DATE DUE

DEMCO 38-296

BRANDS
and Their
Companies

ISSN 1047-6407

A Gale Trade Names Directory

BRANDS
and Their
Companies

**Consumer Products and Their
Manufacturers with Addresses
and Phone Numbers**

Nineteenth Edition

In Two Volumes
Volume 1
A-R

Donna Craft and Sheila M. Dow, Editors

The Gale Group

DETROIT · SAN FRANCISCO · LONDON · BOSTON · WOODBRIDGE, CT

Editors: Donna Craft and Sheila M. Dow

Managing Editor: Diane Maniaci

Contributors: Susan J. Cindric, Sarah E. DeMar, Christine A. Kesler,
Jane A. Malonis, Rebecca Marlow-Ferguson, Terry Peck,
Holly M. Selden, Mike Weaver

Manufacturing Manager: Dorothy Maki
Senior Buyer: Wendy Blurton

Production Director: Mary Beth Trimper
Assistant Production Manager: Evi Seoud

Product Design Manager: Cynthia Baldwin
Graphic Artist: Gary Leach

Supervisor of Systems and Programming: Theresa Rocklin
Programmer: Natasha Mikheyeva

Copyright © 1999 by
The Gale Group
27500 Drake Rd.
Farmington Hills, MI 48331-3535

Library of Congress Catalog Card Number 84-643242
ISBN 0-7876-2290-7 (3 Vol. set)
ISBN 0-7876-2291-5 (Vol. 1)
ISBN 0-7876-2292-3 (Vol. 2)
ISSN 1047-6407

Printed in the United States of America

CONTENTS

Volume 1: A - R

Volume 2: S - Z and Company Listings

CONTENTS

Volume 1: A - R

Volume 2: S - Z and Company Listings

HIGHLIGHTS

Comprehensive Coverage

☞ Extensive Updating -- includes more than:
- ◆ 84,000 manufacturers and distributors
- ◆ 358,000 consumer brands
- ◆ 20,000 brands new to this edition

☞ Variety of sources:
- ◆ Company literature
- ◆ United States Patent and Trademark Office (PTO)
- ◆ Trade journals

☞ Includes brands that are not registered with the PTO

☞ Includes 1999 data

Easy Access

☞ Alphabetical arrangement

☞ Includes company contact information in Company Listings

Historical Information

☞ Indicates companies that are out of business

☞ Indicates a last known address for a company

☞ Indicates brands that are no longer in production

☞ Includes brands that are now considered generic

INTRODUCTION

The vast number of consumer products available today often makes it very difficult to find information about U.S. brands and tradenames, particularly those not registered with the U.S. Patent and Trademark Office (PTO). The *Brands and Their Companies (BTC)* series responds to this need, providing current, accurate and easily accessible tradename information. *BTC* provides the answers to questions such as which company manufactures brand "x", whether a U.S. company imports a product that is manufactured overseas, and which products are marketed by a specific company. Used by business owners, lawyers, students and others, *BTC* is the primary source for consumer brand information. When users need to know if a tradename is currently in use and by whom, *BTC* is the perfect starting point for their search. *BTC* is unique among sources in that it contains many tradenames that are not registered with the PTO, or which are no longer in production, making it extremely difficult to find information on them elsewhere.

The entries in this edition were compiled from company literature, the U.S. Patent and Trademark Office information, and trade journals. Our extensive revision process ensures the accuracy and timeliness of this information, and provides comprehensive coverage of consumer products. The *BTC* staff makes every attempt to stay abreast of current market trends so that *BTC* will include the latest products and offer comprehensive coverage of swiftly developing industries, such as computer software and health care. *BTC* contains the obvious and the elusive--from apparel to zithers, and everything in between.

The *BTC* staff's commitment to continuously improving our database is evident in our extended Resource Listing, which includes trade journals and other publications that have been identified by the editor as important sources of tradename information. These sources are now alphabetized under subject categories.

Approximately 20,000 new brands were researched and collected for this edition of *BTC*. In total, there are more than 358,000 consumer brands included. The more than 84,000 manufacturers and distributors of these brands include small businesses and large corporations, representing both the public and private sector.

The *BTC* series maintains a historical perspective. Brand names that are no longer being produced, as well as those that have become generic, are included. They are indicated as such in the appropriate entries. In the Company Listings section, any companies that are now out of business are so indicated.

Users will find the nineteenth edition contains more essential brand name and company information in one place than previous editions. The *BTC* staff is committed to expanding our database in order to provide our users with the most accurate and current information possible.

Arrangement of *Brands and Their Companies*

Brands and Their Companies is arranged in two separate sections: Brands and Company listings. This makes searching and cross-referencing easy.

The Brand Listings section is an alphabetical listing of all brands collected for this edition. Entries include the trade name, a description of the product, and the manufacturer or distributor. With this format, users can quickly discover who makes what. In addition, there is no need to contact the company in order to determine the type of product.

The Company Listings section contains company name, address, and phone number. Fax and toll-free numbers have been provided when available. URL and e-mail addresses have also been added when available.

Each section contains a Numerical listing for brands and companies beginning with an Arabic numeral, which precedes the alphabetical arrangement.

Electronic Formats Available

Diskette/Magnetic Tape. *Brands and Their Companies* is available for licensing on magnetic tape or diskette in a fielded format. Either the complete database or a custom selection of entries may be ordered. The database is available for internal data processing and non-publishing purposes only. For more information, please call 800-877-GALE.

Online. *BTC* (along with *International Brands and Their Companies*) is accessible as file 116 through Knight-Ridder Information Inc.'s DIALOG service. For more information, contact Knight-Ridder Information Inc., 2440 El Camino Real, Mountain View, CA 94040; phone: (415) 254-7000; toll-free: 800-3-DIALOG.

CD-ROM. *BTC* is available on CD-ROM as part of the Gale Business Resources CD-ROM. For more information, please call 1-800-877-GALE.

GaleNet. *Brands and Their Companies* information is available as part of the Gale Business Resources database accessible through GaleNet, an online information resource that features an easy-to-use end-user interface, the powerful search capabilities of BRS/SEARCH retrieval software, and ease of access through the World-Wide Web. For more information, please call 1-800-877-GALE.

Suggestions Are Welcome

Comments and suggestions for *Brands and Their Companies* are always welcome and can be addressed:

Editor
Brands and Their Companies
The Gale Group
27500 Drake Rd.
Farmington Hills, MI 48331-3535
Phone: (248) 699-4253
Fax: (248) 699-8070
URL: http://www.galegroup.com

USER'S GUIDE

All brand names are alphabetized by the first letter of the first word. Brand names beginning with articles **a, an,** or **the** are alphabetized both under the article and under the following word. This is also true of foreign articles such as **la.**

Most characters, including **&** (and) and **#** (number), are treated as if they were spelled out and are alphabetized accordingly. Spacing affects alphabetizing and causes hyphenated terms (**-**), and terms including a slash mark (**/**), to be treated as separate words. Periods and parentheses, however, are ignored. Groups of initials are treated as if they were actual words.

When the company name is a personal name, it is alpabetized by the surname unless the first name or initial(s) are part of a trade name. The editors have made every effort to distinguish between first names, initials, acronyms, and trade names or multiple surnames; where the editors were unable to make the determination, the company name is alphabetized by the first element in its name. The user is advised to try to locate a company first by surname, and if unsuccessful, to try the first element in the name. Cross-references are provided to indicate corporate name changes and relationships.

Brand Listing examples:	Company Listing examples:
A/D...	B & G Equipment Co. ...
A-HA!...	Baker Hughes Inc. ...
ACCU-BAKERY...	W.M. Barr & Co. ...
ACCU LIFT...	Big Fun Toy Co. ...
ACCUGRIP...	B.O.G. Ltd. ...
THE ACE...	Boo-Boo-Baby, Inc. ...

In each section, entries beginning with an Arabic numeral are located in the Numerical section that precedes the alphabetical arrangement.

In the Company Listings section, companies that are now out of business are indicated by a ☐ after the company name. Companies with a last known address are indicated by a ○ after the address.

Sample Brand Entry

The brand name ① appears first and is highlighted in bold type. The product description ② and the company name ③ (may be manufacturer or distributor) follow the brand. Brands that are no longer in production are indicated with a ☆ after the product description.

    ①   ②   ③

SMITTY'S - Candy - John Smith and Co.

USER'S GUIDE

All brand names are alphabetized by the first letter of the first word. Brand names beginning with articles a, an, or the are alphabetized both under the article and under the following word. This is also true of foreign articles such as la.

Most characters, including & (and) and # (number), are treated as if they were spelled out and are alphabetized accordingly. Spacing affects alphabetizing and causes hyphenated terms (--) and terms including a slash mark (/) to be treated as separate words. Periods and parentheses, however, are ignored. Groups of initials are treated as if they were actual words.

When the company name is a personal name, it is alphabetized by the surname unless the first name or initial(s) are part of a trade name. The editors have made every effort to distinguish between first names, initials, acronyms and trade names or multiple surnames where the editors were unable to make the determination, the company name is alphabetized by the first element in its name. The user is advised to try to locate a company first by surname, and if unsuccessful to try the first element in the name. Cross references are provided to indicate complete name changes and relationships.

Company Listing examples:	Brand Listing examples:
B & G Equipment Co....	A.O....
Baker Hughes Inc....	A-HA!
W M Barr & Co....	ACCU-BAKERY
Big Fun Toy Co....	ACCU-LIFT
B.O.B., Ltd.	ACCUGRIP
Boo-Boo Baby, Inc....	THE ACE

In each section, entries beginning with an Arabic numeral are located in the numerical section that precedes the alphabetical arrangement.

In the Company Listings section, companies that are now out of business are indicated by a ⊡ after the company name. Companies with a last known address are indicated by a ◇ after the address.

Sample Brand Entry

The brand name ① appears first and is highlighted in bold type. The product description ② and the company name ③ (may be manufacturer or distributor) follow the brand. Brands that are no longer in production are indicated with a ⚹ after the product description.

SMITTY'S - Candy - John Smith and Co.

Resource Listing
(Prices quoted are current as of March 1999)

AIR CONDITIONING AND HEATING EQUIPMENT

Air Conditioning, Heating and Refrigeration News - Directory Issue
Business News Publishing Co., 755 W. Big Beaver Rd., 10th Fl., Troy, MI 48084
Tel: (800) 837-7370
Price: $35.00, plus $2.50 shipping.

APPAREL AND ACCESSORIES

American Apparel Manufacturers Association - Directory of Members/Associate Members
American Apparel Manufacturers Association, 2500 Wilson Blvd., Ste. 301, Arlington, VA 22201
Tel: (800) 520-AAMA
Price: $100.00.

American Shoemaking Directory
Shoe Trades Publishing Co., PO Box 198, Cambridge, MA 02140
Tel: (781) 648-8160
E-mail: info@shoetrades.com
Price: $49.00, payment must accompany order.

Athletic Footwear Association - Trademark Directory
Athletic Footwear Association, 200 Castlewood Dr., North Palm Beach, FL 33408
Tel: (561) 842-4100
E-mail: jhsgma@aol.com
Price: Available to members only.

Body Fashions/Intimate Apparel - Directory Issue
Advanstar Communications Inc., 7500 Old Oak Blvd., Cleveland, OH 44130
Tel: (440) 243-8100
Price: $40.00, plus $3.50 shipping.

Earnshaw's Infants, Girls, Boys Wear Review - Children's Wear Directory Issue
Earnshaw Publications, Inc., 225 W. 34th St., Rm. 1212, New York, NY 10122
Tel: (212) 563-2742
Price: $10.00, plus $3.00 shipping, available to trade only.

Hat Life Directory
Hat Life Directory, 66 York St., Jersey City, NJ 07302
Tel: (201) 434-8322
Price: $21.00, includes shipping.

Juvenile Merchandising—Directory and Buyers Guide
Columbia Communications, Inc. 2125 Center Ave., Ste. 305, Fort Lee, NJ 07024-5859
Tel: (201) 532-9290
Price: $20.00

SoleSource
Footwear Industries of America, 1420 K St. NW, Ste. 600, Washington, DC 20005
Tel: (800) 688-SOLE
URL: http://www.fig.org
Price: $45.00, plus $5.95 shipping.

APPLIANCES

Association of Home Appliance Manufacturers - Directory
Association of Home Appliance Manufacturers, 20 N. Wacker Dr., Chicago, IL 60606
Tel: (312) 984-5800
Price: $7.50; $150.00 (Diskette or Magnetic Tape).

ART AND CRAFT SUPPLIES

Craft and Needlework Age - Trade Directory Issue
Krousy Publications, 700 E. State St., Iola, WI 54990
Tel: (732) 446-4900
Price: $40.00.

Graphic Arts Blue Book
A.F. Lewis and Co., Inc., 245 5th Ave., New York, NY 10016
Tel: (212) 519-7398
Price: $85.00, plus $5.00 shipping.

Knitting Times Buyers' Guide
National Knitwear & Sportswear Association, 386 Park Ave. S, New York, NY 10016
Tel: (212) 683-7520
Price: $25.00, plus $2.50 shipping.

Who's Who in Art Materials
National Art Materials Trade Association, 178 Lakeview Ave., Clifton, NJ 07011
Tel: (800) 746-2682
Price: free to members; $100.00 for nonmembers.

AUTOMOTIVE AND RECREATIONAL VEHICLES, PARTS, AND ACCESSORIES

Automotive News Market Data Book
Crain Communications, 1400 Woodbridge Ave., Detroit, MI 48207
Tel: (800) 992-9970
Price: $10.00.

Car and Driver
Hachette Magazines, 1633 Broadway, New York, NY 10019
Tel: (212) 767-6000
Price: $21.94 per year.

Dealernews - Buyers Guide Issue
Advanstar Communications Inc., 7500 Old Oak Blvd., Cleveland, OH 44130
Tel: (440) 243-8100
Price: $29.95, plus $3.50 shipping.

Gale's Auto Sourcebook
The Gale Group, 27500 Drake Rd., Farmington Hills, MI 48331-3535
Tel: (800) 877-GALE
URL: http://www.galegroup.com
Price: $98.00.

Motorcycle Product News - Trade Directory Issue
M.H. West, Inc., 1846 Hoffman St., Madison, WI 53704-2522
Tel: (800) 234-8255
Price: $45.00.

Recreational Vehicle Blue Book
National Hunter Market Reports Inc., Maclean Hunter Bldg., 29 N. Wacker Dr., Chicago, IL 60606
Tel: (800) 621-9907
Price: $110.00.

RV Business – RV Industry Directory Issue
TL Enterprises, Inc., 3675 Vista Del Mar Dr., Ventura, CA 93001
Tel: (805) 667-4100
Price: $14.95, plus $2.95 shipping.

Tire Review - Sourcebook and Directory Issue
Babcox Publications, 11 S. Forge St., Akron, OH 44304
Tel: (303) 535-6117
URL: http://www.tirereview.com
Price: $5.00.

Who Makes It and Where
Tire Guides Inc., 1101-6 S. Rogers Cir., Boca Raton, FL 33487
Tel: (561) 997-9229
Price: $7.00, plus $3.00 shipping.

BEVERAGES

Beverage Industry--Annual Manual Issue
Stagnito Publishing Co., 1935 Shermer Rd., Ste. 100, Northbrook, IL 60062
Tel: (847) 205-5660
Price: $60.00, plus $3.50 shipping.

Beverage Marketing Directory
Beverage Marketing Corp., PO Box 126, Mingo Junction, OH 43938
Tel: (800) 332-6222
Price: $815.00 (hardcover); $795.00 (softcover).

Brewer's Resource Directory
Brewers Publications, Association of Brewers, PO Box 1679, Boulder, CO 80306-1679
Tel: (303) 447-0816
Price: $60.00, plus shipping (members), $100.00, plus shipping (nonmembers).

Distilled Spirit, Wine and Beer Directories
Distilled Spirits Council of the United States, Inc., 1250 I St. NW, Ste. 900, Washington, DC 20005
Tel: (202) 682-8897
Price: $250.00 (spirit); $500.00 (wine); $175.00 (beer).

Wines & Vines - Directory of the Wine Industry in North America Issue
Hiaring Co., 1800 Lincoln Ave., San Rafael, CA 94901
Tel: (415) 453-9700
Price: $75.00.

ELECTRONIC EQUIPMENT

Access Control - Buyers' Guide
Argus Business, 6151 Powers Ferry Rd. NW, Atlanta, GA 30339-2941
Tel: (770) 955-2500
Price: $63.95, payment must accompany order.

Best's Safety Directory
A.M. Best Co., Ambest Rd., Oldwick, NJ 08858
Tel: (908) 439-2200
URL: http://www.ambest.com
Price: $49.95, plus $15.95 shipping.

Billboard International Buyer's Guide
Billboard, 1515 Broadway, 39th Fl., New York, NY 10036
Tel: (800) 344-7119
Price: $130.00, plus $6.00 shipping.

Boxoffice Buyers' Directory Issue
RLD Communications Inc., 6640 Sunset Blvd., Ste. 100, Beverly Hills, CA 90028-7159
Tel: (323) 465-1186
Price: $6.95.

Directory of Computer Software Retailers
Chain Store Guide Information Services, 3922 Coconut Palm Dr., Tampa, FL 33619
Tel: (800) 927-9292
Price: $290.00.

Hearing Journal Directory Issue
Williams & Wilkins, 428 E. Preston St., Baltimore, MD 21202-3993
Tel: (410) 528-4000
Price: $73.00 per year (individual); $43.00 per year (student).

Solid State Technology Resource Guide
PennWell Publishing Co., 10 Tara Blvd., 5th Fl., Nashua, NH 03062-2801
Tel: (603)891-0123
Price: $95.00.

Sound and Communications - Blue Book Issue
Testa Communications, 25 Willowdale Ave., Port Washington, NY 11050
Tel: (516) 767-2500
Price: $15.00 per year.

FOOD PRODUCTS

American Frozen Food Institute - Membership Directory & Buyers' Guide
American Frozen Food Institute, 1764 Old Meadow Ln., Ste. 350, McLean, VA 22102
Tel: (703) 821-0770
Price: $100.00.

Baking Buyer - Yearbook Issue
Sosland Publishing Co., 4800 Main, Ste. 100, Kansas City, MO 64112-2513
Tel: (816) 756-1000
Price: $75.00, payment must accompany order.

Candy Buyer's Directory
Manufacturing Confectioner Publishing Co., 175 Rock Rd., Glen Rock, NJ 07452
Tel: (201) 652-2655
Price: $65.00, payment must accompany order.

Deli News-Directory Issue
Pacific Rim Publishing, 12631 E. Imperial Hwy., Ste. 215A, Santa Fe Springs, CA 90670
Tel: (562) 929-6788
Price: $2.00, payment must accompany order.

Directory of Foodservice Distributors
Chain Store Guide Information Services, 3922 Coconut Palm Dr., Tampa, FL 33619
Tel: (800) 927-9292
Price: $290.00.

Directory of the Canning, Freezing, Preserving Industries
Edward E. Judge & Sons, Inc., PO Box 866, Westminster, MD 21158
Tel: (410) 876-2052
Price: $175.00, standard edition; $275.00, deluxe edition; $680.00 electronic (includes copy of standard edition).

Fancy Food - Buyers Guide Issue
Talcott Communications Corp., 20 N. Wacker Dr., Ste. 3230, Chicago, IL 60606
Tel: (312) 849-2220
Price: $5.00 per issue; $26.00 per year.

Foodservice Equipment and Supplies Specialists - Product Source Guide
Cahners Publishing Co., 1350 E. Touhy Ave., Des Plaines, IL 60017-5080
Tel: (847) 635-8800
Price: $35.00.

National Frozen Food Association - Directory
National Frozen Food Association, 4755 Linglestown Rd., Ste. 300, Harrisburg, PA 17112
Tel: (717) 657-8601
Price: $195.00, plus $5.00 shipping.

Quick Frozen Foods Annual Directory of Frozen Food Processors & Buyers Guide
Saul Beck Publications, 271 Madison Ave., Ste. 1104, New York, NY 10016
Tel: (212) 557-8600
Price: $130.00, includes shipping.

Thomas Food Industry Register
Thomas Publishing Co., 5 Penn Plz., 15th Fl., New York, NY 10001
Tel: (212) 290-7341
Price: $215.00, three-volume set or CD-ROM, includes shipping.

Whole Foods - Source Book Issue
Whole Foods Communications, Inc., 3000 Hadley Rd., South Plainfield, NJ 07080
Tel: (908) 769-1160
Price: $60.00, plus $3.20 shipping.

Who's Who in the Snack Food Industry
Snack Food Association, 1711 King St., Ste. 1, Alexandria, VA 22314
Tel: (703) 836-4500
E-mail: sfa@sfa.org
Price: $20.00 (member); $150.00 (nonmember), plus $6.00 shipping, payment must accompany order.

FRANCHISES

Directory of Franchising Organizations
Pilot Books, 127 Sterling Ave., PO Box 2102, Greenport, NY 11944
Tel: (516) 477-1094
Price: $12.95.

Worldwide Franchise Directory
The Gale Group, 27500 Drake Rd., Farmington Hills, Detroit, MI 48331-3535
Tel: (800) 877-GALE
URL: http://www.galegroup.com
Price:$129.50.

GENERAL

Advertising Age
Crain Communications, Inc., 740 N. Rush St., Chicago, IL 60611-2590
Tel: (800) 992-9970
Price: $119.00

ADWEEK - Client/Brand Directory
ADWEEK Directories, 1515 Broadway, 12th Fl., New York, NY 10036
Tel: (800) 468-2395
E-mail: mtebo@interport.net
Price: $295.00, plus $12.00 shipping.

Consumer Reports Buying Guide Issue
Consumer Report Books, 9180 Le Saint Dr., Fairfield, OH 45014
Tel: (800) 272-0722
Price: $8.95, prepaid.

Consumer Sourcebook
The Gale Group, 27500 Drake Rd., Farmington Hills, MI 48331-3535
Tel: (800) 877-GALE
URL: http://www.galegroup.com
Price: $304.75.

Directory of U.S. Trademarks
Thomson and Thomson, 500 Victory Rd., North Quincy, MA 02171-3145
Tel: (800) 692-8833
URL: http://www.thomson-thomson.com
Price: $1,395.00.

Leading National Advertisers Ad & Summary
Leading National Advertisers/BAR, 11 W. 42nd St., New York, NY 10036-8088
Tel: (212) 789-1400
Price: $780.00, quarterly.

MacRae's Blue Book
MacRae's Blue Book, Inc., 65 Bleecker St., New York, NY 10012-2420
Tel: (800) 622-7237
URL: http://d-net.com/macraes
Price: $170.00, includes shipping.

Official Gazette of the United States Patent and Trademark Office: Trademarks
Government Printing Office, Washington, DC 20402-9371
Tel: (202) 512-1800
Price: $672.00 per year.

PRODUCTSCAN [Database]
Marketing Intelligence Service Ltd., 6473D Rte. 64, Naples, NY 14512
Tel: (800) 836-5710
E-mail: mktgintel@cis.compuserve.com
Price: $3,995.00 per year.

Sources of Supply Buyers Guide
Wm. O. Dannhausen Corp., PO Box 795, Park Ridge, IL 60068
Tel: (847) 823-3145
Price: $81.00.

GIFTWARE AND NOVELTY ITEMS

Gifts and Decorative Accessories Buyers Directory
Geyer-McAllister Publications, Inc., 51 Madison Ave., New York, NY 10010
Tel: (212) 572-9636
Price: $42.00; subscription price includes directory.

Souvenirs and Novelties Magazine - Party Supply and Stationery Buyers Guide Issue
Kane Communications, 7000 Terminal Sq., Ste. 210, Upper Darby, PA 19082
Tel: (610) 734-2420
Price: $5.00.

GLASS PRODUCTS

American Glass Review - Glass Factory Directory Issue
Doctorow Communications, Inc., 1011 Clifton Ave., Clifton, NJ 07013
Tel: (973) 779-1600
Price: $25.00, subscription price includes directory.

Architects' Guide to Glass, Metal & Glazing
Key Communications Inc., PO Box 569, Garrisonville, VA 22463
Tel: (540) 720-5584
E-mail: usglass@aol.com
Price: $10.00, plus $1.50 shipping.

Glass Digest-Buyers Guide Issue
Ashlee Publishing Co., 18 E. 41st St., New York, NY 10017-6222
Tel: (212) 376-7722
Price: $30.00.

HARDWARE AND TOOLS

Directory and Buyer's Guide of the Door and Hardware Institute
Door and Hardware Institute, 14170 Newbrook Dr., Chantilly, VA 22021-2223
Tel: (703) 222-2010
Price: $35.00 (members); $150.00 (non-members).

HEALTH, HYGIENE, AND FITNESS PRODUCTS

American Salon's Green Book
Advanstar Communications, Inc., 7500 Old Oak Blvd., Cleveland, OH 44130
Tel: (212) 243-8100
Price: $130.00, plus $5.00 shipping.

Beauty Fashion - Body/Bath/Sun Issue
Beauty Fashion, Inc., 530 5th Ave., Ste. 430, New York, NY 10036
Tel: (212) 840-8800
Price: $10.00.

Beauty Fashion - Cosmetic Directory Issue
Beauty Fashion Inc., 530 5th Ave., Ste. 430, New York, NY 10036
Tel: (212) 840-8800
Price: $10.00.

Beauty Fashion - Cosmetic, Toiletry, and Fragrance Association (CTFA) Convention Issue
Beauty Fashion, Inc., 530 5th Ave., Ste. 430, New York, NY 10036
Tel: (212) 840-8800
Price: $10.00.

Beauty Fashion - Men's Issue
Beauty Fashion, Inc., 530 5th Ave., Ste. 430, New York, NY 10036
Tel: (212) 840-8800
Price: $10.00.

Beauty Fashion - Women's Fragrance Issue
Beauty Fashion, Inc., 530 5th Ave., Ste. 430, New York, NY 10036
Tel: (212) 840-8800
Price: $10.00.

Beauty Fashion - Women's Treatment Issue
Beauty Fashion, Inc., 530 5th Ave., Ste. 430, New York, NY 10036
Tel: (212) 840-8800
Price: $10.00.

Cosmetics and Toiletries - Cosmetic Bench Reference
Allured Publishing Corp., 362 S. Schmale Rd., Carol Stream, IL 60188-2787
Tel: (603) 653-2155
Price: $177.00.

Drug and Cosmetic Industry Catalog
Advanstar Communications, Inc., 7500 Old Oak Blvd., Cleveland, OH 44130
Tel: (800) 225-4569
Price: $25.00, plus $5.00 shipping.

Health Foods Business - Purchasing Guide Issue
Cygnus Publishing, 2 University Plz., Ste. 204, Hackensack, NJ 07601
Tel: (201) 487-7800
Price: $45.00, plus $3.50 shipping.

Homecare Product Directory and Buyers' Guide
Miramar Publishing Co., 23815 Stuart Ranch Rd., Malibu, CA 90265
Tel: (800) 543-4116
Price: $25.00.

Industrial Launderer - Buyer's Guide Issue
Institute of Industrial Launderers, 1730 M St. NW, Ste. 610, Washington, DC 20036
Tel: (800) 486-6745
Price: $60.00.

Red Book
Medical Economics, 5 Paragon Dr., Montvale, NJ 07645-1742
Tel: (800) 222-3045
Price: $59.95, plus $5.95 shipping.

Safety and Health - Industrial Hygiene Buyers' Guide Issue
National Safety Council, 1121 Springlake Dr., Itasca, IL 60143-3201
Tel: (800) 621-7615
Price: $3.75 (members); $4.70 (nonmembers).

Safety and Health - Safety Equipment Buyers' Guide Issue
National Safety Council, 1121 Springlake Dr., Itasca, IL 60143-3201
Tel: (800) 621-7615
Price: $3.75 (members); $4.70 (nonmembers).

Soap/Cosmetics/Chemical Specialties--Blue Book Issue
Cygnus Publishing Inc., 445 Broad Hollow Rd., Ste. 21, Melville, NY 11747-3601
Tel: (516) 845-2700
Price: $15.00.

Unlisted Drugs Index - Guide
Pharmaco Medical Documentation, Inc., PO Box 429, Chatham, NJ 07928
Tel: (973) 822-9200
Price: $680.00, 1998 edition.

HOME FURNISHINGS

Architectural Woodwork Institute - Source Book
Architectural Woodwook Institute, 1952 Isaac Newton Sq. W, Reston, VA 20190
Tel: (703) 733-0600
Price: Free to members, architects, and designers; $100.00 to others.

Decorating Registry
National Decorating Products Association, 1050 N. Lindbergh Blvd., St. Louis, MO 63132-2994
Tel: (800) 737-0107
E-mail: info@ndpa.hygexpo.com
Price: $15.00.

Directory of Discontinued Tableware Replacement Services
Joyful Ventures, Box 5297, Ocala, FL 34478
Tel: (352) 622-4077
Price: $5.00, postpaid.

Draperies & Window Coverings - Directory & Buyer's Guide
L.C. Clark Publishing Co., 840 US Hwy. 1, Ste. 330, North Palm Beach, FL 33408
Tel: (800) 833-9056
Price: $15.00.

Flooring - Buying and Resource Guide Issue
Douglas Publications, Inc., 2807 N. Parham Rd., Ste. 200, Richmond, VA 23294
Tel: (804) 762-9600
Price: $35.00, plus $3.50 shipping.

IDH-Interior Decorators Handbook
Columbia Communications, Inc., 2125 Center Ave., Ste. 305, Fort Lee, NJ 07024-5659
Tel: (212) 532-9290
Price: $15.00 per issue.

Kitchen and Bath Business - Buyers' Guide
Miller Freeman, Inc., 1515 Broadway, New York, NY 10036
Tel: (800) 250-2430
Price $7.00.

National Floor Trend - Buyers Guide and Directory Issue
Specialist Publications, Inc., 17835 Ventura Blvd., Ste. 312, Encino, CA 91316
Tel: (800) 835-4398
Price: $25.00.

Wallcoverings Association - Directory of Members
Wallcoverings Association, 401 N. Michigan Ave., Chicago, IL 60611
Tel: (312) 644-6610
Price: Available to members only.

Wallcoverings, Windows, and Interior Fashions—Directory Issue
Cygnus Publishing Inc., 445 Broad Hollow Rd., Ste. 21, Melville, NY 11747-3601
Tel: (516) 845-2700
Price: $25.00.

JEWELRY AND CLOCKS

Jewelers Circular/Keystone Brand Name and Trademark Guide
Chilton Co., 1 Chilton Way, Radnor, PA 19089
Tel: (800) 866-0206
Price: $49.95.

Watch & Clock Review Clock Directory and Watch Directory
Bell Publications, 2403 Champa St., Denver, CO 80205
Tel: (303) 296-1600
Price: $19.50 per year.

LIGHTING EQUIPMENT

Lighting Dimensions - Industry Resources
Entertainment Technology Communications Corp., 32 W. 18th St., New York, NY 10011-4612
Tel: (212) 229-2965
Price: $20.00, postpaid.

LODGING AND TRAVEL

Directory of Hotel & Motel Companies
American Hotel & Motel Association Directory Corp.
1201 New York Ave. NW, Washington, DC 20005-3931
Tel: (202) 289-3157
Price: $82.00, plus shipping.

Travelware Magazine-Travelware Resources Directory Issue
Business Journals, Inc., 50 Day St., Norwalk, CT 06854
Tel: (203) 853-6015
Price: $25.00, payment must accompany order.

METAL PRODUCTS

Die Casting Industry Buyer's Guide
Die Casting Industry Publications, 415 Bennett Rd., Elk Grove Village, IL 60007
Tel: (847) 364-1222
Price: $44.95, plus $3.00 shipping.

Iron and Steel Works of the World
Metal Bulletin Inc., 220 5th Ave., 19th Fl., New York, NY 10001
Tel: (800) METAL-25
Price: $423.00.

Welding and Fabricating Data Book
Penton Publishing Co., 1100 Superior Ave., Cleveland, OH 44114-2543
Tel: (216) 696-7000
Price: $35.00.

MUSIC

Musical Merchandise Review Music Industry Directory
The Larkin Group, 100 Wells Ave., Box 9103, Newton, MA 02159-9103
Tel: (800) 869-7469
Price: $135.00.

PAINT, PIGMENTS, AND INK PRODUCTS

American Ink Maker - Buyers' Guide Issue
Cygnus Publishing Inc., 445 Broad Hollow Rd., Melville, NY 11747
Tel: (516) 845-2700
Price: $15.00.

American Painting Contractor - Buyers' Guide Issue
Douglas Publications, Inc., 2807 N. Parham Rd., Ste. 200, Richmond, VA 23294
Tel: (804) 762-9600
Price: $33.00.

Modern Paint and Coatings - Paint Red Book
Cygnus Publishing, 6151 Powers Ferry Rd. NW, Atlanta, GA 30339-2941
Tel: (920) 563-1766
Price: $89.95.

Rauch Guide to the U.S. Ink Industry
Impack Marketing Group, PO Box 1226, Manchester Center, VT 05255
Tel: (802) 362-2325
Price: $389.00.

Textile Chemist and Colorist - Buyer's Guide Issue
American Association of Textile Chemists and Colorists, PO Box 12215, Research Triangle Park, NC 27709
Tel: (919) 549-8141
Price: $45.00 (members); $65.00 (nonmembers).

PAPER, STATIONERY, AND WRITING IMPLEMENTS

Greeting Card Industry Directory
Greeting Card Association, 1200 G St. NW, Ste. 760, Washington, DC 20005
Tel: (202) 393-1778
Price: Please inquire.

Marking Industry Magazine - Marking Products and Equipment Buyer's Guide Issue
Marking Devices Publishing Co., 136 W. Vallette, Ste. 6, Elmhurst, IL 60126
Tel: (603) 832-5200
Price: $30.00.

PIMA Buyers Guide & Directory
Paper Industry Management Association, 2400 E. Oakton St., Arlington Heights, IL 60005
Tel: (847) 956-0250
Price: $140.00.

Walden's Paper Catalog
Walden-Mott Corp., 225 N. Franklin Tpke., Ramsey, NJ 07446-1600
Tel: (201) 818-8630
Price: $50.00 per issue; $75.00 per year.

Directory of Manufacturers Supporting the Writing and Marking Instrument Industry
Writing Instrument Manufacturers Association, 236 Rte. 38 W, Ste. 100, Moorestown, NJ 08057
Tel: (609) 231-8500
Price: $50.00.

PET PRODUCTS

Petfood Industry-Directory Reference Issue
Watt Publishing Co., 122 S. Wesley Ave., Mt. Morris, IL 61054-1497
Tel: (815) 734-4171
Price: $25.00.

Pet Supplies Marketing Directory
Fancy Publications, PO Box 6050, Mission Viejo, CA 92690
Tel: (949) 855-8822
Price: $75.00, plus $5.00 shipping.

PETROLEUM PRODUCTS

National Petroleum News-Market Facts Issue
Adams/Hunter Publishing, 2101 S. Arlington Heights Rd., Ste. 150, Arlington Heights, IL 60005
Tel: (847) 427-9512
E-mail: 102615.55@CompuServe.com
Price: $64.00.

PLASTIC AND RUBBER PRODUCTS

Modern Plastics Encyclopedia-Directory of Trade Names
McGraw-Hill, Inc., 2 Penn Plz., New York, NY 10121-2298
Tel: (212) 512-2000

Rubber and Plastics News - Rubbicana Issue
Crain Communications Inc., 1725 Merriman Rd., Ste. 300, Akron, OH 44313-5251
Tel: (330) 836-9180
Price: $89.00, plus $6.00 shipping.

SPORTING GOODS

Shooter's Bible
Stoeger Publishing Co., 5 Mansard Ct., Wayne, NJ 07470-6040
Tel: (800) 631-0722
Price: $23.95, payment with order; postpaid.

SIA Ski, Snowboard, and Outdoor Sports Show Directory
Ski Industries America, 8377 B Greensboro Dr., McLean, VA 22102
Tel: (703) 556-9020
Price: $250.00.

Sports Market Place
SportsGuide Inc., 2400 E. Arizona Biltmore Ctr., Bldg. 2, Ste. 1270, Phoenix, AZ 85016
Tel: (800) 776-7877
Price: $209.00, plus shipping and sales tax.

TEXTILES

Davison's Textile Blue Book
Davison Publishing Co., Inc., PO Box 1289, Concord, NC 28026-1209
Tel: (800) DAVISON
Price: $140.00, plus shipping.

Fairchild's Textile & Apparel Financial Directory
Fairchild Books & Visuals, 7 W. 34th St., New York, NY 10001
Tel: (212) 630-3880
Price: $85.00, plus $5.00 shipping.

International Directory of the Nonwoven Fabrics Industry
INDA, Association of the Nonwoven Fabrics Industry,
1001 Winstead Dr., Ste. 460, Cary, NC 27513
Tel: (919) 677-0060
Price: $135.00 (members); $195.00 (nonmembers).

World Directory of Manufactured Fiber Producers
Fiber Economics Bureau, Inc., 1150 17th St. NW, Ste. 306, Washington, DC 20036
Tel: (202) 467-0916
Price: $80.00.

TOBACCO PRODUCTS

Tobacco International Annual International Directory & Buyer's Guide
Lockwood Trade Journal Co., 130 W. 42nd St., Ste. 2200, New York, NY 10036
Tel: (212) 391-2060
E-mail: lockmin@aol.com
Price: $40.00.

U.S. Distribution Journal—Source Book
McFadden Trade Publishing, 233 Park Ave. S, New York, NY 10003
Tel: (212) 979-4800
Price: $95.00, payment must accompany order.

TOYS

International Toy Center Directory
RobToy, Inc., 177 Sound Beach Ave., PO Box 173, Old Greenwich, CT 06870-0173
Tel: (203) 637-5466
Price: $15.00 (by mail); $10.00 (picked up).

Playthings - Who Makes It Issue
Geyer-McAllister Publications, Inc., 51 Madison Ave., New York, NY 10010-1603
Tel: (212) 689-4411
Price: $50.00.

TEXTILES

Davison's Textile Blue Book
Davison Publishing Co., Inc., PO Box 1289, Concord, NC 28026-1289
Tel. (800) DAVISON
Price: $140.00, plus shipping.

Fairchild's Textile & Apparel Financial Directory
Fairchild Books & Visuals, 7 W. 34th St., New York, NY 10001
Tel. (212) 630-3880
Price: $30.00, plus $5.00 shipping.

International Directory of the Nonwoven Fabrics Industry
INDA, Association of the Nonwoven Fabrics Industry
1001 Winstead Dr., Ste. 460, Cary, NC 27513
Tel. (919) 677-0060
Price: $132.00 (members); $495.00 (nonmembers)

World Directory of Manufactured Fiber Producers
Fiber Economics Bureau, Inc., 1150 17th St. NW, Ste. 305, Washington, DC 20036
Tel. (202) 857-0315
Price: $30.00

TOBACCO PRODUCTS

Tobacco International Annual International Directory & Buyer's Guide
Lockwood Trade Journal Co., 130 W. 42nd St., Ste. 2200, New York, NY 10036
Tel. (212) 391-2060
E-mail: lockinc@aol.com
Price: $40.00

U.S. Distribution Journal—30-rpe B&K
MacLean Hunter Publishing, 233 Park Ave. S, New York, NY 10003
Tel. (212) 979-4860
Price: $15.00, payment must accompany order.

TOYS

International Toy Center Directory
Rinaldy, Inc., 171 Sound Beach Ave., PO Box 174, Old Greenwich, CT 06870-0174
Tel. (203) 637-8408
Price: $15.00 (by mail); $10.00 (picked up).

Playthings—Who Makes It issue
Geyer McAllister Publications, Inc., 51 Madison Ave., New York, NY 10010-1603
Tel. (212) 689-4411
Price: $8.00.

Numerical Brands

Addresses and phone numbers for the companies cited in the brands below
are available in the Company Listings section immediately following the brands listings.

0-2 SOLUTION - Ophthalmic goods ✩ - Whitby Pharmaceuticals, Inc.

0-3 - Ophthalmic goods - Whitby Pharmaceuticals, Inc.

0-4 IRRIGATION SOLUTION - Ophthalmic goods ✩ - Whitby Pharmaceuticals, Inc.

0/40 LOVE/ FORTY - Apparel–athletic - Love/40 Tennis Collection Inc.

00ECTRICAL WATCH DOG USES, THE - Electrical equipment - Uses Mfg Inc.

1 - Adhesives and sealants - Tile Perfect

1 - Apparel–athletic - Soccer Madness

1 - Baby foods - Ralston Purina Co.

#1 - Chickens - Perdue Holdings, Inc.

1-1-2 - Cleaning preparations - Finger Lakes Chemicals, Inc.

1 + 1 4 SCHOOLS - Computer software - Maxis, Inc.

1-2-3 - Golfing equipment - Hillerich & Bradsby Co.

1-2-3 - Health care products ✩ - Emerson Laboratories

1-2-3 - Nail care products - Opi Products, Inc.

1-2-3 - Yarn - Bernat Yarn & Craft Corp.

1-2-3 BASEBALL - Toys - Playskool, Inc.

1, 2, 3 DISCOVER - Toys - Toy Biz, Inc.

1 2 3'S - Adhesives and sealants ✩ - Mactac Inc. (Packaging Closures Systems Div.)

1-2-99 - Lubricants ✩ - Ashland Oil, Inc.

1/2 PRICE MOVERS - Consulting services - Chad Miller

1/2KX2 - Golfing equipment - James I. Park

1/4 - Medical apparatus - Philadelphia Cervical Collar Co.

1 800 8 KAMALI - Apparel and accessories - Norma Kamali, Inc.

1-800-COOKIES - Cookies - R & R Bourbon Street, Inc.

1-800-DIAL-WORD 1-800-342-5967 - Computer software - David M. Ronson

1-800 DIRECTORY - Computer software - Parsons Technology, Inc.

1-800-FAN-EARS - Radios - Sportronics Radios, Inc.

1 - 800 - PETUNIA - Flowers, plants, and seeds - 1-800-Petunia

1-800-SCHOLASTIC - Educational materials - Scholastic Inc.

1-888-NO-HASSLE - Medical apparatus - Brooke R. Weisleder

1-888-TAX-LAWS - Accounting services - P.J. Greco Associates, Ltd.

#1 ALL AMERICAN CHEW - Meat products - Enjoy Foods International, Inc.

1 ALL IN ONE - Adhesives and sealants - Tile Perfect

#1 ALL SYSTEMS - Pet products - Ken Alta Inc.

1 & 1 - Hair care products - Helene Curtis Industries Inc.

1 BAG, THE - Infant product - Forrester Industries Inc.

1¢ POPS - Candy ✩ - American Candy Co.

1 COAT LTX - Paints - Mac-O-Lac Paints Inc.

1 CONTROL - Television equipment ✩ - Jasco Products Co. Inc.

1-DAY ACUVUE - Contact lenses - Johnson & Johnson

1 DIR + - Computer software - Bourbaki Inc.

1 DIR, THE - Computer software ✩ - Bourbaki Inc.

1 DROP - Adhesives and sealants - Union Laboratories Inc.

1 DYNAMIC AUTOLOAD SYSTEMS - Motor vehicles–trucks - Dynamic Autoload Systems

'01 EQUAL - Games - Merit Industries

1 FIRST - Binders - First Products, Inc.

1 FITS ALL - Inks - Eversharp Pen Co.

1-FITS-ALL - Pens - Astro Pen Co.

1 FOR YES, 2 FOR NO - Telephone accessories - Active Voice Corp.

1-HOUR - Patterns–clothing - Mccall Pattern Co.

#1-ISS - Computer hardware ✩ - Netrix Corp.

#1 KIDS BRICK BUILDER'S LOCAL FOR FUN - Toys–blocks - Nickel Industries, Inc.

1 LOCK - Metals - Enclosures, Inc.

1 M - Calendars - Mach 1, Inc.

1 MINUTE SET-UP - Furniture - System 3R USA, Inc.

1 MURALO - Paints - Muralo Co. Inc.

#1 NETWORK - Film - #1 Network, Inc.

1 ONE-UPS - Electrical equipment - Exide Electronics Corp.

1 OPTIMUM NUTRIENT ENHANCER - Dietary supplement - Genesis 2000 Biologic Systems, Inc.

1 + 1 - Pharmaceutical preparations - Dunhall Pharmaceuticals Inc.

1 POUND PLUS - Yarn - Caron International Inc.

1 QUALITEE - Golf equipment - Quality Golf Products Inc.

1-SHOT - Lettering and poster paints - Consumers Paint Factory Inc.

1-STEP - Chemical preparations - Accurate Chemical and Scientific Corp.

1-STEP - Housewares - A-Step Products Inc.

1 STEP - Paper–transfer - Chemical Design Co.

1 STEP - Pet products ✩ - Jungle Laboratories Corp.

1-STEP MEALS - Pasta - Pasta USA Inc.

1 TO 10 PANEL - Toys - Lauri Inc.

1 VARNISH - Varnishes ✩ - Gilman Co. Inc.

1-WIRE - Computer software - Dallas Semiconductor Corp.

1 X 1 - Vacuum cleaners and accessories - Shop Vac Corp.

1 X 1 RIB - Fabrics–broadcloth - Desire Mills Co. Inc.

1K - Air transportation–passengers - United Air Lines, Inc.

1MAGE - Computer software - Image Software, Inc.

1Q2000 - Computer software - Ird Mechanalysis, Inc.

1SOFT - Computer software - 1soft Corp.

1ST - Fruits and vegetables ✩ - Snokist Growers

1ST ACTION - Health care products - Vector Products Inc.

1ST ADE - Beverages - Daily Juice Products Inc.

1ST ADE - Confections - American Beverage Corp.

1ST AID - Flashlights - Zelco Industries, Inc.

1ST & 10 - Sporting goods - Mueller Sports Medicine Inc.

1ST & TEN - Games - International Gamco, Inc.

1ST & TEN - Games - Packerland Toys and Sports Inc.

1ST ANNUAL S.O.B. TOURNAMENT - T-shirts–men's - World Cup USA 1994, Inc.

1ST AUTO - Wiring devices - Kmart Properties, Inc.

1ST CHOICE - Cigarettes - R.J. Reynolds Tobacco Co.

1ST CLASS CRITTERS - Toys–stuffed - Fun World Inc.

1ST DATE - Soap - L.P.I. Far East Inc.

1ST DEFENSE - Medical apparatus - 1st Defense Safety Corp.

1ST DESK - Computer software - 1st Desk Systems, Inc.

1ST EYE CARE - Cases–eyeglass - 1st Eye Care Inc.

1ST FIRST CHOICE - Cleaning preparations - First Choice Chemicals

1ST INDIANA - Wines ✩ - Banholzer Winecellars Ltd.

1ST INTERSTATE INN - Hotels and motels - Rite-A-Way Industries Inc.

1ST KISS - Computer peripheral equipment - QMS, Inc.

1ST LOOK - Video equipment - Fonet Inc.

1ST MATE - Horns–motor vehicle ✩ - Falcon Safety Products, Inc.

1ST MEDICAL RESPONSE - Computer storage devices–optical - Micromedex, Inc.

1ST NATIONAL BAGEL COMPANY - Bagels - Bagels Forever Inc.

1ST NATIONAL CHECK - Fabrics - Dan River Inc.

1ST NOTE - Musical instruments - Trophy Music Co.

1ST NUTRIENTS - Food products - Ultra Life

1ST PRIORITY - Apparel–children's - RSK Industries, Inc.

1ST PUR! - Bags - Flying Tigers Assn., Inc.
1ST RESPONSE - Knives - Taylor Cutlery Co.
1ST SELECTION - Fabrics–tapestry - Comark Wallcoverings
1ST STEP - Hand cleaning preparations - Sherman Pharmaceuticals, Inc.
1ST SURPRISE - Dolls - Mattel, Inc.
1ST TEAM - Footwear - Angel-Etts of California, Inc.
1ST TECH - Computer peripheral equipment - 1st Tech Corp.
1ST TRACK - Computer software - Ageless Software Co.
1ST WINNER'S CIRCLE - Brushes - Champion Brush, Inc.
1ST WORD - Computer software - Atari Games Corp.
1STBASE - Computer software - 1st Desk Systems, Inc.
1XCEL - Medical apparatus - One Xcel, Inc.
1XTNG CAM - Tools - Cepco Tool Co.
2 - Baby foods - Ralston Purina Co.
02 - Smoke detectors - Generation II Smoke Detector Inc.
2-1 - Toys - Goldberger Doll Manufacture Co.
2-1 FORMULA - Spot remover compound - R.R. Street & Co. Inc.
2 + 2 - Skin care products - Backscratchers, Inc.
2 3 4 5 - Apparel and accessories - Peggy Ann Lee
2-4-1 - Electronic equipment - Signal Transformer Co., Inc.
2-4-1 - Gloves - Midwest Glove Co.
2-ALARM CHILI SEASONING MIX - Food products - Reily Foods
2 BADD - Bicycles ☆ - Huffy Corp.
2-BARREEL - Food products - Jardine's Texas Foods
2-BOND-2 - Archery equipment - Saunders Archery Co.
2-CALORIE QUEST - Beverages–carbonated - Joseph E. Seagram & Sons, Inc.
2 CHEFS BRAND - Oils–edible - Sovrana Trading Corp.
2-COL-A-PAD - Stamps–hand ☆ - Eaton Allen Ko-Rec-Type Corp.
2 CREEMY - Candy - Stanico, Inc.
2-CYCLE - Oils–lubricating - Castrol, Inc.
2-CYCLE MOLY - Lubricants - Pacific Lubricants
2 CYCLES - Golfing equipment - Graman USA Inc.
2-D - Pet products ☆ - Penn-Plax, Inc.
2-D RIDER - Greeting cards - Curtis Randolph and Steven Randolph Partnership
2-DEX - Telephone directories - The Union Group
2-FEES - Candy - Standard Candy Co. Inc.
2 FROOTY - Candy - Stanico, Inc.
2/G - Pharmaceutical preparations - Marion Merrell Dow
2 GOOD - Golfing equipment - Tommy Armour Golf Co.
2 GOOD - Tortillas - Recot, Inc.
2 HIP - Apparel stores–children's - Just for Wraps, Inc.
2-HOUR - Patterns–clothing - Mccall Pattern Co.
2 HR WEED ERASER - Herbicides - Security Products Co.
2 IN 1 - Automotive parts and accessories - G.H. Meiser & Co.
2 IN 1 - Cigarette paper - Republic Tobacco L.P.
2-IN-1 - Pet collars - Hartz Mountain Corp.
2-IN-1 - Rope - Samson Cordage Works
2-IN-1 PLUS - Pet collars - Hartz Mountain Corp.
2 IN 1'S - Clothing - CPC (Aztec)
2 IN ONE - Deodorizers - Surco Products Inc.
2-J - Recording label ☆ - Ozark Opry Records
2 LEES SQUARED - Floor coverings–carpet and rugs - Burlington Industries, Inc.
2 LIVE CREW, THE - Compact discs–prerecorded - Chinaman Enterprises
2 MINUTE MAGIC - Skin care products - Dorothy Gray Cosmetics Ltd.
2-MINUTE NAIL ICING - Skin care products ☆ - Gefden International Inc.
2-N-1 - Bowling balls - 2-N-1 Grip Inc.
2 'N 1 - Pens - K-9 Pen Co.
2 'N 1 - Screw drivers ☆ - Channellock, Inc.
2 NAZTY - Recording label - Down Payment Records, Inc.
2 OZ. - Apparel and accessories ☆ - Glamorise Foundations Inc.
2 OZ. CRIPPLED HERRING - Fishing tackle - Luhr Jensen & Sons, Inc.
2-PLEX - Embossing machines - New Hermes Inc.
2 + 4 - Automotive parts and accessories - Outboard Marine Corp.
2 PLUS - Food products - Nanci Corp. International
2+1 - Cosmetics - Sebastian International, Inc.
2-PLY - Adhesives and sealants - Woodtape Co.
2.5 - Apparel and accessories - Wemco, Inc.
2-SPEED GRIPPERS - Toy cars - Intex Recreation Corp.
2 STAGE - Chairs–plastic - Evenflo Juvenile Furniture Co.
2-STEP - Housewares - A-Step Products Inc.
2 STICKS - Wallcovering - 2 Sticks Manufacturing
2 TABLE - Drafting supplies - Martin Universal Design Inc.
2 TANTALIZING PUZZLES - Puzzles - Binary Arts Corp.

2 TEMP - Hardware - Black & Decker Corp.
2-THIOCURACIL - Pharmaceutical preparations - City Chemical Corp.
2-TIME WORLD CHAMPION - Food products - Milnot Co.
2 TO GO - Paint rollers ☆ - Bestt-Liebco
2 TO GO! - Sandwiches–prepackaged ☆ - J.T.M. Provisions Co.
2-TON - Adhesive - Devcon Consumer Products (ITW Devcon)
2-TONE - Dental compounds - Lorvic Corp.
2-WAY GREEN POWER - Fertilizers - Greenview Lawn & Garden Products
2 WAY TRAINER - Infant product - Century Products Co.
II WAY TUFF SLIDER - Bedding–linen ☆ - Atwell Industries Inc.
2-WAY WINTER GREEN - Fertilizers - Greenview Lawn & Garden Products
2-XL - Toys ☆ - Mego Financial Corp.
2A TO A DEGREE - Apparel–men's - Frederick W. Welch
2B! - Hats - 2B! Worldwide Productions
2X4 - Candy bars - Standard Candy Co. Inc.
2C - Pens - Zebra Pen Corp.
2CD - Computer hardware - 2CD-ROM, LLC
2D-AIMS - Computer software - GX Technology L.P.
IIDA - Banjos - Kaman Music Corp.
2FOR1.COM - Advertising agencies - Unlimited Card Corp.
2G/DM - Pharmaceutical preparations - Marion Merrell Dow
2H - Jewelry - Two Hands, Inc.
2ND CENTURY - Fans–electric ☆ - Hunter Fan Co.
2ND CENTURY ORIGINAL - Fans–electric - Hunter Fan Co.
2ND DEGREE, THE - Thermometers - Zelco Industries, Inc.
2ND FLEET - Games - Avalon Hill Game Co.
2ND FOODS - Juices - Gerber Products Co.
2ND GLOVE - Skin care products - A to Z Marketing, Inc.
2ND NAIL - Manicure preparations - Max Factor & Co.
2ND SKIN - Gel dressing - Spenco Medical Corp.
2+2 - Refrigerators - Amana Refrigeration Inc.
2R - Tables–wood - Domore/DO3
2TEK - Musical instruments - 2tek Corp.
2TONE MFG. - Apparel and accessories - 2 Tone Manufacturing Co.
2X5 - Computer peripheral equipment - Videomedia, Inc.
2XS - Electronic equipment - AudioControl
2XTNG CAM - Tools - Cepco Tool Co.
3 - Baby foods - Ralston Purina Co.
3 - Vases - Lladro USA, Inc.
3-2-1 CONTACT: WILD THINGS - Games - Children's Television Workshop
3/4 TIME - Clocks - Largely Literary Designs, Inc.
3/4 WEED - Rackets–tennis - Weed USA Inc.
3/4 XL-125 - Rackets–tennis - Weed USA Inc.
3 ALARM FIRE - Snack foods ☆ - Reser's Fine Foods Inc.
3 & 1 - Hardware - Barrett Varnish Co.
3 & 1 TRI-STAR SPINDLE BEARING PULLER - Tools–hand-operated - Charles E. Vanbibber
3 BAGS BY MEE - Travel bags - Marlene Mee
3 BALLOONS - Computer software ☆ - Knowledge Adventure
3 BIOLOGICAL RECOVERY CONCENTRATE - Vitamin and mineral supplement - Genesis 2000 Biologic Systems, Inc.
3 BLIND MICE - Games - International Gamco, Inc.
3-BUTTON POWER - Computer software - Mouse Systems Corp.
3-C - Food products - Clement Pappas and Co.
3 C - Recording label - Continental Communications Corp.
3 CARAT LOOK - Jewelry - Sterling Inc.
3 CASTLES - Tobacco–chewing or smoking - James B. Russell Inc.
3 CHEERS - Footwear ☆ - R.G. Barry Corp.
3 COUNT BOUT - Video games - Snk Corp. of America
3-D - Cleaning preparations - Harley Chemicals
3-D - Detergents - Big Star Food Stores
3-D - Mattresses - Vinyl Products
3-D - Paints - Sherwin-Williams Automotive Finishes Corp.
3-D - Pet products ☆ - Penn-Plax, Inc.
3-D ACCUSCAN - Medical apparatus - Implantech Associates, Inc.
3-D BLUE - Ammunition - 3-D Investment, Inc.
3-D CLASSIC COMICS - Books–comic - Determined Productions, Inc.
3-D EMBOSSED SCULPTURE PRINT - Shirts - Artwear, Inc.
3 D EYEWITNESS - Designware, Inc.
3-D HOMETOWN COLLECTION - Puzzles - Warren Industries Inc.
3-D JUNGLE TRAIN - Computer software ☆ - Knowledge Adventure
3-D LUX BY MARK SCHNEIDER - Computer software - Ventura Educational Systems
3 D OCR - Computer software - Caere Corp.
3-D OFFICE - Computer software - Designware, Inc.
3-D ONE SHOT - Cleaning preparations - ATM America Corp.

☆ = Now out of production

3-D POOL - Computer software ☆ - Microprose Software, Inc.
3-D POPS - Candy ☆ - Nellson Candies Inc.
3-D SENSATION - Games - THQ Inc.
3-D YARN ART - Hobby kits ☆ - Revell-Monogram, Inc.
III DAY MBA - Computer software - Executive Conversation, Inc.
3 DAYS OF PEACE & MUSIC - Posters - Woodstock Ventures LC
3 DIAMONDS - Food products - Mitsubishi Foods
3 DIMENSIONAL - Hair care products - Helene Curtis Industries Inc.
3 DIMENSIONS II - Wallpaper ☆ - Pickhardt & Siebert USA Inc.
3 DOT - Apparel and accessories - Indiana Knitwear Corp.
3-DROP - Sweeteners–artificial ☆ - Mid-America Chemical Co.
3 FLAGS - Food products - Vegetable Growers Supply Co.
3 FLOWERS BRILLANTINE - Hair care products - Warner-Wellcome
3-FOLD - Stools–metal - Cosco, Inc.
3 FOR 1 - Paints - Dean and Barry Co.
3 FOR ME - Games - Patch Products, Inc.
3 FOR THE ROAD - Cookies - Interstate Brands Corp.
3 FT. 6 PAK - Computer storage devices–optical - Sirius Publishing, Inc.
3 G MERMET - Blinds–vertical - Vertical Blind Factory
3 G RECORDS - Recording label - Ichiban Records, Inc.
3 GREAT FOODS - Cat food - CC Pollen Co.
3 G'S - Recording label - 3 G's Industries Inc.
3 HOUR - Paints - Eaglo Paint & Varnish Corp.
3-HOUR - Patterns–clothing - Mccall Pattern Co.
3 IN 1 - Brooms - M.B. Walton, Inc.
3-IN-1 - Chemical preparations - Personal Safety Corp.
3-IN-1 - Coffee - Handee International
3-IN-1 - Cosmetics - Ladyfingers
3 IN 1 - Hair care products ☆ - Capitol Novelty Co.
3 IN 1 - Health care products ☆ - Grandpa Brands Co.
3-IN-1 - Pet products ☆ - Helmac Products Corp.
3-IN-1 - Rustproofing compounds - WD-40 Co.
3-IN-1 BRUSH - Makeup brush ☆ - Cosrich Inc.
3-IN-1 FLIPPIT DOLL - Dolls - Kappelerhof Trading (USA), Inc.
3 IN 1 JOB-SITE - Buckets–plastic - Hometown Advantage, Inc.
3-IN-1 TOON CAR - Toys - Mattel, Inc.
3 IN 1 VERI TOOL - Screw drivers - Alexander Manufacturing Co.
3-IN-ONE - Bathroom fixtures - Moen Inc.
3-IN-ONE - Cleaning preparations–household - Boyle-Midway
3-IN-ONE - Printers–computer - Toshiba America Information Systems, Inc.
3-IN-ONE - Wall-mounted brackets and hangrods - Capital Hardware Inc.
3 ISLANDS - Wines - Meier's Wine Cellars Inc.
3 ISLANDS - Wines - Paramount Distillers Inc.
3-KING GINSENGS CAPSULES - Teas - Prestige Chinese Teas Co.
3-KING GINSENGS TEA - Teas - Prestige Chinese Teas Co.
3-LIEVE - Apparel and accessories - Lemelle, Becerra and Johnson
3-M BEAUTY MARK - Hair care products - Fromm Industries
3-M STRIPS - Adhesives and sealants - Phil Marano Inc.
3-MINUTE - Cleaning preparations - Fast Industries, Inc.
3-MINUTE - Popcorn - National Oats Co. Inc.
3 MINUTE MIRACLE - Hair care products - Redmond Products, Inc.
3 MINUTE OATS - Cereal ☆ - Agway Country Foods Inc.
3 MIX COMBI - Kitchen appliances ☆ - Robert Krups North America
3 MUSKETEERS - Candy bars - Mars, Inc.
3 N 1 - Brush - Morris-Flamingo Inc.
3 NUNS - Tobacco–chewing or smoking - James B. Russell Inc.
3 O'CLOCK FOOD BARS - Candy bars - Richard B. Hill
3 O'CLOCK SOCK - Apparel and accessories - Douglas K. Winzeler and C.S. Collier Partnership
3 ON 3 - Apparel–athletic - Nancy Kahn Designs, Inc.
3-PACK - Brakes–locomotive - Mosebach Manufacturing Co.
3 PHASE - Building materials - North American Green, Inc.
3 PLEXXX - Golfing equipment - Ram Golf Corp.
3-POINT - Sporting goods - Porter Athletic Equipment Co.
3 POUNDER - Pizzas–frozen - Nazzio's Corp.
3 PUTT-SNAKE - Flags - Swing Tips, Inc.
3 RAMS - Cleavers - Darwell Import Co. Inc.
3 R'S - Apparel–women's - Zebulon Manufacturing Inc.
III SETS - Apparel–women's - Sport Chalet Inc.
3 SHAPE HAN-SAN - Tools ☆ - Ali Industries, Inc.
3 STAR - Seafood products–canned or cured - Gulf Food Products Co.
3 STAR CLASSIC - Mirrors ☆ - Colonial Mirror and Glass Corp.
3-STEP - Artists' materials - Logan Graphic Products Inc.
3-STEP - Binders - The Union Group
3 STRIKES - Apparel and accessories - 3 Strikes Custom Design USA
3-T - Hardware - Dowman Products

3 THREE CENTURY DESIGNS - Greeting cards - Pre-Emptive Products, Inc.
3 TIMES EASIER TO PUNCH! - Office supplies - Acco World Corp.
3-TOT ROCKER - Rocking chairs - Flexible Flyer Co.
3-VU ART - Artists' materials - Scratch-Art Co., Inc.
3-WAY - Paints - Nowstar
3 WAY CALCIUM COMPLEX - Dietary supplements - Life Services Supplements, Inc.
3 WAY PACK - Luggage - Luggage America Inc.
3-WAY SUPREME - Food products - Varallo Foods Inc.
3-WAY THREADRAK - Thread - June Tailor Inc.
3-WAY VAC - Vacuum cleaners and accessories - Bissell Inc.
3-WINDOW '34 - Toys–automobiles - Mattel, Inc.
3 WISE GUYS - Greeting cards - Expressions in the Spirit
3-X - Pet products - Happy Jack, Inc.
3BALL - Computer peripherals - Polhemus Inc.
3BC - Computer software - Integrated Credit Services
3C-TV - Video cameras ☆ - Olympus America Inc.
3COM - Computer software - 3Com Corp.
3D - Diving vests - Sea Quest, Inc.
3D - Laser scanners - 3D Technology, Inc.
3D - Maps - 3D Promotions, Inc.
3D ACOUSTICS - Amplifiers - Dahlquist Inc.
3D BIT STREAM - Compact disc players - Harman Kardon Inc.
3D BUILDER - Toys - Play Hut, Inc.
3D-CAL - Decals and transfers - Printmark Industries, Inc.
3D DESIGN PLUS - Computer software - Computer Easy International, Inc.
3D/EYE - Computer software - 3D/Eye, Inc.
3D F/X - Computer software - Asymetrix Corp.
3D FX - Cameras - Image Technology International, Inc.
3D HOME ARCHITECT - Computer software - Broderbund Software, Inc.
3D HUT - Department stores - David R. Shymatta
3D MAGIC - Cameras - Image Technology International, Inc.
3D MAGIC PLUS - Cameras - Image Technology International, Inc.
3D MOVIE MAKER - Computer software - Microsoft Corp.
3D-O'S - Artists' materials - Scratch-Art Co., Inc.
3D REALMS ENTERTAINMENT - Computer software - Apogee Software Ltd.
3D-ROM - Computer storage devices–optical - 3D-Rom Multimedia, Inc.
3D-ROM - Recording label - 3D-Rom Multimedia, Inc.
3D STEREO POSTCARDS (GERMANY) - Postcards - Fotofolio Inc.
3D TRIO - Cameras - Image Technology International, Inc.
3D WIZARD - Photographic equipment ☆ - Image Technology International, Inc.
3DEYEWITNESS - Computer peripheral equipment - Designware, Inc.
3DG - Spectrometers - Hitachi Instruments, Inc.
3DLABS - Integrated circuits - 3Dlabs Inc.
3DMAGIC - Photographic equipment - Image Technology International, Inc.
3DO - Shirts - 3do Co.
3DPC - Computer software - Forte' Advanced Management Software, Inc.
3D'S - Snack foods - Recot, Inc.
3DSCOPE - Medical equipment - American Surgical Technologies Corp.
3DTTT - Computer software - SourceView Software International
3DV TECHNOLOGY - Computer software - 3DV Technology, Inc.
3G GRAPHICS - Publishing software - 3G Graphics, Inc.
3M - Abrasive products - Minnesota Mining & Manufacturing Co.
3M - Medical apparatus - Rockford Medical & Safety Co.
3M - Skin care products ☆ - Hess Hair Milk Laboratories Inc.
3M MAGIC BOW TYER - Hairpins - Ribbon Magic, Inc.
3M STAR BOW MAKER - Hairpins - Ribbon Magic, Inc.
3MUSKETEERS - Confections - Mars, Inc.
3NET - Computer software - 3Net Systems Inc.
3+1 - Housewares - Amana Refrigeration Inc.
3R - Roofing materials–slate - Colonial Refining and Chemical Co.
3RD & LONG - Recording label - 3rd & Long, Inc.
3RD DEGREE - Apparel–athletic - Sleeping Giants Promotions
3RD DIMENSION - Skin care products - J.K. Templeton Inc.
3RD FLEET - Games - Avalon Hill Game Co.
3RD GENERATION - Knives–pocket - Imperial Schrade Corp.
3RD GENERATION - Sunglasses - Sunny Days Marketing, Inc.
3RD MOBILE - Radios - Northeast Telecom, Inc.
3RD RAIL - Apparel–men's - Drummond Knitwear Ltd.
3V CAPS - Veterinary nutritional supplements - DVM Pharmaceuticals, Inc.
3X3 GENUINE CARPET SQUARES - Pulpboard - David Gordon Londagin
3XF - Petroleum ☆ - Shell Oil Co.
3XS - Electronic equipment - AudioControl
3XTWIN/2 - Computer software - Andrew Corp.

☆ = Now out of production

3XYCRO MICRO-FIBERS - Sports rackets and accessories - Wilson Sporting Goods Co.

3Z - Compost - Celite Corp.

4 - Apparel–athletic - Elaine Liss

4% - Beverages - 4% Co.

4-1 - Cleaning preparations–carpet and rug ☆ - Bissell Inc.

4 + 4 - Hair care products - Alberto-Culver Co.

4-4-1 - Lubricants ☆ - Gold Eagle Co.

4-5-6 PICK UP STICKS - Games - Lakeside Games

4 ALARM - Food products ☆ - S & W Fine Foods, Inc.

4-ALARM FIRE ENGINE - Toys - CBS Toys

4-ALLER-G - Pharmaceutical preparations - Vita-Fore Products Co.

4 BALLS - Candy ☆ - American Candy Co.

4 BIRDS - Pet products - Animal Lovers

4-BRASS - Sunglasses - Optica Italee

4-BROTHERS - Seafood products–fresh or frozen - Salasnek Fisheries Inc.

4 X 4 - Hunting equipment - Wildlife Research Center, Inc.

4 X 4 - Wheelchairs ☆ - X-L Manufacturing Co. Inc.

4 X 4 MAGNUM - Kites ☆ - Hi-Flier Manufacturing Co.

4 BY 5 - Apparel and accessories - Isaac Dean

4-C - Food products - 4C Foods Corp.

4 CATS - Cat food - Animal Lovers

4 CLASSIC HOOVES - Veterinary pharmaceutical preparations - Bee Natural Leathercare Co.

4-COLORFUL - Glassware–household ☆ - Himark Enterprises Inc.

4 COMFORT - Footwear - H.H. Brown Shoe Co., Inc.

4 COMFORT CUSHION TECH SYSTEM - Footwear ☆ - H.H. Brown Shoe Co., Inc.

4-CYTE - Games - McGraw-Hill Companies, Inc.

4-D OPTICS - Lenses–optical - New Wave Partners, Inc.

4 DELTA FOUR - Filters–oil - Water Distribution Systems

4 DIRTY PAWS - Pet products - Doggone Pet Products

4 DOGS - Pet products - Animal Lovers

4 EDGE - Scrapers - Allway Tools Inc.

4 EVER CLEAR - Skin-care products - Tiro Industries, Inc.

4 FERRETS - Pet products - Animal Lovers

4-FISHERMEN - Seafood products–fresh or frozen ☆ - Gorton Group

4 FOOD - Apparel and accessories - Split Tee, Inc.

4 FOR 4 - Apparel and accessories - George W. Lamping

IV GEORGE - Apparel–women's - Jean St. Germain, Inc.

4-HAIR - Hair care products - Marlyn Co. Inc.

4 HER 2 - Shirts - Buffalo, Inc.

4-HI - Electronic equipment ☆ - H. Wilson Co.

4-HOUR - Cough medicines - Dorsey Laboratories

4-HOUR - Patterns–clothing - Mccall Pattern Co.

4 HOUR 4 EVERY-WEAR - Paints - Cloverleaf Paint & Varnish

4 HR - Varnishes ☆ - H. Behlen & Bro. Inc.

4 IN 1 - Brushes - Mill Rose Co.

4 IN 1 - File folders - Gussco Manufacturing Inc.

4-IN-1 - Finishing agents - Dial Corp.

4 IN 1 - Mats - New Pendulum Corp.

4 IN 1 - Paints - United States Refining Co.

4-IN-1 - Projection screens - Brumberger Co. Inc.

4-IN-1 - Screw drivers - Allway Tools Inc.

4-IN-1 BUSY ACTIVITY CENTER - Toys - Playskool, Inc.

4-IN-1 SYSTEM - Infant product - Century Products Co.

4-IN-ONE - Snack products - Reser's Fine Foods Inc.

4 LAKES - Labels–paper - Four Lakes Label & Printing Co. Inc.

4-MAX - Tires - Carlisle Tire & Rubber Co.

4-MIN - Adhesives and sealants ☆ - Champion International Corp.

4-N-1 - Percussion-instrument accessory - Mike Balter Mallets

4 'N 1 - Screw drivers ☆ - Channellock, Inc.

4-NAILS - Nail care products - Marlyn Co. Inc.

4-O2 - Medical apparatus - Cal West Trading Inc.

4-PAC - Toys–trains - K-Line

4 PLAY - Novelty items - Barnetts Inc.

4 PLEX - Computer hardware - Plextor Corp.

4 PLUS - Trays - Packaging Corp. of America

4 PLUS POINT - Screws - Parker-Kalon Inc.

4 PLY QUATRO - Tissues - NPM Healthcare Products, Inc.

4 POINT 0 - Apparel and accessories - Roxbury Mills, Inc.

4-POINT GRAPHICS - Computer software ☆ - IMSI

4-POWER - Fuel additives - Conklin Co., Inc.

4-QUART - Cheese - Land O'Lakes Inc.

4 REEL - Footwear - Stride Rite Corp.

4 RENEGADE - Slacks–men's ☆ - Haggar Corp.

4 SALE - Window coverings - John M. Sanders

4-SEASONS - Controls–heating systems - Classic Corp.

4-SEASONS - Garden equipment - Teknor Apex Co.

4 SEASONS - Napkins–paper - Citrin-Pitoscia Co. Inc.

4 SECURITY - Cameras - Stanford Computer Optics Inc.

4 SQUARE INC. - Tubes–steel - 4 Square Inc.

4 STAGE - Chairs–plastic - Evenflo Juvenile Furniture Co.

4 STAR - Flowers, plants, and seeds - Proprietary Seeds, Inc.

4-SURE - Animal feeds - Carl S. Akey Inc.

4 SURE - Incontinence product - Boston and Pacific Medical Inc.

4 SURE - Infant product - Gerry Baby Products Co.

4 TEAS - Teas - Xcell International Corp.

4 THE BIRDS - Garden equipment - J.T. Eaton and Co.

4 THE ROACH - Garden equipment - J.T. Eaton and Co.

4 THE SQUIRREL - Garden equipment - J.T. Eaton and Co.

4 VALVE - Automotive parts and accessories - Fueling Engineering Inc.

4-WAY - Cold remedies - Bristol-Myers Squibb Co.

4 WAY - Lubricants - Minnesota Mining & Manufacturing Co.

4 WAY - Nail care products - Claire Topper Enterprises

4 WAY - Skin care products - Sogo Inc.

4-WAY COMBO - Easels - House of Doolittle

4-WAY DOLL TENDER - Toys - Today's Kids Inc.

4 WAY STOP - Boots - Rocky Shoes & Boots, Inc.

4 WAY SUPER LUBE - Lubricants - ITW Fluid Products

4-X - Film - Eastman Kodak Co.

4X4 - Audio equipment - ADA Signal Processors Inc.

4X4 BAJA JEEP - Toys–automobiles - Tyco Toys

4X4 TUFF COVERS - Seat covers ☆ - Palsa Outdoor Products Inc.

4C+ - Goggles–safety - Uvex Safety LLC

4C - Soups and cheeses - 4C Foods Corp.

4CR - Computer software - Exide Electronics Group, Inc.

4CT - Goggles–safety - Uvex Safety LLC

4DTV - Digital encoders - Nextlevel Systems, Inc.

4FRONT - Computer software - Deloitte & Touche

4G - Apparel and accessories - Ray Strauss Unlimited Inc.

4H - Meat products–pork ☆ - J & B Sausage Co., Inc.

4H - Partitions–metal - Lumberlok

4I - Computer software - 4I Solutions Inc.

4J - Jewelry - Original Designs/Famor Inc.

4KIDZ - Balls - 4 Kidz, Inc.

4LW - Tools–hand-operated - American Tool Companies Inc.

4N6XPRT PED & BIKE CALCS - Computer software - 4n6xprt Systems

4N6XPRT SYSTEMS - Computer software - Daniel W. Vomhof

4RUNNER - Furnace - Goettl Air Conditioning Inc.

4RUNNER - Motor vehicles–sport-utility - Toyota Motor Sales USA Inc.

4SIGHT - Scientific apparatus - Teradyne, Inc.

4SITE - Computer software - 4I Solutions Inc.

4SUM - Sunblocks - Sunshine Health Group, Inc.

4TH & BROADWAY - Recording label - Island Records Inc.

4TH & INCHES - Computer software ☆ - Accolade Inc.

4TH MONKEY - Novelty items - Cal Themes Inc.

4TH QUARTER - Computer software - Braided Matrix Inc.

4U - Greeting cards - Avanti Press, Inc.

4U2C - Golfing equipment - 4u2c Inc.

4U2C - Sportswear - 4U2C Lifestyles Inc.

4UR-GAME - Apparel–athletic - William H. Eggers, Jr.

4X - Bacon ☆ - Fischer Packing Co.

4X PATENT - Fibers–cellulose ☆ - Pillsbury Co.

4X4 - Footwear - H.H. Brown Shoe Co., Inc.

4XS - Electronic equipment - AudioControl

5-7-9 - Apparel–women's - Edison Brothers Stores, Inc.

5:18 SPECIAL, THE - Floor coverings–carpet and rugs ☆ - Hollytex Carpet Mills Inc.

5 BEST - Candy ☆ - Brock Candy Co. Inc.

5 BLADER, THE - Fans–electric ☆ - Aluminum Co. of America

5 BRANCHES - Vitamins and nutritional supplements - Ethical Nutrients

5 D - Fruits and vegetables - Shafer Lake Fruit Inc.

5-D - Paper products - Hartford House, Ltd.

5-D MYSTIGRAPHICS - Greeting cards - Blue Mountain Arts Inc.

5-D STEREOGRAMS - Greeting cards - Blue Mountain Arts Inc.

5 EASY PIECES - Cookie bars ☆ - Intersweet Candy Inc.

5 GRAND - Candy - Leaf, Inc.

5-HYDROXYTRYPTOPHAN - Vitamins and nutritional supplements - Vitamin Research Products Inc.

5-IN-1 - Animal feeds - Menu Foods Inc. Cadillac Foods Div.

5-IN-1 - Cleaning preparations–carpet and rug - HMI Industries Inc.

☆ = Now out of production

5-MINUTE - Cleaning preparations ☆ - Bissell Inc.

5-MINUTE - Epoxy adhesive - Devcon Consumer Products (ITW Devcon)

5 MINUTE DETAILER - Waxes–sealing - Eagle One Industries

5 MINUTE FRAME - Playground equipment - Wonderline

5 MINUTE MOTOR FLUSH - Cleaning preparations - Gold Eagle Co.

5 MINUTE PURSE - Handbags ☆ - Mats Etc. Inc.

5 NR - Automotive parts and accessories - Bridgestone/Firestone, Inc.

5 OF THE BEST - Publisher's imprints - Cherry Lane Music Co. Inc.

5 ON 5 - Video games now out of production - Konami (America) Inc.

5-PT. - Seats–automobile - Cosco, Inc.

5 SATIS-5 - Figurines - Satis-5 Merchandise Inc.

5-SECOND - Adhesives and sealants - International Beauty Design, Inc.

5 SOMES - Candy - Leaf, Inc.

5 SPRINGS - Water–bottled or canned ☆ - Hinckley & Schmitt (Bottled Water Group)

5-STAR - Barbecue sauce - Jardine's Texas Foods

5 STAR - Detergents - Five Star Chemical Corp.

5 STAR - Frozen foods - Five Star Frozen Foods, Inc.

5-STAR - Musical instrument accessories - Stewart-MacDonald Manufacturing

5-STAR - Pans - Wilton Industries, Inc.

5-STAR - Seafood products–canned or cured ☆ - Tampa Maid Seafoods, Inc.

5-WAY - Electrical equipment - Warner Electric/Superior Electric

5-WAY - Lamps - Ever-Ready Co.

5-WAY - Paints - Nowstar

5A - Tape–adhesive - Arlon, Inc.

5B - Projectors–photographic - Star Parts Inc.

5F5 - Paint removers - Sterling-Clark-Lurton Corp.

5FT. 10 PAK - Computer peripheral equipment - Sirius Publishing, Inc.

5G - Display cases–plastic - Hamilton Fixture Co.

5HTP - Vitamins and nutritional supplements - M.M.R.C., Ltd. Co.

5.0 FIVE LITER WEAR - Apparel and accessories - William R. Turpin

5TH AVENUE - Beverages–carbonated - L and A Juice Co. Inc.

5TH AVENUE - Boats–houseboats ☆ - Holiday Mansion

5TH AVENUE - Skin care products ☆ - Christine Valmy, Inc.

5TH AVENUE BAR - Candy - Luden's Inc.

5TH AVENUE DESIGNS - Wallpaper - Covington Fabrics Corp.

5TH FLEET - Games - Avalon Hill Game Co.

5TH SEASON - Spices and extracts - McCormick & Co., Inc.

5TH WHEEL - Racks - Fifth Wheel Co.

5W34T - Apparel and accessories - Lloyd M. Hughes Enterprises, Inc.

5XPRESS - Computer software - At&T Corp.

5XXXXX BEAVER QUALITY - Hats - W. Alboum Hat Co., Inc.

6-12 - Insecticides ☆ - D-Con Co. Inc.

6-40 - Disinfectants - Hilex Co.

6 X 6 HIGH RISERS - Toys - CBS Toys

6 X 6 SEEKER - Toys - CBS Toys

6 DAY - Primers - X-I-M Products Inc.

6 IMMORTALS - Vitamins and nutritional supplements - Ethical Nutrients

6-IN-1 - Animal feeds - Menu Foods Inc. Cadillac Foods Div.

6 IN 1 - Food products - Escalon Frozen Foods

6-IN-1 - Publisher's imprints - Matthew Bender & Co., Inc.

6 IN 1 - Toys ☆ - Tradis Inc.

6 'N 1 - Hair care products - One Bottle Products Inc.

6-N-1 - Pharmaceutical preparations - Holistic Laboratories Inc.

6-PAKS - Beverages ☆ - Hawkhaven Greenhouse Int'l.

6 TILE - Clay–firebrick - Dry Branch Kaolin Co.

6-WAY - Hair spray - Lori Davis Hair, Inc.

6-WHEELERS - Toys - Tonka Corp.

6IX - Fibers–synthetic - BASF Corp.

6K - Locks, keys, etc. - Best Lock Corp.

6PLEX - Computer hardware - Plextor Corp.

6+PLUS - Transmissions–motor vehicle - Navistar International Transportation Corp.

6TH AVENUE - Recording label - RCA Records

6TH FLEET - Games - Avalon Hill Game Co.

6:1 MOTOR LIFT - Brackets - General Boats Corp.

6.0V JET TURBO - Toys–automobiles - Tyco Industries, Inc.

7 - Jewelry - 7th Sense Inc.

7-11 - Floor coverings–carpet and rugs ☆ - Karastan-Bigelow Inc.

7-11 - Insecticides - Cenol Co. Inc.

7-11 - Pencils - Dur-O-Lite Inc.

7/11 - Tomato pastes and sauces - Stanislaus Food Products Co.

7-11 POOL PRODUCTS - Swimming pools - 7-11 Pool Products

7/14 - Contact lenses - O.S.I. Corp.

7:45 - Toothpaste - Mark Allen Co.

7-ACRES - Aquariums–household - Willinger Bros., Inc.

7-ACRES - Pet products ☆ - Tetra Sales USA

7 BELLO - Tiles–ceramic - Federal Tile Imports Inc.

7 BELOW - Golfing equipment - Sports Coolers Unlimited, Inc.

7 CALORIE CANDY, THE - Candy - Golden Apples Candy Co., Inc.

7-CLEANING PREPARATIONS - Cleaning preparations - Armor All Products Corp.

7 CROWN - Whiskey - House of Seagram

7-DAY MOISTURIZER - Hair care products ☆ - Roberts Research Laboratories, Inc.

7 DAY PERM - Hair care products ☆ - Roberts Research Laboratories, Inc.

7 DAY PILL REMINDER - Boxes - Bridge Plastics Co.

7 EAST - Footwear - Lee International Ltd.

7-ELEVEN - Convenience stores - Southland Corp.

7-FARMS - Food products - S.M. Flickinger Co. Inc.

7-FARMS - Food products - Tyler & Simpson Co.

7-FLEX - Cables - MacWhyte Co.

7-FOOTER - Socks - Wigwam Mills Inc.

7 GRAIN HERB - Breads - Natural Ovens of Manitowoc Inc.

7-GRAIN STONE-WHEAT - Crackers - Health Valley Food

7-GRAINERS - Crackers - Auburn Farms, Inc.

7 IN 1 - Cleaning preparations - Kent Investment Corp.

7 IN 1 SMOKER - Cooking equipment–household - Masterbuilt Manufacturing, Inc.

7 IN 7 - Office furniture–plastic - Domore/DO3

7 MAG - Coatings - Merix Chemical Co.

7 O'CLOCK - Handbags - 7's Enterprises, Inc.

7 POWERS CHAKRAS, THE - Jewelry - Victor Flores Designs

7 SHORES - Seafood products–fresh or frozen - International Pacific Seafoods, Inc.

7 SISTERS OF NEW ORLEANS - Cleaning preparations–household - Indio Products, Inc.

7 STAR - Flowers, plants, and seeds - Proprietary Seeds, Inc.

7 UP - Beverages–carbonated - Dr. Pepper/Seven Up, Inc.

7 UP - Ice cream - Eskimo Pie Corp.

7-UP - Key rings ☆ - Gift Creations, Inc.

7-UP - Watches - Western Watches International

7 UP GOLD - Beverages–carbonated ☆ - Dr. Pepper/Seven Up, Inc.

7-UP SPOT - Toys–stuffed ☆ - Commonwealth Toy and Novelty Co. Inc.

7 VALLEYS - Pet products - United Pacific Packers

7 WONDERS - Health care products - Century Systems Inc.

7 YEAR BITCH - Apparel and accessories - 7 Year Bitch

7BY24 - Publisher's imprints - T-Squared, Inc.

7MXS - Skis - Rossignol Ski Co., Inc.

7TH AVENUE - Apparel and accessories ☆ - Wemco, Inc.

7TH DAY - Skin care products ☆ - Molina International

7TH DIMENSION - Hair care products - Zotos International Inc.

7TH FLEET - Games - Avalon Hill Game Co.

7TH GUEST, THE - Games - Virgin Interactive Entertainment, Inc.

7TH INNING STRETCH - Computer software - Kroftware

7TH LEVEL - Computer software - 7th Level, Inc.

7TH ON SIXTH - Apparel and accessories - Seventh on Sixth, Inc.

7TH SAGA II, THE - Video games - Enix America Corp.

7TH STAGE - Hair care products - Clairol Inc.

7TH STREET STOUT - Beverages–alcohol - Riverside Brewing Co.

7UP - Chewing gum ☆ - Amurol Confections Co.

8-1-8 - Pet products - Rael Co.

8 BAL - Watches - I.D. Enterprises

8-HOUR - Cosmetics - Revlon Consumer Products Corp.

8-IN-1 - Infant product - Small World Toys

8 IN 1 - Pet products - 8 in 1 Pet Products Inc.

8 MATE - Projection screens ☆ - Buhl Optical Co.

:08 MIN. - Recording label - Telamerica Media Inc.

8 OZ. TUB O' FUN - Cheese - Brackman Brothers, Inc.

8 PAK BRAND - Packaging–foam - Free-Flow Packaging Corp.

8-SERIES - Motor vehicles–automobiles - BMW of North America Inc.

8 TREASURES - Vitamins and nutritional supplements - Ethical Nutrients

8-WAY - Water treating compounds - Stewart-Hall Chemical Corp.

8D8 - Toys - Lucasfilm Ltd.

9 - Eveready Battery Co., Inc.

9-1-1 - Apparel and accessories ☆ - Unitog Co.

9-1-1 - First aid kits ☆ - Rydelle Laboratories Inc.

9-1-1 - Golfing equipment - Hillerich & Bradsby Co.

9-2-5 COLLECTION, THE - Footwear–women's - J.C. Penney Co., Inc.

9 2 8 TO - Apparel and accessories - Oxford Industries, Inc.

9 18 - Apparel and accessories - La Mode Inc.

9 & CO. - Handbags - Nine West Group Inc.

☆ = Now out of production

9-GRAIN - Pretzels ☆ - Barbara's Bakery, Inc.
9-LIVES - Cat food - Heinz Pet Products Co.
9-LIVES CRUNCHY MEALS - Cat food - Heinz Pet Products Co.
9-LIVES MEATY MORSELS - Pet food ☆ - Star-Kist Foods, Inc.
9-LIVES TENDER MEALS - Cat food - Heinz Pet Products Co.
9 PUTTS PERFECT - Toys - G.M. Inc.
9 TO 5 - Apparel stores–lingerie ☆ - Formfit Rogers
9 TO 5 - Dolls - Mattel, Inc.
9 TO 5 - Lunch boxes ☆ - Aladdin Industries, Inc.
9 TO 5 TYPING - Computer software - Epyx Inc.
9 WEST - Shoes - Fisher Camuto Corp.
9A - Tape–adhesive - Arlon, Inc.
9FX - Computer peripheral equipment - Number Nine Visual Technology Corp.
9FX VISION - Computer peripheral equipment - Number Nine Visual Technology Corp.
9GXE - Computer software - Number Nine Visual Technology Corp.
9K - Dinnerware–glass ☆ - Cyclamen Studio
9K - Locks and keys - Best Lock Corp.
9MM - Insecticides - Loveland Industries, Inc.
9V - Steel - Crucible Materials Corp.
10 - Nail care products - Allercare Inc.
10-0 TEN-O - Apparel–women's - GMR Gymnastics Sales Inc.
10-1 - Pet products - Tomlyn Products
10-4 - Floor coverings–carpet and rugs ☆ - Karastan-Bigelow Inc.
10-10 - Lighting equipment - Gam Products, Inc.
10/11 AGAINST THE VIOLENCE - Broadcasting stations–television - Busse Broadcasting Corp.
10-20 - Filters–industrial - Gam Products, Inc.
10-20 - Sporting goods - Jeff Ellis & Associates, Inc.
10/22 - Rifles - Sturm, Ruger & Co., Inc.
10-30 - Lighting equipment - Gam Products, Inc.
10-40 - Filters–industrial - Gam Products, Inc.
10-50 - Lighting equipment - Gam Products, Inc.
10-55 - Filters–industrial - Gam Products, Inc.
10-60 - Filters–industrial - Gam Products, Inc.
10-70 - Lighting equipment - Gam Products, Inc.
10-75 - Filters–industrial - Gam Products, Inc.
10-90 - Filters–industrial - Gam Products, Inc.
10 DAY BOUQUET - Chemical preparations - Abbott Laboratories
10 DAY MIXTURE - Flowers, plants, and seeds - Seed Corp. of America
10 DAY SHINE - Nail care products - Del Pharmaceuticals, Inc.
10-E-C - Food products - Pitsweet Inc.
10-FOR-1 - Pet products - Lambert-Kay
10 HOUR - Insecticides - Tec Laboratories, Inc.
10-HOUR INSECT REPELLENT, THE - Insecticides - Zebra Books/Kensington Corp.
10 IN 1 MULTI-TOOL - Tools–hand-operated - Sun Metal Products, Inc.
10-K - Beverages - Suntory Water Group. Inc.
10-K - Water–mineral - Kentwood Spring Water
10-K PLUS - Beverages - Suntory Water Group. Inc.
10-K THIRST QUENCHER - Fruit drinks–bottled or canned - 10-K Thirst Quencher
10 MIN. INSTRUMENT DISINFECTANT - Disinfectants - Ultronics
10 MINUTE HAIR CLOG REMOVER - Cleaning preparations - Enforcer Products Inc.
10 N - Musical instrument accessories - Westheimer Corp.
10 PARK - Shoes - Montgomery Ward & Co. Inc.
10 PERCENT PRODUCTIONS - Greeting cards - Nimer Business Development, Inc.
10 POINT MONITOR - Electronic equipment - Flight Systems, Inc.
10-POINT POSTURE CONTROL - Chairs–upholstered - Bodybilt Seating
10-RING REST - Archery equipment - Martin Archery Inc.
10 SECOND - See START
10 SECOND - Cleaning preparations - Guardsman Products, Inc.
10 SECOND - Skin care products - Monaco Import/Export Inc.
10/SQUARE - Photographic equipment ☆ - Hudson Photographic Industries Inc.
10 STORAGE - Closet organizers - Windquest Companies, Inc.
10 TO 2 - Bathing suits - 10 to 2
10-YARD FIGHT - Video games - Taito America Corp.
10-YEAR - Paints ☆ - Frazee Paint
10B - Tape–adhesive - Arlon, Inc.
10C - Paper - Canson-Talens Inc.
10K - Apparel and accessories - Michael B. Gotfredson
10K - Apparel–athletic - Michael B. Gotfredson
10LW - Tools–hand-operated - American Tool Companies Inc.

10MAX - Tubes–steel - Trent Tube
10TH GEAR - Apparel–men's - Caldor Corp.
10V - Floor coverings–carpet and rugs - Playfield International Inc.
10W - Paper - Canson-Talens Inc.
10X - Apparel and accessories - Walls Industries, Inc.
11 - Shoes–athletic - L.A. Gear, Inc.
11-A - Boilers–hot water ☆ - Colonial Co.
11 MILLION BUSINESSES PHONE BOOK - Computer storage devices– optical - American Business Information, Inc.
11 UP - Game machines - Merit Industries, Inc.
11TH FINGER, THE - Surgical instruments - Guardian Angel Health Care Products, Inc.
11TH HOUR: THE SEQUEL TO THE 7TH GUEST, THE - Computer software - Virgin Interactive Entertainment, Inc.
12 - Chewing gum - Philadelphia Chewing Gum Corp.
12/4 SUPER DUCK - Coveralls - Walls Industries, Inc.
12/24 HEAVY TRUCK - Automotive parts and accessories - K & K Jump Start/ Chargers, Inc.
12-BAR TUNESMITH - Computer software - Electronic Courseware Systems Inc.
12 DAYS OF CHRISTMAS - Games - Universal Manufacturing Co., Inc.
12 GA - Glassware–household - Larry C. Cundieff
12 GAMES IN 1 - Games ☆ - Western Publishing Co., Inc.
12 HORSE - Beverages–malt ☆ - Genesee Brewing Co., Inc.
12-HOUR NASAL SPRAY - Cold remedies - Reese Chemical Co.
12 VOLT LIGHTS - Lighting equipment - Sign-Up Corp.
12-VOLTAIR - Compressors–air - Goertzen Enterprises
12AX7 WXT - Tubes–vacuum - New Sensor Corp.
12AX7WB - Tubes–vacuum - New Sensor Corp.
12TH MAN - Jewelry - Texas A&M University
12X - Lenses - Navitar, Inc.
13 DEAD END DRIVE - Games - Hasbro, Inc.
13 OZ. BLUES, THE - Fabrics - West Point-Pepperell Inc.
13 SPORT - Apparel and accessories - Bottom Line Images, Inc.
13MWZ - Apparel and accessories - Blue Bell, Inc.
13TH FLOOR - Apparel and accessories - Dave Parmley
13TH STREET - Apparel–women's - WS Adnil Inc.
14 GRAINS - Cereal ☆ - Barbara's Bakery, Inc.
14-IN-ONE - Tools - Penguin Industries, Inc.
14 KARAT BAR - Candy, nut and confectionery stores ☆ - Nellson Candies Inc.
14 KT. CELI - Jewelry - Celi Domenico Inc.
14 PLUS - Patterns–clothing ☆ - Mccall Pattern Co.
14K - Jewelry - Leach & Garner Co.
14K A, A - Jewelry - A. Alland Inc.
14K PLUS - Jewelry–precious - Dalow Industries, Inc.
14KUL - Jewelry - Ultimar Creations Inc.
1,4SIGHT - Chemical preparations - Di14, Inc.
14U - Computer software - Peopleware, Inc.
15 MINUTE COOKING TIME - Soups–mixes - Bri-AL, Inc.
15 PUZZLE - Puzzles ☆ - Milton Bradley Co.
15A PROP A - Fishing lures - Bomber Bait Co.
15V - Steel - Crucible Materials Corp.
16 - Shoes–athletic - L.A. Gear, Inc.
16-1 - Shampoos - K.C. Pharmacal Inc.
16/8 - Computers–personal - Xerox Corp.
16-32 - Sanders and grinders - Performax Products, Inc.
16 PAD - Steel wool - American Steel Wool Manufacturing Co. Inc.
16TH AVENUE - Recording label ☆ - Acuff-Rose Music Publishing, Inc.
17 MILE DRIVE - Giftware - Pebble Beach Co.
17 NORTH - Apparel–women's - WS Adnil Inc.
17X4 - Dental equipment - AFP Imaging Corp.
18 - Radios–citizens' band - Cobra Electronics Corp.
18 CARAT - Cleaning preparations - Chemed Corp.
18 CARET - Finishing agents ☆ - Calgon Vestal Laboratories
18 DANIEL - Stationery - Al-Dan Trading, Inc.
18 EZ STEP GOLF SHOES - Shoes - TSP of Manatee, Inc.
18 HOUR - Apparel and accessories - Playtex Apparel, Inc.
18 HOUR LIGHTS - Apparel and accessories - Playtex Apparel, Inc.
18 HOUR LOVELY LOOK - Brassieres (Bras) ☆ - Playtex Apparel, Inc.
18 VUE - Packaging–paper - Packaging Corp. of America
18 WATT GOLD - Lighting equipment - Trimble House Corp.
18I - Motor vehicles - Renault Inc.
18TH CENTURY - Cosmetics - May Cove Inc.
18TH CENTURY - Flatware - Reed and Barton Corp.
18TH CENTURY - Furniture - Three Mountaineers Inc.

☆ = Now out of production

18TH CENTURY - Health care products ☆ - Sunrise Medical
18TH CENTURY - Thread - Blumenthal/Lansing Co.
18TH CENTURY - Yarn - Lily Craft Products
18TH CENTURY EMPIRE - Furniture ☆ - Vaughan Furniture Co. Inc.
19 LTD II - Radio communications equipment - Cobra Electronics Corp.
19-P MIXTURE - Tobacco products - Shepherd Tobacco Co.
19 SHOT MACHINE GUN SHELL - Fireworks - B.J. Alan Co. Inc.
1.9L - Motor vehicles–automobiles - BMW of North America Inc.
19TH HOLE - Floor coverings–carpet and rugs - Burtco Enterprises Inc.
19TH HOLE - Floor coverings–carpet and rugs - Richmond Carpet Mills
19TH HOLE - Floor coverings–carpet and rugs ☆ - Porter Carpet Mills Inc.
19TH HOLE - Glassware–household - Ceraglass Inc.
19TH HOLE - Golfing equipment - Brandell Products, Inc.
19TH HOLE - Jewelry - Telux-Pioneer Inc.
19TH STREET - Recording label - Lorenz Creative Services Corp.
20 - Trading cards and stamps - AAA Sports Inc.
20/10 - Antifreeze - 20/10 Products, Inc.
20/20 - Archery equipment ☆ - Ranging Inc.
20/20 - Automotive parts and accessories ☆ - Midwest Sunroofs
20/20 - Cleaning preparations - Craftics Inc.
20/20 - Cleaning preparations–window - Sanitek Products Inc.
20/20 - Doors–metal - CDI Window Manufacturing
20/20+ - Electronics equipment - Ampex Corp.
20/20 - Eyeglasses ☆ - Sellstrom Manufacturing Co.
20-20 - Filters–industrial - Farr Co.
20/20 - Lamps–desk - Park Sherman
20/20 - Lubricants - Telios Pharmaceuticals Inc.
20/20 - Markers–felt-tip - Sanford Corp.
20/20 - Ophthalmic goods - S.S.S. Co.
20/20 - Shampoos - Giovanni Cosmetics Inc.
20/20 - Watches - Textron Inc.
20/20 COLLECTION - Watches ☆ - Hirsch Speidel Inc.
20-20 DIET CITRUS - Wines ☆ - Wine Group Inc.
20/20 EAR - Hearing aids ☆ - Beltone Electronics Corp.
20/30 COLLECTION - Apparel–men's - Mavest Inc.
20 BELOW - Foil–aluminum - KVP Group
20 % BREEDER RATION NIBBLETS - Animal feeds - Bluebonnet Milling Co.
20 CARATS - Perfumes ☆ - Dana Perfumes Corp.
20 GRAM DIET, THE - Publisher's imprints - Linx, Corp.
20 MINUTE WORKOUT - Exercising equipment - Australian Body Works
20 PLUS - Sealing compounds ☆ - Tec Inc.
20 SECOND - Insecticides - Enforcer Products Inc.
20-TEN - Electronics equipment - Grass Valley Group Inc.
20 TO 1 - Cleaning preparations - Viking Manufacturing Co. Inc.
20 WILD STALLIONS - Wines - Regent Champagne Cellars, Inc.
20TH CENTURY - Apparel–men's - Nulook Fashions Menswear Inc.
20TH CENTURY - Musical instruments ☆ - Fred Gretsch Enterprises
20TH CENTURY - Photo albums - 20th Century Plastics
20TH CENTURY BAROQUE - Flatware - Godinger Silver Art Ltd.
20TH CENTURY FARO - Computer software - Robert L. Nicolai
20TH CENTURY-FOX - Recording label - 20th Century-Fox Record Corp.
20TH CENTURY FOX - Video production - Twentieth Century Fox Film Corp.
20TH CENTURY FOX HOME ENTERTAINMENT - Recording label - Twentieth Century Fox Film Corp.
20TH TELEVISION - Video production - Twentieth Century Fox Film Corp.
21 - Beverages - McKesson Home Health Care
21 - Decals and transfers - Glen Wood Co. Corp.
21-1 PLUS - Skin care products - Pro-Capa Products Inc.
21 AGAIN - Medical apparatus - Innovative Medical Devices
21 C - Engine oil - Universal Motor Oils Co., Inc.
21 CLUB - Colognes - Frances Denney
21-DAY HABIT MAKING PROGRAM, THE - Printed matter - Mark David's Interactive Training Programs, Inc.
21 DERFUL YEARS - T-shirts–men's - Blueberry Hill
21 OR BUST - Games - The Learning Experience Inc.
21 PLUS - Hair coloring preparations - Pro-Capa Products Inc.
21DERFUL YEARS - Toys - Blueberry Hill
21ST CENTURY - Cleaning preparations - Christman Chemical Co. Inc.
21ST CENTURY - Electronic equipment - Descent Control Inc.
21ST CENTURY - Fans–electric - Dan's Fan City
21ST CENTURY - Food products - 21st Century Foods Inc.
21ST CENTURY - Golfing equipment - Golfsmith International Inc.
21ST CENTURY - Paint sets–hobby - Coverite
21ST CENTURY - Paint sets–hobby - U.S. Hobby Co.
21ST CENTURY - Recording label - RCI Records
21ST CENTURY - Shoes ☆ - Titleist & Foot-Joy Worldwide

21ST CENTURY - Vitamins and nutritional supplements - 21st Century Products
21ST CENTURY - Wheelchairs - 21st Century Scientific Inc.
21ST CENTURY ELOQUENCE - Communications equipment - 21st Century Eloquence, Inc.
21ST CENTURY LIMITED - Metals - 21st Century Limited Productions, Inc.
21ST CENTURY LOADIES - Games - Darryl L. Jones
21ST CENTURY-PLAYING & READING - Computer software - Electronic Courseware Systems Inc.
21ST CENTURY SOLUTIONS - Plumbing fixtures–plastic - Normandy Products Co.
21ST CENTURY TREND SETTER - Medical equipment - Cow Industries, Inc.
21ST PEOPLE BINGO - Games - 21st Century Ideas, Ltd.
21ST SENTRY, THE - Computer software - Advantageware, Inc.
22/22 - Skin care products - Ya-Man Ltd.
22 K. GOLD - Floor waxes - Harley Chemicals
22% PROFESSIONAL - Finishing agents - Analab Inc.
22 TWICE TURF FERTILIZER - Fertilizers - Agri-Urban Inc.
22 WEAR - Apparel–women's - Cinema Etoile
22MAG - Firearms, accessories, and parts ☆ - Blount International, Inc. (Sporting Equipment Group)
23 KT - Trading cards and stamps - Bleachers Card Corp.
23 NIGHT - Apparel and accessories - Jordan/Silverberg Apparel Inc.
024 - Motor vehicles ☆ - Chrysler Corp. (Dodge Car Div.)
24 DAY COUNTDOWN - Calendars - Morris National Inc.
24 DIAMOND 21 TURF - Footwear ☆ - Nike, Inc.
24-HOUR - Electronic equipment ☆ - West Bend Co.
24 HOUR + - Shorts–men's - Footwear International Corp.
24-HOUR - Skin care products - Estee Lauder Inc.
24 HOUR BROKER - Banks–commercial - Ameritrade, Inc.
24 HOUR COMFORT - Shoes - Footwear International Corp.
24 HOUR DIET PLAN - Vitamins and nutritional supplements - General Nutrition Investment Co.
24 HOUR GOLFER'S SURVIVAL KIT - Balls–golf - Pick Point Sports
24-HOUR MANAGER - Clocks - General Time Corp. (Westclox/Seth Thomas Div.)
24 K - Analgesics - North American Sales, Inc.
24 KARAT - Fungicides - Bally Gaming International, Inc.
24 KARAT - Skin care products - Paula Payne Products Co. Inc.
24 KARATS - Yarn - Rainbow Gallery, Inc.
24-KARROT GEMS - Desserts - Natural Ovens of Manitowoc Inc.
24 SELECT - Beverages - Store 24, Inc.
24C - Tobacco - Fred Stoker & Sons, Inc.
24K - Luggage - Ventura Travelware Inc.
24K B.C. - Vitamins and nutritional supplements - Sandy Shaw
24K GOLD - Shampoos ☆ - Cheveux Inc.
24K POLAR PUFF - Toys–stuffed - Mighty Star Inc. (Special Effects Div.)
24K VISION - Sunglasses - Golden Optics Inc.
24KT FRIEND - Toys–stuffed - Russ Berrie and Co., Inc.
24U BOOKS - Publisher's imprints - G.R. Beyer
24V BEAM - Electrical equipment - W.F. Harris Lighting, Inc.
24X7 - Computer software - Legent Corp.
24XS - Electronic equipment - AudioControl
25 BELOW - Deicing fluid - North American Salt Co.
25 C BEAM O S - Sporting goods - Lisco, Inc.
25 CHANNEL - Telephone apparatus - Motorola, Inc. (Land Mobile Products Sector)
25 GRAND - Floor waxes - Harley Chemicals
25 LTD - Radio communications equipment - Cobra Electronics Corp.
25TH ANNIVERSARY - Glassware–household ☆ - Lotus Glass Co.
27TH STREET - Apparel and accessories - India Ink
28 1/2 - Jewelry - Mel Bernie and Co., Inc.
28 II - Jewelry - Mel Bernie and Co., Inc.
28 SHOP - Apparel and accessories - Dayton Hudson Corp.
2.8L - Motor vehicles–automobiles - BMW of North America Inc.
29 CLASSIC - Motor vehicles–motor homes - Airstream Inc.
29-P MIXTURE - Tobacco products - Shepherd Tobacco Co.
30 - Cleaning preparations - Lee Products Co.
30/30 - Filters–industrial - Farr Co.
30 DAY BEAUTY SECRET - Health care products - Futurebiotics
30 PLUS - Vitamins and nutritional supplements - Pacific Mineral Industries
30 + 4 - Containers - Rubbermaid Inc.
30 SECOND CURL, THE - Hair care products - Celeste Co. Inc.
32 WOOD - Band-saw blade - American Saw & Manufacturing Co.
32M - Motor vehicle parts and accessories - Tcom, L.P.
33 - Apparel and accessories - Latrobe Brewing Co.

☆ = Now out of production

33 - Finishing agents - Dap Products Inc.

33, A - Vitamins and nutritional supplements - Kroeger Herb Products Co. Inc.

33 BRAND - Toys - Lancer Industries Inc.

33 DOLLAR BABY - Games - Universal Manufacturing Co., Inc.

33 EAST - Handbags - Etra Handbags Inc.

34 B - Harmonicas - Hohner Inc.

35 PLUS - Health care products - Futurebiotics

35 SUR CHILEAN - Wines - Shaw-Ross International Importers

36 FORD - Toys - Kingsbury Mini Motors of America Inc.

36 VALVE - Valves–industrial - Spraying Systems Co.

38 - Varnishes - Pratt & Lambert, Inc.

38 KOREAN WAR VETERANS 25 JUNE 1950 KOREA 27 JULY 1953 - Apparel and accessories - PFC Stanley A. Gogoj Chapter No. 38, Inc.

.38 MASTER - Revolvers - Smith & Wesson Corp.

.38 SPECIAL - Fishing lures - Strike King Lure Co.

38 SPECIAL - Goggles–safety - Outdoor Optics, Inc.

39 CLOTH - Apparel–athletic - Powers Manufacturing Co.

39 KIDS ON THE BLOCK - Publisher's imprints - Scholastic Inc.

39 SEASONINGS - Meat products–poultry - Hester Industries, Inc.

40+ - Vitamins and nutritional supplements - Solgar Vitamin and Herb Co., Inc.

40/4 CHAIR - Chairs–metal - GF Office Furniture Ltd.

4.0 COLLECTION - Diaries - Concept One International, Inc.

40 KNOTS - Games ✩ - Cathay International

40 POWER OBSERVER - Telescopes - CBS Toys

40 THUNDERBIRD ANNIVERSARY 1955-1995 - Buckles - Ford Motor Co.

40 VELVET - Paints - Wellborn-DE Corp.

40 WINKS - Apparel and accessories - Bentley Lingerie, Inc.

40 WINKS - Pharmaceutical preparations - Roberts/Hauck Pharmaceuticals Inc.

40 WINKS - Vitamins and nutritional supplements ✩ - Makers of Kal, Inc.

40DS - Tennis nets - Edwards Sports Products

40'S WOODIE - Toys–automobiles - Mattel, Inc.

42ND STREET - Skin care products - Comfort Manufacturing Co.

.42S - Goggles–sun - Oakley, Inc.

44 - Solder - Kester Solder Co.

44-20 - Scissors–hand-operated - Economy Supply Co. Inc.

44-20 ECONOMY - Pet products - Shear Perfection

44-20 MASTER - Pet products - Shear Perfection

44-20 PHILIPPINE - Pet products - Shear Perfection

44-20 SARGENT - Pet products - Shear Perfection

44-20 TAPER FINE - Pet products - Shear Perfection

44 MAGNUM - Beverage dispensing equipment - Starr Novelty Products

44 MAGNUM - Pharmaceutical preparations - BDI Pharmaceuticals

44TH ST. ATHLETIC CLUB - Apparel–women's - Weekend Exercise Co., Inc.

44TH STREET - Apparel–athletic - Weekend Exercise Co., Inc.

45/15 - Evaporation apparatus–laboratory - Hexacomb Corp.

45/45 - Evaporation apparatus–laboratory - Hexacomb Corp.

45CT - Wire - Tafa Inc.

47 - Helicopters ✩ - Bell Helicopter Textron Inc.

47 TEK - Computer software - 47-Tek, Inc.

048 - Automotive parts and accessories - C.B. Performance Products

48 - Garment racks–metal - Vogel Peterson Furniture Co.

48 CHORD - Harmonicas - Hohner Inc.

49-BODY-SHINE - Cleaning preparations - Auto Wax Co., Inc.

49 RECORDS - Compact discs–prerecorded - Njall Helle Productions

49 STAR - Seafood products–fresh or frozen - Penguin Frozen Foods, Inc.

49ER - Sporting goods - 49er Products Inc.

49ER GOLD CALIFORNIA ORANGES - Agricultural products - Stan Pilegard

49'ERS - Boats–dinghies ✩ - C-G Industries Inc.

49'ERS, THE - Computer software - Hartley Courseware Inc.

49'RS CLUB - Apparel - 49er Shops, Inc.

49TH STAR - Seafood products–fresh or frozen - North Pacific Seafoods

50 - Trading cards and stamps - AAA Sports Inc.

50-50 - Carbonated beverage - Cotton Club Bottling Co.

50/50 - Computers - 50/50 Micro Electronics Inc.

50-50 - Gasoline - Getty Petroleum Marketing, Inc.

50/50 - Paint rollers - Wooster Brush Co.

50/50 - Stoves ✩ - Malm Fireplaces Inc.

50-50 BAR - Food products ✩ - Knudsen Dairy Products

50 BELOW - Deicing fluid - Kafko International Ltd.

50 GOLD - Electrical equipment - International Connectors and Cable Corp.

50% LIL' SALT - Frankfurters ✩ - Russer Foods

50 NIFTY - Publisher's imprints - Lowell House

50 PEAKS - Footwear - Hi-Tec Sports USA Inc.

50 + 4 - Containers - Rubbermaid Inc.

50 SERIES - Furniture - Harter

50'S CLASSICS - Footwear - Shoe Show, Inc.

'50'S FAVORITES - Toys–automobiles - Mattel, Inc.

50'S INTERNATIONAL - Posters - Domino Ltd.

50TH ANNIVERSARY - Glassware–household ✩ - Lotus Glass Co.

52 - Publisher's imprints - Lynn Gordon

52ND STREET - Bedding–linen - Dan River Inc.

'56 FLASHSIDER - Toys–automobiles - Mattel, Inc.

'56 HI-TAIL HAULER - Toys–automobiles - Mattel, Inc.

57 - Barbecue sauce - H.J. Heinz Co.

57 CLASSIC - Musical instrument accessories - Gibson Strings & Accessories

57 T-BIRD - Toys - Kingsbury Mini Motors of America Inc.

57 VARIETIES - Apparel and accessories - H.J. Heinz Co.

57TH STREET - Skin care products ✩ - Avon Products, Inc.

'59 MODEL - Musical instrument accessories - Seymour Duncan Pickups

59TH STREET COLLECTION, THE - Apparel - Phillips-Van Heusen Corp.

60/40/20 - Hair care products - Thompson and Formby

60/40 PARKA - Sporting goods - Kellwood Co.

60:60 RINSE - Health care products - Pascal Co. Inc.

60-MINUTE PATTERNS - Patterns–clothing - Mccall Pattern Co.

60-SECOND SPA - Hair care products - Dowbrands L.P.

60 SUPER SIMPLE - Publisher's imprints - Lowell House

61 - Paints - Pratt & Lambert, Inc.

61-SO - Fuel systems–motor vehicle - Dover Corp.

62 EAST - Apparel and accessories - Kellwood Co.

62 EAST SPORT - Women's apparel - A.J. Brandon, Inc.

63 LONDRES - Cigars - National Cigar Corp.

64/128 - Computer software - Central Point Software Inc.

64 CHROMONICA - Harmonicas - Hohner Inc.

65 MUSTANG - Toys–automobiles - Kingsbury Mini Motors of America Inc.

66 - Adhesives and sealants - Sprayway Inc.

66-B - Detergents - Imperial Manufacturing Co. Inc.

67 - Markers–felt-tip ✩ - Pentel of America, Ltd.

68-A - Degreasing solvents - State Chemical Manufacturing Co.

68 AUTOMAG - Air guns - Airgun Designs, Inc.

69 - Sporting goods - Wellington Leisure Products, Inc.

#70 - Inks - Ranger Industries

70M - Valves - ITT Corp.

70'S WOMAN, THE - Dolls ✩ - Effanbee Doll Corp.

72-10 DON'T MEAN A THING WITHOUT THE RING - Apparel and accessories - Kick 10 Promotions, Inc.

72 HOUR BLIND FACTORY - Window coverings - Window Enhancement, Inc.

73 EASTING - Computer software - Novalogic, Inc.

74-40 - Tomato pastes and sauces - Stanislaus Food Products Co.

75/75 - Lubricants - Telios Pharmaceuticals Inc.

75B - Wire–aluminum - Tafa Inc.

76 - Beverages–carbonated - American 76 Co.

76 - Gasoline - Unocal Corp.

'76 FREEDOM SPIRIT - Boats–pontoons ✩ - Riviera Cruiser

77 - Markers–felt-tip ✩ - Marsh Co.

77/22 - Rifles - Sturm, Ruger & Co., Inc.

77 AUTOMOTIVE - Lubricants - ATM America Corp.

77 QUADRANTS - Puzzles - Kadon Enterprises Inc.

78TH STREET - Greeting cards - American Greetings Corp.

#79 SINUS COMBS - Homeopathic remedies - Washington Homeopathic Products

80 - Motor vehicles–automobiles - Audi of America Inc.

80-10-10 - Chemical preparations - Liferich Limited Co.

80/20 BRONZE - Musical instrument accessories - J. D'Addario & Co. Inc.

80/20 BRONZE - Musical instrument accessories - Gibson Strings & Accessories

80-40 - Vegetables–canned - Lico Brands, Inc.

80 BELOW - Vodka - Archer Daniels Midland Co.

80 OTHERS - Vitamins and nutritional supplements - Lifessence Labs

80 WEST END - Jewelry ✩ - K & M Associates

80'S COLLECTION - Furniture ✩ - Virginia House Furniture Corp.

81ST & PARK - Apparel–women's - Nordstrom, Inc.

82 TRACING - Paper ✩ - Canson-Talens Inc.

83RD INDIANAPOLIS 500 MAY 30, 1999 - Apparel and accessories - Indianapolis Motor Speedway Corp.

84-40 TUBE - Musical instrument accessories - Seymour Duncan Pickups

84-50 TUBE - Musical instrument accessories - Seymour Duncan Pickups

85/15 GREAT AMERICAN - Musical instrument accessories - J. D'Addario & Co. Inc.

85/80 - Flowers, plants, and seeds - Jacklin Seed

85 PLUS - Heating equipment - Yukon Energy Corp.

87 SPAR - Varnishes - Devoe & Raynolds Co.

87 ULTRA - Printing trades machinery - Day International Inc.

✩ = Now out of production

88 - Motor vehicles–automobiles ☆ - General Motors Corp. (Oldsmobile Div.)

88 - Solder - Kester Solder Co.

88 LS - Motor vehicles–automobiles - General Motors Corp. (Oldsmobile Div.)

88 LSS - Motor vehicles–automobiles - General Motors Corp. (Oldsmobile Div.)

88 ROYALE - Motor vehicles–automobiles - General Motors Corp. (Oldsmobile Div.)

88TH STREET - Apparel–women's - Weekend Exercise Co., Inc.

89< slash>03 - Veterinary pharmaceutical preparations - Intervet, Inc.

89ERS - Apparel - 89er Baseball L.P.

89TH ST. PIZZA - Apparel–men's - 89th St. Pizza Corp.

90 - Motor vehicles–automobiles - Audi of America Inc.

90 - Rackets–tennis - Yamaha Corp. of America (Sporting Goods Div.)

90-II - Sealing compounds - Edison Coatings, Inc.

90-75 - Faucets - Bradley Corp.

90/90 BACKTRAC - Traction apparatus–medical - Lossing Orthopedic Co.

90-MINUTE FASHION - Patterns–clothing ☆ - Mccall Pattern Co.

90 PLUS - Gasoline - Xcel Ventures, Inc.

90% PROTEIN PLUS - Vitamins and nutritional supplements - Universal Protein Supplements, Inc.

90 SHILLING ALE - Beverages–malt - Odell Brewing Co., Inc.

90 SUPREME - Adhesives and sealants - Capitol Adhesives Inc.

90 W - Sealing compounds - Edison Coatings, Inc.

9.2 - Automotive parts and accessories - Trustee of American Inventory Services

92 - Electrical equipment - Ideal Industries Inc.

95/85 - Flowers, plants, and seeds - Jacklin Seed

96 - Apparel–men's - Eileen Byrne

98% FUNNY - Greeting cards ☆ - Recycled Paper Products, Inc.

99 - Markers–felt-tip - Marsh Co.

99 - Shoes–athletic - L.A. Gear, Inc.

99 BANANAS - Liquors - Canandaigua Wine Co. Inc.

99 LEMON LIME - Beverages–carbonated - Hello Cola Co.

99 PLUS - Hair conditioner ☆ - Costec 20 Inc.

99ER - Awnings ☆ - Carefree of Colorado

100+ - Automotive parts and accessories - Midwest Power Concepts Ltd.

100 - Beverages–carbonated - A.J. Canfield Co.

$100 - Confections - Madelaine Chocolate Novelties, Inc.

100 - Motor vehicles–automobiles - Audi of America Inc.

100 - Pet products - Ralston Purina Co.

100 - Trading cards and stamps - AAA Sports Inc.

100 - Yogurt - Old Home Foods Inc.

100 ACRE POOH - Handbags - Pyramid Handbags Inc.

100 ASTM - Tape–adhesive - Plymouth Rubber Co., Inc.

100 ATLANTA 1996 - Knives–pocket - Atlanta Committee for the Olympic Games, Inc.

100% BRAN - Cereal - Nabisco Foods Group

100% COTTON EQUIPMENT - Apparel and accessories - Chazwas Internationale, Inc.

100 DELTA PROFESSIONAL - Film - ILFORD Photo Corp.

100% EGG PROTEIN - Vitamins and nutritional supplements - Healthy 'N Fit Nutritionals

100% EXTREME LAND AIR WATER PERCENT - Apparel and accessories - Revatex, Inc.

100 GRAND - Candy - Nestle USA

100% GUILT FREE - Snack foods - New Generation Foods Inc.

100% INSANE - Apparel–athletic - Kevin T. Moulton

100% JUST FOR KIDS - Video series - Celebrity Home Entertainment Inc.

100% MAUI GROWN COFFEE - Coffee - AMFAC/JMB Hawaii, Inc.

100% NATURAL HARDWOOD NATURE'S OWN CHUNK CHARWOOD - Briquettes - Treestock Ltd.

100% PEOPLE - Greeting cards - Creatif Licensing Corp.

100 PIPERS - Liquors - Heaven Hill Distilleries, Inc.

100 PLAY CARROM - Games - Carrom Co.

100 PLUS - Cereal - Topco Associates, Inc.

100 PROOF ARAK SHELLELET ZAHLE - Beverages–alcohol - Lebanese Arak Co.

100% PURE ESSENTIAL OILS - Oils–essential - Elizabeth Van Buren Aromatherapy

100% PURE STUFF - Apparel and accessories - Nordstrom, Inc.

100% SOLIDS - Epoxy ☆ - Custom Building Products

100% WHEY PRO AMINO - Vitamins and nutritional supplements - Healthy 'N Fit Nutritionals

100% WHOLE WHEAT - Breads - Natural Ovens of Manitowoc Inc.

100-YEAR NITE-LITE - Lamps - Solid Electric Corp.

100 YEARS OU 1895-1995 - Apparel and accessories - Board of Regents of the University of Oklahoma

100LX PALMTOP - Computers–personal - Hewlett-Packard Co.

100% - Food products - Natural Nectar Corp.

100% NATURAL - Cereal - Quaker Oats Co.

101 - Apparel and accessories ☆ - Noble Apparel, Inc.

101 - Floor coverings–carpet and rugs - No-Muv Corp., Inc.

101 - Tape–adhesive - Arlon, Inc.

101 - Thread - Blue Ribbon Paint Co.

101 ATTRAK - Apparel and accessories ☆ - Noble Apparel, Inc.

101 CHESTERFIELD - Cigarettes ☆ - Liggett Group Inc.

101 DALMATIONS - Games - Milton Bradley Co.

101 DALMATIONS - Wallpaper - Priss Prints Inc.

101 GREAT IDEAS - Publisher's imprints - Tulip Productions

101 MEDICATED FACIAL CREAM - Cosmetics ☆ - Andrew Jergens Co.

101ST ANNIVERSARY - Wallpaper ☆ - Thomas Strahan Wallcoverings

104 - Tape–adhesive - Arlon, Inc.

108 NOTTINGHAM PLACE - Fabrics–tapestry ☆ - Columbus Coated Fabrics Co.

110 AIR - Aquariums–household - Marine Metal Products

110 ALERT - Alarm systems - PC Power and Cooling, Inc.

111 NORTH MAIN - Handbags - Marilyn USA

111 STATE - Apparel and accessories - Dayton Hudson Corp.

112 - Computer software - Smartpatents, Inc.

112G - Toys ☆ - Wham-O Manufacturing Co.

120 DAY - Cleaning preparations–household ☆ - Blue Lustre, LLC

121 - Jewelry - Centoventuno USA Inc.

122 - Rubber-tape - Plymouth Rubber Co., Inc.

123 - Bicycles - Playskool, Inc.

1*2*3* HEART RATE MONITOR - Health care products - Heart Rate Inc.

123 LOTION - Skin care products - European Touch Co.

128XP/4 - Medical apparatus - Acuson Corp.

140 - Boats–fishing - McDaniel Boats Inc.

14.4 COMMUNICATOR - Computer peripheral equipment - Simple Technology, Inc.

150 - Tires - Bridgestone/Firestone, Inc.

150 BASS - Boats - McDaniel Boats Inc.

150 FISH-N-SKI - Boats - McDaniel Boats Inc.

150 SWEEPER - Carpet sweepers ☆ - Bissell Inc.

150 WEST - Apparel and accessories - Breton Industries

151 - Audio equipment - Bose Corp.

151 WIPEOUT - Beverages–alcohol - Daiquiri Shoppe, Inc.

160 BASS - Boats - McDaniel Boats Inc.

164 - Motor vehicles–automobiles - Alfa Romeo Distributors of North America

164 LUXURY - Motor vehicles–automobiles - Alfa Romeo Distributors of North America

164 SPORT - Motor vehicles–automobiles - Alfa Romeo Distributors of North America

170K - Audio equipment - M & M Electronics

171 - Amplifiers–public address - Bose Corp.

180 ABOVE - Apparel and accessories - Brooklyn Apparel Group, Inc.

180 BASS - Boats - McDaniel Boats Inc.

180 FISH-N-SKI - Boats - McDaniel Boats Inc.

180 FROM ANYWHERE - Apparel and accessories - Coed Sportswear, Inc.

187 WEAR - Apparel and accessories - Robert Suarez

190 - Motor vehicles–automobiles - Mercedes-Benz of North America Inc.

190 OCTANE - Beverages–alcohol - David Briggs Enterprises, Inc.

200 - Motor vehicles–automobiles - Audi of America Inc.

200 - Watches - Bulova Corp.

200 MPH - Tape–adhesive - Manco, Inc.

200 PLUS - Health care products - Jen-On Pharmaceutical Enterprises Corp.

200GX - Printers–computer - Citizen America Corp.

200SX - Motor vehicles–automobiles ☆ - Nissan Motor Corp. USA

201SA - Lighting fixtures - General Electric Co.

204 - Helicopters and helicopter parts ☆ - Bell Helicopter Textron Inc.

#205 - Inks - Ranger Industries

206 - Bell Helicopter Textron Inc.

206 - Vitamins and nutritional supplements - North American Laboratory Co.

#208-ADIRONDACK INK - Inks - Ranger Industries

210 - Boats - Marblehead Boatyard Associates

#210 - Inks - Ranger Industries

210 - Motor vehicles–automobiles ☆ - Nissan Motor Corp. USA

212 - Helicopters - Bell Helicopter Textron Inc.

#213 - Inks - Ranger Industries

#213D-DECORIT - Inks - Ranger Industries

213'S - Sunglasses - Face 2 Face Corp.

☆ = Now out of production

9

214 - Helicopters ☆ - Bell Helicopter Textron Inc.
220 CUDDY FISH - Boats - Pro-Line Boats Inc.
221 BAKER STREET - Tobacco–chewing or smoking - Gesty Trading & Manufacturing Corp.
222 - Boats–canoes - Sawyer Composite Products
222 - Helicopters and helicopter parts ☆ - Bell Helicopter Textron Inc.
222 - Plaster–patching ☆ - United Gilsonite Laboratories
222 - Rice - Connell Co.
228 - Motor vehicles–automobiles - Maserati Automobiles Inc.
230 - Adhesives and sealants - Dap Products Inc.
#236 - Inks - Ranger Industries
240 DL - Motor vehicles–automobiles - Volvo Cars of North America Inc.
240 FAMILY FISHERMAN - Boats - Stamas Yacht Inc.
240 GL - Motor vehicles–automobiles - Volvo Cars of North America Inc.
240 TARPON - Boats - Stamas Yacht Inc.
240E - Motor vehicles–automobiles ☆ - Mercedes-Benz of North America Inc.
240SX - Motor vehicles–automobiles - Nissan Motor Corp. USA
24.7 CHRIST - Apparel and accessories - 24.7 Christ and Moragz
250 G - Rackets–racquetball - Ektelon
260E - Motor vehicles–automobiles ☆ - Mercedes-Benz of North America Inc.
280ZX - Motor vehicles–automobiles ☆ - Nissan Motor Corp. USA
28.8 COMMUNICATOR - Computer peripheral equipment - Simple Technology, Inc.
290 EXPRESS - Boats - Stamas Yacht Inc.
290 TARPON - Boats - Stamas Yacht Inc.
300 - High chairs - Century Products Co.
300 - Musical instruments - Getzen Co.
300 ZX - Motor vehicles–automobiles - Nissan Motor Corp. USA
300BP - Adhesive liner - Mactac Inc. (Packaging Closures Systems Div.)
300XK - Projectors–photographic - Kopykake
301 - Computer software - Deerfield Development Corp.
301 - Forms–preprinted - E-Z Legal Forms, Inc.
303 - Mops - Golden Star Inc.
305 - Golf clubs - Merit Golf Co.
307 - Hunting equipment - Wildlife Research Center, Inc.
307 5TH AVENUE - Shorts–women's - J. Steiner Imports Inc.
308GTBI/GTSI - Motor vehicles–automobiles - Ferrari North America Inc.
310 - Motor vehicles–automobiles ☆ - Nissan Motor Corp. USA
310 EXPRESS - Boats - Stamas Yacht Inc.
314 - Bicycles ☆ - Huffy Corp.
318TI SPORT - Motor vehicles–automobiles ☆ - BMW of North America Inc.
320 - Astringents - Stephan Co.
321 - Shampoos ☆ - Flo-Pac Corp.
321-QUIT - Publisher's imprints - TLC Inc.
323 - Motor vehicles–automobiles ☆ - Mazda Motor of America Inc.
325I - Motor vehicles–automobiles ☆ - BMW of North America Inc.
328 - Apparel and accessories - Noble Apparel, Inc.
328 QUATTROVALVOLE - Motor vehicles–automobiles - Ferrari North America Inc.
328I - Motor vehicles–automobiles - BMW of North America Inc.
328IC - Motor vehicles–automobiles - BMW of North America Inc.
328IS - Motor vehicles–automobiles - BMW of North America Inc.
331 +SMOKERS - Cigars - F.X. Smiths Sons Co.
333 HT - Fishing lines - Cortland Line Co., Inc.
340 LOW VOC - Paints ☆ - X-I-M Products Inc.
341 - Electrical equipment - Ideal Industries Inc.
342 - Electrical equipment - Ideal Industries Inc.
350 - Machinery - Tymco, Inc.
350 - Motor vehicles–automobiles - Mercedes-Benz of North America Inc.
350 CLX - Primers - X-I-M Products Inc.
350 HIGHWAY KIT - Metals - Yew Corp.
350 RS - Golfing equipment - Pinseeker Golf Corp.
360 - Electronic equipment - 360o Communications Co.
360 - Pens ☆ - Anson Inc.
360 - Perfumes - Perry Ellis Sportswear Inc.
360° - Perfumes - Sanofi Beaute Inc.
360 - Primers - X-I-M Products Inc.
360 EXPRESS - Boats - Stamas Yacht Inc.
360 SYSTEMS - Musical instrument accessories - 360 Systems
360 TO GO - Telephones - 360o Communications Co.
360° - Recording label - Jazz Composer's Orchestra Association Inc.
365 COLLECTION, THE - Footwear - Dunham Boot Makers
375 - Toys–erector sets - CBS Toys
380 - Motor vehicles–automobiles ☆ - Mercedes-Benz of North America Inc.
386/486 - Computer hardware - Cyrix Corp.
388 - Cleaning preparations - AMF Bowling Worldwide

400 - Kitchen utensils–aluminum ☆ - West Bend Co.
400 - Motor vehicles ☆ - Chrysler Corp. (Dodge Car Div.)
400 - Musical instruments - Selmer Co. Inc.
400 CLEAR - Primers - X-I-M Products Inc.
400 DELTA - Film - ILFORD Photo Corp.
400/MANAGER - Computer software - Imaging Technology Solutions, LLC
400 OIL - Oils–lubricating - Quincy Oil Inc.
400 SEDGEFIELD COLLECTION - Furniture–public buildings - Myrtle Desk Co.
400, THE - Watches - Elgin Watch Co.
400 WHITE - Primers - X-I-M Products Inc.
401(K) ADVISOR - Computer storage devices - Smith Barney Shearson Inc.
405 - Motor vehicles–automobiles - Peugeot Motors of America Inc.
406 INJECTOR PERFECTOR - Fuel additives - Primrose Oil Co., Inc.
407 - Aircraft–helicopters - Bell Helicopter Textron Inc.
409 - Electronics equipment - Grass Valley Group Inc.
409 FLOW-MASTER - Fuel additives - Primrose Oil Co., Inc.
410 OCTAHELIX - Sporting goods - Lisco, Inc.
411ACRYLIC - Nail care products - Thuan Van Hoang
412 - Helicopters and helicopter parts - Bell Helicopter Textron Inc.
417 - Hosiery–men's - Phillips-Van Heusen Corp.
420 - Apparel and accessories - John Marvin Rowland
420 - Motor vehicles–automobiles - Mercedes-Benz of North America Inc.
420 - Pliers - Channellock, Inc.
420 EYEWEAR - Sunglasses - John Marvin Rowland
422 TRI - Balls–golf - Lisco, Inc.
425 - Motor vehicles–automobiles - Maserati Automobiles Inc.
427 - Aircraft–helicopters - Bell Helicopter Textron Inc.
430 - Aircraft–helicopters - Bell Helicopter Textron Inc.
430 - Motor vehicles–automobiles - Maserati Automobiles Inc.
430 - Pliers - Channellock, Inc.
440 - Pistols ☆ - Precise International/Wenger
440 - Pliers - Channellock, Inc.
440 - Shoes–athletic - Sears, Roebuck and Co.
444 - Fishing lines - Cortland Line Co., Inc.
450 GYM - Finishing agents - Hillyard Enterprises, Inc.
452 FIFTH - Apparel–athletic - Morsly Inc.
454 - Analgesics - Signal Investment & Management Co.
454SS - Motor vehicles–trucks - General Motors Corp. (Chevrolet Motor Div.)
484 TACKY - Glue–household or industrial - Bond Adhesives Co.
488 - Sealing compounds - Sealwall Products Inc.
500 - Motor vehicles–automobiles - Mercedes-Benz of North America Inc.
500 - Playing cards - United States Playing Card Co.
500 - Sport shirts, etc. - Botany 500
500 - Tires - Bridgestone/Firestone, Inc.
500 COBALT SHEAR - Scissors–hand-operated - Dubl Duck/Jet Set Inc.
500 CUSTOM - Steering mechanisms–motor vehicle - Superior Industries International, Inc.
500 NATIONS - Video production - 500 Nations Productions
500 PATROL - Tires - Bridgestone/Firestone, Inc.
500 POUNDER - Fishing lures - B-17 Fly Tackle Ltd.
500 PSI - Apparel–athletic - Pharmatronics, Inc.
500 SPORT GRIP - Steering mechanisms–motor vehicle - Superior Industries International, Inc.
500I - Sporting goods ☆ - Dunlop Maxfli Sports Corp.
500T - Electronic equipment - Seal Products Inc.
501 - Jeans - Levi Strauss & Co.
501 - Office supplies - Bates Manufacturing Co.
502 - Amplifiers–public address - Bose Corp.
502 LAUBE GERMAN TRANSFORMER - Barber shop equipment - Kim Laube & Co. Inc.
502 LAUBE UNIVERSAL - Barber shop equipment - Kim Laube & Co. Inc.
505 - Jeans - Levi Strauss & Co.
505 - Motor vehicles–automobiles - Peugeot Motors of America Inc.
506 - Jeans - Levi Strauss & Co.
507 - Adhesives and sealants ☆ - Leech Products Inc.
509 - Jeans - Levi Strauss & Co.
517 - Jeans - Levi Strauss & Co.
520 - Skin care products - Ritornelle Inc.
525 HOMEWEAR - Blankets - Bock & Steinberg Associates, Inc.
525 MADE IN AMERICA - Blankets - Bock & Steinberg Associates, Inc.
525I OLYMPIC GAMES EDITION - Motor vehicles–automobiles ☆ - BMW of North America Inc.
527 - Glue–household or industrial - Bond Adhesives Co.
528E - Motor vehicles–automobiles ☆ - BMW of North America Inc.
528I - Motor vehicles–automobiles - BMW of North America Inc.

☆ = Now out of production

535I - Motor vehicles–automobiles ☆ - BMW of North America Inc.
540I - Motor vehicles–automobiles ☆ - BMW of North America Inc.
547 XL - Machine tools - Atotech Usa Inc.
550 - Cordage and twine - Sunset Line and Twine Co.
550 - Jeans - Levi Strauss & Co.
550 MUSIC - Recording label - Sony Music Entertainment Inc.
555 - Batteries - Mercury Radio & Battery Corp.
555 EAST - Meat extracts - URG Corp.
557 - Jeans - Levi Strauss & Co.
560 - Motor vehicles–automobiles - Mercedes-Benz of North America Inc.
565 - Infant product - Century Products Co.
565 PREFERRED CARE - Medical apparatus - Lumex, Inc.
570 SERIES SEATING - Chairs–metal - GF Office Furniture Ltd.
590 - Infant product - Century Products Co.
598 ULTRA BLACK - Adhesives and sealants - Loctite Corp.
600 - Motor vehicles ☆ - Chrysler Corp. (Dodge Car Div.)
600 - Street sweeper - Tymco, Inc.
600 BUSINESS EDITION - Cameras - Polaroid Corp.
600 ES - Motor vehicles ☆ - Chrysler Corp. (Dodge Car Div.)
600 PLUS - Adhesives and sealants ☆ - Loctite Corp.
601 - Darts and dart games ☆ - Accudart
601 MUSIC - Recording label - Malaco Records Inc.
604 - Motor vehicles–automobiles ☆ - Peugeot Motors of America Inc.
609 - Aircraft–helicopters - Bell Helicopter Textron Inc.
609 - Apparel and accessories - Bugle Boy Industries, Inc.
609 BUFFALOGRASS - Turfgrass - Crenshaw & Doguet Turfgrass, Inc.
615 COLLECTION - Apparel–men's - Venture Stores, Inc.
626 - Motor vehicles–automobiles - Mazda Motor of America Inc.
630 - Tires - Bridgestone/Firestone, Inc.
640 - Staplers - Bates Manufacturing Co.
640 - Tires - Bridgestone/Firestone, Inc.
652 TACKS - Skates–ice - SLM Inc.
666 - Cold remedies - Monticello Drug Co.
686CPT - Welding equipment - Inco Alloys International, Inc.
700 SERIES - Filing cabinets–metal - Krueger International, Inc.
700 SERIES - Musical instruments - Getzen Co.
700 SERIES ADJUSTABLE - Sporting goods - O'Brien International
701 - Loudspeakers - Bose Corp.
707 - Aircraft–airplanes - Boeing Co.
707 - Vans–conversion ☆ - Seven O Seven Industries Inc.
707 CORPORATE COMMUTER - Vans–conversion - Seven O Seven Industries Inc.
707 EXECUTIVE CARRIER - Vans–conversion - Seven O Seven Industries Inc.
707 EXPOSITION - Vans–conversion - Seven O Seven Industries Inc.
712 - Depilatories - K.B.K. Products Inc.
718-ER - Nickel products - Teledyne Industries Inc.
720 POWERBASE - Wheelchairs - Fortress Inc.
721 - Tires - Bridgestone/Firestone, Inc.
721 ASR - Tires - Bridgestone/Firestone, Inc.
721 METRIX - Tires - Bridgestone/Firestone, Inc.
725 - Sporting goods - Donnay USA
725NDUR - Welding equipment - Inco Alloys International, Inc.
727 - Aircraft–airplanes - Boeing Co.
729 SUPER - Rackets–tennis - Estusa Corp.
730 POWERBASE - Wheelchairs - Fortress Inc.
735I - Motor vehicles–automobiles ☆ - BMW of North America Inc.
737 - Housewares - Boeing Co.
740 - Motor vehicles–automobiles - Volvo Cars of North America Inc.
740 GLE - Motor vehicles–automobiles ☆ - Volvo Cars of North America Inc.
740 TURBO - Motor vehicles–automobiles - Volvo Cars of North America Inc.
740IA - Motor vehicles–automobiles - BMW of North America Inc.
740IL - Motor vehicles–automobiles - BMW of North America Inc.
744 - Jewelry - Van Cleef & Arpels, Inc.
745 - Electronic equipment - Polyfusion Electronics Inc.
745 COLLECTION - Apparel and accessories - Neiman Marcus Co.
747 - Aircraft–airplanes - Boeing Co.
747 - Candy ☆ - Leaf, Inc.
747 - Floor coverings–carpet and rugs ☆ - Mohawk Carpet Corp.
747 - Luggage ☆ - Hartmann Luggage Co.
747-XL - Golfing equipment - Golfsmith International Inc.
749 - Cake flour ☆ - Pillsbury Co.
750 - Sporting goods - Donnay USA
750 RIDER - Video games - Taito America Corp.
750IL - Motor vehicles–automobiles ☆ - BMW of North America Inc.
757 - Aircraft–airplanes - Boeing Co.

760 - Motor vehicles–automobiles - Volvo Cars of North America Inc.
764 MODEL II - Beds–hospital - Sci-O-Tech Inc.
767 - Aircraft–airplanes - Boeing Co.
767 - Luggage ☆ - Shalam Imports Inc.
769 - Paints - Rust-Oleum Corp.
770 POWERBASE - Wheelchairs - Fortress Inc.
775 ADJUSTABLE - Sporting goods - O'Brien International
777 - Aircraft–airplanes - Boeing Co.
777 - Vitamins and nutritional supplements - Nutritech
777XTRA - Vitamins and nutritional supplements ☆ - Nutritech
780 - Motor vehicles–automobiles - Volvo Cars of North America Inc.
790 SURE UNIVERSAL - Lubricants - Texas Refinery Corp. (Lubricants Div.)
800-CALL-NOW - Advertising agencies - New England 800 Co.
800 CARD, THE - Business cards - H & C Concepts
800 CONVERTIBLE - Sporting goods ☆ - Ponsness-Warren
800I - Sporting goods ☆ - Dunlop Maxfli Sports Corp.
810 - Dental equipment - AFP Imaging Corp.
810 MAXIMA - Motor vehicles–automobiles ☆ - Nissan Motor Corp. USA
812 - Photographic equipment - Tiffen Manufacturing Corp.
818 - Fuel additives - MacMillan Ring-Free Oil Co. Inc.
845 - Hats - Tommy Armour Golf Co.
845 FLEXO - Brushes–hair - Comare Corp.
850 - Motor vehicles–automobiles - Volvo Cars of North America Inc.
851 - Water–mineral - Charoen Pokphand (USA) Inc.
855 - Golfing equipment - Tommy Armour Golf Co.
855 SILVER SCOT - Golfing equipment - Tommy Armour Golf Co.
860 - Office machines - Xerox Corp.
880 - Pistols ☆ - Precise International/Wenger
890 ADJUSTABLE - Sporting goods - O'Brien International
890 VARI-PURPOSE - Lubricants - Texas Refinery Corp. (Lubricants Div.)
900 - Toys–models - Saab-Scania of America Inc.
900 SC - Medical equipment - Corometrics Medical Systems Inc.
900 SUPER PREMIUM - Beverages–malt ☆ - Pearl Brewing Co.
907 COMPANY - Apparel and accessories - Cloth to Clothing, Inc.
911 - Cleaning preparations - Booda Products, Inc.
911 - Food products - Sanctuary Much
911 - Hair care products - All Ways Natural Industries Inc.
911 - Self-defense spray - Guardian Personal Security Products, Inc.
911 ALERT - Lighting equipment - Ek-Ris Enterprises, Inc.
911 EMERGENCY - Toy vehicles - Play Power Inc.
911 EMERGENCY PAK - Hair care products - Hayashi for Hair Inc.
911-EMS - Gloves–rubber - Satari Corp.
911 ENTERTAINMENT - Computer peripheral equipment - 911 Entertainment
911 NUMBERING - Hardware - Number-It, Inc.
911 PIGEON - Lamps - 911 Flasher Co.
911 RELIEF - Pharmaceutical preparations - PBJ, Inc.
911 RESCUE - Costumes - European Touch Co.
911 RESCUE TEAM - Hats - Rose Marie Mercadante
911 SEATS INCORPORATED - Motor vehicle parts and accessories - Seats Inc.
+911 +STRESS CONTROL - Vitamins and nutritional supplements - King Bio Pharmaceuticals, Inc.
916 DESIGN - Computer software - 916 Design
.925 - Jewelry - Watch Us, Inc.
926, THE - Containers - Stack-On Products Co.
927 DESIGNS - Apparel and accessories - Bergman Enterprises Inc.
928 - Golfing equipment - Renaissance Golf Products, Inc.
929 - Motor vehicles–automobiles - Mazda Motor of America Inc.
934 TURBO - Watches - Accusplit Inc.
955 ORIGINALS - Backpacks - Mercantile Stores Co., Inc.
960 - Electronic equipment - Polyfusion Electronics Inc.
960 - Motor vehicles–automobiles - Volvo Cars of North America Inc.
970 SERIES - Floor coverings - Robbins Inc.
990 COLLECTION - Jewelry - E.B. Harvey and Co., Inc.
999 - Meat extracts - Real Kosher Sausage Co. Inc.
999 - Tools - Vaughan & Bushnell Manufacturing Co.
999 FABRIC STAIN REMOVER - Cleaning preparations - W.R. Rayson Co., Inc.
1000 - Motor vehicles–automobiles ☆ - General Motors Corp. (Pontiac/GMC Div.)
1000 - Trading cards and stamps - AAA Sports Inc.
1000 BC - Pharmaceutical preparations ☆ - Solvay Pharmaceuticals Inc.
1000 DE JEAN PATOU - Perfumes - Jean Patou, Inc.
1000 F AQUA TEMP - Paints ☆ - Zynolyte Products Co.
1,000 KISSES - Skin-care products - Positive Response Marketing, Inc.
1000 PLUS - Adhesives and sealants - Loctite Corp.

1000 PLUS - Lubricants - Ox-Yoke Originals, Inc.
1000 PORTHOLES - Colognes - Key West Aloe Inc.
1000 SPRINGS - Fish–fresh or frozen - Clear Springs Trout Co.
1000 STE - Infant product - Century Products Co.
1000SL - Vans–conversion ☆ - Turtle Top Specialty Products
1001 NIGHTS - Wallpaper ☆ - Old Deerfield Fabrics Inc.
1010AE - Artists' materials ☆ - LogEtronics Corp.
1011 - Jewelry - J.K. Jewelry, Inc.
1012 - Finishing agents - Dap Products Inc.
1033 CONNECTICUT - Cigars - House of Windsor Inc.
1040WORKS - Computer software - National AppleWorks Users Group
1059 - Paper ☆ - Canson-Talens Inc.
1059 WATERCOLOR - Paper - Canson-Talens Inc.
1065 SOLUTION, THE - Computer software - Creative Solutions, Inc.
1100 D SUPER CARAYED - Nutritional Research Associates Inc.
1100 HSS - Communications equipment - Alcatel Titn Inc.
1115 - Labels–gummed - Monarch Marking Systems, Inc.
1130 - Paper ☆ - Canson-Talens Inc.
1166 GREEN MACHINE - Machine tools - Monarch Marking Systems, Inc.
1176 - Labels–paper - Monarch Marking Systems, Inc.
1177 EPOXY - Epoxy - W.J. Ruscoe Co.
1200 - Furniture - Boling Co.
1200 DEGREES - Paints ☆ - United Gilsonite Laboratories
1200 GEAR EFFECT - Golfing equipment - Wilson Sporting Goods Co.
1226 VI - Jewelry - Roberto Coin, Inc.
1250 - Abrasive products - Park Metallurgical Corp.
1270 - Adhesives and sealants - Jones Blair Co.
1311 - Apparel–children's - Pixie Playmates, Inc.
1349 - Adhesives and sealants - Jones Blair Co.
1431 - Furniture - Boling Co.
1441 SPORT - Apparel and accessories - Jayco Sales International, Inc.
1500SP - Vans–conversion ☆ - Turtle Top Specialty Products
1700 - Boats - McDaniel Boats Inc.
1700 - Metal sealer - Coricone Corp.
1700FS - Scouring pads - Fortress Inc.
1704FS - Scouring pads - Fortress Inc.
1750 - Abrasive products - Park Metallurgical Corp.
1750 ARCH - Recording label - Jazz Composer's Orchestra Association Inc.
1752 - Colognes - Caswell-Massey Co. Ltd.
1761 GIN 94 - Gin ☆ - Frank Sutton & Co.
1776 - Bread product ☆ - Interstate Brands Corp.
1776 - Cabinets - Interior Design Inc.
1776 - Cigarettes ☆ - West Park Tobacco Inc.
1776 - Games - Avalon Hill Game Co.
1776 - Paint removers - Reliable Finishing Products, Inc.
1776 - Steel products - Salem China Co.
1776 BY SEAGRAM - Liquors - House of Seagram
1776 GEORGE WASHINGTON - Games - Classic Games Co. Inc.
1776 QUEUE - Cosmetics ☆ - Leon J.A. Buchheit Inc.
1789 - Furniture ☆ - Vaughan Furniture Co. Inc.
1800 - Flatware - Reed and Barton Corp.
1800FS - Scouring pads - Fortress Inc.
1809: NAPOLEON'S DANUBE CAMPAIGN - Games - Avalon Hill Game Co.
1810 - Flatware - International Silver Co.
1833 SHOP - Guitars - C.F. Martin & Co., Inc.
1835 R WALLACE - Flatware ☆ - Wallace International Silversmiths, Inc.
1849 AUTHENTIC RANCHWEAR MADE IN U.S.A. - Apparel and accessories - Tiffara International, Inc.
1849 EMPORIUM AN AMERICAN PIONEER SPIRIT U.S.A. - Apparel and accessories - Cu Tran
1850 - Furniture - Boling Co.
1851 - Perfumes - Kiehl's Since 1851, Inc.
1852 - Honey - Honey Acres Inc.
1856 - Games - Mayfair Games, Inc.
1857 PREMIUM LAGER - Beverages–malt - Lion Brewery, Inc.
1860 AUTHENTIC - Apparel and accessories - Cactus Apparel, Inc.
1865 - Apparel and accessories - Alchem Capital Corp.
1869 - Biscuits - Pillsbury Co.
1870 - Games - Mayfair Games, Inc.
1871 - Coats–men's - Gordon & Ferguson of Delaware, Inc.
1872 - Apparel and accessories - Montgomery Ward & Co. Inc.
1874 - Watches - Gruen Marketing Corp.
1877 - Sausages - Armour Swift-Eckrich
1880 HI-WHEEL - Bicycles - Rideable Bicycle Replicas Inc.
1881 - Silver compounds - Oneida Ltd.
1881 - Wines - MPW, Inc.

1881 SELECT - Top soil, organic fertilizer - Earthgro Inc.
1882 - Fabrics - Dan River Inc.
1886 - Cigar boxes–wood - Consolidated Cigar Corp.
1886 SERIES - Fans–electric - Hunter Fan Co.
1890 - Candy - Price Candy Co. Inc.
1890 CARAMEL CORN CO. - Popcorn - Welch's Shops Inc.
1895 - Food products - Sauk City Canning Co.
1896 - Harmonicas - Hohner Inc.
1897 - Sporting goods ☆ - Shaw & Tenney Inc.
1898 RECIPE - Pickles - Aunt Jane's Foods
1898 RECIPE - Pickles - Kraft Food Ingredients Corp.
1900 - Furniture ☆ - Lane Co. Inc.
1911A1 - Pistols - Gun Parts Corp.
1916 SV - Beverages–malt - Dole Food Co., Inc.
1919 - Root beer–bottled or canned - August Schell Brewing Co.
1920 - Brandy - Admiral Wine Merchants
1928 - Jewelry - 1928 Jewelry Co.
1928 TIMEPIECES - Jewelry - Mel Bernie and Co., Inc.
1932 OLYMPIC TEAM LAKE PLACID USA - Pins–jewelry - United States Olympic Committee
1940 - Apparel and accessories - John Reahl
1942 - Dinnerware–glass - Metlox Pottery Shoppe
1942 THE PACIFIC AIR WAR - Computer software - Microprose Software, Inc.
1944 - Publisher's imprints ☆ - Gamescience
1949 HAVANA MEMORIES - Posters - Gloria Silverstein
1950-127 - Cheese - AMPI/Morning Glory Farms
1950'S BUNNY GINNY - Dolls - Dakin Inc.
1954 - Office supplies - Faber-Castell Corp.
1960 - Office supplies - Faber-Castell Corp.
1983 MACHINE, THE - Machinery - A-10 Equipment Corp.
1984 - Recording label - Miller & Kreisel Sound Corp.
1984 LOS ANGELES USA U.S. OLYMPIC TEAM - Pins–jewelry - United States Olympic Committee
1985 TEAM SET-RADIO BASEBALL - Computer software ☆ - Electronic Arts Inc.
1985 TEAM SET-WEAVER BASEBALL - Computer software - Electronic Arts Inc.
1994 CONGRESSIONAL PIG BOOK - Publisher's imprints - Citizens Against Government Waste
2000 - Adhesives and sealants - Dap Products Inc.
2000 - Motor vehicles–automobiles ☆ - General Motors Corp. (Pontiac/GMC Div.)
2000 - Office furniture–metal - Invincible Metal Furniture Co.
2000 - Office supplies - Bates Manufacturing Co.
2000 CALORIE - Cosmetics - Max Factor & Co.
2000 FLUSHES - Cleaning preparations - Block Drug Co., Inc.
2000 ISLAND - Salad dressings–bottled - Ott Food Products
2000 LSI - Boats - Harris-Kayot Inc.
2000 PLUS - Self-inking daters, time stamps, etc. - Consolidated Stamp Manufacturing Co. Inc.
2000 PROCESS NO WRINKLES - Apparel - Farah Inc.
2000 STE - Infant product - Century Products Co.
2000 YEARS - Toiletries - Richard Barrie Fragrances, Inc.
2000AD - Dryers–hair - Double K Industries, Inc.
2000FS - Scouring pads - Fortress Inc.
2000PD - Health care products - Fortress Inc.
2000S - Scouring pads - Fortress Inc.
2001 - Automotive parts and accessories ☆ - Ben Tunis Co. Inc. (U.S. Car Mat Div.)
2001 - Beds–wood - Richards Quality Bedding
2001 - Cleaning preparations - Turtle Wax, Inc.
2001 - Fabrics - F. Schumacher & Co.
2001 - Floor coverings–carpet and rugs ☆ - Karastan-Bigelow Inc.
2001 - Musical instrument accessories - E. & O. Mari Inc.
2001 - Sprinklers–lawn - Toro Co.
2001 HIGH TECK - Boats - Mariner Co.
2001 ODYSSEY - Health care products - Integrity Health Systems Corp.
2001 SKINODYSSEY - Skin care products - Viviane Woodard Industries, Ltd.
2001, THE - Furniture - Expo Displays
2001LX - Scouring pads - Fortress Inc.
2001LXS - Scouring pads - Fortress Inc.
2002 - Razor blades ☆ - Warner-Lambert Co.
2002 BY SHEAFFER - Office supplies - Sheaffer Inc.
2010 - Paints - California Products Corp.
2020 - Fishing tackle - Zebco Corp.
2020 SUPER BASEBALL - Video games - Snk Corp. of America

☆ = Now out of production

2020 TRIGON CORP. - Canes - 2020 Trigon Corp.
2100 - Watches - Blancpain (Time Products Inc.)
2100 - Watches - Elgin Watch Co.
2110 - Apparel and accessories - Breton Industries
2150 - Computer software - VHT Amplification
2200, THE - Golfing equipment - Bobby Grace Golf Design, Inc.
#2201 - Inks ☆ - Ranger Industries
#2202 - Inks - Ranger Industries
#2209 - Inks - Ranger Industries
#2240- FABRA-CA-DABRA - Inks - Ranger Industries
2400 - Floor coverings–carpet and rugs - J and J Industries Inc.
2400 A.D. - Video games - Origin Systems, Inc.
2500 - Polishes - Park Metallurgical Corp.
2500 MAG II - Washing machines–commercial - Colman Manufacturing Co.
2520 - Photocopy machines - Xerox Corp.
2600 - Audio equipment ☆ - Telequest Inc.
3000 - Faucets - Kallista Inc.
3000 - Transmitting apparatus - Wescom, Inc.
3000 GT - Motor vehicles–automobiles - Mitsubishi Motor Sales of America Inc.
3000 PATRIOT - Artists' materials - Day International Inc.
3000 STE - Infant product - Century Products Co.
3000BC - Health care products - 3000 B.C., Ltd.
3000GT - Motor vehicles–automobiles - Mitsubishi Motor Sales of America Inc.
3001 - Automotive parts and accessories - K & K Jump Start/Chargers, Inc.
3006 - Office machines - Xerox Corp.
3030 - Photocopy machines - Xerox Corp.
3054 - Mufflers–motor vehicle - AP Parts
3060 - Photocopy machines - Xerox Corp.
3120 - Computer peripheral equipment - Echelon Corp.
3150 - Semiconductors - Echelon Corp.
3164 - Mufflers–motor vehicle - AP Parts
3188 - Mufflers–motor vehicle - AP Parts
3197 - Mufflers–motor vehicle - AP Parts
3200 - Rifles - Redfield Co.
3226 - Mufflers–motor vehicle - AP Parts
3277 - Mufflers–motor vehicle - AP Parts
3500 - Mufflers–motor vehicle - AP Parts
3500 MAG II - Pressure washers - Custom Marine
3500 STE - Infant product ☆ - Century Products Co.
4000 - Adhesives and sealants - Dap Products Inc.
4000 - Floor coverings–carpet and rugs ☆ - Karastan-Bigelow Inc.
4000 - Motor vehicles–automobiles ☆ - Audi of America Inc.
4000, 3600 - Blenders - Vita-Mix Corp.
4000CS - Vans–conversion ☆ - Turtle Top Specialty Products
4004 - Printers–computer - Xerox Corp.
4011 - Printers–computer - Xerox Corp.
4050 - Computer peripheral equipment - Xerox Corp.
4100 SERIES, THE - Globes ☆ - Replogle Globes Inc.
4197 MICR - Printers–computer - Xerox Corp.
4220 - Printers–computer - Xerox Corp.
4250/MRP - Printers–computer - Xerox Corp.
4450 - Printers–computer - Xerox Corp.
4500SCOUT - Medical apparatus - Invivo Research, Inc.
4505 - Printers–computer - Xerox Corp.
4510 - Printers–computer - Xerox Corp.
4520 - Printers–computer - Xerox Corp.
4600 - Sports apparel - Reebok International Ltd.
4635 - Printers–computer - Xerox Corp.
4700 - Printers–computer - Xerox Corp.
4711 - Skin care products - Frances Denney
4890 - Printers–computer - Xerox Corp.
4900 - Printers–computer - Xerox Corp.
5000 - Furniture ☆ - Athens Furniture Industries Inc.
5000 - Motor vehicles–automobiles - Audi of America Inc.
5000 - Paints - Buten Paint & Wallpaper
5000 - Staples - ACCO USA, Inc.
5000 CX - Drums–musical instruments - Drum Workshop, Inc.
5000 SERIES - Drive shafts–motor vehicle - Snow-Nabstedt Power Transmissions
5000 SERIES - Tools - Jural Manufacturing Co.
5000 STE - Infant product - Century Products Co.

5000 TURBO - Drums–musical instruments - Drum Workshop, Inc.
5002 - Drums–musical instruments - Drum Workshop, Inc.
5009 - Photocopy machines - Xerox Corp.
5053 - Photocopy machines - Xerox Corp.
5080 - Photocopy machines - Xerox Corp.
5100 - Photocopy machines - Xerox Corp.
5150 SNOWBOARDS - Apparel and accessories - 5150 Co., Inc.
5201 - Photocopy machines - Xerox Corp.
5203 - Photocopy machines - Xerox Corp.
5205 - Photocopy machines - Xerox Corp.
5305 - Photocopy machines - Xerox Corp.
5306 - Photocopy machines - Xerox Corp.
5309 - Photocopy machines - Xerox Corp.
5310 - Photocopy machines - Xerox Corp.
5313 - Office supplies - Xerox Corp.
5340 - Photocopy machines - Xerox Corp.
5343C - Photocopy machines - Xerox Corp.
5350 - Photocopy machines - Xerox Corp.
5352C - Photocopy machines - Xerox Corp.
5365 - Photocopy machines - Xerox Corp.
5380 - Photocopy machines - Xerox Corp.
5390 - Duplicating machines - Xerox Corp.
5500 CENTURY - Bathroom accessories - Franklin Brass Manufacturing Co.
5500 STE - Infant product ☆ - Century Products Co.
5600 - Sports apparel - Reebok International Ltd.
5680 - Photocopy machines - Xerox Corp.
5775 - Office supplies - Xerox Corp.
5850 - Apparel and accessories ☆ - Edison Brothers Stores, Inc.
5950, THE - Hats - New Era Cap Co., Inc.
6000 - Motor vehicles–automobiles - General Motors Corp. (Pontiac/GMC Div.)
6000 SERIES - Tools - Jural Manufacturing Co.
6000 STE - Motor vehicles–automobiles - General Motors Corp. (Pontiac/GMC Div.)
6003 SRC 1000 - Cameras - Rollei of America Inc.
6008 SRC 1000 - Cameras - Rollei of America Inc.
6125 - Asphalt - American Hydrotech, Inc.
6300 - Computers–personal - At&T Corp.
6300 - Microfiche equipment - Bell & Howell Co.
7000 - Sporting goods ☆ - Shakespeare Fishing Tackle
7033 - Facsimile equipment - Xerox Corp.
7041 - Facsimile equipment - Xerox Corp.
7720 - Computer peripheral equipment - Bytex Corp.
7730 - Matrix switch for computer network - Bytex Corp.
7760 - Computer peripherals - Bytex Corp.
7769 - Paints - Rust-Oleum Corp.
7800 - Video games - Atari Games Corp.
7800 CONTEMPORARY - Furniture - Henredon Furniture Industries Inc.
8400/9400 SERIES - Filters–air - Controls Corp. of America
008550ORLD - Computer software - International Data Group, Inc.
8900 - Adhesives and sealants ☆ - Reliable Finishing Products, Inc.
9000 - Dental equipment - AFP Imaging Corp.
9000 - Office supplies - Faber-Castell Corp.
9000 - Staplers - Bates Manufacturing Co.
9000 - Toys–models - Saab-Scania of America Inc.
9001 - Apparel and accessories ☆ - Kellwood Co.
9001 - Apparel–women's - A.J. Brandon, Inc.
9100 - Film - Dale Laboratories, Inc.
9400 - Film - Dale Laboratories, Inc.
9700 CALLING CARD BOXLINE - Boxes - Creative Cookie Inc. (American Dream Enterprises)
9999 FINE-GOLD U.S.A VIETNAM-VIENTIANE HONGKONG-PNOMPENN - Gold products - Phi Thi Nguyen
10,000 FLOWERS - Pollen extracts - CC Pollen Co.
10,000 LAKES PASTA - Pasta - Homestead, Inc.
10,001 - Ventilation equipment - Syntech Products Corp.
12000F HI-TEMP - Paints ☆ - Zynolyte Products Co.
12345 ARCHIVET - Computer software - Archivet Corp.
014620 - Fishing lures - William R. Conine, Jr.
$20,000 PYRAMID - Games ☆ - Milton Bradley Co.
021110 - Protec International
23456 - Computer software - T.L. Ashford & Associates, Inc.
90210 ENTANGLE GAME - Games - Cardinal Industries, Inc.

A

Addresses and phone numbers for the companies cited in the brands below
are available in the Company Listings section immediately following the brands listings.

A - Apparel and accessories - Acceleration Products, Inc.
A - Apparel and accessories - Albany Professional Baseball Club, Inc.
A - Apparel–athletic - Hockey Acceleration Products, Inc.
A - Apparel–athletic - Texas Professional Baseball, Inc.
A - Automotive parts and accessories - AMBAC International Corp.
A+ - Battery testers - High Voltage Engineering Corp.
A+ - Beverages - Atlantic Refining & Marketing Corp.
A - Coffee - ARA Services Inc.
A+ - Computer hardware - Accelgraphics Inc.
A - Computer software - Access Data Inc.
A - Computer software - Ace Software Corp.
A - Computer software - Jung/Brannen Research & Development Corp.
A - Computer software - Medio Multimedia, Inc.
A - Goggles–safety - American Ultraviolet Co.
A - Jewelry - Alessi Jewelry Ltd.
A - Jewelry - Angelo Inc.
A - Jewelry - K. Papazian Inc.
A - Jewelry - Sunwest Silver, Inc.
A - Laboratory apparatus - Atto Instruments, Inc.
A - Measuring instruments - Anders Lowe Inc.
A - Organizers - Advantus, Corp.
A - Paints ☆ - Allpro Corp.
A - Plastics film - Atlantis Group Inc.
A+ - Publisher's imprints - Aluminum Co. of America
A - Sheet metal products - Atco Rubber Products Inc.
A+ - Skin care products - Aramis Inc.
A - Stationery ☆ - Mead Corp.
A-1 - Adhesives and sealants - Pratt & Lambert, Inc.
A-1 - Bathroom accessories - R-Z Co. of America Inc.
A-1 - Beverages–malt ☆ - The Stroh Brewery Co.
A-1 - Bleach - James Austin Co.
A-1 - Fibers–elastomeric ☆ - Pillsbury Co.
A-1 - Food products - Nabisco Foods Group
A-1 - Paint removers ☆ - M.L. Campbell Co.
A-1 - Paints - Allentown Paint Manufacturing Co. Inc.
A-1 - Paints - Standard Brands Paint Co.
A-1 - Paper–tissue ☆ - Plainwell Tissue
A-1 - Pickles - Gourmet Specialties
A-1 - Vegetables–canned - Kennebec Bean Co. Inc.
A-1 BOLD - Food products - Nabisco Foods Group
A-1 CORNBROOMS - Brooms - The Lassen Companies
A-1 MAGIC - Paints - Standard Brands Paint Co.
A-2 - Office supplies ☆ - Ideal Stencil Machine and Tape Co.
A-4 ALPHA HYDROXY - Skin care products - Sports Research Corp.
A-9 - Lubricating oils - Relton Corp.
A-10 - Computer software - Spectrum Holobyte, Inc.
A-10 WARTHOG - Computer software - Spectrum Holobyte, Inc.
A 14K A - Jewelry - A. Alland Inc.
A-21 - Decals and transfers - Rubbermaid Inc.
A 33 - Vitamins and nutritional supplements - Kroeger Herb Products Co. Inc.
A-55 - Gasoline - Rudolf W. Gunnerman
A-100 - Paints - Sherwin-Williams Automotive Finishes Corp.
A 111 - Pens - Alexander Manufacturing Co.
A-200 PYRINATE - Pharmaceutical preparations ☆ - Smithkline Beecham Corp.
A-411 - Luggage - Samsonite Corp.

A-1000 - Epoxy - Rawlplug Co., Inc.
A/A - Almond pastes - American Almond Products Co., Inc.
A/A - Pharmaceutical preparations - Alva-Amco Pharmacal Co.
A/A - Religious artifacts - American Metalcraft Inc.
A/A DRAIN LINER - Liners and covers–pond, pit, and landfill - A/A Manufacturing Inc.
A/A GRIP LINER - Liners and covers–pond, pit, and landfill - A/A Manufacturing Inc.
A ACADEMY BROADWAY - Shovels - Academy Broadway Corp.
A ACTIVE ANKLE - Bandages–orthopedic - Active Ankle Systems, Inc.
A ADOBE - Computer software - Adobe Systems Inc.
A AEROLIGHT - Electric lighting equipment - Londavia Inc.
A ALAMO - Machinery ☆ - Alamo Industrial
A ALEMITE - Machinery - Stewart Warner Alemite Licensco Inc.
A ALICE ANN DESIGNS - Clothing - Hanold Co.
A ALTON HOUSE - Furniture - Alton Industries Inc.
A-AMERICA - Furniture - A-America, Inc.
A AMERICAN HOP ALE - Beverages–malt - Anheuser-Busch Companies Inc.
A AMERICAN MADE - Furniture–upholstered - Park & Sell Co., Inc.
A AMERIGO - Clocks - Lasercraft, Inc.
A & A - Paints - L.D. Sterns Corp.
A & B - Candy ☆ - Adams & Brooks, Inc.
A & B - Coffee - A & B Coffee Co.
A & B - Electronic equipment - A and B Enterprises Inc.
A & D - Skin care products - Schering-Plough Healthcare Products
A & E - Awnings - Dometic Corp.
A & E - Vitamins and nutritional supplements - Naturally Vitamin Supplements Inc.
A & EAGLE - Beverages–malt - Anheuser-Busch Companies Inc.
A & M - Alarm systems–burglar - A & M Jewelry Co.
A & M - Footwear–men's ☆ - A & S Imports Inc.
A & M - Hearing aids - Electone Inc.
A & M - Musical instrument accessories - David Wexler & Co.
A & M - Recording label - A and M Records, Inc.
A & M - Seafood products–fresh or frozen - Pocasset Seafoods Inc.
A & O - Mayonnaise - A & O Specialty Foods
A & S - Containers–shipping - A & S Case Co. Inc.
A & T - Apparel and accessories - A & T Ski Co. Inc.
A & W - Beverages–carbonated - A and W Brands Inc.
A & W - Beverages–carbonated - Dr. Pepper/Seven Up, Inc.
A & W - Chewing gum ☆ - Amurol Confections Co.
A & W - Publisher's imprints - A & W Publishers Inc.
A & W ROOT BEER FLOAT ON A STICK - Confections - Merritt Foods Co.
A & W ROOTBEER - Candy - Glenn Confections Inc.
A & W VISUAL LIBRARY - Publisher's imprints - A & W Publishers Inc.
A & Z - Giftware - A & Z/Hayward
A ANDERSON MARSHALL - Paperboard–corrugated - Inland Container Corp.
A APPLICATION PLUS - Computer software - Daly and Wolcott, Inc.
A ART LEATHER - Photo albums - Art Leather Manufacturing Co., Inc.
A+ AUDIO - Computer software - Atlantic Records
A AUI - Machinery - Ace USA, Inc.
A-B - Beverages–malt - Anheuser-Busch Companies Inc.
A/B - Dairy products - Christian Hansen's Laboratory Inc.
A-B-A - Aluminum paints - American Paints
A-B-C - Bathing suits ☆ - Roxanne Swim Suits Co. Inc.
A-B-C - Food products - L. Karp & Sons, Inc.

A-B-C - Veterinary pharmaceutical preparations ☆ - Pfizer Inc.
A-B-C/1-2-3 - Puzzles - Milton Bradley Co.
A B C D E F G H - Bowling balls - Ebonite International, Inc.
A. B. DICK - Office machines - A.B. Dick Co.
A B H - Hardware - Architectural Builders Hardware Manufacturing Co., Inc.
A-B-S CLOTHING COLLECTION - ABS Clothing Collection Inc.
A-B TEX - Paints - United States Gypsum Co.
A BAG FOR ALL REASONS - Paper–gift wrap - Loretta L. Stenovich
A BALANCED BODY - Exercising equipment - Current Concepts Corp.
A-BAR - Automotive parts and accessories - Answer Products Inc.
A BATCH OF ENDINGS - Computer software ☆ - Right on Programs
A BEDTIME STORY - Wallpaper - Old Stone Mill
A. BERGAMO - Apparel–men's ☆ - Edison Brothers Stores, Inc.
A BETA CARE - Vitamins and nutritional supplements - Aloe Vera of America, Inc.
A-BETTA - Saddles - Donald Marshall Motsenbocker
A BETTER BLIND - Window coverings - Vertical Blind Factory
A BETTER DESIGN - A BETTER WORLD - Computer hardware - Commercial and Industrial Design Co. Inc.
A BETTER POWDER - Cosmetics - Estee Lauder Inc.
A BETTER WAY TO CATCH SOME Z'S - Bedding - Ohio Mattress Co.
A. BIANCHI - Wines - Vintwood International Ltd.
A BIG PART OF BETTER PERFORMANCE. - Motor vehicle parts and accessories - Horton Holdings, Inc.
A BIG TOP CHRISTMAS - Giftware - Schmid Inc.
A BITE OF CHOCOLATE YOU CAN REALLY SINKYOUR TEETH INTO - Candy - Homestead, Inc.
A BITE OF NATURE - Health care products - Ion Laboratories Inc.
A BLAST FROM THE PAST - Giftware - Gary Zachary Lerner
A BOAR 150 - Animal feeds - Carl S. Akey Inc.
A-BOOM - Lawn mowers - Alamo Industrial
A BOOTS - Publisher's imprints - Kidsbooks, Inc.
A BOTTLE A MOTHER COULD LOVE! - Infant product - Munchkin Bottling, Inc.
A BOY & HIS DOG - Calendars - Brown and Bigelow Inc.
A. BRANDT - Furniture - A. Brandt Co. Inc.
A BRIGHTER DAY - Televisions - Jan D. D'atri
A BRUSH WITH SUCCESS - Brushes–hair - Spornette International, Inc.
A/C - Deodorizers - Ryter Corp.
A/C - Jewelry–precious - A/C Import
A-C CARBAMIDE - Food products - Standard Process Inc.
A/C/E - Sporting goods - Easton Aluminum Inc.
A-C FORMULA 90 - Garden equipment - J.T. Eaton and Co.
A CAPPELLA PUBLISHING - Publisher's imprints - A Cappella Publishing
A CARD FOR ALL AGES - Greeting cards - Designer Greetings Inc.
A CAT'S EYE VIEW - Calendars - American Greetings Corp.
A CHANCE FOR SURVIVAL - Jewelry - Felley Inc.
A CHANGE FOR THE BUTTER - Margarine - Western Family Foods, Inc.
A CHILD'S GIFT OF BEDTIME STORIES - Recording label - Someday Baby, Inc.
A CHILD'S GIFT OF LULLABYES - Frames–picture - Someday Baby, Inc.
A CHILD'S GIFT OF LULLABYES - Recording label - Child's Gift of Lullabyes
A CHORUS OF CULTURES - Recording label - Hampton-Brown Co., Inc.
A CHRISTMAS DREAM - Christmas tree ornaments ☆ - Roman, Inc.
A CHRISTMAS SAMPLER - Computer software ☆ - Cross Educational Software Inc.
A CHUCKLE A DAY... - Calendars - E.P. Publishing
A CIRCLE A - Saddles - American Saddlery, Inc.
A CLASSIC IDEA IN COFFEE CONCEPTS - Sweeteners–artificial - Mr. Coffee Concepts, Inc.
A CLASSICAL STYLE - Wallpaper ☆ - Sanitas Wallcoverings
A+ +CLIENT/SERVER - Computer software - Daly and Wolcott, Inc.
A COMMON THREAD - Apparel and accessories - Bugle Boy Industries, Inc.
A COMPANY OF FRIENDS - Giftware - Determined Productions, Inc.
A COMPUJET - Office supplies - American Ink Jet Corp.
A COMPUTER USER'S BEST FRIEND - Computer storage devices–optical - Kris Jamsa Software, Inc.
A CONTEMPORARY TOUCH - Fabrics–tapestry ☆ - Coloroll Inc.
A COUNTRY WELCOME - Wallcovering - Fashon Wallcoverings
A CUP ABOVE - Coffee - Saramar Corp.
A CURRENT EVENT - Apparel stores–women's - Lady Ester Lingerie Corp.
A. CUSTOM-CYMBALS - Cymbals - Avedis Zildjian Co.
A CUT ABOVE - Apparel stores–lingerie - Formfit Rogers
A CUT ABOVE - Knives - A & W Products Co., Inc.
A CUT ABOVE - Seasonings - A Cut Above Foods, Inc.
A CUT ABOVE AT ANY ANGLE - Motor vehicles–all-terrain - UST Corp.

A CUT ABOVE THE CROWD - Wallpaper - K.M.L. Industries
A CUT ABOVE THE REST - Apparel–women's - HCS International Inc.
A CUT ABOVE THE REST - Cabinets–wood - Coastal Wood Products, Inc.
A-CUTE DERM - Skin care products - Esta Kronberg
A-CYSTO - Health care products - Equi-Tron Inc.
A/D - Pet food - Colgate-Palmolive Co.
A + D - Pharmaceutical preparations - Schering Corp.
A-D-A - Veterinary pharmaceutical preparations ☆ - Pfizer Inc.
A/D/F - Vitamins and nutritional supplements - Freeman Industries LLC
A-D-R - Pharmaceutical preparations - Lincoln Diagnostics
A DALLA COSTA - Postcards ☆ - Classico San Francisco Inc.
A DAY AT PLAY - Computer software - Don Johnston Inc.
A DAY AT THE PARK - Games - Treat Entertainment, Inc.
A DAY AT THE PARK - Trading cards and stamps - ANCO Collector Supplies, Inc.
A DAY AT THE SLOPES - Health care products - Production Plus Inc.
A DAY IN THE SUN - Suntan lotions - Matrix Essentials, Inc.
A DAY TO FIND OUT - Computer software ☆ - Orange Cherry Software
A DEPENDENT SOCIETY - Recording label - Peter Mahoney
A DICTIONARY FOR THE REST OF US! - Computer software - International Data Group, Inc.
A DIET EMPORIUM - Food products - Muffin Lady Inc.
A DIFFERENT PERSPECTIVE - Furniture - Different Perspective, Inc.
A DIFFERENT VIEWPOINT - Fabrics–tapestry ☆ - Columbus Coated Fabrics Co.
A-DOOR-ABLES - Pillows - Russ Berrie and Co., Inc.
A. E. C. - Musical instrument accessories - Seymour Duncan Pickups
A F - Jewelry - American Fulfillment Trading Corp.
A. F. BISCHOFF - Posters - Sloan Glass Inc.
A F R - Ashtrays–metal - One Eleven Corp.
A FAIRY BOX BOOK - Publisher's imprints - Wendy Wallin Malinow
A FARMHOUSE IN PROVENCE - Wallpaper ☆ - Raintree Designs Inc.
A FESTIVAL OF FLOWER FAIRIES - Giftware ☆ - Enesco Corp.
A FIELD TRIP TO THE RAINFOREST - Computer software - Sunburst Communications, Inc.
A-FIL - Pharmaceutical preparations - Texas Pharmacal Co.
A FINISH 52 - Animal feeds - Carl S. Akey Inc.
A FINISH 58 - Animal feeds - Carl S. Akey Inc.
A FLUID - Antiseptics - Elysee Scientific Cosmetic Co.
A. FONTAINE - Musical instruments ☆ - Fred Gretsch Enterprises
A FOOT OF BUBBLEGUM - Chewing gum - Sahagian & Associates, Inc.
A-FRAME - Apparel and accessories ☆ - Jantzen Inc.
A-FREE PRENATAL - Vitamins and nutritional supplements - Freeda Vitamins Inc.
A FRIEND OF THE FAMILY - Toys - Spalding & Evenflo Companies, Inc.
A FROSTY FRUIT SENSATION! - Beverages - Parrot Ice Drink Products of America, Inc.
A FUNNY CARD - Greeting cards - Pawprints Greeting Cards
A-G ALLISON-GRAY COLLECTION - Apparel–women's - Swat Fame, Inc.
A. G. BEAR - Toys–electronic - Axlon Inc.
A. G. +RUSSELL - Knives - A.G. Russell Knives Inc.
A GARDEN OF GOOD EATIN' - Spices and extracts - To Market to Market
A GARDEN OF GOOD THINGS - Crock pots - Rival Manufacturing Co.
A GARDEN ROMANCE - Wallpaper - Pickhardt & Siebert USA Inc.
A GARDEN VIEW - Wallpaper - Sterling Prints
A GARDENERS CHRONICLE - Wallpaper ☆ - Old Deerfield Fabrics Inc.
A GATEWAY STORY - Compact discs–prerecorded - Texas Caviar, Inc.
A GENERATION AHEAD - Firearms, accessories, and parts ☆ - Modern Muzzle Loading, Inc.
A-GENT - Pharmaceutical preparations - Abbott Laboratories
A. GEOFFREY LTD. - Apparel–men's - Alan Stuart, Inc.
A. GIANETTI - Handbags - TJX Companies, Inc.
A GIFT FOR YOU - Flowers, plants, and seeds - Plant Promotions, Inc.
A GIFT FROM THE AGES - Vitamins and nutritional supplements - Benchmark USA, Inc.
A GIFT FROM THE ENVIRONMENT - Paper–gift wrap - Earthelp Inc.
A GIFT OF CREATION - Bottled spring water - Gentleman Jim's, Inc.
A GIFT OF TIME - Greeting cards - M.S. Strong, LLC
A-GIRL - Books–comic - Elizabeth Sirikanya Watasin
A GIRL'S BEST FRIEND - Apparel and accessories ☆ - Glamorise Foundations Inc.
A GO GLO - Clocks - Indiglo Corp.
A. GOLD E. - Clothing - A.G.E.
A GOLDEN EASY READER - Publisher's imprints ☆ - Western Publishing Co., Inc.

☆ = Now out of production

A GOLDEN LITTLE SUPER SHAPE BOOK - Publisher's imprints - Golden Books Publishing Co., Inc.

A GOLDEN MYSTERY PUZZLE? - Games ☆ - Western Publishing Co., Inc.

A GOLDEN NAPTIME TALE - Publisher's imprints - Western Publishing Co., Inc.

A GOLDEN PREMIER PUZZLE - Games ☆ - Western Publishing Co., Inc.

A GOLDEN STAR READER - Publisher's imprints ☆ - Western Publishing Co., Inc.

A GOLDEN TAKE-A-LOOK BOOK - Publisher's imprints - Western Publishing Co., Inc.

A GOLDEN VERY EASY READER - Publisher's imprints - Western Publishing Co., Inc.

A GRATEFUL NATION REMEMBERS 1941-1945 E - Awards, plaques and medals - Department of the Army

A GREAT DAY AT THE RACES - Computer software - Philips Interactive Media of America

A GREAT FIT - Brassieres (Bras) - Playtex Apparel, Inc.

A GREAT VARIETY - Recording label - Jay Jay Record & Tape Co.

A GREENPATCH BOOK - Publisher's imprints - Harcourt Brace & Co.

A GROW-FINISH 65 - Animal feeds - Carl S. Akey Inc.

A-H - Adhesives and sealants - Anti Hydro International Inc.

A-H 3 WAY SEALER - Adhesives and sealants - Anti Hydro International Inc.

A. H. BROOKING - Leather goods - Korchmar Case Co.

A-H EMERY - Caulking compounds - Anti Hydro International Inc.

A-H POLYSEALANTS - Caulking compounds - Anti Hydro International Inc.

A-H PVC WATERSTOP - Adhesives and sealants - Anti Hydro International Inc.

A-H SEAMLESS MEMBRANE - Adhesives and sealants - Anti Hydro International Inc.

A-H SUPER CAN-CRETE - Adhesives and sealants ☆ - Anti Hydro International Inc.

A-HA! - Apparel–women's - Miss India, Inc.

A HALF MOON BOOK - Children's books - Simon & Schuster, Inc.

A. HARDY - Beverages–alcohol - Paterno Imports, Ltd.

A HEALTHIER BALANCE FOR A HEALTHIER PET - Pet food - Colgate-Palmolive Co.

A HEALTHY SNACK TO GROW ON - Cheese - Frigo Cheese Corp.

A HENRY HOLT MYSTERY - Publisher's imprints - Henry Holt and Co.

A. HOFFMAN CO. - Tarpaulins - John Hoffman Awning Co.

A. HOLTHE - Dinnerware–glass ☆ - Henriksen Imports Inc.

A HOUSE IN THE HAMPTONS - Wallpaper ☆ - Raintree Designs Inc.

A HUG - Novelty items - St. Clair & Co.

A-HUG-AWAY - Dolls - A-Hug-Away, Inc.

A I C - Jewelry - American Inns of Court Foundation

A. J. BOYD - Window blinds - A.J. Boyd Industries Inc.

A-J PINK LIQUID - Cleaning preparations - Mione Manufacturing Co.

A J R - Jewelry - Reeds Corporate Services, Inc.

A. #JAFFE - Jewelry - Sandberg & Sikorski Diamond Corp.

A JOURNEY INTO DARKNESS - Computer software ☆ - Earthware Computer Services

A JULI JR. - Underwear and nightwear ☆ - Slumbertogs Inc.

A-JUST-A-CUT ABOVE THE REST! - Envelopes - New York Envelope Corp.

A-JUST-A-FLAME - Lighters - Butane Products Corp.

A-JUST-A-RIBBON - Ribbons ☆ - Equality/Stribbons

A-JUST-O-RAKE - Rakes - Oak Lawn Industries Inc.

A. K. COBURG - Compact discs–prerecorded - Coburg CDs

A KIDS - Recording label - Peter W. Hickey

A KIDS COMPANION - Vitamins and nutritional supplements - Natrol, Inc.

A KINDER LINER - Cosmetics - Dolly Parton Inc.

A KITCHEN FOR THE MIND - Recording label - Intellectual Equities, Inc.

A. KNILLING - Musical instrument accessories - St. Louis Music Supply Co.

A-KONO-FLO - Filters–air - Air Kontrol Inc.

A. KRAMLING - Musical instrument accessories ☆ - John M. Connolly & Co. Inc.

A LA CART - Carts - Clifford Pierce Inc.

A LA CARTE - Apparel and accessories ☆ - Imperial Knitting Co. Inc.

A LA CARTE - Credit-card wallet - Hugo Bosca Co., Inc.

A LA CARTE - Frames–eyeglass - May Optical Co. Inc.

A LA CARTE - Furniture ☆ - Bernhardt Industries

A LA CARTE - Furniture–wood - Ficks Reed Co. Inc.

A LA CARTE - Ovens–industrial - Lincoln Foodservice Products, Inc.

A LA CARTE - Tiles–ceramic - Epro Inc.

A LA CARTE - Underwear and nightwear - Maidenform Inc.

A LA CAT - Greeting cards - American Greetings Corp.

A LA FRANCAIS - Yogurt - Weight Watchers International, Inc.

A LA HENRI - Meat and poultry - Pocono Foods Inc.

A LA MAUVE - Nail care products - Cosmair Inc.

A LA MODE - Apparel–children's - Venture Stores, Inc.

A LA MODE - Food products - Van Den Bergh Foods Co.

A LA MODE - Food products ☆ - American Fruit Processors

A LA MODE - Frames–eyeglass - Zylo Ware Corp.

A LA MODE - Nail care products - Orly International Inc.

A LA PERRUCHE - Sugar–granulated, refined, or powdered - Dean & Deluca Inc.

A LA POURSUITE DE CARMEN SANDIEGO - Computer software - Gessler Publishing Co., Inc.

A LA TREND - Hair care products ☆ - Spilo/Mehaz Worldwide

A-LAB - Recording label - ABX Records

A LADY'S PARADISE - Apparel–women's - Henri Bendel, Inc.

A. LAURANCE - Wines ☆ - Cannon Wines Ltd.

A. LE MARTEAU & FILS - Beverages–alcohol - Hammer Co.

A LEGEND IN A NUTSHELL - Nuts–salted, roasted, cooked, or canned - Virginia Diner, Inc.

A LEGEND IN SOUND - Amplifiers–public address - Klipsch and Associates Inc.

A LEMONATED - Liqueurs - Mango Bottling, Inc.

A LESSON OF SORTS - Computer software ☆ - Earthware Computer Services

A LETTER FROM HOME COOKIE COMPANY - Bakery products - A Letter from Home Cookie Co.

A LIBRARY OF LITERARY CRITICISM - Publisher's imprints ☆ - Crossroad

A LI'L ANNIE FRANNIE - Dolls - S & P Industries

A LIL' PEACE OF HEAVEN CLOUD CUTIES - Playing cards - Bethann Shannon

A LINE - Apparel–women's - Anne Klein & Co.

A LINE - Hosiery - Pennaco Hosiery Inc.

A LINE A DAY - Diaries - Samuel Ward Manufacturing Inc.

A-LIST - Apparel–women's - Just for Wraps, Inc.

A LITTLE ANGEL CREATION - Crocheted and knitted items - Baby Togs, Inc.

A LITTLE BIT OF LUCK - Giftware - Russ Berrie and Co., Inc.

A LITTLE CHRISTMAS VILLAGE AT LA VILLITA - Broadcasting stations–television - Waterman Broadcasting Corp. of Texas, Inc.

A LITTLE CURIOSITY - Hobby kits - Curiosity Development, Inc.

A LITTLE JAZZ - Hair coloring preparations ☆ - Clairol Inc.

A LITTLE MESSAGE OF LOVE - Giftware - Russ Berrie and Co., Inc.

A LITTLE NUDEY - Apparel and accessories ☆ - Warnaco Inc.

A LITTLE OFF THE TOP - Hair care products - Salon Development Corp.

A LITTLE PERFECTION GOES A LONG WAY - Bakery products - Anthony Bonviso

A LITTLE PIECE OF ART - Greeting cards - Constance Kay

A LITTLE PUSHY - Apparel and accessories ☆ - Warnaco Inc.

A LITTLE ROMANCE - Greeting cards - American Greetings Corp.

A LITTLE ROMANCE.TO REMIND YOU OF ME - Greeting cards - AGC, Inc.

A LITTLE SLEEPYTIME BOOK - Publisher's imprints - Kidsbooks, Inc.

A LITTLE SOMETHING - Giftware ☆ - Brushcreek Creative Co.

A LITTLE SOMETHING - Jewelry - Monmouth Capital Corp.

A LITTLE SOMETHING FOR EVERYONE - Candy - Homestead, Inc.

A-LIVE - Laces–boot and shoe - Pepperell Braiding Co. Inc.

A LOCAL - Apparel and accessories - Dehylton Studio

A-LOK - Hardware - Predator Industries, Inc.

A L'OLIVIER - Olive oil - De Medici Imports Ltd.

A LONGABERGER HOMETOWN CHRISTMAS - Christmas tree ornaments - Longaberger Co.

A LOTTA CHILADAS - Sauces - David W. Kienzle

A LP FINISH 15 - Animal feeds - Carl S. Akey Inc.

A LP FINISH 60 - Animal feeds - Carl S. Akey Inc.

A-LUM-O - Aluminum products - Carey Electronic Engineering Co.

A-LUM-O-AIRE - Filters–air - Carey Electronic Engineering Co.

A-LUMI-CAULK - Caulking compounds - Sterling-Clark-Lurton Corp.

A-LUMI-GLAZE - Finishing agents - Sterling-Clark-Lurton Corp.

A-LURE - Boats - Glen-L Marine Designs

A-M - Cabinets - Akro-Mils Inc.

A M ANDREW MCCLINTOCK COLLECTION - Apparel and accessories - Scott Andrew McClintock

A-M-T - Pharmaceutical preparations ☆ - Wyeth-Ayerst Laboratories

A MAG ZINC - Vitamins and nutritional supplements - Garcoa Labs/Vitamin Classics

A MAGICAL BLEND OF MUSIC AND THE SOUNDSOF NATURE - Recording label - Metacom Inc.

A-MAIZE-ING DELIGHT - Ice cream - Desco Foods Inc.

A MAJOR - Recording label ☆ - Parr-X Corp.

A MARILYN BURNS BRAINY DAY BOOK - Publisher's imprints - Marilyn Burns Education Associates

☆ = Now out of production

A MASTERPIECE IN A MOMENT - Spices and extracts - To Market to Market

A MASTER'S PORTFOLIO - Wallpaper - Andover Wallcovering

A-MAUI-CAN - Apparel and accessories - Robert A. Abrahams

A-MAZE-ING BUGS - Toys - Educational Insights, Inc.

A-MAZE-MENT - Games - Tyco Toys

A MAZE 'N MONEY - Games - Dittler Brothers, Inc.

A. MEAKIN - Glassware–household ✩ - Crownford Giftware Co. Inc.

A+ MEDICAL PRODUCTS - Medical apparatus - A+ Medical Products, Inc.

A-MERC - Ammunition - F & F Equipment, Inc.

A MERRIGOLD PRESS TELL-A-TALE - Publisher's imprints - Western Publishing Co., Inc.

A MERRY LITTLE MURDER - Puzzles - Hasbro, Inc.

A MHS - Computer software - Data Systems Analysts, Inc.

A MICHAEL & CORNELIA BESSIE BOOK - Publisher's imprints - Harper & Row Publishers Inc.

A MIND FOREVER VOYAGING - Computer software - Activision, Inc.

A MOMENT'S PAUSE - Greeting cards - Kokohar Publications, Inc.

A. MONMOUSSEAU - Wines - C & B Vintage Cellars

A. MONTEUX FLOWER WATER - Spices and extracts - Europa Foods Ltd.

A MONTH OF SUNDAYS - Anvils - Psychographic Design Group, Inc.

A MOTHER'S HEART - Jewelry - Sandberg & Sikorski Diamond Corp.

A MOTHER'S LOVE - Giftware - Avon Products, Inc.

A MOTHER'S SPECIAL LOVE - Jewelry - Peter Brams Designs, Ltd.

A MOVEABLE FEAST OF TEXAS - Meat sauces - A Moveable Feast, Inc.

A-MTS - Office supplies - Ed-Tech Service Co.

A MUPPET BABIES BIG STEPS BOOK - Publisher's imprints - Jim Henson Productions, Inc.

A/N/W - Artists' materials - Andrews/Nelson/Whitehead

A NATROL HIGH - Vitamins and nutritional supplements - Natrol, Inc.

A NATURAL RESPONSE TO THE SUN - Outlook Eyewear Co.

A-NET - Computer software ✩ - Apple Computer Inc.

A NEW ANGLE ON SNACKING - Potato chips ✩ - Keebler Co.

A NEW LEGACY - Wallpaper - Beachwood Wallcoverings

A NEW LIFE TO LIVE - Computer software - A New Life to Live, Inc.

A NEW LOOK FOR HEALTH PROFESSIONALS - Apparel and accessories - Avery Medical Fashions, Inc.

A NEW WAY TO TELL - Clocks - By Design Corp.

A NEW WAY TO TELL TIME - Clocks - Charles S. Coster

A+ NEW YORK - Apparel and accessories - A+ Ltd.

A NIGHT ON THE HUDSON - Dolls ✩ - Effanbee Doll Corp.

A NIGHTMARE ON ELM STREET - Games - Avalon Hill Game Co.

A-NIL - Pharmaceutical preparations ✩ - Vangard Labs Inc.

A. NONINI PREMIUM - Wines - A. Nonini Winery

A NOVEL ALTERNATIVE - Publisher's imprints - Adams Book Co., Inc.

A-NURIC - Diuretics - Alvin Last Inc.

A O C ANGELS OF COLOR - Ornaments - Reva W. Broomer

A-O-K - Cleaning preparations - Bison Laboratories (Central OB Products Division)

A/O MAT - Building materials - A/Ogeo Products, Inc.

A O-MATIC - Key cases - Co-Ray Inc.

A-O-Q10 MAXIPOWER FORMULA - Vitamins and nutritional supplements - Solgar Vitamin and Herb Co., Inc.

A-OK - Apparel–women's ✩ - Bali Co. Inc.

A OK - Candy - Auburn Farms, Inc.

A-O.K. - Putties ✩ - BASF Corp.

A-OK APPLIANCE - Refrigerator repair shops - Darryl I. Katz

A-ONE - Office supplies - McGill Inc.

A-ONE - Veterinary pharmaceutical preparations - Vital Nutrition Products

A+ +ONSITE - Computer software - Daly and Wolcott, Inc.

A-P - Pickles ✩ - Green Bay Foods Co.

A PAGE A DAY - Diaries - Samuel Ward Manufacturing Inc.

A PASSPORT - Food products ✩ - Flagship Foods Inc.

A PEACE-ABLE PLACE - Publisher's imprints - C.E. Mendez Foundation, Inc.

A PEACHY PLACE TO BE - Postcards - Aerial Photography Services, Inc.

A-PEN-DEX - Binders - Cel-U-Dex Corp.

A. PETITE - Croissants - Sherwood Brands, Inc.

A-PEX - Enamels - Morris Paint & Varnish Co.

A PIECE OF MIND - Computer software - Floyd Victor Etienne

A PIED - Ballet slippers - Wolowick Shoe Co.

A PLACE FOR YOU - Prophylactics - Healthwise Foundation, Inc.

A PLAN FOR SUCCESS - Calendars - Diaco Sales, Inc.

A PLAYER - Sporting goods ✩ - Dunlop Maxfli Sports Corp.

A PLAYMATE TODAY. A TREASURE TOMORROW - Toys - Robin Woods Inc.

A-PLEX - Cleaning preparations - Malter International Corp.

A-PLEX - Paints - Cowman-Campbell Paint Co.

A PLUS - Frames–eyeglass - May Optical Co. Inc.

A PLUS - Gasoline ✩ - Ashland Oil, Inc.

A PLUS VALUE - Cleaning preparations - AmeriPlus Inc.

A PORTION OF CHAPTER FIVE - Calendars - Gabby D. Gaborik

A-POXIDE - Pharmaceutical preparations ✩ - Abbott Laboratories

A-PRODUCTS - Sealants, repair materials, etc. - Devcon Consumer Products (ITW Devcon)

A+ PUBLISHER - Computer software - Carr Publishing Co.

A PUZZLING SURPRISE - Puzzles - Henry J. Legendre, Jr.

A QC GROUP - Toners - AQC Group Corp.

A QC GROUP - Toners - AQC Group Corp.

A QUESTION OF SCRUPLES - Games ✩ - Milton Bradley Co.

A. R. MORROW - Brandy - Beaver Wine Co.

A/R TRAK - Health care products ✩ - Healthcare Automation Inc.

A. R. V. CONDOR - Toys–models - Estes Industries

A-+RAY OF PETALS - Hobby kits ✩ - Mangelsen's (VDI)

A REASON FOR WRITING - Educational materials - Concerned Group, Inc.

A REFERENCE BOOK II - Wallpaper - Jack Denst Designs

A REFERENCE FOR THE REST OF US! - Publisher's imprints - International Data Group, Inc.

A. REGNARD ET FILS - Wines ✩ - Kobrand Corp.

A-REX - Pharmaceutical preparations - C.S. Ruckstuhl Co. Inc.

A RHYME IN TIME - Games - Jill Renee Lenhart

A-RITE - Vitamins and nutritional supplements - Dobbs and Associates

A ROAST OF OLD NEW YORK - Coffee - Noah's New York Bagels, Inc.

A. RODET BURGUNDIES - Wines - Winesellers Ltd.

A ROOM WITH A VIEW - Compact discs–prerecorded - Shore Bets Inc.

A ROSE IS A ROSE - Posters ✩ - Edward Weston Fine Arts

A ROYAL ROBE - Robes - Royal Robes Inc.

A ROYAL WEDDING - Computer software - Digital Matrix Corp.

A-S - Hardware - Allen-Stevens Corp.

A/S - Recording label ✩ - Alshire International Inc.

A. S. BARNES - Publisher's imprints - Oak Tree Publications Inc.

A-S-D - Golfing equipment - Aldila, Inc.

A SALAD IN HAND - Vitamins and nutritional supplements ✩ - Pines International, Inc.

A. SANOMA CO. - Novelty items - J. Kenneth Zahn

A SANTE - Cosmetics - RBI Beauty Industries, Inc.

A SANTE - Nail care products - A Sante Inc.

A-SCAN PLUS - Measuring instruments - Sonic Industries, Inc.

A SEAL THAT COULD FLY - Electronic equipment - Texas Instruments Inc.

A SECRET ADMIRER'S KIT - Paper products - Musleh, Susan

A SENSE OF HUMOR - Greeting cards - Kalan Inc.

A SERIES & DESIGN - Circuit breakers - General Electric Co.

A SHADE BETTER - Drapery hardware - Granite State Innovations, Inc.

A SHAPED LITTLE NUGGET BOOK - Publisher's imprints - Western Publishing Co., Inc.

A SHAPED NAPTIME TALE - Publisher's imprints - Western Publishing Co., Inc.

A SHOT IN THE DARK - Candy - That's My Favorite Inc.

A SIMPLER TIME - Games - Michael Riggs

A. +SIWEK - Jewelry - Arlene Siwek

A SKIN KISS WITH LOVE - Cosmetics ✩ - Madeleine Mono Ltd.

A SLEEPY HOLLOW BOOK - Publisher's imprints - Fordham University Press

A SLEEPYTIME BOOK - Publisher's imprints - Kidsbooks, Inc.

A SLICE ABOVE THE REST - Pizzas–frozen - Gianni's Food Concepts, Inc.

A SLICE OF BREAKFAST - Bakery products - Morton Scott, Ltd.

A SLICE OF FAMILY FUN - T-shirts–men's - Papa's Pizza Parlor

A SOCCER SLEUTHS MYSTERY - Puzzles ✩ - Lombard Marketing, Inc.

A SOCIABLE LIGHT ALE - Beverages - Bridgeport Brewing Co.

A SOLID CONNECTION - Adhesives and sealants - MKT Fastening, LLC

A SONG IN BLOOM - Recording label - Creative Ventures, Inc.

A SOURCE OF PRIDE - Apparel and accessories ✩ - Jantzen Inc.

A SOW 96 - Animal feeds - Carl S. Akey Inc.

A SOW 106 - Animal feeds - Carl S. Akey Inc.

A SOW 110 - Animal feeds - Carl S. Akey Inc.

A SOW BOOSTER 40 - Animal feeds - Carl S. Akey Inc.

A SOW BOOSTER 65 - Animal feeds - Carl S. Akey Inc.

A SPECIAL FIT - Brassieres (Bras) - Playtex Apparel, Inc.

A SPECIAL SEASON - Spices and extracts - To Market to Market

A SPECIAL VINTAGE - Wallpaper - Somerville Designs

A. SPORT - Apparel and accessories - Andrews' Sport Co., Inc.

A SQUIRREL'S TALE - Publisher's imprints - Bien Productions, Inc.

A STAR - Computer peripheral equipment - Astar, Inc.

A STAR IS BORN! - Paper products - C.R. Gibson Co.

A START 200 - Animal feeds - Carl S. Akey Inc.

✩ = Now out of production

A START 300 - Animal feeds - Carl S. Akey Inc.

A START 400 - Animal feeds - Carl S. Akey Inc.

A STATE OF MIND - Apparel and accessories - T. Enterprises Inc.

A. STAUB & CO. - Beverages–alcohol - Leonard Kreusch Inc.

A STEP ABOVE - Hair care products - Waverly Beauty Products

A STEP BEYOND - Wallpaper - Essex Wallcoveringss

A STEP FURTHER - Hair care products - Helene Curtis Industries Inc.

A STONE'S THROW - Calendars - Jared A. Miller

A STONE'S THROW - Wallpaper - J. Chesterfield Studio

A STORY-TO-COLOR - Publisher's imprints - Stemmer House Publishers Inc.

A STORYBOOK CHRISTMAS - Christmas tree ornaments - Enchanted Gold, Inc.

A STREAMLINE - Playing cards - United States Playing Card Co.

A-STRIKE LEADER & LURE - Fishing lures - A-Strike Leader & Lure, Ltd.

A STROKE OF BRILLIANCE - Paints - Benjamin Moore & Co.

A STROKE OF GENIUS - Correction fluid - Wite-Out Products, Inc.

A SURVIVAL GUIDE FOR THE REST OF US! - Publisher's imprints - International Data Group, Inc.

A SWITCH FOR THE HOLIDAYS - Christmas tree ornaments - Lamson & Sessions Co.

A SWITCH IN ART - Switches–electric - A Switch in Art

A-T - Surgical supplies - A-T Surgical Manufacturing Co. Inc.

A-T FINANCIAL - Computer software - A-T Financial Information, Inc.

A T H ALL TERRAIN HUMIDOR - Cases–cigar - Controlled Environments, Inc.

A/T/S - Pharmaceutical preparations - Hoechst-Roussel Pharmaceuticals Inc.

A T T I T U D E - Perfumes - Mahender M. Sabhnani

A-TACH - Bodyboards - Earth & Ocean Sports, Inc.

A-TACH BODYBOARDS - Bodyboards - Earth & Ocean Sports, Inc.

A TAIL WE COULD WAG - Pet products - Wendel Wirth

A-TAPER - Hammers - Hawera Inc.

A TASTE FOR KNOWLEDGE - Video production ☆ - Canandaigua Wine Co. Inc.

A TASTE OF AFRICA - Coffee - Barnie's Coffee & Tea Co., Inc.

A TASTE OF BARNIE'S - Coffee - Barnie's Coffee & Tea Co., Inc.

A TASTE OF BRAZIL - Coffee - Barnie's Coffee & Tea Co., Inc.

A TASTE OF CHRISTMAS - Coffee - Barnie's Coffee & Tea Co., Inc.

A TASTE OF COSTA RICA - Coffee - Barnie's Coffee & Tea Co., Inc.

A TASTE OF FRANCE - Bakery products ☆ - McGlynn Bakeries Inc.

A TASTE OF GUATEMALA - Coffee - Barnie's Coffee & Tea Co., Inc.

A TASTE OF HEAVEN - Baked goods - Divine Delights Inc.

A TASTE OF HOLLAND - Vegetables–canned - Deboer & Co., Inc.

A TASTE OF LAS VEGAS - Candy - Ethel M. Chocolates, Inc.

A TASTE OF LIFE - Mustard - HSN Lifeway Health Products Inc.

A TASTE OF OLD NEW YORK - Bagels - Noah's New York Bagels, Inc.

A TASTE OF PARADISE - Candy - K & L Associates, Inc.

A TASTE OF TAPESTRY - Fabrics–tapestry - Jeppson Galleries Inc.

A TASTE OF THAI - Seasonings - Andre Prost Inc.

A-TEAM - Eyeglasses - Martin-Copeland Eyewear Corp.

A-TEAM - Games ☆ - Ben Cooper Inc.

A-TEAM - Toys ☆ - ERTL Co., Inc.

A-TEAM RACING - Toys–electronic ☆ - Tyco Toys

A-TEAM, THE - Games ☆ - Parker Brothers

A-TECH - Lighting fixtures - American Lantern Co.

A. TEDDY B - Apparel and accessories - Theodore Bazzini, III

A TEDDY BEAR LANE CHRISTMAS - Toys - Those Characters from Cleveland, Inc.

A TENNIS TWINS MYSTERY - Games ☆ - Lombard Marketing, Inc.

A-TENS - Health care products - American Imex

A-TEX - Ophthalmic goods - Select Optical

A-TEX - Wallpaper - Quality House Inc.

A THE ARROW COMPANY - Shirts - Cluett, Peabody & Co.

A-THERM - Window frames - Acorn Window Systems Inc.

A THOUSAND FLOWERS - Wines - Hop Kiln Winery

A TIME FOR NATIVE AMERICANS - Playing cards - Aristoplay, Ltd.

A TIME TO LAUGH - Greeting cards - David C. Cook Publishing Co.

A TIME TO REMEMBER - Apparel–children's - Children's Hour, Inc.

A TIMELESS COLLECTION - Wallpaper ☆ - Manuscreens

A TIMES MIRROR COMPANY - Computer software - Time Mirror Co.

A TO ZAP? - Computer software - Sunburst Communications, Inc.

A-TO-ZOO - Bedding–linen - Dan River Inc.

A TOKEN OF OUR SOUTHERN HOSPITALITY - Nuts–salted, roasted, cooked, or canned - Young Pecans Sales Corp.

A TOUCH OF AFRICA COLLECTION - Greeting cards - Creative Diversity Designs

A TOUCH OF BRASS - Key rings - Russ Berrie and Co., Inc.

A TOUCH OF CHARM - Wallpaper ☆ - Decor International Wallcovering Inc.

A TOUCH OF CHEESE - Electronic equipment - Bakertowne Co., Inc.

A TOUCH OF CHRISTMAS - Novelty items - Best Products Co., Inc.

A TOUCH OF CLASS - Wallpaper - Sunnyside Prints

A TOUCH OF COUNTRY - Giftware - Russ Berrie and Co., Inc.

A TOUCH OF EILEEN - Apparel and accessories - Gentry Inc.

A TOUCH OF SUN - Hair care products - Clairol Inc.

A TOUCH OF VELVET - Dolls ☆ - Effanbee Doll Corp.

A TOUCH OF VELVET - Pillows - Pillowtex Corp.

A TOUT PRIX - Clothing - Creative Design Parkway, Inc.

A TRADITION OF SERVICE TO DERMATOLOGY - Pharmaceutical preparations - Oclassen Pharmaceuticals, Inc.

A-TREAT - Beverages–carbonated - A-Treat Bottling Co.

A-TREAT - Beverages–carbonated - Reading A-Treat Bottling Co. Inc.

A TREE FOR THEE - Trees–artificial ☆ - Vermillion Inc.

A TRUE TO NATURE COMPANY - Cakes - Food Integrated Technologies, Inc.

A TWO Z - Shoes - JBI Inc.

A-UNIFIED - Duplicating machines - Heyer Inc.

A:UTODRIVE - Computer software - Trademark Systems Corp.

A/V MASTER - Video tapes–blank - Fuji Photo Film USA Inc.

A/V PARAGON - Electronics equipment - Universal Tape Co. Inc.

A. VAHAN - Jewelry - Alwand Vahan Jewelry Ltd.

A VIEW TO A KILL - Games - Avalon Hill Game Co.

A-VIT-A - Hair care products - Evita Marketing Inc.

A. VOGEL'S - Pharmaceutical preparations - Bioforce of America Ltd.

A. W. BUCHAN - Earthenware - De Greve Associates

A. W. FABER - Office supplies - Faber-Castell Corp.

A WARNER ORIGINAL - Apparel and accessories ☆ - Warnaco Inc.

A WAY OF LIFE - Christmas tree ornaments - Cracker Box Inc.

A WEDDING ALBUM - Photo albums ☆ - Chase

A WEEK OF TREATS - Candy ☆ - Bissinger's Inc.

A WHALE OF A SNACK - Bakery products ☆ - Goodmark Foods, Inc.

A WHOLE LOT OF MEXICAN - Restaurants–fast food - Taco John's International Inc.

A. WILLIAMS - Giftware - Roman, Inc.

A-WING FIGHTER - Toys–automobiles - Lucasfilm Ltd.

A WINNER EVERY TIME - Game machines - Advanced Games & Engineering, Inc.

A WINNING BALANCE - Publisher's imprints - Professional Development Group, Inc.

A WOMAN'S NATURAL - Vitamins and nutritional supplements - Thompson Nutritional Products

A WONDERFUL YEAR - Greeting cards - American Greetings Corp.

A WORLD OF CORROSION PROTECTION - Coatings - Bronz-Glow Technologies, Inc.

A WORLD OF DIFFERENCE - Video production - Anti-Defamation League of B'nai B'rith

A WORLD OF EDUCATION IN YOUR HANDS - Computer peripheral equipment - Bayer Corp.

A WORLD OF FLOWERS - Calendars ☆ - Amcal Inc.

A WORLD OF FRIENDS - Greeting cards - Morehead, Inc.

A XXI S INFORMATION SYSTEMS FOR THE 21ST CENTURY - Electronic equipment - Southeast Information Retrieval Systemsco.

A YARD OF BUBBLEGUM - Chewing gum - Sahagian & Associates, Inc.

A YARD OF LICORICE STICKS - Candy - Sahagian & Associates, Inc.

A-Z - Cleaning preparations ☆ - Lee Products Co.

A-Z - Electrical equipment ☆ - Triangle Wire & Cable, Inc.

A-Z - Tools - Abbeon Cal. Inc.

A-Z BEAR - Toys–stuffed - Trendmasters, Inc.

A-Z BIG SUCKER - Candy ☆ - Spangler Candy Co.

A-Z PANEL - Toys - Lauri Inc.

A ZERO WASTE COMPANY - Containers–metal - Bulk Tank, Inc.

A-ZOOM - Microscopes - Ready Products Corp.

A1FREE - Computer software - Echosoft Corp.

A2 - Pharmaceutical preparations - Allergan Elite, Inc.

A2F ALL ABOUT FASHION - Women's apparel - Adrienne Vittadini, Inc.

A2M - Bicycles - Barracuda Bicycle Co.

A2T - Bicycles - MRI, Inc.

A2Z - Furniture - Domore/DO3

A³ - Computer peripheral equipment - Mouse Systems Corp.

A3 PLUS - Printers–computer - Lasermaster Corp.

A4 - Motor vehicles–automobiles - Audi of America Inc.

A5 - Sporting goods - North Face, Inc.

A6 - Motor vehicles–automobiles - Audi of America Inc.

A100 - Colognes - Agustin Reyes, Inc.

A.320 - Golfing equipment - Kent Sports, Inc.

A2000 - Sporting goods - Wilson Sporting Goods Co.
AA - Cables - Achilles Aerospace Products, Inc.
AA - Enamels - Fuller-O'Brien Paints Inc.
AA - Grinders - Active Automation, Inc.
A.A. - Rice - Comet American Marketing
AA - Targets - Reagent Chemical and Research Inc.
AA - Teas - Wisconsin AA Co. Ltd. (USA)
AA - Wines - Laird and Co.
A.A. CALEM - Wines - House of Burgundy Inc.
AA CELLULAR - Accessories - AA Cellular Accessories
AA CELLULAR ACCESSORIES - Telephone apparatus - AA Cellular Accessories
AA CONCEPTS - Skin care products - Shear World International
AA DIETS - Pet products - Apples Aviary & Supply Co.
AA PYRAMID PARTS AMERICAN ALLOY CORP. - Machine parts - American Alloy Corp.
AAA - Cutting blades - Sunbeam Corp.
AAA - Shrimp–fresh or frozen - Central Seaway Co.
AAA - Telephones–cellular - American Automobile Assn., Inc.
AAA - Wire - Triple-A Specialty Co.
AAA ALSTYLE APPAREL & ACTIVEWEAR - Sweatshirts - Alstyle Apparel & Activewear Manufacturing Co.
AAA GLASS - Glassware, ashtrays, bar supplies, etc. - AAA Glass Corp.
AAA HEALTHCARE - Health care products - AAA Healthcare Equipment Co.
AAA TRIPWWIZARD - Calculators - Ultradata Systems, Inc.
AAA1 - Paints - Masury Paint Co.
AAAHH!!! REAL MONSTERS - Cups–plastic - Viacom International Inc.
AAAHH!!! REAL MONSTERS - Dolls - Happiness Express Inc.
A.A.C.T. - Hair care products - Redken Laboratories, Inc.
AAD - Medical device - Incontrol Inc.
AADA - Games - Steve Jackson Games Inc.
AAE - Sporting goods - Aluminum Athletic Equipment
A.A.F. - Flowers–artificial - European Imports of California Inc.
A.A.F. GOLD LABEL - Flowers–artificial - Aldik Artificial Flower Co. Inc.
AAG LEASE EXPRESS ACCEPTANCE CORPORATION - Motor vehicle dealers - Automotive Assistance Group, Inc.
AAGAARD PROPOLIS - Health care products - Oakmont Investments Co.
AAGARD - Alarm systems–burglar - National Guardian Security Services Corp.
AAH THAT'S PERFECT - Pasta - San Francisco Spice Co.
AAHHH! - Juices - Upstate Farms Cooperative, Inc.
AAI - Adhesives and sealants ☆ - Ridlen Manufacturing Inc.
AAI - Eyeglasses - AAI/ACCESSORIES Associates Inc.
AAI - Sporting goods - American Athletic Inc.
AAL - Audio equipment - MTX
AALBORG AKVAVIT - Whiskey - Jim Beam Brands Co.
AALBORG JUBILAEUMS AKVAVIT - Whiskey - Jim Beam Brands Co.
AAM - Axles - American Axle & Manufacturing, Inc.
AAMAD - Apparel and accessories - Jennifer Mills
AAMCO - Oils–lubricating - Aamco Transmissions, Inc.
AAMW - Apparel–athletic - African American Men of Westchester, Inc.
A&A PLUSH - Toys–stuffed - A & A Plush, Inc.
A&E HOME VIDEO - Video production - A & E Television Network
A&L +METAL FRAMES FOR BEDDING - Mattresses - High Point Bedding, Inc.
AANGAMIK-DMG - Health care products - Foodscience Laboratories Inc.
AANYTIME - Publisher's imprints - Coda Publications
AAON - Heating equipment - Aaon, Inc.
AAONAIRE - Heating equipment - Aaon, Inc.
A.A.P. - See MAXAIR
AAR-II - Epoxy - Cambridge Tile Manufacturing Co.
AARDVARK - Windows–vinyl - Gentek Building Products, Inc.
AARDVARK 'ARRY - Furs–artificial - Cross at the Green...Not in Between Enterprises
AARDWOOF - Recording label - Jazz Composer's Orchestra Association Inc.
AARGH - Toys ☆ - Those Characters from Cleveland, Inc.
AARIKKA OF FINLAND - Jewelry - Scandia Specialties Inc.
AARK - Skin care products - Regent Bond Inc.
AARON - Ophthalmic goods ☆ - Luxottica
AARON - Recording label - Terock Records
AARON BRANDS - Pharmaceutical preparations - Aaron Industries Inc.
AARON'S BEST - Meat products - Agriprocessors Inc.
AARQUE - Duplicating machines - R.Q.O. Holding Co. Inc.
AARS - Implants–surgical - Biomet, Inc.
AART - Computer peripheral equipment - RTC Industries, Inc.
AARTIK - Dinnerware–glass ☆ - Dansk International Designs, Ltd.

AARTRONICS - Computer hardware - Aartronics Corp.
AAS - Pharmaceutical preparations ☆ - Rugby Laboratories Inc.
AASAN - Food products - Caltex Trading, Inc.
AASCO - Automobile burglar-alarm accessories - Auto Alarm Supply Corp.
AAT - Recording label - Hope International
AATCC - Textile machinery - American Association of Textile Chemists and Colorists
AATO - Shoes - American Asian Trading Co.
AATRIX - Computer software - Aatrix Software Inc.
AAU USA - Apparel and accessories - Amateur Athletic Union of the United States, Inc.
AAURA - Jewelry - AAURA Inc.
AAVS - Electronic equipment - Sencore, Inc.
AB - Artists' materials - Paasche Airbrush Co.
A.B. - Food products ☆ - Baumer Foods, Inc.
A.B. - Inks ☆ - Specialty Ink Co. Inc.
AB - Jewelry - Buvin Jewelry of Florida Inc.
A.B. - Recording label - A.B. Records
AB - Trading cards and stamps - Olive Enterprises, Inc.
AB & A - Drains - American Brass & Aluminum Foundry Inc.
AB ANTIBACTERIAL - Pet products - A & M Products Inc.
AB BLASTER - Exercising equipment - Bodyshaping, Inc.
AB ELECTROSTATIC - Floor coverings - American Biltrite Inc.
AB MASTER - Exercising equipment - Hilary Michael Milko
AB MAT - Exercising equipment - Frederick W. Koch Jr.
AB-ORIGINALS - Exercising equipment - Modern Body Design
AB ROLLER PLUS SUPER SET - Video production - Concord-Chase, Inc.
AB/SCENT - Deodorizers - Pettibone Laboratories Inc.
AB-SORBS-ALL - Floor coverings–linoleum ☆ - Goodall Manufacturing Co.
AB WORKS - Exercising equipment - Kor-One, Ltd.
ABA - Medical instruments - Adeza Biomedical Corp.
ABA MEMPHIS PROS - Apparel and accessories - NBA Properties, Inc.
ABA-USA - Athletic footwear - Converse Inc.
ABACO CONCH FARMS - Agricultural products - Lawrence A. Keller
ABACO JOE FROZEN FRUIT DRINKS - Beverages - Abaco Joe
ABACUS - Floor coverings–carpet and rugs - Atlas Carpet Mills Inc.
ABACUS - Floor coverings–carpet and rugs - Mohawk Industries Inc.
ABACUS - Glassware–household ☆ - Ceraglass Inc.
ABADA - Brass giftware - Israeli Handicrafts Importing Co.
ABADA INTERNATIONAL - Nativity sets, etc. - Israeli Handicrafts Importing Co.
ABADDON - Photocopy machines - Abaddon, Inc.
ABADDON COPYSHOP - Photocopy machines - Abaddon, Inc.
ABADDON MANAGER - Photocopy machines - Abaddon, Inc.
ABADDON NETWORK CONTROLLER - Photocopy machines - Abaddon, Inc.
ABADDON REPORTER - Photocopy machines - Abaddon, Inc.
ABADDON TCII - Photocopy machines - Abaddon, Inc.
ABADDON TRANSITOR - Photocopy machines - Abaddon, Inc.
ABADOX - Games ☆ - Milton Bradley Co.
ABANA - Skin care products ☆ - Abana Pharmaceuticals, Inc.
ABANDA - Apparel and accessories - Abanda Inc.
ABANDON - Frames–eyeglass - Liberty Optical Manufacturing Co.
ABANO - Skin care products ☆ - Prince Matchabelli
ABAPHAGE - Pharmaceutical preparations - Rexar Pharmacal Corp.
ABAQUS - Computer software - Karlsson Hibbitt & Soresen, Inc.
ABAR - Manicure preparations - ABAR Beauty Supply Inc.
ABARBANEL - Alcoholic beverage - Howard S. Barbanel
ABARIS - Floor coverings–carpet and rugs ☆ - Hollytex Carpet Mills Inc.
ABARIS BOOKS - Publisher's imprints - Abaris Books Inc.
ABARTA - Water–bottled or canned - Abarta, Inc.
ABAXIS - Diagnostic apparatus - Abaxis, Inc.
ABB - Veterinary medical equipment - Animal Blood Bank
ABBA - Fish–canned or cured - Haram-Christensen Corp.
ABBA - Pet products - Abba Products Corp.
ABBA-ZABA - Candy - Annabelle Candy Co. Inc.
ABBE - Paints - Paris Paint & Varnish Co.
ABBE DESIGNS - Place mats and napkins - Coordinated Products Corp.
ABBEVILLE - Cabinets ☆ - Yorktowne Inc.
ABBEVILLE COLLECTION - Men's shirts - Abbeville Shirtmaker Inc.
ABBEVILLE KIDS - Publisher's imprints - Abbeville Press, Inc.
ABBEVILLE PRESS - Publisher's imprints - Abbeville Press, Inc.
ABBEY - Floor coverings - Mannington Resilient Floors
ABBEY - Floor coverings–carpet and rugs ☆ - Interloom Ltd.
ABBEY - Marzipan - Daprano & Co.
ABBEY - Trailers–travel ☆ - Starcraft Corp.

☆ = Now out of production

ABBEY COLLECTION - Giftware - Lenox, Inc.
ABBEY COURT - Apparel–women's - Mileace General Trading (USA) Inc.
ABBEY DESIGNS - Glassware–household - Kover Klad Products Inc.
ABBEY DRIVE - Electrical controls - Abbey Etna Machine Co.
ABBEY ENGLISH BRIDLES - Saddles - Thornhill Enterprises, Inc.
ABBEY GRAPE - Beverages–carbonated - Hello Cola Co.
ABBEY LANE - Apparel–women's - G.P.O. Inc.
ABBEY ROSE - House furnishings ✩ - Dan River Inc.
ABBEY STONE - Finishing agents ✩ - Flintkote Co.
ABBEY STONE - Floor coverings ✩ - Azrock Commercial Flooring
ABBEY STONE - Paints ✩ - GS Roofing Products Co.
ABBEY, THE - Wines - The Missouri Winery Warehouse Outlet
ABBI - Surgical supplies - United States Surgical Corp.
ABBIE'S JIFFY 6 PACK - Patterns–clothing ✩ - Simplicity Pattern Co., Inc.
ABBINGTON - Furniture ✩ - Bassett Furniture Industries, Inc.
ABBINGTON ROW - Furniture ✩ - Hammary Furniture Co. Inc.
ABBI*TAYLOR - Apparel and accessories - Fashion Initiatives
ABBOKINASE - Pharmaceutical preparations - Abbott Laboratories
ABBOTT - Cooking equipment–household - Abbott Industries Inc.
ABBOTT - Food products - Abbotts Meat Inc.
ABBOTT - Measuring instruments - Abbott Tachograph
ABBOTT - Uniforms–tailored - Abbott Military Tailors Inc.
ABBOTT ENERGIZER - Intravenous apparatus - Abbott Laboratories
ABBOTT-ROBINSON - Rotary polishing brushes - Buffalo Dental Manufacturing Co. Inc.
ABBOTTS - Dairy products ✩ - Leehi Dally Dairies
ABBOTT'S - Food products - Abbott's Lobsters Inc.
ABBOTT'S - Health care products - Abbott Laboratories
ABBOTTS - Ice cream - Lehigh Valley Dairies Inc.
ABBRA-CADABRA - Skin care products - Sogo Inc.
ABBREVIATE - Apparel–women's - Susan Burrowes, Ltd.
ABBY - Dolls - Russ Berrie and Co., Inc.
ABBY MICHAEL - Apparel–women's ✩ - Bobbie Brooks Inc.
ABC - Brassieres (Bras) ✩ - Warnaco Inc.
ABC - Cleaning equipment - Babcock & Wilcox Co.
ABC - Cleaning preparations–household - A.B.C. Market Corp.
ABC - Computer storage devices–optical - ABC Inc.
ABC - Confections ✩ - Bahlsen Inc.
ABC - Cosmetics ✩ - Shiseido Cosmetics (America) Ltd.
ABC - Dental equipment - Endslip Products Co.
ABC - Display cases–metal - B. Yaffe & Sons, Inc.
ABC - Fasteners–snap - Alpha Bolt Co.
ABC - Food products - Scrivner, Inc.
ABC - Food products - Bob White Organization
A.B.C. - Fruits and vegetables - G.A.C. Produce Co. Inc.
ABC - Furniture - Flexible Flyer Co.
ABC - Jewelry - American Bracelet & Chain Co. Inc.
ABC - Novelty items ✩ - Lemberger Candy Corp.
ABC - Ophthalmic goods - Durasol Drug & Chemical Co.
ABC - Paints - Grow Group, Inc.
ABC - Railroad equipment - ABC Rail Products Corp.
ABC - Recording label - MCA Universal Studios
ABC - Ships–sailing vessels - International Trading Connection, Inc.
ABC - Socks - Adams-Millis Corp.
ABC - Teas - Cathay International
ABC - Toothbrushes - Pacific Man Corp.
ABC - Towels - Keuffel & Esser Co.
ABC - Vitamins and nutritional supplements - Culture Systems Inc.
ABC ALREADY BEEN CHEWED GUM - Chewing gum - Joseph M. Bowe
ABC AMERICAN BICYCLE CLUB - Apparel and accessories - American Bicycle Club
ABC AMERICAN BUILDING COMPONENTS - Paints - Metal Building Components, Inc.
ABC & 123 - Pasta - American Home Food Products Inc.
ABC BLEND - Tobacco–chewing or smoking - Amar Blends Co.
ABC BLOCK EXPRESS - Toys - Playskool, Inc.
ABC CORROSION BUSTER - Cleaning preparations - Marine Development & Research Corp.
ABC DOPHILUS - Vitamins and nutritional supplements - Solgar Vitamin and Herb Co., Inc.
ABC DUMP TRUCK - Toys - Playskool, Inc.
ABC FLUORIDE - Toothpaste - Pacific Man Corp.
ABC NEWS INTERACTIVE - Computer storage devices–optical - ABC Inc.
ABC POOLS - Swimming pools - Pam Tipton
ABC ROCK RADIO NETWORK - Broadcasting stations–radio - ABC Radio Network, Inc.

ABC SPORTS - Footwear–athletic - ABC Sports Inc.
ABC SPORTS - Luggage - La Rue International, Inc.
ABC SPORTS - Sunglasses - International Tropic-Cal Inc. (I SKI Div.)
ABC STICK-ONS - Wallpaper - Priss Prints Inc.
ABC TOYS - Toys–automobiles - P.W. Woo & Sons, Inc.
ABC VIEWER - Computer software - Micrografx, Inc.
ABC WIDE WORLD OF SPORTS - Posters ✩ - Thought Factory
ABC WINDOW, THE - Windows - ABC, Inc.
ABC WRITER - Computer software ✩ - Digital Marketing Corp.
ABCD - Coffee - Thomas A. Campbell Co.
ABCO - Lamp bulbs–incandescent - Angelo Brothers Co.
ABCO - Pharmaceutical preparations ✩ - Abco Dealers Inc.
ABCO GLOWESCENT - Lamp bulbs–incandescent - Angelo Brothers Co.
ABC'S - Wallpaper - Priss Prints Inc.
ABC'S FOR LIVING - Posters - John Alan O'Bine
ABC'S MONDAY NIGHT FOOTBALL - Bird feeds - ABC Sports Inc.
ABC'S OF SCRIPTURE BIBLE CUP SERIES, THE - Cups–paper - Arrow Publicity Co.
ABCYCLE - Bicycles - Dynacraft Industries Inc.
ABDEC - Vitamins and nutritional supplements ✩ - Parke-Davis
ABDOLIFT - Corsets - Sears, Roebuck and Co.
ABDOMIN ALL - Girdles - Crown Foundations Inc.
ABDULLA - Tobacco products - Philip Morris Companies Inc.
ABDX - Valves - Westinghouse Air Brake Co.
ABDX-L - Valves - Westinghouse Air Brake Co.
ABE - Frames–eyeglass - Rozin Optical Export Corp.
ABEA - Olive oil - Oliva, Ltd.
ABEC - Recording label - Goldwax Record Co. Inc.
ABEDA - Wood products - Woodland Products Inc.
ABEDON - Bedding–linen - Dan River Inc.
ABEL - Apparel and accessories - Abel Industries Inc.
ABEL - Apparel–athletic - Abel Automatics, Inc.
ABEL - Office supplies ✩ - Abel Products
ABEL - Pharmaceutical preparations ✩ - Nortech Laboratories
ABEL II - Can openers–hand-operated - Norstar Enterprises
ABEL STIX - Drumsticks - JTA Products
ABELCET - Pharmaceutical preparations - Liposome Co. Inc.
ABELL - Elevators - Abell Elevator International
ABERCROMBIE & FITCH - Skin care products - A & F Trademark, Inc.
ABERDEEN - Apparel and accessories - Aberdeen Sportswear Inc.
ABERDEEN - Cabinets - American Woodmark Corp.
ABERDEEN - Fabrics - Dan River Inc.
ABERDEEN - Floor coverings - Mannington Resilient Floors
ABERDEEN - Floor coverings–carpet and rugs - Porter Carpet Mills Inc.
ABERDEEN - Floor coverings–carpet and rugs ✩ - Customweave Carpets Inc.
ABERDEEN - Floor coverings–carpet and rugs ✩ - Daltonian Carpet & Cushion Inc.
ABERDEEN - Hair care products ✩ - Fromm Industries
ABERDEEN & DUNBAR - Apparel and accessories - Aberdeen & Dunbar Ltd.
ABERDEEN HEATHER - Candles - Scarborough and Co. Inc.
ABERDEEN JR. - Fabrics - Dan River Inc.
ABERLOUR - Scotch whiskey - Austin, Nichols & Co., Inc.
ABERNATHY - Oils–edible - Rosebrier, Inc.
ABE'S BAR B Q DRIVE-IN - Sauces - George P. Davis Sr.
ABESTEX - Paints ✩ - Mac-O-Lac Paints Inc.
ABESTO - Adhesives and sealants - Miller Purcell Co.
ABESTOSHIELD - Apparel and accessories - Durafab Inc.
ABETA - Pet products - Abeta Products Inc.
ABEX - Brake drums - Abex Corp. (Friction Products Group)
ABEX - Exercising equipment - Keys Fitness Products, Inc.
ABEX - Musical instruments ✩ - Meisel Music Inc.
ABG - School supplies - Wescosa Inc.
ABI - Automotive parts and accessories - Judsen Rubber Works, Inc.
ABI - Pet products - Aquatic Biotechnologies Inc.
ABI PRISM - Chemical preparations - Perkin Elmer Corp.
ABIDOS - Footwear–athletic ✩ - E.S. Originals, Inc.
ABIDS - Computer software - Computer Data Systems, Inc.
ABIGAIL - Ophthalmic goods - Swank Optical
ABIGAIL - Tableware–china - Lenox, Inc.
ABIGAIL MAGIC TAIL - Candy ✩ - R.M. Palmer Co.
ABIGAIL'S HEIRLOOMS - Jewelry - Abigail's Heirlooms Ltd.
ABIGAIL'S LEGACIES - Jewelry - Golden Cove, Inc.
ABILENE - Boots - B.B. Walker Co.
ABILENE - Floor coverings–carpet and rugs ✩ - Galaxy Carpet Mills Inc.
ABILENE - Optical services ✩ - U.S. Optical Frame Co.
ABILENE - Sporting goods - O.F. Mossberg & Sons, Inc.

ABILIS - Golfing equipment - Prime Golf Co., Inc.
ABILITY DEVELOPMENT - Music–sheet - Learning One Inc.
ABINGTON - Floor coverings - Mannington Resilient Floors
ABINGTON - Rings–jewelry - Artcarved Inc.
ABINO MILLS - Breads - Abino Mills LLC
ABISANTE - Liquors ☆ - House of Seagram
ABITA - Water–bottled or canned - Abita Water Co. Inc.
ABITA - Water–bottled or canned ☆ - Ozone Spring Water Co.
ABITA BEER - Beverages–malt - Abita Brewing Co., Inc.
ABITAR - Toys–trains - Abitar Inc.
ABKCO - Recording label - ABKCO Records
ABL LIGHTS - Lamps - ABL Lights, Inc.
ABLC - Pharmaceutical preparations - Liposome Co. Inc.
ABLE - Doors–garage - Able Manufacturing and Wholesale Garage Door Co.
ABLE - Frames–eyeglass - Liberty Optical Manufacturing Co.
ABLE - Insecticides - Ciba-Geigy Corp.
ABLE - Machinery - Mekatronics Inc.
ABLE - Ships–sailing vessels - Able Custom Yachts (Div. of Trenton Marine Inc.)
ABLE ANCHORS - Hardware ☆ - Teco/Lumberlok
ABLE AND YOYO - Computer programming services - Berta-Max Inc.
ABLE FABLEHOPPER - Video production - Kids Comedy Theatre, Inc.
ABLE FAMILY, THE - Greeting cards - Wings & Wheels
ABLE-PHONE - Telephones - DQP
ABLE-RUB - Erasers - Alvin and Co. Inc.
ABLE TABLE - Furniture - Able Table Co.
ABLEAIDE - Computer software - Meeting the Challenge, Inc.
ABLESYS - Computer software - Ablesys Corp.
ABLEWARE - Health care products - Maddak Inc.
ABLON - Finishing agents - Ablon Finishes Inc.
ABLOY - Locks–door - Abloy Security Inc.
ABM - Fabrics - Gates-Mills, Inc.
ABN - Nuts and bolts - Auto Bolt & Nut
ABOCAST - Adhesive, casting and coating product - Abatron, Inc.
ABOCLAD - Antiskid coatings, etc. - Abatron, Inc.
ABOCOAT - Epoxy coating - Abatron, Inc.
ABOCRETE - Masonry patching and resurfacing product - Abatron, Inc.
ABODIA - Containers - Elden Enterprises, Inc.
ABOJET - Crack fillers - Abatron, Inc.
ABOMINABLE SNOWMAN, THE - Sleds - Jack Gasnick, The Virtuous Locksmith
ABOSEAL - Adhesives and sealants - Abatron, Inc.
ABOSOLV - Solvents - Abatron, Inc.
ABOUND - Fungicides - Zeneca Inc.
ABOUT FACE - Skin-care products - Bronson Pharmaceuticals
ABOUT FACE - Video production - About Face, Inc.
ABOUT FLAGS! - Flags - Marilyn A. Chipollini
ABOUT THE LAW - Keychains - Snyder Marketing Group, Inc.
ABOUT TIME - Recording label - Jazz Composer's Orchestra Association Inc.
ABOUT-TIME - Skin care products - Allan Palmer Laboratories, Inc.
ABOUT TOWN - Frames–eyeglass ☆ - Universal/Univis Inc.
ABOVE ALL - Frames–eyeglass - Pathway Optical Prods.
ABOVE AVERAGE - Apparel–men's - Hampton Industries, Inc.
ABOVE AVERAGE - Shirts - Pennshire Shirt Corp.
ABOVE-IT-ALL - Frames–eyeglass - Pathway Optical Prods.
ABOVE THE AVERAGE - Cigars ☆ - Havatampa Inc.
ABOVEALL - Can openers–electric - National Presto Industries, Inc.
ABOVELAN - Computer software - Above Software Inc.
ABOVEMEM - Computer software - Above Software Inc.
ABOVO - Miniature word processor - Abovo, Inc.
ABOWELD - Adhesives and sealants - Abatron, Inc.
ABOXABLOX - Wood products - House of Fara Inc.
ABP - Faucets - Arrowhead Brass Products, Inc.
A.B.P. - Labels, label dispensers - Automatic Business Products, Inc.
ABR-A-SAW - Saws–power ☆ - Rothenberger USA, Inc.
ABRA! - Computer peripheral equipment - Abra Cadabra Software, Inc.
ABRA - Jewelry - Abra Inc.
ABRA - Ophthalmic goods ☆ - Luxottica
ABRA 2000 - Computer software - Best Software Inc., Abra Products
ABRA APPLICANT - Computer software - Best Software Inc., Abra Products
ABRA ATTENDANCE - Computer software - Best Software Inc., Abra Products
ABRA-CADABRA - Frames–eyeglass - May Optical Co. Inc.
ABRA CADABRA - Novelty items - S.S. Adams Co.
ABRA-CADABRA - Stain removers - Fast Industries, Inc.
ABRA-CARDABBLE - Games - Willie L. Glenn
ABRA HR - Computer software - Best Software Inc., Abra Products

ABRA LINK - Computer software - Best Software Inc., Abra Products
ABRA MULTI-SITE CONSOLIDATION - Computer software - Best Software Inc., Abra Products
ABRA PAYROLL - Computer software - Best Software Inc., Abra Products
ABRA PCS - Computer software - Best Software Inc., Abra Products
ABRA PEOPLE MANAGER - Computer software - Best Software Inc., Abra Products
ABRA PORT - Computer software - Best Software Inc., Abra Products
ABRA RECRUITING SOLUTION - Computer software - Best Software Inc., Abra Products
ABRA RESUME SCAN - Computer software - Best Software Inc., Abra Products
ABRA THERAPEUTIC BATHS - Skin care products - Warren Raysor
ABRA TOOLKIT - Computer software - Best Software Inc., Abra Products
ABRA TRAIN - Computer software - Best Software Inc., Abra Products
ABRA TRAK - Computer software - Best Software Inc., Abra Products
ABRACADABRA - Health care products - ABRA Inc.
ABRACADABRA - Wallpaper - Jack Foley Associates Inc.
ABRACADABRA - Wallpaper - W.H.S. Lloyd
ABRACADABRA II - Wallpaper - Jack Foley Associates Inc.
ABRACADABRA JOKE SHOP - Toys - Umsi Inc.
ABRACADATA - Computer storage devices - Abracadata Ltd.
ABRACOR - Dental equipment - Eutectic Corp.
ABRAHAM - Hams - Haram-Christensen Corp.
ABRAHAM - Meat products–pork - De Choix Specialty Foods Co.
ABRAHAM'S SOY DELITES - Food products - Soy Delites Inc.
ABRALON - Brushes - Hahl Filaments, Inc.
ABRASION KING - Hoses - Pullman Co.
ABRAX - Thermostats ☆ - Abbeon Cal. Inc.
ABRAXAS - Colognes - Romane Inc.
ABRAXAS - Computer software - Abraxas Software, Inc.
ABRAXAS - Housewares - Glendon R. Good
ABRAXAS - Publisher's imprints - NPT Publishing Group, Inc.
ABRAXIS - Cymbals - On-Site Music Group
ABREZ - Hair care products - Image Laboratories, Inc.
ABRUZZI - Frames–eyeglass ☆ - Universal/Univis Inc.
ABS - Combs - Capitol Novelty Co.
ABS - Computer software - American Business Systems
ABS - Containers - American Bureau of Shipping
ABS - Fiberboard ☆ - Fibre Glass-Evercoat Co. Inc.
ABS BRAKESAFE - Brake system pressure control - BST Enterprises, Inc.
ABS CEMENT/CLEANERS - Cleaning preparations - Comstar International Inc. (IPC Div.)
ABS COMTRAK - Antennas - Advanced Business Sciences, Inc.
A.B.S. DRESS COLLECTION - Apparel - ABS Clothing Collection Inc.
ABS OF STEEL - Publisher's imprints - Maier Group Inc.
ABS SAFEHULL - Computer software - American Bureau of Shipping
ABS USA - Apparel–women's - ABS Clothing Collection Inc.
ABSAN - Resins–synthetic - General Electric Co.
ABSCO - Automotive parts and accessories - Midland Brake Inc.
ABSENTA - Paints - Hempel Coatings USA Inc.
ABSOCLEAR - Water purification systems - Absopure Water Co.
ABSOCLEAR - Water–mineral - Aqua Pure Drinking Waters
ABSOLITE - Luggage - Samsonite Corp.
ABSOLUT - Furniture ☆ - Athens Furniture Industries Inc.
ABSOLUT - Vodka - Joseph E. Seagram & Sons, Inc.
ABSOLUT VODKA CAKES - Snack foods - Downey's Products
ABSOLUTE - Computer software - Absolute Entertainment, Inc.
ABSOLUTE - Finishing agents - Absolute Coatings Inc.
ABSOLUTE - Floor coverings–carpet and rugs - Johnson's Carpets Inc.
ABSOLUTE - Floor coverings–carpet and rugs - Whitecrest Carpet Mills
ABSOLUTE - Flowers, plants, and seeds - Jacklin Seed
ABSOLUTE - Gloves–safety - Jason Marketing Co.
ABSOLUTE - Hair care products - Waverly Beauty Products
ABSOLUTE - Skin care products - Lancome
ABSOLUTE - Tiles–ceiling ☆ - Armstrong World Industries, Inc.
ABSOLUTE CONTROL - Machinery - Vertex Technologies, Inc.
ABSOLUTE FRUIT - Candy - Ragold Inc.
ABSOLUTE MUSIC - Computer peripheral equipment - Reindeer Co.
ABSOLUTE PERFORMANCE - Valves - Pall Corp.
ABSOLUTE RECALL - Computer software - Absolute Solutions, Inc.
ABSOLUTE RINSE - Hair care products - Chenice Beverly Hills
ABSOLUTE SUN - Tannery machines - Interlectric Corp.
ABSOLUTELY ABIGAIL - Dolls ☆ - Effanbee Doll Corp.
ABSOLUTELY AFFORDABLE HOMES - Real estate agencies - Absolutely Affordable Homes, Inc.

☆ = Now out of production

ABSOLUTELY ALMOND - Candy - Chocolate House, Inc.
ABSOLUTELY ALOE - Skin care products - Natural Laboratories Corp.
ABSOLUTELY AMERICAN - Water–bottled or canned - Sports Beverage, Inc.
ABSOLUTELY COTTON - Apparel–women's - P.S. Knits Inc.
ABSOLUTELY ENCHANTING MAGIC WAND - Toy stores ☆ - Dynatec International Inc.
ABSOLUTELY FRESH - Prestige Leather Creations
ABSOLUTELY GEORGE'S - Wallpaper - Sellers & Josephson
ABSOLUTELY GEORGE'S II - Wallpaper - Sellers & Josephson
ABSOLUTELY INCREDIBLE FLYING THINGS - Toys–airplanes ☆ - Martin Carbone Inc.
ABSOLUTELY KIDS - Apparel and accessories - Prestige Leather Creations
ABSOLUTELY PARFAIT - Vitamins and nutritional supplements - SPR Pharmaceuticals Corp.
ABSOLUTELY THE BEST - Cleaning preparations - Sparta Brush Co., Inc.
ABSOLUTES - Filters–air - Farr Co.
ABSOLUTION - Dietary food supplements - Rosalba Emanuel-King
ABSOMATIC - Stamps–hand - Dayton Stencil Works Co.
ABSOPURE - Food products - California Citrus Processors
ABSOPURE - Water–bottled or canned - Absopure Water Co.
ABSORB AN ODOR - Deodorizers - Atmosphere Products Co. Inc.
ABSORB-EZE - Housewares ☆ - Scott Paper Co.
ABSORB-F - Chemical preparations - Trend Scientific, Inc.
ABSORB-IT MOP - Mops - Ekco Housewares, Inc.
ABSORB-MOR - Sports rackets and accessories - Winn, Inc.
ABSORB-O-MAT - Mats–grass, reed, and jute - Pioneer Medical, Inc.
ABSORB-X - Bags - Excell Products Corp.
ABSORBA - Apparel–children's ☆ - Poron Ltd.
ABSORBAFIL - Health care products - Dundee Mills, Inc.
ABSORBAID - Vitamins and nutritional supplements - Nature's Sources, L. L. C.
ABSORBAL - Paper–toweling - Cleveland Cotton Products Co.
ABSORBALL - Fabrics - Veratec
ABSORBEEZE - Towels - QVC, Inc.
ABSORBENT GP - Pet products - Absorption Corp.
ABSORBENT W - Pet products - Absorption Corp.
ABSORBER, THE - Handlebars–motorcycle - M/C Enterprises
ABSORBINE - Veterinary pharmaceutical preparations - W.F. Young, Inc.
ABSORBINE JR. - Antiseptics - W.F. Young, Inc.
ABSORBINE POWER GEL - Skin care products - W.F. Young, Inc.
ABSORBITOL - Vitamins and nutritional supplements - Genesis Research Corp.
ABSORBOND - Fabrics - Texwipe Co. LLC
ABSORBS-IT-ALL - Hardware - Excel-Mineral Co. Inc.
ABSORBSHIN WRAP - Bandages–orthopedic - Professional's Choice Sports Medicine Products, Inc.
ABSORENE - Cleaning preparations–household - Absorene Manufacturing Co.
ABSTRACT - Dinnerware–glass ☆ - Nikko Ceramics Inc.
ABSTRACT - Footwear–women's ☆ - Joyce Shoes
ABSTRACT - Furniture ☆ - Bassett Furniture Industries, Inc.
ABSTRACTION - Floor coverings–carpet and rugs - Trend Carpet
ABSTRACTIONS - Cases–eyeglass - California Optical Leather Inc.
ABSTRACTIONS - Floor coverings–carpet and rugs ☆ - Concepts International
ABSTRACTIONS - Kaleidoscopes - Gemini Kaleidoscopes
ABSTRAKT WORKSHOP - Recording label - Shadow Records Corp.
ABSTRAX - Shoes - Marx & Newman Co. Inc.
ABSTRAX BREAKTHROUGH - Brakes–motor vehicle - ABS Tech Sciences, Inc.
ABSTRAXIONS - Greeting cards ☆ - Brett-Forer Greetings Inc.
ABT - Art markers - American Tombow Inc.
ABT - Flowers, plants, and seeds - AgriBioTech, Inc.
ABT - Skates–roller - Rollerblade, Inc.
ABT GRABBER - Machinery - Advanced Belt Technology
ABTCO - Construction equipment - ABT Co., Inc.
ABTONER - Exercising equipment - CSA, Inc.
ABTOX - Baskets–steel - Abtox, Inc.
ABT'S - Seafood products–fresh or frozen ☆ - Winter Harbor Fisheries
ABUELITA - Food products - Abuelita Mexican Foods
ABUNDANCE - Dinnerware - Corning Inc.
ABUNDANCE - Lenses–optical - Ditto Industries Inc.
ABUNDANT ENERGY - Health care products - Above All Health Inc.
ABUNDVITA - Food products - Nutri-Metics International (USA) Inc.
ABUS DISKUS - Locks–padlocks - Abus Lock Co.
ABUSE - Computer software - Crack Dot Com. Inc.
ABUSED DENIM - Handbags - Bagland

ABUVAL - Sunblocks - Beta Dermaceuticals, Inc.
ABVANTAGE - Exercising equipment - Ort Tool & Die Corp.
ABX - Recording label - ABX Records
ABYDOS - Apparel and accessories - Loyd Anthony Inc.
ABYSS - Publisher's imprints - Bantam Doubleday Dell Publishing Group, Inc.
ABYSS, THE - Apparel and accessories - John J. Boyle, III
ABZ VALVE - Valves - ABZ Manufacturing, Inc.
ABZORBANDS - Hair care products - Judi Williams
AC - Apparel and accessories - Unionbay
AC - Automotive parts and accessories - General Motors Corp.
AC - Cabinets–wood - AC Products Inc.
AC - Cement ☆ - Atlas Chemical Co.
AC - Computers - Alectron Corp.
AC - Food products - Atlantic Coast Fisheries Corp.
AC - Paints - Radiant Color Div.
AC - Spark plugs - General Motors Corp. (AC Spark Plug Div.)
AC-3 - Electrical equipment - Dolby Laboratories Licensing Corp.
AC-8 AQUARIUM CLEANSER - Aquarium accessories - Kordon
AC-8 AQUARIUM CLEANSER - Cleaning preparations - Novalek, Inc.
AC-200E - Electrical equipment - General Electric Co.
AC-300 - Electrical equipment - General Electric Co.
AC-500 - Electrical equipment - General Electric Co.
AC 556 - Rifles - Sturm, Ruger & Co., Inc.
AC ALVIN CHIN - Housewares - A2 House Inc.
AC ANALYTICAL CONTROLS - Computer software - Analytical Controls, Inc.
AC-CAY-LAC - Hardware - Sherwin-Williams Automotive Finishes Corp.
AC-CEL - Gasoline - Livingston Chemicals, Inc.
AC-CORD-IAN - Fabrics - Dan River Inc.
AC/DC ELECTRIC CIRCUIT - Games - Ampersand Press
AC-DELCO PACKARD - Automotive parts and accessories - Packard Electric Div.
AC DETECTIVE - Greenlee Textron Inc.
AC HYDROSEAL 3000 - Asphalt - Northern Elastomeric, Inc.
AC-KRO-GRUV - Rifles - O.F. Mossberg & Sons, Inc.
AC LIGHTING DESIGN - Lighting fixtures - Brijor Acquisition Corp.
A.C. PLUG - Fishing lures - Fred Arbogast Co. Inc.
AC STAYFLAT - Asphalt - Northern Elastomeric, Inc.
AC-TIV-OLOGY - Women's sportwear - Rousso Apparel Group, Inc.
AC TOUGHSEAL - Asphalt - Northern Elastomeric, Inc.
A.C.A. - Pet products - Natural Animal Nutrition Inc.
ACA - Shoe polish - L & F Consumer Products
ACA JOE - Shoes - Atsco Footwear Inc.
ACA PRESS - Publisher's imprints - American Chiropractic Association
ACACIA - Fabric for vertical window blinds - Home Fashions Inc.
ACACIA - Wines - Acacia Winery
ACADEMIA - Footwear - Academia Inc.
ACADEMIC - Floor coverings–carpet and rugs - Dorsett Carpet Mills Inc.
ACADEMIC - Microscopes - Bausch & Lomb Inc.
ACADEMIC EDGE - Publisher's imprints - Information Architecture Associates
ACADEMIC ENTERPRISES - Publisher's imprints - Academic Enterprises
ACADEMIC JEOPARDY - Computer software - Orange Cherry Software
ACADEMIC PRESS PROFESSIONAL - Publisher's imprints - Harcourt Brace & Co.
ACADEMIC WALL - Partitions–wood - Dowcraft Corp.
ACADEMIE - Cosmetics - Nailtex Inc.
ACADEMIE BOOKS - Publisher's imprints ☆ - Zondervan Publishing House
ACADEMY - Cleaning preparations–carpet and rug - AC Products Inc.
ACADEMY - Clocks ☆ - General Time Corp. (Westclox/Seth Thomas Div.)
ACADEMY - Cotton–balls - National Patent Medical
ACADEMY - Floor coverings–carpet and rugs - Karastan-Bigelow Inc.
ACADEMY - Furniture - Omni International Inc.
ACADEMY - Glassware–household - Crisa Corp.
ACADEMY - Guitars - Ovation Instruments
ACADEMY - Hardware - Harloc, Inc.
ACADEMY - Loud speakers - Klipsch and Associates Inc.
ACADEMY - Mobile homes - Skyline Corp.
ACADEMY - Paints–artists' - Koh-I-Noor, Inc.
ACADEMY - Tires - Private Brands Ltd.
ACADEMY - Toys–models ☆ - Minicraft Models Inc.
ACADEMY - Water colors - M. Grumbacher Inc.
ACADEMY - Wiring devices - Academy Electrical Products Corp.
ACADEMY ARTS - Wallpaper ☆ - Intercraft Industries
ACADEMY AWARD - Floor coverings–carpet and rugs ☆ - Criterion Mills Inc.
ACADEMY AWARDS - Apparel and accessories - Academy of Motion Picture Arts and Sciences
A ACADEMY BROADWAY - Shovels - Academy Broadway Corp.

ACADEMY HANDPRINTS - Wallcovering - Capital Carousel Inc.
ACADEMY MYSTERY - Publisher's imprints - Academy Publications Ltd.
ACADEMY SERIES BY BALFOUR - Jewelry - L.G. Balfour Co., Inc.
ACADIA - Bathroom fixtures ☆ - Artesian Industries
ACADIA - Beverages–malt - Anheuser-Busch Companies Inc.
ACADIA - Boats–canoes ☆ - Old Town Canoe Co.
ACADIA - Campers - American Sterling Corp.
ACADIA - Fabrics - Acadia Co. Inc.
ACADIA - Floor coverings - Mannington Resilient Floors
ACADIA - Floor coverings–carpet and rugs - Karastan-Bigelow Inc.
ACADIA - Furniture - Moosehead Manufacturing Co.
ACADIA - Housewares - Pfaltzgraff Investment Co.
ACADIA - Lighting fixtures ☆ - Hubbell Lighting, Inc. (Lighting Div.)
ACADIA - Luggage - American Tourister, Inc.
ACADIA - Milk - Acadia Dairy
ACADIA - Sardines–canned - Stinson Seafood Co.
ACADIAN - Food products - Vlasic Foods Inc.
ACADIAN - Food products - Wally Sea Products Corp.
ACADIAN - Giftware - Acadian Religious
ACADIAN GOURMET - Seafood products–fresh or frozen - Ecrevisse Acadienne USA
ACADIAN GOURMET PREMIUM - Food products - Ecrevisse Acadienne USA
ACADIAN SUPREME - Seafood - Clouston Foods USA
ACALA - Hoses - Goodyear Tire & Rubber Co.
ACAN - Housewares - Matthew Rutland, Jr.
ACANTHUS - Furniture - Lane Co. Inc.
ACANTHUS - Wallcoverings - Ben Rose Ltd.
ACAPPELLA - Hearing aids - Telex Communications, Inc.
ACAPPELLA COMPANY, THE - Recording label - Acappella Co., Inc.
ACAPULCO - Glassware–household - Crisa Corp.
ACAPULCO - Glassware–household ☆ - Oneida Ltd.
ACAPULCO - Lamps - Sperti Sunlamp
ACAPULCO - Musical instrument accessories - Westheimer Corp.
ACAPULCO - Radios - Robert Bosch Corp.
ACAPULCO - Tableware–earthenware - Villeroy and Boch Tableware Ltd.
ACAPULCO - Window shades ☆ - Colony Shade Co.
ACC - Computer software - Advanced Computer Communications
ACC - Electrical equipment - Array Connector Corp.
A+CC - Medical apparatus - Promedic, Inc.
ACC - Motors - American Contex Corp.
ACC/ME - Chemical preparations - Drew Chemical Corp.
ACC-U-SIZE - Computer software - A.O. Smith Corp.
ACC-U-WIND FILAMENT WINDING MACHINE - Machinery - G & S Machine Tool, Inc.
ACCAR - Jewelry - Accar Limited, Inc.
ACCEL - Automotive-ignition products - Echlin Inc.
ACCEL - Motor vehicle parts and accessories - Rivera Engineering, Inc.
ACCEL - Veterinary nutritional supplements - Vita Flex Nutrition Co., Inc.
ACCEL - Wheels–motor vehicle - Aerosport, Inc.
ACCEL-A-GRAPHIX - Printers–computer ☆ - Xante Corp.
ACCEL-A-WRITER 3DN - Printers–computer - Xante Corp.
ACCEL-A-WRITER 3G - Printers–computer - Xante Corp.
ACCEL-A-WRITER 3N - Printers–computer - Xante Corp.
ACCEL THE COMPUTER COMPANY - Computers–personal - Mantech Solutions Corp.
ACCELATAN - Health care products ☆ - Active Organics Inc.
ACCELERASE - Correction fluid - Wirth International Inc.
ACCELERASE - Pharmaceutical preparations ☆ - Organon Inc.
ACCELERATE - Dental compounds - Den-Mat Corp.
ACCELERATED EXPERIENCE - Construction equipment rental services - Sterling Institute
ACCELERATED FREEZE DRY - Food products - Gourmet Club Corp.
ACCELERATED READER, THE - Computer peripheral equipment - Advantage Learning Systems, Inc.
ACCELERATED SYSTEM DEVELOPMENT - Computer software - Ernst & Young LLP
ACCELERATO - Fruits–canned - Lico Brands, Inc.
ACCELERATOR - See **KINSMAN**
ACCELERATOR - Ammunition - Remington Arms Co., Inc.
ACCELERATOR - Animal feeds - Cargill, Inc.
ACCELERATOR - Fishing tackle - Cecily C. Pearson Vincent
ACCELERATOR I - Athletic shoes - Reebok International Ltd.
ACCELERATOR MID - Athletic shoes - Converse Inc.
ACCELERATOR, THE - Containers - Hold Em, Inc.
ACCELERATOR, THE - Tools - Imco Carbide Tool Inc.
ACCELERATOR TUBE - Toys - Mattel, Inc.

ACCENT - Awnings - Rainbow Awnings
ACCENT - Beauty aids ☆ - London International U.S. Holdings
ACCENT - Cabinets ☆ - Canyon Creek Cabinet Co.
ACCENT - Cabinets ☆ - Karman Kitchens Inc.
ACCENT - Cabinets–wood - Tradeways Inc.
ACCENT - Clocks - General Time Corp. (Westclox/Seth Thomas Div.)
ACCENT - Cooking utensils–aluminum - Regal Ware, Inc.
ACCENT - Craft supplies ☆ - Zorba Frame & Moulding
ACCENT - Desks ☆ - Invincible Metal Furniture Co.
ACCENT - Dinnerware–glass ☆ - WMF/USA
ACCENT - Doors–vinyl - Panelfold Inc.
ACCENT - Enamels - Camco Paints Inc.
ACCENT - Faucets - Sterling Plumbing Group Inc.
ACCENT - Fireplace equipment ☆ - Majestic Co.
ACCENT - Floor coverings - Congoleum Corp.
ACCENT - Floor coverings–carpet and rugs ☆ - Blue Ridge Carpet Mills
ACCENT - Flowers, plants, and seeds - Jacklin Seed
ACCENT - Giftware ☆ - Gorham Inc.
ACCENT - Glassware–household - Owens-Illinois Inc. (Libbey Div.)
ACCENT - Hair care products - Trionics Systems Corp.
ACCENT - Lamps–desk - Cannon Products Inc.
ACCENT - Luggage - Airway Industries, Inc.
ACCENT - Markers–felt-tip - Sanford Corp.
ACCENT - Motor vehicles–automobiles - Hyundai Motor America
ACCENT - Paints - Lasting Paints, Inc.
ACCENT - Paints - St. Louis Paint Manufacturing Co.
ACCENT - Paints ☆ - Frazee Paint
ACCENT - Plastics–laminated - Plaskolite Inc.
ACCENT - Primers - Koh-I-Noor, Inc.
ACCENT - Prosthetic apparatus - Freeman Manufacturing Co.
ACCENT - Recording label - Accent Records
ACCENT - Recreational buoyance vests - JWA Scubapro Undersea Industries, Inc.
ACCENT - Rings–jewelry - Artcarved Inc.
AC'CENT - Seasonings - Pet Inc.
ACCENT - Shoes - Interco Inc.
ACCENT - Telephones - At&T Corp.
ACCENT - Thread - Coats and Clark Inc.
ACCENT - Tiles–ceramic ☆ - American Olean Tile Co.
ACCENT - Wallets ☆ - Enger-Kress Co.
ACCENT - Wood products - Klise Manufacturing Co.
ACCENT II - Floor coverings–carpet and rugs - Patrick Carpet Mills
ACCENT II - Hardware ☆ - Amerock Corp.
ACCENT II - Tiles–ceramic ☆ - Latco Products
ACCENT 70'S - Giftware ☆ - Seymour Mann Inc.
ACCENT AMERICA - Sweaters - Sweaters USA Inc.
ACCENT BEBE - Apparel–children's - Celebrity International, Inc.
ACCENT BOARDS - Office supplies - Universal Cork, Inc.
ACCENT BRIGHT - Markers–felt-tip - Sanford Corp.
ACCENT DESIGN - Beads - Petersen-Arne
ACCENT FHA - Floor coverings–carpet and rugs - Johnson's Carpets Inc.
ACCENT FLAIR - Floor coverings–carpet and rugs ☆ - Karastan-Bigelow Inc.
ACCENT GLO - Lighting fixtures–swimming pool - Fiberstars, Inc.
ACCENT GOLDEN ELITE - Artists' materials - Koh-I-Noor, Inc.
ACCENT I - Audio equipment ☆ - Pyle Industries Inc.
ACCENT II - Paints - Gilbert Spruance Co.
ACCENT III - Floor coverings–carpet and rugs - Sheridan Carpet Mills
ACCENT LAB - Computer software - Accent Technologies
ACCENT LITE - Markers–felt-tip ☆ - Sanford Corp.
ACCENT MASQUE - Skin care products - Fanie International
ACCENT MATS - Frames–picture ☆ - Hunt Manufacturing Co.
ACCENT ON ART - Apparel–women's - KWBL Clothing & Apparel Corp.
ACCENT ON DETAILS - Apparel and accessories - Montgomery Ward & Co. Inc.
ACCENT ON NATURE - Giftware - Enesco Corp.
ACCENT PLUS - Floor coverings–carpet and rugs - Criterion Mills Inc.
ACCENT PLUS - Health care products - Huntington Laboratories Inc.
ACCENT STUDIOS - Posters - Accent Studios Inc.
ACCENT SUPREME - Floor coverings ☆ - Congoleum Corp.
ACCENT SYSTEMS - Computer integrated systems design services - Accent Systems, Inc.
ACCENTA - Pens - Accutec Inc.
ACCENTART - Stencils ☆ - Hunt Manufacturing Co.
ACCENTE' - Apparel–women's - Roy Smith Shoes, Inc.
ACCENTRICS - Hosiery–men's - Clovermere Sales Corp.
ACCENTS - Automotive parts and accessories - Rally Accessories, Inc.

ACCENTS - Bathroom accessories - Wilardy Originals Inc.
ACCENTS - Cigar boxes—wood - Consolidated Cigar Corp.
ACCENTS - Floor coverings—carpet and rugs - Richmond Carpet Mills
ACCENTS - Floor coverings—carpet and rugs ☆ - Orian Rugs Inc.
ACCENTS - Flowers—artificial - Coppersource/Halves Inc.
ACCENTS - Footwear—women's ☆ - Avanti Shoe
ACCENTS - Frames—eyeglass - Kenmark Optical Co.
ACCENTS - Furniture - Lane Co. Inc.
ACCENTS - Giftware ☆ - Quality Artworks Inc.
ACCENTS - Hardware ☆ - Amerock Corp.
ACCENTS - Housewares - Vincent Lippe Co.
ACCENTS - Jewelry—costume - Hallmark Cards Inc.
ACCENTS - Lighting fixtures - Juno Lighting Inc.
ACCENTS - Office supplies - Datacom Inc.
ACCENTS - Scales - Counselor Co.
ACCENTS - Tablecloths - Town & Country Linen Corp.
ACCENTS - Tiles—ceramic - Latco Products
ACCENTS - Underwear and nightwear - Maidenform Inc.
ACCENTS - Wallpaper ☆ - Prelude Designs
ACCENTS - Watchbands—base metal - Chisco, Inc.
ACCENTS BY A. LOCK & CO. - Furniture ☆ - Oak Land Furn. Manufacturing, Inc.
ACCENTS BY HERITAGE - Furniture ☆ - Drexel Heritage Furnishings, Inc.
ACCENTS BY LILIBET - Jewelry - Accents by Lilibet Inc.
ACCENTS BY PAKULA - Jewelry - Pakula & Co.
ACCENTS BY STANLEY - Furniture - Stanley Furniture Co. Inc.
ACCENTS IN PINE - Furniture ☆ - Henredon Furniture Industries Inc.
ACCENTS OF LOVE - Candles - San Francisco Candle Co.
ACCENTS ON EVERYTHING - Paints—artists' - Plaid Enterprises, Inc.
ACCENTS ON SHADES - Drapery hardware ☆ - Newell Window Furnishing Co.
ACCENTS TEMPRA - Hardware ☆ - Amerock Corp.
ACCENTS VALUE PLUS - Hardware ☆ - Amerock Corp.
ACCENTUATE - Eyeglasses - Art-Craft Optical Co.
ACCENTUER - Floor coverings—carpet and rugs - J.L. Benson Co.
ACCENTUETTE - Brassieres (Bras) - Blue Bay Inc.
ACCENTUETTE - Underwear and nightwear - LANZ, Inc.
ACCENTUOUS - Cosmetics - Cosmair Inc.
ACCENT'Z - Hardware - Amerock
ACCEPTANCE - Paper—bond ☆ - Fox River Paper Co.
ACCEPTANCE - Rings—jewelry - Feature Enterprises
ACCES - Telephones—cellular - Mitsubishi International Corp.
ACCESS - Computer equipment - ITT Corp.
ACCESS - Computer software - Lionville Systems, Inc.
ACCESS - Computer software - Microsoft Corp.
ACCESS - Computers - Miles Inc.
ACCESS - Dental equipment - Centrix, Inc.
ACCESS - Diapers—cloth ☆ - Salk Co. Inc.
ACCESS - Filing cabinets—wood ☆ - Sam Flax
ACCESS - Frames—eyeglass - Pathway Optical Prods.
ACCESS - Lenses—optical - Sola International Inc.
ACCESS - Padding—foam - Responsive Medical Applications, Inc.
ACCESS - Projection screens - Draper Shade and Screen Co. Inc.
ACCESS - Towels - Kimberly-Clark Corp.
ACCESS - Vitamins and nutritional supplements - Melaleuca, Inc.
ACCESS 911 BY OEC - Radio communications equipment - Independent Living/Emergency Response Network, Inc.
ACCESS 3000 - Computer software - SEI Corp.
ACCESS 5000 RACEWAY - Electrical equipment - Wiremold Co.
ACCESS-A-LIFT - Health care products - Maddak Inc.
ACCESS ABILITY - Elevators - Access-Ability, Inc.
ACCESS ABILITY - Remote control devices - Wikk Industries, Inc.
ACCESS BLUE - Pharmaceutical preparations - Centrix, Inc.
ACCESS DISCLOSURE - Computer storage devices—optical - Disclosure Inc.
ACCESS-GARD - Health care products - PRN Services Inc.
ACCESS GOLD - Computer software - Access Specialties, Inc.
ACCESS GOLD - Pharmaceutical preparations - Centrix, Inc.
ACCESS LIFT - Swimming pools ☆ - Recreonics, Inc.
ACCESS MOBILITY SYSTEM - Wheelchairs - Quest Technologies Corp.
ACCESS/OPEN - Computer peripheral equipment - Ungermann-Bass, Inc.
ACCESS-ORIES - Floor mats - R.W. & Able, Inc.
ACCESS PLUS - Computer peripheral equipment - Jo-Dan International, Inc.
ACCESS-PLUS - Locks—door - Cellular Control Systems
ACCESS-POINT - Medical apparatus - Access Surgical International, Inc.
ACCESS PURPLE - Pharmaceutical preparations - Centrix, Inc.
ACCESS SOLUTIONS - Computer software - BBM Office Products

ACCESS SQUARE - Floor coverings—tile - Philadelphia Carpets
ACCESS TO MATH - Computer software - Don Johnston Inc.
ACCESS TO PLATINUM - Computer software - Advanced Business Microsystems Inc.
ACCESS UNLIMITED, INC. - Computer software - Access Unlimited
ACCESS VERTICALS - Window coverings - Blind Design Inc.
ACCESS WORLD - Credit institutions - Access World Communications, Inc.
ACCESS30 - Computer peripheral equipment - Telco Systems, Inc.
ACCESS60 - Electronic equipment - Telco Systems, Inc.
ACCESS.ABL - Computer software - Westlake Technologies Inc.
ACCESSALITE - Lighting fixtures ☆ - Hubbell Lighting, Inc. (Lighting Div.)
ACCESSBUILDER - Computer peripheral equipment - 3Com Corp.
ACCESSCARD - Computer peripheral equipment - Wireless Access, Inc.
ACCESSCERT - Computer software - Transcender Corp.
ACCESSIBILITY INFORMATION MANAGEMENT SYSTEM (AIMS) - Computer software - Access Unlimited
ACCESSIBILITY LIFT - Elevators - Inclinator Co. of America
ACCESSIBILITY WITH STYLE - Motor vehicles—vans - Ricon Corp.
ACCESSIBLE ARCHIVES - Computer peripherals - Accessible Archives Inc.
ACCESSIT - Electronic equipment ☆ - Connectronics Corp.
ACCESSLAW - Computer software - Virginia J. Halican
ACCESSLINE SYSTEM - Computers - Access Plus Colorados Inc.
ACCESSMANAGER - Computer software - Engineering and Business Systems, Inc.
ACCESSMASTER - Machinery - JLG Industries Inc.
ACCESSMAX - Computer software - Boston Technology Inc.
ACCESSO - Metals - Crane Nuclear, Inc.
ACCESSO - Trays - Yawman and Erbe of California Corp.
ACCESSOCRAFT - Giftware - Accessocraft Products Corp.
ACCESSORAMA - Crocheted and knitted items ☆ - Ben Berger LLC.
ACCESSORIES BY ACRICITE - Desk sets - Acricite Co. Inc.
ACCESSORIES PLUS - Bags—cosmetic - A.J. Siris Products Corp.
ACCESSORIZE! - Bathroom accessories - General Marble Co.
ACCESSORY BOUTIQUE - Jewelry boxes - Laverne Thompson
ACCESSORY CAFE - Display cases—plastic - Health O Meter, Inc.
ACCESSORY CLUB, THE - Patterns—clothing ☆ - Simplicity Pattern Co., Inc.
ACCESSORY CORP., THE - Garment hangers - Accessory Corp.
ACCESSORY DECORATING PARTY - Paint sets—hobby ☆ - Tulip Productions
ACCESSORY DESIGN GROUP - Hosiery—women's - TBAC-Prince Gardner Inc.
ACCESSORY INSTITUTE, THE - Apparel and accessories - Durlacher & Co., Inc.
ACCESSORY NETWORK - Jewelry - Gitano Licensing, Ltd.
ACCESSORY PERFORMANCE PAC - Telephones—cellular - Cellstar, Ltd.
ACCESSORY WORKS - Umbrellas - Accessory Network Group, Inc.
ACCESSPLUS COMMUNICATIONS - Computer software - Accessline Technologies, Inc.
ACCESSPOST - Dental equipment - Essential Dental Systems, Inc.
ACCESSPOST OVERDENTURE - Dental equipment - Essential Dental Systems, Inc.
ACCESSPRO - Radio magnetic instrumentation - Linear Corp.
ACCESSWORKS - Computer software - Digital Equipment Corp.
ACCIDENTAL FINE DINING INC. - Sauces - Accidental Fine Dining Inc.
ACCIDENTS CAUSE PEOPLE. - Apparel and accessories - Sandra Mangione
ACCIDENTS HAPPEN! - Stain removers - USA-Petrx
ACCINTE - Footwear - Bee-Gee Shoe Corp
ACCLAIM - Brushes—hair - Spornette International, Inc.
ACCLAIM - Cigarettes - Philip Morris Companies Inc.
ACCLAIM - Clocks - General Time Corp. (Westclox/Seth Thomas Div.)
ACCLAIM - Computer software - Acclaim Entertainment Inc.
ACCLAIM - Fabrics—broadcloth - Collins & Aikman Corp.
ACCLAIM - Fabrics—tapestry ☆ - Columbus Coated Fabrics Co.
ACCLAIM - Floor coverings - Mannington Resilient Floors
ACCLAIM - Floor coverings—carpet and rugs ☆ - Blue Ridge Carpet Mills
ACCLAIM - Floor coverings—carpet and rugs ☆ - Criterion Mills Inc.
ACCLAIM - Frames—eyeglass ☆ - Universal/Univis Inc.
ACCLAIM - Furniture - Hammary Furniture Co. Inc.
ACCLAIM - Furniture - Krueger International, Inc.
ACCLAIM - Furniture ☆ - Vaughan Furniture Co. Inc.
ACCLAIM - Hair care products - Zotos International Inc.
ACCLAIM - Jewelry - Leach & Garner Co.
ACCLAIM - Lighting equipment - Lighting Methods Inc.
ACCLAIM - Luggage - Samsonite Corp.
ACCLAIM - Manicure preparations - Fromm Industries

☆ = Now out of production

ACCLAIM - Motor vehicles–automobiles ☆ - Chrysler Corp. (Chrysler-Plymouth Div.)

ACCLAIM - Paper - Butler Paper Co.

ACCLAIM - Recording label - Acclaim Music

ACCLAMATION - Floor coverings - Congoleum Corp.

ACCLAMATION - Floor coverings–carpet and rugs - Coronet Carpets Inc.

ACCLAMATION - Floor coverings–carpet and rugs - Philadelphia Carpets

ACCLIMATE - Apparel and accessories - Russ Knits, Inc.

ACCLIMATE - Skin care products - Ilona, Inc.

ACCLIMATOR - Pet products ☆ - Aquarium Products Inc.

ACCO - Cleaning preparations–carpet and rug - Windsor Wax Co. Inc.

ACCO - Cotton batting - Absorbent Cotton Co.

ACCO - Dog collars and chains, sporting goods - Babcock Industries Inc. (Babcock Control Group)

ACCO - Fasteners–snap - ACCO USA, Inc.

ACCOBIND - Paper - ACCO USA, Inc.

ACCODATA - Binders - ACCO USA, Inc.

ACCODATA MATE - Binders - ACCO USA, Inc.

ACCOFILTER - Water purification systems ☆ - Rothco Inc.

ACCOFLEX - Insulating materials - Armstrong World Industries, Inc.

ACCOHIDE - Binders - ACCO USA, Inc.

ACCOLADE - Cleaning preparations–carpet and rug ☆ - Richmond Carpet Mills

ACCOLADE - Computer software - Accolade Inc.

ACCOLADE - Dishes–china ☆ - Gorham Inc.

ACCOLADE - Flatware - Utica Cutlery Co.

ACCOLADE - Floor coverings–carpet and rugs ☆ - Lees Carpets

ACCOLADE - Floor coverings–carpet and rugs ☆ - Royalweve Carpet Mills

ACCOLADE - Furniture - Haworth, Inc.

ACCOLADE - Margarine - Kraft Food Ingredients Corp.

ACCOLADE - Paints - Pratt & Lambert, Inc.

ACCOLADE - Paper - International Paper Co.

ACCOLADE - Surgical supplies - Tidi Products, Inc.

ACCOLADES - Fabrics ☆ - Gretchen Bellinger Inc.

ACCOLADES - Floor coverings–carpet and rugs - Patcraft Mills Inc.

ACCOLADES - Furniture ☆ - Bassett Furniture Industries, Inc.

ACCOLADES - Greeting cards - American Greetings Corp.

ACCOLADES - Wallpaper - Peacock Papers, Inc.

ACCOLADES - Wallpaper ☆ - Capital Carousel Inc.

ACCOLADE'S COMICS - Computer software ☆ - Accolade Inc.

ACCOLAID - Skin care products ☆ - Avon Products, Inc.

ACCOLOY II - Hardware - Babcock Industries Inc. (Babcock Control Group)

ACCOMODATOR - Tables–metal - Counterpoint

ACCOMPLI - Desk sets - Boling Co.

ACCOMPLICE - Apparel stores–lingerie - Formflex Foundations Inc.

ACCOMPLICE - Rackets–tennis - Spalding Sports Worldwide

ACCOMPLISH - Cleaning preparations - Ecolab Inc.

ACCOMPLISH - Fertilizers - Platte Chemical Co.

ACCOMPRA 120 - Orthopedic products - Smith & Nephew Richards, Inc.

ACCOPAC - Packaging–foam - Armstrong World Industries, Inc.

ACCOPRESS - Binders - ACCO USA, Inc.

ACCORD - Audio equipment - KLH

ACCORD - Cabinets ☆ - Medallion Kitchens of Minnesota Inc.

ACCORD - Clocks - General Time Corp. (Westclox/Seth Thomas Div.)

ACCORD - Clothing - Amtex Inc.

ACCORD - Fabrics–broadcloth - Kimberly-Clark Corp.

ACCORD - Floor coverings–carpet and rugs ☆ - Regal Rugs Inc.

ACCORD - Furniture - Mersman Furniture Co.

ACCORD - Luggage - Samsonite Corp.

ACCORD - Motor vehicles–automobiles - American Honda Motor Co. Inc. (Acura Div.)

ACCORD - Musical instruments - E.K. Blessing Co. Inc.

ACCORD - Recording label - Musidisc SA

ACCORD - Siding–insulating ☆ - Aluminum Co. of America

ACCORD - Tobacco products - Philip Morris Companies Inc.

ACCORD-A-PAC - Containers - Information Packaging Corp.

ACCORD BRAND - Fruits and vegetables - Golden State Citrus Packers

ACCORD KEYBOARD - Computer peripheral equipment - Lite-On Peripherals, Inc.

ACCORD TRIM-ALL - Siding–insulating ☆ - Aluminum Co. of America

ACCORDE - Nutrition product - Welcon

ACCORDEX - Wallets - Kleer-Vu Plastics Inc.

ACCORDIA - Aircraft parts - MSA Aircraft Interior Products, Inc.

ACCORDIA - Blinds–venetian - Kirsch Inc.

ACCORDIA - Tiles–ceramic - WesekPalley Tile Inc.

ACCORDIA - Window shades - Kirsch Co.

ACCORDIA-FOLD - Draperies - Kirsch Co.

ACCORDIANA - Musical instruments - Excelsior Accordions Inc.

ACCORDION - Office supplies - Globe-Weis

ACCORDION CASES WITH ROLLERS - Cases–musical instrument - Castiglione Accordion

ACCORDION TRIPOD STANDS - Musical instrument accessories - Castiglione Accordion

ACCORDIX - Musical instruments ☆ - Multivox/Sorkin Music Co. Inc.

ACCORGAN - Accordions - Syn-Cordion Musical Instruments Corp.

ACCORN - Combs - Hess Hair Milk Laboratories Inc.

ACCORNERO - Biscuits ☆ - Bell'amore Imports Inc.

ACCOSEAL - Gaskets - Armstrong World Industries, Inc.

ACCOST - Pesticides–agricultural - Platte Chemical Co.

ACCOTEX - Aprons - Armstrong World Industries, Inc.

ACCOTONE - Floor coverings - Armstrong World Industries, Inc.

ACCOUNTABILITY NOTEBOOK - Notebooks and notepads - Jeff L. Noblit

ACCOUNTANT 210 - Adding machines ☆ - Citizen America Corp.

ACCOUNTANT INC. - Computer software - Softsync Inc.

ACCOUNTING FOR NONPROFITS - Computer software - Blackbaud, Inc.

ACCOUNTING PLUS - Computer software - Systems Plus Inc.

ACCOUNTLINK - Computer software - Cellular Technical Services Inc.

ACCOUNTVUET - Computer software - Cellular Technical Services Inc.

ACCOUST-ARRAY - Audio equipment - Electro-Voice, Inc.

ACCOUSTIC FOAM - Paint rollers - Corona Brushes Inc.

ACCRA LAB - Research–scientific - Biochemical Sciences, Inc.

ACCRA-SHOT - Firearms, accessories, and parts - Anderson Manufacturing Co.

ACCROSEAL - Sealing devices - Kalplas, Inc.

ACCS - Snowmobiles - Polaris Industries Partners LP

ACCT - Pet products ☆ - Aquatronics-Filtronics

ACCTV - Electronic equipment - Puritan-Bennett Corp.

ACCU ARM - Agricultural machinery - Osborne Industries Inc.

ACCU-BACK - Medical apparatus - Accu-Back, Inc.

ACCU-BAKERY - Housewares - Salton/Maxim Housewares, Inc.

ACCU-BEADS - Beads - Hamilton-Thorn Research

ACCU-BEEP - Thermometers - Becton, Dickinson and Co.

ACCU-BLEND - Machinery - Accurate Metering Systems, Inc.

ACCU-BLEND - Vitamins and nutritional supplements - Tishcon Corp.

ACCU-BOLT - Electronic equipment - Sherikon, Inc.

ACCU-BORE - Tools - ILCO Unican Corp.

ACCU-CHART - Video production - Nalpak Video Sales, Inc.

ACCU-CHEK - Golfing equipment - Universal Fountain Pen & Pencil Co.

ACCU-CHEK EASY - Health care products - Boehringer Mannheim Corp.

ACCU-CHOKE - Sporting goods - O.F. Mossberg & Sons, Inc.

ACCU-CLEANSE - Skin care products - Allan Palmer Laboratories, Inc.

ACCU CORE - Golfing equipment - Golfsmith International Inc.

ACCU-CURL - Hair care products - Kenra Laboratories, Inc.

ACCU-CUT - Firearms, accessories, and parts ☆ - Modern Muzzle Loading, Inc.

ACCU-CUT - Packaging–paper - Sealed Air Corp.

ACCU/CUT - Scissors–hand-operated - S & S Medical Supply Co.

ACCU-DOSE - Veterinary pharmaceutical preparations - Genesis Industries Inc.

ACCU-EDGE - Rulers–metal - Alvin and Co. Inc.

ACCU-FAST - Pool tables - Olhausen Billiard Manufacturing, Inc.

ACCU-FIT - Floor coverings ☆ - Congoleum Corp.

ACCU-FIT - Plugs–ear - Mine Safety Appliances Co.

ACCU FLEX - Paints - Gregory F. Konrad

ACCU-FLITE - Sporting goods - Pro Select, Inc.

ACCU FLO - Painting supplies - Cotter & Co.

ACCU-FLOW - Medical apparatus - Salter Labs

ACCU-FRESH - Chickens - ConAgra Broiler Co.

ACCU GAGE - Automotive parts and accessories - G.H. Meiser & Co.

ACCU-GAP - Machinery - Bluffton Agri/Industrial Corp.

ACCU-GRID - Mat boards - Extra Special Products Corp.

ACCU-GRINDER - Grinders - Salton/Maxim Housewares, Inc.

ACCU-JET - Machine parts - Thermo Fibertek Inc.

ACCU-KLEAR - Paints - OEM Paints, Inc.

ACCU-KOTE - Paints - Kwal-Howells Inc.

ACCU-L - Electronic equipment - AVX Corp.

ACCU LIFT - Back support belts - Fla. Orthopedics, Inc.

ACCU-LINE - Electrical equipment - GB Electrical Inc.

ACCU-LINK - Machine parts - Jason Industrial Inc.

ACCU-LITE - Firearms, accessories, and parts ☆ - Modern Muzzle Loading, Inc.

ACCU-MARKER - Floor coverings ☆ - Congoleum Corp.

ACCU-MASSAGE - Sandals - Genki USA

☆ = Now out of production

ACCU MEASURE - Measuring instruments - Riley Manufacturing Co., Inc.
ACCU-MISER - Barbecues and grills - Middleby Marshall Inc.
ACCU-MIX - Vitamins and nutritional supplements - Tishcon Corp.
ACCU-MIXER - Chemical compounds - Accurate Chemical and Scientific Corp.
ACCU-NET - Sporting goods - Howard Silagy
ACCU-PAK - Circuit boards - Zierick Manufacturing Corp.
ACCU-PIN - Dowels - Accu-Systems Inc.
ACCU-PLANT - Seed planter - Rawson Control Systems, Inc.
ACCU-POD - Firearms, accessories, and parts - Bausch & Lomb Inc.
ACCU-POINT - Pens - Gillette Co.
ACCU-PORT - Microphones - Shure Brothers, Inc.
ACCU-RAM - Machinery - TT Technologies, Inc.
ACCU-RANGE - Telescopes - Redfield Co.
ACCU-RATER - Computer software - Accu-Rater, Inc.
ACCU-READ - Scales–bathroom - Sunbeam Corp.
ACCU RED - Glassware - Corning Inc.
ACCU RULE - Measuring instruments - United Machining Services, Inc.
ACCU SCAN - Television equipment ☆ - J.C. Penney Co., Inc.
ACCU-SENSOR - Electrodes - Lynn Medical Instrument Co.
ACCU SERIES - Archery equipment - Golden Key Futura, Inc.
ACCU-SET - Clock radios - Matsushita Consumer Electronics Co.
ACCU-SET - Sights–gun - Pachmayr Ltd.
ACCU-SHAPER - Cosmetics - Revlon Consumer Products Corp.
ACCU-SHARP - Tools - Parkwood Products Co., Inc.
ACCU SHOT - Computer software - Accusport International, Inc.
ACCU-SLIDE - Video production ☆ - Nalpak Video Sales, Inc.
ACCU-SONIC - Golfing equipment - TourEdge Golf Manufacturing Inc.
ACCU-SORB - Medical apparatus - Medline, Industries, Inc.
ACCU-SPOUT - Dishwashers–commercial - Benckiser Consumer Products Inc.
ACCU-SPRAY - Sprayers - Root-Lowell Manufacturing Co.
ACCU-STAND - Record stores ☆ - American Acoustics
ACCU-STEP - Golfing equipment - Wilson Sporting Goods Co.
ACCU-STOP - Machine parts - Ryobi America Corp.
ACCU-SURG - Surgical instruments - TTI Medical, Inc.
ACCU-TECH - Epoxy - Angelo Miozza
ACCU-TECTURE - Computer terminals ☆ - Accu-Time Systems, Inc.
ACCU-TEE - Golfing equipment - Accu-Tee, Inc.
ACCU-TEMP - Aquariums–household - GM Aquatics
ACCU-TEMP - Refrigerator thermometer - American Thermometer Co.
ACCU-TEMP - Thermometers - Republic Drug Co. Inc.
ACCU-TEMP - Thermostats - BKI, Inc.
ACCU-THERM - Skin care products - Paula Payne Products Co. Inc.
ACCU-TIME - Computer terminals ☆ - Accu-Time Systems, Inc.
ACCU-TIME - Hair care products - Nexxus Products Co.
ACCU-TIMER - Electronic equipment - Time-Cal Systems Inc.
ACCU-TONE - Paints - Kwal-Howells Inc.
ACCU-TOSS - Toys - Moneywon Inc.
ACCU-TRAC - Computer peripheral equipment - Micro Chemical, Inc.
ACCU-TRAC - Medical apparatus - Clinical Concepts
ACCU-TRAC - Rifles - Redfield Co.
ACCU-TRAX - Handlebars–motorcycle - Answer Products Inc.
ACCU-TRIMMER - Floor coverings ☆ - Congoleum Corp.
ACCU-TROLL - Fishing tackle ☆ - Wright & McGill Co.
ACCU-TRU - Medical apparatus - Bristoline Inc.
ACCU-VAC - Valves - Thermo Fibertek Inc.
ACCU-VAL - Film - Weber-Valentine Co.
ACCU-VELVET - Dental Impression material - Dyna Group, Inc.
ACCU-WRIST - Medical apparatus - Accu-Back, Inc.
ACCU-ZONE - Alarm systems - Stevens Industries Inc.
ACCU-ZONE - Labels–gummed - Graphic Technology, Inc.
ACCUBAKE - Controls–heating systems - Flynn Burner Corp.
ACCUBAR - Golfing equipment - Ram Golf Corp.
ACCUBOND - Medical apparatus - GAC International, Inc.
ACCUBORE - Musical instrument accessories - Deg Music Products Inc.
ACCUBORE - Tools - ILCO Unican Corp.
ACCUBRAN - Cylinders - Compact Air Products, Inc.
ACCUCAL - Laboratory apparatus - Cole-Parmer Instrument Co.
ACCUCARE - Cosmetics - Medline, Industries, Inc.
ACCUCARE - Health care products - Aedline, Industries, Inc.
ACCUCENTRIC - Electronic equipment - Optical Gaging Products, Inc.
ACCUCHOICE - Staples - Georgia-Pacific Corp.
ACCUCLAMP - Fasteners–snap - Hadady Corp.
ACCUCLEAR - Tape–adhesive ☆ - Permacel
ACCUCOLOR - Electronic equipment ☆ - NEC Technologies, Inc.
ACCUCOPY - Computer hardware - Media Logic, Inc.

ACCUCORE - Golfing equipment - Golfsmith International Inc.
ACCUDART - Darts and dart games - Accudart
ACCUDATA - Medical apparatus - Boehringer Mannheim Corp.
ACCUDATA - Photographic equipment - Eastman Kodak Co.
ACCUDESIGN - Computer software - PPG Architectural Finishes, Inc.
ACCUDOSE - Dental equipment - Centrix, Inc.
ACCUDOT - Sights–gun - Tasco Sales, Inc.
ACCUDRIVE - Gears - Cone Drive Operations Inc.
ACCUFAX - Paper - PM Co. (Office Products Div.)
ACCUFEED - Tools–garden - Toro Co.
ACCUFIT - Exercising equipment ☆ - Raleigh USA Bicycle Co.
ACCUFIT - Plugs–ear - MSA
ACCUFIT WELDED - Filters–industrial - Mechanical Manufacturing Corp.
ACCUFLEX - Eyeglasses - Marchon and Marcolin Eyewear Inc.
ACCUFLY - Machinery - Extrusion Services, Inc.
ACCUFORCE - Rackets–tennis - Forten Corp.
ACCUFRET - Musical instrument accessories - Dunlop Manufacturing, Inc.
ACCUGLIDE - Tape–masking - Minnesota Mining & Manufacturing Co.
ACCUGLOW - Watches - Accutime Watch Corp.
ACCUGRAPH - Computer software - Accugraph Corp.
ACCUGRAVE - Tools - Standex International Corp.
ACCUGRIP - Golf gloves - MDM Golf Worldwide
ACCUGUARD - Bottle caps - Phoenix Closures, Inc.
ACCUGUIDE - Cables–coaxial - Control Concepts Corp.
ACCUJECT - Dental equipment - Astra Pharmaceutical Products, Inc.
ACCUJET - Paper - International Paper Co.
ACCULAB - Audio equipment ☆ - RTR Speaker Co.
ACCULAB PRODUCTS GROUP - Electronic equipment - Summit Controls
ACCULAM - Machinery - D & K Custom Machine Design, Inc.
ACCULDR - Laboratory apparatus - Gen-Probe Inc.
ACCULIGHT - Furniture - Bretford Manufacturing, Inc.
ACCULINE - Desk sets - Accu-Line
ACCULINE - Tape–adhesive ☆ - Permacel
ACCULINE - Tools - Johnson Level & Tool Manufacturing Co. Inc.
ACCULITE - Computer software - Accutron Inc.
ACCULITE - Photographic equipment - Eastman Kodak Co.
ACCULOC - Hardware - American Cord & Webbing Co., Inc.
ACCULON - Sporting goods - Accu Cutter Co.
ACCULYTE - Lighting fixtures - Accudyne Corp.
ACCUMAG STRIPE - Magnetic tape–blank - CFC International, Inc.
ACCUMAP SPORT - Radios - Lowrance Electronics, Inc.
ACCUMARK - Rifles - Weatherby, Inc.
ACCUMAT - Insulating materials - Scosche Industries, Inc.
ACCUMATCH - Computer storage devices - Exactech, Inc.
ACCUMATCH IMPLANT SELECTION SYSTEM - Computer software - Exactech, Inc.
ACCUMAX - Blood pressure apparatus - Graham-Field Inc.
ACCUMAX - Film - Eastman Kodak Co.
ACCUMAX - Motor vehicle parts and accessories - Bob Bartlett & Associates Inc.
ACCUMENTOR - Health care products - Omron Healthcare, Inc.
ACCUMETRIX - Computer software - Information Technology Group, Inc.
ACCUMILL - Treadmills - Pacer Fitness Systems
ACCUMIX - Marine rigging - Outboard Marine Corp.
ACCUMOLD - Gloves - Bianchi International
ACCUMULATOR - Health care products - Permatron Corp.
ACCUNAV - Electronic equipment - Guided Boring Systems, Inc.
ACCUNAV SPORT - Electronic equipment - Lowrance Electronics, Inc.
ACCUNET - Computer software - TMA Technologies, Inc.
ACCUNO - Internal combustion engines–mobile - Precision Engine Controls Corp.
ACCUNOX - Internal combustion engines–mobile - Precision Engine Controls Corp.
ACCUPAK - Giftware - Accurate Flannel Bag Co.
ACCUPART - Brake parts - Accupart International
ACCUPATCH - Pharmaceutical preparations ☆ - The Hymed Group Corp.
ACCUPATH - Computers - ABL Electronics Corp.
ACCUPHASE - Audio equipment ☆ - Madrigal Ltd.
ACCUPIC - Machinery - Si Handling Systems, Inc.
ACCUPLEX - Chemical preparations - Western Water Management, Inc.
ACCUPLUS - Medical apparatus - Del Mar Avionics
ACCUPOST - Posters - Accupost, Inc.
ACCUPOWER - Automotive parts and accessories - Echlin Inc.
ACCUPRIL - Pharmaceutical preparations - Parke-Davis
ACCUPRINT - Printers–computer - Avery Dennison Corp.
ACCUPRO - Multi-image stand - Pacific Innovations

ACCUPRO - Speedometers - Airguide Instrument Co.

ACCUPULSE - Exercising equipment - Precise International/Wenger

ACCUQUAD - Kurt J. Lesker Co.

ACCUQUARTZ - Watches - Bulova Corp.

ACCUR - Computer software ☆ - Humphrey Systems

ACCURA - Photo albums - SP Systems/Saratons

ACCURA - Sonic depth finder - Lowrance Electronics, Inc.

ACCURA - Watches - Bella Time Corp.

ACCURACY - Stationery ☆ - Mead Corp.

ACCURACY - RELIABILITY - SAFETY KNIGHT - Firearms, accessories, and parts - Modern Muzzle Loading, Inc.

ACCURAID - Computer peripheral equipment - Antrone Research, Inc.

ACCURAIL - Toy models - Accurate Finishing, Inc.

ACCURATE - Hardware - Accurate Lock & Hardware Co.

ACCURATE - Pencils ☆ - Faber-Castell Corp.

ACCURATE - Sporting goods - HO Sports Inc.

ACCURATE - Surgical instruments - James R. Kendrick Co. Inc.

ACCURATE - Toys–models - Accurate Miniatures

ACCURATE 2230 - Gunpowder - Accurate Arms Co., Inc.

ACCURATE AUDIO - Audio equipment - Sanus Systems

ACCURATE IMAGE - Audio equipment - Cerwin-Vega Inc.

ACCURATE PROTECTS - Bags–storage - Accurate Flannel Bag Co.

ACCURATE RELEASE - Vitamins and nutritional supplements - Nature's Bounty, Inc.

ACCURATE TRANSMISSIONS - Transmissions–motor vehicle - Accurate Transmissions, Inc.

ACCURATER - Computer software - S.F. Checkosky & Associates

ACCURATONE - Hearing aids - Telex Communications, Inc.

ACCURATRONIC - Watches - Bulova Corp.

ACCURBRON - Pharmaceutical preparations - Marion Merrell Dow

ACCURE - Cleaning preparations - Chemed Corp.

ACCUREADER - Computer software - Ultima Electronics Corp.

ACCUREAMER - Machine tools - SGS Tool Co.

ACCUREL - Circuit boards - Accurel Systems International Corp.

ACCUREX - Heart monitors ☆ - Polar Electro Inc.

ACCUREX II - Heart monitors - Polar Electro Inc.

ACCURIBBON - Cables - Minnesota Mining & Manufacturing Co.

ACCURIST - Watches - Bulova Corp.

ACCURON - Machinery - Dearborn Gage Co.

ACCURX PLUS - Computer software - Humphrey Systems

ACCUSAFE - Paper cutters - Quartet Manufacturing Co.

ACCUSCAN - Computer hardware - AccuScan Inc.

ACCUSCORE - Books–blank - Accuscore

ACCUSEAL - Containers - Phoenix Closures, Inc.

ACCUSEAL - Varnishes - AMK Inc.

ACCUSET - Dental compounds - Essential Dental Systems, Inc.

ACCUSIGN - Pharmaceutical preparations - Princeton Biomeditech Corp.

ACCUSITE PH - Medical apparatus - Zinetics Medical Technology Corp.

ACCUSIZE - Machine parts - Madison Cutting Tools Inc.

ACCUSKETCH - Computer software - E for M Corp.

ACCUSKI - Electronic equipment - GK Aviation, Inc.

ACCUSLITTER - Mailing machines - Staplex Co.

ACCUSNAP - Medical apparatus - Lynn Medical Instrument Co.

ACCUSOFT - Water purification systems - Flint & Walling Industries, Inc.

ACCUSONIC - Musical instruments - Fender Musical Instruments

ACCUSPLIT - Watches - Accusplit Inc.

ACCUSPOT - Diagnostic substances - Specialty Biosystems, Inc.

ACCUSPOT - Flashlight - Eveready Battery Co., Inc.

ACCUSTAIR - Computer software - L.J. Smith Co., Inc.

ACCUSTAK - Machinery - Thermoguard Equipment, Inc.

ACCUSTAR - Laboratory apparatus - Lucas Industries, Inc.

ACCUSTOCK - Electronic equipment - Electronic Retailing Systems International, Inc.

ACCUSTRIP - Medical apparatus - Jant Pharmacal Corp.

ACCUSTRIP SYSTEM - Abrasive products - Schmidt Manufacturing, Inc.

ACCUSURE - Surgical supplies - Qualitest Products, Inc.

ACCUSWAY - Medical apparatus - Advanced Mechanical Technology Inc.

ACCUSWING - Golfing equipment - J. Don Reed

ACCUSYSTEM - Golfing equipment - Clubmasters Golf, Inc.

ACCUSYSTEMS - Implants–surgical - Accusystems, Inc.

ACCUTAB - Computer peripheral equipment - Gtco Corp.

ACCUTANE - Pharmaceutical preparations - Hoffmann-La Roche Inc.

ACCUTEC - Office supplies - Accutec Inc.

ACCUTECH - Animal feeds - Hubbard Milling Co.

ACCUTECH - Electronic equipment - VMI Industries

ACCUTECH - Electronic equipment ☆ - Fyrnetics Inc.

ACCUTECH - Golf clubs - Austad Co.

ACCUTECH SYSTEMS CORPORATION - Computer software - Accutech Systems Corp.

ACCUTEK - Humidifiers - Accutek Products Corp.

ACCUTEL - Computer software - Electronic Selection Systems Corp.

ACCUTEST - Computer software - Accuware Inc.

ACCUTEST - Diagnostic apparatus - Jant Pharmacal Corp.

ACCUTEST - Pregnancy test kits ☆ - Reese Chemical Co.

ACCUTHERM - Watches - Bulova Corp.

ACCUTIDE - Computer software - Palindrome Software

ACCUTIME - Watches ☆ - Accutime Watch Corp.

ACCUTINT - Computer peripheral equipment - Zenith Electronics Corp.

ACCUTINTER - Machinery - Fluid Management

ACCUTIP - Mortars–clay - CCPI Inc.

ACCUTONE - Musical instruments - Widener Engineering

ACCUTONE - Toners - Accutone, Inc.

ACCUTOWER - Electrical equipment - Liebert Corp.

ACCUTRAC - Computer software - Pacific Telematics, Inc.

ACCUTRAC - Elevators - Delaware Capital Formation Inc.

ACCUTRAC - Lawn mowers - Fuqua Industries Inc.

ACCUTRACK - Boats - Boston Whaler, Inc.

ACCUTRACK - Clocks - Specialty Instruments Corp.

ACCUTRACK - Computer software - At&T Corp.

ACCUTRACKER - Medical apparatus - Suntech Medical Instruments, Inc.

ACCUTRAK - Tape players ☆ - Califone International Inc.

ACCUTREX - Clocks - Franklin Instrument Co. Inc.

ACCUTRIEVE - Industrial machinery - Richards-Wilcox Manufacturing Co.

ACCUTROL - Pumps - Tuthill Corp.

ACCUTRON - Watches - Bulova Corp.

ACCUTRON - Water treating compounds ☆ - Aquatronics-Filtronics

ACCUTRUST - Computer storage devices - Accutech Systems Corp.

ACCUTUNE - Musical instrument accessories - Hansen House Inc.

ACCUTUPH - Electrodes - Fisher Scientific Co.

ACCUVAC - Veterinary medical equipment - Select Laboratories, Inc.

ACCUVAR - Electrical surge protectors - Control Concepts Corp.

ACCUVIEW - Machinery - Fluid Management

ACCUVIEW - Paper - PM Co. (Office Products Div.)

ACCUVITE - Vitamins and nutritional supplements - Integrated Health, Inc.

ACCUWALL - Glass products - EGL Co. Inc.

ACCUWAY - Farm machinery - Spyker Spreader Works

ACCWARE - Computer software - Nobel International

ACD-A-CITRATE BASED - Pharmaceutical preparations - Cytosol Laboratories, Inc.

ACD AIR COOLED DESIGN - Bags–duffel - Franklin Sports, Inc.

ACE - Aquariums–household - Jungle Laboratories Corp.

ACE - Automotive parts and accessories - Kanei, Inc.

ACE - Automotive parts and accessories ☆ - Champion Laboratories, Inc.

ACE - Bicycles - Wheelsmith Fabrications Inc.

ACE - Binders - Ace Loose Leaf Bindery Co.

ACE - Boat hoist - Ace Lab, Inc.

ACE - Brooms - F.M. Thorpe Manufacturing Co.

ACE - Brushes - Ace Wire Brush Co.

ACE - Brushes–hair - Spilo/Mehaz Worldwide

ACE - Combs - Ace Comb Co. Inc.

ACE - Computer peripheral equipment - Wellfleet Communications, Inc.

ACE - Computer software - Loctite Corp.

ACE - Electrical equipment - Fostec, Inc.

ACE - Electronic equipment - Precision Systems, Inc.

ACE - Electronic equipment - Toro Co.

ACE - Exhaust systems–motor vehicle - Associated Equipment Corp.

ACE - Fishing tackle ☆ - Frabill Inc.

ACE - Fruit - Florida Fresh

ACE - Gliders–metal - Turner and Seymour Manufacturing Co.

ACE - Guitars - N.H.F. Musical Merchandise Corp.

ACE - Hair care products - Marianna Imports, Inc.

ACE - Hardware stores - Ace Hardware Corp.

ACE - Hoists - Ace Boat Hoist

ACE - Jewelry - Stan-Lee Corp.

ACE - Knives - Ace Services Inc.

ACE - Lighting equipment - Dura Electric Lamp Co. Inc.

ACE - Medical apparatus - Ace Orthopedic Manufacturing, Inc.

ACE - Medical apparatus - Diemolding Corp.

ACE - Mops - Piedmont Mop Co.

ACE - Motorcycles - Ace Motorcycle Corp.

ACE - Nozzles - Aeronautical Concept of Exhaust, Ltd.

ACE - Office supplies - Ace Fastener

ACE - Office supplies ☆ - Ace Hose and Rubber Co.
ACE - Paints ☆ - Hampton Paint Manufacturing Co.
ACE - Pens - Rosa Pen Co.
ACE - Pesticides–household - Bekins Co.
ACE - Photographic equipment - Ace Products Enterprises Inc.
ACE - Pistols ☆ - Colt's Manufacturing Co. Inc.
ACE - Publisher's imprints - Berkley Publishing Corp.
ACE - Rackets–tennis - Pro Kennex, Inc.
ACE - Recording label - Ace Records
ACE - Sporting goods - Spalding Sports Worldwide
ACE - Surgical supplies - Becton, Dickinson and Co.
ACE - Tools–hand-operated ☆ - Durall-Eagle Tools
ACE - Toothpaste ☆ - Comfort Manufacturing Co.
ACE - Toys - Tonka Corp.
ACE - Toys–automobiles - 1992 Mathre Family Trust
ACE - Wrenches - Covers Co. Inc.
ACE 2000 - Computers ☆ - Franklin Computer Corp.
ACE ANTENNA - Antennas - Ace Antenna Co.
ACE APPLE CIDER - Cider - Thames America Trading Co. Ltd.
ACE COMPUTERS - Computers - J.C. Technology, Inc.
ACE DETECTIVE - Computer software - Mind Play
ACE EXPLORER - Computer software - Mind Play
ACE-GRIP - Exercising equipment - IMC Products Corp.
ACE/HANSON - Tools ☆ - American Tool Companies Inc.
ACE-HESIVE - Health care products ☆ - Becton, Dickinson and Co.
ACE-HI - Flour–blended - California Milling Corp.
ACE HI FEEDS - Animal feeds - Star Milling Co.
ACE HIGH - Animal feeds ☆ - Foster Canning Inc.
ACE HIGH - Wines - Monarch Wine Co. of Georgia
ACE HONEY CIDER - Cider - Thames America Trading Co. Ltd.
ACE HURLER - Exercise equipment - Scott E. Elson
ACE-IN-THE-HOLE - Pumps - Simer Pump Co.
ACE IN THE HOLE - Sporting goods ☆ - Bear Archery Inc.
ACE INQUIRER - Computer software - Mind Play
ACE IT - Apparel–athletic - Texace Corp.
ACE MASTER - Sporting goods - Eclectic Creations, Inc.
ACE MATES - Combs ☆ - Ace Comb Co. Inc.
ACE MCCLOUD - Toys - Tonka Corp.
ACE O SPADES - Food products - SPADA enterprise, ltd.
ACE OF ACES - Computer software - Accolade Inc.
ACE OF CHERRY - Housewares - Amaza Laboratories Inc.
ACE OF CLUBS SWING TECH AUTOMATIC - Golfing equipment - Frederick
   E. Barber
ACE OF DIAMONDS - Garden equipment - Valley View Specialties Co.
ACE OF SPADES - Giftware - Gessner Products Co. Inc.
ACE OF SPADES - Playing cards ☆ - Pacific Game Co.
ACE PEAR CIDER - Cider - Thames America Trading Co. Ltd.
ACE + Z - Pharmaceutical preparations - Legere Pharmaceuticals Inc.
ACE PROGRAMMER - Computer software - Mind Play
ACE RAY - Jewelry - Ace Green Products Corp.
ACE REPORTER - Computer software - Cellular Technical Services Inc.
ACE REPORTER - Computer software - Mind Play
ACE REPORTER DELUXE - Computer software - Mind Play
ACE RIKER - Toys - Tonka Corp.
ACE/SERVER - Alarm systems - Security Dynamics Technologies Inc.
ACE SPORTS WASHERS - Games - Ace Sports & Products Co.
ACE TETRAPLOID ANNUAL RYEGRASS - Flowers, plants, and seeds -
   Jacklin Seed
ACE, THE - Sporting goods - Lisco, Inc.
ACE TITE - Oakum - Ace Jute Packing Co.
ACE TONE - Musical instruments ☆ - Multivox/Sorkin Music Co. Inc.
ACE-TUF - Wheels - Hamilton Caster & Manufacturing Co.
ACE VENTURA - Recording label - Morgan Creek Productions, Inc.
ACE WAY - Ladders–metal - Ace Way Ladder Co. Inc.
ACEA - Pharmaceutical preparations - Acea Pharmaceuticals, Inc.
ACECAP - Insecticides - Creative Sales Inc.
ACECOMM - Computer hardware - American Computer and Electronics Corp.
ACEDOVAL - Pharmaceutical preparations ☆ - Pal-Pak Inc.
ACEDYNE - Pharmaceutical preparations ☆ - Pal-Pak Inc.
ACELA - Apparel and accessories - Christopher Arcella
ACELINER - Office supplies - Ace Fastener
ACENGINES - Engines–motor vehicle - Acengines, Inc.
A'CENOL - Pharmaceutical preparations - Kay Pharmacal Co. Inc.
ACEO TECHNOLOGY - Computer software - ACEO Technology Inc.
ACEPHEN - Health care products - G and W Laboratories Inc.
ACER - Computers - Acer America Corp.

ACER - Footwear - Vans, Inc.
ACER SACCHARUM FALLRED - Trees - Platt's Inc.
ACERBIS - Furniture - Roche-Bobois USA
ACERBIS - Motorcycle accessories ☆ - Cosmopolitan Motors Inc.
ACERO - Footwear - Kinney Shoe Corp.
ACEROLA CHERRY - Health care products - Above All Health Inc.
ACES - Computer software - Gulf State Computer Services Inc.
ACES - Cookies - Nabisco Foods Group
ACES - Footwear–athletic ☆ - American Athletic Shoe Co.
ACES - Monitors–electronic - Technology for Energy Corp.
ACES - Vitamins and nutritional supplements - J.R. Carlson Laboratories Inc.
ACES OF THE DEEP - Games - Dynamix, Inc.
ACES OVER EUROPE - Computer software - Dynamix, Inc.
ACES+ZN - Vitamins and nutritional supplements - J.R. Carlson Laboratories
   Inc.
ACETA - Pharmaceutical preparations - Century Pharmaceuticals Inc.
ACETA-GESIC - Pharmaceutical preparations - Rugby Laboratories Inc.
ACETA - GRAN - Pharmaceutical - Barrington Chemical Corp.
ACETACO - Pharmaceutical preparations - Legere Pharmaceuticals Inc.
ACETANOL - Health care products - Esquire Pharmaceuticals Inc.
ACETARSONE - Pharmaceutical preparations - City Chemical Corp.
ACETASOL - Pharmaceutical preparations - Barre-National, Inc.
ACETEST - Chemical preparations - Miles Inc.
ACETOCOT - Pharmaceutical preparations - C.O. Truxton Inc.
ACETOGRAPH - Pens ☆ - Koh-I-Noor, Inc.
ACETOHIST - Pharmaceutical - IDE-Interstate Inc.
ACETOSPAN - Pharmaceutical preparations ☆ - Solvay Pharmaceuticals Inc.
ACETYL-L-CARNITINE - Vitamins and nutritional supplements - Vitamin
   Research Products Inc.
ACEVEDO - Jewelry - Mano A Mano Inc.
ACEY DUECY - Food products - SPADA enterprise, ltd.
ACFOAM - Roofing insulation - Atlas Roofing Corp.
ACG - Footwear–athletic - Nike, Inc.
ACG NIKE - Backpacks - Nike, Inc.
ACHAIA CLAUSS - Wines - Blair Importers Ltd.
ACHAIA CLAUSS - Wines - David Sherman Corp.
ACHIEVA - Jewelry - Gold Lance Inc.
ACHIEVA S - Motor vehicles–automobiles - General Motors Corp. (Oldsmobile
   Div.)
ACHIEVA SC - Motor vehicles–automobiles - General Motors Corp.
   (Oldsmobile Div.)
ACHIEVA SCX - Motor vehicles–automobiles - General Motors Corp.
   (Oldsmobile Div.)
ACHIEVA SL - Motor vehicles–automobiles - General Motors Corp.
   (Oldsmobile Div.)
ACHIEVE - Beverages - Basic Organics, Inc.
ACHIEVE! - Computer software - Valusoft, Inc.
ACHIEVE - Plastics - Exxon Corp.
ACHIEVE-A-GOAL - Sporting goods - Fabrication Enterprises
ACHIEVEMENT - Contact lenses - Art Optical Contact Lens, Inc.
ACHIEVEMENT - Flatware ☆ - Oneida Ltd.
ACHIEVEMENT - Floor coverings - Aladdin Mills, Inc.
ACHIEVEMENT - Floor coverings–carpet and rugs - Philadelphia Carpets
ACHIEVEMENT - Floor coverings–tile - Flexco Co.
ACHIEVEMENT - Watches - Gruen Marketing Corp.
ACHIEVEMENT AWARD - Watches - Gruen Marketing Corp.
ACHIEVER - Animal feed - Spartan Grain & Feed Co.
ACHIEVER - Floor coverings–carpet and rugs ☆ - Blue Ridge Carpet Mills
ACHIEVER - Machinery - General Binding Corp.
ACHIEVER - Mattresses - Simmons USA
ACHIEVER - Sporting goods - Nordictrack, Inc.
ACHIEVER 11 - Air conditioning equipment - Rheem Manufacturing Co.
ACHIEVER 13 - Air conditioning equipment - Rheem Manufacturing Co.
ACHIEVER II - Floor coverings–carpet and rugs - Walter Carpet Mills
ACHIEVER, THE - Desks - Virco Manufacturing Corp.
ACHIEVERS UNLIMITED - Vitamins and nutritional supplements - Achievers
   Unlimited, Inc.
ACHIEVING YOUR POTENTIAL - Video production - Pacific Institute Inc.
ACHILLES - Boats - Achilles USA Inc.
ACHILLES - Stamps–hand - Superior Marking Equipment Co.
ACHME COMPUTER INC. - Computer hardware - Achme Computer Inc.
ACHOL - Pharmaceutical preparations - Enzyme Process Co. Inc.
ACHROMYCIN - Antibiotics - Lederle Laboratories
ACI - Gauging instruments - Energy Services, Inc.
ACI - Hair care products - American Chemical Industries, Ltd.
ACI-JEL - Pharmaceutical preparations ☆ - Ortho Pharmaceutical Corp.

ACI-RIST - Enamels ☆ - Waterlox Coatings Corp.
ACICHLOR - Putties - Pecora Chemical Corp.
ACID - Coveralls - Distributors Service Corp.
ACID-A-CAL - Health care products - Enzymatic Therapy, Inc.
ACID BUFFER - Pet products - Seachem Laboratories
ACID-EASE - Vitamins and nutritional supplements - Prevail Corp.
ACID-FAST BACTISTAIN - Diagnostic kit - Polysciences, Inc.
ACID JAZZ - Recording label ☆ - Instinct Records Corp.
ACID MANTLE - Pharmaceutical preparations - Dorsey Laboratories
ACID NEUTRALIZER - Chemical preparations - Highside Chemicals Inc.
ACID-R - Mortars–clay - Mapei East Corp.
ACID STICKS - Chemical preparations - Select Industries, Inc.
ACID SURF - Apparel and accessories - C.W. Surf & Sport Inc.
ACID TEST - Recording label - Continuum Records Inc.
ACIDEX - Pharmaceutical preparations - Lunsco Inc.
ACIDEX - Waterproofing compounds ☆ - A.C. Horn Co.
ACIDI - Pet products ☆ - Tomlyn Products
ACIDI JEL - Pet products - Tomlyn Products
ACIDINE - Cleaning preparations - State Chemical Manufacturing Co.
ACIDIZE - Varnishes ☆ - H. Behlen & Bro. Inc.
ACIDONE - Paints - Heil Process Equipment Corp.
ACIDOPHILASE - Vitamins and nutritional supplements - Wakunaga of America Co., Ltd.
ACIDOPHILUS TRIO - Vitamins and nutritional supplements - Wakunaga of America Co., Ltd.
ACIDULIN - Pharmaceutical preparations - Eli Lilly and Co.
ACIES - Sunglasses - Russell Todd Lidbury
ACIM - Video production - Foundation for Inner Peace
ACIN - Apparel and accessories - Shawn Koutahi and Michael Peymaan Koutahi Partnership
A'CINO - Skin care products - Cac North America Inc.
A.C.I.T. - Ceramic tile ☆ - Integrity Tile Co.
ACITABS - Antacids ☆ - Chex Co.
ACK - Apparel and accessories - Francie Z. Bovers
ACKAPON - Food products - Amende and Schultz
ACKERMAN - Anchors - Ackerman Johnson Fastening Systems Inc.
ACKERMAN - Wines - Ackerman Winery Inc.
ACKERMANN - Calendars - Sormani Inc.
ACKLEY - Food products ☆ - Stokely USA, Inc.
ACKNOWLEDGE THE DISH - Apparel and accessories - Passionplay, Inc.
ACL - Chlorine - Monsanto Co.
ACL - Cleaning preparations - Occidental Chemical Corp.
ACLAIM - Mouthwashes - Lever Brothers Co. Inc.
ACLAM - Motor vehicle parts and accessories - Alliedsignal Inc.
ACLORAL - Aquarium accessories ☆ - Sera Aquaristik USA Inc.
ACM - Office supplies - Allstate/Copymate Imaging Supply
ACM GAME CARD - Computer software - Thrustmaster, Inc.
ACM JIFFY SLATE - Braille slates,now out of production - Howe Press
ACMA - Computers–personal - ACMA Computers Inc.
ACME - Apparel and accessories - L & M Adjustable Dress Form Co.
ACME - Beef - Blue Diamond Meat Co.
ACME - Boots - Acme Boot Co., Inc.
ACME - Building materials - Acme Brick Co.
ACME - Clips–gun - Acme Industries Inc.
ACME - Door frames - Stanley Hardware Div.
ACME - Dusters - Wright-Bernet
ACME - Easels ☆ - Anco Wood Specialties Inc.
ACME - Electrical equipment - Acme Battery Manufacturing Co.
ACME - Fertilizers - PBI/Gordon Corp.
ACME - Food products - Acme Continental Foods Inc.
ACME - Food products - Acme Poultry Co.
ACME - Food products - Acme Steak Co. Inc.
ACME - Food products - American Stores Co.
ACME - Food products - Smith & Nelson Inc.
ACME - Furniture ☆ - ACME Design Technology
ACME - Hitches–trailer - Acme Products Co. Inc.
ACME - Housewares - Acme International
ACME - Ladders–metal ☆ - Rich Ladder Co.
ACME - Ledgers ☆ - ACCO USA, Inc.
ACME - Lighting equipment - Acme-Lite Manufacturing Co.
ACME - Lime products ☆ - First Preference Products Corp.
ACME - Machinery - American Precision Industries Inc.
ACME - Mirrors - Acme Specialty Manufacturing Co.
ACME - Musical instrument accessories - Rothco Inc.
ACME - Pet products - Ancol Pet Products Inc.
ACME - Pet products - Mr. Mutt Pet Products Inc.

ACME - Pet products - Pet Supply Imports Inc.
ACME - Scissors–hand-operated - Arthur H. Gaebel Inc.
ACME - Spices and extracts - Ottens Flavors
ACME - Sporting goods - Acme Tackle Co.
ACME - Sporting goods - Pennsylvania Sporting Goods Co.
ACME - Stamp pads - Consolidated Stamp Manufacturing Co. Inc.
ACME 800 - Office supplies ☆ - ACME Design Technology
ACME A - Footwear - Acme Boot Co., Inc.
ACME CONTINENTAL - Meat products–poultry - Acme Continental Foods Inc.
ACME GOURMET - Food products - Acme Continental Foods Inc.
ACME GREETINGS - Greeting cards - Recycled Paper Products, Inc.
ACME HOLDER, THE - Bathroom fixtures - Acme Holder Co. Inc.
ACME INTERNATIONAL - Housewares - Acme International
ACME JUICERATOR - Kitchen appliances - Waring Products Div.
ACME LEATHER WORKS - Footwear - Acme Boot Co., Inc.
ACME-LITE - Lighting equipment - Acme-Lite Manufacturing Co.
ACME OF CANADA - Apparel stores–sports ☆ - Kombi Ltd.
ACME ROAD GEAR - Air purification systems - Medo Industries, Inc.
ACME ROCKET - Brushes–paint - Wooster Brush Co.
ACME SIGNALS - Markers–felt-tip ☆ - ACME Design Technology
ACME SNAPPY - Pipes - Standex International Corp.
ACME STEEL - Steel products - Acme Steel Co.
ACME SYNCHRO-SHUTTER - Ophthalmic goods ☆ - Ilex Optical Co. Inc.
ACME THUNDERER - Whistles - Tide-Rider Inc.
ACME UNITED - Scissors–hand-operated - Acme United Corp.
ACMELOID - Filing cabinets–metal ☆ - ACME Design Technology
ACMO - Thread ☆ - Belding Heminway Co. Inc.
A.C.N. - Pharmaceutical preparations ☆ - Person and Covey Inc.
ACNE-AID - Skin care products - Stiefel Laboratories, Inc.
ACNE ATTACK - Skin-care products - Peter M. Wallach
ACNE-DOME - Skin care products - Miles Inc.
ACNEDERM - Skin care products - Lannett Co. Inc.
ACNEGUARD - Acne treatment preparations - Lazarus Dermatologic Products
ACNELEN - Skin care products - Lendan USA Co.
ACNEMED - Skin care products ☆ - Vitarine Pharmaceuticals Inc.
ACNEPACK - Skin care products - Magick Mud
ACNESARB - Pharmaceutical preparations ☆ - C&M Pharmacal, Inc.
ACNETRACIN - Skin care products ☆ - Halsey Drug Co. Inc.
ACNIXX - Health care products - Pharma Botanixx
ACNO - Skin care products - Baker Cummins Dermatologicals Inc.
ACNOID-LAPODO - Pharmaceutical preparations - Sargeant Acnoid Pharmaceutical Co.
ACNOMEL - Skin care products ☆ - Smithkline Beecham Corp.
ACNOTEX - Pharmaceutical preparations - C&M Pharmacal, Inc.
ACO - Concrete products - Aco Polymer Products Inc.
ACO - Floor coverings–carpet and rugs ☆ - Capel, Inc.
ACO COMFORT - Footwear ☆ - Conjac Inc.
ACOLITE - Paper–coated - Appleton Papers Inc.
ACONDI NO BASE - Beauty shop equipment ☆ - Summit Laboratories
ACONITE - Pharmaceutical preparations - Sherwood Laboratories Inc.
ACONOMY - Doors–metal - Acorn Window Systems Inc.
ACOOLADE III - Furniture - Drexel Heritage Furnishings, Inc.
ACOR - Orthopedic footwear - Acor Orthopaedic, Inc.
ACORD - Computer software - Acord Corp.
ACORE - Doors–metal - Acorn Window Systems Inc.
ACORK - Novelty items–glass - Mike Schweitzer
ACORN - Hardware - Acorn Manufacturing Co., Inc.
ACORN - Health care products - Marquest Medical Products Inc.
ACORN - Mobile homes - Deck House, Inc.
ACORN - Paper clips - Labelon Corp.
ACORN - Pet products ☆ - Curzon Designs Ltd.
ACORN - Recording label - Freddie Records
ACORN - Siding–insulating ☆ - Champion International Corp.
ACORN - Slippers - Acorn
ACORN - Tools - Greenfield Tap & Die
ACORN - Water purification systems - Recovery Engineering, Inc.
ACORN BALL - Novelty items - Heiss Concepts
ACORN FORGED IRON - Hardware - Acorn Manufacturing Co., Inc.
ACORN HUT SCUFF - Slippers - Acorn
ACORN MOCCASIN - Slippers - Acorn
ACORN SOX - Hosiery - Acorn
ACORN SOX2 - Slippers - Acorn
ACORNMEDIA - Video production - Acorn Media Publishing, Inc.
ACORTO - Coffee and espresso machines - Caffe Acorto Inc.
ACOTUS - Pharmaceutical preparations - Whorton Pharmaceuticals Inc.
ACOUST-BRITE - Lighting equipment ☆ - Enersys3 Inc.

☆ = Now out of production

ACOUSTA-PANE - Glass products - Globe-Amerada Glass Co.
ACOUSTA WALLS - Wallcoverings - Designtex Fabrics Inc.
ACOUSTACADD - Computer software - Altech Lansing Corp.
ACOUSTALLOY - Diaphragms - Electro-Voice, Inc.
ACOUSTAQWIK - Computer software - Altech Lansing Corp.
ACOUSTAR - Audio equipment - Holcomb & Hoke Manufacturing Co., Inc.
ACOUSTAT - Electrical equipment - Acoustat Corp.
ACOUSTEX - Audio equipment - Martin Picard Inc.
ACOUSTEX - Paints ☆ - Thomas Waterproof Coatings Co.
ACOUSTEX-1600 - Hardware - Enersys3 Inc.
ACOUSTEX EEC - Hardware - Enersys3 Inc.
ACOUSTI-CENTER - Learning aid ☆ - L & M Auto Supply
ACOUSTI-CORDER - Tape recorder ☆ - L & M Auto Supply
ACOUSTI-CURTAIN - Paneling - Inplant Enviro Systems 2000, Inc.
ACOUSTI-FLOR - Insulating materials ☆ - Laticrete International Inc.
ACOUSTI GARD - Siding–metal ☆ - Globe Building Materials Inc.
ACOUSTI GP COR - Sackner Products Inc.
ACOUSTI-GUM - Adhesives and sealants - W.W. Henry Co.
ACOUSTI-K27 - Ducts–metal - United McGill Corp.
ACOUSTI-KOTE - Stucco ☆ - GS Roofing Products Co.
ACOUSTI-LECTRIC - Guitars - Guild Music Corp.
ACOUSTI-MAT - Rubber–synthetic - Maxxon Corp.
ACOUSTI-MATE - Insulation materials - RPR Products, Inc.
ACOUSTI-PLAYER - Tape player ☆ - L & M Auto Supply
ACOUSTI-SEAL - Partitions–metal - Modernfold, Inc.
ACOUSTI-SHIELD - Sound containment panels - Conserv-A-Therm Corp.
ACOUSTI-WALL - Acoustically treated wall covering - Acousti Inc.
ACOUSTIC - Amplifiers–public address - Wagner Group Inc.
ACOUSTIC - Covers–seat - Anthes Universal
ACOUSTIC APPRAISER - Audio equipment - Qualitone
ACOUSTIC BIT CORRECTION - Audio equipment - Db Technologies, Inc.
ACOUSTIC BOND - Adhesives and sealants ☆ - Continental Brands Inc.
ACOUSTIC-COATER - Paints - Synkoloid Co.
ACOUSTIC DISC 100% HANDMADE MUSIC - Recording label - Acoustic Disc
ACOUSTIC DYNAMIC - Audio equipment - TDK Electronics Corp.
ACOUSTIC LIFE - Recording label - Jazz Composer's Orchestra Association Inc.
ACOUSTIC MODEL - Guitars - Dimarzio, Inc.
ACOUSTIC MOODS - Recording label - Carmel Records
ACOUSTIC PLUS - Musical instrument accessories - Ridge Runner
ACOUSTIC QUICK MOUNT - Musical instrument accessories - Dimarzio, Inc.
ACOUSTIC RESEARCH - Audio equipment - Teledyne Acoustic Research
ACOUSTIC SIMULATOR - Musical instruments - XL Specialty Percussion
ACOUSTIC TUBE - Musical instrument accessories - Seymour Duncan Pickups
ACOUSTIC WAVE - Stereo system - Bose Corp.
ACOUSTICAL - Wallcoverings - Technique Textiles Inc.
ACOUSTICAL SOURCE BOOK - Wallpaper - Capital Carousel Inc.
ACOUSTICEL - Insulating materials - Eften Inc.
ACOUSTICORD - Floor coverings–carpet and rugs - Eurotex Inc.
ACOUSTICOTE - Paints ☆ - Frost Paint and Oil Corp.
ACOUSTICRAFT - Musical instrument accessories - Grover/Trophy Musical Products Inc.
ACOUSTICS - Musical instrument accessories - E. & O. Mari Inc.
ACOUSTICTOOLS - Audio equipment - RPG Diffusor Systems, Inc.
ACOUSTIDYM - Electronic equipment - Electro-Voice, Inc.
ACOUSTIFLOR - Floor coverings - Tarkett, Inc.
ACOUSTIFOAM - Window coverings - Electro-Voice, Inc.
ACOUSTIGRAPHIC - Tiles–ceiling - Yorkraft Inc.
ACOUSTIKOTE - Paints - Dunn Edwards Corp.
ACOUSTILE - Tiles–ceiling - Armstrong World Industries, Inc.
ACOUSTILEAD - Audio equipment - Alpha Audio Acoustics
ACOUSTIQUES - Wallpaper ☆ - Playfield International Inc.
ACOUSTIROC - Building materials - Illbruck, Inc.
ACOUSTISCORE - Medical apparatus - Del Mar Avionics
ACOUSTOGRAPHIC - Recording label - Acoustographic Records
ACOUSTOLIGHT - Paints - PPG Industries, Inc.
ACOUSTONE - Audio equipment - Acoustone Corp.
ACOUSTONE - Tiles–ceiling - United States Gypsum Co.
ACOUSTONE - Wallpaper - Newcastle Fabrics Corp.
ACOUSTOQUAD - Recording label - Acoustographic Records
ACP - Adhesives and sealants - PJH Brands
ACP - Paints ☆ - Parker & Amchem
ACPI BUILDER - Systemsoft Corp.
ACQUA-BAN - Thread - Needlecraft Industries
ACQUA DE FELSINA - Colognes - J. Palazzolo Son Inc.
ACQUA DELLA MADONNA - Water–mineral - Chris Payne International

ACQUA MIA - Water–bottled or canned - Tama Trading
ACQUACILS - Cosmetics - Cosmair Inc.
ACQUERELLO - Wallpaper ☆ - Wallquest, Inc.
ACQUERELLO ITALIANO - Recording label - Champs-Elysees Inc.
ACQUIRE - Games - Avalon Hill Game Co.
ACQUIRE 1 - Computer software - Jon D. Gillen
ACQUISITION - Apparel–women's ☆ - J.C. Penney Co., Inc.
ACQUISITION - Clocks - General Time Corp. (Westclox/Seth Thomas Div.)
ACQUISITIONS MANAGER - Computer software - Right on Programs
ACQULAB - Electrical equipment - Gould Instrument Systems, Inc.
ACR - Electronic equipment - ACR, Electronics, Inc.
ACR - Screws - Phillips Screw Co.
ACR-1 - Adhesives and sealants - Permalite Plastics Corp.
ACR/FILE - Computer software - Unitech Systems Inc.
ACR-LATEX - Paints - Remien & Kuhnert Co.
ACR/PC WORKBENCH - Computer software - Unitech Systems Inc.
ACR/PLUS - Computer software - Unitech Systems Inc.
ACRA - Balls–golf - Hansberger Precision Golf Worldwide
ACRA - Floor coverings ☆ - Oregon Lumber Products Inc.
ACRA - Paints–artists' - Binney & Smith Inc.
ACRA-CLAD - Paints - Briner Paint Manufacturing Co. Inc.
ACRA-FLEX - Paints - Briner Paint Manufacturing Co. Inc.
ACRA FUR - Golfing equipment - Korex Corp.
ACRA HIDE - Paints - M.A. Bruder & Sons Inc.
ACRA-KOTE - Paints - Briner Paint Manufacturing Co. Inc.
ACRA-LASTIC - Paints - M.A. Bruder & Sons Inc.
ACRA-LUX - Paints ☆ - M.A. Bruder & Sons Inc.
ACRA-SEAL - Waterproofing compounds - Radiator Specialty Co.
ACRA-TUNE - Antennas - Shure Brothers, Inc.
ACRA-VECTOR - Electronic equipment - Shure Brothers, Inc.
ACRA-VEL - Paints - Olympic Paint & Varnish Co.
ACRAFLEX - Tillers–rotary - Acra-Plant, Inc.
ACRAGLAS - Firearms, accessories, and parts - Brownells, Inc.
ACRAJOINT - Glass block - Acrymet Industries Inc.
ACRALITE - Paints ☆ - United Coatings Inc.
ACRASIL - Skin care products - Alberto-Culver Co.
ACRATEK - Furniture ☆ - Telescope Casual Furniture Inc.
ACRAVIN - Paints - Nu-Brite Chemical Co. Inc.
ACRECKO - Recording label - Starman Records
ACRI-COLOR - Paints - Sinclair Paint Co.
ACRI-FIL - Adhesives and sealants - Porter Paint Co.
ACRI-FLAT - Paints - Dunn Edwards Corp.
ACRI-FLEX - Caulking compounds ☆ - Fulton Co.
ACRI-HUES - Paints - Dunn Edwards Corp.
ACRI-KOTE - Paints - Tresco Paint Co. Inc.
ACRI-LIFE - Paints - Chemical Coating Corp.
ACRI-NALL - Paints ☆ - Pratt & Lambert United, Inc.
ACRI-PAVE - Adhesives and sealants ☆ - Pratt & Lambert United, Inc.
ACRI-PRIME - Paints ☆ - Pratt & Lambert United, Inc.
ACRI-SEAL - Adhesives and sealants - Black & Puryear Paint Manufacturing Co. Inc.
ACRI-STONE - Wall-matrix system - Construction Adhesives Co.
ACRI-TEC - Paints - Frazee Paint
ACRI-THANE - Varnishes - Dunn Edwards Corp.
ACRI-TILE - Enamels ☆ - Pratt & Lambert United, Inc.
ACRI-TONE - Paints - Chemical Coating Corp.
ACRI-TRIM - Paints ☆ - Frazee Paint
ACRI-VIN - Paints - Sinclair Paint Co.
ACRICLEAR - Adhesives and sealants - Vitricon
ACRIDEL - Yarn - Delaine Worsted Mills
ACRIFIL - Paints - Suntec Paint Inc.
ACRIFLAVIN PLUS - Aquatic pharmacuetical preparations ☆ - Aquatronics-Filtronics
ACRIFLEX - Paints - Suntec Paint Inc.
ACRIGLO - Paints - Suntec Paint Inc.
ACRIL-ITE - Paints - Vanguard Paints & Finishes Inc.
ACRILAN - Fibers–acrylic - Monsanto Polymer Products
ACRILAN 2000+ - Fibers–acrylic - Monsanto Polymer Products
ACRILAN PLUS - Fibers–acrylic - Monsanto Polymer Products
ACRILIAN MARBLE - Pet products - Imperial Pet Products
ACRILITE - Enamels - Frazee Paint
ACRILON - Paints - Conco Paint Co.
ACRILUX - Paints - Sampson Coatings Inc.
ACRILUX - Wainscotting ☆ - Georgia-Pacific Corp.
ACRIMETAL - Paints - Miller Paint Co., Inc.
ACRINAMEL - Paints - Miller Paint Co., Inc.

ACRISHEEN - Paints - Sampson Coatings Inc.
ACRITUF - Paints - Suntec Paint Inc.
ACRO - Fabrics–canvas - Crown Textile Co.
ACRO - Fabrics–canvas - Handler Textile Corp.
ACRO-BAT - Kites ☆ - Gayla Industries Inc.
ACRO LATEX ENAMEL - Paints - Miller Paint Co., Inc.
ACRO-LINE - Bathroom accessories ☆ - Alford Packaging
ACROBASE - Adhesives and sealants - Premix-Marbletite Manufacturing Co.
ACROBAT - Computer software - Adobe Systems Inc.
ACROBAT ! - Computer software ☆ - Fenton Music
ACROBAT - Fungicides - American Cyanamid Co.
ACROBAT - Kites - Llumar Star Kites Inc.
ACROBAT PLANES - Toys ☆ - Tomy America, Inc.
ACROBATS - Dining room furniture ☆ - Daystrom Furniture Inc.
ACROBATS - Games ☆ - Pressman Toy Corp.
ACROBOT - Toys ☆ - Tomy America, Inc.
ACROBUNNY - Toys–stuffed ☆ - Fun World Inc.
ACROCOTE - Paints - Premix-Marbletite Manufacturing Co.
ACRODISC - Laboratory apparatus - Pall Gelman Sciences
ACROEDITIONS - Fabrics–tapestry - Jeppson Galleries Inc.
ACROFINISH - Stucco - Premix-Marbletite Manufacturing Co.
ACROFLEX - Paints ☆ - Fuller-O'Brien Paints Inc.
ACROGRAPHICS - Artists' materials - Jeppson Galleries Inc.
ACROLAC - Abrasive products - Park Metallurgical Corp.
ACROLOCK - Locks–door - Abloy Security Inc.
ACROLOK - Paints - Key Laboratories Inc.
ACRONETIC - Clocks ☆ - General Time Corp. (Westclox/Seth Thomas Div.)
ACRONYMBLE - Games - Acronymwits, Inc.
ACROPOLIS - Cheese - Wiskerchen Cheese Inc.
ACROPOLIS - Computers - Acropolis Systems Inc.
ACROPOLIS - Floor coverings–carpet and rugs ☆ - Mannington Carpets, Inc.
ACROPOLIS - Frames–picture - Terragrafics Inc.
ACROPOLIS SOFTWARE - Computer storage devices–magnetic - Acropolis Software, Inc.
ACROPOOL - Swimming pools ☆ - Premix-Marbletite Manufacturing Co.
ACROSONIC - Pianos - Baldwin Piano & Organ Co.
ACROSOUND - Audio equipment - Kathry Petrich-Lafevre
ACROSS AMERICA WOMAN - Women's sweaters and shirts - Knit Maven Ltd.
ACROSS THE BOARD - Games ☆ - Mph Games Co.
ACROSS THE COUNTER - Lighting equipment - General Electric Co.
ACROSS THE SEA - Shrimp - Continental Seafoods Inc.
ACROSS THE STREET - Apparel and accessories ☆ - Kellwood Co.
ACROTEX - Paints ☆ - Steelcote Manufacturing Corp.
ACROVYN - Wallcovering - C/S Group/DecoGard Products
ACRY-BOND - Paints - Dunn Edwards Corp.
ACRY-CLEAR - Skin care products - Plasto Tech Co. International
ACRY-CRETE - Paints - Kwal-Howells Inc.
ACRY-FLOR - Varnishes - Paragon Paint & Varnish Corp.
ACRY-GARD - Siding–metal ☆ - Alcan Aluminum Corp. Alcan Building Products Div.
ACRY-GLOSS - Adhesives and sealants ☆ - Consolidated Coatings Corp.
ACRY-LITE - Paints - Gilman Co. Inc.
ACRY-LOK - Paints - Morwear Paint Co.
ACRY-NIZERS - Skin care products - Plasto Tech Co. International
ACRY-OIL - Paper - Canson-Talens Inc.
ACRY-PRIME - Paints - Frazee Paint
ACRY-SHEEN - Enamels - Frazee Paint
ACRY-SHIELD - Enamels - Columbia Paint and Coatings, Inc.
ACRY-TONE - Paints - Kwal-Howells Inc.
ACRY-TRAC - Paints - Dunn Edwards Corp.
ACRY-TUFF - Wainscotting ☆ - Georgia-Pacific Corp.
ACRY-URETHANE - Varnishes - Sav-Cote Chemical Laboratories Inc.
ACRYBIND - Fabric binding - Manart-Hirsch Co. Inc.
ACRYBRONZ - Paints - Finnaren & Haley Inc.
ACRYCLAD - Wood products ☆ - Pluswood Inc.
ACRYCOLOR - Paints ☆ - Triangle Coatings Inc.
ACRYDERM - Bandages–surgical - Acrymed, Inc.
ACRYFIL - Sleeping bags ☆ - Coleman Co., Inc.
ACRYFLEX - Paint - Interstate Paint Corp.
ACRYGAURD - Paints - Gray Seal Paint Manufacturing Co. Inc.
ACRYGLAS - Resins–polymer - Georgia-Pacific Corp.
ACRYL 1500 - Hardware - Qromtek Inc.
ACRYL-3000 - Glue–household or industrial ☆ - Custom Building Products
ACRYL-4000 - Glue–household or industrial ☆ - Custom Building Products
ACRYL-A-CUT - Saw blades - Heinemann Saw Corp.
ACRYL-EX - Paints - Kentucky Paint Manufacturing Co.

ACRYL-GLAZE - Paints - Synkoloid Co.
ACRYL-ITE - Paints - Perry & Derrick Co.
ACRYL-NAIL - Nail care products - H & H Products
ACRYL-THANE - Adhesives and sealants ☆ - Consolidated Coatings Corp.
ACRYLAGLAZE - Manicure preparations ☆ - Cameo Inc.
ACRYLAGRAPH - Decals and transfers - August Art Co.
ACRYLAGRAPH ON FINE ART CANVAS - Paints–artists' - August Art Co.
ACRYLAMASTER - Canvas–artists' - Master Woodcraft Inc.
ACRYLASTIC - Adhesives and sealants - Davlin Coatings Inc.
ACRYLETTE - Artists' materials - Robert Simmons Inc.
ACRYLEZE - Paints - Standard T Chemical Co. Inc.
ACRYLI-CLEAN - Wax removers - PPG Industries, Inc.
ACRYLIC CLASSICS LTD. - Clocks - Today's Acrylic Classics
ACRYLIC IMPRESSIONS - Office supplies ☆ - Alltrista Corp.
ACRYLIC MORTAR ADMIX - Cement - Custom Building Products
ACRYLIC ONE - Adhesives and sealants - Gibson-Homans Co. (Sealant Technology)
ACRYLICLEAN - Cleaning preparations - Isolab, Inc.
ACRYLICOLOR - Pencils - Blackfeet Writing Instruments Inc.
ACRYLICORK - Gaskets - AE Clevite Inc.
ACRYLICS - Housewares - Two's Co. Inc.
ACRYLINE - Denture materials - Smithkline Beecham Corp.
ACRYLIPOLISH - Cleaning preparations - Isolab, Inc.
ACRYLITE - Molding compounds–plastics - Cyro Industries
ACRYLITE PLUS - Molding compounds–plastics - Cyro Industries
ACRYLITHANE C - Paints - Jones Blair Co.
ACRYLIX - Brushes–paint - Wooster Brush Co.
ACRYLLIUM - Bowling balls - Ebonite International, Inc.
ACRYLMEL - Hardware - Sherwin-Williams Automotive Finishes Corp.
ACRYLMELT - Skin care products - Nails Naturally, Inc.
ACRYLMIX 290 - Glue–household or industrial ☆ - Custom Building Products
ACRYLO - Frames–picture - Recyco
ACRYLOFLEX - Exercising equipment - Gerstung/Gym-Thing Inc.
ACRYLPRO - Adhesives and sealants - Custom Building Products
ACRYLUCENT LTD - Artists' materials - Robert L. Funk
ACRYLUME - Lighting fixtures - National Service Industries, Inc.
ACRYLURE - Paints - Ponderosa Paint Manufacturing Co. Inc.
ACRYLUX - Hardware - Diffusa-Lite Co.
ACRYMAX - Coatings - Acrymax Technologies Inc.
ACRYMED - Pharmaceutical preparations - Acrymed, Inc.
ACRYNAIL - Skin care products - Rudolph International, Inc.
ACRYPAK - Lenses - Alcon Laboratories, Inc.
ACRYPLEX - Paints - Graham Paint and Varnish Co.
ACRYSEAL - Caulking compounds - L.D. Sterns Corp.
ACRYSEAL - Coatings - Johnson-Doppler Lumber
ACRYSEAL - Motor vehicle parts and accessories - BASF Corp.
ACRYSEAL - Paints - Triangle Coatings Inc.
ACRYSHELL - Paints - Sherwin-Williams Automotive Finishes Corp.
ACRYSHIELD - Acrylic ceiling panels - Artcrest Products Co. Inc.
ACRYSTONE - Acrylic sheeting - Aristech Chemical Corp.
ACRYTEX - Paints - Fuller-O'Brien Paints Inc.
ACS - Computer software - Systore Companies, Inc.
ACS - Metals - American Containment Systems, Inc.
ACS - Office supplies - Letraset USA Inc.
ACS - Vacuum cleaners and accessories - Hako Minuteman Inc.
ACS INDUSTRIES, INC. - Metals - ACS Industries Inc.
ACS MULTI-LINK - Medical apparatus - Advanced Cardiovascular Systems, Inc.
ACS PRISM - Medical apparatus - Advanced Cardiovascular Systems, Inc.
ACSETERATOR - Chemical preparations - Wayne Sallee
ACT - Amplifiers - Lin Wei
ACT - Apparel and accessories - Action Clothing Technology
A.C.T. - Aquarium accessories - Mardel Laboratories, Inc.
ACT - Beverages–alcohol - Archer Daniels Midland Co.
ACT - Chocolate candy - Topographic Chocolate Co.
ACT - Detergents ☆ - Clorox Co.
ACT - Electronic equipment - Advanced Conversion Technology, Inc.
A.C.T. - Hair care products - Dena Corp.
ACT - Health care products - Johnson & Johnson
ACT - Identification tags - Envirometrics Products Inc.
ACT - Motor vehicle parts and accessories - Alliedsignal Inc.
ACT - Recording label - Elliot W. Stone
ACT 600 - Sports apparel - Reebok International Ltd.
ACT FAST - Nuts and bolts - Accurate Fasteners, Inc.
ACT FOR IBM & APPLE - Computer software - Krell Software Corp.
ACT I - Conference tables - Atlantic Furniture Systems

☆ = Now out of production

ACT I - Dinnerware–plastic ☆ - Plastics Manufacturing Co.

ACT I - Fabrics - Greenwood Mills Inc.

ACT I - Furniture ☆ - Bassett Furniture Industries, Inc.

ACT I - Popcorn - Golden Valley Microwave Foods, Inc.

ACT I - Wallpaper ☆ - David & Dash

ACT II - Fabrics - Greenwood Mills Inc.

ACT II - Furniture ☆ - Lexington Furniture Industries, Inc.

ACT II - Popcorn - Golden Valley Microwave Foods, Inc.

ACT III - Apparel–women's - Jonathan Logan Inc.

ACT III - Dinnerware–plastic ☆ - Plastics Manufacturing Co.

ACT III - Furniture ☆ - Bassett Furniture Industries, Inc.

ACT III - Popcorn - Golden Valley Microwave Foods, Inc.

ACT IV - Floor coverings–carpet and rugs ☆ - Mannington Carpets, Inc.

ACT NETWORKS - Computer hardware - Act Networks, Inc.

ACT-O-MATIC - Plumbing fixtures - Sloan Valve Co.

ACT-ON - Analgesics - Keystone Laboratories Inc.

ACT V - Nail care products ☆ - Joico Laboratories, Inc.

ACT VIEW - Computer software - Advanced Compression Technology, Inc.

ACTA - Apparel and accessories ☆ - Playtex Apparel, Inc.

ACTA - Computer software - Symmetry Corp.

ACTA-FLO - Bedding–linen ☆ - Grant Airmass Corp.

ACTA-FLO - Water treating compounds - Actagro, Inc.

ACTABS - Controls–air conditioning systems - Stewart-Hall Chemical Corp.

ACTACIN - Pharmaceutical preparations ☆ - Vangard Labs Inc.

ACTAGEN - Pharmaceutical preparations - Goldline Laboratories, Inc.

ACTAHIST - Pharmaceutical preparations - H.R. Cenci Laboratories Inc.

ACTAHIST C - Pharmaceutical preparations - H.R. Cenci Laboratories Inc.

ACTAMIN - Analgesics - Buffington

ACTAMIN EXTRA - Analgesics - Buffington

ACTAMIN SUPER - Analgesics - Buffington

ACTAMINE - Pharmaceutical preparations - Moore Medical Corp.

ACTAR - Computers–mainframe - Actar Computer Corp.

ACTAR 911 TROOPER - Mannequins - Vital Signs, Inc.

ACTAR AIRFORCE OF THE UNIVERSE - Medical apparatus - Vital Signs, Inc.

ACTASAL - Pharmaceutical preparations ☆ - Purdue Frederick Co.

ACTCONNECT - Advertising agencies - Actmedia, Inc.

ACTEVES - Underwear and nightwear - Henson-Kickernick Inc.

ACTH-40 - Pharmaceutical preparations ☆ - Roberts/Hauck Pharmaceuticals Inc.

ACTHAR - Pharmaceutical preparations ☆ - Armour Pharmaceutical Co.

ACTHRON 80 - Pharmaceutical preparations ☆ - Legere Pharmaceuticals Inc.

ACTI-FLEX - Vitamins and nutritional supplements - Freelife International LP

ACTI-GEST - Health care products - Nature's Concept Inc.

ACTI-PAKS - Aquariums–household ☆ - Jungle Laboratories Corp.

ACTI-VITA - Skin care products - Monteil Paris

ACTIBATH - Bath salts - Andrew Jergens Co.

ACTIBINE - Pharmaceutical preparations - Consolidated Midland Corp.

ACTIBIOTIC - Vitamins and nutritional supplements - Vitamin Research Products Inc.

ACTICHROM - Vitamins and nutritional supplements - Solaray

ACTICIDE - Pesticides–agricultural - Thor Americas, Inc.

ACTICISE - Vitamins and nutritional supplements - Enrich Corp.

ACTICON - Chemical preparations - Robert Lehrer Associates, Inc.

ACTICORT 100 - Skin care products - Baker Cummins Dermatologicals Inc.

ACTIDIL - Antihistamine preparations - Burroughs Wellcome Co.

ACTIDOSE - Pharmaceutical preparations - Paddock Laboratories Inc.

ACTIF - Skin care products - Monteil Paris

ACTIFED ALLERGY - Antihistamine preparations - Warner-Wellcome

ACTIFED COLD & ALLERGY - Antihistamine preparations - Warner-Wellcome

ACTIFED COLD & SINUS - Cold remedies - Warner-Wellcome

ACTIFED HEAD COLD & ALLERGY - See **ACTIFED COLD & ALLERGY**

ACTIFED PLUS - See **ACTIFED COLD & SINUS**

ACTIFED SINUS - Antihistamine preparations - Warner-Wellcome

ACTIFILE - Computers - Active Files Inc.

ACTIFIRM TS - Cosmetics - Active Organics Inc.

ACTIFLO - Pharmaceutical preparations - American Home Products Corp.

ACTIGEN - Health care products - Active Organics Inc.

ACTIGLIDE - Cosmetics - Active Organics Inc.

ACTIGLOW - Cosmetics - Active Organics Inc.

ACTILIFT - Health care products - Midwest Contracting & Manufacturing Inc.

ACTILINE - Cosmetics ☆ - P-Ryton Corp.

ACTIMAR - Cough medicines ☆ - Marlop Pharmaceuticals Inc.

ACTIMED - Diagnostic apparatus - Actimed Laboratories, Inc.

ACTIMED - Pharmaceutical preparations - Parmed Pharmaceuticals, Inc.

ACTIMEM - Vitamins and nutritional supplements - Nature's Way Products, Inc.

ACTIMETER - Photographic equipment - Eastman Kodak Co.

ACTIMIN FORTE - Pharmaceutical preparations - Vartex Pharmaceuticals Inc.

ACTIMOIST BIO 2 - Health care products - Active Organics Inc.

ACTING UP - Apparel–women's ☆ - Jonathan Logan Inc.

ACTINIC - Inks - Phillips Process Co. Inc.

ACTION - Apparel–men's - Levi Strauss & Co.

ACTION - Apparel–women's - AnnTaylor, Inc.

ACTION - Asphalt felts and coatings ☆ - DMF Industries Inc. (Al-Chroma Div.)

ACTION - Automotive parts and accessories ☆ - Lancaster Colony Automotive Group

ACTION - Badminton equipment ☆ - Anderson Manufacturing Co.

ACTION - Beverages - Crown Brands Inc.

ACTION - Binoculars - Nikon Inc.

ACTION - Brassieres (Bras) ☆ - Lovable Co.

ACTION - Cold remedies - Michigan Pharmaceutical

ACTION + - Cosmetics - Circle of Beauty, Inc.

ACTION - Cushions - Action Products Inc.

ACTION - Detergents - Colgate-Palmolive Co.

ACTION - Electronic equipment - Califone International Inc.

ACTION - Gasoline - Western Petroleum Co.

ACTION - Health care products - Invacare Corp.

ACTION - Hoes - Ames Lawn & Garden Tool Co.

ACTION - Locks–padlocks - Hampton International

ACTION - Markers–felt-tip - Quality Die Co.

ACTION - Organizers, marine seats, etc. - Action Products Co.

ACTION - Paints - Aco Inc.

ACTION - Paper–toweling - Nice-Pak Products, Inc.

ACTION - Recliners - Lane Co. Inc.

ACTION - Recording label - Action Records

ACTION - Sporting goods ☆ - All-Luminum Products Inc.

ACTION - Stationery ☆ - Mead Corp.

ACTION - Tape–adhesive - National Tape Corp.

ACTION - Thread ☆ - Perfect Thread Co. Inc.

ACTION - Tools ☆ - GC Thorsen, Inc.

ACTION - Watches - Bulova Corp.

ACTION - Yarn ☆ - William Unger & Co. Inc.

ACTION 2 - Computer software - Mead Corp.

ACTION 52 - Video games - Active Enterprises Ltd.

ACTION 75 - Vitamins and nutritional supplements - Consac Industries, Inc.

ACTION ART - Posters - Successories, Inc.

ACTION ATV - Microscopes–proton - San Diego Cycle Supply Distributing

ACTION AWARDS - Trophies–metal - Action Athletics Inc.

ACTION B-50 - Vitamins and nutritional supplements - Consac Industries, Inc.

ACTION B-100 - Vitamins and nutritional supplements - Consac Industries, Inc.

ACTION BAC - Clay products - Amoco Fabrics and Fibers Co.

ACTION BACK - Apparel–women's - Bi-Flex International

ACTION BACK - Automotive parts and accessories ☆ - Lancaster Colony Automotive Group

ACTION BAGS - Luggage - Sirco International Corp.

ACTION BALANCED - Hair care products - Helene Curtis Industries Inc.

ACTION BAR - Computer software - Datastorm Technologies, Inc.

ACTION BASEBALL - Games - Tudor Inc.

ACTION BELT - Braces–orthopedic - Accu-Back, Inc.

ACTION BLOCKS - Toys–blocks - Mattel, Inc.

ACTION BOWLGAME - Games - Tudor Inc.

ACTION BRACKET - Hardware - Outboard Performance, Inc.

ACTION BRAND TAPES - Tape–masking ☆ - National Tape Corp.

ACTION CAP, THE - Hats - Lynnabeth Martinez

ACTION CLEANING PACK - Water treating compounds - Jungle Laboratories Corp.

ACTION CLOTHING TECHNOLOGY - Apparel and accessories - Action Clothing Technology

ACTION COMMAND - Toys–automobiles - Mattel, Inc.

ACTION DANCER - Giftware - Beistle Co.

ACTION DOLLIKIN - Dolls ☆ - Uneeda Doll Co., Inc.

ACTION ENVIRONMENTAL PRODUCTS - Hair care products - Action Environmental Products

ACTION ERGONOMICS - Braces–orthopedic - Action Ergonomics, Inc.

ACTION EYES - Goggles ☆ - Bausch & Lomb Inc.

ACTION EYEWEAR - Eyeglasses - BP Partners

ACTION FILE - File folders - Anthes Universal

ACTION FLOOR SYSTEMS - Flooring–hardwood - Action Floor Systems, Inc.

ACTION FLUID - Fly swatters - Trap-a-Fly

ACTION FOR MEN - Vitamins and nutritional supplements - Action Labs, Inc.

ACTION-FREE - Apparel and accessories - Vanity Corset Co. Inc.

ACTION-FREE - Gloves - Good Luck Glove Co.

ACTION FREESTYLER - Scooters–motorized - Action Sports

☆ = Now out of production

ACTION FURNITURE BY LANE - Furniture - Lane Co. Inc.
ACTION GEAR - Apparel–athletic - Action Gear, Inc.
ACTION GRAPHICS - Bags - Algoma Net Co.
ACTION-HIP - Girdles ☆ - Q-T Foundations Co. Inc.
ACTION HOCKEY - Games ☆ - Parker Brothers
ACTION JACKETS - Apparel–athletic - Catalina
ACTION JACKSON - Toys ☆ - Mego Financial Corp.
ACTION KIDS - Bakery products - Roush Products Co., Inc.
ACTION KIDS - Wheelchairs ☆ - Invacare Corp.
ACTION-KNIT - Crocheted and knitted items ☆ - Hampshire Hosiery, Inc.
ACTION KNIT - Fabrics–broadcloth - Desire Mills Co. Inc.
ACTION LANE - Furniture–upholstered - Lane Co. Inc.
ACTION-LANE - Recliners - Action Industries Inc.
ACTION LANE COMFORT SHOWCASE - Chairs–upholstered - Lane Co. Inc.
ACTION LANGUAGE - Computer software - Keytex Corp.
ACTION-LASH - Cosmetics - Revlon Consumer Products Corp.
ACTION LIFT - Brassieres (Bras) - Moore Products
ACTION LINE - Apparel and accessories - Workwear Corp. Inc.
ACTION LINE - Dictating machines ☆ - Lanier Voice Products
ACTION LINE - Floor coverings–carpet and rugs - Coronet Carpets Inc.
ACTION LINE - Office accessories - ArtMold Products Corp.
ACTION LOCK - Latex - Queen Carpet Corp.
ACTION LUBE PLUS - Lubricants - Brownells, Inc.
ACTION MAGIC II - Lubricants - Brownells, Inc.
ACTION MAINTENANCE - Computer software - Jake Marshall Service Inc.
ACTION MAPS - Games - Gamescience
ACTION MARKER - Markers–felt-tip - Mark-Tex Corp.
ACTION MASTER - Slacks–men's - J.C. Penney Co., Inc.
ACTION MASTER - Tools–hand-operated - Action Industries Inc.
ACTION MASTER NATURALS - Slacks–men's - J.C. Penney Co., Inc.
ACTION MASTERS - Toys - Tonka Corp.
ACTION MATES - Recliners - Action Industries Inc.
ACTION MAX - Vitamins and nutritional supplements - Consac Industries, Inc.
ACTION MEDIA BOARD - Electrical equipment - Action Media Technologies, Inc.
ACTION NAMES - Computer software - Barbara Prince
ACTION NOTE - Notebooks and notepads - Productive Environments, Inc.
ACTION OFFICE - Office furniture–metal - Herman Miller, Inc.
ACTION OPTICS - Sunglasses - Smith Sport Optics Inc.
ACTION PACK - Batteries - GNB Inc. (Automotive Battery Div.)
ACTION PACK - Toys - Fisher-Price, Inc.
ACTION PAGE/ALL - Communications equipment–mobile - Action Systems Co.
ACTION PARK - Cases–plastic - Great American Recreation, Inc.
ACTION PATRIOT - Wheelchairs ☆ - Invacare Corp.
ACTION PATROL - Toys–guns - Tyco Toys
ACTION PEN - Pens ☆ - Scripto-Tokai Corp.
ACTION PLATFORM - Exercising equipment - Gerstung/Gym-Thing Inc.
ACTION PLUS INTAKE MANIFOLDS - Manifolds–motor vehicle - Weiand Automotive Industries
ACTION PLUS WATER PUMPS - Pumps–motor vehicle - Weiand Automotive Industries
ACTION POP - Popcorn - Golden Valley Microwave Foods, Inc.
ACTION PRO - Athletic footwear - International Seaway Trading Corp.
ACTION RATION - Astringents ☆ - Agway Country Foods Inc.
ACTION RIDER - Toys - Roadmaster Corp.
ACTION RINGS - Fishing tackle - Mason Tackle Co.
ACTION SANTA - Toys–stuffed - Fun World Inc.
ACTION SCENE - Apparel–women's - Jonathan Logan Inc.
ACTION SCRATCHER - Pet products - Southern California Foam, Inc.
ACTION-SHAPE - Apparel–women's - Champion Jogbra
ACTION SHOT! - Games - Gelhaar Uniform Co.
ACTION SNACKS - Snack foods - Action Products International Inc.
ACTION-SPECS - Tools - Fibre-Metal Products Co.
ACTION SPORT - Sunblocks - Sun Pharmaceuticals Corp.
ACTION SPORT - Sunglasses and goggles - Bolle' America, Inc.
ACTION SPORTS - Headphones - Maxell Corp. of America
ACTION SPORTS - Skateboards - Action Sports
ACTION SPORTSWEAR - Apparel and accessories ☆ - Jantzen Inc.
ACTION STAINLESS - Steel products - Action Stainless & Alloys, Inc.
ACTION STEPS - Notebooks and notepads - American Society for Quality Control, Inc.
ACTION STORM - Wheelchairs ☆ - Invacare Corp.
ACTION STRAP - Apparel–women's - Bi-Flex International
ACTION STRESS - Vitamins and nutritional supplements - Natural Organics, Inc.

ACTION SUPPORT - Underwear and nightwear - Spencer Supports Ltd.
ACTION SYSTEM - Footwear - Morse Shoe, Inc.
ACTION SYSTEM - Toys - Matchbox Toys (USA) Ltd.
ACTION-TECH - Apparel–women's - Champion Jogbra
ACTION-TECH - Brassieres (Bras) - Playtex Apparel, Inc.
ACTION TECHNOLOGY - Pens - Action Technology Co.
ACTION, THE - Toothbrushes - Advanced Dental Technology, Inc.
ACTION TRACTION - Health care products - Staodyn, Inc.
ACTION WARM-UP - Skin care products - Fanie International
ACTION WRAP - Tape–adhesive - State Chemical Manufacturing Co.
ACTION ZONE - Shirts - Capital Mercury Shirt Corp.
ACTIONADE - Fruit drinks–bottled or canned - Green Spot Packaging, Inc.
ACTIONAIRE - Clocks ☆ - General Time Corp. (Westclox/Seth Thomas Div.)
ACTIONARE OVEN - Cooking equipment–household - Kent Television Marketing Inc.
ACTIONBAC - Fabrics–coated - Amoco Oil Co.
ACTIONBATH - Health care products ☆ - W.R. Medical Electronics Co.
ACTIONBOARD - Computer software - Park City Group, Inc.
ACTIONCAPS - Novelty items–paper ☆ - Western Publishing Co., Inc.
ACTIONEAR - Amplifiers - Silver Creek Industries
ACTIONFLEX - Carpeting - Danube Carpet Mills Inc.
ACTIONMAP - Maps ☆ - Rand McNally & Co.
ACTIONMEDIA - Computer software - Intel Corp.
ACTIONPACKER - Coolers - Diversified Recycling Systems
ACTIONPACKER - Tool boxes - Rubbermaid Inc.
ACTIONRIDER - Frames–eyeglass ☆ - Universal/Univis Inc.
ACTION'S - Boxes ☆ - Rothco Inc.
ACTIONWALL - Wood products ☆ - Georgia-Pacific Corp.
ACTIONWARE - Computer software - Appintec Corp.
ACTIONWEAR - Apparel–athletic - Monsanto Polymer Products
ACTIONWEAR - Shoes - Kid Power USA Inc.
ACTIONWORKFLOW - Computer software - Action Technologies Inc.
ACTIPAR - Pharmaceutical preparations - Parmed Pharmaceuticals, Inc.
ACTIPHYTE - Health care products - Active Organics Inc.
ACTIPLEX - Hair care products ☆ - Alleghany Pharmacal Corp.
ACTIPLEX - Health care products - Active Organics Inc.
ACTIQUENCH GTP - Cosmetics - Active Organics Inc.
ACTISEA 100 - Cosmetics - Active Organics Inc.
ACTISITE - Pharmaceutical preparations - Alza Corp.
ACTISOMES - Cosmetics - Estee Lauder Inc.
ACTISORB - Chemical preparations - Robert Lehrer Associates, Inc.
ACTIV - Vitamins and nutritional supplements - Unipro Inc.
ACTIV-8 - Apparel–women's - Jacques Moret, Inc.
ACTIV-8 - Cough medicines ☆ - Chesapeake Pharmacal Corp.
ACTIV-8 - Detergents - Imperial Manufacturing Co. Inc.
ACTIV-AID - Detergents - Imperial Manufacturing Co. Inc.
ACTIV-KIDZ - Diapers–disposable - Kimberly-Clark Corp.
ACTIVA - Dog food - Valley Feed and Supply, Inc.
ACTIVA - Glaze - Activa Products Inc.
ACTIVA - Scuba diving equipment - Beuchat-USA Inc.
ACTIVADA - Computer software - Alsys, Inc.
ACTIVAIR - Batteries - Activair
ACTIVAIR - Hearing aids - Duracell Co. USA
ACTIVAN - Motor vehicles–vans - Ricon Corp.
ACTIVAN - Skin care products - I. Sekine Co. Inc.
ACTIVANCE - Skin care products - Monteil Paris
ACTIVANT - Pet products ☆ - Sera Aquaristik USA Inc.
ACTIVASE ALTEPLASE - Pharmaceutical preparations - Genentech, Inc.
ACTIVATE - Garden equipment - Pace International Corp.
ACTIVATE - Hair care products - Redken Laboratories, Inc.
ACTIVATED BOTANICALS - Health care products - Activated Botanicals Ltd.
ACTIVATED QUERCETIN - Vitamins and nutritional supplements - Source Naturals
ACTIVATEUR - Hair care products - Mastey De Paris
ACTIVATION FRAMEWORK - Computer software - Real-Time Intelligent Systems Corp.
ACTIVATOR - Housewares - Amaza Laboratories Inc.
ACTIVATOR - Washing machines–commercial - General Electric Co.
ACTIVATOR - Window shades - Verosol
ACTIVATOR II - Electronic equipment - Draw-Tite, Inc.
ACTIVATOR 711 - Adhesives and sealants - Loctite Corp.
ACTIVATOR COMPLEXION SCRUB - Skin care products - Viviane Woodard Industries, Ltd.
ACTIVATOR C.T. - Athletic footwear ☆ - Autry Industries Inc.
ACTIVATOR, THE - Fruit drinks–bottled or canned - Smoothie King Franchises, Inc.

☆ = Now out of production

ACTIVATORS - Audio equipment - Alembic Inc.

ACTIVE - Computer accessories - Quantum Data Systems (USA), Inc.

ACTIVE - Floor coverings–carpet and rugs ☆ - Alexander Smith Carpets

ACTIVE - Recording label - Select Records

ACTIVE - Skin care products - Dr. Babor Natural Cosmetics

ACTIVE - Skin care products - Excelcis

ACTIVE - Toothpaste ☆ - Carter-Wallace, Inc.

ACTIVE - Wheelchairs ☆ - Activeaid Inc.

ACTIVE 8 - Apparel and accessories - Indiana Knitwear Corp.

ACTIVE 8 - Lemonade - Amway Corp.

ACTIVE A - Vitamins and nutritional supplements - Source Naturals

ACTIVE AMERICAN - Ambulatory aid - American Wheelchair

ACTIVE ANKLE - Health care products - Cramer Products Inc.

A ACTIVE ANKLE - Bandages–orthopedic - Active Ankle Systems, Inc.

ACTIVE AREA CARPETS - Floor coverings - Queen Carpet Corp.

ACTIVE ARTS - Computer software - Active Arts, Inc.

ACTIVE ATTITUDES - Apparel and accessories - Jacobson Stores Inc.

ACTIVE AUDIO - Automotive parts and accessories - General Motors Corp.

ACTIVE BRAKE TECHNOLOGY - Skates–roller - Rollerblade, Inc.

ACTIVE BRIGHTS - Apparel–women's ☆ - Jantzen Inc.

ACTIVE BRITES - Cosmetics ☆ - Bonne Bell, Inc.

ACTIVE BY P.F.I. - Footwear - Diesse Shoes Inc.

ACTIVE CAN - Electrodes - Medtronic, Inc.

ACTIVE CLUB - Luggage - Shalam Imports Inc.

ACTIVE CODE - Apparel and accessories - C.S.F. Corp.

ACTIVE COMPLEX - Skin care products - Gap Inc.

ACTIVE CONDITIONER SPRAY - Hair care products - Chenice Beverly Hills

ACTIVE DUTY - Apparel–children's - Federated Department Stores, Inc.

ACTIVE DUTY - Floor coverings–carpet and rugs ☆ - Karastan-Bigelow Inc.

ACTIVE ENERGY - Activewear - Caldor Corp.

ACTIVE ENTERTAINMENT - Recording label - Active Entertainment

ACTIVE E.Q. - Musical instrument accessories - Seymour Duncan Pickups

ACTIVE EXCHANGE - Apparel and accessories - Frederick Atkins, Inc.

ACTIVE EXPOSURE - Apparel–athletic - Kuma Sport, Inc.

ACTIVE FLEX - Footwear - United States Shoe Corp.

ACTIVE GEAR - Audio equipment - Casio, Inc.

ACTIVE GROW - Nail care products - Revlon Consumer Products Corp.

ACTIVE HANDS - Skin care products - Matrix Essentials, Inc.

ACTIVE HERBAL - Vitamins and nutritional supplements - McZand Herbal, Inc.

ACTIVE I - Apparel–men's - Tropical Garment Manufacturing Co.

ACTIVE INVESTOR - Computer software - SourceView Software International

ACTIVE KIDS - Handbags - Romar International Corp.

ACTIVE KIDS SUNBLOCK - Sunblocks - Sun Pharmaceuticals Corp.

ACTIVE LEGS - Hosiery–women's ☆ - J.C. Penney Co., Inc.

ACTIVE LIFE - Hair care products - LaDove Inc.

ACTIVE LIFE - Wallpaper ☆ - Imperial Wallcoverings, Inc.

ACTIVE LIFE - Wheelchairs ☆ - Fortress Inc.

ACTIVE LIFE PLUS SPORTS - Wheelchairs ☆ - Fortress Inc.

ACTIVE LIFESTYLE - Yogurt ☆ - Ryan Foods Co.

ACTIVE MAGNETICS - Conveyors - Kenneth B. Caulkins

ACTIVE MIND - Vitamins and nutritional supplements - Amrion, Inc.

ACTIVE MOIST - Pharmaceutical preparations ☆ - Dermalogica Inc.

ACTIVE PACK - Luggage - Shalam Imports Inc.

ACTIVE PARTNER - Computer software - R.B. Van LP

ACTIVE PEARLS - Skin care products - Ya-Man Ltd.

ACTIVE PHYTOCONTOUR - Skin care products - Sothys USA Inc.

ACTIVE PICKUP FOR JAZZ BASS - Musical instrument accessories ☆ - Seymour Duncan Pickups

ACTIVE PROTECTION - Cosmetics - Max Factor & Co.

ACTIVE RADIATOR - Radiators–motor vehicle - Active Radiator Supply Co.

ACTIVE READER-WORLD OF NATURE - Computer software - Orange Cherry Software

ACTIVE REASONING - Computer software - American MSI Corp.

ACTIVE RELEASE TECHNIQUES - Recording label - Champion Health Associates, LLC

ACTIVE-SCRAPE - Traps–animal - Wildlife Research Center, Inc.

ACTIVE SOLUTIONS - Skin care products - Matrix Essentials, Inc.

ACTIVE STICK WEAR - Apparel and accessories - Active Stick Wear

ACTIVE STUFF - Apparel and accessories - Outerstuff, Ltd.

ACTIVE SUN SPRAY - Suntan lotions ☆ - Sothys USA Inc.

ACTIVE SUPPORT - Hosiery - Sara Lee Corp.

ACTIVE TAN - Sunblocks - Eurotan International

ACTIVE TEEN - Soap - Teen Care Inc.

ACTIVE TIMES - Apparel–women's - NCC Industries, Inc.

ACTIVE VAULT - Bathing suits - Authentic Fitness Corp.

ACTIVE VOICE - Communications equipment–satellite - Active Voice Corp.

ACTIVE WEAR - Cosmetics - Maybelline Co.

ACTIVE WOMAN - Perfumes - Luzier Personalized Cosmetics, Inc.

ACTIVE WOMAN - Vitamins and nutritional supplements - Unipro Inc.

ACTIVE WOMAN BRA, THE - Apparel stores–lingerie - Formfit Rogers

ACTIVE WOMAN COLLECTION, THE - Apparel stores–lingerie - Formfit Rogers

ACTIVE YOU, THE - Apparel stores–lingerie - Formfit Rogers

ACTIVE ZONE - Shirts - Capital Mercury Shirt Corp.

ACTIVEAID - Health care products - Activeaid Inc.

ACTIVEAIRE - Shirts - Dolfin Corp.

ACTIVEBOOK - Computer software - Vertigo Development Group, Inc.

ACTIVEEZE - Vitamins and nutritional supplements - Ultravit Enterprises, Inc.

ACTIVELITE - Antennas - Allen Telecom Group, Inc.

ACTIVELITE - Apparel and accessories - Dolfin Corp.

ACTIVEMOVIE - Computer software - Microsoft Corp.

ACTIVENET - Computer software - Activenet, Corp.

ACTIVENT - Apparel and accessories - W.L. Gore & Associates, Inc.

ACTIVERA - Cosmetics - Active Organics Inc.

ACTIVEWEAR - Nail care products - Cosmair Inc.

ACTIVEWEAR BY SENECA - Socks - Seneca Knitting Mills Corp.

ACTIVEWEAR FOR WOMEN. ONLY. - Apparel and accessories - Weekend Exercise Co., Inc.

ACTIVEX - Computer software - Microsoft Corp.

ACTIVFILTER - Deodorizers - Lewcott Corp.

ACTIVIDEO - Electronic equipment - Akai America Ltd.

ACTIVIEW - Computer software - At&T Corp.

ACTIVISION - Computer software - Activision, Inc.

ACTIVISION DECATHLON - Computer software - Activision, Inc.

ACTIVIST - Lamps–desk ☆ - Luxo Corp.

ACTIVITEASE - Orthopedic products ☆ - Deroyal Industries, Inc.

ACTIVITIES PROUD TO MAKE A DIFFERENCE - Jewelry - Briggs Medical Services, Inc.

ACTIVITIES TO GO - Toys - Mattel, Inc.

ACTIVITY - Toys–blocks - Fisher-Price, Inc.

ACTIVITY ANALYZER - Computer software - Lead Software, Inc.

ACTIVITY CENTER - Toys - Fisher-Price, Inc.

ACTIVITY LOCKER - Containers - Igloo Products Corp.

ACTIVITY PACK - Electronic equipment - Texas Instruments Inc.

ACTIVITY PAKS BY BERNICE - Games - Birthdays by Bernice Co.

ACTIVITY PROFILER - Computer software - The Alexander Group, Inc.

ACTIVITY RATTLE - Toys - Fisher-Price, Inc.

ACTIVITY ROLL-ALONG - Toys - Mattel, Inc.

@ACTIVITYBASE - Computer software ☆ - Workflow Designs, Inc.

ACTIVIZE - Vitamins and nutritional supplements - Lifetronix, Inc.

ACTIVSLEEVE - Prosthetic apparatus - Performance Prosthetics and Orthotics Centers, Inc.

ACTIVSPORT - Hair care products - I. Sekine Co. Inc.

ACTIVSTYLE - Health care products - FCI-American Health

ACTIVTAN - Suntan lotions - Mastey De Paris

ACTIVUS - Pharmaceutical preparations - Colgate-Palmolive Co.

ACTOFIN - Pharmaceutical preparations - Dener Management Inc.

ACTOL - Pharmaceutical preparations ☆ - Smithkline Beecham Corp.

ACTON STACKER - Furniture - American Seating Co.

ACTOR BY LEE STRASBERG - Glassware–household - Executrix of the Estate of Lee Strasberg

ACTOSOL - Fertilizers - ARCTECH Inc.

ACT!PAK! - Computer software - Symantec Corp.

ACTROL - Hair care products - Matrix Essentials, Inc.

ACTRON - Analgesics - Bayer Corp. (Consumer Care Div.)

ACTRON - Cigarettes - Brown & Williamson Tobacco Corp.

ACTRON - Pharmaceutical preparations - Bayer Corp.

ACTS - Electrical industrial apparatus - Communications Technology Corp.

ACTUAL ENTERTAINMENT - Computer software - Actual Entertainment, Inc.

ACTUAL REALITY - Video equipment - Wintriss Engineering Corp.

ACTUATE - Computer peripheral equipment - Actuate Software Corp.

ACTUATOR - Hair care products - Trionics Systems Corp.

ACTUELLES - Fabrics–canvas ☆ - DMC Corp.

ACTUS - Health care products - Omron Healthcare, Inc.

ACTV - Computer software - ACTV, Inc.

ACTVIEW - Computer software - Act Networks, Inc.

ACU - Nail care products - Nailmate Inc.

ACU-ARC - Hardware - Hoyle Products Inc.

ACU-BOND - Nail care products - Nailmate Inc.

ACU-CAUTERY - Surgical equipment - Acuderm Inc.

ACU-CHEM - All purpose cleaners - Acu-Chem, Inc.

ACU-COAT - Nail care products - Nailmate Inc.

ACU-COVER - Garden equipment - L.R. Nelson Corp.

ACU-CUSHION - Automotive parts and accessories - Trends Worldwide Inc.

ACU-CUT - Scissors–hand-operated - Diane Products Inc.

ACU-DISPO-CE - Surgical supplies - Acuderm Inc.

ACU-E D & C - Surgical instruments - Acuderm Inc.

ACU-E-PUNCH - Surgical supplies - Acuderm Inc.

ACU-EVAC - Medical equipment - Acuderm Inc.

ACU-EXPERT - Computer software - Grace-Comp Systems, Ltd.

ACU GRIP - Nail care products - Nailmate Inc.

ACU-GUARD - Medical equipment - Acuderm Inc.

ACU-HALT - Surgical instruments - Cygnus Inc.

ACU-HERB - Toothpaste - Murphy's Import

ACU-I - Photographic equipment - Acufine Inc.

ACU-I-TANE - Vitamins and nutritional supplements - Alacer Co.

ACU-LOCK SYRINGE - Surgical instruments - Acuderm Inc.

ACU-MASK - Surgical supplies - Acuderm Inc.

ACU-MASSAGE - Automotive parts and accessories - Trends Worldwide Inc.

ACU MEASURE - Window shades - Solar-Screen Corp.

ACU-MIN - Tools - Moody Tools Inc.

ACU-RITE - Thermometers - John L. Chaney Instrument Co.

ACU-SHOT - Sporting goods - Acu-Shot, Inc.

ACU-SYSTEMS - Skin care products - Nailmate Inc.

ACU-TEST - Pregnancy test kits ☆ - Smithkline Beecham Corp.

ACU-VET - Medical apparatus - Integra Health International

ACU-VIBE - Cosmetics - HWE Inc.

ACU-ZYME - Vitamins and nutritional supplements - Lotus Brands Inc.

ACUAIR - Ventilation equipment - York International Corp.

ACUAIR AIR SYSTEMS - Air purification systems - Weather-Rite Inc.

ACUCAM - Electronics equipment - New Image Industries, Inc.

ACUCRON - Pharmaceutical preparations - Seatrace Co.

ACUDATA - Computer software - MicroStim Inc.

ACUDIAL - Pencils ☆ - MacPherson Sales Co.

ACUDOME - Electrical equipment - Jayco Interface Technology Inc.

ACUDYNE - Chemical preparations - Rohm and Haas Co.

ACUET - Watches - Ruby International, Inc.

ACUFINDER - Computer peripheral equipment - Cognex Corp.

ACUFINE - Photographic equipment - Acufine Inc.

ACUITY - Computer hardware - Acuity Imaging, Inc.

ACUITY-27 WITH BCG - Vitamins and nutritional supplements ☆ - Great Life Laboratories Inc.

ACUITY IMAGING, INC. - Computer hardware - Acuity Imaging, Inc.

ACUMAT - Photographic equipment - Acufine Inc.

ACUMED - Orthopedic products - Acumed, Inc.

ACUMEN 100 - Exercising equipment - Precise International/Wenger

ACUMEN 110 - Exercising equipment - Precise International/Wenger

ACUMEN 500 - Exercising equipment ☆ - Precise International/Wenger

ACUMEN 600 - Exercising equipment ☆ - Precise International/Wenger

ACUMEN 660 - Exercising equipment - Precise International/Wenger

ACUPLEASURE - Skin care products - Matrix Essentials, Inc.

ACUPOINT - Pens - Paper Mate Co.

ACUPRESS - Pharmaceutical preparations - Thera Research Consultants

ACURA - Apparel–men's - Haspel Brothers Inc.

ACURA - Aquariums–household - Willinger Bros., Inc.

ACURA - Floor coverings–carpet and rugs - Cumberland Mills Inc.

ACURA - Health care products - Her-Mar Inc.

ACURA - Motor vehicles–automobiles - American Honda Motor Co. Inc. (Acura Div.)

ACURA - Pens - Idea International Inc.

ACURA - Tables–metal - Alvin and Co. Inc.

ACURA THERMOMETERS - Pet products - Tetra Sales USA

ACURICON - Adhesives and sealants - Anti Hydro International Inc.

ACURISK - Computer software - United Guaranty Residential Insurance Co.

ACUROLLER - Exercising equipment - Health Yourself

ACURUS - Audio equipment - Mondial Designs Ltd.

ACUSHNET - Golfing equipment - Acushnet Co.

ACUSNARE - Medical apparatus - Wilson-Cook Medical Inc.

ACUSTEK - Motors–air - Ametek, Inc.

ACUTE - Scarves - Vera Co.

ACUTE THERAPY - Skin care products ☆ - Pfizer Inc.

ACUTESCRUB - Soap - Stahmer Weston Scientific

ACUTHIN - Aircraft parts - Hughes Aircraft Co.

ACUTIP - Nail care products - Nailmate Inc.

ACUTO - Jewelry - Acuto Ltd.

ACUTRAK - Medical apparatus - Acumed, Inc.

ACUTRIM 16 HOUR - Pharmaceutical preparations - Ciba-Geigy Corp.

ACUTRIM II - Pharmaceutical preparations - Ciba-Geigy Corp.

ACUTRIM LATE DAY - Pharmaceutical preparations - Ciba-Geigy Corp.

ACUTRON - Pencils - MacPherson Sales Co.

ACUVUE - Contact lenses - Johnson & Johnson

ACV - Hair care products - Mahdeen Laboratory

ACV - Valves - Diversified Energy Products, Inc.

ACV PLUS - Hair care products - Mahdeen Laboratory

ACV TRIPLE - Shampoos - Mahdeen Laboratory

ACVATIC - Watches - Movado Time Corp.

ACW SYSTEMS - Computers - Computer Warehouse of Central Florida, Inc.

ACWORTH - Vegetables–canned - M.W. Acworth & Son Inc.

ACX - Heating equipment - Astro Metallurgical, Inc.

ACX TECHNOLOGIES - Machine tools - ACX Technologies, Inc.

ACXIOM MARKETIMAGE - Computer storage devices - Acxiom Corp.

ACXIOM MARKETREADY - Computer software - Acxiom Corp.

ACXIOM MARKETSCORE - Computer software - Acxiom Corp.

ACXIOM MARKETSELECT - Computer software - Acxiom Corp.

ACXIOM MARKETTRANSFER - Computer storage devices - Acxiom Corp.

AD - Jewelry–precious - Ashi Diamonds Inc.

AD - Markers–felt-tip - Chartpak

AD - Tableware–earthenware - Andersen Design Inc.

AD-A-LASH - Cosmetics - Mehron Inc.

AD-A-PAD - Calendars - Goes Lithographing Co.

AD-A-RACK - Housewares ☆ - Akro-Mils Inc.

AD-A-RATTLE - Recording label - Ad-A-Rattle

AD A-TAB - Office supplies - Do-It Corp.

AD AGENCY IN A BOX - Paints–artists' - I.C.E.D. Management, Inc.

AD ART - Paper ☆ - Hunt Manufacturing Co.

AD BAC - Fabrics - Amoco Fabrics and Fibers Co.

AD BANDS - Office supplies ☆ - Faber-Castell Corp.

AD BANDS - Rubber bands - Alliance Rubber Co.

AD BOND - Adhesives and sealants - Dayton Superior Corp.

AD-CEBRIN - Pharmaceutical preparations ☆ - Eli Lilly and Co.

AD/CYCLE - Computer software - International Business Machines Corp.

AD DIRECTOR - Computer software - Managing Editor Software Inc.

AD-EASE - Computer peripheral equipment - Moore Business Forms, Inc.

AD IMPRESSION - Novelty items - Pioneer Balloon Co.

AD IN THE HOLE - Plastics - Ad in the Hole International, Inc.

AD LIB - Apparel and accessories - Charles B. Martin

AD LIB BY CHARACTER - Apparel stores–lingerie - Character Foundations Inc.

AD LIB CROSS WORD CUBES - Games ☆ - Milton Bradley Co.

AD-LITHO - Inks - Newspaper Association of America

AD MAKER - Computer software ☆ - Integrated Software

AD MATE - Pens - Gillette Co.

AD-MAX - Signs - Ad Art Marquees

A.D. MCGILL - Sporting goods - Wright & McGill Co.

AD MIX - Hardware - Bondex International Inc.

AD-ON - Office accessories - Phenix Group, Inc.

AD PLANNER - Computer software - Integrated Software

AD REM - Computer software - Ad Rem Technologies, Inc.

AD-SAN - Pigments–paint - Proko Industries Inc.

AD SHADE - Plastics film - International Mercantile Industries, Inc.

A.D. STARR - Sporting goods - A.D. Starr

AD-TECH - Adhesives and sealants - Adhesive Technologies Inc.

AD-TY - Ribbons–inked - Paperwork Ltd.

AD-TYPE - Paper–photographic - Eastman Kodak Co.

AD4 - Computers - Integrated Network Corp.

ADA - Pharmaceutical preparations ☆ - Richie Pharmacal Co. Inc.

ADA - Rackets–tennis - Ada, Inc.

ADA ALTERNATIVE - Signs - Rowmark Inc.

ADA MABEL - Apparel stores–women's - Ada Mabel, Inc.

ADA-XXX - Sporting goods - ADA Tennis

ADABEE - Vitamins and nutritional supplements ☆ - A.H. Robins Co. Inc.

ADAC - Alarm systems–fire - Fire Control Instruments, Inc.

ADAGIO - Cabinets - Aristokraft, Inc.

ADAGIO - Chairs–upholstered ☆ - La-Z-Boy Chair Co.

ADAGIO - Dishes–china - Taylor, Smith & Taylor Co.

ADAGIO - Footwear - Leo's Dancewear, Inc.

ADAGIO - Rings–jewelry - Artcarved Inc.

ADAGIO - Skin care products - Better Living Products Inc.

ADAGIO - Wines - John P. Sutton

ADAHELP - Computer software ☆ - David William Kelley

ADAK - Hats - Adak Outerwear

ADALOX - Paper–sand - Norton Co.

ADAM - Computer software - Leasing Systems International Ltd.

ADAM - Computer software - Pesus Group Inc.

☆ = Now out of production

ADAM - Flatware - Gorham Inc.
ADAM - Furniture ☆ - Bassett Furniture Industries, Inc.
ADAM - Housewares - Alvin and Co. Inc.
ADAM - Monitors–electronic - Survivair, Inc.
ADAM - Musical instruments - MBT International, Inc.
ADAM - Ophthalmic goods - Rozin Optical Export Corp.
ADAM - Sporting goods - Nichols Wrestling Products Inc.
ADAM & EVE - Health care products - Scott Specialties, Inc.
ADAM & EVE/PEOPLE TREE - Games - Creatnetics
ADAM AND THE ANTS - Apparel and accessories - Merchandising Corp. of America Inc.
ADAM COLLECTION - Wallpaper - Stroheim & Romann, Inc.
ADAM FURST - Socks ☆ - MMG Corp.
ADAM GOLD - Fruits and vegetables - Adam Farms, Inc.
ADAM +HARRINGTON - Clocks - License Products, Inc.
ADAM PLATE - Floor coverings–carpet and rugs - Milliken & Co. Inc.
ADAMANT - Varnishes - Seagraves Coatings
ADAMANTIUM RAGE - Computer software - Marvel Characters, Inc.
ADAMAS - Flatware ☆ - Kirk Stieff Co.
ADAMAS - Guitars - Kaman Music Corp.
ADAMAS - Guitars - Ovation Instruments
ADAMBA - Food products - Adamba Imports International Inc.
ADAMI COLLECTION, THE - Gourmet cooking utensils - Atlas Metal Spinning Co.
ADAMO - Wines ☆ - Winesellers Ltd.
ADAMO I - Shower rods - Theodore Efron Manufacturing Co.
ADAMS - Beverages–carbonated - Royal Crown Cola Co.
ADAMS - Candy ☆ - American Chicle Co.
ADAMS - Citrus fruits - Florida Global Citrus Ltd.
ADAMS - Drums–musical instruments - Orpheus Music Inc.
ADAMS - Earthenware ☆ - Waterford Wedgewood USA, Inc.
ADAMS - Electronic equipment - Adams Electronics Inc.
ADAMS - Fireplace equipment - The Adams Co.
ADAMS - Floor coverings–carpet and rugs - Capel, Inc.
ADAMS - Floor coverings–carpet and rugs ☆ - Colonial Mills Inc.
ADAMS - Food products - Adams Extract Co. Inc.
ADAMS - Fruit drinks–bottled or canned - Citrus World Inc.
ADAMS - Hats - Resistol Hats
ADAMS - Musical instrument accessories ☆ - McMillan Music Co.
ADAMS - Office supplies - Adams Manufacturing Corp.
ADAMS - Peanut butter - Nalley's Fine Foods
ADAMS - Pet products - Mr. Mutt Pet Products Inc.
ADAMS - Photographic equipment - Adams Retouching Machine Co.
ADAMS - Watches - Bulova Corp.
ADAMS/400 - Computer software - Namtrig, Inc.
ADAMS & BROOKS - Candy - Adams & Brooks, Inc.
ADAM'S APPLE - House furnishings - Dan River Inc.
ADAMS APPLE SPARKLING APPLE JUICE - Fruit juices - Fred G. Farago
ADAMS BEST - Food products - Adams Extract Co. Inc.
ADAM'S BEST - Fruit and vegetable markets - Sandoe's Fruit Market
ADAMS COUNTY DAIRIES - Cheese - Grande Cheese Co.
ADAMS COUNTY WINERY - Wines - Adams County Winery
ADAMS FAMILY, THE - Greeting cards - Paramount Pictures Corp.
ADAMS HEALTH COLONY-N-DAIRY FARM - Cheese - Market Finders
ADAM'S LEAF - Prosthetic apparatus - RWB Novelty
ADAMS MAGNETIC - Audio blank tapes, diskettes - Adams Magnetic Products Inc.
ADAMS NO-MO - Veterinary pharmaceutical preparations - Adams No-Mo Dog Medicine Supply Co.
ADAM'S NO-STIK - Peanut butter - Nalley's Fine Foods
ADAMS NO-STIR - Peanut butter - Curtice-Burns Foods, Inc.
ADAMS OLD-FASHIONED - Peanut butter - Curtice-Burns Foods, Inc.
ADAM'S ORGANIC COFFEES - Coffee - Adam Teitelbaum
ADAMS PRIDE - Produce - Adams Brothers Produce Co. Inc.
ADAM'S RIB - Apparel and accessories ☆ - Playtex Apparel, Inc.
ADAMS RITE - Hardware - Adams Rite Manufacturing Co.
ADAMS ROW - Apparel and accessories - Richman Brothers Co.
ADAM'S SECRET DREAMS - Dolls - Gary Bengston
ADAM'S SOURS - Candy ☆ - American Chicle Co.
ADAMS SPEEDFLAME - Gas machinery - Adams Manufacturing Co.
ADAMS STREETWISE - Computer software - Adams Media Corp.
ADAMS STRINGS - Guitars - Kaman Music Corp.
ADAMS - WESTLAKE - Hardware - Blaine Window Hardware Inc.
ADAMSMILLS - Publisher's imprints - Adamsmill Stationers, Inc.
ADAMS'S FARM - Furniture ☆ - Bassett Furniture Industries, Inc.
AD&D - Games - Tsr, Inc.

ADANTE - Hair care products - Matrix Essentials, Inc.
ADANTE - Shoes - Harris Chernin, Inc.
ADANTE - Wallpaper - Capital Carousel Inc.
ADANTI-UMBRIA - Wines - Dreyfus Ashby Inc.
ADAORA - Dolls - Motherland International Inc.
ADAPETTES - Ophthalmic goods - Alcon Laboratories, Inc.
ADAPIN - Health care products ☆ - Fisons Corp.
ADAPT - Office furniture–wood - Joyce International Inc.
ADAPT - Ophthalmic goods ☆ - Alcon Laboratories, Inc.
ADAPT - Shelving units–metal - Tennsco Corp.
ADAPT-A-BRACKET - Brackets ☆ - California Concepts
ADAPT-A-CASE - Cases–compacts - Fiberbilt Cases Inc.
ADAPT-A-GRID - Construction equipment - Alcan Aluminum Corp. Alcan Building Products Div.
ADAPT-A-LITE - Lighting fixtures - Swivelier Co. Inc.
ADAPT A PAKS - Pet products - Picture Perfect Parrot
ADAPT-A-RAIL - Artists' materials - Logan Graphic Products Inc.
ADAPT-A-SCREEN - Rear-projection screen ☆ - Audiscan Products Co.
ADAPT-A-SYSTEM - Easels - Chief Manufacturing Co.
ADAPT-A-TOTE - Trays ☆ - Olympic Plastics Co. Inc.
ADAPT IMPROVISE OVERCOME - Apparel and accessories - AIO Enterprises
ADAPT-IT - Paper–thermoplastics coated - Unnatural Resources Inc.
ADAPT-TIX - Publisher's imprints - Grt Productions, Inc.
ADAPTA - Health care products - Chattanooga Group, Inc.
ADAPTA-SNAP - Wallets - Prince Gardner Inc.
ADAPTABILITY - Health care products - S and S Worldwide Inc.
ADAPTABLE ANNIE - Wheelchairs ☆ - Ventura Enterprises, Inc.
ADAPTABLE AUDIO - Electronic equipment - Rutgers Group, Ltd.
ADAPTABLE PERM - Hair care products - Gillette Co.
ADAPTABLES - Furniture - Broyhill Furniture Industries, Inc.
ADAPTABOWL - Containers–glass ☆ - Anchor Hocking Glass, Inc.
ADAPTAFILE - Office furniture–metal ☆ - Borroughs Corp.
ADAPTAHORN - Electrical equipment - Edwards Co. Inc.
ADAPTAMAT - Projectors–photographic ☆ - Buhl Optical Co.
ADAPTAPACK - Electrical equipment - Crown International, Inc.
ADAPTAR - Eyeglasses - Essilor of America, Inc.
ADAPTAR NO-LINE LENS - Lenses–optical - Essilor of America, Inc.
ADAPTATIONS - Window frames - Reynolds Metals Co.
ADAPTEC - Computer software and peripherals - Adaptec, Inc.
ADAPTIC - Bandages - Johnson & Johnson
ADAPTIVE ADDRESSING - Computer hardware - Positive Technologies
ADAPTIVE COMMODE - Orthopedic products - Ortho-Kinetics, Inc.
ADAPTIVE HOT PLUNGE - Welding equipment - Emhart Inc.
ADAPTIVE RECOGNITION TECHNOLOGY - Computer software - Caere Corp.
ADAPTIVE SWITCHES - Electronic equipment - APT Technology, Inc.
ADAPTIVE WORKS - Health care products - National Home Health Care Exposition
ADAPTLICATIONS - Computer software - Powercerv Technologies Corp.
ADAPTO - Vases - Retko Products Co.
ADAPTO-DISC - Exercising equipment ☆ - Camp Forest Springs
ADAPTOR - Furniture - Gaylord Bros. Inc.
ADAPTOR - Ribbons–inked - Standard Manifold Co.
ADAPTOR CENTER - Audio equipment - Pro-Co. Sound Co. Inc.
ADAPTOSODE - Vitamins and nutritional supplements - Hobon
ADAPT'R - Signboards - Eddy Associates
ADAPTRIN - Health care products - Pacific BioLogic Inc.
ADAR - Giftware - Adar Pewter Products Co.
ADARA - Toilets–porcelain - Universal-Rundle Corp.
ADARE - Earthenware ☆ - Waterford Wedgewood USA, Inc.
ADARE - Floor coverings–carpet and rugs ☆ - Navan Carpets Inc.
ADAS - Food products ☆ - Empire Kosher Poultry Inc.
ADA'S CANDY CREATIONS - Candy - Ada's Candy Creations
ADATABAS - Office supplies - Southern Folder & Index Co.
ADATRACER - Computer software and accessories - TeleSoft Inc.
ADATTO - Coffee - Coffee Time, Inc.
ADB - Jewelry - Clover Chain Co.
ADBAN - Bandages - Avcor Health Care Products, Inc.
ADBEON - Pharmaceutical preparations - Forest Pharmaceuticals Inc.
ADBOX - Publisher's imprints - Adbox, Inc.
ADBUG - Computer software - Carthage Systems Inc.
ADC - Audio equipment ☆ - ARS Electronics
A.D.C. - Coffee - Maxwell House
ADC - Detergents ☆ - Conklin Co., Inc.
ADC - Hair care products - Waverly Beauty Products
A.D.C. - Window coverings - Nelson Beck of Washington

ADC AMERICAN DRYER CORP. - Dryers–commercial - American Dryer Corp.

ADC FAS TERM - Connectors–electronic - ADC Telecommunications, Inc.

ADC SOUNDSHAPER - Audio equipment - ADC

ADC THE MAP PEOPLE - American Map Corp.

ADCAPS - Caps–baseball - Dunn Manufacturing Corp.

ADCHEM - Adhesives and sealants - Adchem Corp.

ADCLOCK - Computer software - ZML Software Systems, Inc.

ADCO - Adhesives and sealants - Adhesive Products, Inc.

ADCO - Beverage dispensing equipment - Minstar Inc.

ADCO - Covers for recreational vehicles and accessories - American Door Co. Inc.

ADCOM - Computer peripheral equipment - Adcom Technologies Corp.

ADCOMOLD - Hearing-aid product - American Overseas Trading Corp.

ADCOMP - Computer software - Eastman Kodak Co.

ADCOOL - Hardware - Ashland Oil, Inc.

ADCO'S VIVIA! - Starch–laundry - ADCO Inc.

ADCS - Containers–metal - Advanced Delivery & Chemical Systems, Ltd.

ADD - Veterinary pharmaceutical preparations - F.C. Sturtevant Co.

ADD-1 - Vitamins and nutritional supplements ☆ - Nutritech

ADD-A-BASKET - Baskets–steel - Clairson International Corp.

ADD-A-BASKET - Containers–plastic - Clairson, Inc.

ADD A BED - Sofabeds - Bean Station Furniture Factory Inc.

ADD-A-BELT - Belts–apparel - J. B. Belts

ADD-A-BOB - Surveying machinery - Trueplumb Tool Co.

ADD-A-BOND - Adhesives and sealants - Allpro Corp.

ADD-A-BOND - Paints - Olympic Paint & Varnish Co.

ADD-A-CLASP - Jewelry ☆ - Napier Co.

ADD-A-CLEAT - Sporting goods - C. Sherman Johnson Co. Inc.

ADD-A-CLOSET - Racks - Hirsh Co.

ADD-A-COMB - Racks - Add-A-Comb Inc.

ADD-A-DIAMOND - Jewelry - Kaspar & Esh Inc.

ADD-A-DRAWER - Racks - Hirsh Co.

ADD-A-DUCT - Air conditioning equipment - Lambro Industries Inc.

ADD A FENCE - Fencing–wood ☆ - Akay Corp.

ADD A FILE - Office supplies - Rubbermaid Office Products Inc.

ADD-A-FLUSH - Toilets–portable - Polyjohn Enterprises Corp.

ADD-A-FURNACE - Heating equipment - Monarch Ranges & Heaters

ADD-A-GLO - Fishing lures - Palsa Outdoor Products Inc.

ADD-A-HOOK - Racks - Clairson International Corp.

ADD-A-LINK - Jewelry - Kaspar & Esh Inc.

ADD-A-MAT - Artists' materials - Reeves Photo Sales Inc.

ADD-A-METER - Electrical equipment - General Electric Co.

ADD-A-PACK - Fishing lures - Thomas and Thomas Rodmakers Inc.

ADD-A-PAD - Brassieres (Bras) ☆ - Lovable Co.

ADD-A-PAD - Firearms, accessories, and parts - Palsa Outdoor Products Inc.

ADD-A-PAGE - Books–blank - Success Business Industries, Inc.

ADD-A-PANEL - Wood products ☆ - Grosfillex Inc.

ADD-A-PEARL - Jewelry - Juergens & Andersen Co.

ADD-A-PIPE - Lighting fixtures - Swivelier Co. Inc.

ADD-A-RACK - Shelving units–plastic - Lapin Products Inc.

ADD-A-RAK - Thread - June Tailor Inc.

ADD-A-SHADE - Lighting fixtures - Swivelier Co. Inc.

ADD-A-SHADE - Sporting goods ☆ - Harold Cunningham & Co.

ADD-A-SHROUD - Plugs–electric - Hubbell Inc.

ADD-A-SLING - Firearms, accessories, and parts - Palsa Outdoor Products Inc.

ADD A STACK - Shelving units–metal - Tennsco Corp.

ADD A STAR TO YOUR MENU - Cheese - Stella Foods, Inc.

ADD-A-STONE - Pet products - Penn-Plax, Inc.

ADD-A-STONE FAMILY RING - Jewelry - Ullenberg Corp.

ADD-A-TANK - Pet products - Penn-Plax, Inc.

ADD-A-TAP - Wiring devices - Academy Electrical Products Corp.

ADD-A-TIER - Shelving units–metal - Storex Division

ADD-A-TRACK - Tape recorders - V-M Corp.

ADD-A-VALVE - Plumbing fittings - Jomar International, Ltd.

ADD AN OUTLET - Plastic conduit - Hubbell Lighting, Inc. (Lighting Div.)

ADD & SUB OF WHOLE NUMBERS - Computer software - Orange Cherry Software

ADD-CRETE - Adhesives and sealants - Missouri Paint & Varnish Co.

ADD-IN - Apparel and accessories ☆ - Bausch & Lomb Inc.

ADD-N-EYE - Fishing lures - Palsa Outdoor Products Inc.

ADD 'N' STAC - Audio equipment - Royal Sound Co. Inc.

ADD-O-MIST - Air purification systems ☆ - United Technologies Corp.

ADD-O-RITE - Paper–rolls ☆ - Rite-Made Paper Converters Inc.

ADD-ON - Antifreeze - Monson Companies, Inc.

ADD-ON - Electrical equipment - Quick Cable Corp.

ADD-ON - Electronic equipment - Sound-Craft Systems Inc.

ADD-ON - Heating equipment - Easy Heat Inc.

ADD-ON - Signs - Zax Corp.

ADD ON EYES - Eyeglasses - Eyes of Tomorrow, Inc.

ADD-R SYSTEM - Insulating materials - Rockwool Industries Inc.

ADD-R-VALUE - Insulating materials - Rockwool Industries Inc.

ADD-SORBS - Infant product - Koalakins Inc.

ADD-TOO - Toys - Mattel, Inc.

ADD-VANTAGE - Pharmaceutical preparations - Abbott Laboratories

ADD-VENTS - Brassieres (Bras) ☆ - Lovable Co.

ADD-VENTURE IV - Wallpaper - Peacock Papers, Inc.

ADD VERB - Sound equipment - Peavey Electronics Corp.

ADD-X - Paints - Zehrung Corp.

ADDAMS FAMILY - Cereal - Ralston Purina Co.

ADDAMS FAMILY, THE - Candy - Bee International

ADDAPRIN - Pharmaceutical preparations - Dover Pharmaceutical Inc.

ADDAX - Footwear - Weiner's Stores, Inc.

ADDAX - Machine parts - Addax, Inc.

ADDCO - Chemicals - Gateway Additive Co.

ADDDEPTH - Computer software - Ray Dream Inc.

ADDED ATTRACTION - Apparel–women's ☆ - Bali Co. Inc.

ADDED DIMENSION - Floor coverings–carpet and rugs - Trend Carpet

ADDED TOUCH - Floor coverings–carpet and rugs - Alexander Smith Carpets

ADDED TOUCH - Floor coverings–carpet and rugs ☆ - Mannington Carpets, Inc.

ADDED TOUCH, THE - Apparel and accessories - Sita II Inc.

ADDENDUM - Furniture–laboratory - Wright Line Inc.

ADDER - Guitar-enhancer equipment - Adder Plus Corp.

ADDI TURBO - Crochet hooks - Skacel Collection Inc.

ADDICON - Camera flashes - Arkon Resources Inc.

ADDICTED TO SPEED - Apparel and accessories - Mass Apparel Trading, Inc.

ADDICTION - Apparel and accessories - Vertical Apparel Ltd.

ADDIGRAM - Scales–industrial ☆ - Robert Krups North America

ADDING MACHINE - Computer software - Dynacomp Inc.

ADDIPAK - Health care products - Hudson Respiratory Care Inc.

ADDISON - Cosmetics - Addison Laboratories, Inc.

ADDISON - Flatware - Pfaltzgraff Investment Co.

ADDISON - Floor coverings - Congoleum Corp.

ADDISON - Sinks–metal - Kohler Co.

ADDISON HOUSE - Photo albums - Addison House Interiors Inc.

ADDISON TECHNOLOGY - Computer equipment - Addison Technology

ADDISON-WESLEY - Publisher's imprints - Addison-Wesley Publishing Co.

ADDIT - Cleaning preparations–carpet and rug - Sanitek Products Inc.

ADDITION CIRCUS - Computer software - Gamco Industries Inc.

ADDITION TUTOR - Computer software - SourceView Software International

ADDITIONS - Belts, hair accessories, jewelry, etc. - Honey Fashions Ltd.

ADDITIONS - Prefinished needlework ovals - Daniel Enterprises

ADDITIONS BY CHU - Apparel and accessories - Kellwood Co.

ADDITIONS BY CHU - Shirts - AJ Brandon

ADDITIONS BY IVY - Apparel and accessories ☆ - Kellwood Co.

ADDITIONS BY RONNIE - Apparel and accessories - House of Ronnie, Inc.

ADDITIVE M - Calcium compounds - Georgia-Pacific Corp.

ADDLIFE - Pet products - Wysong Corp.

ADDQ - Chemical preparations ☆ - Ecogen Inc.

ADDRESS AGLOW - Signs - Joe Leighton & Associates, Inc.

ADDRESS-BLOCK - Signs - Builders' Art, Inc.

ADDRESS BOOK - Computer software - Parsons Technology, Inc.

ADDRESS CORRECTION AND ENCODING LIBRARY - Computer software - i.d. Centric

ADDRESS CORRECTION AND ENCODING LIBRARY - Computer software - Postalsoft, a Firstlogic Technology

ADDRESS EXPRESS, THE - Giftware - Cross Country Group Inc.

ADDRESS-O-LITE - Lighting fixtures - Digecon Plastics Internatiional Inc.

ADDRESS OF DISTINCTION - Mail boxes - Cedar Works Inc.

ADDRESS-SAVER - Envelopes - Tension Envelope Corp.

ADDRESS UNKNOWN - Men's apparel - India Garments Inc.

ADDRESSEASE - Printers–computer - Addressease, Inc.

ADDRESSWRITER - Printers–computer - CoStar Corp.

ADDVANTAGE - Computer software - Addvantage, Inc.

ADDVANTAGE - Hearing aids - Omni Hearing Systems

ADDVANTAGE SERIES - Headsets–telephone - GN Netcom Inc.

ADDVOX - Medical apparatus - Stanton Magnetics Inc.

A.D.D.X. - Health care products - Healthwatchers System

ADDY WALKER - Publisher's imprints - Pleasant Co.

ADE - Computer software - Autodesk Inc.

ADE - Paints - Mateson Chemical Corp.

ADE - Skin care products ☆ - J.R. Carlson Laboratories Inc.
ADE-O-MATIC - Housewares - Zim Manufacturing Co.
ADE OIL - Pet products - Nutritional Research Associates Inc.
ADECO - Seafood - Bayside Imports Inc.
ADEECON - Pharmaceutical preparations - Consolidated Midland Corp.
ADEFLOR - Vitamins and nutritional supplements - Upjohn Co.
ADEL VER PHLICHTET - Games ☆ - Avalon Hill Game Co.
ADELAIDES - Candy - Russell Stover Candies, Inc.
ADELCO - Paints - Adelphi Coatings Co.
ADELE SIMPSON - Dresses–women's ☆ - Adele Simpson Inc.
ADELGADINA - Pharmaceutical preparations - Tarmac Products Inc.
ADELINA - Cosmetics ☆ - Zauder Bros. Inc.
ADELINE'S - Food products - Adeline's Gourmet Foods
ADELMAN - Hardware - Blaine Window Hardware Inc.
ADELPHI - Flowers, plants, and seeds - J. & L. Adikes Inc.
ADELPHI - Flowers, plants, and seeds - Jacklin Seed
ADELPHI - Paints - Adelphi Coatings Co.
ADELPHI RECORDS, INC. - Recording label - Adelphi Records Inc.
ADELPHIA - Floor coverings - Mannington Resilient Floors
ADELSHEIM - Wines - Adelsheim Vineyard
ADELSHEIM VINEYARD - Wines - Adelsheim Vineyard
ADEM - Skin care products - Alexandra De Markoff, Ltd.
ADENINE - Pharmaceutical preparations - Spectrum Chemical Manufacturing Corp.
ADENOCREST - Pharmaceutical preparations - Nutrition Control Products
ADENOLIN FORTE - Pharmaceutical preparations - Lincoln Diagnostics
ADENOMUNE - Veterinary pharmaceutical preparations - Oxford Veterinary Laboratories, Inc.
ADENOSINE-ADENSINE - Pharmaceutical preparations - Legere Pharmaceuticals Inc.
ADEPA - Health care products - Valentine Enterprises Inc.
ADEPT - Bicycles - Klein Bicycle Corp.
ADESEDA - Medical apparatus - Intramedica, Corp.
ADESSO - Cabinets - Pannebaker Custom Cabinet Corp.
ADESSO - Jewelry–precious - Skalet Inc.
ADESSO - Lamps - MTLS Lighting, Inc.
ADESSO - Perfumes - Luzier Personalized Cosmetics, Inc.
ADEVINA ! - Apparel and accessories - Adevina!, Inc.
ADEVINA! - Apparel–women's - Adevina!, Inc.
ADEX - Tiles–ceramic - Amsterdam Corp.
ADEXOL - Cough medicines - Dayton Laboratories, Inc.
ADEYEME - Recording label - Jazz Composer's Orchestra Association Inc.
ADF - Animal feeds - American Dehydrated Foods Inc.
ADFLAP - Computer hardware - Transkrit
ADFLEX - Cement - Adhesive Products, Inc.
ADFLEX - Electrical equipment - Adflex Solutions, Inc.
ADG - Waterproof outerwear - Omni Consolidated Services, Inc.
ADGC - Antennas–satellite - KVH Industries, Inc.
ADH - Dehumidifiers - Environmental Technology, Inc.
ADH - Heart monitors - ADH Health Products
ADHARA - Ships–sailing vessels - Adhara Industrial Polishing Co.
ADHAWK - Computer software - Management Information Technology, Inc.
ADHEEZ - Adhesives and sealants ☆ - Dick Blick Co.
ADHER-O-FLEX - Lacquers ☆ - R and A Coatings. Inc.
ADHERE - Bandages - Aso Corp.
ADHERE - Glue–household or industrial ☆ - Craft World International Inc.
ADHERE-O - Adhesives and sealants - Scratch-Art Co., Inc.
ADHERES - Medical apparatus ☆ - FNC Medical Corp.
ADHERETO - Paints - House of Kolor, Inc.
ADHERON - Nail care products - Revlon Consumer Products Corp.
ADHERZAL - Enamels - Akron Paint and Varnish, Inc.
ADHESIUM - Adhesives and sealants - Muralo Co. Inc.
ADHESIVE ENGINEERING & SUPPLY - Adhesives and sealants - Adhesive Engineering & Supply, Inc.
ADHESIVE SOLVENT - Hair care products - Vapon, Inc.
ADHESTIK - Paints - Republic Powdered Metals, Inc.
ADHEZO - Adhesives and sealants ☆ - Milton Bradley Co.
ADHEZOLITH - Lubricating oils - Pennzoil Products Co.
ADI - Alarm systems - Airflow Direction Inc.
ADI - Computer peripheral equipment - Applied Dynamics International Inc.
ADI - Computers - Advanced Digital Imaging
ADI - Jewelry - Aspen Designs, Inc.
ADI - Machine parts - Associated Dynamics, Inc.
ADI - Photographic equipment - Argraph Corp. (Samigon Div.)
ADI-STAT - Pharmaceutical preparations ☆ - C.O. Truxton Inc.
ADI-ZYME - Cleaning preparations - E.R. Squibb & Sons, Inc.

ADIC - Computer hardware - Adic
ADICIA - Rings–jewelry - Artcarved Inc.
ADICOTE - Adhesives and sealants - Premix-Marbletite Manufacturing Co.
ADIDAS - Eyeglasses - Adidas America, Inc.
ADIDAS - Shaving preparations - Quintessence Inc.
ADIDAS - Shoes–athletic - Adidas USA Inc.
ADIDAS HELSINKI - Shoes–athletic - Adidas USA Inc.
ADIDAS ROTTERDAM - Shoes–athletic - Adidas USA Inc.
ADIDAS WAITZ - Shoes–athletic - Adidas USA Inc.
ADIDAS WEB - Shoes–athletic - Adidas USA Inc.
ADIDAS ZX 500 - Shoes–athletic - Adidas USA Inc.
ADIEU MILDEW - Chemical preparations - Gordon Feron & Co., Inc.
ADIEU MILDEW PREVENTATIVE PART 2 - Chemical preparations - Gordon Feron & Co., Inc.
ADIEU RIDES - Skin care products - Lancome
ADIMEC CAMERAS B.V. - Cameras - Atlantic International Products & Services Co.
ADINA - Bottles–glass - Drug Plastic and Glass Co.
ADINA - Wigs - Adina Wigs Inc.
ADIO - Shoes–athletic - K2 Inc.
ADIOS - Cleaning preparations–carpet and rug ☆ - Puritan-Churchill Chemical Co.
ADIOS - Insecticides - Micro-Flo Co.
ADIOS - Insecticides ☆ - Blue Cross Laboratories Inc.
ADIOS - Manicure preparations - Gena Laboratories Inc.
ADIOS NACHOS - Vegetables–frozen - Lamb-Weston, Inc.
ADIPEX-P - Pharmaceutical preparations - Lemmon Co.
ADIPICACID - Pharmaceutical preparations - Spectrum Chemical Manufacturing Corp.
ADIPOST - Health care products ☆ - B.F. Ascher & Co. Inc.
ADIPOST - Pharmaceutical preparations - Jones Medical Industries, Inc. (Medical Div.)
ADIRONDACK - Bases–baseball - Rawlings Sporting Goods Co., Inc.
ADIRONDACK - Bird feeders - Morris & Broderick, Inc.
ADIRONDACK - Doors–storm - Duo-Temp
ADIRONDACK - Fabrics - Gretchen Bellinger Inc.
ADIRONDACK - Fabrics - Stonebridge Co.
ADIRONDACK - Gloves - Gates Gloves
ADIRONDACK - Knives - Precise International/Wenger
ADIRONDACK - Moccasins - E and W Moccasin Co. Inc.
ADIRONDACK - Recording label - Michele Audio Corp.
ADIRONDACK - Slippers - Tru-Stitch Footwear (Div. of Wolverine World Wide)
ADIRONDACK - Wood products ☆ - Log Cabin Homes Ltd.
ADIRONDACK CAMP PILLOWS - Pillows - Christy B. Roeber
ADIRONDACK CHOCOLATES - Candy - Leonard A. & Charlene S. Matarese Partnership
ADIRONDACK MT. - Siding ☆ - Log Cabin Homes Ltd.
ADIRONDACK TRAILS - Jewelry - Frederick Atkins, Inc.
ADIRONICK - Wood products - Weyerhaeuser Co.
ADIRONSTACK - Chairs–stacking - Aleksis Lahti
ADIS 360 - Compasses–magnetic - VDO Instruments Inc.
ADJ - Golfing equipment - Plop Golf Co.
ADJACENT - Computer software - Adjacent Market Systems, Inc.
ADJECTIVES AND OPPOSITES: LEARNING AT THE CIRCUS - Computer software - Laureate Learning Systems Inc.
ADJEL - Detergents - AmeriPlus Inc.
ADJUST - Pharmaceutical preparations - Bioherb Inc.
ADJUST-A-BEAM - Lighting fixtures - Quality Lighting Corp.
ADJUST-A-BIN - Shelving units–metal ☆ - Tennsco Corp.
ADJUST A BOX - Electrical equipment - Veco Products, Inc.
ADJUST-A-BOX - Tools–hand-operated ☆ - Danaher Tool Group
ADJUST-A-BRUSH - Extension handles - Boden Co.
ADJUST-A-CORD - Cordage and twine - King Cotton Cordage Co.
ADJUST - A - CUP - Kitchen utensils–enameled - Robbins Industries, Inc.
ADJUST-A-CUT - Hair-clipper attachments - Wahl Clipper Corp.
ADJUST-A-DESK - Adjustable typewriter desks ☆ - Inwood Office Furniture
ADJUST-A-DISH - Hardware - CJ&J Enterprises
ADJUST-A-DRAIN - Plumbing fixtures–plastic - Waxman Industries Inc.
ADJUST-A-DRAPE - Drapery hardware - Fabritec International Corp.
ADJUST-A-FIT - Bedding–linen - Pillowtex Corp.
ADJUST-A-FLOW - Surgical instruments - Marlen Manufacturing & Developing Co.
ADJUST-A-FLUSH - Plumbing fixtures - Fluidmaster, Inc.
ADJUST-A-FRAME - Paint rollers - Arsco International Inc.
ADJUST-A-GLIDE - Cleaning preparations - Flo-Pac Corp.
ADJUST-A-LEG - Wire products - Caldwell Group, Inc.

ADJUST-A-MATIC - Beds–metal - L & P Property Management Co.
ADJUST-A-MATIC - Cabinets–metal - Fort Howard Corp.
ADJUST-A-NOSE - Rubber–synthetic - R.C.A. Rubber Co.
ADJUST-A-PEG - Racks - Richard L. Sheriff
ADJUST-A-PERCH - Pet products - Animal Lovers
ADJUST-A-PITCH - Window coverings ☆ - Leslie-Locke, Inc.
ADJUST-A-PORTER - Bicycles ☆ - Graber Products, Inc.
ADJUST-A-POWER - Garden equipment - Slip Seal Co.
ADJUST-A-SHELF - Shelving units–plastic - Minnesota American, Inc.
ADJUST-A-SHIELD - Infant product - Lisco, Inc.
ADJUST-A-SINK - Sinks–porcelain - B.J. Industries, Inc.
ADJUST-A-SPOUT - Gutters–plastic - Ronald L. Sweers
ADJUST-A-SPRAY - Plumbing fixtures–metal ☆ - Peerless Faucet Co.
   (Plumbing Products Div.)
ADJUST-A-STRIKE - Locks–padlocks - M.A.G. Engineering & Manufacturing
   Co. Inc.
ADJUST-A-STROBE - Lighting equipment - National Artcraft Co.
ADJUST-A-TABLE - Tools ☆ - Hirsh Co.
ADJUST-A-THIGH - Apparel–women's ☆ - Bali Co. Inc.
ADJUST-A-TRUSS - Metals - Wilian Holding Co.
ADJUST-ALL - Novelty items–paper - Angler's Roslyn Group Ltd.
ADJUST-ANGLE - Cooking equipment–household - Weksler Instruments
   Corp.
ADJUST-EZE - Apparel and accessories - Glamorise Foundations Inc.
ADJUST-O-CART - Health care products ☆ - Marquest Medical Products Inc.
ADJUST-O-GRIP - Scissors–hand-operated - Diane Products Inc.
ADJUST-O-MATIC - Hardware - National Manufacturing Co.
ADJUST-O-MATIC - Toys - Azrak-Hamway International, Inc.
ADJUST-O-VINYL - Hardware - Ames Metal Moulding Co. Inc.
ADJUST-RITE - Window shades - Spring Window Fashions Division, Inc.
ADJUST TIGHT - Trailers–truck ☆ - Durbin Industries
ADJUST-TO-FIT - Apparel–women's - Exquisite Form Industries
ADJUST TO FIT - Patterns–clothing ☆ - Simplicity Pattern Co., Inc.
ADJUSTA - Office supplies - Adjusta Bulletin Board System Inc.
ADJUSTA-BAR - Playground equipment ☆ - Kane Products, Inc.
ADJUSTA-BLADE - Tools–garden ☆ - Wallace Manufacturing Corp.
ADJUSTA-CUT - Photographic equipment - Hudson Photographic Industries
   Inc.
ADJUSTA-FLO - Paint sprayers - Speeflo Manufacturing Corp.
ADJUSTA-GROOM - Scissors–hand-operated - Sunbeam Corp.
ADJUSTA-HEM - Slips - Beverly Vogue Co.
ADJUSTA-LEAD - Pet products - Penn-Plax, Inc.
ADJUSTA-LOC - Garment hangers - Batts, Inc.
ADJUSTA-MATIC - Serving carts ☆ - Quaker Industries Ltd.
ADJUSTA-RULE - Rulers–metal - Ideal Creations Products, Inc.
ADJUSTA-SET - Easels - Chief Manufacturing Co.
ADJUSTA-SHELF - Shelving units–metal ☆ - Lomanco Inc.
ADJUSTA-TRIM - Metal door frames - General Products Co. Inc.
ADJUSTABELS - Skin care products - R & R International Corp.
ADJUSTABLE - Tables–metal - Metal Masters Foodservice Equipment Co.,
   Inc.
ADJUSTABLE - Tools - Adjustable Clamp Co. Inc.
ADJUSTABLE EYEGLASS HOLDER - Ophthalmic goods - Karlen
   Manufacturing, Inc.
ADJUSTABLE SIGHTS ASS SNOWBOARDS - Snowboards - Bryant Harrison
ADJUSTABLE TUBE TREE - Medical apparatus - Trademark Corp.
ADJUSTABLES - Tables–metal - Space Tables Inc.
ADJUSTAFIT - Door frames - General Products Co. Inc.
ADJUSTAFIT - Pet collars - Leatherite-Nylorite Manufacturing Inc.
ADJUSTAFLOW - Aquarium accessories - Aquarium Systems, Inc.
ADJUSTAMAGIC - Electric beds - L & P Property Management Co.
ADJUSTER, THE - Tree climbing stands - Amacker International Inc.
ADJUSTITE - Cabinet catches - H.B. Ives
ADJUSTO - Furniture - James Bright Backgrounds
ADJUSTO - Lawn mowers - Tee & Gee Sales
ADJUSTO - Musical instrument accessories - Remle Musical Products Inc.
ADJUSTO-DISSOLVE - Electronic equipment ☆ - MacKenzie Laboratories Inc.
ADJUSTO-EASE - Railings–metal - Elite Products Co.
ADJUSTO-FLEX - Watchbands–base metal - Regal Industries, Inc.
ADJUSTO-LOCK - Clippers–barber - Wahl Clipper Corp.
ADJUSTO-MATIC - Curling irons–electric - Helene Curtis Industries Inc.
ADJUSTO SR. - Drafting supplies ☆ - Teledyne Post
ADJUSTO-STAND - Tables–metal ☆ - Squibb-Taylor Inc.
ADJUSTO-TIP - Blinds–venetian - Spring Window Fashions Division, Inc.
ADJUSTO-WAVE - Hair care products ☆ - Spilo/Mehaz Worldwide
ADJUSTOBRACE - Bandages–orthopedic - Tecnol Medical Products, Inc.

ADJUSTOMATIC - Lighters - Colibri Inc.
ADJUSTRETTE - Hearing aids - Qualitone
ADJUTANT - Garden equipment - H.D. Hudson Manufacturing Co.
ADJUTANT - Thread ☆ - SCT Yarns Inc.
ADKIN'S - Blueberries - Adkin Blue Ribbon Packing Co.
ADKLEN - Cosmetics - Research Council of Make-Up Artists Inc.
ADKS - Electrical equipment - Easy Heat Inc.
ADL - Hardware - Mailhawk Manufacturing Co.
ADL-II - Frames–eyeglass - Hoya Corp. USA
ADLER - Apparel and accessories - Crystal Brands Inc.
ADLER - Cheese - C. & J. Willenborg Inc.
ADLER - Hosiery - Kayser-Roth Corp.
ADLER - Typewriters - Adler-Royal Business Machines Inc.
ADLER-ART - Novelty items–paper - Bob Adler
ADLER BARBOUR/CROSBY - Refrigerators - Kenyon Marine, Inc. (Adler/
   Barbour Div.)
ADLER FELS - Wines - Adler Fels
ADLER-ROYAL - Office supplies - Adler-Royal Business Machines Inc.
ADLERIKA - Laxatives ☆ - Alvin Last Inc.
ADLERS - Jewelry - Coleman E. Adler and Sons Inc.
ADLETTER - Office supplies - Adletter Co.
ADLEY EXPRESS CO. - Toys–models - Toy Truck Lines, Inc.
ADLIB - Computer software - Computer Associates International, Inc.
ADLON - Cigar boxes–wood - Consolidated Cigar Corp.
ADLON - Faucets - Interbath, Inc.
ADLUH - Breads–mixes - Allen Bros. Milling Co./ADLUH Flour Mills
ADM PLUS - Computer software - Pleier & Associates
ADM WHOLE WHEAT - Flour–blended - Western Star Mill Co.
ADMARK - Printers–computer - Eastman Kodak Co.
ADMAT - Placemats - Fort Howard Corp.
ADMATIC - Machinery - Richard F. Nestler & Associates, Inc.
ADMIN TOOLBOX - Computer software - Netpro Computing, Inc.
ADMINISTER - Computer software - Advantage Systems
ADMINISTRATOR - Containers ☆ - Sentry Group
ADMINISTRATOR - Floor coverings–carpet and rugs ☆ - Mannington Carpets,
   Inc.
ADMINISTRATOR - Watches - Gruen Marketing Corp.
ADMINSITE - Computer software - Xenergy Inc.
ADMIRA - Corsets - Sears, Roebuck and Co.
ADMIRABLE - Cleaning preparations–carpet and rug - Uncle Sam Chemical
   Co., Inc.
ADMIRAL - Apparel and accessories - Modern Jacket Co. Inc.
ADMIRAL - Binoculars - Pioneer Marketing & Research, Inc.
ADMIRAL - Boats–houseboats ☆ - Kennedy Inc.
ADMIRAL - Boats–motor ☆ - Crestliner Boats Inc.
ADMIRAL - Boats–motor ☆ - Larson Boat Div.
ADMIRAL - Boats–pontoons - Harris-Kayot Inc.
ADMIRAL - Cigars - National Cigar Corp.
ADMIRAL - Clocks - General Time Corp. (Westclox/Seth Thomas Div.)
ADMIRAL - Computer software - Cruise Associates, Inc.
ADMIRAL - Fish–canned or cured - R.J. Peacock Canning Co.
ADMIRAL - Fishing tackle - Trophy Products Inc.
ADMIRAL'S - Flag stands - Annin and Co.
ADMIRAL - Flatware - Utica Cutlery Co.
ADMIRAL - Freezers - Frigibar Industries Inc.
ADMIRAL - Glassware–household - Svend Jensen of Denmark Inc.
ADMIRAL - Insecticides - H.D. Hudson Manufacturing Co.
ADMIRAL - Kitchen appliances - Magic Chef Inc.
ADMIRAL - Paint sprayers - Speeflo Manufacturing Corp.
ADMIRAL - Paints ☆ - Dutch Boy Group
ADMIRAL - Seafood products–fresh or frozen - Nordic Delights Foods Inc.
ADMIRAL - Televisions - Maytag Corp.
ADMIRAL - Thread ☆ - SCT Yarns Inc.
ADMIRAL - Toys–stuffed ☆ - Gund, Inc.
ADMIRAL - Watchbands–precious metal - Admiral Watchband Co. Inc.
ADMIRAL ACKBAR - Toys - Lucasfilm Ltd.
ADMIRAL BEAR - Toys–stuffed - Russ Berrie and Co., Inc.
ADMIRAL BENBOW INN - Hotels and motels - Admiral Benbow Inns
ADMIRAL BLACKIE'S - Life preservers - Schoellkopf Sports Inc.
ADMIRAL COLLECTION - Frames–picture - Fetco International Corp.
ADMIRAL DAY - Boats–motor ☆ - Larson Boat Div.
ADMIRAL DEWEY - Water–distilled - Suntory Water Group. Inc.
ADMIRAL H - Housewares - Alvin and Co. Inc.
ADMIRAL LIMITED - Boats–pontoons - Harris-Kayot Inc.
ADMIRAL NELSON - Rum - David Sherman Corp.
ADMIRAL PIERPONT - Food products - Amdiral Pierpont

☆ = Now out of production

ADMIRAL SOLUTIONS - Detergents - Adsolution, Inc.
ADMIRAL WOOD - Lumber - Georgia-Pacific Corp.
ADMIRAL ZIP - Sleds ✩ - General Foam Plastics Corp.
ADMIRALS CORNER - Furniture - Brill Manufacturing Co.
ADMIRAL'S QUINTA PETITE SIRAH PORT - Wines ✩ - Fife Vineyards LLC
ADMIRALTY - Boats–motor ✩ - Bayliner Marine Corp.
ADMIRALTY - Floor coverings–carpet and rugs - Quaker Inc.
ADMIRALTY - Floor coverings–carpet and rugs ✩ - Catalina Carpet Mills Inc.
ADMIRATION - Cigars ✩ - Phillies Cigar Co.
ADMIRATION - Cosmetics - Morris-Flamingo Inc.
ADMIRATION - Dishwashing compounds - PYA/Monarch Inc.
ADMIRATION - Glassware–household - Riedel Crystal of America Inc.
ADMIRATION - Paints ✩ - North Jersey Paint Co.
ADMIRE - Furniture polish and wax ✩ - Blue Cross Laboratories Inc.
ADMIRE - Insecticides - Bayer Corp. (Agriculture Div.)
ADMISSIONS OFFICE - Computer software - Blackbaud, Inc.
ADMIT - Computer software - Admit Computer Services Inc.
ADMIT ONE - Apparel and accessories - American Argo Corp.
ADMIX-101 - Concrete products - Larsen Products Corp.
ADNAP - Napkins–paper - Fort Howard Corp.
ADNEXT - Computer peripheral equipment - Radio Data Group, Inc.
ADNIK - Recreational vehicle dealers - Adnik
ADNX - Computer software - Network Equipment Technologies Inc.
ADO PRODUCTS - Ventilation products - Ado Inc.
ADOBE - Floor coverings–carpet and rugs ✩ - Regal Rugs Inc.
ADOBE - Siding–insulating - Weyerhaeuser Co.
ADOBE - Wallpaper ✩ - Koroseal Wallcoverings
A ADOBE - Computer software - Adobe Systems Inc.
ADOBE ACCURATE SCREENS - Integrated circuits - Adobe Systems Inc.
ADOBE BRILLIANT - Computer software - Adobe Systems Inc.
ADOBE CANYON II - Swimming pools - Doughboy Recreational Inc.
ADOBE CELLARS - Wines - Chateau Diana
ADOBE CHARGED - Computer hardware - Adobe Systems Inc.
ADOBE DIMENSIONS - Computer software - Adobe Systems Inc.
ADOBE FURNITURE - Furniture - Adobe Furniture Manufacturing, Inc.
ADOBE HOUSE - Snack foods - Adobe House
ADOBE IRON - Hardware - Acorn Manufacturing Co., Inc.
ADOBE MEMORY BOOSTER - Circuit boards - Adobe Systems Inc.
ADOBE NATURALS - Skin care products - C.E.D.A. Corp.
ADOBE PREMIERE - Computer software - Adobe Systems Inc.
ADOBE PROPANE - Gasoline - Adobe Propane Inc.
ADOBE ROSE - Apparel–women's - Nitches, Inc.
ADOBE TEACH - Computer software - Adobe Systems Inc.
ADOBEAIR - Air conditioning equipment - Adobe Air Inc.
ADOBERA - Cheese - Los Altos Food Products, Inc.
ADOBO - Seasonings - Lipton Investments, Inc.
ADOCAINE - Pharmaceutical preparations ✩ - Wesley Pharmacal Co. Inc.
ADOHR FARMS - Dairy products - Adohr Milk Farms
ADOLA - Underwear and nightwear ✩ - Lovable Co.
ADOLFO - Apparel and accessories - Sanmark-Stardust Inc.
ADOLFO - Apparel and accessories - Sigallo Ltd.
ADOLFO - Apparel–men's - Leon of Paris Co. Inc.
ADOLFO - Colognes - Frances Denney
ADOLFO - Footwear - Americal Corp.
ADOLFO - Underwear and nightwear - Nantucket Industries Inc.
ADOLFO - Underwear and nightwear ✩ - J.E. Morgan Knitting Mills
ADOLFO - Underwear and nightwear ✩ - Spirite Industries Inc.
ADOLFO - Wigs - Revlon General Wig Manufacturers, Inc.
ADOLFO BY AETNA - Shirts - Aetna Shirt Corp.
ADOLFO COIFFURES - Wigs - Revlon General Wig Manufacturers, Inc.
ADOLFO EXCIZZO - Apparel–women's - Adolfo Inc.
ADOLFO II - Hats - Aldo Hat Corp.
ADOLFO INTERNATIONAL - Apparel–men's - Adolfo Inc.
ADOLFO JEANSWEAR - Apparel and accessories - Braxton Jeans Inc.
ADOLFO MASTERPIECE - Wigs - Revlon General Wig Manufacturers, Inc.
ADOLFO MODA - Apparel–men's - Adolfo Inc.
ADOLFO PREMIER - Wigs - Revlon General Wig Manufacturers, Inc.
ADOLFO SALON COLLECTION - Wigs - Revlon General Wig Manufacturers, Inc.
ADOLFO STUDIO - Slacks–men's - Adolfo Inc.
ADOLPH SCHUMAN - Apparel–women's - Lilli Ann Corp.
ADOLPHE SANDOLE - Publisher's imprints - Theodore Presser Co.
ADOLPH'S - Meat sauces - Adolph's Ltd.
ADOLPHUS - Rice - Comet American Marketing
ADONIS - Floor coverings - Aladdin Mills, Inc.
ADONIS - Floor coverings–carpet and rugs - Coronet Carpets Inc.

ADONIS - Pharmaceutical preparations - Sherwood Laboratories Inc.
ADONIS - Whirlpool bath ✩ - Jacuzzi Inc.
ADONIS COLLECTION - Jewelry ✩ - Hobe Cie. Ltd.
ADONNA - Underwear and nightwear - J.C. Penney Co., Inc.
ADONNA WOMAN - Underwear and nightwear - J.C. Penney Co., Inc.
ADOORNMENTS - Novelty items - Vintage Images
ADOPHYLLIN - Pharmaceutical preparations ✩ - JMI-Canton Pharmaceuticals
ADOPT-A-BALL - Novelty items - Scott Wathen
ADOPT A SCHOOL - Advertising agencies - Adopt-A-School, Inc.
ADOPT-A-WORRY - Novelty items - Stands Etc., Inc.
ADOPT AN ATHLETE - Shirts - U.K.-Lasalle, Inc.
ADORA - Peanut butter - Nabisco Foods Group
ADORA - Skin care products - Carr Products Co. Inc.
ADORABLE - Combs - Waldor Products
ADORABLE - Diapers–disposable - Paragon Trade Brands, Inc.
ADORABLE - Floor coverings–carpet and rugs ✩ - World Carpets, Inc.
ADORABLE - Watches - Bulova Corp.
ADORABLE DRESS-ME - Skin care products ✩ - Grant Plastics Inc.
ADORABLE ORIGINALS - Apparel and accessories - Adorable Originals, Inc.
ADORABLE SANTA - Novelty items - Rennoc Corp.
ADORABLE STORABLES - Glassware–household ✩ - Anchor Hocking Glass, Inc.
ADORABLE SWEET HEART - Bedding–linen - Hollander Home Fashions Inc.
ADORABLES - Figurines - Anna-Perenna Inc.
ADORABLES, THE - Colognes - Schnapp Enterprises Inc.
ADORATION - Manicure preparations - Morris-Flamingo Inc.
ADORATION - Pillows - Hollander Home Fashions Inc.
ADORATION - Watches ✩ - SMH (US) Inc.
ADORDER ENGRY - Computer software - Digital Technology International
ADORE - Hair care products - Waverly Beauty Products
A'DORE - Lipsticks - Lancome
ADORING - Floor coverings–carpet and rugs - Lees Carpets
ADORISSE - Perfumes - Jafra Cosmetics Inc.
ADORN - Christmas tree ornaments - Cracker Box Inc.
ADORN - Finishing agents ✩ - Flintkote Co.
ADORN - Floor coverings–carpet and rugs - Queen Carpet Corp.
ADORN - Floor coverings–carpet and rugs ✩ - American Carpet Mills
ADORN - Hair care products - Gillette Co.
ADORN - Paints ✩ - GS Roofing Products Co.
ADORN-A-TRIM - Trimmings–fabric ✩ - Novtex Corp.
ADORNA - Watchbands–base metal - Hirsch Speidel Inc.
ADORNABLES - Boxes - Greene Plastics Corp.
ADORNAMENTS - Christmas tree ornaments ✩ - Danalco
ADORNEAU - Floor coverings–carpet and rugs ✩ - Karastan-Bigelow Inc.
ADORNO FILTER CIRGARETTES - Cigarettes - Maia Tobacco Corp.
ADORO - Jewelry - Circle Jewelry Products Inc.
ADOROS - Floor coverings–carpet and rugs - Concepts International
ADOSS - Computer software - Portland Cement
ADOX - X-ray film - E.I. Dupont de Nemours and Co.
ADP - Meters–water - Sontek, Inc.
ADPAC - Toys - Jac Enterprises Inc.
ADPHEN - Health care products ✩ - Ferndale Laboratories, Inc.
ADPIX - Food products - Adpix
ADPRIN B - Pharmaceutical preparations - Pfeiffer Pharmaceuticals Inc.
ADR - Audio equipment ✩ - Electro-Voice, Inc.
ADR - Food processing machines - Key Technology, Inc.
ADRAIN PARRY - Tablecloths ✩ - Odin Ltd.-Scan Am Imports Inc.
ADRAN - Tires–automobile - K & S Engineering Inc.
ADRAWABLES - Lawn mowers - Natco Products Corp.
ADRAWABLES - Puzzles - Compoz-A-Puzzle Inc.
ADRENAGEN - Vitamins and nutritional supplements - Great Life Laboratories Inc.
ADRENAID - Vitamins and nutritional supplements - Nature's Way Products, Inc.
ADRENAL GLANDULAR PLUS - Vitamins and nutritional supplements - Ethical Nutrients
ADRENAL PLUS - Health care products - Futurebiotics
ADRENALIN - Pharmaceutical preparations - Parke-Davis
ADRENALIN - Video games - Western Technologies, Inc.
ADRENALINE - Computer peripheral equipment - Kofax Image Products, Inc.
ADRENALINE - Jackets - Brian Robbins
ADRENALINE - Sporting goods - Seneca Sports, Inc.
ADRENALINE RUSH. - Apparel and accessories - Clinton B. Simons
ADRENATROPHIN - Vitamins and nutritional supplements - Vitamin Research Products Inc.
ADRENO-MIST - Inhalers ✩ - Nephron Pharmaceuticals

ADRENOCHROME - Pharmaceutical preparations - City Chemical Corp.
ADRENOCOT - Pharmaceutical preparations - C.O. Truxton Inc.
ADRENUCLEO - Pharmaceutical preparations - Enzyme Process Co. Inc.
ADRI - Shoes - Futura Shoe Corp.
ADRIA - Flatware - Gorham Inc.
ADRIA - Wines - World Wide Wine and Spirits Inc.
ADRIA GOLD - Tableware–china - Gorham Inc.
ADRIAN - Perfumes and jewelry - Adrian Designs of Pompono, Inc.
ADRIAN - Rings–jewelry - Artcarved Inc.
ADRIAN CROOK'S INFLEX - Video production - Adrian Crook
ADRIAN HALL - Floor coverings - Congoleum Corp.
ADRIAN JORDAN - Apparel–women's - The Avenue Inc.
ADRIANA - Furniture - Drexel Heritage Furnishings, Inc.
ADRIANA - Games - Treat Entertainment, Inc.
ADRIANA - Jewelry - Selected Trading Corp.
ADRIANNA - Glassware–household ☆ - Dansk International Designs, Ltd.
ADRIANNA PAPELL - Handbags and small leather goods - Pantera International Corp.
ADRIANNA PAPELL - Scarves - Ashear Brothers
ADRIANO - Footwear - M & R Shoes Inc.
ADRIAN'S BARBECUE COLLECTION - Barbecue sauce - Adrian's Merchandising, Inc.
ADRIANTITAS - Shoes - Futura Shoe Corp.
ADRIATIC - Bathtubs–enameled - Briggs Plumbing Products, Inc.
ADRIELLA - Television equipment–cable - Wal-Mart Stores Inc.
ADRIEN ARPEL - Cosmetics - Alfin Inc. Adrien Arpel
ADRIENNE - Glassware–household - Crate and Barrel
ADRIENNE - Rings–jewelry - Artcarved Inc.
ADRIENNE - Tableware–china ☆ - Lenox, Inc.
ADRIENNE PICARD - Eyeglasses - AAI/ACCESSORIES Associates Inc.
ADRIENNE VITTADINI - Apparel and accessories - Heckler Manufacturing & Investment Group Inc.
ADRIENNE VITTADINI - Apparel–children's - Her Majesty Industries Inc.
ADRIENNE VITTADINI - Cosmetics - Vittadini Ltd.
ADRIENNE VITTADINI - Handbags - Mutterperl Group Inc.
ADRIENNE VITTADINI - Hobby kits - JCA, Inc.
ADRIENNE VITTADINI - Scarves - Accessory Street Inc.
ADRIENNES - Breads - Lavosh Hawaii
ADRIENNE'S MINI BITES - Breads - Lavosh Hawaii
ADRIENNE'S SPECIALTY CRACKERS - Breads - Lavosh Hawaii
ADRO - Food products - Adro International, Inc.
ADROIT - Bicycles - Klein Bicycle Corp.
ADROLAZINE - Pharmaceutical preparations - H.R. Cenci Laboratories Inc.
ADRONICS/ELROB - Electronic equipment - Adronics/Elrob Manufacturing Corp.
ADROYD - Pharmaceutical preparations ☆ - Parke-Davis
ADRUB - Cement - Adhesive Products, Inc.
ADRUB RTV - Hobby kits - Adhesive Products, Inc.
ADS - Alarm systems - Electronic Security Services Co.
ADS - Computer peripheral equipment - Advanced Digital Systems
ADS - Motor vehicle parts and accessories - ADS Superchip
ADS - Personal computers, printers, etc. - International Antex Inc.
ADS - Stereos - Analog and Digital Systems Inc.
ADS 1000 - Veterinary medical equipment - Engler Engineering Corp.
ADS ACCOUNTING DATA SOLUTIONS - Computer software - Accounting Data Solutions, Inc.
ADS IN MOTION - Advertising agencies - H.A. Steen Industries, Inc.
ADSORB - Charcoal - Wysong Corp.
ADSORBA - Pipes–tobacco - Denicotea, Inc.
ADSORBIT - Air purification systems - Barnebey and Sutcliffe Corp.
ADSORBOCARPINE - Ophthalmic goods - Alcon Laboratories, Inc.
ADSORBONAC - Ophthalmic goods - Alcon Laboratories, Inc.
ADSORBOTEAR - Ophthalmic goods - Alcon Laboratories, Inc.
ADSPEED - Computer software - Digital Technology International
ADSTAR - Computer peripheral equipment - International Business Machines Corp.
ADSTAT - Computer software - Community Health Computing, Inc.
ADSU - Communications equipment - ADC Telecommunications, Inc.
ADSUM - Trays - Horne of Engineering Ltd.
ADT TRAILBLAZER - Footwear - Ecco USA, Inc.
ADTEC HEX - Sporting goods - Georgia's Tennis
ADTEES - Apparel and accessories - Adtees Corp.
ADTIQUES - Giftware - Pre-Emptive Products, Inc.
ADTOOL - Computer software - Jamison Bothwell Carr, Ltd.
ADTOOLS - Computer software - Avery Dennison Corp.
ADULT CARE - Hair care products - Thompson and Formby

ADULT LOCK - Health care products - Apothecary Products, Inc.
ADULT NEW IMAGE - Pharmaceutical preparations - Vita Plus Industries Inc.
ADULTS CAN SEW - Patterns–clothing - Kids Can Sew & Craft
ADV - Meters–water - Sontek, Inc.
A.D.V. A.D.V. FILMS - Video production - A.D. Vision, Inc.
ADVABATCH - Computer peripheral equipment - ABB Process Automation Corp.
ADVABUILD - Computer software - ABB Process Automation Corp.
ADVAC - Circuit breakers - ABB Power T&D Co. Inc.
ADVACOMMAND - Computer software - ABB Process Automation Corp.
ADVAINFORM - Computer software - ABB Process Automation Corp.
ADVALUE - Pharmaceuticals - Albers Inc.
ADVANCE - Artists' materials - Advance Process Supply Co.
ADVANCE - Boats–motor - Grady-White Boats, Inc.
ADVANCE - Cakes–mixes - L. Karp & Sons, Inc.
ADVANCE - Computer software - Lighten, Inc.
ADVANCE - Hair care products - Major/Advance International
ADVANCE - Hobby kits - Needlecraft Industries
ADVANCE - Nail care products - Pacer Technology
ADVANCE - Paper - L.L. Brown Paper Co.
ADVANCE - Pregnancy test kits - Ortho Pharmaceutical Corp.
ADVANCE - Recording label - Jazz Composer's Orchestra Association Inc.
ADVANCE - Shoes ☆ - Hyde Athletic Industries Inc.
ADVANCE - Ski boat - American Skier Boat Co.
ADVANCE - Televisions - Advance Products Co. Inc.
ADVANCE - Vitamins and nutritional supplements - Milk Specialties Co.
ADVANCE - Vitamins and nutritional supplements - Ross Laboratories
ADVANCE - Wallpaper - Advance Wallcoverings
ADVANCE - Watches - Advance Watch Co. Ltd.
ADVANCE - Water purification systems - Capital Controls Co.
ADVANCE 90 - Pesticides–agricultural - Countrymark Cooperative, Inc.
ADVANCE CARBO PLUS - Animal feeds - Milk Specialties Co.
ADVANCE COMMERCIAL III - Wallpaper ☆ - Advance Wallcoverings
ADVANCE CRAFT - Hardware - W.H. Group, Inc.
ADVANCE DESIGNS - Wigs - It's a Wig!
ADVANCE FAST FIXIN - Meat products - Advance Meat Co.
ADVANCE FAVORITES - Wallpaper - Advance Wallcoverings
ADVANCE GRASS CLOTH - Wallpaper - Advance Wallcoverings
ADVANCE GUARD - Finishing agents - Pioneer Manufacturing Co.
ADVANCE LAMB MILK REPLACER - Animal feeds - Milk Specialties Co.
ADVANCE NET - Cables–coaxial - Mohawk Cable & Wire Corp.
ADVANCE PIG MILK REPLACER - Veterinary pharmaceutical preparations - Milk Specialties Co.
ADVANCE POWER - Generators - Winco, Inc.
ADVANCE PRO - Rackets–tennis - Pro Kennex, Inc.
ADVANCE TO BOARDWALK - Games ☆ - Parker Brothers
ADVANCE XXI - Skin care products - Scentsations Perfumes International, Inc.
ADVANCED 25 - Pet products - Rolf C. Hagen (USA) Corp.
ADVANCED ACADEMY OF GEORGIA, THE - Publisher's imprints - Board of Regents of the University System of Georgia
ADVANCED AGILITY DOG - Pet products - United States Dog Agility Association Inc.
ADVANCED ATHLETIC SYSTEMS - Sporting goods - Advanced Athletic Systems Inc.
ADVANCED BASE CAMP - Sporting goods - Liberty Mountain Sports
ADVANCED BIOLOGICAL CONCEPTS - Animal feed supplements - Advanced Biological Concepts
ADVANCED BOTANICS - Vitamins and nutritional supplements - Natrix International, Llc
ADVANCED CARE - Health care products - Johnson & Johnson
ADVANCED COLOR LOGIC - Machinery - M.K. Products, Inc.
ADVANCED CONCEPT - Infant product - Lisco, Inc.
ADVANCED DATABASE ENVIRONMENT ADE - Computer software - Marasco Newton Group, Ltd.
ADVANCED DETECTION SYSTEMS - Electrical equipment - Carnes Co., Inc.
ADVANCED DISCOVERIES - Electronic equipment - Texas Instruments Inc.
ADVANCED DUNGEONS & DRAGONS - Games - Tsr, Inc.
ADVANCED ENERGIZING EXTRACT - Skin care products - Elizabeth Arden Inc.
ADVANCED ENVIRONMENTAL SYSTEMS AES - Water purification systems - Advanced Environmental Systems, Inc.
ADVANCED ESSENTIAL MINERALS - Vitamins and nutritional supplements - Vitamin Research Products Inc.
ADVANCED FAT BURNING SYSTEM - Vitamins and nutritional supplements - Healthy 'N Fit Nutritionals

☆ = Now out of production

ADVANCED FIBRE COMMUNICATIONS - Computer peripheral equipment - Advanced Fibre Communications

ADVANCED FITNESS - Apparel and accessories - John B. Bellucci III

ADVANCED FORMULA - Nail care products - Revlon Consumer Products Corp.

ADVANCED FORMULA - Pet products - Marine Enterprises International, Inc.

ADVANCED FORMULA - Vitamins and nutritional supplements - Leiner Health Products Inc.

ADVANCED FORMULA THERMOGENICALLY ASSISTED FAT BURNING SYSTEM - Food products - Physicians Weight Loss Centers of America, Inc.

ADVANCED FRAGRANCE BOOSTER - Perfumes - Scentex Inc.

ADVANCED GOLF TECHNOLOGIES - Golfing equipment - Advanced Golf Technologies, Inc.

ADVANCED GROWTH FORMULA - Animal feeds - Manna Pro Corp.

ADVANCED HARDWARE ARCHITECTURES - Computers - Advanced Hardware Architectures, Inc.

ADVANCED HEALTH SCIENCES - Health care products - Bios

ADVANCED HEALTH SYSTEMS - Vitamins and nutritional supplements - Food Sciences Corp.

ADVANCED HEALTHCARE - Dean Distributors, Inc.

ADVANCED IDEAS - Candy - Bissinger's Inc.

ADVANCED INSOL-8 - Windows–storm - Hurd Millwork Co. Inc.

ADVANCED IRON - Vitamins and nutritional supplements - Rexall Sundown, Inc.

ADVANCED KINETICS - Vitamins and nutritional supplements - Amrion, Inc.

A+DVANCED LEARNING SYSTEM - Computer software - American Education Corp.

ADVANCED-LOGIC - Computer peripheral equipment - Valentine Research, Inc.

ADVANCED MECHANICAL TECHNOLOGY, INC. - Electronic equipment - Advanced Mechanical Technology Inc.

ADVANCED MEDICAL NUTRITION, INC. - Vitamins and nutritional supplements - Advanced Medical Nutrition, Inc.

ADVANCED MEMORY - Cassettes, computer boards - ISI International

ADVANCED MIND TECHNOLOGY - Recording label - Futurehealth Inc.

ADVANCED MOISTURE - Skin care products ☆ - Avon Products, Inc.

ADVANCED MOISTURE SYSTEM - Medicated topical preparations - Blistex Inc.

ADVANCED MOTOR-CARE - Lubricants - Thermoil Distribution

ADVANCED NIGHT REPAIR - Skin care products - Estee Lauder Inc.

ADVANCED NUTRITION FORMULA - Dog food - Pet Specialties International

ADVANCED NUTRITIONAL TECHNOLOGY - Vitamins and nutritional supplements - Banner-Pharmacaps Inc. (Advanced Nutritional Technology Division)

ADVANCED PEER-TO-PEER NETWORKING - Publisher's imprints - International Business Machines Corp.

ADVANCED PERFORMANCE - Ovens–microwave - Nordic Ware

ADVANCED PERFORMANCE DYMETADRINE 25 - Vitamins and nutritional supplements - AST Research, Inc.

ADVANCED PERFORMANCE EPH 833 - Vitamins and nutritional supplements - AST Research, Inc.

ADVANCED PERFORMANCE VYOPRO WHEY PROTEIN - Vitamins and nutritional supplements - AST Research, Inc.

ADVANCED PHOTO SYSTEM - Photographic equipment - Eastman Kodak Co.

ADVANCED RADIO TELECOM - Communications equipment - Advanced Radio Telecom Corp.

ADVANCED RESEARCH LABS - Vitamins and nutritional supplements - Taylormade Hair Replacement

ADVANCED SAFETY SYSTEMS - Safety products - Advanced Safety Systems, Inc.

ADVANCED SALON FORMULA - Hair care products - Vidal Sassoon Inc.

ADVANCED SHOW SUPREME - Animal feeds - Bluebonnet Milling Co.

ADVANCED SIGNAL - Communications equipment–marine - Advanced Signal Corp.

ADVANCED SPORT OPTICS - Sunglasses ☆ - International Tropic-Cal Inc. (I SKI Div.)

ADVANCED SQUAD LEADER - Games - Avalon Hill Game Co.

ADVANCED SUBLIMINAL TECHNOLOGY - Recording label - Futurehealth Inc.

ADVANCED SUPER PRODUCTS - Paper–writing - Stuart Hall Co., Inc.

ADVANCED SUPEREX - Health care products - General Nutrition Inc.

ADVANCED TARGET DRONE - Toys–models ☆ - Estes Industries

ADVANCED TELECONFERENCING SOLUTIONS - Electronic equipment - Polycom, Inc.

ADVANCED THERAPY GELCREME - Skin care products - Warner-Wellcome

ADVANCED THINKING GAMES - Computer software ☆ - Optimum Resource, Inc.

ADVANCED VOCABULARY - Computer software - Cross Educational Software Inc.

ADVANCED WARNING - Apparel and accessories - Kellwood Co.

ADVANCED WOMAN'S FORMULA MULTI VITAMIN ENERGY PLUS - Vitamins and nutritional supplements - Pdk Labs, Inc.

ADVANCED WYNN'S - Lubricants ☆ - Wynn Oil Co.

ADVANCEDALERT - Computer software ☆ - DLI Engineering Corp.

ADVANCEMENT - Floor coverings–carpet and rugs - Alexander Smith Carpets

ADVANCEMENT - Floor coverings–carpet and rugs ☆ - Blue Ridge Carpet Mills

ADVANCEMENT - Ophthalmic goods - Foremost Optical Products

ADVANCER - Pencils–mechanical - Paper Mate Co.

ADVANCES IN CHIROPRACTIC - Publisher's imprints - Mosby-Year Book, Inc.

ADVANCES IN OBSTETRICS AND GYNECOLOGY - Publisher's imprints - Mosby-Year Book, Inc.

ADVANCESTACK - Computer hardware - Hewlett-Packard Co.

ADVANCETRIM - Valves–industrial - Anchor-Darling Valve Co.

ADVANCEWARE - Computer software - Advanced System Products, Inc.

ADVANCING THE SCIENCE OF FOOTCARE - Footcare products - Dr. Fabricant's Foot Health Products, Inc.

ADVANCOM - Radio communications equipment - Advancom, Inc.

ADVANEDGE TECHNOLOGIES - Computer software ☆ - Advanedge Technologies, Inc.

ADVANSCSI - Circuit boards - Advanced System Products, Inc.

ADVANSEAL - Pressure seal gaskets - Anchor-Darling Valve Co.

ADVANSIL - Chemical preparations - Rodel, Inc.

ADVANTA - Fishing tackle - Outdoor Technologies Group

ADVANTA - Flowers, plants, and seeds - Advanta Seeds, Inc.

ADVANTAGE - Audio equipment - Rauland-Borg Corp.

ADVANTAGE - Bathroom fixtures - Leonard Valve Co.

ADVANTAGE - Bicycles - Klein Bicycle Corp.

ADVANTAGE - Boats - Advantage Boats, Inc.

ADVANTAGE - Boats–fishing - Klamath Boat Co. Inc.

ADVANTAGE - Bricks - Pacific Coast Building Products, Inc.

ADVANTAGE - Brushes–paint - Wooster Brush Co.

ADVANTAGE - Cleaning preparations ☆ - Gent-L-Kleen Products Inc.

ADVANTAGE - Computer software - RTS Electronics Inc.

ADVANTAGE - Dentifrices - Oral B Laboratories

ADVANTAGE - Detergents - Cleaning Systems, Inc.

ADVANTAGE - Eyeglasses - Crews, Inc.

ADVANTAGE - Fireplaces ☆ - Heatilator Inc.

ADVANTAGE - Floor coverings–carpet and rugs - Conquest Carpet Mills Inc.

ADVANTAGE - Floor coverings–carpet and rugs - Johnson's Carpets Inc.

ADVANTAGE - Floor coverings–carpet and rugs - Whitecrest Carpet Mills

ADVANTAGE - Furniture ☆ - Vaughan Furniture Co. Inc.

ADVANTAGE - Hair coloring preparations - Cosmair Inc.

ADVANTAGE - Housewares ☆ - Kidde Consumer Durables Corp.

ADVANTAGE - Infant product - Graco Children's Products

ADVANTAGE - Insulator pads - L & P Property Management Co.

ADVANTAGE - Luggage - Samsonite Corp.

ADVANTAGE - Manufactured homes - Redman Industries, Inc.

ADVANTAGE - Mats - Rubbermaid Office Products Inc.

ADVANTAGE - Medical apparatus - Boehringer Mannheim Corp.

ADVANTAGE - Medical apparatus ☆ - Biosearch Medical Products Inc.

ADVANTAGE - Musical instrument accessories - Mechanical Music Corp.

ADVANTAGE - Notebooks and notepads - SCM Corp.

ADVANTAGE - Office supplies ☆ - Faber-Castell Corp.

ADVANTAGE - Oils–edible - C. & T. Refinery, Inc.

ADVANTAGE - Paints - Universal Protective Coatings

ADVANTAGE - Paper–bond - Georgia-Pacific Corp.

ADVANTAGE - Paper–newsprint - Advantage Engineering, Inc.

ADVANTAGE - Paper–toilet - Wisconsin Tissue Mills Inc.

ADVANTAGE - Photographic equipment - Amergraph Corp.

ADVANTAGE - Rackets–tennis - Wilson Sporting Goods Co.

ADVANTAGE - Respirators - Mine Safety Appliances Co.

ADVANTAGE - Rubber bands - Alliance Rubber Co.

ADVANTAGE - Seat covers - Rubbermaid Inc.

ADVANTAGE - Shower stalls–metal - Sterling Plumbing Group Inc.

ADVANTAGE - Siding–insulating - Alcan Aluminum Corp. Alcan Building Products Div.

ADVANTAGE - Socks - WorkAbles for Women

ADVANTAGE - Sporting goods - O'Brien International

ADVANTAGE - Thread ☆ - Perfect Thread Co. Inc.

ADVANTAGE - Tires - Uniroyal Goodrich Tire Co.

ADVANTAGE - Toothbrushes - Gillette Co.

ADVANTAGE - Trailers–industrial - Alumatech, Inc.

ADVANTAGE - Vacuum cleaners and accessories ☆ - The Hoover Co.

ADVANTAGE - Valves - Anchor-Darling Valve Co.

ADVANTAGE - Wallets ☆ - Enger-Kress Co.

ADVANTAGE - Wallpaper - Carlton-Metro Wallcoverings

ADVANTAGE - Water purification systems ☆ - Aqua Drip Innovations, Inc.

ADVANTAGE - Wood products - Trus Joist MacMillan L.P.

ADVANTAGE 24 - Pharmaceutical preparations - Columbia Laboratories Inc.

ADVANTAGE 24 - Pharmaceutical preparations - Lake Consumer Products

ADVANTAGE 100 - Steel - Metaltech

ADVANTAGE 900 - Paints - Porter Paint Co.

ADVANTAGE 2000 - Office supplies - Esselte Corp.

ADVANTAGE 2000 M2 - Electronic equipment - Card Technology Corp.

ADVANTAGE 2000 M3 - Electronic equipment - Card Technology Corp.

ADVANTAGE AMERICA - Eyeglasses - Opsales, Inc.

ADVANTAGE BASKETBALL - Games ☆ - Advantage Games Inc.

ADVANTAGE BY RICHARD SIMMONS - Apparel and accessories - Breton Industries

ADVANTAGE CAMOUFLAGE - Archery equipment - Martin Archery Inc.

ADVANTAGE C.I.A.I. - Paint thinners - Collision Industry Alliance, Inc.

ADVANTAGE COLLECTION - Cooking utensils–stoneware ☆ - Farberware Inc.

ADVANTAGE COMPUTING SYSTEM - Computer software - T and B Computing, Inc.

ADVANTAGE FOOTBALL - Games ☆ - Advantage Games Inc.

ADVANTAGE FORMULA ONE - Fertilizers - Wabash Soil and Plant, Inc.

ADVANTAGE GOURMET - Cheese - Advantage International Food Corp.

ADVANTAGE H - Chemical preparations - Boehringer Mannheim Corp.

ADVANTAGE HOCKEY - Games ☆ - Advantage Games Inc.

ADVANTAGE LEARNING SYSTEMS, INC. - Computer software - Advantage Learning Systems, Inc.

ADVANTAGE PACK - Pharmaceutical preparations - Western Family Foods, Inc.

ADVANTAGE SERIES - Cabinets - Diamond Cabinets

ADVANTAGE SERIES - Vacuum cleaners and accessories - Sle, Inc.

ADVANTAGE SPIN-IT - Games ☆ - Advantage Games Inc.

ADVANTAGE S.S. - Boats–fishing - Klamath Boat Co. Inc.

ADVANTAGE T/A, THE - Tires - Uniroyal Goodrich Tire Co.

ADVANTAGE TENNIS - Games ☆ - Advantage Games Inc.

ADVANTAGE, THE - Saddles - Pard's Western Shop, Inc.

ADVANTAGED SOLUTIONS - Tools - Kennametal Inc.

ADVANTAGES - Floor coverings - Congoleum Corp.

ADVANTAGES ARE CLEAR, THE - Lenses - Signet Armorlite, Inc.

ADVANTASSESS - Computer software - AdvantaCare, Inc.

ADVANTEC - Sealing devices - Greene & Co.

ADVANTECH - Polysulfides - Lawter International Inc.

ADVANTEDGE - Bulletin boards–wood - Marsh Chalkboard Co.

ADVANTEDGE - Computer peripheral equipment - Xerox Corp.

ADVANTEDGE - Garden equipment - Master Mark Plastic Products

ADVANTEX - Computer software - Solution Technology Inc.

ADVANTEX - Glass products - Owens Corning

ADVANTGARDE - Razors–electric - Parks Products Inc.

ADVANTIS - Computer software - Advantis

ADVANTIS PASSPORT - Computer software - Advantis

ADVANTIX - Computer software - General Automation Inc.

ADVANTIX - Photographic equipment - Eastman Kodak Co.

ADVANTOR - Alarm systems–fire - Advantor Corp.

ADVANTOUCH - Communications equipment - Square D Co.

ADVANTUS - Health care products - American Cyanamid Co.

ADVATALK - Computer peripheral equipment - ABB Process Automation Corp.

ADVENSURE - Computer programs - Skillmaster Software, Inc.

ADVENT - Audio components, projection-TV systems, etc ☆ - International Jensen Inc.

ADVENT - Flowers, plants, and seeds - Jacklin Seed

ADVENT - Hair care products - Jheri Redding Products Inc.

ADVENT - Medical apparatus - Mentor O & O Inc.

ADVENT - Publisher's imprints - Advent Books Inc.

ADVENT - Recording label ☆ - Roots and Rhythm

ADVENT - Sporting goods - Service Cycle Supply Co.

ADVENT - Telescopes - Northern Telecom, Inc.

ADVENT - Wallcovering - Capital Carousel Inc.

ADVENT AUDIO CINEMA - Loudspeakers - Recoton Audio Corp.

ADVENT AUDIO FOCUS - Loudspeakers - International Jensen Inc.

ADVENT FURNITURE - Furniture - Douglas Furniture of California, Inc.

ADVENT - HOME AUDIO & HOME THEATER SPEAKERS - Audio equipment - International Jensen Inc.

ADVENT INTERNATIONAL, INC. - Fans–electric - Advent International, Inc.

ADVENT VIDEOBEAM - Televisions ☆ - International Jensen Inc.

ADVENTURE - Brassieres (Bras) - Goddess Bra

ADVENTURE - Compasses–gyroscopic ☆ - Tedco Inc.

ADVENTURE - Computer software - SourceView Software International

ADVENTURE - First aid kits - Eric A. Weiss

ADVENTURE - Floor coverings–carpet and rugs ☆ - World Carpets, Inc.

ADVENTURE - Floor game mats ☆ - Coloron Industries

ADVENTURE - Furniture ☆ - Bassett Furniture Industries, Inc.

ADVENTURE - Games - Flying Buffalo Inc.

ADVENTURE - Paper - Ideal School Supply Corp.

ADVENTURE - Rings–jewelry - Artcarved Inc.

ADVENTURE - Strollers–baby - Century Products Co.

ADVENTURE - Video games - Atari Games Corp.

ADVENTURE 16 OUTDOOR & TRAVEL OUTFITTERS 30 YEARS - Apparel and accessories - Adventure 16, Inc.

ADVENTURE ALPHA - Computer software ☆ - Milliken Publishing Co. (Computer Software Div.)

ADVENTURE AWAITS... - Footwear - Pic 'n Pay Stores, Inc.

ADVENTURE BOUND - Briefcases - Wilsons House of Suede, Inc.

ADVENTURE CITY - Apparel and accessories - Adventure City, Inc.

ADVENTURE CONSTRUCTION SET - Computer software - Electronic Arts Inc.

ADVENTURE DISC, THE - Audio equipment - Mountain Travel Sobek

ADVENTURE FOLD-UP - Games ☆ - Tsr Inc.

ADVENTURE IN PARADISE - Slacks - Newstar Group, Inc.

ADVENTURE ISLAND - Towels - Busch Entertainment Corp.

ADVENTURE LOG - Paper products - International Padi, Inc.

ADVENTURE MASTER - Computer software - CBS Software

ADVENTURE PACK - Yogurt - General Mills, Inc.

ADVENTURE PALS - Recording label - Christian Children's Associates, Inc.

ADVENTURE PEOPLE - Toys - Fisher-Price, Inc.

ADVENTURE PHOTOS - Publisher's imprints - Joseph L. Fellin

ADVENTURE QUENCHER - Beverages - Jel Sert Co.

ADVENTURE SERIES - Luggage - Samsonite Corp.

ADVENTURE TOOL - Toys - Wild Planet Toys, Inc.

ADVENTURE TRAIL - Luggage - Shalam Imports Inc.

ADVENTURE WALKAROUND - Boats–motor - Grady-White Boats, Inc.

ADVENTURELAND - Computer software - Adventure International

ADVENTURELAND - Games ☆ - Milton Bradley Co.

ADVENTURER - Bicycles - Roadmaster Corp.

ADVENTURER - Boats ☆ - Valco Aluminum Boats

ADVENTURER - Boats–canoes - Black River Canoes

ADVENTURER - Boats–motor - Thompson Boat Co.

ADVENTURER - Boats–motor ☆ - Bluewater

ADVENTURER - Boats–motor ☆ - Cruisers

ADVENTURER - Boats–motor ☆ - Sport-Craft Inc.

ADVENTURER - Handbags - Esprit De Corp.

ADVENTURER - Knives - Precise International/Wenger

ADVENTURER - Luggage - United States Luggage Corp.

ADVENTURER - Motor vehicles–motor homes - Winnebago Industries, Inc.

ADVENTURER - Motorcycles ☆ - Suzuki of America Automotive Corp.

ADVENTURER - Perfumes - Quintessence Inc.

ADVENTURER - Seats–automobile - Cosco, Inc.

ADVENTURER - Tires ☆ - Cooper Tire & Rubber Co.

ADVENTURER - Tool boxes ☆ - Flambeau Products Corp.

ADVENTURER - Trading cards and stamps - Treat Entertainment, Inc.

ADVENTURER - Trailers–travel - Snowy Mountain Recreational Products

ADVENTURER - Trailers–travel ☆ - Shasta Industries Inc.

ADVENTURERS, INC. - Publisher's imprints - Kensington Publishing Corp.

ADVENTURES - Floor coverings–tile ☆ - Monarch Tile Inc.

ADVENTURES AROUND THE WORLD - Computer software - Orange Cherry Software

ADVENTURES FROM THE BOOK OF VIRTUES - Video production - William J. Bennett

ADVENTURES IN ARTS, SCIENCES AND WORLD CULTURES - Hobby kits - Curiosity Development, Inc.

ADVENTURES IN COLORLAND: SPACE SAGAS - Computer software ☆ - Spinnaker Software Corp.

ADVENTURES IN DESKTOP PUBLISHING - Publisher's imprints - Parsons Technology, Inc.

ADVENTURES IN FLESH - Computer software ☆ - Krell Software Corp.

ADVENTURES IN LEATHER - Leather goods - Tandy Leather Co.

ADVENTURES IN MAINE! - Games - Escapade Games, Inc.

☆ = Now out of production

ADVENTURES IN MUSICLAND - Computer software - Electronic Courseware Systems Inc.

ADVENTURES IN ODYSSEY - Film–motion picture - Focus On The Family

ADVENTURES IN PUBLISHING - Computer software - Wright Group Publishing, Inc.

ADVENTURES IN SCIENCE - Video production - WGBH Educational Foundation

ADVENTURES IN STAMP COLLECTING - Toys - ZOE Arts

ADVENTURES IN THE LAND OF O - Plush toys - Beta Toys Inc.

ADVENTURES OF BILLY BEE, THE - Publisher's imprints - Billy Bee Productions, Inc.

ADVENTURES OF NIKKO, THE - Computer software - Mindscape Software Inc.

ADVENTURES OF ROBIN HOOD, THE - Games - Avalon Hill Game Co.

ADVENTURES OF ROCKY AND BULLWINKLE AND FRIENDS - Toys–stuffed - Ward Productions, Inc.

ADVENTURES OF ROCKY AND BULLWINKLE AND FRIENDS, THE - Apparel and accessories - Ward Productions, Inc.

ADVENTURES OF SINBAD, THE - Computer software - Unicorn Software

ADVENTURES OF THE BAILEY SCHOOL KIDS, THE - Publisher's imprints - Scholastic Inc.

ADVENTURES OF THE C-PATROL - Educational product - St. Luke's Hospital of Kansas City

ADVENTURES UNLIMITED - Computer software - Lindy Enterprises, Inc.

ADVENTURESS - Floor coverings–carpet and rugs ✩ - Karastan-Bigelow Inc.

ADVENTUREVISION - Board games and accessories - Tsr, Inc.

ADVERA - Health care products - Abbott Laboratories

ADVERMAT - Floor coverings - Devon Corp.

ADVERSARIES - Figurines - Game Designers' Workshop, Inc.

ADVERSARY - Video games ✩ - National Semiconductor Corp.

ADVERSITY - Recording label - Jazz Composer's Orchestra Association Inc.

ADVERTAG - Labels–paper - Printed Systems

ADVERTAINMENT - Computer software - Inmar Communications, Inc.

ADVERTEASING - Games ✩ - Cadaco Div.

ADVERTEASING II - Games ✩ - Cadaco Div.

ADVERTEASING JUNIOR - Games ✩ - Cadaco Div.

ADVERTISER - Electronic equipment - CNC Automation, Inc.

ADVERTISING SPECIALTIES - Office supplies - Risto Inc.

ADVET - Dental equipment ✩ - Schroer Manufacturing Co.

ADVIL - Cold remedies - American Home Products Corp.

ADVIL - Pharmaceutical preparations - Whitehall Laboratories

ADVINET - Consulting services - Advinet, Inc.

ADVISE! - Computer software - EX Machina, Inc.

ADVISOR - Clocks - General Time Corp. (Westclox/Seth Thomas Div.)

ADVISOR - Golfing equipment - Daiwa Corp.

ADVISOR - Trailers–travel - Royals International

ADVISOR CHANNEL - Computer software - FMR Corp.

ADVISOR PRO - Radios–citizens' band - Motorola, Inc.

ADVISORSOFT - Computer software - Providian Corp.

ADVISORY BOARD - Signs - Recomm International Display Corp.

ADVISTA - Computer software - Advista Group, Inc.

ADVITOL - Vitamins and nutritional supplements - Petland, Inc.

ADVOCAAT - Liquors - Adamba Imports International Inc.

ADVOCACY AND COMMUNICATIONS TECHNIQUES - Recording label - Elliot W. Stone

ADVOCACY GAME, THE - Games - Jewish Vocational Service Cincinnati

ADVOCARE - Skin care products - Advocare International, LLC

ADVOCATE - Floor coverings–carpet and rugs ✩ - Karastan-Bigelow Inc.

ADVOCATE - Office supplies - Esselte Corp.

ADVOCATE - Tables–wood - Riverside Furniture Corp.

ADVOCATE - Telephone apparatus - Lanier Voice Products

ADVOCATE - Tires - Uniroyal Goodrich Licensing Services, Inc.

ADVOCATE HEATHER - Floor coverings–carpet and rugs - Karastan-Bigelow Inc.

ADVOCATE PLUS - Floor coverings–carpet and rugs ✩ - Karastan-Bigelow Inc.

ADVOCATES - Hardware - Scott Sign Systems, Inc.

ADVOCEL - Pharmaceutical preparations - Abbott Laboratories

ADVOCIN - Veterinary pharmaceutical preparations - Pfizer Inc.

ADWRAP - Paper–newsprint - Champion International Corp.

ADX - Fire extinguishers - Ad-X Corp.

ADYAR - Publisher's imprints - Theosophical Publishing House

ADZORBSTAR - Air purification systems - Davstar California, Inc.

ADZUMOS KITCHEN - Crackers - Adzumos Kitchen Inc.

AE - Wheel rims–motor vehicle - Advent Enterprises Inc.

AE-2 - Computer software - Artisoft, Inc.

AE-55 - Artists' materials ✩ - LogEtronics Corp.

AE INFO 2010 - Computer software - American Engineering Corp.

AE2100 - Engines - Allison Engine Co.

AE3007 - Engines - Allison Engine Co.

AEARO - First aid kits - Cabot Safety Intermediate Corp.

AEBS+ZN - Vitamins and nutritional supplements ✩ - J.R. Carlson Laboratories Inc.

AEC - Artists' materials - Paasche Airbrush Co.

AEC - Electrical equipment - Andon Electronics Corp.

AEC AUTHORITY, THE - Computer software - Softdesk, Inc.

AEC-X - Computer peripheral equipment - Softdesk, Inc.

AEC826004NE - Electronic equipment - Humidial Corp.

AECD ELECTRODES - Medical apparatus - Cardiac Science, Inc.

AECO - Office supplies - National Service Industries, Inc.

AECS - Computer software - Intessera, LP

AEDERNA - Skin care products - Tri-Tec, Inc.

AEGEAN - Bathroom fixtures ✩ - Artesian Industries

AEGEAN - Bathtubs–enameled - Briggs Plumbing Products, Inc.

AEGEAN - Beverages–malt ✩ - Stanley Stawski Distributing Co.

AEGEAN - Dinnerware–glass ✩ - Gorham Inc.

AEGEAN - Floor coverings–carpet and rugs ✩ - Regal Rugs Inc.

AEGEAN - Glassware–household - Oneida Ltd.

AEGEAN - Watches - Seiko Corp. of America

AEGEAN COBALT - Tableware–china ✩ - Lenox, Inc.

AEGEAN FOLIO - Furniture - Henredon Furniture Industries, Inc.

AEGEAN ISLES - Suntan lotions - Aegean Isles, Inc.

AEGEAN MIST - Floor coverings - Armstrong World Industries, Inc.

AEGEAN STONE - Floor coverings - Azrock Commercial Flooring

AEGEAN STRIKE - Games - Avalon Hill Game Co.

AEGEAN WEAVE - Flatware - Wallace International Silversmiths, Inc.

AEGINA - Furniture ✩ - Bassett Furniture Industries, Inc.

AEGIS - Bicycle parts and accessories - DLCI

AEGIS - Clocks - Timex Corp.

AEGIS - Computer hardware - Acuson Corp.

AEGIS - Computer software - Guaranty Asset Protection Services, Inc.

AEGIS - Computer software - Pesus Group Inc.

AEGIS - Electronic equipment - Kalglo Electronics Co. Inc.

AEGIS - Fabrics - Precision Fabrics Group, Inc.

AEGIS - Light-sensitive coatings - Shipley Co. Inc.

AEGIS - Paints - Surface Protection Industries, Inc.

AEGIS - Recording label - Little Major Record Distributors Inc.

AEGIS - Telephone accessories - Scitec, Inc.

AEGIS - Tires - Yokohama Tire Corp.

AEGIS ECF - Padding–foam - Sonoco Products Co.

AEGIS GUARDIAN OF THE FLEET - Computer software - Writing Wizardry, Inc.

AEI - Hair care products - Allen Edwards International Inc.

AEL - Wheelchairs - Adaptive Engineering Lab Inc.

AEM - Electronic equipment - Aem, Inc.

AEM - Medical apparatus - Electroscope, Inc.

AEMME - Tiles–ceramic - TJ Imports

A.E.M.S. (AIR EMISSION MANAGEMENT SYSTEM) - Computer software - EnviroMetrics Software Inc.

AENICAID - Pharmaceutical preparations - P. & S. Laboratories Inc.

AEO - Watches - American Eagle Outfitters, Inc.

AEOLIAN - Pianos - Aeolian Pianos Inc.

AEOLIAN AMERICAN - Pianos - Aeolian Pianos Inc.

AEOLUS - Musical instrument accessories - Player Piano Co. Inc.

AEON FLUX - Apparel and accessories - Viacom International Inc.

AEONIAN PRESS INC. - Publisher's imprint - Amereon Ltd.

AEOR-LAN - Electronic equipment - William Bal Corp.

AEORGLAS GEL - Firearms, accessories, and parts - Brownells, Inc.

A.E.P. - Pharmaceutical preparations - Reaco Products Inc.

AEP - Plastics film - AEP Industries, Inc.

AEP/SPAN - Siding–metal - Meyer Furnace Co.

AEQUITRON - Medical apparatus - Aequitron Medical, Inc.

A.E.R. - Surgical supplies - Birchwood Laboratories, Inc.

AER ENERGY - Batteries - Aer Energy Resources, Inc.

AER-FOIL - Marine rigging ✩ - Woolsey Marine Industries

AER-O-WAY - Deodorizers - Puritan-Churchill Chemical Co.

AER-TUF - Marine rigging ✩ - Woolsey Marine Industries

AERA-VATOR - Agricultural machinery - First Products, Inc.

AERDIL - Pharmaceutical preparations ✩ - Econo Med Pharmaceuticals Inc.

AEREATED - Hosiery ✩ - Sheffield Industries Inc.

AERECON - Film - Eastman Kodak Co.

AEREON - Antistatic and dust-control equipment - Cumming Corp.

AEREX - Hardware - SPS Technologies, Inc.
AERFLYTE - Skates–ice - Roller Derby Skate Corp.
AERIAL - Floor coverings–carpet and rugs - Roxbury Carpet Co.
AERIAL - Footwear–athletic - Puma Inc.
AERIAL - Goggles–safety - Ektelon
AERIAL - Recording label - Jazz Composer's Orchestra Association Inc.
AERIAL - Trees - Willet N. Wandell
AERIALS - Apparel and accessories - Tighe Industries Inc.
AERIE - Automotive parts and accessories - Hop-Cap Inc.
AERIE - Golfing equipment - Falcon Golf Inc.
AERIELLE - Pillows - E.I. Dupont de Nemours and Co.
AERIKA - Handbags - BCW Enterprises Inc.
AERLAK - Imitation leather ☆ - Ivy International Ltd.
AERLIGHT - Imitation leather ☆ - Ivy International Ltd.
AERLUZ - Imitation leather ☆ - Ivy International Ltd.
AERMOTOR - Pumps - Aermotor Pumps Inc.
AERO - Automotive parts and accessories ☆ - Hop-Cap Inc.
AERO - Balls - Biotech Corp.
AERO - Boats–motor ☆ - Four Winns Inc.
AERO - Computers - Compaq Computer Corp.
AERO - Fabrics - Greenwood Mills Inc.
AERO - Film - Eastman Kodak Co.
AERO - Floor finishing machines–commercial - United Floor Machine Co.
AERO - Furniture - RMF/DLO Group, Inc.
AERO - Hot tubs–fiberglass ☆ - Jacuzzi Inc.
AERO - Kites - Gayla Industries Inc.
AERO - Locks–padlocks - Transmission Technology Inc.
AERO - Machine parts - Rosa Pen Co.
AERO - Motor vehicle parts and accessories - ABC Compounding Co. Inc.
AERO - Motor vehicles–automobiles - American Honda Motor Co. Inc. (Acura Div.)
AERO - Paints ☆ - M. Grumbacher Inc.
AERO - Publisher's imprints - Tab Books
AERO - Sporting goods ☆ - Gold Eagle/Arnold Palmer
AERO - Sporting goods ☆ - Ski Accessories Co.
AERO - Thread ☆ - United Thread Mills Corp.
AERO - Vacuum cleaners and accessories ☆ - The Eureka Co.
AERO - Wallcoverings - Ben Rose Ltd.
AERO - Window coverings - Aero Drapery Corp.
AERO 1200 - Dryers–hair - Helene Curtis Industries Inc.
AERO-6000 - Brakes–motor vehicle - Dico, Inc.
AERO ATLAS - Maps - Aero Surveys of Georgia, Inc.
AERO BAR - Chocolate candy - Nestle USA
AERO-BELT - Exercising equipment - Nurge Fitness Systems, Inc.
AERO-BLEND - Food processor components - Sales Magic, Inc.
AERO-BRAND - Inks - Specialty Ink Co. Inc.
AERO CATI-COAT - Paints ☆ - Sherwin-Williams Automotive Finishes Corp.
AERO CLASSIC - Bicycles - Columbia Manufacturing Inc.
AERO-CLEAN - Chemical preparations - Maxi-Blast Inc.
AERO COMP - Computer software - United States Research and Development Corp.
AERO CORE - Artists' materials - Pickett Industries
AERO COSMETICS - Cleaning preparations - Aero Cosmetics
AERO DARTS - Sporting goods ☆ - General Sportcraft Co. Ltd.
AERO-DISPERSER - Laboratory apparatus - Amherst Process Instruments, Inc.
AERO DRIVER - Tufting machines - Tuftamatic, Inc.
AERO DYNE - Bicycles - Columbia Manufacturing Inc.
AERO DYNE-AMIC - Pesticides–agricultural - Helena Chemical Co.
AERO-FAC - Water treating compounds - Lake Aid, Inc.
AERO FAIR - Deodorizers - Atmosphere Products Co. Inc.
AERO-FIN - Toys–models ☆ - Estes Industries
AERO-FLAX - Automotive parts and accessories - Razzi Corp.
AERO FLITE - Bicycles - Columbia Manufacturing Inc.
AERO FORCE - Golfing equipment - Golfsmith International Inc.
AERO-GARD - Health care products - Inhalation Plastic Inc.
AERO-GARD IT - Health care products - Inhalation Plastic Inc.
AERO-GLIDE - Athletic footwear - Converse Inc.
AERO-GLIDE SYSTEM 7 - Footwear - H.H. Brown Shoe Co., Inc.
AERO GLOSS - Paints - Testor Corp.
AERO-JET - Athletic footwear - Converse Inc.
AERO JR. - Floor finishing machines–commercial - United Floor Machine Co.
AERO K - Gasoline - Circle K
AERO KING - Lawn mowers - Textron Inc.
AERO KOOL CORPORATION - Aircraft repairing services - Aero Kool Corp.
AERO LAID - Stationery ☆ - Mead Corp.

AERO LINE - Bicycles - Columbia Manufacturing Inc.
AERO LITE HOME HEALTH CARE PRODUCTS - Medical apparatus - Medical Industries America, Inc.
AERO M - Capacitors ☆ - Aerovox Inc.
AERO MARINE SEARCH TEAM - Toys - Fisher-Price, Inc.
AERO-METRIC - Pens ☆ - Parker Pen USA
AERO-MIST - Health care products - Inhalation Plastic Inc.
AERO-N-AQUA - Bathroom accessories - Anaco
AERO-NEG - Photographic equipment - Eastman Kodak Co.
AERO-ONE - Mattresses - Integrated Therapy Products, Inc.
AERO-PAK - Luggage ☆ - Seward Luggage Co.
AERO PRO - Bicycles - Columbia Manufacturing Inc.
AERO PRO - Sporting goods - Riddell, Inc.
AERO PUBLISHERS - Publisher's imprints - McGraw-Hill Companies, Inc.
AERO QUALITY - Batteries - Smiths Industries Aerospace & Defense Systems Inc.
AERO SERIES - Dryers–hair - Remington Products Co.
AERO-SHAFT PUSHRODS - Craft supplies - Sig Manufacturing Inc.
AERO SPORT - Apparel and accessories - Montgomery Ward & Co. Inc.
AERO SPORT - Computer peripheral equipment - Archie Joseph Snider
AERO SPORT - Kites - Gayla Industries Inc.
AERO-SPOT - Paints - Nelson Paint Co., Inc.
AERO SPRITZ - Hair care products - Demert & Dougherty, Inc.
AERO-STEP - Exercising equipment - Maxxim Medical Inc.
AERO STUN PEPPER SPRAY - Safety products - Steele Security International Corp.
AERO-TEMP - Health care products ☆ - Marquest Medical Products Inc.
AERO-THANE - Motor vehicle parts and accessories - Razzi Corp.
AERO, THE - Crocheted and knitted items ☆ - Reliable of Milwaukee
AERO THE ACRO-BAT - Video games - Sun Corp. of America
AERO-TIP - Hardware - Nylok Fastener Corp.
AERO TRAINER - Tires–airplane - Polymer Enterprises Corp.
AERO TURBO - Bicycles - Kung Hsue She, Inc.
AERO-WHIRL - Sprinklers–lawn - La Fayette Brass Co. Inc.
AERO WHITE - Paints–artists' - M. Grumbacher Inc.
AEROAID - Pharmaceutical preparations - Graham-Field Inc.
AEROASTRO - Rocket motors–aircraft - Aeroastro LLC
AEROBA FLEX - Ophthalmic goods - Foremost Optical Products
AEROBAIT THE AERATED BAIT SAVER - Sporting goods - Magic Products, Inc.
AEROBALL - Exercising equipment - Maze Inc.
AEROBAR - Air purification systems - Ion Systems
AEROBAT - Toys–models - Cox Products Inc.
AEROBIANA - Women's aerobic shoes ☆ - Jaclar
AEROBIC - Aquariums–household - Willinger Bros., Inc.
AEROBIC - Health care products ☆ - East Earth Herb Inc.
AEROBIC 16 - Food products - Tomsun Foods Inc.
AEROBIC FITNESS - Exercising equipment - Twinson Co.
AEROBIC KNIT - Fabrics–broadcloth - Desire Mills Co. Inc.
AEROBIC POINT - Sporting goods - Bollinger Industries
AEROBIC SPEEDWALKER - Shoes–athletic - Brown Shoe Co.
AEROBIC SPONGE - Pet products - Tetra Sales USA
AEROBIC SQUARE - Exercising equipment - Gerstung/Gym-Thing Inc.
AEROBIC STRIDER - Sporting goods - Diversified Products Corp.
AEROBICGLIDE - Exercising equipment - Icon Health & Fitness, Inc.
AEROBICGLIDE PLUS - Exercising equipment - Icon Health & Fitness, Inc.
AEROBICOUNTRY - Recording label - Aerobicountry Records, Inc.
AEROBICS - Floor coverings–carpet and rugs - Porter Carpet Mills Inc.
AEROBICYCLES - Exercising equipment - Universal Gym Equipment, Inc.
AEROBID - Pharmaceutical preparations - Forest Pharmaceuticals Inc.
AEROBISKATE - Skates–roller - Sure Grip International Inc.
AEROBIX - Watches - Timex Corp.
AEROBLADE - Skates–roller - Rollerblade, Inc.
AEROBOX - Shirts - Aerobox Athletic Enterprises, Inc.
AEROBOXER - Sporting goods - Century Martial Art Supply, Inc.
AEROBRAKE - Auxiliary braking systems - American Technology & Development Corp.
AEROCAB - Motor vehicle parts and accessories - Kenworth Truck Co.
AEROCAINE - Pharmaceutical preparations - Graham-Field Inc.
AEROCARD - Greeting cards - Aerobal Corp.
AEROCARRIER - Bicycles ☆ - National Cycle Inc.
AEROCELL - Deodorizers - Graham-Field Inc.
AEROCEUTICALS - Deodorizers - Graham-Field Inc.
AEROCHAMBER - Pharmaceutical preparations - Forest Pharmaceuticals Inc.
AEROCHROME - Film - Eastman Kodak Co.
AEROCIDE - Pharmaceutical preparations - Graham-Field Inc.

☆ = Now out of production

AEROCOL - Pharmaceutical preparations ☆ - Graham-Field Inc.

AEROCOLOR - Film - Eastman Kodak Co.

AEROCON - Automotive parts - American Technology & Development Corp.

AEROCOS - Hair care products ☆ - Gem Inc.

AEROCOVER - Truck beds - Warn Industries, Inc.

AEROCRUISER - Stroller - Tri Industries, Inc.

AEROCYCLE - Exercising equipment - Maxxim Medical Inc.

AERODANCER - Footwear - Bata Shoe Co. Inc.

AERODINE - Deodorizers ☆ - Graham-Field Inc.

AERODYNAMIC COMPETITIVE EDGE - Bicycles - Wheelsmith Fabrications Inc.

AERODYNAMICS - Exercise apparel - Weekend Exercise Co., Inc.

AERODYNE - Athletic footwear - Converse Inc.

AERODYNE RESEARCH - Electronic equipment - Aerodyne Research, Inc.

AEROEDGE - Wheelchairs - Fortress Inc.

AEROEXCHANGE - Computer software - Aerospace Development, Inc.

AEROFAST - Bicycles - Emory Manufacturing Co.

AEROFECT - Deodorizers ☆ - Graham-Field Inc.

AEROFIL - Food products - Beatrice Cheese Inc.

AEROFIL - Food products - Rich Products Corp.

AEROFIRE - Golfing equipment - Outdoor Technologies Group

AEROFIRE - Tires - Bridgestone/Firestone, Inc.

AEROFIXX - Hair care products - Amethyst Investment Group, Inc.

AEROFLASH - Toys–automobiles - Mattel, Inc.

AEROFLASH SIGNAL - Lighting equipment–aircraft - Mellish & Murray Co., Inc.

AEROFLATE - Health care products ☆ - Marquest Medical Products Inc.

AEROFLEX - Golfing equipment - Outdoor Technologies Group

AEROFLEX - Insulating materials - Owens Corning

AEROFLIGHT - Bicycle parts and accessories - Schwinn Cycling & Fitness Inc.

AEROFLOAT - Fishing tackle ☆ - Gladding Braided Products Inc.

AEROFLOW - Valves - Watts Investment Co.

AEROFLOW ULTRA - Lighting fixtures - Guth Lighting

AEROFLY - Fishing lures - Renny Mason Co.

AEROFOIL - Ventilation equipment - Triangle Metal and Manufacturing Inc.

AEROFREEZE - Deodorizers - Graham-Field Inc.

AEROFUSE - Health care products ☆ - Marquest Medical Products Inc.

AEROGEL - Hairstyling product - Tri-Institute of Trichology

AEROGEL - Toys - Applied Elastomerics, Inc.

AEROGLAS - Antennas - Alliance Telecommunications Corp.

AEROGLAS RM - Filters–air - AIFCO Co.

AEROGLOVE - Exercising equipment - Aerobic Glove, Inc.

AEROGRAPHIC - Film - Eastman Kodak Co.

AEROGRAPHICS - Posters - Kersten Bros. Studios

AEROHALOR - Pharmaceutical preparations ☆ - Abbott Laboratories

AEROHEAD AEROCAP - Helmets–athletic ☆ - Giro Sport Design

AEROHEAD SHARKSKIN - Helmets–athletic ☆ - Giro Sport Design

AEROHEAD WILDTHING - Helmets–athletic ☆ - Giro Sport Design

AEROHIDE - Paints ☆ - PPG Industries, Inc.

AEROHOT - Trays–warming - Duke Manufacturing Co.

AEROKROIL - Oils–lubricating - Kano Laboratories Inc.

AEROLAK - Hair care products - Demert & Dougherty, Inc.

AEROLATE - Pharmaceutical preparations - Fleming & Co.

AEROLIGHT - Bicycles - Columbia Manufacturing Inc.

A AEROLIGHT - Electric lighting equipment - Londavia Inc.

AEROLITE - Bicycles - North American Cycles

AEROLITE - Binoculars ☆ - Swift Instruments, Inc.

AEROLITE - Glass–safety - PPG Industries, Inc.

AEROLITE - Medical apparatus - Mentor O & O Inc.

AEROLITE - Motor vehicles–motor homes ☆ - Thor Industries West

AEROLITE - Recording label - Vandor Motion Pictures, Phonorecords & Music Publishing Group

AEROLOFT - Golfing equipment - Sandy Seeman

AEROLONE COMPOUND - Pharmaceutical preparations - Eli Lilly and Co.

AEROLUX - Window shades - Aeroshade Inc.

AEROLUX VUDOR - Window coverings - Aeroshade Inc.

AEROMARINE - Varnishes ☆ - Thibaut & Walker Co. Inc.

AEROMAT - Insulating materials - Owens Corning

AEROMAT - Mattresses - Integrated Therapy Products, Inc.

AEROMATE - Health care products - Muscle Dynamics USA

AEROMATIC OVEN - Pressure cookers - Aroma Manufacturing Co. Inc.

AEROMAX - Electrical equipment - Aerovox Inc.

AEROMAX - Medical apparatus - Medical Industries America, Inc.

AEROMAX 120 - Motor vehicles–semi-trucks - Ford Motor Co.

AEROMET - Guns ☆ - Remington Arms Co., Inc.

AEROMETER - Sporting goods - Bollinger Industries

AEROMIKE - Microphones - J & M Corp.

AEROMILL - Sporting goods - Bollinger Industries

AEROMILLE - Crocheted and knitted items ☆ - Roosevelt Mills Inc.

AEROMIX - Water purification systems - Aeromix Systems, Inc.

AEROMOUSSE - Hair care products - Artec Systems Group, Inc.

AERON - Chairs–plastic - Herman Miller, Inc.

AERONAUT - Watches - Bulova Corp.

AERONEB ONE - Home-health-care products - Ivex Corp.

AEROPENNE - Pens - Salis International, Inc.

AEROPOSTALE - Apparel and accessories - R.H. Macy & Co.

AEROPREP - Deodorizers - Graham-Field Inc.

AEROPRO - Motor vehicle parts and accessories ☆ - National Cycle Inc.

AEROPURE - Cleaning preparations–household ☆ - Graham-Field Inc.

AEROQUATIC - Boats–kayaks - Noah Corp.

AEROS - Bicycles - Klein Bicycle Corp.

AEROS - Health care products - Camp, Inc.

AEROS - Seats–automobile - Cramer Inc.

AEROSCREEN - Motorcycles ☆ - National Cycle Inc.

AEROSEB-DEX - Pharmaceutical preparations - Allergan, Inc.

AEROSEB-HC - Pharmaceutical preparations - Allergan, Inc.

AEROSHADE - Automotive parts and accessories - Auto Ventshade Co.

AEROSHADE - Window shades - Aeroshade Inc.

AEROSHELL - Lubricating oils - Shell Oil Co.

AEROSHIELDS - Vehicle ground effects - Automotive Restyling Products, Inc.

AEROSMITH - Knives–pocket - Svengali Merchandising Inc.

AEROSMITH - Tools - Danair, Inc.

AEROSOFT - Hair care products - Image Laboratories, Inc.

AEROSOL ONE + TWO - Health care products ☆ - Medical Industries America, Inc.

AEROSOL TWO - Health care products - Medical Industries America, Inc.

AEROSOLV - First aid kits ☆ - Graham-Field Inc.

AEROSOLV - Tools–hand-operated - Katec

AEROSOMES - Pharmaceutical preparations - Imarx Pharmaceutical Corp.

AEROSONIC - Ultrasonic scanning devices ☆ - Sunrise Medical (Respiratory Products Division)

AEROSPA - Lotions - Main Marketing, Inc.

AEROSPACE - Aircraft parts - Birken Manufacturing Co.

AEROSPACE - Cases–plastic - Andiamo Inc.

AEROSPACE - Ships–cargo vessels - Seaco Inc.

AEROSPELL - Computer software - American Institute of Aeronautics and Astronautics

AEROSPORIN - Antibiotics ☆ - Burroughs Wellcome Co.

AEROSPORT - Bicycles ☆ - National Cycle Inc.

AEROSPORT - Footwear - Gator Industries, Inc.

AEROSPRAY - Laboratory apparatus - Wescor, Inc.

AEROSPRAY - Paints - Valspar Corp.

AEROSTAR - Bicycles - Schwinn Cycling & Fitness Inc.

AEROSTAR - Golfing equipment - Outdoor Technologies Group

AEROSTAR - Motor vehicles–vans - Ford Motor Co.

AEROSTAR - Trailers–travel - Starcraft Corp.

AEROSTAT - Pharmaceutical preparations - Afasco

AEROSTAT - Static eliminator - Simco

AEROSTICH - Bags–duffel - Aero Design and Manufacturing Co. Inc.

AEROTECH - Health care products - Cadema Medical Products

AEROTECH - Motor vehicles–trucks - Reading Body Works, Inc.

AEROTECH - Transducers ☆ - Krautkramer-Branson Inc.

AEROTEK - Hockey equipment - Mylec, Inc.

AEROTEL - Communications equipment - Technical Advantage, Inc.

AEROTEMP - Heaters–swimming pool - R & D Technologies

AEROTHERM - First aid kits ☆ - Graham-Field Inc.

AEROTREK - Computer software ☆ - Estes Industries

AEROTYPE - Footwear–athletic ☆ - Prince Sports Group, Inc.

AEROWAVE - Welding equipment - Miller Electric Manufacturing Co.

AEROWAX - Furniture polish and wax - Boyle-Midway

AEROWEDGE - Furniture - HWE Inc.

AEROWING - Awnings - Coleman Co., Inc.

AEROXON - Fly sprays - Roxide International, Inc.

AEROZOIN - Health care products ☆ - Graham-Field Inc.

AERPEL - Imitation leather ☆ - Ivy International Ltd.

AERS - Lighting fixtures - Holophane Corp.

AERVOE - Paints - Aervoe-Pacific Co. Inc.

AES - American Companies, Inc.

AES INTELLINET - Transceivers - AES Corp.

AESCO - Signs ☆ - American Electronic Sign Co.

AESCULAFORCE - Health care products - Bioforce of America Ltd.

AESOP'S FABLE - Wines - Post Winery Inc.

AESOP'S FABLES - Computer software - Unicorn Software
AESTELANCE - Hair care products - Inestra, Inc.
AESTHETI-COAT - Paints ☆ - Flood Co.
AESTHETIC BABIES - Dolls - Donna Jean Piper
AESTHETICARE SKIN REJUVENATION SYSTEME - Skin care products - Aestheticare Medical Corp.
AET - Window coverings ☆ - Courtaulds Performance Plus
AETEC - Rifles - Simmons Outdoor Corp.
AETERNUM - Housewares - Miracle Exclusives Inc.
AETNA - Food products - Chas. F. Cates & Sons Inc.
AETNA - Footwear - Jaclyn, Inc.
AETNA - Paints ☆ - Adelphi Coatings Co.
AETNA - Plumbing fixtures–metal - Hooper Industries Inc.
AETNA - Rope - Samson Cordage Works
AETNA - Shirts - Aetna Shirt Corp.
AEUROFIAMMA - Coffee makers–electric - G.O. Aeurofiamma, Inc.
AEXCEL - Adhesives and sealants - Aexcel Corp.
AF - Cosmetics - Research Council of Make-Up Artists Inc.
AF - Flowers–artificial - PPG Industries, Inc.
AF - Jackets - Tighe Industries Inc.
AF - Jewelry - Tafco Inc.
AF - Nozzles - Accu-Flow Tech, Inc.
AF - Nuts and bolts - Accurate Threaded Fasteners, Inc.
AF - Nuts and bolts - Aerotech Fasteners, Inc.
AF - Plastics film - Autofeeds, Inc.
AF - Stain removers ☆ - H. Behlen & Bro. Inc.
AF-250E - Electrical equipment - General Electric Co.
AF-300 - Electrical equipment - General Electric Co.
AF-400 - Electrical equipment - General Electric Co.
AF ARTURO FILLIPO - Frames–eyeglass - Vernon Optical Co. Inc.
AF TELE - Cameras ☆ - Minolta Corp.
AFA - Fertilizers - AFA Products, Inc.
AFA - Jewelry - Air Force Academy Athletic Association
AFAS-COLD - Health care products - Afasco
AFB - Bells - AFB Manufacturing & Sales Corp.
AFC - Filters–industrial - F.B. Leopold Co. Inc.
A.F.C. - Golfing equipment - Golf International, Inc.
AFC ADVANCED FIBRE COMMUNICATIONS - Communications equipment - Advanced Fibre Communications
A.F.C. BLINKY - Toys - Continuity Graphic Associates, Inc.
AFC FOOTBALL - Toys ☆ - Tyco Toys
AFCO - Audio equipment - Afco Electronics
AFCO - Copper products - Afco Products Inc.
AFCO - Flags - Eagle Regalia Co. Inc.
AFCO - Housewares - Camp Chef
AFELTRA - Macaroni - Vincent Russo
A.F.F. - Pharmaceutical preparations - Lyphomed Inc.
AFFABLE ANIMALS - Toys–stuffed - Kay Mathews Designs
AFFAIR - Flatware - Yamazaki Tableware Inc.
AFFAIR - Whipped topping–powdered - Presto Food Products, Inc.
AFFAIR GOLD ACCENT - Flatware - Yamazaki Tableware Inc.
L'AFFAIRE - Colognes - Regency Cosmetics Inc.
AFFAIRS - Confections - Affairs Inc.
AFFAIRS OF THE HEART - Greeting cards - Fairchild Art
AFFECTION - Christmas tree ornaments - Cracker Box Inc.
AFFECTION - Floor coverings–carpet and rugs ☆ - Columbus Mills, Inc.
AFFECTION - Glassware–household - Owens-Illinois Inc. (Libbey Div.)
AFFECTION - Sponges - Affection Co.
AFFECTIONATELY YOURS - Candy - Ethel M. Chocolates, Inc.
AFFILIATE - Computer software - Uni-Mail List Corp.
AFFILIATE VENTURE PUBLISHING - Computer software - Microleague Multimedia, Inc.
AFFILIATED - Food products - Blum & Bergeron Inc.
AFFINE - Skin care products - Mastey De Paris
AFFINITI - Lubricants - Amsted Industries Inc.
AFFINITI - Pens - Accutec Inc.
AFFINITROL - Ventilation equipment - Alcan Aluminum Corp. Alcan Building Products Div.
AFFINITY - Fada Industries Inc.
AFFINITY - Brassieres (Bras) - Coloplast Corp.
AFFINITY - Chairs–wood - Globe Business Furniture, Inc.
AFFINITY - Clocks - General Time Corp. (Westclox/Seth Thomas Div.)
AFFINITY - Computer hardware - IPC Technologies, Inc.
AFFINITY - Electronics equipment - Omega Organization International (Laser Concepts Div.)
AFFINITY - Fabrics - Pioneer-Leimel Fabrics, Inc.

AFFINITY - Flatware - Reed and Barton Corp.
AFFINITY - Flatware ☆ - Yamazaki Tableware Inc.
AFFINITY - Floor coverings - Congoleum Corp.
AFFINITY - Floor coverings–carpet and rugs - Hollytex Carpet Mills Inc.
AFFINITY - Frames–eyeglass - Kenmark Optical Co.
AFFINITY - Shampoos - Johnson & Johnson
AFFINITY - Tires - Bridgestone/Firestone, Inc.
AFFINITY - Wallpaper - Bob Mitchell Designs
AFFINITY BY COUNTRY COACH - Motor vehicles–buses - Country Coach, Inc.
AFFINITY COLLECTION - Medical apparatus - Coloplast Corp.
AFFINITY GOLD ACCENT - Flatware ☆ - Yamazaki Tableware Inc.
AFFIRM - Chemical preparations - MicroProbe Corp.
AFFIRM - Floor coverings–carpet and rugs - J and J Industries Inc.
AFFIRM - Sanitary napkins - Kmart Properties, Inc.
AFFIRMATION - Floor coverings–carpet and rugs - Lees Carpets
AFFIRMATION STATION, THE - Clocks - Now & Zen, Inc.
AFFIRMATION TREASURES - Jewelry - Wave to Grandma, Inc.
AFFIRMATIVE - Cosmetics - Jheri Redding Products Inc.
AFFIRMED - Floor coverings–carpet and rugs - Philadelphia Carpets
AFFIX - Seats–automobile - Cramer Inc.
AFFLIGEM - Beverages–malt - Victor Sales & Marketing
AFFLUENCE - Floor coverings–carpet and rugs - V & B Carpet
AFFLUENCE - Floor coverings–carpet and rugs ☆ - Regal Rugs Inc.
AFFLUENT - Floor coverings–carpet and rugs ☆ - Columbus Mills, Inc.
AFFOLDABLE - Display cases–wood - Stellar Holdings, Inc.
AFFORDABLE - Wallpaper - Norwall Wallcoverings
AFFORDABLE COLLECTION - Jewelry–precious - United Services Automobile Association
AFFORDABLE LUXURY IN EYEWEAR - Eyeglass frames and cases - Atlantic Optical Co., Inc.
AFFORDABLE PORTABLE, THE - Heaters–space - Desa International, Inc.
AFFORDABLE PORTABLES - Bags–cosmetic - Paris Presents Ltd.
AFFORDABLE TREASURE, THE - Jewelry - Mallorca Pearls Ltd., Inc.
AFFORDABLES - Chairs–upholstered - Joyce International Inc.
AFFY TAPPLE - Snack foods - Affy Tapple Inc.
AFGHAN MAKER, THE - Hobby kits ☆ - Latham Studios
AFI - Computer software - Anacomp Inc.
AFI - Marine horns - American Foreign Industries
AFI - Meat products - Agri-Products, Inc.
AFICIONADO - Games - Ricorso
AFIX - Computer hardware - Phoenix Group, Inc.
AFJC - Jewelry - Ambras Fine Jewelry Corp.
AFKA - Furniture - Krueger International, Inc.
AFKO - Ear oil - American Pharmaceutical Co.
AFKO-CILLIN - Prescription drug - American Pharmaceutical Co.
AFKO-LUBE - Pharmaceutical - American Pharmaceutical Co.
AFM - Asphalt - Protecto Wrap Co.
AFM FABTEK - Metal finishing equipment - AFM (USA), Inc.
AFN - Computer peripheral equipment - Wellfleet Communications, Inc.
AFN - Fabrics - Veratec
AFO - Medical equipment - Langer Biomechanics Group, Inc.
AFRAFYL - Hair care products - Organifyl Laboratories
AFRC - Apparel–athletic - Raven Industries Inc.
AFRI-Q - Sauces - Country Cottage Savories Inc.
AFRICA - Tableware–earthenware - Anacapa Corp.
AFRICA COLLECTION, THE - Wines - Nicolass P. J. Steyn
AFRICA SAFARI SCENERY - Computer software - Abacus Software, Inc.
AFRICA SELECTION - Wines ☆ - HDT Importers Inc.
AFRICA TRAIL - Computer software - Minnesota Educational Computing Corp.
AFRICA TRAIL - Computer software - Softkey International Inc.
AFRICAN - Pencils ☆ - Faber-Castell Corp.
AFRICAN AMERICAN HERITAGE CHECK SERIES - Checkbooks - Marshall Johnson Agency
AFRICAN AMERICAN INVENTORS - T-shirts–men's - Graphics by Sellers
AFRICAN AMERICANS: VOICES OF TRIUMPH - Publisher's imprints - Time Life Inc.
AFRICAN BEAUTY - Hair care products - Goody Products, Inc.
AFRICAN EYE INC. COLLECTION - Apparel and accessories - African Eye, Inc.
AFRICAN FORMULA - Toiletries - Jacob Aini
AFRICAN GOLD - Cosmetics - Posner Laboratories Inc.
AFRICAN HAIR CARE - Hair care products - B & S Beauty Products, Inc.
AFRICAN HONEYWOOD - Wood products ☆ - Georgia-Pacific Corp.
AFRICAN KENTE - Toys - Playskool, Inc.
AFRICAN KINGS AND QUEENS - Cosmetics - Terrance Michael Davie

☆ = Now out of production

AFRICAN MANICURE - Nail care products ✩ - Nina International, Inc.
AFRICAN MOOD - Floor coverings ✩ - Congoleum Corp.
AFRICAN NATURAL - Hair care products - B and J Sales & Marketing Inc.
AFRICAN ORIGINALS - Games ✩ - Webway, Inc.
AFRICAN PRIDE - Cosmetics - A.P. Products Ltd.
AFRICAN PRIDE - Dolls - Shark Products Inc.
AFRICAN QUEEN - W. Atlee Burpee and Co.
AFRICAN ROYALE - Hair care products - Bronner Bros. Manufacturing Co., Inc.
AFRICAN SUNSHINE - Beverages–carbonated - Sparkle Group Inc.
AFRICAN SURF - Seafood products–fresh or frozen - Trans World Seafood Inc.
AFRICAN VILLAGE, THE - Apparel and accessories - P.A.C. Imports Inc.
AFRICAN VITAL - See BLACKWATER EXTRACT
AFRICAN WAVE - Hair care products - W. Henry Lee
AFRICANA - Giftware - Africana Colors Inc.
AFRICANA - Giftware - Enesco Corp.
AFRICANA - Wallpaper - Carlton-Metro Wallcoverings
AFRICARE - Skin care products - Cococare Products Inc.
AFRICE - Bedding–linen - Dan River Inc.
AFRICO - Cosmetics - Nino Originals
AFRICORD - Sporting goods ✩ - Babolat
AFRIKA - Floor coverings–carpet and rugs - Regal Rugs Inc.
AFRIKA KORPS - Games - Avalon Hill Game Co.
AFRIKAN LOVE FRAGRANCES UNLIMITED THE WORLD'S BEST NO-BURN INCENSE - Incense - Kofi Khemet
AFRIN - Cold remedies - Schering-Plough Healthcare Products
AFRIN - Pharmaceutical preparations - Schering Corp.
AFRINOL - Cold remedies - Schering-Plough Healthcare Products
AFRINOPOLY - Games - Eugene D. Alexander
AFRIQUE - Wallpaper - Capital Carousel Inc.
AFRO PERCUSSION - Musical drums - Pearl Corp.
AFRO PIK N LIFT - Hair care products - Capitol Novelty Co.
AFRO SHAVE - Shaving preparations ✩ - Johnson Products Co., Inc.
AFRO SHEER - Hosiery - TGC Inc.
AFROCENTRIC - Paper - Lewis Black
AFROROMAN - Computer software - Payne Loving Trust
AFROSHEEN - Hair care products - Johnson Products Co., Inc.
AFROSOUND - Percussion instruments - Tropical Music and Pro Audio
AFS - Hearing aids - Otosonic Corp.
AFS - Jewelry - A. Fishman & Son Jewelry Inc.
AFS MASTER SYSTEM - Computer software - American Financial Systems, Inc.
AFSHAM - Hair care products - Stephan Co.
AFSI - Seafood - American Fish & Seafood Inc.
AFSXPRESS - Computer software - Automated Financial Systems, Inc.
AFSXPRESS SOFTWARE - Computer software - Automated Financial Systems, Inc.
AFT - Boats–motor ✩ - Cruisers
AFT - Jewelry - American Foreign Trade Inc.
AFT CABIN - Boats–motor - Carver Boat Corp.
AFTA - Cleaning preparations - Guardsman Products, Inc.
AFTA SHAVE - Shaving preparations - Mennen Co.
AFTAB - Rice - Basmati Rice Imports Inc.
AFTADIN - Oral antiseptic-anesthetic - Universal Laboratories, Inc.
AFTALENE - Cleaning preparations - Guardsman Products, Inc.
AFTATE - Pharmaceutical preparations - Schering-Plough Healthcare Products
AFTER - Pet products ✩ - Roussel-Uclaf Corp.
AFTER 9 - Recording label - Touchwood Records LLC
AFTER 35 - Skin care products ✩ - Noxell Corp.
AFTER 40 - Vitamins and nutritional supplements - Fleetwood Co.
AFTER ALL IT TAKES A BAKER - Shortening - Bunge Foods Corp.
AFTER BALM - Skin care products - Alvin Last Inc.
AFTER BATH - Pet products - Professional Pet Products
AFTER BITE - Health care products - Tender Corp.
AFTER DARK - Computer software - Berkeley Systems, Inc.
AFTER DARK - Dresses–women's - Evening Visions Apparel, Lt'd.
AFTER DARK - Reflectors–vehicular - Fastech Corp.
AFTER DARK COMPATIBLE - Computer software - Berkeley Systems, Inc.
AFTER DEATH - Sauces - Gardner Resources, Inc.
AFTER DINNER - Candy - Richardson Brands
AFTER DINNER MINT - Teas–herbal - Traditional Medicinals, Inc.
AFTER DINNER MINTS - Cigarettes ✩ - Nat Sherman, Inc.
AFTER EFFECTS - Publisher's imprints - Aldus Corp.
AFTER-FIRE - Deodorizers - Surco Products Inc.
AFTER FIVE - Glassware–household ✩ - Crisa Corp.

AFTER GLO - Automotive parts and accessories - Barcolene Inc.
AFTER GLOVE - Skin care products - Sharpe Lines, Inc.
AFTER GLOW CHANGE OF LIFE ESSENTIALS - Dietary supplement - Heart Foods Co., Inc.
AFTER GOLF - Apparel - David Geoffrey & Associates
AFTER GYM PAK - Deodorants–personal - Bertsherm Products Inc.
AFTER HOURS - Apparel and accessories - Genesco Inc.
AFTER HOURS - Christmas tree ornaments - Cracker Box Inc.
AFTER HOURS - Recording label - Ichiban Records, Inc.
AFTER HOURS - Tobacco products ✩ - Lane Ltd.
AFTER-PUMPS - Infant product - HT Marketing, Inc.
AFTER RUN - Cleaning preparations - Pacer Technology
AFTER SHOCK - Bowling balls - Columbia Industries, Inc.
AFTER SHOCK - Game machines - Lazer-Tron Corp.
AFTER SHOCK - Liqueurs - Jim Beam Brands Co.
AFTER SHOCK - Vitamins and nutritional supplements - Weider Nutrition Group, Inc.
AFTER SHOT - Cleaning preparations - Nomax, Inc.
AFTER SIX - Furniture ✩ - Singer Furniture Co.
AFTER SIX - Tuxedos ✩ - After Six Inc.
AFTER SUN LOTION - Suntan lotions - Sothys USA Inc.
AFTER SUN SILK - Nail care products - Revlon Consumer Products Corp.
AFTER SUN TAN EXTENDER - Suntan lotions - John Paul Mitchell Systems
AFTER SWIM - Skin care products - Ledimar Inc.
AFTER TAN - Skin care products - Aloe Creme Laboratories
AFTER TENS - Health care products - Pharmaceutical Innovations
AFTER THE FALL - Fruit drinks–bottled or canned - After the Fall Products Inc.
AFTER THE GAME - Footwear ✩ - E.S. Originals, Inc.
AFTER THOUGHTS - Handbags - F.W. Woolworth Co.
AFTERBUMER - Vitamins and nutritional supplements - Vitamin Research Products Inc.
AFTERBURNER - Amplifiers - Afterburner Industries
AFTERBURNER - Sporting goods ✩ - Wellington Leisure Products, Inc.
AFTERBURNER P.W.C. - Sporting goods ✩ - Wellington Leisure Products, Inc.
AFTERCARE - Computer software - Micromedex, Inc.
AFTERGLOW - Christmas tree ornaments - Cracker Box Inc.
AFTERGLOW - Wallpaper ✩ - Artisan Handprints Inc.
AFTERIMAGE - Recording label - Strategic Records
AFTERLIFE - Computer software - Lucasarts Entertainment Co.
AFTERLOCK - Adhesives and sealants - Permatex Industrial Corp.
AFTERNOON DELIGHT - Candy - Horizon-West Marketing Corp.
AFTERNOON DELIGHT - Teas ✩ - Nature's Way Products, Inc.
AFTERNOON TEA - Dolls ✩ - Effanbee Doll Corp.
AFTERNOON TEA - Wallpaper - Seabrook Wallcoverings, Inc.
AFTERPERM - Hair care products - Modafini Inc.
AFTERPOOL - Hair care products - Niki Bryan Companies Inc.
AFTERSCHOOL - Recording label - Afterschool Publishing Co.
AFTERSUN - Skin care products - Chasalco Inc.
AFTERTHOUGHT - Dictating machines - Dictaphone Corp.
AFTEX-90 - Floor coverings - American Floor Products Co. Inc.
AFTHAID - Mouthwashes ✩ - Campbell Laboratories Inc.
AFTON - Dinnerware–glass ✩ - Royal China & Porcelain Companies Inc.
AFTON MOUNTAIN VINEYARDS - Wines - Afton Mountain Vineyards
AFTR - Publisher's imprints - Lazer-Tron Corp.
AFTROL - Electrical equipment - General Electric Co.
AFUCHE/CABASA - Drums–musical instruments - LP Music Group
AFV - Sporting goods - Babolat
AFV STRATEGIST - Computer software - Runzheimer International Ltd.
AG - Drill bits - Cooper Industries, Inc.
AG - Jewelry - Abad Gold, Inc.
AG - Jewelry - August Gem Corp.
AG - Jewelry - Anthony Gerard
AG - Jewelry - Arthur Groom & Co.
AG - Tape–adhesive - Applied Graphics Corp.
AG ALUMNI SEED - Flowers, plants, and seeds - AG Alumni Seed Improvement Association, Inc.
AG AUBURN GEAR - Machine parts - Auburn Gear, Inc.
AG-BAG SQUARE BALE BAGGER - Machinery - Ag-Bag International Limited
AG BOARD DOW STYROFOAM - Insulating materials–foam - Dow Chemical Co.
AG-CIDAL - Pharmaceutical preparations - Natrition, Inc.
AG-CRETE - Concrete–ready-mix - Cemstone Products Co.
AG-DERMAL - Pharmaceutical preparations - Natrition, Inc.
AG INTERNATIONAL - Sporting goods - Guterman International Inc.
AG-TUFF - Containers - Southwest Agri-Plastics, Inc.

✩ = Now out of production

AG300 - Computer hardware - Accelgraphics Inc.
AG500 - Computer hardware - Accelgraphics Inc.
AGA - Floor coverings - AGA Corp.
AGA - Food products - Mira International Foods Inc.
AGA JOHN - Floor coverings–carpet and rugs - Aga John Oriental Rugs
AGAFAR - Medical apparatus - Infection Control Products, Inc.
AGAIN - Fabricated metal products - Group Three, Inc.
AGAIN & AGAIN - Batteries - Saft America Inc.
AGAINST ALL ODDS - Apparel and accessories - Against All Odds Inc.
AGAINST GRAVITEE - Apparel–women's - Against Gravity Apparel, Inc.
AGAINST THE GRAIN - Frames–picture - Mathias Enterprises Inc.
AGAPE - Dolls - Agape Toys, Inc.
AGAPE - Shoes - Tree Import/Export, Corp.
AGAPI - Slacks–men's - H.R. Kaminsky & Sons Inc.
AGAPO - Apparel and accessories - Sid International Inc.
AGAR - Food products - Patrick Cudahy Inc.
AGAR-GRAN - Vitamins and nutritional supplements - Freeda Vitamins Inc.
AGARIC - Recording label - Jazz Composer's Orchestra Association Inc.
AGARO - Doughnut and danish pastry glaze - American Flavor & Fragrance Corp.
AGASSIZ - Watches ☆ - Longines-Wittnauer Watch Co.
AGAST - Floor coverings–carpet and rugs - V & B Carpet
AGATE - Dinnerware - Bennington Potters
AGATE - Flatware ☆ - Denby USA Limited
AGATE - Floor coverings–carpet and rugs - Regal Rugs Inc.
AGATEEN - Lacquers - Agate Lacquer Manufacturing Co. Inc.
AGATEEN ACQUATIC - Lacquers - Agate Lacquer Manufacturing Co. Inc.
AGATES THE ROCK GROUP - Computer software - Multiwave Innovation, Inc.
AGATHA - Bedding–linen - Dan River Inc.
AGATHA - Dolls - Uneeda Doll Co., Inc.
AGAVE 4 X 4 - Sandals - Playazul International Inc.
AGAVE LOCO TEQUILA - Liquors - Jim Beam Brands Co.
AGAVE SISALANA GENUINUS - Twine - Universal Cooperative Inc.
AGAWAM - Paper–bond ☆ - Fox River Paper Co.
AGAWAM - Thread - Threads USA Div.
AGB - Fabrics - Tetko Inc.
AGBIN - Containers - Perstorp Xytec Inc.
AGC - Games - Metal Art of California, Inc.
AGC CONNECT! - Computer software - Texas Building Branch Associated General Contractors of America, Inc.
AGCO - Agricultural machinery - Agco Corp.
A.G.E. - Apparel and accessories - A.G.E.
AGE - Hardware ☆ - M.A.G. Engineering & Manufacturing Co. Inc.
AGE DEFYING COMPLEX - Skin care products - Chesebrough-Pond's USA Co.
AGE DEFYING MAKEUP - Skin care products - Revlon Consumer Products Corp.
AGE ERASER - Skin care products - Clientele, Inc.
AGE-ETERNAL - Skin care products - Rainco Co. Inc.
AGE ETERNAL - Vitamins and nutritional supplements ☆ - Nutri-West
AGE IN REVERSE - Exercising equipment - Yoga World, Inc.
AGE-LESS - Skin care products - Revlon Consumer Products Corp.
AGE-LESS FORMULA 1 - Vitamins and nutritional supplements ☆ - Nutri-West
AGE MANAGEMENT - Skin care products - European Skin & Haircare
AGE MANAGEMENT SERUM - Skin care products ☆ - La Prairie Inc.
AGE OF ADVENTURE - Computer software ☆ - Electronic Arts Inc.
AGE OF AQUARIUS - Recording label - American Music Co.
AGE OF ELEGANCE - Dolls ☆ - Effanbee Doll Corp.
AGE OF ELEGANCE - Wallpaper ☆ - Winfield Design Associates, Inc.
AGE OF EMPIRES - Computer peripheral equipment - Microsoft Corp.
AGE OF INFORMOTION - Computer software - Digital Communications Associates, Inc.
AGE OF INNOCENCE - Dolls ☆ - Effanbee Doll Corp.
AGE RECOVERY - Skin care products - Matrix Essentials, Inc.
AGE RELIEF - Skin care products - ACI, Inc.
AGE SHIELD - Cosmetics - Max Factor & Co.
AGE TESTER - Novelty items - Adams Apple Distributing L.P.
AGE WARS ALPHA COMPLEX - Skin care products ☆ - Victoria Vogue, Inc.
AGE-ZONE - Skin care products - Charles of the Ritz Group Ltd.
AGE ZONE - Skin care products - Yves St. Laurent Parfum Corp.
AGEAN AVANTI - Floor coverings–carpet and rugs - Customweave Carpets Inc.
AGED - Colognes - Brandy Harvest
AGELESS - Floor coverings–carpet and rugs - Coronet Carpets Inc.
AGELESS BEAUTY - Health care products - Biotec Foods
AGELESS BEAUTY - Skin care products - Arizona Natural Resources

AGELESS BODY, TIMELESS MIND - Skin care products - Quantum Publications, Inc.
AGENA - Key rings - Agena Manufacturing Corp.
AGENA - Musical instruments ☆ - Deg Music Products Inc.
AGENCY COLLECTION, THE - Computer storage devices–optical - Compuvision Development Services, Inc.
AGENCYLINK - Computer software - Paragon Interface, Inc.
AGENDA - Briefcases - Heritage Springfield Inc.
AGENDA - Calendars - North Hollywood Manufacturing Co.
AGENDA - Floor coverings–carpet and rugs - Whitecrest Carpet Mills
AGENDA - Floor coverings–carpet and rugs ☆ - Walter Carpet Mills
AGENDA - Hair care products - Graf Skin Care, Inc.
AGENDA - Skin care products ☆ - Avon Products, Inc.
AGENDA MASTER - Computer software - SourceView Software International
AGENOR - Bathtubs–enameled - Kallista Inc.
AGENT - Revolvers ☆ - Colt's Manufacturing Co. Inc.
AGENT 13 - Publisher's imprints ☆ - Tsr, Inc.
AGENT TRAINER - Computer software - Edify Corp.
AGENT USA - Computer software - Scholastic Software Inc.
AGENT95 - Computer software - Connectix Corp.
AGENTSCRIPT - Computer software - I-Kinetics, Inc.
AGEPROOF - Drafting materials - Dietzgen Corp.
AGERA - Cosmetics - Biosyn, Inc.
AGERA PRO - Skin care products - Biosyn, Inc.
AGES & STAGES - Toys - Playskool, Inc.
AGEWARS - Cleaning preparations–household - Survival Corp.
AGEWELL - Recording label - Agewell Communications Ltd.
AGFA - Photographic equipment - Miles Inc. (Agfa Div.)
AGFA AUTOMATIC 66 - Cameras ☆ - Miles Inc. (Agfa Div.)
AGFA DIAMATOR - Projectors–photographic ☆ - Miles Inc. (Agfa Div.)
AGFA-GEVAERT - Photographic equipment - Miles Inc. (Agfa Div.)
AGFA ISOPAN - Film ☆ - Miles Inc. (Agfa Div.)
AGFA MICROFLEX - Cameras–motion picture ☆ - Miles Inc. (Agfa Div.)
AGFA OPTIMA - Cameras ☆ - Miles Inc. (Agfa Div.)
AGFA REFLEX - Cameras ☆ - Miles Inc. (Agfa Div.)
AGFA SILETTE - Cameras ☆ - Miles Inc. (Agfa Div.)
AGFACHROME - Film - Miles Inc. (Agfa Div.)
AGFACOLOR - Film - Miles Inc. (Agfa Div.)
AGFALEX - Cameras ☆ - Miles Inc. (Agfa Div.)
AGFAMATIC 100 SENSOR - Cameras ☆ - Miles Inc. (Agfa Div.)
AGFAPAN RAPID - Film ☆ - Miles Inc. (Agfa Div.)
AGFAST - Fasteners - Nylon Agtex Corp.
AGGIE ICE CREAM - Ice cream - Utah State University
AGGLOSIMPLEX - Marble products - Verona Marble Co.
AGGOS - Jewelry - John Joseph Schlosser, Sr.
AGGOSTINO - Clocks - Tindle Mills Inc.
AGGPREP - Industrial machinery - Portec Inc.
AGGRAND - Fertilizers - Amsoil, Inc.
AGGRASTAT - Pharmaceutical preparations - Merck & Co., Inc.
AGGRAVATION - Games - Lakeside Games
AGGRAVATION - Games - Milton Bradley Co.
AGGRAVATOR - Fishing lures - Aggravator Lure Co., Inc.
AGGRE-SKIN - Polyester contact paste ☆ - Boiardi Products Corp.
AGGRECEL - Construction equipment - Greengrove Corp.
AGGRESSION SPORTSWEAR - Apparel and accessories - Erich B. Whiteford
AGGRESSIVE COURT EQUIPMENT - Apparel and accessories - In the Zone, Inc.
AGGRESSIVE COURT EQUIPMENT A.C.E. - Apparel–athletic - In the Zone, Inc.
AGGRESSOR - Bicycles - Kent International Inc.
AGGRESSOR - Fishing rods - Zebco Corp.
AGGRESSOR - Golfing equipment - Wilson Sporting Goods Co.
AGGRESSOR - Saw blades ☆ - Capewell Components Co. L.P.
AGGRESSOR - Tires–bicycles ☆ - Carlisle Tire & Rubber Co.
AGGRESSR - Cleaning equipment - Contec, Inc.
AGHTAMAR BRANDY - Liquors - Saharex, Inc.
AGI - Audio equipment - Audio General Inc.
AGI - Computers - Everex Systems, Inc.
AGI - Gloves - Adams Global Industries, Inc.
AGI - Musical instrument accessories - Actodyne General, Inc.
AGIFTCORP - Giftware - American Gift Corp.
AGIL - Surgical supplies - C.R. Bard, Inc.
AGILE - Bicycles - Klein Bicycle Corp.
AGILITY - Children's shoes - Reebok International Ltd.
AGILITY - Vitamins and nutritional supplements - Marine Biotherapies
AGILITY DOG - Pet products - United States Dog Agility Association Inc.

☆ = Now out of production

AGILITY SYSTEM - Office furniture–plastic - Rosemont Office Systems Inc.

AGINCOURT - Apparel–men's - Omnisport Inc.

AGINCOURT - Furniture - Hickory Manufacturing Co.

AGING TO PERFECTION - Greeting cards - American Greetings Corp.

AGITANK - Photographic equipment - Yankee Photo Products Inc.

AGITATOR - Fishing lures - Mann's Bait Co.

AGITRAY - Photographic equipment - Yankee Photo Products Inc.

AGL SUPREME - Sauces - AGL Distributing, Inc.

AGLAZE - Hair care products - Tressa, Inc.

AGLIA - Fishing lures - Sheldons', Inc.

AGLIA LONG - Fishing lures - Sheldons', Inc.

AGLOW CANDLES - Candles - Aglow Inc.

AGLOW PUBLICATIONS - Publisher's imprints - Aglow Publications

AGNES B. - Sunglasses - Michel Loubiere

AGNETA - Jewelry–precious - Agneta Imports Inc.

AGNOLOTTI AL PESCE - Food products ✩ - Dean & Deluca Inc.

AGOBYL - Pharmaceutical preparations ✩ - Consolidated Midland Corp.

AGON - Recording label - Dragon Records (Div. of Agon Productions)

AGONY OF THE FEET, THE - Shoe insoles ✩ - Professional Product Research, Inc.

AGORA - Wallpaper - Koroseal Wallcoverings

AGORA II - Floor coverings ✩ - Armstrong World Industries, Inc.

AGORA PUBLICATIONS, INC. - Educational materials - Agora Publications, Inc.

AGORAL - Laxatives - Warner-Wellcome

A.G.P. - Exterior protective coating - A.G.P. Surface Control Systems Inc.

AGP GRAIN LTD. - Animal feeds - AGP, L.P.

AGPAK WATER SOLUBLE PACK - Pesticides–agricultural - Griffin Corp.

AGR - Golfing equipment - Mohawk Carpet Corp.

AGR - Hair care products - Andis Co.

AGRA ZONE - Chemical preparations - Loveland Industries, Inc.

AGRAIN & AGRAIN - Cereal ✩ - Arrowhead Mills, Inc.

AGRAL - Fruits and vegetables - Marglo Products Corp.

AGREE - Cigarettes - Brown & Williamson Tobacco Corp.

AGREE - Hair care products - Dep Corp.

AGREE + - Shampoos - Dep Corp.

AGRELLOS - Wines - W.J. Deutsch & Sons Ltd.

AGRESSOR - Bicycles - Roadmaster Corp.

AGRESSOR - Motorcycles ✩ - National Cycle Inc.

AGRESTE - Fruits and vegetables - Agreste Marketing Co.

AGRESTORE - Fertilizers - Agrestore Inc.

AGRI-AIDE - Agricultural machinery - Osborne Industries Inc.

AGRI BOND - Pet products - Theodore M. Kiebke

AGRI-COAT - Adhesives and sealants - Duracool Roofing Systems

AGRI-COVER - Truck cabs - Agri-Cover Inc.

AGRI-DIESEL - Fuel additives - Index Industries Inc.

AGRI-FAN - Fans–ceiling - Northwest Envirofan

AGRI-FLOW - Pipes - Hancor Inc.

AGRI/GARD - Paints - Valspar Corp.

AGRI-GATE - Computer software - James V. Hurson Associates, Inc.

AGRI-GUARD - Chemical preparations - Ch2o, Inc.

AGRI-HEP - Fertilizers - Agri-Business Technologies, Inc.

AGRI PAK - Motor vehicle parts and accessories - Springfield Remanufacturing Corp.

AGRI-POLY - Polyethylene film sheets - Carlisle Plastics, Inc.

AGRI-STABLE - Veterinary nutritional supplements - Balchem Corp.

AGRI-STARTER - Fertilizers - Agri-Business Technologies, Inc.

AGRI-SUL - Fertilizers ✩ - Eagle-Picher Industries Inc.

AGRI SUN NURSERY - Flowers, plants, and seeds - Stark Nursery Co.

AGRI TIME - Clocks - CTB, Inc.

AGRI-TORQUE - Agricultural machinery - Goodyear Tire & Rubber Co.

AGRICHARGED V-P - Batteries - Farmland Industries Inc.

AGRICHERRY - Flowers, plants, and seeds - Agrisales, Inc.

AGRICULTURAL PRODUCTS - Agricultural products - Seeds of Change Inc.

AGRIDYNE TECHNOLOGIES - Fertilizers - Agridyne Technologies, Inc.

AGRIFAX ON-FARM - Computer storage devices - Farm Credit Bank of Springfield

AGRIGATOR - Agricultural products - Ghassan Alireza

AGRILAND EXPO - Consulting services - Farm Progress Companies, Inc.

AGRILUBE - Oils–lubricating - SF Services, Inc.

AGRIMER - Polymers and copolymers - ISP Investments Inc.

AGRIMONTANA - Jams and jellies - Royal Pacific Foods

AGRIMONTANA - Nuts–salted, roasted, cooked, or canned ✩ - De Choix Specialty Foods Co.

AGRINUTRIENTS - Fertilizers - Agri-Business Technologies, Inc.

AGRIPEG TRACTOR - Scooters–children's - Peg Perego USA Inc.

AGRIPLEX MICRO-MIX - Fertilizers - Lisa Products Corp.

AGRISET SEED - Flowers, plants, and seeds - Agrisales, Inc.

AGRISOLV - Chemical preparations - ISP Investments Inc.

AGRISYSTEMS INTERNATIONAL - Containers - George Hoeffner

AGRO-FILL - Agricultural products - Ranpak Corp.

AGRO-LITE - Lamps - Philips Lighting Co.

AGROB - Tiles–ceramic - Amsterdam Corp.

AGROFABRIC - Garden equipment - PCK, Inc.

AGROMAC INTERNATIONAL - Agricultural machinery - Agromac International, Inc.

AGRONET - Hardware - Weldotron Corp.

AGROSOKE - Sealing compounds - Agrosoke Intl.

AGROTAIN - Chemical preparations - Freeport-McMoran Resource Partners L.P.

AGS - Dripless oil, automotive flashers, and auto bulbs - American Grease Stick Co.

AGSAFE - Fertilizers - Agcal Research Inc.

AGSTAR - Fencing–gates and posts - Behlen Manufacturing Co.

AGSTAR - Vitamins and nutritional supplements - Furman E. Hendrix Inc.

AGT - Tape–adhesive ✩ - Arlon, Inc.

AGTECH - Peanut shells - Agtech Co.

AGUA DIVINA - Cosmetics ✩ - Caswell-Massey Co. Ltd.

AGUAMIEL - Sweetener, syrup ✩ - Botanical Products

AGUARDIENTE ANTIOQUENO - Wines - Blair Importers Ltd.

AGUILA - Flour–blended - Cahokia Flour Co.

AGUIRRE - Colognes - Bourjois Ltd.

AGUSTA - Flooring–hardwood - Mannington Wood Floors

AGUSTE - Hair care products - Aguste Personal Care Products, Inc.

AGV HELMETS - Motorcycle helmets - Cosmopolitan Motors Inc.

AGVANTAGE SOFTWARE - Computer software - Udenberg & Associates, Inc.

AGVEST - Fruits–frozen - Agvest, Inc. (Northeastern Packing Div.)

AH - Games - Avalon Hill Game Co.

AH! - Shampoos - Gillette Co.

AH-64D - Aircraft–helicopters - McDonnell Douglas Helicopter Co.

AH-BON - Apparel–athletic - Ah-Bon Athletics, Inc.

AH-CHEW - Antihistamine preparations - We Pharmaceuticals, Inc.

AH-H - Brassieres (Bras) - Sears, Roebuck and Co.

AH HARD - Perfumes - Commercial Properties, Inc.

AH-ONE - Spices and extracts - Michele Adrian

AH-SHOOT SPLATTER REMOVER - Paint removers - Enviro-Chem Inc.

AH-SO - Food products - Edlin Sales

AH-SO - Housewares - SCI Scandicrafts Inc.

AH SOY - Beverages - Westbrae Natural Foods, Inc.

AHA - Computer circuits and peripherals - Adaptec, Inc.

AHA ACTIVATOR - Skin care products - Viva America Marketing, Inc.

AHA BOOSTER COMPLEX - Lotions - Guthy-Renker Corp.

AHA HYDROXY GOLD PLUS - Skin care products - Creative Laboratories Inc.

AHAB - Fishing tackle - Fin-Nor Corp.

AHAB BY FIN-NOR - Fishing tackle - United Sports Secialists Corp.

AHACK PACK - Golfing equipment - Ryobi-Toski Corp.

AHB - Audio equipment - Allen & Heath Brenell USA Ltd.

AHB - Hardware - Associated Hardware Buyers Inc.

AHB - Heating equipment - Easy Heat Inc.

AHCO - Hats - American Hat Co. Inc.

AHEAD - Bicycles - Dia-Compe USA, Inc.

AHEAD - Brushes–hair ✩ - M-F-G Corp.

AHEAD DRUMSTICKS - Drums–musical instruments - Big Bang Distribution/A.P.I.

AHERN WINERY - Wines - Ahern Winery

AHH! - Pet products - Farnam Cos. Inc.

AHH. KEDS - Footwear - SR Holdings Inc.

AHH SHUCKS - Popcorn - Story's Popcorn Co.

AHH-SOME GOURMET - Coffee - Ahh-Some Gourmet Coffee, Inc.

AHH SUPER - Corkscrews - Franmara Co. Inc.

AHI - Toys - Azrak-Hamway International, Inc.

AHI PAKA - Novelty items - Hawaii Calls Inc.

AHJ - Neckwear - Fashion Neckwear Co. Inc.

AHK - Containers–glass - Kerr Group, Inc.

AHLGREN VINEYARD - Wines - Ahlgren Vineyard

AHMED HALAL - Meat products–canned - Star of Ocean Inc.

AHNTECH - Electrical equipment - Ahntech, Inc.

AHOY! - Computer peripheral equipment - Bradley W. Bennett

AHOY - Frames–eyeglass - May Optical Co.

AHP - Publisher's imprints - Jain Publishing Co.

AHP - Rings–jewelry - Artcarved Inc.

AHS 100 - Flooring–parquet - Bruce Hardwood Floors

AHS 200 - Floor coverings - Bruce Hardwood Floors
AHS 300 - Floor coverings - Bruce Hardwood Floors
AHS 400 - Floor coverings - Bruce Hardwood Floors
AHS 500 - Floor coverings - Bruce Hardwood Floors
AHT SYSTEM - Golfing equipment - Golfsmith International Inc.
AHU - Film - Eastman Kodak Co.
AHUMS - Flight recorders - Teledyne Industries Inc.
AI - Adhesives and sealants - Accumetric, Inc.
AI - Antipyretics ☆ - Wahyet Inc.
AI - Car-care product - Automotive International, Inc.
AI - Lighting fixtures - Atelier International Inc.
A.I.-AN EXPERIENCE WITH ARTIFICIAL INTELLIGENCE - Computer
  software - Scholastic Software Inc.
AI TROPICS - Food products - Aesquivel Corp. of California
AIA ELECTRONIC DOCUMENTS SERVICE - Computer software - American
  Institute of Architects
AIBORG - Cameras ☆ - Konica USA Inc.
A.I.C. - Seafood products–fresh or frozen - Alpine International
AICE - Computer software - Infection Control and Prevention Analysts, Inc.
AICO - Office supplies - Avery Label Systems
AICO-CELL - Office supplies ☆ - Avery Label Systems
AICO-LOID - Office supplies ☆ - Avery Label Systems
AICO-PRINT - Office supplies ☆ - Avery Label Systems
AICORITE - Watches ☆ - Assurance Industries Co. Inc.
AID - Automotive parts and accessories - Aid Auto Stores Inc.
AID - Latex gloves - Regaltex International, Inc.
AIDA - Accordions - Ideal Musical Merchandise Co.
AIDA - Glassware–household - Spiegelau Inc.
AIDA - Wallpaper - Scalamandre Silks Inc.
AIDA - Wines - Frank Sutton & Co.
AIDA GREY - Hair care products - Douglas and Aida Behrend Family Trust
AIDA THIBIANT - Skin care products - Thibiant International
AIDA THIBIANT PHYTOTHERAPY - Skin care products - Aida Thibiant, Inc.
AIDA THIBIANT PROFESSIONAL - Skin care products - Aida Thibiant, Inc.
AIDACO - Dental equipment - Temrex Corp.
AIDANT - Pharmaceutical preparations ☆ - P.J. Noyes Co., Inc.
AIDE GREY - Skin care products - Helen of St. Moritz
AIDE MEMOIRE - Office supplies - Blue Star Leather Inc.
AIDEES DEVON VIOLETS - Skin care products ☆ - Freund-Mayer & Co. Inc.
AIDELLS - Sausages - Aidells Sausage Co.
AIDELLS AUTHENTIC - Sausages - Aidells Sausage Co.
AIDELLS LOWFAT - Sausages - Aidells Sausage Co.
A.I.D.H.M. - Doghouses - American International Dog House Manufacturing Inc.
AIDJUSTOR - Hearing aids - Hearing Health Group Inc.
A.I.D.S. AUTOMOBILE INTERACTIVE DEFENSESYSTEM - Alarm systems -
  Joseph A. Resnick
AIDS AVENGER - Video games - Raya Systems, Inc.
AIDS LINGO - Publisher's imprints - Neighborhood Service Organization
AIDS TEST DROPS - Pharmaceutical preparations - Vita Elixir Co. Inc.
AIELLO - Food products - Nicola International, Inc.
AIELLO'S - Food products - Silver State Foods Inc.
AIEO - Skin care products - IT&LY Hairfashion NA Inc.
AIFOS - Footwear ☆ - Skea Ltd.
AIFP - Medical apparatus - Microstrain Co.
AIG - Sporting goods - O.F. Mossberg & Sons, Inc.
AIG - Umbrellas - American International Group Inc.
AIGLE - Footwear - Sebago Inc.
L'AIGLON - Apparel–men's - Swank Inc.
AIGNER - Leather - Etienne Aigner, Inc.
AIGNER - Office supplies - Avery Label Systems
AIGNER INTERNATIONAL - Apparel and accessories - United Merchants and
  Manufacturers Inc.
AII - Jewelry - Aurora Imports Inc.
AIIS - Computer software - Decision Research Corp.
AIKIDO FORCE - Toys - Mattel, Inc.
AIKO - Electronic equipment - Aiko Corp.
AIKON - Cooking equipment–household - International Home Tech, Inc.
AIKYROL - Oils–edible ☆ - Scandinavian Natural Health & Beauty Products,
  Inc.
AIL - Jewelry–precious - Aluma USA Inc.
AILEEN - Apparel–women's - Aileen Inc.
AILEEN - Frames–eyeglass - Pathway Optical Prods.
AILEEN GIRL - Apparel and accessories - Aileen Inc.
AILEEN OSER - Apparel–women's - Aileen Oser, Inc.
AILEEN SPORT - Apparel–women's - Aileen Inc.
AIM - Adhesives and sealants ☆ - Macklanburg-Duncan Co.

AIM - Archery equipment - Hoyt
AIM - Computer software - Alexander Utility Engineering, Inc.
AIM - Computer software - Applied Information for Marketing, Inc.
AIM - Computer software - Biles and Associates
AIM - Computer software - Cramer Products Inc.
AIM - Computer software ☆ - Abtech Corp.
AIM - Electric lighting equipment - Wybron, Inc.
AIM - Electronic equipment - Aim Electronics Corp.
AIM - Hardware - Aim Products Inc.
AIM - Lubricants - Robert E Wikel
AIM - Mailing machines - Bell & Howell Phillipsburg Co.
AIM - Medical apparatus - Ace Orthopedic Manufacturing, Inc.
AIM - Medical apparatus - Acoustic Imaging Technologies Corp.
AIM - Ovens–microwave - Lincoln Foodservice Products, Inc.
AIM - Toothpaste - Chesebrough-Pond's USA Co.
AIM - Toothpaste - Lever Brothers Co. Inc.
AIM-9 SIDEWINDER - Toys–models - Estes Industries
AIM AIR - Ventilation equipment - Air-Perme-Ator Inc.
AIM ALOE GOLD - Beverage - Aim International, Inc.
AIM BEAR PAW GARLIC - Vitamins and nutritional supplements - Aim
  International, Inc.
AIM GOLF - Golfing equipment - Climax Clothing Industries, Inc.
AIM HIGH - Apparel–athletic - Mark L. Mccann
AIM HOST SOFTWARE - Computer software - American Innovations, Ltd.
AIM IDR MODULE - Computer hardware - American Innovations, Ltd.
AIM MODULE - Computer hardware - American Innovations, Ltd.
AIM 'N FLAME - Lighters - Scripto-Tokai Corp.
AIM REDIBEETS - Vitamins and nutritional supplements - Aim International,
  Inc.
AIM REVOLUTION! THE LIFESTYLE BAR - Vitamins and nutritional
  supplements - Aim International, Inc.
AIM-RITE - Targets - McKenzie Supply
AIMCO - Automotive parts and accessories - Echlin Inc.
AIME - Cosmetics - RH Cosmetics Corp.
AIME BOUCHER LOIRE - Beverages–alcohol - World Shippers & Importers
AIME COLOR COMBS - Hair care products - Valmor Products Co.
AIMEE - Dolls - Russ Berrie and Co., Inc.
AIMEE - Frames–eyeglass ☆ - Universal/Univis Inc.
AIMEX - Camera - Aimex Camera Inc.
AIMEZ-VOUS - Beverages–alcohol - Joseph E. Seagram & Sons, Inc.
AIMLINE - Golfing equipment - Independent Golf Research Corp.
AIMS - Bathroom fixtures - Aims-Abrams Fixture Corp.
AIMS - Computer software - Cable Computerized Management Systems, Inc.
AIMS - Electronic equipment - PMS Sales and Leasing Inc.
AIM'S LIFESTYLE WEIGHT MANAGEMENT PROGRAM - Publisher's imprints
  - Aim International, Inc.
AIMTECH - Computer software - Aimtech Corp.
AINSBROOKE - Apparel and accessories - Genesco Inc.
AINSLEY - Cabinets - Actua
AINSLEY - Flatware - Utica Cutlery Co.
AINSLEY - Floor coverings–carpet and rugs ☆ - Gulistan Carpet Inc.
AINSLEY - Saddles - Toklat Originals, Inc.
AINSLEY BLAKE - Footwear–men's - Atsco Footwear Inc.
AIN'T NO WAY - Apparel and accessories ☆ - Vanderbilt Shirt Co.
AIN'T SHE SWEET - Bicycles - Roadmaster Corp.
AIO WIN - Computer software - Knowledge Based Systems, Inc.
AIOLA - Wines - C. Daniele & Co., Inc.
AIP - Computer software - Centigram Communications Corp.
AIP PRESS - Publisher's imprints - American Institute of Physics Inc.
AIPLA - Recording label - American Intellectual Property Law Association, Inc.
AIR - Computer peripheral equipment - Advanced Integration Research Inc.
A.I.R. - Computer software - Ithaca Software Inc.
A.I.R. - Garden equipment - Metromedia International Group, Inc.
AIR 17 - Guns ☆ - Crosman Corp.
AIR 21 TURF - Footwear ☆ - Nike, Inc.
AIR 24 DIAMOND - Footwear ☆ - Nike, Inc.
AIR 4000 - Batteries - Rayovac Corp.
AIR-A-LATOR - Fireplace equipment - Bernard Dalsin Manufacturing
AIR-A-PLANE - Air conditioning equipment - Wm. L. Shepheard Co.
AIR ACCELERATOR - Compressors–air - Black & Decker Corp.
AIR ACTION - Toys - Remco Baby Inc.
AIR AID - Compressors–air ☆ - Universal Security Instruments Inc.
AIR ALL - Compressors–air ☆ - Goodall Manufacturing Co.
AIR AMERICA - Clothing - Kennedy Marketing Communications Corp.
AIR AMERICA - Compressors–air - Devilbiss Air Power Co.
AIR & REPAIR - Automotive repair shops - Gold Eagle Co.

AIR ASSAULT - Footwear–athletic ☆ - Nike, Inc.

AIR ASSAULT - Toys–automobiles - Hasbro, Inc.

AIR ATTACK - Toys - Mattel, Inc.

AIR-BALL - Golfing equipment - Airball Enterprises, LLC

AIR BAND - Dryers–hair ☆ - General Cage Corp.

AIR BEAR - Golfing equipment - Golden Bear International, Inc.

AIR BEAR - Kites - Gayla Industries Inc.

AIR BEDS - Exercising equipment - CSA, Inc.

AIR BLASTER GUN - Toys ☆ - Wham-O Manufacturing Co.

AIR BLUSH - Skin care products - Revlon Consumer Products Corp.

AIR BOHEMIAN - Footwear ☆ - Nike, Inc.

AIR BOOSTER - Ventilation equipment - Field Controls Corp.

AIR BOOT - Furnaces–electric - Pettibone Corp.

AIR BOSS - Air freshener - Affiliated Paper Companies, Inc.

AIR BOSS - Air purification systems - Trion, Inc.

AIR BOSS - Machinery - Athey Products Corp.

AIR BOX - Packaging–paper - Air Packaging Technologies Inc.

AIR BRACE - Sporting goods - Cliff Keen Wrestling Products, Inc.

AIR-BROOM - Portable blowers - Lesco, Inc.

AIR BRUSH - Mats - Royal Rubber & Manufacturing Co.

AIR BUBBLE - Envelopes - Manco, Inc.

AIR-BUOY - Skin diving equipment ☆ - Outboard Marine Corp.

AIR BUS - Luggage - Welsh Sporting Goods Corp. (Boyt Div.)

AIR CAM - Braces–orthopedic - United States Manufacturing Co.

AIR CARE - Air purification systems ☆ - Medo Industries, Inc.

AIR CARE - Ventilating hoods, fans, and heaters - Aubrey Manufacturing Inc.

AIR CAVALRY - Toys - Tyco Toys

AIR CEL - Fishing tackle - Minnesota Mining & Manufacturing Co.

AIR CHAIR - Medical apparatus - Creative Medical, Inc.

AIR CHAIR, THE - Hammocks - Interworld Corp.

AIR-CHEM TECHNOLOGIES - Identification tags - Envirometrics Products Inc.

AIR CHIEF - Air conditioning equipment - Bridgestone/Firestone, Inc.

AIR CLASSIC - Musical instrument accessories - Dimarzio, Inc.

AIR CLEAN - Deodorizers - Bishop-Wisecarver Corp.

AIR-COAT - Paint sprayers - Wagner Spray Tech Corp.

AIR COIL TECHNOLOGIES - Air conditioning equipment - International Environmental Corp.

AIR COMFORT - Footwear ☆ - E.S. Originals, Inc.

AIR COMMAND - Housewares - Amana Refrigeration Inc.

AIR COMMAND FORCE - Footwear ☆ - Nike, Inc.

AIR CONDITIONER - Footwear–athletic ☆ - Nike, Inc.

AIR CONTROL - Air conditioning equipment - Leigh

AIR-CONTROL - Pipes–tobacco ☆ - S.M. Frank & Co. Inc. (Kaywoodie-Yello-Bole-Medico)

AIR CONTROLLER - Air transportation - Pollenex Corp.

AIR CONTROLLER - Deodorizers - Origins Natural Resources Inc.

AIR-COOL - Shoe soles - L. Karno & Co.

AIR COOLED DESIGN ACD - Sporting goods - Franklin Sports, Inc.

AIR COPLANAR PROBE - Measuring instruments - Cascade Microtech, Inc.

AIR CRAFT - Footwear–athletic ☆ - Nike, Inc.

AIR CREATIVE GROUP - Advertising agencies - Jacobs & Gerber, Inc.

AIR CRIB - Cribs–metal - Jeffrey H. Hine

AIR CRISPS - Crackers - Nabisco Holdings Corp.

AIR CRUISERS - Toys - Mattel, Inc.

AIR CUP - Packaging–paper - Sealed Air Corp.

AIR CUSHION - Cases–binocular - Pioneer Marketing & Research, Inc.

AIR CUSHION - Medical apparatus - Apex Medical Corp.

AIR-CUSHION - Pocket stamps - Consolidated Stamp Manufacturing Co. Inc.

AIR CUSHION EAR PLUGS - Plugs–ear - Karlen Manufacturing, Inc.

AIR DANCER - Boomerangs - Gutmann Cutlery Inc.

AIR DEFENSE - Deodorizers - Fuller Brush Co.

AIR-DEVIL - Ventilation equipment - Triangle Metal and Manufacturing Inc.

AIR DIAMOND TURF - Footwear ☆ - Nike, Inc.

AIR DOME - Aluminum products - N.H. Rudeen Co.

AIR DONJOY - Braces–orthopedic - Smith & Nephew DonJoy Inc.

AIR DRI - Dehumidifiers - Coughlan Products Corp.

AIR DRI - Medical apparatus - Paper-Pak Products, Inc.

AIR DRY - Nail care products - Pro Finish USA, Ltd.

AIR DRY - Waterproof outerwear - Servus Footwear Co.

AIR DUFFLE BAG - Bags–duffel - Pro Screen

AIR DURACRAFT - Fans–electric - Duracraft Corp.

AIR DYNAMICS - Toys - Wal-Mart Stores Inc.

AIR-DYNE - Exercising equipment - Schwinn Cycling & Fitness Inc.

AIR E ATOR - Socks - Shane K. Cooper

AIR EAGLE - Binoculars - Davis Brothers & Madison Ltd.

AIR EASE - Heating equipment ☆ - Magic Chef Inc.

AIR EASE - Sporting goods ☆ - Dacon Manufacturing

AIR EAST - Frames–eyeglass - U.S. Optical Frame Co.

AIR ENHANCED - Yarn - Spanco Industries Inc.

AIR-ENTRAINED - Lime products - Western Lime Corp.

A.I.R. EQUIPPED - Parachutes - John A. Dunham

AIR ESCAPE - Footwear–athletic ☆ - Nike, Inc.

AIR-EVAC - Containers - Falcon Safety Products, Inc.

AIR EXPRESS - Furniture - Wise Co., Inc.

AIR EXPRESS - Helmets–athletic - Specialized Bicycle Components, Inc.

AIR EXPRESS VALUE - Golfing equipment - Harrison Sports, Inc.

AIR-EZE - Food products - Sherwood Medical Co.

AIR FAULTLESS - Wheels - Faultless Caster Co.

AIR FILLED WRIST WREST - Computer hardware - Medic-Air Corp. of America

AIR FILTER TECHNOLOGY - Filters–air - Air Filter Technology, Inc.

AIR FLARES - Automotive parts and accessories - National Cycle Inc.

AIR FLEX - Musical-instrument-case handles - American Handle Co. Inc.

AIR FLEX - Sporting goods - Lisco, Inc.

AIR FLEX 400 - Exercising equipment - Gerstung/Gym-Thing Inc.

AIR FLEX PONY TAILS - Shoes - Shoe Show, Inc.

AIR-FLIER - Toys ☆ - Hi-Flier Manufacturing Co.

AIR FLIGHT - Footwear–athletic - Nike, Inc.

AIR FLIGHT LITE - Footwear–athletic ☆ - Nike, Inc.

AIR FLITE - Cages–wire ☆ - General Cage Corp.

AIR-FLO - Garden equipment ☆ - Pro Inc.

AIR-FLO - Health care products ☆ - Inbrand Corp.

AIR-FLO - Hockey equipment - Mylec, Inc.

AIR-FLO - Lubricants - Relton Corp.

AIR FLOAT - Automotive parts and accessories ☆ - Dinsmore Instrument Co.

AIR FLOTE - Cushions–foam - Schnadig Corp.

AIR FLOW - Brushes–hair ☆ - Modern Research Laboratories

AIR-FLOW - Musical instruments ☆ - Barclay Music

AIR-FLOW - Thread - Cincinnati Thread Co.

AIR FLOW TELS - Weather tracking equipment - Davis Instruments Corp.

AIR FORCE - Games - Avalon Hill Game Co.

AIR FORCE - Tools–boring - Trade Associates, Inc.

AIR FORCE II - Sprayers - Emson Research Inc.

AIR FORCE MAX - Footwear–athletic ☆ - Nike, Inc.

AIR FORCE ONE - Cylinders–pneumatic - Clippard Instrument Laboratory, Inc.

AIR FORM - Medical apparatus - Royce Medical Co.

AIR FOSC - Electrical equipment - Raychem Corp.

AIR FRESH PAC - Deodorizers - PortionPac Chemical Corp.

AIR FRIES - Food products - Good Earth Corp.

AIR GENERAL - Dryers–household - General Cage Corp.

AIR GLIDE - Cushions - Saddleman, Inc.

AIR GLO - Thread - A. Lewis Thread Co. Inc.

AIR-GUARD - Alarm systems - Seatt Corp.

AIR GUARD - Deodorizers - Lester Laboratories Inc.

AIR GUARD - Deodorizers ☆ - Promaster

AIR GUARD - Sporting goods - Brine Inc.

AIR GUARD - Water purification systems - Stanley M. White

AIR GUARD MISTER - Insect repellant - R & M Products

AIR HAMMER - Rackets–racquetball - Wilson Sporting Goods Co.

AIR HANDLER - Filters–air - Grainger Division

AIR-HAWK - Cupolas ☆ - Aluminum Co. of America

AIR HELMET II - Medical apparatus - Breathing Systems Inc.

AIR HOCKEY - Games ☆ - Brunswick Corp.

AIR HOTRONIX - Adhesives and sealants - Stahls' Inc.

AIR HUARACHE - Footwear–athletic ☆ - Nike, Inc.

AIR ICARUS - Footwear–athletic ☆ - Nike, Inc.

AIR INTERNATIONAL - Footwear–athletic ☆ - Nike, Inc.

AIR INVADERS - Toys - Worldwide Properties, Inc.

AIR JACK - Shock absorbers–motor vehicle ☆ - Goodyear Tire & Rubber Co.

AIR JAMMER CYCLE SCRAMMER - Toys ☆ - Tomy America, Inc.

AIR JAMMER ROAD RAMMER - Toys ☆ - Tomy America, Inc.

AIR JET - Air conditioning equipment - General Products Co. Inc.

AIR JET QUENCH - Surface Combustion, Inc.

AIR JOCK - Novelty items - Air Wear

AIR JORDAN - Footwear–athletic - Nike, Inc.

AIR KING - Dehumidifiers - Lasko Metal Products Inc.

AIR KING - Hardware - Dixon Valve and Coupling Co.

AIR KING - Watches - Bulova Corp.

AIR KING AMERICA - Dental equipment - Medidenta International, Inc.

AIR-KRAFT - Envelopes - Astro-Valcour, Inc.

AIR KRAFT - Envelopes - Marvin Envelope & Paper Co.

AIR LAND AND SEA - Cases–vanity - Romanoff Products Inc.

AIR-LEC - Door openers–electronic - Air-Lec Industries Inc.
AIR LIFT - Carburetors ✰ - Outboard Marine Corp.
AIR LIFT - Health care products - Air Lift Unlimited Inc.
AIR LIGHT - Dryers–hair - Sunbeam-Oster Household Products
AIR LINE - Fans–electric ✰ - Dorothy Biddle Service
AIR-LINK - Electronics equipment - Grass Valley Group Inc.
AIR-LITE - Caulking guns - Vital Products Inc.
AIR-LITE - Goggles–safety - Aearo Co.
AIR-LITE - Housewares ✰ - Franzus Co. Inc.
AIR LITE - Prosthetic apparatus - A.D. Craig Co. Inc.
AIR-LITE - Sporting goods - Bike Athletic Co.
AIR-LITE - Tools ✰ - Goldblatt Tool Co.
AIR LOCK - Heating equipment - Venstar, Inc.
AIR-LOK - Windows–storm - The Southard Corp.
AIR LUBE - Petroleum - Non-Fluid Oil Corp.
AIR LUMBAR - Chairs–wood - Bodybilt Seating
AIR MACH FORCE - Footwear–athletic ✰ - Nike, Inc.
AIR-MAGIC - Vacuum cleaners - Harold J. Schoettler
AIR MAIL - Food products - Lodi Canning Inc.
AIR MASTER - Air conditioning equipment ✰ - Houston Fearless 76 Inc.
AIR MASTER - Automotive parts and accessories ✰ - MasterForce Inc.
AIR MASTER - Compressors–air - Kopykake
AIR MASTIC - Paint sprayers - Speeflo Manufacturing Corp.
AIR-MATE - Compressors–air - Emglo Products L.P. (Emglo Air Compressors)
AIR MATE SEAT - Motor vehicle parts and accessories - Lancaster Colony Automotive Group
AIR MAX - Footwear–athletic - Nike, Inc.
AIR MAX SQUARED - Footwear–athletic ✰ - Nike, Inc.
AIR MAZING GAMES - Games ✰ - Tomy America, Inc.
AIR MEDIC - Filters–air - Air Kontrol Inc.
AIR MIST - Stationery ✰ - T.V. Allen Co.
AIR MOWABB - Footwear–athletic ✰ - Nike, Inc.
AIR NAUTIQUE - Boats - Correct Craft Inc.
AIR NORTON - Musical instrument accessories - Dimarzio, Inc.
AIR NOSTALGIA - Posters - Art Services, Inc.
AIR NURSE - Watches - Bulova Corp.
AIR-O - Frames–eyeglass - Hoya Corp. USA
AIR-O - Musical instrument accessories ✰ - Selmer Co. Inc.
AIR-O-EASE - Air mattresses - Mason Medical Products
AIR-O-MA - Incense - Auroma International Inc.
AIR-O-MAGIC - Footwear - Rocky Shoes & Boots, Inc.
AIR-O-MATIC - Medical apparatus - Genesis Industries Inc.
AIR-O-MATIC - Projection screens - Brumberger Co. Inc.
AIR-O-MATIC - Tools–garden - Gilmour Manufacturing Co.
AIR-O-PAD - Health care products - HNE Healthcare
AIR-OBIK - Footwear - Kisco International Corp.
AIR ONE - Air purification systems - Penox Technologies Inc.
AIR-OPAGUE - Hardware - Badger Air-Brush Co.
AIR-PAC - Compressors–air - Thomas Industries Inc.
AIR-PAK - Medical apparatus - Scott Aviation
AIR PATROL - Air purification systems - Holmes Products, Corp.
AIR PEN - Tools–hand-operated - Richard R. Scott
AIR-PERME-ATOR DRY HUMIDIFICATION SYSTEM - Humidifiers - Air-Perme-Ator Inc.
AIR-PILLO - Shoe accessories - Schering-Plough Healthcare Products
AIR PILLOW - Tape–adhesive - Manco, Inc.
AIR PILOT - Tools - R.E. Dietz Co.
AIR PIONEER - Skin care products - Air Pioneer Ltd.
AIR PLAY - Apparel–women's - Melbeth, Inc.
AIR PLAY - Broadcasting equipment - Avid Technology, Inc.
AIR POGO - Playground equipment - Hypergee, Inc.
AIR PORT - Pumps - Coleman Co., Inc.
AIR POWER - Sporting goods ✰ - Schutt Manufacturing Co.
AIR PRO - Compressors–air - Art Materials West
AIR-PRO - Plastic pipe - Asahi/America Inc.
AIR PRO - Skin care products - Premiere Salon Products
AIR PRO - Toys - Mattel, Inc.
AIR PRO QUALITY PARTS - Steering mechanisms–motor vehicle - C & M Core Distributors, Inc.
AIR PRO-TEC - Shoe insoles - Sparco, Inc.
AIR-PURE - Cleaning preparations - Viking Manufacturing Co. Inc.
AIR QC - Filters–air - Howard C. Smith, Inc.
AIR QUEEN - Watches - Bulova Corp.
AIR RAID - Fireworks - American Promotional Events, Inc.
AIR RAID - Footwear–athletic ✰ - Nike, Inc.
AIR RANCHO - Shock absorbers - Monroe Auto Equipment Co.

AIR-RATE - Meters–gas - Accurate Metering Systems, Inc.
AIR RELEASE - Sporting goods - Gear 2000, Ltd.
AIR REPAIR - Deodorizers - Deltatrak, Inc.
AIR RIDER - Motorcycle parts and accessories - Ooltewah Manufacturing, Inc.
AIR RUNNER - Footwear - Cerwin Shoes Corp.
AIR-RX - Filters–air - Dust Free Inc.
AIR-SAVERS - Deodorizers - Surco Products Inc.
AIR SAVERS - Guns–BB - Lonn Manufacturing Co. Inc.
AIR-SCENT - Deodorizers - Surco Products Inc.
AIR SCHOOMS - Sporting goods - MascoTech Accessories
AIR-SEA BATTLE - Video games - Atari Games Corp.
AIR SENTRY - Air purification systems - Pollenex Corp.
AIR SENTRY-IMS - Monitors–electronic - Molecular Analytics, LLC
AIR SEW - Thread ✰ - Perfect Thread Co. Inc.
AIR-SHIELD - Adhesives and sealants - W.R. Meadows Inc.
AIR SO CLEAR - Deodorizers - Avon Products, Inc.
AIR SOURCE ONE - Aircraft parts - Air Source One, Inc.
AIR SOUTH - Apparel and accessories - Air South Airlines, Inc.
AIR SPACE - Deodorizers - Ecolab Inc.
AIR SPORTS - Stereos - S.N.S.T., Inc.
AIR SPRING - Cushions - Roho, Inc.
AIR SQUADRON - Ophthalmic goods - Robin Optical
AIR STAR - Footwear - Eurostar Inc.
AIR STEP - Shoes - Brown Shoe Co.
AIR-STIK 160 - Fans–electric - A.J. Carlow Inc.
AIR-STOP - Hardware - Portaseal Inc.
AIR STOP - Insulating materials - K2 Inc.
AIR STREAM - Garden equipment - McCulloch Corp.
AIR STREAM - Thread ✰ - Perfect Thread Co. Inc.
AIR STREET DEFENDER - Shoes–athletic ✰ - Nike, Inc.
AIR STREET DEKE - Shoes–athletic ✰ - Nike, Inc.
AIR-STRIKE - Golfing equipment - Echelon, Golf Inc.
AIR STRIP - Cleaning preparations - Ecolab Inc.
AIR STRIP - Mats - JCH International Inc.
AIR SUPERIORITY - Games - Game Designers' Workshop, Inc.
AIR SUPPLY VENTILATOR - Air purification systems - Condar Co.
AIR SWEEP - Air conditioning equipment - White Consolidated Industries, Inc.
AIR SWEET - Deodorizers - Uncle Sam Chemical Co., Inc.
AIR SWITCH - Electronic equipment ✰ - ITC, Inc.
AIR SYSTEMS INTERNATIONAL - Filters–air - Air Systems, Inc.
AIR-TABS GG - Pharmaceutical preparations ✰ - Scrip-Physician Supply Co.
AIR TASER - Projectiles - Air Taser, Inc.
AIR TECH - Exercising equipment - Formula Ventures
AIR TECH - Footwear - Ambassador Shoe Corp.
AIR TECH - Skates–roller ✰ - National Sporting Goods Corp.
AIR TECHNOLOGIES - Air-conditioner repair shops - Ohio Transmission Corp.
AIR-TECHNOLOGY SERIES - Sporting goods - Lisco, Inc.
AIR-TEMP - Thermometers - Sea-Temp Instruments Ltd.
AIR-TEX - Hardware - Badger Air-Brush Co.
AIR TEX - Luggage - Airline Textile Manufacturing Co.
AIR-TEX - Thread - Elmore-Pisgah, Inc.
AIR THEE WELL - Deodorizers - Atmosphere Products Co. Inc.
AIR THERAPY - Air purification systems - Mia Rose Products Inc.
AIR THORSEN - Tools - GC Thorsen, Inc.
AIR THREADING - Clutches–industrial - Logan Clutch Corp.
AIR-THRU - Ophthalmic goods - Salvatori Ophthalmics Inc.
AIR TIME - Apparel and accessories - New Boys Inc.
AIR-TIPS - Cigar boxes–wood - Consolidated Cigar Corp.
AIR-TITE - Tobacco pouches - Allied Products Corp.
AIR TRAINER - Footwear–athletic - Nike, Inc.
AIR TRAK 90 - Audio equipment - Broadcast Electronics, Inc.
AIR TRANSPORT - Footwear ✰ - E.S. Originals, Inc.
AIR TRANSPORT INTERNATIONAL - Airports - USA Jet Airlines, Inc.
AIR TREAD - Mats - U.S. Mat & Rubber Co.
AIR TREADS - Tires - Goodyear Tire & Rubber Co.
AIR UPTEMPO - Footwear ✰ - Nike, Inc.
AIR-VAC - Air conditioning equipment - Kohler Co.
AIR VAC - Cleaning preparations - Penn-Plax, Inc.
AIR VAC - Vacuum cleaners and accessories - M and S Systems Inc.
AIR VACUATE - Air purification systems - Knight International Holdings, Inc.
AIR VENT - Floor coverings ✰ - Texas Aluminum Industries Inc.
AIR WALKER - Orthopedic braces - Centec Orthopaedics
AIR WAR - Fireworks - American Promotional Events, Inc.
AIR-WATER X-15 CAR - Toys - Park Plastics Co.
AIR WAVE - Helmets–athletic - Specialized Bicycle Components, Inc.
AIR WAVES - Deodorizers - Reckitt & Colman, Inc.

54   ✰ = Now out of production

AIR WAVES - Hair care products - Redken Laboratories, Inc.
AIR WEDGE - Medical apparatus - Medical Plastics Laboratory, Inc.
AIR-WEIGH - Scales–truck - Hi-Tech Transport Electronics
AIR WEIGHTS - Exercising equipment - Sports Step Inc.
AIR-WEST - Frames–eyeglass - Hudson Optical Corp.
AIR WEST - Frames–eyeglass - U.S. Optical Frame Co.
AIR WINGS - Motorcycle parts and accessories - Baker Built Products Inc.
AIR WUZZY - Toys–stuffed ☆ - Gund, Inc.
AIR ZONE - Musical instrument accessories - Dimarzio, Inc.
AIR ZONE II - Electrical testing instruments - Enzone Inc.
AIRACOBRA - Toys–airplanes - Cox Products Inc.
AIRADON - Paints - Mankind Research Unltd. Inc.
AIRAGEOUS - Sporting goods - O'Brien International
AIRAMMER - Soil compactor - M-B-W Inc.
AIRASSIST - Braces–orthopedic - Medassist-Op, Inc.
AIRAZOR - Toys - Hasbro, Inc.
AIRBAG AND STEERING WHEEL SHIELD - Automotive parts and accessories - Winner International Corp.
AIRBAKE - Cooking equipment–household - Mirro Corp.
AIRBAKE - Metal enamel - Iowa Paint Manufacturing Co. Inc.
AIRBAND - Saws–power - CS Unitec Inc.
AIRBEAM - Aluminum products - Enviroquip, Inc.
AIRBEAM - Boating equipment and accessories - Electromechanical Research Laboratories Inc.
AIRBIRD - Medical apparatus - Bird Products Corp.
AIRBLADE - Knives - Wells Technology Inc.
AIRBLOCK - Boating equipment and accessories - Harken, Inc.
AIRBOAT - Boats - Glen-L Marine Designs
AIRBONS - Candy - Pet Inc. (Whitman's Chocolates Div.)
AIRBORN - Recording label - Airborn Records
AIRBORNE - Fabrics - Greenwood Mills Inc.
AIRBORNE - Frames–eyeglass - Hoya Corp. USA
AIRBORNE - Photographic equipment - American Photographic Instrument Co.
AIRBORNE - Shoes ☆ - Brown Shoe Co.
AIRBORNE - Skates–roller - First Team Sports, Inc.
AIRBORNE - Sporting goods - O'Brien International
AIRBORNE - Vitamins and nutritional supplements - Thomas John McDowell
AIRBORNE NEW ZEALAND - Honey - Masterpeace Food Imports
AIRBORNE RANGER - Computer software ☆ - Microprose Software, Inc.
AIRBORNE SURVEILLANCE MISSILE - Toys–models ☆ - Estes Industries
AIRBOSS - Firefighting apparatus - National Draeger, Inc.
AIRCAP - Lawn mowers ☆ - Aircap Industries Corp.
AIRCARE - Hair care products - Conair Corp.
AIRCARE - Medical apparatus - Apotheus Laboratories, Ltd.
AIRCAST - Sporting goods - Mueller Sports Medicine Inc.
AIRCAT - Boats - Aircat Airboats
AIRCEIL - Air purification systems - Envirco Corp.
AIRCEL SUPREME - Fishing tackle - Minnesota Mining & Manufacturing Co.
AIRCEL SYSTEMS - Dryers–commercial - Robert L. Olson
AIRCELL - Mattresses - Marcon Group, Inc.
AIRCISER - Exercising equipment - Diversified Products Corp.
AIRCLEAN - Hoods–industrial - Susan L. Fischer
AIRCLEAN 2000 - Health care products - Euroclean
AIRCLIPPER - Motor vehicle parts and accessories ☆ - National Cycle Inc.
AIRCOMASTER - Welding equipment - Controls Corp. of America
AIRCOMITE - Welding equipment - Controls Corp. of America
AIRCOMMUNICATOR - Computer peripheral equipment - Air Communications, Inc.
AIRCON - Glass products - PPG Industries, Inc.
AIRCON - Industrial gases - Airosol Co. Inc.
AIRCONTROLLER - Computer software - Air Communications, Inc.
AIRCORPS - Apparel and accessories - Mercury International Trading Corp.
AIRCOS - Luggage ☆ - Platt Luggage Inc.
AIRCRAFT - Musical instrument accessories - Stephen P. Poorman
AIRCRAFT - Watches - Bulova Corp.
AIRCRAFT FACTORY - Computer software - Abacus Software, Inc.
AIRCURE - Bandages - Pacific Exploration Inc.
AIRCYCLE - Sporting goods - Diversified Products Corp.
AIRDEMON - Filters–air - AAF-Mcquay Inc.
AIRDEMON - Filters–air - American Air Filter International (Replacement Filter Products)
AIRDO II - Hair care products - Helene Curtis Industries Inc.
AIRDO UNIMIST - Hair care products - Helene Curtis Industries Inc.
AIRDOCK - Computer hardware - Farallon Computing, Inc.
AIRDRI - Socks - William L. Staley
AIRDRIVER - Pumps - Schwinn Cycling & Fitness Inc.

AIRDRYVE - Machinery - ETM, Inc.
AIRE - Hosiery - Aire Hosiery Inc.
AIRE CELL - Mouthwashes - Gerbig Engineering Co.
AIRE FORCE - Deodorizer ☆ - Intex Chemical Inc.
AIRE-LITE - Uniforms–tailored - Angelica Uniform Group
AIRE-LITE - Wigs - Revlon General Wig Manufacturers, Inc.
AIRE PAK - Bags - Promotional Marketing Enterprises, Inc.
AIRE-REST - Mattresses - Intex Recreation Corp.
AIRE ROYALE - Ceiling fans - Smartel Inc.
AIRE SERV - Heaters–space - Aire Serv Heating & Air Conditioning, Inc.
AIRE-SWEEP - Compressors–air - Abatement Technologies Inc.
AIRE-TITE - Bags–paper - Bemis Co. Inc.
AIREBRUSH - Bookmarks ☆ - Blue Mountain Arts Inc.
AIREBRUSH FEELINGS - Greeting cards - Blue Mountain Arts Inc.
AIRECTOR - Racks - Jarke Corp.
AIREDALE - Eyeglasses - Art-Craft Optical Co.
AIRELITE - Furniture - Expo Displays
AIRELLE - Fabric stores - Jaunty Textile Div.
AIRELOOM - Mattresses - Aireloom Bedding Co.
AIRELOOM - Mattresses - Eastman House of California
AIREPEATER - Audio equipment - Colorado Computer Associates, Inc.
AIRES - Gadget bags - Kalimar, Inc.
AIRES - Jewelry - Aires Jewelry Co.
AIRESS - Jewelry - Airess, Inc.
AIREX - Television equipment ☆ - Lance Industries
AIRFIT - Footwear - Mercury International Trading Corp.
AIRFITNESS - Filters–air - Dust Free Inc.
AIRFLARE - Motor vehicle parts and accessories - National Cycle Inc.
AIRFLO PLEAT - Filters–air - Stephen Schlesinger
AIRFLOAT - Housewares - Airfloat Systems of Decatur, Inc.
AIRFLOTEK - Filters–air - Stephen Schlesinger
AIRFLOW - Goggles–safety - U.S. Safety Corp.
AIRFLOW - Mattresses - Paramount Industrial Companies Inc.
AIRFLOW - Sporting goods - Placo Products Co.
AIRFLOW - Varnishes ☆ - Kyanize Paint Co.
AIRFLOW 2000 - Business furniture - CenterCore Inc.
AIRFLOW BY CASABLANCA - Fans–electric - Casablanca Fan Co.
AIRFLOW FLEX - Brushes–hair ☆ - Spilo/Mehaz Worldwide
AIRFLOW POWER - Guns–dart - Placo Products Co.
AIRFLOW SYSTEMS, INC. - Filters–air - Airflow Systems, Inc.
AIRFLY - Machinery - Extrusion Services, Inc.
AIRFLYTE - Clocks - Tropar Manufacturing Co., Inc.
AIRFOIL - Golfing equipment - Dunlop Maxfli Sports Corp.
AIRFOIL - Sunglasses - Popside Inc.
AIRFORCE - Air purification systems - Ion Systems
AIRFRAME - Computer hardware - Crown International, Inc.
AIRFRAMES - Frames–eyeglass ☆ - Universal/Univis Inc.
AIRGAS - Packaging machines - ETM, Inc.
AIRGATOR - Boats - Alumitech Inc.
AIRGLIDE - Mattresses - Montgomery Ward & Co. Inc.
AIRGLIDE - Pneumatic locking devices - W.S.A., Inc.
AIRGLIDE - Shock absorbers–motor vehicle - Fluidrive Inc.
AIRGOMETER - Exercising equipment - Diversified Products Corp.
AIRGRIT DRY ETCHER - Inks - Matthews International Corp.
AIRGUIDE - Automotive parts and accessories - Airguide Instrument Co.
AIRGUN 40 - Piccolos - Paratech Inc.
AIRGUN DESIGNS - Sporting goods - Airgun Designs, Inc.
AIRHAWK - Motorcycles ☆ - National Cycle Inc.
AIRHAWK - Ventilation equipment - Enamel Products and Plating Co.
AIRHEAD - Aquariums–household - Marine Metal Products
AIRHEAD - Games - Mattel, Inc.
AIRHEADS - Candy - Van Melle Inc.
AIRHEADSET - Bicycles - Klein Bicycle Corp.
AIRHEART - Computer software ☆ - Broderbund Software, Inc.
AIRID - Hobby kits - Deep Flex Plastic Molds Inc.
AIRIEL - Deodorizers - Ecolab Inc.
AIRIES - Fabrics - Greenwood Mills Inc.
AIRILEE - Apparel stores–lingerie - Goddess Bra
AIRILY - Air freshener - Janalyn Laboratories Inc.
AIRIS - Water–bottled or canned - Sparkletts Water Co.
AIRJET - Chemical preparations - GC Thorsen, Inc.
AIRJET - Nozzles - Spraying Systems Co.
AIRJET - Yarn - Parkdale Mills, Inc.
AIRJUGS - Housewares - Kenco Incentives
AIRKEM - Cleaning preparations - Ecolab Inc.
AIRKLEEN - Filters–air - Fiberbond Corp.

AIRLAN CAN - Computer hardware - Solectek Corp.
AIRLENS - Contact lenses ☆ - Wesley-Jessen Co.
AIRLESSCO - Paint sprayers - Desco Manufacturing Co. Inc.
AIRLIE GARDENS - Floor coverings–carpet and rugs - Shaheen Carpet Mills
AIRLIFT COPTER - Toys - Fisher-Price, Inc.
AIRLINE - Televisions ☆ - Montgomery Ward & Co. Inc.
AIRLINE-61 RECORDS - Recording label - Airline 61 Records, Inc.
AIRLINE CARGO SERVICES, INC. - Air transportation - Airline Cargo Services, Inc.
AIRLITE - Brushes–hair ☆ - I. Sekine Co. Inc.
AIRLITE - Dialing devices–telephone - Baltimore Luggage Co.
AIRLITE - Hot tubs–fiberglass - Starlite Leisure Products, Inc.
AIRLITE - Medical apparatus - Racal Health and Safety Inc.
AIRLITE - Medical apparatus - Roho, Inc.
AIRLITE - Ophthalmic goods - Foremost Optical Products
AIRLOC - Office supplies - Scripto-Tokai Corp.
AIRLOCK - Tobacco pouches - Allied Products Corp.
AIRLOFT - Sleeping bag - CW Group
AIRLOGIC - Beds–hospital - Lectus, Inc.
AIRLOOM - Floor coverings - Congoleum Corp.
AIRLUM - Candles - Miracle Candle Co.
AIRMAN - Radio communications equipment - Netro Corp.
AIRMAP - Navigational instruments - Lowrance Electronics, Inc.
AIRMARK - Tools - Diamond West & Associates
AIRMASTER - Frames–eyeglass ☆ - Universal/Univis Inc.
AIRMASTER - Pumps - Eugene G. Danner Manufacturing Inc.
AIRMASTER PLUS - Compressors–air - Kopykake
AIRMATE - Health care products - Spinal Technologies
AIRMATE - Medical apparatus - Mentor O & O Inc.
AIRMAX - Footwear - Nike, Inc.
AIRMAX - Motor vehicle parts and accessories - David Lee Stevenson
AIRMAX - Motor vehicle parts and accessories - James P. Wright
AIRMEDIA - Computer software - EX Machina, Inc.
AIRMOLD - Containers - W.R. Grace & Co.
AIRMONT CLASSICS - Publisher's imprints - Airmont Publishing Co. Inc.
AIRMOUSE - Remote control devices - Selectech Ltd.
AIRMOVES - Dryers–hair - Windmere Corp.
AIRMULTI - Air conditioning equipment - Mitsubishi Electronics America Inc.
AIRNXRAD - Computer software - Airnxrad, Inc.
AIRO-FLO - Filters–air - Air Kontrol Inc.
AIRO NATURAL SOLUTIONS - Air purification systems - Norman Gittelman
AIRO NATURAL SOLUTIONS FOR LIFE'S SMELLY PROBLEMS MARINE FRESH - Filters–air - Norman Gittelman
AIRO NATURAL SOLUTIONS FOR LIFE'S SMELLY PROBLEMS MIGHTY FRESH - Air purification systems - Norman Gittelman
AIROBIC BALL - Exercising equipment - Caroline Corning Creager
AIROFLY - Machinery - Airofly USA International, Inc.
AIROGRATE - Pipes–tobacco - S.M. Frank & Co. Inc. (Kaywoodie-Yello-Bole-Medico)
AIROKILL - Insecticides - Airosol Co. Inc.
AIROMAX - Air purification systems - Airomax Corp.
AIRONE - Telephones - Claircom Communications Group, Inc.
AIROS BY CAMP - Compressors - Camp, Inc.
AIROSCENT - Deodorizers - Airosol Co. Inc.
AIROSOL - Industrial gases - Airosol Co. Inc.
AIROSPACE - Tents - Coleman Co., Inc.
AIROTEX - See **SUPERTEX**
AIROWISP - Crocheted and knitted items - Puritan Sportswear Corp.
AIRPAC - Compressors–air ☆ - Goodall Manufacturing Co.
AIRPAINTER - Sprayers - Testor Corp.
AIRPEL - Machine parts - Airpot Corp.
AIRPEN - Chemical preparations - Michele Hester
AIRPLANE SPECTACULAR - Games - Addison-Wesley Publishing Co.
AIRPLANE STATION - Toys–airplanes - Paul K. Guillow Inc.
AIRPLAY - Computers - Avid Technology, Inc.
AIRPLUS - Motor vehicle parts and accessories - James P. Wright
AIRPLUS - Shoe accessories - Implus Corp.
AIRPLY - Plywood - Harbor Sales Co.
AIRPOCKETS - House furnishings ☆ - Gear Holdings, Inc.
AIRPORT - Computer software - Windata, Inc.
AIRPORT - Dinnerware–glass ☆ - WMF/USA
AIRPORT - Raisins - Enoch Packing Co. Inc.
AIRPORT AMBASSADOR - Pins–jewelry - Service Institute, USA Nice
AIRPORT & SCENERY DESIGNER - Computer software - Abacus Software, Inc.
AIRPORT-TOWER - Window shades ☆ - View-Guard Shade Co.

AIRPOT - Machine parts - Airpot Corp.
AIRPOTS - Housewares - Kenco Incentives
AIRPOWER - Batteries - Best Laboratories
AIRPOWER - Batteries - R & T Distributors, Inc.
AIRPOWER - Pumps ☆ - Big Boy Products Inc.
AIRPRINT - Computer hardware - Whitaker Corp.
AIRPRO - Machine parts - Taiyo America, Inc.
AIRQUEST - Heating and cooling systems - Inter-City Products Corp. (USA)
AIRR PONY - Apparel and accessories - Larry T. Ziegler
A.I.R.S. - Medical apparatus - Omron Healthcare, Inc.
AIRS - Perfumes - Airs International, Inc.
AIRSCREEN - Conveyors - Ohio Blow Pipe Co.
AIRSEAL - Bicycle parts - Delta Cycle Corp.
AIRSEAL - Electric lighting equipment - Genlyte Group Inc.
AIRSEAL - Electrical equipment - Kearney
AIRSEAL - Lighting fixtures - Thomas Lighting (Accent Division)
AIRSET - Hair care products - Redken Laboratories, Inc.
AIRSET - Paints ☆ - Fuller-O'Brien Paints Inc.
AIRSHARE - Computer peripheral equipment - National Semiconductor Corp.
AIRSHIELD - Nail care products - American Consolidated Manufacturing Co., Inc.
AIRSHOW NETWORK - Electronic equipment - Airshow, Inc.
AIRSLOT - Boats ☆ - Wellcraft Marine Corp.
AIRSO - Thread ☆ - Perfect Thread Co. Inc.
AIRSOC - Headwear - Airsoc, Inc.
AIRSOURCE - Automotive parts and accessories - Mathews Equipment, Inc.
AIRSOURCE - Computer software - Silverlake Communications, Inc.
AIRSPACE - Glass–flat - Guardian Industries Corp. (Architectural Glass Div.)
AIRSPORT - Sporting goods ☆ - USA Sport Eyewear
AIRSPRAY - Hair care products - Vidal Sassoon Inc.
AIRSPUN - Brassieres (Bras) ☆ - Playtex Apparel, Inc.
AIRSPUN - Cosmetics - Coty Inc.
AIRSPUN POWDERESSENCE - Cosmetics - Coty Inc.
AIRSTAR - Hoists - Columbus Mckinnon Corp.
AIRSTAR 99 - Navigational instruments - Satloc, Inc.
AIRSTAR 2000 - Navigational instruments - Satloc, Inc.
AIRSTATION - Compressors–air - Black & Decker Corp.
AIRSTOP - Tires - Michelin Tire Corp.
AIRSTREAM - Compressors–air - Emglo Products L.P. (Emglo Air Compressors)
AIRSTREAM - Motor vehicles–motor homes - Airstream Inc.
AIRSTRIKE ROCKET ASSORTMENT - Fireworks - B.J. Alan Co. Inc.
AIRSTRIP - Paint removers - Inventive Machine Corp.
AIRSTRIP-INTERLOCK - Floor coverings - American Floor Products Co. Inc.
AIRSTYLER - Curling irons–electric - Andis Co.
AIRSTYLER - Hair care products - Fromm Industries
AIRSUPPLY - Footwear - Marlboro Footworks, Ltd.
AIRSUPPLY COMFORT - Footwear - Marlboro Footworks, Ltd.
AIRSURFER - Computer peripheral equipment - Netwave Technologies, Inc.
AIRTEC - Agricultural machinery - Airtec Sprayers, Inc.
AIRTECH - Motor vehicle parts and accessories - Pro Air, Inc.
AIRTEMP - Air conditioning equipment - Fedders North America Inc.
AIRTEX ULTRAFLO - Automotive parts and accessories - UIS, Inc.
AIRTIGHT GARAGE - Books–comic - Starwatcher Graphics, Inc.
AIRTIQUE - Boats - Correct Craft Inc.
AIRTOUCH - Computer software - Airtouch Communications, Inc.
AIRTRAN - Aircraft - Airtran Airways, Inc.
AIRTRAN AIRWAYS - Aircraft–airplanes - Airtran Airways, Inc.
AIRTRANS FUEL TESTERS - Electrical testing instruments - Airtrans, Inc.
AIRTRED - Floor coverings ☆ - Tarkett, Inc.
AIRTROL - Plasters - United States Gypsum Co.
AIRTRON - Air purification systems - Space Biospheres Venture
AIRTRUE - Computer software - Air Communications, Inc.
AIRUG - Mats - Superior Manufacturing Group/Notrax Floor Matting
AIRVENT - Floor coverings ☆ - Tarkett, Inc.
AIRWALK - Forms–preprinted - Items International Airwalk Inc.
AIRWALKER - Toys - Dye-namic Movement Products, Inc.
AIRWALKER - Toys–models - Estes Industries
AIRWALKERS - Aircraft–balloons - Anagram International, Inc.
AIRWARE - Pagers - Pronet
AIRWARES - Kites - What's Up
AIRWASH - Deodorizers - E. Davis Inc.
AIRWATCH - Medical apparatus - Enact Products
AIRWAVE - Hair care products - Kenra Laboratories, Inc.
AIRWAVE ADVENTURE - Toys–electronic - Tiger Media Inc.
AIRWAVE COMMUNICATIONS - Pagers - Thomas E. Mack

☆ = Now out of production

AIRWAX - Recording label - Airwax Records Productions
AIRWAY - Coffee ✩ - Safeway Stores Inc.
AIRWAY - Compasses–magnetic - Sherrill Corp.
AIRWAY - Luggage - Airway Industries, Inc.
AIRWAY - Medical uniforms - OTC Professional Appliances
AIRWAY - Recording label - Earwig Music Co. Inc.
AIRWAY EXPRESS - Envelopes - Quality Park Products Co.
AIRWAYS - Watches - Gruen Marketing Corp.
AIRWEAR - Frames–eyeglass - Liberty Optical Manufacturing Co.
AIRWEIGHT - Revolvers - Smith & Wesson Corp.
AIRWEIGHT - Tools–hand-operated - Armament Systems and Procedures, Inc.
AIRWELL - Fabrics - Greenwood Mills Inc.
AIRWICK - Deodorizers - Airwick Industries
AIRWICK - Deodorizers - Reckitt & Colman, Inc.
AIRWOLF - Toys–airplanes - Cox Products Inc.
AIRWOLF - Toys–models ✩ - ERTL Co., Inc.
AIRWORKS - Air mattresses - Kinetic Concepts, Inc.
AIRWORTHY - Luggage - American Flyer
AIRX - Deodorizers - Bullen Companies Inc.
AIRY TALES - Deodorizers - Atmosphere Products Co. Inc.
AIS - Medical apparatus - Applied Immune Sciences, Inc.
AIS ADVANCED INFORMATION SYSTEMS LLC FUELING TALKER - Electrical industrial apparatus - Advanced Information Systems (A.I.S.), LLC
AISHA - Recording label - Jazz Composer's Orchestra Association Inc.
AISLE GLIDER - Luggage - Monarch Luggage Co., Inc.
AISLE LIGHTER - Lighting fixtures - Hubbell Lighting, Inc. (Lighting Div.)
AISLE RANGER - Forklifts - Baker Material Handling Corp.
AIT - Computer software - Advanced Interconnection Technology, Inc.
AIT - Transducers - Ait, Inc.
AITA - Bedding–linen - Dan River Inc.
AITLESS - Apparel–women's ✩ - Bali Co. Inc.
AIWA - Audio equipment - Aiwa America Inc.
AIX/ESA - Computer software - International Business Machines Corp.
AIYANA - Skin care products - Oxyfresh Worldwide, Inc.
AJ - Furniture–wood - Bassett Furniture Industries, Inc.
AJ - Jewelry - Astoria Jewelry Manufacturing Co., Inc.
A.J. BRANDON - Apparel and accessories - Kellwood Co.
A.J. BRANDON - Apparel–women's - A.J. Brandon, Inc.
AJ COLOURS - Shirts - Alexander Julian Inc.
A.J. DOG - Toys–banks - A.J. Renzi Plastic Corp.
A.J. TREMONT - Apparel - Boston Trading Ltd. Inc.
AJACCIO - Glassware–household - Durand International
AJAHA - Cymbals ✩ - Fred Gretsch Enterprises
AJANTA - Giftware - Ajanta Enterprises
AJAX - Brushes–paint - Corona Brushes Inc.
AJAX - Cleaning preparations–household - Colgate-Palmolive Co.
AJAX - Combs - Ajax Comb Co. (Div. of Antonio's Manufacturing, Inc.)
AJAX - Envelopes - ATAPCO Office Products Group
AJAX - Gutters–metal ✩ - American Building Components Co.
AJAX - Hardware - Herr & Co. Inc.
AJAX - Jewelry - Stainless Steelcraft Co.
AJAX - Ladders–metal - Rich Ladder Co.
AJAX - Paper - Fay Paper Products Inc.
AJAX - Thread - Threads USA Div.
AJAX - Tools - O.P. Link Handle Co. Inc.
AJAX - Varnishes ✩ - Sherwin-Williams Automotive Finishes Corp.
AJAX CON EXPEL - Cleaning preparations - Colgate-Palmolive Co.
AJAX EXPERT - Cleaning preparations–household - Colgate-Palmolive Co.
AJB-5 - Musical instrument accessories - Seymour Duncan Pickups
AJBOYD - Doors - Leucadia, Inc.
AJE - Perfumes - Revlon Consumer Products Corp.
AJENIS - Computer software - Plansoft, Inc.
AJI-CO - Japanese hors d'oeuvres - Ajinomoto USA, Inc.
AJINOMOTO - Chemical preparations - Ajinomoto USA, Inc.
AJIRO - Wallpaper - Maya Romanoff Corp.
A.J.K. MUSIC - Labels–paper - K-Tel International, Inc.
AJOUTER - Apparel–athletic - Ajouter, Inc.
AJP - Jewelry - Leer Gem Ltd.
AJ'S - Hobby kits - Twinn-K Hobbies Inc.
A.J.S. - Wines - Foxwood Wine Cellars
A.J.'S FRISCO - Barbecue sauce - Golden Whisk Pasta Partners
AJUST-A-RAIL - Rails–iron - Leslie-Locke, Inc.
AJUSTA - Pumps–water - Rosemond Manufacturing, Inc.
AJUSTA FLEX - Lamps - Cannon Products Inc.
AJUSTA-HEAD - Slips - Beverly Vogue Co.

AJUSTAFIT - Braces–orthopedic - Slim-Ez Mr. America Manufacturing, Inc.
AK - Electronic equipment - Avantek, Inc.
AK - Food products - Avo-King International, Inc.
AK - Jewelry–precious - Atasay Gold, Inc.
AK - Steel products - AK Steel Corp.
AK - Thread - Scandinavian House Imports Inc.
AK-1 - Audio equipment - R & T Enterprises
AK:BA - Recording label - Jazz Composer's Orchestra Association Inc.
AK-CIDE - Pharmaceutical preparations - Akorn Inc.
AK-CON-A - Antihistamine preparations ✩ - Akorn Inc.
AK-DEX - Pharmaceutical preparations - Akorn Inc.
AK-DILATE - Pharmaceutical preparations - Akorn Inc.
AK-FLUOR - Pharmaceutical preparations - Akorn Inc.
AK-HOMATROPINE - Pharmaceutical preparations ✩ - Akorn Inc.
AK-MYCIN - Pharmaceutical preparations ✩ - Akorn Inc.
AK-NACL - Pharmaceutical preparations - Akorn Inc.
AK-NEFRIN - Pharmaceutical preparations - Akorn Inc.
AK-NEO-CORT - Pharmaceutical preparations ✩ - Akorn Inc.
AK-NEO-DEX - Pharmaceutical preparations - Akorn Inc.
AK-PENTOLATE - Pharmaceutical preparations - Akorn Inc.
AK-POLY-BAC - Pharmaceutical preparations - Akorn Inc.
AK-PRED - Pharmaceutical preparations - Akorn Inc.
AK-RAMYCIN - Pharmaceutical preparations ✩ - Akorn Inc.
AK-RATABS - Pharmaceutical preparations ✩ - Akorn Inc.
AK-RINSE - Pharmaceutical preparations - Akorn Inc.
AK-SPORE - Pharmaceutical preparations - Akorn Inc.
AK-SPORE HC - Pharmaceutical preparations - Akorn Inc.
AK STEEL - Steel - AK Steel Corp.
AK-SULF - Pharmaceutical preparations - Akorn Inc.
AK-T-CAINE - Pharmaceutical preparations - Akorn Inc.
AK-TAINE - Pharmaceutical preparations ✩ - Akorn Inc.
AK-TATE - Pharmaceutical preparations ✩ - Akorn Inc.
AK-TRACIN - Pharmaceutical preparations - Akorn Inc.
AK-TROL - Pharmaceutical preparations - Akorn Inc.
AK-VERNACON - Pharmaceutical preparations ✩ - Akorn Inc.
AK-ZOL - Pharmaceutical preparations ✩ - Akorn Inc.
AK8 - Paints - Triangle Coatings Inc.
A.K.A. - Paints - Van Aken International
AKA KIDS - Apparel and accessories - Rhobbe Inc.
A.K.A. WEAR - Apparel and accessories - Breton Industries
AKABUKA - Hair care products ✩ - J. Frey Enterprises Inc.
AKADAMA - Wines - Suntory International Corp.
AKADAMA PLUM ROYALE (PLUME WINE) - Wines - Suntory International Corp.
AKADEMUS - Computer software - Companion Corp.
AKAI - Electronic equipment - Akai America Ltd.
AKAMAI - Apparel and accessories - Timothy J. Bedison
AKANTUS - Dinnerware–glass ✩ - Henriksen Imports Inc.
AKARI - Lamps - Isamu Noguchi Foundation, Inc.
AKAROGUE - Apparel and accessories - Sport 1 Multimedia
AKARPINE - Pharmaceutical preparations - Akorn Inc.
AKASHA - Recording label - Akasha Records
AKASHIC - Labels–paper - Akashic Records
AKASHIC CONCEPTS - Computer software - FF255, Inc.
AKASHIC RECORDING STUDIO - Recording label - Timothy Bishop-Prasanna
AKBAR MASHTI - Ice cream - Akbar Mashti Corp.
AKBETA - Pharmaceutical preparations - Akorn Inc.
AKBTF - Apparel and accessories - A & K International
AKC - Recording label - Sonotone Corp.
AKD - Seats–automobile ✩ - Cramer Inc.
AKE-A-WAY - Health care products - Fleetwood Co.
AKEMI - Fabrics–polyester - Hastings Plastics Co.
AKEMPUCKY - Lubricants - Nuresearch
AKER - Bathroom fixtures - Aker Plastics Co. Inc.
AKERS - Pens - J.E. Akers Co. Inc.
AKERS RECORDING COMPANY - Recording label - William Akers Douglass
AKG - Audio equipment - AKG Acoustics Inc.
AKG FUEL - Vitamins and nutritional supplements - Twinlab
AKH - Helmets–athletic - Ankel International, Inc.
AKH - Machine tool dies - AKH Inc.
AKICA - Cameras - Akica Corp.
AKIKO ON THE PLANET SMOO - Books–comic - Sirius Entertainment, Inc.
AKILA - Sandals - Playazul International Inc.
AKILEINE - Skin care products - Nailtex Inc.
AKIN - Skin care products - Helene Curtis Industries Inc.
AKINA - Hair care products - Worldwide Cosmetics

AKINETON - Pharmaceutical preparations - Knoll Pharmaceutical Co.
AKITA OTOME - Food products - Nishimoto Trading Co. Ltd.
AKKO - Furniture polish and wax - Akko Inc.
AKKRO-7T - Glue–household or industrial - Tamms Industries Co.
AKLO - Glass–window - Corning Inc.
A.K.M. - Apparel–men's - Swank Inc.
AKN SKINCARE - Vitamins and nutritional supplements - Nature's Way Products, Inc.
AKNE-MYCIN - Antibiotics - Center Laboratories/Hermal Dermatology Group
AKNE-ZYME - Health care products - Enzymatic Therapy, Inc.
AKNEKAPS - Pharmaceutical preparations - Alto Pharmaceuticals Inc.
AKO - Crab meat–canned or cured - Amtorg Trading Corp.
AKO - Heating equipment - Ako-Ismet Electrical Appliances, Inc.
AKO - Recording label - AKO Records
AKONA - Concrete products - Akona Chemical Corp.
AKONA - Life preservers - Akona Adventure Gear, Inc.
AKONA FLEX - Caulking compounds - Akona Chemical Corp.
AKONAKOTE - Concrete repair products - Akona Chemical Corp.
AKORN ANTIOXIDANTS - Pharmaceutical preparations - Akorn Inc.
AKPRO - Pharmaceutical preparations ☆ - Akorn Inc.
AKRINOL - Pharmaceutical preparations - Schering-Plough Healthcare Products
AKRO - Mats - Akro Corp.
AKRO - Paints - Akron Paint and Varnish, Inc.
AKRO-NST - Cabinets - Akro-Mils Inc.
AKROL - Adhesives and sealants - C.B. Dolge Co.
AKROMATIC - Paints ☆ - Akron Paint and Varnish, Inc.
AKRON - Tiles–ceramic - Dal-Tile Corp.
AKRON - Varnishes - Akron Paint and Varnish, Inc.
AKRON - Water–bottled or canned - Akron Mineral Spring Water Co.
AKRONAMEL - Enamels - Akron Paint and Varnish, Inc.
AKRONT RIMS - Motorcycle-tire rims - Cosmopolitan Motors Inc.
AKROPOLIS - Olive oil - John's Import Foods, Inc.
AKROS - Pharmaceutical preparations - Lumex, Inc.
AKROS - Recording label - Clone Records
AKROS - Varnishes ☆ - Akron Paint and Varnish, Inc.
AKROS DFD GELL CELL - Medical apparatus - Lumex, Inc.
AKROSPAR - Varnishes ☆ - Akron Paint and Varnish, Inc.
AKROTEX - Pharmaceutical preparations - Lumex, Inc.
AKROTITE - Enamels - Akron Paint and Varnish, Inc.
AKS - Sporting goods - Omni Scientific Inc.
AKSARBEN - Flour–blended ☆ - ADM Milling Co.
AKSHUN - Laxatives - Seatrace Co.
AKT AXIS - Apparel–men's - Richard Solomon
AKTA - Skin care products - Gunilla of Sweden
AKTAR PARIS - Cosmetics - Paris Designs, Inc.
AKTEX - Skin care products ☆ - Fox Pharmacal Inc.
AKTI-TABS - Pet products - Gerard-Pellham Co.
AKTIGEN - Pet products - Gerard-Pellham Co.
AKTILURE - Pet products - Gerard-Pellham Co.
AKTINOL - Disinfectants - Gerard-Pellham Co.
AKTOB - Pharmaceutical preparations ☆ - Akorn Inc.
AKTOLEUM - Pet products - Gerard-Pellham Co.
AKTON - Cushions - Action Products Inc.
AKU - Fishing lures - Boone Bait Co. Inc.
AKUA - Boating equipment and accessories - Alan Kinkead
AKURET - Tools–hand-operated - Kastar Inc.
AKWA-TEARS - Pharmaceutical preparations - Akorn Inc.
AKWATEK - Fabrics–polyester - Comfort Technologies, Inc.
AKX CLEANER - Cleaning preparations - Air Kontrol Inc.
AKX COIL CLEANER - Cleaning preparations - Air Kontrol Inc.
AL - Jewelry - Rogers Ltd.
AL - Recording label - Starbound Publishing
AL - Tool boxes - Artcadi Products
AL-1 - Lubricants - Envir-O-Lube, Inc.
AL AFFILIATED LABORATORIES NVIRO MASTER - Disinfectants - Affiliated Paper Companies, Inc.
AL AMIR - Vegetables–canned - Tut's International Export and Import Co.
AL & REED'S - Ice cream - Reed's Dairy, Inc.
AL AUDIOLOGIC - Medical apparatus - Audiologic, Inc.
AL-AY - Pharmaceutical preparations - JMI-Canton Pharmaceuticals
AL BASHA - Olives–canned - Nicola International, Inc.
AL CAFE - Coffee - Herold & Miller Inc.
AL CAPONE - Cigars ☆ - Swisher International, Inc.
AL-CAROID - Antacids ☆ - Sterling Winthrop Inc.
AL CELL - Vitamins and nutritional supplements - Natural Organics, Inc.

AL-CHROMA - Asphalt felts and coatings - DMF Industries Inc. (Al-Chroma Div.)
AL DENTE - Pasta - Al Dente Inc.
AL +DENTE - Tomato pastes and sauces - Stanislaus Food Products Co.
AL DI MEOLA - Guitars ☆ - Dimarzio, Inc.
AL E. - Apparel and accessories - Al E. Productions
AL E GATOR - Toys–stuffed - Metro Private Investigations, Inc.
AL E KAT - Toys–stuffed - Russ Berrie and Co., Inc.
AL FALAHA PAR EXCELLENCE - Rice - Producers Rice Mill, Inc.
AL FRESCO - Lipsticks - Estee Lauder Inc.
AL FRESCO - Paper - Riverside Paper Corp.
AL FRESCO - Spaghetti sauces ☆ - Campbell Soup Co.
AL GROUP - Office furniture–metal ☆ - Metier Furniture Corp.
AL-JAX - Swimming-pool algicide - Value Line Laboratories
AL-KO-LAK - Shellac ☆ - Mantrose-Haeuser Co. Inc.
AL-MATT - Mats - George A. Keith
AL-NAL - Pharmaceutical preparations ☆ - Cumberland Pharmacal Co. Inc.
AL-PA-KA - Yarn - Lion Brand Yarn Co.
AL PIERSON - Recording label ☆ - Telemark Dance Records
AL-PRO-COTE - Paints - Floquil-Polly S Color Corp.
AL-QADIM - Games - Tsr, Inc.
AL-R - Pharmaceutical preparations - Saron Pharmacal Corp.
AL-RITE - Food products - Al-Rite Fruits & Syrups
AL SIMMONS - Toys - TMP International, Inc.
ALA-BATH - Bath salts - Del-Ray Labs, Inc.
ALA CARTE - Earthenware ☆ - Trend Pacific Inc.
ALA-CARTE - Strollers–baby ☆ - Evenflo Co.
ALA-CORT - Pharmaceutical preparations - Del-Ray Labs, Inc.
ALA-DINER - Novelty items ☆ - Aladdin Industries, Inc.
ALA LAB SYSTEM - Computer software ☆ - American Language Academy Inc.
ALA-QUIN - Pharmaceutical preparations - Del-Ray Labs, Inc.
ALA SANTE - Wines - Bella Napoli Winery
ALA-SCALP HP - Pharmaceutical preparations - Del-Ray Labs, Inc.
ALA-SEB - Shampoos - Del-Ray Labs, Inc.
ALA SEBT - Shampoos - Del-Ray Labs, Inc.
ALA-TET - Pharmaceutical preparations ☆ - Del-Ray Labs, Inc.
ALA TEX - Seafood products–fresh or frozen - Mobile Freezers Inc.
ALABAM GIRL - Pickles - Green Bay Foods Co.
ALABAM GIRL - Pickles ☆ - Whitfield Foods, Inc.
ALABAMA - Processed meats - Saramar Corp.
ALABAMA SLAMMER - Liquors - White Rock Distilleries Inc.
ALABAMACARBONATES - Chemicals - Alabama Carbonates, L.P.
ALABASTER - Cabinets - Schrock
ALABASTER - Dinnerware–glass ☆ - Nikko Ceramics Inc.
ALABASTER DUST - Resins–epoxy ☆ - Deep Flex Plastic Molds Inc.
ALABIN - Health care products - Aseptico Laboratories Inc.
ALACAZAM - Recording label - Alcazar Productions
ALACAZAR - Watches - Elgin Watch Co.
ALACEN - Nutritional product - New Zealand Milk Products Inc.
ALACID - Food products - New Zealand Milk Products Inc.
ALACO - Cheese - New Zealand Milk Products Inc.
ALACRA - Recording label - Jazz Composer's Orchestra Association Inc.
ALACRITY - Boats ☆ - Wells Yachts Inc.
ALACRON - Circuit boards - Alacron Inc.
ALADAN - Computer software - General Electric Co.
ALADAN GOLD - Gloves–rubber - Aladan Corp.
ALADAN GOLD - Gloves–rubber - Durex Consumer Products
ALADDIN - Automotive parts and accessories - Automatic Equipment Manufacturing Co.
ALADDIN - Binders - Dennison National Co.
ALADDIN - Black & White video magnifier - Telesensory Systems Inc.
ALADDIN - Candy - Alyamani Delicacy
ALADDIN - Floor waxes - Puritan-Churchill Chemical Co.
ALADDIN - Frames–eyeglass - May Optical Co. Inc.
ALADDIN - Hosiery - Kayser-Roth Corp.
ALADDIN - Housewares - Aladdin Industries, Inc.
ALADDIN - Lawn mowers - Orbex Inc.
ALADDIN - Lawn mowers ☆ - Hoffco Inc.
ALADDIN - Snack foods - Grist Mill Co.
ALADDIN - Tools ☆ - New England Carbide
ALADDIN - Yarn - Henry's Attic
ALADDIN ACTIVITY CENTER - Computer storage devices–optical - Walt Disney Co.
ALADDIN BOOKS - Publisher's imprints - MacMillan Publishing Co. Inc.
ALADDIN DELIGHTS - Candy - Alyamani Delicacy

☆ = Now out of production

ALADDIN LAMP - Deodorizers - Quality of Life Associates

ALADDIN RECORDS - Recording label - Caltex Trading, Inc.

ALADDIN STORYBOOKS - Publisher's imprints - MacMillan Publishing Co. Inc.

ALADDINEETTS - Lanterns–kerosene ☆ - Aladdin Industries, Inc.

ALADDIN'S BROWN BAGGER W.M. - Containers–insulated - Aladdin Industries, Inc.

ALADDIN'S GENIE - Cleaning preparations - Aladdin Products Inc.

ALADDIN'S LAMP - Games - International Gamco, Inc.

ALADDIN'S LAMP GAME, THE - Board game - University Games Corp.

ALADERM - Skin care products - Princess Pharmaceuticals

ALADIN - Scuba diving equipment - Johnson Worldwide Associates, Inc.

ALADIN - Wallpaper - Surface Industries Inc.

ALADRINE - Pharmaceutical preparations ☆ - Schering-Plough Healthcare Products

ALAGA - Syrup - Whitfield Foods, Inc.

ALAGA BUTTER LITE - Syrup - Whitfield Foods, Inc.

ALAGA LITE - Syrup - Whitfield Foods, Inc.

ALAGEL - Pharmaceutical preparations - Century Pharmaceuticals Inc.

ALAIN - Sporting goods - FTM Sports

ALAIN COURT CASUALS - Apparel and accessories ☆ - L & M Distribution Inc.

ALAIN MIKLI - Sunglasses - Alain Mikli

ALAIN PIRRAUX - Watches - Majesti Watch Co. Inc.

ALAIN SILBERSTEIN - Watches - Chatom Collection

ALAKEF - Coffee - Alakef Coffee Roasters, Inc.

ALAMAC - Fabrics - West Point-Pepperell Inc.

ALAMAG - Pharmaceutical preparations - Barre-National, Inc.

ALAMAG - Pharmaceutical preparations - United Research Laboratories, Inc.

ALAMANCE - Furniture - Boling Co.

ALAMBA - Apparel–men's - Alps Sportswear Manufacturing Co.

ALAMBIC - Type faces - John S. Hicks

ALAMBRE - Cases–eyeglass - G.R.V. Associates, Ltd.

ALAMEDA - Clocks - Ridgeway Clock Co.

ALAMEDA - Coffee - Merchants Coffee Co.

ALAMIN - Milk - New Zealand Milk Products Inc.

ALAMINE - Pharmaceutical preparations ☆ - Vortech Pharmaceuticals

ALAMINE-C - Pharmaceutical preparations ☆ - Vortech Pharmaceuticals

ALAMO - Amplifiers ☆ - Castiglione Accordion

ALAMO - Blinds–venetian - Alamo Distributors

ALAMO - Cigars - Finck Cigar Co.

ALAMO - Darts and dart games - Dart World Inc.

ALAMO - Food products - Alamo Masa Co.

ALAMO - Footwear - Acme Boot Co., Inc.

ALAMO - Frames–eyeglass - Hudson Optical Corp.

ALAMO - Furniture - Bean Station Furniture Factory Inc.

ALAMO - Handbags - Honey Fashions Ltd.

ALAMO - Musical instruments and accessories - Alamo Music Products

ALAMO - Pet products - ALPO Petfoods Inc.

ALAMO - Tortillas - Magic Wand Food Products, Inc.

ALAMO - Toys–stuffed - Russ Berrie and Co., Inc.

A ALAMO - Machinery ☆ - Alamo Industrial

ALAMO BASIC - Pet products - ALPO Petfoods Inc.

ALAMO E - Flowers, plants, and seeds - Jacklin Seed

ALAMO STREET - Vegetable sauces - Sauces Unlimited Inc.

ALAMO SWEET - Cigars - Finck Cigar Co.

ALAMO, THE - Computer hardware and software - Omnicomp Graphics Corp.

ALAMO WIRE WORKS - Eyeglasses - Sugerose, Inc.

ALAMODOME - Clothing - Via Metropolitan Transit

ALAMODOME SAN ANTONIO - Seat cushions - Via Metropolitan Transit

ALAN - Dolls - Mattel, Inc.

ALAN & COMPANY - Apparel and accessories - Alan Stuart, Inc.

ALAN BUCKINGHAM - Shirts - Pacific Teaze

ALAN FLUSSER - Apparel - Alan Flusser

ALAN FLUSSER - Hosiery–men's - S.L. Gilbert Co.

ALAN INTERNATIONAL - Skin care products - Denman Inc.

ALAN LEBOW - Apparel–men's - Hartz & Co., Inc.

ALAN LEBOW - Neckties - Alan Lebow, Inc.

ALAN MALEY - Calendars ☆ - Amcal Inc.

ALAN SPORT - Apparel - Alan Stuart, Inc.

ALAN STUART - Apparel–men's - Alan Stuart, Inc.

ALANA - Earthenware ☆ - Waterford Wedgewood USA, Inc.

ALANA - Fans–electric - Casablanca Fan Co.

ALANA - Toys–stuffed - Dakin Inc.

ALANA GALE - Apparel stores–lingerie - Gold Seal Garter Corp.

ALANAP - Herbicides - Uniroyal Chemical Co. Inc. (Crop Protection Div.)

ALANATE - Food products - New Zealand Milk Products Inc.

ALANITE - Games - Jax Ltd.

ALANNA - Frames–eyeglass - U.S. Optical Frame Co.

ALANNA - Sauces - Bewley Irish Imports

ALAN'S BAKERY SHOPPE - Doughnuts - Rich Products Corp.

ALAN'S X-TENDA FORK - Novelty items - Clayton Charles Enterprizes, Inc.

ALANTE - Hair care products - Avanti International Ltd.

ALANTE - Rackets–racquetball - Ektelon

ALANTEC - Computers - Alantec Corp.

ALANTEL - Health care products - DQP

ALAPRO - Food products - New Zealand Milk Products Inc.

ALAQUA - Wines - Alaqua Vineyards

ALAR - Plant growth regulators - Uniroyal Chemical Co. Inc. (Crop Protection Div.)

ALAREN - Food products - New Zealand Milk Products Inc.

ALARIS - Circuit boards–printed - Alaris, Inc.

ALARM-A-GRIP - Personal alarms - Invention Marketing Inc.

ALARM-A-LITE - Medical apparatus ☆ - Lumex, Inc.

ALARM BUSTERS - Toy vehicles - Intex Recreation Corp.

ALARM CENTER - Computer software - Security Information Systems Inc.

ALARM GUARD - Alarms–personal - 21st Century Innovations, Inc.

ALARM GUARD - Fire-detection devices ☆ - In/Comm

ALARM LOCK SYSTEMS - Alarm systems - Napco Security Systems Inc.

ALARM RANGER - Antenna - Antenna World, Inc.

ALARM95 - Computer software - Parsons Technology, Inc.

ALARMA - Recording label - Frontline Records

ALARMINATOR - Safety products - Alarminator, Inc.

ALARMING CONCEPTS, INC. - Alarms–personal - Alarming Concepts, Inc.

ALARON - Electronic equipment - Alaron Inc.

ALASED - Antacids ☆ - Norgine Laboratories Inc.

ALASIKA - Water–bottled or canned - Edward Hsi-Hua Wang

ALASKA - Ammunition ☆ - Federal Cartridge Co.

ALASKA - Fertilizers - Alaska Fish Fertilizer Co.

ALASKA - Floor coverings–carpet and rugs - Edgecrest Carpet Mills

ALASKA - Lubricating oils - Lubricating Specialties Co.

ALASKA - Seafood products–fresh or frozen - Alaskan Seafood Co. Inc.

ALASKA - Sporting goods ☆ - USA Sport Eyewear

ALASKA - Teas - Alaska Herb & Tea Co., Inc.

ALASKA - Window coverings ☆ - Vertilux-Louverlux Inc.

ALASKA ADVENTURE - Frames–eyeglass - Euro-Frames Inc.

ALASKA-ARCTIC FURS - Apparel–athletic - Alaska-Arctic Furs

ALASKA BAIT - Fishing tackle - Cossack Caviar Inc. (Alaska Premier Bait)

ALASKA BEACHCOMBER - Seafood products–fresh or frozen - Alaska Beachcomber Seafoods

ALASKA BEAR - Apparel and accessories - Young One Fashions, Inc.

ALASKA CAPTAIN - Food products - Ursin Seafoods Inc.

ALASKA FJORD - Seafood products–fresh or frozen - Salamatof Seafoods Inc.

ALASKA FRESH - Seafood products–fresh or frozen - Ocean Fresh Seafoods Inc.

ALASKA GEAR ALERT STOP DON'T WALK IN THIS AREA - Apparel and accessories - Young One Fashions, Inc.

ALASKA GLACIER - Cosmetics - Alaska Glacier Products

ALASKA GOLD - Fishing rods - V.F. Grace, Inc.

ALASKA GOLD - Seafood products–fresh or frozen - Seafood Producers Cooperative

ALASKA LOX - Seafood - Alaska Fresh Seafoods Inc.

ALASKA ONE - Broadcasting stations–television - Alaska Public Broadcasting Service

ALASKA PREMIER - Fishing tackle - Cossack Caviar Inc. (Alaska Premier Bait)

ALASKA PRIDE - Food products - Carr-Gottstein Foods Co.

ALASKA SEAFOOD WORLD'S FINEST - Seafood products–fresh or frozen - Alaska Seafood Marketing Institute

ALASKA SEAS - Food products - Sea-Alaska Products Inc.

ALASKA SHELL - Seafood products–fresh or frozen - G.F. Higgins

ALASKA STATEWIDE - Games - Universal Manufacturing Co., Inc.

ALASKA TESTED - Footwear - Stuart R. Chalfin, a U.S. Citizen, AS Trustee of the Bell Boys Irrevocable Trust

ALASKA TOP PRO - Paints - Alaskan Paint Manufacturing Co. Inc.

ALASKA TWO - Broadcasting stations–television - Alaska Public Broadcasting Service

ALASKA WILD - Teas - Alaska Herb & Tea Co., Inc.

ALASKABITS - Food products - Alaska Food Group

ALASKAN - Beer and ale - Alaskan Brewing and Bottling Co.

ALASKAN - Boats–motor - Klamath Boat Co. Inc.

ALASKAN - Boats–motor - Lund Boat Co.

ALASKAN - Crocheted and knitted items ☆ - Schuessler Knitting Mills Inc.
ALASKAN - Food products - Seward Fisheries
ALASKAN - Garden equipment ☆ - H.D. Hudson Manufacturing Co.
ALASKAN - Gloves - Good Luck Glove Co.
ALASKAN - Guns - Weatherby Inc.
ALASKAN - Meat products–beef - Alaska Meat Co.
ALASKAN - Paints - Alaskan Paint Manufacturing Co. Inc.
ALASKAN - Pet products - Rae's Harness Shop
ALASKAN - Sporting goods ☆ - Bear Archery Inc.
ALASKAN CAMPER - Motor vehicles - Alaskan Campers
ALASKAN CLASSICS - Dairy products - General Container Co. of Michigan, Inc.
ALASKAN DENALI - Bicycles - Thomas C. Ritchie
ALASKAN FALLS - Water–bottled or canned - Alaskan Falls Bottling Co.
ALASKAN FISH - Fertilizers - Lawn & Garden Supply Co.
ALASKAN FUR COMPANY - Coats–fur - Alaskan Fur Co.
ALASKAN GOLD RUSH, THE - Games - Alaskan Gold Rush, Inc.
ALASKAN GOURMET - Salmon–smoked, salted, dried, or pickled - Alaskan Gourmet Inc.
ALASKAN GUIDE MODEL - Tents - Cabela's Inc.
ALASKAN HARVEST - Seafood products–fresh or frozen - Sitka Sound Seafoods, Inc.
ALASKAN ICE COMPANY - Shirts - Pennshire Shirt Corp.
ALASKAN MARK III - Tools - Granberg International
ALASKAN MIST - Seafood products–fresh or frozen - G.F. Higgins
ALASKAN PAK - Sporting goods ☆ - Bear Archery Inc.
ALASKAN SEA-LECT - Salmon–smoked, salted, dried, or pickled ☆ - Keener Packing Co. Inc.
ALASKAN SNOW LEGS - Meat products - Sugiyo Usa, Inc.
ALASKAN, THE - Building materials - Herbert Malarkey Roofing Co.
ALASKAN WATER - Seafood products–fresh or frozen - Milfico Foods Inc.
ALASKA'S BEST DEFENSE - Personal defense products - Security Equipment Corp.
ALASKA'S CHOICE - Seafood products–canned or cured - Alaska Sausage Co. Inc.
ALASKA'S FINEST COFFEE - Coffee - Franklin Wood
ALASKIMO - Sporting goods - Stearns Manufacturing Co.
ALASKOVA - Salmon–smoked, salted, dried, or pickled - Anco Foods Corp.
ALASTIK - Dental compounds - Minnesota Mining & Manufacturing Co.
ALATAL - Food products - New Zealand Milk Products Inc.
ALATATE - Food products ☆ - New Zealand Milk Products Inc.
ALATEX - Shirts - Cluett, Peabody & Co.
ALAURA - Beverages–alcohol - Heublein, Inc.
ALAVOX - Recording label - International Record Corp.
ALAZAR WINERY - Wines - Geerlings & Wade, Inc.
ALB - Jewelry - Albithel Jewelry Manufacturing Inc.
ALBA - Cocoa–powders or mixes - H.J. Heinz Co.
ALBA - Computer software - Alba Editorial, Inc.
ALBA - Erasers ☆ - Bright Boy Abrasives
ALBA - Giftware ☆ - Alpine Crafts Co. Inc.
ALBA - Milk–canned or powdered - Alba Foods Co. Inc.
ALBA - Skin care products - La Natura
ALBA - Spices and extracts - Acme Food Specialties Inc.
ALBA - Tableware–earthenware - Villeroy and Boch Tableware Ltd.
ALBA - Underwear and nightwear - Alba-Waldensian, Inc.
ALBA 66 - Cocoa–powders or mixes - Alba Foods Co. Inc.
ALBA '77 FIT 'N FROSTY - Beverages - Alba Foods Co. Inc.
ALBA BOTANICA - Cosmetics - Alba Products Group Inc.
ALBA-DAIRY LIGHT - Milk–canned or powdered - Alba Foods Co. Inc.
ALBA DUE - Tiles–ceramic ☆ - Maxsam Sales, Inc.
ALBA IU LIA - Dinnerware–glass ☆ - M & M Associates Ltd.
ALBA LABS - Health care products - Alba Products Group Inc.
ALBA LYBE - Vitamins and nutritional supplements - Alba Pharmacal
ALBAC - Veterinary pharmaceutical preparations - Alpharma Inc.
ALBACILLIN - Veterinary pharmaceutical preparations - Upjohn Co.
ALBACORE - Boats - Allen Boat Co.
ALBACORE - Watches - Gruen Marketing Corp.
ALBADORA - Pasta - Borden, Inc.
ALBADRY PLUS - Veterinary pharmaceutical preparations - Upjohn Co.
ALBADURE - Tape measures ☆ - Keuffel & Esser Co.
ALBALON-A - Ophthalmic goods ☆ - Allergan, Inc.
ALBAMIX - Veterinary pharmaceutical preparations - Upjohn Co.
ALBAMYCIN - Pharmaceutical preparations - Upjohn Co.
ALBANAMEL - Enamels ☆ - Impervious Paint Industries Ltd.
ALBANENE - Paper–transfer - Keuffel & Esser Co.
ALBANIZED - Paper–photographic - Keuffel & Esser Co.

ALBANY - Cleaning preparations - Autozone, Inc.
ALBANY - Daters and time stamps - Consolidated Stamp Manufacturing Co. Inc.
ALBANY - Flatware - Wallace International Silversmiths, Inc.
ALBANY - Furniture - Haworth, Inc.
ALBANY POLECATS - Trading cards and stamps - Albany Professional Baseball Club, Inc.
ALBAPLEX - Veterinary pharmaceutical preparations - Upjohn Co.
ALBASULPHIDI - Skin care products ☆ - Ferndale Laboratories, Inc.
ALBATA - Brushes–paint ☆ - Winsor & Newton
ALBATONE - Paints ☆ - Impervious Paint Industries Ltd.
ALBATROS DV - Hobby kits ☆ - Testor Corp.
ALBATROS MINI TOAST - Bakery products - Europa Foods Ltd.
ALBATROSS - Bicycles - Huffy Corp.
ALBATROSS - Watches - Bulova Corp.
ALBEAR - Food products - Golden Whisk Pasta Partners
ALBEMARLE - Agricultural products - Ronald W. Harvey and Co.
ALBEMARLE - Furniture ☆ - Bassett Furniture Industries, Inc.
ALBERENE - Stones–synthetic - New Alberene Stone Co. Inc.
ALBERIC - Crocheted and knitted items - Beldoch Industries Corp.
ALBERMARLE COUNTY - Wallpaper - Seabrook Wallcoverings, Inc.
ALBERO DI PRIMAVERA - Sauces - Spring Tree Corp.
ALBEROY - Crocheted and knitted items - Beldoch Industries Corp.
ALBERT - Giftware - Albert Findings Inc.
ALBERT - Toys - Russ Berrie and Co., Inc.
ALBERT-DS - Fire retardant - American Vamag Co. Inc.
ALBERT E. - Boats - Glen-L Marine Designs
ALBERT MENES - Spices and extracts ☆ - Made in France
ALBERT NAPON - Apparel and accessories ☆ - Swirl II Ltd.
ALBERT NIPON - Apparel and accessories - International Designer Accessories
ALBERT NIPON - Apparel–men's - Castle Neckwear Inc.
ALBERT NIPON - Apparel–women's - Leslie Fay Companies Inc.
ALBERT NIPON - Belts–apparel ☆ - Echo Design Group
ALBERT NIPON - Scarves - Collection XIIX Ltd.
ALBERT NIPON BOUTIQUE - Apparel–women's - Leslie Fay Companies Inc.
ALBERT NIPON GIRLS - Girls' apparel ☆ - Atlanta Apparel Group Ltd.
ALBERT NIPON PETITES - Apparel–women's - Leslie Fay Companies Inc.
ALBERT NURNBERGER - Musical instrument accessories ☆ - Scherl & Roth Inc.
ALBERT PIC - Wines ☆ - Kobrand Corp.
ALBERT PIC CHABLIS - Wines ☆ - Kobrand Corp.
ALBERT ROBIN - Beverages–alcohol - Star Liquor Imports Inc.
ALBERT SWEETSER'S - Snuff ☆ - Byfield Snuff Co.
ALBERTA - Glassware–household ☆ - Lotus Glass Co.
ALBERTA SPRINGS - Whiskey - Jim Beam Brands Co.
ALBERTA'S - Vegetables–pickled or brined - Desert Rose Foods, Inc.
ALBERTA'S PEPPERS - Vegetables–canned - Desert Rose Corp.
ALBERTINA - Tableware–earthenware - Villeroy and Boch Tableware Ltd.
ALBERTO - Ophthalmic goods ☆ - Luxottica
ALBERTO NATURAL SILK - Hair care products - Alberto-Culver Co.
ALBERTO VARGAS - Posters - Icart Vendor Graphics Inc.
ALBERTO VO5 - Hair care products - Alberto-Culver Co.
ALBERT'S - Salad dressings–bottled - Louis Albert & Son Foods Co.
ALBERT'S - Vegetable seasonings - Harvest States Cooperatives
ALBERT'S FINEST - Food products - Louis Albert & Son Foods Co.
ALBERTSONS - Food products - Albertson's Inc.
ALBERTSON'S - Food products - Indian Summer
ALBI - Chairs–stacking - Fixtures Furniture
ALBI - Handbags - Apollo Handbag Co.
ALBI - Paints - Stan Chem Inc. (Albi Div.)
ALBI CLAD - Paints - Stan Chem Inc. (Albi Div.)
ALBI COTE - Paints - Stan Chem Inc. (Albi Div.)
ALBI CRETE - Paints - Stan Chem Inc. (Albi Div.)
ALBI DURASPRAY - Paints - Stan Chem Inc. (Albi Div.)
ALBI TYCLAD - Paints - Stan Chem Inc. (Albi Div.)
ALBIN - Boats–motor - Albin Marine Inc.
ALBION - Insulating materials ☆ - Thermal Ceramics Inc.
ALBION - Ophthalmic goods - Styl-Rite Optical Manufacturing Co., Inc.
ALBION - Soap ☆ - Caswell-Massey Co. Ltd.
ALBION - Thread - Threads USA Div.
ALBION - Tools–hand-operated - Albion Engineering Co.
ALBION CHELAZOMES - Vitamins and nutritional supplements - Albion Laboratories, Inc.
ALBION MAAC'S - Animal feed supplements - Albion Laboratories, Inc.
ALBION METALOSATES - Fertilizers - Albion Laboratories, Inc.

☆ = Now out of production

ALBOLENE - Skin care products - Smithkline Beecham Corp.

ALBORG - Cabinets - Mutschler European

ALBORG - Glassware–household - Dansk International Designs, Ltd.

ALBRA - Brushes - Braun Bruch Co.

ALBRADELLA - Recording label ☆ - Soul-Po-Tion Records

ALBRAYE - Furniture - National/Mt. Airy Furniture

ALBRECHT'S - Eggs - Double A Poultry Farm

ALBRO - Syrup ☆ - Majestic Drug Co., Inc.

ALBROM - Chemical preparations - Ethyl Corp.

ALBUCONN - Pharmaceutical preparations ☆ - Elkins-Sinn Inc.

ALBUM EASEL - Photo albums - Pioneer Photo Albums, Inc.

ALBUM-ETTES - Photo albums ☆ - JM Co.

ALBUM-UNLIMITED - Photo albums ☆ - JM Co.

ALBUMARC - Pharmaceutical preparations - American National Red Cross

ALBUMINAR - Pharmaceutical preparations ☆ - Armour Pharmaceutical Co.

ALBUMISOL - Pharmaceutical preparations ☆ - Merck & Co., Inc. (Merck Research Laboratories)

ALBURY PARK - Dishes–china - Viletta China Co.

ALBUSPAN - Pharmaceutical preparations ☆ - Parke-Davis

ALBUSTIX - Chemical preparations - Miles Inc.

ALBUTEIN - Pharmaceutical preparations - Alpha Therapeutic Corp.

ALC - Electronics equipment - Auernheimer Labs Corp.

ALC - Industrial machinery - S & H Industries, Inc.

ALC - Ships–sailing vessels - A. Le Comte Co. Inc.

ALCA MAX - Aluminum products - Aluminum Co. of America

ALCAINE - Ophthalmic goods - Alcon Laboratories, Inc.

ALCALYTE - Bicycle parts and accessories - Aluminum Co. of America

ALCAMA - Apparel–men's - Alps Sportswear Manufacturing Co.

ALCAMO - Sausages - Potok Packing Co.

ALCAN - Construction equipment - Alcan Aluminum Corp. Alcan Building Products Div.

ALCAN - Sporting goods ☆ - Bombardier Corp.

ALCAREZ - Adhesives and sealants ☆ - PPG Industries, Inc.

ALCASHA - Apparel–men's - Alps Sportswear Manufacturing Co.

ALCATRAZ - Paints - Sampson Coatings Inc.

ALCAZAR - Dinnerware–glass ☆ - WMF/USA

ALCAZAR - Floor coverings–tile ☆ - Kentile Floors Inc.

ALCAZAR RECORDS - Recording label - Alcazar Productions

ALCAZAR: THE FORGOTTEN FORTRESS - Computer software - Activision, Inc.

ALCAZAR U.S.A. - Apparel–women's - Parsons Place Apparel Co. Ltd.

ALCET - Ammunition - Remington Arms Co., Inc.

ALCHEMIST - Computer software - Omniview, Inc.

ALCHEMISTS - Jewelry - Alchemists, Inc.

ALCHEMY - Computer software - Information Management Research, Inc.

ALCHEMY - Frames–eyeglass - Hudson Optical Corp.

ALCHEMY - Recording label - Rough Trade Inc.

ALCHEMY - Wallcovering - Innovations in Wallcoverings, Inc.

ALCHEMY 101 - Musical instrument accessories - Dimarzio, Inc.

ALCHROMATE - Paints - Burgess Fobes Paint Co.

AL+CLEAR - Chemical preparations - General Chemical Corp.

ALCO - Aluminum products ☆ - Seymour Mann Inc.

ALCO - Coatings - DMF Industries Inc. (Al-Chroma Div.)

ALCO - Lamps - Angelo Brothers Co.

ALCO - Office machines ☆ - Eaton Allen Ko-Rec-Type Corp.

ALCO - Pet products - Alco Carrying Cases Inc.

ALCO - Seat covers - Alco Manufacturing Co. Inc.

ALCO - Stationery - Al Nyman and Son

ALCO-ANALYZER - Health care products - U.S. Alcohol Testing of America Inc.

ALCO BEST - Seafood products–fresh or frozen - Hip Shing Trading, Inc.

ALCO-BRITE - Fireplace equipment - Alco-Brite, Inc.

ALCO-GEL - Chalk ☆ - Tweezerman Corp.

ALCO-LITE - Hardware - Aluminum Ladder Co.

ALCO-LITE - Ophthalmic goods - Styl-Rite Optical Manufacturing Co., Inc.

ALCO-MET - Solder - Dexter Corp.

ALCO-SCREEN - Health care products - Chematics Inc.

ALCO-SCREEN - Pharmaceutical preparations - Chem-Elec Inc.

ALCO SCRUB INSTANT ANTISEPTIC HAND CLEANSER - Skin care products - Stahmer Weston Scientific

ALCOA - Aluminum products - Aluminum Co. of America

ALCOA ALCA PLUS - Aluminum products - Aluminum Co. of America

ALCOA ALCALYTE - Bicycle parts and accessories - Aluminum Co. of America

ALCOA DUTCH OAK - Siding–metal - Aluminum Co. of America

ALCOA HC - Bottle caps - Aluminum Co. of America

ALCOA IMAGES - Siding - Aluminum Co. of America

ALCOA SYBMOL - Aluminum products - Aluminum Co. of America

ALCOBACA - Pottery ☆ - Penco Industries Inc.

ALCOBATH - Pharmaceutical preparations ☆ - Ulmer Pharmacal Co.

ALCOHOL-FREE FINAL NET - Hair care products - Clairol Inc.

ALCOHOL GRAPHICS - Cleaning preparations - Federal Mining & Manufacturing Co.

ALCOHOLADO MARAVILLA 70 - Pharmaceutical preparations - Humphreys Pharmacal Inc.

ALCOHOLMAN - Measuring instruments - Seponix Corp.

ALCOIZE - Varnishes ☆ - H. Behlen & Bro. Inc.

ALCOJET - Detergents - Alconox Inc.

ALCOKLIN - Medical apparatus - Intramedica, Inc.

ALCOLADO RELAMPAGO - Analgesics - Larkspur Group Inc.

ALCOLADO RELAMPAGO - Health care products - Hair Specialty Co.

ALCOLEC - Lecithin - American Lecithin Co. Inc.

ALCOM - Telephone apparatus ☆ - Lenmar Enterprises, Inc.

ALCON - Ophthalmic goods - Alcon Laboratories, Inc.

ALCON - Video games ☆ - Taito America Corp.

ALCON-EFRIN - Pharmaceutical preparations ☆ - Alcon Laboratories, Inc.

ALCON ENZYMATIC - Health care products - Alcon Laboratories, Inc.

ALCON ENZYMATIC FOR EXTENDED WEAR - Health care products - Alcon Laboratories, Inc.

ALCON SALINE FOR SENSITIVE EYES - Health care products - Alcon Laboratories, Inc.

ALCONOX - Detergents - Alconox Inc.

ALCOPAD - Health care products - Mason-Keller Corp.

ALCOPHOBIN - Pharmaceutical preparations ☆ - Consolidated Midland Corp.

ALCOQUEST - Chemical preparations - Indopco, Inc.

ALCOR - Cabinets ☆ - Lane Co. Inc.

ALCOR - Clocks ☆ - General Time Corp. (Westclox/Seth Thomas Div.)

ALCOR - Envelopes - Alling & Cory Co.

ALCOR - Fishing tackle ☆ - Best Tackle Manufacturing Co.

ALCORENSE - Tiles–ceramic ☆ - Maxsam Sales, Inc.

ALCORUB - Pharmaceutical preparations - Purepac Pharmaceutical Co.

ALCOTABS - Detergents - Alconox Inc.

ALCOTROL - Health care products - Desert Health Products, Inc.

ALCOTT - Sinks–metal - Kohler Co.

ALCOVE - Bathroom fixtures - Artesian Industries

ALCOVE VIEW - Floor coverings - Armstrong World Industries, Inc.

ALD 750 - Jewelry - Albert Lipten Designs et Cie. Ltd.

ALDA HM - Golfing equipment - Aldila, Inc.

ALDA V - Golfing equipment - Aldila, Inc.

ALDA VIII - Golfing equipment ☆ - Aldila, Inc.

ALDACTAZIDE - Pharmaceutical preparations - G. D. Searle & Co.

ALDACTONE - Pharmaceutical preparations - G. D. Searle & Co.

ALDALITE - Golfing equipment - Aldila, Inc.

ALDAREX PLUS - Pharmaceutical preparations - C.S. Ruckstuhl Co. Inc.

ALDA'S FOREVER - Soap - Alda's Forever Soap

ALDEAO - Fish–fresh or frozen ☆ - Corte & Co.

ALDEMAX - Food products - Givaudan Roure

ALDEN - Boats - John G. Alden Inc.

ALDEN - Boats - Alden Ocean Shells Inc.

ALDEN - Footwear - Alden Shoe Co.

ALDEN - Greeting cards ☆ - Doehla Greeting Cards Inc.

ALDEN - Lighting fixtures ☆ - Liteway

ALDEN - Silver products - Wallace International Silversmiths, Inc.

ALDEN - Watches - Hampden Corp.

ALDEN HOWARD - Handbags - Benjamin Worth Inc.

ALDEN MARTIN - Boats–skiffs - Alden Ocean Shells Inc.

ALDEN MERRELL - Bakery products - Alden Merrell Corp.

ALDEN OCEAN SHELL - Boats–skiffs - Alden Ocean Shells Inc.

ALDEN OCEAN SHELL DOUBLE - Boats–skiffs - Alden Ocean Shells Inc.

ALDEN PEDIC - Footwear - Alden Shoe Co.

ALDEN SMITH'S - Sauerkraut - Shiocton Kraut Co.

ALDEN STAR - Boats - Alden Ocean Shells Inc.

ALDEN SUPERCOMP - Oars - Alden Ocean Shells Inc.

ALDENS - Paints - Alden's Inc.

ALDER - Brushes–paint - Allpro Corp.

ALDER COVE - Seafood products–canned or cured - Kirkland Custom Seafood

ALDER CREEK COFFEE - Coffee - N.W. Specialty Roasters, Inc.

ALDER SQUARE - Cabinets - Riviera Cabinets Inc.

ALDERBROOK - Wines - Alderbrook Winery

ALDERMAN - Ophthalmic goods - Embassy Creations Inc.

ALDERMERE - Cattle - A.H. Chatfield, Jr.

ALDERWOOD CELLARS - Wines - Haviland Vintners
ALDI - Ice cream - Roney-Oatman Inc.
ALDI - Salad dressings–bottled - Mrs. Clark's Foods
ALDILA - Golfing equipment ☆ - Aldila, Inc.
ALDO - Lenses–optical - Ditto Industries Inc.
ALDO CONTROLS - Automotive parts and accessories ☆ - MJR Industries, Inc.
ALDO FAZIO COLLECTION - Figurines ☆ - Reco International Corp.
ALDO VELANI - Pipes–tobacco - Mastercraft Pipes Inc.
ALDOCLOR - Pharmaceutical preparations - Merck & Co., Inc. (Merck Research Laboratories)
ALDOMET - Pharmaceutical preparations - Merck & Co., Inc. (Merck Research Laboratories)
ALDON - Floor coverings–carpet and rugs - Concord/Aldon Industries Inc.
ALDON ACCESSORIES - Apparel and accessories - Aldon Accessories
ALDONS - Food products - Van Den Bergh Foods Co.
ALDOR - Spark plugs - A.L. Doering Spark Plug Corp.
ALDORIL - Pharmaceutical preparations - Merck & Co., Inc. (Merck Research Laboratories)
ALDO'S - Spices and extracts - Aldo's Spices
ALDRICH DAIRY - Milk - Aldrich Dairy Inc.
ALDYL - Pipes–plastic - E.I. Dupont de Nemours and Co.
ALE - Frames–eyeglass - Zylo Ware Corp.
A.L.E. - Paints ☆ - PPG Industries, Inc.
ALE STREET NEWS - Packaging–paper - Tuscarora Inc.
ALEA - Cosmetics - Kaemark Inc.
ALEAR - Recording label - Sounds of Winchester
ALEC - Skin care products - Imperial Inc.
ALEDRYL - Health care products - Esquire Pharmaceuticals Inc.
ALEEDA - Apparel and accessories - Aleeda Wetsuits
ALEENE'S - Glue–household or industrial - Aleene's
ALEENE'S - Stamps–hand - Artis, Inc.
ALEENE'S GLITTER COLORS - Craft supplies - Artis, Inc.
ALEENE'S PAPER NAPKIN APPLIQUE GLUE - Adhesives and sealants - Artis, Inc.
ALEENE'S SHRINK-IT - Craft kits - Artis, Inc.
ALEFAR - Lenses–photographic ☆ - Heitz Service Corp.
ALEGIS - Golf bags - Datrek Professional Bags, Inc.
ALEGRA - Faucets - Sterling Plumbing Group Inc.
ALEGRE - Wines - Konocti Winery
ALEJANDRO - Glassware–household - Crisa Corp.
ALEKI - Lenses–optical - National Optical Co.
ALEMANY PRESS - Publisher's imprints - Paramount Publishers
ALEMBIC - Musical instruments - Alembic Inc.
ALEMITE - Lubrication equipment and accessories - Stewart Warner Alemite Licensco Inc.
A ALEMITE - Machinery - Stewart Warner Alemite Licensco Inc.
ALEMITE A - Machine parts - Stewart Warner Alemite Licensco Inc.
ALEN - Cereal - Alen Imports & Trade Corp.
ALENA - Floor coverings–carpet and rugs ☆ - Evans-Black Carpet Mills
ALENA - Hot tubs–fiberglass ☆ - Jacuzzi Inc.
ALENA - Lenses–optical - National Optical Co.
ALENAX - Bicycles - Alenax Corp.
ALENCO - Windows–plastic - Alenco Div.
ALENCON - Perfumes ☆ - Treasure Masters
ALENCON - Rings–jewelry - Artcarved Inc.
ALEPPO - Rings–jewelry ☆ - Artcarved Inc.
ALER-C - Vitamins and nutritional supplements - J.R. Carlson Laboratories Inc.
ALER-DRYL - Pharmaceutical preparations - Reese Chemical Co.
ALER-DRYL ELIXIR - Cold remedies - Reese Chemical Co.
ALER-KEY - Vitamins and nutritional supplements ☆ - J.R. Carlson Laboratories Inc.
ALER-RELEAF - Pharmaceutical preparations - Reese Chemical Co.
ALERION-EXPRESS - Ships–sailing vessels - Harbor Boat Co. Inc.
ALERT - Alarm systems - Tandy Corp.
ALERT - Auto alarm - Bulldog Distributing
ALERT - Chemical preparations - La-Co Industries, Inc.
ALERT - Deodorants–personal - Lever Brothers Co. Inc.
ALERT - Detergents - Western Family Foods, Inc.
ALERT - First aid kits - Carter-Wallace, Inc.
ALERT - Gasoline - Exxon Corp.
ALERT - Heaters–space - Adobe Air Inc.
ALERT - Insecticides - American Cyanamid Co.
ALERT - Sporting goods ☆ - Outdoor Technologies Group
ALERT - Toothbrushes - Bioware, Inc.
ALERT-ALONG - Identification tags - Weiss Works

ALERT-BOLT - Locks–door - Pease Industries, Inc.
ALERT CENTRAL - Computer software - Motorola, Inc. (Land Mobile Products Sector)
ALERT-LOCK - Locks–door - Pease Industries, Inc.
ALERT TABS - Pharmaceutical preparations - Rexall Sundown, Inc.
ALERTCAPS - Pharmaceutical preparations ☆ - Church and Dwight Co. Inc.
ALERTCARE - Alarm systems - Care Technologies, Inc.
ALERTLINK - Emergency device - Linear Corp.
ALERTMASTER - Alarm systems - American Phone Products, Inc.
ALERTMASTER - Alarm systems - Ameriphone
ALERTO - Pharmaceutical preparations - Brenner Pharmacal Co./Pharma Kwik
ALERTONIC - Pharmaceutical preparations ☆ - Marion Merrell Dow
ALES - Tableware–plastic - Durand International
ALESHIA - Ophthalmic goods ☆ - Luxottica
ALESIA - Bathtubs–enameled - Americh Corp.
ALESIS - Audio equipment - Alesis Corp.
ALESSANDRA - Bedding–linen - Dan River Inc.
ALESSANDRO - Eyeglasses - Art-Craft Optical Co.
ALESSANDRO COLLECTION - Furniture ☆ - Baker, Knapp & Tubbs
ALESSANDRO COLLECTION - Wallpaper ☆ - Manuscreens
ALESSI - Kitchen appliances - Markuse Corp.
ALESSI PIGNOLI - Nuts–salted, roasted, cooked, or canned - Vigo Importing Co. Inc.
ALESSI-VACCHIANO - Musical instrument accessories - G. Leblanc Corp.
ALESSIO SAVON - Skin care products - Alessio International
ALETA - Rings–jewelry - Artcarved Inc.
ALEUR - Toilets–porcelain - Mansfield Plumbing Products, Inc.
ALEUTIAN - Fish–fresh or frozen - Unisea, Inc.
ALEUTIAN - Gloves - Swan Enterprises, Inc.
ALEUTIAN - Watches - Croton Watch Co., Inc.
ALEVAIRE - Pharmaceutical preparations - Sterling Winthrop Inc.
ALEVE - Analgesics - Procter & Gamble Co.
ALEVR - Toilets–enameled - Mansfield Plumbing Products, Inc.
ALEX - Apparel–women's - ATLB Sportswear, Inc.
ALEX - Caulking compounds - Dap Products Inc.
ALEX - Computer software - Logos Corp.
ALEX - Electronic equipment - Lexicon, Inc.
ALEX - Food products - Alex Foods, Inc.
ALEX - Frames–eyeglass ☆ - Rozin Optical Export Corp.
ALEX - Ophthalmic goods ☆ - Luxottica
ALEX - Stamps–hand - Panline USA, Inc.
ALEX - Toys - Tonka Corp.
ALEX ACUNA - Musical instruments - St. Louis Music Supply Co.
ALEX ACUNA SIGNATURE - Musical instruments - Vic Firth Inc.
ALEX & IVY - Furniture ☆ - Bombay Co. Inc.
ALEX & ME - Apparel and accessories - Alex & Me Sportswear, Inc.
ALEX BY ALEXANDER JULIAN - Suits–men's - Alexander Julian, Inc.
ALEX COLMAN - Apparel–women's - Alex Colman Inc.
ALEX-DUNCAN SHRIMP CHEF - Shrimp-preparing knife - Alex-Duncan Shrimp Chef Inc.
ALEX EVENINGS - Dressing gowns - Alex Apparel Group Inc.
ALEX INTERNATIONAL SALAD - Salads–prepackaged - Orval Kent Food Co., Inc.
ALEX LTD. - Games - Alex Cramer Co.
ALEX NICOLE - Jewelry ☆ - 1928 Jewelry Co.
ALEX PLUS - Caulking compounds - Dap Products Inc.
ALEX REED - Apparel and accessories - A.C. Reed
ALEX SECTOR - Toys - Tonka Corp.
ALEX SEPKUS - Jewelry - Alex Sepkus
ALEX THE ALLIGATOR - Toys - Imperial Toy Corp.
ALEXA - Frames–eyeglass - Hudson Optical Corp.
ALEXA - Housewares - Doranne
ALEXA - Spas–home - Jacuzzi Inc.
ALEXA - Wedding gowns - Atlantis Trading Corp.
ALEXA GOLD - Crystal stemware - May Department Stores Co.
ALEXA GRACE - Blouses–women's - Home Shopping Club, Inc.
ALEXANDER - Clocks - Ridgeway Clock Co.
ALEXANDER - Fireplace equipment - Majestic Co.
ALEXANDER - Pens - Alexander Manufacturing Co.
ALEXANDER 2 - Pens - Alexander Manufacturing Co.
ALEXANDER AND FRIENDS - Shirts - Pablo A. Diaz-Cruz
ALEXANDER BONNET CHA - Wines ☆ - Prestige Wine Corp.
ALEXANDER CONCERTO - Footwear - Leo's Dancewear, Inc.
ALEXANDER DIANA - Food products - Diana Fruit Preserving Co.
ALEXANDER GRAHAM PLANE - Telescopes - Northern Telecom, Inc.
ALEXANDER GRAPPA - Wines - Francis A. Bonanno, Inc.

☆ = Now out of production

ALEXANDER JULIAN - Apparel–women's - Alexander Julian Inc.
ALEXANDER JULIAN - Hosiery–men's - Marum Knitting Mills
ALEXANDER JULIAN BESPOKE - Apparel–men's - Alexander Julian Inc.
ALEXANDER JULIAN COLOURS - Shoes - Coleman
ALEXANDER JULIAN HOME COLOURS - Mattresses - Alexander Julian, Inc.
ALEXANDER JULIAN WOMENSWEAR - Perfumes - Paul Sebastian, Inc.
ALEXANDER LTD. - Shoes - R.B. Alexander & Co. Ltd.
ALEXANDER MARTIN - Apparel and accessories - Supreme International
　Corp.
ALEXANDER PESKANOV - Publisher's imprints - Willis Music Co.
ALEXANDER QUINT - Hair care products - Mahdeen Laboratory
ALEXANDER ROSS - Apparel–men's ☆ - Edison Brothers Stores, Inc.
ALEXANDER SMITH - Floor coverings–carpet and rugs - Alexander Smith
　Carpets
ALEXANDER THE GRAPE - Candy - Ferrara Pan Candy Co., Inc.
ALEXANDER THE GRAPE - Towels - National Pax Corp.
ALEXANDER THE GREAT - Computer software ☆ - Krell Software Corp.
ALEXANDER THE GREAT - Dinnerware–glass ☆ - WMF/USA
ALEXANDER THE GREAT - Games ☆ - Avalon Hill Game Co.
ALEXANDER VALLEY VINEYARDS - Wines - Alexander Valley Vineyards
ALEXANDER'S - Housewares ☆ - Chase Collection, Inc.
ALEXANDER'S - Ice cream - John Huff Ice Cream, Inc.
ALEXANDER'S - Ice cream ☆ - Kay's Ice Cream
ALEXANDER'S BELTS & BUCKLES - Jewelry - Ashraf Khalaf
ALEXANDER'S LIQUOR - Jams and jellies - Bewley Irish Imports
ALEXANDRA - Floor coverings–carpet and rugs - Stanton Carpet Corp.
ALEXANDRA - Giftware - Filene's Basement Corp.
ALEXANDRA - Glassware–household ☆ - Lenox Crystal, Inc.
ALEXANDRA - Lighting fixtures - Illumilite Inc.
ALEXANDRA - Perfumes - Alexandra De Markoff, Ltd.
ALEXANDRA - Tableware–china - Pfaltzgraff Investment Co.
ALEXANDRA BRILLIANT - Paper–writing - Strathmore Paper Co.
ALEXANDRA DE MARKOFF - Cosmetics - Yves St. Laurent Parfum Corp.
ALEXANDRA GOLD ACCENT - Flatware - Yamazaki Tableware Inc.
ALEXANDRA JORDYN - Sweaters - Little Funky Knits, Inc.
ALEXANDRA SCOTT - Apparel–women's - Frederick Atkins, Inc.
ALEXANDRA STUART - Towels - Alexandra Stuart Marketing, Inc.
ALEXANDRA'S - Mayonnaise - Cortina Corp.
ALEXANDRIA - Apparel–women's - C.F.S. Alexandria Blouses Inc.
ALEXANDRIA - Carpets and rugs - Couristan Inc.
ALEXANDRIA - Computer software - Western Automation Laboratories, Inc.
ALEXANDRIA - Floor coverings - Mannington Resilient Floors
ALEXANDRIA - Floor coverings–carpet and rugs - Barrett Carpet Mills Inc.
ALEXANDRIA - Floor coverings–carpet and rugs ☆ - Regal Rugs Inc.
ALEXANDRIA - Mattresses - Simmons USA
ALEXANDRIA - Tiles–ceramic - Epro Inc.
ALEXANDRIA II - Floor coverings - Armstrong World Industries, Inc.
ALEXANDRIA ACES - Apparel and accessories - Texas Professional Baseball,
　Inc.
ALEXANDRIA DRAFTING CO. - Maps and atlases ☆ - American Map Corp.
ALEXIA - Bedding–linen - Dan River Inc.
ALEXIA - Dolls - Mattel, Inc.
ALEXIA - Jewelry - Roman Co.
ALEXIA - Lubricating oils - Shell Oil Co.
ALEXIA - Ophthalmic goods ☆ - Luxottica
ALEXIA ALEXANDER - Hair care products - Alexia Alexander Inc.
ALEXIS - Apparel–women's - Alexis Fashions Inc.
ALEXIS - Cabinets - Merillat Industries, Inc.
ALEXIS - Dolls - Bob's Surplus Sales, Inc.
ALEXIS - Dryers–hair - Marianna Imports, Inc.
ALEXIS - Floor coverings–carpet and rugs - Eligere Carpets
ALEXIS - Floor coverings–carpet and rugs - Alexander Smith Carpets
ALEXIS - Frozen foods - Alexis, Inc.
ALEXIS - Fruits and vegetables - Cal-Western Farming Co.
ALEXIS - Furniture - Stanley Furniture Co. Inc.
ALEXIS - Luggage ☆ - Samsonite Corp.
ALEXIS - Nail care products ☆ - Orly International Inc.
ALEXIS - Novelty items - Kash N' Gold, Ltd.
ALEXIS - Paper–writing ☆ - Strathmore Paper Co.
ALEXIS ASHLEY - Jewelry - Weingeroff Enterprises, Inc.
ALEXIS BAILLY VINEYARD - Wines - Alexis Bailly Vineyard Inc.
ALEXIS PARK - Trailers–travel - Fleetwood Enterprises, Inc.
ALEXIS REED - Jewelry - Bon-Ton Trade Corp.
ALEXWEB - Computer software - Alexander & Alexander Services Inc.
ALF - Candy ☆ - Topps Co., Inc.
ALF - Fuses–electric ☆ - Littelfuse, Inc.

ALF - Games ☆ - Ben Cooper Inc.
ALF - Hobby kits - Distinctive Design
ALF IN THE COLOR CAVES - Computer software - Spinnaker Software Corp.
ALFA - Boots - Erik Sports Inc.
ALFA - Lenses–optical ☆ - Signet Armorlite, Inc.
ALFA - Tiles–terrazzo - Imperial Tile and Marble Corp.
ALFA - Trailers–travel - Alfa Leisure Inc.
ALFA - Umbrellas - Alfa Umbrella Co. of America
ALFA BITS - Pet products - L/M Animal Farms, Inc.
ALFA BLOCKS - Pet products - Petland, Inc.
ALFA CHEWS - Pet products - L/M Animal Farms, Inc.
ALFA-CON - Nutritional supplement - Barth's Nutra Products
ALFA GOLD - Motor vehicles - Alfa Leisure, Inc.
ALFA ITALY, FRANCE - Tiles–terrazzo - Imperial Tile and Marble Corp.
ALFA-LITTER - Pet products ☆ - Alfa-Pet Inc.
ALFA MAX - Vitamins and nutritional supplements - Nature's Way Products,
　Inc.
ALFA PET - Pet products - Alfa-Pet Inc.
ALFA PLUS - Animal feeds - Buckeye Feed Mills, Inc.
ALFA ROMEO - Motor vehicles–automobiles - Alfa Romeo Distributors of
　North America
ALFAJUICE - Vitamins and nutritional supplements - Solaray
ALFALCO TONIC - Pharmaceutical preparations - Boericke & Tafel
ALFALFA - Apparel trimmings - Dan River Inc.
ALFALFA - Labels–paper - King Walk Inc.
ALFALFA - Pet products - Golden West Bird Farm Inc.
ALFALFA-ALA CARTE - Pet products - Golden West Bird Farm Inc.
ALFALFA BITS - Animal feeds ☆ - Alfa-Pet Inc.
ALFALFA COMPLEET - Vitamins and nutritional supplements - J.R. Carlson
　Laboratories Inc.
ALFALFA PELLET WORMER - Veterinary pharmaceutical preparations -
　Farnam Cos. Inc.
ALFANI - Sunglasses - R.H. Macy & Co.
ALFARO'S CAFE & BAKERY - Bakery products - Alfaro's Cafe & Bakery
ALFATAC - Pharmaceutical preparations - Consolidated Midland Corp.
ALFATONIC - Pharmaceutical preparations - Standard Homeopathic Co., Inc.
ALFCO - Filters–air - AIFCO Co.
ALFCOATER - Filters–air ☆ - AIFCO Co.
ALFENTA - Analgesia - Janssen Pharmaceutica Inc.
ALFERON LDO - Oral interferon - Interferon Sciences, Inc.
ALFERON N GEL - Pharmaceutical preparations - Interferon Sciences, Inc.
ALFERON N INJECTION - Medical apparatus - Interferon Sciences, Inc.
ALFEX - Watches - Memox
ALFIE - Apparel and accessories - Kennington Limited Inc.
ALFIE - Computer software - Cramer Products Inc.
ALFIE - Ophthalmic goods - Robin Optical
ALFIE ALLIGATOR - Toys - Imperial Toy Corp.
ALFILLE - Jewelry - Eve J. Alfille, Ltd.
ALFINAR - Lenses–photographic ☆ - Heitz Service Corp.
ALFINON - Lenses–photographic ☆ - Heitz Service Corp.
ALFONS MUCHA - Dishes–china ☆ - WMF/USA
ALFONSO - Hair care products ☆ - Stanley Fay Co.
ALFONSO - Lenses–optical - Ditto Industries Inc.
ALFONSO F. BISCEGLIA - Wines - Bisceglia Bros. Wine Co.
ALFONSO REGE - Wines - Diamond Oaks Vineyard
ALFRED - Ophthalmic goods ☆ - Luxottica
ALFRED A. KNOPF - Publisher's imprints - Alfred A. Knopf Inc.
ALFRED ANGELO - Wedding gowns - Alfred Angelo Inc.
ALFRED ANGELO INTERNATIONAL - Wedding gowns - Alfred Angelo Inc.
ALFRED BUTLER - Jewelry - Alfred Butler Inc.
ALFRED DUNHILL - Ophthalmic goods ☆ - Carrera Eyewear Corp.
ALFRED DUNHILL OF LONDON - Apparel–men's - Alfred Dunhill of London
　Inc.
ALFRED SCHYLER - Wines ☆ - House of Burgundy Inc.
ALFRED SUNG - Bath salts - Riviera Concepts
ALFRED SUNG - Frames–eyeglass - Carrera Eyewear Corp.
ALFRED SUNG - Scarves - Basha Scarves Inc.
ALFRED SUNG - Sunglasses - Outlook Eyewear Co.
ALFREDA - Dresses–women's - Anne Klein & Co.
ALFREDO - Wines - Banfi Vintners
ALFREDO'S - Bakery products - Neighborhood Baking Co.
ALFRED'S THE GOURMET BUTTER - Butter - Rowal Foods, Inc.
ALFRESCO - Floor coverings - Armstrong World Industries, Inc.
ALFRESCO - Footwear - JBI, Inc.
ALFRESCO - Wines ☆ - Renwood Winery, Inc.
ALFRESCO SALSA - Sauces - Hunt-Wesson, Inc.

ALFRY - Clocks - Alfry Manufacturing Inc.
ALG FARMERS BEST FEED - Animal feed supplements - A.L. Gilbert & Co.
ALG SINCE 1892 - Veterinary nutritional supplements - A.L. Gilbert & Co.
ALGAE-A-WAY - Pesticides–household ☆ - Aquatronics-Filtronics
ALGAE CLEAR - Chemical preparations - Locey Swim Pool Co.
ALGAE DESTROYER - Water treating compounds - Aquarium Pharmaceuticals, Inc.
ALGAE-EASE - Chemical preparations ☆ - Mydor Industries Inc.
ALGAE GALORE - Pet products - Nippon Pet Food
ALGAE GROW - Pet shops - Florida Aqua Farms Inc.
ALGAE GUARD - Pet products - Seachem Laboratories
ALGAE REMOVER - Aquariums–household - Jungle Laboratories Corp.
ALGAE-TROL - Chemical preparations ☆ - Barton Chemical Corp.
ALGAE-X - Water treating compounds - Great Lakes Biochemical Co., Inc.
ALGAEGON-9 - Cleaning preparations - Stewart-Hall Chemical Corp.
ALGAEGONE-12 - Cleaning preparations - Stewart-Hall Chemical Corp.
ALGAEMEC - Agricultural products - PBI/Gordon Corp.
ALGAEN-X - Agricultural fungicides - Grace-Sierra Crop Protection Co.
ALGAETRINE - Herbicides - Applied Biochemists, Inc.
ALGAL TURF SCRUBBER - Water filters - Ecological Systems, Inc.
ALGALATOR - Chemical preparations - Aqua Clear Industries Inc.
ALGARID - Artists' materials - LogEtronics Corp.
ALGAYU - Brandy ☆ - Shaw-Ross International Importers
ALGCO - Gaskets - Auburn Manufacturing Co.
ALGE-BLASTER 3 - Computer software ☆ - Knowledge Adventure
ALGE-BLASTER PLUS! - Computer software ☆ - Knowledge Adventure
ALGEBRA ARCADE - Computer software - Queue Inc.
ALGEBRA CONCEPTS - Computer software - Ventura Educational Systems
ALGEBRA PIECES - Publisher's imprints - Math Learning Center
ALGEBRA SYSTEM, THE - Computer software - E. David & Associates
ALGEBRAMASTER - Computer software - SourceView Software International
ALGEL - Pharmaceutical preparations ☆ - Wayne Medical Co. Inc.
ALGENIC ALKA - Pharmaceutical preparations - Rugby Laboratories Inc.
ALGER - Housewares - Alger Creations Inc.
ALGI - Soap ☆ - B. Shackman & Co.
ALGI-CURE - Swimming pools - Great Lakes Biochemical Co., Inc.
ALGI-EATER - Pet products - Silco Pet Products
ALGI-KLEER - Fungicides ☆ - E-Z Clor Systems
ALGI-NOX - Pesticides–household ☆ - Aquatrol, Inc.
ALGICON - Antacids - Rhone-Poulenc Rorer Pharmaceuticals Inc.
ALGIE - Toys - Mattel, Inc.
ALGIERS - Floor coverings–carpet and rugs - Trend Carpet
ALGIRAL - Floor coverings–carpet and rugs ☆ - Eurotex Inc.
ALGITAB - Antacids ☆ - Upsher-Smith Laboratories, Inc.
ALGLAS - Adhesives and sealants - General Electric Co.
ALGM COMPUTER SAYS: - Board game - Deborah Graham
ALGOLI - Soap - Nature de France
ALGOMA - Bags–canvas - Gleason Corp.
ALGOMA - Hammocks - Algoma Net Co.
ALGONQUIN - Beverages–malt - Frank's Distributing Co. Inc.
ALGONQUIN - Paints - Reliance Paint Co. Inc.
ALGONQUIN - Sporting goods ☆ - Shaw & Tenney Inc.
ALGOOD - Peanut butter - Algood Food Co.
ALGOPUR - Pet products ☆ - Sera Aquaristik USA Inc.
ALGORITHMIC COMPUTING ENGINE - Computer peripheral equipment - Fostex Corp. of America
ALGOSON - Pharmaceutical preparations ☆ - McNeil Pharmaceuticals
ALGULAR - Lenses–photographic ☆ - Heitz Service Corp.
ALGY BAR 40 - Chemical preparations - Chem Lab Products, Inc.
ALGY COP - Chemical preparations - Chem Lab Products, Inc.
ALHAMBRA - Dinnerware–glass ☆ - Lenox, Inc.
ALHAMBRA - Floor coverings–carpet and rugs - Artistic Rugs Inc.
ALHAMBRA - Floor coverings–carpet and rugs - Cabin Crafts Carpets
ALHAMBRA - Floor coverings–carpet and rugs - Patusan Trading Co., Inc.
ALHAMBRA - Recording label - Sonotone Corp.
ALHAMBRA - Roofing materials–slate - Zion Services Corp.
ALHAMBRA - Water–bottled or canned - Alhambra National Water
ALHAMBRA - Wines - Gibson Wine Co.
ALI - Colognes - Brandy Harvest
ALI ABA - Recording label - American Law Institute
ALI BABA - Bread and pastries - Ali Baba Middle Eastern Bakery
ALI BABA - Headwear - Benkel Manufacturing Co.
ALI CAT - Toys–stuffed - Russ Berrie and Co., Inc.
ALI DESIGN ANALYZER - Computer software - ALI Technologies Inc.
ALI DI FARFELLA - Crackers ☆ - Crystal Food Import Corp.
ALI-GATOR-GRIT - Tools - Ali Industries, Inc.

ALI MAC - Apparel–children's - Mack & Moore, Inc.
ALI MILES - Apparel–women's - Jerell, Inc.
ALI-SHINE - Tools ☆ - Ali Industries, Inc.
ALIA - Apparel–women's - Nygard, Inc.
ALIA - Recording label - Jazz Composer's Orchestra Association Inc.
ALIAGE - Perfumes - Estee Lauder Inc.
ALIAS - Recording label - Alias Records, Inc.
ALIBI - Food products ☆ - Tour Eiffel
ALIBI - Games - Mayfair Games, Inc.
ALICANTE - Floor coverings–carpet and rugs ☆ - Orian Rugs Inc.
ALICE - Computer software - Apple Computer Inc.
ALICE - Dolls - Alexander Doll Co. Inc.
ALICE - Ophthalmic goods ☆ - Rozin Optical Export Corp.
A ALICE ANN DESIGNS - Clothing - Hanold Co.
ALICE BEST - Candy ☆ - Williams & Randolph Inc.
ALICE DARLING - Games - Alexander Doll Co. Inc.
ALICE IN RUBBERLAND - Stamps–hand - Paul Decker
ALICE IN WONDERLAND - Computer software - Queue Inc.
ALICE IN WONDERLAND - Dolls - Dakin Inc.
ALICE IN WONDERLAND - Flowers, plants, and seeds - White Swan, Ltd.
ALICE IN WONDERLAND - Toys–stuffed - Toy Works, Inc.
ALICE LIN - Giftware ☆ - Henriksen Imports Inc.
ALICE MACRAY'S - Candy - S.L. Kaye Co., Inc.
ALICE 'N THUNDERLAND - Apparel and accessories - Alice 'n Thunderland
ALICE PETITES - Blouses–women's - Jonathan Logan Inc.
ALICE STUART - Apparel–women's - Jonathan Logan Inc.
ALICE TOWNE - Floor coverings ☆ - Armstrong World Industries, Inc.
ALICE'S - Table linens - Alice's
ALICE'S FLOWER GARDEN - Flowers, plants, and seeds - White Swan, Ltd.
ALICI - Food products - Bel Canto Fancy Foods Ltd.
ALICIA - Blouses–women's - J.C. Penney Co., Inc.
ALICIA - Olive oil ☆ - Southern Import Distributors
ALICIA-MILTRIX - Recording label - Jazz Composer's Orchestra Association Inc.
ALICON - First aid kits - Alimed, Inc.
ALICOOL - First aid kits - Alimed, Inc.
ALICOVER - Bandages - Alimed, Inc.
ALIDA - Rings–jewelry - Artcarved Inc.
ALIDA INDUSTRIES - Needlework kits - Alida Industries
ALIE GAETA'S FOODS - Salad dressing - Gaeta's Restaurant, Inc.
ALIEN - Electronic equipment - Focus Electronic Corp.
ALIEN - Games ☆ - Kenner Products
ALIEN - Trading cards and stamps - Twentieth Century Fox Film Corp.
ALIEN ACTION - Computer software - SRA/McGraw-Hill (Div. of The McGraw-Hill Companies)
ALIEN ADDITION - Computer software - SRA/McGraw-Hill (Div. of The McGraw-Hill Companies)
ALIEN ADVENTURE - Fireworks - Ingram Enterprises, Inc.
ALIEN COMMAND - Video games - Jaleco USA, Inc.
ALIEN CRAFT - Computer software - Educational Adventures, Inc.
ALIEN CREATURES - Erasers - Diener Industries Inc.
ALIEN ENERGY NODES - Candy - Toucan Confections Inc.
ALIEN EXPLORER - Toys–models ☆ - Estes Industries
ALIEN FRIENDLY? - Games - Carol Jo Gustafson
ALIEN INVADERS-PLUS - Toys–electronic ☆ - Philips Consumer Electronics Co.
ALIEN PIES - Novelty items - Tom and Sally's Handmade Chocolates, Inc.
ALIEN PIZZA RAIDERS - Costumes - McCain Ellio's Foods, Inc.
ALIEN SPACE - Games - Gamescience
ALIEN SPACE PROBE - Toys–models ☆ - Estes Industries
ALIEN SPORT - Golfing equipment - Alien Sport, Inc.
ALIEN STORM - Games - Sega of America, Inc.
ALIEN TALES - Computer software ☆ - Broderbund Software, Inc.
ALIEN, THE - Games ☆ - Avalon Hill Game Co.
ALIEN WARS, THE - Games ☆ - Konami (America) Inc.
ALIEN WORKSHOP - Skateboards - Wormtrap, Inc.
ALIENATOR - Toys–automobiles - Nikko America, Inc.
ALIENCOUNTER/FACE FLASH - Computer software ☆ - Milliken Publishing Co. (Computer Software Div.)
ALIENS WITH ATTITUDE - Notebooks and notepads - Norcom Inc.
ALIENTO DEL SOL - Wines - San Antonio Winery Inc.
ALIESA - Chairs–wood - Jami, Inc.
ALIESA - Furniture - Harter
ALIGN - Insecticides - Agridyne Technologies, Inc.
ALIGN-A-DRAIN - Plumbing fixtures–plastic - Webstone Co. Inc.
ALIGN A SIGN - Hardware ☆ - Cole Consumer Products Inc.

☆ = Now out of production

ALIGNER - Tools - Diamond Machining Technology Inc.

ALIGNING THE TOWER OF BABEL - Publisher's imprints - Block Petrella Weisbord, Inc.

ALIGNMASTER - Electronic equipment - Laser Alignment, Inc.

ALIGNSIDE - Siding ☆ - ABT Co., Inc.

ALIITE - Cement - E. Khashoggi Industries

ALILA GUARD - Repellent - Alila, Inc.

ALIMAR - Food products - Liberty Fish Co.

ALIMED - Health care products - Alimed, Inc.

ALIMENTOS BALANCEADOS PARA ANIMALES - Magazines - Watt Publishing Co.

ALIMOLD - Fabrics—gauze - Alimed, Inc.

ALIMONY ALE - Ale - Buffalo Bill's Brewery

ALINA - Bedding—linen - Dan River Inc.

ALINABAL ACHIEVING EXCELLENCE-WORLDWIDE - Metals - Alinabal, Inc.

ALINCOURT - Glassware—household - Durand International

ALINE - Floor coverings—carpet and rugs - Regal Rugs Inc.

ALINE - Surgical instruments - Smith & Nephew Richards, Inc.

ALINE/ANNE KLEIN - Shoes - Schwartz & Benjamin Inc.

ALINK - Computer software - Experior Corp.

ALINOSI - Candy - Alinosi French Ice Cream Co.

ALIPLAST - Foam rubber - Alimed, Inc.

ALIPLAST XPE - Medical apparatus - Alimed, Inc.

ALIQUIS - Hair care products - Tressa, Inc.

ALISA - Olives—pickled or brined - V.M. Calderon Inc.

ALISAL - Computer software - Carter and Cone Type Inc.

ALISED - Pharmaceutical preparations ☆ - ICN Pharmaceuticals Inc.

ALISE'S BOUQUET - Floor coverings ☆ - Tarkett, Inc.

ALISHAN - Jewelry - Alishan Designer Jewelry

ALISON - Mail boxes - Gordon Associates

ALISON ROBERTS - Crocheted and knitted items - Valor

ALISTRAN - Fibers—fluorocarbons - Multi-Tex Products INC.

ALISTRAP - Medical apparatus - Alimed, Inc.

ALISUN - Skin care products - Falcon Health & Fitness Systems Inc.

ALISYN - Musical-instrument oil, cleaner, etc. - Aerospace Lubricants Inc.

ALITA - Macaroni - D. Merlino & Sons

ALITA - Pasta - Merlino & Sons

ALIVE - Artillery - Defensive Living Systems, Inc.

ALIVE - Bicycles - Klein Bicycle Corp.

ALIVE - Cereal ☆ - General Mills, Inc.

ALIVE - Computer storage devices—optical - CD Technology, Inc.

ALIVE - Health care products - Lotus Brands Inc.

ALIVE - Hosiery - Sara Lee Corp.

ALIVE - Recording label - Jazz Composer's Orchestra Association Inc.

ALIVE! - Toys ☆ - Brunswick Corp.

ALIVE '55 - Toys—automobiles - Mattel, Inc.

ALIVE & KICKIN' - Bakery products - Port City Bakery, Inc.

ALIVE & WELL - Hair care products - Gillette Co.

ALIVE & WELL - Housewares - Bemis Manufacturing Co.

ALIVE ENERGY - Vitamins and nutritional supplements - Lotus Brands Inc.

ALIVE WITH COLOR - Wallpaper ☆ - Sanitas Wallcoverings

ALIX - Furniture - Haworth, Inc.

ALIX - Sporting goods - Action & Leisure

ALIX PAIGE - Apparel—women's - Alix Paige Ltd.

ALIX TAYLOR - Apparel—women's - Jamie Brooke Inc.

ALIX USA - Bags—duffel - Action & Leisure

ALIYAH - Game - Contemporary Designs

ALIZA - Cabinets - Kabom Kitchen & Bath Manufacturing

ALIZE - Beverages—alcohol - Kobrand Corp.

ALJIM - See SCHAFFER

ALJO - Dyes and pigments - Aljo Manufacturing Co.

ALJOCOTE - Paints ☆ - St. Louis Paint Manufacturing Co.

ALJON - Jewelry - Aljon Jewelry, Inc.

ALK - Computer software - Alk Associates, Inc.

ALK ASSOCIATES - Computer software - Alk Associates, Inc.

ALKA 2 - Antacids - Miles Inc.

ALKA-BRITE - Cleaning preparations - Nu-Calgon Wholesaler, Inc.

ALKA-FAT - Agricultural products - CS Animal Feeds, Inc.

ALKA-LINE - Vitamins and nutritional supplements - Best Process, Inc.

ALKA-MED - Health care products ☆ - Halsey Drug Co. Inc.

ALKA-MIN - Agricultural products - CS Animal Feeds, Inc.

ALKA-MINTS - Antacids - Miles Inc.

ALKA-PHEN - Pharmaceutical preparations ☆ - Solvay Pharmaceuticals Inc.

ALKA PLEX - Vitamins and nutritional supplements - Natural Organics, Inc.

ALKA PRO - Paints - Wilson Paint Co.

ALKA-SEAL - Paints - Diamond/Kuhn Paint Co.

ALKA-SELTZER - Antacids - Bayer Corp. (Consumer Care Div.)

ALKA-SELTZER - Antacids - Miles Inc.

ALKA-TUSSIN - Cough medicines - Maxim Chemicals Ltd.

ALKADINE - Oils—lubricating ☆ - Shell Oil Co.

ALKALINE BELL - Pharmaceutical preparations - Hollings-Smith Co. Inc.

ALKALINE BUFFERED - Veterinary pharmaceutical preparations - International Stock Food Corp.

ALKALINE BUFFES - Pet products - Seachem Laboratories

ALKALINITY FIRST - Chemical preparations - Church and Dwight Co. Inc.

ALKALINITY UP - Chemical preparations - Great Lakes Biochemical Co., Inc.

ALKALIZER - Pet products ☆ - Aquatronics-Filtronics

ALKALOL - Mouthwashes - Alkalol Co.

ALKALON - Varnishes - Heil Process Equipment Corp.

ALKANE - Pharmaceutical preparations ☆ - JMI-Canton Pharmaceuticals

ALKARAU - Antihistamine preparations ☆ - Ferndale Laboratories, Inc.

ALKARIGHT - Pet products ☆ - Jungle Laboratories Corp.

ALKASANS - Pharmaceutical preparations ☆ - P.J. Noyes Co., Inc.

ALKASIL - Antacids - Ralph Winton Co. Inc.

ALKATITE - Paints - Pratt & Lambert, Inc.

ALKEN - Cosmetics - Gary Farn Ltd.

ALKENITE - Paints - Tenax Finishing Product

ALKERAN - Pharmaceutical preparations - Burroughs Wellcome Co.

ALKETS - Pharmaceutical preparations ☆ - Upjohn Co.

ALKHOBAR - Floor coverings - Bellbridge Carpets

ALKI ALE - Beverages—malt - West Seattle Brewing Co.

ALKISHEEN - Paints ☆ - Induron Coatings Inc.

ALKOLAVE - Pharmaceutical preparations ☆ - Schering-Plough Healthcare Products

ALKOLAVE GEL - Astringents ☆ - Schering-Plough Healthcare Products

ALKON - Machine parts - Alkon Corp.

ALKPHASE-B - Medical apparatus - Metra Biosystems, Inc.

ALKRYLIC - Paints - Long Island Paint & Chemical Co.

ALKYD CHARM - Paints - Pervo Paint Co.

ALKYD DULAMEL - Paints - Benjamin Moore & Co.

ALKYD-KOTE - Paints ☆ - United States Refining Co.

ALKYFLAT - Paints - Seagraves Coatings

ALKYLSEAL - Paints - Dunn Edwards Corp.

ALKYROL - Vitamins and nutritional supplements - Scandinavian Natural Health & Beauty Products, Inc.

ALKYVAR - Varnishes - Multi-Coat Corp.

ALL - Cigars - G.A. Georgopulo & Co. Inc.

ALL - Detergents - Lever Brothers Co. Inc.

ALL - Posters - All Group, Inc.

ALL-4-ONE - Recording label - Brookhill Records Corp.

ALL-4-ONE - Transformers—electric - Signal Transformer Co., Inc.

ALL-A-GLOW - Lighting fixtures - Meijer, Inc.

ALL-A-ROUND - Pape towel dispenser - James A. Hall

ALL ABOUT AMERICA - Computer software - Unicorn Software

ALL ABOUT DINOSAURS - Computer software - Orange Cherry Software

ALL ABOUT LIGHT AND SOUND - Computer software - Ventura Educational Systems

ALL ABOUT MATTER - Computer software - Ventura Educational Systems

ALL ABOUT ME - Children's health journal - Informative Amenities Inc.

ALL ABOUT ME - Educational materials - Options, Inc.

ALL ABOUT ME - Electronic equipment - Texas Instruments Inc.

ALL ABOUT ME - Publisher's imprints - Gerber Products Co.

ALL ABOUT SCIENCE - Computer software - Ventura Educational Systems

ALL ABOUT SIMPLE MACHINES - Computer software - Ventura Educational Systems

ALL ABOUT THE SOLAR SYSTEM - Computer software - Ventura Educational Systems

ALL ABOUT TIME - Computer software - Orange Cherry Software

ALL ABOUT US - Publisher's imprints - Sunny Skyes

ALL-ABOUTS - Shoes ☆ - Edison Brothers Stores, Inc.

ALL ACTION - Apparel—women's - NCC Industries, Inc.

ALL ALASKAN - Seafood products—fresh or frozen - All Alaskan Seafoods Inc.

ALL AMERICA - Fireworks - Freedom Fireworks, Inc.

ALL AMERICAN - Bags—canvas - Risto Inc.

ALL AMERICAN - Beverages—carbonated - Krier Foods Inc.

ALL AMERICAN - Bicycles - Gulf Cycle Corp.

ALL AMERICAN - Boats—motor - Glastex Inc.

ALL AMERICAN - Boats—motor - Larson Boat Div.

ALL AMERICAN - Chocolate candy - Maxfield Candy Co.

ALL AMERICAN - Cordage and twine ☆ - Winchester-Auburn Mills Inc.

ALL AMERICAN - Darts and dart games - Dart Mart Inc.

ALL-AMERICAN - Decals and transfers - Dyer Specialty Co. Inc.
ALL AMERICAN - Dog food ☆ - Buckeye Feed Mills, Inc.
ALL AMERICAN - Exercising equipment ☆ - American Athletic Inc.
ALL AMERICAN - Fertilizers - Vigoro Consumer & Professional Products Group
ALL-AMERICAN - Fertilizers - Vigoro Industries, Inc.
ALL-AMERICAN - Film - W.J.M. Plastics, Inc.
ALL AMERICAN - Floor coverings–carpet and rugs - Cabin Crafts Carpets
ALL AMERICAN - Food products - V. & E. Kohnstamm Inc.
ALL AMERICAN - Food products - Siritop, Inc.
ALL AMERICAN - Glass–optical - Criss Optical Manufacturing Co.
ALL AMERICAN - Glassware–household - Benner Glassware Inc.
ALL AMERICAN - Handkerchiefs ☆ - Carolina Manufacturing Inc.
ALL-AMERICAN - Hardware - Blaine Window Hardware Inc.
ALL-AMERICAN - Kitchen appliances - Wisconsin Aluminum Foundry Co.
ALL-AMERICAN - Knives–pocket - Imperial Schrade Corp.
ALL-AMERICAN - Mechanical pencils - Autopoint Inc.
ALL AMERICAN - Nuts–salted, roasted, cooked, or canned - Los Angeles Nut House
ALL AMERICAN - Office machines - All American
ALL AMERICAN - Paint rollers - Bestt-Liebco
ALL AMERICAN - Paints - St. Louis Paint Manufacturing Co.
ALL AMERICAN - Prefabricated buildings–wood - All American Homes Inc.
ALL AMERICAN - Pressure cookers - R & R Mill Co. Inc.
ALL AMERICAN - Prosthetic apparatus - RWB Novelty
ALL AMERICAN - Recording label - D.S.M. Producers Inc.
ALL AMERICAN - Saunas - Pollenex Corp.
ALL AMERICAN - Scoreboards - Austin Athletic Equipment Corp.
ALL AMERICAN - Seasonings - All American Seasonings Inc.
ALL AMERICAN - Seat covers - Alco Manufacturing Co. Inc.
ALL-AMERICAN - Sporting goods - Lyman Products Corp.
ALL AMERICAN - Sporting goods - Midwest Sporting Goods Manufacturing Co.
ALL-AMERICAN - Tool boxes ☆ - Waterloo Industries Inc.
ALL-AMERICAN - Tools - Great Neck Saw Manufacturers, Inc.
ALL AMERICAN - Tools–hand-operated ☆ - Durall-Eagle Tools
ALL AMERICAN - Toys ☆ - Wham-O Manufacturing Co.
ALL AMERICAN - Toys–guns - Tyco Toys
ALL AMERICAN - Truck-window grille, ramp - Bloomfield Manufacturing Co.
ALL AMERICAN - Varnishes - McCloskey Corp.
ALL AMERICAN - Veterinary medical equipment - Y-Tex Corp.
ALL-AMERICAN BEAUTIES - Furniture–factory ☆ - Clayton Marcus Co. Inc.
ALL-AMERICAN COLLECTION - Fabric basket linings - Longaberger Co.
ALL AMERICAN FOOTBALL - Games - Cadaco Div.
ALL AMERICAN FOOTLOCKER - Lockers–metal - All American Industries, Inc.
ALL AMERICAN IRRIGATOR - Irrigation equipment - Hendrickson Bros.
ALL AMERICAN LADDER - Hardware - Werner Co.
ALL AMERICAN LOOK - Nail care products - Revlon Consumer Products Corp.
ALL AMERICAN MINI HOOPSTER - Easels - Hutch Sports USA Inc.
ALL AMERICAN MODEL 2000 - Pistols - Colt's Manufacturing Co. Inc.
ALL AMERICAN SANTA - Paper products - Giordano Art, Ltd.
ALL AMERICAN SNACK WHITE TRASH - Chocolate syrup - BLM Enterprises Inc.
ALL AMERICAN SUPER BONE, THE - Dog food - Pet Center, Inc.
ALL AMERICAN SUPER CHEWS - Pet food - Pet Center, Inc.
ALL AMERICAN SUPERCHEWS - Dog food - Pet Center, Inc.
ALL AMERICAN XMAS BONE - Dog food - Pet Center, Inc.
ALL AROUND PLUS - Sporting goods - Trace Athletic Corp.
ALL-AROUND, THE - Pillows - Camp Kazoo, Ltd.
ALL AROUND THE CITY! - Games - Addison-Wesley Publishing Co.
ALL AROUND TOWN WITHOUT WAKING OR DISTURBING BABY - Strollers–baby - Lisco, Inc.
ALL AROUNDER - Flowers, plants, and seeds ☆ - Applewood Seed & Garden Group
ALL-ART - Artists' materials - All-Art Products Inc.
ALL-ART BRUSHGUARD - Artists' materials ☆ - All-Art Products Inc.
ALL ART JAZZ - Recording label - Jazz Alliance, Inc.
ALL-ART OVERPOINTS - Pens ☆ - All-Art Products Inc.
ALL ARTS STUDIO - Statuary ☆ - Hillside House of Originals
ALL B - Vitamins and nutritional supplements - Naturally Vitamin Supplements Inc.
ALL BODY ACTION - Exercising equipment - Exercycle Corp.
ALL BRASS - Computer software - Harden Industries Inc.
ALL BREED - Dog food - Armada Grain Co.

ALL-BRIGHT - Cleaning preparations ☆ - Promaster
ALL BY MYSELF - Footwear - Toddler University
ALL-CAMERA RAINCOAT - Photographic equipment - SP Systems/Saratons
ALL-CLAD LTD. - Pans - All-Clad Metalcrafters Inc.
ALL-CLARK - Food products - Evans Enterprises
ALL CLEAN - Cosmetics - Estee Lauder Inc.
ALL CLEAR - Chemical preparations - First Brands Properties Inc.
ALL CLEAR - Motor vehicle parts and accessories - Reflectory
ALL-CLEAR - Pet products - Golden West Bird Farm Inc.
ALL CLIMATE - Inks ☆ - Specialty Ink Co. Inc.
ALL CLIMATE - Paints - Black & Puryear Paint Manufacturing Co. Inc.
ALL-CLIMATE HD - Oils–lubricating - Valvoline Oil Co.
ALL COLORS EQUAL - Apparel and accessories - All Colors Equal Clothing
ALL COMFORT - Climate-control products - Interdynamics, Inc.
ALL CONDITIONS GEAR - Footwear–athletic - Nike, Inc.
ALL CONFERENCE - Apparel–athletic - All Conference, Inc.
ALL COUNTRY - Tires–automobile - Hercules Tire & Rubber Co.
ALL COURT SPORTS - Sporting goods - Joseph M. Trippodo, Jr.
ALL-CRAFT - Paints ☆ - Briner Paint Manufacturing Co. Inc.
ALL CRAFT - Tools–hand-operated - Arthur Zakarian
ALL CRISP - Pickles - B & G Foods Inc.
ALL-DAIRY BLEND - Dairy products - Land O'Lakes Inc.
ALL-DAY - Cosmetics ☆ - Noxell Corp.
ALL DAY - Deodorants–personal - Schering Corp.
ALL DAY - Hair care products ☆ - Nu-Tress Laboratories Inc.
ALL-DAY - Hosiery - Mayer/Berkshire Corp.
ALL-DAY - Lipsticks - Estee Lauder Inc.
ALL-DAY - Pharmaceutical preparations - Barth's Nutra Products
ALL DAY - Vitamins and nutritional supplements ☆ - Columbia Laboratories Inc.
ALL DAY COMFORT - Footwear–athletic - Lowell Shoe, Inc.
ALL DAY COMFORT SHOES, THE - Footwear - Lowell Shoe, Inc.
ALL DAY LONG - Underwear and nightwear - Alba-Waldensian, Inc.
ALL-DAY ORANGE - Juices - Smith's Dairy Products Co.
ALL-DAY SHADOWLINER - Cosmetics - Almay Inc.
A.L.L. DESIGNS - Jewelry - Amy L. Levine
ALL DRESSED UP - Apparel and accessories - Kmart Properties, Inc.
ALL-DRY - Dryers–household - Loroman Co.
ALL DRY - Nail care products - RTS Laboratories, Inc.
ALL-ETCH - Dental compounds - Bisco, Inc.
ALL EYE NEED - Cases–eyeglass - TEC Vision, Inc.
ALL EYES KIT - Cosmetics - Maybelline Co.
ALL FALL, THE - Wigs - Helene Curtis Industries Inc.
ALL FAMILY - Vitamins and nutritional supplements ☆ - Xttrium Laboratories Inc.
ALL-FLEET EXTRA - Oils–lubricating - Valvoline Oil Co.
ALL-FLEET PLUS - Oils–lubricating - Valvoline Oil Co.
ALL-FLEX - Mortars–clay - Bil-Dry Corp.
ALL-FLEX - Pharmaceutical preparations - Ortho Pharmaceutical Corp.
ALL-FLORA - Vitamins and nutritional supplements - New Moon Extracts, Inc.
ALL FREE & CLEAR - Detergents - Lever Brothers Co. Inc.
ALL FRESH - Food products - All Fresh Products Inc.
ALL FRESH - Food products - Cako Development Corp.
ALL-FRESH - Pet products - Nickers International Ltd.
ALL GIRL BAND, THE - Apparel stores–lingerie - Formfit Rogers
ALL GIRL SPORTSWEAR - Apparel and accessories - William Charles Moore
ALL-GLASS - Aquariums–household - All Glass Aquarium Co. Inc.
ALL GOD'S CREATURES - Pet products - Northeastern Products Corp.
ALL GONE! - Insecticides - Eagle-Picher Minerals, Inc.
ALL-GRIP - Cargo handling equipment - Western Sling Co.
ALL-GUARD - Giftware - Wyler Sales Corp.
ALL-GUARD - Goggles–safety - Allan Enterprises
ALL-HERBAL - Cough drops - F & F Laboratories, Inc.
ALL HOLD - Adhesives and sealants - National Artcraft Co.
ALL IN A DAZE WORK - Calendars ☆ - American Greetings Corp.
ALL-IN-ONE - Aquarium accessories - HTZ Investment Corp.
ALL-IN-ONE - Bandages - Avcor Health Care Products, Inc.
ALL-IN-ONE - Cleaning preparations - International Bullion & Metal Brokers (USA) Inc.
ALL-IN-ONE - Conveyors - Kvp Systems, Inc.
ALL IN ONE - Cutting oil - Comstar International Inc. (IPC Div.)
ALL-IN-ONE - Detergents - Imperial Manufacturing Co. Inc.
ALL IN ONE - Food products ☆ - United Citrus Products Corp.
ALL IN ONE - Fuel additives - Star Brite
ALL IN ONE - Hardware - Abus Lock Co.
ALL-IN-ONE - Invitations ☆ - Lemon Tree Stationery Corp.

☆ = Now out of production

ALL-IN-ONE - Kitchen appliances - Vaughan Manufacturing Co. Inc.

ALL-IN-ONE - Office supplies ☆ - Esselte Corp.

ALL IN ONE - Ovens–microwave - Nordic Ware

ALL-IN-ONE - Paper–gift wrap - American Greetings Corp.

ALL-IN-ONE - Pet products - Golden West Bird Farm Inc.

ALL-IN-ONE - Pharmaceutical preparations - Michigan Pharmaceutical

ALL-IN-ONE - Posters - Federal Wage and Labor-Law Institute

ALL IN ONE - Remote control devices - Universal Electronics Inc.

ALL-IN-ONE - Rice ☆ - Mystic Lake Dairy Inc.

ALL IN ONE - Shampoos - Chesebrough-Pond's USA Co.

ALL-IN-ONE GREENHOUSE - Garden equipment - Carefree Garden Products

ALL IN ONE POTTY - Infant product - Summer Infant Products Inc.

ALL IN ONE SYSTEM - Mattresses - Flexi-Mat Corp.

ALL-IN-ONE TOOTHPASTE - Toothpaste - Colgate-Palmolive Co.

ALL-IN-ONE TRAVELITE - Luggage ☆ - Postcraft Co.

ALL JUICE - Juices - Green Spot Packaging, Inc.

ALL KIDS ARE NUMBER ONE - Apparel–children's - All Kids Are Number One, Inc.

ALL KITCHEN - Eggs - Almark Inc.

ALL KITCHENS - Canned goods, paper products, soup bases, spices - Brown and Joiner Inc.

ALL KITCHENS - Meat products–poultry - O.K. Foods Inc.

ALL KITCHENS - Preserved foods–prepackaged - Anchor Food Products, Inc.

ALL KITCHENS - Turkeys - Watson Quality Foods Inc.

ALL-KLEEN - Cleaning preparations - PLC

ALL LENNON - Wallpaper - Norwall Wallcoverings

ALL LIVER - Vitamins and nutritional supplements - Vita-Fore Products Co.

ALL-LUMINUM - Tables–metal - All-Luminum Products Inc.

ALL MADMEN TEAM - Games - Universal Manufacturing Co., Inc.

ALL MAG - Electronic equipment ☆ - Magna Visual, Inc.

ALL MEDIA - Office supplies - Ames Safety Envelope Co.

ALL MEN ARE PIGS - Shirts - Mark L. Thomas

ALL METAL GARD - Paints - Kelly-Moore/Preservative Paints

ALL MY CHILDREN - Games ☆ - Decipher Inc.

ALL NATURAL FARMS - Fruits and vegetables - All Natural Farms, Inc.

ALL NATURAL GOURMET - Iced tea, coffee, soft drinks ☆ - Brooklyn Bottling Corp.

ALL NATURAL GREENE'S FARM - Sauces - Stokes Canning Co.

ALL NATURAL SPRING GREEN - Fertilizers - Spring Green Enterprises, Inc.

ALL NATURAL VEGETARIAN DELIGHT - Dinners–frozen - Deep Foods, Inc.

ALL NIGHT MEDIA - Rubber stamps, inkpads and ink - All Night Media, Inc.

ALL-NIGHTER, THE - Fireplace logs–treated - Meeks Firewood Co., Ltd.

ALL-NU - Floor waxes - R.M. Hollingshead Corp.

ALL-NUTRIENT - Hair care products - Chuckles Inc.

ALL-O-ROUND - Spaghetti ☆ - Fantastic Foods Inc.

ALL OCCASION - Candy - Zachary Confections Inc.

ALL OF LIFE'S ANSWERS - Giftware - Ideas, Inc.

ALL OFF - Cleaning preparations–household - Hertron International Inc.

ALL-OFF - Floor cleanser - Klein & Co.

ALL ONE - Vitamins and nutritional supplements ☆ - Nutritech

ALL ONE SEA - Apparel and accessories - Allayna Kahan

ALL ONE VITAMIN C CRYSTALS - Vitamins and nutritional supplements - Nutritech

ALL ORGANIC - Furniture polish and wax - Amrep Inc.

ALL OUR KIDS - Furniture - Draco Corp.

ALL OUT - Cleaning preparations - Iron Out, Inc.

ALL OUTDOORS - Canes - All Outdoors, Inc.

ALL-OVER - Roofing materials–slate - United Hardware

ALL OVER THE WORLD - Jewelry - Studex USA Inc.

ALL PACKA - Sporting goods - Nett Designs, Inc.

ALL-PEN - Pens–fountain ☆ - Sanford Corp.

ALL-PHASE ELECTRIC SUPPLY CO. - Electrical equipment - All-Phase Electric Supply Co.

ALL POINTS - Food products - Epicure Foods Inc.

ALL POINTS - Pencil sharpeners - Revlon Consumer Products Corp.

ALL-POINTS - Skin care products - Ilona, Inc.

ALL POINTS SOFTWARE - Computer software - Penstuff, Inc.

ALL PRIME - Paints - Triangle Coatings Inc.

ALL-PRO - Automotive parts and accessories - Rite Autotronics Corp.

ALL PRO - Bathtubs–enameled - Sterling Plumbing Group Inc.

ALL PRO - Computer software - Freightliner Corp.

ALL PRO - Footwear - Seaway Importing Co.

ALL PRO - Gloves - Ektelon

ALL PRO - Laces–boot and shoe - Hickory Industries, Inc.

ALL PRO - Mops - Rubbermaid Cleaning Products Inc.

ALL PRO - Rackets–tennis ☆ - Wimbledon

ALL PRO - Shirts - Cluett, Peabody & Co.

ALL PRO - Weightlifting equipment - All Pro Exercise Products, Inc.

ALL PRO BIG SHOTS - Toys - Hot Properties, Inc.

ALL-PRO BY ALLISON - Apparel and accessories - Allison Manufacturing Co.

ALL-PRO TABS - Vitamins and nutritional supplements - Solgar Vitamin and Herb Co., Inc.

ALL-PROOF - Watches ☆ - Longines-Wittnauer Watch Co.

ALL PURE - Cosmetics - Demert & Dougherty, Inc.

ALL PURPOSE - Coffee - Mr. Coffee, Inc.

ALL PURPOSE - Egg substitutes - Olson Farms Inc. (Liquid Egg Div.)

ALL PURPOSE - Lenses–magnifying - Edroy Products Co.

ALL PURPOSE - Pet products - Novalek, Inc.

ALL-PURPOSE - Photographic equipment ☆ - Tiffen Manufacturing Corp.

ALL PURPOSE - Sponges - A.J. Kicks Corp.

ALL PURPOSE BOQUET - Health care products ☆ - Halsey Drug Co. Inc.

ALL PURPOSE GOURMET SPRINKLE - Spices and extracts - Finest Kind Spices

ALL-RANGE - Musical instruments - Fred Gretsch Enterprises

ALL READY - Food products - Pillsbury Co.

ALL REDS - Glass products - Vitro Agate Corp.

ALL-RITE - Pens - Empire Berol USA

ALL ROOKIE TEAM - Trading cards and stamps - Upper Deck Co.

ALL-ROUND - Bearings–industrial - EDT Corp.

ALL 'ROUND - Meat products ☆ - Texxstar Resources (USA), Inc.

ALL ROUND FOODS - Pastries - All Round Foods, Inc.

ALL SAINTS - Pharmaceutical preparations - Lorrie Schulte

ALL SEASON - Doors–garage - Clopay Millwork

ALL SEASON - Fertilizers - Howard Johnson's Enterprises, Inc.

ALL SEASON - Motor vehicle parts and accessories - Lancaster Colony Automotive Group

ALL-SEASON - Oils–lubricating - Marathon Oil Co.

ALL SEASON - Salad dressings–bottled - Korbro Oil Corp.

ALL SEASON KING - Tires - Uniroyal Goodrich Licensing Services, Inc.

ALL SEASONALS - Greeting cards - Kersten Bros. Studios

ALL SEASONS - Beverages–carbonated ☆ - America's Best Beverages Inc.

ALL SEASONS - Brooms - Zephyr Manufacturing Co.

ALL SEASONS - Cooking equipment–household ☆ - Nordic Ware

ALL SEASONS - Floor coverings–carpet and rugs ☆ - Callaway Carpets

ALL SEASONS - Frames–eyeglass - Zylo Ware Corp.

ALL SEASONS - Hair care products - Waverly Beauty Products

ALL SEASONS - Indoor-outdoor carpets and rugs - Instant Turf Industries Inc.

ALL SEASONS - Mattresses - Spring Air Bedding Inc.

ALL SEASONS - Mattresses - Spring Air Co.

ALL SEASONS - Meat products–poultry - El Jay Poultry Corp.

ALL SEASONS - Pesticides–household - Bonide Products, Inc.

ALL SEASONS - Plastic shutters ☆ - Contico International Inc.

ALL SEASONS - Thermostats - Quad Six Inc.

ALL SEASON'S FELT - Hats–felt ☆ - Bollman Hat Co.

ALL-SET - Adhesives and sealants - Bil-Dry Corp.

ALL SET - Hair care products - Demert & Dougherty, Inc.

ALL SET BRAND - Hair care products - Demert & Dougherty, Inc.

ALL SET GOLD - Cosmetics - Demert & Dougherty, Inc.

ALL SHADY - Lawn mowers ☆ - Kellogg Inc.

ALL-SHIELD - Varnish - Robert E. Diefendorf

ALL SIGN - Signs - All Sign Products, Inc.

ALL-SIZE - Shutters ☆ - Selfix, Inc.

ALL SKINS - Cosmetics - Estee Lauder Inc.

ALL SMILES - Health care products - Liberty Natural Products

ALL SOL - Soldering equipment - L.B. Allen Co. Inc.

ALL SORTS OF SPORTS - Giftware - Fort USA

ALL SPORT - Beverages–carbonated - Pepsi-Cola Co.

ALL SPORT - Binoculars ☆ - Swift Instruments, Inc.

ALL SPORT - Scoreboards - Daktronics Inc.

ALL SPORT 2200 - Scoreboards ☆ - Daktronics Inc.

ALL SPORT 2300 - Scoreboards ☆ - Daktronics Inc.

ALL SPORT 2400 - Scoreboards ☆ - Daktronics Inc.

ALL SPORT 2500 - Scoreboards ☆ - Daktronics Inc.

ALL SPORT 2600 - Scoreboards ☆ - Daktronics Inc.

ALL SPORT 3000 - Scoreboards ☆ - Daktronics Inc.

ALL SPORT 6000 - Scoreboards ☆ - Daktronics Inc.

ALL SPORT LITE - Beverages–carbonated - Pepsico, Inc.

ALL SPORTS - Apparel stores–sports - Jefferies Socks

ALL SPORTS - Skin care products - Tennis Elbow Corp.

ALL-SPORTS CALENDAR - Calendars - Unique Images, Inc.

ALL-SPRAY - Paints ☆ - Allpro Corp.

ALL SQUARE - Office supplies ☆ - Boorum & Pease Co.

ALL STAR - Candy ☆ - Leaf, Inc.
ALL STAR - Cleaning preparations - Five Star Chemical Corp.
ALL STAR - Cleaning preparations - Saxon Paper Co.
ALL-STAR - Climate-control product, now out of production - GSW Jackes-Evans Manufacturing Co.
ALL-STAR - Concrete–mixture - Quikrete Cos.
ALL STAR - Floor coverings–carpet and rugs ☆ - World Carpets, Inc.
ALL STAR - Flowers, plants, and seeds - Jacklin Seed
ALL-STAR - Food products - Cap's Italian Foods Inc.
ALL-STAR - Gloves - All Star Industries
ALL STAR - Guitars - MBT International, Inc.
ALL STAR - Motor vehicles–trucks - Mack Trucks Inc.
ALL STAR - Perfumes - Winsome Fragrance Co.
ALL STAR - Protective liners - Durakon Industries Inc.
ALL STAR - Toys - Today's Kids Inc.
ALL STAR - Toys ☆ - Wham-O Manufacturing Co.
ALL-STAR BASEBALL - Games - Cadaco Div.
ALL STAR BLEACHERS - Chairs–wood - All Star Bleachers
ALL-STAR BOWLING - Games - Munro Games Inc.
ALL-STAR HOCKEY - Games - SLM Inc.
ALL STAR NBA WEEKEND CLEVELAND '97 - Apparel and accessories - NBA Properties, Inc.
ALL STAR SAUCER-TOSSER - Toys - Concept Products Inc.
ALL-STAR SPORTS - Wallcovering - Colortree Designs
ALL-STAR SPORTS - Wallpaper - W.H.S. Lloyd
ALL STAR SPORTS - Wallpaper ☆ - Eisenhart Wallcoverings Co.
ALL-STAR SPORTS CENTER - Toys ☆ - Today's Kids Inc.
ALL-STAR TEAM - Toys–stuffed - Fun World Inc.
ALL STAR TOY COMPANY - Toys - All Star Toy Co.
ALL STAR WRESTLERS - Toys - Azrak-Hamway International, Inc.
ALL-STARS - Sports apparel - Converse Inc.
ALL-STATE INTERNATIONAL - Audio tapes–blank - All-State International, Inc.
ALL STATES MOTOR OIL - Motor vehicle parts and accessories - Donald R. Schulke
ALL STATES QUALITY - Chicken bi-products - All States Quality Foods
ALL-STEEL - Furniture - Allsteel, Inc.
ALL STEER - Automotive parts and accessories - Oshkosh Truck Corp.
ALL STRONG - Window coverings - All Strong Industry (USA) Inc.
ALL SURFACE - Paper - M. Grumbacher Inc.
ALL SURFACE PRIMER - Paints - Gray Seal Paint Manufacturing Co. Inc.
ALL-SYN - Mops - Golden Star Inc.
ALL TAME - Bird feeds - Judee K. Creations, Inc. (Crazy Corn Division)
ALL TECHNIQUE - Paper - M. Grumbacher Inc.
ALL TECHNIQUES - Skin care products - Lendan USA Co.
ALL TECK - Blinds–venetian - Custom Shade
ALL-TECK - Window shades - Distinctive Window Fashions
ALL TEMP - Antifreeze - Marcus International Inc.
ALL-TEMP - Chemical preparations - Baker Hughes Inc.
ALL-TEMP - Thermostats - Harper-Wyman Co.
ALL-TEMP ROOFLON - Roofing materials–clay ☆ - Master's Choice Inc.
ALL TERRAIN PUZZLES - Puzzles - Coburn Designs
ALL-TERRAIN SUPERTABLET - Computer hardware - Tusk, Inc.
ALL-TERRAIN TREKKER - Footwear - AmAsia International Ltd.
ALL TERRAIN VEHICLE - Sandals - Earth & Ocean Sports, Inc.
ALL-TEST/CWT II - Testing instruments - B.J.M. Corp.
ALL-TEX - Sealing compounds ☆ - Briner Paint Manufacturing Co. Inc.
ALL THAT GLITTERS - Fabrics–tapestry ☆ - Comark Wallcoverings
ALL THAT GLITTERS - Floor coverings–carpet and rugs ☆ - American Carpet Mills
ALL THAT GLITTERS - Games ☆ - Mayfair Games, Inc.
ALL THAT GLITTERS - Paints - Greenstreet Co., Inc.
ALL THAT GLITTERS - Pet products - Mustang Products, Inc.
ALL THAT JAZZ - Apparel and accessories - Chorus Line Corp.
ALL THAT JAZZ - Figurines ☆ - Enesco Corp.
ALL THAT JAZZ - Wallpaper ☆ - David & Dash
ALL THAT SHIMMERS - Paints - Greenstreet Co., Inc.
ALL THE ALIEN WARRIOR NAMES - Toys - Henry Gordy International Inc.
ALL THE BEST - Wallpaper - James Seeman Studios
ALL THE BEST III - Wallpaper - James Seeman Studios
ALL THE COMFORTS OF HOME - Bedding–linen - Pillowtex Corp.
ALL THE GOODNESS OF HAWAII - Cookies - C Brewer Co. Limited
ALL THE GOODS TO BAKE THE GOODS - Raisins - Frank A. Serio and Sons Inc.
ALL THE HUES THAT'S FIT TO PRINT - Wallpaper - Manhattan Creations Ltd.

ALL THE HUES THAT'S FIT TO PRINT - Wallpaper - Michele Wallpaper Inc.
ALL THE KING'S MEN - Toys - Tonka Corp.
ALL THE TIME - Underwear and nightwear - Maidenform Inc.
ALL THE WAY - Fabrics–ramie ☆ - Dan River Inc.
ALL-THE-WAY REDS - Lipsticks - Estee Lauder Inc.
ALL THIS & DOLLY TOO - Dolls - Goldberger Doll Manufacture Co.
ALL-THREE SUNSHINE - Pet products - Rich Health
ALL THROUGH THE HOUSE - Figurines - Department 56 Inc.
ALL THROUGH THE HOUSE - Wallpaper ☆ - Imperial Wallcoverings, Inc.
ALL-TOGETHER - Games - Mattel, Inc.
ALL TOGETHER - Handbags ☆ - Buxton Inc.
ALL TRACK - Computer software - Capricorn Systems Associates Corp.
ALL TRACTION - Tires - Bridgestone/Firestone, Inc.
ALL TRUMPS HI-GLUTEN - Flour–blended ☆ - General Mills, Inc.
ALL TUB - Drains - Gerber Plumbing Fixtures Corp.
ALL TUNE TRANSMISSIONS - Automotive repair shops–transmission - ATL International, Inc.
ALL TURF - Footwear–athletic - Puma Inc.
ALL TYPES - Cosmetics - La Femme Cosmetics Inc.
ALL VOTE - Prefabricated buildings–metal - Smurfit Packaging Corp.
ALL WAVE - Computer software - Fogg System Co., Inc.
ALL-WAY - Cash registers ☆ - Auer Register Co.
ALL-WAY - Ladders–metal - White Metal Rolling & Stamping Corp.
ALL WAYS - Easels - MagnaPlan Corp.
ALL WAYS - Wallcovering ☆ - Gilford Corp.
ALL WAYS SOFT - Fabric softeners ☆ - Dowbrands L.P.
ALL-WEATHER - Aluminum products - N.H. Rudeen Co.
ALL-WEATHER - Archery equipment - Ames Industries
ALL WEATHER - Automotive parts and accessories - Stant Corp.
ALL WEATHER - Barbecues and grills - Thermos Co.
ALL WEATHER - Climate-control products - Interdynamics, Inc.
ALL WEATHER - Paints - Continental Products Co.
ALL-WEATHER - Paints - Devoe & Raynolds Co.
ALL-WEATHER - Paints - Martin Paint Stores
ALL-WEATHER - Pens - La-Co Industries, Inc.
ALL-WEATHER - Pet products - Novalek, Inc.
ALL WEATHER - Rifles - Sturm, Ruger & Co., Inc.
ALL WEATHER - Shoe soles - Goodyear Tire & Rubber Co.
ALL WEATHER - Sunglasses - Style Eyes of California
ALL WEATHER ANTIFREEZE - Antifreeze - Old World Industries, Inc.
ALL WEEK LONG - Apparel–women's - Eddie Bauer Inc.
ALL WELL - Vegetables–frozen - Double Green Produce Inc.
ALL WEST - Garden equipment - Far West Forests
ALL-WOOD - Floor coverings - Horner Flooring Co. Inc.
ALL YOU FEEL IS THE WARMTH - Sports apparel - Medalist Apparel Inc.
ALL YOU NEED - Skin-care products - Estee Lauder Inc.
ALL YOU NEED FOR DRIER SKIN - Skin care products - Prescriptives
ALL YOU SEE IS YOU - Hosiery - Sara Lee Corp.
ALLA PRIMAVERA - Food products - Golden Whisk Pasta Partners
ALLADIN - Rings–jewelry - Artcarved Inc.
ALLADINWARE - Housewares - Alladin Plastics Inc.
ALLAGASH - Beverages–alcohol - Allagash Brewing Co.
ALLAGASH - Boats–canoes - Stowe Canoe and Snowshoe Co. Inc.
ALLAGASH - Cots–metal - Byer of Maine
ALLAGASH - Footwear–athletic - New Balance Athletic Shoe, Inc.
ALLAGASH - Log cabins–prefabricated - Ward Log Homes
ALLAIRE - Flowers, plants, and seeds - Jonathan Green, Inc.
ALLAN - Dolls - Mattel, Inc.
ALLAN EDWARD - Handbags - Studio Imports Ltd., Inc.
ALLAN HOLDSWORTH - Musical instrument accessories ☆ - Seymour Duncan Pickups
ALLANN BROTHERS - Coffee - Allann Brothers Coffee Co.
ALLANTE - Area rugs - Couristan Inc.
ALLANTE - Boats–motor ☆ - Cobia Boat Co.
ALLANTE - Cooking equipment–household ☆ - Anchor Hocking Glass, Inc.
ALLANTE - Floor coverings–carpet and rugs - Cabin Crafts Carpets
ALLANTE - Golfing equipment - Knight Golf, Inc.
ALLANTE - Motor vehicles–automobiles - General Motors Corp. (Cadillac Motor Car Div.)
ALLANTOIN - Pharmaceutical preparations - City Chemical Corp.
ALLAROUND - Vacuum cleaners and accessories - Shop Vac Corp.
ALLAY - Skin care products - Studex USA Inc.
ALLAY - Vitamins and nutritional supplements - Vitamin Research Products Inc.
ALLBALL - Rackets–racquetball - David J. Todoroff
ALLBECON - Pharmaceutical preparations - Consolidated Midland Corp.

☆ = Now out of production

ALLBEE - Vitamins and nutritional supplements - A.H. Robins Co. Inc.

ALLBLACK - Brushes–paint - Wright-Bernet

ALLBRANDS - Wax removers - L & F Consumer Products

ALLCACHE - Computers - Kendall Square Research Corp.

ALLCASE - Surface Combustion, Inc.

ALLCLEAR - Water treating compounds - Wardley Corp.

ALLCOCK - Plaster–wallboard - Caswell-Massey Co. Ltd.

ALLCORE - Thread - Toowain Co. Inc.

ALLCORK - Finishing agents - Allcork, Inc.

ALLCOTT - Thread - Toowain Co. Inc.

ALLDAY - Cosmetics ☆ - Palm Beach Beauty Products

ALLE - Floor coverings - Armstrong World Industries, Inc.

ALLE GIANT GUI - Surveillance equipment - Combi International Corp.

ALLEE - Trees - Tree Introductions, Inc.

ALLEE - Vitamins and nutritional supplements ☆ - Wesley Pharmacal Co. Inc.

ALLEGHENY - Beverages–malt - Old European Brewery Co.

ALLEGHENY - Crocheted and knitted items ☆ - S. Schwab Co., Inc.

ALLEGHENY - Seafood products–fresh or frozen - Virginia Trout Co. Inc.

ALLEGHENY METALS AND MINERALS, INC. - Chemicals - Allegheny Metals and Minerals, Inc.

ALLEGIANCE - Computer software - Stores Automated Systems, Inc.

ALLEGIANCE - Floor coverings–carpet and rugs ☆ - Columbus Mills, Inc.

ALLEGIANCE ADVANTAGE - Publisher's imprints - Allegiance Advantage Inc.

ALLEGIANT - Surveillance equipment - Philips Communication & Security Systems Inc.

ALLEGIANT GUI - Surveillance equipment - Philips Communication & Security Systems Inc.

ALLEGIS - Furniture ☆ - Harter

ALLEGIS - Recording label - Nazarene Publishing House

ALLEGRA - Golf clubs - Austad Co.

ALLEGRA - Whirlpools - Kohler Co.

ALLEGRA DESIGNS - Apparel and accessories - Sylvia Lichauco

ALLEGRA GOLD ACCENT - Flatware - Yamazaki Tableware Inc.

ALLEGRA'S WINDOW - Apparel and accessories - Viacom International Inc.

ALLEGRE - Floor coverings–carpet and rugs ☆ - Karastan-Bigelow Inc.

ALLEGRE - Shoes - MSF Corp.

ALLEGRETTO - Confections - Flavor-ONE Inc.

ALLEGRETTO - Recording label - Essex Entertainment Inc.

ALLEGRINI - Wines - Paterno Imports, Ltd.

ALLEGRO - See ALLEGIS

ALLEGRO - Accordions - Ideal Musical Merchandise Co.

ALLEGRO - Aircraft - Mooney Aircraft Corp.

ALLEGRO - Audio equipment - Zenith Electronics Corp.

ALLEGRO - Bar code label printers - DATAMAX Corp.

ALLEGRO - Boats - Glen-L Marine Designs

ALLEGRO - Cabinets - Aristokraft, Inc.

ALLEGRO - Chimes ☆ - J.W. Stannard Co.

ALLEGRO - Cleaning preparation - Allegro, Inc.

ALLEGRO - Dishes–china - Brastoff Designs Inc.

ALLEGRO - Dyes and pigments - Allegro Rug Weaving Co.

ALLEGRO - Floor coverings–carpet and rugs - World Carpets, Inc.

ALLEGRO - Food products - Allegro Fine Foods, Inc.

ALLEGRO - Footwear - Samuels Shoe Co.

ALLEGRO - Frames–picture - Intercraft Industries

ALLEGRO - Furniture ☆ - Halcyon Inc.

ALLEGRO - Furniture ☆ - Hammary Furniture Co. Inc.

ALLEGRO - Glassware–household - Lenox Crystal, Inc.

ALLEGRO - Glassware–household - Owens-Illinois Inc. (Libbey Div.)

ALLEGRO - Glassware–household ☆ - National Housewares

ALLEGRO - Hardware - National Lock Cabinet Hardware

ALLEGRO - Hearing aids - Beltone Electronics Corp.

ALLEGRO - Jewelry - Jacoby-Bender Inc.

ALLEGRO - Liquors - Stoller Wholesale Wines & Spirits, Inc.

ALLEGRO - Luggage ☆ - Andiamo Inc.

ALLEGRO - Motor vehicles - Tiffin Motor Homes, Inc.

ALLEGRO - Musical instrument accessories - John M. Connolly & Co. Inc.

ALLEGRO - Musical instrument accessories ☆ - Pro-Mark Corp.

ALLEGRO - Paper - Gilbert Paper Co.

ALLEGRO - Personal telephones - American Telecommunications Corp.

ALLEGRO - Recording label - Moss Music Group Inc.

ALLEGRO - Rings–jewelry - Artcarved Inc.

ALLEGRO - Stationery ☆ - Mead Corp.

ALLEGRO - Toilets–porcelain - Mansfield Plumbing Products, Inc.

ALLEGRO - Wallpaper ☆ - Singer Wallcoverings, Inc.

ALLEGRO GOLD BUCKLE BRISKET SAUCE - Seasonings - Allegro Fine Foods, Inc.

ALLEGRO PC LIBRARY - Computer storage devices–optical - Allegro New Media, Inc.

ALLEGRO REFERENCE SERIES - Computer storage devices–optical - Allegro New Media, Inc.

ALLEGRO TIME BRACELETS - Watches - Austern & Paul/Orgel-Shorr Inc.

ALLEGRO VINEYARDS - Wines - Allegro Vineyards

ALLELIX - Flowers, plants, and seeds - Pioneer Hi-Bred International, Inc.

ALLELUIA! - Recording label - Integrity Music, Inc.

ALLEN - Automotive parts and accessories - R.A. Allen Co.

ALLEN - Flowers, plants, and seeds - Allen Plant Co.

ALLEN - Fruits and vegetables - G.M. Allen & Son Inc.

ALLEN - Hardware - Holo-Krome Co.

ALLEN - Organs–musical instrument - Allen Organ Co.

ALLEN - Soldering equipment ☆ - L.B. Allen Co. Inc.

ALLEN - Stirrups - Allen Medical Systems Inc.

ALLEN-A - Sports apparel - Medalist Apparel Inc.

ALLEN ALLEN - Apparel–men's - Allen Allen USA Corp.

ALLEN ALLEN USA - Apparel and accessories - Allen Allen USA Corp.

ALLEN & HEATH - Audio equipment - Allen & Heath Brenell USA Ltd.

ALLEN & HEATH BRENELL - Audio equipment - Allen & Heath Brenell USA Ltd.

ALLEN ARTHUR - Hair-replacement product and services - International Hairgoods Inc.

ALLEN, BENNINGTON BOOKS - Publisher's imprints - Hyst'ry Myst'ry House

ALLEN DAIRY - Milk - Allen Dairy Products Inc.

ALLEN-EDMONDS - Shoes - Allen-Edmonds Shoe Corp.

ALLEN EDMONDS LIFESTYLES - Apparel and accessories - Allen-Edmonds Shoe Corp.

ALLEN HOLLANDER - Hardware ☆ - Litton Industrial Automation Systems

ALLEN MILK - Food products - T. Marzetti Co.

ALLEN PRIDE - Food products - Allen Foods Inc.

ALLEN ROMEO - Travel bags - Locomotor USA, Inc.

ALLEN ROYAL - Fruits and vegetables - Allen International Inc.

ALLEN SCOOPER, THE - Pet products - Four Paws Products Ltd.

ALLEN TELECOM GROUP - Radio communications equipment - Allen Telecom Group, Inc.

ALLEN WERTZ - Confections - National Confectionery Brands Inc.

ALLENBY - Cabinets - Actua

ALLENCOATER - Paints - Allentown Paint Manufacturing Co. Inc.

ALLENDALE - Food products - J.W. Allen & Co.

ALLENDALE - Switchboard apparatus - Integrated Network Corp.

ALLENEZE - Paints - Allentown Paint Manufacturing Co. Inc.

ALLENFIL - Sealing compounds - Allentown Paint Manufacturing Co. Inc.

ALLENHOLM FARM - Fruits and vegetables - Allenholm Farm

ALLENKALK - Caulking compounds ☆ - Allentown Paint Manufacturing Co. Inc.

ALLENLUX - Enamels ☆ - Allentown Paint Manufacturing Co. Inc.

ALLENPLEX - Paints ☆ - Allentown Paint Manufacturing Co. Inc.

ALLEN'S - Brandy - M.S. Walker Inc./Seacoast

ALLEN'S - Food products - J.W. Allen & Co.

ALLENS - Food products - Allen Canning Co.

ALLEN'S - Fruits and vegetables - Allen International Inc.

ALLEN'S - Fruits–frozen - Allen's Blueberry Freezer Inc.

ALLEN'S - Poultry - Allen Family Foods Inc.

ALLEN'S SHELLARAMA - Novelty items - Allen's Shell-A-Rama

ALLENSEAL - Sealing compounds - Allentown Paint Manufacturing Co. Inc.

ALLENSHIELD - Paints - Allentown Paint Manufacturing Co. Inc.

ALLENT - Health care products - B.F. Ascher & Co. Inc.

ALLENTEX - Paints - Allentown Paint Manufacturing Co. Inc.

ALLENTILE - Epoxy coatings - Allentown Paint Manufacturing Co. Inc.

ALLENTITE - Paints ☆ - Allentown Paint Manufacturing Co. Inc.

ALLENTOWN - Cabinets - Prestige Inc.

ALLENTOWN - Paints - Allentown Paint Manufacturing Co. Inc.

ALLER-BROM - Pharmaceutical preparations - Rugby Laboratories Inc.

ALLER-CHLOR - Pharmaceutical preparations - Rugby Laboratories Inc.

ALLER-DERM - Skin care products - Allercare Inc.

ALLER-EASE - Health care products - Long Life Herb Classics

ALLER-FREE - Vitamins and nutritional supplements - Williams Marketing Group International, Inc.

ALLER-G - Pharmaceutical preparations ☆ - Goldline Laboratories, Inc.

ALLER-G-PLUS - Pharmaceutical preparations - Vita Plus Industries Inc.

ALLER MINS - Vitamins and nutritional supplements - Natural Organics, Inc.

ALLER PLEX - Vitamins and nutritional supplements - Natural Organics, Inc.

ALLER-TABS - Herbal products - Maharishi Ayur-Ved Products International, Inc.

ALLER VITE - Vitamins and nutritional supplements - Natural Organics, Inc.

ALLERACT - Antihistamine preparations - Burroughs Wellcome Co.
ALLERAIDE - Pharmaceutical preparations - Boericke & Tafel
ALLERCAINE - Pet products - Tomlyn Products
ALLERCIDIN - Pharmaceutical preparations ☆ - Schering-Plough Healthcare Products
ALLERCLEAR - Pharmaceutical preparations - Amrion, Inc.
ALLERCOLD - Health care products - Leiner Health Products Inc.
ALLERCORT - Pharmaceutical preparations ☆ - Lunsco Inc.
ALLERCREME - Skin care products ☆ - Carme Inc.
ALLERDERM - Infant product - Protex
ALLERDERM EFA-CAPS - Veterinary nutritional supplements - Virbac, Inc.
ALLERDRYL - Pharmaceutical preparations ☆ - Legere Pharmaceuticals Inc.
ALLERELIEF - Cold remedies ☆ - Nature's Herbs
ALLEREST - Health care products - Fisons Corp.
ALLEREX - Pharmaceutical preparations ☆ - Nature's Way Products, Inc.
ALLERFED - Antihistamine preparations - Private Formulations, Inc.
ALLERFREE - Cleaning preparations - Tatung Co. of America Inc.
ALLERFREE - Pillowcases - Perfect Fit Industries, Inc.
ALLERFRIN - Pharmaceutical preparations - Rugby Laboratories Inc.
ALLERG-ENS - Enzyme immunoassay - Dexall Biomedical Labs, Inc.
ALLERGAN - Ophthalmic goods ☆ - Allergan, Inc.
ALLERGAN ENZYMATIC - Ophthalmic goods - Allergan, Inc.
ALLERGAN HYDROCARE - Ophthalmic goods - Allergan, Inc.
ALLERGAN SORBI-CARE - Ophthalmic goods ☆ - Allergan, Inc.
ALLERGEN - Health care products - Goldline Laboratories, Inc.
ALLERGEND - Antihistamine preparations - Miles Inc.
ALLERGESIC - Skin care products ☆ - Vitarine Pharmaceuticals Inc.
ALLERGEX - Health care products - Healthwatchers System
ALLERGEX - Pharmaceutical preparations - Bayer Corp. (Pharmaceutical Division)
ALLERGONE - Health care products ☆ - Halsey Drug Co. Inc.
ALLERGROOM - Shampoos - Allerderm Inc.
ALLERGUARD - Vitamins and nutritional supplements ☆ - Bio San Laboratories Inc.
ALLERGY 4 - Filters–air - Dust Free Inc.
ALLERGY 4 - Filters–air - Eramco
ALLERGY 911 - Vitamins and nutritional supplements - Bioenergy Nutrient's Inc.
ALLERGY A & D CAPS - Vitamins and nutritional supplements - Twinlab
ALLERGY A CAPS - Vitamins and nutritional supplements - Twinlab
ALLERGY ALERT - Labels–paper - Patty Metcalf Design
ALLERGY ANSWER - Jewelry - Donley Co.
ALLERGY-C - Vitamins and nutritional supplements - Twinlab
ALLERGY CONTROL - Health care products - Allergy Control Products Inc.
ALLERGY D CAPS - Vitamins and nutritional supplements - Twinlab
ALLERGY-FREE TOYS FOR ME - Toys–stuffed - Allergy-Free Toys for Me Inc.
ALLERGY GOLD - Filters–air - Dust Free Inc.
ALLERGY RESEARCH GROUP - Vitamins and nutritional supplements - Allergy Research Group
ALLERGY SEASON PLUS - Cold remedies - Quantum, Inc.
ALLERGYN - Pharmaceutical preparations - Alva-Amco Pharmacal Co.
ALLERHIST - Pharmaceutical preparations ☆ - Pharmex Inc.
ALLERMAX - Pharmaceutical preparations - Pfeiffer Pharmaceuticals Inc.
ALLERMUNE - Vitamins and nutritional supplements - Vitamin Science Inc.
ALLERNADE - Pharmaceutical preparations ☆ - Rugby Laboratories Inc.
ALLERPET - Pet products - Allerpet
ALLERPET - Pet products - Farnam Cos. Inc.
ALLERPHEN - Pharmaceutical preparations ☆ - Legere Pharmaceuticals Inc.
ALLERPROP - Pharmaceutical preparations - Rugby Laboratories Inc.
ALLERSEB T - Shampoos - Allerderm Inc.
ALLERSONE - Pharmaceutical preparations - Roberts/Hauck Pharmaceuticals Inc.
ALLERSPRAY - Veterinary pharmaceutical preparations - Evsco Pharmaceuticals
ALLERSTAT - Pharmaceutical preparations ☆ - Lemmon Co.
ALLERSTOP - Health care products - Enzymatic Therapy, Inc.
ALLERTEX - Pharmaceutical preparations ☆ - Veratex Group
ALLERVAC - Health care products - Euroclean
ALLES GUTE - Video cassettes - Eurotel Inc.
ALLEVIA - Soap - Alexandra De Markoff, Ltd.
ALLEVIATE - Pet products - Roussel-Uclaf Corp.
ALLEVIATOR - Plumbing fixtures - P.J. Pappas Co., Inc.
ALLEX - Scissors–electric ☆ - Acme United Corp.
ALLEX JANE COSMETICS - Lipsticks - William O. Kil
ALLEY CAT - Apparel and accessories - Alley Cat

ALLEY CAT - Cat food - Ralston Purina Co.
ALLEY CAT AMBER - Beverages–malt - Table Bluff Brewing, Inc.
ALLEY CAT MUSIC - Recording label - Alley Cat Music, Inc.
ALLEY CATS - Dolls - N.S. Gustin Co.
ALLEY CATS POPOUT - Puppets ☆ - Dakin Inc.
ALLEY CATZ - Sporting goods - Garry V. Turpin
ALLEY COURT - Sporting goods - Indian Industries Inc.
ALLEY OOP - Publisher's imprints - Creative Enterprises
ALLEY PRIDE & GARDENS LEARNING IS FUN - Publisher's imprints - Barbara Warren-Mattingly
ALLEYCAT - Boats ☆ - Aircat Airboats
ALLEY'S - Potato chips ☆ - Weaver Potato Chip Co.
ALLEYSIDE PRESS - Publisher's imprints - Highsmith Press LLC
ALLEYWAY - Video games - Nintendo of America Inc.
ALLEZ - Fruit drinks–bottled or canned - Van Tone Co., Inc.
ALLFINE - Food products ☆ - Norpac Services, Inc.
ALLFLOR - Enamels - California Products Corp.
ALLFORMS WORDBOOKS - Publisher's imprints ☆ - Bandanna Books
ALLGAUER LATSCHENKIEFER - Pharmaceutical preparations - Merz Apothecary Inc.
ALLGUARD - Paints - Triangle Coatings Inc.
ALLIANCE - Audio equipment - Dukane Corp.
ALLIANCE - Bicycles ☆ - Huffy Corp.
ALLIANCE - Detergents - Lan-O-Sheen, Inc.
ALLIANCE - Diagnostic apparatus - E.I. Dupont de Nemours and Co.
ALLIANCE - Flatware - Couzon USA
ALLIANCE - Floor coverings–carpet and rugs - Mohawk Carpet Corp.
ALLIANCE - Floor coverings–carpet and rugs - Philadelphia Carpets
ALLIANCE - Floor coverings–carpet and rugs - Quaker Inc.
ALLIANCE - Floor coverings–carpet and rugs ☆ - Robertex Associates Inc.
ALLIANCE - Flowers, plants, and seeds - Turf-Seed, Inc.
ALLIANCE - Footwear ☆ - Asics Tiger Corp.
ALLIANCE - Linen - Artex International, Inc.
ALLIANCE - Motor vehicles ☆ - DaimlerChrysler
ALLIANCE - Office supplies ☆ - Faber-Castell Corp.
ALLIANCE - Packaging machines - Integrated Industrial Services, Inc.
ALLIANCE - Rackets–tennis - Lisco, Inc.
ALLIANCE - Rings–jewelry - Artcarved Inc.
ALLIANCE - Surgical instruments - Biomet, Inc.
ALLIANCE - Tables–wood - Howe Furniture Corp.
ALLIANCE - Tires - Solcoor Inc.
ALLIANCE - Wallets - American Trading and Production Corp.
ALLIANCE - Watches - Accusplit Inc.
ALLIANCE - Water heaters–household - Burnham Corp.
ALLIANCE II - Floor coverings–carpet and rugs ☆ - Mannington Carpets, Inc.
ALLIANCE 90 - Pesticides–agricultural - Countrymark Cooperative, Inc.
ALLIANCE 1100 - Floor coverings–carpet and rugs - Alliance Industries Inc.
ALLIANCE AMERICA - Office supplies - Alliance America
ALLIANCE COURIER NETWORK - Courier services–land - H.L.B. Transportation Services, Inc.
ALLIANCE ENHANCER - Floor coverings–carpet and rugs - Philadelphia Carpets
ALLIANCE FARMS - Meats–luncheon - John Liber & Co. Inc.
ALLIANCE GENERATION - Communications equipment–satellite - Natural Microsystems
ALLIANCE GOLD - Flatware - Couzon USA
ALLIANCE LAW ENFORCEMENT NETWORK - Computer software - Glen Haimovitz and John Roevekamp Partnership
ALLIANCE PD CENTRAL - Computer software - Glen Haimovitz and John Roevekamp Partnership
ALLIANCE PERIPHERAL SYSTEMS - Computer hardware - APS Technologies
ALLIANCEPLUS - Computer software - Healthworks Alliance, Inc.
ALLIANT - Wines - Alliant Foodservice, Inc.
ALLIANT-LINK - Computer software - Alliant Foodservice, Inc.
ALLIANT POWDER - Gunpowder - Alliant Techsystems Inc.
ALLIANT PREMIER - Meat products - Alliant Foodservice, Inc.
ALLIANT TECHSYSTEMS - Electronic equipment - Alliant Techsystems Inc.
ALLIANZ - Watches - Oryx International Ltd.
ALLIBAR - Floor coverings–carpet and rugs - Masland Corp.
ALLIBERT - Cabinets - Rubbermaid-Allibert Inc.
ALLIE - Aerobic footwear ☆ - Autry Industries Inc.
ALLIE - Frames–eyeglass - U.S. Optical Frame Co.
ALLIED - Audio equipment - Allied Plastics
ALLIED - Bakery products - Allied Bakers Co.
ALLIED - Bicycle parts and accessories - Poor Boy

ALLIED - Floor coverings–tile - Allied Tile Manufacturing Corp.

ALLIED - Food products - Allied Foods Inc.

ALLIED - Motor vehicle parts and accessories - Alliedsignal Inc.

ALLIED - Ribbons–inked - Eaton Allen Ko-Rec-Type Corp.

ALLIED - Thread - United Thread Mills Corp.

ALLIED - Tools - Allied Specialty and Manufacturing Corp.

ALLIED - Tools ✩ - GC Thorsen, Inc.

ALLIED - Window shades - Vertical Images Inc.

ALLIED ADVANTAGE - Banks–commercial - Allied Supply Co.

ALLIED ALL-TECH - Blinds–vertical - Vertical Blind Factory

ALLIED ARTS - Stationery ✩ - Wards Printing & Stationery

ALLIED-AU NATURAL - Allied Tile Manufacturing Corp.

ALLIED BRASS - Bathroom accessories - Allied Brass Manufacturing Co.

ALLIED EXTRUSIONS - Window shades - Allied Extrusions

ALLIED GENERAL - Computer software - Strategic Simulations, Inc.

ALLIED GOLF - Golfing equipment - Allied Golf Co.

ALLIED INGREDIENTS - Honey - Allied Processors, Inc.

ALLIED LABS - Health care products ✩ - Robinette Inc.

ALLIED-MED VITAGRAN - Vitamins and nutritional supplements ✩ - Pharmed Group Corp.

ALLIED-ROTA-GATOR - Machinery - Allied Gator, Inc.

ALLIED SECURITY - Safes - Allied Safe and Vault Co. Inc.

ALLIE'S PLAYHOUSE - Opcode Systems, Inc.

ALLIGATOR - Boats–motor ✩ - Kay Park Rec Corp.

ALLIGATOR - Computer equipment and accessories - Infiniti Manufacturing, Inc.

ALLIGATOR - Electrical equipment - Porcelain Products Co.

ALLIGATOR - Motorcycles - All American Racers, Inc.

ALLIGATOR - Paint removers ✩ - Klean-Strip

ALLIGATOR - Recording label - Alligator Records and Artist Management Inc.

ALLIGATOR ADVENTURE - Zoos - Barefoot Zoological Gardens, LLC

ALLIGATOR ALLEY - Computer software - SRA/McGraw-Hill (Div. of The McGraw-Hill Companies)

ALLIGATOR MIX - Computer software - SRA/McGraw-Hill (Div. of The McGraw-Hill Companies)

ALLIGATORS - Candy ✩ - Bohemian Biscuit Co.

ALLIGRO - Surveillance equipment - Philips Communication & Security Systems Inc.

ALLIMIN - Pharmaceutical preparations - Health Care Industries Inc.

ALLINI - Wines - M.S. Walker Inc./Seacoast

ALLIONE - Food products ✩ - Gourmet Club Corp.

ALLIOOP - Toys–stuffed ✩ - Gund, Inc.

ALLIRICH - Spices and extracts - Arizona Natural Products

ALLIS-CHALMERS - Garden equipment - Allis-Chalmers Corp.

ALLIS CHALMERS - Toys - ERTL Co., Inc.

ALLISAN - Fungicides - Gowan Co.

ALLISON - Apparel and accessories - Allison Manufacturing Co.

ALLISON - Audio equipment - Allison Acoustics Inc.

ALLISON - Beverages–alcohol ✩ - Blair Importers Ltd.

ALLISON - Dolls - Uneeda Doll Co., Inc.

ALLISON - Dolls ✩ - Effanbee Doll Corp.

ALLISON - Floor coverings ✩ - Tarkett, Inc.

ALLISON - Frames–eyeglass - U.S. Optical Frame Co.

ALLISON - Hardware - Amerock

ALLISON - Hardware - Amerock Corp.

ALLISON - Trailers–travel ✩ - Giles Industries

ALLISON - Window coverings - Allison-Erwin Co.

ALLISON ANN - Dresses–girls' - J.C. Penney Co., Inc.

ALLISON DALEY NO-IRON COTTON - Apparel–women's - Eddie Haggar Ltd., Inc.

ALLISON DALEY STRETCH TECH - Apparel–women's - Eddie Haggar Ltd., Inc.

ALLISON DALY - Apparel–women's ✩ - Haggar Corp.

ALLISON GRAY - Apparel and accessories - Swat Fame, Inc.

ALLISON LIBRARY - Publisher's imprints - Willis Music Co.

ALLISON PAIGE - Apparel–women's - May Department Stores Co.

ALLISON REED - Jewelry–costume ✩ - Sarah Coventry Fashion Jewelry

ALLISON SMITH COLLECTION - Textiles - Frederick Atkins, Inc.

ALLISON TRANSMISSION GENUINE RETRAN - Motor vehicle parts and accessories - General Motors Corp.

ALLISTER - Electronic equipment - Alliedsignal Inc.

ALLITH - Hardware ✩ - Midwest Manufacturing Co.

ALLKORE - Pencils ✩ - Koh-I-Noor, Inc.

ALLLPRO GOLD - Brushes–paint - Allpro Corp.

ALLMAN - Palettes ✩ - Winsor & Newton

ALLMARK - Rubber-stamp ink - J.P. Cooke Co.

ALLMED - First aid kits - Alliance Medical, Inc.

ALLMETAL - Metals - Allmetal, Inc.

ALLNODE - Computer software - International Business Machines Corp.

ALLOCCASION PETS - Pens ✩ - A.D. Sutton & Sons Inc.

ALLOPAC - Medical apparatus - Allosource

ALLORA - Apparel–men's - Michael Isaacson

ALLORGANIC TRACE MINERALS-B12 - Vitamins and nutritional supplements - Standard Process Inc.

ALLOTRAP - Pharmaceutical preparations - Sangstat Medical Corp.

ALLOVER - Heaters–space - Master Appliance Corp.

ALLOWANCE - Sweeteners–artificial - JP Foodservice, Inc.

ALLOWANCE - Underwear and nightwear ✩ - Lovable Co.

ALLOWANCE CALCULATOR, THE - Educational materials - TBSC Learning Systems, Inc.

ALLOY NEW YORK CITY - Clocks - Bromate Corp.

ALLOY WHEEL GUARDIAN - Automotive parts and accessories - Hennessy Technology Corp., Inc.

ALLPARTS - Guitars - Allparts

ALLPATH - Communications equipment - Panamax

ALLPEN - Computer software - Newtonian Technologies, Inc.

ALLPOLY - Thread - Toowain Co. Inc.

ALLPRIME - Wallpaper - Allpro Corp.

ALLPRO - Paints - Wallauer Paint & Wallpaper

ALLPRO - Pesticides–household - Sureco, Inc.

ALLPRO - Wallpaper - Allpro Corp.

ALLPRO SILVER - Brushes–paint - Allpro Corp.

ALLPRO SV+A27 - Brushes–paint - Allpro Corp.

ALLPURE - Water purification systems - Richard M. Arikian, Jr.

ALLRESPONSE - Chemical preparations - Spill 911, Inc.

ALLRITE - Food products ✩ - John Morrell & Co.

ALLROAD - Tires - Bridgestone/Firestone, Inc.

ALLSAFE - Automotive parts and accessories - Echlin Inc.

ALLSAFE - Shutters–plastic - B & H Industries of Southwest Florida, Inc.

ALLSEASONS - Fans–electric - Seattle Lighting Fixtures Co.

ALLSHEEN - Enamels - California Products Corp.

ALLSLOW - Artists' materials - Rea Art Inc.

ALLSON T. SEYMOUR - Floor coverings–carpet and rugs - Matworks

ALLSOP - Sporting goods - Allsop, Inc.

ALLSOP 3 - Audio equipment - Allsop, Inc.

ALLSPICE - Dishes–earthenware ✩ - Louisville Stoneware Co.

ALLSPORT - Footwear–athletic - Stride Rite Corp.

ALLSPORT - Radios - Hanig & Co.

ALLSPORTS - Underwear and nightwear - Champion Jogbra

ALLSTAR - Beverages - Florida Bottling Inc.

ALLSTAR - Cleaning preparations - Unisource Worldwide, Inc.

ALLSTAR - Trailers–travel ✩ - Starcraft Corp.

ALLSTAR GOLD - Photo albums - 20th Century Plastics

ALLSTATE - Tires - Sears, Roebuck and Co.

ALLSTEEL - Scales–industrial - Triner Scale and Manufacturing Co. Inc.

ALLSTON - Crocheted and knitted items ✩ - Pilgrim Sportswear Inc.

ALLSTRETCH - Apparel and accessories ✩ - Playtex Apparel, Inc.

ALLSWEET - Margarine - Armour Swift-Eckrich

ALLTALK - Computer software - Tangram Enterprise Solutions, Inc.

ALLTANK - Measuring instruments - Mid-Town Petroleum Inc.

ALLTERMAX - Tires - Carlisle Tire & Rubber Co.

ALLTOUCH - Remote control devices - Scientific-Atlanta, Inc.

ALLTRAK - Games - Bingo Card Minder Corp.

ALLUPRIM - Pharmaceutical preparations ✩ - Lexis Laboratories Inc.

ALLUR - Computers and accessories - I. Morley Drucker

ALLURA - Brassieres (Bras) ✩ - Gem-Dandy, Inc.

ALLURA - Fabrics ✩ - West Point-Pepperell Inc.

ALLURA - Floor coverings - Congoleum Corp.

ALLURA - Floor coverings–carpet and rugs - Whitecrest Carpet Mills

ALLURA - Lamp bulbs - Satco Products, Inc.

ALLURA - Plastics–laminated - Plaskolite Inc.

ALLURE - Adhesives and sealants - Dymax Corp.

ALLURE - Adhesives and sealants - Morgan Adhesives Co.

ALLURE - Candles - Kameyama USA Ltd.

ALLURE - Christmas tree ornaments ✩ - Cracker Box Inc.

ALLURE - Cosmetics - Advance Magazine Publishers Inc.

ALLURE - Floor coverings–carpet and rugs - Dorsett Carpet Mills Inc.

ALLURE - Floor coverings–carpet and rugs - Regal Rugs Inc.

ALLURE - Floor coverings–carpet and rugs - Sweetwater Carpet Corp.

ALLURE - Floor coverings–carpet and rugs ✩ - Hollytex Carpet Mills Inc.

ALLURE - Furniture - Lane Co. Inc.

ALLURE - Glassware–household ✩ - Lenox Crystal, Inc.

ALLURE - Hair care products - Fromm Industries
ALLURE - Jewelry - Jacoby-Bender Inc.
ALLURE - Occasional tables - JDI Group, Inc.
ALLURE - Perfumes - Chanel Inc.
ALLURE - Rings–jewelry - Mercury Ring Corp.
ALLURE - Shoes - Caressa Inc.
ALLURE - Wallpaper - Camelot Design Studios
ALLURE - Wallpaper - Queens Decorative Wallcoverings Inc.
ALLURE - Watches ☆ - SMH (US) Inc.
ALLURE - Wood beautifier ☆ - ChemRex Inc.
ALLURE - Yarn - William Unger & Co. Inc.
ALLURE BY ATLAS - Jewelry chains - Atlas Chain Co.
ALLURE BY COUNTRY COACH - Motor vehicles–buses - Country Coach, Inc.
ALLURESSA - Apparel and accessories - Burlington Industries, Inc.
ALLURING - Floor coverings–carpet and rugs - Lees Carpets
ALLURING - Floor coverings–carpet and rugs - Tuftex Carpet Mills, Inc.
ALLURING - Floor coverings–carpet and rugs ☆ - Downs Carpet Co. Inc.
ALLURING - Floor coverings–carpet and rugs ☆ - Royalweve Carpet Mills
ALLURING - Wallpaper ☆ - Vymura
ALLURING IMAGES - Greeting cards - Krafft, Lord & Walters Publishing
ALLURON - Curtains–shower ☆ - Kleinert's Inc.
ALLUSIAN - Whirlpool bath ☆ - Jacuzzi Inc.
ALLUSION - Bathroom accessories - Tsumura International Inc.
ALLUSION - Floor coverings–carpet and rugs ☆ - Kelly Group Inc.
ALLUSION - Office furniture - Gaylord Bros. Inc.
ALLUSIONS - Floor coverings - Mannington Resilient Floors
ALLUSIONS - Furniture - Collingwood Furniture
ALLUSIONS - Soap - Carolina Designs Ltd.
ALLUSIONS OF GRANDEUR - Trees–artificial - Madeleine B. Newman
ALLVAT - Thread - Lewis Threads Inc.
ALLWALKERS - Footwear–athletic - C. & J. Clark America, Inc.
ALLWALL - Paints - California Products Corp.
ALLWAY - Tools - Allway Tools Inc.
ALLWHIP - Food products - New Zealand Milk Products Inc.
ALLY - Computer software - Ally Software Inc.
ALLY - Health care products - Lotus Brands Inc.
ALLY - Herbicides - E.I. Dupont de Nemours and Co.
ALLYANSE - Spices and extracts - Continnuus
ALLYLGESIC - Pharmaceutical preparations ☆ - ICN Pharmaceuticals Inc.
ALLYLVON - Pharmaceutical preparations ☆ - ICN Pharmaceuticals Inc.
ALLYN ST. GEORGE - Apparel and accessories - Wemco, Inc.
ALLYN ST. GEORGE - Apparel–men's - Hartmarx Corp.
ALLYN ST. GEORGE - Belts–apparel - Lyntone Belts Inc.
ALLYN ST. GEORGE - Hosiery–men's - McCubbin Hosiery Inc.
ALLYN ST. GEORGE - Slacks–men's - Glen Oaks Industries Inc.
ALLYSON NAGEL SANTAS - Giftware - Roman, Inc.
ALM - Computer hardware - Affinity Financial Group, Inc.
ALMA - Calendars - Alfred Mainzer Inc.
ALMA - Compact discs–prerecorded ☆ - Original Sound Record Co. Inc.
ALMA - Girdles - Jo La Foundations Inc.
ALMA - Vegetables–canned - Allen Canning Co.
ALMA LEO - Candy - Alma-Leo USA Inc.
ALMA-MAG - Pharmaceutical preparations - Rugby Laboratories Inc.
ALMA SLADE DESIGNS - Fabrics - Lieff Textile & Mill Supply Co. Inc.
ALMACONE - Pharmaceutical preparations - Rugby Laboratories Inc.
ALMADA - Floor coverings - Mannington Resilient Floors
ALMADA - Furniture ☆ - White Furniture Co.
ALMADEN - Wines - Canandaigua Wine Co. Inc.
ALMAGEL - Pharmaceutical preparations ☆ - ICN Pharmaceuticals Inc.
ALMANAC - Hobby kits - Craft World International Inc.
ALMANAC - Stoneware dinnerware - Iron Mountain Stoneware Inc.
ALMANAC, THE - Fabrics–tapestry ☆ - Coloroll Inc.
ALMANACK - Wood products ☆ - Georgia-Pacific Corp.
ALMANOR - Bedding–linen - Dan River Inc.
ALMANTE - Wines ☆ - Canandaigua Wine Co. Inc.
ALMAR - Brushes–hair - Almar Sales Co., Inc.
ALMAR - Hair curlers - Burmax Co. Inc.
ALMAR - Pickles - Chas. F. Cates & Sons Inc.
ALMARLA - Wines - Almarla Vineyards
ALMARLA BLACK LIGHTNIN - Wines - Almarla Vineyards
ALMARLA SOUL TRAIN - Wines - Almarla Vineyards
ALMART - Paints ☆ - Salem Paint Inc.
ALMA'S - Pasta - Alma Food Imports, Inc.
ALMAY - Cosmetics - Almay Inc.
ALMAY AGE CONTROL - Cosmetics - Almay Inc.

ALMEBEX - Pharmaceutical preparations - Glaxo Wellcome Inc.
ALMEDAHL - Fabrics–linen ☆ - Odin Ltd.-Scan Am Imports Inc.
ALMEDAHLS - Fabrics–linen - Bergquists
ALMEDAHLS - Wallpaper ☆ - Wallquest, Inc.
ALMEIDA - Cigarettes - Gesty Trading & Manufacturing Corp.
ALMEIDA - Flutes - Edward Almeida Flutes
ALMENA - Publisher's imprints - Almena King-Raven
ALMERIA - Glassware–household ☆ - Oneida Ltd.
ALMET - Fishing tackle - U.S. Line Co.
ALMET - Varnishes - Ranbar Technology Inc.
ALMEX - Skin care products - Rogers' Drug Co.
ALMEZYME - Pharmaceutical preparations - Glaxo Wellcome Inc.
ALMHURST - Rings–jewelry - Artcarved Inc.
ALMIERA - Finishing agents ☆ - Flintkote Co.
ALMIERA - Paints ☆ - GS Roofing Products Co.
ALMIGHTY - Recording label - Refuge Music Group
ALMOCARPINE - Pharmaceutical preparations - Wyeth-Ayerst Laboratories
ALMOG - Wines ☆ - Seagram's Chateau & Estate Wines Co.
ALMOND - Jewelry–precious - Almond Jewelers Inc.
ALMOND - Shaving preparations - Caswell-Massey Co. Ltd.
ALMOND BREEZE - Beverages - Blue Diamond Growers
ALMOND BUTTERCRUNCH - Candy - Brown & Haley
ALMOND COCONUT - Candy - Tom's Foods Inc.
ALMOND COCONUT DELIGHT - Candy - Tom's Foods Inc.
ALMOND CREAM - Skin care products - Sterling Winthrop Inc.
ALMOND CRUNCH - Snack foods ☆ - Wyandot, Inc.
ALMOND DELIGHT - Cereal - Ralston Purina Co.
ALMOND DELIGHT - Glassware–household - Owens-Illinois Inc. (Libbey Div.)
ALMOND DELIGHTS - Candy - Russell Stover Candies, Inc.
ALMOND DREAM EGG - Candy ☆ - Russell Stover Candies, Inc.
ALMOND EXPRESSIONS - Chocolate novelties - Bortz Chocolate Co.
ALMOND GEM - Candy ☆ - Melster Candies Inc.
ALMOND GLOW - Skin care products - Home Health Products, Inc.
ALMOND HARVEST - Pretzels - Pretzelmaker, Inc.
ALMOND HORNS - Pastries - Joey's Fine Foods
ALMOND JOY - Candy bars - Peter Paul
ALMOND KISSES - Candy - Boyer Candy Co., Inc.
ALMOND LOVERS' BREAKFAST, THE - Cereal - Ralston Foods, Inc.
ALMOND MEAL - Skin care products - Elysee Scientific Cosmetic Co.
ALMOND MIST - Beverages - Blue Diamond Growers
ALMOND PLEASURE - Teas–herbal - Lipton Investments, Inc.
ALMOND RELLA - Food products - Rella Good Cheese Co.
ALMOND ROCA - Candy - Prince of Peace Enterprises Inc.
ALMOND ROCA - Food products - Brown & Haley
ALMOND SUNSET - Teas–herbal - Celestial Seasonings, Inc.
ALMOND SUPREME - Cookies ☆ - Campbell Soup Co.
ALMOND SUPREME - Popcorn - American Home Food Products Inc.
ALMOND TREE - Nuts–salted, roasted, cooked, or canned ☆ - Liberty Richter Inc.
ALMOND WINDMILL - Cookies - Nabisco Foods Group
ALMONDETTES - Candy - Price Candy Co. Inc.
ALMONDFRUIT - Food products - Cambridge House
ALMONDINE - Nail care products - Cosmair Inc.
ALMONDO - Handbags - Mid-Continent Ltd./MCL
ALMONDO ORIGINALS - Belts - Accessories Place
ALMONDOLAS - Candy - Koppers Chocolate Specialty Co. Inc.
ALMONDRELLA - Cheese - Rose International
ALMONDS CABERCHINO - Chocolate candy ☆ - Gil's Gourmet Gallery
ALMONDS N' WHITE - Confectionery - Bortz Chocolate Co.
ALMONETTE - Tobacco–chewing or smoking - Amar Blends Co.
ALMOPHEN - Health care products ☆ - JMI-Canton Pharmaceuticals
ALMORA - Apparel and accessories - Caledonia Knitwear Co.
ALMORA - Pharmaceutical preparations - Forest Pharmaceuticals Inc.
ALMOST ALMOND - Lipsticks ☆ - Honey & Spice Toiletries
ALMOST BASIC - Apparel and accessories - Joe Boxer Corp.
ALMOST CHILI - Food products - Brooks Foods
ALMOST FAMOUS - Toys - Russ Berrie and Co., Inc.
ALMOST FOREVER - Novelty items - Accord, Inc.
ALMOST FOREVER ENVELOPE, THE - Envelopes - Poly Pak America Inc.
ALMOST-HEAVEN - Food products - Pierce Foods Corp.
ALMOST HEAVEN - Water–bottled or canned - Virginia Water Conditioning, Inc.
ALMOST HOME - Cookies - Nabisco Foods Group
ALMOST MAKEUP - Cosmetics - Clinique Laboratories, Inc.
ALMOST MOCHA - Lipsticks ☆ - Honey & Spice Toiletries
ALMOST NATURAL - Pillows - Bicor Processing Corp.

☆ = Now out of production

ALMOST PERFECT - Drums–musical instruments - Tamarkin Co.

ALMOST READY TO WEAR - Greeting cards - Countdown Enterprises, Inc.

ALMSYS - Computer software - Information Center, Co.

ALMUD - Spices and extracts ☆ - Liberty Richter Inc.

ALMUD SAFFRON - Spices and extracts - Europa Foods Ltd.

ALNAHSA - Seafood products–fresh or frozen ☆ - Southeast Foods Inc.

ALNICO II PRO - Musical instrument accessories - Seymour Duncan Pickups

ALNIDE - Chemical preparations - Dow Chemical Co.

ALNIMAG - Tools - General Tools Manufacturing Co. Inc.

ALNORAL - Apparel–women's - Noral Fashion Partners, Inc.

A.L.N.Y. - Apparel and accessories - At Last Sportswear Inc.

ALNYTE - Pharmaceutical preparations - Mayer Laboratories, Inc.

ALO-BEAUTY MATTE - Skin care products - Aloe Creme Laboratories

ALO-COSMETICS - Skin care products - Aloe Creme Laboratories

ALO-ETTE - Hair care products - Paula Payne Products Co. Inc.

ALO-EYES - Skin care products - Aloe Creme Laboratories

ALO-FACE - Skin care products - Aloe Creme Laboratories

ALO-LIP-SHIELD - Skin care products - Aloe Creme Laboratories

ALO-MOISTURE PLUS - Skin care products - Aloe Creme Laboratories

ALO-OINTMENT - Skin care products - Aloe Creme Laboratories

ALO PRO - Skin care products - Alo Pro of Chicago Inc.

ALO-RELIEF - Skin care products - Aloe Creme Laboratories

ALO SUN - Tanning agents - Aloe Creme Laboratories

ALO-SUN TOP KOTE - Tanning agents - Aloe Creme Laboratories

ALO-TONE - Skin care products - Aloe Creme Laboratories

ALO-TRIUMPH - Skin care products - Aloe Creme Laboratories

ALO-TUSS - Pharmaceutical preparations ☆ - Vortech Pharmaceuticals

ALOAIDE - Beverages–carbonated - Columbine Beverage

ALOBA - Skin care products - Frances Denney

ALODAR SYSTEMS - Computer software - Alodar Systems, Inc.

ALODINE - Adhesives and sealants - Parker & Amchem

ALODIZED - Finishing agents ☆ - Parker & Amchem

ALODROPS - Cosmetics - Royal Bodycare, Inc.

ALOE 99 - Skin care products - Alivio Products Inc.

ALOE-A - Skin care products - Key West Aloe Inc.

ALOE ACCELERATOR - Health care products - Creative Laboratories Inc.

ALOE AID - Skin care products - Caribia, Cosmetic Research Laboratories Inc.

ALOE AID - Skin care products - Set-N-Me-Free Aloe Vera Co.

ALOE ALL OVER - Pharmaceutical preparations - Jess Clarke & Sons Inc.

ALOE ALL OVER - Skin care products - Winning Solutions Inc./Miracle of Aloe

ALOE BETA - Health-care products - Omnitrition International, Inc.

ALOE BURST - Beverages - Aloe Laboratories, Inc.

ALOE BURST - Beverages ☆ - J. Benson Corp.

ALOE-CARA - Pet Shampoo - Natra Pet Inc.

ALOE CARE - Cosmetics - ICN Pharmaceuticals Inc.

ALOE CARE - Skin care products - Roberts Research Laboratories, Inc.

ALOE-CELTZER - Pharmaceutical preparations - Charles H. Robson

ALOE COMFREY - Skin care products - Set-N-Me-Free Aloe Vera Co.

ALOE-CON - Pollen extracts - Florida Food Products Inc.

ALOE COVER - Skin care products - Robert F. Berlucchi

ALOE CURE - Hair care products - Select Brands

ALOE DELIGHT - Cosmetics - Rainco Co. Inc.

ALOE DERM - Pet products ☆ - Fermenta Animal Health

ALOE E - Skin care products - Alivio Products Inc.

ALOE-ECONOMICS - Lotions - Southern Exposure International, Inc.

ALOE EVER-SHIELD - Deodorants–personal - Aloe Vera of America, Inc.

ALOE FALLS - Beverages - Yerba Prima, Inc.

ALOE FARMS - Health care products - Aloe Farms

ALOE FIRST - Skin care products - Aloe Vera of America, Inc.

ALOE-FLEX - Skin care products - Tennis Elbow Corp.

ALOE GINSENG - Fruit drinks–bottled or canned - Health One Corp.

ALOE-GLO - Pet products - Glo-Marr Products Inc.

ALOE GOLD - Health care products - Creative Laboratories Inc.

ALOE GRANDE - Skin care products - Gordon Laboratories

ALOE HEAL - Veterinary pharmaceutical preparations - Farnam Cos. Inc.

ALOE ICE - Skin care products ☆ - Aloe Laboratories, Inc.

ALOE IN THE PINK - Skin care products - Key West Aloe Inc.

ALOE KIDS - Cosmetics - Fruit of the Earth, Inc.

ALOE KING - Flowers, plants, and seeds - Southern Fields Aloe Inc.

ALOE KOTE - Skin care products ☆ - Aloe Laboratories, Inc.

ALOE KOTE PLUS - Pharmaceutical preparations ☆ - Aloe Laboratories, Inc.

ALOE LABS - Skin care products - Aloe Laboratories, Inc.

ALOE LIFE - Health care products - Aloe Farms

ALOE LIFE - Health care products ☆ - Texas Best Unlimited, LP

ALOE LIFE - Juices - Aloe-Life International

ALOE LIPS - Lipsticks - Sarah Aloe Essence Cosmetics & Accessories, Inc.

ALOE LITE - Health care products ☆ - Texas Best Unlimited, LP

ALOE LOTION - Skin care products - Para Laboratories Inc.

ALOE MAX 100 - Skin care products - Key West Aloe Inc.

ALOE-MED - Pet products - Glo-Marr Products Inc.

ALOE-MOIST - Pharmaceutical preparations - Terry Laboratories

ALOE N' ICE - Skin care products - Garcoa Labs/Vitamin Classics

ALOE PLEX - Vitamins and nutritional supplements - Natural Organics, Inc.

ALOE POTIONS - Cosmetics - Conifer, Inc.

ALOE POWER - Beverages–carbonated ☆ - J. Benson Corp.

ALOE PRO JERI JACOBUS - Cosmetics - Aloe Pro International Co.

ALOE PRO-SET - Hair care products - Aloe Vera of America, Inc.

ALOE RAIN - Hair care products ☆ - J. Benson Corp.

ALOE RICH - Soft drinks and concentrates - Golden Aloe Products, Inc.

ALOE RICH 399 - Skin care products - Viva Vera Aloe Vera

ALOE/RID - Hair care products - Nexxus Products Co.

ALOE SELECT - Vitamins and nutritional supplements - General Nutrition Investment Co.

ALOE SHAVE - Shaving preparations - Caribia, Cosmetic Research Laboratories Inc.

ALOE-SOFT - Skin care products - Geri Gentle Corp.

ALOE SPLASH - Beverages–carbonated - Grant Wesley Burke

ALOE SPORT - Cosmetics and hair-care productss - Fruit of the Earth, Inc.

ALOE STIC - Skin care products - Set-N-Me-Free Aloe Vera Co.

ALOE SUPREME - Skin care products - Carr Products Co. Inc.

ALOE-THERA - Skin care products - Key West Aloe Inc.

ALOE TO THE RESCUE - Pharmaceutical preparations - Jess Clarke & Sons Inc.

ALOE TONER - Skin care products - Blackmores

ALOE UP - Skin care products ☆ - Aloe Laboratories, Inc.

ALOE VERA - Skin care products - Fruit of the Earth, Inc.

ALOE VERA 80 COLLECTION - Health care products - Naturade Inc.

ALOE VERA BODYCARE - Hair care products ☆ - Terry Laboratories

ALOE VERA JUICES - Juices - Aloe Laboratories, Inc.

ALOE VERA MOISTURIZING BODY BALM - Skin care products - Viviane Woodard Industries, Ltd.

ALOE VESTA - Skin care products - Calgon Vestal Laboratories

ALOE VITE - Vitamins and nutritional supplements - Natural Organics, Inc.

ALOEBARE - Depilatories - Pastels International, Inc.

ALOEBROSIA - Vitamins and nutritional supplements - Amrion, Inc.

ALOECAINE - Pharmaceutical preparations - Winning Solutions Inc./Miracle of Aloe

ALOECARE PLUS 3 - Lotions - Cross Country Paper Products, Inc.

ALOEDAN - Hair care products - Key West Aloe Inc.

ALOEDENT - Toothpaste - Winning Solutions Inc./Miracle of Aloe

ALOEDERM - Skin care products - Aloe Creme Laboratories

ALOEDINE - Pet products - Farnam Cos. Inc.

ALOEGATOR - Suntan lotions - Aloe Gator Suncare Co.

ALOEGEN - Hair care products - Levlab, Inc.

ALOEGEN BIOTREATMENT 22 - Hair care products - Levlab, Inc.

ALOEGUARD - Soap - Barrow Riddell & Associates

ALOELABS - Skin care products - Aloe Laboratories, Inc.

ALOELAX - Laxatives - Nature's Way Products, Inc.

ALOEMINT - Skin care products - Indiana Botanic Gardens, Inc.

ALOEPET - Pet products - Natra Pet Inc.

ALOESEPT - Lotions - Walter G. Legge Co., Inc.

ALOESOAP - Soap - Aloe Laboratories, Inc.

ALOESPA - Bath salts - Aloette Cosmetics, Inc.

ALOEX - Medicated shampoo - Key West Fragrance & Cosmetics Inc.

ALOEZONE - Skin care products - Key West Aloe Inc.

ALOGENETICS - Skin care products - Key West Aloe Inc.

ALOGROOM - Pet products - Best n' Show Pet Products Inc.

ALOHA - Dialing devices–telephone - Baltimore Luggage Co.

ALOHA - Floor coverings–carpet and rugs ☆ - Playfield International Inc.

ALOHA - Food products - Aloha Produce Corp.

ALOHA - Food products - Dole Food Co., Inc.

ALOHA - Jewelry - Pakula & Co.

ALOHA - Liqueurs - Jenkins Spirits Corp., Ltd.

ALOHA - Sandals - Aloha Sandal Co.

ALOHA - Shoes ☆ - Daniel Green Co.

ALOHA - Yarn ☆ - William Unger & Co. Inc.

ALOHA GOLD MACADAMIA - Oils–edible - Golden Whisk Pasta Partners

ALOHA HAWAIIAN SHAVE ICE - Beverages - Aloha Hawaiian Shave Ice Distributors

ALOHA MELT - Sandwiches–prepackaged - Denny's Inc.

ALOHA NETWORKS - Computers - Aloha Networks, Inc.

☆ = Now out of production

ALOHA PATCHWORKS - Patches, insignia, and emblems - Aloha Candle Manufacturing Co. Inc.

ALOHA RINGS - Candlesticks ✩ - Aloha Candle Manufacturing Co. Inc.

ALOHA ROUNDS - Candles - Aloha Candle Manufacturing Co. Inc.

ALOHA SPIRIT HAWAII - Decals and transfers - Hello Hawaii Inc.

ALOHA STICK - Cosmetics - Jason & Jean Products Inc.

ALOHAN - Floor coverings - Mannington Resilient Floors

ALOIS POSCHL - Tobacco products - Alfred & Christian Petersen U.S. Ltd.

ALOLAC - Lacquers ✩ - Parker & Amchem

ALOMIDE - Health care products - Alcon Laboratories, Inc.

ALON - Paints ✩ - Allentown Paint Manufacturing Co. Inc.

ALON - Sound equipment - Acarian Systems Ltd.

ALONDE - Footwear ✩ - Trico International Inc.

ALONDRA - Furniture ✩ - Landes Manufacturing Co.

ALOOF - Skin care products - MNI Products Inc.

ALOPHEN - Laxatives - Warner-Wellcome

ALOR - Pharmaceutical preparations - Atley Pharmaceuticals, Inc.

ALORA - Pharmaceutical preparations - Procter & Gamble Co.

ALORA - Skin care products - Superior Marketing Corp.

ALORAR - Lenses–photographic ✩ - Heitz Service Corp.

ALORIS - Machine tools - Aloris Tool Co., Inc.

ALOTTAFUN - Candy - Sirprize, Inc.

ALOUETTE - Bathroom fixtures - Kohler Co.

ALOUETTE - Cheese - Bongrain Cheese USA

ALOUETTE - Furniture ✩ - Lea Industries Inc.

ALOUETTE - Wines - Moquet Ltd.

ALOUETTE - Yarn ✩ - Joseph Galler Inc.

ALOUETTE BABY BRIE - Cheese - Bongrain Cheese USA

ALOUETTE ELEGANTE - Cheese - Bongrain Cheese USA

ALOUF ARAK - Cordials - Kedem Royal Wine Corp.

ALOX - Dinnerware - Standex International Corp.

ALOX - Dishes–china - H.F. Coors China Co.

ALOXITE - Paper–sand ✩ - Carborundum Abrasives North America

ALOXXI - Hair coloring preparations - Nexxus Products Co.

ALOXXI BLOCK - Skin care products - Nexxus Products Co.

ALOXXI BOOST - Dyes–cosmetic - Nexxus Products Co.

ALOXXI CHROMA - Hair coloring preparations - Nexxus Products Co.

ALOXXI H2O2 - Dyes–cosmetic - Nexxus Products Co.

ALOXXI LIGHTENER - Hair care products - Nexxus Products Co.

ALOXXI LOCK - Hair care products - Nexxus Products Co.

ALP - Communications equipment - Swedcom Corp.

ALP - Footwear - Golden Fox International Corp.

ALP - Sandals - ALP Sport Sandals

ALP AND DELL - Meat extracts - Roth Kase USA, Ltd.

ALP BOOTS - Shoes - Golden Fox International Corp.

ALP-INTERNATIONAL - Sandals - ALP Sport Sandals

ALP SEA BEES - Sandals - ALP Sport Sandals

ALP SPORT - Sandals - ALP Sport Sandals

ALPA - Photographic equipment - Heitz Service Corp.

ALPA ROTO - Cameras - Heitz Service Corp.

ALPACA - Computer diskettes–blank - Alpaca Corp.

ALPACA FUR - Floor coverings–carpet and rugs - La Casa De Carlo

ALPACA II - Floor coverings–carpet and rugs - Galaxy Carpet Mills Inc.

ALPACA PETE'S - Floor coverings–carpet and rugs - Alpaca Pete's, Inc.

ALPACAN - Crocheted and knitted items ✩ - Jacques De Loux Inc.

ALPADUR - Silver products - Michael Feinberg Inc.

ALPAK - Food products - Duso Food Distributors

ALPAMARE - Seasonings - Bioforce of America Ltd.

ALPAN - Alarm systems - Alpan, Inc.

ALPATIR - Telescopes ✩ - Heitz Service Corp.

ALPEN - Cereal - Young's Market Co.

ALPEN ICE - Candy - Ragold Inc.

ALPEN SECRETS - Skin care products - Solar Cosmetic Labs, Inc.

ALPENA - Sausages - Dairy Fresh Products Co.

ALPENECHO - Harmonicas - Hohner Inc.

ALPENGEIST - Amusement parks - Busch Entertainment Corp.

ALPENGLOW - Cider - Linden Beverage Co. Inc.

ALPENGRIP - Fabrics–rubberized - Outdoor Research, Inc.

ALPENJANKER - Apparel–men's - Alps Sportswear Manufacturing Co.

ALPENJOY - Cheese - Swissrose International Inc.

ALPENKRAUTER - Laxatives - Dr. Peter Fahrney & Sons Co.

ALPENKRONE - Mushrooms - Ernest L. Fischel Co.

ALPENLITE - Motor vehicles–motor homes - Western Recreational Vehicles Inc.

ALPENROSE - Milk - Alpenrose Dairy, Inc.

ALPENTALER - Cheese ✩ - Swissrose International Inc.

ALPENTOP - Cheese - Galaxy Trading Co.

ALPENWALKER - Shoes–athletic - Dexter Shoe Co.

ALPERN - Manicure preparations - Alpern Laboratories

ALPERNA - Apparel–athletic ✩ - Sportcaster Co. Inc.

ALPETORA - Apparel and accessories - Alpetora Imports Inc.

ALPEX - Photographic equipment ✩ - AIC International Inc.

ALPH/SIM - Computer software - Alphatech, Inc.

ALPHA - Apparel–athletic ✩ - Sportcaster Co. Inc.

ALPHA - Audio-cassette copiers ✩ - International Audio Inc.

ALPHA - Beverages–alcohol - Alpha Industries, Inc.

ALPHA - Bicycles - Ross Bicycles USA, Ltd.

ALPHA - Cabinets–wood ✩ - Kemper

ALPHA - Chairs–upholstered - United Chair Co., Inc.

ALPHA - Chalk - Quartet Manufacturing Co.

ALPHA - Coats - Rothco Inc.

ALPHA - Electrodes - Omega Engineering, Inc.

ALPHA - Electronic equipment - ABB Power T&D Co. Inc.

ALPHA - Electronics equipment - RTI Research Technology International

ALPHA - Fabrics - Interface, Inc.

ALPHA - Fabrics ✩ - Superior Shade & Blind Co. Inc.

ALPHA - Fibers–fluorocarbons - Amoco Fabrics and Fibers Co.

ALPHA - Flatware - Dansk International Designs, Ltd.

ALPHA - Flatware ✩ - W.M.F. of America Inc.

ALPHA - Floor coverings - Tek Stil Concepts Inc.

ALPHA - Floor coverings–carpet and rugs ✩ - Regal Rugs Inc.

ALPHA - Flowers, plants, and seeds ✩ - J. & L. Adikes Inc.

ALPHA - Furniture - Weiman Co.

ALPHA - Furniture ✩ - Lane Co. Inc.

ALPHA - Furniture–public buildings - Myrtle Desk Co.

ALPHA - Golfing equipment - All American Golf Sales, Inc.

ALPHA - Hair care products - Rusk Inc.

ALPHA - Hardware ✩ - Alside Div.

ALPHA - Infant product - Today's Kids Inc.

ALPHA - Musical instruments - Paiste America, Inc.

ALPHA - Occasional tables ✩ - JDI Group, Inc.

ALPHA - Pencils - Empire Berol USA

ALPHA - Pet products - Alpha Tech Pet Inc.

ALPHA - Pharmaceutical preparations ✩ - Columbia Laboratories Inc.

ALPHA - Pipes–tobacco - Mastercraft Pipes Inc.

ALPHA - Racks - Alpha Enterprises, Inc.

ALPHA - Skin care products ✩ - Neoteric Cosmetics, Inc.

ALPHA - Sporting goods - Oceanic

ALPHA - Sporting goods - Shakespeare Fishing Tackle

ALPHA - Telephones–cellular - Penn Central Corp.

ALPHA - Tents - Coleman Co., Inc.

ALPHA - Toys–models - Estes Industries

ALPHA - Vitamins and nutritional supplements - Bio San Laboratories Inc.

ALPHA - Wallpaper - Pickhardt & Siebert USA Inc.

ALPHA - Watches - Alpha Watch Co.

ALPHA-1 - Yogurt–frozen - Alpha-1 Products Inc.

ALPHA 2 - Boats - Glen-L Marine Designs

ALPHA 2 - Sprinklers–lawn - L.R. Nelson Corp.

ALPHA 2 - Vacuum cleaners and accessories - Baracuda International Corp.

ALPHA 2.5 - Hair care products - Revlon Consumer Products Corp.

ALPHA 3 - Plant growth regulators - Swallowtail Corp.

ALPHA III - Toys–models - Estes Industries

ALPHA 4 PLUS - Skin care products - Jason Natural Products, Inc.

ALPHA 5 - Toys - Saban Entertainment, Inc.

ALPHA 5 IN 1 - Hair care products - Revlon Consumer Products Corp.

ALPHA 6 PLUS - Skin care products - Jason Natural Products, Inc.

ALPHA-7 - Hand cleaner - Dynacco, Inc.

ALPHA-7 - Veterinary pharmaceutical preparations - Boehringer Ingelheim Animal Health, Inc.

ALPHA 8 - Blood coagulation preparations - Alpha Therapeutic Corp.

ALPHA 9 - Manicure preparations - Alpha 9

ALPHA 10 PLUS - Skin care products - Jason Natural Products, Inc.

ALPHA 12 - Skin care products - Jason Natural Products, Inc.

ALPHA 40 - Telephone apparatus ✩ - RF Communications Div.

ALPHA 100 - Hair care products - Revlon Consumer Products Corp.

ALPHA 1000 - Hoists - Sky Climber, Inc.

ALPHA 2001 MD TMA - Crash barrier components - Energy Absorption Systems, Inc.

ALPHA AND OMEGA - Hair care products - Waverly Beauty Products

ALPHA AUDIO - Audio equipment - Alpha Audio Acoustics

ALPHA BASS - Amplifiers–musical instrument - Peavey Electronics Corp.

ALPHA BETA - Coffee - Tetley Inc.

✩ = Now out of production

ALPHA BETA - Neckties - Joscar Industries Inc.
ALPHA BETTE - Crocheted and knitted items ☆ - Alpha Mills Corp.
ALPHA-BIOPLEX - Skin care products - Biocare Labs, Inc.
ALPHA BITS - Crocheted and knitted items ☆ - Alpha Mills Corp.
ALPHA BITS FOR CHILDREN - Publisher's imprints ☆ - Summit Univ. Press
ALPHA-BLOCKS - Hobby kits ☆ - Accento Plastic Manufacturing Inc.
ALPHA BLOCKS - Toys - Tyco Toys
ALPHA-BORDER - Wallpaper - Smart Kids
ALPHA BRICKS - Toys - Earle Industries, Inc.
ALPHA-CARE - Computer software - Healthcare Computer Corp.
ALPHA CARE - Skin care products - Jason Natural Products, Inc.
ALPHA CAROTENE PLUS - Vitamins and nutritional supplements - Source Naturals
ALPHA CEUTICALS - Cosmetics - Beauty for All Seasons Inc.
ALPHA CF - Pharmaceutical preparations - Boericke & Tafel
ALPHA CHYMAR - Ophthalmic goods - Barnes-Hind Inc.
ALPHA CLEAR - Skin care products - North Pacific Naturals, Inc.
ALPHA COMMUNICATIONS - Telephone apparatus - Alpha Communications
ALPHA COMPLEX - Cosmetics - Survival Corp.
ALPHA COMPLEX - Skin care products - Orjene Natural Cosmetics
ALPHA CRITTERS - Toys–stuffed ☆ - Mighty Star Inc. (Special Effects Div.)
ALPHA-E - Vitamins and nutritional supplements - Advanced Nutritional Technology
ALPHA FACTORS - Apparel–athletic - Tighe Industries Inc.
ALPHA FASTENING SYSTEM - Fasteners - Barrett Manufacturing Co.
ALPHA-FRY - Solder - Fry Technology
ALPHA-GEMS - Costume jewelry - Michael Assile
ALPHA GLUTAMINE - Vitamins and nutritional supplements - Bionutritional Research Group, Inc.
ALPHA HYDRACTIVE - Skin care products - Aida Thibiant, Inc.
ALPHA HYDROX - Skin care products - Neoteric Cosmetics, Inc.
ALPHA HYDROXY BAR - Soap - Karlen Manufacturing, Inc.
ALPHA I - Cameras ☆ - Polaroid Corp.
ALPHA I - Guitars - Music Distributors Inc.
ALPHA INTERNATIONAL - Recording label - Capitol-EMI Music Inc.
ALPHA INTERNATIONAL - Recording label - Sigma Alpha Entertainment Group Ltd.
ALPHA JET - Dryers–hair ☆ - Dynex International
ALPHA-KERI - Pharmaceutical preparations - Westwood-Squibb Pharmaceuticals, Inc.
ALPHA LETTER DROP - Computer programming services - Berta-Max Inc.
ALPHA LINE - Transmitting apparatus–radio - Broadcast Electronics, Inc.
ALPHA-LINKS - Wood products - Mangelsen's (VDI)
ALPHA LITE - Hair care products - Revlon Consumer Products Corp.
ALPHA MAGIC - Cosmetics - CBI Laboratories, Inc.
ALPHA MIRACLE - Hair care products - Avanza Corp.
ALPHA NINE - Pharmaceutical preparations - Alpha Therapeutic Corp.
ALPHA-NUMBER SET - Puzzles - Lauri Inc.
ALPHA NUTRIUM - Skin care products - Chesebrough-Pond's USA Co.
ALPHA NUTRIUM - Skin care products - Conopco, Inc.
ALPHA OMEGA - Curling irons–electric - Select Brands
ALPHA OMEGA - Games ☆ - Avalon Hill Game Co.
ALPHA OMEGA - Infant product - Cosco, Inc.
ALPHA-OMEGA - Pens - Olde Windjammer
ALPHA PERM - Fabrics - Hollingsworth & Vose Co.
ALPHA PETS - Toys–stuffed - Fun World Inc.
ALPHA-PHED - Pharmaceutical preparations ☆ - Lexis Laboratories Inc.
ALPHA-POS - Computer software - Healthcare Computer Corp.
ALPHA PROBE - Toys - Fisher-Price, Inc.
ALPHA PYRAMIS - Spices and extracts - Continnuus
ALPHA REMEDIES - Pharmaceutical preparations - Boericke & Tafel
ALPHA-RIDGE - Padding–foam - Innovative Flooring Systems Inc.
ALPHA SAN 300 - Pet products ☆ - Alpha Tech Pet Inc.
ALPHA SECURITY - Containers–plastic - Alpha Enterprises, Inc.
ALPHA SERUM - Skin care products - Sothys USA Inc.
ALPHA SET - Hair care products - Revlon Consumer Products Corp.
ALPHA SH - Pharmaceutical preparations - Boericke & Tafel
ALPHA-STIM - Health care products - Electropedic Manufacturing Corp.
ALPHA SUN - Vitamins and nutritional supplements - New Algae Co.
ALPHA SYSTEM 2000 - Steel products - Kewaunee Scientific Corp.
ALPHA TAU DELTA - Jewelry - Alpha Tau Delta
ALPHA-TET - Pharmaceutical preparations ☆ - Perry Laboratories
ALPHA-VITA - Pharmaceutical preparations - Barrows Pharmacal Inc.
ALPHA-WOODY STICKEMS - Wood products - Russ Berrie and Co., Inc.
ALPHA-Z - Labels–gummed - Smead Manufacturing Co.
ALPHABASIC - Computer software - Alpha Microsystems

ALPHABATTLE - Games - Robert Mendell
ALPHABEADS - Spices and extracts - Pharmachem Laboratories, Inc.
ALPHABEAR - Toys ☆ - Toy Works, Inc.
ALPHABEARS - House furnishings ☆ - Gear Holdings, Inc.
ALPHABED - Health care products - HNE Healthcare
ALPHABEE - Computer software ☆ - Orange Cherry Software
ALPHABET - Brassieres (Bras) ☆ - Warnaco Inc.
ALPHABET - Cookies - Dairy State Foods Inc.
ALPHABET ACADEMY - Computer software - Hartley Courseware Inc.
ALPHABET AVALANCHE - Toys - Lauri Inc.
ALPHABET BLOCKS - Wallpaper ☆ - Priss Prints Inc.
ALPHABET BOARD - Toys - Fisher-Price, Inc.
ALPHABET CIRCUS - Computer software - SRA/McGraw-Hill (Div. of The McGraw-Hill Companies)
ALPHABET COMPANY, THE - Housewares - Stephanie Johns Brewer
ALPHABET EXPRESS - Computer software - Gamco Industries Inc.
ALPHABET FUN - Electronic equipment - Texas Instruments Inc.
ALPHABET GAME, THE - Games - Smethport Specialty Co.
ALPHABET LAND - Games - Cadaco Div.
ALPHABET LAND - Games - Rapid Mounting and Finishing Co.
ALPHABET PHONE - Toys–musical - Mattel, Inc.
ALPHABET PRESS - Posters ☆ - Picture Book Studio
ALPHABET SOUNDS - Computer software - Orange Cherry Software
ALPHABET SOUP - Games - Parker Brothers
ALPHABET VITAMINS - Vitamins and nutritional supplements - Retired Persons Services, Inc.
ALPHABET WITH TOM & ANDY, THE - Computer software - Dunamis Inc.
ALPHABET ZOO - Bedding–linen - Dan River Inc.
ALPHABET ZOO - Computer software ☆ - Queue Inc.
ALPHABETEPHANT - Toys - Lauri Inc.
ALPHABETICAL BIBLE AB, THE - Publisher's imprints - David Lewis Staton
ALPHABETTER - Paper–writing - MCM Co.
ALPHABITE - Bicycles - Ritchey Design Inc.
ALPHABLEND - Skin care products - Barbara Salomone and Associates, Inc.
ALPHABOND - Chemical preparations - Alcoa Alumina & Chemicals, LLC
ALPHABONK FARM - Computer software - Headbone Interactive, Inc.
ALPHABRITE - Paints - Quartet Manufacturing Co.
ALPHABUILDER - Computer software - Barra, Inc.
ALPHACATS - Clothing - Jeb Biemiller
ALPHACODE - Stationery - Tab Products Co.
ALPHACOLOR - Paints - Quartet Manufacturing Co.
ALPHACOPY - Electronic equipment - Equitrac Corp.
ALPHADERM - Pharmaceutical preparations ☆ - Lemmon Co.
ALPHADROL - Pharmaceutical preparations ☆ - Upjohn Co.
ALPHAEX - Chemical preparations - Etrac Inc.
ALPHAFAX - Facsimile equipment - Equitrac Corp.
ALPHAGAN - Ophthalmic goods - Allergan, Inc.
ALPHAGENERATION - Computer hardware - Digital Equipment Corp.
ALPHAGLASS - Resins–synthetic - Alpha & Omega Fiberglass Finishes
ALPHAKEY - Computer programming services - Berta-Max Inc.
ALPHALAB - Doilies - Alpha Omega Technologies, Inc.
ALPHALAIN - Dinnerware - Homer Laughlin China Co.
ALPHALERT - Radio communications equipment - Motorola, Inc. (Paging Products Group)
ALPHALIN - Vitamins and nutritional supplements - Eli Lilly and Co.
ALPHALINE - Electronic equipment - Leteron
ALPHAMARK - Paints ☆ - Quartet Manufacturing Co.
ALPHAMAT - Mat boards - Nielsen & Bainbridge
ALPHAMATE - Radio communications equipment - Motorola, Inc. (Paging Products Group)
ALPHAMAX - Skin care products - Richard M. Salit
ALPHAMIN - Pharmaceutical preparations ☆ - Vortech Pharmaceuticals
ALPHAMOUNT - Mat boards - Nielsen & Bainbridge
ALPHAMUL - Pharmaceutical preparations - Lannett Co. Inc.
ALPHANATE - Pharmaceutical preparations - Alpha Therapeutic Corp.
ALPHANUMERAL - Band stamps - Consolidated Stamp Manufacturing Co. Inc.
ALPHAPOINTE - Pens - Alphapointe Association for the Blind
ALPHAQUEST - Audio equipment ☆ - Telequest Inc.
ALPHARAG - Mat boards - Nielsen & Bainbridge
ALPHAREDISOL - Vitamins and nutritional supplements ☆ - Merck & Co., Inc. (Merck Research Laboratories)
ALPHARPL - Computer software - Alpha Software Corp.
ALPHASAT - Cloth–asbestos - Texwipe Co. LLC
ALPHASAURS - Paper products - Shadowind, Inc.
ALPHASCAN - File folders - Kardex Systems, Inc.
ALPHASITE - Chalk ☆ - Quartet Manufacturing Co.

ALPHASMART - Computer keyboards - Intelligent Peripheral Devices, Inc.
ALPHASONIK - Audio equipment - Alphasonik Inc.
ALPHASPEC - Safety products - Uvex Safety LLC
ALPHASTATION - Computer hardware - Digital Equipment Corp.
ALPHATEC EXTRUSION - Containers–plastic - Creative Forming, Inc.
ALPHATEC III - Health care products - Alphatec Research Institute
ALPHATEX - Leather–vellum - National Printfast
ALPHATOONS - Video production - Jack Wohl
ALPHATOR - Electronic equipment - Educational Insights, Inc.
ALPHATREX - Pharmaceutical preparations - Savage Laboratories Inc.
ALPHAVILLE - Recording label - Alphaville, Inc.
ALPHAWASH - Skin care products - Passepartout, Inc.
ALPHAWORKS - Skin care products - U.K. Abba Products, Inc.
ALPHAZOMES - Skin care products - C'est Belle Societe
ALPHEN CELLARS - Wines - Blair Importers Ltd.
ALPHIE II - Toys–electronic - Playskool, Inc.
ALPHIE RIDER - Infant product - Alphie Enterprises
ALPHIX - Electrical equipment - General Electric Co.
ALPHONSE MELLOT - Wines - House of Burgundy Inc.
ALPHONSE MELLOT - Wines ☆ - Dreyfus Ashby Inc.
ALPHONSE MUCHA - Posters - Icart Vendor Graphics Inc.
ALPHOSYL - Eczema and psoriasis treatments ☆ - Reed & Carnrick
ALPIN - Binoculars ☆ - Heitz Service Corp.
ALPINA - Furniture - Dinaire Corp.
ALPINA - Sporting goods ☆ - Regina Imports
ALPINA - Teas–herbal - Wunderlich-Diez Corp.
ALPINE - Air purification systems - Norwalk Sales & Service
ALPINE - Antifreeze - Prestone Products Corp.
ALPINE - Archery equipment - Archer Sports Inc.
ALPINE - Audio equipment - Alpine Electronics of America Inc.
ALPINE - Backpacks - Travel Professionals Corp.
ALPINE - Beverages - Continental Mills, Inc.
ALPINE - Beverages–malt - Berghoff-Huber Brewing Co. Ltd.
ALPINE - Beverages–malt ☆ - Joseph Huber Brewing Co., Inc.
ALPINE - Bicycles ☆ - Huffy Corp.
ALPINE - Bicycles ☆ - Murray, Inc.
ALPINE - Brushes - Wright-Bernet
ALPINE - Cabinets - Quality Cabinets
ALPINE - Cabinets - Yorktowne Inc.
ALPINE - Cabinets ☆ - Medallion Kitchens of Minnesota Inc.
ALPINE - Cabinets ☆ - H.J. Scheirich Co.
ALPINE - Chocolate syrup - J. Hungerford Smith Co.
ALPINE - Cigarettes - Philip Morris Companies Inc.
ALPINE - Cooking equipment–household ☆ - Mirro Corp.
ALPINE - Cosmetics - Stephan Co.
ALPINE - Curtains - Bay State Curtain Manufacturing Co. Inc.
ALPINE - Cushions - Saddleman, Inc.
ALPINE - Detergents - Stanson Corp.
ALPINE - Dinnerware–glass - Nikko Ceramics Inc.
ALPINE - Door frames - Canyon Creek Cabinet Co.
ALPINE - Doors–storm - Quaker Window Products Co.
ALPINE - Electrical equipment - Adobe Air Inc.
ALPINE - Fabrics–velvet - Dan River Inc.
ALPINE - Fans–electric - Casablanca Fan Co.
ALPINE - Floor coverings–carpet and rugs - Bloomsburg Carpet Industries
ALPINE - Floor coverings–carpet and rugs - Cabin Crafts Carpets
ALPINE - Floor coverings–carpet and rugs ☆ - Foreign Accents
ALPINE - Flowers, plants, and seeds - Jacklin Seed
ALPINE - Furniture - American Woodmark Corp.
ALPINE - Furniture - Lea Industries Inc.
ALPINE - Furniture–children's ☆ - Child Craft Industries Inc.
ALPINE - Kilns - A.R.T. Studio Clay Co. (Alpine Div.)
ALPINE - Lighting fixtures ☆ - Hubbell Lighting, Inc. (Lighting Div.)
ALPINE - Manufactured homes - Redman Industries, Inc.
ALPINE - Motor vehicles–motor homes - Western Recreational Vehicles Inc.
ALPINE - Musical instruments - Trophy Music Co.
ALPINE - Musical instruments ☆ - L.A. Sax Co.
ALPINE - Office supplies - Faber-Castell Corp.
ALPINE - Oxygen - Caire
ALPINE - Paints - The White Co.
ALPINE - Paints ☆ - True-Tagg Paint Co.
ALPINE - Picnic equipment ☆ - Poloron Products Inc.
ALPINE - Recording label - JR Sound Productions Inc.
ALPINE - Seafood products–fresh or frozen - Alpine International
ALPINE - Sponges ☆ - Schroeder & Tremayne, Inc.
ALPINE - Sporting goods - Ski Accessories Co.

ALPINE - Stepladders - W.W. Babcock Co. Inc.
ALPINE - Watches - Precise International/Wenger
ALPINE 525 - Oxygen - Caire
ALPINE BLOSSOM - Dinnerware ☆ - Corning Inc.
ALPINE BLOSSOM - Floor coverings ☆ - Congoleum Corp.
ALPINE BOY - Fruits and vegetables ☆ - Heeren Brothers Inc.
ALPINE CLIMBER - Playground equipment - Child Life Inc.
ALPINE COOL - Cosmetics - Stephan Co.
ALPINE COTTON - Yarn - Henry's Attic
ALPINE CRAFTS - Apparel and accessories ☆ - Alpine Crafts Co. Inc.
ALPINE CRISP - Food products - Gilbert Orchards Inc.
ALPINE DRY - Gloves ☆ - Swany America Corp.
ALPINE EAGLE - Macaroni product - Cumberland Macaroni Manufacturing Co.
ALPINE EXPRESS - Luggage - Travel Professionals Corp.
ALPINE FLEECE - Jackets - Victoria's Secret Catalogue, Inc.
ALPINE FRESH - Fruits–canned - Chief Tonasket Growers
ALPINE FRESH - Sponges - Reckitt & Colman, Inc.
ALPINE HEIGHTS - Cabinets - Alpine Cabinet Co.
ALPINE HERBS - Cosmetics ☆ - Divina Products Co.
ALPINE HIKERS - Dolls ☆ - Effanbee Doll Corp.
ALPINE HIKERS - Footwear–men's - B. Levy & Son
ALPINE HOLIDAY - Floor coverings–carpet and rugs ☆ - Mohawk Carpet Corp.
ALPINE LACE - Cheese - Alpine Lace Brands, Inc.
ALPINE MINT - Cosmetics ☆ - Nutrine Ltd.
ALPINE MINT CARE FREE - Chewing gum - Nabisco Holdings Corp.
ALPINE PETITE - Yarn - Henry's Attic
ALPINE PIONEER - Footwear - TKW Trading Corp.
ALPINE PREMIER - Containers–plastic - Laclede Chain Manufacturing Co.
ALPINE ROWER - Rowing machine ☆ - CSA, Inc.
ALPINE SKI - Video games - Taito America Corp.
ALPINE SPORT - Containers–plastic - Laclede Chain Manufacturing Co.
ALPINE SPRING - Housewares ☆ - Himark Enterprises Inc.
ALPINE STAR BOOTS - Motorcycle boots - Cosmopolitan Motors Inc.
ALPINE STRUCTURES - Wood trusses and joists - Trus Joist MacMillan L.P.
ALPINE SUPER SPORT - Containers–plastic - Laclede Chain Manufacturing Co.
ALPINE, THE - Calendars - Sormani Inc.
ALPINE TRAVELERS - Luggage - Travel Professionals Corp.
ALPINE VALLEY - Water–bottled or canned - Alpine Valley Waters
ALPINE VILLAGE SERIES - Figurines - Department 56 Inc.
ALPINE VINEYARDS - Wines - Alpine Vineyards
ALPINE WALKER - Treadmills ☆ - CSA, Inc.
ALPINE WHITE - Candy bars - Nestle USA
ALPINE WOODS - Footwear - C.P. International Corp.
ALPINE XC SKIER - Exercising equipment ☆ - CSA, Inc.
ALPINLOOP - Sporting goods - Life Style Concepts
ALPINO - Cheese - Swissrose International Inc.
ALPINO BIANCO - Wines - Joseph E. Seagram & Sons, Inc.
ALPINO ROSSO - Wines - Joseph E. Seagram & Sons, Inc.
ALPINOR - Spices and extracts ☆ - Liberty Richter Inc.
ALPITRIX - Telescopes ☆ - Heitz Service Corp.
ALPLEX - Adhesives and sealants - Adhesive Products, Inc.
ALPO - Enamels - Standard T Chemical Co. Inc.
ALPO - Pet products - ALPO Petfoods Inc.
ALPO - Pet products - Pillsbury Co.
ALPO SNAPS - Pet products - ALPO Petfoods Inc.
ALPREP - Cleaning preparations ☆ - Parker & Amchem
ALPRESS LP - Pharmaceutical preparations - Pfizer Inc.
ALPRIMA - Saddles - St. Lawrence Sales Inc.
ALPRINE - Pharmaceutical preparations ☆ - Ulmer Pharmacal Co.
ALPRO - Audio equipment - Alpro Acoustics
ALPROSE - Chocolate candy - H & H International Co. USA
ALPS - Apparel–men's - Alps Sportswear Manufacturing Co.
ALPS - Cheese - Normark & Associates
ALPS - Footwear - A.S. Associates
ALPS ACTIVE LIFESTYLE - Handbags - Alps, Inc.
ALPS BREEZE - Deodorizers - Surco Products Inc.
ALPS LTD. - Apparel and accessories - Springfoot, Inc.
ALPSBERG - Cheese - Galaxy Trading Co.
ALPSCHMIEDE - Sporting goods ☆ - Liberty Mountain Sports
ALQUAVIMA - Skin care products - Alessio International
ALR EVOLUTION V - Computers and microcomputers - Advanced Logic Research Inc.
ALR EXPRESS - Computers - Advanced Logic Research Inc.
ALRAD - Computer software - Alden Electronics, Inc.

☆ = Now out of production

ALRAY - Paints - Impervious Paint Industries Ltd.

ALREADY A LEGEND - Apparel and accessories - MGRR, Inc.

ALRECORDS - Recording label - Sonotone Corp.

ALREDASE - Diabetes preparation - American Home Products Corp.

ALS SCAN - Computer peripheral equipment - ALS Scan, Inc.

ALSA - Juices ☆ - Mira International Foods Inc.

ALSACE - Blinds–venetian ☆ - Hunter Douglas, Inc.

ALSACE II - Furniture ☆ - Stanley Furniture Co. Inc.

ALSACE WILLM - Wines - Frederick Wildman and Sons Ltd.

ALSE - Candy - Ford's Produce Co., Inc.

ALSETAR - Lenses–photographic ☆ - Heitz Service Corp.

ALSHIRE - Recording label ☆ - Alshire International Inc.

ALSICAL - Pharmaceutical preparations - Dorsey Laboratories

ALSIP - Boats - Channel Craft

ALSOL - Automotive parts and accessories - Scott Associates Inc.

ALSOL TRU-GLO - Automotive parts and accessories - Scott Associates Inc.

ALSONS - Bathroom fixtures - Alsons Corp.

ALSONS - Plumbing fixtures–metal - Masco Corp.

ALSPRAY - Bathroom fixtures - Alsons Corp.

ALSTON - Floor coverings–carpet and rugs ☆ - Atlas Carpet Mills Inc.

ALSTON - Floor coverings–carpet and rugs ☆ - Mannington Carpets, Inc.

ALSTON ENTERTAINMENT - Computer peripheral equipment - Alston Entertainment, Inc.

ALSYNITE - Hardware - Sequentia Inc. (Reinforced Plastics Div.)

ALT AMSTERDAM - Tableware–earthenware - Villeroy and Boch Tableware Ltd.

ALT DEUTSCHER - Cheese - Swissrose International Inc.

ALT NOUVEAU BEER - Beverages–malt - North Coast Brewing Co., Inc.

ALTA - Bicycles - American Recreation Co., Inc.

ALTA - Cigar boxes–wood ☆ - Consolidated Cigar Corp.

ALTA - Cosmetics - Alta Health Products

ALTA - Floor coverings–carpet and rugs - Regal Rugs Inc.

ALTA - Golfing equipment - Dunlop Maxfli Sports Corp.

ALTA - Hair care products - Waverly Beauty Products

ALTA - Peanut butter ☆ - Sweet Candy Co.

ALTA - Prefabricated buildings–wood - Alta Log Homes

ALTA - Sewing machines–household ☆ - Bernina Sewing Machine Co. Inc.

ALTA - Thread - Van Waters and Rogers Inc.

ALTA & OMEGA - Hair care products - Waverly Beauty Products

ALTA CUCINA - Tomato pastes and sauces - Stanislaus Food Products Co.

ALTA DENA - Frozen dairy confections - Alta-Dena Certified Dairy, Inc.

ALTA-DENA CLASSIC - Ice cream - Alta-Dena Certified Dairy, Inc.

ALTA DENA NATURAL SELECT - Dairy products - Alta-Dena Certified Dairy, Inc.

ALTA MAR - Sardines–canned - Crown Prince Inc.

ALTA MIRA - Slacks–women's - Tony Marterie & Associates

ALTA RACER - Tires–airplane - Greenball Corp.

ALTA SELENIUM PLUS - Health care products - Alta Health Products

ALTA SIL-X SILICA - Health care products - Alta Health Products

ALTA VALTELLINA - Jams and jellies - Lettieri

ALTA VINEYARD CELLAR - Wines - Alta Vineyard Cellar

ALTA WAVE - Hair care products - Waverly Beauty Products

ALTA WRAP - Plastics - Alta Industries Inc.

ALTACE - Pharmaceutical preparations - Hoechst-Roussel Pharmaceuticals Inc.

ALTADYNE - Mattresses - Mul Acquisition Corp. II

ALTAGAMMA - Wallpaper - Textile Wallcoverings International Ltd.

ALTAIR - Eyewear - Altair Holding Co.

ALTAIR - Floor coverings–tile - Monarch Tile Inc.

ALTAIR - Frames–eyeglass - Altair Eyewear

ALTAIR - Telephones - TT Systems Corp.

ALTAIR VISTA POINT - Radio communications equipment - Motorola, Inc. (Land Mobile Products Sector)

ALTAMA - Apparel and accessories - Altama Footwear

ALTAMAR - Seafood products–fresh or frozen ☆ - Penguin Frozen Foods, Inc.

ALTAMIRA - Floor coverings–carpet and rugs ☆ - Karastan-Bigelow Inc.

ALTAMIRA - Lamps - Brownlie-Lamar Design Group, Inc.

ALTAMIRA - Tomato pastes and sauces - Caragol, Esformes & Phelan Corp.

ALTAMONT - Thread - Elmore-Pisgah, Inc.

ALTAMURA - Wines - Frank Altamura

ALTARIS - Computer software - PRC Inc.

ALTAS ZOO DADS - Plastics - Alta Industries Inc.

ALTAVISTA - Computer hardware - Digital Equipment Corp.

ALTCO - Thread - A. Lewis Thread Co. Inc.

ALTEA - Housewares ☆ - Berarducci Bros. Manufacturing Co. Inc.

ALTEC - Brakes–motor vehicle - Motion Control Industries, Inc.

ALTEC LANSING - Electronic equipment - Altec

ALTEC LANSING - Furniture - Altec Lansing Consumer Products

ALTENEDER - Office supplies - Theodore Alteneder & Sons

ALTEON - Medical apparatus - Alteon Inc.

ALTER - Apparel–men's - Zanella Ltd.

ALTER - Computer software - BMC Software, Inc.

ALTER EGO - Computer software - Activision, Inc.

ALTER EGO - Jewelry - Donley Co.

ALTER EGO THE PERSONAL CARE COMPANION - Skin care products - Club Amenities International, Inc.

ALTERED - Recording label - Multi-Sound Records International

ALTERED FACES - Toys - Spearhead Industries Inc.

ALTERED SPACE - Games - Sony Imagesoft Inc.

ALTERED STATES - Wines ☆ - Bully Hill Vineyards, Inc.

ALTERIS BUSINESS MANAGEMENT - Computer software - Novatek Corp.

ALTERN8 - Medical apparatus - Pegasus Airwave Inc.

ALTERNA - Faucets - Kohler Co.

ALTERNA - Fireplace equipment - Preway Industries Inc.

ALTERNA - Musical instrument accessories - Deg Music Products Inc.

ALTERNAGEL - Antacids - McNeil Pharmaceuticals

ALTERNASCENTS - Banks–commercial - Good Sense

ALTERNATE ACTION DEMINERALIZING TREATMENT - Hair care products - Matrix Essentials, Inc.

ALTERNATE CHOICE - Fruits and vegetables - Phoenix Foods Marketing, Inc.

ALTERNATIVE - Hair-replacement product - International Hairgoods Inc.

ALTERNATIVE 301 NAIL SYSTEMS - Cosmetics - I-301 Systems Inc.

ALTERNATIVE DESIGNER - Colognes - Carlton

ALTERNATIVE MEDICINE CENTER - Vitamins and nutritional supplements - King Bio Pharmaceuticals, Inc.

ALTERNATIVE NATION - Shirts - Viacom International Inc.

ALTERNATIVE PARADISE - Apparel and accessories - Cori Langdon

ALTERNATIVE POSTURES - Furniture - John Larson

ALTERNATIVES - Apparel and accessories - Swirl II Ltd.

ALTERNATIVES - Cakes ☆ - Awrey Bakeries, Inc.

ALTERNATIVES - Floor coverings - Congoleum Corp.

ALTERNATIVES - Prosthetic apparatus - Alternatives, Intl. Inc.

ALTERNATIVES - Salad dressings–bottled - Kraft Foods, Inc.

ALTERNATIVES - Wallpaper - Dunridge Industries Inc.

ALTERNATIVES BY NATURAL ISSUE - Apparel and accessories - Supreme International Corp.

ALTERNATIVES IN AMERICAN MUSIC - Recording label - Jazz Composer's Orchestra Association Inc.

ALTERNECARE HEALTH PRODUCTS - Vitamins and nutritional supplements - Alternecare Health Products, Inc.

ALTERNITY - Games - Tsr, Inc.

ALTERRA - Hoses - Alterra Holdings Corp.

ALTERRA - Vitamins and nutritional supplements - Upsher-Smith Laboratories, Inc.

ALTERVISION POINT OF FIT SYSTEM - Computer software - D & L, Inc.

ALTES - Beverages–malt ☆ - The Stroh Brewery Co.

ALTES LIGHT - Beverages–malt ☆ - The Stroh Brewery Co.

ALTESINO - Beverages–alcohol ☆ - Palm Bay Imports, Inc.

ALTESSE - Apparel–women's - Lily of France Inc.

ALTESSE - Brushes–hair - Karina Inc.

ALTEX - Pharmaceutical preparations - H.R. Cenci Laboratories Inc.

ALTEXIDE - Pharmaceutical preparations - H.R. Cenci Laboratories Inc.

ALTEZZA - Furniture - Arbek Furniture Manufacturing Inc.

ALTHANE - Paints - Allentown Paint Manufacturing Co. Inc.

ALTHEA - Giftware ☆ - Gorham Inc.

ALTHEA - Glassware–household ☆ - Dansk International Designs, Ltd.

ALTHUSER - Apparel–women's - Althuser Co.

ALTIA - Computer software - Altia Inc.

ALTIA - Footwear - Five Ten

ALTICORT - Vitamins and nutritional supplements - Bio-Therapeutics, Inc.

ALTIGWELD - Welding equipment - Aluminum Co. of America

ALTIMA - Computers - Altima Systems, Inc.

ALTIMA - Golfing equipment - Triumph Golf Co.

ALTIMA - Motor vehicles–automobiles - Nissan Motor Corp. USA

ALTIMASTER - Electronic equipment - SSE Inc.

ALTIMATE CUSTOM STYLING - Apparel–women's - Altimate Custom Styling, Inc.

ALTIMATE SERIES CONTROLERS - Computer hardware - Proprietary Controls Systems Corp.

ALTIMIX - Faucets - Briggs Plumbing Products, Inc.

ALTINI-ASTI SPUMANTE - Beverages–alcohol - HDT Importers Inc.

☆ = Now out of production

ALTIS - Electrical equipment - Altis Audio Ltd.

ALTITRAK - Toys–models - Estes Industries

ALTITUDE AM - Bags - Altitude Marketing, Inc.

ALTIVAR - Regulators–power - Square D Co.

ALTLAND HOUSE - Vegetables–frozen ☆ - Hanover Foods Corp.

ALTLANDER - Sausages - Fresh Mark, Inc.

ALTMAN - Food products - A.J. Altman Distributing Co.

ALTMP-EP - Lubricants - Unocal Corp.

ALTO - Apparel and accessories ☆ - Glamorise Foundations Inc.

ALTO - Brushes - Wright-Bernet

ALTO - Flatware - Wallace International Silversmiths, Inc.

ALTO - Glass–plate - Sasaki

ALTO - Hearing aids - Beltone Electronics Corp.

ALTO - Paints - Dozier & Gay Paint Co.

ALTO - Photographic equipment - Miles Inc.

ALTO - Toilets–porcelain - Mansfield Plumbing Products, Inc.

ALTO - Watchcases - Fada Industries Inc.

ALTO - Watches - QVC, Inc.

ALTO - Whey - Alto Dairy Cooperative

ALTO DEL CARMEN - Beverages–alcohol ☆ - Shaw-Ross International Importers

ALTO GRANDE - Coffee - Garrido Alto Grande Corp.

ALTO-MARKS - Rubber stamps - Kelly Morgan, Art Works

ALTO REY - Tortillas - Lookout Enterprises, Inc.

ALTOBELLA - Hair care products - Altobella Hair Products Inc.

ALTOBELLA MAXIMUM SHINE - Hair care products - Altobella Hair Products Inc.

ALTOCOF - Vitamins and nutritional supplements - Oxford Laboratories Inc.

ALTOIDS - Candy - Callard & Bowser USA Inc.

ALTON - Paper - Fay Paper Products Inc.

A ALTON HOUSE - Furniture - Alton Industries Inc.

ALTONE - Recording label - American Tape Corp.

ALTORAN - Apparel–women's - Non No International Corp.

ALTOS - Furniture ☆ - Lane Co. Inc.

ALTO'S - Tools - Alto's EZ/Mat Inc.

ALTRA - Computer software - Adaptec, Inc.

ALTRA - Vacuum cleaners and accessories - CFR Corp.

ALTRA FLUX - Medical apparatus - Althin Medical Inc.

ALTRA-FORM - Paper–thermoplastics coated - Unnatural Resources Inc.

ALTRA LINK - Computer software - Althin Medical Inc.

ALTRA SERIES - Printing presses - Accel Graphic Systems

ALTRACOLOR - Paints - Aftermarket Appearance Industries, Inc.

ALTRACRAFT - Doors–metal - Van Horn Home Improvements

ALTRASEAL - Sealing compounds - Maurer-Shumaker Inc.

ALTRESS - Golfing equipment - Triumph Golf Co.

ALTREX - Golfing equipment - Triumph Golf Co.

ALTRO CLASSIC 25 - Floor coverings - Altro Floors

ALTRO DESIGNER 25 - Floor coverings - Altro Floors

ALTRO GRIDLOK - Floor coverings ☆ - Altro Floors

ALTRO IMPRESSIONAL 20 + 25 - Floor coverings - Altro Floors

ALTRO MARINE 20 - Floor coverings - Altro Floors

ALTRO PRISMATIC 20 - Floor coverings - Altro Floors

ALTRO STRONGHOLD 35 - Floor coverings - Altro Floors

ALTRO WALKWAY 20 - Floor coverings - Altro Floors

ALTRON 7000 - Bicycles ☆ - Raleigh USA Bicycle Co.

ALTRUM - Detergents - Amsoil, Inc.

ALTSPOT - Lighting equipment - Altman Stage Lighting Co. Inc.

ALTSTAR - Lighting equipment - Altman Stage Lighting Co. Inc.

ALTSYS FONT-O-MATIC - Computer software - Altsys Corp.

ALTURA - Floor coverings–carpet and rugs - Milliken & Co. Inc.

ALTUS - Aircraft - General Atomics

ALTUS - Flutes ☆ - Jupiter Band Inst. Inc.

ALTUS - Hairpieces, hair-care product and services - International Hairgoods Inc.

ALTYMID - Machine parts - Greene, Tweed of Delaware, Inc.

ALU - Photographic equipment - ALU Systems Inc.

ALU-CAP - Antacids - Minnesota Mining & Manufacturing Co.

ALU-FLAKE - Paints - Glitterex Corp.

ALU-K-H - Pharmaceutical preparations ☆ - Mill-Mark Pharmaceuticals Inc.

ALU-LINE - Sporting goods - Freedom Golf Co.

ALU-MO-PASTE - Skin care products - Claflin Co.

ALU-SOL - Tools - Multicore Solders

ALU-TAB - Antacids - Minnesota Mining & Manufacturing Co.

ALUBLETS - Vitamins and nutritional supplements ☆ - Chase Laboratories Inc.

ALUCEN - Pharmaceutical preparations ☆ - Central Pharmaceutical Inc.

ALUCINE - Bedding–linen - Dan River Inc.

ALUCUT EP - Oils–lubricating - R.G. Shannon Co.

ALUDROX - Antacids - Wyeth-Ayerst Laboratories

ALUFLEX - Gaskets - Auburn Manufacturing Co.

ALUFOIL - Paper - Alufoil Products Co. Inc.

ALUFUSE - Adhesives and sealants - Kwik-Affix Products

ALUGEL - Pharmaceutical preparations - Ralph Winton Co. Inc.

ALUKON - Hardware - Aluplast Roll Shutter Systems Inc.

ALULUX - Shutters–metal - Galaxy Security Shutters Inc.

ALUM-A-BRACES - Hardware - Alum-A-Pole Corp.

ALUM-A-FOAM - Insulating materials ☆ - Deflecto Corp.

ALUM-A-JACK - Hardware - Alum-A-Pole Corp.

ALUM-A-JOINTS - Hardware - Alum-A-Pole Corp.

ALUM-A-KOTE - Paints - Columbia Paint Co.

ALUM A LUB - Housewares - Alum A Lub Lubricant Corp.

ALUM-A-POLES - Hardware - Alum-A-Pole Corp.

ALUM-A-SCAFFS - Hardware - Alum-A-Pole Corp.

ALUM-A-SLATE - Sporting goods ☆ - Penn's Woods Products Inc.

ALUM-A-WELD - Automotive parts and accessories ☆ - Fibre Glass-Evercoat Co. Inc.

ALUM C90 - Bicycles - Columbia Manufacturing Inc.

ALUM COATING - Hardware - Aluminum Coating Manufacturers Inc.

ALUM. COMP - Bicycles - Columbia Manufacturing Inc.

ALUM-EN-ESSENCE - Paints ☆ - Masury Paint Co.

ALUM-PLY II - Tools - Alumax Aluminum Corp.

ALUM ROCK - Cheese - Atlas Horn Food Service

ALUMA - Computers - Motionex, Inc.

ALUMA - Garden equipment - Rome Industries

ALUMA-CARE - Protectant for aluminum - Coricone Corp.

ALUMA-CORE - Hardware - Alumatic Corp. of America

ALUMA COUPE - Motor vehicles–automobiles - Hot Rods by Boyds

ALUMA CRAFT - Ornamental products–metal - Florida Rock Industries Inc.

ALUMA/GLASS - Automotive parts and accessories ☆ - Fibre Glass-Evercoat Co. Inc.

ALUMA GUARD - Boating equipment and accessories - Rupp Marine Inc.

ALUMA LAM - Ladders–metal ☆ - Howard Manufacturing Co.

ALUMA-LATTICE - Metals - Valley Aluminum Co.

ALUMA LITE - Hockey equipment - Christian Brothers, Inc.

ALUMA LITE - Motor vehicles - Holiday Rambler Corp.

ALUMA LOK - Hardware - Deco Products Co. (Fast-Lok Div.)

ALUMA-ROLL - Awnings ☆ - Nichols-Homeshield Inc.

ALUMA SEAL - Epoxy coatings ☆ - Steelcote Manufacturing Corp.

ALUMA-SLIDE - Door frames ☆ - Macklanburg-Duncan Co.

ALUMA SNACK'N - Garden equipment - Rome Industries

ALUMA-TILT - Sashes–window - Caldwell Manufacturing Co.

ALUMA TRI-DOG HOT HOT-DOG COOKER - Cooking equipment–household - Rome Industries

ALUMA-WOOD - Ladders–metal - Howard Manufacturing Co.

ALUMACAULK - Caulking compounds - Republic Powdered Metals, Inc.

ALUMACIDE - Adhesives and sealants ☆ - Pettit Paint Co. Inc.

ALUMACOAT - Adhesives and sealants - Pettit Paint Co. Inc.

ALUMACRAFT - Boats–motor - Alumacraft Boat Co.

ALUMADRINE - Pharmaceutical preparations - Fleming & Co.

ALUMAFLEX - Building materials - Republic Powdered Metals, Inc.

ALUMAGLAS - Glass–safety - Republic Powdered Metals, Inc.

ALUMAGLASS - Abrasive products - Conversion Technologies International, Inc.

ALUMAGUARD - Adhesives and sealants ☆ - Pettit Paint Co. Inc.

ALUMAHIST - Pharmaceutical preparations - C.S. Ruckstuhl Co. Inc.

ALUMALINE - Jewelry–costume - Nelson B. Boone Co., Inc.

ALUMALURE - Siding–metal - Aluminum Co. of America

ALUMANA - Office equipment - Katun Corp.

ALUMANATION - Adhesives and sealants - Republic Powdered Metals, Inc.

ALUMANATION 301 - Roofing materials–slate - Republic Powdered Metals, Inc.

ALUMAPAK - Boxes - Electronic Precepts of Florida, Inc.

ALUMAPOOL - Swimming pools - Cascade Pools

ALUMARAIL - Rails–aluminum - Anodizing, Inc.

ALUMARK - Hardware - Alumark Building Products

ALUMASAL - Pharmaceutical preparations ☆ - Columbia Drug Co. Inc.

ALUMASCAPE - Motor vehicles–motor homes - Monaco Coach Corp.

ALUMASOL - Roof coatings - Universal Protective Coatings

ALUMASPRAY - Paints - Kop-Coat, Inc.

ALUMASTAR - Trailers–horse - Merhow Industries

ALUMASTEP - Ladders–metal - Material Control Inc.

ALUMASTIC - Epoxy - Sigma Coatings USA BV.

ALUMAT - Housewares - Reliance Plastic & Chemical Corp.

ALUMATIC - Hardware - Alumatic Corp. of America
ALUMATONE - See **CRES-LITE**
ALUMAX - Hardware - Alumax Aluminum Corp.
ALUMAX - Nozzles - Spraying Systems Co.
ALUMAX/SAILOR - Doors–metal ✩ - Phillips Products
ALUMDAMP - Waterproofing compounds - The White Co.
ALUME DUST - Paints - OEM Paints, Inc.
ALUMESTATE - Hardware - Aluminum Hardgoods Inc.
ALUMET - Aluminum products - Alumet Building Products, Inc.
ALUMEX - Adhesives and sealants ✩ - Sperry Owens Inc.
ALUMI-DOOR - Doors–garage - Stevens-Thuet Co.
ALUMI GLO - Cleaning preparations ✩ - Servaas Laboratories Inc.
ALUMI-LINER - Sealing compounds - W.W. Henry Co.
ALUMI-LITE - Machine parts - Alinabal, Inc.
ALUMI-LITE - Skylights - Bristolite Skylights
ALUMI-NON - Paints - Rust-Oleum Corp.
ALUMI-ROOF - Paints - Sheffield Bronze Paint Corp.
ALUMI-SHIELD - Fabricated metal products ✩ - Pabco Metals Corp.
ALUMI-SODER - Solder - L.B. Allen Co. Inc.
ALUMI-SPAN - Piers and accessories - Alumi-Span Inc.
ALUMICLAD - Paints - Strathmore Products, Inc.
ALUMID - Pharmaceutical preparations ✩ - Vangard Labs Inc.
ALUMIDOCK - Docks - Metallic Ladder Manufacturing Corp.
ALUMIDOCK - Piers, ramps, floats, etc. - Alumidock
ALUMIFY - Aluminum products - Conklin Co., Inc.
ALUMIGRIP - Adhesives and sealants - Grow Group, Inc.
ALUMIHAB - Pharmaceutical preparations ✩ - JMI-Canton Pharmaceuticals
ALUMILADDER - Ladders–metal - Werner Co.
ALUMILITE - Handlebars–motorcycle - Answer Products Inc.
ALUMILITES - Lighting equipment - Hobby Hill Inc.
ALUMIN-NU - Cleaning preparations - Alumin-Nu Corp.
ALUMIN-NU X-521 - Cleaning preparations - Alumin-Nu Corp.
ALUMIN-X - Furniture–metal - Specialized Banking Furniture International Inc.
ALUMINA - Bicycles - Huffy Corp.
ALUMINATION - Blinds–venetian ✩ - Hunter Douglas, Inc.
ALUMINATOR - Motorcycle parts and accessories - Harley-Davidson, Inc.
ALUMINATOR - Sporting goods - Brimms Inc.
ALUMINEX - Pharmaceutical preparations - Michael C. Slade
ALUMINITE - Clipboards - Metalite Corp.
ALUMINOSTOMY - Pharmaceutical preparations ✩ - Richards Pharmaceutical Co.
ALUMINUM BRAID - Adhesives and sealants - Gemini Braids, Inc.
ALUMINUM CARBON AC - Sporting goods - Easton Aluminum Inc.
ALUMINUM JELLY - Cleaning preparations–household - Loctite Corp.
ALUMINUM, STAINLESS STEEL & Z-LOK JACKETING - Fabricated metal products - Pabco Metals Corp.
ALUMIPREP - Cleaning preparations - Parker & Amchem
ALUMIRAMP - Health care products - Alumiramp Inc.
ALUMITECH - Boats - Alumitech Inc.
ALUMITHANE - Paints - Gray Seal Paint Manufacturing Co. Inc.
ALUMITITE - Aluminum-roof coating - Coopers Creek Chemical Corp.
ALUMNI - Fabrics - Dan River Inc.
ALUMNI - Floor coverings–carpet and rugs - Specialty Carpets
ALUMNI - Frames–eyeglass - U.S. Optical Frame Co.
ALUMNI - Office supplies - Atico International Inc.
ALUMOGRIT - Trimmings–metal - Wooster Products Inc.
ALUMSOL - Automotive parts and accessories ✩ - Richland Manufacturing Co.
ALUNDUM - Abrasive products - Norton Co.
ALUPENT - Pharmaceutical preparations - Boehringer Ingelheim Pharmaceuticals Inc.
ALUPRIN - Pharmaceutical preparations ✩ - Lemmon Co.
ALURA - Boats–motor - Luhrs Co.
ALURA - Cording - Novelty Cord and Tassel Co. Inc.
A'LURA - Shampoos ✩ - Head Shampoo, Inc.
ALURA SUEDE - Wallpaper - Carlton-Metro Wallcoverings
ALURATE - Pharmaceutical preparations - Roche Laboratories
A'LURE - Apparel and accessories ✩ - Warnaco Inc.
ALUSASH - Finishing agents - Sterling-Clark-Lurton Corp.
ALVA - Hair care products - Tu-K Industries Inc.
ALVA - Recording label - Golden Boy Records
ALVA-BLU-LINE - Paper - Alvin and Co. Inc.
ALVA-LINE - Vellum - Alvin and Co. Inc.
ALVA-QUAT - Hair care products - Tu-K Industries Inc.
ALVA-SAK - Luggage - Alvin and Co. Inc.
ALVA-TRAN - Pharmaceutical preparations - Alva-Amco Pharmacal Co.
ALVA-TRANQUIL - Pharmaceutical preparations - Alva-Amco Pharmacal Co.

ALVA-TRANQUIL-SPAN - Pharmaceutical preparations - Alva-Amco Pharmacal Co.
ALVAC - Vaccines - Virogenetics Corp.
ALVACAST - Museum reproductions - Alva Museum Replicas Inc.
ALVAFLEX - Office supplies - Alvin and Co. Inc.
ALVANIA - Lubricating oils - Shell Oil Co.
ALVAR SPAR - Varnishes ✩ - Pettit Paint Co. Inc.
ALVARADO - Apparel and accessories - Neutral, Inc.
ALVARADO - Floor coverings - Azrock Commercial Flooring
ALVAREZ - Musical instruments - St. Louis Music Supply Co.
ALVAS - Recording label - Jazz Composer's Orchestra Association Inc.
ALVAS - Sporting goods - Victoria's Dance-Theatrical Supply
ALVASTONE - Casting compounds - Alva Museum Replicas Inc.
ALVEMA - Health care products ✩ - Invacare Corp.
ALVERA - Skin care products - Texas Best Unlimited, LP
ALVIN - Giftware ✩ - Alvin Co.
ALVIN - Office supplies - Alvin and Co. Inc.
ALVIN AARDVARK - Toys–stuffed ✩ - Kenner Products
ALVIN BULK-PAK - Drafting supplies - Alvin and Co. Inc.
ALVIN CLIPP II - Printers–computer - Alvin and Co. Inc.
ALVIN G. & CO. - Games - Alvin G. & Co.
ALVIN VSPM SERIES - Scales–industrial - Alvin and Co. Inc.
ALVINITE - Office supplies - Alvin and Co. Inc.
ALVINO - Pizzas–frozen - Little Lady Foods Inc.
ALVISE - Wallpaper ✩ - Wallquest, Inc.
ALVITA - Teas ✩ - Alvita Products Co.
ALVORADA - Recording label ✩ - Penco Industries Inc.
ALVUNA - Apparel–men's - Alps Sportswear Manufacturing Co.
ALWAYS - Beverages–carbonated - Coca-Cola Co.
ALWAYS - Colognes - Renee Distributors
ALWAYS - Frames–picture - Terragrafics Inc.
ALWAYS - Health care products - Procter & Gamble Co.
ALWAYS - Rings–jewelry - Artcarved Inc.
ALWAYS A PERFECT MARK - Ribbons–inked - Uneq, Inc.
ALWAYS ABLOOM - Housewares - Wal-Mart Stores Inc.
ALWAYS ACTIVE - Skin care products - Tennis Elbow Corp.
ALWAYS ALLDAYS - Underwear and nightwear - The Procter & Gamble Co.
ALWAYS & FOREVER - Jewelry–precious - Wal-Mart Stores Inc.
ALWAYS BE GUARANTEE - Apparel–children's - Liberty Childrenswear Co., LLC
ALWAYS CALENDAR - Calendars - Slencil Co.
ALWAYS CLEAN - All purpose cleaners - Associated Wholesale Grocers, Inc.
ALWAYS CLEAR - Optical goods - National Vision Associates, Ltd.
ALWAYS COOL NO MATTER HOW HOT IT GETS! - Books–comic - Modern Thought Combine
ALWAYS CURVES - Health care products - Procter & Gamble Co.
ALWAYS FRESH - Food products ✩ - Shurfine International, Inc.
ALWAYS FRIENDS - Stationery - Troll Associates, Inc.
ALWAYS GOOD - Food products - Associated Wholesale Grocers, Inc.
ALWAYS GOOD - Food products ✩ - Pillsbury Co.
ALWAYS HOME - Tea - United Service Organizations, Inc.
ALWAYS MAGIC - Cosmetics - LM Cosmetics Inc.
ALWAYS NATURAL - Apparel and accessories ✩ - Playtex Apparel, Inc.
ALWAYS ON MY MIND - Greeting cards - American Greetings Corp.
ALWAYS OPEN - Food products - Always Open, Inc.
ALWAYS PLUS - Health care products - Procter & Gamble Co.
ALWAYS QUALITY ALWAYS FUN - Apparel–children's - Mcdonald's Corp.
ALWAYS QUICKWRAPS - Health care products - Procter & Gamble Co.
ALWAYS SAVE - Food products - Associated Wholesale Grocers, Inc.
ALWAYS SHARP - Tools - General Housewares Corp.
ALWAYS SISTERS - Toys - Tonka Corp.
ALWAYS SLENDER - Health care products - Procter & Gamble Co.
ALWAYS SMOOTH - Skin care products - Avon Products, Inc.
ALWAYS SOFT - Toilet tissue - Cascades Industries, Inc.
ALWAYS TENDER - Pork - Hormel Foods Corp.
ALWAYS TWENTY-ONE - Apparel and accessories - Strouse, Adler Co.
ALWAY$ VALUE - Lenses–optical - National Vision Associates, Ltd.
ALWAYS WITH CHANNELS - Sanitary napkins - Procter & Gamble Co.
ALWAYS YOUNG - Floor coverings–carpet and rugs - Lees Carpets
ALWAYS...IN ALL WAYS - Pet products - Eagle Products, Inc.
ALWAYSWIN - Recording label - Dr. Gallatin Presents
ALWELD - Boats - Alweld Commercial Boats, Inc.
ALWINE - Bricks - Glen-Gery Corp.
ALWYN NO SEE UM - Insecticides - Alwyn Co., Inc.
ALX - Jewelry - Alexandra Designs, Inc.
ALX - Photographic chemicals - Ulano Corp.

ALY - Motor vehicles - Skyline Corp.

ALYCE - Blouses–women's - Jonathan Logan Inc.

ALYCE - Frames–eyeglass - U.S. Optical Frame Co.

ALYCE DESIGNS - Wedding gowns - Alyce Designs

ALYDAR - Whirlpools - Lasco Products Group

ALYO CHILDREN'S DANCE THEATRE - Apparel–children's - Alyo Children's Dance Theater

ALYSSA ASHLEY - Cosmetics - Houbigant, Inc.

ALYSSA CARR - Apparel–women's - Alyssa Carr Inc.

ALYSSA MILANO - Watches - Chatom Collection

ALZAK - Aluminum products - Aluminum Co. of America

ALZEES - Shoes - A & F Shoes

ALZENE - Pharmaceutical preparations - Baker Norton Pharmaceuticals, Inc.

ALZET - Medical apparatus - Alza Corp.

ALZIP - Sheet metal products - Aluminum Co. of America

AM - Bakery machines - A.M. Manufacturing Co., Inc.

AM - Food products ☆ - Plumrose Inc.

AM - Furnaces–electric - Ajax Magnethermic Corp.

A.M. - Giftware - A.M. Designs

AM - Miniature airplanes - AeroMini Inc.

A.M. - Yogurt - Natural Nectar Corp.

AM-A-FLAGE - Camouflage netting - Amacker International Inc.

AM AGRA - Agricultural products - Am Agra Inc.

AM AMAZING MEDIA - Computer software - Amazing Media, Inc.

AM & E - Golfing equipment - Arizona Manufacturing & Embroidery Inc.

AM COLLECTION - Clothing - Apparel Industries, Inc.

A.M. COMPLETE - Beverages - Colombo Inc. (Frozen Desserts Div.)

AM-CUT - Tools - Vermont American Corp.

AM-DONE - Bags - Pro Hygiene

AM-E-POX - Enamels - Ellis Paint Co.

AM FAB - Furniture - AM Fab Inc.

AM-FLEX - Machine parts - Appleton Mills

AM-FM - Apparel and accessories - Rays Apparel, Inc.

AM/FM - Computer software ☆ - Donovan Data Systems, Inc.

AM GUARD - Pet products - Seachem Laboratories

. AM I NORMAL NOW? - Video production - Realtree Outdoor Products, Inc.

AM-LON - Hosiery - Goldstone Hosiery Co.

AM-MAC - Kitchen appliances - Am-Mac Inc.

AM MAG - Archery equipment ☆ - High Country American

AM PLUS PM - Sunblocks - Stephen Marcus Inc.

AM PM - Apparel–women's - Celeste Turner, Inc.

A.M.-P.M. - Health care products - Brite Years Vitamins

AM PM - Snack foods - Atlantic Richfield Co.

AM/PM - Vitamins and nutritional supplements - Schiff Products, Inc.

AM PM BBQRIB - Sandwiches–prepackaged - Atlantic Richfield Co.

AM:PM CORPORATE SAFE - Computer software - Tangram Enterprise Solutions, Inc.

AM-RAY - Cleaning supplies ☆ - American Textile Products Co.

AM-SASH - Sashes–window - American Home Improvement

AM SPORTS - Apparel–men's - A.M. Player, Inc.

AM-STRENGTH - Heat-strengthened glass - American Tempering Inc. (Laminating Div.)

AM TECH - Veterinary preparations - Amtech Group, Inc.

AM-TEMP - Tempered glass - American Tempering Inc. (Laminating Div.)

AM ZZIPPER - Apparel and accessories - Zzip Designs

AM5X86 - Semiconductors ☆ - Advanced Micro Devices, Inc.

AM75 - Heart monitors - ADH Health Products

AM486 - Computer peripherals ☆ - Advanced Micro Devices, Inc.

AMA - Educational books - American Management Association

AMACLATE - Vitamins and nutritional supplements - Liferich Limited Co.

AMACO - Artists' materials - American Art Clay Co. Inc.

AMACOM - Publisher's imprints - Amacom

AMACOR - Windows–storm ☆ - Norandex, Inc.

AMADA - Musical instruments - Geneva International Corp.

AMADAS - Farm machinery - Amadas Industries, Inc.

AMADEO - Recording label - Apon Record Co., Inc.

AMADEUS - Bedding–linen - Artworks, Inc.

AMADEUS - Harmonicas - Hohner Inc.

AMADEUS - Recording label - Michele Audio Corp.

AMADEUS - Watches - Seville Watch Corp.

AMADILLO - Leather goods - Casecraft Inc.

AMADO - Tableware–china ☆ - Villeroy and Boch Tableware Ltd.

AMADO - Wines - Renwood Winery, Inc.

AMADOR - Floor coverings ☆ - Tarkett, Inc.

AMADOR FOOTHILL WINERY - Wines - Amador Foothill Winery

AMADOR WINERY - Wines - Amador Foothill Winery

AMAGER - Glassware–household ☆ - Svend Jensen of Denmark Inc.

AMAHUG - Pillows - Loovitz, Inc.

AMAIZE - Cleaning preparations - Amaize Corp.

AMAIZE-ING - Corn chips - Sumptious Selection

AMAIZING TASTE - Tortillas - Gates Enterprises Inc.

AMAIZO - Baking product - American Maize-Products Co.

AMAIZO - Starch–edible - American Maize Technology, Inc.

AMAK - Motor vehicle parts and accessories - Amak Brake Corp.

AMAKUCHI MUGI - Miso - American Miso Co.

AMALACT - Animal feed supplements ☆ - Central Soya Co. Inc.

AMALEE ITALY - Belts - La Ceeho International

AMALFI - Dishes–china - Pasmantier Co. Inc.

AMALFI - Floor coverings–tile ☆ - Monarch Tile Inc.

AMALFI - Giftware ☆ - WMF/USA

AMALFI - Medical apparatus - OTC Professional Appliances

AMALFI - Shoes - Marx & Newman Co. Inc.

AMALFI - Toys - Peg Perego USA Inc.

AMALFI COLLECTION - Furniture ☆ - Evenflo Juvenile Furniture Co.

AMALGAM - Seafood products–fresh or frozen ☆ - Gourmet Club Corp.

AMALGAM 624 - Plant growth regulators - Hydrogrowth Technology, Inc.

AMALGAMATED - Apparel and accessories - Graj & Gustavsen

AMALIE - Oils–lubricating - Witco Corp.

AMALIENBURG - Tableware–china ☆ - Villeroy and Boch Tableware Ltd.

AMALITSA - Perfumes - Coty Inc.

AMANA - Housewares - Amana Refrigeration Inc.

AMANA TOOL - Machine parts - Amana Tool Corp.

AMANDA - Bedding–linen - Dan River Inc.

AMANDA - Candy bars ☆ - Brocks Candy Co.

AMANDA - Dolls - Russ Berrie and Co., Inc.

AMANDA - Dolls ☆ - Effanbee Doll Corp.

AMANDA - Footwear - D. Myers and Sons Inc.

AMANDA - Glassware–household - Anchor Hocking Glass, Inc.

AMANDA - Tableware–china ☆ - Lenox, Inc.

AMANDA AND JEREMY - Toys–stuffed - Dakin Inc.

AMANDA FIELDING - Handbags - J.C. Penney Co., Inc.

AMANDA GRAY - Apparel–women's - Bay Crest Industries

AMANDA HILLS - Water–bottled or canned - Amanda Hills Distribution, Inc.

AMANDA KAYE - Shoes - Steve Slaughter

AMANDA STAR - Dolls - Fred Meyer, Inc.

AMANDA WENTWORTH - Perfumes ☆ - Treasure Masters

AMANDA WEST - Apparel–athletic - Montgomery Ward & Co. Inc.

AMANDA'S - Dolls - Ponce's Creations

AMANDA'S GARDEN - Bedding–linen - Dan River Inc.

AMANECER - Cosmetics - Darling Corp.

AMANO - Footwear–women's - Cels Enterprises Inc.

AMANO - Shoes - Robert L. Goldman

AMANO CINCINNATI - Computer software - Amano Cincinnati Inc.

AMANTE - Wines - Bardenheier Wine Cellars

AMANTEX - Pharmaceutical preparations - Verex Laboratories, Inc.

AMANTI - Greeting cards - Joche Davila Studio

AMAPOLA - Flour–blended - Conagra, Inc.

AMAPOLA - Tableware–china - Villeroy and Boch Tableware Ltd.

AMAR - Floor coverings–carpet and rugs ☆ - Trans-Ocean Import Co. Inc.

AMAR BLENDS - Tobacco–chewing or smoking - Amar Blends Co.

AMARA - Perfumes - Jonathan International, Inc.

AMARA-TEX - Wallpaper - Walls Alive

AMARAD - Floor coverings–carpet and rugs ☆ - Eurotex Inc.

AMARANT - Awnings - Dills-Challstrom Inc.

AMARANTH - Breads - Health Valley Food

AMARANTH MINUTE MEAL - Food products - Health Valley Food

AMARELLE - Upholstery leather - American Leather Manufacturing Co.

AMARETTA - Fabrics - Charter Fabrics Inc.

AMARETTE - Floor coverings–carpet and rugs ☆ - Eurotex Inc.

AMARETTI - Cookies - Ferrara Food Co., Inc.

AMARETTI - Seasonings ☆ - Andre Prost Inc.

AMARETTO - Bidets - Kohler Co.

AMARETTO CORSO - Beverages–alcohol - Consolidated Distilled Products Inc.

AMARETTO CREME DI AMORE - Beverages–alcohol - Barton Inc.

AMARETTO DA VINCI - Cordials - Laird and Co.

AMARETTO DE SABROSO - Beverages–alcohol - Barton Brands, Ltd.

AMARETTO DE SABROSO - Liqueurs - Canandaigua Wine Co. Inc.

AMARETTO DELL'ORSO - Liquors - Disusa Imports Co.

AMARETTO DI AMORE - Beverages–alcohol - Barton Inc.

AMARETTO DI AMORE - Liqueurs - Canandaigua Wine Co. Inc.

AMARETTO DI PADRINO - Cordials - Sazerac Co. Inc.

☆ = Now out of production

AMARETTO DI SARONNO - Beverages–alcohol - Paddington Corp.
AMARETTO DI SARONNO - Ice cream - Haagen-Dazs Co. Inc.
AMARETTO DI TORINO - Liquors - House of Seagram
AMARETTO E'DOLCE - Liquors - White Rock Distilleries Inc.
AMARETTO ESSENCE - Coffee ☆ - Boyd Coffee Co.
AMARETTO NIGHTS - Teas–herbal ☆ - Celestial Seasonings, Inc.
AMARETTO ORCHARDS - Nuts–salted, roasted, cooked, or canned - Cal-Fruit (Frozen Foods Div.)
AMARETTO PECANS - Food products - Mrs. Powell's Gourmet Pecans
AMARIL D - Pharmaceutical preparations ☆ - Vortech Pharmaceuticals
AMARIL D SPANTAB - Pharmaceutical preparations ☆ - Vortech Pharmaceuticals
AMARILIS - Bathroom faucets - American Standard Inc.
AMARILLO - Trailers–travel ☆ - Marathon Homes Corp.
AMARILLO DILLAS - Apparel and accessories - Texas Professional Baseball, Inc.
AMARILLO LONGFELLOW - Cigars - Gesty Trading & Manufacturing Corp.
AMARMICH'S - Jewelry - Ramodi's
AMARNICK - Water–mineral - Erba Food Products Inc.
AMARO - Wood products ☆ - Decorative Woods
AMART - Artists' materials - Ampad Corp.
AMARTJIA - Cosmetics - Xerion Import Export, Inc.
AMATE - Flowers, plants, and seeds - Oglesby Plants International, Inc.
AMATEUR CUP, THE - Athletic associations - Amateur Cup, Inc.
AMATEX - Floor-finish applicator - American Textile Products Co.
AMATI - Saxophones - Ideal Musical Merchandise Co.
AMATO - Apparel and accessories - Decorp Inc.
AMATO - Apparel and accessories ☆ - Kellwood Co.
AMATROL - Pharmaceutical preparations ☆ - Vortech Pharmaceuticals
AMAX - Radio communications equipment - Electronic Industries Association
AMAZA - Housewares ☆ - Amaza Laboratories Inc.
AMAZAKE - Food products - Grainaissance
AMAZAKE - Pies–frozen - Creative Kitchens
AMAZALL - Housewares ☆ - Amaza Laboratories Inc.
AMAZASHAPE - Apparel–women's - Sally Hampton
AMAZE - Fertilizers - International AG Labs, Inc.
AMAZE - Hair care products - Ellen Voss
AMAZE - Herbicides - Green Light Co.
AMAZE-A GLAZE - Hobby kits ☆ - DecoArt, Inc.
AMAZE-N-TOW - Transportation vehicles and equipment - Angie G. Walker
AMAZEMENT - Publisher's imprints - Creative Publications Inc.
AMAZEN KITTY MAZE - Pet products - R.A.F. Trading Inc.
AMAZIN' - Sauces - Montego Foods, Inc.
AMAZIN' FRUIT - Candy - Hershey Chocolate USA
AMAZIN RAISIN BELLS - Candy ☆ - R.M. Palmer Co.
AMAZING - Video production - Motivational Media
AMAZING ACROCATS, THE - Publisher's imprints - Tigerboy Entertainment
AMAZING ALPHABET - Calendars - Richard Charles Wixo
AMAZING ANIMALS - Computer software ☆ - Broderbund Software, Inc.
AMAZING ANIMATION - Computer software - Claris Corp.
AMAZING ARTICHOKE - Vitamins and nutritional supplements ☆ - Natural Balance, Inc.
AMAZING BAKES - Tortillas ☆ - Barbara's Bakery, Inc.
AMAZING BEAD MACHINE - Toys - Natural Science Industries, Ltd.
AMAZING BODY - Museums - Foundation for the Museum of Medical Science
AMAZING BRA, THE - Brassieres (Bras) - NCC Industries, Inc.
AMAZING COACHELLA - Fruits and vegetables - Peter Rabbit Farms, Inc.
AMAZING COLORACERS - Toys - Rapid Mounting and Finishing Co.
AMAZING ELECTRONICS STORE AES - Forms–preprinted - Sales Creators, Inc.
AMAZING ELECTRONICS STORE AES - Paper - Sales Creators, Inc.
AMAZING ENGINE - Games - Tsr, Inc.
AMAZING GLAZE - Popcorn ☆ - E.A. Sween Co.
AMAZING GLOVE - Popcorn ☆ - E.A. Sween Co.
AMAZING GOOP - Adhesives and sealants - Eclectic Products Inc.
AMAZING GOOP, THE - Adhesives and sealants - Eclectic Products Inc.
AMAZING GRACE - Apparel–women's - Noah Enterprises, Ltd.
AMAZING GRACE - Calendars - Mach 1, Inc.
AMAZING GRACE - Dolls - Fagan International
AMAZING GRACE - Recording label - Fred Rice Productions
AMAZING GRAINS - Skin care products - Elizabeth Van Buren Aromatherapy
AMAZING I-LINER - Cosmetics - Revlon Consumer Products Corp.
AMAZING IMAGINATION MACHINE - Playground equipment - Custom Swings of Texas, Inc.
AMAZING KONG, THE - Pet products - Kong Co.
AMAZING LASTING - Cosmetics - Revlon Consumer Products Corp.

AMAZING MAGNETS - Magnets - Norstar Enterprises
AMAZING NUMBER LAND GAME - Games - Rapid Mounting and Finishing Co.
AMAZING PANORAMIC PHOTOS - Photofinishing laboratories - Advanced Innovations, Inc.
AMAZING PICTURES - Computer hardware and software - Colorvision International, Inc.
AMAZING PLANT FOOD! - Fertilizers - Alljack & Co.
AMAZING SCIENCE FICTION & HORROR TRIVIA GAME, THE - Games - Dann Russkett Games, Inc.
AMAZING SKY BOOK, THE - Calendars - Skyshapers, Inc.
AMAZING SPIDER-MAN IN THE SKYSCRAPER CAPER - Learning aids ☆ - Texas Instruments Inc.
AMAZING THERMO-PADS - Heating pads–electric - Dr. B's Natural Products, Inc.
AMAZING UNIVERSE - Computer software - Hopkins Technology LLC
AMAZING WHITE - Cosmetics - Amwhite Labs, Inc.
AMAZING WRITING MACHINE - Computer software - Broderbund Software, Inc.
AMAZINGLY DELICIOUS - Pastries ☆ - Wonderslim
AMAZINGLY SWIM DIAPER, THE - Bathing suits - Gulbenkian Swim Inc.
AMAZ'N BLAZ'N - Video games - Honeyword Foundation, Inc.
AMAZON - Beverages–carbonated - Laurel Hill, Inc.
AMAZON - Bicycles - Ross Bicycles USA, Ltd.
AMAZON - Bicycles ☆ - Huffy Corp.
AMAZON - Computer software - Advanced Computer Communications
AMAZON - Computer software - Trillium Research Inc.
AMAZON - Computer software ☆ - Access Software Inc.
AMAZON - Flowers, plants, and seeds - Jacklin Seed
AMAZON - Thread - Threads USA Div.
AMAZON ACIDIFIER - Pet products - Aquatronics-Filtronics
AMAZON ADVENTURE - Bath salts - Jason Natural Products, Inc.
AMAZON ANNIE - Games - Universal Manufacturing Co., Inc.
AMAZON BASIN BROWNIE - Cookies ☆ - Michael D's Cookies
AMAZON BUFFER - Pet products - Aquatronics-Filtronics
AMAZON EXTRACT - Aquatic pharmacuetical preparations - Aquarium Pharmaceuticals, Inc.
AMAZON GUARDIANS OF EDEN - Computer software ☆ - Access Software Inc.
AMAZON MIST - Beverages - Laurel Hill, Inc.
AMAZON QUEEN - Coffee - De Choix Specialty Foods Co.
AMAZON RECORDS - Record stores - Ah Entertainment, Inc.
AMAZON RIVER PEAT PELLETS - Pet products - Aquatronics-Filtronics
AMAZON TRAIL - Computer software - Softkey International Inc.
AMAZON TREASURE - Health care products ☆ - Futurity Products
AMAZON VINEYARD - Wines - Ahlgren Vineyard
AMAZONA - Tableware–china - Villeroy and Boch Tableware Ltd.
AMAZONAS - Footwear - Sonic Shoe Corp.
AMAZONAS - Photographic equipment ☆ - H.P. Marketing Corp.
AMAZONAS - Seafood products–fresh or frozen - J.F. Clarke Corp.
AMAZONIA SORBEIJA - Fruit pops–frozen - Howler Products, Inc.
AMAZONS - Games - Kadon Enterprises Inc.
AMB - Jewelry - Ambel Diamond Importers
AMBAR - Barbituates ☆ - A.H. Robins Co. Inc.
AMBAR - Chemicals - AMBAR Inc.
AMBAR - Containers–plastic - Amko Plastics Inc.
AMBASSADOR - Apparel and accessories - Manhattan International
AMBASSADOR - Audio equipment - Sanyo Fisher (USA) Corp.
AMBASSADOR - Bathroom accessories - Associated Marketing Concepts
AMBASSADOR - Batteries - Douglas Battery Manufacturing Co.
AMBASSADOR - Bicycles - Ross Bicycles USA, Ltd.
AMBASSADOR - Boats–motor ☆ - Checkmate Boats Inc.
AMBASSADOR - Boats–motor ☆ - Regal Marine Industries Inc.
AMBASSADOR - Boats–pontoons ☆ - Boatel Marine, Inc.
AMBASSADOR - Curtain rods - Newell Window Furnishing Co.
AMBASSADOR - Desk sets - Stanton's Quills
AMBASSADOR - Dishes–china ☆ - Pickard Inc.
AMBASSADOR - Fabrics–tapestry ☆ - Coloroll Inc.
AMBASSADOR - Flags - Annin and Co.
AMBASSADOR - Floor coverings–carpet and rugs - Coronet Carpets Inc.
AMBASSADOR - Floor coverings–carpet and rugs - Providence Rug Co.
AMBASSADOR - Floor coverings–carpet and rugs ☆ - Porter Carpet Mills Inc.
AMBASSADOR - Floor coverings–carpet and rugs ☆ - Royalweve Carpet Mills
AMBASSADOR - Furniture ☆ - Lane Co. Inc.
AMBASSADOR - Furniture ☆ - Mersman Furniture Co.
AMBASSADOR - Glassware–household - Federal Glass

☆ = Now out of production

AMBASSADOR - Glassware–household - Lenox, Inc.

AMBASSADOR - Gloves - George Glove Co. Inc.

AMBASSADOR - Golf clubs, carts - Austad Co.

AMBASSADOR - Greeting cards - Ambassador Cards

AMBASSADOR - Hardware - Ambassador Industries

AMBASSADOR - Hoses - Goodyear Tire & Rubber Co.

AMBASSADOR - Infant product - Tailored Baby Inc.

AMBASSADOR - Lighting fixtures - Edison Price Lighting

AMBASSADOR - Lockers–metal - American Locker Security Systems

AMBASSADOR - Luggage - United States Luggage Corp.

AMBASSADOR - Motor vehicles ☆ - DaimlerChrysler

AMBASSADOR - Motor vehicles–motor homes - Thor Tech, Inc.

AMBASSADOR - Motor vehicles–motor homes ☆ - Honey Recreational Vehicles Inc.

AMBASSADOR - Office furniture–metal ☆ - Joyce International Inc.

AMBASSADOR - Pens - Accutec Inc.

AMBASSADOR - Pens - Union Pen Co.

AMBASSADOR - Projection screens - Draper Shade and Screen Co. Inc.

AMBASSADOR - Projectors–photographic - Buhl Industries, Inc.

AMBASSADOR - Recording label - Ambassador Recording Corp.

AMBASSADOR - Salad dressings–bottled - Food Specialties Inc.

AMBASSADOR - Shoes - Interco Inc.

AMBASSADOR - Slippers - L.B. Evans' Son Co.

AMBASSADOR - Stepladders - W.W. Babcock Co. Inc.

AMBASSADOR - Thread - Needlecraft Industries

AMBASSADOR - Tobacco–chewing or smoking - Amar Blends Co.

AMBASSADOR - Trailers–travel - Airstream Inc.

AMBASSADOR - Trailers–travel - Royals International

AMBASSADOR - Upholstery leather - American Leather Manufacturing Co.

AMBASSADOR - Vacuum cleaners and accessories - Hako Minuteman Inc.

AMBASSADOR - Watches - Accusplit Inc.

AMBASSADOR - Wheels ☆ - Faultless Caster Co.

AMBASSADOR - Wood products - Mission Industries Inc.

AMBASSADOR - Wood products - States Industries Inc.

AMBASSADOR 100 - Cigarettes - Philip Morris Companies Inc.

AMBASSADOR III - Wallpaper ☆ - Marburg Wallcoverings Inc.

AMBASSADOR JR. - Vacuum cleaners and accessories - Hako Minuteman Inc.

AMBASSADOR OF LIFE - Video production - Deano's, Inc.

AMBASSADOR SHAKE - Shingles–asphalt or tar - Celotex Corp.

AMBASSADOR SOFTWARE - Compact discs–prerecorded - Peter Pan Industries

AMBASSADOR STRIPE - Floor coverings–carpet and rugs - Roxbury Carpet Co.

AMBASSADOR SUITE 18 - Floor coverings–carpet and rugs - Eagle Carpets Inc.

AMBASSADOR, THE - Projectors–photographic - Buhl Industries, Inc.

AMBASSADOR, THE - Hotel-motel franchise - Radisson Hotels International Inc.

AMBASSADOR'S GALLERY - Blinds–vertical ☆ - Ambassador Industries

AMBATRAK - Blinds–vertical ☆ - Ambassador Industries

AMBE - Computer hardware - Digital Voice Systems, Inc.

AMBE+ - Computer software - Digital Voice Systems, Inc.

AMBENYL - Pharmaceutical preparations - Forest Pharmaceuticals Inc.

AMBENYL - Pharmaceutical preparations ☆ - Marion Merrell Dow

AMBENYL-D - Pharmaceutical preparations - Marion Merrell Dow

AMBER - Computer peripheral equipment - Oxford Molecular Group

AMBER - Dolls - Justin Products, Inc.

AMBER - Hams - Smithfield Ham Products Co. Inc.

AMBER - Knives–hunting - Queen Cutlery Co.

AMBER - Skin care products - Amber Products Co.

AMBER - Tobacco–chewing or smoking - Amar Blends Co.

AMBER - Tools - Fuller Tool Co. Inc.

AMBER - Wigs - Jean Paree Weegs Inc.

AMBER BAY - Bathing suits ☆ - Beach Patrol, Inc.

AMBER CREST - Fruits and vegetables - Sun World International

AMBER CUISINE - Cooking equipment–household ☆ - Anchor Hocking Glass, Inc.

AMBER DAWN - Hair care products - Redmond Products, Inc.

AMBER FLASH - Flowers, plants, and seeds - J. Benjamin Williams

AMBER FONG - Brushes–paint - Wooster Brush Co.

AMBER GLO - Brushes–paint - Wooster Brush Co.

AMBER-GLO - Candles ☆ - Eastern Seaboard Products Inc.

AMBER JEWEL - Trees - Brandt's Fruit Trees, Inc.

AMBER LAMB - Educational materials - Pensacola Christian College, Inc.

AMBER OIL - Cosmetics ☆ - Divina Products Co.

AMBER OIL - Skin care products - Waverly Beauty Products

AMBER OWL! - Beverages–malt - 2426 Dunstan, L.C.

AMBER PUP - Toys–stuffed - Russ Berrie and Co., Inc.

AMBER ROAD, THE - Jewelry - Irene Patkowski

AMBER ROSE - Rings–jewelry - Artcarved Inc.

AMBER SCIENCE INC. - Measuring instruments - Amber Science Inc.

AMBER SPLASH - Lipsticks ☆ - Honey & Spice Toiletries

AMBER STIK - Tongue depressors - Precision Dynamics Corp.

AMBER STONE - Apparel–women's - Federated Department Stores, Inc.

AMBER STREET INN - Wallcovering - Gencorp Inc.

AMBER WAVES - Floor coverings–tile - Interface, Inc.

AMBERCRAFT - Jewelry - Maria Larimer

AMBERDALE - Wallpaper - Seabrook Wallcoverings, Inc.

AMBERESQUE - Skin-care products - Colin Ingram Co.

AMBEREX - Vitamins and nutritional supplements - Universal Foods Corp.

AMBERFECTIONS - Confections - Novelart Manufacturing Co.

AMBERFLAKES - Yeast - Universal Foods Corp.

AMBERG - Office supplies - Esselte Corp.

AMBERG SHOWFOLIO - Office supplies - Esselte Corp.

AMBERGLOW - Clocks - Equity Industries Corp.

AMBERHILL - Wines - Raymond Vineyard and Cellar Inc.

AMBERIDGE - Floor coverings–carpet and rugs - Quaker Inc.

AMBERJACK - Boats–motor - Sea Ray Boats

AMBERLEY - Floor coverings - Congoleum Corp.

AMBERLEY - Greeting cards - Amberley Greeting Card Co.

AMBERLEY BABY - Greeting cards ☆ - Amberley Greeting Card Co.

AMBERLIGHT - Barbecues and grills ☆ - Temtex Products Inc.

AMBERMATIC - Eyeglasses - Bausch & Lomb Inc.

AMBERMIDE - Pharmaceutical preparations - Dolgin Acme Foods

AMBERSHADES - Glass–optical - DTR Associates, LP

AMBERSKIM - Dairy products - Universal Foods Corp.

AMBERTUF - Tools ☆ - Mayhew Steel Products

AMBERWARE - Cooking equipment–household - Wingknife, Inc.

AMBERWAY - Whey - Universal Foods Corp.

AMBERWOOD - Blinds–venetian - Alabama Venetian Blind Co. Inc.

AMBERYEAST - Yeast - Universal Foods Corp.

AMBEZE - Pharmaceutical preparations - Whitestone Products Inc.

AMBI - Chairs–upholstered - Herman Miller, Inc.

AMBI - Cosmetics - Kiwi Brands, Inc.

AMBI - Gloves - Edmont

AMBI - Infant product - Small World Toys

AMBI 10 - Skin care products - Kiwi Brands, Inc.

AMBI-24 - Medical apparatus ☆ - Biosearch Medical Products Inc.

AMBI FIVE - Cleaning preparations ☆ - Hertron International Inc.

AMBI-GARD - Skin care products - Saf-T-Gard International, Inc.

AMBI-PURE - Deodorizers - Kiwi Brands, Inc.

AMBI TOYS - Toys - Learning Curve Toys, LLC

AMBIA - Computer software - Software Partners, Inc.

AMBIANCE - Bernhardt Industries

AMBIANCE - Aquarium accessories - Blue Ribbon Pet Products, Inc.

AMBIANCE - Bathroom fittings - American Standard Inc.

AMBIANCE - Blinds–venetian ☆ - Hunter Douglas, Inc.

AMBIANCE - Cleaning preparations–household - Roxide International, Inc.

AMBIANCE - Cookies ☆ - Pillsbury Co.

AMBIANCE - Floor coverings - Mannington Resilient Floors

AMBIANCE - Floor coverings–carpet and rugs ☆ - Hollytex Carpet Mills Inc.

AMBIANCE - Floor coverings–tile - Monarch Tile Inc.

AMBIANCE - French doors - Glass Unlimited of High Point, Inc.

AMBIANCE - Furniture - Broyhill Furniture Industries, Inc.

AMBIANCE - Furniture–wood ☆ - Ficks Reed Co. Inc.

AMBIANCE - Luggage - American Tourister, Inc.

AMBIANCE - Wallpaper - Source Five

AMBIANCE I - Wallpaper - Royson's Corp.

AMBIANCE II - Luggage - American Tourister, Inc.

AMBIANT - Cabinets - Actua

AMBICO - Electronic equipment - Recoton Corp.

AMBIDERM - Latex gloves - Meditex Inc.

AMBIDEXTORS - Scissors–hand-operated - Lois Noyes California Unusuals

AMBIDEXTROUS - Antennas - American Electronic Laboratories Inc.

AMBIENCE - Occasional tables - JDI Group, Inc.

L'AMBIENCE - Wallpaper ☆ - David & Dash

AMBIENT - Microfiche equipment - Taylor-Merchant Corp.

AMBIENT - Wallpaper - Mari V Inc.

AMBIENTE - Cigars - D. Marshall, Inc.

AMBIENTE - Flatware ☆ - W.M.F. of America Inc.

AMBIENTE - Wallcoverings - Sherman & Associates International

☆ = Now out of production

AMBIETROL - Detergents - Bristol-Myers Squibb Co.
AMBIT - Computer software - Ambit Design Systems, Inc.
AMBITEX - Gloves–safety - Tradex International, Inc.
AMBITION - Colognes - AZ Product Co.
AMBITIONS - Apparel–women's - Irving S. Camens
AMBITIONS - Floor coverings–carpet and rugs - Philadelphia Carpets
AMBITOYS - Toys - DGI/Buki
AMBIVAN - Motor vehicles–automobiles - Nissan Motor Corp. USA
AMBLA - Fibers–vinyl ☆ - ICI Americas Inc.
AMBLERS - Shoes - Endicott Johnson Corp.
AMBLESIDE - Beverages–malt - Ambleside Brewing Co.
AMBODRYL - Antihistamine preparations ☆ - Parke-Davis
AMBOISE - Glassware–household - Durand International
AMBON - Cakes - First Indo-American Corp.
AMBOUND - Resins–synthetic - Georgia-Pacific Corp.
AMBRA - Apparel and accessories - Winona Knitting Mills, Inc.
AMBRE BEIGE - Nail care products - Cosmair Inc.
AMBRE L'ARTISTE PERLE - Lipsticks - Cosmair Inc.
AMBRETTA - Bakery products - Boboli International, Inc.
AMBRIA - Floor coverings–carpet and rugs - World Carpets, Inc.
AMBRIA - Floor coverings–carpet and rugs ☆ - Zenith Carpets
AMBRICO - Bricks - Williams Panel Bricks Inc.
AMBRIDGE - Floor coverings ☆ - Tarkett, Inc.
AMBRIOLA - Cheese - Coronet Brokerage Co. Inc.
AMBRIOLA PICCANTE - Cheese - Ambriola Co. Inc.
AMBRITE - Crayons - Dixon Ticonderoga Co.
AMBROID - Hardware - Ambroid Co.
AMBROID ORIGINAL - Hardware - Ambroid Co.
AMBROSIA - Bird feeds - Petland, Inc.
AMBROSIA - Bowls ☆ - Lenox Crystal, Inc.
AMBROSIA - Christmas tree ornaments ☆ - Cracker Box Inc.
AMBROSIA - Fabrics - Burlington House Fabrics Group
AMBROSIA - Floor coverings - Mannington Resilient Floors
AMBROSIA - Food products - ADM Cocoa
AMBROSIA - Fruits–canned - Schreiber Foods International, Inc.
AMBROSIA - Fruits–frozen ☆ - Agvest, Inc. (Northeastern Packing Div.)
AMBROSIA - Giftware ☆ - Dodge Trophies
AMBROSIA - Housewares - Shafford Co. Inc.
AMBROSIA - Milk ☆ - Cedarburg Dairy Inc.
AMBROSIA - Pins–jewelry - W.R. Grace & Co.
AMBROSIA - Rings–jewelry - Artcarved Inc.
AMBROSIA - Shampoos - Lenaco Corp.
AMBROSIA - Skin care products - Ambrosia Cosmetics Inc.
AMBROSIA - Skin care products - Ca Botana International, Inc.
AMBROSIA - Snack foods - Hershey Import Co. Inc.
AMBROSIA - Wallpaper - Advance Wallcoverings
AMBROSIA - Wallpaper - Koroseal Wallcoverings
AMBROSIA - Wallpaper ☆ - Morton Jonap Co. Inc.
AMBROSIA BLUE - Bathing suits ☆ - Jantzen Inc.
AMBROSIA CAKE IN A JAR - Confections - Grandma Pfeiffer's
AMBROSIA DAMASK - Wallpaper - Koroseal Wallcoverings
AMBROSIA GIFTS - Candles - Ottoman's, Inc.
AMBROSIA GOURMET FROZEN YOGURT - Yogurt–frozen - Instantwhip Foods Inc.
AMBROSIA LITE - Wallpaper - Koroseal Wallcoverings
AMBROSIA LUX - Pet products - Nutritional Research Associates Inc.
AMBROSIA RICHE - Food products ☆ - ADM Cocoa
AMBROSIA SLIM - Yarn ☆ - Tahki Imports Ltd.
AMBROSIA STRIPE - Wallpaper - Koroseal Wallcoverings
AMBROSOLI - Candy - Andre Prost Inc.
AMBROSSIA - Frozen yogurt - Instantwhip-Chicago Inc.
AMBRU - Coffee ☆ - American Ace LLC
AMBRY - Watches - La Marque Watch Co. Inc.
AMBULATOR - Medical apparatus - AA Sales Inc.
AMBULATORY ELECTROCARDIOLOGY - Medical apparatus - Del Mar Avionics
AMBULIFT - Health care products - Arjo Manufacturing Co.
AMBUSH - Bicycles - Kent International Inc.
AMBUSH - Fabrics - Burlington House Fabrics Group
AMBUSH! - Games - Avalon Hill Game Co.
AMBUSH - Golfing equipment - King Par Corp.
AMBUSH - Skin care products - Dana Perfumes Corp.
AMBUSH - Sporting goods - Anthony Newman
AMBUSH DEER - Hunting equipment - Anthony Newman
AMBUSH RIP ROCKETS - Toys - Hasbro, Inc.
AMBUTRON - Braces–orthopedic - Kirschner Medical Corp.

AMC - Lubrication equipment–industrial - Aetna Manufacturing Co.
AMC - Plumbing fixtures–metal - Anderson Metals Corp. Inc.
AMCA - Heaters–space ☆ - Desa International, Inc.
AMCA - Pharmaceutical preparations - Amca Pharmaceutical Co., Inc.
AMCAP - Pharmaceutical preparations ☆ - Circle Pharmaceuticals Inc.
AMCC - Computer software - Applied Micro Circuits Corp.
AMCEL - Packaging–paper - American Excelsior Co.
AMCHEM - Chemical preparations - Parker & Amchem
AMCHRON - Apparel and accessories - Associated Merchandising Corp.
AMCICO - Surgical equipment - Ben Gee Tan
AMCIL - See **WARNER-CHILCOTT**
AMCLEAN - Cleaning equipment - Amclean, Inc.
AMCM - Electronic equipment - Integrated System Assemblies Corp.
AMCO - Artists' materials - American Blueprint Co. Inc.
AMCO - Hardware - Amarillo Hardware Co.
AMCO/STRAP - Tools ☆ - American Manufacturing Co. Inc.
AMCOM D - Telephone devices and light signals for the deaf - American Communications Corp.
AMCOM I - Telephone devices and light signals for the deaf - American Communications Corp.
AMCOM P - Telephone devices and light signals for the deaf - American Communications Corp.
AMCOR - Automotive parts and accessories ☆ - Masco Corp.
AMCOR - Housewares - Amcor Group Ltd.
AMCOR PRECAST - Concrete products - Oldcastle Precast, Inc.
AMCORT - Pharmaceutical preparations - Keene Pharmaceuticals Inc.
AMCRON - Audio equipment - Crown International, Inc.
AMD - Exercising equipment - American Medical Devices, Inc.
AMD-K6 - Semiconductors - Advanced Micro Devices, Inc.
AMD-K6-2 - Semiconductors - Advanced Micro Devices, Inc.
AMDEK - Floor coverings - American Safety Technology
AMDESK - Electronics equipment - American Desk Manufacturing Co.
AMDEX - Mats - Robert Godfrey, Ltd.
AME - Audio equipment - Fiducci Electronics, Inc.
AME - Computer software - Autodesk Inc.
L'AME - Recording label - Wood'n Music Inc.
AME - Sporting goods - AME
AMEA - Whirlpools - Jacuzzi Inc.
AMECO - Dart game sets - American Eagle Co./Teacher's Discovery
AMEGA - Electronic equipment - Rangertone Research Inc.
AMEGA - Toilets–porcelain - Universal-Rundle Corp.
AMEK - Beauty shops - Amek/Tac U.S. Operations
AMEKINE - Rubber–synthetic ☆ - Dykema Rubber Band Co.
AMELIA - Bedding–linen - Dan River Inc.
AMELIA - Clocks - General Time Corp. (Westclox/Seth Thomas Div.)
AMELIA - Glassware–household ☆ - Lenox Crystal, Inc.
AMELIA EARHART - Dialing devices–telephone - Baltimore Luggage Co.
AMELIA'S SECRET - Private-label perfume - Butler-Burlingame
AMELIA'S SUGARFREE SHOPPE - Food products - EMAC International, Inc.
AMELOGEN - Dental instruments - Ultradent Products, Inc.
AMELOTTE - Apparel and accessories - Amelotte International Corp.
AMEN - Hormone preparations - Carnick Laboratories Inc.
AMEN - Recording label - Amen Records, Inc.
AMENDE - Cabinets - American Woodmark Corp.
AMENOPHIS SKIN CARE - Health care products - Select Brands
AMENTA - Hair care products - Walneir Group, Inc.
AMENTA - Recording label - Amenta Records
AMER. ARTISTS - Giftware - Viking Import House Inc.
AMER. COLL - Attache cases ☆ - H.C. Meyers Co.
AMER-FLINT II - Paints ☆ - Lilly Industries, Inc.
AMER-GLAS - Filters–air ☆ - American Air Filter International (Replacement Filter Products)
AMER. LEATHER - Attache cases ☆ - H.C. Meyers Co.
AMER LINE - Tires–automobile - General Tire, Inc.
AMER-THANE - Poly-urethane coatings ☆ - Lilly Industries, Inc.
AMERA - Cabinets - Masco Corp.
AMERA - Cabinets - Merillat Industries, Inc.
AMERA-BOND - Fencing - American Fence Co. Inc.
AMERA SPORT - Luggage - Steven H. Fisch
AMERACRYL - Cabinets - Ameracryl Inc.
AMERAFRI - Apparel and accessories - Robert L. Harris
AMERAMAX - Construction machinery - AMPAC Machinery Co.
AMERAMAX P33/24 - Construction machinery - AMPAC Machinery Co.
AMERATHON - Tires - Carlisle Tire & Rubber Co.
AMERCARE - Gloves–safety - Amercare, Inc.
AMEREC - Saunas - Cedarbrook Sauna Inc.

AMEREC - Saunas, steambath generators, and accessories - Nasscor Inc.

AMEREON HOUSE - Publisher's imprints - Amereon Ltd.

AMEREQUIP - Paper products - Amerequip Corp.

AMERESSE - Pharmaceutical preparations - American Pharmacal Inc.

AMEREX - Dishwashers–household - Amerex Inc.

AMEREX - Fire extinguishers - Ad-X Corp.

AMERFOND - Health care products - Domino Sugar Corp.

AMERGLOSS - Inks–letterpress - American Inks and Coatings Corp.

AMERHIST T.D. - Pharmaceutical preparations ☆ - American Pharmacal Inc.

AMERI - See ROCKIN' HORSE

AMERI - Tires–automobile ☆ - General Tire, Inc.

AMERI 400 SL - Tires - General Tire, Inc.

AMERI-550 AS - Tires–automobile - General Tire, Inc.

AMERI-550 TR - Tires–automobile - General Tire, Inc.

AMERI BALL - Balls–football - National Sports Properties

AMERI-CLASSIC - Tires–automobile - General Tire, Inc.

AMERI-DRAIN - Roofing and siding materials - American Building Components Co.

AMERI-EZP - Pharmaceutical preparations ☆ - Roberts/Hauck Pharmaceuticals Inc.

AMERI-FAX - Paper–thermoplastics coated - Saxon Nuco Inc.

AMERI-FLEX - Gas reliner and connector - American Metal Products

AMERI-FLOW - Registers, diffusers, grilles, etc. - American Metal Products

AMERI G4S - Tires - Continental General Tire, Inc.

AMERI GARD II - Tires–automobile - General Tire, Inc.

AMERI-GLAZE - Adhesives and sealants ☆ - Consolidated Coatings Corp.

AMERI-GLIDE - Stairway lift ☆ - Access Industries, Inc.

AMERI-GLOSS - Flags - Dettra Flag Co. Inc.

AMERI GRIP - Tires–automobile - General Tire, Inc.

AMERI-GRIP LT - Tires–automobile - General Tire, Inc.

AMERI-PAC - Vitamins and nutritional supplements - Ameri-Pac, Inc.

AMERI-PET INC. - Pet collars - Ameri-Pet Inc.

AMERI-PHEROL - Animal feed supplements - Ameri-Pac, Inc.

AMERI S330 - Tires–automobile - General Tire, Inc.

AMERI SD400 - Tires - Continental General Tire, Inc.

AMERI-SEAL - Adhesives and sealants ☆ - Consolidated Coatings Corp.

AMERI-SPORT - Tires–automobile - General Tire, Inc.

AMERI-SPRINT - Tires–automobile ☆ - General Tire, Inc.

AMERI-STEEL - Tires - General Tire, Inc.

AMERI-STEEL A/S - Tires - General Tire, Inc.

AMERI-STEEL LT - Tires - General Tire, Inc.

AMERI-TEC - Chimney - American Metal Products

AMERI-TECH 4 - Tires - General Tire, Inc.

AMERI-TECH ST - Tires - General Tire, Inc.

AMERI-THANE - Adhesives and sealants ☆ - Consolidated Coatings Corp.

AMERI-TRAC - Tires–automobile - General Tire, Inc.

AMERI-TRAC LT - Tires–automobile - General Tire, Inc.

AMERI-VENT - Gas vents - American Metal Products

AMERI-VET - Vitamins and nutritional supplements - Ameri-Pac, Inc.

AMERI-WAY - Tires–automobile - General Tire, Inc.

AMERI-WAY S/T - Tires–automobile - General Tire, Inc.

AMERI-WAY SE - Tires–automobile - General Tire, Inc.

AMERI-WAY XT - Tires–automobile - General Tire, Inc.

AMERI-WELD PLUS - Adhesives and sealants ☆ - Consolidated Coatings Corp.

AMERI-XL4 - Tires–automobile - General Tire, Inc.

AMERIBEAN STYLE - Mustard - Hot Head Sauceworks, Llc

AMERIBEAR - Toys–stuffed - Ric Paul Enterprises Inc.

AMERIBOND - Adhesives and sealants ☆ - Consolidated Coatings Corp.

AMERIBRITE SYSTEMS - Building and remodeling franchise - Ameribrite Systems

AMERICA - Cabinets ☆ - Les-Care Kitchens Inc.

AMERICA - Clocks - General Time Corp. (Westclox/Seth Thomas Div.)

AMERICA - Flowers, plants, and seeds - Jacklin Seed

AMERICA - Furniture - Lane Co. Inc.

AMERICA - Kites - Gayla Industries Inc.

AMERICA - Motorcycles ☆ - Commerce Overseas Corp.

AMERICA - Recording label - Musidisc SA

AMERICA - Toys–models - Estes Industries

AMERICA ADVENTURE - Games - Knowledge Adventure, Inc.

AMERICA CABLE SYSTEMS - Wiring devices - WPFY, Inc.

AMERICA CLASSIC - Clocks - General Time Corp. (Westclox/Seth Thomas Div.)

AMERICA COAST-TO-COAST - Computer software - CBS Software

AMERICA COLLECTION - Tableware–china ☆ - Pfaltzgraff Investment Co.

AMERICA COLLECTION - Trays - Wallace International Silversmiths, Inc.

AMERICA COOKS - Cutlery - Robinson Knife & Fiddlers Plastics

AMERICA-DIRECT - Computer software - Bretton Woods Group, Inc.

AMERICA FIRST IN MATH - Games - Suntex

AMERICA GET IT OFF YOUR CHEST! - Apparel and accessories - America's Voice Communications Corp.

AMERICA IS TURNING US ON - Electric lighting equipment - L.D. Kichler Co.

AMERICA-LAND OF BEAUTY - Calendars - American Greetings Corp.

AMERICA L.I.O.L.I. - Clothing - Asis, Inc.

AMERICA MARK - Placemats - Bright of America Inc.

AMERICA MOVES WEST - Computer software - Orange Cherry Software

AMERICA, OUR HOME - Calendars - American Greetings Corp.

AMERICA OUTDOORS - Apparel and accessories - Jackster Inc.

AMERICA REMEMBERS - Firearms, accessories, and parts - Ahl, Inc.

AMERICA ROCK - Video production - ABC Inc.

AMERICA THE BEAUTIFUL - Flowers, plants, and seeds - White Swan, Ltd.

AMERICA THE BEAUTIFUL COLLECTION - Floor coverings–carpet and rugs ☆ - Karastan-Bigelow Inc.

AMERICA TROUSER - Apparel–men's - American Trouser Inc.

AMERICA WEST - Furniture - Lane Co. Inc.

AMERICA WORKS! - Apparel and accessories - BMW Enterprises

AMERICA WORKS - Drill bits - Cleveland Twist Drill Co.

AMERICA3 - Bags–duffel - America3 Foundation

AMERICAD - Furniture ☆ - Mayline/Hamilton

AMERICADE - Apparel and accessories - De Marigny Music, Inc.

AMERICAINE - Anesthetics - Fisons Corp.

AMERICAINE OTIC - Health care products - Fisons Corp.

AMERICAL - Stone products - Arroyo Stone Co., Inc.

AMERICAN - Ammonia - American Bluing Co. Inc.

AMERICAN - Aprons - Dunn Manufacturing Corp.

AMERICAN - Bakery products - American Bakeries Co.

AMERICAN - Bathtubs–enameled - American Bidet Inc.

AMERICAN - Beverages–alcohol ☆ - David Sherman Corp.

AMERICAN - Beverages–malt - Pittsburg Brewing Co.

AMERICAN - Beverages–malt - William and Scott Co.

AMERICAN - Bicycles - Columbia Manufacturing Inc.

AMERICAN - Boats ☆ - Wellcraft Marine Corp.

AMERICAN - Boats–motor ☆ - Starcraft Corp.

AMERICAN - Brooms - American Water Broom Co.

AMERICAN - Brushes–paint - American Brush Co. Inc.

AMERICAN - Cabinets - Schuler Corp.

AMERICAN - Cases–musical instrument - M & M Distributing Co.

AMERICAN - Caviar - Tsar Nicoulai Caviar

AMERICAN - Cigarettes - American Tobacco Co.

AMERICAN - Coffee - American Coffee Co. Inc.

AMERICAN - Crayons ☆ - Dixon Ticonderoga Co.

AMERICAN - Crocheted and knitted items - AMF Head Sportswear

AMERICAN - Desk sets - Artistic Office Products

AMERICAN - Dryers–commercial - American Dryer Inc.

AMERICAN - Dryers–photographic - Johnke Manufacturing Co.

AMERICAN - Exercising equipment - Professional Gym Inc.

AMERICAN - Fasteners–hook and eye - Morris-Flamingo Inc.

AMERICAN - Fifes - American Plating & Manufacturing Co.

AMERICAN - Flints ☆ - Red Devil Products Inc.

AMERICAN - Floor coverings–carpet and rugs - Superior American Plastics Co.

AMERICAN - Floor coverings–carpet and rugs - Whitecrest Carpet Mills

AMERICAN - Flooring–hardwood - Mannington Wood Floors

AMERICAN - Food products - AMK for Service

AMERICAN - Furniture - Lowy Group Inc.

AMERICAN - Furniture - Tomlinson of High Point Inc.

AMERICAN - Garden equipment ☆ - True Temper Hardware Co.

AMERICAN - Glass ☆ - D & L Stained Glass Supply, Inc.

AMERICAN - Hardware - Washington Products Inc.

AMERICAN - Hardware ☆ - Servistar Corp.

AMERICAN - Horseshoes - St. Pierre Manufacturing Corp.

AMERICAN - Kitchen cabinets–metal ☆ - Haas Cabinet Co. Inc.

AMERICAN - Laces–boot and shoe ☆ - Hickory Industries, Inc.

AMERICAN - Lawn mowers - American Lawn Mower Co.

AMERICAN - Leather goods - Torel Inc.

AMERICAN - Machinery - American Laundry Machinery, Inc.

AMERICAN - Manicure preparations - American Manicure Corp.

AMERICAN - Manufactured homes - Redman Industries, Inc.

AMERICAN - Measuring instruments ☆ - Macklanburg-Duncan Co.

AMERICAN - Motor vehicles–motor homes ☆ - Forest River, Inc.

AMERICAN - Office supplies - Faber-Castell Corp.

AMERICAN - Office supplies - R.A. Stewart Superior

☆ = Now out of production

AMERICAN - Paper - Scott Paper Co.
AMERICAN - Peanut butter - Clements Food Co. Inc.
AMERICAN - Pencils - Sanford Corp.
AMERICAN - Perforators - American Perforator Co.
AMERICAN - Pet products ☆ - Windmill Nursery (L & M Farm)
AMERICAN - Petroleum - Amoco Oil Co.
AMERICAN - Pianos ☆ - Universal Player Piano Co.
AMERICAN - Playground equipment - American Playground Corp.
AMERICAN - Poultry product - American Poultry Co.
AMERICAN - Pumps–oil well - Lufkin Industries Inc.
AMERICAN - Rope and twine - American Manufacturing Co. Inc.
AMERICAN - Rope ☆ - Waterbury Rope Mills
AMERICAN - Salt - North American Salt Co.
AMERICAN - Sinks–metal ☆ - Federal Home Products
AMERICAN - Stamps–hand - American Stamp & Marking Products, Inc.
AMERICAN - Steel-wool pads - American Steel Wool Manufacturing Co. Inc.
AMERICAN - Stones–synthetic ☆ - Perfecto Products Co.
AMERICAN - Trophies–metal - Artistic Gifts
AMERICAN - Tuna–canned - Tri-Union International, LLC
AMERICAN - Water heaters–household - Mor-Flo Industries Inc.
AMERICAN - Wines - Schloss Doepken Winery
AMERICAN ACCENT - Cheese - Great Lakes Cheese Co., Inc.
AMERICAN ACCENT - Wallpaper ☆ - Three Sisters Studio
AMERICAN ACCENT 2 - Wallpaper ☆ - Three Sisters Studio
AMERICAN ACCENTS - Paints - Rust-Oleum Corp.
AMERICAN ACCESSORIES - Suspenders - Reborn Products Co., Inc.
AMERICAN ACE - Beverages - American Ace LLC
AMERICAN ACE - Harmonicas - Hohner Inc.
AMERICAN ACOUSTICS - Audio equipment - MTX
AMERICAN AESTHETIC, THE - Lamps - Boyd Lighting Co.
AMERICAN AIRE - Water beds - American Thermoseal Inc.
AMERICAN AIRLINES - Air transportation–passengers - American Airlines Inc.
AMERICAN AIRLINES - Luggage ☆ - Skyway Luggage Co.
AMERICAN ALBUM & TAPE - Recording label - Hope International
AMERICAN ALL PURPOSE - Footwear–athletic - American Athletic Shoe Co.
AMERICAN ALMOND - Food products - American Almond Products Co., Inc.
AMERICAN ANAGLYPH - Paper products - Lin Howard
AMERICAN ANGEL - Handbags ☆ - Integrated Handbags
AMERICAN ANGLER - Sporting goods - Douglas/Quikut
AMERICAN ART-WARE - Trays ☆ - Social Supper Inc.
AMERICAN ARTIST - Novelty items - Pat Dellacroce Studio
AMERICAN ARTISTS - Greeting cards - American Artists Group Inc.
AMERICAN ARTISTS JUNIORS - Stationery - American Artists Group Inc.
AMERICAN ARTS - Greeting cards ☆ - American Artists Group Inc.
AMERICAN ARTWARE - Giftware ☆ - Pfaltzgraff Investment Co.
AMERICAN ASHLEY - Handbags - Ames International Group
AMERICAN ASSETS - Fabrics - West Point-Pepperell Inc.
AMERICAN ATHLETIC - Exercising equipment - American Athletic Inc.
AMERICAN ATHLETIC - Sporting goods - Victoria's Dance-Theatrical Supply
AMERICAN ATHLETIC, INC. - Exercising equipment - American Sports International, Ltd.
AMERICAN AUTUMN - Kitchen cabinets–metal - Haas Cabinet Co. Inc.
AMERICAN AVIATOR - Audio equipment - Wing Aero Products, Inc.
AMERICAN BAKER - Flour - Inland Mills Co.
AMERICAN BAND - Rubber bands - B.F. Goodrich Co.
AMERICAN BANDSTAND - Dolls ☆ - Totsy Manufacturing Co., Inc.
AMERICAN BANDSTAND - Trading cards - Olive Enterprises, Inc.
AMERICAN BANDSTAND GRILL - Apparel, towels, etc. - Olive Enterprises, Inc.
AMERICAN BANKCARD CENTER - Electronic equipment - Bankcard America, Inc.
AMERICAN BARBERSHOP - Men's toiletries - Cosrich Inc.
AMERICAN BARNS - Wallpaper ☆ - Imperial Wallcoverings, Inc.
AMERICAN BASICS - Wallpaper - Belmont Wallcoverings
AMERICAN BASS SUB-WOOFERS - Amplifiers - Five Star Car Audio Svs. Inc.
AMERICAN BATH COLLECTION - Hardware ☆ - Artistic Brass
AMERICAN BEARING & CLUTCH CO. - Automotive parts and accessories - L & S Bearing Co.
AMERICAN BEAUTIES - Candy ☆ - New England Confectionery Co.
AMERICAN BEAUTIES - Cigarettes - Nat Sherman, Inc.
AMERICAN BEAUTIES - Dolls - Mattel, Inc.
AMERICAN BEAUTY - Breads - Maier's Sunbeam Bakery
AMERICAN BEAUTY - Cabinets - Kent Moore Cabinets Inc.
AMERICAN BEAUTY - Cakes - Plaza Sweets Bakery
AMERICAN BEAUTY - Dolls ☆ - Effanbee Doll Corp.

AMERICAN BEAUTY - Flatware ☆ - Lifetime Hoan Corp.
AMERICAN BEAUTY - Floor coverings - American Floor Products Co. Inc.
AMERICAN BEAUTY - Food products - American Beauty
AMERICAN BEAUTY - Food products - Hillshire Farm Co.
AMERICAN BEAUTY - Food products - Homestead, Inc.
AMERICAN BEAUTY - Food products - Shawnee Milling Co.
AMERICAN BEAUTY - Giftware ☆ - Colony Glass
AMERICAN BEAUTY - Greeting cards - Norcross Inc.
AMERICAN BEAUTY - Incense - Excelsior Incense Works
AMERICAN BEAUTY - Nuts–salted, roasted, cooked, or canned - Zaloom Brothers Co. of New Jersey
AMERICAN BEAUTY - Paper–gift wrap - American Greetings Corp.
AMERICAN BEAUTY - Pasta - American Beauty Macaroni
AMERICAN BEAUTY - Pasta - Hershey Pasta Group
AMERICAN BEAUTY - Rings–jewelry - Artcarved Inc.
AMERICAN BEAUTY - Seafood products–canned or cured ☆ - Star-Kist Foods, Inc.
AMERICAN BEAUTY - Soldering irons and equipment - American Electrical Heater Co. (American Beauty Div.)
AMERICAN BEAUTY - Vegetables–frozen - Morgan Foods Inc.
AMERICAN BEAUTY - Wallpaper - Atlas Wallpaper & Paint Co.
AMERICAN BEAUTY - Wallpaper ☆ - Fabricut Inc.
AMERICAN BEAUTY - Wet mops ☆ - American Textile Products Co.
AMERICAN BEAUTY - Wheat–flour or meal - Conagra, Inc.
AMERICAN BEAUTY FETTUCCINI FLORENTINE - Pasta - Homestead, Inc.
AMERICAN BEAUTY SPAGHETTI AND ALFREDO SAUCE MIXES - Sauces - Williams Foods Inc.
AMERICAN BEAUTY VINYL STRINGS - Wallpaper - Atlas Wallpaper & Paint Co.
AMERICAN BEDDING - Beds–metal - Santino Antinori
AMERICAN BEDDING AND BATH COMPANY - Linen - Frederick Atkins, Inc.
AMERICAN BEEF - Food products - American Beef Packers Inc.
AMERICAN BELLE - Candy - Farley Candy Co.
AMERICAN BELT COMPANY - Belts–apparel - American Belt Co.
AMERICAN BELTING BY BOSCA - Leather goods - Hugo Bosca Co., Inc.
AMERICAN BERKSHIRE GOLD - Meat products–pork - American Berkshire Association
AMERICAN BEST - Air conditioning equipment - Goettl Air Conditioning Inc.
AMERICAN BEST QUALITY - Paints ☆ - Servistar Corp.
AMERICAN BILTRITE - Shoe repair shops - American Biltrite Inc.
AMERICAN BIOGRAPHICAL INSTITUTE - Books - American Biographical Institute, Inc.
AMERICAN BLADE COLLECTORS ASSOCIATION - Trading cards and stamps - American Blade, Inc.
AMERICAN BLUE - Apparel–men's - Berkley Shirt Co. Inc.
AMERICAN BODY BUILDING GEAR - Sweatshirts - Mordecai P. Williams Jr.
AMERICAN BOY - Apparel and accessories - Barrel-Marvin Apparel, Inc.
AMERICAN BOY - Rice - Connell Co.
AMERICAN BRAKEBLOK - Automotive parts and accessories - Echlin Inc.
AMERICAN BRAKEBLOK - Brake linings - Abex Corp. (Friction Products Group)
AMERICAN BREAKFAST - Teas ☆ - R.C. Bigelow, Inc.
AMERICAN BRONZE - Tires - American Car Care Centers Inc.
AMERICAN BUSINESS - Recording label - Simitar Entertainment, Inc.
AMERICAN BUSINESS COLLECTION - Floor coverings–carpet and rugs - Karastan-Bigelow Inc.
AMERICAN BYWAYS - Furniture - Cochrane Furniture Co. Inc.
AMERICAN CABIN - Furniture - Bob Timberlake Collection, Inc.
AMERICAN CABIN - House furnishings - Lexington Furniture Industries, Inc.
AMERICAN CAFE EXPRESS, THE - Food products - American Cafe
AMERICAN CAFE, THE - Restaurant franchise - American Cafe
AMERICAN CALICO - Wallpaper - Style-Tex Wallcoverings
AMERICAN CAMPER - Backpacks - American Camper
AMERICAN CAMPER - Bags - American Camper
AMERICAN CAMPING COMPANY - Sporting goods - Kellwood Co.
AMERICAN CARIBBEAN - Hair care products - American Caribbean Beauty Product
AMERICAN CARVER - Cutlery - General Housewares Corp.
AMERICAN CARVER PROFESSIONAL SERIES - Cutlery - General Housewares Corp.
AMERICAN CATHEDRAL - Kitchen cabinets–metal - Haas Cabinet Co. Inc.
AMERICAN CEDAR - Siding - Aluminum Co. of America
AMERICAN CENTURY - Magazines - Farrar, Straus and Giroux Inc.
AMERICAN CHALLENGE: A SAILING SIMULATION - Computer software - Mindscape Software Inc.

☆ = Now out of production

AMERICAN CHALLENGE, THE - Computer software - Mindscape Software Inc.

AMERICAN CHAMPION - Jewelry - Jacoby-Bender Inc.

AMERICAN CHARM - Floor coverings–carpet and rugs ☆ - Gulistan Carpet Inc.

AMERICAN CHEESEMEN - Cheese, dairy products - American Cheeseman Inc.

AMERICAN CHEF - Cutlery - General Housewares Corp.

AMERICAN CHEF - Food products - American Beef Packers Inc.

AMERICAN CHEF - Meat products–canned ☆ - Groezinger Provision Inc.

AMERICAN CHEMICALS COMPANY, INC. - Lubricants - ACC, Inc.

AMERICAN CHERRY - Furniture - Pennsylvania House

AMERICAN CHINESE NATURAL HERBS HEALTH FOOD - Herbal dietary supplements - American Chinese Natural Herbs

AMERICAN CHOICE - Window coverings - Tempo Industries Inc.

AMERICAN CHRISTMAS TREE - Dinnerware–glass - Cuthbertson Imports Inc.

AMERICAN CHRISTMAS TREE, THE - Giftware ☆ - Fenton Art Glass Co.

AMERICAN CLASS - Truck cab and sleeper liner - Peterbilt Motors Co.

AMERICAN CLASSIC - Balls ☆ - Mikasa Sports

AMERICAN CLASSIC - Barbecue sauce ☆ - Louis Maull Co.

AMERICAN CLASSIC - Beverages–carbonated - Strategic Brands, Inc.

AMERICAN CLASSIC - Bird cages - Ameriguard Corp.

AMERICAN CLASSIC - Candles ☆ - Arizona Natural Resources

AMERICAN CLASSIC - Cookies - Nabisco Foods Group

AMERICAN CLASSIC - Floor coverings–carpet and rugs - Calladium & Marglen

AMERICAN CLASSIC - Floor coverings–carpet and rugs - Lees Carpets

AMERICAN CLASSIC - Floor coverings–carpet and rugs ☆ - Masland Corp.

AMERICAN CLASSIC - Flooring–hardwood - Mannington Wood Floors

AMERICAN CLASSIC - Food products - Salyer American Fresh Foods

AMERICAN CLASSIC - Footwear - De La Rentis Imports Inc.

AMERICAN CLASSIC - Furniture - Statesville Chair Co. Inc.

AMERICAN CLASSIC - Guns - Crosman Corp.

AMERICAN CLASSIC - Ice cream cones - Affiliated Ice Cream Distributors, Inc.

AMERICAN CLASSIC - Musical instruments - Vic Firth Inc.

AMERICAN CLASSIC - Paints - Distribution America, Inc.

AMERICAN CLASSIC - Paints - Valspar Corp.

AMERICAN CLASSIC - Sporting goods - Lindy Little Joe Inc.

AMERICAN CLASSIC - Teas - Charleston Tea Plantation Inc.

AMERICAN CLASSIC - Turkeys - Christensen Processing & Marketing, Inc.

AMERICAN CLASSIC - Watches - SMH (US) Inc.

AMERICAN CLASSIC CHOCOLATE COMPANY - Candy - American Trends Corp.

AMERICAN CLASSIC HOLIDAY FAIR AND DESIGN - Handbags - Holiday Fair, Inc.

AMERICAN CLASSIC JR. - Bird cages - Ameriguard Corp.

AMERICAN CLASSICS - Bathroom accessories - Nutone Inc.

AMERICAN CLASSICS - Boxes - American Classics/Mimbreno Trading Co.

AMERICAN CLASSICS - Cakes - Boyer Printing Co.

AMERICAN CLASSICS - Computer software - Harden Industries Inc.

AMERICAN CLASSICS - Figurines ☆ - Ideal Originals

AMERICAN CLASSICS - Furniture ☆ - Lane Co. Inc.

AMERICAN CLASSICS - Furniture ☆ - Stanley Furniture Co. Inc.

AMERICAN CLASSICS - Hobby kits ☆ - Craft House Corp.

AMERICAN CLASSICS - Lighting fixtures - American Lantern Co.

AMERICAN CLASSICS - Marble products - Georgia Marble Co.

AMERICAN CLASSICS - Patterns–clothing ☆ - Simplicity Pattern Co., Inc.

AMERICAN CLASSICS - Publisher's imprints ☆ - Crossroad

AMERICAN CLASSICS - Toys–automobiles - Jak-Pak Inc.

AMERICAN CLASSROOM - Diaries - Concept One International, Inc.

AMERICAN CLAVE - Recording label - Jazz Composer's Orchestra Association Inc.

AMERICAN CLIPPER - Watches - Bulova Corp.

AMERICAN COLLARS AND COUPLINGS - Hardware - American Collars and Couplings, Inc.

AMERICAN COLLECTION - Cookies - Pepperidge Farm Inc.

AMERICAN COLLECTION - Neckties - World Wide Ties Inc.

AMERICAN COLLECTION, THE - Artists' materials - Artoptic International Corp.

AMERICAN COLLECTION, THE - Apparel and accessories - Kellwood Co.

AMERICAN COLONIAL - Wallpaper - Capital Carousel Inc.

AMERICAN COLONIAL - Wallpaper ☆ - Richard E. Thibaut, Inc.

AMERICAN COMFORT - Building materials - Napco Inc.

AMERICAN COMFORT - Siding–metal - National Aluminum Products Co.

AMERICAN COMPANY WITH EUROPEAN ROOTS, THE - Vitamins and nutritional supplements - Ultravit Enterprises, Inc.

AMERICAN CONCEPT - Musical instrument accessories - Vic Firth Inc.

AMERICAN CONNECTION - Apparel and accessories - Fashion Boom Inc.

AMERICAN CONNOISSEUR GOURMET - Oils–edible - Birmingham Marketing, Inc.

AMERICAN CONSERVATION CLUB - Toys–blocks - K & M International, Inc.

AMERICAN CONSUMER WHOLESALE DIAMONDS - Jewelry - Shar-Ko International Co.

AMERICAN COONER - Boots ☆ - Servus Footwear Co.

AMERICAN CORNER CASTLE - Cages–wire - Ameriguard Corp.

AMERICAN COTTONS - Apparel and accessories - Century Place Inc.

AMERICAN COUNTRY - Automotive parts and accessories ☆ - Allied Plastics

AMERICAN COUNTRY - Boots - L.B. Evans' Son Co.

AMERICAN COUNTRY - Chocolate - Sweet Shop

AMERICAN COUNTRY - Dinnerware–glass - Nikko Ceramics Inc.

AMERICAN COUNTRY - Flowers, plants, and seeds - White Swan, Ltd.

AMERICAN COUNTRY - Kitchen cabinets–metal ☆ - Haas Cabinet Co. Inc.

AMERICAN COUNTRY - Leather goods - Enger-Kress Co.

AMERICAN COUNTRY - Wallpaper - Imperial Wallcoverings, Inc.

AMERICAN COUNTRY - Wines - Door Peninsula Winery

AMERICAN COUNTRY CHRISTMAS - Publisher's imprints - Oxmoor House Inc.

AMERICAN COUNTRY COLLECTION - Furniture ☆ - Lea Industries Inc.

AMERICAN COUNTRY GEAR - House furnishings ☆ - Gear Holdings, Inc.

AMERICAN COUNTRY KIDS - House furnishings - Gear Holdings, Inc.

AMERICAN COUNTRY WEST - Furniture - Lexington Furniture Industries, Inc.

AMERICAN COWBOY SONGS - Recording label - American Cowboy Songs Inc.

AMERICAN COWBOY, THE - Craft supplies ☆ - VIP/VIP Crafts

AMERICAN CRAFT - Faucets - Peerless Faucet Co. (Plumbing Products Div.)

AMERICAN CRAFTSMAN COLLECTION - Furniture - Stanley Furniture Co. Inc.

AMERICAN CRAFTSMEN - Leather goods - Leatherform Ltd.

AMERICAN CREME - Liquors - Heublein, Inc.

AMERICAN CREW - Hair care products - American Crew, Inc.

AMERICAN CROSSROADS - Apparel and accessories - Hide Tech Clothing Co.

AMERICAN CUSTOM - Musical instruments - Vic Firth Inc.

AMERICAN DAYSAILER - Sailboat - American Sail

AMERICAN-DE ROSA LAMPARTS, INC. - Lighting fixtures - American-De Rosa Lamparts, Inc.

AMERICAN DECO - Tableware–china ☆ - Lenox, Inc.

AMERICAN DENIM - Apparel and accessories - USA Enterprises/Fifth Ave.

AMERICAN DENTAL - Dental equipment - American Dental Laser Inc.

AMERICAN DENTAL HYGIENICS - Toothpaste - American Dental Hygienics Inc.

AMERICAN DENTAL TECHNOLOGIES - Dental equipment - American Dental Laser Inc.

AMERICAN DERRINGER CORP. - Firearms, accessories, and parts - American Derringer Corp.

AMERICAN DESIGN - Fans–attic - Fasco Industries Inc. (Consumer Products Div.)

AMERICAN DESIGN GROUP - Paper–gift wrap - Gear Holdings, Inc.

AMERICAN DESIGNERS - Greeting cards ☆ - Nu-Art Inc.

AMERICAN DESIGNERS COLLECTION - Jewelry - Kaspar & Esh Inc.

AMERICAN DIARY DOLLS - Dolls - Georgetown Collection, Inc.

AMERICAN DIETARY LABS - Health care products - Energen Products Inc.

AMERICAN DIGEST - Furniture - Hickory Chair Co.

AMERICAN DJ - Lighting fixtures - American DJ Supply, Inc.

AMERICAN DOUBLE EAGLE - Bicycles - Rideable Bicycle Replicas Inc.

AMERICAN DREAM - Archery equipment - High Country American

AMERICAN DREAM - Comforters - Summit Textiles Inc.

AMERICAN DREAM - Fireplaces - Temtex Products Inc.

AMERICAN DREAM - Floor coverings–carpet and rugs - Philadelphia Carpets

AMERICAN DREAM - Floor coverings–carpet and rugs ☆ - American Carpet Mills

AMERICAN DREAM - Motor vehicles–motor homes - Fleetwood Enterprises, Inc.

AMERICAN DREAM SPA - Hot tubs–plastic - CTA Corp.

AMERICAN DREW - Furniture - American Drew

AMERICAN DREW - Furniture - LADD Furniture Inc.

AMERICAN DRY - Beverages–carbonated - Polar Corp.

AMERICAN DUST SERIES - Publisher's imprints - Dustbooks

AMERICAN DYNASTY - Floor coverings–carpet and rugs ☆ - American Carpet Mills

☆ = Now out of production

AMERICAN DYNASTY - Floor coverings–carpet and rugs ☆ - Columbus Mills, Inc.

AMERICAN EAGLE - Ammunition - Federal Cartridge Co.

AMERICAN EAGLE - Bicycles - Coastal Trading Enterprises, Inc.

AMERICAN EAGLE - Bicycles - Ross Bicycles USA, Ltd.

AMERICAN EAGLE - Boats - American Eagle Marine Inc.

AMERICAN EAGLE - Faucets - Sterling Plumbing Group Inc.

AMERICAN EAGLE - Golfing equipment ☆ - Western Golf Inc.

AMERICAN EAGLE - Optical machinery - Night Vision Equipment Co., Inc.

AMERICAN EAGLE - Shoes - Jimlar Corp.

AMERICAN EAGLE - Stoves ☆ - Lancaster Fabricating Co. Inc.

AMERICAN EAGLE - Tools–power-driven - American Abrasives, Inc.

AMERICAN EAGLE - Trailers–travel - Fleetwood Enterprises, Inc.

AMERICAN EAGLE - Watches - Bulova Corp.

AMERICAN EAGLE - Water - American Eagle Water Co.

AMERICAN EAGLE INSTRUMENTS - Dental equipment - American Eagle Instruments, Inc.

AMERICAN EAGLE OUTFITTERS - Leather goods - American Eagle Outfitters, Inc.

AMERICAN EAGLE SAILPLANE - Toys–models ☆ - Cox Products Inc.

AMERICAN EAGLES - Handbags ☆ - Sarne Co. Inc.

AMERICAN EDGE - Fabrics–cotton - Delta Mills Inc.

AMERICAN ELEGANCE - Floor coverings–carpet and rugs ☆ - Callaway Carpets

AMERICAN ELEGANCE - Furniture–factory - Clayton Marcus Co. Inc.

AMERICAN ELEGANCE - Greeting cards - American Greetings Corp.

AMERICAN ELEGANCE - Wallpaper - Taylor Wallcoverings Inc.

AMERICAN ELITE - Luggage - American Poly Vinyl Corp.

AMERICAN ENFORCER - Toys–guns - Parris Manufacturing Co.

AMERICAN ENTERTAINMENT - Recording label - Hope International

AMERICAN ESPRESSO - Coffee - Gillies Coffee Co.

AMERICAN ESSENTIALS - Panty hose - American Essentials Inc.

AMERICAN EXIT DEVICE - Hardware - American Device Manufacturing Co. Inc.

AMERICAN EXPRESS TRAVEL GUIDES - Publisher's imprints - Simon & Schuster, Inc.

AMERICAN EXPRESSIONS - Floor coverings–carpet and rugs - American Rug Craftsmen Inc.

AMERICAN EXPRESSIONS - Furniture ☆ - Hammary Furniture Co. Inc.

AMERICAN EYELAND - Eyeglasses - E-M International

AMERICAN FAMILY - Craft supplies - Marketing Action Group Inc. (American Family Crafts Div.)

AMERICAN FAMILY - Photo albums - Kleer-Vu Plastics Inc.

AMERICAN FAMILY - Scales–bathroom - Healthometer

AMERICAN FAMILY - Watchbands–precious metal - Peterson's Health Products

AMERICAN FAMILY LODGE - Hotel/motel chain - American Family Lodge Inc.

AMERICAN FARE - Food products - Conagra, Inc.

AMERICAN FASHION COLLECTION BY H.I.S. - Apparel–men's - H.I.S. Sportswear

AMERICAN FASHION FIRST - Watches - Gruen Marketing Corp.

AMERICAN FAST FINISH - Paints - Altawood Inc.

AMERICAN FAVORITES - Fabrics–tapestry ☆ - Columbus Coated Fabrics Co.

AMERICAN FED - Beef - AMK for Service

AMERICAN FEDERAL - Flatware - Reed and Barton Corp.

AMERICAN FIBER INDUSTRIES - Pillows - American Fiber Industries Corp.

AMERICAN FIBERFILL - Bed pillows - American Foam Latex Corp.

AMERICAN FIELD - Apparel and accessories - Fair Haven Industries Inc.

AMERICAN FIELD - Backpacks - Allen Co., Inc.

AMERICAN FISHERMAN - Fishing tackle - American Camper

AMERICAN FITNESS CLASSIC A HIGH ENERGY BAR - Snack food - Bakery Products Distributors

AMERICAN FITNESS FACTORY - Shirts - American Fitness Factory

AMERICAN FIXTURE - Display fixture ☆ - Lozier Corp.

AMERICAN FLAGSHIP - Fireworks - L. W. Loyd Co., Inc.

AMERICAN FLASH - Cleaning preparations - ATM America Corp.

AMERICAN FLORAL SERVICES - Educational materials - American Floral Services, Inc.

AMERICAN FLYER - Motor vehicles–motor homes ☆ - Fleetwood Enterprises, Inc.

AMERICAN FLYER - Sleds - Paris Co. Inc.

AMERICAN FLYER - Toys–trains - Lionel Trains Inc.

AMERICAN FLYERS - Musical instrument accessories - Dean Markley

AMERICAN FOLKLORE - Greeting cards ☆ - Kristin Elliott Inc.

AMERICAN FOOTWEAR - Shoes - L.B. Evans' Son Co.

AMERICAN FORGE - Furniture ☆ - Bassett Furniture Industries, Inc.

AMERICAN FORGE & FOUNDRY - Tools - Intermarket Imports Inc.

AMERICAN FORMULAS - Hair care products - Pyramid Beauty Labs, Inc.

AMERICAN FORTUNE - Shirts–flannel - American Fortune Inc.

AMERICAN FREEDOM - Slacks–men's - Gitano Fashions Ltd

AMERICAN FREEZERS - Food products - Harry H. Bell and Sons Inc.

AMERICAN FRONTIER - Furniture - Broyhill Furniture Industries, Inc.

AMERICAN FRUIT CLASSICS - Snack foods ☆ - Boyer Printing Co.

AMERICAN GALLERY - Apparel and accessories - Tandy Brands Accessories Inc.

AMERICAN GALLERY - Art councils - Fabulous Forgeries Ltd.

AMERICAN GARDEN - Flatware - Tiffany and Co.

AMERICAN GARDENER - Tools–hand-operated - Consolidated Stores Corp.

AMERICAN GEM COLLECTION, THE - Dolls ☆ - Uneeda Doll Co., Inc.

AMERICAN GENTLEMAN - Shoes - Craddock-Terry Inc.

AMERICAN GENTLEMAN - Watches - Hampden Corp.

AMERICAN GENTLEMEN - Wallcovering - Fashon Wallcoverings

AMERICAN GEOGRAPHICAL SOCIETY AROUND THE WORLD PROGRAM - Publisher's imprints - American Geographical Society

AMERICAN GIFT - Giftware - American Gift Corp.

AMERICAN GINSENG - Health care products - Prince of Peace Enterprises Inc.

AMERICAN GIRL - Rice - Connell Co.

AMERICAN GIRL - Trading cards and stamps - Pleasant Co.

AMERICAN GIRL - Watches - Bulova Corp.

AMERICAN GIRL GEAR - Jewelry - Pleasant Co.

AMERICAN GIRL LIBRARY - Publisher's imprints - Pleasant Co.

AMERICAN GIRL OF TODAY - Dolls - Pleasant Co.

AMERICAN GIRL, THE - Spaghetti sauces - The American Girl Inc.

AMERICAN GIRLS HISTORIAN - Paper products - Pleasant Co.

AMERICAN GIRLS, THE - Publisher's imprints - Pleasant Co.

AMERICAN GLACE - Ice cream - American Glace Inc.

AMERICAN GLADIATOR - Candy bars - Ferrara Food Co., Inc.

AMERICAN GLADIATORS - Umbrellas - Shaw Creations Inc.

AMERICAN GLASSWORKS - Glass products - Import Associates

AMERICAN GLIDER - Swings–metal - Evenflo Co.

AMERICAN GLOBAL PUBLISHING - Publisher's imprints - Alam E. Hammad

AMERICAN GOLD - Fruits and vegetables - Paramount Citrus Association

AMERICAN GOLD - Recording label - Bellaire Record Sales

AMERICAN GOLDSMITHS - Product description unknown - Wright and Lato Inc.

AMERICAN GOLF CLASSICS - Apparel–athletic - American Golf Corp.

AMERICAN GOTHIC - Building materials–concrete - Joanna Western Mills Co.

AMERICAN GOTHIC - Furniture - Romweber Co.

AMERICAN GRAMAPHONE - Recording label - American Gramaphone Records

AMERICAN GREAT 18 - Bags–canvas - Dick Clark Productions Inc.

AMERICAN GREETINGS - Greeting cards - American Greetings Corp.

AMERICAN GREETINGS GET ALONG GANG - Toys - Chilton-Globe, Inc.

AMERICAN GRILL - Food products - Lightlife Foods, Inc.

AMERICAN GRIP - Apparel and accessories - Ogio International, Inc.

AMERICAN GROOVE - Apparel and accessories - Erica W. Zohar

AMERICAN HABITAT - Fabrics–tapestry ☆ - Columbus Coated Fabrics Co.

AMERICAN HAIRLINES - Hairpieces - American Hairlines

AMERICAN HARVEST - Deodorizers - Scarborough and Co. Inc.

AMERICAN HARVEST - Portable ovens - Alternative Pioneering Systems Inc.

AMERICAN HARVEST RECORDING SOCIETY - Recording label - Terrace Entertainment Corp.

AMERICAN HEARTH - Floor coverings–carpet and rugs - Milliken & Co. Inc.

AMERICAN HEARTLAND - Figurines - Gare Inc.

AMERICAN HEARTLAND COLLECTION - Craft supplies - Mangelsen's (VDI)

AMERICAN HEARTLAND COMPANY LTD. - Bags–duffel - American Heartland Co. Ltd.

AMERICAN HEIRLOOM - Furniture ☆ - Vaughan Furniture Co. Inc.

AMERICAN HEIRLOOMS - Bernhardt Industries

AMERICAN HEMP - Apparel and accessories - Sean Travers Casey

AMERICAN HEMP MERCANTILE - Luggage - American Hemp Mercantile, Inc.

AMERICAN HERALD - Siding–metal - National Aluminum Products Co.

AMERICAN HERBAL SCIENCE - Vitamins and nutritional supplements - Dr. Clayton's Herbs

AMERICAN HERITAGE - Bakery products - American Bakeries Co.

AMERICAN HERITAGE - Brushes–paint - E-Z Paintr Corp.

AMERICAN HERITAGE - Cabinets - Nutone Inc.

AMERICAN HERITAGE - Cheese - Schreiber Foods, Inc.

AMERICAN HERITAGE - Desk sets ☆ - Postamatic Co. Inc.

AMERICAN HERITAGE - Floor coverings–carpet and rugs - Philadelphia Carpets

AMERICAN HERITAGE - Floor coverings–carpet and rugs ☆ - Playfield International Inc.

AMERICAN HERITAGE - Furniture - Hammary Furniture Co. Inc.

AMERICAN HERITAGE - Furniture - Stanley Furniture Co. Inc.

AMERICAN HERITAGE - Greeting cards - American Artists Group Inc.

AMERICAN HERITAGE - History, art, and architecture books - American Heritage

AMERICAN HERITAGE - Kitchen cabinets–metal ☆ - Haas Cabinet Co. Inc.

AMERICAN HERITAGE - Nutcrackers ☆ - Roman, Inc.

AMERICAN HERITAGE - Publisher's imprints - Houghton Mifflin Co.

AMERICAN HERITAGE - Shutters - American Heritage Shutters Inc.

AMERICAN HERITAGE - Snack foods ☆ - Sunshine Biscuits, Inc.

AMERICAN HERITAGE - Tents - Coleman Co., Inc.

AMERICAN HERITAGE - Watches - Forbes, Inc.

AMERICAN HERITAGE COLLECTION - Toys - Forbes, Inc.

AMERICAN HERO - Apparel and accessories - Blue Bell, Inc.

AMERICAN HERO - Toys - Ben Cooper Inc.

AMERICAN HERO MEDALS - Jewelry - U.S. Consumer Products Corp.

AMERICAN HEROES AND LEGENDS - Firearms, accessories, and parts - Ahl, Inc.

AMERICAN HICKORY - Tools - O.P. Link Handle Co. Inc.

AMERICAN HIKERS - Boots - Amwelt Corp.

AMERICAN HISTORY EXPLORER - Computer software - Parsons Technology, Inc.

AMERICAN HISTORY I - Wallpaper ☆ - Artisan House Inc.

AMERICAN HISTORY REVIEW BANK II - Computer software ☆ - Technical Educational Consultants

AMERICAN HISTORY REVIEW BANK I - Computer software ☆ - Technical Educational Consultants

AMERICAN HISTORY SMART - Publisher's imprints - Princeton Review Publishing, LLC

AMERICAN HOBNAIL - Glass products - Westmoreland Glass Co.

AMERICAN HOME - Dinnerware–glass - Lenox, Inc.

AMERICAN HOME - Furniture ☆ - Bernhardt Industries

AMERICAN HOME - Sofas - La-Z-Boy Chair Co.

AMERICAN HOME COLLECTION - Glassware–household - Federal Glass

AMERICAN HOME GARDEN CENTER QUALITY - Fertilizers - Tessman Seed, Inc.

AMERICAN HOME REPAIR - Broadcasting stations–television - Bruce Leon Lamb

AMERICAN HOMECOMING - Ornamental products–metal - May Department Stores Co.

AMERICAN HOMESTEAD - Furniture - Cochrane Furniture Co. Inc.

AMERICAN HOMESTEAD COLLECTION - Candy - Archibald Candy Corp.

AMERICAN HOMESTYLE - Wallpaper - Surface Industries Inc.

A AMERICAN HOP ALE - Beverages–malt - Anheuser-Busch Companies Inc.

AMERICAN HORMONE - Hair care products ☆ - Samlo

AMERICAN HORSESHOES - Video games - Taito America Corp.

AMERICAN HUNTER - Archery equipment - High Country American

AMERICAN HUNTER - Knives ☆ - Tru-Balance Knife Co.

AMERICAN HYBRID - Flowers, plants, and seeds - Golden State Bulb Growers

AMERICAN HYDRO-SURGICAL - Surgical supplies - American Hydro-Surgical Instruments, Inc.

AMERICAN IC EXCHANGE TECHNOLOGY'S CLEARINGHOUSE - Electronics stores - Bally Micro

AMERICAN IMAGE - Apparel and accessories ☆ - Horace Small Apparel Co.

AMERICAN INDEPENDENCE COLLECTION - Furniture - American Drew

AMERICAN INDIAN COLLECTION - Toys - Imperial Toy Corp.

AMERICAN INDUSTRIAL CONTROLS - Electronic equipment - Amicon, Inc.

AMERICAN INSPIRATION - Apparel and accessories ☆ - Edison Brothers Stores, Inc.

AMERICAN INSPIRATIONS - Giftware - Wilton Co.

AMERICAN INSTANTS - Coffee, tea - American Instants Inc.

AMERICAN INTELLECTUAL PROPERTY LAW ASSOCIATION - Recording label - American Intellectual Property Law Association, Inc.

AMERICAN INTERNATIONAL COLLECTION - Floor coverings–carpet and rugs - Milliken & Co. Inc.

AMERICAN INTERNATIONAL GROUP, INC. - Apparel and accessories - American International Group Inc.

AMERICAN INTERNATIONAL RENT-A-CAR - Auto-rental franchise - American International Rent-a-Car

AMERICAN INTIMATES - Underwear and nightwear - LCA Intimates

AMERICAN JAC - Apparel and accessories - California Manufacturing Co. Inc.

AMERICAN JAZZ - Mallets - Mike Balter Mallets

AMERICAN JERUSALEM - Food products - Deboles Nutritional Foods Inc.

AMERICAN JOINT COMMITTEE ON CANCER - Publisher's imprints - American College of Surgeons

AMERICAN JUNCTION - Eyeglasses - Atlantic Optical Co., Inc.

AMERICAN JUSTICE - Video production - Arts & Entertainment Network

AMERICAN KIDS - Apparel–children's ☆ - Melton Shirt Co., Inc.

AMERICAN KIDS - Furniture - Studio RTA, Inc.

AMERICAN KITCHEN & BATH - Wallpaper ☆ - Sanitas Wallcoverings

AMERICAN KITCHEN & BATH II - Wallpaper - Sanitas Wallcoverings

AMERICAN LADY - Food products - General Grocer Co.

AMERICAN LAFRANCE - Fire extinguishers - Badger Powhatan

AMERICAN LAFRANCE PUMPER - Toys–models ☆ - ERTL Co., Inc.

AMERICAN LARD - Lard - American Lard Co.

AMERICAN LASER GAMES, INC. - Video games - American Laser Games, Inc.

AMERICAN LEADER - Food products - United Stores

AMERICAN LEADER - Musical instruments - Hershman Musical Instrument

AMERICAN LEADERSHIP - Watches - Gruen Marketing Corp.

AMERICAN LEGACY - Floor coverings–carpet and rugs - Capel, Inc.

AMERICAN LEGACY - Furniture - National/Mt. Airy Furniture

AMERICAN LEGACY - Meat products - John Morrell & Co.

AMERICAN LEGACY - Wallpaper - Bayview Wallcoverings

AMERICAN LEGACY - Wallpaper - Madison Wallcoverings

AMERICAN LEGACY TRADING CO. - Trading cards and stamps - American Legacy Trading Co.

AMERICAN LEGACY TRADING COMPANY - Trading cards and stamps - American Legacy Trading Co.

AMERICAN LEGEND CRAZY HORSE - Apparel and accessories - L.C. Licensing, Inc.

AMERICAN LEGENDS - Tables–wood - Riverside Furniture Corp.

AMERICAN LEWA ECODOS - Meters–electric - American Lewa, Inc.

AMERICAN LIFE - Books - American Life Foundation & Study Institute

AMERICAN LIFESTYLE - Fabrics - Burlington Industries, Inc.

AMERICAN LIFESTYLE - Window coverings - Eastern Standard Corp.

AMERICAN LIGHT - Beverages–malt - Keystone Brewers Holding Co.

AMERICAN LIGHTING - Lamps - American Lighting Industry Inc.

AMERICAN LIGHTS - Cigarettes - American Tobacco Co.

AMERICAN LIGHTWAVE SYSTEMS - Microwave components - American Lightwave Systems, Inc.

AMERICAN-LINCOLN - Cleaning equipment - Clarke Industries, Inc.

AMERICAN LINE - Personal-care product Now out of production ☆ - American Safety Razor Co.

AMERICAN LIVING - Fabrics–tapestry ☆ - Columbus Coated Fabrics Co.

AMERICAN LOCK COMPANY - Locks–padlocks - Junkunc Bros. American Lock Co.

AMERICAN LOCK CO. - Padlocks - American Lock Co.

AMERICAN LOOSE LEAF - Binders - American Loose Leaf Business Products Inc.

AMERICAN LOVE - Dresses–women's - Tocca Ltd.

AMERICAN LURE COLLECTION - Fishing lures - TradeTech International Trading Inc.

AMERICAN MADE - Garden equipment - Ames Lawn & Garden Tool Co.

A AMERICAN MADE - Furniture–upholstered - Park & Sell Co., Inc.

AMERICAN MADE/AMERICAN OWNED - Lawn mowers - MTD Products Inc.

AMERICAN MADE WORLD PLAYED - Guitars - Gibson Guitar Corp.

AMERICAN MADRAS - Bedding–linen - Dan River Inc.

AMERICAN MAID - Bathroom fixtures ☆ - American Shower Door Co.

AMERICAN MAID - Carriages–doll - South Bend Toy Manufacturing Co.

AMERICAN MAID - Clothespins - Penley Corp.

AMERICAN MAID - Food products ☆ - Red Wing Co., Inc.

AMERICAN MAID - Wood products - M. Kamenstein, Inc.

AMERICAN MAJESTY - Floor coverings–carpet and rugs ☆ - Gulistan Carpet Inc.

AMERICAN MALE, THE - Coats–men's - Gallron

AMERICAN MANHATTAN - Kitchen cabinets–metal - Haas Cabinet Co. Inc.

AMERICAN MANOR COLLECTION - Furniture - Pinnacle Furniture Co.

AMERICAN MANSION - Trailers–travel - Fleetwood Enterprises, Inc.

AMERICAN MAP - American Map Corp.

AMERICAN MAPLE - Cutlery - General Housewares Corp.

AMERICAN MAPLE - Syrup, candy, bread and pancake mixes, etc. - American Maple Products Corp.

AMERICAN MAPLE CUTTER - Paper cutters - Dahle USA

AMERICAN MASTERPIECE COLLECTION - Furniture - Hickory Manufacturing Co.

AMERICAN MASTERS - Musical instrument stores - Educational Broadcasting Corp.

☆ = Now out of production

AMERICAN MATES - Footwear - Alta Products Corp.
AMERICAN MELODY - Recording label - American Melody Records
AMERICAN MEMORIES - Furniture - A-America, Inc.
AMERICAN METAL PRODUCTS - Dampers - Masco Corp.
AMERICAN METRIC - Transmission equipment–industrial - American-Metric Corp.
AMERICAN MILLS - Paints - Keller Industries Inc.
AMERICAN MISS - Cosmetics - AAI/ACCESSORIES Associates Inc.
AMERICAN MIXTURES - Vegetables–frozen - Pillsbury Co.
AMERICAN MODE - Apparel and accessories ☆ - Horace Small Apparel Co.
AMERICAN MODERN HOME FIRST - Computer software - American Modern Home Insurance Co.
AMERICAN MODULARS - Window frames - Bellwether Corp.
AMERICAN MONOFIL - Sporting goods - American Wholesale Hardware Co.
AMERICAN MOOD - Linen - Thomaston Mills Inc.
AMERICAN MOUNTAIN - Hobby kits - Harper-Lee International
AMERICAN MUSCLE - Vitamins and nutritional supplements - American Muscle Inc.
AMERICAN MUSCLE CARS - Toys–models - ERTL Co., Inc.
AMERICAN MUSEUM BRASS COLLECTION - Giftware - Baldwin Hardware Corp.
AMERICAN MUSEUM COLLECTION - Silver products - Kirk Stieff Co.
AMERICAN MUSIC - Musical instruments - American Music Group Ltd.
AMERICAN MUSIC - Recording label - Jazzology-GHB Records
AMERICAN NATIONAL - Water beds and accessories - American National Watermattress Corp.
AMERICAN NATIVES - Posters - Marigold Graphics
AMERICAN NATURAL - Apparel and accessories - American Laundry Machinery, Inc.
AMERICAN NATURAL - Furniture ☆ - Bassett Furniture Industries, Inc.
AMERICAN NATURALS - Skin care products - Mana Products, Inc.
AMERICAN NATURALS - Wallpaper ☆ - J.M. Lynne Co. Inc.
AMERICAN NEEDLECREST - Floor coverings–carpet and rugs ☆ - Playfield International Inc.
AMERICAN NORSE - Flatware - Royal Silver Manufacturing Co. Inc.
AMERICAN NOSTALGIA - Recording label - Hope International
AMERICAN NURSE - Watches - Bulova Corp.
AMERICAN NUTRICEUTICALS - Vitamins and nutritional supplements - Natural Resource
AMERICAN NUTRITIONALS - Vitamins and nutritional supplements - Marcham Laboratories, Inc.
AMERICAN OAK - Cabinets–wood - Haas Cabinet Co. Inc.
AMERICAN OAK COLLECTION - Furniture - Thomasville Furniture Industries Inc.
AMERICAN OAK COLLECTION - Furniture ☆ - Evenflo Juvenile Furniture Co.
AMERICAN OARS - Sportswear - Douglas H. Keeffe
AMERICAN OF MARTINSVILLE - Furniture - American Furniture Co. Inc.
AMERICAN OLEAN - Tiles–ceramic - American Olean Tile Co.
AMERICAN OPULENCE - Giftware - Yale-Forman Designs
AMERICAN OPULENCE - Wallcoverings - Sherman & Associates International
AMERICAN ORCHARD - Mayonnaise and salad dressings - Mouloud Baira
AMERICAN ORCHARD - Water–bottled or canned - Heublein, Inc.
AMERICAN ORIGINAL - Food products - American Original Foods
AMERICAN ORIGINAL - Seafood products–fresh or frozen - Sea Watch International Ltd.
AMERICAN ORIGINALS - Beverages–malt - Anheuser-Busch Companies Inc.
AMERICAN ORIGINALS - Blankets - Pillowtex Corp.
AMERICAN ORIGINALS - Glassware–household - Pfaltzgraff Investment Co.
AMERICAN ORIGINALS - Novelty items ☆ - Webway, Inc.
AMERICAN OUTBACK - Apparel and accessories - American Artwear, Inc.
AMERICAN OUTERWEAR - Apparel and accessories - American Outerwear Group, Ltd.
AMERICAN OUTPOST - Apparel and accessories - Forman Enterprises, Inc.
AMERICAN PACIFIC - Quilts - American Pacific Enterprises, Inc.
AMERICAN PACIFIC SPAS - Spas–home - American Pacific Spas, Ltd.
AMERICAN PAINTER - Artists' materials - Loew-Cornell Inc.
AMERICAN PAJAMA COMPANY - Apparel and accessories - Bentley Lingerie, Inc.
AMERICAN PANTS - Apparel and accessories - World Trading Inc.
AMERICAN PAPER & TWINE CO. - Cleaning preparations–household - American Paper & Twine Co.
AMERICAN PAPER PRODUCTS - Mailing tubes, tubular containers - American Paper Products Co.
AMERICAN PASSAGE - Advertising agencies - Network Event Theater, Inc.
AMERICAN PATCHWORKS - Wallcovering ☆ - Colortree Designs
AMERICAN PATCHWORKS - Wallpaper ☆ - Eisenhart Wallcoverings Co.

AMERICAN PATRIOT - Jewelry - Jacoby-Bender Inc.
AMERICAN PAVER - Floor coverings ☆ - Tarkett, Inc.
AMERICAN PETCARE - Pet products ☆ - Waters Corp.
AMERICAN PETROLEUM INSTITUTE CERTIFIED - Lubricating oils ☆ - American Petroleum Institute
AMERICAN PEWTER GUILD - Jewelry - Sycamore Pewtersmith
AMERICAN PHYTOTHERAPY RESEARCH LABORATORY APRL - Vitamins and nutritional supplements - American Phytotherapy Research Laboratory
AMERICAN PIE - Kitchen utensils–aluminum - Bonny Products Inc.
AMERICAN PIE - Recording label - American Pie
AMERICAN PINE COLLECTION - Giftware - Cornwall Industries Inc.
AMERICAN PLAINS - Underwear and nightwear - Tect, Inc.
AMERICAN PLAY HOUSE - Apparel and accessories - Goldenwood International, Inc.
AMERICAN PLAYBOY - Recording label - Music Enterprises Inc.
AMERICAN PLAYWORLD - Sporting goods - Roadmaster Corp.
AMERICAN PLEASURE CURL - Hair care products ☆ - Samlo
AMERICAN POLYMER - Paints ☆ - American Polymer Corp.
AMERICAN POLYTREL - Bed pillows - American Foam Latex Corp.
AMERICAN POP - Jewelry - American Pop, Inc.
AMERICAN PORTRAIT - Apparel and accessories - Charles Komar and Sons Inc.
AMERICAN PORTRAITS - Dolls - Susan Wakeen Doll Co., Inc.
AMERICAN POULTRY INTERNATIONAL LTD. - Chickens - American Poultry International Ltd.
AMERICAN POWER CONVERSION - Power switching equipment - American Power Conversion Corp.
AMERICAN PRAIRIE - Food products - Mercantile Food Co.
AMERICAN PREFERENCE - Furniture–wood - Cardinal American Corp.
AMERICAN PREMIER - Bakery products - Lucky Stores, Inc.
AMERICAN PREMIER - Beverages–alcohol - American Stores Co.
AMERICAN PREMIER BEDDING - Mattresses - High Point Bedding, Inc.
AMERICAN PREMIUM - Meat products–beef - Highland Beefalo Farms, Inc.
AMERICAN PREMIUM - Tires - Hanco Corp.
AMERICAN PRESS - Pencils ☆ - Koh-I-Noor, Inc.
AMERICAN PRESTIGE - Flowers–artificial - Vincent Lippe Co.
AMERICAN PRETZEL A NEW TRADITION, THE - Pretzels - Atlanta Pretzel Co., Inc.
AMERICAN PRIDE - Fireworks - American Promotional Events, Inc.
AMERICAN PRIDE - Jewelry - Landstrom's Original Black Hills Gold Creations
AMERICAN PRIDE - Shutters–plastic - Aluminum Co. of America
AMERICAN PRIDE BELT COMPANY - Belts–apparel - RKP Industries
AMERICAN PRIMITIVE - Floor coverings–carpet and rugs ☆ - Mohawk Industries Inc.
AMERICAN PRIMITIVES - Posters - One-of-a-Kind Workshop
AMERICAN PRINCESS - Apparel and accessories - Mamiye Brothers, Inc.
AMERICAN PRIORITY SWEATERS LTD. - Apparel and accessories - American Priority Sweaters, Ltd.
AMERICAN PRO - Footwear–athletic - American Athletic Shoe Co.
AMERICAN PRO - Golfing equipment - Prostar L.P.
AMERICAN PRODUCTION SERVICES - Recording label - Conrad W. Denke
AMERICAN PRODUCTS - Pickles - Green Bay Foods Co.
AMERICAN PROFILE - Broadcasting stations–television - National Cable Satellite Corp.
AMERICAN PROFILES - Magazines - Farrar, Straus and Giroux Inc.
AMERICAN PROFILES - Wastebaskets - American Profiles, Inc.
AMERICAN PUBLISHING - Puzzles - Warren Industries Inc.
AMERICAN QUEEN - Glassware–household - Delta Queen Steamboat Co.
AMERICAN QUEEN - Leather goods - St. Thomas Inc.
AMERICAN QUILT CLASSICS - Greeting cards ☆ - Evergreen Press
AMERICAN QUILT STORY - Wallpaper - J. Josephson, Inc.
AMERICAN RACE TRUCKS - Motor vehicles–trucks - Motorsports Promotions, Inc.
AMERICAN RACER - Toys ☆ - Servistar Corp.
AMERICAN RACING - Wheels–motor vehicle - American Racing Equipment Inc.
AMERICAN RADIO - Recording label - Caprice International Records
AMERICAN RAG CIE - Apparel and accessories - Industries Werts, Inc.
AMERICAN RAMP SYSTEMS - Ramps - American Ramp Systems
AMERICAN REBEL - Apparel and accessories - Kelley A. Doyle
AMERICAN RECIPE - Food products - Whole Food Marketing
AMERICAN RECIPE - Soups–canned - Campbell Soup Co.
AMERICAN RECREATION PRODUCTS - Sporting goods - Kellwood Co.
AMERICAN REDNECK ASSOCIATION - Apparel and accessories - Benny H. Pellom
AMERICAN RENAISSANCE - Windows–storm - Norco Windows, Inc.

☆ = Now out of production

AMERICAN REPRINT CO. - Publisher's imprints - Amereon Ltd.
AMERICAN RESCUE TECHNOLOGY INCORPORATED - Tools–machine - American Rescue Technology Inc.
AMERICAN RESERVE - Socks - Wrangler Apparel Co.
AMERICAN ROMAN - Apparel and accessories - Matthew K. Valenzuela
AMERICAN ROMANTIC - Greeting cards - Blue Mountain Arts Inc.
AMERICAN ROPE - Jewelry–precious - Michael Anthony Jewelers, Inc.
AMERICAN ROSE - Candles - Princess House, Inc.
AMERICAN ROYALTY - Glassware–household - Saladmaster Corp.
AMERICAN RUNNER - Floor coverings–carpet and rugs - Superior American Plastics Co.
AMERICAN SADDLERY - Saddles - American Saddlery, Inc.
AMERICAN SAFETY - Boots - L.B. Evans' Son Co.
AMERICAN SAILOR - Apparel and accessories - Embroidery Services Inc.
AMERICAN SALAMANDER HEATER, THE - Heaters–gas - Vogelzang International Corp.
AMERICAN SALTBOX - Wallpaper - Shelbourne Wallcoverings
AMERICAN SALTBOX II - Wallpaper - Shelbourne Wallcoverings
AMERICAN SAMPLER - Tableware–china ☆ - Villeroy and Boch Tableware Ltd.
AMERICAN SANDERS - Washing machine parts - Alto U.S. Inc.
AMERICAN SANITARY - Hardware - Blaine Window Hardware Inc.
AMERICAN SANTAS BY GALLERIA LUCCHESE - Giftware - Roman, Inc.
AMERICAN SCANDIA - Cabinets - Haas Cabinet Co. Inc.
AMERICAN SEAFOODS COMPANY - Seafood products–fresh or frozen - American Seafoods Co.
AMERICAN SELECT - Barbecues and grills - Char-Broil
AMERICAN SENTINEL - Rubber–molded ☆ - Lancaster Colony Automotive Group
AMERICAN SETTINGS COLLECTION - Dinnerware - FFSC, Inc.
AMERICAN SETTLER - Furniture - Universal Flooring
AMERICAN SHORES - Wallpaper - Imperial Wallcoverings, Inc.
AMERICAN SHORES II - Wallpaper ☆ - Imperial Wallcoverings, Inc.
AMERICAN SHOWCASE - Carpet - Shaw Industries Inc.
AMERICAN SHOWER & BATH - Plumbing fixtures–metal - Masco Corp.
AMERICAN SHOWER DOOR - Bathroom fixtures - American Shower Door Co.
AMERICAN SHOWLINE GAME - Trailers–travel - Trailer Craft
AMERICAN SIGNATURE - Coats - Kent Street Group, Inc.
AMERICAN SIGNATURE - Cosmetics - E & M Atlantic Partners, Inc.
AMERICAN SILHOUETTES - Furniture - Cochrane Furniture Co. Inc.
AMERICAN SILKS - Wallpaper ☆ - Vymura
AMERICAN SIMPLICITY - Wallpaper ☆ - Glidden Co.
AMERICAN SKETCHBOOK III - Wallpaper ☆ - Imperial Wallcoverings, Inc.
AMERICAN SKIER - Powerboat ☆ - American Skier Boat Co.
AMERICAN SKULLS - Footwear - De La Rentis Imports Inc.
AMERICAN SNAP - Knives - American Brush Co. Inc.
AMERICAN SOCCER - Games ☆ - Tudor Inc.
AMERICAN SOCK EXCHANGE - Socks - Hit or Miss Inc.
AMERICAN SOUND - Recording label - Jazz Composer's Orchestra Association Inc.
AMERICAN SOUTHWEST - Wallpaper ☆ - Imperial Wallcoverings, Inc.
AMERICAN SPECIAL - Tools - American Wholesale Hardware Co.
AMERICAN SPECIALTIES - Novelty items - Risto Inc.
AMERICAN SPEED - Apparel and accessories - American Speed, Inc.
AMERICAN SPEED-READERS ASSOCIATION - Publisher's imprints - Krestmont Group
AMERICAN SPICE - Floor coverings–carpet and rugs - Downs Carpet Co. Inc.
AMERICAN SPICE - Wallpaper - Shelbourne Wallcoverings
AMERICAN SPICE II - Wallpaper - Shelbourne Wallcoverings
AMERICAN SPICE SHELF - Seasonings - Cross Border Enterprises
AMERICAN SPIRIT - Floor coverings–carpet and rugs - Cabin Crafts Carpets
AMERICAN SPIRIT - Game machines ☆ - WMS Gaming Inc.
AMERICAN SPIRIT - Nail care products - CCA Industries, Inc.
AMERICAN SPIRIT - Tobacco–chewing or smoking - Santa Fe Natural Tobacco Co.
AMERICAN SPIRIT - Women's apparel - India Garments Inc.
AMERICAN SPIRIT, THE - Fans–ceiling - Fasco Industries Inc. (Consumer Products Div.)
AMERICAN SPOON - Cherry gooseberry chutney - American Spoon Foods Inc.
AMERICAN SPORTER II TRAP - Sporting goods - Blount International, Inc. (Sporting Equipment Group)
AMERICAN SPORTFISHING ASSOCIATION - Apparel–athletic - American Sportfishing Association
AMERICAN SPORTS - Air purification systems ☆ - Medo Industries, Inc.
AMERICAN SPORTS - Giftware - Sasaki

AMERICAN SPORTS - Ski racks - American Sports Inc.
AMERICAN SPORTSMAN - Air purification systems ☆ - Medo Industries, Inc.
AMERICAN SQUAD - Golfing equipment - International Sports Cns, Inc.
AMERICAN SQUARE - Finishing agents ☆ - Flintkote Co.
AMERICAN SQUARE - Paints ☆ - GS Roofing Products Co.
AMERICAN STANDARD - Musical instrument accessories - D'Andrea Manufacturing Co. Inc.
AMERICAN-STANDARD - Plumbing fixtures - American Standard Inc.
AMERICAN STANDARD - Watches - Bulova Corp.
AMERICAN STANDARD GOLF - Golfing equipment - Carolina Custom Golf
AMERICAN STAR - Apparel - Alakh Sportswear, Inc.
AMERICAN STAR - Trailers–travel - Newmar Corp.
AMERICAN STAR - Water–bottled or canned - American Water Co., Inc.
AMERICAN STATEMENTS ORIGINAL ACTIVE WEAR - Apparel and accessories - Lavaille Metoyer
AMERICAN STEEL SPAN - Prefabricated buildings–metal - Steel Factory Corp.
AMERICAN STENCIL - Floor coverings–carpet and rugs ☆ - Concepts International
AMERICAN STENCIL - Pens, markers ☆ - American Coated Products Inc.
AMERICAN STERLING PEWTER - Picture frames - Elias Artmetal, Inc.
AMERICAN STONE - Finishing agents ☆ - Flintkote Co.
AMERICAN STONE - Paints ☆ - GS Roofing Products Co.
AMERICAN STORM - Apparel–men's - Charles Navasky & Co. Inc.
AMERICAN STORY - Wallpaper - J. Josephson, Inc.
AMERICAN STORYTELLER - Wallpaper - Surface Industries Inc.
AMERICAN STOVE PRODUCTS - Ventilation equipment - GSW Jackes-Evans Manufacturing Co.
AMERICAN STREETWISE - Boots - Amwelt Corp.
AMERICAN STUDIO GLASS - Glassware–household ☆ - National Housewares
AMERICAN STYLE - Toiletry cases and tote bags - Living Things Manufacturing Co., Inc.
AMERICAN STYLE - Wallpaper - Sanitas Wallcoverings
AMERICAN SUCCESS CO. - Books–blank - Harold-Lawrence Associates Inc.
AMERICAN SUNSETS - Wallcovering ☆ - Fashon Wallcoverings
AMERICAN SUNSETS II - Wallcovering ☆ - Fashon Wallcoverings
AMERICAN SUNSETS III - Wallcovering - Fashon Wallcoverings
AMERICAN SUPREME - Pharmaceutical preparations - T.N. Dickinson Co.
AMERICAN SUPREME - Window coverings - American Window Fabricators Inc.
AMERICAN TARTAN - Bedding–linen - Dan River Inc.
AMERICAN TEAM SPORTS PRO CELEBRITY - Apparel–athletic - Tee Top of California, Inc.
AMERICAN TEAM, THE - Plastics - American Team
AMERICAN TERMINAL EXCHANGE - Electronic equipment - American Terminal Exchange, Inc.
AMERICAN TERRAIN - Apparel–men's - Robert Peritz
AMERICAN TERRITORIES - Apparel and accessories - Unlimited Avenues Inc.
AMERICAN TESTLINER - Paperboard - International Paper Co.
AMERICAN THATCH - Asbestos products ☆ - GAF Corp.
AMERICAN, THE - Saddles - American Saddlery, Inc.
AMERICAN THERMOSEAL - Water-bed mattresses - American Thermoseal Inc.
AMERICAN THREE LINE - Abrasive products ☆ - American Hone Co.
AMERICAN TOBACCO CO. LIGHTS QUALITY BLEND - Cigarettes - Brown & Williamson Tobacco Corp.
AMERICAN TOMAHAWK CO. - Knives–hunting - Cold Steel Inc.
AMERICAN TOOL - Machine tools - Devlieg-Bullard Services Group
AMERICAN TOUR - Golfing equipment - GMT Golf, Inc.
AMERICAN TOURISTER - Automotive parts and accessories - Samsonite Corp.
AMERICAN TOURISTER - Luggage - American Tourister, Inc.
AMERICAN TOURISTER MAKING TRAVEL LESS PRIMITIVE. - Automotive parts and accessories - Samsonite Corp.
AMERICAN TRADITION - Breads–mixes - Dawn Food Products Inc.
AMERICAN TRADITION - Floor coverings–carpet and rugs ☆ - Gulistan Carpet Inc.
AMERICAN TRADITION - Paints - Valspar Corp.
AMERICAN TRADITIONAL - Furniture - Singer Furniture Co.
AMERICAN TRADITIONAL - Furniture–children's ☆ - Child Craft Industries Inc.
AMERICAN TRADITIONAL - Roofing materials–concrete - GAF Corp.
AMERICAN TRADITIONAL - Stencils - American Traditional Stencils
AMERICAN TRADITIONS - Apparel–men's - Superba, Inc.

☆ = Now out of production

AMERICAN TRADITIONS - Food products - Turner Gourmet & International Foods

AMERICAN TRADITIONS - Furniture ☆ - Broyhill Furniture Industries, Inc.

AMERICAN TRAIL - Footwear - Westwood Shoe Corp.

AMERICAN TRAIL, THE - Video production - Jeffrey J. Harsh

AMERICAN TRAVELER - Slacks - Hart Schaffner & Marx

AMERICAN TREASURES - Fabrics–tapestry - Comark Wallcoverings

AMERICAN TREASURES - Floor coverings–carpet and rugs ☆ - Karastan-Bigelow Inc.

AMERICAN TREASURES - Furniture ☆ - Stanley Furniture Co. Inc.

AMERICAN TREASURES - Wallpaper ☆ - Thomas Strahan Wallcoverings

AMERICAN TRIUMPH - Jewelry - Jacoby-Bender Inc.

AMERICAN TURBO - Tires - American Car Care Centers Inc.

AMERICAN TWIST DRILLS - Drills - Production Tool Supply International

AMERICAN UNIFORM - Boots - L.B. Evans' Son Co.

AMERICAN URBAN LIGHTS - Boots - Amwelt Corp.

AMERICAN URN - Vases - American Urn, Inc.

AMERICAN VACATION VIDEOS - Prerecorded videocassettes - Clark's Video Group, Inc.

AMERICAN VALANCE - Window shades - Quakermaid Products

AMERICAN VALLEY - Food products - Mouloud Baira

AMERICAN VALUE - Paper–tissue - Allen & Co., Inc.

AMERICAN VELVET - Floor coverings–carpet and rugs ☆ - Lees Carpets

AMERICAN VETERINARY FORMULA - Pet products - Cardinal Laboratories, Inc.

AMERICAN VICTORY - Toys–automobiles - Mattel, Inc.

AMERICAN VINTAGE - Furniture - Borkholder Corp.

AMERICAN VINTAGE - Furniture ☆ - Vaughan Furniture Co. Inc.

AMERICAN VINTAGE CYCLES - Trading cards and stamps - Custom Graphics, Inc.

AMERICAN VINYLS VOL. 2 - Wallpaper - I. Gottlieb & Associates

AMERICAN V.I.P. - Furniture - American Furniture Co. Inc.

AMERICAN VISION CENTERS - Pharmaceutical preparations - American Vision Centers

AMERICAN WALKER - Apparel–women's ☆ - David Smith

AMERICAN WALL DECOR - Posters - Fabulous Forgeries Ltd.

AMERICAN WALNUT - Giftware - Jacksonville Manufacturing

AMERICAN WASH - Apparel - Blue Bell, Inc.

AMERICAN WATCH CO. - Watches - American Watch Co.

AMERICAN WATERFOWL COLLECTION - Decoys - Jibco Industries Inc.

AMERICAN WATERPROOF +PLUS - Boots - L.B. Evans' Son Co.

AMERICAN WAY - Floor coverings–carpet and rugs - Alexander Smith Carpets

AMERICAN WAY II - Wallpaper ☆ - Sanitas Wallcoverings

AMERICAN WAY, THE - Recording label - Pony Venture Project

AMERICAN WEAVE - Wallpaper ☆ - J. Josephson, Inc.

AMERICAN WEAVERS - Linen - American Weavers, LLC

AMERICAN WEAVES & LANDSCAPE - Wallpaper - J. Josephson, Inc.

AMERICAN WEEKEND - Apparel and accessories - Montgomery Ward & Co. Inc.

AMERICAN WEST - Handbags ☆ - Sarne Co. Inc.

AMERICAN WEST - Toys–guns - Strombecker Corp.

AMERICAN WHIRLPOOL - Bathtubs–enameled - American Trading and Production Corp.

AMERICAN WHITEHALL - Pressed glassware - Indiana Glass Co.

AMERICAN WHITEHALL PEACH COLLECTION - Pressed glassware ☆ - Indiana Glass Co.

AMERICAN WICK - Computer hardware - Cans Unlimited, Inc.

AMERICAN WIDGEON - Apparel–children's - Sara's Prints, Inc.

AMERICAN WILDLIFE - Knives–hunting - Camillus Cutlery Co.

AMERICAN WILDLIFE COLLECTION - Hobby kits - Craft-Tex Inc.

AMERICAN WINDING - Musical instrument accessories - Dean Markley Strings, Inc.

AMERICAN WOMAN - Hair care products - AAI/ACCESSORIES Associates Inc.

AMERICAN WOMAN - Handbags - Marilyn USA

AMERICAN WOOD BLINDS - Window coverings - M & B Mini-Blind Corp.

AMERICAN WOODS - Furniture ☆ - Tacony Corp.

AMERICAN WORKHORSE - Toys–trains - Life-Like Products Inc.

AMERICAN X-RAY - X-ray apparatus - Panoramic Corp.

AMERICAN XT - Motor vehicle parts and accessories - Family Dollar Services, Inc.

AMERICAN XT - Oils–lubricating - Family Dollar Services, Inc.

AMERICAN ZEBRA - Exercising equipment - Douglas R. Matthews

AMERICAN ZETTLER - Diodes - American Zettler, Inc.

AMERICANA - Apparel and accessories - SKL Co. Inc.

AMERICANA - Artists' materials ☆ - Hamilton Industries

AMERICANA - Bathroom accessories ☆ - Franklin Brass Manufacturing Co.

AMERICANA - Book club - American Life Foundation & Study Institute

AMERICANA - Brooms - Royal Maid Association for the Blind Inc.

AMERICANA - Cabinets - Continental Kitchen Corp.

AMERICANA - Cabinets ☆ - Merillat Industries, Inc.

AMERICANA - Calendars - Amcal Inc.

AMERICANA - Candles ☆ - Candle-Lite Co.

AMERICANA - Computer software - Aris Multimedia Entertainment, Inc.

AMERICANA - Desks - Vanguard Corp.

AMERICANA - Dining room furniture - John Boos and Co. Inc.

AMERICANA - Dining room furniture ☆ - Imperial Manufacturing Co.

AMERICANA - Dishwashers–household - General Electric Co.

AMERICANA - Dolls - Alexander Doll Co. Inc.

AMERICANA - Dolls ☆ - Effanbee Doll Corp.

AMERICANA - Door frames - Fenestra Corp.

AMERICANA - Doors–garage - General American Door Co.

AMERICANA - Drapery hardware - Kirsch Co.

AMERICANA - Fabrics–broadcloth - Desire Mills Co. Inc.

AMERICANA - Floor coverings - American Floor Products Co. Inc.

AMERICANA - Floor coverings - Congoleum Corp.

AMERICANA - Floor coverings–carpet and rugs - Sheridan Carpet Mills

AMERICANA - Food products - Pierce Foods Corp.

AMERICANA - Frames–eyeglass - U.S. Optical Frame Co.

AMERICANA - Furniture ☆ - American Toy & Furniture Co.

AMERICANA - Furniture ☆ - Lexington Furniture Industries, Inc.

AMERICANA - Furniture–children's ☆ - Child Craft Industries Inc.

AMERICANA - Furniture–wood ☆ - Flanders Industries Inc.

AMERICANA - Giftware - Russ Berrie and Co., Inc.

AMERICANA - Glassware–household - Durand International

AMERICANA - Health care products - Sunrise Medical

AMERICANA - Hobby kits ☆ - Craft World International Inc.

AMERICANA - Housewares ☆ - Gemco Ware, Inc.

AMERICANA - Iron products ☆ - Roesch Inc.

AMERICANA - Lamps ☆ - Prestigeline Inc.

AMERICANA - Lighting fixtures - Leviton Manufacturing Co., Inc.

AMERICANA - Manicure sets ☆ - London International U.S. Holdings

AMERICANA - Melamine dinnerware - Boonton Molding Co. Inc.

AMERICANA - Mobile homes ☆ - Wick Building Systems Inc. (Manufactured Home Div./North)

AMERICANA - Novelty items - Americana Art China Co.

AMERICANA - Nutcrackers - Grain Processing Corp.

AMERICANA - Nuts–salted, roasted, cooked, or canned - Leavitt Corp.

AMERICANA - Oils–illuminating ☆ - Klean-Strip

AMERICANA - Paints ☆ - DecoArt

AMERICANA - Paper - Strathmore Paper Co.

AMERICANA - Sandwiches–prepackaged - Denny's Inc.

AMERICANA - Seafood products–fresh or frozen - Demerico Corp.

AMERICANA - Sinks–porcelain - Artesian Industries

AMERICANA - Sporting goods - Cut 'n Jump Ski Corp.

AMERICANA - Thermometers - Taylor Environmental Instruments

AMERICANA - Thread ☆ - American & Efird, Inc.

AMERICANA - Toys–banks ☆ - Doranne

AMERICANA - Underwear and nightwear - Bestform Foundations, Inc.

AMERICANA - Wallpaper ☆ - Artisan House Inc.

AMERICANA - Watches - Bulova Corp.

AMERICANA - Wines - Americana Vineyards Estate Winery

AMERICANA - Wines - Kendall Jackson Winery, Ltd.

AMERICANA BEARS - See **BEAR HUGS**

AMERICANA BIRD COLLECTION - Giftware - Arnart Imports Inc.

AMERICANA BOW RIDER - Boats–motor ☆ - Yar-Craft, Inc.

AMERICANA CHRISTMAS ORNAMENT COLLECTION - Christmas tree ornaments - Gloria Duchin Inc.

AMERICANA CLASSICS - Candles - Candle-Lite Co.

AMERICANA COLLECTION - Fabrics - Interials Inc.

AMERICANA COLLECTION - Floor coverings–carpet and rugs ☆ - Custom Decor Inc.

AMERICANA COLLECTION - Luggage - Lollypop Import and Export of Brooklyn

AMERICANA COLLECTION BY BILL JAUQUET - Giftware - Roman, Inc.

AMERICANA COLLECTION, THE - Containers–paper - Earle Industries, Inc.

AMERICANA COLLECTION, THE - Apparel and accessories ☆ - Martingale & Co.

AMERICANA DESIGNS - Figurines - Designs Americana

AMERICANA HEARTLAND TRADITIONS - Candles - Anagada Corp.

AMERICANA HOME - Giftware - Arnart Imports Inc.

AMERICANA II - Bathroom accessories - Franklin Brass Manufacturing Co.
AMERICANA II-D - Bells and chimes - Schulmerich Carillons Inc.
AMERICANA III - Bathroom accessories - Franklin Brass Manufacturing Co.
AMERICANA OUTDOOR RECEPTACLES - Wastebaskets - United Receptacle Inc.
AMERICANA PALING - Fencing–wood - Machalk Enterprises Inc.
AMERICANA PRINTS - Placemats - Cascade Fibers Co.
AMERICANA ROOT BEER TRADITIONAL CREAM STYLE - Beverages–carbonated - Orca Beverage, Inc.
AMERICANA SCRAPBOOK - Giftware - S.S. Sarna Inc.
AMERICANA SIGNATURE COLLECTION - Giftware - Arnart Imports Inc.
AMERICANA VINEYARDS - Wines - Americana Vineyards Estate Winery
AMERICANAS - Shoes - Beacon Shoe Co.
AMERICANCHURCH - Paper products - American Paper Group, Inc.
AMERICANDLES - Candles - Armadilla Wax Works, Inc.
AMERICANDRY - Beverages–carbonated - Polar Corp.
AMERICANLEVEL - Tools–hand-operated - Macklanburg-Duncan Co.
AMERICANMADE - Recording label - Stylette Plastics Inc.
AMERICANO, THE - Ventilation equipment ✰ - Leslie-Locke, Inc.
AMERICANS - Cigar boxes–wood - Consolidated Cigar Corp.
AMERICANS - Mats, matting ✰ - American Floor Products Co. Inc.
AMERICAN'S BEST - Popcorn - American Pop Corn Co.
AMERICARD - Greeting cards - American Greetings Corp.
AMERICARPS - Musical instrument accessories - Pro-Mark Corp.
AMERICA'S #1 DRILLMAKER - Drill bits - Precision Twist Drill Co.
AMERICA'S 1ST BASEBALL COMPANY - Sporting goods - Lisco, Inc.
AMERICA'S ALL-TIME FAVORITE CRAFTS CARDS - Hobby kits - Atlas Editions, Inc.
AMERICA'S ALTERNATIVE - Apparel and accessories - Seattle Pacific Industries, Inc.
AMERICA'S BASEBALL TEMPLES - Posters - Brad Bennett
AMERICA'S BEST - Apparel–women's - Newton Manufacturing Corp.
AMERICA'S BEST - Chocolate candy - Cocoline Chocolate Co.
AMERICA'S BEST - Cleaning preparations - Quality Products International Corp.
AMERICA'S BEST - Coffee - America's Best Beverages Inc.
AMERICA'S BEST - Crackers - Mark Group Ltd., Inc.
AMERICA'S BEST - Flour–blended - The Wall-Rogalsky Milling Co.
AMERICA'S BEST - Food products - The Kroger Co.
AMERICA'S BEST - Housewares - Moore-Handley Inc.
AMERICA'S BEST - Roofing materials - Georgia-Pacific Corp.
AMERICA'S BEST - Shorts–men's - America's Best, Inc.
AMERICAS BEST - Snack foods - Gateway Candy Corp.
AMERICA'S BEST ANTIOXIDANT - Vitamins and nutritional supplements - First Security of Destin, Inc.
AMERICA'S BEST-LOVED QUILT BOOKS - Publisher's imprints - Martingale & Co.
AMERICA'S BEST NATURALLY - Crackers - Fort Biscuit Co.
AMERICA'S BEST PORK - Advertising agencies - Farmland Foods, Inc.
AMERICA'S BEST!WIPE-ON - Finishing agents - Woodshed Furniture Restoration Enterprises, Ltd.
AMERICA'S BOOTMAKER - Footwear - United States Shoe Corp.
AMERICA'S BOUNTY - Soups–canned ✰ - Campbell Soup Co.
AMERICA'S BREWER OF FRUIT BEER - Beverages - Aldo A. Stanton
AMERICA'S CARPET GALLERY - Floor coverings–carpet and rugs - Magic Marketing, Inc.
AMERICA'S CHOICE - Cutting tools - Precision Twist Drill Co.
AMERICA'S CHOICE - Food products - Great Atlantic & Pacific Tea Co., Inc.
AMERICA'S CHOICE - Food products - Silver Foods Corp.
AMERICA'S CHOICE - Packaging machines - Infra Pak, Inc.
AMERICA'S CHOICE EYEWEAR - Frames–eyeglass - United Optical Corp.
AMERICA'S CLASSIC FOODS - Yogurt–frozen - America's Classic Foods
AMERICA'S CUP - Fiberboard ✰ - Fibre Glass-Evercoat Co. Inc.
AMERICA'S CUP - Floor coverings–carpet and rugs - Alexander Smith Carpets
AMERICA'S CUP - Sporting goods - America's Cup Inc.
AMERICA'S CUP - Sporting goods - Wellington Leisure Products, Inc.
AMERICA'S CUP - Watches - Hampden Corp.
AMERICA'S CUP SAILING SIMULATION - Computer software ✰ - Electronic Arts Inc.
AMERICA'S DOORMAKER - Doors–garage - Taylor Building Products Co.
AMERICA'S DREAM EXTERIOR - Siding–insulating - K-Designers
AMERICA'S FAMILY CUPS - Cups–plastic - Scott Paper Co.
AMERICA'S FAMILY PLATES - Paper - Scott Paper Co.
AMERICA'S FAVORITE - Cigars - Swisher International, Inc.
AMERICA'S FAVORITE - Electrical equipment - West Bend Co.

AMERICA'S FAVORITE - Trading cards - Unified Product Marketing
AMERICA'S FAVORITE MUSHROOM - Food products - Giorgifred Co.
AMERICA'S FAVORITE SINCE FBI - Candy - Favorite Brands International, Inc.
AMERICA'S FAVORITE SPORTSMEN - Video production - Tom Miranda Outdoors, Inc.
AMERICA'S FINEST - Food products - Ipswich Shellfish Co. Inc.
AMERICA'S FINEST - Novelty items - Charles Products Inc.
AMERICA'S FINEST COFFEE - Coffee - Ireland Coffee and Tea Inc.
AMERICA'S FINEST CONFECTION - Candy - Brown & Haley
AMERICA'S FINEST COOKIES - Cookies - BF USB Inc.
AMERICA'S FINEST JELLIES - Candy - Ben Myerson Candy Co.
AMERICA'S FIRST - Food products - ICCO Cheese Co., Inc.
AMERICA'S FIRST CHOICE - Lighting equipment - Bright Star Industries Inc.
AMERICA'S FIRST MALL FOR CHILDREN - Real estate agencies - Deborah L. Colvin
AMERICA'S GUITAR - Guitars - C.F. Martin & Co., Inc.
AMERICA'S GUNSMITH - Firearms, accessories, and parts - H & R 1871, Inc.
AMERICA'S GYM - Playground equipment ✰ - Hedstrom Corp.
AMERICA'S HERITAGE - Air purification systems ✰ - Medo Industries, Inc.
AMERICA'S HISTORY MULTICULTURAL CONTRIBUTIONS TO AMERICA - Computer software - Richard Robinson
AMERICA'S HOME REMEDY - Antacids - Miles Inc.
AMERICA'S INDOOR OUTDOOR CERAMIC TILE - Tiles–ceramic - Metropolitan Industries, Inc.
AMERICA'S KID TIMES - Paper–newsprint - Dean Paradise
AMERICA'S KIDS - Toys - Azrak-Hamway International, Inc.
AMERICA'S LIVING NATIONAL TREASURE - Paper products - Ringling Bros.-Barnum & Bailey Combined Shows, Inc.
AMERICA'S MOST DURABLE CARPET - Floor coverings–carpet and rugs - Carpet Co-Op of America Association
AMERICAS MOST WANTED BEARS - Toys - Sarcastic Toy Co.
AMERICA'S NATURAL CHICKEN - Poultry products - Seaboard Corp.
AMERICA'S NATURAL LEGACY - Watches ✰ - Longines-Wittnauer Watch Co.
AMERICA'S ORGANIC COMPANY - Grain products–rice - Arrowhead Mills, Inc.
AMERICA'S ORIGINAL MARCH MADNESS - Apparel and accessories - Illinois High School Assn.
AMERICA'S PEOPLE - Air purification systems ✰ - Medo Industries, Inc.
AMERICA'S PEOPLE SUCCESS EXPERTS - Paper products - Phase II, Inc.
AMERICA'S PERSONAL TRAINER - Vitamins and nutritional supplements - Tony Little Enterprises, Inc.
AMERICA'S PRECISION - Watches - Gruen Marketing Corp.
AMERICA'S PREMIER PAINT STORE - Paints - Kmart Properties, Inc.
AMERICA'S PRIDE - Apparel and accessories - Melton Shirt Co., Inc.
AMERICA'S SOURCE FOR SMALL COMMERCIAL MORTGAGES - Banks–commercial - Parallel Commercial Capital LLC
AMERICA'S SPORT TEAM - Apparel and accessories - H.H. Cutler Co.
AMERICA'S SPORTS VOICE - Broadcasting stations–radio - CBS Inc.
AMERICA'S TASTERS - Glassware–household ✰ - Crisa Corp.
AMERICA'S TEAM - Apparel and accessories - Meob Inc.
AMERICA'S THANKSGIVING PARADE DETROIT - Jackets - Parade Co.
AMERICA'S TRADEMARK - Apparel and accessories - Leo R. Estopare
AMERICA'S TRAVEL AUTHORITY - Computer software - Rand McNally & Co.
AMERICATONE - Recording label - Americatone Records International
AMERICATONE INTERNATIONAL USA - Recording label - Christy Records International
AMERICAWARE - Housewares and dinnerware - Feltman-Langer Co., Inc.
AMERICELL - Antennas - Scala Electronic Corp.
AMERICHILLER - Ice chests - Ohio Valley A.F.M. Inc.
AMERICLAD - Metals - Crown Partnership
AMERICO - Paints - Grow Group, Inc.
AMERICOINA - Penny banks - Valleau Brass Foundry
AMERICOLA - See **AMERICAN DRY**
AMERICOLD - Compressors–refrigeration - White Consolidated Industries, Inc.
AMERICOLORS - Jewelry - Mike Lemonakis
AMERICONE - Ice cream cones - Ohio Valley A.F.M. Inc.
AMERICOR - Framing board - Creative Industries, Inc.
AMERICORE - Machinery - Americore Technologies, Inc.
AMERICOREMASTER - Machinery - Americore Technologies, Inc.
AMERICRAFT - Bells - Bevin Brothers Manufacturing Co.
AMERICRAFT - Boxes–paperboard - Americraft Carton Group Inc.
AMERICRAFT - Cabinets - Newell Operating Co.
AMERICRAFT - Floor coverings–tile - Florida Brick & Clay Co.
AMERICRAFT - Furniture - Norwalk Furniture Corp.

✰ = Now out of production

AMERICRAFTS - Novelty items - Root Candle Co.
AMERICUS - Beverages - Tri-State Natural Food Products, Inc.
AMERICUS - Recording label - Americus Records, Inc.
AMERICUS - Water–bottled or canned - Tri-State Natural Food Products, Inc.
AMERICUT - Hardware - Alside Div.
AMERIDOCS - Consulting services - New America Financial, Inc.
AMERIDOWN - Comforters - Co. Store Holdings, Inc.
AMERIFITTERS - Apparel and accessories - Cummington-Ford, Inc.
AMERIFOAM - Novelty items - Brooklyn Products, Inc.
AMERIFOLD - Folding doors - American Fold Doors Inc.
AMERIGAMES - Toys ☆ - Jak-Pak Inc.
AMERIGAMES INTERNATIONAL - Games - Amerigames International Corp.
AMERIGIFT - Toys - Pacific Balloon Co., Inc.
AMERIGO - Frames–picture - Lasercraft, Inc.
AMERIGO - Trailers–travel - Amerigo-Gardner Inc.
AMERIGRAPH - Pens - American Graphics Inc.
AMERIGRO - Fruits and vegetables - Danny & Sons Inc.
AMERIKICK - Publisher's imprints - Amerikick, Inc.
AMERIKIT - Educational materials - Elenco Electronic, Inc.
AMERILUBE - Apparel and accessories - Amerilube, Inc.
AMERIMATCH - Cigarette lighters - Ohio Valley A.F.M. Inc.
AMERIMELT - Rods–steel - Empire Metal Supply Inc.
AMERIMULCH - Fertilizers - Kurtz Bros., Inc.
AMERIND-MACKISSIC - See **MACKISSIC**
AMERIPANE - Insulating glass - Insulated Glass Specialties Inc.
AMERIPHONE - Communications equipment - American Phone Products, Inc.
AMERIPOXY - Floor waxes ☆ - Consolidated Coatings Corp.
AMERIQUAD - Audio equipment - Pro-Co. Sound Co. Inc.
AMERIRAMP - Loading ramps for pick-up trucks - American Road Equipment Co.
AMERISEAL - Motor vehicle parts and accessories - American Rubber Products Corp.
AMERISENG - Teas - Progenix Corp.
AMERISOFT - Contact lenses - Surgitec, Inc.
AMERISONG - Recording label - AmeriSong Records
AMERISPORT - Floor coverings–tile - Tarkett, Inc.
AMERISPORT ALWAYS MADE IN THE U.S.A. - Bags - Hardcastle/East Sports Inc.
AMERISTACK - Cages–wire - Ameriguard Corp.
AMERISTAR - Building materials - Ameristar Industries, Inc.
AMERISTAR - Motor vehicles–motor homes - Eldorado Motor Corp.
AMERISTAR - Shirts - Marble Sportswear, Inc.
AMERISTART - Storage batteries - O.I.S. Tire, Inc.
AMERISTEEL - Steel products - Ameristeel Corp.
AMERISTONE - Finishing agents - Dryvit Systems, Inc.
AMERITEES - Apparel and accessories - Ramstar Mills, Inc.
AMERITEX - Fabrics–cotton - Cohn-Hall-Marx Co.
AMERITOGS - Crocheted and knitted items - Valor
AMERITONE - Paints - Grow Group, Inc.
AMERITONER - Photocopy machine products - Nu-Deluxe Corp.
AMERITRADE ONLINE - Computer peripheral equipment - Ameritrade, Inc.
AMERITRON - Amplifiers - MFJ Enterprises Inc.
AMERITRON - Lighting fixtures - Service Lighting Associates, Inc.
AMERIVAP - Electronic equipment - AmeriVap Systems Inc.
AMERLUX LIGHTING SYSTEMS - Lighting fixtures - Amerlux, Inc.
AMERO - Housewares - Lescoa Inc.
AMEROCK - Hardware - Amerock
AMEROCK - Hardware - Amerock Corp.
AMEROCRAFT - Toys–trains ☆ - Polk's Model Craft Hobbies, Inc.
AMERON - Beverages - Cameron Coca-Cola Bottling Co., Inc.
AMEROSA - Skin care products - Ambrosia Cosmetics Inc.
AMEROSPORT - Boats–motor ☆ - Chris Craft Boats
AMEROX - Compressors–gas - Ashchem I.P. Inc.
AMERSIA - Apparel and accessories - Amersia International, Inc.
AMERTAC - Fasteners, now out of production - American Tack & Hardware Co., Inc.
AMERTAN - Pharmaceutical preparations - Eli Lilly and Co.
AMERTRICA - Paper–bond ☆ - Georgia-Pacific Corp.
AMERTRON - Briefcases and portfolios - American Portfolio Co. Inc.
AMERWOOD - Lumber ☆ - Georgia-Pacific Corp.
AMES - Garden equipment - Ames Lawn & Garden Tool Co.
AMES II - Computer software - Xenometrix, Inc.
AMES CARANI - Sporting goods - O. Ames Co.
AMES/DAY - Artists' materials - Olson Manufacturing and Distribution Inc.
AMES DRAFT-PAK - Artists' materials - Olson Manufacturing and Distribution Inc.

AMES LETTERING GUIDE - Artists' materials - Olson Manufacturing and Distribution Inc.
AMESBURY - Apparel–men's - Montgomery Ward & Co. Inc.
AMESBURY - Dinnerware–glass ☆ - WMF/USA
AMESBURY - Floor coverings - Armstrong World Industries, Inc.
AMESBURY FLORAL - Floor coverings ☆ - Armstrong World Industries, Inc.
AMESCO - Office supplies ☆ - Ames Supply Co.
AMESEC - Pharmaceutical preparations ☆ - Eli Lilly and Co.
AMESTYLE - Office supplies - Ames Safety Envelope Co.
AMETEX - Fabric stores - Ametex/Robert Allen Contract Fabrics
AMETHYST - Amplifiers - Essence
AMETHYST - Hair- and skin-care products, fragrance, etc. - Benjamin Ansehl Co.
AMETHYST - Tableware–china ☆ - Lenox, Inc.
AMETHYST HOUR - Christmas tree ornaments - Cracker Box Inc.
AMETHYST KORDE - Craft supplies - Textile Enterprises Inc.
AMETHYST RECORDS - Recording label - Amethyst Records
AMEX - Plastic bottles and jars - Amex Packaging Ltd.
AMF - Gymnastic equipment - Austin Athletic Equipment Corp.
AMF - Sporting goods - National Sporting Goods Corp.
AMF - Toys - Minstar Inc.
AMF 2100 - Ships–sailing vessels ☆ - Sunfish Laser Inc.
AMF REECE - Sewing machines–industrial - AMF Reece Inc.
AMFAC - Fruits–frozen - Amfac Tropical Products
AMFED - Pharmaceutical preparations - Legere Pharmaceuticals Inc.
AMFI - Lighting equipment–boat and ship ☆ - Falcon Safety Products, Inc.
AMFICOT - Pharmaceutical preparations - C.O. Truxton Inc.
AMFLO - Packaging–foam - American Excelsior Co.
AMFLO RE-GREEN - Packaging–foam - American Excelsior Co.
AMFOROL - Veterinary pharmaceutical preparations - Bristol-Myers Squibb Co.
AMGARD - Alarm systems - Amway Corp.
AMGENAL - Health care products - Goldline Laboratories, Inc.
AMGLO - Cameras - Amglo-Kemlite
AMGUARD - Asphalt felts and coatings - American Stone-Mix Inc.
AMHERST - Blinds–vertical - Tontine/VyTech Industries Inc.
AMHERST - Cabinets - Legeis Corp.
AMHERST - Cabinets ☆ - Merillat Industries, Inc.
AMHERST - Cabinets–wood ☆ - Kemper
AMHERST - Clocks - Ridgeway Clock Co.
AMHERST - Computers - Amherst International Enterprises Co.
AMHERST - Dishes–china - Waterford Wedgewood USA, Inc.
AMHERST - Floor coverings - National Floor Products Co., Inc.
AMHERST - Floor coverings–carpet and rugs - Atlas Carpet Mills Inc.
AMHERST - Furniture - Dinaire Corp.
AMHERST - Ophthalmic goods - Foremost Optical Products
AMHERST - Paper products - Georgia-Pacific Corp.
AMHERST - Recording label - Amherst Records
AMHERST - Wallpaper - Koroseal Wallcoverings
AMHERST - Weather tracking equipment ☆ - Bausch & Lomb Inc.
AMHERST CATHEDRAL - Cabinets–wood ☆ - Kemper
AMHERST FIBER OPTICS - Electronic equipment - Amherst International Inc.
AMHERST LITE - Chimes ☆ - Nutone Inc.
AMHERST OLDIES - Recording label - Amherst Records
AMHERST SPORT - Apparel stores–sports ☆ - Amherst Sportswear Co. Inc.
AMHURST - Clocks - Sunbeam Precision Measurement
AMI - Apparel and accessories - Renee Stein
AMI - Business-card holders, desk accessories, key chains, etc. - Automated Marking Inc.
AMI - Computer software - Lotus Development Corp.
AMI - Electronics equipment - RTI Research Technology International
AMI MODO - Apparel–women's - Difusion Purificacion Garcia
AMI PROFESSIONAL - Computer software - Lotus Development Corp.
AMIABLE - Floor coverings–carpet and rugs - Ashley Commercial Carpets
AMICA - Cosmetics - RH Cosmetics Corp.
AMICA - Sewing machines–household ☆ - Nelco Sewing Machine Sales Corp.
AMICAP - Vitamins and nutritional supplements - Gides-NuLife Inc.
AMICO - Christmas tree lights ☆ - Noma International, Inc.
AMICO - Health care products ☆ - Graham-Field Inc.
AMICO - Metals - Alabama Metal Industries Corp.
AMICO - Snack foods - Millner Trading Co. Inc.
AMICO EYEWEAR - Frames–eyeglass - United States Shoe Corp.
AMICO SHERPA - Toys - Peg Perego USA Inc.
AMID-SAL - Pharmaceutical preparations - Glenwood LLC
AMIDE - Pharmaceutical preparations ☆ - Scrip-Physician Supply Co.
AMIE - Ophthalmic goods - Swank Optical
AMIE & ALEXIS - Apparel–children's - Kids R Us Co.

AMIFAST - Hardware - Amifast Corp.

AMIFASTENERS - Hardware - Amifast Corp.

AMIFLEX - Cameras ☆ - Luminos Photo Corp.

AMIGA - Computers–personal - Commodore Business Machines Inc.

AMIGA - Food products ☆ - Darik Enterprises Inc.

AMIGA - Hot tubs–fiberglass ☆ - Jacuzzi Inc.

AMIGLYDE-V - Veterinary pharmaceutical preparations - Bristol-Myers Squibb Co.

AMIGO - Beverages–carbonated - Florida Brewing Co.

AMIGO - Boats - Glen-L Marine Designs

AMIGO - Flowers, plants, and seeds - Jacklin Seed

AMIGO - Lemonade - Delaware Punch Co.

AMIGO - Medical apparatus - Amigo Mobility International Inc.

AMIGO - Motor vehicles–automobiles - American Isuzu Motors Inc.

AMIGO - Pens - Yafa Pen Co.

AMIGO - Recording label - Jazz Composer's Orchestra Association Inc.

AMIGO - Shoes ☆ - Daniel Green Co.

AMIGO - Tableware–china - Villeroy and Boch Tableware Ltd.

AMIGO 620 - Cameras - Polaroid Corp.

AMIGO DE ORO - Cheese - Friendship Dairies, Inc.

AMIGO DEL SOL - Sunblocks - Jarphens International Inc.

AMIGO HERMANOS - Wines ☆ - Safeway Stores Inc.

AMIGO MOBILITY CENTERS - Health care products - Amigo Mobility International Inc.

AMIGO PRINTS - Posters ☆ - Henry R. Mockel's

AMIGO SUPREME - Medical apparatus - Amigo Mobility International Inc.

AMIGOS - Food products - Amigos Canning Co. Inc.

AMIGOS - Food products - Chiquita Brands, Inc.

AMIGOS - Pizzas–frozen - Chicago Brothers, Inc.

AMIGOS CASUALS - Footwear–men's ☆ - Edison Brothers Stores, Inc.

AMIGRO - Agricultural products - Donlar Corp.

AMIGWELD - Wire - Aluminum Co. of America

AMIKEY - Circuit boards - American Megatrends, Inc.

AMILOY - Plastics - Amicon Plastics Inc.

AMILUX - Yarn - Amital Spinning Corp.

AMIMATIC - Cameras ☆ - Edixa Camera Co.

AMINEOPT - Computer software - Dow Chemical Co.

AMINESS - Pharmaceutical preparations - Kabi Pharmacia Inc.

AMINET - Walnut Creek CD ROMs, Inc.

AMINEX 700 - Vitamins and nutritional supplements - Winning Laboratories Corp.

AMINO 75 - Vitamins and nutritional supplements - Solgar Vitamin and Herb Co., Inc.

AMINO 2000 - Health care products - Nature Health

AMINO 2000 - Vitamins and nutritional supplements - Weider Health and Fitness

AMINO ACID 1000 - Health care products - Above All Health Inc.

AMINO ATHLETE - Vitamins and nutritional supplements - Source Naturals

AMINO BLEND - Health care products - Marcor Development Corp.

AMINO-CERV - Pharmaceutical preparations - Milex Products Inc.

AMINO CHERRY - Cosmetics ☆ - Nutrine Ltd.

AMINO COLORS - Hair care products - Redken Laboratories, Inc.

AMINO COOLER - Vitamins and nutritional supplements - Sports Beverage, Inc.

AMINO DAY - Vitamins and nutritional supplements - Source Naturals

AMINO + DERM - Skin care products - Aminoderm Laboratories Inc.

AMINO DRIVER - Health care products ☆ - Marcor Development Corp.

AMINO EDGE - Vitamins and nutritional supplements - Vitamin Research Products Inc.

AMINO FORCE - Vitamins and nutritional supplements - American Body Building Products, Inc.

AMINO FUEL BAR - Snack foods - Twinlab

AMINO GLO - Skin care products ☆ - Majestic Drug Co., Inc.

AMINO HEALTH - Vitamins and nutritional supplements - Integrated Health, Inc.

AMINO HIGH - Health care products - Resurrection Laboratories

AMINO LEAN - Vitamins and nutritional supplements - Amino Age, Inc.

AMINO-LITE - Veterinary pharmaceutical preparations ☆ - Boehringer Ingelheim Animal Health, Inc.

AMINO-LITE 34X - Veterinary pharmaceutical preparations ☆ - Boehringer Ingelheim Animal Health, Inc.

AMINO MASS - Vitamins and nutritional supplements - Source Naturals

AMINO MAX 21 - Health care products - Foodscience Laboratories Inc.

AMINO MAX 2000 - Vitamins and nutritional supplements - Sportpharma USA, Inc.

AMINO MINT - Cosmetics ☆ - Nutrine Ltd.

AMINO NIGHT - Vitamins and nutritional supplements - Source Naturals

AMINO-OPTI-C - Vitamins and nutritional supplements - Integrated Health, Inc.

AMINO ORGANIC - Cosmetics ☆ - Palm Beach Beauty Products

AMINO PLEX - Health care products - Universal Nutritional Systems

AMINO PLEX - Shampoos ☆ - Cassidy Inc.

AMINO-PLEX - Veterinary pharmaceutical preparations ☆ - Boehringer Ingelheim Animal Health, Inc.

AMINO PLUS - Cosmetics - Nu-Tress Laboratories Inc.

AMINO PON - Hair care products - Redken Laboratories, Inc.

AMINO POWER - Vitamins and nutritional supplements - American Body Building Products, Inc.

AMINO PRO - Vitamins and nutritional supplements - Integrated Health, Inc.

AMINO QUEST - Vitamins and nutritional supplements - Nutri-West

AMINO SCIENCE - Animal feeds - Hubbard Milling Co.

AMINO STRENGTH - Vitamins and nutritional supplements - Source Naturals

AMINO-TECH - Vitamins and nutritional supplements - JBN Enterprises, Inc.

AMINO V.I.L. - Vitamins and nutritional supplements ☆ - J.R. Carlson Laboratories Inc.

AMINO XCELERATOR - Vitamins and nutritional supplements - Juice Pak

AMINOBLEND - Pharmaceutical preparations - Pro Cap

AMINOBRAIN PLUS - Pharmaceutical preparations - Medical Products Panamericana Inc.

AMINOBUILDER - Pharmaceutical preparations - Pro Cap

AMINODUR DURA-TABS - Pharmaceutical preparations ☆ - Berlex Laboratories, Inc.

AMINODYNE - Pharmaceutical preparations - JMI-Canton Pharmaceuticals

AMINOFEN - Pharmaceutical preparations - Dover Pharmaceutical Inc.

AMINOFEN MAX - Pharmaceutical preparations - Dover Pharmaceutical Inc.

AMINOFOL - Fertilizers - Wilbur-Ellis Co.

AMINOFORM - Vitamins and nutritional supplements - Integrated Health, Inc.

AMINOGEN - Food supplement - Triarco Industries, Inc.

AMINOLATE - Vitamins and nutritional supplements - Albion Laboratories, Inc.

AMINOLIFE - Vitamins and nutritional supplements - Integrated Health, Inc.

AMINOLINE - Pharmaceutical preparations ☆ - Mericon Industries Inc.

AMINOMIN - Pharmaceutical preparations ☆ - Pharmex Inc.

AMINOMINE - Health care products - Tyson & Associates, Inc.

AMINOMUNE - Vitamins and nutritional supplements - Integrated Health, Inc.

AMINOPHASE - Vitamins and nutritional supplements - Metaphaz Sports Nutrition Inc.

AMINOPLEX - Health care products - Tyson & Associates, Inc.

AMINOPLEX PLUS - Health care products - Tyson & Associates, Inc.

AMINOPLUS - Vitamins and nutritional supplements - Integrated Health, Inc.

AMINOPREL - Pharmaceutical preparations - Pasadena Research Laboratories, Inc.

AMINOPRO - Vitamins and nutritional supplements - Integrated Health, Inc.

AMINOS PLUS - Health care products ☆ - Nature Health

AMINOSTASIS - Health care products - Tyson & Associates, Inc.

AMINOSYN - Pharmaceutical preparations - Abbott Laboratories

AMINOTATE - Health care products - Tyson & Associates, Inc.

AMINOTRATE - Vitamins and nutritional supplements - Integrated Health, Inc.

AMINOTROPIN-6 - Vitamins and nutritional supplements - A. Glenn Braswell

AMINOVIROX - Health care products - Tyson & Associates, Inc.

AMINOZYME - Vitamins and nutritional supplements - Natural Organics, Inc.

AMINPURE - Hair care products - Temp Technologies

AMIO AQUEOUS - Pharmaceutical - Academic Pharmaceuticals

AMIOGUM - Starch–edible - American Maize-Products Co.

AMIPAQUE - Pharmaceutical preparations - Winthrop Pharmaceuticals

AMIR - Olive oil - International Delicacies

AMIR - Recording label - Jazz Composer's Orchestra Association Inc.

AMIR BY ZILDJIAN - Cymbals - Avedis Zildjian Co.

AMIRACLE - Pet products - Amiracle Plastics, Inc.

AMIRON - Pharmaceutical preparations - Misemer Pharmaceuticals Inc.

AMISH - Bakery products - Amish Country Bakery

AMISH COLLECTION - Furniture - Borkholder Corp.

AMISH COUNTRY - Furniture - Mary Anne Collins-Svoboda

AMISH COUNTRY - Jams and jellies - Williams Cheese Co.

AMISH COUNTRY GAZEBOS - Lawn pavilions - Amish Country Gazebos

AMISH FAMILY RECIPES - Fruit butters - Jake & Amos Co.

AMISH FOOD FACTORY - Fruit butters - Jake & Amos Co.

AMISH HERITAGE - Cheese - Alpine Cheese Factory, Inc.

AMISH HERITAGE COLLECTION, THE - Figurines ☆ - Willitts Design International, Inc.

AMISH KRAFT - Brass products - Amish Kraft Co.

AMISH PRIDE - Cheese - Williams Cheese Co.

AMISH PRIDE - Meat products - Brookside Foods

AMISHWARE - Lamps - Kaadan Ltd.

☆ = Now out of production

AMISYS - Computer software - Amisys, Inc.

AMITEE DEEP THERAPY - Hair conditoner ☆ - Advanced Research Laboratories

AMITEE GROUPE OUT - Hair care products ☆ - Advanced Research Laboratories

AMITEE THICK-FIXX - Hair care products ☆ - Advanced Research Laboratories

AMITONE - Pharmaceutical preparations - Smithkline Beecham Corp.

AMITRIL - Pharmaceutical preparations ☆ - Parke-Davis

AMITY - Diapers–disposable - Mark One Healthcare Products Inc.

AMITY - Hobby kits - Amity Inc.

AMITY - Leather goods - AR Accessories Group Inc.

AMITY - Paints - Minuteman, Inc.

AMITY 1-2-3 - Hobby kits - Amity Inc.

AMITY LIFESTYLES - Wallets - AR Accessories Group Inc.

AMITY VINEYARDS - Wines - Amity Vineyards

AMIVA - Eyeglasses - Art-Craft Optical Co.

AMIX - Computer software - American Information Exchange Corp.

AMJET - Computer peripheral equipment - Amjet, Inc.

AMK - See KARAT

AMKEY - Tapioca flours, starches - American Key Products Inc.

AMKEY DIVA EXTRA - Tapioca flours ☆ - American Key Products Inc.

AMKLEER - Envelopes - Champion Envelope Corp.

AML - Computer software - Pacific Scientific Co.

AMLAB - Antipruritic, eardrops, etc. - American Laboratories Inc.

AMLING'S ORIGINALS - Florists - Amlings Flowerland

AMLOGIC - Computer hardware - Amlogic, Inc.

AMM AMERICAN MILITARY MARKETING - Jewelry - Michael Cohen Enterprises Inc.

AMM-AWAY - Chemical preparations - Petcetera Inc.

AMMATE - Herbicides - E.I. Dupont de Nemours and Co.

AMMATEX - Pesticides–household ☆ - Bonide Products, Inc.

AMMCO FLEX - Electrical wire - American Metal Moulding

AMMEND - Hair care products - Nemesis Inc.

AMMENS - Pharmaceutical preparations - Bristol-Myers Squibb Co.

AMMEX - Motorcycles - Apache Ltd.

AMMEZZATI - Cigars - Avanti Cigar Co.

AMMO - Bowling balls - AMF Bowling Worldwide

AMMO - Toys–automobiles - Mattel, Inc.

AMMO - Water treating compounds - Aquarium Pharmaceuticals, Inc.

AMMO-CARB - Water treating compounds - Aquarium Pharmaceuticals, Inc.

AMMO-CAT - Pet products - Aquarium Pharmaceuticals, Inc.

AMMO-CHIPS - Pet products - Aquarium Pharmaceuticals, Inc.

AMMO-LITTER - Pet products - Aquarium Pharmaceuticals, Inc.

AMMO-LOCK - Water treating compounds - Aquarium Pharmaceuticals, Inc.

AMMO MASTER - Ammunition - Blount International, Inc. (Sporting Equipment Group)

AMMO MASTER - Pet products - Aquarium Pump & Piping Systems

AMMO-PAD - Pet products - Aquarium Pharmaceuticals, Inc.

AMMO-ROCKS - Aquarium accessories - Aquarium Pharmaceuticals, Inc.

AMMOGUARD - See WOODSTREAM

AMMONEX - Aquatic pharmacuetical preparations ☆ - Aquatronics-Filtronics

AMMONIA ALERT - Pet products - Seachem Laboratories

AMMONIA CHLORAMINE REMOVER - Water treating compounds - Jungle Laboratories Corp.

AMMONIA CLEAR - Aquariums–household - Jungle Laboratories Corp.

AMMONIA-EASE - Chemical preparations - Mydor Industries Inc.

AMMONIA SORB - Aquariums–household - Jungle Laboratories Corp.

AMMONIA SORBER - Pet products ☆ - Jungle Laboratories Corp.

AMMONIA-X - Pet products - Penn-Plax, Inc.

AMMS - Electronics equipment - RTI Research Technology International

AMNESIA - Computer software ☆ - Electronic Arts Inc.

AMNESIA - Fishing lures - Sunset Line and Twine Co.

AMNESTY - Hardware - W.W. Grainger, Inc.

AMNI - Computer hardware - Avant Marketing Network, Inc.

AMO-DERM - Soap ☆ - High Chemical Co.

AMO PRESTIGE - Surgical instruments - Allergan, Inc.

AMOBELL - Pharmaceutical preparations ☆ - Bock Pharmacal Co.

AMOCHLOR - Pet products ☆ - Aquatronics-Filtronics

AMOCO - Floor coverings–carpet and rugs - Amoco Fabrics and Fibers Co.

AMOCO - Floor coverings–carpet and rugs - Ashley Commercial Carpets

AMOCO - Insulating materials ☆ - Illinois Fastening Systems

AMOCO - Petroleum - Amoco Oil Co.

AMOCO HOUSEWRAP - Insulating materials ☆ - Illinois Fastening Systems

AMOCO RACING - Apparel and accessories - Amoco Oil Co.

AMOCO SILVER - Gasoline - Amoco Oil Co.

AMOCO V-1 - Gas pump nozzles - Amoco Oil Co.

AMOCOR-PLYGOOD - Sheathing - Amoco Fabrics and Fibers Co.

AMODEX - Stain removers - Amodex Products Inc.

AMODIN-25 - Pharmaceutical preparations ☆ - Vortech Pharmaceuticals

AMODRINE - Pharmaceutical preparations - G. D. Searle & Co.

AMOEBA WARS - Games ☆ - Avalon Hill Game Co.

AMOENA - Brassieres (Bras) - Coloplast Corp.

AMOFOAM - Insulation board - Amoco Fabrics and Fibers Co.

AMOFOAM - Petroleum - Amoco Oil Co.

AMOGEL PG - Pharmaceutical preparations ☆ - Vortech Pharmaceuticals

AMOIRE - Blinds–venetian ☆ - Hunter Douglas, Inc.

AMOLE - Hair care products - Amole Inc.

AMOLUBE - Lubricants ☆ - Amoco Oil Co.

AMON - Brackets - G.H. Meiser & Co.

AMONG THE STARS - Christmas tree ornaments - Cracker Box Inc.

AMONIDRIN - Pharmaceutical preparations ☆ - Forest Pharmaceuticals Inc.

AMOPHED - Pharmaceutical preparations ☆ - Vangard Labs Inc.

AMOR - Ophthalmic goods - Silor Optical Inc.

AMORA - Artists' materials - Andrews/Nelson/Whitehead

AMORCLAD - Giftware - Wyler Sales Corp.

AMORE - Cat food - Heinz Pet Products Co.

AMORE - Combs - Amore Comb Products Inc.

AMORE - Cosmetics - Pacific Corp. of America

AMORE - Food products - Universal Foods Corp.

AMORE - Pasta - Liberty Richter Inc.

AMORE - Rings–jewelry - Artcarved Inc.

AMORE ARBORIO RICE - Rice - Europa Foods Ltd.

AMORE BEAR - Toys–stuffed - Russ Berrie and Co., Inc.

AMORE CANNOLI SHELLS - Bakery products - Europa Foods Ltd.

AMORE MIO - Frozen pizza - Continental Food Products Inc.

AMORE NATURAL - Pet food - Star-Kist Foods, Inc.

AMORE TEA - Vitamins and nutritional supplements - Goodlife Network, Inc.

AMORETTE - Floor coverings–carpet and rugs ☆ - Galaxy Carpet Mills Inc.

AMORETTE - Rings–jewelry - Artcarved Inc.

AMORILLION - Jewelry–precious - Am Gold Products, Inc.

AMORINI - Cookies - Amorini Bakery Confections

AMORINO - Vinegar - Melanie Lane Farms, Inc.

AMORITA - Cigars - A.J. Golden Inc.

AMORLITE - Vitamins and nutritional supplements - Fuisz Technologies Ltd.

AMOROUS - Eyeglasses - Martin-Copeland Eyewear Corp.

AMOROUS - Floor coverings–carpet and rugs ☆ - Royalweve Carpet Mills

AMOROUS - Floor coverings–carpet and rugs ☆ - World Carpets, Inc.

AMOROUSAPES - Toys–stuffed ☆ - Mighty Star Inc. (Special Effects Div.)

AMORPHIUM - Computer software - Play Inc.

AMORTON - Calculators - Sanyo Fisher (USA) Corp.

AMOS - Frames–eyeglass - Pathway Optical Prods.

AMOS & SARA'S - Pet products - Amos & Sara's Enterprises, Inc.

AMOS FEER'S - Lubricating oils - Rectorseal Corp.

AMOS FEER'S FAMOUS FLUID - Deicing fluid - Rectorseal Corp.

AMOS FEER'S FAMOUS FLUX - Chemical preparations - Rectorseal Corp.

AMOSENE - Tranquilizers ☆ - Ferndale Laboratories, Inc.

AMOSOL - Veterinary medical equipment ☆ - Kay Pharmacal Co. Inc.

AMOSPEC - Computer software - Amoco Oil Co.

A'MOST REALS - Flowers, plants, and seeds - D.C. Frisbey Perma-Flora Imports

AMOSTAT - Pharmaceutical preparations ☆ - Vortech Pharmaceuticals

AMOUR - Floor coverings–carpet and rugs - Gulistan Carpet Inc.

AMOUR - Floor coverings–carpet and rugs - Karastan-Bigelow Inc.

AMOUR - Greeting cards - Joche Davila Studio

AMOUR - Wallpaper ☆ - Jolie Papier

AMOUR - Yarn ☆ - William Unger & Co. Inc.

AMOURETTES, THE - Apparel stores–lingerie ☆ - Formfit Rogers

AMOUREX - Perfumes - Amourex International, Inc.

AMOWEVE - Wallpaper - Amoco Fabrics and Fibers Co.

AMOXIL - Antibiotics - Smithkline Beecham Corp.

AMOZON - Pharmaceutical preparations ☆ - Chase Laboratories Inc.

AMP - Computer software - Whitaker Corp.

AMP - Electrical equipment - AMP Inc.

AMP - Hearing aids - Audiotone, Inc.

AMP - Motor vehicle parts and accessories - Rivera Engineering, Inc.

AMP - Recording label - Alternative Music Productions Inc.

AMP - Shampoos - KMS Research Inc.

AMP SUPERSEAL 1.5 SERIES - Electronic equipment - Whitaker Corp.

AMP-TRAP - Electrical equipment - Gould Shawmut Inc.

AMP-TRAP II - Electrical equipment - Gould Shawmut Inc.

AMP-TWIST - Cables - Whitaker Corp.

☆ = Now out of production

AMP TY - Electrical equipment - AMP Inc.

AMP-X2 - Hearing aids - Audiotone, Inc.

AMPAC - Luggage - Ampac Enterprise

AMPAC - Power transformers - SGS-Thomson Microelectronics, Inc.

AMPAD - Paper - Ampad Corp.

AMPCLIENT - Computer software - Belobox Systems, Inc.

AMPCO - Automotive parts and accessories ☆ - Wells Manufacturing Corp.

AMPCO - Cabinets–metal - Ampco/Rosedale Fabricators

AMPCO - Cabinets–wood - Ampco Products Inc.

AMPCO - Food products - American Products Co. Inc.

AMPCO-STANDARDIZD - Automotive parts and accessories ☆ - Wells Manufacturing Corp.

AMPEC BELT - Lighting equipment–bicycles - Ampec & Associates Inc.

AMPEG - Amplifiers–musical instrument - Ampeg

AMPERASE - Medical apparatus - Roche Molecular Systems, Inc.

AMPEREX - Audio equipment - Philips Components

AMPERIL - Pharmaceutical preparations - Armenpharm Ltd.

AMPET - Pet products - Amturf

AMPEX - Video equipment - Ampex Corp.

AMPFILES - Computer software - Belobox Systems, Inc.

AMPHA-QUAD - Pharmaceutical preparations ☆ - Harvey Laboratories Inc.

AMPHCAPS - Pharmaceutical preparations ☆ - Kenneth A. Manne Co.

AMPHEDRINE - Pharmaceutical preparations - Lannett Co. Inc.

AMPHETAMINE REPTILE - Recording label - Twin/Tone Records Inc.

AMPHETRIM - Diet aid - American Pharmaceutical Co.

AMPHIBIAN - Electronic equipment - White's Electronics, Inc.

AMPHIBIAN - Recording label - Morgan Martin

AMPHIBIFLOAT - Mattress pads - Basic Designs, Inc.

AMPHIBIFLOAT - Sporting goods - Stearns Manufacturing Co.

AMPHIBIGEAR - Sporting goods - Stearns Manufacturing Co.

AMPHIBIOUS MOMENTOUS - Apparel and accessories - Lifeforms International, Inc.

AMPHICOL - Pharmaceutical preparations - McKesson Home Health Care

AMPHITEO - Furniture - Haworth, Inc.

AMPHOCAPS - Health care products - Halsey Drug Co. Inc.

AMPHODERM - Veterinary pharmaceutical preparations - Bristol-Myers Squibb Co.

AMPHOJEL - Antacids - Wyeth-Ayerst Laboratories

AMPHOPLEX - Pharmaceutical preparations - E.R. Squibb & Sons, Inc.

AMPHORA - Floor coverings–carpet and rugs - Masland Corp.

AMPHORA STRIPES - Floor coverings–carpet and rugs - Masland Corp.

AMPHOTO ART - Publisher's imprints - Watson-Guptill Publications

AMPHOTO BOOKS - Publisher's imprints - Watson-Guptill Publications

AMPHYL - Pharmaceutical preparations - L & F Consumer Products

AMPI - Dairy products - Associated Milk Producers Inc.

AMPICILLEX - Aquatic pharmacuetical preparations ☆ - Aquatronics-Filtronics

AMPICILLIN - Pharmaceutical preparations - Legere Pharmaceuticals Inc.

AMPINE - Paper products - Georgia-Pacific Corp.

AMPION - Electric lighting equipment - Lutron Electronics Co., Inc.

A.M.P.L. - Lighting equipment - Cornerstone/Clearlight

AMPLE POWER - Motor vehicle parts and accessories - Ample Technology

AMPLE POWER - Motor vehicle parts and accessories - Powertap, Inc.

AMPLI-SOUND - Audio equipment - Ampli-Sound

AMPLI-TWIN - Hearing aids - Telex Communications, Inc.

AMPLI-VOX - Audio equipment - Perma Power Electronics Inc.

AMPLIBASS - Marimbas ☆ - Selmer Co. Inc.

AMPLIBOX - Tape recorders ☆ - Paso Sound Products Inc.

AMPLICALL - Electronic equipment - Rauland-Borg Corp.

AMPLICOLUMN - Amplifiers–public address - Paso Sound Products Inc.

AMPLIF - Hair care products - Matrix Essentials, Inc.

AMPLIFICATOR - Musical instruments - Ernest Deffner Inc.

AMPLIFIED - Publisher's imprints - Lockman Foundation

AMPLIFIED BIBLE, THE - Publisher's imprints - Zondervan Publishing House

AMPLIFIER RESEARCH - Amplifiers - Amplifier Research Corp.

AMPLIFIEUR - Hair care products - La Coupe

AMPLIFIRE - Fireplace equipment - Thomas Industries Inc. (Portland Willamette Div.)

AMPLIN - Pharmaceutical preparations ☆ - Roberts/Hauck Pharmaceuticals Inc.

AMPLIPHONE - Television equipment - Television Equipment Associates

AMPLIPHONICS - Audio equipment ☆ - King Musical Instruments

AMPLISEAL - Electrical equipment ☆ - AMP Inc.

AMPLITONE - Hearing aids - Telex Communications, Inc.

AMPLITRON - Coolers–electric - Barnstead Thermolyne Corp.

AMPLITUDE - Golfing equipment - Dunlop Maxfli Sports Corp.

AMPLIVOICE - Amplifiers–public address - Paso Sound Products Inc.

AMPLON - Hosiery - Kayser-Roth Corp.

AMPNET - Computer software - Belobox Systems, Inc.

AMPORT FOODS - Dates, dried fruits, fillings, and snack foods - American Importing Co.

AMPOS - Computer software - Belobox Systems, Inc.

AMPOWER - Pumps–water - American Advantech Corp.

AMPRIDE - Fuel - Farmland Industries Inc.

AMPRO - Alarm systems–burglar - Seco-Larm U.S.A., Inc.

AMPRO - Electronic equipment - Telex Communications, Inc.

AMPRO - Hair care products - Ampro Industries, Inc.

AMPRO - Video equipment - AmPro Corp.

AMPROL - Veterinary pharmaceutical preparations - Merck & Co., Inc. (Merck Agvet Division)

AMPROVINE - Veterinary pharmaceutical preparations - Merck & Co., Inc. (Merck Agvet Division)

AMPTHREADS - Computer software - Belobox Systems, Inc.

AMPTOOLS - Computer software - Belobox Systems, Inc.

AMPU-TEE'S - Apparel and accessories - Gwen R. Jensen

AMPULATOR - Audio equipment - ADA Signal Processors Inc.

AMPURE - Water–bottled or canned - CR Springwater Co.

AMQUEL - Aquarium accessories - Kordon

AMQUEL - Water treating compounds - Novalek, Inc.

AMR AUTOMOTIVE MANAGEMENT RESOURCES - Trade Associations - Tony Radoci

AMRAD - Veterinary medical equipment - Americomp, Inc.

AMRES - Resins–polymer - Georgia-Pacific Corp.

AMRIT KALASH - Vitamins and nutritional supplements - Maharishi Ayurveda Products International Inc.

AMRITA - Perfumes - Amrita Aromatherapy, Inc.

AMRITA - Publisher's imprints ☆ - Amrita Foundation, Inc.

AMRITA CHYAVANPRASH - Herbal jam - Auromere Inc.

AMRITE - Photo albums ☆ - Fotofolio Inc.

AMROC - Motors - American Rocket Co.

AMRON - Jewelry - Amron Manufacturing Jewelers Inc.

AMROX - Fiberboard - Roxite Fiberglass

AMROX/BROOKLINE CARRIAGE - Bricks - Roxite Fiberglass

AMS - Braces–orthopedic - Innovation Sports, Inc.

AMS - Machinery - Svedala Industries, Inc.

AMS - Microphones - Shure Brothers, Inc.

AMS - Scooters–motorized - AMS Imports Inc.

AMS ADVANTAGE - Computer software - American Management Systems, Inc.

AMS AMBICOR - Prosthetic apparatus - American Medical Systems, Inc.

AMS EXECUTECH - Cellular telephone cases - A.M.S. Cellular Products, Inc.

AMS HOHHY'S - AMS Imports Inc.

AMS IMPORTS - House furnishings - AMS Imports Inc.

AMSA - Food products - Empacadora Anahuac SA

AMSBURY WINERY - Wines - Geerlings & Wade, Inc.

AMSCO - Publisher's imprints - Amsco School Publications Inc.

AMSCO - Window glass - AMSCO Windows

AMSCO - Wire products - Amsco Wire Products Corp.

AMSCO PUBLICATIONS - Musical instrument accessories - Music Sales Corp.

AMSELFELDER - Wines - Dieter Steinmann Inc.

AMSI - Sporting goods - Activation Inc.

AMSINO - Medical apparatus - Amsino International, Inc.

AMSNACK - Vinegar - Amsnack, Inc.

AMSODYNE - Pharmaceutical preparations ☆ - ICN Pharmaceuticals Inc.

AMSOIL - Lubricants - Amsoil, Inc.

AMSPRAY - Paint sprayers - Wagner Spray Tech Corp.

AMSTAR - Apparel and accessories - Scott Xung Thach

AMSTAR - Powdered drink mix - Ireland Coffee and Tea Inc.

AMSTAR - Toys–electronic - Amstar Electronics Corp.

AMSTAR - Watches - Timestar, Inc.

AMSTEG - Frames–eyeglass ☆ - Universal/Univis Inc.

AMSTEL - Beverages–malt - Van Munching and Co. Inc.

AMSTEL LIGHT - Beverages–malt - Van Munching and Co. Inc.

AMSTERDAM - Clocks - General Time Corp. (Westclox/Seth Thomas Div.)

AMSTERDAM - Cooking utensils–enameled ☆ - Denby USA Limited

AMSTERDAM - Floor coverings–carpet and rugs - V & B Carpet

AMSTERDAM - Floor coverings–carpet and rugs ☆ - Kelly Group Inc.

AMSTERDAM - Paints–artists' - Canson-Talens Inc.

AMSTERDAM - Paper ☆ - M. Grumbacher Inc.

AMSTERDAM COLLECTION - Luggage - Universal Trav-ler Inc.

AMSTERDAM USA 1928 TEAM - Jewelry - United States Olympic Committee

AMSTERDAMER - Tobacco–chewing or smoking ☆ - G.A. Georgopulo & Co. Inc.

☆ = Now out of production

AMSTONE - Concrete products - American Stone-Mix Inc.

AMSTONE - Giftware - A.M. Designs

AMSYS COMPUTER - Computer peripheral equipment - Krisam Marketing Co., Inc.

AMT - Electric lighting equipment - Action Media Technologies, Inc.

AMT - Hobby kits - ERTL Co., Inc.

AMT - Microphones - David Wexler & Co.

AMT - Power tools - American Machine and Tool Co. Inc.

AMT (AIR MOTION TRANSFORMER) - Audio equipment - ESS Laboratory Inc.

AMT ALTERNATIVE MATERIALS TECHNOLOGY - Lacquers - Alternative Materials Technology Inc.

AMT ERTL - Toys–models - ERTL Co., Inc.

AMTECH - Ammunition - Amtech International, Inc.

AMTECH - Welding equipment - American Technology, Inc.

AMTEX - Electronic equipment - American Terminal Exchange, Inc.

AMTICON - Floor coverings - American Biltrite Inc.

AMTOY - Toys - Those Characters from Cleveland, Inc.

AMTURF LIQUA-LIME - Fertilizers - Amcorn Hybrids Inc.

AMTUSSIN - Pharmaceutical - American Laboratories Inc.

AMUN - Colognes - Frances Denney

AMUREX - Pharmaceutical preparations ☆ - Solvay Pharmaceuticals Inc.

AMUROL - Chewing gum ☆ - Amurol Confections Co.

AMUSEMENT PARK LEMONADE, THE - Lemonade - Slush Puppie Corp.

AMUTRONICS, INC. - Game machines - Amutronics, Inc.

AMV-RT - Chemical preparations - Seikagaku America, Inc.

AMVAC - Containers–plastic - Amko Plastics Inc.

AMVIK - Aluminum windows - American Viking Co.

AMWAC - Watches - Bulova Corp.

AMWAL - Gun stocks - American Walnut Co. Inc.

AMWAY - Water purification systems - Amway Corp.

AMWAY GROOMING GEAR - Skin care products - Amway Corp.

AMWAY QUEEN - Cutlery - Amway Corp.

AMWHITE 90 - Lighting fixtures - Amalco Metals, Inc.

AMX - See **JAVELIN AMX**

AMX - Computer software - AMX Corp.

AMX - Ophthalmic goods - Foremost Optical Products

AMX SCHEDULE! - Computer software - AMX Corp.

AMX SYNERGY - Computer software - AMX Corp.

AMY - Fabrics - Pepperell Braiding Co. Inc.

AMY - Frames–eyeglass ☆ - Universal/Univis Inc.

AMY - Frames–picture - Terragrafics Inc.

AMY - House furnishings - Dan River Inc.

AMY - Pens - Louis A. Amy Co. Inc.

AMY - Shoes - Shoe Masters Inc.

AMY - Toys - Knickerbocker Toy Co. Inc.

AMY - Watches - Bulova Corp.

AMY ADAMS - Apparel–women's - Jonathan Logan Inc.

AMY ALLIGATORS - Dolls - Mattel, Inc.

AMY ALLISON - Greeting cards - American Greetings Corp.

AMY ALLISON CARD SHOP, THE - Greeting cards - American Greetings Corp.

AMY BARR - Apparel–women's - Harper Shirt Co.

AMY BETH - Hosiery - Mayer/Berkshire Corp.

AMY JOY - Doughnut shops - American Snacks Inc.

AMY LEE - Wedding gowns - Hilton Bridal Corp.

AMYABLE - Greeting cards - Amyable Cards

AMYLATE - Health care products ☆ - Halsey Drug Co. Inc.

AMYLIN - Pharmaceutical preparations - Amylin Pharmaceuticals, Inc.

AMYLOCAINE - Pharmaceutical preparations - City Chemical Corp.

AMYLON - Starch–laundry - Indopco, Inc.

AMYLYTE - Pharmaceuticals - Editha Scientific, Inc.

AMY'S - Meat products–canned ☆ - SOPAKCO

AMY'S ORGANIC - Pies–frozen - Old Chicago Pizza

AMY'S ORGANIC FROZEN MEALS - Frozen foods - Amy's Kitchen, Inc.

AMYTAL - Barbituates - Eli Lilly and Co.

AMYTAL SODIUM - Barbituates - Eli Lilly and Co.

AN - Computer hardware - Bay Networks, Inc.

AN - Vitamins and nutritional supplements - Banner-Pharmacaps Inc. (Advanced Nutritional Technology Division)

AN +ADVANCED STATE OF COMFORT - Beds–metal - Ohio Mattress Co.

AN +AFRIKAN AMERICAN PRINCESS - Doll - Norman & Norman Inc.

AN +AMERICAN CLASSIC - Perfumes - White Scarf, Inc.

AN +AMERICAN LEGACY - Furniture - Yale-Forman Designs

AN +AMERICAN LEGEND - Garden equipment - Garden Way Inc.

AN +AMERICAN MAKEUP - Cosmetics - American Makeup Inc.

AN +AMERICAN SALT - Salt - North American Salt Co.

AN +AMERICAN TAIL - Computer software - Capstone Software

AN +AMERICAN TAIL: FIEVEL GOES WEST - Toys–models - U-Drive Productions, Inc.

AN +AMERICAN TRADITION - Giftware - Baldwin Hardware Corp.

AN ANGEL'S TORCH - Greeting cards - American Greetings Corp.

AN +ASPEN PUBLICATION - Publisher's imprints - Aspen Systems Corp.

AN +ASSOCIATED FEATURES BOOK - Publisher's imprints - Associated Features Inc.

AN-DU-SEPTIC - Crayons - Binney & Smith Inc.

AN +EDEN GIFT - Toys - Eden LLC

AN +ELEMENT OF DANGER - Games ☆ - Mayfair Games, Inc.

AN +ENCHANTED WEDDING - Computer software - An Enchanted Wedding

AN +EVENING CUP OF TEA - Teas - Village Herbalist

AN +IDEA TO LIVE WITH - Apparel and accessories - Earth Patrol, Inc.

AN +INTIMATE WORLD - Apparel–women's - J.T. Voulgaris Enterprises, Inc.

AN MEI - Furniture - Singer Furniture Co.

AN +ORIGINAL AMERICAN DESIGN - Eyeglasses - California Design Studio Inc.

AN +OUNCE OF PREVENTION - Skin care products - Frances Denney

AN +OUT OF THIS WORLD PRODUCTION - Publisher's imprints - Shelley Kaehr

AN +OWLET BOOK - Publisher's imprints - Henry Holt and Co.

AN +UMBRELLA OF CLEAN AIR - Office partitions - CenterCore Inc.

ANA - Bakery products - Ana's Gourmet Fare Bakery

ANA BOATS - Bakery products - Ana's Gourmet Fare Bakery

ANA-GUARD - Pharmaceutical preparations - Bayer Corp. (Pharmaceutical Division)

ANA-KIT - Pharmaceutical preparations - Bayer Corp. (Pharmaceutical Division)

ANA-KIT - Pharmaceutical preparations - Miles Inc.

ANA LA QUINCEANERA - Dolls - Tyco Industries, Inc.

ANA-SAL - Diagnostic substances - Americare Biologicals, Inc.

ANABELLA - Dolls - Uneeda Doll Co., Inc.

ANABELLA - Whirlpools - Jason International, Inc.

ANABOL - Pharmaceutical preparations ☆ - Keene Pharmaceuticals Inc.

ANABOLIC AMINO 10,000 - Vitamins and nutritional supplements - Healthy 'N Fit Nutritionals

ANABOLIC CARBO - Health care products ☆ - Nature Health

ANABOLIC CUTS - Vitamins and nutritional supplements - Weider Health and Fitness

ANABOLIC DIET, THE - Recording label - Strength & Conditioning Technologies

ANABOLIC EDGE - Vitamins and nutritional supplements - Nutri Science Inc.

ANABOLIC ENERGY - Vitamins and nutritional supplements - Weider Health and Fitness

ANABOLIC PRE-WORKOUT PAK - Pharmaceutical preparations - Pro Cap

ANACAINE - Pharmaceutical preparations - Gordon Laboratories

ANACAPA - Floor coverings–carpet and rugs - Catalina Carpet Mills Inc.

ANACAPA - Fruits and vegetables - Saticoy Lemon Association

ANACAPA - Tableware–earthenware - Anacapa Corp.

ANACET - Analgesics - Whitby Pharmaceuticals, Inc.

ANACETIN - Veterinary pharmaceutical preparations ☆ - Boehringer Ingelheim Animal Health, Inc.

ANACIN - Pharmaceutical preparations - Whitehall Laboratories

ANACIN-3 - Pharmaceutical preparations - Whitehall Laboratories

ANACONDA - Bicycles - Python USA, Inc.

ANACONDA - Foil–aluminum ☆ - Arco Aluminum Co.

ANACONDA - Musical instrument accessories ☆ - Mapes Piano String Co.

ANACONE - Bathroom fixtures ☆ - Crane Plumbing/Fiat Products

ANADAMA - Food products - Bakers Franchise Corp.

ANADISQ 200 - Recording label - Mobile Fidelity Sound Lab

ANADROL - Pharmaceutical preparations - Syntex USA, Inc.

ANAFED - Health care products ☆ - Everett Laboratories Inc.

ANAFIND - Computer software - Anacomp Inc.

ANAGAMMON - Games - Feb Grumman

ANAGLIDE - Braces–orthopedic - Clinitex Medical Corp.

ANAGLYPTA - Wallpaper - Bentley Brothers

ANAGRAM - Toys - Anagram International, Inc.

ANAHEIM - Furniture - Taylor-Ramsey Corp.

ANAHEIM - Musical instrument accessories - Sottile Manufacturing Co.

ANAHEIM AMIGOS - Apparel and accessories - John A. Busch

ANAHIST - Pharmaceutical preparations ☆ - Warner-Lambert Co.

ANAHUAC - Food products - Empacadora Anahuac SA

ANAHUAC - Processed herbs - Mayda Hernandez

ANAIDS - Pharmaceutical preparations ☆ - Forest Pharmaceuticals Inc.

ANAIS - Ophthalmic goods - Swank Optical

ANAIS ANAIS - Cosmetics - Cosmair Inc.
ANALASER - Smoke detectors - Kidde-Fenwal, Inc.
ANALBALM - Analgesics - Central Pharmaceutical Inc.
ANALDIN - Pharmaceutical preparations ☆ - Harvey Laboratories Inc.
ANALGESICS - Pharmaceutical preparations - Global Pharmaceutical Corp.
ANALGESINE - Pharmaceutical preparations ☆ - ICN Pharmaceuticals Inc.
ANALGEX - Health care products ☆ - JMI-Canton Pharmaceuticals
ANALIG - Chemical preparations - Ibc Advanced Technologies, Inc.
ANALJEL - Pharmaceutical preparations - Detroit First Aid Co.
ANALOG - Fabrics - Interface, Inc.
ANALOG ARTIST - Computer software - Cadence Design Systems, Inc.
ANALOG ENGINE - Engines - That Corp.
ANALOGUE - Recording label - Acoustic Sounds
ANALOGY - Floor coverings–carpet and rugs - Hollytex Carpet Mills Inc.
ANALOGY HDL - Computer software - Analogy, Inc.
ANALYSEUR - Eyeglasses - Martin-Copeland Eyewear Corp.
ANALYST - Cameras–video - Eastman Kodak Co.
ANALYST - Computer hardware - Cochran Consulting, Inc.
ANALYST - Frames–eyeglass ☆ - Universal/Univis Inc.
ANALYTIX - Computer software - Customer Insight Co.
ANALYTIX - Computer software - Saltire Software, Inc.
ANALYZE AND APPLY - Educational materials - Analyze and Apply, Inc.
ANALYZE DISCHARGE CONDITION - Battery chargers ☆ - Alexander Manufacturing Co.
ANALYZED - Paints - Harrison Paint Corp.
ANALYZER - Electronic equipment - Lafayette Instrument Co. Inc.
ANALYZER - Electronic equipment - Republic Controls Corp.
ANALYZING OFFICE PRODUCTIVITY - Computer terminals and software - Danyl Corp.
ANAMATE - Computer software - Technimetrics, Inc.
ANAMINE - Cleaning preparations - Analab Inc.
ANAMINE - Pharmaceutical preparations - Merz Inc.
ANANASE - Pharmaceutical preparations - Rhone-Poulenc Rorer Pharmaceuticals Inc.
ANANCONDA - Revolvers - Colt's Manufacturing Co. Inc.
ANANDA - Incense ☆ - The Ananda Collection (CinTrac Enterprises, Ltd.)
ANANDA - Recording label - Jazz Composer's Orchestra Association Inc.
ANANDA-BLISS SAN FRANCISCO - Crocheted and knitted items ☆ - Saha-Union International USA Inc.
ANAPAMU CELLARS - Wines - E. & J. Gallo Winery
ANAPATH - Medical equipment and pharmaceuticals - Stat Lab Medical Products, Inc.
ANAPLEX - Cough medicines - ECR Pharmaceuticals
ANAPLEX - Veterinary pharmaceutical preparations ☆ - Boehringer Ingelheim Animal Health, Inc.
ANAPLEX HD - Pharmaceutical preparations - ECR Pharmaceuticals
ANAPROX - Analgesics - Syntex USA, Inc.
ANARCHY - Apparel and accessories - Alan Hamu
ANARCHY - Snowboards - Amu Hamu
ANA'S ACCOUTREMONTS - Costumes - Ruth's Custom Sewing
ANASAZI - Beans - Adobe Milling
ANASAZI - Clothing and footwear - Five Ten
ANASAZI - Hair care products - Anasazi Salon System, Inc.
ANASMA - Pharmaceutical preparations ☆ - Lunsco Inc.
ANASPAZ - Pharmaceutical preparations - B.F. Ascher & Co. Inc.
ANASTAR - Phototransmission equipment - Eastman Kodak Co.
ANASTASIA - Dishes–china - Pickard Inc.
ANASTASIA - Lighting fixtures - Illumilite Inc.
ANASTASIA - Ophthalmic goods - Styl-Rite Optical Manufacturing Co., Inc.
ANASTON - Phototransmission equipment - Eastman Kodak Co.
ANATECH - Computer software - Intergraph Corp.
ANATHESIA-MOP - Anesthetics ☆ - Durham's Products Co.
ANATOLE - Toilets–enameled - Kohler Co.
ANATOMIC SLEEP SUPPORT SURFACE TECHNOLOGY - Mattresses - Anatomic Concepts, Inc.
ANATOMICAL CONSOLE - Footwear - Wolverine World Wide, Inc.
ANATOMICALLY CORRECT FEMALE - Novelty items - Voodoo To You Inc.
ANATOMICALLY CORRECT MALE - Novelty items - Voodoo To You Inc.
ANATOMIGRAPHICS - Publisher's imprints - American Medical Art for Litigation, Inc.
ANATOMY OF A FISH - Computer software - Ventura Educational Systems
ANATOMY OF A SHARK - Computer software - Ventura Educational Systems
ANATONE HEALTH BELT - Belts–apparel - Magic Mold Inc.
ANATONIC - Vitamins and nutritional supplements - Pannox Health Products, Inc.
ANATOX - Pharmaceutical preparations - Anatox Co.

ANATRAC - Computer software - Anacomp Inc.
ANATRANS - Computer software - Anacomp Inc.
ANATTENE - Food products ☆ - Penick Corp.
ANATUSS - Pharmaceutical preparations - Merz Inc.
ANATYM - Health care products ☆ - Everett Laboratories Inc.
ANAVAR - Pharmaceutical preparations - G. D. Searle & Co.
ANAVIAN GALLERY - Pottery products - Habib Anavian & Sons Ltd.
ANAWERK - Ceramic tile ☆ - Integrity Tile Co.
ANBESOL - Pharmaceutical preparations - Whitehall Laboratories
ANCEF - Pharmaceutical preparations - Smithkline Beecham Corp.
ANCEL - Beverages–carbonated - Ancel Products Inc.
ANCENIS - Glassware–household - Durand International
ANCESTOR - Playing cards - Harry Leonard Johnson
ANCESTORS AND DESCENDANTS - Computer software - Adventures in Ancestry, Inc.
ANCESTRAL JEWELS - Dishes–china - Portmeirion USA
ANCESTRY - Furniture - Hickory Manufacturing Co.
ANCHIANO - Eyeglasses - Pacific Vision Network, Inc.
ANCHO MULATO - Chili peppers–powdered ☆ - Frieda's, Inc.
ANCHOR - See PLEASANT BAY
ANCHOR - Adhesives and sealants - Anti Hydro International Inc.
ANCHOR - Amplifiers–musical instrument - Bob White Associates
ANCHOR - Audio equipment and accessories - Anchor Audio Inc.
ANCHOR - Beverages–malt - Anchor Brewing Co.
ANCHOR - Brushes–hair - Anchor Brush Co.
ANCHOR - Buckles - North and Judd Inc.
ANCHOR - Cooking equipment–household - Anchor Hocking Glass, Inc.
ANCHOR - Cutlery - Lamson and Goodnow Manufacturing Co.
ANCHOR - Fencing–gates and posts - Anchor Fence Co. Inc.
ANCHOR - Floor coverings - American Floor Products Co. Inc.
ANCHOR - Food products - Union Fish Co.
ANCHOR - Heating equipment - Radiator Specialty Co.
ANCHOR - Mops - Lighthouse Industries
ANCHOR - Paints - Crop Production Services Inc.
ANCHOR - Paints - Klee Chemical Coatings
ANCHOR - Paper–carbon ☆ - Eaton Allen Ko-Rec-Type Corp.
ANCHOR - Plumbing fixtures–metal - Moen Inc.
ANCHOR - Preserved foods–prepackaged - Anchor Food Products, Inc.
ANCHOR - Recording label - MCA Universal Studios
ANCHOR - Syrup ☆ - H.B. Hunter Co.
ANCHOR - Thread - Coats and Clark Inc.
ANCHOR - Tools - Lufkin Rule Co.
ANCHOR - Veterinary pharmaceutical preparations - Boehringer Ingelheim Animal Health, Inc.
ANCHOR - Window shades - Anchor American Enterprises Inc.
ANCHOR - Yarn - Ports of Scandinavia Inc.
ANCHOR-ALL - Fasteners–hook and eye - VSI Fasteners, Inc.
ANCHOR BAG - Sporting goods - Randall R. Olguin
ANCHOR BALL, THE - Boating equipment and accessories - Alan M. Simon
ANCHOR BLUE - Colognes - Hub Distributing Inc.
ANCHOR CLIP - Building materials–concrete - Lumberlok
ANCHOR COAT - Paints - Grow Group, Inc.
ANCHOR-DOWN - Hardware - Maze Nails
ANCHOR EASE - Marine rigging - Powerwinch Co.
ANCHOR EDGER - Building materials–concrete - Anchor Wall Systems, Inc.
ANCHOR/FAST - Hardware - Bondex International Inc.
ANCHOR FAST - Marine rigging - Windline Marine
ANCHOR FLANGE - Shoes - Interco Inc.
ANCHOR FLEX - Concrete–ready-mix - Sakrete Inc.
ANCHOR GARD - Fishing tackle - Wenco Products
ANCHOR H - Cooking equipment–household - Anchor Hocking Glass, Inc.
ANCHOR HANKER - Brackets - C. Sherman Johnson Co. Inc.
ANCHOR HOCKING - Glassware–household - Anchor Hocking Glass, Inc.
ANCHOR-IT - Adhesives and sealants - Anti Hydro International Inc.
ANCHOR KRETE - Cement ☆ - Tamms Industries Inc.
ANCHOR-LOCK - Concrete products - Gates & Sons Inc.
ANCHOR MAN - Lenses–optical - Ditto Industries Inc.
ANCHOR MAT - Mats - E.S. Robbins Corp.
ANCHOR PAD - Computer peripheral equipment - Anchor Pad International Inc.
ANCHOR POINT - Apparel–men's - Big & Tall Associates
ANCHOR PRESS - Publisher's imprints - Bantam Doubleday Dell Publishing Group, Inc.
ANCHOR-PRO - Hoists - Campbell Group (Wayne Home Equipment Div.)
ANCHOR-RITE - Anchors - Sac Corp.
ANCHOR-SET - Building materials - Anchor-Set Products, Inc.

☆ = Now out of production

ANCHOR-SET - Cement - Atlas Chemical Co.
ANCHOR STAT - Mats - E.S. Robbins Corp.
ANCHOR STEAM BEER - Beverages–malt - Anchor Brewing Co.
ANCHOR STRIP - Mats - E.S. Robbins Corp.
ANCHOR-TITE - Cement - CGM Inc.
ANCHOR-TITE - Cement - Sealwall Products Inc.
ANCHOR TITE - Marine rigging - Windline Marine
ANCHOR/WALLACE - Calendars - Anchor/Wallace Publishers
ANCHOR WHEAT BEER - Beverages–malt - Anchor Brewing Co.
ANCHORFAST - Annular-thread monel nails - Independent Nail Inc.
ANCHORGLASS - Glassware–household - Anchor Hocking Glass, Inc.
ANCHORMASK - Tape–adhesive - Anchor Continental, Inc.
ANCHORMATE - Anchors - Worth Co.
ANCHORMATE - Mats - E.S. Robbins Corp.
ANCHORS-A-WAIST - Underwear and nightwear ✰ - Lovable Co.
ANCHORS AWAY - Anchors - Anchors Away Co.
ANCHORS AWAY - Bathing suits ✰ - Jantzen Inc.
ANCHORS AWAY - Water treating compounds - Jungle Laboratories Corp.
ANCHORS AWAY SEAFOOD MEAT COMPANY - Seafood products–fresh or frozen - Anchors Away Seafood, Inc.
ANCHORS AWEIGH - Dolls ✰ - Effanbee Doll Corp.
ANCHORS AWEIGH - Food products ✰ - Shurfine International, Inc.
ANCHORSTONE - Cement - W.W. Henry Co.
ANCHORWHITE - Cooking equipment–household - Anchor Hocking Glass, Inc.
ANCI - Needlework supplies - American Needlework Co. Inc.
ANCIEN - Wines - Ancien Wines
ANCIENT AGE - Beverages–alcohol - Sazerac Co. Inc.
ANCIENT AGE 10 STAR - Beverages–alcohol - Sazerac Co. Inc.
ANCIENT AGE BOURBON - Beverages–alcohol - SPAR Inc.
ANCIENT AGE PREFERRED - Beverages–alcohol - Sazerac Co. Inc.
ANCIENT AMERICA - Film–motion picture - Camera One
ANCIENT ART OF WAR AT SEA, THE - Computer software ✰ - Broderbund Software, Inc.
ANCIENT ART OF WAR, THE - Computer software ✰ - Broderbund Software, Inc.
ANCIENT CARTOUCHE, THE - Jewelry - Aurafin Corp.
ANCIENT ECHOES - Jewelry - Hofstadter Co.
ANCIENT ECHOES - Rugs - Chris O'Connell, Inc.
ANCIENT EMPIRES - Computer software ✰ - The Learning Co., Inc.
ANCIENT FUTURE ARTIFACTS - Shirts - Laurel Burch Inc.
ANCIENT HARVEST QUINOA - Flour–blended - Quinoa Corp.
ANCIENT IMAGES - Jewelry - Kyle Design, Inc.
ANCIENT MYSTERIES - Video production - A & E Television Network
ANCIENT REALMS - Electronic game - Tantalus Inc.
ANCIENT REMEDIES - Hair care products ✰ - Marianna Imports, Inc.
ANCIENT REMEDY - Hair care products - Native American Naturals
ANCIENT ROME - Computer software - Teach Yourself By Computer Software Inc.
ANCIENT ROSE - Flatware - Utica Cutlery Co.
ANCIENT SECRETS - Skin care products - Lotus Brands Inc.
ANCIENT TREASURE - Vitamins and nutritional supplements - Benchmark USA, Inc.
ANCIENT TREASURES - Paper–lithograph - Ancient Treasures
ANCIENT WATERS - Skin care products - En Fleur, Inc.
ANCIENT WORLD 2000 - Educational materials - Decision Development Corp.
ANCILIN - Skin care products - Skin Biology, Inc.
ANCO - Automotive parts and accessories - Cooper Industries (Cooper Automotive)
ANCO - Cheese - Anco Foods Corp.
ANCO - Food products - Dole Food Co., Inc.
ANCO-BILT - Tables–wood - Anco Wood Specialties Inc.
ANCO BRIE DE MEAUX - Cheese - Anco Foods Corp.
ANCO DELUXE - Toys–electronic - Bird Bromiticous Inc.
ANCO STRETCHER STRIPS - Artists' materials ✰ - Winsor & Newton
ANCOBON - Pharmaceutical preparations - Roche Laboratories
ANCON - Electrical equipment - Frederic J. Lowell
ANCONA - Apparel and accessories - Charles P. Ancona
ANCONA - Fruits–canned - Ancona Brothers Co.
ANCONA - Lenses–optical ✰ - Nassau Lens Co. Inc.
ANCONA - Yarn - William Unger & Co. Inc.
ANCOR - Chemical preparations - Air Products and Chemicals, Inc.
ANCOR-EEZ - Anchors - Woodmack Products Inc.
ANCORA - Bathroom accessories - Kohler Co.
ANCORA - Food products - Moore & Co. Soups Inc.
ANCORA COFFEE ROASTERS - Coffee - Ancora Coffee Roasters, Inc.

ANCOROCK - Paints - Key Laboratories Inc.
ANCOSUL - Veterinary pharmaceutical preparations ✰ - Boehringer Ingelheim Animal Health, Inc.
ANCOV - Coatings - Kimberton Enterprises, Inc.
ANCRA - Pet products - Foster Corp.
ANCRIS - Drums–musical instruments - Ancris-Cana-Sonic Inc.
ANCUBES - Pet products ✰ - Ancare Corp.
ANCY - Floor coverings - Parquet de France Inc.
AND - Clocks - And, Inc.
AND... - Colognes ✰ - Avon Products, Inc.
AND 1 - Apparel and accessories - Basketball Marketing Co., Inc.
& COMPANY - Apparel and accessories - Carter Hawley Hale Stores Inc.
AND I MADE IT MYSELF - Bags–paper - Mangelsen's (VDI)
AND NOW HERE'S... - Greeting cards - Oatmeal Studios, Inc.
AND/OR PRESS - Publisher's imprints - And/Or Press
& SONS - Apparel and accessories - Barney's Inc.
AND THEN THERE WERE THREE.... - Posters - A Different Angle Inc.
A & W - Beverages–carbonated - Dr. Pepper/Seven Up, Inc.
ANDAC - Battery chargers ✰ - Marine Electric Systems Inc.
ANDANTE - Boats - Glen-L Marine Designs
ANDANTE - Bottles–glass - Demptos Glass Corp.
ANDANTE - Dishes–china - Gorham Inc.
ANDANTE - Floor coverings–tile - Porcelanite, Inc.
ANDANTE - Frames–eyeglass ✰ - Universal/Univis Inc.
ANDANTE - Glassware–household ✰ - National Housewares
ANDANTE - Rings–jewelry - Artcarved Inc.
ANDANTE - Tableware–china ✰ - Villeroy and Boch Tableware Ltd.
ANDANTE GOLD - Glassware–household - Gorham Inc.
ANDARELLA - Footwear - Shandong Inc.
ANDCO - Wire products - Andfel Corp.
ANDE - Leather goods - McCrackin Industries, Inc.
ANDE ROONEY INC. - Paper–lithograph - Ande Rooney Inc.
ANDEAN ALPACA - Yarn ✰ - JCA, Inc.
ANDEAN ALPACA REGAL - Yarn ✰ - JCA, Inc.
ANDEAN VINEYARDS - Wines - Vinos Argentinos Imports USA
ANDECHS - Beverages–malt ✰ - Joseph Huber Brewing Co., Inc.
ANDEE - Yarn - Henry's Attic
ANDEK - Adhesives and sealants - Plastics & Resins Ltd.
ANDEK 950 - Adhesives and sealants - Andek Corp.
ANDEK WALKWAY - Floor coverings - Andek Corp.
ANDEKER - Beverages–malt - Pabst Brewing Co.
ANDELOT - Frames–eyeglass ✰ - Universal/Univis Inc.
ANDER-LIGN - Brass products - Anderson-Barrows Metals Corp.
ANDER-PAK - Hay - Anderson Hay & Grain Co., Inc.
ANDERBERG - Hardware - Owatonna Tool Co.
ANDERCRAFT - Ships–sailing vessels - Andercraft Products
ANDERLEX - Abrasive products - Anderson Products, Inc.
ANDERLEX - Polishing wheels - Wilton Corp.
ANDERS - Frames–eyeglass - Hoya Corp. USA
ANDERSEN - Tableware–earthenware - Andersen Design Inc.
ANDERSEN - Window frames - Andersen Corp.
ANDERSEN ART GLASS - Glass products - Andersen Corp.
ANDERSEN DAIRY - Milk - Andersen Dairy Inc.
ANDERSEN LIGHT - Windows - Andersen Corp.
ANDERSEN'S - Soups–canned - Real Fresh, Inc.
ANDERSON - Floor coverings - L.D. Brinkman & Co. Inc.
ANDERSON - Hosiery - Ithaca Industries Inc.
ANDERSON - Pretzels - Anderson Bakery Co. Inc.
ANDERSON - Sporting goods ✰ - Omni Scientific Inc.
ANDERSON - Tools–power-driven - Wilton Corp.
ANDERSON - Window walls - Aztec Door Manufacturing Co.
ANDERSON BEAN - Boots - Rios of Mercedes Handmade Boots
ANDERSON CLASSIC - Floor coverings ✰ - Anderson Hardwood Floors Inc.
ANDERSON-ERICKSON - Juices - Anderson Erickson Dairy Co.
ANDERSON FITTINGS - Plumbing fixtures–metal - Anderson Copper & Brass
ANDERSON KNEE STABLER - Sporting goods - Omni Scientific Inc.
ANDERSON-LITTLE - Apparel–men's - F.W. Woolworth Co.
A ANDERSON MARSHALL - Paperboard–corrugated - Inland Container Corp.
ANDERSON VALLEY WINERY - Wines - Edmeades Inc.
ANDES - Candy - Andes Candies Inc.
ANDES - Fabrics ✰ - N. Erlanger, Blumgart & Co. Inc.
ANDES - Floor coverings–carpet and rugs - Atlas Carpet Mills Inc.
ANDES CANDE CARDS - Candy - Andes Candies Inc.
ANDES CERVEZA - Beverages–alcohol - Best Brands Inc.
ANDI - Optical scanners–computer - Tart Optical
ANDIAMEAU - Floor coverings - Mohawk Carpet Corp.

ANDIAMEAU - Floor coverings—carpet and rugs ☆ - Karastan-Bigelow Inc.

ANDIAMO - Fragrance - Borghese Cosmetics Inc.

ANDIAMO - Luggage - Andiamo Inc.

ANDIAMO - Shoes - Craddock-Terry Inc.

ANDIE - Eyeglasses - Art-Craft Optical Co.

ANDIS - Health care products - Andis Co.

ANDIS ACTION - Razors ☆ - Andis Co.

ANDIS BEAUTYTRIM - Clippers—barber ☆ - Andis Co.

ANDIS BRUSH N CURL - Brushes—hair ☆ - Andis Co.

ANDIS ELITE - Dryers—hair ☆ - Andis Co.

ANDIS EURO PRO TURBO - Dryers—hair - Andis Co.

ANDIS FOLD N GO - Dryers—hair - Andis Co.

ANDIS HANG-UP - Dryers—hair - Andis Co.

ANDIS JERICO - Dryers—hair ☆ - Andis Co.

ANDIS LADYTRIM - Clippers—barber ☆ - Andis Co.

ANDIS MASTER - Clippers—barber - Andis Co.

ANDIS POWER GROOM - Clippers—barber - Andis Co.

ANDIS PRO - Brushes—hair ☆ - Andis Co.

ANDIS SELECTAIRE - Dryers—hair - Andis Co.

ANDIS SOFTSET - Brushes—hair - Andis Co.

ANDIS SPEED MASTER - Clippers—barber - Andis Co.

ANDIS STYLINER - Health care products - Andis Co.

ANDIS TEMP II - Curling irons—electric - Andis Co.

ANDIS TREND SETTER - Brushes—hair - Andis Co.

ANDIS TUCKAWAY - Brushes—hair ☆ - Andis Co.

ANDIS ULTRA - Dryers—hair - Andis Co.

ANDMORE - Apparel and accessories - Andmore Sportswear Corp.

AND...NOW DESSERT - Candy - Tootsie Roll Industries, Inc.

ANDO GIOTTO - Apparel and accessories ☆ - Edison Brothers Stores, Inc.

ANDOAS - Glass—plate - Sasaki

ANDOIN - Pharmaceutical preparations ☆ - Ulmer Pharmacal Co.

ANDONNES - Seafood products—fresh or frozen ☆ - Penguin Frozen Foods, Inc.

ANDORA - Furniture ☆ - A.A. Laun Furniture Co.

ANDORA WALLS - Wallcoverings - Designtex Fabrics Inc.

ANDORRA - Floor coverings—carpet and rugs - Atlas Carpet Mills Inc.

ANDORRA - Floor coverings—carpet and rugs - Bellbridge Carpets

ANDORRA - Floor coverings—carpet and rugs - Milliken & Co. Inc.

ANDORRA - Floor coverings—carpet and rugs ☆ - Eurotex Inc.

ANDORRA - Rings—jewelry - Artcarved Inc.

ANDORRA - Water—mineral - Andorra Spring Water

ANDORRA - Yarn ☆ - William Unger & Co. Inc.

ANDOVER - Apparel—men's - Andover Togs, Inc.

ANDOVER - Bicycles - Columbia Manufacturing Inc.

ANDOVER - Cabinets - American Woodmark Corp.

ANDOVER - Cabinets - Imperial Cabinet Co. Inc.

ANDOVER - Cabinets—wood - UltraCraft Co.

ANDOVER - Cigarettes - Brown & Williamson Tobacco Corp.

ANDOVER - Fireplace equipment ☆ - Majestic Co.

ANDOVER - Floor coverings ☆ - Congoleum Corp.

ANDOVER - Floor coverings—carpet and rugs - Atlas Carpet Mills Inc.

ANDOVER - Furniture - Lane Co. Inc.

ANDOVER - Glassware—household - Seneca Glass Co.

ANDOVER - Lighting fixtures - Swivelier Co. Inc.

ANDOVER - Ophthalmic goods - Swank Optical

ANDOVER - Tableware—china ☆ - Lenox, Inc.

ANDOVER COLLECTION BY CAMBRIDGE MEMBERS - Apparel and accessories - Cambridge, U.S., Ltd.

ANDOVER FOLK ART - Wallpaper - Andover Wallcovering

ANDOVER GARDENS - Wallpaper ☆ - Andover Wallcovering

ANDOVER GARDENS II - Wallpaper ☆ - Andover Wallcovering

ANDOVER KITCHEN & BATH - Wallpaper - Andover Wallcovering

ANDOVER KITCHEN & BATH II - Wallpaper ☆ - Andover Wallcovering

ANDOVER MINIATURES - Wallpaper ☆ - Andover Wallcovering

ANDOVER MINIATURES III - Wallpaper ☆ - Andover Wallcovering

ANDOVER SLATE - Floor coverings - Congoleum Corp.

ANDRAE - Footwear - Her-Man Imports Inc.

ANDRE - Beverages—alcohol - Ernest and Julio Gallo Winery

ANDRE - Frames—eyeglass ☆ - Universal/Univis Inc.

ANDRE - Hair care products - Andre Fantasies Inc.

ANDRE - Musical instrument accessories ☆ - Rico International

ANDRE - Toiletries - Andre Corp.

ANDRE ASSOUS - Footwear - Andre Assous Inc.

ANDRE BINI - Apparel and accessories - St. Michel Sportswear Ltd.

ANDRE BOUCHE - Watches - Weissman Watch Corp.

ANDRE CHAMBORD - Watches - Belair Watch Corp.

ANDRE DEUTSCH - Publisher's imprints - E.P. Dutton Inc.

ANDRE DOUGLAS - Wigs ☆ - It's a Wig!

ANDRE FANTASIES - Hair care products - Andre Fantasies Inc.

ANDRE GASTON - Wines - Leonard Kreusch Inc.

ANDRE GIANNI - Neckties - A. Schreter & Sons Co. Inc.

ANDRE GIROUD - Watches - Croton Watch Co., Inc.

ANDRE LARIN - Men's suits and blazers - International Clothing of Florida Inc.

ANDRE LURTON - Wines - Classic Wine Imports Inc.

ANDRE LURTON - Wines - W.J. Deutsch & Sons Ltd.

ANDRE MONCIER - Wines - Gold Seal Vineyards Inc.

ANDRE PAILET - Watches - Sterling Jewelry & Distributing Co. Inc.

ANDRE PERON - Musical instruments ☆ - Hershman Musical Instrument

ANDRE PIERRE - Wines ☆ - Winesellers Ltd.

ANDRE POURAT - Wines - European Beverage Co., Inc.

ANDRE REVAN - Musical instruments - J.M. Sahlein Music Co. Inc.

ANDRE RICHARD - Bathroom accessories - Andre Richard

ANDRE ROMARE - Recording label - Sabteca Records

ANDRE-TISSERAND - Pet products - Classic Products

ANDREA - Coats—women's - Sharilove Fashions Inc.

ANDREA - Communications equipment—mobile - Andrea Electronics Corp.

ANDREA - Cosmetics - American International Industries

ANDREA - Dolls - Cap Toys, Inc.

ANDREA - Figurines - Charles Sadek and Jay Willfred Import Co.

ANDREA - Floor coverings—carpet and rugs - Queen Carpet Corp.

ANDREA - Frames—eyeglass - U.S. Optical Frame Co.

ANDREA - Furniture - Weiman Co.

ANDREA - Handbags - Imax Hand Bags

ANDREA - Ophthalmic goods ☆ - Luxottica

ANDREA - Watches - Bulova Corp.

ANDREA ANTI-NOISE - Microphones - Andrea Electronics Corp.

ANDREA BY SADEK - Dishes—china - Charles Sadek and Jay Willfred Import Co.

ANDREA CORBIN - Apparel and accessories - Corbin Ltd.

ANDREA DEPTHMETER - Communications equipment—marine ☆ - Andrea Electronics Corp.

ANDREA GAYLE - Apparel—women's - Leslie Fay Companies Inc.

ANDREA KAY - Apparel and accessories - Blair Holdings, Inc.

ANDREA LAUREN - Crocheted and knitted items - Beldoch Industries Corp.

ANDREA RICCI - Apparel and accessories ☆ - Italian Classics Inc.

ANDREA SINAI - Towels ☆ - Terrisol Corp.

ANDREA VICCARO - Apparel—women's - Bon-Ton Trade Corp.

ANDREAS MORELLI - Musical instruments - Ideal Musical Merchandise Co.

ANDREA'S PERFECT BROWNIE - Baked goods - Andrea's Perfect Bakery, Inc.

ANDRELUX - Handbags - Senix Group

ANDRENO ARGENTI - Sweaters - Rainbow Sports

ANDRES - Footwear - Rod-Man Children's Footwear Corp.

ANDRESEN-RYAN - Coffee - Andresen-Ryan Coffee Co.

ANDREST - Pharmaceutical preparations - Seatrace Co.

ANDRETTI - Shoes - Emilio's Fashion Shoes

ANDREW - Frames—eyeglass ☆ - Universal/Univis Inc.

ANDREW AMERICA - Apparel and accessories - Brittany Sportswear's, Inc.

ANDREW BEAR - Toys—stuffed - Russ Berrie and Co., Inc.

ANDREW G. - Neckties ☆ - Charles S. Gelles & Son

ANDREW HARVEY - Apparel and accessories ☆ - Kellwood Co.

ANDREW HARVEY - Apparel—women's - Robert Scott Ltd. Inc.

ANDREW MURRAY VINEYARDS - Wines - Andrew Murray Vineyards

ANDREW PEARSON DESIGN - Sculptured glass furniture - Easy Investment, Inc.

ANDREW SCHROETTER - Musical instruments - Boosey & Hawkes Buffet Crampon USA

ANDREW STEVENS - Footwear - Elle Footwear Inc.

ANDREW TOBIA$ - Computer software - Meca Software, Inc.

ANDREW TOBIAS' FINANCIAL ADVISOR - Computer software - Meca Software, Inc.

ANDREWS - Beef - E.W. Knauss & Son, Inc.

ANDREWS - Motor vehicle parts and accessories - Rivera Engineering, Inc.

ANDREWS - Sprinklers—lawn - A.M. Andrews Co.

ANDREWS & MCMEEL - Publisher's imprints - Andrews and McMeel

ANDREWS MUSIC - Recording label - Jazz Composer's Orchestra Association Inc.

ANDREWS PREMIUM - Food products - E.W. Knauss & Son, Inc.

ANDRINA - Oils—edible - A & J Cheese Co., Inc.

ANDRIZZI'S - Pancakes—mixes - ADC

ANDRO - Pharmaceutical preparations ☆ - Forest Pharmaceuticals Inc.

ANDRO-CYP - Pharmaceutical preparations ☆ - Keene Pharmaceuticals Inc.

☆ = Now out of production

ANDRO/FEM - Pharmaceutical preparations - Pasadena Research Laboratories, Inc.

ANDRO L.A. - Pharmaceutical preparations - Forest Pharmaceuticals Inc.

ANDRO-MEDICONE - Pharmaceutical preparations ☆ - E.E. Dickinson Co.

ANDRO-SPLICE - Tools–hand-operated - Andro-Splice Systems Inc.

ANDROAC - Pharmaceutical preparations ☆ - Morton Pharmaceuticals Inc.

ANDROBAN - Beauty shop equipment - Focus 21 International Inc.

ANDROCK - Hardware - Androck Hardware Corp.

ANDRODERM - Pharmaceutical preparations - Theratech, Inc.

ANDROGYN - Pharmaceutical preparations ☆ - Forest Pharmaceuticals Inc.

ANDROHEP - Pharmaceutical preparations - Minitube of America, Inc.

ANDROID - Watches - OKO International Co.

ANDROLAN - Pharmaceutical preparations - Lannett Co. Inc.

ANDROLIN - Pharmaceutical preparations - Lincoln Diagnostics

ANDROLONE - Pharmaceutical preparations ☆ - Keene Pharmaceuticals Inc.

ANDROMAX - Vitamins and nutritional supplements - Natural Balance, Inc.

ANDROMEDA - Apparel and accessories - Thurman Manufacturing Co.

ANDROMEDA - Floor coverings - American Floor Products Co. Inc.

ANDROMEDA - Floor coverings–carpet and rugs ☆ - Hollytex Carpet Mills Inc.

ANDROMEDA - Mattresses - Namaco Industries, Inc.

ANDROMEDA - Ophthalmic goods ☆ - Luxottica

ANDROMEDA - Telescopes ☆ - Steven Manufacturing Co.

ANDROMEDA - Toys–models ☆ - Estes Industries

ANDROMEDA - Yarn - Henry's Attic

ANDROMEDA CONQUEST - Games ☆ - Avalon Hill Game Co.

ANDRON - Cigarettes - G.A. Georgopulo & Co. Inc.

ANDRON - Perfumes - Quintessence Inc.

ANDRON EGYPTIAN - Cigarettes - G.A. Georgopulo & Co. Inc.

ANDRONAQ - Pharmaceutical preparations ☆ - Central Pharmaceutical Inc.

ANDRONAQ-50 - Pharmaceutical preparations ☆ - Central Pharmaceutical Inc.

ANDRONAQ-LA - Pharmaceutical preparations ☆ - Central Pharmaceutical Inc.

ANDRONATE - Pharmaceutical preparations - Pasadena Research Laboratories, Inc.

ANDROSPHINX - Cheese - F.M. Van Tol

ANDROSPRAY - Vitamins and nutritional supplements - Vitamin Research Products Inc.

ANDROSTENEDIONE CAPS - Vitamins and nutritional supplements - Vitamin Research Products Inc.

ANDROSTRONE - Pharmaceutical preparations ☆ - Coast Laboratories Inc.

ANDRUS - Wines - R. Gary Andrus

ANDRYL - Pharmaceutical preparations ☆ - Keene Pharmaceuticals Inc.

ANDRY'S - Food products - Eckerty Flour Mill

ANDUIN - Floor coverings–carpet and rugs - Masland Corp.

ANDY - Frames–eyeglass - Rozin Optical Export Corp.

ANDY - Ophthalmic goods ☆ - Luxottica

ANDY ACORN - Flooring–hardwood - Triangle Pacific Corp.

ANDY BOY - Coleslaw - D'Arrigo Brothers Co.

ANDY BOY ORIGINAL BRAND SINCE 1927 - Salads–prepackaged - D'Arrigo Brothers Co.

ANDY CAPP - Darts and dart games ☆ - Dart World Inc.

ANDY CAPP'S - Snack foods - Goodmark Foods, Inc.

ANDY DANDYTALE - Character ☆ - Druther's System Inc.

ANDY HILLENBURG - Greeting cards - Andrew Hillenburg, IV

ANDY K - Drums–musical instruments - Leo Quan Badass Musical Products

ANDY ROO'S - Seasonings - Andy Roo's Cajun Enterprise, Inc.

ANDYLATE - Pharmaceutical preparations - Vita Elixir Co. Inc.

ANDY'S - Ice cream - Andrew Miller Jackson

ANDY'S LANDING - Meat products - National Carpet Equipment, Inc.

ANDY'S OTHER KID - Apparel–children's ☆ - Kahn Lucas Lancaster Inc.

ANECAL - Skin care products - Lannett Co. Inc.

ANECORD - Thread - American & Efird, Inc.

ANECOT - Thread - American & Efird, Inc.

ANECOT PLUS - Thread - American & Efird, Inc.

ANEE CALVADOS - Beverages–alcohol - Victoire Imports Co.

ANEFIL NYLON - Thread - American & Efird, Inc.

ANEFIL POLY - Thread - American & Efird, Inc.

ANEGADA'S COLLECTION - Apparel and accessories - Orient Arts Inc.

ANELLO/CEXTON - Recording label - Cexton Entertainment Group

ANERGAN - Pharmaceutical preparations ☆ - Forest Pharmaceuticals Inc.

ANES CHIRPER - Alarm systems - Anes Electronics Burglar Alarm Systems

ANES PROTECT ALERT - Alarm systems - Anes Electronics Burglar Alarm Systems

ANESCO - Veterinary medical equipment - Anesco, Inc.

ANESI - Skin care products - Divi International Co.

ANESONE - Liquors - Disusa Imports Co.

A+NET - Computer software - American Education Corp.

ANEW - Skin care products - Avon Products, Inc.

ANEX - Health care products ☆ - E. Fougera & Co. Inc.

ANEXSIA - Pharmaceutical preparations - Smithkline Beecham Corp.

ANF - Animal feeds - Pet Specialties International

ANF-22 - Vitamins and nutritional supplements - Great Life Laboratories Inc.

ANF ADVANTAGE - Pet products - Pet Specialties International

ANF TAMI - Pet products - Pet Specialties International

ANG-O-SPAN - Pharmaceutical preparations ☆ - Scrip-Physician Supply Co.

ANGE DAMOUR - Apparel–women's - Sui-Chun Lam

ANGEC - Musical instruments - Kaman Music Corp.

ANGEEZE - Apparel and accessories - Jameric Inc.

ANGEION - Catheters - Angeion Corp.

ANGEL - Beverages–malt - EFCO Importers

ANGEL - Bicycles ☆ - Raleigh USA Bicycle Co.

ANGEL - Computer software - Alive Systems, Inc.

ANGEL - Food products - F. Malatesta

ANGEL - Footwear–athletic ☆ - Puma Inc.

ANGEL - Hair care products ☆ - Betty Dain Creations Inc.

ANGEL - Handbags - American Angel Corp.

ANGEL - Handbags - Angel Hands, Inc.

ANGEL - Health care products - Skymart Enterprises Inc.

ANGEL - Musical instrument accessories - Kaman Music Corp.

ANGEL - Perfumes - Chesebrough-Pond's USA Co.

ANGEL - Pet products - Nippon Pet Food

ANGEL - Recording label - Capitol-EMI Music Inc.

ANGEL - Shrimp–fresh or frozen - Caleb Haley and Co. Inc.

ANGEL - Skin care products - Lotus Brands Inc.

ANGEL-ABRA - Candles ☆ - Colonial Candle of Cape Cod

ANGEL BABES - Giftware - Brushcreek Creative Co.

ANGEL BABIES - Figurines ☆ - United Design Corp.

ANGEL BABIES - Magnets - Kling Magnetics Inc.

ANGEL BABY SHOES - Footwear - Im-Link Corp.

ANGEL BARS - Cookies - Stella D'Oro Biscuit Co. Inc.

ANGEL BELLS - Jewelry - Peter Brams Designs, Ltd.

ANGEL BOWZ - Toys - E-Z Bowz, LLC

ANGEL-BRITE - Cleaning preparations - Angelica Uniform Group

ANGEL BRITE - Dolls - Imagi-Toy Group Inc.

ANGEL BUNNY - Toys - Mattel, Inc.

ANGEL CAKE - Frames–eyeglass - Liberty Optical Manufacturing Co.

ANGEL CLOTH - Paper–gift wrap - Angel Cloth Creations Inc.

ANGEL CURLS - Christmas tree ornaments - Old World Trading, Inc.

ANGEL DEVOID - Computer software - Tyke Studios, LLC

ANGEL DEVOID - Video games - Electric Dreams, Inc.

ANGEL DEW - Perfumes - Angel Dew

ANGEL DREAMS - Perfumes - Airs International, Inc.

ANGEL EYES - Eyeglasses - Art-Craft Optical Co.

ANGEL FACE - Dolls - J.C. Toys Group, Inc.

ANGEL FACE - Frames–eyeglass ☆ - Universal/Univis Inc.

ANGEL FACTORY - Confections - Tabitha A. Yothers

ANGEL FAIRIES OF THE SEASONS - Figurines ☆ - Rawcliffe Corp.

ANGEL-FLEX - Uniforms–tailored - Angelica Uniform Group

ANGEL-FOAM - Uniforms–tailored - Angelica Uniform Group

ANGEL FOOD - Candy - Melster Candies Inc.

ANGEL FOOD - Wheat–flour or meal - Pioneer Flour Mills

ANGEL FORMULA - Pet products - Ocean Nutrition Corp.

ANGEL FRIENDS - Dolls - Gabrielle Productions

ANGEL GLO - Toys - Imagi-Toy Group Inc.

ANGEL GUARD - Pet products ☆ - Jungle Laboratories Corp.

ANGEL HAIR - Packaging–paper - J.P. Paper Shredders

ANGEL HAIR - Yarn - Melrose Yarn Co. Inc.

ANGEL HANDS - Medical apparatus - Angel Hands, Inc.

ANGEL HARP - Harps - Angel Harp Corp.

ANGEL HAT - Hats - Laura Rothstein

ANGEL HEAVEN - Dolls - Estee Productions, Inc.

ANGEL ICE - Beverages–carbonated ☆ - R.S. Wells Enterprises

ANGEL IN TRAINING - Figurines - American Greetings Corp.

ANGEL IN YOUR CORNER - Figurines - United Design Corp.

ANGEL JOY - Greeting cards - Morehead, Inc.

ANGEL KISSED CHOCOLATE - Chocolate candy - Angel Kissed Chocolate Inc.

ANGEL-KNIT - Uniforms–tailored - Angelica Uniform Group

ANGEL-LIFE - Juice extracting devices - Angel Life Corp.

ANGEL-LIGHT - Candles - Terra Studios

ANGEL LIGHT - Lamps - Lamplight Farms, Inc.

ANGEL LIGHT - Stationery - Zorn Design

ANGEL LIGHTS - Dolls - Mattel, Inc.

☆ = Now out of production

ANGEL LITE - Pet products - Colorado Aggregate Co. of New Mexico
ANGEL MAGIC - Paper products - Giordano Art, Ltd.
ANGEL MESSAGES - Paper products - Angelic Dimensions
ANGEL MINISTRIES - Publisher's imprints - Angel Ministries, Inc.
ANGEL MINT - Candy - Florida Candy Factory, Inc.
ANGEL OF FORTUNE - Games - Carol Chaiken
ANGEL OF VISION - Jewelry - Treasures & Trinkets, Inc.
ANGEL ON MY SHOULDER - Jewelry - Charles Loeb & Co., Inc.
ANGEL ON MY SHOULDER - Pins—jewelry - Papel Freelance, Inc.
ANGEL QUEST - Games - Donna Gwen Craig
ANGEL RINSE - Automotive parts and accessories ☆ - Turtle Wax, Inc.
ANGEL SKIN - Fabrics - Burlington House Fabrics Group
ANGEL SOFT - Paper—tissue - Georgia-Pacific Corp.
ANGEL SOFT KID'S PRINTS - Paper—toilet - Georgia-Pacific Corp.
ANGEL SONG - Rings—jewelry - Artcarved Inc.
ANGEL SOUP - Dolls - Angel Soup, LLC
ANGEL-STAT - Uniforms—tailored - Angelica Uniform Group
ANGEL TATTOO - Apparel and accessories - Major Motion Sportswear
ANGEL-TEX - Uniforms—tailored - Angelica Uniform Group
ANGEL THREADS - Patterns—clothing - Strasburg Petite Couterie, Inc.
ANGEL TIME - Watches - Kirk's Folly, Inc.
ANGEL TOUCH - Apparel and accessories ☆ - Glamorise Foundations Inc.
ANGEL TOY - Toys—stuffed - Angel Toy Corp.
ANGEL TREADS - Footwear - R.G. Barry Corp.
ANGEL WALK - Floor coverings—carpet and rugs - Lees Carpets
ANGEL WATER - Novelty items—glass - Cato & Newby, Inc.
ANGEL-WEAVE - Uniforms—tailored - Angelica Uniform Group
ANGEL WINGS - Candles ☆ - Carolina Designs Ltd.
ANGEL WINGS - Christmas tree ornaments ☆ - Cracker Box Inc.
ANGEL WINGS - Greeting cards - Treasures & Trinkets, Inc.
ANGEL WINGS - Pillows - Wee Wonders
ANGEL WORKS - Figurines - Angelworks
ANGEL ZIMICK SLEEP ZZZ - Bedding—linen - Asa Nisi Masa, Ltd.
ANGEL ZIMICK SLEEP ZZZ - Linen - Asa Nisi Masa, Ltd.
ANGELA - Dolls - Russ Berrie and Co., Inc.
ANGELA - Food products - SD Fisheries Enterprises Inc.
ANGELA - Ophthalmic goods ☆ - Luxottica
ANGELA MARIE'S - Snack foods - Heritage Brands Holdings, Inc.
ANGELA MIA - Tomato pastes and sauces - Hunt-Wesson, Inc.
ANGELA MIA PRIMA CHOICE - Tomato pastes and sauces ☆ - Hunt-Wesson, Inc.
ANGELA PAGANONI - Apparel and accessories - Lilia Villanueva
ANGELA TRIPI - Novelty items - Roman, Inc.
ANGELCHIMES - Giftware - Scandia Specialties Inc.
ANGELE PARLANGE - Furniture—upholstered - Angele Parlange
ANGELFIRE - Perfumes - Mary Kay Cosmetics Inc.
ANGELIC - Floor coverings—carpet and rugs - Carpeting Concepts
ANGELIC - Frames—eyeglass - Zylo Ware Corp.
ANGELIC ALPHABET, THE - Jewelry - Michael Anthony Jewelers, Inc.
ANGELIC COMPANIONS COLLECTION - Dolls - Heritage Mint, Ltd.
ANGELIC HARMONIES - Giftware - Russ Berrie and Co., Inc.
ANGELIC INNOCENCE - Giftware - Russ Berrie and Co., Inc.
ANGELIC LIGHT - Video production - Peter Pan Industries
ANGELIC MELODIES - Figurines - Schmid Inc.
ANGELIC PIGASUS - Figurines - Calabar Creations
ANGELICA - Apparel and accessories - Angelica Corp.
ANGELICA - Frames—eyeglass - U.S. Optical Frame Co.
ANGELICA - Rings—jewelry - Artcarved Inc.
ANGELICA - Skin care products ☆ - Natural Thoughts Inc.
ANGELICA - Toys - Heaven on Earth, Inc.
ANGELICA - Uniforms—tailored - Angelica Uniform Group
ANGELICA-PREST - Uniforms—tailored - Angelica Uniform Group
ANGELICAPERS - Uniforms—tailored - Angelica Uniform Group
ANGELICARE - Uniforms—tailored - Angelica Uniform Group
ANGELICREATION - Uniforms—tailored - Angelica Uniform Group
ANGELICRON - Uniforms—tailored - Angelica Uniform Group
ANGELIKA FILMS - Recording label - Angelika Film Centers, Inc.
ANGELINA - Fabrics - Meadowbrook Inventions Inc.
ANGELINA - Women's hosiery and intimate apparel - Vida Enterprise Corp.
ANGELINE - Wines - Codera Wine Group
ANGELINO - Dolls - Cardinal Industries, Inc.
ANGELINO - Footwear - O & B Shoe Co.
ANGELIQUE - Dolls - Russ Berrie and Co., Inc.
ANGELIQUE - Glassware—household ☆ - Durand International
ANGELIQUE - Jewelry - Angelique Inc.
ANGELITE - Flour—blended - Acme-Evans/A.D.M. Milling Co.

ANGELITE - Uniforms—tailored - Angelica Uniform Group
ANGELITE-MADONNA - Candles - Empire Manufacturing Co.
ANGELITOS - Dolls - Matrix Investment Corp.
ANGELITOS - Statuary—marble - Angelitos Alumicolor
ANGELLA - Toys - Mattel, Inc.
ANGELO - Food products - A.F.I. Food Service Distributors Inc.
ANGELO - Frames—eyeglass - U.S. Optical Frame Co.
ANGELO DE DRAW - Paper - Riverside Paper Corp.
ANGELO DONGHIA - Fabrics—linen ☆ - West Point-Pepperell Inc.
ANGELO GHIGI - Pasta - Flora's Food Distributor Inc.
ANGELO LAMPARTS - Hardware ☆ - Angelo Brothers Co.
ANGELO OF ROME - Apparel—men's ☆ - After Six Inc.
ANGELO PAPAGNI - Wines - Papagni Vineyards
ANGELO SPINAZZE - Wines - Tabor Hill Winery
ANGELO'S GARLIC - Food products - Tucuru
ANGELO'S HOT - Food products - Tucuru
ANGELOSUITE - Lighting fixtures - Angelo Brothers Co.
ANGELS - Candles - Hanna's Potpourri Specialties, Inc.
ANGELS - Computer software - LIVE Entertainment Inc.
ANGELS - Kaleidoscopes - Gemini Kaleidoscopes
ANGEL'S BLUSH - Flowers, plants, and seeds - Monrovia Nursery Co.
ANGELS BY CARRIE ANNE - Jewelry - Carrie Anne Corso
ANGEL'S CARESS - Perfumes - My Sweet Dreams, Inc.
ANGELS COLLECTION - Novelty items - UniteDesign
ANGEL'S DUST, THE - Giftware - Costa Enterprises
ANGELS NOW - Publisher's imprints - Jane Payne
ANGELS OF THE WORLD - Christmas tree ornaments - Noma International, Inc.
ANGELS ON HIGH - Christmas tree ornaments - Seasonal Specialties Electrics, Inc.
AN ANGEL'S TORCH - Greeting cards - American Greetings Corp.
ANGELS UNLIMITED - Figurines ☆ - Panation Inc.
ANGELSILK - Artificial flowers and foliage - Corham Artificial Flower Co.
ANGELSPUN - Yarn ☆ - William Unger & Co. Inc.
ANGELTONE - Chimes ☆ - Angelo Brothers Co.
ANGELUS - Doors—metal - Angelus Manufacturing
ANGELUS - Food products - Gerawan Foods Inc.
ANGELVISION - Skin care products - Imperial Inc.
ANGELWISHES - Greeting cards ☆ - Vivian Greene Inc.
ANGENIEUX - Lamps - Alm Surgical Equipment Inc.
ANGENIEUX - Lenses—photographic - Heitz Service Corp.
ANGER - Shirts - Ripz
ANGER BLOCK - Toys - Uniquity
ANGERMEIER'S - Spices and extracts - T.H. Angermeier & Co.
ANGERS - Glassware—household - Durand International
ANGI - Natural gas - Associated Natural Gas Corp.
ANGI - Pumps - Angi International
ANGICON - Pharmaceutical preparations ☆ - Lunsco Inc.
ANGIDIL - Pharmaceutical preparations ☆ - Saron Pharmacal Corp.
ANGIE - Ophthalmic goods ☆ - Luxottica
ANGIE ANGORA - Toys—stuffed - Dakin Inc.
ANGIE BABY - Lenses—optical - Ditto Industries Inc.
ANGIE DECO-ART - Glassware—household - Angie Deco-Arts, Inc.
ANGIE'S SPECIALTEAS & ACCESSORIES - Teas - Padomi, Inc.
ANGINADOL - Cough drops - Polam Wholesale Inc.
ANGIO-CONRAY - Pharmaceutical preparations ☆ - Mallinckrodt Medical, Inc.
ANGIO-SEAL - Pharmaceutical preparations - Quinton Instrument Co.
ANGIOLO DEL GOBBO - Leather goods - Italian Classics Inc.
ANGIPEC - Pharmaceutical preparations ☆ - Jones Medical Industries, Inc. (Medical Div.)
ANGLE - Apparel and accessories - AMF Bowling Worldwide
ANGLE - Skin care products - Takara Belmont USA, Inc.
ANGLE - Work benches - Metal Components Inc. (Flexible Furniture Div.)
ANGLE ACTION - Brassieres (Bras) - Bi-Flex International
ANGLE-CAD - Work benches - Metal Components Inc. (Flexible Furniture Div.)
ANGLE CLAMP - Cables - General Cable Corp.
ANGLE-CUT - Brushes—paint - Corona Brushes Inc.
ANGLE-D - Binders - Samsill Corp.
ANGLE-DRIVER - Hardware - E. Mishan & Sons, Inc.
ANGLE IRON, THE - Golfing equipment - Tour Experience, Inc./Long & Strong Inc.
ANGLE-JET - Plastics - Polytop Corp.
ANGLE KING - Brushes—paint - Corona Brushes Inc.
ANGLE-LOC - Closures - Gregory Environmental Systems
ANGLE POWER - Work benches - Metal Components Inc. (Flexible Furniture Div.)

☆ = Now out of production

ANGLE STEP - Footwear - Hershberg Shoe Co. Inc.
ANGLE STIK - Exercising equipment - Jugglebug
ANGLE TECH - Work benches - Metal Components Inc. (Flexible Furniture Div.)
ANGLE TECH SUPER ZZIPPER - Apparel and accessories - Zzip Designs
ANGLE TRED - Footwear - Bell Boys Irrevocable Trust
ANGLE WORM - Fishing lures - Creme Lure Co.
ANGLEFIX - Measuring instruments - Glass Inc.
ANGLEMATIC - Motors–outboard ☆ - Outboard Marine Corp.
ANGLER - Boats ☆ - Lanness K. McKee & Co.
ANGLER - Boats–motor - Alumacraft Boat Co.
ANGLER - Boats–motor - Lund Boat Co.
ANGLER - Brooms - Drackett Co.
ANGLER - Display cases–metal - Kathleen Romano
ANGLER - Pontoons–aircraft - Forester Boats Inc.
ANGLER - Toothbrushes - Playtex Beauty Care, Inc.
ANGLER - Trailers–truck - Fleetwood Enterprises, Inc.
ANGLER - Watches - Cooper & Co., Inc.
ANGLER TE - Boats–motor - Glasstream Boats Inc.
ANGLER TECHNOLOGIES - Fishing lures - Larren T. Wood
ANGLER, THE - Archery equipment - Saunders Archery Co.
ANGLEROD - Beauty shop equipment - Total Woman Salon
ANGLERS' CHOICE - Boating equipment and accessories - Suncoast of America, Inc.
ANGLER'S CONNECTION WOODSTOCK POWERSTRIKE, THE - Fishing lures - Woodstock Line Co.
ANGLER'S PRIDE - Sporting goods - Highland Group
ANGLES - Dinnerware ☆ - Corning Inc.
ANGLES - Floor coverings–carpet and rugs - Daltonian Carpet & Cushion Inc.
ANGLES - Floor coverings–carpet and rugs - Trend Carpet
ANGLESCOPE - Photographic equipment - SP Systems/Saratons
ANGLESENSOR - Sporting goods ☆ - Zircon Corp.
ANGLESEY - Toilets–enameled - Kohler Co.
ANGLETERRE - Flatware - Dansk International Designs, Ltd.
ANGLEWALL - Wallpaper - PCI Industries Inc.
ANGLIA - Olive oil - Liberty Richter Inc.
ANGLIER - Water–bottled or canned - Rifle Ice/Mountain Pure Drinking Water
ANGLING ON AUDIO - Recording label - North American Outdoor Group, Inc.
ANGLO - Fabrics–cotton - Anglo Fabrics Co. Inc.
ANGLO - Leather–chamois ☆ - Schroeder & Tremayne, Inc.
ANGLO - Ophthalmic goods - Styl-Rite Optical Manufacturing Co., Inc.
ANGLO - Paints - Wallauer Paint & Wallpaper
ANGLO-AMERICAN - Wrenches ☆ - Anglo American Enterprises Corp.
ANGLUX - Lighting fixtures - Edison Price Lighting
ANGOLA - Ophthalmic goods - Styl-Rite Optical Manufacturing Co., Inc.
ANGONOA - Breads - A. Angonoa Inc.
ANGORA - Craft supplies - Canson-Talens Inc.
ANGORA - Eyeglasses - Martin-Copeland Eyewear Corp.
ANGORA - Fabric softeners - Stearns Packaging Corp.
ANGORA - Hats - Aris Isotoner Inc.
ANGORA - Tiles–ceiling ☆ - Wenczel Tile Co.
ANGORA - Tools - Ton-Tex Corp.
ANGORA MOHAIR COVER - Paint rollers - Corona Brushes Inc.
ANGORLON - Crocheted and knitted items ☆ - Schuessler Knitting Mills Inc.
ANGOSTURA - Beverages - Angostura
ANGRY SALAD - Recording label - Hale Pulsifer
ANGRY WIZARD, THE - Games ☆ - Mayfair Games, Inc.
ANGSTOM - Aquariums–household - Echo Services
ANGSTROM - Aquariums–household - Hawaiian Marine Imports Inc.
ANGSTROMLAP - Abrasive products - Fiber Optic Center, Inc.
ANGULAR WHITE FITCH - Brushes–paint - Corona Brushes Inc.
ANGULON - Lenses–photographic ☆ - Schneider Optics, Inc.
ANGUS - Electronic equipment - Esterline Technologies Corp.
ANGUS - Meat pies - Angus Meat Pies Inc.
ANGUS - Towels - Arden Corp.
ANGUS - Towels - Benhar Products International
ANGUS - Toys - Russ Berrie and Co., Inc.
ANGUS BRAND - Cheese - Angus Brands, Inc.
ANGUS MACBRIDE - Beverages–alcohol - Hy-Vee Food Stores Inc.
ANGUS MCDOUGAL - Beverages–malt - Old European Brewery Co.
ANGY'S - Pasta - Angy's Tortellini Inc.
ANHEUSER - Beverages–malt - Anheuser-Busch Companies Inc.
ANHEUSER-BUSCH - Fans–electric ☆ - Homestead Products
ANHEUSER BUSCH - Neckties - MMG Corp.
ANHEUSER-BUSCH - Telephones - Pierre Cardin Electronique

ANHEUSER-BUSCH BREWING ASSOCIATION - Beverages–carbonated - Anheuser-Busch Companies Inc.
ANHEUSER-BUSCH GOLF CLASSIC - Apparel and accessories - Anheuser-Busch Companies Inc.
ANHEUSER-BUSCH TIES - Neckties - Global Neckwear Marketing Inc.
ANHEUSER LIGHT - Beverages–malt - Anheuser-Busch Companies Inc.
ANHOLT - Ashtrays–metal - Willert Home Products, Inc.
ANHYDRON - Pharmaceutical preparations - Eli Lilly and Co.
ANI - First aid kits - Ani Distribution Inc.
ANI-COMM AUTOMATIC DIALER - Pet products - Amtek Pet Behavior Products
ANI-MALL - Pet shops - Albert L. Wilding
ANI-MATE - Footwear - Melville Corp.
ANI-MURALS - Toys - Milton Bradley Co.
ANI-PACTOR - Machinery - Ani America Inc.
ANI-SPACE - Toys ☆ - Lauri Inc.
ANIAR RECORDS - Recording label - Aniar Records
ANIBOARD - Pet products - Ancare Corp.
ANIBOTS - Toys - Trendmasters, Inc.
ANICHINE-ITALY - Porcelain electrical supplies - Murmac Importing Corp.
ANICOM - Electrical equipment - A-Z Anicom Inc.
ANIDA - Ophthalmic goods ☆ - Luxottica
ANIKA - Water–bottled or canned - Desert West Sales, L.C.
ANIMA - Recording label - Jazz Composer's Orchestra Association Inc.
ANIMAAL CRACKERS - Toys–stuffed - Mighty Star Inc. (Special Effects Div.)
ANIMADROIDZ - Games - Creatif Licensing Corp.
ANIMAGIC - Video production - Marcos Sebastian Ferrer
ANIMAL - Amplifiers - VMI Industries
ANIMAL - Bicycles - Huffy Corp.
ANIMAL - Giftware - Sasaki
ANIMAL - Toys - Jim Henson Productions, Inc.
ANIMAL ACCENTS - Giftware ☆ - Cast Art Industries, Inc.
ANIMAL ACCENTS - Tiles–ceramic - Demery Designs
ANIMAL ACT - Games - Smethport Specialty Co.
ANIMAL AWARENESS - Puzzles - Kingdom Puzzles
ANIMAL BALL PARK - Toys - Tomy America, Inc.
ANIMAL BINGO - Games - Smethport Specialty Co.
ANIMAL BUDDIES - Cookies - Premiere Brands
ANIMAL CHARACTERS - Toys - Knickerbocker Toy Co. Inc.
ANIMAL CHATTER - Greeting cards ☆ - American Greetings Corp.
ANIMAL CHATTER - Toys–stuffed - Russ Berrie and Co., Inc.
ANIMAL CHECKERS - Games ☆ - Milton Bradley Co.
ANIMAL CLASSICS - Figurines - United Design Corp.
ANIMAL CLUB - Shirts - Animal Gear
ANIMAL CONCERN - Publisher's imprints - Stanyan Record Co.
ANIMAL COOKIES - Cookies - Pure's Food Specialities Inc.
ANIMAL COOKIES - Cookies ☆ - Barbara's Bakery, Inc.
ANIMAL COUPLES - Giftware - Russ Berrie and Co., Inc.
ANIMAL CUT-UPS - Toys - Tonka Corp.
ANIMAL DELITES - Pet products - American Cat Emporium
ANIMAL FACES - Toys - Spearhead Industries Inc.
ANIMAL FAIR - Toys–stuffed - Animal Fair Inc.
ANIMAL FAMILIES - Games - Aristoplay, Ltd.
ANIMAL FAMILIES MEMORY - Games - Milton Bradley Co.
ANIMAL FARM - Greeting cards ☆ - Recycled Paper Products, Inc.
ANIMAL FARM - Lamps - Animal Farm Inc.
ANIMAL FRACKERS - Cookies - R.W. Frookies Inc.
ANIMAL FRIENDS - Electronic equipment - Texas Instruments Inc.
ANIMAL FRIENDS - Fabrics–tapestry ☆ - Coloroll Inc.
ANIMAL FRIENDS - Toys–stuffed - Little Tikes Co.
ANIMAL FRIENDS - Vitamins and nutritional supplements - Twinlab
ANIMAL GEAR - Apparel - Animal Gear
ANIMAL GOLF - Games - Golf Gifts, Inc.
ANIMAL GRABBERS - Toys - Fisher-Price, Inc.
ANIMAL GRAHAMS - Cookies - Tree of Life, Inc.
ANIMAL HOUSE - Vending machines - Rainbow Crane, Inc.
ANIMAL INN - Publisher's imprints - Scholastic Inc.
ANIMAL INSTINCTS - Greeting cards ☆ - Kersten Bros. Studios
ANIMAL INSTINX - Apparel and accessories - Witness Wear Christian Clothiers, Inc.
ANIMAL JAX - Slippers - Ben Berger LLC.
ANIMAL JAZZ BAND PONY PIANO - Toys - Tomy America, Inc.
ANIMAL JAZZ BAND WHALE XYLOPHONE - Toys - Tomy America, Inc.
ANIMAL KINGDOM - Candy - Superior Fruit & Confections
ANIMAL KINGDOM - Computer software - Unicorn Software

☆ = Now out of production

ANIMAL KINGDOM - Computer storage devices–optical - Aris Multimedia Entertainment, Inc.
ANIMAL KINGDOM - Glass products - Westmoreland Glass Co.
ANIMAL KINGDOM - Neckties - Superba, Inc.
ANIMAL KINGDOM - Toys - Imperial Toy Corp.
ANIMAL KINGDOM - Umbrellas - Avon Products, Inc.
ANIMAL KLAKERS - Slippers ☆ - Cathay International
ANIMAL LOVERS SKIN & COAT - Pet products - Animal Lovers
ANIMAL LOVIN' BARBIE - Dolls - Mattel, Inc.
ANIMAL MAGNETISM - Magnets - United Design Corp.
ANIMAL MAGNETISM - Medical apparatus - Kenneth Alan Teichmann
ANIMAL ODYSSEY - Apparel and accessories - Atma Enterprises, Inc.
ANIMAL PACKERS - Backpacks - Weekend Warrior Designs, Inc.
ANIMAL PAK - Vitamins and nutritional supplements - Universal Nutritional Systems
ANIMAL PALS - Toys - Fisher-Price, Inc.
ANIMAL PARADE - Vitamins and nutritional supplements - Nature's Plus
ANIMAL PEOPLE - Dolls - C.M. Paula Co.
ANIMAL PERFORMANCE LABS - Vitamins and nutritional supplements - Unipro Inc.
ANIMAL PHOTO FUN - Computer software - SRA/McGraw-Hill (Div. of The McGraw-Hill Companies)
ANIMAL PLANET - Pet food - Howard M. Cohen
ANIMAL RESCUE FARM - Publisher's imprints - Scholastic Inc.
ANIMAL RING - Toys - Fisher-Price, Inc.
ANIMAL SHOPPING CLUB, THE - Broadcasting stations–cable television - Tanya J. James
ANIMAL SKINS - Pens - Bic Corp.
ANIMAL SNACKERS - Candy - Gertrude Hawks Chocolate Inc.
ANIMAL SNACKERS - Dolls - Coppersource/Halves Inc.
ANIMAL SNAPS - Cookies - Health Valley Food
ANIMAL SOUNDS BARN - Toys - Fisher-Price, Inc.
ANIMAL SUEDES - Wallpaper - Walls Alive
ANIMAL SURVIVAL - Computer software - Hartley Courseware Inc.
ANIMAL TIMES - Pet products ☆ - Trendco Inc.
ANIMAL TOONS - Apparel and accessories - Michael Beau Lawson
ANIMAL 'TOONS' - Apparel and accessories - Michael Beau Lawson
ANIMAL TOTS - Potato flakes - Ore-Ida Foods, Inc.
ANIMAL TRACKORS - Toys ☆ - Proll Toy Co.
ANIMAL TRACKS - Notebooks and notepads - Animal Tracks, Inc.
ANIMAL TRAINER - Sporting goods - Vitronics Inc.
ANIMAL WHIMSIES - Acrylic paint-by-number sets ☆ - Coloron Industries
ANIMAL WONDERLAND - Toys - Mattel, Inc.
ANIMAL X-ING - Apparel and accessories - Lifeforms International, Inc.
ANIMAL XING - Apparel and accessories - Lifeforms International, Inc.
ANIMALENS - Veterinary pharmaceutical preparations - NNQ Inc.
ANIMALIA - Puzzles ☆ - Kingdom Puzzles
ANIMALS AND THINGS - Computer software ☆ - Knowledge Access International, Inc.
ANIMALS BY ME - Toys–models - Chenille Kraft Co.
ANIMALS IN THE BASKET - Toys–stuffed ☆ - Gund, Inc.
ANIMALS IN THE ZOO - Toys - Dakin Inc.
ANIMALS OF THE WILDLANDS - Jewelry - Wieck Family L.P.
ANIMALS OF THE WORLD - Jewelry and watches - Shube's Manufacturing, Inc.
ANIMALS!, THE - Computer programs - Software Toolworks, Inc.
ANIMALTALK - Playing cards - Tabletalk
ANIMANIACS - Apparel and accessories - Warner Bros. Inc.
ANIMANIACS - Footwear - S. Goldberg and Co. Inc.
ANIMANIACS - Publisher's imprints - Time Warner Entertainment Co., L.P.
ANIMANTICS - Buttons - U.S. Souvenir & Novelty
ANIMATE - Computer software ☆ - Broderbund Software, Inc.
ANIMATE - Hair care products - Redken Laboratories, Inc.
ANIMATED EYES - Cosmetics - Revlon Consumer Products Corp.
ANIMATED HANDWRITING - Video production - Robert Bruce McCumsey
ANIMATED HERO CLASSICS - Video production - Warner Nest Animation
ANIMATIC - Computer software - Digital Promotions, Inc.
ANIMATIC CONVAR - Electronic equipment - Leica USA Inc.
ANIMATION - Floor coverings–carpet and rugs ☆ - Alexander Smith Carpets
ANIMATION FARM, THE - Computer programming services - Animation Farm
ANIMATION QUEST - Video production - Sam Lee
ANIMATION TOOLKIT 1 - Computer software - Ann Arbor Software
ANIMATIONS - Apparel–children's - Caldor Corp.
ANIMATIONS - Hair care products - Wella Corp. (Consumer Products Div.)
ANIMATOR - Electronics equipment - Kimchuk Inc.
ANIMATOR - Helmets–athletic - Giant Bicycle, Inc.

ANIMATOR STUDIO - Computer software - Autodesk Inc.
ANIME YOUR WAY - Video production - Animeigo, Inc.
ANIMEALS - Paper products - Chicago Zoological Society
ANIMEC - Health care products - FutureMed America Inc.
ANIMEIGO - Prerecorded video cassettes - Animeigo, Inc.
ANIMOBILES - Toys–stuffed - Fun World Inc.
ANIMOPS - Greeting cards ☆ - Fran Mar Greeting cards Ltd.
ANIPADS - Pet products - Ancare Corp.
ANIS DE L'ABBAYE DE FLAVIGNY - Candy - Roth & Liebmann Inc.
ANIS ISAN - Jewelry - Lieberfarb, Inc.
ANISIMOV EGGS - Novelty items - Andrew D. Darvas Inc.
ANISTICS - Computer software - Alexander & Alexander Services Inc.
ANITA - Ophthalmic goods ☆ - Rozin Optical Export Corp.
ANITA - Watches - Bulova Corp.
ANITA - Water–bottled or canned - Tyler Mountain Water Co., Inc.
ANITA - Water–mineral - Anita Spring Water Co.
ANITA BECK CARDS & SUCH - Novelty items - Anita Beck Cards & Such Inc.
ANITA GOOD BUY - Office furniture–wood - Krueger International, Inc.
ANITA SELINGER - Jewelry - Anita Selinger
ANITA'S - Food products - Queen International Foods
ANITRA'S - Pet food - Halo Purely for Pets
ANIWORLD - Computer software - Aniworld, Inc.
ANJA - Pens - Anja Engineering Corp.
ANJALEX - Pens - Anja Engineering Corp.
ANJU - Jewelry - Town & Country Fine Jewelry Group, Inc.
ANK-L-RAP - Bandages–orthopedic - Cramer Products Inc.
ANKARA - Cigars - G.A. Georgopulo & Co. Inc.
ANKERTITE - Cement - Dayton Superior Corp.
ANKLE ARMOR - Braces–orthopedic - Swede-O, Inc.
ANKLE LOK - Braces–orthopedic - Swede-O, Inc.
ANKLE SHEERS - Socks ☆ - Dan River Inc.
ANKLESPORT - Health care products - Camp, Inc.
ANKLIZER - Orthopedic products - Bird & Cronin, Inc.
ANKOR-MAT - Masts–wood - Condux Corp.
ANKOR-SET - Cement - Rock-Tred Corp.
ANKORITE - Packaging machines - Anchor Packing Co.
ANKR-TRIM - Hardware - Ames Metal Moulding Co. Inc.
ANLA - Recording label - Goldband Recording Corp.
ANN - Eyeglasses - Art-Craft Optical Co.
ANN - Ophthalmic goods ☆ - Rozin Optical Export Corp.
ANN ARBOR - Publisher's imprints - University of Michigan Press
ANN DOROTHY - Jewelry ☆ - Charles Zahn-Import Merchant
ANN ELIZABETH - Food products - B. Sessler Co.
ANN GERLIN - Apparel–women's - Laus Apparel, Inc.
ANN GISH AG - Fabrics - Ann Gish
ANN GISH AG - Pillows - Ann Gish
ANN HARVEY - Floor coverings–carpet and rugs - Marketing Resources Inc.
ANN HILL PETITES - Apparel–women's - Kmart Properties, Inc.
ANN IRVINE - Stationery ☆ - Key West Aloe Inc.
ANN LOY ORIGINALS - Apparel–women's - Ann Loy Originals, Inc.
ANN #MICHAELS - Eyeglasses - Eyetel Optics, Inc.
ANN 'N ANDY - Giftware ☆ - Rubens Originals
ANN RASKAS - Candy - Gilliam Candy Brands
ANN RASKAS - Candy - Square Shooter Candy Co.
ANN TAYLOR. - Perfumes - AnnTaylor, Inc.
ANN W - Apparel–women's - Combined Interest Inc.
ANNA - Floor coverings–carpet and rugs - Robertex Associates Inc.
ANNA - Footwear - Swedish Clogs Inc.
ANNA - Occasional tables ☆ - JDI Group, Inc.
ANNA - Photo albums - International Silver Co.
ANNA B - Apparel–women's - Argentum USA Inc.
ANNA BABY CLUB - Toys–stuffed - IBTT
ANNA DE CODORNIU - Wines - Codorniu USA Inc.
ANNA G. - Apparel–women's - Anise Corp.
ANNA GRAY - Clothing - Anna Group Inc.
ANNA, IDA & ME - Bakery goods - Anna, Ida & Me, Ltd.
ANNA LAURA - Tiles–ceramic ☆ - Mediterranean Exports
ANNA-PERENNA - Figurines - Anna-Perenna Inc.
ANNABEL - Ophthalmic goods ☆ - Luxottica
ANNABELLE - Candy bars ☆ - Annabelle Candy Co. Inc.
ANNABELLE - Tableware–earthenware - Pfaltzgraff Investment Co.
ANNABELLE - Toys–stuffed ☆ - Gund, Inc.
ANNABELLE'S - Ice cream - Annabelle's Handmade Ice Cream
ANNABELLE'S NATURAL ICE CREAM - Ice cream - Annabelle's Handmade Ice Cream

☆ = Now out of production

ANNABELLE'S SOUTHERN MOMENTS COLLECTION - Hair care products - Annabelle's Inc.
ANNACLAIRS - Candy - Price Candy Co. Inc.
ANNALEE - Dolls - Annalee Mobilitee Dolls Inc.
ANNALEE MOBILITEE DOLLS - Dolls and accessories - Annalee Mobilitee Dolls Inc.
ANNAPOLIS - Eyeglasses - Art-Craft Optical Co.
ANNAPOLIS - Glassware–household ✰ - Lenox Crystal, Inc.
ANNAPOLIS - Luggage - Samsonite Corp.
ANNAPOLIS - Yarn - Henry's Attic
ANNAPOLIS BLUE - Tableware–china ✰ - Lenox, Inc.
ANNA'S COLLECTION - Apparel and accessories - Printworks Inc.
ANNA'S CUPBOARD - Jams and jellies - Dillman Farm, Inc.
ANNA'S DESIGN - Novelty items - Swe-Den Inc.
ANNA'S PEPS - Cookies - Skandia Foods Inc.
ANNASTASIA - Cosmetics - Annastasia Cosmetics
ANNATTO - Dyes–food - Christian Hansen's Laboratory Inc.
ANNE - Jewelry - Anne Jewelry
ANNE CARSON - Apparel and accessories - Chung Hwa Tai
ANNE COLE - Bathing suits - Authentic Fitness Corp.
ANNE COLE COLLECTION - Bathing suits - Cole of California Inc.
ANNE COLE LOCKER - Apparel and accessories - Anne Cole Design Studio, Ltd.
ANNE E. DWYER THE CAKE LADY - Bakery products - Anne E. Dwyer
ANNE GEDDES - Puzzles - Ceaco, Inc.
ANNE KINGSLEY - Jewelry - Anne Kingsley
ANNE KLEIN - Apparel–women's - Anne Klein & Co.
ANNE KLEIN - Bath salts - Parlux Inc.
ANNE KLEIN - Gloves - Aris Isotoner Inc.
ANNE KLEIN - Hosiery - Camp Hosiery
ANNE KLEIN - Hosiery–women's - Pennaco Hosiery Inc.
ANNE KLEIN - Jewelry - Swank Inc.
ANNE KLEIN - Leather goods ✰ - St. Thomas Inc.
ANNE KLEIN - Ophthalmic goods - Luxottica
ANNE KLEIN - Scarves - Vera Co.
ANNE KLEIN - Shoes - Schwartz & Benjamin Inc.
ANNE KLEIN - Sunglasses ✰ - Riviera Trading, Inc.
ANNE KLEIN - Watches - E. Gluck Corp.
ANNE KLEIN II - Apparel–women's - Anne Klein & Co.
ANNE KLEIN II - Watches - E. Gluck Corp.
ANNE KLEIN FOR CALDERON - Handbags - Ann Klein for Oroton
ANNE KLEIN FOR NEW ASPECTS - Apparel and accessories - Salant/Manhattan Industries
ANNE KLEIN II - Shoes - Schwartz & Benjamin Inc.
ANNE KLEIN II PETITES - Apparel–women's - Anne Klein & Co.
ANNE KLEIN II - Gloves - Aris Isotoner Inc.
ANNE LESLIE - Apparel–women's - Sanmark-Stardust Inc.
ANNE MARIE - Apparel - Best Wear Inc.
ANNE MARIE - Cosmetics - Burmax Co. Inc.
ANNE MARIE - Furniture ✰ - Singer Furniture Co.
ANNE MICHELLE - Footwear - J.P. Original Corp.
ANNE MOORE - Hats - Anne C. Moore
ANNE RASKAS - Candy - Square Shooter Candy Co.
ANNE WILD - Paper ✰ - Chase Collection, Inc.
ANNE WILKINSON DESIGNS - Toys ✰ - European Toy Collection/Crocodile Creek
ANNECHARICO - Apparel and accessories - BOCCE by Annecharico Inc.
ANNECY - Glassware–household - Durand International
ANNEKE VAN ZANTEN - Apparel–women's - Anneke Van Zanten, Inc.
ANNELIESE'S - Salad dressings–bottled - Running Deer Ranch
ANNEMARIE BORLIND - Skin care products - Borlind of Germany
ANNE'S OF VERMONT - Salad dressings–bottled ✰ - Tidelands Sales Co. Inc.
ANNE'S TAKE N' BAKE - Cookie doughs - Rhino Foods Inc.
ANNETTE - Confections ✰ - Bahlsen Inc.
ANNETTE - Corsets - John Wanamaker Inc.
ANNETTE - Dolls - Goldberger Doll Manufacture Co.
ANNETTE - Glassware–household - Van Dow-Fenton Inc.
ANNETTE - Watches - Bulova Corp.
ANNETTE BEHRE - Ashtrays–glass - Mandala Productions
ANNEX - Books–comic ✰ - Marvel Entertainment Group, Inc.
ANNI & CO. - Jewelry–costume - Anni & Co.
ANNIE - Footwear - Shoe Wind International Corp.
ANNIE - Frames–eyeglass - U.S. Optical Frame Co.
ANNIE - Lamps - W.R.B. Johnson Co.
ANNIE - Skin care products - Renee A. Gabet

ANNIE - Toys - Knickerbocker Toy Co. Inc.
ANNIE H. - Belts ✰ - Prestige Leather Creations
ANNIE OAKLEY - Skin care products - Renee A. Gabet
ANNIE, OH! - Apparel and accessories - Annie, Oh! Originals, Inc.
ANNIE REVA - Jackets–men's - Current Affairs, Inc.
ANNIE'S - Pasta - Annie's Homegrown, Inc.
ANNIE'S BOOK STOP - Book stores - Little Professor Book Center
ANNIE'S BOUQUET - Bedding–linen - Dan River Inc.
ANNIE'S CALENDAR BED DOLL SOCIETY - Dolls - Annie's Attic, Inc.
ANNIES CHOICE - Yarn - Annie's Attic, Inc.
ANNIE'S COLLECTION - Fabrics–linen - Peking Handicraft, Inc.
ANNIE'S GRANNIE'S - Barbecue sauce - Mullein Ridge Co.
ANNIE'S HOMEGROWN - Pasta - Annie's Homegrown, Inc.
ANNIE'S PRIDE - Cookies - Springwater Cookie
ANNIE'S TREASURES - Vases - Peking Handicraft, Inc.
ANNIHALATOR - Floor coverings–carpet and rugs - World Carpets, Inc.
ANNIHILATOR - Loudspeakers, amplifiers, and signal processors - Earthquake Sound Corp.
ANNIK - Ophthalmic goods - Swank Optical
ANNIN & CO. - Flags - Flags International Inc.
ANNIQUE - Apparel–women's - Duck Head Apparel Co., Inc.
ANNIVERSARY - Floor coverings–carpet and rugs - Regal Rugs Inc.
ANNIVERSARY - Floor coverings–carpet and rugs - Trend Carpet
ANNIVERSARY - Floor waxes - Fuller Brush Co.
ANNIVERSARY - Frames–eyeglass - Zylo Ware Corp.
ANNIVERSARY - Glassware–household - Fenton Art Glass Co.
ANNIVERSARY - Glassware–household - Seneca Glass Co.
ANNIVERSARY - Hardware - Amerock Corp.
ANNIVERSARY - Music boxes ✰ - Papel Freelance, Inc.
ANNIVERSARY - Paper–bond ✰ - Fox River Paper Co.
ANNIVERSARY - Watches - Gruen Marketing Corp.
ANNIVERSARY - Wines ✰ - Bardenheier Wine Cellars
ANNIVERSARY 101 - Fabrics–tapestry - Comark Wallcoverings
ANNIVERSARY 101 YEARS - Wallpaper - Decorative Coverings Inc.
ANNIVERSARY BABY - Dolls - Horsman
ANNIVERSARY BEAR - Toy stores ✰ - Gund, Inc.
ANNIVERSARY COLLECTION - Wallpaper - Richard E. Thibaut, Inc.
ANNIVERSARY COLLECTION - Wallpaper ✰ - Thomas Strahan Wallcoverings
ANNIVERSARY SIGNET COLLECTION, THE - Jewelry - CJC Holdings, Inc.
ANNIVERSARY STAR - Dolls - Mattel, Inc.
ANNJALL - Leather goods - Charlotte Richmond
ANNONDALE - Floor coverings ✰ - Kentile Floors Inc.
ANNOUNCEMENT BACKGROUNDS - Posters - Clement Communications Inc.
ANNOUNCEMENTS - Apparel–women's - Wal-Mart Stores Inc.
ANNOUNCEMENTS - Computer software - Parsons Technology, Inc.
ANNOUNCEMENTS - Paneling - Armstrong World Industries, Inc.
ANNOUNCER - Audio equipment - Perma Power Electronics Inc.
ANN'S - Wines ✰ - Robert Keenan Winery
ANN'S WEDDING STATIONERY - Stationery - Taylor Corp.
ANNTAYLOR - Jewelry - AnnTaylor, Inc.
ANNUAL EDITIONS - Publisher's imprints - Dushkin Publishing Group Inc.
ANNUAL PHOTO ORGANIZER - Photo albums - Rothkopf Enterprises, Inc.
ANNUALS - Giftware - Waterford Wedgewood USA, Inc.
ANNUFLEX - Corrugated hose - Hose Master, Inc.
ANNUITY! - Computer software - Recreational Mathemagical Software
ANNUITY PRO - Computer software - Professional Data Management Associates, Inc.
ANNULAR EXPANSION (A/E) - Laboratory apparatus - EM Industries, Inc.
ANO - Turpentine ✰ - Reliable Finishing Products, Inc.
ANOCAINE - Pharmaceutical preparations ✰ - Roberts/Hauck Pharmaceuticals Inc.
ANODAL - Lighting fixtures - Hubbell Lighting, Inc. (Lighting Div.)
ANODYNE - Publisher's imprints - Lowell House
ANODYNOS - Pharmaceutical preparations - Buffington
ANODYNOS FORTE - Pharmaceutical preparations - Buffington
ANOGESIC - Pharmaceutical preparations - Stephen R. Gorfine
ANOGLAS - Lighting fixtures ✰ - Hubbell Lighting, Inc. (Lighting Div.)
ANOINTING OIL - Colognes - Brandy Harvest
ANOLIFT - Health care products - Anodyne Inc.
ANONYME - Handbags - Anonyme Inc.
ANONYMOUSLY YOURS - Greeting cards - Recycled Paper Products, Inc.
ANOQUAN - Pharmaceutical preparations - Roberts/Hauck Pharmaceuticals Inc.
ANORALP - Apparel and accessories ✰ - Skis Dynastar, Inc.
ANOREX - Pharmaceutical preparations - Dunhall Pharmaceuticals Inc.
ANOREXIN - Pharmaceutical preparations ✰ - S.D.A. Pharmaceuticals Inc.

ANOTHER - Snowboards - Alfa-Row, Inc.
ANOTHER BUSY WEEKEND - Games - Mattel, Inc.
ANOTHER GWT SPECIAL GIFT IDEA - Aquariums–household - Great Western Trading Co., Inc. ✱
ANOTHER ONE OF THOSE DAYS - Teas - Village Herbalist
ANOTHER ORIGINAL - Greeting cards - Another Original
ANOTHER WORLD - Eyeglasses - Martin-Copeland Eyewear Corp.
ANOXINE-AM - Pharmaceutical preparations ☆ - Roberts/Hauck Pharmaceuticals Inc.
ANOXINE-T - Pharmaceutical preparations ☆ - Roberts/Hauck Pharmaceuticals Inc.
A.N.P. - Health care products - Arizona Natural Products
ANR - Vitamins and nutritional supplements - Trans Mins by Nutrilogic
ANRI - Giftware ☆ - Schmid Inc.
ANSA - Infant product - Ansa Co. Inc.
ANSA SPORT - Sport bottle - Ansa Co. Inc.
ANSAC - Liquors - Heaven Hill Distilleries, Inc.
ANSAFONE - Telephone answering machines - Dictaphone Corp.
ANSAI - Television equipment - Aiko Corp.
ANSAID - Pharmaceutical preparations - Upjohn Co.
ANSBACH - Beverages–malt ☆ - The Stroh Brewery Co.
ANSCO - Electronic equipment - GAF Corp.
ANSCOCHROME - Electronic equipment - GAF Corp.
ANSCOFLEX - Electronic equipment - GAF Corp.
ANSCOMATIC - Electronic equipment - GAF Corp.
ANSCORAMA - Electronic equipment - GAF Corp.
ANSCOVISION - Electronic equipment - GAF Corp.
ANSEHL'S - Cosmetics - Benjamin Ansehl Co.
ANSEL - Antiseborrheic lotion ☆ - Allergan Skin Care
ANSELL - Novelty items ☆ - Ansell Inc. (Personal Products Div.)
ANSELL-EDMONT - Gloves–rubber - Rockford Medical & Safety Co.
ANSELL EDMONT TOOLS FOR HANDS - Gloves - Ansell Edmont Industrial Inc.
ANSELMI - Wines ☆ - Pellegrini Bros. Wines Inc.
ANSEMCO - Pharmaceutical preparations ☆ - ICN Pharmaceuticals Inc.
ANSER - Cleaning preparations–carpet and rug - Castex Industries Inc.
ANSETT OF SEYMOUR - Apparel and accessories - Mariner Resource Corp.
ANSEWN - Footwear–men's - L.B. Evans' Son Co.
ANSILEX - Clay products - Engelhard Corp.
ANSIMAG - Pumps - Ansimag Inc.
ANSLEY - Floor coverings–carpet and rugs ☆ - Regal Rugs Inc.
ANSO - Fabrics–nylon - Allied Fibers
ANSO TRIOMPHE - Yarn - Alliedsignal Inc.
ANSON - Furniture - Boling Co.
ANSON - Jewelry - Anson Inc.
ANSON - Publisher's imprints - Willis Music Co.
ANSONIA - Clocks - Ansonia Clock Co. Inc.
ANSONIA - Flatware - Pfaltzgraff Investment Co.
ANSONIA - Recording label - Ansonia Records Inc.
ANSPACH EFFORT, THE - Medical apparatus - Anspach Effort, Inc.
ANSPOR - Antibiotics - Smithkline Beecham Corp.
ANSUL - Fire extinguishers - Ansul, Inc.
ANSUL AUTOMAN - Alarm systems–fire - Ansul, Inc.
ANSULEX - Fire extinguishers - Ansul, Inc.
ANSULITE - Fire extinguishers - Ansul, Inc.
ANSULITE ARC - Fire extinguishers - Ansul, Inc.
ANSWER - Audio equipment ☆ - St. Louis Music Supply Co.
ANSWER - Hair care products - Helene Curtis Industries Inc.
ANSWER - Health care products - Gillette Co.
ANSWER - Helmets–athletic - Answer Products Inc.
ANSWER - Pregnancy test kits - Carter-Wallace, Inc.
ANSWER - Thermostats - National Stove Works Inc.
ANSWER 2 - Pregnancy test kits - Carter-Wallace, Inc.
ANSWER:ARCHITECT - Computer software - Sterling Software, Inc.
ANSWER BACK - Telephone answering machines ☆ - Cobra Electronics Corp.
ANSWER BLANKET, THE - Fabrics - West Point-Pepperell Inc.
ANSWER CAKE - Flour–blended ☆ - General Mills, Inc.
ANSWER CLOCK - Toys - Tomy America, Inc.
ANSWER FUN WITH NUMBERS - Games - Lowell E. Jack
ANSWER PAD - Computer terminals - Mind Path Technologies Inc.
ANSWER PLUS - Pregnancy test kits - Carter-Wallace, Inc.
ANSWER QUICK & SIMPLE - Pregnancy test kits - Carter-Wallace, Inc.
ANSWER STORE, THE - Computer software - Answer Store
ANSWER, THE - Floor coverings–carpet and rugs - Beaulieu of America, Inc.
ANSWER, THE - Doors–screen - Columbia Manufacturing Corp.
ANSWER, THE - Computers–personal - Comark, Inc.

ANSWER, THE - Shoes–athletic - Ektelon
ANSWER, THE - Archery equipment - Golden Key Futura, Inc.
ANSWER, THE - Stoves–wood-burning - Travis Industries
ANSWER:ZIM - Computer software - Sterling Software, Inc.
ANSWERING SERVICE - Greeting cards ☆ - Recycled Paper Products, Inc.
ANSWERQUEST - Computer software - Segal Co., (Eastern States), Inc.
ANSWERS ON DEMAND - Computer software - Brouwer Software Solutions, Inc.
ANSWERTIME - Telephone apparatus - Answer/Line Associates Inc.
ANSWERWARE - Computer software - Applied Intelligence Group, Inc.
ANSYS - Laboratory apparatus - Ansys, Inc.
ANSYS/PROFEA - Computer software - Swanson Analysis Systems Inc.
ANT-BOB - Vitamins and nutritional supplements - Scot-Tussin Pharmacal Co.
ANT CITY - Science kits - Natural Science Industries, Ltd.
ANT CITY - Toys - Natural Science Industries, Ltd.
ANT COLONY - Toys - Natural Science Industries, Ltd.
ANT DOOM - Insecticides ☆ - Fairfax Biological Laboratory
ANT DUST - Pesticides–household - Bonide Products, Inc.
ANT EATER - Games - Brown and Bigelow Inc.
ANT FACTORY - Toys - Educational Insights, Inc.
ANT FARM - Computer software ☆ - Sunburst Communications, Inc.
ANT FARM - Pet products - Uncle Milton Industries Inc.
ANT-GO - Insecticides ☆ - W.R. Sweeney Manufacturer Inc.
ANT HOUSE - Toys - Natural Science Industries, Ltd.
ANT N ROACH - Insecticides - Vitarroz
ANT-NOT - Insecticides - Nott Manufacturing Co. Inc.
ANT RANCH - Toys - Natural Science Industries, Ltd.
ANT/ROACH-NIP - Insecticides - Roccorp, Inc.
ANT-STOP - Pesticides–agricultural - Chevron Chemical Co.
ANTA-GEL - Health care products - Halsey Drug Co. Inc.
ANTABUSE - Pharmaceutical preparations - Wyeth-Ayerst Laboratories
ANTACHE - Medical apparatus ☆ - Biosig Instruments Inc.
ANTACID DOPHILUS - Vitamins and nutritional supplements - Nutrition Now, Inc.
ANTAEUS - Colognes - Chanel Inc.
ANTALIA - Apparel–women's - Campagna Co.
ANTAR - Pharmaceutical preparations ☆ - Ulmer Pharmacal Co.
ANTARA - Apparel and accessories - Fashion Initiatives
ANTARA II - Apparel and accessories - Fashion Initiatives
ANTARCTIC - Watches - Croton Watch Co., Inc.
ANTARCTIC QUEEN - Fish–fresh or frozen - Wholey International (Robert Wholey)
ANTARCTICA - Novelty items - Museum of Science and Industry
ANTARCTICA GUARANA - Juices - Brooklyn Bottling Corp.
ANTARES - Electronic equipment - Intermec Corp.
ANTARES - Musical instruments - VMI Industries
ANTARES - Toys–models ☆ - Estes Industries
ANTARES - Whirlpools - Lasco Products Group
ANTARTICA - Recording label - Jazz Composer's Orchestra Association Inc.
ANTAYA - Medals, badges, insignia - American Metalcraft Inc.
ANTAZINE - Pharmaceutical preparations - H.R. Cenci Laboratories Inc.
ANTBOXX - Machinery - Saginaw Information Management Services
ANTEATER - Games - Mattel, Inc.
ANTEBELLUM - Shutters–wood - Pinecrest, Inc.
ANTEC - Broadcasting stations–television - Antec Corp.
ANTECH - Coats - Antigua Sportswear Inc.
ANTELL - Floor coverings - Bruce Hardwood Floors
ANTELL - Floor coverings–carpet and rugs - Evans-Black Carpet Mills
ANTELOPE - Ophthalmic goods - Embassy Creations Inc.
ANTELOPE TALK - Sporting goods - E.L.K., Inc.
ANTENNA - Apparel–children's - Charles Greenberg & Sons Inc.
ANTENNA - Computer software - Goldenwood International, Inc.
ANTENNA - Recording label - Antenna Records/Cornerstone Management
ANTENNA GUARD - Telephone apparatus - Cellular Safety Systems Inc.
ANTENNA MATE - Electronics equipment - Marine Motions, Inc.
ANTENNA MULTIPLIER - Television picture booster - Rothkopf Enterprises, Inc.
ANTENNA SPECIALISTS - Telephone apparatus - Allen Telecom Group, Inc.
ANTENNACO INC. - Antennas - Antennaco Inc.
ANTENNACRAFT - Antennas - Antennacraft Co.
ANTENORI - Footwear - Antenori Footwear Inc.
ANTENSE - Medical apparatus - Biosig Instruments Inc.
ANTEPAR - Pharmaceutical preparations ☆ - Burroughs Wellcome Co.
ANTER - Measuring instruments - Anter Corp.
ANTERION - Sporting goods - D.L.C. Fabricating Co. Inc.
ANTERO - Chairs–upholstered - La-Z-Boy Chair Co.

☆ = Now out of production

ANTERO - Computer software - Evolving Video Technologies Corp.
ANTEX - Personal computers and peripherals - International Antex Inc.
ANTEX - Tools–soldering - Hot Tools Inc.
ANTFARM - Postcards - Fotofolio Inc.
ANTHATEST - Health care products - Kay Pharmacal Co. Inc.
ANTHEM-C - Hearing aids - Starkey Labs Inc.
ANTHEM-E - Hearing aids - Starkey Labs Inc.
ANTHEM-S - Hearing aids - Starkey Labs Inc.
ANTHES - File folders - Anthes Universal
ANTHES - Tools ✰ - Gleason Corp.
ANTHING GOES - Hair accessories, jewelry - Bead Shoppe
ANTHOLOGY - Wallpaper - Capital Carousel Inc.
ANTHOLOGY - Wines - Stimson Lane Vineyards & Estates
ANTHONY - Lumber - Anthony Forest Products Co.
ANTHONY - Ophthalmic goods ✰ - Luxottica
ANTHONY - Skin care products - Imperial Inc.
ANTHONY ALEXANDER - Hair accessories and jewelry - Spencer Jewelry & Accessories Manufacturing Inc.
ANTHONY BARTON - Wines - W.J. Deutsch & Sons Ltd.
ANTHONY MARTIN - Frames–eyeglass - Ambassador Eyewear Group
ANTHONY REED - Footwear–men's ✰ - Univshoe Inc.
ANTHONY ROBBINS' PERSONAL POWER! - Recording label - Anthony J. Robbins
ANTHONY ROBBINS' POWERTALK! - Video and audio cassette tapes - Anthony J. Robbins
ANTHONY STERN - Glass products ✰ - Westminster Trading Corp.
ANTHONY'S - Apparel and accessories ✰ - C.R. Anthony Co.
ANTHRA-DERM - Pharmaceutical preparations ✰ - Dermik Laboratories Inc.
ANTHRAROBIN - Pharmaceutical preparations ✰ - City Chemical Corp.
ANTHRASOME - Pharmaceutical preparations - Igen, Inc.
ANTHRO - Furniture - Harter
ANTHRONE - Pharmaceutical preparations - City Chemical Corp.
ANTI-ANT - Insecticides - Farnam Cos. Inc.
ANTI-BACCO - Cough drops ✰ - Pharmex Inc.
ANTI-BACT - See SWISS TOUCH
ANTI-BASIC - Apparel and accessories - Lazeon Corp.
ANTI-BASICX DAILY JEANS - Apparel and accessories - Lazeon Corp.
ANTI-CAL - Health care products ✰ - Halsey Drug Co. Inc.
ANTI-CATABOLIC FUEL - Vitamins and nutritional supplements - Twinlab
ANTI-CERNES LINE CORRECTOR - Skin care products - Victoria Vogue, Inc.
ANTI DRIFT MINI FIN - Sporting goods - O'Brien International
ANTI-ELEMENTS - Cosmetics - Victoria Jackson Cosmetics, Inc.
ANTI-EM/GP - Hosiery–women's - Jobst Institute Inc.
ANTI-FATIGUE ENERGY FORMULA - Vitamins and nutritional supplements ✰ - Naturade Inc.
ANTI-FLAT KAP - Beverage bottle stopper - Converse Distributing
ANTI-G - Finishing agents - Flexi-Wall Systems
ANTI-GERM 50 - Veterinary pharmaceutical preparations ✰ - Pfizer Inc.
ANTI - GERM CONTROL - Disinfectants - Clean Control Corp.
ANTI-HEAT - Pharmaceutical preparations - Specialty Products Co.
ANTI-HIGHJACKER - Chemical preparations - Auto Security Systems, Inc.
ANTI-HYDRO - Adhesives and sealants - Anti Hydro International Inc.
ANTI-MERGE - Hunting equipment - M.L.R. Enterprises, Inc.
ANTI-MONOPOLY - Games - Talicor Inc.
ANTI-MONOPOLY - Toys - Tonka Corp.
ANTI-NAUSEA/REKEMATOL - Pharmaceutical preparations - Reese Chemical Co.
ANTI NAUSEANT - Pharmaceutical preparations - Global Pharmaceutical Corp.
ANTI-NUCLEAR WAR HEAD - Apparel and accessories - Andrew H. Krasnow
ANTI-OA-519 - Chemical preparations - Chektec Corp.
ANTI-OXIDANT EDGE - Teas - Gary R. Harlem
ANTI-OXIDANT PLUS PHYSICIAN'S FORMULA - Vitamins and nutritional supplements - Healthy America Campaign Inc.
ANTI PERSPIRANT, ROLL-ON DEODRANT - Deodorants–personal - Viviane Woodard Industries, Ltd.
ANTI-RESIDUE SHAMPOO, THE - Hair care products - Neutrogena Corp.
ANTI RUST-1 - Rust removers - Dynamic Development
ANTI-RUST POWDER - Pharmaceutical preparations - Gordon Laboratories
ANTI SALT - Vitamins and nutritional supplements - Nature Mart, Inc.
ANTI-SEIZE - Lubricants - Loctite Corp.
ANTI-SHOK - Sports rackets and accessories - Winn, Inc.
ANTI-SHOX - Footcare products - Apex Foot Health Industries, Inc.
ANTI-SLIP-SLOP - Adhesives and sealants - Michael Beau Lawson
ANTI-SOUND/PLUS-SOUND - Amplifiers - Projectapix-II
ANTI-SPARK - Cleaning preparations–carpet and rug - Multi-Care Corp.
ANTI SSSSSSKID - Traction apparatus–medical - Rohrer's Quarry Inc.

ANTI-STAT - Cleaning preparations ✰ - Edwal Scientific Products Corp.
ANTI-STAT - Cleaning preparations–carpet and rug - Hillyard Enterprises, Inc.
ANTI-STATIC - Plastics - Westinghouse Electric Corp. (Decorative Micarta Div.)
ANTI-STATIC #79 CONCENTRATE - Static eliminator - Merix Chemical Co.
ANTI-STATIC #79-OL - Static eliminator - Merix Chemical Co.
ANTI-STATIC PRO - Hair care products - Bobby Co.
ANTI TANK LAUNCHER - Fireworks - China Pyrotechnics, Inc.
ANTI-TERGE - Skin care products - Comfort Manufacturing Co.
ANTI-THERM - Pharmaceutical preparations ✰ - Scrip-Physician Supply Co.
ANTI-TIGHTS - Slacks - Norm Thompson Outfitters, Inc.
ANTI-TUSS - Pharmaceutical preparations - Century Pharmaceuticals Inc.
ANTI-TUSS DM - Pharmaceutical preparations - Century Pharmaceuticals Inc.
ANTI-TUSSIN - Pharmaceutical preparations ✰ - Pharmex Inc.
ANTI WEAR-1 - Automotive parts and accessories - Dynamic Development
ANTIALL - Hair care products ✰ - Framesi USA/Roffler Industries Inc.
ANTIBACTERIAL LEVER 2000 - Soap - Lever Brothers Co. Inc.
ANTIBACTERIAL PLUS - Soap - Andrew Jergens Co.
ANTIBES - Bedding–linen - Dan River Inc.
ANTIC - Pharmaceutical preparations - C.S. Ruckstuhl Co. Inc.
ANTICA - Ceramic tile ✰ - Integrity Tile Co.
ANTICA ITALIA - Food products - Group International of Italian Aliments, Inc.
ANTICA ITALIA - Food products - Med-USA Corp.
ANTICA MURINA - Jewelry - Alice Sturzinger Ltd.
ANTICA TERRA - Wines - Antica Terra Ltd.
ANTICIPATION - Floor coverings–carpet and rugs - Tuftex Carpet Mills, Inc.
ANTICIPATION - Floor coverings–carpet and rugs ✰ - Columbus Mills, Inc.
ANTICIPATION - Furniture ✰ - Bassett Furniture Industries, Inc.
ANTICIPATION - Maternity clothing - Mercantile Stores Co., Inc.
ANTICLOT - Pharmaceutical preparations - G.O. Spanner Inc.
ANTICO DOCCIA - Dishes–china - Pasmantier Co. Inc.
ANTICO TOSCANO - Cigars - G.A. Georgopulo & Co. Inc.
ANTICS - Decals and transfers - P & S GA Co. Inc.
ANTIDOTE - Apparel - At Last Sportswear Inc.
ANTIFOAM - Cleaning preparations - Analab Inc.
ANTIGA PARCH - Paper - Howard Paper Mills Inc.
ANTIGONE - Bedding–linen - Dan River Inc.
ANTIGONE II - Floor coverings–carpet and rugs - Regal Rugs Inc.
ANTIGUA - Bathroom accessories - Franklin Brass Manufacturing Co.
ANTIGUA - Bathroom fixtures - Artesian Industries
ANTIGUA - Boats ✰ - Wellcraft Marine Corp.
ANTIGUA - Briefcases - David M. Weiselman
ANTIGUA - Carpets and rugs ✰ - Couristan Inc.
ANTIGUA - Dinnerware–glass ✰ - Johnson Brothers, USA, Inc.
ANTIGUA - Furniture ✰ - Telescope Casual Furniture Inc.
ANTIGUA - Glassware–household ✰ - Culver Glass Inc.
ANTIGUA - Thread ✰ - YLI Corp.
ANTIGUA - Wallpaper ✰ - Winfield Design Associates, Inc.
ANTIGUA - Wines - Merryvale Vineyards
ANTIGUA CLASSIC - Jewelry ✰ - Hirsch Speidel Inc.
ANTIGUA SPORT - Sporting goods - Antigua Sportswear Inc.
ANTIGUA WINDS - Musical instruments - Antigua Winds, Inc.
ANTIHEMM - Veterinary pharmaceutical preparations - Vineland Laboratories Inc.
ANTIHESIVE - Electronic equipment - Apollo Audiovisual Div.
ANTILIRIUM - Pharmaceutical preparations - Forest Pharmaceuticals Inc.
ANTILLES - Recording label - Island Records Inc.
ANTILOPE - Perfumes ✰ - Classic Fragrances Ltd.
ANTIMINTH - Pharmaceutical preparations - J.B. Roerig & Co.
ANTINEA - Topical fungicide - American Dermal Corp.
ANTINORI - Olive oil ✰ - Dean & Deluca Inc.
ANTINORI - Wines - Hiram Walker & Sons, Inc.
ANTIO & NUEVO - Wallpaper - Carlton-Metro Wallcoverings
ANTIOCH - Novelty items–paper ✰ - Antioch Publishing Co.
ANTIOCH FARMS - Food products - Aspen Foods, a division of Koch Poultry
ANTIOCH FARMS - Meat products–poultry - Koch Poultry Co., Inc.
ANTIOQUENO - Beverages–alcohol - Blair Importers Ltd.
ANTIOXIDANT ARSENAL - Vitamins and nutritional supplements - Lifetrends International
ANTIOXIDANT DEFENDERS - Pharmaceutical preparations - Barth's Nutra Products
ANTIOXIDANT FORMULA 2500 - Vitamins and nutritional supplements - Earth Industries Inc.
ANTIOXIDANT PLUS - Pharmaceutical preparations - Vita Plus Industries Inc.
ANTIOXIDANT SKIN CARE DERMS - Skin care products - Osmotics Corp.
ANTIPASTO ITALIANO - Food products - Homemade Brand Foods

✰ = Now out of production

ANTIPHLOGISTINE - Veterinary pharmaceutical preparations - W.F. Young, Inc.

ANTIPHOLGISTINE - Veterinary pharmaceutical preparations - W.F. Young, Inc.

ANTIQ-KIT - Paints ☆ - M.A. Bruder & Sons Inc.

ANTIQA PARCH - Paper–bond ☆ - Fox River Paper Co.

ANTIQUA - Bathing suits - Ocean Pool Co.

ANTIQUA - Dinnerware–glass ☆ - Nikko Ceramics Inc.

ANTIQUA - Flatware - Antiqua, Ltd.

ANTIQUA - Floor coverings - Tarkett, Inc.

ANTIQUA - Office supplies ☆ - Sheaffer Inc.

ANTIQUA - Shelving units–wood - Woodland Products Inc.

ANTIQUA - Whirlpool bath ☆ - Jacuzzi Inc.

ANTIQUA BAY - Floor coverings–carpet and rugs - Whitecrest Carpet Mills

ANTIQUARIAN - Mats - Potomac Corp.

ANTIQUARIAN FOSSILS - Moldings–plaster of paris - Antiquarian Fossils, Inc.

ANTIQUARIAN SCRAPBOOK - Greeting cards - Lovelace Family Ltd.

ANTIQUARY - Furniture - Tomlinson of High Point Inc.

ANTIQUE - Artists' materials - Andrews/Nelson/Whitehead

ANTIQUE - Clocks ☆ - General Time Corp. (Westclox/Seth Thomas Div.)

ANTIQUE - Faucets - Kohler Co.

ANTIQUE - Glassware–household - Durand International

ANTIQUE - Paper–toweling ☆ - Fort Howard Corp.

ANTIQUE - Recording label - Antique-Catfish Records

ANTIQUE - Wood products - Mountain Lumber Co., Inc.

ANTIQUE - Yarn - Lily Craft Products

ANTIQUE ANTICS - Trading cards and stamps ☆ - Comstock Cards Inc.

ANTIQUE BEARS - Toys–stuffed - Dakin Inc.

ANTIQUE BLACK - Coatings - Birchwood Casey

ANTIQUE BLEND - Furniture polish - Black's Products of High Point Inc.

ANTIQUE BLUE - Glassware–household ☆ - Lenox Crystal, Inc.

ANTIQUE BRICK - Floor coverings - Tarkett, Inc.

ANTIQUE BRICK - Tiles–facing - Design Brick Products Inc.

ANTIQUE BROWN - Glassware–household ☆ - Lenox Crystal, Inc.

ANTIQUE CHARM - Lamps - Kaadan Ltd.

ANTIQUE CLASSICS - Glassware–household - Jeannette Corp.

ANTIQUE CLEAR - Glassware–household ☆ - Lenox Crystal, Inc.

ANTIQUE CRANBERRY - Glass products - Pilgrim Glass Corp.

ANTIQUE FLOWERS - Wallcovering ☆ - Colortree Designs

ANTIQUE GALERIE - Watches - Bulova Corp.

ANTIQUE GARDEN - Dinnerware ☆ - Corning Inc.

ANTIQUE GLASS LTD. - Glassware–household ☆ - Knobler International Ltd.

ANTIQUE GRAPE - Dinnerware–glass - Metlox Pottery Shoppe

ANTIQUE GREEN - Glassware–household ☆ - Lenox Crystal, Inc.

ANTIQUE HANDGUNS - Patterns–clothing - Ann's Cottage

ANTIQUE-IT - Varnishes ☆ - Magicolor Co.

ANTIQUE KIRMAN - Floor coverings–carpet and rugs - Capel, Inc.

ANTIQUE LACE - Christmas tree ornaments - Cracker Box Inc.

ANTIQUE LINEN - Envelopes - Western States Envelope Co.

ANTIQUE MARBLE - Floor coverings–tile - Kentile Floors Inc.

ANTIQUE MARBLE - Tiles–ceramic - KPT Inc.

ANTIQUE 'N GLAZE - Paints ☆ - American Art Clay Co. Inc.

ANTIQUE OAK - Wood products ☆ - Vermillion Inc.

ANTIQUE PAVER - Floor coverings - Armstrong World Industries, Inc.

ANTIQUE ROAD - Floor coverings - Armstrong World Industries, Inc.

ANTIQUE ROSE - Glassware–household ☆ - Fenton Art Glass Co.

ANTIQUE ROSE EMPORIUM, THE - Flowers, plants, and seeds - Antique Rose Emporium

ANTIQUE RUST - Glassware–household ☆ - Lenox Crystal, Inc.

ANTIQUE SATIN - Underwear and nightwear - Maidenform Inc.

ANTIQUE SHOP - Wallpaper - Warner Co.

ANTIQUE SILVER - Dishes–china - Pickard Inc.

ANTIQUE WASH - Jeans - Blue Bell, Inc.

ANTIQUE YELLOW - Glassware–household ☆ - Lenox Crystal, Inc.

ANTIQUEGLAZE - Floor coverings ☆ - Armstrong World Industries, Inc.

ANTIQUER'S CHOICE - Furniture polish and wax - Piedmont Care Products

ANTIQUES & COLLECTIBLES - Wallcovering ☆ - Colortree Designs

ANTIQUES & OLD LACE - Wallpaper - Milbrook Wallcoverings

ANTIQUITY - Apparel–women's - Jezebel-Renee of Hollywood

ANTIQUITY - Furniture ☆ - Stanley Furniture Co. Inc.

ANTIQUITY - Glassware–household - Wilton Co.

ANTIQUITY - Musical instrument accessories - Seymour Duncan Pickups

ANTIQUITY - Recording label - Narada Productions Inc.

ANTIQUITY II - Musical instrument accessories - Seymour Duncan Pickups

ANTIQUITY COLLECTION - Furniture ☆ - Evenflo Juvenile Furniture Co.

ANTIQUITY OF MUSIC - Figurines ☆ - E.M.I. Inc.

ANTIROLL PAK - Tubes–plastic - VisiPak

ANTIS - Health care products - Halsey Drug Co. Inc.

ANTISEPTIC LANELLE - Soap - Sanitary Soap Co. Inc.

ANTISOLAIRE - Suntan lotions ☆ - Sothys USA Inc.

ANTISPAS - Pharmaceutical preparations ☆ - Keene Pharmaceuticals Inc.

ANTISTAT - Floor coverings - Tarkett, Inc.

ANTISTOCK - Computer storage devices–optical - Digital Stock Corp.

ANTITEN - Pharmaceutical preparations - Century Pharmaceuticals Inc.

ANTIVERT - Antihistamine preparations - J.B. Roerig & Co.

ANTIVIRUS - Computer software - International Business Machines Corp.

ANTIZOL-VET - Pharmaceutical preparations - Orphan Medical, Inc.

ANTLER - Antennas - Newtronics Antenna Corp.

ANTLER - Recording label - Lamon Records

ANTLER - Shirts - M. Rubin & Sons Inc.

ANTLER - Thread - Threads USA Div.

ANTLER ATHLETIC - Health care products - East Earth Herb Inc.

ANTLER-GRO - Veterinary pharmaceutical preparations - Julius N. Norris, Jr.

ANTLER SUBWAY - Recording label - Caroline Records, Inc.

ANTOCIN - Health care products - Johnson & Johnson

ANTOGIANNI - Wines - House of Burgundy Inc.

ANTOINE CLOUTIER - Wines - Chatam Imports Inc.

ANTOINE GUILBAUD - Wines - House of Burgundy Inc.

ANTOINES - Canned vegetables - Aunt Nellie's Farm Kitchens Inc.

ANTOINE'S - Pasta - Liberty Richter Inc.

ANTOINETTE - Dolls - Horsman

ANTOINETTE - Giftware - Arnart Imports Inc.

ANTOINETTE - Luggage - American Flyer

ANTOINETTE - Watches - Bulova Corp.

ANTOINETTE COLLECTION - Floor coverings–carpet and rugs - Nourison

ANTON - Ophthalmic goods ☆ - Rozin Optical Export Corp.

ANTON BERG - Chocolate candy - FCW Imports

ANTON PAAR USA - Computer software - Anton Paar USA, Inc.

ANTON RIEMERSCHMID - Beverages–alcohol - Joseph Gies Import

ANTON SCHUSTER - Musical instrument accessories - M & M Distributing Co.

ANTON STOHR - Cellos - St. Louis Music Supply Co.

ANTONE'S FINEST BRAND - Food products - Antone's Import Co.

ANTONETTE - Skin care products - Imperial Inc.

ANTONIO - Fabrics–cotton ☆ - Stylecrest Fabrics Ltd.

ANTONIO - Footwear - O & B Shoe Co.

ANTONIO - Musical instruments - Dealer's Photo Supply, Inc.

ANTONIO - Olive oil - LFI, Inc.

ANTONIO BORSATO - Porcelain figurines - Intercontinental Industries Inc.

ANTONIO COLLECTION - Fabrics ☆ - Stylecrest Fabrics Ltd.

ANTONIO MORENO MIAMI - Apparel and accessories - Antonio Lazaro Moreno

ANTONIO VIOLINS - Violins - Dealer's Photo Supply, Inc.

ANTONIO Y CLEOPATRA - Cigar boxes–wood - Consolidated Cigar Corp.

ANTONIO ZENGARA - Footwear–men's - Harbor Footwear Group Ltd.

ANTONIOLO GATTINARA - Wines - Banfi Vintners

ANTONIOS - Cigar boxes–wood - Consolidated Cigar Corp.

ANTONIO'S - Combs - Ajax Comb Co. (Div. of Antonio's Manufacturing, Inc.)

ANTONIOS AFRO-PIK - Combs - Ajax Comb Co. (Div. of Antonio's Manufacturing, Inc.)

ANTONIOU - Hair care products - Shampoo, Ltd.

ANTRATE - Pharmaceutical preparations - C.S. Ruckstuhl Co. Inc.

ANTRIM - Kitchen cabinets–metal - Richwood

ANTRIN - Pharmaceutical preparations ☆ - Pal-Pak Inc.

ANTRON - Fabrics–nylon - E.I. Dupont de Nemours and Co.

ANTRON III - Fabrics–nylon - E.I. Dupont de Nemours and Co.

ANTRON PLUS - Fabrics–nylon - E.I. Dupont de Nemours and Co.

ANTS - Display cases–plastic - Gastro-Gnomes, Inc.

ANTS IN THE PANTS - Games - Milton Bradley Co.

ANTSY - Games ☆ - Talicor Inc.

ANTTRON - Antennas - Twin*Tronics, Inc.

ANTUITRIN-S - Pharmaceutical preparations ☆ - Parke-Davis

ANTURANE - Pharmaceutical preparations - Ciba-Geigy Corp.

ANTWERP - Wallcoverings - Stretchwall Fabrics Co.

ANTWORKS - Computer software - Miaco Corp.

ANTWORKS - Toys - Educational Insights, Inc.

ANUCORT - Health care products - G and W Laboratories Inc.

ANUDERM - Pharmaceutical preparations - Macsil Inc. (Balmex Div.)

ANUGARD - Pharmaceutical preparations ☆ - Vangard Labs Inc.

ANUGESIC - Pharmaceutical preparations ☆ - Warner-Lambert Co.

ANUJECT - Pharmaceutical preparations ☆ - Roberts/Hauck Pharmaceuticals Inc.

☆ = Now out of production

ANUKI - Vitamins and nutritional supplements - Unique Products Co.

ANULAN - Pharmaceutical preparations - Lannett Co. Inc.

ANULL - Deodorants–personal ☆ - Carter-Wallace, Inc.

ANUS-OID - Pharmaceutical preparations - Raway Pharmacal Inc.

ANUSERT - Health care products - G and W Laboratories Inc.

ANUSOL - Pharmaceutical preparations - Warner-Wellcome

ANUSOL HC - Pharmaceutical preparations - Parke-Davis

ANUSOL HC-1 - Pharmaceutical preparations - Warner-Wellcome

ANVARI - Floor coverings–carpet and rugs - Evans-Black Carpet Mills

ANVIL - Apparel–athletic - McCrory Corp.

ANVIL - Apparel–athletic ☆ - Rothco Inc.

ANVIL - Cases–musical instrument - Anvil Cases

ANVIL - Flatware - Dansk International Designs, Ltd.

ANVIL - Insecticides - Vectec, Inc.

ANVIL - Knives–pocket - Colonial Knife Co. Inc.

ANVIL - Lamps ☆ - Tensor Corp.

ANVIL - Paints - Anvil Paints & Coatings Inc.

ANVIL - Publisher's imprints - Krieger Publishing Co.

ANVIL - Snowboards - Anvil Snowboard Corp.

ANVIL - T-shirts–men's - Midstates Sportswear

ANVIL - Thread ☆ - Coats and Clark Inc.

ANVIL - Window coverings - Bellwether Corp.

ANVIL F - Adhesives and sealants - Formica Corp.

ANVIL FIRST SPRING WHEAT CLEAR - Flour - Inland Mills Co.

ANVIL HEAD - Fishing lures - Eugene W. Kaecker

ANVIL INTELLIGENT MODELER - Computer software - Manufacturing and Consulting Services, Inc.

ANVIL UTILITY - Paints - United Hardware

ANVILITE - Cases–musical instrument ☆ - Anvil Cases

ANVILLAR - Locks–door - Anvillar International, Ltd.

ANVILOK I - Machine parts - Dicar, Inc.

ANVILOK III - Machine parts - Dicar, Inc.

ANVILOK VI - Machine parts - Dicar, Inc.

ANVILOK VIII - Machine parts - Dicar, Inc.

ANX - Pharmaceutical preparations - Econo Med Pharmaceuticals Inc.

ANXANIL - Pharmaceutical preparations - Econo Med Pharmaceuticals Inc.

ANXIETY CONTROL - Vitamins and nutritional supplements - M.M.R.C., Ltd. Co.

ANY D'AVRAY - Wigs - International Hairgoods Inc.

ANY MACHINE...ONE PAPER - Paper products - Georgia-Pacific Corp.

ANY MOMENT - Apparel–women's - Dobie Industries Inc.

ANY ONE CAN PAINT - Artists' materials - Dahle USA

ANY PRODUCT - Cosmetics - L.T. York Co.

ANY SIDE UP - Containers - Any Side Up Inc.

ANY SIZE - Hoses ☆ - Melnor Inc.

ANY TIME - Cleaning preparations - W.W. Grainger, Inc.

ANYA - Apparel–women's - Anya & Co. Inc.

ANYA BY MANDY - Apparel and accessories ☆ - Toll-Gate Garment Co.

ANYCASE - Computer peripheral equipment - Securtech Co.

ANYCSE - Anchors - Securtech Co.

ANYDAY - Sanitary napkins - Kimberly-Clark Corp.

ANYDAY - Sporting goods - Jack Martin Co.

ANYLITE - Calculators - Texas Instruments Inc.

ANYNET - Computer hardware - International Business Machines Corp.

ANYPLACE - Watches - Elgin Watch Co.

ANYPRINT! - Computer software - ETI USA

ANYSIZE-ANYTIME - Metal frames and components - Pro-De-Co Inc.

ANYSTREAM - Bathroom fixtures - Speakman Co. (Manufacturing Div.)

ANYTHING GOES - Baskets - Russ Berrie and Co., Inc.

ANYTHING GOES - Containers - Rubbermaid Inc.

ANYTHING GOES - Fabrics - VIP/VIP Crafts

ANYTHING GOES - Toys - Tonka Corp.

ANYTHING LESS JUST WON'T CUT IT - Garden equipment - Fuqua Industries Inc.

ANYTHING'S POSSIBLE - T-shirts–men's - KDK Inc.

ANYTIME - Glassware–household ☆ - Crisa Corp.

ANYTIME - Lemonade - Food Sciences Corp.

ANYTIME - Meat products - Greenwood Packing Plant

ANYTIME - Syrup - Dearborn

ANYTIME - Vegetables–canned - Loyal Canning Corp.

ANYTIME - Vegetables–frozen - Bellingham Frozen Foods

ANYTIME ANYWHERE - Containers–plastic - Insta-Heat, Inc.

ANYTIME ANYWHERE NURSING APRON - Apparel–women's - Oakes Design Group

ANYTIME BOOKS - Publisher's imprints - E.P. Dutton Inc.

ANYTIME CAKE - Cakes ☆ - Creative Bakers Inc.

ANYTIME CARDS - Greeting cards - American Greetings Corp.

ANYTIME IS PINEAPPLE PIZZA TIME DOLE - Vegetables–canned - Dole Food Co., Inc.

ANYTIME MUFFINS - Bakery products - Boyer Printing Co.

ANYTIME PERM - Hair care products - Gillette Co.

ANYTIME TAN - Suntan lotions - Scandinavian Sun

ANYVIEW - Computer software - Binar Graphics, Inc.

ANYWEAR - Brassieres (Bras) - Sara Lee Corp.

ANYWHERE - Garment hangers - Vogel Peterson Furniture Co.

ANYWHERE - Shelving units–wood ☆ - Kirsch Co.

ANYWHERE, ANYTIME GENERATOR, THE - Electrical equipment - Active Technologies, Inc.

ANYWHERE CHAIR - Office furniture–metal - Hon Co.

ANYWHERE DOOR, THE - Doors–wood - Maywood Inc.

ANYWHERE SUITCASE SHOWER - Shower stalls–plastic - Mininome Inc.

ANZA - Bicycles - Dynacraft Industries Inc.

ANZAC - Yarn ☆ - National Spinning Co., Inc.

ANZEA - Wallpaper - Ambiance Textiles Inc.

AO - Apparel and accessories - Alpha Omega Sports, Inc.

AO - Ophthalmic goods - American Optical Corp.

AO - Refractometers - Aquaculture Research/Environmental Associates Inc.

AO - Tiles–ceramic ☆ - American Olean Tile Co.

AO - Vitamins and nutritional supplements - E.R. Squibb & Sons, Inc.

AO 7 STAR - Respirators - American Optical Corp.

AO ADULTS ONLY - Computer software - Interactive Digital Software Association

AO FENG - Apparel and accessories - Ao Feng USA, Inc.

AO PRO - Ophthalmic goods - American Optical Corp.

AO-SR99 - Ophthalmic goods - American Optical Corp.

AO-XT - Lenses–optical - American Optical Corp.

AO-XT16 - Ophthalmic goods - American Optical Corp.

AO3 - Ophthalmic goods - American Optical Corp.

AOA - Medical laboratories - Biomedical Design, Inc.

AOE - Deodorizers - Thornell Corp.

AOIS - Computer software - AOIS Transaction Tracking, Inc.

AOIS TRANSACTION TRACKING - Computer software - AOIS Transaction Tracking, Inc.

A.O.K. - Motor vehicle parts and accessories - Pyroil Co. Inc.

AOLITE - Ophthalmic goods - American Optical Corp.

AOLNET - Computer software - America Online Inc.

AOPLANO - Ophthalmic goods - American Optical Corp.

AORACILLIN B - Pharmaceutical preparations - Vita Elixir Co. Inc.

AOSAFETY - Safety products - Aearo Co.

AOSR99 - Ophthalmic goods - American Optical Corp.

AOSS - Gloves–safety - Alpha Omega Systems & Services, Inc.

AOT - Medical apparatus - American Orthopedic Technologies, Inc.

AOT AMERICAN ORTHOPEDIC TECHNOLOGIES - Medical apparatus - American Orthopedic Technologies, Inc.

AOTEC - Goggles–safety - American Optical Corp.

AP - Apparel and accessories - Austen Payne Co.

AP - Automotive parts and accessories - AP Parts

AP - Chemical preparations - Paxon Manufacturing Co.

AP - Nuts and bolts - Askew Hardware Products, Inc.

AP - Pumps - Clean Environment Engineers, Inc.

AP - Sporting goods - Roadmaster Corp.

AP - Water purification systems - Autopilot Systems, Inc.

AP 24 - Dental equipment - Nu Skin International, Inc.

AP-50 - Compressors–refrigeration - Sunrise Medical (Respiratory Products Division)

AP-80 - Printers–computer ☆ - Epson America, Inc.

AP AMPC - Food products - Ampac Seed Co.

AP APC - Vitamins and nutritional supplements - Ampac Seed Co.

AP-GU-GA - Recording label - Jazz Composer's Orchestra Association Inc.

AP MACPHERSON - Automotive parts and accessories - AP Parts

AP NEWSCENTER - Computer software - Associated Press

AP NEWSCLIP - Computer software - Associated Press

AP NEWSHOUND - Computer software - Associated Press

AP NONTOXIC - Artists' materials - Art & Creative Materials Institute, Inc.

APA AMERICAN PADDLE ASSOCIATION - Apparel–athletic - American Paddle Association

APA AUTOMOTIVE PARTS ASSOCIATE - Automotive parts and accessories - Automotive Parts Assoc., Inc.

APAC - Pharmaceutical preparations ☆ - Vortech Pharmaceuticals

APAC - Photographic equipment - American Photographic Appliance Corp.

APACET - Analgesics - Parmed Pharmaceuticals, Inc.

APACHE - Automotive parts and accessories - Apache

APACHE - Bicycles - Columbia Manufacturing Inc.
APACHE - Boats - Indian Head Products Inc.
APACHE - Boats–motor ☆ - Thunderbird Products
APACHE - Clocks - General Time Corp. (Westclox/Seth Thomas Div.)
APACHE - Filters–industrial - Reading Technologies, Inc.
APACHE - Floor coverings - American Floor Products Co. Inc.
APACHE - Food products - Mid-America Potato Co.
APACHE - Footwear - Apache of California
APACHE - Gates - Cool Attic
APACHE - Insecticides - Farnam Cos. Inc.
APACHE - Medical equipment - Apache Medical Systems Inc.
APACHE - Motor vehicle parts and accessories - Titan Security
APACHE - Motorcycles ☆ - Suzuki of America Automotive Corp.
APACHE - Pet collars ☆ - Leatherite-Nylorite Manufacturing Inc.
APACHE - Shoes ☆ - Bostonian Shoe Co.
APACHE - Snack foods - Terra Prima, Inc.
APACHE - Sporting goods - Apache Products Inc.
APACHE - Sporting goods - Rollin Wilson Co. Inc.
APACHE - Thermal and acoustical insulators - Apache Products Co.
APACHE - Tires–automobile - General Tire, Inc.
APACHE - Wet mops ☆ - American Textile Products Co.
APACHE 2 - Toys–models ☆ - Estes Industries
APACHE ARROWHEADS - Jewelry - Beads & More
APACHE DAD-N-ME - Sporting goods - Apache Products Inc.
APACHE-GRIP - Floor coverings - Apache Mills Inc.
APACHE HIDE-OUT - Sporting goods - Apache Products Inc.
APACHE HUNT-N-HUT - Sporting goods - Apache Products Inc.
APACHE MOCS - Men's footwear ☆ - Bostonian Shoe Co.
APACHE OF CALIFORNIA - Footwear–women's - Apache of California
APACHE PORT-A-STAND - Sporting goods - Apache Products Inc.
APACHE RIB - Floor coverings - Apache Mills Inc.
APACHE TRANSFORMER - Computer hardware - CPU Industries, Inc.
APACHE TRI-POD - Sporting goods - Apache Products Inc.
APACHE WAR EAGLE - Trailers–travel - Apache
APACHE WARRIOR - Archery equipment - Rollin Wilson Co. Inc.
APACHESTAT - Floor coverings - Apache Mills Inc.
APACOMP - Pharmaceutical preparations - Lannett Co. Inc.
APADAC - Paints - Chilton Paint Co.
APADINE - Pharmaceutical preparations ☆ - Vangard Labs Inc.
APADON - Pharmaceutical preparations ☆ - ICN Pharmaceuticals Inc.
APAMIDE - Pharmaceutical preparations - Miles Inc.
APANDA - Lighting fixtures - America's Lighting Distributors, Inc.
AP&E SYSTEMS - Metal construction materials - Drosihn, Inc.
APANOL FAVORIT - Cigars - Gesty Trading & Manufacturing Corp.
APAP - Pharmaceutical preparations ☆ - Lunsco Inc.
APART - Women's apparel - Spiegel, Inc.
APATATE - Vitamins and nutritional supplements - Kenwood Laboratories Inc.
APATCHE-TOTEM - Patches, insignia, and emblems - Apatche-Totem Badge & Emblem Ltd.
A.P.B. - Apparel–women's - KWBL Clothing & Apparel Corp.
APB - Motor vehicles–construction - Louis Berkman Co.
A.P.C. - Aspirin, cod-liver oil, etc. - American Pharmaceutical Co.
A.P.C. - Cleaner - Contact Industries Inc.
APC - Cleaning preparations - Roebic Laboratories Inc.
A.P.C. - Cleaning preparations ☆ - Paxon Manufacturing Co.
APC - Musical instrument accessories - Adder Plus Corp.
APC-240 - Kitchen utensils–aluminum ☆ - R & R Mill Co. Inc.
APC-816 - Cleaning preparations - Unival Corp.
APC AMERICAN POWER CONVERSION - Electrical equipment - American Power Conversion Corp.
APC AMPLE POWER COMPANY - Motor vehicle parts and accessories ☆ - Powertap, Inc.
APC AUTOBODY PRODUCTS CORPORATION - Automotive parts and accessories - Baf Industries
APC III - Computers–personal ☆ - NEC Technologies, Inc.
APC LIFELINE - Animal feed supplements - American Protein Corp.
APCEDINE - Pharmaceutical preparations - Blair Pharmacal
APCIS - Computer software - Allegheny Power Service Corp.
APCO - Cleaning preparations–carpet and rug - Marshlin Inc.
APCO - Doors–garage - Arrow Tru-Line, Inc.
APCO - Gasoline - Total Petroleum Inc.
APCO - Housewares ☆ - Commercial Plastics Co.
APCO - Life jackets - Atlantic-Pacific
APCO - Paints ☆ - Adhesive Products, Inc.
APCO - Tools–pruning - Arett Sales Corp.
APCO WILLAMETTE - Sewerage systems - Valve and Primer Corp.

APCORETIC - Pharmaceutical - American Pharmaceutical Co.
APCS - Filters–air - Cotton Machinery, Inc.
APD - Pet products - Breeder's Choice Pet Foods, Inc.
APD ADVANCED PET DIETS - Animal feeds - Breeder's Choice Pet Foods, Inc.
APD ADVANCED PET DIETS RENEW FORMULATED FOR HEALTHY SKIN & COAT - Pet food - Breeder's Choice Pet Foods, Inc.
APE - Integrated circuits - United Technologies Corp.
APE NINJAZORD - Toys–automobiles - Saban Entertainment, Inc.
APEC - Glassines - American Printing & Envelope Co.
APECS - Computer software - Complete Business Solutions Inc.
APECTOL - Pharmaceutical preparations ☆ - Legere Pharmaceuticals Inc.
APEDA - Measuring instruments - Fullen Systems, Inc.
APEM - Electronic equipment - Apem Components, Inc.
APEQS - Computer software - Duart Group, Ltd.
APERIODIC ENHANCER - Electronic equipment - Electro-Voice, Inc.
APERITIF - Cigars - Gesty Trading & Manufacturing Corp.
APERITIF - Sinks–metal - Kohler Co.
APERITINE - Pharmaceutical preparations ☆ - Edom Laboratories Inc.
APEROL - Beverages–alcohol - Paterno Imports, Ltd.
APERTURA - Computer software - Alaris Corp.
APERTURE - Communications equipment - Primary Access Corp.
APERTURE - Postcards - Aperture Foundation Inc.
APETIMAR - Pharmaceutical preparations - Marlop Pharmaceuticals Inc.
APETITO - Dog food - Valley Feed and Supply, Inc.
APEX - Abrasive products - Minnesota Mining & Manufacturing Co.
APEX - Blinds–vertical - Moody-Carlson Associates Inc.
APEX - Boats–liferafts - Intercoastal, Inc.
APEX - Circuit boards–printed - Shipley Co. Inc.
APEX - Computer software - Apex Software Corp.
APEX - Exercising equipment - Marcy Fitness Products
APEX - Fertilizers - J.R. Simplot Co.
APEX - Flowers, plants, and seeds - Jacklin Seed
APEX - Golfing equipment ☆ - Ben Hogan Co.
APEX - Hardware - Arnold Precision Manufacturers
APEX - Hardware - Cooper Industries, Inc.
APEX - Knives–pocket - Imperial Schrade Corp.
APEX - Locks–padlocks ☆ - Fort Lock Corp.
APEX - Mats ☆ - Austin Athletic Equipment Corp.
APEX - Medical apparatus - Apex Medical Corp.
APEX - Medical apparatus - Marquette Electronics, Inc.
APEX - Modems - Apex Data, Inc.
APEX - Musical instrument accessories - Ultimate Support Systems Inc.
APEX - Novelty items - Delfino Products Inc.
APEX - Office supplies - Mead Corp.
APEX - Packaging machines - Heat and Control, Inc.
APEX - Paints - Dunn Edwards Corp.
APEX - Paints - Jones Blair Co.
APEX - Paints - Triangle Coatings Inc.
APEX - Pharmaceutical preparations - Apex Bioscience, Inc.
APEX - Projection screens - Draper Shade and Screen Co. Inc.
APEX - Shrimp–fresh or frozen - Apex Marine Products, Inc.
APEX - Sporting goods - Indian Industries Inc.
APEX - Sporting goods ☆ - O'Brien International
APEX - Stoves - Coleman Co., Inc.
APEX - Tables - Impact Furniture
APEX - Tables–wood - Riverside Furniture Corp.
APEX - Tables–wood ☆ - Anco Wood Specialties Inc.
APEX - Thread - Blue Mountain Industries, Inc.
APEX - Toys - Apex Manufacturing Co.
APEX - Weightlifting equipment - Ektelon
APEX - Wines - WHC Inc.
APEX 7000 - Medical apparatus - Plasma & Materials Technologies, Inc.
APEX AMPULATOR - Footwear - Apex Foot Health Industries, Inc.
APEX BOOKS - Publisher's imprints - Abingdon Press
APEX DATA - Computer peripheral equipment - Apex Data, Inc.
APEX FITNESS AND NUTRITION ANALYSIS SYSTEMS - Vitamins and nutritional supplements - Apex Fitness, Inc.
APEX ONE - Bags - Apex One, Inc.
APEX-STROBOS - Switches–electric - General Datacomm, Inc.
APEX ZX - Floor coverings–carpet and rugs - Patrick Carpet Mills
APEXIOR - Paints - Dampney Co., Inc.
APF - Televisions - Zenith Electronics Corp.
APFA - Frames–eyeglass - Teco/Lumberlok
APFELSCHUSS - Computer software - Gessler Publishing Co., Inc.
APFFEL - Coffee - Apffel Coffee Co.

☆ = Now out of production

APFS - Electronic equipment - Sharp Electronics Corp.
APG - Lubricants - Fiske Brothers Refining Co. (Lubriplate Div.)
APG - Thermostats ☆ - Field Controls Co.
APG/LYSINE CAPS - Vitamins and nutritional supplements - Vitamin Research Products Inc.
APHCO - Hemorrhoidal suppositories - American Pharmaceutical Co.
APHEX - Audio equipment - Aphex Systems, Ltd.
APHRO TEASIAC CHAI - Beverages–alcohol - Masala Chai Co.
APHRODAC - Health care products ☆ - Kay Pharmacal Co. Inc.
APHRODISIA - Cosmetics - Faberge Co.
APHRODYNE - Pharmaceutical preparations - Star Pharmaceuticals Inc.
APHTHASOL - Pharmaceutical preparations - Block Drug Co., Inc.
API - Conveyors - Automation Packaging, Inc.
A.P.I. - Footwear - Alta Products Corp.
API ADVANCED PRODUCTS, INC. - Vitamins and nutritional supplements - Advanced Products, Inc.
API LIBRARY, THE - Computer software - Application Partners, Inc.
API SERVICE - Oils–lubricating ☆ - American Petroleum Institute
API SERVICE SG/CD SAE 30 - Oils–lubricating ☆ - American Petroleum Institute
API TONE ZONES - Skin care products - Acufacial Products Inc.
APIA - Furniture - Haworth, Inc.
APIANA - Soap - Baudelaire Inc.
APIARY - Computer software - Intelec Systems Corp.
APIC - Industrial machinery - Auxiliary Power International Corp.
APIDENT - Toothpaste ☆ - Futurebiotics
APIK - Jewelry - Apik Jewelry Inc.
APIKAL - Health care products ☆ - Futurebiotics
APILCO CHINA - Tableware–earthenware - Charles F. La Malle
APILCO PORCELAINE - Dinnerware - Cuthbertson Imports Inc.
APISCARE - Pharmaceutical preparations - Dolisos America, Inc.
APITON 1200 - Vitamin supplements - Winning Laboratories Corp.
APL - Audio equipment - APL Technology Corp.
A.P.L. - Pharmaceutical preparations - Wyeth-Ayerst Laboratories
APL SYNETICS - Computer software - APL-Synetics, Inc.
APL2 - Computer software - International Business Machines Corp.
APL2/6000 - Computer software - International Business Machines Corp.
APLA-PUMP - Tools–masonry - Apla-Tech, Inc.
APLA-TAPER - Tools–masonry - Apla-Tech, Inc.
APLA-TAPER II - Tools–hand-operated - Apla-Tech, Inc.
APLD - Electronic equipment - Sharp Electronics Corp.
APLETS - Candy - Liberty Orchards Co., Inc.
APLEX - Hardware - Aplex Industries, Inc.
APLI-PADS - Fabrics ☆ - Veratec
APLIFAST - Tape–adhesive - Permacel
APLISOL - Pharmaceutical preparations - Parke-Davis
APLITEST - Pharmaceutical preparations - Parke-Davis
APLOMB - Floor coverings–carpet and rugs ☆ - Mohawk Industries Inc.
APLOMB - Floor coverings–carpet and rugs ☆ - Regal Rugs Inc.
APLON - Hair care products - Zoulla Inc.
APLUM - Cosmetics - Lancome
APLUS - Computer hardware - Alpus Computer, Inc.
APM - Concrete products - Architectural Precast Masonry Inc.
APM - Flowers, plants, and seeds - Jacklin Seed
APM - Hardware - Arnold Precision Manufacturers
APM - Paper–toilet - Atlas Paper Mills, Ltd.
APM 5 - Pharmaceutical preparations ☆ - Warner-Lambert Co.
APM 10 - Pharmaceutical preparations ☆ - Warner-Lambert Co.
APMS - Electronic equipment - Sharp Electronics Corp.
APNEA MONITOR - Medical apparatus - Nellcor Puritan Bennett
APNEA THERAPY - Medical apparatus - Nellcor Puritan Bennett
APO - Projectors–photographic - Apollo Audiovisual Div.
A.P.O. - Tools ☆ - National Aerosol Products Co.
APO-REPRO - Lenses–photographic ☆ - Heitz Service Corp.
APO-RODAGON - Photographic equipment - H.P. Marketing Corp.
APO-RONAR - Photographic equipment - H.P. Marketing Corp.
APOC - Roofing materials - Gardner Asphalt Corp.
APOCALYPSE ATTACKCOPTER - Toys - Troma, Inc.
APOCLYPSE - Recording label - Rough Trade Inc.
APOGEE - Computer software - Apogee Software Ltd.
APOGEE - Golfing equipment ☆ - Wilson Sporting Goods Co.
APOGEE - Medical apparatus - Alcon Laboratories, Inc.
APOGEE - Perfume - Bourjois Ltd.
APOGEE II - Toys–models ☆ - Estes Industries
APOGEE BOOKS - Publisher's imprints - Omnigraphics Inc.
APOGEN - Antibiotics ☆ - Smithkline Beecham Corp.

APOKOLIPS SOURCEBOOK - Games - Mayfair Games, Inc.
APOLAN - Machine tools - Apolan International
APOLLINARIS - Water–mineral - Shaffer, Clark & Co. Inc.
APOLLO - Artists' materials ☆ - Keuffel & Esser Co.
APOLLO - Automotive parts and accessories ☆ - Fibre Glass-Evercoat Co. Inc.
APOLLO - Bicycles - Ross Bicycles USA, Ltd.
APOLLO - Binoculars ☆ - Swift Instruments, Inc.
APOLLO - Boats–motor - Glastex Co.
APOLLO - Boats–motor ☆ - Crestliner Boats Inc.
APOLLO - Boats–motor ☆ - Seajay Boats Inc.
APOLLO - Candy - Leaf, Inc.
APOLLO - Clocks ☆ - Robertshaw Controls Co.
APOLLO - Cooking equipment–household - Packaging Corp. of America
APOLLO - Corn starch - Penford Products Co.
APOLLO - Dinnerware–glass ☆ - Nikko Ceramics Inc.
APOLLO - Drums–musical instruments ☆ - St. Louis Music Supply Co.
APOLLO - Fabrics - Superior Shade & Blind Co. Inc.
APOLLO - Fabrics ☆ - Greenwood Mills Inc.
APOLLO - Firearms, accessories, and parts - Arnold Arms Co., Inc.
APOLLO - Flatware - Reed and Barton Corp.
APOLLO - Floor coverings - American Floor Products Co. Inc.
APOLLO - Floor coverings–carpet and rugs - V & B Carpet
APOLLO - Floor waxes - Chemical Products Co.
APOLLO - Furniture - Lane Co. Inc.
APOLLO - Furniture ☆ - Bassett Furniture Industries, Inc.
APOLLO - Garden equipment ☆ - Valley View Specialties Co.
APOLLO - Glass–optical - Criss Optical Manufacturing Co.
APOLLO - Glassware–household ☆ - Owens-Illinois Inc. (Libbey Div.)
APOLLO - Hair brushes - Apollo Products, Inc.
APOLLO - Handbags - Apollo Handbag Co.
APOLLO - Hoists - Columbus Mckinnon Corp.
APOLLO - Housewares ☆ - Bissell Inc.
APOLLO - Lamps - Art Specialty Co. Inc.
APOLLO - Lawn mowers - Lambert Manufacturing Corp.
APOLLO - Lighting fixtures - Kenall Manufacturing Co.
APOLLO - Mobile homes - Wick Building Systems Inc. (Manufactured Home Div./North)
APOLLO - Motor vehicles–automobiles ☆ - General Motors Corp. (Buick Motor Div.)
APOLLO - Paint sprayers - Apollo Sprayers International, Inc.
APOLLO - Paints ☆ - Kelly-Moore Paint Co. Inc.
APOLLO - Paper - Light Impressions Corp.
APOLLO - Paper–rolls - Willamette Industries, Inc.
APOLLO - Pastries - Athens Foods
APOLLO - Pastries - Kalil Mediterranean Pastries
APOLLO - Pet products - Apollo Enterprises Inc.
APOLLO - Pipes–tobacco - S.M. Frank & Co. Inc. (Kaywoodie-Yello-Bole-Medico)
APOLLO - Projectors–photographic - Apollo Audiovisual Div.
APOLLO - Publisher's imprints ☆ - Harper Junior Books Group
APOLLO - Recording label - Athena Productions
APOLLO - Recording label - Malaco Records Inc.
APOLLO - Seeds–salted, roasted, cooked, or canned ☆ - Moscow Idaho Seed Co.
APOLLO - Ships–sailing vessels ☆ - Sunfish Laser Inc.
APOLLO - Skin care products - Bettina Creations Inc.
APOLLO - Sporting goods ☆ - Daiwa Corp.
APOLLO - Strollers–baby - Daust Juvenile Products Inc.
APOLLO - Toilets–porcelain - Universal-Rundle Corp.
APOLLO - Tripods–photographic - QuickSet International Inc.
APOLLO - Watches - Aristo Import Co. Inc.
APOLLO - Water purification systems - RainSoft Water Conditioning Co.
APOLLO - Water–distilled - Water Technologies Inc.
APOLLO - Yarn - Henry's Attic
APOLLO - Yarn ☆ - Plymouth Yarn Co.
APOLLO 3 - Exercising equipment - California Gym Equipment
APOLLO 3 - Medical apparatus - C. R. Bard, Inc.
APOLLO 14 - Toys - Park Plastics Co.
APOLLO 18 - Computer software ☆ - Accolade Inc.
APOLLO BOOKS - Publisher's imprints - Adam Starchild
APOLLO-COAT - Paints - Apollo Sprayers International, Inc.
APOLLO JR. - Carts - R.A. Industries Inc.
APOLLO SR. - Carts - R.A. Industries Inc.
APOLLO SILVER - Sporting goods ☆ - Daiwa Corp.
APOLLO, THE - Uniforms–athletic ☆ - Felco Athletic Wear Co.
APOLLO WHIRL - Playground equipment - Miracle Recreation Equipment Co.

APOLLOCAST - Sporting goods ☆ - Daiwa Corp.
APOLLON - Pharmaceutical preparations - Apollon, Inc.
APOLO - Dialing devices–telephone - Baltimore Luggage Co.
APOLOGIE - T-shirts–men's - Allan & Marcy, Inc.
APON - Recording label - Apon Record Co., Inc.
APOPTEST - Chemical preparations - Oncor, Inc.
APOTEK - Wigs - Apollo Products, Inc.
APOTHECA - Skin care products - Apotheca Inc.
APOTHECALC - Calculators - Stokes Publishing Co., Inc.
APOTHECARE - Computer peripheral equipment - Etreby Computer Co., Inc.
APOTHECARE - Medical apparatus - American Clicical Industries
APOTHECARIST - Publisher's imprints - Apothecarist Institute
APOTHECARY - Furniture ☆ - Pulaski Furniture Corp.
APOTHECARY PRODUCTS, INC. - Health care products - Apothecary Products, Inc.
APOTHECARY, THE - Antiseptics - Mitech Laboratories, Inc.
APOTHECON - Pharmaceutical preparations - Bristol-Myers Squibb Co.
APOTHIA - Toiletries - Ron Robinson, Inc.
APPALACHIA - Novelty items ☆ - Royal Cathay Trading Co.
APPALACHIAN - Boats - Phoenix Products Inc.
APPALACHIAN - Boats–canoes - Old Town Canoe Co.
APPALACHIAN - Floor coverings - Stuart Flooring Corp.
APPALACHIAN - Furniture ☆ - Virginia House Furniture Corp.
APPALACHIAN - Musical instruments ☆ - St. Louis Music Supply Co.
APPALACHIAN GOLD - Floor coverings - Stuart Flooring Corp.
APPALACHIAN LIGHTS - Candles - Candle Station, Ltd.
APPALACHIAN PREMIUM SODA - Soft drink - Quibell Corp.
APPALACHIAN STOVE, THE - Stoves–wood-burning - Appalachian Stove & Fabricators, Inc.
APPALACHIAN TRAIL - Shirts - Hills Department Store Co.
APPALACHIAN VALLEY - Furniture ☆ - Kincaid Furniture Co. Inc.
APPALOOSA - Computer software - Appaloosa Interactive Corp.
APPALOOSA HORSE CLUB - Watches - Appaloosa Horse Club
APPALSHOP - Motion picture distributors–prerecorded - Appalshop Inc.
APPARATELLE - Apparel–women's - Marie's Fashion Discounts, Inc.
APPARATUS - Apparel and accessories - J.C. Penney Co., Inc.
APPARATUS - Apparel and accessories - Phillips-Van Heusen Corp.
APPAREL TECHNOLOGIES - Outerwear - Odyssey USA Inc.
APPAREL UNLIMITED - Shirts - Signal Art Wear
APPARELLINE - Apparel and accessories - Rodin Industries Inc.
APPARELND SKIN - Apparel - Barry Trading Corp.
APPARENZA - Apparel and accessories - United Merchants and Manufacturers Inc.
APPARITION - Recording label - Jazz Composer's Orchestra Association Inc.
APPARITION DECK, THE - Playing cards - Thomas A. Gagnon, Jr.
APPARITIONS - Apparel–athletic - Tighe Industries Inc.
APPARITIONS - Games - Mayfair Games, Inc.
APPBASE - Computer software - Powerbase Systems Composed
APPCO - Envelopes - American Paper Products Co.
APPCO - Toilet seats - Appco Seats
APPE-TRIM - Health care products - Traco Laboratories Inc.
APPE-TRIM - Vitamins and nutritional supplements ☆ - First Security of Destin, Inc.
APPEAL - Apparel and accessories - Nanwani International Ltd.
APPEAL - Floor coverings–tile - Flexco Co.
APPEAL - Toothpaste - Colgate-Palmolive Co.
APPEALING - Spices and extracts - Herbert Marmorek & Son, Inc.
APPEAR - Shaving preparations ☆ - Demert & Dougherty, Inc.
APPEARANCE - Floor waxes - Fuller Brush Co.
APPEARANCE - Hair care products - Marianna Imports, Inc.
APPEARANCE 2000 - Floor waxes - Fuller Brush Co.
APPEARANCE PLUS - Floor waxes - Fuller Brush Co.
APPEARANCES - Wallpaper ☆ - Wallquest, Inc.
APPEARGEAR - Apparel–athletic - Colour Haus Inc.
APPEAR'S - Skin care products - Sara Lee Corp.
APPECON - Pharmaceutical preparations - Lunsco Inc.
APPEDRINE - Pharmaceutical preparations ☆ - Thompson Medical Co., Inc.
APPEL - Apparel and accessories - I. Appel Corp.
APPELLA - Apple product ☆ - Vacu-Dry Co.
APPELLATE PINSTRIPE - Floor coverings–carpet and rugs ☆ - Mohawk Carpet Corp.
APPELTISE - Beverages - Sundor Brands Inc.
APPEND - Hats - Mascotech Accessories, Inc.
APPENZELL - Pens - Bycin Industries, Inc.
APPENZELLER - Beverages–alcohol - Paterno Imports, Ltd.
APPESATE - Health care products ☆ - Concord Chemists

APPESTATIN - Vitamins and nutritional supplements - Tishcon Corp.
APPETEASERS - Crackers - Lavosh Hawaii
APPETIZE - Food products - Source Food Technology, Inc.
APPEVITE - Fish food - Hawaiian Marine Imports Inc.
APPIAN HYDRAVISION - Computer software - ETMA Corp.
APPIAN WAY - Floor coverings ☆ - Congoleum Corp.
APPIAN WAY - Furniture ☆ - Athens Furniture Industries Inc.
APPIAN WAY - Pizzas–mixes - Dial Corp.
APPLAUD - Footwear - L.C. Licensing, Inc.
APPLAUSE - Apparel and accessories - Lewis Frimel Co. Inc.
APPLAUSE - Bedding–linen ☆ - Dan River Inc.
APPLAUSE - Brassieres (Bras) - Goddess Bra
APPLAUSE - Clocks - General Time Corp. (Westclox/Seth Thomas Div.)
APPLAUSE - Crackers - Meijer, Inc.
APPLAUSE - Fabrics - Gretchen Bellinger Inc.
APPLAUSE - Floor coverings - Mannington Resilient Floors
APPLAUSE - Floor coverings–carpet and rugs - Alliance Industries Inc.
APPLAUSE - Floor coverings–carpet and rugs - S and S Mills Inc.
APPLAUSE - Floor coverings–carpet and rugs ☆ - Porter Carpet Mills Inc.
APPLAUSE - Floor coverings–carpet and rugs ☆ - Royalweve Carpet Mills
APPLAUSE - Fruits and vegetables - Adam Bros. Farming, Inc.
APPLAUSE - Furniture - Almet/Lawnlite
APPLAUSE - Furniture ☆ - Lane Co. Inc.
APPLAUSE - Furniture ☆ - Tropitone Furniture Co. Inc.
APPLAUSE - Furniture–upholstered - Kinder Manufacturing Corp.
APPLAUSE - Guitars - Kaman Music Corp.
APPLAUSE - Guitars - Ovation Instruments
APPLAUSE - Headsets–telephone - ACS Wireless, Inc.
APPLAUSE - Snack foods - Mars, Inc.
APPLAUSE - Toys–stuffed - Applause, Inc.
APPLAUSE - Wallcoverings - Worldwalls International Inc.
APPLAUSE - Wallpaper - Gamrod-Harman
APPLAUSE - Window coverings - Hunter Douglas, Inc.
APPLAUSE - Window coverings - Hunter Douglas Intermountain Fabrication Co.
APPLAUSE - Windows–vinyl - Gentek Building Products, Inc.
APPLAUSE APPLAUSE - Wallpaper - Essex Wallcoveringss
APPLE - Computer software - Apple Computer Inc.
APPLE - Cosmetics - Tristar Corp.
APPLE - Dinnerware–glass - Franciscan by Johnson Brothers, USA, Inc.
APPLE - Dishes–china - Waterford Wedgewood USA, Inc.
APPLE - Envelopes - Appleson Press Inc.
APPLE - Footwear - Interco Inc.
APPLE - Furniture polish and wax - Apple Polishes Inc.
APPLE - Publisher's imprints - Scholastic Inc.
APPLE - Restaurants–pizzerias - U.S. Trading Enterprise, Inc.
APPLE - Skin care products - Lado Co. of America
APPLE - Tableware–earthenware - Maurice Ceramics of California
APPLE - Tobacco products - John Middleton Inc.
APPLE - Tobacco–chewing or smoking - Swedish Math North America Inc.
APPLE-A-DAY - Food products - Robert A. Sultzbaugh
APPLE ACES - Fruits and vegetables - Red Hook Cold Storage Co.
APPLE ADE - Beverages - Sundor Brands Inc.
APPLE AMARANTH - Cereal ☆ - Arrowhead Mills, Inc.
APPLE AMY - Dolls - Mattel, Inc.
APPLE & CINNAMON - Shampoos - Demert & Dougherty, Inc.
APPLE & CINNAMON TOASTED OATS - Breakfast cereal - Malt-O-Meal Co.
APPLE & EVE - Juices - Apple and Eve Inc.
APPLE ANDY - Candy ☆ - R.M. Palmer Co.
APPLE ANNIE - Cakes ☆ - Christopher's Chewies
APPLE ANNIE - Juices ☆ - National Fruit Product Co., Inc.
APPLE-APPLE - Juices - Pokka, Inc.
APPLE ARMOR - Electronic equipment - Omni-Tech Group, Inc.
APPLE AVENUE - Juices - Nabisco Foods Group
APPLE BARREL - Beverages–alcohol - Jim Beam Brands Co.
APPLE BARREL - Paints - Plaid Enterprises, Inc.
APPLE BAY - Fruit and vegetable markets - Fruit Growers Cooperative
APPLE BEE - Fruit drinks–bottled or canned - Eve Sales Co.
APPLE BERRY BURST - Juices ☆ - Dole Food Co., Inc.
APPLE BLOSSOM - Deodorizers - Analab Inc.
APPLE BLOSSOM - Dishes–china ☆ - WMF/USA
APPLE BLOSSOM - Hair care products - Beauty Brands Group
APPLE BLOSSOM - Hair care products - Marianna Imports, Inc.
APPLE BLOSSOM - Skin care products - Avon Products, Inc.
APPLE BLOSSOM - Teas - Farmer Bros. Co.
APPLE BLOSSUM - Bacon - Patrick Cudahy Inc.

☆ = Now out of production

APPLE/BLUEBERRY SPLITS - Candy - Nabisco Holdings Corp.
APPLE BOBBERS - Cereal - Moran Foods, Inc.
APPLE-BREEZE - Cleaning preparations - Georgia-Pacific Corp.
APPLE BULLETIN BOARD - Computer software - Software Sorcery Inc.
APPLE BUTTER - Food products - New Morning
APPLE CANYON CENTER - Campgrounds - Ronald Mcdonald House Charities of Southern California, Inc.
APPLE CART - Bicycles ✩ - Murray, Inc.
APPLE CHEEKS - Dolls ✩ - Corham Artificial Flower Co.
APPLE CIDER - Tobacco–chewing or smoking - Amar Blends Co.
APPLE CINNAMON - Teas–herbal - R.C. Bigelow, Inc.
APPLE CINNAMON CHEERIOS - Cereal - General Mills, Inc.
APPLE CINNAMON CIRCLES - Cereal - Weetabix Co., Inc.
APPLE CITY - Food products - Knouse Foods Cooperative, Inc.
APPLE CLASSICS - Publisher's imprints - Scholastic Inc.
APPLE CONCENTRATE - Cosmetics ✩ - Para Laboratories Inc.
APPLE CONDITIONER - Shampoos - Kim Laube & Co. Inc.
APPLE CORE - Fabrics–felt - Apple Felt & Wiping Systems, Inc.
APPLE CORNS - Cereal - Arrowhead Mills, Inc.
APPLE COUNTRY - Beverages–alcohol - Joseph E. Seagram & Sons, Inc.
APPLE COUNTRY - Fruits and vegetables - New York Apple Association, Inc.
APPLE CRISP - Cookies - Nabisco Foods Group
APPLE CRISP - Juices - Snapple Beverage Corp.
APPLE CRISP - Wines - Schloss Doepken Winery
APPLE CRISP MIX - Doughnuts–mixes - Dawn Food Products Inc.
APPLE CRUNCHIES - Snack food ✩ - Auroma International Inc.
APPLE DANDY - Food products - Hudson Valley Apple Products Co. Inc.
APPLE DANDY APPLE JUICE - Juices - Brooklyn Bottling Corp.
APPLE DELIGHT - Fruit drinks–bottled or canned - Green Spot Packaging, Inc.
APPLE DELIGHT - Fruits and vegetables - Valley Fruit
APPLE DESKTOP BUS - Computer software - Apple Computer Inc.
APPLE DIETS - Pet products - Apples Aviary & Supply Co.
APPLE ESSENCE - Shampoos - Alberto-Culver Co.
APPLE FAIR - Fruits and vegetables - Price Cold Storage & Packing Co.
APPLE FRESH - Beverages - Sundor Brands Inc.
APPLE FRESH - Chemical preparations - Extended Product Life, Inc.
APPLE GARLIC JAM - Jams and jellies - Lillieville Farm Foods Inc.
APPLE GRANDE - Desserts - Taco John's International Inc.
APPLE HARVEST - Dinnerware ✩ - Corning Inc.
APPLE HILL - Fruits and vegetables - Apple Hill Growers Association
APPLE HOLLER - Fruit butters - Apple Farm Management, Inc.
APPLE-HONEY - Tobacco–chewing or smoking - Amar Blends Co.
APPLE IIC - Computers–personal - Apple Computer Inc.
APPLE IIE - Computers–personal - Apple Computer Inc.
APPLE IIGS - Computers–personal - Apple Computer Inc.
APPLE JACK - Cheese - Warren Cheese Plants
APPLE JILL - Fruit drinks–bottled or canned ✩ - Yakima Valley Grape Producers Inc.
APPLE JUICE - Candy ✩ - Topps Co., Inc.
APPLE KEG - Juices - Comstock Michigan Fruit
APPLE KIDS - Fruits–dried ✩ - Cowiche Growers Inc.
APPLE KNOCKERS - Games - Gregory J. Hendrick
APPLE LAND - Food products - Knouse Foods Cooperative, Inc.
APPLE LAND - Food warming equipment ✩ - Ultra Seal Corp.
APPLE LANE - Games - Avalon Hill Game Co.
APPLE LEATHER CARE - Leather tanning and finishing - Apple Polishes Inc.
APPLE LIGHT - Beverages - Hansen Beverage Co.
APPLE LURE - Sporting goods ✩ - Kolpin Manufacturing, Inc.
APPLE MADE FOR KIDS, THE - Fruits and vegetables - New York Apple Association, Inc.
APPLE MAGIC - Teas - Harris Tea Co.
APPLE MAN, THE - Food products ✩ - Barney's Produce Inc.
APPLE MOUNTAIN - Fruits and vegetables - Mountain Orchard Cooperative Inc.
APPLE MUNCHIES - Fruits–dried ✩ - Vacu-Dry Co.
APPLE 'N CINNAMON COUNTRY SAUSAGE - Sausages - Johnsonville Foods Co.
APPLE-N-CINNAMON OATIOS - Cereal - New Morn, Inc.
APPLE-N-CINNAMON OATIOS - Cereal - New Morning
APPLE NECTAR - Shampoos - Freeman Cosmetics Corp.
APPLE NEWTONS - Cookies - Nabisco Foods Group
APPLE OS - Candy - Trolli, Inc.
APPLE PARIS - Shirts - Aqil Davidson
APPLE PEEL MOBILE - Toys ✩ - Tomy America, Inc.
APPLE PICKER JUNIOR - Shovels - Port-a-Stall

APPLE PICKER, THE - Computer software - AV Systems Inc.
APPLE PIE - Fabrics–tapestry ✩ - Coloroll Inc.
APPLE PIE - Food products - Bainbridge Corp.
APPLE PIE - Toys - Milton Bradley Co.
APPLE PIE PRESS - Publisher's imprints ✩ - Ten Speed Press
APPLE PIE RIDGE - Vinegar ✩ - National Fruit Product Co., Inc.
APPLE POPS - Candy ✩ - Earl's Candy Co.
APPLE QUENCHERS - Beverages - Veryfine Products, Inc.
APPLE RIDGE - Food products - Jack Brown Produce Inc.
APPLE RINGS - Cereal - Ralston Foods, Inc.
APPLE ROLLS - Cereal - Jasper Foods, Inc.
APPLE-ROOS - Cookies - McKee Foods Corp.
APPLE-SATIN - Pet products - RHB Enterprises
APPLE SAUCE - Greeting cards - American Greetings Corp.
APPLE SHEEN - Pet products - RHB Enterprises
APPLE SIDRA - Beverage - Cosco International Inc.
APPLE SOURS - Candy - Judson-Atkinson Candies
APPLE STAMPEDE - Juices - Clement Pappas & Co., Inc.
APPLE-STIX - Adhesives and sealants - Apple Felt & Wiping Systems, Inc.
APPLE STIX - Candy - Leaf, Inc.
APPLE STROODLES - Cereal - U.S. Mills, Inc.
APPLE SUPERDRIVE - Computer equipment - Apple Computer Inc.
APPLE TEMPTATION - Wines - Laird and Co.
APPLE, THE - Candy - Attivo
APPLE THERM - Hair care products - Paula Payne Products Co. Inc.
APPLE TIME - Fruits and vegetables - Knouse Foods Cooperative, Inc.
APPLE TREAT - Fruits and vegetables - Valley Fruit
APPLE TREE - Golfing equipment - Apple Tree Partnership
APPLE TREE - Water–bottled or canned - Water House
APPLE-TRU - Food products ✩ - Seneca Foods Corp.
APPLE VALLEY - Cider - S. Martinelli and Co.
APPLE VALLEY - Wallpaper ✩ - Decorative Coverings Inc.
APPLE VALLEY INN - Bakery products - Rewco, Inc.
APPLE WHITE - Pet products - Professional Pet Products
APPLE WRITER II - Computers–personal - Apple Computer Inc.
APPLE-X - Sporting goods - Ole Time Woodsman
APPLEASY - Cakes–mixes ✩ - Pillsbury Co.
APPLEBEE'S - Food products - Sea Harvest Packing Co.
APPLEBY - Apparel - Babyfair Inc.
APPLECOPTER - Recording label - Van Horne Services
APPLECRISP - Deodorizers - Crabtree & Evelyn, Ltd.
APPLEDESIGN - Computer speakers - Apple Computer Inc.
APPLEDISIACS - Bakery goods - Appledisiacs
APPLEDOLLY ✩ - Dolls ✩ - Tender Heart Treasures, Ltd.
APPLEDORE - Boats - Alden Ocean Shells Inc.
APPLEDORE POD - Boats - Alden Ocean Shells Inc.
APPLEFAX - Computer peripheral equipment - Apple Computer Inc.
APPLEGATE FARMS - Meat products - Weiser Inc.
APPLEHEAD - Candy - Ferrara Pan Candy Co., Inc.
APPLELINE - Computer software - Apple Computer Inc.
APPLELINK - Computer software - Apple Computer Inc.
APPLEMAIL - Computer software - Apple Computer Inc.
APPLEMAN - Fruits and vegetables ✩ - Elwin R. Mann
APPLEMOUSE - Computer peripheral equipment - Apple Computer Inc.
APPLEPLY - Plywood - States Industries Inc.
APPLES - Toys–stuffed - Gund, Inc.
APPLES BY DOC BURRELL - Food products - Burrell Orchards Inc.
APPLES FOR YOU - Novelty items ✩ - Iwasaki Images of America
APPLES 'N SPICE - Cooking equipment–household ✩ - Mirro Corp.
APPLESCRIPT - Computer software - Apple Computer Inc.
APPLESEARCH - Computer software - Apple Computer Inc.
APPLESOFT - Computer software - Apple Computer Inc.
APPLESOFT MULTIWASH - Cleaning preparations - W.L. Young Inc.
APPLESSENCE - Hair care products ✩ - E.T. Browne Drug Co. Inc.
APPLESTACKS - Computer software - Apple Computer Inc.
APPLETALK - Computer peripheral equipment - Apple Computer Inc.
APPLETIZIN' - Fruits and vegetables - Yakima Fruit & Cold Storage Co.
APPLETON - Paper ✩ - Riverside Paper Corp.
APPLETON - Rum - Schieffelin and Somerset Co.
APPLETON - Yarn - American Crewel & Canvas Studio
APPLETON DUEL - Rum - Carriage House Imports Ltd.
APPLETON ESTATE - Rum - Rums International, Inc.
APPLETON FARMS - Animal feeds - Appleton Farms, Inc.
APPLETON FARMS ESTABLISHED 1638 IPSWICH, MASSACHUSETTS - Animal feeds - Appleton Farms, Inc.
APPLETON PATCH - Rum - Carriage House Imports Ltd.

APPLETON SPECIAL - Rum - Carriage House Imports Ltd.
APPLETON WHITE - Rum - Carriage House Imports Ltd.
APPLETOWN - Fruits and vegetables - Yakima Fruit & Cold Storage Co.
APPLETTE - Food products - Sebastopol Apple Growers United
APPLEWAYS - Fiber supplement - R.W. Frookies Inc.
APPLEWOOD - Smoked meats - American Cafe
APPLEWOOD HERB GARDEN - Flowers, plants, and seeds - Applewood Seed & Garden Group
APPLEWOOD HOLLOW - Deodorizers - Reckitt & Colman, Inc.
APPLEWOOD'S CHERRY PAK - Fruits and vegetables ☆ - Applewood Orchards Inc.
APPLEWOOD'S PRIME PAK - Fruits and vegetables - Applewood Orchards Inc.
APPLEWOOD'S WASHINGTON PAK - Fruits and vegetables ☆ - Applewood Orchards Inc.
APPLEWORKS MANAGEMENT TEMPLATES - Computer software - Electronic Courseware Systems Inc.
APPLEWRITER ENHANCER - Computer software - SourceView Software International
APPLI-COIL - Fibers–synthetic - Veratec
APPLI-HESIVE - Adhesives and sealants - Sew-Art International
APPLI KAT - Label applicator - B.C.E. Technologies, Inc.
APPLI-TIQUE - Appliques - Patches of Joy
APPLIANCE INNOVATIONS - Kitchen appliances - Mr. Coffee, Inc.
APPLICA - Computer software - Concurrent Controls, Inc.
APPLICANTS NAVIGATOR - Computer software - Automating Peripherals, Inc.
APPLICATION BRIDGE - Computer software - Aspect Telecommunications Corp.
APPLICATION LIBRARIAN - Computer storage devices–magnetic - HDC Computer Corp.
A APPLICATION PLUS - Computer software - Daly and Wolcott, Inc.
APPLICATIONEX TENDER - Computer software ☆ - OTG Software
APPLICATIONS - Floor coverings–carpet and rugs ☆ - Alexander Smith Carpets
APPLICATIONXTENDER - Computer peripheral equipment - OTG Software
APPLICATOR SYSTEMS - Electrically heated hoses - Applicator Systems, Inc.
APPLICATOR, THE - Paint rollers - Wooster Brush Co.
APPLIED AFTS - Publisher's imprints - Applied Arts Publishers
APPLIED ARTS - Computer software - Applied Arts Limited
APPLIED BIOCHEMISTS - Water treating compounds - Great Lakes Biochemical Co., Inc.
APPLIED CHEMICAL SOLUTIONS - Machinery - Applied Chemical Solutions
APPLIED COMPUTER TECHNOLOGY - Electronics equipment - Applied Computer Technology, Inc.
APPLIED DIGITAL ACCESS - Communications equipment - Applied Digital Access, Inc.
APPLIED FIBEROPTICS - Cables–fiber optic - Applied Fiberoptics, Inc.
APPLIED INFORMATION GROUP'S MAILEASY - Computer peripheral equipment - Applied Information Group, Inc.
APPLIED LOGIC - Computer hardware - Applied Logic
APPLIED LOGIC - Floor waxes - Midlab, Inc.
APPLIED MEDICAL RESOURCES - Surgical supplies - Applied Medical Resources Inc.
APPLIED NUTRITION - Vitamins and nutritional supplements - Irwin Naturals
APPLIED PHYSICS RESEARCH - Plastics film - Applied Physics Research, L.P.
APPLIEDVIEW - Computer software - Applied Innovation Inc.
APPLIQUE - Clocks ☆ - General Time Corp. (Westclox/Seth Thomas Div.)
APPLIQUE - Glassware–household - Durand International
APPLIQUE - Health care products ☆ - Mason-Keller Corp.
APPLIQUE - Tiles–ceramic - Latco Products
APPLIQUE BY CLESTRA HAUSERMAN - Paneling - Clestra Hauserman Inc.
APPLIQUES - Underwear and nightwear - Maidenform Inc.
APPLIQUILT - Publisher's imprints - Martingale & Co.
APPLISTIK - Labels–fabric - Appleson Press Inc.
APPLIX - Machine tools - Union Butterfield Corp.
APPLIX BUILDER - Computer software - Applix, Inc.
APPLIX REALTIME - Computer software - Applix, Inc.
APPLIXDATA - Computer software - Applix, Inc.
APPLIXWARE - Computer software - Applix, Inc.
APPLWOOD'S WASHED PAK - Fruits and vegetables - Applewood Orchards Inc.
APPLY - Petroleum ☆ - Vi-Jon Laboratories, Inc.
APPLY AND DRY - Skin soaps - Apply and Dry Laboratories, Inc.
APPLY & DRY - Toiletries - Micro-Pak, Inc.
APPLY TO THE LINE - Beauty shop equipment - Focus 21 International Inc.

APPMANAGER - Computer software - Netiq Corp.
APPOINT - Computers–mainframe - Machine Control Systems Inc.
APPOINTBOOK - Diaries - Success Business Industries, Inc.
APPOINTMENTS - Wood products - Ornamental Mouldings Limited
APPOINTMENTS PLUS - Computer software - I.D.S.C. Rental Co. Inc.
APPOLLO - Artists' materials - Bee Paper Co. Inc.
APPOLO - Thread - Threads USA Div.
APPRAISAL EXPRESS, INC. - Real estate agencies - Appraisal Express, Inc.
APPRAISAL WORKSTATION - Computer software - Dataquick Information Systems
APPRAISE - Medical apparatus - Osborn Laboratories, Inc.
APPRAISE AMERICA - Real estate agencies - Appraise America, Inc.
APPRECIATE A TROLLOPE - Novelty items - Caledonia Press
APPRECIATION - Vases - Crisa Corp.
APPREMMAT - Roofing materials - Cedar Crest Roofing & Distributing Co.
APPREMOVE/VB - Computer software - Spinoza Limited
APPRENTICE - Computer software - James Martin & Co., Inc.
APPRENTICE - Knives - Precise International/Wenger
APPRESSANT - Pharmaceutical preparations - Rugby Laboratories Inc.
APPRO - Watches - Hata Corp.
APPROACH - Bicycles - L.L. Bean Inc.
APPROACH - Shoes–athletic - Titleist & Foot-Joy Worldwide
APPROS - Connectors–electrical - Appros, Inc.
APPROVAL - Computer software - FormAtion Technologies Inc.
APPROVED ORGANIC HOME & GARDEN ASSOCIATION - Fertilizers - Grow More, Inc.
APPROXIMATE JIM - Cement - Rectorseal Corp.
APPSOLUTIONS - Computer software - Appsolutions, Inc.
APPSTANDARD - Computer software - Powersware Group
APPWARE - Computers - Novell, Inc.
APPZAP - Computer software - Collegeview Partnership
APR - Measuring instruments - APR Corp.
APRA BATH - Body cleansers - Polychem Corp.
APRE TAN - Suntan lotions - Estee Lauder Inc.
APRENDE CON NOSOTROS - Recording label - Custom Duplication, Inc.
APRES - Chipurnoi Inc.
APRES - Vases - Crisa Corp.
APRESAZIDE - Pharmaceutical preparations - Ciba-Geigy Corp.
APRESODEX - Pharmaceutical preparations - Rugby Laboratories Inc.
APRESOLINE - Pharmaceutical preparations - Ciba-Geigy Corp.
APRESOLINE ESIDRIX - Diuretics - Ciba-Geigy Corp.
APRESPORT - Boots ☆ - Riedell Shoes Inc.
APRESREX - Pharmaceutical preparations - C.S. Ruckstuhl Co. Inc.
APREX - Medical apparatus - Aprex Corp.
APRICA - Strollers–baby - Aprica Kassai USA Inc.
APRICADABRA - Jams and jellies - Sarabeth's Kitchen
APRICORN A - Computer hardware - Apricorn Inc.
APRICOT BRANDY - Tobacco–chewing or smoking - Amar Blends Co.
APRICOT CREME - Skin care products - Fanie International
APRICOT EASE - Hair care products - Dena Corp.
APRICOT GROVE - Dinnerware - Corning Inc.
APRICOT JULEP - Wines ☆ - Jack Poust & Co. Inc.
APRICOT KERNEL - Beauty shop equipment ☆ - Freeman Cosmetics Corp.
APRICOT MANGO MONTEGO - Frozen yogurt - Alta-Dena Certified Dairy, Inc.
APRICOT ORCHARD - Perfumes - Aromatique, Inc.
APRICOT SCRUBBLE - Shampoos - Jason Natural Products, Inc.
APRICOT SHORTIES - Cookies - Royal Court Cookie Co.
APRICOT SUPREME - Rouges ☆ - Elysee Scientific Cosmetic Co.
APRICOT ZING - Cookies ☆ - Natural Nectar Corp.
APRIKOL - Health care products - Bell Flavors & Fragrances Inc.
APRIL - Dinnerware ☆ - Corning Inc.
APRIL - Dinnerware–glass - Franciscan by Johnson Brothers, USA, Inc.
APRIL - Frames–eyeglass ☆ - Rozin Optical Export Corp.
APRIL - Tableware–china - Pfaltzgraff Investment Co.
APRIL - Tableware–china ☆ - Lenox, Inc.
APRIL - Toilets–porcelain ☆ - Crane Plumbing/Fiat Products
APRIL - Wigs - Jean Paree Weegs Inc.
APRIL BATH & SHOWER - Toiletries - Dollar Tree Stores, Inc.
APRIL BUNNY - Toys–stuffed - Russ Berrie and Co., Inc.
APRIL CORNELL - Apparel - ACC Enterprises, LLC
APRIL GLO - Fruits and vegetables ☆ - Sun World International
APRIL HILL - Cookies - Grocers Baking Co.
APRIL HILL - Food products - April Hill Inc.
APRIL IN PARIS - Colognes - Schnapp Enterprises Inc.
APRIL LOVE - Floor coverings–carpet and rugs ☆ - World Carpets, Inc.
APRIL LOVE - Rings–jewelry ☆ - Artcarved Inc.

☆ = Now out of production

APRIL ORCHARDS - Food products - Eatmor Cranberries Inc.
APRIL RIVER - Recording label - Stanyan Record Co.
APRIL ROSE - Apparel and accessories - Goldenwood International, Inc.
APRIL SHOWER - Floor coverings–carpet and rugs ☆ - Regal Rugs Inc.
APRIL SHOWERS - Blinds–vertical - Tontine/VyTech Industries Inc.
APRIL SHOWERS - Christmas tree ornaments - Cracker Box Inc.
APRIL SHOWERS - Perfumes - R.T. French Co.
APRIL SHOWERS - Perfumes ☆ - Houbigant, Inc.
APRIL SHOWERS - Personal hand showers ☆ - Jaclo Inc.
APRILAIRE - Humidifiers - Research Products Corp.
APRILGUARD - Lotions - Chester Labs, Inc.
#L'APRINA - Pharmaceutical preparations - Patricia M. Van Engelen
APRIS - Watches - Margrove Industries Inc.
APRISA - Computer hardware - Video Technics, Inc.
APRISA - Computer software - Cygnus Multimedia Group, Inc.
APRISAUCE - Food products - William H. Leahy & Associates Inc.
APRON POCKET - Jewelry - Cheryl Lampton
APROPO - Beverages ☆ - Pabst Brewing Co.
APROPO - Paints ☆ - Decorative Coverings Inc.
APROPOS - Computer software - Unitek Computer Systems, Inc.
APROPOS - Fabrics–chambray - Dan River Inc.
APROPOS - Furniture - Tomlinson of High Point Inc.
APROPOS - Mattresses - National Patient Care Systems, Inc.
APROPOS - Wallpaper - First Editions Wallcoverings & Fabrics Inc.
APROTEN - Pasta - Dietary Specialties
APS - Backpacks - Lowe Alpine Systems, Inc.
APS - Packaging–blisterwrap - Autovend Packaging Systems
APS - Pre-fabricated sound absorbing wall and ceiling panels - Acoustical
    Panel Systems, Inc.
APS ACADEMY OF PUBLIC SERVICE - Publisher's imprints - National
    Academy Foundation
APS CHECKS - Computer software - National Credit Management Corp.
APS-DRGS - Computer software - HCIA Software Systems, Inc.
APS TECHNOLOGIES - Computer peripheral equipment - APS Technologies
APSARA - Jewelry - India Jewelry & Gifts Inc.
APSCO - Hinges - Advance Group
APSCO - Pencil sharpeners - Empire Berol USA
APSCO - Piano-tuning/regulating tools - American Piano Supply Co.
APSCO - Sporting goods - Apsco Enterprises
APSILON - Cameras - Ansco Photo-Optical Products Corp.
APSS - Computer software - Aristo Computers, Inc.
APSS - Electronic equipment - Sharp Electronics Corp.
APT - Computer software - Microcom Systems, Inc.
APT - Computer software - Siemens Industrial Automation, Inc.
APT - Tape–adhesive ☆ - Arlon, Inc.
APT-LOK - Bicycle parts and accessories - Sunshine U-Lok Corp.
APTECON - Paper products - Georgia-Pacific Corp.
APTEIN - Pharmaceutical preparations ☆ - Pharmex Inc.
APTIVA - Computers–personal - International Business Machines Corp.
APTOS SEMICONDUCTOR - Integrated circuits - Aptos Semiconductor Corp.
APTOS VINEYARD - Wines ☆ - Thomas Kruse Winery
APTROL - Pharmaceutical preparations - Misemer Pharmaceuticals Inc.
APTS - Computer software - APT Systems, Inc.
APU'S BOTTOM LINE - Paper–catalog - Urbano America Corp.
APX - Containers - Hoffman
APX - Targets - Johnson Matthey Electronics, Inc.
APY CHECKER - Computer software - Bankers Systems Inc.
APYREXIN - Pharmaceutical preparations ☆ - U.S. Ethicals Inc.
AQ-200 - Epoxy ☆ - Allied Compositions
AQ PLUS+ - Heat exchanger and air cleaner ☆ - Berner International Corp.
    (Miniveil Air Curtain Div.)
AQ4B - Pharmaceutical preparations - Western Research Laboratories
AQ10 - Fungicides - Ecogen Inc.
AQABA - Perfumes - Miriam Gilbert
AQC - Nutritional supplements - Advanced Physicians Products, Inc.
AQCB - Computer software - U.S. West Communications Inc.
AQI - Ultrasonic scanning devices - Hewlett-Packard Co.
AQL - Printing trades machinery - E.I. Dupont de Nemours and Co.
AQM - Printing trades machinery - E.I. Dupont de Nemours and Co.
AQP - Hoses - Aeroquip Corp.
AQS - Air purification systems - Dust Free Inc.
AQS - Computer software - United Chambers Administrators, Inc.
AQS AMES - Office supplies - Ames Supply Co.
AQT PLUS - Animal feeds - Standard Manufacturing Co.
AQU PAC - Containers–plastic - Aqumix, Inc.
AQUA - Herring–smoked, salted, dried, or pickled - Lyon Food Products Inc.

AQUA - Inks - Crown Art Products
AQUA - Lamps - Voltarc Technologies, Inc.
AQUA - Seafood products–fresh or frozen - Aqua Star, Inc.
AQUA - Skin care products - Excelcis
AQUA - Sponges - Acme Sponge & Chamois Co., Inc.
AQUA - Sporting goods - Aqua-Leisure Industries, Inc.
AQUA - Watches - Rolex Watch USA, Inc.
AQUA - Water–bottled or canned - Aqua Vie Beverage Corp.
AQUA - Window coverings - Lewis Hyman, Inc.
AQUA-4 - Water purification systems - Smith and Loveless Inc.
AQUA-A - Lamps - Voltarc Technologies, Inc.
AQUA-ACRYLIC - Enamels - Lilly Perfection Paint
AQUA-ACTIN - Vitamins and nutritional supplements - Natural Organics, Inc.
AQUA AID - Chemical preparations - World Resources Co.
AQUA AID - Water purification systems - Plastics Development Corp.
AQUA AIRE - Humidifiers - Aqua-Aire, Inc.
AQUA ALERT - Electronic equipment - Light Engineered Displays, Inc.
AQUA AMP - Pet products - Animal Majesty Ltd.
AQUA ANTICS - Games ☆ - Tomy America, Inc.
AQUA ARM - Garbage disposal units–commercial - Thompson Manufacturing
    Co.
AQUA ARMOR - Epoxy - Permagile Industries Inc.
AQUA-BALANCE - Water treating compounds - Wardley Corp.
AQUA BALL - Stationery - Martin Yale Industries, Inc.
AQUA-BAN - Diapers–cloth ☆ - Salk Co. Inc.
AQUA-BAN - Pharmaceutical preparations - Thompson Medical Co., Inc.
AQUA BAR - Roof coating - Continental Products Co.
AQUA BATH - Shower stalls–plastic - Aqua Bath Co., Inc.
AQUA BEAMS - Footwear ☆ - E.S. Originals, Inc.
AQUA BELLS - Exercising equipment - Scott E Silverman
AQUA BIKE - Boats ☆ - Harris-Kayot Inc.
AQUA BLOX - Water purification systems - St. Thomas Beverage Inc.
AQUA BLUE - Cleaning preparations - Thermax, Inc.
AQUA BLUE - Cleaning preparations–household - Herbert Stanley Co.
AQUA BLUES - Apparel–children's - Shane Hunter Inc.
AQUA BODY - Hair care products - Faberge Co.
AQUA-BOMB - Toys - Poof Toy Products, Inc.
AQUA-BOND - Paints ☆ - Atlas Chemical Co.
AQUA BOND - Vinyl - Aquacide
AQUA BOWL - Housewares - Thetford Corp.
AQUA BRA - Boating equipment and accessories - Aqua Bra
AQUA BRAID - Adhesives and sealants - Gemini Braids, Inc.
AQUA BREATHE - Apparel and accessories - Bob Allen Sportswear
AQUA BRILLIANT - Swimming pools - Muskin Leisure Products Inc.
AQUA BRITE - Mouthwashes - Vi-Jon Laboratories, Inc.
AQUA-BRITE - Water treating compounds ☆ - Aquatronics-Filtronics
AQUA BRITES - Plugs–ear - Earmold Design Inc.
AQUA BUDDIES - Toys–stuffed ☆ - Russ Berrie and Co., Inc.
AQUA-BUFF - Hawkeye Industries, Inc.
AQUA B.U.M. - Apparel–men's - Chauvin International Ltd.
AQUA BUOYZ - Air mattresses - Aqua Buoyz, Inc.
AQUA C - Pet products - Nutritional Research Associates Inc.
AQUA CAL - Agricultural chemicals - United States Gypsum Co.
AQUA CALK - Caulking compounds ☆ - Boatlife Inc.
AQUA CALM - Vitamins and nutritional supplements - Oxygen for Life, Inc.
AQUA-CARBON - Aquariums–household ☆ - Hawaiian Marine Imports Inc.
AQUA CARE - Water treating compounds - Wardley Corp.
AQUA CAT - Boats - Glen-L Marine Designs
AQUA CATALYST - Water purification systems - Fountainhead Technologies,
    Inc.
AQUA-CAULK - Caulking compounds - Sterling-Clark-Lurton Corp.
AQUA-CEL - Health care products - Aqua-Cel Corp.
AQUA-CELL/MATE - Ophthalmic goods ☆ - Barnes-Hind Inc.
AQUA CHAISE - Cushions - Better Sleep, Inc.
AQUA CHARGE - Vitamins and nutritional supplements - Oxygen for Life, Inc.
AQUA CHECK WATER ANALYZER - Analyzers–industrial - O.I. Corp.
AQUA CHEM - Chemical preparations - Great Lakes Chemical Corp.
AQUA CHEM - Chemical preparations - Grow Group, Inc.
AQUA-CHEX - Paints - Klee Chemical Coatings
AQUA-CHILL - Coolers–electric - Elkay Manufacturing Co.
AQUA CHILL - Refrigeration units - Printers' Service, Inc.
AQUA-CHILLER - Aquariums–household - Jewel Industries Inc.
AQUA CHLOR - Chemical preparations - Aqua Clear Industries Inc.
AQUA-CICHLID - Pet products ☆ - Aquatronics-Filtronics
AQUA CLEAN - Cleaning preparations - Wade Jones Co.
AQUA-CLEAN - Laundries–coin-operated - Foremost Chemicals Inc.

AQUA-CLEAN - Marine protective coating - Kop-Coat, Inc.
AQUA CLEAN MD-4 - Water purification systems - Pure Water Inc.
AQUA CLEANSE - Medical apparatus - Space Focus, Inc.
AQUA CLEAR - Chemical preparations - Aqua Clear Industries Inc.
AQUA CLEAR - Pet products - Rolf C. Hagen (USA) Corp.
AQUA CLEAR - Water—bottled or canned - A.J. Canfield Co.
AQUA-COAT - Epoxy coatings - Sterling-Clark-Lurton Corp.
AQUA COAT - Varnishes - Gilbert Spruance Co.
AQUA COATER - Enamels - Sinclair Paint Co.
AQUA COOL - Apparel and accessories - Prism Enterprises, Inc.
AQUA COOL - Containers—insulated - Stephen Flasch
AQUA-COOL - Infant product ☆ - Binky-Griptight Co.
AQUA COOL - Water—bottled or canned - Aqua Cool Bottled Water
AQUA-CRAFT - Scuba diving equipment - Underwater Diving Inc.
AQUA CRYLIC - Adhesives and sealants - Biddle Co.
AQUA CURE - Pharmaceutical preparations ☆ - Poly-Bio-Marine Inc.
AQUA-CURE - Pigments—metallic - Gilbert Spruance Co.
AQUA/CURE BY TRITON - Water purification systems - Nimbus Water Systems, Inc.
AQUA-CURL - Hair curlers - Remington Products Co.
AQUA CYCLE - Bicycles - Aqua Cycle International
AQUA CYCLINE - Pet products - Animal Majesty Ltd.
AQUA CYLINDER - Aquarium accessories ☆ - Cole Enterprises
AQUA D 2000 - Water purification systems - Pure Water Inc.
AQUA DECK - Boats—pontoons - Weeres Industries Corp.
AQUA DESIGN INCORPORATED - Water purification systems - Aqua Design, Inc.
AQUA-DIVE - Sporting goods - T.G. Sports Co.
AQUA DOG - Pet products - Black Sheep Inc.
AQUA DRIP - Purification unit - Gig Drewery
AQUA DRIP - Water purification systems - Aqua Drip Innovations, Inc.
AQUA-DUCK - Bedding—linen - Gotham Industries II
AQUA DUCT - Gutters—plastic - National Aluminum Products Co.
AQUA-DUCT - Pet products ☆ - Penn-Plax, Inc.
AQUA EAR - Pharmaceutical preparations ☆ - A.H. Robins Co. Inc.
AQUA-EASE - Medical apparatus - Lumex, Inc.
AQUA EDITION - Tires - Reinalt-Thomas Corp.
AQUA ELITE - Pumps—water - U.S. Sales and Marketing Corp.
AQUA EXPLORER - Sporting goods - Aqua-Leisure Industries, Inc.
AQUA EZ - Chemicals - Associated Leisure Products, Inc.
AQUA FABULON - Varnishes ☆ - Pratt & Lambert, Inc. (Specialty Products Div.)
AQUA FALLS - Water—bottled or canned - B & R Water Corp.
AQUA-FARMS - Seafood ☆ - Winter Harbor Fisheries
AQUA FEED - Lawn irrigation systems - Herbert Stephen Wallace
AQUA FILL - Paints - Sherwin-Williams Automotive Finishes Corp.
AQUA-FILM - Pharmaceutical preparations - Maurry Biological Co. Inc.
AQUA FINN - Sailboat - American Sail
AQUA FIRM - Beds—wood ☆ - Classic Corp.
AQUA FIZZZZ - Pet products - Rolf C. Hagen (USA) Corp.
AQUA FLARE - Flashlights - Princeton Tectonics, Inc.
AQUA FLAT - Paints - Diamond/Kuhn Paint Co.
AQUA-FLAVE - Pharmaceutical preparations ☆ - Nutritional Research Associates Inc.
AQUA FLEECE - Apparel and accessories - Descente North America, Inc.
AQUA FLEET-DRY - Metal surface enamels - Vogel Paint and Wax Co., Inc.
AQUA-FLEX - Floor coverings - Tarkett, Inc.
AQUA-FLEX - Garden equipment - Teknor Apex Co.
AQUA-FLINT - Epoxy - Briner Paint Manufacturing Co. Inc.
AQUA FLITE DECK - Boats—pontoons - Weeres Industries Corp.
AQUA-FLO - Plumbing fixtures—enameled - Aqua-Flo Corp.
AQUA FLO - Water purification systems - Water Conditioning, Inc.
AQUA FLOAT - Boats—motor - Godfrey Marine Co.
AQUA FLOAT - Thermometers - Coastal Industries Inc.
AQUA FLORA - Pet products - Rolf C. Hagen (USA) Corp.
AQUA-FLOW - Contact-lens solution ☆ - CooperVision Inc.
AQUA-FLOW - Paints - Talon Paint Inc.
AQUA FLOW - Tires - TBC Corp.
AQUA FOG 3300 - Machinery - City Theatrical Inc.
AQUA FOUNTAIN - Water purification systems - Pure Water Inc.
AQUA FRESH - Gloves - Murine Co.
AQUA FRESH - Seafood - Catfish Wholesale Inc.
AQUA FYNE - Enamels - Fyn Paint & Lacquer Co. Inc.
AQUA-GARD - Facial tissues - Marcal Paper Mills, Inc.
AQUA-GAUGE - Sprinklers—lawn - Melnor Inc.
AQUA-GEL - Diapers—cloth - Salk Co. Inc.

AQUA-GEM-E - Vitamins and nutritional supplements - J.R. Carlson Laboratories Inc.
AQUA GEMS - Pet products - Now Pet Products
AQUA GLASS - Bathtubs—enameled - Masco Corp.
AQUA GLASS - Tub and shower units - Aqua Glass Corp.
AQUA GLAZE - Finishing agents - Sterling-Clark-Lurton Corp.
AQUA GLOSS - Paints - Pratt & Lambert, Inc.
AQUA-GLOSS - Paints ☆ - Old World Art
AQUA GLOSS - Polishes - Aqua Glass Corp.
AQUA GLYCOLIC - Skin care products - Allergan Skin Care
AQUA GLYDE - Skin care products ☆ - Allergan Skin Care
AQUA GOLD - Filters—water - N.R.G. Enterprises, Inc./Mistra Inc.
AQUA GOLF - Games - Dean F. Peabody
AQUA GRIP - Apparel and accessories - Todd Schmidt
AQUA GUARD - Chemical preparations - Chem Lab Products, Inc.
AQUA-GUARD - Paints - Ponderosa Paint Manufacturing Co. Inc.
AQUA GUARD - Tires ☆ - Kelly-Springfield Tire Co.
AQUA GUARD - Water purification systems - Bruner Corp.
AQUA GUIDE - Radiofrequency measuring equipment ☆ - Rule Industries, Inc.
AQUA-GUN - Hoses - Melnor Inc.
AQUA HERBAL - Health care products ☆ - Earthnet
AQUA-HIDE - Shoe accessories ☆ - E.S. Originals, Inc.
AQUA HOBBY - Aquariums—household - Ginger, Inc.
AQUA HOME - Boats—motor - Holiday Mansion
AQUA HOUNDS, THE - Books—comic - Barry Alan Kraus
AQUA ILLUMINATORS - Aquariums—household - Petland, Inc.
AQUA-IMAGE - Photographic equipment - Eastman Kodak Co.
AQUA JADE - Soap - Swat Enterprise, Inc.
AQUA-JEL - Animal feeds - Transport Container Corp.
AQUA-JET - Sealing compounds - Passonno Paints
AQUA-JET - Tires—automobile - Jetzon/Telstar Tire
AQUA-JET POWER MASSAGE TABLE - Medical apparatus - Backman Products, Inc.
AQUA JEWELS - Glass products - Vitro Agate Corp.
AQUA JOY - Pumps—water - Beckett Corp.
AQUA KEM - Health care products - Thetford Corp.
AQUA KEM GREEN - Health care products - Thetford Corp.
AQUA KEM TOSS-INS - Health care products - Thetford Corp.
AQUA-KID - Toys - Kilgore Corp.
AQUA KILLER - Sporting goods - Bear Archery Inc.
AQUA KITE - Kites ☆ - Raven Industries Inc.
AQUA-KLEAN - Tools - Shop Vac Corp.
AQUA KLEAR - Water purification systems - Beckett Corp.
AQUA LAC - Hair care products - Faberge Co.
AQUA-LAC - Paints - C.M. Athey Paint Co.
AQUA LACTEN - Skin care products - Allergan Skin Care
AQUA-LAK - Finishing agents - Lenmar Inc.
AQUA LASH - Mascara - Noxell Corp.
AQUA LAV - Glassware—household ☆ - Aqua Glass Corp.
AQUA-LAWN - Sprinklers—lawn - Goulds Pumps, Inc.
AQUA-LEARN SWIMAID - Infant product - Aqua Learn Inc.
AQUA-LEEN - Diuretics - Ray Drug Co.
AQUA LEISURE - Sporting goods - Aqua-Leisure Industries, Inc.
AQUA-LIFT - Elevators - Reynold's Holding's, Inc.
AQUA LINE - Paints - Paris Paint & Varnish Co.
AQUA LINE - Pumps—water - Lin's Aqua Corp.
AQUA-LINER - Boats—pontoons ☆ - Duracraft Boats Inc.
AQUA-LIST EPOXY-ESTER - Polishing rouge - Williams-Hayward Protective Coatings Inc.
AQUA LITE - Fertilizers ☆ - Anchor Swan
AQUA-LITE - Paints - KCI Coatings, Inc.
AQUA-LITE - Vinyl - Manart-Hirsch Co. Inc.
AQUA-LITER - Toys - Gary M. Stern
AQUA-LOCK - Cleaning preparations - First Brands Properties Inc.
AQUA-LOK - Bottle caps - Aluminum Co. of America
AQUA-LOSE PLUS - Pharmaceutical preparations - Parmed Pharmaceuticals, Inc.
AQUA LOVE - Apparel and accessories ☆ - Swatch Watch USA
AQUA LUBE - Lubricants - Mayer Laboratories, Inc.
AQUA-LUNG - Skin diving equipment - U.S. Divers Co., Inc.
AQUA LUSTER - Enamels - Frazee/Deer-O Paints
AQUA-LUSTRE - Paints - C.M. Athey Paint Co.
AQUA-LUX - Lamp bulbs - Vo-Toys Inc.
AQUA LYTE - Pharmaceutical preparations - Nutritional Research Associates Inc.
AQUA-M - Lamps - Voltarc Technologies, Inc.

☆ = Now out of production

AQUA MAGIC - Bath salts - Frances Denney
AQUA MAGIC - Recreational vehicle dealers - Thetford Corp.
AQUA MAID - Bathroom fixtures - American Shower Door Co.
AQUA MAID - Food products - Carmine Foods Inc.
AQUA-MAID - Pet products - Tetra Sales USA
AQUA-MAR - Sporting goods - Alvimar Manufacturing Co. Inc.
AQUA-MARIN - Salt ☆ - Aquatrol, Inc.
AQUA MASSAGE - Skin care products - Aqua Massage International Inc.
AQUA MASTER - Lithographic plates - Western Litho Plate & Supply Co.
AQUA-MASTER - Skin diving equipment - U.S. Divers Co., Inc.
AQUA MASTER - Tires–automobile ☆ - Summit Tire and Battery, Inc.
AQUA MATE - Heating equipment - Aqua Queen
AQUA MATE - Marine rigging - Thetford Corp.
AQUA MATE - Paints - Pratt & Lambert, Inc.
AQUA MATE - Pool and spa chemicals - Little Chemical Co., Inc.
AQUA-MATE - Tanks–water - Thermal Concepts, Inc.
AQUA-MATIC - Life preservers ☆ - Gladding Braided Products Inc.
AQUA MATTE - Paints - Pratt & Lambert, Inc.
AQUA MED - Dental equipment - Innovative Industries, Inc.
AQUA METER - Speedometers - Rule Industries, Inc.
AQUA-MISER - Hardware - Carolina Equipment & Supply Co., Inc.
AQUA MIST - Bathroom accessories - Better Sleep, Inc.
AQUA-MIST - Pet products - Penn-Plax, Inc.
AQUA MISTIQUE - Water–bottled or canned - Carr Products Co. Inc.
AQUA MOIST - Skin care products - Jason Natural Products, Inc.
AQUA-MOTIVE - Polishing rouge - Williams-Hayward Protective Coatings Inc.
AQUA MOX - Pet products - Animal Majesty Ltd.
AQUA MULCHER - Lawn mowers - TGMI Inc.
AQUA MYCIN - Pet products - Animal Majesty Ltd.
AQUA NAILS - Manicure preparations - DeEnterprises Inc.
AQUA-NAMEL - Paints - Black & Puryear Paint Manufacturing Co. Inc.
AQUA NATURAL - Electronic water filter - Aquanatural Co.
AQUA NET - Fabrics - French Textiles Co.
AQUA NET - Hair care products - Chesebrough-Pond's USA Co.
AQUA NET - Hair care products - CPI Fab, Inc.
AQUA NET - Swimming pool covers - Aqua Net
AQUA-NET - Water purification systems - Aqua-Net, Inc.
AQUA NET COMPLETE CONTROL - Hair care products - Faberge Co.
AQUA NIQUE FINE COSMETICS - Cosmetics - Aquanique Fine Cosmetics, Inc.
AQUA NOVA - Cement - American Helmitin Corp.
AQUA NOXSTAIN - Cleaning preparations - Pioneer Manufacturing Co.
AQUA-NURSERY - Pet products - Penn-Plax, Inc.
AQUA NYMPH CYCLE - Boats–skiffs - Aqua Cycle International
AQUA ODOR CURB - Pet products - Nutritional Research Associates Inc.
AQUA-OPTICALS - Aquariums–household ☆ - Poly-Optical Products, Inc.
AQUA PAC - Fruits and vegetables - Ready Pac Produce, Inc.
AQUA PACK - Chemical preparations - McCalla Co.
AQUA-PAK - Aquariums–household - Valco International Inc.
AQUA PANNA - Beverages - San Pellegrino USA
AQUA PATIO - Boats–liferafts - Godfrey Marine Co.
AQUA PEDS - Exercising equipment - Aquastyle Inc.
AQUA PEL - Adhesives and sealants - Porter Paint Co.
AQUA-PEL - Finishing agents - Camp Co. Inc.
AQUA-PEN - Pens–fountain ☆ - Universal Fountain Pen & Pencil Co.
AQUA PEN AND PAD - Waterproofing compounds - Roca Productions Inc.
AQUA PENN - Water–mineral - Aquapenn Spring Water Co., Inc.
AQUA-PLANE - Sporting goods ☆ - Gladding Braided Products Inc.
AQUA-PLANT - Flowers, plants, and seeds - Penn-Plax, Inc.
AQUA PLAQUE - Signs - Holiday Craft
AQUA PLASTIC - Finishing agents - Coronado Paint Co.
AQUA-PLATE - Filters–water - Aquarium Systems, Inc.
AQUA PLATE - Waterproofing compounds - Bruning Paint Co.
AQUA PLEX - Vitamins and nutritional supplements - Natural Organics, Inc.
AQUA PLUG - Cement - L & F Products Inc.
AQUA-POND - Pet products ☆ - Tetra Sales USA
AQUA-POOL - Pet products - Tetra Sales USA
AQUA POWER - Carpet cleaning machines - Kent Investment Corp.
AQUA POWER - Water heaters–household - Mechanical Ingenuity Corp.
AQUA-PREP - Water treating compounds - Novalek, Inc.
AQUA PRIME - Paints - Buten Paint & Wallpaper
AQUA-PRIME - Paints - Dunn Edwards Corp.
AQUA PRIMER - Enamels - Sinclair Paint Co.
AQUA PRO - Enamels - Foy-Johnston Inc.
AQUA PROBE - Fathometers - Rule Industries, Inc.
AQUA PROOF - Waterproofing product - Construction Adhesives Co.

AQUA PROOFS - Infant product - Dundee Mills, Inc.
AQUA-PROTECH - Water purification systems - Crystalstil, Inc.
AQUA PRUF - Waterproofing compounds - Bruning Paint Co.
AQUA PRYME - Paints - C.M. Athey Paint Co.
AQUA PT - Health care products - Aqua Massage International Inc.
AQUA PULSE - Health care products ☆ - Black & Decker Corp.
AQUA PURA - Bathroom fixtures - Universal Spanish Communications, Inc.
AQUA-PURE - Food products - Kennerly Co.
AQUA PURE - Health care products ☆ - Blue Magic Products Inc.
AQUA-PURE - Water purification systems - Minstar Inc.
AQUA PURE - Water–mineral - Aqua Pure Drinking Waters
AQUA QUARTZ - Epoxy coatings - W.P. Hickman Systems
AQUA QUEEN - Heating equipment - Aqua Queen
AQUA QUEEN - Sprinklers–lawn ☆ - Melnor Inc.
AQUA QUEEN - Watches - Bulova Corp.
AQUA RAMP - Ramps - Aqua Ramp Industries
AQUA RELAXA - Pillows ☆ - Alger Creations Inc.
AQUA-RELIEF - Health care products - Aqua-Cel Corp.
AQUA REST - Mattresses - Perfect Dreamer
AQUA RICH - Hair care products - Helene Curtis Industries Inc.
AQUA RID - Pharmaceutical preparations - Goldline Laboratories, Inc.
AQUA-RITE - Floor coverings ☆ - Congoleum Corp.
AQUA ROCK - Epoxy coatings - W.P. Hickman Systems
AQUA-ROOT - Horticultural prepration - Aqua-Aid, Inc.
AQUA ROUND - Aquariums–household - Midwest Tropical Inc.
AQUA-ROYAL - Paints - Pratt & Lambert, Inc.
AQUA-RUNNER - Footwear - Excel Sports Science Inc.
AQUA SAFE - Mattresses - Land and Sky Manufacturing Inc.
AQUA SAND - Filters–water - Muskin Leisure Products Inc.
AQUA SASH - Enamels - Sinclair Paint Co.
AQUA-SATIN - Enamels - Pratt & Lambert, Inc.
AQUA SATIN - Enamels - Sinclair Paint Co.
AQUA SAUNA - Bath salts - Creative Leisure Inc.
AQUA-SAVA - Bathroom fixtures - Beacon Valves
AQUA SAVER - Garbage disposal units–commercial - Emerson Electric Co.
AQUA-SCAN - Surgical instruments - Marlen Manufacturing & Developing Co.
AQUA SCAPER - Pet products - Rolf C. Hagen (USA) Corp.
AQUA-SCRIP - Pharmaceutical preparations ☆ - Scrip-Physician Supply Co.
AQUA SCRUB - Cleaning preparations–household - Aqua Glass Corp.
AQUA SCRUB - Machinery - Usher Oil Co.
AQUA SCUTUM - Apparel and accessories - Morgan Shirt Corp.
AQUA-SEA - Seafood products–fresh or frozen - Aqua Sea Products, Inc.
AQUA SEAL - Electrical equipment - Kearney
AQUA SEAL - Paints - Frazee Paint
AQUA-SEAL - Paints - Sherwin-Williams Automotive Finishes Corp.
AQUA SEAL - Varnishes - Gilbert Spruance Co.
AQUA-SEARCH - Sporting goods ☆ - Gladding Braided Products Inc.
AQUA SELECT - Fish food - Blue Ribbon Pet Products, Inc.
AQUA-SENSOR - Water purification systems - Culligan International Co.
AQUA SERVE - Water–bottled or canned - Stone Mountain Water Co.
AQUA-SET - Hair care products - Faberge Co.
AQUA-SHED - Floor waxes ☆ - Uncle Sam Chemical Co., Inc.
AQUA-SHEEN - Waterproof outerwear - Aqua Sheen
AQUA SHELL - Paints - Pratt & Lambert, Inc.
AQUA SHIELD - Aquariums–household - Northwest Aquarium Supply Ltd.
AQUA SHIELD - Doors - Aqua Glass Corp.
AQUA-SHIELD - Paints - Farwest Paint Manufacturing Co. Inc.
AQUA-SHIELD - Waterproofing compounds - Camp Co. Inc.
AQUA SHINE - Waxes–mineral - Aqua Glass Corp.
AQUA SHUTTLE - Water purification systems - Poaul European, Inc.
AQUA-SIGNAL - Lighting fixtures–underwater - Aqua Signal Corp.
AQUA SILK - Hair care products - Pantresse Inc.
AQUA SINK - Fishing tackle ☆ - Gladding Braided Products Inc.
AQUA-SLIK - Paint ☆ - Hawkeye Industries, Inc.
AQUA-SLING - Hammocks - Goodlife Designs
AQUA-SMARTE - Water purification systems - King Technology, Inc.
AQUA SNAPPY - Cameras ☆ - Canon USA, Inc.
AQUA SOFT - Recreational vehicle dealers - Thetford Corp.
AQUA-SOIL - Soil–potting - Ace Products, Inc.
AQUA-SOL - Detergents - Imperial Manufacturing Co. Inc.
AQUA-SOL - Fertilizers - Plant Marvel Laboratories
AQUA SOLARIUM - Bathroom fixtures ☆ - Aqua Glass Corp.
AQUA-SOLV - Cleaning preparations ☆ - Grace Construction Products
AQUA SOLV - Fabrics - Sew-Art International
AQUA SPARKLE - Water treating compounds - Distributors Processing Inc.
AQUA SPLASH - Fruit drinks–bottled or canned - All-American Bottling Corp.

☆ = Now out of production

AQUA SPORT - Footwear–athletic ☆ - E.S. Originals, Inc.
AQUA SPRINGS - Bathroom fixtures ☆ - Aqua Glass Corp.
AQUA SPRINTER - Sporting goods - Rothhammer International Inc.
AQUA-STATI - Electrical equipment - Wagner Spray Tech Corp.
AQUA STEAM - Bathroom fixtures - Aqua Glass Corp.
AQUA STEEL - Cleaning preparations - Carroll Co.
AQUA STILL - Water purification systems - Pure Water Inc.
AQUA-STOCK - Aquarium accessories - Aqua Stock/Petcetera Inc.
AQUA-STOCK - Pet products - Petcetera Inc.
AQUA STOP - Footwear - SBC/Sporto Corp.
AQUA STOP-IT - Waterproofing compounds - Coronado Paint Co.
AQUA-STORM - Cleaning preparations–household ☆ - Wagner Spray Tech Corp.
AQUA STRIP - Paint removers - Sterling-Clark-Lurton Corp.
AQUA SUEDE - Enamels - Sinclair Paint Co.
AQUA SUL - Pet products - Weco Products Inc.
AQUA-SUN PRODUCTS - Garden furniture - Mr. Bean Bag Co.
AQUA SUPREME - Water–bottled or canned - Carr Products Co. Inc.
AQUA SWEEP - Brooms ☆ - Kleer Flo Co. Inc.
AQUA SWIMSCHOOL - Sporting goods - Aqua-Leisure Industries, Inc.
AQUA-TAINER - Bathroom fixtures - Aqua-Tainer Co.
AQUA-TARIUMS - Pet products - Pets International, Ltd.
AQUA TEC - Skin care products ☆ - Teledyne Water Pik
AQUA TECH - Aquariums–household - Advanced Aquatic Technologies Inc.
AQUA TECH - Chemical preparations - TBA Graphics, Inc.
AQUA TECH - Finishing agents - Dura Seal
AQUA-TECH - Tires - Ganin Tire Inc.
AQUA-TEMP - Pet products - Penn-Plax, Inc.
AQUA TERRAZZO - Bathroom fixtures ☆ - Aqua Glass Corp.
AQUA-TEX - Gloves - Olympia Sports Co. Inc.
AQUA-TEX - Pharmaceutical preparations - Syosset Laboratories Inc.
AQUA-THANE - Varnishes - Lilly Perfection Paint
AQUA-THERM - Food processors - Oliver Products Co.
AQUA TINT - Epoxy coatings - W.P. Hickman Systems
AQUA-TITE - Adhesives and sealants ☆ - McCloskey Corp.
AQUA-TITE - Hardware stores ☆ - Epmar Corp.
AQUA-TITE - Silicon products - Marchem Coated Fabrics, Inc.
AQUA TOP - Epoxy coatings - W.P. Hickman Systems
AQUA TOUCH - Printing trades machinery - Republic Roller Corp.
AQUA TOWER - Aquariums–household - Midwest Tropical Inc.
AQUA TOWER - Health care products - Medical Industries America, Inc.
AQUA TRAIL - Playground equipment - Miracle Recreation Equipment Co.
AQUA TRAINER - Whirlpools - Fort Wayne Plastics, Inc.
AQUA TRAK - Apparel and accessories - Alpha Protech, Inc.
AQUA-TREAT - Clippers–nail - W.W. Grainger, Inc.
AQUA TRED - Tires - Goodyear Tire & Rubber Co.
AQUA-TREE - Pet products - Penn-Plax, Inc.
AQUA-TRETE - Concrete waterproofing treatment - Huls America Inc.
AQUA TRU - Water treating compounds - Novalek, Inc.
AQUA TURF - Floor coverings–carpet and rugs ☆ - Proffitt Manufacturing Co.
AQUA-VAC - Decoys - Carry-Lite, Inc.
AQUA VAC - Pet products - Rolf C. Hagen (USA) Corp.
AQUA-VAC - Pharmaceutical preparations - Republic Drug Co. Inc.
AQUA-VAC - Vacuum cleaners and accessories - Shop Vac Corp.
AQUA VALET - Containers–paper ☆ - Moeller Products Co. Inc.
AQUA VELVA - Shaving preparations - J.B. Williams Co. Inc.
AQUA VELVET - Floor coverings–carpet and rugs ☆ - Proffitt Manufacturing Co.
AQUA-VELVET - Paints ☆ - Old World Art
AQUA-VEND - Water–bottled or canned - McKesson Home Health Care
AQUA VENTURES - Aquarium accessories - Blue Ribbon Pet Products, Inc.
AQUA VIE JAVA - Flavored spring water - Aqua Vie Beverage Corp.
AQUA VIE PARADISE - Flavored spring water - Aqua Vie Beverage Corp.
AQUA-VIEW - Vinyl - Manart-Hirsch Co. Inc.
AQUA VITE - Veterinary pharmaceutical preparations - Nutritional Research Associates Inc.
AQUA-VIVE - Water purification systems - Cassco Products, Inc.
AQUA WACKY POOLVERIZERS - Toys - Little Kids, Inc.
AQUA WALL - Bathroom fixtures - Aqua Glass Corp.
AQUA/WHIRL - Health care products - Thermo-Electric Co.
AQUA WIND UPS - Toys - Imperial Toy Corp.
AQUA WING TRAINER - Sporting goods - Flents Products Co. Inc.
AQUA WITCH - Industrial machinery - Aqua Witch, Inc.
AQUA WOOD - Swimming pools - Aqua Wood Pools
AQUA Z - Skin care products - Aloe Gator Suncare Co.
AQUA ZAR - Coatings - United Gilsonite Laboratories

AQUA ZOLE - Pet products - Animal Majesty Ltd.
AQUA ZYME - Recreational vehicle dealers - Thetford Corp.
AQUAAIR - Filtration units - AquaAir Environmental, Inc.
AQUABAC - Insecticides - Becker Microbial Products, Inc.
AQUABALANCE - Vitamins and nutritional supplements - Intelligent Nutrients, Inc.
AQUABALANCE - Water treating compounds - Ecolab Inc.
AQUABANK - Water treating compounds - Greywater Management
AQUABARS - Exercising equipment - Aquastyle Inc.
AQUABASE - Pharmaceutical preparations - Paddock Laboratories Inc.
AQUABASE - Pharmaceutical preparations ☆ - Pal-Pak Inc.
AQUABATIC - Dishes–china - Waterford Wedgewood USA, Inc.
AQUABEE - Paper - Bee Paper Co. Inc.
AQUABEST - Toners - Radiant Color Div.
AQUABEST - Water purification systems - Emerson Electric Co.
AQUABLOK - Poison–rat - Roussel-Uclaf Corp.
AQUABON - Deodorizers - Pettibone Laboratories Inc.
AQUABOND - Adhesives and sealants - Kyanize Paint Co.
AQUABOND - Golfing equipment - Anchor Continental, Inc.
AQUABOND - Solder - Kester Solder Co.
AQUABOX - Mattresses - Del Astra Industries Inc.
AQUABROME - Water treating compounds - Bio-Lab, Inc.
AQUABUG - Motors–outboard - Seaborne Systems Inc.
AQUACAP - Valves - Zurn Industries, Inc.
AQUACARE - Water purification systems - Aquacare Systems, Inc.
AQUACAT - Paint driers - Ultra Additives, Inc.
AQUACEL - Chemical preparations - Ecofoster Biomaterial, Inc.
AQUACEL - Paints - Aexcel Corp.
AQUACHEK - Adhesives and sealants ☆ - Gibson-Homans Co.
AQUACHLOR - Pharmaceutical preparations - Armenpharm Ltd.
AQUACIDE - Waterproofing compounds ☆ - Pratt & Lambert United, Inc.
AQUACILLIN G - Pharmaceutical preparations - Armenpharm Ltd.
AQUACILS - Cosmetics - Lancome
AQUACISER - Exercise equipment - AquaCiser Inc.
AQUACISER - Medical apparatus - Ferno Washington, Inc.
AQUACLEAN - Carpet cleaning equipment - Advance Machine Co.
AQUACLEAR - Paints - Suntec Paint Inc.
AQUACLEAR - Skin care products - Chasalco Inc.
AQUACLOUD - Health care products - Graham-Field Inc.
AQUACOAT - Artists' materials - International Paper Co.
AQUACOIL - Mattresses - Kingsdown, Inc.
AQUACOL - Health care products ☆ - Kay Pharmacal Co. Inc.
AQUACORR - Boxes ☆ - Georgia-Pacific Corp.
AQUACOT - Pharmaceutical preparations - C.O. Truxton Inc.
AQUACREAM - Lotions - ADM Tronics Unlimited, Inc.
AQUACUBE - Pet products - Advanced Aquaculture Systems Inc.
AQUACURE - Chemical preparations - Deatrick & Associates, Inc.
AQUACYCLINE - Pharmaceutical preparations - Armenpharm Ltd.
AQUADAM - Waterproofing compounds - Blue Ridge Talc Co. Inc.
AQUADEMIC - Paper - Hunt Manufacturing Co.
AQUADENT - Mouthwashes - Vi-Jon Laboratories, Inc.
AQUADERM - Skin care products - Baker Cummins Dermatologicals Inc.
AQUADEX 50 - Stain removers - Bio-Dex Laboratories
AQUADINE - Water purification systems - Aquascience Research Group Inc.
AQUADIVE - Watches - I.D. Enterprises
AQUADOME - Swimming pools - Cascade Pools
AQUADONNA - Skin care products - Pauser, Inc.
AQUAD'OR - Water–mineral - Aquad'or
AQUADOZE - Anesthetics - Novalek, Inc.
AQUADOZE - Aquarium accessories - Aquaculture Aquavet
AQUADRATE - Pharmaceutical preparations - Norwich-Eaton Pharmaceuticals
AQUADRIL - Diuretics - Pharmex Inc.
AQUADROID ELITE - Cleaning preparations - Aquanaut Inc.
AQUADUCT - Bathroom fixtures - Kallista Inc.
AQUADUCT - Plastic conduits - Composite Concepts, Inc.
AQUADURO - Paints ☆ - Standard Paints Inc.
AQUAETTES - Apparel–women's - Blue Bay Inc.
AQUAFAX - Chemical preparations - Gaines Industries, Inc.
AQUAFIBE - Vitamins and nutritional supplements - Cer-Burg Enterprises, Inc.
AQUAFILM - Plastics–laminated - Color Communications, Inc.
AQUAFILTER - Tobacco products - Aquafilter Corp.
AQUAFINA - Water–mineral - Pepsico, Inc.
AQUAFITNESS - Exercising equipment - Aqua-Leisure Industries, Inc.
AQUAFLARE - Lighting equipment–boat and ship ☆ - Soderberg Manufacturing Co. Inc.
AQUAFLARE - Paints–artists' ☆ - Winsor & Newton

☆ = Now out of production

AQUAFLECK - Paints - California Products Corp.

AQUAFLEX - Contact lenses - Wesley-Jessen Co.

AQUAFLEX - Machine parts - Amarillo Pump & Supply Co., Inc.

AQUAFLEX - Paints - Savannah Paint Manufacturing Co.

AQUAFLEX - Sporting goods ☆ - Hedstrom Corp.

AQUAFLO - Fabrics–spandex - H. Warshow & Sons, Inc.

AQUAFLO - Printing trades machinery - Printers' Service, Inc.

AQUAFLO - Surgical supplies - Flexbar Machine Corp.

AQUAFLOR - Floor coverings ☆ - Pratt & Lambert, Inc. (Specialty Products Div.)

AQUAFLUR - Paints - Valspar Corp.

AQUAFOAM - Foam rubber - Syndicate Sales, Inc.

AQUAFOAM - Hair care products - Amole Inc.

AQUAFOAM - Life preservers - Stearns Manufacturing Co.

AQUAFOIL - Inks - U.S. Aluminum

AQUAFRESH - Toothpaste - SmithKline Beecham Consumer Healthcare

AQUAFRESH - Toothpaste - Smithkline Beecham Corp.

AQUAFRESH FLEX - Toothbrushes - SmithKline Beecham Consumer Healthcare

AQUAFRESH FLEX - Toothbrushes - Smithkline Beecham Corp.

AQUAFRESH FLEX DIRECT - Toothbrushes - SmithKline Beecham Consumer Healthcare

AQUAFRESH FLEX DIRECT - Toothbrushes - Smithkline Beecham Corp.

AQUAFRESH SENSITIVE - Toothpaste - SmithKline Beecham Consumer Healthcare

AQUAFRESH WHITENING - Toothpaste - Smithkline Beecham Corp.

AQUAFUGE - Cigarette paper - G.A. Georgopulo & Co. Inc.

AQUAFUREN - Pharmaceutical preparations - Armenpharm Ltd.

AQUAGAITER - Medical apparatus - Ferno Washington, Inc.

AQUAGARD - Floor coverings - Tarkett, Inc.

AQUAGARD - Motor vehicle parts and accessories ☆ - National Cycle Inc.

AQUAGARD - Paints - Flexbar Corp.

AQUAGEL - Food products - Marcel Trading Corp.

AQUAGEM - Inks–letterpress - Sun Chemical Corp.

AQUAGEMS - Fish–fresh or frozen - Aquacultural Research Corp.

AQUAGEN - Pet products - Evert-Fresh Corp.

AQUAGENIC - Pharmaceutical preparations - Syosset Laboratories Inc.

AQUAGENIE - Water purification systems - Jacuzzi Brothers

AQUAGLIDE - Lubricants - Exxon Corp.

AQUAGLO - Paints - Benjamin Moore & Co.

AQUAGLO - Paints - Triangle Coatings Inc.

AQUAGRIP - Paints - Benjamin Moore & Co.

AQUAGRO - Fish food - Martek Corp.

AQUAGUARD - Apparel and accessories ☆ - Terramar Sports Worldwide, Ltd.

AQUAGUARD - Floor coverings - Domco Industries Ltd.

AQUAGUARD - Lubricants - SF Services, Inc.

AQUAGUARD - Photographic equipment - Sureguard, Inc.

AQUAHAWAII - Toys - Aqua-Leisure Industries, Inc.

AQUAHOOP - Toys - Cleanaids Inc.

AQUAJET - Health care products - Hydrotherapy Systems

AQUAJET - Watches - Bulova Corp.

AQUAJOGGER - Exercising equipment - Excel Sports Science Inc.

AQUAKING - Aquariums–household - Eugene G. Danner Manufacturing Inc.

AQUAKNIT - Crocheted and knitted items - Puritan Sportswear Corp.

AQUAKOTE - Paints - Royal Lustre Brands

AQUALAB I - Aquarium accessories - Mardel Laboratories, Inc.

AQUALAB II - Aquarium accessories - Mardel Laboratories, Inc.

AQUALAB III - Aquarium accessories - Mardel Laboratories, Inc.

AQUALAB IV - Aquarium accessories - Mardel Laboratories, Inc.

AQUALAND - Watches - Citizen Watch Co. of America Inc.

AQUALAQ - Paints - Savannah Paint Manufacturing Co.

AQUALARM - Alarm systems - Aqualarm

AQUALAX - Pharmaceutical preparations - Parmed Pharmaceuticals, Inc.

AQUALEEN - Plastics film - Norpak Corp.

AQUALENS - Contact lenses - O.S.I. Corp.

AQUALIFE - Faucets - Waxman Industries Inc.

AQUALIFE - Vitamins and nutritional supplements ☆ - Optimal Nutrients

AQUALIFT - Mufflers–motor vehicle - Onan Corp.

AQUALIGHT - Pet products - Aquapro

AQUALILY - Cosmetics - Revlon Consumer Products Corp.

AQUALIN - Skin care products - Micro Balanced Products Inc.

AQUALIN SUPPRETTES - Pharmaceutical preparations ☆ - M. Polymedica Corp.

AQUALINE - Faucets ☆ - U.S. Brass Corp.

AQUALINE - Regulators–voltage - Hehr International Inc.

AQUALINE - Swimming pools ☆ - Doughboy Recreational Inc.

AQUALINK - Agricultural products - Scotts Co. (Organics Business Group)

AQUALINK - Controls–heating systems - Jandy Industries, Inc.

AQUALIPID - Animal feed supplements - Central Soya Co. Inc.

AQUALITE - Clocks ☆ - Toastmaster Inc.

AQUALITE - Watches - Advance Watch Co. Ltd.

AQUALITE - Wheels - Hamilton Caster & Manufacturing Co.

AQUALITY - Tools - Sta-Rite Industries Inc.

AQUALIZER - Pet products ☆ - Jungle Laboratories Corp.

AQUALLOY - Paints - Tresco Paint Co. Inc.

AQUALOCK - Adhesives and sealants - B.F. Goodrich Co.

AQUALOCK - Paints and coatings - Insl-X Products Corp.

AQUALOCKIT - Absorbant powder - J.V. Manufacturing Co., Inc.

AQUALOCO BRAZIL - Swimwear - Aqualoco International Swimwear, Ltd.

AQUALOGIC - Lubricants - Terresolve Technologies Ltd.

AQUALOGY - Pet products - Rolf C. Hagen (USA) Corp.

AQUALOID - Paints - Essex Specialty Products, Inc.

AQUALUBE - Lubricants - Armenpharm Ltd.

AQUALUX - Paints - Orleans Paint Co. Inc.

AQUAMAID - Cleaning preparations - Chesco Inc.

AQUAMAR - Fish–fresh or frozen - Aquamar, Inc.

AQUAMARINE - Aquariums–household - California Aquarium Supply Corp.

AQUAMARINE - Cosmetics - Revlon Consumer Products Corp.

AQUAMARINE INC. - Water purification systems - Aquamarine, Inc.

AQUAMART - Vending machines - Aquamart Manufacturing, Inc.

AQUAMASTER - Aquariums–household - Eugene G. Danner Manufacturing Inc.

AQUAMASTER - Water purification systems - Aquamaster International Inc.

AQUAMAT - Liners and covers–pond, pit, and landfill - American Colloid Co.

AQUAMAT - Medical apparatus - Aquamat Partners

AQUAMATCH - Water treating compounds - Aquamatch Inc.

AQUAMATE - Carpet cleaning equipment - Rexair, Inc.

AQUAMATE - Dyes and pigments - Morton International Inc. (Morton Salt Div.)

AQUAMATE - Tray table - Softub, Inc.

AQUAMATES - Aquariums–household - Marineland Aquarium Products

AQUAMATES - Sporting goods - Foster Grant Co. Inc.

AQUAMATIC - Watches - Croton Watch Co., Inc.

AQUAMAX - Cleaning preparations - Aqua Products Inc.

AQUAMAX - Inks - Sun Chemical Corp.

AQUAMAX - Paints - Triangle Coatings Inc.

AQUAMED - Pharmaceutical preparations - Legere Pharmaceuticals Inc.

AQUAMED - Skin care products - Allergan Skin Care

AQUAMEDICO - Watches - Croton Watch Co., Inc.

AQUAMEG - Vitamins and nutritional supplements ☆ - Enzyme Process Co. Inc.

AQUAMEMBRANE - Filters–industrial - Separation Technologists

AQUAMEND - Epoxy - Polymeric Systems, Inc.

AQUAMEPHYTON - Pharmaceutical preparations - Merck & Co., Inc. (Merck Research Laboratories)

AQUAMILE - Tires - Pirelli Armstrong Tire Corp.

AQUAMINT - Mouthwashes - Aquamint Laboratories Inc.

AQUAMIST - Pharmaceutical preparations ☆ - R.A. McNeil Co.

AQUAMIST - Sprinklers–lawn - Grinnell Corp.

AQUAMITT - Aquarium accessories - Corina Kazarian

AQUAMOC - Footwear - H.H. Brown Shoe Co., Inc.

AQUAMOD - Printing trades machinery - Printers' Service, Inc.

AQUAMOTION - Hydrotherapy equipment - Aquamotion, Inc.

AQUAMULSION - Chemicals–photographic - Universal Engraving, Inc.

AQUAMYCIN - Pharmaceutical preparations - Armenpharm Ltd.

AQUAN D - Water–mineral ☆ - Absopure Water Co.

AQUANAMEL - Paints - Grow Group, Inc.

AQUANAUT - Adhesives and sealants - Induron Coatings Inc.

AQUANAUT - Boats - Rotocast International Inc.

AQUANEO - Paints ☆ - PPG Industries, Inc.

AQUANET - Sporting goods - J.A. Cissel Manufacturing Co.

AQUANIL - Skin care products - Person and Covey Inc.

AQUANINE - Pharmaceutical preparations - Armenpharm Ltd.

AQUANOMICS - Bathtubs–enameled - Unique Bathing Supplies Inc.

AQUANYLON - Paints ☆ - Jay Bee Paint Co.

AQUAOXY - Pharmaceutical preparations - Armenpharm Ltd.

AQUAPAK - Health care products - Hudson Respiratory Care Inc.

AQUAPASTO - Paints–artists' - Winsor & Newton

AQUAPEARL - Paints - Benjamin Moore & Co.

AQUAPEDIC - Health care products - Graham-Field Inc.

AQUAPEL - Chemical preparations - PPG Industries, Inc.

AQUAPELLA - Figurines - Takar USA Corp.

AQUAPET - Pet products - President Trading USA Inc.

AQUAPEX - Tools–hand-operated - Wirsbo Co.

AQUAPHANE - Coatings - Sun Chemical Corp.

AQUAPHENICOL - Pharmaceutical preparations - Armenpharm Ltd.

AQUAPHILIC - Pharmaceutical preparations - Medco Lab Inc.

AQUAPHOR - Health care products - Beiersdorf Inc.

AQUAPIB - Adhesives and sealants - Mozel Inc.

AQUAPILL - Humidifier-water treatment ☆ - Hamilton Home Products Inc.

AQUAPILL 8 - Pet products - Etani International Inc.

AQUAPLAST - Orthopedic products - Smith & Nephew Inc. (Rehabilitation Div.)

AQUAPLAST ORIGINAL RESILIENT - Splints - Smith & Nephew Inc. (Rehabilitation Div.)

AQUAPLAST PRODRAPE - Splints - Smith & Nephew Inc. (Rehabilitation Div.)

AQUAPLAST RESILIENT-T - Splints - Smith & Nephew Inc. (Rehabilitation Div.)

AQUAPLAST ULTRA THIN - Splints - Smith & Nephew Inc. (Rehabilitation Div.)

AQUAPLAST WATERCOLORS - Splints - Smith & Nephew Inc. (Rehabilitation Div.)

AQUAPLATE - Glassware–household - Precision Bache Glass

AQUAPLEZ - Paints - Gilbert Spruance Co.

AQUAPLY - Plywood - Harbor Sales Co.

AQUAPON - Paints - PPG Industries, Inc.

AQUAPRENE - Adhesives and sealants - Sta'-Put Inc.

AQUAPRIME - Paints - Triangle Coatings Inc.

AQUAPRIME 211Z - Paints - Edison Coatings, Inc.

AQUAPRIN - Pharmaceutical preparations - Teresa Phykitt

AQUAPRINT - Inks–lithographic ☆ - Martin F. Weber Co.

AQUAPRO - Aquariums–household - World Trade Union & Co.

AQUAPRO - Pet products - KP Trading USA

AQUAPULSE - Faucets - Sunbeam-Oster Household Products

AQUAPURE - Solder - Lukens Manufacturing Co.

AQUARAY 20 - Suntan lotions - Allergan Skin Care

AQUARELLE - Artists' materials - M. Grumbacher Inc.

AQUARELLE - Floor coverings–carpet and rugs - Atlas Carpet Mills Inc.

AQUARELLE - Wallpaper - Seabrook Wallcoverings, Inc.

AQUAREM - Pet products - Tetra Sales USA

AQUARESIN - Pet products - Aquapro

AQUARESIN - Spices and extracts - Kalsec, Inc.

AQUARESS - Shampoos - SBS Products, Inc.

AQUARI CLEAN - Water treating compounds - Jungle Laboratories Corp.

AQUARI-LUX - Lighting equipment - Penn-Plax, Inc.

AQUARI-SOL - Veterinary pharmaceutical preparations - Aquarium Products Inc.

AQUARI-YUMS - Fish food - Wardley Corp.

AQUARIAN - Air conditioning equipment - Air-O-Lator Corp.

AQUARIAN - Bathroom fittings ☆ - American Standard Inc.

AQUARIAN - Boats - Glen-L Marine Designs

AQUARIAN - Drums–musical instruments - Aquarian Accessories Corp.

AQUARIAN - Fish food ☆ - Mardel Laboratories, Inc.

AQUARIAN - Novelty items–paper - Morgan & Morgan

AQUARIAN - Sporting goods ☆ - Stearns Manufacturing Co.

AQUARIAN BODYSCIENCE - Vitamins and nutritional supplements - Aquarian Bodyscience

AQUARINE - Cosmetics - Lancome

AQUARIUM - Computer software - Cross Educational Software Inc.

AQUARIUM - Soap - Softsoap Enterprises, Inc.

AQUARIUM MASTER - Pet products - Aquarium Industrial Inc.

AQUARIUM SALT - Aquariums–household - Jungle Laboratories Corp.

AQUARIUM SERIES - Soap - Softsoap Enterprises, Inc.

AQUARIUM SYSTEM, THE - Aquariums–household - Aquarium Systems, Inc.

AQUARIUS - Cabinets ☆ - Triangle Pacific Corp. (Cabinet Division)

AQUARIUS - Cleaning equipment - Sonicstar International, Ltd.

AQUARIUS - Computer software - Environmental Testing and Certification Corp.

AQUARIUS - Computer software - HNC Inc.

AQUARIUS - Dehumidifiers - Oasis Corp.

AQUARIUS - Diving boards - American Playground Corp.

AQUARIUS - Fabrics ☆ - Greenwood Mills Inc.

AQUARIUS - Floor coverings - American Floor Products Co. Inc.

AQUARIUS - Floor coverings ☆ - Azrock Commercial Flooring

AQUARIUS - Floor coverings–carpet and rugs ☆ - Mannington Carpets, Inc.

AQUARIUS - Freezers ☆ - Frigibar Industries Inc.

AQUARIUS - Furniture ☆ - Bassett Furniture Industries, Inc.

AQUARIUS - Ice boxes–household - Deer Park Spring Water Inc.

AQUARIUS - Luggage - Airway Industries, Inc.

AQUARIUS - Markers–felt-tip ☆ - Sakura of America

AQUARIUS - Mobile homes - Golden West Homes

AQUARIUS - Powerboat ☆ - Invader Marine Inc.

AQUARIUS - Pumps ☆ - Alexander-Roberts Co.

AQUARIUS - Shower rods - Kenney Manufacturing Co.

AQUARIUS - Skin care products - Imperial Inc.

AQUARIUS - Soil–potting - Decorative Rock Specialties and Equipment Inc.

AQUARIUS - Sporting goods ☆ - Outdoor Technologies Group

AQUARIUS - Tiles–ceramic - Dal-Tile Corp.

AQUARIUS - Trailers–travel - Travel Units Inc.

AQUARIUS - Water–mineral ☆ - Wheeler Spring Water

AQUARIUS - Wine - Unique Wines, Inc.

AQUARIUS II - Paper–lithograph - International Paper Co.

AQUARIUS II - Fabrics ☆ - Greenwood Mills Inc.

AQUARIUS II - Paper–writing - Strathmore Paper Co.

AQUARIUS RAIN CURTAINS - Lasers - Laser Fantasy International, Inc.

AQUAROBICS - Pet products - Bounce Inc.

AQUAROBICS - Pet products - Kong Co.

AQUAROYALE - Seafood products–fresh or frozen - Tuna House, Inc.

AQUARUNNERS - Exercising equipment - Excel Sports Science Inc.

AQUASAFE - Filters–air - Hydrotechnology, Inc.

AQUASAFE - Pet products - Tetra Sales USA

AQUASALINE - Aquariums–household - Wardley Corp.

AQUASAVER - Plumbing fixtures–enameled - Aqua Smart, Inc.

AQUASAVER - Toilets–porcelain - Gerber Plumbing Fixtures Corp.

AQUASCUTUM - Neckties - Mallory and Church Corp.

AQUASEA - Fishing tackle - Aquasea Inc.

AQUASEAL - Adhesives and sealants - McNett Corp.

AQUASEAL - Vitamins and nutritional supplements - Seal Products Inc.

AQUASEARCH - Sporting goods ☆ - Gladding Braided Products Inc.

AQUASEAT - Health care products - Graham-Field Inc.

AQUASELECT - Pet food - Blue Ribbon Pet Products, Inc.

AQUASENTIALS - Cosmetics - American Telecast Corp.

AQUASHADE - Dyes–synthetic - Applied Biochemists, Inc.

AQUASHADOW - Dyes–synthetic - Applied Biochemists, Inc.

AQUASHAVE - Shaving preparations - G.I. Drug Co.

AQUASHEEN - Paints ☆ - Royal Lustre Brands

AQUASHIELD - Paints - Sigma Coatings USA BV.

AQUASIL - Pigments - Silberline Manufacturing Co., Inc.

AQUASITE - Eye drops - InSite Vision Inc.

AQUASKATE - Exercising equipment - Aquastyle Inc.

AQUASOL - Chemical preparations - Specialty Products, Inc.

AQUASOL - Skin care products ☆ - Rhone-Poulenc Rorer Pharmaceuticals Inc.

AQUASOL A - Pharmaceutical preparations - Rhone-Poulenc Rorer Pharmaceuticals Inc.

AQUASOL PLUS - Aquatic pharmacuetical preparations ☆ - Aquatronics-Filtronics

AQUASOL WATER PUMP - Pumps–water - USA Exports Inc.

AQUASOLE - Shoe accessories - Micro Balanced Products Inc.

AQUASOLVE - Degreasing solvents - Xklen Corp.

AQUASONIC - Housewares - Black Diamond Industries, Ltd.

AQUASONIX - Electronic equipment - Alexander G. Langer

AQUASORB - Chemical preparations - Stewart-Hall Chemical Corp.

AQUASORB - Shoe insoles - Zapendar Labs Inc.

AQUASORB - Skin care products - Kobayashi International Inc.

AQUASORB - Wound dressing - Deroyal Industries, Inc.

AQUASOX - Sporting goods - Everett Giants, Inc.

AQUASPHERE - Skin care products - Estee Lauder Inc.

AQUASPORT - Hair care products - I. Sekine Co. Inc.

AQUASPUN - Fabrics ☆ - International Paper Co.

AQUASSAGE - Bathroom fixtures - Pacific Spirit Corp.

AQUASSAGE - Housewares ☆ - Dacon Manufacturing

AQUASSAGER - Electronic equipment - Pollenex Corp.

AQUASTAIN - Wood products - Tamms Industries Co.

AQUASTAIN PLUS - Wood products ☆ - Tamms Industries Co.

AQUASTAR - Faucets - Moen Inc.

AQUASTATIC - Mattresses ☆ - E & S Vinyl Manufacturing Inc.

AQUASTONE - Paving materials–stone - Roberta A. Hair

AQUASTREAM - Plugs–nose - Moen Inc.

AQUASTRIDE - Exercising equipment - Aquastyle Inc.

AQUASTRIPE - See SPORTSTRIPE

AQUASTRIPE - Paints - Triangle Coatings Inc.

AQUASULF - Pharmaceutical preparations - Armenpharm Ltd.

AQUASURE - Detergents - Ecolab Inc.

AQUASURE - Wet suits–rubber - McNett Corp.

AQUASWITCH - Regulators–power - Jandy Industries, Inc.

AQUATACK - Gloves - New York, Inc.

AQUATAG - Health care products ☆ - Solvay Pharmaceuticals Inc.

AQUATAN - Pet products ☆ - Sera Aquaristik USA Inc.

AQUATANK - Pet products - Hawkeye Corp.

AQUATANK V - Pet products - Hawkeye Corp.

AQUATAPE - Gauging instruments - Metritape, Inc.

AQUATAR - Skin care products - Allergan, Inc.

AQUATEC - Health care products - Aquatec Healthcare Products

AQUATEC - Paints - Bocour Artist Colors Inc.

AQUATECH - Contact lenses - O.S.I. Corp.

AQUATECH - Paints - Triangle Coatings Inc.

AQUATECH - Watches - Advance Watch Co. Ltd.

AQUATENSEN - Pharmaceutical preparations - Wallace Laboratories

AQUATERRA - Sporting goods - Perception Inc.

AQUATEX - Fabrics–coated - Herculite Products, Inc.

AQUATEX - Glass products - AFG Industries Inc. (Glass Group Div.)

AQUATEX - Glue–household or industrial - Golden Harvest Adhesives

AQUATEX - Lubricants - Texaco, Inc.

AQUATHANE - Enamels - Bruning Paint Co.

AQUATHANE - Floor waxes - Coatings Lab

AQUATHANE - Paints - Triangle Coatings Inc.

AQUATHANE - Resins–polymer - Reichhold Chemicals, Inc.

AQUATHANE 210 - Finishing agents - Edison Coatings, Inc.

AQUATHERM - Health care products - Graham-Field Inc.

AQUATHERM - Pumps–water ☆ - Heat Controller Inc.

AQUATIC ADVANTAGE - Exercising equipment - Aquatic Advantage, Inc.

AQUATIC GARDENS - Aquariums–underwater museums - Petco Animal Supplies, Inc.

AQUATIC GREEN - Pet products ☆ - Aquatronics-Filtronics

AQUATIC LIFE SAVER - Aquarium accessories - Kordon

AQUATIC LIFE SAVER - Water treating compounds - Novalek, Inc.

AQUATIC PLANT FOOD TABS - Water treating compounds - Jungle Laboratories Corp.

AQUATICA - Water treating compounds - Wardley Corp.

AQUATILE - Moisture-proof paneling - ABT Co., Inc.

AQUATILIS - Bicycles - Ecosports America, Inc.

AQUATIME ROPE - Clocks - Zelco Industries, Inc.

AQUATINIC - Lamps - Duro-Test Corp.

AQUATINIC - Lighting equipment - Duro-Lite Lamps Inc.

AQUATINT - Wood products ☆ - Tamms Industries Co.

AQUATONE - Paints - Bridges Smith & Co.

AQUATONE - Tiles–ceiling ☆ - Flintkote Co.

AQUATONE - Tiles–ceiling ☆ - GS Roofing Products Co.

AQUATOOLS - Chemical preparations - Sta-Rite Industries Inc.

AQUATOWEL - Ink - Aarberg Printing Inks Co.

AQUATOX - Computer software - Burlington Research, Inc.

AQUATOX - Paints - Conco Paint Co.

AQUATRAP - Freezers–laboratory - APD Cryogenics, Inc.

AQUATRED - Tires - Goodyear Tire & Rubber Co.

AQUATREX - Cleaning preparations - L & R Manufacturing Co.

AQUATRINE - Herbicides - Applied Biochemists, Inc.

AQUATRINE OA - Herbicides - Applied Biochemists, Inc.

AQUATROL - Finishing agents ☆ - Flood Co.

AQUATROLS - Soil testing kits - Aquatrols Corp. of America, Inc.

AQUATRON - Heating equipment - Slant/Fin Corp.

AQUATRON - Housewares - Advance Machine Co.

AQUATRON - Watches - Bulova Corp.

AQUATRONICS - Pet products - Aquatronics-Filtronics

AQUATROX - Adhesives and sealants - Advance Cleaning Products Inc.

AQUATRU - Aquarium accessories - Kordon

AQUATTRACT - Chemical preparations - International Flavors & Fragrances Inc.

AQUATUBE - Toys - Rapco

AQUATUBES - Orthopedic products - Smith & Nephew Inc. (Rehabilitation Div.)

AQUATWILL - Raincoats - Tomen Apparel Group Inc.

AQUAUDIO - Recording label - Dennis Kraynik

AQUAVAC 42 - Water heaters–household - Aquavac

AQUAVANTAGE - Cleaning preparations - Brulin & Co., Inc.

AQUAVAR - Paints ☆ - Cowman-Campbell Paint Co.

AQUAVELVET - Paints - Benjamin Moore & Co.

AQUAVERT - Degreasing solvents - Detrex Corp.

AQUAVISION - Aquariums–household - Midwest Tropical Inc.

AQUAVISIONS - Pet products - Blue Ribbon Pet Products, Inc.

AQUAVISTA AV - Water–bottled or canned - Fremont Beverages Inc.

AQUAVITE - Pharmaceutical preparations - Armenpharm Ltd.

AQUAVITE - Vitamins and nutritional supplements - Great American Natural Products Inc.

AQUAVON - Drinking water ☆ - Aqua Systems Inc.

AQUAWELD - Cement - Dap Products Inc.

AQUAWIPE - Markers–felt-tip - Sakura of America

AQUAWOOL - Crocheted and knitted items ☆ - Puritan Sportswear Corp.

AQUAYUMS - Pet products - Ocean Nutrition Corp.

AQUAZ - Skin care products - Minnesota Mining & Manufacturing Co.

AQUAZIDE - Pharmaceutical preparations ☆ - Roberts/Hauck Pharmaceuticals Inc.

AQUAZOL - Pharmaceutical preparations - Armenpharm Ltd.

AQUAZOLE - Pet products - Seachem Laboratories

AQUAZONE - Toys–erector sets - Lego Systems Inc.

AQUAZYME - Pet products - Tetra Sales USA

AQUEDUCT - Agricultural products - Aquatrols Corp. of America, Inc.

AQUEOUS - Footwear–athletic - Ryka, Inc.

AQUEPOXY 250 - Epoxy coatings - Edison Coatings, Inc.

AQUEST - Pharmaceutical preparations ☆ - C.O. Truxton Inc.

AQUEX - Pharmaceutical preparations ☆ - Lunsco Inc.

AQUIA - Skin care products - Skyline Northwest Corp.

AQUIESSENCE - Skin care products - Redmond Products, Inc.

AQUIFER - Chemical preparations - Aqua-Aid, Inc.

AQUILA - Cabinets - Imperial Cabinet Co. Inc.

AQUILA - Cheese - Cerami Sales Co. Inc.

AQUILA - Food products - Victoria Packing Corp.

AQUILA - Hats - Aquila Inc.

AQUILA - Wines - Thackrey & Co.

AQUILA BIOPHARMACEUTICALS - Pharmaceutical preparations - Cambridge Biotech Corp.

AQUINAS - Floor coverings–tile ☆ - Fieldturf & Carpet Inc.

AQUIS - Fishing rods - L.L. Bean Inc.

AQUISTAR - Diagnostic apparatus - Instrumentation Northwest, Inc.

AQUO-MATIC - Swimming pools - Quiet Automatic Burner Corp.

AQUPOND - Pet products ☆ - Sera Aquaristik USA Inc.

AQUQPOXY - Paints - Triangle Coatings Inc.

AQUUS - Bathtubs–enameled ☆ - Lasco Products Group

AQWESINE - Pharmaceutical preparations ☆ - Wesley Pharmacal Co. Inc.

AR - Adhesives and sealants - C-Cure Corp.

AR - Amplifiers–radio - Amplifier Research Corp.

AR - Audio equipment - Teledyne Acoustic Research

AR - Figurines - Another Rainbow, Inc.

AR - Filaments–electric lamps - Energy Beam Sciences Inc.

A.R. - Pharmaceutical preparations - Medco Lab Inc.

AR - Screws - Aerospace Rivet Manufacturers Corp.

AR - Sporting goods - Ark-Rod, Inc.

AR 1 - Tires - Bridgestone/Firestone, Inc.

AR 2 - Tires - Bridgestone/Firestone, Inc.

AR-5 - Measuring instruments - Acu-Rite Inc.

AR-7 EXPLORER - Guns - Charter Arms

AR-10 PLUS - Measuring instruments - Acu-Rite Inc.

AR (ACOUSTIC RESEARCH) - Audio equipment - Recoton Corp.

AR/DI - Ophthalmic goods - Volk Optical, Inc.

AR-DOLL - Dolls - Standard Doll Co.

AR-DOLLETTE - Dolls - Standard Doll Co.

AR-EX - Cosmetics - Ar-Ex Ltd.

AR-JAY - Toy trucks - Ar-Jay Sales Co.

AR-KAY - Food products - Home Style Foods Inc.

AR KLEEN - Ophthalmic goods - Amcon Laboratories, Inc.

AR LIMITED - Audio equipment - International Jensen Inc.

AR-M-PAC - Veterinary pharmaceutical preparations - Schering Corp.

AR PLUS - Medical apparatus - Caliber Medical Corp.

AR-TIK - Electronic equipment - Arion Corp.

AR.1000 - Exercising equipment - Nautilus Acquisition Inc.

AR2000 - Bostik Inc.

ARA: EPI-GUIDE - Dental compounds - THM Biomedical, Inc.

ARA-SHIELD - Fabrics - Southern Mills Inc.

ARA-Z LAVASH - Breads - Ara-Z Inc.

ARAB-ISRAELI WARS - Games ☆ - Avalon Hill Game Co.

ARABAN - Coffee - Araban Coffee Co. Inc.

ARABEL - Window coverings - Vertical Blind Factory

ARABEL - Window shades - Vertical Designs Inc.

ARABELLA - Floor coverings–carpet and rugs - Queen Carpet Corp.

ARABESQUE - Artists' materials - Stangren Co.

ARABESQUE - Christmas tree ornaments ☆ - Cracker Box Inc.

ARABESQUE - Dinnerware–glass ☆ - Nikko Ceramics Inc.

ARABESQUE - Floor coverings ☆ - Congoleum Corp.

ARABESQUE - Floor coverings–carpet and rugs - Philadelphia Carpets

ARABESQUE - Floor coverings–carpet and rugs ☆ - Customweave Carpets Inc.

ARABESQUE - Glassware–household ☆ - Denby USA Limited

ARABESQUE - Hardware ☆ - Ballack Corp.

ARABESQUE - House furnishings ☆ - Burwood Products Co.

ARABESQUE - Kitchenware–earthenware ☆ - Arita Sales Co. Inc.

ARABESQUE - Publisher's imprints - Kensington Publishing Corp.

ARABESQUE - Recording label - Arabesque Recording

ARABESQUE - Recording label - Rebot Corp.

ARABESQUE - Rings–jewelry - Artcarved Inc.

ARABESQUE - Tiles–ceramic - Monarch Tile Inc.

ARABESQUE - Toilets–enameled - Kohler Co.

ARABESQUE - Wallpaper - Koroseal Wallcoverings

ARABESQUE - Wallpaper - Bill Villetto Designs Inc.

ARABIAN - Boats–motor - Century Boat Co.

ARABIAN KNIGHTS - Publisher's imprints - Hard Hat Records

ARABIAN LIGHTS - Cosmetics - Madeleine Mono Ltd.

ARABIAN NIGHTS - Christmas tree ornaments ☆ - Cracker Box Inc.

ARABIAN NIGHTS - Fabrics–linen - West Point-Pepperell Inc.

ARABICA COFFEE - Coffee - Barrington Coffee Roasting Co., Inc.

ARACHNOROD - Toys–automobiles - Mattel, Inc.

ARACOM - Rope - Yale Cordage, Inc.

ARAFLEX - Fabrics - Second Chance Body Armor, Inc.

ARAFLO - Fabrics - Lion Apparel, Inc.

ARAG - Adhesives and sealants - ViewSonic Corp.

ARAGANCE - Health care products - Saxony Products Inc.

ARAGLIN - Glassware–household - Waterford Wedgewood USA, Inc.

ARAGON - Audio equipment - Mondial Designs Ltd.

ARAGON - Axles–motor vehicle - Aragon Engineering, Inc.

ARAGON - Dinnerware–glass - Franciscan by Johnson Brothers, USA, Inc.

ARAGON - Floor coverings–carpet and rugs - Hollytex Carpet Mills Inc.

ARAGON - Tableware–china - Villeroy and Boch Tableware Ltd.

ARAGOSTA - Dishes–china - Pasmantier Co. Inc.

ARAK - Floor coverings–carpet and rugs - Orian Rugs Inc.

ARAK EL-DALIA - Beverages–alcohol - Black Prince Distillery, Inc.

ARAK RAZZOUK - Alcoholic beverage - Austin, Nichols & Co., Inc.

ARAL - Floor coverings–carpet and rugs ☆ - Trans-Ocean Import Co. Inc.

ARALEN - Pharmaceutical preparations - Winthrop Pharmaceuticals

ARALIA - Exercise programs - Northern Telecom, Inc.

ARALIA - Furniture - Tropitone Furniture Co. Inc.

ARALINE - Panty hose - Arrowood Mills Inc.

ARAMARK - Apparel and accessories - Ara Group, Inc.

ARAMARK - Apparel and accessories - Aramark Corp.

ARAMAX - Automotive parts and accessories - Dayco Products, Inc.

ARAMID-SHIELD - Safety products - Top-Line USA Inc.

ARAMINE - Pharmaceutical preparations - Merck & Co., Inc. (Merck Research Laboratories)

ARAMIS - Cosmetics - Aramis Inc.

ARAMIS 900 - Colognes - Aramis Inc.

ARAMIS A+ - Skin care products - Aramis Inc.

ARAMIS DIRECT BENEFITS - Skin care products - Aramis Inc.

ARAMIS LAB SERIES - Skin care products - Aramis Inc.

ARANCIATA - Beverages - San Pellegrino USA

ARANDAS - Beverages–alcohol - Hiram Walker & Sons, Inc.

ARANGO - Tobacco products - Arangold Corp.

ARANJUEZ - Guitars - Juan Orozco Corp.

ARAPAHO - Knives–pocket ☆ - W.R. Case & Sons Cutlery Co.

ARAPAHO TRADING COMPANY - Apparel and accessories - Hawe Yue Inc.

ARAPAHOE - Tiles–ceramic - Monarch Tile Inc.

ARARAT - Brandy - Monsieur Henri Wines Ltd.

ARASCO - Pharmaceutical preparations - Martek Corp.

ARATEX - Vegetable oil - Indopco, Inc.

ARAUCANA COLORS - Paints - Time Publishing Ventures Inc.

ARAX - Pliers, wrenches, vises, hammers, etc. - Intercontinental Machinery Co.

ARAX - Solder - Multicore Solders

ARAZZO - Floor coverings–carpet and rugs - Patcraft Mills Inc.

ARB - Musical instrument accessories - Remle Musical Products Inc.

A.R.B. DESIGN - Apparel–women's - A.R.B., Inc.

ARBEE BARS - Confections - Arbee Fine Foods Imports

ARBELOS - Electronic equipment - Monolith Technologies Corp.

ARBELOS SOUND - Electronic equipment - Monolith Technologies Corp.

ARBISI'S - Salad dressings–bottled - Ar-B-C's, Inc.

ARBITOR - Goggles–safety - Ektelon

ARBITRON RSVP - Computer software - The Arbitron Co.

ARBOGA - Marine rigging ☆ - Hyde Products Inc.

ARBOGAST - Fishing lures - Fred Arbogast Co. Inc.

ARBOGASTER - Fishing lures - Fred Arbogast Co. Inc.

ARBOLITO - Knives–hunting - Boker USA Inc.

ARBON - Health care products ☆ - Forest Pharmaceuticals Inc.

ARBOR - Computer software - Arbor Software Corp.

ARBOR - Dinnerware–glass ☆ - Johnson Brothers, USA, Inc.

ARBOR - Floor coverings–carpet and rugs ☆ - Regal Rugs Inc.

ARBOR - Food products - California-Omega Foods Inc.

ARBOR - Footcare products - Washington Homeopathic Products

ARBOR - Guitars - Midco International

ARBOR - Lumber ☆ - Georgia-Pacific Corp.

ARBOR & CONSERVATORY - Housewares - Wilton Co.

ARBOR BLOSSOMS - Glassware–household ☆ - Fenton Art Glass Co.

ARBOR CREST - Wines - Arbor Crest Wine Cellars

ARBOR GATE - Floor coverings–carpet and rugs - Karastan-Bigelow Inc.

ARBOR GOLD - Rope - Columbian Rope Co.

ARBOR HILL - Jams and jellies - Arbor Hill Associates, Inc.

ARBOR LANE - Garden equipment - Garden Pals, Inc.

ARBOR LOVE - Rings–jewelry - Artcarved Inc.

ARBOR MIST - Beverages–alcohol - Canandaigua Wine Co. Inc.

ARBOR OAK - Furniture - Singer Furniture Co.

ARBOR OAK - Lumber ☆ - Georgia-Pacific Corp.

ARBOR RIDGE - Wallpaper - Gagne Wallcovering, Inc.

ARBOR ROAD - Floor coverings - Armstrong World Industries, Inc.

ARBOR SNOWBOARDS - Snowboards - Arbor Snowboards

ARBOR SPRINGS - Water–bottled or canned - Arbor Springs Water Co. Inc.

ARBOR TERRACE - Manufactured homes - Redman Industries, Inc.

ARBORESQUE - Dishes–china - Taylor, Smith & Taylor Co.

ARBORETUM - Cosmetics - Starbased Technologies Inc.

ARBORETUM - Flowers, plants, and seeds - Mangelsdorf Seed Co.

ARBORGOLD SOFTWARE - Computer software - Tree Management Systems

ARBORGROW - Fertilizers - Agway Country Foods Inc.

ARBORIA - Trellises - L.W.O. Corp.

ARBORTAPE - Tape–adhesive - Neptco Inc.

ARBORVINE - Tableware–china - Pfaltzgraff Investment Co.

ARBORWARE - Computer software - M. Smith & Associates

ARBOUR PARK - Floor coverings ☆ - Armstrong World Industries, Inc.

ARBOUR TERRACE - Floor coverings - Congoleum Corp.

ARBUTIN - Pharmaceutical preparations - City Chemical Corp.

ARBY - Fishing lures ☆ - Fred Arbogast Co. Inc.

ARBY'S - Barbecue sauce ☆ - Golden Specialty Foods Inc.

A.R.C. - Motoman, Inc.

ARC - Audio equipment - Shahinian Acoustics Ltd.

ARC - Boats–kayaks - Phoenix Products Inc.

ARC - Building materials - Gerald D. Myers

ARC - Filing cabinets–metal - ACME Design Technology

ARC - Glassware–household - Durand International

ARC - Hair care products - KMS Research Inc.

ARC - Motor vehicle parts and accessories - Morse Controls

ARC - Pet products - Decker Manufacturing Co.

ARC - Pharmaceutical preparations - International Enzymes, Inc.

ARC - Recording label - Rashid Sales Co.

ARC - Recording label ☆ - Spina Music

ARC - Sporting goods ☆ - Prince Sports Group, Inc.

ARC COM - Fabrics - Arc-Com Fabrics, Inc.

ARC-COM - Window coverings - Covoc Corp.

ARC DETECT - Electronic equipment - Contemporary Control Systems, Inc.

ARC EYE - Motoman, Inc.

ARC INTERNATIONAL - Musical instruments ☆ - Jackman Music Corp.

ARC-MAX - Computer software - Interscan Corp.

ARC-T SYSTEM - Surgical supplies - Chiron Corp.

ARC TUBE - Metals - Form Rite Corp.

ARCA-SWISS - Cameras - Tekno Inc.

ARCABALENI - Hair care products - Lipid Technologies, Inc.

ARCACHON - Wines - Oak Knoll Winery Inc.

ARCADA - Computer software - Conner Peripherals, Inc.

ARCADE - Cabinets - Classic Bath Products

ARCADE - Cleaning preparations–household - Brite-House Co.

ARCADE - Floor coverings - Mannington Resilient Floors

ARCADE - Floor coverings–carpet and rugs - Johnson's Carpets Inc.

ARCADE - Floor coverings–carpet and rugs - Trend Carpet

ARCADE - Floor coverings–carpet and rugs ☆ - Blue Ridge Carpet Mills

ARCADE - Furniture ☆ - Bassett Furniture Industries, Inc.

ARCADE - Glassware–household - Durand International

ARCADE - Novelty items - Beistle Co.

ARCADE - Publisher's imprints - Arcade Publishing Inc.

☆ = Now out of production

ARCADE - Recording label - Arcade Record Co./Arzee Record Co.
ARCADE - Video games - Hasbro, Inc.
ARCADE - Wainscotting - Georgia-Pacific Corp.
ARCADE - Wallpaper - Carlton-Metro Wallcoverings
ARCADE POKER - Computer software - Robert L. Nicolai
ARCADE POWERWEAR MJK - Apparel and accessories - Oxford Industries, Inc.
ARCADE TIME & FUN - Toys–electronic - Video Technology U.S. Inc.
ARCADE TOYS - Toys - Valu-Cast Products, Inc.
ARCADIA - Cabinets - Sunny Wood Products Co. Inc.
ARCADIA - Construction equipment - Alcan Aluminum Corp. Alcan Building Products Div.
ARCADIA - Dinnerware–glass - Royal China & Porcelain Companies Inc.
ARCADIA - Doors–glass - Robertson-Ceco Corp.
ARCADIA - Doors–glass - Therma-Tru Corp.
ARCADIA - Fabrics - Gretchen Bellinger Inc.
ARCADIA - Flatware - Wallace International Silversmiths, Inc.
ARCADIA - Floor coverings–carpet and rugs - Trans-Ocean Import Co. Inc.
ARCADIA - Flowers, plants, and seeds - Jacklin Seed
ARCADIA - Furniture - Henredon Furniture Industries Inc.
ARCADIA - Furniture ✩ - Landes Manufacturing Co.
ARCADIA - Furniture ✩ - Lane Co. Inc.
ARCADIA - Guitars ✩ - Grossman Music Corp.
ARCADIA - Lighting fixtures - Holophane Corp.
ARCADIA - Pencils - Empire Berol USA
ARCADIA - Rings–jewelry - Artcarved Inc.
ARCADIA - Trailers–travel ✩ - Fleetwood Enterprises, Inc.
ARCADIA - Wallpaper ✩ - Osborne & Little
ARCADIA - Water–bottled or canned ✩ - Arcadia Farms Inc.
ARCADIA - Wines - Stag's Leap Wine Cellars
ARCADIA - Wines - Wildhurst Winery
ARCADIAN - China cabinets–wood - C.H. Stuart & Co. Inc.
ARCADIAN - Fertilizers - Hartwell Brothers Handle Co.
ARCADIAN - Video games - KBM Enterprises, Inc.
ARCADIAN - Water colors ✩ - Binney & Smith Inc.
ARCALTITUDE - Sporting goods - Dana Design Ltd.
ARCANO - Cameras–video - Good Times Home Video Corp.
ARCARE - Tape–adhesive - Adhesives Research, Inc.
ARCAS ISLAND - Seafood products–fresh or frozen - Meridian Products
ARCEE - Watches - Frontier Incentive Business Corp.
ARCENCIEL - Paints–artists' - New York Central Art Supply Co.
ARCET - Pharmaceutical preparations - Econo Med Pharmaceuticals Inc.
ARCFLEX - Backpacks - Dana Design Ltd.
ARCGATE - Computer software - Arcsys, Inc.
ARCH - Pillows - Arch Associates, Inc.
ARCH BRIDGE - Footwear - Prince Manufacturing Inc.
ARCH CROWN - Labels–paper - Arch Crown Inc.
ARCH DARTS - Games - Mark Tuzinsky
ARCH-DECO - Christmas tree lights - Continental Lighting Ind., Inc.
ARCH-EASE - Shoe accessories - Professional Foot Care Products Inc.
ARCH-LOK - Bicycle parts and accessories - Sunshine U-Lok Corp.
ARCH MADNESS - Apparel and accessories - Missouri Valley Conference
ARCH MATE - Massage products - Remington Products Co.
ARCH RING - Binders - Dennison National Co.
ARCHAEOGRAPHICS BY WILL MCGEER - Frames–picture - Distinctive Design
ARCHANGEL - Books–comic ✩ - Marvel Entertainment Group, Inc.
ARCHEO - Faucets - Kallista Inc.
ARCHEO PRINTS - Shirts - Marilu Jibaja
ARCHER - Adhesives and sealants - A.W. Archer Co. Inc.
ARCHER - Bicycles - Ross Bicycles USA, Ltd.
ARCHER - Electronic equipment - Tandy Corp.
ARCHER - Hosiery ✩ - Signal Knitwear Co.
ARCHER - Lubricants - Witco World Headquarters
ARCHER - Novelty items - Archer Worldwide
ARCHER - Paper–gift wrap ✩ - Plus Mark Inc.
ARCHER - Shirts - Cluett, Peabody & Co.
ARCHER ACE - Computer software - Cybergraham Interactive, Inc.
ARCHER II - Aircraft - New Piper Aircraft, Inc.
ARCHER ROAD PATROL - Radios - Tandy Corp.
ARCHER SPACE PATROL - Radios - Tandy Corp.
ARCHERKIT - Electronic equipment - Tandy Corp.
ARCHEROTOR - Electronic equipment - Tandy Corp.
ARCHERY - Fruits and vegetables - Goodell Packing Corp.
ARCHES - Paper - Canson-Talens Inc.
ARCHES - Wedding set - Oldcastle Associates Inc.

ARCHES FIELD WATERCOLOR BOOKS - Notebooks and notepads - Canson-Talens Inc.
ARCHES PORTFOLIO - Paper - Canson-Talens Inc.
ARCHETYPE RECORDS - Compact discs–prerecorded - Archetype Records, Inc.
ARCHETYPE, THE - Lighting fixtures - Kim Lighting Inc.
ARCHGAUGE - Exchangers–heat - Archxerciser Corp.
ARCHGEN - Computer software - C.A.E. Plus, Inc.
ARCHIBALD BROS. - Beverages–carbonated - Archibald Bros. Fine Beverages, Inc.
ARCHIBALD CAMPBELL - Posters ✩ - One-of-a-Kind Workshop
ARCHIBALD KNOX-PAPERS - Wallpaper - Christopher Hyland
ARCHIDEK - Trading cards and stamps - Greenway Communications, Llc.
ARCHIE COLLECTION - Belts - Bobtron International Inc.
ARCHIE COMICS - Postcards ✩ - Classico San Francisco Inc.
ARCHIE COMICS & DIGEST MAGAZINES - Archie Comic Publications Inc.
ARCHIE EYEWEAR - Eyeglasses - Windsor Optical Inc.
ARCHIE MOORE'S - Food products - Archie Moore's Foods Inc.
ARCHIES - Prerecorded audio/video tapes - Archie Comic Publications Inc.
ARCHIFOLD - Drapery hardware - Kirsch Co.
ARCHIMEDEAN DYNASTY - Computer software - Blue Byte Software, Inc.
ARCHIMEDIA - Computer software - CKI Inc.
ARCHIPELAGOS - Computer software - Compton's NewMedia
ARCHITALK - Computer software - Wygant Scientific, Inc.
ARCHITECT - Audio equipment - Sanyo Fisher (USA) Corp.
ARCHITECT - Drafting supplies - Martin Universal Design Inc.
ARCHITECT - Floor coverings ✩ - Congoleum Corp.
ARCHITECT - Safety glasses - Crews, Inc.
ARCHITECT 70 - Shingles–asphalt or tar ✩ - Bird Inc.
ARCHITECT 80 - Shingles–asphalt or tar ✩ - GS Roofing Products Co.
ARCHITECT 80'S - Shingles–asphalt or tar ✩ - Globe Building Materials Inc.
ARCHITECT MARK 25 - Shingles–asphalt or tar ✩ - Bird Inc.
ARCHITECT, THE - Electronic equipment - AudioControl
ARCHITECTONIC - Shutters–wood - Pinecrest, Inc.
ARCHITECT'S CHOICE - Floor coverings - Mannington Resilient Floors
ARCHITECT'S CHOICE - Floor coverings–carpet and rugs - Olympic Carpets Inc.
ARCHITECTS FOR HUMAN RESILIENCE - Video production - O.D. Resources, Inc.
ARCHITECTURAL - Floor coverings–tile - Tarkett, Inc.
ARCHITECTURAL - Paints ✩ - McCloskey Corp.
ARCHITECTURAL ACCENTS - Floor coverings–tile ✩ - Kentile Floors Inc.
ARCHITECTURAL BORDERS - Wallpaper - Robert Crowder & Co.
ARCHITECTURAL CONSERVATORIES - Roofing materials - Texas Aluminum Industries Inc.
ARCHITECTURAL CRITERION - Floor coverings - Kentile Floors Inc.
ARCHITECTURAL CUTTERS - Tools - LRH Enterprises Inc.
ARCHITECTURAL DETAILS - Wallpaper - Sterling Prints
ARCHITECTURAL EFFECTS - Wallpaper - Manuscreens
ARCHITECTURAL ENHANCEMENTS - Moldings and trim - R & R Woodworking
ARCHITECTURAL FOLD - Window shades - Protech Shading Inc.
ARCHITECTURAL FOREST ENTERPRISES - Wood products - Architectural Forest Enterprises
ARCHITECTURAL POLE SYSTEM - Shelving units–wood - Naomi Gale Wall Systems
ARCHITECTURAL PORTFOLIO - Fabrics–tapestry ✩ - Coloroll Inc.
ARCHITECTURAL PRODUCT MASTER - Computer software - YKK Corp. of America
ARCHITECTURAL SERIES - Fireplace equipment - Design Specialties Inc.
ARCHITECTURAL SERIES - Floor coverings–tile ✩ - Kentile Floors Inc.
ARCHITECTURAL STYLIST - Fabrics–tapestry ✩ - Coloroll Inc.
ARCHITECTURAL TAMBOUR - Wallpaper - National Products Inc.
ARCHITECTURAL, THE - Lighting fixtures - Crystal Clear Importing Co. Inc.
ARCHITECTURAL THRU-CHIP - Floor coverings - Tarkett, Inc.
ARCHITECTURALE - Floor coverings–carpet and rugs ✩ - Karastan-Bigelow Inc.
ARCHITECTURALLY YOURS - Cabinets–metal - Horizon Steel Products Inc.
ARCHITECTURE - Bedding–linen - Dan River Inc.
ARCHITECTURE - Wallcoverings - Flexcell Wallcoverings
ARCHITEK - Toys - Creatnetics
ARCHITENT - Fabrics - Astrup Co.
ARCHITENT - Fabrics–coated - Herculite Products, Inc.
ARCHITERRA - Paints ✩ - Parks Corp.
ARCHITEXT - Computer software - Architext, Inc.
ARCHITEXTURE - Fabrics - Valley Forge Fabrics Inc.

ARCHITEXTURE - Hair care products - Logics International
ARCHITEXTURES - Floor coverings - Mannington Resilient Floors
ARCHITEXTURES - Wallpaper - Capital Carousel Inc.
ARCHITEXTURES GEO - Floor coverings - Mannington Resilient Floors
ARCHITRAC - Drapery hardware - Kirsch Co.
ARCHITRAVE - Furniture - J. Kenneth Zahn
ARCHITUTUAL COATINGS - Adhesives and sealants - Mac-O-Lac Paints Inc.
ARCHITYPES - Lithographs - Cappelano Design Co.
ARCHIVAL CLEANING SYSTEM, THE - Cleaning preparations - Photographic
  Solutions, Inc.
ARCHIVAL COMPANY, THE - Boxes–corrugated paperboard - University
  Products, Inc.
ARCHIVAL MOUNT - Electronic equipment - Seal Products Inc.
ARCHIVAL NON-CRACKING ARTIST OILS - Paints–artists' - Chroma
  Acrylics Inc.
ARCHIVE - Recording label - Polygram Records, Inc.
ARCHIVE LIBRARIAN - Computer software - Digital Technology International
ARCHIVE LINENS - Mat boards - Archive Paper Co.
ARCHIVE OF FOLK & JAZZ MUSIC - Recording label - Everest Record Group
ARCHIVE OF PIANO MUSIC - Recording label - Everest Record Group
ARCHIVE QUARRY STONE - Mat boards - Archive Paper Co.
ARCHIVE SILKS - Mat boards - Archive Paper Co.
ARCHIVE ST - Computer peripheral equipment - Archive Corp.
ARCHIVE SUEDE - Mat boards - Archive Paper Co.
ARCHIVES - Fabrics - Piedmont Collections
ARCHIVES - Floor coverings–carpet and rugs - Atlas Carpet Mills Inc.
ARCHIVES - Floor coverings–carpet and rugs ☆ - Patcraft Mills Inc.
ARCHIVES - Lighting fixtures ☆ - Thomas Industries Inc.
ARCHIVES - Music–sheet - J. D'Addario & Co. Inc.
ARCHIVES NEUTRALS - Floor coverings–carpet and rugs - Atlas Carpet Mills
  Inc.
ARCHLITE - Doors–glass - Therma-Tru Corp.
ARCHMATES - Shoe insoles - Benchmark Brands
ARCHON - Computer software ☆ - Electronic Arts Inc.
ARCHON - Measuring instruments - Dynatech Precision Sampling Corp.
ARCHON BOOKS - Publisher's imprints - Shoe String Press Inc.
ARCHON II: ADEPT - Computer software ☆ - Electronic Arts Inc.
ARCHRON - Clocks - Niobrara
ARCHTONE - Guitars, etc ☆ - International Music Corp.
ARCHTRUSS - Brackets - Western Support Systems
ARCHWAY - Computer software - Centec Corp.
ARCHWAY - Cookies - Archway Cookie Co.
ARCHWAY - Floor coverings–carpet and rugs - Atlas Carpet Mills Inc.
ARCHWAY - Publisher's imprints - Simon & Schuster, Inc.
ARCHWAY CLASSIC - Cookies ☆ - Archway Cookie Inc.
ARCHWAY HOMESTYLE - Cookies - Archway Cookie Inc.
ARCIN - Analgesics - Pharmex Inc.
ARCLAD - Tape–adhesive - Adhesives Research, Inc.
ARCLAND - Computer software - Arcland Inc.
ARCLIGHT - Backpacks - Dana Design Ltd.
ARCLITE - Lighting fixtures - Edison Price Lighting
ARCM CORP. AUTOMATIC REMOTE CONTROL MIRROR - Remote control
  devices - Arcm Corp.
ARCO - Charcoal - Atlantic Richfield Co.
ARCO - Coffee - Andresen-Ryan Coffee Co.
ARCO - Lumber - Arcata Redwood Co.
ARCO - Marine rigging - Alexander-Roberts Co.
ARCO - Mirrors - Capitol Novelty Co.
ARCO - Office supplies ☆ - Faber-Castell Corp.
ARCO - Oils–lubricating - Lyondell Petrochemical Co.
ARCO - Pencils - Empire Berol USA
ARCO - Publisher's imprints - Simon & Schuster, Inc.
ARCO - Ribbons and carbons - American Ribbon & Carbon Co.
ARCO - Tools–power-driven - Arco Products Corp.
ARCO - Vitamins and nutritional supplements - Nature's Bounty, Inc.
ARCO - Watches ☆ - Aristo Import Co. Inc.
ARCO-CEE - Health care products - Nature's Bounty, Inc.
ARCO COFFEE - Coffee - Andresen-Ryan Coffee Co.
ARCO-EE - Health care products - Nature's Bounty, Inc.
ARCO-FLEX - Tape–adhesive - Arcon Coating Mills Inc.
ARCO GOLD - Tableware–china ☆ - Villeroy and Boch Tableware Ltd.
ARCO-LASE - Antacids - Nature's Bounty, Inc.
ARCO-LITH - Carbon-paper ribbons - American Ribbon & Carbon Co.
ARCO POWDER - Jewelry - Arco Powder, Inc.
ARCO STARTING & CHARGING SPECIALISTS - Generators/motors and
  starters - Arco Starting and Charging Specialists

ARCO-USA - Winches - Alexander-Roberts Co.
ARCO WEISS - Tableware–china - Villeroy and Boch Tableware Ltd.
ARCOAIRE - Heating and cooling systems - Inter-City Products Corp. (USA)
ARCOBALENO - Toys - Learning Materials Workshop
ARCOBALENO - Wallpaper ☆ - Blumenthal
ARCOBEE - Pharmaceutical preparations - Nature's Bounty, Inc.
ARCOFLAM - Cooking equipment–household - Durand International
ARCOFLEET - Oils–lubricating - Lyondell Petrochemical Co.
ARCOGRAPHITE - Oils–lubricating - Lyondell Petrochemical Co.
ARCOM - Circuit boards–printed - Arcom Control Systems, Inc.
ARCOM - Communications equipment - Arrow Communication Laboratories,
  Inc.
ARCOMAGICO - Brassieres (Bras) - Playtex Apparel, Inc.
ARCOPAL - Dinnerware–glass - Durand International
ARCOPEDICO - Footwear ☆ - Conjac Inc.
ARCOR - Confections - R.L. Albert & Son, Inc.
ARCORET - Pharmaceutical preparations - Nature's Bounty, Inc.
ARCOROC - Glassware–household - Durand International
ARCOSET PRINTER - Labeling machinery - Archon Co.
ARCOSUPREME - Oils–lubricating - Lyondell Petrochemical Co.
ARCOTEX - Gloves–rubber ☆ - Capitol Novelty Co.
ARCOTINIC - Pharmaceutical preparations - Nature's Bounty, Inc.
ARCSAFE - Tools - EOA Systems, Inc.
ARCSEAL - Fittings–cast iron - Aeroquip Corp.
ARCSOLO - Computer software - Cheyenne Software, Inc.
ARCSTREAM - Lamps - General Electric Co.
ARCTEA - Brushes–paint ☆ - Winsor & Newton
ARCTI-COOL - Building materials - Yancey Co.
ARCTIC - Flatware ☆ - Towle Silversmiths
ARCTIC - Floor coverings–tile - ECC International
ARCTIC - Recording label - Universal Record
ARCTIC - Rope - Wellington Leisure Products, Inc.
ARCTIC - Snow tools - Cotter & Co.
ARCTIC - Thread - Threads USA Div.
ARCTIC - Underwear and nightwear - Woods
ARCTIC ADVENTURE - Apparel and accessories - Tricraft Groups Ltd.
ARCTIC AIR - Refrigerators - Broich Enterprises, Inc.
ARCTIC AIRE - Fans–electric ☆ - Fasco Industries Inc. (Consumer Products
  Div.)
ARCTIC ALGAE - Hair care products - Barbara Salomone & Associates, Inc.
ARCTIC ANTICS - Figurines ☆ - Schmid Inc.
ARCTIC AVENGER - Motor vehicle parts and accessories - J. Thomas
  Distributors, Inc.
ARCTIC BEACH - Coats–men's - Custom Furs, Inc.
ARCTIC BLAST - Fruit pops–frozen - Oberlin Farms Dairy Inc.
ARCTIC BLAST - Snack foods - J & J Snack Foods Corp.
ARCTIC BLOOM COLLECTION - Giftware - Lenox, Inc.
ARCTIC CAPE - Fish–fresh or frozen ☆ - Frionor USA Inc.
ARCTIC CAT - Snowmobiles - Arctco, Inc.
ARCTIC CHERRY - Beverages - Refreshments International
ARCTIC CHILLER - Beverages–alcohol - Sierra Wine Corp.
ARCTIC CIRCLE - Electrical equipment - Adobe Air Inc.
ARCTIC CLEAR - Water purification systems - Arctic Clear Products, Inc.
ARCTIC COLADA - Beverages - Refreshments International
ARCTIC COOLER - Milk - Clovervale Foods, Inc.
ARCTIC-COR - Extension cords - General Cable Corp.
ARCTIC DAWN - Food product - Interocean Inc.
ARCTIC DELIGHT - Food product - Interocean Inc.
ARCTIC D'LITES - Ice cream - Weight Watchers International, Inc.
ARCTIC DOWN - Bedding–linen - Hollander Home Fashions Inc.
ARCTIC DREAMS - Fabrics ☆ - VIP/VIP Crafts
ARCTIC EXPRESS - Apparel and accessories - Tri-North Department Stores,
  Inc.
ARCTIC FADEGUARD - Tape–adhesive - Chief Supply Corp.
ARCTIC-FILL - Fibers–synthetic - Nirock International Inc.
ARCTIC FLEECE - Archery equipment - Martin Archery Inc.
ARCTIC FLEECE - Fabrics - B.W. Harris Manufacturing Co.
ARCTIC-FLEX - Electrical equipment - Bicc Cables Corp.
ARCTIC-FLEX - Gloves - Southern Glove Manufacturing Co., Inc.
ARCTIC FLOW - Containers–plastic - Packaging Products Corp.
ARCTIC FORMULA - Sealing compounds ☆ - Ultraseal International Inc.
ARCTIC FOX - Measuring instruments - Arctic Fox Heaters, Inc.
ARCTIC FREEZE - Frozen foods - J & J Snack Foods Corp.
ARCTIC FRESH - Codfish–smoked, salted, dried, or pickled - Royal Seafoods
  Inc.
ARCTIC FROSTING - Frosting - H.C. Brill Co., Inc.

☆ = Now out of production

ARCTIC GOLD - Seafood products–fresh or frozen - Coast to Coast Seafood Inc.

ARCTIC GUARD - Antifreeze - Hi-Lex Corp.

ARCTIC HARVEST - Seafood products–fresh or frozen - US Foodservice

ARCTIC ICE - Ice - Arctic Ice

ARCTIC ICE - Seafood products–fresh or frozen - Arctic Alaska Fisheries Corp.

ARCTIC ICE EAGLE - Sporting goods ☆ - Wright & McGill Co.

ARCTIC KING - Watches - Bulova Corp.

ARCTIC LEMON - Beverages - Refreshments International

ARCTIC LIGHTS - Cigarettes - Brown & Williamson Tobacco Corp.

ARCTIC LIGHTS - Glassware–household - Mikasa Licensing, Inc.

ARCTIC NIGHT - Dishes–china - Taylor, Smith & Taylor Co.

ARCTIC POWER - Generators–electric - Arctco, Inc.

ARCTIC SAN JAMAR - Housewares - Lake Geneva Spindustries, Inc.

ARCTIC-SEA - Vitamins and nutritional supplements - Aloe Vera of America, Inc.

ARCTIC SEAL - Waterproofing compounds - Herbert Malarkey Roofing Co.

ARCTIC SPURS - Sporting goods - Ack-Shun Lure

ARCTIC SQUEEZ - Bottles–plastic - Wawa Inc.

ARCTIC STAR - Ice cream - Allied Marketing, Inc.

ARCTIC STORM - Fireworks - L. W. Loyd Co., Inc.

ARCTIC STRAWBERRY - Beverages - Refreshments International

ARCTIC SUN - Beverages–carbonated - Faygo Beverages, Inc.

ARCTIC SWORD - Toys - LCD International

ARCTIC TERN - Ships–sailing vessels - Devlin Designing Boat Builders Inc.

ARCTIC-THERM - Underwear and nightwear - Jockey International, Inc.

ARCTIC TREATS - Food products - Land O'Lakes Inc.

ARCTIC-WRAP - Health care products ☆ - CAH Industries Inc.

ARCTIC ZONE - Apparel and accessories - Walls Industries, Inc.

ARCTIC ZONE - Food containers - Outer Circle Products, Ltd.

ARCTICA - Bicycles - Huffy Corp.

ARCTICFOX - Computer software - Electronic Arts Inc.

ARCTICICE - Laboratory apparatus - USA/Scientific Plastics, Inc.

ARCTICREEL - Fishing nets - Colorado Tent Co.

ARCTICWEAR - Apparel and accessories - Arctco, Inc.

ARCTICWELD - Cement - Genova Products Inc.

ARCTURUS - Publisher's imprints - Southern Illinois University Press

ARCTURUS - Telescopes ☆ - Steven Manufacturing Co.

ARCUATE - Exercising equipment - Pacific Fitness Corp.

ARCUATE - Exercising equipment - Stairmaster Sports/Medical Products, Inc.

ARCUISINE - Cooking equipment–household - Durand International

ARCUS - Computer peripheral equipment - Tech 101 Office Automation Inc.

ARCUS - Integrated circuits - Arcustech, Inc.

ARCUS ODYSSEY - Games - Sega of America, Inc.

ARCVIEW - Computer software - Environmental Systems Research Institute Inc.

ARCWORLD - Motoman, Inc.

ARCYLATE - Pharmaceutical preparations ☆ - Roberts/Hauck Pharmaceuticals Inc.

ARCYLIC - Pharmaceutical preparations ☆ - Jones Medical Industries, Inc. (Medical Div.)

A.R.D. - Surgical supplies - Birchwood Laboratories, Inc.

ARDA - Office supplies - Alvin and Co. Inc.

ARDAT - Computer peripheral equipment - Ardat Inc.

ARDCO - Furniture - Ard Manufacturing Co. Inc.

ARDCO - Giftware - H.T. Ardinger & Son Co.

ARDEBEN - Pharmaceutical preparations - Physician Sales & Service

ARDEC - Construction equipment ☆ - Showerlux USA

ARDECAINE - Pharmaceutical preparations - Physician Sales & Service

ARDEE - Floor coverings–carpet and rugs - Navan Carpets Inc.

ARDEE - Sinks–metal ☆ - Werner Co.

ARDEFEM - Pharmaceutical preparations - Physician Sales & Service

ARDELL - Cosmetics - American International Industries

ARDELL - Cosmetics - Ardell International Inc.

ARDELL - Jewelry - T. Sardelli and Sons Inc.

ARDELL - Lard - Armour Dairy Co.

ARDELL - Tools - Ardell Industries Inc.

ARDEN - Food products - Arden International Kitchens Inc.

ARDEN - Jewelry - Arden-Belmar

ARDEN - Watches - Bulova Corp.

ARDEN MARBLE - Floor coverings - Congoleum Corp.

ARDEN WOODS - Wines - Admiral Wine Merchants

ARDEN'S - Pharmaceutical preparations ☆ - P. & S. Laboratories Inc.

ARDEPRED - Pharmaceutical preparations - Physician Sales & Service

ARDERONE - Pharmaceutical preparations - Physician Sales & Service

ARDESIA - Floor coverings–tile ☆ - Monarch Tile Inc.

ARDESIA - Tiles–ceramic - KPT Inc.

ARDEX - Concrete resurfacing, acrylic mortars, etc ☆ - Ardex, Inc.

ARDEX - Vitamins and nutritional supplements - Archer Daniels Midland Co.

ARDEX FEATHER FINISH - Cement ☆ - Ardex, Inc.

ARDI - Computer software - Abacus Research and Development Inc.

ARDICO - Glassware–household - Edward P. Paul & Co. Inc.

ARDIOL - Pharmaceutical preparations - Physician Sales & Service

ARDIS - Augers - Ardisam, Inc.

ARDIS - Computer software - Ardis Co.

ARDIS BOOKS - Publisher's imprints - Ardis Publishers

ARDLEY - Bicycles - Columbia Manufacturing Inc.

ARDMAUISION - Deodorizers ☆ - Vaportek, Inc.

ARDMORE - Cabinets - Contempri Kitchens

ARDMORE - Clocks - General Time Corp. (Westclox/Seth Thomas Div.)

ARDMORE - Floor coverings - Armstrong World Industries, Inc.

ARDMORE - Glassware–household - Seneca Glass Co.

ARDMORE - Knitting machines - Colonial Corp. of America

ARDMORE - Prefabricated buildings–wood - Champion Enterprises Inc.

ARDMORE - Rings–jewelry - Artcarved

ARDMORE - Thread ☆ - SCT Yarns Inc.

ARDMORE - Watches ☆ - SMH (US) Inc.

ARDMORE FARMS - Juices - Ardmore Farms Inc.

ARDMORE STRIPE - Bedding–linen - Dan River Inc.

ARDO - Health care products ☆ - HNE Healthcare

ARDOL - Photographic equipment ☆ - GAF Corp.

ARDOR - Paper–bond - Georgia-Pacific Corp.

ARDOR - Pipes–tobacco - Mastercraft Pipes Inc.

ARDOX - Nails–horseshoe - National Nail Corp.

ARDOX SPIRAL - Nails–horseshoe - National Nail Corp.

ARDOX SPIRAL DECK - Nails–horseshoe - National Nail Corp.

ARDSLEY - Bird feeds ☆ - Hyde's Birdfeeder

ARDSLEY - Giftware - M & R Manufacturing Inc.

ARDSLEY - Musical instruments - Ardsley Musical Instrument Co.

ARDSLEY - Watches - Bulova Corp.

ARDSLEY WOW WOW - Musical instruments - Ardsley Musical Instrument Co.

ARDTARAIG - Salmon–smoked, salted, dried, or pickled ☆ - De Choix Specialty Foods Co.

ARDURA - Photographic equipment ☆ - GAF Corp.

ARDVAN - Pharmaceutical preparations - Organon Inc.

ARDYNE - Paint rollers - Arsco International Inc.

ARDYTH ARTS - Giftware - W.C. Bunting Co.

ARE - Automotive parts and accessories - Toppertown Inc.

ARE - Jewelers' findings - ARE Inc.

A.R.E. - Truck cabs - A.R.E. Inc.

ARE YOU TOO CHICKEN TO TRY LIPS? - Lip balms - Solaray

AREA - Cases–vanity - Area International, Inc.

AREA - Computer software - CB Commercial Holdings, Inc.

AREA 51 - Computer software - Atari Games Corp.

AREA 51 - Signs - 800 Trekker, Inc.

AREA GOLF - Computer software - Compuvision, Inc.

AREA II - Floor coverings–carpet and rugs - Coronet Carpets Inc.

AREA LOCATOR - Maps - Stanley Sanders

AREA SECURITY - Lighting fixtures ☆ - General Electric Co.

AREA SI TECHNOLOGIES - Musical instrument accessories - Mechanical Music Corp.

ARECOLINE - Pharmaceutical preparations - City Chemical Corp.

AREDIA - Pharmaceutical preparations - Ciba-Geigy Corp.

ARENA - Bathing suits - Arena USA Inc.

ARENA - Computer software - Arena Systems

ARENA - Computer software - Eidetics Corp.

ARENA - Furniture–metal - Krueger International, Inc.

ARENA - Publisher's imprints - Berkley Publishing Corp.

ARENA - Recording label - RCI Records

ARENA - Sporting goods ☆ - Swift Instruments, Inc.

ARENA - Windows–screen - MW Manufacturers, Inc.

ARENA DESIGN - Bathroom fixtures ☆ - Aqua Glass Corp.

ARENA DRAFT - Beverages–malt - CRB Co.

ARENA PUCK - Hockey equipment - Sun Hockey, Inc.

ARENDAL - Furniture–children's ☆ - Child Craft Industries Inc.

ARENDINE - Apparel–women's - Jeri-Jo Knitwear Inc.

ARENIX - Computer software - North Coast Logic, Inc.

ARENS - Boats ☆ - Federal Marine Motors Co.

AREO - Apparel–women's - Young Stuff Apparel Group

AREPA QUEEN - Breads - South American Delights, Inc.

AREPO - Computer software - Stone Type Foundry Inc.

☆ = Now out of production

ARES - Detergents - First Preference Products Corp.
ARES - Mats–rattan ☆ - Golden Star Inc.
ARES - Vases - Durand International
ARESDA - Wallpaper - Aresda Design Associates
ARETAE - Oils–essential - Redmond Products, Inc.
ARETAE DAILY ESSENTIAL - Hair care products - Redmond Products, Inc.
AREZZO - Jewelry - Arezzo Gold & Silver Jewelry Center
AREZZO GOLD - Jewelry - Arezzo Gold & Silver Jewelry Center
AREZZO JEWELRY - Jewelry - Arezzo Gold & Silver Jewelry Center
ARF - Communications equipment–mobile ☆ - A.R.F. Products Inc.
ARF ARF DOGGIE - Toys–stuffed - Trendmasters, Inc.
ARF SCARFS - Pet products ☆ - Precious Paws
ARFABET - Clothing - Jeb Biemiller
ARFANGO - Shoes - Footgear
ARFCO - Roofing materials - Arfco Products, Inc.
ARFONAD - Pharmaceutical preparations - Roche Laboratories
ARG-DRI - Cleaning equipment - J.V. Manufacturing Co., Inc.
ARGENION - Water purification systems - Marketers International Inc.
ARGENT - Lubricants - Third Coast Packaging, Inc.
ARGENTA - Handbags ☆ - Integrated Handbags
ARGENTAGE - Wines - Vinos USA, Inc.
ARGENTI - Faucets - Barclay Products Ltd.
ARGENTINE LIVER - Health care products - Above All Health Inc.
ARGESIC - Pharmaceutical preparations - Econo Med Pharmaceuticals Inc.
ARGESIC-SA - Pharmaceutical preparations - Econo Med Pharmaceuticals Inc.
ARGIANO - Wines - Frederick Wildman and Sons Ltd.
ARGILE BLANCHE - Soap - Nature de France
ARGILE ROSE - Soap - Nature de France
ARGILET - Soap - Nature de France
ARGILLA - Skin care products - Rene Furterer
ARGIMIEL - Soap - Nature de France
ARGINA - Lubricating oils - Shell Oil Co.
ARGININE/ORNITHINE CAPS - Vitamins and nutritional supplements - Vitamin Research Products Inc.
ARGINMAX - Vitamins and nutritional supplements - Wellness Beverage Co.
ARGIS - Computer software - Janus Technologies, Inc.
ARGITONI - Cheese - Arthur Schuman Inc.
ARGO - Apparel and accessories - American Argo Corp.
ARGO - Corn starch - CPC International Inc.
ARGO - Preserved foods–canned - Del Monte Corp.
ARGO - Recording label - London Records Inc.
ARGO BOOKS - Publisher's imprints ☆ - Maxwell/McMellan Inc.
ARGOGEL - Chemical preparations - Argonaut Technologies, Inc.
ARGOLD - Glass–leaded - Argold Inter Ltd.
ARGON - Camera ☆ - Saul Bower Inc.
ARGON - Eyeglasses ☆ - Cable Car Eyeware
ARGON PATHFINDER - Medical apparatus - Maxxim Medical Inc.
ARGONAUT - Computer hardware - Advanced Techsource
ARGONAUT - Fabrics - Glen Raven Mills Inc.
ARGONAUT - Floor coverings–tile - Burke Flooring Products
ARGONAUT - Swimming-pool pumps - ITT Marlow
ARGONAUT - Watches - Bulova Corp.
ARGONAUT TECHNOLOGIES - Chemical preparations - Argonaut Technologies, Inc.
ARGOS - Posters - Aegis Entertainment, Inc.
ARGOSY - Boats - Glen-L Marine Designs
ARGOSY - Cabinets - Imperial Cabinet Co. Inc.
ARGOSY - Hearing aids - Acoustic Devices Inc.
ARGOSY - Luggage - York Luggage Co.
ARGOSY - Rings–jewelry - Artcarved Inc.
ARGOSY - Seafood products–fresh or frozen - Meridian Products
ARGOSY - Seafood products–fresh or frozen - Meridian Products, Inc.
ARGOSY - Toys–models ☆ - Estes Industries
ARGOSY BLACK - Tobacco products - House of Windsor Inc.
ARGOSY CCA - Hearing aids - Argosy Electronics, Inc.
ARGOSY HS - Hearing aids - Argosy Electronics, Inc.
ARGOSY SHADO - Hearing aids - Argosy Electronics, Inc.
ARGUATI - Window shades ☆ - Vertical Blind Factory
ARGUESO - Wines - Jack Poust & Co. Inc.
ARGUILE - Games - Hersch and Co.
ARGUS - Aircraft parts - Eventide
ARGUS - Calendars - Argus Communications
ARGUS - Electronic data encryptors - Litronic Industries
ARGUS - Glass products - Pittsburgh Corning Corp.
ARGUS - Gloves–rubber - Playtex Beauty Care, Inc.
ARGUS - Goggles–safety - Ektelon

ARGUS - Lawn mowers - Lambert Manufacturing Corp.
ARGUS - Mirrors - Hardee-Pickard, Inc.
ARGUS - Pet products - Code 26 Group Inc.
ARGUS - Thread - Threads USA Div.
ARGUS - Tires - Argus Products, Inc.
ARGUS - Wallets ☆ - Enger-Kress Co.
ARGUSTO - Wines - Banfi Vintners
ARGYLE - Floor coverings–carpet and rugs - Barrett Carpet Mills Inc.
ARGYLE - Floor coverings–carpet and rugs - Porter Carpet Mills Inc.
ARGYLE - Floor coverings–carpet and rugs ☆ - American Excelsior Co.
ARGYLE - Floor coverings–carpet and rugs ☆ - Regal Rugs Inc.
ARGYLE - Health care products - Sherwood Medical Co.
ARGYLE - Recording label - Spina Music
ARGYLE - Wines - Dreyfus Ashby Inc.
ARGYLES - Ceramic tile - Latco Products
ARGYROL S.S. - Ophthalmic pharmaceutical ☆ - Iolab Pharmaceuticals
ARHOOLIE - Recording label - Arhoolie Productions Inc.
ARI IMPORTS - Beads - Ari Imports, Inc.
ARIA - Apparel and accessories - Charles Komar and Sons Inc.
ARIA - Boats–motor - Cruisers
ARIA - Cabinets - HomeCrest Corp.
ARIA - Cabinets ☆ - Medallion Kitchens of Minnesota Inc.
ARIA - Data storage software - Control Data Systems Inc.
ARIA - Fans–electric - Casablanca Fan Co.
ARIA - Floor coverings–carpet and rugs - Addison/Dicus Co., Inc.
ARIA - Furniture ☆ - Broyhill Furniture Industries, Inc.
ARIA - Glassware–household - Lenox Crystal, Inc.
ARIA - Hair care products - Dellaria International Inc.
ARIA - Hearing aids - Beltone Electronics Corp.
ARIA - Musical instruments - Scott Music Supply Inc.
ARIA - Office furniture–metal - Anthro International Inc.
ARIA - Office furniture–metal - Joyce International Inc.
ARIA - Paper - Mead Corp.
ARIA - Respirators - Respironics, Inc.
ARIA - Tableware–china ☆ - Villeroy and Boch Tableware Ltd.
ARIA - Wallpaper - Koroseal Wallcoverings
ARIA COLLECTION - Jewelry - Sheng Horng Enterprise USA Inc.
ARIA PRO II - Guitars - On-Site Music Group
ARIA SENZA VOCE - Recording label ☆ - Alshire International Inc.
ARIADNI - Electric lighting equipment - Lutron Electronics Co., Inc.
ARIAKE - Pet products - Pets Pacifica Inc.
ARIAL - Tiles–ceramic - Porcelanite, Inc.
ARIANA - Bedding–linen - Dan River Inc.
ARIANA - Citrus fruits ☆ - Florida Global Citrus Ltd.
ARIANA - Dishes–china ☆ - Gorham Inc.
ARIANA - Flatware - Yamazaki Tableware Inc.
ARIANA - Tiles–ceramic ☆ - Maxsam Sales, Inc.
ARIANA GOLD ACCENT - Flatware - Yamazaki Tableware Inc.
ARIANA GOURMET - Giftware ☆ - Gorham Inc.
ARIANE - Colognes - Avon Products, Inc.
ARIANE - Pet product - Interwood Corp.
ARIANE - Yarn - William Unger & Co. Inc.
ARIANNA - Toys - Peg Perego USA Inc.
ARIANNA SHERPA - Toys - Peg Perego USA Inc.
ARIAS - Chimes - QMT Associates Inc.
ARIAS - Pistons - Rivera Engineering, Inc.
ARIAT - Scuba diving equipment - Ariat International Inc.
ARID - Flowers, plants, and seeds - Jacklin Seed
ARID II-E - Flowers, plants, and seeds - Jacklin Seed
ARIDOL - Adhesives and sealants - Missouri Paint & Varnish Co.
ARIDSIL - Adhesives and sealants - Anti Hydro International Inc.
ARIEL - Bicycles ☆ - Raleigh USA Bicycle Co.
ARIEL - Computer peripheral equipment - Ariel Corp.
ARIEL - Dinnerware–glass - Franciscan by Johnson Brothers, USA, Inc.
ARIEL - Doors–glass - Peachtree Doors and Windows Inc.
ARIEL - Dryers–hair - P.S. Pibbs Inc.
ARIEL - Fabrics - Superior Shade & Blind Co. Inc.
ARIEL - Flatware - Reed and Barton Corp.
ARIEL - Floor coverings–carpet and rugs - Eligere Carpets
ARIEL - Floor coverings–carpet and rugs ☆ - Hollytex Carpet Mills Inc.
ARIEL - Furniture - Allsteel, Inc.
ARIEL - Glassware–household ☆ - Lenox Crystal, Inc.
ARIEL - Gutters–metal - Gazelle Inc.
ARIEL - Musical instruments - Barclay Music
ARIEL - Rings–jewelry - Artcarved Inc.
ARIEL - Toys - Tonka Corp.

☆ = Now out of production

ARIEL - Whirlpools - Lasco Products Group

ARIEL - Wines - Ariel Vineyards

ARIEL BLANC - Juices ☆ - Ariel Vineyards

ARIEL INDUSTRIES - Soil testing kits - Ariel Delaware Inc.

ARIELLE - Apparel—women's - Bedford Fair Industries

ARIELLE - Jewelry—costume - Crystal Clear Importing Co. Inc.

ARIENS - Lawn mowers - Ariens Co.

ARIENS PLUS - Snowblowers - Ariens Co.

ARIES - Cabinets - Belwood Inc.

ARIES - Cabinets - Triangle Pacific Corp. (Cabinet Division)

ARIES - Electronic monitoring equipment - Aries Industries, Inc.

ARIES - Floor coverings—carpet and rugs - Hartford Carpet Mills

ARIES - Floor coverings—carpet and rugs ☆ - Regal Rugs Inc.

ARIES - Footwear - Sunroad International, Inc.

ARIES - Furniture ☆ - Bassett Furniture Industries, Inc.

ARIES - Golfing equipment - Ram Golf Corp.

ARIES - Motor vehicles ☆ - Chrysler Corp. (Dodge Car Div.)

ARIES - Oils—lubricating - Texaco, Inc.

ARIES - Ophthalmic goods ☆ - Rozin Optical Export Corp.

ARIES - Paper products - Consolidated Papers, Inc.

ARIES - Perfumes - Advertising to Women, Inc.

ARIES - Sausages - Aries Prepared Beef Co.

ARIES - Skin care products - Veeco Manufacturing Co.

ARIES - Stools—wood ☆ - Krueger International, Inc.

ARIES - Teas—herbal - Calvin Thornton

ARIES - Wines - Sinskey Vineyards Inc.

ARIES - Yarn - William Unger & Co. Inc.

ARIES - Yarn ☆ - JCA, Inc.

ARIES CUSTOM - Motor vehicles ☆ - Chrysler Corp. (Dodge Car Div.)

ARIES ONLINE ENTERTAINMENT - Computer software - Kesmai Aries, Ltd.

ARIES SPECIAL EDITION - Motor vehicles ☆ - Chrysler Corp. (Dodge Car Div.)

ARIES S.S.T. - Toys—models ☆ - Estes Industries

ARIES TECHNOLOGY - Electronic equipment - Coco Distributing Co., Inc.

ARIETTE - Accordions - Hohner Inc.

ARIETTE - Musical instruments - Hohner, Inc.

ARIMEX - Food processors - Am-Mac Inc.

ARIMPEX - Amceco International Corp.

ARINO - Shirts - Fateh International Inc.

ARIOLA - Recording label ☆ - Arista Records Inc.

ARION - Electronic equipment - Evets Corp.

ARION - Floor coverings—carpet and rugs - Calladium & Marglen

ARIOSO - Rings—jewelry - Artcarved Inc.

ARIOSO CLASSICS INTERNATIONAL - Recording label - Thomas York Concert Marketing Inc.

ARIOSTEA - Tiles—ceramic - Capitol Tile Import Co.

ARIRANG - Beverages—carbonated - Dong-A America Corp.

ARIRANG KOREAN GINSENG DRINK - Beverages—carbonated - Dong-A America Corp.

ARIS - Beverages—malt - Fantis Foods, Inc.

ARIS - Computer software - Ascent Technology, Inc.

ARIS - Gloves - Aris Isotoner Inc.

ARI'S - Pizzas—frozen - Ari's Pizza

ARIS - Rackets—racquetball - Ektelon

ARIS/AV - Computer software - Ascent Technology, Inc.

ARIS BOOKS - See **ADDISON-WESLEY**

ARIS/CX - Computer software - Ascent Technology, Inc.

ARIS/DBU - Computer software - Ascent Technology, Inc.

ARIS ENTERTAINMENT - Electronics equipment - Aris Multimedia Entertainment, Inc.

ARIS/GMA - Computer software - Ascent Technology, Inc.

ARIS/MU - Computer software - Ascent Technology, Inc.

ARIS/PX - Computer software - Ascent Technology, Inc.

ARIS/SP - Computer software - Ascent Technology, Inc.

ARISE - Colognes - A-Veda Corp.

ARIST-O-KRATT - Harmonicas - William Kratt Co.

ARISTA - Apparel—women's - Bi-Flex International

ARISTA - Apparel—women's - Exact Change Only Corp.

ARISTA - Electronic equipment - Arista Enterprises Inc.

ARISTA - Frames—eyeglass - Bausch & Lomb Inc.

ARISTA - Hair care products - Gillette Co.

ARISTA - Recording label - Arista Records Inc.

ARISTA - Shrimp—canned or cured - Arista Industries Inc.

ARISTA - Sporting goods - Texon Inc.

ARISTA - Wallpaper - Koroseal Wallcoverings

ARISTA - Whirlpool bath ☆ - Jacuzzi Inc.

ARISTA WALLS - Wallcoverings - Designtex Fabrics Inc.

ARISTAR - Frames—eyeglass - Charmant Inc., USA

ARISTEX - Finishing agents - Proko Industries Inc.

ARISTO - Musical instruments - Woodwind & Brasswind

ARISTO - Photographic equipment - Aristo Grid Lamp Products Inc.

ARISTO - Recording label - Creav Inc. USA

ARISTO - Watches - Aristo Import Co. Inc.

ARISTO-BILT - Furniture - Union City Chair Co.

ARISTO-CAT - Pet products ☆ - Golden Cat Corp.

ARISTO CHROME - Bathroom accessories - Nutone Inc.

ARISTO-COAT - Pigments—synthetic - Chemical Coatings, Inc.

ARISTO-CRAFT - Cooking utensils—aluminum - West Bend Co.

ARISTO-CRAFT - Toys—electronic - Polk's Model Craft Hobbies, Inc.

ARISTO-CRAT - Hardware - Windor Security Manufacturing Inc.

ARISTO PANE - Glass products - Norandex, Inc.

ARISTO-RAY - Kitchen appliances - Broaster Co.

ARISTOCALE - Bedding—linen - Dan River Inc.

ARISTOCALE - Computer software - Atlantic Rim Information Systems, Inc.

ARISTOCAT - Pet products - Interwood Corp.

ARISTOCOB - Pipes ☆ - Missouri Meerschaum Co.

ARISTOCON - Floor coverings - Mannington Resilient Floors

ARISTOCRAFT - Figurines ☆ - Polk's Model Craft Hobbies, Inc.

ARISTOCRAFT - Hair care products - Fromm Industries

ARISTOCRAFT - Paints ☆ - Dunn Edwards Corp.

ARISTOCRAFT - Thread - Needlecraft Industries

ARISTOCRAT - Accordions - Atlas Accordions Inc.

ARISTOCRAT - Amplifiers ☆ - Electro-Voice, Inc.

ARISTOCRAT - Bicycles - Ross Bicycles USA, Ltd.

ARISTOCRAT - Brushes—paint - Solo-Horton Brush Co.

ARISTOCRAT - Butter ☆ - Hotel Bar Foods Inc.

ARISTOCRAT - Cabinets - Nutone Inc.

ARISTOCRAT - Cleaning preparations - L & A, Inc.

ARISTOCRAT - Dinnerware—plastic - Genpak Corp.

ARISTOCRAT - Exercising equipment - York Barbell Co., Inc.

ARISTOCRAT - Filing cabinets—metal - Kardex Systems, Inc.

ARISTOCRAT - Flatware ☆ - Lifetime Hoan Corp.

ARISTOCRAT - Floor coverings - American Floor Products Co. Inc.

ARISTOCRAT - Floor coverings—carpet and rugs - Ebsco Carpet Mills

ARISTOCRAT - Giftware - Endicott-Seymour of Ann Arbor

ARISTOCRAT - Giftware ☆ - Charles Zahn-Import Merchant

ARISTOCRAT - Glassware—household - Crisa Corp.

ARISTOCRAT - Glassware—household - Durand International

ARISTOCRAT - Glassware—household - Federal Glass

ARISTOCRAT - Guitars ☆ - International Music Corp.

ARISTOCRAT - Hair care products - Burmax Co. Inc.

ARISTOCRAT - Hearing aids - Argosy Electronics, Inc.

ARISTOCRAT - Heels—boot and shoe ☆ - O'Sullivan Corp.

ARISTOCRAT - Jewelry - Jacoby-Bender Inc.

ARISTOCRAT - Lighting fixtures - Lava-Simplex Internationale

ARISTOCRAT - Liquors - Heaven Hill Distilleries, Inc.

ARISTOCRAT - Luggage - United States Luggage Corp.

ARISTOCRAT - Masonry blocks - Trenwyth Industries Inc.

ARISTOCRAT - Motor vehicles—motor homes ☆ - Thor Industries West

ARISTOCRAT - Musical instruments - Selmer Co. Inc.

ARISTOCRAT - Occasional furniture ☆ - JDI Group, Inc.

ARISTOCRAT - Office supplies ☆ - Victor Systems & Equipment Co.

ARISTOCRAT - Ovens—convection - Kienhwa International Corp.

ARISTOCRAT - Paper—toweling - Wisconsin Tissue Mills Inc.

ARISTOCRAT - Playing cards - United States Playing Card Co.

ARISTOCRAT - Playpens—metal ☆ - Graco Children's Products

ARISTOCRAT - Projection screens - Claridge Products and Equipment Inc.

ARISTOCRAT - Salad dressings—bottled ☆ - American Specialty Foods Inc.

ARISTOCRAT - Siding - Norandex, Inc.

ARISTOCRAT - Signs - Best Manufacturing Co.

ARISTOCRAT - Spices and extracts - Herbert Marmorek & Son, Inc.

ARISTOCRAT - Tableware—china ☆ - Lenox, Inc.

ARISTOCRAT - Tires - Bridgestone/Firestone, Inc.

ARISTOCRAT - Toys—stuffed - Regina Products Inc.

ARISTOCRAT - Trailers—travel ☆ - Commodore Corp.

ARISTOCRAT - Vegetables—frozen - D.M. Camp & Sons

ARISTOCRAT - Wigs - New Image

ARISTOCRAT CATERERS - Kosher food products - Aristocrat International Corp.

ARISTOCRAT EAGLE - Sporting goods ☆ - Wright & McGill Co.

ARISTOCRAT OF CORSETS - Apparel—women's ☆ - Lady Mac Corset Co. Inc.

ARISTOCRAT OF FINE CHOCOLATES, THE - Candy - Sweet Candy Co.
ARISTOCRAT, THE - Hair care products ☆ - Giovanni Cosmetics Inc.
ARISTOCRAT VELLUM - Stationery ☆ - Pratt & Austin Co.
ARISTOFF - Caviar - Caviar & Fine Foods Inc.
ARISTOFF - Vodka - Crown Holdings, Inc.
ARISTOKRAFT - Cabinets - Aristokraft, Inc.
ARISTOKRAFT - Envelopes ☆ - Kimberly-Clark Corp. (Karolton Envelope Div.)
ARISTOLITE - Paints - Dunn Edwards Corp.
ARISTON - Electronic equipment - Bell & Howell Co.
ARISTOROBES - Apparel–women's - Town Fashions
ARISTOSEXIVA - Vitamins and nutritional supplements - Fast Break Esoterics
ARISTOTLE'S LOGICAL LYNX - Computer software ☆ - Krell Software Corp.
ARISTOWAX - Waxes–paraffin - Unocal Corp.
ARISTROCRAT - Doors–wood ☆ - Raynor Manufacturing Co.
ARITA - Kitchenware–earthenware - Arita Sales Co. Inc.
ARITA - Musical instruments - Newark Musical Merchandise Co.
ARITEX - Fabrics–tapestry - Art Metal-U.S. Corp.
ARITH-MAGIC - Computer software - Quality Educational Designs Inc.
ARITH-MAGIC II - Computer software - Quality Educational Designs Inc.
ARITHMECHECK - Games - Palmer Johnson Enterprises Inc.
ARITHMEFACTS - Computer software ☆ - EMC Publishing Corp.
ARITHMEFONTS - Computer software - Mountain Lake Software, Inc.
ARITHMEKICKS - Computer software - Houghton Mifflin Co.
ARITHMETICKLE - Computer software - Houghton Mifflin Co.
ARITHMIN - Pharmaceutical preparations - Lannett Co. Inc.
ARIUS - Labels–paper - Arius Tiles
ARIUS - Skin care products - Arius-Eickert Co. Inc.
A'RIVA - Boats–motor - Glassmaster Co.
ARIX - Computer software - ARIX Corp.
ARIZA - Cheese - Ariza Cheese Co., Inc.
ARIZE - Vitamins and nutritional supplements - Lifewell Inc.
ARIZONA - Cigarettes - Philip Morris Companies Inc.
ARIZONA - Iced tea–bottled or canned - Ferolito, Vultaggio and Sons
ARIZONA BEST - Barbecue sauce - Sunset Food & Beverage Corp.
ARIZONA CALM - Men's skin-care products - Aramis Inc.
ARIZONA CARDINALS - Posters - B & B Holdings, Inc.
ARIZONA CELLARS - Wines - R.W. Webb Winery
ARIZONA DATABASE PROJECT INC., THE - Computer software - Arizona Database Project Inc.
ARIZONA DIET - Teas - Ferolito, Vultaggio and Sons
ARIZONA GOLD - Skin care products - Jojoba Resources Inc.
ARIZONA GOLF - Golfing equipment - National Sporting Goods Corp.
ARIZONA IMPRESSIONS - Jewelry - American Business Systems, Inc.
ARIZONA INDIAN CORN - Snack foods - Cowboy Vittles & More
ARIZONA JEAN CO, THE - Apparel and accessories - J.C. Penney Co., Inc.
ARIZONA MIST OUTDOOR COOLING SYSTEMS, INC. - Agricultural machinery - Arizona Mist
ARIZONA MIST SYSTEM 2000 - Hoses - Arizona Mist
ARIZONA NATURAL - Vitamins and nutritional supplements - Arizona Natural Products
ARIZONA NATURAL CIRCULATION PLUS - Vitamins and nutritional supplements - Arizona Natural Products
ARIZONA NATURALS - Cosmetics - Arizona Natural Resources
ARIZONA PORTLAND CEMENT - Mortars–clay - Arizona Portland Cement Co.
ARIZONA STONE - Tiles–ceramic - Porcelanite, Inc.
ARIZONA SUN - Flour–blended ☆ - Central Milling Co.
ARIZONA SUN BREWED STYLE ICED TEA - Beverages - Hornell Brewing Co. Inc.
ARIZONA SUNRISE - Floor coverings–carpet and rugs ☆ - Regal Rugs Inc.
ARIZONA TILE - Floor coverings–tile - Arizona Tile Supply Inc.
ARIZONA VINEYARDS - Wines - Arizona Vineyards
ARIZONA'S BEST - Garden equipment - Lawn & Garden Supply Co.
ARJ - Jewelry–costume - Nick Curto Jewelers
ARJEM - Jewelry - A.R. Jester Co.
ARJO GLOSS - Paper ☆ - Arjo Wiggins USA
ARK - Publisher's imprints - Routledge
ARK - Recording label - Sparrow Corp.
ARK-A-BET - Toys - Lauri Inc.
ARK BRITE - Paper products - Green Bay Packaging, Inc.
ARK INTERFACE - Computer software - Ark Interface Inc.
ARK SPECIAL - Food products - Bush Brothers and Co.
ARK WHITE - Paperboard ☆ - Green Bay Packaging, Inc.
ARK WORKSPACE - Computer software - Ark Interface II , Inc.
ARKADY - Food products - Archer Daniels Midland Co.
ARKANOID - Video games - Taito America Corp.

ARKANSAS - Juices - Speaco Foods Inc.
ARKANSAS CAN OPENER - Rifles - Daisy Manufacturing Co.
ARKANSAS' FINEST - Food products - Bush Brothers and Co.
ARKANSAS PERFECT - Stones–synthetic - Normark Corp.
ARKANSAS ROSE - Rice - Producers Rice Mill, Inc.
ARKANSAUCE - Sauces - Kerwin S. Koerper
ARKAY - Electronic equipment - Comspace Corp.
ARKAY - Photographic equipment - Omega/Arkay
ARKAY/SPRINT - Photographic equipment ☆ - Omega/Arkay
ARKHAM HORROR - Games - Chaosium Inc.
ARKHAM HOUSE - Publisher's imprints - Arkham House Publishers Inc.
ARKIDTECTURE - Tiles–ceiling - La Crosse Acoustical Tile, Inc. (Interior Systems)
ARKIN A-OK - Toys - Arkin A-Ok Products Co.
ARKLA - Exercising equipment - Preway Industries Inc.
ARKLA - Gasoline - Arkla Chemical Corp. (Petroleum Div.)
ARKLA-SERVEL - Air conditioning equipment - Preway Industries Inc.
ARKLAMATIC - Barbecues and grills - Preway Industries Inc.
ARKLAMATIC - Barbecues and grills - Sunbeam Outdoor Products Inc.
ARKO - Health care products - Arkopharma Inc.
ARKO-BOOST - Vitamins and nutritional supplements - Arkopharma Inc.
ARKO-MIGRAINE - Pharmaceutical preparations - Arkopharma Inc.
ARKO-RHEUMA - Pharmaceutical preparations - Arkopharma Inc.
ARKO-SLEEP - Pharmaceutical preparations - Arkopharma Inc.
ARKO-SLIM - Pharmaceutical preparations - Arkopharma Inc.
ARKO-STRESS - Pharmaceutical preparations - Arkopharma Inc.
ARKS - See **BOLLETJE**
ARKSUITE - Computer software - Information International, Inc.
ARL - Pharmaceutical preparations - Alva-Amco Pharmacal Co.
ARLAM - Paint rollers - Arsco International Inc.
ARLAN SPRINGS - Filters–air - Dalessandro Enterprises Inc.
ARLAREX - Pharmaceutical preparations - C.S. Ruckstuhl Co. Inc.
ARLEN - Dinnerware–glass - Arlen China Co.
ARLEN NESS - Structural motorcycle parts - Arlen Ness Enterprises, Inc.
ARLEQUIN - Flatware ☆ - Couzon USA
ARLEQUIN - Floor coverings - Parquet de France Inc.
ARLES - Floor coverings–carpet and rugs - Atlas Carpet Mills Inc.
ARLIDIN - Pharmaceutical preparations - Rhone-Poulenc Rorer Pharmaceuticals Inc.
ARLIE - Greeting cards - Recycled Paper Products, Inc.
ARLIN - Apparel–children's - Rasamny Mills Inc.
ARLIN - Hats - Arlington Hat Co. Inc.
ARLIN-TEX - Hats - Arlington Hat Co. Inc.
ARLINGTON - Cabinets - Yorktowne Inc.
ARLINGTON - Cages–wire - Ameriguard Corp.
ARLINGTON - Coffee - Earl Gill Coffee Co. Inc.
ARLINGTON - Cribs–wood ☆ - Welsh Co.
ARLINGTON - Doors–metal - Emhart Industries Inc.
ARLINGTON - Floor coverings ☆ - Azrock Commercial Flooring
ARLINGTON - Furniture - Vermont Tubbs Inc.
ARLINGTON - Garden equipment - Parker Sweeper Co.
ARLINGTON - Glassware–household - Arlington Crystal Inc.
ARLINGTON - Glassware–household - Dalzell-Viking
ARLINGTON - Lighting fixtures - Holophane Corp.
ARLINGTON - Motor vehicle parts and accessories - Lancaster Colony Automotive Group
ARLINGTON - Pens ☆ - Empire Berol USA
ARLINGTON - Shoes ☆ - Allen-Edmonds Shoe Corp.
ARLINGTON - Thread - Threads USA Div.
ARLINGTON - Windows - Louisiana-Pacific Corp.
ARLINGTON HILLS - Dinnerware–glass ☆ - Lenox, Inc.
ARLINGTON HOUSE - Furniture–metal - General Housewares Corp.
ARLINGTON II - Bells and chimes - Schulmerich Carillons Inc.
ARLINGTON SQUARE - Furniture ☆ - Bassett Furniture Industries, Inc.
ARLINGTON, THE - Fencing–plastic - Nebraska Plastics, Inc.
ARLINTEX - Crocheted and knitted items - Rasamny Mills Inc.
ARLOTTA - Apparel–men's - John Arlotta
ARLY - Jewelry - Aarly Jewelry Co.
ARLY IMPORTERS - Jewelry–precious - Arly Diamond Co.
ARLYN - Fabrics - Phifer Wire Products Inc.
ARM-A-DOR - Locks–door - Sargent & Greenleaf, Inc.
ARM-A-REST - Motor vehicle parts and accessories - Northern Industrial Tool Co.
ARM ADVANCE SENTRY - Machinery - A.O. Smith Harvestore Products, Inc.
ARM & HAMMER - Cleaning preparations–household - Church and Dwight Co. Inc.

☆ = Now out of production

ARM & HAMMER POTPOURRI - Deodorizers - Church and Dwight Co. Inc.
ARM & HAMMER THE STANDARD OF PURITY - Deodorants–personal - Church & Dwight Co.
ARM BUSTER, THE - Exercising equipment - Joseph Kennedy Co., Inc.
ARM-GUARD - Sporting goods - Trace Athletic Corp.
ARM-LITE - Lighting equipment–bicycles ☆ - Wonder Corp. of America
ARM MASTER - Golfing equipment - R.M. & G. Products, Inc.
ARM OF HARM, THE - Dolls - Intext Diversified Sales, Inc.
ARM PETS - Toys–stuffed - Dakin Inc.
ARM-R-CLAD - Glass products - HGP Industries Inc.
ARM-R-SECUR - Glass products - HGP Industries Inc.
ARM SOK - Plastics - Spray Sok Co. Inc.
ARMA - Coatings - Arma Coatings, Inc.
ARMA-KLEEN - Chemical preparations - Arma-Kleen International Inc.
ARMA KOTE - Nuts and bolts - Bontel Fastener Corp.
ARMA-SOL - Cleaning preparations - PDG Precision, Inc.
ARMACRYL - Paints - Kallista Inc.
ARMADA - Cleaning preparations–household - Diversey Wyandotte Corp.
ARMADA - Luggage - United States Luggage Corp.
ARMADA - Varnishes - Boatek, Inc.
ARMADA PIRATE FIGHTER - Wallpaper - Bon-Ton Wallcoverings Inc.
ARMADILLO - Attache cases - Alvin and Co. Inc.
ARMADILLO - Bicycle tires - Specialized Bicycle Components, Inc.
ARMADILLO - Computers - Pulse Electronics, Inc.
ARMADILLO - Luggage - Case Products, Inc.
ARMADILLO - Protective coatings - New Malter Inc.
ARMADILLO - Skin care products - Roly International
ARMADILLO - Toys–automobiles ☆ - Hasbro, Inc.
ARMADILLO AMBER - Beverages–malt - Willie C's Cafe and Bar, Inc.
ARMADILLO MAN - Novelty items - Cross at the Green...Not in Between Enterprises
ARMADILLO WASHERS - Games - Dillo, Inc.
ARMADURA - Notebooks and notepads - Norcom Inc.
ARMAFELT - Floor coverings - Armstrong World Industries, Inc.
ARMAFLEX - Insulating materials–foam - Armstrong World Industries, Inc.
ARMAGEDDON - Apparel and accessories - Hawaii-Pacific Apparel Group, Inc.
ARMAGEDDON - Computer software - SourceView Software International
ARMAGNAC - Tobacco–chewing or smoking - James B. Russell Inc.
ARMALARM - Alarms–personal - James K. Bahcall
ARMALUME - Fencing–steel - Semmerling Fence and Supply Inc.
ARMALY - Sponges - Armaly Sponge Co.
ARMALY BRANDS - Sponges - Armaly Sponge Co.
ARMAND - Cosmetics - Cabot Laboratories Inc.
ARMAND DUVAL - Watches - Nicolet International Inc.
ARMAND ROUX - Wines - Bercut-Vandervoort & Co.
ARMANI EAU POUR HOMME - Colognes - Cosmair Inc.
ARMANINO FARMS - Frozen foods ☆ - SUPHERB
ARMANO'S - Meat products - Hormel Foods Corp.
ARMAN'S - Health care products - Medicine Shoppe International Inc.
ARMASHIELD - Tiles–ceiling - Armstrong World Industries, Inc.
ARMASPORT - Foam rubber ☆ - Armstrong World Industries, Inc.
ARMATEX - Insulating fabric - Mid-Mountain Materials Inc.
ARMATO'S - Pizzas–frozen - Armato's Pizza Co.
ARMATRON - Toys ☆ - Tomy America, Inc.
ARMATUFF - Tiles–ceiling - Armstrong World Industries, Inc.
ARMAX - Vitamins and nutritional supplements - Enzymatic Therapy, Inc.
ARMDOR - Paper–toilet - Clark Paper Converting Corp.
ARMEASE - Medical apparatus - American Health Specialties Inc.
ARMED - Electronic equipment - Digequip Security Industries Inc.
ARMED FORCE - Toys - Mattel, Inc.
ARMED FORCES COMMEMORATIVE SOCIETY - Firearms, accessories, and parts - Ahl, Inc.
ARMENIAN - Breads - Young's Market Co.
ARMENIAN BLEND - Coffee - Brewing Market, Ltd.
ARMETALE - Giftware - Wilton Co.
ARMEX - Cleaning preparations - Church & Dwight Co.
ARMINIUS - Revolvers - Fie Corp.
ARMIS - Computer software - Zurich Insurance Co.
ARMITAGE ES ES - Heating equipment ☆ - Aqua Stock/Petcetera Inc.
ARMITRON - Watches - Armitron Corp.
ARMITRON - Watches - E. Gluck Corp.
ARMIX - Shortening - Armour Dairy Co.
ARMO - Fabrics–canvas - Crown Textile Co.
ARMO-DUR - Microphones - Shure Brothers, Inc.
ARMO FLEECE - Fabrics - Crown Textile Co.
ARMO-PRESS - Fabrics - Crown Textile Co.

ARMO-RITE - Fabrics–canvas - Crown Textile Co.
ARMO WEFT - Fabrics - Handler Textile Corp.
ARMO-WEFT - Fabrics–canvas - Crown Textile Co.
ARMO WOOL - Fabrics–canvas - Crown Textile Co.
ARMOFLEXXX - Fabrics–canvas - Crown Textile Co.
ARMOLA - Shortening - Armour Dairy Co.
ARMOLUBE - Abrasive products - SIA America
ARMOND - Musical instruments - Newark Musical Merchandise Co.
ARMONICHE - Pasta ☆ - Dean & Deluca Inc.
ARMONT - Floor coverings - Armstrong World Industries, Inc.
ARMOR - Antigens - Babson Bros. Co.
ARMOR - Cases–eyeglass - Fidelity Case Corp.
ARMOR - Floor coverings - American Floor Products Co. Inc.
ARMOR - Floor coverings–carpet and rugs - Coronet Carpets Inc.
ARMOR - Hardware - W.W. Grainger, Inc.
ARMOR - Uniforms–tailored - Angelica Uniform Group
ARMOR 75 X-TRA LITE - Footwear - Iron Age Corp.
ARMOR-AISLE - Floor coverings - American Floor Products Co. Inc.
ARMOR-ALL - Cleaning preparations - Armor All Products Corp.
ARMOR ALL - Waterproofing compounds - Klean-Strip
ARMOR BOND - Siding–insulating - Armor Bond Building Products, Inc.
ARMOR-BRITE - Paints - Wattyl Paint Corp.
ARMOR CAST - Concrete storage containers - Del Zotto Manufacturing
ARMOR-CEMENT - Floor coverings - American Floor Products Co. Inc.
ARMOR-CLAD - Electronic equipment - General Electric Co.
ARMOR-CLAD - Swimming pool covers - Aqua Fab Industries Inc.
ARMOR COAT - Plastics film - MSC Specialty Films Inc.
ARMOR-CRETE - Epoxy ☆ - Fosroc Inc.
ARMOR-CURE - Concrete products ☆ - Fosroc Inc.
ARMOR EDGE - Drafting supplies - Mayline/Hamilton
ARMOR-EDGE - Furniture - Sico Inc.
ARMOR-FLEX - Floor coverings - American Floor Products Co. Inc.
ARMOR FLEX - Pennants - National Banner Co., Inc.
ARMOR GARD - Plastics film - MSC Specialty Films Inc.
ARMOR-GUARD - Hardware - Brook-National Hardware Co. Inc.
ARMOR KOTE - Projection screens - Draper Shade and Screen Co. Inc.
ARMOR LAME - Floor coverings - Parquet de France Inc.
ARMOR LININGS - Automotive repair shops - Tough Trucks & Accessories, Inc.
ARMOR-LINK - Floor coverings - American Floor Products Co. Inc.
ARMOR-LUXE - Floor coverings - Parquet de France Inc.
ARMOR MAIL - Computer software - LJL Enterprises, Inc.
ARMOR-NOSE - Floor coverings - American Floor Products Co. Inc.
ARMOR OF GOD - Jewelry - Lord & Miller Creations
ARMOR PLASTIC - Adhesives and sealants - Missouri Paint & Varnish Co.
ARMOR PLATE - Cleaning preparations - Armor All Products Corp.
ARMOR-PLATE - Protective covers for machinery - Milwaukee Slide and Spindle, Inc.
ARMOR-R GLAS - Insulating materials - Alliedsignal Inc.
ARMOR-R PLUS - Insulations - Alliedsignal Inc.
ARMOR-SEAL - Weather stripping - E.S. Robbins Corp.
ARMOR-SHEEN - Plastics–laminated ☆ - Lawson Marden Post Card
ARMOR/SPAR - Paints - Perry & Derrick Co.
ARMOR-SPRAY - Paints ☆ - Valspar Corp.
ARMOR SYSTEMS - Computer software - Armor Systems, Inc.
ARMOR-TAR - Epoxy coatings - Pratt & Lambert, Inc.
ARMOR-TECH - Toys - Hasbro, Inc.
ARMOR-THANE - Adhesives and sealants - Missouri Paint & Varnish Co.
ARMOR-TILE - Floor coverings - American Floor Products Co. Inc.
ARMOR-TITE - Adhesives and sealants - Missouri Paint & Varnish Co.
ARMOR-TOUGH - Sporting goods - Kellwood Co.
ARMOR-TREDS - Floor coverings - American Floor Products Co. Inc.
ARMOR-WELD - Adhesives and sealants - Missouri Paint & Varnish Co.
ARMORBARB - Wire - Page Aluminized Steel Corp.
ARMORCARD - Trading cards and stamps - Sportworld Distributing Inc.
ARMORCAST - Cables - Minnesota Mining & Manufacturing Co.
ARMORCLAD - Bags - K-L Industries (Knickerbocker Case Div.)
ARMORCLAD - File folders ☆ - Kardex Systems, Inc.
ARMORCLAD - Kitchen cabinets - Miller Building Supply Co. Inc.
ARMORCORE - Plywood - States Industries Inc.
ARMORCORE - Rubber–vulcanized - Hunt Holdings, Inc.
ARMORCOTE - Floor coverings–carpet and rugs - Barrett Carpet Mills Inc.
ARMORCRYLIC - Adhesives and sealants - Missouri Paint & Varnish Co.
ARMORED - Garden equipment ☆ - Cox and Co. Inc.
ARMORED ENCOUNTER - Toys–electronic ☆ - Philips Consumer Electronics Co.

ARMORED FIST - Computer software - Novalogic, Inc.
ARMORED MARLIN - Binoculars ☆ - Swift Instruments, Inc.
ARMORED PROTECTION - Coatings - International Paper (Decorative Products Division)
ARMORED SEA HAWK - Binoculars - Swift Instruments, Inc.
ARMORED SWIFT FOCUS - Binoculars ☆ - Swift Instruments, Inc.
ARMORFLEX - Scrapers - Imperial Paint Applicators Ltd.
ARMORGLIDE - Medical apparatus - St. Jude Medical Inc.
ARMORGLOSS - Enamels - Pratt & Lambert United, Inc.
ARMORGUARD - Adhesives and sealants - John L. Armitage & Co.
ARMORGUARD - Adhesives and sealants - Induron Coatings Inc.
ARMORHIDE - Adhesives and sealants - John L. Armitage & Co.
ARMORINES - Books–comic - Voyager Communications Inc.
ARMORITE - Paints - John L. Armitage & Co.
ARMORIZED - Lamp bulbs–incandescent - Duro-Test Corp.
ARMORKOTE - Waterproof outerwear - Jomac Products Inc.
ARMORLINE - Doors–metal - Kawneer Co., Inc.
ARMORLINK - Fencing–chain link - Page Aluminized Steel Corp.
ARMORLITE - Firearms, accessories, and parts - Bausch & Lomb Inc.
ARMORLITE - Floor coverings ☆ - Azrock Commercial Flooring
ARMORLOCK - Locks–door - Master Lock Co.
ARMORLON - Adhesives and sealants ☆ - Missouri Paint & Varnish Co.
ARMORLON - Tarpaulins - Reef Industries, Inc.
ARMORLUX - Adhesives and sealants - Induron Coatings Inc.
ARMORLUX - Fiber optic cable - Sumitomo Electric Fiber Optics
ARMORPLATE - Adhesives and sealants - John L. Armitage & Co.
ARMORSEAL - See **CONCRETE SEALER**
ARMORSHIELD - Door frames - Robertson-Ceco Corp.
ARMORTOP - Adhesives and sealants - Anti Hydro International Inc.
ARMORTOP - Plastics - Westinghouse Electric Corp. (Decorative Micarta Div.)
ARMORWIRE - Wire - Page Aluminized Steel Corp.
ARMOUR - Epoxy - Sigma Coatings USA BV.
ARMOUR - Glass–tempered - Armour Worldwide Glass
ARMOUR - Hats - Tommy Armour Golf Co.
ARMOUR - Meats–luncheon - Armour Swift-Eckrich
ARMOUR - Pharmaceutical preparations - Armour Pharmaceutical Co.
ARMOUR - Pharmaceutical preparations - Forest Pharmaceuticals Inc.
ARMOUR CLASSIC - Sporting goods - Tommy Armour Golf Co.
ARMOUR CLASSIC LITE - Dinners–frozen - Conagra, Inc.
ARMOUR-DIAL - Cleaning preparations–household - Dial Corp.
ARMOUR DINNER CLASSICS - Dinners–frozen - Conagra, Inc.
ARMOUR ETCH - Tools - Armour Products
ARMOUR GOLDEN STAR - Meats–luncheon - Armour Swift-Eckrich
ARMOUR MEAT GLAZES AND DIPPING SAUCES - Sauces - Williams Foods Inc.
ARMOUR MEAT MARINADES - Meat sauces - Williams Foods Inc.
ARMOUR STAR - Meats–luncheon - Armour Swift-Eckrich
ARMOUR TREET - Meat products–canned - Dial Corp.
ARMOURFLEX - Floor coverings–linoleum ☆ - Forbo Industries, Inc.
ARMOURFLEX - Floor coverings–tile - Gerbert Ltd.
ARMOURTILE - Floor coverings–linoleum - Gerbert Ltd.
ARMOURTILE - Floor coverings–linoleum ☆ - Forbo Industries, Inc.
ARMOURTUFF - Enamels - Bo-Nash, Inc.
ARMPUBLISHER - Computer software - FormAtion Technologies Inc.
ARMS AUTOMATED ROBOTIC MAINTENANCE SYSTEM - Robots–industrial - Waterjet Systems, Inc.
ARMSAVER - Trailer jack - Atwood Mobile Products
ARMSTONE - Marble products - Permagrain Products, Inc.
ARMSTRONG - Bags–plastic - Asari Plastic Corp.
ARMSTRONG - Bicycles ☆ - Roadmaster Corp.
ARMSTRONG - Building materials–concrete - Hallett Building Materials Inc.
ARMSTRONG - Cleaning preparations–carpet and rug - S.C. Johnson & Son, Inc.
ARMSTRONG - Cutlery - Lifetime Hoan Corp.
ARMSTRONG - Floor coverings - Armstrong World Industries, Inc.
ARMSTRONG - Flowers, plants, and seeds - Armstrong Nurseries Inc.
ARMSTRONG - Glass - D & L Stained Glass Supply, Inc.
ARMSTRONG - Heating equipment ☆ - Magic Chef Inc.
ARMSTRONG - Latex - Columbia Paint Inc.
ARMSTRONG - Musical instruments - Armstrong Woodwinds
ARMSTRONG - Musical instruments - United Musical Instruments USA Inc.
ARMSTRONG - Pagers - Monitor Crystal Service
ARMSTRONG - Tires - Armtec Industries Inc.
ARMSTRONG CLEANER - Cleaning preparations - Armstrong World Industries, Inc.
ARMSTRONG FORGE - Cutlery - Lifetime Hoan Corp.

ARMSTRONG SMITH - Paints - Wattyl Paint Corp.
ARMSTRONG'S - Vials–glass - Kerr Group, Inc.
ARMTEC - Ammunition - Esterline Technologies Corp.
ARMX - Medical appliance - Product Innovation, Inc.
ARMY - Firearms, accessories, and parts - Texas Longhorn Arms, Inc.
ARMY 1860 - Guns - Euroarms of America
ARMY GEAR - Toys–guns - Lewis Galoob Toys, Inc.
ARMY HAWK - Toys–models ☆ - Estes Industries
ARMY PRESERVE - Rust removers ☆ - W.J. Hagerty & Sons Ltd. Inc.
ARNART - Giftware - Arnart Imports Inc.
ARNAUD - Olives–canned - Gourmet America
ARNBEE - Flatware - Reed and Barton Corp.
ARNDT & HERMAN - Window frames - East Coast Millwork Distributors, Inc.
ARNESIA - Recording label - Eucharist Films Distribution
ARNETTE - Sunglasses - Arnet Optic Illusions, Inc.
ARNETT'S - Candy - Arway Confections Inc.
ARNEX - Watches - Lucien Piccard/Arnex
ARNI - Cookies - Liberty Richter Inc.
ARNI PALM LEAVES - Food products ☆ - Liberty Richter Inc.
ARNICA - Shampoos ☆ - Image Laboratories, Inc.
ARNICA 30 INJURY - Homeopathic remedies - Washington Homeopathic Products
ARNICA GEL - Pharmaceutical preparations - Boiron Inc.
ARNICAID - Health care products - Standard Homeopathic Co., Inc.
ARNICALM - Pharmaceutical preparations - Boiron Inc.
ARNICARE - Pharmaceutical preparations - Dolisos America, Inc.
ARNIE - Apparel–men's - Sears, Roebuck and Co.
ARNIE'S - Dips - Arnie's
ARNIE'S BAGELICIOUS - Bagels - Arnie's Bagelicious Bagels, Inc.
ARNIFLORA ARNICA - Pharmaceutical preparations - Boericke & Tafel
ARNO - Hair care products - Phil Marano Inc.
ARNOLD - Bread crumbs - CPC International Inc.
ARNOLD - Industrial machinery - Arnold Industries Inc.
ARNOLD - Magnets - SPS Technologies, Inc.
ARNOLD - Pens - Arnold Pen Co. Inc.
ARNOLD - Polishing wheels - S.M. Arnold Inc.
ARNOLD - Power switching equipment - MTD Products Inc.
ARNOLD - Recording label - Carrie Records
ARNOLD BAKERY - Breads - Best Foods Baking Group
ARNOLD BAKERY LIGHT - Breads - CPC International Inc.
ARNOLD BRICK OVEN - Breads - Best Foods Baking Group
ARNOLD-COUNTRY - Breads - CPC International Inc.
ARNOLD EHRET - Publisher's imprints - Ehret Literature Publishing Co. Inc.
ARNOLD GROUP - Wallpaper - K.M.L. Industries
ARNOLD PALMER - Apparel–men's - TMG Corp.
ARNOLD PALMER - Apparel–men's ☆ - Harwood Companies Inc.
ARNOLD PALMER - Footwear - Arnold Palmer Enterprises, Inc.
ARNOLD PALMER - Golfing equipment - Arnold Palmer Golf Co.
ARNOLD PALMER - Neckties - Salem Neckwear Corp.
ARNOLD PALMER AQUATOR - Apparel–men's - TMG Corp.
ARNOLD RIEGGER - Coats ☆ - Centralia Knitting Mills Inc.
ARNOLD SORENSIN - Sardines–canned - Mitsui & Co. Inc.
ARNOLD ZIMBERG - Apparel and accessories - Zimberg Group, Inc.
ARNOLD'S - Sausages - Arnold's Meat Food Products Inc.
ARNOLD'S - Vegetables–pickled or brined - Arnold Pickle & Olive Co.
ARNOLD'S BRAN'NOLA - Breads - Best Foods Baking Group
ARNOLFO DI CAMBIO - Glassware–household - Puiforcat
ARNOTT'S - Cookies - Pepperidge Farm Inc.
ARNUCLANS - Pharmaceutical preparations ☆ - Wesley Pharmacal Co. Inc.
ARO - Recording label - Sounds-Vision Music
ARO - Sporting goods ☆ - Sport Obermeyer Ltd.
ARO AROMATIQUE - Perfumes - Aromatique, Inc.
ARO MODULE/AIR 2000 - Aircraft parts - ARO Corp.
ARO-OIL - Oils–vulcanized - Commercial Chemical Co. Inc.
ARO-SPAR - Varnishes ☆ - Frazee Paint
ARO-THANE - Varnishes ☆ - Frazee Paint
ARO-TRON - Paints ☆ - Frazee Paint
ARO-VAR - Varnishes ☆ - Frazee Paint
AROCHRON - Watches - Bulova Corp.
AROLENE - Paints - Commercial Chemical Co. Inc.
AROLITE - Insulating materials - Schuller International, Inc.
AROM-COT - Medical apparatus - Utah Medical Products, Inc.
AROMA - Cigarettes - G.A. Georgopulo & Co. Inc.
AROMA - Coffee - Aroma Coffee Co. Inc.
AROMA - Cooking equipment–household - Aroma Manufacturing Co. Inc.
AROMA - Meat products–canned ☆ - Design Foods

☆ = Now out of production

AROMA - Seasonings - Josephine Inc.
AROMA AIR - Deodorizers - Tina Rocca
AROMA ART - Bath salts - Natural Body Bath Aroma Art
AROMA CLASSICS - Cosmetics - Warren Raysor
AROMA DISC - Perfumes - Karen Carson Creations
AROMA ELEGANT - Skin care products - Boutique D'elite USA, Inc.
AROMA ESSENCE - Pharmaceutical preparations - Desert Essence Cosmetics
AROMA GARDEN - Deodorizers - Great American Herb Co.
AROMA GARDEN - Flowers, plants, and seeds - Puget Sound Seed Co.
AROMA GLO - Candles ☆ - Our Secret, Ltd.
AROMA GLOW - Air fresheners - Countryside Fragrances Inc.
AROMA LOTION - Skin care products - Elizabeth Van Buren Aromatherapy
AROMA MEDICA - Toiletries - Scentsational, Inc.
AROMA MIST - Skin care products - Elizabeth Van Buren Aromatherapy
AROMA NATURALS - Cosmetics - Tina Rocca
AROMA-NOTES - Greeting cards - Green Field Paper Co.
AROMA POLY - Polysulfides - Aroma Tech, Inc.
AROMA-SENSUALS - Bath salts - Feeling Fine Institute, Inc.
AROMA SHOWER - Hardware - Life Essences, Inc.
AROMA TERRA - Hair care products - Redmond Products, Inc.
AROMA THERAPY - Bath salts - Wives Tales
AROMA-THERAPY - Deodorizers - Aroma Design Group Inc.
AROMA THERAPY BEARS - Figurines - Gilbertie's Herb Gardens, Inc.
AROMA VERA - Hair care products - Aroma Vera Inc.
AROMA WRAP - Bandages - Nature's Spa, Inc.
AROMABLEND - Skin care products - Natural Attitudes Inc.
AROMABODY - Skin care products - Supre, Inc.
AROMACLEAN - Pet products - Best n' Show Pet Products Inc.
AROMACOTE - Perfumes - International Flavors & Fragrances Inc.
AROMAFLORIA - Bath salts, gels, and lotions - California Fragrance Co.
AROMAGEMS - Jewelry - Nature's Geometry
AROMAHAT - Hats - Danica Siegel
AROMAHOP - Beverages–malt - Pfizer Inc.
AROMAIRE - Deodorizers - Viking Manufacturing Co. Inc.
AROMALITE - Deodorizers - Sitara Aromatica, Inc.
AROMALITE - Lamp bulbs - Miracle Products
AROMANCE - Deodorizers - Boars Leap Marketing, Inc.
AROMANCE - Deodorizers ☆ - Charles of the Ritz Group Ltd.
AROMANTIX - Skin care products - Brant Corp.
AROMAPET - Pet products - Danklied Laboratories Ltd.
AROMAPHORIC PROTECTOR - Hair care products - Revlon Consumer Products Corp.
AROMAPHYTE - Botanical extracts - Active Organics Inc.
AROMAPLEX - Botanical extracts - Active Organics Inc.
AROMAPLEX - Oils–essential - Natural Thoughts Inc.
AROMAPLUS - Skin care products - H2O Plus, L.P.
AROMAPOWER DIET - Vitamins and nutritional supplements - Aroma Therapy Research Institute, Inc.
AROMASAURUS REX - Health care products - Warren Raysor
AROMASOAK - Health care products - Roux Laboratories, Inc.
AROMASPA - Skin care products - Avon Products, Inc.
AROMASPA - Spas–home - Softub, Inc.
AROMASSAGE - Skin care products - Khalsa Sunshine Corp.
AROMASTONE - Fragrance containers - Aromatique, Inc.
AROMASTROLOGY - Perfumes - Advertising to Women, Inc.
AROMASYS - Deodorizers - Aromasys, Inc.
AROMATHERAPA - Candles - Hanna's Potpourri Specialties, Inc.
AROMATHERAPY - Hair care products - Aveda Corp.
AROMATHERAPY - Inhalers - Nature's Apothecary Inc.
AROMATHERAPY - Skin care products - La Natura
AROMATHERAPY BODY OILS - Skin care products - F. Cousteaux Co., Inc.
AROMATHERAPY INSTITUTE - Sachets - L'Herbier De Provence Ltd.
AROMATHERAPY OF ROME, THE - Candles - Aromatherapy of Rome
AROMATHETICS - Colognes - Conopco, Inc.
AROMATHETICS - Skin care products - Chesebrough-Pond's USA Co.
AROMATIC DELIGHT - Tobacco–chewing or smoking - Gesty Trading & Manufacturing Corp.
AROMATIC MUSIC - Recording label - Creative Ventures, Inc.
AROMATIC SPIRITS - Colognes - Luzier Personalized Cosmetics, Inc.
AROMATIC VOLCANIC BATH PEBBLES - Bath salts - Echelle, Inc.
AROMATICA - Rice ☆ - Uncle Ben's, Inc.
AROMATIQUE - Decorative fragrances - Aromatique, Inc.
AROMATIQUE BATH - Soap - Aromatique, Inc.
AROMATRAN - Measuring instruments - MOCON/Modern Controls, Inc.
AROMAVIE - Oils–essential - Herbalife International, Inc.
AROMAVISION - Deodorizers ☆ - Vaportek, Inc.

AROMAWEST - Oils–lubricating - Jaime Dworin
AROMAX - Incense - S.S.I. Fragrances, Inc.
AROME VIVANT - Oils–essential - International Flavors & Fragrances Inc.
AROMES VIVANTS - Oils–essential - International Flavors & Fragrances Inc.
AROMESENTIALS - Skin care products - Freeman Cosmetics Corp.
AROMIN - Vitamins and nutritional supplements - Earth Science Products Inc.
AROMIZER - Air purification systems - Amcor Group Ltd.
ARONDALE - Cabinets - Yorktowne Inc.
ARONDIA - Photo albums - General Products
ARONNEX - Watches - Gruen Marketing Corp.
AROOLU - Apparel and accessories - Elizabeth's Originals, Ltd.
AROOSTOOK JACK - Cheese - State of Maine Cheese
ARORA - Shoes ☆ - Genesco Inc.
AROSA - Floor coverings–carpet and rugs ☆ - Eurotex Inc.
AROSCI - Hair care products - Revlon Consumer Products Corp.
AROUND & ABOUT CIVIL WAR - Computer software - Orange Cherry Software
AROUND THE CORNER - Window coverings - Vermont American Corp.
AROUND-THE-DOOR DECOR - Paperboard - Trend Enterprises, Inc.
AROUND THE HOUSE - Lighting fixtures - Big Beam Emergency Systems Inc.
AROUND THE WORLD - Computer software - Abacus Software, Inc.
AROUND THE WORLD IN LINENS - Furniture ☆ - Foley & Robinson Inc.
AROUND TOWN - Apparel and accessories - H.L. Miller and Son, Inc.
AROUND TOWN - Hosiery - Van Raalte Gloves
AROUND TOWN - Pet products - City Dog Designed Co., Inc.
AROUND TOWN - Wallpaper - Sandpiper Studios
AROUND YOUR NECK - Neckties - Around Your Neck Inc.
AROUSE VIGOR - Health care products - East Earth Herb Inc.
ARP - Heat pumps - Meyer Furnace Co.
ARP - Synthesizers–musical instrument - Fender Musical Instruments
ARP SAFETY PRODUCTS - Sporting goods - Kellwood Co.
ARPA - Tiles–ceramic - Maxsam Sales, Inc.
ARPAD - Meats–luncheon ☆ - Liberty Richter Inc.
ARPAGE - Floor coverings–carpet and rugs - Philadelphia Carpets
ARPAGE ENCORE - Floor coverings–carpet and rugs - Philadelphia Carpets
ARPEGE - Floor coverings - Parquet de France Inc.
ARPEGE - Floor coverings–carpet and rugs - Kelly Group Inc.
ARPEGGIO COLLECTION - Fabrics ☆ - Decorative Aides Co. Inc.
ARPELLS - Floor coverings–carpet and rugs ☆ - Royalweve Carpet Mills
ARPIN - Cheese ☆ - Dan Carter Inc.
ARPIN STRIP - Cheese ☆ - Dan Carter Inc.
ARPINO - Apparel–women's - United Fashion Industries Inc.
ARPO - Dinnerware–glass ☆ - M & M Associates Ltd.
ARPOCOX - Veterinary pharmaceutical preparations ☆ - Merck & Co., Inc. (Merck Agvet Division)
ARPS - Garden equipment - Amerequip Corp.
ARQUATI - Blinds–vertical - Vertical Blind Factory
ARQUATI - Window coverings - Arquati Inc.
ARQUEST - Sanitary napkins - Arquest, Inc.
ARRA SMITH - Nuts–salted, roasted, cooked, or canned - Arra Smith Co.
ARRAN BRONTE - Biscuits - Bri-AL, Inc.
ARRANAGA - Tomato pastes and sauces - Robert Arranaga & Co.
ARRANGE - Computer software - Common Knowledge, Inc.
ARRANGE - Computer software - General Electric Co.
ARRANGE - Hair care products - Shaklee Corp.
ARRANGE-IT - Craft supplies ☆ - Clayton Corp.
ARRANGEMENTS - Wallcovering - Wall Trends, Inc.
ARRANGEMENTS CAN BE MADE - Flowers, plants, and seeds - Rosewood
ARRANGER - Computer software - Texas Instruments Inc.
ARRAS - Floor coverings–carpet and rugs - Arras Wall Illusions
ARRAY - Contact lenses - Allergan, Inc.
ARRAY - Hair care products - Gillette Co.
ARRAY - Orthopedic products - Orthopedic Technology, Inc.
ARRAY - Paper–bond - Riverside Paper Corp.
ARRAYGUIDE - Computer software - Data General Corp.
ARRCO - Playing cards - United States Playing Card Co.
ARREST - Fungicides ☆ - Uniroyal Chemical Co. Inc. (Crop Protection Div.)
ARREST - Paints ☆ - Red Devil Paints
ARREST-ME - Harnesses - W.T. Ayres & Associates
ARREST YOUR CURIOSITY WITH DETECTIVE HOWIE DUNN - Computer storage devices–optical - How It's Done, Inc.
ARRESTEAR - Paper–looseleaf - Dennison National Co.
ARRESTED - Apparel–women's - Harkham Industries, Inc.
ARRESTIN - Pharmaceutical preparations ☆ - Vortech Pharmaceuticals
ARRESTORPORT-PLUS - Plates–steel - Andrew Corp.
L'ARRET - Bakery products - L'arret French Cafes

☆ = Now out of production

ARREZZIO - Napkins–paper - Sysco Corp.
ARRI - Lighting equipment ✩ - Arriflex Corp.
ARRIBA - Bicycles - REI
ARRIBA - Floor coverings–carpet and rugs ✩ - Customweave Carpets Inc.
ARRIBA - Flowers, plants, and seeds - Jacklin Seed
ARRIBA! - Food products - Riba Foods
ARRIBA - Imitation leather ✩ - Ivy International Ltd.
ARRIBA CAJETA - Candy ✩ - Jackson-Mitchell Inc.
ARRICCIO - Hair care products - Modafini Inc.
ARRID - Deodorants–personal - Carter-Wallace, Inc.
ARRID ALOE ESSENCE - Deodorants–personal - Carter-Wallace, Inc.
ARRID CLEAR - Deodorants–personal - Carter Products Co.
ARRID EXTRA DRY - Deodorants–personal - Carter-Wallace, Inc.
ARRID SHAPE - Deodorants–personal - Carter-Wallace, Inc.
ARRID TEEN IMAGE - Deodorants–personal - Carter-Wallace, Inc.
ARRID-XX - Deodorants–personal - Carter-Wallace, Inc.
ARRIDEL - Shoes - Cara Lee Corp.
ARRIFLEX - Cameras–motion picture ✩ - Arriflex Corp.
ARRIO - Furniture - Herman Miller, Inc.
ARRIS - Paneling ✩ - Domore/DO3
ARRIVA - Computer peripheral equipment - Creative Computers, Inc.
ARRIVA - Cribs–wood ✩ - Cosco, Inc.
ARRIVA - Floor coverings - Congoleum Corp.
ARRIVA - Floor coverings–carpet and rugs ✩ - Galaxy Carpet Mills Inc.
ARRIVA - Goggles–safety - Parmelee Industries, Inc.
ARRIVA - Goggles–safety - U.S. Safety Corp.
ARRIVA - Tires - Goodyear Tire & Rubber Co.
ARRIVANTO - Belts - Crown Pacific Accessories
ARRIVO - Ophthalmic goods - Foremost Optical Products
ARRMAPLAST - Chemical preparations - Arr-Maz Products, Inc.
ARRMASHIELD - Waterproofing compounds - Arr-Maz Products, Inc.
ARRO-MARKER - Markers–felt-tip - Mark-Tex Corp.
ARROGANT RECORDS - Nutcrackers - Kendrick W. Wells
ARROGLYPHS - Computer software - Arro International
ARROKA - Giftware ✩ - Alpine Crafts Co. Inc.
ARROSTO - Food products - Koo Koo Roo, Inc.
ARROW - Ammunition ✩ - Remington Arms Co., Inc.
ARROW - Apparel and accessories - Cluett, Peabody & Co.
ARROW - Bakery products ✩ - Scranton Baker Supply Co.
ARROW - Beverages–alcohol - Heublein, Inc.
ARROW - Boats–canoes ✩ - Black River Canoes
ARROW - Boats–fishing - Doyle/Boston Sailmakers
ARROW - Brushes–paint - Greenview Manufacturing Co.
ARROW - Fireplaces - Heatilator Inc.
ARROW - Glassware–household - Precision Bache Glass
ARROW - Health care products ✩ - Invacare Corp.
ARROW - Hobby kits - Helenor Industries
ARROW - Horseradish ✩ - Gold Pure Food Products Inc.
ARROW - Lighting equipment - Arrow Safety Device Inc.
ARROW - Mops - Bouras Mop Manufacturing Co.
ARROW - Motor vehicles ✩ - Chrysler Corp. (Chrysler-Plymouth Div.)
ARROW - Musical instruments ✩ - Grossman Music Corp.
ARROW - Office supplies - Arrow Rubber Products Inc.
ARROW - Pens ✩ - Parker Pen USA
ARROW - Plastic coatings - Arthur Blank and Co. Inc.
ARROW - Prefabricated buildings–metal - Arrow Group Industries
ARROW - Rings–jewelry - Artcarved Inc.
ARROW - Seafood products–fresh or frozen - Arrowac Fisheries Inc.
ARROW - Ships–sailing vessels ✩ - Johnson Boat Works
ARROW - Skates–ice - Up in the Air, Inc.
ARROW - Sporting goods - F.A. Baker Co. Inc.
ARROW - Staplers - Arrow Fastener Co. Inc.
ARROW - Surveying machinery - Apache Technologies, Inc.
ARROW - Thread ✩ - Coats and Clark Inc.
ARROW - Tires - Carlisle Tire & Rubber Co.
ARROW - Tools - Chickasaw Handle Co. Inc.
ARROW - Tools - Grobet File Co. of America, Inc.
ARROW - Tools ✩ - Mascot Precision Tools
ARROW - Tools–hand-operated ✩ - Durall-Eagle Tools
ARROW - Tools–machine ✩ - Cincinnati Machine
ARROW - Toys - Mattel, Inc.
ARROW - Toys - North Pacific Products Inc.
ARROW - Toys–models ✩ - Estes Industries
ARROW - Vegetables–dried - Arrow Industries, Inc.
ARROW 1851 - Shirts - Cluett, Peabody & Co.
ARROW ALLEY - Game machines ✩ - Coastal Amusement, Inc.

ARROW & ARROW II - Skates–roller - Seneca Sports, Inc.
ARROW BENCH SCRAPER - Cutlery - Pfeil & Holing, Inc.
A THE ARROW COMPANY - Shirts - Cluett, Peabody & Co.
A THE ARROW COMPANY - Shirts - Cluett, Peabody & Co.
ARROW DESIGN - Paints ✩ - Unocal Corp.
ARROW DYNAMICS: THE PROGRAMMING GAME - Computer software ✩ - Sunburst Communications, Inc.
ARROW EXPRESS - Ammunition ✩ - Remington Arms Co., Inc.
ARROW-FLEX - Medical instruments - Arrow International Investment Corp.
ARROW-FLITE - Bicycles - Ross Bicycles USA, Ltd.
ARROW HART - Wiring devices - Cooper Industries, Inc.
ARROW HOT MELT - Tools - Arrow Fastener Co. Inc.
ARROW IV - Aircraft - New Piper Aircraft, Inc.
ARROW-KLIPS - Paper clips - Baumgarten's
ARROW LEATHER - Hobby kits - Craft House Corp.
ARROW-LOCK - Plastic sheeting - Ameron Inc.
ARROW MAP, INC. - American Map Corp.
ARROW MATE - Archery equipment - Saunders Archery Co.
ARROW PUTT - Sporting goods - M.B.I. Enterprises, Inc.
ARROW TEX - Draperies - Arrow Textile Corp.
ARROW-THERMO - Bags - Pfeil & Holing, Inc.
ARROW TRAX - Mats - Superior Manufacturing Group/Notrax Floor Matting
ARROW-WOOD - Prefabricated buildings–wood ✩ - Arrow Group Industries
ARROWFIELD - Wines - Crown Capital USA Inc.
ARROWG+ARD BLUE - Catheters - Arrow International Investment Corp.
ARROWGLASS - Boats–motor - Eldocraft
ARROWHEAD - Cereal - Deer Valley Farm
ARROWHEAD - Dinnerware–glass ✩ - Nikko Ceramics Inc.
ARROWHEAD - Electrical equipment - Mallinckrodt Medical, Inc.
ARROWHEAD - Envelopes - Western States Envelope Co.
ARROWHEAD - Erasers - Faber-Castell Corp.
ARROWHEAD - Floor coverings–carpet and rugs ✩ - Cumberland Mills Inc.
ARROWHEAD - Floor coverings–carpet and rugs ✩ - Walter Carpet Mills
ARROWHEAD - Food products ✩ - Goodmark Foods, Inc.
ARROWHEAD - Leather–chamois - S.M. Arnold Inc.
ARROWHEAD - Musical instruments ✩ - Grossman Music Corp.
ARROWHEAD - Nurseries and garden stores - Dyna Corp.
ARROWHEAD - Plumbing fixtures - Arrowhead Brass Products, Inc.
ARROWHEAD - Recording label ✩ - Oakridge Music Recording Service
ARROWHEAD - Rice ✩ - Gourmet House Inc.
ARROWHEAD - Roof coating - American Paints
ARROWHEAD - Wallpaper - Koroseal Wallcoverings
ARROWHEAD - Water–bottled or canned - Arrowhead Drinking Water Co.
ARROWHEAD - Window coverings - Vertical Blind Factory
ARROWHEAD CRUNCH - Cereal - Arrowhead Mills, Inc.
ARROWHEAD MILLS - Cereal - Arrowhead Mills, Inc.
ARROWHEAD MOUNTAIN - Water–mineral - Perrier Group of America Inc.
ARROWHEAD SPARKLING - Water–bottled or canned - Arrowhead Drinking Water Co.
ARROWHEAD VALLEY - Jewelry - Carlton Russ Greer
ARROWSMITH - Luggage - Arrowsmith Leather Goods Inc.
ARROWSTAR - Sporting goods ✩ - Bear Archery Inc.
ARROWSTONE - Dinnerware–glass - Sango Co. Ltd. (Sango USA Div.)
ARROWSTRAIGHT - Electrical equipment - Southwire Co.
ARROYO - Bicycles ✩ - Raleigh USA Bicycle Co.
ARROYO - Frames–picture - Terragrafics Inc.
ARROYO - Furniture - Romweber Co.
ARROYO GRANDE II - Floor coverings–carpet and rugs ✩ - Walter Carpet Mills
ARROYO SONOMA - Wines - California Wine Co.
ARROYOS - Boots - Boot Royalty Co., LP
ARRYTHMIAGRAPH - Medical apparatus - Del Mar Avionics
ARS - Amplifiers–musical instrument ✩ - ARS Electronics
ARS - Footwear - Hi-Tec Sports USA Inc.
ARS - Heating equipment - American Residential Services, Inc.
ARS - Jewelry - Jess Jewelry Designs Inc.
ARS - Radiators–motor vehicle - Auto Radiator Sales, Inc.
ARS - Tools–garden - Dorothy Biddle Service
ARS AMERICAN READING SYSTEMS - Publisher's imprints - American Reading Systems, Inc.
ARS VIVENDI - Tableware–china - Villeroy and Boch Tableware Ltd.
ARSAN-45 - Veterinary nutritional supplements ✩ - Bingman Laboratories, Inc.
ARSAW - Machine parts - Arsaw, Inc.
ARSAW SUPERBIT-MAN - Tools–power-driven - Darlene M. Collett
ARSCO PRO - Paint rollers - Arsco International Inc.
ARSE-PHENO - Veterinary pharmaceutical preparations ✩ - C.J. Martin Co.

✩ = Now out of production

ARSENAL - Chemical preparations - Foxlabs, Inc.
ARSENAL - Fireworks - American Promotional Events, Inc.
ARSENAL - Fireworks - China Pyrotechnics, Inc.
ARSENAL - Golf clubs - Austad Co.
ARSENAL CITY - Paints - Passonno Paints
ARSHO - Handbags - Stuart Weitzman Inc.
ARSPEC - Wallpaper - Fidelity Industries, Inc.
ARSPEC 54 - Wallpaper - Rigo Wallcoverings Inc.
ARSTYL - Moldings–plaster of paris - NMC Decoration Inc.
ARSYN - Recording label - Jazz Composer's Orchestra Association Inc.
ART - Artists' materials - UDI Corp.
ART - Embossing machines - A.D. Joslin Manufacturing Co.
ART - Jewelry–precious - Arthur Boginsky
ART - Motorcycles - Advanced Racing Technology, Inc.
ART - Recording label - Art Records Manufacturing Co.
ART A LA CARTE - Computer software - 3G Graphics, Inc.
ART-A-MATIC - Toys - Brumberger Co. Inc.
ART-A-RONI - Hobby kits - Roylco Inc.
ART A SQUAD - Employment agencies–temporary help - Wordtemps, Inc.
ART ABC'S - Video production - Mia Kangas
ART ADVANCED RELEASE TECHNOLOGY - Vitamins and nutritional
    supplements - Rexall Sundown, Inc.
ART AMERICANA - Posters - Edward Weston Fine Arts
ART AND CRAFT OF HAVING FUN!, THE - Hobby kits - Jim Henson
    Productions, Inc.
ART & FACTS - Games - Smethport Specialty Co.
ART AND SCIENCE OF PURE FLOWER AND PLANT ESSENCES, THE -
    Hair care products - A-Veda Corp.
ART ATTACKS - Pens - Bic Corp.
ART BANK - Toys–banks - Maruzen Co. Ltd.
ART-BAR - Eyeglasses - Art-Craft Optical Co.
ART BARN - Artists' materials - Karen K. Lewis
ART BEATS - Greeting cards - Art Beats, Inc.
ART BEEPER - Crayons - E.K. Success Ltd.
ART-BILT - Eyeglasses - Art-Craft Optical Co.
ART-BILT CIRCLES - Eyeglasses - Art-Craft Optical Co.
ART BIN - Boxes - Flambeau Products Corp.
ART BITS - Electronic games - N.A.T.T.
ART-BLEND - Paints - Payson Corp.
ART BONES - Sporting goods ☆ - Powell Skateboards
ART-BROW - Eyeglasses - Art-Craft Optical Co.
ART BROWN - Artists' materials - Arthur Brown and Bros. Inc.
ART-CEMENT - Cement ☆ - Atlas Chemical Co.
ART CENTER - Electronics equipment - AZTEK Inc.
ART CETERA - Furniture - Lexington Furniture Industries, Inc.
ART CLAD - Eyeglasses - Art-Craft Optical Co.
ART COLLECTION - Artists' materials - Art Collection by Simi
ART COLLECTION, THE - Novelty items ☆ - Chrishawn Associates Inc.
ART COLLECTION, THE - Office supplies ☆ - McBee Loose Leaf Binders
ART CONCEPT - Plastics–laminated ☆ - Advanced Technology Inc.
ART-CONTEMPO - Jewelry - Kaspar & Esh Inc.
ART-CRAFT - Eyeglasses - Art-Craft Optical Co.
ART CRAFT - Wallets - Art Craft Wallets Inc.
ART CREATION - Artists' materials - Georgia Art Supply Co.
ART CREPE - Paper–crepe - Bemiss-Jason Corp.
ART-CREST - Eyeglasses - Art-Craft Optical Co.
ART CUT - Glassware–household - Federal Glass
ART CZECHOSLOVAKIA - Glassware–household - Superlux Ltd.
ART/DARTS - Games ☆ - Ben Cooper Inc.
ART-DAWN - Eyeglasses - Art-Craft Optical Co.
ART DECO - Bathroom accessories ☆ - Wilardy Originals Inc.
ART DECO - Cigars - Miami Cigars & Co.
ART DECO - Cosmetics - Pauli of Vienna
ART DEPARTMENT, THE - Computer software - ASDG, Inc.
ART DIFFUSOR - Building materials - Systems Development Group
ART DIRECTOR - Drafting supplies - Martin Universal Design Inc.
ART ENAMEL - Enameled ware - Brastoff Designs Inc.
ART ENTERPRISE - Computer software - Inference Corp.
ART ETCH - Crystal etching - Jonal Crystal Ltd.
ART EXPLORER - Computer software - Adobe Systems Inc.
ART-FLEX - Eyeglasses - Art-Craft Optical Co.
ART-FOLIO - Briefcases - Fellowes Manufacturing Co.
ART FOR A NEW AGE. - Posters - Gallery 92, Inc.
ART FOR GOD - Publisher's imprints - Art For God
ART FOR HEAVEN'S SAKE - Posters - Carpentree, Inc.
ART FOR THE YOUNG - Giftware - Artisan House Inc.

ART-FORM - Eyeglasses - Art-Craft Optical Co.
ART FOUNDATION - Figurines - Anna-Perenna Inc.
ART FRAME - Frames–picture - North American Enclosures Inc.
ART FROM THE HEART - Paints–artists' - Bill Jewell
ART FUN - Paper - Bemiss-Jason Corp.
ART GALLERY - Computer software ☆ - Spectrum Universal
ART GALLERY - Fabrics - Piedmont Collections
ART-GEM - Eyeglasses - Art-Craft Optical Co.
ART-GLAZE - Clear polystyrene sheets ☆ - Artcrest Products Co. Inc.
ART-GLO - Eyeglasses - Art-Craft Optical Co.
ART-GLO FOIL - Novelty items - Beistle Co.
ART-GO-ROUND - Lazy Susan for art materials ☆ - Coloron Industries
ART-GO-ROUND - Trays - Brite-Tone Co.
ART GRABBER - Computer software - Spinnaker Software Corp.
ART GRID - Aluminum products - Artcrest Products Co. Inc.
ART GROUP, LONDON - Posters ☆ - Fotofolio Inc.
ART GUILD - Paints ☆ - Dick Blick Co.
ART-GUILD - Pencils ☆ - Faber-Castell Corp.
ART HISTORIAN, THE - Computer peripheral equipment - Reindeer Co.
ART IN CONCERT - House furnishings - Greenwich Workshop, Inc.
ART IN CORRESPONDENCE - Stationery - American Artists Group Inc.
ART IN DESIGN - Wallpaper - Scalamandre Silks Inc.
ART IN HEAVEN - Stationery - Pegge Lynn Butenhoff
ART INSTITUTE/COUNTRY FANCIES - Wallpaper - Warner Co.
ART-KING - Eyeglasses - Art-Craft Optical Co.
ART-KLAD - Eyeglasses - Art-Craft Optical Co.
ART KRAFT - Paper–construction - Bemiss-Jason Corp.
ART LABOE COLLECTION - Compact discs–prerecorded - Original Sound
    Record Co. Inc.
ART-LAD - Eyeglasses - Art-Craft Optical Co.
A ART LEATHER - Photo albums - Art Leather Manufacturing Co., Inc.
ART LIBRARY - Publisher's imprints ☆ - M. Grumbacher Inc.
ART-LINE - Eyeglasses - Art-Craft Optical Co.
ART-LITE - Eyeglasses - Art-Craft Optical Co.
ART-LITE - Lighting equipment - Hobby Hill Inc.
ART-LURE - Eyeglasses - Art-Craft Optical Co.
ART MADE - Wallpaper - Pickhardt & Siebert USA Inc.
ART MARKETING - Greeting cards - Kensington Cards
ART MASTER - Paper–construction - Pen-Tab Industries
ART/MXR - Audio equipment - Applied Research & Technology Inc.
ART 'N FACT - Apparel and accessories - China Trade & Research, Inc.
ART N GOLD - Rings–jewelry - Benjamin Spergel Co.
ART N' SOUL - Recording label - Frederick Dion Riley
ART NOISE - Recording label - Jazz Composer's Orchestra Association Inc.
ART NOUVEAU - Apparel and accessories ☆ - Jantzen Inc.
ART NOUVEAU - Foil–aluminum - Highland Supply Corp.
ART NOUVEAU - Iron - French & Pacific Trading Corp.
ART NOUVEAU - Wallpaper ☆ - Eisenhart Wallcoverings Co.
ART-O-CRAFT - Hobby kits ☆ - Boin Arts & Crafts Co.
ART-O-GRAPH - Projectors–photographic - Artograph Inc.
ART-O-LITE - Picture reflectors - American Reflector & Lighting Co.
ART-O-LOPE - Novelty items–paper - Angler's Roslyn Group Ltd.
ART OF BORDERS - Wallpaper - Jolie Papier
ART OF CALLIGRAPHY, THE - Wallpaper - Kirk-Brummel
ART OF CHRISTMAS FRAGRANCE, THE - Deodorizers - Countryside
    Fragrances, Inc.
ART OF DISCOVERY, THE - Posters - Greenwich Workshop, Inc.
ART OF GAMING, THE - Game tables - Harrah's Las Vegas, Inc.
ART OF GLYNDA TURLEY, THE - Soap - Glynda Turley Prints Inc.
ART OF HOME FRAGRANCE, THE - Air fresheners - Countryside Fragrances
    Inc.
ART OF MACWORLD, THE - Compact discs–prerecorded - Sumeria, Inc.
ART OF MARTELL, THE - Beverages–alcohol - J. & F. Martell Inc.
ART OF MOVEMENT, THE - Fabrics–denim - Dan River Inc.
ART OF MOVEMENT, THE - Footwear - Hongson, Inc.
ART OF ORGANIZATION, THE - Racks - Creative Point Inc.
ART OF SERIES - Music–sheet - Summy-Birchard Inc.
ART OF SEWING: BASICS & BEYOND, THE - Publisher's imprints - Sewing
    Arts, Inc.
ART OF SEWING COLLARS, THE - Video production - Sewing Arts, Inc.
ART OF SEWING WELT POCKETS & BOUND BUTTONHOLES, THE - Video
    production - Sewing Arts, Inc.
ART OF SILK, THE - Wallpaper ☆ - Kingfisher Wallcoverings
ART OF THE 21ST CENTURY, THE - Greeting cards - Hartford House, Ltd.
ART OF THE AGES - Dinnerware - Pfaltzgraff Investment Co.
ART OF THE CRAFTSMAN, THE - Floor coverings - Chris O'Connell, Inc.

ART OF THE GAME, THE - Apparel and accessories - BOCCE by Annecharico Inc.

ART OF THE SEA - Advertising agencies - Red Farm Studio Co.

ART OPAQUE - Paper–bond - Badger Paper Mills, Inc.

ART OUT - Correction fluid - Liquid Paper Corp.

ART PAC - Bags–storage - Herbarium Supply Co.

ART PARTS - Computer software - Electronic Arts Inc.

ART PARTS RON JOE - Computer software - Art Parts

ART PLAYHOUSE - Paper dolls ☆ - Coloron Industries

ART PORTFOLIO - Computer software ☆ - Axlon Inc.

ART-QUEEN - Eyeglasses - Art-Craft Optical Co.

ART-RAY - Eyeglasses - Art-Craft Optical Co.

ART-RIM - Eyeglasses - Art-Craft Optical Co.

ART-ROCK - Aquariums–household - Great American Color Co.

ART SCHOOL - Artists' materials - Sculpture House Inc.

ART SERIES - Furniture - Davis Furniture Industries, Inc.

ART SHEETS - Decals and transfers - Letraset USA Inc.

ART SHOWCASE - Frames–picture ☆ - Two's Co. Inc.

ART-SKOR - Leather goods ☆ - Amceco International Corp.

ART-SOFT - Eyeglasses - Art-Craft Optical Co.

ART-STIK - Markers–felt-tip - Micropoint Inc.

ART STIX - Crayons - Empire Berol USA

ART STREET - Paper - Riverside Paper Corp.

ART STUDIO - Product description unknown - Amav Sales Ltd.

ART STUDIO, THE - Computer software ☆ - Spectrum Holobyte, Inc.

ART STYLE - Eyeglasses - Art-Craft Optical Co.

ART, STYLE & COLOR - Wallpaper - Advent Industries Inc.

ART SUBLIME - Recording label - Art Sublime

ART TACHE - File folders - Angler's Roslyn Group Ltd.

ART TAPE - Tape–adhesive - Bemiss-Jason Corp.

ART TEX - Paper - Bemiss-Jason Corp.

ART TEXTURES ART TO WEAR - Artists' materials - Art Textures, Inc.

ART TILE - Floor coverings–tile - Shep Brown Associates Inc.

ART TIME - Crayons - Sargent Art, Inc.

ART-TISSUE - Novelty items–paper - Beistle Co.

ART TO ART - Wallpaper ☆ - J.C. Prints

ART TO BURN - Candles - Cloene

ART TO GO - Computer software - Multi-Image Network

ART-TONE - Paints - American Paints

ART TOPS - T-shirts–men's - Portal Publications, Ltd.

ART-TOUCH - Eyeglasses - Art-Craft Optical Co.

ART TRAK - Computer software - Art Trak Inc.

ART-TRATION - Games - Kay McVey Nethery

ART UNLIMITED - Postcards - Fotofolio Inc.

ART UTILITY - Artists' materials - J.L. Hammett Co.

ART VEL - Paper ☆ - Hunt Manufacturing Co.

ART VERRIER, THE - Lighting fixtures - Crystal Clear Importing Co. Inc.

ART-VUE - Giftware - Art-Vue Inc.

ART WATCH - Jewelry, watches - Walsh V.P. Group Organization

ART WEAR BY JONAS INC. - Buttons - Art Wear by Jonas Inc.

ART WOOD - Giftware ☆ - Warner Press, Inc.

ART WORKS - Greeting cards and calendars - Weedn Design Ltd.

ART WORKSHOP - Artists' materials - Binney & Smith Inc.

ART WORX - Artists' materials - E.K. Success Ltd.

ART YARN - Yarn - Bemiss-Jason Corp.

ART Z CARD - Greeting cards - Hico Products, Inc.

ARTA CLOAKS - Fabrics - Donna Maltony and Lori L. Pickering Partnership

ARTABEL - Sewing machines–household ☆ - Fleur De Paris

ARTABRAS - Publisher's imprints - Abbeville Press, Inc.

ARTACHE - Artists' materials - Custom Case Co.

ARTAFFECTS - Giftware - Ebeling and Reuss Co.

ART&STUFF - Publisher's imprints - Mission Media, Inc.

ARTAPE - Paper–gummed ☆ - Tape Inc.

ARTAR - Lenses–photographic ☆ - Schneider Optics, Inc.

ARTATTACK - Apparel and accessories - Artattack

ARTBEAT - Musical instruments - Southwest Products, Ltd.

ARTBIN - Boxes - Flambeau Products Corp.

ARTBOARD - Medical apparatus - Artboard Corp.

ARTCADI - Artists' materials - Artcadi Products

ARTCAPS - Toys - Images International Direct Sales Corp.

ARTCARE - Filters–air - Nielsen & Bainbridge

ARTCARVED - Building materials - Entol Industries Inc.

ARTCARVED - Rings–jewelry - Artcarved Inc.

ARTCHEM - Laboratory apparatus - Artchem, Inc.

ARTCO - Desk sets - Artistic Office Products

ARTCO - Hobby kits - Art Chemical Products Inc.

ARTCOR - Artists' materials - Amoco Fabrics and Fibers Co.

ARTCOR - Panels - Harbor Sales Co.

ARTCRAFT - Artists' materials - M. Grumbacher Inc.

ARTCRAFT - Artists' materials - Dick Blick Co.

ARTCRAFT - Coffee mugs, etc. - AAA Glass Corp.

ARTCRAFT - Containers - Rubbermaid Inc.

ARTCRAFT - Dryers–household - Mapes Industries Inc.

ARTCRAFT - Games - Saalfield Publishing Co.

ARTCRAFT - Hobby kits - Great Lakes Crafts

ARTCRAFT - Mail boxes - Enamel Products and Plating Co.

ARTCRAFT - Metals - Artcraft Industries, Inc.

ARTCRAFT - Musical instrument accessories - J. D'Addario & Co. Inc.

ARTCRAFT - Paper ☆ - Erving Paper Products Inc.

ARTCREST - Tiles–ceiling - Artcrest Products Co. Inc.

ARTDINK - Computer software - Seika Corp.

ARTE DE DULCE - Candy - Mojave Foods Corp.

ARTE II - Communications equipment - Qualop Systems Corp.

ARTEC - Floor coverings–carpet and rugs - Burtco Enterprises Inc.

ARTEC - Furniture - Kimball International, Inc.

ARTEC - Hair care products - Artec Systems Group, Inc.

ARTEC - Varnishes - Remien & Kuhnert Co.

ARTEC COLORIST COLLECTION - Hair care products - Artec Systems Group, Inc.

ARTECH - Easels - Art Supply & Instrument Co.

ARTECH - Wallpaper - Fidelity Industries, Inc.

ARTECH DESIGNS - Apparel and accessories ☆ - H.C. Meyers Co.

ARTECH HOUSE - Computer software - Artech House, Inc.

ARTECNICA - Frames–picture - Artecnica

ARTECO - Jewelry - Stewart Webb

ARTEFACTS - Furniture ☆ - Henredon Furniture Industries Inc.

ARTEL - Frames–picture - Designer Moulding

ARTEL - Measuring instruments - Artel, Inc.

ARTEMIA - Pet products - Artemia Inc.

ARTEMIDE - Bedding–linen - Dan River Inc.

ARTEMIS - Ophthalmic goods ☆ - Luxottica

ARTEMIS - Publisher's imprints - Rizzoli International Publications Inc.

ARTEMIS - Rings–jewelry ☆ - Artcarved Inc.

ARTEMIS - Underwear and nightwear ☆ - Signal Knitwear Inc.

ARTEMIS - Vitamins and nutritional supplements - Cell Life Corp.

ARTERBERRY - Wines ☆ - Duck-Pond Cellars

ARTERBERRY CIDERWORKS, THE - Beverages ☆ - Duck-Pond Cellars

ARTERIL - Pharmaceutical preparations ☆ - U.S. Ethicals Inc.

ARTES MONTE AZUL - Greeting cards - Blue Mountain Arts Inc.

ARTESANIA RINCONADA - House furnishings - John Madison Co. Inc.

ARTESANO - Furniture ☆ - Bassett Furniture Industries, Inc.

ARTESANO - Guitars - Juan Orozco Corp.

ARTESIA - Flatware - Pfaltzgraff Investment Co.

ARTESIA - Frames–eyeglass - Hoya Corp. USA

ARTESIA - Furniture ☆ - Mersman Furniture Co.

ARTESIA - Musical instruments - United Musical Instruments USA Inc.

ARTESIA - Recording label - International Record Corp.

ARTESIA - Water–distilled - Artesia Waters Inc.

ARTESIAN - Bathroom fixtures ☆ - Artesian Industries

ARTESIAN - Paper–bond ☆ - Fox River Paper Co.

ARTESON - Wood products ☆ - R & R Woodworking

ARTEX - Cooking equipment–household - Companion Group

ARTEX - Erasers ☆ - Bright Boy Abrasives

ARTEX - Fabrics–linen - Artex International, Inc.

ARTEX - Housewares - The Companion Group

ARTEX - Paints - Josten's Sportswear

ARTEX - Paper–photographic ☆ - Miles Inc. (Agfa Div.)

ARTEX - Sporting goods - Exel Marketing Inc.

ARTEX - Tables–metal - Artex-Green Corp. of N.Y.

ARTEX MAJESTIC - Fabrics - Artex International, Inc.

ARTFAIRE - Giftware - Artfaire

ARTFAIRE - Paper–gift wrap - CPS Corp.

ARTFILE - Computer software - Frambach Software Systems

ARTFLOSS 6 - Thread - Sew-Art International

ARTFORMS - Floor coverings - Armstrong World Industries, Inc.

ARTFUL BALANCE - Recording label - JCI

ARTFUL ORNAMENTS - Christmas tree ornaments - Enesco Corp.

ARTGEL - Paint removers - Winsor & Newton

ARTGLAS - Display cases–wood - Photran Corp.

ARTGLAS - Jars–glass - RTC Industries, Inc.

ARTGUARD - Alarm systems - Andra Systems Inc.

ARTGUARD - Skin care products - Winsor & Newton

ARTGUM - Erasers - Faber-Castell Corp.
ARTH-HERBS - Pharmaceutical preparations - Dr. Clayton's Herbs
ARTH RITE - Vitamins and nutritional supplements - Dobbs and Associates
ARTHA-G - Pharmaceutical preparations ☆ - T.E. Williams Pharmaceutical Inc.
ARTHAFFECT - Vitamins and nutritional supplements - Reliv' International, Inc.
ARTHAREX - Pharmaceutical preparations - C.S. Ruckstuhl Co. Inc.
ARTHERBAL - Vitamins and nutritional supplements - Solaray
ARTHFREE - Vitamins and nutritional supplements - International Medical Research, Inc.
ARTHITROL - Pesticides–agricultural - Avitrol Corp.
ARTHO-FLEX - Health care products ☆ - Enzymatic Therapy, Inc.
ARTHO GENIC - Health care products - Pacific Genesis Inc.
ARTHONUL - Pharmaceutical preparations - Ray Drug Co.
ARTHORITE II - Health care products - Futurebiotics
ARTHOVIMS TABS - Vitamins and nutritional supplements - Great Life Laboratories Inc.
ARTHRA-ZENE - Pharmaceutical preparations ☆ - Xttrium Laboratories Inc.
ARTHRAHERB - Vitamins and nutritional supplements ☆ - J.R. Carlson Laboratories Inc.
ARTHRALGEN - Analgesics - A.H. Robins Co. Inc.
ARTHREADS - Silk scarves - Circle Fine Art Corp.
ARTHRED - Vitamins and nutritional supplements - Traco Labs, Inc.
ARTHRELIEF - Pharmaceutical preparations - Johnston Pharmaceuticals Co.
ARTHREX - Pharmaceutical preparations - Alva-Amco Pharmacal Co.
ARTHRI-ASSIST - Medical apparatus - Alimed, Inc.
ARTHRI-GRIP - Golfing equipment - Royal Grip, Inc.
ARTHRIBALM - Vitamins and nutritional supplements - Bioenergy Nutrient's Inc.
ARTHRIBAN - Pharmaceutical preparations - Vita-Fore Products Co.
ARTHRICARE - Analgesics - Del Pharmaceuticals, Inc.
ARTHRIGEL - Pharmaceutical preparations - Vita-Fore Products Co.
ARTHRIN - Pharmaceutical preparations ☆ - Saron Pharmacal Corp.
ARTHRISOOTHE - Veterinary nutritional supplements - Garmon Corp.
ARTHRISTEP - Shoe insoles - Benchmark Brands
ARTHRITA BLOCK - Pharmaceutical preparations - Equi-Flite Technologies, Inc.
ARTHRITEN - Pharmaceutical preparations - Alva-Amco Pharmacal Co.
ARTHRITIS HOT - Health care products - Thompson Medical Co., Inc.
ARTHRITIS PAIN FORMULA - Pharmaceutical preparations - Whitehall Laboratories
ARTHRITIS RELIEF - Veterinary pharmaceutical preparations - Dr. Goodpet
ARTHRITIS STRENGTH BUFFERIN - Analgesics - Bristol-Myers Squibb Co.
ARTHRITISAIDE - Pharmaceutical preparations - Boericke & Tafel
ARTHRITISAN - Pharmaceutical preparations ☆ - Bioforce of America Ltd.
ARTHRIX - Health care products - Healthwatchers System
ARTHRIZINE - Vitamins and nutritional supplements - Bioenergy Nutrient's Inc.
ARTHRO - Health care products - Maddak Inc.
ARTHRO MUFF - Heating pads–electric - Sunbeam-Oster Household Products
ARTHROCARE - Surgical instruments - Arthrocare Corp.
ARTHROGESIC - Pharmaceutical preparations - Rotex Pharmaceuticals Inc.
ARTHROGOLF - Clothing - Scott Orthopedic Center
ARTHRONICS - Prosthetic apparatus - Arthronics Inc.
ARTHROPAN - Analgesics - Purdue Frederick Co.
ARTHROSAL - Health care products - Halsey Drug Co. Inc.
ARTHROWAND - Surgical instruments - Arthrocare Corp.
ARTHUR - Computer software - Broderbund Software, Inc.
ARTHUR - Footwear - S. Goldberg and Co. Inc.
ARTHUR - Toys–stuffed - Marc Brown
ARTHUR - Toys–stuffed - Eden LLC
ARTHUR - Toys–stuffed ☆ - Russ Berrie and Co., Inc.
ARTHUR-ARTHUR - Apparel–women's ☆ - En Chante
ARTHUR ASHE - Apparel–athletic - Catalina
ARTHUR BLANK & COMPANY - Publisher's imprints - Arthur Blank and Co. Inc.
ARTHUR COURT DESIGNS - Housewares - Arthur Court Designs Inc.
ARTHUR EARL - Arthur Earl
ARTHUR FULMER - Automotive parts and accessories - Arthur Fulmer Co.
ARTHUR GROOM & CO. - Jewelry - Arthur Groom & Co.
ARTHUR HOLLAND - Candy - Murray-Allen International Inc.
ARTHUR I. MAIER ASSOCIATES - Jewelry - Arthur I. Maier Associates
ARTHUR ITIS - Analgesics - Stellar Health Products, Inc.
ARTHUR PRICE OF ENGLAND - Flatware ☆ - Boardman Silversmiths Inc.
ARTHUR RANK - Recording label - Creav Inc. USA
ARTHUR TREACHER'S - Restaurants–fast food - Arthur Treacher's Fish & Chips
ARTHUR WOOD - Tea kettles–nonelectric - Ebeling and Reuss Co.

ARTHUR'S COURT - Floor coverings ☆ - Tarkett, Inc.
ARTHWRITER - Health care products - Maddak Inc.
ARTI & MESTIERI - Novelty items - Italianissimo Inc.
ARTI SETS - Pens - Alvin and Co. Inc.
ARTIA - Musical instruments - Ideal Musical Merchandise Co.
ARTIC - Floor coverings–carpet and rugs - Regal Rugs Inc.
ARTIC - Giftware ☆ - Therma-Tru Corp.
ARTIC - Shirts - Commander Garment Co.
ARTIC 50 - Footwear - Chippewa Shoe Co.
ARTIC CIRCLE - Floor coverings–carpet and rugs - Trend Carpet
ARTIC CIRCLE - Fruits and vegetables ☆ - McMullen Food Bank Inc.
ARTIC FLEXWING - Hoses - Goodyear Tire & Rubber Co.
ARTIC HIGHLIGHT - Speech-synthesis computer software - Artic Technologies International Inc.
ARTIC ICE - Beverages–malt - Adolph Coors Co.
ARTIC ICE - Seafood products–fresh or frozen - Arctic Ice Inc.
ARTIC LINED - Gloves - Netz Glove & Mitten Co.
ARTIC MINT LISTERMINT - Mouthwashes ☆ - Warner-Wellcome
ARTIC MIST - Talcum powders - Luzenac America Inc.
ARTIC SUN - Apparel–children's - Montgomery Ward & Co. Inc.
ARTICHOKE - Recording label - Jazz Composer's Orchestra Association Inc.
ARTICHOKE EXTRACT - Vitamins and nutritional supplements - Vitamin Research Products Inc.
ARTICHOKE-POWER - Vitamins ☆ - Nature's Herbs
ARTICOM - Computer software - Artisoft, Inc.
ARTICULATED SNOUT RINGS - Machine parts - IMO Industries, Inc.
ARTICULATIONS II - Wallpaper - Winfield Design Associates, Inc.
ARTICULATIONS I - Wallpaper ☆ - Winfield Design Associates, Inc.
ARTICULATIONS III - Wallpaper - Winfield Design Associates, Inc.
ARTICULOSE - Pharmaceutical preparations - Seatrace Co.
ARTICWEAR - Apparel and accessories - Answer Products Inc.
ARTIE'S - Juices ☆ - Warner Vineyards Inc.
ARTIFACT NEW YORK - Apparel and accessories - Charivari Holding Corp.
ARTIFACTS - Recording label - Jazz Composer's Orchestra Association Inc.
ARTIFACTS - Wallpaper - B. Berger Co.
ARTIFACTS - Wallpaper - J.C. Prints
ARTIFAX - Artists' materials ☆ - Plano Molding Co.
ARTIFICIAL HORIZONS - Computer software - Artificial Horizons Inc.
ARTIFICIAL LIFE - Science kits - Dynamic Development
ARTIFICIAL TEARS - Pharmaceutical preparations ☆ - Reese Chemical Co.
ARTIFICIAL WORK ENVIRONMENT - Computer software - Up & Running Computer Consultants, Inc.
ARTIGARLICO - Food products - Golden Whisk Pasta Partners
ARTILLA - Toys–automobiles - Mattel, Inc.
ARTIME - Clocks ☆ - Recyco
ARTIQUE - Cabinets - Merillat Industries, Inc.
ARTIQUE - Glass products - Artique Inc.
ARTIQUE - Paper - Bee Paper Co. Inc.
ARTIQUE COLLECTION - Floor coverings–carpet and rugs - Milliken & Co. Inc.
ARTIS - Greeting cards - Paper Magic Group Inc.
ARTISAN - Audio equipment - Sanyo Fisher (USA) Corp.
ARTISAN - Brushes–paint - Bestt-Liebco
ARTISAN - Cabinets - HomeCrest Corp.
ARTISAN - Eyeglasses - Art-Craft Optical Co.
ARTISAN - Fans–electric - Casablanca Fan Co.
ARTISAN - Flatware - Crate and Barrel
ARTISAN - Flatware ☆ - Dansk International Designs, Ltd.
ARTISAN - Floor coverings–tile - Monarch Tile Inc.
ARTISAN - Frames–picture - Artisan Frame & Moulding Co. Inc.
ARTISAN - Furniture ☆ - Bassett Furniture Industries, Inc.
ARTISAN - Furniture ☆ - Hooker Furniture Corp.
ARTISAN - Guitars - Cobble Hill International
ARTISAN - Key rings - Craft Supplies USA
ARTISAN - Musical instruments - Gemeinhardt Co., Inc.
ARTISAN - Paints - Evans Paint
ARTISAN - Paper–writing - Butler Paper Co.
ARTISAN - Pet products - Ronnie DaVinci Inc.
ARTISAN - Projection screens - Draper Shade and Screen Co. Inc.
ARTISAN - Projectors–photographic ☆ - Rigyt-Damar
ARTISAN - Tools - Lufkin Rule Co.
ARTISAN - Tools–garden ☆ - Gamble-Skogmo Inc.
ARTISAN - Wallpaper - Dekortex Inc.
ARTISAN - Wood products - Georgia-Pacific Corp.
ARTISAN BRUSHES - Brushes–paint - Winsor & Newton
ARTISAN COLLECTION - Bathroom fixtures ☆ - Test-Rite Products Corp.

ARTISAN COLLECTION, THE - Hobby kits ☆ - Accent Studios Inc.
ARTISAN COLLECTION, THE - Decorative hardware - H.B. Ives
ARTISAN FROST - Cabinets - HomeCrest Corp.
ARTISAN GLASS BOWL - Pet products - Novalek, Inc.
ARTISAN HOUSE - Giftware - Artisan House Inc.
ARTISAN STONE CARE PRODUCTS - Cleaning preparations - Chemique Inc.
ARTISAN WAY - Dolls - Artisan Way Inc.
ARTISANAT - Floor coverings—carpet and rugs - Artistic Rugs Inc.
ARTISANDS - Hobby kits - Hue Inc.
ARTISANS - Apparel - Artisans Inc.
ARTISAVE - Computer software - Artisoft, Inc.
ARTISCRIBE - Computer software - Artisoft, Inc.
ARTISHAMMY - Polishing cloths - Liberty Advisors Interiors
ARTISSTIX - Office supplies - Artistic Greetings, Inc.
ARTIST - Computer peripherals - Control Systems Inc.
ARTIST - Musical instrument accessories - Dean Markley Strings, Inc.
ARTIST - Musical instruments - E.K. Blessing Co. Inc.
ARTIST - Notebooks and notepads - Alvin and Co. Inc.
ARTIST - Paper - Strathmore Paper Co.
ARTIST-AID - Artists' materials - Artist Aid Transfer Lettering Co.
ARTIST AWARD - Guitars - Guild Music Corp.
ARTIST CHOICE - Glass—flat - Knights Industries Corp.
ARTIST TOUCH - Hobby kits - Craft House Corp.
ARTIST XJS - Computer-graphics controllers - Control Systems Inc.
ARTISTA - Artists' materials ☆ - Binney & Smith Inc.
ARTISTA - Curling irons—electric - Helen of Troy Corp.
ARTISTA - Guitars - MBT International, Inc.
ARTISTA - Tiles—ceramic - Classic International Ceramics, Inc.
ARTISTA II - Artists' materials - Binney & Smith Inc.
ARTISTA VISITATORE - Mirrors - Italianissimo Inc.
ARTISTE - Brushes—hair - Nino Originals
ARTISTE - Frames—eyeglass - Hudson Optical Corp.
ARTISTE - Musical instruments ☆ - Deg Music Products Inc.
ARTISTE DE FRANCE - Wines - Allied Management, Inc.
ARTISTIC - Faucets - Norris Industries Inc.
ARTISTIC - Floor coverings—carpet and rugs - Artistic Rugs Inc.
ARTISTIC - Floor coverings—carpet and rugs - Quaker Inc.
ARTISTIC - Frames—eyeglass ☆ - Vanity Optical Manufacturing Co. Inc.
ARTISTIC - Greeting cards - Artistic Greetings, Inc.
ARTISTIC - Hair care products - Renbow International Ltd. USA
ARTISTIC - Labels—paper - Sue Records Inc.
ARTISTIC - Leather ☆ - K & M Associates
ARTISTIC - Nail care products - Major International Inc.
ARTISTIC - Office supplies - Artistic Office Products
ARTISTIC - Wallpaper - Queens Decorative Wallcoverings Inc.
ARTISTIC ACCENTS - Handbags - Bagland
ARTISTIC BRASS - Faucets - Masco Corp.
ARTISTIC CHECKS - Checkbooks - Artistic Greetings, Inc.
ARTISTIC EXPRESSIONS - Shirts - Prophet Corp.
ARTISTIC EXPRESSIONS - Wallpaper - Unique Wall Fashions Inc.
ARTISTIC GLASS - Glassware—household - Artistic Glass Decorators Inc.
ARTISTIC GLASS - Glassware—household - Superlux Ltd.
ARTISTIC GREETINGS - Labels and stationery - Artistic Greetings, Inc.
ARTISTICK - Wallpaper - Eisenhart Wallcoverings Co.
ARTISTICO - Paper - Fabriano America Inc.
ARTISTIK - Tape—adhesive - Flormel Adhesive Products Inc.
ARTISTIX - Wallpaper - Spare Me the Details Inc.
ARTISTRY - Bathroom accessories - Wilardy Originals Inc.
ARTISTRY - Floor coverings - Aladdin Mills, Inc.
ARTISTRY - Furniture - Schnadig Corp.
ARTISTRY - Furniture ☆ - Bassett Furniture Industries, Inc.
ARTISTRY COLLECTION - Giftware - Grainware Co.
ARTISTRY EDITION - Wallcoverings - Beverly Stevens Ltd.
ARTISTS & WRITERS GUILD - Publisher's imprints - Western Publishing Co., Inc.
ARTISTS' CHOICE - Artists' materials ☆ - Anthes Universal
ARTIST'S EDITION - Dolls - Georgetown Collection, Inc.
ARTISTS' OIL COLORS - Artists' materials - Winsor & Newton
ARTISTS' OILBAR - Artists' materials - Winsor & Newton
ARTISTS' WATER COLOURS - Artists' materials - Winsor & Newton
ARTIVA - Figurines - Possible Dreams, Ltd.
ARTIVITY - Paper—kraft - Pacon Corp.
ARTKO - Posters and art prints - IMS Corp.
ARTLAID - Paper ☆ - Strathmore Paper Co.
ARTLEY - Musical instruments - United Musical Instruments USA Inc.
ARTLIGHT - Lamps - Recyco

ARTLINE - Computer software ☆ - Novell, Inc.
ARTLINE - Construction equipment ☆ - Showerlux USA
ARTLINE - Fabrics—tapestry - Comark Wallcoverings
ARTLINE - Pens - Shachihata Inc. USA
ARTLINE - Wallpaper - Surface Industries Inc.
ARTLINES - Greeting cards ☆ - Chase Collection, Inc.
ARTLITE SIML - Lighting fixtures ☆ - CSL Lighting Manufacturing, Inc.
ARTLOC - Eyeglasses - Art-Craft Optical Co.
ARTLON - Health care products - Bell-Horn
ARTMAN - Eyeglasses - Art-Craft Optical Co.
ARTMAR - Artists' materials ☆ - A.I. Friedman Inc.
ARTMASK - Photographic equipment ☆ - Artype Inc.
ARTMASTER - Paper—construction - Pen-Tab Industries
ARTMASTER - Tables—metal ☆ - Roconex Corp.
ARTMASTER STUDIOS - Lighting fixtures - Merchandise Sales, Inc.
ARTMATE - Luggage - Excel Products Corp.
ARTMATIC - Cosmetics - Arthur Matney Co., Inc.
ARTMATS - Place mats - Convergence Corp.
ARTMEDIA - Computers - Corion Industrial Corp., USA
ARTNERS (PARTNERS IN ART) - Greeting cards - Remigraphics, State of the Heart
ARTNEWS - Publisher's imprints ☆ - ARTnews Books
ARTNEWS MAGAZINE - Magazines - Artnews
ARTNIC - Stamps—hand - Tsukineko, Inc.
ARTO - Office supplies - Alvin and Co. Inc.
ARTOBELLO - Footwear—women's - JBI, Inc.
ARTOGRAPH - Projectors—photographic - Artograph Inc.
ARTOLEUM - Floor coverings—linoleum - Forbo Industries, Inc.
ARTONA - Paper—photographic ☆ - Miles Inc. (Agfa Div.)
ARTONA-RAPID - Paper—photographic ☆ - Miles Inc. (Agfa Div.)
ARTONE - Musical instrument accessories - Sklenarik Musical String Co.
ARTONE - Office supplies ☆ - Faber-Castell Corp.
ARTONE PETER MAX - Office supplies ☆ - Faber-Castell Corp.
ARTONE VENUS - Clay—modeling - American Art Clay Co. Inc.
ARTOPIA CERAMICS - Figurines - Artopia
ARTOPTIC - Artists' materials ☆ - Artoptic International Corp.
ARTOX - Paints ☆ - John L. Armitage & Co.
ARTPEN - Pencils - Koh-I-Noor, Inc.
ARTPOINT - Greeting cards ☆ - Regency Thermographers Inc.
ARTPOST - Postcards - Fotofolio Inc.
ARTPRESS - Publisher's imprints ☆ - ARTnews Books
ARTPRINTS - Giftware ☆ - Quality Artworks Inc.
ARTRA - Easels - Art Supply & Instrument Co.
ARTRA - Skin care products - J. Strickland & Co.
ARTRA ASHY - Skin care products ☆ - Schering-Plough Healthcare Products
ARTRAGEOUS - Computer software - Future Vision Holding, Inc.
ARTRAIL - Construction equipment - Caddcon Designs
ARTRAN - Tiles—ceiling ☆ - Armstrong World Industries, Inc.
ARTRAY - Artists' materials - Martin Universal Design Inc.
ARTRON PRODUCTS - Electronic equipment - David R. Hausten
ART'S - Food products - Art's Tamales
ART'S - Nuts—salted, roasted, cooked, or canned - Bob Ostrow Co.
ARTS AMANTIS - Window coverings - Arts Amantis Corp.
ARTS AND COMMERCE - Computer software - Byron Preiss Multimedia Co., Inc.
ARTS & CRAFTS COLLECTION - Wallpaper - Bradbury & Bradbury Wallpapers
ARTS & ENTERTAINMENT NETWORK - Broadcasting stations—cable television - Arts & Entertainment Network
ARTS & FLOWERS - Giftware - Arts & Flowers
ARTS & KIDS - T-shirts - Arts & Kids, Inc.
ART'S & MARY'S - Snack foods - Art's Tater Chip Co. Inc.
ART'S BBQ - Food products - Art's Tamales
ARTS DU MONT BLEU - Greeting cards - Blue Mountain Arts Inc.
ARTS' LINE - Greeting cards - Brian Arthur Gilna
ARTS 'N CRAFTS - Hardware - Baker Brush Co. Inc.
ART'S PARTYTIME - Food products - Art's Tamales
ARTS PATRONAGE - Publisher's imprints - Washington International Arts Letter
ARTSCARE - Pharmaceutical preparations - Pilates, Inc.
ARTSCREENS - Computer software - Trident Software, Inc.
ARTSE - Computer software - Sparta Inc.
ARTSENSE - Coupons - Art$ Ense, Inc.
ARTSHARP - Artists' materials ☆ - Portage Newspaper Supply Co.
ARTSTART - Credit institutions - H.J. Heinz Co.
ARTSTIR - Bar fixtures—plastic - Spir-it Inc.

☆ = Now out of production

ARTSTOP - Posters - Graphique De France, Ltd.
ARTSTOR - Binders - Oblique Filing Systems
ARTSTOR SYSTEMS - Computer software - Oblique Filing Systems
ARTSZONE - Broadcasting stations–television - Ovation, Inc.
ARTTEC - Artists' materials - Loew-Cornell Inc.
ARTU - Sporting goods - Universal Gym Equipment, Inc.
ARTUR TELLER - Violins ☆ - Ideal Musical Merchandise Co.
ARTURA - Ceramic wall tile - Florida Tile Industries, Inc.
ARTURA IMAGERY - Tiles–ceramic - Florida Tile Industries, Inc.
ARTURA LUMINA - Tiles–ceramic ☆ - Florida Tile Industries, Inc.
ARTURO - Footwear–men's - Baker-Benjes, Inc.
ARTURO FUENTE - Cigars - Tampa Sweetheart Cigar Co.
ARTURO VALDEZ - Musical instruments - Valdez
ARTUSIO - Wines - Pellegrini Bros. Wines Inc.
ARTVAULT - Computer software - Mediamagic Solutions, Inc.
ART*VELOPE - Artists' materials ☆ - Dahle USA
ARTVELOPS - Luggage - Multiple Choice
ARTWARE IN BRASS - Candlesticks - Biedermann & Sons Inc.
ARTWATCH - Clocks - Art Watch International, Inc.
ARTWATCH - Computer peripheral equipment - Ferguson Taylor Group, Inc.
ARTWAX - Adhesives and sealants - Portage Newspaper Supply Co.
ARTWAXER - Adhesives and sealants - Portage Newspaper Supply Co.
ARTWIPES - Paint removers - Winsor & Newton
ARTWISE - Maps - Streetwise Maps Inc.
ARTWORK - Eyeglasses - Art-Craft Optical Co.
ARTWORKS - Computer software - Dynamic Graphics Inc.
ARTWORKS - Jewelry - Rolo Manufacturing Co., Inc.
ARTWORKS - Wallpaper ☆ - Imperial Wallcoverings, Inc.
ARTWORKS COLLECTION - Floor coverings–carpet and rugs - Daltonian Carpet & Cushion Inc.
ARTWORKS I - Wallpaper ☆ - Archetonic
ARTWORKS LIGHTING ARTISTRY - Lighting fixtures - Angelo Brothers Co.
ARTWORKS ONE - Wallpaper - Artique Design
ARTWORTHY - Artists' materials - Datacom Inc.
ARTY SEAL - Toys–stuffed - Dakin Inc.
ARTZNER - Food products - Young's Market Co.
ARUBA - Audio equipment - Robert Bosch Corp.
ARUBA - Bathing suits - Pierre Cardin Electronique
ARUBA - Bathroom fixtures ☆ - Artesian Industries
ARUBA - Boats - Lanness K. McKee & Co.
ARUBA - Boats ☆ - Wellcraft Marine Corp.
ARUBA - Boats–houseboats ☆ - Bluewater
ARUBA - Furniture ☆ - Homecrest Industries Inc.
ARUBA - Glass–optical - Welling International
ARUBA - Shoes ☆ - Allen-Edmonds Shoe Corp.
ARUBA PLAID - Bedding–linen - Dan River Inc.
ARUBACAT - Pet products - Sheri Mitchell
ARUM - Glassware–household ☆ - Spiegelau Inc.
ARUNGO - Games - Little Harbor Corp.
ARUP SYSTEM 2000 - Computer hardware - Associated Regional and University Pathologists, Inc.
ARUSH - Apparel and accessories - Arush Apparel
ARVEE - Health care products - International Biomedical, Inc.
ARVEE - Recording label - Everest Record Group
ARVIDA - Ophthalmic goods - Styl-Rite Optical Manufacturing Co., Inc.
ARVIN - Electrical equipment - Arvin Industries Inc.
ARVIN TIME SENTRY - Electrical equipment ☆ - Adobe Air Inc.
ARVON - Paints - Monsey Products Co.
ARX - Locks–door - Medeco Security Locks, Inc.
ARY COOPER - Apparel and accessories ☆ - Seattle Pacific Industries, Inc. (UNIONBAY Sportswear)
ARYA LAYA - Health care products - Skin Care Centre Inc.
ARYLIFT PATIENT SUPPORT SYSTEM - Medical apparatus - Arylift, Inc.
ARYLZENE - Resins–synthetic - Georgia-Pacific Corp.
ARZACH - Publisher's imprints - Starwatcher Graphics, Inc.
ARZBERG - Dishes–china - WMF/USA
ARZEE - Recording label - Arcade Record Co./Arzee Record Co.
ARZUMAN - Meats - Mikailian Meat Products, Inc.
AS - Construction equipment - Appleton Supply Co. Inc.
AS - Cutlery - Salm-Harley Corp.
AS - Eyeglasses - Jackson Products, Inc.
AS-5 OATS - Flowers, plants, and seeds - Jacklin Seed
AS/20 - Cleaning preparations–carpet and rug ☆ - Wallerstein Co.
AS/400 - Computers - International Business Machines Corp.
AS ACROSS SPORT - Apparel and accessories - Chet Starling
AS B4 - Apparel and accessories - Fateh International Inc.

AS-CAFF - Pharmaceutical preparations - Rugby Laboratories Inc.
AS CLOSE AS TWO RINGS CAN BE - Jewelry - Sandberg & Sikorski Diamond Corp.
AS GENTLE WITH YOUR BABY AS YOU ARE - Paper - Scott Paper Co.
AS INDIVIDUAL AS YOU ARE - Colognes - Parfum de Coeur Ltd.
AS-MA-PA - Pharmaceutical preparations - Lanpar Co.
AS/MANAGER - Computer software - MBA Inc.
AS/MANAGER - Computer software - Mersch-Bacher Associates, Inc.
A.S. RIGGER - Footwear - CMA Marketing Corp.
AS-TILE - Tiles–enamel - Lucky America Inc.
AS TIME GOES BY - Floor coverings–carpet and rugs - Mohawk Industries Inc.
AS TIME GOES BY - Wallpaper - Gagne Wallcovering, Inc.
AS TOUGH AS THE ATHLETES WHO WEAR IT - Fabrics - Yarrington Mills Corp.
AS YOU LIKE IT - Cigars - Swisher International, Inc.
AS YOU LIKE IT - Furniture - Erwin-Lambeth Inc.
AS YOU LIKE IT - Wallpaper - Pantasote Inc. (Wallcovering Div.)
AS.2000 - Exercising equipment - Nautilus Acquisition Inc.
A.S.A. - Analgesics - Eli Lilly and Co.
ASA - Pet products - John A. Van Den Bosch Co.
ASA-312 - Computer software - Digital Lightwave, Inc.
ASA-4795 - Toys - Amateur Softball Association of America
ASAHI - Postcards - Asahi Trading Co.
ASAHI - Sporting goods - Yamaha Corp. of America (Sporting Goods Div.)
ASAHI NAMAICCHO - Beverages–malt - Century Importers Inc.
ASAHI PENTAX - Cameras - Pentax Corp.
ASAHI SUPER DRY - Beverages–malt - Century Importers Inc.
ASAMERA - Gasoline - Asamera Oil U.S. Inc.
ASANA - Insecticides - E.I. Dupont de Nemours and Co.
ASANTE FASHIONS - Apparel and accessories - Asante Fashions International, Inc.
ASAP - Bathroom accessories - General Marble Co.
ASAP - Computer software - QMS, Inc.
ASAP - Computer software - Wonderlic Personnel Test, Inc.
ASAP - Fibers–acrylic - Chemdal Corp.
A.S.A.P. - Nail care products - Salon Sciences Inc.
ASAP - Screws - Olympic Manufacturing Group, Inc.
ASAP RESPONDER - Computer peripheral equipment - Command Communications, Inc.
ASAT - Apparel and accessories - Brigade Quartermasters Ltd.
ASB - Wheelchairs - Labac Systems, Inc.
ASB GROWER MIX - Synthetic soil - ASB Greenworld, Inc.
ASBACH - Confections - Acme Food Specialties Inc.
ASBESTALUME - Paints - Standard T Chemical Co. Inc.
ASBESTITE - Roof coating - Coopers Creek Chemical Corp.
ASBESTOCOTE - Paints - Morris Paint & Varnish Co.
ASBESTOLITE - Roofing materials–clay - L.D. Sterns Corp.
ASBESTOS SEAL - Paints ☆ - Verflex Co. Inc.
ASBRON-G - Pharmaceutical preparations - Dorsey Laboratories
ASBURY - Cabinets - Yorktowne Inc.
ASBURY - Frames–eyeglass ☆ - U.S. Optical Frame Co.
ASBURY - Machine parts - American Coupler Systems, Inc.
ASBURY FERST - Crayons - Asbury Ferst
ASBURY PARK - Floor coverings - Mannington Resilient Floors
ASC - Computer programs - Advanced Software Concepts
ASC - Computer software - Healthcare Design Systems
ASC - Skin care products - Geritrex Corp.
ASC ADVANCED SOFTWARE CONCEPTS - Computer programs - Advanced Software Concepts
ASC ELECTRONIC - Tape recorders–cassette ☆ - Meteor Light & Sound Co.
ASCALBAR - Pharmaceutical preparations ☆ - C.O. Truxton Inc.
ASCAP - Analgesics - Maxim Chemicals Ltd.
ASCAREL - Pharmaceutical preparations - Pfeiffer Pharmaceuticals Inc.
ASCARITE - Chemicals - Thomas Scientific
ASCEND - Braces–orthopedic - Kirschner Medical Corp.
ASCEND - Drums–musical instruments - LP Music Group
ASCEND - Golfing equipment - Triumph Golf Co.
ASCEND - Herbicides - BASF Corp.
ASCENDA - Wheelchairs - Access Industries, Inc.
ASCENDANCY - Computer software - Broderbund Software, Inc.
ASCENSION - Dinnerware–glass ☆ - Nikko Ceramics Inc.
ASCENSION - Floor coverings–carpet and rugs - Patcraft Mills Inc.
ASCENSION - Wheelchairs - Ascension, L.C.
ASCENSION - Wines - York Mountain Winery
ASCENT - Computer software - Kofax Image Products, Inc.

☆ = Now out of production

ASCENT - Furniture - Haworth, Inc.
ASCENT - Integrated circuits - United Technologies Microelectronics Center, Inc.
ASCENT - Sporting goods - Lisco, Inc.
ASCENT CAPTURE - Computer software - Kofax Image Products, Inc.
ASCENT DESCENT - Apparel and accessories - Fila USA, Inc.
ASCENT TEAM - Apparel–athletic - Statusworks International
ASCIIPAD - Computer peripherals - ASCII Entertainment Software Inc.
ASCIIWARE - Joysticks - ASCII Entertainment Software Inc.
ASCIRAM - Computer software - ASCI
ASCLEROL - Pharmaceutical preparations - G.O. Spanner Inc.
ASCO - Artists' materials - Artists Supply Co.
ASCO - Bags–duffel - Asco Group Limited
ASCO - Jewelry–precious - Capitol Ring Co., Inc.
ASCOBRIC - Toys - Learning Products Inc.
ASCOM HASLER - Mailing machines ☆ - Better Packages
ASCOR-B.I.D. - Vitamins and nutritional supplements - Pharmex Inc.
ASCORBALOX - Spices and extracts - Kalsec, Inc.
ASCORBATE BIO-C - Vitamins and nutritional supplements - NutriBiotic
ASCORBE A VITE - Vitamins and nutritional supplements - Natural Organics, Inc.
ASCORBIC ACID - Vitamins and nutritional supplements - Vitamin Research Products Inc.
ASCORBIC-B - Health care products - Health Maintenance Programs Inc.
ASCORBIN/II - Pharmaceutical preparations - Pasadena Research Laboratories, Inc.
ASCORBINEED - Pharmaceutical preparations - Hanlon Drug Products
ASCORBISOL-K - Veterinary pharmaceutical preparations - Vineland Laboratories Inc.
ASCORBUF - Pharmaceutical preparations ☆ - JMI-Canton Pharmaceuticals
ASCOT - Dinnerware–glass ☆ - Lenox, Inc.
ASCOT - Drinkware - Corbell & Co.
ASCOT - Floor coverings - Mannington Resilient Floors
ASCOT - Floor coverings–carpet and rugs - Glen Eden Wool Carpets
ASCOT - Floor coverings–carpet and rugs - Tuftex Carpet Mills, Inc.
ASCOT - Floor coverings–carpet and rugs ☆ - Stanton Carpet Corp.
ASCOT - Furniture ☆ - Lane Co. Inc.
ASCOT - Luggage - Skyway Luggage Co.
ASCOT - Motorcycles ☆ - American Honda Motor Co. Inc. (Acura Div.)
ASCOT - Ophthalmic goods - Styl-Rite Optical Manufacturing Co., Inc.
ASCOT - Tires - Bridgestone/Firestone, Inc.
ASCOT - Wallets - Enger-Kress Co.
ASCOT - Whirlpools - Lasco Products Group
ASCOT CLUB - Gin - Old Boone Distillery Co.
ASCOT MARK I - Binoculars ☆ - Swift Instruments, Inc.
ASCOT POINT - Floor coverings–carpet and rugs - Karastan-Bigelow Inc.
ASCOT STRIPE - Bedding–linen - Dan River Inc.
ASCP IMAGEBASE - Computer software - American Soccer Co. Inc.
ASCRIPTIN - Analgesics - Rhone-Poulenc Rorer Pharmaceuticals Inc.
ASCTREND - Computer software - Ablesys Corp.
ASD - Computer software - ASD Software Inc.
A.S.D INTERNATIONAL - Apparel - Arlette International Inc.
ASDAN - Recording label ☆ - Dana Publishing Co.
ASEBORREIC - Skin care products - Lendan USA Co.
ASELLACRIN - Pharmaceutical preparations ☆ - Serono Laboratories Inc.
ASEP - Bags–laundry - Angelica Corp.
ASEPBOND - Dental equipment - KHS Polymer Technologies, Inc.
ASEPTAIR - Air filters - Aston Technologies Corp.
ASEPTEC - Dental equipment - MDT Corp.
ASEPTEX - Dental equipment - Minnesota Mining & Manufacturing Co.
ASEPTICO - Health care products - Aseptico Laboratories Inc.
ASEPTO - Medical apparatus - Becton, Dickinson and Co.
ASEPTO CATCH - Health care products - Medi Inc.
ASEPTOPLAST - Contact lenses ☆ - Wesley-Jessen Co.
ASEPTOR - Ophthalmic apparatus - Bausch & Lomb Inc.
ASEPTRON - Ophthalmic apparatus - Bausch & Lomb Inc.
A*S*EXEC - Computer software - EDP Systems, Inc.
A.S.F. - Vitamins and nutritional supplements - Solaray
ASF135 - Duplicating machines - Xerox Corp.
ASG-IMPACT - Computer software - Allen Systems Group, Inc.
ASGARD SOFTWARE - Computer software - Asgard Software Inc.
ASH - Hosiery - Ash Handkerchief Corp.
ASH - Jams and jellies - Ash Enterprises, Inc.
ASH - Jewelry - Asher Jewelry Co. Inc.
ASH 087 - Leather - Classic Soft Trim Inc.
ASH-BUOY - Housewares - Orbex Inc.

ASH CADDY - Musical instrument accessories - Mechanical Music Corp.
ASH HOE - Fireplace equipment - O'Hagin's Inc.
ASH-LOK - Wood products - Aspen Valley Lumber Co. Inc.
ASH MEADOW - Furniture ☆ - Stanley Furniture Co. Inc.
ASH 'N TRASH - Wastebaskets - Witt Co.
ASH PUMP - Valves–intake - Baker Hughes Inc.
ASHA - Dolls - Mattel, Inc.
ASHA FOR LIFE - Skin care products - Decar, Ltd.
ASHANTI - Iced tea–bottled or canned - Ashanti Holding Co., Inc.
ASHANTI - Perfume - Flori Roberts Inc.
ASHANTI KINGDOM, THE - Toys–stuffed - ABC International Co.
ASHAWAY - Sporting goods - Ashaway Line & Twine Manufacturing Co.
ASHBOURNE - Liqueurs - Marie Brizard Et Roger, Inc.
ASHBOURNE BISCUITS - Cookies - Christopher Brookes Distinctive Foods
ASHBOURNE IRISH CREAM - Beverages–alcohol - Marie Brizard Wines & Spirits, USA
ASHBROOK - Water purification systems - Ashbrook Corp.
ASHBURTON - Glassware–household - Owens-Illinois Inc. (Libbey Div.)
ASHBURY - Confections - Beacon Sweets, Inc.
ASHBURY - Floor coverings–carpet and rugs - Tuftex Carpet Mills, Inc.
ASHBURY - Statuary - Service Merchandise Co., Inc.
ASHBURY HALL - Furniture - Universal Flooring
ASHBURY PARK - Floor coverings–carpet and rugs - Hollytex Carpet Mills Inc.
ASHBURY PLACE - Wallpaper - Seabrook Wallcoverings, Inc.
ASHBURY SPRAYS - Dishes–china - Waterford Wedgewood USA, Inc.
ASHBY PARK - Recording label - Smarty Pants Audio and Video Inc.
ASHBY'S NO REGRETS - Ice cream - Tom Davis & Sons Dairy Co., Inc.
ASHCRAFT - Furniture–wood - Chaircraft Div.
ASHCROFT - Gauging instruments - Dresser Industries, Inc.
ASHCROFT - Lumber - Georgia-Pacific Corp.
ASHDKA - Pizzas–frozen - Indian Foods Co.
ASHDOWN - Wallpaper - Dekortex Inc.
ASHE - Recording label ☆ - Rounder Records Corp.
ASHER - Apparel–men's - Asher Co.
ASHER - Candy - Asher Candy Co.
ASHER BERNJAMIN - Furniture - Harden Furniture Co. Inc.
ASHER SPORT - Apparel–men's - Asher Co.
ASHEVILLE - Cabinets ☆ - Marsh Furniture Co.
ASHEVILLE - Furniture - Haworth, Inc.
ASHEVILLE TRAVELER - Publisher's imprints - Gray Matter Publishing
ASHEX - Skin care products ☆ - Sheila Brit Ltd.
ASHFIELD - Furniture ☆ - Lane Co. Inc.
ASHFORD - Bathroom fixtures - Artesian Industries
ASHFORD - Floor coverings ☆ - Congoleum Corp.
ASHFORD - Floor coverings–carpet and rugs ☆ - Navan Carpets Inc.
ASHFORD - Frames–eyeglass ☆ - U.S. Optical Frame Co.
ASHFORD - Furniture - Homecrest Industries Inc.
ASHFORD - Puppets - Dakin Inc.
ASHFORD - Wallpaper - Ashford House
ASHFORD - Watches - Bulova Corp.
ASHFORD II - Wallpaper ☆ - Ashford House
ASHFORD BEAR - Toys–stuffed - Dakin Inc.
ASHFORD IV - Wallpaper ☆ - Ashford House
ASHFORD PLUS - Bathroom fixtures - Artesian Industries
ASHGROVE 32 - Floor coverings–carpet and rugs - Eagle Carpets Inc.
ASHLAND - Clocks ☆ - General Time Corp. (Westclox/Seth Thomas Div.)
ASHLAND - Drums–musical instruments ☆ - Grossman Music Corp.
ASHLAND - Floor coverings–carpet and rugs ☆ - Criterion Mills Inc.
ASHLAND - Furniture - American Woodmark Corp.
ASHLAND - Furniture ☆ - Bassett Furniture Industries, Inc.
ASHLAND - Housewares - Ashland Products Co. Inc.
ASHLAND - Lubricants - Ashland Oil, Inc.
ASHLAND - Shoes ☆ - Allen-Edmonds Shoe Corp.
ASHLAND - Tools - Electro Engineering Products Co. Inc.
ASHLAND-DAVIS - Siding–insulating - Ashland-Davis Co.
ASHLAND MART - Gasoline - Ashland Inc.
ASHLAND STATION - Figurines - Linda Mc Co.
ASHLAR - Dinnerware–glass - Arita Sales Co. Inc.
ASHLAWN - Floor coverings–carpet and rugs ☆ - Capel, Inc.
ASHLEIGH - Furniture - Stanley Furniture Co. Inc.
ASHLEIGH BRILLIANT - Postcards - Brilliant Enterprises
ASHLEY - Apparel stores–children's - Goodman Knitting Co. Inc.
ASHLEY - Apparel–women's - Kellwood Co.
ASHLEY - Cabinets ☆ - Merillat Industries, Inc.
ASHLEY - Cabinets ☆ - Nutone Inc.

☆ = Now out of production

ASHLEY - Cabinets ☆ - Wellborn Cabinet, Inc.
ASHLEY - Cabinets–wood - Kemper
ASHLEY - Dishes–china ☆ - Gorham Inc.
ASHLEY - Dolls ☆ - Hasbro, Inc.
ASHLEY - Floor coverings–carpet and rugs ☆ - Regal Rugs Inc.
ASHLEY - Floor coverings–carpet and rugs ☆ - Richmond Carpet Mills
ASHLEY - Glassware–household - Dalzell-Viking
ASHLEY - Heaters–gas - Martin Industries, Inc.
ASHLEY - Tableware–china ☆ - Lenox, Inc.
ASHLEY - Trailers–boat - Hustler Boat Trailers
ASHLEY - Wallcoverings ☆ - Wallstars
ASHLEY - Wallpaper ☆ - Wolf-Gordon Inc.
ASHLEY - Wigs - Jean Paree Weegs Inc.
ASHLEY AMES - Apparel–women's - Montgomery Ward & Co. Inc.
ASHLEY ARBOR - Floor coverings–carpet and rugs - Downs Carpet Co. Inc.
ASHLEY HALL - Floor coverings–carpet and rugs ☆ - Mannington Carpets, Inc.
ASHLEY HALL - Furniture ☆ - Bernhardt Industries
ASHLEY HEIGHTS - Floor coverings–carpet and rugs - Gulistan Carpet Inc.
ASHLEY HEIGHTS - Floor coverings–carpet and rugs - Whitecrest Carpet Mills
ASHLEY MARIE - Footwear - Bee-Gee Shoe Corp
ASHLEY MOORE - Leather goods - Leather Loft Stores, Inc.
ASHLEY TAYLOR - Lamp shades–fabric - Kmart Properties, Inc.
ASHLEYROSE - Drapery hardware - Kenney Manufacturing Co.
ASHLEY'S - Food products - Bruce Foods Corp.
ASHLING - Earthenware ☆ - Waterford Wedgewood USA, Inc.
ASHLING - Floor coverings–carpet and rugs - Navan Carpets Inc.
ASHLYN HALL - Floor coverings ☆ - Congoleum Corp.
ASHMANS - Boots - Accessory Distributors Inc.
ASHMONT - Flatware - Reed and Barton Corp.
ASHMORE - Floor coverings–carpet and rugs - Karastan-Bigelow Inc.
ASHORE - Apparel and accessories - Kellwood Co.
ASHRAM - Incense - Auromere Inc.
ASHTON - Bedding–linen - Dan River Inc.
ASHTON - Cabinets - American Woodmark Corp.
ASHTON - Floor coverings–carpet and rugs - Karastan-Bigelow Inc.
ASHTON - Floor coverings–carpet and rugs ☆ - Regal Rugs Inc.
ASHTON - Furniture - Inwood Office Furniture
ASHTON - Pens - Ashton Holdings, Inc.
ASHTON - Printing presses - Didde Web Press Corp.
ASHTON - Shoes - Allen-Edmonds Shoe Corp.
ASHTON-DRAKE - Novelty items - Bradford Exchange, Ltd.
ASHTON-DRAKE GALLERIES - Dolls - Ashton-Drake Galleries, Ltd.
ASHTON FALLS - Tables–wood - Riverside Furniture Corp.
ASHTON HUMIDIGUIDE - Thermometers - Taylor Environmental Instruments
ASHTON PARK - Tableware–china ☆ - Lenox, Inc.
ASHTRON - Furniture polish and wax - Ashley Furniture Industries, Inc.
ASHVILLE - Floor coverings - Armstrong World Industries, Inc.
ASHWELL - Machine parts - Ashwell Label Dies, Inc.
ASHWIN - Computer software - Seagate Enterprise Management Software
ASHWORTH - Apparel and accessories - Ashworth, Inc.
ASHWORTH - Apparel and accessories - Charter Golf, Inc.
ASHWORTH - Conveyors - Ashworth Bros., Inc.
ASHY - Skin care products ☆ - Sheila Brit Ltd.
ASI - Audio equipment - Parts Express International, Inc.
ASI - Paint sprayers - Wagner Spray Tech Corp.
ASI - Structural trusses and joists - Trus Joist MacMillan L.P.
ASI SOY YO - Spanish children's-health journal - Informative Amenities Inc.
ASIA - Frames–eyeglass - May Optical Co. Inc.
ASIAN ACCENTS - Wallpaper - Seabrook Wallcoverings, Inc.
ASIAN ALMOND - Vegetables–frozen - Flowers Industries Inc.
ASIAN BASICS - Wallpaper - Seabrook Wallcoverings, Inc.
ASIAN CLASSICS - Wallpaper - Seabrook Wallcoverings, Inc.
ASIAN CLASSICS II - Wallpaper - Seabrook Wallcoverings, Inc.
ASIAN CONNECTIONS - Catalogs - Asian Connections
ASIAN COURT - Furniture ☆ - Hammary Furniture Co. Inc.
ASIAN ELEGANCE - Wallpaper - Seabrook Wallcoverings, Inc.
ASIAN EXPRESSIONS - Wallpaper - Seabrook Wallcoverings, Inc.
ASIAN FAVORITES - Wallpaper - Seabrook Wallcoverings, Inc.
ASIAN GOLD - Seafood products–fresh or frozen - Coast to Coast Seafood Inc.
ASIAN GOURMET - Food products - Tidelands Sales Co. Inc.
ASIAN HARVEST - Shrimp–fresh or frozen - U.S. Foodsvervice Inc.
ASIAN HARVEST - Shrimp–fresh or frozen - US Foodservice
ASIAN HUMANITIES PRESS - Publisher's imprints - Jain Publishing Co.

ASIAN IMAGES - Wallpaper - Seabrook Wallcoverings, Inc.
ASIAN IMPROV - Recording label - Carmel Records
ASIAN JEWELS - Wallpaper - Seabrook Wallcoverings, Inc.
ASIAN SILK CREAM - Skin care products - Entre-Nous Fragrances Ltd.
ASIAN STAR - Fish–fresh or frozen - Zaloom Marketing Corp.
ASIAN TAMARIND SAUCE - Sauces - Cinnabar Specialty Foods, Inc./Neera's Products
ASIAN TEXTILES - Fabrics–broadcloth - A.R. Lawrence & Associates
ASIAN TEXTILES - Wallpaper ☆ - Seabrook Wallcoverings, Inc.
ASIAN TEXTURES - Wallpaper - Seabrook Wallcoverings, Inc.
ASIAN TREASURES - Wallpaper - Seabrook Wallcoverings, Inc.
ASIAN WEAVES - Wallpaper - Seabrook Wallcoverings, Inc.
ASIAN WEAVES II - Wallpaper - Seabrook Wallcoverings, Inc.
ASIAN YARNS - Wallpaper - Seabrook Wallcoverings, Inc.
ASIANA - Wallpaper - Advance Wallcoverings
ASIANCE - Hair care products - William M. Wong
ASIASCRIPT - Computer storage devices - Payne Loving Trust
ASIATICA - Wallpaper - Surface Industries Inc.
ASIC TIME TO MARKET SOLUTION, THE - Integrated microcircuits - Chip Express Corp.
ASICS - Footwear - Asics Tiger Corp.
ASICS - Sporting goods - Nichols Wrestling Products Inc.
ASIST - Computer software - Summa Four, Inc.
ASK - Video production - Accom, Inc.
ASK APPLE: SCIENCE - Computer software - AV Systems Inc.
ASK-IT - Computer software - True Basic, Inc.
ASK ME MULTIMEDIA CENTER - Computer peripheral equipment - Ask Me Multimedia, Inc.
ASK RX - Computer software - Camdat Corp.
ASK TAROT - Games - Danuta Christine Miller
ASK ZANDAR - Toys - Hasbro, Inc.
ASK?EM - Computer software - Infonetics Corp.
ASKIT - Computer software - ASK Computer Systems Inc.
ASK'N ANSWER - Toys ☆ - Creative Playthings Ltd.
ASL+ - Lenses–optical - Sola Optical USA, Inc.
ASL - Lighting fixtures - American Scientific Lighting
ASL ASPHERIC FLAT-TOP 28 - Lenses–optical - Sola Optical USA, Inc.
ASL IN POLYCARBONATE - Lenses–optical - Sola Optical USA, Inc.
ASL IN SPECTRALITE - Lenses–optical - Sola Optical USA, Inc.
ASLAN MEDICAL - Surgical instruments - Aslan Medical Technologies
ASLAN MINILAPAROSCOPY - Surgical instruments - Aslan Medical Technologies
ASLANIS BRAND, THE - Seafood products–fresh or frozen - Aslanis Seafoods Inc.
ASLESEN - Fruits–canned - Aslesen Co.
ASLEX - Computer peripheral equipment - Aslex, Inc.
ASLI ARTS - Furniture - J. Kenneth Zahn
ASM - Antennas - Allen Telecom Group, Inc.
A.S.M. - Emulsifiers - Chromaline Corp.
ASM - Water purification systems - Recovery Engineering, Inc.
ASM PRESS - Publisher's imprints - American Society for Microbiology
ASMA-EZE - Pharmaceutical preparations - Parmed Pharmaceuticals, Inc.
ASMA-TUSS - Health care products - Halsey Drug Co. Inc.
ASMAC - Pharmaceutical preparations ☆ - Vitarine Pharmaceuticals Inc.
ASMACOL - Pharmaceutical preparations ☆ - Pal-Pak Inc.
ASMADIL - Pharmaceutical preparations ☆ - Solvay Pharmaceuticals Inc.
ASMAKOL - Cough medicines - D'Franssia Corp.
ASMANEX - Pharmaceutical preparations - Schering Corp.
ASMAVERT - Inhalers ☆ - Nephron Pharmaceuticals
ASMOLIN - Pharmaceutical preparations - Lincoln Diagnostics
ASMUS - Spices and extracts - Asmus Spice Co.
ASNACA - Dental equipment ☆ - Freeda Vitamins Inc.
ASNY - Frames–picture - Alfred Schiftan Inc.
ASOLO SPORT - Footwear - Kenko International Inc.
ASP - Cabinets–metal - Richards-Wilcox Manufacturing Co.
ASP - Computer peripheral equipment - Oxford Molecular Group
ASP - Electronic equipment - ASP Computer Products Inc.
ASP - Fasteners–hook and eye - Huck International, Inc.
ASP - Golf clubs ☆ - Raymon W. Cook
ASP - Medical apparatus - Johnson & Johnson
ASP - Stationery - C.M. Paula Co.
A.S.P. - Toys–models ☆ - Estes Industries
ASP HOMBLAD - Candles - Bergquists
ASPA - Lubricating oils ☆ - Shell Oil Co.
ASPARAGO - Pasta - Hagerty Foods, Inc.

ASPARTAMINS - Vitamins and nutritional supplements - Solgar Vitamin and Herb Co., Inc.

ASPAS - Pharmaceutical preparations - Hyrex Pharmaceuticals

ASPCA - Jewelry - American Society for the Prevention of Cruelty to Animals

ASPCQ COLLECTION - Toys–stuffed - Mighty Star Inc. (Special Effects Div.)

ASPEC TECHNOLOGY - Integrated circuits - Aspec Technology, Inc.

ASPECT - Computer software - Aspect Telecommunications Corp.

ASPECT - Frames–eyeglass - May Optical Co. Inc.

ASPECT - Loudspeakers - Aura Systems, Inc.

ASPECT - Publisher's imprints - Warner Books, Inc.

ASPECT DIGITAL FORMATTER - Cameras - Aspect Electronics, Inc.

ASPECT MINI IMAGER - Ultrasound cameras and equipment - Aspect Electronics, Inc.

ASPECT RATIO - Rackets–tennis - Spalding Sports Worldwide

ASPEN - Apparel and accessories - Abel Industries Inc.

ASPEN - Bicycles - Roadmaster Corp.

ASPEN - Brushes–paint - Allpro Corp.

ASPEN - Building materials - Sealmaster, Inc.

ASPEN - Candlesticks ☆ - Lenox Crystal, Inc.

ASPEN - Clocks - General Time Corp. (Westclox/Seth Thomas Div.)

ASPEN - Colognes - Quintessence Inc.

ASPEN - Cutlery ☆ - National Housewares

ASPEN - Dinnerware–glass - Durand International

ASPEN - Flatware - Trend Pacific Inc.

ASPEN - Floor coverings–carpet and rugs - Quaker Inc.

ASPEN - Floor coverings–carpet and rugs ☆ - American Carpet Mills

ASPEN - Floor coverings–carpet and rugs ☆ - Blue Ridge Carpet Mills

ASPEN - Floor coverings–carpet and rugs ☆ - Lowe's Carpet Corp.

ASPEN - Flowers, plants, and seeds - Jacklin Seed

ASPEN - Food products - Aspen Foods, a division of Koch Poultry

ASPEN - Frames–eyeglass - Denver International Eyewear Inc.

ASPEN - Frames–picture - Ammak Manufacturing Corp.

ASPEN - Furniture - American Woodmark Corp.

ASPEN - Furniture - Stanley Furniture Co. Inc.

ASPEN - Furniture ☆ - Bassett Furniture Industries, Inc.

ASPEN - Furniture ☆ - Lea Industries Inc.

ASPEN - Goggles–safety - U.S. Safety Corp.

ASPEN - Guitars ☆ - International Music Corp.

ASPEN - Hobby kits - Craft World International Inc.

ASPEN - Motor vehicles ☆ - Chrysler Corp. (Dodge Car Div.)

ASPEN - Motor vehicles–motor homes - Aspen Coach Corp.

ASPEN - Occasional tables ☆ - JDI Group, Inc.

ASPEN - Perfumes - Coty Inc.

ASPEN - Pet products - Reptilia

ASPEN - Shoes - KangaROOS USA Inc.

ASPEN - Skin care products - Takara Belmont USA, Inc.

ASPEN - Splints - International Healthcare Devices

ASPEN - Strollers–baby - Aspen International Inc.

ASPEN - Sunglasses - Aspen Licensing International, Inc.

ASPEN - Swimming pools ☆ - Doughboy Recreational Inc.

ASPEN - Thread - Van Waters and Rogers Inc.

ASPEN - Veterinary pharmaceutical preparations - Lextron, Inc.

ASPEN - Watches ☆ - Brokoe Manufacturing Co. Inc.

ASPEN - Water–bottled or canned - Cable Car Beverage Corp.

ASPEN - Window coverings ☆ - Vertilux-Louverlux Inc.

ASPEN - Yarn ☆ - Brunswick Yarns

ASPEN 1940'S - Apparel and accessories - Abel Industries Inc.

ASPEN AIRE - Floor coverings–carpet and rugs - Milliken & Co. Inc.

ASPEN BARBEQUE CHIPS - Wood products ☆ - Spear Engineering Co.

ASPEN CLASSIC - Watches ☆ - Brokoe Manufacturing Co. Inc.

ASPEN COVE - Toilets–porcelain - Mansfield Plumbing Products, Inc.

ASPEN CRACKER - Jackets - Richton International Corp.

ASPEN FOR WOMEN - Colognes - Quintessence Inc.

ASPEN FURNITURE - Furniture - Aspen Furniture, Inc.

ASPEN GLOW - Jams and jellies - Mountain Maid Gourmet Jelly

ASPEN GOLD - Eyeglass frames - Denver International Eyewear Inc.

ASPEN GROVE - Floor coverings - Congoleum Corp.

ASPEN HIGHLANDS - Furniture ☆ - Bassett Furniture Industries, Inc.

ASPEN III - Oxygen ☆ - Caire

ASPEN LANE - Furniture ☆ - Bassett Furniture Industries, Inc.

ASPEN LIDS - Hats - Moriarty Hat and Sweater Co.

ASPEN-LOK - Wood products - Aspen Valley Lumber Co. Inc.

ASPEN MINTS - Candy - Aspen Pharmaceuticals and Distributing Inc.

ASPEN MOUNTAIN - Bakery products - Our Name is Mud, Inc.

ASPEN PERFECT CONDITIONS - Colognes - Quintessence Inc.

ASPEN RUNNERS - Apparel and accessories - Richton International Corp.

ASPEN SKIING COMPANY SKI SCHOOL - Patches, insignia, and emblems - Aspen Skiing Co.

ASPEN SPECIALTY FOODS - Mustard - Aspen Specialty Foods, Inc.

ASPEN SPECIALTY FOODS MUSTARD SAUCE - Mustard - Aspen Specialty Foods, Inc.

ASPEN SPRINGERS - Apparel and accessories - Richton International Corp.

ASPEN WOODS - Handbags ☆ - Tandem Imports Corp.

ASPENCADE - Motorcycles - American Honda Motor Co. Inc. (Acura Div.)

ASPENELLE - Water–bottled or canned - High Aspenelle Natural Springs Inc.

ASPENITE - Plaster–wallboard - MacMillan Bloedel Building Materials

ASPENITE FLORDEK - Flooring–hardwood - MacMillan Bloedel Building Materials

ASPENITE RUFFDEK - Roofing materials–clay - MacMillan Bloedel Building Materials

ASPENITE U-DEK - Plywood - MacMillan Bloedel Building Materials

ASPENS - Shoes - Trans-World Shoe Import Corp.

ASPENTONES - Craft supplies - American Excelsior Co.

ASPERBUF - Photo albums ☆ - JMI-Canton Pharmaceuticals

ASPERCIN - Analgesics - Otis Clapp & Son Inc.

ASPERCIN EXTRA - Analgesics - Otis Clapp & Son Inc.

ASPERCREME - Pharmaceutical preparations - Thompson Medical Co., Inc.

ASPERGEL - Health care products - Thompson Medical Co., Inc.

ASPERGUM - Pharmaceutical preparations - Schering-Plough Healthcare Products

ASPERMIN - Health care products - Buffington

ASPERMIN EXTRA - Pharmaceutical preparations - Buffington

ASPHAC-G - Pharmaceutical preparations ☆ - Central Pharmaceutical Inc.

ASPHACOLOR - Chemical preparations - Asphacolor Corp.

ASPHALASTIC - Paints - Remien & Kuhnert Co.

ASPHALT - Sunglasses - Asphalt Motorcycle Eyewear

ASPHALT ASSAULT - Apparel and accessories - Winterland Concessions Co.

ASPHALT ATHLETIC CLUB, THE - Apparel and accessories - Advanced Athletes Inc.

ASPHALT BOMBER - Apparel and accessories - Out W Designs, LLC

ASPHALT COWBOYS - Apparel and accessories - B & D Metal Rodeo Promotions, Inc.

ASPHALUME - Paints - Standard T Chemical Co. Inc.

ASPHERCON - Contact lenses ☆ - Wesley-Jessen Co.

ASPHEREYES - Ophthalmic lenses - BMC Industries, Inc.

ASPHERICAL - Lenses–photographic - Tamron Industries Inc.

ASPHERLITE - Ophthalmic goods - American Optical Corp.

ASPI-COR - Analgesics - Health Products Corp.

ASPIR-10 - Pharmaceutical preparations ☆ - Pal-Pak Inc.

ASPIR-D - Pharmaceutical preparations - Lannett Co. Inc.

ASPIR - GRAN - Pharmaceutical - Barrington Chemical Corp.

ASPIR LOW - Aspirin - Major Pharmaceuticals

ASPIR-PULSE - Medical apparatus - Sherwood Medical Co.

ASPIR-PULSE GOLD - Medical apparatus - Sherwood Medical Co.

ASPIRA - Office furniture–plastic - Newell Office Products

ASPIRA - Office furniture–plastic - Rubbermaid Office Products Inc.

ASPIRALOE - Health care products - Aloe Laboratories, Inc.

ASPIRATION - Floor coverings–carpet and rugs - Gulistan Carpet Inc.

ASPIRATION - Floor coverings–carpet and rugs - Karastan-Bigelow Inc.

ASPIRATIONS - Floor coverings–carpet and rugs - Philadelphia Carpets

ASPIRBAR - Pharmaceutical preparations - Lannett Co. Inc.

ASPIRE - Computers - Acer America Corp.

ASPIRE - Fungicides - Ecogen Inc.

ASPIRE - Furniture ☆ - Bassett Furniture Industries, Inc.

ASPIRE - Motor vehicles–automobiles - Ford Motor Co.

ASPIRE - Skates–roller ☆ - Rollerblade, Inc.

ASPIRE AUTOMATED SYSTEM - Computer software - Incentive Solutions, Inc.

ASPIRE ICE CAFE - Coffee ☆ - O-AT-KA Milk Products Cooperative Inc.

ASPIRE MINUS - Lenses–optical - X-Cel Optical Co.

ASPIRE PLUS - Lenses–optical - X-Cel Optical Co.

ASPIRIN -

ASPIRIN-FREE EXCEDERIN GELTABS - Analgesics - Bristol-Myers Squibb Co.

ASPIRIN-FREE EXCEDRIN PM MEDICINE - Analgesics - Bristol-Myers Squibb Co.

ASPIRIN REGIMEN BAYER - Analgesics - Bayer Corp. (Consumer Care Div.)

ASPIRLOZENGE - Health care products - G.I. Drug Co.

ASPIRO - Pharmaceutical preparations ☆ - C.O. Truxton Inc.

ASPIRSED - Pharmaceutical preparations - Bio-Factor Laboratories

ASPIRTAB - Pharmaceutical preparations - Dover Pharmaceutical Inc.

ASPIRTAB MAX - Pharmaceutical preparations - Dover Pharmaceutical Inc.

☆ = Now out of production

ASPOROTATE - Vitamins and nutritional supplements - Solaray

ASPRAI - Hair care products - Tressa, Inc.

ASPRI-ACTIN - Vitamins and nutritional supplements - Natural Organics, Inc.

ASPRISTICK - Pharmaceutical preparations ☆ - Palm Beach Beauty Products

ASPROJECT - Pharmaceutical preparations - Merz Inc.

ASQ-10 - Uniforms–tailored ☆ - Angelica Uniform Group

ASQ-100 - Uniforms–tailored - Angelica Uniform Group

ASR - Tires - Bridgestone/Firestone, Inc.

ASRT - Computer software - Proteon, Inc.

ASRX - Generators–gas - Surface Combustion, Inc.

ASS KICKIN' CHILI - Chili sauce - Southwest Specialty Foods

ASS KICKIN' CORN BREAD - Breads–mixes - Southwest Specialty Foods

ASS KICKIN' JELLY BEANS - Candy - Southwest Specialty Foods

ASS KICKIN' SALSA - Vegetable sauces - Southwest Specialty Foods

ASSA - Audio equipment - Alberee Products Inc.

ASSA - Locks–padlocks - Assa High Security Locks

ASSASSIN - Alarm systems–burglar - Norje Electronics Corp.

ASSASSINS - Darts and dart games ☆ - Dart World Inc.

ASSAULT - Cleaning preparations - Hillyard Enterprises, Inc.

ASSAULT - Floor coverings–carpet and rugs - Mohawk Industries Inc.

ASSAULT - Games - Game Designers' Workshop, Inc.

ASSAULT - Recording label - Outrage Music, Inc.

ASSAULT - Sporting goods - Skis Dynastar, Inc.

ASSAULT 18 - Balls - Spalding & Evenflo Companies, Inc.

ASSAULT CRAWLER - Toys–automobiles - Mattel, Inc.

ASSAULT LIGHT - Rackets–tennis - Spalding & Evenflo Companies, Inc.

ASSAULT ON CRETE - Games ☆ - Avalon Hill Game Co.

ASSAULT SHIELDS - Goggles–safety - Outdoor Optics, Inc.

ASSEMBLAGE - Bookcases–wood - National/Mt. Airy Furniture

ASSEMBLAGE - Floor coverings - Armstrong World Industries, Inc.

ASSEMBLAGE - Furniture ☆ - Fancher Furniture Co. Inc.

ASSEMBLAGE - Shirts - Capital Mercury Shirt Corp.

ASSEMBLAGE CULINAIRE - Meat products - Vie De France Corp.

ASSEMBLY - Work benches - Metal Components Inc. (Flexible Furniture Div.)

ASSEMBLY LINE, THE - Hardware ☆ - Stanley Hardware Div.

ASSENT - Floor coverings–carpet and rugs - Hollytex Carpet Mills Inc.

ASSERTION II - Floor coverings–carpet and rugs - J and J Industries Inc.

ASSERTIVE DISCIPLINE - Video production - Canter and Associates, Inc.

A+SSESS - Computer software - American Education Corp.

ASSESS - Health care products - Healthscan Products Inc.

ASSET - Computer software - Texas Instruments Inc.

ASSET - Fertilizers - Helena Chemical Co.

ASSET - Floor coverings–carpet and rugs - Hollytex Carpet Mills Inc.

ASSET - Floor coverings–carpet and rugs ☆ - J and J Industries Inc.

ASSET - Furniture - Allsteel, Inc.

ASSET ADVANTAGE - Computer software - Tangram Enterprise Solutions, Inc.

ASSET INSIGHT - Computer software - Tangram Enterprise Solutions, Inc.

ASSET INSIGHT - Computer software - Tangram Enterprise Solutions, Inc.

ASSET PROTECTION DEVICE - Computer peripheral equipment - Anthony J. Rietkerk

ASSET PROTECTION SYSTEM - Alarm systems–burglar - Anthony J. Rietkerk

ASSET SURVEYOR - Navigational instruments - Trimble Navigation Ltd.

ASSETNET - Computer software - International Business Machines Corp.

ASSETPLUS - Software - At&T Corp.

ASSETS - Hair care products - Helene Curtis Industries Inc.

ASSETS - Publisher's imprints - Score Board Holding Corp.

ASSETS LONDON - Apparel and accessories - Assets London (USA) Corp.

ASSI BRAND - Food products - Rhee Bros., Inc.

ASSIGNABLE 88 - Electronics equipment - AMS Industries Inc.

ASSIMILAID - Nutritional supplements - Sunrider International

ASSIS - Food products - A & A Food Products Corp.

ASSIST - Chemical preparations - Bio-Lab, Inc.

ASSIST - Veterinary nutritional supplements - Continental Grain Co.

ASSIST-A-LIFT - Home-health-care products - Action Engineering Inc.

ASSIST-MATE - Wheelchairs - Medreco Inc.

ASSISTANTMANAGER - Computer software - Coconut Code, Inc.

ASSIST'EM - Seasonings - Delta Spice Works

ASSISTRAP - Golfing equipment - Lisco, Inc.

ASSISTWARE - Computer software - Softweave Corp.

ASSOCIATE - Eyeglasses - Martin-Copeland Eyewear Corp.

ASSOCIATE - Floor coverings–carpet and rugs - Mohawk Carpet Corp.

ASSOCIATE PRODUCER - Computer software - Comprehensive Video Supply Corp.

ASSOCIATED - Battery testers - Associated Equipment Corp.

ASSOCIATED - Food products - Associated Food Stores Inc.

ASSOCIATED - Office supplies - Boise Cascade Corp.

ASSOCIATED BISCUITS - Cookies ☆ - Gilway Co. Ltd.

ASSOCIATED ENAMEL ARTISTS - Enameled ware - Brastoff Designs Inc.

ASSOCIATES - Footwear - G.S.I. Ltd.

ASSOCIATES - Wallpaper - Sanitas Wallcoverings

ASSOCIATES, THE - Luggage ☆ - American Tourister, Inc.

ASSOCIATION PRESS - Publisher's imprints - New Century Education

ASSOLUTI! - Cheese - Louis Piancone

ASSORT-O-MINT - Candy ☆ - Planters LifeSavers Co.

ASST DISCS - Candy - Judson-Atkinson Candies

ASSUMPTION - Wines - Pliska Winery

ASSUMPTION ABBEY - Wines - Brookside Enterprises Inc.

ASSURANCE - Calculators - Assurance Industries Co. Inc.

ASSURANCE - Cleaning preparations - Hillyard Enterprises, Inc.

ASSURANCE - Floor coverings - Congoleum Corp.

ASSURANCE - Floor coverings–carpet and rugs - Calladium & Marglen

ASSURANCE - Floor coverings–carpet and rugs - J and J Industries Inc.

ASSURANCE - Floor coverings–carpet and rugs - Patrick Carpet Mills

ASSURANCE - Fruits and vegetables - Orange Cove-Sanger Citrus Association

ASSURANCE - Medical apparatus - Nellcor Puritan Bennett

A+SSURANCE PLUS - Building materials - Bill Erickson Trading Co.

ASSURANCE PLUS - Floor coverings–tile - Flexco Co.

ASSURE - Agricultural products ☆ - Hogan Associates

ASSURE - Computer software - Centel Federal Systems Inc.

ASSURE - Herbicides - E.I. Dupont de Nemours and Co.

ASSURE - Sanitary napkins - Johnson & Johnson

ASSURE - Shampoos - Nexxus Products Co.

ASSURE - Sinks–metal - Kohler Co.

ASSURE 425 - Adhesives and sealants - Loctite Corp.

ASSURE NATURAL FIT - Sanitary napkins - Johnson & Johnson

ASSURED CAPITAL TRANSFER - Publisher's imprints - John J. Lenz

ASSURED COMFORT - Incontinence products ☆ - Scott Health Care

ASSURED TIME - Clocks - Sunbeam Precision Measurement

AST - Computers–personal - AST Research

AST - Tape–adhesive - Arlon, Inc.

AST - Watches - Accusplit Inc.

AST-5 - Toys - Lucasfilm Ltd.

AST ADEPTA - Sporting goods - Adepta Sport Technologies, Inc.

ASTA - Jewelry - Asta-Tittman Jewelry Manufacturing Inc.

ASTAIRE - Glassware–household ☆ - Crisa Corp.

ASTAR - Video equipment - Astar, Inc.

ASTARTE - Floor coverings–carpet and rugs ☆ - Hollytex Carpet Mills Inc.

ASTARTE WOMAN BY DESIGN - Apparel and accessories - Astarte Woman by Design

ASTATIC - Microphones - C.T.I. Audio Inc.

ASTEA - Computer software - Astea International Inc.

ASTEC - Computers ☆ - Taylor-Merchant Corp.

ASTECH - Peak flow meters - EM Industries, Inc.

ASTELIN NASAL SPRAY - Pharmaceutical preparations - Wallace Laboratories

ASTEN - Shirts - Tux Shop Inc.

ASTER - Dishes–earthenware ☆ - Royal China & Porcelain Companies Inc.

ASTER - Nuts–candied - Aster Nut Products Co. Inc.

ASTER - Tiles–ceramic ☆ - Dal-Tile Corp.

ASTERISK - Vases–ceramic - Bennington Potters

ASTERISKS - Apparel ☆ - Levi Strauss & Co.

ASTERISM - Recording label - Jazz Composer's Orchestra Association Inc.

ASTERMA - Pharmaceutical preparations - Mecin Co.

ASTEROID - Floor coverings - American Floor Products Co. Inc.

ASTEROID - Skates–roller ☆ - Rollerblade, Inc.

ASTEROID EXPLORER - Toys–models ☆ - Estes Industries

ASTEROIDS - Video games - Atari Games Corp.

ASTGMD - Surveillance equipment - Combi International Corp.

ASTGMD - Surveillance equipment - Philips Communication & Security Systems Inc.

ASTHMA ADVENTURE, THE - Games - Barnes West County Hospital

ASTHMA-AID - Vitamins and nutritional supplements - Amrion, Inc.

ASTHMA BACKPACK - Medical apparatus - Asthma Backpack Corp.

ASTHMA TABS - Pharmaceutical preparations ☆ - Reese Chemical Co.

ASTHMA TABS - Pharmaceutical preparations ☆ - Veratex Group

ASTHMACALM - Vitamins and nutritional supplements - Desert Health Products, Inc.

ASTHMACON - Pharmaceutical preparations - Consolidated Midland Corp.

ASTHMAHALER - Pharmaceutical preparations - Smithkline Beecham Corp.

ASTHMAID - Pharmaceutical preparations - Pharmex Inc.

☆ = Now out of production

ASTHMALIXIR - Pharmaceutical preparations ☆ - Reese Chemical Co.

ASTHMANEFRIN - Pharmaceutical preparations - Smithkline Beecham Corp.

ASTHMASAN - Pharmaceutical preparations ☆ - Bioforce of America Ltd.

ASTI - Ice buckets ☆ - Heller Inc.

ASTI - Tomato pastes and sauces - Salvati Foods, Inc.

ASTI - Wines - M.S. Walker Inc./Seacoast

ASTI BANFI - Wines - Banfi Vintners

ASTI SPUMANTE - Wines - Kobrand Corp.

ASTIN - Pianos - Astin-Weight Piano Makers

ASTIN-WEIGHT - Pianos - Astin-Weight Piano Makers

ASTLEY - Dinnerware–glass ☆ - Royal China & Porcelain Companies Inc.

ASTON - Dishes–china ☆ - Royal China & Porcelain Companies Inc.

ASTON BEACH - Floor coverings ☆ - Armstrong World Industries, Inc.

ASTON COURT - Furniture - Henredon Furniture Industries Inc.

ASTON MARTIN - Eyeglasses - Private Eyes Sunglass Corp.

ASTON MARTIN - Motor vehicles - Aston Martin Lagonda of North America Inc.

ASTONISHING - Floor coverings–carpet and rugs - World Carpets, Inc.

ASTOPHOLIQUE - Skin care products - Ritornelle Inc.

ASTOR - Brushes–paint - Corona Brushes Inc.

ASTOR - Chocolate candy - Astor Chocolate Corp.

ASTOR - Cigarettes - G.A. Georgopulo & Co. Inc.

ASTOR - Coffee - Astor Products Co.

ASTOR - Dinnerware–glass - Crystal Clear Importing Co. Inc.

ASTOR - Fruit drinks–bottled or canned - Golden Gem Growers Inc.

ASTOR - Pianos - Kohler & Campbell Inc.

ASTOR - Playing cards - Astor Playing Card Co.

ASTOR - Wallpaper - Pantasote Inc. (Wallcovering Div.)

ASTOR 100'S - Cigarettes - G.A. Georgopulo & Co. Inc.

ASTOR BOUTIQUE - Wallpaper ☆ - Pantasote Inc. (Wallcovering Div.)

ASTOR INTERNATIONAL - Cigarettes - G.A. Georgopulo & Co. Inc.

ASTOR PLACE - Bathroom accessories - Melard Manufacturing Corp.

ASTOR PLACE - Dinnerware - Philip Whitney, Ltd.

ASTOR PLACE - Floor coverings - Mannington Resilient Floors

ASTOR PLACE - Wallpaper ☆ - Pantasote Inc. (Wallcovering Div.)

ASTOR RIGHT STUFF - Wallpaper ☆ - Pantasote Inc. (Wallcovering Div.)

ASTOR SQUARE - Floor coverings - Mannington Resilient Floors

ASTOR TONES 'N TEXTURES - Wallpaper ☆ - Pantasote Inc. (Wallcovering Div.)

ASTORIA - Bathroom fixtures - Universal-Rundle Corp.

ASTORIA - Computer software - Xerox Corp.

ASTORIA - Cribs–wood ☆ - Welsh Co.

ASTORIA - Drums–musical instruments ☆ - Grossman Music Corp.

ASTORIA - Fabrics ☆ - Greenwood Mills Inc.

ASTORIA - Floor coverings - Mannington Resilient Floors

ASTORIA - Tableware–china - Pfaltzgraff Investment Co.

ASTORIA - Wigs - Paula Young

ASTORIA - Window frames - Louisiana-Pacific Corp.

ASTORIA COURT - Wallcovering - Gencorp Inc.

ASTORIAPRO - Windows–vinyl - Louisiana-Pacific Corp.

ASTORLOID - Furniture - Astorloid Manufacturing Co.

ASTOUNDING GRAPHICS - Postcards - Fotofolio Inc.

ASTRA - Cabinets - Aristokraft, Inc.

ASTRA - Cabinets ☆ - Decora

ASTRA - Corsets - Abraham & Straus/Jordan Marsh Co.

ASTRA - Fabrics - Superior Shade & Blind Co. Inc.

ASTRA - Firearms, accessories, and parts ☆ - International Armament Corp.

ASTRA - Flowers, plants, and seeds - J. Benjamin Williams

ASTRA - Furniture ☆ - Bassett Furniture Industries, Inc.

ASTRA - Health care products - Power Plus Systems Inc.

ASTRA - Luggage ☆ - Gateway Travelware

ASTRA - Pumps - Gasboy International, Inc.

ASTRA - Teas–herbal - Health Concerns

ASTRA - Tools ☆ - Joseph Caragol Inc.

ASTRA 8 - Teas–herbal - Health Concerns

ASTRA 2000 - Pens - Union Pen Co.

ASTRA-BOLT - Door frames - Combo Aluminum Products

ASTRA COLLECTION - Bathroom accessories - Franklin Brass Manufacturing Co.

ASTRA CT 2000 - Skis - Wellington Leisure Products, Inc.

ASTRA LAV - Sinks–porcelain - Artesian Industries

ASTRA LINE - Upholstery material - American Leather Manufacturing Co.

ASTRA ORIGINALS - Jewelry ☆ - Jewelry Fashions Inc.

ASTRADA - International Violin Co. Ltd.

ASTRAFLEX - Cameras ☆ - Luminos Photo Corp.

ASTRAGALOS - Health care products - East Earth Herb Inc.

ASTRAGALUS EXTRACT - Vitamins and nutritional supplements - Vitamin Research Products Inc.

ASTRAGALUS-POWER - Vitamins and nutritional supplements - Natur-Pharma, Inc.

ASTRAGON - Lenses–photographic - Luminos Photo Corp.

ASTRAIIIB - Sextants–navigational - Celestaire

ASTRAKAN - Yarn ☆ - YLI Corp.

ASTRAL - Building materials - Burns & Russell Co.

ASTRAL - Glassware–household ☆ - WMF/USA

ASTRAL - Wallpaper - Norman/Baer Associates

ASTRAL FORECAST - Publisher's imprints - Astral Research, Inc.

ASTRAL GUIDE - Publisher's imprints - Astral Research, Inc.

ASTRAL MASTER - Rackets–tennis - Head Sports USA

ASTRAL PORTRAIT - Publisher's imprints - Astral Research, Inc.

ASTRALI PARIS - Skin care products - Societe RNA D'Esthetique Inc.

ASTRALITE - Hardware - Astralite Inc.

ASTRALON - Ribbons–inked - Buckeye Business Products Inc.

ASTRALUX - Enlargers–photographic ☆ - Luminos Photo Corp.

ASTRALWERKS - Recording label - Caroline Records, Inc.

ASTRANAR PANORAMIC - Lenses–photographic ☆ - Luminos Photo Corp.

ASTRASCOPE - Projectors–photographic - Luminos Photo Corp.

ASTRE - Motor vehicles–automobiles ☆ - General Motors Corp. (Pontiac/GMC Div.)

ASTREX F-3 - Diet supplements - Natur-Pharma, Inc.

ASTRID - Dolls - Estee Productions, Inc.

ASTRID - Glassware–household - Seneca Glass Co.

ASTRID - Glassware–household ☆ - ACC

ASTRID - Handbags - Astrid Creations Ltd.

ASTRING-O-SOL - Mouthwashes - Mentholatum Co.

ASTRING-O-SOL - Mouthwashes ☆ - Winthrop Pharmaceuticals

ASTRINGYN - Astringents - Cooper Companies Inc.

ASTRIO - Cookies ☆ - Purepak Foods Inc.

ASTRO.- Automotive parts and accessories - Rite Autotronics Corp.

ASTRO - Boats - Brunswick Corp.

ASTRO - Brushes - Perfex Corp.

ASTRO - Cameras ☆ - Star Parts Inc.

ASTRO - Chairs–stacking - Fixtures Furniture

ASTRO - Chewing gum - Ford Gum and Machine Co.

ASTRO - Computers - DMS Computers Inc.

ASTRO - Cutlery - Lifetime Hoan Corp.

ASTRO - Door openers–electronic - Stanley Home Automation Inc.

ASTRO - Flatware ☆ - Stanley Roberts, Inc.

ASTRO - Insecticides - FMC Corp.

ASTRO - Lenses–photographic - Ercona Corp.

ASTRO - Mops ☆ - Helen Keller Services for the Blind

ASTRO - Motor vehicle dealers ☆ - General Motors Corp.

ASTRO - Motor vehicles - General Motors Corp. (Chevrolet Motor Div.)

ASTRO - Shoes - Endicott Johnson Corp.

ASTRO - Sporting goods - Astro Nautics Co. Inc.

ASTRO - Starch–edible - Penford Products Co.

ASTRO - Telescopes - Bausch & Lomb Inc.

ASTRO - Thread ☆ - Belding Heminway Co. Inc.

ASTRO - Toys–models ☆ - Estes Industries

ASTRO - Yogurt ☆ - Upstate Farms Cooperative, Inc.

ASTRO 14 - Bags–duffel ☆ - Innovo Inc.

ASTRO AB BRIGHTS - Paper–writing ☆ - Wausau Paper Mills Co.

ASTRO-AID - Computer software - Zephyr Services

ASTRO ALGEBRA - Computer peripheral equipment - Edmark Corp.

ASTRO-AMP - Amplifiers ☆ - RMS Electronics, Inc.

ASTRO-ARCTIC - Packaging–blisterwrap ☆ - Astro-Valcour, Inc.

ASTRO AWESOME - Candy ☆ - Spangler Candy Co.

ASTRO-BLASTER - Toys–models - Estes Industries

ASTRO BLENDER - Blenders - Commercial Refrigeration Co., Inc.

ASTRO-BOND - Padding–foam - Bondafoam Inc.

ASTRO-CELL - Packaging–blisterwrap - Astro-Valcour, Inc.

ASTRO-CELL LITE - Packaging–blisterwrap - Astro-Valcour, Inc.

ASTRO CHASE - Computer software - First Star Software Inc.

ASTRO COLOR - Paints ☆ - Testor Corp.

ASTRO-COMPACT - Chairs–stacking - Fixtures Furniture

ASTRO CONFETTI POP - Candy ☆ - Spangler Candy Co.

ASTRO CRUNCH-TOP - Yogurt ☆ - Upstate Farms Cooperative, Inc.

ASTRO DESTINY - Games - Meyers List Inc.

ASTRO-DOME - Maps - Solensten/Sunstone Inc.

ASTRO-DOTS - Toys - Solensten/Sunstone Inc.

ASTRO-FECT - Coatings - Coronado Paint Co.

ASTRO FIRE - Toys–airplanes ☆ - Paul K. Guillow Inc.

☆ = Now out of production

ASTRO-FLEX - Gloves–safety - Comasec Safety, Inc.
ASTRO FLYER - Bicycles - Western Auto Supply Co.
ASTRO FOAM - Padding–foam - Astro-Valcour, Inc.
ASTRO-FOLD - Doors–metal - Republic Industries Inc.
ASTRO FORECAST - Toys - Twelve Signs Inc.
ASTRO-GROVER - Computer software - CBS Software
ASTRO-GUARD - Alarm systems - Astro-Guard Industries Inc.
ASTRO I.D.S - Paper–gummed - Wry Idea Co.
ASTRO-JET - Pens ☆ - Eversharp Pen Co.
ASTRO LINE - Cabinets–metal - Horizon Steel Products Inc.
ASTRO LION - Toys - Mattel, Inc.
ASTRO LITE - Automotive parts and accessories ☆ - TBC Corp.
ASTRO-LITE - Fittings–cast iron ☆ - Semmerling Fence and Supply Inc.
ASTRO MAT - Pet products - Astro Pet Industries Inc.
ASTRO METAL - Eyeglasses - Uvex Safety LLC
ASTRO NAIL - Manicure preparations - GG's Nail Systems
ASTRO NOTES - Greeting cards ☆ - Regency Thermographers Inc.
ASTRO NYLON - Musical instrument accessories - Deg Music Products Inc.
ASTRO OTG - Eyeglasses - Uvex Safety LLC
ASTRO-PAK - Bicycles ☆ - Astro Nautics Co. Inc.
ASTRO-PAK - Fruit drinks–bottled or canned ☆ - Magnetic Springs Water Co.
ASTRO-PEN - Pens - Eversharp Pen Co.
ASTRO PILOT - Toys - Super Science Ltd.
ASTRO POOL - Swimming pool covers - Astro-Valcour, Inc.
ASTRO POPS - Candy ☆ - Spangler Candy Co.
ASTRO PRINTS - Astrological signs - IMS Corp.
ASTRO-PROFILES - Publisher's imprints - Pygmy Fund, Inc.
ASTRO PUNCH - Fasteners–snap - Astro Punch Corp.
ASTRO-RITER - Pens ☆ - Empire Berol USA
ASTRO ROVER - Kites - Gayla Industries Inc.
ASTRO ROVER - Toys - Mattel, Inc.
ASTRO-SCIENCE - Magnetic recording equipment - Eastman Kodak Co.
ASTRO-SCOPE - Computer software - Astrolabe Software
ASTRO SCOUT - Toys - Park Plastics Co.
ASTRO-SHADE - Umbrellas - Wellington Home Products (Plastic Woven Products Div.)
ASTRO SHIELD - Automotive parts and accessories - Nord-Viscount Corp.
ASTRO-SHIELD - Goggles–safety - Uvex Safety LLC
ASTRO SHOOTER - Toys - Tomy America, Inc.
ASTRO SKY-WHEEL - Pet products ☆ - R.A.F. Trading Inc.
ASTRO-SOLAR - Sporting goods ☆ - Astro-Valcour, Inc.
ASTRO-SPEC - Eyeglasses - Uvex Safety LLC
ASTRO STAR - Computer software - Astrolabe Software
ASTRO STAR - Trading cards - Space WIF Corp.
ASTRO STAR - Trailers–travel ☆ - Travel Line Enterprises Inc.
ASTRO SUNDAE POP - Candy ☆ - Spangler Candy Co.
ASTRO-SUPRABUBBLE - Packaging–blisterwrap - Astro-Valcour, Inc.
ASTRO-TAC - Apparel–athletic - Motorola, Inc. (Land Mobile Products Sector)
ASTRO TALK - Computer software - Matrix Software, Inc.
ASTRO T&O - Insecticides - FMC Corp.
ASTRO-TEC - Pens - Astro Pen Co.
ASTRO-TEC PEN - Pens - Eversharp Pen Co.
ASTRO-TOUCH - Pens - Astro Pen Co.
ASTRO-TOUCH - Pens - Eversharp Pen Co.
ASTRO-VAC - Vacuum cleaners and accessories ☆ - Lindsay Manufacturing Inc.
ASTRO-VAR - Varnishes - Martin-Senour Co.
ASTRO-VIOLET - Packaging–blisterwrap - Astro-Valcour, Inc.
ASTRO-WRAP - Packaging–blisterwrap ☆ - Astro-Valcour, Inc.
ASTRO ZAPPER - Toys - Tyco Toys
ASTROANALYST, THE - Computer software - Astrolabe Software
ASTROBASE - Computer software - Zephyr Services
ASTROBEE - Toys–models ☆ - Estes Industries
ASTROBLADE - Skates–roller ☆ - Rollerblade, Inc.
ASTROBRIGHTS - Paper - Wausau Paper Mills Co.
ASTROCAD - Computer software - Estes Industries
ASTROCALC - Computer software - Zephyr Services
ASTROCAM 110 - Toys–models - Estes Industries
ASTROCAP - Hats - Henschel Manufacturing Co.
ASTROCHOC - Watches - Hampden Corp.
ASTROCOLORS - Footwear–athletic - San Shoe Trading Corp.
ASTROCOM - Stereos - Astrocom Electronics Inc.
ASTRODOME - Electrical equipment - General Electric Co.
ASTRODOME THE ORIGINAL - Decals and transfers - Houston McLane Co., Inc.
ASTRODYNE - Solar energy collectors - Astrodyne Corp.

ASTROFINDER - Computer software ☆ - Zephyr Services
ASTROFLEX - Office supplies - Martin Universal Design Inc.
ASTROGEM - Jewelry - Avi Raz
ASTROGRAPH - Watches - Movado Time Corp.
ASTROGRASS - Floor coverings - Southwest Recreational Industries, Inc.
ASTROJAX - Balls - Laurence Jay Shaw
ASTROJET - Watches - Hampden Corp.
ASTROLAN - Dust-mop refills - American Textile Products Co.
ASTROLIGHT - Toys ☆ - Flambeau Products Corp.
ASTROLINE - Rope ☆ - Crow Rope Industries LLC
ASTROLITE - Flour–blended - Cahokia Flour Co.
ASTROLITE - Paper–writing - Monadnock Paper Mills Inc.
ASTROLITE - Television equipment - Television Equipment Associates
ASTROLITE - Trailers–travel - Starcraft Corp.
ASTROLITE - Wire - Astro Metallurgical, Inc.
ASTROLO - Games - Creatnetics
ASTROLOGER'S COMPANION, THE - Computer software - Astrolabe Software
ASTROLOGON - Toys - Advanced Design Concepts Inc.
ASTROMATIC - Clocks ☆ - General Time Corp. (Westclox/Seth Thomas Div.)
ASTROMATIC - File folders ☆ - ACME Design Technology
ASTRON - See **PULSAR**
ASTRON - Cameras–video ☆ - Elmo Manufacturing Corp.
ASTRON - Floor coverings ☆ - Congoleum Corp.
ASTRON - Toys–models ☆ - Estes Industries
ASTRON COMDESK - Office furniture–plastic - John J. Lee
ASTRONAUT - Food products - Small World Toys
ASTRONAUT - Pens - Eversharp Pen Co.
ASTRONAUT BEAR - Toys–stuffed - Dakin Inc.
ASTRONAUT GUNTHER - Hardware - Werner Co.
ASTRONAUT PEN - Pens - Eversharp Pen Co.
ASTRONIC - Watches - Movado Time Corp.
ASTRONOMY - Computer software - Orange Cherry Software
ASTRONOMY BOOK CLUB - Publisher's imprints - MacMillan Publishing Co. Inc.
ASTRONOMY SMART - Publisher's imprints - Princeton Review Publishing, LLC
ASTRONON - Jewelry - Gold Lance Inc.
ASTROPACK - Cases–eyeglass - Uvex Safety LLC
ASTROPARCHE - Paper - Wausau Paper Mills Co.
ASTROPLAN - Banks–commercial - Southwest Recreational Industries, Inc.
ASTROPULSE - See **MARSHALL**
ASTROS - Apparel and accessories - Astrodome USA
ASTROSNIK - Toys - Tyco Toys
ASTROSNIKS - Stationery - Bullyland Inc.
ASTROSTAR - Trailers–travel ☆ - Starcraft Corp.
ASTROSTELL - Computer software - Zephyr Services
ASTROSUB - Toys - Mattel, Inc.
ASTROTEMP - Thermometers - Omron Healthcare, Inc.
ASTROTUFF - Rope ☆ - Wellington Leisure Products, Inc.
ASTROTURF - Door mats - Monsanto Co.
ASTROTURF - Floor coverings - Southwest Recreational Industries, Inc.
ASTROTURF - Floor coverings–carpet and rugs - Ludlow Composites Corp.
ASTROTURF XL - Floor coverings - AstroTurf Industries Inc.
ASTROVISIONS - Kaleidoscopes - Gemini Kaleidoscopes
ASTROVOLITE - Flashlights - Accutec Inc.
ASTRUP - Hardware - Astrup Co.
ASTURIAS - Guitars - JTG of Nashville
ASTYPTODYNE - Antiseptics - Astyptodyne Chemical Co.
ASU - Bowling balls - Award Skores Unlimited Inc.
ASULAM - Pharmaceutical preparations - Goldline Laboratories, Inc.
ASUNCION CHARME - Skin care products - Motofumi Watanabe
ASUNCION SCHON - Hair care products - Motofumi Watanabe
ASUPIRIN - Pharmaceutical preparations - Suppositoria Laboratories
ASURE - Rodenticides - Warren Chemical Products Co.
ASV - Recording label - Creav Inc. USA
ASYA GRAPHICS - Stamps–hand - Asya Graphics
ASYLUM - Apparel and accessories - Brad Whitney Sportswear Manufacturing
ASYLUM - Recording label - Warner Music International
ASYMETRIX INFOMODELER - Computer software - Asymetrix Corp.
ASYMETRIX WEBPUBLISHER - Computer software - Asymetrix Corp.
ASYMMETRIC - Bicycle parts and accessories - Litespeed Titanium Components, Inc.
ASYMMETRIC - Lamps - Luxo Corp.
ASYN-A-LYTE - Lighting fixtures - Voigt Lighting Industries Inc.
ASYNK - Toys - Mattel, Inc.

☆ = Now out of production

AT - Apparel–women's - AnnTaylor, Inc.
AT - Audio equipment - Cerwin-Vega Inc.
AT - Automotive parts and accessories - Punch Press Products, Inc.
AT - Gaskets - Accutrex Products, Inc.
AT-A-GLANCE - Calendars - Keith Clark Inc.
AT-A-GLANCE ORGANIZER - Diaries - Cullman Ventures Inc.
AT-A-GLANCE ORGANIZER - Display cases–plastic ☆ - Design Northwest
AT-AT (IMPERIAL ALL-TERRAIN ARMORED TRANSPORT) - Toys–models - ERTL Co., Inc.
@BASE - Computer software - PERSONICS Corp.
A.T. CLEAN SPOON - Pharmaceutical preparations - Apothecary Products, Inc.
AT DENIM - Apparel - AnnTaylor, Inc.
AT EASE - Coats–women's - Colberts, Inc.
AT-EASE - Furniture–upholstered - Simmons USA
AT EASE - Housewares - Shaklee Corp.
AT EASE - Pharmaceutical preparations ☆ - Tranzonic Cos.
AT-EASE - Shirts - Apparel Group, Ltd.
AT EASE 2X - Vitamins and nutritional supplements - Frye Co.
AT-FA - Paints - American Turpentine Farmers Association
AT FIRST SIGHT - Toys–stuffed ☆ - Gund, Inc.
AT HAND - Office supplies - Bodge Engineering
AT HOME - Apparel stores–lingerie - Formflex Foundations Inc.
AT HOME - Computer software - Seven Hills Software
AT HOME - Housewares - Lillian Vernon Corp.
AT HOME - Phonographs ☆ - Fantasy Inc.
AT-HOME - Pregnancy test kits - Carter-Wallace, Inc.
AT HOME - Wallpaper - James Seeman Studios
AT HOME III - Wallpaper - James Seeman Studios
AT HOME IN AMERICA - Furniture ☆ - La-Z-Boy Chair Co.
AT HOME IN PROVENCE - Wallpaper - Imperial Wallcoverings, Inc.
AT-HOME PROFESSIONS - Publisher's imprints - Weston Enterprises Inc.
AT HOME WITH FLORALS - Wallpaper ☆ - Lifestyle Studios
AT HOME WITH JEANNE-MARC - Robes ☆ - Periphery Loungewear Inc.
AT HOME WITH STICKYBEAR - Computer software - Optimum Resource, Inc.
AT/LANTIC - Computer hardware - National Semiconductor Corp.
AT LAST - Hair care products - Colgate-Palmolive Co.
AT LAST. NEW YORK BAGELS - Food products - Primary Capital Group Inc.
AT-MATIC - Pencils–mechanical ☆ - Sakura of America
AT RANDOM - Floor coverings–carpet and rugs ☆ - Playfield International Inc.
@RISK - Computer software - Palisade Corp.
A.T. STEELER - Shock absorbers–motor vehicle - Works Performance Products
AT THE BEACH - Advertising agencies - At the Beach Enterprises, Inc.
AT THE DANCE - Dolls - Seymour Mann Inc.
AT THE PARTY - Dolls - Seymour Mann Inc.
AT THE SIGN OF THE CHRISTMAS TREE - Christmas tree ornaments - Cracker Box Inc.
AT THE SOUND OF MY NAME - Apparel and accessories - Florentine Corp.
AT THE SOUND OF THE BEEP - Audio tapes–blank - Great American Audio Corp.
AT THE ZOO - Computer software - Gessler Publishing Co., Inc.
AT WHEELER - Toys - Tonka Corp.
AT WOOD - Sporting goods ☆ - Sea Spike Marine Supply Co. Inc.
AT WORK< slash> PLAY - Shirts - Cluett, Peabody & Co.
AT WORK UNIFORMS - Apparel and accessories - Export Performance Corp.
AT YOUR FINGERTIPS - Publisher's imprints - McClanahan Book Co., Inc.
AT YOUR LEISURE - Apparel–women's - QVC, Inc.
AT1200 - Projection screens - Draper Shade and Screen Co. Inc.
ATA - Apparel and accessories - Campus Crusade for Christ, Inc.
A.T.A. - Cases–musical instrument - Anvil Cases
ATA - Chemical preparations - Midwest Industrial Supply, Inc.
ATA - Jewelry - Atamant Inc.
ATA - Musical instrument accessories - Viking Cases
ATA - Spices and extracts - Herbert Marmorek & Son, Inc.
ATA-31 - Toys–models ☆ - Estes Industries
ATA FAX! - Computer software - Eas Technologies, Inc.
ATA STAR - Boxes - Star Case Manufacturing Co. Inc.
ATABOARD - Computer peripheral equipment - Kingston Technology Corp.
ATABRINE - Pharmaceutical preparations - Winthrop Pharmaceuticals
ATAC - Pharmaceutical preparations ☆ - Reese Chemical Co.
ATAC - Skin care products - Sween Corp.
ATAK - Medical apparatus - Performance Wrap Inc.
ATALA - Bicycles - Corso Bicycle Distributor Inc.
ATALHEA - Floor coverings–carpet and rugs - Robertex Associates Inc.
ATAMET - Pharmaceutical preparations - Athena Neurosciences, Inc.
AT&G - Tools–hand-operated - A.T. & G. Co., Inc.

AT&T - Telecommunications devices - At&T Corp.
AT&T MAIL ACCESSKIT - Computer software - At&T Corp.
AT&T SDN NETWORK MANAGER - Computer software - At&T Corp.
AT&T UNIPLAN BILLING EDGE - Computer software - At&T Corp.
AT&T VIDEOPHONE 2500 - Telephones - At&T Corp.
AT&T VOICESPAN - Communications equipment - At&T Corp.
ATARA - Hair care products - Cosmair Inc.
ATARA - Jewelry - Atara Designs Inc.
ATARAX - Antihistamine preparations - J.B. Roerig & Co.
ATARI - Video games - Atari Games Corp.
ATARI 800XL - Computers–personal - Atari Games Corp.
ATARI 1030 - Computer software - Atari Games Corp.
ATARI 5200 - Video games - Atari Games Corp.
ATARI BATTERY ELIMINATOR - Electronic equipment - Atari Games Corp.
ATARI ST - Computers–personal - Atari Games Corp.
ATARIN - Pharmaceutical preparations - Athena Neurosciences, Inc.
ATARISOFT - Computer software - Atari Games Corp.
ATARIWRITER - Computer software - Atari Games Corp.
ATARIWRITER PLUS - Computer software - Atari Games Corp.
ATAVIO - Drapery rods - Kirsch Co.
ATB - Circuit breakers - General Electric Co.
ATB - Motors - American Contex Corp.
ATB AUTHENTIC WESTERN WEAR - Apparel and accessories - C.R. Anthony Co.
ATC - Antennas–satellite - Antenna Technology Communications, Inc.
ATC - Automotive fuses - Cooper Industries, Inc.
ATC - Carts - Litton Industrial Automation Systems
ATC - Chemical preparations - Minnesota Mining & Manufacturing Co.
ATC - Electronics equipment - Assurance Technology Corp.
ATC - Motor vehicles–all-terrain - American Honda Motor Co. Inc. (Acura Div.)
ATC - Software product - L & M Auto Supply
ATC-3 - Water treating compounds - Bio-Lab, Inc.
ATC 5000 - Auto diagnostic device ☆ - Cooper Industries, Inc.
ATC-COMM - Computer software - Sycon Corp.
ATC WATT-SAVER - Lamp bulbs–incandescent - Duro-Test Corp.
ATCH-80 - Pharmaceutical preparations - Roberts/Hauck Pharmaceuticals Inc.
ATCO - Medical apparatus - Atco Truelife International
ATCO - Metal products - Atco Rubber Products Inc.
ATCO - Packaging supplies - Royal Packaging Inc.
ATCO - Recording label - Atlantic Records
ATCO - Tiles–ceramic - Atco Ceramics Corp.
ATCO - Tools ☆ - Atlas Group
ATCO BREST - Prosthetic apparatus - Atco Truelife International
ATD - Audio equipment - All-Test Devices Corp.
ATD ACTUATOR - Machine parts - Milwaukee Protective Covers
ATEC - Electronic equipment - Fry's Metals, Inc.
ATEC - Sporting goods - Grand Slam USA
ATEC DIAMOND DEMON, THE - Sporting goods - Grand Slam USA
ATEC GRAND SLAM USA - Apparel stores–sports - Grand Slam USA
ATECO - Cake-decorating accessories - August Thomsen Corp.
ATEGRA - Computer software - Ategra Systems, Inc.
ATEL-O-GRAM - Consulting services - Atel Capital Group
ATEL-O-GRAPH - Consulting services - Atel Capital Group
ATELICA - Wallpaper - Jolie Papier
ATELIER - Floor coverings–carpet and rugs - Mannington Carpets, Inc.
ATELIER - Paints ☆ - Chroma Acrylics Inc.
ATELIER ARTIST'S ACRYLICS & MEDIUMS - Paints–artists' - Chroma Acrylics Inc.
ATELIER CHRISTIANE - Food products - Bellini Imports Ltd.
ATELIER DES HURETS - Housewares - Elon Inc.
ATELIER DES TOURNELLES - Frames–picture ☆ - Chase Collection Inc.
ATELIER ESTHETIQUE - Cosmetics - Atelier Esthetique
ATELIER MARTEX - Fabrics–linen - West Point-Pepperell Inc.
ATEMI - Computer software - Atemi Corp.
ATENCO - Paper file folders - National Service Industries, Inc.
ATEPRINT - Resins–polymer - Boehme Filatex, Inc.
ATEX - Adhesives and sealants ☆ - Adhesive Products, Inc.
ATEX - Computer software - Eastman Kodak Co.
ATF - Food products - Auro Tech, Inc.
ATF - Pharmaceutical preparations - Advanced Vision Research, Inc.
ATF - Toys - American Toy & Furniture Co.
ATF 2000+ - Transmission equipment–motor vehicle - Flo-Dynamics, Inc.
ATF-XTRA - Transmission fluids - Conklin Co., Inc.
ATGAM - Pharmaceutical preparations - Upjohn Co.
ATH-LEISURE-THOTIC - Medical apparatus - Northwest Podiatric Laboratory, Inc.

☆ = Now out of production

ATHALON - Soft luggage ☆ - Hartmann Luggage Co.
ATHCOM - Amplifiers - Communications Sales Co.
ATHEMOL - Pharmaceutical preparations - Glaxo Wellcome Inc.
ATHENA - Athletic shoes - Converse Inc.
ATHENA - Bathing suits - Ocean Pool Co.
ATHENA - Bathing suits ☆ - Raj Manufacturing, Inc.
ATHENA - Candlesticks ☆ - Carolina Designs Ltd.
ATHENA - Clocks - Terragrafics Inc.
ATHENA - Computer graphics software - MVIS Corp.
ATHENA - Dinnerware–glass ☆ - Johnson Brothers, USA, Inc.
ATHENA - Electric lighting equipment - Lutron Electronics Co., Inc.
ATHENA - Electronic equipment - Athena Controls, Inc.
ATHENA - Fireplaces ☆ - Majestic Co.
ATHENA - Flatware - Crate and Barrel
ATHENA - Floor coverings–carpet and rugs ☆ - Regal Rugs Inc.
ATHENA - Fuel additives - Athena International
ATHENA - Giftware ☆ - Athena Products Corp.
ATHENA - Glassware–household - Block China Co.
ATHENA - Guns - Weatherby Inc.
ATHENA - Housewares - Aervoe-Pacific Co. Inc.
ATHENA - Housewares - Oneida Ltd.
ATHENA - Lamps - Kaadan Ltd.
ATHENA - Olive oil ☆ - Kiss My Face
ATHENA - Projectors–photographic - L-W Athena Inc.
ATHENA - Recording label - Athena Productions
ATHENA - Rings–jewelry ☆ - Artcarved Inc.
ATHENA - Statuary - Lansing Regional Chamber of Commerce Athena Foundation
ATHENA - Telescopes - Northern Telecom, Inc.
ATHENA - Tiles–ceramic - Kowa Texas Inc.
ATHENA - Tiles–ceramic - Monarch Tile Inc.
ATHENA - Toys–models - Estes Industries
ATHENA - Vases ☆ - Lenox Crystal, Inc.
ATHENA - Watches - Bulova Corp.
ATHENA - Whirlpool bath ☆ - Jacuzzi Inc.
ATHENA ALEXANDER - Footwear - J & A Shoe Co., Inc.
ATHENA COLLECTION - Bathing suits - Raj Manufacturing, Inc.
ATHENA-ESE - Projectors–photographic - L-W Athena Inc.
ATHENA TECHNOLOGY - Dental equipment - Athena Technology, Inc.
ATHENAEUM - Computer software - Fox Post Production Services, Inc.
ATHENAEUM - Wallpaper - Imperial Wallcoverings, Inc.
ATHENAS - Window coverings - Vertilux-Louverlux Inc.
ATHENE - Cocktail tables ☆ - JDI Group, Inc.
ATHENEUM - Publisher's imprints - MacMillan Publishing Co. Inc.
ATHENIAN - Coffee tables - Landes Manufacturing Co.
ATHENIAN - Dishes–china ☆ - Pickard Inc.
ATHENIAN - Floor coverings - Mannington Resilient Floors
ATHENIAN - Food products - GDF, Inc.
ATHENIAN COLLECTION - Giftware - Lenox, Inc.
ATHENS - Cabinets - Canyon Creek Cabinet Co.
ATHENS - Dinnerware–glass - Block China Co.
ATHENS - Floor coverings–carpet and rugs - Atlas Carpet Mills Inc.
ATHENS - Floor coverings–carpet and rugs ☆ - LaVelle Textile Marketing Inc.
ATHENS - Food products - Athens Foods
ATHENS - Furniture - Athens Furniture Industries Inc.
ATHENS - Glassware–household ☆ - Lotus Glass Co.
ATHENS - Tableware–china - Pfaltzgraff Investment Co.
ATHENS - Wigs - Paula Young
ATHENS ARCH - Door frames - Canyon Creek Cabinet Co.
ATHENS COLLECTION - Furniture - Telescope Casual Furniture Inc.
ATHERSTONE - Floor coverings ☆ - Azrock Commercial Flooring
ATHERTON - Apparel and accessories - Sun Mountain Sports, Inc.
ATHERTON - Flatware ☆ - Pfaltzgraff Investment Co.
ATHERTON CLASSICS - Apparel and accessories - Sun Mountain Sports, Inc.
ATHERTON HOUSE - Greeting cards ☆ - Paper Magic Group Inc.
ATHERTON PLACE - Floor coverings–carpet and rugs - Catalina Carpet Mills Inc.
ATHEY - Paints - C.M. Athey Paint Co.
ATHEY - Window shades - Eli Custom Window Treatment, Ltd.
A'THIA - Crocheted and knitted items - Collins & Aikman Corp.
ATHLEISURE - Apparel stores–sports - Rugged Wear Ltd.
ATHLETE - Bicycles - Columbia Manufacturing Inc.
ATHLETE - Flour–blended - Hubbard Milling Co.
ATHLETE, THE - Sporting goods - Hogue Tool & Manufacturing Corp.
ATHLETE'S CHOICE - Beverages - American Eagle Beverages, Inc.
ATHLETE'S CHOICE - Footwear - Sunbelt Footwear Corp.

ATHLETES CHOICE - Sporting goods ☆ - Bee Natural Leathercare Inc.
ATHLETE'S CHOICE - Vitamins and nutritional supplements ☆ - Optimal Nutrients
ATHLETE'S FOOT, THE - Apparel, footwear, and sporting goods franchise - Athlete's Foot Marketing Associates Inc.
ATHLETES IN MOTION - Pins–jewelry - Imprinted Products Corp.
ATHLETE'S MANNA - Food products - Leslie E. Nunn
ATHLETES ONLY - Apparel and accessories - Athletes Only, Inc.
ATHLETE'S PAK - Health care products - Above All Health Inc.
ATHLETIC 3 - Vitamins and nutritional supplements ☆ - Weider Health and Fitness
ATHLETIC ADDICTION - Apparel–athletic - Steven Dennis Schwartz
ATHLETIC ATTIC, THE - Sporting-goods franchise - Athletic Attic National
ATHLETIC CLUB - Colognes - Brandy Harvest
ATHLETIC CLUB - Hosiery - Desoto Hosiery Mills, Inc.
ATHLETIC CLUB - Hosiery–women's - Desoto Mills, Inc.
ATHLETIC LADY - Athletic apparel franchise - Athletic Attic National
ATHLETIC PRESS - Publisher's imprints - Golden West Books
ATHLETIC RAGS - Apparel and accessories - House of Ronnie, Inc.
ATHLETIC RECOVERY OIL - Pharmaceutical preparations - Econatural Solutions
ATHLETIC SUPPORTER - Apparel, novelties - J & J Enterprises
ATHLETIC TAPES - Sporting goods - Medi Inc.
ATHLETIC TRAINING ACTION - Computer software - Cramer Products Inc.
ATHLETIC TRAINING SUPPLIES - Sporting goods - Medi Inc.
ATHLETIC TURF - Floor coverings–carpet and rugs - Playfield International Inc.
ATHLETIC WORLD ADVERTISING - Advertising agencies - Tri-State Publications, Inc.
ATHLETICARE - Health care products - Johnson & Johnson
ATHLEX - Fungicides - Sani-Mist Inc.
ATHOL - Tools - L.S. Starrett Co. Inc. (Consumer Products Div.)
ATHON - Tiles–ceramic ☆ - Federal Tile Imports Inc.
ATHOS - Faucets - Kallista Inc.
ATHROMBIC PUMP - Compressors–gas - Jobst Institute Inc.
ATHROMBIN-K - Pharmaceutical preparations ☆ - Purdue Frederick Co.
ATHTEX - Apparel stores–sports ☆ - Tultex Corp.
ATI - Artists' materials - Artoptic International Corp.
ATI - Bicycles - Applied Tectonics Inc.
ATI - Computers - Atronics International, Inc.
ATI - Electrical generators - Active Technologies, Inc.
ATI - Health care products ☆ - Trimline Medical Products Corp.
ATI - Jewelry - Athra Trading
ATI - Sheet material - Alucobond Technologies Inc.
ATI - Toys–trains - Model Power
ATI-TEST - Health care products ☆ - Trimline Medical Products Corp.
ATILIER K - Glassware–household - Spiegelau Inc.
ATILLA THE HUNTER - Toys - Tonka Corp.
ATINATRIB - Watches - Bulova Corp.
ATIRIZ - Footwear ☆ - Conjac Inc.
ATIS - Tire inflators - Pressure System International, Inc.
ATITLAN ACCENTS - Apparel and accessories ☆ - Sales Marketing Services, Inc.
ATIVAN - Pharmaceutical preparations - Wyeth-Ayerst Laboratories
ATK - Recreational vehicles - American Dirt Bike Inc.
ATKINS - Pickles - Green Bay Foods Co.
ATKINS - Thermostats - Atkins Technical Inc.
ATKINSON - Blankets - Imperial Childrens Wear Inc.
ATKINSON - Gift wrap - Atkinson Sales Co.
ATKINSON ROYAL IRISH POPLIN - Neckties ☆ - Salant/Manhattan Industries
ATL - Recording label - Jazz Composer's Orchestra Association Inc.
ATL 14K - Jewelry - Atlantic Jewelry Co. Inc.
ATLAB - Computer software - Data Translation, Inc.
ATLANDIA - Apparel and accessories - Atlandia Imports, Inc.
ATLANTA - Accordions - Hohner Inc.
ATLANTA - Dairy product - Atlanta Dairies Co-Operative Inc.
ATLANTA - Dolls ☆ - Effanbee Doll Corp.
ATLANTA - Floor coverings–carpet and rugs - Stanton Carpet Corp.
ATLANTA - Heaters–space - Martin Industries, Inc.
ATLANTA - Yarn ☆ - Joseph Galler Inc.
ATLANTA BLACK CRACKERS ABC - Apparel and accessories - Negro Leagues Baseball Museum, Inc.
ATLANTA BURNING - Sauces - Robert A. Witt
ATLANTA CARPET MILLS - Floor coverings–carpet and rugs - Royalty Carpet Mills, Inc.
ATLANTA COTTON DUCK - Canvas–artists' ☆ - Winsor & Newton

ATLANTA CUTLERY - Hardware - Atlanta Cutlery Corp.
ATLANTA HAWKS - Apparel and accessories - Atlanta Hawks, Ltd.
ATLANTA ROASTERY COFFEE - Coffee - Atlanta Coffee Roastery, Inc.
ATLANTA TEA - Teas - Atlanta Coffee & Tea Co.
ATLANTALAWN - Flowers, plants, and seeds - Sunbelt Seeds Inc.
ATLANTE - Leather goods - Bugatti Inc.
ATLANTEK - Printers–computer - Atlantek Inc.
ATLANTES - Toilets–porcelain - Raritan Engineering Co. Inc.
ATLANTEX - Fabrics and notions - Atlanta Textile Co. Inc.
ATLANTIC - Accordions - Hohner Inc.
ATLANTIC - Amplifiers–musical instrument - Newark Musical Merchandise Co.
ATLANTIC - Bicycles - Ross Bicycles USA, Ltd.
ATLANTIC - Boats–motor - Gilman Marine Inc.
ATLANTIC - Boats–motor ☆ - Grady-White Boats, Inc.
ATLANTIC - Brooms - France Broom Co.
ATLANTIC - Brooms ☆ - Harbor Manufacturing
ATLANTIC - Crayons ☆ - Binney & Smith Inc.
ATLANTIC - Frozen blueberries - Atlantic Blueberry Co.
ATLANTIC - Giftware - Atlantic-Paulson Inc.
ATLANTIC - Horseradish - Silver Spring Gardens Inc.
ATLANTIC - Ladders–metal - John S. Tilley Ladders Co. Inc.
ATLANTIC - Luggage - Airway Industries, Inc.
ATLANTIC - Mops ☆ - Helen Keller Services for the Blind
ATLANTIC - Nails, fencing product ☆ - Atlantic Steel Co.
ATLANTIC - Pier ladders, davits and boatlifts - Atlantic Boatlifts Inc.
ATLANTIC - Prefabricated buildings–wood - Champion Enterprises Inc.
ATLANTIC - Racks - Atlantic Representations, Inc.
ATLANTIC - Recording label - Atlantic Records
ATLANTIC - Roller skates - Atlantic Skates Inc.
ATLANTIC - Seafood products–canned or cured - A.M. Look Canning Co.
ATLANTIC - Ships–sailing vessels - Seafarer Yachts Inc.
ATLANTIC - Sporting goods - Bennett Brothers Yachts Inc.
ATLANTIC - Stoves - Portland Franklin Stove Foundry Inc.
ATLANTIC - Tableware–china ☆ - Villeroy and Boch Tableware Ltd.
ATLANTIC - Teas ☆ - Old Mansion Foods Inc.
ATLANTIC - Vertical blinds - Atlantic Venetian Blind & Drapery Co.
ATLANTIC BEACH LEATHER COAT WORKS - Apparel and accessories - Derby Enterprises Corp.
ATLANTIC BEDFORD - Coffee and snack bags - AB Specialty Package Inc.
ATLANTIC BLUEBERRY CO. - Blueberries and blueberry products - Atlantic Blueberry Co.
ATLANTIC CHALLENGE CUP - Athletic associations - New York Yacht Club
ATLANTIC CITY - Colognes - Brandy Harvest
ATLANTIC CITY BLEND - Coffee - Wayne Coffee Co.
ATLANTIC COAST - Fruits–frozen - Gay Brothers Inc.
ATLANTIC COAST - Seafood products–fresh or frozen - Atlantic Coast Fisheries Corp.
ATLANTIC COAST - Seafood products–fresh or frozen - Ruggiero Seafood, Inc.
ATLANTIC COAST CONFERENCE - Apparel–athletic - Atlantic Coast Conference
ATLANTIC COAST CONFERENCE 1953 - Apparel and accessories - Atlantic Coast Conference
ATLANTIC FRESH - Agricultural products - Atlantic Fresh, Inc.
ATLANTIC FURNITURE SYSTEMS - Furniture and accessories - Atlantic Furniture Systems
ATLANTIC HARBOR TRADING COMPANY - Seafood products–fresh or frozen - Giant Eagle, Inc. (By Itself and Through Related Companies)
ATLANTIC ISLES - Salmon–smoked, salted, dried, or pickled - Friendly Fruit, Inc.
ATLANTIC MONTHLY PRESS - Publisher's imprints - Grove/Atlantic, Inc.
ATLANTIC OCEAN - Seafood products–fresh or frozen - F.W. Bryce Inc.
ATLANTIC PEARL - Scallops - Sea-Rich Seafoods, Inc.
ATLANTIC PEARL - Seafood products–fresh or frozen - G.F. Higgins
ATLANTIC PRIDE - Shrimp–fresh or frozen - Sea Harvest Packing Co.
ATLANTIC SEACOAST - Paints - C.M. Athey Paint Co.
ATLANTIC STANDARD - Herbicides - BASF Corp.
ATLANTIC TOWERS - Boats–motor - Atlantic Fabricators of Rhode Island Inc.
ATLANTICA - Board games - American Sports Games Corp.
ATLANTICA - Floor coverings–carpet and rugs ☆ - Royalweve Carpet Mills
ATLANTICA - Sailboat - Atlantica Yachts Ltd.
ATLANTIS - Aquarium product - Sergeant's Pet Products, Inc.
ATLANTIS - Bathing suits - Ocean Pool Co.
ATLANTIS - Bathroom fixtures - Crane Plumbing/Fiat Products
ATLANTIS - Bathroom fixtures ☆ - Artesian Industries
ATLANTIS - Boats–motor ☆ - Old Town Canoe Co.

ATLANTIS - Carpets - Couristan Inc.
ATLANTIS - Ceiling fans - HPD Acquisition Corp.
ATLANTIS - Clocks - Ridgeway Clock Co.
ATLANTIS - Computer software - Atlantis Technologies, Inc.
ATLANTIS - Fabrics–tapestry ☆ - Coloroll Inc.
ATLANTIS - Floor coverings - Mannington Resilient Floors
ATLANTIS - Floor coverings–carpet and rugs - Playfield International Inc.
ATLANTIS - Floor coverings–carpet and rugs ☆ - Mannington Carpets, Inc.
ATLANTIS - Food products - Armour Dairy Co.
ATLANTIS - Food products - Stache Foods
ATLANTIS - Furniture - Lane Co. Inc.
ATLANTIS - Glassware–household - Block China Co.
ATLANTIS - Seafood products–fresh or frozen - State Fish Co., Inc.
ATLANTIS - Sporting goods - U.S. Divers Co., Inc.
ATLANTIS - Tiles–ceramic - Dal-Tile Corp.
ATLANTIS - Water–mineral - Laureate Imports Co.
ATLANTIS - Waterproof outerwear ☆ - Imtra Corp.
ATLANTIS CLUB - Floor coverings–carpet and rugs - Playfield International Inc.
ATLANTIS FILMS - Plastics film - Atlantis Group Inc.
ATLANTIS II - Tiles–ceramic - Buchtal USA
ATLANTIS-PRESTIGIO - Glassware–household - Block China Co.
ATLANTIS SKIN DRINK - Cosmetics - Rachel Perry, Inc.
ATLAS - Automotive batteries, tires, accessories - Atlas Supply Co.
ATLAS - Automotive parts and accessories - Amoco Oil Co.
ATLAS - Bicycles ☆ - Murray, Inc.
ATLAS - Bricks - Pacific Coast Building Products, Inc.
ATLAS - Brooms - Lighthouse Industries
ATLAS - Cement ☆ - Lehigh Portland Cement Co.
ATLAS - Cookies - Atlas Biscuit Co. Inc.
ATLAS - Cymbals - Jim Atlas Cymbal Works
ATLAS - Dinnerware - Pfaltzgraff Investment Co.
ATLAS - Electronic storage medium - National Biomedical Research Foundation
ATLAS - Envelopes ☆ - Marvin Envelope & Paper Co.
ATLAS - Flags ☆ - Flags International Inc.
ATLAS - Floor coverings–carpet and rugs - Mohawk Industries Inc.
ATLAS - Floor coverings–carpet and rugs ☆ - Eurotex Inc.
ATLAS - Floor coverings–carpet and rugs ☆ - Quaker Inc.
ATLAS - Garden equipment - Ames Lawn & Garden Tool Co.
ATLAS - Garden equipment ☆ - Lawn & Garden Supply Co.
ATLAS - Gelatin - Vyse Gelatin Co.
ATLAS - Hardware - Atlas Products Co.
ATLAS - Housewares - SCI Scandicrafts Inc.
ATLAS - Insulation board - Atlas Roofing Corp.
ATLAS - Jewelry chains - Atlas Chain Co.
ATLAS - Labels–fabric ☆ - Rand McNally & Co.
ATLAS - Ladders–metal - John S. Tilley Ladders Co. Inc.
ATLAS - Ladders–metal ☆ - Rich Ladder Co.
ATLAS - Machinery - Polyfibron Technologies, Inc.
ATLAS - Matches - Atlas Match Co.
ATLAS - Medical apparatus - Kirschner Medical Corp.
ATLAS - Medical products - Miles Inc.
ATLAS - Musical instruments and music stands - Atlas Accordions Inc.
ATLAS - Office supplies - The Union Group
ATLAS - Paint sprayers - Speeflo Manufacturing Corp.
ATLAS - Pencil sharpeners - Empire Berol USA
ATLAS - Pharmaceutical preparations - Duro Med Industries Inc.
ATLAS - Pocket stamps, hand-printing presses - Consolidated Stamp Manufacturing Co. Inc.
ATLAS - Post hole diggers–hand-operated - Seymour Manufacturing Co.,Inc.
ATLAS - Sealing compounds - Monsey Products Co.
ATLAS - Sports apparel - Medalist Apparel Inc.
ATLAS - Tape measures - Lufkin Rule Co.
ATLAS - Tiles–ceramic ☆ - Federal Tile Imports Inc.
ATLAS - Tiles–terrazzo - Imperial Tile and Marble Corp.
ATLAS - Tobacco–chewing or smoking - Cornell & Diehl Inc.
ATLAS - Toilets–porcelain - Universal-Rundle Corp.
ATLAS - Toys, stationery, sporting goods, health and beauty aids - Atlas Group
ATLAS - Toys–trains - Atlas Model Railroad Co., Inc.
ATLAS - Washcloths ☆ - Clean-Rite Products Co.
ATLAS - Woodworking machines - Clausing Industrial Inc.
ATLAS AMERICAN - Furniture ☆ - The Coleman Co.
ATLAS BAG - Tarpaulins - Atlas Bag, Inc.
ATLAS BAG INC. - Tarpaulins - Atlas Bag, Inc.
ATLAS BRADFORD - Couplings - Grant TFW, Inc.

☆ = Now out of production

ATLAS CHINA 1918 - Giftware - Bernard W. Bernthal Inc.
ATLAS-COOL - Paints ☆ - Atlas Chemical Co.
ATLAS CURE-ROT - Sealer and restorer for dry-rotted wood - Atlas Minerals & Chemicals, Inc.
ATLAS II - Musical instruments ☆ - Selmer Co. Inc.
ATLAS MARINE SERVICES - Storage racks, lockers, and cabinets - Atlas Marine Services, Inc.
ATLAS METAL - Woks, copperware, etc. - Atlas Metal Spinning Co.
ATLAS MODEL RAILROAD CO., INC. - Toys–trains - Atlas Model Railroad Co., Inc.
ATLAS OF THE DC UNIVERSE - Games - Mayfair Games, Inc.
ATLAS PASTA - Pasta - Yknot in Madison, Inc.
ATLAS PELLETS - Fireplace logs–treated - Atlas Marketing, LLC
ATLAS PRO - Lawn mowers - Cotter & Co.
ATLAS ROLL-LITE - Shutters–metal - Atlas Roll-Lite Door Corp.
ATLAS-SEAL - Cement ☆ - Atlas Chemical Co.
ATLAS SOUND - Microphone accessories - American Trading and Production Corp.
ATLAS/SOUND - Microphones - Atlas/Soundolier
ATLAS/SOUNDOLIER - Communications equipment - Atlas/Soundolier
ATLAS SUPPORT BELTS - Orthopedic products - Atlas Support Belts, Inc.
ATLASEAL - Coatings ☆ - Atlas Chemical Co.
ATLASFLEX - Paints ☆ - Atlas Chemical Co.
ATLASGUARD - Enamels ☆ - Atlas Chemical Co.
ATLASHIELD - Paints ☆ - Atlas Chemical Co.
ATLASITE - Furniture - Bassick Casters
ATLASMAT - Housewares - Reliance Plastic & Chemical Corp.
ATLASTACRETE - Concrete repair products - Atlas Minerals & Chemicals, Inc.
ATLUS - Video and computer games - Asuka Technologies Inc.
ATM - Lawn mowers - DewEze Manufacturing Inc.
ATM - Vans–conversion ☆ - Turtle Top Specialty Products
ATM-9 SUPERLIFE - Lamp bulbs–incandescent - Duro-Test Corp.
ATM EXPRESS - Computer software - Optical Data Systems, Inc.
ATM TOPPER - Signs - Dallman Industrial Corp.
ATM UNIVERSE SWITCH - Communications equipment - Fujitsu Business Communication Systems,Inc.
ATMA - Electronic equipment - Applied Power Inc.
ATMAN - Jewelry - Atman Jewelry Co. Inc.
ATMANIKETAN ASHRAM - Spiritual books and journals ☆ - Auromere Inc.
ATMIZED - Computer hardware - Lsi Logic Corp.
ATMOS - Clocks - Jaeger-Le Coultre SA
ATMOSFEAR - Games - Mattel, Inc.
ATMOSFERA - Wallpaper - Walldesigns
ATMOSFERS II - Wallpaper - Advance Wallcoverings
ATMOSPHEAR - Recording label ☆ - Mystic Records
ATMOSPHERE - Computer terminals - Fibermux Corp.
ATMOSPHERE FURNACE CO. - Furnaces–industrial - Atmosphere Furnace Co.
ATMOSPHERE RECORDS - Recording label ☆ - Northcott Productions Ltd.
ATMOSPHERICS COLLECTION - Wallcoverings - Ben Rose Ltd.
ATMSIM - Computer software - Wandel & Goltermann Technologies, Inc.
ATMX - Communications equipment - Network Equipment Technologies Inc.
ATO - Fuses–electric - Littelfuse, Inc.
ATO-MIZOR - Housewares ☆ - H.D. Hudson Manufacturing Co.
ATOKA - Clocks - Ridgeway Clock Co.
ATOLECTRIC - Watches - Bulova Corp.
ATOM - Braces–orthopedic - Swede-O, Inc.
ATOM - Fishing lures - Den Manufacturing Co.
ATOM - Transformers–electric - Advanced Optical Controls, Inc.
ATOM BOB - Books–comic - Malibu Comics Entertainment, Inc.
ATOM BOMB - Perfumes - Andrew Jergens Co.
ATOMACHRON - Watches - Bulova Corp.
ATOMAL - Photographic equipment - Miles Inc. (Agfa Div.)
ATOMATRON - Watches - Bulova Corp.
ATOMIC - Amplifiers - SJA Industries Inc.
ATOMIC - Bicycles ☆ - Huffy Corp.
ATOMIC - Fireworks - L. W. Loyd Co., Inc.
ATOMIC - Flints ☆ - Red Devil Products Inc.
ATOMIC - Lotions - Cramer Products Inc.
ATOMIC - Tortillas - Atomic Wings
ATOMIC - Video games - Atomic Games, Inc.
ATOMIC - Video production - Atomic Video, LLC
ATOMIC AFTERGLOW - Fireworks - B.J. Alan Co. Inc.
ATOMIC ARCADE - Toys - Tomy America, Inc.
ATOMIC CLOCK - Computer software - Parsons Technology, Inc.

ATOMIC DOG SOFTWARE - Computer storage devices–magnetic - Atomic Dog Software Corp.
ATOMIC FIREBALL - Candy - Ferrara Pan Candy Co., Inc.
ATOMIC GOLDEN SHARP - Cheese ☆ - Bruder Dairy Products Co.
ATOMIC GREEN TANGERINE - Beverages–carbonated - J & H Food and Beverage, Inc.
ATOMIC SHARP - Cheese - Bruder Dairy Products Co.
ATOMIC THEORY - Recording label - Flying Fish Records Inc.
ATOMICRONIC - Watches - Gruen Marketing Corp.
ATOMIDINE - Antiseptics - Heritage Store Inc.
ATOMIK ANGELS - Publisher's imprints - William Elliott Tucci
ATOMIST - Atomizers - RL Flo-Master
ATOMIX - Fuel additives - Bell Additives, Inc.
ATOMLAB - Medical products - Biodex Medical Systems Inc.
ATONE - Hair care products - Biocare Labs, Inc.
ATONE WITH NATURE - Hair care products - Biocare Labs, Inc.
ATOPAC - Tools - Atlas Tool Co. Inc.
ATORON ELECTRO - Cameras ☆ - Yashica Inc.
ATOZCO - Video production - AtoZco
ATP - Computer software - Flightlogic, Inc.
ATP - Hair care products - Genesis Research International
ATP - Hoses - Advanced Technology Products, Inc.
ATP - Screws - Action Threaded Products Inc.
ATP - Sporting goods - Adidas USA Inc.
ATP - Sporting goods - FTM Sports
A.T.P. - Vitamins and nutritional supplements - Integrated Health, Inc.
ATP/CASEMATE - Controls–heating systems - Surface Combustion, Inc.
ATP MAINTENANCE DIRECTOR - Computer software - Aircraft Technical Publishers, Inc.
ATP NAVIGATOR - Computer software - Aircraft Technical Publishers, Inc.
ATP TOUR - Rackets–tennis - ATP Tour, Inc.
ATP=E - Pharmaceutical preparations - Carni-Ray Research
ATPI - Computer peripheral equipment - Mr. Fax
ATR - Rivets–metal - Allied Tubular Rivet, Inc.
ATRA - Fasteners–snap - Reynolds Consumer Products, Inc.
ATRA - Shaving preparations - Gillette Co.
ATRA - Tools - Nitto Kohki USA Inc.
ATRA ELITE - Shaving preparations - Gillette Co.
ATRA INVITATION - Shaving preparations - Gillette Co.
ATRA-PLUS - Clay–kiln - ECC International
ATRA PLUS - Shaving preparations - Gillette Co.
ATRAC - Racks - Mirland Corp.
ATRAC-TAIN - Skin care products - Sween Corp.
ATRANS - Computer software - ACEO Technology Inc.
ATREVETE CON MOUNTAIN DEW - Beverages - Pepsico, Inc.
ATRIA - Computer storage devices - Atria Software Inc.
ATRIA - Wallcoverings - Ben Rose Ltd.
ATRIDINE - Prescription drug - IDE-Interstate Inc.
ATRIDOX - Pharmaceutical preparations - Atrix Laboratories, Inc.
ATRIGEL - Motor vehicles - Atrix Laboratories, Inc.
ATRIO - Frames–eyeglass - Windsor Optical Inc.
ATRISORB - Dental equipment - Atrix Laboratories, Inc.
ATRIUM - Dinnerware–glass ☆ - Nikko Ceramics Inc.
ATRIUM - Floor coverings - Congoleum Corp.
ATRIUM - Floor coverings–carpet and rugs ☆ - Whitecrest Carpet Mills
ATRIUM - Floor coverings–carpet and rugs ☆ - World Carpets, Inc.
ATRIUM - Glassware–household ☆ - Lenox Crystal, Inc.
ATRIUM - Luggage - American Tourister, Inc.
ATRIUM - Mats - Matworks
ATRIUM - Paints - Duron, Inc.
ATRIUM - Vitamins and nutritional supplements - Atrium Nutrition
ATRIUM COLLECTION - Suits–men's - Dress Barn Inc.
ATRIUM COURT - Furniture ☆ - Bernhardt Industries
ATRIUM EMPOWERMENT - Computer software - Innovative Business and Training Solutions, Inc.
ATRIUM PLAZA - Furniture - Singer Furniture Co.
ATRIUS - Computer software - Atrius Technologies, Inc.
ATRIX - Pharmaceutical preparations ☆ - Atrix Laboratories, Inc.
ATRO - Motor vehicle parts and accessories - Atro Engineered Systems, Inc.
ATROBAN - Veterinary pharmaceutical preparations - Schering-Plough Animal Health
ATROBARBITAL - Pharmaceutical preparations ☆ - Wesley Pharmacal Co. Inc.
ATROCHOLIN - Pharmaceutical preparations - Glaxo Wellcome Inc.
ATROHIST - Antihistamine preparations - Adams Laboratories Inc.
ATROL - Measuring instruments - Abbott Tachograph

☆ = Now out of production

ATROMID-S - Pharmaceutical preparations - Wyeth-Ayerst Laboratories
ATROPHYSINE - Pharmaceutical preparations - Lannett Co. Inc.
ATROPINE CARE - Pharmaceutical preparations - Akorn Inc.
ATROPISOL - Prescription ophthalmic - Iolab Pharmaceuticals
ATS - Apparel and accessories - Carolon Co.
ATS - Computer terminals ☆ - Accu-Time Systems, Inc.
ATS - Sporting goods - Lisco, Inc.
ATS-1 - Skis - Wellington Leisure Products, Inc.
ATS6 - Tools–power-driven - Phillips Screw Co.
ATS8 - Tools–power-driven - Phillips Screw Co.
ATS10 - Tools–power-driven - Phillips Screw Co.
ATSERVER - Computer software - Automatic Time Systems Corp.
ATSL-4 - Tools–power-driven - Phillips Screw Co.
ATT901 - Tires - Goodyear Tire & Rubber Co.
ATTA-BOY! - Diapers–disposable - Kimberly-Clark Corp.
ATTA BOY - Dog food - American Nutrition, Inc.
ATTA BOY - Harmonicas - Hohner Inc.
ATTA CAT - Pet food - American Nutrition, Inc.
ATTA-GIRL! - Diapers–disposable - Kimberly-Clark Corp.
ATTAC - Pharmaceutical preparations - Barrows Pharmacal Inc.
ATTACH-A-BAG - Bags - J & J Sport Products
ATTACH-A-MATIC - Lawn mowers - Toro Co.
ATTACH-A-PATCH - Games - Centsable Toys Inc.
ATTACH-A-TAB - Office supplies ☆ - Barkley Filing Supplies
ATTACH 'N GO - Toys ☆ - Playskool, Inc.
ATTACH 'N GO BYE BYE BEARS - Toys ☆ - Playskool, Inc.
ATTACHABLES - Toys - Playskool, Inc.
ATTACHE - Bags - AEP Industries, Inc.
ATTACHE - Compressors–air - Caire
ATTACHE - Diaries ☆ - Sheaffer Inc.
ATTACHE - Electric lighting equipment - Lutron Electronics Co., Inc.
ATTACHE - Floor coverings–carpet and rugs - Roxbury Carpet Co.
ATTACHE - Jewelry - Gentry Inc.
ATTACHE - Medical apparatus - Caire Inc.
ATTACHE - Pens - Accutec Inc.
ATTACHE - Tape recorders–cassette - Lanier Voice Products
ATTACHE - Trailers–travel - Royals International
ATTACHE - Wallpaper ☆ - Bob Mitchell Designs
ATTACHE CASE - Pipes–tobacco ☆ - Buescher's Industries Inc.
ATTACHE CORONA - Cigars - Gesty Trading & Manufacturing Corp.
ATTACHE-PHONE - Leather goods - Leather Sophisticates
ATTACHE-VUE - Projectors–photographic ☆ - JM Co.
ATTACHES - Footwear–men's - Allen-Edmonds Shoe Corp.
ATTACHMENTS - Jewelry - Imperial Pearl Syndicate Inc.
ATTACK - Detergents - PYA/Monarch Inc.
ATTACK - Insecticides ☆ - Reuter Manufacturing inc.
ATTACK - Rackets–racquetball ☆ - Rackets International (Racket Sports Div.)
ATTACK BOLLE. - Sunglasses - Bolle' America, Inc.
ATTACK COBRA - Toys–models - Cox Products Inc.
ATTACK CROC - Toys - Mattel, Inc.
ATTACK CRUISER - Toys–automobiles - Hasbro, Inc.
ATTACK-FOAM - Fire extinguishing compositions - Baroid Technology, Inc.
ATTACK FORCE - Athletic shoes - Payless Shoesource Worldwide, Inc.
ATTACK FORCE - Toys - Placo Products Co.
ATTACK OF THE TIMELORD - Toys–electronic ☆ - Philips Consumer Electronics Co.
ATTACK PACK - Toys–automobiles - Mattel, Inc.
ATTACK PACK DINOSAURS - Toys–automobiles - Mattel, Inc.
ATTACK RAFT - Toys - Mattel, Inc.
ATTACK SUB - Games - Avalon Hill Game Co.
ATTACK SUPER STRONG SHOCK - Water treating compounds - Bio-Dex Laboratories
ATTACK VEST - Sporting goods ☆ - Suplay Products-Wrestling World
ATTACKER - Grinders - United Abrasives, Inc.
ATTACKER - Staples - Interchange Brands, Inc.
ATTACKING ANXIETY - Video production - Midwest Center for Stress and Anxiety, Inc.
ATTACKTICS - Games - Walshing Machine Inc.
ATTAIN - Cosmetics ☆ - Divina Products Co.
ATTAIN - Health care products - Sherwood Medical Co.
ATTAIN - Insecticides - Whitmire Research Laboratories, Inc.
ATTAIN - Shampoos - Naturelle, Inc.
ATTAKISKA - Vodka - Alaska Mountaintop Spirits Co.
ATTAR - Handbags - Mid-Continent Ltd./MCL
ATTAR BAZAAR - Perfumes - Chishti Co.
ATTASORB - Coatings - Engelhard Corp.

ATTC - Machinery - American Torch Tip Co.
ATTEND - Computer peripheral equipment - Indata Corp.
ATTENDANCE CONTROLLER - Business forms - G. Neil Companies
ATTENDANT - Floor coverings–carpet and rugs - Mohawk Carpet Corp.
ATTENDANT - Floor coverings–carpet and rugs ☆ - Mannington Carpets, Inc.
ATTENDANT, THE - Wheelchairs - Alden B. Davis
ATTENDORE - Floor mats ☆ - Cooper Industries, Inc.
ATTENDORE - Security alarm - Signal-U Manufacturing
ATTENDS - Health care products - Procter & Gamble Co.
ATTENTION - Office supplies ☆ - Ames Safety Envelope Co.
ATTENTION MAILER - Envelopes - Esselte Corp.
ATTENUVAX - Vaccines - Merck & Co., Inc. (Merck Research Laboratories)
ATTERRACK - Recording label - Vandor Motion Pictures, Phonorecords & Music Publishing Group
ATTEST - Consulting services - Attest National Drug Testing, Inc.
ATTEST - Medical apparatus - Minnesota Mining & Manufacturing Co.
ATTESTED - Jewelry - Frederick Modell Inc.
ATTEX - Squeegees, ice scrapers, etc ☆ - Clean-Rite Products Co.
ATTIC AIRE - Ventilation equipment - Certainteed
ATTIC BLANKET - Insulating materials - Owens Corning
ATTIC BREEZE - Ventilators - Cool Attic
ATTIC CAP - Insulating materials - Reliable Plastics
ATTIC MASTER - Ladders–wood - Werner Co.
ATTIC PRO - Fans–attic - Leslie-Locke, Inc.
ATTICUBE - Novelty items - Judith La Rue & Co.
ATTIKA - Trees - Van Well Nursery Inc.
ATTILA - Sporting goods - Attila Juhasz
ATTITUDE - Bicycles - Klein Bicycle Corp.
L'ATTITUDE 39 - Wines - Fife Vineyards LLC
ATTITUDE ADJUSTING HOT STUFF - Spices and extracts - Bruce A. Pinnell
ATTITUDE ADJUSTMENT - Apparel and accessories - Bryant D. Nevitt
ATTITUDE APPAREL - Apparel and accessories - Successories, Inc.
ATTITUDE EQUIPMENT - Apparel–athletic - Reynolds & Brumfield Co.
ATTITUDE IS EVERYTHING - Recording label - Harrell & Associates, Ltd.
ATTITUDE SAVERS - Computer software - Celebrating Excellence, Inc.
ATTITUDE SAVERS - Computer software - Successories, Inc.
ATTITUDES - Footwear–women's - Hawaii Shoe Co.
ATTITUDES - Occasional tables - JDI Group, Inc.
ATTITUDES BY LEYLA MITRA - Apparel–women's - Jacobson Stores Inc.
ATTITUDES ONLY - Apparel–men's - Harper Shirt Co.
ATTITUDES UNLIMITED - Hair care products - Attitudes Unltd.
ATTITYPE - Artists' materials - Anthes Universal
ATTO INSTRUMENTS - Electronic equipment - Atto Instruments, Inc.
ATTOFLUOR - Electronic equipment - Atto Instruments, Inc.
ATTORNEY, THE - Novelty items - Voodoo To You Inc.
ATTRACT - Animal feeds - F.M. Brown's Sons, Inc.
ATTRACTION PACK - Computer software - Rand McNally & Co.
ATTRACTIONS - Hair care products - Helene Curtis Industries Inc.
ATTRACTIVE - Health care products - JUZO
ATTRACTIVE LIVING KASUALS - Wallpaper ☆ - Marburg Wallcoverings Inc.
ATTRAK - Apparel and accessories - Noble Apparel, Inc.
ATTRAK JEANS - Apparel and accessories - Noble Apparel, Inc.
ATTRAK ORIGINAL 328 - Slacks–children's ☆ - Noble Apparel, Inc.
ATTWOOD - Marine hardware and accessories - Attwood Corp.
ATTWOOD COLLECTION - Jewelry - Collections International
ATU TELECOMMUNICATIONS - Telephones - Municipality of Anchorage
ATUNE - Hair care products - Helene Curtis Industries Inc.
ATUS - Audio equipment - Audio-Technica U.S., Inc.
ATV - Cases–plastic - Doskocil Manufacturing Co., Inc.
ATV 7 - Vacuum cleaners and accessories - Douglas/Quikut
ATV EXPLORER - Toys - Fisher-Price, Inc.
ATVOICE - Computer software - UFA, Inc.
ATW - Alarm systems - Mascon, Inc.
ATWAY - Chemical preparations - A&T Development Corp.
ATWOOD - Floor coverings–carpet and rugs ☆ - Dorsett Carpet Mills Inc.
ATWOOD - Trailer jack - Atwood Mobile Products
ATWOODAIR - Recreational-vehicle air conditioning - Atwood Mobile Products
ATX - Fuel additives - Bell Additives, Inc.
ATX - Helmets–athletic - Giant Bicycle, Inc.
ATX - Screws - All-Tex Industries, Inc.
ATX - Tires - Bridgestone/Firestone, Inc.
AU - Apparel and accessories - Auburn University
AU - Jewelry–precious - Aurafin Corp.
AU BON - Pet products - Old Mother Hubbard Dog Food Co., Inc.
AU COURANT COSMETICS - Suntan lotions - Ramirez Partnership
AU CURRANT - Nail care products ☆ - Cosmair Inc.

☆ = Now out of production

AU GOURMET - Salad dressings–bottled - Robert's American Gourmet
AU NATURAL - Fish–fresh or frozen ☆ - Campbell Soup Co.
AU NATUREL - Bakery products - Miss Kings Kitchen Inc.
AU NATUREL - Floor coverings ☆ - Kentile Floors Inc.
AU NATUREL - Meat products–poultry - Pierce Foods Corp.
AU REVOIR - Cosmetics - Lancome
AU ROAR - Recording label - Jazz Composer's Orchestra Association Inc.
AU STUDIO - Men's apparel - India Garments Inc.
AU VINAIGRE - Food products - Continental Food Corp.
AUBEL - Chemical preparations - Uyemura International Corp.
AUBERGE - Wines ☆ - Chateau St. Jean
AUBERGINE RECORDS - Recording label - Aubergine Records, L.C.
AUBERNE - Watches - Israel Levy Diamond Cutters, Inc.
AUBERT - Musical instruments ☆ - Multivox/Sorkin Music Co. Inc.
AUBESTON - Gaskets - Auburn Manufacturing Co.
AUBIN - Footwear–athletic - Vans, Inc.
AUBREY - Bedding–linen - Dan River Inc.
AUBREY - Ventilating hoods, fans, and heaters - Aubrey Manufacturing Inc.
AUBREY ORGANICS - Beauty aids, pet products - Aubrey Organics, Inc.
AUBURN - Bicycling products ☆ - GT Bicycles Inc.
AUBURN - Bond paper ☆ - Copco Papers Inc.
AUBURN - Buttermilk and sour cream ☆ - Auburn Dairy Products, Inc.
AUBURN - Cabinets–wood - UltraCraft Co.
AUBURN - Jackets ☆ - Crown Prince Inc.
AUBURN - Leather pet supplies - Auburn Leathercrafters Inc.
AUBURN - Recording label - Auburn Records & Tapes
AUBURN - Shoes ☆ - Allen-Edmonds Shoe Corp.
AUBURN - Tires - John Kelsey
AUBURN - Trailers–travel - Fleetwood Enterprises, Inc.
AUBURN FAN - Fans–electric - Combustion Service & Equipment Co.
AUBURN GEAR - Automotive parts - Auburn Gear, Inc.
AUBURN HILLS - Swimming pools - Hoffinger Industries, Inc.
AUBURN UNIVERSITY - Publisher's imprints - Auburn University
AUBURN WOODS - Tandem Imports Corp.
AUBUSSON - Dinnerware–glass - Noritake Co. Inc.
AUBUSSON - Floor coverings–carpet and rugs ☆ - Capel, Inc.
AUBUSSON - Luggage ☆ - Samsonite Corp.
AUCHENTOSHAN - Beverages–alcohol - White Rock Distilleries Inc.
AUCLAIR - Gloves ☆ - Leisure Leather Ltd.
AUCOM - Computer software - Automation Unlimited, Inc.
AUCORD - Cordage and twine ☆ - Winchester-Auburn Mills Inc.
AUCS - Ice making machines - Manitowoc Co. Inc.
AUCTION - Games - Avalon Hill Game Co.
AUDALLION - Hearing aids - Audiologic, Inc.
AUDAX - Audio equipment - Polydax Speaker Corp.
AUDAX - Recording label - Music and Arts Programs of America Inc.
AUDE BOOKS - Publisher's imprints - MacMillan Publishing Co. Inc.
AUDEEN - Boats - Glen-L Marine Designs
AUDEK - Clock radios - Audek Corp.
AUDEMARS PIGUET - Watches - Audemars Piguet Ltd.
AUDEOCAM - Electronic equipment - Kobishi America, Inc.
AUDES PRIDE - Food products - Reede International Seafood Corp.
AUDI - Motor-vehicles–automobiles - Audi of America Inc.
AUDI-BUHL - Electronic equipment - Buhl Industries, Inc.
AUDIBLE ANIMALS - Toys ☆ - Tomy America, Inc.
AUDIBLE PURITY - Wire–insulated - Kordex, Inc.
AUDIBLE-TONE - Electronic equipment - Benjamin Electroproducts Inc.
    (Robins Div.)
AUDIENCE - Apparel and accessories - Stephen Resnick
AUDILENS - Hearing aids - Widex Hearing Aid Co., Inc.
AUDIMAX - Electronic equipment - Apollo Audiovisual Div.
AUDINA - Hearing aids - Audina Hearing Instruments, Inc.
AUDIO 2000 - Audio equipment - WavePhore Inc.
AUDIO 2000'S - Audio equipment - H & F Technologies, Inc.
AUDIO ACCENTS - Audio cabinets–wood - Kmart Corp.
AUDIO ADDICT - Recording label - Juggler Records Ltd.
AUDIO ADVANTAGE - Computer hardware - Integrated Circuit Systems
AUDIO ARCHIVES - Recording label - Stanyan Record Co.
AUDIO ARTS - Recording label - Audio Arts Records
AUDIO AUTHORITY - Audio equipment - Audio Authority Corp.
AUDIO BOOKS - Compact discs–prerecorded - Rezound International, Inc.
AUDIO BUSINESS CARD - Recording label - Cold Call Cowboy Productions
AUDIO CENTRON - Audio equipment - St. Louis Music Supply Co.
AUDIO-CHECK - Electrical testing instruments - Paladin Tools Weidmuller Inc.
AUDIO CHOICE - Hearing aids ☆ - Dahlberg, Inc.

AUDIO CITY MOBILE ELECTRONIC SPECIALISTS - Electronic equipment - Boo Yun Kim
AUDIO-COM - Electronics equipment - Audio-Sine Inc.
AUDIO D - Hearing aids - Hearing Solutions, Inc.
AUDIO ENERGY - Hearing-aid batteries - Audio Energy Inc.
AUDIO ESTATE PLANNER - Recording label - American Law Institute
AUDIO-EX - Hearing aids - Sharper Image Corp.
AUDIO EXPERT - Hearing aids - Beltone Electronics Corp.
AUDIO FENCE - Pet products - Biological Engineering/High Tech Pet Products
AUDIO FIDELITY - Recording label ☆ - Alshire International Inc.
AUDIO GALLERY - Computer storage devices–optical ☆ - Korg USA
AUDIO GODS - Electronic equipment - Hollywood Audio Products
AUDIO GOSPEL - Recording label - Audio Arts Records
AUDIO GROOME - Audio equipment ☆ - Empire Scientific Corp.
AUDIO-GUARD - Headphones - Hamilton Electronics Corp.
AUDIO GUARD - Lighting equipment - Cable Electric Products
AUDIO INK - Prerecorded audio cassettes - Simitar Entertainment, Inc.
AUDIO INTERFACE - Audio equipment - Audio Interface Inc.
AUDIO KING - Communications equipment–mobile - Van Ordt Inc.
AUDIO LAB - Recording label - Creav Inc. USA
AUDIO LOGIC - Audio equipment - Dod Electronics
AUDIO MASTER - Audio equipment - Shure Brothers, Inc.
AUDIO MATE - Computer software - Media Vision Technology Inc.
AUDIO/MATE 580 - Electrical equipment - Montage Productions Inc.
AUDIO/MATIC - Electrical equipment - Montage Productions Inc.
AUDIO MEMORY - Recording label - Audio Memory Publishing
AUDIO MIRROR - Computer software - Electronic Courseware Systems Inc.
AUDIO PAGES - Publisher's imprints - Zondervan Publishing House
AUDIO PAK - Audio equipment - J & M Corp.
AUDIO-PHONE - Electronic equipment - Hamilton Electronics Corp.
AUDIO PLUS - Audio equipment - AVAS Corp.
AUDIO PLUS - Audio equipment - Valiant IMC
AUDIO + VIDEO - Home-entertainment systems ☆ - International Jensen Inc.
AUDIO PRISM - Antennas - GNP Audio Video Inc.
AUDIO PRO 16 - Computer hardware - Keep It Simple Technology, Inc.
AUDIO PRO GREEN 16 - Computer hardware - Keep It Simple Technology, Inc.
AUDIO PROFILE - Audio equipment ☆ - Speakerkits Inc.
AUDIO REAL ESTATE LAWYER - Recording label - American Law Institute
AUDIO RESEARCH - Audio equipment - Audio Research Corp.
AUDIO-SAFE - Electrical equipment - Rebel Electronics Inc.
AUDIO SCOUT - Hearing aids - Beltone Electronics Corp.
AUDIO SEAL - Audio equipment - Alpha Audio Acoustics
AUDIO-SLIDE - Electronic equipment - Kalart Victor Corp.
AUDIO SPECTRUM - Microphones - Music People Inc.
AUDIO SPECTRUM - Recording label ☆ - Alshire International Inc.
AUDIO TECHNA - Microphones - Castiglione Accordion
AUDIO-TECHNICA - Audio equipment - Audio-Technica U.S., Inc.
AUDIO TRAINER - Electronic equipment - Telex Communications, Inc.
AUDIO-TREASURY - Recording label - MCA Universal Studios
AUDIO TREMORS - Audio equipment - Sammi Sound Technology Corp. USA
AUDIO-VATION - Computer software - International Business Machines Corp.
AUDIO VAULT - Audio equipment - Broadcast Electronics, Inc.
AUDIO VOIS - Electronic equipment ☆ - Import Audio
AUDIO-VU - Electronic equipment ☆ - Lectrosonics Inc.
AUDIO-VUE - Electronic equipment - Telex Communications, Inc.
AUDIO-WALL - Partitions–metal - Modernfold, Inc.
AUDIOACCESS - Amplifiers - JBL Inc.
AUDIOADVENTURES - Audio equipment - MCP Davisound
AUDIOCANNON - Motorcycles ☆ - National Cycle Inc.
AUDIOCARD - Sewing machine cabinets–wood - Revox Systems Inc.
AUDIOCARE - Hearing aids - Jon Bain
AUDIOCELL - Batteries - Audiotone, Inc.
AUDIOCOM - Communications equipment–mobile - Telex Communications, Inc.
AUDIOCONTROL - Electronic equipment - AudioControl
AUDIOCRAFT - Guitars ☆ - Chandler Industries
AUDIOCUPS - Hearing-aid product - American Overseas Trading Corp.
AUDIODIGITAL - Electronics equipment - Studio Magnetics Co. Inc.
AUDIOEASE - Computer hardware - Audioease, Inc.
AUDIOFAX - Electronic equipment - AudioFax Inc.
AUDIOFICHE - Electrical equipment - Revox Systems Inc.
AUDIOFILE - Stereo-housing systems - AMS Industries Inc.
AUDIOFILE - Stereos ☆ - Meteor Light & Sound Co.
AUDIOGRAPH - Recording label - Physicians Postgraduate Press, Inc.
AUDIOIMAGE - Computers and computer peripherals - ImagiMedia Corp.

AUDIOIMAGE - Recording label - Richmark Production Services, Inc.

AUDIOLINK - Electronic equipment - National Captioning Institute

AUDIOLOGIC - Audio equipment ☆ - Randix Industries Inc.

AUDIOLOGIST'S CHOICE - Health care products - Oaktree Products, Inc.

AUDIOMASTER - Intercoms - Federal Signal Corp.

AUDIOMATIC - Audio-level control - Blonder-Tongue Laboratories Inc.

AUDION - Organs–musical instrument ☆ - Strydel Inc.

AUDION TEMPO - Organs–musical instrument ☆ - Strydel Inc.

AUDIOPAD - Switches–electric ☆ - Hershman Musical Instrument

AUDIOPHILE - Recording label - Jazzology-GHB Records

AUDIOPHILE CAR STEREO - Apparel and accessories - Monster Cable Products, Inc.

AUDIOPLATE - Audio equipment - Barcus-Berry Inc.

AUDIOPLEX TECHNOLOGY - Audio equipment - Audioplex Technology, Inc.

AUDIOPRO - Amplifiers - Yorkville Sound

AUDIOQ - Electronic equipment - Gettech, Inc.

AUDIOQUEST - Audio equipment - GNP Audio Video Inc.

AUDIORAMA - Recording label - Audiorama Records Corp.

AUDIOSCIENCE - Hearing aids - AudioScience Inc.

AUDIOSELL - Tape recorder - Audio Visual Dynamics, Inc.

AUDIOSHOP - Computer software - Opcode Systems, Inc.

AUDIOSIGHTS - Recording label - Penell Braide Skinner

AUDIOSOURCE - Audio equipment - Audiosource

AUDIOSPEC - Audio equipment - D.A.S. Distributors, Inc.

AUDIOSTATION - Computer software - Voyetra Technologies Inc.

AUDIOTECH PROBE - Diagnostic apparatus - Sonic Technology Products Inc.

AUDIOTEX - Audio equipment ☆ - GC Thorsen, Inc.

AUDIOTONE - Hearing aids - Audiotone, Inc.

AUDIOTONE - Hearing aids ☆ - Dahlberg, Inc.

AUDIOTOWER - Loudspeakers - NEC Technologies, Inc.

AUDIOTRACK - Tape recorder - L & M Auto Supply

AUDIOTRONICS - Electronics equipment - L & M Auto Supply

AUDIOVAULT 100 - Audio equipment - Broadcast Electronics, Inc.

AUDIOVIDEO INTERNATIONAL - Magazines - Dempa Publications, Inc.

AUDIOVIEWER - Electronic equipment - Eastman Kodak Co.

AUDIOVISION - Computer peripheral equipment - Avid Technology, Inc.

AUDIOVOICE - Amplifiers–public address - Paso Sound Products Inc.

AUDIOVOX - Car-stereo components, telephones, security systems, etc. - Audiovox Corp.

AUDIOWARE - Computer peripheral equipment - VTech Computers Inc.

AUDIOWAVE - Computer hardware - Multiwave Innovation, Inc.

AUDIOWIZ - Computer peripheral equipment - Audio Highway Corp.

AUDIOWORKS - Audio tapes–blank - Simon & Schuster, Inc.

AUDIOZINE - Magazine series on tape ☆ - Audio Books on Cassette Distributors, Inc.

AUDIRE - Audio equipment - Audire Inc.

AUDISSEY - Electronic equipment - Bell Atlantic Corp.

AUDIT PRO - Computer programs - Professional Data Management Associates, Inc.

AUDITGARD - Computer software - Legalgard, Inc.

AUDITION - Amplifiers–musical instrument - Peavey Electronics Corp.

AUDITION - Computer software - Adobe Systems Inc.

AUDITION - Floor coverings–carpet and rugs ☆ - Blue Ridge Carpet Mills

AUDITION CHORUS - Amplifiers–musical instrument - Peavey Electronics Corp.

AUDITION PLUS - Amplifiers–musical instrument - Peavey Electronics Corp.

AUDITIONER - Computer software - Bose Corp.

AUDITIONS - Games ☆ - Decipher Inc.

AUDITIONS - Shoes - Craddock-Terry Inc.

AUDITORS - Pens - K-9 Pen Co.

AUDITPOWER - Computer software - Environmental Resources Management

AUDITRACK - Computer software - Pharm/Dur Inc.

AUDITRON - Health care products - Omron Healthcare, Inc.

AUDITVISION - Computer software - CCH Inc. (Wolters Kluwer)

AUDITWARE - Computer software - Preferred Systems, Inc.

AUDITWORKS - Computer software - Primatech Inc.

AUDIVISETTE - Hearing aids - Siemens Hearing Instruments Inc.

AUDIX - Amplifiers, microphones, speakers, and monitors - Audix Corp. of America

AUDIX - Telephones - At&T Corp.

AUDOGRAPH - Dictating machines ☆ - Lanier Voice Products

AUDRA THE SQUIRREL - Furniture–children's - Maze Inc.

AUDREY - Giftware - American Commercial Inc.

AUDREY - Placemats ☆ - Designers Collection

AUDREY CHILDRESS - Housewares - Sewing Organizer

AUDREY JONES - Handbags - Audrey Jones Inc.

AUDREY MORRIS - Cosmetics - Audrey Morris Cosmetics International Inc.

AUDREY SMITH - Women's apparel - Hub Distributing Inc.

AUDREY'S COOKIE BOUTIQUE AND CHEESECAKE - Bakery products - Cookie Boutique Inc.

AUDRIE - Skin care products - Hanah Beauty & Health Inc.

AUDTEX-85 - Hearing aids - Mid-States Laboratories Inc.

AUDUA - Audio equipment ☆ - TDK Electronics Corp.

AUDUBON - Binoculars - Swift Instruments, Inc.

AUDUBON - Flowers, plants, and seeds - Jacklin Seed

AUDUBON - Greeting cards - Renaissance Greeting Cards Inc.

AUDUBON - Neckties ☆ - A. Schreter & Sons Co. Inc.

AUDUBON COLLECTION - Wine - Audubon Cellars Inc.

AUDUBON PARK - Bird feeds - Audubon Park Co.

AUDUBON PARK - Bird feeds - Lawn & Garden Supply Co.

AUDUBON WILDLIFE ADVENTURES - Computer software ☆ - Advanced Ideas

AUER - Cash registers - Continental Industries Inc.

AUER PAK - Garlic and shallots - Maurice A. Auerbach Inc.

AUFERMANN - Hardware - Erich M. Reich Inc.

AUFFRAY & CO. INC. - Furniture - Auffray & Co., Inc.

AUFOND - Bathroom fixtures - Regent International, Inc.

AUG FORSTER - Pianos - Hanseatic Overseas Trading Inc.

AUGA - Breads ☆ - Bel Canto Fancy Foods Ltd.

AUGI - Guitars - Augustino Guitars Inc.

AUGILA - Flour–blended - Cahokia Flour Co.

AUGLER - Cases–plastic ☆ - Sazerac Co. Inc.

AUGMENTIN - Antibiotics - Smithkline Beecham Corp.

AUGSBURG BOOKS - Publisher's imprints - Augsburg Fortress Publishers

AUGSBURGER - Beverages–malt ☆ - The Stroh Brewery Co.

AUGSBURGER ALT - Beverages–malt ☆ - The Stroh Brewery Co.

AUGSBURGER BAVARIAN STYLE - Beverages–malt - Augsburger Brewing Co., Inc.

AUGSBURGER BOCK - Beverages–malt ☆ - The Stroh Brewery Co.

AUGSBURGER DARK - Beverages–malt ☆ - The Stroh Brewery Co.

AUGSBURGER DOPPELBOCK - Beverages–malt ☆ - The Stroh Brewery Co.

AUGSBURGER GOLDEN - Beverages–malt ☆ - The Stroh Brewery Co.

AUGSBURGER LIGHT - Beverages–malt ☆ - The Stroh Brewery Co.

AUGSBURGER OKTOBERFEST - Beverages–malt ☆ - The Stroh Brewery Co.

AUGSBURGER RED - Beverages–malt ☆ - The Stroh Brewery Co.

AUGSBURGER WEISS - Beverages–malt ☆ - The Stroh Brewery Co.

AUGSBURGER WINTER FESTBIER - Beverages–malt ☆ - The Stroh Brewery Co.

AUGSTINE - Baskets–wood ☆ - Royal Cathay Trading Co.

AUGUR - Computer software - Panoptic Solutions Corp.

AUGUST - Banks–commercial - August Capital Management, LLC

AUGUST ART CANVAS ACRYLAGRAPH GENUINE CERTIFIED PH BALANCED UV PROTECTION - Decals and transfers - August Art Co.

AUGUST BROTHERS - Breads - Best Foods Baking Group

AUGUST MAX - Apparel–women's - Selby Shoe Co.

AUGUST MAX WOMAN - Apparel - United States Shoe Corp.

AUGUST RECORDS INC. - Recording label - August Records, Inc.

AUGUST SCHELL - Beverages–malt - August Schell Brewing Co.

AUGUST SCHWER - Clocks - La Crosse-McCormick

AUGUST SEBASTIANI - Wines ☆ - Sebastiani Vineyards, Inc.

AUGUST THOMSEN - Cooking equipment–household ☆ - Bernard W. Bernthal Inc.

AUGUSTA - Apparel–athletic - Midstates Sportswear

AUGUSTA - Cabinets - Aristokraft, Inc.

AUGUSTA - Cabinets - Imperial Cabinet Co. Inc.

AUGUSTA - Floor coverings - Armstrong World Industries, Inc.

AUGUSTA - Floor coverings–carpet and rugs - Playfield International Inc.

AUGUSTA - Floor coverings–carpet and rugs - Sweetwater Carpet Corp.

AUGUSTA - Flooring–hardwood - Mannington Wood Floors

AUGUSTA - Giftware ☆ - Gorham Inc.

AUGUSTA - Locks–door - Weiser Lock Corp.

AUGUSTA COUNTY - Furniture ☆ - Bassett Furniture Industries, Inc.

AUGUSTA MANOR - Furniture - Pilliod Co.

AUGUSTA MILLS - Linen - Atd-American Co.

AUGUSTA NATIONAL - Hats - Augusta National Golf Club

AUGUSTA PLUS - Floor coverings–carpet and rugs - Playfield International Inc.

AUGUSTA ROMAN ARCH - Cabinets - Aristokraft, Inc.

AUGUSTIN - Beverages–malt - Victor Sales & Marketing

AUGUSTINAS - Cookies - Veronika A. Luke

AUGUSTINE - Guitar strings - American Music Export Co. Inc.

☆ = Now out of production

AUGUSTINO - Guitars - Augustino Guitars Inc.

AUGUSTINO - Meat products–beef ☆ - Chef Italia Inc.

AUGUSTUS - Apparel–men's - Augustus Fashions, Ltd.

AUGUSTUS - Dishes–china - Waterford Wedgewood USA, Inc.

AUGUSTUS - Food products - Losurdo Foods, Inc.

AUGUSTUS FIRE TOOL - Firefighting apparatus - Augustus Fire Tool Corp.

AUI - Lighting equipment - Advertising Unlimited Inc.

A AUI - Machinery - Ace USA, Inc.

AUK - Drilling anchors ☆ - ITW Ramset/Red Head

AULD - Awards, jewelry, etc. - Auld Crafters Inc.

AULD ACQUAINTANCE SPICE ALE - Beverages–malt - The Pike Brewing Co.

AULD LANG SYNE - Beverages–malt - Coast Range Brewing Co.

AULSEBROOKS - Crackers - FCW Imports

AULSEBROOKS - Crackers ☆ - Masterpeace Food Imports

AUMISH MAID - Candy - Polish Mountain Maple Products Inc.

AUNT ASPARAGUS - Greeting cards - Larson II

AUNT BEA'S - Bakery products - Southland Corp.

AUNT BEA'S - Liquors - NWS, Inc.

AUNT BEE'S - Candles - Vicky Mcwilliams

AUNT BEE'S ROYAL LIP JELLY - Lip balms - Aunt Bee's Royal Associates

AUNT BELLE'S - Pickles - Benjamin Lipitz Co.

AUNT BRONNIE'S - Peanut brittle - Aunt Bronnie's Brittle

AUNT B'S BLUE RIBBON SALAD - Salads–prepackaged - Brinker Restaurant Corp.

AUNT CHILOTTA - Fast-food franchise - Aunt Chilotta Systems Inc.

AUNT CHOVIE - Games - Todd R. Sichelstiel

AUNT CLARA'S - Fruit butters - Nestle USA

AUNT CORA'S DOWN HOME SEASONINGS - Seasonings - Mary Ellen Strong

AUNT DEE'S SAUSAGE - Meat products–poultry - Aunt Dee's Sausage Co.

AUNT ELDERBEARY & DEWDROP - Toys–stuffed ☆ - Gund, Inc.

AUNT ELLEN'S - Candy - Palmer Candy Co.

AUNT ENNA'S DOWN HOME STYLE - Syrup - CNN Enterprises, Inc.

AUNT FANNY'S - Bakery products - Pet Inc.

AUNT GINNIE'S - Baked goods - Perfection Bakeries, Inc.

AUNT GLADYS' - Calendars - Martin Carbone Inc.

AUNT GOLDIE'S GOLDIES - Bakery products - Aunt Goldie's Goldies Inc.

AUNT GRACE'S - Snack foods ☆ - Robison Ranch

AUNT HATTIES - Food products - Cooks Processed Foods Inc.

AUNT IRMA'S UDDER BALM - Skin care products - Crystal Springs Pharmaceutical, Inc.

AUNT JANE'S - Pickled vegetables - Aunt Jane's Foods

AUNT JEMIMA - Flour–blended - Quaker Oats Co.

AUNT JEMIMA LITE - Syrup - Quaker Oats Co.

AUNT JEMIMA WHOLE GRAIN - Pancakes–mixes - Quaker Oats Co.

AUNT JENNY'S - Cooking equipment–household ☆ - Anchor Hocking Glass, Inc.

AUNT JENNY'S - Seasonings - Melba Food Specialties Inc.

AUNT KERRI'S INCREDIBLES - Cookie dough - Cascade Cookie Co., Inc.

AUNT KITTY'S - Food products ☆ - Hanover Foods Corp.

AUNT LUCY - Toys–stuffed - Eden LLC

AUNT LYDIA'S - Thread - Susan Bates Inc.

AUNT LYDIA'S - Yarn - Caron International Inc.

AUNT MABLE'S - Apparel and accessories - Aunt Mable's Accessories, Inc.

AUNT MARTHA'S - Bakery products - Giant Eagle, Inc.

AUNT MARTHA'S - Craft supplies - Colonial Patterns Inc.

AUNT MEG'S - Spices and extracts - Clover Hill Candies

AUNT MID - Vegetables - Aunt Mid Produce Co.

AUNT MILLIE'S - Breads - Perfection Bakeries, Inc.

AUNT MILLIE'S - Sauces - Borden/Prince Foods (Canning Div.)

AUNT MILLIE'S LIGHT - Breads - Perfection Bakeries, Inc.

AUNT MINNIE'S HOME STYLE - Seafood products–fresh or frozen - Southern Belle Frozen Foods Inc.

AUNT NELLIE'S - Vegetables and drinks - Aunt Nellie's Farm Kitchens Inc.

AUNT NELLIE'S FARM KITCHEN - Food products - Pillsbury Co.

AUNT NETTIE - Apparel - Annette Vann

AUNT PATTY'S - Molasses - Glorybee Food Inc.

AUNT PENNY'S - Food products - Lindsay Olive Growers

AUNT SALLY'S - Milk - Customer Co.

AUNT SCARLOTTA - Dolls - Destiny Designs, Inc.

AUNT SUE'S - Honey - Sioux Honey Association

AUNT VI'S - Food products - Warren's Frozen Food Inc.

AUNT WICK'S - Root beer–bottled or canned - Jel Sert Co.

AUNTIE ANNE'S - Coffee - Auntie Anne's, Inc.

AUNTIE EM COLLECTION - Dinnerware–glass ☆ - Treasure Craft Co.

AUNTIE JANE'S - Apparel–children's - JHS Designs, Inc.

AUNTIE TANK - Toys ☆ - Tomy America, Inc.

A.U.P. CONSORT - Hearing aids - Widex Hearing Aid Co., Inc.

AUQA-PREP - Aquarium accessories - Kordon

AURA - Air curtain - Berner International Corp. (Miniveil Air Curtain Div.)

AURA - Communications equipment - Aura Communications, Inc.

AURA - Hair care products - Helene Curtis Industries Inc.

AURA - Hair care products - Naturelle, Inc.

AURA - Insulating materials - Owens Corning

AURA - Insulation board - Owens Corning Fiberglass Technology Inc.

AURA - Leather goods ☆ - AR Accessories Group Inc.

AURA - Lighting fixtures ☆ - Hubbell Lighting, Inc. (Lighting Div.)

AURA - Medical apparatus - Active, Inc.

AURA - Skin care products - Richardson-Vicks USA

AURA - Tableware–earthenware - Pfaltzgraff Investment Co.

AURA - Toys - Tonka Corp.

AURA - Whirlpools - Jacuzzi Inc.

AURA - Yarn ☆ - JCA, Inc.

AURA 2 - Wallpaper ☆ - Walldesigns

AURA-BELL - Pharmaceutical preparations ☆ - Lexis Laboratories Inc.

AURA CANDLE COLOR - Paints - Carnival Arts, Inc.

AURA-CLEAN - Machinery - General Hearing Instrument, Inc.

AURA-FLEX - Jewelry - Aurafin Corp.

AURA GALAXY AG - Lamps - Aura Galaxy Co., Inc.

AURA GLOW - Skin care products - Heritage Store Inc.

AURA-LITE - Nail care products ☆ - E.O.H. Industries, Inc.

AURA OF AROMA - Colognes - International Flavors & Fragrances Inc.

AURA OF LIVING FLAVOR - Spices and extracts - International Flavors & Fragrances Inc.

AURA OF LIVING FRAGRANCE - Colognes - International Flavors & Fragrances Inc.

AURA OF MUSK - Colognes - International Flavors & Fragrances Inc.

AURA WAX - Waxes–dental - Dentifax International, Inc.

AURADEX - Calculators, personal computers, etc ☆ - Aurora Corp. of America

AURAFIN - Jewelry - Aurafin Corp.

AURAGEN ARCHITECT - Computer software - Auragen Communications, Inc.

AURAL ACUTE - Pharmaceutical preparations - Saron Pharmacal Corp.

AURAL EXPLORER - Recording label ☆ - MMO Music Group Inc.

AURAL SKILLS TRAINER - Computer software - Electronic Courseware Systems Inc.

AURALCORT - Pharmaceutical preparations - Wesley Pharmacal Co. Inc.

AURALGAN - Analgesics - Wyeth-Ayerst Laboratories

AURALGESIC - Pharmaceutical preparations - Wesley Pharmacal Co. Inc.

AURALON - Crocheted and knitted items ☆ - Hampshire Hosiery, Inc.

AURAPHENE-B - Pharmaceutical preparations - Reese Chemical Co.

AURASOL - Pharmaceutical preparations ☆ - JMI-Canton Pharmaceuticals

AURATONE - Speaker systems - Auratone Corp.

AURATONE - Tiles–ceiling - United States Gypsum Co.

AUREA - Crystal stemware - RCR

AUREAL SOFSHADES - Furniture - Tempo

AUREATE - Flatware ☆ - Gorham Inc.

AURELI - Violins - VMI Industries

AURELIA - Rings–jewelry - Artcarved Inc.

AURELIA - Tiles–ceramic - United Ceramic Tile Corp.

AURELIE - House furnishings - Dan River Inc.

AURENA - Computer peripheral equipment - Superpower Supply, Inc.

AUREOMYCIN - Antibiotics - Lederle Laboratories

AURES - Colognes - Avon Products, Inc.

AUREUS - Apparel and accessories - Sun Ice USA

AUREX-3 - Medical apparatus - ADM Tronics Unlimited, Inc.

AURI - Cleaning preparations - Lombard Management, Inc.

AURI-SEPT - Pharmaceutical preparations ☆ - Vitarine Pharmaceuticals Inc.

AURIC - Floor coverings–carpet and rugs ☆ - Columbus Mills, Inc.

AURICCHIO - Cheese - Fred Montesi Super Markets

AURICLE - Recording label - Jazz Composer's Orchestra Association Inc.

AURICULINA - Hearing aids - Siemens Hearing Instruments Inc.

AURIFERITE - Paints - Philadelphia Ceramics Inc.

AURIGA - Recording label ☆ - Prince/SF Productions

AURIGA - Tea kettles–nonelectric ☆ - Robinson Knife & Fiddlers Plastics

AURO - Pharmaceutical preparations - Del Pharmaceuticals, Inc.

AURO - Scissors–hand-operated - Shear World International

AURO-DRI - Pharmaceutical preparations - Del Pharmaceuticals, Inc.

AURO TECH - Food products - Auro Tech, Inc.

AUROBOND - Electronic equipment - Enthone-OMI

AUROCAINE - Pharmaceutical preparations - Republic Drug Co. Inc.

AUROCAINE-2 - Pharmaceutical preparations - Republic Drug Co. Inc.

AUROLATE - Pharmaceutical preparations - Pasadena Research Laboratories, Inc.

AUROMERE - Publisher's imprint, incense, incense burners, herbal toothpaste, herbal soap, massage oil - Auromere Inc.

AUROMID - Pharmaceutical preparations ☆ - Vangard Labs Inc.

AURORA - See **SHREDZ**

AURORA - Awnings - Alcan Aluminum Corp. Alcan Building Products Div.

AURORA - Bathroom tissue - James River Corp.

AURORA - Beef - Aurora Packing Co. Inc.

AURORA - Boats - Glen-L Marine Designs

AURORA - Boats–pontoons - Triton Industries, Inc.

AURORA - Breads - Bell'amore Imports Inc.

AURORA - Calculators ☆ - Aurora Corp. of America

AURORA - Candles - Faroy Sales

AURORA - Cases–eyeglass - Fidelity Case Corp.

AURORA - Cigarettes - G.A. Georgopulo & Co. Inc.

AURORA - Cleaning preparations - IVAX Industries, Inc.

AURORA - Computer software - Data Translation, Inc.

AURORA - Dinnerware ☆ - Corning Inc.

AURORA - Dinnerware–glass ☆ - Nikko Ceramics Inc.

AURORA - Doors–storm - Canyon Creek Cabinet Co.

AURORA - Electric lighting equipment - Lutron Electronics Co., Inc.

AURORA - Fabrics–coated ☆ - Duracote Corp.

AURORA - Flatware - Yamazaki Tableware Inc.

AURORA - Floor coverings - Mannington Resilient Floors

AURORA - Floor coverings–carpet and rugs ☆ - Regal Rugs Inc.

AURORA - Floor coverings–tile - ECC International

AURORA - Hair- and skin-care products - Aurora Henna Co.

AURORA - Hair care products - American Hairlines

AURORA - Hardware - Blaine Window Hardware Inc.

AURORA - Heating equipment - Bowles Fluidics Corp.

AURORA - Jewelry - Mel Bernie and Co., Inc.

AURORA - Marble products - Kohler Co.

AURORA - Medical apparatus - Advanced Mammography Systems, Inc.

AURORA - Motor vehicles–automobiles - General Motors Corp. (Oldsmobile Div.)

AURORA - Office furniture–wood ☆ - Haskell of Pittsburgh, Inc.

AURORA - Paper ☆ - Hunt Manufacturing Co.

AURORA - Semolina - Italgrani USA, Inc.

AURORA - Shelving units–metal - Richards-Wilcox Manufacturing Co.

AURORA - Signs - Marketing Displays, Inc.

AURORA - Skates–roller - Rollerblade, Inc.

AURORA - Stationery ☆ - Superior Marking Equipment Co.

AURORA - Tires - Hankook Tire America Corp.

AURORA - Wallpaper - Koroseal Wallcoverings

AURORA - Wallpaper - Seabrook Wallcoverings, Inc.

AURORA - Wines - Bully Hill Vineyards, Inc.

AURORA - Wines - Leonard Kreusch Inc.

AURORA - Yarn ☆ - William Unger & Co. Inc.

AURORA BOREALIS - Christmas tree ornaments - Cracker Box Inc.

AURORA CANDLERS - Candles - N.S. Gustin Co.

AURORA COFFEE - Coffee - Aurora Coffee

AURORA CREATIONS - Greeting cards - Advantage/Aurora Publications

AURORA FASHION PLEAT - Drapery hardware - Spring Window Fashions Division, Inc.

AURORA II - Yarn ☆ - William Unger & Co. Inc.

AURORA NUIT - Lipsticks - Lancome

AURORA PLUS - Floor coverings - Mannington Resilient Floors

AURORA STAR - Patent flour - Italgrani USA, Inc.

AURORA, THE - Stoves–wood-burning - Dovre Inc.

AURORA TIMOTHY - Flowers, plants, and seeds - Jacklin Seed

AURORE - Wines - Ziem Vineyards

AUROSHIKHA - Incense - Auroma International Inc.

AUROTO - Pharmaceutical preparations - Barre-National, Inc.

AUROVILLE - Stationery ☆ - Auroma International Inc.

AURUM - Au Pharmaceuticals Inc.

AURUM - Jewelry - Aurum Design Jewelry

AUS-BEN - Figurines - Aus-Ben Studios

AUS-BEN ACCESSORIES - Sculptures and bookends - Aus-Ben Studios

AUS-BEN LIMITEDS - Bronze figurines - Aus-Ben Studios

AUS JENA - Electronic equipment - Ercona Corp.

AUSABLE - Fabrics - Gretchen Bellinger Inc.

AUSBALL - Apparel and accessories - Ausball Properties, Inc.

AUSCO - Brakes, clutches, valves, jacks - Ausco Products Inc.

AUSELBROOK - Crackers - Castle Food Products

AUSKEY - Computer software - Animal Ultrasound Services, Inc.

AUSPICE - Apparel and accessories - Jeffrey Scott Busche

AUSSIE - Ammunition ☆ - Olin Corp. (Winchester Div.)

AUSSIE - Apparel and accessories - Texace Corp.

AUSSIE - Bicycling apparel - Aussie Racing Apparel

AUSSIE - Boomerangs - 49er Products Inc.

AUSSIE - Food products machinery - Four 'n Twenty-Australia

AUSSIE - Hair care products - Redmond Products, Inc.

AUSSIE - Medical apparatus - Kransco Manufacturing Inc.

AUSSIE APPAREL - Apparel and accessories - Down Under Saddle Supply, Inc.

AUSSIE CITRIFIER - Shampoos - Redmond Products, Inc.

AUSSIE COLORWISE SHAMPOO - Hair care products - Redmond Products, Inc.

AUSSIE CURING MUDDY - Hair care products - Redmond Products, Inc.

AUSSIE CUSTARD APPLE - Shampoos - Redmond Products, Inc.

AUSSIE FRUIT SPARKLER - Juices - Koala Springs International Inc.

AUSSIE GLOSS - Hair care products - Redmond Products, Inc.

AUSSIE GOLD - Health care products ☆ - Jason Natural Products, Inc.

AUSSIE GOLD - Shampoos - Redmond Products, Inc.

AUSSIE HAIR INSURANCE - Hair care products - Redmond Products, Inc.

AUSSIE HOT CURING OIL - Hair care products - Redmond Products, Inc.

AUSSIE INSTANT - Hair care products - Redmond Products, Inc.

AUSSIE INTERMISSIONS - Shampoos - Redmond Products, Inc.

AUSSIE KOALA - Toys–stuffed - Russ Berrie and Co., Inc.

AUSSIE LAMB BRAND PRODUCT OF AUSTRALIA - Lamb - Foodcomm International, Inc.

AUSSIE MEGA - Hair care products - Redmond Products, Inc.

AUSSIE MOIST - Hair care products - Redmond Products, Inc.

AUSSIE PERMANENT WAVE INSURANCE - Shampoos - Redmond Products, Inc.

AUSSIE PIE - Pies–fresh - Aussie Foods Ltd.

AUSSIE POUCH - Furniture - Aussie Pouch Co., Inc.

AUSSIE SAUCE - Food products - Garden Complements Inc.

AUSSIE SLAMMER - Juices - Koala Springs International Inc.

AUSSIE SPEEDSLICK - Medical apparatus - Kransco Manufacturing Inc.

AUSSIE-TIZERS - Food products - Outback Steakhouse of Florida, Inc.

AUSSIEMATE - Candy - Grifair Co.

AUSSOM AUSSIE PRODUCTS - Barbecue sauce - $Alesabroad, Inc.

AUSSY KOALA - Toys ☆ - Dakin Inc.

AUST - Seafood products–fresh or frozen - C.E. Lixie Fisheries Inc.

AUSTAD - Golf bags, clubs, and shoes - Austad Co.

AUSTEN - Flatware - Yamazaki Tableware Inc.

AUSTERE BEAUTY - Jewelry - Austin Wahl Co.

AUSTEX - Meat products–canned - Castleberry's Food Co.

AUSTIN - Blinds–vertical ☆ - Kittrich Corp.

AUSTIN - Crackers - Bahlsen Inc.

AUSTIN - Food products - Schaffer Food Service Co.

AUSTIN - Furniture - Bean Station Furniture Factory Inc.

AUSTIN - Motor vehicles–automobiles ☆ - Sterling Motor Cars

AUSTIN - Musical instrument accessories - Kaman Music Corp.

AUSTIN - Publisher's imprints - Willis Music Co.

AUSTIN - Radios - Robert Bosch Corp.

AUSTIN - Rings–jewelry - Artcarved Inc.

AUSTIN - Watches - Zale Corp.

AUSTIN - Watches - Zale Delaware, Inc.

AUSTIN 1938 - Watches - Zale Delaware, Inc.

AUSTIN CELLARS - Wines - Los Olivos Vintners

AUSTIN CHEESE ON CHEESE - Crackers - Bahlsen Inc.

AUSTIN COLLECTION - Apparel and accessories - Austin Collection

AUSTIN-HAYNE CORPORATION - Computer software - Austin-Hayne Corp.

AUSTIN HILL - Apparel and accessories - Palm Beach Co., Inc.

AUSTIN HOUSE - Travel accessories - Austin House Inc.

AUSTIN ICE BATS - Apparel and accessories - Austin Hockey Group, Ltd.

AUSTIN ICEBATS - Apparel and accessories - Austin Hockey Group, Ltd.

AUSTIN-JAMES - Computer software - Austin-Brett, Inc.

AUSTIN KANE - Apparel stores–sports - Brawn of California, Inc.

AUSTIN MANOR - Apparel and accessories - J.C. Penney Co., Inc.

AUSTIN MANOR - Furniture ☆ - Bassett Furniture Industries, Inc.

AUSTIN NICHOLS - Beverages–alcohol - Deinhard & Partners

AUSTIN NOW - Cosmetics - Austin Now Inc.

AUSTIN PLANK - Floor coverings - Robbins Inc.

AUSTIN PRODUCTIONS - Sculpture reproductions, decorative accessories - Austin Sculpture Inc.

AUSTIN QUALITY - Cookies - Austin Quality Foods, Inc.

AUSTIN REED - Apparel–women's - Hartmarx Corp.

AUSTIN REED - Neckties ☆ - Mallory and Church Corp.

☆ = Now out of production

AUSTIN REED OF REGENT STREET - Waterproof outerwear - Hartmarx Corp.
AUSTIN SCIENTIFIC - Pumps–vacuum - Austin Scientific Co.
AUSTIN SMACKERS - Crackers - Bahlsen Inc.
AUSTIN-TAYLOR - Travel accessories - Austin House Inc.
AUSTIN TRADING - Apparel and accessories - Austin Collection
AUSTIN VALLEY - Meat products–canned - SOPAKCO
AUSTIN/WRIGHT - Flatware - Estia Corp.
AUSTIN'S - James Austin Co.
AUSTIN'S - Dog food ✩ - Sunshine Biscuits, Inc.
AUSTIN'S A-1 - James Austin Co.
AUSTIN'S OWN - Barbecue sauce - Austin's Own Inc.
AUSTRAL - Canned meats - Austral Foods Corp.
AUSTRAL - Propellers - Alexander-Roberts Co.
AUSTRALIA DOWN UNDER - Apparel–athletic - Ron Jon Surf Shop
AUSTRALIA RUGBY - Apparel–athletic - DeLong Sportswear Inc.
AUSTRALIA: THE LAND DOWN UNDER - Games - S. Alden Inc.
AUSTRALIAN - Pet products - Mr. Christal's
AUSTRALIAN - Wood products ✩ - States Industries Inc.
AUSTRALIAN 3 MINUTE MIRACLE, THE - Hair care products - Redmond Products, Inc.
AUSTRALIAN-A.C.A. - Vitamins and nutritional supplements - Pharmakon USA, Inc.
AUSTRALIAN ALPS - Cheese - Normark & Associates
AUSTRALIAN BODYCARE - Computer software - Australian Bodycare Enterprises, Inc.
AUSTRALIAN COMPLETE - Hair care products - Revlon Consumer Products Corp.
AUSTRALIAN FORTUNE - Hair care products - Helene Curtis Industries Inc.
AUSTRALIAN GOLD - Sunblocks - European Tanning Systems Inc.
AUSTRALIAN HAIR INSURANCE - Hair care products - Redmond Products, Inc.
AUSTRALIAN KD - Beverages–malt - Mission Imports Inc.
AUSTRALIAN NATURALS - Vitamins and nutritional supplements - Vitamin Classics, Inc.
AUSTRALIAN ORANGE PEEL - Candy bars - Cloud Nine
AUSTRALIAN OUTBACK - Beverages–alcohol ✩ - Jim Beam Brands Co.
AUSTRALIAN OUTBACK COLLECTION, THE - Apparel–athletic - Australian Outback Collection
AUSTRALIAN RAILS - Games - Mayfair Games, Inc.
AUSTRALIAN SOURDOUGH BREAD - Breads - Stahl's Bakery, Inc.
AUSTRALIAN SUN BARS - Snack foods - Finnfoods Div.
AUSTRALIAN TEA TREE - Skin care products ✩ - Roberts Research Laboratories, Inc.
AUSTRALIAN TOTAL DIETS - Bird feeds - Sunshine Bird Supplies, Inc.
AUSTRALIS - Boats–pontoons ✩ - Dynamic Plastics Inc.
AUSTRIA - Eyeglasses ✩ - Private Eyes Sunglass Corp.
AUSTRIALPIN - Sporting goods - Climb High Inc.
AUSTRIAN - Tobacco–chewing or smoking - Amar Blends Co.
AUSTRIAN ALPS - Cheese - M.H. Greenebaum Inc.
AUSTRIAN SNOWSCENES - Giftware - Charles Zahn-Import Merchant
AUSTRIAN STAR - Cheese - Noon Hour Food Products
AUSTRIETTE - Cheese - Lactoprot USA, Inc.
AUSTRO-COMBI - Skis ✩ - Miller Ski and Camp
AUSTROFLAMM - Hardware - Austroflamm USA, Inc.
AUTEC - Automotive parts and accessories - International AutoCare Services Inc.
AUTECH - Chemical preparations - Au Technologies, Inc.
AUTEL - Bathroom fixtures - Kohler Co.
AUTEL - Computer hardware - Autel, Inc.
AUTENTICA COMO TU! - Beverages–malt - Anheuser-Busch Companies Inc.
AUTENTICO - Restaurants–pizzerias - Pizzeria Uno Corp.
AUTHENTIC - Apparel and accessories - Authentic Imports Inc.
AUTHENTIC - Footwear - Vans, Inc.
AUTHENTIC - Meats–luncheon - Oscar Mayer Foods Corp.
AUTHENTIC - Recording label - Sonic Arts Corp.
AUTHENTIC AMERICAN - Toys - Channel Craft
AUTHENTIC AMERICAN JEANSWEAR COMPANY, THE - Shirts - Authentic American Jeanswear Co.
AUTHENTIC AMERICAN SOUL FOOD - Vegetables–canned - Uncle Wiley's Inc.
AUTHENTIC ART CO. - Apparel and accessories - Equity Southern Financial Corp.
AUTHENTIC BABY - Infant product - Marshalls, Inc.
AUTHENTIC BARFLY SPORTSWEAR EST. 1994 - Shirts - Barfly Productions
AUTHENTIC BASS-TAB - Music books - Warner Bros. Publications
AUTHENTIC BIG BLUES - Apparel–men's - D. Stone Industries, Inc.

AUTHENTIC CHINO CASUALS - Apparel and accessories - Tropical Sportswear International Corp.
AUTHENTIC CLEVELAND STADIUM MUSTARD, THE - Mustard - Davis Food Co.
AUTHENTIC COWBOY BEEF STICK - Beef product - NJJ Corp.
AUTHENTIC COWBOY SALOON - Cakes - Cowboy Vittles & More
AUTHENTIC GUITAR TAB - Textbooks - Warner Bros. Publications
AUTHENTIC HOMES - Precut log-home kits - Authentic Log Homes, Inc.
AUTHENTIC KHAKI COMPANY, THE - Apparel and accessories - Tropical Sportswear International Corp.
AUTHENTIC KIDS A K - Apparel–children's - Marshalls, Inc.
AUTHENTIC MODELS - Games - Classic Brasscraft Ltd.
AUTHENTIC PHARAONIC SPORTS APPAREL - Apparel and accessories - Loyd Anthony Inc.
AUTHENTIC PRODUCTS QUALITY SERVICE - Apparel and accessories - Western-English Trademark, Inc.
AUTHENTIC REEF - Sandals - South Cone, Inc.
AUTHENTIC RUGGED GEAR - Luggage - VT International Ltd.
AUTHENTIC SAN FRANCISCO SOURDOUGH SINCE 1856 - Breads - Parisian Bakeries Inc.
AUTHENTIC SPIRAL SLICED - Chickens - HBH L.P.
AUTHENTIC STONE - Hobby kits ✩ - Creative Concepts of Raleigh Inc.
AUTHENTIC VINTAGE CLOTHING CO. OF AMERICA - Apparel and accessories - Capital Pants Co.
AUTHENTICHEK - Forms–preprinted - Standard Register Co.
AUTHENTICO - Food products - Authentico, Ltd.
AUTHENTICS - Apparel and accessories - Levi Strauss & Co.
AUTHOR! AUTHOR! - Computer software - Mind Play
AUTHOR PLUS COLOR, THE - Computer software - Daines Associates
AUTHOR PLUS, THE - Computer software - Daines Associates
AUTHOR, THE - Computer software - Daines Associates
AUTHORITY - Cases–plastic ✩ - Jesse Jones Box Corp.
AUTHORITY - Fabrics - Greenwood Mills Inc.
AUTHORITY - Floor coverings–carpet and rugs - Dan River Inc.
AUTHORITY - Locks - American Lock & Supply, Inc.
AUTHORITY - Pet products - Petstuff, Inc.
AUTHORITY II - Floor coverings–carpet and rugs ✩ - Callaway Carpets
AUTHORITY REFERENCE TOOL - Computer programs - J. Paul Getty Trust
AUTHORITY/SURE CHOICE - Padding–foam - Milliken-Sommer
AUTHORIZED SELECT - Siding - Heartland Building Products Inc.
AUTHORS - Paper–writing - P.H. Glatfelter Co.
AUTHOR'S AID - Computer software - SourceView Software International
AUTHORSOFT - Computer software - Spirit of St. Louis Software Co.
AUTHORSOFT MULTIMEDIA PRESENTATIONS - Computer software - Spirit of St. Louis Software Co.
AUTHORWARE - Computer software - Macromedia, Inc.
AUTHORWARE STAR - Computer software - Macromedia, Inc.
AUTO - Thread - Threads USA Div.
AUTO ADJUST - Converters–electric - Franzus Co. Inc.
AUTO AID PARTS SUPER STORE - Automotive parts and accessories - Auto Aid Stores, Inc.
AUTO APRON - Coveralls - William W. Carpenter
AUTO AVIONICS INSTRUMENT RESEARCH - Gauging instruments - Auto Avionics Instrument Reseach Inc.
AUTO BANDER - Antennas - Valor Enterprises, Inc.
AUTO-BELL - Bells and chimes - Schulmerich Carillons Inc.
AUTO BINGO - Games ✩ - Cathay International
AUTO BOND - Adhesives and sealants - Super Glue Corp.
AUTO BOOK PRESS - Publisher's imprints - Auto Book Press
AUTO BOOK PRESS - Publisher's imprints - Coda Publications
AUTO-BRAIN COMPUTER SYSTEM - Computer peripheral equipment - Francis D. McGrath
AUTO CADDY - Toys - Forty Four International, Inc.
AUTO-CAL - Watches - Elgin Watch Co.
AUTO CHARGE - Battery chargers - Kussmaul Electronics Co., Inc.
AUTO CHISEL - Tools - Nitto Kohki USA Inc.
AUTO CHOCK - Trailers–truck - Kelley Co., Inc.
AUTO-CHUTE BINGO - Games ✩ - Milton Bradley Co.
AUTO/CLAMP - Electrical equipment - Pass & Seymour, Inc.
AUTO CLEEN - Polishing rouge - Red Spot Paint & Varnish Co., Inc.
AUTO CLIP - Knives–pocket - Sog Specialty Knives, Inc.
AUTO CLN - Electronic equipment ✩ - Scholz Research & Development, Inc.
AUTO CLUB - Umbrellas - Totes, Inc.
AUTO COLORS - Flags - Atlas Flags Inc.
AUTO-COTE - Bostik Inc.
AUTO CYCLE - Bicycles - Schwinn Cycling & Fitness Inc.

AUTO DATA - Computer storage devices - Electro-Sensors, Inc.

AUTO-DRAFT - Air conditioning equipment - Tjernlund Products Inc.

AUTO-DRIVE - Racks - Sharper Image Corp.

AUTO DRIVE - Vacuum cleaners and accessories - The Hoover Co.

AUTO DRY - Automotive parts and accessories ☆ - Turtle Wax, Inc.

AUTO-EQUALIZER - Door openers–electronic - LCN Closers

AUTO ETCH - Tools - Armour Products

AUTO-EVERYTHING - Cameras - Vivitar Corp.

AUTO EXPRESS - Automotive parts and accessories - Montgomery Ward & Co. Inc.

AUTO-EYE - Optical machinery - Kollmorgen Instruments Corp.

AUTO-FADE - Electronics equipment - Kimchuk Inc.

AUTO-FAULT - Electronic equipment - Benz Airborne Systems

AUTO FILM ID - Medical apparatus - Lorad Corp.

AUTO FIRE - Toys ☆ - Henry Gordy International Inc.

AUTO-FLASHLITE - Motor vehicle parts and accessories ☆ - SAFCO Corp.

AUTO-FLITE - Tires - Target Tire and Automotive Corp.

AUTO-FLO - Humidifiers - American Metal Products

AUTO-FLO - Pet products ☆ - Marineland Aquarium Products

AUTO-FLOOR - Floor cleaning equipment - Indopco, Inc.

AUTO-FLOW - Artists' materials ☆ - Keuffel & Esser Co.

AUTO FLOW - Milking machines - Babson Bros. Co.

AUTO FLUSH - Electronic equipment - Technical Concepts LP

AUTO-FOCUS - Projectors–photographic - Eiki International Inc.

AUTO FOLD - Beds–metal ☆ - Evenflo Co.

AUTO-FOLD - Electrical equipment - D/A Manufacturing Co., Inc.

AUTO-FOLD - Ladders–metal ☆ - Michigan Ladder Co. Inc.

AUTO/FT - Computer software - Phoenix Computer Corp.

AUTO-GARD - Automotive parts and accessories - Metallized Products Inc.

AUTO-GEN - Generators–power - Mercantile Manufacturing Co. Inc.

AUTO-GRAPH - Computer software - Auto-Graph Computer Design Systems Inc.

AUTO-GRAPH COMPUTER DESIGNING SYSTEMS - Computer software - Masco Corp.

AUTO-GRIP - Pens ☆ - Zebra Pen Corp.

AUTO HOOKERS - Automotive parts and accessories - Norski of America Ltd.

AUTO INSIGHT - Computer software - Informative Graphics Corp.

AUTO JOHN - Novelty items - Cal Themes Inc.

AUTO-JUST - Hardware - Marshalltown Trowel Co.

AUTO KING - Automotive parts and accessories - Pirelli Power Transmission Corp.

AUTO-LANCET - Medical apparatus - Palco Laboratories

AUTO LEDGER - Computer peripheral equipment - Transportation Recording Systems, Inc.

AUTO LERT - Tape recorder - L & M Auto Supply

AUTO-LEVEL - Building materials–concrete - Croft Metals Inc.

AUTO-LIFT - Filters–water - Cuno Inc.

AUTO-LITE - Torches - Bernzomatic

AUTO-LOC - Electrical equipment - McGill Manufacturing Co. Inc.

AUTO LOC - Lighters–cigarette - Scripto-Tokai Corp.

AUTO-LOCK - Paperboard - Sonoco Products Co.

AUTO-MAGIC - Electronic equipment - Tandy Corp.

AUTO-MAGIC - Polishes - Auto Wax Co., Inc.

AUTO-MAGIC RUB - Erasers - Faber-Castell Corp.

AUTO MASTER - Ammunition ☆ - Remington Arms Co., Inc.

AUTO MASTER - Automotive parts and accessories - International Development Corp.

AUTO-MAT - Electronic equipment - Brumberger Co. Inc.

AUTO-MATE - Compressors–air - Midwest Products Inc.

AUTO-MATE - Computer software - Beacon Hill Technologies, Inc.

AUTO-MATE - Recreational vehicles - Auto-Mate Recreational Products Inc.

AUTO MATT SHIELD - Mats ☆ - Sealright Co., Inc.

AUTO-MATTE - Drafting supplies ☆ - Teledyne Post

AUTO MAXX - Alarm systems - Maxi-Guard

AUTO METER - Tachometers - Auto Meter Products Inc.

AUTO METER III - Photographic equipment - Minolta Corp.

AUTO-MIX - Coatings, etc. - Devcon Consumer Products (ITW Devcon)

AUTO MOCS - Footwear - Wolverine World Wide, Inc.

AUTO MOIST - Air conditioning equipment - Skuttle Manufacturing Co.

AUTO-MOLY - Lubricants - Pacific Lubricants

AUTO-MORPH - Computer software - Advantageware, Inc.

AUTO MORPHIN POWER RANGERS - Toys - Saban Entertainment, Inc.

AUTO-NAILER - Machinery - Stanley-Bostitch Inc.

AUTO-NEON - Automotive accessories - Street Glow, Inc.

AUTO OFFICE - Portable desk - Auto Office Co.

AUTO-ONE ACCESSORIES AND GLASS - Automotive-services franchise - Auto-One Accessories & Glass Inc.

AUTO OPTIMIZE - Computer software - Amergraph Corp.

AUTO ORDER - Computer software - Parts Inc.

AUTO ORGANIZER - Automotive parts and accessories ☆ - Velcro USA Inc. (Consumer Products Div.)

AUTO-PAK - Automotive parts and accessories - Minnesota Mining & Manufacturing Co.

AUTO-PAK TOPPER - Electrical equipment - Bridges Electric, Inc.

AUTO PANEL - Paints - Krylon/Dupli-Color

AUTO-PEAK - Tents - Colorado Mineral Strike, Inc.

AUTO-PILE - Pile weather strip - Bailey Corp.

AUTO PILLOW - Pillows - Blue Ridge International Products Co., Inc.

AUTO PILOT PROFITS - Recording label - Financial Freedom Report, L.C.

AUTO-PLUNGE - Welding equipment - Emhart Inc.

AUTO POCKETS - Automotive parts and accessories ☆ - Lancaster Colony Automotive Group

AUTO-PREG - Fabrics–coated - Airtech International, Inc.

AUTO PRESERVATION - Auto protection compounds - Auto Preservation, Inc.

AUTO-PRO - Computer terminals ☆ - Mead-Hatcher, Inc.

AUTO-PROTECTIVE PERM, THE - Hair care products - Cosmair Inc.

AUTO PULSE - Automotive parts and accessories ☆ - Walbro Corp.

AUTO-PURGE LNX - Gas machinery - Semi-Gas Systems, Inc.

AUTO-PURGER - Rope - Hansen Technologies Corp.

AUTO REGISTRATION TRACKING SYSTEM (ARTS), THE - Computer software - Trans Union/Dateq

AUTO REL - Measuring instruments - Beckman Industrial Corp.

AUTO RELAXER - Medical apparatus - Standex International Corp.

AUTO RETRACT - Seats–automobile ☆ - Cosco, Inc.

AUTO REVERSING - Toys–trains - Digitrax, Inc.

AUTO-RISE - Timers–appliance - Comfortex Corp.

AUTO ROMA - Cleaning preparations - Vita Chlor Corp.

AUTO ROTATE - Blinds–vertical - Louverdrape Inc.

AUTO SAVER - Computer software - Ronald H. Sorel

AUTO SCENT - Deodorizers - Home Specialties

AUTO SEAL - Doors - Lindgren RF Enclosures, Inc.

AUTO SEAL - Envelopes - Champion Envelope Corp.

AUTO SELECT - Antennas - Peterson Manufacturing Co.

AUTO-SENTRY - Automotive parts and accessories ☆ - CSI/Speco

AUTO SENTRY - Electrical equipment - Gardner Denver Machinery Inc.

AUTO SENTRY ES - Monitors–electronic - Gardner Denver Machinery Inc.

AUTO-SERI-GRAPH - Novelty items–paper - A Separate Ability, Inc.

AUTO - SERV - Computer software - Auto Services Co., Inc.

AUTO-SET - Electronic equipment - Chief Manufacturing Co.

AUTO SHOE - Sporting goods ☆ - Woodstream Corp.

AUTO-SIZER - Apparel–children's - Norm Thompson Outfitters, Inc.

AUTO SKEW - Electronic equipment - Lectrosonics Inc.

AUTO-SKIM - Swimming pools - Hayward Pool Products Inc.

AUTO-SLUSH - Medical apparatus - O.R. Solutions, Inc.

AUTO SOCKET - Electronic equipment - Power Star Products, Inc.

AUTO SOURCE - Motor vehicle parts and accessories - Auto Source, Inc.

AUTO SPRAY - Paints - Krylon/Dupli-Color

AUTO STICK 3 - Automotive parts and accessories - Hurst Performance Inc.

AUTO-STIR - Medical apparatus - O.R. Solutions, Inc.

AUTO-STOP - Medical apparatus - Lumex, Inc.

AUTO-STOP - Pencil sharpeners - Matsushita Consumer Electronics Co.

AUTO STRIP - Paint removers - Klean-Strip

AUTO SUN SHIELD - Automotive parts and accessories ☆ - Sta-Put Industries Corp.

AUTO-SWEEP - Housewares ☆ - Normark Corp.

AUTO TAGS - Deodorizers - Natural Products Corp.

AUTO-TAPE - Electronic equipment - Telex Communications, Inc.

AUTO TASER - Alarm systems–burglar - Air Taser, Inc.

AUTO TAX - Computer software - Tax Link, Inc.

AUTO TECH 1000 - Footwear ☆ - H.H. Brown Shoe Co., Inc.

AUTO TEMP - Thermostats - Hunter Fan Co.

AUTO TEMP PLUS - Thermostats - Hunter Fan Co.

AUTO-TERRA - Cameras ☆ - Edixa Camera Co.

AUTO THERM - Health care products - Mettler Electronics Corp.

AUTO THERMIC - Cosmetics ☆ - Duart Industries Ltd.

AUTO-THREAD - Electronics equipment - RTI Research Technology International

AUTO-TIMER - Automotive parts and accessories ☆ - Pacific Lubricants

AUTO-TOPPER - Electrical equipment - Bridges Electric, Inc.

AUTO-TRAC - Computer software - Auto-Trac, Inc.

AUTO-TRAC - Humidifiers - Research Products Corp.

☆ = Now out of production

AUTO-TRAC - Photographic equipment - Houston Fearless 76 Inc.
AUTO TRANS - Chemical preparations - Petrolon Management, Inc.
AUTO TREND - Tools—hand-operated - Meijer, Inc.
AUTO TRIP - Drains - Gerber Plumbing Fixtures Corp.
AUTO TRUST - Batteries - Exide Corp.
AUTO-TUFF - Tools - K-Line Industries
AUTO-TUNE - Automotive parts and accessories - Echlin Inc.
AUTO-TWIN - Photocopy machines - Eastman Kodak Co.
AUTO-UP - Cameras ☆ - Konica USA Inc.
AUTO-VALVE - Harmonicas - Hohner Inc.
AUTO VANCE - Audio equipment - Telex Communications, Inc.
AUTO-VARIABLE - Fans—exhaust - Hudson Products Corp.
AUTO-VECTOR - Electrical equipment - Bridges Electric, Inc.
AUTO-VENT - Ventilation equipment - Maid-o-Mist
AUTO VISIONS - Automotive parts and accessories - Autovisions, Inc.
AUTO VU - Automotive parts and accessories - Barcolene Inc.
AUTO WIPE - Automotive parts and accessories - J.R. Hunt Ventures
AUTO WIZARD - Computer software - Oz Software Inc.
AUTO WORLD - Model cars - Mailcorp
AUTO WRAP - Hair care products ☆ - W.R. Rayson Co., Inc.
AUTO YOKE - Machinery - City Theatrical Inc.
AUTO-ZONE - Machinery - Wattmaster Co. Inc.
AUTOADJUST - Seats—automobile ☆ - Cosco, Inc.
AUTOBAHN - Leather goods - David Kirk (London)
AUTOBAHN - Wallcoverings - Ben Rose Ltd.
AUTOBERNZ - Lighters - Bernzomatic
AUTOBIKE - Bicycles - AutoBike Inc.
AUTOBIKE - Bicycles - Ross Bicycles USA, Ltd.
AUTOBIKE - Fully automatic shifting bicycle. - CSA, Inc.
AUTOBLOT - Glass products - Bellco Glass Inc.
AUTOBODY EXPRESS - Apparel and accessories - Fred Imus Car Gallery, Inc.
AUTOBODY EXPRESS EL PASO, TEXAS - Apparel and accessories - Fred Imus Car Gallery, Inc.
AUTOBOOK - Electronics equipment - RTI Research Technology International
AUTOBRAKE - Machine tools - Roper Whitney of Rockford, Inc.
AUTOBRAKE-2000 - Brakes—motor vehicle - Roper Whitney Co.
AUTOBRUSH - Toothbrushes—electric - Oralgiene USA, Inc.
AUTOCAD - Computer software - Autodesk Inc.
AUTOCAD DATA EXTENSION - Computer software - Autodesk Inc.
AUTOCAD LT - Computer software - Autodesk Inc.
AUTOCAR - Motor vehicles - Western-White GMC (Sales Div.)
AUTOCARB - Controls—heating systems - Surface Combustion, Inc.
AUTOCARE - Cleaning preparations - Guardsman Products, Inc.
AUTOCARE COVERAGE AT EVERY TURN - Motor vehicle dealers - Autocare Dealer Service Contracts Inc.
AUTOCATH - Medical apparatus - HK Medical Technologies, Inc.
AUTOCELL - Transmitting apparatus - Allen Telecom Group, Inc.
AUTOCHILL - Medical apparatus - Aircast, Inc.
AUTOCINEMA - Electronic equipment - Bob Bartlett & Associates Inc.
AUTOCLAM - Cranes - WEC Co.
AUTOCLASS - Photographic equipment - Eastman Kodak Co.
AUTOCLERK - Electronic equipment - American Registration Systems, Inc.
AUTOCLOCK - Tape players—video - Sony Electronics Inc.
AUTOCODE - Computer software - Lancomm, Inc.
AUTOCOMP - Engines—motor vehicle - Consolidated Manufacturing, Inc.
AUTOCONTROLLER - Computer peripheral equipment - Software Recording Corp. of America
AUTOCORD - Cameras ☆ - Minolta Corp.
AUTOCRAT - Coffee - Autocrat, Inc.
AUTOCRAT - Ice cream - Kraft Foods, Inc.
AUTOCRAT - Stationery ☆ - Mead Corp.
AUTOCRAT - Tires - Bridgestone/Firestone, Inc.
AUTOCRAT - Watches ☆ - Toastmaster Inc.
AUTOCYCLE - Electronic equipment - Delaware Capital Formation Inc.
AUTODAPTIVE - Electrical equipment - Beckwith Electric Co.
AUTODAT - Audio equipment - Tallgrass Technologies Corp.
AUTODESK - Computer software - Autodesk Inc.
AUTODESK VIEW - Computer software - Autodesk Inc.
AUTODESK WORKCENTER - Computer software - Autodesk Inc.
AUTODEX - Stationery - Rolodex Corp.
AUTODEX SLIDE-O-MAGIC - Stationery - Rolodex Corp.
AUTODIAL - Telephones ☆ - RF Communications Div.
AUTODIFF - Computer software ☆ - Software Toolworks, Inc.
AUTODOC PLUS - Computer software - Corbel
AUTODOC PRO - Computer storage devices - Corbel

AUTODOCK - Computer peripheral equipment - Oxford Molecular Group
AUTODOME - Surveillance equipment - Philips Communication & Security Systems Inc.
AUTODRAW - Computer software - AI Systems, Inc.
AUTODRAW - Computer software - SourceView Software International
AUTODUEL - Computer software ☆ - Electronic Arts Inc.
AUTODUEL - Games - Steve Jackson Games Inc.
AUTODUEL - Toys—models ☆ - Grenadier Models
AUTODUEL - Video games - Origin Systems, Inc.
AUTOENHANCE - Computer software - Wordstar Atlanta Technology Center Inc.
AUTOEXCEL - Chemical preparations - Anacomp Inc.
AUTOFAST - Staples, scales, tackers, etc. - Automation Fastening Co. Inc.
AUTOFAX - Duplicating machines - Toshiba America Medical Systems Inc.
AUTOFEED II - Clippers—barber - Vermeer Manufacturing Co.
AUTOFILL - Bathtubs—enameled - Kohler Co.
AUTOFILTER - Computer peripheral equipment - Gatan, Inc.
AUTOFIRE - Fishing tackle - Superior Sports Products, Inc.
AUTOFIT - Electrical equipment - Raynet Corp.
AUTOFLATOR - Compressors—air - W.R. Brown Co.
AUTOFLEX - Eyeglasses - Marchon and Marcolin Eyewear Inc.
AUTOFLEX - Health care products - Chattanooga Group, Inc.
AUTOFLEX - Steel products - Brainard Strapping
AUTOFLUSH - Electronic control unit - Sussman-Automatic Corp.
AUTOFOCUS - Enlargers—photographic ☆ - Heitz Service Corp.
AUTOFORM - Rubber—vulcanized - McNeil & NRM, Inc.
AUTOGAS - Electronic equipment - Auto-Gas Systems, Inc.
AUTOGATE - Window shades - Sol-R-Veil Inc.
AUTOGENESIS - Medical equipment - Autogenesis, Inc.
AUTOGRAPH - Doors—garage - Stanley Works
AUTOGRAPH - Electronic equipment - Peavey Electronics Corp.
AUTOGRAPH - Golfing equipment ☆ - Northwestern Golf Co.
AUTOGRAPH - Office supplies ☆ - Faber-Castell Corp.
AUTOGRAPH - Recording label - Sonic Arts Corp.
AUTOGRAPH - Sporting goods - Rawlings Sporting Goods Co., Inc.
AUTOGRAPH COLLECTION - Leather goods - St. Thomas Inc.
AUTOGRAPH HOUND - Pet products - Pupperwear Inc.
AUTOGRAPH PRODUCTIONS - Stationery - Autograph Productions
AUTOGRAPH SPORTS - Sporting goods - Autograph Sports, Inc.
AUTOGRAPHS - Nameplates—engraved - Metalcraft Inc.
AUTOGRAVER - Machinery ☆ - Scott Machine Development Corp.
AUTOGUARD - Batteries - Netco International, Inc.
AUTOGUARD - Brake fluids - Quaker State Oil Refining Corp.
AUTOGUARD - Catheters - Becton, Dickinson and Co.
AUTOGUIDE - Motor vehicles—trucks - Clark Material Handling Co.
AUTOGYRO - Electronic equipment - Andrew Corp.
AUTOHARP - Zithers ☆ - Oscar Schmidt International Inc.
AUTOHELP - Computer software - DS Technologies, Inc.
AUTOIDE - Computer software - Bus Logic Inc.
AUTOIMAGE - Computer software - Medic Computer Systems, Inc.
AUTOIMMUNE TEST SYSTEMS - Pharmaceutical preparations - Wampole Laboratories Div.
AUTOJECTOR - Health care products ☆ - Ulster Scientific Inc.
AUTOJECTORS - Machinery - Autojectors, Inc.
AUTOJET - Paint sprayers - Spraying Systems Co.
AUTOKNIP - Photographic self-timer ☆ - Saul Bower Inc.
AUTOLASER - Tools - David White Inc.
AUTOLET II - Health care products ☆ - Ulster Scientific Inc.
AUTOLET LITE - Health care products ☆ - Ulster Scientific Inc.
AUTOLINK - Electrical equipment - Prince Corp.
AUTOLINK - Telephone apparatus ☆ - RF Communications Div.
AUTOLITE - Motor vehicle parts and accessories - Alliedsignal Inc.
AUTOLOAD - Electronic equipment - Eiki International, Inc.
AUTOLOAD - Motor vehicles—trucks - Dynamic Autoload Systems
AUTOLOCATE - Distance measuring equipment—aeronautical - Garmin Corp.
AUTOLOG - Ledgers - Beach Publishing Co.
AUTOLOG - LWD - Computer software - TDS, Inc.
AUTOLOGO - Computer software - Preco Industries Inc.
AUTOLOK - Power tapes ☆ - U.S. Tape Co.
AUTOLOO - Pet products - R.C. Steele Co.
AUTOLOO - Pet products ☆ - Dogloo Inc.
AUTOLOSS - Computer software - Telecommunications Techniques Corp.
AUTOLUX - Automotive window insulating film - Madico, Inc.
AUTOLYFE - Engine cleaning machinery - Motorvator International Ltd.
AUTOMADDAK - Health care products - Maddak Inc.
AUTOMAGIC - Hearing aids - Telex Communications, Inc.

AUTOMAGIC - Umbrellas - Shedrain Corp.
AUTOMAGIC PUTTING - Video tapes - Bob Mann
AUTOMAP STREETS - Computer software - Microsoft Corp.
AUTOMAR - Lenses–projection ☆ - Kalart Victor Corp.
AUTOMASK - Tape–masking - RBL Products Inc.
AUTOMASTER - Projection screens - Brumberger Co. Inc.
AUTOMATABLES - Labels–paper - Ever-Ready Label Corp.
AUTOMATCH - Housewares - Hiac/Royco Co.
AUTOMATCH - Telephone apparatus - Antenna Systems Corp.
AUTOMATE - Bottles–plastic - Microbar Systems Inc.
AUTOMATE - Electronic equipment - Peavey Electronics Corp.
AUTOMATED INDUSTRIAL MACHINERY - Welding equipment - Automated Industrial Machinery, Inc.
AUTOMATED PRODUCTION ENVIRONMENT - Computer software - Iguide, Inc.
AUTOMATED WEATHER SOURCE - Computer hardware - Automated Weather Source Inc.
AUTOMATIC - Furniture - Automatic Inc.
AUTOMATIC - Golfing equipment ☆ - Browning Manufacturing Co.
AUTOMATIC - Thread - Cincinnati Thread Co.
AUTOMATIC ACCESS CONTROLS - Safety products - Integrated Security Systems Inc.
AUTOMATIC BIRD BATH - Pet products - Molor Products Co.
AUTOMATIC BUILDING MACHINE - Machinery - M.I.C. Industries, Inc.
AUTOMATIC DUSTPAN, THE - Vacuum cleaners and accessories - Plastiflex Co. Inc.
AUTOMATIC E-Z- WELLTESTERS - Oilfield equipment - Oilfield Controls, Inc.
AUTOMATIC FILE - Office supplies ☆ - Knoll Group
AUTOMATIC HOUSEKEEPER - Air purification systems ☆ - Trion, Inc.
AUTOMATIC INVEST-O-METER - Computer software - Oscar Leary
AUTOMATIC MANUFACTURING - Pharmaceutical preparations - Automatic Manufacturing
AUTOMATIC PRODUCTS INTERNATIONAL, LTD. - Vending machines - Automatic Products International, Ltd.
AUTOMATIC RADIO - Audio equipment ☆ - Flowtron Outdoor Products
AUTOMATIC SHUTOFF, THE - Irons–electric - Black & Decker Corp.
AUTOMATIC-TAKE-AWAY - Golfing equipment - DGR Golf Products Corp.
AUTOMATIC TRADE RELEASE - Computer software - Omr Systems Corp.
AUTOMATIC TUBE - Adhesives and sealants - Loctite Corp.
AUTOMATIC VANISH - Cleaning preparations - Drackett Co.
AUTOMATIC VANISH - Cleaning preparations–household - S.C. Johnson & Son, Inc.
AUTOMATIC WASHERS - Underwear and nightwear - Exquisite Form Industries
AUTOMATIFIED - Thread ☆ - Belding Heminway Co. Inc.
AUTOMATION CERTIFIED - Laboratory apparatus - Zymark Corp.
AUTOMATOR - Garden equipment - Dalen Products Inc.
AUTOMATOR - Medical apparatus - Autogenesis, Inc.
AUTOMAX - Antifreeze - Superior Blends Inc.
AUTOMAX - Computer software - Reliance Electric Co.
AUTOMAXI - Bicycle carrier - Automaxi Inc.
AUTOMEG INSULATION TESTERS - Measuring and dispensing pumps - Automeg, Inc.
AUTOMELT - Packaging machines - Westpac Packaging Systems, Inc.
AUTOMETER - Motor vehicle parts and accessories - Rivera Engineering, Inc.
AUTOMILL - Computer software - Autodesk Inc.
AUTOMIX - Health care products - Baxter International Inc.
AUTOMIX - Valves - Cooney Brothers, Inc.
AUTOMOBILI LAMBORGHINI - Video games - Titus Software Corp.
AUTOMODEM - Computer software ☆ - Commodore Business Machines Inc.
AUTOMOIST - Hoses - Plastic Specialties and Technologies, Inc.
AUTOMOTIVE AFTERMARKET OF THE AMERICAS - Oil machinery - Fag Bearings Corp.
AUTOMOTIVE GOOP - Adhesives and sealants - Eclectic Products Inc.
AUTOMOTIVE QUALITY PREMIUM GRADE - Carburetor and throttle parts, etc. - SDI Operating Partners
AUTOMOTIVE RESTORE - Lubricants - Restore Inc.
AUTOMOVE - Computer software - Vantageware
AUTOMUG LITE - Dishes–earthenware - Teledyne Water Pik
AUTONAIRE - Fiber measuring instruments - Motion Control, Inc.
AUTONAME - Computer software - Stratcode Information Systems, Inc.
AUTONAV - Computer software ☆ - American Technologies, Inc.
AUTONET - Computer software - Nemasoft, Inc.
AUTONGS - Computer software - Pafmap Consulting
AUTONOMOUS RECORDS - Recording label - Split Nickel Entertainment
AUTOOCR - Computer software - STF Technologies, Inc.

AUTOPACE - Computer software - At&T Corp.
AUTOPACK - Luggage racks–automotive - Automotive Accessories Manufacturers, Inc.
AUTOPAD - Audio equipment ☆ - Electro-Voice, Inc.
AUTOPAINT - Computer software - First Light Products, Inc.
AUTOPAK - Automotive parts and accessories - Springfield Remanufacturing Corp.
AUTOPAK - Computers–personal - Infopak, Inc.
AUTOPAK - Medical apparatus - On-Gard Systems, Inc.
AUTOPAP - Computer software and hardware - Neopath Inc.
AUTOPAY - Computer software - Municipal Management Associates, Inc.
AUTOPICK - Electronic equipment - Electronic Design Inc.
AUTOPILOT - Computer hardware - Gammagraphx, Inc.
AUTOPILOT - Lighting fixtures–stage - Wybron, Inc.
AUTOPLAN II - Computer software - Digital Tools, Inc.
AUTOPLAN II PROFESSIONAL - Computer software - Digital Tools, Inc.
AUTOPLY - Thread ☆ - Belding Heminway Co. Inc.
AUTOPOINT - Writing and office supplies - Autopoint Inc.
AUTOPORT - Trailers–truck - U.S. Cargo, Inc.
AUTOPORTABLE - Electronic equipment ☆ - Tandy Corp.
AUTOPOSITIVE - Film - Eastman Kodak Co.
AUTOPOST - Computer software ☆ - Icam Technologies Corp. U.S.A.
AUTOPOWER - Computer software - Mazda Motor of America Inc.
AUTOPREP - Finishing agents ☆ - Carborundum Abrasives North America
AUTOPRIDE - Computer software - Bankers Insurance Co.
AUTOPRIME - Primers - PPG Industries, Inc.
AUTOPRO - Automotive parts and accessories - APS Big A
AUTOPRO - Automotive parts and accessories - A.P.S., Inc.
AUTOPROPANE - Gasoline - Sunmarks, Inc.
AUTOPULSE - Alarm systems–fire - Ansul, Inc.
AUTOPUTTER - Golfing equipment - Autoputter
AUTOQUALITY - Computer software - Applied Automation Techniques, Inc.
AUTOQUIP - Automotive parts and accessories - One Stop Undercar, Inc.
AUTOQUIP - Machinery - Autoquip Corp.
AUTORAILER - Trailers - Wabash National Corp.
AUTOREEL - Machinery - Reel-Neat Systems, Inc.
AUTOREL - Automotive parts and accessories - CLA Associates Inc.
AUTORESPONSE - Computers - Western National Warranty Corp.
AUTOROTOR - Oscillators - Jackson Machine Products, Inc.
AUTOSCAN - Automobile thermometer - American Thermometer Co.
AUTOSCAN - Computer software - Municipal Management Associates, Inc.
AUTOSCOPE - Steel - Image Sensing Systems, Inc.
AUTOSCORE - Computer software - Scobra Software Solutions, Ltd.
AUTOSCREEN - Film - Eastman Kodak Co.
AUTOSDI - Measuring instruments - Purification Products Co.
AUTOSEAL - Forms–preprinted - Laser Substrates, Inc.
AUTOSEAL - Machine parts - Wormser Systems, Inc.
AUTOSEAL - Machinery - Bescorp Inc.
AUTOSECURE - Computer software - Platinum Technology, Inc.
AUTOSERT - Fasteners–snap - Textron Inc.
AUTOSET - Electronic equipment - Philips Communication & Security Systems Inc.
AUTOSET - Watches - Gruen Marketing Corp.
AUTOSHAPE - Machinery - Cincinnati Inc.
AUTOSHIELD - Alarm systems - Kobishi America, Inc.
AUTOSHIP - Computer software - Applied Automation Techniques, Inc.
AUTOSIPHON - Pumps - Autosiphon
AUTOSIZE - Computer software - Raychem Corp.
AUTOSLIDE - Automotive parts and accessories - American Seating Co.
AUTOSMART - Publisher's imprints - National Auto Lock Service, Inc.
AUTOSMEAR - Machinery - QualMark Corp.
AUTOSNEAK ON BOARD - Electrical surge protectors - Diversified Technology Group, Inc.
AUTOSOFT - Computer software - David F. Snider
AUTOSOL RTU 2000 - Computer hardware - Automation Solutions, Inc.
AUTOSONIK - Automotive electronics - Hurricane Acoustics Ltd.
AUTOSORT - Computer hardware - Positek, Inc.
AUTOSOUND 2000 - Audio equipment - Autosound 2000, Inc.
AUTOSPEC - Computer software - MediaPlan, Inc.
AUTOSPEC - Fasteners–snap - Penn Engineering and Manufacturing Corp.
AUTOSPECIALTY - Automotive parts and accessories - S.B.C. Ltd., Inc.
AUTOSPELL - Typewriters - Smith Corona Corp.
AUTOSPOOL - Film ☆ - T.M. Visual Industries Inc.
AUTOSTAMP - Office supplies - IDL Corp.
AUTOSTART - Batteries - Hensley Battery and Electrical Supply Inc.
AUTOSTAT - Thermostats ☆ - BRK Electronics Inc.

☆ = Now out of production

AUTOSUCKER - Pumps–hydraulic - Pengwyn
AUTOSURF - Computer software - Autodesk Inc.
AUTOSWITCH - Cigarette lighters - SAFCO Corp.
AUTOTAB - Computer hardware - Autodisc Inc.
AUTOTALK - Electronic equipment - Telestar Interactive Corp.
AUTOTEAM - Computer software - Digital Tools, Inc.
AUTOTENNA - Motor vehicle parts and accessories - Jet Sound Electronics
AUTOTHIN - Watches - Hampden Corp.
AUTOTRACER - Alarm systems - United States Auto Security
AUTOTRACK - Surveillance equipment ✩ - Philips Communication & Security Systems Inc.
AUTOTRAINER - Computer software - Software Recording Corp. of America
AUTOTRAK - Computer software - Suprex Corp.
AUTOTRAY - Conveyors - Electrocom Automation Inc.
AUTOTRIM - Packaging machines - Bemis Co. Inc.
AUTOTUNE - Electronic equipment - General Electric Co.
AUTOTUNE - Electronic equipment - Rodix, Inc.
AUTOTYPE - Computer software - Now Software, Inc.
AUTOVAC - Vacuum cleaners and accessories ✩ - Randal Marketing Corp.
AUTOVAL - Computer software - Vintek, Inc.
AUTOVAP - Analyzers–industrial - O.I. Corp.
AUTOVAP - Evaporation apparatus–laboratory ✩ - Standard-Keil Hardware Manufacturing Co.
AUTOVIEW - Computer hardware - Autodisc Inc.
AUTOVISION - Computer software - Autodesk Inc.
AUTOWAGON - Trailers–travel - Wells Cargo Inc.
AUTOWASH - Electronic equipment - Fit Group, Inc.
AUTOWORKS - Motor vehicle parts and accessories - Metra Electronics Corp.
AUTOZORB - Insulating materials - Recycled Fibre Industries, Inc.
AUTRA - Electronic equipment - Delco Electronics Corp.
AUTRONEX - Electronic equipment - Enthone-OMI
AUTRONIC - Binoculars ✩ - Luminos Photo Corp.
AUTRONIC EYE - Lighting equipment–automotive - General Motors Corp. (Fisher Guide Div.)
AUTRY - Athletic footwear - Autry Industries Inc.
AUTRY - Corn–flour or meal - House-Autry Mills, Inc.
AUTRY SHOX - Athletic footwear - Autry Industries Inc.
AUTTOCOM - Automotive parts and accessories - Auttocom LLC
AUTUMAIRE - Fans ✩ - Autumaire Fan Co.
AUTUMN - Bedding–linen - Dan River Inc.
AUTUMN - Cabinets - Karman Kitchens Inc.
AUTUMN - Glassware–household - Lenox Crystal, Inc.
AUTUMN - Margarine - Lever Brothers Co. Inc.
AUTUMN - Tableware–china - Lenox, Inc.
AUTUMN BLEND - Jams, jellies and fruit preserves - J.M. Smucker Co.
AUTUMN BLOSSOM II - Floor coverings - Armstrong World Industries, Inc.
AUTUMN CHERRY - Cabinets–wood ✩ - Kemper
AUTUMN DAY - Toys - Tonka Corp.
AUTUMN EARTH - Hair care products ✩ - Natural Thoughts Inc.
AUTUMN FANTASY - Floor coverings–carpet and rugs - Evans-Black Carpet Mills
AUTUMN FIRES - Cosmetics - Elizabeth Arden Inc.
AUTUMN FOLIAGE - Kitchenware–earthenware - Watt Pottery Co.
AUTUMN FRESH - Fruits–canned - Larson Fruit Co.
AUTUMN GLORY - Melamine product - Boonton Molding Co. Inc.
AUTUMN GLOW - Dinnerware–glass - Salem China Co.
AUTUMN GOLD - Christmas tree ornaments - Cracker Box Inc.
AUTUMN GOLD - Jewelry ✩ - Hirsch Speidel Inc.
AUTUMN GOLD - Lenses–optical - X-Cel Optical Co.
AUTUMN GOLD - Trees - Columbia Basin Nursery
AUTUMN GOLD - Turkeys ✩ - Continental Grain Co.
AUTUMN GRAIN - Bakery products - American Bakeries Co.
AUTUMN-HARP - Lip and face balm, body lotion - Autumn-Harp, Inc.
AUTUMN HARVEST - Dishes–china - Taylor, Smith & Taylor Co.
AUTUMN HARVEST - Floor coverings–carpet and rugs - Evans-Black Carpet Mills
AUTUMN HARVEST - Florists - Florists' Transworld Delivery Association, Inc.
AUTUMN HARVEST - Furniture - Artesian Industries
AUTUMN HARVEST - Giftware - Russ Berrie and Co., Inc.
AUTUMN HARVEST - Juices ✩ - Hunt-Wesson, Inc.
AUTUMN HARVEST - Juices ✩ - Warner Vineyards Inc.
AUTUMN HARVEST - Mixing bowls ✩ - Corning Inc.
AUTUMN HAZE - Dishes–china - Pickard Inc.
AUTUMN HAZE - Floor coverings–carpet and rugs ✩ - Playfield International Inc.
AUTUMN HILL SOFTWARE - Computer software - Autumn Hill Software Inc.

AUTUMN HUNTER - Sporting goods - Easton Aluminum Inc.
AUTUMN LEAVES - Candy - Brach and Brock Confections Inc.
AUTUMN LEAVES - Cooking utensils–enameled ✩ - National Housewares
AUTUMN LEAVES - Deodorizers - Claire Manufacturing Co.
AUTUMN LEAVES - Dinnerware–glass ✩ - Metlox Pottery Shoppe
AUTUMN LEAVES - Floor coverings–carpet and rugs - Stanton Carpet Corp.
AUTUMN LEAVES - Floor coverings–carpet and rugs ✩ - Mohawk Carpet Corp.
AUTUMN LEAVES - Glassware–household ✩ - Fenton Art Glass Co.
AUTUMN LEAVES - Paper–book - American Tissue Corp.
AUTUMN LEAVES - Watches - Hampden Corp.
AUTUMN LITES - Cosmetics ✩ - Bonne Bell, Inc.
AUTUMN LOVE - Rings–jewelry - Artcarved Inc.
AUTUMN MATE - Mulchers - Highway Equipment Co.
AUTUMN MEADOW - Dinnerware ✩ - Corning Inc.
AUTUMN MIST - Boats–canoes - Sawyer Composite Products
AUTUMN MORN - Rings–jewelry ✩ - Artcarved Inc.
AUTUMN PINE - Tables - Impact Furniture
AUTUMN PRIDE - Fruit and vegetable markets - Fruit Growers Marketing Association
AUTUMN RAINBOW - Servingware ✩ - Corning Inc.
AUTUMN ROSE - Books–blank - Antioch Publishing Co.
AUTUMN ROSE - Deodorizers - Reynolds Consumer Products, Inc.
AUTUMN ROSE - Perfumes ✩ - Carolina Designs Ltd.
AUTUMN SEED - Food products - Autumn Seed Inc.
AUTUMN SHADOWS - Floor coverings–carpet and rugs - Queen Carpet Corp.
AUTUMN SPICE - Deodorizers - Reckitt & Colman, Inc.
AUTUMN SPIRAL - Dishes–china - Taylor, Smith & Taylor Co.
AUTUMN SPLENDOR - Dishes–china - Taylor, Smith & Taylor Co.
AUTUMN SPLENDOR - Floor coverings–carpet and rugs - Alexander Smith Carpets
AUTUMN VILLAGE FROM THE CRANSTON COLLECTIONS - Fabrics ✩ - VIP/VIP Crafts
AUTUMN VINE - Floor coverings–carpet and rugs - Couristan Inc.
AUTUMN WOODLANDS - Skin care products - Earth Preserv, Ltd.
AUTUMN WOODS - Floor coverings–carpet and rugs ✩ - Walter Carpet Mills
AUTUMN ZINFANDEL - Wines - Franzia Winery
AUTUMNFOGG - Beverages–malt - Olde Heurich Brewing Co.
AUTUMNS DELIGHT - Dinnerware–glass ✩ - Johnson Brothers, USA, Inc.
AUX - Generators–electric - Onan Corp.
AUX ANYSETIERS DU ROY - Candles ✩ - Estus Export-Import
AV - Audio equipment - Artisticover
AV - Jewelry - Act V Inc.
AV - Pens - Staedtler, Inc.
A.V. - Recording label - Soundmasters Studio
AV - Spring water beverage - Aqua Vie Beverage Corp.
AV - Wines - Columbia Winery
AV 100 - Broadcasting equipment - Broadcast Electronics, Inc.
AV-2000 - Facepiece for scuba and gas masks - Figgie Licensing Corp.
AV ALARM - Repellent - Weitech Inc.
AV ARCHITECTURE - Furniture–wood - AV Arcitecture
AV ARMORVISION PLASTICS & GLASS - Plastics - Armorvision Plastics & Glass
AV BLUEBOOK - AVBluebook
AV-COM - Electronics equipment - Jerome Menell Co.
AV E - Food products ✩ - Helga Van Dyke Skin Care
AV-EXPRESSIONS - Computer software - AV-Expressions
AV/FONE - Audio equipment - Califone International Inc.
AV IMAGE - Computer software - Data General Corp.
AV-LINE - Switchboards–power - General Electric Co.
AV-MATIC - Projectors–photographic - Dukane Corp.
AV PRODUCTS INC. - Computer software - AV Products Inc.
AV-UNIFIER - Electronic equipment - Radmar Inc.
AV8 - Compact discs–prerecorded - AV8 Records, Corp.
AV8R - Electronic equipment - J.L. Cooper Electronics
AVA - Audio and video accessories - AVA Electronics Corp.
AVA - Balls - Lisco, Inc.
AVA - Electronic equipment ✩ - Childs Corp.
AVA - Flowers, plants, and seeds - Ava Associates Inc.
AVA BERGMAN - Apparel and accessories ✩ - Swirl II Ltd.
AVA BERGMAN - Fabrics–linen ✩ - West Point-Pepperell Inc.
AVACADO - Brooms - Zephyr Manufacturing Co.
AVACADOL - Hair care products - Beauty Brands Group
AVACCI - Leather goods - Glotone Enterprising Corp., Inc.
AVACUN - Invitations - Classic Thermographers Ltd.
AVADEX - Herbicides - Monsanto Co.

AVADYNE - Adhesives and sealants - Pierce & Stevens Corp.
AVAIL - Apparel and accessories - Vail Trademarks, Inc.
AVAIL - Furniture - Cramer Inc.
AVAIL - Vitamins and nutritional supplements - Smithkline Beecham Corp.
AVAILA - Veterinary nutritional supplements - Zinpro Corp.
AVAILABILITY COMMAND CENTER - Computer peripheral equipment - Candle Corp.
AVAILABLE PRESS - Publisher's imprints - Ballantine Books Inc.
AVAILWORKS - Computer peripheral equipment - Avail Technology, Inc.
AVAIT SPORTIF - Apparel - Pan Pacific Textile Group, Inc.
AVALAN - Computer software - Avalan Technology, Inc.
AVALANCHE - Apparel and accessories - Pat Fashions Industries Inc.
AVALANCHE - Apparel–men's - Barrel-Marvin Apparel, Inc.
AVALANCHE - Beverages - Southland Corp.
AVALANCHE - Gloves - Avon Glove Corp.
AVALANCHE - Ice chests - Charles E. Jones
AVALANCHE - Motor vehicles - Thrall Car Manufacturing Co.
AVALANCHE - Recording label - Avalanche Records
AVALANCHE - Skates–roller - Fremont International Trading, Inc.
AVALANCHE - Skin care products - Helene Curtis Industries Inc.
AVALANCHE - Sporting goods - Avalanche Snowboards, Inc.
AVALANCHE - Yarn - Henry's Attic
AVALANCHE ABLAZE - Apparel - Avalanche International, Inc.
AVALANCHE PUBLISHING - Calendars - Apex Press, Inc.
AVALAR - Eyeglasses - Bausch & Lomb Inc.
AVALGESIC - Pharmaceutical preparations - Barre-National, Inc.
AVALON - Bathroom fixtures ☆ - Artesian Industries
AVALON - Cabinets - Dewills Industries Inc.
AVALON - Cabinets ☆ - Medallion Kitchens of Minnesota Inc.
AVALON - Cigarettes - Brown & Williamson Tobacco Corp.
AVALON - Cleaning preparations - Wesco Foods Co.
AVALON - Computer software - Steinberg/Jones Corp.
AVALON - Dishes–china ☆ - Royal China & Porcelain Companies Inc.
AVALON - Door frames - Jeld-Wen, Inc.
AVALON - Fabrics - Capital Carousel Inc.
AVALON - Floor coverings ☆ - Congoleum Corp.
AVALON - Floor coverings–tile - KPT Inc.
AVALON - Garters - Marcus & Wiesen Inc.
AVALON - Golf clubs - King Par Corp.
AVALON - Guitars - Hershman Musical Instrument
AVALON - Ice buckets ☆ - Lenox Crystal, Inc.
AVALON - Luggage - American Tourister, Inc.
AVALON - Motor vehicles - Toyota Motor Sales USA Inc.
AVALON - Paints - Sinclair Paint Co.
AVALON - Pens ☆ - Herco Products
AVALON - Perfumes - Shiara Holdings, Inc.
AVALON - Porous-point pens ☆ - Coloron Industries
AVALON - Publisher's imprints - Airmont Publishing Co. Inc.
AVALON - Spring water - Loverseas Inc.
AVALON - Tires - Target Tire and Automotive Corp.
AVALON - Trailers–travel ☆ - Fleetwood Enterprises, Inc.
AVALON - Wallpaper - Marburg Wallcoverings Inc.
AVALON - Watches - Webster Watch Co. Associates
AVALON - Wood desks - Inwood Office Furniture
AVALON 30 - Floor coverings–carpet and rugs ☆ - Catalina Carpet Mills Inc.
AVALON ACOUSTICS - Amplifiers - Avalon Acoustics
AVALON BAY - Floor coverings–carpet and rugs ☆ - Catalina Carpet Mills Inc.
AVALON BAY - Food products - Avalon Bay Foods Inc.
AVALON BOOKS - Publisher's imprint - Thomas Bouregy & Co. Inc.
AVALON COLLECTION - Furniture ☆ - Armstrong World Industries, Inc.
AVALON HILL - Games - Avalon Hill Game Co.
AVALONIA - Floor coverings–carpet and rugs - Lees Carpets
AVALRT - Sporting goods - Ramer Products, Ltd.
AVAN - Hair care products - Framesi USA/Roffler Industries Inc.
AVANCE - Vitamins and nutritional supplements - Spa Health Consultants
AVANGUARDIA - Shoes - Jimlar Corp.
AVANSTAR - Computer peripheral equipment - Star-Gate Technologies, Inc.
AVANT - Food products machinery - Leedal Inc.
AVANT - Health care products - ETAC USA Inc.
AVANT - Musical instrument accessories - Chartier Reeds
AVANT - Photographic equipment - Avant Inc.
AVANT - Recording label - Crystal Records Inc.
AVANT - Video equipment - Optical Gaging Products, Inc.
AVANT CARDS - Games - Franklin Merchandising Co.
AVANT GARDE - Floor coverings–carpet and rugs - Whitecrest Carpet Mills

AVANT GARDE - Furniture - Lea Industries Inc.
AVANT GARDE - Furniture ☆ - Singer Furniture Co.
AVANT-GARDE - Placemats ☆ - Scott Paper Co.
AVANT-GARD'N - Lighting fixtures - Fleco Industries Inc.
AVANT GAUZE - Gauze–surgical - Medline, Industries, Inc.
AVANTA - Coffee makers–electric - Old Dutch International Ltd.
AVANTAGE - Apparel–women's ☆ - Jonathan Logan Inc.
AVANTAGE - Computer software - Accolade Inc.
AVANTAGE - Hair coloring preparations - Cosmair Inc.
AVANTE - Bathroom fixtures ☆ - Price Pfister Co.
AVANTE - Blinds–vertical - Kittrich Corp.
AVANTE - Cabinets - American Woodmark Corp.
AVANTE - Floor coverings–carpet and rugs ☆ - Mohawk Industries Inc.
AVANTE - Housewares ☆ - Seasia
AVANTE - Lighting fixtures - National Service Industries, Inc.
AVANTE - Luggage - Airway Industries, Inc.
AVANTE - Rings–jewelry - Artcarved
AVANTE-GARDE - Wallpaper - Marburg Wallcoverings Inc.
AVANTGARD - Glassware–household - Spiegelau Inc.
AVANTI - Audio equipment - Avanti Products Inc.
AVANTI - Cabinets - Contempri Kitchens
AVANTI - Centrifuges–laboratory - Beckman Industrial Corp.
AVANTI - Cigars - Avanti Cigar Co.
AVANTI - Cups–paper - Imperial Bondware Inc.
AVANTI - Cushions ☆ - Invacare Corp.
AVANTI - Cutlery ☆ - Lifetime Hoan Corp.
AVANTI - Cymbals - Ace Product
AVANTI - Doors–glass - Peachtree Doors and Windows Inc.
AVANTI - Floor coverings–carpet and rugs - Coronet Carpets Inc.
AVANTI - Floor coverings–carpet and rugs - Customweave Carpets Inc.
AVANTI - Floor coverings–tile - Kentile Floors Inc.
AVANTI - Footwear - Circle Shoe Co.
AVANTI - Footwear - Unico, Inc.
AVANTI - Furniture - Lane Co. Inc.
AVANTI - Furniture ☆ - Broyhill Furniture Industries, Inc.
AVANTI - Glassware–household ☆ - Denby USA Limited
AVANTI - Hair care products - Conair Corp.
AVANTI - Handbags - A.D. Sutton & Sons Inc.
AVANTI - Hardware ☆ - Advanced Affiliates Inc.
AVANTI - Hearing aids - Beltone Electronics Corp.
AVANTI - Hot tubs–fiberglass - Novi American Inc.
AVANTI - Lamps–desk - Lightolier Inc.
AVANTI - Lighters - Scripto-Tokai Corp.
AVANTI - Lighting fixtures - Big Beam Emergency Systems Inc.
AVANTI - Luggage - Tumi Luggage, Inc.
AVANTI - Motor vehicles–automobiles - AAC Inc.
AVANTI - Novelty items - Avanti Press, Inc.
AVANTI - Occasional tables ☆ - JDI Group, Inc.
AVANTI - Paints - Paris Paint & Varnish Co.
AVANTI - Pens - Union Pen Co.
AVANTI - Prophylactics - London International U.S. Holdings
AVANTI - Recording label - Reflection Sound Studios
AVANTI - Safety products - Trecom Safety Corp.
AVANTI - Sausages - Foodbrands America, Inc.
AVANTI - Skin care products - Veeco Manufacturing Co.
AVANTI - Televisions - Mackle Co.
AVANTI - Toys–stuffed ☆ - Applause, Inc.
AVANTI - Wallpaper - Style-Tex Wallcoverings
AVANTI - Watches - Advance Watch Co. Ltd.
AVANTI - Watches - Nicolet International Inc.
AVANTI ENGINEERING - Screws - Avanti Engineering, Inc.
AVANTI SPORTS - Motor vehicles–automobiles - AAC Inc.
AVANTI VEE - Boats–motor ☆ - Cruisers
AVANTIQUE - Floor coverings–carpet and rugs ☆ - Customweave Carpets Inc.
AVANTOS - Computer software - Avantos Performance Systems Inc.
AVANTRA - Electronic equipment - Miles Inc.
AVANZA - Boats–motor ☆ - Sport-Craft Inc.
AVANZA - Firearms, accessories, and parts - Precision Sales International Inc.
AVANZA - Skin-care products - Avanza Corp.
AVANZA - Whirlpool bath/spa ☆ - Jacuzzi Inc.
AVARAY - Floor coverings–carpet and rugs - Patcraft Mills Inc.
AVARI CREME GLACE - Desserts - Honey Hill Farms Frozen Yogurt
AVARUS - Bedding–linen - Dan River Inc.
AVAS - Audio equipment - AVAS Corp.
AVASOL - Pharmaceutical preparations ☆ - Wesley Pharmacal Co. Inc.

☆ = Now out of production

AVAST - Deodorizers - AgroPlus Inc.
AVATAR - Faucets - Kohler Co.
AVATAR - Health care products ✰ - Wheel Ring Inc.
AVATAR - Hearing aids - Audiotone, Inc.
AVATAR - Paper–bond - Labelon Corp.
AVATAR - Publisher's imprints - Origin Systems, Inc.
AVATAR - Synthesizers–musical instrument - Fender Musical Instruments
AVATAR - Watches ✰ - Siemens Components Inc. (Optoelectronics Div.)
AVATAR COLLECTION - Occasional furniture ✰ - IPF International
AVATAR COMPONENTS CORP. - Motor vehicle parts and accessories - Avatar Components Corp.
AVATREL - Electronic equipment - B.F. Goodrich Co.
AVAZYME - Pharmaceutical preparations ✰ - Wallace Laboratories
AVBLEND - Lubricants - Edzoil Co.
AVC - Antibiotics - Marion Merrell Dow
A.V.C. - Pet products - Glo-Marr Products Inc.
AVC - Recording label - AVC Entertainment Inc.
AVC - Toys - Victor M. Bulgarelli Associates Inc.
A.V.C. - Wines - American Vineyards Co. Inc.
AVCO - Motor vehicles–motor homes ✰ - Avco Aerostructures Inc.
AVCO - Valves–engine - United Pacific Industries Inc.
AVCOAT - Plastics–laminated - Avery Dennison Corp.
AVCOFLEX - Combs - Accessories International
AVCOM - Electronic equipment - Avcom of Virginia Inc.
AVCOM - Photographic equipment - Avcom Systems Inc.
AVCON CORP. - Electrical equipment - Avcon Corp.
AVCON CORPORATION - Electrical equipment - Avcon Corp.
AVCOR - Electronic equipment ✰ - George R. Snell Associates, Inc.
AVD - Medical products - Applied Medical Resources Inc.
AVDEL - Hardware - Textron Aerospace Fasteners
AVE. - See also AVENUE
A.V.E. - Electronic equipment - Rangertone Research Inc.
AVE - Video production - Asiaview Entertainment, Inc.
AVE MARIA - Beads - A.F. Grenci Co. Inc.
$AVE-STRAP - Belts–industrial - Safe-Strap Co., Inc.
AVEBE - Chimes ✰ - Arnold Larson Inc.
AVEC - Hair care products - Demert & Dougherty, Inc.
AVEC AMOUR - Soap and toiletries - Country Lane Enterprises Inc.
AVEDA - Bathroom accessories - Aveda Corp.
AVEDA - Floor coverings–carpet and rugs - Tuftex Carpet Mills, Inc.
AVEDA - Hair care products - A-Veda Corp.
AVEDA PRO - Skin care products - Aveda Corp.
AVEDIS ZILDJIAN - Cymbals - Avedis Zildjian Co.
AVEDON - Jewelry - Park Lane Associates, Inc.
AVEENO - Skin care products - S.C. Johnson & Son, Inc.
AVEENO ANTI-ITCH - Health care products - S.C. Johnson & Son, Inc.
AVEN - Tweezers - Aven International, Inc.
AVENA - Cookies - Sunshine/Salerno Inc.
AVENA - Dishes–china ✰ - Pickard Inc.
AVENCASA - Seafood products–fresh or frozen ✰ - J.F. Clarke Corp.
AVENCASA - Shrimp–fresh or frozen ✰ - Darik Enterprises Inc.
AVENGER - Bicycles ✰ - Roadmaster Corp.
AVENGER - Boats–motor - Penn Yan Boats Inc.
AVENGER - Brushes–paint - Allpro Corp.
AVENGER - Cleaning preparations - ChemPlus
AVENGER - Dirt bike - American Dirt Bike Inc.
AVENGER - Fishing lures ✰ - Church Tackle Co.
AVENGER - Footwear - Reebok International Ltd.
AVENGER - Machine tools ✰ - Cincinnati Machine
AVENGER - Motor vehicles–automobiles - Chrysler Corp. (Dodge Car Div.)
AVENGER - Paints - Paint Equipment People
AVENGER - Photographic equipment - Bogen Photo Corp.
AVENGER - Radios - E.F. Johnson Co.
AVENGER - Skates–roller - Seneca Sports, Inc.
AVENGER - Sporting goods ✰ - Outdoor Technologies Group
AVENGER - Tires - Carlisle Tire & Rubber Co.
AVENGER - Toys–models ✰ - Estes Industries
AVENGER, THE - Boats–motor - Cee Bee Manufacturing Inc.
AVENGER, THE - Toys–airplanes ✰ - Life-Like Products Inc.
AVENGERS - Books–comic - Marvel Entertainment Group, Inc.
AVENGING SPIRIT - Games - Jaleco USA, Inc.
AVENIR - Bicycle parts and accessories - Diamondback
AVENIR - Office furniture–metal - Steelcase Inc.
AVENTA - Automotive parts and accessories - Automatic Equipment Manufacturing Co.
AVENTS - Dairy products - Avents Dairy Inc.

AVENTURA - Automotive parts and accessories ✰ - Lancaster Colony Automotive Group
AVENTURA - Publisher's imprints - Random House, Inc.
AVENTURA - Shoes ✰ - Brown Shoe Co.
AVENTURA - Window shades - Eli Custom Window Treatment, Ltd.
AVENTURA SHOWER AND SOAK - Bathtubs–enameled - Kohler Co.
AVENTYL - Pharmaceutical preparations - Eli Lilly and Co.
AVENUE - See also AVE.
AVENUE - Apparel and accessories - Sutton Shirt Corp.
AVENUE - Flower pots–plastic - Krueger International, Inc.
AVENUE - Glassware–household - Oneida Ltd.
AVENUE - Jewelry–costume - Jewelry Fashions Inc.
AVENUE - Paper–gift wrap - Field Container Corp.
AVENUE - Recording label ✰ - Malaco Records Inc.
AVENUE ACE - Toys - Tonka Corp.
AVENUE-E - Balls–basketball - Voit Corp.
AVENUES - Apparel and accessories - Russ Togs Inc.
AVENUES - Shoes - Interco Inc.
AVERNA - Beverages–alcohol - Paterno Imports, Ltd.
AVERT - Paper–tissue - Kimberly-Clark Corp.
AVERT - Sporting goods - Camp-Cap Products
AVERT II - Sporting goods - Camp-Cap Products
AVERY - Beverages–alcohol - John Gross & Co.
AVERY - Cabinets–wood - Parcraft Distinctive Cabinetry
AVERY - Computer software - Avery Dennison Corp.
AVERY - Floor coverings ✰ - Tarkett, Inc.
AVERY - Furniture - Boling Co.
AVERY - Labels–paper - Avery Label Systems
AVERY - Wallpaper ✰ - Gilford Corp.
AVERY BOARDMAN - Sofas - Carlyle Custom Convertibles Ltd.
AVERY BOARDMAN INTERNATIONAL - Mattresses - Carlyle Custom Convertibles Ltd.
AVERY CARDOZA'S CASINO - Computer software - Cardoza Entertainment, Inc.
AVESTA 2000 - Ophthalmic goods - Lens Dynamics, Inc.
AVESTA 3000 - Ophthalmic goods - Lens Dynamics, Inc.
AVESTA LENZ CARE II CLEANING AND WETTING SYSTEM - Cleaning preparations - Lens Dynamics, Inc.
AVEX - Computer software - AV-Expressions
AVEX BLIND RIVETS - Rivets–metal - Auto Vehicle Parts Co.
AVGARD - Chemical preparations - Rhone-Poulenc Inc.
AVGARD - Trisodium phosphate food cleanser - Rhone-Poulenc Specialty Chemicals Co.
AVI - Dairy products - Avi Food Systems, Inc.
AVI - Recording label - A.V.I. Entertainment Group
AVI-CAKES - Bird feeds - Lafeber Co.
AVI-CAL - Animal feed supplements - Rep-Cal Research Labs
AVI-DINE - Pet products - Bay-Mor Pet Feeds
AVI-DROPS - Pet products - Gerard-Pellham Co.
AVI-ERA - Bird feeds ✰ - Lafeber Co.
AVI-TRAIL - Pet products ✰ - For the Birds
AVI-VITE - Pet products - Rich Health
AVIA - Cabinets - Merillat Industries, Inc.
AVIA - Veterinary pharmaceutical preparations - Nutra-Vet Research Corp.
AVIA 590 - Footwear–athletic ✰ - Avia Athletic Footwear
AVIA 600 - Footwear–athletic ✰ - Avia Athletic Footwear
AVIA AEROBIC 440 - Footwear–athletic ✰ - Avia Athletic Footwear
AVIAN - Pet products - Rolf C. Hagen (USA) Corp.
AVIAN-FARE - Pet products - Reliable Protein Products
AVIAN FARMS - Chickens - Avian Farms Inc.
AVIAN PLUS - Veterinary pharmaceutical preparations - Zoo Med Laboratories, Inc.
AVIAN SCIENCE - Bird feeds - C.M. Volkman Co. Inc.
AVIAN SELECT - Bird feeders - Petco Animal Supplies, Inc.
AVIANCE - Jewelry - Pakula & Co.
AVIANCE - Perfumes - Prince Matchabelli
AVIANCE NIGHT - Skin care products - Prince Matchabelli
AVIANNE - Lotions - W.L. Young Inc.
AVIANT - Veterinary nutritional supplements - Diamond V Mills Inc.
AVIANT A10 - Veterinary nutritional supplements - Diamond V Mills Inc.
AVIANT P10 - Veterinary nutritional supplements - Diamond V Mills Inc.
AVIANT P20 - Veterinary nutritional supplements - Diamond V Mills Inc.
AVIARY - Figurines - Doranne
AVIARY - Sinks–metal - Kohler Co.
AVIATION ADVENTURE - Computer peripheral equipment - Knowledge Adventure, Inc.

✰ = Now out of production

AVIATION COLLECTIONS - Postcards ☆ - Kustom Quality
AVIATION FORM-A-GASKET - Adhesives and sealants - Loctite Corp.
AVIATOR - Infant product - Evenflo Co.
AVIATOR - Ophthalmic goods - Rozin Optical Export Corp.
AVIATOR - Pencils ☆ - Koh-I-Noor, Inc.
AVIATOR - Pet products - Dogloo Inc.
AVIATOR - Playing cards - United States Playing Card Co.
AVIATOR BY ZERO KING - Coats - B.W. Harris Manufacturing Co.
AVIATOR CLOTHING COMPANY - Medical uniforms - Donald J. Wardle
AVIATOR SPORT - Coats - B.W. Harris Manufacturing Co.
AVIATOR'S CLUB, THE - Apparel and accessories - David Mosteller
AVICIDIN - Pharmaceutical preparations - Neorx Corp.
AVICO - Food products - Avico Distributing Inc.
AVID - Bicycle parts and accessories - Avid Enterprises, Inc.
AVID - Golfing equipment - Mega Pro, Inc.
AVID - Latex - Avid Inc.
AVID - Mattresses - Avid Outdoor LLC
AVID - Strollers–baby ☆ - Combi International Corp.
AVID OUTDOOR - Tents - Avid Outdoor LLC
AVIDAY ENTERTAINMENT - Recording label - Ichiban Records, Inc.
AVIDENE - Disinfectants ☆ - Viro Research International Inc.
AVIDESK - Electronic equipment - Avid Corp.
AVIDIA - Computer peripheral equipment - Avidia Systems, Inc.
AVIDIA SYSTEMS - Computer peripheral equipment - Avidia Systems, Inc.
'AVIE - Skin moisturizers/replenishers - Life Energy Resources Ltd.
AVIEMORE - Dinnerware–glass - Franciscan by Johnson Brothers, USA, Inc.
AVIEX - Cleaning preparations - K & W Products
AVIEX - Fuel additives - K & W Products
AVIGAL - Hair care products - Avigal Henna
AVIGNON - Dishes–earthenware ☆ - Denby USA Limited
AVIGNON - Earthenware - Shafford Co. Inc.
AVIGNON - Furniture - CTH/Sherrill Occasional
AVIGNON - Glassware–household - Durand International
AVIGNON - House furnishings - Dan River Inc.
AVIGRON - Glassware–household ☆ - Colony Glass
AVILA - Guitars - Music Imports Ltd.
AVILA - Seafood products–fresh or frozen - J.F. Clarke Corp.
AVILAC - Pet products - 8 in 1 Pet Products Inc.
AVILIFE - Pet products - L/M Animal Farms, Inc.
AVILOCK - Fasteners–snap - Avibank Manufacturing Inc.
AVIMIN - Pet products - Lambert-Kay
AVIMYCIN - Pet products - Lambert-Kay
AVINANTI - Amplifiers ☆ - SJA Industries Inc.
AVINGTON PARK - Furniture ☆ - Henredon Furniture Industries Inc.
AVIOGYRO - Antennas–satellite - KVH Industries, Inc.
AVION - Bicycles - Schwinn Cycling & Fitness Inc.
AVION - Floor coverings–carpet and rugs - Calladium & Marglen
AVION - Luggage - French Co.
AVION - Medical apparatus - Avionix Medical Devices
AVION - Motor vehicles - Avion Coach Corp.
AVION - Trailers–travel - Fleetwood Enterprises, Inc.
AVIONICS - Medical apparatus - Del Mar Avionics
AVIONICS SALES CORPORATION - Electronics stores - Eduardo Marquez
AVIREX - Apparel and accessories - Avirex Ltd.
AVIREX USA - Apparel and accessories - Avirex Ltd.
AVIS CARES CONCIERGE SERVICE - Consulting services - Wizard Co., Inc.
AVIS SPORTS - Fishing tackle - Avis Enterprises, Inc.
AVISTA - Computer software - Peachtree Software Inc.
AVISTART - Bird feeds - L/M Animal Farms, Inc.
AVITA - Penederm Inc.
AVITA - Health care products - Avita Health & Fitness Products Inc.
AVITA 950 - Health care products - Avita Health & Fitness Products Inc.
AVITAR - Bicycle parts and accessories - VII of California, Inc.
AVITAR - Bicycles - Avitar Sports International
AVITRA - Giftware - Avitra Corp.
AVITRON - Pet products - Lambert-Kay
AVIV - Jewelry - Aviv Inc.
AVIVA - Automotive parts and accessories ☆ - Hyundai Motor America
AVIVA - Pharmaceutical preparations - Du Pont Merck Pharmaceutical Co.
AVIVA - Pharmaceutical preparations - Dupont Merck Pharmaceutical Co.
AVIVA - Toys - Avia Group International Inc.
AVIVA JAFFA NEWELS - Fruits–canned ☆ - Caltex Trading, Inc.
AVIX - Batteries - Aviall
AVKAR - Electronic equipment ☆ - General Audio-Visual Inc.
AVL - Chemical preparations - Aviation Laboratories, Inc.
AVLON - Hair care products - Avlon Industries Inc.

AVLOSULFON - Pharmaceutical preparations ☆ - Wyeth-Ayerst Laboratories
AVMAC - Connectors–electrical - At&T Corp.
AVN - Video production - First Methodist Church of Shreveport, Louisiana
AVO - Cigars - Avo Cigars and Avo Uvezian Cigars
AVO - Veterinary pharmaceutical preparations - Breeder's Choice Pet Foods, Inc.
AVO CAT - Pet food - Breeder's Choice Pet Foods, Inc.
AVO-DERM - Dog food - Breeder's Choice Pet Foods, Inc.
AVO-DIETS - Dog food - Breeder's Choice Pet Foods, Inc.
AVO FRESCO - Fruits–frozen - Calavo Growers of California
AVO HEALTH FOOD FOR CATS - Cat food - Breeder's Choice Pet Foods, Inc.
AVO-KING SOUTHWESTERN GUACAMOLE - Sauces - Avo-King International, Inc.
AVO-MAINTENANCE - Pet products - Breeder's Choice Pet Foods, Inc.
AVO-MED - Veterinary pharmaceutical preparations - Glo-Marr Products Inc.
AVO UVEZIAN - Cigars - Uvezian Cigars
AVOCADO - Skin care products - Helga Van Dyke Skin Care
AVOCADO - Tableware–earthenware ☆ - Seymour Mann Inc.
AVOCADO 7 OILS - Skin care products - Orjene Natural Cosmetics
AVOCADO CLENZ - Hair care products - Image Laboratories, Inc.
AVOCET - Giftware - N.S. Gustin Co.
AVOCET - Recording label - Jazz Composer's Orchestra Association Inc.
AVOID - Cleaning preparations - Coughlan Products Corp.
AVOLITES - Switches–electric - U.S. Avo
AVON - Apparel–women's - Bi-Flex International
AVON - Bathroom fixtures - Artesian Industries
AVON - Brooms - Wright-Bernet
AVON - Brushes–paint - Corona Brushes Inc.
AVON - Brushes–paint - Rubberset Co.
AVON - Cabinets–wood ☆ - Kemper
AVON - Cooking utensils–aluminum - Gemco Ware, Inc.
AVON - Floor coverings–carpet and rugs - Stephen-Leedom Carpet Co.
AVON - Furniture - Avon Co.
AVON - Gloves - Avon Glove Corp.
AVON - Health care products - Avon Products, Inc.
AVON - Housewares ☆ - Scio Pottery Co.
AVON - Microphones ☆ - Ercona Corp.
AVON - Playing cards ☆ - United States Playing Card Co.
AVON - Publisher's imprints - Hearst Corp.
AVON - Sporting goods - Avon Marine
AVON - Threads ☆ - International Thread Co.
AVON - Tires - Avon America
AVON - Tires - Cooper Tire & Rubber Co.
AVON COLOR - Cosmetics - Avon Products, Inc.
AVON KIDS - Skin care products - Avon Products, Inc.
AVON LIFE - Vitamins and nutritional supplements - Avon Products, Inc.
AVON LITE - Plumbing fixtures–metal - CR-PL L.P.
AVON PARK - Floor coverings - Mannington Resilient Floors
AVON ROSE - Flatware ☆ - Washington Forge Inc.
AVON STYLE - Apparel and accessories - Avon Products, Inc.
AVON TECHNIQUES - Hair care products - Avon Products, Inc.
AVON ULTIMATE EFFECT - Cosmetics - Avon Products, Inc.
AVONA - Corsets - Abraham & Straus/Jordan Marsh Co.
AVONDALE - Dinnerware–glass - Nikko Ceramics Inc.
AVONDALE - Dishes–china ☆ - WMF/USA
AVONDALE - Dishes–earthenware - Royal China & Porcelain Companies Inc.
AVONDALE - Floor coverings ☆ - Armstrong World Industries, Inc.
AVONDALE - Floor coverings–carpet and rugs - Atlas Carpet Mills Inc.
AVONDALE - Mattresses - Simmons USA
AVONDALE - Thread - Cincinnati Thread Co.
AVONDALE II - Floor coverings - Armstrong World Industries, Inc.
AVONIQUE - Vitamins and nutritional supplements - Armenpharm Ltd.
AVONITE - Rouges - Avonite Inc.
AVONLEA - Floor coverings–carpet and rugs - Barrett Carpet Mills Inc.
AVONLEIGH PLACE - Wallpaper ☆ - Gagne Wallcovering, Inc.
AVOPLEX - Skin care products - Opi Products, Inc.
AVORO - Plates–paper ☆ - Potlatch Corp.
AVOSET - Food products - Avoset Food Corp.
AVP - Resins–synthetic - General Electric Co.
AVR - Suntan lotions - Key West Aloe Inc.
AVRIL - Fabrics - Avtex Fibers Inc.
AVRIL PRIMA - Fabrics ☆ - Avtex Fibers Inc.
AVS - Office accessories - Advac Signs
AVS/EXPRESS - Computer software - Advanced Visual Systems Inc.
AVSEP - Medical apparatus - Del Mar Avionics

☆ = Now out of production

AVSIX - Electronic equipment - J.L. Cooper Electronics
AVSPUN - Thread ✰ - American & Efird, Inc.
AVTEX - Fabrics - Avtex Fibers Inc.
AVTR - Electronic equipment - Teac America, Inc.
AVTRAK - Computer software - Advanced Vehicle Tracking Corp.
AVUS - Computer peripheral equipment - Avus Systems and Peripherals, Inc.
AVVIO - Water–bottled or canned - Whitney Group
AVVIO COLA BIANCA - Soft drinks - Whitney Group
AW - Jewelry - A. Warmbrand Jewelers
AW-SOME - Pharmaceutical preparations ✰ - Bricker Laboratories
AWA - Apparel–athletic - First String, Inc.
AWA - Cleaning preparations - Carbona Products Co.
AWAFLEX - Shingles - Tamko Roofing Products, Inc.
AWAKE - Crocheted and knitted items ✰ - Glen Raven Mills Inc.
AWAKE N ESCAPE - Luggage ✰ - Ronde
AWAKEN FOOD PRODUCTS - Food products - Sweet Earth Natural Foods
AWAKENING - Floor coverings–carpet and rugs - Mattel Carpet & Rug Inc.
AWAKENING - Pharmaceutical preparations - Body Alive International Inc.
AWAKENING SERIES - Recording label - Walsh-Haloska
AWAKENINGS - Greeting cards - American Greetings Corp.
AWAPLAN 170 - Shingles - Tamko Roofing Products, Inc.
AWAPLAN PREMIUM - Shingles - Tamko Roofing Products, Inc.
AWAPUHI - Hair care products - Jheri Redding Products Inc.
AWARD - Clocks - General Time Corp. (Westclox/Seth Thomas Div.)
AWARD - Computer software - Blackbaud, Inc.
AWARD - Cosmetics - Colgate-Palmolive Co.
AWARD - Fishing tackle - Trophy Products Inc.
AWARD - Floor coverings–carpet and rugs - Mohawk Industries Inc.
AWARD - Floor coverings–carpet and rugs ✰ - Barrett Carpet Mills Inc.
AWARD - Floor coverings–carpet and rugs ✰ - Royalweve Carpet Mills
AWARD - Flowers, plants, and seeds - Jacklin Seed
AWARD - Food products - Conagra, Inc.
AWARD - Fruits and vegetables - Yakima Fruit & Cold Storage Co.
AWARD - Insecticides - Ciba-Geigy Corp.
AWARD - Paints - Dehart Paint & Varnish Co.
AWARD - Pens - Sheaffer Holdings Inc.
AWARD - Puzzles - JTG of Nashville
AWARD - Recording label - RCI Records
AWARD - Wigs - Helene Curtis Industries Inc.
AWARD - Window coverings - Award Fabrics Inc.
AWARD - Window shades - Newell Window Furnishing Co.
AWARD 500 - Motor vehicle parts and accessories - Superior Industries International, Inc.
AWARD COLLECTION - Faucets - Peerless Faucet Co. (Plumbing Products Div.)
AWARD CONTINENTAL - Motor vehicles–trucks - Superior Industries International, Inc.
AWARD FEE MONITOR - Computer software - BD Systems, Inc.
AWARD SOFTWARE INTERNATIONAL - Computer software - Award Software International, Inc.
AWARD, THE - Jackets - Howe K. Sipes Co.
AWARD WINNER - Floor coverings–carpet and rugs - Patcraft Mills Inc.
AWARD WINNER'S - Pet products - Gabel's Cosmetics Inc.
AWARDROBE - Uniforms–tailored - Hartmarx Corp.
AWARDS OF DIMENSION - Awards, plaques and medals - Bruce Fox, Inc.
AWARDS OF THE YEAR - Posters ✰ - Stevenson Industries Inc.
AWARE - Drug-testing kit - American Drug Screens Inc.
AWARE - Food-flavoring product - American Flavor & Fragrance Corp.
AWARE - Infant product - Aware Diaper Inc.
AWARE - Paper ✰ - Uarco Inc.
AWARE - Recording label - Gregg Alan Corp.
AWARE - Vegetable oil - Ventura Foods LLC (Lou Ana Division)
AWARE SPEED-OF-SOUND LIBRARY - Computer software - Aware, Inc.
AWARENESS - Greeting cards - Gibson Greetings, Inc.
AWARF SERIES - Toys–airplanes - Hobbico Inc.
AWAY - Deodorants–personal - Colgate-Palmolive Co.
AWAY - Wallpaper - Tattersalls
AWC - Doors–wood - SNE Enterprises Inc.
AWC - Watches - American Watch Case Corp.
AWD - Motor vehicles - Subaru of America, Inc.
AWDP - Postcards - Fotofolio Inc.
AWE-SUM - Spray bottle - Intex Chemical Inc.
AWESOME - Belts - West Unity
AWESOME - Bicycles - Giant Bicycle, Inc.
AWESOME - Cosmetics - Jaclyn Michaels Ltd.
AWESOME - Floor coverings–carpet and rugs - Quaker Inc.

AWESOME ALL-STARS - Chewing gum - Leaf, Inc.
AWESOME ANGELS - Dolls - Tandler Design, Inc.
AWESOME CHICKEN SANDWICH - Sandwiches–prepackaged - Qsc, Inc.
AWESOME COMBINATION - Meat products - Allen Bros., Inc.
AWESOME EGGS - Candy ✰ - R.M. Palmer Co.
AWESOME GAMES - Games - Mark Dale Keener
AWESOME GOLF - Video games - Atari Games Corp.
AWESOME GRAPHICS - T-shirts–women's - Tanles Inc.
AWESOME HOLD - Hair care products - Dial Corp.
AWESOME ORANGE - Fruit drinks–bottled or canned - Green Spot Packaging, Inc.
AWESOMEWEAR - Apparel stores–women's - Awesome Clothing Outlets Inc.
AWI - Computer software - Addison Wesley Longman, Inc.
AWI - Game machines - Video Lottery Technologies, Inc.
AWI - Locks–door - Abloy Security Inc.
AWICK - Wicking - Hooper Industries Inc.
AWL AUTOMATIC WIPER LIGHT - Lighting equipment - Ken-Lor Controls, Inc.
AWL-BRITE - Varnishes - U.S. Paint Corp.
AWL-FAIR - Paints - Grow Group, Inc.
AWLCRAFT - Paints - U.S. Paint Corp.
AWLGARD - Paints - Grow Group, Inc.
AWLGRIP - Adhesives and sealants - Grow Group, Inc.
AWLSTAR - Paints - Grow Group, Inc.
AWNAIR - Window coverings - Awnair Aluminum Awnings
AWNING - Fabrics - Gretchen Bellinger Inc.
AWNING - Floor coverings–carpet and rugs ✰ - Regal Rugs Inc.
AWNLIT - Fabrics–coated - Duracote Corp.
AWNTEX - Vinyl - Astrup Co.
AWNTOP - Fabrics–coated - Duracote Corp.
AWNTUBE - Hardware - Astrup Co.
AWREY - Bakery products - Awrey Bakeries, Inc.
AWREY'S AMERICA'S HOMETOWN BAKERY - Breads - Awrey Bakeries, Inc.
AWREY'S BEST - Bakery products - Awrey Bakeries, Inc.
A.W.S.A. TOURNAMENT - Sporting goods ✰ - Outdoor Technologies Group
AWSCO - Glass–window - AWSCO
AWST - Tape–adhesive ✰ - Arlon, Inc.
A.W.T. - Diagnostic substances ✰ - Warner-Lambert Co.
AWT - Tape–adhesive - Arlon, Inc.
AWT - Turbines - Advanced Wind Turbines, Inc.
AWT 2 - Tape–adhesive - Arlon, Inc.
AWW - Wheels–motor vehicle - Hulcher Enterrpise, Inc.
A.X. - Inks - Specialty Ink Co.
AX - Jewelry - Hallmark Healy Group
AX-1200 SCANTOUCH - computer scanner - Nikon Inc.
AX A DENT - Stain removers - Ryter Corp.
AX-IT - Floor finishing machines–commercial - Betco Corp.
A.X. LLOYD - Apparel and accessories - JBI, Inc.
AX, MAX - Filters–industrial - Surface Combustion, Inc.
AX WAX - Guitars - Super Star Products
AXAREL - Cleaning preparations - Tech Spray, Inc.
AXBAR - Recording label - TMC Productions
AXBRIDGE - Beverages - Inlet Inc.
AXCEL - Musical instrument accessories - Ultimate Support Systems Inc.
AXCELERATOR - Musical instruments - Peavey Electronics Corp.
AXCENT2 - Computer hardware - AMX Corp.
AXCENTWIRE - Computer software - AMX Corp.
AXCESS - Apparel and accessories - Limited Inc.
AXCESS - Computer software - AMX Corp.
AXCESS - Golfing equipment - Triumph Golf Co.
AXCESS 21 - Medical apparatus - Wilson-Cook Medical Inc.
AXCESS GLOBAL - Radio communications equipment - Axcess Global Communications Corp.
AXCIS - Electronic equipment - Axcis Pocket Information Network, Inc.
AXDESIGN - Computer software - AMX Corp.
AXDS - Computer software - Ariel Corp.
AXE - Bowling balls - J.P.F., Inc.
AXE & ARROW - Games - Gamescience
AXE CRADLE - Musical instrument accessories - Dennis William Broersma
AXE HANDLER - Musical instrument accessories ✰ - Herco Products
AXELROD - Food products - Crowley Foods, Inc.
AXEMAN - Abrasive products - American Hone Co.
AXEMAN'S PRIDE - Handles–wood ✰ - Hartwell Brothers Handle Co.
AXENT - Helmets–athletic ✰ - E.D. Bullard Co.
AXESSIMO - Leather goods - Westport Corp.
AXESSORIUM - Sunglasses - Idea Nuova, Inc.
AXI-MAP - Computer software - Axios Products, Inc.

AXIAL - Electronic equipment - Accom, Inc.
AXIAL SERIAL KNOWLEDGE - Electronic equipment - Accom, Inc.
AXIBASIC - Computer software - Cleveland Motion Controls, Inc.
AXIDYNE - Electrical equipment - Tol-O-Matic, Inc.
AXILERATE - Computer hardware - Axil Computer, Inc.
AXIMATE - Computer hardware - Cleveland Motion Controls, Inc.
AXINUS - Lubricants ☆ - Shell Oil Co.
AXIOM - Apparel and accessories - Carter Hawley Hale Stores Inc.
AXIOM - Floor coverings–carpet and rugs - Billy J. Wann, Jr.
AXIOM - Floor coverings–carpet and rugs ☆ - Dorsett Carpet Mills Inc.
AXIOM - Furniture - Axiom
AXIOM - Golfing equipment - Arnold Palmer Golf Co.
AXIOM - Medical equipment - Siemens Medical Systems, Inc.
AXIOM - Prosthetics - Orthomet, Inc.
AXIOM - Telephone apparatus - Gemini Industries, Inc.
AXIOM - Tiles–ceiling - Armstrong World Industries, Inc.
AXIOM - Transformers–electric - Sergio Hamernik
AXIOM II - Floor coverings–carpet and rugs ☆ - Walter Carpet Mills
AXIOM PROJECT MANAGER - Computer software - Marsh Software Systems
AXIOM, THE - Books–comic - Icon Creations
AXION - Detergents - Colgate-Palmolive Co.
AXIS - Apparel–men's - Media Industries
AXIS - Bicycles - Yin Ping Kwan
AXIS - Deodorants–personal - Lever Brothers Co. Inc.
AXIS - Flatware - Dansk International Designs, Ltd.
AXIS - Floor coverings–carpet and rugs ☆ - Regal Rugs Inc.
AXIS - Furniture - Haworth, Inc.
AXIS - Lighting fixtures - Illuminating Concepts, Ltd.
AXIS - Lighting fixtures - Thomas Lighting (Accent Division)
AXIS - Metals - Chris Scott PTC
AXIS - Oils–lubricating - Conklin Co., Inc.
AXIS - Rackets–racquetball - Ektelon
AXIS - Soil conditioner - Eagle-Picher Minerals, Inc.
AXIS - Surgical supplies - Danek Medical, Inc.
AXIS & ALLIES - Games - Milton Bradley Co.
AXLE WORKS - Clothing - New Boys Inc.
AXLELESS - Motor vehicles - DBX Engineering Corp.
AXLESS - Conveyors ☆ - Precision Handling Devices, Inc.
AXO - Paper–photographic ☆ - Eastman Kodak Co.
AXOCET - Analgesics - Altana, Inc. (Savage Laboratories, Div.)
AXOKINE - Pharmaceutical preparations - Regeneron Pharmaceuticals Inc.
AXON - Golfing equipment - Axon Sports, Inc.
AXON - Rackets–racquetball - Ektelon
AXP - Apparel stores–sports - Kinney Shoe Corp.
AXPANDCRETE - Adhesives and sealants ☆ - Anti Hydro International Inc.
AXPANDCRETE S HI-FLOW - Adhesives and sealants - Anti Hydro International Inc.
AXS - Bags–duffel - Photoco, Inc.
AXS - Computer peripheral equipment - Dynaflo Systems, Inc.
AXS - Computer software - Electric Works Corp.
AXSYM - Medical apparatus - Abbott Laboratories
AXSYS APPLICATIONS SYSTEM - Computer software - Information Advantage, Inc.
AXTIVE - Computer software - Axtive Software Corp.
AXTRAX - Music–sheet ☆ - Warner Bros. Publications
AXTRON - Guitars - LPD Music International
AXWIRE - Computer software - AMX Corp.
AXXE - Synthesizers–musical instrument - Fender Musical Instruments
AXXESS+ - Keys - Axxess Technologies Inc.
AXXESS PC - Machinery - Axxess Technologies Inc.
AXXION - Cases–plastic - Axxion Group Corp.
AXXIS - Golfing equipment - Climax Clothing Industries, Inc.
AXYS - Computer software - McCaw Cellular Communications, Inc.
AY CARAMBA - Food products - The Brown Adobe Inc.
AYA - Jewelry - Andin International Inc.
AYA AZRIELANT 18K GOLD - Jewelry - Andin International Inc.
AYD - Golfing equipment - Karsten Solheim
AYDS - Pharmaceutical preparations ☆ - Dep Corp.
AYE - Yeast - Gist-Brocades Food Ingredients Inc.
AYE PORT - Footwear - Im-Link Corp.
AYECUE - Mushrooms - Joseph Caragol Inc.
AYER WAFERS - Candy - Sterling Candy Corp.
AYGESTIN - Pharmaceutical preparations - Wyeth-Ayerst Laboratories
AYINGER - Beverages–alcohol - Merchant du Vin Corp.
AYITIAN FORMULA - Cosmetics - One World, Inc.
AYITIANA - Water–bottled or canned - Wilner Lamour

AYLA'S ORGANICS - Snack foods ☆ - Spectrum Naturals, Inc.
AYLESFORD - Wallpaper - Seabrook Wallcoverings, Inc.
AYNSLEY - Rings–jewelry - Artcarved
AYOTTE'S ARTISTRY IN GLASS - Glassware–household - Ayotte's Artistry in Glass
AYR - Pharmaceutical preparations - B.F. Ascher & Co. Inc.
AYRLYN - Fabrics–nylon ☆ - Rohm and Haas Co.
AYSO - Athletic footwear - Converse Inc.
AYUMI - Computer software - Qualitas Trading Co.
AYURVEDA SCIENCE OF LIFE - Toiletries - Abbas Syed Qutab
AYURVEDIC - Health care products - Auroma International Inc.
AYURVEDIC - Health care products - Nature's Herbs
AYURVEDIC - Tea - Yogi Tea
AZ - Lighting equipment - American Zettler, Inc.
AZ - Pharmaceutical preparations - Hoechst-Roussel Pharmaceuticals Inc.
AZ-KAP - Pharmaceutical preparations ☆ - Keene Pharmaceuticals Inc.
AZ ONE - Recording label - Willis J. Wilson
AZ-PLUS - Apparel and accessories - Tiger Button Co., Inc.
AZ-TUFT - Floor coverings - Azrock Commercial Flooring
AZA - Toys–stuffed - American Zoo and Aquarium Association
AZACTAM - Pharmaceutical preparations - Bristol-Myers Squibb Co.
AZAD - Food products - Bestovall Foods Inc.
AZALEA - Dinnerware–glass ☆ - Nikko Ceramics Inc.
AZALEA - Food products - H.M. Thames Nut House
AZALEA - Vases - Crisa Corp.
AZALEA QUEEN - Food products - Supreme Foods Inc.
AZALEA SPRINGS - Wines - Azalea Springs Wine Co., Inc.
AZALEE - Lipsticks ☆ - Cosmair Inc.
AZAR - Footwear - Azar Industries Inc.
AZAR - Nuts - Azar Nut Co.
AZDEL - Fiberglass-reinforced plastic sheeting - Azdel Inc.
AZDEN - Microphones - Bob White Associates
AZDONE - Analgesics - Central Pharmaceutical Inc.
AZELEX - Skin care products - Allergan, Inc.
AZELON - Brushes - Corona Brushes Inc.
AZIENDA ABBONA - Beverages–alcohol - Trebon Wine & Spirit Corp.
AZIENDA AGRARIA PACINA - Wines - Pellegrini Bros. Wines Inc.
AZIENDA AGRICOLA MAISANO - Wines - Tempo Imports Ltd.
AZIENDA PROVENZA - Beverages–alcohol - Trebon Wine & Spirit Corp.
AZIENDE AGRICOLE APRUTINE - Wines - Tempo Imports Ltd.
AZIMUTH - Antennas–satellite - KVH Industries, Inc.
AZIRONAL - Pharmaceutical preparations ☆ - U.S. Ethicals Inc.
AZIZA - Cosmetics - Prince Matchabelli
AZIZA CLEAR AND NATURAL - Cosmetics - Prince Matchabelli
AZLIDON - Pharmaceutical preparations ☆ - U.S. Ethicals Inc.
AZLIMED - Pharmaceutical preparations ☆ - U.S. Ethicals Inc.
AZLIN - Antibiotics - Miles Inc.
AZLYCORT - Pharmaceutical preparations ☆ - U.S. Ethicals Inc.
AZLYSPRAY - Pharmaceutical preparations ☆ - U.S. Ethicals Inc.
AZLYTAL - Pharmaceutical preparations ☆ - U.S. Ethicals Inc.
AZMADRINE - Pharmaceutical preparations ☆ - U.S. Ethicals Inc.
AZMIR - Floor coverings–carpet and rugs - Foreign Accents
AZO - Floor coverings - Tek Stil Concepts Inc.
AZO - Paper–photographic - Eastman Kodak Co.
AZO CRANBERRY - Vitamins and nutritional supplements - M. Polymedica Corp.
AZO-ENTUSIL - Pharmaceutical preparations ☆ - Rhone-Poulenc Rorer Pharmaceuticals Inc.
AZO GANTANOL - Analgesics - Roche Laboratories
AZO GANTRISIN - Analgesics - Roche Laboratories
AZO-JEFAZOLE - Health care products ☆ - Halsey Drug Co. Inc.
AZO-KOTE - Fertilizer - Encore Technologies, Inc.
AZO-MANDELAMINE - Pharmaceutical preparations ☆ - Parke-Davis
AZO-METHALATE - Pharmaceutical preparations ☆ - Vortech Pharmaceuticals
AZO-METHENAMINE MANDELATE - Pharmaceutical preparations - C.S. Ruckstuhl Co. Inc.
AZO-STANDARD - Analgesics - M. Polymedica Corp.
AZO-SULFAGAN - Pharmaceutical preparations - C.S. Ruckstuhl Co. Inc.
AZO-SULFAPYRIDINE - Pharmaceutical preparations - Robinson Laboratories Inc.
AZO-SULFISOCON - Pharmaceutical preparations - Consolidated Midland Corp.
AZO TEST STRIPS - Pharmaceutical preparations - M. Polymedica Corp.
AZO-TRUXAZOLE - Pharmaceutical preparations ☆ - C.O. Truxton Inc.
AZODINE - Pharmaceutical preparations ☆ - Vortech Pharmaceuticals
AZOGRAPH - Paper–carbon - A.B. Dick Co.

☆ = Now out of production

AZOLA BABY BASS - Musical instruments - Stephen J. Azola
AZOLID - Analgesics - Rhone-Poulenc Rorer Pharmaceuticals Inc.
AZON - Insulating materials - Azon USA, Inc.
AZONE - Tranquilizers ☆ - Du Pont Pharmaceuticals
AZOOMER - Fabrics - Dan River Inc.
AZORES - Shoes - Soft Shoe, Inc.
AZOSTIX - Chemical preparations - Miles Inc.
AZOSUL - Pharmaceutical preparations ☆ - Solvay Pharmaceuticals Inc.
AZOTREX - Pharmaceutical preparations ☆ - Bristol-Myers Squibb Co.
AZPAN - Pharmaceutical preparations ☆ - Zenith Laboratories, Inc.
AZRA - Recording label - Ready to Rock Records
AZRA - Whirlpools - Lasco Products Group
AZRAEL'S TEAR - Computer software - Mindscape Software Inc.
AZROCK - Floor coverings - Azrock Commercial Flooring
AZROCK LUXURY - Floor coverings - Azrock Commercial Flooring
AZRON - Computer software - Azron, Inc.
AZTEC - Abrasive products - Norton Co.
AZTEC - Aircraft ☆ - New Piper Aircraft, Inc.
AZTEC - Artists' materials - Leisurecrafts
AZTEC - Blinds–vertical - Steelwood Extruding Corp.
AZTEC - Cabinets ☆ - Classic Bath Products
AZTEC - Cereal - U.S. Mills, Inc.
AZTEC - Computer software - Arizona Packaging Software Inc.
AZTEC - Darts and dart games - Dart World Inc.
AZTEC - Dinnerware–glass ☆ - Metlox Pottery Shoppe
AZTEC - Dinnerware–glass ☆ - Nikko Ceramics Inc.
AZTEC - Dinnerware–glass ☆ - Salem China Co.
AZTEC - Dishes–china - Waterford Wedgewood USA, Inc.
AZTEC - Fireplaces ☆ - Majestic Co.
AZTEC - Floor coverings - American Floor Products Co. Inc.
AZTEC - Floor coverings - Congoleum Corp.
AZTEC - Floor coverings–carpet and rugs - Foreign Accents
AZTEC - Floor coverings–carpet and rugs - Quaker Inc.
AZTEC - Floor coverings–carpet and rugs ☆ - Regal Rugs Inc.
AZTEC - Floor coverings–tile - WesekPalley Tile Inc.
AZTEC - Food products - Sauces & Salsas, Ltd.
AZTEC - Garden furniture–metal - Samsonite Furniture Co. (Consumer Products Div.)
AZTEC - Handles–wood - Sequatchie Handle Works Inc.
AZTEC - Heating panels - Marley Electric
AZTEC - Insecticides - Bayer Corp. (Agriculture Div.)
AZTEC - Lamps ☆ - Lamplight Farms, Inc.
AZTEC - Recording label - AKO Records
AZTEC - Tiles–ceramic - Monarch Tile Inc.
AZTEC - Vitamins and nutritional supplements - Michael's Naturopatic Products
AZTEC - Wallpaper ☆ - Pickhardt & Siebert USA Inc.
AZTEC - Water–bottled or canned ☆ - Hinckley & Schmitt (Bottled Water Group)
AZTEC BASIC - Security devices - Aztec Security Products

AZTEC-COVE - Heaters - Marley Electric
AZTEC FLEXEL - Heating system - Marley Electric
AZTEC GOLD - Dinnerware–glass ☆ - Nikko Ceramics Inc.
AZTEC HARVESTS - Coffee - Thanksgiving Coffee Co.
AZTEC LEATHERWORKS - Handwoven leather sandals and shoes - International Imports
AZTEC QUALITY EYEWEAR - Sunglasses - Glennco Marketing, Inc.
AZTEC RTA - Cabinets - Classic Bath Products
AZTEC SECRET - Food products - Hemisphere Minerals
AZTEC SILVER - Paper–gift wrap - Heller & Usdan Inc.
AZTEC TERRA COTTA - Outdoor light - Lamplight Farms, Inc.
AZTECA - Cookware - Azteca Foods, Inc.
AZTECA - Floor coverings–carpet and rugs - Burlington House Carpets
AZTECA - Health care products - D'Franssia Corp.
AZTECA - Liquors - David Sherman Corp.
AZTECA - Recording label ☆ - Alshire International Inc.
AZTECA DE ORO - Brandy - Domecq Importers Inc.
AZTECA PICANTE - Salsa - Azteca Foods, Inc.
AZTECH WARE - Computer software - A to Z Systems, Inc.
AZTECS, THE - T-shirts–children's - Cross at the Green...Not in Between Enterprises
AZTEK - Games - Stephan Daubney
AZTEK - Paint sprayers - Eastman Kodak Co.
AZTLAN - Apparel and accessories - Aztlan Graphics
AZTRA - Mouldings - ABT Co., Inc.
AZU-QUITA - Sweeteners–artificial - Dieta Foods, Inc.
AZUL - Apparel and accessories - Apparel Ventures, Inc.
AZUL - Hair care products - Chenice Beverly Hills
AZULEJERA AKCORENSE - Tiles–terrazzo - Imperial Tile and Marble Corp.
AZULEV - Tiles–ceramic - United Ceramic Tile Corp.
AZULFIDINE - Pharmaceutical preparations - Kabi Pharmacia Inc.
AZUMAYA - Egg rolls, noodles, tofu, etc. - Azumaya Inc.
AZUR - Dinnerware–glass ☆ - WMF/USA
AZUR - Watches - Pearl Times, Inc.
AZURA - Dishes–china - Taylor, Smith & Taylor Co.
AZURA STS - Shoes ☆ - Hyde Athletic Industries Inc.
AZURE - Jewelry–precious - Hoover & Strong, Inc.
AZURE HAND PAINTED - Wallpaper - Artique Design
AZURE SCROLL - Glassware–household ☆ - Culver Glass Inc.
AZURE SEAS - Christmas tree ornaments - Cracker Box Inc.
AZURE TECHNOLOGIES - Computer software - Azure Technologies, Inc.
AZUREE - Perfumes - Estee Lauder Inc.
AZUREL - Rings–jewelry - L & M Castings Inc.
AZURINE - Fabrics - Eclipse International
AZURINE - Toys–stuffed ☆ - Gund, Inc.
AZUVI - Tiles–ceramic - Capitol Tile Import Co.
AZZALI - Oars ☆ - Phoenix Products Inc.
AZZURO BLUE - Glass–plate - Sasaki
AZZURRO - Giftware - Sasaki
AZZURRO - Pasta - LaPace Imports, Inc.

B

Addresses and phone numbers for the companies cited in the brands below
are available in the Company Listings section immediately following the brands listings.

B - Apparel - BB Acquisition Corp.
B - Apparel and accessories - Bison Baseball Inc.
#B - Apparel and accessories - James Ronald Scriber
B - Clothing - Boathouse Row Sports, Ltd.
B - Desserts - Boccone's Inc.
B - Floor coverings–carpet and rugs - Bashian Bros., Inc.
B - Floor coverings–carpet and rugs - Beaulieu of America, Inc.
B - Furniture - Baker, Knapp & Tubbs
B - Glassware–household - Guernsey Glass Co. Inc.
B - Hair care products - Big Beans, Inc.
B - Hair care products - Dial Corp.
B - Jewelry - CJC Holdings, Inc.
B - Jewelry - RasDiam Inc.
B - Jewelry - Benjamin Singer
B - Luggage - Boyt L.P.
B - Machinery - Belgium Tool and Die Co.
B - Medical products - Birtcher Medical Systems Inc.
B - Posters ✰ - Super Products, Inc.
B - Shirts - Maurice T. Saffor
B - Signs - Advantus, Corp.
B - Skin care products - Dri-Kleen, Inc.
B - Wines - Bridgeview Vineyards, Inc.
B-1 - Bronze products - Magnolia Metal Corp.
B-1, C & N-ACETYL CYSTEINE - Vitamins and nutritional supplements - Vitamin Research Products Inc.
B-1 NUCLEAR BOMBER - Games ✰ - Avalon Hill Game Co.
B-4 - Cleaning preparations–carpet and rug - Windsor Wax Co. Inc.
B-5 PANTETHINE - Vitamins and nutritional supplements - Vitamin Research Products Inc.
B-7 CHEMSEAL - Automotive repair shops–transmission - Berryman Products Inc.
B-8 - Cymbals - Atlas Accordions Inc.
B-8T SPECIAL FORMULA - Cymbals - Jim Atlas Cymbal Works
B-9 CHEMDIP - Automotive parts and accessories - Berryman Products Inc.
B-11 LUBREX - Automotive parts and accessories - Berryman Products Inc.
B-12 CHEMTOOL - Carburetors - Berryman Products Inc.
B-12 PLEX - Pharmaceutical preparations ✰ - Vortech Pharmaceuticals
B-17 - Fishing lures - B-17 Fly Tackle Ltd.
B-17 - Games - Monarch Avalon, Inc.
B-17 QUEEN OF THE SKIES - Games - Avalon Hill Game Co.
B-20 - Sunglasses - Bausch & Lomb Inc.
B-20 CM - Sunglasses - Bausch & Lomb Inc.
B-22 - The Stroh Brewery Co.
B-33 - Automotive parts and accessories - Berryman Products Inc.
B-50 GEL - Vitamins and nutritional supplements - J.R. Carlson Laboratories Inc.
B-52 - Stereos - E.T.I. Sound Systems Inc.
B-105 - Cleaning preparations ✰ - Omega Products Corp.
B-200 - Thermostats - Bilbee Controls, Inc.
B ACTIVE FASHIONS - Dolls - Mattel, Inc.
B AN' G - Seasonings - B & G Foods Inc.
B & A - Health care products - Eastern Research Laboratories
B & B - Containers - B & B Manufacturing Co., Inc.
B & B - Footwear–men's - Baker-Benjes, Inc.
B & B - Hair care products - B & B Distributors
B & B - Jewelry - B & B Jewelry Manufacturing

B & B - Leather goods - Brown and Bigelow Inc.
B. & B. - Office supplies ✰ - JM Co.
B. & B. LTD. - Giftware - Baekgaard Ltd.
B & C - Nuts and bolts ✰ - Brink & Cotton
B & D - Housewares - Barth-Dreyfuss of California
B & D - Window coverings - Vertical Blind Factory
B. & D. BEAUCHAMP - Apparel–men's ✰ - Edison Brothers Stores, Inc.
B & D GOURMET MARKET - Housewares - Barth-Dreyfuss of California
B & F - Beverages–alcohol - Margolis Wines & Spirits
B & G - Extracts, coloring - Diamond Crystal Salt Co.
B & G - Giftware - Royal Copenhagen Porcelain Inc.
B & G - Nautical instruments - IMI Electronics, Inc.
B & G - Pickles - Bloch & Guggenheimer, Inc.
B & G - Portable water fountain - B & G Equipment Co.
B & G - Wines ✰ - Seagram's Chateau & Estate Wines Co.
B & H - Deodorizers - Travaco Laboratories Inc.
B & H - Pizza ✰ - B & H Pizza Co.
B & H - Projectors–photographic - Eiki International Inc.
B & I - Health care products ✰ - CTS Laboratories Inc.
B & J - Antiseptics ✰ - Pfeiffer Pharmaceuticals Inc.
B & J BARTLES & JAYMES - Wine coolers - Ernest and Julio Gallo Winery
B & K - Audio equipment - GNP Audio Video Inc.
B & K - Corned beef - Berns & Koppstein
B & L - Adhesives and sealants - Brummer & Lundeen Diversified Inc.
B & M - Baked beans–canned - Pet Inc.
B & M - Window shades, shutters, and blinds - B & M Venetian Blinds Inc.
B & N - Jewelry–precious - B & N Jewelry, Inc.
B & O - Electronic equipment - Bang & Olufsen of America Inc.
B & O NO. 16A - Pharmaceutical preparations - M. Polymedica Corp.
B & P - Office supplies - Boorum & Pease Co.
B & R - Apparel–children's - Garward Associates Inc.
B & R - Bakery products - Omaha Bakers Supply Co.
B & R - Furniture ✰ - Barden & Robeson Corp.
B & R - Processed fruits - B & R Packing Co.
B & R MICROCONTROL - Hardware - B & R Industrial Automation Corp.
B & R PUBLISHING - Publisher's imprints - Factory Beat Records Inc.
B & S - Breads - Morabito Baking Co. Inc.
B & S - Musical instruments - Custom Music Co.
B & T - Cough medicines - Boericke & Tafel
B & V - Food products - International Bakers Services Inc.
B & W - Electronic equipment ✰ - H.P. Marketing Corp.
B & W - Fruit juices - Florida Select Citrus Inc.
B & W - Sporting goods ✰ - Bremer Manufacturing Co. Inc.
B & W EXTRA - Cigarettes - Brown & Williamson Tobacco Corp.
B & W SUN CURED - Tobacco–chewing or smoking - Brown & Williamson Tobacco Corp.
B-ATLAS - Recording label - Jody Record Corp.
B-B-BATS - Candy - Gilliam Candy Brands
B B BIRDS BREW - Beverages–malt - Sports Beers L.C.
B-B-S - Shortening - Karlshamns USA Inc.
B. B. SHOTZ - Beverages–alcohol - M.S. Walker Inc./Seacoast
B BAD - T-shirts–women's - Wholesale Fitness Inc.
B BALTIMORE PICTURES - Apparel and accessories - Baltimore Pictures, Inc.
B BERNARDS, INC. - Furniture - Bernards, Inc.
B-BETWEEN - Vitamins and nutritional supplements - J.R. Carlson Laboratories Inc.

✰ = Now out of production

165

B BIND-A-BOOK - Binders - Bind-A-Book Inc.

B BIO LUC - Eyeglasses - Bio Luc USA Inc.

B BIOMIXOTEK - Health care products - Optimox Corp.

B-BITES - Vitamins and nutritional supplements - Twinlab

B. BLASS - Apparel and accessories - Tropical Garment Manufacturing Co.

B BLEYER INDUSTRIES, INC. - Toys - Bleyer Industries (Peoria Plastics Div.)

B BLOND AMERICA - Apparel–athletic - Capital Distribution, Inc.

B-BOP'S - Potatoes - B-Bop's, Inc.

B BOURGEAU-RICHARDS - Artists' materials - Bourgeau B. Richards Collection

B' BOX - Skin care products - Michel Roochel

B BRAUM'S - Eggs - Braum Ice Cream Stores, Inc.

B BRIGGS - Bathroom accessories - Briggs Plumbing Products, Inc.

B-BRO - Scarves - B-Bro, Inc.

B. BRONSON - Apparel and accessories - Bronson's L.A. Action, Inc.

B. BROWN PRODUCTIONS - Recording label - MCA Universal Studios

B BRUMLEVE CANVAS PRODUCTS - Tents - Brumleve Industries, Inc.

B BTI - Batteries - Battery Technology Inc.

B BUCCANEERS - Paper products - Salem Professional Baseball Club, Inc.

B-BURGER - Food products - Dairy Cheer Stores

B. C. AMES - Gauging instruments - Arthur H. Gaebel Inc.

B-C-BID - Vitamins and nutritional supplements - Geriatric Pharmaceutical Corp.

B C COVER - Paper products - Fox River Paper Co.

B C CREATIONS - Linen - B & C Creations

B. C. LIFE - Cleaning preparations - McNett Corp.

B. C. RICH - Guitars - Class Acts

B-CAP - Connectors–electronic - Buchanan Construction Products, Inc.

B-CAPSAI - Pharmaceutical preparations - Bristol-Myers Squibb Co.

B-CASUAL - Apparel–women's - Cupid Foundations Inc.

B-CEE 50 - Pharmaceutical preparations ☆ - Legere Pharmaceuticals Inc.

B-CLEAN - Cleaning preparations - Build-All Corp.

B-CODER - Computer software - Tal Technologies, Inc.

B-COLOR - Hair coloring preparations - Vienna Beauty Products Co.

B-COMPLEET - Vitamins and nutritional supplements - J.R. Carlson Laboratories Inc.

B-COMPLEX - Pharmaceutical preparations - Physician Sales & Service

B-COMPLEX - Vitamins and nutritional supplements - Uptime

B-D - Medical apparatus - Becton, Dickinson and Co.

B-D - Wallpaper - Brod-Dugan Co./Sherwin Williams Co.

B-D-ACRYLASTIC - Paints - Brod-Dugan Co./Sherwin Williams Co.

B. D. BAGGIES - Apparel and accessories - Damon Creations Inc.

B D C USA - Sporting goods - Black Diamond Equipment, Ltd.

B-D PENTHOUSE - Paints - Brod-Dugan Co./Sherwin Williams Co.

B. DALTON - Book stores - B. Dalton Bookseller Inc.

B. DALTON JR. - Book stores - B. Dalton Bookseller Inc.

B. DAVID - Jewelry - B. David Co.

B. DE CHATELLIAC - Beverages–alcohol - Hiram Walker & Sons, Inc.

B. DESVIGNES - Wines - Winesellers Ltd.

B-DOX - Pharmaceutical preparations - Lannett Co. Inc.

B-DPRS - Diagnostic apparatus - Leonard R. Derogatis

B-E-C-Z - Pharmaceutical preparations - Republic Drug Co. Inc.

B-ELEGANT - Pet product - B-Elegant Products

B ELITES - Apparel and accessories - Negro Leagues Baseball Museum, Inc.

B F EXPORTS - Apparel and accessories ☆ - Ajanta Enterprises

B. F. GOODRICH - Tires - Uniroyal Goodrich Tire Co.

B. F. MCKERNIN - Metals - B.F. McKernin Co. Inc.

B-FAMILY - Yeast - Modern Products, Inc.

B. FAMOUS ON STAGE - Computer software - New Stuff Inc.

B-FREE - Chemical preparations - Midwest Industrial Supply, Inc.

B-G - Pickles - Castle Food Products

B. GELAS ET FILS - Beverages–alcohol - Paterno Imports, Ltd.

B-GOLD STUDIO - Apparel–women's - Bimoteur Inc.

B-GRIP SILICA - Automotive parts and accessories - Bridgestone/Firestone, Inc.

B-GUARD - Vitamins and nutritional supplements - Schiff Products, Inc.

B HIP - Shirts - Bodacious Apparel, Inc.

B I A PROFESSIONAL - Computer software - Strohl Systems, Inc.

B-I-N - Paints - William Zinsser & Co. Inc.

B. IDEAS - Jewelry - Brilliant I.D.E.A.S. Inc.

B IN B - Food products - Pillsbury Co.

B IN KEYSTONE - Stationery ☆ - Mead Corp.

B. J. HOLLADAY - Beverages–alcohol - Mccormick Distilling Co., Inc.

B-JECT 100 - Pharmaceutical preparations - Hyrex Pharmaceuticals

B-JEWELED - Trimmings–fabric ☆ - Novtex Corp.

B-K - Archery equipment - Archer Sports Inc.

B-K LIGHTING - Electric lighting equipment - B-K Lighting, Inc.

B KENMPO B - Shirts - Bowie Enterprises

B/L - Aluminum doors, sidelights - Unique Industries

B. L. & V. - Bakery products - International Bakers Services Inc.

B. L. O. & V. - Bakery products - International Bakers Services Inc.

B-LEVEL - Pharmaceutical preparations ☆ - DDI Pharmaceuticals Inc.

B LINE - Bulletin boards–cork - Staver Westport Inc.

B LINE - Paper–book - Butterick Co. Inc.

B-LINE - Toys - Processed Plastic Co.

B-LINE SYSTEMS INC. - Metal hardware - B-Line Systems, Inc.

B-LUX - Luggage - Hunting World, Inc.

B MAJOR ROCK 'N' ROLL GEAR - Apparel and accessories - B Major Inc.

B MAX - Men's jackets, pants, shorts, etc. - In Private Inc.

B-MAX - Microscopes ☆ - Olympus America Inc.

B-MAXI - Vitamins and nutritional supplements - Sundown Vitamins, Inc.

B. MEV - Shoes - Bernie Mev Shoes Inc.

B. MICHAEL - Hats - Aldo Hat Corp.

B. MOSS CLOTHING COMPANY - Apparel and accessories - Moray, Inc.

B. MOSS CLOTHING COMPANY AROUND SINCE NINETEEN THIRTY-NINE - Apparel and accessories - Moray, Inc.

B-NATURAL - Apparel–women's - Cupid Foundations Inc.

B-NATURAL - Vitamins and nutritional supplements ☆ - Nature's Way Products, Inc.

B NATURAL TOTAL BODY MOISTURIZER - Skin care products - B-Natural Products

B-O-D-Y XPRESSIONS - Apparel–women's - Urban Issue, Inc.

B-O-O-K-M-A-N - Computers–micro - Sherwin M. Borsuk

B-OK - Health care products - Bissell Inc.

B ORIGINAL - Apparel–women's - Joseph and Feiss Co.

B-PENDULES - Clocks - Dilliplane Sales Inc.

B. PEPPER PLUS - Spices and extracts - Continnuus

B-PLEX - Pet products - Aquatronics-Filtronics

B-PLEX - Pharmaceutical preparations - Goldline Laboratories, Inc.

B-PLUS - Thread ☆ - Belding Heminway Co. Inc.

B-PLUS - Vitamins and nutritional supplements - Enzyme Process Co. Inc.

B PLUS - Vitamins and nutritional supplements - Phoenix Unlimited, Inc.

B. PORTNOY - Musical instrument accessories - B. Portnoy Clarinet Accessories

B-POTEN - Vitamins and nutritional supplements - Vita-Fore Products Co.

B-P'S - Ostomy product - Torbot-Gricks

B-R - Housewares - Melvin E. Acott

B-R BEST RESULT - Enamels ☆ - Blue Ribbon Paint Co.

B-REDI/RED HEARTS/RED ROOSTERS - Vitamins and nutritional supplements - Reese Chemical Co.

B. ROBERT'S COUNTRY OVEN RECIPES - Food products - Susan L. Lurz

B-ROW, INC. - Educational materials - B-Row

B-S-P - Pharmaceutical preparations - Legere Pharmaceuticals Inc.

B SAFE ANTI-SLIP FORMULA - Chemical preparations - Capital Chemical Corp.

B. SCENE - Clothing - MGRR, Inc.

B-SCORBIC - Pharmaceutical preparations - Pharmics Inc.

B SHARPE - Coats–down-filled - Sharpe Manufacturing Co.

B-SLIM - Vitamins and nutritional supplements - Twinlab

B-SMOOTH - Skin care products - Waverly Beauty Products

B-SOFT - Skin care products - Waverly Beauty Products

B. STONE - Jewelry - B. Stone Jeweler

B-STRESS - Vitamins and nutritional supplements - Solaray

B-STRESS A.M. - Vitamins and nutritional supplements - Solaray

B-STRESS P.M. - Vitamins and nutritional supplements - Solaray

B. STUART & CO. - Apparel and accessories - B. Stuart & Co., Inc.

B-TAP - Electrical equipment - Buchanan Construction Products, Inc.

B-TOOLS - Computer software - American Star Software Systems, Inc.

B-TRIM - Pharmaceutical - American Laboratories Inc.

B-TWEEN - Cleaning preparations ☆ - Duchess Royale Inc.

B-U-C-K-Y - Pillows - Bucky Products Inc.

B-U-G KILLER - Insecticides - Devpro Machine Inc. (Insectocutor Div.)

B UNEEK - Fabrics - Embroidery Systems International, Inc.

B-V - Paper punches - Bonney-Vehslage Tool Co.

B-VAT - Ophthalmic apparatus - Mentor O & O Inc.

B-VAT II - Medical apparatus - Mentor O & O Inc.

B-VIT - Pharmaceutical preparations ☆ - Bluco Inc.

B-VITE - Pharmaceutical preparations - Rugby Laboratories Inc.

B W - Pumps - Blue White Industries

B. W. M. BENN - Harpsichords - B.W.M. Benn Harpsichords

B WARE - Apparel and accessories - Bugle Boy Industries, Inc.

B-WEST - Firearms, accessories, and parts - B-West Imports, Inc.

☆ = Now out of production

B-WING - Computer software - Lucasfilm Ltd.

B-WING FIGHTER - Toys - Lucasfilm Ltd.

B. YOUNG - Apparel and accessories - Texcraft International, Inc.

B. YOUNG - Footwear - Tempo Enterprises Inc.

B. +ZOL - Apparel–women's - B. Zol Inc.

B2 - Amplifiers–musical instrument - Pearce Amplification Ltd.

B2 - Surfboards - Earth & Ocean Sports, Inc.

B2-BASIC BROWNIE - Bakery products - Boulder Brownie Co.

B3 - Apparel and accessories - Bikes, Blades & Boards Inc.

B3 - Jewelry - HVR, Inc.

B4 SPORT - Apparel and accessories - Finish Line, Inc.

B8 - Bird feeds - Metz Farms

B8 - Staplers - Stanley-Bostitch Inc.

B12 RED WONDER VITAMIN - Vitamins and nutritional supplements - Freeda
Vitamins Inc.

B52 - Apparel and accessories - Ruben Archilla

B500B - Audio equipment - ADA Signal Processors Inc.

B2000 - Motor vehicles–automobiles ☆ - Mazda Motor of America Inc.

B2200 - Motor vehicles–automobiles - Mazda Motor of America Inc.

B2600 - Motor vehicles–automobiles - Mazda Motor of America Inc.

B4000 - Motor vehicles–automobiles - Mazda Motor of America Inc.

BA-A-ALLERINA WOOL - Fabrics–wool - Karyl Lynn Buchholz

BA-BA BOTTLE - Infant product - Pacesetter

BA BA LOO - Pet products ☆ - Dogloo Inc.

BA CLOWN - Dolls ☆ - Totsy Manufacturing Co., Inc.

BA MINI AIR CARTON STAPLER - Staplers - Salco, Inc.

BA-SA-KA - Potato chips - Adeline's Gourmet Foods

BA TAMPTE - Pickles - SWB Co. Inc.

B.A. TREE - Sporting goods - Hunter's Edge, Inc.

BAA BAA BLANKIE - Toys–stuffed ☆ - Gund, Inc.

BAA BAA-Q'S - Dog food - Monfort, Inc.

B.A.A. BOSTON MARATHON - Jewelry - Boston Athletic Association

BAADE II - Jewelry - Mary Ann Paul

BAARTMANS - Bakery products - Holland-American Importing Co. Inc.

BAB - Exercising equipment - American Athletic Inc.

BAB-O - Cleaning preparations - Tri-Par Corp.

BABA YAGA AND THE MAGIC GEESE - Computer software ☆ - Knowledge
Adventure

BABALOT US - Sporting goods - Georgia's Tennis

BABALU - Cigars - Babalu, Inc.

BABAR - Handbags - Dover Handbag Corp.

BABAR - Toys–stuffed - Gund, Inc.

BABAR - Toys–stuffed - Toy Works, Inc.

BABA'S MARKETPLACE - Decorations - BARD International, Inc.

BABB - Jewelry - D & W Jewelry Manufacturing Inc.

BABBITT - Clarinet and saxophone mouthpieces - J.J. Babbitt Co. Inc.

BABBITT SUPREME - Clarinet and saxophone mouthpieces - J.J. Babbitt Co.
Inc.

BABBLE - See TITTLE TATTLE

BABBLE - Games - Lewis Galoob Toys, Inc.

BABCO - Bench vises, bolt cutters, etc. - Babcock Manufacturing Co.

BABCOCK - Wines - Babcock Enterprises, Inc.

BABCOCK & BABCOCK - Salad dressings–bottled - Melba Food Specialties
Inc.

BABE - Perfumes - Faberge Co.

BABE BEAR - Toys–stuffed ☆ - Dakin Inc.

BABE BEE - Toys–automobiles - Cox Products Inc.

BABE-CHUCKS - Health care products - Pratt Medical Inc.

BABE EASE - Health care products - Healthteam

BABE-EASE - Health care products - Labeltape Meditect Inc.

BABE EASE COLLECTION - Infant product - Pacesetter

BABE-N-SUIT - Bathing suits - Peter C. Tomassetti

BABE RUTH - Dolls ☆ - Effanbee Doll Corp.

BABE RUTH - Sporting goods - CMG Worldwide

BABE RUTH - Toys - Empire of Carolina Inc.

BABE SHADES - Apparel–children's - USA Sport Eyewear

BABE, THE - Frames–picture - Framemica Co.

BABEE - Cold remedies - Pfeiffer Pharmaceuticals Inc.

BABEL - Recording label - Jazz Composer's Orchestra Association Inc.

BABES - Knit goods - Infanta Knitting Mills

BABES IN THE HOOD - Dolls - Well-Made Toy Manufacturing Corp.

BABES IN TOYLAND - Games ☆ - Milton Bradley Co.

BABETTA - Mopeds ☆ - American Jawa Ltd.

BABETTE - Chocolate bars ☆ - Dae Julie, Inc.

BABETTE - Dolls ☆ - Effanbee Doll Corp.

BABETTE - Dolls ☆ - Goldberger Doll Manufacture Co.

BABETTE - Ophthalmic goods ☆ - Luxottica

BABIBAGS - Bags - Romar International Corp.

BABIBEAR SCRUBS - Uniforms–tailored - Richard D. Crawshaw

BABIES' ALLEY - Baby bottles, and pacifiers - LaRue Distributors, Inc.

BABIES' ALLEY - Infant product - La Rue International, Inc.

BABIES & BOWS COLLECTIBLES - Dolls - Mary Beth Chamberlain

BABIES REST - Publisher's imprints - Weingart Design Inc.

BABINEAU - Food products - Wally Sea Products Corp.

BABO 4-IN-1 - Fabric binding - B.T.B. Corp.

BABOL - Racket grips - Babolat

BABOLAT - Sports watches and caps ☆ - Babolat

BABOO - Toys - Saban Entertainment, Inc.

BABOOM - Apparel–children's - Bambini Elegante Inc.

BABOR - Skin care products - Dr. Babor Natural Cosmetics

BABOR 28 - Perfumes - Dr. Babor Natural Cosmetics

BABOR MEN - Perfumes - Dr. Babor Natural Cosmetics

BABORISAN - Skin care products - Dr. Babor Natural Cosmetics

BAB'S - Mayonnaise - Orval Kent Food Co., Inc.

BABS - Ophthalmic goods ☆ - Luxottica

BABS - Yarn - Melrose Yarn Co. Inc.

BABUETTE CREATIONS - Jewelry - Diamond & Jewelry Syndicate Corp.

BABY - Baby foods - Chiquita Brands, Inc.

BABY - Candy ☆ - Topps Co., Inc.

BABY - Flowers, plants, and seeds - Rod McLellan Co.

BABY - Food products - Blum & Bergeron Inc.

BABY - Infant product - Magick Mud

BABY - Seafood products–canned or cured ☆ - Robinson Canning Co. Inc.

BABY 1 YEAR OLD - Dolls - Eugene Doll & Novelty Co. Inc.

BABY 2 YEAR OLD - Toys - Eugene Doll & Novelty Co. Inc.

BABY 10-H SPEAKER SYSTEM - Sound equipment - PRO Manufacturing

BABY ACTIVATOR - Toys ☆ - Creative Playthings Ltd.

BABY ACTIVITY COMPUTER - Toys–electronic - Toy Biz, Inc.

BABY ALIVE - Dolls - Kenner Products

BABY-ALL - Infant product ☆ - Barden & Robeson Corp.

BABY ALL GONE - Dolls - Hasbro, Inc.

BABY AMY - Dolls - Jolly U.S.A., Inc.

BABY & DUCKIE - Dolls - Mattel, Inc.

BABY & ME - Toys–stuffed - Dakin Inc.

BABY & ME - Vitamins and nutritional supplements - Bio San Laboratories Inc.

BABY ANGEL - Dolls - Jolly U.S.A., Inc.

BABY ANIMALS - Stationery - Vagabond Creations Inc.

BABY ANN & HER CARE SET - Dolls - Fisher-Price, Inc.

BABY ANNOUNCEMINTS - Candy - Mints-Ing Words, Inc.

BABY B - Infant product - Nogatco International Inc.

BABY BACI - Jewelry - Janis, Inc.

BABY BACKERS - Cushions - Baby Backers, Inc.

BABY BACKSEAT BEAR - Toys–stuffed ☆ - Dakin Inc.

BABY BACKUPS - Infant product - Sheri Dawn Apache

BABY BAG - Apparel–children's - Baby Bag of Maine

BABY-BARES - Underwear and nightwear ☆ - Lovable Co.

BABY BARTER THE BABY-SITTING TRADING KIT - Novelty items - Baby
Barter

BABY BAT - Kites - Gayla Industries Inc.

BABY BATH PETS - Toys–stuffed - Gund, Inc.

BABY-BATHE-A-LOT - Toys - Animal Fair Inc.

BABY BATHER - Infant product - Sanitoy Inc.

BABY BATHER - Infant product ☆ - Century Products Co.

BABY BE MINE - Apparel–children's - Antigua Knits, Inc.

BABY BEANS - Dolls - Adolph Eddy Goldfarb

BABY BEANS - Dolls - Mattel, Inc.

BABY BEAR FEET - Footwear - Bear Feet

BABY BEARHEART - Toys–stuffed ☆ - Gund, Inc.

BABY BEARS - Cookies ☆ - Keebler Co.

BABY BEARS - Giftware - Brushcreek Creative Co.

BABY BEATS - Apparel–women's - Donald A. Baker

BABY BEE - Soap - Burt's Bees Inc.

BABY BEEPERS - Apparel–women's - Andover Togs, Inc.

BABY BEGINNINGS - Bottles–glass - Meijer, Inc.

BABY BELLA - Vegetables–pickled or brined - Phillips Mushroom Farms

BABY BEN - Clocks - General Time Corp. (Westclox/Seth Thomas Div.)

BABY BEST - Infant product - Velsco Inc.

BABY B'GOSH - Brushes–hair - Oshkosh B'gosh, Inc.

BABY BIBI - Toys–stuffed - Russ Berrie and Co., Inc.

BABY BIBSY - Dolls - Mattel, Inc.

BABY BIG EYES - Dolls - Uneeda Doll Co., Inc.

BABY BIGGIE BEAR - Toys ☆ - Those Characters from Cleveland, Inc.

BABY BINGO - Flowers, plants, and seeds - Panamerican Seed
BABY BINKS - Candy - R.M. Palmer Co.
BABY BISTRO - Infant product ☆ - Cosco, Inc.
BABY BITES - Prepackaged cheesecakes - Seventy West Cheesecakes, Inc.
BABY BITS - Computer software - Dax Technologies, Inc.
BABY BITS - Toys–stuffed ☆ - Gund, Inc.
BABY BLANKIE BEAR - Blankets - Toy Biz, Inc.
BABY BLISS - Apparel–children's - Baby Bliss Inc.
BABY BLOCK - Suntan lotions - Estee Lauder Inc.
BABY BLOCKS - Comforters - Triboro Quilt Manufacturing Corp.
BABY BLOOMERS - Flowers, plants, and seeds - Ten West Inc.
BABY BLUE - Heaters–space - Desa International, Inc.
BABY BLUE - Toys - Tonka Corp.
BABY BLUE SAGA - Cheese - Tholstrup Cheese USA Inc.
BABY BLUES - Eyeglasses and sunglasses - Sunglass Designs, Inc.
BABY BLUES - Greeting cards - Baby Blues Partnership
BABY BOARDS - Infant product - Sentry Medical Products
BABY BONGO - Apparel and accessories - Michael Caruso & Co., Inc.
BABY-BONNET - Apparel–children's - Sherwood Medical Co.
BABY BONNY'S - Toy stores ☆ - Fun World Inc.
BABY BOOM - Infant product - Mitzi International Handbags & Accessories Ltd.
BABY BOOMER - Cooking equipment–household ☆ - Nordic Ware
BABY BOOMER - Furniture stores - Baby Boomer Corp.
BABY BOOMER - Toy stores ☆ - Gund, Inc.
BABY BOOMER - Toys - Southern States Marketing, Inc.
BABY BOOMER CLASSICS - Recording label - Warner Special Products Inc.
BABY BOP - Plush toys - Lyons Partnership, L.P.
BABY BOPPER - Toys - Shelcore Inc.
BABY BO'S BONES - Pet products - Misha-Sterling Inc.
BABY BOTTOMS - Dolls - Goldberger Doll Manufacture Co.
BABY BOUNCE-UP - Infant product - Sanitoy Inc.
BABY BRAKES - Infant product ☆ - Today's Kids Inc.
BABY BRIGHT EYES - Toys - Eugene Doll & Novelty Co. Inc.
BABY BRIGHTS - Floodlights ☆ - RAB Electric
BABY BRIGHTS BOOKS - Publisher's imprints - Lowell House
BABY BROCATO - Hair care products - Brocato International
BABY-BRUTE - Amplifiers ☆ - Polytone Musical Instruments Inc.
BABY BUDDY - Infant product - Baby Buddies Inc.
BABY BUFFET - Infant product - Iris Inc.
BABY BUG - Storm Manufacturing Co.
BABY BUGGY - Toys–electronic - Meritus Industries, Inc.
BABY BUMPKIN - Dolls - Uneeda Doll Co., Inc.
BABY BUNCH - Jewelry–costume - Lawrence Jewelry Co.
BABY BUNDLE BUNNY - Toys–stuffed - Dakin Inc.
BABY BUNDLER - Infant product - Baby Bundler, Inc.
BABY BUNDLES - Dolls ☆ - Kenner Products
BABY BUNDLES - Toys - Playskool, Inc.
BABY BUNDT - Pans - Nordic Ware
BABY BUNGO - Toys–stuffed - Russ Berrie and Co., Inc.
BABY BUNKY - Toys–stuffed ☆ - Gund, Inc.
BABY BUNNY - Toys–stuffed - Gerber Products Co.
BABY BUNS CINNAMON ROLLS - Bakery products - Jeanne Golden Scott
BABY BUNTING BEANS - Dolls - Mattel, Inc.
BABY BUTTERFLY - Toys - Fisher-Price, Inc.
BABY BUTTON NOSE - Dolls ☆ - Effanbee Doll Corp.
BABY BYTES - Greeting cards - Advanced Research Corp.
BABY CAKES - Food products - Baby Watson Cheesecake Inc.
BABY CARE - Dolls - Meritus Industries, Inc.
BABY CARE - Infant product - Baby Care
BABY CARRIE - Dolls - Goldberger Doll Manufacture Co.
BABY CASCADE - Toys - Tonka Corp.
BABY CASERO BY VIRGINIA - Apparel and accessories - Casero's & Associates
BABY CASSIE - Apparel–children's - Cassie Cotillion Inc.
BABY CHANGER - Infant product ☆ - Barden & Robeson Corp.
BABY CHEE CHEE - Toys–stuffed - Russ Berrie and Co., Inc.
BABY CHEESECAKE - Food products - Baby Watson Cheesecake Inc.
BABY CHEX - Dolls - Horsman
BABY CHICKS - Candy - American Chewing Gum Inc.
BABY CHUGGER SPOOK - Sporting goods - James Heddon's Sons
BABY CLAIRE - Optical scanners–computer - Tart Optical
BABY CLASSICS - Diapers–disposable - Pace Membership Warehouse, Inc.
BABY CLASSICS - Dolls ☆ - Effanbee Doll Corp.
BABY COLOR - Yarn - Tahki Imports Ltd.
BABY-COM - Transmitting apparatus–radio ☆ - Fanon Courier Inc.
BABY CONNECTIONS - Infant product - Pacesetter

BABY COOL - Containers–insulated - Stephen Flasch
BABY COOL - Fabrics - Fashion Promotions Limited
BABY COOL - Fabrics - Dan River Inc.
BABY CORPS - Apparel–children's - Venture Stores, Inc.
BABY COTTON - Yarn - Tahki Imports Ltd.
BABY COTTON COLOR - Yarn - Tahki Imports Ltd.
BABY COURTELLE - Yarn - William Unger & Co. Inc.
BABY CRATES - Toys ☆ - Henry Gordy International Inc.
BABY CRIES-A-LOT - Toy stores ☆ - Fun World Inc.
BABY CRISSY - Toys–stuffed - CBS Toys
BABY CRY - Telephone devices and light signals for the deaf - American Communications Corp.
BABY CUB - Tripods–photographic - Camera Mart Inc.
BABY CUDDLES - Dolls ☆ - Effanbee Doll Corp.
BABY CURTSY - Toys - Tonka Corp.
BABY DANA - Dolls ☆ - Uneeda Doll Co., Inc.
BABY DAYS - Infant product - Blue Cross Laboratories Inc.
BABY DAYS - Infant product - Edison Industries Inc.
BABY DAYS DAILY JOURNAL - Books–blank - Baby Days
BABY DEAR - Dolls - Vogue Dolls Inc.
BABY DEAR - Toys - Playmates World Wide Inc.
BABY DEAR ONE - Dolls - Vogue Dolls Inc.
BABY DEB - Frames–eyeglass - May Optical Co. Inc.
BABY DEER - Shoes - Endicott Johnson Corp.
BABY DENTAPAINE - Pharmaceutical preparations ☆ - Reese Chemical Co.
BABY DESIGN - Diapers–disposable - Weyerhaeuser Co.
BABY DESIGNS - Tote bags and backpacks - Steven's Baby Boom Ltd.
BABY DINA - Dolls - Meritus Industries, Inc.
BABY DINO-ROARRRRR - Toys - Fisher-Price, Inc.
BABY DIOR - Apparel–children's - William Carter Co.
BABY DOG - Pet products - Cardinal Laboratories Inc.
BABY DOLL - Apparel–women's - Lady Marlene
BABY DOLL - Cosmetics - Nu-Art Beauty Products
BABY DOLL - Recording label - Sweet 'N Smooth Productions
BABY DOLLY - Tripods–photographic - Camera Mart Inc.
BABY DOVE - Soap - Lever Brothers Co. Inc.
BABY DREAM - Toys - Peg Perego USA Inc.
BABY DREAMS - Infant product ☆ - Bibb Co.
BABY DRI - Mattress pads - Kolcraft Enterprises, Inc.
BABY DUCK - Cosmetics - Dubl Duck/Jet Set Inc.
BABY DUCK HEAD - Diapers–cloth - Duck Head Apparel Co., Inc.
BABY DUCKLINGS - Toys–stuffed - Fun World Inc.
BABY DUMPLING - Dolls - Horsman
BABY DUMPTRUCK - Toys - Playskool, Inc.
BABY DUTCH - Brushes–paint ☆ - Wooster Brush Co.
BABY ELEPHANT - Toys - Tyco Toys
BABY ESSENTIALS - Apparel–children's - Primex International Corp.
BABY EXPRESS - Apparel–women's - CR & ME Ltd.
BABY FACE - Dolls - Lewis Galoob Toys, Inc.
BABY FACE - Dolls ☆ - Effanbee Doll Corp.
BABY FACE - Infant product - Dakin Inc.
BABY FINELLA - Toys - Tonka Corp.
BABY FINES - Cosmetics - Revlon Consumer Products Corp.
BABY FIRST - Towels - Sufolla Industries Inc.
BABY FIRST BORN - Dolls - Uneeda Doll Co., Inc.
BABY FIRST WORDS - Dolls - Toymax Inc.
BABY FLAPS - Publisher's imprints - McClanahan Book Co., Inc.
BABY FLO - Toys - Tonka Corp.
BABY FLOAT - Toys - Kransco Manufacturing Inc.
BABY FLUTTER - Toys - Tonka Corp.
BABY FOX - Bakery products - Baby Fox Enterprises Inc.
BABY FRESH - Paper - Scott Paper Co.
BABY FRESH ORIGINAL - Paper - Scott Paper Co.
BABY FRIENDS - Toys - Mattel, Inc.
BABY GAP - Apparel–children's - Gap Inc.
BABY GAP - Apparel–children's - GPS, Inc.
BABY-GARD - Pharmaceutical preparations - Lyphomed Inc.
BABY GET WELL - Dolls - Tyco Industries, Inc.
BABY GIGGLES 'N GO - Toys - Those Characters from Cleveland, Inc.
BABY GLOVE - Apparel–children's - Dive N' Surf, Inc.
BABY-GO-ROUND - Infant product - Leachco Inc.
BABY-GO-TO-SLEEP - Infant product - Flying Colors, Inc.
BABY-GO-TO SLEEP - Recording label - Baby-Go-to-Sleep Center
BABY GOLD BOND MEDICATED POWDER - Skin care products - Martin Himmel Inc.
BABY GRAND - Hunting equipment - Paul Meeks

☆ = Now out of production

BABY GRANDS - Cakes - Miss Kings Kitchen Inc.
BABY GUARD - Notebooks and notepads - Bay Katie Products Inc.
BABY GUARDS - Infant product - Playskool Baby Inc.
BABY GUMBALLS - Toys - Playskool, Inc.
BABY GWORK - Toys-stuffed - Russ Berrie and Co., Inc.
BABY HEADSTAND SURPRISE - Dolls - Toy Biz, Inc.
BABY HEARTBEAT - Dolls ☆ - Kenner Products
BABY HEATHER - Dolls - Mattel, Inc.
BABY HI-LO - High chairs ☆ - Cosco, Inc.
BABY HIDE-OUT - Pet products - Penn-Plax, Inc.
BABY HONEYKINS - Toys - Eugene Doll & Novelty Co. Inc.
BABY HOOD - Carriages-baby - Babyhood, (USA) Inc.
BABY IN A BASKET - Dolls - Goldberger Doll Manufacture Co.
BABY IN TRAVEL TRUNK - Dolls - Goldberger Doll Manufacture Co.
BABY IRIS - Footwear - De Osu Inc.
BABY, IT'S YOU! - Apparel-children's - Baby, It's You! Distinctive Clothing, Ltd.
BABY JACKS - Infant product - Jumping-Jacks Shoes Inc.
BABY JAMA - Bedding-linen - Alan Lloyd Schaechter
BABY JANE - Watches - Bulova Corp.
BABY JAY - Apparel-children's - Growing Feet, Inc.
BABY JOGGER - Strollers-baby - Racing Strollers Inc.
BABY JOSELLE - Dolls ☆ - Barval Toys Inc.
BABY JOURNAL, THE - Calendars - Conceivable Concepts
BABY JOY - Furniture ☆ - Tradis Inc.
BABY KARE - Infant product ☆ - Peg Perego USA Inc.
BABY KEEPSAKES - Giftware - Bradson Press, Inc.
BABY KICKLE - Dolls - Mattel, Inc.
BABY KING - Infant product - Regent Baby Products Corp.
BABY KISSES - Apparel-children's - Frederick Atkins, Inc.
BABY KISSES - Dolls - Georgetown Collection, Inc.
BABY KRIBBERS - Footwear - Shoeware Ltd.
BABY LACE - Apparel and accessories ☆ - Jantzen Inc.
BABY LAMBSDOWN - Bedding-linen - Crestwood Industries Inc.
BABY LASH - Cosmetics - Maybelline Co.
BABY LAUGH'N CRY - Dolls - Horsman
BABY LAWYER'S TEETH - Novelty items - Robert Edward Benedict
BABY LENZ - Sunglasses - Solar Sense USA, Inc.
BABY LINDA - Toys - Eugene Doll & Novelty Co. Inc.
BABY LINE - Furniture ☆ - Evenflo Juvenile Furniture Co.
BABY LISA - Dolls ☆ - Effanbee Doll Corp.
BABY-LITE - Health care products - Pratt Medical Inc.
BABY LITTLE LOVE - Dolls - Animal Fair Inc.
BABY LITTLE ONE - Dolls - Goldberger Doll Manufacture Co.
BABY LOCK - Sewing machines-household - Tacony Corp.
BABY LOO - Infant product - G.W. DMKA Inc./Best Days Inc.
BABY LOONEY TUNES - Footwear - S. Goldberg and Co. Inc.
BABY LOONEY TUNES - Wallpaper - Priss Prints Inc.
BABY LORRIE - Toys - Eugene Doll & Novelty Co. Inc.
BABY LOTION - Skin care products - Geritrex Corp.
BABY LOVE - Eyeglasses - Art-Craft Optical Co.
BABY LOVE - Hair care products - Soft Sheen Products Co.
BABY LOVES - Infant product - Yarn Kits Inc.
BABY LOVES TO TALK - Dolls - Toy Biz, Inc.
BABY LUCKY 13 - Sporting goods - James Heddon's Sons
BABY LULLABERRY PIE - Dolls ☆ - American Greetings Corp.
BABY LULU - Apparel and accessories - Baby Lulu, Inc.
BABY LUV - Apparel-children's - Bend 'n Stretch Inc.
BABY MAGIC - Health care products - Mennen Co.
BABY-MAGIK - Diapers-cloth ☆ - Reese Chemical Co.
BABY-MATE - Furniture - Baby-Tenda Corp.
BABY MATES - Crocheted and knitted items ☆ - Manchester Knitted Fashion Inc.
BABY MATTERS - Educational materials - Child Matters
BABY ME - Blankets - Comfort Silkie Co. Inc.
BABY ME - Dolls - Marie Green
BABY-ME-NOW - Vitamins and nutritional supplements - Solaray
BABY MEMOIRS - Publisher's imprints ☆ - McMillin Foley Publishing Co.
BABY MICKEY - Infant product - Mattel, Inc.
BABY MILD & KIND - Skin care products ☆ - Borlind of Germany
BABY MINE - Dolls - Goldberger Doll Manufacture Co.
BABY MONARCH - Towels - Monarch Towel Co.
BABY MORGAN - Apparel-children's - J.E. Morgan Knitting Mills
BABY MOVES - Apparel-children's - Winning Moves, Inc.
BABY N - Fishing lures - Howe Now Inc.
BABY-NAMER! - Computer software - Daniel A. Richman

BABY NAPPING - Toys - Eugene Doll & Novelty Co. Inc.
BABY NATURALS - Perfumes ☆ - Chase Collection, Inc.
BABY NEEDS ME - Toys - Tonka Corp.
BABY NETWORKS - Infant product - Railnet Corp.
BABY NINE - Footwear - Nine West Group Inc.
BABY NOTIONS - Baskets-wood ☆ - Royal Cathay Trading Co.
BABY O BABY - Apparel-children's - Roxanne Weiner
BABY OH-NO - Dolls - Hasbro, Inc.
BABY OIL - Skin care products - Geritrex Corp.
BABY ORAJEL - Pharmaceutical preparations - Del Pharmaceuticals, Inc.
BABY ORAJEL NIGHTTIME - Pharmaceutical preparations - Del Pharmaceuticals, Inc.
BABY ORAJEL TOOTH AND GUM CLEANSER - Health care products - Del Pharmaceuticals, Inc.
BABY PADUKE - Candy - Gilliam Candy Co. Inc. (Gilliam Candy Brands)
BABY PAN!PAN! - Food products - Little Caesar Enterprises, Inc.
BABY PEARL - Toys - Tonka Corp.
BABY PEE WEE - Dolls - Uneeda Doll Co., Inc.
BABY PENS - Pens - Arnold Pen Co. Inc.
BABY PLACE - Apparel and accessories - Children's Place Retail Stores, Inc.
BABY PLACE - Infant product - Graco Children's Products
BABY PLEX - Vitamins and nutritional supplements - Natural Organics, Inc.
BABY PLUMPEE - Dolls - Uneeda Doll Co., Inc.
BABY POUNDING BENCH - Toys - Playskool, Inc.
BABY PRANCER - Dolls - Mattel, Inc.
BABY PRINTS - Diapers-disposable - Weyerhaeuser Co.
BABY PRO - Toys - Kenneth Gerald Lockard
BABY PROPER - Infant product - Mericon Corp.
BABY PUFF - Toys-stuffed ☆ - Gund, Inc.
BABY PUFFALUMPS - Toys - Fisher-Price, Inc.
BABY PURE - Filters-water - Ultrapure Systems, Inc.
BABY PUSS - Ophthalmic goods - Styl-Rite Optical Manufacturing Co., Inc.
BABY Q - Bedding-linen ☆ - Quiltex
BABY REBELS - Apparel-children's - Cradle Togs, Inc.
BABY REINDEER STINKYS - Chocolate candy - Christine Niedermier
BABY REST - Infant product - Velsco Inc.
BABY REX - Fishing lures - Weezel Bait Co.
BABY-ROO - Infant product - Century Products Co.
BABY RORY - Toys - Tonka Corp.
BABY ROSE - Dolls - Mattel, Inc.
BABY RUTH - Candy - Nabisco Foods Group
BABY SAFE - Scissors-hand-operated - Mehaz International, Inc.
BABY-SAFE LITTLE TREASURES - Infant product ☆ - Treasure Masters
BABY SAFE SIT - Infant product - Intermark Inc.
BABY SAGA - Cheese - Tholstrup Cheese USA Inc.
BABY SALEM - Apparel-children's - Salem Sportswear Inc.
BABY SANTA - Greeting cards, apparel, etc. - Al-Sheikh
BABY SEABRINA - Toys - Tonka Corp.
BABY SEEDS - Paper - Ann Weimer Baumgardner
BABY SHADES - Infant product - Sentry Medical Products
BABY SHADES - Visors - Russ Berrie and Co., Inc.
BABY SHARON - Dolls ☆ - Horsman
BABY SHOP - Dolls - Multi Toys Corp.
BABY SIP AND SLURP - Dolls - Hasbro, Inc.
BABY SIT - Toys - Peg Perego USA Inc.
BABY SITTER - Infant product - Candy Kisses of Florida, Inc.
BABY SITTER - Infant product - Stork Stuff
BABY-SITTERS CLUB - Puzzles - Milton Bradley Co.
BABY-SITTERS CLUB, THE - Children's toiletries - Cosrich Inc.
BABY-SITTERS CLUB, THE - Bags-duffel - Scholastic Inc.
BABY-SITTER'S LITTLE SISTER - Publisher's imprints - Scholastic Inc.
BABY SKATES - Dolls - Mattel, Inc.
BABY SMURF - Puzzles ☆ - Milton Bradley Co.
BABY SNOW PUFF - Dolls - Urban Retail Properties Co.
BABY SNUFFLES - Toys-stuffed - Gund, Inc.
BABY SNUFFY - Toys-stuffed - Gund, Inc.
BABY SNUFFY RATTLE - Toys-stuffed - Gund, Inc.
BABY SNUFFY WRIST RATTLE - Toys-stuffed - Gund, Inc.
BABY-SNUGGLEHEADS - Infant product - Rock-A-Bye Baby Inc.
BABY SNUGGLEHEADS - Infant product - Startech Inc.
BABY SO BEAUTIFUL - Dolls - Playmates World Wide Inc.
BABY SO REAL - Dolls - Toy Biz, Inc.
BABY SOFSKIN - Dolls - Horsman
BABY SOFT BY PUREX - Detergents - Dial Corp.
BABY SOFT EXPRESSION - Dolls - Dan-Dee International Ltd.
BABY SOFT LOVE - Dolls - Horsman

BABY SOFT SOUNDS - Dolls - Fisher-Price, Inc.
BABY SOFT STUFF - Toys - Eugene Doll & Novelty Co. Inc.
BABY SOOTHER, THE - Audio tapes–blank - Quiet Tymes, Inc.
BABY SPARKLER - Toys - Marlin Toy Products Inc.
BABY SPARKLES - Dolls - Mattel, Inc.
BABY SQUEAKERS - Swim rings - Intex Recreation Corp.
BABY STAMPIN' PLAYGROUND - Toys - Mattel, Inc.
BABY STEP - Furniture - Rochelle Furniture Manufacturing Co.
BABY STEPS - Diapers–disposable - Kimberly-Clark Corp.
BABY STORKLINE - Dolls - Goldberger Doll Manufacture Co.
BABY STRAWBERRY SHORTCAKE - Dolls ☆ - American Greetings Corp.
BABY STRIDES - Diapers–disposable - Arquest, Inc.
BABY STUFF - Towels - Baby Stuff, Inc.
BABY SUNBLOCK - Sunblocks - Sun Pharmaceuticals Corp.
BABY SUNSHADE - Toys - Aqua-Leisure Industries, Inc.
BABY SUPER SWEET - Infant product - Simmons Juvenile Products Co., Inc.
BABY SUPERSTORE - Linen - Baby Superstore, Inc.
BABY SURE - Window shades - Zuoliang Chen
BABY SUSAN - Infant product - Pansy Ellen Products, Inc.
BABY SWEET - Stain removers - Fast Industries, Inc.
BABY SWEETUMS - Dolls - Uneeda Doll Co., Inc.
BABY TALK - Dolls - Lewis Galoob Toys, Inc.
BABY TEARDROP - Hams - Cloverdale Foods Co. Inc.
BABY TEARS - Dolls - Mattel, Inc.
BABY TECH - Footwear - SRL, Inc.
BABY TEE HEE - Dolls - Mattel, Inc.
BABY-TENDA - Furniture - Baby-Tenda Corp.
BABY TENDER LOVE - Dolls - Mattel, Inc.
BABY TERRY - Infant product - Terry Products, Inc.
BABY THATAWAY - Dolls - Mattel, Inc.
BABY THINGS - Infant product - Dakin Inc.
BABY THOUGHTS - Greeting cards - Martha J. Hurse
BABY THUNDERSTICK - Fishing lures - Storm Manufacturing Co.
BABY TICKLE TOES - Toys - Eugene Doll & Novelty Co. Inc.
BABY TITE - Infant product - Baby Tite, Inc.
BABY TO LOVE - Dolls ☆ - Effanbee Doll Corp.
BABY TOGS - Crocheted and knitted items - Baby Togs, Inc.
BABY TONES - Tape players - Caramia Francais
BABY TOOTHIE - Dolls ☆ - Mangelsen's (VDI)
BABY TORPEDO - Sporting goods - James Heddon's Sons
BABY TRAIN - Infant product ☆ - Peg Perego USA Inc.
BABY TREASURE - Dolls - Uneeda Doll Co., Inc.
BABY TREND - Infant product - Baby Trend Inc.
BABY TRIX - Dolls ☆ - Uneeda Doll Co., Inc.
BABY TUM - Pharmaceutical preparations - Rex Research Laboratories
BABY TURTLE TOTS - Dolls - Mattel, Inc.
BABY TWEEKS - Dolls - Horsman
BABY UGGS - Footwear–children's - Ugg Holdings, Inc.
BABY UH-OH - Dolls - Hasbro, Inc.
BABY VELVET - Infant product - Cameo Inc.
BABY VERSA - Pumps–water - Beckett Corp.
BABY VITE - Vitamins and nutritional supplements - Natural Organics, Inc.
BABY WAGGLE - Dolls - Mattel, Inc.
BABY WANNA WALK - Dolls - Hasbro, Inc.
BABY WASH 'N PLAY - Dolls - Horsman
BABY WATCH - Mirrors - JMS Colonial Corp.
BABY WATSON - Bakery products - Specialty Desserts LLC
BABY WATSON - Food products - Baby Watson Cheesecake Inc.
BABY WEST - Infant product - Baby West, Inc.
BABY WET N' CARE - Dolls ☆ - Kenner Products
BABY WETS - Dolls - Mattel, Inc.
BABY WHALE - Pumps ☆ - Imtra Corp.
BABY WHIRL - Toys - Tonka Corp.
BABY WIGGLES 'N GIGGLES - Dolls - Tyco Industries, Inc.
BABY WINKIE - Dolls ☆ - Effanbee Doll Corp.
BABY WORLD - Infant product - Baby World Co. Inc.
BABY WORLD CO. INC. - Infant product - Baby World Co. Inc.
BABY YAWNIE - Dolls ☆ - Kenner Products
BABY YOUR CAR - Automotive parts and accessories - International Beauty and Fitness Concepts
BABY ZARA - Sporting goods - James Heddon's Sons
BABY ZEECURL - Cosmetics ☆ - Spilo/Mehaz Worldwide
BABYBEL - Cheese - Fromageries Bel, Inc.
BABYBELL - Toys–stuffed ☆ - Gund, Inc.
BABYBELLE - Clocks - General Time Corp. (Westclox/Seth Thomas Div.)
BABYBIRD - Medical apparatus - Bird Products Corp.

BABYBOAT - Toys - Aqua-Leisure Industries, Inc.
BABYBOTTE - Footwear–children's - Bidegain Inc.
BABYBRIC - Toys - Learning Products Inc.
BABYCAKES - Soap - Only Natural Inc.
BABYCAM - Monitors–electronic - Ultrak, Inc.
BABYCARE - Bedding–linen ☆ - Mount Vernon Mills Inc.
BABYCARE - Diapers–disposable ☆ - Plainwell Tissue
BABYCISE - Exercising equipment - Matchbox Toys USA
BABYCOLOGY - Infant product - Leiner Health Products Inc.
BABYCREST - Infant product - Associated Merchandising Corp.
BABYDRY - Infant product - Rock-A-Bye Baby Inc.
BABYFACE SHIELD - Health care products - Physician Engineered Products
BABYGRO - Apparel–children's - Kleinert's Inc.
BABYKIN - Dolls ☆ - Effanbee Doll Corp.
BABYKING - Infant product - Regent Baby Products Corp.
BABYKINS - Infant product - HT Marketing, Inc.
BABYLAND - Apparel–children's - Woods & Gray, Ltd.
BABYLAND GENERAL HOSPITAL - Dolls - Original Appalachian Artworks, Inc.
BABYLAX - Laxatives - C.B. Fleet Co. Inc.
BABYLIFE - Infant product - Solaray
BABYLIN - Dolls - Doll Factory, Inc.
BABYLISS - Beauty shop equipment ☆ - JRC Products Inc.
BABYLON - Floor coverings–carpet and rugs - Edgecrest Carpet Mills
BABYLON 5 - Toys - Time Warner Entertainment Co., L.P.
BABYLONE - Bedding–linen - Dan River Inc.
BABYLOVE - Analgesic - American Pharmaceutical Co.
BABYMUGS! - Video production - Three Friends Productions
BABYPIES - Novelty items - Shelby Nichols
BABYPRINT - Infant product ☆ - Sisiby Co.
BABYRAGEOUS - Blankets - Impact Imports International, Inc.
BABY'S 1ST BIRTHDAY - Dolls - Gata Box Ltd.
BABY'S 1ST EASTER - Toys–stuffed - Russ Berrie and Co., Inc.
BABY'S 1ST SOFSKIN - Dolls - Horsman
BABY'S 1ST TEDDY BEAR - Toys–stuffed - Russ Berrie and Co., Inc.
BABY'S BALLERINA - Toys–stuffed ☆ - Gund, Inc.
BABY'S BEST - Apparel–children's - Baby Bliss Inc.
BABY'S BEST - Skin care products - Liberty Natural Products
BABY'S BEST - Toys–stuffed - Kamar International Inc.
BABY'S BOTTLE SACK - Infant product - Jack Friedman
BABY'S BREAKFAST ROAST - Coffee - Baby's Place Coffee Bar
BABY'S BREATH - Lipsticks - Essie Cosmetics Ltd.
BABY'S BREATH - Vaporizers - Duracraft Corp.
BABY'S BUNS - Infant accessories - Art for the Heart, Inc.
BABY'S CHOICE - Diapers–disposable - VMG Products Inc.
BABY'S DELIGHT - Diapers–disposable ☆ - Certified Grocers Midwest Inc.
BABY'S DREAM FURNITURE, INC. - Furniture–children's - Baby's Dream Furniture, Inc.
BABY'S FAVORITES - Diapers–disposable - Dayton Hudson Corp.
BABY'S FIRST - Baby foods ☆ - Beech-Nut Nutrition Corp.
BABY'S FIRST - Dolls ☆ - Effanbee Doll Corp.
BABY'S FIRST - High chairs - Safe-Strap Co., Inc.
BABY'S FIRST BABY - Dolls - Horsman
BABY'S FIRST BLOCKS - Toys - Fisher-Price, Inc.
BABY'S FIRST BOOK CLUB - Children's books - Sandvik Publishing Ltd.
BABY'S FIRST BUNNY - Toys–stuffed - Russ Berrie and Co., Inc.
BABY'S FIRST CHOICE - Toys - Tot Inc.
BABY'S FIRST CHRISTMAS - Glassware–household ☆ - Fenton Art Glass Co.
BABY'S FIRST CHRISTMAS - Toys - Eugene Doll & Novelty Co. Inc.
BABY'S FIRST CHRISTMAS - Toys–stuffed - Gund, Inc.
BABY'S FIRST CURL - Frames–picture - Agent Andy Inc.
BABY'S FIRST KWAANZA - Toys - Prestige Toy Corp.
BABY'S FIRST PLAYMATE - Toys–stuffed ☆ - Russ Berrie and Co., Inc.
BABY'S FIRST PURSE - Toys - Playskool, Inc.
BABY'S FIRST RATTLE - Toys–stuffed ☆ - Gund, Inc.
BABY'S FIRST ROCKER - Toys - Little White House Inc.
BABY'S FIRST SILLY SOUNDS - Toys–stuffed - Gund, Inc.
BABY'S FIRST TOY - Toys–stuffed - Russ Berrie and Co., Inc.
BABY'S FIRST XMAS - Christmas tree ornaments - Cracker Box Inc.
BABY'S FIRST YEAR - Calendars - Rock-A-Bye Baby Inc.
BABYS FRIEND - Footwear–children's ☆ - Livonia Catalog
BABY'S H20 - Water purification systems - ClearBrook Labs Inc.
BABY'S IMAGE - Apparel–children's - Steven Mohler
BABY'S KEEPSAKE COLLECTION, THE - Baby books, gift items for babies - Michel & Co.

☆ = Now out of production

BABY'S NEST - Bed pads - Intromark Inc.
BABY'S NURSERY - Toys - Tyco Toys
BABY'S OWN - Water–bottled or canned - Sparkling Spring Mineral Water Co.
BABY'S PERSONAL TIME CAPSULE - Containers - Dan M. Adler
BABY'S PRIVATE BUZZ - Coffee - Baby's Place Coffee Bar
BABY'S RAINBOW - Toys - Mattel, Inc.
BABY'S TROPICAL ISLAND - Sporting goods - Kransco Manufacturing Inc.
BABY'S VIDEO DEBUT - Video tapes–blank - Meeting Services Inc.
BABY'S VIEW - Infant product - Fisher-Price, Inc.
BABY'S WORLD - Publisher's imprints - McClanahan Book Co., Inc.
BABYSAFE - Posters - Forever Yours, Inc.
BABYSCOTT - Diapers–disposable ☆ - Scott Paper Co.
BABYSHADES - Automotive parts and accessories - Two Little Girls Inc.
BABYSITTER PLAYHOUSE - Dolls - Mattel, Inc.
BABYSITTER, THE - Infant product - Babyhood Manufacturing Inc.
BABYSITTERS CLUB - Publisher's imprints - Scholastic Inc.
BABYSITTERS LITTLE SISTER - Publisher's imprints - Scholastic Inc.
BABYSLING - Infant product - Noel Joanna, Inc.
BABYSMART - Infant product - Diane M. Zissu
BABYSMASH - Computer software - Aniworld, Inc.
BABYTAB - Electrodes - Ludlow Technical Products
BABYTENDER - Bags–duffel - Babytender Totes
BABYTIME - Publisher's imprints ☆ - Small World Toys
BABYTIME FUN - Toys - Mattel, Inc.
BABYVISION - Cameras–video - CCTV Corp./GBC
BABYWATCH - Monitors–electronic - Ultrak, Inc.
BABYWOOD - Apparel–children's - Goldenwood International, Inc.
BAC - Health care products - Luconex Inc.
BAC-A-BELL - Alarm systems ☆ - Preco Inc.
BAC-A-LARM - Alarm systems - Preco Inc.
BAC-AIR - Cushions - Alimed, Inc.
BAC-AZAP - Chemical preparations - Nisus Corp.
BAC-O-BITS - Food products - General Mills, Inc.
BAC-ON-SNAPS - Snack foods - Beatrice Cos. Inc.
BAC-OS - Food products - General Mills, Inc.
BAC-OS MAKES EVERY BITE BETTER - Food products - General Mills, Inc.
BAC RAC PLUS - Bicycles ☆ - Graber Products, Inc.
BAC ROCKER - Exercising equipment - Robert Fuller
BAC-SAFE - Motor vehicle parts and accessories - PublicSafety Equipment Inc.
BAC-SEAT - Health care products ☆ - Rinz-L-O Pillow Co.
BAC STOP - Floor coverings - Congoleum Corp.
BAC-T-DERM - Pet products ☆ - Fermenta Animal Health
BAC-TALK - Motor vehicle parts and accessories - PublicSafety Equipment Inc.
BAC-TERRA - Fertilizers - Fifco International, Inc.
BAC-TIVATOR - Sewage treatment equipment - Boyer Corp.
BACARATE - Pharmaceutical preparations ☆ - Solvay Pharmaceuticals Inc.
BACARDI - Beverages–alcohol - Coca-Cola Co.
BACARDI - Rum - Bacardi Imports Inc.
BACARDI BREEZER - Rum - Bacardi Imports Inc.
BACCARA - Wallpaper - Bayview Wallcoverings
BACCARA - Wallpaper - Madison Wallcoverings
BACCARAT - Apparel and accessories - Phillips-Van Heusen Corp.
BACCARAT - Eyeglasses - Martin-Copeland Eyewear Corp.
BACCARAT - Furniture ☆ - Tropitone Furniture Co. Inc.
BACCARAT - Glassware–household - Haviland Limoges
BACCESS - Robes - Arthella Isaacs
BACCHINI - Food products - Bacchini USA, Inc.
BACCHUS - Glassware–household ☆ - Neuwirth Co.
BACCHUS - Toiletries ☆ - Coty Inc.
BACCIO - Mouthwashes - Concord Chemists
BACCO BUCCI - Footwear–men's - Cable & Co.
BACCO-RESIST - Pharmaceutical preparations - Vita Elixir Co. Inc.
BACCONE - Cookies - Baccone
BACCTO - Soil–potting - Michigan Peat Co.
BACCTO LITE - Soil–potting - Michigan Peat Co.
BACH - Calendars - Mach 1, Inc.
BACH - Computer software - Bach Group, Inc.
BACH - Hearing aids ☆ - Magnatone Hearing Aid Corp.
BACH - Musical instruments ☆ - Selmer Co. Inc.
BACH FLOWER ESSENCES - Petroleum refinement equipment - Nelson Bach USA
BACH FLOWER REMEDIES - Health care products - Ellon Bach USA Inc.
BACH REMEDIES - Health care products - Ellon Bach USA Inc.
BACH SONGBOOK - Computer software - Dr. T's Music Software Inc.
BACH TO ROCK - Clocks ☆ - Dunlop Manufacturing, Inc.
BACHATS - Recording label - Kubaney Publishing Corp.

BACHELOR - Colognes - J. Palazzolo Son Inc.
BACHELOR - Eyeglasses - Art-Craft Optical Co.
BACHELOR BUTTON - Dishes–china - Taylor, Smith & Taylor Co.
BACHELOR BUTTONS - Bathing suits ☆ - Jantzen Inc.
BACHELOR PAD - Shaving preparations ☆ - Givaudan-Roure Corp.
BACHI - Machinery - Bachi, L.P.
BACHMAN - Snack foods - Bachman Co.
BACHMAN JAX - Snack foods - Bachman Co.
BACHMANN - Musical instruments - General Electro Music Corp.
BACHMANN - Toys - Bachmann Industries Inc.
BACHMANN/TAIYO - Toys ☆ - Bachmann Industries Inc.
BACHRI'S SAMBAL TUMIS - Sauces - Syamsul Bachri
BACHSCHMIDT - Cigars - G.A. Georgopulo & Co. Inc.
BACI - Chocolate candy - Perugina Chocolate & Confections Inc.
BACI - Mirrors - Remcraft Lighting Products
BACIBELLA - Apparel–athletic ☆ - Double J of Broward Inc.
BACID - Health care products - Fisons Corp.
BACIGALUPI VINEYARDS - Wines ☆ - Belvedere Winery
BACIGUENT - Pharmaceutical preparations ☆ - Upjohn Co.
BACILLIUM - Vitamins and nutritional supplements - Barth-Spencer Corp.
BACIMYCIN - Pharmaceutical preparations - Marion Merrell Dow
BACK 2 BACK - Apparel–women's - Richwil Corp.
BACK AID - Apparel–women's ☆ - Bali Co. Inc.
BACK ALLEY DESIGNS - Film–motion picture - Backstreet Tees
BACK ANCHOR - Underwear and nightwear - Youthcraft-Charmfit
BACK & FORTH - Luggage ☆ - Innovative Manufacturing Corp.
BACK & NECK AIDE - Pharmaceutical preparations - Boericke & Tafel
BACK AT THE RANCH - Apparel and accessories - Square Dance Collection, Inc.
BACK AT THE RANCH - Cosmetics - Revlon Consumer Products Corp.
BACK-ATTACKER - Skin care products - Richard S. Henderson
BACK BAY - Frames–eyeglass - Pathway Optical Prods.
BACK BAY - Furniture - Tropitone Furniture Co. Inc.
BACK BAY - Musical instrument accessories - Kaman Music Corp.
BACK BAY U.S.A. - Frames–eyeglass - Marine Optical, Inc.
BACK BITER - Toys–automobiles - Mattel, Inc.
BACK BONE - Fishing lures - Backbone Inc.
BACK BRACER - Mattresses ☆ - Kingsdown, Inc.
BACK BUDDY - Tools–hand-operated - O's Marine International, Inc.
BACK BUDDY - Wheelchairs ☆ - Fortress Inc.
BACK BURNER - Deodorizers - Herbal Holding Co.
BACK BURNER - Toys–automobiles - Mattel, Inc.
BACK COUNTRY - Lumber ☆ - Georgia-Pacific Corp.
BACK-COUNTRY - Motor vehicle parts and accessories - Design Automotive Group, Inc.
BACK COUNTRY - Oars ☆ - Plaza Enterprises Inc. (Magnador Div.)
BACK COUNTRY BOOKS - Publisher's imprints - Chatham Press
BACK DANGLES - Jewelry - Idaho Opal & Gem Corp.
BACK DOOR - Recording label ☆ - Rounder Records Corp.
BACK EASER - Garden-tool handles - Invention Prototypes & Marketing Corp.
BACK EASER - Medical apparatus - Nelkin/Piper Health Products
BACK-ERCISER - Health care products ☆ - Chattanooga Group, Inc.
BACK-EZE - Cushions ☆ - Better Sleep, Inc.
BACK-EZE - Shovels - Frank A. Barone
BACK-FIRM - Bandages–orthopedic - Richards/Dillion Inc.
BACK FIXER - Health care products - Remington Products Co.
BACK GUARD - Shoe accessories - Schering-Plough Healthcare Products
BACK HAPPY - Underwear and nightwear - Exquisite Form Industries
BACK HOME - Wallpaper - Lin-Gor Wallcoverings
BACK HOME COLLECTION - Furniture ☆ - Vaughan Furniture Co. Inc.
BACK-HUGGAR - Health care products - Bodyline Comfort Systems
BACK IN A FLASH! - Computer software - CCT Inc.
BACK IN ORDER - Medical apparatus - Carol A. Sullivan
BACK IN SHAPE - Vitamins and nutritional supplements - Anabolic Laboratories, Inc.
BACK-IT-UP OFF-SITE - Computer software - Intellectual Capital Repository, Inc.
BACK-JACK - Chairs–upholstered ☆ - La-Z-Boy Chair Co.
BACK JAM - Basketball shoes - Converse Inc.
BACK LOGIC - Medical apparatus - Perfect Fit Industries, Inc.
BACK MACHINE, THE - Health care products - Kingstar International America, Inc.
BACK MAGIC - Apparel–women's - Lady Lynne Lingerie Inc.
BACK MASTER - Medical apparatus - Back-Jack, Inc.
BACK ME UP - Medical apparatus - Roloke Co.
BACK MECHANIC - Medical apparatus - Maven Labs, Inc.

BACK NINE - Golfing equipment - Customputt, Inc.

BACK OFF - Decals and transfers - Plasticolor Molded Products, Inc.

BACK OFF! BUZZARD - Games - Milton Bradley Co.

BACK OFFICE - Computer software - Restaurant Accounting Systems, Inc.

BACK-PAC - Frames–eyeglass - Liberty Optical Manufacturing Co.

BACK PACK WHEELCHAIR ACCESSORIES - Wheelchairs - Ventura Enterprises, Inc.

BACK-PACKABLES - Umbrellas - Collegiate Umbrellas, Inc.

BACK PACKER - Cooking equipment–household ☆ - Mirro Corp.

BACK PACKER - Knives–pocket ☆ - Imperial Schrade Corp.

BACK PACKERS - Footwear–children's - Step Master Shoes

BACK PAL - Cushions - Better Sleep, Inc.

BACK PLEASER - Massage products - Homedics Inc.

BACK PORCH - Teas - Eastern Shore Tea Co.

BACK-QUELL - Pharmaceutical preparations - Buffington

BACK-QUELL - Pharmaceutical preparations - Otis Clapp & Son Inc.

BACK REST, THE - Health care products - Cascade Designs, Inc.

BACK ROOM CLUB - Apparel–men's ☆ - Edison Brothers Stores, Inc.

BACK SAFER - Railroad equipment - G & B Specialities, Inc.

BACK-SAVER - Shovels - Rugg Manufacturing Co. Inc.

BACK-SAVER/LITE - Shovels - Rugg Manufacturing Co. Inc.

BACK-SAVER/SWEEPER - Brooms - Rugg Manufacturing Co. Inc.

BACK-SAVER/WEEDER - Tools–garden - Rugg Manufacturing Co. Inc.

BACK SEAT BEAR - Toys–stuffed ☆ - Dakin Inc.

BACK SLAPPERS - Novelty items - Cal Themes Inc.

BACK STAGE - Apparel and accessories - Hi Joon Woo

BACK STAGE - Frames–eyeglass - Pathway Optical Prods.

BACK STAGE BOOKS - Publisher's imprints - Watson-Guptill Publications

BACK SUPPORTER - Mattresses - Spring Air Bedding Inc.

BACK SWING - Apparel and accessories ☆ - Jantzen Inc.

BACK TALK - Alarm systems - Directed Electronics, Inc.

BACK TO AMERICA - Wines - Old South Winery

BACK-TO-BACK - Cigarettes - Clanel Inc.

BACK TO BACK - Health care products - Bell-Horn

BACK-TO-BACK-PACK - Backpacks - A.I.P. Products, Inc.

BACK TO BASICS - Cosmetics - Graham Webb International

BACK TO BASICS - Dinnerware - Gibson Overseas Inc.

BACK-TO-BASICS - Glass products - Bellco Glass Inc.

BACK TO BASICS - Hosiery - Sara Lee Corp.

BACK TO BASICS - Toiletries ☆ - Smith & Vandiver, Inc.

BACK TO BASICS - Wallpaper ☆ - Fidelity Industries, Inc.

BACK TO BASICS - Wallpaper ☆ - Quality House Wallcoverings

BACK TO BASICS TOYS - Toys - Back to Basics Toys

BACK-TO-BLACK - Cleaning preparations - Mothers Polishes Waxes Cleaners

BACK TO CAMELOT - Christmas tree ornaments - Cracker Box Inc.

BACK TO CLASSICS - Fabrics - Stonebridge Co.

BACK TO NATURE - Cereal - Organic Milling

BACK TO NATURE - Jewelry - The Diamond Registry

BACK TO NATURE - Pharmaceutical preparations - Alva-Amco Pharmacal Co.

BACK TO NATURE - Wallpaper - Wallpaper Imports Inc.

BACK TO NEW - Cleaning preparations–carpet and rug - Eplo Products Corp.

BACK TO NORMAL - Girdles - Jeunique International, Inc.

BACK TO SLEEP - Fasteners–snap - Prince Lionheart, Inc.

BACK TO THE FARM - Games - Animal Town

BACK TRACK - Exercising equipment - M.T.I. Corp.

BACK TROLLER - Boats–motor ☆ - Yar-Craft, Inc.

BACK-UP - Back supports - Victor Toso

BACK-UP - Braces–orthopedic - Nada-Chair

BACK-UP - Health care products - Span-America Medical Systems, Inc.

BACK-UP - Underwear and nightwear - Maidenform Inc.

BACK-UPS - Power switching equipment - American Power Conversion Corp.

BACK UPS - Sunglasses - Eyesore Enterprises Inc.

BACK-UPS OFFICE - Electrical surge protectors - American Power Conversion Corp.

BACK-UPS PRO - Electrical equipment - American Power Conversion Corp.

BACK YARD BIRDS - Novelty items ☆ - United Design Corp.

BACK2BACK - Medical apparatus - Wilen Companies, Inc.

BACKAID - Pharmaceutical preparations - Alva-Amco Pharmacal Co.

BACKBAY - Beverages - Lenox-Martell, Inc.

BACKBEAT - Recording label - MCA Universal Studios

BACKBONE - Medical apparatus - Case Medical, Inc.

BACKCARE - Infant product - Simmons Juvenile Products Co., Inc.

BACKCOUNTRY GOURMET - Freeze dried foods - Eastern Mountain Sports, Inc.

BACKCOUNTRY PUBLICATIONS - Publisher's imprints - Countryman Press Inc.

BACKCOURT PLAYERS - Apparel–athletic - Mark L. Mccann

BACKCYCLE - Bicycles - Perfect Season, Inc.

BACKCYCLER CPM - Furniture - Ergomedics, Inc.

BACKDRAFT - Exercising equipment - Schwinn Cycling & Fitness Inc.

BACKDRAFT, THE - Gloves–work - Marmon Holdings, Inc.

BACKDROPS & BORDERS - Wallcoverings - Atrium Industries Inc.

BACKERTRACKER - Computer software - ViewPlan Inc.

BACKEYE - Ophthalmic goods - Embassy Creations Inc.

BACKFIRE - Toys ☆ - Tomy America, Inc.

BACKFLASH MOUNTAIN - Fireworks - Ingram Enterprises, Inc.

BACKFLIP - Puzzles - Binary Arts Corp.

BACKFLIPS - Bathing suits - Backflips

BACKFLOW - Golfing equipment - Golfsmith International Inc.

BACKGAMMON - Outdoor furniture - Rubbermaid Inc.

BACKGAMMON IN-THE-ROUND - Games - True Image Audio

BACKGAMMON TUTOR - Games ☆ - Milton Bradley Co.

BACKGAMMON4 - Games - Wow Toys, Inc.

BACKGROUNDS - Wallpaper - B. Berger Co.

BACKGROUNDS - Wallpaper ☆ - Sanitas Wallcoverings

BACKGROUNDS & BRUSHSTROKES - Wallpaper - Brewster Wallcovering Co.

BACKGROUNDS & FOREGROUNDS - Wallpaper - Carlton-Metro Wallcoverings

BACKGROUNDS FROM PARIS - Wallpaper ☆ - Fairwinds Studio

BACKGROUNDS II - Wallpaper - Sanitas Wallcoverings

BACKGROUNDS III - Wallpaper - Sanitas Wallcoverings

BACKHAND, THE - Cosmetic applicators - Asher Cloyd Enterprises

BACKHOME! - Computer software - ETI USA

BACKING CLASS - Sporting goods - Outdoor Technologies Group

BACKJOY - Orthopedic products - Preston Willingham

BACKLASH - Toys - Tonka Corp.

BACKLASH - Trading cards and stamps - Wildstorm Productions

BACKMAG - Health care products - Michael J. Alberts

BACKMAN POWER MASSAGE TABLE - Massage products - Backman Products, Inc.

BACKNACK - Tools–hand-operated - Myra Per-Lee

BACKOVICH - Vodka - Glencourt Products

BACKPACK - Envelopes - Farrell-Towt International, Inc.

BACKPACK - Filing cabinets–metal - Knoll, Inc.

BACKPACKER - Fishing rods - Zebco Corp.

BACKPACKER - Guitars - C.F. Martin & Co., Inc.

BACKPACKER - Guns - Crosman Corp.

BACKPACKER - Knives–pocket - Precise International/Wenger

BACKPACKER'S PANTRY - Food products - Back Packers Pantry

BACKPACKING IS IN-TENTS - Apparel and accessories - GNP Graphics & Design

BACKPAX! - Publisher's imprints - Backpax International Ltd.

BACKPOCKET - Bags - Armament Systems and Procedures, Inc.

BACKPORCH - Floor coverings–carpet and rugs ☆ - Trans-Ocean Import Co. Inc.

BACKRIDER - Travel bags - ENRGE Sports Inc.

BACKRITE - Tables–wood - Hugh's Co. Inc.

BACKROAD BLUES - Apparel and accessories - Wal-Mart Stores Inc.

BACKROAD RACERS - Toys - Revell-Monogram, Inc.

BACKROADS - Bicycles - Raleigh USA Bicycle Co.

BACKROADS - Footwear–men's ☆ - Thom McAn Shoe Co.

BACKRUB - Electrical equipment - Kinsei Shiatsu, Inc.

BACKSAVER - Caulking compounds ☆ - Ardisam, Inc.

BACKSAVER - Medical apparatus - Chiroventures Ltd.

BACKSAVER - Pizzas–frozen - Farberware Inc.

BACKSAVER - Tools - Burton C. Harlan

BACKSAVER PRODUCTS - Seats–automobile - Nepsco, Inc.

BACKSAVER, THE - Chairs–upholstered - Dealers Business Forms Co. Inc.

BACKSAVER, THE - Medical apparatus - Standex International Corp.

BACKSCRATCHERS - Manicure preparations - Backscratchers, Inc.

BACKSEAT BOOKS - Publisher's imprints - Rand McNally & Co.

BACKSEAT WEBBIE - Infant product - Children on the Go, Inc.

BACKSIDERS - Apparel and accessories ☆ - Edison Brothers Stores, Inc.

BACKSOOTHER - Cushions - David B. Gardner

BACKSPIN - Apparel and accessories - Carolina Custom Golf

BACKSPLASH - Glassware–household - Julie Ueland

BACKS'PORT - Health care products - Camp, Inc.

BACKSTAGE - Amplifiers–musical instrument ☆ - Peavey Electronics Corp.

BACKSTOP - Boats–canoes - Neil Enterprises

BACKSTOP - Medical apparatus - Merit Medical Systems Inc.

BACKSTREET - Snack foods - Comfort Foods, Inc.

☆ = Now out of production

BACKSTREET MCA - Recording label - MCA Universal Studios
BACKSTROKE - Back massage device - David M. Vitko
BACKSTROKER - Skin care products - David Wood
BACKSWING - Exercising equipment ☆ - Moving Books Inc.
BACKSYS - Medical apparatus - Foot Levelers, Inc.
BACKTALK - Telephone apparatus - M.O.O. Corp.
BACKTECH - Exercise equipment - Back Technologies, Inc.
BACKTROLLOR - Boats–motor - Alumacraft Boat Co.
BACKUP BASICS - Computer software - Conner Peripherals, Inc.
BACKUP.UNET - Computer software - Unitech/Raxco, Inc.
BACKWARDS UNIVERSITY - T-shirts–men's - Danny Jessie Wolf and Lorrie Louise Wolf Partnership
BACKWASH - Water treating compounds - Robarb Inc.
BACKWATERS BY ATS - Motor vehicles–all-terrain - American Travel Systems, Inc.
BACKWATER'S FISHING APPAREL - Apparel and accessories - Christine M. Gorman
BACKWOODS - Cigar boxes–wood - Consolidated Cigar Corp.
BACKWOODS BOMB - Toys–automobiles - Mattel, Inc.
BACKWOODS BUCK - Hunting equipment - WPC Holdings, Inc.
BACKWOODS CUTTER - Insecticides - Miles Inc. (Agriculture Div.)
BACKWORDS - Hats - Patrick Sullivan
BACKYARD - Recording label - All American Music Group
BACKYARD BABIES - Fruits and vegetables - Natural Selection Foods
BACKYARD BANQUET FOR BIRDS - Bird feeds - Agway Country Foods Inc.
BACKYARD BARBECUE - Toys - Playskool, Inc.
BACKYARD BEAUTIES - Fruits and vegetables - Natural Selection Foods
BACKYARD BIRDS - Statuary - United Design Corp.
BACKYARD BUDDIES - Garden equipment - Cobraco Manufacturing, Inc.
BACKYARD GRILL - Turkeys - Jennie-O Foods, Inc.
BACKYARD KICKER - Toys - Poof Toy Products, Inc.
BACKYARD SCIENTIST - Publisher's imprints ☆ - Small World Toys
BACKYARD, THE - Computer software - Broderbund Software, Inc.
BACKYARD WILD, THE - Video production - Kaytee Products Inc.
BACKYARDER - Hammocks - Gleason Corp.
BACO - Furniture - Bassick Casters
BACON - Office supplies - Bacon Felt Co. Inc.
BACON B & D - Banjos ☆ - Fred Gretsch Enterprises
BACON BITS PIG - Toys–stuffed - Dakin Inc.
BACON CURLS - Snack foods - Curtice-Burns Foods, Inc.
BACON-EEZ - Meat products–pork - Columbia Products Inc.
BACON IN THE ROUND - Computer software - Patcud Investments, Inc.
BACON IN THE SUN - Toys–stuffed - Dakin Inc.
BACON-QUIK - Meat products–pork - Columbia Products Inc.
BACON SLICE - Candy ☆ - Gilliam Candy Co. Inc. (Gilliam Candy Brands)
BACONER - Barbecues and grills ☆ - Hamilton Beach/Proctor-Silex Inc.
BACON'S C-K TEA - Pharmaceutical preparations - Brown Manufacturing Co.
BACONWAVE - Cookware - E. Mishan & Sons, Inc.
BACOTOL - Pharmaceutical preparations - Ray Drug Co.
BACPAC - Health care products - Comfy-Back/E.J. Evans
BACPLAQUE - Chemical preparations - Novagen, Inc.
BACQUET - Games - Let's Play...
BACSTAXBILL - Computer software - Barrie Adsett Computer Services, Inc.
BACT-X - Cleaning preparations - Knight Marketing Corp.
BACTA CLEAN - Cleaning preparations - Coughlan Products Corp.
BACTA SCREEN - Cleaning preparations - Coughlan Products Corp.
BACTA-STAT - Deodorizers - Coughlan Products Corp.
BACTAL - Soap ☆ - Redi Products Laboratories
BACTALIN - Mouthwashes ☆ - Redi Products Laboratories
BACTEC - Pesticides–agricultural - Bactec Corp.
BACTER PLUS - Pet products ☆ - Aquatronics-Filtronics
BACTERNA - Pharmaceutical preparations ☆ - U.S. Ethicals Inc.
BACTI-CLEANSE - Pharmaceutical preparations - Pedinol Pharmacal Inc.
BACTI-GROW - Vitamins and nutritional supplements - NRG, Inc.
BACTI-STAT - Health care products - Huntington Laboratories Inc.
BACTICORT - Pharmaceutical preparations - Rugby Laboratories Inc.
BACTINE - Pharmaceutical preparations - Bayer Corp. (Consumer Care Div.)
BACTISHIELD - Fibers–nylon - Fiber Industries, Inc.
BACTIZIN - Pet products - Aquatic Biotechnologies Inc.
BACTIZYME - Cleaning preparations - Nyco Products Co.
BACTOCILL - Antibiotics - Smithkline Beecham Corp.
BACTOID - Veterinary pharmaceutical preparations - Texas Vet Lab, Inc.
BACTOPUR - Pet products ☆ - Sera Aquaristik USA Inc.
BACTRASTAT - Filters–air - Home Care Industries, Inc.
BACTRIM - Antibiotics - Roche Laboratories
BACTROBAN - Antibiotics - Smithkline Beecham Corp.

BACTROBAN NASAL - Skin care products - Smithkline Beecham Corp.
BACTURCULT - Pharmaceutical preparations - Wampole Laboratories Div.
BACULOGOLD - Chemical preparations - Pharmingen
BACVECTOR - Chemical preparations - Novagen, Inc.
BAD - Prophylactics - Finley Co.
BAD AIR SPONGE - Chemical preparations - Mateson Chemical Corp.
BAD-ATTITUDES - Publisher's imprints - Creative Excellence, Inc.
BAD AZZ - Toys - Walter J. McGivney
BAD BEARD ACOUSTIC DESIGN - Audio equipment - Michael H. Beard
BAD BIRD - Toys - Tonka Corp.
BAD BLOOD - Video games - Origin Systems, Inc.
BAD BONES - Motorcycle parts and accessories - Stephen Dobernic
BAD BOY - Apparel–men's - Platypus Wear, Inc.
BAD BOY - Toys - Tonka Corp.
BAD BOY MADE GOOD - Apparel–men's - Laurentian Group
BAD BOYS - Recording label ☆ - Prince/SF Productions
BAD CALL - Apparel and accessories - Gregory V. Moss
BAD DOG RANCH - Wines - Salmon Creek Cellars Inc.
BAD FROG - Beverages - Wauldron Corp.
BAD GUY - Cakes ☆ - Christopher's Chewies
BAD GUYS - Toys - Azrak-Hamway International, Inc.
BAD HABIT - Toys - Tonka Corp.
BAD HAIR DAY - Apparel and accessories - L.A. Sweats
BAD HARE DAYS - Bakery products - Capital Concepts, Inc.
BAD IDEA - Decals and transfers - Phil Monty Hennessee
BAD IMAGE, INC. - Apparel and accessories - Bad Image, Inc.
BAD INFLUENCE - Apparel and accessories - Kelsey Enterprises, Inc.
BAD JUJU - Decals and transfers - Phil Monty Hennessee
BAD KITTY PRESS - Publisher's imprints - Boom Boom Wiz
BAD LANDER - Toys - Tonka Corp.
BAD MAX - T-shirts–men's - SR Concepts, Ltd.
BAD MISTER FROSTY - Computer software - Interplay Productions
BAD MOJO - Games - Drew Pictures
BAD TO THE BONE - Publisher's imprints - Shelia Mason
BADA - Eyeglasses - Bada USA, Inc.
BADASH - Glass products - Badash Jack Inc.
BADASS - Musical instruments - Leo Quan Badass Musical Products
BADAVICI - Jewelry - David Badowich & Associates
BADDEST OF THE BAD POSSE - Recording label - Baddest of the Bad Posse Records
BADEN - Wines - Dieter Steinmann Inc.
BADENIA - Shoes ☆ - Mengen-Ulla
BADFOOT - Toys ☆ - Tomy America, Inc.
BADGE - Apparel and accessories - R.H. Macy & Co.
BADGEBUILDER - Computer software - New England Security & Communications, Inc.
BADGECAM - Cameras - Polaroid Corp.
BADGEMASTER - Computer peripheral equipment - Amtech Corp.
BADGER - Bicycles ☆ - Huffy Corp.
BADGER - Brushes–paint - Wooster Brush Co.
BADGER - Chairs–folding - E-Z Sales & Manufacturing, Inc.
BADGER - Cosmetics - William F. Whyte
BADGER - Furniture - Badger Basket Co.
BADGER - Hardware - Badger Air-Brush Co.
BADGER - Pencils - General Pencil Co.
BADGER - Recording label - Jazz Composer's Orchestra Association Inc.
BADGER - Rope - John Rauschenberger Co.
BADGER - Shovels - Keller Manufacturing Co. Inc.
BADGER FARMS - Food products ☆ - Maple Leaf Farms Inc.
BADGER-GLAS - Shovels - Keller Manufacturing Co. Inc.
BADGER/MAGNUM - Exercising equipment - Badger Fitness Equipment
BADGER STICK - Sausages - Fred Usinger, Inc.
BADIA A. COLTIBUONO - Olive oil - De Medici Imports Ltd.
BADLANDER - Motorcycle parts and accessories - H-D Michigan, Inc.
BADLANDS TRAIL - Toys–automobiles - Tyco Toys
BADOUX - Wines - Dreyfus Ashby Inc.
BADROCK - Toys - Rob Liefeld, Inc.
BAEDEKER - Publisher's imprints - Simon & Schuster, Inc.
BAEKGAARD LTD. - Giftware - Baekgaard Ltd.
BAETIS - Apparel–athletic - Samuel A. Bakke
BAFFETTE - Accordions - Castiglione Accordion
BAFFIN - Food products - Robert W. Hayman Inc.
BAFFLER, THE - Alarm systems - Reflectory
BAFLUX - Lighting fixtures - Edison Price Lighting
BAFO! - Software - Netbase Corp.
BAFPE - Health care products - Maddak Inc.

BAFRA - Cigarettes - G.A. Georgopulo & Co. Inc.
B.A.G. - Apparel and accessories - Bag Industries Inc.
BAG-A-GIFT - Paper–gift wrap - Crystal Tissue Co. Inc.
BAG A SPORT - Luggage - Mary Irons Kersey
BAG-AGE - Handbags ☆ - Pyramid Handbags Inc.
BAG AUTHORITY, THE - Bags–duffel - Sports Authority, Inc.
BAG BALM - Veterinary pharmaceutical preparations - Dairy Association Co. Inc.
BAG BLASTERS - Backpacks - Hedstrom Corp.
BAG BOY - Golf carts - Bag Boy Inc.
BAG BUDDIES - Aquariums–household - Jungle Laboratories Corp.
BAG BUTLER - Containers–plastic - Bag Butler, Inc.
BAG COLLECTOR, THE - Bags - Dawne Alumbaugh Williams
BAG FOR ALL REASONS, A - Paper–gift wrap - Loretta L. Stenovich
BAG HOG - Trash containers - Form Farm Inc.
BAG KEEPER, THE - Plastics - Shawn K. Halverson
BAG KING - Golf carts - Montgomery Ward & Co. Inc.
BAG LADY DOLLS - Dolls - Bag Lady Dolls, Inc.
BAG LOK - Tape–masking ☆ - Mystik Corp.
BAG N BOW - Paper–gift wrap - Crystal Tissue Co. Inc.
BAG-N-SEASON - Seasonings - McCormick & Co., Inc.
BAG 'N TRAIN - Toys–trains ☆ - Century Products Co.
BAG-O-BALSA - Wood products ☆ - Paul K. Guillow Inc.
BAG O' BATS - Candy - Gilliam Candy Co. Inc. (Gilliam Candy Brands)
BAG O' BEANS - Soups–mixes - ACB/Richard Watson
BAG O BITS - Hardware - Eazypower Corp.
BAG-O-BONES - Pet treats - Items Inc.
BAG O BOOKS - Publisher's imprints - Ottenheimer Publishers, Inc.
BAG O' BOWS - Pet products - Wee Waggers
BAG O' CHILI FIXIN'S KIT - Food products - Jardine's Texas Foods
BAG-O-FLAVOR - Seasonings - Pacific Foods Inc.
BAG O GOLD - Food products - Armour Dairy Co.
BAG O' KITS - Candy - Gilliam Candy Co. Inc. (Gilliam Candy Brands)
BAG-O-MATIC - Bags–plastic - Durabag Co. Inc.
BAG O'BLOCKS - Pet products - Golden West Bird Farm Inc.
BAG O'BUGS - Pet products - Golden West Bird Farm Inc.
BAG OF BONES - Dog food - Lisa M. Breitenbach
BAG OF TRICKS - Computer software ☆ - DataPak Software Inc.
BAG OF TUNES - Motorcycle parts and accessories - Davis Designs, Inc.
BAG OF WHIM - Handbags - Gianna Majzler
BAG O'STUFF - School supplies - Block and Co., Inc.
BAG SNAGS - Housewares - Tyz-All Plastics Inc.
BAG SPECIALISTS - Handbags - Bag Specialists Inc.
BAG STAND CO., THE - Bags–laundry - Bag Stand Co.
BAG STIK - Traps–animal - Fuhrman Diversified
BAG TECH - Golfing equipment - Dynasty Golf Co. Inc.
BAG TENDERS - Bags–canvas - Susan B. Licata
BAG, THE - Pet products - Seachem Laboratories
BAG THE PEAKS - Games - C.W. Heileg & Associates
BAG TO BASICS - Handbags ☆ - Gold Medal Inc.
BAG-TO-GO - Pet products ☆ - Hawkeye Corp.
BAG TOTER - Luggage - Aparco Inc.
BAG TRAY - Motor vehicle parts and accessories - Winfield Consumer Products, Inc.
BAG WORLD - Handbags - Hazan Imports Corp.
BAGACEIRA DO MINHO - Wines - Admiral Wine Merchants
BAGCRAFT - Bags - Bagcraft Corp. of America
BAGEASY - Health care products - Respironics, Inc.
BAGEL BABYS - Bakery products - Bagel Boys Bakery & Deli Co.
BAGEL BAR - Counter tops–laminated - Leisure Craft Inc.
BAGEL BARREL - Bakeries - Bagel Barrel Corp.
BAGEL BARREL - Containers - RF Nature Farm Foods, Inc.
BAGEL BARS - Bakery products - Broadmoor Baker, Inc.
BAGEL BITER - Food products machinery - Larien Products
BAGEL BITES - Food products - Ore-Ida Foods, Inc.
BAGEL BLENDS - Cheese - Raskas Foods, Inc.
BAGEL BONES - Dog food - Julia S. Mickum
BAGEL BOTTOMS - Food products - KT Kitchens
BAGEL BREAK - Food products - Bagl Corp.
BAGEL BUTLER - Housewares - Larien Products
BAGEL CRISPS - Snack foods - Swissrose International Inc.
BAGEL FACTORY - Bakery products - Bagel Factory
BAGEL HAPPY - Jewelry - Judith H. Blau
BAGEL HUGGER - Housewares - John A. Mcleod
BAGEL MASTER - Food products machinery - M & E Manufacturing Co., Inc.
BAGEL/MEISTER - Food products machinery - M & E Manufacturing Co., Inc.

BAGEL SMASH - Sandwiches–prepackaged - Nancy Hope Gallo
BAGEL STOP - Bagels - Nabco, Inc.
BAGEL STUFFS - Bagels - Bessin Corp.
BAGEL TEMPTATIONS - Cheese - Rondele Foods, LLC
BAGEL THAT WON THE WEST, THE - Bagels - Western Bagel Baking Corp.
BAGEL TIME - Bagels - Sara Lee Corp.
BAGEL TOPPER - Cheese ☆ - Scott's, Inc.
BAGEL TRAP - Kitchen utensils–aluminum - Bagel Trap, Inc.
BAGEL TREATS - Snack foods ☆ - Gourmet Club Corp.
BAGEL WORLD - Breads and pastries - Bagel World, Inc.
BAGELBREAD - Breads - Robin W. Bissell
BAGELBY'S - Bakery products - Bagel Bros., Inc.
BAGELDOG - Frankfurters - Vienna Sausage Manufacturing Co.
BAGELETTA - Bagel sandwiches - Janson's Foods Inc.
BAGELOG - Cream cheese - Sodiaal North America Corp.
BAGELROL - Bakery products - John Morrongiello
BAGELS - Toys–stuffed - Gund, Inc.
BAGELS AND LOCKS - Jewelry - AB Designs, Inc.
BAGELS FOREVER - Bagels - Bagels Forever Inc.
BAGELTIME - Bagels - Bageltime Inc.
BAGELWICH - Bagel sandwiches - Janson's Foods Inc.
BAGELZ THE BAGEL BAKERY - Bagels - Bagelz Franchising Corp.
BAGETELLE - Floor coverings–carpet and rugs ☆ - Regal Rugs Inc.
BAGFUL OF BAGELS - Bakery products - Bagful of Bagels, Inc.
BAGFUL OF FITNESS - Exercising equipment - Twinson Co.
BAGGALLINI - Bags - Baggallini
BAGGER - Thread - Threads USA Div.
BAGGETT - Thread - Threads USA Div.
BAGGETTE - Apparel–athletic - Patagonia, Inc.
BAGGIES - Apparel and accessories - Patagonia, Inc.
BAGGIES - Bags–plastic - Mobil Chemical Co. Plastics Div.
BAGGO - Games ☆ - Pressman Toy Corp.
BAGIT SYSTEM - Containers - Bag Connection Inc.
BAGLADY - Educational materials - Baglady Press, LLC
BAGMAN - Tools - Arcoa Industries
BAGMANAGER - Housewares - The Clean Advantage, Inc.
BAGMASTER - Firearm holsters, belts, and cases - Bagmaster Manufacturing, Inc.
BAG'MS - Plastic bags - Instrument Systems Corp.
BAGODA - Leather goods - Bagoda, Inc.
BAGPIPER - Robes - Mcgregor Corp.
BAGS AGAIN - Plastics - Strout Plastics Inc.
BAGS BY PINKY - Handbags - P & R Handbag Inc.
BAGS BY PONCE - Bags - Ponce's Creations
BAGS FOR KEEPS - Vases–ceramic - Bonnie Lee Creations, Inc.
BAGS HOOK-UP - Electronic equipment - Hook-Up, Inc.
BAGS ON BOARD - Bags–trash - Martim Group, Inc.
BAGS ON TIME - Bags–plastic - Essex Plastics, Inc.
BAGUETTE - Flatware - Couzon USA
BAGUETTE - Floor coverings–carpet and rugs ☆ - Masland Corp.
BAGUETTE - Glassware–household ☆ - Dansk International Designs, Ltd.
BAGUETTE - Mirrors ☆ - Floral Glass & Mirror Inc.
BAGUETTE - Rings–jewelry - Artcarved Inc.
BAGUETTE - Wainscotting - A.P.F. Master Framemaker
BAGUETTE DE PARIS - Breads - P.K.M. International, Inc.
BAGUETTES - Bakery products - Lunds, Inc.
BAGUIO - Bathmats - Ramar International Corp.
BAGZILLA - Bags–trash - Sears, Roebuck and Co.
BAH KOO - Toys–stuffed - Robert V. Rhodes
BAH-RUM - Food products - H.C. Brill Co., Inc.
BAHA - Card game - International Games
BAHA - Seafood products–canned or cured ☆ - Lyon Food Products Inc.
BAHAMA - Bakery products - Fuchs Bakery Co.
BAHAMA - Bicycles ☆ - Murray, Inc.
BAHAMA - Boats–motor - Glastex Co.
BAHAMA - Floor coverings - Congoleum Corp.
BAHAMA - Floor coverings–carpet and rugs - Barrett Carpet Mills Inc.
BAHAMA - Frames–eyeglass - May Optical Co. Inc.
BAHAMA - Tiles–ceramic - Payless Cashways Inc.
BAHAMA BAY - Fabrics - Greenwood Mills Inc.
BAHAMA BEAUTY - Apparel stores–lingerie - Goddess Bra
BAHAMA BLUSH - Nail care products ☆ - Cosmair Inc.
BAHAMA BREEZE - Apparel–athletic - Darden Corp.
BAHAMA BREEZE - Deodorizers - W.W. Grainger, Inc.
BAHAMA BREEZE - Hair care products - Mennen Co.
BAHAMA BRONZE - Skin care products - Anjuli Cosmetics

☆ = Now out of production

BAHAMA CLASSIC - Seafood products–fresh or frozen - L.M. Sandler & Sons, Inc.
BAHAMA MAMA - Suntan lotions - Gregory Guccione
BAHAMA MIAMI - Meat products–pork - Hot 'n Spicey, Inc.
BAHAMA PLAID - Bedding–linen - Dan River Inc.
BAHAMA WHITE - Wines - Bardenheier Wine Cellars
BAHAMAS COLLECTION - Furniture–wood - Fran's Basket House
BAHIA - Brushes–paint - Corona Brushes Inc.
BAHIA - Floor coverings–carpet and rugs ☆ - Providence Rug Co.
BAHIA - Furniture ☆ - Bassett Furniture Industries, Inc.
BAHIA - Liquors ☆ - Heublein, Inc.
BAHIA - Swimming pools ☆ - Doughboy Recreational Inc.
BAHIA - Tableware–earthenware - Johnson Brothers, USA, Inc.
BAHIA BREEZE CUSHION COLLECTION - Furniture - Telescope Casual Furniture Inc.
BAHIA DE ORO - Seafood products–fresh or frozen - Coast to Coast Seafood Inc.
BAHIA ENTERTAINMENT - Labels–paper - Bahia Entertainment
BAHIA MAR - Seafood products–fresh or frozen - ICD Group Inc.
BAHIA REEF - Floor coverings–carpet and rugs ☆ - Catalina Carpet Mills Inc.
BAHIM - Foot aid - Jamol Laboratories Inc.
BAHL - Cheese - Fennimore Cheese
BAHLSEN - Crackers - Bahlsen Inc.
BAHLSEN AFRIKA - Confections - Bahlsen Inc.
BAI - Batteries - Douglas Battery Manufacturing Co.
BAI - Luggage - Buenos Aires Imports
BAIER - Food products - De Choix Specialty Foods Co.
BAIGISH - Electronic equipment - INT Traders, Inc.
BAIKAL - Sporting goods - Commercial Trading Imports Inc.
BAIKO YOGURTS - Yogurt - Crystal Food Import Corp.
BAIL-A-WAY - Buckets–plastic ☆ - Moeller Products Co. Inc.
BAIL-OUT - Toys–models - Estes Industries
BAILA - Recording label - Worldwide Entertainment
BAILEN - Helmets–athletic ☆ - E.D. Bullard Co.
BAILES - Dog food - Bailes Pet Food Co. Inc.
BAILEY - Hats - Bailey Hat Co.
BAILEY - Toys–stuffed ☆ - Russ Berrie and Co., Inc.
BAILEY FARM - Food products - Bailey Farm Dairy Co.
BAILEY RESEARCH, INC. - Vitamins and nutritional supplements - Bailey Research, Inc.
BAILEYS - Meat products - Clarence Bailey
BAILEY'S BOOK HOUSE - Educational materials - Edmark Corp.
BAILEY'S IRISH CREAM - Ice cream - Haagen-Dazs Co. Inc.
BAILEYS ORIGINAL - Beverages–alcohol - Paddington Corp.
BAILIWICK - Games - Bailiwick Enterprises, Inc.
BAILPRO - Computer storage devices - Bailpro Software
BAIN DE BEAUTE - Cosmetics - Arizona Natural Resources
BAIN DE SOLEIL - Cosmetics - Revlon Consumer Products Corp.
BAIN DE SOLEIL - Frames–eyeglass - May Optical Co. Inc.
BAIN DE SOLEIL - Sunglasses - International Tropic-Cal Inc. (I SKI Div.)
BAIN DE TERRE SPA - Hair care products - Zotos International Inc.
BAIN DES FLEURS - Skin care products - Conair Corp.
BAIN DOUCEUR - Cosmetics - Cosmair Inc.
BAINBRIDGE - Cabinets - American Woodmark Corp.
BAINBRIDGE - Clocks - Ridgeway Clock Co.
BAINBRIDGE - Eyeglasses - Bausch & Lomb Inc.
BAINBRIDGE - Floor coverings–carpet and rugs ☆ - Lees Carpets
BAINBRIDGE - Food products - Bainbridge Corp.
BAINBRIDGE - Recording label - Bainbridge Entertainment Co. Inc.
BAINBRIDGE - Wallpaper - United Wallcoverings
BAINBRIDGE BEARS - Greeting cards - American Greetings Corp.
BAINBRIDGE ISLAND - Apparel–children's ☆ - Pacific Trail, Inc.
BAINBRIDGE ISLAND WINERY - Skin care products - Bainbridge Island Vineyards & Winery
BAIRD - Fabrics - Hamilton Adams Imports Ltd.
BAIT BAG, THE - Feed bags - Bait Bag
BAIT CARE - Aquatic pharmacuetical preparations - Aquarium Pharmaceuticals, Inc.
BAIT CARRIER - Sporting goods - Magic Products, Inc.
BAIT CHLOR - Pet products ☆ - Jungle Laboratories Corp.
BAIT DRAPES - Fishing tackle - Area Rule Engineering Inc.
BAIT KEEPER, THE - Bags - Sportmans Advantage, Inc.
BAIT LIFE - Pet products ☆ - Jungle Laboratories Corp.
BAIT-N-A-BOTTLE - Sporting goods - Gapen Co.
BAIT SAVER - Aquariums–household - Marine Metal Products

BAIT SEDATE - Veterinary pharmaceutical preparations - Professional Sporting Goods, Inc.
BAIT SHUTTLE - Fishing lures - Frabill Inc.
BAIT SHUTTLE - Fishing tackle - Palm Leaf Products, Inc.
BAIT SPORT - Fishing tackle - Ashaway Line & Twine Manufacturing Co.
BAIT TANNINS - Water purification systems - Professional Sporting Goods, Inc.
BAIT WALKER - Sporting goods - Gapen Co.
BAITDATA - Fishing equipment - Baitdata, Inc.
BAITER-AID - Bait-well aerators - Coleman Co., Inc.
BAITFISH - Fishing lures - Lindy Little Joe Inc.
BAITMATE - Fishing lures - Wisconsin Pharmacal Co. Inc.
BAITMATE ULTIMATE - Fishing lures - Wisconsin Pharmacal Co. Inc.
BAIT'S ALIVE - Aquarium accessories - Aquaculture Aquavet
BAIT'S ALIVE! - Aquarium accessories - Sportfishing Aquavet
BAIT'S ALIVE! - Water treating compounds - Novalek, Inc.
BAJA - Bicycles ☆ - Murray, Inc.
BAJA - Boats–motor - Baja Marine Corp.
BAJA - Cases–eyeglass - Majorca, Inc.
BAJA - Desk sets - Micropoint Inc.
BAJA - Floor coverings–carpet and rugs - Dan River Inc.
BAJA - Floor coverings–carpet and rugs - Wunda Weve Carpet Co.
BAJA - Fruits and vegetables - Lakeview Farms
BAJA - Glassware–household - Crisa Corp.
BAJA - Gocarts - Commonwealth Inc.
BAJA - Hydrotherapy equipment - Baja Products, Ltd.
BAJA - Liquors - Frank-Lin Distillers Products
BAJA - Motor vehicles–trucks - General Motors Corp. (Chevrolet Motor Div.)
BAJA - Recording label - TSR Records
BAJA 200 - Gocarts - Commonwealth Inc.
BAJA 1000 - Frames–eyeglass ☆ - Universal/Univis Inc.
BAJA BACKROADS - Toys–automobiles - Mattel, Inc.
BAJA BOARD - Skateboards - U.S. Bendables Corp.
BAJA BREAKER - Toys–automobiles - Mattel, Inc.
BAJA BUG - Bicycles ☆ - Murray, Inc.
BAJA BULLIES - Decals and transfers - Lawrence Bettencourt
BAJA BUSTER - Bicycles ☆ - Murray, Inc.
BAJA BUSTER - Toys–automobiles - Mattel, Inc.
BAJA CRUISER - Trailers–travel - Compact Equipment Co.
BAJA DUNE CRAWLERS - Toys - Tonka Corp.
BAJA ENSALADA - Food products - Triune Corp.
BAJA GRABBER - Tires - Bridgestone/Firestone, Inc.
BAJA GRIPS - Sporting goods - Baja Products
BAJA RADIAL - Tires - Max-Trac Tire Co.
BAJA RUNNER - Tires - Bridgestone/Firestone, Inc.
BAJA SPORT GRIP - Steering mechanisms–motor vehicle - Superior Industries International, Inc.
BAJA USA - Motor vehicle parts and accessories ☆ - Cobbs Manufacturing Co.
BAJEE - Apparel and accessories - Bajee, Inc.
BAJISTA SOUTHWEST - Bean dish - MT OSO Trading Co.
BAJONET - Water purification systems - Structural Fibers
BAK CHEK - Plumbing fixtures - Sloan Valve Co.
BAK-KLENE - Oils–edible - Par-Way Group
BAK-KLENE - Oils–edible - Tryson Co.
BAK-O-FLEX - Brushes–paint - Baker Brush Co. Inc.
BAK-O-PLAST - Brushes–paint - Baker Brush Co. Inc.
BAK-O-TEK - Brushes–paint - Baker Brush Co. Inc.
BAK-O-TEX - Paint rollers - E-Z Paintr Corp.
BAK-O-TIP - Brushes–paint - Baker Brush Co. Inc.
BAK PAK - Electrical equipment - GB Electrical Inc.
BAK-SPAR - Varnishes - Pettit Paint Co. Inc.
BAK-TA-BASIX - Apparel–men's - High Wide & Handsome Designer Ltd.
BAK-V-SPAR - Varnishes - Pettit Paint Co. Inc.
BAKALON - Cooking equipment–household - Chicago Metallic Products Inc.
BAKE-A-DINNER - Dinners–frozen ☆ - Green Giant Co.
BAKE-A-TATER - Food products - Prestige American Foods
BAKE A TREAT - Pans - E-Z-Por Corp.
BAKE & SERVE - Pies–frozen - Sara Lee Corp.
BAKE & TASTE - Computer software - Mind Play
BAKE FRESH - Cups–paper - Rockline Industries Inc.
BAKE-IN-BAG - Turkeys - Land O'Lakes Inc.
BAKE IN GOOD HEALTH - Cereal - Nabisco Foods Group
BAKE-IN-THE-BAG - Turkey breast - Carolina Turkeys
BAKE-INS - Cooking equipment–household ☆ - Dansk International Designs, Ltd.

☆ = Now out of production

BAKE-IT-EASY AUTOMATIC BREADMAKER - Cooking equipment–household - High Performance Appliances, Inc.

BAKE IT FRESH - Pastries - Pepperidge Farm Inc.

BAKE-ITOS - Snack foods - Mexi-Snax Inc.

BAKE-KING - Cooking equipment–household - Chicago Metallic Products Inc.

BAKE-KING MAGIC - Cooking equipment–household ☆ - Chicago Metallic Products Inc.

BAKE-KING'S ANSWER - Cooking equipment–household ☆ - Chicago Metallic Products Inc.

BAKE 'N BACON - Cooking equipment–household - Nordic Ware

BAKE 'N' CARRY - Covered bakeware ☆ - Corning Inc.

BAKE N ROASTER, THE - Ovens–roaster - Gemco Ware, Inc.

BAKE 'N' SERVE - Bakeware - Corning Inc.

BAKE 'N SHOW - Cookware - Genpak Corp.

BAKE 'N' STORE - Bakeware ☆ - Corning Inc.

BAKE 'N TAKE - Cooking equipment–household ☆ - Mirro Corp.

BAKE 'N TAKE - Pans - E-Z-Por Corp.

BAKE NJOY - Bakery products–frozen - Bake-N-Joy Foods, Inc.

BAKE-OFF - Desserts - Rich Products Corp.

BAKE-OFF COLLECTION - Cakes–mixes ☆ - Pillsbury Co.

BAKE 'R BROIL - Fish–fresh or frozen - Nordic Fisheries

BAKE-RITE - Aluminum products - E-Z-Por Corp.

BAKE SHOP - Food products - General Mills, Inc.

BAKE SHOPPE - Bakery products - B. Manischewitz Co.

BAKE SHOPPE - Bakery products ☆ - Specialty Bakers Inc.

BAKE TOPS - Cakes - Pillsbury Co.

BAKEALL - Shortening ☆ - Swift Edible Oil Co.

BAKED BEADS - Jewelry - David Cohen

BAKED CHEX MIX - Snack foods - Ralston Purina Co.

BAKED LAYS - Snack foods - Frito-Lay, Inc.

BAKED PERFECT - Pies–frozen - Sara Lee Corp.

BAKED POCKETS - Food products - Continental Delight/Ore-Ida

BAKED TOSTITOS - Snack foods - Frito-Lay, Inc.

BAKED TOSTITOS COOL RANCH - Snack foods - Frito-Lay, Inc.

BAKED TOSTITOS ORIGINAL - Snack foods - Frito-Lay, Inc.

BAKED WITH ALOHA - Cookies - Uncle Noname Cookie Co.

BAKEEZ PAN - Oils–edible - Concept Foods

BAKEL CHIPS - Bagels - Pride of the Plains, Ltd.

BAKELITE - Cigarette holders - Gesty Trading & Manufacturing Corp.

BAKELITE - Cigarette holders ☆ - Bryn Mawr Smokers Sundries Inc.

BAKELITE - Resins–synthetic - Georgia-Pacific Corp.

BAKELITE 21 - Fish–fresh or frozen - Trident Seafoods Corp.

BAKELON - Bakery products - Sibille Dalle Inc.

BAKEN-ETS - Pork rinds - Frito-Lay, Inc.

BAKENAMEL - Hardware - National Manufacturing Co.

BAKEPACKER - Camping products - Strike 2 Industries, Inc.

BAKER - Bakery products - Sokol and Co.

BAKER - Food products - Baker Brands

BAKER - Furniture - Baker, Knapp & Tubbs

BAKER - Trailers–travel ☆ - Giles Industries

BAKER - Window coverings - Covoc Corp.

BAKER & JONES - Cookies - K & D Enterprises, Inc.

BAKER-BENJES - Footwear–men's - Baker-Benjes, Inc.

BAKER BOY - Flour–blended - International Market Brands, Inc.

BAKER CAC - Computer software - Baker Hughes Inc.

BAKER CUMMINS DERMATOLOGICALS, INC. - Skin care products - Baker Norton Pharmaceuticals, Inc.

BAKER-EZE - Bakery products - G & S Metal Products Co., Inc.

BAKER-EZE INSULATED - Bakery products - G & S Metal Products Co., Inc.

BAKER IN A BASKET - Baking dishes with baskets ☆ - Corning Inc.

BAKER NORTON - Pharmaceuticals - Baker Norton Pharmaceuticals, Inc.

BAKER REFRACTORIES - Bricks - J.E. Baker Co.

BAKER ST. - Watches ☆ - Danecraft, Inc.

BAKER STREET - Scotch - International Wine & Spirits Inc.

BAKER STREET COLLECTION, THE - Apparel and accessories - Phillips-Van Heusen Corp.

BAKER VALLEY FARMS - Ice cream - Quality Food Centers, Inc.

BAKERLOC - Furniture–restaurant - R. Baker Enterprises, Inc.

BAKERLOG - Cream cheese - Sodiaal North America Corp.

BAKER'S - Beverages–alcohol - Jim Beam Brands Co.

BAKER'S - Health care products - John C. Baker Co.

BAKER'S - Mustard - Gold Pure Food Products Inc.

BAKERS - Shoes - Edison Brothers Stores, Inc.

BAKERS - Whipped topping–frozen - Presto Food Products, Inc.

BAKERS' ADVANTAGE - Breads–mixes - Dawn Food Products Inc.

BAKER'S AID - Ovens–bakery - M. Raubvogel Co., Inc.

BAKERS AND CHEFS - Bakery products - Wal-Mart Stores Inc.

BAKER'S ANGEL FLAKE - Food products - Baker's Coconut

BAKER'S AWARD - Bakery products–frozen - Rykoff-Sexton, Inc.

BAKER'S BATCH - Biscuit mix - Pioneer Flour Mills

BAKER'S BEST - Shampoos - Schering-Plough Healthcare Products

BAKER'S BLEND - Margarine - Nabisco Foods Group

BAKERS-BLEND - Milk–canned or powdered - Bongards Creameries

BAKER'S BONUS - Cookies - Nabisco Foods Group

BAKER'S BOUQUET, THE - Bakery products - Baker's Basket Franchise System, Inc.

BAKER'S CATALOGUE - Flour–blended - Taylor & Wood Sands

BAKERS CHOICE - Computer software - Computer Services Co.

BAKER'S CHOICE - Cookies - Baker's Choice Co.

BAKER'S CHOICE - Cookies - Simmers Products

BAKER'S CHOICE - Cooking equipment–household - West Bend Co.

BAKER'S CHOICE - Cooking equipment–household ☆ - Chicago Metallic Products Inc.

BAKERS CHOICE - Honey ☆ - Heins Marketing

BAKER'S CHOICE - Oils–edible - Baker's Choice, Inc.

BAKER'S CHOICE BAKE CUPS - Cups–paper - Reynolds Metals Co.

BAKER'S COLLECTION - Bread - Interstate Brands Corp.

BAKER'S CORNER - Breads–mixes - Aldi Inc.

BAKER'S CORNER - Food products - Goodhue's Inc.

BAKER'S CRUST - Breads - S & H Investments, Inc.

BAKER'S CUT - Pies–fresh - Vicorp Restaurants, Inc.

BAKERS DAIRY - Food products - Baker's Dairy Co.

BAKER'S DELUXE - Margarine - Nabisco Foods Group

BAKER'S DOZEN - Cooking utensils–aluminum ☆ - Himark Enterprises Inc.

BAKERS DOZEN - Furniture ☆ - Baker, Knapp & Tubbs

BAKER'S EDGE - Cooking utensils–aluminum ☆ - Himark Enterprises Inc.

BAKER'S ESTATE - Cookies - Baders Dutch Biscuit Co., Inc.

BAKER'S FIND, THE - Pans - Dressner Sales Co. Inc.

BAKER'S FINEST - Cakes - McKee Foods Corp.

BAKER'S FINISHING TOUCH - Whipped topping–frozen - Instantwhip Foods Inc.

BAKER'S HARVEST - Cookies - Bremner, Inc.

BAKER'S HEARTH - Sandwiches–prepackaged - Sabatasso Foods Inc.

BAKERS HEAVEN - Bakery mixes - International Multifoods Corp.

BAKERS HELPER - Kitchen utensils–aluminum - Bonny Products Inc.

BAKERS HERITAGE - Cooking equipment–household - Chicago Metallic Products Inc.

BAKER'S JOY - Oils–edible - Alberto-Culver Co.

BAKERS KNEAD - Food products - Armour Dairy Co.

BAKER'S LABEL - Bakery products - M-Cap Technologies International

BAKER'S OWN - Cookies ☆ - Nabisco Foods Group

BAKER'S PERFECTION INC. - Bakery products - Baker's Perfection, Inc.

BAKER'S PLUS - Frozen foods - Pillsbury Co.

BAKER'S PRIDE - Egg substitutes - Papetti's Hygrade Egg Products, Inc.

BAKER'S RAWHIDE - Dog food - Pet Products, Inc.

BAKER'S RESERVE - Bakery products - Gordon Food Service, Inc.

BAKER'S SANCO - Shortening ☆ - Swift Edible Oil Co.

BAKER'S SECRET - Housewares - Ekco Housewares, Inc.

BAKER'S SECRET PRO - Cookware - Ekco Housewares, Inc.

BAKER'S SELECT - Yeast - Burns Philp Food Inc.

BAKERS SPECIAL - Dairy products - Foremost Farms USA

BAKER'S SPECIAL - Shortening - Armour Dairy Co.

BAKERS SQUARE RESTAURANT & PIES - Pies–fresh - Vicorp Restaurants, Inc.

BAKER'S SUPREME - Bakery products - Park Corp.

BAKER'S TOPPING - Food products - Presto Food Products, Inc.

BAKER'S TOUCH - Cooking equipment–household ☆ - Mirro Corp.

BAKER'S TRADITION - Cookies - Bake-Line Products Inc.

BAKER'S TREAT - Bakery products - Aldi Inc.

BAKER'S VALUE CARD - Advertising agencies - Fleming Companies, Inc.

BAKERS WARE - Bakery machines ☆ - National Housewares

BAKERSAVER - Milk–canned or powdered - Good Source, Inc.

BAKERSFIELD - Sinks–metal - Kohler Co.

BAKERSMATE - Egg substitutes - New Zealand Milk Products Inc.

BAKERY BOYS, THE - Pet products ☆ - Novapet, Inc.

BAKERY CART - Bakery franchise - Cookie Factory of America

BAKERY CRAFT - Bakery products - Lotus Manufacturing Co.

BAKERY LIGHT - Breads - Best Foods Baking Group

BAKERY MAGIC - Oils–edible - Par-Way Group

BAKERY NEW ORLEANS - Bakery products - Dobake, Inc.

BAKERY PRO - Food products machinery - M & E Manufacturing Co., Inc.

BAKERY, THE - Cooking equipment–household ☆ - Mirro Corp.

☆ = Now out of production

BAKERY WAGON - Cookies - Mother's Cake & Cookie Co.
BAKEWARE OF THE 90'S - Cookware - Oscarware, Inc.
BAKEWICHES - Food products - American Frozen Foods Inc.
BAKIN' EASY - Seasonings - Conagra, Inc.
BAKIN' MAGIC - Seasonings ☆ - Little Crow Foods
BAKIN' MIRACLE - Seasonings - Little Crow Foods
BAKIN' TIME - Deodorizers - Willert Home Products, Inc.
BAKING BASICS - Cakes–mixes - Sovex Foods, Inc.
BAKING BREAK - Chocolate candy ☆ - Sunlight Foods, Inc.
BAKING MAGIC - Spices and extracts ☆ - McCormick & Co., Inc.
BAKING SODA - Mouthwashes - Tec Laboratories, Inc.
BAKING TIME - Breads–mixes - Pan-O-Rama Baking, Inc.
BAKING'S ANSWER - Cooking equipment–household ☆ - Chicago Metallic
 Products Inc.
BAKIT - Frosting - B. Manischewitz Co.
BAKKER BROS. - Flowers, plants, and seeds - Bakker Brothers of Idaho, Inc.
BAKON - Food products - Bakon Yeast Inc.
BAKON DELITES - Pork rinds - Wise Foods
BAKON STRIPS - Dog food - Gimborn U.S., Inc.
BAKONY - Food products - Bakon Yeast Inc.
BAKOTE - Paints - Triangle Coatings Inc.
BAKOTEX - Food products - General Spice
BAKOUA - Cookies - Sunshine/Salerno Inc.
BAK'S BLACKBERRY FLAVORED BRANDY - Liquors - Adamba Imports
 International Inc.
BAKTEC - Belts–industrial - Baktec Inc.
BAKU - Floor coverings–carpet and rugs ☆ - Evans-Black Carpet Mills
BAKUBA - Ophthalmic goods - Styl-Rite Optical Manufacturing Co., Inc.
B.A.L. - Veterinary pharmaceutical preparations - Zirin Laboratories
 International
BAL A VERSAILLES BY JEAN DESPREZ - Perfumes - Alfin Fragrances Inc.
BAL-CO-MUL - Varnishes ☆ - Ranbar Technology Inc.
BAL DE BAIN - Colognes - Regency Cosmetics Inc.
BAL-FLANGE - Ophthalmic goods - Salvatori Ophthalmics Inc.
BAL-FOCAL - Ophthalmic goods - Salvatori Ophthalmics Inc.
BAL-GUARD - Ophthalmic apparatus ☆ - Bausch & Lomb Inc.
BAL HARBOR - Boats–motor ☆ - Glastron Boats
BAL HARBOR - Wallpaper - Frankford Wallcoverings Inc.
BAL HARBOR II - Wallpaper - Frankford Wallcoverings Inc.
BAL HARBOR, THE - Frames–eyeglass ☆ - Universal/Univis Inc.
BAL HARBOUR - Floor coverings–carpet and rugs - Richmond Carpet Mills
BAL HARBOUR - Footwear - Sperry Top-Sider, Inc.
BAL HARBOUR - Furniture - American Furniture Co. Inc.
BAL-TUCK - Apparel and accessories - Harwood Companies Inc.
BALA - Balls - Lisco, Inc.
BALA - Motor vehicles–construction - Tuff-S-Nails Inc.
BALA CLUB - Beverages - American Stores Co.
BALACLAVA - Apparel–athletic - Reliable of Milwaukee
BALAFRE - Cosmetics - Lancome
BALAHE PERFUMES - Perfumes - Classic Fragrances Ltd.
BALANCE - Bedding–linen - Dan River Inc.
BALANCE - Candles - Merrill-West Publishing
BALANCE - Computer software - Wiseport Data Systems, Inc.
BALANCE - Computer software ☆ - Queue Inc.
BALANCE - Housewares - A-Bee Syndicate Inc.
BALANCE - Pencils ☆ - Faber-Castell Corp.
BALANCE - Vitamins and nutritional supplements - Vitamin Research Products
 Inc.
BALANCE 40 50 30 - Vitamins and nutritional supplements - Roseal
BALANCE BLEND - Margarine - Lever Brothers Co. Inc.
BALANCE BOARD - Games - Carrom Co.
BALANCE COLLECTION, THE - Vitamins and nutritional supplements -
 Organic Health Natural Labs
BALANCE COLOGNES - Pet products - Landco
BALANCE MASTER - Sporting goods - Mantua/Cosom Sporting Goods
BALANCE OF NATURE - Food products - Norganic Foods USA Inc.
BALANCE OF POWER - Computer software - Mindscape Software Inc.
BALANCE PLUS - Adhesives and sealants - PJH Brands
BALANCE PLUS - Cutlery - Gerber Legendary Blades
BALANCE SHAMPOOS - Pet products - Landco
BALANCE WATER - Hair care products - Big Beans, Inc.
BALANCE YOUR GAME - Apparel and accessories - Educational Wear Inc.
BALANCED - Blood pressure apparatus - Trimline Medical Products Corp.
BALANCED - Health care products - American Natural Snacks
BALANCED-ACTION - Saxophones ☆ - Selmer Co. Inc.
BALANCED BLEND - Coffee - Compass Foods Inc.

BALANCED BODY, A - Exercising equipment - Current Concepts Corp.
BALANCED BRAND - Health care products - Tree of Life, Inc.
BALANCED-FIT - Foundation garments - Jodee, Inc.
BALANCED-FLOW - Water purification systems - Goulds Pumps, Inc.
BALANCED KAKE - Animal feeds - Bluebonnet Milling Co.
BALANCED NEUROTRANSMITTER COMPLEX - Vitamins and nutritional
 supplements - M.M.R.C., Ltd. Co.
BALANCED PHASE - Audio equipment - Barcus-Berry Inc.
BALANCED POWER - Cleaning preparations - Ecolab Inc.
BALANCED SALT SOLUTION - Pharmaceutical preparations - Akorn Inc.
BALANCED STATE - Skin care products - Charles Revson Inc.
BALANCELINE - Saddles - Equine Balance System
BALANCER, THE - Fishing tackle - Fishing Designs, Inc.
BALANCING ACT - Computer software - Ventura Educational Systems
BALANCING ACT - Cosmetics - Noxell Corp.
BALANCING ACT, THE - Games - Little Harbor Corp.
BALANCING BEAR - Toys–stuffed - Schylling Associates Inc.
BALANCING INFUSION - Oils–essential - A-Veda Corp.
BALAO - Seafood products–fresh or frozen ☆ - J.F. Clarke Corp.
BALATA - Apparel and accessories - Anthony Marino
BALATA LB - Balls–golf - Hansberger Precision Golf Worldwide
BALATON - Trees - Board of Trustees Operating Michigan State University
BALATRIN - Vitamins and nutritional supplements ☆ - U.S. Ethicals Inc.
BALBOA - Apparel - Maimonides Licensing Group Ltd.
BALBOA - Cakes - Balboa Dessert Co., Inc.
BALBOA - Fireplaces - Dyna Corp.
BALBOA - Floor coverings–carpet and rugs - Tuftex Carpet Mills, Inc.
BALBOA - Footwear–men's - L.B. Evans' Son Co.
BALBOA - Frames–eyeglass - May Optical Co. Inc.
BALBOA - Glassware–household - Edward P. Paul & Co. Inc.
BALBOA - Transducers - Balboa Instruments, Inc.
BALBOA - Vegetables–canned - Case-Swayne Co. Inc.
BALBOA - Window shades - Castec Window Shading Inc.
BALBOA PARK - Trailers–travel - Fleetwood Enterprises, Inc.
BALCAR - Lighting fixtures - Tekno Inc.
BALCOLD - Electronic equipment - Bausch & Lomb Inc.
BALCONES - Floor coverings–tile ☆ - Monarch Tile Inc.
BALCOR - Ophthalmic goods ☆ - Bausch & Lomb Inc.
BALCOTE - Eyeglasses - Bausch & Lomb Inc.
BALCREST - Frames–eyeglass ☆ - Bausch & Lomb Inc.
BALD HEADED - Recording label - Winners Circle Records
BALD HEADS - Cosmetics - Paper Magic Group Inc.
BALD MOUNTAIN - Vitamins and nutritional supplements - Summa
 Pharmaceutical Laboratories Inc.
BALD MTN. - Wines - Carter P. Thacher
BALDANZA - Food products - Baldanza Bakery Inc.
BALDINELLI ESTATE - Wines - Baldinelli Winery
BALDINELLI VINEYARDS - Wines - Baldinelli Winery
BALDINGER'S - Food products - Baldinger's Truffade Co. Ltd.
BALDOM - Sauces - Otto Knuper
BALDOR - Engines–motor vehicle - Baldor Electric Co.
BALDOR MOTORS AND DRIVES - Engines–motor vehicle - Baldor Electric
 Co.
BALDRIGE MAP - Computer software - Pacesetter Group
BALDUR - Gloves–rubber - Baldur Systems Corp.
BALDWIN - Film processing chemicals - E.G. Baldwin and Associates, Inc.
BALDWIN - Frames–eyeglass - Pathway Optical Prods.
BALDWIN - Giftware - Baldwin Hardware Corp.
BALDWIN - Pianos - Baldwin Piano & Organ Co.
BALDWIN - Thread - Threads USA Div.
BALDWIN AMER. - Attache cases - H.C. Meyers Co.
BALDWIN COUNTY'S BEST - Fruits and vegetables - Schermer Potato Co.
BALDWIN HARDWARE - Housewares - Masco Corp.
BALDWIN HILL - Bakery products - Baldwin Hill Corp.
BALDWIN HILL SINCE 1975 - Breads - Baldwin Hill Corp.
BALDWIN PARK - Floor coverings–carpet and rugs ☆ - Hollytex Carpet Mills
 Inc.
BALDWIN SILVER - Giftware - Baldwin Hardware Corp.
BALDWIN.COM - Advertising agencies - Michael Baldwin
BALDWIN'S VICTORIAN OVENS - Food products - Ludy D. Frew
BALDY CLOWN - Dolls ☆ - Dakin Inc.
BALDY GARD - Suntan lotions - Act-M Inc.
BALE - Emblematic awards, class rings, school jewelry, etc. - Bale Co.
BALE CAP - Tarpaulins - Bale Caps, LLC
BALE EATER - Textile machinery - Osprey Corp.
BALE-LOK PLUS - Twine - Exxon Corp.

BALE MILL - Wines - Charles F. Shaw Vineyard & Winery
BALE-SAFE - Agricultural products ☆ - Bio Huma Netics, Inc.
BALEM CIAZA - Eyeglasses ☆ - B. Robinson Sunglasses
BALENCED COUNSEL - Computer software - Elan Associates (GreenLight Software Division)
BALENCIAGA - Neckties ☆ - Remington Apparel Co. Inc.
BALENCIAGA LUNETTES - Ophthalmic goods - Robin Optical
BALENCIEGA - Watches - Andre Victor America Ltd.
BALENE - Needles–sewing ☆ - Boye Needle
BALENO - Sporting goods - Baleno Inc.
BALFCLAT - Sporting goods - Mark Schuster
BALFOR - Gaskets - Balfor Industries Inc.
BALFOUR - Floor coverings–carpet and rugs ☆ - Royalweve Carpet Mills
BALFOUR - Giftware - L.G. Balfour Co.
BALFOUR - Jewelry - L.G. Balfour Co., Inc.
BALFOUR - Wines - Foreign Vintages Inc.
BALGRES - Tiles–ceramic - Balgres Distributing Co.
BALGRIP - Frames–eyeglass ☆ - Bausch & Lomb Inc.
BALHSEN - Cookies - FCW Imports
BALI - Apparel–women's - Bali Co. Inc.
BALI - Apparel–women's - Saramar Corp.
BALI - Blinds–venetian ☆ - Spring Window Fashions Division, Inc.
BALI - Cribs–wood ☆ - Welsh Co.
BALI - Dishes–china - Pickard Inc.
BALI - Floor coverings–carpet and rugs ☆ - Karastan-Bigelow Inc.
BALI - Frames–eyeglass - May Optical Co. Inc.
BALI - Games - Avalon Hill Game Co.
BALI - Giftware - Sasaki
BALI - Lighting fixtures - Swivelier Co. Inc.
BALI - Rings–jewelry - Artcarved Inc.
BALI - Wallpaper - Surface Industries Inc.
BALI - Wallpaper ☆ - Capital Carousel Inc.
BALI - Wallpaper ☆ - Marburg Wallcoverings Inc.
BALI - Yarn ☆ - William Unger & Co. Inc.
BALI 2 - Wallpaper - Marburg Wallcoverings Inc.
BALI III - Wallpaper - Advance Wallcoverings
BALI BASICS - Blinds–venetian ☆ - Spring Window Fashions Division, Inc.
BALI BLAST - Fruit drinks–bottled or canned - Snapple Beverage Corp.
BALI BLUE STRIPE - Bathing suits ☆ - Jantzen Inc.
BALI BOW-BRA - Apparel–women's - Bali Co. Inc.
BALI CLASSICS - Blinds–venetian ☆ - Spring Window Fashions Division, Inc.
BALI GO ACTIVE - Apparel–women's ☆ - Bali Co. Inc.
BALI GO-LIGHTLY - Apparel–women's - Bali Co. Inc.
BALI GO-NATURAL - Apparel–women's ☆ - Bali Co. Inc.
BALI GRABEN - Blinds–venetian - California Textiles Inc.
BALI/GRABER - Blinds–vertical - Amsterdam Fabricators
BALI HAI - Floor coverings–carpet and rugs - Queen Carpet Corp.
BALI HAI - House furnishings - Link-Taylor Corp.
BALI HAI - Housewares ☆ - Shafford Co. Inc.
BALI HAI - Wines ☆ - Heublein, Inc.
BALI-HI - Bathroom fixtures - Crane Plumbing/Fiat Products
BALI LIGHT - Candles - American Candle Co. Inc.
BALI-LO - Apparel–women's ☆ - Bali Co. Inc.
BALI MICRO BLINDS - Blinds–venetian ☆ - Spring Window Fashions Division, Inc.
BALI PRIVATE COLLECTION - Blinds–venetian ☆ - Spring Window Fashions Division, Inc.
BALI SOFTONES - Blinds–venetian ☆ - Spring Window Fashions Division, Inc.
BALI SOFTRIMS - Window coverings ☆ - Spring Window Fashions Division, Inc.
BALI-SONG - Knives–pocket - Benchmade Knife Co., Inc.
BALI SPORTS - Underwear and nightwear - Saramar Corp.
BALI ULTRA - Blinds–venetian ☆ - Spring Window Fashions Division, Inc.
BALIC - Wines - Balic Winery
BALKAN - Tobacco–chewing or smoking - Amar Blends Co.
BALKAN SOBRANIE - Tobacco–chewing or smoking - James B. Russell Inc.
BALKANTON - Recording label ☆ - Worldtone Music Inc.
BALKIN CREST - Wines - Monsieur Henri Wines Ltd.
BALL - Cleaning preparations - Grainger Division
BALL - Cleaning preparations - W.W. Grainger, Inc.
BALL - Food containers - Alltrista Corp.
BALL - Markers–felt-tip - Markal Co.
BALL 100 % NATURAL - Food products - Alltrista Corp.
BALL A BOUT - Toys - Doskocil Manufacturing Co., Inc.
BALL & CHAIN - Cables–steel - Kryptonite Corp.

BALL & CHAIN - Musical instrument accessories - Sottile Manufacturing Co.
BALL-B-Q - Barbecues and grills ☆ - Shepherd Products U.S. Inc.
BALL BUCKET - Sporting goods - Lob-Ster Inc.
BALL BUSTER - Apparel–athletic - Ken Linkfield
BALL BUSTER - Games ☆ - Mego Financial Corp.
BALL BUSTER - Golfing equipment - Golf Star Inc.
BALL CAPS - Hats - Dyot Ventures, Inc.
BALL CAPS BY DYOT - Caps–baseball - Dyot Ventures, Inc.
BALL CERTIFIED PLANTS - Flowers, plants, and seeds - Ball Floraplant
BALL DOCTOR - Sporting goods - Unique Sports Products Inc.
BALL-ET BAG - Bags - Agri-Concepts Inc.
BALL GRINDING - Printing lables - Bower Manufacturing Co. Inc.
BALL HAWKER - Sporting goods ☆ - Chesal Golf
BALL-HEX-L - Keys - Eklind Tool Co.
BALL HOPPERS - Sporting goods - Rocky Mountain Sports
BALL KORT - Shoes–athletic - Precious Mements Co., Inc.
BALL LINER - Pens - Pilot Pen Corp. of America
BALL LITE - Lamps - Satco Products, Inc.
BALL-LOK - Pins–straight - Avibank Manufacturing Inc.
BALL MASON - Jar tops–metal - Alltrista Corp.
BALL-O-FOOT - Shoe accessories - Schering-Plough Healthcare Products
BALL-O-HIDE - Pet toys - Items Inc.
BALL-O-SOLV - Cleaning preparations - W.W. Grainger, Inc.
BALL-OCITY - Apparel and accessories - Totally Texas Technologies
BALL O'FIRE - Chewing gum - Leaf, Inc.
BALL PAINT MARKER - Paints - La-Co Industries, Inc.
BALL PARK - Food products - European Bakers
BALL PARK - Frankfurters - Hygrade Food Products Corp.
BALL PARK FUN FRANKS - Frankfurters - Hygrade Food Products Corp.
BALL PARK MINI FRANKS - Sandwiches–prepackaged - Sara Lee Corp.
BALL PARK PRETZEL DOGS - Snack foods - Sara Lee Corp.
BALL PARK SINGLES - Sandwiches–prepackaged - Hygrade Food Products Corp.
BALL PENTEL - Pens - Pentel of America, Ltd.
BALL POCKET - Sporting goods - Unique Sports Products Inc.
BALL POINT - Paper–writing - Cavert Wire Co. Inc.
BALL POINT - Pet products - Lixit Animal Care Products
BALL POINT - Underwear and nightwear - Bentley Lingerie, Inc.
BALL POWDER - Ammunition - Olin Corp. (Winchester Div.)
BALL PRESS - Balls–tennis - Edgeroy Co. Inc.
BALL RESEARCH - Computer software - Ball Research Inc.
BALL-RITER - Pens ☆ - Empire Berol USA
BALL ROOM - Apparel and accessories - Bentley Lingerie, Inc.
BALL SHOOTER - Golfing equipment - Hollrock Engineering, Inc.
BALL STALL - Framing supplies - Binfort Corp.
BALL STUDIO - Jewelry - Lillian Ball
BALL SWAPPERS - Motor vehicle parts and accessories - Lloyd G. Wass
BALL, THE - Bags–duffel - Neil Kuslansky
BALL TOP - Hair care products - Capitol Novelty Co.
BALL VIGOR INDEX - Flowers, plants, and seeds - Ball Horticultural Co.
BALLA - Footwear - Wolverine World Wide, Inc.
BALLACK - Ceramic tile - Ballack Corp.
BALLAD - Sinks–metal - Kohler Co.
BALLAD - Watches - Bulova Corp.
BALLADEER - Guitars - Ovation Instruments
BALLANTINE - Beverages–alcohol - Falstaff Brewing Corp.
BALLANTINE - Publisher's imprints - Ballantine Books Inc.
BALLANTINE INDIA PALE - Beverages–alcohol - Falstaff Brewing Corp.
BALLANTINE LIGHT - Beverages–alcohol ☆ - Falstaff Brewing Corp.
BALLANTINE YOUNG ADULTS - Publisher's imprints - Ballantine Books Inc.
BALLANTINE'S - Beverages–alcohol - Hiram Walker & Sons, Inc.
BALLANTINE'S FINEST - Beverages–alcohol - Sunbelt Beverage Corp.
BALLANTRAE - Wallpaper - Gilford Corp.
BALLARD - Biscuits - Pillsbury Co.
BALLARD BITTER - Beverages–malt - Redhook Ale Brewery, Inc.
BALLARD CANYON - Wines - Ballard Canyon Corp.
BALLARD EGG ISLAND - Food products - Virginia Seafoods Inc.
BALLARINI - Cookware - Epoca, Inc./Ballarini
BALLAST - Fabrics - Dan River Inc.
BALLATORE - Wines - Ernest and Julio Gallo Winery
BALLBANK - Children's toy bats, rackets, and golf clubs - Catco, Inc.
BALLBLAZER - Computer software - Epyx Inc.
BALLBLAZER - Computer software - Lucasarts Entertainment Co.
BALLBLAZER - Video games - Lucasfilm Ltd.
BALLBOARD - Curtains - Barrett Enclosures, Inc.
BALLBUSTER - Apparel–athletic ☆ - Earth & Ocean Sports, Inc.

☆ = Now out of production

BALLCO 66 - Sporting goods - Ballco Products Inc.
BALLDRIVER - Tools - Bondhus Corp.
BALLENA - Thread - New Bedford Thread Co. Inc.
BALLENA - Wines - Stone Cellars
BALLENA BAY PEWTER - Glassware–household - Ballena Bay Pewter
BALLENTINE - Wines - Ballentine Vineyard
BALLENTINE'S - Beverages–alcohol - Domecq Importers Inc.
BALLERINA - Artists' materials - Stangren Co.
BALLERINA - Bicycles - Columbia Manufacturing Inc.
BALLERINA - Christmas tree ornaments ☆ - Cracker Box Inc.
BALLERINA - Floor coverings ☆ - Dayco Products Inc.
BALLERINA - Floor coverings–carpet and rugs ☆ - Playfield International Inc.
BALLERINA - Frames–eyeglass - May Optical Co. Inc.
BALLERINA - Glassware–household ☆ - ACC
BALLERINA - Jewelry ☆ - Hirsch Speidel Inc.
BALLERINA - Jewelry–costume - B.B. Greenberg Co.
BALLERINA - Rings–jewelry - Artcarved Inc.
BALLERINA - Sinks–metal - Just Manufacturing Co.
BALLERINA - Watches - Bulova Corp.
BALLERINA BEAR - Sleeping bags - Lillian Vernon Corp.
BALLERINA BLUSH - Toys - Tonka Corp.
BALLERINA BUNNIES - Stationery - Lisa Frank, Inc.
BALLERINA PAL - Dolls - Mattel, Inc.
BALLERINA SATIN SLIPPER - American International Industries
BALLEROY - Dishes–china - Viletta China Co.
BALLET - Frames–eyeglass ☆ - Universal/Univis Inc.
BALLET - Hosiery - Kayser-Roth Corp.
BALLET - Jewelry - Ballet Jewels Inc.
BALLET - Mattresses and box springs - Ohio Mattress Co.
BALLET - Tables–wood - Steelcase Inc.
BALLET BRIEFS - Underwear and nightwear - Sylray Inc.
BALLET BUDDIES - Leotards ☆ - Leo's Dancewear, Inc.
BALLET FUN CLASS - Dolls - Justin Products, Inc.
BALLET PLEAT - Blinds–venetian ☆ - Hunter Douglas, Inc.
BALLET RUSSE - Ballet slippers - Leo's Dancewear, Inc.
BALLETS RUSSES - Fabrics - Gretchen Bellinger Inc.
BALLGAL - Varnishes - Ranbar Technology Inc.
BALLGIRL ATHLETIC - Apparel and accessories - ballgirl Athletic, Inc.
BALLHEADS - Apparel and accessories - SS Gear International, Ltd.
BALLIGATOR - Game machines - Bally Gaming International, Inc.
BALLINGER-GOLD - Apparel - Bimoteur Inc.
BALLISTIC - Books–comic - Top Cow Productions, Inc.
BALLISTIC - Computer software - Accolade Inc.
BALLISTIC - Golfing equipment ☆ - Daiwa Corp.
BALLISTIC - Sporting goods ☆ - Wellington Leisure Products, Inc.
BALLISTIC SHOOTING BAG - Guns - Hughes Products Co., Inc.
BALLISTIC TECHNOLOGIES - Medical apparatus - Ballistic Technologies, Inc.
BALLISTICLEAN - Cartridges–ammunition - Federal-Hoffman, Inc.
BALLKYDVAR - Varnishes ☆ - Ranbar Technology Inc.
BALLMATE - Adhesives and sealants - Top Star Inc.
BALLOGRAF EPOCA - Pens - Bic Corp.
BALLOGRAF EPOCA DELUXE - Pens - Bic Corp.
BALLOMATIC - Pens ☆ - Universal Fountain Pen & Pencil Co.
BALLON - Tableware–china ☆ - Villeroy and Boch Tableware Ltd.
BALLOON - Air purification systems - Medo Industries, Inc.
BALLOON - Beverages ☆ - Juice Bowl Products Inc.
BALLOON-A-SCENT - Novelty items - Dipcraft Manufacturing Co.
BALLOON-A-STICKS - Toys - U.S. Balloon Manufacturing Co.
BALLOON BAGS BY RAINBOWRAPPER - Bags - Balloon Bags by Rainbowrapper
BALLOON BANDIT - Computer software - Orange Cherry Software
BALLOON BARON - Toys - Williams Products Inc.
BALLOON BAZOOKA - Toys - Todd R. Hartzell
BALLOON BEAR GREETINGS - Novelty items - Celebrations of America
BALLOON BEARS - Infant product - Pansy Ellen Products, Inc.
BALLOON DANCERS - Novelty items - Beistle Co.
BALLOON DELIGHTS - Novelty items - Balloon Delights
BALLOON-FIL - Welding equipment - Controls Corp. of America
BALLOON GREETINGS - Novelty items - Pioneer Balloon Co.
BALLOON KID - Video games - Nintendo of America Inc.
BALLOON MAGIC - Novelty items - Pioneer Balloon Co.
BALLOON MESSAGE TEDDIES - Toys–stuffed - Russ Berrie and Co., Inc.
BALLOON RIDE - Toys–models ☆ - Century Products Co.
BALLOON SADDLE - Decorations - A.J. Ganz Co. Inc.
BALLOON SEAT - Apparel–athletic - Knothe Corp.
BALLOONS STIK-EMS - Decorations - A.J. Ganz Co. Inc.

BALLOON SWEETS - Novelty items - M & D Balloons, Inc.
BALLOON WAREHOUSE - Toys - Balloon Arts, Inc.
BALLOON WEIGHTS - Figurines - Miller Studio
BALLOON ZONE - Toys - American Greetings Corp.
BALLOONATICS - Ornamental figures - Balloonatics Enterprises Inc.
BALLOONCLOTH - Fabrics - Greenwood Mills Inc.
BALLOONLINE - Toys - Rodin Industries Inc.
BALLOONS - Floor coverings–carpet and rugs - Customweave Carpets Inc.
BALLOONS - Footwear - Thom McAn Shoe Co.
BALLOONS - Statuary ☆ - Blue Ridge International Products Co., Inc.
BALLOONS & CLOUDS - Wallpaper ☆ - Priss Prints Inc.
BALLOONS AWAY! - Toys - Systemax Network, Inc.
BALLOONS BY NAME - Novelty items ☆ - Pacific Balloon Co., Inc.
BALLOONS NATURE'S FINEST - Decorations - Tilly Balloon Inc. / Center Stage Productions
BALLOONS THAT COUNT - Novelty items ☆ - Securitag Corp.
BALLOONTEX - Novelty items - Pacific Balloon Co., Inc.
BALLOONY - Decorations - C.M. Estes Enterprises, Inc.
BALLOTMASTER - Computer peripheral equipment - Gregory R. Chumbley
BALLOW'S - Seasonings - Barzizza Brothers
BALLOW'S CHILI - Seasonings - Barzi Foods
BALLPARK - Flowers, plants, and seeds - Weyerhaeuser Co.
BALLPARK - Office supplies - Rubbermaid Office Products Inc.
BALLPARK - Toys - Mel Appel Group, Inc.
BALLPARK BUNNIES - Toys–stuffed - International Silver Co.
BALLPOINT - Computer peripheral equipment - Microsoft Corp.
BALLPORT - Sporting goods - Unique Sports Products Inc.
BALLROOM BEAUTIES COLLECTION - Dolls - Mattel, Inc.
BALLS - Paper - Bonanza Press, Inc.
BALLS-A-POPPIN' - Balls ☆ - Kenner Products
BALLS OF FIRE - Candles - W and F Products Inc.
BALLS O'FIRE - Chickens - Pierce Foods Corp.
BALLS TO THE WALL - Apparel–men's - Frank J. Portera, Jr.
BALLWALL - Sporting goods - Ballwall, Inc.
BALLY - Frames–eyeglass ☆ - U.S. Optical Frame Co.
BALLY - Metals - Bally Engineered Structures, Inc.
BALLY GAMING - Gaming equipment - Bally Manufacturing Corp.
BALLY OF SWITZERLAND - Apparel, leather goods - Bally of Switzerland
BALLYBRAE - Yarn - Brunswick Yarns
BALLYHAGEN INTERNATIONAL - Meat products–cured - Gemini Food Industries Inc.
BALLYHOO - Computer software - Activision, Inc.
BALLYMALOE - Relishes - Bewley Irish Imports
BALLY'S BIG BUCKS - Game machines - Bally Manufacturing Corp.
BALLYSHANNON - Floor coverings–carpet and rugs - Masland Corp.
BALLZOOKA - Games - Tonka Corp.
BALM ARGENTA - Skin care products - Washburn Laboratories
BALM BARR - Skin care products - Mennen Co.
BALMAC - Doors–glass ☆ - ODL, Inc.
BALMENACH - Beverages–malt - European Beverage Co., Inc.
BALMEX - Talcum powders - Macsil Inc. (Balmex Div.)
BALMFORTH - Sporting goods - Pacifico Co.
BALMITE - Electronic equipment - Bausch & Lomb Inc.
BALMORAL - Bathroom fixtures - Showerlux USA
BALMORAL - Floor coverings–carpet and rugs - Queen Carpet Corp.
BALMORAL - Frames–eyeglass - May Optical Co. Inc.
BALMORAL INTERNATIONAL - Cigars - James B. Russell Inc.
BALNEOL - Health care products - Solvay Pharmaceuticals Inc.
BALNETAR - Pharmaceutical preparations - Westwood-Squibb Pharmaceuticals, Inc.
BALNUL - Tiles–ceramic - WesekPalley Tile Inc.
BALOMATIC - Electronic equipment - Bausch & Lomb Inc.
BALOPTICON - Electronic equipment - Bausch & Lomb Inc.
BALOPTIK - Ophthalmic goods ☆ - Bausch & Lomb Inc.
BALORAMA - Eyeglasses - Bausch & Lomb Inc.
BALPLAN - Microscopes - Bausch & Lomb Inc.
BALPRO - Pet products - Kage Co. Inc.
BALREX - Eyeglasses ☆ - Bausch & Lomb Inc.
BALRIM - Frames–eyeglass ☆ - Bausch & Lomb Inc.
BALSA - Electronic equipment - Estes Industries
BALSA BIN - Wood products ☆ - Paul K. Guillow Inc.
BALSAM ALGAS - Hair care products - Lendan USA Co.
BALSAM & BODY - Hair care products - Helene Curtis Industries Inc.
BALSAM & PROTEIN - Skin care products - Waverly Beauty Products
BALSAM-BALM - Pet products - Gerard-Pellham Co.
BALSAM COLOR - Hair coloring preparations - Clairol Inc.

☆ = Now out of production

BALSAM EVE - Deodorizers - Gilbertie's Herb Gardens, Inc.
BALSAM FRESH - Deodorizers - Pro Industries Inc.
BALSAM MIST - Sachets - Andre Richard
BALSAM PLUS - Hair care products - Helene Curtis Industries Inc.
BALSAM-WOOL - Insulation ☆ - Conwed Plastics
BALSAMICO VIGNOLA - Vinegar - Gourmet America
BALSAMICO VIGNOLA - Vinegar - Hormel Foods Corp.
BALSAMS - Water - Balsams Water Co. Inc.
BALSTON - Hardware - Balston, Inc.
BALT A CLASS ACT - Computer peripheral equipment - Balt, Inc.
BALTA - Floor coverings–carpet and rugs - Princeton Carpets
BALTA - Office furniture ☆ - Inwood Office Furniture
BALTAR - Electronic equipment - Bausch & Lomb Inc.
BALTEKMAT - Boat-building materials - Baltek Corp.
BALTER - Mallets - Mike Balter Mallets
BALTEX - Apparel–women's - Maillot Baltex, Inc.
BALTHASAR RESS - Wines - Niche Marketing Corp.
BALTIC - Bathtubs–enameled - Briggs Plumbing Products, Inc.
BALTIC - Floor coverings–carpet and rugs ☆ - Colonial Mills Inc.
BALTIC - Frames–eyeglass ☆ - Universal/Univis Inc.
BALTIC CLEAR - Flour–blended - ConAgra Grain Co.
BALTIC MINNOW - Fishing lures - Howe Now Inc.
BALTIMORE - Tape–adhesive - Select Brands
BALTIMORE BEAUTIES - Fabrics–cotton - Eleanor P.H. Sienkiewicz
BALTIMORE CHAMPIONS OF LOYAL TEAM SPIRIT, THE - Shirts - Ron Free
BALTIMORE CHIPPER - Bakery products - Baltimore Chipper, Inc.
BALTIMORE CLIPPER - Teas - Eastern Shore Tea Co.
BALTIMORE INGREDIENTS - Food products - Alan R. Brunn
BALTIMORE ORIOLES - Apparel and accessories - Baltimore Orioles Ltd. Partnership
BALTIMORE PICTURES B - Figurines - Baltimore Pictures, Inc.
BALTIMORE SPECIAL - Brushes–paint ☆ - PPG Industries, Inc.
BALTIMORE WHARF RAT, THE - Pet products - St. John's Herb Garden Inc.
BALTO - Pins–jewelry - Cleveland Museum of Natural History
BALTONNA - Beverages–carbonated - Hampton Associates and Son, Inc.
BALTRON - Pharmaceutical preparations ☆ - Solvay Pharmaceuticals Inc.
BALUSTAIR - Wood products - M.I.M. Architecturals
BALUSTER - Flatware ☆ - Gorham Inc.
BALVAR - Firearms, accessories, and parts - Bausch & Lomb Inc.
BALVENIE, THE - Liquors - William Grant & Sons, Inc.
BALVERNE CELLARS - Wines - Balverne Cellars
BALWIN - Cups–paper - Evergreen Products
BALZAC - Games - Milton Bradley Co.
BALZAC BALLOON BALLS - Toys - Catco, Inc.
BALZAC BRAT - Games - Milton Bradley Co.
BALZIG - Apparel and accessories - X-S Look Graphic Design
BALZOLA - Cookies - Crystal Food Import Corp.
BALZOUT - Apparel and accessories - Balzout, Inc.
BAM - Chemical preparations ☆ - Senoret Chemical Co.
BAM - Floor coverings–carpet and rugs ☆ - Hollytex Carpet Mills Inc.
BAM - Jewelry - Burdett A. Milkins
BAM-340 - Chemical preparations - Boiardi Products Corp.
BAM-340 ANTI-FRACTURE/CRACK SUPPRESSION MEMBRANE - Waterproofing compounds - Boiardi Products Corp.
BAM BAM BHOLE - Perfumes - R. Expo (USA) Ltd.
BAM BY ANY MEANS - Apparel and accessories - Titan Enterprises Inc.
BAM DE BEAUTY - Skin care products - Arizona Natural Resources
BAMA - Dog food - AGP Petfoods
BAMA - Food products - Bama Food Products
BAMA - Food products - Bama Pie Ltd.
BAMA - Food products machinery - Florence Frozen Foods
BAMA - Footwear–athletic - A Business Contracting Corp.
BAMA - Seafood - Bama Sea Products
BAMA DRAGON - Seafood - Bama Sea Products
BAMALASTIC - Crocheted and knitted items - Bama Mills Inc.
BAMAMAHAMA - Liqueurs - Mango Bottling, Inc.
BAMBER - Musical instruments - Woodwind & Brasswind
BAMBI - Accordions - Pancordion Inc.
BAMBI - Campers - American Sterling Corp.
BAMBI - Frames–eyeglass - Pathway Optical Prods.
BAMBINA - Musical instruments - JTG of Nashville
BAMBINETO - Infant product - Bambineto Products International
BAMBINI - Apparel–children's - Daydreamers Inc.
BAMBINI - Infant product - Baudelaire Inc.
BAMBINI - Yarn - Brunswick Yarns
BAMBINO - Bedding–linen - Crestwood Industries Inc.

BAMBINO - Dinnerware ☆ - Corning Inc.
BAMBINO - Electronic equipment - GAF Corp.
BAMBINO - Wallpaper - Bayview Wallcoverings
BAMBINO CLUB - Ophthalmic goods - Optikos Shami, Inc.
BAMBINO HUEY - Bakery products - Boccone's Inc.
BAMBOLA - Sand and water toys ☆ - International Playthings Inc.
BAMBOLA - T-shirts - Jakob Schlaepfer Inc.
BAMBOLINAS - Footwear - Southern Leather & Shoe Co.
BAMBOLINO'S - Pizzas–frozen - Ninfa's Inc.
BAMBOO - Bathing suits - Gottex Industries Inc.
BAMBOO - Dishes–china ☆ - Dansk International Designs, Ltd.
BAMBOO - Dishes–china ☆ - Royal China & Porcelain Companies Inc.
BAMBOO - Flatware ☆ - Lifetime Hoan Corp.
BAMBOO - Floor coverings–carpet and rugs - Artistic Rugs Inc.
BAMBOO - Fruits–dried - Suma Fruit International (USA) Inc.
BAMBOO - Glassware–household - Owens-Illinois Inc. (Libbey Div.)
BAMBOO - Glassware–household ☆ - Anchor Hocking Glass, Inc.
BAMBOO - Pottery ☆ - Rubens Originals
BAMBOO-2 - Rakes - Rugg Manufacturing Co. Inc.
BAMBOO ABBOTT - Window coverings ☆ - Bamboo Abbott Florida Corp.
BAMBOO-ABBOTT MOTORIZATION - Window coverings ☆ - Bamboo Abbott Florida Corp.
BAMBOO BAY - Apparel–women's - North American Cornerstone Group, Ltd.
BAMBOO CANE - Flatware ☆ - Lifetime Hoan Corp.
BAMBOO CASUALS - Glassware–household - Federal Glass
BAMBOO COMFORT-FIT - Jewelry - Tosyali International, Inc.
BAMBOO CURTAIN - Apparel and accessories - Neosport Inc.
BAMBOO EAST - Furniture ☆ - Lexington Furniture Industries, Inc.
BAMBOO HARDWOODS - Flooring–hardwood - Bamboo Hardwoods, Inc.
BAMBOO HOP DANCE - Educational materials - Twinson Co.
BAMBOO MARIE-HELENE MILLER NEW YORK - Women's apparel - Bamboo Inc.
BAMBOO PANDA - Toys–stuffed - Russ Berrie and Co., Inc.
BAMBOO SILK - Yarn ☆ - Joseph Galler Inc.
BAMBU - Cigarette paper - Bambu Sales, Inc.
BAMBU - Coffee substitutes - Bioforce of America Ltd.
BAMBU - Waxes–sealing ☆ - Zecol Inc.
BAMBUCA - Beverages–alcohol - Consolidated Distilled Products Inc.
BAMINI - Floor coverings ☆ - Tarkett, Inc.
BAMM BAMM - Ophthalmic goods - Styl-Rite Optical Manufacturing Co., Inc.
BAMM-BAMM - Toys - Hanna-Barbera Productions, Inc.
BAMMENTAL - Housewares - Bammental Wallcoverings Inc.
BAMMENTAL - Wallcoverings ☆ - Wallstars
BAMO - Pharmaceutical preparations - Misemer Pharmaceuticals Inc.
BAMO 400 - Pharmaceutical preparations - Misemer Pharmaceuticals Inc.
BAMS KNITS-SAN FRANCISCO - Crocheted and knitted items ☆ - Saha-Union International USA Inc.
BAN - Deodorants–personal - Bristol-Myers Squibb Co.
BAN-A-STAIN - Denture cleaners - Brimms Inc.
BAN ACHE - Health care products ☆ - Reese Chemical Co.
BAN BASIC - Deodorants–personal - Bristol-Myers Squibb Co.
BAN CLEAR A.P. - Deodorants–personal - Bristol-Myers Squibb Co.
BAN DAN ART - T-shirts–men's - Eli Africa
BAN DUST - Dusters - Argraph Corp. (Samigon Div.)
BAN FOR MEN - Deodorants–personal - Bristol-Myers Squibb Co.
BAN FOR MEN CLEAR - Deodorants–personal - Bristol-Myers Squibb Co.
BAN FROST 2000 - Antifreeze - Camco Manufacturing, Inc.
BAN GLARE - Photographic equipment - Argraph Corp. (Samigon Div.)
BAN-M - Plastics - Spill-Stop Manufacturing LLC
BAN-O - Deodorizers - Hill Manufacturing Co. Inc.
BAN-O-DOR - Deodorizers - Surco Products Inc.
BAN-O-TRAY - Ashtrays–glass ☆ - Kingwood Ceramics
BAN-ROL - Waistbands and waistband components - Atlantic Bias Products Inc.
BAN SENSITIVE TOUCH - Deodorants–personal - Bristol-Myers Squibb Co.
BAN-SMOKE - Pharmaceutical preparations ☆ - Thompson Medical Co., Inc.
BANA-BEE - Peanut butter - Nabisco Foods Group
BANACID - Pharmaceutical preparations - Buffington
BANALG - Pharmaceutical preparations - Forest Pharmaceuticals Inc.
BANAMINE - Veterinary pharmaceutical preparations ☆ - Schering-Plough Animal Health
BANAN-ZA - Candy - Leaf, Inc.
BANANA - Boats–motor - Banana Boat Co.
BANANA - Cosmetics ☆ - Nutrine Ltd.
BANANA - Recording label - Jazz Composer's Orchestra Association Inc.
BANANA 0S - Cereal - U.S. Mills, Inc.

☆ = Now out of production

BANANA ADD-ON - Wigs - Jean Paree Weegs Inc.
BANANA BAG - Bags–plastic - Warp Bros.
BANANA BAY HAWAII - Apparel and accessories - Aloha Candle Manufacturing Co. Inc.
BANANA BLADE - Knives - Better Tools, Inc.
BANANA BLISS - Sherbet - Cascadian Farm, Inc.
BANANA BOAT - Suntan lotions - Sun Pharmaceuticals Corp.
BANANA BOAT ALOE VERA - Skin care products - Sun Pharmaceuticals Corp.
BANANA BOAT OIL FREE - Suntan lotions - Sun Pharmaceuticals Corp.
BANANA BOAT SUNLESS - Suntan lotions - Sun Pharmaceuticals Corp.
BANANA BOAT VITAMIN E GEL - Skin care products - Sun Pharmaceuticals Corp.
BANANA BOATS - Candy - Nestle USA
BANANA CONDOMS - Condoms - Banana Products, Inc.
BANANA CREAM - Cookies - Khong Guan
BANANA DIAMONDS - Candy - Leaf, Inc.
BANANA FACTORY - Apparel and accessories - Bethlehem Musikfest Association
BANANA JACKS - Candy ☆ - Leaf, Inc.
BANANA JIMMY - Footwear–men's - Delta Shoe Group
BANANA-LYCHEE - Teas - Eastern Shore Tea Co.
BANANA MAN POPS - Candy - Creative Specialties Inc.
BANANA NUT PLUS - Pet products - Hansen's Pet Products Co.
BANANA-O'S - Cereal - U.S. Mills, Inc.
BANANA PEEL - Bicycles - Trailmate Inc.
BANANA PEELS - Candy - Tootsie Roll Industries, Inc.
BANANA-RAMA - Ice cream - H.P. Hood & Sons Inc.
BANANA REPUBLIC - Apparel and accessories - Banana Republic
BANANA REPUBLIC - Linen - GPS, Inc.
BANANA REPUBLIC - Sunglasses - GPS, Inc.
BANANA ROYAL - Candy ☆ - Stark Candy Co.
BANANA SPLIT - Brushes–hair - Belson Products
BANANA SPLIT - Infant product - Toddle Tyke Co.
BANANA SPLIT - Kites ☆ - Hi-Flier Manufacturing Co.
BANANA SPLIT - Lipsticks ☆ - Tinkerbell
BANANA TARTS - Candy ☆ - Chex Co.
BANANA TREE - Housewares - Original Products Co., Inc.
BANANA-WHAM - Vitamins and nutritional supplements - Nutri-West
BANANABERRY SPLIT - Candy - Planters LifeSavers Co.
BANANAPPLES - Juices - Peter R. Desantis
BANANARAMAS - Cookies - Delicious Cookies
BANANAS - Frames–eyeglass - Zylo Ware Corp.
BANANAS AT LARGE - Recording label - Bananas at Large
BANANAS IN PAJAMAS - Shoes ☆ - S. Goldberg and Co. Inc.
BANANAS IN PAJAMAS - Toys - Tomy America, Inc.
BANANAS OVER YOU - Toys–stuffed - Dakin Inc.
BANANAS TROPICAL - Food products - Pollo Tropical, Inc.
BANANAWIG - Brushes–hair - Capitol Novelty Co.
BANANCY - Dolls - Mattel, Inc.
BANANERGY - Fruits and vegetables - David Damlich
BANARAMA - Paper–crepe ☆ - Kalan Inc.
BANARES - Rings–jewelry ☆ - Artcarved Inc.
BANASIL - Pharmaceutical preparations ☆ - Ulmer Pharmacal Co.
BANBURY - Dishes–china - Viletta China Co.
BANBURY CROSS - Floor coverings–carpet and rugs - Milliken & Co. Inc.
BANBURY CROSS - Neckties - Charles S. Gelles & Son
BANCAP - Analgesics ☆ - Forest Pharmaceuticals Inc.
BANCAP H.C. - Analgesics - Forest Pharmaceuticals Inc.
BANCES - Cigars - Danby-Palicio
BANCROFT - Frames–eyeglass - Hudson Optical Corp.
BANCROFT - Hardware ☆ - Vance Industries Inc.
BANCROFT - Hats - Bancroft Cap Co.
BANCROFT - Milk - Bancroft Dairy Co.
BANCROFT - Pagers - Courtaulds Aerospace Inc.
BANCROFT - Rackets–tennis - Etonic Inc.
BANCROFT WAY - Floor coverings ☆ - Tarkett, Inc.
BANCSTAR SPECTRUM - Computer software - Broadway & Seymour, Inc.
BAND - Shoes - Lowell Shoe, Inc.
BAND - Tables–wood ☆ - Krueger International, Inc.
BAND I - Artists' materials ☆ - Dick Blick Co.
BAND-A-BLU - Stoves - Coleman Co., Inc.
BAND - ADE - Machinery - Indian Country Inc.
BAND-AID - Bandages - Johnson & Johnson
BAND-AID HOT COLORS - Bandages - Johnson & Johnson
BAND AROOS - LD Weiss, Inc. (Bandaroos, Inc.)

BAND BAR - Jewelry - Jacoby-Bender Inc.
BAND BORDERS - Floor coverings–carpet and rugs - Bloomsburg Carpet Industries
BAND BOX - Desk sets ☆ - Park Sherman
BAND BOX - Ice cream cones - Safeway Stores Inc.
BAND BOX - Jewelry - Jacoby-Bender Inc.
BAND BOX - Pet products - Aaronco Grooming Products
BAND BOX - Recording label - Band Box Record Co.
BAND-GUARD - Bottle caps - White Cap, Inc.
BAND-IT - Clamps - Band-It-Idex Inc.
BAND IT - Crocheted and knitted items ☆ - Schuessler Knitting Mills Inc.
BAND-IT - Pet products - Northcutt Enterprises
BAND-ITS - Office supplies ☆ - Faber-Castell Corp.
BAND-M - Tubes–glass - Chase Instruments Corp.
BAND OF LIFE, THE - Recording label - Paul Glover
BAND STAND - Musical instrument accessories - Trophy Music Co.
BAND SUPPLIES - Musical instrument accessories - Ardsley Musical Instrument Co.
BAND, THE - Jewelry - Chisco, Inc.
BAND WAGON - Floor coverings–carpet and rugs ☆ - Quaker Inc.
BANDA LOS LAGOS - Compact discs–prerecorded - Luna Music Corp.
BANDA NOVILLERA - Computer software - Luna Music Corp.
BANDA PACHUCO - Recording label - Luna Music Corp.
BANDA POTRERO - Recording label - Luna Music Corp.
BANDA R-15 - Recording label - Luna Music Corp.
BANDA SUPERBANDIDO - Recording label - Andrea Music, Inc.
BANDAGE ART - Bandages - Colossus Corp.
BANDAGE IN A BOTTLE - Water treating compounds - Novalek, Inc.
BANDAGE IN A DROP, THE - Adhesives and sealants - Medlogic Global Corp.
BANDAI AMERICA - Toys–electronic ☆ - Bandai America Inc.
BANDAI GAME PAKS - Toys–electronic - Bandai America Inc.
BANDANA - Cakes ☆ - Christopher's Chewies
BANDANA - Frames–eyeglass - May Optical Co. Inc.
BANDANA - Vinegar - Roanoke Apple Products Co.
BANDANA BEAR - Toys–stuffed ☆ - Dakin Inc.
BANDANA BUFFET-PATIO - Dinnerware–glass ☆ - Kenro Inc.
BANDANA CLASSICS - Fabrics ☆ - VIP/VIP Crafts
BANDANAS - Sandals ☆ - Bear Feet
BANDANA'S A. PEPPERHEAD - Vegetable sauces - Bandana's Inc.
BANDANGO - Apparel and accessories - Bandango, Inc.
BANDANIMALS - Toys - Bandanna
BANDANNA MEXICAN LINE - Cooking utensils–earthenware - Reco International Corp.
BANDANNA WORLD/USA - Scarves - Paris Accessories, Inc.
BANDAROOS - Handkerchiefs - LD Weiss, Inc. (Bandaroos, Inc.)
BANDAUX - Hair care products - Capitol Novelty Co.
B&B DRY GOODS - Apparel–athletic - J. Chandler & Co., Inc.
B&D POTPOURRI - Deodorizers - Mcauley's, Inc.
BANDED ANTIQUEGLAZE - Floor coverings ☆ - Armstrong World Industries, Inc.
BANDED DECO - Floor coverings ☆ - Armstrong World Industries, Inc.
BANDED PACK - Metals - Tee-Lok Corp.
BANDED PAVER - Floor coverings ☆ - Armstrong World Industries, Inc.
BANDELIER DESIGHS - Paper - ANW-Crestwood Paper Co.
BANDERA - Floor coverings–carpet and rugs ☆ - Callaway Carpets
BANDERO - Dinnerware–glass ☆ - Metlox Pottery Shoppe
BANDGUARD - Veterinary pharmaceutical preparations - Schering Corp.
B&H - Recording label - Sunday School Board of the Southern Baptist Convention
BANDIDO - Boats - Glen-L Marine Designs
BANDIDO - Dinnerware–glass ☆ - Cyclamen Studio
BANDIDO - Pizzas–frozen - Sabatasso Foods Inc.
BANDIERA - Wines - California Wine Co.
BANDIT - Amplifiers–musical instrument ☆ - Peavey Electronics Corp.
BANDIT - Apparel and accessories - Gentry Inc.
BANDIT - Automotive parts and accessories ☆ - Echlin Inc.
BANDIT - Bicycles ☆ - Huffy Corp.
BANDIT - Boats–motor ☆ - Alumacraft Boat Co.
BANDIT - Bumpers–motor vehicle - Wedgestone Automotive Corp.
BANDIT - Catheters - Scimed Life Systems, Inc.
BANDIT - Communications equipment–mobile - Twinpoint Inc.
BANDIT - Eyeglasses - Art-Craft Optical Co.
BANDIT - Floor coverings–carpet and rugs ☆ - Lowe's Carpet Corp.
BANDIT - Lubricants - American Rescue Technology Inc.
BANDIT - Pet collars - Jet Products
BANDIT - Sporting goods - Gexco Enterprises

BANDIT - Sporting goods ☆ - O'Brien International
BANDIT - Toys - Tonka Corp.
BANDIT - Toys–models - Estes Industries
BANDIT - Toys–stuffed - Dakin Inc.
BANDIT - Toys–stuffed ☆ - Gund, Inc.
BANDIT COON - Sporting goods - Wellington Leisure Products, Inc.
BANDIT LURES - Fishing lures - Bandit Lures, Inc.
BANDIT SERIES - Sporting goods ☆ - Hyde Athletic Industries Inc.
BANDIT-WEAR - Apparel and accessories - Rember O. Burthey III
BANDITO - Food products - Newman's Own Inc.
BANDITO - Toys–guns - Barnett International, Inc.
BANDITO DIAVOLO - Food products - Newman's Own Inc.
BANDITS - Dental equipment - Wykle Research, Inc.
BANDITS - Footwear - Markon Footwear Inc.
BANDITS - Rubber bands - Alliance Rubber Co.
BANDITS - Underwear and nightwear - Maidenform Inc.
BANDITS - Watchbands–base metal - Chisco, Inc.
BANDITS OF NATCHEZ TRACE - Puzzles - Parris Manufacturing Co.
B&J BARTLES & JAYMES - Wine coolers - Ernest and Julio Gallo Winery
BANDJII - Floor coverings–carpet and rugs ☆ - Regal Rugs Inc.
B&L - Contact lenses - Bausch & Lomb Inc.
BANDLE - Tools - Columbine International
BANDLEADER, THE - Jewelry ☆ - Hirsch Speidel Inc.
BANDLESS - Envelopes–paper - Smead Manufacturing Co.
BANDLINE - Housewares - Doranne
BANDMASTER - Accordions - Castiglione Accordion
BANDMASTER - Accordions - Sho-Bud Pedal Steel Guitar
BANDMASTER - Antennas - Wintenna Inc.
BANDMASTER - Fabrics - Burlington House Fabrics Group
BANDMASTER - Fabrics - Minnetonka Mills Inc.
BANDMASTER - Office supplies - Ever-Ready Co.
BANDMASTERS - Watchbands–base metal - Duchess Industries Inc.
B&N SOFTWARE - Computer software - B & N Companies, Inc.
BANDOLEER - Frames–eyeglass - May Optical Co. Inc.
BANDOLERO - Floor coverings–carpet and rugs ☆ - Cumberland Mills Inc.
BANDOLERO - Watches - Hausen Associates, Inc.
BANDOLIER - Recording label - Suncountry Productions Inc.
BANDOLINE - Hair care products - Alvin Last Inc.
BANDOLINO - Shoes - Marx & Newman Co. Inc.
BANDOLINO - Shoes - United States Shoe Corp.
BANDOLITE - Sporting goods ☆ - Kenyon Consumer Products Inc.
BANDON - Food products - Bandon Fisheries
BANDOR - Filters–air ☆ - American Air Filter International (Replacement Filter Products)
B&P - Office supplies - Esselte Corp.
BANDS & IVY - Tiles–ceramic - Wenczel Tile Co.
BANDS OF LOVE - Rings–jewelry - Feature Enterprises
BANDSTAND - Computer software - Olive Enterprises, Inc.
BANDSTAND - Musical instrument accessories - Grover Musical Products, Inc.
BANDSTAND U.S.A. - Recording label - Goldwax Record Co. Inc.
B&T CHILDREN'S COUGH AND BRONCHIAL - Cough medicines - Boericke & Tafel
BANDU - Games - Hasbro, Inc.
B&W - Amplifiers - J. Atkins Holdings Ltd.
B&W - Fruits and vegetables - B & W Quality Growers, Inc.
BANDWAGON - Eyeglasses - Art-Craft Optical Co.
BANDWAGON - Toys - Play-Tech, Inc.
BANDWIDTH XTENDER - Electrical devices - First Pacific Networks
BANDY - Toys–stuffed - Dakin Inc.
BANDY BALL - Rubber bands - Alliance Rubber Co.
BANDYBALL - Balls–rubber - Bandyball Corp.
BANESIN - Pharmaceutical preparations ☆ - Forest Pharmaceuticals Inc.
BANFF - Flowers, plants, and seeds - Jacklin Seed
BANFF BREWERY/CANADA - Beverages–malt - HDT Importers Inc.
BANFF ICE - Vodka - Jim Beam Brands Co.
BANFF SPRINGS CHAMPIONSHIP COURSE - Computer software - Access Software Inc.
BANFI BRUT - Wines - Banfi Vintners
BANFLEX INJECTABLE - Pharmaceutical preparations - Forest Pharmaceuticals, Inc.
BANFORTH PRODUCTS - Recording label - Holy Bible Gospel Ministry of The Body of Christ, Yeshua, of the Holy Land,
BANG - Chewing gum - Carbonated Candy Ventures
BANG - Fruit drinks–bottled or canned - Orange Bang Inc.
BANG - Health care products - Lang Naturals
BANG - Radiation shielding equipment - MGS Research Inc.

BANG - Recording label ☆ - Web IV Music Inc.
BANG - Toys–guns - Kilgore Corp.
BANG & OLUFSEN - Electronic equipment - Bang & Olufsen of America Inc.
BANG BANG - Candy - Richardson Brands
BANG BANG - Jewelry - Hi-Fashion
BANG BEEF - Meat products and pet foods - Central Meat Packing
BANG CHANG - Spices and extracts - Eastland Food Corp.
BANG-UP JOB - Toys–automobiles - Mattel, Inc.
BANGALORE - Soap ☆ - Avon Products, Inc.
BANGESIC - Pharmaceutical preparations - Barre-National, Inc.
BANGKOK - Hardware - Bangkok International Inc.
BANGKOK - Men's hats ☆ - American Hat Co. Inc.
BANGKOK BEER - Beverages–malt - Chaupaya Trading Corp.
BANGKOK CUISINE - Sauces - Paul Messino
BANGLE'EAR - Cases–plastic - PKS Design Inc.
BANGLES - Cosmetics - Spearhead Industries Inc.
BANGLET - Jewelry - Unigem International
BANGOR - Frames–eyeglass ☆ - U.S. Optical Frame Co.
BANGOR - Shoes ☆ - Allen-Edmonds Shoe Corp.
BANGORA - Hats - American Hat Co. Inc.
BANGS AWAY - Hair care products - Stage One Designs
BANGSITE! - Ammunition - The Conestoga Co., Inc.
BANGUARD - Fabrics - Dickson Elberton Mills, Inc.
BANGUARD 30 - Fabrics - Dickson Elberton Mills, Inc.
BANHOLZER WINECELLARS - Wines - Banholzer Winecellars Ltd.
BANISH - Cleaning preparations - Garon Products Inc.
BANISHING CREAM - Skin care products - Avon Products, Inc.
BANISTER - Shoe stores - United States Shoe Corp.
BANJI - Apparel and accessories ☆ - Accessories International
BANJO - Golfing equipment - Yost Innovations
BANJO - Grass seed - International Seeds, Inc.
BANJO - Tape recorders - Goldblatt Tool Co.
BANJO FLATS - Toys–trains - Mattel, Inc.
BANJOR - Novelty items ☆ - Cathay International
BANJOS - Notebooks and notepads - Robert Thomas
BANK-O-MATIC - Toys ☆ - Arrow Industries, Inc.
BANK-ON-IT - Computer software - Learned-Mahn, Inc.
BANK SHOT - Toys - Tonka Corp.
BANK SHOT - Toys–electronic ☆ - Parker Brothers
BANK STREET SCHOOL FILER - Computer software ☆ - Sunburst Communications, Inc.
BANK STREET WRITER - Computer software ☆ - Broderbund Software, Inc.
BANK STREET WRITER PLUS - Computer software ☆ - Broderbund Software, Inc.
BANK-TIQUES - Toys–banks ☆ - Dakin Inc.
BANKABLE - Cigars - National Cigar Corp.
BANKABLE - Frames–eyeglass - Pathway Optical Prods.
BANKER - Floor coverings–carpet and rugs ☆ - Atlas Carpet Mills Inc.
BANKER - Watches - Bulova Corp.
BANKER II - Floor coverings–carpet and rugs - Milliken & Co. Inc.
BANKERS - Cigar boxes–wood - Consolidated Cigar Corp.
BANKERS - Pens - Bankers Pens Inc.
BANKERS BOX - Filing cabinets–metal - Fellowes Manufacturing Co.
BANKERS CHOICE - Cigars - National Cigar Corp.
BANKER'S CHOICE - Cigars ☆ - Avanti Cigar Co.
BANKERS CLUB - Whiskey - Laird and Co.
BANKERS LINE - Pens - Creative Learning Products Inc.
BANKERS LINEN - Paper - Southworth Co.
BANKER'S RUN - Computer software ☆ - Orange Cherry Software
BANKER'S WINDOW - Computer software - Xyquad, Inc.
BANKERS' WORKSTATION - Computer software - Chemical Bank
BANKIT - Toys - Matchbox Toys USA
BANKLINE - Paints - Synkoloid Co.
BANKLINE - Publisher's imprints - Probus Publishing Co.
BANKNOTES - Computer software - Joseph Madison Associates Inc.
BANKRUPTCY MATE - Publisher's imprints - Little, Brown and Co., Inc.
BANKSHOT - Apparel and accessories - Neutral, Inc.
BANLEP - Insecticides - Merck & Co., Inc.
BANNER - Adhesives and sealants - Colorado Paint Co.
BANNER - Apparel–men's - Montgomery Ward & Co. Inc.
BANNER - Binders - Boorum & Pease Co.
BANNER - Candy - Banner Candy Manufacturing Corp.
BANNER - Clocks - General Time Corp. (Westclox/Seth Thomas Div.)
BANNER - Faucets - Woodmark International, Inc.
BANNER - Firearms, accessories, and parts - Bausch & Lomb Inc.
BANNER - Food products - Bunge Foods Corp.

☆ = Now out of production

BANNER - Fruits–dried ☆ - Johnston Farms
BANNER - Glue–household or industrial - Evans Adhesive Corp.
BANNER - Hunting equipment - Worldwide Sports & Recreation, Inc.
BANNER - Mats and runners - Banner Mat Inc.
BANNER - Meat products–beef - Armour Swift-Eckrich
BANNER - Paints - Midwest Paint Manufacturing Co.
BANNER - Paper–toilet - Procter & Gamble Co.
BANNER - Recreational vehicle dealers ☆ - Commodore Corp.
BANNER - Watches - Avalon Watch Corp.
BANNER - Watches - Webster Watch Co. Associates
BANNER BAND - Printers–computer - Sunshine Business Forms Inc.
BANNER BLUE - Musical instruments ☆ - Fred Gretsch Enterprises
BANNER BRAND - Flowers, plants, and seeds - Hub Floral Corp.
BANNER BUDDY - Construction machinery - Security Lighting Systems, Inc.
BANNER FAIR - Food products - Beckman and Gast Co. Inc.
BANNER HOUSE - Cosmetics ☆ - Fashion Express
BANNER LINE - Saws–power - DBNA Trademarks Holding Inc.
BANNER MACHINE, THE - Computer software - Virginia Micro Computer Systems
BANNER MANIA - Computer software ☆ - Broderbund Software, Inc.
BANNER PHARMACAPS - Cosmetics - Banner Pharmacaps Inc.
BANNER - S - Drills–dental - Professional Manufacturing Corp.
BANNER-UP - Fabrics - Weblon Inc.
BANNER VINEYARDS - Wines - Giumarra Vineyards
BANNER YEARS BOSTON GARDEN 1928-1995 - Calendars - New Boston Garden Corp.
BANNERLINE - Fabrics - Industrial Coatings Group, Inc.
BANNERS PLUS - Banners - Trend Enterprises, Inc.
BANNERS WITH APPEAL - Banners - Randy Nash
BANNERS WITH APPEAL CABANA BANNERS - Banners - Randy Nash
BANNIS - Dermatological preparations - Pickett Investments, Inc.
BANNISTER AND BEALE - Apparel and accessories - Jaymar-Ruby Inc.
BANNON - Sinks–metal - Kohler Co.
BANOM BRAND - Gloves–work - Commodity Glove Co., Inc.
BANQUET - Cheese - Nelson-Ricks Creamery Co.
BANQUET - Dinners–frozen - Conagra, Inc.
BANQUET - Fish food - Aquatrol, Inc.
BANQUET - Food products - Dairy Fresh Products Co.
BANQUET - Food products ☆ - Baron Seafoods
BANQUET - Milk - Banquet Dairy Products
BANQUET - Pasta - Shreveport Macaroni Co.
BANQUET - Plastic silverware - Van Brode Milling Co. Inc.
BANQUET - Teas ☆ - McCormick & Co., Inc.
BANQUET BASIC - Fish food ☆ - Aquatrol, Inc.
BANQUET GOURMET - Dinners–frozen - Conagra, Inc.
BANQUET KID'S CUISINE - Dinners–frozen - Conagra, Inc.
BANQUET PASTA FAVORITES - Pasta - Conagra, Inc.
BANQUET TABLE - Fruits–canned - Aslesen Co.
BANQUO BOOKS - Publisher's imprints - Woodbridge Press Publishing Co.
BANROL - Thread - Staple Sewing Aids Corp.
BANSECT - Pet collars - Sergeant's Pet Products, Inc.
BANSECT - Pet products - A.H. Robins Co. Inc.
BANSHEE - Alarm systems - Whistler Acquistion Corp.
BANSHEE - Bicycles - Ross Bicycles USA, Ltd.
BANSHEE - Computer peripheral equipment - Adobe Systems Inc.
BANSHEE - Sporting goods - Skis Dynastar, Inc.
BANSHEE BOMBER - Toys–guns - Kenner Products
BANSHEE, THE - Darts and dart games - Dart World Inc.
BANSI - Vegetables–pickled or brined - Deep Foods, Inc.
BANTA - Vitamins and nutritional supplements - Vita Source, Inc.
BANTAM - Bicycles - Schwinn Cycling & Fitness Inc.
BANTAM - Brake parts - Adams Machine & Tool Co.
BANTAM - Brushes–paint ☆ - PPG Industries, Inc.
BANTAM - Cameras - Eastman Kodak Co.
BANTAM - Chemical preparations - Starkey Chemical Process Co.
BANTAM - Cigars - G.A. Georgopulo & Co. Inc.
BANTAM - Clocks - General Time Corp. (Westclox/Seth Thomas Div.)
BANTAM - Doors–vinyl - Rytec Corp.
BANTAM - Health care products ☆ - Wheel Ring Inc.
BANTAM - Motor vehicles–buses - Collins Bus Corp.
BANTAM - Portable overhead projectors - Audiscan Products Co.
BANTAM - Publisher's imprints - Bantam Doubleday Dell Publishing Group, Inc.
BANTAM - Shovels - True Temper Hardware Co.
BANTAM - Soldering equipment - Hexacon Electric Co.
BANTAM - Staplers ☆ - Hunt Manufacturing Co.
BANTAM - Toys–stuffed - Bantam Collections Inc.

BANTAM - Umbrellas - Storm Hero Umbrella Co. Inc.
BANTAM - Window coverings - Levolor Inc.
BANTAM 2000 - Lighting fixtures - Holophane Corp.
BANTAM/BRITANNICA - Publisher's imprints - Encyclopaedia Britannica Inc.
BANTAM CLASSICS - Publisher's imprints - Bantam Doubleday Dell Publishing Group, Inc.
BANTAM PATHFINDERS - Publisher's imprints ☆ - Bantam Doubleday Dell Publishing Group, Inc.
BANTAM PLUG - Screws - Rawlplug Co., Inc.
BANTAM PLUS - Umbrellas - Storm Hero Umbrella Co. Inc.
BANTAM WEIGHT - Wire products - Vector Enterprises
BANTAMWATE CHAMPION - Lighting fixtures - Acme-Lite Manufacturing Co.
BANTEX - Fabrics–coated - Herculite Products, Inc.
BANTHINE - Pharmaceutical preparations - G. D. Searle & Co.
BANTRON - Pharmaceutical preparations ☆ - Dep Corp.
BANTRY BAY - Furniture ☆ - Henredon Furniture Industries Inc.
BANTU - Hair care products - Johnson Products Co., Inc.
BANUS - Musical instruments - Tropical Music and Pro Audio
BANYAN BOOKS - Publisher's imprints - Banyan Books Inc.
BANYAN RECORDS - Recording label - Burton A. Borrok
BANZA - Headwear - Zant Products Inc.
BANZAI - Apparel and accessories ☆ - Edison Brothers Stores, Inc.
BANZAI - Games - Avalon Hill Game Co.
BANZAI - Toys - Hasbro, Inc.
BAOBAB - Recording label - Jazz Composer's Orchestra Association Inc.
BAOBAB TREE - Greeting cards - AGC, Inc.
BAOBAB TREE - Greeting cards - American Greetings Corp.
BAPPTRACK - Computer software - Behavioral Science Technology, Inc.
BAPS - Medical apparatus - Camp, Inc.
BAPTEN - Pharmaceutical preparations - Alaco, Inc.
BAPTISTE GELAS - Beverages–alcohol - Paterno Imports, Ltd.
BAR - Pharmaceutical preparations ☆ - Scrip-Physician Supply Co.
BAR 3 - Veterinary pharmaceutical preparations ☆ - Boehringer Ingelheim Animal Health, Inc.
BAR 3/SOMNUS - Veterinary pharmaceutical preparations ☆ - Boehringer Ingelheim Animal Health, Inc.
BAR 4 - Veterinary pharmaceutical preparations - Boehringer Ingelheim Animal Health, Inc.
BAR 4/SOMNUS - Veterinary pharmaceutical preparations - Boehringer Ingelheim Animal Health, Inc.
BAR-B-BOSS - Barbecues and grills - Regent Sheffield, Ltd.
BAR-B-BRIC - Charcoal - Pacer Technology
BAR-B-CHEF - Barbecues and grills - Barbeques Galore Inc.
BAR-B-CHEK - Thermometers - Maverick Industries, Inc.
BAR-B-CUBE - Briquettes - California Alfalfa Cube
BAR-B-DOG - Sandwiches–prepackaged - Donald P. Kobielush
BAR-B-FORK - Barbecues and grills - Regent Sheffield, Ltd.
BAR-B-GRILL - Barbecues and grills - Dazey Corp.
BAR-B-KETTLE - Barbecues and grills - Weber-Stephen Products Co.
BAR-B-MATE - Barbecues and grills - Regent Sheffield, Ltd.
BAR-B-Q BOX - Charcoal - Caldo International, Inc.
BAR-B-Q LITERS - Lighters - Meteor Inc.
BAR-B-QUE - Barbecue-grill cleaner ☆ - Chase Products Co.
BAR-B-SKEWS - Barbecues and grills ☆ - M.E. Heuck Co. Inc.
BAR-B-TONGS - Barbecues and grills - Regent Sheffield, Ltd.
BAR BABY - Bar fixtures–metal ☆ - Life Time Faucets Inc.
BAR-BAC - Uniforms–tailored - Angelica Uniform Group
BAR BAG COLORADO U.S.A. - Bags–duffel - Bar Bag
BAR BQ - Pork - Big B Distributors Inc.
BAR-BUOY - Ashtrays–glass - Orbex Inc.
BAR C - Apparel and accessories - Duck Head Apparel Co., Inc.
BAR C - Meat products–beef - Schweigert Foods
BAR CODE BASICS - Computer software - Percon Acquisition, Inc.
BAR CODE PRO - Computer software - Synex
BAR CODE PUBLISHER - Computer software - Strandware, Inc.
BAR CRAWL - Apparel and accessories - Lindy Promotions Inc.
BAR DK - Waterproofing compounds ☆ - Samuel Cabot Inc.
BAR END SYSTEM - Bicycles - Ornate Acquisition Corp.
BAR ESSENTIALS - Housewares stores - Innovative Beverage Products
BAR FLIES - Darts and dart games - Dart Mart Inc.
BAR FLIES - Pet products - Lambert-Kay
BAR-GRAIN - Hair curlers - Paperwork Ltd.
BAR GUARD-99 - Veterinary pharmaceutical preparations - Boehringer Ingelheim Animal Health, Inc.
BAR HARBOR - Bells - North Country Wind Bells Inc.
BAR HARBOR - Boats–motor ☆ - Cruisers

BAR HARBOR - Calendars - House of Doolittle
BAR HARBOR - Cough drops - New England Lozenge Co., Inc.
BAR HARBOR - Floor coverings–carpet and rugs ☆ - Trans-Ocean Import Co. Inc.
BAR HARBOR - Foul-weather gear - Bliss Marine
BAR HARBOR - Furniture - A. Brandt Co. Inc.
BAR HARBOR - Furniture - Moosehead Manufacturing Co.
BAR HARBOR - Glassware–household - Owens-Illinois Inc. (Libbey Div.)
BAR HARBOR - Seafood products–canned or cured - A.M. Look Canning Co.
BAR-HARBOR - Shoes - Cole-Haan
BAR HARBOR - Toilets–porcelain - Mansfield Plumbing Products, Inc.
BAR I BUD - Veterinary pharmaceutical preparations ☆ - Boehringer Ingelheim Animal Health, Inc.
BAR-IT - Pharmaceutical preparations - Lanpar Co.
BAR KEEPERS FRIEND - Cleaning preparations - Servaas Laboratories Inc.
BAR KING - Beverages–carbonated - Great Western Juice Co.
BAR-LE-DUC - Teas - Eastern Shore Tea Co.
BAR-LEG - Automotive hand tool - Cascade Marketing Associates
BAR-LOC - Binders - Steego Corp.
BAR-LOCK - Jewelry - Unigem International
BAR LOK - Aluminum products - Aluminum Co. of America
BAR-M - Beef ☆ - Murco Inc.
BAR/MET - Paints - Valspar Corp.
BAR MITZVAH BEAR - Toys–stuffed - Russ Berrie and Co., Inc.
BAR MIX - Snack foods - Amsnack, Inc.
BAR MOBILE - Housewares - Beverage-Air
BAR NONE - Candy - Hershey Chocolate USA
BAR-O - Firearms, accessories, and parts - Benjamin Sheridan Corp.
BAR-O-BEX - Pharmaceutical preparations - Barrows Pharmacal Inc.
BAR O FARM - Fruits–frozen - Bar O Farms
BAR-ONE - Computer software - Vertical Technologies, Inc.
BAR-OX - Paints - Devoe & Raynolds Co.
BAR S - Food products - Bar S Food Co. Inc.
BAR-S - Recording label - Flat Town Music Co.
BAR-SCHEEZ - Cheese - Win Schuler Foods
BAR-SCHIPS - Snack foods - Win Schuler Foods
BAR SHOP - Bar accessories - John A. Peterson Co.
BAR SOMNUS - Veterinary pharmaceutical preparations - Boehringer Ingelheim Animal Health, Inc.
BAR SOMNUS 2P - Veterinary pharmaceutical preparations - Boehringer Ingelheim Animal Health, Inc.
BAR SOMNUS/LEPTO-5 - Veterinary pharmaceutical preparations ☆ - Boehringer Ingelheim Animal Health, Inc.
BAR-SPAR - Varnishes - Remien & Kuhnert Co.
BAR STOOL - Beverages–alcohol - Pontiac Beer Co., Inc.
BAR-TENDER'S - Beverages–alcohol - Brady Enterprises Inc.
BAR-TENDERS - Chickens - Hester Industries, Inc.
BAR-V - Fixtures - Benjamin Sheridan Corp.
BAR VAC 7 - Veterinary pharmaceutical preparations - Boehringer Ingelheim Animal Health, Inc.
BAR-VAC-7/SOMNUS - Veterinary pharmaceutical preparations - Boehringer Ingelheim Animal Health, Inc.
BAR VAC CD/T - Veterinary pharmaceutical preparations - Boehringer Ingelheim Animal Health, Inc.
BAR WARS - Games - Avalon Hill Game Co.
BAR-X - Food products - Valley Distributing Co.
BARABOO - Food products ☆ - Melson Meat Co. Inc.
BARACUDA - Tires–motorcycle - Greenball Corp.
BARACUTA - Apparel–men's - Phillips-Van Heusen Corp.
BARAD - Apparel and accessories - Barad & Co.
BARAHIST - Pharmaceutical preparations ☆ - Consolidated Midland Corp.
BARAKA - Paper products - Midway Manufacturing Co.
BARAKA BOOKS LTD. - Publisher's imprints - Baraka Press Inc.
BARANCA - Floor coverings - Mannington Resilient Floors
BARANOFF - Fragrance products - Richard Barrie Fragrances, Inc.
BARANZELLI - Housewares - Baranzelli House
BARASOL - Pharmaceutical preparations - Consolidated Midland Corp.
BARAT BITS - Confections - L.T. Plant, Inc.
BARAT NOVELLE - Tofu - L.T. Plant, Inc.
BARATEX - Apparel and accessories - Baratex, Inc.
BARATTI & MILANO - Candy ☆ - De Medici Imports Ltd.
BARAZET - Cookies - Damascus Baking
BARB-TY - Electrical equipment - Panduit Corp.
BARBA-CUE SPECIALS - Publisher's imprints - Harian Creative Press-Books
BARBACINE - Pharmaceutical preparations ☆ - Wayne Medical Co. Inc.
BARBADOS - Bathroom accessories - Kohler Co.

BARBADOS - Dinnerware - Corning Inc.
BARBADOS - Floor coverings–carpet and rugs ☆ - Callaway Carpets
BARBADOS - Furniture - Homecrest Industries Inc.
BARBADOS - Furniture ☆ - Southern Furniture Co. of Conover
BARBADOS - Shoes ☆ - Allen-Edmonds Shoe Corp.
BARBADOS - Wallpaper ☆ - Winfield Design Associates, Inc.
BARBADOS GLASSWORKS - Bathroom fixtures - Kohler Co.
BARBADOS HONEY PEPPER SAUCE - Sauces - Cinnabar Specialty Foods, Inc./Neera's Products
BARBADOS JACK - Food products - Royal Distributors
BARBARA - Frames–eyeglass - U.S. Optical Frame Co.
BARBARA - Glassware–household - ACC
BARBARA - Rings–jewelry - Artcarved Inc.
BARBARA BERGER - Greeting cards - Berger Silkscreen Cards
BARBARA BROOKS - Apparel–women's - Nardis, Inc.
BARBARA DEE - Cookies - Barbara Dee Bakery (Div. of President Baking)
BARBARA GERWIT - Apparel and accessories - Barbara Gerwit
BARBARA IRRI - Ribbons - Princess Ribbon Corp.
BARBARA LEE FASHIONS - Sewing machine cabinets–wood - Tex-Craft Co. Inc.
BARBARA MONIGAN - Apparel and accessories - Barbara A. Monigan
BARBARA STITT'S - Pancakes–mixes ☆ - Natural Ovens of Manitowoc Inc.
BARBARA TAYLOR FOUTS - Jewelry - Gregory G. Fouts
BARBARA WOODHOUSE - Pet products - Whitco Manufacturing Inc.
BARBARAMAC - Apparel and accessories - California Concepts, Inc.
BARBARA'S - Food products - Barbara's Bakery, Inc.
BARBARA'S CRACKLESNAX - Crackers ☆ - Barbara's Bakery, Inc.
BARBARESCO RISERVA - Wines - Kobrand Corp.
BARBARIAN - Toys - Tonka Corp.
BARBARIAN BLAST - Fireworks - B.J. Alan Co. Inc.
BARBARIAN GOLF - Golfing equipment - John M. Correlli
BARBAROSSA - Beverages–alcohol - Consolidated Distilled Products Inc.
BARBAROSSA - Footwear - Italian Leather Co. Inc.
BARBARRIER - Guard for chain saw - K & M Industries, Inc.
BARBARY COAST - Fabrics - Dan River Inc.
BARBARY COAST - Floor coverings–carpet and rugs ☆ - Cumberland Mills Inc.
BARBASOL - Shaving preparations - Pfizer Inc.
BARBATIA - Lubricants ☆ - Shell Oil Co.
BARBAZANGE - Stationery - Barbazange
BARBECUE MASTER - Housewares - Companion Group
BARBECUE RUB 21 - Seasonings - North American Laboratory Co.
BARBECUE VITTLES - Snack foods ☆ - General Mills, Inc.
BARBED WIRE - Cables–steel - Kryptonite Corp.
BARBEE - Food products ☆ - Maple Leaf Farms Inc.
BARBEE - Fruits and vegetables - Nuchief Sales Inc.
BARBEE - Skin care products - Spilo/Mehaz Worldwide
BARBEE BEAUTY COIL - Skin care products - Graham Medical Products
BARBELL - Cookies - James D. Rogers
BARBELLA - Wines - Blair Importers Ltd.
BARBELLA - Wines - David Sherman Corp.
BARBELLS - Wallpaper ☆ - Koroseal Wallcoverings
BARBELOID - Pharmaceutical preparations ☆ - Pal-Pak Inc.
BARBER - Milk - Barber Pure Milk Co.
BARBER - Razor blades - Barber Blade Co.
BARBER BLADE - Razor blades - Barber Razor Blade Co.
BARBER FOODS - Frozen foods - Barber Foods
BARBER POLES - Candy - Gilliam Candy Co. Inc. (Gilliam Candy Brands)
BARBERA - Olive oil - Bel Canto Fancy Foods Ltd.
BARBERA - Wines - Fife Vineyards LLC
BARBERA - Wines - Renwood Winery, Inc.
BARBERA D'ASTI SUPERIORE - Wines - Kobrand Corp.
BARBERAMI - Wines - Pellegrini Bros. Wines Inc.
BARBERINI - Wines - Wine Imports Ltd.
BARBER'S SECRET - Shaving preparations - Tarieek Punter
BARBERS, THE - Razor blades - City Looks International
BARBES - Milk - Barbe's Dairy Inc.
BARBET - Hosiery - Virginia Maid Hosiery Mills Inc.
BARBICIDE - Disinfectants - King Research, Inc.
BARBICIDE PLUS - Disinfectants - King Research, Inc.
BARBIDONNA - Pharmaceutical preparations - Wallace Laboratories
BARBIE - Apparel and accessories - Breton Industries
BARBIE - Bathroom accessories - Tsumura International Inc.
BARBIE - Computer software - Epyx Inc.
BARBIE - Cosmetics ☆ - Andrew Jergens Co.
BARBIE - Decals and transfers ☆ - Creative Teaching Press

☆ = Now out of production

BARBIE - Dolls - Mattel, Inc.
BARBIE - Footwear - Pagoda Trading Co.
BARBIE - Handbags - Pyramid Handbags Inc.
BARBIE - Lamps - Dolly, Inc.
BARBIE - Lunch boxes - Thermos Co.
BARBIE - Pet products - Precious Paws
BARBIE - Shoes - Sidney Rich Associates Inc.
BARBIE - Shoes–athletic ☆ - Coast Shoes Inc.
BARBIE - Socks - High Point Knitting Inc.
BARBIE - Sunglasses - Riviera Trading, Inc.
BARBIE - Toys - Chilton-Globe, Inc.
BARBIE - Wallpaper - Priss Prints Inc.
BARBIE - Wheelchairs ☆ - Everest and Jennings International Ltd.
BARBIE & THE ROCKERS - Games ☆ - Ben Cooper Inc.
BARBIE AND THE ROCKERS - Shoes ☆ - Sidney Rich Associates Inc.
BARBIE CHARMS THE WORLD - Games - Mattel, Inc.
BARBIE COLLECTIBLES - Dolls - Mattel, Inc.
BARBIE DREAM CYCLE - Bicycles ☆ - Murray, Inc.
BARBIE DREAM HORSE - Dolls - Mattel, Inc.
BARBIE FASHION DESIGNER - Computer software - Mattel Media Inc.
BARBIE FOR GIRLS - Dolls - Mattel, Inc.
BARBIE FOR PRESIDENT - Dolls - Mattel, Inc.
BARBIE JEWEL SECRETS - Dolls - Mattel, Inc.
BARBIE MAGIC FAIRY TALES - Computer software - Mattel Media Inc.
BARBIE MILLICENT ROBERTS - Dolls - Mattel, Inc.
BARBIERI RANCH - Wines - Deloach Vineyards
BARBIPIL - Pharmaceutical preparations ☆ - Vortech Pharmaceuticals
BARBITA - Pharmaceutical preparations ☆ - Vortech Pharmaceuticals
BARBIZON - Apparel–women's - Barbizon Lingerie
BARBIZON - Floor coverings–carpet and rugs - Atlas Carpet Mills Inc.
BARBIZON - Hosiery - Vanities Unlimited, Inc.
BARBIZON - School franchise, cosmetics - Barbizon International Inc.
BARBKOA - Sauces - Roco Foods, Inc.
BARBOUR - Tiles–terrazzo ☆ - Maxsam Sales, Inc.
BARBOUR'S - Thread - Blue Mountain Industries, Inc.
BARBOURSVILLE VINEYARDS - Wines - Barboursville Winery Inc.
BARBQ MATE - Cooking utensils–cast iron - Jopco, Inc.
BARBWIRE'S - Vegetable sauces - Shoney's, Inc.
BARC - Pharmaceutical preparations ☆ - Del Pharmaceuticals, Inc.
BARCA - Wines - Barca Wine Cellars of California
BARCA - Wines - Barcamerica International Corp. USA
BARCALOUNGER - Furniture - Barcalounger Co.
BARCARDS - Educational materials - Stephen A. Mendel
BARCART - Serving carts ☆ - Artex-Green Corp. of N.Y.
BARCEL - Leather goods - REXAM DSI
BARCELONA - Beverages–alcohol - Juba Beverages Corp.
BARCELONA - Cigars ☆ - General Cigar Co., Inc.
BARCELONA - Dishes–china ☆ - Pickard Inc.
BARCELONA - Flatware - International Silver Co.
BARCELONA - Floor coverings - Congoleum Corp.
BARCELONA - Furniture–upholstered - Maharam Vertical Surfaces
BARCELONA - Giftware - Sasaki
BARCELONA - Wallpaper - Pickhardt & Siebert USA Inc.
BARCELONA - Wines ☆ - Bardenheier Wine Cellars
BARCELONA COLLECTION - Bathing suits - Authentic Fitness Corp.
BARCLAY - Cabinets - Del Mar Cabinets
BARCLAY - Cigarettes - Brown & Williamson Tobacco Corp.
BARCLAY - Fabrics - Dan River Inc.
BARCLAY - Flatware - Reed and Barton Corp.
BARCLAY - Flatware - Utica Cutlery Co.
BARCLAY - Furniture - Barclay Home Products Corp.
BARCLAY - Glassware–household ☆ - Lenox Crystal, Inc.
BARCLAY - Hardware - Baldwin Hardware Corp.
BARCLAY - Preserved foods–canned ☆ - Sundor Brands Inc.
BARCLAY - Shoes - Endicott Johnson Corp.
BARCLAY - Tableware–china ☆ - Lenox, Inc.
BARCLAY - Tuxedos ☆ - After Six Inc.
BARCLAY - Wallpaper ☆ - Eisenhart Wallcoverings Co.
BARCLAY - Window coverings - Norman Lacoff & Associates Inc.
BARCLAY 5 - Wallpaper ☆ - Eisenhart Wallcoverings Co.
BARCLAY CLUB - Men's and boys' sweaters - Barclay Sportswear Inc.
BARCLAY COURT - Floor coverings–carpet and rugs - Queen Carpet Corp.
BARCLAY FIBERGLASS RECEPTCLES - Wastebaskets - United Receptacle Inc.
BARCLAY FROST - Cabinets - Del Mar Cabinets
BARCLAY-GENEVE - Cutlery ☆ - Lifetime Hoan Corp.

BARCLAY SQUARE - Floor coverings - Mannington Resilient Floors
BARCLAY SQUARE - Floor coverings ☆ - Congoleum Corp.
BARCLAY'S - Liquors - Canandaigua Wine Co. Inc.
BARCO - Medical uniforms - Barco of California
BARCO - Tools - Barco Industries, Inc.
BARCO OF CALIFORNIA - Uniforms–tailored ☆ - Barco of California
BARCOCOID - Paints - Barrett Varnish Co.
BARCODATA - Electronics equipment - Barco Inc.
BARCODE - Apparel and accessories - Conic Enterprises Ltd.
BARCODE LABELER II - Computer software - Videx, Inc.
BARCOFLAT - Paints - Barrett Varnish Co.
BARCOFLO - Paints - Barrett Varnish Co.
BARCOGRAPHICS - Electronics equipment - Barco Inc.
BARCOLENE - Cleaning preparations - Barcolene Inc.
BARCOMP - Steel - Theis Precision Steel Corp.
BARCON 1000 - Air purification systems - Marine Shale Processors, Inc.
BARCOPLEX - Lacquers - Barrett Varnish Co.
BARCOTEX - Enamels - Barrett Varnish Co.
BARCOTONE - Varnishes - Barrett Varnish Co.
BARCOVAR - Varnishes - Barrett Varnish Co.
BARCOVISION - Electronics equipment - Barco Inc.
BARCUS-BERRY - Audio equipment - Barcus-Berry Inc.
BARCUS-BERRY - Electrical equipment - Bbe Sound, Inc.
BARD - Cigars ☆ - General Cigar Co., Inc.
BARD - Health care products - C.R. Bard, Inc.
BARD - Sporting goods - Gold Eagle/Arnold Palmer
BARD - Sporting goods ☆ - Georgia's Tennis
BARD AERO CERAMIC - Sporting goods ☆ - Gold Eagle/Arnold Palmer
BARD AFTER TENNIS - Sporting goods ☆ - Gold Eagle/Arnold Palmer
BARD BOOKS - Publisher's imprints ☆ - Hearst Corp.
BARD JADE ELITE - Sporting goods ☆ - Gold Eagle/Arnold Palmer
BARD MIRAGE - Sporting goods ☆ - Gold Eagle/Arnold Palmer
BARD TRI FORCE - Sporting goods ☆ - Gold Eagle/Arnold Palmer
BARDAHL - Chemical preparations - Bardahl Manufacturing Corp.
BARDCO - Health care products - C.R. Bard, Inc.
BARDENHEIER'S - Wines - Bardenheier Wine Cellars
BARDEX - Health care products - C.R. Bard, Inc.
BARDIA - Health care products - C.R. Bard, Inc.
BARDIC - Health care products - C.R. Bard, Inc.
BARDIN - Food products - Bardin Farms Corp.
BARDNEY - Faucets - Kohler Co.
BARDOLINO CLASSICO SUPERIORE - Wines ☆ - Kobrand Corp.
BARDON - Urinals–enameled - Kohler Co.
BARDS - Smoked salmon - International Marketing Services Inc.
BARD'S TALE - Computer software - Electronic Arts Inc.
BARD'S TALE II: DESTINY KNIGHT - Computer software - Electronic Arts Inc.
BARDURA - Office supplies - Labelon Corp.
BARDWIN - Floor coverings - Armstrong World Industries, Inc.
BARE & BEAUTIFUL - Cosmetics ☆ - Rubigo Cosmetics Inc.
BARE & SMOOTH - Pharmaceutical preparations ☆ - Thompson Medical Co., Inc.
BARE AROMA - Lotions - Barry Alan
BARE ASSETS - Bathing suits - Pierre Cardin Electronique
BARE BASICS B - Underwear and nightwear - Sheena 61st Lingerie Corp.
BARE BLUSHER - Cosmetics - Coty Inc.
BARE BODY ILLUSION - Apparel–women's - Brazabra Corp.
BARE BONES - Bicycles - Dynacraft Industries Inc.
BARE BONES - Dog food - Sherre Taylor Cammack
BARE BONES - Floor waxes - Mission Kleensweep Products, Inc.
BARE BONES - Sauces and seasonings - Joseph J. Reese
BARE BOTTOMS - Women's shoes - International Seaway Trading Corp.
BARE BRA - Brassieres (Bras) ☆ - Vanity Fair Mills Inc.
BARE CARE - Vacuum cleaners and accessories - The Eureka Co.
BARE COVER - Cosmetics - Charles Revson Inc.
BARE D' LITES - Brassieres (Bras) ☆ - Playtex Apparel, Inc.
BARE ELEGANCE - Shampoos - Gillette Co.
BARE EMBRACE - Apparel–women's - Carnival Creations
BARE ESSENTIAL - Brassieres (Bras) ☆ - Vanity Fair Mills Inc.
BARE ESSENTIAL - Razors - Wahl Clipper Corp.
BARE FACTS - Apparel–women's ☆ - Carnival Creations
BARE FOOT - Skin care products - Freeman Cosmetics Corp.
BARE IS BACK - Apparel and accessories - Warnaco Inc.
BARE MINIMUM - Underwear and nightwear ☆ - Lovable Co.
BARE NECESSITY - Apparel–women's - Jezebel-Renee of Hollywood
BARE SHOULDER ELEGANCE - Underwear and nightwear - Maidenform Inc.
BARE SPOT R - Flowers, plants, and seeds - Seed Corp. of America

☆ = Now out of production

BARE TRAPS - Footwear ☆ - G.H. Bass and Co.
BAREBACK - Prophylactics - Ansell Inc. (Personal Products Div.)
BAREBACK - Skin care products ☆ - Blistex Inc.
BAREFOOT - Boats–motor - Master Craft Boat Co.
BAREFOOT - Floor coverings–carpet and rugs ☆ - Mohawk Carpet Corp.
BAREFOOT - Wines - Michael C. Houlihan
BAREFOOT - Wines ☆ - Parliament Import Co.
BAREFOOT ARCH SUPPORTS - Orthopedic products - Bio-Orthotics International, Inc.
BAREFOOT BALLERINA - Publisher's imprints - Panache Productions Inc.
BAREFOOT BY FLORIDA - Sandals - Florida Shoe Inc.
BAREFOOT BYNUM - Wines ☆ - Parliament Import Co.
BAREFOOT FREEDOM - Footwear - Drew Shoe Corp.
BAREFOOT MISS OF CALIFORNIA - Bathing suits - Raj Manufacturing, Inc.
BAREFOOT NAUTIQUE - Boats ☆ - Correct Craft Inc.
BAREFOOT ORIGINALS - Footwear–women's - Wolff Shoe Co.
BAREFOOT SIMULATOR - Footwear - Toddler University
BAREFOOT SKIER - Ski boat ☆ - American Skier Boat Co.
BAREFOOTIN' - Exercising equipment ☆ - Raleigh USA Bicycle Co.
BARELY LEGAL - Magazines - HG Publications, Inc.
BARELY ME - Intimate apparel - Maidenform Inc.
BARELY NOTHINGS - Underwear and nightwear - Barely Nothings Inc.
BARELY THERE - Apparel–women's - Bi-Flex International
BARELY THERE - Pharmaceutical preparations - Texas Pharmacal Co.
BARELY YOURS - Underwear and nightwear - Bestform Foundations, Inc.
BAREMAN'S - Food products - Bareman Dairy Inc.
BAREN - Noodles - Kreiner Imports
BARENE - Varnishes - Standard T Chemical Co. Inc.
BARENGO - Wine vinegar - American Foods Corp.
BARENGO - Wines - Lost Hills Winery
BARENGO RESERVE - Wines ☆ - Lost Hills Winery
BARENJAGER - Liquors - Sidney Frank Importing Co., Inc.
BAREUTHER - Giftware - Wara Intercontinental Co.
BAREUTHER PLATES - Giftware - Viking Import House Inc.
BARFBAN - Deodorizers - Surco Products Inc.
BARFEDRINE - Pharmaceutical preparations ☆ - Wendt-Bristol Co.
BARFO - Candy - Topps Co., Inc.
BARFOOT - Snow boards - Atlantic Skates Inc.
BARFOOT - Surfboards - Charles Lee Barfoot
BARGAIN BAG - Hosiery - Desoto Hosiery Mills, Inc.
BARGAIN BITES - Pet products - HTZ Investment Corp.
BARGAIN BUY - Cigarettes - R.J. Reynolds Tobacco Co.
BARGAIN HUNTER - Games ☆ - Milton Bradley Co.
BARGAIN MIX - Fasteners–hook and eye - VSI Fasteners, Inc.
BARGARD - Fabrics - JD Fabrics Ltd.
BARGE - Adhesives and sealants - Smith & Nephew Inc. (Rehabilitation Div.)
BARGELLO - Floor coverings–carpet and rugs - Milliken & Co. Inc.
BARGELLO - Glassware–household ☆ - Spiegelau Inc.
BARGELLO BELT - Toys - Milton Bradley Co.
BARGETTO - Wines - Bargetto's Santa Cruz Winery
BARGREEN - Coffee - Bargreen Coffee Co.
BARI - Bathtubs–enameled - Lasco Products Group
BARI - Instrument mouthpieces - Bari Associates, Inc.
BARI - Musical instrument accessories - CTC Music Inc.
BARI-KAID - Paints - Grow Group, Inc.
BARICELLA - Rice - Gourmet America
BARIDIUM - Analgesics - Pfeiffer Pharmaceuticals Inc.
BARIELLE - Nail care products - The Wilkes Group
BARIENT - Sporting goods - Barient Inc.
BARIENT - Winches - International Marine Marketing, Inc.
BARIKARE - Medical apparatus - Kinetic Concepts, Inc.
BARILLA - Vegetable sauces - Campbell Soup Co.
BARILOT - Wines - Kobrand Corp.
BARISOL - Pharmaceutical preparations - Barre-National, Inc.
BARISTA BRAVA - Coffee - Barista, Inc.
BARITHRICIN - Pharmaceutical preparations ☆ - Barre-National, Inc.
BARIUM TECHNOLOGY - Batteries - Exide Corp.
BARIVITE, JR. - Pharmaceutical preparations ☆ - Barre-National, Inc.
BARIVITE T - Pharmaceutical preparations ☆ - Barre-National, Inc.
BARK - Pet treats - Items Inc.
BARK - Wallpaper - Maya Romanoff Corp.
BARK BARS - Pet food - American Health Kennels, Inc.
BARK BUDDIES - Plush toys - Heritage Gifts Inc.
BARK BUSTER - Pet products - Classic Products
BARK DIMINISHER - Pet products - R.C. Steele Co.
BARK DIMINISHER - Pet products - Tri-Tronics Inc.

BARK ELIMINATOR - Pet products - R.C. Steele Co.
BARK ELIMINATOR - Pet products - Tri-Tronics Inc.
BARK 'N' BAKE - Pet products - Penn-Plax, Inc.
BARK TO GO - Bark - Lee's Forest Products, Inc.
BARKA - Olive oil - Nicola International, Inc.
BARKAMO - Apparel and accessories - Hawe Yue Inc.
BARKER - Window coverings ☆ - Hunter Douglas Intermountain Fabrication Co.
BARKER BREAKER - Pet products - Amtek
BARKER BREAKER - Pet products - Amtek Pet Behavior Products
BARKER BREAKER - Pet products - R.C. Steele Co.
BARKER'S - Frankfurters - Sahlen Packing Co. Inc.
BARKERS, THE - Novelty items - West Coast Wood Specialties
BARKER'S TRU-FRUIT - Juices–frozen - Cronin Vineyards
BARKERSVILLE - Toys - Carolyn A. Franks
BARKHOUSE - Prefabricated buildings–wood - Doskocil Manufacturing Co., Inc.
BARKHUIS - Cakes - Holland-American Importing Co. Inc.
BARKIE - Pet products - Maine Nature Products
BARKIES - Dog food ☆ - Central Soya Co. Inc.
BARKING DOG - Tobacco products - House of Windsor Inc.
BARKING FISH - Apparel–men's - Mark Rowen & Co., Inc.
BARKING PUMPKIN - Recording label - Capitol-EMI Music Inc.
BARKLEY - Office supplies ☆ - Barkley Filing Supplies
BARKMAN'S OLD COUNTRY TRADITION - Honey - Barkman Honey Co. Inc.
BARKO-KNUCLEBOOM LOADERS - Forklifts - Pettibone Corp.
BARKOFF CONTAINER & SUPPLY CO. - Containers–paper - Barkoff Container & Supply Co.
BARKUM RIFF - Tobacco products - Swedish Math North America Inc.
BARKUS - Toys–stuffed ☆ - Gund, Inc.
BARKWOOD - Siding–insulating - Aluminum Co. of America
BARKY - Toys–stuffed - Gund, Inc.
BARKY BUCKS - Wood products - Forest Time Products Inc.
BARKY TREETOT - Toys - Tonka Corp.
BARLEKORN - Animal feeds - Cole Grain Co.
BARLETTA - Knitting machines ☆ - Colonial Corp. of America
BARLEY BEAR - Puppets - Dakin Inc.
BARLEY BREW - Coffee substitute - Sundance Roasting Co.
BARLEY BURGOO - Chowders–canned - Buckeye Beans & Herbs, Inc.
BARLEY DOG - Pharmaceutical preparations - Green Foods Corp.
BARLEY ESSENCE - Barley ☆ - Green Foods
BARLEY GREEN - Barley - Green Foods
BARLEY HARVEST - Vitamins and nutritional supplements - Vital Food Sources, Inc.
BARLEY MILL - Floor coverings - Mannington Resilient Floors
BARLEY PLUS - Cereal - U.S. Mills, Inc.
BARLEY SUGAR SWEETS - Candy - Shelly Bros. Inc.
BARLOW - Toys–stuffed ☆ - Dakin Inc.
BARLOW'S - Food products - Barlow Co.
BARMOBILE - Racks - Jarke Corp.
BARN DOOR - Furniture - Finger Furniture Co., Inc.
BARN DOORS - Lighting fixtures ☆ - Hubbell Lighting, Inc. (Lighting Div.)
BARN LANTERNS - Candles - American Candle Co. Inc.
BARN RED - Wines - Hopkins Vineyard
BARN, THE - Fabrics - Lieff Textile & Mill Supply Co. Inc.
BARN YARD - Housewares ☆ - Shafford Co. Inc.
BARN YARD - Toys–models ☆ - Century Products Co.
BARNABUS - Toys–stuffed ☆ - Gund, Inc.
BARNABY BEAR - Toys–stuffed - Dakin Inc.
BARNABY BUNNY - Toys–stuffed - Dakin Inc.
BARNACLE BARRIER - Paints - DSBG, Inc.
BARNACLEAN - Electrical equipment - Clean Seas Co.
BARNARD & SONS SINCE 1897 - Socks - Foot Traffic, Inc.
BARNART - Hobby kits ☆ - Blumenthal/Lansing Co.
BARNASOLVE - Cleaning preparations - Robert Louis Associates of Newtown, Inc.
BARNDAZZLERS - Dolls - Meritus Industries, Inc.
BARNDINO - Floor coverings–carpet and rugs - Foreign Accents
BARNEGAT - Boats–motor ☆ - Cruisers
BARNEGAT - Lighting equipment - Barnegat Light
BARNEGAT BAY - Food products - Brokers Choice Inc.
BARNES - Bakery products ☆ - Allied Bakers Co.
BARNES - Pumps - Barnes Pumps Inc.
BARNES & NOBLE - Publisher's imprints - Barnes & Noble, Inc.
BARNES & WATSON FINE TEAS - Teas - Tea Clipper Ltd
BARNES DE COLUMBIA - Fluid power pumps - Barnes Pumps Inc.

☆ = Now out of production

BARNES-HIND - Ophthalmic goods - Barnes-Hind Inc.
BARNES STORM - Apparel and accessories - Oxford Industries, Inc.
BARNETT - Food products - Barnett Spices Inc.
BARNETT - Plumbing fixtures–metal - Barnett Brass & Copper, Inc.
BARNETT - Sporting goods - Barnett Boat Co. Inc.
BARNETT 1400 - Sporting goods - Barnett Boat Co. Inc.
BARNETT CAPITAL ADVISORS, INC. - Banks–commercial - Barnett Banks, Inc.
BARNETT INTERNATIONAL - Condoms - Barnett International Corp.
BARNEY - Footwear - S. Goldberg and Co. Inc.
BARNEY - Lunch boxes - Thermos Co.
BARNEY - Pet products - Dogloo Inc.
BARNEY - Skin care products - Tsumura International Inc.
BARNEY - Tableware–plastic - Unique Industries, Inc.
BARNEY - Video production - Lyons Partnership, L.P.
BARNEY - Wallpaper - Priss Prints Inc.
BARNEY AND CLYDE - Toys–guns - Cross at the Green...Not in Between Enterprises
BARNEY BAG, THE - Craft supplies - Lyons Partnership, L.P.
BARNEY BEAGLE - Toys–stuffed - Dakin Inc.
BARNEY GREENGRASS THE STURGEON KING - Food products - Barney Greengrass, Inc.
BARNEY MUSIC - Recording label - Lyons Partnership, L.P.
BARNEY OLDFIELD - Toys–stuffed ✩ - Bijou Enterprises Inc.
BARNEY PUZZLES WOODBOARD - Puzzles - Playskool, Inc.
BARNEY TALKING PHONE - Toys - Playskool, Inc.
BARNEY WATER PALS - Toys - Playskool, Inc.
BARNEY'S - Food products - Barney's Foods
BARNEY'S - Nuts - Northampton Peanut Co.
BARNEYS - Tobacco products - Faber, Coe & Gregg Inc.
BARNEY'S DINNER CLASSICS - Food products ✩ - Barney's Foods
BARNEY'S MUSICAL BATON - Toys - Playskool, Inc.
BARNEY'S NEW YORK - Apparel and accessories - Barney's Inc.
BARNEY'S TOWN AND COUNTRY - Snack foods - Fancy Foods of Virginia Inc.
BARNHIDE - Paints ✩ - PPG Industries, Inc.
BARNIE'S - Coffee makers–electric - Barnie's Coffee & Tea Co., Inc.
BARNIE'S COFFEE & TEA COMPANY - Beverage franchise - Barnie's Coffee & Tea Co., Inc.
BARNIE'S. THE COFFEE PERFECTIONISTS. - Coffee - Barnie's Coffee & Tea Co., Inc.
BARNIE'S WEEKENDER - Tea - Barnie's Coffee & Tea Co., Inc.
BARNIMALS - Dolls - Meritus Industries, Inc.
BARNLIFE - Pet products ✩ - Merrick's Inc.
BARNPLANK - Paneling - Georgia-Pacific Corp.
BARNSTABLE - Wood products ✩ - Masonite Corp.
BARNSTABLE CAT - Ships–sailing vessels - Howard Boat Shop Inc.
BARNSTEAD - Bedding–linen - Dan River Inc.
BARNSTORMERS - Children's apparel ✩ - Levi Strauss & Co.
BARNSTORMING MICROSTATION 3-D - Computer software - Electronic Courseware Systems Inc.
BARNSVILLE - Dresses–women's - Anne Klein & Co.
BARNUM'S ANIMALS - Crackers - Nabisco Foods Group
BARNUM'S ANIMALS ENDANGERED COLLECTION - Bakery products - Nabisco Holdings Corp.
BARNWALL - Lumber ✩ - Georgia-Pacific Corp.
BARNWOOD BIRDS - Garden furniture - Forest Time Products Inc.
BARNYARD - Wines - Bully Hill Vineyards, Inc.
BARNYARD ANIMALS - Figurines - Aus-Ben Studios
BARNYARD BASKET COLLECTION DESIGNED BY BELLE - Baskets–wood - Belle Gifts, Inc.
BARNYARD BINKS - Candy - R.M. Palmer Co.
BARNYARD BUDDIES - Toys–stuffed ✩ - Gund, Inc.
BARNYARD BUDDIES, THE - Children's storybooks, sweatshirts, etc. - Stardom Co. Ltd.
BARNYARD BUDDY - Toys–stuffed ✩ - Gerber Products Co.
BARNYARD FRIENDS - Housewares - Franco Manufacturing Co., Inc.
BARNYARD GROUP - Housewares - Doranne
BARO-SEAL - Chemical preparations - Baroid Technology, Inc.
BAROCA - Rum - White Rock Distilleries Inc.
BAROCCO - Beverages–alcohol - Baldotec Corp
BAROCEL - Measuring instruments - BOC Group Inc.
BARODA - Dishes–china ✩ - Royal China & Porcelain Companies Inc.
BARODYN - Pumps–vacuum - Danielson Vacuum Products, Inc.
BAROFLAVE - Pharmaceutical preparations - Lannett Co. Inc.
BAROK - Floor coverings–carpet and rugs - Stanton Carpet Corp.

BAROLO RISERVA, D.O.C. AND D.O.C.G. - Wines - Kobrand Corp.
BARON - Aircraft–airplanes - Beech Aircraft Corp.
BARON - Boats–motor - Lund Boat Co.
BARON - Boats–motor ✩ - Larson Boat Div.
BARON - Boats–motor ✩ - Skeeter Products Inc.
BARON - Brushes–paint - Corona Brushes Inc.
BARON - Brushes–paint ✩ - Linzer Products Corp.
BARON - Cabinets–wood ✩ - Kemper
BARON - Footwear - Southern Shoe Importers Inc.
BARON - Golfing equipment - Golfco, Inc.
BARON - Hardware - Shepherd Products U.S. Inc.
BARON - Locks–door - Alvi, Inc.
BARON - Motor vehicles–motor homes - Baron Motor Homes Inc.
BARON - Trailers–horse - Real Trailers Inc.
BARON - Waterproof outerwear - Distributors Service Corp.
BARON - Wigs - Jean Paree Weegs Inc.
BARON DE CASTERAC - Beverages–alcohol ✩ - Twelve Stone Flagons Ltd.
BARON DE LA LIGNE - Wines - Blair Importers Ltd.
BARON DE MARTINAY - Wines - Wines Ltd.
BARON DE ROTHSCHILD - Cigars - General Cigar Co., Inc.
BARON DE SIGOGNAC - Beverages–alcohol - European Beverage Co., Inc.
BARON DUSSAUT - Brandy - Crown Capital USA Inc.
BARON HERZOG - Wines - Kedem Royal Wine Corp.
BARON HERZOG - Wines - Royal Wine Corp.
BARON PHILIPPE DE BOISREDON - Wines - Bercut-Vandervoort & Co.
BARON PHILIPPE DE ROTHSCHILD - Wines - Heublein, Inc.
BARON ROTHSCHILD - Gin - Hood River Distillers Inc.
BARON, THE - Perfumes - Evyan Perfumes Inc.
BARON, THE - Colognes - LTL Fragrances, LLC
BARON VON JOY - Toys - Tonka Corp.
BARON VON REDBERRY - Cereal ✩ - General Mills, Inc.
BARON VON SCHEUTERS - Beverages–alcohol - Jim Beam Brands Co.
BARONCINI - Wines - Admiral Wine Merchants
BARONDORF - Salad dressings–bottled - Tidelands Sales Co. Inc.
BARONDORF - Salad dressings–bottled ✩ - Chelten House Products Inc.
BARONE FINI - Wines ✩ - House of Burgundy Inc.
BARONESS - Brushes–hair - Phillips Brush Corp.
BARONESS - Cabinets–wood ✩ - Kemper
BARONESS - Christmas tree ornaments - Cracker Box Inc.
BARONESS - Flatware - Towle Manufacturing Co.
BARONESS - Floor coverings–carpet and rugs - Queen Carpet Corp.
BARONESS - Glassware–household ✩ - Colony Glass
BARONESS - Hair care products - Helene Curtis Industries Inc.
BARONESS - Opera glasses ✩ - Swift Instruments, Inc.
BARONESS - Rings–jewelry - Artcarved Inc.
BARONESS - Watches - Bulova Corp.
BARONESS COLLECTION - Fabric stores - Conso Products Co.
BARONESS DE WAYNE - Apparel–women's - Arizona Mail Order Co., Inc.
BARONESSE - Dishes–china - WMF/USA
BARONET - Amplifiers ✩ - Electro-Voice, Inc.
BARONET - Apparel and accessories - International Designer Accessories
BARONET - Footwear–men's - L.B. Evans' Son Co.
BARONET - Motor vehicles–motor homes - Beaver Coaches Inc.
BARONET - Musical instruments ✩ - Barclay Music
BARONET - Tables–wood - Riverside Furniture Corp.
BARONET - Wallpaper - Riverside Silkscreen
BARONET BABY - Apparel and accessories - International Designer Accessories
BARONET BOOKS - Publisher's imprints - Playmore Inc. Publishers
BARONET COFFEE - Coffee - Baronet Coffee, Inc.
BARONI - Shoes - Delta Shoe Group
BARONIAL - Chimes - Nutone Inc.
BARONIAL - Dinnerware–glass ✩ - Gorham Inc.
BARONIAL PLAID - Floor coverings–carpet and rugs ✩ - Mohawk Carpet Corp.
BARONIE - Chocolate candy - Dae Julie, Inc.
BARONOF - Vodka - Jim Beam Brands Co.
BARONS - Beverages - Dairy Fresh Products Co.
BARONS - Beverages–alcohol - Coastal Wine Merchants
BARON'S - Food products ✩ - Baron Seafoods
BARON'S - Fruit drinks–bottled or canned - Specialty Beverages Inc.
BARON'S CLASSIC PEPPER SAUCE - Food products - MEB Distributing
BARON'S MEAT CO. - Meat products–beef - Pioneer Food Sales Inc.
BARONS NAPA VALLEY - Wines ✩ - Coastal Wine Merchants
BARON'S WEST INDIAN HOT SAUCE - Food products - MEB Distributing
BARONSCOURT - Dishes–china ✩ - Gorham Inc.

✩ = Now out of production

BARONWAX - Waxes–paraffin ☆ - BP America Inc.
BARONY - Crocheted and knitted items - Majestic Mills Inc.
BARONY - Flatware - Utica Cutlery Co.
BAROPHEN - Pharmaceutical preparations - Barre-National, Inc.
BAROPLEX - Pharmaceutical preparations - Consolidated Midland Corp.
BAROQUE - Artists' materials - Artoptic International Corp.
BAROQUE - Christmas tree ornaments ☆ - Cracker Box Inc.
BAROQUE - Clocks ☆ - General Time Corp. (Westclox/Seth Thomas Div.)
BAROQUE - Dinnerware - Denby USA Limited
BAROQUE - Floor coverings - Bellbridge Carpets
BAROQUE - Glass products - Spectrum Glass Co.
BAROQUE - Glassware–household - Crate and Barrel
BAROQUE - Housewares ☆ - Doranne
BAROQUE - Thread - DMC Corp.
BAROQUE BLOSSOM - Musical instrument accessories - Dimarzio, Inc.
BAROQUE LEAF - Musical instrument accessories - Dimarzio, Inc.
BAROQUE STRIPE - Wallpaper - Maya Romanoff Corp.
BAROSORB - Vacuum cleaners and accessories ☆ - Danielson Vacuum Products, Inc.
BAROSSA VALLEY - Wines ☆ - Safeway Stores Inc.
BARPIX - Food products - Adpix
BARPRINE - Pharmaceutical preparations ☆ - Ulmer Pharmacal Co.
BARQNET - Recording label - Westwood Entertainment Group
BARQ'S - Beverages–carbonated - Barq's Inc.
BARQUETTE - Rings–jewelry - Artcarved Inc.
BARQUITO ROJO - Frozen foods - Schwan's Sales Enterprises, Inc.
BARQUITO ROJO - Frozen foods - SSE Foods, Inc.
BARR - Balls ☆ - Rubber Queen
BARR - Engines - Barr Marine Products Co.
BARR - Pharmaceutical preparations - BARR Laboratories Inc.
BARRA - Computer software - Barra, Inc.
BARRA - Food products ☆ - Vincent Food Industries Inc.
BARRACUDA - Bicycles - MRI Inc.
BARRACUDA - Bicycles - Ross Bicycles USA, Ltd.
BARRACUDA - Boats - McKenzie Boat Manufacturing Co.
BARRACUDA - Boats–canoes - Fishin' Ski Barge
BARRACUDA - Boats–motor - Arctco, Inc.
BARRACUDA - Boats–motor - Holiday Mansion
BARRACUDA - Boats–motor - Penn Yan Boats Inc.
BARRACUDA - Computer storage devices - Seagate Technology, Inc.
BARRACUDA - Floor coverings–carpet and rugs - Roxbury Carpet Co.
BARRACUDA - Goggles - Skyline Northwest Corp.
BARRACUDA - Measuring instruments - MTI Corp.
BARRACUDA - Motor vehicles–automobiles ☆ - Chrysler Corp. (Chrysler-Plymouth Div.)
BARRACUDA - Radio-controlled toy vehicle - Nikko America, Inc.
BARRACUDA - Wheelchairs - Everest and Jennings International Ltd.
BARRACUDA ALL TUBE - Audio equipment - ADA Signal Processors Inc.
BARRACUDA HOT SAUCE - Sauces - Patrick M. Cooke
BARRACUDA SPORT FINS - Toys - Skyline Northwest Corp.
BARRAGE - Bicycles - Kent International Inc.
BARRAGE - Herbicides - Helena Chemical Co.
BARRAL - Food products - Europa Foods Ltd.
BARRAZONI - Cooking equipment–household - Robert D. Murray & Associates
BARRE - Pharmaceutical preparations ☆ - Barre-National, Inc.
BARRE - Tools - Trow & Holden Co.
BARRE CHOCOLAT - Cookies - Sunshine/Salerno Inc.
BARRE SLATE - Floor coverings–tile - Kentile Floors Inc.
BARRECRAFTERS - Sporting goods - Barrecrafters
BARREL - Apparel–children's - Barrel-Marvin Apparel, Inc.
BARREL - Furniture - Haworth, Inc.
BARREL - Golfing equipment - Nassau Precision Casting Co., Inc.
BARREL BAGGER - Lawn mowers ☆ - Homelite, Inc.
BARREL BLASTER - Toys–automobiles - Mattel, Inc.
BARREL BURNERS GILLIAM - Candy - Gilliam Candy Co. Inc. (Gilliam Candy Brands)
BARREL-LITE - Firearms, accessories, and parts - Bravo International Corp.
BARREL-LITE - Firearms, accessories, and parts - J Bar Products
BARREL OF FUN - Candy ☆ - L.M. Becker & Co.
BARREL OF FUN - Ice chests–plastic - Igloo Products Corp.
BARREL OF MONKEYS - Games - Lakeside Games
BARREL OF MONKEYS - Games - Milton Bradley Co.
BARREL SEAL - Sealing devices - Greene, Tweed of Delaware, Inc.
BARRELED SUNLIGHT - Paints ☆ - PPG Industries, Inc.
BARRELHEAD - Beverages–carbonated - Canada Dry Corp.

BARRELL - Vinegar - Speaco Foods Inc.
BARREN - Herbicides - Dexol Industries
BARRENS, THE - Food products - Shaw Orchards
BARRETT - Hardware - Barrett Manufacturing Co.
BARRETT GROUP - Men's suits - Britches of Georgetowne, Inc.
BARRETTE BUDDIES - Hairpins - John C. Fallin
BARRETTE FOR YOUR PET - Pet products - Wee Waggers
BARRI - Window coverings - Covoc Corp.
BARRI-CARE - Skin care products - Care-Tech Laboratories Inc.
BARRICADE - Doors - Harloc, Inc.
BARRICADE - Hardware - U.S. Home Security Systems
BARRICADE - Insulating materials - Simplex Products Div.
BARRICADE - Mops - Golden Star Inc.
BARRICADE - Synthetic adhesive film - Brunswick Bowling & Billiards Corp.
BARRICADE GLOVE LINER - Gloves–rubber - Robert J. Kilcullen
BARRICADER - Locks–door ☆ - Lori Lock
BARRICINI - Coffee - Barricini Foods Inc.
BARRICINI - Ice cream - Velda Farms
BARRICK - Recording label - Jazz Composer's Orchestra Association Inc.
BARRICKS BOARDS - Bulletin boards–wood - Premier Metal Products Co.
BARRIE-AIRE - Pet products - Kennel-Aire Inc.
BARRIE BEAN - Toys–stuffed - Barrie House Coffee Co., Inc.
BARRIE HOUSE - Coffee - Barrie House Coffee Co., Inc.
BARRIE HOUSE COFFEE KIDS BLEND - Coffee - Barrie House Coffee Co., Inc.
BARRIE HOUSE COOL BREW CAFE ESPRESSO - Coffee - Barrie House Coffee Co., Inc.
BARRIER - Bags–plastic - W.R. Grace & Co.
BARRIER - Cleaning preparations - Ecolab Inc.
BARRIER - Coats - Roffe Inc.
BARRIER - Locks–door - Lori Lock
BARRIER - Windows–storm - ICI Acrylics Inc.
BARRIER BUBBLE - Packaging–paper - Sealed Air Corp.
BARRIER DIP 2000 - Seasonings - Newly Weds Foods, Inc.
BARRIER FREE LIFTS - Health care products - Barrier Free Lifts, Inc.
BARRIER-GUARD - Chemical preparations - Reichhold Chemicals, Inc.
BARRIER-LOK - Fabrics - Polylok Corp.
BARRIER-LOK PLUS - Fabrics - Polylok Corp.
BARRIER REEF - Watches - North American Watch Corp.
BARRIER WEAVE - Comforters - Pacific Coast Feather Co.
BARRIERBOND - Floor coverings - General Felt Industries, Inc.
BARRIERCOAT - Bags - International Paper Co.
BARRIERGATE - Cushions - Energy Absorption Systems, Inc.
BARRINGER'S - Chocolate candy - Godiva Chocolatier
BARRINGTON - Cabinets - H.J. Scheirich Co.
BARRINGTON - Cabinets ☆ - American Woodmark Corp.
BARRINGTON - Cabinets ☆ - Medallion Kitchens of Minnesota Inc.
BARRINGTON - Cabinets–wood ☆ - Kemper
BARRINGTON - Floor coverings–carpet and rugs - Criterion Mills Inc.
BARRINGTON - Garden furniture - Jack-Post Corp.
BARRINGTON - Guitars ☆ - L.A. Sax Co.
BARRINGTON - Hardware - National Lock Hardware
BARRINGTON - Occasional tables ☆ - JDI Group, Inc.
BARRINGTON - Tableware–china - Lenox, Inc.
BARRINGTON - Toilets–enameled - Kohler Co.
BARRINGTON - Trailers–travel - Fleetwood Enterprises, Inc.
BARRINGTON BASSET - Toys–stuffed ☆ - Dakin Inc.
BARRINGTON COLLECTION - Furniture - Williamsburg Furniture
BARRINGTON COURT - Floor coverings - Congoleum Corp.
BARRINGTON COURT - Furniture ☆ - Singer Furniture Co.
BARRINGTON HALL: BY DUFOUR - Wallpaper - Sterling Prints
BARRINGTON HOUSE - Giftware - Arnart Imports Inc.
BARRINGTON PIERCED COLLECTION - Giftware - Lenox, Inc.
BARRINGTON WOODWINDS AND BRASSWINDS - Musical instruments - L.A. Sax Co.
BARRISTAT - Medical apparatus - E.I. Dupont de Nemours and Co.
BARRISTER - Clocks ☆ - General Time Corp. (Westclox/Seth Thomas Div.)
BARRISTER - Floor coverings–carpet and rugs - Mohawk Carpet Corp.
BARRISTER - Tobacco–chewing or smoking - Amar Blends Co.
BARRISTER'S - Beverages–alcohol - Kasser Laird Distilling Co.
BARRON - Flowers, plants, and seeds - Jacklin Seed
BARRON - Tables–wood - Krueger International, Inc.
BARRON'S - Publisher's imprints - Barron's Educational Series, Inc.
BARRON'S BOOK NOTES - Educational testing and reference books - Barron's Educational Series, Inc.
BARROW - Apparel and accessories - Barrow Manufacturing Co., Inc.

☆ = Now out of production

BARRY - Palettes - Art Supply & Instrument Co.
BARRY - Wines - Eagle Crest Vineyard Inc.
BARRY & HENRY - Vitamins and nutritional supplements ☆ - Pharmavite Corp.
BARRY BAGELS - Bagels - Bagel Place, Inc.
BARRY BONDS - Sporting goods - Franklin Sports, Inc.
BARRY CUDA - Toys - Ronnie Kaylin Ladoux
BARRY FLECHER'S LIQUID MOISTURE - Hair and skin moisturizer - Barry Flecher
BARRY II - Pharmaceutical preparations - EM Industries, Inc.
BARRY KIESELSTEIN-CORD - Apparel and accessories - Barry Kieselstein-Cord
BARRY RESERVE - Wines ☆ - Eagle Crest Vineyard Inc.
BARRYMORE - Floor coverings–carpet and rugs ☆ - Blue Ridge Carpet Mills
BARRY'S - Food products ☆ - Turf Cheesecake Corp.
BARRY'S BLENDS - Coffee ☆ - San Francisco Herb & Natural Food Co.
BARRY'S TRICOPHEROUS - Hair care products - Lanman & Kemp-Barclay & Co. Inc.
BARRYTON - Apparel–men's - Nulook Fashions Menswear Inc.
BAR'S LEAKS - Adhesives and sealants - Fre-Bar, Inc.
BARSAIVE - Games - Fasa Corp.
BARSAL - Pharmaceutical preparations ☆ - Wendt-Bristol Co.
BARSEB HC - Health care products - Barnes-Hind Inc.
BARSEB THERA-SPRAY - Ophthalmic goods - Barnes-Hind Inc.
BARSKA - Binoculars - Micro World Corp.
BARSTAR - Detergents - Ecolab Inc.
BART - Guitars ☆ - L.A. Sax Co.
B.A.R.T. - Toys–guns - Toymax Inc.
BART SCRAPER-SANDER - Tools–hand-operated - Barton Industries
BART SIMPSON - Apparel and accessories - Twentieth Century Fox Film Corp.
BART SIMPSON - Candy - Street Kids
BART SIMPSON - Chewing gum ☆ - Amurol Confections Co.
BART SIMPSON, GO FOR IT DUDE - Kites ☆ - Hi-Flier Manufacturing Co.
BARTAB - Pharmaceutical preparations ☆ - C.O. Truxton Inc.
BARTEC - Housewares - Lifetime Hoan Corp.
BARTELS - Beverages–malt - Lion Brewery, Inc.
BARTEMP-B - Steel - Theis Precision Steel Corp.
BARTENDERS - Beverages - Hamilton Foods Co. Inc.
BARTENDER'S CHOICE - Containers - Kraftware Corp. (Morgan Div.)
BARTENDER'S CHOICE, THE - Sauces - Demitri Pallis
BARTENDER'S GUIDE - Cooking equipment–commercial ☆ - Kraftware Corp. (Morgan Div.)
BARTENDERS PRIDE - Beverages–carbonated - Western Syrup Co.
BARTENURA - Wines - Kedem Royal Wine Corp.
BARTENURA - Wines - Royal Wine Corp.
BARTENURA KOSHER - Vinegar - Kedem Food Products Co.
BARTEST - Pharmaceutical preparations - Glenwood LLC
BARTEX - Steel - Theis Precision Steel Corp.
BARTH - Motor vehicles–motor homes - Barth Inc.
BARTH & DREYFUSS - Towels - Barth-Dreyfuss of California
BARTHA/GI PRV - Veterinary pharmaceutical preparations ☆ - Boehringer Ingelheim Animal Health, Inc.
BARTH'S NATURALLY - Food products - Barth's Nutra Products
BARTH'S NUTRAFOODS - Food products - Barth's Nutra Products
BARTILE ULTRALITE - Roofing materials - Evans Brothers Investments
BARTLES & JAYMES - Wine coolers - Ernest and Julio Gallo Winery
BARTLETT - Tools–garden - Bartlett Manufacturing Co.
BARTLETT-COLLINS - Glassware–household - Bartlett-Collins Co.
BARTLETT SPRINGS - Water–mineral - Nestle USA
BARTLETT SQUARE - Floor coverings–carpet and rugs - Collins & Aikman Corp.
BARTO - Furniture - Domore/DO3
BARTOLI - Handbags - Bartoli Handbags
BARTOLINI - Footwear–women's - Olem Shoe Corp.
BARTOLO MASCARELO - Wines ☆ - Diamond Wine Merchants
BARTON - Brandy - Barton Brands, Ltd.
BARTON - Door frames ☆ - Dunbarton Corp.
BARTON - Lighting fixtures ☆ - Liteway
BARTON - Liquors - Canandaigua Wine Co. Inc.
BARTON & GUESTIER - Wines - Seagram's Chateau & Estate Wines Co.
BARTON BUNNY - Dolls - Russ Berrie and Co., Inc.
BARTON CREEK - Floor coverings–carpet and rugs - Gulistan Carpet Inc.
BARTON CREEK CHAMPIONSHIP COURSE - Computer software - Access Software Inc.
BARTON PREMIUM BLEND - Whiskey - Barton Brands, Ltd.
BARTON RESERVE - Whiskey - Barton Brands, Ltd.
BARTON WOOD VALVE COMPANY - Valves - ERC Industries, Inc.

BARTONELLI - Men's suits and blazers - International Clothing of Florida Inc.
BARTONETTES - Candy - Boyer Candy Co., Inc.
BARTON'S - Stain removers - C.A. Zoes Manufacturing Co. Inc.
BARTONS BONBONNIERE - Candy - Boyer Candy Co., Inc.
BARTON'S CANADIAN - Whiskey - Barton Brands, Ltd.
BARTON'S QT - Whiskey - Barton Brands, Ltd.
BART'S - Health care products ☆ - Park Surgical Co. Inc.
BARTUS - Pharmaceutical preparations ☆ - Consolidated Midland Corp.
BARUFFALDI GOGGLES - Goggles - Cosmopolitan Motors Inc.
BARUKA GOURMET KAFFA - Coffee - Beanhead International
BARUM - Tires–motorcycle - American Jawa Ltd.
BARVAL - Dolls - Barval Toys Inc.
BARVAR - Varnishes - Dunn Edwards Corp.
BARVIANI DESIGNS - Apparel–women's - BarViani Designs Ltd.
BARWANG WINES - Wines - Geyser Peak Winery
BARWICK - Clocks ☆ - Howard Miller Clock Co.
BARYSHNIKOV - Apparel–athletic - Physical Fashions
BARYSHNIKOV - Bags–duffel - Mikhail Baryshnikov
BARYSHNIKOV POUR FEMME - Perfumes - Richard Barrie Fragrances, Inc.
BARZ - Games - Electro-Mech Inc.
BARZI - Food products - Barzizza Brothers
BARZI - Seasonings - Barzi Foods
BARZI CANTERBURY - Food products - Barzizza Brothers
BARZI CHILI FIX - Food products - Barzizza Brothers
BARZI MIAMI RICE - Food products - Barzizza Brothers
BARZI OLD #16 - Food products - Barzizza Brothers
BAS-KET - Games - Cadaco Div.
BAS-RELIEF - Floor coverings–carpet and rugs - Carpet Graphics Inc.
BAS RELIEF - Floor coverings–carpet and rugs ☆ - Regal Rugs Inc.
BASAGRAN - Herbicides - BASF Corp.
BASALJEL - Antacids - Wyeth-Ayerst Laboratories
BASARA - Cosmetics - Shiseido Cosmetics (America) Ltd.
BASCH'S - Cider ☆ - Ranson Fruit Co. Inc.
BASCO - Bathroom accessories - B.A.S.C.O., Inc.
BASCO - Catalogs - Barrel Accessories and Supply Co. Inc.
BASCO - Chemical preparations - Milwhite, Inc.
BASCO - Machinery - American Precision Industries Inc.
BASCO COLLECTION - Apparel and accessories - Basco Sportswear Inc.
BASCOMS - Seasonings - Heartline Foods
BASE/7 - Phone switching gear - Phone Base Systems, Inc.
B.A.S.E. BEDINI AUDIO SPACIAL ENVIRONMENT - Audio equipment - John Bedini
BASE-BOAR-ZIT - Drill bits - Labor Saving Devices, Inc.
BASE COMMANDER - Antennas - Allen Telecom Group, Inc.
BASE FURNITURE LINE - Angeles Group, Inc.
BASE GRADE - Floor coverings–carpet and rugs - No-Muv Corp., Inc.
BASE HIT - Bakery goods - Schmidt-Cannon, Inc.
BASE HIT - Furs–artificial ☆ - Quaker Inc.
BASE HIT II - Adhesives and sealants - Hercules Chemical Co. Inc.
BASE-IT - Housewares - Plastec Industries
BASE-KOTE - Paints ☆ - Briner Paint Manufacturing Co. Inc.
BASE LINE - Trading cards and stamps - Treat Entertainment, Inc.
BASE-N-PLY - Shingles - Tamko Roofing Products, Inc.
BASE PAC - Finishing agents - PortionPac Chemical Corp.
BASE PURETE - Skin care products - Chanel Inc.
BASE-RAY - Boilers–gas - Burnham Corp.
BASE RUNNER - Hardware - W.W. Grainger, Inc.
BASE SAVER - Building materials - Roger D Wilson
BASE TEN BLOCKS - Computer software - Ventura Educational Systems
BASE WARS - Toys–electronic - Ultra Software Corp.
BASEBALL - Floor coverings–carpet and rugs - Regal Rugs Inc.
BASEBALL BUCKET - Sporting goods - Lob-Ster Inc.
BASEBALL BUCKET, JR. - Sporting goods - Lob-Ster Inc.
BASEBALL B.U.M. - Apparel–men's - Chauvin International Ltd.
BASEBALL BUN - Cushions–foam - Tri-Bun Corp.
BASEBALL CARDS - Playing cards - Novelti Playing Cards
BASEBALL CHEW - Seeds–salted, roasted, cooked, or canned - Variety Foods, Inc.
BASEBALL GOT ME HOOKED NOT DRUGS - Apparel and accessories - Dick Leon
BASEBALL GOT ME HOOKED NOT DRUGS - Apparel and accessories - Palace Sports Center
BASEBALL GREATS - Toys - Tonka Corp.
BASEBALL PASTA - Pasta - Buckeye Beans & Herbs, Inc.
BASEBALL POWER - Computer software - SourceView Software International
BASEBALL STARS 2 - Video games - Snk Corp. of America

BASEBALL STRATEGY - Games - Avalon Hill Game Co.
BASEBALL TODAY - Trading cards and stamps - Treat Entertainment, Inc.
BASEBALL TONIGHT - Video game - ESPN, Inc.
BASEBALLOPOLY - Board game - Scott C. Blanke
BASEBALLS - Snack cakes - Interstate Brands Corp.
BASEBALL'S GREAT ESTATES - Reproduced correspondence - ANCO
 Collector Supplies, Inc.
BASEBURNER - Baseball/softball shoes ☆ - Jaclar
BASELINE - Animal feeds - Continental Grain Co.
BASELINE - Apparel and accessories - Baseline Sportswear
BASELINE - Furniture - Meridian, Inc.
BASELINE BOOKS - Publisher's imprints - New York Zoetrope
BASELINER - Wallpaper - Gencorp Inc.
BASELLI - Sporting goods ☆ - AC International
BASEMASTER - Chemical preparations - Pharmacia P-L Biochemicals Inc.
BASEMENT CLEAR - Deodorizers - Enviro-Dynamics Inc.
BASEMENT-DRI - Paints ☆ - Nowstar
BASEMENT SEAL - Waterproofing compounds - Master's Choice Inc.
BASEMENT STOP-LEAK - Hardware - Sears, Roebuck and Co.
BASER - Sound equipment - SRS Labs, Inc.
BASES - Jewelry ☆ - American Mineral Gift Co.
BASES HOME RUN - Food products - Bases Better Burgers of America, Inc.
BASES LOADED - Video game - Jaleco USA, Inc.
BASEWORX - Computer software - At&T Corp.
BASF - Audio equipment ☆ - BASF Corp.
BASF - Wallcoverings - Ben Rose Ltd.
BASH 'N SMASH - Toys–automobiles - Mattel, Inc.
BASHAS - Food products ☆ - Victoria's Treasure Inc.
BASHASAURUS - Toys–automobiles - Mattel, Inc.
BASHER - Toys–automobiles - Mattel, Inc.
BASHFUL - Recording label - Jazz Composer's Orchestra Association Inc.
BASHFUL - Toys–stuffed ☆ - Russ Berrie and Co., Inc.
BASHFUL BEAR - Toys ☆ - Tomy America, Inc.
BASHFUL BEN - Toy stores ☆ - Fun World Inc.
BASHGUARD - Gears–bicycle - BSL Design
BASHIT - Games - Sipa Sipa Games
BASIC - Amplifiers–musical instrument ☆ - Peavey Electronics Corp.
BASIC - Bicycles - Fred Chesnut
BASIC - Food products - Basic Vegetable Products Inc.
BASIC - Notebooks and notepads - Alvin and Co. Inc.
BASIC - Notebooks and notepads - Norcom Inc.
BASIC - Paper–tissue - Kimberly-Clark Corp.
BASIC - Skin care products - ElectroDerma International Inc.
BASIC - Tiles–ceramic ☆ - Latco Products
BASIC - Wigs - Helene Curtis Industries Inc.
BASIC II - Ophthalmic goods ☆ - Rozin Optical Export Corp.
BASIC 4 - Cereal - General Mills, Inc.
BASIC 4 - Pharmaceutical preparations ☆ - Dermalogica Inc.
BASIC 100'S - Cigarettes - Philip Morris Companies Inc.
BASIC ADVANTAGE - Eyeglasses - Wal-Mart Stores Inc.
BASIC AIRPAINTER - Paint sprayers - Testor Corp.
BASIC AMERICAN - Prepared foods - Basic American Frozen Foods
BASIC BARRELS - Barrels–wood - Bradbury Barrel Co.
BASIC BEAT - Musical instruments - West Music Co., Inc.
BASIC BEAUTY - Hair care products - Demert & Dougherty, Inc.
BASIC BLACK - Artists' materials - M. Grumbacher Inc.
BASIC BLACK - File folders - Angler's Roslyn Group Ltd.
BASIC BLACK - Perfumes - Revlon Consumer Products Corp.
BASIC BLACK - Stoneware dinnerware - Iron Mountain Stoneware Inc.
BASIC BLACK - Toys–stuffed ☆ - Dakin Inc.
BASIC BLOCK - Skin care products - Elizabeth Arden Inc.
BASIC BROWN BEAR FACTORY - Department stores - Basic Brown Bears,
 Inc.
BASIC BUILDERS - Electronic equipment - Texas Instruments Inc.
BASIC BUILDING BLOCKS - Computer software - Meca Software, Inc.
BASIC CARE - Hair care products - Helene Curtis Industries Inc.
BASIC COMFORT - Pillows - American Fiber Industries Corp.
BASIC CONCEPTS IN SCIENCE - Computer software - Orange Cherry
 Software
BASIC COUNTRY GOODNESS - Vegetables–frozen - Pacific Valley Foods
BASIC-D - Vitamins and nutritional supplements - Shaklee Corp.
BASIC DESIGNS - Sporting goods - Stearns Manufacturing Co.
BASIC ELEMENTS - Cosmetics - Info Media Productions Group, Inc.
BASIC ELEMENTS - Wallpaper - Blumenthal
BASIC ENGLISH - Computer software - Orange Cherry Software
BASIC EQUIPMENT - Handbags - Bagland

BASIC EQUIPMENT - Men's clothing - Gitano Licensing, Ltd.
BASIC ESSENTIALS - Apparel–women's - Montgomery Ward & Co. Inc.
BASIC FACE, THE - Cosmetics - Cosmedic Concepts, Inc.
BASIC-FLAKE - Pet products - Worldwide Aquatics
BASIC FRIDAY - Apparel and accessories - Americo Group, Inc.
BASIC FUN - Toys - Basic Fun, Inc.
BASIC-G - Vitamins and nutritional supplements - Shaklee Corp.
BASIC GAME - Games ☆ - Avalon Hill Game Co.
BASIC GEOMETRY - Wallpaper - Blumenthal
BASIC GRACE - Apparel–children's - Grace Co.
BASIC-H - Vitamins and nutritional supplements - Shaklee Corp.
BASIC-I - Vitamins and nutritional supplements - Shaklee Corp.
BASIC ID - Safety goggles - H.L. Bouton Co. Inc.
BASIC ILLUMINATIONS - Lighting fixtures - Meyda Tiffany Inc.
BASIC IMAGE - Apparel and accessories - Wal-Mart Stores Inc.
BASIC IMPACT - Handbags - Basic Impact, Inc.
BASIC IMPRESSIONS - Floor coverings - Gencorp Inc.
BASIC INGREDIENTS - Containers–metal - Amco Corp.
BASIC IV - Safety goggles - H.L. Bouton Co. Inc.
BASIC-L - Vitamins and nutritional supplements - Shaklee Corp.
BASIC LIFE - Vitamins and nutritional supplements - American Vitamin
 Products, Inc.
BASIC LUXE - Apparel and accessories - Melissa McElrath Wyatt
BASIC NAIL - Cosmetics - Nu-Art Beauty Products
BASIC NEEDS - Apparel and accessories - Basic Needs Inc.
BASIC ONE - Vitamins and nutritional supplements ☆ - ICN Pharmaceuticals
 Inc.
BASIC PEOPLE - Apparel–athletic - Basic People Inc.
BASIC PLUS - Pet food - American Nutrition, Inc.
BASIC PREVENTIVE - Vitamins and nutritional supplements - Advanced
 Medical Nutrition, Inc.
BASIC PRIMER, THE - Computer software - International Business Machines
 Corp.
BASIC RESEARCH - Vitamins and nutritional supplements - Basic Research,
 Llc
BASIC-RX - Computer software - Healthcare Computer Corp.
BASIC SCENTS - Sachets - Franco Manufacturing Co., Inc.
BASIC SOFT SEAT, THE - Toilet seats - Magnolia Products
BASIC SOLUTIONS - Office furniture–plastic - Rosemont Office Systems Inc.
BASIC SOURCE INC., THE - Lighting fixtures - Basic Source, Inc.
BASIC SPICE - Seasonings - Continnuus
BASIC STRUCTURES - Floor coverings–tile - Tarkett, Inc.
BASIC SUPERPAC - Hair care products - Mastey De Paris
BASIC TEACHER, THE - Computer software - AV Systems Inc.
BASIC, THE - Cushions - Jay Medical Ltd.
BASIC THIO - Hair care products ☆ - Joico Laboratories, Inc.
BASIC TOUCH - Electronic equipment - Basic Touch
BASIC TRAINING - Apparel and accessories - Guy Wells & Co., Inc.
BASIC V - Dinnerware–glass ☆ - Trend Pacific Inc.
BASIC V - Ophthalmic goods ☆ - Rozin Optical Export Corp.
BASIC VII - Ophthalmic goods ☆ - Rozin Optical Export Corp.
BASIC VIII - Ophthalmic goods ☆ - Rozin Optical Export Corp.
BASIC VI - Ophthalmic goods ☆ - Rozin Optical Export Corp.
BASIC WHITE - Hair care products - Clairol Inc.
BASIC XPL - Computer software - SourceView Software International
BASIC1 - Floor waxes - Basic Coatings, Inc.
BASICALC - Calculators - Texas Instruments Inc.
BASICALLY BASIL - Food products - Golden Whisk Pasta Partners
BASICALLY NORDSTROM - Apparel–children's - Nordstrom, Inc.
BASICOAT - Paints - Payson Corp.
BASICS - Aprons - Now Designs
BASICS - Brushes–hair - I. Sekine Co. Inc.
BASICS - Floor coverings–carpet and rugs - Mannington Carpets, Inc.
BASICS - Floor tiles - Tarkett, Inc.
BASICS - Pillows - Hollander Home Fashions Inc.
BASICS - Vitamins and nutritional supplements - Shaklee Corp.
BASICS - Wallcoverings - Cork Products Co. Inc.
BASICS - Wallcoverings - Stretchwall Fabrics Co.
BASIC'S BEST BUY - Underwear and nightwear ☆ - Lady Ester Lingerie Corp.
BASICS COLLECTION - Floor coverings - Tarkett, Inc.
BASICS I - Floor coverings–carpet and rugs - Columbus Mills, Inc.
BASICS PLUS III - Floor coverings–tile - Interface, Inc.
BASICS, THE - Office furniture–wood - Anderson Desk Inc.
BASICSCRIPT - Computer storage devices - Summit Software Co.
BASICWARE - Disposable dinnerware - Curry Sales, Inc.
BASIGUN - Chemical preparations - Premier Services Corp.

☆ = Now out of production

BASIKBENCH - Furniture - Kewaunee Scientific Corp.

BASIL BESLER - Posters - One-of-a-Kind Workshop

BASIL BRAVADO - Salad dressings–bottled ☆ - Santa Barbara Olive Co.

BASIL HAVARTI SAGA - Cheese - Tholstrup Cheese USA Inc.

BASIL HAYDEN'S - Whiskey - Jim Beam Brands Co.

BASILE - Lenses–optical ☆ - Ambassador Eyewear Group

BASILICA - Cordials - Marie Brizard Wines & Spirits, USA

BASILICA - Tiles–ceramic - American Marazzi Tile, Inc.

BASILICAN II-D - Bells and chimes - Schulmerich Carillons Inc.

BASILICO - Shoes ☆ - Intershoe Inc.

BASILIT - Finishing agents ☆ - Osmose Wood Preserving Inc.

BASILLO QUADRINI - Footwear - Footlinks/CEJ Corp.

BASILOLIO - Food products - Colavita USA, Inc.

BASIL'S - Sporting goods ☆ - Basil's Bavarian Bakery

BASIL'S CAFE - Oils–edible - C.C. Village Commons Inc.

BASIN BEST - Fruits and vegetables - Grigg and Sons

BASIN STREET BRICK - Floor coverings - Tarkett, Inc.

BASINGWERK - Artists' materials ☆ - Andrews/Nelson/Whitehead

BASIRAN - Floor coverings–carpet and rugs - E. Basmadjian & Co., Inc.

BASIS - Computer software - Information Dimensions, Inc.

BASIS - Skin care products - Beiersdorf Inc.

BASIS - Thermometers - M. Polymedica Corp.

BASIS DESKTOP - Computer software - OCLC Online Computer Library Center

BASIS SHAMPOO - Hair care products - Peter Hantz Co.

BASIS TECHLIB - Computer software - Information Dimensions, Inc.

BASISLINE - Seats–automobile - Charvoz

BASIX - Doors–metal - Caradon Doors and Windows, Inc.

BASIX - Furniture ☆ - International Paper (Decorative Products Division)

BASIX - Knives–hunting - Basix Manufacturing Corp.

BASIX - Medical apparatus - Empi Inc.

BASIX - Modular power supplies - Computer Products, Inc.

BASIX - Paper - Mead Corp.

BASIX - Skin care products ☆ - Fox Pharmacal Inc.

BASIX - Telephones - Maher & Maher Inc.

BASIX - Wallpaper ☆ - Ozite Corp.

BASIX SERIES - Display cases–metal - Structural Concepts Corp.

BASK - Apparel and accessories - Cluett, Peabody & Co.

BASK-IT - Sporting goods - Excel Sports Products

BASKEEBOWL - Toys - Mattel, Inc.

BASKERVILLE - Dog food - Baskerville Biscuits Ltd.

BASKET - Tableware–china - Villeroy and Boch Tableware Ltd.

BASKET & BALLOONS - Aircraft–balloons - Anagram International, Inc.

BASKET BELLS - Toys - Hasbro, Inc.

BASKET BOUNCE - Games - Smethport Specialty Co.

BASKET BOWL - Bowls - A. Aronson, Inc.

BASKET BUDDIES - Toys–stuffed - Spearhead Industries Inc.

BASKET BUFFET - Cooking equipment–household - Anchor Hocking Glass, Inc.

BASKET BUGGY - Carts ☆ - Selfix, Inc.

BASKET BUNNIES - Candy - R.M. Palmer Co.

BASKET BUNNIES - Toys–stuffed - Fun World Inc.

BASKET CASE - Bathroom accessories - FPI Thermoplastic Technologies

BASKET EVERYTHING - Baskets–wood - Pot Co., Inc.

BASKET FILLER - Flowers, plants, and seeds - Timbuk Farms, Inc.

BASKET OF ANIMALS - Toys–stuffed ☆ - Gund, Inc.

BASKET OF BEARS - Toys–stuffed ☆ - Gund, Inc.

BASKET OF BEAUTY - Toys - Mattel, Inc.

BASKET OF LOVE - Flowers, plants, and seeds - Florists' Transworld Delivery Association, Inc.

BASKET PALS - Toys–stuffed - Pacific Balloon Co., Inc.

BASKET PETS - Toys–stuffed - Fun World Inc.

BASKET TONE - Paint sets–hobby ☆ - Carnival Arts, Inc.

BASKETBALL - Floor coverings–carpet and rugs - Regal Rugs Inc.

BASKETBALL GOT ME HOOKED NOT DRUGS - Apparel and accessories - Dick Leon

BASKETBALL GOT ME HOOKED NOT DRUGS - Apparel and accessories - Palace Sports Center

BASKETBALL HIGHWAY, THE - Computer programming services - Alan Lambert

BASKETBALL STRATEGY - Games - Avalon Hill Game Co.

BASKETBALL TODAY - Trading cards and stamps - Treat Entertainment, Inc.

BASKETEENIES - Toys–stuffed ☆ - Fun World Inc.

BASKETMATH - Computer software - Science Academy Software

BASKETRY HOOPS - Fabrics–quilted - Gibbs Manufacturing Co.

BASKETS OF LOVE - Giftware - Russ Berrie and Co., Inc.

BASKETS OF OLD WORLD CREATIONS, THE - Baskets–steel - Old World Creations

BASKETVILLE - Sporting goods - Basketville Inc.

BASKETWEAVE - Flatware ☆ - Dansk International Designs, Ltd.

BASKETWEAVE - Floor coverings ☆ - Bellbridge Carpets

BASKETWEAVE - Floor coverings ☆ - Congoleum Corp.

BASKIN - Toys–stuffed ☆ - Russ Berrie and Co., Inc.

BASKIN-ROBBINS - Ice cream - Baskin-Robbins USA Co.

BASKING BUOY - Pet products ☆ - Tetra Sales USA

BASKING LITE - Lighting equipment - Duro-Lite Lamps Inc.

BASLE - Apparel–women's - C & Y Sportswear, Inc.

BASMATI SUPREME - Rice - Jyoti Cuisine India

BASO - Lumber - Johnson Controls Inc.

BASQUE - Apparel and accessories ☆ - Alpine Crafts Co. Inc.

BASQUETTES - Sporting goods - Babolat

B.A.S.S. - Bags–canvas - B.A.S.S., Inc.

BASS - Beverages–malt - Guinness Import Co.

BASS - Electrical equipment - Bass Products

BASS - Footwear - G.H. Bass and Co.

BASS - Knives - Precise International/Wenger

BASS 4000 - Musical instrument accessories - Seymour Duncan Pickups

BASS ACKWARDS - Games - International Gamco, Inc.

BASS ALIVE - Aquarium accessories - Aquaculture Aquavet

BASS ALIVE! - Aquarium accessories - Sportfishing Aquavet

BASS ALIVE! - Water treating compounds - Novalek, Inc.

BASS AND COHO - Fishing lures - Joe's Flies

BASS & SKI - Boats–fishing - Glasstream Boats Inc.

BASS ASSASSIN - Fishing lures - Bass Assassin Lures Inc.

BASS BABY - Boats - Schafer Systems Inc.

BASS BANDIT - Boats–motor ☆ - Ebbtide Corp.

BASS BANDIT II - Fishing lures - Shannon Lure Co.

BASS BOAT - Boats - Glen-L Marine Designs

BASS BOMB - Recording label - Thump Records, Inc.

BASS BOMB - Sporting goods - Weber Industries Inc.

BASS BOMBER - Audio equipment - E.T.I. Sound Systems Inc.

BASS BOSS - Boats–motor - Starcraft Corp.

BASS CATCHER - Boats - O.M.C. Aluminum Boat Group

BASS CLASS - Fishing tackle - Fenwick

BASS CLASS - Sporting goods ☆ - Outdoor Technologies Group

B.A.S.S. CLASSIC - Apparel and accessories - B.A.S.S., Inc.

BASS COMPASS, THE - Footwear - G.H. Bass and Co.

BASS DECKER - Boats - H & H Molded Products

BASS ELECTRONICS - Television equipment–closed circuit - Bass Electronics, Inc.

BASS-FEX - Amplifiers - Peavey Electronics Corp.

BASS HARASSER - Fishing lures - Armstrong's Cricket Farm

BASS HOG - Fishing lures - Storm Manufacturing Co.

BASS HOSS - Fishing nets - Four Rivers Tackle Co.

BASS II - Musical instruments - Leo Quan Badass Musical Products

BASS KIDS - Footwear - G.H. Bass and Co.

BASS KILLER - Fishing lures - Sheldons', Inc.

BASS LINE CONDUCTORS - Audio equipment ☆ - Monster Cable Products, Inc.

BASS LINES - Wallpaper - K.M.L. Industries

BASS LITES - Footwear ☆ - G.H. Bass and Co.

BASS-MASTER - Boats–motor ☆ - Ebbtide Corp.

BASS-MASTER - Fishing lures - L & S Bait Co. Inc.

BASS-N-BUCKS - Fish–canned or cured - Bass-N-Bucks, Inc.

BASS NAUTIQUE - Boats ☆ - Correct Craft Inc.

BASS-ON - Fishing tackle - Mason Tackle Co.

BASS ONLY - Fishing lures - Maurice Sporting Goods, Inc.

BASS-ORENO - Sporting goods ☆ - Gladding Braided Products Inc.

BASS PATROL - Recording label - Joey Boy Records Corp.

BASS PONY - Fishing nets - Four Rivers Tackle Co.

BASS POWER - Musical instruments - Bass Power

BASS PUMP - Loudspeakers and amplifiers - Concept Enterprises, Inc.

BASS-QUAKE - Audio equipment - Earthquake Sound Corp.

BASS RAIDER - Boats–motor ☆ - Cobia Boat Co.

BASS ROCKMAN - Amplifiers ☆ - Scholz Research & Development, Inc.

BASS SEARCHER - Boats ☆ - McDaniel Boats Inc.

BASS SPINNER - Fishing lures - Joe's Flies

BASS STRIKER - Boats–motor - Bayliner Marine Corp.

BASS TACKS - Footwear ☆ - G.H. Bass and Co.

BASS TALK - T-shirts–men's - Dean Sanderson and Peter Cowley Partnership

BASS TRACKER - Boats–motor ☆ - Ebbtide Corp.

☆ = Now out of production

BASS V - Boats–motor - Starcraft Corp.
BASS VI - Guitars - Fender Musical Instruments
BASSETT - Furniture - Bassett Furniture Industries, Inc.
BASSETT - Manicure preparations - W.E. Bassett Co.
BASSETT BEDDING - Mattresses - Bassett Furniture Industries, Inc.
BASSETT-WALKER - Apparel–athletic - Bassett-Walker Inc.
BASSETTI - Accordions - Giulietti Accordion Corp.
BASSETT'S - Candy - Callard & Bowser USA Inc.
BASSETT'S - Meat products - Wimmer's Meat Products, Inc.
BASSETTS ALL SORTS - Candy - Y & S Candies Inc.
BASSFINDER - Boats - Monark Boat Co.
BASSICK - Furniture - Bassick Casters
BASSICS - Musical instrument accessories - GHS Strings
BASSIN' MAN - Sporting goods ☆ - Gladding Braided Products Inc.
BASSIST - Electronic equipment - Peavey Electronics Corp.
BASSLINE RECORDS - Recording label - Bassline Records
BASSLINES - Musical instrument accessories - Seymour Duncan Pickups
BASSMASTER - Boats–motor ☆ - Glassmaster Co.
BASSMATE - Boats–motor ☆ - Checkmate Boats Inc.
BASSMATE - Boats–motor ☆ - Glassmaster Co.
BASSON - Musical instruments - Ardsley Musical Instrument Co.
BASSPIRATOR - Air purification systems - Mayfair Molded Products
BASSSTAR - Guitars - Modulus Graphite Products
BASSTUB - Boats - Westgate Research Inc.
BASSWOOD - Window coverings - Decorator's Service Inc.
BASSWORM - Bicycle parts and accessories - Sram Corp.
BASSXPANDER - Audio equipment - Sanyo Fisher (USA) Corp.
BASSXPANDERS - Audio equipment ☆ - Pyle Industries Inc.
BASTA SOLE - Umbrellas - ATA Industries, Inc.
BASTAD - Shoes - Three Crown Import Inc.
BASTAID - Canker sore treatment - American Hygienic Laboratories Inc.
BASTANCHURY - Water ☆ - Yosemite Water Co.
BASTARI - Accordions - Castiglione Accordion
BASTARRI - Food products ☆ - Dean & Deluca Inc.
BASTIAN - Dolls - Mattel, Inc.
BASTILLE - Dinnerware–glass - WMF/USA
BASTILLE - Floor coverings–carpet and rugs ☆ - Blue Ridge Carpet Mills
BASTILLE - Floor coverings–carpet and rugs ☆ - Patcraft Mills Inc.
BASTING GUN - Cooking equipment–household - Hutzler Manufacturing Co.
BASTION - Floor coverings–carpet and rugs - Philadelphia Carpets
BASTION - Hardware - Liberty Hardware Manufacturing Corp.
BASTON - Furniture - Baston Kitchen Systems, Inc.
BASUS - Veterinary pharmaceutical preparations - Ciba-Geigy Corp.
BASYS - Construction equipment rental services - Howell Training Co.
BASZIO - Blouses–women's - All American Apparel Inc.
BAT - Medical apparatus - Mentor O & O Inc.
BAT - Novelty items - Uh-Oh Games Inc.
BAT-A-HAWK - Novelty items - Penner/Mcfall Enterprises
BAT-A-RAT - Pet products ☆ - Kong Co.
BAT-A-ROUND - Games - Schaefsco, Inc.
BAT BOUTIQUE - Apparel - Gloria J. Cast-Gray
BAT BOY - Housewares - J. Paul Donnelly
BAT CHIPS - Snack foods - Street Kids
BAT 'N BALL - Chewing gum - Philadelphia Chewing Gum Corp.
BAT-N-CATCH! - Games - Bravo International Corp.
BAT OUT OF HELL - Recording label - Bat out of Hell, Inc.
BAT-SAVERS - Prophylactics - Stuart Weissman
BAT SEAT - Planar device - Bat Seat Inc.
BAT TEETH - Candy - Glenn Confections Inc.
BAT, THE - Toys–models ☆ - Estes Industries
BAT-WING FLAPPER - Kites - Hi-Flier Manufacturing Co.
BATA - Footwear - Bata Shoe Co. Inc.
BATA SPORTS - Footwear - Bata Shoe Co. Inc.
BATAAN - Toys ☆ - War House
BATAILLE DE MOTS - Computer software - Gessler Publishing Co., Inc.
BATALLA DE PALABRAS - Computer software - Gessler Publishing Co., Inc.
BATANDO - Health care products - Knobble Associates
BATANDO, THE - Tools - Knobble Associates
BATARO - Cigarettes - G.A. Georgopulo & Co. Inc.
BATAVIA - Cabinets - Imperial Cabinet Co. Inc.
BATAVIA - Furniture - Homecrest Industries Inc.
BATAVIA - Seafood products–fresh or frozen - Penguin Frozen Foods, Inc.
BATAYA WEAVE - Apparel–men's - Palm Beach Co., Inc.
BATCH OF ENDINGS, A - Computer software ☆ - Right on Programs
BATCH-PAK - Measuring and dispensing pumps - Gate City Equipment Co. Inc.

BATCHERS - Potato chips ☆ - Season's Enterprises Ltd.
BATCHLOADER - Freezers - Societe De Gestion Et Diffusion North America, Inc.
BATCHMASTER - Furnaces–industrial - Surface Combustion, Inc.
BATCHPIPES - Computer software - International Business Machines Corp.
BATDORF & BRONSON ROASTERS - Coffee - Challain Inc.
BATE MATE - Tools - Syrvet, Inc.
BATEMAN - Holloware - Corbell & Co.
BATEMAN'S - Insulating materials - Bateman's Inc.
BATEN - Jewelry - Baten Corp.
BATENBURG LACE - Tablecloths - American Trading Co.
BATES - Apparel–children's ☆ - Gerber Products Co.
BATES - Bedspreads - Bates Mill Store
BATES - Emery products - Capitol Novelty Co.
BATES - Hosiery - Wolverine World Wide, Inc.
BATES - Manicuring implements ☆ - London International U.S. Holdings
BATES - Musical instrument accessories - McMillan Music Co.
BATES - Office supplies - Bates Manufacturing Co.
BATES - Shoes - Coleman
BATES - Wire - Cavert Wire Co. Inc.
BATES-JAMA - Apparel–children's - Gerber Products Co.
BATES MUNKEE - Inks - Specialty Ink Co. Inc.
BATES WATERSPRE - Fabrics ☆ - Bates Mill Store
BATEX - Skin care products - Ella Bache Inc.
BATH ACTIVITY CENTER - Toys - Fisher-Price, Inc.
BATH AHOY - Infant product - Pansy Ellen Products, Inc.
BATH-AID - Bathroom accessories - Guardian Products Inc.
BATH AND BLUES - Skin care products - Mercedes and Grace Partnership
BATH & BODY EXCELLENCE - Skin care products - Cosmyl, Inc.
BATH & BODY LUXURIES - Beauty aids - Paul Sebastian, Inc.
BATH & BODY THERAPIES - Skin care products - Cosmyl, Inc.
BATH & BOUDOIR - Bathroom fixtures ☆ - Hamilton Glass Products Inc.
BATH & BOUTIQUE - Deodorizers - Dial Corp.
BATH & EARTH - Skin care products - Solar Cosmetic Labs, Inc.
BATH BASICS - Bath salts - Helene Curtis Industries Inc.
BATH BLAST - Dolls - Mattel, Inc.
BATH BOUQUET - Housewares ☆ - Venturi, Inc.
BATH BOUTIQUE - Floor coverings–carpet and rugs - Concord/Aldon Industries Inc.
BATH BUDDIES - Infant soaps, shampoos, etc. - Intercontinental Enterprises Ltd.
BATH BUDDY - Health care products - Temco Health Care
BATH BUDDY - Toys ☆ - Gerber Products Co.
BATH CLUB - Hot tubs–fiberglass - Novi American Inc.
BATH CREATIONS - Floor coverings - Colmar Industries, Inc.
BATH EASE BENCH - Bathroom accessories - Frohock-Stewart Inc.
BATH EFFECTS - Racks - Leucadia, Inc.
BATH ESSENCES - Bathroom accessories - Weleda Inc.
BATH-EZE - Infant product ☆ - Reliance Products Corp.
BATH FAIR - Hot tubs–fiberglass - Novi American Inc.
BATH FASHION - Dolls - Mattel, Inc.
BATH FULL OF BUBBLES - Bubble-bath sets ☆ - Cosrich Inc.
BATH IMPRESSIONS - Sponges - Acme Sponge & Chamois Co., Inc.
BATH INSTITUTE - Skin care products - La Natura
BATH JOY - Aprons - La Joy Products, Inc.
BATH MAGIC - Dolls - Mattel, Inc.
BATH MASTER - Bathroom accessories - Tub-Master Corp.
BATH 'N COUNTER - Bathroom accessories ☆ - Selfix, Inc.
BATH NATURALS - Health care products - SGI Inc.
BATH-O-MATIC - Health care products ☆ - International Healthcare Products
BATH OF THE MONTH CLUB - Bath salts - Jill Cury
BATH OREN - Bath salts - Tawn Ltd.
BATH PAC - Manicuring implements ☆ - London International U.S. Holdings
BATH PAK - Plumbing fixtures–plastic ☆ - Genova Products Inc.
BATH PARTY BABY - Dolls - Mattel, Inc.
BATH PETS - Toys–stuffed - Gund, Inc.
BATH RACK, THE - Skin care products - Nordstrom, Inc.
BATH SPA - Housewares ☆ - Bissell Inc.
BATH TISSUE - Paper–toilet ☆ - Georgia-Pacific Corp.
BATH TRED - Housewares ☆ - ARK Laboratory, Inc.
BATH TUB BREW - Skin care products - Waverly Beauty Products
BATH WAYS - Hot tubs–fiberglass - Novi American Inc.
BATH WORKS - Towels - Barth-Dreyfuss of California
BATH WRAPS - Plastics–laminated - Plaskolite Inc.
BATHCARE - Bathroom accessories - Frohock-Stewart Inc.
BATHE AH WAY - Soap holders - Abel Benitez

☆ = Now out of production

BATHE IN BEAUTY - Bathroom fixtures ☆ - ABT Co., Inc.
BATHER 2001, THE - Bathroom fixtures - Silcraft Corp.
BATHERAPY - Bath salts - General Therapeutics Inc.
BATHERAPY MINERAL BATH SALTS - Skin care products - Para Laboratories Inc.
BATHETTE - Bathroom accessories - Lee-Rowan Co.
BATHETTE - Clocks ☆ - General Time Corp. (Westclox/Seth Thomas Div.)
BATHFORMS - Saunas - Trayco, Inc.
BATHINETTE - Infant product ☆ - Century Products Co.
BATHING BABES - Apparel–children's - Rubbies for Kids, Inc.
BATHING BABY - Dolls - Mattel, Inc.
BATHING BEAUTIES - Dolls - Tonka Corp.
BATHING BEAUTY - Dolls - Mattel, Inc.
BATHING BEAUTY - Shaving preparations - Clairol Inc.
BATHING BEAUTY PAGEANT - Dolls - Mattel, Inc.
BATHLINE - Containers - FPI Thermoplastic Technologies
BATHMATE - Clocks ☆ - General Time Corp. (Westclox/Seth Thomas Div.)
BATHMOODS - Skin care products - Levlab, Inc.
BATHOSPHERE - Plumbing fixtures - Electric Outlet, Inc.
BATHROOM BEAUTY - Faucets - Bathroom Beauty Co., Ltd.
BATHROOM BUDDY - Toys - All American Toy Co.
BATHROOM DUCK - Cleaning preparations–household - S.C. Johnson & Son, Inc.
BATHROOM ELEGANCE - Curtains–shower - Showeray Corp.
BATHROOM FINESSE - Curtains–shower - Showeray Corp.
BATHROOM GUARD - Deodorizers ☆ - Frank J. Curran-Esquire Chemical Co.
BATHROOM PETS - Housewares - V-Link, Inc.
BATHROOM SPLENDOR - Curtains–shower - Showeray Corp.
BATHROOMDISC HEATER, THE - Heaters–gas - Pelonis USA Ltd.
BATHS & KIDS - Wallpaper - Prelude Designs
BATHS OF UTICA, THE - Towels - West Point-Pepperell Inc.
BATHSAFE - Bathroom accessories - Venturi, Inc.
BATHSOAKS - Bath salts - Avalon Natural Cosmetics Inc.
BATHSTILES - Floor coverings–carpet and rugs - Habitat International Inc.
BATHTILE - Bathroom fixtures ☆ - Swan Corp.
BATHTIME - Brushes - Paris Presents Inc.
BATHTIME BABY - Infant product - Rock-A-Bye Baby Inc.
BATHTIME BOOTIES - Infant product - Rock-A-Bye Baby Inc.
BATHTIME BUDDIES - Toys–stuffed - Russ Berrie and Co., Inc.
BATHTIME FUN - Dolls - Mattel, Inc.
BATHTIME MARINA - Toys - Playskool, Inc.
BATHTUB BABY - Dolls - Uneeda Doll Co., Inc.
BATHTUB GIN - Shaving preparations ☆ - Tinkerbell
BATHTUBBIES - Toys - Tomy America, Inc.
BATHWATCH - Water monitor - CRA Inc.
BATIK - Artists' materials - Artoptic International Corp.
BATIK - Dinnerware ☆ - Corning Inc.
BATIK - Floor coverings–carpet and rugs ☆ - Kelly Group Inc.
BATIK - Waxes–paraffin - Siphon Art Products
BATIK DESIGNS - Sponges - Loofa Brite
BATIK IMPORTS - Fabrics–broadcloth - A.R. Lawrence & Associates
BATIK WAVE - Bathing suits ☆ - Jantzen Inc.
BATIKIT - Clay–modeling - American Art Clay Co. Inc.
BATISCO - Toys - Learning Products Inc.
BATKAT - Lighting fixtures - GTE Corp.
BATLEASH - Pet collars - Plastec Design Corp.
BATMAN - Air purification systems ☆ - Medo Industries, Inc.
BATMAN - Bath product - Cosrich Inc.
BATMAN - Bathroom accessories - Tsumura International Inc.
BATMAN - Candy - Topps Co., Inc.
BATMAN - Cereal - Ralston Purina Co.
BATMAN - Games - Mayfair Games, Inc.
BATMAN - Leather goods - RGA Accessories Inc.
BATMAN - Lunch boxes - Thermos Co.
BATMAN - Tableware–plastic - Unique Industries, Inc.
BATMAN - Umbrellas - Essex Manufacturing Inc.
BATMAN - Video games - Sun Corp. of America
BATMAN - Wallpaper ☆ - Priss Prints Inc.
BATMAN - Watches ☆ - Genender International, Inc.
BATMAN DC COMICS - Key rings ☆ - Gift Creations, Inc.
BATMAN RETURNS - Cereal - Ralston Purina Co.
BATMOBILE - Toys–automobiles - Kingsbury Mini Motors of America Inc.
BATON - Accordions - Pancordion Inc.
BATON - Drapery hardware - Hang-Well Corp.
BATON - Lamps–desk - Lightolier Inc.
BATON ROMPU - Floor coverings - Parquet de France Inc.

BATON ROUGE - Soups–mixes - Bon Melange Inc.
BATONNADE - Floor coverings - Parquet de France Inc.
BATORAY - Batteries - Batoray Co.
BATRON - Rubber–vulcanized - Atlantic Construction Fabrics, Inc.
BAT'RY CHEKKER - Battery testers ☆ - Birken Manufacturing Co.
BATT CAT - Battery chargers - Galvanix Corp.
BATT-MAT - Cleaning equipment - Calicorp, Inc.
BATT-PAK - Seafood - Battistella's Seafood Inc.
BATTAGLIA BEVERLY HILLS - Apparel–men's - Battaglia Shops, Inc.
BATTAGLIA OUTDOORS - Apparel and accessories - World Class Footwear, Inc.
BATTALIA NATURALS - Skin care products - Battalia
BATTALION - Cleaning preparations - W.W. Grainger, Inc.
BATTALION - Floor coverings–carpet and rugs ☆ - Customweave Carpets Inc.
BATTALION - Luggage ☆ - Lark Luggage Co. Inc.
BATTALION - Transmission fluids - Conklin Co., Inc.
BATTALION - Watches - Precise International/Wenger
BATTALION, THE - Luggage ☆ - Samsonite Corp.
BATTAT - Toys - Battat Inc.
BATTENLOK - Roofing materials–slate - Metal Building Components, Inc.
BATTER BADGE - Musical instrument accessories - Eric J. Behrenfeld
BATTER BRILLIANCE - Bakery products - Classic Bakery
BATTER MAGIC - Vegetables–frozen - Stilwell Foods
BATTER-TEX - Starch–edible - American Maize-Products Co.
BATTER UP - Toys - Sports Sciences, Inc.
BATTER UP - Trading cards - ANCO Collector Supplies, Inc.
BATTERIES AND TOOLS FOR THE MOBILE EXECUTIVE - Batteries - Battery Express, Inc.
BATTERLITE - Dietetic cake mixes - TKI Foods, Inc.
BATTER'S BOX - Apparel–children's - Buster Brown Apparel Inc.
BATTER'S BOX, THE - Mail boxes - Enamel Products and Plating Co.
BATTERSEA - Wallpaper - Piedmont Collections
BATTERY BEER - Beverages–malt - Battery Beer
BATTERY BOOST - Computer software - Lucid Corp.
BATTERY BUDDY - Electronic equipment - Bob Bartlett & Associates Inc.
BATTERY-CARD - Batteries - Ever Corp.
BATTERY CONNECTION - Batteries - WS Battery and Sales Co., Inc.
BATTERY GUARD - Battery chargers - Ray Jefferson
BATTERY-MATE - Battery case ☆ - Attwood Corp.
BATTERY NETWORK - Batteries - WS Battery and Sales Co., Inc.
BATTERY PAL - Magnetic pickup device - Thomas C. Crawford, Jr.
BATTERY PARK - Battery chargers - Cad Forms Technology, Inc.
BATTERY PATROL - Batteries - John Willemsen Corp.
BATTERY RECYCLER - Containers - Frank Galasso
BATTERY SAVER - Cleaning preparations - Tender Corp.
BATTERY SENTINEL - Electronic equipment - Tandy Corp.
BATTERY TRACKER - Computer program ☆ - Systemsoft Corp.
BATTERY-VAC - Pet products ☆ - Penn-Plax, Inc.
BATTERY WASH - Cleaning preparations - Zorbite Corp.
BATTERYDISK - Computer software - National Systems Corp.
BATTLE - Vit-E-Men Co., Inc. (Life Products)
BATTLE - Insecticides - Zeneca Inc.
BATTLE ARMOR - Toys - Mattel, Inc.
BATTLE AT ROARING PASS - Toys–models - CPG Products Corp.
BATTLE AT SARLACC'S PIT - Games - Lucasfilm Ltd.
BATTLE BEAST - Toys - Hasbro, Inc.
BATTLE BELT - Toys - Hasbro, Inc.
BATTLE BIKE - Games - Saban Entertainment, Inc.
BATTLE BIRD - Dolls - Mattel, Inc.
BATTLE BIRDS - Toys - Mattel, Inc.
BATTLE BLADE - Knives - Tru-Balance Knife Co.
BATTLE BLADE - Toys - Mattel, Inc.
BATTLE BOARD - Electronic equipment - Mitek Corp.
BATTLE BONES - Toys - Mattel, Inc.
BATTLE BOY - Sporting goods - Minnie S. Booth
BATTLE BRAWLERS - Toys - Tonka Corp.
BATTLE BUGS - Computer software - Bridgestone Management Group, Inc.
BATTLE CARS - Games - Namco Hometek, Inc.
BATTLE CAT - Toys–automobiles - Mattel, Inc.
BATTLE CREEK - Exercising equipment - Battle Creek Equipment Co.
BATTLE CREEK - Food products ☆ - Worthington Foods Inc.
BATTLE DAMAGE - Toys - Hasbro, Inc.
BATTLE DOME - Games - Hasbro, Inc.
BATTLE FLAGS - Flags - Concepts, Inc.
BATTLE FOR ETERNIA - Games - Mattel, Inc.

BATTLE FOR ITALY - Games ☆ - Avalon Hill Game Co.
BATTLE FOR TOBRUK - Toys ☆ - War House
BATTLE HYMN - Games - Avalon Hill Game Co.
BATTLE LANE! VOL. 5 - Video games - Taito America Corp.
BATTLE MASTER - Knives ☆ - Tru-Balance Knife Co.
BATTLE MASTERS - Games - Hasbro, Inc.
BATTLE OF BRITAIN - Games - Gamescience
BATTLE OF CHICKAMAUGA - Computer software - Electronic Arts Inc.
BATTLE OF FLOWERS - Jewelry - Battle of Flowers Association
BATTLE OF MIDWAY - Fireworks - American Promotional Events, Inc.
BATTLE OF PORK CHOP HILL - Games - Multi Toys Corp.
BATTLE OF THE BULGE - Games - Avalon Hill Game Co.
BATTLE ON HOTH ACTION SCENE - Toys–models - ERTL Co., Inc.
BATTLE ON THE BAYOU - Apparel and accessories - Sugar Bowl
BATTLE PLAN - Games - Flying Buffalo Inc.
BATTLE PUNCH - Toys - Mattel, Inc.
BATTLE RAM - Toys–automobiles - Mattel, Inc.
BATTLE READY - Toys - Tonka Corp.
BATTLE READY COTS - Computers - Mercury Computer Systems Inc.
BATTLE ROAD PRESS - Puzzles - Battle Road Press
BATTLE RUGGED - Toys - Tonka Corp.
BATTLE SPHERE - Video games - 4 Play Inc.
BATTLE STREEX - Toys–automobiles - Mattel, Inc.
BATTLE SWING - Toys - Mattel, Inc.
BATTLE SWORD - Toys–guns - Mattel, Inc.
BATTLE TOADS - Video games - Nintendo of America Inc.
BATTLE TRACK - Toys - Tonka Corp.
BATTLE TWIN - Motorcycle parts and accessories - Buell Motorcycle Co.
BATTLEBOOK - Publisher's imprints - Arsenal Publishing, Inc.
BATTLECRY - Games ☆ - Milton Bradley Co.
BATTLEDROME - Games - Dynamix, Inc.
BATTLEFRONT - Computer software ☆ - Electronic Arts Inc.
BATTLEHAWKS - Toys ☆ - Spearhead Industries Inc.
BATTLEMENT - Roof coatings and primer - Trans-X Corp.
BATTLENAUTS - Toys - Tonka Corp.
BATTLESHIP - Apparel–men's - Dan River Inc.
BATTLESHIP - Floor coverings ☆ - Congoleum Corp.
BATTLESHIP - Floor coverings–carpet and rugs - Barrett Carpet Mills Inc.
BATTLESHIP - Floor coverings–linoleum - Gerbert Ltd.
BATTLESHIP - Games - Milton Bradley Co.
BATTLESHIP - Toys–electronic - Hasbro, Inc.
BATTLESHIP PADS - Games - Twinson Co.
BATTLSPORT - Computer software - 3do Co.
BATTLESTATIONS - Games ☆ - Gamescience
BATTLESTICKS - Golfing equipment - MacGregor Golf Co.
BATTLESYSTEM - Figurines - Tsr, Inc.
BATTLEVIEW - Computer software - Network Connection, Inc.
BATTLEVIEW ORCHARDS - Food products - Battleview Orchards
BATTLEVISION - Toys–electronic - Tiger Electronics, Inc.
BATTLEWAGON SALVO - Games - Gamescience
BATTLEWEAR - Apparel and accessories - Battlewear USA, Inc.
BATTLEWHEELS - Computer software - Kris N. Johnson
BATTLEZONE - Video games - Atari Games Corp.
BATTLIN' BELT - Toys - Mattel, Inc.
BATTMARK - Computer software - Business Applications Performance Corp.
BATTS BATTS BATTS CLASSICS - Garment hangers–wire - Batts, Inc.
BATTS GOH - Garment hangers - Batts, Inc.
BATTSLIDE - Boats - Sailpower Systems, Inc.
BATTUE - Saddles - Hunting World, Inc.
BATTY BERRIES - Chewing gum - Fleer Corp.
BATTY BUGGIES - Toys ☆ - Henry Gordy International Inc.
BATUTIL - Computer software - CTRLALT Associates
BATZ SNAPS - Pet products - Batz Corp.
BAUBLE, THE - Christmas tree ornaments - Sangray Corp.
BAUBLES - Underwear and nightwear - Maidenform Inc.
BAUBLES & BEADS - Cosmetics - Maybelline Co.
BAUBLES, BANGLES & BEADS - Christmas tree ornaments - Cracker Box Inc.
BAUDAUX - Headbands - Accessories International
BAUDELAIRE - Sponges - Baudelaire Inc.
BAUDVILLE - Computer software - Baudville, Inc.
BAUER - Boats–dinghies - Bauteck Marine Co. Inc.
BAUER - Photographic equipment ☆ - AIC International Inc.
BAUER - Sporting goods - Canstar Sports USA
BAUER & BLACK - Medical apparatus - Becton, Dickinson and Co.
BAUER BETTER WATER - Water purification systems - M. J. Bauer Co., Inc.

BAUER COMPRESSORS - Compressors–air - EKS Enterprises, Inc.
BAUERHAUS - Frankfurters ☆ - Max Bauer Meat Packer Inc.
BAUERKLAUS - Figurines - Nancy A. Bauer
BAUERMSTOLZ - Cheese - Crystal Food Import Corp.
BAUERS ALL AMERICAN - Frankfurters ☆ - Max Bauer Meat Packer Inc.
BAUERS DELI INTERNATIONAL - Meats–luncheon ☆ - Max Bauer Meat Packer Inc.
BAUGRID - Steel products - Baumann Engineering
BAUHAUS - Dinnerware–glass - Trend Pacific Inc.
BAUM - Wines - Baum Wine Imports
BAUMANN - Blinds–venetian - Baumann Inc.
BAUMANN'S BEST - Food products - Moran Foods, Inc.
BAUMANOMETER - Health care products - W.A. Baum Co. Inc.
BAUMAN'S - Food products - The Bauman Family
BAUMARD - Wines - Classic Wine Imports Inc.
BAUME & MERCIER - Watches - David G. Steven Inc.
BAUME DE LA FERTE - Lip balms - Guerlain Inc.
BAUMESH - Masonry equipment - Baumann Engineering
BAUMGARTEN'S ELITE - Calendars ☆ - Baumgarten's
BAUMGARTEN'S PERPETUAL - Calendars ☆ - Baumgarten's
BAUMGARTEN'S UNIVERSAL - Calendars ☆ - Baumgarten's
BAUMODYNE - Pharmaceutical preparations ☆ - Vortech Pharmaceuticals
BAUM'S - Beef - Daniel Weaver Co.
BAUR - Food products - George C. Brown's Biscuits & Confections
BAUSCH - Musical instrument accessories ☆ - Scherl & Roth Inc.
BAUSCH & LOMB - Hearing aids ☆ - Dahlberg, Inc.
BAUSCH & LOMB - Pharmaceutical preparations - Bausch & Lomb Inc.
BAUSMAN - Pet products - Bausman Pet Supplies
BAUTEE COMPACT MAKE-UP MIRROR - Cosmetics - Beautee Sense Inc.
BAUTEEN - Giftware - Kellerman Manufacturing Co. Inc.
BAUTEX - Hardware ☆ - AM-Source International
BAUTEX - Window shades - Bautex Inc.
BAUXCAST - Building materials - Refractory Technology, Inc.
BAVALP - Cheese - Lactoprot USA, Inc.
BAVARIA - Door frames - Canyon Creek Cabinet Co.
BAVARIA BLU - Cheese - Swissrose International Inc.
BAVARIAN - Meat products–beef - North Star Foods Inc.
BAVARIAN - Pretzels - Toad-Ally Snax Inc.
BAVARIAN - Pretzels ☆ - Barbara's Bakery, Inc.
BAVARIAN BERTHAL - Glassware–household - Imperial Crystal and China Inc.
BAVARIAN BRASSCUTTER - Brass products - Biedermann & Sons Inc.
BAVARIAN BREAD - Breads ☆ - Liberty Richter Inc.
BAVARIAN CHOCOLATE ORANGE - Teas–herbal ☆ - Celestial Seasonings, Inc.
BAVARIAN CLUB - Beverages–malt - Joseph Huber Brewing Co., Inc.
BAVARIAN COLD MASTER - Ice chests–plastic - Glacier Ware Inc.
BAVARIAN CREME - Cream ☆ - Presto Food Products, Inc.
BAVARIAN FINGERS - Cookies ☆ - Sunshine Biscuits, Inc.
BAVARIAN KREME - Food products - H.C. Brill Co., Inc.
BAVARIAN SCHWEIZERHOF - Beverages–malt - HDT Importers Inc.
BAVARIAN SPECIALTY FOODS - Food products - Ore-Ida Foods, Inc.
B.A.W. - Jewelry–precious - B.A.W. Manufacturing Inc.
BAWANA GORILLA - Toys–stuffed ☆ - Dakin Inc.
B.A.W.B. - Apparel and accessories - B.A.W.B.
BAWDY - Beads ☆ - Greene Plastics Corp.
BAXIS - Apparel and accessories - Baxis Inc.
BAXPIN - Sporting goods - Carbite, Inc.
BAXTER - Clocks ☆ - General Time Corp. (Westclox/Seth Thomas Div.)
BAXTER - Pharmaceutical preparations - Baxter International Inc.
BAXTER - Shoes - Dayton Hudson Corp.
BAXTER - Toys–stuffed - Russ Berrie and Co., Inc.
BAXTER - Toys–stuffed ☆ - Gund, Inc.
BAXTER & WELLS WOMAN - Apparel stores–women's - Frederick Atkins, Inc.
BAXTER BRAND NATURAL CLOTHING CO. - Apparel and accessories - Baxter International, Ltd.
BAXTER COMPANY - Apparel and accessories - Baxter International, Ltd.
BAXTER STREET - Floor coverings–carpet and rugs ☆ - Hollytex Carpet Mills Inc.
BAXTER'S - Soups–canned - Source Atlantique
BAXTER'S HEALTHY REWARDS - Soups–canned - Source Atlantique
BAY - See **MY-K**
BAY - Boats - Bay Manufacturing
BAY - Brushes–paint - Corona Brushes Inc.
BAY - Fireplaces - Majestic Co.

☆ = Now out of production

BAY - Gasoline - Tenneco Oil Co.
BAY - Vegetables–canned ☆ - Lyons Canning Co. Inc.
BAY 1 - Apparel stores–sports - Bay 1 Swimwear Inc.
BAY AREA CHINESE TELEPHONE BOOK/YELLOW PAGES - Telephone directories - Bay Area Chinese News, Inc.
BAY AREAS BEST - Meat products–beef - Nicholas A. Drabec
BAY AREA'S BEST COUPON BOOK - Coupons - Bay Area's Best Coupon Book
BAY-ASE - See **MYPHENTOL**
BAY BAGS - Luggage - I.J.K. Sales Corp.
BAY BEAUTY - Salmon–smoked, salted, dried, or pickled - Ocean Beauty Seafood, Inc.
BAY BIRDS - Meat products–poultry - Pierce Foods Corp.
BAY BOULEVARD - Apparel–women's - United States of America
BAY BREEZE - Beverages–carbonated - Schooner's International, Inc.
BAY BREEZE - Bicycles - Roadmaster Corp.
BAY BREEZE - Floor coverings - Armstrong World Industries, Inc.
BAY BREEZE - Furniture ☆ - Singer Furniture Co.
BAY BREEZE - Garden furniture–rattan - Lloyd/Flanders Industries
BAY BREEZE - Tableware–earthenware - Pfaltzgraff Investment Co.
BAY BREEZE - Wallpaper ☆ - Carey Lind Designs
BAY BREEZE 2 - Wallpaper - York Wall Coverings Inc.
BAY BRIDGE - Apparel and accessories - Bay Bridge Sportswear Co.
BAY BRIDGE - Bakeries - San Francisco French Bread Co.
BAY BRIDGE - Floor coverings–carpet and rugs - Hollytex Carpet Mills Inc.
BAY CELLARS - Wines - Bay Cellars
BAY CHAMPAGNE - Wallpaper - Sherburne Ewing Wallcovering Co.
BAY CITY - Bakery products - United States Bakery
BAY CITY - Recording label - Victory Media Group
BAY CITY - Seafood - Bama Sea Products
BAY CITY PLAIDS - Fabrics - Dan River Inc.
BAY CLUB - Glassware–household - Ceraglass Inc.
BAY COLONY - Floor coverings–carpet and rugs - Monticello Carpet Mills
BAY COLONY/- Footwear - Atsco Footwear Inc.
BAY COLOR - Paper - Bay Color Products
BAY CORPORATION - Medical apparatus - Bay Corp.
BAY COUNTRY - Paints - Bruning Paint Co.
BAY COUNTRY - Vegetables–canned - Clifton Canning Co.
BAY COUNTRY BY J.G. HOOK - Apparel and accessories - J.G. Hook, Inc.
BAY COUNTRY WOODCRAFTS - Hobby kits ☆ - Stoney Point Decoys Ltd.
BAY CREEK - Apparel–men's - Edison Brothers Stores, Inc.
BAY CREST - Furniture - Homecrest Industries Inc.
BAY FIRE - Fireplace equipment - Design Specialties Inc.
BAY FRONT - Floor coverings–carpet and rugs ☆ - Columbus Mills, Inc.
BAY-GALE - Musical instrument accessories ☆ - Bay Woodwind Mouthpieces
BAY GEM - Seafood - Sahlman Seafoods, Inc.
BAY GEM - Seafood products–fresh or frozen - Sahlman Seafoods, Inc.
BAY HARBOR - Furniture ☆ - Lane Co. Inc.
BAY HARBOR - Real estate agencies - Bay Harbor Co., LLC
BAY HARBOUR - Seafood products–fresh or frozen - Staff Supermarket Associates, Inc.
BAY HAWK - Boats–fishing - Gulf Master, Inc.
BAY HILL - Floor coverings–carpet and rugs - Patcraft Mills Inc.
BAY ISLAND - Slacks–women's - Kentogs Corp.
BAY LINENS - Linen - Bay Linens, Inc.
BAY-LITE - Lighting fixtures - Hubbell Lighting, Inc. (Lighting Div.)
BAY MASTER - Boats–motor ☆ - Holiday Mansion
BAY MEADOWS - Floor coverings–carpet and rugs ☆ - Hollytex Carpet Mills Inc.
BAY MEADOWS - Sportswear ☆ - Levi Strauss & Co.
BAY MIST - Wines - J. Lohr Winery
BAY-MOR - Pet products - Bay-Mor Pet Feeds
BAY NETWORKS - Computer software - Synoptics Communications, Inc.
BAY PAD CLASSIC - Notebooks and notepads - Blind Industries and Services of Maryland
BAY PAD LEGAL ELITE - Notebooks and notepads - Blind Industries and Services of Maryland
BAY PATH - Paper–bond - Strathmore Paper Co.
BAY POINT - Floor coverings–carpet and rugs - Tuftex Carpet Mills, Inc.
BAY POINT - Furniture - Homecrest Industries Inc.
BAY POINT THREADS - Apparel and accessories - Kenneth Too Inc.
BAY POINTE - Cabinets–wood ☆ - Kemper
BAY POINTE - Furniture - Universal Furniture Industries, Inc.
BAY RUM - Colognes - Stephan Co.
BAY RUNNER - Apparel and accessories - Tropical Garment Manufacturing Co.

BAY SHORE - Lobster bisque - Yankee Specialty Foods
BAY SHORE - Seafood products–fresh or frozen - W.H. Harris Seafood Inc.
BAY SIDE ICED TEA - Iced tea–bottled or canned - Archibald Bros. Fine Beverages, Inc.
BAY/SPARTAN - Flags - Flags International Inc.
BAY SPRINGS - Prefabricated buildings–wood - Skyline Corp.
BAY STATE - Brushes–paint ☆ - PPG Industries, Inc.
BAY STATE CHOWDA COMPANY - Soups–canned - Bay State Chowda
BAY STATE STERLING - Grinders - Abrasive Industries, Inc.
BAY STATE/STERLING - Machine parts - Bay State/Sterling Inc.
BAY STONE - Floor coverings ☆ - Congoleum Corp.
BAY TIGER - Boats–motor - Moorman Manufacturing Co.
BAY TO BAY - Apparel and accessories - Tropical Garment Manufacturing Co.
BAY TO BAY CREW - Apparel and accessories - Tropical Sportswear International Corp.
BAY TOWN - Wallpaper - Sherburne Ewing Wallcovering Co.
BAY TREE - Furniture ☆ - Broyhill Furniture Industries, Inc.
BAY TREE - Vinegar - Food Service/Specialty Product
BAY VIEW - Milk - Crowley Foods, Inc.
BAY VILLAGE I - Wallpaper ☆ - Imperial Wallcoverings, Inc.
BAY WEAR - Bathing suits - Bodylines Inc.
BAY WINDS - Furniture ☆ - Bassett Furniture Industries, Inc.
BAY WINDS - Wallpaper - Marburg Wallcoverings Inc.
BAY WINDS - Wallpaper - Sherburne Ewing Wallcovering Co.
BAYAMINIC - See **MYMINIC**
BAYAMINICOL - See **MYMINICOL**
BAYAMO - Floor coverings–carpet and rugs ☆ - Evans-Black Carpet Mills
BAYANIHAN - Jewelry - Bayanihan, Ltd.
BAYAPAP - See **MYAPAP**
BAYARD SPORT - Apparel–women's ☆ - Vera Sportswear
BAYBEE FRESH - Deodorizers - Sterling Co.
BAYBERRY - Jewelry–costume ☆ - Safari Ltd.
BAYBERRY COURT - Floor coverings - Mannington Resilient Floors
BAYBERRY DOWNS - Floor coverings - Armstrong World Industries, Inc.
BAYBERRY MIST - Sachets - Andre Richard
BAYBRY'S - Wines ☆ - Anheuser-Busch Companies Inc.
BAYCADRON - See **MYMETHASONE**
BAYCOMINE - See **MYHYDROMINE**
BAYCOR - Paperboard plug - Newark Group Industries, Inc.
BAYCORT - Pharmaceutical preparations ☆ - Parnell Pharmaceuticals Inc.
BAYCOTUSSEND - See **MYCOTUSSIN**
BAYCREST - Floor coverings–carpet and rugs - Evans-Black Carpet Mills
BAYCREST - Food products - VS Tampa Inc.
BAYDANCER - Boats–fishing - Palm Beach Marinecraft, Inc.
BAYDEC - See **MYCADEC DM**
BAYEL CRYSTAL - Giftware - Ebeling and Reuss Co.
BAYER - Analgesics - Bayer Corp. (Consumer Care Div.)
BAYER - Health care products - American Threshold Industries Inc.
BAYER FAMILY, THE - Toys–stuffed - Lois Hall Creations
BAYER PLUS - Analgesics - Bayer Corp. (Consumer Care Div.)
BAYER SELECT - Analgesics - Bayer Corp. (Consumer Care Div.)
BAYERNLAND - Cheese - Galaxy Trading Co.
BAYERNPRISE - Snuff - James B. Russell Inc.
BAYERNWALD - Mushrooms ☆ - Liberty Richter Inc.
BAYFEDRINE - See **MYFEDRINE**
BAYFEDRINE PLUS - See **MYFEDRINE PLUS**
BAYFEO - See **MYFED**
BAYFIELD - Crock pots ☆ - Wonderknit
BAYFIELD - Floor coverings–carpet and rugs - Burlington House Carpets
BAYFIELD - Furniture ☆ - Bassett Furniture Industries, Inc.
BAYFIELD - Jams and jellies - Bayfield
BAYFIELD - Paper ☆ - Silver Leaf Paper Co.
BAYFIRE - Fireplaces ☆ - Earth Stove Inc.
BAYFLITE - Boats–motor ☆ - Glastron Boats
BAYGON - Insecticides ☆ - Bayer Corp. (Agriculture Div.)
BAYHARBOR - Floor coverings–carpet and rugs ☆ - Walter Carpet Mills
BAYHEAD - Fabrics ☆ - Greenwood Mills Inc.
BAYHILL CLUB CHAMPIONSHIP COURSE - Computer software - Access Software Inc.
BAYHISTINE - See **MYHISTINE**
BAYHISTINE DH - See **MYHISTINE DH**
BAYIDYL - See **MYIDYL**
BAYLETON - Fungicides - Bayer Corp. (Agriculture Div.)
BAYLEY - Hardware - Blaine Window Hardware Inc.
BAYLEY - Luggage - French Co.
BAYLEY'S - Seafood - Bayley's Quality Seafood

☆ = Now out of production

BAYLIGHT - Lighting fixtures - Ampac Industries Inc.
BAYLINE - Food products - Justrite Food Service Inc.
BAYLINER - International Yachting Center
BAYLINER - Boats–motor - Bayliner Marine Corp.
BAYLOCAINE - See **MYLOCAINE**
BAYLOR - Cigarettes - Brown & Williamson Tobacco Corp.
BAYLOR - Dinnerware - Baylor University
BAYLOR - Floor coverings–carpet and rugs - Hollytex Carpet Mills Inc.
BAYLOR UNIVERSITY - Rings–jewelry - Baylor University
BAYLUSCIDE - Exterminating products ☆ - Bayer Corp. (Agriculture Div.)
BAYLY - Apparel and accessories - Bayly Corp.
BAYMASTER - Fishing rods - Penn Fishing Tackle Manufacturing Co.
BAYONET - Apparel–athletic - Joe Kang
BAYOU - Seafood products–fresh or frozen - John's Pass Seafood Co.
BAYOU - Soups–mixes - Bon Melange Inc.
BAYOU BLUE - Recording label - Great Southern Record Co. Inc.
BAYOU BOOGIE - Fishing lures - Plastics Research and Development Co.
BAYOU BOOK DISTRIBUTORS - Publisher's imprints - Pelican Publishing Co. Inc.
BAYOU CHICKEN - Food products - Pearl's Oyster Bar, Inc.
BAYOU CLASSIC - Barbecues and grills - Barbour International, Inc.
BAYOU CLASSICS - Recording label - Master-Trak Sound Recorders
BAYOU COOK - Seafood - Bayou Cook Food Corp.
BAYOU COUNTRY - Food products - Whistlin' Dixie Fried Chicken Inc.
BAYOU CRUNCH - Food products - Dearborn
BAYOU LAND - Food products - Bayou Land Seafood
BAYOU MAID - Honey - Bessonet Bee Co. Inc.
BAYOU MAPLE - Plywood - Georgia-Pacific Corp.
BAYOU SPORT - Apparel–athletic - State-O-Maine, Inc.
BAYOU TECHE - Food products - Bayou Teche Canning Co. Inc.
BAYOUS OF LOUISIANA BRAND - Food products - Daedalus Corp.
BAYPOINTE - Floor coverings–carpet and rugs - Mannington Carpets, Inc.
BAYPORT - Floor coverings–carpet and rugs - Rugby Rugs Inc.
BAYPORT - Luggage - Airway Industries, Inc.
BAYPORT - Recording label ☆ - Bayport Records
BAYPORT - Trailers–travel - Fleetwood Enterprises, Inc.
BAYPRIDE - Seafood products–fresh or frozen ☆ - L.N. White & Co. Inc.
BAYRIDGE - Wallpaper - Sherburne Ewing Wallcovering Co.
BAYRUNNER - Boats - Valco Aluminum Boats
BAYS - Food products - Bays Corp.
BAY'S FORMULA 77 - See **MY-K FORMULA 77**
BAY'S FORMULA 77D - See **MY-K FORMULA 77D**
BAYSCAPE - Dinnerware ☆ - Corning Inc.
BAYSHORE - Food products ☆ - C-Corp.
BAYSHORE - Furniture ☆ - Bassett Furniture Industries, Inc.
BAYSHORE - Garden furniture - Winston Furniture Co. Inc.
BAYSHORE - Seafood - Bayshore Group Ltd.
BAYSHORE - Seafood products–fresh or frozen - Missouri Fish Co.
BAYSIDE - Food products - Bayside Shellfish Inc.
BAYSIDE - Seafood - Bayside Imports Inc.
BAYSIDE - Siding–insulating ☆ - Masonite Corp.
BAYSIDE - Vegetables–frozen - Exmore Foods Inc.
BAYSIDE II - Floor coverings–carpet and rugs ☆ - Mannington Carpets, Inc.
BAYSIDE BAGELS - Bakery products - Bayside Bagels, Inc.
BAYSIDE DESIGN WALLCOVERINGS - Wallpaper - Gagne Wallcovering, Inc.
BAYSOFT - Computer software - Baytech Systems, Inc.
BAYSTAR - Boats - Palm Beach Marinecraft, Inc.
BAYSTATE - Toilets–enameled ☆ - Ecos/Water Conservation System Inc.
BAYSTONE - Furniture - Hooker Furniture Corp.
BAYSTONE - Paving materials–stone - Fergus Concrete Products Co., Inc.
BAYSWATER ROAD - Wallpaper - Seabrook Wallcoverings, Inc.
BAYTEC - Computers and peripherals - Baytec Inc.
BAYTECH - Pet products - California Aquarium Supply Corp.
BAYTECH AQUARIUM - Aquariums–household - California Aquarium Supply Corp.
BAYTEX - Insecticides ☆ - Bayer Corp. (Agriculture Div.)
BAYTHROID - Insecticides - Bayer Corp. (Agriculture Div.)
BAYTOWN - Floor coverings–carpet and rugs ☆ - Cumberland Mills Inc.
BAYTREE MANOR - Furniture ☆ - Universal Flooring
BAYTUSSIN - See **MYTUSSIN**
BAYTUSSIN AC - See **MYTUSSIN AC**
BAYTUSSIN DAC - See **MYTUSSIN DAC**
BAYTUSSIN DM - See **MYTUSSIN DM**
BAYVIEW - Dairy products - Super Store Industries
BAYVIEW - Fireplace equipment ☆ - Earth Stove Inc.
BAYVIEW - Fireplace screens - Jack-Post Corp.

BAYVIEW - Floor coverings–carpet and rugs ☆ - Blue Ridge Carpet Mills
BAYVIEW - Floor coverings–carpet and rugs ☆ - Catalina Carpet Mills Inc.
BAYVIEW - Floor coverings–carpet and rugs ☆ - Dorsett Carpet Mills Inc.
BAYVIEW - Furniture ☆ - Hooker Furniture Corp.
BAYVIEW CELLARS - Wines - House of Burgundy Inc.
BAYVIEW VINYLS - Wallpaper - Bayview Wallcoverings
BAYVILLE FARMS - Ice cream - Bayville Farms Associates
BAYWATCH - Apparel and accessories - Baywatch Production Co.
BAYWATCH LIFEGUARD - Apparel and accessories - Baywatch Production Co.
BAYWEST - Floor coverings–carpet and rugs - Gulistan Carpet Inc.
BAYWINDS - Floor coverings–carpet and rugs - Catalina Carpet Mills Inc.
BAYWOOD - Nuts–salted, roasted, cooked, or canned - Old Dominion Peanut Inc.
BAZA - Skin care products - Sween Corp.
BAZEL - Toys - Playskool, Inc.
BAZOOKA - Candy - Topps Co., Inc.
BAZOOKA - Floor cleaning equipment - Edic
BAZOOKA - Golfing equipment - David Glod
BAZOOKA - Golfing equipment - TourEdge Golf Manufacturing Inc.
BAZOOKA - Tools - Ames Taping Tool Systems Co.
BAZOOKA BITS - Candy ☆ - Topps Co., Inc.
BAZOOKA BURSTS - Chewing gum - Topps Co., Inc.
BAZOOKA LOLLIPOPS - Candy ☆ - Topps Co., Inc.
BAZOOKA SYSTEM - Medical apparatus - Innovative Medical Systems, Inc.
BAZOOKLETS - Candy ☆ - Topps Co., Inc.
BAZZ BUZZ - Fishing lures - Hildebrandt Corp.
BAZZINI - Snack foods - A.L. Bazzini Co. Inc.
BAZZITTLE - Candy - A.L. Bazzini Co. Inc.
BB - Doors–metal - Better-Bilt Aluminum Products Co.
BB - Fishing rods - Zebco Corp.
BB - Hitches–trailer - Robert L. Liland
BB - Luggage - BB Systems Products
BB-9 - Nuts and bolts - Big Bolt Corp.
BB - Shoes - Bill Blass, Ltd.
BB - Vegetables–frozen - Delicious Foods Co.
BB-9 - Adhesives and sealants - Daige Products Inc.
BB-10 - Boats - BB-10 Class Association
B.B. BATS - Candy - Gilliam Candy Co. Inc. (Gilliam Candy Brands)
BB BILCO BRICK - Building materials - Bilco Corp.
BB BLACK BERRY TECHNOLOGIES - Wheelchairs - Blackberry Technologies, Inc.
BB BULLET BUSTER - Bulletproof vests - East-West Executives, Inc.
BB EUC - Flowers, plants, and seeds - Matsui Nursery Inc.
BB KING - Pins–jewelry - Kingsid Ventures, Ltd.
B.B. KING - Posters - Kingsid Ventures, Ltd.
B.B. KING - Recording label - King-Sas Communications, Inc.
BB KING: KING OF THE BLUES - Shirts - Kingsid Ventures, Ltd.
BB KING LUCILLE - Jewelry - Kingsid Ventures, Ltd.
BB MARKS DESIGNS - Giftware - Marks Designs
BB-MATIC - Guns–BB ☆ - Crosman Corp.
BB/PC - Computer software - Mai Systems Corp.
BB PROGRESSION/2 - Computer software - Basis International Ltd.
BB PROGRESSION/3 - Computer software - Basis International Ltd.
BB PROGRESSION/4 C LIBRARY - Computer software - Basis International Ltd.
BB SATIN STAR - Pet products - Stearns Technical Textiles Co.
BB SCOUT - Guns–BB - Crosman Corp.
B.B. SHOTS - Candy ☆ - Ferrara Pan Candy Co., Inc.
BBAND - Apparel–athletic - George J. Schaffer
BBC - Apparel and accessories - Bugle Boy Industries, Inc.
BBC - Apparel–women's ☆ - CB North America Inc.
BBC - Cameras - Nu Arc Co. Inc.
BBC - Cookies - Bud's Best Cookies Inc.
BBC - Luggage - Nick Berian
BBD AITP - Recording label - Street Street Communications Inc.
BBE - Amplifiers–musical instrument ☆ - Bob White Associates
BBE - Electronic equipment - Bbe Sound, Inc.
BBF - Buckles ☆ - Erich M. Reich Inc.
BBF MAXERCISE - Exercising equipment - Sports Research Corp.
BBI - Bags–plastic - Better Bags, Inc.
BBI - Fruits and vegetables - Biggers Brothers Inc.
BBP - Recording label ☆ - Ray Lawrence Ltd.
BBP - Ribbons–inked - Buckeye Business Products Inc.
BBPROGRESSION/4 DATA SERVER - Computer software - Basis International Ltd.

☆ = Now out of production

BBQ BAG - Charcoal - Kingsford Co.
BBQ BOMBER - Toys - Mattel, Inc.
BBQ CHAMPS - Barbecue sauce - Uncle Ben's, Inc.
BBQ DOG - Clocks ☆ - General Time Corp. (Westclox/Seth Thomas Div.)
BBQ FLAME MASTER - Barbecue and grill accessories - Janco Products Inc.
BBQ GRILL - Food products - Lightlife Foods, Inc.
BBQ HALL OF FLAME - Bread crumbs - Goode-Cook, Inc.
BBQ RIBS - Bathing suits - Jantzen Inc.
BBQ ROUND-UPS - Pizzas–frozen - Sabatasso Foods Inc.
BBQER CHOICE - Barbecues and grills - Modern Home Products Corp.
BB'S - Cough drops - Alacer Co.
BBS - Health care products ☆ - Solvay Pharmaceuticals Inc.
BBS 900 - Computer software - Audiotext Services, Inc.
BBS SYSTEMS - Stainless steel - BBS Systems International, Inc.
BBSB - Publisher's imprints - McGraw-Hill Companies, Inc.
BBXPROGRESSION/4 - Computer software - Basis International Ltd.
BC - Cleaning preparations - Roebic Laboratories Inc.
BC - Furniture - Universal Furniture Industries, Inc.
B.C. - Greeting cards - Field Enterprises Inc.
B.C. - Health care products - Block Drug Co., Inc.
BC - Jewelry - Buyer's Choice Corp.
BC - Jewelry - Kathryn Carlislen Craven
BC - Juices ☆ - Musselman Fruit Products
BC - T-shirts–women's - Bethune-Cookman College
BC - Tables–wood - Anderson Desk Inc.
BC - Vegetable oil - Bunge Corp.
BC-A - Tobacco products - Lane Ltd.
BC BENCHCRAFT - Furniture - Universal Furniture Industries, Inc.
B.C. BOULDERS - Candy - Zeebs Enterprises, Inc.
B.C. COTTON - Apparel–men's - Glacier Group, Inc.
B.C. COVER - Paper - Howard Paper Mills Inc.
B.C. ETHNIC - Apparel–men's - Ceteris Paribus Inc.
BC PAL - Paperboard–corrugated - Boise Cascade Corp.
BC1 - Amplifiers–musical instrument - Pearce Amplification Ltd.
BCA - Automotive parts and accessories - Federal-Mogul Corp.
BCA - Bicycles - Bicycle Corp. of America
BCAD - Computer software - Open Engineering Inc.
BCAS - Electrical equipment - ENDEVCO Corp.
BCB - Sporting goods - Rothco Inc.
B.C.B.G. - Apparel and accessories - Max Azria
BCBG MAX AZRIA SWIM - Bathing suits - Raj Manufacturing, Inc.
B.C.C. - Tobacco–chewing or smoking - Sterling Tobacco Co.
BCC BLUES - Apparel and accessories - Bob's HC, Inc.
BCD - Cleaning prepartion - RPS International, Inc.
BCD - Computer software - BCD Technology, Inc.
BCD - Machine parts - Best Cutting Die Co.
BCDMAX - Computer hardware - Powertec Industrial Corp.
BCE - Health care products ☆ - Geneva Generics Inc.
BCE 2000 - Labeling machines - B.C.E. Technologies, Inc.
BCE 2003 - Printing presses - B.C.E. Technologies, Inc.
B.C.F.P. - Construction equipment - Woodex Lumber Corp.
BCI - Batteries - Battery Center, Inc.
BCI BURKE - Playground equipment - BCI Burke Co., Inc.
BCI CLOTHING COMPANY - Apparel stores–women's - Nitches, Inc.
BCM - Shirts - Boom Club Inc.
BCM2 - Games - Bingo Card Minder Corp.
BCMS VU - Computer software - Lucent Technologies Inc.
BCN - Computer peripheral equipment - Wellfleet Communications, Inc.
BCO - Cleaning preparations–window - Bill Clark Oil Co. Inc.
BCODE/DBS - Computer software - Specific Designs, Inc.
BCOM - Jewelry - Boom Fancies Inc.
BCOYZ - Apparel and accessories - Boom Club Inc.
BCR - Office supplies - American Tombow Inc.
BCS - Chemical preparations - Arnold Laboratories
BCS - Housewares ☆ - Amaza Laboratories Inc.
B.C.'S QUEST FOR TIRES - Computer software - Sierra On-Line, Inc.
BCTA C - Medical apparatus - Capintec, Inc.
BCW - Health care products - Wheelchair Institute of Kansas
BCW - Wheelchairs - Raye's, Inc. (Wheelchairs of Kansas)
B.C.W.-13 - Food products - Brokay Products Inc.
BCW 600 - Wheelchairs - Raye's, Inc. (Wheelchairs of Kansas)
BCW POWERCHAIR - Wheelchairs - Raye's, Inc. (Wheelchairs of Kansas)
BD - Screws - Safety Socket Screw Corp.
BD BOTANICAL DESIGNS INTERNATIONAL INC - Flowers–artificial - Botanical Designs International Inc.
BD SCRIBBLES - Watches - Richard J. White

BDA - Amplifiers–radio - Radio Frequency Systems, Inc.
BDC - Apparel - Black Dress Co.
BDGX - Pet products - Golden Pond Inc.
BDL - Machine parts - BDL USA, Inc.
BDR - Electronic equipment - High Voltage Engineering Corp.
BD'S BY LA MODE - Fabrics ☆ - Blumenthal/Lansing Co.
BDX-1000 - Hardware - Bondex International Inc.
BE - Computer hardware - BE Inc.
B.E. - Electrical equipment - Buhl Industries, Inc.
BE - Hair care products - Ronnie E. Ward
BE - Sporting goods - Best Equipment International, Inc.
BE - Water treating compounds - Beckart Environmental, Inc.
BE A BUDDY TO YOUR BACK - Video production - National Automatic Merchandising Association
BE-A-CLOWN - Dolls - Davis Brothers & Madison Ltd.
BE-ALERT AWAKENERS - Pharmaceutical preparations ☆ - Barre-National, Inc.
BE ALIVE - Greeting cards - Leanin' Tree Inc.
BE BEAU ENS - Cosmetics - Kathy Y.S. Nam
BE BEAUTIFUL - Cosmetics ☆ - Avon Products, Inc.
BE-BO - Hair care products - Nino Originals
BE-BOB - Musical instrument accessories ☆ - Sottile Manufacturing Co.
BE BOP - Candy - Bradley Candy Manufacturing Co.
BE-BOP - Pencils ☆ - Faber-Castell Corp.
BE-BOP BAGGY - Apparel–women's - P.J. Henry Inc.
BE-C 800 - Vitamins and nutritional supplements - Schein Pharmaceutical Inc.
BE-CE-PLEX FORTE - Pharmaceutical preparations - Consolidated Midland Corp.
BE COOL EAT AT SCHOOL - Aprons - Food Services of America, Inc.
BE COOL PRE-SCHOOL - Compact discs–prerecorded - Everland Entertainment
BE COOL PRESCHOOL - Recording label - Everland Entertainment
BE FOOLED - Toys - Alsip & Co.
BE FREE - Apparel–women's - Fitzgerald Underwear Corp.
BE GONE - Hair care products - Gold Medal Hair Products Inc.
BE GOOD TO YOURSELF - Skin care products - J. Gaunt Woodman Co.
BE GREEN - Toiletries - GPS, Inc.
BE HAPPY - Wallcoverings - Sherman & Associates International
BE HI - Shoes - Famolare Inc.
BE-LONG - Manicure preparations - Del Pharmaceuticals, Inc.
BE MINE VALENTINES - Figurines - American Greetings Corp.
BE MY VALENTINE - Christmas tree ornaments ☆ - Cracker Box Inc.
BE NATURAL - Skin care products - Prolinc Cosmetics, Inc.
BE NOT AFRAID - Recording label - Apostolate for Family Consecration, Inc.
BE OK - Health care products ☆ - Sammons Preston
BE OK THERO-GEL - Health care products ☆ - Sammons Preston
BE-PEN - Pens ☆ - Zebra Pen Corp.
BE PREPARED TO SURVIVE - First aid kits - Category 5, Inc.
BE SAFE - Health care products - Advantage Life Products Inc.
BE-SAFE - Medical apparatus - Mathis-Koolpe, Inc.
BE S.A.F.E. - Pamphlets - Cain Consulting Associates
BE-SHUR TEE PLACER - Golfing equipment - Glenn O. Axne
BE SMUG-DE-BUG - Insecticides - Sidwell Enterprises Inc.
BE SOMEBODY - Apparel and accessories - Be Somebody Sportwear, Inc.
BE SOMEBODY BE YOURSELF - T-shirts–men's - Continnuus
BE SURE - Health care products - Syntron Bioresearch Inc.
BE SURE ANTI-FLATULENT - Vitamins and nutritional supplements - Kyolic/Wakunaga
BE THE GAME - Apparel and accessories - Kevin Cantwell
BE TRUE - Paper products - DRL Enterprises, Inc.
BE YOURSELF - Apparel and accessories ☆ - Strouse, Adler Co.
BEA - Computer software - Bea Systems, Inc.
BEA CHERUB - Publisher's imprints - AABC Angels, Inc.
BEA HAVEN - Motor vehicles–motor homes ☆ - Honey Recreational Vehicles Inc.
BEACH - Floor coverings–carpet and rugs ☆ - Regal Rugs Inc.
BEACH - Recording label - Extra Sensory Productions
BEACH-AID - Pharmaceutical preparations - Bethurum Research & Development Inc.
BEACH BABIES - Bathing suits ☆ - Health-Tex Inc.
BEACH BABIES - Dolls - Doll Factory, Inc.
BEACH BABIES - Recording label - Maureen O'Sullivan Bryant
BEACH BABY BEARS - Infant product - Pansy Ellen Products, Inc.
BEACH-BALL - Games - Drybranch Inc./Sport Design
BEACH BALL CLASSIC - Apparel and accessories - Dan D'Antoni
BEACH BALLS - Chewing gum - Zeebs Enterprises, Inc.

BEACH BANANA - Yogurt–frozen - Alta-Dena Certified Dairy, Inc.
BEACH BASICS - Fabrics - Beach Basic Enterprises
BEACH BASTER - Cosmetic applicators - Joseph G. Angeletta
BEACH BED - Sporting goods - Carolyn V. Watson
BEACH BLANKET BABYLON - Shirts - Steve Silver Productions Inc.
BEACH BLAST - Dolls - Mattel, Inc.
BEACH BLASTER - Suntan lotions - Sun Pharmaceuticals Corp.
BEACH BOMBER - Bicycles - Emory Manufacturing Co.
BEACH BOY - Apparel and accessories - Andmore Sportswear Corp.
BEACH BREW - Beer - Southern Wine & Spirits of America, Inc.
BEACH BRITE - Paper–crepe - Beach Products
BEACH BROS. - Sporting goods - Coming Attractions
BEACH BUBBLE MAGNETS - Magnets - Visionary Products, Inc.
BEACH BUBBLES - Ornamental products–glass - Visionary Products, Inc.
BEACH BUDDIES - Towels - Jay Franco and Sons Inc.
BEACH BUGGY - Toys–automobiles - Kransco Manufacturing Inc.
BEACH BUM - Fabrics - Greenwood Mills Inc.
BEACH BUM - Toys - Russ Berrie and Co., Inc.
BEACH BUM BY MCGREGOR - Shirts - Mcgregor Corp.
BEACH BUM VOLLEYBALLS - Balls - Seneca Sports, Inc.
BEACH BUSTERS - Apparel–children's - Buster Brown Apparel Inc.
BEACH BUTLER - Chairs–folding - Matthew F. Walsh
BEACH CASTLE - Toys - Trendmasters, Inc.
BEACH CHAMP - Balls - Mikasa Sports
BEACH CHUMS - Toys - Advanced Design Concepts Inc.
BEACH CITIES - Leather goods - Borsack Group, Inc.
BEACH CLASSIC - Balls - Mikasa Sports
BEACH CLEANER BY HARLEY - Machine parts - Glenmac Inc.
BEACH CLEAT - Sporting goods - Suncoast Products
BEACH CLIFF - Sardines–canned - Stinson Seafood Co.
BEACH CLIFF GOLD LABEL - Sardines–canned - Stinson Seafood Co.
BEACH CLIPPER - Bicycles - Columbia Manufacturing Inc.
BEACH CLUB - Balls - Brine Inc.
BEACH CLUB - Beverages ☆ - The Stroh Brewery Co.
BEACH CLUB - Cosmetics - Randall Products International
BEACH-COMB - Bathing suits - Catalina
BEACH COMBERS - Bathing suits - Ocean Pool Co.
BEACH CRAFT - Hobby kits - Frederick H. Beach & Co. Inc.
BEACH CREATURES - Children's water pistols, balls, etc. - Namkung
    Promotions Inc.
BEACH DAYS - Toys - Mattel, Inc.
BEACH DAZZLE - Dolls - Mattel, Inc.
BEACH-DESIGN - Toys - Drybranch Inc./Sport Design
BEACH FRIES - Food products - Lancer Corp.
BEACH FROGS - Footwear - Lee International Ltd.
BEACH FRONT II - Floor coverings–carpet and rugs - Galaxy Carpet Mills Inc.
BEACH FUN - Dolls - Mattel, Inc.
BEACH GIRL - Apparel and accessories - Ben Elias Industries Corp.
BEACH GUIDE - Sporting goods - IHK International Corp.
BEACH HAVEN - Food products - Mrs. Paul's Kitchen
BEACH HEAD - Computer software ☆ - Access Software Inc.
BEACH HOUSE - Candles - Gps, Inc.
BEACH HOUSE - Furniture - Bassett Furniture Industries, Inc.
BEACH IN A BOX - Novelty items - Martin Willem Asmus
BEACH INVESTIGATIONS INTERNATIONAL - Apparel–athletic - Beach
    Investigations International
BEACH LINGO - Bathing suits - Raj Manufacturing, Inc.
BEACH LINGO BABES - Bathing suits - Raj Manufacturing, Inc.
BEACH LINGO GIRLS - Bathing suits - Raj Manufacturing, Inc.
BEACH LINGO 'TWEENS - Bathing suits - Raj Manufacturing, Inc.
BEACH MANIA - Apparel - Bradlees Stores, Inc.
BEACH 'N - Racks - Kent L. Dees
BEACH N BEYOND - Bathing suits ☆ - Cole of California Inc.
BEACH 'N' STREETS - Bicycles - Emory Manufacturing Co.
BEACH-N WEAR - Apparel and accessories - Jim Samp
BEACH PAINT - Suntan lotions ☆ - A.H. Robins Co. Inc.
BEACH PARTY - Apparel–women's - Jonathan Logan Inc.
BEACH PARTY - Bicycles - Columbia Manufacturing Inc.
BEACH PARTY - Bicycles ☆ - Huffy Corp.
BEACH PARTY - Toys - Tonka Corp.
BEACH PATROL - Apparel–women's - Daffy Waterwear
BEACH PATROL - Toys–automobiles - Mattel, Inc.
BEACH PATROL SUN-SYSTEMS - Skin care products - Beach Patrol Sun
    Systems Inc.
BEACH PEACH - Dolls - Mattel, Inc.
BEACH PEBBLES - Health care products - Dorothy Gray Cosmetics Ltd.

BEACH PET - Pet products - American Pacific Pet
BEACH PLUM - Jewelry–costume ☆ - Safari Ltd.
BEACH PRO - Balls - Mikasa Sports
BEACH PUFFS - Pillows - Sandlake Enterprises, Inc.
BEACH RAKE - Machine parts - Glenmac Inc.
BEACH RIDER - Bicycles - Ross Bicycles USA, Ltd.
BEACH SCENE - Apparel and accessories - Dave Goldberg, Inc.
BEACH SOCCER - Balls ☆ - Mikasa Sports
BEACH STOP - Bathing suits - Manhattan Beachwear, Inc.
BEACH STREAK - Dolls - Mattel, Inc.
BEACH TABLE - Furniture - Michael T. Credle, Sr.
BEACH TAXI - Toys–automobiles - Mattel, Inc.
BEACH TREE - Skin care products ☆ - Noxell Corp.
BEACH TRIBE - Apparel and accessories - Dominick D'Ercole
BEACH VOLLEY - Games - Drybranch Inc./Sport Design
BEACH WAGON - Toys - Processed Plastic Co.
BEACH WEAR FOR EVERYWHERE - Apparel stores–men's - Darden Corp.
BEACH WHITE - Paints - Camco Paints Inc.
BEACHBALL BEARS - Bedding–linen - Pansy Ellen Products, Inc.
BEACHBOWL - Games - David H. Ottley
BEACHBOX - Playground equipment - Wonderline
BEACHCO BEADS - Candy - Beach Co.
BEACHCOBOARD - Artists' materials - Beach Co.
BEACHCOMBER - Boats–motor ☆ - Cruisers
BEACHCOMBER - Boats–pontoons - Lakes Manufacturing Inc.
BEACHCOMBER - Desk sets ☆ - Park Sherman
BEACHCOMBER - Fabrics - Greenwood Mills Inc.
BEACHCOMBER - Floor coverings–carpet and rugs - Catalina Carpet Mills
    Inc.
BEACHCOMBER - Furniture - Stanley Furniture Co. Inc.
BEACHCOMBER - Lamps - Lamplight Farms, Inc.
BEACHCOMBER - Sandals - Gerber Products Co.
BEACHCOMBER - Tiles–ceramic ☆ - Porcelanite, Inc.
BEACHED - Clothing - Sears, Roebuck and Co.
BEACHGLOO - Adhesives and sealants - Beach Co.
BEACHIE KEEN - Bathing suits - Riviera Sales Corp.
BEACHLEY - Wallpaper - K.M.L. Industries
BEACHLIFT - Conveyors - Inclinator Co. of America
BEACHLOVER - Apparel and accessories - Cup Graphics
BEACHMASTER - Bicycles - Emory Manufacturing Co.
BEACHMASTER - Fishing tackle - Penn Fishing Tackle Manufacturing Co.
BEACHMASTER - Wheelchairs - Beach Wheels Inc.
BEACHNIKS - Cosmetics - Max Factor & Co.
BEACHSTAR BEAUTY - Toys - Tonka Corp.
BEACHTREE - Umbrellas - Richard Gurney
BEACHTREE BOOKS - Publisher's imprints - William Morrow and Co. Inc.
BEACHWOOD - Floor coverings–carpet and rugs - Cabin Crafts Carpets
BEACHWOOD - Recording label - Chameleon Music Group Inc.
BEACHWOOD - Skin care products - ABAR Beauty Supply Inc.
BEACHWORKS - Novelty items - Eagle Affiliates, Inc.
BEACON - Bedding–linen - Beacon Manufacturing Co.
BEACON - Beverages–malt - Judge Marketing Inc.
BEACON - Candy - Beacon Sweets, Inc.
BEACON - Cleaning preparations–household - Sterling Winthrop Inc.
BEACON - Electronic equipment - Heatcraft Inc.
BEACON - Fabrics - Uniroyal Engineered Products
BEACON - Flatware - Utica Cutlery Co.
BEACON - Pagers - NEC America, Inc.
BEACON - Paints ☆ - Wescon Products Co.
BEACON - Paper - Fay Paper Products Inc.
BEACON - Pet products - Woodstream Corp.
BEACON - Petroleum - Ultramar Inc.
BEACON - Projectors–photographic - General Audio-Visual Inc.
BEACON - Seafood products–canned or cured ☆ - Bumble Bee Seafoods,
    Inc.
BEACON - Shoes - Beacon Shoe Co.
BEACON - Sporting goods - Beacon Industries, Inc.
BEACON - Windows–plastic - Norandex, Inc.
BEACON 400 - Remote control devices ☆ - GMI Photographic Inc.
BEACON BAY - Floor coverings - Armstrong World Industries, Inc.
BEACON-FLEX - Shoes - Beacon Shoe Co.
BEACON-FLEX LITE II - Shoes ☆ - Beacon Shoe Co.
BEACON GOOF-PROOF - Lubricating oils ☆ - Ultramar Inc.
BEACON HALL - Lumber - Georgia-Pacific Corp.
BEACON HILL - Bedding–linen - Sardo Textile Corp.
BEACON HILL - Fans–electric - Nutone Inc.

☆ = Now out of production

BEACON HILL - Floor coverings ☆ - Congoleum Corp.
BEACON HILL - Fruits and vegetables - S & W Fine Foods, Inc.
BEACON HILL - Furniture - Tomlinson of High Point Inc.
BEACON HILL - Furniture ☆ - Kincaid Furniture Co. Inc.
BEACON HILL - Glassware–household ☆ - Lenox Crystal, Inc.
BEACON HILL - Greeting cards - Harrison-Simpson Co.
BEACON HILL - Lighting fixtures - Collins International Co., Ltd.
BEACON HILL - Luggage ☆ - Samsonite Corp.
BEACON HILL - Tableware–china ☆ - Lenox, Inc.
BEACON HILL - Trailers–travel - Fleetwood Enterprises, Inc.
BEACON HILL PRESS OF KANSAS CITY - Publisher's imprints - Nazarene
    Publishing House
BEACON HOUSE - Lamps - Service Merchandise Co. Inc.
BEACON LITE - Chimes ☆ - Nutone Inc.
BEACON RIDGE - Wines - ASV Wines, Inc.
BEACON SQUARE PRESS - Greeting cards - American Greetings Corp.
BEACON STREET - Floor coverings–carpet and rugs ☆ - Mohawk Carpet
    Corp.
BEACONETTES - Shoes ☆ - Beacon Shoe Co.
BEACONSFIELD - Cigars - Danby-Palicio
BEACONSFIELD - Furniture ☆ - Harden Furniture Co. Inc.
BEAD - Flatware - Gorham Inc.
BEAD - Flatware - Wallace International Silversmiths, Inc.
BEAD BIN - Beads - Pepperell Braiding Co. Inc.
BEAD BOPS - Hobby kits - Lisa Frank, Inc.
BEAD CHAIN - Hardware - Bead Industries Inc. (Bead Chain Div.)
BEAD CONNECTION, THE - Artists' materials - Decorator and Craft Corp.
BEAD DANGLER - Toys - Natural Science Industries, Ltd.
BEAD EASY - Craft sets ☆ - Faultless Starch/Bon Ami Co.
BEAD-EZE - Automotive parts and accessories - Summit Tool Co.
BEAD-FEEDER - Hobby kits ☆ - Accento Plastic Manufacturing Inc.
BEAD FUN - Dolls - Mattel, Inc.
BEAD HAPPY - Jewelry - Bead Happy
BEAD MAGIC - Toys - ERTL Co., Inc.
BEAD MAGIC MINDY - Dolls - ERTL Co., Inc.
BEAD POINT - Hobby kits - Quincrafts Corp.
BEAD SAVER SYSTEM - Tools–hand-operated - Gaither Tool Co., Inc.
BEAD SMITH - Jewelry - M & Y Helby Import Co., Inc.
BEAD WAREHOUSE, THE - Catalogs - Marvin A. Schwab
BEADANGLED - Jewelry - Melanie S. Weinstein
BEADAZZLED - Jewelry - Diamanti, Inc.
BEADBOX - Beads - Beadbox, Inc.
BEADED - Musical instrument accessories - Dimarzio, Inc.
BEADED - Wood products - States Industries Inc.
BEADED ANTIQUE - Cutlery - Carvel Hall Inc.
BEADED ANTIQUE - Dinnerware–glass - Towle Silversmiths
BEADED ANTIQUE - Flatware - Towle Manufacturing Co.
BEADED DRAMA - Apparel and accessories - Sapna Sood
BEADED EDGE - Glass products - Westmoreland Glass Co.
BEADED GRAPE - Glass products - Westmoreland Glass Co.
BEADERETTE - Looms - Aleene's
BEADERY, THE - Hobby kits - Greene Plastics Corp.
BEADLE - Apparel and accessories - Louis R. Beadle
BEADLES - Jewelry - Beadles/Three Ring Circuits
BEADMAGIC - Tools–hand-operated - Beadwear, Inc.
BEADS & BEADS - Waterproofing compounds - Sterling-Clark-Lurton Corp.
BEADS 'N BAUBLES - Toys - Lauri Inc.
BEADS O' BLEACH - Bleach - Dial Corp.
BEADS-O-FASHION - Hobby kits - C-Mor Co.
BEADS OF LIGHT - Candles - Smith & Vandiver, Inc.
BEADS, THE - Apparel and accessories - Red Beads Outlet
BEADSMART - Beads - Euro Tool, Inc.
BEADY BUDDY'S - Craft supplies - Western Trimming Corp.
BEADY BUDDY'S - Craft supplies - Westrim Crafts
BEAGLE - Magnetic resonance imaging devices - Multi Products Co.
BEAGLE - Racks - Beagle Manufacturing Co. Inc.
BEAGLE BAGELS - Pet shops - Gimborn U.S., Inc.
BEAGLES - Sunglasses - Beagles, Inc.
BEAKER-KEEPER - Pet products - Products Carousel Inc.
BEAKEY BUZZARD THE EARTH KID - Apparel and accessories - John R.
    Sunzeri
BEAKMAN'S WORLD - Computer software - Elp Communications
BEAKS - Fishing tackle - Michael R. Hurt
BEAL - Rope - Climb High Inc.
BEALE STREET - Beverages–alcohol - Juba Beverages Corp.

BEALE STREET CARAVAN - Broadcasting stations–radio - Blues Foundation,
    Inc.
BEALE STREET U.S.A. - Recording label - Goldwax Record Co. Inc.
BEAM - Office accessories - Omnimed Inc.
BEAM - Vacuum cleaners and accessories - White Consolidated Industries, Inc.
BEAM ALIGNER - Lasers - Laser Alignment, Inc.
BEAM BIKE - Bicycles - Softride, Inc.
BEAM BUTLER - Vacuum cleaners and accessories - White Consolidated
    Industries, Inc.
BEAM MACHINE - Saws–chain ☆ - Hal E. Verble & Son Inc. (Veri Products
    Div.)
BEAM-O-MATIC - Lighting fixtures - Big Beam Emergency Systems Inc.
BEAM SENSOR - Cigarette lighters - Park Lane Associates, Inc.
BEAMAN MILLET - Giftware - Vincent Lippe Co.
BEAMASTER - Antennas - Recoton Corp.
BEAMATIC - Office accessories - Omnimed Inc.
BEAMAX - Lighting fixtures - Thomas Lighting (Accent Division)
BEAMAX - Track lighting fixtures ☆ - Thomas Industries Inc.
BEAMBALL - Balls - Pick Point Sports
BEAMCALC - Computer software - Trus Joist MacMillan L.P.
BEAME & WHITESIDE SOFTWARE - Computer software - Beame &
    Whiteside Software, Inc.
BEAMERO - Beverages–alcohol - Jim Beam Brands Co.
BEAMERS - Apparel and accessories - D.A.F. Management, Inc.
BEAMGRID - Construction equipment - Alcan Aluminum Corp. Alcan Building
    Products Div.
BEAMISH IRISH CREAM - Beverages–alcohol ☆ - Century Importers Inc.
BEAMISH IRISH STOUT - Beverages–malt - Martlet Importing Co.
BEAMISH IRISH STOUT - Beverages–malt - Scottish & Newcastle Importers
    Co.
BEAM'S 8 STAR BLEND - Beverages–alcohol - Jim Beam Brands Co.
BEAM'S BLACK LABEL - Beverages–alcohol - Jim Beam Brands Co.
BEAM'S CHOICE - Beverages–alcohol - Jim Beam Brands Co.
BEAMSCOPE - Television monitors - Florida New Concepts Marketing Inc.
BEAMSCREEN - Infant product - Children on the Go, Inc.
BEAN - Sporting goods - L.L. Bean Inc.
BEAN BAG BABY - Dolls ☆ - Goldberger Doll Manufacture Co.
BEAN BAG BETTY - Furniture - Bean Bag Betty & Co.
BEAN BAG GOODIES - Toys ☆ - Horsman
BEAN BAG HYDE - Furniture - Betty P. Rogers
BEAN BAG SOFTEZE - Toys–stuffed ☆ - Fun World Inc.
BEAN BALLS - Candy - American Candy Co.
BEAN BALLS-JUGGLING SUPER SET - Exercising equipment - Jugglebug
BEAN BAR - Coffee - Bean Bar, Inc.
BEAN BOOTS BY L.L. BEAN - Footwear - L.L. Bean Inc.
BEAN BOYS - Toys - Sheram Puppets Inc.
BEAN BUSH BOUQUET - Flowers, plants, and seeds - NTS Co.
BEAN CLASSICS - Beans - C & F Foods Inc.
BEAN CUISINE - Beans - W.J. Clark & Co.
BEAN CUISINE SOUPS - Food products - Reily Foods
BEAN KLEEN - Deodorizers - G.G. Bean Inc.
BEAN POT - Food products - Bush Brothers and Co.
BEAN SPICE SUPERIOR - Seasonings - Continnuus
BEAN SPROUTS - Toys - Great American Fun Corp.
BEAN STATION FURNITURE FACTORY, THE - Furniture - Bean Station
    Furniture Factory Inc.
BEANBAG MADNESS - Games - Gary Buck and Mark R. Hockridge
    Partnership
BEANBAGS - Toys–stuffed ☆ - Russ Berrie and Co., Inc.
BEANBLOSSOM - Wines - Oliver Wine Co. Inc.
BEANE BAG - Filters–industrial - Beane Filter Media, Inc.
BEANEE BOPPERS - Candy - Carol V. Barilone
BEANERY BLEND - Coffee - Coffee Beanery Ltd.
BEANHEAD INTERNATIONAL - Coffee - Beanhead International
BEANIE BABIES - Toys–stuffed - Ibssl, Inc.
BEANIE FLYERS - Kites - Llumar Star Kites Inc.
BEANILOO - Pet products ☆ - Dogloo Inc.
BEANO - Computer software ☆ - SRA/McGraw-Hill (Div. of The McGraw-Hill
    Companies)
BEANO - Pharmaceutical preparations - Lactaid Inc.
BEANS & BREWS - Coffee - Arabica Inc.
BEANS FERMIERE CASSOULET - Bean casserole - MT OSO Trading Co.
BEANS MCGEE - Apparel and accessories - J.G. Hook, Inc.
BEANTOWN COFFEE - Coffee - Garber Bros., Inc.
BEANY - Dolls - Fun World Inc.
BEANY BOY - Vegetables–canned - Meridian Foods

BEAR - Ammonia ☆ - American Bluing Co. Inc.
BEAR - Archery equipment - Bear Archery Inc.
BEAR - Fruits and vegetables - Upland Lemon Co.
BEAR - Giftware - Bear Enterprises USA Inc.
BEAR - Kites ☆ - Hi-Flier Manufacturing Co.
BEAR - Paper–sand - Norton Co.
BEAR - Raisins ☆ - Sun-Maid Growers of California
BEAR - Recording label - Bear Creek Entertainment Group
BEAR - Sprinklers–lawn - Grizzle Y Hunter Plastic, Inc.
BEAR - Tires - Gillette Tire Co.
BEAR & JENNINGS - Archery equipment - Bear Archery Inc.
BEAR ATHLETIC WARE - Sporting goods - Steve Van, Inc.
BEAR BAG - Bags–duffel - Benjamin R. Groeser
BEAR BAGS - Bags–plastic - Flexwrap Corp.
BEAR BEANS - Dolls - Mattel, Inc.
BEAR BODY SUPPORT SYSTEMS - Braces–orthopedic - Steve Van, Inc.
BEAR BOTTOMS - Toys–stuffed ☆ - Bradley Import Co.
BEAR BRASS BAND - Christmas tree ornaments - Mr. Christmas, Inc.
BEAR BUDDI - Candy ☆ - L.E.G. Inc.
BEAR CAMO - Archery equipment ☆ - Bear Archery Inc.
BEAR CAT - Fishing tackle - Williamson & Co. Inc.
BEAR CAT - Garden equipment - Crary Co.
BEAR CLAW - Golfing equipment - Golden Bear International, Inc.
BEAR CLAW - Ice cream - General Container Co. of Michigan, Inc.
BEAR CLAW BAGS - Trash-can liners - Bland Co.
BEAR CLAW BEEFALO - Meat products - Bear Claw Cattle Co.
BEAR CLAW TRACTION MATS - Mats - Traveler's Checklist
BEAR CLAWS - Nuts–candied - NMS, Inc.
BEAR COUNTRY - Toys–stuffed - Kamar International Inc.
BEAR COUNTRY BAVARIAN BRAND HEFE WEIZENBEER - Beverages–
  malt - Southern California Brewing Co.
BEAR COVER-UPS - Wallpaper ☆ - Northern California Imports Inc.
BEAR CREEK - Fruits–canned ☆ - Harry and David Inc.
BEAR CREEK BANQUETS - Food products - Harry and David Inc.
BEAR CREEK GARDENS - Flowers, plants, and seeds - Bear Creek Gardens,
  Inc.
BEAR CUB - Archery equipment - Bear Archery Inc.
BEAR CUB - Firearms, accessories, and parts - Beeman Precision Airguns
BEAR DANCE - Wines - Harry's Farmers Market, Inc.
BEAR E. SLEEPY - Soap - Copperchase Productions, Inc.
BEAR ELEGANCE - Wallpaper ☆ - Northern California Imports Inc.
BEAR ELEGANCE COLLECTION - Furniture - Evenflo Juvenile Furniture Co.
BEAR ESCENTS - Air purification systems ☆ - Medo Industries, Inc.
BEAR EXPRESSIONS - Signs - Bear Expressions, Inc.
BEAR FACTS - Toys - Educational Insights, Inc.
BEAR FEET - Footwear - Bear Feet
BEAR FLAG - Cheese - Vella Cheese Co. Inc.
BEAR FLARE - Archery equipment ☆ - Bear Archery Inc.
BEAR FORCE - Giftware - Russ Berrie and Co., Inc.
BEAR-GLUV - Archery equipment - Bear Archery Inc.
BEAR GRIP - Sporting goods - Barrett Lee Cruthirds, Sr.
BEAR HUG - Archery equipment - Bear Archery Inc.
BEAR HUG - Cording - Global Fury, Inc.
BEAR HUG - Sporting goods - Unique Sports Products Inc.
BEAR HUG GREETINGS - Envelopes - Pup-Pak Production and Marketing Inc.
BEAR HUGS - Paper–gift wrap - Papercraft Corp.
BEAR HUGS - Publisher's imprints ☆ - Warren Publishing House, Inc.
BEAR HUGS - Stationery - Giordano Art, Ltd.
BEAR HUGS - Toys–stuffed - Russ Berrie and Co., Inc.
BEAR HUGS - Wallpaper ☆ - Imperial Wallcoverings, Inc.
BEAR IN A BAG - Toys–stuffed - Great American Fun Corp.
BEAR-IN-A-TUBE - Toys - Gerber Products Co.
BEAR ISLAND OUTFITTERS - Leather goods - Bear Island Outfitters, Ltd.
BEAR JAM - Computer software - Dunamis Inc.
BEAR KAT - Gloves - Shelby Group International, Inc.
BEAR LAKE - Food products - Sundor Brands Inc.
BEAR LIGHTARGET II - Archery equipment - Bear Archery Inc.
BEAR MOUNTAIN - Footwear–men's - Shoe Tree, Inc.
BEAR MUSH - Cereal - Arrowhead Mills, Inc.
BEAR MY LOVE - Toys–stuffed - Fun World Inc.
BEAR NECESSITIES - Footwear ☆ - Bear Feet
BEAR NECESSITIES - Wallpaper ☆ - Northern California Imports Inc.
BEAR NINJAZORD - Toys–automobiles - Saban Entertainment, Inc.
BEAR PAKS - Candy - Brock Candy Co. Inc.
BEAR PAW - Sporting goods - Bear Paw Tackle Co.
BEAR PAW LAPIDARY - Jewelry - Bear Paw Lapidary Corp.

BEAR PAWS - Candy - Doman, Inc.
BEAR PAWSE - Toys–stuffed ☆ - Gund, Inc.
BEAR PRO - Sporting goods ☆ - Bear Archery Inc.
BEAR RIVER INDUSTRIES - Sporting goods - Bear River Industries, Inc.
BEAR SOCIETY - Toys–stuffed - Russ Berrie and Co., Inc.
BEAR STONES - Sporting goods ☆ - Bear Paw Tackle Co.
BEAR TALK - Games ☆ - Great Graphic Originals
BEAR TARGET - Archery equipment ☆ - Bear Archery Inc.
BEAR-TEX - Non-woven products - Norton Co.
BEAR TEXTURES - Wallpaper ☆ - Northern California Imports Inc.
BEAR, THE - Golfing equipment - Golden Bear International, Inc.
BEAR VALLEY - Bicycles - Marin Mountain Bikes, Inc.
BEAR VALLEY - Snack food - Inter Mountain Trading Co.
BEAR WHISKERS - Archery equipment - Bear Archery Inc.
BEARABLES - Pencils - National Pen & Pencil Co.
BEARABLES - Toys–stuffed ☆ - Bearables Ltd.
BEARATONE BEAR - Toys–stuffed - Dakin Inc.
BEARBAC - Floor coverings–carpet and rugs - GFF Holding Co.
BEARBATH - Toys - Bear Care Co.
BEARBERRY - Toys–stuffed ☆ - Dakin Inc.
BEARBOAT - Wines - Piper Sonoma
BEARBOTTOMS - Toys–stuffed ☆ - Gund, Inc.
BEARCAPS - Automotive parts and accessories - Egl 1, Inc.
BEARCAT - Archery equipment - Bear Archery Inc.
BEARCAT - Bicycles - Ross Bicycles USA, Ltd.
BEARCAT - Boats–pontoons - Bearcat Corp.
BEARCAT - Electronic equipment ☆ - Uniden America Corp.
BEARCAT - Mats - Matworks
BEARCAT - Motor vehicles–all-terrain - Arctco, Inc.
BEARCAT - Motor vehicles–all-terrain - Arctic Cat Inc.
BEARCAT - Revolvers - Sturm, Ruger & Co., Inc.
BEARCAT - Tools - Bruner Ivory Handle Co.
BEARD - Publisher's imprints - Willis Music Co.
BEARFEAT - Toys–stuffed ☆ - Gund, Inc.
BEARFIELD FAMILY, THE - Toys–stuffed - Seventh Avenue, Inc.
BEARFLEX - Giftware - Bear Enterprises USA Inc.
BEARFOOT - Figurines - Marty Sculpture
BEARFOOT - Toys–stuffed - Dakin Inc.
BEARFOOTIN' BY CREATURE COMFORTS - Shoes - JBI, Inc.
BEARFOOTS - Figurines - Singing Tree Farms, Inc.
BEARHAIR - Archery equipment - Bear Archery Inc.
BEARHEART - Toys–stuffed - Gund, Inc.
BEARHUNTER, THE - Computer software - Discovery Channel
BEARIN' SEAL - Automotive parts and accessories - Radiator Specialty Co.
BEARING GARD - Engines - Tecumseh Products Co. Engine and
  Transmission Group
BEARING LIFE - Bearings–motor vehicle - Fulton Manufacturing Corp.
BEARINGS - Computer software - Zephyr Services
BEARINGS - Containers–paper - David Leinberger
BEARISH - Toys–stuffed ☆ - Gund, Inc.
BEARITONE - Toys–stuffed ☆ - Gund, Inc.
BEARITOS - Snack foods - Little Bear Organic Foods, Inc.
BEARITOS FRUIT SOURS - Candy ☆ - Little Bear Organic Foods, Inc.
BEAR*LERINA - Ballet slippers - Bear Feet
BEARLICIOUS GREETINGS - Candy - Securitag Corp.
BEARLOONS - Dolls - Mattel, Inc.
BEARLOTS - Toys–stuffed ☆ - Gund, Inc.
BEARLY - Toys–stuffed ☆ - Gund, Inc.
BEARLY ARABESQUE - Posters - Heartprint Inc.
BEARLY TAME - Toys - Tonka Corp.
BEARLY THERE - Figurines - Ellen Lisa Pavelka
BEARLY THINKING - Greeting cards - Sharon's Stuff Greeting Cards & Stuff
BEARLY YOURS - Novelty items–paper ☆ - Antioch Publishing Co.
BEARMAIL - Greeting cards - Recycled Paper Products, Inc.
BEARMAIL - Toys–stuffed ☆ - Gund, Inc.
BEARNARD - Toys–stuffed ☆ - Gund, Inc.
BEARNIE - Toys–stuffed ☆ - Gund, Inc.
BEAROBICS - Magnets - Russ Berrie and Co., Inc.
BEARRIFIC BEAR FACTORY, THE - Toys–stuffed - Bearrific Bear Factory,
  Inc.
BEARS FROM THE PAST - Toys–stuffed - Russ Berrie and Co., Inc.
BEARS OF COZY HAVEN, THE - Apparel and accessories - Brumfield
  Studios, Inc.
BEARS OF THE MONTH - Toys–stuffed - Russ Berrie and Co., Inc.
BEARS ONLY - Wallpaper - United Wallcoverings
BEARS REPEATING - Calendars ☆ - American Greetings Corp.

☆ = Now out of production

BEARS WITH LOVE - Toys–stuffed ☆ - Imperial Toy Corp.
BEARSPOT - Toys–stuffed ☆ - Gund, Inc.
BEARSTONE COLLECTION, THE - Figurines - Boyds Collection Ltd.
BEARSVILLE - Recording label - Bearsville Records
BEARSY - Toys–stuffed ☆ - Dakin Inc.
BEARTH CERTIFICATE - Toys–stuffed - Bearrific Bear Factory, Inc.
BEARTOOTH RANCH BEEF - Beef - Beartooth Meats
BEARWEAR - Toys–stuffed ☆ - Gund, Inc.
BEARY BEST FRIENDS - Toys–stuffed - Frivals n Friends
BEARY DU FRAISE - Dolls - Destiny Designs, Inc.
BEARY GELATIN - Gelatin - Bela Corp.
BEARY SPECIAL BEAR - Toys–stuffed - Dakin Inc.
BEARY SPECIAL BUNNIES - Toys–stuffed - Russ Berrie and Co., Inc.
BEARY SPECIAL GREETINGS - Greeting cards ☆ - Marsyl Inc. (Marsyl Enterprises, Inc.)
BEARY SWEET MIX - Snack foods - A.L. Schutzman Co., Inc.
BEARY'S - Novelty items - Edward C. Labarre
BEARZ 'N THE HOOD - Broadcasting stations–television - Orbit Productions, Inc.
BEA'S - Pork rinds and crackins - R & R Sunshine
BEAST - Books–comic - Marvel Entertainment Group, Inc.
BEAST - Motors–outboard - Zebco Corp.
BEAST - Rackets–racquetball - Gexco Enterprises
BEAST - Trash compactors–household - The Genie Co.
BEAST BLASTER - Toys - Wild Planet Toys, Inc.
BEAST MAN - Toys - Mattel, Inc.
BEAST, THE - Hardware - Centrum Products Co.
BEAST, THE - Bowling balls - Columbia 300 Inc.
BEAST, THE - Sleds - Emsco Inc.
BEAST, THE - Bicycles - Ross Bicycles USA, Ltd.
BEAST, THE - Vitamins and nutritional supplements - Ultra-Lab Nutrition, Inc.
BEAST WALKER - Toys - Mattel, Inc.
BEAST WAR - Games ☆ - Avalon Hill Game Co.
BEAST WARS - Toys - Hasbro, Inc.
BEAST WITHIN, THE - Games - Mayfair Games, Inc.
BEAST WITHIN, THE - Computer software - Sierra On-Line, Inc.
BEASTEES - Apparel - Avant Sportswear
BEASY II - Medical apparatus - Robert F. Brantman, Inc.
BEASY II EASY TRANSFER SYSTEM - Medical apparatus - Robert F. Brantman, Inc.
BEASYTRANS - Handicap transfer apparatus - Robert F. Brantman, Inc.
BEAT - Recording label - Orange Record Co. Inc.
BEAT IT - Pet products ☆ - Senoret Chemical Co.
BEAT SEAT - Seat covers - Red Comet Productions, Inc.
BEAT THE BELTWAY - Games - Larry A. Bowring
BEAT THE CHAMP - Video production - Konami (America) Inc.
BEAT THE CLOCK - Games ☆ - Milton Bradley Co.
BEATER - Apparel–athletic - Exodus International
BEATLES, THE - Watches - Temlex/Jupiter Watch Corp.
BEATMASTER - Watches - Elgin Watch Co.
BEATNIK - Apparel and accessories - Edward S. Evans
BEATNIK - Computer peripheral equipment - Thomas Dolby
BEATNIK - Computer software - Headspace, Inc.
BEATNIK BETTE - Apparel and accessories - Beatnik Brand Inc.
BEATNIKS - Toys–stuffed - Jack Gasnick, The Virtuous Locksmith
BEATO - Drummer's gloves - Fred Beato
BEATO BAGS - Cases–musical instrument - Fred Beato
BEATO U.S.A. - Cases–musical instrument - Fred Beato
BEATRICE - Food products - Beatrice Cos. Inc.
BEATRICE - Glassware–household ☆ - Oneida Ltd.
BEATRICE - Nuts–salted, roasted, cooked, or canned - August Battaglia Processing Co.
BEATRICE - Toys–stuffed ☆ - Edumundo Productions, Inc.
BEATRICE BUNNY - Puppets - Dakin Inc.
BEATRIX POTTER - Bedding–linen - Quiltex
BEATRIX POTTER - Computer software - Frederick Warne & Co., Inc.
BEATRIX POTTER - Figurines - Royal Doulton-Somerset UK Ltd.
BEATRIX POTTER - Giftware - Schmid Inc.
BEATRIX POTTER - Hobby kits ☆ - Activa Products Inc.
BEATRIX POTTER - Posters - One-of-a-Kind Workshop
BEATRIX POTTER - Rubber stamps - All Night Media, Inc.
BEATRIX POTTER - T-shirts–children's - Prelude Designs
BEATRIX POTTER COLLECTION - Toys–stuffed - Toy Works, Inc.
BEATRIX POTTER COLLECTION, THE - Toys–stuffed - Eden LLC
BEATRIX POTTER COLLECTION, THE - Glassware–household - C.R. Gibson Co.

BEATRIX POTTER COLLECTION, THE - Recording label - Frederick Warne & Co., Inc.
BEATRIX POTTER CREATIONS - Buttons - JHB International Inc.
BEATRIX POTTER'S COUNTRY WORLD - Dishes–earthenware - Frederick Warne & Co., Inc.
BEATRIX SAINT LAMONT - Apparel and accessories ☆ - Swirl II Ltd.
BEATS ALL - Pencils ☆ - Faber-Castell Corp.
BEATS BUTTER - Vitamins and nutritional supplements - Tishcon Corp.
BEATS SALT - Seasonings - Tishcon Corp.
BEATS SUGAR - Vitamins and nutritional supplements - Tishcon Corp.
BEATS THE NAIL - Adhesives and sealants - Dap Products Inc.
BEATS THE NAILS - Adhesives and sealants - Dap Products Inc.
BEATS-UM-ALL - Cleaning preparations - Bodyguard Chemical
BEAU - Apparel stores–lingerie - Formflex Foundations Inc.
BEAU - Pet products - Plee-Zing Inc.
BEAU BASIX - Hair care products - Kimberly F. Sublett
BEAU BELLE - Paper - Bee Paper Co. Inc.
BEAU BLOC - Rubber utility mats ☆ - Ace Rubber Products Inc.
BEAU-BRIAN - Recording label ☆ - Acoustographic Records
BEAU BRILLIANT - Paper - Strathmore Paper Co.
BEAU BRILLIANT - Rings–jewelry ☆ - Artcarved Inc.
BEAU BRUMMEL - Leather goods - RGA Accessories Inc.
BEAU BRUMMEL - Scissors–hand-operated ☆ - Dubl Duck/Jet Set Inc.
BEAU BRUMMELL - Apparel–men's - Mcgregor Corp.
BEAU BRUMMELL - Beauty aids - American Mercantile Co.
BEAU BRUMMELL - Watches - Bulova Corp.
BEAU BUNNY - Chocolate candy - Superior Fruit & Confections
BEAU CHATEAU - Floor coverings–carpet and rugs ☆ - Karastan-Bigelow Inc.
BEAU CREST - Floor coverings–carpet and rugs ☆ - Karastan-Bigelow Inc.
BEAU DANDIES - Toys–stuffed ☆ - Fun World Inc.
BEAU DOG - Toys–stuffed - Russ Berrie and Co., Inc.
BEAU GESTE - Apparel and accessories - Orion Pacific Corp.
BEAU GESTE - Giftware - Bamboo Inc.
BEAU HIDES - Wallets - Le Baron Manufacturing Corp.
BEAU JACK - Boats–motor ☆ - Glastron Boats
BEAU JACQUES - Wines ☆ - Alimar & Cie. Inc.
BEAU JEST - Office supplies - Samuel Ward Manufacturing Inc.
BEAU-KAY - Apparel stores–lingerie - Formflex Foundations Inc.
BEAU MARK - Sporting goods - Ektelon
BEAU MONDE - Eyeglasses - Biba Optique Inc.
BEAU MONDE - Rings–jewelry - Artcarved Inc.
BEAU MONTE - Floor coverings–carpet and rugs ☆ - Galaxy Carpet Mills Inc.
BEAU PEAR - Desserts ☆ - Sarabeth's Kitchen
BEAU PRE - Wines - Laird and Co.
BEAU RIVAGE - Floor coverings ☆ - Tarkett, Inc.
BEAU RIVAGE - Frames–eyeglass - Zylo Ware Corp.
BEAU SQUIRE - Furniture - Dinaire Corp.
BEAU-T-WALL - Paints ☆ - Dunn Edwards Corp.
BEAU TECH - Tools–hand-operated - Peter B. Garsoe
BEAU TIES - Shoes - Etonic Inc.
BEAU TYE - Ribbons - Artistic Manufacturing Co.
BEAU VAL - Wines - Beau Val Wines Inc.
BEAU-VEL - Ribbons - W.F.R. Ribbon Corp.
BEAUBIEN - Bedding–linen - Dan River Inc.
BEAUCAIRE - Apparel–men's ☆ - MMG Corp.
BEAUCANON - Wines ☆ - Parliament Import Co.
BEAUCHAMP PLACE - Wallpaper - Ashford House
BEAUCLAIR - Skin care products - Goddess Co.
BEAUFLAIRE - Floor coverings - Mannington Resilient Floors
BEAUFOR - Mustard - De Choix Specialty Foods Co.
BEAUFORT - Dishes–china - Royal China & Porcelain Companies Inc.
BEAUFORT - Furniture ☆ - Lane Co. Inc.
BEAUFORT - Rings–jewelry - Artcarved Inc.
BEAUFORT ISLAND - Furniture ☆ - Lane Co. Inc.
BEAUGENCY - Glassware–household - Durand International
BEAUGNIER - Saxophones - Fred Gretsch Enterprises
BEAUJE - Hairpins - Dcnl, Inc.
BEAUJOLAIS - Furniture ☆ - Stanley Furniture Co. Inc.
BEAUJOLAIS VILLAGE - Wines - Kedem Royal Wine Corp.
BEAULASTIQUE - Corsets - Bonwit Teller & Co.
BEAULIEU - Glassware–household - Durand International
BEAULIEU - Wines - Beaulieu Vineyard
BEAULIEU VINEYARD - Wines - IDV Wines (Beaulieu Vineyard)
BEAULITE - Sporting goods ☆ - Shakespeare Fishing Tackle
BEAUMONT - Clocks - Ridgeway Clock Co.
BEAUMONT - Coffee - Aldi Inc.

BEAUMONT - Furniture - Weiman Co.
BEAUMONT - Wallpaper ☆ - J.M. Lynne Co. Inc.
BEAUMONT BRICK - Floor coverings ☆ - Azrock Commercial Flooring
BEAUMONT III - Wallpaper ☆ - J.M. Lynne Co. Inc.
BEAUPRE - Floor coverings–carpet and rugs ☆ - Evans-Black Carpet Mills
BEAUS ART - Playing cards ☆ - United States Playing Card Co.
BEAUS 'N BELLES - Toys–stuffed - Dakin Inc.
BEAUSHARD - Floor coverings–tile - Kentile Floors Inc.
BEAUT' BOOTS - Footwear - Inter-American Sheepskins, Inc.
BEAUT 'E' CREAM - Vitamin E cream - American Hygienic Laboratories Inc.
BEAUTE - Cosmetics - Demert & Dougherty, Inc.
BEAUTE - Crocheted and knitted items - Hoffman Mills Inc.
BEAUTE - Floor coverings–carpet and rugs - Karastan-Bigelow Inc.
BEAUTE - Wallpaper - Carlton-Metro Wallcoverings
BEAUTE BENETTON - Costumes - Benetton
BEAUTE EXTRA - Cosmetics - Demert & Dougherty, Inc.
BEAUTE LIFT - Skin care products - Helen of St. Moritz
BEAUTEE - Cosmetics - Beautee Sense Inc.
BEAUTEE HAIR BRUSHES - Hair care products - Beautee Sense Inc.
BEAUTEE LASH - Cosmetics - Beautee Sense Inc.
BEAUTEE LOOFAH PRODUCTS - Skin care products - Beautee Sense Inc.
BEAUTEE SENSE - Cosmetics - Beautee Sense Inc.
BEAUTI-BATH - Bath salts - Ray Drug Co.
BEAUTI-BLEND - Fabrics–linen - West Point-Pepperell Inc.
BEAUTI-FI - Cleaning preparations - Herbert Stanley Co.
BEAUTI-FULL BY KIKI - Underwear and nightwear ☆ - Kiki International
BEAUTI-GLIDE - Furniture–metal - Seymour Housewares Corp.
BEAUTI-GLO - Rings–jewelry - Feature Enterprises
BEAUTI-LITE - Eyeglasses - Art-Craft Optical Co.
BEAUTI-MOULD - Wood products - Visador Co.
BEAUTI-NAIL - Nail care products - Magna Inc.
BEAUTI PLEAT - Drapery hardware - Beauti Pleat Hardware Inc.
BEAUTI-SLIM - Pharmaceutical preparations - Ray Drug Co.
BEAUTI-VUE - Window coverings - Beauti-Vue Products Corp.
BEAUTIATOR - Manicure preparations - ABAR Beauty Supply Inc.
BEAUTICALE - Fabrics–linen ☆ - West Point-Pepperell Inc.
BEAUTICIANS FORMULA - Skin care products - Monaco Import/Export Inc.
BEAUTICONTROL - Cosmetics - BC International Cosmetics & Image Services, Inc.
BEAUTIDEAL - Window coverings - Steven Fabrics Co.
BEAUTIES - Candy - Square Shooter Candy Co.
BEAUTIFAIR - Cosmetics - Ray Drug Co.
BEAUTIFLEX - Housewares - Dial Industries Inc.
BEAUTIFLOR - Cleaning preparations–carpet and rug - S.C. Johnson & Son, Inc.
BEAUTIFUL - Floor coverings–carpet and rugs ☆ - World Carpets, Inc.
BEAUTIFUL - Frames–eyeglass ☆ - Universal/Univis Inc.
BEAUTIFUL - Perfumes - Estee Lauder Inc.
BEAUTIFUL AMERICA - Calendars ☆ - Sormani Inc.
BEAUTIFUL BAGELS - Bagels ☆ - Natural Nectar Corp.
BEAUTIFUL BALANCE - Hair care products - Helene Curtis Industries Inc.
BEAUTIFUL BALI - Apparel–women's - Bali Co. Inc.
BEAUTIFUL BATH - Skin care products - Freeman Cosmetics Corp.
BEAUTIFUL BATHS - Faucets - Sepco-Industries Inc.
BEAUTIFUL BEADS! - Hobby kits - Hasbro, Inc.
BEAUTIFUL BEAUTIFUL WOMEN - Computer storage devices–optical - Marin Media Works, Inc.
BEAUTIFUL BEGINNING - Apparel–women's - Wacoal America Inc.
BEAUTIFUL BEGINNINGS - Hair care products - Carson Products Co.
BEAUTIFUL BEGINNINGS - Jewelry - Sandberg & Sikorski Diamond Corp.
BEAUTIFUL BERGAMOT - Hair care products - House of Excellence
BEAUTIFUL BLONDES - Hair coloring preparations - Clairol Inc.
BEAUTIFUL BODY - Hair care products - Helene Curtis Industries Inc.
BEAUTIFUL BOTTOMS COLLECTION - Apparel–women's - Miracle Max, Inc.
BEAUTIFUL BRIDES BY BRADLEY - Dolls ☆ - Bradley Import Co.
BEAUTIFUL BRIGHTS - Hair coloring preparations - Clairol Inc.
BEAUTIFUL BROWN LEGS - Hosiery - Noe-Equal Hosiery Corp.
BEAUTIFUL BROWNS - Hair coloring preparations - Clairol Inc.
BEAUTIFUL BRYANS - Footwear - Beautiful Bryans Inc.
BEAUTIFUL COLLECTION - Cosmetics - Bristol-Myers Squibb Co.
BEAUTIFUL COLLECTION - Hair coloring preparations - Clairol Inc.
BEAUTIFUL COLORS NAIL POLISH - Nail care products - RTS Laboratories, Inc.
BEAUTIFUL DREAMER - Aquarium accessories ☆ - Cole Enterprises
BEAUTIFUL EYES - Frames–eyeglass ☆ - Universal/Univis Inc.
BEAUTIFUL FEET - Skin care products - Beautiful Feet

BEAUTIFUL FOOD - Food products - Beautiful Food
BEAUTIFUL HAIR ARIEL - Dolls - Walt Disney Co.
BEAUTIFUL HOMES - Floor coverings–carpet and rugs - Mohawk Carpet Corp.
BEAUTIFUL IMAGES - Foundation garments–women's - Beautiful Images, Inc.
BEAUTIFUL IRELAND - Calendars ☆ - Sormani Inc.
BEAUTIFUL LADY - Cosmetics - Maynard Inc.
BEAUTIFUL LADY - Eyeglasses - Art-Craft Optical Co.
BEAUTIFUL MAGIC HAIR GRO - Hair care products - Evangeline Williams
BEAUTIFUL MOODS - Greeting cards ☆ - Regency Thermographers Inc.
BEAUTIFUL MOONSTONE - Wallpaper - Seabrook Wallcoverings, Inc.
BEAUTIFUL NAILS - Nail care products - Nu-Nails
BEAUTIFUL NATURALS - Cosmetics - Victoria Jackson Cosmetics, Inc.
BEAUTIFUL ONES - Apparel and accessories - Playtex Apparel, Inc.
BEAUTIFUL OREGON PUBLICATIONS INCORPORATED - Publisher's imprints - Beautiful America Publishing Co.
BEAUTIFUL PEOPLE - Frames–eyeglass ☆ - Universal/Univis Inc.
BEAUTIFUL PLANTS BRAND - Fertilizers - Beautiful Plants Brand
BEAUTIFUL REDS - Hair coloring preparations - Clairol Inc.
BEAUTIFUL REFLECTIONS - Mirror with makeup palettes ☆ - Cosrich Inc.
BEAUTIFUL ROOM - Wallpaper - Bon-Ton Wallcoverings Inc.
BEAUTIFUL ROSE, THE - Frames–picture - Amlings Flowerland
BEAUTIFUL SHAPES - Brassieres (Bras) - Sara Lee Corp.
BEAUTIFUL SKIN - Skin care products - Freeman Cosmetics Corp.
BEAUTIFUL SUPPORT - Apparel and accessories - Playtex Apparel, Inc.
BEAUTIFUL THIGHS - Skin care products - Cosmania, Inc.
BEAUTIFUL THOUGHTS - Cosmetics - Revlon Consumer Products Corp.
BEAUTIFUL THOUGHTS - Stationery - Sangamon Co.
BEAUTIFUL TOUCH - Skin care products ☆ - Honey & Spice Toiletries
BEAUTIFUL VISIONS - Carpeting - Shaw Industries Inc.
BEAUTIFUL WEST PUBLISHING CO. - Publisher's imprints - Beautiful America Publishing Co.
BEAUTIFUL WORLD BY JEAN B. - Wallpaper ☆ - James Seeman Studios
BEAUTIFUL YOUNG THING - Hair care products - Helene Curtis Industries Inc.
BEAUTIFULLY BASIC - Fabrics–tapestry ☆ - Columbus Coated Fabrics Co.
BEAUTIFULLY BERKSHIRE - Hosiery - Mayer/Berkshire Corp.
BEAUTIFULLY EASY - Hair care products ☆ - Avon Products, Inc.
BEAUTIFULLY TOUGH - Paints - Cotter & Co.
BEAUTIFYING BODY - Cosmetics - Sothys USA Inc.
BEAUTIFYING CLEANSER - Lipsticks - Revlon Consumer Products Corp.
BEAUTIHOME - Paper - Millen Industries Inc.
BEAUTILITY SEAT - Bathroom accessories - Tub-Master Corp.
BEAUTIPATCH - Pharmaceutical preparations - Transdermal Products, Inc.
BEAUTIQUE - Apparel and accessories - Trina/Genie
BEAUTIQUE - Cosmetics - Sally Beauty Co., Inc.
BEAUTIQUE - Floor coverings–carpet and rugs ☆ - Customweave Carpets Inc.
BEAUTIQUE - Wood-panel cleaner - Contact Industries Inc.
BEAUTIWALL - Wallpaper - Queens Decorative Wallcoverings Inc.
BEAUTIWALL TEXTURES - Wallpaper - Queens Decorative Wallcoverings Inc.
BEAUTOUR - Wines - IDV Wines (Beaulieu Vineyard)
BEAUTY - Cleaning preparations - Erbrich Products Co. Inc.
BEAUTY - Dishes–earthenware ☆ - Denby USA Limited
BEAUTY - Floor coverings–carpet and rugs - Barrett Carpet Mills Inc.
BEAUTY - Frames–eyeglass ☆ - Universal/Univis Inc.
BEAUTY - Gloves - George Glove Co. Inc.
BEAUTY - Hair care products - Norjac Manufacturing Corp.
BEAUTY - Hams - Fresh Mark, Inc.
BEAUTY - Handles–wood - Turner, Day and Woolworth Handle Corp.
BEAUTY - Health care products ☆ - ETAC USA Inc.
BEAUTY - Health care products ☆ - Carolina Absorbent Cotton
BEAUTY - Paper–gift wrap ☆ - Cleo Inc.
BEAUTY - Spices and extracts - Herbert Marmorek & Son, Inc.
BEAUTY - Toys ☆ - Hedstrom Corp.
BEAUTY AID - Dryers–hair - Helene Curtis Industries Inc.
BEAUTY AIDS - Cosmetics - Beauty Aids Inc.
BEAUTY AM/BEAUTY PM - Vitamins and nutritional supplements - Hall Laboratories, Inc.
BEAUTY & THE BEAST - Computer software - Orange Cherry Software
BEAUTY AND THE BEAST - Footwear - Pagoda Trading Co.
BEAUTY AND THE BEAST - Games - Milton Bradley Co.
BEAUTY & THE BEAST - Paper dolls, sewing cards - Coloron Industries
BEAUTY-ART - Napkins–paper - Erving Paper Products Inc.
BEAUTY BACKS - Apparel–women's - Milady Brassiere & Corset Co., Inc.

☆ = Now out of production

BEAUTY BANQUET - Cosmetics - Wendy Marsten Martin
BEAUTY BASICS - Cosmetics - Shaklee Corp.
BEAUTY BASICS - Skin care products - Spilo/Mehaz Worldwide
BEAUTY BASKET - Flowers–artificial ☆ - Reliance Trading Corp. of America
BEAUTY BATH - Dolls - Mattel, Inc.
BEAUTY BELLS - Exercising equipment - California Gym Equipment
BEAUTY BEYOND BELIEF WILDFLOWER SEED - Flowers, plants, and seeds - Eversoll Enterprises, Inc.
BEAUTY BLACK - Pet products ☆ - Gerard-Pellham Co.
BEAUTY BLENDERS - Cosmetics - Karlen Manufacturing, Inc.
BEAUTY BLITZ - Bags–cosmetic - Paris Presents Ltd.
BEAUTY BLOCK - Skin care products - Norstar Consumer Products Co., Inc.
BEAUTY BORDER - Mattresses - Simmons USA
BEAUTY BOUQUET - CABBAGE PATCH pin with cologne and lipstick ☆ - Cosrich Inc.
BEAUTY BOUQUET - Underwear and nightwear ☆ - Lovable Co.
BEAUTY BOX - Skin care products - Excelcis
BEAUTY BREEZE - Dryers–hair ☆ - Sunbeam-Oster Household Products
BEAUTY-BRITE - Christmas tree lights - General Enterprises Inc.
BEAUTY BROWN - Pet products ☆ - Gerard-Pellham Co.
BEAUTY BUFFS - Skin care products - Karlen Manufacturing, Inc.
BEAUTY BUILDERS - Lipsticks - Honey & Spice Toiletries
BEAUTY BUTTERFLY - Cosmetic set ☆ - Cosrich Inc.
BEAUTY BY ME - Manicure preparations - MJE & Associates Inc.
BEAUTY CENTER - Dolls - Mattel, Inc.
BEAUTY CITY - Dolls - Mattel, Inc.
BEAUTY CLASSICS - Skin care products - Garcoa Labs/Vitamin Classics
BEAUTY COAT - Pet products ☆ - Gerard-Pellham Co.
BEAUTY CONNECTION, THE - Apparel–women's - Normandy Manufacturing Co. Inc.
BEAUTY CORSAGE CONTAINER - Plastic bags - Highland Supply Corp.
BEAUTY-CRAFT - Eyeglasses - Art-Craft Optical Co.
BEAUTY CRYSTAL - Seasonings - Woo Jung Natural Food Co., Ltd.
BEAUTY CURL - Curling irons–electric ☆ - Dazey Corp.
BEAUTY CURL - Curling irons–electric ☆ - Standard Products Corp.
BEAUTY ESSENTIALS - Cosmetics - Perfectly Beautiful, Inc.
BEAUTY FARM - Shampoos - King Research, Inc.
BEAUTY FLAME - Lighters - Butane Products Corp.
BEAUTY FLEX - Housewares ☆ - All Power Manufacturing Co.
BEAUTY-FLO - Floor coverings ☆ - Diasyde Corp.
BEAUTY FLO - Paints ☆ - DecoArt, Inc.
BEAUTY FOLD - Musical instrument accessories - Humes & Berg Manufacturing Co. Inc.
BEAUTY FOLD - Tables–metal ☆ - All-Luminum Products Inc.
BEAUTY-FORM - Shutters–metal ☆ - Lomanco Inc.
BEAUTY FORM - Underwear and nightwear - Valu-Plus, Inc.
BEAUTY FOURSOME - Shower cap and personal-care product ☆ - Cosrich Inc.
BEAUTY FROM THE CHEMISTRY OF NATURE - Skin care products - Nonie of Beverly Hills, Inc.
BEAUTY FROM THE SEA - Skin care products - Sarkli-Repechage, Ltd.
BEAUTY FROM WITHIN - Skin care products ☆ - Scandinavian Natural Health & Beauty Products, Inc.
BEAUTY GARD - Coatings - Uniroyal Technology Corp.
BEAUTY GARD - Hair coloring preparations - Graham Medical Products
BEAUTY GIFT - Cosmetics - Darling Corp.
BEAUTY GRASS - Foil–aluminum - Highland Supply Corp.
BEAUTY GUARD - Furniture - American Woodmark Corp.
BEAUTY GUILD - Hair care products ☆ - Beauty Guild Inc.
BEAUTY IN A BAG - Cosmetics - Kris Evans
BEAUTY IN ACTION - Ophthalmic goods - Embassy Creations Inc.
BEAUTY IN GARBAGE - Trays - P.T.M. Interiors Unlimited Designs, Inc.
BEAUTY LATHER - Shampoos ☆ - Stanley Fay Co.
BEAUTY-LIGHT - Lighting fixtures–underwater - Aquarium Products Inc.
BEAUTY LIGHTS - Cosmetics - Clairol Inc.
BEAUTY LIGHTS - Cosmetics - Viviane Woodard Industries, Ltd.
BEAUTY-LINE - Awnings ☆ - Andersen Corp.
BEAUTY-LOK - Hardware - Sherwin-Williams Automotive Finishes Corp.
BEAUTY LUSTRE - Cosmetics ☆ - Avon Products, Inc.
BEAUTY MARK - Hair care products - Spilo/Mehaz Worldwide
BEAUTY MARKS - Jewelry ☆ - Towle Silversmiths
BEAUTY NAILS - Manicure preparations - SRA Industries Inc.
BEAUTY NECTAR - Cosmetics - Caswell-Massey Co. Ltd.
BEAUTY NITE - Skin care products - Excelcis
BEAUTY OF CALIFORNIA SLIM, THE - Vitamins and nutritional supplements - California Slim Inc.

BEAUTY OF COMFORT, THE - Underwear and nightwear - Vanity Fair, Inc.
BEAUTY OF GOLD - Wigs - Baek, in Taek
BEAUTY ON THE BEACH - Suntan lotions ☆ - Carter-Wallace, Inc.
BEAUTY ON THE MOVE - Ophthalmic goods - Embassy Creations Inc.
BEAUTY PAGENT - Dolls - Mattel, Inc.
BEAUTY PART - Wigs - Helene Curtis Industries Inc.
BEAUTY PARTNERS - Lip gloss and nail polish ☆ - Cosrich Inc.
BEAUTY PLUS - Underwear and nightwear ☆ - Lovable Co.
BEAUTY PLUS GOLD K - Wigs - Beauty Plus Trading Co., Inc.
BEAUTY POINT SYSTEM, THE - Cosmetics - Kerstin Skin Care
BEAUTY PUFFS - Cosmetics - Karlen Manufacturing, Inc.
BEAUTY QUEEN - Cabinets–metal ☆ - Triangle Pacific Corp. (Cabinet Division)
BEAUTY QUEEN - Underwear and nightwear ☆ - Lovable Co.
BEAUTY RAVISH - Perfumes - Proverbial Inc.
BEAUTY RECOVERY PRINCIPLES - Skin care products - Shaklee Corp.
BEAUTY REST - Frames–eyeglass - Zylo Ware Corp.
BEAUTY RITUALS - Skin care products - Cosmyl, Inc.
BEAUTY ROUNDS - Cosmetics - Karlen Manufacturing, Inc.
BEAUTY RUGS - Automotive parts and accessories ☆ - Sta-Put Industries Corp.
BEAUTY-SHAPE - Apparel and accessories - Playtex Apparel, Inc.
BEAUTY SLEEP - Dolls - Mattel, Inc.
BEAUTY SLEEP - Pillows - Simmons USA
BEAUTY SLEEP - Skin care products - Gold Medal Hair Products Inc.
BEAUTY SOLUTIONS - Skin care products - Blair Corp.
BEAUTY SPONGE - Skin care products - Absorbent Cotton Co.
BEAUTY SPOTS - Decals and transfers - Metra Inc.
BEAUTY SQUARES - Mirrors ☆ - Gardner Mirror Corp.
BEAUTY/TECH - Cosmetics - Home Shopping Club, Inc.
BEAUTY TIPS - Nail care products - H.K. Simon Co.
BEAUTY TONE - Lamps - Philips Lighting Co.
BEAUTY TOOLS - Cosmetics - Shaklee Corp.
BEAUTY TOUCH - Cosmetics - Karlen Manufacturing, Inc.
BEAUTY TRENDS - Wigs - Revlon General Wig Manufacturers, Inc.
BEAUTY TUK - Window coverings - Dale's Draperies
BEAUTY U. - Cosmetics - Cosrich Inc.
BEAUTY VIBES - Vibrators ☆ - Jason Natural Products, Inc.
BEAUTY WALL - Mirrors ☆ - Fred Silver and Co. Inc.
BEAUTY-WALL - Wood products ☆ - Bradley Plywood Corp.
BEAUTY WEDGE - Cosmetics - Karlen Manufacturing, Inc.
BEAUTY WHITE - Pet products - Gerard-Pellham Co.
BEAUTY WOOD - Window shades ☆ - C-Mor Co.
BEAUTY WRAP - Paper–gift wrap ☆ - Cleo Inc.
BEAUTY ZONE - Skin care products - Pavion Ltd.
BEAUTYBASKET - Baskets–wood - Reliance Trading Corp. of America
BEAUTYCOLOGY - Skin care products - Beautycology Inc.
BEAUTYCRAFT - Flowers–artificial - Reliance Trading Corp. of America
BEAUTYCREST - Jewelry - SKL Co. Inc.
BEAUTYDRIED - Flowers, plants, and seeds - Reliance Trading Corp. of America
BEAUTYFACTS - Publisher's imprints - U.S. Equities Inc.
BEAUTYLINE - Baskets–wood ☆ - Reliance Trading Corp. of America
BEAUTYMASTER - Cosmetics ☆ - Andis Co.
BEAUTYMIST - Hosiery ☆ - Sara Lee Corp.
BEAUTYREST - Mattresses - Simmons USA
BEAUTYREST FEELINGS - Mattresses - Simmons USA
BEAUTY'S ROSE PETAL - Cosmetics - Fairytale Fragrances, Inc.
BEAUTYSCOPE - Cabinets - Nutone Inc.
BEAUTYSILK - Flowers–artificial - Reliance Trading Corp. of America
BEAUTYSMART - Hair coloring preparations - Beaurline Co., Inc.
BEAUTYSTONE - Pumice - Glass Mtn. Pumice Inc.
BEAUTYTRIM - Hardware - Trendlines Inc.
BEAUTYWOOD - Varnishes - Dean and Barry Co.
BEAUVELLE - Floor coverings–carpet and rugs ☆ - Eligere Carpets
BEAUVEX - Perfumes and colognes - Parfums Givenchy, Inc.
BEAUVIGNOT - Wines - Beauvignot International Inc.
BEAUVIGNY - Building materials–concrete - Walker & Zanger (West Coast), Ltd.
BEAUVILLE - Tablecloths - Necessities
BEAUVOORDE - Cheese - Swissrose International Inc.
BEAUX ART - Accordions, guitars, brass, woodwinds - Atlas Accordions Inc.
BEAUX ART - Greeting cards ☆ - Papercraft Corp.
BEAUX ARTS - See **DECOR ELEGANCE**
BEAUX ARTS - Artists' materials - M. Grumbacher Inc.
BEAUX ARTS - Floor coverings–tile ☆ - Kentile Floors Inc.

BEAUX ARTS - Paints ☆ - Tara Materials Inc.
BEAUX ARTS COLLECTION - Lighting fixtures - Fredrick Ramond Inc.
BEAUX ARTS DU MONDE - Statuary - Fabulous Forgeries Ltd.
BEAUX FINESSE - Artists' materials ☆ - M. Grumbacher Inc.
BEAUX FRERES - Wines - Beaux Freres
BEAUX REVES - Apparel and accessories - Kellwood Co.
BEAUX TIE - Frames—eyeglass - Zylo Ware Corp.
BEAUX VILLAGES - Cheese ☆ - Swissrose International Inc.
BEAUX-WRAPS - Paper—gift wrap - Canover Industries Inc.
BEAUXARTS - Publisher's imprints - Alan Wofsy Fine Arts
BEAVE - Toys—stuffed - Dakin Inc.
BEAVER - Adding machines ☆ - Kanematsu USA Inc. (High-Tech Div.)
BEAVER - Bicycles - Ross Bicycles USA, Ltd.
BEAVER - Brushes—paint - Allpro Corp.
BEAVER - Cleaning preparations - Beaver Research Co.
BEAVER - Generators—electric - Clarke Mosquito Equipment, Inc.
BEAVER - Hardware - Beaver Industries
BEAVER - Lubricants - M. Spiegel & Sons Oil Corp.
BEAVER - Recreational vehicle dealers - Beaver Camper Co.
BEAVER - Rope - Samson Cordage Works
BEAVER - Sauces - Beaverton Foods
BEAVER - Towels ☆ - Durafab Inc.
BEAVER - Toys - Tyco Toys
BEAVER BALLS - Archery equipment - Mountain Man Furs
BEAVER BRAND - Pet products - Hill Top Enterprises
BEAVER COACH - Motor vehicles - Beaver Coaches Inc.
BEAVER CREEK - Furniture - Pilliod Co.
BEAVER FALLS - Meat products—beef - Hatfield, Inc.
BEAVER FREEZE POPS - Confections - Leader Candies Inc.
BEAVER KING - Vegetables—dried - Classe Onions, Inc.
BEAVER PRODUCTIONS - Bags - Beaver Productions, Inc.
BEAVER-SEAL - Adhesives and sealants - Beaver Industries
BEAVER SEAL - Roofing materials - Pinnell, Inc.
BEAVER VALLEY - Skis - Collins Ski Products Inc.
BEAVERITE - Binders - Beaverite Products Inc.
BEAVERPRINTS - Paper - Beaverprints, Inc.
BEAVIS AND BUTT-HEAD - Recording label - Viacom International Inc.
BEBAX - Shoes - Camp, Inc.
BEBE - Cosmetics - Cosmair Inc.
BEBE - Negligees - Bebe Girdle Corp.
BEBE - Water—bottled or canned - Bebe, Inc.
BEBE BY CRADLECRAFT - Apparel and accessories - Federated Department Stores, Inc.
BEBE DENISE - Dolls ☆ - Effanbee Doll Corp.
BEBE GENEVIEVE - Dolls ☆ - Effanbee Doll Corp.
BEBE MARIANNE - Dolls ☆ - Effanbee Doll Corp.
BEBE NANNETTE - Dolls ☆ - Effanbee Doll Corp.
BEBE SAN FRANCISCO - Apparel and accessories - Bebe, Inc.
BEBE SOUNDS - Medical apparatus - Unisar, Inc.
BEBE XOXO - Toys - Xoxo International, Inc.
BEBE'S ORIGINALS - Socks - Bebbian F. Wilson
BEBON - Yarn ☆ - Dixie Yarns, Inc.
BEBOP - Bicycles - Bebop Inc.
BEBOP - Toys - Playmates World Wide Inc.
BEC COLOR MOMENT - Hair coloring preparations - King Research, Inc.
BECAUSE - Apparel and accessories - Michael A. Paulsen
BECAUSE - Pharmaceutical preparations - Schering-Plough Healthcare Products
BECAUSE CHILDREN LEARN BY DOING - Educational materials - Delta Education, Inc.
BECAUSE EMERGENCIES DO HAPPEN - First aid kits - Top Safety Products Co. Inc.
BECAUSE EVERYTHING'S RELEVANT - Computers - Compuzone, Inc.
BECAUSE I CARE - Greeting cards - Paramount Cards Inc.
BECAUSE IT'S YOUR STUFF - Computer peripheral equipment - Iomega Corp.
BECAUSE NATURE WORKS AT A CELLULAR LEVEL - Building materials—concrete - Presto Products Co.
BECAUSE OF YOU - Greeting cards - American Greetings Corp.
BECAUSE THE WORLD IS NOT FLAT - Computer software - Forte' Advanced Management Software, Inc.
BECAUSE TIME FLIES, INC. - Calendars - Because Time Flies, Inc.
BECAUSE WE'RE ALL NAKED UNDER OUR CLOTHES - Apparel and accessories - Boing Clothing
BECAUSE WINNING IS EVERYTHING - Vitamins and nutritional supplements - Caroline Owens

BECAUSE YOU CAN - Paper products - Area Code Where? Ltd.
BECAUSE YOUR SKIN NEEDS TO LAST A LIFETIME - Skin-care products - Benchmark Enterprises
BECCA - Nail care products - Spilo/Mehaz Worldwide
BECCO - Candy - H. Hamstra & Co.
BECCON - Cooking utensils—aluminum ☆ - Holland-American Importing Co. Inc.
BECEEVITES - Health care products - Halsey Drug Co. Inc.
BECHAMEL - Handbags - Dillard Department Stores Inc.
BECHARAS - Coffee - Becharas Coffee Co.
BECHER - Beverages—alcohol - Stanley Stawski Distributing Co.
BECH'S CLASSIC SHARP - Mustard - J.N. Bech, Ltd.
BECHTENE - Pharmaceutical preparations - Alva-Amco Pharmacal Co.
BECHTLE - Noodles - Haram-Christensen Corp.
BECK - Recording label - Beck Records
BECK/ARNLEY WORLD PARTS - Automotive parts and accessories - Echlin Inc.
BECK-TOP47 - Cement - Edison Coatings, Inc.
BECKER - Automotive parts and accessories - Becker of North America, Inc.
BECKER - Food products - Becker Food Co. Inc.
BECKER - Musical instruments - Kaman Music Corp.
BECKER - Office supplies ☆ - Hampton-Haddon Marketing
BECKER - Radios - Walter Odemer Co. Inc.
BECKER - Xylophones - Marimba Productions Inc.
BECKER GROVES - Fruits and vegetables - Becker Holding Corp.
BECKETT - Computer software - Beckett Publications, Inc.
BECKETT - Furniture ☆ - Athens Furniture Industries Inc.
BECKETT EXPRESSION - Stationery - International Paper Co.
BECKHAM - Clocks - Ridgeway Clock Co.
BECKLEY - Shoes ☆ - Allen-Edmonds Shoe Corp.
BECKMAN PLACE - Floor coverings—carpet and rugs - Queen Carpet Corp.
BECKMAN PLACE - Floor coverings—carpet and rugs ☆ - Eligere Carpets
BECKMANS - Food products - Beckman and Gast Co. Inc.
BECKMAN'S - Skin care products - Therapon Inc.
BECK'S - Beverages—malt - Beck's North America
BECK'S - Beverages—malt - Dribeck Importers, Inc.
BECKS & NESSI - Clothing - Steven Ross, Inc.
BECK'S DARK - Beverages—malt - Beck's North America
BECK'S FOR OKTOBERFEST - Beverages—malt - Beck's North America
BECK'S LIGHT - Beverages—malt ☆ - Dribeck Importers, Inc.
BECKSON - Nautical instruments - Beckson Marine Inc.
BECKSTOFFER RANCH - Wines - Stag's Leap Wine Cellars
BECKY - Apparel—children's - Elder Manufacturing Co., Inc.
BECKY - Dolls - Mattel, Inc.
BECKY BEAVER - Dolls - Mattel, Inc.
BECKY LITTLE & COMPANY - Children's clothing - Roanna Togs, Inc.
BECKY STERMEN COLLECTION - Novelty items - Rennoc Corp.
BECKY SUMMERS - Patterns—clothing - McCarn Enterprises Inc.
BECKY THATCHER - Apparel—children's - Elder Manufacturing Co., Inc.
BECKY THATCHER - Dolls ☆ - Effanbee Doll Corp.
BECKY, THE - Aerobic footwear - Autry Industries Inc.
BECKYLEE - Greeting cards ☆ - Lee Frey Enterprises
BECKY'S - Figurines ☆ - Gallo Pewter Sculptures Corp.
BECLOVENT - Lubricants - Glaxo Wellcome Inc.
BECO - Automotive parts and accessories ☆ - Beckett Corp.
BECOCOM - Construction equipment rental services - Beckwith Electric Co.
BECOMING - Rings—jewelry - Artcarved Inc.
BECOMING A LOVE AND LOGIC PARENT - Recording label - Cline-Fay Institute, Inc.
BECOMING A TOTAL PERSON - Recording label - Rutherford Publishing, Inc.
BECOMJECT/100 - Pharmaceutical preparations ☆ - Merz Inc.
BECOMP-C - Pharmaceutical preparations - H.R. Cenci Laboratories Inc.
BECOOL - Chemical preparations - Brush Wellman, Inc.
BECOPLOT - Construction equipment rental services - Beckwith Electric Co.
BECORA - Watches - Ballandra Corp.
BECOTIN - Pharmaceutical preparations ☆ - Dista Products Co.
BECTON DICKINSON - Medical apparatus - Becton, Dickinson and Co.
BECUZ BEARS - Greeting cards - Vivian Greene Inc.
BED-A-WAY - Beds—wood - Kentucky Woodcrafts Co. Inc.
BED-ALL - Chemical preparations - Chem-Pak Inc.
BED & BATH - Fabrics—tapestry ☆ - Columbus Coated Fabrics Co.
BED & BATH - Wallpaper - Kingfisher Wallcoverings
BED AND BATH BOOK, THE - Wallpaper ☆ - Kingfisher Wallcoverings
BED & BOARD - Furniture - Universal Flooring
BED AND BREAKFAST - Garden furniture - Forest Time Products Inc.
BED AND BREAKFAST - Housewares - Barth-Dreyfuss of California

☆ = Now out of production

BED & BREAKFAST BOARDING PASS - Invitations - Wry Idea Co.
BED & BREAKFAST INN - Wallpaper ☆ - Imperial Wallcoverings, Inc.
BED-BAR - Health care products - Brown Engineering Co., Ltd.
BED BATH & BEYOND - Linens, housewares, and home furnishings - Bed Bath & Beyond Inc.
BED, BATH, & BREAKFAST - Wallpaper - United Wallcoverings
B.E.D. BIG EASY DREAMS - Apparel and accessories - Bentley Lingerie, Inc.
BED BUDDIES - Pet products - Pet Food Warehouse, Inc.
BED BUDDY - Heating pads—electric - Lisa Capprelli Wagner
BED BUGS - Candy ☆ - Fleer Corp.
BED BUGS - Games - Milton Bradley Co.
BED CONTROL - Medical apparatus - APT Technology, Inc.
BED ESSENTIALS - Draperies - Crown Crafts, Inc.
BED FELLOWS - Beds—wood ☆ - Landes Manufacturing Co.
BED IN A BAG - Bedding—linen - Dan River Inc.
BED-JACKET - Bedding—linen - Perfect Fit Industries, Inc.
BED 'N BUBBLES - Dolls - Mattel, Inc.
BED-O'COBS - Pet products - Andersons Management Corp.
BED OF ROSES - Wallpaper - Imperial Wallcoverings, Inc.
BED POK-IT - Housewares ☆ - Blue Ridge International Products Co., Inc.
BED RAT - Industrial machinery - Knaack Manufacturing Co.
BED RIZER, THE - Housewares - A-1 Manufacturing Corp.
BED RUG - Truck beds - Wise Industries Inc.
BED SAVER - Mattress pads - Morning Glory Products
BED, THE - Pet products - Kalico Enterprises
BED TRENDS - Bedding—linen - Springs Industries, Inc.
BED TUB - Medical apparatus - Lotus Health Care Products/Connecticut Art Craft
BED WRAP - Bedding—linen - Perfect Fit Industries, Inc.
BED&BODY WARMER - Heating pads—electric - Auntiea's, Inc.
BEDAZZLE - Nail care products - SRA Industries Inc.
BEDAZZLE - Ophthalmic goods - Foremost Optical Products
BEDAZZLED - Bicycles - Dynacraft Industries Inc.
BEDAZZLED - Floor coverings—carpet and rugs ☆ - Mohawk Carpet Corp.
BEDAZZLER - Toys - Natural Science Industries, Ltd.
BEDBASE, THE - Furniture - Leggett & Platt/Hartex
BEDDAR WITH CHEDDAR - Sausages - Johnsonville Foods Co.
BEDDERREST - Mattresses - Valwhat Enterprises Inc.
BEDDIE BUDDIES - Toys - Azrak-Hamway International, Inc.
BEDDY BY - Tea - Boston Tea Co.
BEDDY-BYE BUNNIES - Toys—stuffed ☆ - Fun World Inc.
BEDDYBYE BEAR - Greeting cards - Vivian Greene Inc.
BEDE PRODUCTIONS - Publisher's imprints - Stemmer House Publishers Inc.
BEDE VENT - Ventilation equipment ☆ - Oatey Co.
BEDFORD - Bathroom fixtures - Crane Plumbing/Fiat Products
BEDFORD - Boats—motor ☆ - Holiday Distributing Co.
BEDFORD - Cabinets - American Woodmark Corp.
BEDFORD - Cabinets—wood ☆ - Kemper
BEDFORD - Candlesticks ☆ - Anchor Hocking Glass, Inc.
BEDFORD - Eyeglasses - Art-Craft Optical Co.
BEDFORD - Fireplace equipment - Design Specialties Inc.
BEDFORD - Floor coverings - Congoleum Corp.
BEDFORD - Floor coverings—carpet and rugs ☆ - Patrick Carpet Mills
BEDFORD - Flowers, plants, and seeds - Jonathan Green, Inc.
BEDFORD - Frames—picture - Frank A. Edmunds and Co.
BEDFORD - Furniture ☆ - Mersman Furniture Co.
BEDFORD - Furniture ☆ - Universal Flooring
BEDFORD - Furniture—children's ☆ - Child Craft Industries Inc.
BEDFORD - Kitchen, vanity, and bathroom cabinets - IXL Furniture Co. Inc.
BEDFORD - Lighting fixtures - Liteway
BEDFORD - Occasional tables - JDI Group, Inc.
BEDFORD - Paint sprayers - Bedford Precision Parts Corp.
BEDFORD - Tuxedos ☆ - After Six Inc.
BEDFORD BRITCHES - Men's and boy's apparel - Palm Beach Co., Inc.
BEDFORD CHEESE - Dairy products - Bedford Cheese, Inc.
BEDFORD HILLS - Floor coverings—carpet and rugs ☆ - Columbus Mills, Inc.
BEDFORD OAK FROST - Cabinets - Del Mar Cabinets
BEDFORD PARK - Floor coverings—carpet and rugs ☆ - Blue Ridge Carpet Mills
BEDFORD PLACE - Handbags - Mutterperl Group Inc.
BEDFORD PLACE - Handbags ☆ - Contessa Accessories Corp.
BEDFORD PLAID - Floor coverings—carpet and rugs ☆ - Trans-Ocean Import Co. Inc.
BEDFORD TECHNOLOGY - Packaging machines - Bedford Industries, Inc.
BEDFORD VILLAGE - Paneling - Georgia-Pacific Corp.
BEDI - Jewelry - Beck-Dillenius Inc.

BEDKINS - Comforters ☆ - Kellwood Co.
BEDLAM RECORDS - Recording label - Alcazar Productions
BEDLITE HI-LITE - Lamps ☆ - Eagle Electric Manufacturing Co., Inc.
BEDMATE - Mattress pads - Pillowtex Corp.
BEDMATES - Window coverings - Norman's of Salisbury
BEDMINISTER - Floor coverings - Mannington Resilient Floors
BEDMINSTER - Bedding—linen - Dan River Inc.
BEDOUIN - Carpets, now out of production - Couristan Inc.
BEDOUIN - Floor coverings - Aladdin Mills, Inc.
BEDROCK - Chemical preparations - Jevco, Inc.
BEDROCK - Computer software - Symantec Corp.
BEDROCK - Ophthalmic goods - Styl-Rite Optical Manufacturing Co., Inc.
BEDROCK N ROLLIN - Kites - Hi-Flier Manufacturing Co.
BEDROCK PRESS - Publisher's imprints - Turner Publishing, Inc.
BEDROCK SPRAYED LINERS - Motor vehicle parts and accessories - Jevco, Inc.
BEDROOM BABIES - Dolls - San Francisco Necessities
BEDROOM BUNGEE - Novelty items - Julie B. Bandy
BEDROOM BUTLER - Furniture - Tell City Chair Co.
BEDROOM CHOICES - Wallpaper - Studio Designs
BEDROOM EXPRESSIONS - Furniture stores - Big Sur Waterbeds, Inc.
BEDS THAT BRIDGE THE GAP, THE - Mattresses ☆ - California Concepts
BEDSACK - Bedding—linen - Perfect Fit Industries, Inc.
BEDSCAPES - Curtains - Healing Environments International, Inc.
BEDSIDE ASSISTANT - Handles—metal - Bed Handles, Inc.
BEDSIDE BASSINET - Bassinets - Century Products Co.
BEDSIDE-CARE - Skin care products - Sween Corp.
BEDSIDE MANOR - Comforters - Hollander Home Fashions Inc.
BEDSIDE PAL - Toys—stuffed - Happiness Express Inc.
BEDSIDE TENDER - Housewares ☆ - Alger Creations Inc.
BEDSPECS - Eyeglasses - Swift Instruments, Inc.
BEDTIME - Furniture - Romweber Co.
BEDTIME BEAR - Toys - Those Characters from Cleveland, Inc.
BEDTIME BOTTLE BABY - Dolls - Tyco Industries, Inc.
BEDTIME BUDDIES - Bedding—linen - Triboro Quilt Manufacturing Corp.
BEDTIME BUNNIES - Toys—stuffed ☆ - Dolly, Inc.
BEDTIME BUNNY - Candy ☆ - R.M. Palmer Co.
BEDTIME BUNNY - Toys—stuffed - Fun World Inc.
BEDTIME FORMULA - Vitamins and nutritional supplements - Re-Vita Manufacturing Co., Inc.
BEDTIME FUN - Dolls - Mattel, Inc.
BEDTIME KENYA - Dolls - Tyco Industries, Inc.
BEDTIME ORIGINALS - Bedding—linen - Lambs & Ivy
BEDTIME STORAGE - Furniture - Thomasville Furniture Industries Inc.
BEDTIME STORY - Dolls ☆ - Effanbee Doll Corp.
BEDTIME STORY - Frames—picture - Terragrafics Inc.
BEDTIME STORY, A - Wallpaper - Old Stone Mill
BEDTIME TEDDY - Toys—stuffed - Russ Berrie and Co., Inc.
BEDWARMER - Blankets—electric - Sunbeam-Oster Household Products
BEDWARMER WITH A BRAIN - Blankets—electric - Sunbeam Corp.
BEE - Apparel and accessories - Bee Hat Co.
BEE - Candy - Bee International
BEE - Cigarettes - R.J. Reynolds Tobacco Co.
BEE - Fruits and vegetables - Johnston Farms
BEE - Leather goods - Bee Electronics Inc.
BEE - Playing cards - United States Playing Card Co.
BEE - Salt - McCormick & Co., Inc.
BEE A CHAMPION - Vitamins and nutritional supplements - CC Pollen Co.
BEE-ALIVE QUEEN'S - Vitamins and nutritional supplements - Bee-Alive Inc.
BEE & FLOWER - Soap - Darwell Import Co. Inc.
BEE AR SPAR - Varnishes - Blue Ribbon Paint Co.
BEE-BAK - Boomerang - Allied Toy Co.
BEE BALL - Apparel and accessories - Idea 101, Inc.
BEE BALM - Skin care products - Old World Honey
BEE-BOP - Footwear - Orly Shoe Corp.
BEE BOPPER - Insecticides - ARI
BEE COOL - Hats - Bee Hat Co.
BEE EXCELLENT - Honey - Roso Honey, Inc.
BEE-FORTE - Pharmaceutical preparations - Rugby Laboratories Inc.
BEE GEE - Artists' materials ☆ - Artoptic International Corp.
BEE GEE - Seafood products—fresh or frozen - J.F. Clarke Corp.
BEE-GEE - Seafood products—fresh or frozen - Sahlman Seafoods, Inc.
BEE HAPPY - Apparel—children's - Martin Romero
BEE HEALTHY - Apparel—children's - Martin Romero
BEE HIVE - Games - Smethport Specialty Co.
BEE HIVE - Popcorn - National Oats Co. Inc.

BEE HOLDER - Beeswax - Greater Good Co.
BEE HOUSE - Dinnerware, housewares - Bee House Co., Ltd.
BEE KIND - Health care products - Withers Mill
BEE LIGHT - Candles - Bee-Light Candles Corp.
BEE LINE - Golfing equipment - Golfsmith International Inc.
BEE-LINE - Musical instrument accessories - Pro-Mark Corp.
BEE-LINE - Novelty items - Beistle Co.
BEE LINE - Paints - Somay Products Inc.
BEE LINE RECORDS - Recording label - Brentwood Music, Inc.
BEE LINE ROCKY T. - Golfing equipment - Golfsmith International Inc.
BEE LINE RULER - Golfing equipment - Golfsmith International Inc.
BEE NATURALE - Skin care products - Beautymasters
BEE-NIP - Insecticides - Roccorp, Inc.
BEE NO. 92 CLUB STANDARD SPECIAL - Playing cards - United States Playing Card Co.
BEE POLEN FROM ENGLAND - Health care products - Oakmont Investments Co.
BEE POLLEN PLUS - Skin care products ☆ - Palm Beach Beauty Products
BEE POPULARITY - Gloves - Bee Hat Co.
BEE PROPOLIS - Health care products - Above All Health Inc.
BEE-PROPOLIS - Pharmaceutical - IDE-Interstate Inc.
BEE QUEENS - Soap - Tai Wing Hong Importer, Inc.
BEE RIGHTEOUS - Honey - Neshaminy Valley Distributors Ltd.
BEE SAFE - Apparel–children's - Martin Romero
BEE SEAL - Sporting goods - Sierra West
BEE SMART - Veterinary pharmaceutical preparations - Farnam Cos. Inc.
BEE SMART YELLOW OIL - Health care products - Farnam Cos. Inc.
BEE SNACKS - Nuts–candied - Aster Nut Products Co. Inc.
BEE SWEET - Fruits and vegetables - Producer Marketing Corp.
BEE SWEETNER - Tobacco products - S.M. Frank & Co. Inc. (Kaywoodie-Yello-Bole-Medico)
BEE-T-VITES - Pharmaceutical preparations - Rugby Laboratories Inc.
BEE-THI - Pharmaceutical preparations - Physician Sales & Service
BEE-THIN - Pollen extracts - CC Pollen Co.
BEE-TOPS - Veterinary pharmaceutical preparations - Zirin Laboratories International
BEE VICTORIOUS! - Games - Mountain Creek Ranch Prod.
BEE WISE - Cookies ☆ - New Life Bakery Inc.
BEE-YOUNG - Vitamins and nutritional supplements - CC Pollen Co.
BEE-ZEE - Pharmaceutical preparations - Rugby Laboratories Inc.
BEEBE-APPLE - Fruits and vegetables - Wenatchee-Beebe Orchard Co.
BEEBO - Snack foods - Flowers Industries Inc.
BEEBOP! - Snack foods ☆ - Futurebiotics
BEECH AVENUE - Apparel and accessories - Breton Industries
BEECH-NUT - Baby foods - Beech-Nut Nutrition Corp.
BEECH-NUT - Chewing gum - Planters LifeSavers Co.
BEECH-NUT - Coffee - Tetley Inc.
BEECH-NUT - Tobacco products - Lorillard Tobacco Co.
BEECH NUT COFFEE - Coffee - Tetley Inc.
BEECHBROOK - Furniture - Krivaja Beechbrook Corp.
BEECHBROOK - Furniture ☆ - Hooker Furniture Corp.
BEECHIES - Chewing gum - Planters LifeSavers Co.
BEECHJET - Aircraft–airplanes - Beech Aircraft Corp.
BEECHLER - Musical instruments - Remle Musical Products Inc.
BEECHLER BELLITE - Musical instrument accessories - Remle Musical Products Inc.
BEECHLER GOLD - Musical instrument accessories - Remle Musical Products Inc.
BEECHWOOD - Floor coverings–carpet and rugs ☆ - Karastan-Bigelow Inc.
BEECHWOOD - Furniture - Winsome Trading, Inc.
BEECHWOOD - Recording label - Little Giant Records
BEECHWOOD BLEND - Bird feeds - Audubon Society of Western Pennsylvania
BEECHWOOD PUBLICATIONS - Greeting cards - Beechwood Publications
BEECOM-5 - Pharmaceutical preparations ☆ - Pasadena Research Laboratories, Inc.
BEEF-ADELPHIA - Sandwiches–prepackaged - Denny's Inc.
BEEF & BRUNCH - Restaurant chain - Interstate Inns
BEEF & CHICKEN KITTY STARS - Cat food - Mardel Laboratories, Inc.
BEEF & LIVER DOG TREATS - Dog food - Mardel Laboratories, Inc.
BEEF BITES - Pet products - ALPO Petfoods Inc.
BEEF BITES DINNER - Pet products ☆ - ALPO Petfoods Inc.
BEEF BREEDER - Animal feed supplements - Stevens Industries Inc.
BEEF CHIP COOKIES - Dog food - Tapf, Inc.
BEEF CREEP - Animal feeds - Bluebonnet Milling Co.
BEEF DAKOTA - Sandwiches–prepackaged - Southland Corp.

BEEF HIDE - Pet treats - Items Inc.
BEEF INTERNATIONAL - Meat products–beef - Fancy Foods of Virginia Inc.
BEEF JUMP START - Animal feed supplements - Agri-King Inc.
BEEF-LIKE - Food products ☆ - Worthington Foods Inc.
BEEF-LYX - Animal feed supplements - Hubbard Milling Co.
BEEF-MATE - Spices and extracts - David Michael & Co.
BEEF MULTI-FACTORS - Animal feed supplements - Agri-King Inc.
BEEF 'N BEAN - Food products - Lipton Investments, Inc.
BEEF 'N MORE - Dog food - Merrick Petfoods Inc.
BEEF-O-GETTI - Pasta - American Home Food Products Inc.
BEEF PRO - Dog food - Merrick Petfoods Inc.
BEEF REVOLUTION, THE - Meat products - GFI America, Inc.
BEEF RIBSTEER - Food products - Janson's Foods Inc.
BEEF SIZZLERS - Meat products–beef - C.E. Stehouwer Co. Inc.
BEEF SNAPS - Dog food - Tapf, Inc.
BEEF STEW - Meat products–beef - My Own Meals Inc.
BEEF WOOFINGTON - Dog food ☆ - Kal Kan Foods, Inc.
BEEFAMATO - Beverages - Mott's Inc.
BEEFARONI - Food product - American Home Food Products Inc.
BEEFBREAK - Food products - Beatrice Cos. Inc.
BEEFEATER - Beverages–alcohol - Hiram Walker & Sons, Inc.
BEEFEATER - Food products - AMK for Service
BEEFEATER - Gin - Domecq Importers Inc.
BEEFEATERS - Dog food - R.C. Steele Co.
BEEFEATERS - Pet products - Petrapport, Inc.
BEEFEATERS BARBECUE - Beef - Holiday Foods Corp.
BEEFED-UP BARLEY - Soups–canned - Buckeye Beans & Herbs, Inc.
BEEFIES - Food products - Chip Steak Co. of Buffalo
BEEFIT BLANKIT - Tarpaulins - Beefit Services
BEEFNOT! - Meat extracts - Dixie, USA, Inc.
BEEFORCAN - Food products - Beatrice Cos. Inc.
BEEFSTEAK - Bread - Interstate Brands Corp.
BEEFSTEAK - Toys - Mattel, Inc.
BEEFSTEAK CHARLIE'S BURGERS - Meat products–beef - Burger Maker Inc.
BEEFSTEAK PUMPERNICKEL - Bread - Interstate Brands Corp.
BEEFSTEAK ROBUST - Bread - Interstate Brands Corp.
BEEFTON - Health care products ☆ - Cumberland-Swan, Inc.
BEEFY - Apparel - Sara Lee Corp.
BEEFY BABY II SKID STEER - Tires–automobile - Galaxy Tire & Wheel, Inc.
BEEFY BABY CLASSIC SKID STEER - Tires–automobile - Galaxy Tire & Wheel, Inc.
BEEFY BASEBALL - Dog food ☆ - Omega Products Corp.
BEEFY-T - Underwear and nightwear - Sara Lee Corp.
BEEGUM - Recording label - Jazz Composer's Orchestra Association Inc.
BEEHIVE - Glassware–household - Nourot Glass Studio
BEEHIVE BOTANICALS - Food products - Beehive Botanicals Inc.
BEEHIVE PRESS, THE - Publisher's imprints - Beehive Press
BEEKEEPER'S BEST - Honey - Honey Acres Inc.
BEEKEEPERS GARDEN - Wallpaper - Imperial Wallcoverings, Inc.
BEEKMAN - Bicycles - Ross Bicycles USA, Ltd.
BEEKMAN - Frames–eyeglass - Hudson Optical Corp.
BEEKMAN - Hardware - Gordon Associates
BEELINE - Golfing equipment ☆ - Square Two Golf
BEELITH - Pharmaceutical preparations - Beach Pharmaceuticals, Inc.
BEEMAN - Firearms, accessories, and parts - Beeman Precision Airguns
BEEMAN'S - Candy ☆ - American Chicle Co.
BEEMAX - Brass products - Daden Distributing Co.
BEENE BAG - Apparel and accessories ☆ - Bobbie Brooks Inc.
BEENERGIZED - Pharmaceutical preparations - Longevity Pure Medicine
BEENUT BUTTER - Peanut/honey blend - American Natural Foods Inc.
BEEP - Recording label - Jazz Composer's Orchestra Association Inc.
BEEP BEEP THE ROAD RUNNER - Games - Warner Bros. Inc.
BEEP FOR BREAKFAST - Fruit drinks–bottled or canned - Universal Flavor USA
BEEPEN-VK - Antibiotics - Smithkline Beecham Corp.
BEEPER - Navigational instruments ☆ - Ray Jefferson
BEEPER - Toys–stuffed ☆ - Gund, Inc.
BEEPER BUDDY - Leather goods - St. Dennis Accessories, Inc.
BEEPER CONNECTION - Telephones–cellular - Aries Manufacturing, Inc.
BEEPER PAGES, THE - Publisher's imprints - Beeper Pages, Inc.
BEEPER STUFF - Communications equipment–mobile - A.G. Findings & Manufacturing Co.
BEEPERKID - Electronic equipment - Comtrad Industries Inc.
BEEPERKID - Transceivers - A & H International, Inc.
BEEPERS - Apparel–children's - Andover Togs, Inc.

☆ = Now out of production

BEEPERS - Games - Tiger Electronics, Inc.
BEER - Frames—eyeglass - Zylo Ware Corp.
BEER BOTTLE - Sausages - Heid Meat Service & Catering Ltd.
BEER CANS - Apparel and accessories - Sutton Shirt Corp.
BEER CHEST - Beverages—malt ✩ - Pabst Brewing Co.
BEER CITY GRILLERS - Sausages - Johnsonville Foods Co.
BEER GEAR - Housewares - Panache Marketing, Inc.
BEER GOGGLES - Eyeglasses - Laura Ann Bettencourt
BEER-GUARD - Electrical testing instruments - John William Ljepava
BEER IS MY LIFE - Beverages—malt - Summit Brewing Co.
BEER-JOINTS - Meat products—poultry ✩ - Pierce Foods Corp.
BEER KING - Beverage dispensing equipment - Oregon Specialty Co. Inc.
BEER LOVERS TASTING SERIES - Beverages—carbonated - Hops and Barley Beer Corp.
BEER MATS - Housewares - Sonoco-Rixie Coaster Division
BEER 'N BRAT - Horseradish - Silver Spring Gardens Inc.
BEER 'N BRATWURST - Sausages - Johnsonville Foods Co.
BEER NUTS - Nuts—salted, roasted, cooked, or canned - Beer Nuts Inc.
BEER O'CLOCK - Apparel and accessories - Archibald H. Green
BEER-PAL - Plastics - Nucon Corp.
BEER SPIKES - Snack foods - Dolefam Corp.
BEERCOLA - Beverages—malt - A.C.M.
BEERY'S BEASTS - Fabrics - Jana D. Beery
BEES - Shoes ✩ - Beacon Shoe Co.
BEE'S KNEES - Apparel—women's - Nicole Noelani Lee
BEES KNEES - Wallpaper ✩ - Linden Street Gallery
BEESILK - Skin care products - Beequest Inc.
BEESIX - Pharmaceutical preparations ✩ - Forest Pharmaceuticals Inc.
BEESWAX EXPRESS - Candles - 1-800-Candles, Inc.
BEETHOVEN - Floor coverings—carpet and rugs ✩ - Columbus Mills, Inc.
BEETHOVEN - Hearing aids - Magnatone Hearing Aid Corp.
BEETHOVEN - Toys—stuffed - MCA Universal Studios
BEETHOVEN'S 2ND - Publisher's imprints - Universal City Studios, Inc.
BEETLE - Bicycles - Ross Bicycles USA, Ltd.
BEETLE - Motor vehicles—automobiles ✩ - Volkswagen of America Inc.
BEETLE - Thread - New Bedford Thread Co. Inc.
BEETLE BAILEY - Publisher's imprints - Comicana Inc.
BEETLE BONDER - Toys—guns - Saban Entertainment, Inc.
BEETLE BUB - Insecticides - Del's
BEETLE BUG - Apparel and accessories - Spencer's Inc. of Mount Airy, North Carolina
BEETLE BUSTER - Insecticides ✩ - Dalen Products Inc.
BEETLE CAT - Boat dealers ✩ - Concordia Custom Yachts Inc.
BEETLE CAT - Boats - Concordai Custom Yachts Inc.
BEETLE MEGABUG - Toys - Tonka Corp.
BEETLEBORGS - Footwear - S. Goldberg and Co. Inc.
BEETLEJUICE - Candy - Glenn Confections Inc.
BEETLES, MOTHS, & BUMBLEBEES - Puzzles - Robert W. Fathauer
BEETRIM - Bicycles ✩ - Korex Corp.
BEEVEL - Tools—woodworking - Leisurecrafts
BEF - Fuel additives - Belvieu Environmental Fuels
BEFINE - Food products - Richard A. Jennings
BEFORE AND AFTER - Cosmetics - Transamerica Mailings, Inc.
BEFORE & AFTER - Publisher's imprints - Allan Chochinov
BEFORE & AFTER - Shaving preparations - Triumph Associates
BEFORE & AFTER - Vitamins and nutritional supplements - Min Tong Herbs, Inc.
BEFORE DAWN - Recording label - Touchwood Records LLC
BEFORE SIX - Apparel—men's ✩ - After Six Inc.
BEFORE TAN - Suntan lotions ✩ - Oakmont Investments Co.
BEFORE THE BABY - Underwear and nightwear - Glamorise Foundations Inc.
BEFORE THE RAIN FLOWERY JASMINE - Teas - Grace Tea Co. Ltd.
BEFORE YOU BUILD .... HOMEWORK-ITINERARY - Publisher's imprints - Peter A. Jeswald
BEFOREPERM - Hair care products - Modafini Inc.
BEFRESH - Cleaning preparations—household ✩ - S.C. Johnson & Son, Inc.
BEFRY 100 - Shortening - Hormel Foods Corp.
BEG-A-BONE - Pet food - B.G.B. Pet Supply Inc.
BEGA'S BATTLE - Toys—electronic - Data East USA Inc.
BEGGAR DOG BISCUITS - Dog food - BD International Corp.
BEGGARS BANQUET - Recording label - RCA Records
BEGGIN' STRIPS - Dog food - Ralston Purina Co.
BEGIN AGAIN - Hair care products ✩ - Mahdeen Laboratory
BEGINNER - Baby foods - H.J. Heinz Co.
BEGINNER PUZZLES - Puzzles - Lauri Inc.
BEGINNERS - Paints—artists' ✩ - Martin F. Weber Co.

BEGINNERS - Pencils - Dixon Ticonderoga Co.
BEGINNER'S BIBLE - School supplies - James R. Leininger
BEGINNERS' CHOICE - Patterns—clothing ✩ - Simplicity Pattern Co., Inc.
BEGINNERS' LUCK - Apparel—women's - Wacoal America Inc.
BEGINNERS LUCK - Toys ✩ - Real Good Toys
BEGINNING - Rings—jewelry ✩ - Artcarved Inc.
BEGINNING GEOMETRY - Computer software - Ventura Educational Systems
BEGINNING LITERACY - Publisher's imprints - Scholastic Inc.
BEGINNING MATH CONCEPTS - Computer software - Orange Cherry Software
BEGINNING MATH KIT - Toys ✩ - Lauri Inc.
BEGINNING SPELLING - Puzzles ✩ - Lauri Inc.
BEGINNINGS - Floor coverings—carpet and rugs - Monticello Carpet Mills
BEGINNINGS - Furniture - Bean Station Furniture Factory Inc.
BEGINNINGS - Glassware—household ✩ - Anchor Hocking Glass, Inc.
BEGO - Apparel and accessories - Marijana Begovic
BEGONIA - Dinnerware—glass - Nikko Ceramics Inc.
BEGUILING - Frames—eyeglass - Hudson Optical Corp.
BEGUILING - Perfumes - Avon Products, Inc.
BEGY'S MUSTARINE - Pharmaceutical preparations - Brown Manufacturing Co.
BEHAR NEW YORK - Apparel and accessories - A.R.B., Inc.
BEHAVE - Frames—eyeglass - Pathway Optical Prods.
BEHAVE - Health care products - Gillette Co.
BEHAVIOR BEASTS - Publisher's imprints - Michael Cohen
BEHAVIOR DESCRIPTION SYSTEMS - Printed products for employers - Personnel Decisions Inc.
BEHAVIORAL TECHNOLOGY - Computer software - Behavioral Technology, Inc.
BEHAVIORAL TECHNOLOGY FINDING ANSWERS IN ACTIONS - Computer software - Behavioral Technology, Inc.
BEHIND CLOSED DRAWERS - Apparel and accessories - Jaclyn, Inc.
BEHIND THE GLASS - Trading cards and stamps - Upper Deck Co.
BEHIND THE SCENES - Computer software - Chemeketa Community College
BEHKOL - Solvents - H. Behlen & Bro. Inc.
BEHNING - Pianos - Kohler & Campbell Inc.
BEHOLD - Furniture polish and wax - Drackett Co.
BEHR - Magnifying loupe - Behr Manufacturing Inc.
BEHR - Pianos - Kohler & Campbell Inc.
BEHR - Varnishes - Behr Process Corp.
BEHR-CAT - Tape—masking ✩ - Norton Co.
BEHR EXPRESSIONS - Varnishes - Behr Process Corp.
BEHRHORST - Salad dressings—bottled - Hudson Industries, Inc.
BEHRINGER - Audio equipment - Samson Technologies Inc.
BEICH'S - Beverages - Inventory Auditors Inc.
BEICH'S - Candy - Nestle-Beich Inc.
BEIERSDORF - Bandages - Roberts/Hauck Pharmaceuticals Inc.
BEIGE BOOK - Wallpaper ✩ - Imperial Wallcoverings, Inc.
BEIGE GRAPE - Pottery ✩ - Rubens Originals
BEIGEL'S - Bakery products - SGFW Bakers, Inc.
BEIJA FLOR - Apparel and accessories - Hummingbird, Inc.
BEIJING - Furniture - Singer Furniture Co.
BEIJING - Vegetables—frozen ✩ - VIP Sales Co. Inc.
BEILE MEADE - Bicycles ✩ - Murray, Inc.
BEINFORMED! - Computer software - Saga Solutions, Inc.
BEING - Apparel - New Issues Inc.
BEING B - Books—comic - Anthony Masino
BEING THE BEST COMES NATURALLY - Vitamins and nutritional supplements - Green Foods Corp.
BEING YOU - Cosmetics - Sears, Roebuck and Co.
BEINGTHERE - Computer software - Intelligence at Large, Inc.
BEJECTAL - Pharmaceutical preparations ✩ - Abbott Laboratories
BEJEWELED - Frames—eyeglass ✩ - Universal/Univis Inc.
BEJEWELER - Tools—jewelers - Creative Crystal Co., LLC
BEJEX - Pharmaceutical preparations ✩ - Abbott Laboratories
BEJING - Wallpaper - Pickhardt & Siebert USA Inc.
BEKA - Cooking equipment—household - Waba Co.
BEKA - Wood products - Beka Inc.
BEKAERT - Fabrics - W.R. Grace & Co.
BEKAFECT - Fencing—steel - Bekaert Corp. (Wire & Wire Products Div.)
BEKAL - Spices and extracts - Alberto R. Abrante
BEKAMAN - Fencing—steel - Bekaert Corp. (Wire & Wire Products Div.)
BEKATEN - Fencing—steel - Bekaert Corp. (Wire & Wire Products Div.)
BEKKA - Statuary - National Graphic Gift Souvenir
BEKO - Apparel and accessories - Robert Gregory Beliveau
BEL - Dryers—hair ✩ - Belson Products

BEL-AD - Recording label ☆ - Ray Lawrence Ltd.
BEL AIR - Appliance parts - Meteor Inc.
BEL AIR - Beauty aids - European Cosmetics Inc.
BEL AIR - Fans–electric - Casablanca Fan Co.
BEL AIR - Flatware - Reed and Barton Corp.
BEL-AIR - Floor coverings–carpet and rugs - Atlas Carpet Mills Inc.
BEL-AIR - Floor coverings–carpet and rugs ☆ - Blue Ridge Carpet Mills
BEL AIR - Floor coverings–carpet and rugs ☆ - S and S Mills Inc.
BEL-AIR - Food products - Bel Air Markets
BEL-AIR - Food products - Safeway Stores Inc.
BEL-AIR - Food products - Townsend Farms
BEL-AIR - Fruits–frozen - Glencourt Products
BEL-AIR - Furniture–upholstered ☆ - Patrician Furniture Co.
BEL AIR - Motor vehicles ☆ - General Motors Corp. (Chevrolet Motor Div.)
BEL-AIR - Paper - CST Office Products, Inc.
BEL-AIR - Projection screens - Brumberger Co. Inc.
BEL AIR - Salads–prepackaged - R.T. French Co.
BEL AIR - Shutters–wood - Ohline Corp.
BEL-AIR K42 - Cameras ☆ - Keystone Camera Corp.
BEL AIR MIX - Candy - Nabisco Foods Group
BEL-AIRE - Compressors–air - American IMC Inc.
BEL-AIRE - Floor coverings–carpet and rugs - Philadelphia Carpets
BEL AIRE - Furniture–wood ☆ - Ficks Reed Co. Inc.
BEL AIRE - Wallpaper - Lawrence Wallcoverings
BEL ARBORS - Wines - Fetzer Vineyards Inc.
BEL ARIA - Food products - Bel Canto Fancy Foods Ltd.
BEL ARIA ARBORIO - Food products - Bel Canto Fancy Foods Ltd.
BEL B COMPLEX - Vitamins and nutritional supplements ☆ - Freeda Vitamins Inc.
BEL-BARI - Food products - Losurdo Foods, Inc.
BEL BOLT - Fasteners - Jess L. Belser
BEL CANTEAY - Floor coverings–carpet and rugs - Karastan-Bigelow Inc.
BEL CANTO - Floor coverings–carpet and rugs ☆ - Lees Carpets
BEL CANTO - Glassware–household ☆ - Lenox Crystal, Inc.
BEL CANTO - Rings–jewelry - Artcarved Inc.
BEL CANTO - Tableware–china ☆ - Villeroy and Boch Tableware Ltd.
BEL-CAP - Oils–essential - Belmay Inc.
BEL-CAPRI - Food products - Losurdo Foods, Inc.
BEL CUCINA - Food products ☆ - Mesa International
BEL-DECK - Lumber - Belco
BEL DOLCA - Pasta - Hickory Farms, Inc.
BEL DOMAINE II - Floor coverings–carpet and rugs - Lees Carpets
BEL FIORE - Tableware–china ☆ - Villeroy and Boch Tableware Ltd.
BEL-FIT - Music stands ☆ - Micro Musical Products Corp.
BEL-FLEUR - Fabrics - Dan River Inc.
BEL-MAR - Shoes - Bata Shoe Co. Inc.
BEL-MIN - Vitamins and nutritional supplements - Freeda Vitamins Inc.
BEL NORMANDE - Cider - Made in France
BEL-RAY - Lubricants - Bel-Ray Co. Inc.
BEL-RAY TOTAL PERFORMANCE LUBRICANTS - Lubricant - Bel-Ray Co. Inc.
BEL-RINGER - Housewares - Floyd Bell Inc.
BEL-TRONICS - Radar detectors - Bel-Tronics Corp.
BEL-VUE - Meat products–canned - Zehner Packing Co.
BELAGIO - Dinnerware–plastic - Gibson Overseas Inc.
BELAIR - Cigarettes - Brown & Williamson Tobacco Corp.
BELAIR - Jewelry - Tru-Kay Manufacturing Co.
BELAIR - Motor vehicles–motor homes - Baron Motor Homes Inc.
BELAIR - Office supplies - Needlecraft Industries
BELAIR - Wallpaper - Koroseal Wallcoverings
BELAIR - Watches - Belair Watch Corp.
BELAIR - Window coverings - Superior Shade & Blind Co. Inc.
BELAIR BY ATS - Motor vehicles–all-terrain - American Travel Systems, Inc.
BELAIRE - Boats - Clark Craft Boat Co.
BELAIRE - Cooking equipment–household - Welbilt Appliances Inc.
BELAIRE - Underwear and nightwear - Bestform Foundations, Inc.
BELAIRE - Wallpaper ☆ - Wolf-Gordon Inc.
BELAIRE CREEK - Wines ☆ - Canandaigua Wine Co. Inc.
BELAM - Electrical equipment - R.H. Belam Co., Inc.
BELANGOR - Yarn - Joseph Galler Inc.
BELAP - Pharmaceutical preparations ☆ - Lemmon Co.
BELARDI - Wine - B.O.G., Ltd.
BELARIA - Spices and extracts - Bel Canto Fancy Foods Ltd.
BELARUS - Farm machinery - Belarus Machinery of U.S.A., Inc.
BELATOL - Pharmaceutical preparations - H.R. Cenci Laboratories Inc.
BELAVI - Cosmetics - Belavi Facelift Massage System, Inc.

BELBOB - Thread - Belding Heminway Co. Inc.
BELCA - Food products ☆ - Skylark Co.
BELCLEAR - Thread ☆ - Belding Heminway Co. Inc.
BELCOBALSA - Balsa wood for boat-building - Baltek Corp.
BELCORA - Thread ☆ - Belding Heminway Co. Inc.
BELCORDION - Accordions ☆ - Bell Duovox Corp.
BELCORT - Thread ☆ - Belding Heminway Co. Inc.
BELCREST - Dishes–china - Arrow International, Inc.
BELCREST - Musical instruments - LPD Music International
BELCREST COURT - Wallpaper - Gagne Wallcovering, Inc.
BELDEN - Cables - ARS Electronics
BELDEN - Cables - Cooper Industries (Cooper Automotive)
BELDEN - Electronic and automotive wires, cables, etc. - Cooper Industries, Inc.
BELDEN INFINITY - Cables - Belden Wire & Cable Co.
BELDIN - Health care products - Halsey Drug Co. Inc.
BELDING - Thread - Belding Heminway Co. Inc.
BELDING BUTTERFLY - Thread ☆ - Belding Heminway Co. Inc.
BELDOCH - Crocheted and knitted items - Beldoch Industries Corp.
BELDOCH-POPPER - Apparel–women's - Beldoch Industries Corp.
BELDORO - Thread - Belding Heminway Co. Inc.
BELE CHERE - Cups–plastic - City of Asheville
BELEVEDERE - Cosmetics - Marianna Imports, Inc.
BELEX - Skin care products - Lendan USA Co.
BELEXA - Pharmaceutical - American Pharmaceutical Co.
BELEXAL - Pharmaceutical preparations ☆ - Pal-Pak Inc.
BELEXON FORTE - Pharmaceutical - American Pharmaceutical Co.
BELFAB - Machine parts - John Crane Inc.
BELFAST - Food products - Penobscot Frozen Foods Inc.
BELFAST - Frames–eyeglass - Pathway Optical Prods.
BELFER - Pharmaceutical preparations ☆ - Forest Pharmaceuticals Inc.
BELFLEX - Cables–signal - Belden Wire & Cable Co.
BELFLEX - Floor coverings - Belting Associates Inc.
BELFLOR - Floor coverings ☆ - Congoleum Corp.
BELFOCA - Cameras ☆ - Edixa Camera Co.
BELFORD - Apparel–women's - USA Peninsula, Inc.
BELFORD - Eyeglasses - Art-Craft Optical Co.
BELFORT - Frames–eyeglass ☆ - Universal/Univis Inc.
BELFRY - Hosiery ☆ - Danskin, Inc.
BELFRY CHAMPIONSHIP COURSE, THE - Computer software ☆ - Access Software Inc.
BELGA - Licorice - Holland-American Importing Co. Inc.
BELGA ROYALE - Floor coverings–carpet and rugs - Rugby Rugs Inc.
BELGARD - Hardware ☆ - Aqualarm
BELGIAN-BLOCK - Floor coverings ☆ - American Floor Products Co. Inc.
BELGIAN CAFE - Coffee - Western Family Foods, Inc.
BELGIAN CHEF - Waffles–frozen - Chef America, Inc.
BELGIAN CLASSICS - Wallpaper ☆ - Wall Fashion Inc.
BELGIAN CREMES - Candy - Brown & Haley
BELGIAN FORMULA - Hair care products - Revlon Consumer Products Corp.
BELGIAN SNOW - Floor coverings–carpet and rugs ☆ - Masland Corp.
BELGIAN WAFFLER - Waffle irons - Nordic Ware
BELGIMERE - Bathing suits - Catalina
BELGIQUE - Canvas–artists' - New York Central Art Supply Co.
BELGIQUE - Floor coverings–carpet and rugs ☆ - Trans-Ocean Import Co. Inc.
BELGIUM - Ophthalmic goods - Embassy Creations Inc.
BELGIUM RIB - Wallpaper ☆ - Armstrong World Industries, Inc.
BELGIUM TRUFFLES - Wallcoverings - Cork Products Co. Inc.
BELGRADE - Floor coverings–carpet and rugs - Barrett Carpet Mills Inc.
BELGRADE - Floor coverings–carpet and rugs ☆ - Callaway Carpets
BELGRADE GLOSS - Paper - Scott Paper Co.
BELGRANO - Office supplies ☆ - Alliance America
BELGRAVIA - Floor coverings–carpet and rugs - Bentley Mills, Inc.
BELGRAVIA - Floor coverings–carpet and rugs - Glen Eden Wool Carpets
BELGRAVIA - Frames–eyeglass - Hudson Optical Corp.
BELGRAVIA ROYALE - Floor coverings–carpet and rugs - Bentley Mills, Inc.
BELGROVE - Food products - King George Packing Co. Inc.
BELHAVEN - Cabinets - Marsh Furniture Co.
BELI - Ophthalmic goods - Styl-Rite Optical Manufacturing Co., Inc.
BELICIA - Whirlpools - Lasco Products Group
BELIEVE - Margarine - Moran Foods, Inc.
BELIEVE - Posters - Wormtrap, Inc.
BELIEVE IN YOURSELF! - Publisher's imprints - Phun from Phoenix! Inc.
BELIEVE-IT - Cleaning preparations–carpet and rug - Core Products Co., Inc.
BELINDA - Cigars - Villazon and Co.

☆ = Now out of production

BELINDA - Dolls - Mattel, Inc.
BELINDA - Floor coverings - Armstrong World Industries, Inc.
BELINDA - Floor coverings–carpet and rugs - Regal Rugs Inc.
BELINDA BUNNY - Dolls - Russ Berrie and Co., Inc.
BELINDAS - Cigars - Faber, Coe & Gregg Inc.
BELITA - Electrical equipment - R.H. Belam Co., Inc.
BELITE - Pharmaceutical preparations - Longevity Pure Medicine
BELIVRON - Pharmaceutical preparations ☆ - Vitarine Pharmaceuticals Inc.
BELK - Apparel and accessories - Belk Stores Services, Inc.
BELKIN COMPONENTS - Computer peripheral equipment - Belkin
    Components
BELL - Brushes–paint - Corona Brushes Inc.
BELL - Dairy products - Dean Foods Co.
BELL - Electrical equipment - Hubbell Electrical Products
BELL - Food products - Bell-Carter Foods Inc.
BELL - Frames–eyeglass - May Optical Co. Inc.
BELL - Fruitcake mix, glace fruits - Aunt Nellie's Farm Kitchens Inc.
BELL - Helmets–athletic - Bell Sports Corp.
BELL - Hobby kits - Bell Ceramics, Inc.
BELL - Kitchen utensils–aluminum ☆ - R & R Mill Co. Inc.
BELL - Mirrors - Bell Glass & Mirror Co.
BELL - Musical-instrument strings - International Music Corp.
BELL - Potato chips - Bell Brand Foods Inc.
BELL - Shingles–shakes - North Hoquiam Cedar Products Inc.
BELL ACCORDIONS ACCOUSTIC - Accordions - Bell Duovox Corp.
BELL ACCORDIONS MIDI - Accordions - Bell Duovox Corp.
BELL-ANS - Health care products ☆ - Grandpa Brands Co.
BELL/ANS ANTACID TABLETS - Antacids ☆ - Grandpa Brands Co.
BELL BOTTLE - Pet products - Novalek, Inc.
BELL BOY - Olives–canned - Lee, Thompson & Fawcett Co.
BELL BROS. - Shoes - Genesco Inc.
BELL BUOY - Food products - Bell Buoy Crab Co.
BELL CANYON CELLARS - Wines ☆ - Burgess Cellars
BELL DAIRY - Milk - Bell Dairy Products Inc.
BELL DUOVOX - Accordions ☆ - Bell Duovox Corp.
BELL EQUIPMENT SONECOR - Telephones - TT Systems Corp.
BELL FLOWER - Flatware ☆ - Utica Cutlery Co.
BELL-HORN - Health care products - Bell-Horn
BELL JAR BOUTIQUE CRAFT - Hobby kits ☆ - Natural Science Industries,
    Ltd.
BELL LINES - Toys - Toy Truck Lines, Inc.
BELL MEDLEY - Giftware - Fenton Art Glass Co.
BELL MOUNTAIN - Wines - Bell Mountain Vineyards Inc.
BELL O'TEXAS - Shrimp–fresh or frozen - Atalanta Corp.
BELL OUTDOOR - Electrical equipment - Hubbell Inc.
BELL PLUCKER - Sporting goods ☆ - Georgia's Tennis
BELL RINGER - Balls–basketball - Logan Electric Specialty Manufacturing Co.
BELL RINGER - Calendars - Kurtz Bros. Inc.
BELL RINGER - Game machines - Bally Gaming International, Inc.
BELL RINGERS - Apparel and accessories ☆ - Levi Strauss & Co. (Accessory
    Div.)
BELL TOWER - Publisher's imprints - Random House, Inc.
BELL TOY - Toys–stuffed - Winner International Inc.
BELLA - Cosmetics - RJM International
BELLA - Floor coverings–carpet and rugs ☆ - J.L. Benson Co.
BELLA - Food products - Henry Bresky & Sons Inc.
BELLA - Frames–eyeglass - Pathway Optical Prods.
BELLA - Manicure sets ☆ - London International U.S. Holdings
BELLA - Pizzas–frozen ☆ - H.P. Hood & Sons Inc.
BELLA BISCOTTI LTD. - Confections - Bella Biscotti, Ltd.
BELLA CERAMICA - Dinnerware–glass - Tienshan, Inc.
BELLA CREMA - Candy - Log House Foods Inc.
BELLA CREMA - Coffee - Coffee Masters, Inc.
BELLA DESIGNS - Jewelry - Bella Designs
BELLA DI CERIGNOLA - Olives–canned - Bel Canto Fancy Foods Ltd.
BELLA DIOSA COLLECTION - Dresses–women's - Bella Diosa Group, Inc.
BELLA DONNA - Tableware–china - Pfaltzgraff Investment Co.
BELLA FEMINA - Lenses–optical - Ditto Industries Inc.
BELLA FLORA - Pottery ☆ - Rubens Originals
BELLA GENTO - Cheese - Olympia Cheese Co. LLC
BELLA ITALIA - Hair care products - Organifyl Laboratories
BELLA ITALIANE - Breads - Charles Freihofer Baking Co.
BELLA KARA COSMETICS - Skin care products - Bella Kara, Inc.
BELLA MARIA - Wine - Italian and French Wine Co. of Buffalo Inc.
BELLA MIA - Cheese ☆ - Stella Foods, Inc.
BELLA NONNA - Pizzas–mixes - Lunar Visions Cuisine, Inc.

BELLA NOTTE - Wines - Kenneth Volk
BELLA PRONTO - Pasta - Purple Onion Products, Inc.
BELLA ROSSA - Tomato pastes and sauces - Escalon Frozen Foods
BELLA SUN LUCI - Tomatoes - Mooney Farms
BELLA VIA - Pasta - Tree of Life, Inc.
BELLA VISTA - Floor coverings ☆ - Congoleum Corp.
BELLA VISTA - Food products - Furman Foods, Inc.
BELLABARB - Pharmaceutical preparations ☆ - Veratex Group
BELLACICCO - Bakery products - Bellacicco Inc.
BELLACOTTA - Cheese - H.P. Hood & Sons Inc.
BELLADENAL - Pharmaceutical preparations - Sandoz Pharmaceuticals Corp.
BELLAFEDROL A-H - Pharmaceutical preparations - Lannett Co. Inc.
BELLAFLEX - Paper - Miami Valley Paper Co. Inc.
BELLAFOLINE - Pharmaceutical preparations - Sandoz Pharmaceuticals Corp.
BELLAGIO - Apparel and accessories - Kellwood Co.
BELLAGIO - Food products - John Sexton and Co.
BELLAGIO - Food products - US Foodservice
BELLAGIO - Wallpaper ☆ - Capital Carousel Inc.
BELLAGIO - Wines - Banfi Vintners
BELLAGUSTO - Butter - Lov-It Creamery Inc.
BELLAIR EXPRESS - Air transportation - Bellair Expediting Service, Inc.
BELLAIRE - Floor coverings - Congoleum Corp.
BELLAIRE - Furniture - Mersman Furniture Co.
BELLAIRE - Musical instrument accessories - Hershman Musical Instrument
BELLAIRE - Recording label - Bellaire Record Sales
BELLAIRE - Rings–jewelry - Artcarved Inc.
BELLAIRE - Tableware–china ☆ - Lenox, Inc.
BELLALPHEN - Pharmaceutical preparations - Consolidated Midland Corp.
BELLAMONTE - Bathroom accessories - Kohler Co.
BELL'AMORE - Cookies - Bell'amore Imports Inc.
BELLAMY - Dishes–china ☆ - Gorham Inc.
BELL+HOWELL - Computer software - Bell & Howell Co.
BELLARENA - Floor coverings - Mannington Resilient Floors
BELLARI - Amplifiers - Rolls Corp.
BELLASTAL - Pharmaceutical preparations ☆ - U.S. Ethicals Inc.
BELLATEX - Fabrics - Seaward International Inc.
BELLAVIA - Floor coverings–carpet and rugs ☆ - Gulistan Carpet Inc.
BELLAVISTA - Manufactured homes - Bonnavilla Homes
BELLBOY - Pencils ☆ - Dur-O-Lite Inc.
BELLBROOK FARMS - Desserts - Eastern Foods, Inc.
BELLCELL - Batteries - At&T Corp.
BELLCO - Nameplates–engraved - Bell Co. Inc.
BELLCRAFT - Apparel and accessories - Bellcraft Manufacturing Co.
BELLE - Dolls - K.B. Brothers Inc.
BELLE - Glassware–household ☆ - Dansk International Designs, Ltd.
BELLE - Ophthalmic goods ☆ - Luxottica
BELLE - Recording label - La Louisiane Records & Studio
BELLE AIR - Product description unknown - Sports Belle Inc.
BELLE ARBOR - Novelty items - Belle Arbor Promotion Co. Inc.
BELLE AUBERGE - Flatware ☆ - Kirk Stieff Co.
BELLE BAIE - Food products - Wally Sea Products Corp.
BELLE BONNE - Liquors - House of Seagram
BELLE BRUMMEL - Leather goods - RGA Accessories Inc.
BELLE BUNNY - Toys–stuffed - Russ Berrie and Co., Inc.
BELLE-CAMP - Candy - Standard Candy Co. Inc.
BELLE CHANDELLE - Candles ☆ - Colonial Candle of Cape Cod
BELLE CLASSIQUE - Skin care products - Jafra Cosmetics Inc.
BELLE DE BRILLET - Wines ☆ - Dreyfus Ashby Inc.
BELLE DE JOVAN - Perfumes ☆ - Quintessence Inc.
BELLE EPOQUE - Food products - Made in France
BELLE-FILLE - Frames–eyeglass - Hudson Optical Corp.
BELLE FLEUR - Carpets and rugs - Couristan Inc.
BELLE FLEUR - Rings–jewelry - Artcarved Inc.
BELLE GROVE - Dinnerware ☆ - Corning Inc.
BELLE HARBOR - Floor coverings–carpet and rugs - Criterion Mills Inc.
BELLE HAVEN - Furniture - Athens Furniture Industries Inc.
BELLE HELENA - Wines - Charles F. Shaw Vineyard & Winery
BELLE KLIPSCH - Amplifiers–public address - Klipsch and Associates Inc.
BELLE-LITE - Eyeglasses - Art-Craft Optical Co.
BELLE MEADE - Fabrics–tapestry ☆ - Coloroll Inc.
BELLE MEADE - Mobile homes ☆ - Wescon Products Co.
BELLE MONDE - Ophthalmic goods - Foremost Optical Products
BELLE OF BELDING - Food products - Bell Harvest Sales Inc.
BELLE OF MAINE - Vegetables–frozen - W.S. Wells & Son
BELLE OF THE FARM - Food products ☆ - Old Ranchers Canning Co. Inc.
BELLE POINT - Furniture ☆ - Riverside Furniture Corp.

BELLE POINTE - Floor coverings—carpet and rugs - Collins & Aikman Corp.
BELLE PROVENCALE - Wines - Vineyard Brands, Inc.
BELLE REVE SOURCEBOOK - Games ☆ - Mayfair Games, Inc.
BELLE ROSE - Wines - Diamond Wine Merchants
BELLE-SHARMEER - Hosiery - Hampshire Hosiery, Inc.
BELLE SPIRIT - Rings—jewelry - Artcarved Inc.
BELLE STAR - Rings—jewelry - Artcarved Inc.
BELLE SUISSE - Watches - Lucien Piccard/Arnex
BELLE-VUE - Beverages—malt - Labatt Importers Inc.
BELLE-VUE - Typewriter covers - American Guard-It Manufacturing Co. Inc.
BELLE-WEATHER - Shrink-film window system ☆ - Oatey Co.
BELLEAIR - Wallpaper ☆ - Schooner Prints Inc.
BELLEBUE - Dishes—china ☆ - Gorham Inc.
BELLEGEM - Waffle irons ☆ - Bellegem Waffle Corp.
BELLEJOUR - Wines - Kobrand Corp.
BELLEMEADE - Cabinets ☆ - Wellborn Cabinet, Inc.
BELLEMMS - Pharmaceutical preparations ☆ - C.O. Truxton Inc.
BELLEPOINTE - Apparel—women's - Bellepointe Inc.
BELLERGAL - Barbituates - Dorsey Laboratories
BELLERIVE - Cheese - Fromark
BELLEROSE VINEYARD - Wines - Bellerose Vineyard
BELLE'S - Flour—blended ☆ - Climax Mills Inc.
BELLES & WHISTLES - Apparel—children's - Rose Cage Ink, Inc.
BELLES & WHISTLES - Linen - Levinsohn Textile Co., Inc.
BELLES ROUGES - Fruits and vegetables - California Vegetable Specialties, Inc.
BELLEVILLE - Footwear—men's - Belleville Shoe Manufacturing Co.
BELLEVILLE - Toys—erector sets - Lego Systems Inc.
BELLEVOIR - Skin care products - Bellevoir, Inc.
BELLEVUE - Dishes—china ☆ - WMF/USA
BELLEVUE - Flatware - Reed and Barton Corp.
BELLEVUE - Floor coverings—carpet and rugs - West Point-Pepperell Mill Store
BELLEVUE MATTE - Flatware - Reed and Barton Corp.
BELLEWOOD - Chimes - Nutone Inc.
BELLEWOOD - Furniture ☆ - Bernhardt Industries
BELLEZZA - Oils—edible - Costello Oil Packers Corp.
BELLFLOWER - Rings—jewelry ☆ - Artcarved Inc.
BELLGOTRAL - Pharmaceutical preparations ☆ - U.S. Ethicals Inc.
BELLGRANDE BURRITOS - Food products - Taco Bell Corp.
BELLHOP - Motor vehicles - Ransomes-Cushman-Ryan
BELLINA - Lenses—optical - Ditto Industries Inc.
BELLINEAU - Floor coverings—carpet and rugs ☆ - Karastan-Bigelow Inc.
BELLINGHAM - Dishes—china ☆ - Gorham Inc.
BELLINGHAM - Frames—eyeglass ☆ - Universal/Univis Inc.
BELLINGHAM - Shoes ☆ - Allen-Edmonds Shoe Corp.
BELLINGHAM PARK - Furniture - CTH/Sherrill Occasional
BELLINI - Cosmetics ☆ - P.S. Pibbs Inc.
BELLINI - Footwear—women's - Bellini Imports Ltd.
BELLINI - Paints - Bocour Artist Colors Inc.
BELLINO - Breads - Patrick M. Ciccotelli
BELLINO - Briefcases ☆ - Korchmar Case Co.
BELLINO - Food products - Alanric Food Distributors Inc.
BELLINO - Footwear - Wadiwalkers Inc.
BELLINO PARIS MODE - Clothing - Azriel Altman
BELLINS WONDERSTOEN - Pharmaceutical ☆ - Benjamin Ansehl Co.
BELLISIMA - Apparel and accessories - Her Majesty Industries Inc.
BELLISSIMA - Apparel and accessories - Heckler Manufacturing & Investment Group Inc.
BELLISSIMA - Wigs - Bellissima Beauty World
BELLISSIMO - Cosmetics ☆ - Nino Originals
BELLISSIMO - Floor coverings - Armstrong World Industries, Inc.
BELLISSIMO - Floor coverings—carpet and rugs ☆ - J.L. Benson Co.
BELLISSIMO - Food products - Health Valley Food
BELLISSIMO - Wallpaper - Parkview Designs
BELLKATAL - Gastroscopes ☆ - Ferndale Laboratories, Inc.
BELLMARK - Recording label - Capitol-EMI Music Inc.
BELLMARK RECORDS - Compact discs—prerecorded - Isbell Records, Inc.
BELLMORE - Food products - Staff Supermarket Associates, Inc.
BELLMORE - Musical instruments ☆ - Grossman Music Corp.
BELLO - Briefcases - Tomac International Inc.
BELLO - Food products - Overseas Trading & Shipping
BELLO DUPLISCOPE - Photographic equipment - SP Systems/Saratons
BELLO UOMO - Knit, woven apparel - Frederick Atkins, Inc.
BELLOPHEN - Pharmaceutical preparations ☆ - Vortech Pharmaceuticals
BELLOREX - Pharmaceutical preparations ☆ - Rex Research Laboratories

BELLOWS - Bellows - Centryco Inc.
BELLOWS - Beverages—alcohol - Jim Beam Brands Co.
BELLOWS - Recording label - Jazz Composer's Orchestra Association Inc.
BELLOWS CHECK - Computer software - DSD Associates, Inc.
BELLOWS CLUB - Beverages—alcohol ☆ - Jim Beam Brands Co.
BELLOWS PARTNERS CHOICE - Whiskey ☆ - Jim Beam Brands Co.
BELLOWSCOPE - Photographic equipment - SP Systems/Saratons
BELLOWSMASTER - Photographic equipment - SP Systems/Saratons
BELLOWSMATE - Photographic equipment - SP Systems/Saratons
BELLROCK - Floor coverings—carpet and rugs ☆ - Daltonian Carpet & Cushion Inc.
BELL'S - Seasonings - William G. Bell & Co.
BELL'S FAMILY - Vitamins and nutritional supplements ☆ - Oakmont Investments Co.
BELLS OF SARNA - Giftware - S.S. Sarna Inc.
BELLS OF THE MONTH - Giftware - Russ Berrie and Co., Inc.
BELLS OF THE TAJ MAHAL - Bells - Taj Importing Co.
BELLSOL - Solvents - Georgia-Pacific Corp.
BELLSOUTH CLASSIC - Umbrellas - Bellsouth Corp.
BELLSOUTH.NET - Computer software - Bellsouth Corp.
BELLSTIR - Bar fixtures—plastic - Spir-it Inc.
BELLVEDERE - Lighting fixtures ☆ - Hubbell Lighting, Inc. (Lighting Div.)
BELLVIEW - Floor coverings—carpet and rugs - Gloria of America Inc.
BELLWETHER - Fabrics ☆ - Dan River Inc.
BELLWETHER - Frames—eyeglass - Liberty Optical Manufacturing Co.
BELLWETHER - Grinders - Advanced Grinding Concepts, Inc.
BELLWETHER - Sporting goods - Bellwether Inc.
BELLWORK - Educational materials - Bellwork Enterprises, Inc.
BELLWRINGR - Cleaning equipment - Contec, Inc.
BELLY - Apparel and accessories - Tanya Donelly
BELLY BAGS - Novelty purse with cologne and lip gloss ☆ - Cosrich Inc.
BELLY BAND - Apparel—athletic - Bodyslimmers Inc.
BELLY BLISTERIN PEPPER SAUCE - Vegetable sauces - Philip R. Hagadorn
BELLY BUDDY - Apparel and accessories - SGI Inc.
BELLY BUMPER - Dolls, doll accessories, and plush toys ☆ - Hart Enterprises, Inc.
BELLY BUSTER GANG - Pet products - Penn-Plax, Inc.
BELLY BUTTON - Housewares - Mary Brooks Pittman
BELLY BUTTONS - Apparel stores—children's - Barbara A. Tubbs
BELLY BUTTONS - Candy ☆ - Haribo of America Inc.
BELLY DANCE - Recording label ☆ - Rashid Sales Co.
BELLY DIVER - Fishing lures - Paul Warner Industries
BELLY FLOPS - Candy - Herman Goelitz Candy Co., Inc.
BELLY FULL OF CATNIP - Pet products - R.A.F. Trading Inc.
BELLY UP - Apparel - Belly Up Tavern, Inc.
BELLY UP - Fishing lures - Richard S. Sisco
BELLYBOARD - Exercising equipment ☆ - World Famous Trading Co., Ltd.
BELLYBUSTER BOYLEG - Apparel and accessories - Warnaco Inc.
BELLYMASTER - Sporting goods - Muriel Gwinner
BELMAR - Chocolate candy - Belmar Candy Co.
BELMAR - Food products ☆ - Skylark Co.
BELMAR - Water—bottled or canned - Belmar Spring Water Co.
BELMERIT - Electronic equipment ☆ - ARS Electronics
BELMO - Thread - Belding Heminway Co. Inc.
BELMONDO - Floor coverings ☆ - Congoleum Corp.
BELMONDO - Wines - A.V. Imports, Inc.
BELMONT - Artists' materials - Solo-Horton Brush Co.
BELMONT - Bacon ☆ - Fischer Packing Co.
BELMONT - Binders - Steego Corp.
BELMONT - Cabinets - Triangle Pacific Corp. (Cabinet Division)
BELMONT - Cigarettes - G.A. Georgopulo & Co. Inc.
BELMONT - Cigarettes - Philip Morris Companies Inc.
BELMONT - Curtain rods - Newell Window Furnishing Co.
BELMONT - Floor coverings—carpet and rugs - Glen Eden Wool Carpets
BELMONT - Floor coverings—carpet and rugs - Philadelphia Carpets
BELMONT - Floor coverings—carpet and rugs ☆ - Regal Rugs Inc.
BELMONT - Footwear—men's - L.B. Evans' Son Co.
BELMONT - Frames—eyeglass ☆ - Universal/Univis Inc.
BELMONT - Furniture—upholstered ☆ - Mersman Furniture Co.
BELMONT - Glassware—household ☆ - Lenox Crystal, Inc.
BELMONT - Leather goods ☆ - AR Accessories Group Inc.
BELMONT - Mops - Piedmont Mop Co.
BELMONT - Perfumes - Irving W. Rice & Co. Inc.
BELMONT - Pickles - Pikle-Rite Co. Inc.
BELMONT - Projectors—photographic ☆ - Keystone Camera Corp.
BELMONT - Recording label - Belmont Records

☆ = Now out of production

BELMONT - Skin care products - Takara Belmont USA, Inc.
BELMONT - Soups–mixes - Empire Dehydrated Products Inc.
BELMONT - Thread - Threads USA Div.
BELMONT - Wallpaper - Wolf-Gordon Inc.
BELMONT - Watches - Bulova Corp.
BELMONT - Whirlpools - Lasco Products Group
BELMONT HALL - Floor coverings–carpet and rugs - Milliken & Co. Inc.
BELMONT PARK - Floor coverings–carpet and rugs ☆ - World Carpets, Inc.
BELMONT PRESIDENT - Cheese - Besnier USA, Inc.
BELMONT SHORES - Floor coverings–carpet and rugs ☆ - Hollytex Carpet Mills Inc.
BELMONT SPRINGS - Water–bottled or canned - Belmont Springs Water Co. Inc.
BELMONT STRIP - Floor coverings - Robbins Inc.
BELMONTE - Musical instruments - Kaman Music Corp.
BELMONTE - Wines - Palm Bay Imports, Inc.
BELMORE - Flatware - Delco Tableware International, Inc.
BELMORE - Thread - Belding Heminway Co. Inc.
BELNAP - Napkins–paper - Fort Howard Corp.
BELNORD - Giftware - Swiss Harmony Inc.
BELONGING - Rings–jewelry - Artcarved Inc.
BELOUX - Clothing - Beloux, Inc.
BELOVABLES - Toys ☆ - Bleyer Industries (Peoria Plastics Div.)
BELOVED - Colognes ☆ - Prince Matchabelli
BELOVED - Rings–jewelry - Artcarved Inc.
BELOW THE BELT - Apparel and accessories - Sweetheart Products Inc.
BELOW ZERO - Coats–men's - Gallron
BELOWDECKS - Frames–eyeglass - Liberty Optical Manufacturing Co.
BELSIZE - Canvas–artists' ☆ - Winsor & Newton
BELSON - Hair care products - Windmere Corp.
BELSONO - Musical instruments - Lo Duca Bros. Musical Instruments Inc.
BELSTAFF - Apparel and accessories - Accessory Distributors Inc.
BELT A GLASS - Tires - Bridgestone/Firestone, Inc.
BELT BAG - Leather goods - AR Accessories Group Inc.
BELT BUCKLE GUARD - Musical instrument accessories - Artist Showcase Inc.
BELT BUSTER - Food products ☆ - Pierre Frozen Foods Inc.
BELT-EASE - Lubricants - American Grease Stick Co.
BELT MASTER - Ophthalmic goods - Fidelity Case Corp.
BELT-PAKS - Belts–industrial - Crosman Corp.
BELT RACER - Toys - Tyco Toys
BELTABLES - Belt ornaments - Cityside Inc.
BELTBLOX - Wood products - Nasco Handcrafters
BELTCRETE - Conveyors - Rotec Industries, Inc.
BELTDANGLE - Telephones–cellular - Bugatti Inc.
BELTEX - Pharmaceutical preparations - Duro Med Industries Inc.
BELTEZE - Sanitary-napkin belts - Mills Products Inc.
BELTGRIP - Adhesives and sealants - Imperial Adhesives Inc.
BELTMATE - Controls–heating systems - Surface Combustion, Inc.
BELTO - Belts - Waist Wear Ltd.
BELTON - Apparel and accessories - Rice Mills Inc.
BELTON - T-shirts–men's ☆ - Midstates Sportswear
BELTON - Tools - Nitto Kohki USA Inc.
BELTONE - Hearing aids - Beltone Electronics Corp.
BELTONE - Musical instruments - Entertainment Music Marketing Corp.
BELTRAMINI - Footwear–men's - Atsco Footwear Inc.
BELTUNA - Accordions - Castiglione Accordion
BELTWAY - Alarm systems - ADT Inc.
BELUGA BY SKIVERTEX - Paper products - REXAM DSI
BELUGA CAVIAR - Caviar - Tsar Nicoulai Caviar
BELVEDERE - Bathroom fixtures - American Standard Inc.
BELVEDERE - Cigarettes - G.A. Georgopulo & Co. Inc.
BELVEDERE - Floor coverings–carpet and rugs - Gulistan Carpet Inc.
BELVEDERE - Floor coverings–carpet and rugs ☆ - Kelly Group Inc.
BELVEDERE - Frames–eyeglass - Hudson Optical Corp.
BELVEDERE - Furniture–children's ☆ - Child Craft Industries Inc.
BELVEDERE - Mattresses - Ohio Mattress Co.
BELVEDERE - Motor vehicles–automobiles ☆ - Chrysler Corp. (Chrysler-Plymouth Div.)
BELVEDERE - Pet products - Rolf C. Hagen (USA) Corp.
BELVEDERE - Soap ☆ - Stahl Soap Corp.
BELVEDERE - Vacuum cleaners and accessories - Tacony Corp.
BELVEDERE VIRGINIA - Cigarettes - G.A. Georgopulo & Co. Inc.
BELVEDERES - Cigar boxes–wood - Consolidated Cigar Corp.
BELVIDERE - Tableware–china ☆ - Lenox, Inc.
BELVIVA - Fabrics–broadcloth - Collins Σ Aikman Corp.

BELWAXED - Thread - Belding Heminway Co. Inc.
BELWITH - Doors–metal - Belwith International, Ltd.
BEMA - Exercising equipment - Bema USA Inc.
BEMA AMBIDEX - Exercising equipment ☆ - Bema USA Inc.
BEMA CORRIGEN - Pillows ☆ - Bema USA Inc.
BEMA DECUPAD - Furniture ☆ - Bema USA Inc.
BEMA SWIM WINGS - Apparel and accessories - Bema USA Inc.
BEMAC - Gloves - Jomac Products Inc.
BEMAR - Pharmaceutical preparations - Duro Med Industries Inc.
BEMCO - Mattresses and box springs - Bemco Associates, Inc.
BEMCO POSTURE - Mattresses and box springs - Bemco Associates, Inc.
BEMEX GENEX - Exercising equipment ☆ - Bema USA Inc.
BEMIDJI - Paneling - Georgia-Pacific Corp.
BEMINAL - Vitamins and nutritional supplements - Whitehall Laboratories
BEMINAL-500 - Vitamins and nutritional supplements - Whitehall Laboratories
BEMINAL FORTE - Vitamins and nutritional supplements - Whitehall Laboratories
BEMINAL STRESS PLUS - Vitamins and nutritional supplements - Whitehall Laboratories
BEMIS - Housewares - Bemis Manufacturing Co.
BEMISIA BLASTER - Insecticides - Florikan-E.S.A. Corp.
BEMOT - Health care products ☆ - Everett Laboratories Inc.
BEN - Frames–eyeglass - Rozin Optical Export Corp.
BEN & BILL'S - Candy - Ben & Bill's Chocolate Emporium
BEN & BILL'S CHOCOLATE EMPORIUM - Chocolate candy - Ben & Bill's Chocolate Emporium
BEN & HENRY'S - Pet products - Sharon B. Wilson
BEN & JERRY'S - Ice cream - Ben and Jerry's Homemade, Inc.
BEN & JERRY'S ICE CREAM - Ice cream - Ben and Jerry's Homemade, Inc.
BEN & JERRY'S LIGHT - Ice milk - Ben and Jerry's Homemade, Inc.
BEN & JERRY'S SMOOTH NO CHUNKS! - Ice cream - Ben and Jerry's Homemade, Inc.
BEN-AQUA - Pharmaceutical preparations - Syosset Laboratories Inc.
BEN BERGER - Gloves - Ben Berger LLC.
BEN BEY - Cigars - National Cigar Corp.
BEN BIO - Furniture - Ben Big Group America Inc.
BEN-CAINE B-B - Pharmaceutical preparations ☆ - Ulmer Pharmacal Co.
BEN COOPER - Games - Ben Cooper Inc.
BEN CRENSHAW - Golfing equipment - Brunswick Corp.
BEN D. BIGTOP - Toys - Russ Berrie and Co., Inc.
BEN D. BONES - Toys - Russ Berrie and Co., Inc.
BEN DAVIS - Clothing - Ben Davis Co.
BEN E. KEITH - Salad dressings–bottled - Hudson Industries, Inc.
BEN ELLIS - Greeting cards - Benjamin Franklin Ellis, Jr.
BEN-FIT SOFT TOUCH MIRACLE BRIDGE - Ophthalmic goods - Benson Optical Co., Inc.
BEN FRANKLIN - Cigar boxes–wood - Consolidated Cigar Corp.
BEN FRANKLIN - Clocks ☆ - Ridgeway Clock Co.
BEN FRANKLIN - Department stores - Ben Franklin Stores Inc.
BEN FRANKLIN - Fruits and vegetables - Nelson and Co. Inc.
BEN FRANKLIN - Pencils - Empire Berol USA
BEN-GAY - Analgesics - Pfizer Inc.
BEN GULLION - Beverages–malt ☆ - European Beverage Co., Inc.
BEN HOGAN TOUR - Golfing equipment ☆ - Ben Hogan Co.
BEN HUNT - Hobby kits ☆ - Crafters
BEN HUR - Garden equipment - Van Camp Hardware & Iron Co. Inc.
BEN HUR - Perfumes - Andrew Jergens Co.
BEN HUR - Pizzas–mixes - Akins Foods, Inc.
BEN HUR - Slippers - Okawa Trading
BEN HUR - Thread - Threads USA Div.
BEN LEE - Sporting goods - Wellington Leisure Products, Inc.
BEN LOMOND - Beverages - Juba Beverages Corp.
BEN MATTE - Finishing agents - Daly's Inc.
BEN MOORE - Chocolate syrup - I.J. White Corp.
BEN NEVIS - Beverages–malt - European Beverage Co., Inc.
BEN NYE - Cosmetics - Ben Nye Inc.
BEN NYE - Cosmetics - Victoria's Dance-Theatrical Supply
BEN PEARSON - Archery equipment - Pearson Archery
BEN-REX - Pharmaceutical preparations - C.S. Ruckstuhl Co. Inc.
BEN RICHTER - Pet products - Ben Richter Co.
BEN RICKERT - Collar buttons - Ben Rickert, Inc.
BEN ROSE - Window coverings - Covoc Corp.
BEN VENUE FARM THE TACK HOUSE KITCHEN - Vegetables–pickled or brined - Heidi Eastham
BEN-WA - Health care products - Ben-Wa International Inc.
BEN WADE - Pipes–tobacco ☆ - Lane Ltd.

BENA-D - Pharmaceutical preparations - Seatrace Co.

BENADRYL - Pharmaceutical preparations - Warner-Lambert Co.

BENADRYL - Pharmaceutical preparations - Warner-Wellcome

BENADRYL ALLERGY - Antihistamine preparations - Warner-Wellcome

BENADRYL ALLERGY CHEWABLES - Antihistamine preparations - Warner-Lambert Co.

BENADRYL ALLERGY/COLD - Pharmaceutical preparations - Warner-Wellcome

BENADRYL ALLERGY/SINUS - Antihistamine preparations - Warner-Wellcome

BENADRYL COLD/FLU - See BENADRYL ALLERGY/COLD

BENADRYL DYE FREE ALLERGY - Antihistamine preparations - Warner-Wellcome

BENADRYL ITCH STICK - Pharmaceutical preparations - Warner-Wellcome

BENADRYL ITCH STOPPING GEL - Pharmaceutical preparations - Warner-Wellcome

BENAHIST - Pharmaceutical preparations ☆ - Keene Pharmaceuticals Inc.

BENAMINE - Pharmaceutical preparations ☆ - Vita-Fore Products Co.

BENASE - Health care products ☆ - Ferndale Laboratories, Inc.

BENASEPT - Pharmaceutical preparations - Glaxo Wellcome Inc.

BENAT-12 - Pharmaceutical preparations ☆ - Roberts/Hauck Pharmaceuticals Inc.

BENCH - Combs - Robert Main & Sons Inc.

BENCH & FIELD - Cat food - Martin's Feed Mills, Inc.

BENCH & FIELD - Dog food - Bench & Field

BENCH BOX - Boxes - Igloo Products Corp.

BENCH BRUTE - Tool boxes - Flambeau Products Corp.

BENCH BUDDY - Firearms, accessories, and parts - Hughes Products Co., Inc.

BENCH BUDDY - Tools - Disston Co.

BENCH CRAFT - Furniture - Bench Craft Inc.

BENCH-MADE - Golfing equipment - Falcon Golf Inc.

BENCH MADE - Upholstered furniture - Jackson of Danville Inc.

BENCH-MARK - Gloves–work - Pioneer Industrial Products Co.

BENCH MARK COMPOSITE - Krautkramer-Branson Inc.

BENCH-MART - Glass products - Poly-Tex, Inc.

BENCH-MATE - Shelving units–metal ☆ - Akro-Mils Inc.

BENCH TOP - Brackets - Kmart Properties, Inc.

BENCH TOP - Tools–hand-operated - Kmart Corp.

BENCH WARMER - Trading cards and stamps - Bench Warmer International, Inc.

BENCHBUILT - Luggage - Altman Luggage Co.

BENCHCRAFT - Luggage - Airway Industries, Inc.

BENCHCRAFTERS - Toys - Princess Soft Toys

BENCHELEY - Teas - Premium Coffee

BENCHLAND - Wines - Cakebread Cellars, Inc.

BENCHLAND WINE ESTATE - Wines - Michel-Schlumberger Partners, L.P.

BENCHLEY - Cabinets - Actua

BENCHLINE - Apparel and accessories - Americo Group, Inc.

BENCHLINK - Computer software - Hewlett-Packard Co.

BENCHMADE - Chairs–wood - Les Brown Chair Co.

BENCHMADE - Knives - Benchmade Knife Co., Inc.

BENCHMADE BY BOSCA - Leather goods - Hugo Bosca Co., Inc.

BENCHMARK - Adhesives and sealants - Hot Melt Technologies

BENCHMARK - Cabinets - Starmark, Inc.

BENCHMARK - Clocks - Benchmark Clock Co.

BENCHMARK - Doors–storm - General Products Co. Inc.

BENCHMARK - Exercising equipment ☆ - American Athletic Inc.

BENCHMARK - Flatware - Reed and Barton Corp.

BENCHMARK - Giftware - Baldwin Hardware Corp.

BENCHMARK - Hoses - Aeroquip Corp.

BENCHMARK - Luggage - Airway Industries, Inc.

BENCHMARK - Paneling - Lamit Industries, Inc.

BENCHMARK - Rifle accessories - Aspen Outdoors, Inc.

BENCHMARK - Thermometers - Benchmark Industries, Inc.

BENCHMARK - Tools–power-driven ☆ - Shopsmith Inc.

BENCHMARK - Varnishes - Standard Brands Paint Co.

BENCHMARK - Vinyl - Wolverine Technologies

BENCHMARK - Wallpaper - Decorative Coverings Inc.

BENCHMARK BOOKS - Publisher's imprints - Van Nostrand Reinhold Inc.

BENCHMARK NATURALLY - Wallpaper ☆ - Benchmark Preferred Wallcoverings

BENCHMARK SERIES I - Partitions–wood - Dowcraft Corp.

BENCHMARK SINGLE BARREL - Beverages–alcohol ☆ - Sazerac Co. Inc.

BENCHMARK SOUR MASH - Liquors - Sazerac Co. Inc.

BENCHMARQ - Electronic equipment - Bench Marq Controls Inc.

BENCHMASTER - Tools - Structural Plastics Corp.

BENCHMATE - Chemical preparations - Burns Philp Food Inc.

BENCHPRO - Adhesives and sealants - Syntronic Instruments, Inc.

BENCHWARMER - Shoes - C.O. Lynch Enterprises, Inc.

BENCHWARMER, THE - Jackets - Howe K. Sipes Co.

BENCO - Capes–fur - Benco Manufacturing Co.

BENCO - Jewelry - Ed Benjamin & Sons Inc.

BENCO - Publisher's imprints - Benjamin Co.

BENCO PEAK - Food products - Trinidad/Benham Holding Co.

BENCONE - Apparel and accessories - Bencone Uniforms

BENCOTE - Ophthalmic goods - Benson Optical Co., Inc.

BEND-A-BEAM - Lighting equipment - Bridgeport Metal Goods Manufacturing Co.

BEND-A-BITTYS - Dolls ☆ - Diener Industries Inc.

BEND-A-LITE FLEXIBLE NEON - Lighting equipment - Richard H. Schwarz

BEND-A-PET - Toys–stuffed ☆ - Fun World Inc.

BEND-A-TWISTS - Dolls ☆ - Diener Industries Inc.

BEND BAND - Toys - Allied Toy Co.

BEND EASY - Oils–essential - Maharishi Ayur-Ved Products International, Inc.

BEND-ENDER - Shovels ☆ - Cobraco Manufacturing, Inc.

BEND-IT - Frames–picture ☆ - Bendix Mouldings Inc.

BEND-LOK SYSTEM - Tires–bicycles - Skyway Recreation Products

BEND 'N POSE - Dolls - Santa's Best

BEND 'N STRETCH - Apparel–children's - Bend 'n Stretch Inc.

BEND OVER - Women's slacks - Levi Strauss & Co.

BEND OVER MATE - Women's apparel ☆ - Levi Strauss & Co.

BEND-PAK - Machinery - Bend-Pak

BENDABLES - Footwear - L.A. Gear, Inc.

BENDABLES, THE - Toys - Henry Gordy International Inc.

BENDECTIN - Pharmaceutical preparations ☆ - Marion Merrell Dow

BENDER & TRAUB - Mustard - Bender & Traub Foods, Inc.

BENDEROIDS - Toys–models - Toymax Inc.

BENDERS - Hair curlers - Clairol Inc.

BENDI BOYS - Skin care products - Dome Cosmetics

BENDIGO - Apparel and accessories - Bendigo International Inc.

BENDING BRANCHES - Hockey sticks and canoe paddles - Bending Branches

BENDITO - Pharmaceutical preparations - Humphreys Pharmacal Inc.

BENDIX - Brakes–bicycle - Mark Worksman Bicycle Brake Corp. International

BENDIX - Frames–picture - Bendix Mouldings Inc.

BENDIX - Motor vehicle parts and accessories - Alliedsignal Inc.

BENDIX - Refrigerators - White Consolidated Industries, Inc.

BENDIX CUP - Frames–eyeglass ☆ - Universal/Univis Inc.

BENDY RABBIT - Toys–stuffed ☆ - Fun World Inc.

BENDY SANTA - Toys–stuffed - Fun World Inc.

BENDY TOYS - Toys ☆ - South Bend Toy Manufacturing Co.

BENDY WENDY - Dolls - Toy Biz, Inc.

BENDYLATE - Pharmaceutical preparations ☆ - Solvay Pharmaceuticals Inc.

BENE-BAC - Pet products - Pet-Ag, Inc.

BENEATH IT ALL - Apparel–women's - Julius Corn & Co.

BENEATH THE SEA - Christmas tree ornaments - Cracker Box Inc.

BENEATH TWO SUNS - Games - Mayfair Games, Inc.

BENECOMP - Computer software - Marlin Capital, Inc.

BENEDETTO - Guitars - Robert Benedetto

BENEDETTO PICKUPS - Musical instrument accessories - Robert Benedetto

BENEDICT LUST LIBRARY PRESS - Publisher's imprints - Benedict Lust Publications

BENEDICTINE - Beverages–alcohol - Benedictine USA Corp.

BENEE - Occasional tables - JDI Group, Inc.

BENEFACTOR - Floor coverings–carpet and rugs ☆ - Lees Carpets

BENEFICIAL BOOKS - Publisher's imprints - Benedict Lust Publications

BENEFICIAL INTERNATIONAL - Skin care products - Beneficial International

BENEFIN - Vitamins and nutritional supplements - Lane Labs-USA, Inc.

BENEFIT - Cereal ☆ - General Mills, Inc.

BENEFIT - Frames–eyeglass - Liberty Optical Manufacturing Co.

BENEFIT - Insecticides - Scotts-Sierra Horticultural Products Co.

BENEFIT - Paper–writing - Champion International Corp.

BENEFIT ASSESSOR - Computer peripheral equipment - Eri Economic Research Institute, Inc.

BENEFIT BAGS - Bags–trash - James M. Alderden

BENEFIT BALL - Dolls - Mattel, Inc.

BENEFIT PERFORMANCE - Dolls - Mattel, Inc.

BENEFIT SYSTEM - Bathing suits - Apparel America, Inc.

BENEFITS NAVIGATOR - Computer software - Automating Peripherals, Inc.

BENEFOOT - Orthopedic products - Benefoot, Inc.

BENEGYN - Pharmaceutical preparations ☆ - Vortech Pharmaceuticals

BENEKE - Toilet seats - Sanderson Plumbing Products, Inc.

BENELLE - Watches - Hampden Corp.

BENELLI - Motorcycles - Benelli/Moto Guzzi North America

☆ = Now out of production

BENELLI MOTORCYCLES - Cosmopolitan Motors Inc.
BENEMID - Pharmaceutical preparations - Merck & Co., Inc. (Merck Research Laboratories)
BENEPURE - Water-purification units - Benelec Corp.
BENESSERE - Wines - Benessere Vineyards, Ltd.
BENETEAU FIRST - Sporting goods - Beneteau USA Inc.
BENETTI - Fabrics - Benetti, Inc.
BENETTON - Apparel and accessories - Benetton
BENETTON - Watches - Bulova Corp.
BENEVENTO - Beverages–alcohol - Consolidated Distilled Products Inc.
BENEVIEW - Computer software - ViewPlan Inc.
BENEVOX - Computer software - Surveytools Corp.
BENFIELD - Tools - Klein Tools Inc.
BENFITAL - Veterinary pharmaceutical preparations ✩ - Boehringer Ingelheim Animal Health, Inc.
BENGAL - Archery equipment - Martin Archery Inc.
BENGAL - Craft supplies - James Thompson and Co. Inc.
BENGAL - Leather goods - Casecraft Inc.
BENGAL - Machinery - Flow International Corp.
BENGAL - Tape–adhesive - Permacel
BENGAL - Tobacco–chewing or smoking - James B. Russell Inc.
BENGAL - Twine ✩ - John Rauschenberger Co.
BENGAL PEARL - Shrimp - Continental Seafoods Inc.
BENGAL SPICE - Teas–herbal - Celestial Seasonings, Inc.
BENGAL SWIRL - Wallcoverings - Stretchwall Fabrics Co.
BENGALA - Floor coverings–carpet and rugs ✩ - Eurotex Inc.
BENGALE - Glassware–household - Durand International
BENGALI - Floor coverings–carpet and rugs - Cameron Pande and Co. of New York, Inc.
BENGALI - Floor coverings–carpet and rugs ✩ - LaVelle Textile Marketing Inc.
BENGE - Musical instruments - United Musical Instruments USA Inc.
BENGE - Trumpets - King Musical Instruments
BENGT - Glassware–household - Van Dow-Fenton Inc.
BENGT BLOMQUIST - Jewelry - Swedish Products Inc. (Sojo Inc.)
BENICIA - Apparel and accessories - T.I.E. Industries, Inc.
BENIHANA FRESH 'N NATURAL - Noodles ✩ - Benihana Inc.
BENIOTOME - Beverages–alcohol - Wine of Japan Import Inc.
BENITE - Adhesives and sealants - Daly's Inc.
BENITO J. - Apparel and accessories ✩ - Edison Brothers Stores, Inc.
BENJ. - See also BENJAMIN
BENJ. N. CONN - Giftware - Benjamin N. Conn
BENJAMIN - See also BENJ.
BENJAMIN - Electronic equipment - Benjamin International Inc.
BENJAMIN - Firearms, accessories, and parts - Benjamin Sheridan Corp.
BENJAMIN - Toys–stuffed - Dakin Inc.
BENJAMIN ADAM - Bookcases–wood - Naomi Gale Wall Systems
BENJAMIN & MEDWIN - Automotive repair shops–tires - Benjamin & Medwin Inc.
BENJAMIN BEAR - Dinnerware–plastic - Design Imports Ltd.
BENJAMIN BEAR - Toys–stuffed - Russ Berrie and Co., Inc.
BENJAMIN COMPANY BOOK - Publisher's imprints - Benjamin Co.
BENJAMIN FRANKLIN - Desk sets - Stanton's Quills
BENJAMIN LAMBERT - Recording label ✩ - Acoustographic Records
BENJAMIN MARTIN - Frames–picture - Benjamin Martin Corp.
BENJAMIN MOORE - Paints - Benjamin Moore & Co.
BENJAMIN/SHERIDAN - Guns - Crosman Corp.
BENJAMIN-SHERIDAN - Sporting goods ✩ - Rothco Inc.
BENJAMIN SIGNALS - Lighting fixtures ✩ - Thomas Industries Inc.
BENJAMIN SISKO - Novelty items - Paramount Pictures Corp.
BENJAMIN TWIGGS - Food products - Benjamin Twiggs
BENJANE - Novelty items - Benjane Arts
BENJANE ARTS - Novelty items - Benjane Arts
BENJI - Toys–stuffed - Dakin Inc.
BENJI'S MOIST 'N CHUNKY - Dog food - Ralston Purina Co.
BENLATE - Fungicides - E.I. Dupont de Nemours and Co.
BENLOLO - Jewelry - David Benlolo
BENMAR - Electronic equipment - Benmar Marine Electronics
BENMAR FMS 300 - Electronic equipment - Benmar Marine Electronics
BENMARL - Wines - Benmarl Wine Co. Ltd.
BENNE - Candy - Byrd Cookie Co.
BENNER - Glassware–household - Benner Glassware Inc.
BENNER - Teas - Aldi Inc.
BENNETT - Dinnerware–glass - Arita Sales Co. Inc.
BENNETT - Gasoline - Bennett Pump Co.
BENNETT - Health care products - Puritan-Bennett Corp.
BENNETT - Tools - Bennett Marine Inc.

BENNETT - Watches - Bennett Brothers Inc.
BENNETT BILT - Wastebaskets - Bennett Manufacturing Co. Inc.
BENNETT/IGLOO - Recording label - Jazz Composer's Orchestra Association Inc.
BENNETT MARINE - Tools - Bennett Marine Inc.
BENNETTE - Paints - Bennette Paint Manufacturing Co.
BENNETTS - Food products - Serv-Agen Corp.
BENNETT'S - Paints - Devoe Paint Co.
BENNIE'S TOE TREATS - Socks - Ben Berger LLC.
BENNIGAN'S - Barbecue sauce - S & A Restaurant Corp.
BENNINGTON - Bathroom fixtures ✩ - Artesian Industries
BENNINGTON - Cabinets ✩ - Decora
BENNINGTON - Cabinets–wood - Parcraft Distinctive Cabinetry
BENNINGTON - Dinnerware - Bennington Potters
BENNINGTON - Furniture–children's - Child Craft Industries Inc.
BENNINGTON - Golfing equipment - Bennington Golf Co.
BENNINGTON - Soap - Bennington Design Inc.
BENNINGTON - Tableware–china ✩ - Lenox, Inc.
BENNINGTON - Travel bags and accessories - Jameslee Corp.
BENNINGTON BASIC - Dinnerware–glass - Bennington Potters
BENNINGTON BEAR - Toys–stuffed - Russ Berrie and Co., Inc.
BENNINGTON BRONZE - Tools - Virginia Metalcrafters Inc.
BENNINGTON CLASSIC - Dinnerware–glass - Bennington Potters
BENNINGTON ESTATES - Furniture - Singer Furniture Co.
BENNINGTON FORGE - Cutlery - Lifetime Hoan Corp.
BENNOU, LTD. - Calendars - Bennou, Ltd.
BENNY - Frames–eyeglass - U.S. Optical Frame Co.
BENNY BLANKET - Toys–stuffed - Rumpus Corp.
BENNY GOODMAN - Musical instrument accessories ✩ - Selmer Co. Inc.
BENNY GOODMAN - Recording label - Estate of Benny Goodman
BENNY-THE-BUG - Toys - Roxide International, Inc.
BENNY'S BRAND - Fruits and vegetables - R.B. Packing Inc.
BENO - Fishing lures - Mill Run Products Co.
BENO J. GUNDLACH - Tools - Impo Glaztile Inc.
BENOJECT - Pharmaceutical preparations ✩ - Merz Inc.
BENOL - Lubricants - Klotz Special Formula Products, Inc.
BENOMINE - Pharmaceutical preparations - C.S. Ruckstuhl Co. Inc.
BENOMYL - Pesticides–household - Bonide Products, Inc.
BENOQUIN - Skin care products - ICN Pharmaceuticals Inc.
BENORA - Wines ✩ - Possum Trot Vineyards
BENOXYL - Pharmaceutical preparations - Stiefel Laboratories, Inc.
BENOXYL 5 ACNE LOTION - Skin care products - Stiefel Laboratories, Inc.
BENOXYL 10 ACNE LOTION - Skin care products - Stiefel Laboratories, Inc.
BENRIACH - Beverages–malt - European Beverage Co., Inc.
BENRINNES - Beverages–malt - European Beverage Co., Inc.
BENRUS - Watches ✩ - Hampden Corp.
BEN'S - Computers - Owl Software Corp.
BEN'S - Insecticides - Rothco Inc.
BEN'S BACKYARD 23 % DEET INSECT REPELLENT - Repellent - Tender Corp.
BEN'S MAX - Repellent - Tender Corp.
BENS PRIDE - Fruits and vegetables - London Fruit Inc.
BEN'S WILDERNESS - Repellent - Tender Corp.
BENSDORP - Chocolate candy - W.L.M. Bensdorp Co.
BENSDORP - Cocoa–powders or mixes - Dean & Deluca Inc.
BENSDORP - Confectioneries - Cosmo Food USA
BENSON - Recording label - Benson Music Group
BENSON & HEDGES - Cigarettes - Philip Morris Companies Inc.
BENSON & HEDGES DELUXE ULTRA LIGHTS - Cigarettes - Philip Morris Companies Inc.
BENSON & HEDGES LIGHTS - Cigarettes - Philip Morris Companies Inc.
BENSON & HEDGES PARK AVENUE - Cigarettes - Philip Morris Companies Inc.
BENSON SCRIPTS - Computer software - Adobe Systems Inc.
BENSON'S - Beverages - Aloe Laboratories, Inc.
BENSULFOID - Skin care products - ECR Pharmaceuticals
BENT - Recording label - Jazz Composer's Orchestra Association Inc.
BENT ARM OAK - Tables–metal - Taylor-Ramsey Corp.
BENT ARROW - Shirts - Cluett, Peabody & Co.
BENT BRYLON - Pipes–tobacco ✩ - S.M. Frank & Co. Inc. (Kaywoodie-Yello-Bole-Medico)
BENT SPECIAL FERTILIZER - Fertilizers - Plant Marvel Laboratories
BENT WING - Toys - Tonka Corp.
BENTECH - Chemical preparations - Bentley Mills, Inc.
BENTHIAZIDE - Pharmaceutical preparations - Parmed Pharmaceuticals, Inc.
BENTHIC - Recording label - Rustron Music Productions

✩ = Now out of production

BENTHIN - Blinds–vertical - Vertical Blind Factory
BENTLEY - Blinds–vertical - Tontine/VyTech Industries Inc.
BENTLEY - Cabinets ☆ - American Woodmark Corp.
BENTLEY - Clocks ☆ - Ridgeway Clock Co.
BENTLEY - Flatware - Washington Forge Inc.
BENTLEY - Floor coverings–carpet and rugs - Bentley Mills, Inc.
BENTLEY - Flowers, plants, and seeds - Bentley Seeds Inc.
BENTLEY - Furniture ☆ - Universal Flooring
BENTLEY - Gin - Majestic Distilling Co.
BENTLEY - Mattresses - Ohio Mattress Co.
BENTLEY - Motor vehicles–automobiles - Bentley Motors Inc.
BENTLEY - Shirts - Tica Industries Inc.
BENTLEY - Tables–wood - Krueger International, Inc.
BENTLEY - Wallpaper - Wolf-Gordon Inc.
BENTLEY - Wallpaper ☆ - Advent Industries Inc.
BENTLEY BEAR - Toys–stuffed - Dakin Inc.
BENTLEY BUNNY - Toys–stuffed - Russ Berrie and Co., Inc.
BENTLEY SYSTEMS, INC. - Computer software - Bentley Systems, Inc.
BENTLEY'S BEST - Pet food - Old Mother Hubbard Dog Food Co., Inc.
BENTLEYS CONFECTIONERY - Candy - British American Imports
BENTLITE - Glass products ☆ - Laminated Glass Corp.
BENTLY - Guitars - St. Louis Music Supply Co.
BENTLY - Toys–stuffed - Eden LLC
BENTO - Computer software - Apple Computer Inc.
BENTOEL INTERNATIONAL - Cigarettes - G.A. Georgopulo & Co. Inc.
BENTON - Flowers, plants, and seeds - Jonathan Green, Inc.
BENTON - Office supplies - Benton Announcements Inc.
BENTON - Shoes - Allen-Edmonds Shoe Corp.
BENTON & SMITH - Apparel–women's - Perry Manufacturing Co.
BENTON BEAR - Dolls - Mattel, Inc.
BENTON CENTER - Floor coverings - Armstrong World Industries, Inc.
BENTON HARBOR - Floor coverings–carpet and rugs - Philadelphia Carpets
BENTONY - Luggage - Bentony, Inc.
BENTRAC - Pharmaceutical preparations ☆ - Kenyon Drug Co. Inc.
BENTWOOD - Furniture - Haworth, Inc.
BENTYL - Pharmaceutical preparations - Marion Merrell Dow
BENTZKNIT - Bathing suits - Catalina
BENULFOID CREAM - Pharmaceutical preparations - ECR Pharmaceuticals
BENVENUTO CELLINI - Watches - Rolex Watch USA, Inc.
BENWAL - Oboes - Ben Storch Corp.
BENWOOD - Varnishes - Benjamin Moore & Co.
BENYLIN - Cough medicines - Parke-Davis
BENYLIN - Cough medicines - Warner-Wellcome
BENYLIN MULTI-SYMPTOM - Cough medicines - Warner-Wellcome
BENYLIN PEDIATRIC - Cough medicines - Warner-Wellcome
BENYOR - Cigarettes - Brown & Williamson Tobacco Corp.
BENZ - Recording label ☆ - J.R. Records
BENZ-ALL - Cleaning preparations ☆ - Xttrium Laboratories Inc.
BENZ-G - Contact lenses - Benz Research and Development Corp.
BENZ-PIC - Health care products ☆ - JMI-Canton Pharmaceuticals
BENZA - Pharmaceutical preparations - Century Pharmaceuticals Inc.
BENZAC - Pharmaceutical preparations - Owen/Galderma Laboratories Inc.
BENZAGEL - Pharmaceutical preparations - Dermik Laboratories Inc.
BENZALL - Skin care products ☆ - Tweezerman Corp.
BENZAMYCIN - Pharmaceutical preparations - Dermik Laboratories Inc.
BENZEDRINE - Pharmaceutical preparations - Smithkline Beecham Corp.
BENZEL'S - Pretzels ☆ - Benzel's Bretzel Bakery, Inc.
BENZER - Apparel and accessories - Yogi International, Inc.
BENZHYDROL - Pharmaceutical preparations ☆ - City Chemical Corp.
BENZIE-PAK - Pharmaceutical preparations - Dermik Laboratories Inc.
BENZIGER - Publisher's imprints - MacMillan Publishing Co. Inc.
BENZIGER - Wines - Glen Ellen Winery
BENZO-CREME - Pharmaceutical preparations ☆ - Reese Chemical Co.
BENZO-MENTH - Pharmaceutical preparations ☆ - Pal-Pak Inc.
BENZO-SAL - Pharmaceutical preparations ☆ - Ulmer Pharmacal Co.
BENZO-TROCHES - Cold remedies ☆ - Reese Chemical Co.
BENZOCOL - Pharmaceutical preparations - Roberts/Hauck Pharmaceuticals Inc.
BENZODENT - Pharmaceutical preparations - Richardson-Vicks USA
BENZODYNE - Health care products - Kay Pharmacal Co. Inc.
BENZOIN - Pet products - Morton Pharmaceuticals Inc.
BENZOKAL - Skin care products - Gigi Laboratories
BEOCENTER - Electronic equipment - Bang & Olufsen of America Inc.
BEOCORD - Electronic equipment - Bang & Olufsen of America Inc.
BEOGRAM - Electronic equipment - Bang & Olufsen of America Inc.
BEOLINK - Electronic equipment - Bang & Olufsen of America Inc.

BEOMASTER - Electronic equipment - Bang & Olufsen of America Inc.
BEOSYSTEM 5500 - Electronic equipment ☆ - Bang & Olufsen of America Inc.
BEOVOX - Electronic equipment - Bang & Olufsen of America Inc.
BEP - Computer software - Hospice of Southeastern Michigan
BEP - Electrical equipment - Flow Measurement, Inc.
BEPI - Wines - Vintwood International Ltd.
BEPPE SPADACIMC - Apparel and accessories - Jerry Kohn Inc.
BEPUZZLED - Games - Lombard Marketing, Inc.
BEPUZZLED JR. - Games - Lombard Marketing, Inc.
BEQUEST - Clocks ☆ - General Time Corp. (Westclox/Seth Thomas Div.)
BEQUEST - Floor coverings–carpet and rugs ☆ - Regal Rugs Inc.
BEQUIPCO - Insecticides - Breeders Equipment Co.
BER-BO-ZIN - Antiseptics ☆ - Washington Homeopathic Products
BER-EX - Pharmaceutical preparations - Dolgin Acme Foods
BERA - Wines - Pellegrini Bros. Wines Inc.
BERASINI - Milk - Oak Farms Dairies
BERAWAGEN - Watches - Cooper & Co., Inc.
BERBER - Mats - Interstate Mat & Rubber
BERBER - Skin care products ☆ - Hess Hair Milk Laboratories Inc.
BERBER II - Floor coverings ☆ - Bellbridge Carpets
BERBER ACCENT - Floor coverings–carpet and rugs - Galaxy Carpet Mills Inc.
BERBER CLASSIC - Floor coverings–carpet and rugs ☆ - Karastan-Bigelow Inc.
BERBER INTERNATIONALS - Floor coverings–carpet and rugs ☆ - Concepts International
BERBER KING - Floor coverings–carpet and rugs - Barrett Carpet Mills Inc.
BERBER KNIT - Floor coverings–carpet and rugs - Porter Carpet Mills Inc.
BERBER-TAK - Floor coverings–carpet and rugs - Carpet Crafts Inc.
BERBER-TEK - Floor coverings–carpet and rugs ☆ - Customweave Carpets Inc.
BERBER TREND - Floor coverings–carpet and rugs ☆ - Karastan-Bigelow Inc.
BERBER TWIST - Floor coverings–carpet and rugs ☆ - Porter Carpet Mills Inc.
BERBER WEAVE - Blinds–venetian ☆ - Hunter Douglas, Inc.
BERBERA - Floor coverings–carpet and rugs - Artistic Rugs Inc.
BERBERE - Floor coverings–carpet and rugs ☆ - Patrick Carpet Mills
BERBEREAU - Floor coverings–carpet and rugs - Karastan-Bigelow Inc.
BERBEREAU CHECK - Floor coverings–carpet and rugs ☆ - Karastan-Bigelow Inc.
BERBEREAU PRISMS - Floor coverings–carpet and rugs ☆ - Karastan-Bigelow Inc.
BERBERESQUE - Floor coverings–carpet and rugs ☆ - Cabin Crafts Carpets
BERBERPLUSH - Floor coverings–carpet and rugs ☆ - Eurotex Inc.
BERBERTEK - Floor coverings–carpet and rugs - Daltonian Carpet & Cushion Inc.
BERBERTEX - Floor coverings–carpet and rugs - Gulistan Carpet Inc.
BERBERTEX SUPREME - Floor coverings–carpet and rugs - Gulistan Carpet Inc.
BERCHET - Sand and water toys - International Playthings Inc.
BERCLON - Floor coverings–carpet and rugs - Princeton Carpets
BERCO - Work clothes - Berco, Inc.
BERCONA - Watches - Belair Watch Corp.
BERDEL - Ophthalmic goods ☆ - Luxottica
BERDOVES - Soap - Nailtex Inc.
BERDY SMARTCLINIC - Computer storage devices–magnetic - Berdy Medical Systems, Inc.
BERDY SMARTMED - Computer storage devices - Berdy Medical Systems, Inc.
BEREA - Chimes ☆ - Nutone Inc.
BEREK - Apparel - Jack Berek Ltd.
BERELIS TROPICAL GLACE' - Ice cream - Bernardo Perez & Asociados, Inc.
BERELLA - Yarn - Bernat Yarn & Craft Corp.
BERELLA 4 - Handwork supplies - Bernat Yarn & Craft Corp.
BERELLA SPORTSPUN - Yarn - Bernat Yarn & Craft Corp.
BERELSON - Seafood products–fresh or frozen ☆ - Nichirei Foods America
BERENICE - Glassware–household - Durand International
BERENSTAIN BEARS - Cookies - D.F. Stauffer Biscuit Co., Inc.
BERENSTAIN BEARS - Wallpaper ☆ - Priss Prints Inc.
BERENSTAIN BEARS' OLYMPICS, THE - Electronic equipment ☆ - Texas Instruments Inc.
BERENSTAIN BEARS ON THE JOB, THE - Electronic equipment ☆ - Texas Instruments Inc.
BERENSTAIN GUMMI BEARS - Candy - Murray-Allen International Inc.
BERENTZEN - Liquors - William Grant & Sons, Inc.
BERET - Colognes - Chesebrough-Pond's USA Co.

☆ = Now out of production

BERETTA - Food products - Bel Canto Fancy Foods Ltd.
BERETTA - Furniture - Lane Co. Inc.
BERETTA - Motor vehicles - General Motors Corp. (Chevrolet Motor Div.)
BERETTA GTZ - Motor vehicles - General Motors Corp. (Chevrolet Motor Div.)
BERETTA U.S.A. - Distilling apparatus–laboratory - Beretta USA Corp.
BERG - Automotive parts and accessories - Echlin Inc.
BERG - Cables - Berg Technology, Inc.
BERGADER - Cheese - Peacock Foods Inc.
BERGAMO - Floor coverings - Mannington Resilient Floors
BERGAMO - Furniture - Broyhill Furniture Industries, Inc.
BERGAMO - Leather goods - Korchmar Case Co.
BERGAMO - Shoes - Allen-Edmonds Shoe Corp.
BERGAMO - Wallets - Avalon Resources Group Inc.
BERGAMOT - Hair care products - Ampro Industries, Inc.
BERGDALAGLAS - Figurines - Charles Norman Inc.
BERGDORF - Frames–picture - Terragrafics Inc.
BERGDORF GOODMAN - Apparel and accessories - Neiman-Marcus Group, Inc.
BERGELIN LONGSTRING - Rackets–tennis - MacGregor Sport Products Inc.
BERGEN - Brushes–paint ☆ - PPG Industries, Inc.
BERGEN - Lighting fixtures ☆ - Liteway
BERGEN - Marzipan - Haram-Christensen Corp.
BERGEN BEAR - Toys–stuffed - Russ Berrie and Co., Inc.
BERGEN NURSERIES - Trees - Recyc, Inc.
BERGEY - Dairy products - Bergey's Dairy Farm
BERGFELD - Wines ☆ - Golden State Vintners
BERGGREN ORIGINALS - Dishes–china - Bergquists
BERGGREN TRAYNER - Dishes–china - Bergquists
BERGHAUS - Sporting goods - Denali International Inc.
BERGHOF - Housewares ☆ - Washington Forge Inc.
BERGHOFF - Beverages–malt - Joseph Huber Brewing Co., Inc.
BERGHOFF - Root beer–bottled or canned - Berghoff Restaurant Co. of Delaware
BERGHOFF BOCK - Beverages–malt - Joseph Huber Brewing Co., Inc.
BERGHOFF DARK - Beverages–malt - Joseph Huber Brewing Co., Inc.
BERGHOFF LIGHT - Beverages–malt - Joseph Huber Brewing Co., Inc.
BERGQUIST - Napkins–paper - Bergquists
BERGS - Flowers, plants, and seeds - Access Denmark
BERGSMA - Paper products - Jody Bergsma Galleries, Inc.
BERGUMMER - Cheese - Swissrose International Inc.
BERIDOX - Electronic equipment - Fuji Photo Film USA Inc.
BERING - Cigars - Swisher International, Inc.
BERING CIGARILLO - Cigars - Swisher International, Inc.
BERINGER - Wines - Wine World Inc.
BERISON - Battery chargers - Berison Industries Inc.
BERJUSA - Dolls - J.C. Toys Group, Inc.
BERK - Cooking utensils–aluminum ☆ - Holland-American Importing Co. Inc.
BERK-LITE - Sporting goods ☆ - Outdoor Technologies Group
BERKELEY - Curtains–shower - Dawson Home Fashions, Inc.
BERKELEY - Floor coverings–carpet and rugs ☆ - Royalweve Carpet Mills
BERKELEY - Furniture - Berkeley Upholstering Co.
BERKELEY - Housewares - Associated Products Inc.
BERKELEY - Housewares - Educational Products Co.
BERKELEY - Pencils ☆ - Faber-Castell Corp.
BERKELEY FARMS - Milk - Berkeley Farms Inc.
BERKELEY FORGE - Garden furniture–wood - Berkeley Products Inc.
BERKELEY HALL COLLECTION - Furniture - Broyhill Furniture Industries, Inc.
BERKELEY JET DRIVE - Engines–marine - Hardin Marine Inc.
BERKELEY REVIEW, THE - Publisher's imprints - Dale Schmidt
BERKELEY SPRINGS - Water–bottled or canned - Berkeley Club Beverages
BERKELEY SQUARE - Furniture - National/Mt. Airy Furniture
BERKLEIGH - Pet products - Val-A Co.
BERKLEY - Apparel–men's - Berkley Shirt Co. Inc.
BERKLEY - Cribs–wood ☆ - Welsh Co.
BERKLEY - Floor coverings–carpet and rugs ☆ - Atlas Carpet Mills Inc.
BERKLEY - Neckties - Salant/Manhattan Industries
BERKLEY - Publisher's imprints - Berkley Publishing Corp.
BERKLEY - Shoes - Allen-Edmonds Shoe Corp.
BERKLEY - Sporting goods - Outdoor Technologies Group
BERKLEY - Tools–plumbing - Embassy Industries Inc.
BERKLEY BIONIX - Sporting goods - Outdoor Technologies Group
BERKLEY LANE MEMORIES - Apparel and accessories - Bertie I. Arnhols
BERKLEY MEDALLION BOOKS - Publisher's imprints - Berkley Publishing Corp.
BERKLEY SELECT - Fishing tackle - Outdoor Technologies Group

BERKLEY SQUARE - Floor coverings–carpet and rugs - Hollytex Carpet Mills Inc.
BERKLEY SQUARE - Paper–toilet ☆ - Warren Chemical Products Co.
BERKLEY STRIKE - Fishing lures ☆ - Outdoor Technologies Group
BERKLEY, THE - Recliners - Lane Co. Inc.
BERKLEY VECTRA - Sporting goods ☆ - Outdoor Technologies Group
BERKLINE - Recliners - Berkline Corp.
BERKS - Meat products - Berks Packing Co., Inc.
BERKSHIRE - Cabinets ☆ - H.J. Scheirich Co.
BERKSHIRE - Cabinets ☆ - Yorktowne Inc.
BERKSHIRE - Calendars - Berkshire Stationery Inc.
BERKSHIRE - Candy - Berkshire Candy Co.
BERKSHIRE - Clocks - General Time Corp. (Westclox/Seth Thomas Div.)
BERKSHIRE - Clocks - Ridgeway Clock Co.
BERKSHIRE - Cutlery - Washington Forge Inc.
BERKSHIRE - Floor coverings–carpet and rugs - Atlas Carpet Mills Inc.
BERKSHIRE - Floor coverings–carpet and rugs - Bloomsburg Carpet Industries
BERKSHIRE - Floor coverings–tile ☆ - Kentile Floors Inc.
BERKSHIRE - Furniture - Haworth, Inc.
BERKSHIRE - Glassware–household - Seneca Glass Co.
BERKSHIRE - Gliders–metal - Turner and Seymour Manufacturing Co.
BERKSHIRE - Hosiery–women's - Mayer/Berkshire Corp.
BERKSHIRE - Mat boards - Potomac Corp.
BERKSHIRE - Mattresses - Stearns & Foster Bedding Co.
BERKSHIRE - Mushrooms - Mt. Laurel Canning Corp.
BERKSHIRE - Ophthalmic goods - Foremost Optical Products
BERKSHIRE - Shoes ☆ - Allen-Edmonds Shoe Corp.
BERKSHIRE - Tools - Great Neck Saw Manufacturers, Inc.
BERKSHIRE - Trailers–travel - Fleetwood Enterprises, Inc.
BERKSHIRE - Watches - Bulova Corp.
BERKSHIRE FARMS - Sausages - Joseph Decosta Inc.
BERKSHIRE HILLS - Food products - Butler Wholesale Products
BERKSHIRE LITES - Hosiery - Mayer/Berkshire Corp.
BERKSHIRE PERFORMANCE - Panty hose - Mayer/Berkshire Corp.
BERKSHIRE PLACE - Floor coverings–carpet and rugs - Queen Carpet Corp.
BERKSHIRE SILKY - Hosiery - Mayer/Berkshire Corp.
BERKSHIRE SPRINGS - Water–bottled or canned - Berkshire Springs Inc.
BERKSHIRE ULTRA - Hosiery - Mayer/Berkshire Corp.
BERKWEAVE - Window shades - Berkshire Industries Inc.
BERLANA - Floor coverings–carpet and rugs - Collins & Aikman Corp.
BERLAND - Giftware - Joseph Berland
BERLANTI COSMETICS CORP. - Cosmetics - Berlanti Cosmetics Corp.
BERLECO - Hobby kits - Berman Leather Co. Inc.
BERLEI - Brassieres (Bras) - Biflex International, Inc.
BERLIN - Furniture - Haworth, Inc.
BERLIN - Leather–glove - Berlin Glove Co. Inc.
BERLIN - Saddles - Thornhill Enterprises, Inc.
BERLIN CLASSICS - Recording label - Edel America Records, Inc.
BERLIN FLYER - Toys - Berlin Wood Products
BERLIN GLOVE - Gloves - Berlin Glove Co. Inc.
BERLIN PLATES - Giftware - Viking Import House Inc.
BERLIN WALL - Apparel and accessories - Berlin Wall
BERLINA - Motor vehicles–automobiles ☆ - Alfa Romeo Distributors of North America
BERLINER BAR - Beverages–alcohol - Carradale Import Co.
BERLINGOT - Floor coverings–carpet and rugs ☆ - Foreign Accents
BERLITE - Brushes–paint - Wright-Bernet
BERLITZ - Toys–electronic - Berlitz Investment Corp.
BERLITZ INTERPRETER - Computer software - Microlytics Inc.
BERLITZ PUBLICATIONS INC. - Publisher's imprints - MacMillan Publishing Co. Inc.
BERLON - Skin care products - Freeman Cosmetics Corp.
BERLUCCH - Wines - Vinvino Wine Co. Inc.
BERMUDA - Brushes–paint - Corona Brushes Inc.
BERMUDA - Floor coverings–carpet and rugs - Playfield International Inc.
BERMUDA - Furniture - Halcyon Inc.
BERMUDA - Giftware - Sasaki
BERMUDA - Glassware–household ☆ - Oneida Ltd.
BERMUDA - House furnishings - Dan River Inc.
BERMUDA - Lighting fixtures - Swivelier Co. Inc.
BERMUDA - Motor vehicles–motor homes - Baron Motor Homes Inc.
BERMUDA - Window shades ☆ - Colony Shade Co.
BERMUDA 40 - Ships–sailing vessels - The Hinckley Co.
BERMUDA CASUALS - Apparel and accessories - USA Enterprises Inc.
BERMUDA CUP - Colognes ☆ - Gary Farn Ltd.

BERMUDA DUNES - Floor coverings–carpet and rugs ☆ - World Carpets, Inc.

BERMUDA DUNES - Floor coverings–carpet and rugs ☆ - Zenith Carpets

BERMUDA GENTLEMAN - Colognes ☆ - Gary Farn Ltd.

BERMUDA ISLES - Beverages–alcohol - Holiday Food & Beverage Ltd.

BERMUDA PLUS - Floor coverings–carpet and rugs - Playfield International Inc.

BERMUDA RAIN - Water–bottled or canned - Jerome J. Gilels

BERMUDA RINGS - Snack foods ☆ - Bachman Co.

BERMUDA SHORTS - Flowers, plants, and seeds - Agrono-Tec Seed Co.

BERMUDA TRIANGLE - Games ☆ - Milton Bradley Co.

BERN CONRAD - Apparel–women's - Bern Conrad

BERN-THAL - Giftware - Bernard W. Bernthal Inc.

BERN VAN DOESBURG - Biscuits - Roth & Liebmann Inc.

BERNADAUD - Dinnerware - Bernardaud Manufacture de Limoges, N.A.

BERNAFON - Medical apparatus - Bernafon Inc.

BERNARD - Apparel and accessories - Bernard Cap Co. Inc.

BERNARD HOLA! - Beverages - Bernard Food Industries Inc. (Consumer Products Div.)

BERNARD OF HOLLYWOOD - Apparel and accessories - Renaissance Roads Productions, Inc.

BERNARD PRADEL - Wines - House of Burgundy Inc.

BERNARDAUD - Giftware - Bernardaud Limoges

BERNARDI - Food products - Bernardi Italian Foods Co.

BERNARDI - Frozen foods - Windsor Quality Food Co. Ltd.

BERNARDI FROZEN ITALIAN SPECIALTIES - Frozen foods - Windsor Quality Food Co. Ltd.

BERNARDIN - Jar tops–metal - Alltrista Corp.

BERNARDI'S - Coffee - Bernardi's Fresh Roast Inc.

BERNARDO - Footwear - E.S. Originals, Inc.

BERNARDO - Footwear–women's - Bernardo Brands

BERNARDO - Giftware ☆ - Bernard W. Bernthal Inc.

BERNARDO WINERY - Wines - Bernardo Winery

BERNARDS - Furniture - Bernards, Inc.

BERNARD'S BAKE SHOPPE - Cookies - Rich Products Corp.

BERNARDUS - Wines - Baylaurel Corp.

BERNAT - Yarn - Bernat Yarn & Craft Corp.

BERNE - Furniture - Berne Furniture Co.

BERNEESE - Cheese - Noon Hour Food Products

BERNER - Air curtain doors - Berner International Corp. (Miniveil Air Curtain Div.)

BERNER - Cheese - Berner Cheese Corp.

BERNER CHEESE - Cheese - Berner Cheese Corp.

BERNE'S - Snack foods - That's Entertainment

BERNHARD ALTMANN - Apparel and accessories - Neema Clothing, Ltd.

BERNHARD ALTMANN - Crocheted and knitted items - Mcgregor Corp.

BERNHARDT PECK - Meats–luncheon - Emmber Foods, Inc.

BERNI - Pepper - De Choix Specialty Foods Co.

BERNIE FUELETTES HOME FUELS CORPORATION - Agricultural products - Home Fuels Corp.

BERNIE KOSAR - Candy ☆ - Chris Candies Inc.

BERNIE'S - Bagels ☆ - Barney's Foods

BERNIE'S BEST BAGEL BITS - Snack foods - Joshua Enterprises Ltd.

BERNIE'S EAST BAGEL DOG - Food products ☆ - Barney's Foods

BERNINA - Dishes–china ☆ - Royal China & Porcelain Companies Inc.

BERNINA - Sewing machines–household - Bernina Sewing Machine Co. Inc.

BERNINI - Accordions - Newark Musical Merchandise Co.

BERNINI - Mirrors - Mechanical Mirror Works Inc.

BERNOULLI BOX - Computer-disk drives - Iomega Corp.

BERNRAIN - Chocolate bars ☆ - Dae Julie, Inc.

BERNSTEIN'S - Salad dressings–bottled - Curtice-Burns Foods, Inc.

BERNSTEINS - Salad dressings–bottled - Nalley's Fine Foods

BERNSTEIN'S LIGHT FANTASTIC - Salad dressings–bottled - Curtice-Burns Foods, Inc.

BEROCCA - Vitamins and nutritional supplements - Roche Laboratories

BEROCCA-C - Pharmaceutical preparations ☆ - Roche Laboratories

BEROL - Markers–felt-tip - Empire Berol USA

BEROL 8200 - Markers–felt-tip - Empire Berol USA

BEROL MARKER 8800 - Markers–felt-tip - Empire Berol USA

BEROL TIP - Markers–felt-tip ☆ - Empire Berol USA

BEROLINA - Lighters - Berolina Imports

BERONIA - Wines - House of Burgundy Inc.

B.E.R.P. - Musical instrument accessories - Musical Enterprises

BERRI BAGS - Luggage - Mercury Luggage Manufacturing Co.

BERRI-MAGIC - Flowers, plants, and seeds - Monrovia Nursery Co.

BERRIE POP - Candy - Nabisco Foods Group

BERRIES - Floor coverings–carpet and rugs ☆ - Regal Rugs Inc.

BERRIES & GOATS B G THE LEGEND OF COFFEE - Sandwiches–prepackaged - Retail Design & Licensing, Inc.

BERRIES JUBILEE - Nail care products ☆ - Noxell Corp.

BERRIES, THE - Candy ☆ - Topps Co., Inc.

BERRIGAN - Boats–canoes ☆ - Old Town Canoe Co.

BERRILY - Barbecue sauce - Wisconsin Wilderness Food

BERRINGER - Motor vehicles–trucks - Keith Huber, Inc.

BERRY - Jewelry–costume ☆ - Safari Ltd.

BERRY-A-LET - Candy - Adams & Brooks, Inc.

BERRY & CREME KISSES - Candy - Glade Taffy Town, Inc.

BERRY B. WILD - Beverages - General Mills, Inc.

BERRY BABIES - Playthings, coloring books, dolls, etc ☆ - American Greetings Corp.

BERRY BASKET - Tableware–earthenware - Pfaltzgraff Investment Co.

BERRY BEACHY - Doll clothing ☆ - American Greetings Corp.

BERRY BEARS - Snack foods - General Mills, Inc.

BERRY BERRY KIX - Cereal - General Mills, Inc.

BERRY BLEND - Tobacco–chewing or smoking - Amar Blends Co.

BERRY BLENDER - Beverages - Logret Import & Export Co.

BERRY BLUSH - Teas–herbal - Lipton Investments, Inc.

BERRY BOSS - Fruits and vegetables - BBI Produce Inc.

BERRY BUNCH - Dolls - Goldberger Doll Manufacture Co.

BERRY BUSY-BUG - Coloring books, toys, etc, now out of production - American Greetings Corp.

BERRY BUTTER - Fruit butters - Nestle USA

BERRY CRAZY CRUNCH - Cereal - Malt-O-Meal Co.

BERRY-DACTYL - Fruit drinks–bottled or canned - Cliffstar Corp.

BERRY DIPPER - Food products - Naturipe Berry Growers

BERRY FANCY FUN ROOM - Doll accessories ☆ - American Greetings Corp.

BERRY GO ROUND - Amusement rides - Bruce A. Sellner

BERRY GROWN UP PURSE - Toy purse and accessories ☆ - American Greetings Corp.

BERRY HILL - Recording label - Track America

BERRY HILL BEARS - Figurines - Youngs Inc.

BERRY HOT - Food products - Mary K. Graves

BERRY JAMBOREE - Teas - Eastern Shore Tea Co.

BERRY KING - Fruits–canned ☆ - California Farm Products Div.

BERRY KOOL - Beverages - Mackie International, Inc.

BERRY NICE DESIGNS - Pottery - A Berry Nice Design, Inc.

BERRY PATCH - Doll clothing ☆ - American Greetings Corp.

BERRY PATCH - Needles–sewing - The Berry Patch

BERRY PATCH - Skin-care products - Crabtree & Evelyn, Ltd.

BERRY PATCH COLLECTION - Stationery - Determined Productions, Inc.

BERRY PEACH SMOOTHIE - Fruit drinks–bottled or canned - Hansen Beverage Co.

BERRY QUEEN - Fruits–canned ☆ - California Farm Products Div.

BERRY-SET - Garden equipment - Science Products Co. Inc.

BERRY SWIRL - Ice cream - Nestle USA

BERRY TASTY - Beverages - Chevy's Inc.

BERRY TIME - Housewares - Shafford Co. Inc.

BERRY TREAT - Fruits–frozen - Shuksan Frozen Foods Inc.

BERRY VEAL - Food products - Dennis J. Alba & Co.

BERRY WILD CRITTERS - Candy ☆ - Sunlight Foods, Inc.

BERRYBRIDGE - Pet products - Kingdom Puzzles

BERRYESSA - Wines - Heublein, Inc.

BERRYKINS - Coloring books, modeling compound, dolls, etc ☆ - American Greetings Corp.

BERRYS BEST - Veal - Berry Veal Corp.

BERRYWINE - Wines - Berrywine Plantations Winery

BERSANO - Wines ☆ - Seagram's Chateau & Estate Wines Co.

BERSERKER - Games - Flying Buffalo Inc.

BERSERKER - Publisher's imprints - Blassingame-Spectrum Corp.

BERSTED'S SUPER MIX - Papier-mache articles - Bersted's Hobby-Craft

BERT - Food products - Bridgford Foods Corp.

BERT - Toys - Jim Henson Productions, Inc.

BERT & JOE'S - Skin care products - A K Cosmetics, Inc.

BERT GRANT'S ALE MASTER COLLECTION - Beverages - Yakima Brewing & Malting Co.

BERT GRANT'S AMBER ALE - Beverages - Yakima Brewing & Malting Co.

BERT GRANT'S FRESH HOP ALE - Beverages - Yakima Brewing & Malting Co.

BERT GRANT'S HEFE WEIZEN - Beverages - Yakima Brewing & Malting Co.

BERT GRANT'S IMPERIAL STOUT - Beverages - Yakima Brewing & Malting Co.

BERT GRANT'S INDIA PALE ALE - Beverages - Yakima Brewing & Malting Co.

☆ = Now out of production

BERT GRANT'S PERFECT PORTER - Beverages - Yakima Brewing & Malting Co.

BERT GRANT'S SCOTTISH ALE - Beverages - Yakima Brewing & Malting Co.

BERT GRANT'S SPRING FEST ALE - Beverages - Yakima Brewing & Malting Co.

BERT GRANT'S SUMMER ALE - Beverages - Yakima Brewing & Malting Co.

BERT GRANT'S WINTER ALE - Beverages - Yakima Brewing & Malting Co.

BERT PULITZER - Apparel and accessories - Neema Clothing, Ltd.

BERT PULITZER - Apparel and accessories - Sunrise Apparel, Inc.

BERT PULITZER - Apparel–men's - McCrory Corp.

BERT PULITZER - Coats–men's - Gallron

BERT PULITZER - Handkerchiefs - Mcgregor Corp.

BERT PULITZER BY AETNA - Shirts - Aetna Shirt Corp.

BERT PULITZER COLLECTORS EDITION - Apparel and accessories - Mcgregor Corp.

+BERT +RODGERS - Educational materials - Bert Rodgers Schools of Real Estate, Inc.

BERT RODGERS REAL ESTATE COURSES - Educational materials - Bert Rodgers Schools of Real Estate, Inc.

BERTAGNI - Tomato pastes and sauces ☆ - Liberty Richter Inc.

BERTAGNIR - Food products - Bel Canto Fancy Foods Ltd.

BERTANI VERONESE WINES - Wines - Palm Bay Imports, Inc.

BERTELLI - Shoes ☆ - Jack Schwartz Shoes, Inc.

BERTHA BASSET - Toys–stuffed - Russ Berrie and Co., Inc.

BERTHIOT - Lenses–photographic ☆ - Edixa Camera Co.

BERTHOLD - Computer software - Berthold Direct Corp.

BERTIE - Furniture - Boling Co.

BERTINI - Artists' materials - Andrews/Nelson/Whitehead

BERTOLINO - Meats–luncheon - Bert Packing Co.

BERTOLLI - Olive oil - Bertolli USA, Inc.

BERTOLLI CLASSICO - Olive oil - Bertolli USA, Inc.

BERTOLLI LUCCA - Breads - Speikermann's Bakery

BERTONE - Motor vehicles–automobiles - RVD International Distributors Inc.

BERTONI - Bicycles - Lawee Inc.

BERTRAM - Boats–motor - Bertram Yachts

BERTRAM BOND - Paper–bond - Tension Envelope Corp.

BERTRAND - Brandy ☆ - David Sherman Corp.

BERTUCCI'S BRICK OVEN PIZZERIA - Food products - Bertucci's Inc.

BERTUGLIA & SON - Olive oil - Bertuglia & Son, Inc.

BERUBIGEN - Pharmaceutical preparations ☆ - Upjohn Co.

BERWICK - Candy - Florence Candy Co. Inc.

BERWICK - Glassware–household ☆ - Anchor Hocking Glass, Inc.

BERWYN - Cabinets - Contempri Kitchens

BERYL - File folders - Imperial Rivets and Fasteners Co., Inc.

BERZERK - Video games - Atari Games Corp.

BERZERK CANDY WERKS - Candy - Kraft Food Ingredients Corp.

BERZERK CANDY WERKS - Candy - Philip Morris Companies Inc.

BES - Audio equipment - Bertagni Electroacoustic Systems Inc.

BES-PAK - Bags–plastic - Webster Industries

BES-PAK ZIPPER SEAL - Bags–plastic - Webster Industries

BES-PLAK - Laminated plaques - Classic Plaques Inc.

BESCO - Adhesives and sealants - Besco Marketing & Sales

BESCO - Crayons ☆ - Binney & Smith Inc.

BESCO - Vitamins - B & E Sales Co. Inc.

BESCOR - Video tapes–blank - New Products Group

BESELER - Photographic equipment - Charles Beseler Co.

BESFILE - Boxes - Charles Beseler Co.

BESITOS - Breads - El Tesoro Foods Inc.

BESKINE - Cosmetics - Pacific Corp. of America

BESLAR - Lenses–photographic - Charles Beseler Co.

BESNIER - Cheese - Made in France

BESO DE LUNA DREAM TOOLS AND COMFORTS - Candles - Beso De Luna, Inc.

BESPECO - Musical instrument accessories - Kaman Music Corp.

BESS - Construction equipment rental services - Logica North America Inc.

BESS - Floor coverings–carpet and rugs ☆ - Regal Rugs Inc.

BESS EATON - Bakery products - Bess Eaton Donut Flour Co. Inc.

BESS MUSIC - Recording label - Malaco Records Inc.

BESS TYLE - Invitations - Bess Tyle Wedding Stationery Co.

BESSEAL - Envelope stuffing and sealing machines - Besline Corp.

BESSER - Sporting goods - A & T Ski Co. Inc.

BESSERABIAN KELIM - Floor coverings–carpet and rugs - Stark Carpet Corp.

BESSEY - Clamps and vises - American Clamping Corp.

BESSEY'S - Food products - Sundor Brands Inc.

BESSIE - Flour–blended - Birkett Mills

BESSIE - Footwear - Glamour Footwear

BESSIE BEAR - Toys–stuffed - Russ Berrie and Co., Inc.

BESSIE BROWNS - Cookies - Simmers Products

BESSIE COW - Toys–stuffed ☆ - Dakin Inc.

BESSIE PEASE GUTMANN - Novelty items - Balliol Corp.

BESSIE PEASE GUTMANN - Pillows - Toy Works, Inc.

BESSINGER'S OL'FASHIONED - Pickles - Bessinger Pickle Co.

BESSON - Musical instruments - Boosey & Hawkes Buffet Crampon USA

BESSWOOD - Food products ☆ - Stemley Canning Co.

BEST - Air conditioning equipment - General Signal Power Systems, Inc.

BEST - Aircraft - Best Aviation Sales, Inc.

BEST - Apparel–athletic - Julie Hat Co. Inc.

BEST - Cheese - Holland-American Importing Co. Inc.

BEST - Chemical preparations ☆ - Woolsey Marine Industries

BEST - Computer software ☆ - Krell Software Corp.

BEST - Fishing tackle - Best Tackle Manufacturing Co.

BEST - Fishing tackle - Best Water

BEST - Flags - Valley Forge Flag

BEST - Flour–blended - Mercer Milling Co.

BEST - Fruits and vegetables - Heeren Brothers Inc.

BEST - Gasoline - Total Petroleum Inc.

BEST - Mayonnaise - Best Foods/Mueller Co.

BEST - Medical productss - Best Industries, Inc.

BEST - Sausages - Bessin Corp.

BEST - Signs - Best Manufacturing Co.

BEST - Strollers–baby - Inglesina Baby Ltd.

BEST - T-shirts–women's - Fruit of the Loom Inc.

BEST - Tobacco products ☆ - Philip Morris Companies Inc.

BEST - Vitamins and nutritional supplements - Set-N-Me-Free Aloe Vera Co.

BEST - Wallpaper - Unique Wall Fashions Inc.

BEST - Yeast - Burns Philp Food Inc.

BEST 6 CORD - Thread - Coats and Clark Inc.

BEST ALBUM YOU'VE NEVER HEARD, THE - Advertising agencies - Columbia House Co.

BEST AMERICAN CLOTHING COMPANY - Apparel–women's - Brooks Fashion Stores Inc.

BEST & JUICY - Meat products - Bristol Valley Foods, Inc.

BEST ASIC SOLUTION, THE - Computer hardware - Chip Express Corp.

BEST ASSETS - Hair care products - Helene Curtis Industries Inc.

BEST AUTOMOTIVE - Automotive parts and accessories - Oxford Speakers Co.

BEST BAGELS - Bakery products - Best Bagels L.P.

BEST BAKERS SPECIAL PATENT - Wheat–flour or meal - Pillsbury Co.

BEST BALANCE - Photographic equipment - Spectracolor, Inc.

BEST BALL - Pet products - Hueter Toledo, Inc.

BEST BATTERY, THE - Batteries - Best Battery Co., Inc.

BEST BEAR - Toys–stuffed ☆ - Gund, Inc.

BEST BEEF ON THE BLOCK, THE - Beef - Sysco Corp.

BEST BEGINNINGS - Apparel–children's - S. Schwab Co., Inc.

BEST BEGINNINGS - Toys - Mattel, Inc.

BEST BEHAVIOR - Veterinary pharmaceutical preparations - PETS 'N PEOPLE, INC.

BEST BET - Computer software - Lotto Software, Ltd.

BEST BET - Floor coverings–carpet and rugs - Calladium & Marglen

BEST BETTER GOOD - Tools–hand-operated - Uniontools, Inc.

BEST BITES - Rice cakes - U.S. Farm, Inc.

BEST BLEND - Shortening ☆ - Hunt-Wesson, Inc.

BEST BOND - Glue–household or industrial - H.B. Fuller Co. (North American Adhesives, Sealants and Coatings Group)

BEST BOOK SERIES - Publisher's imprints ☆ - Bantam Doubleday Dell Publishing Group, Inc.

BEST BOOKS - Publisher's imprints - Price Stern Sloan Inc.

BEST BRANDS - Fabrics - Best Brands Home Products, Inc.

BEST BRANDS PLUS - Housewares - Best Brands Plus, Inc.

BEST BROS. - Housewares stores - Best Bros.

BEST BUDDY - Apparel–children's - Good Lad Co.

BEST BUY - Beverages–malt ☆ - Eastern Brewing Corp.

BEST BUY - Cheese - Safeway Stores Inc.

BEST BUY - Containers–insulated - Aladdin Industries, Inc.

BEST BUY - Dog food - Freeport Roller Mills Inc.

BEST BUY - Hardware - Brown-Rogers-Dixson Co.

BEST BUY AMERICAN - Fruits and vegetables - American Growers Inc.

BEST BUY ON THE AMERICAN LANDSCAPE, THE - Garden equipment - MTD Products Inc.

BEST BUY TORTS - Bakery products - Bob Ostrow Co.

BEST-BY-TEST - Mops ☆ - Helen Keller Services for the Blind

BEST-C - Pharmaceutical preparations ☆ - Roberts/Hauck Pharmaceuticals Inc.

BEST CALIFORNIAN, THE - Soups–mixes - Amerex International Trading

BEST CAMPAIGN BETTER EDUCATION STARTS TODAY - Publisher's imprints - Educorp Systems, Inc.

BEST CHANCE - Floor coverings–carpet and rugs - Patcraft Mills Inc.

BEST CHOICE - Food products - Associated Wholesale Grocers, Inc.

BEST CHOICE - Thread - Quality Thread Co.

BEST CLUTCH BALL - Pet products - Hueter Toledo, Inc.

BEST CONNECTED E-MAIL IN THE WORLD, THE - Glassware–household - Qualcomm Inc.

BEST CRAFT - Apparel stores–lingerie - Best Manufacturing Inc.

BEST CURE FOR DRYNESS, THE - Humidifiers - Research Products Corp.

BEST CUTTING DIE COMPANY - Machinery - Best Cutting Die Co.

BEST DEMO - Consulting services - Marketing Force, Inc.

BEST EFFORT - Posters - Clement Communications Inc.

BEST ESP - Computer software - A.M. Best Co.

BEST EVER - Milk - Best-Ever Dairy Product

BEST EVER - Paints - Dean and Barry Co.

BEST FACE FORWARD - Cosmetics ☆ - Honey & Spice Toiletries

BEST FEEDS - Dog food - Best Feeds and Farm Supplies Inc.

BEST FIT - Pet products - Coastal Pet Products, Inc.

BEST FITTINGS IN THE JOINT, THE - Tubes–copper - Mueller Industries, Inc.

BEST FLEX - Jewelry - Best Products Co., Inc.

BEST FOODS - Margarine - Best Foods/Mueller Co.

BEST FOOT FORWARD - Wallcoverings - Cork Products Co. Inc.

BEST FRIEND - Jewelry - Joseph Nudelman Inc.

BEST FRIEND - Soap - Brookside Soap Inc.

BEST FRIEND - Veterinary nutritional supplements - Hamilton Horse Cookie Co.

BEST FRIEND PET TAGS - Pet products - Salco Enterprises

BEST FRIENDS - Apparel–children's - Buster Brown Apparel Inc.

BEST FRIENDS - Greeting cards - Recycled Paper Products, Inc.

BEST FRIENDS - Hobby kits ☆ - Martin F. Weber Co.

BEST FRIENDS - Puzzles ☆ - Milton Bradley Co.

BEST FRIENDS - Wallpaper - Pickhardt & Siebert USA Inc.

BEST FRIENDS - Wallpaper ☆ - Glidden Co.

BEST FRIENDS - Wallpaper ☆ - Imperial Wallcoverings, Inc.

BEST FROM OREGON, THE - Fruits–canned - Oregon Fruit Products Co., Inc.

BEST FROM START TO FINISH, THE - Lawn mowers - Ariens Co.

BEST GLOVES - Gloves–rubber - Rockford Medical & Safety Co.

BEST HAIR IMPORTS - Hair-replacement product - International Hairgoods Inc.

BEST HEALTH - Iced tea–bottled or canned - Brooklyn Bottling Co.

BEST HEALTH BEVERAGES - Beverages–carbonated - Brooklyn Bottling Corp.

BEST HEALTH WATER - Water–mineral - Brooklyn Bottling Corp.

BEST HEALTH'S ALL NATURAL - Iced tea–bottled or canned - Brooklyn Bottling Co.

BEST HOOF - Veterinary pharmaceutical preparations - Farnam Cos. Inc.

BEST INSTANT SIGN COMPANY, THE - Signs - Best Franchising Co. in the World

BEST KEPT SECRETS - Candles - Chase Collection, Inc.

BEST KEPT SECRETS - Stationery - Current, Inc.

BEST KOSHER - Meat products–beef - SWB Co. Inc.

BEST LABS - Hearing aids - Best Laboratories

BEST LIFE - Salad dressings–mixes - Best Life Co.

BEST LOAF - Desserts - Conagra, Inc.

BEST LOOK FORWARD - Hair care products - BLF, Inc.

BEST LOTTO PIZZA, THE - Pizzas–frozen - Heck's Landing Inc.

BEST MADE CUTTING TOOLS IN THE WORLD - Knife blades - General Housewares Corp.

BEST-MAID - Cleaning preparations–household - Ever-Ready Appliance Manufacturing Co.

BEST MAID - Cookies - Best Maid Cookie Co.

BEST MAID - Pickles - Mrs. Dalton's Best Maid Products

BEST MOULDING - Silk-screen stretchers - Best Molding Frames

BEST N' SHOW - Pet products - Best n' Show Pet Products Inc.

BEST NAILS NEXT TO YOUR OWN - Nail care products - Pacific World Corp.

BEST NEVER REST, THE - Clocks - Ford Motor Co.

BEST O' CORN - Margarine - Ventura Foods

BEST O' THE WHEAT - Flour–blended - Roland Industries Inc.

BEST O' VEG - Margarine - Ventura Foods

BEST OF ALYCIA - Fabrics–tapestry - Comark Wallcoverings

BEST OF AMERICA - Puzzles ☆ - Milton Bradley Co.

BEST OF BAVARIA - Health care products ☆ - Norganic Foods USA Inc.

BEST OF BOTH - Fabrics ☆ - Cone Mills Corp.

BEST OF BOTH WORLDS - Floor coverings ☆ - Armstrong World Industries, Inc.

BEST OF BREED - Flags - Chad Management Inc.

BEST OF BROCK - Candy - Brock Candy Co. Inc.

BEST OF EVERYTHING - Floor coverings–carpet and rugs - Monticello Carpet Mills

BEST OF FRIENDS - Dolls - Lloyderson Dolls & Toys

BEST OF FRIENDS - Wallpaper - Cavalier Handprints Ltd.

BEST OF HEALTH! - Food products - Amaranth Resources, Inc.

BEST OF MAINE - Moccasins - Wolverine World Wide, Inc.

BEST OF SEAFOOD - Food products - Health Valley Food

BEST OF SELLERS - Wallpaper - Sellers & Josephson

BEST OF, THE - Food products ☆ - Dole Food Co., Inc.

BEST OF THE BEST - Meat products–beef - Best of the Best

BEST OF THE BEST - Trading cards and stamps - Treat Entertainment, Inc.

BEST OF THE BEST CHAMPIONSHIP KARATE - Toys - Electro Brain Corp.

BEST OF THE BEST, THE - Calendars - Mach 1, Inc.

BEST OF THE BLUES - Flowers, plants, and seeds - Turf-Seed, Inc.

BEST OF THE EGG - Eggs - Safeway Inc.

BEST OF THE HARVEST - Peanut oil - Nabisco Holdings Corp.

BEST OF THE MAGAZINE MARKETS, THE - Directories - Institute, Inc.

BEST OF THE MOUNTAINS - Salad dressings–bottled - Best of the Mountains, Inc.

BEST OF THE NORTHWEST GOURMET COFFEE & CHOCOLATE CLUB - Coffee - Best of the Northwest

BEST OF THE PAST, THE - Calendars - Mach 1, Inc.

BEST OF THE TWENTIETH THE OFFICIAL NATIONAL SURVEY, THE - Compact discs–prerecorded - Best of the Twentieth Century, Inc.

BEST OF THE WEST - Charcoal - Salco, Inc.

BEST OF THE WEST - Flowers, plants, and seeds - Agway Country Foods Inc.

BEST O'VEG - Oils–edible - Harvest States Cooperatives

BEST OVERALL BEARS - Novelty items - At the Zoo

BEST-PAC - Patches, insignia, and emblems ☆ - Best Emblem & Insignia Co. Inc.

BEST PALS - Apparel–children's - Little Laura of California, Inc.

BEST PITSCH - Fruits and vegetables - Edward Pitsch Produce Inc.

BEST PLACES - Wallpaper - Pantasote Inc. (Wallcovering Div.)

BEST PLACES TO STAY - Publisher's imprints - Houghton Mifflin Co.

BEST PRACTICES BENCHMARKING - Educational materials - Best Practices Benchmarking & Consulting, Inc.

BEST PRESSED - Irons–electric - Windmere Corp.

BEST QUALITY - Breads - Sal A. Scafidi

BEST REAL ESTATE - Real estate agencies - Best Real Estate, Inc.

BEST REGARDS - Floor coverings–carpet and rugs - Lees Carpets

BEST REGARDS - Wallpaper - Essex Wallcoveringss

BEST REGARDS CARDS - Greeting cards - John Henry Co.

BEST REST - Camping products - Associated Marketing, Inc.

BEST REST - Mattresses - Sealy Inc.

BEST RESULTS - Housewares - Ekco Housewares, Inc.

BEST-RITE - Paneling - Best-Rite Manufacturing

BEST SELLER - Colognes - Brandy Harvest

BEST SELLER - Floor coverings–carpet and rugs - World Carpets, Inc.

BEST SELLER - Fruits and vegetables - Hemphill & Wilson Enterprises

BEST-SET - Brackets - Kurtz Enterprises, Inc.

BEST SHOT - Apparel and accessories ☆ - Jantzen Inc.

BEST SLEEP SYSTEMS - Mattresses - Paramount Industrial Companies Inc.

BEST-STRETCH - Thread - American & Efird, Inc.

BEST STRIKE - Food products - Mitchell Madesko

BEST SUNGLASS VALUE MONEY CAN BUY, THE - Eyeglasses - Solar-Mates Sunglasses

BEST TEST - Rubber cement - Union Rubber, Inc.

BEST-TEST ART PRODUCTS GRADE SCHOOL GLUE - Glue–household or industrial - Union Rubber, Inc.

BEST, THE - Floor coverings–carpet and rugs ☆ - Daltonian Carpet & Cushion Inc.

BEST, THE - Candy - Ph. Wunderle Inc.

BEST THINGS IN LIFE ARE ALMOST FAT FREE!, THE - Cookies - Interbake Foods Inc.

BEST TO YOU - Greeting cards - Outreach Publications Inc.

BEST UNITED GARMENT COMPANY - Apparel and accessories - C.S.F. Corp.

BEST VALUE - Nuts–candied - Aster Nut Products Co. Inc.

BEST VALUE - Paper - Plainwell Tissue

BEST VALUE IN LIGHTING - Wiring devices - National Service Industries, Inc.

☆ = Now out of production

BEST-VUE - Mirrors - Best Industries
BEST WATER - Water purification systems - Shaklee Corp.
BEST-WAY - Communications equipment - PMS Sales and Leasing Inc.
BEST WAY - Food products - United Citrus Products Corp.
BEST-WAY - Musical instrument accessories - Bestway Musical Products
BEST-WAY - Recording label - Holy Bible Gospel Ministry of The Body of
  Christ, Yeshua, of the Holy Land,
BEST WAY TO TRAVEL WITHOUT WAKING OR DISTURBING BABY, THE -
  Infant product - Lisco, Inc.
BEST WEIGHT, THE - Soybean oil - Earth's Resources, Inc.
BEST WISHES - Apparel and accessories - Yes Clothing Co.
BEST WISHES - Floor coverings–carpet and rugs ✰ - Gulistan Carpet Inc.
BEST WISHES - Greeting cards - Leanin' Tree Inc.
BEST YET - Food products - Pay Cash Grocery Co.
BESTA - Pharmaceutical preparations ✰ - Roberts/Hauck Pharmaceuticals Inc.
BESTAIR - Filters–air - RPS Products Inc.
BESTASTE - Food products - J.G. Pieri Co. Inc.
BESTBAKE - Kitchen utensils–aluminum - Bonny Products Inc.
BESTBODY - Vitamins and nutritional supplements - New Reality Products, Inc.
BESTBOOKS - Computer software - Best! Ware, Inc.
BESTBUY - Brushes–paint - Wright-Bernet
BESTBUY - Fabrics–canvas - Wolsey Co.
BESTBUY - Laxatives - Brenner Pharmacal Co./Pharma Kwik
BESTCARE - Health care products - Marketing Management, Inc.
BESTCARE - Pet products - Ameriguard Corp.
BESTCLAD - Window frames - Biltbest Windows
BESTECH BIOFEED - Chemical preparations - Bestechnologies, Inc.
BESTEST - Medical apparatus - Medix Biotech Inc.
BESTEVER - Combs - Ajax Comb Co. (Div. of Antonio's Manufacturing, Inc.)
BESTEX - Thread - Witten Sales Corp.
BESTFIT - Computer software - Palisade Corp.
BESTFIT - Jewelers' tools and supplies - Vigor Co.
BESTFITNESS - Apparel and accessories - Fitness Equip USA
BESTFORM - Underwear and nightwear - Bestform Foundations, Inc.
BESTFRONT - Paper - Chartpak
BESTI ZESTI - Sauces - Slush Puppie Corp.
BESTIEN - Handbags - Robert Bestien
BESTIEN BOUTIQUE - Handbags - Robert Bestien
BESTIEN INTERNATIONAL - Handbags - Robert Bestien
BESTINE - Rubber cement - Union Rubber, Inc.
BESTLIFE - Food products - Better Living Products Inc.
BESTLINE - Tools–machine - Bestline Products, Inc.
BEST*LITE - Badges–uniform - Best Emblem & Insignia Co.
BESTMADE - Sporting goods and fishing tackle - American Import Co.
BESTMARX - Crayons ✰ - Walbuck Crayon Co., Inc.
BESTOFALL - Fruits–canned - Johnson-Middleby Co. (Karp's Manufactured
  Products Div.)
BESTOIL - Oils–illuminating - Teledyne Landis Machine
BESTOL - Mouthwashes - Etna Products Co. Inc.
BESTOVALL - Food products - Bestovall Foods Inc.
BESTPAK - Insulating materials - Manville/Schuller
BESTPAL - Computer software - Sheng Labs, Inc.
BESTPLAN - Computer software - BestPlan Group Inc.
BESTPLEAT - Tape–adhesive - Conso Products Co.
BESTREED - Switches–electric - General Equipment & Manufacturing Co.,
  Inc.
BESTROCK - Plaster–wallboard - Georgia-Pacific Corp.
BESTRON - Electronic equipment, tapes - B & E Sales Co. Inc.
BESTRONE - Pharmaceutical preparations ✰ - Bluco Inc.
BEST'S FOREST PINE - Cleaning preparations–household - Canton
  Industries, Inc.
BESTSPUN - Thread - Threads USA Div.
BESTT COATER - Paint rollers - Bestt-Liebco
BESTT-LIEBCO - Brushes–paint - Bestt-Liebco
BESTT-LOK - Paint rollers - Bestt-Liebco
BESTT ROLLR - Paint rollers - Bestt-Liebco
BESTTOP - Soil - Morie Co. Inc.
BESTUVALL - Rubber–synthetic - Dykema Rubber Band Co.
BESTWALL - Plaster–wallboard - Georgia-Pacific Corp.
BESTWARE, THE - Containers–plastic - Hyun Kim
BESTWAY - Bakery products–frozen - Herold & Miller Inc.
BESTWAY - Food products - Marketing Management, Inc.
BESTWAY - Scales–bathroom ✰ - Healthometer
BESTWAY - Swimming pools - Diversified Products & Services Co.
BESTWAY - Thread - Jeanette Crews Designs

BESTWELL OPTICAL - Photographic equipment - Bestwell Optical Instrument
  Co.
BESTYET - Food products - Scrivner, Inc.
BESTYETTE - Hair care products - N.B. Cohen Co.
BESWICK - Figurines - Royal Doulton-Somerset UK Ltd.
BET-A-MILLION - Games ✰ - Milton Bradley Co.
BET-A-WAVE - Hair care products - Waverly Beauty Products
BET BORGESON - Greeting cards - Roseville Press
BET ON MUSIC - Recording label - Black Entertainment Television, Inc.
BET URBAN CONTEMPORARY CHANNEL - Broadcasting stations–cable
  television - Black Entertainment Television, Inc.
BETA - Amplifiers - Yorkville Sound
BETA - Chairs–upholstered - United Chair Co., Inc.
BETA - Cushions - Commander-Omni Co. Inc.
BETA - Doors–metal - United Dominion Industries, Inc.
BETA - Fabrics - Interface, Inc.
BETA - Fertilizers - Howard Fertilizer Co., Inc.
BETA - Floor coverings–carpet and rugs - Lotus Carpets
BETA - Floor coverings–carpet and rugs ✰ - Regal Rugs Inc.
BETA - Floor coverings–tile ✰ - Mannington Carpets, Inc.
BETA - Food products - Louis Rich Co.
BETA - Frames–eyeglass - Rozin Optical Export Corp.
BETA - Hair care products - Rusk Inc.
BETA - Hair care products - Waverly Beauty Products
BETA - Handbags - Beta Handbag Corp.
BETA - Helmets - Willson/Dalloz Safety
BETA - Microphones - Shure Brothers, Inc.
BETA - Moped - Michael Bondy Inc.
BETA - Motor vehicles–motor homes ✰ - Eldorado Motor Corp.
BETA - Staplers - ACCO USA, Inc.
BETA - Toys–models - Estes Industries
BETA - Vacuum cleaners and accessories - Baracuda International Corp.
BETA-2 - Pharmaceutical preparations - Nephron Pharmaceuticals
BETA 2 - Sprinklers–lawn ✰ - L.R. Nelson Corp.
BETA 52 - Microphones - Shure Brothers, Inc.
BETA 56 - Microphones - Shure Brothers, Inc.
BETA 57A - Microphones - Shure Brothers, Inc.
BETA 58A - Microphones - Shure Brothers, Inc.
BETA-B-PLEX - Pharmaceutical preparations ✰ - Roberts/Hauck
  Pharmaceuticals Inc.
BETA BOOST - Vitamins and nutritional supplements - Naturally Vitamin
  Supplements Inc.
BETA C - Sporting goods - Klein Bicycle Corp.
BETA-C - Vitamins and nutritional supplements - Body Wise International, Inc.
BETA-C-PLEX - Pharmaceutical preparations - Roberts/Hauck Pharmaceuticals
  Inc.
BETA CARE, A - Vitamins and nutritional supplements - Aloe Vera of America,
  Inc.
BETA CARROT - Juices - Green Foods
BETA-GINSENG - Skin care products - Kristine M. Schoenauer
BETA-GOLD REHYD - Skin care products - Jason Natural Products, Inc.
BETA GREEN - Microphones - Shure Brothers, Inc.
BETA LAUNCH VEHICLE - Toys–models ✰ - Estes Industries
BETA-LIFTX - Pharmaceutical preparations - Medicis Pharmaceutical Corp.
BETA-LOK - Saw blades - Belcar Products, Inc.
BETA MASSIVE - Pharmaceutical preparations - Eastern Research
  Laboratories
BETA MED - Shampoos - Beta Dermaceuticals, Inc.
BETA-PARVENZYME - Vitamins and nutritional supplements ✰ - Freeda
  Vitamins Inc.
BETA PEPTIDE - Vitamins and nutritional supplements - Bodyonics, Ltd.
BETA-PHED - Pharmaceutical preparations ✰ - Lexis Laboratories Inc.
BETA PILE - Medical apparatus - Alimed, Inc.
BETA PLUS - Cushions - Commander-Omni Co. Inc.
BETA POWER - Health care products - Nature Health
BETA PRO CAP - Vitamins and nutritional supplements - Natural Organics, Inc.
BETA PROTECTION FACTOR - Vitamins and nutritional supplements - Head
  Start Vitamin Products
BETA RAIN - Sprinklers–lawn ✰ - L.R. Nelson Corp.
BETA TENE - Vitamins and nutritional supplements - Natural Organics, Inc.
BETA-THIN - Bird coloring - Sunshine Bird Supplies, Inc.
BETA TONE - Bird coloring - Sunshine Bird Supplies, Inc.
BETA TRIAL MOTORCYCLES - Motorcycles - Cosmopolitan Motors Inc.
BETA TRON - Toys–models - Estes Industries
BETA-VAL - Pharmaceutical preparations - Lemmon Co.

BETA-VITE - Vitamins and nutritional supplements ☆ - Vortech Pharmaceuticals
BETABASIC - Chemical preparations - Keystone Scientific, Inc.
BETABEADS - Spices and extracts - Pharmachem Laboratories, Inc.
BETABED - Health care products - HNE Healthcare
BETACAROTENE CAPS - Vitamins and nutritional supplements - Vitamin Research Products Inc.
BETACIDE - Antiseptics ☆ - Purdue Frederick Co.
BETACOTE - Paints - Essex Specialty Products, Inc.
BETACREST - Vitamins and nutritional supplements - Nutrition Control Products
BETACUT - Electrodes - Intech Technology Corp.
BETADINE - Antiseptics - Purdue Frederick Co.
BETADINE - Surgical supplies - Alcon Laboratories, Inc.
BETAGAN - Ophthalmic goods - Allergan, Inc.
BETAGEN - Pharmaceutical preparations - Enzyme Process Co. Inc.
BETAGUN - Tools–power-driven - Essex Specialty Products, Inc.
BETALIN - Pharmaceutical preparations - Eli Lilly and Co.
BETAMARK - Paints ☆ - Quartet Manufacturing Co.
BETAMAX - Tape players–video - Sony Corp. of America
BETAMAX CAROTENE + - Vitamins and nutritional supplements - Nutra-Source Corp.
BETAMETH - Health care products - Kay Pharmacal Co. Inc.
BETAPAR - Pharmaceutical preparations ☆ - Parke-Davis
BETAPEN - Antibiotics - Bristol-Myers Squibb Co.
BETAPEN-VK - Penicillin preparations - Bristol-Myers Squibb Co.
BETAPLEX - Vitamins and nutritional supplements ☆ - U.S. Ethicals Inc.
BETAR - Medical apparatus - Dimensional Sciences, Inc.
BETASAL - Shampoos - Beta Dermaceuticals, Inc.
BETASCAN - Electronic equipment - Sony Corp. of America
BETASEAL - Adhesives and sealants - Essex Specialty Products, Inc.
BETASIL - Chemical preparations - Keystone Scientific, Inc.
BETASITE - Pharmaceutical preparations - InSite Vision Inc.
BETASOFT - Soap - Purdue Frederick Co.
BETASONE - Veterinary pharmaceutical preparations - Schering-Plough Animal Health
BETASTACK - Electronic equipment - Sony Corp. of America
BETASTAY - Adhesives and sealants - Essex Specialty Products, Inc.
BETATEN - Vitamins and nutritional supplements - Henkel Corp. (Fine Chemicals Div.)
BETATHIOLIN - Pharmaceutical preparations - Lincoln Diagnostics
BETATOP - Paints - Essex Specialty Products, Inc.
BETATREX - Pharmaceutical preparations - Savage Laboratories Inc.
BETAVARON - Lenses–photographic - Schneider Optics, Inc.
BETAZYME - Pharmaceutical preparations - Barrows Pharmacal Inc.
BETCHA' LIFE - Candy - James P. Linette Inc.
BETCO - Cleaning preparations - Betco Corp.
BETCO EXPRESS - Cleaning preparations - Betco Corp.
BETH - Shoes - Daniel Green Co.
BETH BAILEY - Candy - Fritz Co., Inc.
BETH FORM 400 - Metals - Bethlehem Steel Corp.
BETH ILYSSA - Dolls - Bradley Import Co.
BETH MICHAEL'S - Underwear and nightwear - J.C. Penney Co., Inc.
BETHANY - Cabinets–wood - Kemper
BETHANY - Flatware - Pfaltzgraff Investment Co.
BETHANY BAY - Wallpaper - Dekortex Inc.
BETHANY BRICK - Floor coverings - Mannington Resilient Floors
BETHANY MANOR - Wallpaper ☆ - Mirage Wallcovering Co.
BETHEA - Electrical equipment - MacLean-Fogg Co.
BETHEL - Computer storage devices–magnetic - Payne Loving Trust
BETHEL HEIGHTS VINEYARD - Wines - Winesellers Ltd.
BETHEL LAMB - Toys–musical - Dakin Inc.
BETHLEHEM - Bakery products - Neighborhood Baking Co.
BETHLEHEM - Steel - Bethlehem Steel Corp.
BETHLEHEM WIRE ROPE - Rope - Williamsport Wirerope Works, Inc.
BETH'S BOTANICS - Skin care products - Beth C. Gurin
BETHWOOD - Lamps - Beth Weissman Co. Inc.
BETHY'S BAKERY - Bakery products - Stew Leonard's
BETLAR - Infant product - BetLar, Inc.
BETOL - Pharmaceutical preparations - Upsher-Smith Laboratories, Inc.
BETOPTIC - Health care products - Alcon Laboratories, Inc.
BET'R COAT - Lacquers - Porter Warner Industries
BETRAYAL AT BOGWATER - Games ☆ - Mayfair Games, Inc.
BETSEY HALL - Stationery - Royal Imprints Corp.
BETSY - Dinnerware–glass - Franciscan by Johnson Brothers, USA, Inc.
BETSY - Napkins–paper - Wisconsin Tissue Mills Inc.

BETSY & BOBBY - Apparel–children's - Buster Brown Apparel Inc.
BETSY BLOOMINGDALE - Apparel and accessories ☆ - Swirl II Ltd.
BETSY BOBBIT - Dolls and Christmas ornaments - Elizabeth T. McManus
BETSY CAMERON'S CHILDREN - Furniture - Lexington Furniture Industries, Inc.
BETSY MCCALL - Patterns–clothing - Mccall Pattern Co.
BETSY PINK OUTRAGEOUS CHIC - Apparel and accessories - Frank Jay Delano
BETSY ROSS - Apparel–women's ☆ - Carmen Foundations Inc.
BETSY ROSS - Bakery products - Flowers Bakeries (West Virginia Div.)
BETSY ROSS - Bicycles - Ross Bicycles USA, Ltd.
BETSY ROSS - Cigars - F.X. Smiths Sons Co.
BETSY ROSS - Dolls ☆ - Effanbee Doll Corp.
BETSY ROSS - Elastic ☆ - Hickory Industries, Inc.
BETSY ROSS - Floor coverings–carpet and rugs - Capel, Inc.
BETSY ROSS - Housewares - Rex Venetian Blind Co.
BETSY ROSS - Watches - Bulova Corp.
BETSY ROSS COLLECTION, THE - Rocking chairs - Brooks Furniture Manufacturing Inc.
BETSY ROSS NEEDLEWORK - Hobby kits - Betsy Ross Needlework
BETSY WETSY - Toys–stuffed - CBS Toys
BETSY'S - Cookies ☆ - Barbara's Bakery, Inc.
BETSY'S TEMPEH - Food products - S & P Farms
BETTA - Candy ☆ - Walden Farms, Inc.
BETTA - Novelty items–paper - Betta Products, Inc.
BETTA BARRACKS - Pet products - Rolf C. Hagen (USA) Corp.
BETTA BITS - Pet products - Nippon Pet Food
BETTAMAX - Pet products ☆ - Aquatronics-Filtronics
BETTATANK - Pet products - Hawkeye Corp.
BETTCHER PANELBLOC - Heating equipment ☆ - Bettcher Manufacturing Corp.
BETTE APPEL - Apparel and accessories - Bette Appel Inc.
BETTE BALL - Dolls - Goebel of North America
BETTEJON - Jewelry - Bettejon of Dallas
BETTER - Office supplies - E.W. Pike & Co.
BETTER 4U FOODS - Fish–canned or cured - Better 4U Foods Inc.
BETTER ALTERNATIVE - Paper products - Georgia-Pacific Corp.
BETTER BAKED - Food products - Lincolnland Food Sales
BETTER BALLPOINT PEN - Pens - Pilot Pen Corp. of America
BETTER BARLEY - Soups–canned - Buckeye Beans & Herbs, Inc.
BETTER BASICS - Apparel and accessories ☆ - Kellwood Co.
BETTER BASICS - Health care products - D.D. Williamson & Co., Inc.
BETTER BEAGLING - Magazines - Robert G. Baker
BETTER BECAUSE YOU BAKE THEM - Food products - Van Den Bergh Foods Co.
BETTER-BILT - Doors–garage - Fimbel Door Corp.
BETTER BITES - Food products - Austin Quality Foods, Inc.
BETTER BLIND - Window coverings - Golden Image Inc.
BETTER BLIND, A - Window coverings - Vertical Blind Factory
BETTER BLUE CHEESE - Crackers - Nabisco Foods Group
BETTER BOND - Tiles–ceramic ☆ - United States Ceramic Tile Co.
BETTER BOTTOMS - Apparel and accessories ☆ - Warnaco Inc.
BETTER BRAIDS - Hair-care products - Keystone Laboratories Inc.
BETTER BUILT - Machinery - American Sterilizer Co.
BETTER BURGER, THE - Food products - Woodstock Whole Earth Foods, Inc.
BETTER BURRITO - Food products - Chapin's Supreme Foods
BETTER BUY - Detergents - Provigo Corp.
BETTER BUY - Fish–fresh or frozen - North Atlantic Fish Co.
BETTER BY DESIGN - Machinery - Bishamon Industries Corp.
BETTER CHEDDARS - Crackers - Nabisco Foods Group
BETTER CHEESES - Crackers - Nabisco Foods Group
BETTER COOKING BY DESIGN - Cookware - Corning Inc.
BETTER DESIGN - A BETTER WORLD, A - Computer hardware - Commercial and Industrial Design Co. Inc.
BETTER DIRECTION. - Computer software - Mindsolve Technologies, Inc.
BETTER EGG - Eggs - Specialty Foods Investment Co.
BETTER ENTERTAINMENT - Video production - Lavin McCauley, Inc.
BETTER FOR BREAD - Flour–blended - General Mills, Inc.
BETTER FOR YOU - Meat and fruit products - Saramar Corp.
BETTER-FUNN - Herbal products - Ying's Herbal Teas, Inc.
BETTER GOLF - Golfing equipment - Better Golf Inc.
BETTER GRIP - Pens - Pilot Pen Corp. of America
BETTER HALF - Bakery products–frozen - Dawn Food Products Inc.
BETTER HALF - Hair care products - Roux Laboratories, Inc.
BETTER HOMES - Paints ☆ - Cowman-Campbell Paint Co.
BETTER HOMES AND GARDENS - Fencing–plastic - Meredith Corp.

☆ = Now out of production

BETTER HOMES & GARDENS - Patterns–clothing ✩ - Simplicity Pattern Co., Inc.

BETTER HOMES & GARDENS - Publisher's imprints - National Plan Service

BETTER HOMES & GARDENS - Tools–garden - Better Homes & Gardens

BETTER HOMES & GARDENS REAL ESTATE SERVICE - Real estate agencies - Better Homes & Gardens

BETTER HOUSEWARE - Housewares - Better Houseware Corp.

BETTER IMAGING THROUGH ELECTROCHEMISTRY - Microscopes - Molecular Imaging Corp.

BETTER LETTER - Decals and transfers - C-Thru Ruler Co.

BETTER LITE - Snap-in door lights - Unique Industries

BETTER LOUVER - Snap-in door louvers - Unique Industries

BETTER MADE - Potato chips - Cross & Peters Co.

BETTER MAID - Flour–blended - Houchens Industries, Inc.

BETTER MOLD - Footwear - Better Mold Shoe Co.

BETTER MOUSETRAP, THE - Awards - Stanton's Quills

BETTER 'N BENS' - Stoves–wood-burning ✩ - EBM

BETTER NACHOS - Crackers - Nabisco Foods Group

BETTER-OFF - Skin care products - Dorothy Gray Cosmetics Ltd.

BETTER PACK - Office supplies - Better Packages

BETTER PACKAGES - Office supplies - Better Packages

BETTER PLACE RECORDS - Recording label - Better Place Records, Inc.

BETTER POWDER, A - Cosmetics - Estee Lauder Inc.

BETTER SHAVE - Shaving preparations - Medtech Laboratories, Inc.

BETTER SLEEP - Bathroom accessories - Better Sleep, Inc.

BETTER SOUND THROUGH RESEARCH - Loudspeaker system - Bose Corp.

BETTER SWISS CHEESE - Crackers - Nabisco Foods Group

BETTER SYSTEM, THE - Floor brushes - Harper Brush Works

BETTER THAN BAKERY - Breads - Better than Bakery

BETTER THAN BARE - Panty hose - Mayer/Berkshire Corp.

BETTER THAN BOTTLED - Water purification systems - DTR Associates, LP

BETTER THAN BOUILLON - Soups - Superior Quality Foods, Inc.

BETTER THAN BURGER? - Food products - Sovex Foods, Inc.

BETTER THAN BUTTER - Vegetable oil - Nabisco Foods Group

BETTER THAN CHEESECAKE - Food products ✩ - Tofutti Brands Inc.

BETTER THAN CREAM CHEESE - Food products - Tofutti Brands Inc.

BETTER THAN EVER - Underwear and nightwear ✩ - Lovable Co.

BETTER THAN FRESH! - Seafood products–fresh or frozen - California Specialty Products, Inc.

BETTER THAN KETCHUP - Food products - Doxsee Food Corp.

BETTER THAN MILK - Beverages - Sovex Foods, Inc.

BETTER THAN SUN - Cosmetics - Transamerica Mailings, Inc.

BETTER THAN YOGURT - Yogurt - Tofutti Brands Inc.

BETTER VISION BETTER GRADES - Frames–eyeglass - Marine Optical, Inc.

BETTER VUE - Covers–seat - Jay Plastics Inc.

BETTER WAY - Breads - Metz Baking Co.

BETTER WAY - Cleaning preparations - Loew-Cornell Inc.

BETTER WAY - Pet products - Sanex Corp.

BETTER WAY TO CATCH SOME Z'S, A - Bedding - Ohio Mattress Co.

BETTER WORLD - Apparel and accessories - Take the Lead Inc.

BETTER WORLD - Coffee - Frontier Cooperative Herbs

BETTERBACK - Health care products - Orthopedic Products Corp.

BETTERBAKE - Tableware–china - Pfaltzgraff Investment Co.

BETTERBEAD - Hand tool - Myro, Inc.

BETTERBODY - Health care products - Healthwatchers System

BETTERBOTTOM - Covers–seat - Phifer Wire Products Inc.

BETTERCREME - Food products - Rich Products Corp.

BETTERGRIP - Pens - Pilot Corp. of America

BETTERLINE - File folders - Better Office Products, Inc.

BETTERMADE - Containers - Sportsmen's Plastics, Inc.

BETTER'N BURGERS - Food products - Specialty Foods Investment Co.

BETTER'N EGGS - Egg substitutes - Worthington Foods Inc.

BETTERWEAR - Hosiery - Rudin & Roth Inc.

BETTERYET - Candy - Old Dominion Peanut Inc.

BETTE'S - Food products - Bette's Diner Products

BETTI TERRELL - Apparel–children's - Johnston Inc.

BETTINA - Skin care products - Bettina Creations Inc.

BETTR'N BONES - Pet food - Golden Sun Feeds, Inc.

BETTS SMART SPLICE - Electrical equipment - Betts Industries Inc.

BETTS SNAP SEAL - Motor vehicle parts and accessories - Betts Industries Inc.

BETTY - Footwear - Blue Jasper Inc.

BETTY - Shoes–athletic - Coast Shoes Inc.

BETTY ADAMS - Food products ✩ - Adams Extract Co. Inc.

BETTY ANN - Food products - Monticello Canning Co. Inc.

BETTY ANN - Markers–felt-tip ✩ - K-Tel International, Inc.

BETTY BAKER - Pasta - Pasta USA Inc.

BETTY BAKER PASTA ITALIAN CHEF - Pasta - Pasta USA Inc.

BETTY BALL - Toys - Tonka Corp.

BETTY BARCLAY - Apparel–women's - Hooper Associates Ltd.

BETTY BARRETTE - Barrette holder, barrettes, and cologne - Cosrich Inc.

BETTY BENSON - Candy ✩ - Fine Products Co. Inc.

BETTY BERRY - Dolls - Mattel, Inc.

BETTY BEST - Cooking equipment–commercial - G & S Metal Products Co., Inc.

BETTY BITS - Chocolate candy ✩ - Betty Bits Inc.

BETTY BLUE - Apparel and accessories - Regaliti Inc.

BETTY BOOP - Air purification systems - Medo Industries, Inc.

BETTY BOOP - Footwear - S. Goldberg and Co. Inc.

BETTY BOOP - Hair care products ✩ - Lander Co., Inc.

BETTY BOOP - Postcards ✩ - Classico San Francisco Inc.

BETTY BOOP - Wallets - Strand Enterprises

BETTY BOOP - Watches - I.D. Enterprises

BETTY BOOP - Watches - Western Watches International

BETTY BRITE - Paper ✩ - Scott Paper Co.

BETTY CLARK'S - Snack foods - California Snack Foods, Inc.

BETTY CROCKER - Bakery products - General Mills, Inc.

BETTY CROCKER - Novelty items - Signature Brands, LLC

BETTY CROCKER - Publisher's imprints - Simon & Schuster, Inc.

BETTY CROCKER - Puzzles - Milton Bradley Co.

BETTY CROCKER BACOS - Meat products–dried - General Mills, Inc.

BETTY CROCKER BROWNIE SUNDAE - Desserts - General Mills, Inc.

BETTY CROCKER CREAMY CHILLED DESSERT - Desserts - General Mills, Inc.

BETTY CROCKER DUNKAROOS - Cookies - General Mills, Inc.

BETTY CROCKER EASY BAKE OVEN - Toys–electronic - Kenner Products

BETTY CROCKER EASY DELICIOUS DESSERTS - Cakes–mixes - General Mills, Inc.

BETTY CROCKER - ESPECIALLY FOR THE KITCHEN - Wallpaper ✩ - Imperial Wallcoverings, Inc.

BETTY CROCKER GINGERBREAD FUN KIT - Food products - General Mills, Inc.

BETTY CROCKER JUICER BLENDER - Toys–electronic ✩ - Kenner Products

BETTY CROCKER MAKING A HOME HOUSEWARES COLLECTION - Catalogs - General Mills, Inc.

BETTY CROCKER RECIPE SAUCES - Food products - General Mills, Inc.

BETTY CROCKER SERVABLES - Containers - Eagle Affiliates, Inc.

BETTY CROCKER SIGNATURE SERIES - See **BETTY CROCKER SERVABLES**

BETTY CROCKER SUPREME - Desserts - General Mills, Inc.

BETTY CROCKER SWEET REWARDS - Pastries - General Mills, Inc.

BETTY DAIN - Apparel and accessories - Betty Dain Creations Inc.

BETTY G - Kitchen appliances - Abbott Industries Inc.

BETTY KAY - Pharmaceutical preparations - Duro Med Industries Inc.

BETTY KAY - Sweaters - Binghamton Knitting Co.

BETTY LEE - Food products ✩ - Vita Food Products, Inc.

BETTY LEWIS - Bakery products - Flowers Bakeries (West Virginia Div.)

BETTY LOU - Bags–cosmetic - A.J. Siris Products Corp.

BETTY LOU - Potato chips - Granny Goose Foods Inc.

BETTY RIDES - Apparel and accessories - Cow Co.

BETTY WHITE - Recording label - Conversa-Phone Institute Inc.

BETTY ZANE - Popcorn - National Oats Co. Inc.

BETTY'S - Food products - Van Bennett Food Inc.

BETTY'S BEAUTY PARLOR - Dolls - Horsman

BETTYS IMPORTS - Lamps - Hillside House of Originals

BETULINE - Health care products - Ferndale Laboratories, Inc.

BETWEEN - Hair care products - KMS Research Inc.

BETWEEN-GLASS - Blinds–venetian ✩ - Hunter Douglas, Inc.

BETWEEN HEAVEN AND HELL - Computer diskettes–blank - Bureau Development Inc.

BETWEEN PERMS - Hair care products - Epitomi, Inc.

BETWEEN ROUNDS - Prepared foods - Between Rounds Franchise Corp.

BETWEEN THE ACTS - Cigars - Havatampa Inc.

BETWEEN THE COVERS - Broadcasting stations–radio - Peter C. Wensberg

BETWEEN THE LINES - Bathing suits ✩ - Jantzen Inc.

BETWEEN THE SHEETS - Greeting cards - Recycled Paper Products, Inc.

BETWEENERS - Dental floss - Informative Amenities Inc.

BETWEENI - Underwear and nightwear - Henson-Kickernick Inc.

BETZ CONCEALMENT SYSTEMS - Apparel and accessories - Betz Concealment Systems, LLC

BEUKERS & REINEKEN - Chocolate candy ✩ - Holland-American Importing Co. Inc.

BEULON - Zippers - YKK USA Inc.

BEUR - Cookies ☆ - Holland-American Importing Co. Inc.

BEUTHANASIA - Veterinary pharmaceutical preparations - Schering-Plough Animal Health

BEUY PRO - Combs - B.W. Boyd Shears Inc.

BEV-RICH - Beverages - Bev-Rich Co.

BEV-TABS - Labels–paper - Bev-Tabs, Inc.

BEVCO - Chairs–upholstered - Bevco Precision Manufacturing Co.

BEVEL-8 - Siding–insulating ☆ - Aluminum Co. of America

BEVEL-AIR - Floor coverings - American Floor Products Co. Inc.

BEVEL AIRE - Mats - Ludlow Composites Corp.

BEVEL GAUGE - Measuring instruments - National Electrical Carbon Products Inc.

BEVEL TILE - Paneling - ABT Co., Inc.

BEVELITE - Plastics - D. D. Butler, Ltd

BEVELLINE - Doors–glass - Therma-Tru Corp.

BEVERAGE BILLBOARD - Cups–paper - Coalewrap Co.

BEVERAGE BOOT - Containers–plastic - Design Innovator, Inc.

BEVERAGE BREWER - Coffee makers–electric ☆ - Hamilton Beach/Proctor-Silex Inc.

BEVERAGE CENTER 2000 - Beverage dispensing equipment - Fountain Fresh International

BEVERAGE MATE - Motor vehicle parts and accessories - Bob Bartlett & Associates Inc.

BEVERAGE OF CHOICE, THE - Coffee - Cafe Au Lait

BEVERAGEMASTER - Beverage holder - International Ventures, Ltd.

BEVERLEE'S - Paints ☆ - United Gilsonite Laboratories

BEVERLEY TAYLOR - Cosmetics - Moore Beauty Inc.

BEVERLY - Cymbals ☆ - Harris-Teller, Inc.

BEVERLY - Footwear–children's ☆ - Bidegain Inc.

BEVERLY - Meat products–pork - Foell Packing Co.

BEVERLY - Polishing cloths - Beverly Manufacturing Corp.

BEVERLY - Wigs - Paula Young

BEVERLY ANN - Skin care products - Scentsational Products Corp.

BEVERLY BUNNY - Toys–stuffed - Russ Berrie and Co., Inc.

BEVERLY DINGHY - Ships–sailing vessels - Cape Cod Shipbuilding Co.

BEVERLY FARMS QUALITY FOODS - Meat products–poultry - Hamilton Meat Pies Co., Inc.

BEVERLY HEIGHTS - Floor coverings–carpet and rugs - Catalina Carpet Mills Inc.

BEVERLY HILLBILLIES, THE - Computer software - Capstone Software

BEVERLY HILLBILLIES, THE - Paper products - CBS Inc.

BEVERLY HILLS - Bicycles ☆ - Huffy Corp.

BEVERLY HILLS - Colognes ☆ - La Parfumerie Inc.

BEVERLY HILLS - Floor coverings–carpet and rugs - Calladium & Marglen

BEVERLY HILLS - Floor coverings–carpet and rugs - Mandate-Dawn Carpet Mills

BEVERLY HILLS - Footwear - International Seaway Trading Corp.

BEVERLY HILLS - Games - Jax Ltd.

BEVERLY HILLS - Hair care products - Rescue Marketing Group

BEVERLY HILLS - Recording label - Holy Bible Gospel Ministry of The Body of Christ, Yeshua, of the Holy Land,

BEVERLY HILLS - Wallpaper - Frankford Wallcoverings Inc.

BEVERLY HILLS - Window coverings ☆ - Vertilux-Louverlux Inc.

BEVERLY HILLS 2000 - Footwear - Pacific Trading Co. Citizens

BEVERLY HILLS 90210 - Apparel and accessories - Torand Productions Inc.

BEVERLY HILLS, 90210 - Games - Milton Bradley Co.

BEVERLY HILLS 90210 - Perfumes ☆ - Tsumura International Inc.

BEVERLY HILLS APPAREL DESIGN - Apparel and accessories - Joel Brooks Associates Inc.

BEVERLY HILLS BEAUTY - Skin care products - Thibiant International

BEVERLY HILLS CONFECTION COLLECTION - Chocolate and cookies - Cortina Corp.

BEVERLY HILLS FARMERS MARKET - Pastries - Dana Lynn Slatkin

BEVERLY HILLS GEM - Jewelry - OroAmerica Inc.

BEVERLY HILLS GLAMOUR - Cookies ☆ - Vegetarian Health Inc.

BEVERLY HILLS III - Wallpaper - Frankford Wallcoverings Inc.

BEVERLY HILLS JEWELS - Jewelry - OroAmerica Inc.

BEVERLY HILLS KIDS - Jewelry - OroAmerica Inc.

BEVERLY HILLS LIGHTING - Lighting fixtures - Beverly Hills Fan Co.

BEVERLY HILLS MANICURE - Nail care products - Orly International Inc.

BEVERLY HILLS MUSIC PUBLISHING - Music–sheet - Holy Bible Gospel Ministry of The Body of Christ, Yeshua, of the Holy Land,

BEVERLY HILLS NATURAL - Cosmetics - Beverly Hills Natural Products Inc.

BEVERLY HILLS POLO CLUB - Apparel and accessories - BHPC Marketing, Inc.

BEVERLY HILLS POLO CLUB - Apparel stores–children's ☆ - D. Glasgow & Sons Inc.

BEVERLY HILLS POLO CLUB - Footwear - Mag Shoe Corp.

BEVERLY HILLS POLO CLUB - Leather goods ☆ - Prince Gardner Inc.

BEVERLY HILLS SPA - Skin care products - Jheri Redding Products Inc.

BEVERLY HILLS SPORTS CLUB - Apparel and accessories - BHPC Marketing, Inc.

BEVERLY HILLS: THE GOLDEN TRIANGLE - Games - S. Alden Inc.

BEVERLY JANE - Hosiery - Adams-Millis Corp.

BEVERLY MANOR - Floor coverings–carpet and rugs ☆ - Walter Carpet Mills

BEVERLY MINIS - Posters ☆ - Henry R. Mockel's

BEVERLY STEVENS - Wallcoverings - Beverly Stevens Ltd.

BEVERLY VOGUE - Slips - Beverly Vogue Co.

BEVERLY'S YO YUMMY - Cookies - Beverly Waters

BEVILL'S - Health care products - I.L. Bevill Co.

BEVNAP - Napkins–paper - Fort Howard Corp.

BEVRON - Hair care products - Bevron Laboratories, Inc.

BEVS - Apparel and accessories - Beverly Vogue Co.

BEVTEND - Blenders - Tessco Inc.

BEVY - Polishing cloths - Beverly Manufacturing Corp.

BEWARE THE PENGUINS - Beverages–malt - Anheuser-Busch Companies Inc.

BEWITCHED - Christmas tree ornaments ☆ - Cracker Box Inc.

BEWITCHED - Floor coverings–carpet and rugs ☆ - Mohawk Carpet Corp.

BEWITCHIN' WITCH - Toys–stuffed - Fun World Inc.

BEWITCHING - Floor coverings–carpet and rugs ☆ - Lees Carpets

BEWITCHING BEADCRAFT - Hobby kits - Greene Plastics Corp.

BEWLEY - Food products - Lockport Canning Co.

BEWLEY'S - Candy - Bewley Irish Imports

BEWLEY'S IRISH CREME - Coffee - Fairwinds Gourmet Coffee Co. Inc.

BEWO - Saws–power - BEWO/USA

BEWON ELIXIR - Pharmaceutical preparations ☆ - Wyeth-Ayerst Laboratories

BEXIBEE - Pharmaceutical preparations ☆ - Vortech Pharmaceuticals

BEXLEY - Floor coverings–carpet and rugs - Karastan-Bigelow Inc.

BEXOMAL-C - Pharmaceutical preparations ☆ - Roberts/Hauck Pharmaceuticals Inc.

BEXOPHENE - Pharmaceutical preparations - Roberts/Hauck Pharmaceuticals Inc.

BEY-BERK - Clocks - Bey-Berk International

BEY-BERK - Giftware - H.C. Meyers Co.

BEYER - Microphones - Beyerdynamic Inc.

BEYERDYNAMIC - Headphones - GNP Audio Video Inc.

BEYOND - See **BEYOND SEVEN**

BEYOND - Milk - Meadow Brook Dairy Co.

BEYOND - Recording label - Allegiance Records Ltd.

BEYOND - Rings–jewelry - Artcarved Inc.

BEYOND - Skin care products - Alberto-Culver Co.

BEYOND BAGGY - Dickeys - Hub Distributing Inc.

BEYOND BASICS KIDS - Apparel–children's - Beyond Basics Kids, Inc.

BEYOND BEAUTIFUL - Apparel - Saramar Corp.

BEYOND BERBER - Floor coverings–carpet and rugs - Philadelphia Carpets

BEYOND BIZARRE - Greeting cards - Leanin' Tree Inc.

BEYOND BLACK - Cosmetics - Maybelline Co.

BEYOND BLUE - Fabrics–denim - Swift Textiles, Inc.

BEYOND BREAKFAST - Food products ☆ - Energy Food Factory Inc.

BEYOND CASTLE WOLFENSTEIN - Computer software - Muse Software

BEYOND COLOR TRIPLE BENEFIT LIPSTICK - Cosmetics - Avon Products, Inc.

BEYOND COMFORT - Pillows - Pacific Coast Feather Co.

BEYOND CONCEPTION FURNITURE CO. - Furniture–children's - Beyond Conception, Inc.

BEYOND CONCEPTION THE PREGNANCY STORE - Apparel–children's - Beyond Conception, Inc.

BEYOND DISTANCE - Balls–golf - Dunlop Maxfli Sports Corp.

BEYOND EARTH - Computer software - Optical Data Corp.

BEYOND ESSENCE - Cosmetics - Elaine Seneca

BEYOND GAMES - Computer software - Kris N. Johnson

BEYOND GARLIC LIQUIGELS - Vitamins and nutritional supplements - Makers of Kal, Inc.

BEYOND INDULGENCE - Soap - Bed Bath & Beyond Inc.

BEYOND MOISTURE - Lipsticks - Physicians Formula Cosmetics Inc.

BEYOND PERFORMANCE - Bags–duffel - Kinney Shoe Corp.

BEYOND PHONICS - Computer software - Interactive Software, Inc.

BEYOND PINK - Nail care products ☆ - Cosmair Inc.

BEYOND RECORDS - Recording label - Beyond Records Corp.

BEYOND SCRUBS - Medical uniforms - Barco of California

BEYOND SEVEN - Prophylactics - Okamoto USA Inc.

BEYOND SEVEN PLUS - Prophylactics - Okamoto USA Inc.

BEYOND SILENCE - Computer storage devices–optical ✩ - Hadda Little Production Co.

BEYOND SUCCESS - Apparel and accessories - Joni Saito

BEYOND THE ARC BTA - Apparel and accessories - Beyond the Arc

BEYOND THE BLUE - Cosmetics - Estee Lauder Inc.

BEYOND THE HEADLINES - Advertising agencies - Film House, Inc.

BEYOND THE LINES - Apparel and accessories - Majestic Athletic Wear, Ltd.

BEYOND THE ORDINARY - Golfing equipment - King Par Corp.

BEYOND THE RAINBOW - Wallpaper - Norwall Wallcoverings

BEYOND THE WALL - Posters - Posters Preferred, Inc.

BEYOND UTOPIA SOLAR ZONE - Skin care products - Creative Laboratories Inc.

BEYOND VALOR - Games - Avalon Hill Game Co.

BEYOND VITAMINS - Vitamins and nutritional supplements - Leiner Health Products Inc.

BEYOND WOODS - Blinds–venetian - Hunter Douglas, Inc.

BEYOND WORDS - Computer software - Liafail, Inc.

BEYONDNOW TECHNOLOGIES - Computer software - BeyondNow Technologies, Inc.

BEYRITH - Cabinets - Actua

BEZ SAFE - Housewares - Mechanical Mirror Works Inc.

BEZARC - Computer software - Kandu Software Corp.

BEZEL - Fabrics - Dan River Inc.

BEZEL - Measuring tapes - U.S. Tape Co.

BEZIER - Pickles - Made in France

BEZIQUE - Floor coverings–carpet and rugs - Atlas Carpet Mills Inc.

BF - Apparel and accessories - M & A Operations, Inc.

BF & C - Vitamins and nutritional supplements - Nature's Way Products, Inc.

BF EXPORTS - Giftware ✩ - Ajanta Enterprises

B.F.B. ROYAL GLAZED STEEL - Cooking equipment–household ✩ - Herman Dodge & Son Inc.

BFCO - Weightlifting equipment - Bell Foundry Co.

BFCS - Computer software - Stockholder Systems, Inc.

BFD BIG FAT DADDY - Apparel and accessories - Tillman I. Segal

B.F.I. - Antiseptics - Smithkline Beecham Corp.

BFI - Audio equipment ✩ - Washburn International

BFI - Metals - Briarwood Fasteners, Inc.

BFI ORGANICS - Agricultural products - Browning-Ferris Industries, Inc.

BFIX - Jewelry - Bristol Seamless Ring Corp.

BFJ - Jewelry - Blanche Fine Jewelry

BFS - Food products - Bozzuto's Food Services

BFS - Jewelry - XOX, Inc.

B.F.S. - Sporting goods - O'Brien International

BG - Golfing equipment - Buster Golf Devices, Inc.

BG - Nuts and bolts - B & G Manufacturing Co., Inc.

BG 14K - Jewelry - Baby Gold Jewelry, Inc.

BG 300 - Gloves - Ektelon

B.G. TWIST - Tobacco products - Scott Tobacco Co.

BGA - Semiconductors - Tessera, Inc.

BGB - Golfing equipment - Mammoth Industries, Inc.

BGC - Apparel and accessories - Broadway Garment Co. Inc.

BGI - Automotive additives - BGI

BGI - Shelving units–metal - Burke Gibson Inc.

BGM - Recording label - BGM Records

BGR - Clipboards - Andis Co.

BGT - Tools–hand-operated - Marshalltown Trowel Co.

BGW - Audio equipment - BGW Systems Inc.

BH - Floor coverings ✩ - Congoleum Corp.

BH - Wines - Heublein, Inc.

BH & G - Publication series - Better Homes & Gardens

BH BURNS HARBOR BETHLEHEM - Steel products - Bethlehem Steel Corp.

BH DE-NIC - Cigarettes - Philip Morris Companies Inc.

BH ELECTRONICS - Electronic equipment - BH Electronics, Inc.

BH GOLD FASHIONS - Jewelry - Black Hills Jewelry Manufacturing Co.

BH MINI HAND CARTON STAPLER - Staplers - Salco, Inc.

BH453 - Binoculars - INT Traders, Inc.

B*H*A*D - Apparel and accessories - Joel Brooks Associates Inc.

BHAKTAPUR - Floor coverings–carpet and rugs ✩ - Foreign Accents

B'HAVE - Pet products - Farnam Cos. Inc.

BHC - Honey - Christopher Brookes Distinctive Foods

BHCC - Apparel - Knight Development Corp.

BHE - Electronic equipment - BH Electronics, Inc.

BHI - Desk accessories - Brochure Holders, Inc.

BHI - Pharmaceutical preparations - Heel, Inc.

BHI - Sporting goods - Blackhawk Industries, Inc.

BHJ - Recording label - Seaside Records

BHP-2000 - Vitamins and nutritional supplements - Better Health Products

BHP-3000 - Vitamins and nutritional supplements - Better Health Products

BHR - Recording label - Rosalie Gerut

BHS - Jewelry–costume - BH Star Enterprises, Inc.

BHS VIDEO GUM - Candy - Zeebs Enterprises, Inc.

BI - Jewelry–precious - Brilliant I.D.E.A.S. Inc.

BI - Recording label - Bollman International Records

BI - Vitamins and nutritional supplements - Zuellig Botanicals, Inc.

BI AGLUT - Breads - Dietary Specialties

BI-BAND - Saw blades - Sandvik Saws & Tools

BI BI CAFE - Beverages–carbonated - Kittridge & Frederickson

BI-BLADE - Hockey sticks - Hughes Sports Inc.

BI BUNGEE - Cords, straps, and tie-downs - Bungee International Manufacturing Corp.

BI-CO-REX - Pharmaceutical preparations - C.S. Ruckstuhl Co. Inc.

BI-DI - Tape–adhesive ✩ - Central Products Co.

BI DIRECTIONAL MICROSTATIC ALBUMS - Photo albums - Pioneer Photo Albums, Inc.

BI-FILE - Shelving units–wood - Spacesaver Corp.

BI-FLEX - Apparel–women's - Bi-Flex International

BI-FLEX - Garden equipment - Teknor Apex Co.

BI-FOLIO - Office supplies - Design-A-Day, Inc.

BI-K - Potassium compounds - Rhone-Poulenc Rorer Pharmaceuticals Inc.

BI-LEVEL - Electric lighting equipment - Genlyte Group Inc.

BI-LEVEL - Medical apparatus - Puritan-Bennett Corp.

BI-LINGUAL SECURITY THAT SPEAKS FOR ITSELF - Alarm systems - Electronic Security Products of California

BI-LITE - Glass–safety - Buchmin Industries

BI-LO - Food products - The Kroger Co.

BI-LO - Jams and jellies - Bi-Lo, Inc.

BI-LO - Lubricants - Ashland Oil, Inc.

BI-LOFT - Fibers–acrylic - Monsanto Polymer Products

BI-NELL - Blankets - E.I. Dupont de Nemours and Co.

BI-O-KAL - Pharmaceutical preparations ✩ - Ulmer Pharmacal Co.

BI-OCULAR - Guns ✩ - Trius Products Co.

BI OX - Aquariums–household - Marine Environment/Aqua Craft

BI-PAS - Griffin Industries Inc.

BI-PERM - Contact lenses - Contact Lens Technology

BI PHASIC - Skin care products - Cosmetic Solutions, Inc.

BI-PLANE - Kites - Hi-Flier Manufacturing Co.

BI-PLY - Sports apparel - Medalist Apparel Inc.

BI-RADIAL - Electronics equipment - JBL Inc.

BI-RIB - Siding–metal - Metal Sales Manufacturing Corp.

BI-RITE - Super Valu Inc.

BI-RITE - Food products - Wetterau Inc.

BI-SECTOR - Toys–automobiles - Mattel, Inc.

BI-TA BISCUITS - Pet products - ALPO Petfoods Inc.

BI-TEC - Medical apparatus - Edward Weck & Co. Inc.

BI TECHNOLOGIES - Electronic equipment - Beckman Industrial Corp.

BI-TEX - Paper–toilet - Fort Howard Corp.

BI THE WAY - Apparel and accessories - Judy A. Piccione

BI-THERM - Thermometers - Taylor Environmental Instruments

BI/TRI - File folders - Supreme Equipment & Systems Corp.

BI-TRONICS - Computers–personal - Hewlett-Packard Co.

BI-ZETS - Health care products ✩ - Reese Chemical Co.

BI-ZETS/BENZO-TROCHES - Pharmaceutical preparations - Reese Chemical Co.

B.I.A. CORDON BLEU INTERNATIONAL - Cooking equipment–household - B.I.A. Cordon Bleu Inc.

BIACTRIN - Hair care products - Thompson and Formby

BIAGGIO CASUALWEAR - Apparel and accessories - Matteo International, Inc.

BIAGI - Jewelry ✩ - Anne Klein Jewelry

BIALETTI - Housewares ✩ - Delfino Products Inc.

BIALOGUE - Games - Barbara Joann Resimont

BIALOSKY BEAR - Toys–stuffed - Alan-Peggy Promotions, Inc.

BIALOSKY BEAR - Toys–stuffed ✩ - Gund, Inc.

BIAMINE - Pharmaceutical preparations ✩ - Forest Pharmaceuticals Inc.

BIAMP 8000 - Musical instrument accessories - Seymour Duncan Pickups

BIANCA - Cheese - Joseph Campagna & Sons Inc.

BIANCA - Dishes–china - Waterford Wedgewood USA, Inc.

BIANCA - Floor coverings - Armstrong World Industries, Inc.

BIANCA - Occasional tables - JDI Group, Inc.

BIANCA - Rings–jewelry - Artcarved Inc.

BIANCA - Whirlpool bath ☆ - Jacuzzi Inc.
BIANCA CAT - Toys–stuffed ☆ - Russ Berrie and Co., Inc.
BIANCA NYGARD - Apparel–women's - Nygard, Inc.
BIANCHI - Coffee - Astoria Expresso & Cappuccino Machine Corp.
BIANCHI - Hats - Miller Bros. Industries Inc.
BIANCHI - Holsters - Bianchi International
BIANCHI - Motor vehicles - Bianchi USA
BIANCHI - Wedding gowns - House of Bianchi Inc.
BIANCHI - Wines - Bianchi Vineyards
BIANCHI - Wines - Pellegrini Bros. Wines Inc.
BIANCHI MADEIRAS - Beverages–alcohol - John Gross & Co.
BIANCO - Accordions - Bianco Accordions
BIANCO - Cheese - Swissrose International Inc.
BIANCO - Fabrics–tapestry ☆ - Coloroll Inc.
BIANCO - Food products - Homestead Ravioli Co.
BIANCO - Hair care products ☆ - Framesi USA/Roffler Industries Inc.
BIANCO BROS. - Scissors–hand-operated - John's Sharpening Service
BIANCO BROTHERS EXCALIBUR - Clippers–nail - Bianco Brothers Instruments
BIANCO BROTHERS INSTRUMENTS - Pet products - Bianco Brothers Instruments
BIANCO'S SPECIAL - Fruits and vegetables - Anthony Vineyards, Inc.
BIAROM - Cheese - Swissrose International Inc.
BIARRITZ - Bathroom fixtures - Crane Plumbing/Fiat Products
BIARRITZ - Boats - Ebko Industries Inc.
BIARRITZ - Cookies - Pepperidge Farm Inc.
BIARRITZ - Dinnerware–glass - Nikko Ceramics Inc.
BIARRITZ - Floor coverings - Mannington Resilient Floors
BIARRITZ - Floor coverings–carpet and rugs - Customweave Carpets Inc.
BIARRITZ - Floor coverings–carpet and rugs ☆ - Galaxy Carpet Mills Inc.
BIARRITZ - Shoes - MSF Corp.
BIARRITZ - Strollers–baby ☆ - Welsh Co.
BIAS - Wines - Bias Vineyards & Winery
BIAS FOLD - Girdles - Rago Foundations Inc. LLC
BIAS-MOLD - Girdles - Rago Foundations Inc. LLC
BIAS SQUARE - Quilts - Martingale & Co.
BIAS STRIPPER - Measuring instruments - Martingale & Co.
BIAS Y - Girdles - Beverly Vogue Co.
BIASSAC - Jams and jellies - De Choix Specialty Foods Co.
BIAVAX II - Vaccines - Merck & Co., Inc. (Merck Research Laboratories)
BIAX - Lamps - General Electric Co.
BIAX - Lighting fixtures - Thomas Lighting (Accent Division)
BIAXIN - Pharmaceutical preparations - Abbott Laboratories
BIAZZO - Cheese - Biazzo Dairy Products, Inc.
BIB BRACES - Infant product - Elf Childrens' Products, Inc.
BIB-KIN - Infant product - M.G. Schloeman Manufacturing Co.
BIB 'N BUMP - Infant product - Rock-A-Bye Baby Inc.
BIB 'N BURP - Infant product - Rock-A-Bye Baby Inc.
BIB/RITE - Computer software - Robert E. Litke Associates
BIB TIES - Paper products - Bedford Industries, Inc.
BIB X - Tires - Michelin Tire Corp.
BIBA - Cookies - Sunshine/Salerno Inc.
BIBB - Housewares - Alford Home Products Inc.
BIBELITE - Office supplies ☆ - Estus Export-Import
BIB'EMS - Disposable bibs - Disposable Products Corp.
BIBI - Beverages - Ready Made Fun Imports
BIBI - Novelty items–paper ☆ - Jobar International Inc./Bibi Products
BIBITS - Dental equipment - PSM, Inc.
BIBLE BAFFLE - Games - Talicor Inc.
BIBLE BAGELS - Bagels - Garden of Eatin', Inc.
BIBLE BOOKS - Publisher's imprints ☆ - Cross Educational Software Inc.
BIBLE BREAD - Breads - Garden of Eatin', Inc.
BIBLE BURGERS - Breads - Garden of Eatin', Inc.
BIBLE GEAR - Book covers and binders - Gregg Manufacturing
BIBLE GREATS - Toys - Rainfall Inc.
BIBLE ILLUSTRATOR - Computer software - Parsons Technology, Inc.
BIBLE LEAVES - Stationery ☆ - Warner Press, Inc.
BIBLE MATCH - Computer software - Hartley Courseware Inc.
BIBLE-OP - Games - Late for the Sky Productions Co., Inc.
BIBLE PEEL & PLAY - Toys - Rainfall Inc.
BIBLE PLAY-ALONGS - Audio tapes–blank - Rainfall Inc.
BIBLE TEASERS - Recording label - Travel Teasers, Inc.
BIBLE TEXT - Stationery - Warner Press, Inc.
BIBLE TO GO - Audio cassettes - Clearline Concepts Corp.
BIBLE TRIVIA - Games - Cadaco Div.
BIBLE TRIVIA - Games - Rapid Mounting and Finishing Co.

BIBLEMAN - Recording label - Pamplin Entertainment Corp.
BIBLEMASTER - Computer software ☆ - Lockman Foundation
BIBLESOURCE - Computer storage devices–magnetic - Zondervan Publishing House
BIBLICAL INSPIRATIONS - Jewelry - Mel Bernie and Co., Inc.
BIBLIO-LINKS - Computer software - Personal Bibliographic Software Inc.
BIBLIOGRAPHY - Computer software - Digital Marketing Corp.
BIBO - Apparel–children's - Garan, Inc.
BIBO - Belts - Benjamin Worth Inc.
BIBS 4 LITTLE KIDS - Apparel–children's - Mother of Invention
BIBSEAL - Tires - Michelin Tire Corp.
BIBSTERS - Paper products - Procter & Gamble Co.
BIC - Floor coverings–carpet and rugs - Concepts International
BIC - Housewares ☆ - Bic Corp.
BIC - Salmon–smoked, salted, dried, or pickled - SWB Co. Inc.
BIC 2000 - Lighters ☆ - Bic Corp.
BIC BANANA - Pens ☆ - Bic Corp.
BIC BOSS - Pens ☆ - Bic Corp.
BIC BRITE LINER - Pens - Bic Corp.
BIC CLASSIC STIC - Pens - Bic Corp.
BIC CLIC - Pens - Bic Corp.
BIC CLIC STIC - Pens - Bic Corp.
BIC ROUND STIC - Pens - Bic Corp.
BIC SENSITIVE SHAVER - Shaving preparations - Bic Corp.
BIC SPORT - Sporting goods - Bic Sport USA
BIC STIC - Pens ☆ - Bic Corp.
BIC TOPPING - Whipped topping–frozen - Instantwhip Foods Inc.
BIC TWIN - Bic Corp.
BIC VALENTINES - Pens ☆ - Bic Corp.
BICE - Apparel–women's - Kellwood Co.
BICENTENNIAL - Bread - Roush Products Co., Inc.
BICENTENNIAL - Candles ☆ - American Candle Co. Inc.
BICENTENNIAL BEER - Beverages–alcohol - CRB Co.
BICEP LITE II MAGNUM - Agricultural products - Ciba-Geigy Corp.
BICEPS-POWER - Exercising equipment - All Pro Exercise Products, Inc.
BICHOLAX - Pharmaceutical preparations ☆ - ICN Pharmaceuticals Inc.
BICICCO - Beverages–alcohol - R.V. D'Alfonso Co.
BICILLIN - Pharmaceutical preparations - Wyeth-Ayerst Laboratories
BICILLIN C-R - Pharmaceutical preparations - Wyeth-Ayerst Laboratories
BICITRA - Pharmaceutical preparations - Willen Drug Co.
BICK - Apparel and accessories - Wolverine World Wide, Inc.
BICK 4 LEATHER - Leather conditioner - Bickmore Inc.
BICKETT'S TICKET CADDY - Office supplies - E.H. Bickett Co. Inc.
BICKFORD - Food products - Bickford Flavors Inc.
BICKHAM SCRIPT - Computer peripheral equipment - Adobe Systems Inc.
BICKMORE - Soap - Bickmore Inc.
BICKMORINE - Veterinary medical equipment - Bickmore Inc.
BICNU - Pharmaceutical preparations - Bristol-Myers Squibb Co.
BICO-KINZUA - Lumber ☆ - Cavenham Forest Industries Inc.
BICOAXIAL - Pipes–plastic - Phillips Petroleum Co.
BICONIC - Sporting goods - Pro Kennex, Inc.
BICOR - Sewing machines–household - Brother International Corp.
BICS CLIPS - Cosmetics - Nino Originals
BICYCLE - Beverages–alcohol - Bicycle Beverage Corp.
BICYCLE - Playing cards - United States Playing Card Co.
BICYCLE - Wines - Nevada City Winery
BICYCLE CLUB - Alarm systems - Winner International Corp.
BICYCLE DAY - Cloth patches - Thomas B. Roberts
BICYCLE ENGINEERING - Tools–hand-operated - William Earl Crisick
BICYCLE JAMS - Semi-fitted bicycle covers - Michael C. Ballard
BICYCLE MUSIC COMPANY, THE - Record stores - Bicycle Music Co.
BICYCLES IRON HORSE - Bicycles - Bike Rack Inc.
BICYCOOL - Containers–insulated - Stephen Flasch
BID LINE - Golfing equipment - Outdoor Technologies Group
BID-TO-BID - Computer software - Darold P. Francis
BIDDEFORD - Fabrics ☆ - Warnaco Inc.
BIDDLES RICE CHIPS - Snack foods ☆ - Pepsico, Inc.
B.IDEAS - Jewelry - Brilliant I.D.E.A.S. Inc.
BIDETTE - Sanitary napkins - Clinipad Corp.
BIDFORM - Computer software - BT Systems Ltd.
BIDHERB - Vitamins and nutritional supplements - Bioherb Inc.
BIDIL - Pharmaceutical preparations - Medco Research, Inc.
BIDIM - Fibers–polyester - Monsanto Polymer Products
BIDJAR - Floor coverings–carpet and rugs - Rugby Rugs Inc.
BIDLINE - Computer software - Demand Systems, L.C.
BIDMAGIC - Computer software - Turtle Creek Software

☆ = Now out of production

BIDMASTER - Calendars - Kurtz Bros. Inc.
BIDRITE - Computer software - Progressive Programming, Inc.
BIDWARE - Computer software - Freemarkets Online, Inc.
BIDWORK - Computer programs - Spectra-Physics Laserplane, Inc.
BIEDERMANN & SONS INC. - Candles - Root Candle Co.
BIEFFE - Furniture—metal - Sam Flax
BIEGA COFFEE CO. - Coffee - Biega Limited
BIEL - Tools - Paratech Inc.
BIEN - Apparel and accessories - Bien Internationale Corp.
BIEN JOLIE - Apparel stores—lingerie - H.F. Robbins
BIEN JOLIE JRS. - Apparel stores—lingerie - H.F. Robbins
BIEN PADRE - Food products ✩ - Queen International Foods
BIEN PADRE - Potato chips - Bien Parde Foods
BIENFAIT - Skin care products - Lancome
BIENFAIT DU MATIN - Skin care products - Cosmair Inc.
BIENFANG - Paper - Hunt Manufacturing Co.
BIENVILLE - Clocks ✩ - General Time Corp. (Westclox/Seth Thomas Div.)
BIER - Religious items - Israeli Accents
BIERLING BROS. - Pastries - Creme Curls Bakery Inc.
BIERMANN - Confections - C. & J. Willenborg Inc.
BIFF - Toys—stuffed ✩ - Russ Berrie and Co., Inc.
BIFF BARFBALL - Toys - Those Characters from Cleveland, Inc.
BIFF KARDS - Postcards ✩ - Fotofolio Inc.
BIFFAR - Food products - George C. Brown's Biscuits & Confections
BIFFI - Food products ✩ - De Medici Imports Ltd.
BIFFS - Food products - Country Lane Foods Inc.
BIFFY - Food products ✩ - Red Gold Inc.
BIFIDO BALANCE - Dietary supplement ✩ - Omega Nutrition USA Inc.
BIFIDO FACTOR - Health care products - Natren Inc.
BIFIDOPHILUS FLORA FORCE - Vitamins and nutritional supplements - Lifetrends International
BIFIDYN - Vitamins and nutritional supplements - Source Naturals
BIFLEX - Furniture ✩ - Altec Lansing Consumer Products
BIFLOW - Health care products ✩ - Marquest Medical Products Inc.
BIFOCALS - Posters - Corman S. Drumm and Judith C. Drumm, Partnership
BIFORM - Medical apparatus - Tumble Forms, Inc.
BIFRAME - Bicycles - Montague Corp.
BIFS - Computer software ✩ - CONDUIT
BIFUSE - Health care products - MedFusion Systems Inc.
BIG - Recording label - Big Productions & Publishing Co. Inc.
BIG - Recording label - BMG Music
B.I.G. - Trays - P.T.M. Interiors Unlimited Designs, Inc.
BIG 1 - Tires - Bridgestone/Firestone, Inc.
BIG 3 - Air conditioning equipment - Grant Wilson Inc.
BIG 3 - Chemical preparations - Big Three Industries, Inc.
BIG 4 - Compressors - Dunham Bush, Inc.
BIG 4 - Hardware ✩ - National Manufacturing Co.
BIG 4 - Wheelbarrows - Kelley Manufacturing Co.
BIG 5 - Games ✩ - Milton Bradley Co.
BIG 5 - Lawn mowers ✩ - Kelley Manufacturing Co.
BIG 8 - Frankfurters - Seitz Foods Inc.
BIG 8 - Pickles - Mrs. Dalton's Best Maid Products
BIG 8 - Tables—wood ✩ - Kestell Furniture Co. Inc.
BIG 8 BALLS - Candy ✩ - American Candy Co.
BIG 10 - Screw drivers - Alexander Manufacturing Co.
BIG 10 - Wheelbarrows - True Temper Hardware Co.
BIG 29, THE - Games - Pacific Game Co.
BIG '76 - Books—blank - Sax Arts & Crafts
BIG 98 - Tools - Smith Equipment
BIG A - Gloves - Midwest Glove Co.
BIG A - Hair care products - Gillette Co.
BIG A - Hardware ✩ - Servistar Corp.
BIG ACE - Apparel—women's ✩ - Wilkins Industries Inc.
BIG AIR - Apparel and accessories - Brian Condon & Brian Finn Partnership
BIG AL STICKS - Candy ✩ - American Candy Co.
BIG ALASKA - Ice cream - Wells' Dairy, Inc.
BIG ALPHA - Oils—edible - Krinos Foods, Inc.
BIG AL'S - Food products ✩ - Cap's Italian Foods Inc.
BIG & BEAUTIFUL - Apparel and accessories - Together Crafts Inc.
BIG AND COMPANY - Apparel—men's - Men of Measure Inc.
BIG & EASY - Paint sets—hobby ✩ - Tulip Productions
BIG & JUICY - Freezers - Oscar Mayer Foods Corp.
BIG AND LITTLE JERK - Fishing lures ✩ - Lindy Little Joe Inc.
BIG APE - Chore gloves - Boss Manufacturing Co.
BIG APPLE - Bagels - Big Apple Baking Co.
BIG APPLE - Fruit drinks—bottled or canned - Big Apple Juice & Drink

BIG APPLE BAGELS - Bagels - BAB Holdings, Inc.
BIG APPLE CIRCUS - Housewares - Big Apple Circus, Ltd.
BIG APPLE COOLER - Juices - Dellwood Foods, Inc.
BIG APPLE, THE - Computer software - AV Systems Inc.
BIG ASS BASKETBALL - Apparel and accessories - Thomas Wilkolak
BIG B - Animal feeds - Bluebonnet Milling Co.
BIG B - Boats - N.A. Taylor Co. Inc.
BIG B - Dust mops - Bouras Mop Manufacturing Co.
BIG B - Fruits and vegetables ✩ - Stemilt Growers, Inc.
BIG B - Hardware - Barrett Manufacturing Co.
BIG B - Juvenile product - Jamy Inc.
BIG B - Paints ✩ - H. Behlen & Bro. Inc.
BIG B - Pork - Big B Distributors Inc.
BIG BAD BULL - Containers - Dairy Mart Convenience Stores, Inc.
BIG BAD BURRITOS - Food products - Sweet Earth Natural Foods
BIG BAD DENIM - Fabrics - Dan River Inc.
BIG BAG - Footwear ✩ - S. Goldberg and Co. Inc.
BIG BAKE - Bakery products - Saramar Corp.
BIG BALL - Cotton—balls ✩ - King Cotton Cordage Co.
BIG BALL SPORTS - Apparel and accessories - Big Ball Sports, Inc.
BIG BALLOON - Catheters - Scimed Life Systems, Inc.
BIG BALLOON - Chewing gum - Lotte USA Inc.
BIG BAMBINO - Toys ✩ - A.J. Renzi Plastic Corp.
BIG BANANA - Chewing gum ✩ - Fleer Corp.
BIG BAND - Candy - Murray-Allen International Inc.
BIG BAND - Exercising equipment - Gerstung/Gym-Thing Inc.
BIG BAND - Floor coverings—carpet and rugs - Patcraft Mills Inc.
BIG BAND - Identification tags - Precision Dynamics Corp.
BIG BAND JUMP - Recording label - Crawford Houston Group, Inc.
BIG BAND PAK - Rubber bands - Alliance Rubber Co.
BIG-BANG - Candy and chewing gum - Carbonated Candy Ventures
BIG BANG BODY ZOOM JUICE, THE - Juices - Fresh Samantha Inc.
BIG BANG CANNONS - Cannon - The Conestoga Co., Inc.
BIG BANG PIGGY BANKIN' - Video games - WMS Gaming Inc.
BIG BARGAIN - Paper—writing - Mafcote Industries, Inc.
BIG BASS - Fishing lures - Blue Fox Tackle Co.
BIG-BASS - Fishing tackle ✩ - Frabill Inc.
BIG BATCH - Cookies - General Mills, Inc.
BIG BATH - Chemical preparations - GC Thorsen, Inc.
BIG BEAM - Lighting fixtures - Big Beam Emergency Systems Inc.
BIG BEAN - Baked beans—canned ✩ - S & W Fine Foods, Inc.
BIG BEAR - Beverages—malt - Pabst Brewing Co.
BIG BEAR BOOSTER - Chairs—plastic ✩ - Steven Manufacturing Co.
BIG BEARS - Candy ✩ - Brock Candy Co. Inc.
BIG BEAT - Toys - Brumberger Co. Inc.
BIG BEAVER - Brooms - Perfex Corp.
BIG BEAVER - Food products - Mid-America Potato Co.
BIG BEE - Artists' materials - Bee Paper Co. Inc.
BIG BELLY - Toys—banks - John M. Chesnut
BIG BELTER - Toys—automobiles ✩ - Mattel, Inc.
BIG BEN - Cigarettes - Brown & Williamson Tobacco Corp.
BIG BEN - Clocks - General Time Corp. (Westclox/Seth Thomas Div.)
BIG BEN - File folders - Hedges Manufacturing Co.
BIG BEN - Golfing equipment - Ben Hogan Co.
BIG BEN - Pens ✩ - Eastern Seaboard Products Inc.
BIG BEN - Puzzles - Milton Bradley Co.
BIG BEN - Recording label ✩ - Rounder Records Corp.
BIG BEN - Wheelchairs - Ventura Enterprises, Inc.
BIG BEN II - Yarn - Henry's Attic
BIG BEN BY WRANGLER - Uniforms—tailored - Red Kap
BIG BEND - Seafood products—canned or cured - Lombardi's Seafood Inc.
BIG BEND COUNTRY - Fruits and vegetables - Grigg and Sons
BIG BERELLA BULKY - Handwork supplies - Bernat Yarn & Craft Corp.
BIG BERTHA - Games - Smart Industries Corp.
BIG BERTHA - Hobby kits - Centuri Corp.
BIG BERTHA - Toys—models - Estes Industries
BIG BERTHA CALLAWAY IRONS USA - Golfing equipment - Callaway Golf Co.
BIG BERTHA GOLD - Golfing equipment - Callaway Golf Co.
BIG BERTHA PEPPER - Flowers, plants, and seeds - Grace's Gardens, Inc.
BIG BERTHA WAR BIRD - Golfing equipment - Callaway Golf Co.
BIG BET - Pet products - Deep Run Packing Co. Inc.
BIG-BI - Gasoline - Mobil Oil Corp.
BIG! BIG! - Food products - Little Caesar Enterprises, Inc.
BIG BIG LOADER - Toys - Tomy America, Inc.
BIG BIG TOOLBENCH - Toys - Playskool, Inc.

BIG BILL - Cement - Rectorseal Corp.

BIG BILL - Food products - W.M. Meador Co. Inc.

BIG BILL'S BRIC' BUILDERS - Toys–erector sets - Good Ideas Enterprises Inc.

BIG BIN - Containers - Georgia-Pacific Corp.

BIG BIN - Garden equipment - Dalen Products Inc.

BIG BIN - Pet products - Kane Manufacturing Co.

BIG BIRD - Stand-up/sit-down easel ☆ - Coloron Industries

BIG BIRD - Toys - Jim Henson Productions, Inc.

BIG BIRD DRIVER - Toys ☆ - Playskool, Inc.

BIG BIRD JACK IN THE BOX - Toys - Playskool, Inc.

BIG BIRD SKY-RIDE - Playground equipment - Wonderline

BIG BIRD STOVE & SINK - Toys - Playskool, Inc.

BIG BIRD SUPERGYM - Playground equipment - Wonderline

BIG BIRD'S FUNHOUSE - Computer software - CBS Software

BIG BIRD'S SPECIAL DELIVERY - Computer software - CBS Software

BIG-BITE - Mops - Zephyr Manufacturing Co.

BIG BITE - Sandwiches–prepackaged - Southland Corp.

BIG BITES - Pet products - Gimborn U.S., Inc.

BIG BIX - Dog food - Mardel Laboratories, Inc.

BIG BIX - Dog food - USA-Petrx

BIG BLACK CAPE, THE - Toys–stuffed - Fun World Inc.

BIG BLAST - Chewing gum ☆ - Fleer Corp.

BIG BLAST, THE - Horns–motor vehicle - Anes Electronics Burglar Alarm Systems

BIG BLOCK - Candy - Hershey Chocolate USA

BIG BLOCK BATTLERS - Toys - Tomy America, Inc.

BIG BLOW - Chewing gum - R.L. Albert & Son, Inc.

BIG BLUE - Cleaning preparations ☆ - Senoret Chemical Co.

BIG BLUE - Computers - Big Blue Products, Inc.

BIG BLUE - Filters–water - Ametek, Inc.

BIG BLUE - Gloves–rubber ☆ - Ansell Inc. (Personal Products Div.)

BIG BLUE - Toys - Tonka Corp.

BIG BLUE - Wheelbarrows ☆ - Kelley Manufacturing Co.

BIG BOAR - Rifles ☆ - Thompson/Center Arms

BIG BOB - Pillows - Camp Kazoo, Ltd.

BIG BOGGLE - Games - Parker Brothers

BIG BOGIE - Candy ☆ - Fenn Brothers Inc.

BIG BOL - Chewing gum - R.L. Albert & Son, Inc.

BIG BOLT - Food products - Hot'n Now, Inc.

BIG BOLT - Toys ☆ - Tomy America, Inc.

BIG BONES - Toys–automobiles - Mattel, Inc.

BIG BOOKS - Publisher's imprints - Scholastic Inc.

BIG BOOMER - Golfing equipment ☆ - Rainbow Sports

BIG BOOMER - Toys–guns - Jak-Pak Inc.

BIG BOOST - Fuel additives - K & W Products

BIG BOPPER - Heat pumps - Aqua Cal, Inc.

BIG BOPPER - Ice cream - Wells' Dairy, Inc.

BIG BORE - Sporting goods ☆ - Olin Corp. (Winchester Div.)

BIG BOSS - Bicycles - Columbia Manufacturing Inc.

BIG BOSS - Calculators ☆ - Delfino Products Inc.

BIG BOSS - Chewing gum - Philadelphia Chewing Gum Corp.

BIG BOSS - Embossing tool - International Rotex Inc.

BIG BOSS - Tires - Bridgestone/Firestone, Inc.

BIG BOSS BRUISER - Tires - Bridgestone/Firestone, Inc.

BIG BOSS LITTLE BOSS - Games - Minocqua Games

BIG BOSS, THE - Footwear - West Coast Shoe Co.

BIG BOWL - Shirts - Lettuce Entertain You Enterprises

BIG BOY - Barbecues and grills - Paramount Housewares

BIG BOY - Food products ☆ - All Fresh Products Inc.

BIG BOY - Frames–picture - Framemica Co.

BIG BOY - Novelty items - Elias Brothers Restaurants, Inc.

BIG BOY - Pencils - General Pencil Co.

BIG BOY - Pet products - Strongheart Products, Inc.

BIG BOY - Plumbing fixtures - Jameco Industries, Inc.

BIG BOY - Pumps - Big Boy Products Inc.

BIG BOY - Toys–banks - A.J. Renzi Plastic Corp.

BIG BOY - Toys–trains - Digitrax, Inc.

BIG-BOY - Water-ski harness ☆ - Indiana Mills & Manufacturing, Inc.

BIG BRACKETS - Window shades - Solar-Screen Corp.

BIG BREAKER - Tools ☆ - Goldblatt Tool Co.

BIG BRITE - Electrical equipment ☆ - Electripak

BIG-BRONC - Toys - Empire of Carolina Inc.

BIG BROTHER - Alarm systems - Astro-Guard Industries Inc.

BIG BROTHER - Pencils - National Pen & Pencil Co.

BIG BROWN BAG - Bags–paper - Danco Products, Inc.

BIG BRUCE'S GUNPOWDER CHILI - Seasonings - Bruce A. Pinnell

BIG BRUISER - Toys–automobiles - Buddy L Inc.

BIG BRUTE - Electronic equipment - Mueller Electric Co.

BIG BRUTE - Hardware ☆ - Weil Service Products Corp.

BIG BRUTE - Toys–models - Estes Industries

BIG BRUTES - Toys–automobiles - Buddy L Inc.

BIG BRUTUS - Recording label - Antique-Catfish Records

BIG BUBBA - Colognes - Charleston Catalog Co.

BIG BUCK$ - Chocolate candy - Lemberger Candy Corp.

BIG BUCKET - Paints ☆ - United Coatings Inc.

BIG BUCKS - Toys - Tonka Corp.

BIG BUCKS BASEBALL - Games - Kitchen Table Games, Inc.

BIG BUCKSHOT - Toys ☆ - Princess Soft Toys

BIG BUD - Sporting goods - James Heddon's Sons

BIG BUDDY - Candy ☆ - Topps Co., Inc.

BIG BUG - Fishing lures - Storm Manufacturing Co.

BIG BUILDINGS - Toys - Natural Science Industries, Ltd.

BIG BULL - Feeders and other livestock equipment - Econo-Recut

BIG BULLY - Cleaning preparations - Marikate Ship Shape, Inc.

BIG BULLY - Food products - G & W Packing Co., Inc.

BIG B.U.M. - Apparel–men's - Chauvin International Ltd.

BIG BUNS CINNAMON ROLLS - Bakery products - Jeanne Golden Scott

BIG BURLY - Flowers, plants, and seeds - Gro-N-Sell, Inc.

BIG BURST - Beverages - Sunburst Fruit Juices

BIG BUSTER - Brushes–paint - E-Z Paintr Corp.

BIG BUSTER - Bubble gum - American Chewing Gum Inc.

BIG BUSTER - Flashlights ☆ - Zelco Industries, Inc.

BIG BUSTER - Popcorn - TV Time Foods Inc.

BIG BUTCH - Garden equipment - Fimco Inc.

BIG BUTT CIGAR CO. - Cigars - Big Butt Cigar Co., Inc.

BIG BUTTON - Remote control devices - Jasco Products Co. Inc.

BIG BY LP - Drums–musical instruments ☆ - LP Music Group

BIG C - Food products - Central Grocery Co. Inc.

BIG: CALC - Computer software - Don Johnston Inc.

BIG CANYON EXPLORER - Toys - Tonka Corp.

BIG CAT - Beverages–malt ☆ - Pabst Brewing Co.

BIG CAT - Cookies - Sarah Lingwood's Kitchens

BIG CAT - Machine tools - Weiler Corp.

BIG CATS - Footwear - Wolverine World Wide, Inc.

BIG CHECK - Food products - Smith & Nelson Inc.

BIG CHECK - Fruits and vegetables - Nuchief Sales Inc.

BIG CHEESE - Dolls - Mattel, Inc.

BIG CHEESE - Food products - Graziano Zazzara

BIG CHEESE SHOPPE, THE - Cheese - Brewster Dairy Inc.

BIG CHEESE, THE - Frankfurters - Chiquita Brands, Inc.

BIG CHERRY - Candy - Ben Myerson Candy Co.

BIG CHIEF - Barbecues and grills ☆ - Lifetime Hoan Corp.

BIG CHIEF - Brooms - Hamburg Broom Works Inc.

BIG CHIEF - Cleaning preparations ☆ - Patterson Laboratories Inc.

BIG CHIEF - Food products - Valley Distributing Co.

BIG CHIEF - Food products ☆ - Pierre Frozen Foods Inc.

BIG CHIEF - Knives–pocket - Queen Cutlery Co.

BIG CHIEF - Paper–writing ☆ - Union Camp Corp. (Fine Paper Division)

BIG CHIEF - Peanut butter - American Ace LLC

BIG CHIEF - Spices and extracts - Cajun Chef Products Inc.

BIG CHIEF - Stationery - Mead Corp.

BIG CHIEF - Sugar–granulated, refined, or powdered - Monitor Sugar Co.

BIG CHILL - Toys–automobiles - Mattel, Inc.

BIG CHIPPER - Toys - A.J. Renzi Plastic Corp.

BIG CHOICE - Chewing gum - Philadelphia Chewing Gum Corp.

BIG CHUNK - Chili–canned - Nalley's Fine Foods

BIG CIS - Trees - J. Frank Schmidt & Son Co.

BIG CITY BAGELS - Bakery goods - Big City Bagels, Inc.

BIG CLAW - Fishing lures ☆ - Wright & McGill Co.

BIG CLEAN - Automotive parts and accessories - Bloch/New England, Inc.

BIG COLA - Candy - American Chewing Gum Inc.

BIG COLOR - Paper–coated - Lasermaster Corp.

BIG COMFORT - Cushions - L & P Property Management Co.

BIG COUNTRY - Biscuits - Pillsbury Co.

BIG COUNTRY - Food products - Hardee's Food Systems, Inc.

BIG COUNTRY - Furniture ☆ - Lea Industries Inc.

BIG COUNTRY - Knives–pocket - Pamida, Inc.

BIG CRUNCH - Food products - Conagra, Inc.

BIG CRUNCH - Snack foods ☆ - Wyandot, Inc.

BIG D - Food products ☆ - State Fair Foods, Inc.

☆ = Now out of production

BIG DADDY - Automotive parts and accessories - Marson Creative Fastener Group
BIG DADDY - Bats–baseball ☆ - Hillerich & Bradsby Co.
BIG DADDY - Flowers, plants, and seeds - Smith Seed Services
BIG DADDY - Golfing equipment - Kliker Golf Co.
BIG DADDY - Housewares - Vantage Tool Inc.
BIG DADDY - Meat products–beef - Clark Meat Co.
BIG DADDY - Mufflers ☆ - International Parts Corp.
BIG DADDY - Vegetables–frozen - Norpac Services, Inc.
BIG DADDY POPS - Candy - Gladstone Candies
BIG DADDY'S - Beverages - Sumptious Selection
BIG DADDY'S - Rice - Big Daddy's Foods
BIG DANS - Games - Universal Manufacturing Co., Inc.
BIG DEAL - Chewing gum - Philadelphia Chewing Gum Corp.
BIG DEAL - Dairy products - Southland Corp.
BIG DEAL - Health care products ☆ - Medical Science Products Inc.
BIG DEAL - Pillows - Pillowtex Corp.
BIG DEAL - Sponges - S.M. Arnold Inc.
BIG DEAL - Sunglasses - Arnet, Inc.
BIG DEAL - Yarn - Lily Craft Products
BIG DEAL BAKERY - Bakery products - International Baking Co.
BIG DEAL VEAL - Food products - Little Caesar Enterprises, Inc.
BIG DECKER - Boats - H & H Molded Products
BIG DINOSAUR - Cookies - Mother's Cake & Cookie Co.
BIG DIPPER - W. Atlee Burpee and Co.
BIG DIPPER - Apparel–women's - Jezebel-Renee of Hollywood
BIG DIPPER - Bicycles - Columbia Manufacturing Inc.
BIG DIPPER - Cookies - San Anselmo's Cookies
BIG DIPPER - Kitchen utensils–aluminum - Bonny Products Inc.
BIG DIPPER - Lighting fixtures - Westinghouse Electric Corp.
BIG DIPPER - Pumps–water ☆ - Woolsey Marine Industries
BIG DIPPER - Tortillas - Terry's Inc.
BIG DIPPER - Toys - Tonka Corp.
BIG DIPPER - Trays - Argee Corp.
BIG DIPPER & LITTLE DIPPER - Toys–stuffed ☆ - Gund, Inc.
BIG DIX - Sauces - Delbert Richard Fields
BIG DOG - Frankfurters - A & R Foods Inc.
BIG DOG - Frankfurters - Bryan Foods, Inc.
BIG DOG - Golfing equipment - Ray Cook Co.
BIG DOG MOTORCYCLES - Motorcycle dealers - Big Dog Motorcycles, LLC
BIG DOGS - Sunglasses - Fortune Dogs Inc.
BIG DON - Sandwiches–prepackaged - Donatos Pizza, Inc.
BIG DOT - Office machines - Adaptive Micro Systems, Inc.
BIG DRAGGER - Toys - Tonka Corp.
BIG DRAW - Ice cream cones ☆ - Pet Dairy
BIG DUCT KIT - Boats - GPL Enterprises, Inc.
BIG DUKE - Tobacco products ☆ - Swedish Math North America Inc.
BIG DUTY DEADBOLT - Locks–door - U.S. Lock Corp.
BIG-E - Beef - Armour Swift-Eckrich
BIG E - Vegetables–canned - Big E Produce
BIG E-Z BOOKKEEPING - Accounting machines - Big E-Z Bookkeeping Co.
BIG EAGLE - Apparel–children's ☆ - Eagle Knitting Mills Inc.
BIG EAR MUSIC - Recording label - DCC Compact Classics, Inc.
BIG EARS - Microphones - Connectronics Corp.
BIG EARS - Vegetables–frozen - Kraft Foods, Inc.
BIG EASY, THE - Iced tea–bottled or canned - Conwell & Laniado
BIG EASY, THE - Computer software - On-Site Systems Inc.
BIG ED - Fishing lures - Eppinger Manufacturing Co.
BIG EDGE - Frames–eyeglass ☆ - Universal/Univis Inc.
BIG EVENT - Floor coverings–carpet and rugs ☆ - World Carpets, Inc.
BIG EVENT GOLF - Video games ☆ - Taito America Corp.
BIG EYE - Golfing equipment - Ram Golf Corp.
BIG-EYE - Hardware - U.S. Home Security Systems
BIG EYE - Sporting goods - Orvis Co., Inc.
BIG-EYE II - Hardware - U.S. Home Security Systems
BIG FARM - Toys - ERTL Co., Inc.
BIG FAT DADDY - Apparel and accessories - Tillman I. Segal
BIG FEET - Toys–stuffed - Kamar International Inc.
BIG FIG - Advertising agencies - Dane Petersen
BIG FIN SPINNER BAIT - Fishing lures - Lindy Little Joe Inc.
BIG FISH - Watches - Paul Marable
BIG FISH-LITTLE FISH - Toys - Tyco Toys
BIG FLIPPER - Plumbing products - Thermaco, Inc.
BIG FLIPPER, THE - Novelty items - Digital Expressions Corp.
BIG-FLO - Pipes - Anderson-Barrows Metals Corp.
BIG FLO - Pumps - Marley Pump Co.

BIG FOOT - Air purification systems ☆ - Medo Industries, Inc.
BIG FOOT - Communications equipment–mobile - Mid-West Electronics Inc.
BIG FOOT - Footwear - Etta-Kit Enterprises
BIG FOOT - Games - Scramb-L-Gram, Inc.
BIG FOOT - Garden equipment - Master Mark Plastic Products
BIG-FOOT - Lighting equipment - Lowel-Light Manufacturing Inc.
BIG FOOT - Musical instrument accessories - XL Specialty Percussion
BIG FOOT - Nail care products - Simplicity Nail Products
BIG FOOT - Office supplies - Master Caster Co.
BIG FOOT - Pizzas–mixes - Pizza Hut Inc.
BIG FOOT - Sewing machine equipment - Little Foot, Ltd.
BIG FOOT - Shovels - Emsco Inc.
BIG FOOT - Tires–automobile - Big O Tires, Inc.
BIG FOOT - Toys ☆ - Playskool, Inc.
BIG FOOT - Toys–models ☆ - Estes Industries
BIG FOUR YELLOW - Paints - Perry & Derrick Co.
BIG FRANK - Toys - Playskool, Inc.
BIG FREEZE - Ice chests–plastic - Igloo Products Corp.
BIG FRUIT - Chewing gum - Philadelphia Chewing Gum Corp.
BIG FUN - Sweaters - Shah Safari, Inc.
BIG FUN SOUNDS - Publisher's imprints ☆ - Western Publishing Co., Inc.
BIG G - Cereal - General Mills, Inc.
BIG G - Fruits and vegetables - Schermer Potato Co.
BIG G - Mayonnaise ☆ - B.G. Grocery & Nut Co.
BIG G - Scouring pads ☆ - Royal Paper Products Inc.
BIG G IMPORTS - Apparel and accessories - Island G Ltd.
BIG GALS - Apparel–women's - Exquisite Form Industries
BIG GASSER, THE - Rodenticide, pesticide ☆ - Atlas Chemical Corp.
BIG GEM - Flowers, plants, and seeds - New Tomorrow Inc.
BIG GEORGE - Food products - Eisenberg Co.
BIG GLOW - Pens ☆ - Uchida of America Corp.
BIG GOLD TOP - Breads - Grand Union Co.
BIG GOOD WOLF, THE - Pet products ☆ - Gone to the Dogs
BIG GOSPEL - Recording label - McDowell Records
BIG GREEN - Cleaning equipment - Bissell Inc.
BIG GRID - Hobby kits - Extra Special Products Corp.
BIG GRIPPER - Fasteners–snap - Lord & Hodge, Inc.
BIG GULP - Housewares - Hako Minuteman Inc.
BIG GUN - Golfing equipment - Golfsmith International Inc.
BIG GUNS - Motorcycle parts and accessories - San Luis Industrial Innovations, Inc.
BIG GUY - Cookies - James D. Rogers
BIG GUY - Glassware–household - James A. Wold
BIG GUY - Sunglasses - Jack Martin Co.
BIG H - Vegetable sauces ☆ - CPC International Inc.
BIG HEAD TODD AND THE MONSTERS - Posters - Big Head Todd and the Monsters, Inc.
BIG HEADS - Figurines - Dennis Dillman
BIG HEAT - Heaters–space - Air Care Industries Inc.
BIG HED - Apparel and accessories - Lana Inc.
BIG HED DESIGNS - Apparel and accessories - Lana Inc.
BIG HELP, THE - Apparel–children's - Viacom International Inc.
BIG HIT - Chewing gum - Leaf, Inc.
BIG HIT - Sporting goods ☆ - J. De Beer & Son Inc.
BIG HITTER - Bats–baseball - Mantua/Cosom Sporting Goods
BIG HOLD - Hair care products ☆ - Gefden International Inc.
BIG HORN - Binoculars - Pioneer Marketing & Research, Inc.
BIG HORN - Saddles ☆ - Outdoor Sports Industries
BIG HORN - Slacks - Tropical Sportswear International Corp.
BIG HORN - Water–bottled or canned - WJP, Inc.-Big Horn Water
BIG HUG - Juices - Daily Juice Products Inc.
BIG HUG - Pillows - American Fiber Industries Corp.
BIG HUNK - Boats - Glen-L Marine Designs
BIG HUNK - Candy - Annabelle Candy Co. Inc.
BIG HURT - Greeting cards - Frank Thomas
BIG HURT, THE - Trading cards and stamps - Leader Enterprises, Inc.
BIG HURT, THE - Apparel and accessories - Frank Thomas
BIG I - Food products - Western Farmers Association
BIG IDEA - Apparel and accessories ☆ - Warnaco Inc.
BIG IMPRESSIONS - Pins–jewelry - Imprinted Products Corp.
BIG INCH - Office supplies - Better Packages
BIG INCH - Pencils–mechanical - Alexander Manufacturing Co.
BIG INCH MOTOR - Motors - Haydon Switch and Instrument Inc.
BIG INK - Computer peripheral equipment - Lasermaster Corp.
BIG ISLAND - Computer hardware - Big Island Communication, Inc.
BIG J - Apparel and accessories ☆ - Jantzen Inc.

BIG J - Fruit - Malcolm & Burtt Jacobs
BIG J - Toys - Tonka Corp.
BIG JAM - Musical instrument accessories ☆ - Multivox/Sorkin Music Co. Inc.
BIG JAW - Candy - Leaf, Inc.
BIG JAWS - Clamps - Paine Co.
BIG JEWEL STONE - Tiles–ceramic - Capitol Tile Import Co.
BIG JIG - Puzzles - Kingdom Puzzles
BIG JIM - Candy - Bobs Candies Inc.
BIG JIM'S - Barbecue sauce - Clark Foods, Inc.
BIG JINX - Insecticides - Claire Manufacturing Co.
BIG JOB - Motor vehicle parts and accessories ☆ - Delta Industries
    International, Inc.
BIG JOB - Rubber bands - B.F. Goodrich Co.
BIG JOB - Swimming pools - Coastal Industries Inc.
BIG JOHN - Bread, dairy product, potato chips - Martin and Bayley Inc.
BIG JOHN - Pumps - Little Giant Pump Co.
BIG JOHN - Rods–aluminum - Fulton Corp.
BIG JOHN - Sporting goods ☆ - Marty Gilman Inc.
BIG JOHN'S 01' WEST - Sauces - The James Valley Co. Inc.
BIG JOHN'S BEANS 'N FIXINS - Food products ☆ - Hunt-Wesson, Inc.
BIG JOHN'S OL' WEST - Sauces - John C. Collins
BIG JOHNSON - Apparel and accessories - Maryland Screen Printers, Inc.
BIG JON - Boats - O.M.C. Aluminum Boat Group
BIG JUG - Beverages–malt - Hudepohl-Schoenling Brewing Co.
BIG K - Combs - Kim Laube & Co. Inc.
BIG K BURGER - Sandwiches–prepackaged - Kmart Properties, Inc.
BIG KAHUNA - Automotive batteries - Batteries, Inc.
BIG KAHUNA - Skis - K-2 Corp.
BIG KATUNA - Apparel and accessories - Pacific Motion Corp.
BIG KICK - Tobacco - Conwood Co. L.P.
BIG KICK BERRY - Juices - Chiquita Brands, Inc.
BIG KID TRAINER - Infant product - Century Products Co.
BIG KIDS - Suntan lotions - Cumberland-Swan, Inc.
BIG KIDS ENTERPRISES - Toys–models - Big Kids Enterprises
BIG KIDS, THE - Dolls - Doll Factory, Inc.
BIG KISS - Printers–computer - QMS, Inc.
BIG LAKES - Boats–motor ☆ - Lund Boat Co.
BIG LASH - Cosmetics - Revlon Consumer Products Corp.
BIG LEAGUE - Balls–baseball - Jim Bouton Corp.
BIG LEAGUE - Recording label - Priority Records
BIG LEAGUE - Toys - Pick Point Sports
BIG LEAGUE CHEW - Chewing gum - Amurol Confections Co.
BIG LEAGUE PLUG - Chocolate bars ☆ - Amurol Confections Co.
BIG LED - Pencils - Empire Berol USA
BIG LICK - Candy - Tom's Foods Inc.
BIG LIDS - Apparel and accessories - Samii Clothes
BIG LIFTER - Toys - Tonka Corp.
BIG LI'L HOE - Tillers–rotary - Hoffco Inc.
BIG LI'L SNACK - Potato chips - Humpty Dumpty Potato Chip Co.
BIG-LITTLE ACTIVITY BOX - Toys - Natural Science Industries, Ltd.
BIG/LITTLE GAMES - Games ☆ - Smethport Specialty Co.
BIG-LITTLE PEGBOARD - Toys - Lauri Inc.
BIG LOADER - Toys - Tomy America, Inc.
BIG LOCK - Toys - Tyco Toys
BIG LOOK - Mirrors - Spilo/Mehaz Worldwide
BIG LOOK, THE - Mirrors - Femme Manufacturing Corp.
BIG LOUIE - Ladders–metal - Louisville Ladder Group LLC
BIG LUG - T-shirts–men's - Take Me out to the Ballgame, LLC
BIG M - Footwear - Scottie Industries Inc.
BIG M - Fruits and vegetables - Muir-Roberts Co. Inc.
BIG M - Meat products - Big M Supermarkets, Inc.
BIG M - Pens - Micropoint Inc.
BIG M MIDSTATE - Breads - Big M Supermarkets, Inc.
BIG MAC - Apparel–men's - J.C. Penney Co., Inc.
BIG MAC - Bicycles - Columbia Manufacturing Inc.
BIG MAC - Fishing lures - Storm Manufacturing Co.
BIG MAC - Fruits and vegetables - Agri Sales Inc.
BIG MAC - Paper punches ☆ - Rolodex Corp.
BIG MAC - Rope ☆ - Wellington Leisure Products, Inc.
BIG MAC - Sandwiches–prepackaged - Mcdonald's Corp.
BIG MAC - Snow-cleaning brush ☆ - Clean-Rite Products Co.
BIG MAC III - Snow-cleaning brush ☆ - Clean-Rite Products Co.
BIG MACK - Recording label ☆ - Thomas E. Mack
BIG MAMA - Food products - Goodmark Foods, Inc.
BIG MAMA - Hosiery - Sheffield Industries Inc.
BIG MAMA BUGS - Novelty items ☆ - Lemberger Candy Corp.

BIG MAMA G - Beverages–alcohol - Gaetano Specialties Ltd.
BIG MAMA JAMA - Bedding–linen - Alan Lloyd Schaechter
BIG MAN - Ophthalmic goods - Foremost Optical Products
BIG MAN - Work clothes - Key Industries, Inc.
BIG MAN STICKS - Candy - Wellons Candy Co. Inc.
BIG MAN, THE - Toys - Kraft Foods, Inc.
BIG MAT - Mats - Storall Inc.
BIG MAT - Truck beds - Durakon Industries Inc.
BIG MATE - Tote bags - S.I. Jacobson Manufacturing Co.
BIG MAX - Multiple vitamins - Basic Organics, Inc.
BIG MAX - Skis - Skis Dynastar, Inc.
BIG MAX - Travel accessories - American Guard-It Manufacturing Co. Inc.
BIG MEDICINE - Meat products - R.C. Western Meats Inc.
BIG MIKE - Housewares - Smyth Manufacturing Co.
BIG MIKE - Paint rollers - Bestt-Liebco
BIG MINT - Candy - Bobs Candies Inc.
BIG MISSISSIPPI MUD - Ice cream - Wells' Dairy, Inc.
BIG MO - Golfing equipment - Slotline Golf
BIG MO TACKLE - Fishing lures - John's Rod & Reel Service
BIG MOGUL - Banjos ☆ - OME Co. Inc.
BIG MOMMA - Antennas - Allen Telecom Group, Inc.
BIG MONEY - Recording label - Big Money Inc.
BIG MONTANA - Sandwiches–prepackaged - Arby's, Inc.
BIG MOUTH - Bottles–plastic - Cramer Products Inc.
BIG MOUTH - Buckets–plastic - Argee Corp.
BIG MOUTH - Candy - Topps Co., Inc.
BIG MOUTH - Plumbing fixtures - Cherne Industries Inc.
BIG MOUTH - Shelving units–metal ☆ - Tennsco Corp.
BIG MOUTH SINGERS - Toys–stuffed - CBS Toys
BIG MUDDER, THE - Wheelbarrows - Trallfa U.S. Inc.
BIG N - Fishing lures - Howe Now Inc.
BIG 'N BEAUTIFUL - Apparel stores–lingerie - Goddess Bra
BIG N' BEEFY - Sausages - Wimmer's Meat Products, Inc.
BIG N BOLD - Clocks - Sunbeam Precision Measurement
BIG 'N BOUNCY - Curling irons–electric - Remington Products Co.
BIG 'N FRIENDLY - Toys - Mattel, Inc.
BIG N LITTLE - Toys ☆ - Henry Gordy International Inc.
BIG 'N PRETTY - Napkins–paper - Georgia-Pacific Corp.
BIG 'N SOFT - Marshmallows - Shaw's Supermarkets, Inc.
BIG 'N SOFT - Paper–toilet ☆ - Georgia-Pacific Corp.
BIG 'N THIRSTY - Paper–toweling ☆ - Georgia-Pacific Corp.
BIG NAME IN SUGAR FREE, THE - Candy - Sorbee International, Ltd.
BIG NEAPOLITAN - Ice cream - Wells' Dairy, Inc.
BIG NICKEL - Golfing equipment - Lawrence Au
BIG NORMIS MAGIC FISH SCALER - Fishing tackle - Cuba Specialty
    Manufacturing Co.
BIG NOSE BREWING COMPANY - Beverages–malt - Premier Ventures, Inc.
BIG NOSE MIGHTY LIGHT - Beverages–malt - Premier Ventures, Inc.
BIG NOSE RED ALE - Beverages–malt - Premier Ventures, Inc.
BIG NUT - Toys - Martin Perl
BIG O - Agricultural machinery - Sioux Steel Co.
BIG O - Lawn mowers ☆ - Orgill Brothers and Co.
BIG O - Paints - Olympic Paint & Varnish Co.
BIG O TIRES - Automotive-services franchise - Big O Tires, Inc.
BIG ONE - Screws - American Mussel Harvesters Inc.
BIG ONE, THE - Locks ☆ - American Lock Co.
BIG ONE, THE - Skin care products - Bonat Inc.
BIG ONE, THE - Mattress pads - Pillowtex Corp.
BIG ORANGE - Hammers - American Clamping Corp.
BIG ORANGE - Health care products - DBA Products Co.
BIG-O'S DEER NIP - Animal feeds - Big-O Deer Products
BIG-O'S DEER PIE - Animal feeds - Big-O Deer Products
BIG OTTO - Pens ☆ - Parker Pen USA
BIG OVINE - Toys ☆ - A.J. Renzi Plastic Corp.
BIG PAL - Angler's clip ☆ - London International U.S. Holdings
BIG PART OF BETTER PERFORMANCE., A - Motor vehicle parts and
    accessories - Horton Holdings, Inc.
BIG PARTY, THE - Gift shops - Big Party, L.P.
BIG PAY - Candy ☆ - Leaf, Inc.
BIG PEACH - Beverage ☆ - Big Red Inc.
BIG PENNY VINEYARDS - Table grapes - Big Penny Vineyards
BIG PETE - Food products - Beatrice Cos. Inc.
BIG PETE - Tools–plumbing - Moen Inc.
BIG PICTURE, THE - Computer software - Panacea, Inc.
BIG PLAY DESK - Toys - Steven Manufacturing Co.
BIG POLY - Sporting goods - Griffith Rubber Mills

                                                                              ☆ = Now out of production

BIG POP - Popcorn - National Oats Co. Inc.
BIG POSSUM GOLF - Shorts–men's - Jeff Oliphant
BIG POWER PUSHERS - Toys ☆ - Tomy America, Inc.
BIG PRINT - Yarn - Tahki Imports Ltd.
BIG PRO - Dryers–hair - Belson Products
BIG PUCKERS - Chewing gum ☆ - Fleer Corp.
BIG PUMPER - Toys - Tonka Corp.
BIG PUNCH - Candy ☆ - Ferrara Pan Candy Co., Inc.
BIG PUTT - Toys ☆ - A.J. Renzi Plastic Corp.
BIG-QIK - Brooms - Zephyr Manufacturing Co.
BIG R - Food products - Roberts Bros. Inc.
BIG RAPIDS - Footwear - Wolverine World Wide, Inc.
BIG RED - Animal feeds - Agway Country Foods Inc.
BIG RED - Beverage ☆ - Big Red Inc.
BIG RED - Chewing gum - Wm. Wrigley Jr. Co.
BIG RED - Food processors - Beehive, Inc.
BIG RED - Food products - Milton G. Waldbaum Co.
BIG RED - Food products ☆ - Springdale Food Co.
BIG RED - Fruits and vegetables - Westin Inc.
BIG RED - Health care products - Ablenet Inc.
BIG RED - Housewares ☆ - Arden Corp.
BIG RED - Nuts–salted, roasted, cooked, or canned ☆ - Dole Dried Fruit & Nut Co.
BIG RED - Paint sprayers ☆ - Wooster Brush Co.
BIG RED - Paints - Colony Paints Div.
BIG RED - Pens–fountain ☆ - Parker Pen USA
BIG RED - Sleeping bags - A. Brandt Sleepworks
BIG RED - Snack foods - Mexican Food Manufacturing of Omaha Inc.
BIG RED - Sporting goods ☆ - Gill Sports Equipment, Inc.
BIG RED - Suspenders - Techno-Optic, Inc.
BIG RED - Tractors - Taylor Machine Works
BIG RED - Vises - Wilton Corp.
BIG RED - Wheelbarrows - Kelley Manufacturing Co.
BIG RED - Work benches - Shure Manufacturing Corp.
BIG RED RACER - Toys - Tyco Toys
BIG RED SMOKEYS - Sausages - Hillshire Farm Co.
BIG RED'S CAN DO KITS - Tools - Red Devil Inc.
BIG REELER - Electronic equipment - Rangertone Research Inc.
BIG RESORTER - Boats–motor ☆ - Lund Boat Co.
BIG RICHARD - Sporting goods ☆ - O'Brien International
BIG RIDER DUMP TRUCK - Toys - Steven Manufacturing Co.
BIG RIG - Lubricants - Bullshot Systems Inc.
BIG RIGGER - Toys–automobiles - Mattel, Inc.
BIG RIG'S - Air purification systems ☆ - Medo Industries, Inc.
BIG RIGS - Toy trucks - Intex Recreation Corp.
BIG RIGS - Toys–automobiles - Empire Industries
BIG RIP-OFF - Carpet- and tile-removal equipment - Inventive Manufacturing
BIG RIVER - Key rings - Hugo Bosca Co., Inc.
BIG RIVER HARP - Harmonicas - Hohner Inc.
BIG ROCK - Apparel and accessories - Blue Sky Corp.
BIG ROCK MOUNTAIN SPRING WATER - Water–bottled or canned - Big Rock Clothing Co.
BIG ROLL - Paper–toweling - Scott Paper Co.
BIG ROLLS - Paper–toweling - Georgia-Pacific Corp.
BIG SAM - Meat products–beef - Schwan's Sales Enterprises, Inc.
BIG SCOOP - Dairy products - Challenge Dairy Co.
BIG SHAPEZ - Paper - Z-Barten Productions
BIG SHAVER - Toys - Tyco Toys
BIG SHOT - Nitrous Oxide Systems, Inc.
BIG SHOT - Beverages - Jefferson Bottling Co. Inc.
BIG SHOT - Cameras ☆ - Polaroid Corp.
BIG SHOT - Candy - American Chewing Gum Inc.
BIG SHOT - Candy ☆ - Glenn Confections Inc.
BIG SHOT - Fire extinguishers - Hawk International, Inc.
BIG SHOT - Fire extinguishers ☆ - Big Boy Products Inc.
BIG SHOT - Fireworks - Alamo Fireworks, Inc.
BIG SHOT - Lenses–optical - Opsales, Inc.
BIG SHOT - Plumbing-line cleaner - Jancyn Manufacturing Corp.
BIG SHOT - Projection screens ☆ - General Audio-Visual Inc.
BIG SHOT - Soil–potting - Sun Gro Horticulture, Inc.
BIG SHOT - Sporting goods - Porter Athletic Equipment Co.
BIG SHOT - Toys ☆ - Henry Gordy International Inc.
BIG SHOT - Vitamins and nutritional supplements - Naturally Vitamin Supplements Inc.
BIG SHOT - Washers–metal ☆ - Mi-T-M Corp.
BIG SHOT - Writing product - Island Pen Manufacturing Corp.

BIG SHOT BUNGEE POOL - Games - Mattel, Inc.
BIG SHOTS - Cannon - Artistry in Motion Entertainment, Inc.
BIG SHOTS - Toys - Recoton Corp.
BIG SHOULDERS BAKING - Pastries - Little Miss Muffin, Inc.
BIG SHOULDERS PORTER - Beverages–malt - Chicago Brewing Co.
BIG SHOW OFF - Glassware–household - Federal Glass
BIG SICILIAN - Pizzas–frozen - Papa Romano's, Inc.
BIG SIG - Pens - Sanford Corp.
BIG SIXTY I - Stoves–gas - LazyMan, Inc.
BIG SIXTY II - Stoves–gas - LazyMan, Inc.
BIG SKI - Sporting goods - Sweco
BIG SKINNY, THE - Skin care products - Cosmedic Concepts, Inc.
BIG SKY - Colognes - Parfum de Coeur Ltd.
BIG SKY - Recording label - SCP Records
BIG SKY COUNTRY - Furniture - Lane Co. Inc.
BIG SKY, THE - Wallpaper - Capital Carousel Inc.
BIG SKY, THE - Wallpaper - Roger Nicholson Designs Ltd.
BIG SKY TROOPER - Computer software - Lucasarts Entertainment Co.
BIG SKY USA DETENTE - Apparel and accessories - Organik Technologies, Inc.
BIG SLAM - Beverages–carbonated - Pepsico, Inc.
BIG SLAMMU - Toys - Mattel, Inc.
BIG SLEEP, THE - Bedding–linen - Dan River Inc.
BIG SMITH - Apparel and accessories - Big Smith Brands Inc.
BIG SMOKE, THE - Golfing equipment - Pro's Edge Wholesale Inc.
BIG SMOKEY - Apparel–men's - U.O.D., Inc.
BIG SOCKS - Yarn - Tahki Imports Ltd.
BIG SOUND - Recording label - TNA Records
BIG SOUND - Toys–musical - Magnus Organ Co.
BIG SPILL - Puzzles - Games Group International Inc.
BIG SPLASH - Bathing suits - Puritan Sportswear Corp.
BIG SPLASH BAIT, THE - Fishing lures - Sports Design and Development, Inc.
BIG SPORT - Shirts - Big Ball Sports, Inc.
BIG SPORTS TAG - Luggage - Dolan Enterprises Inc.
BIG SPRING - Mattresses ☆ - The Coleman Co.
BIG SQUEEEEZE!, THE - Fruit drinks–bottled or canned - Energy Beverage, Inc.
BIG SQUIRTZ - Beverages ☆ - ATGT, Inc.
BIG STAR - Food products - Big Star Food Stores
BIG STATE MUSIC - Publisher's imprints - Green Dog Productions
BIG STEAM - Toys–trains ☆ - Life-Like Products Inc.
BIG STEP - Stools–metal - Cosco, Inc.
BIG STICK - Adhesives and sealants - Dap Products Inc.
BIG STICK - Flypaper - Security Products Co.
BIG STICK - Food products ☆ - Knudsen Dairy Products
BIG STICK - Sporting goods - Rawlings Sporting Goods Co., Inc.
BIG STICK COMPANY, THE - Canes - Cold Steel Inc.
BIG STINKY - Flypaper - J.L. Price Products Inc.
BIG STOP - Alarm systems - Kolin Industries Inc.
BIG STRAPPER, THE - Containers - Barbara Wanat
BIG STRECH - Adhesives and sealants - Sashco Inc.
BIG STRIKE - Fertilizer - Southern States Cooperative Inc.
BIG STRIKE - Games - Little Tikes Co.
BIG STUF - Cookies - Nabisco Foods Group
BIG STUFF - Oil machinery - J.M. Huber Corp.
BIG STUFF - Pillows - Pillowtex Corp.
BIG SUGAR MORE IS BETTER - Sugar–granulated, refined, or powdered - Peter J. Barnes
BIG SUR - Apparel and accessories - San Francisco Sales, Inc.
BIG SUR - Apparel stores–sports - Jem Sportswear Inc.
BIG SUR - Bathtubs–enameled ☆ - Lyons Industries Inc.
BIG SUR - Floor coverings–carpet and rugs - Catalina Carpet Mills Inc.
BIG SUR - Floor coverings–carpet and rugs ☆ - Royalweve Carpet Mills
BIG SUR - Furniture ☆ - Broyhill Furniture Industries, Inc.
BIG SUR - Thread - Van Waters and Rogers Inc.
BIG SUR - Wines - Monterey Peninsula Winery
BIG SUR-PRISE - Toys–automobiles - Mattel, Inc.
BIG SURFER - Furniture - Life-Like Products Inc.
BIG SURFSTIK - Fishing tackle ☆ - Fenwick
BIG SWEDE - Knives–pocket - Normark Corp.
BIG SWEEP - Brooms - Royal Maid Association for the Blind Inc.
BIG SWIM MEET, THE - Games - Addison-Wesley Publishing Co.
BIG SWITCH - Lighting equipment - Carlon
BIG TAG - Luggage - Dolan Enterprises Inc.
BIG TALK TEES - Apparel - Big Ego
BIG TALKER - Dolls - Goldberger Doll Manufacture Co.

☆ = Now out of production

BIG TATE - Potato flakes - R.T. French Co.
BIG TED - Paint rollers - Wooster Brush Co.
BIG-TEE - Hardware ☆ - Leslie-Locke, Inc.
BIG TEE BURGER - Sandwiches–prepackaged - Tastee-Freez International Inc.
BIG TEETER TOTTER - Playground equipment - Little Tikes Co.
BIG TEN - Bicycles - Columbia Manufacturing Inc.
BIG TEN - Fabrics - Dan River Inc.
BIG TEN - Snack foods ☆ - McCleary Inc.
BIG TEX - Candy - Judson-Atkinson Candies
BIG TEX - Fruit drinks–bottled or canned - Texas Citrus Exchange. (Citrus Juice Div)
BIG TEX - Restaurants–fast food - Western Sizzlin Steak House Franchises Inc.
BIG TEX - Rocking horses - Flexible Flyer Co.
BIG THING - Sporting goods ☆ - Bear Paw Tackle Co.
BIG THINGS - Toys–stuffed - Those Characters from Cleveland, Inc.
BIG THINKING IN A LITTLE SIZE - Footwear - Reebok International Ltd.
BIG THREE - Binders ☆ - Korchmar Case Co.
BIG THUMB - Candy - Glenn Confections Inc.
BIG THUMPER - Toys - Tonka Corp.
BIG THUNDER - Toys - Mattel, Inc.
BIG TIMBER - Golfing equipment - Louisville Golf Club Co. Inc.
BIG TIMBER - Wooden pens - Autopoint Inc.
BIG TIME - Apparel and accessories ☆ - Glint Inc.
BIG TIME - Candy ☆ - Leaf, Inc.
BIG TIME - Clocks - General Time Corp. (Westclox/Seth Thomas Div.)
BIG TIME - Dog food - SOPAKCO
BIG TIME - Floor coverings–carpet and rugs - World Carpets, Inc.
BIG TIME TEACHER - Toys - Tyco Toys
BIG TIMER - Clocks - Major/Advance International
BIG-TIMER - Timers–appliance ☆ - Healthometer
BIG TOM - Sporting goods ☆ - Penn's Woods Products Inc.
BIG TOOL - Apparel and accessories - Tanya Willard
BIG TOOTH - Agricultural machinery - Kondex Corp.
BIG TOOTH - Candy ☆ - Topps Co., Inc.
BIG TOP - Bedding–linen - Dan River Inc.
BIG TOP - Candles ☆ - W and F Products Inc.
BIG TOP - Food products - Procter & Gamble Co.
BIG TOP - Kitchen appliances ☆ - Sunbeam-Oster Household Products
BIG TOP - Macaroni ☆ - Borden, Inc.
BIG TOP - Pet products - Fashion Pet Accessories Inc.
BIG TOP - Photographic equipment ☆ - SP Systems/Saratons
BIG TOP - Plastics - Working Products, Inc.
BIG TOP - Tents - Denver Tent Co.
BIG TOP - Toys–stuffed ☆ - Gund, Inc.
BIG TOP CHRISTMAS, A - Giftware - Schmid Inc.
BIG TOP CLOWN COLLECTION, THE - Dolls - Heritage Mint, Ltd.
BIG TOP POPCORN - Popcorn - Twin Valley Development Services Inc.
BIG TOP SORT 'N POP - Toys - Mattel, Inc.
BIG TOP, THE - Apparel and accessories - International Blueprint Inc.
BIG TOP, THE - Umbrellas - Totes, Inc.
BIG TOW - Skis ☆ - Outdoor Technologies Group
BIG TOWN - Recording label - Cadet Records Inc.
BIG TOYS - Video production - Arc Light Productions, Inc.
BIG TREE - Recording label - Atlantic Records
BIG TROUBLE - Toys–stuffed ☆ - Gund, Inc.
BIG TRUCKER'S - Footwear–children's - Durango Boot Co. Inc.
BIG T'S - Fishing tackle - Big T's Mechanical Repairs, Inc.
BIG T'S OUTA' WHERE! - T-shirts - Big T's Outa' Where! and Design
BIG TUB - Food containers ☆ - Reynolds Aluminum Supply Co.
BIG-TWIN - Pumps - Hypro Corp.
BIG-U - Fruits and vegetables - Grand View Heights Citrus Association
BIG UGLY - Tires - Bridgestone/Firestone, Inc.
BIG 'UN - Fishing lures - Big 'un Tackle Co.
BIG 'UNS - Cookies - President Baking Co., Inc.
BIG V - Dog food - Big V Feeds Inc.
BIG V - Fruits–frozen - J.H. Verbridge & Son Inc.
BIG V - Tools–hand-operated - Sumner Manufacturing Co., Inc.
BIG V - Trees - Vans Pines, Inc.
BIG VALLEY - Farm machinery - Behlen Manufacturing Co.
BIG VALLEY - Food products - Sundor Brands Inc.
BIG VALLEY - Food products - Townsend Farms
BIG VALLEY - Fruits and vegetables - Big Valley Marketing Corp.
BIG VALLEY - Fruits and vegetables - J.R. Wood Inc.
BIG-VALU - Fabric softener - James Austin Co.

BIG VALUE - Bread and rolls - Cotton Bros. Baking Co. Inc.
BIG VALUE - Cordage and twine ☆ - Winchester-Auburn Mills Inc.
BIG VALUE - Flour–blended - Western Star Mill Co.
BIG VALUE - Food products - Freemont Co.
BIG VALUE - Food products - Gold Kist Inc.
BIG-VALUE - Food products - Richfood (Pennsylvania Division)
BIG VALUE - Socks - Sockyard Co. Inc.
BIG VALUE - Sporting goods - Ed Cumings Inc.
BIG VANILLA - Ice cream - Wells' Dairy, Inc.
BIG VERSA - Pumps–water - Beckett Corp.
BIG/VOICE - Electronic equipment - Sound-Craft Systems Inc.
BIG VOLUME - Hair care products - Mebco Industries, Inc.
BIG 'W' BRAND - Leather goods - James Cox Saddlery
BIG WAD - Chewing gum ☆ - Fleer Corp.
BIG WALLY - Cleaning preparations - S.C. Johnson & Son, Inc.
BIG WATER - Boats–motor - O.M.C. Aluminum Boat Group
BIG WATER - Boats–motor - Sea Nymph Boats
BIG WAVE, THE - Motor vehicle parts and accessories - CFL Systems, LLC
BIG WHALE CD'S - Record stores - Big Dog Inc.
BIG WHEEL - Agricultural machinery - Osborne Industries Inc.
BIG WHEEL - Cultivator - American Lawn Mower Co.
BIG WHEEL - Dairy products - Southland Corp.
BIG WHEEL - Kitchen utensils–aluminum - Bicycle Tools Inc.
BIG WHEELER - Film–motion picture - Rangertone Research Inc.
BIG WHIP - Candy ☆ - Brock Candy Co. Inc.
BIG WHISTLE - Apparel and accessories - Dennis Cucci
BIG WHITE - Water purification systems - U.S. Water Products, Inc.
BIG WIG - Musical instrument stores - Big Wig
BIG WILLIE - Recording label - Forrest Green Enterprises Inc.
BIG WING - Kites - Toy Biz, Inc.
BIG WONDERS - Housewares - Tupperware Co.
BIG WOODY - Apparel and accessories - Nathan Adam Gowen
BIG WORLD BARS - Cereal - Geebees, Inc.
BIG X - Dust-mop refills - American Textile Products Co.
BIG YANK - Toys–models ☆ - Estes Industries
BIG YANK - Work clothes - Big Yank Corp.
BIG YATES - Food products ☆ - Yates Blodgett
BIG YAZOO - Boats–dinghies ☆ - C-G Industries Inc.
BIG YUMMY - Candy bars ☆ - Confex Inc.
BIG Z - Dairy products ☆ - Zausner Foods Corp.
BIG Z - Golfing equipment - Ram Golf Corp.
BIG Z - Onions - Big Z Pre-Pack Corp.
BIG Z - Pillows - Pacific Coast Feather Co.
BIGA'S - Bakery products - C.B. Breads, Inc.
BIGBALL - Balls–basketball - Advanced Sports Concepts Inc.
BIGBALL, THE - Sporting goods - Advanced Sports Concepts Inc.
BIGBEE - Toys–stuffed ☆ - Gund, Inc.
BIG!BIG! SLICE - Pizza - Little Caesar Enterprises, Inc.
BIGDOG MOTORCYCLES - Motorcycles - Big Dog Motorcycles, LLC
BIGELOIL - Veterinary pharmaceutical preparations - W.F. Young, Inc.
BIGELOW - Floor coverings–carpet and rugs - Karastan-Bigelow Inc.
BIGELOW - Floor coverings–carpet and rugs - Mohawk Carpet Corp.
BIGELOW - Teas - R.C. Bigelow, Inc.
BIGELOW-GRIDLOCK - Floor coverings–carpet and rugs ☆ - Karastan-Bigelow Inc.
BIGELOW TEATIME - Teas - R.C. Bigelow, Inc.
BIGEN - Hair coloring preparations - Capitol Novelty Co.
BIGENS - Balls–rubber - Sport Fun, Inc.
BIGFOOT - Bakery products - Johnson Oil Co., Inc.
BIGFOOT - Beverages–malt - Sierra Nevada Brewing Co.
BIGFOOT - Computer peripheral equipment - Amis International Corp.
BIGFOOT - Crutches ☆ - Ambulatory Products International
BIGFOOT - Games ☆ - Milton Bradley Co.
BIGFOOT - Playground equipment - Game Time, Inc.
BIGFOOT - Toys–models - ERTL Co., Inc.
BIGFOOT BUNNY - Toys–stuffed - Dakin Inc.
BIGFOOT HIGHLANDER SERIES - Shovels - Emsco Inc.
BIGFOOT SMOW MONSTER - Sleds - Emsco Inc.
BIGG & HARRY - Apparel and accessories - Chritian Louis Wanek
BIGG MIXX - Cereal ☆ - Kellogg Co.
BIGGER BADDER BUGS - Toys - Toymax Inc.
BIGGER HARE POCKET - Tobacco - American Tobacco Co.
BIGGER THAN THE BUN - Frankfurters - John Morrell & Co.
BIGGER THE DOT - BETTER THE FISHING - Calendars - Elliott Sales Corp.
BIGGEST LITTLE PHOTO ALBUMS - Photo albums - Pioneer Photo Albums, Inc.

☆ = Now out of production

BIGGEST SUCKER IN TOWN - Candy - Gladstone Candies
BIGGESTPREP - Chemical preparations - 5 Prime - 3 Prime, Inc.
BIGGIE BLUE BOOK - Paper–kraft ✰ - Canson-Talens Inc.
BIGGIES - Candles ✰ - Our Secret, Ltd.
BIGGLET - Toys ✰ - Those Characters from Cleveland, Inc.
BIGG'S - Food products - Super Valu Inc.
BIGGSY - Toys ✰ - Those Characters from Cleveland, Inc.
BIGGY IGGY - Ice cream - Foodmark, Inc.
BIGHORN - Motor vehicles–motor homes ✰ - Mitchell & Sons Inc.
BIGHORN - Snuff - Conwood Co. L.P.
BIGI - Wines - C & B Vintage Cellars
BIGPAC - Power transformers - SGS-Thomson Microelectronics, Inc.
BIGROOM - Electrical equipment - Nady Systems Inc.
BIGSBY - Musical instrument accessories - Bigsby Accessories Inc.
BIGSO BOX OF SWEDEN - Frelonic/Division of Dertek Corp.
BIGSPRING - Farm machinery - Ahrens Agricultural Industries, Inc.
BIGTREE - Computer software - Western Dairy Research, Inc.
BIGWIN - Computer software - Rational Systems Inc.
BII-FIL - Pharmaceutical preparations - Bio-Interfaces, Inc.
BII, LTD. - Jewelry - Mary Ann Paul
BIJA - Recording label - Jazz Composer's Orchestra Association Inc.
BIJAN'S ANIMAL ADVENTURES - Giftware - Bijan Corp.
BIJANS BRONZES - Giftware - Bijan Corp.
BIJOU - Carpets and rugs ✰ - Couristan Inc.
BIJOU - Christmas tree ornaments ✰ - Cracker Box Inc.
BIJOU - Dishes–china - Pickard Inc.
BIJOU - Glassware–household ✰ - Crisa Corp.
BIJOU - Jewelry ✰ - Blumenthal/Lansing Co.
BIJOU - Pens - Accutec Inc.
BIJOU - Shoes - Fortune Footwear Inc.
BIJOU - Tableware–china - Villeroy and Boch Tableware Ltd.
BIJOU - Toys–stuffed - Bijou Enterprises Inc.
BIJOU BEBE - Jewelry - Bijou Bebe
BIJOU PENDANT - Pens - Accutec Inc.
BIJOU, THE - Electronic equipment - AudioControl
BIJOU, THE - Paint sets–hobby - Winsor & Newton
BIJOUX - Furniture–wood - Nucraft Furniture Co.
BIJOUX - Wallpaper ✰ - Capital Carousel Inc.
BIJOUX - Wallpaper ✰ - Jolie Papier
BIJOUX CHRISTIAN DIOR - Jewelry - Grosse Jewels N.Y. Inc.
BIJOUX DE BAIN - Cosmetics - Inne Dispensables, Inc.
BIJOUX DE BOHEME - Glassware–household - Whitehurst Imports
BIJOUX GIVENCHY - Colognes - Richelieu Corp.
BIJOUX GIVENCHY - Jewelry - Victoria International.
BIJOUX ORIGINAL ART TO WEAR - Apparel and accessories - Case Communications
BIJU - Apparel–athletic - Biju Bodywear, Inc.
BIKE - Uniforms–athletic - Bike Athletic Co.
BIKE-A-LITE - Sporting goods - Jog-A-Lite Inc.
BIKE AID - Lubricants - Guardsman Products, Inc.
BIKE B BASICS - Gloves - Promark International, Inc.
BIKE BANK, THE - Bicycle equipment - Graber Products, Inc.
BIKE BEARS - Bicycles - Cycle Products Co.
BIKE BLASTER - Toys–guns ✰ - Imperial Toy Corp.
BIKE BOOTY - Sporting goods - Gator Sports Inc.
BIKE BOXX BIG - Sporting goods - SKIBOXX LTD.
BIKE BOXX I - Sporting goods - SKIBOXX LTD.
BIKE BUDDY - Janko USA, Inc.
BIKE-BUOY - Housewares - Orbex Inc.
BIKE CHAUFFEUR - Bicycles - Graber Products, Inc.
BIKE CLUB - Motorcycle parts and accessories - James E. Winner Jr.
BIKE COMPRESSION - Apparel and accessories - Bike Athletic Co.
BIKE DOCK - Motor vehicle parts and accessories - Ready Access-Div. of Ready Metal Manufacturing
BIKE FOR LIFE - Giftware - Bike for Life Products
BIKE GEAR - Bicycle parts and accessories - J & B Importers, Inc.
BIKE GRIP, THE - Sporting goods ✰ - Bike Athletic Co.
BIKE HIKER - Racks ✰ - Spacemaster Home Products
BIKE KABLE - Bicycles - Weil Service Products Corp.
BIKE MATE - Bicycles ✰ - Cycle Products Co.
BIKE-N-HIKE - Tents - Southern Exchange, Inc.
BIKE-O-MATIC - Sporting goods - Bike-O-Matic Ltd.
BIKE PAJAMAS - Bicycle parts and accessories - Kool Stop Originals, Inc.
BIKE PALS - Bicycles ✰ - Cycle Products Co.
BIKE PRO - Sporting goods ✰ - Schutt Manufacturing Co.
BIKE PRO USA - Bags–duffel - Bike Pro USA

BIKE SAF-T-FLAG - Sporting goods - Molor Products Co.
BIKE SAF-T REFLECTOR - Bicycles - Molor Products Co.
BIKE SAFE - Sporting goods - Patterson-Williams Manufacturing Co. Inc.
BIKE-SHELL - Lockers–metal - Turtle Storage, Ltd.
BIKE SHOP - Sporting goods - Bike Brokers
BIKE SLIDER, THE - Racks - Slider Corp.
BIKE STORY - Computer software - E. David & Associates
BIKE WASH - Cleaning preparations - Finish Line Technologies, Inc.
BIKEBARK - Bicycle parts and accessories - Toren P.B. Orzeck
BIKEBELT - Motor vehicle parts and accessories - FZ Designs
BIKEBLOCK - Clamps - Twofish Unlimited
BIKEBOXX - Motor vehicle parts and accessories - Robert C. Vincent
BIKEE - Bicycles - Bikee Corp.
BIKEMASTER - Bicycles - Western Auto Supply Co.
BIKEN - Footwear ✰ - Kenkoh American Co.
BIKEPORT - Locks–padlocks - Compu-Desk Systems Inc.
BIKER - Watches - Bulova Corp.
BIKER BABE - Jewelry - Dian Malouf
BIKER II - Helmets–athletic ✰ - Bell Sports Corp.
BIKER MICE - Novelty items–paper ✰ - Unique Industries, Inc.
BIKER MICE FROM MARS - Video games - Brentwood Television Funnies, Inc.
BIKER SKINS - Clothing - Nichols Motorcycle Supply, Inc.
BIKER TRASH - Apparel and accessories - T. Bosch Inc.
BIKERMICE FROM MARS - Video games - Nintendo of America Inc.
BIKER'S - Barbecue sauce - Charles Rau
BIKERS IMAGE - Apparel and accessories - Bikers Image, Inc.
BIKERS IMAGE KEY WEST - Apparel and accessories - Bikers Image, Inc.
BIKER'S ONLY - Apparel and accessories - Trinity Products, Inc.
BIKES UP & AWAY - Bicycle-storage systems - IMS Enterprises Inc.
BIKES USA EXPRESS - Bicycle parts and accessories - Bicycle Exchange, Inc.
BIKEWAY - Bicycle parts and accessories - Midway Sales, Inc.
BIKEWAY - Bicycles - Columbia Manufacturing Inc.
BIKEXPERT - Bicycles - Gallop Cycle
BIKEXTRAS - Bicycles - Cycle Products Co.
BIKIN THINGS - Bicycles - R & R Sales
BIKINEEZ - Hosiery ✰ - Mayer/Berkshire Corp.
BIKINI - Dairy products - Harris-Teeter Inc.
BIKINI - Floor waxes ✰ - Uncle Sam Chemical Co., Inc.
BIKINI - Potato chips - Lisa's Gourmet Snacks, Inc.
BIKINI BABY - Razors ✰ - Wahl Clipper Corp.
BIKINI BARE - Shaving preparations - Lee Pharmaceuticals
BIKINI CREME - Skin care products - Hye Cosmetics, Inc.
BIKINI KITS - Luggage - Airline Textile Manufacturing Co.
BIKINI ZONE - Analgesics - CCA Industries, Inc.
BIL-BUILT - Cap rails - Bil-Built Manufacturing Co.
BIL-DRY - Concrete products ✰ - Bil-Dry Corp.
BIL-DRY WATERTIGHT - Masonry waterproofing product - Bil-Dry Corp.
BIL-JAC - Dog food - Bil-Jac Foods Inc.
BIL-JAC SELECT - Dog food - Bil-Jac Foods Inc.
BIL-MAR - Food products - Bil Mar Foods
BILAGOG - Pharmaceutical preparations ✰ - Wesley Pharmacal Co. Inc.
BILAMIDE - Pharmaceutical preparations ✰ - Norgine Laboratories Inc.
BILANGE BODY SPONGE - Cosmetics - Bilange Inc.
BILANGE COMPLETE - Hair care products - Bilange Inc.
BILBERRY - Vitamins and nutritional supplements - Natrol, Inc.
BILBERT - Toys–stuffed ✰ - Russ Berrie and Co., Inc.
BILCO - Doors–metal - Bilco Co.
BILD-N-REPAIR - Hardware - Baden Steelbar & Bolt Co.
BILDO - Apparel and accessories - Shawn R. Knaggs
BILECHOL - Pharmaceutical preparations ✰ - Kenneth A. Manne Co.
BILEZYME - Pharmaceutical preparations - Geriatric Pharmaceutical Corp.
BILEZYME PLUS - Pharmaceutical preparations ✰ - Geriatric Pharmaceutical Corp.
BILFRO - Electrical equipment - Quick Cable Corp.
BILGE BUGS - Cleaning preparations - Life Industries Corp.
BILGE CAPTAIN - Bilge pumps - Gem Products, Inc.
BILGE KING - Bilge pumps ✰ - Attwood Corp.
BILGE OILZORB - Degreasing solvents - Marine Development & Research Corp.
BILGE SORB - Padding–foam - Leucadia, Inc.
BILGE TENDER - Boats ✰ - Raritan Engineering Co. Inc.
BILGEKOTE - Paints - Interlux Yacht Finishes
BILI-LABSTIX - Chemical preparations - Miles Inc.

BILIKEN TETRAPLOID WESTERWORLD RYEGRASS - Flowers, plants, and seeds - Jacklin Seed

BILINGUAL WRITING CENTER, THE - Computer software - The Learning Co., Inc.

BILINGVAL - Computer software - Bilingual Software Co.

BILINSKI'S - Sausages - Bilinski Sausage Manufacturing Co.

BILJOY - Wedding gowns - Biljoy Formals Inc.

BILL - Ophthalmic goods ☆ - Rozin Optical Export Corp.

BILL & BRADS TROPICAL FORMULA - Cleaning preparations - William A. Wade

BILL & TED'S EXCELLENT ADVENTURE - Computer software - Capstone Software

BILL & TED'S EXCELLENT CEREAL - Cereal - Ralston Purina Co.

BILL BAILEYS - Meat products - Clarence Bailey

BILL BLASS - Apparel and accessories - Mcgregor Corp.

BILL BLASS - Apparel–men's - Pincus Bros., Inc.

BILL BLASS - Bathing suits - Jonathan Logan Inc.

BILL BLASS - Chocolate candy ☆ - Godiva Chocolatier

BILL BLASS - Footwear - Bill Blass, Ltd.

BILL BLASS - Gloves ☆ - Grandoe Corp.

BILL BLASS - Leather goods - Gem-Dandy, Inc.

BILL BLASS - Perfumes - Revlon Consumer Products Corp.

BILL BLASS - Scarves ☆ - Baar & Beards

BILL BLASS - Sunglasses - Riviera Trading, Inc.

BILL BLASS - Tuxedos ☆ - After Six Inc.

BILL BLASS - Watches - Gruen Marketing Corp.

BILL BLASS - Waterproof outerwear ☆ - Gordon & Ferguson of Delaware, Inc.

BILL BLASS FOR ROYAL - Robes - Royal Robes Inc.

BILL BURNS - Apparel–women's - Bill Burns New York Inc.

BILL BURNS NEW YORK - Apparel and accessories - Kellwood Co.

BILL DANCE - Boats–motor ☆ - Starcraft Corp.

BILL DING - Toys - Stuhr Enterprises Inc.

BILL E. DUCK - Toys - Mattel, Inc.

BILL EAGAN'S - Frames–picture - Distinctive Design

BILL EDWARDS - Musical instruments ☆ - Kramer

BILL FARNSWORTH - Giftware - Reco International Corp.

BILL JOHNSON'S BOOT PARDNER - Leather tanning and finishing ☆ - Farnam Cos. Inc.

BILL LAIMBEER'S COMBAT BASKETBALL - Video game - Hudson Soft USA Inc.

BILL MARTIN BOOKS - Publisher's imprints - Henry Holt and Co.

BILL MONROE - Musical instrument accessories - Gibson Strings & Accessories

BILL MULLER - Toys ☆ - Handcraft Designs Inc.

BILL OF FARE - Floor coverings–carpet and rugs - Gulistan Carpet Inc.

BILL ROSCOE - Musical instrument accessories - M.M. Meason Inc.

BILL-TAINER - Wallets - Buxton Inc.

BILL THE CAT - Toys–stuffed - Dakin Inc.

BILL TICE FOR SWIRL - Apparel and accessories ☆ - Swirl II Ltd.

BILL-TITE - Adhesives and sealants - Evans Adhesive Corp.

BILL WATSON'S DISCOUNT AUTO OUTLET - Motor vehicle dealers - Bill Watson Nissan, Inc.

BILL WHITAKER'S - Meat products–beef - Whitaker Foods Inc.

BILLABONG - Toys–stuffed - Gund, Inc.

BILLARD - Exercising equipment - Roadmaster Corp.

BILLBOARD BLAST - Toys - Tonka Corp.

BILLBOARD BOOKS - Publisher's imprints - Watson-Guptill Publications

BILLDATS - Computer integrated systems design services - At&T Corp.

BILLDATS II - Computer software - At&T Corp.

BILLET - Sunglasses - Ken Wilson

BILLET-MASTER BLADE - Band-saw blade - American Saw & Manufacturing Co.

BILLFISHER - Fishing tackle - Sea Striker Inc.

BILLI FILTER - Pet products - Tetra Sales USA

BILLIARD BALL FINISH - Floor waxes - C.A. Nash & Son Inc.

BILLIES - Garbage bags - North American Plastics & Chemical Co.

BILLING COMMANDER - Computer software - MCI Communications Corp.

BILLINGS - Milk - Billings Dairy

BILLINGSLEY ROSE - Dishes–earthenware - Royal China & Porcelain Companies Inc.

BILLING*STAR - Computer software - Electronic Data Systems Corp.

BILLINGTON - Sauces - Europa Foods Ltd.

BILLIONAIRE - Apparel and accessories ☆ - Jantzen Inc.

BILLIONAIRE - Games ☆ - Parker Brothers

BILLIONAIRE - Toys - Tonka Corp.

BILLIONAIRES - Chocolate candy - Pangburn Candy Co.

BILLIONTH CAR COLLECTION - Toys–automobiles - Mattel, Inc.

BILLMASTER - Computer software - Customized Business Software

BILLMINDER - Ledgers - Joe Cimino

BILLOW - Paper–toilet - Fort Howard Corp.

BILLOW PILLOWS - Hardware - Sears, Roebuck and Co.

BILLPAK - Leather goods - A & L Seamon Inc.

BILL'S - Pizzas–frozen - Bill's Pizza & Pub Inc.

BILL'S BAG - Garment storage bags - Bill's Bag

BILLTIPS - Pens - Hedra Inc.

BILLUPS - Oils–lubricating ☆ - Charter Marketing Co.

BILLY - Beverages–malt ☆ - The Stroh Brewery Co.

BILLY - Ophthalmic goods ☆ - Luxottica

BILLY ADLEN STUDIO - Belts–apparel - Humphrey's Inc.

BILLY BALDWIN - Furniture - Matthew Patrick Smyth

BILLY BAR - Bicycles - Sears, Roebuck and Co.

BILLY BAROO - Golf putters - Ray Cook Co.

BILLY BASELINE - Apparel - Centennial Sports Promotions, Inc.

BILLY BEAR - Toys–stuffed ☆ - Dakin Inc.

BILLY BEE PRODUCTIONS - Publisher's imprints - Billy Bee Productions, Inc.

BILLY BELCHER - Toys - Mattel, Inc.

BILLY BLUES - Barbecue sauce - Sales Mark Southern California

BILLY BUILDER - Toys - Natural Science Industries, Ltd.

BILLY BUM - Dolls ☆ - Effanbee Doll Corp.

BILLY BUSTER - Footwear - Washington Shoe Co.

BILLY CASPER - Golfing equipment - Wilson Sporting Goods Co.

BILLY CLUB - Golf equipment - King Par Corp.

BILLY DRESSED BUNNY - Toys–stuffed - Russ Berrie and Co., Inc.

BILLY G - Crocheted and knitted items ☆ - Gillman Knitwear Co.

BILLY GOAT - Games ☆ - Tyco Toys

BILLY GOAT - Garden equipment - Billy Goat Industries Inc.

BILLY GOAT - Shorts–children's - Royal Robbins

BILLY JEAN - Eyeglasses - Martin-Copeland Eyewear Corp.

BILLY JOE COW - Novelty items–stitched - A + A

BILLY PENN - Building materials–concrete - Billy Penn Corp.

BILLY STICK - Flashlights - Dynamic Classics Ltd.

BILLY THE KID - Apparel–children's - Mcgregor Corp.

BILLY THE KID - Toys ☆ - Henry Gordy International Inc.

BILLY THE KID - Toys–stuffed - Hortex Inc.

BILLYBOARDS - Posters - Impulse Marketing, Inc.

BILLYCOAT - Coats - William Winters

BILLYS - Cookies ☆ - Parco Foods, Inc.

BILLY'S BLUES - Jams and jellies - Sarabeth's Kitchen

BILLY'S BRETZEL GEMS - Pretzels ☆ - Pepperidge Farm Inc.

BILOCOMP - Pharmaceutical preparations - Lannett Co. Inc.

BILOGEN - Pharmaceutical preparations ☆ - Organon Inc.

BILORA - Camera ☆ - Saul Bower Inc.

BILORA - Photographic equipment ☆ - Argraph Corp. (Samigon Div.)

BILOX - Pharmaceutical preparations ☆ - Wesley Pharmacal Co. Inc.

BILOXI - Cabinets - Belwood Inc.

BILOXI - Chimes ☆ - Nutone Inc.

BILOXI BUCKS - Electronic gaming devices - President Riverboat Casino

BILOXI ROYALE - Seafood products–fresh or frozen - Alphin Bros. Inc.

BILRON - Laxatives - Eli Lilly and Co.

BILSOM COMFORT - Apparel and accessories - Bilsom International Inc.

BILSOM SOUND BAN - Plugs–ear - Willson/Dalloz Safety

BILSOM SOUND BARRIER - Plugs–ear - Willson/Dalloz Safety

BILSOM SOUND SILENCER - Plugs–ear - Willson/Dalloz Safety

BILT-MORE - Food products - Allied Foods Inc.

BILT-TUFF - Shoes - Kobacker Co.

BILT-WELL - Hardware - Blaine Window Hardware Inc.

BILTBEST - Window frames - Biltbest Windows

BILTMORE - Cabinets - Actua

BILTMORE - Cigars ☆ - Avanti Cigar Co.

BILTMORE - Clocks - General Time Corp. (Westclox/Seth Thomas Div.)

BILTMORE - Envelopes - Butler Paper Co.

BILTMORE - Floor coverings–carpet and rugs - Helios Carpets

BILTMORE - Floor coverings–carpet and rugs - Richmond Carpet Mills

BILTMORE - Floor coverings–carpet and rugs ☆ - Callaway Carpets

BILTMORE - Frames–eyeglass ☆ - Universal/Univis Inc.

BILTMORE - Furniture - Bean Station Furniture Factory Inc.

BILTMORE - Furniture - Universal Flooring

BILTMORE - Giftware - Western Buckle Co.

BILTMORE - Housewares - The HammockSource

BILTMORE - Mats - Majestic Mat Co.

BILTMORE - Stationery ☆ - Pratt & Austin Co.

BILTMORE - Tableware–china ☆ - Lenox, Inc.

☆ = Now out of production

BILTMORE - Watches ☆ - Toastmaster Inc.
BILTMORE - Wines ☆ - Biltmore Estate Wine Co.
BILTMORE ESTATE - Furniture ☆ - Bassett Furniture Industries, Inc.
BILTMORE ESTATE - Wines - Biltmore Co.
BILTMORE ESTATE - Wines - Biltmore Estate Wine Co.
BILTRICIDE - Chemical preparations - Miles Inc.
BILTRITE - Hockey equipment - Dare Development Group, Inc.
BILTRITE - Shoe repair shops - American Biltrite Inc.
BILTRITE - Tables—wood - Anco Wood Specialties Inc.
BILTWELL - Refuse cans ☆ - Bowman Metal Deck
BILU - Apparel and accessories - Vogue Originals Inc.
BILU - Footwear - Conjac Inc.
BILZ - Games - T.E. Brangs, Inc.
BIM - Electronic equipment - Incomed, Inc.
BIMARMI - Marble tile - Integrity Tile Co.
BIMAT - Photographic equipment ☆ - Eastman Kodak Co.
BIMAXIN - Analgesics - Smithkline Beecham Corp.
BIMBEAUX VIDEO - Video production - Michael Shores
BIMBO - Breads - Campbell Taggart Inc.
BIMETALIC - Golfing equipment - Golfsmith International Inc.
BIMETALLIC - Golfing equipment - Golfsmith International Inc.
BIMINI - Awnings ☆ - John Boyle & Co., Inc.
BIMINI - Boats—motor - Bayhead Yacht Sales Inc.
BIMINI - Boats—motor - Glastex Co.
BIMINI - Boats—motor ☆ - Magnum Marine Corp.
BIMINI - Frames—eyeglass - May Optical Co. Inc.
BIMINI - Furniture - Homecrest Industries Inc.
BIMINI BAY OUTFITTERS LTD. - Slacks—men's - Folsom Corp.
BIMINI RUN - Electronic game - Nuvision Entertainment Inc.
BIMINI TOPS - Boats—pontoons - Bearcat Corp.
BIMOTA MOTORCYCLES - Motorcycles - Cosmopolitan Motors Inc.
BIN BOARD - Plywood ☆ - Georgia-Pacific Corp.
BIN-CUBE - Nuts and bolts - Elco Industries, Inc.
BIN-PAK - Builders' hardware - H.B. Ives
BIN-TI PRODUCTS - Rope - Robin Knudson and Albin Knudson Partnership
BINA - Musical instruments - Eastern Music Co.
BINACA - Mouthwashes - Ciba-Geigy Corp.
BINACA BLAST - Chewing gum ☆ - Amurol Confections Co.
BINAMEL - Enamels - Sherwin-Williams Automotive Finishes Corp.
BINANCA SUGAR FREE - Health care products - Reckitt & Colman, Inc.
BINAR GRAPHICS - Computer peripheral equipment - Binar Graphics, Inc.
BINARY - Computer software - Binary Software Inc.
BINARY ARTS - Puzzles - Binary Arts Corp.
BINAURA - Audio equipment - Binaura Corp.
BIND - Photo albums - DNA Plant Technology Corp.
BIND-A-FOLIO - File folders - Angler's Roslyn Group Ltd.
BIND-A-VUE - File folders ☆ - Angler's Roslyn Group Ltd.
BIND-IT - Binders - Bind-It Corp.
BIND-IT - Cordage and twine - Gold Glass Group Corp.
BIND-X - Labels—paper - Cel-U-Dex Corp.
BINDAFILE - Office supplies ☆ - Esselte Corp.
BINDER - Thread ☆ - American & Efird, Inc.
BINDER BRAIN - Calculator ☆ - Better Office Products, Inc.
BINDER-BUDDY - Tools—hand-operated - Hodgeon & Anderson, Inc.
BINDER EXPRESS, THE - Office supplies - McBee Loose Leaf Binders
BINDER-KOTE - Paints - Tuff-Kote Co. Inc.
BINDER-MATE - Pens - Rosa Pen Co.
BINDERBOARD - Beekeeping supplies - Jerry Mills
BINDERLINE - Binders, index tabs, etc. - American Loose Leaf Business Products Inc.
BINDERLOK - Ring binders - U.S. Ring Binder Corp.
BINDERSEAL - Finishing agents ☆ - Flintkote Co.
BINDERSEAL - Sealing compounds ☆ - GS Roofing Products Co.
BINDI - Apparel - Bindi Trading
BINDITOL - Vitamins and nutritional supplements - Nature's Products Inc.
BINDVIEW - Computer software - Bindview Development Corp.
BINFORD & MORT - Publisher's imprints - Binford & Mort Publishers
BING - Binders - Boorum & Pease Co.
BING - Candy - Palmer Candy Co.
BING & GRONDAHL - Giftware - Royal Copenhagen Porcelain Inc.
BING & GRONDAHL - Giftware - Viking Import House Inc.
BING BOING KOOSH - Toys - Oddzon Products, Inc.
BING-GO - Dog food - Bing-Go Dog Food Inc.
BINGH2O - Filters—water - Bingh2o, Inc.
BINGHAM - Coffee - S & D Coffee, Inc.
BINGHAM - Motorcycles - Side Strider Inc.

BINGHAM FARMS - Food products ☆ - Hollywood Super Markets
BINGHAMTON - Sweaters - Binghamton Knitting Co.
BINGHAMTON METS - Sporting goods - Sterling Doubleday Enterprises, L.P.
BINGMAN LABORATORIES - Pharmaceutical preparations ☆ - Bingman Laboratories, Inc.
BINGMAN'S - Veterinary pharmaceutical preparations ☆ - Bingman Laboratories, Inc.
BINGO - Boats - Glen-L Marine Designs
BINGO - Candy - Phoenix Confections Inc.
BINGO - Clocks - General Time Corp. (Westclox/Seth Thomas Div.)
BINGO - Detergents - Colgate-Palmolive Co.
BINGO - Flowers, plants, and seeds - Panamerican Seed
BINGO - Frames—eyeglass - Liberty Optical Manufacturing Co.
BINGO - Games ☆ - Warren Industries Inc.
BINGO - Glue—household or industrial - Hayes Specialties Corp.
BINGO - Publisher's imprints - Industrial Printing Co.
BINGO - Stationery ☆ - Superior Marking Equipment Co.
BINGO - Thread - United Thread Mills Corp.
BINGO - Toys—stuffed - Commonwealth Toy and Novelty Co. Inc.
BINGO - Toys—stuffed - Gund, Inc.
BINGO BANDIT - Games ☆ - Pressman Toy Corp.
BINGO BET-IT-ALL BEAVER - Greeting cards ☆ - American Greetings Corp.
BINGO BOOKS - Construction equipment rental services - Truly Friendly Software, Inc.
BINGO BUDDY - Apparel and accessories - Bingo Buddy
BINGO BUTLER - Giftware - Ashbury & Associates, Ltd.
BINGO CARAMEL - Candy - Phoenix Confections Inc.
BINGO NUT - Games - International Gamco, Inc.
BINGOCARDMINDER - Games - Bingo Card Minder Corp.
BINGORILLAS - Ice pops - American Beverage Corp.
BINGS - Golfing equipment and accessories - Bings
BINK - Cleaning preparations - Malter International Corp.
BINKIE PUPPY - Toys—stuffed ☆ - Dakin Inc.
BINKIE TEDDY - Toys—stuffed - Russ Berrie and Co., Inc.
BINKSVILLE FIRE CO. NO. 1 - Candy ☆ - R.M. Palmer Co.
BINKSVILLE NATIONAL BANK - Candy ☆ - R.M. Palmer Co.
BINKSVILLE SHOPPING CENTER - Candy ☆ - R.M. Palmer Co.
BINKY - Infant product - Binky-Griptight Co.
BINKYBELL - Toys—stuffed ☆ - Gund, Inc.
BINKYKIDS - Infant product - Binky-Griptight Co.
BINNEY & SMITH - Artists' materials - Binney & Smith Inc.
BINNIE - Flowers, plants, and seeds - Binnie Enterprises
BINNS - Wines - Binns Vineyards & Winery
BINO BUDDY - Photographic equipment - Classic Outdoor Products Inc.
BINO/CAM - Optical scanners—computer ☆ - Tasco Sales, Inc.
BINOCFLEX - Binoculars - Team Products
BINOCOLORS - Binoculars - Tasco Sales, Inc.
BINOCSOCK - Cases—binocular - M. Dan Andersen
BINOCTAR - Binoculars ☆ - Ercona Corp.
BINOCTARMO - Binoculars ☆ - Ercona Corp.
BINOCTEM - Binoculars ☆ - Ercona Corp.
BINODAPTER - Binoculars - Bausch & Lomb Inc.
BINOLUX - Binoculars - Compass Industries, Inc.
BINOX - Aquariums—household - Jungle Laboratories Corp.
BINSEY HAWKES - Musical instruments - Ardsley Musical Instrument Co.
BINSWANGER - Mirrors - Binswanger Mirror Products
BINTOO - Games - Bintoo America
BINY-BINY - Cosmetics - Cosmetic Center, Inc.
BINZO - Pet products ☆ - Pet Supply Imports Inc.
BIO - Detergents - Malco Products, Inc.
BIO - Golfing equipment - Bio Dynamics Ltd.
BIO - Pharmaceutical preparations - Botanical Laboratories Inc.
BIO - Vitamins and nutritional supplements - Physician Sales & Service
BIO-7 - Hair care products ☆ - Nino Originals
BIO 10 - Aquariums—household - Ginger, Inc.
BIO-ACTION - Drain pipe cleaners - Athea Laboratories, Inc.
BIO AIRE UV - Lighting equipment - Airguard Industries, Inc.
BIO-BAG - Aquariums—household - Willinger Bros., Inc.
BIO-BAG - Pet products - Tetra Sales USA
BIO BALANCE - Cosmetics - Revlon Consumer Products Corp.
BIO-BALANCE - Vitamins and nutritional supplements - Leiner Health Products Inc.
BIO BALE - Filters—water - Creative Plastic Research
BIO BARRIER - Prophylactics - Robin Renee Thill Shlenker
BIO-BEAUTY - Shampoos - Royal Country, Inc.
BIO-BIRDHOUSE - Bird feeders - Innovative Recycled Products, Inc.

BIO BLOCK - Paper - Easy Gardener Acquisition Corp.
BIO BLU - Cleaning preparations - E.W. Smith Chemical Co.
BIO-BODY - Cosmetics - Jheri Redding Products Inc.
BIO-BODY - Skin care products - Nylynn Cosmetic Inc.
BIO BOOT - Implants–surgical - Biomet, Inc.
BIO-BORON - Vitamins and nutritional supplements ☆ - Natrol, Inc.
BIO-BOTANICA - Health care products - Bio-Botanica
BIO-BRITE - Pigments - Magruder Color Co., Inc.
BIO-BRITE LIGHT VISOR, THE - Medical apparatus - Bio-Brite, Inc.
BIO-BUILD - Vitamins and nutritional supplements - Shaklee Corp.
BIO C - Cleaning preparations - Vaportek, Inc.
BIO-C-PLEX - Vitamins and nutritional supplements - Vita-Vista
BIO CARB - Pet products - Ginger, Inc.
BIO-CARE - Health care products - Temco Health Care
BIO-CARPET - Wood products - Super Mulch of Atlanta, Inc.
BIO-CARRIER - Pesticides–agricultural - Smucker Manufacturing Inc.
BIO-CARTILAGE - Vitamins and nutritional supplements - Lescarden, Inc.
BIO-CEE - Vitamins and nutritional supplements ☆ - Fibertone Co.
BIO-CEL I - Filters–air - AAF-Mcquay Inc.
BIO CELL - Computer software - Zephyr Services
BIO-CELL RESEARCH - Vitamins and nutritional supplements - Performance Research & Development, Inc.
BIO-CHA - Skin care products - Clientele, Inc.
BIO-CHECK - Pharmaceutical preparations - Baxter International Inc.
BIO-CHELATED - Health care products - Bio-Botanica
BIO-CHEM - Chemical preparations - Bio-Chem, Inc.
BIO-CHEM - Pet products - Aquarium Pharmaceuticals, Inc.
BIO-CHEM - Pharmaceutical preparations - Summa Pharmaceutical Laboratories Inc.
BIO CHEM STARS - Aquarium accessories - Aquarium Pharmaceuticals, Inc.
BIO-CIDRIN - Analgesics ☆ - Pharm-A-Lab
BIO-CLAIM - Paper–writing - Lincoln Pulp and Paper Co. Inc.
BIO-CLASSICS - Shoes - Freeman Shoe Co.
BIO-CLEAN - Chemical preparations - Kinzie & Payne Biochemical Corp.
BIO CLEANSER - Skin care products - Alleghany Pharmacal Corp.
BIO-CLEAR - Chemical preparations - Aqua Clear Industries Inc.
BIO-CLEAR - Skin care products - Alleghany Pharmacal Corp.
BIO CLEAR HOME AIR & DUCT TREATMENT - Cleaning equipment - Leslie-Locke, Inc.
BIO CLIMAT - Skin care products - Biotherm
BIO COAT - Veterinary pharmaceutical preparations - Nickers International Ltd.
BIO-CON - Diesel-fuel conditioner - CRC Chemicals USA/Siloo
BIO-CONCENTRE - Skin care products - Sanofi Beaute Inc.
BIO-CONTOUR LIFT - Skin care products - Sanofi Beaute Inc.
BIO-CORP - Vitamins - Bio Corp.
BIO-COTE - Veterinary nutritional supplements - Greentree Laboratories, Inc.
BIO-CREST - Vitamins and nutritional supplements - Nutrition Control Products
BIO CRYSTALS - Pet products - Marine Enterprises International, Inc.
BIO-CURVE - Pens - Winning Solutions Inc./Miracle of Aloe
BIO DATA - Computer software - Zephyr Services
BIO-DAYSED - Pharmaceutical preparations - Bio-Factor Laboratories
BIO-DELTA - Veterinary pharmaceutical preparations ☆ - Upjohn Co.
BIO DERM - Health care products - Biomedical Life Systems, Inc.
BIO-DERMA - Skin care products - Barrows Pharmacal Inc.
BIO-DESIGN - Cosmetics - Jheri Redding Products Inc.
BIO-DESIGN - Vitamins and nutritional supplements - Werum Enterprises, Inc.
BIO-DEX - Shampoos ☆ - Jason Natural Products, Inc.
BIO-DEX - Water treating compounds - Bio-Dex Laboratories
BIO-DEXABARB - Pharmaceutical preparations - Bio-Factor Laboratories
BIO-DEXAM - Pharmaceutical preparations - Bio-Factor Laboratories
BIO-DICE - Toys - Aharon G. Aharonian
BIO DIESEL - Fuel additives - Star Brite
BIO-DONNAL - Pharmaceutical preparations - Bio-Factor Laboratories
BIO DRAIN AID - Cleaning preparations–household - Faultless Starch/Bon Ami Co.
BIO-DYNE - Bicycles - Schwinn Cycling & Fitness Inc.
BIO-DYNE - Chemical preparations - Ecosys Inc.
BIO E - Vitamins and nutritional supplements - Solaray
BIO EASE II - Aquariums–household - Cole Enterprises
BIO ELEVEN - Cleaning preparations - Sudden Service, Inc.
BIO-ENERGY - Health care products - Bioenergy Inc.
BIO ESSENCE - Hair care products - Salon Visage
BIO ESSENCE - Vitamins and nutritional supplements - Kris K. S. Yang
BIO-ESTHETIC - Dental equipment - Steri-Oss, Inc.
BIO-ESTYL - Pharmaceutical preparations - Bio-Factor Laboratories
BIO-EXCELERATOR - Chemical preparations - Espoma Co.

BIO-FACTOR - Health care products - Bio-Factor Laboratories
BIO-FAME - Chemical preparations - M & M Livestock Products Co., Inc.
BIO FEED - Hair care products - Flori Roberts Inc.
BIO FEED BACK - Footwear - K-Swiss Inc.
BIO FILTERS - Pet products - Maryland Aquatic Nurseries
BIO-FISH - Fish meal ☆ - Bio-Nutritional Products
BIO FLEA HALT! - Insecticides - Farnam Cos. Inc.
BIO-FLEX - Exchangers–heat - Besicorp Group, Inc.
BIO-FLEX - Health care products - Unicare Health & Fitness Co.
BIO FLO - Aquariums–household - Ginger, Inc.
BIO FLORA ALL FLORA - Health care products - New Moon Extracts, Inc.
BIO-FLOW - Pipes - Hancor Inc.
BIO-FLUSH - Detergents - International Medical, Inc.
BIO-FOAM - Cleaning products - Standard T Chemical Co. Inc.
BIO-FOAM - Packaging–foam - Bio Products International
BIO FOAM - Pet products - Tetra Sales USA
BIO-FORMED - Vitamins and nutritional supplements - Twinlab
BIO FREE - Cleaning preparations ☆ - Seventh Generation Wholesale Inc.
BIO-FRESH - Disinfectants - Nu-Calgon Wholesaler, Inc.
BIO-FRUCEES - Vitamins and nutritional supplements ☆ - Fibertone Co.
BIO GEL - Health care products - Biomedical Life Systems, Inc.
BIO-GENESIS - Vitamins and nutritional supplements - Head Start Vitamin Products
BIO GENETIC HEALTH GROUP - Vitamins and nutritional supplements - Bio Genetic Health Group, Inc.
BIO-GENIC - See **BYOGENIC**
BIO-GENICS - Health care products - Makers of Kal, Inc.
BIO GINKGO - Herbal products - Generation Health
BIO GLOW - Dietary supplement for animals - Omega-3 Marine Foods and Oils, Inc.
BIO-GOLD GOLDFISH FOOD - Pet products - Hikari Sales USA Inc.
BIO-GRADE - Automotive parts and accessories - Berryman Products Inc.
BIO-GRAFT - Medical apparatus - Bio-Vascular, Inc.
BIO-GREEN BIODEGRADER - Disinfectants - Delta Bioproducts International
BIO-GRIPS - Handles–rubber - GripWorks
BIO-GROOM - Pet products - Bio-Derm Laboratories Inc.
BIO GUARD - Chemical preparations - Great Lakes Chemical Corp.
BIO GUARD - Hairpiece adhesives - American Hairlines
BIO GUARD - Slippers - Robin Renee Thill Shlenker
BIO GUARD - Water treating compounds - Bio-Lab, Inc.
BIO-HAIRMIN - Skin care products - Hanah Beauty & Health Inc.
BIO HARMONY - Vitamins and nutritional supplements - Natures Surprise Inc.
BIO-HAZARD RESPONSE KIT - Chemical preparations ☆ - Impact
BIO-HIDE - Metals - Hugo Bosca Co., Inc.
BIO HUMA NETICS - Fertilizers - Bio Huma Netics, Inc.
BIO HY-GARD - Oils–lubricating - Deere & Co.
BIO IMAGE - Photographic equipment - Eastman Kodak Co.
BIO-ION - Water purification systems - GSG Associates, Inc.
BIO KILL - Insecticides - Bio-Environmental Products, Inc.
BIO-KINETIC - Sewage treatment equipment - Norwalk Wastewater Equipment Co.
BIO-KING - Water purification systems - Beckett Corp.
BIO-KLEEN - Cleaning preparations - Kester Solder Co.
BIO-KLEEN 99 - Filters–air - TFC Corp.
BIO-KONTROL - Filter coating - Air Kontrol Inc.
BIO-KUR - Hair care products - Novatrend Inc.
BIO KYSS - Hair care preparations - PI Water, Inc.
BIO-LAB - Aquariums–household - Jewel Industries Inc.
BIO-LAX - Pet products - Watkins Inc.
BIO LEAN FREE - Herbal products - Wellness International Network, Ltd.
BIO LIFE - Pet products - Rolf C. Hagen (USA) Corp.
BIO-LIFT - Temporary wrinkle-removing cream - Suarez Corp.
BIO-LINK - Computer hardware - Biomolecular Separation Inc.
BIO-LOGIC SYSTEMS - Fireplace equipment - Pyro Industries, Inc.
BIO LUME - Aquarium accessories - Rainbow Lifegard Aquarium Products
BIO-LUTEST - Pharmaceutical preparations - Bio-Factor Laboratories
BIO-LUTONE - Pharmaceutical preparations - Bio-Factor Laboratories
BIO-M - Spices and extracts - Grand Stone
BIO-MAGNET - Pet products ☆ - Jungle Laboratories Corp.
BIO-MATE - Aquarium accessories - Rainbow Lifegard Aquarium Products
BIO-MATRIX - Aquariums–household - Eugene G. Danner Manufacturing Inc.
BIO-MECH - Aquarium accessories - Kordon
BIO-MECH - Filters–water - Novalek, Inc.
BIO-MECH II - Golfing equipment - Ralph Maltby Enterprises Inc.
BIO MED - Health care products - Biomedical Life Systems, Inc.
BIO-METHAM - Pharmaceutical preparations - Bio-Factor Laboratories

☆ = Now out of production

BIO-MIRACLE - Skin care products ☆ - Monteil Paris
BIO-MITE - Chemical preparations - Ecosys Inc.
BIO-MOLECULAR PERFECTING FLUID - Skin care products - A-Veda Corp.
BIO-MOLECULAR RECOVERY TREATMENT - Skin care products - A-Veda Corp.
BIO-MOS - Veterinary nutritional supplements - Alltech, Inc.
BIO MULCH - Paper - Paul Owen Davis
BIO-MYCIN - Veterinary pharmaceutical preparations ☆ - Boehringer Ingelheim Animal Health, Inc.
BIO-MYCIN C - Veterinary pharmaceutical preparations - Boehringer Ingelheim Animal Health, Inc.
BIO-NATE - Health care products - Natren Inc.
BIO-NEUTRALIZER - Dechlorination tablets - Norwalk Wastewater Equipment Co.
BIO NEWS - Paper–newsprint - Biotechnology Industry Organization
BIO-NUTRITION FOR THE FUTURE - Vitamins and nutritional supplements - Integrated Health, Inc.
BIO-OPTIC - Vitamins and nutritional supplements - Christine Khemis
BIO-ORB - Garden equipment - Gordon Charles Associates
BIO-OXIDIZER - Incinerator - Eshland Enterprises, Inc.
BIO-OXY - Health care products - Biolife
BIO PACE - Sporting goods - Shimano American Corp.
BIO-PAK - Aquariums–household - Marine Environment/Aqua Craft
BIO-PAK - Pet products - Bio-Pak Associates
BIO-PATH - Insecticides - Ecoscience Corp.
BIO-PEN - Medical apparatus - Mentor O & O Inc.
BIO-PERFORMANCE - Cosmetics - Shiseido Cosmetics (America) Ltd.
BIO-PEX - Heating equipment - Besicorp Group, Inc.
BIO-PHASE 30+ - Vitamins and nutritional supplements ☆ - Quantum, Inc.
BIO-PHASE 50+ - Vitamins and nutritional supplements ☆ - Quantum, Inc.
BIO-PLEX - Chemical preparations - Turf Chemicals Plus, Inc.
BIO-PLEX CUTICLE CREAM - Cosmetics - Colour Grow Cosmetics Intl.
BIO PLUM - Computer software - Bio Plum Inc.
BIO PLUS - Air purification systems - Technovation
BIO PLUS - Flowers, plants, and seeds - Bioplus Manufacturing Inc.
BIO POWER - Golfing equipment - Outdoor Technologies Group
BIO-PRO - Chairs–metal - Stacor Corp.
BIO-PULSE - Medical apparatus - Respond Systems Inc.
BIO-PUMP - Medical apparatus - Medtronic Bio-Medicus, Inc.
BIO PURE - Shampoos - Bio Pure Corp.
BIO-PURE - Skin care products ☆ - Reviva Laboratories
BIO-PURE FROZEN FISH FOOD SERIES - Pet products - Hikari Sales USA Inc.
BIO-Q - Recording label - Futurehealth Inc.
BIO QUANTUM - Medical apparatus - Bio Quantum Technologies Inc.
BIO-RACK - Aquariums–household - Jewel Industries Inc.
BIO-REALITY - Computer software - Kemtec Educational Corp.
BIO-RELAXING EYE GEL - Skin care products - Sothys USA Inc.
BIO-SAFE - Skin care products - Bio-Safe Enterprises, Inc.
BIO-SAFE KWIK SOLDER - Solder - Vibe Records Inc.
BIO ST. JOHN'S - Vitamins and nutritional supplements - Pharmanex, Inc.
BIO-SCOPE - Medical equipment - Physical Health Devices Inc.
BIO-SEA - Aquariums–household - Marine Environment/Aqua Craft
BIO-SEAL - Building materials - Palace Guard, Inc.
BIO-SEAL - Medical apparatus - Tidi Products, Inc.
BIO-SENTRY - Pharmaceutical preparations - Qualis Inc.
BIO-SEPTIC - Skin care products ☆ - Organics Corp. of America (Ambix Laboratories Div.)
BIO-SET - Pigments - Magruder Color Co., Inc.
BIO SEVEN - Cleaning preparations - Sudden Service, Inc.
BIO-SHEAR - Tools–hand-operated - Xuron Corp.
BIO-SHINE - Cosmetics - Jheri Redding Products Inc.
BIO SKIN - Skin care products - Elysee Scientific Cosmetic Co.
BIO-SOK - Fabrics - Petrol Rem, Inc.
BIO SOLVE - Chemical preparations - Westford Chemical Corp.
BIO-SORB - Peat moss - Bio-Natural Products, Inc.
BIO SPRAE - Beauty aids ☆ - Redken Laboratories, Inc.
BIO-START - Chemical preparations - Aqua Clear Industries Inc.
BIO-START - Hair care products ☆ - Head Start Vitamin Products
BIO-STATIC - Skin care products - Elysee Scientific Cosmetic Co.
BIO-STATIC - Water purification systems - Norwalk Wastewater Equipment Co.
BIO-STRIP - Insecticides - Bio-Strip
BIO-SUBSTRATE - Pet products - Ginger, Inc.
BIO SUPER B - Vitamins and nutritional supplements - Vita-Fore Products Co.
BIO-SYN-CUT - Automotive parts and accessories - R.G. Shannon Co.
BIO-SYSTEM - Chemical preparations - Aqua Clear Industries Inc.

BIO SYSTEM - Odor neutralizing preparations - Sysco Corp.
BIO T - Cleaning preparations–household - Golden Technologies Co., Inc.
BIO TAB - Cleaning preparations - Coughlan Products Corp.
BIO-TAL - Veterinary pharmaceutical preparations ☆ - Boehringer Ingelheim Animal Health, Inc.
BIO-TECT - Food products - Fieldcrest Cannon Licensing, Inc.
BIO-TONE - Beverages - Shaklee Corp.
BIO-TONE - Chemical preparations - Espoma Co.
BIO TOUCH - Medical apparatus - Biomedical Life Systems, Inc.
BIO-TOUCH - Skin care products - Bio-Touch, Inc.
BIO-TRAY - Water purification systems - Aquarium Pump & Piping Systems
BIO-TREND - Vitamins and nutritional supplements - CKD International Corp.
BIO-TRIM - Vitamins and nutritional supplements - Vitamin Power Inc.
BIO-TROL - Chemicals - Betz Laboratories, Inc.
BIO ULTRA SHIELD PLUS - Pharmaceutical preparations ☆ - Whitestone Products Inc.
BIO-VASCULAR PROBE - Medical apparatus - Bio-Vascular, Inc.
BIO-VITE - Vitamins and nutritional supplements - Vitamin Power Inc.
BIO WATER - Vitamins and nutritional supplements - Nutrition for Life International, Inc.
BIO-WAVE - Cosmetics ☆ - Redken Laboratories, Inc.
BIO-WHEEL - Pet products - Marineland Aquarium Products
BIO WIRE - Medical apparatus - Maryland Specialty Wire Inc.
BIO-WORM KILLER - Insecticides - Green Light Co.
BIO-ZIN - Vitamins and nutritional supplements - Mobile Milling Service, Inc.
BIO ZINC - Vitamins and nutritional supplements - Solaray
BIO-ZYME - Cleaning preparations - Blitz Manufacturing Co., Inc.
BIO2XYDANT - Cleaning preparations - Bioxy, Inc.
BIOA - Computer software - ABC Development Inc.
BIOAC - Cleaning preparations–household - K-Zyme Laboratories Inc.
BIOACTIVE - Fertilizers - Beautiful Plants Brand
BIOADVANCE BEAUTY RECOVERY SYSTEM - Skin care products - Avon Products, Inc.
BIOALLERS - Health care products - Botanical Laboratories Inc.
BIOANALOGICS - Computers - ABC Development Inc.
BIOARCH - Shoes–orthopedic - J2B2, Inc.
BIOBEE - Pharmaceutical preparations - Goldline Laboratories, Inc.
BIOBELLE - Skin care products - Renbow International Ltd. USA
BIOBIRD - Sporting goods - Deborah Hellings
BIOBITS - Computer software ☆ - Queue Inc.
BIOBLAST - Computer software - Wheeling Jesuit College
BIOBOLIC POWER LIFE - Health care products - Anabol Naturals
BIOBOTTOMS - Catalogs - Biobottoms, Inc.
BIOBRANE II - Pharmaceutical preparations - Dow B. Hickam Inc.
BIOBRIDGE - Chemical preparations - Enzo Biochem, Inc.
BIOCAINE - Pet products - Tomlyn Products
BIOCAL - Chemical preparations - Miles Inc.
BIOCAM - Shampoos - Renbow International Ltd. USA
BIOCAROTTIN - Vitamins and nutritional supplements - Bioforce of America Ltd.
BIOCATH - Health care products - C.R. Bard, Inc.
BIOCEBRIN T - Pharmaceutical preparations - Goldline Laboratories, Inc.
BIOCHANGE CLEANSER - Skin care products - Charles of the Ritz Group Ltd.
BIOCHAVAN - Vitamins and nutritional supplements - Quantum Publications, Inc.
BIOCHEMICS DR. DOG - Pet products - Biochemics, Inc.
BIOCHEWS - Pharmaceutical preparations - Goldline Laboratories, Inc.
BIOCINE - Pharmaceuticals - Biocine Co.
BIOCLATE - Pharmaceutical preparations - Armour Pharmaceutical Co.
BIOCLEAN - Agricultural products - Citrex, Inc.
BIOCLEAN - Cleaning preparations - Twi-Laq Industries Inc.
BIOCLEANSE - Health-care products - NutriCology
BIOCLIMBER - Exercising equipment - Engineering Dynamics Corp.
BIOCLINIC - Health care products - Sunrise Medical Inc.
BIOCLUSIVE - Bandages - Johnson & Johnson
BIOCOLLASPHERES - Skin care products ☆ - Sothys USA Inc.
BIOCOLOR - Paint sets - QTL Corp.
BIOCON - Filters–oil - Advanced Waste Reduction
BIOCORT - Pharmaceutical preparations ☆ - C.O. Truxton Inc.
BIOCRITTERS - Figurines - Environmental Solutions, Inc.
BIODAY - Pharmaceutical preparations - Goldline Laboratories, Inc.
BIODEGREAT - Drain pipe cleaners - Shaklee Corp.
BIODERM - Surgical supplies - Bioderm, Inc.
BIODIESEL - Fuel additives - National Biodiesel Board
BIODIMENSIONAL - Implants–surgical - MdGhan Medical Corp.
BIODOC - Electrical equipment - Westech Engineering Inc.

BIODOCARB - Chemical preparations - G + G International Inc.

BIODONE - Chemicals - ISP Investments Inc.

BIODOPHILUS - Vitamins and nutritional supplements - Viva America Marketing, Inc.

BIODRY - Veterinary pharmaceutical preparations ☆ - Upjohn Co.

BIODYNAMAX - Vitamins and nutritional supplements - Amrion, Inc.

BIOEARTH - X-ray apparatus - Mega Linx Inc.

BIOEASE - Chairs–metal ☆ - Stacor Corp.

BIOELEMENTS - Skin care products - BioElements Skin Care & Conservatory of Esthetics

BIOENGINEERED COMFORT - Fabrics - Protein Polymer Technologies, Inc.

BIOESSENCE - Bathroom accessories ☆ - Tsumura International Inc.

BIOFIELD - Medical apparatus - Biofield Corp.

BIOFIRM FORTIFYING COMPLEX - Cosmetics - Viviane Woodard Industries, Ltd.

BIOFIT - Vitamins and nutritional supplements - Cernitin America Inc.

BIOFLAVOMAX - Vitamins and nutritional supplements - Bioenergy Nutrient's Inc.

BIOFLAVONOID COMPLEX - Vitamins and nutritional supplements - Vitamin Research Products Inc.

BIOFLAVONOIDS - Health care products - Above All Health Inc.

BIOFLUSH - Drain pipe cleaners - Technical Concepts, L.P.

BIOFORCE - Dental equipment - GAC International, Inc.

BIOFORCE - Health care products - Bioforce of America Ltd.

BIOFORCE 7 - Health care products - Bioforce of America Ltd.

BIOFORCE ECHINACEA - Health care products - Bioforce of America Ltd.

BIOFORCE SYMPHYTUM - Health care products - Bioforce of America Ltd.

BIOFORM - Fertilizers - Hallier Enterprises

BIOFORM HC - Pharmaceutical preparations - Goldline Laboratories, Inc.

BIOFRACTALS - Posters - Mitchell Anthony

BIOFREE - Deodorizers ☆ - Horace Small Apparel Co.

BIOFREEZE - Pharmaceutical preparations - Performance Health, Inc.

BIOFUSION - Computer software - Buffalo Capital Corp.

BIOGAN - Fertilizers - Bioproducts Inc.

BIOGEN - Health care products - Dr. Babor Natural Cosmetics

BIOGEN - Pharmaceutical preparations - Biogen Inc.

BIOGENOL - Hair care products - Framesi USA/Roffler Industries Inc.

BIOGERM - Air purification systems - Pollenex Corp.

BIOGESTIN - Vitamins and nutritional supplements - Great Life Laboratories Inc.

BIOGINKGO - Vitamins and nutritional supplements - Pharmanex, Inc.

BIOGLIDE - Medical apparatus - Pudenz-Schulte Medical Research Corp.

BIOGRADE - Engines - Berryman Products Inc.

BIOGRADE - Pet products - Rolf C. Hagen (USA) Corp.

BIOGRAF - Publisher's imprints - Garber Communications Inc.

BIOGRAN - Pet products ☆ - Sera Aquaristik USA Inc.

BIOGRAPH - Recording label - Biograph Records Inc.

BIOGRAPHY IN MUSIC - Recording label - Lyric Distribution Inc.

BIOGRAPHY THROUGH PHOTOGRAPHY - Photo albums - Ilya Tsenter

BIOGRATE - Filters–water - Munters Corp.

BIOGRID - Aquarium accessories - Aquarium Systems, Inc.

BIOGUAR FIBER - Health care products - Bios

BIOGUARD - Floor coverings–carpet and rugs - Lees Carpets

BIOGUARD FOR PETS - Pet products - Biogenetics Food Corp.

BIOGUARD PLUS FOR PETS - Pet products - Biogenetics Food Corp.

BIOHERBAL - Shampoos - Renbow International Ltd. USA

BIOHIST-LA - Antihistamine preparations - Wakefield Pharmaceuticals, Inc.

BIOHISTINE - Pharmaceutical preparations - Goldline Laboratories, Inc.

BIOHORIZONS - Video production - Biohorizons, Inc.

BIOJEC - Veterinary pharmaceutical preparations - Biomed Inc.

BIOJET - Pet products - Aquapro

BIOJOBA - Hair care products - Joico Laboratories, Inc.

BIOKOSMA - Skin care products ☆ - Nature's Answer (Bio Botanica)

BIOLAB - Water treating compounds - Bio-Lab, Inc.

BIOLAC - Pharmaceutical preparations - Goldline Laboratories, Inc.

BIOLANTA - Pharmaceutical preparations - Goldline Laboratories, Inc.

BIOLASER - Laser systems–medical - International Biolaser Corp.

BIOLAST - Health care products - Posture Support Manufacturing Inc.

BIOLAX - Vitamins and nutritional supplements - Body Wise International, Inc.

BIOLECITHIN - Vitamins and nutritional supplements - Viva America Marketing, Inc.

BIOLESTINE - Hair coloring preparations - Paul Penders Co. Inc.

BIOLIC - Vitamins and nutritional supplements - Wakunaga of America Co., Ltd.

BIOLIFE - Computer software - Lifelink, Inc.

BIOLIN - Pharmaceutical - American Hygienic Laboratories Inc.

BIOLINE - Health care products - Goldline Laboratories, Inc.

BIOLINE - Hoses - Netafim Irrigation, Inc.

BIOLINK - Fertilizers - Westbridge Agricultural Products

BIOLINK - Food supplements - Biolink International Inc.

BIOLINX - Computer software - Dynatech Laboratories, Inc.

BIOLOG - Building materials–concrete - Bonterra America, Inc.

BIOLOGIC - Medical apparatus - OrthoLogic Corp.

BIOLOGIC - Notebooks and notepads - Norcom Inc.

BIOLOGIC - Pet products - California Aquarium Supply Corp.

BIOLOGIC COMPACT - Aquariums–household - California Aquarium Supply Corp.

BIOLOGICAL CLOCK - Watches - Rabbit Foot, Inc.

BIOLOGICAL SPHERES - Water purification systems - Aquarium Products Inc.

BIOLOGICAL WEARFARE - Shirts - Biowear, Inc.

BIOLOGICALLY QUIET - Surgical supplies - Biologic, Inc.

BIOLOGICS - Cosmetics - Cosmair Inc.

BIOLOGIX - Health care products - Best Vitamin Inc.

BIOLOGY A2Z - Computer peripheral equipment - Harcourt Brace & Co.

BIOLOGY TODAY - Textbooks - Harcourt Brace & Co.

BIOLOX - Pharmaceutical preparations - Goldline Laboratories, Inc.

BIOLUMBER INC. - Building materials - BioLumber

BIOLURE - Pesticides–agricultural - Santa Cruz Horticultural Supply

BIOLYTE - Veterinary pharmaceutical preparations ☆ - Upjohn Co.

BIOMAG - Golfing equipment - Outdoor Technologies Group

BIOMANI - Cosmetics - Biomani, Inc.

BIOMARINE - Pet products - Aquafauna Bio-Marine, Inc.

BIOMARK SYSTEM - Vitamins and nutritional supplements - Biomark International, Inc.

BIOMASTER - Exercise equipment - Roadmaster Corp.

BIOMASTER - Juice extracting devices ☆ - Robert Krups North America

BIOMAT - Flowers, plants, and seeds - Mid-America Biomat, Inc.

BIOMATE - Exercising equipment - Joseph N. Khazzam

BIOMAX - Chemicals–photographic - Eastman Kodak Co.

BIOMAX - Diapers–disposable - E.I. Dupont de Nemours and Co.

BIOMAX FORTE - Vitamins and nutritional supplements - Ramon E. Iglesias

BIOMEDIC - Skin care products - Cosmedic Concepts, Inc.

BIOMEDICAL 2000 - Medical apparatus - Medserv Group, Inc.

BIOMEDICAL ENGINEERING CITATION INDEX - Computer software - Delaware Licensing Corp.

BIOMEDICAL PLUS - Medical apparatus - Medserv Group, Inc.

BIOMEDICS - Contact lenses - O.S.I. Corp.

BIOMEDISPHERE - Air purification systems ☆ - Bionaire Corp.

BIOMETRIC IMAGING - Medical apparatus - Biometric Imaging, Inc.

BIOMILK - Hair care products - Renbow International Ltd. USA

BIOMIST - Pharmaceutical preparations ☆ - Vita-Fore Products Co.

BIOMOX - Veterinary product - Biocraft Laboratories Inc.

BIOMYDRIN - Pharmaceutical preparations ☆ - Warner-Lambert Co.

BION - Health care products - Alcon Laboratories, Inc.

BION - Soap - DKP, Inc.

BION TECHNOLOGIES - Electronic equipment - Bion Technologies Corp.

BIONADE - Pharmaceutical preparations - Goldline Laboratories, Inc.

BIONAIRE - Air purification systems - Bionaire Corp.

BIONATE - Resins–synthetic - Polymer Technology Group, Inc.

BIONATE 50-2 - Pharmaceutical preparations - Seatrace Co.

BIONATOPS - Toys - Mattel, Inc.

BIONATURAL - Chemical preparations - Life Industries Corp.

BIOND FURY - Publisher's imprints - Biond Fury

BIONDAL - Hair care products - Framesi USA/Roffler Industries Inc.

BIONDO - Apparel and accessories - Susan Elizabeth Longo

BIONEB - Medical apparatus - Templeton Coal Co. Inc.

BIONEEM - Insecticides - W.R. Grace & Co.

BIONET - Agricultural products - North American Green, Inc.

BIONEX - Pharmaceutical preparations - Goldline Laboratories, Inc.

BIONIC - Frames–eyeglass - Hudson Optical Corp.

BIONIC - Freezers and ranges - Crosley Group, Inc.

BIONIC TONIC - Beverages - Biomega, Inc.

BIONIC WOMAN - Toys–stuffed ☆ - Kenner Products

BIONICS - Infant product - Nurturtech

BIONIQ - Cosmetics - Hymedix International, Inc.

BIONITRA - Pet products - Aquapro

BIONOSH - Vegetables–dried ☆ - Jaret Specialties Inc.

BIOORGANIC - Pet products - Aquapro

BIOOX - Medical apparatus - SRE, Inc.

BIOPAK - Laboratory apparatus - National Scientific Supply Co., Inc.

BIOPANEL - Filters–air - A.J. Dralle, Inc.

BIOPAP - Screening test reagents - Enzo Diagnostics Inc.

☆ = Now out of production

BIOPAR FORTE - Pharmaceutical preparations ☆ - Armour Pharmaceutical Co.
BIOPASS - Animal feeds - Bioproducts Inc.
BIOPATCH - Bandages - Johnson & Johnson
BIOPATH - Laboratory apparatus - Biopath Laboratories, Inc.
BIOPET - Pet products - Vitakraft Pet Products Co., Inc.
BIOPHAR - Honey - Haram-Christensen Corp.
BIOPHARM - Pharmaceutical preparations - Biopharmaceutics, Inc.
BIOPLASMA - Vitamins and nutritional supplements - Standard Homeopathic Co., Inc.
BIOPOND - Chemical preparations - Bioenvirotech, Inc.
BIOPRO - Medical apparatus - International Bioproducts, Inc.
BIOPRO - Recording label - Futurehealth Inc.
BIOPRO BAIT EGGS - Fishing lures - Magic Products, Inc.
BIOPRO CAPS - Vitamins and nutritional supplements - Vitamin Research Products Inc.
BIOPROPOLIS - Vitamins and nutritional supplements - Amrion, Inc.
BIOP'S - Cleaning preparations - Laurent G. Guez
BIOP'S - Drain pipe cleaners - Bio Alliance
BIOQUEST - Detergents - Amway Corp.
BIORANDIN - Health care products - Bioforce of America Ltd.
BIOREDUCER - Grinders - Bio Quest Inc.
BIOREPORT - Computer software - Modular Instruments, Inc.
BIORESOURCE - Health care products - Bios
BIORESPONSIBLE - Cleaning preparations - Block Drug Co., Inc.
BIORESPONSIVE - Cleaning preparations–household - Block Drug Co., Inc.
BIORESTORE - Chemical preparations - Oilton, Inc.
BIORGANIC - Oils–essential - Nature's Bounty, Inc.
BIORHYTHM MASTER - Computer software - SourceView Software International
BIORKUDDEN - Figurines - Swe-Den Inc.
BIORUTIN - Vitamins and nutritional supplements - Natural Organics, Inc.
BIOS - Pharmaceutical preparations - Bios
BIOS - Sporting goods - Oceanic
BIOS LIFE DIET - Health care products - Bios
BIOS LIFE2 - Vitamins and nutritional supplements - Rexall Sundown, Inc.
BIOSAFE - Water purification systems - Filtrue Corp.
BIOSAFETY SYSTEMS - Apparel and accessories - BioSafety Systems, Inc.
BIOSCALIN - Hair care products ☆ - Optimal Nutrients
BIOSCAN - Computer hardware - Oryx Press, Inc.
BIOSCENTS - Colognes - Farouk Systems, Inc.
BIOSCRIPT RESEARCH - Vitamins and nutritional supplements - Bioscript International Inc.
BIOSCULPTOR - Computer software - Biosculptor Inc.
BIOSEARCH - Chemical preparations - Millipore Corp.
BIOSEL - Vitamins and nutritional supplements - Nutramax Laboratories, Inc.
BIOSENCE - Hair care products - Andrew Questell
BIOSENSE - Golfing equipment - Outdoor Technologies Group
BIOSEPRIN - Medical apparatus - Biosearch Medical Products Inc.
BIOSHAPE - Pillows - Linda H. Dixon
BIOSHARK-740 - Vitamins and nutritional supplements - Amrion, Inc.
BIOSHIELD - Medical apparatus - Medserv Group, Inc.
BIOSHIELD - Sunblocks - Tanning Research Laboratories Inc.
BIOSILK - Hair care products - Farouk Systems, Inc.
BIOSIM - Computer software - Life Science Associates
BIOSINE COMPLEX - Dermatological preparations - ETS, Inc.
BIOSIS 3001 - Hair care products - Genesis Research International
BIOSLIM - Vitamins and nutritional supplements - Medicus Formulas, Inc.
BIOSODE - Vitamins and nutritional supplements - Hobon
BIOSOFT - Weightlifting equipment ☆ - Spenco Medical Corp.
BIOSOL - Veterinary pharmaceutical preparations ☆ - Upjohn Co.
BIOSOL-M - Veterinary pharmaceutical preparations ☆ - Upjohn Co.
BIOSOLV - Chemical preparations - Spectrum Quality Products, Inc.
BIOSONE - Health care products - Kay Pharmacal Co.
BIOSONIC - Pet products - Biological Engineering/High Tech Pet Products
BIOSOURCE - Body lotions and gel - Natural Attitudes Inc.
BIOSOURCE - Health care products ☆ - Bios
BIOSOURCE GENETICS - Biochemicals - Biosource Genetics Corp.
BIOSPEC - Floor coverings - Mannington Resilient Floors
BIOSPHERE - Cleaning preparations - Gaines Industries, Inc.
BIOSPHERE 2 - Jewelry - Space Biospheres Venture
BIOSPHERE 2 - Video production - Decisions Investment Corp.
BIOSTA - Health care products - Miracle Exclusives Inc.
BIOSTACK - Medical apparatus - SRE, Inc.
BIOSTAKE - Building materials - North American Green, Inc.
BIOSTEP - Footwear - Prism Enterprises, Inc.
BIOSTHETICS - Skin care products - Laboratoire Biosthetique Ltd.

BIOSTICK - Beverages - Interport International, Inc.
BIOSTIM - Medical apparatus - Medserv Group, Inc.
BIOSTRESS - Pharmaceutical preparations - Goldline Laboratories, Inc.
BIOSTRIDE - Shoe insoles - Benchmark Brands
BIOSTRIKE - Filters–air - Giftech Filter Products, Inc.
BIOSTRIP - Test kits - Princeton Biomeditech Corp.
BIOSTRUT - Crutches ☆ - Ambulatory Products International
BIOSUN - Sunblocks - Playtex Beauty Care, Inc.
BIOSURE - Containers - J. Richard Riese
BIOSWEDE - Pet products - Eclipse Biofarm Ltd.
BIOSYN - Dietary supplement - Biosyn Inc.
BIOSYNTHESIS - Hair care products - Alexandria Williamson
BIOT - Giftware - N.S. Gustin Co.
BIOTA - Agricultural products - AlphaBiota Inc.
BIOTANE - Skin care products - L'anza Research International
BIOTEC - Furniture - Hamilton Sorter Co. Inc.
BIOTECH - Apparel and accessories - Joseph N. Khazzam
BIOTECH - Pet products - Rolf C. Hagen (USA) Corp.
BIOTECHNICAL COMPOSITES - Building materials - Synthetic Industries, Inc.
BIOTEIN H-3 - Hair care products - Head Start Vitamin Products
BIOTEK - Medical apparatus - Biotek, Inc.
BIOTENE - Toothpaste - Laclede Research Laboratories
BIOTENE H-24 - Hair care products - Carme Inc.
BIOTERA - Hair care products - Naturelle, Inc.
BIOTHAW - Medical apparatus - Biopore, Inc.
BIOTHERM - Skin care products - Biotherm
BIOTHESIN - Pharmaceutical preparations ☆ - Pal-Pak Inc.
BIOTHRIX - Hair care products - Linart International, Inc.
BIOTIC - Skin care products ☆ - Scrip-Physician Supply Co.
BIOTIC CODE 614 - Vitamins and nutritional supplements - Biotic Code International, Inc.
BIOTIC-T-500 - Antibiotics ☆ - Scrip-Physician Supply Co.
BIOTICS - Vitamins and nutritional supplements - Biotics Research Corp.
BIOTIN - Hair care products - Jason Natural Products, Inc.
BIOTIN - Vitamins and nutritional supplements - Vitamin Research Products Inc.
BIOTIN - Vitamins and nutritional supplements ☆ - Great Life Laboratories Inc.
BIOTIP - Laboratory apparatus - Multi-Technology, Inc.
BIOTOL - Hair care products - Jojoba Resources Inc.
BIOTONE - Massage products - Natural Thoughts Inc.
BIOTONIN PLUS - Health care products - Scandinavian Natural Health & Beauty Products, Inc.
BIOTRAINER - Measuring instruments - Individual Monitoring Systems, Inc.
BIOTREAT - Chemical preparations - International Enviroguard Systems, Inc.
BIOTREATMENT 22 - Hair care products - Levlab, Inc.
BIOTRES - Antibiotics ☆ - Central Pharmaceutical Inc.
BIOTRESS - Hair care products - Universal Biologics, Inc.
BIOTRIM - Food products - Molecular Biologics, Inc.
BIOTTA - Juices ☆ - Liberty Richter Inc.
BIOTUBE - Pumps–water - Orenco Systems, Inc.
BIOTUSSIN - Pharmaceutical preparations ☆ - Bioforce of America Ltd.
BIOVAP - Cleaning preparations - AmeriVap Systems Inc.
BIOVITE OB - Pet products - Crowne Royale, Ltd.
BIOWEIGHTS - Fishing tackle - Outdoor Technologies Group
BIOWINDOW - Computer software - Modular Instruments, Inc.
BIOWIPE - Surgical supplies - Biodyne, Inc.
BIOWOOL - Yarn - Creative Yarns International, Inc.
BIOWORKS - Medical apparatus - Mankind Research Unltd. Inc.
BIOYEAST - Animal feed supplements - Bioproducts Inc.
BIOZEA - Agricultural products - Universal Foods Corp.
BIOZENE - Antipyretics - Sandoz Pharmaceuticals Corp.
BIOZINE II - Deodorizers - Naace Industries Inc.
BIOZINE III - Disinfectants - Naace Industries Inc.
BIOZOME - Chemical preparations - Oppenheimer Environmental Co., Inc.
BIOZONE - Vitamins and nutritional supplements - Surfactant Technologies, Inc.
BIOZONICS - Pet products - Rolf C. Hagen (USA) Corp.
BIOZYEST - Seasonings - Burns Philp Food Inc.
BIOZYME - Pet products - BioZyme Inc.
BIOZYME - Pharmaceutical preparations ☆ - Armour Pharmaceutical Co.
BIOZYME - Water treating compounds - Aquarium Products Inc.
BIOZYME-C - Pharmaceutical preparations ☆ - Armour Pharmaceutical Co.
BIPAP - Health care products - Respironics, Inc.
BIPAP HARMONY - Medical apparatus - Respironics, Inc.
BIPECTOL - Pharmaceutical preparations ☆ - Pal-Pak Inc.
BIPHETAMINE - Health care products - Fisons Corp.

☆ = Now out of production

BIPLANE BOOKS - Publisher's imprints - Stanyan Record Co.
BIPLEXER - Photographic equipment - Buhl Optical Co.
BIPOLAR TECHNOLOGY - Fabrics - ADS Properties Corp.
BIPOLE-S - Pharmaceutical preparations - G.O. Spanner Inc.
BIPOLIGATOR - Surgical instruments - Microsurge, Inc.
BIPOSTO - Infant product - Inglesina Baby Ltd.
BIPPEE - Frames–eyeglass - May Optical Co. Inc.
BIPPY BEANS - Dolls - Mattel, Inc.
BIPYRIDINE - Pharmaceutical preparations - City Chemical Corp.
BIR-D - Golfing equipment - Bailey Enterprises
BIRANGLE - Measuring instruments - Martingale & Co.
BIRCH - Computer software - Adobe Systems Inc.
BIRCH - Drums–musical instruments ☆ - Pearl Corp.
BIRCH - Shampoos - S.C. Johnson & Son, Inc.
BIRCH BARK - Skin care products - Helga Van Dyke Skin Care
BIRCH BAY - Apparel and accessories - Brigata International, Inc.
BIRCH BEER - Soft drink - Briar's USA Inc.
BIRCH BLUFF - Food products - Lodi Canning Inc.
BIRCH CREEK - Wainscotting - Georgia-Pacific Corp.
BIRCH HILLS - Floor coverings–carpet and rugs ☆ - Evans-Black Carpet Mills
BIRCH SAUNA - Bath gel - Crabtree & Evelyn, Ltd.
BIRCHTONE - Cabinets - Leedo Manufacturing Co.
BIRCHWOOD - Floor coverings–carpet and rugs ☆ - Downs Carpet Co. Inc.
BIRCHWOOD TIP - Cigars ☆ - Havatampa Inc.
BIRD - Chili peppers–powdered ☆ - Frieda's, Inc.
BIRD - Computer storage devices - American College of Radiology
BIRD - Mining equipment - Baker Hughes Inc.
BIRD - Siding–metal - Bird Inc.
BIRD A CHIP - Pet products ☆ - Northeastern Products Corp.
BIRD AND REPTILE LITTER - Pet products - Northeastern Products Corp.
BIRD BANQUET - Bird feeds - Aquatrol, Inc.
BIRD BARN - Bird feeders - Eckelman Innovations, Inc.
BIRD BATH - Pet products - Natra Pet Inc.
BIRD BEAKIN' - Bird feeders - Pocket Mountain Enterprises, Inc.
BIRD BELFRY - Bird cages ☆ - Applewood Seed & Garden Group
BIRD BLOCKERS - Bird feeds - Lafeber Co.
BIRD BOLT - Gocarts - Commonwealth Inc.
BIRD BRAIN - Games - Tiger Electronics, Inc.
BIRD BRAINS - Pet products - Pet Brains Inc.
BIRD BUDDIES - Hobby kits ☆ - Greene Plastics Corp.
BIRD BUDDY - Bird feeders - Metal Man, Inc.
BIRD BUDDY - Bird feeders and houses - Richard A. Meitrott
BIRD BUFFET, THE - Bird feeders - Robert L. Brostowicz
BIRD BUNGALOWS - Pet products - Next to Nature
BIRD CADDY - Pet products - Emerald Bird Caddy
BIRD CAGE DEFENDER - Pesticides–household - Rich Health
BIRD COUNTRY - Pet products - Mountain Meadows Pet Products, Inc.
BIRD DELITES - Pet products - American Cat Emporium
BIRD DOG - Radio communications equipment - Westinghouse Electric Corp.
BIRD-E-RITE - Pet products - Lake Products Co. Inc.
BIRD-EE BRICK - Animal feeds - B.G.B. Pet Supply Inc.
BIRD FARM - Pork rinds - PSF Finance L.P.
BIRD GARD - Repellent - Weitech Inc.
BIRD HANDLER, THE - Veterinary medical equipment - Defoy Ranch Products Inc.
BIRD HOME - Pet products ☆ - Circle K Industries Inc.
BIRD IN PARADISE - Cosmetics - Revlon Consumer Products Corp.
BIRD JET WAVE - Toys–electronic - Bird Bromiticous Inc.
BIRD KONG - Pet products - Kong Co.
BIRD LUNCH STATIONS - Garden furniture - Forest Time Products Inc.
BIRD MINI-WHEELS - Toys–electronic - Bird Bromiticous Inc.
BIRD MOTEL - Bird cages - Papagallo Enterprises
BIRD NEPONSET - Roofing materials–slate - Bird Inc.
BIRD OF PARADISE - Frames–eyeglass ☆ - Universal/Univis Inc.
BIRD OF PARADISE - Giftware ☆ - Gorham Inc.
BIRD OF PARADISE - Skin care products - Avon Products, Inc.
BIRD ON A BUDGET - Pet products - Picture Perfect Parrot
BIRD PERFECT - Bird food and seed - Farmers Elevator Co. of Arthur
BIRD PLAYARDS - Pet products - American Cat Emporium
BIRD PROTECTOR - Pet products - 8 in 1 Pet Products Inc.
BIRD SANCTUARY, THE - Figurines - Regency
BIRD SENTRY - Respirators - Bird Products Corp.
BIRD SHOOTER - Footwear–men's - W.C. Russell Moccasin Co.
BIRD SHOOTER - Traps–animal - Trius Products Co.
BIRD SPRINGERS - Toys ☆ - Dakin Inc.
BIRD STOP SIGN - Decals and transfers - Young Ideas

BIRD STUFF - Pet products - Backyard Nature Products Inc.
BIRD SUPPLEMENT - Pet products - Natra Pet Inc.
BIRD TEASER - Fishing lures - Boone Bait Co. Inc.
BIRD THINGS - Bird feeds - Bird-Things Inc.
BIRD TUTOR - Recording label - James K. Lynch
BIRD WHISTLER - Tea kettles–nonelectric ☆ - National Housewares
BIRD-X - Garden equipment - Dalen Products Inc.
BIRD ZERK! - Athletic associations - Birdzerk! Inc.
BIRDALL - Pet products - Animal Lovers
BIRDALURE - Bird feeds - Birdalure Inc.
BIRDANGLE - Pet products - Rednour & Smith Manufacturing Co. Inc.
BIRDBAN - Netting - Beaumont G. Lyons
BIRDBRAINS - Apparel and accessories - Robin Dee Carter
BIRDBRAINS, THE - Apparel and accessories - Robin Dee Carter
BIRDCAGE BARRIER BIRD BRAINS, INC. - Pet products - Pet Brains Inc.
BIRDCYCLINE - Veterinary pharmaceutical preparations - Dyna Pet Inc.
BIRDEZ - Chemical preparations - Monson Companies, Inc.
BIRDFEEDER - Lenses–magnifying - Swift Instruments, Inc.
BIRDHOUSE BASKETS - Flower pots–earthenware - Forest Time Products Inc.
BIRDIE - Apparel–men's - Alps Sportswear Manufacturing Co.
BIRDIE - Apparel–men's - Richard A. Leslie Co. Inc.
BIRDIE - Flowers, plants, and seeds - Turf-Seed, Inc.
BIRDIE - Golfing equipment - Brandell Products, Inc.
BIRDIE - Sporting goods - Donnay USA
BIRDIE - Umbrellas - Haas-Jordan Co.
BIRDIE BAGEL BITES - Pet products - Doggie Bagel Bites
BIRDIE BALL - Toys - Marlin Toy Products Inc.
BIRDIE BLOOMERS - Pet products - JT Industries
BIRDIE KING - Video games - Taito America Corp.
BIRDIE PAK - Food products - Birdie Pak Products Inc.
BIRDIE TREE - Posters - Birdie Tree Productions
BIRDIE VITA DROPS - Veterinary pharmaceutical preparations - Nutritional Research Associates Inc.
BIRDLOCK - Garden equipment - L.E.L. Enterprises LC
BIRDMAN - Toys - Tonka Corp.
BIRDMYCIN - Veterinary pharmaceutical preparations - Dyna Pet Inc.
BIRDNEST - Infant product - Birdland Baby Products Inc
BIRDNEST HOUSE - Infant product - Birdland Baby Products Inc
BIRDOLA - Bird feeds - Metz Farms
BIRDPERCH - Rocking chairs - Birdland Baby Products Inc
BIRD'S - Desserts - Gilway Co. Ltd.
BIRD'S - Food products - One Pie Canning Co.
BIRDS - Kaleidoscopes - Gemini Kaleidoscopes
BIRDS AND BEES - Wallpaper - Somerville Designs
BIRDS & BLOOMS - Calendars - Reiman Publications, LP
BIRDS & THE BEADS, THE - Pet products - Pyramid Bird Toys
BIRDS-AWAY - Garden equipment ☆ - Dalen Products Inc.
BIRDS BED AND BREAKFAST - Bird feeders - Bennington Potters
BIRDS DELITE - See HEATH
BIRDS EYE - Vegetables–frozen - Dean Foods Co.
BIRD'S EYE FRUIT - Fruits–frozen - Dean Foods Vegetable Co.
BIRDS EYE PRODUCTIONS - Greeting cards - Birds Eye Productions, Inc.
BIRD'S EYE VEGETABLES - Vegetables–frozen - Dean Foods Vegetable Co.
BIRDS EYE VIEW - Bird feeders - Cedar Works Inc.
BIRD'S EYE VIEW - Computer software - Hartley Courseware Inc.
BIRD'S FAVORITE MIX - Bird feeds - Kellogg Inc.
BIRDS 'N BEES - Computer software ☆ - Capstone Software
BIRDS OF A FEATHER - Communications equipment - Bradley Madison Co.
BIRDS OF AMERICA - Giftware - Arnart Imports Inc.
BIRDS OF AMERICA - Giftware - Lenox, Inc.
BIRDS OF BRITAIN - Earthenware - Portmeirion USA
BIRDS OF PREY - Computer software - Business Systems Communications, Inc.
BIRDS OF PREY-FARE - Pet products - Reliable Protein Products
BIRDS OF THE WORLD - Toys ☆ - Bachmann Industries Inc.
BIRDS OF WINTER - Glassware–household ☆ - Fenton Art Glass Co.
BIRD'S SELECT - Bird feed - Countrymark Cooperative, Inc.
BIRDSENSE - Computer software - McClendon Enterprises, Inc.
BIRDSEYE - Recording label - Jazz Composer's Orchestra Association Inc.
BIRDSNACK - Bird feeds ☆ - Agway Country Foods Inc.
BIRDSONG - Air purification systems ☆ - Medo Industries, Inc.
BIRDSONG COLLECTION - Chimes - New Creative Enterprises, Inc.
BIRDWATCHER'S GARDEN - Flowers, plants, and seeds - W. Atlee Burpee and Co.

☆ = Now out of production

BIRDWELL BEACH BRITCHES BIRDIE - Apparel and accessories - Birdwell Enterprises, Inc.

BIRDWING - Recording label - Sparrow Corp.

BIRDWIT - Greeting cards - Recycled Paper Products, Inc.

BIRDY - Automotive parts and accessories - Kolin Industries Inc.

BIRELEY'S - Beverages–carbonated - Re-Mi Foods

BIRELL - Beer ☆ - Charles Jacquin et Compagnie Inc.

BIRGITTA - Glassware–household - Crate and Barrel

BIRIDEX - Electronic equipment - Sony Corp. of America

BIRING BOOK SOCIETY, THE - Publisher's imprints ☆ - MacMillan Publishing Co. Inc.

BIRKENSTOCK - Footwear - Birkenstock Footprint Sandals, Inc.

BIRKI - Footwear - Birkenstock Footprint Sandals, Inc.

BIRKMAYER PHARMACEUTICALS - Pharmaceutical preparations - Birkmayer Pharmaceuticals, Inc.

BIRKMAYER USA - Pharmaceutical preparations - Birkmayer USA Corp.

BIRKO - Cleaning preparations - Birko Corp.

BIRKS - Gin and Canadian whiskey - Italian and French Wine Co. of Buffalo Inc.

BIRMADIL - Pharmaceutical - Birkmayer Pharmaceuticals, Inc.

BIRMINGHAM - Musical instruments - C. Bruno & Son Inc.

BIRNBAUM TRAVEL GUIDES - Publisher's imprints - Houghton Mifflin Co.

BIRO - Pens - Bic Corp.

BIRO NO. 3 - Health care products ☆ - Bedard Pharmacy Inc.

BIRTCHER MEDICAL SYSTEMS - Medical equipment - Birtcher Medical Systems Inc.

BIRTH - Recording label - Jazz Composer's Orchestra Association Inc.

BIRTH MARK - Toys - Treva D. Metoyer, Inc.

BIRTH MEDALLION - Jewelry - Dmitri Tatarinov

BIRTH-O-GRAM - Stationery - Birth-O-Gram Co.

BIRTH STUDS - Jewelry - Roman Research, Inc.

BIRTHDAY BAG, THE - Hobby kits - Birthday Bag Inc.

BIRTHDAY BATH - Bathtubs–enameled - Kohler Co.

BIRTHDAY BEAR - Greeting cards - Those Characters from Cleveland, Inc.

BIRTHDAY BEARS - Toys - Those Characters from Cleveland, Inc.

BIRTHDAY BLIMP, THE - Novelty items - Your Special Day, Inc.

BIRTHDAY/CELEBRATION DESIGN - Computer software - Parsons Technology, Inc.

BIRTHDAY CIRCUS CENTER - Novelty items ☆ - Papel Freelance, Inc.

BIRTHDAY CONTROL PILLS - Candy - Marsyl Inc. (Marsyl Enterprises, Inc.)

BIRTHDAY COUNTDOWN - Toys - Unique Industries, Inc.

BIRTHDAY EXPRESS - Paper–gift wrap - Prism Network International, Inc.

BIRTHDAY FORTUNE COOKIES - Cookies - Creative Cookie Inc. (American Dream Enterprises)

BIRTHDAY GAZETTE - Greeting cards - Concepts Direct, Inc.

BIRTHDAY GIRLS - Dolls - Martha Peebles

BIRTHDAY G.S. - Giftware - U.S. Fiberglass Inc.

BIRTHDAY NEWS - Greeting cards - Nadel Worldwide, Inc.

BIRTHDAY OF THE MONTH - Greeting cards ☆ - Amberley Greeting Card Co.

BIRTHDAY PETS - Toys ☆ - Those Characters from Cleveland, Inc.

BIRTHDAY REMINDER - Calendars - Stevenson Industries Inc.

BIRTHDAY SUIT - Apparel and accessories ☆ - Warnaco Inc.

BIRTHDAY SUIT - Skin care products - Origins Natural Resources Inc.

BIRTHDAY SURPRISE - Computer software - Laureate Learning Systems Inc.

BIRTHDAY SURPRISE - Dolls - Mattel, Inc.

BIRTHDAY TRADITIONS - Greeting cards ☆ - American Greetings Corp.

BIRTHDAY TRIBUTES - Greeting cards ☆ - Stevenson Industries Inc.

BIRTHFLOWERS - Novelty items - Thoughtful Impressions, Inc.

BIRTHPATCH - Greeting cards ☆ - Best Emblem & Insignia Co. Inc.

BIRTHRIGHT - Games - Tsr, Inc.

BIRTHSTONE BEARS - Glassware–household - Fenton Art Glass Co.

BIRTHSTONE BEARS - Jewelry - Jackmail Jewelry Inc.

BIRTHSTONE BOW - Jewelry - Avon Products, Inc.

BIRTHSTONE BRATS - Jewelry - Key Item Sales, Inc.

BIRTHSTONE FLOWER SNOWGLOBE - Giftware - Avon Products, Inc.

BIRTHSTONE TEDDYS - Jewelry - Tru-Kay Manufacturing Co.

BIRTHSTONES OF THE MONTH - Dolls - Bradley Import Co.

BIRTHTYPE - Computer software - Brookins Enterprises Inc.

BIS BIS IMPORTS BOSTON - Sinks–porcelain - Bis Bis Imports Boston, Limited

BIS-CAPS - Pharmaceutical preparations ☆ - Parthenon Co. Inc.

BIS-KITS - Biscuits–mixes - Morrison Milling Co.

BIS-MA-CAL - Antacids - Claflin Co.

BIS/NET - Computer software - Basis, Inc.

BIS/SNMP - Computer software - Basis, Inc.

BISAC-EVAC - Laxatives - G and W Laboratories Inc.

BISCA - Files–tools - Clemson Brothers Inc.

BISCAN - Computer software - Business Information Storage, Inc.

BISCARDO - Wines - Wine Shippers Import Co.

BISCAY - Bathtubs–enameled - Briggs Plumbing Products, Inc.

BISCAY - Frames–eyeglass - May Optical Co. Inc.

BISCAY - Furniture - CTH/Sherrill Occasional

BISCAYNE - Apparel and accessories - Smith & Weber Co.

BISCAYNE - Cabinets - Yorktowne Inc.

BISCAYNE - Clocks - General Time Corp. (Westclox/Seth Thomas Div.)

BISCAYNE - Dishes–china - Pickard Inc.

BISCAYNE - Flatware - Pfaltzgraff Investment Co.

BISCAYNE - Floor coverings–carpet and rugs - Stanton Carpet Corp.

BISCAYNE - Furniture - Homecrest Industries Inc.

BISCAYNE - Furniture ☆ - Bassett Furniture Industries, Inc.

BISCAYNE - Glassware–household - Owens-Illinois Inc. (Libbey Div.)

BISCAYNE - Motor vehicles ☆ - General Motors Corp. (Chevrolet Motor Div.)

BISCAYNE - Musical instruments - Tropical Music and Pro Audio

BISCAYNE - Rings–jewelry - Artcarved Inc.

BISCAYNE - Wallpaper ☆ - Capital Carousel Inc.

BISCAYNE - Window coverings ☆ - Vertilux-Louverlux Inc.

BISCAYNE - Windows–storm ☆ - Yale Ogron Manufacturing Co. Inc.

BISCAYNE BAY - Floor coverings–carpet and rugs ☆ - Catalina Carpet Mills Inc.

BISCAYNE BAY - Luggage - Samsonite Corp.

BISCAYNE BAY - Occasional tables - JDI Group, Inc.

BISCEGLIA - Wines - Bisceglia Bros. Wine Co.

BISCHOFF - Glassware–household - Sloan Glass Inc.

BISCHOFF TEXTIL - Embroidery machines - Alice Sturzinger Ltd.

BISCO - Hardware - Bishops Inc.

BISCO-LAX - Laxatives - Schein Pharmaceutical Inc.

BISCOLAN - Pharmaceutical preparations - Lannett Co. Inc.

BISCONOVA - SAVOIARDI - Desserts - Bell'amore Imports Inc.

BISCOS - Cookies - Nabisco Foods Group

BISCOTTI - Cookies - Biscotti Cookie

BISCOTTI - Food products - La Piccolina and Co. Inc.

BISCOTTI AMORE BIANCO - Bakery goods - La Tempesta Bakery Confections, Inc.

BISCOTTI DELLA DOMINICA - Cookies - La Tempesta Bakery Confections, Inc.

BISCOTTI DI ROMA - Cookies - Award Baking International

BISCOTTI MEZZAMORE - Cookies - La Tempesta Bakery Confections, Inc.

BISCOTTI NUCCI - Cookies - Biscotti Nucci

BISCOTTIBITES - Pastries - Marketplace Foods, Inc.

BISCOTTINI ALLO CHAMPAGNE - Baked goods - Dicamillo Baking Co. Inc.

BISCUIT BREAK - Sandwiches–prepackaged - E.A. Sween Co.

BISCUIT FIXIN'S - Biscuits - Design Foods

BISCUIT ST. MICHEL - Bakery products - Jaret Specialties Inc.

BISCUITS 'N' GRAVY - Gravy ☆ - Horseman's Financial Group

BISHARA - Recording label - Jazz Composer's Orchestra Association Inc.

BISHOP - Bird feeds - Welles L. Bishop Co. Inc.

BISHOP - Books–comic - Marvel Entertainment Group, Inc.

BISHOP - Eyeglasses - Goat Eyewear

BISHOP - Floor coverings–carpet and rugs - Galaxy Carpet Mills Inc.

BISHOP - Frames–eyeglass - Hoya Corp. USA

BISHOP - Gun stocks - Reinhart Fajen, Inc.

BISHOP - Thread ☆ - Eddington Thread Manufacturing Co.

BISHOP & ASSOCIATES, INC. - Computer software - Bishop & Associates, Inc.

BISHOP OF RIESLING - Wines - Heublein, Inc.

BISHOP'S BEST - Vegetables–canned - Bishop Co. Inc.

BISIGHT - Contact lenses - Soderberg Inc.

BISILAD - Pharmaceutical preparations ☆ - Central Pharmaceutical Inc.

BISK-CHROME - Paints ☆ - DecoArt, Inc.

BISKAPEC - Pharmaceutical preparations - C.O. Truxton Inc.

BISKINS - Biscuits - Flowers Industries Inc.

BISKIT - Pet products - Novalek, Inc.

BISKIT BASKIT - Pet products - Novalek, Inc.

BISKOCHITO - Crackers - Vista Bakery, Inc.

BISLEY - Filing cabinets–metal - Sam Flax

BISLEY MODELS - Revolvers ☆ - Colt's Manufacturing Co. Inc.

BISMAGEN - Pharmaceutical preparations - Biosante Distributors Inc.

BISMAPEC - Pharmaceutical preparations ☆ - Pal-Pak Inc.

BISMARCK - Games ☆ - Avalon Hill Game Co.

BISMARCK - Trailers–travel ☆ - Coachmen Industries, Inc.

BISMARK - Frames–eyeglass - Pathway Optical Prods.

BISMARK - Furs–artificial - Quaker Inc.

BISMATESIA - Antacids ☆ - P.J. Noyes Co., Inc.
BISODOL - Pharmaceutical preparations - Whitehall Laboratories
BISOLAR - Lamps - Battle Creek Equipment Co.
BISOLATE - Pharmaceutical preparations ☆ - C.O. Truxton Inc.
BISON - Adhesives and sealants - Bison Corp.
BISON - Coffee - Broad Street Coffee Roasters
BISON - Dairy products - Upstate Farms Cooperative, Inc.
BISON - Dairy products - Upstate Milk Cooperatives, Inc.
BISON - Fruits and vegetables - Ben Abatti Farms, LLC
BISON - Hardware - Bison Building Materials Inc.
BISON - Housewares ☆ - King Cotton Cordage Co.
BISON - Machinery - Super Strong Products, Inc.
BISON - Ophthalmic goods - Fidelity Case Corp.
BISON - Thread ☆ - Coats and Clark Inc.
BISON - Vegetables–canned ☆ - Bison Canning Co. Inc.
BISON BOOKS - Publisher's imprints - University of Nebraska Press
BISON BUSINESS SUPPLIES - Catalogs - Able America Supply LLC
BISON PEDESTAL SYSTEMS - Pedestals–wood - United Construction Products, Inc.
BISON THE GREAT COMEBACK - Food products ☆ - King B Jerky
BISON WEIZEN - Shirts - Bricktown Brewery
BISPLAN MASTER - Computer software - SourceView Software International
BISQ-STAIN - Artists' materials - Duncan Enterprises
BISQUE - Cabinets - Merillat Industries, Inc.
BISQUETTES - Seafood products–fresh or frozen - Tampa Maid Seafoods, Inc.
BISQUICK - Food products - General Mills, Inc.
BISQUICK EASY BREADS - Breads–mixes - General Mills, Inc.
BISQUIT - Wines - European Beverage Co., Inc.
BISQUITS - Toys–stuffed - Dakin Inc.
BISSELL - Cleaning preparations - Bissell Inc.
BISSELL ONE STEP - Cleaning preparations - Barcolene Inc.
BISSELL PLUS - Vacuum cleaners and accessories - Bissell Inc.
BISSELL TRIO - Vacuum cleaners and accessories - Bissell Inc.
BISSELLETTE - Carpet sweepers ☆ - Bissell Inc.
BISSINGER'S - Candy - Bissinger's Inc.
BISSON - Wines - Tempo Imports Ltd.
BIST ON BOARD - Computer software - LV Software, Inc.
BISTEFANI - Pastries - Fred Montesi Super Markets
BISTRO - Apparel and accessories - Rays Apparel, Inc.
BISTRO - Baskets–wood ☆ - Knobler International Ltd.
BISTRO - Ceiling panels - Armstrong World Industries, Inc.
BISTRO - Dinnerware–glass - Crisa Corp.
BISTRO - Dinnerware–glass - Dansk International Designs, Ltd.
BISTRO - Floor coverings–carpet and rugs - World Carpets, Inc.
BISTRO - Food products - Vienna Sausage Manufacturing Co.
BISTRO - Giftware - Artex-Green Corp. of N.Y.
BISTRO - Towels - Charles Craft Inc.
BISTRO - Wallpaper - Chapters Wallcoverings
BISTRO - Wines - Heublein, Inc.
BISTRO BISCOTTI - Cookies - Nonni's, Corp.
BISTRO GOURMET - Wines ☆ - Buena Vista Winery, Inc.
BISTRO KITCHEN & BATH - Wallpaper - Chapters Wallcoverings
BISTRO TUMBLERS - Glassware–household - Carlisle Foodservice Products, Inc.
BISTROS - Sandwiches–prepackaged - Multi-National Food Service
BIT BAND - Leather goods - Makita USA, Inc.
BIT-BOT - Computer software - Earthquest Inc.
BIT-COAT - Adhesives and sealants - Bill Morgan Enterprises Inc.
BIT JUGGLERS - Computer software - Bit Jugglers, Inc.
BIT-N-BYTE - Office furniture–metal ☆ - Simon Corp.
BIT-O-HONEY - Candy - Nestle USA
BIT-O-LICORICE - Candy ☆ - Nestle USA
BIT-O-MINT - Candy ☆ - Atkinson Candy Co.
BIT-O-PEANUT BUTTER - Candy ☆ - Nestle USA
BIT-O-SCALLOP - Seafood products–canned or cured - Rose Frozen Shrimp Inc.
BIT-O-SHRIMP - Seafood products–canned or cured - Rose Frozen Shrimp Inc.
BIT O' WAX - Dental equipment - John O.Butler Co.
BIT OF BRIGHTNESS - Underwear and nightwear - Maidenform Inc.
BIT ONE - Musical instruments - Ampeg
BITBANK - Computer storage devices ☆ - BASF Corp.
BITBLITZ - Circuit boards - IGT - North America
BITBUSTER - Integrated circuits - Lsi Logic Corp.
BITCH BYTES - Greeting cards - Advanced Research Corp.

BITE - Adhesives and sealants - Roman Adhesives, Inc.
BITE - Health care products - Sage Products
BITE - Rust removers - Sanitek Products Inc.
BITE - Wallcoverings primer and sealer - Golden Harvest Adhesives
BITE - Wines - Wein-Bauer, Inc.
BITE-A-BONE - Pet products - Phydeaux Enterprises Inc.
BITE AID - Health care products - S.C. Johnson & Son, Inc.
BITE AND ITCH LOTION - Pharmaceutical preparations - Reese Chemical Co.
BITE BLOCK - Sunblocks - Sun Pharmaceuticals Corp.
BITE FREE - Insecticides - Farnam Cos. Inc.
BITE GARD - Health care products - Hudson Respiratory Care Inc.
BITE LITE - Flashlights - Ritam International Ltd.
BITE ME - Bakery products - Bite Me Inc.
BITE MY BEEF - Beef - Bite My Beef Products, L.C.
BITE NOT - Pet products - John B. Moy
BITE OF CHOCOLATE YOU CAN REALLY SINKYOUR TEETH INTO, A - Candy - Homestead, Inc.
BITE OF NATURE, A - Health care products - Ion Laboratories Inc.
BITE RELIEF - First aid kits - Flents Products Co. Inc.
BITE SIZE - Apparel and accessories - Harwood Companies Inc.
BITE SIZE - Food products - Tree of Life, Inc.
BITE SIZE CHIPS DELUXE - Cookies - Keebler Co.
BITE SIZE PECAN SANDIES - Cookies - Keebler Co.
BITE SIZE SHREDDED OATS - Cereal - Barbara's Bakery, Inc.
BITE THE BIG ONE - Chewing gum - Philadelphia Chewing Gum Corp.
BITE THE BULLET - Medical supplies - Jarron Industries
BITE YOUR LIPS - Cosmetics - Origins Natural Resources Inc.
BITE'N BRUSH - Dentifrices - Colgate-Palmolive Co.
BITFIRE - Computer software - Elcomp Publishing, Inc.
BITINE - Dental equipment - Alvin Meyer
BITI'S - Footwear - Biti's USA Inc.
BITLOGIC INC. - Computer software - Bitlogic Inc.
BITMAPPER - Optical scanners–computer - Black & Veatch Architects, Inc.
BITRAN - Bags–plastic - Com-Pac International Inc.
BITRATE - Pharmaceutical preparations - Nature's Bounty, Inc.
BITRINSIC-E - Pharmaceutical preparations ☆ - ICN Pharmaceuticals Inc.
BITRODE - Electrical testing instruments - Bitrode Corp.
BITRONICS - Electronic equipment - Bitronics, Inc.
BITRUNR - Computer hardware - Motorola, Inc. (Land Mobile Products Sector)
BITS - Food products - Bland Farms
BITS - Pet products ☆ - Natural Animal Health Products, Inc.
BITS - Seasonings - Hormel Foods Corp.
BITS-A-GUM - Chewing gum - National Chewing Gum Inc.
BITS & PIECES - Jewelry - Cousin Corp. of America
BITS & POPS - Candy - Bowlby Candy Co. Inc.
BITS & STIX - Pretzels ☆ - Benzel's Bretzel Bakery, Inc.
BITS & YOGURT - Yogurt - Kraft Foods, Inc.
BITS BUSINESS INFORMATION TRACKING SYSTEM - Computer software - CSSI Support Group, Inc.
BITS 'N POPS - Snack foods - Anacon Foods Co.
BITS 'O BRICKLE - Candy - Leaf, Inc.
BITS O' FRUIT - Sherbet - H.P. Hood & Sons Inc.
BITS O' HONEY - Food products ☆ - Universal Frozen Foods Co.
BITS O'BARLEY - Cereal - Arrowhead Mills, Inc.
BITSHARE - Computer software - Cheyenne Communications, Inc.
BITSTREAM - Computer peripheral equipment - Sony Electronics Inc.
BITSURFER - Computer peripheral equipment - Motorola, Inc. (Land Mobile Products Sector)
BITSY BABIES - Toys - Mattel, Inc.
BITSY BALL - Toys - Tonka Corp.
BITSY BEARS - Kites - Hi-Flier Manufacturing Co.
BITSY BOUQUET - Dolls - Mattel, Inc.
BITSY BUDDYS - Toys–automobiles - Buddy L Inc.
BITSY BUNNIES AND BOWS - Toys–stuffed - Brass Key, Inc.
BITSY DOG - Toys–stuffed - Russ Berrie and Co., Inc.
BITTER BITE - .Nail-biting deterrent - Cosmetic Arts Inc.
BITTER BITE - Pet products - JT Industries
BITTER HITTER - Apparel and accessories - Byrd & Associates
BITTER LEMON - Skin care products ☆ - Hirsch Speidel Inc.
BITTER LIME - Pet products - Four Paws Products Ltd.
BITTER ROOT - Food products ☆ - Bitter Root Cannery
BITTER ROOT - Siding–insulating - Champion International Corp.
BITTER SAFE - Fuel additives - ACJ Chemical Co. Inc.
BITTER SC - Motor vehicles–automobiles - Amerispec
BITTERSWEET - Candles - Circle of Beauty, Inc.

☆ = Now out of production

BITTERSWEET - Dinnerware–glass ☆ - Franciscan by Johnson Brothers, USA, Inc.
BITTON - Seafood products–fresh or frozen ☆ - J.F. Clarke Corp.
BITTRA - Candy bars ☆ - Brocks Candy Co.
BITTY BABY - Dolls - Pleasant Co.
BITTY BABY COLLECTION - Publisher's imprints - Pleasant Co.
BITTY BAGS - Bags–plastic - Bag Co.
BITTY BANANA - Dolls - Mattel, Inc.
BITTY BATH TUB BABY - Dolls ☆ - Uneeda Doll Co., Inc.
BITTY BEANS - Dolls - Mattel, Inc.
BITTY BITS - Rubber stamps - Russ Berrie and Co., Inc.
BITTY BOMBS - Candy ☆ - Donruss Co.
BITTY BUNNIES - Toys–stuffed - Dakin Inc.
BITTY BYE BABY - Dolls - Uneeda Doll Co., Inc.
BITTY KITTY - Toys - Mattel, Inc.
BITUBAR - Paints ☆ - Devoe & Raynolds Co.
BITUBLAC - Paints ☆ - Samuel Cabot Inc.
BITUFOIL - Tape–adhesive ☆ - Andek Corp.
BITUGLOSS - Enamels ☆ - Kop-Coat, Inc.
BITULATUM - Paints - Everseal International Sales Co. Inc.
BITUMASTIC - Adhesives and sealants - Carboline Co.
BITUMINOL - Paints ☆ - Everseal International Sales Co. Inc.
BITUMINUM - Paints ☆ - Everseal International Sales Co. Inc.
BITUMOD - Chemicals - Rooftech Products, Inc.
BITUPOX - Finishing agents - Permagile Industries Inc.
BITUPOX ECT - Epoxy - Permagile Industries Inc.
BITURBO - Motor vehicles–automobiles - Maserati Automobiles Inc.
BITUTHENE - Waterproofing compounds - W.R. Grace & Co.
BITUTHENE EDGEGUARD - Tape–adhesive - W.R. Grace & Co.
BITWRITER - Computer software - Tektronix, Inc.
BITZ - Jewelry - Bitz
BITZELS - Pretzels - Vesper Corp.
BIVU - Scuba diving equipment - Oceanic
BIWAKO - Floor coverings - Toli International
BIWELL - Leather tanning and finishing - Climb High Inc.
BIWELL - Waterproofing compounds - Denali International Inc.
BIX - Apparel and accessories - Bicycle Exchange, Inc.
BIX - Franchised furniture-care process - Bix Process Systems
BIX - Paint removers - Bix Manufacturing Co. Inc.
BIX BOARDS - Sporting goods - Markwort Sporting Goods Co.
BIXMIX - Bakery products - Martha White Foods Inc.
BIZ - Detergents - Procter & Gamble Co.
BIZ NOTE EXPRESS - Greeting cards - Traylor Communications Inc.
BIZAC - Pate - American Roland Food Corp.
BIZANZIO II - Giftware - Sasaki
BIZARR - Postcards - Fotofolio Inc.
BIZARRE - Wallpaper ☆ - Osborne & Little
BIZARRE/STRAIGHT - Recording label - Bizarre/Straight Records
BIZARRI - Cookies - Bell'amore Imports Inc.
BIZBAG - Publisher's imprints - National Foundation for Teaching Entrepreneurship
BIZCLIP - Office supplies - Pine River Plastics Inc.
BIZMART - Office furniture–metal - Kmart Corp.
BIZNAU - Pharmaceutical preparations - Lunsco Inc.
BIZOLIN 200 - Veterinary pharmaceutical preparations - Boehringer Ingelheim Animal Health, Inc.
BIZOLIN GEL - Veterinary pharmaceutical preparations ☆ - Boehringer Ingelheim Animal Health, Inc.
BIZOPOLY - Games - The Learning Experience Inc.
BIZOUARD - Beverages–alcohol - Joseph E. Seagram & Sons, Inc.
BIZPLANBUILDER - Computer software - Jian
BIZZIEBOARD - Wood board game - Intromark Inc.
BIZZIT - Apparel–women's - Sutton Creations, Inc.
BIZZY - Toys - Playskool, Inc.
BIZZY-KITTY - Pet products - St. Jon Pet Care Products Inc.
B.J. - Metals - Bel Air Jewelry, Inc.
BJ - Toys–stuffed - Lyons Partnership, L.P.
BJ-1 - Golfing equipment - Callaway Golf Co.
B.J. DESIGNER - Apparel and accessories - Oxford Industries, Inc.
BJ FROG - Apparel–children's - Jane Colby Inc.
BJ SOFTWARE SYSTEMS - Computer software - Baker Hughes Inc.
BJA - Novelty items - Benjane Arts
BJI - Jewelry - Brinker's Manufacturing Jewelers Inc.
BJM - Jewelry - Baharian Jewelry Manufacturing, Inc.
BJORNDAL - Shoes - Rack Room Shoes, Inc.
BK - Apparel and accessories - Jack Schwartz Shoes, Inc.

BK - Insect repellents - Flowtron Outdoor Products
BK - Jewelry - B. Kracht Inc.
BK - Sweaters - Binghamton Knitting Co.
BK-92 BLACK KNIGHT - Firearms, accessories, and parts ☆ - Modern Muzzle Loading, Inc.
BK FARMS - Toys - BK Trading Enterprises Inc.
BK RODS - Backpacks - Jack Schwartz Shoes, Inc.
BKB - Jewelry–costume - Leaves of Gold, Inc.
BKC-USA - Metals - Barry Kieselstein-Cord
BKI - Cosmetics - Ben Lu
BKI - Ovens–bakery - Standex International Corp.
BKP SERIES - Dehumidifiers - Heat Pipe Technology Inc.
BL - Prescription and nonprescription drugs - Biocraft Laboratories Inc.
BL - Thread - Belding Heminway Co. Inc.
BL-5 - Whirlpool bath ☆ - Jacuzzi Inc.
BL ACCESS - Computer software - Baseline II Inc.
BL FILMS - Key rings - Anheuser-Busch Companies Inc.
BL-R NYC - Scarves - Bernardo Laniado-Romero
BLABBER - Parlor games - Wayman Discoveries
BLABBER BLOCK - Novelty items - Wine & Roses
BLABBER MOUTH - Fishing lures - Gaines Co.
BLACK - Laxatives - Monticello Drug Co.
BLACK - Tobacco–chewing or smoking ☆ - Swedish Math North America Inc.
BLACK - Tools ☆ - Regent Sheffield, Ltd.
BLACK 4 EVR - Paints ☆ - Valspar Corp.
BLACK ACE - Paints ☆ - Colonial Refining and Chemical Co.
BLACK ACE - Rackets–tennis - Pro Kennex, Inc.
BLACK ADAPTOR - Motorcycles - Target Motorsports
BLACK AMBER - Frames–eyeglass ☆ - Universal/Univis Inc.
BLACK AND BLUE - Apparel–athletic - Made in the Shade by Prime Time
BLACK AND BLUE - Fabrics–denim - Dan River Inc.
BLACK AND BLUES - Candy - Stanico, Inc.
BLACK AND DECKER - Bathroom fixtures - Price Pfister Co.
BLACK & DECKER - Tools - Black & Decker Corp.
BLACK & DECKER PLUS - Kitchen appliances - Black & Decker Corp.
BLACK AND GOLD - Cigarettes - Nat Sherman, Inc.
BLACK & MILD - Tobacco products - John Middleton Inc.
BLACK & SASSY - Headbands - Spartan Brands, Inc.
BLACK & SILVER - Knives–putty - Hyde Manufacturing Co.
BLACK & TAN - Beverages–malt - Anheuser-Busch Companies Inc.
BLACK & TAN CAV - Tobacco–chewing or smoking - Amar Blends Co.
BLACK & TAN ENGLISH STYLE - Beverages–malt ☆ - D.G. Yuengling & Son Inc.
BLACK & WHITE - Cookies - Joey's Fine Foods
BLACK & WHITE - Recording label - Jazz Composer's Orchestra Association Inc.
BLACK & WHITE - Skin care products - J. Strickland & Co.
BLACK & WHITE - Wallpaper - Imperial Wallcoverings, Inc.
BLACK & WHITE - Whiskey ☆ - Sazerac Co. Inc.
BLACK AND WHITE AND BRIGHT ALL OVER - Infant product - Eden LLC
BLACK X WHITE = GREY - Wallcoverings - Tescoha USA
BLACK & WHITE PLUS - Wallpaper - Capital Carousel Inc.
BLACK & WHITE SOFTWARE - Computer software - Black & White Software, Inc.
BLACK ANGUS - Cereal - Flavorite Laboratories Inc.
BLACK ANGUS - Metal stamping - Black Angus Inc.
BLACK ANVIL - Agricultural machinery - Kondex Corp.
BLACK ANVIL - Books–comic - Top Cow Productions, Inc.
BLACK APPLE - Apparel and accessories - Russell Boles III
BLACK ASPHALTUM - Paints - Jones Blair Co.
BLACK BARON, THE - Epoxy - Coverite
BLACK BASALT - Vases–glass ☆ - Waterford Wedgwood USA, Inc.
BLACK BASS, THE - Computer software - Hot-B USA Inc.
BLACK BAVARIAN - Beverages–malt - Sprecher Brewing Co. Inc.
BLACK BEAN - Snack foods - Garden of Eatin', Inc.
BLACK BEAR - Archery equipment - Bear Archery Inc.
BLACK BEAR - Beer and malt liquor - Golden Pacific Brewing Co., Inc.
BLACK BEAR - Firearms, accessories, and parts - Markesbery Muzzle Loaders, Inc.
BLACK BEAR - Wines ☆ - Wine Group Inc.
BLACK BEAR OF THE BLACK FOREST - Meats–luncheon - Black Bear Enterprises, Inc.
BLACK BEAUTY - Bakery products - G & S Metal Products Co., Inc.
BLACK BEAUTY - Beverages–alcohol - Bridgeview Vineyards, Inc.
BLACK BEAUTY - Bicycles - Columbia Manufacturing Inc.
BLACK BEAUTY - Brushes–paint ☆ - PPG Industries, Inc.

☆ = Now out of production

BLACK BEAUTY - Drill bits - K-Line Industries
BLACK BEAUTY - Drums–musical instruments - LP Music Group
BLACK BEAUTY - Dryers–hair - Humboldt Industries, Inc.
BLACK BEAUTY - Electrodes - Welding Consultants, Inc.
BLACK BEAUTY - File folders - Angler's Roslyn Group Ltd.
BLACK BEAUTY - Fishing tackle - South Bend Sporting Goods Inc.
BLACK BEAUTY - Forms–preprinted - BlumbergExcelsior, Inc.
BLACK BEAUTY - Housewares - Cyclops Industries (Empire-Detroit Steel Div.)
BLACK BEAUTY - Paints - Binford Products, Inc.
BLACK BEAUTY - Rifles - Fie Corp.
BLACK BEAUTY - Rocking horses - Flexible Flyer Co.
BLACK BEAUTY - Sporting goods - Brunswick Corp.
BLACK BEAUTY - Tripods–photographic - Brumberger Co. Inc.
BLACK BEAUTY - Watches - Bulova Corp.
BLACK BEAUTY - Wheelbarrows - Ames Lawn & Garden Tool Co.
BLACK BEAUTY, THE - Frames–picture - Award Maker Inc.
BLACK BELT - Beverages–malt ☆ - Genesee Brewing Co., Inc.
BLACK BELT - Health care products - East Earth Herb Inc.
BLACK BELT - Shaving preparations ☆ - Pfizer Inc.
BLACK BELT CLUB - Apparel–athletic - Otomix Inc.
BLACK BELT PROTECTION - Belts–industrial - CMO Inc.
BLACK BIRDIE - Golfing equipment - M & C Specialties
BLACK BOAR - Health care products - East Earth Herb Inc.
BLACK-BOARD - Computer peripheral equipment - Computer Products, Inc.
BLACK BODY - Ovens–industrial - BBC Industries, Inc.
BLACK BOOK - Wallpaper - Christopher Hyland
BLACK BOOK XPRESS - Computer software - Hearst Corp.
BLACK BOTTOM - Frames–eyeglass - Zylo Ware Corp.
BLACK BOURBON - Tobacco–chewing or smoking - Amar Blends Co.
BLACK BOX - Key rings - BB Technologies, Inc.
BLACK BRANT II - Toys–models - Estes Industries
BLACK BRANT III - Toys–models ☆ - Estes Industries
BLACK BRUTE - See **CHAINSHARP**
BLACK BULL - Beverages–alcohol - John Gross & Co.
BLACK BULLET - Toys–automobiles - Mattel, Inc.
BLACK BUSH - Irish whiskey - Brown-Forman Corp.
BLACK BUTTA - Apparel and accessories - Eric Jones
BLACK BY BAINBRIDGE - Mat boards - Nielsen & Bainbridge
BLACK BY DESIGN - Games - Olmec Toys, Inc.
BLACK CANVAS - Liquid crystal displays - Hughes Aircraft Co.
BLACK CAT - Apparel and accessories - Sierra Lynn, Inc.
BLACK CAT - Cigarettes - G.A. Georgopulo & Co. Inc.
BLACK CAT - Golfing equipment - Golfsmith International Inc.
BLACK CAT - Hair coloring preparations - Cosmair Inc.
BLACK CAT - Heating equipment - Coleman Co., Inc.
BLACK CAT - Inks - Dick Blick Co.
BLACK CAT - Mops - Reit-Price Manufacturing Co.
BLACK CAT - Photographic equipment - Black Cat Photoproducts, Inc.
BLACK CAT - Publisher's imprints - Grove/Atlantic, Inc.
BLACK CAT - Sealing compounds - Monsey Products Co.
BLACK CAULDRON, THE - Computer software - Sierra On-Line, Inc.
BLACK CHERRY - Candy - Charms Co.
BLACK CHERRY ECLIPSE - Fruit drinks–bottled or canned - Hansen Beverage Co.
BLACK CHERRY ROYALE - Juices - Green Spot Packaging, Inc.
BLACK CHROME - Eyeglasses - Bausch & Lomb Inc.
BLACK CLOTHING LTD. - Apparel–athletic - Dangerous Design
BLACK COATS - Pet products - Natra Pet Inc.
BLACK COHOSH - Vitamins and nutritional supplements - Vitamin Research Products Inc.
BLACK COLLECTION, THE - Desk sets ☆ - Recyco
BLACK CONTESSA - Dishes–china ☆ - Gorham Inc.
BLACK COPS AGAINST POLICE BRUTALITY - T-shirts–men's - Dawud Sobers Inc.
BLACK CORAL - Skin care products - Key West Aloe Inc.
BLACK CREEK - Vegetables–canned ☆ - McCall Farms Inc.
BLACK CROW - Brushes–paint ☆ - Linzer Products Corp.
BLACK CROW - Enamels - United Hardware
BLACK CROWS - Candy - Tootsie Roll Industries, Inc.
BLACK CURRANT-POWER - Vitamins and nutritional supplements ☆ - Nature's Herbs
BLACK DAISIES - Skates–roller - FPD Technology
BLACK DANDY - Brushes–paint ☆ - Linzer Products Corp.
BLACK DAWN - Computer software - Black Ops Entertainment, Inc.
BLACK DAWN - Hair care products ☆ - Givaudan-Roure Corp.
BLACK DEATH - T-shirts - Black Death USA Inc.

BLACK DEATH, THE - Computer software ☆ - Krell Software Corp.
BLACK DEVIL - Apparel–men's - Central-Samuels Inc.
BLACK DIAMOND - Ammunition ☆ - Olin Corp. (Winchester Div.)
BLACK DIAMOND - Apparel–men's - Kaufman Footwear
BLACK DIAMOND - Automotive parts and accessories - Warn Industries, Inc.
BLACK DIAMOND - Bakery products - Federal Glass
BLACK DIAMOND - Bowling balls - Brunswick Corp.
BLACK DIAMOND - Brushes–paint - Elder & Jenks, Inc.
BLACK DIAMOND - Cheese - Dan Carter Inc.
BLACK DIAMOND - Combs - Bobby Co.
BLACK DIAMOND - Cosmetics - Sylvia Kay
BLACK DIAMOND - Darts and dart games - Dart World Inc.
BLACK DIAMOND - Fertilizers - Black Industries Inc.
BLACK DIAMOND - File folders - Angler's Roslyn Group Ltd.
BLACK DIAMOND - Fishing rods - Cortland Line Co., Inc.
BLACK DIAMOND - Flatware - Sysco Corp.
BLACK-DIAMOND - Garden equipment - Valley View Specialties Co.
BLACK DIAMOND - Guns - Crosman Corp.
BLACK DIAMOND - Motor vehicle parts and accessories - Rivera Engineering, Inc.
BLACK DIAMOND - Musical-instrument strings - International Music Corp.
BLACK DIAMOND - Rifles - Thompson/Center Arms
BLACK DIAMOND - Roofing materials ☆ - GS Roofing Products Co.
BLACK DIAMOND - Rubber–molded - Hunter Industrial Corp.
BLACK DIAMOND - Saws, files - Cooper Industries, Inc.
BLACK DIAMOND - Tape–adhesive - M.W. Dunton Co.
BLACK DIAMOND - Toners - Uinta National Corp.
BLACK DIAMOND - Tools - Sculpture House Inc.
BLACK DIAMOND - Tools–jewelers - Black Diamond Equipment, Ltd.
BLACK DIAMOND - Wines - Pine Ridge Associates
BLACK DIAMOND RACING - Electronic equipment - Black Diamond Racing, Inc.
BLACK DIAMOND II - Fishing tackle - Cortland Line Co., Inc.
BLACK DIAMONDS - Games - Will Spann
BLACK DOG - Recording label - Black Dog Records
BLACK DOG, THE - Wines - Chateau Morrisette, Inc.
BLACK DOT - Apparel and accessories - Pacific Trail, Inc.
BLACK DOUGLAS - Beverages–malt - Phoenix Imports Ltd.
BLACK DRAGON - Enamels - J.C. Whitlam Manufacturing Co.
BLACK DRAGON - Sporting goods - Sunbo Inc.
BLACK DRAUGHT - Laxatives - Chattem Inc.
BLACK DUCK - Apparel and accessories - Walls Industries, Inc.
BLACK DUCK - Food products - Porter Carpet Mills Inc.
BLACK EAGLE - Apparel and accessories - Egl 1, Inc.
BLACK EAGLE - Golfing equipment - O'Murray Golf Co.
BLACK EAGLE - Health care products ☆ - CTS Laboratories Inc.
BLACK EAGLE - Sporting goods - Wright & McGill Co.
BLACK EAGLE II - Sporting goods ☆ - Wright & McGill Co.
BLACK EAGLE III - Sporting goods ☆ - Wright & McGill Co.
BLACK EMPIRE - Brushes–paint ☆ - PPG Industries, Inc.
BLACK FALCON - Knives–pocket - Compass Industries, Inc.
BLACK FILLER - Brushes–paint ☆ - PPG Industries, Inc.
BLACK FIRE - Recording label - Black Fire Records
BLACK FISH TRADING CO. - Apparel and accessories - Black Fish Trading Co.
BLACK FLAG - Insecticides - Boyle-Midway
BLACK FLASH - Cement - J.C. Whitlam Manufacturing Co.
BLACK FLIX - Hair care products - Gold Medal Hair Products Inc.
BLACK FLYER - Pencils ☆ - Faber-Castell Corp.
BLACK FOREST - Baskets–wood ☆ - Royal Cathay Trading Co.
BLACK FOREST - Candy - Ferrara Pan Candy Co., Inc.
BLACK FOREST - Clocks - Staufen Studio
BLACK FOREST - Clocks ☆ - Coehler-Coptex Co.
BLACK FOREST - Cutlery ☆ - Gutmann Cutlery Inc.
BLACK FOREST - Food products - Hygrade Food Products Corp.
BLACK FOREST - Frames–eyeglass - May Optical Co. Inc.
BLACK FOREST - Noodles - Haram-Christensen Corp.
BLACK FOREST - Steel products - Cold Steel Inc.
BLACK FOREST - Trees–artificial - Kurt S. Adler Inc.
BLACK FOREST GIRL - Pasta - Acme Food Specialties Inc.
BLACK FORUM - Recording label - Motown Record Co. L.P.
BLACK FURY - Fishing lures - Sheldons', Inc.
BLACK GEM - Artists' materials - Angler's Roslyn Group Ltd.
BLACK GOLD - Audio equipment - Mitek Corp.
BLACK GOLD - Bicycles ☆ - Roadmaster Corp.
BLACK GOLD - Brushes–paint - FM Brush Co., Inc.

☆ = Now out of production

BLACK GOLD - Chemical preparations - Petcetera Inc.
BLACK GOLD - Cigars ☆ - H.L. Neff & Co. Inc.
BLACK GOLD - Cleaning preparations - Northern Labs, Inc.
BLACK GOLD - Coffee - Advanced Marketing & Sales
BLACK GOLD - Darts and dart games - Dart Mart Inc.
BLACK GOLD - Electrical equipment - Arcair Co.
BLACK GOLD - Fishing tackle - Cemco Inc.
BLACK GOLD - Frames—eyeglass ☆ - Universal/Univis Inc.
BLACK GOLD - Garden equipment - Lewis International Corp.
BLACK GOLD - Gloves—work - Century Glove, Inc.
BLACK GOLD - Paints - Pioneer Paint of Arizona
BLACK GOLD - Recording label - Jazz Composer's Orchestra Association Inc.
BLACK GOLD - Sporting goods - Major Racquet Strings International
BLACK GOLD - Toys ☆ - Playskool, Inc.
BLACK GOLD MAPLE - Tobacco—chewing or smoking - Amar Blends Co.
BLACK GUARD - Enamels - Jones Blair Co.
BLACK HAMMER - Sporting goods - Easton Aluminum Inc.
BLACK HAWK - Beverages—malt - Mendocino Brewing Co., Inc.
BLACK HAWK - Bicycles - Ross Bicycles USA, Ltd.
BLACK HAWK - Brushes—paint ☆ - Linzer Products Corp.
BLACK HAWK - Cigars - National Cigar Corp.
BLACK HAWK - Engines—marine - Brunswick Corp.
BLACK HAWK - Fishing tackle ☆ - Woodstream Corp.
BLACK HAWK - Foil—aluminum - Knomark, Inc.
BLACK HAWK - Golfing equipment - Golfsmith International Inc.
BLACK HAWK - Lawn equipment - Fuqua Industries Inc.
BLACK HAWK - Pencils ☆ - Faber-Castell Corp.
BLACK HAWK - Shoes - Dynasty Footwear, Ltd.
BLACK HAWK - Toys—models ☆ - Estes Industries
BLACK HAWK STOUT - Beverages—malt - Mendocino Brewing Co., Inc.
BLACK HEART - Greeting cards - Heart Cards
BLACK HILLS - Pool tables - Black Hills Milk Producers
BLACK HOLE - Ball bearings - Rollerblade, Inc.
BLACK HOLE - Surgical supplies - Pierre L. Mombrinie
BLACK HORSE - Beverages—alcohol ☆ - Century Importers Inc.
BLACK HORSE - Brooms ☆ - Harbor Manufacturing
BLACK HORSE CELLARS - Wines - CMR Imports Inc.
BLACK ICE - Bicycles - Roadmaster Corp.
BLACK ICE SOFTWARE - Computer software - Black Ice Software, Inc.
BLACK INC GREETINGS - Greeting cards - Frank T. Williamson, Jr.
BLACK IRISH ROLL - Tobacco products - Faber, Coe & Gregg Inc.
BLACK IRON - Tires - Oliver Rubber Co.
BLACK IS BEAUTIFUL - Beauty shops - Amekor Industries
BLACK-IT - Paints - OEM Paints, Inc.
BLACK JACK - Asphalt felts and coatings - Gibson-Homans Co.
BLACK JACK - Beverages—alcohol - Jacob Ries Bottling Works
BLACK JACK - Beverages—malt - Pittsburgh Brewing Co.
BLACK JACK - Candy - Glenn Confections Inc.
BLACK JACK - Cocktail mixes - James Grantman
BLACK JACK - Game machines - IGT - North America
BLACK JACK - Gloves—work - Shelby Group International, Inc.
BLACK-JACK - Pet products ☆ - Penn-Plax, Inc.
BLACK JACK - Tobacco—chewing or smoking - Sterling Tobacco Co.
BLACK JACK - Toys—stuffed ☆ - Gund, Inc.
BLACK JACK - Work gloves, TEFLON tape, windmill seals and cups - C.F. Adams Inc.
BLACK JACK SLOTS - Games - International Gamco, Inc.
BLACK JACK STUD RUNNER - Stud tools - Power House Tool, Inc.
BLACK JET 500 - Scissors—hand-operated - Dubl Duck/Jet Set Inc.
BLACK JET 1700 - Dryers—hair - Dubl Duck/Jet Set Inc.
BLACK KASE SCHENKE - Food products - Black Kase Schenke Cheese Co.
BLACK KNIGHT - Audio equipment ☆ - Electro-Voice, Inc.
BLACK KNIGHT - Bicycles - Ross Bicycles USA, Ltd.
BLACK KNIGHT - Cutlery ☆ - Regent Sheffield, Ltd.
BLACK KNIGHT - Motor vehicle parts and accessories ☆ - Loctite Corp.
BLACK KNIGHT - Shampoos - Kim Laube & Co. Inc.
BLACK KNIGHT - Tobacco products - Lane Ltd.
BLACK KNIGHTS - Fabrics—denim - Dan River Inc.
BLACK LAB - Wallpaper - Warner Co.
BLACK LAB II - Wallpaper - Warner Co.
BLACK LABEL - Beverages—malt - The Stroh Brewery Co.
BLACK LABEL - Cosmetics - Yardley of London Inc.
BLACK LABEL - Meat products—pork - Hormel Foods Corp.
BLACK LABEL 11-11 - Beverages—malt ☆ - The Stroh Brewery Co.
BLACK LABEL ICE - Beverages—malt ☆ - The Stroh Brewery Co.
BLACK LABEL L.A. - Beverages—malt ☆ - The Stroh Brewery Co.

BLACK LABEL LIGHT - Beverages—malt ☆ - The Stroh Brewery Co.
BLACK LADEL - Candies - Bowlby Candy Co. Inc.
BLACK LAMB - Polishing cloths - Micro-Surface Finishing Products, Inc.
BLACK LEAF - Insecticides - Black Leaf Products Co.
BLACK LEAF - Insecticides - Sureco, Inc.
BLACK LEAF 40 - Insecticides ☆ - Black Leaf Products Co.
BLACK LEMONADE - Fruit drinks—bottled or canned - J & H Food and Beverage, Inc.
BLACK LIGHTNING - Archery equipment - Bear Archery Inc.
BLACK-LINE - Music stands ☆ - Micro Musical Products Corp.
BLACK LOVE - Incense - Olfactory Corp.
BLACK LUSTER - Horseshoes ☆ - Farnam Cos. Inc.
BLACK MAG - Archery equipment ☆ - Bear Archery Inc.
BLACK MAGIC - Adhesives and sealants - Pratt & Lambert, Inc. (Specialty Products Div.)
BLACK MAGIC - Air purification systems - Barnebey and Sutcliffe Corp.
BLACK MAGIC - Coatings - Tresco Paint Co. Inc.
BLACK MAGIC - Cooking utensils—enameled - Jacksonville Manufacturing
BLACK MAGIC - Dinnerware—glass - Nikko Ceramics Inc.
BLACK MAGIC - Film - Engelhard Corp.
BLACK MAGIC - Frames—picture - Glass Baron, Inc.
BLACK MAGIC - Golfing equipment - Elmo-B Co.
BLACK MAGIC - Hair care products - J.M. Products, Inc.
BLACK MAGIC - Hair care products ☆ - Samlo
BLACK MAGIC - Horsemeat - Uniweld Products, Inc.
BLACK MAGIC - Housewares ☆ - Grayline Housewares
BLACK MAGIC - Musical instrument accessories ☆ - Music Accessories Manufacturing Co. Inc.
BLACK MAGIC - Paints - Hercules Chemical Co. Inc.
BLACK MAGIC - Pencils ☆ - Faber-Castell Corp.
BLACK MAGIC - Pet products - Aquarium Pharmaceuticals, Inc.
BLACK MAGIC - Sporting goods - O'Brien International
BLACK MAGIC - Thermostats ☆ - American Building Components Co.
BLACK MAGIC - Toys—stuffed ☆ - Gund, Inc.
BLACK MAGIC II - Automotive parts and accessories ☆ - Echlin Inc.
BLACK MARIA - Chewing tobacco - Conwood Co. L.P.
BLACK MARKET SCENTS - Candles - Village Originals, Inc.
BLACK MAX - Adhesives and sealants - Loctite Corp.
BLACK MAX - Alarm systems ☆ - Maxi-Guard
BLACK MAX - Bicycles - Columbia Manufacturing Inc.
BLACK MAX - Compressors—air - Sanborn Manufacturing Co.
BLACK MAX - Electrical equipment - Zebco Corp.
BLACK MAX - Fishing nets ☆ - Frabill Inc.
BLACK MAX - Motors—outboard - Brunswick Corp.
BLACK MAX - Musical instrument accessories - XL Specialty Percussion
BLACK MAX - Optical machinery - Link Electric and Safety Control Co., Inc.
BLACK MAX - Paint sprayers - Graco Inc.
BLACK MAX - Roofing materials—slate - Hy-C Co. Inc.
BLACK MAX - Scissors—hand-operated - Diane Products Inc.
BLACK MAX - Shaving brushes ☆ - American Safety Razor Co.
BLACK MAX - Sporting goods - Dunlop Maxfli Sports Corp.
BLACK MAX II - Sporting goods ☆ - Dunlop Maxfli Sports Corp.
BLACK MAX LTD. - Sporting goods ☆ - Dunlop Maxfli Sports Corp.
BLACK MAX NATIONAL ROD ENDS - Axles - Tuthill Corp.
BLACK MAX PLUS - Sporting goods ☆ - Dunlop Maxfli Sports Corp.
BLACK MAX PRO - Sporting goods ☆ - Dunlop Maxfli Sports Corp.
BLACK MAX WARRIOR - Alarm systems ☆ - Maxi-Guard
BLACK MEDALLION - Knives—hunting - Normark Corp.
BLACK MIST - Footwear - Americal Corp.
BLACK MOUNTAIN - Cheese - Cudahy Co.
BLACK MOUNTAIN - Dulcimers - Black Mountain Instruments
BLACK MOUNTAIN - Water—bottled or canned - Black Mountain Spring Water Inc.
BLACK MOUNTAIN GOLD - Coffee - Advanced Marketing & Sales
BLACK MOUNTAIN'S PARADISE - Water—bottled or canned - Black Mountain Spring Water Inc.
BLACK 'N BLUE - Bandages - Crackle Creations, Inc.
BLACK 'N BRIGHTS - Shoes - Reebok International Ltd.
BLACK 'N GOLD - Wigs - Kum Kang Trading U.S.A., Inc.
BLACK N' SASSY - Hair care products - Shayonna Enterprises, Ltd.
BLACK-N-STYLE - Appreal - Black-N-Style
BLACK 'N WHITE - Frames—eyeglass ☆ - Universal/Univis Inc.
BLACK NARCISSUS - Perfumes - Kiehl's Since 1851, Inc.
BLACK NUGGETS - Jewelry - Forrest W. Pond Inc.
BLACK OFF - Cleaning preparations - Hydra-Tone Chemicals, Inc.
BLACK ON BLACK - Artists' materials - Hunt Holdings, Inc.

BLACK OPAL - Skin-care products - Mana Products, Inc.
BLACK ORCHID - Dinnerware - Corning Inc.
BLACK ORCHID - Perfumes - Quintessence Inc.
BLACK OUT - Firearms, accessories, and parts - Ox-Yoke Originals, Inc.
BLACK OUT - Pet products - Vo-Toys Inc.
BLACK OX - Tools–hand-operated - Industrial Fasteners, Inc.
BLACK OXIDE - Paints - OEM Paints, Inc.
BLACK PAGES USA - Directories - Thomas-McCants Media Inc.
BLACK PANTHER - Archery equipment ☆ - High Country American
BLACK PANTHER - Archery equipment ☆ - Martin Archery Inc.
BLACK PANTHER - Batteries - Crischell Automotive Products, LLC
BLACK PANTHER - Hunting equipment - David Robert Nelson
BLACK PANTHER - Skin care products - Rudolph International, Inc.
BLACK PANTHER PARTY - Leather goods - Gwendolyn Kennedy
BLACK PANTHERS - Gloves - Boss Manufacturing Co.
BLACK PAW - Luggage - Blue Wheel Corp.
BLACK PEARL - Artists' materials - Angler's Roslyn Group Ltd.
BLACK PEARL - Dinnerware–glass - Block China Co.
BLACK PEARL - Hosiery - Triumph Hosiery Corp.
BLACK PEARL - Lubricants - Chevron Chemical Co.
BLACK PEARL - Recording label - Black Diamond Records, Inc.
BLACK PEARL - Sporting goods - Wright & McGill Co.
BLACK PEARL - Tableware–china - Villeroy and Boch Tableware Ltd.
BLACK PEARLS - Olives–pickled or brined - Musco Olive Products Inc.
BLACK PEARLS - Perfumes - Elizabeth Arden Co.
BLACK PETE - Cigars - National Cigar Corp.
BLACK PHANTOM - Bicycles - Schwinn Cycling & Fitness Inc.
BLACK PLANET - Paper mills - Black Planet Enterprises
BLACK POOL - Frames–eyeglass - May Optical Co. Inc.
BLACK PRINCE - Beverages–alcohol - Black Prince Distillery, Inc.
BLACK RADBERRY - Candy - Nabisco Foods Group
BLACK RANGER - Toys - Saban Entertainment, Inc.
BLACK RAVEN - Teas - Eastern Shore Tea Co.
BLACK RAY - Sporting goods - Georgia's Tennis
BLACK RIPE - Cigars - T.E. Brooks & Co.
BLACK ROBACIDE - Water treating compounds - Robarb Inc.
BLACK ROCK - Compact discs–prerecorded - TRF Production Music Libraries
BLACK ROCK - Dinnerware–glass ☆ - WMF/USA
BLACK ROCK - Footwear - Black Rock Sports, Inc.
BLACK ROCK - Golfing equipment - Golfsmith International Inc.
BLACK ROCK - Guitars - Emmons Guitar Co. Inc.
BLACK ROCK BR - Footwear - Black Rock Sports, Inc.
BLACK ROCK DRIVER - Golfing equipment - Golfsmith International Inc.
BLACK ROCK DRIVER - Golfing equipment - Koala Ventures, LLC
BLACK ROCK MV - Golfing equipment - Golfsmith International Inc.
BLACK ROCK PUTTER - Golfing equipment - Golfsmith International Inc.
BLACK ROYALE - Tableware–china ☆ - Lenox, Inc.
BLACK RUSSIAN - Cigarettes - James B. Russell Inc.
BLACK SABLE - Pencils ☆ - Faber-Castell Corp.
BLACK SAINT - Recording label - Polygram Records, Inc.
BLACK SAPPHIRE - Apparel and accessories - Mink Mart, Inc.
BLACK SAPPHIRE - Artists' materials - Angler's Roslyn Group Ltd.
BLACK SAPPHIRE - Dishes–china - Pickard Inc.
BLACK SAPPHIRE - Perfumes - Revlon Consumer Products Corp.
BLACK SAPPHIRE - Pet products - Tomlyn Products
BLACK SATIN - Audio equipment - Royal Sound Co. Inc.
BLACK SATIN - Dishes–china - Pickard Inc.
BLACK SATIN - Hair care products - Scientific Research Products Inc.
BLACK SATIN - Paper–sand - Virginia Abrasives Corp.
BLACK SATIN - Pens - Anson Inc.
BLACK SATIN - Tobacco–chewing or smoking - Amar Blends Co.
BLACK SATIN MINK - Pelts - Arvid A. Ames
BLACK SCORPION - Engines–marine - Brunswick Corp.
BLACK SEA WINE COMPANY - Wines - Black Sea Wine Co., Inc.
BLACK SEAL - Sealing compounds - Colonial Refining and Chemical Co.
BLACK SHADOW - Agricultural machinery - Double D Sprayers, Inc.
BLACK SHADOW - Firearms, accessories, and parts - U.S. Repeating Arms Co.
BLACK SHADOW - Jackets - Egl 1, Inc.
BLACK SHEEP - Beverages–malt - David and Mark Brewing Co., Inc.
BLACK SHEEP - Life preservers - Schoellkopf Sports Inc.
BLACK SHEEP - Pet products - Black Sheep Inc.
BLACK SHEEP - Tents - Kellwood Co.
BLACK SHIELD - Adhesives and sealants - Kol-Tar Inc.
BLACK SHIELD - Asphalt felts and coatings - Columbia Paint Co.
BLACK SNOW - Sporting goods - SLM Inc.

BLACK SPOT CONTROL - Pet products ☆ - Aquatronics-Filtronics
BLACK SPY - Games ☆ - Avalon Hill Game Co.
BLACK STAR - Automotive transmission parts - Black Star Industries, Inc.
BLACK STAR - Beverages–alcohol - McKenzie River Corp.
BLACK STAR - Luggage - Ventura Travelware Inc.
BLACK STAR - Manicure preparations - GG's Nail Systems
BLACK STEEL - Hockey equipment - Old Line Plastics, Inc.
BLACK STERLING - Jewelry–precious - Gold Force International Ltd.
BLACK STRAP - Adhesives and sealants - Carpet Products Co.
BLACK STREAK REMOVER - Cleaning preparations - Star Brite
BLACK STRIPE - Televisions - Toshiba America Consumer Products, Inc. (Consumer Products Business Sector)
BLACK SUEDE - Colognes - Avon Products, Inc.
BLACK SUEDETTE - Calendars - Advertisers Publishing Co.
BLACK SUN - Musical instrument accessories - Impecco, Ltd.
BLACK SUN - Recording label - Celestial Harmonies
BLACK SUNLIGHT - Perfumes - Helene Curtis Industries Inc.
BLACK SWAN - Food products - Amende and Schultz
BLACK SWAN - Hardware - Black Swan Manufacturing Co.
BLACK SWAN - Recording label - Jazzology-GHB Records
BLACK SYN - Firearms, accessories, and parts - Hunter Co., Inc.
BLACK TALON - Ammunition ☆ - Olin Corp. (Winchester Div.)
BLACK THUNDER - Boats - DonVee Inc.
BLACK TIE - Colognes ☆ - Johnson Products Co., Inc.
BLACK TIE - Floor coverings ☆ - Armstrong World Industries, Inc.
BLACK TIE - Game machines ☆ - IGT - North America
BLACK TIE COLLECTION - Jewelry - Town & Country Corp.
BLACK TIE COLLECTION, THE - Housewares - Scranton Lace Co.
BLACK TITE - Adhesives and sealants - Dap Products Inc.
BLACK-TITE - Pipes - Snappy A.D.P.
BLACK TOP - Recording label ☆ - Rounder Records Corp.
BLACK TOP - Tires–bicycles - Specialized Bicycle Components, Inc.
BLACK TOWER - Wines - Hiram Walker & Sons, Inc.
BLACK TRAC - Tools–hand-operated - Hyde Manufacturing Co.
BLACK TREAT - Water treating compounds - United Chemical Corp.
BLACK TURBO - Golfing equipment - Mizuno Corp. of America
BLACK VELVET - Blacktop sealer - Coopers Creek Chemical Corp.
BLACK VELVET - Game machines - Bally Gaming International, Inc.
BLACK VELVET - Hobby kits ☆ - Craft House Corp.
BLACK VELVET - Pencils - Faber-Castell Corp.
BLACK VELVET - Pens ☆ - Accutec Inc.
BLACK VELVET - Tobacco–chewing or smoking - Amar Blends Co.
BLACK VELVET - Whiskey - Heublein, Inc.
BLACK WALNUT - Hair care products - Holistic Laboratories
BLACK WALNUT KRISP - Candy - Pecan Deluxe Candy Co.
BLACK WARRIOR - Pencils - Empire Berol USA
BLACK WATCH - Beverages–alcohol - Majestic Distilling Co.
BLACK WATCH - Boats–motor - Hood Enterprises, Inc.
BLACK WATCH - Cigars - General Cigar Co., Inc.
BLACK WATCH - Shaving preparations ☆ - Prince Matchabelli
BLACK WHITE - Pens - Schneider Pens USA
BLACK WHITE & BEYOND - Wallpaper - J.C. Prints
BLACK, WHITE AND BLUE - Clothing - East-West Apparel, Inc.
BLACK WHITE & MORE - Wallpaper ☆ - J.C. Prints
BLACK, WHITE, RED & MORE - Wallpaper - Bayview Wallcoverings
BLACK WIDOW - Amplifiers - Peavey Electronics Corp.
BLACK WIDOW - Apparel and accessories - Keith Akiyama
BLACK WIDOW - Bicycles - Columbia Manufacturing Inc.
BLACK WIDOW - Boats–motor - Donzi Marine Corp.
BLACK WIDOW - Darts and dart games - Laser Darts Inc.
BLACK WIDOW - Fishing tackle - Hi-Seas Industries, Inc.
BLACK WIDOW - Games - IGT - North America
BLACK WIDOW - Insulators–electrical - Dare Products Inc.
BLACK WIDOW - Kites ☆ - Hi-Flier Manufacturing Co.
BLACK WIDOW - Toys–automobiles - Cox Products Inc.
BLACK WOLF - Archery equipment - Karen Lee T. Brunner
BLACKARACHNIA - Toys - Hasbro, Inc.
BLACKAZHELL UNIVERSITY - Apparel and accessories - Bryon Curtis James
BLACKBEARD - Games - Avalon Hill Game Co.
BLACKBEARD - Shaving products - C.S.C. Laboratories
BLACKBEARD - Toys–stuffed ☆ - Gund, Inc.
BLACKBERRY - Recording label - Blackberry, Inc.
BLACKBERRY & ND - Pillows - Blackberry & ND
BLACKBERRY BRANDY - Tobacco–chewing or smoking - Amar Blends Co.
BLACKBERRY JULEP - Wines ☆ - Jack Poust & Co. Inc.
BLACKBERRY SUMMER - Skin care products ☆ - Avon Products, Inc.

☆ = Now out of production

BLACKBERRY SUMMER - Teas - Eastern Shore Tea Co.
BLACKBERRY TECHNOLOGIES - Wheelchairs - Blackberry Technologies, Inc.
BLACKBIRD - Bicycles - Ross Bicycles USA, Ltd.
BLACKBIRD - Frames–eyeglass ☆ - Universal/Univis Inc.
BLACKBIRD - Hair curlers - Conair Corp.
BLACKBIRD - Recording label - Lakco Record Co.
BLACKBIRD PLATFORM - Computer software - Cellular Technical Services Inc.
BLACKBOTTOMS CYCLEWEAR - Sporting goods - Blackbottoms
BLACKBOURN - Hair care products - Hess Hair Milk Laboratories Inc.
BLACKBURN - Cosmetics ☆ - Spilo/Mehaz Worldwide
BLACKBURN - Electrical ground connectors - American Electric
BLACKBURN - Sporting goods - Bell Sports Corp.
BLACKBURN'S - Food products - Stache Foods
BLACKBURRY - Nail care products - Cosmair Inc.
BLACKCORE - Mat boards - Crescent Cardboard Co.
BLACKER THAN BLACK - Veterinary pharmaceutical preparations - Farnam Cos. Inc.
BLACKEYE BEAM - Automotive parts and accessories - Optronics Inc.
BLACKFEET - Pencils - Blackfeet Writing Instruments Inc.
BLACKFEET INDIAN - Pencils - Blackfeet Writing Instruments Inc.
BLACKFIRE - Apparel and accessories - International Indigo Inc.
BLACKGLAMA - Eyeglasses - Martin-Copeland Eyewear Corp.
BLACKGOLD - Bird feeds - Metz Farms
BLACKHAWK - Automotive product - Lincoln Automotive
BLACKHAWK - Bicycles - Roadmaster Corp.
BLACKHAWK - Drums–musical instruments ☆ - Fred Gretsch Enterprises
BLACKHAWK - Kites - Airplane Kite Co.
BLACKHAWK - Kites - Hi-Flier Manufacturing Co.
BLACKHAWK - Knives–hunting ☆ - Precise International/Wenger
BLACKHAWK - Ladders–wood - John S. Tilley Ladders Co. Inc.
BLACKHAWK - Revolvers - Sturm, Ruger & Co., Inc.
BLACKHAWK - Sleeping bags - Coleman Co., Inc.
BLACKHAWK - Thread - Threads USA Div.
BLACKHAWK - Tools ☆ - Litton Industries Inc. (New Britain Tool Div.)
BLACKHAWK FURNITURE - Furniture - Blackhawk Furniture, Inc.
BLACKHOOK - Beverages–malt - Redhook Ale Brewery, Inc.
BLACKHORNS - Knives–pocket - W.R. Case & Sons Cutlery Co.
BLACKHORSE - Apparel and accessories - Shirley Ann Oster
BLACKIE - Toys–stuffed ☆ - Gund, Inc.
BLACKJACK - Electrical equipment - Thomas & Betts Holdings, Inc.
BLACKJACK - Food products - Jardine's Texas Foods
BLACKJACK - Frames–eyeglass ☆ - Universal/Univis Inc.
BLACKJACK - Glassware–household - Crisa Corp.
BLACKJACK - Skates–roller - Rollerblade, Inc.
BLACKJACK TUTOR - Computer software - SourceView Software International
BLACKJACKS - Percussion mallets - American Drum
BLACKLAND - Garden equipment ☆ - Union Fork and Hoe Co.
BLACKLINE - Ribbons–inked - Katel Products, Ltd.
BLACKLIST RECORDS - Video tapes–blank - Blacklist Entertainment, Inc.
BLACKLITE - Glue–household or industrial - Woodworker's Supply, Inc.
BLACKLITE - Photographic equipment - American Photographic Instrument Co.
BLACKMAGIC - Bulletin boards–wood - Stempel Manufacturing Co.
BLACKMARK - Inks - Mason Marking Systems Corp.
BLACKMASTER - Briefcases - NSM Industries Inc.
BLACKMAX - Pumps - Gibson Pumping Systems, Inc.
BLACKMIX - Brushes–paint - Wright-Bernet
BLACKMOOR - Games - Tsr, Inc.
BLACKNIFE - Guitars - Modulus Graphite Products
BLACKOAK - Computer software - Adobe Systems Inc.
BLACKOTE - Paper products - Schweitzer-Mauduit International, Inc.
BLACKOUT - Cleaning preparations - Advance Cleaning Products Inc.
BLACKOUT - Cleaning preparations - Hercules Chemical Co. Inc.
BLACKOUT! - Computer software - Gamco Industries Inc.
BLACKOUT - Draperies - Rockland Industries Inc.
BLACKOUT - Eyeglasses - Art-Craft Optical Co.
BLACKOUT - Skin care products - Ballco Products Co.
BLACKOUT - Weed-control blankets - Atlantic Construction Fabrics, Inc.
BLACKOUT CAKE - Cakes - Creative Bakers Inc.
BLACKRIDGE MOUNTAIN - Footwear - Mel Shoe Corp.
BLACKRIDGE MOUNTAIN - Footwear - Timberland Co.
BLACK'S - Jewelry polishes, cleaners, etc. - Black's Products of High Point Inc.
BLACKSBURG - Stoneware dinnerware ☆ - Iron Mountain Stoneware Inc.
BLACKSMITH - Golfing equipments - Golfsmith International Inc.

BLACKSMITH SHOP - Furniture - U.S. Furniture Industries Inc.
BLACKSMITH, THE - Meat products - Michael L. Whalen
BLACKSNAKE - Hoses - Gates Rubber Co. (Automotive Aftermarket/Hardware Sales Div.)
BLACKSPIN - Golfing equipment - Odyssey Sports, Inc.
BLACKSTAR BARREL ACCURIZING - Firearms, accessories, and parts - Delaronde Co.
BLACKSTONE - Cigars - Swisher International, Inc.
BLACKSTONE - Frames–eyeglass ☆ - Universal/Univis Inc.
BLACKSTONE - Games - Jak-Pak Inc.
BLACKSTONE - Paper - Byron Weston Div.
BLACKSTONE - Playing cards ☆ - United States Playing Card Co.
BLACKSTONE - Thread - Threads USA Div.
BLACKSTONE MAGIC - Novelty items ☆ - Pressman Toy Corp.
BLACKSTREAM - Shoes - Calliope International, Inc.
BLACKTHORNE - Computer software - Interplay Productions
BLACKTIE - Dresses–women's - He-Ro Group Inc.
BLACKTOP - Apparel - Reebok International Ltd.
BLACKTRON - Toys–blocks - Lego Systems Inc.
BLACKWATER EXTRACT - Pet products - Tetra Sales USA
BLACKWELDER GROVES - Fruit beverages - Blackwelder Groves Inc.
BLACKWELDER'S - Furniture - Blackwelder's Furniture Co.
BLACKWING - Pencils - Faber-Castell Corp.
BLACKWOOD - Pet food - Blackwood Co.
BLACKWRAP - Paper–transfer - George Vincent Inc.
BLACKWULF - Books–comic ☆ - Marvel Entertainment Group, Inc.
BLACLINE - Paper - Teledyne Post
BLACO-THIN - Hardware - Baron Blakeslee, Inc.
BLACQUE BARD - Sporting goods ☆ - Gold Eagle/Arnold Palmer
BLACQUE FIRE - Sporting goods ☆ - Gold Eagle/Arnold Palmer
BLADDEREX - Vitamins and nutritional supplements - Matrix Health Products, Inc.
BLADDERMANAGER - Medical apparatus - Diagnostic Ultrasound Corp.
BLADE - Books–comic - Marvel Entertainment Group, Inc.
BLADE - Games - Flying Buffalo Inc.
BLADE - Guitars - VMI Industries
BLADE-ADE - Cutlery - T.M. Shea Products Inc.
BLADE-AID - Hand tool - Magnadyne Industries, Inc.
BLADE BATH - Pet products - Best n' Show Pet Products Inc.
BLADE BUSTER - Containers - Universal Industrial Products Co.
BLADE COMB - Barber shop equipment - Kim Laube & Co. Inc.
BLADE GRIPPER - Archery equipment - Saunders Archery Co.
BLADE KLEEN - Cleaning preparations - K.C. Pharmacal Inc.
BLADE MAID - Fans–electric - John R. Bielecki
BLADE-PAK - Semiconductors - DB Design Group Inc.
BLADE RAIDER - Toys - Mattel, Inc.
BLADE RUNNER - Shaving preparations - Origins Natural Resources Inc.
BLADE RUNNER - Skates–roller - Rollerblade, Inc.
BLADE SAFE - Medical apparatus - Trademark Corp.
BLADE-SAVER - Cutting boards - Austin Precision Products Inc.
BLADE, THE - Fishing lures - Hildebrandt Corp.
BLADE, THE - Golfing equipment - Northwestern Golf Co.
BLADE TRADING CARDS - Trading cards and stamps - American Blade, Inc.
BLADE WASH CADDIE - Barber shop equipment - Kim Laube & Co. Inc.
BLADEFORCE - Computer software - 3do Co.
BLADEGEAR - Sporting goods - Rollerblade, Inc.
BLADEMASTER - Knives - Frost Cutlery Co.
BLADEMATIC - Motor vehicle parts and accessories ☆ - Hoffco Inc.
BLADERUNNER - Sponges - Katchall Industries International, Inc.
BLADES - Kites - Hi-Flier Manufacturing Co.
BLADES - Mats - Majestic Mat Co.
BLADES - Sunglasses - Oakley, Inc.
BLADES OF VENGEANCE - Computer software - Electronic Arts Inc.
BLADESAVER - Chemical preparations - Bandon Corp.
BLADESMITH - Industrial machinery - Industrial Blades Unltd.
BLADEZ - Toys - Tonka Corp.
BLADIUM - Skin care products - Age Research, Inc.
BLAGDON - Faucets - Kohler Co.
BLAH BLAH BLAH - Apparel and accessories - Blah Blah Blah, Inc.
BLAINE - Hardware - Blaine Window Hardware Inc.
BLAINE ETHRIDGE BOOKS - Publisher's imprints - Blaine Ethridge Books
BLAINE HOUSE COLLECTION, THE - Tables–wood - Moosehead Manufacturing Co.
BLAINE P.N.F. - Prescription drug ☆ - Blaine Co. Inc.
BLAINTRATE - Prescription drug ☆ - Blaine Co. Inc.
BLAIR - Adhesives and sealants - Loctite Corp.

☆ = Now out of production

BLAIR - Agricultural machinery - Decker Manufacturing Co.

BLAIR - Eyeglasses - Bausch & Lomb Inc.

BLAIR - Fasteners–hook and eye - Seymour Manufacturing Co.,Inc.

BLAIR - Jewelry - Blair Holdings, Inc.

BLAIR - Toys - Tonka Corp.

BLAIR ATHOL - Beverages–malt - European Beverage Co., Inc.

BLAIR CRYSTAL - Paints–artists' - Loctite Corp.

BLAIR HARVEST - Varnishes - Loctite Corp.

BLAIR MILL - Floor coverings - Mannington Resilient Floors

BLAIR REGAL - Paints - Loctite Corp.

BLAIREX - Pharmaceutical preparations - Blairex Laboratories, Inc.

BLAIREX SYSTEM II - Ophthalmic goods ☆ - Blairex Laboratories, Inc.

BLAIRWOOD - Floor coverings–tile ☆ - Kentile Floors Inc.

BLAK - Apparel and accessories - Darren Sugiyama

BLAK BOND - Mortars–clay - BNZ Materials, Inc.

BLAK-RAY - Black-light fixtures and fluorescent materials - UVP Inc.

BLAKANAMEL - Paints ☆ - Everseal International Sales Co. Inc.

BLAKE - Ophthalmic goods - Swank Optical

BLAKE - Toys–stuffed - Eden LLC

BLAKE & HOLLISTER - Apparel and accessories - Shelburne Shirt Co. Inc.

BLAKE & HOLLISTER - Apparel and accessories - Sunrise Apparel, Inc.

BLAKE & MANLEY - Apparel–men's - Kellwood Co.

BLAKE STONE - Toys–electronic - Apogee Software Ltd.

BLAKE UNIVERSAL TECHNOLOGIES - Apparel and accessories - Universal Extremes, Inc.

BLAKELY - Floor coverings–carpet and rugs ☆ - Karastan-Bigelow Inc.

BLAKELY - Ophthalmic goods - Styl-Rite Optical Manufacturing Co., Inc.

BLAKENEY'S PARTY GOURMET - Bakery products ☆ - Cateraid Inc.

BLAMETA - Lubricants ☆ - Shell Oil Co.

BLAMMO - Chewing gum ☆ - Amurol Confections Co.

BLANC DE BLANC - Perfumes - Blanc De Blanc, Ltd.

BLANC DE BLANCS - Wines - Codorniu USA Inc.

BLANC DE CHANEL - Cosmetics - Chanel Inc.

BLANC DE CHINE - Apparel and accessories - Volk Art, Inc.

BLANC DE NOIR - Beverages–alcohol - Thornton Winery

BLANC DU LAC - Wines - Lukens Vineyard Inc.

BLANC IT - Fabrics–coated - Muralo Co. Inc.

BLANCAS - Tortillas - El Aguila Food Products, Inc.

BLANCHARD - Dips–sour cream based - Chase Collection, Inc.

BLANCHARD - Floor coverings–carpet and rugs ☆ - Kelly Group Inc.

BLANCHARD - Wines ☆ - Monsieur Henri Wines Ltd.

BLANCHE - Apparel–women's - Blanche

BLANCHE - Watches - Bulova Corp.

BLANCHE BUNNY - Toys–stuffed - Russ Berrie and Co., Inc.

BLANCHE DE BROOKLYN - Beverages–alcohol - Brooklyn Brewery Ltd.

BLANCHET - Wood products - L & P Property Management Co.

BLANCHEZ - Hair care products - Hanah Beauty & Health Inc.

BLANCO - Food products ☆ - Ocean Beauty Seafood, Inc.

BLANCO BUSTER - Nail care products - Spilo/Mehaz Worldwide

BLANCO VERANO - Wines - Joseph E. Seagram & Sons, Inc.

BLAND - Hair care products - Demert & Dougherty, Inc.

BLANDEX SELECT - Building panels - Potlatch Corp.

BLANEX - Pharmaceutical preparations ☆ - Edwards Pharmaceuticals, Inc.

BLANIMALS - Blankets - Modern Thought Combine

BLANK - Recording label - Polygram Records, Inc.

BLANK-A-ROO - Blankets - Dundee Mills, Inc.

BLANK EXPRESSION - Games - Paul R. Winslow

BLANK MFG. - Apparel and accessories - Tuff Stuff Aggrowear

BLANK OUT - Correction fluid ☆ - Kafko International Ltd.

BLANK SLATES - Greeting cards - Advantage/Aurora Publications

BLANK TORPEDO - Wines ☆ - Bully Hill Vineyards, Inc.

BLANKA - Glassware–household - H. Wittur & Co.

BLANKEASE - Blankets - Marilyn Kesler

BLANKET BRAND, THE - Linen - Beacon Manufacturing Co.

BLANKET BUDDIES - Toys–stuffed ☆ - Century Products Co.

BLANKET MAN-THE ULTIMATE PERSONAL PROTECTOR - Blankets - Raymond Fico

BLANKET NANNY - Bedding–linen - Bayport Products Inc.

BLANKEXPRESSION - Games - Winslow Games

BLANTON - Liquors - Blanton Distilling Co.

BLANTON SINGLE BARREL - Beverages–alcohol - Sazerac Co. Inc.

BLANTON'S BOURBON - Beverages–alcohol - SPAR Inc.

BLARNEY - Teas - Bewley Irish Imports

BLARNEY BALLS - Balls–golf - Russ Berrie and Co., Inc.

BLARNEY BAR - Bakery products - Quillin's, Inc.

BLARNEY BEARS - Toys–stuffed - Russ Berrie and Co., Inc.

BLARNEYSPUN - Handwork supplies - Bernat Yarn & Craft Corp.

BLAS - Frames–eyeglass ☆ - Universal/Univis Inc.

BLASER'S - Cheese - Clara Belle, Inc.

BLASIUS - Wines - Orion Imports Ltd.

BLASS MOUNTAIN - Wines - Markham Vineyards

BLAST - Air purification systems ☆ - Medo Industries, Inc.

BLAST - Computer software - U.S. Robotics Access Corp.

BLAST - Diagnostic substances - E.I. Dupont de Nemours and Co.

BLAST - Food products ☆ - H.P. Hood & Sons Inc.

BLAST - Swimming pools - Coastal Industries Inc.

BLAST - Toys - Tonka Corp.

BLAST - Vitamins and nutritional supplements ☆ - Vitamin Research Products Inc.

BLAST ALERT WARNING SYSTEMS - Mobile alarm - H.C. Stubbs Co., Inc.

BLAST ATTACK PHOENIX - Toys - Mattel, Inc.

BLAST-ATTAK - Toys - Mattel, Inc.

BLAST B-12 - Vitamins and nutritional supplements - Georgia Bariatrics Pc

BLAST CAPS - Vitamins and nutritional supplements - Nutra-Source Corp.

BLAST FROM THE PAST, A - Giftware - Gary Zachary Lerner

BLAST FUDGE FROZEN DESSERT - Confections - Blue Bell Creameries, L.P.

BLAST IT - Cleaning preparations - Grow Group, Inc.

BLAST IT - Games ☆ - Placo Products Co.

BLAST JETS - Toys - Tonka Corp.

BLAST 'N CATCH - Toys - Mattel, Inc.

BLAST-OFF - Abrasive products - Park Metallurgical Corp.

BLAST OFF - Apparel–women's - Tony Marterie & Associates

BLAST-OFF - Toys–models - Estes Industries

BLAST OFF - Vitamins and nutritional supplements - Vitamin Research Products Inc.

BLAST OFF DRINK MIX - Vitamins and nutritional supplements - Vitamin Research Products Inc.

BLAST ROCK - Toys - Tonka Corp.

BLAST TRAX - Toys–automobiles - Mattel, Inc.

BLAST ZONE - Beds–hospital - Dynacraft Industries Inc.

BLASTBOX - Stereos - Long Hall Technologies LLC

BLASTED LANDS, THE - Games ☆ - Mayfair Games, Inc.

BLASTER - Electronic equipment - Thomson Consumer Electronics, Inc.

BLASTER - Inflatable surf riders ☆ - Intex Recreation Corp.

BLASTER - Toys - Tonka Corp.

BLASTER 15 AMP - Amplifiers - PRO Manufacturing

BLASTER BALLS - Novelty items - Placo Products Co.

BLASTER BARS - Food products ☆ - Weider Health and Fitness

BLASTER-BOXX HITS - Publisher's imprints - Hard Hat Records

BLASTER BOXX HITS - Recording label - Blaster Boxx Hits

BLASTERHAWK - Toys–automobiles - Mattel, Inc.

BLASTERS - Fruit drinks–bottled or canned - Juice Bowl Products Inc.

BLASTEXX - Cleaning preparations - Zintexx Corp.

BLASTGEL - Explosives - Ireco Inc.

BLASTICKS - Drums–musical instruments - J.D. Calato Manufacturing Inc.

BLASTING POWDER - Candy - Confex Inc.

BLASTO - Musical instrument accessories - Trophy Music Co.

BLASTOFF - Games - International Gamco, Inc.

BLASTOS - Bubble-blowing toy - Toy Originators Inc.

BLASTPAK - Audio equipment - Long Hall Technologies LLC

BLATZ - Beverages–malt - The Stroh Brewery Co.

BLATZ CREAM ALE - Beverages–malt ☆ - The Stroh Brewery Co.

BLATZ DRAFT - Beverages–malt ☆ - The Stroh Brewery Co.

BLATZ DRAFT LIGHT - Beverages–malt ☆ - The Stroh Brewery Co.

BLATZ ICE - Beverages–malt - The Stroh Brewery Co.

BLATZ L.A. - Beverages–malt ☆ - The Stroh Brewery Co.

BLATZ LIGHT - Beverages–malt - The Stroh Brewery Co.

BLAUD STRUBEL - Pharmaceutical preparations - Strubel Drugs

BLAUER - Coats - Blauer Manufacturing Co., Inc.

BLAUPUNKT - Radios - Robert Bosch Corp.

BLAYMAN - Musical instrument accessories - H.S. Blayman Inc.

BLAZ-BERRY - Candy - Bobs Candies Inc.

BLAZAC BLAST - Breath sprays - Catco, Inc.

BLAZE - Bicycles - Columbia Manufacturing Inc.

BLAZE - Cement ☆ - Gibson-Homans Co.

BLAZE - Computers - Alejandro Sastre

BLAZE - Deicing fluid - Ossian, Inc.

BLAZE - Dinnerware–glass ☆ - Nikko Ceramics Inc.

BLAZE - Glassware–household - U.S. Disabled Athletes Fund, Inc.

BLAZE - Goggles–safety - Parmelee Industries, Inc.

BLAZE - Goggles–safety - U.S. Safety Corp.

BLAZE - Hair care products - Mane Street Products USA

☆ = Now out of production

BLAZE - Musical instrument accessories - Dimarzio, Inc.
BLAZE - Ophthalmic goods - Swank Optical
BLAZE - Tools–boring ☆ - Swan Handle Corp.
BLAZE - Toys - Mattel, Inc.
BLAZE & ROAR - Toys–automobiles - Lewis Galoob Toys, Inc.
BLAZE BRONCO - Dolls - Mattel, Inc.
BLAZE BRUSH - Camouflage fabric - Larry Sanburg Fabrics
BLAZE KING CLASSIC - Heating equipment - Blaze King Industries
BLAZE OF GLORY - Fireworks - American Promotional Events, Inc.
BLAZE OF GLORY - Watches - Elgin Watch Co.
BLAZE ORANGE EGGS - Fishing lures - Brown Bear Bait Co.
BLAZE PRODUCTS - Chemical preparations - Aaper Alcohol and Chemical Co.
BLAZEGUARD - Wood products - Weyerhaeuser Co.
BLAZELITE - Cement - BNZ Materials, Inc.
BLAZER - Ammunition - Blount International, Inc. (Sporting Equipment Group)
BLAZER - Bicycles - Raleigh USA Bicycle Co.
BLAZER - Bicycles ☆ - Muskin Leisure Products Inc.
BLAZER - Boats–skiffs ☆ - Shumway Yacht Sales
BLAZER - Catheters - EP Technologies, Inc.
BLAZER - Floor coverings–carpet and rugs - Trend Carpet
BLAZER - Food products - Glenmark Industries, Ltd.
BLAZER - Footwear, sportswear ☆ - Bostonian Shoe Co.
BLAZER - Kites - Oddzon Products, Inc.
BLAZER - Markers–felt-tip - Faber-Castell Corp.
BLAZER - Model of BENELLI moped ☆ - Cosmopolitan Motors Inc.
BLAZER - Motor vehicles - General Motors Corp. (Chevrolet Motor Div.)
BLAZER - Motorcycles ☆ - Suzuki of America Automotive Corp.
BLAZER - Sports rackets and accessories ☆ - Victor Sports
BLAZER - Tobacco–chewing or smoking - P.T.C. Brands, Inc.
BLAZER - Toys–models ☆ - Estes Industries
BLAZER BUTTON COLLECTION - Buttons - JHB International Inc.
BLAZER MICRO-TORCH - Electronic equipment - Edge Co.
BLAZER PLUS - Modems - Telebit Corp.
BLAZER RODS - Antennas - Wintenna Inc.
BLAZERMAKER - Fabrics - Staflex Harotex
BLAZERS - Ophthalmic goods - Karlen Manufacturing, Inc.
BLAZERS - Trading cards and stamps - Traditional Watercraft Inc.
BLAZERS - Trading cards and stamps - Trail Blazers, Inc.
BLAZERS BY FAIRBROOKE - Apparel–athletic - Fairbrooke Enterprises
BLAZIN' BANNERS - Toys - Tonka Corp.
BLAZIN' BULL - Meat products–beef ☆ - Pierce Foods Corp.
BLAZIN' SADDLE - Food products - Texxstar Resources (USA), Inc.
BLAZIN' SADDLES - Food products - Jardine's Texas Foods
BLAZIN' SADDLES - Toys - International Gamco, Inc.
BLAZIN' TURBOS - Toys–automobiles - Matchbox Toys USA
BLAZIN'96 - Bicycles ☆ - Huffy Corp.
BLAZING - Hair care products - Scruples Professional Salon Products, Inc.
BLAZING 7S - Game machines - Bally Gaming International, Inc.
BLAZING 777 - Game machines - Bally Gaming International, Inc.
BLAZING ARROW - Knives - United Cutlery Corp.
BLAZING BANNERS - Banners - Blazing Banners
BLAZING FURY - Fireworks - American Promotional Events, Inc.
BLAZING FURY - Fireworks - China Pyrotechnics, Inc.
BLAZING RAILS - Toys–trains - Life-Like Products Inc.
BLAZING SAND - Waxes–mineral - Classic Accents
BLAZING STAR - Floor coverings–carpet and rugs - Barrett Carpet Mills Inc.
BLAZING STAR - Fruits–canned - Kelseyville Packing Co.
BLAZING SUN - Tortillas - Ottenberg's Bakers, Inc.
BLAZING THE BASIC TRAIL - Computer software ☆ - Sunburst Communications, Inc.
BLAZIN'S SSP - Toys - Tonka Corp.
BLAZITE - Watches - Elgin Watch Co.
BLAZON - Exercising equipment ☆ - Flexible Flyer Co.
BLAZON E-Z PAK - Water-soluble colorant - Milliken & Co.
BLD - Vitamins and nutritional supplements - Healthy America Campaign Inc.
BLDG. BLOCKS - Vinyl - Arc-Com Fabrics, Inc.
BLE - Apparel–athletic - Michael R. Blemaster
BLEACH DROP-IN - Cleaning preparations–household - Super Brands, Inc.
BLEACH PERFECT - Hair coloring preparations - CCA Industries, Inc.
BLEACH STICK - Detergents - Edwards Creative Products, Inc.
BLEACHER CREATURE - Cushions–foam - Igloo Products Corp.
BLEACHER GEAR - Apparel–athletic - Jock's Nitch Inc.
BLEACHER RECLINER - Seat covers - Bleacher Recliner Corp.
BLEACHERS - Trading cards and stamps - Bleachers Card Corp.
BLEACHTEX - Paper–toilet ☆ - Fort Howard Corp.

BLEAD & GLAZE - Paints - William Zinsser & Co. Inc.
BLED - Musical instrument accessories ☆ - Five Star Entertainment
BLEDSOE - Health care products - Medical Technology Inc.
BLEED - Recording label - Bleed
BLEEDING SHINER - Fishing lures - Sports Design and Development, Inc.
BLEEKER - Microscopes ☆ - Heitz Service Corp.
BLEEKER STREET - Apparel–women's - Jonathan Logan Inc.
BLEEP-BLIP'S - Candy - American Chewing Gum Inc.
BLEEPER - Candy - American Chewing Gum Inc.
BLEM - Cleaning preparations–upholstery ☆ - S.C. Johnson & Son, Inc.
BLEM-DERM - Pharmaceutical preparations - Schein Pharmaceutical Inc.
BLEMISH BUSTER - Pharmaceutical preparations - Guthy-Renker Corp.
BLEMISH GEL - Skin care products - Fanie International
BLEMISH SPECIALIST - Antiseptics - Estee Lauder Inc.
BLEN-VUE - Optical scanners–computer - Titmus Optical, Inc.
BLENBACK - Fabrics–oilcloth ☆ - Columbus Coated Fabrics Co.
BLEND - Hair care products - Gold Medal Hair Products Inc.
BLEND - Headphones - Westone Laboratories Inc.
BLEND 30 - Eggs - Milton G. Waldbaum Co.
BLEND 100 - Tobacco products - Shepherd Tobacco Co.
BLEND 0122 - Tobacco products ☆ - Lane Ltd.
BLEND 2000 - Ophthalmic goods ☆ - Sola Optical USA, Inc.
BLEND-A-COLOR - Paints - Martin-Senour Co.
BLEND A TIP - Skin care products - Rudolph International, Inc.
BLEND ALL - Cream - Presto Food Products, Inc.
BLEND-ALL - Veterinary treatment ☆ - American Equine Products Inc.
BLEND EDGE - Ophthalmic goods - Benson Optical Co., Inc.
BLEND ELEVEN - Tobacco products - Lane Ltd.
BLEND GLO - Skin care products - Goubaud
BLEND-IN-CAN - Dispensers - Fluid Management
BLEND IT - Housewares ☆ - M.E. Heuck Co. Inc.
BLEND-IT - Paints - Prestype Inc.
BLEND-IT - Skin care products ☆ - F.W. Engels Inc.
BLEND MASTER - Blenders - Hamilton Beach/Proctor-Silex Inc.
BLEND MASTER - Food products - Land O'Lakes, Inc.
BLEND-MATES - Bathing suits - Catalina
BLEND MIST - Lacquers - BASF Corp.
BLEND-N'S - Salt - Moran Group Inc.
BLEND-O FRUIT - Glace fruits ☆ - Aunt Nellie's Farm Kitchens Inc.
BLEND POLISH - Ophthalmic goods - Benson Optical Co., Inc.
BLEND-RITE - Hairpins - Sta-Rite Ginnie Lou Inc.
BLEND RITE - Meters–water - Blend-Rite Industries, Inc.
BLEND STICK - Paints - Dap Products Inc.
BLEND-TELS - Paints–artists' ☆ - Dick Blick Co.
BLENDA - Ophthalmic goods ☆ - Luxottica
BLENDAIR - Fabric stores - Jaunty Textile Div.
BLENDAIRE - Apparel–women's - Barbizon Lingerie
BLENDAISE - Salad dressings–bottled ☆ - T. Marzetti Co.
BLENDAURA - Fabric stores - Jaunty Textile Div.
BLENDED BERRIES - Lipstick and nail polish ☆ - Cosrich Inc.
BLENDED DELIGHT - Oils–edible - Kraft Food Ingredients Corp.
BLENDED FAMILIES - Greeting cards - Sheila Brayman-Borgese
BLENDER - Hair care products - Fromm Industries
BLENDER BOX - Ventilation units - Blender Products, Inc.
BLENDER CHEF - Food processors - Hamilton Beach/Proctor-Silex Inc.
BLENDER-PLUS - Blenders - Hamilton Beach/Proctor-Silex Inc.
BLENDER QUEEN - Blenders - Westminster International Co., Inc.
BLENDER SECTION - Ventilation units - Blender Products, Inc.
BLENDERCONE - Ventilation units - Blender Products, Inc.
BLENDERS - Shoes - Tina Yoxtheimer
BLENDERS CHOICE - Tobacco–chewing or smoking - Amar Blends Co.
BLENDERS, THE - Recording label - Blenders, Inc.
BLENDEX - Resins–synthetic - General Electric Co.
BLENDIT - Animal feeds - Simmons Industries Inc.
BLENDLENS - Ophthalmic goods - Benson Optical Co., Inc.
BLENDMAX - Food products - Central Soya Co. Inc.
BLENDOMIX - Mixers - Fluid Management
BLENDOR - Blenders - Waring Products Div.
BLENDORAMA - Dispensers - Fluid Management
BLENDORAMA - Paint sprayers ☆ - H.E.R.O. Industries Ltd.
BLENDS - Dog food - Ralston Purina Co.
BLENDTEX - Thread - Perfect Thread Co. Inc.
BLENDTONE - Epilator - Instantron Co. Inc.
BLENDUP - Mops - Zephyr Manufacturing Co.
BLENDZ-ALL - Paints - Grow Group, Inc.
BLENHEIM - Dishes–china ☆ - WMF/USA

☆ = Now out of production

BLENHEIM - Tobacco–chewing or smoking - Amar Blends Co.
BLENHEIM FARMS - Food products - Dulany Foods Inc.
BLENKO ANTIQUE - Glass products - Blenko Glass Co. Inc.
BLENKO DALLES - Glass products - Blenko Glass Co. Inc.
BLENKO HANDCRAFT - Glass products - Blenko Glass Co. Inc.
BLENOXANE - Pharmaceutical preparations - Bristol-Myers Squibb Co.
BLEPH-10 - Ophthalmic goods - Allergan, Inc.
BLEPHAMIDE - Ophthalmic goods - Allergan, Inc.
BLESS THIS HOUSE - Wallpaper ☆ - Sandpiper Studios
BLESS YOUR HEART - Stationery - Heartland Samplers Inc.
BLESSED - Apparel and accessories - Gloval Systems, Inc.
BLESSED BEAR - Toys–stuffed - Heaven on Earth, Inc.
BLESSED EVENT - Cosmetics - Maynard Inc.
BLESSED MOMENTS - Artists' materials - Sangray Corp.
BLESSING - Musical instruments - E.K. Blessing Co. Inc.
BLESSING BOOK - Books–blank - Bernadette Dirr
BLESSING FROM ABOVE - Toys–stuffed - Russ Berrie and Co., Inc.
BLESSING TREE, THE - Audio tapes–blank - Corinna Corp.
BLESSINGS ABOUND BLESSINGS UNBOUND - Fabrics–tapestry - Lauri Gross
BLEU CHEESE INTERNATIONAL RECIPE - Salad dressings–bottled - Walden Farms, Inc.
BLEU DE CHINE BY MARC DE LA MORANDIERE - Perfumes - Alfin Fragrances Inc.
BLEU ELECTRIQUE - Cosmetics - Lancome
BLEU HAWAII - Cosmetics - Langer Hawaii Corp.
BLEU ICE - Sportswear - K.D. Co. Inc.
BLEU LAGUNE - Cosmetics - Lancome
BLEU NATURALS - Gloves–work ☆ - Pioneer Industrial Products Co.
BLEU ROYAL - Dinnerware–glass ☆ - WMF/USA
BLEU SMOKE - Skin care products - Goubaud
BLEUET - Stoves ☆ - Wonder Corp. of America
BLEVINS - Popcorn - National Oats Co. Inc.
BLEWETT PASS - Fruits–canned - Cashmore Pioneer Growers
BLEYLE - Apparel–women's - Bleyle of America Inc.
BLI - Religious articles - Bliss Manufacturing Co. Inc.
BLICK CITY - Paints ☆ - Dick Blick Co.
BLICKRYLIC - Paints - Dick Blick Co.
BLIMPERS - Apparel–children's - Blimpers Inc.
BLIMPIE BEST - Sandwiches–prepackaged - Metropolitan Blimpie, Inc.
BLIMPIE SUBS & SALADS - Food products - Metropolitan Blimpie, Inc.
BLINCIR - Computer software - Beckwith Electric Co.
BLIND - Backpacks - Blind, Inc.
BLIND AMBITION - Blinds–vertical - Blind Ambition Ltd.
BLIND-BRITE - Cleaning preparations–window - Orange-Sol Inc.
BLIND EARL - Giftware - Royal China & Porcelain Companies Inc.
BLIND FAITH - Beverages–alcohol - Magic Hat Brewing Co. & Performing Arts Center, Inc.
BLIND FROG - Apparel and accessories - Jeffrey C. Maile
BLIND-GLO - Cleaning preparations–household - Blind-Glo Products, Inc.
BLIND JUSTICE - Games - Avalon Hill Game Co.
BLIND MAKER - Window dressing - Blind Maker Inc.
BLIND PIG - Recording label - Blind Pig Records
BLIND PIG - Recording label - Whole Hog, Inc.
BLIND ROBINS - Food products ☆ - Bar Food Products Inc. (O)
BLIND SIDER - Toys–automobiles - Mattel, Inc.
BLIND SPOT - Automotive parts and accessories - James E. Winner Jr.
BLINDED BY THE WHITE - Cosmetics - Cosmair Inc.
BLINDGLO - Cleaning preparations–household - Blind-Glo Products, Inc.
BLINDPRIME - Pigments–paint - Building Protective Industries
BLINDSPOTS - Games - Lynn Collins and Barbara McDuffie Partnership
BLINK-N-CLEAN - Ophthalmic goods ☆ - Allergan, Inc.
BLINK-N-PLAY - Music boxes - National Artcraft Co.
BLINKER BUDDY - Automotive parts and accessories - Harc Mercantile Ltd.
BLINKERS - Footwear ☆ - E.S. Originals, Inc.
BLINKIE - Pins–jewelry - Imprinted Products Corp.
BLINKIE - Toys–stuffed ☆ - Fun World Inc.
BLINKING BEAUTY - Toys - Mattel, Inc.
BLINKING LOCO - Toys - Buddy L Inc.
BLINKING PLANE - Toys - Buddy L Inc.
BLINKY BILL GENERAL STORE - Toys - ERTL Co., Inc.
BLINKY BILL SCHOOL HOUSE PLAYSET - Toys - ERTL Co., Inc.
BLINKY BIRDIE - Toys ☆ - Tomy America, Inc.
BLINX - Ophthalmic goods - Barnes-Hind Inc.
BLINX - Pharmaceutical preparations ☆ - Akorn Inc.
BLIP - Electronic equipment - Tomy America, Inc.

BLIP-CLIP (2) - Lighting equipment - Lowel-Light Manufacturing Inc.
BLIPPY TEDDY - Toys–stuffed - Russ Berrie and Co., Inc.
BLIPS - Lighting equipment - Lowel-Light Manufacturing Inc.
BLIS - Medical apparatus - Suzanne Morrissey
BLIS - Skin care products ☆ - Del Pharmaceuticals, Inc.
BLIS-PAK - Packaging–paper - Federal Paper Board Co., Inc.
BLIS-TO-SOL - Health care products - Chattem Inc.
BLIS-TO-SOL - Health care products - Woolfoam Corp.
BLISS - Floor coverings–carpet and rugs - Mohawk Industries Inc.
BLISS - Frames–eyeglass - Zylo Ware Corp.
BLISS - Marine equipment and accessories - Bliss Marine
BLISS - Musical instrument stores - Importoys
BLISS - Paper products - Aegis Entertainment, Inc.
BLISS - Photographic equipment ☆ - Falcon Safety Products, Inc.
BLISS - Rings–jewelry - Bliss Ring Co. Inc.
BLISS BROTHERS - Milk - Bliss Brothers Dairy Inc.
BLISS GIFT & BRIDAL REGISTRY - Giftware - Bliss, Inc.
BLISSFIELD RED - Food products - Blissfield Canning Co. Inc.
BLISSWARE - Housewares - Lerner Manufacturing Inc.
BLIST-AWAY - Blister cream - American Laboratories Inc.
BLISTA-WAY - Pharmaceutical preparations - Vita Plus Industries Inc.
BLISTER - Garden equipment - Emsco Inc.
BLISTER BAN - Skin care products - Divajex
BLISTER BUSTER, THE - Boat-repair machines - Osmotech US Inc.
BLISTER-CARE - Bandages - Futuro Inc.
BLISTERFILM - Health care products - Sherwood Medical Co.
BLISTEX - Lip balms - Blistex Bracken L.P.
BLISTEX - Skin care products - Blistex Inc.
BLISTEX DCT - Skin care products - Blistex Inc.
BLISTEX LIP MEDEX - Skin care products - Blistex Inc.
BLISTEX ULTRA PROTECTION - Skin care products - Blistex Inc.
BLITHE SPIRIT - Floor coverings–carpet and rugs - Mohawk Industries Inc.
BLITZ - Bicycles - Columbia Manufacturing Inc.
BLITZ - Cleaning preparations - Blitz Manufacturing Co., Inc.
BLITZ - Containers–metal - U.S. Metal Container Co.
BLITZ - Fishing lures - Blitz Lures, Inc.
BLITZ - Footwear–athletic - Puma Inc.
BLITZ - Hair care products - Major International Inc.
BLITZ - Musical instrument accessories - David Wexler & Co.
BLITZ - Skates–roller - Rollerblade, Inc.
BLITZ - Video production - Bruce Blitz
BLITZ-BACKGAMMON - Computer software - American Rare Coin Trading Group
BLITZ CLIP - Garment hangers–wire - Mode Plastics, Inc.
BLITZ FOG - Pesticides–household ☆ - Village Blacksmith
BLITZ 'N SHINE - Skin care products - American Image
BLITZ SILVER CARE - Cleaning preparations - Blitz Manufacturing Co., Inc.
BLITZ VIDEO KIT - Artists' materials - Blitz Art Products, Inc.
BLITZ-WEINHARD - Beverages–malt - The Stroh Brewery Co.
BLITZ-WEINHARD LIGHT - Beverages–malt ☆ - The Stroh Brewery Co.
BLITZKRIEG - Fireworks - American Promotional Events, Inc.
BLITZKRIEG - Games - Avalon Hill Game Co.
BLITZKRIEG - Games ☆ - Mayfair Games, Inc.
BLITZMAIL - Computer software - Dartmouth College
BLITZWING - Toys–erector sets - Hasbro, Inc.
BLITZZ - Apparel–men's - Jean Michaud, Ltd.
BLITZZ STUDIOS - Apparel and accessories - Blitzz International, Ltd.
BLIX MIX - Artists' materials - Dick Blick Co.
BLIXTEX LIP TONE - Lip balms - Blistex Inc.
BLIZKIT - Automotive parts and accessories - Yeoman Co.
BLIZZARD - Automotive parts and accessories - MasterForce Inc.
BLIZZARD - Candy ☆ - American Chicle Co.
BLIZZARD - Cleaning preparations - Block Drug Co., Inc.
BLIZZARD - Footwear–athletic ☆ - Seaway Importing Co.
BLIZZARD BAR - Ice cream - American Dairy Queen Corp.
BLIZZARD BEAR - Toys–stuffed - Russ Berrie and Co., Inc.
BLIZZARD BOMBER - Hats - Mad Bomber Co.
BLIZZARD BRUSH - Snow-cleaning brush ☆ - Clean-Rite Products Co.
BLIZZARD BUSTER - Shovels - Structron Corp.
BLIZZARD ICE MELTER - Deicing fluid - Kmart Corp.
BLIZZARD PIE - Food products - American Dairy Queen Corp.
BLIZZARD-PRUF - Apparel and accessories - Walls Industries, Inc.
BLK - Stoves–wood-burning - GSW Jackes-Evans Manufacturing Co.
BLO - Apparel and accessories - Tim T. Cole
BLO - Chewing gum ☆ - Spangler Candy Co.
BLO BALLS - Chewing gum ☆ - Fleer Corp.

BLO-BOT - Toys ☆ - Imperial Toy Corp.
BLO BUBBLE - Candy ☆ - Spangler Candy Co.
BLO-DENT - Chewing gum ☆ - Leaf, Inc.
BLO-HO-HO - Food products - Fleer Corp.
BLO-STYLER - Combs ☆ - Comare Corp.
BLO-STYLING - Hair care products - Jheri Redding Products Inc.
BLOATERS - Toys ☆ - Jak-Pak Inc.
BLOB ELIMINATOR - Paint removers - Lawrence W. Johnson
BLOBBIE - Toys - Troma, Inc.
BLOC - Amplifiers ☆ - Yorkville Sound
BLOC-HEAT - Tools ☆ - CRC Chemicals USA/Siloo
BLOC-IT - Glue–household or industrial - La-Co Industries, Inc.
BLOC-RUST - Paints - Dunn Edwards Corp.
BLOCADREN - Pharmaceutical preparations - Merck & Co., Inc. (Merck
   Research Laboratories)
BLOCFIL - Hardware - Dunn Edwards Corp.
BLOCH - Shoes–athletic - Victoria's Dance-Theatrical Supply
BLOCH & GUGGENHEIMER - Pickles - B & G Foods Inc.
BLOCK - Candles - Svend Jensen of Denmark Inc.
BLOCK - Dinnerware–glass - Block China Co.
BLOCK - Pens - Block and Co., Inc.
BLOCK AID - Suntan lotions ☆ - ICN Pharmaceuticals Inc.
BLOCK & BARREL - Meat products - Sysco Corp.
BLOCK & CHAIN - Pet products - Golden West Bird Farm Inc.
BLOCK AND TACKLE - Sunblocks - Sports Pharmaceuticals of America Inc.
BLOCK BUSTER - Cleaning preparations - W.W. Grainger, Inc.
BLOCK BUSTER - Drain pipe cleaners ☆ - Uncle Sam Chemical Co., Inc.
BLOCK BUSTER - Fishing tackle - Frabill Inc.
BLOCK BUSTER - Ice cream - Pierre's French Ice Cream Distributing Co. of
   Akron
BLOCK BUSTER - Tools - Norton Co.
BLOCK BUSTERS - Stationery - Mead Corp.
BLOCK BY BLOCK - Puzzles - Binary Arts Corp.
BLOCK CHATEAU - Dinnerware–glass - Block China Co.
BLOCK-CIRCLETOPS - Doors - Myles Fisher
BLOCK FAMILY, THE - Toys–blocks ☆ - Creative Playthings Ltd.
BLOCK FINANCIAL - Computer peripheral equipment - Block Financial Corp.
BLOCK ISLAND - Apparel and accessories - Kellwood Co.
BLOCK ISLAND - Ships–sailing vessels - Migrator Yachts
BLOCK ISLAND PETITE - Apparel and accessories - Kellwood Co.
BLOCK IT - Computer software - Electronic Courseware Systems Inc.
BLOCK-IT - Hair care products - W.R. Rayson Co., Inc.
BLOCK-IT - Paints - Dunn Edwards Corp.
BLOCK-IT - Pharmaceutical preparations - Conserv-a-Dent Inc.
BLOCK-IT - Sporting goods - Excel Sports Products
BLOCK LIMOGES - Dinnerware–glass ☆ - Block China Co.
BLOCK-N-PRIME - Paints - Frazee Paint
BLOCK OIL - Furniture polish and wax - Axiom
BLOCK-OUT - Floor coverings - Sponge-Cushion Inc.
BLOCK-OUT - Paints - Bruning Paint Co.
BLOCK-OUT - Stationery - Diagraph Corp.
BLOCK OUT - Suntan lotions - Faberge Co.
BLOCK-OUT II - Paints - Bruning Paint Co.
BLOCK PARTY - Apparel and accessories - Nancy Riley
BLOCK PARTY - Pizzas–frozen - Sabatasso Foods Inc.
BLOCK SET - Waterproofing compounds - Bil-Dry Corp.
BLOCK STOCK - Stamps–hand - Clearsnap, Inc.
BLOCK THE BLOCK LINE - Dialing devices–telephone - Jerry Bloch Inc.
BLOCKADE - Cleaning preparations–carpet and rug - Von Schrader Co.
BLOCKADE - Coveralls - E.I. Dupont de Nemours and Co.
BLOCKADE - Dips–cattle - West Agro, Inc.
BLOCKADE - Pet products - Hartz Mountain Corp.
BLOCKADE - Pet products - Longlife Pet Products
BLOCKADE - Sporting goods - Camp-Cap Products
BLOCKAGE BUSTER - Containers - Eagle Industries Inc.
BLOCKAID - Blocks–concrete - Glidden Co.
BLOCKAID - Health care products ☆ - Outdoor Technologies Group
BLOCKAID - Vitamins and nutritional supplements - Solaray
BLOCKAIDE - Sporting goods - Marty Gilman Inc.
BLOCKAIN - Pharmaceutical preparations ☆ - Sterling Winthrop Inc.
BLOCKBUSTER - Computer software - Mindscape Software Inc.
BLOCKBUSTER - Computer software ☆ - Milton Bradley Co.
BLOCKBUSTER - Fireworks - Ingram Enterprises, Inc.
BLOCKBUSTER - Games - Blockbuster Entertainment Corp.
BLOCKBUSTER - Hammers–electric - Black & Decker Corp.
BLOCKBUSTER - Nail care products - Spilo/Mehaz Worldwide

BLOCKBUSTER - Ophthalmic goods - Foremost Optical Products
BLOCKBUSTER BOWL - Jewelry - Viacom International Inc.
BLOCKBUSTER GOLF & GAMES - Sunglasses - Blockbuster Entertainment
   Corp.
BLOCKBUSTER VIDEO - Games - Blockbuster Entertainment Corp.
BLOCKBUSTERS - Candy ☆ - Topps Co., Inc.
BLOCKBUSTERS - Toys–blocks - Brrr Products Co. Inc.
BLOCKEM-SOCKEM PADDLE BAT - Paddle ball game - Jack Mack, Inc.
BLOCKER - Fabrics - Burlington Industries, Inc.
BLOCKER - Locks–door - Lori Lock
BLOCKER - Rackets–tennis - Gexco Enterprises
BLOCKERS - Bird feeds - Lafeber Co.
BLOCKHEAD - Games - Pressman Toy Corp.
BLOCKHEAD - Games - Saalfield Publishing Co.
BLOCKHEAD - Toys - Tonka Corp.
BLOCKHEADS - Candy - Gerrit J. Verburg Co.
BLOCKIT - Paper products - Stone Container Corp.
BLOCKOUT - Games - Kadon Enterprises Inc.
BLOCKOUT - Toys–electronic ☆ - Philips Consumer Electronics Co.
BLOCKS - Floor coverings ☆ - Bruce Hardwood Floors
BLOCKS - Floor coverings–carpet and rugs - Quaker Inc.
BLOCKS - Pet products - Golden West Bird Farm Inc.
BLOCKS & MARBLES - Toys - Tedco Inc.
BLOCKS IN MOTION - Computer software - Don Johnston Inc.
BLOCKS 'N' MORE - Toys - Fisher-Price, Inc.
BLOCKS OF COLOR - Cosmetics - Maybelline Co.
BLOCKS OF FUN - Christmas tree ornaments - Prosperity Tree International
BLOCKSET - Adhesives and sealants - L.D. Sterns Corp.
BLOCKWOOD - Floor coverings - Azrock Commercial Flooring
BLOCS - Computer software - Ranco Systems, Inc.
BLOCWELD - Wood products ☆ - Georgia-Pacific Corp.
BLODGETT - Food products - Blodgett Foods Inc.
BLODGETT COMBI - Ovens–convection - G.S. Blodgett Corp.
BLOFISH - Apparel and accessories - Y-Design
BLOHM - Floor coverings - Blohm Floors, Inc.
BLOIS - Glassware–household - Durand International
BLOK-FIL - Concrete products - Kwal-Howells Inc.
BLOK-GUARD - Adhesives and sealants - ProSoCo Inc.
BLOK-LOK - Building materials–concrete - AA Wire Products Co.
BLOK-TRUS - Building materials–concrete - AA Wire Products Co.
BLOK-VENT - Ventilation equipment - Leslie-Locke, Inc.
BLOKES - Apparel and accessories - Lifestyle Retail, Inc.
BLOMATIC - Sporting goods - G & G Innovations, Inc.
BLOMMER - Candy - Blommer Chocolate Co.
BLOND BOARDING THREADS - Apparel and accessories - Vincent De La
   Pena
BLOND-IT - Finishing agents - James B. Day and Co.
BLOND OX - Beverages–alcohol - Yellow Rose Brewing Co
BLONDE - Skin care products - Lendan USA Co.
BLONDE DIMENSIONS - Hair care products - Cosmair Inc.
BLONDE ENUFF - Recording label - Cassandra Elizabeth Eubank
BLONDER-TONGUE - Audio equipment - Blonder-Tongue Laboratories Inc.
BLONDES AMERICAN STYLE - Hair care products - Alberto-Culver Co.
BLONDI-SANTI - Wines - Wilson Daniels Ltd.
BLONDIE - Hair care products - Zotos International Inc.
BLONDIE, THE - Food products - Greenfield Healthy Foods Co.
BLONDIE'S COOKIES - Bakery products - Blondie's Cookies, Inc.
BLONDLY - Hair care products - IT&LY Hairfashion NA Inc.
BLONY KISS - Candy ☆ - Topps Co., Inc.
BLOO - Cleaning preparations - Kiwi Brands, Inc.
BLOOD - Sweatshirts - George A. Powell
BLOOD BAIT STIK - Fishing lures ☆ - Brown Bear Bait Co.
BLOOD BATH AT RED FALLS - Computer software - Underworld Software,
   Inc.
BLOOD BUILDER - Vitamins and nutritional supplements - Bio San
   Laboratories Inc.
BLOOD FEUD - Games ☆ - Mayfair Games, Inc.
BLOOD OF TEN CHIEFS - Publisher's imprints - Warp Graphics, Inc.
BLOOD ORANGE - Marmalade - Sarabeth's Kitchen
BLOOD ORANGE - Teas - Eastern Shore Tea Co.
BLOOD RECORDS - Apparel and accessories - Blood Records, Inc.
BLOOD STOPPER - Health care products ☆ - Farnam Cos. Inc.
BLOOD SUCKERS - Chewing gum - Fleer Corp.
BLOOD WARRIOR - Video games - Kaneko USA, Ltd.
BLOOD WARS - Games - Tsr, Inc.
BLOODBATH - Trading cards and stamps - Malibu Comics Entertainment, Inc.

☆ = Now out of production

BLOODHOUND - Tobacco–chewing or smoking - Brown & Williamson Tobacco Corp.

BLOODLINES - Games ☆ - Konami (America) Inc.

BLOODNET - Computer software - Microprose Software, Inc.

BLOODQUEEN - Posters - Aegis Entertainment, Inc.

BLOODY - Candy - Primrose Candy

BLOODY MARY FROM HELL - Mixer - Southwest Specialty Foods

BLOOM - Recording label - David A. Scheraga

BLOOM N' GROW - Garden equipment - Raindrip, Inc.

BLOOM PLUS - Plant growth regulators - Chemical Dynamics, Inc.

BLOOMBERG - Surgical instruments - Leroy Bloomberg

BLOOMBERG TELEVISION - Broadcasting stations–television - Bloomberg LP

BLOOMBERG TRADEBOOK - Banks–commercial - Bloomberg LP

BLOOMBERG TRAVELER, THE - Computer software - Bloomberg LP

BLOOMCRAFT - Fabrics - Bloomcraft, Inc.

BLOOMCRAFT - Wallpaper - Brewster Wallcovering Co.

BLOOMER BUNNY - Greeting cards - American Greetings Corp.

BLOOMERS! - Flowers, plants, and seeds - Turf-Seed, Inc.

BLOOMERS - Greeting cards - Woodbridge Press Publishing Co.

BLOOMFIELD - Floor coverings - Armstrong World Industries, Inc.

BLOOMFIELD - Food products machinery - Bloomfield Industries Inc.

BLOOMGARD - Cleaning preparations - Bloomcraft, Inc.

BLOOMIES - Flowers, plants, and seeds - CFX, Inc.

BLOOMIN' FLOWERS - Jewelry - Jody Coyote, Inc.

BLOOMIN MIRACLE - See **BLOOM N' GROW**

BLOOMIN PLUGS - Flowers, plants, and seeds - Gro-N-Sell, Inc.

BLOOMING COLOR - Flowers, plants, and seeds - Young's Plant Farm, Inc.

BLOOMING COLORS - Cosmetics - Maybelline Co.

BLOOMING YOUTH - Apparel–women's - Wacoal America Inc.

BLOOMINGBAGS - Sporting goods - Catherine A. Gotfredson

BLOOMINGDALE'S - Apparel and accessories - Federated Department Stores, Inc.

BLOOMINGDALE'S ATHLETIC CLUB - Apparel stores–sports - Federated Department Stores, Inc.

BLOOMINGTON - Occasional - JDI Group, Inc.

BLOOMIX - Pet products ☆ - J.E. Ronicker Labs Inc.

BLOOM'N GARDEN POUCH BLOSSOM - Housewares - Bloom'n Plant Products

BLOOMS - Floor coverings–carpet and rugs - Foreign Accents

BLOOMS GALORE - Bedding–linen - Dan River Inc.

BLOOMSBURY - Tiles–ceramic - H & R Johnson Inc.

BLOOMSBURY BOX - Artists' materials - Winsor & Newton

BLOOMSBURY MARKET - Metals - Bloomsbury Market, Inc.

BLOOMWAY - Women's apparel - Freeway Inc.

BLOOP - Balls - Lewis-Frank Corp.

BLOOPER - Fishing lures - Fred Arbogast Co. Inc.

BLOOPERS - Computer software - Binary Software Inc.

BLOOPY - Video production - Creative Children's Group, Ltd.

BLOPS BEAR - Toys–stuffed - Russ Berrie and Co., Inc.

BLOSSOM - Apparel–women's - Group E. Ltd.

BLOSSOM - Bowls - Federal Glass

BLOSSOM - Computer software - Creative Equipment International

BLOSSOM - Computer software ☆ - Gessler Publishing Co., Inc.

BLOSSOM - Foil–aluminum - Highland Supply Corp.

BLOSSOM - Food products - Oakdale Poultry Co.

BLOSSOM - Food products - Schaffer Food Service Co.

BLOSSOM - Glassware–household - Svend Jensen of Denmark Inc.

BLOSSOM - Nuts–salted, roasted, cooked, or canned - Fairmont Snacks Group Inc.

BLOSSOM - Rings–jewelry - Artcarved Inc.

BLOSSOM - Thread ☆ - Coats and Clark Inc.

BLOSSOM - Tiles–ceramic - Monarch Tile Inc.

BLOSSOM - Toiletries and baby-care product - Continental Crafts Co.

BLOSSOM BEAUTIFUL - Dolls - Mattel, Inc.

BLOSSOM BEAUTY - Dolls - Mattel, Inc.

BLOSSOM BLUE - Apparel and accessories ☆ - Kellwood Co.

BLOSSOM BUNNY - Toys–stuffed - Spearhead Industries Inc.

BLOSSOM CREATIONS - Giftware - Blossom Creations

BLOSSOM HILL - Floor coverings - Armstrong World Industries, Inc.

BLOSSOM HILL - Wines - IDV Wines (Beaulieu Vineyard)

BLOSSOM JR. - Apparel and accessories ☆ - Kellwood Co.

BLOSSOM KIDS - Apparel and accessories ☆ - Kellwood Co.

BLOSSOM LAMPS - Lamps–wall - Light Inc.

BLOSSOM LITES - Sporting goods ☆ - Ziffco

BLOSSOM QUEEN - Food products - Pitsweet Inc.

BLOSSOM SET - Garden equipment - Security Product Co.

BLOSSOM TIME - Dinnerware–glass - Nikko Ceramics Inc.

BLOSSOM TIME - Floor coverings - Mannington Resilient Floors

BLOSSOM TIME - Food products - Safeway Stores Inc.

BLOSSOM TRAIL - Fresh fruits - Gillette Citrus Co.

BLOSSOM VALLEY - Cider - Mayer Bros. Apple Products, Inc.

BLOSSOMS - Candy ☆ - Maillard Corp.

BLOSSOMS - Detergents - Miller's Markets, Inc.

BLOSSOMS - Dinnerware–glass ☆ - Nikko Ceramics Inc.

BLOSSOMS IN LACE - Dinnerware ☆ - Corning Inc.

BLOSSOMTIME - Garden equipment - North States Industries Inc.

BLOSSOMTIME - Wallpaper ☆ - Riverside Silkscreen

BLOT:0 - Apparel and accessories - Anthony Papavero

BLOT-O - Tools - Hercules Chemical Co. Inc.

BLOTTO - Adult game ☆ - American Publishing Corp.

BLOTTO - Computer software - Kuzmich Development

BLOUNT - Tools ☆ - Williams & Hussey Machine Co., Inc.

BLOW A TUNE - Toys - Tonka Corp.

BLOW HARD - Musical instruments - C & R Guitars

BLOW HARD - Mustard - Hudson Valley Homestead

BLOW-IT - Hair care products - Schering-Plough Healthcare Products

BLOW-LOONS - Toys - Strombecker Corp.

BLOW-ME-UPS - Toys–stuffed - Fun World Inc.

BLOW-OUT - Chemical preparations - Coastal Industries Inc.

BLOW OUT - Drain cleaner - Comstar International Inc. (IPC Div.)

BLOW-OUT - Hair care products - Ampro Industries, Inc.

BLOW-OUT-PROOF - Rivets–metal ☆ - J.W. Speaker Corp.

BLOW OUT THE FIRE - Games - World Traveler Ltd.

BLOW POP - Confections - Tootsie Roll Industries, Inc.

BLOW POP CLUSTERS - Candy - Tootsie Roll Industries, Inc.

BLOW POPS - Candy - Tootsie Roll Industries, Inc.

BLOW POPS - Food products - DCA Food Industries, Inc.

BLOW TORCH - Toys–automobiles - Tonka Corp.

BLOW-UP - Furniture - Shane Branker and Mike Hoppe Partnership

BLOW-UP - Men's and women's apparel - India Garments Inc.

BLOW-UP PUZZLE - Games - Franklin Merchandising Co.

BLOW UPS - Giftware - Russ Berrie and Co., Inc.

BLOW WAVE - Hair care products - Nutrine Ltd.

BLOWER-IN-A-DRAWER - Heating equipment - Shenandoah Manufacturing Co., Inc.

BLOWGUN - Toys - Tonka Corp.

BLOWING IN THE WIND - Chimes - Delfino Products Inc.

BLOWN OUTS - Apparel–athletic - G & T Enterprises

BLOWOUTS - Toys ☆ - Tomy America, Inc.

BLOX - Apparel–men's - Chauvin International Ltd.

BLOX-BLAZE - Paints ☆ - Fuller-O'Brien Paints Inc.

BLOX-IT - Paints - Mautz Paint Co.

BLOX-RUST - Paints - Fuller-O'Brien Paints Inc.

BLOX SEAL - Paints - Hirshfield's Paint Manufacturing

BLOXEED - Games - Sega of America, Inc.

BLOXFIL - Concrete products - Devoe & Raynolds Co.

BLOXOUT - Adhesives and sealants - Commercial Chemical Co. Inc.

BLOXSEAL - Paints - Mac-O-Lac Paints Inc.

BLP - Paints - Mobile Paint Manufacturing Co.

BLSYS - Furniture - Sebra

BLT - Dishes–earthenware ☆ - Dansk International Designs, Ltd.

BLT - Sprinklers–lawn - American Tube Co. Inc.

BLT - Telephone accessories - Communications Technology Corp.

BLT - Tools–hand-operated - Marshalltown Trowel Co.

BLT SPORTSWEAR - Apparel and accessories - Lenelta Inc.

BLU-6 - Pharmaceutical preparations ☆ - Bluco Inc.

BLU-BELL - Jewelry–precious - Harry Rotter & Co., Inc.

BLU-BITE - Denture materials - Henry Schein, Inc.

BLU-BLAK - Pencils - Faber-Castell Corp.

BLU BOTOL - Water–bottled or canned - Global Beverage Co.

BLU-BOY - Cleaning preparations - Northwest Sanitation Products

BLU-BOY - Cleaning preparations - Reckitt & Colman, Inc.

BLU CASTELLO - Cheese - Swissrose International Inc.

BLU-DACIOUS! KAMIKAZI - Liquors - Mango Bottling, Inc.

BLU DI BLU - Apparel and accessories - Top-Tex, Inc.

BLU-FLUSH - Cleaning preparations ☆ - Willert Home Products, Inc.

BLU-GRO - Fertilizers - Plant Food Co., Inc.

BLU HARE RECORDS - Compact discs–prerecorded - Blu Hare Records

BLU-HIST - Pharmaceutical preparations ☆ - Bluco Inc.

BLU-LITE - Automotive parts and accessories - Monmouth Corp.

BLU-MOL - Saws–hand-operated - Rule Industries, Inc.

☆ = Now out of production

BLU-PRIDE - Steel products - Parkersburg Steel Co.
BLU-RAY - Rings–jewelry - Hy Spreckman & Sons Inc.
BLU-SCRIBE - Office supplies ✩ - Boorum & Pease Co.
BLU-SHEL - Polishing rouge ✩ - Park Metallurgical Corp.
BLU-TACK - Bostik Inc.
BLU-TACK - Adhesives and sealants ✩ - Black & Decker Corp.
BLU-WATER - Cleaning preparations - Willert Home Products, Inc.
BLU WHITE - Blueing - Dial Corp.
BLUBANDOO - Apparel and accessories - CC Waterworks
BLUBBER - Balls - Imperial Toy Corp.
BLUBLOCKER - Suntan lotions - Blublocker Corp.
BLUBORO - Astringents - Allergan, Inc.
BLUCO - Pharmaceutical preparations ✩ - Bluco Inc.
BLUDGEON - Archery equipment - Saunders Archery Co.
BLUDGEON - Toys - Tonka Corp.
BLUE - Vitamins and nutritional supplements - Frye Co.
BLUE 2000 - Filters–air - Survivair, Inc.
BLUE ACRES - Rope - MSC, Inc.
BLUE AMMONIA - Ammonia - Solkatronic Chemicals, Inc.
BLUE ANCHOR - Coffee - Millstone Coffee, Inc.
BLUE ANCHOR - Food products - Blue Anchor Inc.
BLUE AND GREEN CHECK - Bathroom accessories - Royal Cathay Trading Co.
BLUE & LUCY - Toys–stuffed - Amy Schramm
BLUE ANGEL - Bicycles - Columbia Manufacturing Inc.
BLUE ANGEL - Burners - Bel-Aire Sales Corp.
BLUE ANGEL - Kites ✩ - Hi-Flier Manufacturing Co.
BLUE ANGEL - Pumps–water - Campbell Group (Wayne Home Equipment Div.)
BLUE ANGEL - Toys - Tonka Corp.
BLUE ANGEL - Toys–airplanes - Cox Products Inc.
BLUE ARMADILLO - Apparel and accessories - Blue Armadillo Enterprises
BLUE ASH - Recording label - Summit Enterprises
BLUE ASSASSIN - Insecticides - Fermone Corp., Inc.
BLUE ASTOR - Dishes–china - Taylor, Smith & Taylor Co.
BLUE ATTITUDE - Apparel and accessories - Wal-Mart Stores Inc.
BLUE AWAY - Metals - Competition Chemicals
BLUE BAKERY - Bakery products - Willingham Corp.
BLUE BAND - Glassware–household - Owens-Illinois Inc. (Libbey Div.)
BLUE BAND - Pencils - Faber-Castell Corp.
BLUE BANDANA - Recording label - Hard Hat Records
BLUE BANNER - Pet products - Golden Cat Corp.
BLUE BASE - Cleaning preparations - Neutron Industries, Inc.
BLUE BAY - Colognes ✩ - Avon Products, Inc.
BLUE BAYOU - Dolls ✩ - Effanbee Doll Corp.
BLUE BEAK - Food products - Umatilla Citrus Growers Association
BLUE BEAR USA - Apparel and accessories - Blue Bear
BLUE BELL - Batteries - At&T Corp.
BLUE BELL - Dishes–china - Viletta China Co.
BLUE BELL - Floor coverings - Mannington Resilient Floors
BLUE BELL - Housewares ✩ - Blue Mountain Industries, Inc.
BLUE BELL - Ice cream - Blue Bell Creameries, L.P.
BLUE BELL - Milk ✩ - Hygeia Dairy Co.
BLUE BELL BOTTLING COMPANY, INC. - Beverages–malt - Blue Bell Bottling Co., Inc.
BLUE BELL FREE - Ice cream - Blue Bell Creameries, L.P.
BLUE BELL LIGHT - Ice milk - Blue Bell Creameries, L.P.
BLUE BELLE - Brooms - Zephyr Manufacturing Co.
BLUE BELLE - Decals and transfers - Rubbermaid Inc.
BLUE BELLS - Glassware–household ✩ - Fenton Art Glass Co.
BLUE BIRD - Apparel–children's - Blue Bird Knitwear Co.
BLUE BIRD - Bakery products - Rich Products Corp.
BLUE BIRD - Bicycles - Columbia Manufacturing Inc.
BLUE BIRD - Cutlery - Bergman Tool Manufacturing Co. Inc.
BLUE BIRD - Dishes–earthenware - Royal China & Porcelain Companies Inc.
BLUE BIRD - Fruits and vegetables - Peshastin Fruit Growers Association
BLUE BIRD - Hams ✩ - Prestige Foods Corp.
BLUE BIRD - Housewares ✩ - King Cotton Cordage Co.
BLUE BIRD - Kites ✩ - Airplane Kite Co.
BLUE BIRD II - Apparel–children's - Blue Bird Knitwear Co.
BLUE BIRD OF HAPPINESS - Toys–stuffed - Russ Berrie and Co., Inc.
BLUE BIRD ZERO - Toys–models ✩ - Estes Industries
BLUE BLADE - Razor blades - Gillette Co.
BLUE-BLAZE - Cleaning preparations–window - Champion Chemical Co. of California Inc.

BLUE BLAZES - Floor finishing machines–commercial ✩ - Hako Minuteman Inc.
BLUE BLAZES - Food containers - Farmhouse Foods
BLUE BLEND - Skin care products - Paula Payne Products Co. Inc.
BLUE BLOCK - Plastics ✩ - Martin Carbone Inc.
BLUE BOAR - Beverages–malt - The Stroh Brewery Co.
BLUE BOAR - Fabrics–denim - Dan River Inc.
BLUE BOAR - Hams - Atalanta Corp.
BLUE BOAR - Tobacco - American Tobacco Co.
BLUE BOND - Film - Keystone Jackets, Inc.
BLUE BOND - Tools - Norton Co.
BLUE BONNET - Bicycles - Columbia Manufacturing Inc.
BLUE BONNET - Dairy products - Nabisco Holdings Corp.
BLUE BONNET - Margarine - Nabisco Foods Group
BLUE BONNET BUTTER BLEND - Margarine - Nabisco Foods Group
BLUE BOOK - Wallpaper ✩ - Imperial Wallcoverings, Inc.
BLUE BOW - Dinnerware–glass ✩ - Royal China & Porcelain Companies Inc.
BLUE BOW - Food products - Sun Garden Packing Co., Inc.
BLUE BOY - Vegetables–canned - Curtice-Burns Foods, Inc.
BLUE BRASS - Recording label - Release Records
BLUE BREEZE - Dinnerware–glass ✩ - Lenox, Inc.
BLUE BRUSHSTROKES - Dinnerware–glass ✩ - Lenox, Inc.
BLUE BUMPS - Candy - Doug Johnson, Inc.
BLUE BUNNY - Ice cream - Wells' Dairy, Inc.
BLUE C - Fibers–synthetic - Monsanto Polymer Products
BLUE CACTUS - Footwear - JBI, Inc.
BLUE CALICO - Dinnerware–glass - Crownford Giftware Co. Inc.
BLUE CARNIVAL - Servingware ✩ - Indiana Glass Co.
BLUE CASCADE - Hardware ✩ - Proven Pumps Corp.
BLUE CASTELLO - Cheese - Tholstrup Cheese USA Inc.
BLUE CAT - Beverages–malt - Crooked River, Inc.
BLUE CAT - Fishing tackle ✩ - Gladding Braided Products Inc.
BLUE CELL - Microwave components - RF Prime
BLUE CHELAN - Food products - Blue Chelan Inc.
BLUE CHIP - Exercising equipment - Professional Gym Inc.
BLUE CHIP - Fishing tackle ✩ - Martin Reel Co.
BLUE CHIP - Floor coverings–carpet and rugs - Dan River Inc.
BLUE CHIP - Floor coverings–carpet and rugs - Masland Corp.
BLUE CHIP - Flowers, plants, and seeds - Jacklin Seed
BLUE CHIP - Gloves–rubber ✩ - Granet Inc.
BLUE CHIP - Meat products - Saramar Corp.
BLUE CHIP - Oils–lubricating - Arkla Chemical Corp. (Petroleum Div.)
BLUE CHIP - Pens ✩ - Quill Co. Inc.
BLUE CHIP - Ships–sailing vessels - Cape Cod Shipbuilding Co.
BLUE CHIP - Snack foods - Aster Nut Products Co. Inc.
BLUE CHIP JAZZ - Recording label - Da Music
BLUE CHIP PICK - Games - Charlie Pesiridis
BLUE CHIPS - Snack foods - Garden of Eatin', Inc.
BLUE CIRCLE - Balls–billiard ✩ - Brunswick Corp.
BLUE CIRCLE - Food products - Lodi Canning Inc.
BLUE CIRCLE RAIA, INC. - Concrete products - Blue Circle Raia, Inc.
BLUE CLOUD - Mattress pads - Better Sleep, Inc.
BLUE CLOUDS - Tableware–china ✩ - Villeroy and Boch Tableware Ltd.
BLUE COACH - Food products - Sechler Foods Inc.
BLUE COBRA - Sporting goods - Multi Impact Target Systems Inc.
BLUE COLLAR - Footwear - Lake of the Woods
BLUE COLUMBINE - Dinnerware ✩ - Corning Inc.
BLUE COMET - Musical instruments - Multivox/Sorkin Music Co. Inc.
BLUE CO. BY LE TIGRE - Apparel and accessories - Hampton Industries, Inc.
BLUE CORAL - Automotive parts and accessories - Blue Coral, Inc.
BLUE CORN - Pancake and waffle mix ✩ - Zia Foods
BLUE CORNFLOWER - Dinnerware - Corning Inc.
BLUE CREEK - Apparel - Fingerhut Companies Inc.
BLUE CREEPER - Flowers, plants, and seeds - Monrovia Nursery Co.
BLUE CREST - Food products - Bar O Farms
BLUE CREST - Swimming pools ✩ - Doughboy Recreational Inc.
BLUE CROSS - Health care products - Halsey Drug Co. Inc.
BLUE CROSS - Manicure preparations - Blue Cross Beauty Products Inc.
BLUE CROSS - Paper–toweling - Georgia-Pacific Corp.
BLUE CROWN - Shortening ✩ - CPC International Inc.
BLUE CROWN - Spark plugs - Zeller Corp.
BLUE CRYSTAL - Water–bottled or canned - Blue Crystal Water Co.
BLUE DAHLIA - Dinnerware–glass ✩ - Metlox Pottery Shoppe
BLUE DAISY - Dinnerware–glass ✩ - Salem China Co.
BLUE DAISY MIST - Sachets - Andre Richard
BLUE DANUBE - Dolls ✩ - Effanbee Doll Corp.

✩ = Now out of production

BLUE DANUBE - Harmonicas - Sun Rams Products, Inc.
BLUE DANUBE - Perfumes ☆ - Vi-Jon Laboratories, Inc.
BLUE DANUBE - Tableware–china - Lipper International Inc.
BLUE DANUBE PREMIER CUT - Jewelry - QVC, Inc.
BLUE DAWN - Dishes–earthenware - Denby USA Limited
BLUE DEATH - Pesticides–household - Bonide Products, Inc.
BLUE DELFT - Housewares - Ernest Sohn Creations
BLUE DELFT ROSES - Tiles–ceramic - Monarch Tile Inc.
BLUE DELL - Fruits–canned - Northwest Packing Co.
BLUE DEVIL - Bicycles - Columbia Manufacturing Inc.
BLUE DEVIL - Filters–water - Blue Devil Industries, Inc.
BLUE DEVIL - Sponges - Karlen Manufacturing, Inc.
BLUE DIAMOND - Cleaning preparations ☆ - White Cap Inc.
BLUE DIAMOND - Cosmetics ☆ - Duart Industries Ltd.
BLUE DIAMOND - Food products - Blue Diamond Meat Co.
BLUE DIAMOND - Food products - Henry Bresky & Sons Inc.
BLUE DIAMOND - Food products - Central Fish & Oyster Co.
BLUE DIAMOND - Food products ☆ - Diamond Fruit Growers
BLUE DIAMOND - Frozen food products - Golden Shore Food Processors, Inc.
BLUE DIAMOND - Fruits and vegetables ☆ - Western Idaho Potato Processing Co.
BLUE DIAMOND - Knives–putty ☆ - Hyde Manufacturing Co.
BLUE DIAMOND - Nuts–salted, roasted, cooked, or canned - California Almond Growers Exchange
BLUE DIAMOND - Nuts–salted, roasted, cooked, or canned ☆ - Blue Diamond Growers
BLUE DIAMOND - Pet products - Pillsbury Co.
BLUE DIAMOND - Sporting goods ☆ - Wright & McGill Co.
BLUE DIAMOND CALIFORNIA ALMONDS - Edible nuts - California Almond Growers Exchange
BLUE DOT - Artists' materials - Vemco Corp.
BLUE DOT - Fruits and vegetables - David Oppenheimer California, Inc.
BLUE DOT - Handkerchiefs ☆ - Carolina Manufacturing Inc.
BLUE DOT - Photographic equipment - GTE Corp.
BLUE DOT - Sheet metal products - Aluminum Co. of America
BLUE DOT - Sporting goods - Worth Inc.
BLUE DOTS - Dinnerware–glass ☆ - Nikko Ceramics Inc.
BLUE DRAGON - Insecticides - Dragon Chemical Corp.
BLUE DREAMS - Tableware–china - Villeroy and Boch Tableware Ltd.
BLUE DUCK - Pillows - Pacific Coast Feather Co.
BLUE DUSK - Dinnerware ☆ - Corning Inc.
BLUE EAGLE CALIFORNIA PREMIUM RED WINE SINCE 1935 - Wines - Blue Eagle Vineyards, LLC
BLUE ELEGANCE - Dolls - Mattel, Inc.
BLUE ELEGANCE - Tableware–china ☆ - Villeroy and Boch Tableware Ltd.
BLUE ELEPHANT - Giftware - Waterford Wedgwood USA, Inc.
BLUE ENERGY - Shoe accessories - Mason Shoe Manufacturing Co.
BLUE ESPLANADE - Tableware–china - Pfaltzgraff Investment Co.
BLUE-EYED-BLUES - Recording label - Claiming Race Records
BLUE FALLS - Water–bottled or canned - North American Beverage Enterprises, Inc.
BLUE FIN - Boats - Glen-L Marine Designs
BLUE FIN - Boats–motor - Penn Yan Boats Inc.
BLUE FIN - Sporting goods ☆ - Pompanette Inc.
BLUE FIRE - Sporting goods ☆ - Gold Eagle/Arnold Palmer
BLUE FIRE RECORDS - Compact discs–prerecorded - Hill Country Record Co.
BLUE FLAG - Food products ☆ - Di Giorgio Corp.
BLUE FLAME - Automotive parts and accessories - Teleflex Inc.
BLUE FLAME - Cooking utensils–glass ☆ - Revere Ware Corp.
BLUE FLAME - Flowers, plants, and seeds - Lake Ferns, Inc.
BLUE FLAME - Gasoline - SF Services, Inc.
BLUE FLAME - Lighters - Canterbury Enterprises
BLUE FLAME - Recording label - Blue Flame Records
BLUE FLAME - Wood products ☆ - Woolsey Marine Industries
BLUE FLEUR - Dinnerware - Corning Inc.
BLUE FLOW - Concrete products - Blue Circle Raia, Inc.
BLUE FLOWERS - Dinnerware–glass - WMF/USA
BLUE FOOT - Pet products - National Scent Co.
BLUE FOX - Fabrics–denim - Dan River Inc.
BLUE FOX - Sporting goods - FTM Sports
BLUE FRONT - Barbeque sauce - Blue Front
BLUE GALAXIE - Dinnerware–glass ☆ - Nikko Ceramics Inc.
BLUE GALAXY - Swimming pools - Lomart Industries
BLUE GARLAND - Dishes–china - Martin's Herend Imports Inc.
BLUE GATE - Candles - San Francisco Candle Co.

BLUE GEL - Health care products - Organics Corp. of America (Ambix Laboratories Div.)
BLUE GEM - Cosmetics - House of Lowell Inc.
BLUE GEM - Health care products - Hair Doc Co.
BLUE GIANT - Blueberries ☆ - Adkin Blue Ribbon Packing Co.
BLUE GLACIER - Swimming pools - Doughboy Recreational Inc.
BLUE GLIDER - Trowels - Goldblatt Tool Co.
BLUE GOLD - Seafood products–fresh or frozen - Blue Gold Holdings, Inc.
BLUE GOO - Syrup - Flavor Burst Co.
BLUE GOOSE - Cookies - Sarah Lingwood's Kitchens
BLUE GOOSE - Food products - Western Farmers Association
BLUE GOOSE - Golfing equipment - Ray Cook Co.
BLUE GOOSE - Vegetables–frozen - Pacific Valley Foods
BLUE GOOSE FARMS - Sandwiches–prepackaged - Service America Corp.
BLUE GRANULAR - Fertilizers - Nor-Am Chemical Co.
BLUE GRASS - Candy ☆ - Gilliam Candy Co. Inc. (Gilliam Candy Brands)
BLUE GRASS - Colognes - Elizabeth Arden Inc.
BLUE GRASS - Food products - Paramount Foods Inc.
BLUE GRASS - Musical instrument accessories - Trophy Music Co.
BLUE GRASS BRAND - Food products - Blue Grass Provisions Co., Inc.
BLUE-GREEN CONNECTION - Health care products - Healthwatchers System
BLUE GREY - Floor coverings - Southern Aggregates
BLUE-GRIP - Gloves–work - Pioneer Industrial Products Co.
BLUE GULF - Seafood products–fresh or frozen - Gorton Group
BLUE GULF - Shrimp–canned or cured ☆ - Robinson Canning Co. Inc.
BLUE HAIR - Apparel and accessories - Mj Grant Co.
BLUE HAIR - Paper–gummed - Mj Grant Co.
BLUE HAWAII - Shorts–women's - Joni Albao
BLUE HAZE - Fabrics - Burlington Industries, Inc.
BLUE HEART - Flowers, plants, and seeds - Hooven Allison
BLUE HEATHER - Dinnerware - Corning Inc.
BLUE HEATHER - Glassware–household ☆ - Crisa Corp.
BLUE HEAVEN - Christmas tree ornaments ☆ - Cracker Box Inc.
BLUE HEAVEN - Dolls ☆ - Effanbee Doll Corp.
BLUE HEAVEN - Food products ☆ - Arrowhead Mills, Inc.
BLUE HEAVEN - Hosiery - Blue Heaven Hosiery Co., Inc.
BLUE HEAVEN - Tortillas - Natural Choices Inc.
BLUE HEN - Pickles - San-Del Packing Co.
BLUE HEN - Vegetables–canned - Draper-King Cole Inc.
BLUE HEN BEER - Apparel and accessories - Blue Hen Beer Co., Ltd.
BLUE HERON - Beverages–malt - Mendocino Brewing Co., Inc.
BLUE HERON - Wallpaper ☆ - J. Chesterfield Studio
BLUE HERON PALE ALE - Beverages–malt - Mendocino Brewing Co., Inc.
BLUE HERON PINES - Key rings - Ole Hansen & Sons, Inc.
BLUE HERON PRESS - Publisher's imprints - Blue Heron Group, Inc.
BLUE HILL - Water–bottled or canned - Blue Hill Spring Water Co.
BLUE HILL RECORDINGS - Recording label - Rosalie Gerut
BLUE HILLS STUDIO - Floor coverings–carpet and rugs - Nancy Biggs Thomas
BLUE HOLDEX - Aquariums–household - Jungle Laboratories Corp.
BLUE HONEYCOMB - Dinnerware–glass ☆ - Svend Jensen of Denmark Inc.
BLUE HORSE - Dishes–earthenware - Hadley Pottery Co. Inc.
BLUE HORSE - Office supplies ☆ - Mead Corp.
BLUE HOSE - Cables - Belden Wire & Cable Co.
BLUE HOUR - Glassware–household ☆ - Svend Jensen of Denmark Inc.
BLUE ICE - Dry ice - Rubbermaid Inc.
BLUE ICE - First aid kits - Pelton Shepherd Industries
BLUE ICE - Hair coloring preparations - Helene Curtis Industries Inc.
BLUE ICE - Toys - Remco Baby Inc.
BLUE IMARI - Tableware–china ☆ - Lipper International Inc.
BLUE IN THE FACE - Watch crystals - Paul J. Gabriel
BLUE ITALIAN - Dishes–earthenware - Royal China & Porcelain Companies Inc.
BLUE-J INDI GO - Chemical preparations - IVAX Industries, Inc.
BLUE-J KLEEN-POCKETS - Detergents - IVAX Industries, Inc.
BLUE-J ZONE-FREE SOFTENER - Detergents - IVAX Industries, Inc.
BLUE JACKET - Archery equipment - AcuSport Corp.
BLUE JAY - Boats–canoes - Formula Yachts
BLUE JAY - Cases–musical instrument - M & M Distributing Co.
BLUE JAY - Fruits and vegetables - Johnston Farms
BLUE JAY - Hobby kits - Flora Craft Inc.
BLUE JAY - Recording label - Stark Records & Tape Co.
BLUE JAY - Ships–sailing vessels ☆ - Armstrong Boats
BLUE JEAN - Paper–bond - Esleeck Manufacturing Co., Inc.
BLUE JEAN - Publisher's imprints - Auto Book Press
BLUE JEANS POETRY - Publisher's imprints - Coda Publications

☆ = Now out of production

BLUE JEWEL - Bottled water - Blue Jewel Water Co.
BLUE JOB - Polishes - Glass Restoration Specialists, Inc.
BLUE KNIGHT - Knives–pocket - Buck Knives, Inc.
BLUE LABEL - Artists' materials - Martin F. Weber Co.
BLUE LABEL - Cleaning preparations - DL/Banite
BLUE LABEL - Food products - Curtice-Burns Foods, Inc.
BLUE LABEL - Paper ☆ - A.B. Dick Co.
BLUE LABEL - Pencils ☆ - Koh-I-Noor, Inc.
BLUE LABEL - Pet products - Vital Nutrition Products
BLUE LABEL - Polishes - H. Behlen & Bro. Inc.
BLUE LABEL - Thread - Blue Mountain Industries, Inc.
BLUE LACE - Dishes–china - Taylor, Smith & Taylor Co.
BLUE LAGOON - Christmas tree ornaments ☆ - Cracker Box Inc.
BLUE LAGOON - Dinnerware–glass - WMF/USA
BLUE LAGOON - Dyes and pigments - Parkway Research Corp.
BLUE LAGOON - Hair care products - Cosmair Inc.
BLUE LAKE - Fruits and vegetables - Gold Digger Apple Inc.
BLUE LAKES - Fish–fresh or frozen - Blue Lakes Trout Farm Inc.
BLUE LANTERN PUBLISHING - Publisher's imprints - Blue Lantern Publishing
BLUE LASER - Stencils - American Traditional Stencils
BLUE LEAF DESIGN - Tents - Blue Leaf Design, Inc.
BLUE LEAGUE - Apparel and accessories - Lead Sportswear LLC
BLUE LIGHTING - Dinnerware–glass ☆ - Svend Jensen of Denmark Inc.
BLUE LIGHTNING - Dolls - Mattel, Inc.
BLUE LIGHTNING - Footwear ☆ - E.S. Originals, Inc.
BLUE LILY - Dinnerware - Corning Inc.
BLUE LINE - Trading cards and stamps - Treat Entertainment, Inc.
BLUE LINE - Tubes–steel - Aerotrend Products
BLUE LINE STANDARD - Tape–adhesive - Capitol Adhesives Inc.
BLUE LINER - Adhesives and sealants - Phil Marano Inc.
BLUE LITE - Sporting goods - Jack Martin Co.
BLUE LOTION - Veterinary pharmaceutical preparations - Farnam Cos. Inc.
BLUE LOTION AEROSOL - Veterinary pharmaceutical preparations - Boehringer Ingelheim Animal Health, Inc.
BLUE LUSTRE - Carpet-cleaning system - Blue Lustre, LLC
BLUE LUSTRE DIRT BUSTER - Cleaning preparations - Blue Lustre, LLC
BLUE MAGIC - Adhesives and sealants - J.C. Whitlam Manufacturing Co.
BLUE MAGIC - Craft supplies - Sig Manufacturing Inc.
BLUE MAGIC - Food containers - Luce Corp.
BLUE MAGIC - Hair care products - J. Strickland & Co.
BLUE MAGIC - Housewares - Blue Magic Products Inc.
BLUE MAGIC - Pet products ☆ - Safari Pet Products
BLUE MAGIC - Polishing rouge ☆ - Park Metallurgical Corp.
BLUE MAGIC SOFTWARE - Computer software - Sente Systems, Inc.
BLUE MARACA RECORDS - Recording label - Glen Fortinberry
BLUE MARBLE - Glassware–household ☆ - Fenton Art Glass Co.
BLUE MARBLE GEOGRAPHIC - Computer software - Blue Marble Geographics
BLUE MARK - Recording label - QCA Inc.
BLUE MARK - Rope - Samson Cordage Works
BLUE MARLIN BEER BLUE MARLIN BREWERY MIAMI, FLORIDA - Beverages–alcohol - Dennis L. Valdez
BLUE MARMALADE - Paper products - Blue Marmalade, Inc.
BLUE MAX - Automotive parts and accessories - Brinkmann Corp.
BLUE MAX - Cleaning preparations - SCI Scandicrafts Inc.
BLUE MAX - Compressors–air - Coleman Powermate, Inc.
BLUE MAX - Computer software ☆ - Broderbund Software, Inc.
BLUE MAX - Machine parts - Marathon Electric Manufacturing Corp.
BLUE MAX - Novelty lights - IMS Corp.
BLUE MAX - Oils–lubricating - Kerr-McGee Chemical Corp.
BLUE MAX - Sporting goods ☆ - Dunlop Maxfli Sports Corp.
BLUE MAX - Sunglasses - Telebrands Corp.
BLUE MAX - Tape–masking - Nelson King Inc.
BLUE MAX - Toys–automobiles - Thomas Lowe Ventures, Inc.
BLUE MAX - Waxes–mineral - Ashland Oil, Inc.
BLUE MEADOW - Housewares - Himark Enterprises Inc.
BLUE MEDAL - Fishing rods - American Import Co.
BLUE MESA - Beverages–alcohol - Blue Mesa Management Corp.
BLUE MILL - Fruits and vegetables ☆ - MBG Marketing
BLUE MINT - Cosmetics - Sebastian International, Inc.
BLUE MIRAGE - Markers–felt-tip - Illustrator Pen Products Inc.
BLUE MIST - Baskets–wood ☆ - Royal Cathay Trading Co.
BLUE MIST - Glassware–household ☆ - Lenox Crystal, Inc.
BLUE MIST - Paper–toweling - Von Drehle Corp.
BLUE MIST - Water–bottled or canned - Carolina Beverage Inc.
BLUE MOCCA - Coffee - Products-from-Sweden Inc.

BLUE MONDAY - Candy - Ruth Hunt Candy Co.
BLUE MONDAY - Toys - Tonka Corp.
BLUE MOON - Beverages–malt - Adolph Coors Co.
BLUE MOON - Cheese - Blue Moon Cheese Co. Inc.
BLUE MOON - Christmas tree ornaments ☆ - Cracker Box Inc.
BLUE MOON - Computer software - Blue Moon Software, Inc.
BLUE MOON - Dinnerware–glass ☆ - Nikko Ceramics Inc.
BLUE MOON - Flowers, plants, and seeds - Jacklin Seed
BLUE MOON - Spices and extracts - E.A. Weber & Co.
BLUE MOON - Toys - Tonka Corp.
BLUE MOON - Wallpaper - Mokena Mills Inc.
BLUE MOON MAGIC - Lipsticks - Pavion Ltd.
BLUE MOON REEF - Lighting fixtures–underwater - Aquarium Products Inc.
BLUE MOON SORBET - Frozen foods - Blue Moon Foods Inc.
BLUE MORROW - Meat products–beef ☆ - Normark & Associates
BLUE MOUNTAIN - Blinds–venetian - Wellington Leisure Products, Inc.
BLUE MOUNTAIN - Computer software - Blue Mountain Software, Inc.
BLUE MOUNTAIN - Fish–fresh or frozen - Blue Mountain Brands, Inc.
BLUE MOUNTAIN - Golfing equipment ☆ - Western Golf Inc.
BLUE MOUNTAIN - Pet products - ALPO Petfoods Inc.
BLUE MOUNTAIN ARTS - Paper - Blue Mountain Arts Inc.
BLUE MOUNTAIN ARTS VISIONS - Greeting cards - Hartford House, Ltd.
BLUE MOUNTAIN ARTS VISIONS - Greeting cards ☆ - Blue Mountain Arts Inc.
BLUE MOUNTAIN PRINTMAKERS - Paper–writing - Editions Ltd.
BLUE NEWS - Apparel–children's - New World Kids Co.
BLUE NILE - Apparel and accessories ☆ - Swatch Watch USA
BLUE NORSE - Dinnerware–glass ☆ - Svend Jensen of Denmark Inc.
BLUE NOTE - Cheese ☆ - Tholstrup Cheese USA Inc.
BLUE NOTE - Chimes - Woodstock Percussion, Inc.
BLUE NOTE - Lipsticks - Lancome
BLUE NOTE - Recording label - Capitol-EMI Music Inc.
BLUE NOTE - Recording label - Capitol Records, Inc.
BLUE NOTE BLEND - Coffee - Starbucks Corp.
BLUE NUN - Wines - Schieffelin and Somerset Co.
BLUE NUN LIEBFRAUMILCH - Wines - Shaw-Ross International Importers
BLUE OAK - Tools ☆ - O.P. Link Handle Co. Inc.
BLUE OAKS - Firearms, accessories, and parts - Blue Oaks Inc.
BLUE OCEAN - Food products - Shore Lobster & Shrimp Corp.
BLUE OCEAN - Shower stalls–plastic ☆ - Darik Enterprises Inc.
BLUE ONION - Dishes–china - WMF/USA
BLUE ONION - Earthenware ☆ - Scio Pottery Co.
BLUE OPALESCENT - Glassware–household - Fenton Art Glass Co.
BLUE OPERA - Apparel and accessories - Beston Design Group
BLUE ORCHID - Recording label - DA Music USA
BLUE ORGANDY - Tableware–china - Pfaltzgraff Investment Co.
BLUE OX - Automotive parts and accessories - Automatic Equipment Manufacturing Co.
BLUE OX - Fabrics–denim - Dan River Inc.
BLUE PACIFIC - Food products - Associated Seafood Co., Inc.
BLUE PACIFIC - Seafood products–fresh or frozen - Penguin Frozen Foods, Inc.
BLUE PACIFIC - Sporting goods ☆ - Wright & McGill Co.
BLUE PARROT - Teas - Coffee Bean International, Inc.
BLUE PARROT ICED TEAS - Teas - Coffee Bean International, Inc.
BLUE PEARL - Cosmetics - Merle Norman Cosmetics
BLUE PEARL - Incense - Blue Pearl
BLUE PEARL - Incense - Siddha International Import/Export
BLUE PEONY - Dinnerware–glass - Nikko Ceramics Inc.
BLUE PIG INDUSTRIES - Computer software - Matthew Martin Barnes
BLUE PILOT - Apparel and accessories - Moti Shilon
BLUE PINSTRIPES - Dinnerware–glass - Lenox, Inc.
BLUE PLANET GEMS - Jewelry - Blue Planet Gems
BLUE PLANET PRODUCE - Fruits and vegetables - LGS Specialty Sales Ltd.
BLUE PLANET SURF GEAR - Sporting goods - Robert Stehlik
BLUE PLATE - Mayonnaise - Reily Foods
BLUE PLATE - Recording label - Al Bunetta Management
BLUE PLATE - Seafood products–canned or cured - Southern Shell Fish Co.
BLUE PLATE - Vegetables–canned ☆ - McCall Farms Inc.
BLUE PLATE SPECIAL - Dishwashing compounds - Harley Chemicals
BLUE PLATE SPECIAL - Motor vehicle parts and accessories - Raybestos Aftermarket Products Co.
BLUE POLY - Automotive parts and accessories - Blue Coral, Inc.
BLUE POPPY - Food products - Walla Walla Produce Co.
BLUE PRINCESS - Colognes - Darling Corp.
BLUE PRINT SHUTTLE - Cases–plastic ☆ - Rod Caddy Industries

☆ = Now out of production

BLUE PROSE - Dinnerware–glass - Nikko Ceramics Inc.
BLUE PROTECTION PLUS - Gloves–safety - Great Age Container, Inc.
BLUE RACER - Bicycles ☆ - Huffy Corp.
BLUE RAINBOW - Servingware ☆ - Corning Inc.
BLUE RANGER - Toys - Saban Entertainment, Inc.
BLUE RASPBERRY CREATION - Iced tea–bottled or canned - Hansen Beverage Co.
BLUE RASPBERRY POPS - Candy - Brach and Brock Confections Inc.
BLUE RASPBERRY-REX - Syrup - Givaudan Rare Flavors
BLUE RAZZ - Frozen foods - Charms Co.
BLUE RAZZBERRY - Candy - Phoenix Confections Inc.
BLUE REEF - Scuba diving equipment - Mendel Mendlowits
BLUE REVOLUTION - Apparel and accessories - Bugle Boy Industries, Inc.
BLUE RHAPSODY - Dolls - Mattel, Inc.
BLUE RHINO - Tanks–gas - Blue Rhino Corp.
BLUE RIBBON - Baked goods - Interstate Brands Corp.
BLUE RIBBON - Beverages–alcohol - Premier Malt Products, Inc.
BLUE RIBBON - Bicycles - Columbia Manufacturing Inc.
BLUE RIBBON - Biscuits - Pierre Frozen Foods Inc.
BLUE RIBBON - Blueberries - Adkin Blue Ribbon Packing Co.
BLUE RIBBON - Brooms - France Broom Co.
BLUE RIBBON - Candy ☆ - Bobs Candies Inc.
BLUE RIBBON - Cigars - A.J. Golden Inc.
BLUE RIBBON - Cleaning preparations - Blue Lustre, LLC
BLUE RIBBON - Cleaning preparations - Patterson Laboratories Inc.
BLUE RIBBON - Cleaning preparations–carpet and rug - Rooto Corp.
BLUE RIBBON - Combs ☆ - Comare Corp.
BLUE RIBBON - Dinnerware - Lillian Vernon Corp.
BLUE RIBBON - Dinnerware–glass - Nikko Ceramics Inc.
BLUE RIBBON - Dinnerware–glass ☆ - Franciscan by Johnson Brothers, USA, Inc.
BLUE RIBBON - Eggs ☆ - C.H. James and Co.
BLUE RIBBON - Fibers–synthetic - Stearns Technical Textiles Co.
BLUE RIBBON - Firearms, accessories, and parts - Beeman Precision Airguns
BLUE RIBBON - Fishing poles - American Import Co.
BLUE RIBBON - Flower pots–earthenware - Blue Ribbon Flower Holder Co.
BLUE RIBBON - Flowers, plants, and seeds - Agway Country Foods Inc.
BLUE RIBBON - Food products - Chefmaster Products
BLUE RIBBON - Food products - Conagra, Inc.
BLUE RIBBON - Fruits and vegetables - Snokist Growers
BLUE RIBBON - Furniture - John Mullins & Sons Inc.
BLUE RIBBON - Guitars - Fred Gretsch Enterprises
BLUE RIBBON - Handles–wood - Sequatchie Handle Works Inc.
BLUE RIBBON - Hardware ☆ - Gleason Industrial Products
BLUE RIBBON - Harmonicas - Hohner Inc.
BLUE RIBBON - Lumber - Georgia-Pacific Corp.
BLUE RIBBON - Margarine - Lever Brothers Co. Inc.
BLUE RIBBON - Meat products–canned - Midwest Sausage & Corned Beef
BLUE RIBBON - Meat products–poultry - Simmons Foods
BLUE RIBBON - Milk - Blue Ribbon Dairy
BLUE RIBBON - Motor vehicle parts and accessories ☆ - Budge Industries, Inc.
BLUE RIBBON - Paints - Blue Ribbon Paint Co.
BLUE RIBBON - Pens ☆ - Blue Ribbon Pen & Pencil Co. Inc.
BLUE-RIBBON - Pet products ☆ - Semmerling Fence and Supply Inc.
BLUE RIBBON - Playing cards - United States Playing Card Co.
BLUE RIBBON - Publisher's imprints - Scholastic Inc.
BLUE RIBBON - Rice - Comet American Marketing
BLUE RIBBON - Staples - Markwell Manufacturing Co. Inc.
BLUE RIBBON - Tableware–china ☆ - Lenox, Inc.
BLUE RIBBON - Tires - Bridgestone/Firestone, Inc.
BLUE RIBBON - Twine ☆ - Malow Corp.
BLUE RIBBON - Vacuum cleaners and accessories - The Eureka Co.
BLUE-RIBBON BUDDIES - Publisher's imprints - Sylvia Harding
BLUE RIBBON CHAMPIONS - Toys - Marchon, Inc.
BLUE RIBBON COW - Trusses–surgical - Dakin Inc.
BLUE RIBBON DINNER - Turkeys - Cooper's Turkey Place, Inc.
BLUE RIBBON DOG CO. - Pet products - MX2 Inc.
BLUE RIBBON FARMS - Turkeys ☆ - Continental Grain Co.
BLUE RIBBON LAMB MIX - Veterinary nutritional supplements - A.L. Gilbert & Co.
BLUE RIBBON MILK SHAKES - Ice milk - Hamburger Museum, Inc.
BLUE RIBBON OLD ORCHARD - Fruits–dried - Sun-Diamond Growers of California
BLUE RIBBON ORIGINAL - Breads ☆ - Schmidt Baking Co., Inc.
BLUE RIBBON RECIPE - Cookies - Procter & Gamble Co.

BLUE RIBBON SHOW MIX - Veterinary nutritional supplements - A.L. Gilbert & Co.
BLUE RIBBON STOCK - Salt - Gunther Salt Co.
BLUE RIDGE - Beverages - Frederick Brewing Co.
BLUE RIDGE - Camps–recreational - Foam Design Consumer Products Inc.
BLUE RIDGE - Clocks - Ridgeway Clock Co.
BLUE RIDGE - Doors–storm - Duo-Temp
BLUE RIDGE - Fertilizers - Vigoro Industries, Inc.
BLUE RIDGE - Floor coverings - Southern Aggregates
BLUE RIDGE - Flooring–hardwood - Dixon Lumber Co. Inc.
BLUE RIDGE - Flowers, plants, and seeds - Seed Corp. of America
BLUE RIDGE - Furniture - Lowy Group Inc.
BLUE RIDGE - Furniture - Weiman Co.
BLUE RIDGE - Furniture ☆ - Bassett Furniture Industries, Inc.
BLUE RIDGE - Garden equipment ☆ - Wellington Leisure Products, Inc.
BLUE RIDGE - Glassware–household ☆ - Fenton Art Glass Co.
BLUE RIDGE - Golfing equipment - Wilson Sporting Goods Co.
BLUE RIDGE - Health care products - Stanley Home Products Inc.
BLUE RIDGE - Hot tubs–plastic - Gatsby Spas Inc.
BLUE RIDGE - Pet products - Blue Ridge Fish Hatchery Inc.
BLUE RIDGE - Recording label - Stark Records & Tape Co.
BLUE RIDGE - Stoneware dinnerware - Iron Mountain Stoneware Inc.
BLUE RIDGE - Teas - Blue Ridge Tea & Herb Co.
BLUE RIDGE - Trailers–travel - Clay Camper Co. Inc.
BLUE RIDGE - Yarn - Brunswick Yarns
BLUE RIDGE BEADED - Siding - Amerimark Building Products, Inc.
BLUE RIDGE BIRCH BEER - Beverages–carbonated - Frederick Brewing Co.
BLUE RIDGE FARMS - Food products - Blue Ridge Farms, Inc.
BLUE RIDGE FARMS - Salads–prepackaged - Fancy Foods of Virginia Inc.
BLUE RIDGE LAGER - Beverages–malt - Rainbow Ridge Brewing Co., Inc.
BLUE RIDGE ORCHARDS - Fruits and vegetables - Moore & Dorsey Inc.
BLUE RING - Firearms, accessories, and parts - Beeman Precision Airguns
BLUE ROBIN CRUMBLES - Pet products ☆ - Coicor
BLUE ROCK - Product description unknown - Rap Products Inc.
BLUE ROCK - Sporting goods - Remington Arms Co., Inc.
BLUE ROCK - Water–distilled - Vierk Distributing Co.
BLUE ROCK '78 - Sporting goods - Remington Arms Co., Inc.
BLUE ROOM - Recording label - Jazz Composer's Orchestra Association Inc.
BLUE ROSE - Glassware–household ☆ - Fenton Art Glass Co.
BLUE ROSE - Italian chocolates - Tallon USA
BLUE ROSE - Tea kettles–nonelectric ☆ - Mirro Corp.
BLUE ROSE MUSEUM - Museums - Crystal Rice Plantation, Inc.
BLUE ROYALE - Glassware–household ☆ - Fenton Art Glass Co.
BLUE ROYALE - Tableware–china ☆ - Lenox, Inc.
BLUE RTV - Adhesives and sealants - Loctite Corp.
BLUE RUNNER - Fishing rods - Zebco Corp.
BLUE RUNNER - Food products - Gonzales Products Co. Inc.
BLUE SATIN - Glassware–household ☆ - Fenton Art Glass Co.
BLUE SATIN - Hair care products - Worlds of Curls Inc.
BLUE SEA - Seafood - Bayside Imports Inc.
BLUE SEAL - Automotive repair shops ☆ - Gold Eagle Co.
BLUE SEAL - Bread - Interstate Brands Corp.
BLUE SEAL - Cigars - A.J. Golden Inc.
BLUE SEAL - Dog food - Blue Seal Feeds Inc.
BLUE SEAL - Food products - Ipswich Shellfish Co. Inc.
BLUE SEAL - Sausages - Chicopee Provision Co.
BLUE SEAL DEMAND - Animal feeds - Blue Seal Feeds Inc.
BLUE SEAL NATURAL - Dog food - Blue Seal Feeds Inc.
BLUE SEAL ULTRA - Dog food - Blue Seal Feeds Inc.
BLUE SENTURION - Toys - Saban Entertainment, Inc.
BLUE SERGE - Apparel and accessories - Timeless Designs, Inc.
BLUE SHADOW - Bicycles - Western Auto Supply Co.
BLUE SHADOW - Glassware–household ☆ - Lenox Crystal, Inc.
BLUE SHARK - Electrical equipment - Blue Shark Electronics, Inc.
BLUE SHIELD - Bedding–linen - Standard Mattress Co.
BLUE SHOALS - Seafood products–canned or cured - A.M. Look Canning Co.
BLUE SILICAST - Headphones - Westone Laboratories Inc.
BLUE SKIES - Dinnerware–glass - Franciscan by Johnson Brothers, USA, Inc.
BLUE SKIES - Dinnerware–glass ☆ - Lenox, Inc.
BLUE SKIES - Flowers, plants, and seeds - Monrovia Nursery Co.
BLUE SKIES AHEAD - Apparel and accessories - MGT Industries, Inc.
BLUE SKY - Colognes - A.K.A. Saunders, Inc.
BLUE SKY - Tape players–cassette - Sony Music Entertainment Inc.
BLUE SKY - Traps–animal - Fuhrman Diversified
BLUE SKY - Water–bottled or canned - Blue Sky Natural Beverage Co.
BLUE SKY ADVANTAGE - Computer software - CCH Inc. (Wolters Kluwer)

☆ = Now out of production

BLUE SKY FLYER - Toys–airplanes ☆ - Imperial Toy Corp.
BLUE SKY PRESS, THE - Publisher's imprint - Scholastic Inc.
BLUE SMITH - Apparel and accessories - Armen Co., Inc.
BLUE SNOW - Pet products ☆ - Schering-Plough Animal Health
BLUE SPHERE - Recording label - Jazz Composer's Orchestra Association Inc.
BLUE SPIRIT - Beauty aids - Dome Cosmetics
BLUE SPRINGS - Water–bottled or canned - Blue Springs Water Co.
BLUE SPRUCE - Cleaning preparations–household ☆ - Walton March
BLUE STAR - Apparel and accessories - Jeanjer International Co.
BLUE STAR - Balls–baseball - Star Sports, Inc.
BLUE STAR - Beverages–malt - North Coast Brewing Co., Inc.
BLUE STAR - Beverages–malt ☆ - Labatt Importers Inc.
BLUE STAR - Bicycles - Columbia Manufacturing Inc.
BLUE STAR - Desk sets - Tory Jewel Box
BLUE STAR - Dinnerware ☆ - Corning Inc.
BLUE STAR - Flowers, plants, and seeds - Hooven Allison
BLUE STAR - Food products - Blue Star Growers Inc.
BLUE STAR - Food products - Blue Star Meat Processing
BLUE STAR - Food products - Conagra, Inc.
BLUE STAR - Lumber - International Market Strategies, Inc.
BLUE STAR - Plumbing fixtures - Laredo Hardware Co.
BLUE STAR - Razor blades - American Safety Razor Co.
BLUE STAR - Scissors–hand-operated - Cutlery Associates Inc.
BLUE STAR - Toys–models ☆ - Estes Industries
BLUE STAR - Wines - Blue Star Wine Co.
BLUE STAR EXTREME - Lumber - International Market Strategies, Inc.
BLUE STAR LEATHER - Office supplies - Blue Star Leather Inc.
BLUE STEER - Fabrics–denim - Dan River Inc.
BLUE-STICK - Antennas - Childs Corp.
BLUE STINGER AV - Toys–automobiles - Saban Entertainment, Inc.
BLUE STINGER BEETLEBORG - Apparel and accessories - Saban Entertainment, Inc.
BLUE-STONE - Hosiery - Generra Co.
BLUE STONE - Tableware–earthenware ☆ - Seymour Mann Inc.
BLUE STOPPER - Apparel and accessories - Cobbs Manufacturing Co.
BLUE STORM - Apparel and accessories - Sun Apparel, Inc.
BLUE STRAND - Wire products - Bridon American Corp.
BLUE STRATOS - Health care products ☆ - Procter & Gamble Co.
BLUE STREAK - Automotive parts and accessories - Standard Motor Products, Inc.
BLUE STREAK - Boats–motor ☆ - Hobie Cat Co.
BLUE STREAK - Brushes - Wright-Bernet
BLUE STREAK - Chemical preparations ☆ - Woolsey Marine Industries
BLUE STREAK - Flypaper - Security Products Co.
BLUE STREAK - Gasoline ☆ - J. & L. Oil Inc.
BLUE STREAK - Hardware ☆ - Richards-Wilcox Manufacturing Co.
BLUE STREAK - Paint removers ☆ - Klean-Strip
BLUE STREAK - Paper - Schwartz Manufacturing Co.
BLUE STREAK - Rope - Samson Cordage Works
BLUE STREAK - Sporting goods - Voit Corp.
BLUE STREAK - Sporting goods ☆ - Gill Sports Equipment, Inc.
BLUE STREAK 5 - Archery equipment ☆ - Martin Archery Inc.
BLUE STREAK BAIT STAFION - Flypaper - Security Products Co.
BLUE STREAK II - Sporting goods - Seamco Sporting Goods
BLUE STRIPE - Gaskets - Fel-Pro Inc.
BLUE STRIPPER - Abrasive products - Norton Co.
BLUE STUFF - Deodorizers - Thetford Corp.
BLUE STUFF - Detergents - International Chemical Co.
BLUE SURF - Clam product - American Original Foods
BLUE SWAN - Apparel–women's ☆ - Blue Swan Outline Corp.
BLUE SWISS - Lamps ☆ - Lamplight Farms, Inc.
BLUE SYMPHONY - Building materials–concrete - MS International, Inc.
BLUE-TAC - Reusable adhesive - Keene Manufacturing Inc.
BLUE TAG - Food products ☆ - Dole Food Co., Inc.
BLUE THUMB - Recording label - MCA Universal Studios
BLUE THUNDER - Audio equipment - MTX
BLUE THUNDER - Toys - Multi Toys Corp.
BLUE THUNDER POWER ACTIVATOR - Vitamins and nutritional supplements - American Body Building Products, Inc.
BLUE-TICK - Salad dressings–bottled - Carolina Swamp Stuff, Inc.
BLUE TIP - Cigars - Jacobs Cigar Co.
BLUE TOO - Cleaning preparations–household - Blue Cross Laboratories Inc.
BLUE TOP - Lighting equipment - GTE Corp.
BLUE TRANQUILITY - Skin care products ☆ - Avon Products, Inc.
BLUE TREE - Tableware–china ☆ - Lenox, Inc.

BLUE TUBES - Pharmaceutical preparations - Boiron Inc.
BLUE TULIP - Dinnerware–glass - Nikko Ceramics Inc.
BLUE TWIG - Dishes–china - Taylor, Smith & Taylor Co.
BLUE VELVET - Apparel - Steel Sportswear, Inc.
BLUE VELVET - Cosmetics ☆ - P.S. Pibbs Inc.
BLUE VELVET - Musical instrument accessories - Dimarzio, Inc.
BLUE VELVET - Oils–lubricating - Kerr-McGee Chemical Corp.
BLUE VELVET HI TEMP - Lubricants - Kerr-McGee Chemical Corp.
BLUE VELVET RIDE - Lubricants - Kerr-McGee Chemical Corp.
BLUE VIOLETS - Cosmetics ☆ - Sally Hansen
BLUE VISION - Cleaning preparations–window - Harley Chemicals
BLUE WALTZ - Cosmetics - All Clubman
BLUE WATER - Chemical preparations - Blue Devil Industries, Inc.
BLUE WATER - Food products - Standard Food Service Inc.
BLUE WATER - Paper - Port Huron Paper Co.
BLUE WATER - Paper–toweling - Von Drehle Corp.
BLUE WATER - Pumps - Simer Pump Co.
BLUE WATER CAPITAL, L.L.C. - Banks–commercial - Blue Water Capital, LLC
BLUE WATERS - Fishing tackle ☆ - Frabill Inc.
BLUE WATERS - Perfumes - Container Store, Inc.
BLUE WAVE - Boats - Blue Wave
BLUE WAVE - Recording label - Blue Wave Records
BLUE WAVE - Shrimp–fresh or frozen - Premier International Corp.
BLUE WILLOW - Housewares ☆ - Scio Pottery Co.
BLUE WILLOW - Publisher's imprints - Blue Willow, Inc.
BLUE WILLOW - Teas - Blue Willow Tea Co.
BLUE WILLOW - Wallpaper ☆ - Eisenhart Wallcoverings Co.
BLUE WILLOW 2 - Wallpaper ☆ - Eisenhart Wallcoverings Co.
BLUE WILLOW 3 - Wallpaper ☆ - Eisenhart Wallcoverings Co.
BLUE WOODS - Deodorizers ☆ - Avon Products, Inc.
BLUE WORLD BEVERAGES - Iced tea–bottled or canned - Blue World, Inc.
BLUE WREATH - Dinnerware - Corning Inc.
BLUE XL BLADE - Machine parts - Wagman Metal Products, Inc.
BLUE XS - Silicon products - Pro Seal Products
BLUE Z - Food products - C.M. Holtzinger Fruit Co. Inc.
BLUE ZEBRA - Games ☆ - Small World Toys
BLUE ZINNIAS - Dinnerware–glass ☆ - Metlox Pottery Shoppe
BLUE ZOO - Figurines - O.A. Solbakken Inc.
BLUE ZOO MUSIC - Recording label - Noland Four Creative Services, Inc.
BLUE2 - Computer software - Price Waterhouse Llp
BLUEBEARD - Rum - Blair Importers Ltd.
BLUEBELL - Baskets–wood ☆ - Royal Cathay Trading Co.
BLUEBELL - Glassware–household ☆ - Lenox Crystal, Inc.
BLUEBERRIES - Glassware–household - Crest Studios
BLUEBERRY - Dinnerware ☆ - Corning Inc.
BLUEBERRY - Jewelry–costume ☆ - Safari Ltd.
BLUEBERRY BETTY - Dolls - Mattel, Inc.
BLUEBERRY FIELDS - Salad dressing ☆ - American Spoon Foods Inc.
BLUEBERRY HILL - Artists' materials - Rockwell Shops Ltd.
BLUEBERRY HILL - Furniture - Weiman Co.
BLUEBERRY ICING - Christmas tree ornaments ☆ - Cracker Box Inc.
BLUEBERRY LANE - Apparel–children's - Blue Bird Knitwear Co.
BLUEBERRY MUFFINS - Figurines - Specialty Porcelain
BLUEBERRY 'N CREAM - Food products - Breadshop's Natural Foods
BLUEBERRY NEWTONS - Cookies - Nabisco Foods Group
BLUEBERRY OATIOLA - Cereal - New Morn, Inc.
BLUEBERRY PLASTIC - Pellets - Blueberry Plastic Mill Corp.
BLUEBERRY PROVINCIAL - Dinnerware–glass ☆ - Metlox Pottery Shoppe
BLUEBILL - Apparel–athletic - Red Head Brand Corp.
BLUEBIRD - Bake goods - Flowers Family Bakeries, Inc.
BLUEBIRD - Balls - National Latex Products Co.
BLUEBIRD - Clocks - General Time Corp. (Westclox/Seth Thomas Div.)
BLUEBIRD - Fruit drinks–bottled or canned - Citrus World Inc.
BLUEBIRD - Recording label - RCA Records
BLUEBIRD OF HAPPINESS - Glassware–household - Terra Studios
BLUEBONNET - Paper - Texan House Inc.
BLUEBONNET COMPETITIVE EDGE - Animal feeds - American Superior Feeds, Inc.
BLUEBONNET KENNEL CHOICE - Dog food - American Superior Feeds, Inc.
BLUEBONNET STOCK - Animal feeds - Bluebonnet Milling Co.
BLUECASTER - Guitars - St. Blues Guitars
BLUECOAT - Film - General Electric Co.
BLUECOR - Insulating materials–foam - Dow Chemical Co.
BLUEEYE BEAM - Automotive parts and accessories - Optronics Inc.
BLUEFIELD - Dishes–china ☆ - Pickard Inc.

BLUEFIELD - Tableware–china ☆ - Lenox, Inc.
BLUELINE - Beverages–malt - Redhook Ale Brewery, Inc.
BLUELINE - Pet products - Rolf C. Hagen (USA) Corp.
BLUEMAGIC - Cleaning preparations - Ultra Finish Products
BLUEMARK - Index cards - Stanley-Bostitch Inc.
BLUEMOON - Recording label - Mesa/Bluemoon Recordings Inc.
BLUEMOUND - Lawn product - Kellogg Inc.
BLUENOTE - Carbon and graphite products ☆ - Curtis-Young Corp.
BLUEPHOS - Chemical preparations - Kirkegaard and Perry Laboratories Inc.
BLUEPOINTS - Food products - Bluepoints Co.
BLUEPRINT - Apparel–men's - Chauvin International Ltd.
BLUEPRINT - Audio equipment - Mitek Corp.
BLUEPRINT - Floor coverings–carpet and rugs - Alexander Smith Carpets
BLUEPRINT - Hair care products - Redken Laboratories, Inc.
BLUEPRINT MINIATURES - Toys–automobiles - ERTL Co., Inc.
BLUEPRINT REPLICAS - Toys - ERTL Co., Inc.
BLUEPRINTS - Eyeglasses - United States Shoe Corp.
BLUEPRINTS - Video production - Comprehensive Loss Management, Inc.
BLUEPRINTS COLLECTION - Cosmetics - Estee Lauder Inc.
BLUEPRINTS TWO - Video production - Comprehensive Loss Management, Inc.
BLUERAL - Glass products - Glass Inc.
BLUERIDGE HARDY - Fertilizers - Pursley Inc.
BLUEROO - Toys–stuffed ☆ - Gund, Inc.
B.L.U.E.S. - Apparel and accessories - Chicago B.L.U.E.S., Inc.
BLUES - Audio cabinets - Richmond Hill Corp.
BLUE'S - Barbecue sauce - Tellas W. Fogg
BLUE'S - Pet products ☆ - Dogloo Inc.
BLUES - Travel bags and accessories - Jameslee Corp.
BLUES 2! - Apparel - Golden Rainbow
BLUES & LEGENDS HALL OF FAME MUSEUM - Museums - Robinson Property Group LP
BLUES BABYS - Musical instrument accessories - Patrick Michael Roy
BLUES BAND - Harmonicas - Hohner Inc.
BLUES BAND - Watch crystals - Paul J. Gabriel
BLUES BEER - Beverages–malt - Blues Beer Co.
BLUES BLOOD - Recording label - Jazz Composer's Orchestra Association Inc.
BLUES BOTTLE - Musical instruments - Dunlop Manufacturing, Inc.
BLUES CHANNEL, THE - Computer peripheral equipment - Mai Cramer
BLUE'S CITY LEMONADE - Lemonade - Archibald Bros. Fine Beverages, Inc.
BLUES CLASSIC - Amplifiers–musical instrument - Peavey Electronics Corp.
BLUES CLASSICS - Recording label ☆ - Arhoolie Productions Inc.
BLUES HARP - Harmonicas - Hohner Inc.
BLUES KING - Guitars - Gibson Guitar Corp.
BLUES SARACENO MODEL - Musical instrument accessories - Seymour Duncan Pickups
BLUES TOOLS - Harmonicas - Blues Tools, Inc.
BLUES TRADEMARK JEANS - Apparel and accessories - Bennini, Inc.
BLUES UNLIMITED - Recording label - Master-Trak Sound Recorders
BLUESBERRY - Beverages–alcohol - Jim Beam Brands Co.
BLUESEAL - Disinfectants - Waterless Co.
BLUESKING III - Guitars - St. Blues Guitars
BLUESMASTER - Guitars - St. Blues Guitars
BLUESTAR - Chemical preparations - Novagen, Inc.
BLUESTAR - Recording label - Bluestar Communications Corp.
BLUESTAR - Sporting goods - Georgia's Tennis
BLUESTAR - Tires - Aoyama International Inc.
BLUESVILLE - Phonographs - Fantasy Inc.
BLUETS - Dinnerware–glass ☆ - Lenox, Inc.
BLUETTE - Cleaning preparations–household - Walco Linck Co.
BLUETTE - Dishes–earthenware - Hadley Pottery Co. Inc.
BLUETTES - Gloves–work - Pioneer Industrial Products Co.
BLUEWATER - Boats - Bluewater
BLUEWATER WEAR - Apparel–men's - Aftco Manufacturing Co., Inc.
BLUEWRAP - Paper–transfer - George Vincent Inc.
BLUFFTON - Tomato pastes and sauces ☆ - Fremont Co.
BLUFLEX - Fabrics - Hosokawa Micron International Inc.
BLUHILL - Food products - Green Bay Foods Co.
BLUKO - Cleaning preparations–carpet and rug - Cello Chemical Co.
BLULITE - Cosmetics - Lancome
BLUM & BERGERON - Food products - Blum & Bergeron Inc.
BLUMBERG BLAZER FORMS - Office supplies - BlumbergExcelsior, Inc.
BLUMBERG'S LAW PRODUCTS - Office supplies - BlumbergExcelsior, Inc.
BLUMPKINS - Statuary–wood - Linda Lee & Co.
BLUM'S - Cookies ☆ - Price Candy Co. Inc.

BLUM'S - Food products - Blum & Bergeron Inc.
BLUM'S OF SAN FRANCISCO - Candy - Price Candy Co. Inc.
BLUNDERBUSS - Toys–guns - Parris Manufacturing Co.
BLUNT - Apparel - Blunt Graphix
BLUNT POINTE - Pharmaceutical preparations - American Home Products Corp.
BLUNT RECORDINGS - Compact discs–prerecorded - Tee Vee Toons, Inc.
BLUNT TIPS - Cigar boxes–wood - Consolidated Cigar Corp.
BLUNTCUT - Sporting goods - Toobs, Inc.
BLUNTPORT - Medical apparatus - United States Surgical Corp.
BLUNTS - Cigar boxes–wood - Consolidated Cigar Corp.
BLUPAV - Pharmaceutical preparations ☆ - Bluco Inc.
BLUR - Skates–roller - Rollerblade, Inc.
BLURP BALLS - Toys - ERTL Co., Inc.
BLURT! - Games - Timothy Walsh
BLUSH-A-LITTLE - Cosmetics - Maybelline Co.
BLUSH IN BLOOM - Cosmetics - Max Factor & Co.
BLUSH LIGHTLY - Cosmetics - Circle of Beauty, Inc.
BLUSH LITES - Cosmetics ☆ - Bonne Bell, Inc.
BLUSH MATES - Cosmetics ☆ - Noxell Corp.
BLUSH-ON - Cosmetics - Revlon Consumer Products Corp.
BLUSH-ON - Cosmetics ☆ - Sothys USA Inc.
BLUSH ON BLUE - Apparel–women's - In-Port Ltd.
BLUSH PLASTER - Floor coverings - Aladdin Mills, Inc.
BLUSH SO NATURAL - Cosmetics - Hazel Bishop International
BLUSHABLES - Toys - Robert A. Demars
BLUSHDOMES - Cosmetics - Del Pharmaceuticals, Inc.
BLUSHED - Nail care products - Cosmair Inc.
BLUSHED BEIGE - Cosmetics - Lancome
BLUSHETTES - Cosmetics ☆ - Bonne Bell, Inc.
BLUSHETTES - Paints ☆ - Bell Ceramics, Inc.
BLUSHING BELLE - Wines - Shenandoah Vineyards
BLUSHING BLOSSOMS - Flowers–artificial - Waco Products Corp.
BLUSHING BRIDE - Bathroom accessories ☆ - Tsumura International Inc.
BLUSHING BUNNIES - Toys–stuffed - Fun World Inc.
BLUSHING FRAULEIN - Wines - Guadalupe Valley Winery
BLUSOUND - Telephones - Blusound Electronics, Inc.
BLUSTER BEAR - Dolls - CPG Products Corp.
BLUSTER BEAR - Toys - Tonka Corp.
BLUTEX - Leather–vellum - Teledyne Post
BLUTHNER - Pianos - Kasimoff-Bluthner Piano Co.
BLUVARIA - Cheese - Swissrose International Inc.
BLUWASH - Cleaning preparations - Grasso Marine Service Centers, Inc.
BLUX FOX - Sleeping bags - Coleman Co., Inc.
BLVD - Skates–roller - Advanced Polymer Systems, Inc.
BLY - Vitamins and nutritional supplements - Econo Med Pharmaceuticals Inc.
BLYTHEVILLE - Food products - Blytheville Canning Co. Inc.
BM - Tools - Baldwin Machine Works
BM-10 - Dictating machines - Sony Corp. of America
BM BASEMENT - Apparel–athletic - Jay Bautista
BM FORMULA - Vitamins and nutritional supplements - Vital Energy
BM7 - Kitchen utensils–aluminum - Reston Lloyd Ltd.
BMB - Pet products - Rose America Corp.
BMB - Tablecloths - Scandinavian House Imports Inc.
BMB ESTATE - Lawn mowers - Alamo Group
BMC - Adhesives and sealants - ProSoCo Inc.
BMC - Batteries - Battery Marketing Corp.
BMC - Cash registers - Raymond Packer Co.
BMC - Computer software - BMC Software, Inc.
BMC - Cranes - Broderson Manufacturing Corp.
BMC - Motor vehicles–motor homes - Blue Bird Body Co.
BMC - Vane-type air-deflecting fence - Blackstone Manufacturing Co. Inc.
B.M.E. - Pharmaceutical preparations - Brothers Pharmaceuticals Inc.
BMF - Glassware–household - Primex International Corp.
BMF - Hardware - Buchanan Metal Forming, Inc.
B.M.F., THE - Furniture - Bean Station Furniture Factory Inc.
BMG - Flashlights - Bridgeport Metal Goods Manufacturing Co.
BMG KIDZ - Recording label - BMG Entertainment North America
BMH AMERICAS - Machinery - Babcock Holdings (USA), Inc.
BMI - Capacitors - Barker Microfarads Inc.
BMI - Doors - Building Materials, Inc.
BMI - Electronic equipment - BMI Beaux Merzon Inc.
BMI - Publisher's imprints - Book Margins, Inc.
B.M.I. - Recording label - Sweet Tooth Music Publishing Co.
BMI - Telephones - Barely Making It Inc.
BMI - Twine - Blue Mountain Industries, Inc.

☆ = Now out of production

BMI ROBOTICS - Robots–industrial - Burns Machinery, Inc.
BMJ - Recording label - Southern Sound Productions
BMP - Pet products - Thomas Veterinary Drug
BMR - Recording label - Thomas E. Mack
BMW - Motor vehicles–automobiles - BMW of North America Inc.
BMW OF NORTH - Electrical equipment - Eclipse Inc.
BMX - Frames–eyeglass - Universal/Univis Inc.
BMX - Sporting goods ☆ - Texas Recreation Corp.
BMX BIKE RACE - Games - Smethport Specialty Co.
BMX HARD TAIL - Bicycles - Western Auto Supply Co.
BN - Apparel and accessories - FG Industries, Inc.
BN - Flowers, plants, and seeds - Bork Nurseries, Inc.
BN - Hardware - Bossard International, Inc.
B'NAI MITZVAH - Computer software - Castle Computer Technologies
BNC + GABA - Vitamins and nutritional supplements - M.M.R.C., Ltd. Co.
BND - Jewelry - Barbara Noelle
BNDR - Braces–orthopedic - BNDR Associates
BNI - Shelving units–wood - Brunswick National Inc.
BNM - Pharmaceutical preparations - Enzyme Process Co. Inc.
BNX - Computer hardware - Bay Networks, Inc.
BNZ 1FB - Insulating materials - BNZ Materials, Inc.
BO - Beverages–malt - Bohannon Brewing Co.
BO BAC 2X - Veterinary pharmaceutical preparations - Boehringer Ingelheim Animal Health, Inc.
BO BEAR - Toys–stuffed - Dakin Inc.
BO-BERRY - Biscuits - BJ Acquisition Corp.
BO' BOB'S PORK BARBEQUE IN A BUN - Food products - Stannis Research International Inc.
BO BUNNY - Toys–stuffed - Russ Berrie and Co., Inc.
B.O. BUSTER - Detergents - Ole Time Woodsman
BO-CAR-AL - Pharmaceutical preparations ☆ - Smithkline Beecham Corp.
BO-CYCLOMINE - Pharmaceutical preparations - Bolan Pharmaceutical Inc.
BO DANGOS - Ophthalmic goods - Karlen Manufacturing, Inc.
BO-DU - Ribbons ☆ - Ribbon Magic, Inc.
BO-FLEX - Photographic equipment - Bogen Photo Corp.
BO-HOG - Gloves - Knoxville Glove Co.
BO-JEST - Boats - Glen-L Marine Designs
BO-KAY - Flowers, plants, and seeds - Molded Fiber Glass Tray Co.
BO KNOWS - T-shirts–men's ☆ - Nike, Inc.
BO-LIZ - Fishing lures - Strike King Lure Co.
BO-MAR CUT, THE - Firearms, accessories, and parts - Bo-Mar Tool & Manufacturing Co., Inc.
BO MED - Medical apparatus ☆ - Cramer Products Inc.
BO-PEEP - Ammonia - Dial Corp.
BO-PO - Manicure preparations - Tinkerbell
BO SOCKS - Ophthalmic goods - Karlen Manufacturing, Inc.
BOA - Alarm systems - Directed Electronics, Inc.
BOA - Audio equipment - Recoton Corp.
BOA - Cosmetics ☆ - Nino Originals
BOA - Prosthetic products - DAW Industries, Inc.
BOAGS PREMIUM - Beverages–malt - Beverage America, Inc.
BOANZA - Manufactured homes - Redman Industries, Inc.
BOAR 150, A - Animal feeds - Carl S. Akey Inc.
BOAR GUN - Screw drivers ☆ - S-B Power Tool Co.
BOAR-LIFE - Animal feeds - Consolidated Nutrition, L.C.
BOARD 104 - Elevators - Montgomery Kone Inc.
BOARD AND PLANK - Floor coverings - Armstrong World Industries, Inc.
BOARD BOXX - Sporting goods - SKIBOXX LTD.
BOARD BUDDIES - Tools–hand-operated - Woodstock International, Inc.
BOARD CERTIFIED - Apparel and accessories - Active Imaginations, Inc.
BOARD GAME IN A BOTTLE, THE - Toys - M.J. Moran Co.
BOARD-HIKER - Racks - Ruffolo Enterprises
BOARD OF EDUCATION, THE - Publisher's imprints - Gerald James Crowley
BOARD RIDERS - Boots - International Seaway Trading Corp.
BOARD ROOM - Floor coverings–carpet and rugs - Johnson's Carpets Inc.
BOARD SOC - Sporting goods - Primitive Designs Manufacturing Co.
BOARD SPORTS INTERNATIONAL - Apparel–men's - Ronald Lee Pitsenbarger
BOARD WOMB, THE - Apparel–women's - Board Womb, Inc.
BOARDBOX - Sporting goods - Robert C. Vincent
BOARDBOX COFFIN, THE - Sporting goods - Robert C. Vincent
BOARDCUFF - Snowboards - Aok Inc.
BOARDIE - Pet products - Maine Nature Products
BOARDIN' BUDDY - Tools–hand-operated - Advantedge Products, Inc.
BOARDING HOUSE - Seasonings ☆ - Chefmaster Products
BOARDING PASS BP - Luggage - New Harbor Enterprises, Inc.

BOARDING PLUS - Luggage - Liberty Leather Products Co., Inc.
BOARDLINK - Computer software - The Gale Group
BOARDQUEST - Computer software - Cadence Design Systems, Inc.
BOARDRIDERS CLUB - Apparel and accessories - Quiksilver, Inc.
BOARDROOM - Attache cases - Ventura Travelware Inc.
BOARDROOM - Floor coverings–carpet and rugs - Dan River Inc.
BOARDROOM - Floor coverings–carpet and rugs - Sheridan Carpet Mills
BOARDROOM - Floor coverings–carpet and rugs ☆ - Blue Ridge Carpet Mills
BOARDROOM - Floor coverings–carpet and rugs ☆ - Mannington Carpets, Inc.
BOARDROOM - Office supplies - JM Co.
BOARDROOM - Padding–foam ☆ - Foamex LP
BOARDROOM - Projection screens ☆ - Da-Lite Screen Co. Inc.
BOARDROOM - Wood products ☆ - States Industries Inc.
BOARDROOM BLEND - Coffee - Cascade Coffee Inc.
BOARDROOM COLLECTION, THE - Suits–men's - Hickey-Freeman Co. Inc.
BOARDROOM COLLECTIONS - Office supplies - McBee Loose Leaf Binders
BOARDROOM GREETINGS - Stationery - Brett-Forer Greetings Inc.
BOARDSIM - Computer software - Hyperlynx, Inc.
BOARDWALK - Colognes - Brandy Harvest
BOARDWALK - Furniture - Haworth, Inc.
BOARDWALK - Furniture - Lyon-Shaw Inc.
BOARDWALK - Furniture - Stanley Furniture Co. Inc.
BOARDWALK - Games - Tonka Corp.
BOARDWALK - Pizzas–frozen - Premium Frozen Food Products
BOARDWALK STYLE - Potato chips - UTZ Quality Foods Inc.
BOARDWALKER - Treadmills - Battle Creek Equipment Co.
BOARHIDE - Footwear - Wolverine World Wide, Inc.
BOARLON - Brushes–hair ☆ - Phillips Brush Corp.
BOARS HEAD - Food products - Frank Brunckhorst Co., LP
BOAR'S HEAD - Spices and extracts ☆ - Presco Food Seasonings Inc.
BOASEMI AUTOMATIC - Giftware - Boas Box Co.
BOASSY BEARS - Housewares - Arts Uniq', Inc.
BOASTCARD - Postcards - AML Enterprises
BOAT AND TOTE - Bags–duffel - L.L. Bean Inc.
BOAT ARMOUR - Boats - Fibre Glass-Evercoat Co. Inc.
BOAT BUCKLE - Fasteners–hook and eye - Indiana Mills & Manufacturing, Inc.
BOAT GEAR - Boats - Classic Auto Accessories Inc.
BOAT-KOAT - Varnishes - McCloskey Corp.
BOAT MASTER - Brushes–paint - E-Z Paintr Corp.
BOAT-NU - Adhesives and sealants ☆ - Steelcote Manufacturing Corp.
BOAT SAVER - Boats - Boat Saver
BOAT SHOW VIDEO - Video production - Media Artists Inc.
BOAT STIRRUP - Boats - Ve-Ve Inc.
BOAT-SUNS - Shoes - Endicott Johnson Corp.
BOAT VACS - Marine rigging - Powerwinch Co.
BOAT WORKS - Waterproof outerwear - Fox-Knapp Inc.
BOATABLE - Furniture - Hutton Furniture Co.
BOATANK - Sporting goods ☆ - Bettcher Manufacturing Corp.
BOATAPE - Tape–adhesive - Quick Cable Corp.
BOATBASE'N - Computer software - John T. Harrigan
BOATBUCKLE - Hardware - Indiana Marine Co. (Indiana Mills & Manufacturing)
BOATERIFIC - Toys–stuffed ☆ - CBS Toys
BOATERS - Shoes ☆ - Clarks of England Inc.
BOATERS CHOICE - Boats - Fibre Glass-Evercoat Co. Inc.
BOATER'S CHOICE - Marine rigging - Highland Group Industries LP
BOATER'S JACKET - Life preservers ☆ - Stearns Manufacturing Co.
BOATGUARD - Alarm systems - AJJ, Inc.
BOATHOUSE - Boathouse Row Sports, Ltd.
BOATHOUSE - Fabrics - Gretchen Bellinger Inc.
BOATIC - Shirts - Marble Sportswear, Inc.
BOATING BLUES - Cosmetics - Maybelline Co.
BOATING ESSENTIALS - Boating safety kit - Covert Marine
BOATMAN'S - Food products - Mampeza International Inc.
BOATMASTER - Compasses–magnetic ☆ - Andrea Electronics Corp.
BOATMASTER - Computer software - Examco Inc.
BOAT'N TRAIL - Oils–lubricating - Maxus Energy Corp.
BOATSAFE PRODUCT INC. - Electronic equipment - Boatsafe Products Inc.
BOATSAVER - Hardware - Indiana Marine Co. (Indiana Mills & Manufacturing)
BOATSLIDE - Playground equipment - Learning Products Inc.
BOB - Chromium products - Robert Manufacturing Co.
BOB - Computer software - Microsoft Corp.
BOB - Fruits and vegetables - A.V. Olsson Trading Co., Inc.
BOB - Ophthalmic goods - Chums Ltd.

☆ = Now out of production

BOB ALLEN - Luggage - Bob Allen Sportswear
BOB-ALONG BEAR - Toys - Fisher-Price, Inc.
BOB-BET - Fishing tackle ☆ - Frabill Inc.
BOB BROWNIE - Cakes–mixes - Caravan Products Inc.
BOB-CAT - Clay–modeling - Byrne Ceramic Supply Co. Inc.
BOB CAT - Garden equipment - S.P. Lummus Supply Co. Inc.
BOB-CAT - Lawn mowers - Ransomes-Cushman-Ryan
BOB DUKOFF - Musical instrument accessories - Bobby Dukoff Mouthpieces
BOB ELLIS - Wigs - Bob Ellis Hairpieces
BOB EVANS - Food products - Bob Evans Farms Inc.
B.O.B. FINE JEWELRY - Jewelry - B.O.B. Fine Jewelry
BOB HOPE - Clocks - Hope Enterprises, Inc.
BOB LEE - Apparel and accessories - Robert M. Lee
BOB MACKIE - Apparel–women's - Blanche
BOB MACKIE - Belts - Crown Pacific Accessories
BOB MACKIE - Frames–eyeglass - Diaco
BOB MACKIE - Handbags - Will-Co Products Inc.
BOB MACKIE - Watches - Pedre Co. Inc.
BOB MANN - Golfing equipment - Bob Mann
BOB O' POLES - Candy - Bobs Candies Inc.
BOB OSTROW - Meat products–beef - Bob Ostrow Co.
BOB PIERCE - Decals and transfers - Bob Pierce Pianos and Organs
BOB ROSS - Artists' materials - Martin F. Weber Co.
BOB ROSS - Recording label - Bob Ross Inc.
BOB RUSSEL STUDIOS - Costumes - Rubie's Costume Co., Inc.
BOB SCOUT - Toys–stuffed ☆ - Kenner Products
BOB SMART - Shoes - Craddock-Terry Inc.
BOB THE FISH - Apparel and accessories - Christopher Pelletier
BOB TIMBERLAKE - Giftware ☆ - Goebel of North America
BOB TIMBERLAKE COLLECTION, THE - Flowers–artificial - Bob Timberlake Collection, Inc.
BOB TUO DE PARIS - Beauty aids ☆ - Pierre Jolys' French Imports
BOB UP - Toys ☆ - Tomy America, Inc.
BOB WHITE - Bedding–linen ☆ - Dan River Inc.
BOB WHITE - Rope ☆ - Wellington Leisure Products, Inc.
BOB WHITE - Tools - Railway Handle Corp.
BOB WHITE - Wet mops ☆ - American Textile Products Co.
BOB WOLF - Footwear–athletic - Ken-Pin Inc.
BOBBERALL - Fishing tackle - Thomas P. Burns
BOBBI - Bicycles ☆ - Murray, Inc.
BOBBI - Hair care products - Gillette Co.
BOBBI BAKES - Bakery products - Bobbi Bakes, Inc.
BOBBI BROWN PROFESSIONAL COSMETICS - Cosmetics - Estee Lauder Inc.
BOBBIE - Dolls - Fisher-Price, Inc.
BOBBIE BAIT - Fishing lures - Bobbie Bait Co.
BOBBIE BROOKS - Apparel–women's ☆ - Bobbie Brooks Inc.
BOBBIE-LYNN - Hosiery - Bobbie-Lynn Hosiery Co.
BOBBIES - Hairpins - Accessories International
BOBBINS - Pet products - Boomer Ball
BOBBIPOPS - Candy - Bobs Candies Inc.
BOBBLE BUDDY - Headbands - Russ Berrie and Co., Inc.
BOBBLES - Toys - Tyco Toys
BOBBSEY TWINS - Publisher's imprints - Grosset & Dunlap Inc.
BOBBY - Valves–industrial - Robert Manufacturing Co.
BOBBY AIBELLO - Apparel and accessories ☆ - Abel Industries Inc.
BOBBY ALLISON - Toys ☆ - ERTL Co., Inc.
BOBBY & COMPANY - Housewares - Zak Designs Inc.
BOBBY BEAR - Toys ☆ - Princess Soft Toys
BOBBY BUNNY - Candy ☆ - Keppel's Inc.
BOBBY CHONG'S - Spices and extracts - Bobby Chong's Food Products
BOBBY CLAMPETT - Shoes ☆ - Endicott Johnson Corp.
BOBBY CLARKE - Hockey equipment ☆ - Right Gard Corp.
BOBBY COOKIES - Cookies - Astra Imports
BOBBY EZE WAX - Depilatories ☆ - Bobby Co.
BOBBY GRACE - Golfing equipment - Bobby Grace Golf Design, Inc.
BOBBY G'S - Apparel and accessories - Trinity Products, Inc.
BOBBY HULL - Games - Munro Games Inc.
BOBBY JONES - Apparel and accessories - Hickey-Freeman Co. Inc.
BOBBY LEE - Musical instrument accessories - Sottile Manufacturing Co.
BOBBY LEE-NO-SCRATCH CARRY-ALL - Cases–camera - Sottile Manufacturing Co.
BOBBY-MAC - Toys ☆ - Collier-Keyworth Inc.
BOBBY MACLITE - Infant product ☆ - Evenflo Co.
BOBBY ORR - Games - Munro Games Inc.
BOBBY RECORDS - Recording label - Record-Rama Sound Archives

BOBBY SOCKS - Apparel and accessories - Wal-Mart Stores Inc.
BOBBY STIX-N-DANNY STONES - Apparel–children's - Salmor Import Export Corp.
BOBBY'S WORLD - Toys - Twentieth Century Fox Film Corp.
BOBCAT - Archery equipment - High Country American
BOBCAT - Archery equipment ☆ - Martin Archery Inc.
BOBCAT - Binoculars - Swift Instruments, Inc.
BOBCAT - Mats - Matworks
BOBCAT - Motor vehicles–automobiles ☆ - Ford Motor Co. (Lincoln-Mercury Div.)
BOBCAT - Toys–automobiles - Clark Manufacturing Co. Inc.
BOBCAT - Windshields–glass ☆ - National Cycle Inc.
BOBCAT 2 - Tripods–photographic - Phoenix Corp. of America
BOBCAT TRAIL - Bicycles - Marin Mountain Bikes, Inc.
BOBCO ORIGINALS - Florists - Amlings Flowerland
BOBECHES OF BAVERIA - Candlesticks - Biedermann & Sons Inc.
BOBER - Publisher's imprints - Willis Music Co.
BOBLO - Recording label ☆ - Nationwide Sound Distributors
BOBO - Bakery products - Bobo Baking
BOBO - Dog food - Faribault Foods Inc.
BOBO - Pet products - Precious Paws
BOBO - Poultry - Bobo Poultry Market, Inc.
BOBO CLOWN - Dolls - Russ Berrie and Co., Inc.
BOBO CLOWN - Toys–stuffed ☆ - Dakin Inc.
BOBO MINI - Toys–stuffed - Dakin Inc.
BOBOLI - Food products - Boboli Co.
BOBOLI BOTTOMS - Food products - Boboli Co.
BOBRICKS - Ammonia - Sanitek Products Inc.
BOBS - Candy - Bobs Candies Inc.
BOB'S - Salad dressings - KT Kitchens
BOB'S '47 MUNICH-STYLE LAGER - Beverages–malt - Boulevard Brewing Associates L.P.
BOB'S CLOTHING COMPANY EST. 1954 - Apparel and accessories - Bob's HC, Inc.
BOB'S GARAGE - Apparel and accessories - Robert Stock Designs, Inc.
BOB'S PRINTING, INC. - Business forms - Bob's Printing, Inc.
BOB'S SUGAR FREE - Candy - Bobs Candies Inc.
BOBTAIL - Golfing equipment - Golfsmith International Inc.
BOBY 3 - Electronic equipment ☆ - Leedal Inc.
BOBY-DOG - Pet products - Meblo Inc.
BOBYLON - Sporting goods ☆ - Babolat
BOC - Recording label - AudioLoft Recording Studios
BOCA - Floor coverings - Mannington Resilient Floors
BOCA - Floor coverings–carpet and rugs - Coronet Carpets Inc.
BOCA - Floor coverings–carpet and rugs - LaVelle Textile Marketing Inc.
BOCA - Frames–eyeglass - U.S. Optical Frame Co.
BOCA - Occasional tables ☆ - JDI Group, Inc.
BOCA BOCK LAGER - Beverages–alcohol - Truckee Brewing Co.
BOCA BONS - Candy - Susan Kanter
BOCA CHICA - Rum - Black Prince Distillery, Inc.
BOCA CLASSICS - Apparel–men's - Beall's, Inc.
BOCA RATON - Bedding–linen - Dan River Inc.
BOCA RATON - Enamels–dental ☆ - Fasco Industries Inc. (Consumer Products Div.)
BOCA RATON - Furniture - Lane Co. Inc.
BOCA RATON NEWS - Publisher's imprints - Boca Raton News, Inc.
BOCA RATTAN - Furniture ☆ - Lea Industries Inc.
BOCADOR - Rum - Chatam International Inc.
BOCADOR - Rum, etc. - Charles Jacquin et Compagnie Inc.
BOCAGE - Wines - Mark L. Lemmon
BOCALAV - Mouthwashes - Quintessence Inc.
BOCAMODEM - Modems - Boca Research, Inc.
BOCCA - Shoes - Daniel Green Co.
BOCCACCIO - Furniture ☆ - Tropitone Furniture Co. Inc.
BOCCE - Wines - Robert Mondavi Winery
BOCCE BY ANNECHARICO - Apparel and accessories - BOCCE by Annecharico Inc.
BOCCHARA - Floor coverings–carpet and rugs - Capel, Inc.
BOCCONCINO - Pizzas–frozen - Bocconcino Food Products Inc.
BOCK DESIGNS - Wallpaper - Bock Designs Inc.
BOCK Y CA. - Cigar boxes–wood - Consolidated Cigar Corp.
BOCKINGFORD - Artists' materials - Andrews/Nelson/Whitehead
BOCKTOBERFEST - Beverages–malt - Gambrinus Co.
BOCOUR - Paints - Bocour Artist Colors Inc.
BOCQUET - Mustard ☆ - Liberty Richter Inc.
BOD-ACIOUS - Toys–automobiles - Mattel, Inc.

B.O.D. BUILT ON DISCIPLINE - Apparel and accessories - Creative Apparel, Inc.
BOD POD - Measuring instruments - Life Measurement Instruments
BOD SQUAD - Apparel and accessories - Holiday Fair, Inc.
BODACIOUS - Apparel and accessories - Bodacious Boxers Inc.
BODACIOUS - Food products - Gourmet Blending Co. Inc.
BODACIOUS - Hair care products - Graham Webb International
BODACIOUS - Jewelry - Mangarell Wholesalers Inc.
BODACIOUS - Perfumes - Graham Webb International
BODACIOUS - Wallpaper - Camelot Design Studios
BODACIOUS ONE, THE - Golfing equipment - James T. Moore
BODACIOUS OOZE - Candy - Topps Co., Inc.
BODACIOUS VIDALIA - Food products - Williamsburg Foods, Inc.
BODDINGTONS - Beverages–malt - Labatt Importers Inc.
BODDYSLIDE - Apparel–athletic - Ross Athletic Inc.
BODEGA - Boats–motor ☆ - Bayliner Marine Corp.
BODEGA - Glassware–household - Van Dow-Fenton Inc.
BODEGA BAY - Furniture - Lane Co. Inc.
BODEGAS BROQUEL - Beverages–alcohol - Vinos Argentinos Imports USA
BODEGAS CORRAL - Wines - House of Burgundy Inc.
BODEGAS GURPEGUI - Wines - Admiral Wine Merchants
BODEGAS PALACIO - Wines ☆ - Vintners International Co. Inc.
BODEM - Nail care products - Shannon Cosmetics, Inc.
BODET - Clocks - Franklin Instrument Co. Inc.
BODGE PLUGS - Audio equipment - Connectronics Corp.
BODI - Hair care products - Worlds of Curls Inc.
BODI & SOL - Hair care products - Nu-Tress Laboratories Inc.
BODI-BATH - Skin care products - Geritrex Corp.
BODI-DRI - Skin care products - Geritrex Corp.
BODI-ENDURE - Hair care products - Summit Laboratories
BODI-LOTION - Skin care products - Geritrex Corp.
BODI-LUX - Skin care products - Geritrex Corp.
BODI-OIL W/ALOE - Skin care products - Geritrex Corp.
BODI-PROTECT - Skin care products - Geritrex Corp.
BODI-WHIRL - Skin care products - Geritrex Corp.
BODIE BY EDIE - Apparel–women's - Edie Lee Inc.
BODIES MADE NEW - Lotions - In Tact Equine
BODIFI - Hair care products ☆ - Summit Laboratories
BODIFUL - Cosmetics ☆ - Gefden International Inc.
BODIFYING - Hair care products - Image Laboratories, Inc.
BODIGUARD - Chemical preparations - Guardian Royalty Corp.
BODIMER PLUS - Hair care products ☆ - Redken Laboratories, Inc.
BODINE - Motors–automotive - Bodine Electric Co.
BODIN'S - Food products - Bodin Foods Inc.
BODIN'S FANCY FISH - Food products - Bodin Fisheries
BODITUDE - Jewelry - Roman Research, Inc.
BODNER - Neckties - Resisto Tie Makers
BODO HENNIG - Furniture ☆ - Foley & Robinson Inc.
BODUM - Housewares - Bodum, Inc.
BODWEAR - Apparel and accessories - Terri Schneider Riesenman
BODWOK - Footwear - Boardwalk Imports Inc.
BODY - Apparel–athletic - Gilda Marx Inc.
BODY ABUSE ACTIVEWEAR FOR THE OVERACHIEVER - Apparel–athletic - Body Abuse
BODY ACCENT - Brassieres (Bras) - Wacoal America Inc.
BODY ACTION - Apparel stores–sports - Federated Department Stores, Inc.
BODY ACTION DESIGN - Apparel and accessories - Body Action Design, Inc.
BODY ADORNMENTS - Jewelry–costume - Gregorio W. Goss
BODY ADVANTAGE - Hair care products - Tiro Industries, Inc.
BODY ADVENTURE - Computer peripheral equipment - Knowledge Adventure, Inc.
BODY AFFAIR - Lotions - Body Affair Inc.
BODY-AIDE - Cosmetics ☆ - Beauty Aids Inc.
BODY ALERT - Alarms–personal - Kenneth E. Flick
BODY ALL - Deodorants–personal - L & F Consumer Products
BODY AMMO - Vitamins and nutritional supplements - Protein Research Associates
BODY & BOUNCE - Hair care products ☆ - Dep Corp.
BODY & PLUS - Hair care products - For Perms Only Inc.
BODY & SOUL - Optimum Lifestyles, Inc.
BODY & TEXTURE - Hair care products - Scruples Professional Salon Products, Inc.
BODY ARMOR - Apparel and accessories - Nicholas B. Paffett
BODY ARMOR - Insecticides - Mine Safety Appliances Co.
BODY ARMOR - Surgical supplies - Darco International, Inc.

BODY ARMOR CAST REPLACEMENT SYSTEMS - Orthopedic products - Darco International, Inc.
BODY ART - Apparel and accessories ☆ - Jantzen Inc.
BODY ART - Decals and transfers - Metra Inc.
BODY BALANCERS - Footcare products - Professional Product Research, Inc.
BODY BALANCERS - Health care products - Professional Foot Care Products Inc.
BODY BALL - Exercising equipment - Numex Corp.
BODY BASIC, THE - Apparel and accessories ☆ - Warnaco Inc.
BODY BASTER - Apparel and accessories - Joseph G. Angeletta
BODY BAT - Exercising equipment - Body Bat, Inc.
BODY BEAUTE - Toiletries - Inne Dispensables, Inc.
BODY BENEFITS - Skin care products - Dermac Laboratories, Inc.
BODY BILLFOLD, THE - Leather goods - AR Accessories Group Inc.
BODY BINGO. - Games - D.C. Copeland, Inc.
BODY BLISS BEADS - Skin care products ☆ - Lotus Brands Inc.
BODY BLOX - Exercise equipment - Spencer Gee Wellness Corp.
BODY BLUSHERS - Apparel and accessories - Victoria's Secret Stores, Inc.
BODY BOGGLE - Games ☆ - Parker Brothers
BODY BOLSTER - Pillows - American Fiber Industries Corp.
BODY BOND - Hair care products - Roux Laboratories, Inc.
BODY BOOST - Hair care products - Dowbrands L.P.
BODY BOTANICALS - Cosmetics - CBI Laboratories, Inc.
BODY BOW - Exercising equipment - Raymond S. Braver
BODY BRA - Apparel and accessories - Warnaco Inc.
BODY BRASLIP - Apparel and accessories ☆ - Warnaco Inc.
BODY BRIGHTS - Underwear and nightwear - Maidenform Inc.
BODY BRILLIANCE - Skin care products - Halston Borghese Inc. (North America Div.)
BODY BUDDIES - Cereal - General Mills, Inc.
BODY BUDDY - Massage products - Paris Presents Ltd.
BODY BUILDER - Brushes–hair - Clairol Inc.
BODY BUILDER - Food products - Weider Health and Fitness
BODY BUILDER - Hair care products ☆ - Shape-Up
BODY BUILDER - Pharmaceutical preparations - Health Products Corp.
BODY BUILDER - Toys–automobiles - Mattel, Inc.
BODY BUTTER - Skin care products - The Body Shop
BODY BY BALI - Underwear and nightwear - Saramar Corp.
BODY BY DR. FRANCO COLUMBU - Vitamins and nutritional supplements ☆ - ICN Pharmaceuticals Inc.
BODY BY GILDA - Apparel–athletic - Physical Fashions
BODY BY ISOTONER - Lingerie - Saramar Corp.
BODY BY JAKE - Video production - Body by Jake, Inc.
BODY BY NATURE - Shirts - Matthew L. Frazier
BODY BY THE NUMBERS - Shampoos - Lever Brothers Co. Inc.
BODY CARE - Mattress pads - Span-America Medical Systems, Inc.
BODY CARE - Skin care products - Aveda Corp.
BODY-CARE - Skin care products - Geritrex Corp.
BODY CHAIR II - Chairs–upholstered - GF Office Furniture Ltd.
BODY CHIC - Apparel–women's - Lady Ester Lingerie Corp.
BODY CHROME - Jewelry - Anthony C. Santagate, Jr.
BODY COCKTAIL - Apparel and accessories ☆ - Playtex Apparel, Inc.
BODY COLOR - Skin care products - Island Sun Products, Inc.
BODY CO., THE - Apparel–women's - Kmart Properties, Inc.
BODY CONCEPTS - Shampoos - Pro Naturals, Inc.
BODY CONFORT - Skin care products - Sanofi Beaute Inc.
BODY CONTOUR - Skin care products - Helga Van Dyke Skin Care
BODY CONTROLLER - Girdles - Preferred Foundations
BODY COOL ICE - Apparel–athletic - Reliable Plastics
BODY COOLER - Medical apparatus - Conquest Marketing Corp.
BODY COSMETICS - Apparel and accessories - Warnaco Inc.
BODY COTTONS - Underwear and nightwear - Maidenform Inc.
BODY COUNT - Apparel and accessories - Michael J. Grivet
BODY CREATIONS - Cosmetics and skin-care productss - CBI Laboratories, Inc.
BODY CREMES - Apparel and accessories ☆ - Warnaco Inc.
BODY CUSHION - Shoe soles - Polymer Dynamics Technology, Inc.
BODY CYCLE - Mattresses - Fit For Life Sleep Inc.
BODY DANCE - Perfumes - Dri Mark Products, Inc.
BODY DANCER - Footwear–athletic - L.A. Gear, Inc.
BODY DECADENCE - Skin care products - Parfums International Ltd.
BODY DEFENSE - Vitamins and nutritional supplements - Makers of Kal, Inc.
BODY DRAMA - Apparel–women's - Nitches, Inc.
BODY DRENCH BY NORVELL - Suntan lotions - Designs by Norvell Inc.
BODY ECLIPSE - Skin care products - Ready Razor Inc.
BODY ESSENTIAL - Vitamins and nutritional supplements - Natureworks Inc.

BODY ESSENTIALS - Skin care products - Sebastian International, Inc.
BODY FANTASIES - Toiletries - Parfum de Coeur Ltd.
BODY-FIRST - Health care products - Kimberly-Clark Corp.
BODY FITNESS CREAM - Skin-care products - Alexandra De Markoff, Ltd.
BODY FIX - Underwear and nightwear - Kellwood Co.
BODY FLEX - Fabrics–spandex - Bike Athletic Co.
BODY FLEX - Massage products - Conair Corp.
BODY FLOWERS - Deodorants–personal - Gillette Co.
BODY FOR MEN - Hair care products - Helene Curtis Industries Inc.
BODY FORCE - Apparel - Sara Lee Casualwear
BODY FORM - Chairs–upholstered ☆ - All-Luminum Products Inc.
BODY FORTRESS - Vitamins and nutritional supplements - Nature's Bounty, Inc.
BODY FUEL - Vitamins and dietary supplements - Naturally Vitamin Supplements Inc.
BODY FURNITURE L.A. - T-shirts–men's - Body Furniture
BODY FX - Vitamins and nutritional supplements - First Fitness International, Inc.
BODY GEAR - Watches - Golden State International
BODY GIVING - Hair care products - Victoria Jackson Cosmetics, Inc.
BODY GLAZE - Hair care products - Vidal Sassoon Inc.
BODY GLOVE - Garden furniture–metal - Samsonite Furniture Co. (Consumer Products Div.)
BODY GLOVE - Sunglasses ☆ - International Tropic-Cal Inc. (I SKI Div.)
BODY GRAFFITI - Novelty items - Topstone Industries Inc.
BODY GRAPHICS - Automotive parts and accessories ☆ - Arlon, Inc.
BODY GRO - Vitamins and nutritional supplements - Weider Health and Fitness
BODY GUARD - Musical instruments - Fender Musical Instruments
BODY GUARD - Trailers–truck - E.R. Buske Manufacturing Co. Inc.
BODY GUARD - Veterinary nutritional supplements - Pro-Tec Pet Health
BODY GUARD - Veterinary pharmaceutical preparations ☆ - Farnam Cos. Inc.
BODY HEAT - Pens - Bic Corp.
BODY HEAT 1 - Pens ☆ - Bic Corp.
BODY HEAT 2 - Pens ☆ - Bic Corp.
BODY HOT BADWEAR GEAR - Apparel and accessories - Kenneth A. Livingston
BODY HUG, THE - Pillows - American Fiber Industries Corp.
BODY HUGGER - Apparel–athletic ☆ - Pine Hosiery Mills, Inc.
BODY ICING - Lotions - Mehaz International, Inc.
BODY IMAGE - Hosiery–women's - Ames Department Stores, Inc.
BODY IMAGE - Skin care products - Paris Presents Ltd.
BODY INDULGENCE - Nail care products - Revlon Consumer Products Corp.
BODY INSIGHT - Computer software - Informative Graphics Corp.
BODY JACK - Exercising equipment - Fitness Solutions, Inc.
BODY JAM - Toys - Discovery Toys, Inc.
BODY JERSEY - Fabrics - Down East Fabrics Corp.
BODY JEWELS - Apparel–women's - Jezebel-Renee of Hollywood
BODY-JEWELS - Apparel–women's - Renee of Hollywood, Inc.
BODY-KLEEN - Skin care products - Geritrex Corp.
BODY KNEADER - Health care products - Lotus Brands Inc.
BODY KOOLERS - Apparel and accessories - Co. of Women Inc.
BODY LANGUAGE - Apparel and accessories - Playtex Apparel, Inc.
BODY LANGUAGE - Games ☆ - Milton Bradley Co.
BODY LANGUAGE - Jewelry - F.A.F., Inc.
BODY LANGUAGE - Scented body stickers - International Designs, Inc.
BODY LANGUAGE - Skin care products - CBI Laboratories, Inc.
BODY-LIFT - Cosmetics ☆ - Beauty Aids Inc.
BODY-LIGHT - Automotive parts and accessories ☆ - Marson Creative Fastener Group
BODY LINGO - Surfboards - A.G.S. of Hanover Inc.
BODY LITES - Underwear and nightwear - J.C. Penney Co., Inc.
BODY LOVE - Skin care products - Anthony Wilson
BODY LUXURY - Apparel–women's - NCC Industries, Inc.
BODY MAGIC - Apparel and accessories ☆ - Playtex Apparel, Inc.
BODY MAGIC - Polishes - Auto Wax Co., Inc.
BODY MAGIC - Skin care products - Garcoa, Inc.
BODY MAKEUP - Ladies and girls panties - Alba-Waldensian, Inc.
BODY MANAGEMENT SYSTEM - Vitamins and nutritional supplements - DRM, Inc.
BODY MATE - Deodorants–personal - Body Mate
BODY MATE - Health care products - Encore Products Inc.
BODY MAX - Vitamins and nutritional supplements ☆ - Vitamer Laboratories
BODY MECHANICS - Vitamins and nutritional supplements - Triarco Industries, Inc.
BODY MGR. - Vitamins and nutritional supplements - Momentum Marketing Inc.

BODY MOTION - Apparel and accessories ☆ - Playtex Apparel, Inc.
BODY 'N STYLE - Dryers–hair - Pro Star Salon Products
BODY ON TAP - Shampoos - Bristol-Myers Squibb Co.
BODY PALS - Skin care products - Discovery Toys, Inc.
BODY PARTS - Cardboard - Mosby-Year Book, Inc.
BODY PATTERNS - Apparel and accessories ☆ - Playtex Apparel, Inc.
BODY PERFECT, THE - Skin care products - Normajean Fusco
BODY-PIL-O - Mattress pads - Roloke Co.
BODY PLAY - Removable tattoos ☆ - London International U.S. Holdings
BODY PLEASURES - Skin care products - Chanel Inc.
BODY PLUS - Exercising equipment - Newhall Merchandising Concepts Inc.
BODY PRESS, THE - Publisher's imprints - Price Stern Sloan Inc.
BODY PRINT - Bedding–linen - L & P Property Management Co.
BODY PROFIL - Skin care products - Sanofi Beaute Inc.
BODY PROGRAM - Skin care products - Sanofi Beaute Inc.
BODY PRUF - Vitamins and nutritional supplements - Enviro-Tech International
BODY PUMP - Exercising equipment - Aerex Equipment, Inc.
BODY QUENCHER - Beverages–carbonated - Pepsico, Inc.
BODY QUENCHER - Swimming pools - Dazey Corp.
BODY RACERS - Toys - Hersch and Co.
BODY RE-FORMER - Foundation garments–women's - Strouse, Adler Co.
BODY REPAIR - Skin care products - California Cosmetics, Inc.
BODY RHYTHMS - Underwear and nightwear - Maidenform Inc.
BODY RLF - Vitamins and nutritional supplements - Momentum Health Products Inc.
BODY ROK - Deodorants–personal - Acts II Enterprises, Inc.
BODY ROLLER - Massage tool - Jackson Enterprises Inc.
BODY ROUGE - Brassieres (Bras) - Bestform Foundations, Inc.
BODY SAYS WHAT WORDS CANNOT, THE - Apparel and accessories - Ronald Protas
BODY SCENTSATIONS - Toiletries - Scentsation Development Corp.
BODY SCRUB - Automotive parts and accessories - Meguiar's, Inc.
BODY SENSATION - Leotards - Danskin, Inc.
BODY SENSORS - Apparel and accessories - Terramar Sports Worldwide, Ltd.
BODY SHADOWS - Underwear and nightwear - Maidenform Inc.
BODY SHAMPOO - Shampoos - Viviane Woodard Industries, Ltd.
BODY SHAPER - Hair care products - Gold Medal Hair Products Inc.
BODY SHAPER, THE - Faucets ☆ - Moen Inc.
BODY SHAPING - Exercising equipment - Bodyshaping, Inc.
BODY SHEERS - Underwear and nightwear - Maidenform Inc.
BODY SHIMMERS - Underwear and nightwear - Maidenform Inc.
BODY SHINE - Underwear and nightwear - J.C. Penney Co., Inc.
BODY SHOCKS - Apparel and accessories - Pittsburgh Plastics Manufacturing, Inc.
BODY SHOE - Footwear - Wolverine World Wide, Inc.
BODY SHOP - Automotive parts and accessories - Loctite Corp.
BODY SHOP - Paints - Plasti-Kote Co. Inc.
BODY SHOP, THE - Skin care products - The Body Shop
BODY SHOP, THE - Apparel stores–lingerie - Formfit Rogers
BODY SHOP, THE - Medical apparatus - Occumed International Inc.
BODY SHOWER - Bathroom fixtures - Fan-Fi International Inc.
BODY SIZE - Fabrics - Down East Fabrics Corp.
BODY SLEEKS - Underwear and nightwear - Vanity Fair, Inc.
BODY SMOOTHERS - Apparel and accessories ☆ - Playtex Apparel, Inc.
BODY-SOLID - Exercise, sporting, and fitness equipment - Body-Solid, Inc.
BODY SOLUTIONS - Exercise equipment - Ovation Inc.
BODY SOLUTIONS - Vitamins and nutritional supplements - Spa Health Consultants
BODY SPA - Bathroom fixtures - Fan-Fi International Inc.
BODY SPA - Whirlpools - Kohler Co.
BODY SPLENDOR - Skin care products - Inne Dispensables, Inc.
BODY SUEDE - Apparel–women's - Wacoal America Inc.
BODY SWAPPERS - Toys–automobiles - Mattel, Inc.
BODY SYSTEM - Mattresses - Kingsdown, Inc.
BODY SYSTEM - Vitamins and nutritional supplements - Nutramin International, Inc.
BODY TALK - Calendars - Mach 1, Inc.
BODY TALK - Underwear and nightwear - Maidenform Inc.
BODY-TEC - Adhesives and sealants - Tremco Inc.
BODY TECH - Apparel stores–sports - Brawn of California, Inc.
BODY TEMPLE OF CALIFORNIA - Apparel and accessories - L.A. Gymmees
BODY THERAPIES - Skin care products - Orjene Natural Cosmetics
BODY THING - Underwear and nightwear - Maidenform Inc.
BODY TIME - Skin care products - Lenda Inc.
BODY TODDYS - Apparel stores–lingerie ☆ - Formfit Rogers
BODY TONER - Bathroom fixtures ☆ - H.B. Sherman Manufacturing Co.

☆ = Now out of production

BODY TONERS - Hosiery - Sara Lee Corp.
BODY TONIFIANT - Skin care products - Sanofi Beaute Inc.
BODY TOWER - Plumbing fixtures - Body Tower
BODY TRANSPARENT, THE - Computer peripheral equipment - Compton's NewMedia
BODY TRIM - Apparel and accessories ☆ - Playtex Apparel, Inc.
BODY TRIMMER - Cosmetics - Cellulex Inc.
BODY TUNES - Exercising equipment - William R. Birdsong
BODY VELVET - Apparel and accessories ☆ - Playtex Apparel, Inc.
BODY VELVET - Nail care products - Revlon Consumer Products Corp.
BODY VELVET - Skin care products - Cameo Inc.
BODY VIEWS - Apparel and accessories ☆ - Playtex Apparel, Inc.
BODY WARS - Toys - Those Characters from Cleveland, Inc.
BODY WATCH - Sporting goods ☆ - Precise International/Wenger
BODY WATCH - Watches - Christine J. Chickillo
BODY WATCH II - Sporting goods - Precise International/Wenger
BODY WISE - Vitamins and nutritional supplements - Body Wise International, Inc.
BODY WORK BY HAGGAR - Apparel and accessories ☆ - Haggar Corp.
BODY WORKER DELUXE - Massage products - Bodywork Treatment Center
BODY WORKS - Bags - Romar International Corp.
BODY WORKS - Beverages - Shasta Beverages, Inc.
BODY WRAP - Skin care products - Set-N-Me-Free Aloe Vera Co.
BODY WRAPPERS - Apparel and accessories - Attitudes in Dressing, Inc.
BODYBAG BODYBAG - Bags–canvas - Bodybags Ltd.
BODYBAR - Exercising equipment - Marcy Fitness Products
BODYCARE CONCENTRATE - Nail care products - Revlon Consumer Products Corp.
BODYCARE PAQ - Health care products - Body Care Inc.
BODYCIZER - Health care products - Bodyline Comfort Systems
BODYCOLOGY - Hair care products - Leiner Health Products Inc.
BODYCORD - Exercising equipment - SLM Inc.
BODYCTR.ED - Vitamins and nutritional supplements - Jean D. Miller
BODYCURLER - Skin care products - Olivia Garden International
BODYFLEX - Mattresses ☆ - Kingsdown, Inc.
BODYFUEL - Vitamins and nutritional supplements - Vitex Foods Inc.
BODYGARD - Automotive parts and accessories - Benton Plastics, Inc.
BODYGENICS - Cosmetics - Arizona Natural Resources
BODYGUARD - Bathroom fixtures - Price Pfister Co.
BODYGUARD - Cycling shorts and gloves - AXO Sport-America, Inc.
BODYGUARD - Life preservers - Bart's Water Ski Center, Inc.
BODYGUARD - Mattresses - Vandor Corp.
BODYGUARD - Measuring instruments - Bacharach, Inc.
BODYGUARD - Motor vehicle parts and accessories ☆ - Marson Creative Fastener Group
BODYGUARD - Revolvers - Smith & Wesson Corp.
BODYGUARD - Self-defense spray - 1 Mark Consumer Products, Inc.
BODYGUARD - Small arms - Guardian Royalty Corp.
BODYGUARD - Toys - Tonka Corp.
BODYGUARD ACOUSTIC SENSOR - Motor vehicle parts and accessories - Bodyguard Alarm Systems, Inc.
BODYGUARD SLIDE - Playground equipment - Wonderline
BODYGUARDS - Health care products - Jason Marketing Co.
BODYGUARDS - Vitamins and nutritional supplements ☆ - 21st Century Products
BODYHEALTH - Cosmetics - Exerhealth, Inc.
BODYHEALTH SYSTEMS - Water–bottled or canned - Exerhealth, Inc.
BODYKISS - Sponges - Bynum Concepts Inc.
BODYLACE - Apparel–women's - Olga Co.
BODYLEAD - Pet products - Bodylean Inc.
BODYLIND - Skin care products - Borlind of Germany
BODYLINE SPA - Pharmaceutical preparations ☆ - Dermalogica Inc.
BODYLINES - Prosthetic apparatus - Bodylines Inc.
BODYLUSTRE - Nail care products - Revlon Consumer Products Corp.
BODYMASTER - Computer software - Profit Builder Systems, Inc.
BODYMAT - Exercising equipment - Voltex Inc.
BODYMATE - Cereal - Euro Marketing Systems Ltd.
BODYMATE - Pillows - Pillowtex Corp.
BODYNAMIC - Juices - Mayer Bros. Apple Products, Inc.
BODYODYSSEY - Lotions - Viviane Woodard Industries, Ltd.
BODYOGRAPHY - Sponges and loofas - Shigura, Ltd.
BODYOLOGY - Apparel–women's ☆ - Sara Lee Casualwear
BODYONICS - Vitamins and nutritional supplements - Phoenix Laboratories, Inc.
BODYPRINTS - Underwear and nightwear - Body Prints by MP Inc.
BODY'S - Candy ☆ - Pez Candy Inc.

BODYSATIN STRETCH - Brassieres (Bras) - Olga Co.
BODYSCOPE - Computer software - Softkey International Inc.
BODYSHAPER - Exercising equipment ☆ - Maximus Fitness Products
BODYSHAPING STEP - Exercising equipment - Bodyshaping, Inc.
BODYSILK - Brassieres (Bras) - Olga Co.
BODYSILK ACCENTS - Apparel–women's - Olga Co.
BODYSILK PLUS - Apparel–women's - Olga Co.
BODYSKIN - Brassieres (Bras) ☆ - Warnaco Inc.
BODYSKIN - Fabrics ☆ - Vanity Fair Mills Inc.
BODYSLEEKS - Brassieres (Bras) - Vanity Fair, Inc.
BODYSMARTS - Apparel–women's - Exquisite Form Industries
BODYSOX - Toys - Dye-namic Movement Products, Inc.
BODYSSAGE - Whirlpools - Kohler Co.
BODYSURFER, THE - Bathing suits - Surf Line Hawaii, Ltd.
BODYSYNCHER - Apparel–women's - Laracris Corp.
BODYTAPE - Medical apparatus - USMS, Inc.
BODYTECH - Exercising equipment ☆ - Excel, The Exercise Co.
BODYTHERM - Electrical equipment - Conair Corp.
BODYTONE - Skin care products ☆ - WES Publishing
BODYTONE - Sporting goods - Diversified Products Corp.
BODYWALK - Prerecorded video tapes - Reebok International Ltd.
BODYWATCH - Luggage - Handcraft Manufacturing Corp.
BODYWAVES - Apparel and accessories - Bodywaves, Inc.
BODYWEALTH - Skin care products - Bodywealth
BODYWEAR RE-INVENTED - Apparel–women's - David Guy Kubowitz
BODYWINDER - Exercising equipment - Douglas Lawrence Fielder
BOE JOE - Recording label - Black Diamond Records, Inc.
BOECKELER - Measuring instruments - Boeckeler Instruments, Inc.
BOECKH - Computer peripheral equipment - Thomson Publishing Corp.
BOECKH BUILDING COST CONSULTANTS SINCE 1930 - Computer software - Thomson Publishing Corp.
BOECKLING - Glassware–household - German Products Distributing Inc.
BOEGER - Wines - Boeger Winery Inc.
BOEGH BUILDING SYSTEM - Building materials - Boegh Building Systems
BOEHEMIA - Accordions - Castiglione Accordion
BOEHM OF MALVERN, ENGLAND LTD. - Statuary ☆ - Edward Marshall Boehm Inc.
BOEING - Aircraft–airplanes - Boeing Co.
BOEING COLLECTION BY CARRERA, THE - Sunglasses ☆ - Carrera Eyewear Corp.
BOEKHOUT FARM - Food products - Boekhout Farms
BOEL - Cheese - Walker Foods
BOELLA - Bakery products - Bell'amore Imports Inc.
BOEMER - Golf clubs ☆ - Rainbow Sports
BOEN - Flooring–hardwood - Boen Hardwood Flooring
BOERGER - Pet products - Farm & Country Marketing
BOERSMA - Crackers ☆ - Liberty Richter Inc.
BOESCH - International Yachting Center
BOESENDORFER - Pianos - Kimball International, Inc.
BOETTI - Luggage - Boetti
BOF - Bricks - North American Refractories Co.
BOF - Pharmaceutical preparations ☆ - Saron Pharmacal Corp.
BOFF-O! - Computer software - Marilyn Schoeman Dow
BOFFIN BOOKS - Books–comic - Claypool Comics/Boffin Books, Inc.
B.O.G - Apparel and accessories - Bradlees Stores, Inc.
B.O.G. FOR BABY - Apparel and accessories - Bradlees Stores, Inc.
B.O.G. SPORT - Apparel - Bradlees Stores, Inc.
B.O.G. TRADING CO. - Men's apparel - Bradlees Stores, Inc.
BOG WOGGS - Toys - Mattel, Inc.
BOGA BOARD - Water colors - Boga Board
BOGARI - Apparel–men's - United Pacific Apparel (USA), Inc.
BOGDON - Boxes - Castle Food Products
BOGDON'S - Candy - Bogdon Candy Co.
BOGEN - Electronic equipment - Bogen Communications, Inc.
BOGEN - Photographic equipment - Bogen Photo Corp.
BOGEN-CALL - Electronic equipment - Bogen Communications, Inc.
BOGEN-PHONE - Electronic equipment - Bogen Communications, Inc.
BOGEY - Handbags - Bogey, Inc.
BOGEY BIRD - Apparel and accessories - Bogey Bird, Inc.
BOGEY KIT - First aid kits - Dennco, Inc.
BOGEY'S KNIFE & FORK BURRITO - Food products - Palisades Foods, Inc.
BOGGER - Tires - Interco Tire Corp.
BOGGLE - Games - Tonka Corp.
BOGGLE CHALLENGE - Games - Tonka Corp.
BOGGLE JUNIOR - Games - Tonka Corp.
BOGGS - Liquors - Heublein, Inc.

☆ = Now out of production

BOGGY BOTTOM BAYOU - Dolls - Boondocks Collection, Ltd.
BOGIE PUPPY - Toys–stuffed - Dakin Inc.
BOGLE VINEYARDS - Wines - Bogle Vineyards Inc.
BOGLINS - Toys - Mattel, Inc.
BOGMAT - Agricultural products - Bonterra America, Inc.
BOGO - Jewelry - Jerry Bogo Co.
BOGWORT DEW - Colognes ☆ - Fragranhaus
BOH ICE - Beverages–malt ☆ - The Stroh Brewery Co.
BOH ICE LIGHT - Beverages–malt ☆ - The Stroh Brewery Co.
BOHEME - Chairs–upholstered - United Chair Co., Inc.
BOHEME - Tableware–china ☆ - Lenox, Inc.
BOHEMIA - Beverages–malt - Labatt Importers Inc.
BOHEMIA - Lighting fixtures - Angelo Brothers Co.
BOHEMIAN - Beverages–malt ☆ - The Stroh Brewery Co.
BOHEMIAN CLUB - Beverages–malt - Joseph Huber Brewing Co., Inc.
BOHEMIAN GOLD INGOTS - Candy - Bohemian Biscuit Co.
BOHEMIAN HEARTH - Bakery products - Cardiff Foods
BOHEMIAN HEARTH - Breads - Stroehmann Bakeries Inc.
BOHEMIAN KITCHEN - Food products - Sokol and Co.
BOHEMIAN LIGHT - Beverages–malt ☆ - The Stroh Brewery Co.
BOHEMIAN MAID - Pastries - Frank Korinek & Co.
BOHEMIAN RASPBERRY - Liqueurs - William Grant & Sons, Inc.
BOHIO - Food products - Freiria & Co., Inc.
BOHM & MEINL - Musical instruments - Deg Music Products Inc.
BOHM-MEINL - Musical instruments - Multivox/Sorkin Music Co. Inc.
BOHN - Air conditioning equipment - Heatcraft Inc.
BOHNER - Jewelry - Bohner Enterprises
BOHNING - Sporting goods - Bohning Co. Ltd.
BOHNMATE - Heating equipment - Heatcraft Inc.
BOHNMIZER - Hardware - Heatcraft Inc.
BOI-ING! - Cosmetics - Benefit Cosmetics
BOIARDI - Tiles–terrazzo - Boiardi Products Corp.
BOIARDI CERAMICA EPOXY TEXTURED MONOLITHIC FLOORING - Floor coverings–tile - Boiardi Products Corp.
BOIARDI CERAMICS - Floor coverings–tile - Boiardi Products Corp.
BOIDELS - Greeting cards ☆ - Fran Mar Greeting cards Ltd.
BOIL-A-COIL - Cleaner - Comstar International Inc. (IPC Div.)
BOIL EASE - Pharmaceutical preparations - Del Pharmaceuticals, Inc.
BOIL-N-SOAK - Ophthalmic goods ☆ - Alcon Laboratories, Inc.
BOIL-OUT - Carburetors - Justice Brothers Inc.
BOILER AID - Chemical preparations - Imperial Manufacturing Co. Inc.
BOILER BOSS - Controls–heating systems - Erie Controls
BOILER BOSS - Electronic equipment - Advance Systems, Inc.
BOILER CHEMICALS - Chemical preparations - Black Swan Manufacturing Co.
BOILER TREATMENT - Cleaning preparations - Comstar International Inc. (IPC Div.)
BOILERENE - Chemical preparations - Dacar Chemical Co.
BOILERMAKER - Snuff - Brown & Williamson Tobacco Corp.
BOILFAST - Thread ☆ - Coats and Clark Inc.
BOIL'N BAKE - Bagels - Bagelover's Inc.
BOIN - Preserves - International Marketing Services Inc.
BOING! - Computer software - First Star Software Inc.
BOINGO - Inflatable balls - Oddzon Products, Inc.
BOINKER - Games - Bravo International Corp.
BOIS DE PROVENCE - Furniture ☆ - Romweber Co.
BOIS DES ILES - Perfumes - Chanel Inc.
BOIS D'HIVER - Lipsticks - Lancome
BOIS NOIR - Colognes - Chanel Inc.
BOISE - Fabrics - Dan River Inc.
BOISE CASCADE EXPRESSION - Paper–coated - Boise Cascade Corp.
BOISE HAWKS - Paper products - Diamond Sports, Inc.
BOISSET - Beverages–alcohol - Lion Imports
BOISSIERE - Beverages–alcohol ☆ - Jim Beam Brands Co.
BOISSIERE DC - Beverages–alcohol - Palm Bay Imports, Inc.
BOIVERT - Watches - Belair Watch Corp.
BOIZEL - Beverages–alcohol ☆ - Winesellers Ltd.
BOIZET - Food products - Beatrice Cos. Inc.
BOJANGLES - Wines - Monarch Wine Co. of Georgia
BOJANGLES - Yarn ☆ - JCA, Inc.
BOJA'S - Seafood - Boja's Foods Inc.
BOJE - Craft supplies - Norsk Engros USA Inc.
BOJO - Apparel and accessories - John Brown
BOK-LOK - Binders - BOK Industries Inc.
BOKAR - Coffee - Compass Foods Inc.
BOKAR - Coffee - Great Atlantic & Pacific Tea Co., Inc.
BOKER - Knives–hunting - Boker USA Inc.

BOKMA - Beverages–alcohol - Distilled Trading International
BOKOBSA - Wines - Kedem Royal Wine Corp.
BOKOO - Desserts ☆ - Dannon Co., Inc.
BOKS - Shoes - Reebok International Ltd.
BOKU - Fruit drinks–bottled or canned - McCain Citrus, Inc.
BOKU-EKI - Inks–drawing - Boko-Undo USA Inc.
BOKU MELONGE - Fruit drinks–bottled or canned - McCain Citrus, Inc.
BOLA - Chairs–stacking - Fixtures Furniture
BOLA POPS - Candy - Confex Inc.
BOLA PRESS - Recording label - Jazz Composer's Orchestra Association Inc.
BOLAJET - Toys–airplanes - Mattel, Inc.
BOLAND'S - Biscuits - A & A Food Products Corp.
BOLAND'S - Crackers - Bewley Irish Imports
BOLAR - Toys ☆ - Tomy America, Inc.
BOLD - Clocks - General Time Corp. (Westclox/Seth Thomas Div.)
BOLD - Detergents - Procter & Gamble Co.
BOLD - Floor coverings–carpet and rugs - Patcraft Mills Inc.
BOLD - Luggage - Airway Industries, Inc.
BOLD - Shaving preparations - Schnapp Enterprises Inc.
BOLD 1 - Recording label - Bold 1 Records
BOLD 3 - Detergents - Procter & Gamble Co.
BOLD ACCENT - Veterinary pharmaceutical preparations ☆ - Farnam Cos. Inc.
BOLD & BRASSY - Apparel and accessories - Smith & Weber Co.
BOLD BELT - Belts–industrial - Crown Products
BOLD ENCOUNTER - Floor coverings–carpet and rugs ☆ - Galaxy Carpet Mills Inc.
BOLD EXPRESSIONS - Coffee - Starbucks Corp.
BOLD GOLD - Key rings - Curtis Industries Inc.
BOLD GOLD - Toys - Tonka Corp.
BOLD GOLDS - Watches - Timex Corp.
BOLD GRAPH - Floor coverings–carpet and rugs ☆ - Mohawk Carpet Corp.
BOLD HOLD - Hair care products - Alberto-Culver Co.
BOLD IMAGE - Apparel and accessories - Bold Image, Inc.
BOLD IMAGE - Floor coverings–carpet and rugs - Milliken & Co. Inc.
BOLD LOOK - Floor coverings - Armstrong World Industries, Inc.
BOLD MARK - Pens - National Pen & Pencil Co.
BOLD 'N HEARTY - Barbecue sauce - Reckitt & Colman, Inc.
BOLD 'N RUGGED - Watches - Vogue Watch Strap Creations
BOLD 'N SASSY - Floor coverings ☆ - Azrock Commercial Flooring
BOLD 'N SPICY - Mustard - R.T. French Co.
BOLD ONE, THE - Floor coverings - Mannington Resilient Floors
BOLD PROMISE - Floor coverings–carpet and rugs - Monticello Carpet Mills
BOLD REBEL - Pipes–tobacco - S.M. Frank & Co. Inc. (Kaywoodie-Yello-Bole-Medico)
BOLD REMARKS - Greeting cards - Recycled Paper Products, Inc.
BOLD SPIRIT - Floor coverings–carpet and rugs ☆ - Calladium & Marglen
BOLD SPIRIT - Floor coverings–carpet and rugs ☆ - Lees Carpets
BOLD STRIPES - Mats - Akro Corp.
BOLD TASTE - Barbecue sauce - John E. Cain Co.
BOLD TRIGGER - Firearms, accessories, and parts - Bold Triggers, Inc.
BOLD VENTURE - Floor coverings–carpet and rugs ☆ - Lees Carpets
BOLD VOYAGE - Floor coverings–carpet and rugs ☆ - Lees Carpets
BOLDER BORDERS - Paperboard - Trend Enterprises, Inc.
BOLDER DESIGNS - Sleeping bags - FNF Inc.
BOLDIMAGE - Computer software - Diebold Inc.
BOLDIMAGE - Paper ☆ - Rediform
BOLDLINER - Pens - Empire Berol USA
BOLDOCYNARA - Health care products - Bioforce of America Ltd.
BOLDOOT - Colognes - Holland-American Importing Co. Inc.
BOLDT FARMS SINCE 1880 - Preserved foods–prepackaged - Egg Products Inc.
BOLEN - Aprons–leather - Custom Leathercraft Manufacturing
BOLEN - Locks - Bolen Industries Inc.
BOLENS - Garden equipment - Bolens Corp.
BOLERO - Accordions ☆ - Fred Gretsch Enterprises
BOLERO - Apparel and accessories ☆ - Jantzen Inc.
BOLERO - Bathing suits - Vanity Fair, Inc.
BOLERO - Bicycles - Columbia Manufacturing Inc.
BOLERO - Boats - Glen-L Marine Designs
BOLERO - Cigars - Gesty Trading & Manufacturing Corp.
BOLERO - Fabrics - Vertilux-Louverlux Inc.
BOLERO - Floor coverings - Mannington Resilient Floors
BOLERO - Floor coverings–carpet and rugs - V & B Carpet
BOLERO - Floor coverings–carpet and rugs ☆ - Concord/Aldon Industries Inc.
BOLERO - Floor coverings–carpet and rugs ☆ - Kelly Group Inc.
BOLERO - Food products - Greek Gourmet, Ltd.

☆ = Now out of production

BOLERO - Furniture - Weiman Co.
BOLERO - Glassware–household - Owens-Illinois Inc. (Libbey Div.)
BOLERO - Lighters - Colibri Inc.
BOLERO - Shelving units–wood ☆ - Hirsh Co.
BOLERO - Thread - United Thread Mills Corp.
BOLERO - Toilets–enameled - Kohler Co.
BOLERO - Yarn - Henry's Attic
BOLGO - Electronic equipment - Bolgo Inc.
BOLIDE BRAND - Food products - American Bolide International Corp.
BOLIDO - Men's shirts, neckwear, etc. - Frederick Atkins, Inc.
BOLIND - Giftware - Bolind Inc.
BOLING - Bookcases–wood - Boling Co.
BOLIS - Fruit pops–frozen - Latin Specialties Inc.
BOLITA - Beans ☆ - Adobe Milling
BOLIVAR - Cigars - General Cigar Co., Inc.
BOLIVAR - Flatware - Utica Cutlery Co.
BOLIVIA - Recording label - Known Artist Records
BOLL-O-BOLL - Exercising equipment - Arne Roald Bradstock
BOLLA - Wine - Brown-Forman Corp.
BOLLE' - Luggage - Bolle' America, Inc.
BOLLE ACRYLEX - Sunglasses - Bolle' America, Inc.
BOLLE' EYEZONE - Sunglasses ☆ - Bolle' America, Inc.
BOLLETJE - Bakery products - Europa Foods Ltd.
BOLLETJE - Biscuits - Westdale Foods Co.
BOLLETJE - Breads - Holland-American Importing Co. Inc.
BOLLGAME STAYING IN PLAY NO. 1 - Apparel and accessories - Le Collection Inc.
BOLLINGEN - Publisher's imprints - Princeton University Press
BOLLINGER - Wines - Dreyfus Ashby Inc.
BOLLINI - Wines - Kobrand Corp.
BOLLMAN - Headwear - Bollman Hat Co.
BOLLOX - Games - Rob Nelson Enterprises, Inc.
BOLNER'S - Seasonings - Bolner's Fiesta Products, Inc.
BOLNERS FIESTA BLEND - Spices and extracts - Bolner's Fiesta Products, Inc.
BOLO - Dog food - Simmons Industries Inc.
BOLO - Yarn ☆ - Plymouth Yarn Co.
BOLO BAG - Leather goods ☆ - AR Accessories Group Inc.
BOLO FINO - Yarn ☆ - Plymouth Yarn Co.
BOLONO - Meat extracts - Miles Inc.
BOLOS - Ophthalmic goods - Karlen Manufacturing, Inc.
BOLOTIN - Cleaning preparations - Bolotin, Inc.
BOLOXIE - Medical apparatus - Robert J. Ansert
BOLS - Liquors - William Grant & Sons, Inc.
BOLSHOI - Vodka - House of Seagram
BOLSTAR - Insecticides - Bayer Corp. (Agriculture Div.)
BOLSTER BAR - Chocolate bars - New England Confectionery Co.
BOLT - Bags–trash - Sweet Paper Sales Corp.
BOLT - Caulking compounds - White Lightning Products Corp.
BOLT - Chemical preparations - Ch2o, Inc.
BOLT - Computer software - Sungard Investment Ventures, Inc.
BOLT - Musical instruments - Bolt Guitars Inc.
BOLT - Paper towels ☆ - James River Corp.
BOLT - Toys - Tonka Corp.
BOLT-ACTION - Cutlery - Gerber Legendary Blades
BOLT BUSTER - Oils–lubricating - Coastal Unilube Inc.
BOLT JR. - Food products - Hot'n Now, Inc.
BOLT-MAKER - Hardware - Baden Steelbar & Bolt Co.
BOLT 'N' STEIN - Toys - Tomy America, Inc.
BOLT-SET - Concrete products ☆ - Consolidated Coatings Corp.
BOLT THE COLT - Stuffed toys, canisters, now out of production - American Greetings Corp.
BOLTA - Wallpaper - Bolta Wallcoverings
BOLTA CLASSICS - Wallpaper ☆ - Bolta Wallcoverings
BOLTAFLEX - Vinyl - Gencorp Inc.
BOLTAWALL - Wallcovering - Gencorp Inc.
BOLTAWALL - Wallpaper - Bolta Wallcoverings
BOLTERGEIST - T-shirts–men's - David A. Hibi
BOLTMASTER - Hardware - Medalist Industries Inc.
BOLTON - Gin ☆ - Majestic Distilling Co.
BOLTPRO - Computer software - MPR Associates, Inc.
BOLZ - Toys - Small World Toys
BOM BON D'OR - Candy ☆ - Uniconfis Corp.
BOMACRON - Concrete products - Bomanite Corp.
BOMAN - Radios - Boman Industries
BOMANITE - Concrete products - Bomanite Corp.

BOMAR - Sporting goods - Pompanette Inc.
BOMARC - Bicycles - Ross Bicycles USA, Ltd.
BOMARC - Toys–models - Estes Industries
BOMARK - Sporting goods - Bomark Group Inc.
BOMB POP - Confections - Merritt Foods Co.
BOMB POP JR. - Confections - Merritt Foods Co.
BOMB PROOF - Bicycles - Schwinn Cycling & Fitness Inc.
BOMB SHELLS - Eggs - Roger Wood Foods, Inc.
BOMB SQUAD, THE - Games - Trinity Licensing & Marketing
BOMB TECH. - Knives - Imperial Schrade Corp.
BOMB WARE, THE - Apparel and accessories - Daniel P. Copp
BOMBADIER - Books–comic - Malibu Comics Entertainment, Inc.
BOMBAII CUTTERS - Hair care products - Debbie Lamont
BOMBARD - Insecticides ☆ - Uncle Sam Chemical Co., Inc.
BOMBARDIER - Motor vehicles - Bombardier Corp.
BOMBARDIER JACKET - Jackets ☆ - Horace Small Apparel Co.
BOMBAT - Bats–baseball - Pacers Sports
BOMBAY - Floor coverings–carpet and rugs - Queen Carpet Corp.
BOMBAY - Floor coverings–carpet and rugs ☆ - Rugby Rugs Inc.
BOMBAY - Gin - Carillon Importers Ltd.
BOMBAY - Steel springs–railroad - Needlecraft Industries
BOMBAY BUS CO. - Apparel stores–sports - Surf Line Hawaii, Ltd.
BOMBAY COLLECTION - Lighting fixtures - Fredrick Ramond Inc.
BOMBAY COMPANY, THE - Furniture - BBA Holdings
BOMBAY CO., THE - Furniture - Bombay Co. Inc.
BOMBAY KRINKLE - Fabrics ☆ - Charter Fabrics Inc.
BOMBAY ORIGINAL - Fruit drinks–bottled or canned - H.R. Nicholson Co.
BOMBAY ORIGINAL - Rice - Puran Foods, Ltd.
BOMBAY PREMIUM - Juices - H.R. Nicholson Co.
BOMBAY SAPPHIRE - Gin - Carillon Importers Ltd.
BOMBE - Health care products - Rusk Inc.
BOMBER - Batteries - Bomber Battery, Inc.
BOMBER - Boats–motor - Commander Marine
BOMBER - Fishing lures - Bomber Bait Co.
BOMBER - Golfing equipment - Golfsmith International Inc.
BOMBER - Hats - Mad Bomber Co.
BOMBER - Toys - Tonka Corp.
BOMBER ATTACK - Games ☆ - Avalon Hill Game Co.
BOMBER BLUE - Cosmetics ☆ - Noxell Corp.
BOMBITAS - Gelatin - Piacere International, Inc.
BOMBONIERE! - Ribbons - Wilton Industries, Inc.
BOMBOY - Furniture–wood - Bomboy, Inc.
BOMBSHELL - Apparel and accessories - Jerris Greenblat
BOMBSHELL - Golfing equipment - Pinseeker Golf Corp.
BOMMER - Hardware - Bommer Industries Inc.
BOMP - Film–motion picture - Bomp Entertainment, Inc.
BOMP - Recording label - Bomp Records Inc.
BON-A-D - Pharmaceutical preparations - Barrows Pharmacal Inc.
BON-A-LETS - Pharmaceutical preparations - Barrows Pharmacal Inc.
BON-A-M - Pharmaceutical preparations - Barrows Pharmacal Inc.
BON AIL - Garlic - Maurice A. Auerbach Inc.
BON AIR - Deodorizers - Coughlan Products Corp.
BON-AIRE - Motor vehicle parts and accessories - Bob Bartlett & Associates Inc.
BON AMI - Cleaning preparations - Faultless Starch/Bon Ami Co.
BON AMI - Recording label - MCA Universal Studios
BON-AMI - Steel springs–railroad - Needlecraft Industries
BON AMI SHAMMY - Household cleaning cloth ☆ - Faultless Starch/Bon Ami Co.
BON APPETIT - Candy ☆ - Leaf, Inc.
BON APPETIT - Cooking equipment–household ☆ - Kraftware Corp. (Morgan Div.)
BON APPETIT - Food products - McCormick & Co., Inc.
BON APPETIT - Pastries - Bon Appetit Danish Co., Inc.
BON APPETIT - Tableware–china ☆ - Villeroy and Boch Tableware Ltd.
BON APPETIT COLLECTION - Flatware ☆ - Kraftware Corp. (Morgan Div.)
BON APPETIT ELECTRONIC COOKBOOK - Computer software ☆ - Pinpoint Publishing
BON APPLE TITE - Fruit drinks–bottled or canned - Palm Bay Imports, Inc.
BON-B-TOL - Pharmaceutical preparations - Barrows Pharmacal Inc.
BON BEL - Cheese - Fromageries Bel, Inc.
BON BON - Christmas tree ornaments - Cracker Box Inc.
BON BON - Dolls - Tonka Corp.
BON BON - Girdles - Youthcraft-Charmfit
BON BON - Hosiery - Kartex International Cos. Inc.
BON BON - Watches - Sheva R & D Inc.

☆ = Now out of production

BON BON BUM - Candy - Colombina Candy Co., Inc.
BON-BONE - Dog food - Superior Brands Inc.
BON BONS - Ice cream - Nestle USA
BON CAFE - Coffee - Community Coffee Co., Inc.
BON CAMPO - Vegetables–frozen - Merex Inc.
BON CARAFE - Wines ☆ - Widmer's Wine Cellars Inc.
BON CHEF - Cookware - Bon Chef, Inc.
BON-COIF - Hair care products - L.T. Products Ltd.
BON-DEE - Hardware ☆ - William L. Bonnell Co. Inc.
BON-E - Pharmaceutical preparations - Barrows Pharmacal Inc.
BON-E-CON - Tools–hand-operated ☆ - Triangle Tool Group Inc.
BON-ETTES - Candy ☆ - Leaf, Inc.
BON EVE - Cosmetics - Robert Simmons Inc.
BON FOAM - Fibers–synthetic - Georgia-Bonded Fibers, Inc.
BON GUSTO - Cigars - Avanti Cigar Co.
BON HEUR - Apparel–women's - Lily of France Inc.
BON JOUR - Apparel and accessories - Bon Jour Group, Ltd.
BON JOUR - Floor coverings–carpet and rugs - Mohawk Industries Inc.
BON JOUR - Handbags - Dover Handbag Corp.
BON JOUR - Rice - Estherwood Rice Sales
BON LAIT - Dairy products ☆ - Besnier USA, Inc.
BON LAIT 70 - Dairy products ☆ - Besnier USA, Inc.
BON MELANGE - Soups–canned - Jac Hes & Co.
BON-NUIT - Pharmaceutical preparations - Barrows Pharmacal Inc.
BON-O-LAC - Milk–canned or powdered - Bongards Creameries
BON-PEL - Fibers–synthetic - Georgia-Bonded Fibers, Inc.
BON-RAY - Food products - Venice Maid Co. Inc.
BON SANTE - Food products - Allied International Corp.
BON SANTE - Skin care products ☆ - Carme Inc.
BON SECOUR - Seafood products–fresh or frozen - Bon Secour Fisheries Inc.
BON SOIR - Christmas tree ornaments - Cracker Box Inc.
BON SOL - Wines - Joseph E. Seagram & Sons, Inc.
BON TON - Clocks - Sunbeam Precision Measurement
BON TON - Rice - Estherwood Rice Sales
BON-TON - Toys–stuffed - IBTT
BON TON CHEESE CRUNCHIES - Snack foods - York Foods, Inc.
BON TON CHEESE CURLIES - Snack foods - York Foods, Inc.
BON VIVANT - Cooking equipment–household - Old Dutch International Ltd.
BON VIVANT - Floor coverings–carpet and rugs - Monticello Carpet Mills
BON VIVANT - Food products - Moore & Co. Soups Inc.
BON VIVANT - Glassware–household - Owens-Illinois Inc. (Libbey Div.)
BON VIVANT - Sinks–metal - Kohler Co.
BON VOYAGE - Boats - Glen-L Marine Designs
BON VOYAGE - Christmas tree ornaments ☆ - Cracker Box Inc.
BON VOYAGE - Trailers–travel - Hi-Lo Trailer Co. Inc.
BON VOYAGE TRUNK - Luggage ☆ - Alger Creations Inc.
BONA FIDE - Apparel and accessories - Mark A. Sudermann
BONA FORTUNA - Seafood products–fresh or frozen - Royal Seafoods Inc.
BONA-LISA - Pet products - Bona-Lisa, Inc.
BONA ROMA - Pizzas–frozen - V.I.P. Products, Inc.
BONACAL PLUS - Vitamins and nutritional supplements ☆ - Kenwood Laboratories Inc.
BONACURE - Hair care products - Schwarzkopf Inc.
BONADE - Musical instrument accessories - G. Leblanc Corp.
BONAFCO - Thread - Bond Products Inc.
BONAFIDO COMPANY, THE - Pet products - Bonafido Co.
BONAFILE - File folders - Highsmith Co., Inc.
BONAG - Machinery - Compaction America, Inc.
BONAGE - Apparel and accessories - Fierres, Inc.
BONAIR - Baskets–wood - Royal Cathay Trading Co.
BONAIRE - Floor coverings–carpet and rugs ☆ - Regal Rugs Inc.
BONAIRE - Furniture–children's ☆ - Child Craft Industries Inc.
BONAKEMI - Flooring–hardwood - Roane Co.
BONAMIL - Baby foods - American Home Products Corp.
BONANZA - Aircraft–airplanes - Beech Aircraft Corp.
BONANZA - Aluminum foil wrap - Highland Supply Corp.
BONANZA - Boats - Glen-L Marine Designs
BONANZA - Boats–motor ☆ - Cruisers
BONANZA - Brushes–paint - Wooster Brush Co.
BONANZA - Chewing gum - Fleer Corp.
BONANZA - Cigars - General Cigar Co., Inc.
BONANZA - Cigars ☆ - Phillies Cigar Co.
BONANZA - Craft supplies - Western School Supply Co.
BONANZA - Floor coverings ☆ - Tarkett, Inc.
BONANZA - Floor coverings–carpet and rugs ☆ - Len Dal Carpets
BONANZA - Flowers, plants, and seeds - Panamerican Seed

BONANZA - Food products ☆ - Sunstar Foods Inc.
BONANZA - Hams - Peet Packing Co.
BONANZA - Preserved foods–canned - Del Monte Corp.
BONANZA - Seasonings ☆ - Signature Brands, LLC
BONANZA - Snack foods ☆ - American Candy Co.
BONANZA PEPSI PONTIAC - Toys–electronic - Bird Bromiticous Inc.
BONAPARTE - Apparel and accessories - Leela Industries Ltd.
BONAPARTE - Clocks ☆ - Ridgeway Clock Co.
BONARDI - Beverages–alcohol - Hammer Co.
BONAT - Hair care products - American International Industries
BONAT - Hair care products - Bonat Inc.
BONAT - Pet products - Rapid Electric/R & R Manufacturing
BONATE - Pharmaceutical preparations ☆ - Suppositoria Laboratories
BONAVENTURE - Floor coverings - Mannington Resilient Floors
BONAVENTURE - Furniture ☆ - Bassett Furniture Industries, Inc.
BONAVENTURE - Lamps ☆ - Lamplight Farms, Inc.
BONAVITA - Food products - Liberty Richter Inc.
BONBINO - Cheese - Fromageries Bel, Inc.
BONBONS DE BOURGUIGNON - Candy - Jo-Ann M. Bourguignon
BONCHAMPI - Cheese - Swissrose International Inc.
BONCHARD - Wine ☆ - Palace Brands Co.
BOND - Adhesives and sealants - Bond Adhesives Co.
BOND - Beverages - Bond Chemical Products Co.
BOND - Breads ☆ - General Host Corp.
BOND - Garden equipment - Bond Manufacturing Co. Inc.
BOND - Office supplies ☆ - Arrow Rubber Products Inc.
BOND - Pickles - Green Bay Foods Co.
BOND 8 - Epoxy - Permagile Industries Inc.
BOND-A-MATIC 2000 - Tools–power-driven - Loctite Corp.
BOND-AID - Electrical equipment - GB Electrical Inc.
BOND-AID - Nail care products - Opi Products, Inc.
BOND-ALL - Adhesives and sealants - Faber-Castell Corp.
BOND ASSAULT - Games - Avalon Hill Game Co.
BOND BLEND - Coatings - Creative Maintenance Solutions, Inc.
BOND I - Epoxy - Permagile Industries Inc.
BOND-IT - Adhesives and sealants - Atlas Chemical Co.
BOND-IT - Adhesives and sealants - Comstar International Inc. (IPC Div.)
BOND LITE - Laminated glass - American Tempering Inc. (Laminating Div.)
BOND LITE PLUS - Laminated glass - American Tempering Inc. (Laminating Div.)
BOND MASTER - Epoxy coatings - W.P. Hickman Systems
BOND-ME - Adhesives and sealants - KEL-EEZ
BOND OST - Cheese - Noon Hour Food Products
BOND-RITE - Glue–household or industrial ☆ - Standard Paste & Glue Co.
BOND ST. - Watches - Elgin Watch Co.
BOND STREET - Floor coverings–carpet and rugs ☆ - Atlas Carpet Mills Inc.
BOND STREET - Leather goods - Bond Street
BOND STREET - Tobacco products - House of Windsor Inc.
BOND-TITE - Adhesives and sealants - Commercial Chemical Co. Inc.
BOND-TITE - Archery equipment - Bohning Co. Ltd.
BOND-TITE - Automotive parts and accessories ☆ - Oatey Co.
BONDAIR - Thread - Perfect Thread Co. Inc.
BONDAIRE - Fabrics ☆ - West Point-Pepperell Inc.
BONDALAST - Wheels - Hamilton Caster & Manufacturing Co.
BONDALL - Adhesives and sealants ☆ - Allied Compositions
BONDALL - Adhesives and sealants ☆ - L & F Products Inc.
BONDCORE - Thread - Bond Products Inc.
BONDCOTE - Adhesives and sealants ☆ - Flintkote Co.
BONDCOTE - Adhesives and sealants ☆ - GS Roofing Products Co.
BONDED - Brushes–paint ☆ - PPG Industries, Inc.
BONDED - Food products - Delicious Foods Co.
BONDED - Turkeys - Watson Quality Foods Inc.
BONDED COTTON COMPANY - Apparel–men's - Rome Manufacturing Co. Inc.
BONDENE - Cement - Plastruct Inc.
BONDER - Nail care products - Orly International Inc.
BONDEX - Nail care products - Opi Products, Inc.
BONDEX - Paints ☆ - Bondex International Inc.
BONDEX - Patches, insignia, and emblems - Wm. E. Wright Ltd.
BONDEX - Thread - Gudebrod, Inc.
BONDEX 20 YEAR PROTECTOR - Concrete–mixture ☆ - Bondex International Inc.
BONDFLEX - Leather goods - Schwarz Leather Co.
BONDHEX - Hardware - Bondhus Corp.
BONDI JUNCTION - Beverages–carbonated - D.R. Chilton Inc.
BONDINI PIN-POINT - Nail care products ☆ - Spilo/Mehaz Worldwide

☆ = Now out of production

BONDINI PLUS - Nail care products - Spilo/Mehaz Worldwide
BONDLOC - Thread - Bond Products Inc.
BONDO - Automotive repair shops - Dynatron/Bondo Corp.
BONDOST - Cheese - Swedish Food Products
BONDOT - Computer storage devices - Optical Disc Corp.
BONDRITE - Adhesives and sealants - Imperial Adhesives Inc.
BONDRITE - Wire–aluminum - Plasma Powders & Systems, Inc.
BONDS ON - Concrete repair products - Wall Firma Inc.
BONDSETT - Floor coverings–carpet and rugs ☆ - Lees Carpets
BONDSMAN - Tool boxes - Merriam Manufacturing Co. Inc.
BONDSTAR - Artists' materials - Bondstar Portfolio Inc.
BONDSTAR FRENCH COLLECTION - Artists' materials - Bondstar Portfolio Inc.
BONDTIE - Tying twine ☆ - American Manufacturing Co. Inc.
BONDUELLE - Agricultural products - Holland-American Importing Co. Inc.
BONDUELLE - Food products - De Choix Specialty Foods Co.
BONDUELLE - Wines - Bonduel Pickling Co. Inc.
BONDURA - Artists' materials - Bondstar Portfolio Inc.
BONDURA - Fabrics–cotton - Marigail Hull
BONDWELL - Computers–personal ☆ - Bondwell Industrial Co. Inc.
BONDWOOD - Floor coverings - Harris-Tarkett, Inc.
BONDY/SIDKAR - Footwear ☆ - Conjac Inc.
BONDZ-IT PLUS - Sealing compounds - Stewart-Hall Chemical Corp.
BONE - Books–comic - Jeffrey A. Smith
BONE AGE - Toys - Tonka Corp.
BONE & BELL - Pet products - Polly's Pleasures
BONE & BODY - Pet products - Breeder's Choice Pet Foods, Inc.
BONE & JOINT DEFENSE SYSTEM - Vitamins and nutritional supplements - Barth's Nutra Products
BONE-ANZA - Dog food - Superior Brands Inc.
BONE-APARTS - Meat products–poultry ☆ - Pierce Foods Corp.
BONE APPETIT - Dog food - Ralston Purina Co.
BONE BOUTIQUE - Pet food - Paddiwack Enterprises LLC
BONE BUDDIES - Pet food - Petco Pet Food & Supplies
BONE BUILDER - Vitamins and nutritional supplements - Ethical Nutrients
BONE BUILDER CHEWABLE - Vitamins and nutritional supplements - Ethical Nutrients
BONE-C-DENT - Vitamins and nutritional supplements - Enzyme Process Co. Inc.
BONE COMB - Hair care products - Paul Mazzotta Inc.
BONE COVERS - Apparel and accessories - Becky Leadbetter, Spencer St. Cyr, Steven Leadbetter Partnership
BONE CRUSHER - Garbage disposal units–household - Anaheim Manufacturing Co.
BONE CRUSHER - Toys–automobiles - Tonka Corp.
BONE DENSITY FACTORS - Vitamins and nutritional supplements - Consac Industries, Inc.
BONE-DRI - Sealing compounds - Colonial Refining and Chemical Co.
BONE DRY - Apparel–athletic - Red Head Brand Corp.
BONE DRY - Aprons - Klaas R. Van Der Weg
BONE DRY - Pumps–water - Edson Corp.
BONE DRY - Tents - Kellwood Co.
BONE ESSENTIALS - Vitamins and nutritional supplements - Vital Food Sources, Inc.
BONE HEAD - Watches - Mattel, Inc.
BONE HEADS - Chocolate candy - R.M. Palmer Co.
BONE-MANOUX - Wines ☆ - Sidney Frank Importing Co., Inc.
BONE NOURISHER - Intracell Nutrition Inc.
BONE-O-SAPIEN - Apparel and accessories - Bone-O-Sapien, Inc.
BONE PILE - Pet toys - Items Inc.
BONE POWER - Vitamins and nutritional supplements - Natural Organics, Inc.
BONE STRAIT - Hair care products - Alberto-Culver Co.
BONE SUCKIN' - Barbecue sauce - Ford's Fancy Foods
BONE, THE - Motor vehicle parts and accessories - Pegasus Products Co.
BONE TIE - Pet products - Victoria Meekins
BONE TONE - Vitamins and nutritional supplements - Solaray
BONE-UP - Vitamins and nutritional supplements - Nutrition Headquarters, Inc.
BONE YARD - Apparel and accessories - Bert Schaar
BONE ZONE - Stamps–hand - Rubberstampede Partnership
BONEAFIDE FRIENDS - Toys - Strottman International, Inc.
BONEBREAKER - Toys - Hasbro, Inc.
BONECRUSHER - Toys - Hasbro, Inc.
BONELESS - Apparel and accessories - Park M. Beutler
BONELESS BEEF - Dog food - Fort Morgan Pet Foods
BONELLI - Apparel–men's - Bernardi Financial Inc.
BONES - Eyeglasses - Goat Eyewear

BONES - Sporting goods - Powell Skateboards
BONES AND BITS - Pet food - Hubbard Milling Co.
BONES & JOINTS - Vitamins and nutritional supplements - Re-Vita Manufacturing Co., Inc.
BONES AWAY - Pet products - City Dog Designed Co., Inc.
BONES - CLOTHING - Apparel and accessories - Powell Skateboards
BONES OF POWER - Games - Gamescience
BONES VOYAGE - Computer software - Hartley Courseware Inc.
BONESHAKER - Bicycles - Rideable Bicycle Replicas Inc.
BONESHAKERS - Meat products–pork - Quality Meats and Seafood Inc.
BONEWAY FARMS - Condiments and seasonings - Booneway Farms Inc.
BONEY BENNY - Toys ☆ - Imperial Toy Corp.
BONEZE JR. - Apparel and accessories - Mills Products Inc.
BONFARE - Dairy products - Bonfare Food Stores, Inc.
BONFIELD - Food products - Bonduel Pickling Co. Inc.
BONFIRE - Fish–fresh or frozen - New England Fish Co.
BONFIRE - Recording label - Jay Jay Record & Tape Co.
BONFLEX - Fibers–synthetic - Georgia-Bonded Fibers, Inc.
BONGARDS - Whey - Bongards Creameries
BONGERS - Hand-held massagers - Bongers
BONGIORNO - Wines - Wine Merchants Ltd.
BONGO - Bags - Michael Caruso & Co., Inc.
BONGO - Bicycles ☆ - Burley Design Cooperative
BONGO - Bowls ☆ - Deka Plastics Inc.
BONGO - Ice cream - Thin's Inn Inc.
BONGO BY GENE MONTESANO - Apparel and accessories - Michael Caruso & Co., Inc.
BONGRAIN - Cheese - Bongrain Cheese USA
BONGRAIN - Cheese - Dairy Fresh Products Co.
BONHEUR - Floor coverings–carpet and rugs - Regal Rugs Inc.
BONHEUR - Glassware–household ☆ - Oneida Ltd.
BONICELL - Telephone accessories - Bonicell USA Corp.
BONIFATO - Wines - Joseph Victori Wines Inc.
BONIFAY - Brushes–paint - Corona Brushes Inc.
BONIFAZ - Cheese ☆ - Dan Carter Inc.
BONIFLEX - Paper - Permalin Products Co.
BONIM BOOKS - Publisher's imprints - Hebrew Publishing Co.
BONINE - Pharmaceutical preparations - Pfizer Inc.
BONIO - Pet products - Superior Brands Inc.
BONIQUE - Giftware - Terrace Ceramics Inc.
BONIQUE - Salad dressings–mixes - Sunstar Foods Inc.
BONITA - Bicycles - Ross Bicycles USA, Ltd.
BONITA - Brushes - Corona Brushes Inc.
BONITA - Cigars ☆ - General Cigar Co., Inc.
BONITA - Floor coverings - Tarkett, Inc.
BONITA - Food products - Ecuadorean Tropical Products, Inc.
BONITA - Fruits and vegetables - Pacific Fruit, Inc.
BONITA - Rings–jewelry - Artcarved Inc.
BONITA - Trees - H & H Wholesale Nursery, Inc.
BONITA - Underwear and nightwear - Lovable Co.
BONITO - Boats–motor - Tillotson-Pearson Inc.
BONJOUR - Apparel–men's - Harper Shirt Co.
BONJOUR - Apparel–women's - Newton Manufacturing Corp.
BONJOUR - Apparel–women's - Sanmark-Stardust Inc.
BONJOUR - Cosmetics - Bon Jour Group, Ltd.
BONJOUR - Floor coverings–carpet and rugs - Queen Carpet Corp.
BONJOUR - Food products machinery - Culinary Parts Unlimited, Inc.
BONJOUR - Luggage ☆ - Universal Trav-ler Inc.
BONJOUR - Nuts–salted, roasted, cooked, or canned ☆ - Spring Tree Corp.
BONJOUR - Yarn ☆ - William Unger & Co. Inc.
BONJOUR 8 - Apparel and accessories - Bon Jour Group, Ltd.
BONJOUR LA PARISIENNE - Bar fixtures–plastic - La Parisienne Bakery
BONK - Vitamins and nutritional supplements - Stokely-Van Camp, Inc.
BONKERS - Apparel–men's - Harper Shirt Co.
BONKERS - Candy - Nabisco Foods Group
BONKERS - Cat food - Beatrice Cos. Inc.
BONKERS - Games - Milton Bradley Co.
BONKERS - Games ☆ - Parker Brothers
BONKERS - Toys–stuffed ☆ - Gund, Inc.
BONKERS BAND SHOES - Shoes - Jon Farbman
BONKERS! DINOSAURUS - Snack foods - Richardson Brands
BONLINN - Towels - Chicopee
BONNA - Sporting goods - Allsop, Inc.
BONNAVILLA - Manufactured homes - Bonnavilla Homes
BONNCO ABRASIVES - Steel wool - International Steel Wool Corp.
BONNE BELL - Skin care products ☆ - Bonne Bell, Inc.

BONNE BELLE - Furniture ☆ - Bassett Furniture Industries, Inc.
BONNE CHERE - Food products - Sara Lee Corp.
BONNE CHERE - Salad dressings–mixes - Swiss Chalet Inc.
BONNE FAMILY, THE - Toys–stuffed - Lois Hall Creations
BONNE LEE - Health care products - Bonne Products
BONNE MAISON - Mustard - Berry Best Farm
BONNE MAMAN - Preserves - International Marketing Services Inc.
BONNE TERRE - Wines - Schieffelin and Somerset Co.
BONNEE - Bakery products - Our Own Bakeries Inc.
BONNER - Fruits–dried - Dole Dried Fruit & Nut Co.
BONNET - Cleaning preparations–carpet and rug - Guardsman Products, Inc.
BONNET - Recording label - Country Stream Records
BONNET BABIES - Greeting cards ☆ - Recycled Paper Products, Inc.
BONNET BUNNIES - Candy ☆ - R.M. Palmer Co.
BONNET BUNNIES - Toys–stuffed ☆ - Fun World Inc.
BONNET PETS - Toys–stuffed - Fun World Inc.
BONNETS & BOWS - Dolls ☆ - Gorham Inc.
BONNEVILLE - Motor vehicles–automobiles - General Motors Corp. (Pontiac/GMC Div.)
BONNEVILLE - Pickles - Steinfeld's Products Co.
BONNEVILLE - Tires - Bridgestone/Firestone, Inc.
BONNEVILLE - Watches - Bradley J. Fanshaw
BONNEVILLE BOOKS - Publisher's imprints ☆ - University of Utah Press
BONNEVILLE FAMILY ENTERTAINMENT - Recording label - Bonneville International Corp.
BONNEVILLE MODEL G - Motor vehicles–automobiles ☆ - General Motors Corp. (Pontiac/GMC Div.)
BONNEVILLE WORLDWIDE ENTERTAINMENT - Recording label - Bonneville International Corp.
BONNEY - Food products - Becker Food Co. Inc.
BONNEY - Tools–hand-operated - Triangle Tool Group Inc.
BONNIBEL - Footwear - Shoe Magnate, Inc.
BONNIE - Cleaning preparations–household - Desoto, Inc.
BONNIE - Clocks ☆ - General Time Corp. (Westclox/Seth Thomas Div.)
BONNIE - Cookies - Lance, Inc.
BONNIE - Cording - Pepperell Braiding Co. Inc.
BONNIE - Dolls - Russ Berrie and Co., Inc.
BONNIE - Fruits and vegetables ☆ - Stanley Orchards Sales Inc.
BONNIE - Guns - Charter Arms
BONNIE - Paper–tissue ☆ - Potlatch Corp.
BONNIE - Wheat germ - Niblack
BONNIE AND CLYDE - Candy - Bonnie and Clyde, Inc.
BONNIE AUGUST - Apparel and accessories ☆ - Bonnie Doon
BONNIE AUGUST - Apparel–women's - Jacques Moret, Inc.
BONNIE BAY - Food products ☆ - Slade Gorton and Co. Inc.
BONNIE-BEST - Trees - J.W. Jung Seed Co. Inc.
BONNIE BLAIN - Apparel–women's - Vogue Originals Inc.
BONNIE BLUE - Ice cream - Roundy's Inc.
BONNIE BOOKS - Publisher's imprints - Samuel Lowe Co.
BONNIE BOYNTON - Apparel and accessories - Bonnie Boynton Enterprises Inc.
BONNIE BRAE - Flatware - Pfaltzgraff Investment Co.
BONNIE BRIDE - Dolls - Tonka Corp.
BONNIE BROOK - Wallpaper ☆ - Westchester Prints
BONNIE BROOK - Water–bottled or canned - Johanna Foods, Inc.
BONNIE BROWN DESIGNS - Skin care products ☆ - Bonnie Brown Designs Inc.
BONNIE DOON - Apparel and accessories - Bonnie Doon
BONNIE DUNES - Flowers, plants, and seeds - Turf-Seed, Inc.
BONNIE G - Footwear–women's ☆ - Markon Footwear Inc.
BONNIE GREEN - Flowers, plants, and seeds ☆ - Seaboard Seed Co.
BONNIE HOT POGIE, THE - Gloves - Wildwater Designs Ltd.
BONNIE HUBBARD - Food products - United Grocers Inc.
BONNIE INTERNATIONAL - Handbags - Bonnie International
BONNIE JEAN - Dresses–girls' - Gerson and Gerson Inc.
BONNIE LASS - Bolts, screws, fasteners - Independent Fastener Co.
BONNIE LASS - Soil–potting ☆ - Michigan Peat Co.
BONNIE LASSIE - Toys - Milton Bradley Co.
BONNIE LEE - Crocheted and knitted items - Le Roy Knitted Sportswear Inc.
BONNIE LEE - Popcorn ☆ - Weaver Popcorn Co. Inc.
BONNIE LEE CREATIONS - Giftware - Bonnie Lee Creations, Inc.
BONNIE MAID - Food products - Hannaford Brothers Co.
BONNIEBROOK ORIGINALS - Tiles–ceramic - Bonniebrook Park, Inc.
BONNIES - Brownies - Country Club Food Industries Inc.
BONNIE'S BEST - Food products ☆ - Schulze and Burch Biscuit Co.
BONNIE'S FLOWER - Bedding–linen - Dan River Inc.

BONNY - Floor coverings–carpet and rugs ☆ - Regal Rugs Inc.
BONNY - Giftware - Adept Manufacturing Co.
BONNY - Housewares - P. Hutmacher Enterprises Inc.
BONNY - Kitchen utensils–aluminum - Bonny Products Inc.
BONNY BOUNCER - Infant product - Dorsey and Co.
BONNY BUNTING - Juvenile product - Jaffe Group Inc.
BONNY COLORED - Kitchen utensils–aluminum - Bonny Products Inc.
BONNY DOON VINEYARD - Wines - Bonny Doon Winery Inc.
BONNY G'S - Fruits and vegetables - John R. Gavel Co., Inc.
BONNY LASS - Fruits and vegetables - Comstock Michigan Fruit
BONNY TREE - Product description unknown ☆ - Barth's Nutra Products
BONNYWARE - Kitchen utensils–aluminum - Bonny Products Inc.
BONO - Seafood products–fresh or frozen - Monterey Fish Co.
BONOFIDE - Confections ☆ - R.L. Albert & Son, Inc.
BONOMELLI - Teas–herbal ☆ - Liberty Richter Inc.
BONOMO - Candy ☆ - Tootsie Roll Industries, Inc.
BONS RITMOS - Recording label - Spindletop Records Inc.
BONSAL - Cement - W.R. Bonsal Co.
BONSONS - Food products - Bonham Brothers Inc.
BONSTONE - Adhesives and sealants - Bonstone Materials Corp.
BONTA - Food products - Escalon Frozen Foods
BONTE - Candy ☆ - Leaf, Inc.
BONTE - Floor coverings–carpet and rugs - Milliken & Co. Inc.
BONTE NATUREL - Apparel and accessories - Bonte Sportswear, Inc.
BONTEMPI - Musical instruments - Bontempi Electronic Keyboards
BONTEX - Fibers–synthetic - Georgia-Bonded Fibers, Inc.
BONTJE - Cheese - Galaxy Trading Co.
BONTON - Food products ☆ - Liberty Richter Inc.
BONTONE - Hardware ☆ - Bondex International Inc.
BONTONE - Pesticides–household - Bonide Products, Inc.
BONTRAGER - Bicycle parts and accessories - Bontrager Cycles Inc.
BONTRIL PDM - Pharmaceutical preparations - Carnick Laboratories Inc.
BONTRIL SLOW-RELEASE - Pharmaceutical preparations - Carnick Laboratories Inc.
BONTZ - Wax removers - Conklin Co., Inc.
BONUS - Clocks - General Time Corp. (Westclox/Seth Thomas Div.)
BONUS - Computer diskettes–blank - Verbatim Corp.
BONUS - Containers - Fellowes Manufacturing Co.
BONUS - Detergents - The Procter & Gamble Co.
BONUS - Detergents - Procter & Gamble Co.
BONUS - Fabrics–poplin - Greenwood Mills Inc.
BONUS - Fish–canned or cured - U.S. Trading Enterprise, Inc.
BONUS - Floor coverings–carpet and rugs - Carpet Crafts Inc.
BONUS - Floppy disks - Eastman Kodak Co.
BONUS - Food products - Brooks Foods
BONUS - Furniture–factory ☆ - Clayton Marcus Co. Inc.
BONUS - Garden equipment - Scotts Co. (Organics Business Group)
BONUS - Gasoline - Shelby Petroleum Corp.
BONUS - Heating equipment ☆ - Electric Furnace-Man
BONUS - Playing cards - United States Playing Card Co.
BONUS BLEND - Coffee - Wm. B. Reily & Co. Inc.
BONUS BRANDS - Lamp bulbs - Sunobrands Inc.
BONUS CLUB - Games - Universal Manufacturing Co., Inc.
BONUS CRISS CROSS - Games - International Gamco, Inc.
BONUS JOKER POKER - Playing cards - Universal Manufacturing Co., Inc.
BONUS TWINS - Games - Universal Manufacturing Co., Inc.
BONUS!BONUS! - Pizza - Little Caesar Enterprises, Inc.
BONUTTI - Medical apparatus - Peter M. Bonutti
BONUTTI ORTHOPAEDIC SERVICES - Medical apparatus - Peter M. Bonutti
BONVERRE - Wine - St. Supery Vineyards and Winery
BONZ - Dog food - Ralston Purina Co.
BONZAI - Sporting goods - O'Brien International
BONZERS - Cookies - Michael's Cookies
BONZO DOG - Toys–banks - A.J. Renzi Plastic Corp.
BOO - Recording label - Ron-Dom Productions Inc.
BOO! BAR - Candy ☆ - Chocolate House, Inc.
BOO-BEAR - Infant product - Stephan Enterprises, Inc.
BOO BEEPERS - Costumes - Paper Magic Group Inc.
BOO BERRY - Cereal - General Mills, Inc.
BOO BIBS & BEANIES - Costumes - Paper Magic Group Inc.
BOO BOO - Kites ☆ - Hi-Flier Manufacturing Co.
BOO BOO BABY - Apparel–children's - Boo-Boo-Baby Inc.
BOO BOO BUDDIES - Books–comic - Creative Cartoon Concepts, Inc.
BOO BOO BUDDY - Medical apparatus - Anro, Inc.
BOO-BOO PACS - Health care products - Chattanooga Group, Inc.
BOO-BOO STRIPS - Bandages - Colossus Corp.

☆ = Now out of production

BOO BOO THE CLOWN - Bandages - Medical Surgical Specialties, Ltd.
BOO BUBBLES - Chewing gum - Fleer Corp.
BOO BUNCH - Toys–stuffed - Trendmasters, Inc.
BOO BUNNIE - Infant product - Stephan Enterprises, Inc.
BOO DAN - Food products - Bodin Foods Inc.
BOO-EWE - Infant product - Stephan Enterprises, Inc.
BOO HOO BABY - Dolls - Goldberger Doll Manufacture Co.
BOO-KU - Apparel and accessories - Lifeforms International, Inc.
BOO-LOONS - Toys - American Greetings Corp.
BOO-QUET - Flowers, plants, and seeds - Florists' Transworld Delivery Association, Inc.
BOOBER - Toys - Jim Henson Productions, Inc.
BOOBITES - Candy - Pangburn Candy Co.
BOOBOO MAGIC - Bandages - First Step
BOOBY BIBS - Novelty items - Elizabeth A. McGee
BOOBY BIRD-T - T-shirts–men's - Chums Ltd.
BOOBY TRAP - Games - Lakeside Games
BOODA BONES - Pet products - Booda Products, Inc.
BOODA BYRDY - Pet products - Booda Products, Inc.
BOODA BYRDY CABLE - Pet products - Booda Products, Inc.
BOODA GAL - Pet products - Booda Products, Inc.
BOODA GUY - Pet products - Booda Products, Inc.
BOODA HOOF N' FLOSS - Pet products - Booda Products, Inc.
BOODA LOO - Pet products - Booda Products, Inc.
BOODA MIX 10 - Pet products - Booda Products, Inc.
BOODA SCRATCH - Pet products - Booda Products, Inc.
BOODA SMOKEHOUSE - Dog food - Booda Products, Inc.
BOODA TUG - Pet products - Booda Products, Inc.
BOODA WONDER TUG - Pet products - Booda Products, Inc.
BOODA ZOO - Pet products ☆ - Booda Products, Inc.
BOODABOX - Pet products - Booda Products, Inc.
BOODASCRATCH GYM - Pet products - Booda Products, Inc.
BOODLE BAG - Leather goods ☆ - AR Accessories Group Inc.
BOODLE-BUGGY - Carriages–doll ☆ - Welsh Co.
BOODLES - Gin - House of Seagram
BOOFUL BEANS - Dolls - Mattel, Inc.
BOOGER WEAR - Apparel and accessories - Cassa Enterprises, Inc.
BOOGERMAN - Computer software - Interplay Productions
BOOGIE - Amplifiers - Mesa/Boogie Ltd.
BOOGIE - Apparel and accessories - Kransco Manufacturing Inc.
BOOGIE BACK - Medical apparatus - McShane Medical, Inc.
BOOGIE BUSTER - Novelty items - Austin Innovations, Inc.
BOOGIE CHECKER - Mirrors - Day By Day Inc.
BOOGIE 'N BOP PIZZA SHOP - Toys - Those Characters from Cleveland, Inc.
BOOGIE WOOGIE TRUCK - Caps–baseball - L.K. McGuire
BOOK-A-BED - Giftware ☆ - Bob Stone
BOOK BED, THE - Paper–book - Charles R. Stanely
BOOK BROWSER - Computer software - Instructional Technology Services Inc.
BOOK BUNDLES - Publisher's imprints - Books from Cyberspace Corp.
BOOK BUZZ - Educational materials - Troll Associates, Inc.
BOOK CASTLE - Bookcases–wood - Rainbow Play Systems, Inc.
BOOK COMPANY, THE - Computer programming services ☆ - Berta-Max Inc.
BOOK CONSPIRACY - Publisher's imprints - And/Or Press
BOOK 'EM - Computer peripheral equipment - Crawford Enterprises, Inc.
BOOK-EZE - Book ends - Bert M. Morris Co.
BOOK GEAR - Bags–canvas - Gregg Manufacturing
BOOK MAID - Novelty items - Aparco Inc.
BOOK MATES - Dolls - Listening Library Inc.
BOOK MITTEN, THE - Protective pouch - Edward L. McHugh
BOOK 'N TAPE ALONG - Book and tape carrier - Placo Products Co.
BOOK-NEWS - Paper–newsprint - Fay Paper Products Inc.
BOOK-O-TRON - Electronics equipment - RTI Research Technology International
BOOK OF BOOKS - Publisher's imprints - Omega Engineering, Inc.
BOOK OF LISTS - Games ☆ - Avalon Hill Game Co.
BOOK OF TABLES - Games ☆ - Avalon Hill Game Co.
BOOK OF VIRTUES, THE - Recording label - William J. Bennett
BOOK PINS - Jewelry - Lucinda, Inc.
BOOK RACK, THE - Book stores - Book Rack
BOOK-SAVER - Publisher's imprints - Lilly Industrial Coatings Inc. (Delkote Div.)
BOOK SHELF - Scrapbooks ☆ - Garber Communications Inc.
BOOK SKINS - Paper products - James Hofstede
BOOK SLANT - Bookcases–metal ☆ - Antioch Publishing Co.
BOOK SOX - Paper–book - Tiger Marketing and Manufacturing

BOOK THAT MEANS BUSINESS, THE - Telephone directories - AGI Publishing, Inc.
BOOK TRAY - Office supplies - C-Line Products, Inc.
BOOK VALET - Book holder - Smythe-Whithcomb & Graeves Ltd.
BOOK-WOMAN - Apparel and accessories - Book Woman Inc.
BOOKBINDER'S FOODS - Seafood products–canned or cured - Bookbinder's Foods
BOOKBOARD - Computer peripheral equipment - Kevin M. Conway
BOOKBOW - Office supplies - Far Co.
BOOKBRAIN - Computer software - Oryx Press, Inc.
BOOKCRAFT - Tools–hand-operated - Gaylord Bros. Inc.
BOOKEDGE - Office machines - Xerox Corp.
BOOKENDS - Computer software - Quality Computers and Applications
BOOKENDS EXTENDED - Computer software - Quality Computers and Applications
BOOKER - Fabrics–poplin - Greenwood Mills Inc.
BOOKER - Toys–stuffed - Dakin Inc.
BOOKER NOE'S - Beverages–alcohol ☆ - Jim Beam Brands Co.
BOOKER'S SPECIAL RESERVE - Liquors - Jim Beam Brands Co.
BOOKFOLD - Wallets ☆ - Buxton Inc.
BOOKHOUND EXPRESS - Book stores - Martin News Agency, Inc.
BOOKIE BOOKWORM - Computer software ☆ - Knowledge Adventure
BOOKKEEPING BUDDY - Educational materials - Benecorp, Ltd.
BOOKLEEN - Cleaning preparations - Lilly Industrial Coatings Inc. (Delkote Div.)
BOOKMAGIC - Computer software - Krikorian Miller Associates, Inc.
BOOKMAN - Computers - Sherwin M. Borsuk
BOOKMANS PRESS - Publisher's imprints ☆ - Playmore Inc. Publishers
BOOKMARK - Computer peripheral equipment - Telescan Systems, Inc.
BOOKMARK - Computer software - Morse Data Corp.
BOOKMARK35 - Photocopy machines - Xerox Corp.
BOOKMARKS FOR BOOKWORMS - Publisher's imprints ☆ - Fair Air
BOOKMATE - Office supplies - Electrix Inc.
BOOKOTE - Plastics–laminated - Lilly Industrial Coatings Inc. (Delkote Div.)
BOOKS & READERS - Greeting cards - Green Tiger Press
BOOKS-FOR INDEPENDENT MINDS - Publisher's imprints - Ronin Publishing, Inc.
BOOKS FOR INDEPENDENT PEOPLE - Publisher's imprints - Bandanna Books
BOOKS OF LOVE - Publisher's imprints - Books of Love, Inc.
BOOKS THAT WORK - Computer software - Books That Work
BOOKSCOPE - Computer software - Thomson Information Inc.
BOOKSHARP - Computer software - Educator's Computer Software
BOOKSHELF BUDDIES - Publisher's imprints - Jerome R. Smath
BOOKSHELF MAGNETIC BACKGAMMON - Games ☆ - Milton Bradley Co.
BOOKSHELF SERIES - Computer software - Microsoft Corp.
BOOKSTER - Infant product - Deborah J. Bichimer
BOOKTRAP - Book ends ☆ - Park Sherman
BOOKVILLE - Toys - Tyco Industries, Inc.
BOOKWARE - Computer software - American Financial Directories, Inc.
BOOKWORM - Computer software - Communication and Information Technologies, Inc.
BOOLA HOOTS - Apparel and accessories - CGC Garments, Inc.
BOOM - Computer hardware and software - Fakespace, Inc.
BOOM - Recording label - Boom/Powerplay Records
BOOM BABY - Sports clubs - Pacers Basketball Corp.
BOOM BAG - Electronic equipment - John Amarello
BOOM BALL - Games - Cadaco Div.
BOOM BALL - Toys - Rapid Mounting and Finishing Co.
BOOM BOOM - Candy - S.L. Kaye Co., Inc.
BOOM BOOM - Golfing equipment - Golfsmith International Inc.
BOOM BOOMS - Bakery products - American Bakeries Co.
BOOM BOX - Computer software - Dr. T's Music Software Inc.
BOOM CRANE - Toys - Fisher-Price, Inc.
BOOM DOGGERS - Sweatshirts - Touche 21 Inc.
BOOM LIFT - Machinery - JLG Industries Inc.
BOOM POWERPLAY RECORDS - Recording label - Boom Productions Inc.
BOOM ROOM - Marine rigging - General Boats Corp.
BOOMAROOS - Footwear–athletic - KangaROOS USA Inc.
BOOMCHAKALAKA - Sporting goods - Never Quit Sports, Inc.
BOOMDOGGERS - Shirts - Touche 21 Inc.
BOOMER - Apparel and accessories ☆ - Jantzen Inc.
BOOMER - Audio-component kits - Rockford Corp.
BOOMER - Bicycles - Columbia Manufacturing Inc.
BOOMER - Sporting goods - Cramer Products Inc.
BOOMER - Sporting goods - Davis & Box Manufacturing Co.

BOOMER - Toys - Knickerbocker Toy Co. Inc.
BOOMER - Trailers–travel - Skyline Corp.
BOOMER II - Sporting goods - Davis & Box Manufacturing Co.
BOOMER BAG - Luggage - Runners Diversified Inc.
BOOMER BALL - Pet products - Boomer Ball
BOOMER GRAM - Novelty items - Australia Dreaming, Inc.
BOOMER VEHICLES - Toys - Tonka Corp.
BOOMERANG - Antennas - Wintenna Inc.
BOOMERANG - Electronic equipment - Boomerang Musical Products
BOOMERANG - Pillows - Down Under Products, Inc.
BOOMERANG - Security container - Sensormatic Electronics Corp.
BOOMERANG BITE - Meat snack - Austco Foods
BOOMERANG CORKSCREW - Corkscrews - Franmara Co. Inc.
BOOMERANG RODS - Cosmetics ☆ - P.S. Pibbs Inc.
BOOMERANG, THE - Plastics–laminated - Formica Corp.
BOOMERANGLE - Tools–power-driven - William R. Arends
BOOMERING - Electronic equipment - Kkall, Inc.
BOOMERLINER LOW RIDER - Antennas - Wintenna Inc.
BOOMEROUND - Pet products - Boomer Ball
BOOMERS - Broadcasting stations–television - Dinnertainment Ltd.
BOOMER'S - Candy ☆ - Palmer Candy Co.
BOOMERS - Fertilizers - Ross Daniels Inc.
BOOMERS - Musical instrument accessories - GHS Strings
BOOMERS - Pet products - USA-Petrx
BOOMERS - Pet products ☆ - Mardel Laboratories, Inc.
BOOMER'S HEROES ORIGINAL BBQ SAUCE - Barbecue sauce - Sawyer Industries, Inc.
BOOMER'S OOGIES - Confections - Boomer's Oogies
BOOMER'S SALSA - Sauces - Sawyer Industries, Inc.
BOOMIE - Pillows - Hollander Home Fashions Inc.
BOOMJET - Nozzles - Spraying Systems Co.
BOOMSENTRY - Electrical equipment - General Electric Co.
BOOMSLANG - Sunglasses ☆ - Corning Inc.
BOOMTOWN - Playing cards - Boomtown, Inc.
BOON - Candy - Murray-Allen International Inc.
BOONA - Apparel and accessories - Cobarr Creative Marketing, Inc.
BOONA MUSIC - Compact discs–prerecorded - Cobarr Creative Marketing, Inc.
BOONDOCK BAY - Coffee - Bay Area Coffee, Inc.
BOONDOCK BAY COFFEE GOURMET - Coffee - Bay Area Coffee, Inc.
BOONDOCKERS BY BOYT - Luggage ☆ - Welsh Sporting Goods Corp. (Boyt Div.)
BOONDOGGLE - Hobby kits - Craft Supplies Service
BOONDOGGLE WATCH - Watches - Richard J. White
BOONE - Fishing lures - Boone Bait Co. Inc.
BOONE - Pens - Michael K. Boone Inc.
BOONE COUNTY - Catsup - Brooks Foods
BOONE COUNTY - Furniture - Bassett Furniture Industries, Inc.
BOONE'S CREEK - Furniture ☆ - Vaughan Furniture Co. Inc.
BOONE'S FARM - Wines - Ernest and Julio Gallo Winery
BOONE'S MILL - Furniture ☆ - Bassett Furniture Industries, Inc.
BOONITO - Fishing lures - Boone Bait Co. Inc.
BOONTON - Electronic equipment - Boonton Electronics Corp.
BOONTONWARE - Melamine dinnerware - Boonton Molding Co. Inc.
BOOO THE BAT - Toys ☆ - Imperial Toy Corp.
BOOPEEZ - Greeting cards - Sharon's Stuff Greeting Cards & Stuff
BOORD'S - Liquors - David Sherman Corp.
BOORDY VINEYARDS - Wines - Boordy Vineyards
BOORUM - Binders ☆ - Esselte Corp.
BOORUM & PEASE - Office supplies - Esselte Corp.
BOOSEY & HAWKES - Musical instruments - Boosey & Hawkes Buffet Crampon USA
BOOST - Chemical preparations ☆ - Coastal Industries Inc.
BOOST - Computer software - Pavilion Technologies, Inc.
BOOST - Vitamins and nutritional supplements - Mead Johnson & Co.
BOOST EM - Bluebonnet Milling Co.
BOOST-N-ADJUST - Automotive parts and accessories - Manlee Industries Inc.
BOOSTER - Confections - Special Preparations Co.
BOOSTER - Garden equipment ☆ - H.D. Hudson Manufacturing Co.
BOOSTER - Paper - Fay Paper Products Inc.
BOOSTER - Sleeping bags - Coleman Co., Inc.
BOOSTER BEAR - Motor vehicle parts and accessories - Carma B. Robertson
BOOSTER BUDDY - Automotive parts and accessories - K & K Jump Start/ Chargers, Inc.
BOOSTER BYTES - Computer software - Wyman Co., Inc.

BOOSTER MINERAL - Animal feed supplements - Moorman Manufacturing Co.
BOOSTER PLUS - Hair care products - Trionics Systems Corp.
BOOSTER-PLUS - Veterinary nutritional supplements - Oralx Corp.
BOOSTER, THE - Jackets - Howe K. Sipes Co.
BOOSTERBOX - Electronic equipment - Sima Products Corp.
BOOSTERCAP - Capacitors - United Chemi-Con, Inc.
BOOSTIZER - Archery equipment - Saunders Archery Co.
BOOT - Sporting goods - Ski Accessories Co.
BOOT BOXX - Sporting goods - SKIBOXX LTD.
BOOT BUDDY - Shoe insoles - L & A, Inc.
BOOT CAMP BY HAPPY LEGS - Product description unknown - Happy Legs Inc.
BOOT COUNTRY - Footwear - Acme Boot Co., Inc.
BOOT-EASE - Shoe accessories - Lillian Vernon Corp.
BOOT EZE - Shoe polish - Genesco Inc.
BOOT FACTORY - Apparel and accessories - Genesco Inc.
BOOT-GARD - Waterproofing compounds - Bickmore Inc.
BOOT GUARD LEATHER DRESSING - Leather treatments - Save Your Hide
BOOT HILL - Chewing gum ☆ - Leaf, Inc.
BOOT HILL - Games - Tsr, Inc.
BOOT HILL SALOON - Apparel and accessories - Boot Hill Saloon
BOOT JUICE - Skis - Golconda Industries
BOOT LEGGER - Fireworks - Zenith Specialties, LP
BOOT 'N SKI - Luggage - SGI Inc.
BOOT SAVER - Housewares - Tempress, Inc.
BOOT SNUGGIES - Apparel and accessories - Plastec Industries
BOOT STOP - Trays - MacCourt Products Inc.
BOOT STRAP - Trailers - Carl John Scheef Jr.
BOOT SUIT - Apparel and accessories ☆ - Jantzen Inc.
BOOT T - Sporting goods - Ski Accessories Co.
BOOTBOX - Sporting goods - Robert C. Vincent
BOOTH - Herring–smoked, salted, dried, or pickled - Lyon Food Products Inc.
BOOTH - Seafood products–canned or cured - National Sea Products U.S. Corp.
BOOTH BAY - Floor coverings–carpet and rugs ☆ - Lees Carpets
BOOTH BAY - Toilets–porcelain - Mansfield Plumbing Products, Inc.
BOOTH BROTHERS - Milk - Booth Brothers Dairy
BOOTH MASK - Adhesives and sealants - Aqua Tec Coatings Corp.
BOOTHBAY - Fabrics ☆ - Hamilton Adams Imports Ltd.
BOOTHBAY - Siding–insulating - Champion International Corp.
BOOTHBAY CHALLENGER - Boats ☆ - John G. Alden Inc.
BOOTHBAY EXPLORER - Boats ☆ - John G. Alden Inc.
BOOTHBAY GROUP - Furniture–upholstered ☆ - Moosehead Manufacturing Co.
BOOTHBAY HARBOR - Bells - North Country Wind Bells Inc.
BOOTHILL - Wallpaper - Koroseal Wallcoverings
BOOTH'S - Gin - Schenley Industries Inc.
BOOTIES - Socks - Leininger Mills Inc.
BOOTLEG - Footwear - Sloan Corp.
BOOTLEG RECORDS - Recording label - Mystic Records
BOOTLEGGER - Sauces - Jardine Foods
BOOTLEGGER JIG - Fishing lures - Strike King Lure Co.
BOOTNIKS - Dolls ☆ - Uneeda Doll Co., Inc.
BOOTREES - Shoe trees ☆ - Helmac Products Corp.
BOOTS - Prophylactics - Finley Co.
BOOTS - Publisher's imprints - Kidsbooks, Inc.
BOOTS - Toys–stuffed - Russ Berrie and Co., Inc.
BOOTS, A - Publisher's imprints - Kidsbooks, Inc.
BOOTS AND SADDLE - Colognes - Schnapp Enterprises Inc.
BOOTS N SADDLE - Leather goods - Prime Leather Finishes Co.
BOOTS WITHOUT BOUNDARIES - Footwear - Rugged Footwear Co.
BOOTSIE - Dolls - Horsman
BOOTSKI - Sporting goods - Morning Sun, Inc.
BOOTSTRIPE - Tape–adhesive - Marine Development & Research Corp.
BOOTWORKS - Computer software - Keylabs, Inc.
BOOZE BAG - Luggage - Airline Textile Manufacturing Co.
BOOZEFIGHTERS - T-shirts–men's - Boozefighters Motorcycle Club, Inc.
BOOZE'N SHOES - Luggage - Airline Textile Manufacturing Co.
BOP-A-TUNE DUCK - Toys–stuffed - Great American Fun Corp.
BOP-A-TUNE PIG - Toys–stuffed - Great American Fun Corp.
BOP BAGS - Toys - Hart Enterprises, Inc.
BOP CAR - Toys–automobiles - Buddy L Inc.
BOP 'N POP - Toys - Printmark Industries Inc.
BOP 'N WRESTLE - Computer software - Mindscape Software Inc.
BOPKIN - Toys ☆ - Small World Toys
BOPO KIDS INTERNATIONAL - Clothing - Bopo Kids International, Inc.

☆ = Now out of production

BOPPER - Toys - Park Plastics Co.
BOPPERS - Footwear–children's - Yachett Shoe Manufacturing Corp.
BOPPERS - Pens - Bic Corp.
BOPPIE'S GREAT WORD CHASE - Computer software - SRA/McGraw-Hill
 (Div. of The McGraw-Hill Companies)
BOPPY - Infant product - Camp Kazoo, Ltd.
BOPSY - Dolls - Mattel, Inc.
BOQUET - Apparel–women's - Cupid Foundations Inc.
BOR-AD-ZIN - Pharmaceutical preparations ☆ - Wendt-Bristol Co.
BOR-DO-LAY - Food products - Radich's
BOR INN - Brackets - Dec-Kor, Inc.
BOR-IT - Tools–boring - Bor-It Manufacturing Co., Inc.
BOR-SEAL - Oils–lubricating - G. Leblanc Corp.
BORA - Motor vehicles–automobiles ☆ - Maserati Automobiles Inc.
BORA BORA - Brushes–hair - Windmere Corp.
BORA BORA - Floor coverings–carpet and rugs ☆ - Royalweve Carpet Mills
BORA BORA BERRY - Nail care products - Cosmair Inc.
BORA CARE - Wood products - Nisus Corp.
BORA SAMBÙCA - Liquors - Disusa Imports Co.
BORA-SOLV - Soap - Sanitary Soap Co. Inc.
BORACHO BOYZ - Apparel and accessories - Joseph D. Dominguez
BORAGE - Vitamins and nutritional supplements ☆ - Oakmont Investments Co.
BORAGE-POWER - Diet supplements - Natur-Pharma, Inc.
BORAGE-POWER - Vitamins and nutritional supplements ☆ - Nature's Herbs
BORALITE - Bicycles - Lawee Inc.
BORATEEM - Borax - Dial Corp.
BORAX-SUDZ - Detergents - Reen'o Corp.
BORAXO - Cleaning preparations - Dial Corp.
BORAZON - Chemical preparations - General Electric Co.
BORBA - Wines - Manuel M. Garcia
BORBONESE BY REDWALL - Handbags, belts - Spettacolo Inc.
BORD - Apparel and accessories - Bord Co.
BORD-R-CLING - Adhesives and sealants - Mantrose-Haeuser Co. Inc.
BORD-R-LESS - Easels - The Tiffen Co.
BORDA AZUL - Seafood products–fresh or frozen ☆ - Penguin Frozen Foods,
 Inc.
BORDALO PINHEIRO - Pottery ☆ - Penco Industries Inc.
BORDAY - Soft drinks - Islands International
BORDE - Food products - Bel Canto Fancy Foods Ltd.
BORDE DRIED - Mushrooms ☆ - De Medici Imports Ltd.
BORDEAU - Hardware - American Builders Hardware Corp.
BORDEAU - Toilets–porcelain - Universal-Rundle Corp.
BORDEAU FARMS - Food products - Rogers Foods Inc.
BORDEAUX - Cabinets ☆ - Aristokraft, Inc.
BORDEAUX - Christmas tree ornaments ☆ - Cracker Box Inc.
BORDEAUX - Cosmetics ☆ - Honey & Spice Toiletries
BORDEAUX - Dinnerware–glass - Nikko Ceramics Inc.
BORDEAUX - Floor coverings–carpet and rugs - Nourison
BORDEAUX - Floor coverings–carpet and rugs ☆ - World Carpets, Inc.
BORDEAUX - Flowers, plants, and seeds - Flowerwood Nursery, Inc.
BORDEAUX - Furniture - Weiman Co.
BORDEAUX - Furniture ☆ - Bernhardt Industries
BORDEAUX - Furniture ☆ - Hammary Furniture Co. Inc.
BORDEAUX - Hair care products - Helen of Troy Corp.
BORDEAUX - Lamps - Lamplight Farms, Inc.
BORDEAUX - Lipsticks - Monteil Paris
BORDEAUX - Wines - Kedem Royal Wine Corp.
BORDEAUX - Wines - Wines of the World Inc.
BORDEAUX COUNTRY - Wallpaper ☆ - Tattersalls
BORDEAUX COUNTRY II - Wallpaper - Tattersalls
BORDEAUX WINE PROFESSOR, THE - Computer software - E-8 Publications,
 Inc.
BORDEN - Dairy products - Borden, Inc.
BORDEN - Fruit drinks–bottled or canned - BDH Two, Inc.
BORDEN - Paper - Saxon Paper Co.
BORDEN CAPS - Seasonings - Firmenich Inc.
BORDEN INSTANT BREAKFAST - Food products ☆ - Borden, Inc.
BORDEN SNACKS - Snack foods - Borden, Inc.
BORDENSTYLE - Wallcovering - BDH Two, Inc.
BORDER - Figurines ☆ - Schmid Inc.
BORDER - Food products - Blum & Bergeron Inc.
BORDER - Tiles–ceramic - KPT Inc.
BORDER BOUTIQUE - Fabrics–tapestry ☆ - Coloroll Inc.
BORDER BREAKS - Meat products–poultry - Owens Country Sausage Inc.
BORDER BUDDY - Adhesives and sealants ☆ - Custom Building Products
BORDER COLLECTION, THE - Wallpaper ☆ - Rainbow Creations Inc.

BORDER COUNTRY - Wallpaper ☆ - Newmarket Designs Ltd.
BORDER-EASE - Bottles–plastic - Golden Harvest, Inc.
BORDER HOARDER, THE - Wallpaper ☆ - Richard Schlatter Design (O)
BORDER HOOPS - Fabrics–quilted - Gibbs Manufacturing Co.
BORDER ICES - Fruit pops–frozen - Taco Bell Corp.
BORDER LIGHTS - Food products - Taco Bell Corp.
BORDER LINE - Greeting cards - Paramount Cards Inc.
BORDER MAGIC - Machinery - E. Bergman Co.
BORDER MAGIC - Wallpaper - Warner Co.
BORDER NOTES - Computer peripheral equipment - Intersys, Inc.
BORDER PATROL - Electronic animal restraint system - D.W. Thomas
 Companies, Inc.
BORDER PATROL - Garden equipment - Master Mark Plastic Products
BORDER PATROL - Sporting goods - In-Line Sport Systems, Inc.
BORDER POSTERS - Wallpaper ☆ - Environmental Graphics Inc.
BORDER PROTECTOR - Telephone apparatus - Allen Telecom Group, Inc.
BORDER SILHOUETTES - Decals and transfers - K.J. Miller Corp.
BORDER SOLUTIONS - Garden equipment - Solutions, Inc.
BORDER SPECIAL - Firearms, accessories, and parts - Texas Longhorn Arms,
 Inc.
BORDER SPECIAL - Games - Universal Manufacturing Co., Inc.
BORDER STICK-UPS - Decals and transfers - Hedstrom Corp.
BORDER-TEX - Paper–kraft ☆ - Bemiss-Jason Corp.
BORDER-WELL - Machinery - Paste-Well Corp.
BORDERING ON STRIPES - Wallpaper ☆ - Linden Street Gallery
BORDERING REALITY - Furniture - Mark M. Jones
BORDERITA - Beverages–alcohol - Brinker Restaurant Corp.
BORDERLINE - Electronics equipment - Grass Valley Group Inc.
BORDERLINE - Games - Hidden Hills Productions Inc.
BORDERLOC CONTINUOUS SOLID POLYBLOCK SIDE SUPPORT SYSTEM
 - Mattress pads - Sleepcare, Inc.
BORDERMAKER - Computer software - Monotype Typography Inc.
BORDERMASTER - Enlargers–photographic - SP Systems/Saratons
BORDERS - Floor coverings–carpet and rugs ☆ - Mannington Carpets, Inc.
BORDERS & BACKGROUNDS - Computer software - Parsons Technology,
 Inc.
BORDERS AND BACKGROUNDS - Wallpaper - Capital Carousel Inc.
BORDERS & BACKGROUNDS - Wallpaper - Dekortex Inc.
BORDERS & MORE - Wallpaper - Rainbow Creations Inc.
BORDERS & TEXTURES - Wallcovering - Wall Trends, Inc.
BORDERS, BORDERS, BORDERS - Wallpaper - Sandpiper Studios
BORDERS UNLIMITED - Vinyl wallcoverings - Newmarket Limited, Inc.
BORDERSLINE IMAGES - Novelty items–paper - David Borders
BORDETTE - Paper - Bemiss-Jason Corp.
BORDINO - Wines - Peppinella Import Co.
BORDISPO - Health care products - Borda Products Inc.
BORDO - Citrus product - Bordo Products Co.
BORDOK - Toys - Lucasfilm Ltd.
BORE-COTE - Firearms cleaner and lubricant - Sandaro Industries Inc.
BORE OUT - Septic-tank cleaner ☆ - Jancyn Manufacturing Corp.
BORE-TITE - Automotive parts and accessories - Chicago Rawhide
BOREA - Seafood products–fresh or frozen ☆ - Flag/Westbay Seafood
 Brokers
BOREAL - Watches - Mathey Tissot International
BOREALIS - Dinnerware ☆ - Corning Inc.
BOREALIS BOTANICA - Teas - Alaska Herb & Tea Co., Inc.
BOREALIS YURTS - Building materials - Borealis, Inc.
BOREAS - Floor coverings–carpet and rugs ☆ - Hollytex Carpet Mills Inc.
BORED GAMES - Games - Libbie Cole
BORED W/OUT MY BOARD - Apparel–athletic - Robert Andrew Hosea
BOREDOM BUSTER - Pet products - Teddy Pets
BOREHAWK - Electronic instruments - Metrotech Corp.
BOREL - Watches - Borel Watch Co.
BORELLI - Leather goods - Gerald Biller
BORELLI - Leather goods - Burlington Handbags Inc.
BORELLI - Olive oil - Gondola Foods of New England
BORELLI BORELLI BB - Handbags - Jasmine Ltd.
BORELLI PERFECTION - Macaroni - Perfection Macaroni Co.
BORERKIL - Insecticides - Roxide International, Inc.
BORERSOL - Insecticides ☆ - Dexol Industries
BORG - Bathroom scales - Counselor Co.
BORG - Toys - Paramount Pictures Corp.
BORG COMP - Sporting goods - Donnay USA
BORG TECH - Digital-readout scales - Counselor Co.
BORG-WARNER - Automotive parts and accessories - Echlin Inc.
BORG-WARNER - Electronic equipment - Borg-Warner Security Corp.

☆ = Now out of production

BORG WEIGH VALET - Readout clock and scale ☆ - Counselor Co.
BORGANI - Saxophones - Enzo Pizzi
BORGES - Olive oil - Joseph Caragol Inc.
BORGES - Wallpaper - Sunwall of America
BORGES & IRMAO - Wines ☆ - Banfi Vintners
BORGHESE - Handbags - Borghese Trademarks Inc.
BORGHESE - Wallpaper - Robert Crowder & Co.
BORGHESE WALL - Wallpaper ☆ - Blumenthal
BORGHINI - Wines - Leonard Kreusch Inc.
BORGINI - Neckties - Steinberg Neckwear Corp.
BORGLASKA - Simulated-fur fabrics ☆ - Borg Textile Corp.
BORGLEAM - Knit goods ☆ - Borg Textile Corp.
BORGLUX - Knit goods ☆ - Borg Textile Corp.
BORGO PRESS, THE - Publisher's imprint - Borgo Press
BORGOGNO - Wines - Banfi Vintners
BORGWARNER AUTOMOTIVE - Transmission equipment–motor vehicle - Borg-Warner Automotive Inc. (Transmission Systems Div.)
BORI-MANOUX - Wines - Shaw-Ross International Importers
BORICUA - Rice - Producers Rice Mill, Inc.
BORIDE - Tools - Boride Products Inc.
BORIE-MANOU - Wines - Paterno Imports, Ltd.
BORING UNIVERSITY - Clothing - A to W Enterprises
BORIS - Toys–electronic ☆ - Applied Concepts Inc.
BORIS BEAR - Greeting cards - Current, Inc.
BORIS BECKER - Footwear–athletic ☆ - Puma Inc.
BORJOMI - Water–mineral - Universal Foods Corp.
BORKENGLAS - See **DURIA**
BORKUM RIFF - Tobacco–chewing or smoking - United States Tobacco Co.
BORKUM RIFF ULTRA LIGHT - Tobacco–chewing or smoking - United States Tobacco Co.
BORLA - Exhaust systems–motor vehicle - Borla Performance Industries, Inc.
BORLAND - Computer software - Borland International, Inc.
BORM - Sporting goods ☆ - Chesal Golf
BORMIOLI - Italian glassware - Bormioli Rocco Glass Co. Inc.
BORN - Footwear - H.H. Brown Shoe Co., Inc.
BORN AGAIN - Recording label - Golden Boy Records
BORN AGAIN - Skin care products - Alvin Last Inc.
BORN AGAIN HAIR - Hair care products - Alvin Last Inc.
BORN BEAUTIFUL - Clothing and accessories - Born Beautiful
BORN BEAUTIFUL - Hair care products ☆ - Clairol Inc.
BORN BLONDE - Hair care products - Clairol Inc.
BORN DAY FORTUNE - Apparel and accessories - Young Kyun Jang
BORN FREE - Floor coverings–carpet and rugs - Calladium & Marglen
BORN FREE - Floor coverings–carpet and rugs - Alexander Smith Carpets
BORN FREE - Motor homes, vans - Born Free Motorcoach Div.
BORN FREE - Shampoos - Alberto-Culver Co.
BORN IN AMERICA - Breads - Fornaca Family Bakery Inc.
BORN IN COTTON - Apparel - Michel Benasra
BORN IN THE USA - Amplifiers - Earthquake Sound Corp.
BORN IN THE U.S.A. - Calendars - Brown and Bigelow Inc.
BORN OF NATURE - Skin care products - Natus Corp.
BORN TO BE WILD - Apparel and accessories - Steppenwolf Productions Inc.
BORN TO CODE - Shirts - Touch Technologies Inc.
BORN TO LIVE - Shirts - Made on Earth, Inc.
BORN TO ROCK - Guitars - Burn to Rock Design Inc.
BORN TO RUN - Toilets–enameled - Kohler Co.
BORN TO SHOP BEARS - Toys–stuffed - Cozy's Inc.
BORN TO SUCCEED - Video production - Multnomah County Library
BORNE - Deodorants–personal - Park Lane Associates, Inc.
BORNHOLM - Dishes–earthenware ☆ - Dansk International Designs, Ltd.
BORNHOLM - Floor coverings–carpet and rugs ☆ - Eurotex Inc.
BORNIER - Mustard - Gourmet America
BORNIER FRENCH - Mustard - Gourmet America
BORNOVA - Floor coverings–carpet and rugs - Milliken & Co. Inc.
BORO - Wood kitchen and bathroom cabinets - Legeis Corp.
BORO PHENIQUE - Pharmaceutical preparations - Eastern Research Laboratories
BORO-PHENO-FORM - Biological products - Dr. Pierre Chemical Co.
BOROFAX - Pharmaceutical preparations - Warner-Wellcome
BOROFLUX #1 - Chemicals - Climax Performance Materials Corp.
BOROGARD ZB - Insecticides - U.S. Borax Inc.
BOROLEUM - Pharmaceutical preparations - Sinclair Pharmacal Co.
BOROMAR - Pharmaceutical preparations ☆ - Marlop Pharmaceuticals Inc.
BORON 150 - Sports rackets and accessories - Victor Sports
BORON CAPS - Vitamins and nutritional supplements - Vitamin Research Products Inc.

BORON PLUS - Agricultural products - Kemmer Agricultural Manufacturing Co. Inc.
BORON PLUS - Fishing tackle ☆ - South Bend Sporting Goods Inc.
BORON TOUR - Golfing equipment - Harrison Sports, Inc.
BORON-X - Fishing tackle ☆ - Fenwick
BOROPTAL - Health care products - Afassco
BOROPTIC - Pharmaceutical preparations - Sherwood Laboratories Inc.
BOROSILICATE - Dinnerware–glass - Crisa Corp.
BORRACHO BURGER - Sandwiches–prepackaged - T.C. Management, Inc.
BORRA'S CELLAR - Wines, vinegar - Borra's Cellar
BORREL NOOTJIES - Snack foods - Lever Brothers Co. Inc.
BORROWED - Recording label - Column One Ltd. Music Group
BORROWED TIME - Computer software - Activision, Inc.
BORS - Pumps–water - Moore-Handley Inc.
BORSALINO - Colognes - The Wilkes Group
BORSETTA - Luggage - Pacific Connections of California, Inc.
BORTHWICKS FLAVORS U.S.A. B - Spices and extracts - Borthwicks Flavors USA, Inc.
BORTZ - Candy - Bortz Chocolate Co.
BORTZ BITS - Candy ☆ - Bortz Chocolate Co.
BORTZ GOLD - Chocolate coins - Bortz Chocolate Co.
BORU - Vodka - Shaw-Ross International Importers
BORVIEW - Computer peripheral equipment - Schlumberger Technology Corp.
BORYS - Guitars - Borys Guitars
BORZELLINO - Sauces - Marie Williams
BORZOI SPRINTERS - Publisher's imprints - Alfred A. Knopf Inc.
BOS-BAG - Garden equipment - Kinsman Co. Inc.
BO'S BONE - Pet products - Misha-Sterling Inc.
BO'S CAJUN ROAST - Chicken - Bojangles Restaurants Inc.
BOSA - Apparel and accessories - YGM Inc.
BOSA NOVA - Floor coverings–carpet and rugs - World Carpets, Inc.
BOSANOVA - Computer software - Better On-Line Solutions Inc.
BOSBUILDER - Agricultural products - Land O'Lakes, Inc.
BOSCA - Leather goods - Hugo Bosca Co., Inc.
BOSCA - Wines - Wine Shippers Import Co.
BOSCA-BUILT - Leather goods - Hugo Bosca Co., Inc.
BOSCAINI - Wines - Dreyfus Ashby Inc.
BOSCH - Automotive parts and accessories - Robert Bosch Corp.
BOSCH - Beverages–malt ☆ - Jacob Leinenkugel Brewing Co., Inc.
BOSCH - Paints - Van Aken International
BOSCH - Tools–power-driven - S-B Power Tool Co.
BOSCO - Gloves ☆ - Boss Manufacturing Co.
BOSCO - Novelty items ☆ - Lemberger Candy Corp.
BOSCO - Plates–paper - Tri-Par Corp.
BOSCUL - Coffee ☆ - Chock Full O'Nuts Corp.
BOSE - Amplifiers, speakers, public-address equipment - Bose Corp.
BOSENDORFER - Pianos - Bosendorfer Piano
BOSK - Automotive accessories - Bosk Inc.
BOSKYDEL - Wines - Boskydel Vineyard
BOSLEY BUNNY - Novelty items - Paper Magic Group Inc.
BOSLEY BUNNY - Toys–stuffed - Spearhead Industries Inc.
BOS'N - Seafood products–fresh or frozen - Stavis Seafoods Inc.
BOSOM BUDDY - Prosthetic apparatus - B & B Co. Inc.
BOSOM FRIEND - Brassieres (Bras) - Valmont Inc.
BOSOM FRIEND - Underwear and nightwear - Bestform Foundations, Inc.
BOSS - See **CARPENTERS' CHOICE**
BOSS - Audio equipment - Rolandcorp US
BOSS - Chairs–folding - E-Z Sales & Manufacturing, Inc.
B.O.S.S. - Computer peripheral equipment - Newage Industries, Inc.
BOSS - Computer software - Omnex Engineering & Management Inc.
B.O.S.S. - Computer software - Pelco
BOSS - Computer software - Prograph Bindery Systems, Inc.
B.O.S.S. - Deodorizers - Krueger Enterprises
BOSS - Footwear–men's ☆ - Durango Boot Co. Inc.
BOSS - Gloves - Boss Manufacturing Co.
BOSS - Golfing equipment - Brookhurst, Inc.
B.O.S.S. - Medical apparatus - Peter M. Bonutti
BOSS - Pens - Schwan-STABILO USA Inc.
BOSS - Perfumes - Prestige Fragrances Ltd.
BOSS - Recording label - The Pegasus Group, Inc.
BOSS - Scooters–children's ☆ - Hedstrom Corp.
B.O.S.S. - Sleeping bags - Coleman Co., Inc.
BOSS - Thread ☆ - American & Efird, Inc.
BOSS - Tools - Stanley-Bostitch Inc.
BOSS - Toys–models - Ford Motor Co.

☆ = Now out of production

BOSS - Veterinary pharmaceutical preparations - Schering-Plough Animal Health

BOSS-A-JAVA - Cookware - Sweports Limited

B.O.S.S. ACRYLIC SYSTEMS - Cosmetics - European Touch Co.

BOSS BEAR - Toys–stuffed ☆ - Dakin Inc.

B.O.S.S. BEARDED OLD SPUR STRUTTERS WILD TURKEY INSTITUTE INC. 200 PROOF FIELD - Hunting equipment ☆ - B.O.S.S. Wild Turkey Institute, Inc.

BOSS BUBBLE - Chewing gum - Philadelphia Chewing Gum Corp.

BOSS BULL - Sporting goods - Wellington Leisure Products, Inc.

BOSS CALLS - Hunting equipment - B.O.S.S. Wild Turkey Institute, Inc.

BOSS CONTROL SYSTEMS - Electronic equipment ☆ - Rice Lake Weighing Systems, Inc.

BOSS CRUISER - Bicycles - American Cycle Group

BOSS HAWG - Floor coverings - Etc. of Henderson, Inc.

BOSS LITE - Vacuum cleaners and accessories - White Consolidated Industries, Inc.

BOSS-LOCK - Hardware - Dixon Valve and Coupling Co.

BOSS OF PORTABLE LIGHTING, THE - Lighting fixtures - Specialty Lighting Inc.

BOSS-RIB - Flat rib metal lath - Bostwick Steel Lath Co.

BOSS TE - Boats–fishing - Glasstream Boats Inc.

BOSS, THE - Moldings and trim - Boston Metal Products Corp.

BOSS, THE - Toys–stuffed ☆ - CBS Toys

BOSS, THE - Vacuum cleaners and accessories - The Eureka Co.

BOSS, THE - Sporting goods - Daniel Corrigan Miller Sr.

BOSS, THE - Tools - Red Devil Inc.

BOSS, THE - Toys–stuffed - Russ Berrie and Co., Inc.

BOSS, THE - Footwear - West Coast Shoe Co.

B.O.S.S. THE AQUA MISER BICARBONATE OF SODA STRIPPING - Machinery - Carolina Equipment & Supply Co., Inc.

BOSSA BRAVA - Recording label - Instinct Records Corp.

BOSSA NOVA - Bicycles ☆ - Burley Design Cooperative

BOSSANOVA - Frames–eyeglass - U.S. Optical Frame Co.

BOSSARD MUSCADET - Wines - Chartrand Imports

BOSSI - Shoes - Roger & Barbara Bowman

BOSSMAN - Heating equipment - Bossman, Inc.

BOSSMAN - Jacks–hydraulic - Duff-Norton Co., Inc.

BOSSMASTER WILD TURKEY CALLS 200 PROOF FIELD TESTED - Hunting equipment ☆ - B.O.S.S. Wild Turkey Institute, Inc.

BOSSONS - House furnishings - S.P. Skinner Co. Inc.

BOSSTACK - Bostik Inc.

BOSSTEX - Paper–toilet ☆ - Fort Howard Corp.

BOST - Bread, rolls, and cake - Bost Bakery Inc.

BOSTIK - Glue–household or industrial - FPC Corp.

BOSTIK'S BEST - Bostik Inc.

BOSTITCH - Machine tools - Stanley Works

BOSTITCH - Staplers - Stanley-Bostitch Inc.

BOSTOMATIC - Staplers - Stanley-Bostitch Inc.

BOSTON - Belts–automotive - Dana Corp.

BOSTON - Carts - Boston Metal Products Corp.

BOSTON - Cigars ☆ - Havatampa Inc.

BOSTON - Clocks ☆ - Chelsea Clock Co. Inc.

BOSTON - Diet iced tea - Boston Bottling

BOSTON - Dinnerware - Denby USA Limited

BOSTON - Erasers - Durasol Drug & Chemical Co.

BOSTON - Floor coverings ☆ - Congoleum Corp.

BOSTON - Floor waxes - Butcher Co.

BOSTON - Frames–eyeglass - U.S. Optical Frame Co.

BOSTON - Heels–boot and shoe - Star Heel Plate Co.

BOSTON - Ladders–wood - John S. Tilley Ladders Co. Inc.

BOSTON - Locking devices, locks ☆ - Boston Lock & Safe Co.

BOSTON - Orthopedic products - Hunt Holdings, Inc.

BOSTON - Pencil sharpeners - Hunt Manufacturing Co.

BOSTON - Potato chips ☆ - La Tolteca Foods Inc.

BOSTON - Sails - Doyle/Boston Sailmakers

BOSTON - Tea - Boston Tea Co.

BOSTON - Water–mineral - New England Spring Water Inc.

BOSTON 7 - Contact lenses - Wilmington Partners L.P.

BOSTON ACCENT WEATHERPROOF - Footwear - Elicon Resourcing Group, Inc.

BOSTON ACOUSTICS - Audio equipment - Boston Acoustics Inc.

BOSTON ADVANCE - Contact lenses - Polymer Technology Corp.

BOSTON ADVANCE - Ophthalmic goods - Wilmington Partners L.P.

BOSTON. AMERICA'S WALKING CITY - Apparel and accessories - Massachusetts Convention Center Authority

BOSTON ANTIQUE - Cutlery - Carvel Hall Inc.

BOSTON BAKED BEANS - Candy - Ferrara Pan Candy Co., Inc.

BOSTON BASICS - Prepared entrees - Boston Chicken, Inc.

BOSTON BAY - Apparel and accessories - Tropical Garment Manufacturing Co.

BOSTON BAY - Slacks–men's - Tropical Sportswear International Corp.

BOSTON BLEND - Food products ☆ - Borden, Inc.

BOSTON BODY JACKET - Apparel and accessories - Boston Brace International, Inc.

BOSTON BRACE PEOPLE, THE - Body braces - O & P Systems, Inc.

BOSTON CELTICS - Balls - Celtics L.P.

BOSTON CHICKEN - Magnets - Boston Chicken, Inc.

BOSTON CHICKEN ROTISSERIE - Apparel and accessories - Boston Chicken, Inc.

BOSTON CIGAR CUTTER - Cigars - Boston Cigar Cutter Co., Inc.

BOSTON COBBLER - Shoe trees - Bandwagon, Inc.

BOSTON COBBLESTONE - Cheese - Swissrose International Inc.

BOSTON COMMON - Broadcasting stations–television - Castle Rock Entertainment

BOSTON COMMON - Floor coverings–carpet and rugs - Colonial Mills Inc.

BOSTON CORD - Fabrics - Dan River Inc.

BOSTON CR TEST TOOL - Medical apparatus - Boston Test Tool Co.

BOSTON DESIGNED BY STEINWAY & SONS - Musical instruments - Steinway and Sons Inc.

BOSTON ENVISION - Contact lenses - Cooper Companies Inc.

BOSTON EQUALENS - Contact lenses - Cooper Companies Inc.

BOSTON FEASTS - Prepared entrees - Boston Chicken, Inc.

BOSTON GARDEN - Floor coverings - Tarkett, Inc.

BOSTON HARBOR - Furniture–children's ☆ - Child Craft Industries Inc.

BOSTON HARBOUR - Teas - Jacques F. Weber Co.

BOSTON II - Contact lenses - Cooper Companies Inc.

BOSTON IV - Contact lenses - Cooper Companies Inc.

BOSTON LIGHT - Seafood products–fresh or frozen - O'Donnell-Usen Fisheries Corp.

BOSTON LIGHTSHIP - Beer - Boston Beer Co. LP

BOSTON LITE - Popcorn - Boston Popcorn Co.

BOSTON MAN - Buttons - Boston Man Marketing Inc.

BOSTON MARATHON - Jewelry - Boston Athletic Association

BOSTON MARKET HOME STYLE MEALS - Chickens - Boston Chicken, Inc.

BOSTON PRIDE - Seafood products–fresh or frozen - Stavis Seafoods Inc.

BOSTON PRINTING INK - Inks - Van Son Holland Ink Corp. of America

BOSTON RXD - Contact lenses - Cooper Companies Inc.

BOSTON SELECTS - Apparel–athletic - Minuteman Flames Minor Hockey Association

BOSTON SOFT BODY JACKET - Apparel and accessories - Boston Brace International, Inc.

BOSTON SPORT ACCENT - Footwear - Elicon Resourcing Group, Inc.

BOSTON SQUARE - Floor coverings - Congoleum Corp.

BOSTON SQUARES - Flooring–hardwood - Connor Aga Sports Flooring Corp.

BOSTON TEA PARTY - Fireworks - B.J. Alan Co. Inc.

BOSTON TEE BAG CO., THE - Bags–duffel - Michael H. Sarver

BOSTON, THE - Fencing–chain link - Nebraska Plastics, Inc.

BOSTON TORTOISE - Candy - Bari & Gail

BOSTON TRADERS - Toiletries - Boston Trading Ltd. Inc.

BOSTON TRADERS KIDS - Children's apparel - Boston Trading Ltd. Inc.

BOSTON TRAVELER - Apparel–men's - Fitwel Dress Co., Inc.

BOSTON TRIO - Prepared entrees - Boston Chicken, Inc.

BOSTON WHALER - Boats - Boston Whaler, Inc.

BOSTON WHALER - Tanks–gas ☆ - Bettcher Manufacturing Corp.

BOSTON WHALER - Tobacco products - Sterling Tobacco Co.

BOSTON WITH LATTICE - Fencing–plastic - Nebraska Plastics, Inc.

BOSTONETTE - Pencil sharpeners ☆ - Hunt Manufacturing Co.

BOSTONIA - Locks - Boston Lock & Safe Co.

BOSTONIA - Plumbing fixtures–metal - Hooper Industries Inc.

BOSTONIAN - Apparel and accessories - C. & J. Clark America, Inc.

BOSTONIAN - Apparel–men's ☆ - Central-Samuels Inc.

BOSTONIAN - Doors - Jeld-Wen, Inc.

BOSTONIAN - Dyes–household - Whittemore Polish Co.

BOSTONIAN - Food products ☆ - Whipple Co.

BOSTONIAN - Footwear ☆ - S. Goldberg and Co. Inc.

BOSTONIAN - Locks - Boston Lock & Safe Co.

BOSTONIAN - Men's footwear - Bostonian Shoe Co.

BOSTONIAN - Tobacco–chewing or smoking - 1776 Tobacco Co.

BOSTONIAN BOOTIQUES - Men's footwear ☆ - Bostonian Shoe Co.

BOSTONIAN ELEMENTS - Footwear - C. & J. Clark America, Inc.

BOSTONIAN PACERS - Shoes ☆ - Bostonian Shoe Co.

BOSTROM - Surveying instruments - Bostrom-Brady
BOSUN BOATS - Boats - Reeves International, Inc.
BOSWELLA - Pharmaceutical preparations - Sabinsa Corp.
BOSWELLIA SERRATA EXTRACT - Vitamins and nutritional supplements - Vitamin Research Products Inc.
BOSWELLIN - Pharmaceutical - Sabinsa Corp.
BOSWORTH - Compact discs–prerecorded - TRF Production Music Libraries
BOT - Tiles–ceramic ☆ - Federal Tile Imports Inc.
BOT ERASER - Veterinary pharmaceutical preparations - Farnam Cos. Inc.
BOT-X - Veterinary pharmaceutical preparations - Farnam Cos. Inc.
BOTACLEAR - Skin care products - Gerard Pierre-Louis
BOTANAEASE - Vitamins and nutritional supplements - Nu Skin International, Inc.
BOTANAFLOR - Vitamins and nutritional supplements - Nu Skin International, Inc.
BOTANAGUARD - Vitamins and nutritional supplements - Nu Skin International, Inc.
BOTANAME - Vitamins and nutritional supplements - Nu Skin International, Inc.
BOTANASET - Vitamins and nutritional supplements - General Shelters of Texas, Inc.
BOTANAVIVE - Vitamins and nutritional supplements - Nu Skin International, Inc.
BOTANAVOX - Vitamins and nutritional supplements - Nu Skin International, Inc.
BOTANAZYME - Vitamins and nutritional supplements - Nu Skin International, Inc.
BOTANEE - Skin care products - Reviva Laboratories
BOTANI GARDEN - Floor coverings–carpet and rugs - Regal Rugs Inc.
BOTANIC GARDEN - Earthenware - Portmeirion USA
BOTANICA - Confections - Greater Pacific Food Holdings, Inc.
BOTANICA - Flower pots–earthenware - Gale Group Inc.
BOTANICA - Skin care products - La Natura
BOTANICA - Tableware–china - Villeroy and Boch Tableware Ltd.
BOTANICA - Wallpaper ☆ - Osborne & Little
BOTANICA COLLECTION - Silver products - International Silver Co.
BOTANICA TONIQUE - Skin care products - Pharmagel Corp.
BOTANICAL - Housewares - Himark Enterprises Inc.
BOTANICAL BAY - Hardware - Supreme Building Products, Inc.
BOTANICAL BERRIES - Tiles–ceramic - Monarch Tile Inc.
BOTANICAL DESIGNS INTERNATIONAL - Flowers–artificial - Botanical Designs International Inc.
BOTANICAL GARDENS - Computer software ☆ - Sunburst Communications, Inc.
BOTANICAL GLAZE - Lipsticks - Pfizer Inc.
BOTANICAL KINETICS - Skin care products - Aveda Corp.
BOTANICAL MIST BIJOUX DE BAIN - Skin care products - Savonnerie, Inc.
BOTANICAL MOISTURE-COTE - Hair care products - O. Grayson Co.
BOTANICAL PLEASURES - Health care products - Mangelsen's (VDI)
BOTANICAL PLEASURES - Lotions ☆ - Mangelsen's
BOTANICAL SILK - Hair care products - John Amico Expressive Hair Care Products
BOTANICAL TONIQUE - Skin care products - Gary E. Loest
BOTANICAL TRUST CO. - Syrup - Origins Natural Resources Inc.
BOTANICALS - Deodorizers - Reckitt & Colman, Inc.
BOTANICALS - Hair care products - Pro-Line Corp.
BOTANICALS - Perfumes - Smith & Watson
BOTANICALS, THE - Health care products - Smith & Vandiver, Inc.
BOTANICLAB - Vitamins and nutritional supplements - International Medical Research, Inc.
BOTANICOLOR - Hair care products - Clairol Inc.
BOTANICS OF CALIFORNIA - Skin-care products - Botanic Skin Care
BOTANICURL - Hair care products - Fugi Botanix, Inc.
BOTANIFYING - Hair care products - Amethyst Investment Group, Inc.
BOTANIK - Hair care products - Studio Beauty Salon Inc.
BOTANIKA CLEANSE - Hair care products - Garden Botanika, Inc.
BOTANIKA CONDITION - Hair care products - Garden Botanika, Inc.
BOTANIKABABY - Cosmetics - Garden Botanika, Inc.
BOTANIQUE - Hair care products - Orly International Inc.
BOTANIQUE A - Floor coverings–tile ☆ - Monarch Tile Inc.
BOTANIQUE B - Floor coverings–tile ☆ - Monarch Tile Inc.
BOTANIX - Flowers–artificial - Magicsilk
BOTANOIL - Hair care products - Nexxus Products Co.
BOTANY - Belts–apparel - Lyntone Belts Inc.
BOTANY - Flowers–artificial ☆ - Nature Incentives USA
BOTANY - Men's apparel - Botany 500
BOTANY 500 - Apparel and accessories - Mcgregor Corp.

BOTANY 500 - Apparel and accessories - Sigallo Ltd.
BOTANY 500 - Men's apparel - Botany 500
BOTANY 500 - Neckties ☆ - Belle Neckwear Co.
BOTANY 500 - Slacks - Master Industries Corp.
BOTANY BAY - Apparel–men's - Mcgregor Corp.
BOTANY BAY - Floor coverings–carpet and rugs ☆ - American Carpet Mills
BOTANY FIVE HUNDRED - Apparel and accessories - Mcgregor Corp.
BOTANY FOR BOYS - Apparel–children's - Sandess Manufacturing Co. Inc.
BOTAS ALBACETE - Sporting goods - Ballco Products Inc.
BOTE COTE - Novelty items–paper - Epoca Corp.
BOTETOURT COUNTY - Furniture - Pilliod Co.
BOTKIN - Personalized jewelry - Samuel J. Botkin & Co. Inc.
BOTOLPH GRAPHICS - Greeting cards - Botolph Graphics
BOTOX - Ophthalmic goods - Allergan, Inc.
BOTT FRERES - Wines - Wine Imports Ltd.
BOTT/KENNEDY - Cabinets - Kennedy Manufacturing Co.
BOTTARGA DI TONNO - Food products - Bel Canto Fancy Foods Ltd.
BOTTECCHIA - Bicycles - Corso Bicycle Distributor Inc.
BOTTECCINO COLLECTION - Giftware ☆ - J. Kenneth Zahn
BOTTICELLI - Wine - Charles Jacquin et Compagnie Inc.
BOTTICELLI BLUSH - Lipsticks - Lancome
BOTTICELLI: THE ART OF QUESTIONING - Computer software ☆ - Krell Software Corp.
BOTTICELLINO - Apparel - Retail Trademark Holding Corp.
BOTTICELLI'S FAMOUS NUDELS - Snack foods - Designer Snacks Inc.
BOTTLE A MOTHER COULD LOVE!, A - Infant product - Munchkin Bottling, Inc.
BOTTLE BAG, THE - Bags–plastic - Enviro-Tote, Inc.
BOTTLE BIN - Plastic bottle stands - John Stephen Reynolds
BOTTLE BLANK - Sporting goods - Shakespeare Fishing Tackle
BOTTLE BOOT - Bottle caps - David M. Novak
BOTTLE BOOTIES - Infant product - Prince Lionheart, Inc.
BOTTLE BOSS - Racks - T.G.I. Innovations, Inc.
BOTTLE BRIDLE - Leather goods - Cartom Inc.
BOTTLE BUDDY - Baby bottle holder - Kytel Industries
BOTTLE CAP FISHING LURE - Fishing lures - Paul J. Kordish
BOTTLE CAP KEY HOLDER - Key rings - Paul J. Kordish
BOTTLE CAPS - Candy - Willy Wonka Brands
BOTTLE CAPS - Hats - Hat Attack, Inc.
BOTTLE CHUMMY - Infant product ☆ - Surf More Product
BOTTLE COOLR - Wine bottle cover - Team Products
BOTTLE DICE - Games - Bloomco
BOTTLE KNITS - Apparel and accessories - Schuessler Knitting Mills Inc.
BOTTLE 'N JUG - Handicraft kit ☆ - Coloron Industries
BOTTLE O BUTTER - Cocoa butter - Majestic Drug Co., Inc.
BOTTLE SAVER - Bottles–glass - Hackzines, Inc.
BOTTLE TIME BABY - Dolls - Mattel, Inc.
BOTTLE TOPPERS - Corks - Chase Collection, Inc.
BOTTLE TOPPS - Games - Alsip & Co.
BOTTLED-UP BITSY - Dolls - Fun World Inc.
BOTTLED WATER QUALITY-JUST COLDER - Ice - Krieg Boys Ice Corp.
BOTTLESORT - Containers - Magnetic Separation Systems Inc.
BOTTLEWATCH - Measuring instruments - Zevex, Inc.
BOTTOM BETTER - Skin care products - Derma Rx Corp.
BOTTOM BETTER - Topical ointment - InnoVisions Inc.
BOTTOM BLASTER, THE - Exercising equipment - BUY-ON-TV Shopping Network
BOTTOM BRUSH - Brushes–paint - Corona Brushes Inc.
BOTTOM CRUISER - Fishing lures - Lindy Little Joe Inc.
BOTTOM HALF, THE - Apparel and accessories ☆ - Edison Brothers Stores, Inc.
BOTTOM LINE - Attache cases - Mainland Marketing, Inc.
BOTTOM LINE - Card holders ☆ - Palson Inc.
BOTTOM LINE - Floor coverings–carpet and rugs ☆ - Quaker Inc.
BOTTOM LINE - Office furniture–wood - Panel Concepts, Inc.
BOTTOMKOTE - Boat-bottom coating - Interlux Yacht Finishes
BOTTOMLESS BEER MUG, THE - Glassware–household - Michael V. Badalamente
BOTTOMLINE - Blinds–vertical - Louverdrape Inc.
BOTTOMS B - Apparel–women's - Newton Manufacturing Corp.
BOTTOMS UP - File folders - Angler's Roslyn Group Ltd.
BOTTOMS UP - Infant product - Cosco, Inc.
BOTTOMS-UP - Medical apparatus - Roloke Co.
BOTTOMS UP - Novelty items ☆ - Papel Freelance, Inc.
BOTTOMS UP PUTTERS - Golfing equipment - Swing Thing Inc.
BOU-K-STIX - Air freshener - Gonti, Inc.

☆ = Now out of production

BOUCHAINE - Wines - Bouchaine Vineyards
BOUCHER - Jewelry ✩ - Marcel Boucher
BOUCHER BOYS & THE INDIAN - Blankets - Boucher Boys & The Indian, Inc.
BOUCHERON - Giftware - Bueche-Girod Corp.
BOUCHERON - Wines - Blair Importers Ltd.
BOUCHERON - Wines - David Sherman Corp.
BOUCHON - Wines - Cannon Wines Ltd.
BOUCLE - Fabrics–tapestry ✩ - Coloroll Inc.
BOUCLE - Floor coverings–carpet and rugs - Karastan-Bigelow Inc.
BOUCLE - Floor coverings–carpet and rugs ✩ - Gulistan Carpet Inc.
BOUCLE - Hair care products - Mastey De Paris
BOUCLE - Yarn - Henry's Attic
BOUCLE ACCENTS III - Floor coverings–carpet and rugs - Eligere Carpets
BOUCLE COLLECTION - Fabrics ✩ - Decorative Aides Co. Inc.
BOUCLE GRID - Fabrics - Interface, Inc.
BOUCLE III - Floor coverings–carpet and rugs - Eligere Carpets
BOUCLE STATUS - Floor coverings–carpet and rugs ✩ - Karastan-Bigelow Inc.
BOUCLE TWIST - Floor coverings–carpet and rugs ✩ - Regal Rugs Inc.
BOUCLETTE - Fabrics - Fab. Industries Inc.
BOUDIN BITE - Food products - Bodin Foods Inc.
BOUDOIR BANDIT - Apparel–men's - Boudoir Bebe
BOUDOIR BEAR - Toys–stuffed - Russ Berrie and Co., Inc.
BOUDOIR BEBE - Children's apparel - Boudoir Bebe
BOUDOIR BOUQUET - Perfumes - Karen Carson Creations
BOUFFANT - Jewelry ✩ - Hirsch Speidel Inc.
BOUGAINVILLEA - Cosmetics - Revlon Consumer Products Corp.
BOUILLABAISE - Tableware–china ✩ - Villeroy and Boch Tableware Ltd.
BOUKASTAN - Floor coverings–carpet and rugs - Boukalis & Co. Inc.
BOULDER - Fabrics–denim - Dan River Inc.
BOULDER - Floor coverings–carpet and rugs ✩ - Cumberland Mills Inc.
BOULDER - Frames–eyeglass - U.S. Optical Frame Co.
BOULDER - Toys - Tonka Corp.
BOULDER AMBER ALE - Beverages–malt - Rockies Brewing Co.
BOULDER BAR ENDURANCE - Snack foods - Eric Zapf
BOULDER BASHER - Toys–automobiles - Mattel, Inc.
BOULDER BROWN ALE - Beverages–malt - Rockies Brewing Co.
BOULDER CLIFFHANGER ALE - Beverages–malt - Rockies Brewing Co.
BOULDER DASH - Computer software - First Star Software Inc.
BOULDER EXTRA PALE ALE - Beverages–malt - Rockies Brewing Co.
BOULDER EXTRA SPECIAL BITTER - Beverages–malt - Rockies Brewing Co.
BOULDER FALL FEST ALE - Beverages–malt - Rockies Brewing Co.
BOULDER GEAR - Ski suits–women's - Sport USA, Inc.
BOULDER HILL - Toys - Tonka Corp.
BOULDER IGLOO ALE - Beverages–malt - Rockies Brewing Co.
BOULDER MOOSE - Toys–stuffed - Russ Berrie and Co., Inc.
BOULDER PORTER - Beverages–malt - Rockies Brewing Co.
BOULDER SAUSAGE - Sauage - GBS Partners, Inc.
BOULDER SINGLE-TRACK RYE ALE - Beverages–malt - Rockies Brewing Co.
BOULDER SPRINGS - Floor coverings–carpet and rugs - Gulistan Carpet Inc.
BOULDER STOUT - Beverages–malt - Rockies Brewing Co.
BOULDERS, THE - Shirts - Boulders Joint Venture
BOULE DE NEIGE - Apparel and accessories - Boule De Neige, Inc.
BOULES QUIES - Plugs–ear - Consolidated Midland Corp.
BOULEVARD - Apparel–men's - Hartz & Co., Inc.
BOULEVARD - Floor coverings - Congoleum Corp.
BOULEVARD - Floor coverings–carpet and rugs ✩ - Kelly Group Inc.
BOULEVARD - Greeting cards - Hallmark Cards Inc.
BOULEVARD - Musical instrument accessories - VMI Industries
BOULEVARD - Watches - Bulova Corp.
BOULEVARD BAGEL SUB - Sandwiches–prepackaged - Bagel Blvd. Cafe America, Inc.
BOULEVARD BIKES - Motorcycle parts and accessories - Boulevard Bikes
BOULEVARD BOUTIQUE - Eyeglasses - Hart Specialties Inc.
BOULEVARD BREWING CO - Beverages–malt - Boulevard Brewing Associates L.P.
BOULEVARD BREWING CO. - Beverages–malt - Boulevard Brewing Associates L.P.
BOULEVARD CLUB BY BLOCK - Apparel–athletic - Block Industries, Inc.
BOULEVARD VELVETS - Fabrics - A. Wimpfheimer & Brother Inc.
BOULTON - Watches ✩ - SMH (US) Inc.
BOULVARD - Coffee - Atlanta Coffee Roastery, Inc.
BOUNCE - Detergents - Procter & Gamble Co.
BOUNCE - Footwear - Wolverine World Wide, Inc.

BOUNCE - Socks - Leininger Mills Inc.
BOUNCE BAK - Hair care products - Peter Hantz Co.
BOUNCE BAK FRESH - Hair care products - Peter Hantz Co.
BOUNCE BAK PLUS - Hair care products - Peter Hantz Co.
BOUNCE BARRIER - Integrated circuits - International Microelectronics Products
BOUNCE BLASTER - Toys - Spotlight Toys, Inc.
BOUNCE BONE - Pet products - Weiss Twice Toys, Inc.
BOUNCE HOUSE - Furniture–children's - Maze Inc.
BOUNCE-MASTER - Photographic equipment - SP Systems/Saratons
BOUNCE MOUSE - Pet products - Cosmic Cat Corp.
BOUNCE SAND WEDGE - Golfing equipment - Suarez Corp. Industries
BOUNCE STAINGUARD - Detergents - Procter & Gamble Co.
BOUNCE ULTRA - Detergents - Procter & Gamble Co.
BOUNCEABOUT - Furniture ✩ - Cosco, Inc.
BOUNCEBACK - Apparel and accessories ✩ - Jantzen Inc.
BOUNCEBACK - Beverages - Taste Technologies Beverage
BOUNCEBACK - Footwear - Lehigh Safety Shoe Co.
BOUNCEIN' RIDE - Toys - Mattel, Inc.
BOUNCEMOBILE - Toys - Shelcore Inc.
BOUNCEPROOF - Apparel and accessories - Bounceproof
BOUNCER - Jars–plastic - Rubbermaid Inc.
BOUNCER - Pet products - Peak Pet Products
BOUNCER - Sporting goods ✩ - Unique Sports Products Inc.
BOUNCER - Telephone apparatus - SNI Innovation Inc.
BOUNCER COUPE - Infant product - Century Products Co.
BOUNCER COUPE DELUXE - Infant product - Century Products Co.
BOUNCER II - Floor coverings–carpet and rugs - Trend Carpet
BOUNCES THE BEVERAGE GAME - Games - Mitchener & Upton Games, Inc.
BOUNCI BODY - Skin care products - Paula Payne Products Co. Inc.
BOUNCIN' BABIES - Dolls - Lewis Galoob Toys, Inc.
BOUNCIN' BANANA - Milk–flavored ✩ - Gossner Foods, Inc.
BOUNCIN KIDS - Dolls - Lewis Galoob Toys, Inc.
BOUNCING BANDIT - Game machines - Amutronics, Inc.
BOUNCING BETTY - Sporting goods - Boone Bait Co. Inc.
BOUNCING CURLS - Hair care products - Dep Corp.
BOUNCY - Toys–stuffed ✩ - Dakin Inc.
BOUND BAK - Toys - Allied Toy Co.
BOUND TO REMEMBER - Greeting cards - Bound to Remember Greeting Cards
BOUNDARY - Boots - Servus Footwear Co.
BOUNDARY - Insecticides - Lambert-Kay
BOUNDARY LAKES - Luggage - Welsh Sporting Goods Corp. (Boyt Div.)
BOUNDARY LINE - Apparel and accessories - Stanly Knitting Mills, Inc.
BOUNDARY RED BALL - Footwear - Norcross Footwear, Inc.
BOUNDARY ROUTING - Computer software - 3Com Corp.
BOUNDARY WATERS - Apparel and accessories - Dayton Hudson Corp.
BOUNDER - Motor vehicles–motor homes - Fleetwood Enterprises, Inc.
BOUNDER - Wheelchairs - 21st Century Scientific Inc.
BOUNDERS - Footwear ✩ - Falcon Shoe Manufacturing Co.
BOUNDLESS NETWORK ARCHITECTURE - Communications equipment– satellite - Telco Communications Group, Inc.
BOUNTIFUL - Bakery products - Dawn Food Products Inc.
BOUNTIFUL - Breads ✩ - Campbell Soup Co.
BOUNTIFUL - Chocolate candy - Maxfield Candy Co.
BOUNTIFUL - Dinnerware–glass - Franciscan by Johnson Brothers, USA, Inc.
BOUNTIFUL - Fabrics–broadcloth - Dan River Inc.
BOUNTIFUL - Floor coverings–carpet and rugs - Gulistan Carpet Inc.
BOUNTIFUL - Floor coverings–carpet and rugs - Mohawk Carpet Corp.
BOUNTIFUL - Food products ✩ - Ocean Beauty Seafood, Inc.
BOUNTIFUL - Giftware - World of Porcelain & Glassware
BOUNTIFUL BAGELS - Bagels - PF Brands, Inc.
BOUNTIFUL CHAMPIONSHIP COURSE - Computer software - Access Software Inc.
BOUNTIFUL HARVEST - Vitamins and nutritional supplements - Shaperite Concepts, Ltd.
BOUNTIFUL SNACKS - Raisins ✩ - Warner-Lambert Co.
BOUNTY - Boats–motor ✩ - Bayliner Marine Corp.
BOUNTY - Candy bars - Mars, Inc.
BOUNTY - Chemical preparations ✩ - Woolsey Marine Industries
BOUNTY - Fertilizers - Vigoro Industries, Inc.
BOUNTY - Floor coverings–carpet and rugs - Conquest Carpet Mills Inc.
BOUNTY - Paper–toweling - Procter & Gamble Co.
BOUNTY - Recording label - Boddie Record Manufacturing & Recording Inc.
BOUNTY - Sporting goods ✩ - Outdoor Technologies Group

✩ = Now out of production

BOUNTY - Whiskey - Old Boone Distillery Co.
BOUNTY - Wines - Golden State Vintners
BOUNTY HUNTER - Cleaning preparations - W.W. Grainger, Inc.
BOUNTY HUNTER - Colognes - Bounty Hunter Limited
BOUNTY MICROWAVE - Paper–toweling - Procter & Gamble Co.
BOUNTY O'MAINE - Food products - Prelude Corp.
BOUNTY RINSE AND REUSE - Paper–toweling - Procter & Gamble Co.
BOUQUER - Lamps ☆ - Tensor Corp.
BOUQUET - Astringents - Master Chemical Co.
BOUQUET - Cigars - Gesty Trading & Manufacturing Corp.
BOUQUET - Clocks - General Time Corp. (Westclox/Seth Thomas Div.)
BOUQUET - Dinnerware–glass - Franciscan by Johnson Brothers, USA, Inc.
BOUQUET - Dishes–earthenware - Hadley Pottery Co. Inc.
BOUQUET - Flatware - Washington Forge Inc.
BOUQUET - Flatware ☆ - Utica Cutlery Co.
BOUQUET - Floor coverings - Mannington Resilient Floors
BOUQUET - Floor coverings–carpet and rugs - Masland Corp.
BOUQUET - Floor coverings–carpet and rugs ☆ - Calladium & Marglen
BOUQUET - Floor coverings–carpet and rugs ☆ - Colonial Mills Inc.
BOUQUET - Floor coverings–carpet and rugs ☆ - Regal Rugs Inc.
BOUQUET - Food products - Hillshire Farm Co.
BOUQUET - Food products - Waltkoch Ltd.
BOUQUET - Furniture ☆ - Bassett Furniture Industries, Inc.
BOUQUET - Giftware ☆ - Lenox Crystal, Inc.
BOUQUET - Glassware–household - Seneca Glass Co.
BOUQUET - Glassware–household ☆ - Oneida Ltd.
BOUQUET - Jewelry - Jacoby-Bender Inc.
BOUQUET - Ophthalmic goods - Fidelity Case Corp.
BOUQUET - Recording label - Bouquet-Orchid Enterprises
BOUQUET - Rings–jewelry - Artcarved Inc.
BOUQUET - Wallpaper ☆ - Motif Designs, Inc.
BOUQUET-AIRE - Deodorizers - Willert Home Products, Inc.
BOUQUET COLLECTION - Dinnerware–glass ☆ - Lenox, Inc.
BOUQUET DE FLORES - Soap - Paris Presents Ltd.
BOUQUET D'OR - Candy - Morris National Inc.
BOUQUET OF AMERICA - Seasonings - Life Force Nutrition
BOUQUET OF DESSERTS - Food products - Life Force Nutrition
BOUQUET OF GREECE - Seasonings - Life Force Nutrition
BOUQUET OF ITALY - Seasonings - Life Force Nutrition
BOUQUET OF LOVE - Giftware - Russ Berrie and Co., Inc.
BOUQUET SERIES - Frames–picture - North American Enclosures Inc.
BOUQUET SPECIAL - Tobacco products - F.D. Grave & Son, Inc.
BOUQUETS - Footwear - J. Baker Inc.
BOUQUETS OF SPRING - Flowers, plants, and seeds - Russ Berrie and Co., Inc.
BOURAS - Brushes and brooms - Bouras Mop Manufacturing Co.
BOURBON - Cookies - Lulabelle's Gourmet Cookies
BOURBON - Flatware - Couzon USA
BOURBON BLEND - Tobacco products - Swedish Math North America Inc.
BOURBON COUNTY STOUT - Beverages–alcohol - Jim Beam Brands Co.
BOURBON COUNTY STOUT - Beverages–malt - Goose Island Brewing Co.
BOURBON DELUXE - Whiskey - Jim Beam Brands Co.
BOURBON FALLS - Liquors - Heaven Hill Distilleries, Inc.
BOURBON ST. BOXERS - Apparel–men's - Bourbon St. Boxers, Inc.
BOURBON STREET - Fabrics - Uniroyal Engineered Products
BOURBON STREET - Floor coverings - Mannington Resilient Floors
BOURBON STREET - Liquors ☆ - House of Seagram
BOURBONNAIS - Dinnerware–glass ☆ - Block China Co.
BOURDEAUX - Dinnerware–glass - Arita Sales Co. Inc.
BOURGOGNES FAIVELEY - Wines - Wilson Daniels Ltd.
BOURJOIS - Cosmetics, bath product, cologne - Bourjois Ltd.
BOURNE - Sheet music - Bourne Co.
BOURSIN - Cheese ☆ - ULN America Inc.
BOURSIN LIGHT - Cheese ☆ - ULN America Inc.
BOUSSAC - Apparel and accessories ☆ - Swirl II Ltd.
BOUSSAC - Wallpaper - Imperial Wallcoverings, Inc.
BOUSSAC - Window coverings - Award Fabrics Inc.
BOUSSAC II - Wallpaper - Imperial Wallcoverings, Inc.
BOUTARI - Wines - Paterno Imports, Ltd.
BOUTIQUE - Ashtrays–glass - Couzon USA
BOUTIQUE - Fabrics–broadcloth - Collins & Aikman Corp.
BOUTIQUE - Faucets - Moen Inc.
BOUTIQUE - Floor coverings - Mannington Resilient Floors
BOUTIQUE - Furniture ☆ - Bassett Furniture Industries, Inc.
BOUTIQUE - Lighters - Colibri Inc.
BOUTIQUE - Paper–tissue - Kimberly-Clark Corp.

BOUTIQUE - Tableware–china ☆ - Villeroy and Boch Tableware Ltd.
BOUTIQUE - Toilets–enameled - Kohler Co.
BOUTIQUE - Wallpaper - Unique Wall Fashions Inc.
BOUTIQUE - Watches - Bulova Corp.
BOUTIQUE 1 - Frames–eyeglass - U.S. Optical Frame Co.
BOUTIQUE 2 - Frames–eyeglass - U.S. Optical Frame Co.
BOUTIQUE BY SMITH - Bathroom accessories ☆ - L.E. Smith Glass Co.
BOUTIQUE CINOLE - Apparel and accessories - Hung Fashion (USA) Inc.
BOUTIQUE COLLECTION - Apparel–women's - Wacoal America Inc.
BOUTIQUE D'ELITE - Skin care products - Boutique D'elite USA, Inc.
BOUTIQUE EUROPA - Apparel and accessories - Spiegel, Inc.
BOUTONNIERE - Dishes–china - Taylor, Smith & Taylor Co.
BOUVET - Brandy ☆ - Kobrand Corp.
BOUVET - Doors–metal - Bouvet USA, Inc.
BOUVET BRUT SAPHIR, MILLESIME - Wines - Kobrand Corp.
BOUVET BRUT SIGNATURE - Wines - Kobrand Corp.
BOUVET-LADUBAY - Wines - Kobrand Corp.
BOUVET ROSE BRUT - Wines - Kobrand Corp.
BOUVIER - Recording label - Credence Records
BOUYEA'S - Breads - Fassetts Bakery Inc.
BOUZOUKI - Beer, wine - Attiki Imports & Distributors
BOVA DERM - Veterinary pharmaceutical preparations - W.A. Butler Co.
BOVA-GRAIN - Animal feeds - Bluebonnet Milling Co.
BOVAGAIN - Animal feed supplements ☆ - Central Soya Co. Inc.
BOVAGARD - Veterinary pharmaceutical preparations - Y-Tex Corp.
BOVALYX - Animal feed supplements - PM AG Products Inc.
BOVAMAX - Animal feed supplements - PM AG Products Inc.
BOVAMINE - Animal feed supplements - Nutrition Physiology Corp.
BOVANNAH - Cosmetics - Bovannah International, Inc.
BOVANNAH - Skin care products - Color Me Beautiful, Inc.
BOVANO - Briefcases - Tomac International Inc.
BOVANO OF CHESHIRE - Cloisonne enamels - Bovano of Cheshire
BOVANO ORIGINAL - Luggage - Tomac International Inc.
BOVANOWARE - Copper/ceramic giftware - Bovano of Cheshire
BOVATEC - Animal feeds - Bluebonnet Milling Co.
BOVIDA - Spices and extracts - De Choix Specialty Foods Co.
BOVIK - Fish–canned or cured - Haram-Christensen Corp.
BOVIMS - Pharmaceutical preparations ☆ - JMI-Canton Pharmaceuticals
BOVINE BEAUTIES - Ornamental products–glass ☆ - Forest Time Products Inc.
BOVINE BOOSTER - Veterinary pharmaceutical preparations - Stevens Industries Inc.
BOVINE INSPIRATIONS - Notebooks and notepads - Laif W. Bannon
BOVITEX - Gloves - Patagonia, Inc.
BOW - Dusters - Wright-Bernet
BOW - Sporting goods - Guterman International Inc.
BOW - Sporting goods ☆ - Etonic Inc.
BOW - Toys - Mattel, Inc.
BOW-A-RIBBON - Ribbons ☆ - Equality/Stribbons
BOW-BAG - Mesh bags - Cheryl A. Wald
BOW BOATS INC - Boats - Bow Boats, Inc.
BOW BUDDY - Sporting goods - MascoTech Accessories
BOW DANGLE - Archery equipment - Pro Release, Inc.
BOW-DASHUS - Hairpins - Bow-Dashus Inc.
BOW-FLAGE - Cosmetics - Hunter's Specialties, Inc.
BOW-FLEX - Exercise equipment - Bow-Flex of America, Inc.
BOW MAGIC - Ribbons - Minnesota Mining & Manufacturing Co.
BOW MAKER, THE - Musical instruments - Fiddle Factory Inc.
BOW MASTER - Novelty items - Craig Teuten
BOW-MATIC - Paper industry machinery - Hallmark Cards Inc.
BOW RIDER - Boats–motor - Century Boat Co.
BOW-RIFIC - Ribbons - Fibre-Craft Materials Corp.
BOW STREET STATION - Apparel and accessories - Fidelity Sportswear Co.
BOW T' STERN - Sealing compounds - E and B Marine Inc.
BOW-TIE - Electrodes - Uni-Patch
BOW TIE GIFT BAGS - Bags–plastic - Equitable Bag Co., Inc.
BOW TIE PRODUCTIONS - Greeting cards - Super Products, Inc.
BOW TIES - Hobby kits - JCA, Inc.
BOW-TIQUE - Hair care products - Russ Berrie and Co., Inc.
BOW-TITE - Archery equipment ☆ - Bohning Co. Ltd.
BOW WINGS - Musical instrument accessories - Herco Products
BOW WOW BANDANAS - Pet products - Access Wear Plus, Inc.
BOW WOW BOUTIQUE - Dolls - Lewis Galoob Toys, Inc.
BOW WOW BUDDIES - Toys–stuffed - Russ Berrie and Co., Inc.
BOW WOWS & MEOWS - Greeting cards - American Greetings Corp.
BOW WOWS N' MEOWS - Toys–stuffed ☆ - Dakin Inc.

☆ = Now out of production

BOWA TEAK-DEK - Plywood - Harbor Sales Co.
BOWAPLY - Plywood ☆ - Harbor Sales Co.
BOWATER - Wood products - Bowater Inc.
BOWAX - See **S & A WAX**
BOWBABIES - Apparel–children's - Annie, Oh! Originals, Inc.
BOWCID - Antacids ☆ - JMI-Canton Pharmaceuticals
BOWDEN SPACELANDER BOWDEN - Bicycles - Michael Kaplan
BOWDRIN - Pharmaceutical preparations ☆ - JMI-Canton Pharmaceuticals
BOWEN - Tuning machine for musical instruments - Bowen Music Co.
BOWEN - Watches - Bulova Corp.
BOWEN & WRIGHT - Apparel - TJX Companies, Inc.
BOWENS - Photographic equipment ☆ - Bogen Photo Corp.
BOWER - Tripods, cameras, accessories - Saul Bower Inc.
BOWERS - Cigarette lighters - Bowers Lighter Co.
BOWERS - Electrical equipment ☆ - Masco Corp.
BOWERSHADE - Hockey equipment - Bowers
BOWERSHARROR WINERY - Wines - Chateau Grand Traverse Ltd.
BOWFLEX POWER PRO - Exercising equipment - Bow-Flex of America, Inc.
BOWGUARD 360 - Hardware - Johnson Fishing, Inc.
BOWHUNTER'S ORGANIZER - Sporting goods - Stalkmaster Archery Producdts
BOWIE-AXE - Knives - Tru-Balance Knife Co.
BOWL-A-BALL - Candy ☆ - Leaf, Inc.
BOWL-A-MATIC - Games - Hasbro, Inc.
BOWL-A-ROL - Bowling balls - Master Woodcraft Inc.
BOWL-A-SOUP - Soups–mixes - Lipton Investments, Inc.
BOWL-A-STRIKE - Games ☆ - Milton Bradley Co.
BOWL AND SCORE - Games ☆ - Milton Bradley Co.
BOWL BLUE - Cleaning preparations–household - JBI Inc.
BOWL BOUND - Games - Avalon Hill Game Co.
BOWL BRITE - Cleaning preparations ☆ - Drackett Co.
BOWL BUDDY - Air purification systems - Peter Ragusa
BOWL FRESH - Cleaning preparations - Willert Home Products, Inc.
BOWL KLEEN - Cleaning preparations - PLC
BOWL MAGIC - Detergents - AmeriPlus Inc.
BOWL-O-BEAUTY - Florists - Amlings Flowerland
BOWL O' BEAUTY - Flowers, plants, and seeds ☆ - J. Kenneth Zahn
BOWL-O-SHRIMP - Vegetable sauces ☆ - Sau-Sea Foods Inc.
BOWL OF CREAM - Christmas tree ornaments - Cracker Box Inc.
BOWL O'NUTS - Nuts–salted, roasted, cooked, or canned - Los Angeles Nut House
BOWL O'SWEETS - Candy ☆ - California Peanut Co.
BOWL PAC - Cleaning preparations - PortionPac Chemical Corp.
BOWL PATROL - Cleaning preparations - Stanley Home Products Inc.
BOWL POWER - Cleaning preparations–household - L & F Consumer Products
BOWL QUICK - Cleaning preparations - Procter & Gamble Co.
BOWL SOLUTION - Cleaning preparations - Gulf States Chemical Co., Inc.
BOWLBY - Nut products, candy - Bowlby Candy Co. Inc.
BOWLENE - Cleaning preparations - Malco Products, Inc.
BOWLER - Games ☆ - Avalon Hill Game Co.
BOWLER - Ophthalmic goods - Foremost Optical Products
BOWLER 10 - Ophthalmic goods - Foremost Optical Products
BOWLER PUTTER - Golfing equipment - Spaulding
BOWLERS - Bathroom accessories - Suburbanite Industries
BOWLINE FAMILY PRODUCTS - Garden furniture - Bowline Family Products, Ltd.
BOWLING BELLES - Shoes - Gotham Shoe Manufacturing Co.
BOWLING CONCEPTS - Sporting goods - Bowling Concepts, Inc.
BOWLING ELEPHANT - Games ☆ - Montgomery Schoolhouse
BOWLING GOT ME HOOKED NOT DRUGS - Apparel and accessories - Dick Leon
BOWLING GOT ME HOOKED NOT DRUGS - Sweatshirts - Palace Sports Center
BOWLING GREEN - Beverages–alcohol ☆ - Safeway Stores Inc.
BOWLING GREEN - Colognes - Geoffrey Beene Inc.
BOWLING SECRETARY - Computer software - SourceView Software International
BOWLINKNIT - Apparel and accessories ☆ - Brill Bros. Inc.
BOWL'N ALL - Disinfectants - Caltech Industries, Inc.
BOWLO - Archery equipment ☆ - Martin Archery Inc.
BOWMAN - Analgesics ☆ - JMI-Canton Pharmaceuticals
BOWMAN - Apparel and novelty items - Barnes Group Inc.
BOWMAN - Canned-apple product - Bowman Apple Products Co. Inc.
BOWMAN - Trading cards and stamps - Topps Co., Inc.
BOWMANS - Trading cards and stamps - Topps Co., Inc.

BOWMAN QUAD-CUT 4X4 - Drill bits - Barnes Group Inc.
BOWMANS - Liquors - A. Smith Bowman Distillery Inc.
BOWMAR - Laboratory apparatus ☆ - Bowmar Technologies
BOWMAR/NOBLE - Publisher's imprints - Bowmar/Noble Publishers (McGraw-Hill School Div.)
BOWMASTER - Bow maker, ribbons, and bows - Bowmaster Inc.
BOWMORE - Beverages–alcohol - White Rock Distilleries Inc.
BOWMORE - Liquors ☆ - European Beverage Co., Inc.
BOWPOT - Dishes–earthenware ☆ - Royal China & Porcelain Companies Inc.
BOWRENCH - Tools - Cepco Tool Co.
BOWRETTE - Hair care products - Tomima L. Edmark
BOWS - Snack foods ☆ - General Mills, Inc.
BOWS AND A ROLL - Paper–gift wrap - Ribbon Magic, Inc.
BOWS ARTS - Barrettes - Bows Arts, Inc.
BOWS UP - Barrettes - Beverly Kohn
BOWSAL - Pharmaceutical preparations ☆ - JMI-Canton Pharmaceuticals
BOWSER BALL - Pet products - Phydeaux Enterprises Inc.
BOWSER BONE - Pet products - BenePet Pet Care Products
BOWSER BOWS - Pet products - Pet Concepts
BOWSER NAT TREATS - Dog food - Salubrious Inc.
BOWSTERAL - Disinfectants ☆ - JMI-Canton Pharmaceuticals
BOWSTRING - Thread - Threads USA Div.
BOWTIE - Paper–toilet - Georgia-Pacific Corp.
BOWTIQUE, THE - Apparel and accessories ☆ - Design Circle Ltd.
BOWTUSSIN - Pharmaceutical preparations ☆ - JMI-Canton Pharmaceuticals
BOX A - Ice - Krieg Boys Ice Corp.
BOX & SHIP - Packaging materials - Box & Ship, Inc.
BOX BASICS - Boxes - Whitney Corr-Pak International
BOX BLASTER - Pencil holders - Hedstrom Corp.
BOX BRITES - Giftware ☆ - U.S. Fiberglass Inc.
BOX CANYON - Apparel and accessories - International News, Inc.
BOX INNS - Brackets - Dec-Kor, Inc.
BOX IT OR BAG IT MATHEMATICS - Textbooks - Math Learning Center
BOX-LOC - Brackets - Hubbell Inc.
BOX O BITS - Hardware - Eazypower Corp.
BOX OF RAGS SANITIZED ABSORBENT WASHED - Fabrics - Kamen Wiping Materials Co., Inc.
BOX OF SQUARES - Toys–blocks - Guidecraft Inc.
BOX OFFICE - Boxes - Rubbermaid Inc.
BOX OFFICE - Floor coverings–carpet and rugs - Calladium & Marglen
BOX PLUS - Comforters - Pillowtex Corp.
BOX POCKET - Folding machines–paper - Dick Moll & Sons, Inc.
BOX POPS - Toys ☆ - Tomy America, Inc.
BOX RAKE - Machine parts - Glenmac Inc.
BOX SCORE - Games - Thomas Merritt
BOX STAR - Kites - Hi-Flier Manufacturing Co.
BOX, THE - Wireless transmitters - Box Maker
BOX, THE - Artists' materials - Visual Design Manufacturing Co. Inc.
BOX WORKS, THE - Furniture - J.E. Higgins Lumber Co.
BOXALL - Boxes–paperboard - Ercole Beltramini, Inc.
BOXBAG - Bags–paper - Elpac, Ltd.
BOXBOOK - Paper products - Boxbook Media
BOXCAR - Computer software - Onset Computer Corp.
BOXCAR - Eyeglasses - Goat Eyewear
BOXCAR - Skates–roller - Rollerblade, Inc.
BOXCAR BURGERS - Vending machines - Local Railroad Co.
BOXCAR CHILDREN MYSTERIES - Publisher's imprints - Albert Whitman and Co.
BOXCARS - Luggage - Mainland Marketing, Inc.
BOXDICE GAMES - Publisher's imprints - Opine Consultants
BOXER - Adhesives and sealants - Union Laboratories Inc.
BOXER - Beverages–malt ☆ - Joseph Huber Brewing Co., Inc.
BOXER - Clocks - General Time Corp. (Westclox/Seth Thomas Div.)
BOXER - Hot dogs - Southeast Food Systems, Inc.
BOXER - Snuff - Brown & Williamson Tobacco Corp.
BOXER A LA CARTE - Apparel and accessories - Quitman Manufacturing Co.
BOXER PATROL - Underwear and nightwear - Briefly Stated, Inc.
BOXER, THE - Pharmaceutical preparations - Health Products Corp.
BOXER, THE - Bop bags ☆ - Intex Recreation Corp.
BOXER TOP - Shoes - Genesco Inc.
BOXERBRAND - Vinyl - Almont Co.
BOXEROBICS - Video production - Charles Duffy
BOXERS AMERICA - Apparel–men's - Umbro USA
BOXES N BOXES OF COLORS - Cosmetics ☆ - Cosmetic Firsts Ltd.
BOXES TO GO - Ribbons - Boas Box Co.
BOXIES - Food products - Brice Foods, Inc.

BOXING LEGENDS OF THE RING - Computer software - Electro Brain Corp.
BOXING PUP - Toys–stuffed - Russ Berrie and Co., Inc.
BOXLEY - Artists' materials ☆ - Andrews/Nelson/Whitehead
BOXLIGHT - Computer software - Boxlight Corp.
BOXOUT - Recording label - Nancy DiToro
BOXTOPPER - Box opener - Converse Distributing
BOXVELOPE - Envelopes - Tension Envelope Corp.
BOXX - Apparel–men's - C.J. Two Brothers, Inc.
BOXX, THE - Computer software - Surveyworks, Ltd.
BOXX, THE - Transportation vehicles and equipment - Robert C. Vincent
BOXXLE - Video games - Fujisankei Communications International Inc.
BOY - Watches - Boy London
BOY & HIS DOG, A - Calendars - Brown and Bigelow Inc.
BOY BLUE - Fast-food franchise - Boy Blue of America Inc.
BOY-O-BOYS - Apparel and accessories ☆ - Wrangler Co.
BOYAJIAN - Food products - Boyajian, Inc.
BOYAJIAN - Oils–edible ☆ - Gourmet America
BOYARDS - Cigarettes - G.A. Georgopulo & Co. Inc.
BOYCE GAHAGAN - Hair care products - KE2 Laboratories
BOYCE MCLEON - Apparel and accessories - Leon Johnson
BOYCRAFT - Paints ☆ - Wescon Products Co.
BOYD - Coffee - Boyd Coffee Co.
BOYD - Recording label - Boyd Records
BOYD BEDROOMS - Furniture - Royal Waterbeds, Inc.
BOYD DESIGNS - See **SAFARI DESIGNS**
BOYD FURNITURE - Bedroom and dining-room furniture - Boyd Furniture Co. Inc.
BOYDLINE - Folding doors - A.J. Boyd Industries Inc.
BOYDS - Coffee - Boyd Coffee Co.
BOYD'S - Health care products - Boyd's of Madison Avenue, Inc.
BOYDS BARISTA - Coffee - Boyd Coffee Co.
BOYDS BARISTA COFFEE - Coffee - Boyd Coffee Co.
BOYDS BEARS - Toys–stuffed - Boyds Collection Ltd.
BOYDS BEARS & FRIENDS - Figurines - Boyds Collection Ltd.
BOYDS BEARS & FRIENDS - Toys - Boyds Collection, Ltd.
BOYDS COLLECTION LTD., THE - Jewelry - Boyds Collection Ltd.
BOYDS ULTRA VIOLET - Cleaning preparations - Boyds Wheels, Inc.
BOYDWEIGHT - Window treatments - A.J. Boyd Industries Inc.
BOYER - Cleaning preparations - Starkey Chemical Process Co.
BOYER - Drain pipe cleaners - Boyer Corp.
BOYER BRASS & COPPER POLISH - Polishing rouge - Boyer Corp.
BOYER - FIREWATER - Chemical preparations - Starkey Chemical Process Co.
BOYER RED CROWN - Drain pipe cleaners - Boyer Corp.
BOYER RED CROWN LYE - Cleaning preparations - Boyer Corp.
BOYERTOWN - Bottles–glass - Drug Plastic and Glass Co.
BOYES - Needles–sewing - Gilt Import Co. Inc.
BOYESEN - Motors–outboard - Boyesen Engineering
BOYFRIEND - Eyeglasses - Art-Craft Optical Co.
BOYFRIEND CLUB, THE - Publisher's imprints - Daniel Weiss Associates, Inc.
BOYLAND BRAND BOTTLEWORKS - Beverages–carbonated - Boylan Bottling Co.
BOYLAN'S CREAMY RED BIRCH BEER FLOAT ITTHE NU-BLEND - Beverages–carbonated - Boylan Bottling Co.
BOYLAN'S ORIGINAL BIRCH BEER SINCE 1891 GENUINE DRAUGHT - Beverages–carbonated - Boylan Bottling Co.
BOYLE'S FAMOUS - Corned beef - Boyle's Famous Corned Beef Co. Inc.
BOYLESONIAN - Awnings ☆ - John Boyle & Co., Inc.
BOYNE - Earthenware ☆ - Waterford Wedgewood USA, Inc.
BOYNTON - Greeting cards - Recycled Paper Products, Inc.
BOYNTON - T-shirts–women's - Prelude Designs
BOYNTON - Wallcovering - Sandra Boynton
BOYNTON FOR BABIES - Bedding–linen - Perfect Fit Industries, Inc.
BOYNTON FOR KIDS - Apparel–children's - William Carter Co.
BOYNTON III - Wallpaper - Prelude Designs
BOYNTON TOO - Wallpaper - Prelude Designs
BOYOL - Skin care products - Pfeiffer Pharmaceuticals Inc.
BOYS DOUBLE BARREL - Liquors - William Grant & Sons, Inc.
BOYS FARMERS MARKET, THE - Fruit and vegetable markets - Boys Farmers Market, Inc.
BOYS 'N BERRIES - Apparel–children's - May Apparel Group, Inc.
BOYS OF MOO MESA - Toys - Hasbro, Inc.
BOY'S TOWN - Frames–eyeglass - Hudson Optical Corp.
BOYS WILL BE BOYS - Wallpaper - James Seeman Studios
BOYSCLUB - Eyeglasses - Art-Craft Optical Co.
BOYSENBERRY - Jewelry–costume ☆ - Safari Ltd.

BOYSENBERRY BLISS - Juices - Juice Club, Inc.
BOYSENBERRY SMOOTHIE - Beverages–carbonated - Garratt & Gunn Ltd.
BOYT GLIDER - Luggage - Boyt L.P.
BOYT NO-NONSENSE - Luggage - Welsh Sporting Goods Corp. (Boyt Div.)
BOYT SPORT - Luggage - Boyt L.P.
BOYT TREQ - Luggage - Boyt L.P.
BOYT'S - Briefcases - Welsh Sporting Goods Corp. (Boyt Div.)
BOYZ II MEN - T-shirts–children's - Boyz II Men, Inc.
BOYZ TOYZ - Jewelry - Snails Italian Jewelry Inc.
BOZEMAN PORTER'S LOTION - Skin care products - Gallatin River Products, Inc.
BOZI MLYN - Recording label - Jazz Composer's Orchestra Association Inc.
BOZO - Candy ☆ - Latham Studios
BOZO - Dolls - Goldberger Doll Manufacture Co.
BOZO - Ice cream ☆ - Ace Baking Co. L.P.
BOZO - Music boxes ☆ - Schmid Inc.
BOZO BALL - Candy ☆ - Topps Co., Inc.
BOZO THE CLOWN - Toys ☆ - Knickerbocker Toy Co. Inc.
BOZONS' QUEST - Computer software - Laureate Learning Systems Inc.
BP - Frames–eyeglass ☆ - Universal/Univis Inc.
BP - Gasoline - BP America Inc.
BP - Wines - Braren & Pauli Winery
BP BOCK - Pharmaceutical preparations - Bock Pharmacal Co.
BP BRITCHES - Apparel and accessories - Empire Manufacturing Co.
BP EXPRESS - Convenience stores - BP America Inc.
BP PROCARE - Automotive repair shops - BP America Inc.
BP VANELLUS - Oils–lubricating - BP America Inc.
B.P.A. - Housewares ☆ - Amaza Laboratories Inc.
BPA - Jewelry - Burr Patterson and Auld Co. Inc.
BPA DELUXE - Firearms, accessories, and parts - Beeman Precision Airguns
BPANALYZER - Computer software - Technology Economics International Corp.
BPC - Lighters - Butane Products Corp.
BPG - Machine parts - Buff Polish & Grind Industrial Supply Co., Inc.
BPI - Computer software - BPI Systems Inc.
BPI - Medical apparatus ☆ - Professional Product Research, Inc.
BPI - Photographic equipment - B.P.I. Industries Inc.
BPI - Sporting goods - Basketball Products International Inc.
B.P.K.G.W. - Glass products - Big Pine Glass
BPM - Paper–bond - Badger Paper Mills, Inc.
BPM - Plywood - Harbor Sales Co.
BPN - Health care products - Procter & Gamble Co.
B.P.P.-LEMMON - Pharmaceutical preparations ☆ - Lemmon Co.
BPPROGRESSION/4 DATA SERVER - Computer software - Basis International Ltd.
BPR LITE - Computer software ☆ - Wizdom Systems, Inc.
BPS - Computer software - Software Bullet-Proof Inc.
BPS - Paints - BPS Paint Co.
BP'S PET ODOR ELIMINATOR - Pet products - Beaumont Products, Inc.
BPSIMULATOR - Computer software - Technology Economics International Corp.
BPWIN - Computer graphics program - Logic Works, Inc.
BPX - Automatic teller machines - Stratacom, Inc.
BQ - Chemical preparations - North American Marketing Corp.
BQ - Cold remedies - Bristol-Myers Squibb Co.
BQ - Shelving units–plastic - Burke Gibson Inc.
BQ 6 - Cold remedies ☆ - Keller Co.
BR - Candy - Brach and Brock Confections Inc.
BR - Jewelry - Barnett Robinson, Inc.
BR - Leather goods - Hasbeen, Ltd.
BR - Paneling - Best-Rite Manufacturing
BR - Water purification systems ☆ - Bruner Corp.
B.R. & D.R. - See **SUNSET BAY**
B.R. COHN - Wine - B.R. Cohn Winery
B.R. FLAT - Paints - Lilly Perfection Paint
BR3 - Sporting goods - Georgia's Tennis
BRA BARONE - Wine ☆ - Charles Jacquin et Compagnie Inc.
BRA - D - SUIT - Apparel and accessories - Krystal K. International Inc.
BRA-O-MINE - Apparel–women's - Wacoal America Inc.
BRA-RIFFIC - Apparel–women's - Wacoal America Inc.
BRA-S-LETTE - Brassieres (Bras) - Lady Marlene
BRA $TASH - Wallets ☆ - Apothecary Products, Inc.
BRA, THE - Apparel stores–lingerie - Formfit Rogers
BRA TOPPER - Apparel–women's - NCC Industries, Inc.
BRA-TOS - Meat products–pork - Bee-Lor Enterprises, Inc. Co.
BRA-VADO - Apparel–women's - Jezebel-Renee of Hollywood

BRA-VO - Apparel–women's - Wacoal America Inc.
BRABANTIA - Kitchenware–china ✰ - Loroman Co.
BRACACCIA - Food products - Crestar Food Products, Inc.
BRACCIALINI - Leather accessories ✰ - International Accessories Corp.
BRACCICI - Footwear - Footwear International Corp.
BRACCIS OF VENICE - Statuary - Hillside House of Originals
BRACE - Dental compounds - Smithkline Beecham Corp.
BRACE - Games - Kadon Enterprises Inc.
BRACE - Hair care products - Tressa, Inc.
BRACE - Health care products - Tawn Ltd.
BRACE-AID - Anesthetics ✰ - Del Pharmaceuticals, Inc.
BRACE & CLAMP - Clamps–metal - Sign-Up Corp.
BRACE GARD - Dental-brace-discomfort treatment - Infa-Lab Inc.
BRACE RELIEF - Dental-brace-discomfort treatment - Infa-Lab Inc.
BRACELET - Dishes–china - Pickard Inc.
BRACELET - Glassware–household ✰ - Lotus Glass Co.
BRACELINK - Tools–jewelers - Triumph Enterprises, Inc.
BRACEMATE - See **COMPANION**
BRACEOIL - Pet products - Farnam Cos. Inc.
BRACES BRITE - Toothpaste - Ortho-Care Inc.
BRACH-O-SAURUS - Candy ✰ - Brach and Brock Confections Inc.
BRACHABUBBLE - Candy - Brach and Brock Confections Inc.
BRACHETTO D'ACQUI - Wines - Banfi Vintners
BRACHIOSAURUS - Fireworks - American Promotional Events, Inc.
BRACH'S - Candy - Brach and Brock Confections Inc.
BRACH'S CHAMPS - Candy - Brach and Brock Confections Inc.
BRACH'S MALTS - Candy - Brach Van Houten Holding Inc.
BRACH'S ROCKS - Candy - Brach and Brock Confections Inc.
BRACH'S TD'S - Candy - Brach and Brock Confections Inc.
BRACH'S TWISTERS - Candy - Brach Van Houten Holding Inc.
BRACHTEL - Paper - Brachtel Industries Inc.
BRACKENS - Bicycles - Heartlands Crafters Junction
BRACKEN'S BLAZERS - Apparel–men's ✰ - Gallron
BRACKEN'S BREED - Apparel and accessories ✰ - Gallron
BRACKEN'S BRITCHES - Apparel–men's ✰ - Gallron
BRACKETT - Recording label - Source Records Inc.
BRACKIT - Cables–steel - Kryptonite Corp.
BRACOS - Footwear ✰ - Cara Lee Corp.
BRAD - Billiard-cue-tip scuffers - International Billiards Inc.
BRAD - Frames–eyeglass - Rozin Optical Export Corp.
BRAD-FLEX - Wood products ✰ - Bradley Plywood Corp.
BRAD-GUARD - Plastics–laminated ✰ - Bradley Plywood Corp.
BRAD TURNER - Toys - Tonka Corp.
BRADBERRY - Pipes–tobacco - Bradberry Briar Pipe Corp.
BRADBURY - Dinnerware–glass ✰ - Johnson Brothers, USA, Inc.
BRADBURY - Floor coverings - Tarkett, Inc.
BRADBURY - Floor coverings–carpet and rugs - Tuftex Carpet Mills, Inc.
BRADBURY - Pianos - Aeolian Pianos Inc.
BRADBURY PRESS - Publisher's imprints - MacMillan Publishing Co. Inc.
BRADDOCK - Clocks - Ridgeway Clock Co.
BRADDOCK'S COVE - Furniture - Singer Furniture Co.
BRADE-A-FOAM - Skin care products ✰ - Miles Inc.
BRADEN - Prefabricated buildings–metal - Jason Inc.
BRADENTON - Shoes ✰ - Allen-Edmonds Shoe Corp.
BRADEX - Brushes - Abtex Corp.
BRADFORD - Appliance parts - W.T. Grant Co.
BRADFORD - Bathtubs–enameled - Kohler Co.
BRADFORD - Cabinets - Aristokraft, Inc.
BRADFORD - Doors–glass - Therma-Tru Corp.
BRADFORD - Floor coverings–carpet and rugs ✰ - Atlas Carpet Mills Inc.
BRADFORD - Floor coverings–carpet and rugs ✰ - Mannington Carpets, Inc.
BRADFORD - Furniture ✰ - Lane Co. Inc.
BRADFORD - Glass–window ✰ - Wolverine Technologies
BRADFORD - Hats - Resistol Hats
BRADFORD - Novelty items - Bradford Novelty Co., Inc.
BRADFORD - Occasional furniture ✰ - JDI Group, Inc.
BRADFORD - Tableware–china ✰ - Lenox, Inc.
BRADFORD - Toys–stuffed - Dakin Inc.
BRADFORD BOND - Paper - Fay Paper Products Inc.
BRADFORD EDITIONS - Awards, plaques and medals - Bradford Exchange, Ltd.
BRADFORD ESTATES - Furniture - Bassett Furniture Industries, Inc.
BRADFORD EXCHANGE, THE - Commemorative plates - Bradford Exchange, Ltd.
BRADFORD HOUSE - Manufactured homes - Redman Industries, Inc.
BRADFORD HOUSE - Mobile homes - Western Homes Corp.

BRADFORD LTD. - Apparel–men's ✰ - Rainfair, Inc.
BRADFORD MANOR - Furniture - Bassett Furniture Industries, Inc.
BRADFORD MUSEUM PRESS - Greeting cards - Bradford Exchange, Ltd.
BRADFORD SERIES - Locks–padlocks - Sargent Manufacturing Co.
BRADFORD STONE - Floor coverings–tile - Kentile Floors Inc.
BRADFORD-WHITE - Heating equipment - Bradford-White Corp.
BRADINGTON YOUNG - Furniture–upholstered - Woodmark Originals
BRADLEY - Candy - Bradley Candy Manufacturing Co.
BRADLEY - Flooring–hardwood - Potlatch Corp.
BRADLEY - Frames–eyeglass ✰ - U.S. Optical Frame Co.
BRADLEY - Furniture–children's - Child Craft Industries Inc.
BRADLEY - Office supplies - Jonathan Bradley Pens Inc.
BRADLEY - Paints - C.E. Bradley Laboratories Inc.
BRADLEY - Pet products - Bragina Avian Supply
BRADLEY - Plumbing fixtures - Bradley Corp.
BRADLEY - Toys–stuffed ✰ - Russ Berrie and Co., Inc.
BRADLEY BEAR - Toys–stuffed - Dakin Inc.
BRADLEY BELLES - Dolls ✰ - Bradley Import Co.
BRADLEY/BROWNALL - Fixtures - Bradley Corp.
BRADLEY COLLECTABLES - Dolls - Bradley Import Co.
BRADLEY FARMS - Tomato pastes and sauces - John N. Wright Jr. Inc.
BRADLEY FURRY FRIENDS - Toys–stuffed ✰ - Bradley Import Co.
BRADLEY JONS - Waterproof outerwear - Gruner & Co., Inc.
BRADLEY NATUR-ELLES - Dolls ✰ - Bradley Import Co.
BRADLEY OGDEN - Sausages - Saag's Products Inc.
BRADLEY ROGERS - Clocks - Time Products International
BRADLEY RYAN COLLECTION - Wallpaper - I. Gottlieb & Associates
BRADLEY SPECIAL RESERVE - Flooring–hardwood - Potlatch Corp.
BRADLEY'S - Toys ✰ - Bradley Import Co.
BRADLEY'S FASHION SOPHISTICATES - Dolls ✰ - Bradley Import Co.
BRADLEY'S MUSICALS - Collectable product ✰ - Bradley Import Co.
BRADOR - Beverages–malt ✰ - Martlet Importing Co.
BRAD'S - Soups - Dean Distributors, Inc.
BRADSHAW - Ophthalmic goods - Swank Optical
BRADSHAW'S 3 BEARS - Honey - Sioux Honey Association
BRADTOTE - Boxes and containers - Bradford Co.
BRADWAY - Chocolate syrup - Bradway Chocolate Co.
BRADY - Ophthalmic goods ✰ - Luxottica
BRADY - Publisher's imprints - Simon & Schuster, Inc.
BRADY & SUN - Nurseries and garden stores - Brady & Son Inc.
BRADY B - Chemical preparations - W.H. Brady Co.
BRADY-BUILT - Nurseries and garden stores - Brady & Son Inc.
BRADY FARMS - Fruits–frozen - Brady Farms Inc.
BRADY QUIK - Office supplies - W.H. Brady Co.
BRADYCOR - Pharmaceutical preparations - Cortech, Inc.
BRADY'S - Food products - Brady Farms Inc.
BRAE BURN - Shoes–athletic ✰ - Brookfield Athletic Co. Inc.
BRAEBROOK - Apparel and accessories - Braetan, Inc.
BRAEBURN - Floor coverings–carpet and rugs ✰ - Downs Carpet Co. Inc.
BRAEFAIR - Coats–women's - Braetan Kids
BRAEMOOR - Jewelry - R.F. Simmons Co.
BRAETAN - Coats–women's - Braetan Kids
BRAETAN KIDS - Coats–children's - Braetan Kids
BRAG BADGES - Awards, plaques and medals ✰ - Design Circle Ltd.
BRAG-DESIGNERS CHOICE - Apparel–men's ✰ - Berkley Shirt Co. Inc.
BRAGELETS - Jewelry - Bragelets by Amy, Inc.
BRAGG - Food products - Live Food Products Inc.
BRAGGI - Nail care products - Revlon Consumer Products Corp.
BRAHMA - Automotive parts and accessories ✰ - Toppertown Inc.
BRAHMA - Bags–trash - Carlisle Plastics, Inc.
BRAHMA - Beverages–malt ✰ - EFCO Importers
BRAHMA - Boots - Cowtown Boot Co. Inc.
BRAHMA - Cases–eyeglass - California Optical Leather Inc.
BRAHMA - Men's apparel - India Garments Inc.
BRAHMAN - Cigars - Commonwealth Brands, Inc.
BRAHM'S - Food products - Arbor Hill Associates, Inc.
BRAHMS - Hearing aids - Magnatone Hearing Aid Corp.
BRAHM'S - Juices - Randall-Standish Vineyards
BRAID - Footwear–men's - L.B. Evans' Son Co.
BRAID ECOR - Hair care products - Leon J.A. Buchheit Inc.
BRAID-LOC - Hardware - Broderick & Bascom Rope Co.
BRAID 'N BRAID - Rope ✰ - Western Filament, Inc.
BRAID-O-PAD - Hardware ✰ - American Steel Wool Manufacturing Co. Inc.
BRAIDED BEAUTY - Dolls - Mattel, Inc.
BRAIDED BUNCH - Pet collars - Leatherite-Nylorite Manufacturing Inc.
BRAIDINI - Hair curlers - Bernadine Schach

BRAIDS - Candy ☆ - Y & S Candies Inc.
BRAIDS - Wallpaper - Koroseal Wallcoverings
BRAIDS ARE CLASSIC - Publisher's imprints - Willoughby's, Inc.
BRAIDS LOCKS AND SKIN - Hair care products - Bianca's Botanicals
BRAIDS, THE - Recording label - Stephan Jenkins Productions, Inc.
BRAIDWARE - Apparel and accessories - Edel W. Barrett
BRAIDWATER - Tablecloths ☆ - Hamilton Adams Imports Ltd.
BRAIDWINNERS - Floor coverings–carpet and rugs - Braidwinners Ltd.
BRAILLDOTS - Signs - Scott Sign Systems, Inc.
BRAILLE CUDDLES BEAR - Toys–stuffed - Dakin Inc.
BRAILLE PLAQUES - Signs - Scott Sign Systems, Inc.
BRAILLE-TAC - Publisher's imprints - Advance Corp.
BRAILLEMATE - Computers - Telesensory Systems Inc.
BRAILLEPHABET - Children's blocks - McCauley & Broadfoot
BRAILLETTERS - Hardware - Scott Sign Systems, Inc.
BRAILLWORDS - Hardware - Scott Sign Systems, Inc.
BRAIN - Lawn mowers - Tanaka Ltd.
BRAIN BASH - Toys - Tiger Electronics, Inc.
BRAIN BOOST EVERCOFFEE - Vitamins and nutritional supplements - Desert Health Products, Inc.
BRAIN BRAWL CHALLENGE - Educational materials - Sally K. Bernhisel
BRAIN BREW - Coffee - Richard Saunders International, Inc.
BRAIN BRIEFS - Headwear - Waterbird Co.
BRAIN BUGGY - Toys - Tonka Corp.
BRAIN BUILDERS - Publisher's imprints - Lowell House
BRAIN CHILD - Calculators ☆ - Bowmar Technologies
BRAIN DAMAGE - Computer software - SourceView Software International
BRAIN DRAIN - Sandals - Deckers Outdoor Corp.
BRAIN DROPS - Candy - Doug Johnson, Inc.
BRAIN FACTORY - Calculators ☆ - JS & A National Sales Group
BRAIN FLEX - Vitamins and nutritional supplements - Highland Laboratories
BRAIN-FRIENDLY LITERACY - Educational materials - Nellie Edge Resources, Inc.
BRAIN FUEL - Health care products - Futurebiotics
BRAIN GAME FROM AUSTRALIA, THE - Games ☆ - Decipher Inc.
BRAIN GEAR ?+3 A.B.C. - Computer software - Olivetti Office USA, Inc.
BRAIN III FORMULA FAMILY - Health care products - A-Z Nutrients International
BRAIN I.Q. - Games - Smethport Specialty Co.
BRAIN LORD - Video games - Enix America Corp.
BRAIN PEP - Vitamins and nutritional supplements - Natural Balance, Inc.
BRAIN POWER INC. - Chemical preparations - Brain Power Inc.
BRAIN QUEST - Games - Workman Publishing Co., Inc.
BRAIN STAIN - Hair coloring preparations - BodyFX Co.
BRAIN STORM - Vitamins and nutritional supplements - Nature's Bounty, Inc.
BRAIN TAINMENT - Computer software - New Wave Partners, Inc.
BRAIN TEASER - Puzzles - S.J. Miller Co.
BRAIN TONIC - Vitamins and nutritional supplements - Long Life Herb Classics
BRAIN WORKS - Vitamins and nutritional supplements - Next Generation Nutrition Inc.
BRAINBREAKER - Toys - Maryland Toy Corp.
BRAINBUSTER - Puzzles - Fun, Inc.
BRAINCHILD - Computer peripheral equipment - Brainchild Corp.
BRAINCHILD - Frames–eyeglass - Liberty Optical Manufacturing Co.
BRAINCHILD - Recording label - Nova Records Inc.
BRAINFREEZE - Beverages - Southland Corp.
BRAINIAC - Toys–stuffed - Toy Works, Inc.
BRAINLINK - Amplifiers - Advanced Neurotechnologies, Inc.
BRAINLINK COMPLEX - Vitamins and nutritional supplements - M.M.R.C., Ltd. Co.
BRAINMAP - Computer software - Board of Regents of the University of Texas
BRAINSHARE - Computer peripheral equipment - Novell, Inc.
BRAINSTORM - Computer peripheral equipment - Brainstorm MDE, Inc.
BRAINTEASER PUZZLES - Puzzles - Channel Craft & Dist., Inc.
BRAINTRUST - Frames–eyeglass ☆ - Universal/Univis Inc.
BRAINWARE - Prerecorded audio and video cassettes - Cognitech Corp.
BRAINWAVES - Hair care products - Image Laboratories, Inc.
BRAINWEYES - Advertising agencies - Brainweyes Communications, Inc.
BRAINY BAGELS - Bagels - Natural Ovens of Manitowoc Inc.
BRAINYBALL - Games - Harold J. Hicks
BRAIR TEETHER - Toys - Wimmer-Ferguson Inc.
BRAISER/BROWNER - Cooking equipment–household - Nordic Ware
BRAIZAAI - Apparel and accessories - Variety Knit Corp.
BRAKE - Deodorants–personal - Mennen Co.
BRAKE ALERT - Front-brake light and monitoring system ☆ - I.M.R. Products Inc.

BRAKE & PARTS CLEAN - Automotive products - Cyclo Industries, Inc.
BRAKE BUDDY - Brakes–motor vehicle - Master Concepts Inc.
BRAKE FORCE, THE - Measuring instruments - Central Tools, Inc.
BRAKE KIT - Brake parts - Leeson Electric Corp.
BRAKE LOC - Solenoids and switches - Nitrous Oxide Systems, Inc.
BRAKE MAN - Cleaning preparations - W.W. Grainger, Inc.
BRAKE MATE - Automotive parts and accessories - Y-3 Holdings, Inc.
BRAKE NOISE SOLUTION CENTER - Automotive parts and accessories - Quality Automotive Co., Inc.
BRAKE TECHNOLOGY - Automotive parts and accessories - Echlin Inc.
BRAKEBEST - Brake parts - O'Reilly Automotive, Inc.
BRAKEBUSH - Food products - Brakebush Brothers Inc.
BRAKEMASTER - Automotive parts and accessories - Chicago Rawhide
BRAKETECH - Brake parts - Ceco Friction Products, Inc.
BRAKING - Automotive parts and accessories - Towbar Products Inc.
BRAKINI - Apparel–women's - Blue Bay Inc.
BRAKLEEN - Cleaning preparations - CRC Chemicals USA/Siloo
BRAKNER - Pipes–tobacco - Bradberry Briar Pipe Corp.
BRALUSION - Apparel and accessories ☆ - Warnaco Inc.
BRAMBACH - Pianos - Kohler & Campbell Inc.
BRAMBLE - Bedding–linen - Dan River Inc.
BRAMBLE - Fabrics - Gretchen Bellinger Inc.
BRAMBLE - Floor coverings–carpet and rugs - Barrett Carpet Mills Inc.
BRAMBLE - Siding–insulating - Champion International Corp.
BRAMBLE - Yarn ☆ - Melrose Yarn Co. Inc.
BRAMBLES BUNNY - Toys–stuffed - Russ Berrie and Co., Inc.
BRAMBLEY HEDGE - Giftware ☆ - Enesco Corp.
BRAMBLY HEDGE - Figurines - Royal Doulton-Somerset UK Ltd.
BRAMLEY HALL - Wallcovering ☆ - Fashon Wallcoverings
BRAMLEYS - Jams and jellies - Moran Foods, Inc.
BRAMMER - Cabinets - Brammer Manufacturing Co.
BRAMSTEDT - Medical apparatus - Bramstedt Surgical Instrument, Inc.
BRAN CHEX - Cereal - Ralston Purina Co.
BRAN FLAKES-FLAX/OMEGA3 - Cereal - New Morn, Inc.
BRAN FOR LIFE - Breads - Food For Life Baking Co.
BRAN NEWS - Cereal - Ralston Purina Co.
BRANCA MENTA - Beverages–alcohol - Carillon Importers Ltd.
BRANCH DELIVERY - Computer software - FormAtion Technologies Inc.
BRANCH STRATEGIST - Computer software - Bank Strategy Group Information Systems, Inc.
BRANCO - Furniture ☆ - A. Brandt Co. Inc.
BRAND - Beverages–malt - Brand Beer Inc.
BRAND 5 - Electronic equipment ☆ - Benjamin Electroproducts Inc. (Robins Div.)
BRAND 57 - Shoes ☆ - Edison Brothers Stores, Inc.
BRAND BANDIT - Coupons - Brand Bandit, Inc.
BRAND MANAGER - Advertising agencies - BBI Marketing Systems, Inc.
BRAND NEW - Underwear and nightwear ☆ - Lovable Co.
BRAND NEW RED - Lipstick ☆ - Cosrich Inc.
BRAND NEWS - Apparel and accessories - International News, Inc.
BRAND PROFILER - Computer software - WRC Research Systems
BRAND S - Lumber - Woodex Lumber Corp.
BRAND SPANKING NEW DOUG - Handbags - Pyramid Handbags Inc.
BRAND VIEW - Computer software - Advista Group, Inc.
BRAND X - Apparel–men's ☆ - Duck Head Apparel Co., Inc.
BRAND X - Cigarettes - G.A. Georgopulo & Co. Inc.
BRAND X - Detergents - Bottlewerks Molding, Inc.
BRAND X - Fish food - Brand-X Pet Supply
BRAND X - Paints ☆ - Major Brands Inc.
BRAND-X - Recording label - Sivatt Music Productions
BRANDANNA - Apparel and accessories - Carolina Manufacturing Inc.
BRANDED STAR - Giftware ☆ - E & B Giftware
BRANDEIS UNIVERSITY PRESS - Publisher's imprints - University Press of New England
BRANDELLA - Cheese ☆ - Nelson-Ricks Creamery Co.
BRANDER - Food products - Chiquita Brands, Inc.
BRANDER - Wines - Brander Vineyard
BRANDERS - Jeans–men's - Williamson-Dickie Manufacturing Co.
BRANDI - Toys–stuffed ☆ - CBS Toys
BRANDI - Wigs - Jean Paree Weegs Inc.
BRANDI LEE COLLECTION - Wallpaper - I. Gottlieb & Associates
BRANDIED PECANS - Food products - Mrs. Powell's Gourmet Pecans
BRANDINE WOODCRAFT - Toys - Brandine Woodcraft Co.
BRANDING COUNTRY - Food products - Curtice-Burns Foods, Inc.
BRANDING IRON - Meats - John Morrell & Co.
BRANDING IRON - Ophthalmic goods - Embassy Creations Inc.

☆ = Now out of production

BRANDINI - Apparel and accessories - May Department Stores Co.
BRANDIOSO - Beverages–alcohol - Heublein, Inc.
BRANDISH - Computer software - Koei Corp.
BRANDLI'S - Bakery products - Brandli Enterprises, Inc.
BRANDMAN - Food products - Esco Foods Inc.
BRANDMAP - Computer software - WRC Research Systems
BRANDO - Giftware - Ebeling and Reuss Co.
BRANDO - Ophthalmic goods - Styl-Rite Optical Manufacturing Co., Inc.
BRANDOM - Cabinets - Brandom Manufacturing Inc.
BRANDOM - Floor coverings - Congoleum Corp.
BRANDON - Cosmetics - Brandon Co.
BRANDON - Floor coverings - Bruce Hardwood Floors
BRANDON - Furniture - Vermont Tubbs Inc.
BRANDON - Shoes ☆ - Allen-Edmonds Shoe Corp.
BRANDON COURT - Furniture ☆ - Stanley Furniture Co. Inc.
BRANDON SQUARE - Floor coverings - Congoleum Corp.
BRANDON STREET - Floor coverings–carpet and rugs - Masland Corp.
BRANDONBURY - Clocks - Ridgeway Clock Co.
BRANDOODLES - Games - Proplan, Inc.
BRAND'S HATCH - Frames–eyeglass ☆ - Universal/Univis Inc.
BRANDS LAIRA COONAWARRA NSW - Wines ☆ - Parliament Import Co.
BRANDS OF CALIFORNIA - Fruits–canned - Purcell International
BRANDSTAND - Shoe stores - United States Shoe Corp.
BRANDT - Biscuits - Kreiner Imports
BRANDT - Cookies - Fancy Foods of Virginia Inc.
BRANDTAB - Computer software - Mediamark Research Inc.
BRANDWEIN - Mattresses - Ohio Mattress Co.
BRANDY - Colognes - Brandy Harvest
BRANDY - Cosmetics ☆ - Marianna Imports, Inc.
BRANDY - Frames–eyeglass - Hoya Corp. USA
BRANDY BROWN - Frames–eyeglass - May Optical Co. Inc.
BRANDY HARVEST - Colognes - Brandy Harvest
BRANDY PUP - Dolls - Russ Berrie and Co., Inc.
BRANDY STATION II - Furniture–upholstered ☆ - Webb Furniture Enterprises Inc.
BRANDY WINE - Apparel and accessories - Sherne Lingerie Inc.
BRANDY'S - Footwear - Shonac Corp.
BRANDYWINE - Dinnerware–glass ☆ - Lenox, Inc.
BRANDYWINE - Floor coverings ☆ - Congoleum Corp.
BRANDYWINE - Frames–eyeglass ☆ - Universal/Univis Inc.
BRANDYWINE - Furniture - Pilliod Co.
BRANDYWINE - Mushrooms - Giorgio Foods Inc.
BRANDYWINE - Toys–stuffed ☆ - Gund, Inc.
BRANDYWINE - Wallpaper ☆ - Carey Lind Designs
BRANDYWINE 2 - Wallpaper - York Wall Coverings Inc.
BRANDYWINE COLLECTIBLES - Giftware - Brandywine Woodcrafts Inc.
BRANDYWINE DESIGN FURNITURE - Furniture - Everfast Inc.
BRANDYWYNE ORIGINALS - African apparel and accessories - Rags to Riches
BRANFORD - Bedding–linen - Dan River Inc.
BRANFORD - Mattresses - Stearns & Foster Bedding Co.
BRANFORD & TAYLOR - Apparel–men's - Cliftex Corp.
BRANGOLD - Cereal - Niblack
BRANHAM - Urinals–enameled - Kohler Co.
BRANHAM CREST - Floor coverings ☆ - Congoleum Corp.
BRANNETTE - Crackers - Vista Bakery, Inc.
BRANNOCH - Apparel and accessories - Crystal Brands Inc.
BRAN'NOLA - Breads - CPC International Inc.
BRANS - Nuts–salted, roasted, cooked, or canned - Brans Nut Co.
BRANSON BUG - Fishing lures - Blakemore Sales Corp.
BRANSON CATHEDRAL - Cabinets–wood - Kemper
BRANSON COUNTRY CLUB - Apparel and accessories - Westpac Products Co. Inc.
BRANSON ENTERTAINMENT - Recording label - Counter Culture
BRANSON SQUARE - Cabinets–wood - Kemper
BRANSONBERRY - Jams and jellies - Kerwin S. Koerper
BRANSOUNDS - Recording label - At Work Entertainment, Inc.
BRANSTON - Thread ☆ - Kreinik Manufacturing Co. Inc.
BRANT POINT - Brooms - Lighthouse Industries
BRANTLY - Brassieres (Bras) - Cameo Coutures
BRANTLYE - Shoes ☆ - Allen-Edmonds Shoe Corp.
BRANTWOOD - Wallpaper - Seabrook Wallcoverings, Inc.
BRAQUETTE - Frames–picture - Martin F. Weber Co.
BRAREN-PAULI - Wines - Braren & Pauli Winery
BRAS-MATES - Apparel stores–lingerie - Formflex Foundations Inc.
BRASCH ECONOWATT - Heating equipment - Brasch Manufacturing Co. Inc.

BRASCH ELECTRODUCT - Heating equipment - Brasch Manufacturing Co. Inc.
BRASH - Colognes - Madipac
BRASHEAR - Publisher's imprints - Branden Publishing Co., Inc.
BRASILIA - Figurines ☆ - National Housewares
BRASILIA - Furniture - Tropitone Furniture Co. Inc.
BRASILIA - Musical instruments - Tropical Music and Pro Audio
BRASILIA - Seafood products–fresh or frozen - GE Consultants
BRASILIA 2 - Furniture ☆ - Tropitone Furniture Co. Inc.
BRASIVOL - Skin care products - Stiefel Laboratories, Inc.
BRASS - Furniture - Weiman Co.
BRASS - Posters - Aegis Entertainment, Inc.
BRASS - Shoes - Nunn Bush Shoe Co.
BRASS & BLACK - Apparel–men's - Asher Co.
BRASS AND GLASS - Lighting fixtures - Meyda Tiffany Inc.
BRASS BAND - Bedding–linen - Dan River Inc.
BRASS BAND - Harmonicas - William Kratt Co.
BRASS BILLET - Golfing equipment - Callaway Golf Co.
BRASS BOOT - Shoes - Weyco Group Inc.
BRASS BOTTOM SEAL - Hardware - KEL-EEZ
BRASS COLLECTION, THE - Desk sets - Crystal Promotions Ltd.
BRASS-CRAFT - Plumbing fixtures–metal - Masco Corp.
BRASS-E - Golfing equipment - Pinseeker Golf Corp.
BRASS EAGLE - Toys–guns - Daisy Manufacturing Co.
BRASS FITTINGS - Apparel–men's - Nordstrom, Inc.
BRASS HARMONY - Cribs–wood ☆ - Cosco, Inc.
BRASS INSTRUMENT TUTOR - Computer software - Electronic Courseware Systems Inc.
BRASS KING - Washboards - National Washboard Co.
BRASS LINGUINI - Electrical equipment - Whitaker Corp.
BRASS MASTER - Golfing equipment - Golfsmith International Inc.
BRASS 'N GLASS - Chimes - Nutone Inc.
BRASS RAIL - Apparel–men's - Nordstrom, Inc.
BRASS RING, THE - Computer software - TBR Associates
BRASS TARNISH EATER - Cleaning preparations - Blitz Manufacturing Co., Inc.
BRASS-TECH - Faucets - Sterling Plumbing Group Inc.
BRASS TEE - Hosiery–men's - Keepers International
BRASS TONES - Cymbals - Paiste America, Inc.
BRASSADA - Apparel and accessories - Richard L. White
BRASSBAR - Wallpaper - Klein & Co.
BRASSBOND - Adhesives and sealants - Bedlam Brass Beds, Inc.
BRASSCRAFTERS - Giftware - BARD International, Inc.
BRASSERIE - Dinnerware - Williams-Sonoma, Inc.
BRASSERIE - Kitchen appliances ☆ - National Housewares
BRASSESSORIES - Golfing equipment - SPL International, Inc.
BRASSEUR BIER DE PARIS - Beverages–malt - Merchant du Vin Corp.
BRASSFLAME - Stoves–wood-burning - Earth Stove Inc.
BRASSIE - Pencil sharpeners - Wescosa Inc.
BRASSLINE - Brass products ☆ - A and M Leatherlines Inc.
BRASSO - Metals - R.T. French Co.
BRASSO-RAMA - Brass products - Allied Deals Inc.
BRASSTONES - Mirrors - Hoyne Industries Inc.
BRASSTONG - Paper clips - Charles Leonard Inc.
BRASSWARES - Brass products - Decorative Crafts
BRASSWORKS - Door hardware - Kaba High Security Locks Corp.
BRASSWORKS BY IVES - H.B. Ives
BRASSY & SASSIE - Meat products–canned - D.S.D.A. Inc.
BRASWELL'S - Food products - A.M. Braswell Junior Food Co. Inc.
BRAT - Motor vehicles–automobiles - Subaru of America, Inc.
BRAT - Ophthalmic goods - Embassy Creations Inc.
BRAT - Play balls - Catco, Inc.
BRAT - Watches - M.Z. Berger & Co. Inc.
BRAT BAT - Toys–stuffed - Toy Works, Inc.
BRAT POCKETS - Breads - Johnsonville Foods Co.
BRATIVAC - Veterinary pharmaceutical preparations - Smithkline Beecham Corp.
BRATT'S BAT - Sporting goods - Bratt Corp.
BRATZ - Sausages - Johnsonville Foods Co.
BRATZ - Snowboards - Lisa R. Consoli
BRAU-WEISSE - Beverages–malt - Merchant du Vin Corp.
BRAUER'S BEST - Meat products - Brauer's Best, Inc.
BRAUFELS - Mustard - Jardine's Texas Foods
BRAUMEISTER - Beverages–malt - Joseph Huber Brewing Co., Inc.
BRAUMEISTER LIGHT - Beverages–malt - Joseph Huber Brewing Co., Inc.
BRAUM'S - Food products - W.H. Braum, Inc.

☆ = Now out of production

BRAUN - Audio equipment ☆ - Adcom Technologies Corp.
BRAUN - Housewares - Braun Inc.
BRAUN - Sealing devices - W. Braun Co. Inc.
BRAUN & CIE. - See **GALERIE BRAUN**
BRAUN AROMASTER - Housewares - Braun Inc.
BRAUN AROMATIC - Grinders - Braun Inc.
BRAUN BILT - Shoes–athletic ☆ - Brookfield Athletic Co. Inc.
BRAUN CITROMATIC - Juice extracting devices - Braun Inc.
BRAUN CLICKER - Hair curlers ☆ - Braun Inc.
BRAUN GOLD - Beverages–malt - Walton & Post, Inc.
BRAUN GOLD W&P LAGER BEER - Beverages–malt - Walton & Post, Inc.
BRAUN INDEPENDENT 2000 - Hair curlers - Braun Inc.
BRAUN MULTIPRACTIC - Food processors - Braun Inc.
BRAUN MULTIPRESS - Juice extracting devices - Braun Inc.
BRAUN MULTITOAST - Toasters - Braun Inc.
BRAUN ORAL-B - Dental equipment - Braun Inc.
BRAUNBLUMEN - Kitchenware–earthenware - Charles Zahn-Import Merchant
BRAUN'S - Bread - Interstate Brands Corp.
BRAUN'S STAY FRESH BAGELS - Bagels - Interstate Brands Corp.
BRAUNSPORT - Apparel and accessories - Braun's Fashions Inc.
BRAUNSTYLE - Apparel and accessories - Braun's Fashions Inc.
BRAUURA - Belts - Loom Co.
BRAVA - Coffee - Nestle Beverage Co.
BRAVA - Flour - Italgrani USA, Inc.
BRAVA - Food products - Festin Foods
BRAVA - Helmets–athletic ☆ - Bell Sports Corp.
BRAVA - Motor vehicles–automobiles - Fiat USA, Inc.
BRAVA - Underwear and nightwear - Maidenform Inc.
BRAVA - Whirlpool bath ☆ - Jacuzzi Inc.
BRAVADA - Floor coverings–carpet and rugs - Philadelphia Carpets
BRAVADA - Motor vehicles–automobiles - General Motors Corp. (Oldsmobile Div.)
BRAVADO - Apparel and accessories ☆ - Bausch & Lomb Inc.
BRAVADO - Boats - Glen-L Marine Designs
BRAVADO - Health care products - Saxony Products Inc.
BRAVADO - Luggage - Andiamo Inc.
BRAVADO - Paper - CST Office Products, Inc.
BRAVADO - Wines - Joseph Victori Wines, Inc.
BRAVAVIR - Pharmaceutical preparation - Bristol-Myers Squibb Co.
BRAVE - Boats–canoes - Black River Canoes
BRAVE - Motor vehicles–motor homes - Winnebago Industries, Inc.
BRAVE - Tools - Chickasaw Handle Co. Inc.
BRAVE EAGLE - Sporting goods - Wright & McGill Co.
BRAVE HEART - Apparel and accessories - Stephen Wayne Companies, Inc.
BRAVE NEW WORLD - Bathing suits - Authentic Fitness Corp.
BRAVE STARR - Footwear ☆ - Mercury International Trading Corp.
BRAVE STARR - Toys - Mattel, Inc.
BRAVE THE COLD - Beverages–malt - Anheuser-Busch Companies Inc.
BRAVESTARR - Games ☆ - Ben Cooper Inc.
BRAVISIMEAU - Floor coverings–carpet and rugs ☆ - Karastan-Bigelow Inc.
BRAVISSIMA - Brassieres (Bras) - Bravissima Inc.
BRAVISSIMO! - Combs - Bravo International Corp.
BRAVISSIMO - Frames–eyeglass - May Optical Co. Inc.
BRAVISSIMO - Pizzas–frozen - Little Lady Foods Inc.
BRAVISSIMO PRIMO - Food products - Gourmet Products Inc.
BRAVO - Aircraft - Mooney Aircraft Corp.
BRAVO - Amplifiers–musical instrument - Peavey Electronics Corp.
BRAVO - Automotive parts and accessories ☆ - Lancaster Colony Automotive Group
BRAVO - Bicycles - Raleigh USA Bicycle Co.
BRAVO - Boats - G-W Invader, Inc.
BRAVO - Boats–motor ☆ - Thunderbird Products
BRAVO - Briefcases - World Network Trading Corp.
BRAVO - Cabinets ☆ - Nutone Inc.
BRAVO - Chairs–wood ☆ - Fixtures Furniture
BRAVO - Cheese - Beta II Marketing Corp.
BRAVO - Coffee - Krinos Foods, Inc.
BRAVO - Corkscrews - Franmara Co. Inc.
BRAVO - Desks ☆ - Haskell of Pittsburgh, Inc.
BRAVO - Doors–garage - Taylor Building Products Co.
BRAVO - Floor coverings–carpet and rugs - Galaxy Carpet Mills Inc.
BRAVO - Floor waxes - S.C. Johnson & Son, Inc.
BRAVO - Food products - Specialty Foods Corp.
BRAVO - Frames–eyeglass - May Optical Co. Inc.
BRAVO - Games ☆ - Little Lady Foods Inc.
BRAVO - Glassware–household - Federal Glass

BRAVO - Golfing equipment - All American Golf Sales, Inc.
BRAVO - Golfing equipment - Besco USA
BRAVO - Machinery - Muller Martini Corp.
BRAVO - Motors - Leeson Electric Corp.
BRAVO - Olives–pickled or brined - Musco Olive Products Inc.
BRAVO! - Orthopedic products - Ortho-Kinetics, Inc.
BRAVO - Pagers - Motorola, Inc. (Land Mobile Products Sector)
BRAVO - Pasta - Borden, Inc.
BRAVO - Pens - Accutec Inc.
BRAVO - Pet products - Eagle Products, Inc.
BRAVO - Printers–computer - Comtec Information Systems, Inc.
BRAVO - Tires - Cheng Shin Rubber USA, Inc.
BRAVO - Toys - Peg Perego USA Inc.
BRAVO - Toys–stuffed - Mary Meyer Corp.
BRAVO - Underwear and nightwear - Maidenform Inc.
BRAVO! - Vacuum cleaners and accessories - The Eureka Co.
BRAVO - Wallpaper - Winfield Design Associates, Inc.
BRAVO - Wallpaper ☆ - Advance Wallcoverings
BRAVO - Wallpaper ☆ - Bill Villetto Designs Inc.
BRAVO! - Yarn - Rainbow Gallery, Inc.
BRAVO III - Wallpaper - Advance Wallcoverings
BRAVO IV - Wallpaper - Advance Wallcoverings
BRAVO B BY D'ROSSANA - Footwear - D'Rossana Associates LLC
BRAVO BABY BOY - Toys - Peg Perego USA Inc.
BRAVO BALLETS - Ballet slippers ☆ - Leo's Dancewear, Inc.
BRAVO BATH - Floor coverings–carpet and rugs ☆ - Concord/Aldon Industries Inc.
BRAVO BOSS - Vacuum cleaners and accessories - The Eureka Co.
BRAVO BROWNS - Footwear - Brown's Shoe Shops Inc.
BRAVO ENCORE! - Radio communications equipment - Motorola, Inc. (Land Mobile Products Sector)
BRAVO FLX - Communications equipment - Motorola, Inc. (Land Mobile Products Sector)
BRAVO GIORGIO - Wallpaper - Lawrence Wallcoverings
BRAVO ONE - Engines–marine - Brunswick Corp.
BRAVO! PLUS - Orthopedic products - Ortho-Kinetics, Inc.
BRAVO POWERLINE - Vacuum cleaners and accessories - The Eureka Co.
BRAVO SERGIO! BY SERGIO ZELCER - Shoes - Spanish Creations Shoe Imports, Inc.
BRAVO SMOKES - Cigarettes ☆ - General Nutrition Inc.
BRAVO ULTREX - Fungicides - ISK Biosciences Corp.
BRAVO VINYLS III - Wallpaper - Advance Wallcoverings
BRAVO WEATHER STIK - Pesticides–agricultural - ISK Biosciences Corp.
BRAVO ZN - Fungicides - ISK Biosciences Corp.
BRAVOBLADE - Skates–roller - Rollerblade, Inc.
BRAVOBLADE GL - Skates–roller - Rollerblade, Inc.
BRAVOBLADE GLX - Skates–roller - Rollerblade, Inc.
BRAVOPRENE - Furniture - Bassick Casters
BRAVOTHANE - Furniture - Bassick Casters
BRAVURA - Books–comic - Malibu Comics Entertainment, Inc.
BRAVURA - Cabinets - Actua
BRAVURA - Cigars - General Cigar Co., Inc.
BRAVURA - Fabrics–broadcloth - Dan River Inc.
BRAVURA - Faucets - Kohler Co.
BRAVURA - Floor coverings ☆ - Congoleum Corp.
BRAVURA DEL SOL - Skin care products ☆ - Hirsch Speidel Inc.
BRAWN - Colognes ☆ - Hunt Products Inc.
BRAWN - Deodorants–personal ☆ - Carter-Wallace, Inc.
BRAWN - Underwear and nightwear - Brawn of California, Inc.
BRAWNY - Fabrics–canvas - Wolsey Co.
BRAWNY - Fabrics–cotton - Cone Mills Corp.
BRAWNY - Paper towels - James River Corp.
BRAWNY - Pillows - Hollander Home Fashions Inc.
BRAWNY BEARS - Candy ☆ - Brock Candy Co. Inc.
BRAWNY BOY - Brushes–paint - Laitner Brush Co.
BRAWNY BUNCH, THE - Frames–eyeglass - Liberty Optical Manufacturing Co.
BRAWNY LAD - Sandwiches–prepackaged - Frisch's Restaurants, Inc.
BRAWNY RIB - Tires - Bandag Licensing Corp.
BRAWNY ULTRA-THIRSTY POCKETS - Paper–toweling - James River Corp.
BRAXMAR - Badges and award medals - C.G. Braxmar Co. Inc.
BRAXTON - Desks - HON Industries Inc.
BRAXTON - Footwear ☆ - Rios of Mercedes Handmade Boots
BRAXTON - Ophthalmic goods - Styl-Rite Optical Manufacturing Co., Inc.
BRAY - Hardware products - Bray International, Inc.
BRAY-CHROMNOX - Heating pads–electric - Chromalox

☆ = Now out of production

BRAYCOT - Cookies - Bewley Irish Imports
BRAYTON INTERNATIONAL COLLECTION - Office furniture–wood - Brayton International
BRAYTONE - Shampoos - Jay Co.
BRAZA - Brassieres (Bras) - Brazabra Corp.
BRAZA'S SECRET - Apparel and accessories - Brazabra Corp.
BRAZE-PAK - Soldering equipment - Controls Corp. of America
BRAZEAU - Sweaters - Edan Products, Inc.
BRAZIER - Fast-food products - International Dairy Queen Inc.
BRAZIL - Wallpaper ✩ - Ralph Delmonte & Associates
BRAZIL NUT - Lipsticks - Cosmair Inc.
BRAZIL TOO - Wallpaper ✩ - Ralph Delmonte & Associates
BRAZILIA - Bird feeds - Handley Corp.
BRAZILIA - Floor coverings - American Floor Products Co. Inc.
BRAZILIA - Yarn - William Unger & Co. Inc.
BRAZILIAN BEAT - Footwear ✩ - E.S. Originals, Inc.
BRAZILIAN BOUQUET - Bathing suits ✩ - Jantzen Inc.
BRAZILIAN BRONZE - Suntan lotions - Brazilian Bronze, Inc.
BRAZILIAN BRONZE - Suntan lotions - Sports Research Corp.
BRAZILLA FIRE - Jewelry - Vargas Manufacturing Co.
BRAZILOID - Recording label - Celluloid Records
BRAZILO'S - Shoes - International Seaway Trading Corp.
BRAZOS - Seafood products–fresh or frozen - Brazos Fisheries Inc.
BRAZOS BEEF - Snack foods - Brazos Country Foods
BRC - Apparel–men's ✩ - Edison Brothers Stores, Inc.
BRC - Recording label - Brunswick Record Corp.
B.R.C. - Skin care products - Shaklee Corp.
BRD - Veterinary product - American Home Products Corp.
BRE-PORE - Rubber–vulcanized - Steve Van, Inc.
BREACOL - Cough medicines - Sterling Winthrop Inc.
BREAD - Frames–eyeglass - Zylo Ware Corp.
BREAD AND BUTTER - Frames–eyeglass - Zylo Ware Corp.
BREAD & BUTTER - Wallpaper - York Wall Coverings Inc.
BREAD APPETITE BREADSTICKS - Breads ✩ - Schmidt Baking Co., Inc.
BREAD BOARD, THE - Computer software - Esoft Inc.
BREAD BOX - Bakeries - American Bakeries Co.
BREAD BOX - Bakery machines - Toastmaster Inc.
BREAD BRAIN - Toasters - Hamilton Beach/Proctor-Silex Inc.
BREAD DOUGH ENHANCER - Breads–mixes - Lora Brody Products, Inc.
BREAD DU JOUR - Bread, breadsticks - Interstate Brands Corp.
BREAD FACTORY PLUS, THE - Cooking equipment–household - Sanyo Fisher (USA) Corp.
BREAD FACTORY, THE - Cooking equipment–household - Sanyo Fisher (USA) Corp.
BREAD KABOB - Breads - K-Bob's USA, Inc.
BREAD KEEPER - Containers - Products Resource Group, LLC
BREAD KNIFE, THE - Cutlery ✩ - Gourmet Center
BREAD MAGIC - Food products - Ener-G Foods Inc.
BREAD 'N BOARD - Cooking equipment–household ✩ - Nordic Ware
BREAD PUDDIN' SQUARES - Bakery products - Sweet Street Desserts, Inc.
BREAD PUDDING 1000 - Publisher's imprints - Continnuus
BREAD READY - Meat products - Hormel Foods Corp.
BREAD WIZARD - Ovens–bakery - Barrie Stefel
BREADMAN - Breads–mixes - Trillium Health Products
BREADMAN TRILLIUM HEALTH PRODUCTS - Bread making machines - Trillium Health Products
BREADMASTER - Housewares - Keyline Enterprise
BREADMATES - Toasters ✩ - Hamilton Beach/Proctor-Silex Inc.
BREADS FOR LIFE - Breads - Cybros Inc.
BREADS INTERNATIONAL - Bakery products - Flowers Industries Inc.
BREADSAVER - Containers–paper - Lynn T. Dickinson
BREADSHOP - Food products - Breadshop's Natural Foods
BREADUCATE YOURSELF - Bagels - Spot Bagel Bakery, Inc.
BREADZZTICKS - Breads - Domino's Pizza Inc.
BREAK A' DAWN - Beverages–carbonated - Brands Central Inc.
BREAK A LEG - Apparel and accessories - Sharon Ann Shelton
BREAK A LEG - Novelty items - Break A Leg USA Inc.
BREAK-A-WAY - Safety cockpit for kayaks and canoes - Phoenix Products Inc.
BREAK-A-WAY - Sporting goods - Reliable Racing Supply Inc.
BREAK-A-WAY HOCKEY CLUB - T-shirts–men's - Paige Alexander Lopez
BREAK ALL BARRIERS - Apparel and accessories - Anheuser-Busch Companies Inc.
BREAK & BAKE - Doughs–frozen - Schwan's Sales Enterprises, Inc.
BREAK AWAY - Exercising equipment - R & D Products Inc.
BREAK-AWAY - Games ✩ - CBS Toys
BREAK-AWAY - Hockey equipment - Regent Sports Corp.

BREAK AWAY - Metals - Maxx Marketing, LLC
BREAK AWAY BASE - Exercising equipment - R & D Products Inc.
BREAK CAKES - Cakes ✩ - Anheuser-Busch Companies Inc.
BREAK FREE - Cleaning preparations - Rothco Inc.
BREAK FREE - Lubricants ✩ - Duracell Co. USA
BREAK-FREE CLP - Lubricants - Break-Free Inc.
BREAK GLASS STOPPER - Alarm systems–fire - Safety Technology International, Inc.
BREAK-N-MEND - Tools - Granberg International
BREAK-N-SPIN - Tools - Granberg International
BREAK NO MORE - Hair care products - All Ways Natural Industries Inc.
BREAK-NO-MORE - Health care products - Nature's Products Inc.
BREAK O DAY - Dishes–china - Taylor, Smith & Taylor Co.
BREAK O' MORN - Eggs - Nabisco Foods Group
BREAK-OUT - Chemical preparations - Rectorseal Corp.
BREAK PAR GOLF - Games ✩ - Warren Industries Inc.
BREAK READY - Meat products–pork - Hormel Foods Corp.
BREAK THE CYCLE - Apparel and accessories - Rodriguez & Associates
BREAK THE GLASS CEILING - Office supplies - Co. of Women Inc.
BREAK THE ICE - Greeting cards - Inside-Out Productions
BREAK-THROUGH - Paints - Vanex Inc.
BREAK THRU - Agricultural products - Goldschmidt Chemical Corp.
BREAK THRU - Drain opener ✩ - Jancyn Manufacturing Corp.
BREAK-THRU - Paint removers - Momentum Graphics
BREAK-THRU - Safety products - Hunter Douglas, Inc.
BREAK-THRU - Slacks–men's ✩ - Rome Manufacturing Co. Inc.
BREAK TIME - Recording label - Creav Inc. USA
BREAK TIME (NATIONAL POOL TOUR) - Video games - Fujisankei Communications International Inc.
BREAK UP - Chocolate candy - Hooper's Chocolates
BREAK-UP - Fabrics - Haas Outdoors, Inc.
BREAKAWAY - Von Duprin, Inc.
BREAKAWAY - Cosmetics - Jean Philippe Fragrances, Inc.
BREAKAWAY - Dairy products - Country Lake Foods Inc.
BREAKAWAY - Floor coverings–carpet and rugs ✩ - Calladium & Marglen
BREAKAWAY - Ophthalmic goods - Foremost Optical Products
BREAKAWAY - Pet products - Zoecon Corp.
BREAKAWAY - Pharmaceutical preparations - Winfield Laboratories, Inc.
BREAKAWAY - Recording label - Pandisc Records
BREAKAWAY - Trading cards and stamps - ANCO Collector Supplies, Inc.
BREAKAWAY - Yogurt - Land O'Lakes Inc.
BREAKAWAY HOCKEY - Games - Avalon Hill Game Co.
BREAKCAKE - Bakery products - Campbell Taggart Inc.
BREAKDANCE - Computer software - Epyx Inc.
BREAKDANCE - Floor coverings–carpet and rugs - Eurotex Inc.
BREAKDOWN - Apparel - Pacific Sunwear of California Inc.
BREAKDOWN - Toys–electronic ✩ - Philips Consumer Electronics Co.
BREAKDOWN SIGNVEST - Automotive parts and accessories - Reflectory
BREAKER 19 - Games ✩ - Milton Bradley Co.
BREAKER, BREAKER - Circuit breakers - Breaker, Breaker
BREAKER LOCK - Locks–padlocks - Toloc Systems, Inc.
BREAKERS - Boats ✩ - Lanness K. McKee & Co.
BREAKERS - Computer software ✩ - Broderbund Software, Inc.
BREAKERS - Flatware - Kirk Stieff Co.
BREAKERS - Floor coverings–carpet and rugs - Masland Corp.
BREAKERS - Furniture ✩ - Bassett Furniture Industries, Inc.
BREAKFASK-ON-THE-GO - Food products - Weight Watchers International, Inc.
BREAKFAST AT WARNER'S - Wallpaper - Warner Co.
BREAKFAST BAR - Food products - Nestle USA
BREAKFAST, BATH, AND BORDERS - Wallpaper - Mokena Mills Inc.
BREAKFAST BITE - Sandwiches–prepackaged - Southland Corp.
BREAKFAST BLEND - Coffee - Equal Exchange Inc.
BREAKFAST BRATS - Sausages - Klement Sausage Co. Inc.
BREAKFAST CLUB - Food products - Publix Super Markets, Inc.
BREAKFAST CLUB - Wallpaper ✩ - Imperial Wallcoverings, Inc.
BREAKFAST CLUB, THE - Broadcasting stations–radio - Evergreen Media Corp. of Detroit
BREAKFAST CROWNS - Bakery products - Flowers Family Bakeries, Inc.
BREAKFAST CUP - Food products ✩ - Casbah/Sahara Natural Foods Inc.
BREAKFAST DELIGHT - Egg substitutes - Papetti's Hygrade Egg Products, Inc.
BREAKFAST EXPRESS - Kitchen appliances - Welbilt Corp.
BREAKFAST FUN - Toys - Tonka Corp.
BREAKFAST GOLD - Juices - Osceola Fruit Distributors

BREAKFAST IN A BISCUIT - Preserved foods–prepackaged ☆ - Continental Mills, Inc.
BREAKFAST IN BED - Coffee ☆ - Bon Melange Inc.
BREAKFAST IN THE COUNTRY - Wallcovering - Fashon Wallcoverings
BREAKFAST LINKS - Food products - Miles Inc.
BREAKFAST OF CHAMPIONS FOR KIDS, THE - Cereal - General Mills, Inc.
BREAKFAST ON THE GO! - Food products - Hudson Foods, Inc.
BREAKFAST ON THE RUN - Cereal - Ralston Purina Co.
BREAKFAST O'S - Cereal - Barbara's Bakery, Inc.
BREAKFAST PACK - Cereal - General Mills, Inc.
BREAKFAST PALS - Meat products - Gorges Foodservice, Inc.
BREAKFAST PIZZA - Pizzas–mixes - C.H.L. Enterprises Inc.
BREAKFAST PRODUCTIONS - Bakery products - Breakfast Productions Inc.
BREAKFAST ROUNDS - Pizzas–frozen - Owens Country Sausage Inc.
BREAKFAST STRIPS - Food products - Conagra, Inc.
BREAKFAST TIME - Fruit drinks–bottled or canned - Green Spot Packaging, Inc.
BREAKFAST TOPPERS - Food products - McSteven's
BREAKFAST TREAT - Pastries - Pet Inc.
BREAKFAST WRAP-UPS - Food products ☆ - General Mills, Inc.
BREAKFAST WRAPS - Sausages - Hinsdale Farms Ltd.
BREAKFAST YOPLAIT - Yogurt - Yoplait USA Inc.
BREAKIN' LOOSE - Apparel–women's - T Juniors Inc.
BREAKING BREAD - Bakery products - Bread Station, Inc.
BREAKING POINT, THE - Hair care products - Biomedic Clinical Care
BREAKING THE FAT BARRIER - Publisher's imprints - Genesis Way, Inc.
BREAKMASTER - Switches–railroad - General Electric Co.
BREAKOUT - Computer software - Passport Software, Inc.
BREAKOUT - Publisher's imprints - National Hockey League
BREAKOUT - Video games - Atari Games Corp.
BREAKPOINT - Apparel and accessories - Oshman's Sporting Goods Inc.
BREAKPOINT - Recording label - Prison Fellowship Ministries, Inc.
BREAKSTONE'S - Dairy products - Kraft Foods, Inc.
BREAKTHROUGH - Beverages - Weider Health and Fitness
BREAKTHROUGH - Eyeglasses - Martin-Copeland Eyewear Corp.
BREAKTHROUGH - Floor coverings–carpet and rugs ☆ - Columbus Mills, Inc.
BREAKTHROUGH - Oils–edible - Harvest States Cooperatives
BREAKTHROUGH - Pet products - Golden Cat Corp.
BREAKTHROUGH - Publisher's imprints - University of Missouri Press
BREAKTHROUGH - Shortening - Ventura Foods
BREAKTHRU - Games ☆ - Avalon Hill Game Co.
BREAKUP - Vitamins and nutritional supplements - Synergy Plus
BREAKUP BEAR - Toys ☆ - Tomy America, Inc.
BREAKWATER BEACON - Bathtubs–enameled - Lyons Industries Inc.
BREAKWATER SEAPORT - Bathtubs–enameled ☆ - Lyons Industries Inc.
BREAKWATER STRETCHER - Fishing nets - Brian M. Owens
BREAM FOR BODY - Skin care products - Paul Mazzotta Inc.
BREAST COMFORT PACK - Infant product - Flents Products Co. Inc.
BREAST-EZE - Health care products - Professional Products, Inc.
BREAST IS BEST - Infant product - Natural Choice Co.
BREAST MARKER I - Medical apparatus - Polymedco, Inc.
BREAST O GOLD - Food products - Land O'Lakes Inc.
BREAST VEST - Pharmaceutical preparations - Exu-Dry Wound Care Products, Inc.
BREASTFEEDING SUPPORT NETWORK, INC. - Containers - Breastfeeding Support Network
BREASTHEALTH - Breast exam kits - Active, Inc.
BREASY-CEILING/WALL MOUNT - Deodorizers - Vaportek, Inc.
BREATH ASURE - Pharmaceutical preparations - Breath Asure, Inc.
BREATH ASURE - Pharmaceutical preparations - Breath Asure, Inc.
BREATH-AWAY - Mouthwashes - Melaleuca, Inc.
BREATH CAMO - Cleaning preparations ☆ - Wellington Leisure Products, Inc.
BREATH CHECK - Vitamins and nutritional supplements - United Vitamin Manufacturing Corp.
BREATH CLEAN - Vitamins and nutritional supplements - Tishcon Corp.
BREATH EX - Health care products ☆ - Marquest Medical Products Inc.
BREATH-EZE - Brassieres (Bras) - Valmont Inc.
BREATH-EZE - Pet products - St. Jon Pet Care Products Inc.
BREATH FRESH - Candy - Nature's Way Products, Inc.
BREATH-GARD - Vitamins and nutritional supplements - Sundance Healthcare Products, Inc.
BREATH MATE - Mouthwashes - Daesuk James Choi
BREATH-O-MINT - Disinfectants - Uncle Sam Chemical Co., Inc.
BREATH-O-PINE - Disinfectants - Brondow Inc.
BREATH OF AUTUMN - Sporting goods - Deer Run Products Inc.
BREATH OF LIFE - Resuscitators - Breath of Life

BREATH OF LIFE - Vitamins and nutritional supplements - Bioenergy Nutrient's Inc.
BREATH OF NATURE - Deodorizers - Fred Smith Adhesives, Inc.
BREATH OF SPRING - Curtains–shower - Showeray Corp.
BREATH OF SPRING - Deodorizers - Penn Champ Inc.
BREATH OF SPRING - Rings–jewelry - Artcarved Inc.
BREATH OF SPRING - Toothbrushes - Venturi, Inc.
BREATH OF SPRING - Wallpaper ☆ - Imperial Wallcoverings, Inc.
BREATH O'SPRING - Fruit and vegetable markets - J.P. Sullivan & Co.
BREATH-PLEASERS - Candy ☆ - American Chicle Co.
BREATH SAVERS - Candy - Planters LifeSavers Co.
BREATH SAVERS - Chewing gum - Nabisco Brands Co.
BREATH-SWEET - Pet products - Addlife Products Co. Inc.
BREATHABLE - Hair-replacement tape - International Hairgoods Inc.
BREATHABLE BAG FOR FRESHNESS - Bags - Fresh Express Inc.
BREATHABLES - Diapers–disposable - Hosposable Products, Inc.
BREATHABLES - Wallcovering - BDH Two, Inc.
BREATHABLES WALLCOVERING - Wallcovering - BDH Two, Inc.
BREATHAMINT - Mouthwashes - Leonard J. Wong
BREATHASURE - Toothpaste - Breath Asure, Inc.
BREATHE-A-SEAL - Containers - Tech-Seal Products, Inc.
BREATHE-AID - Expectorant - Nature's Way Products, Inc.
BREATHE EASY - Brassieres (Bras) - Brazabra Corp.
BREATHE-EASY - Health care products - Physician Engineered Products
BREATHE EASY - Infant product - US Family Products Inc.
BREATHE EASY - Motor vehicles - Consolidated Natural Gas Service Co., Inc.
BREATHE EASY - Pharmaceutical preparations - Traditional Medicinals, Inc.
BREATHE EASY - Vacuum cleaners and accessories - The Hoover Co.
BREATHE EASY SINUS PILLOW - Pillows - Elda Originals International, Inc.
BREATHE FREE - Pharmaceutical preparations - Thompson Medical Co., Inc.
BREATHE FREELY - Health care products - Long Life Herb Classics
BREATHE NOW - Cold remedies - Healthcare Laboratories, Inc.
BREATHE RIGHT - Pharmaceutical preparations - CNS Inc.
BREATHE-TEX - Fabrics - Aldan Rubber Co.
BREATHEASY - Health care products - Pascal Co. Inc.
BREATHEEASY - Health care products - Caring Products International Inc.
BREATHEWEAVE - Fabrics - David Guy Kubowitz
BREATHIN' - Footwear - Wolverine World Wide, Inc.
BREATHING - Gloves - Magla Products Inc.
BREATHING AIR CELL CUSHIN - Footwear - Trans-World Instruments, Inc.
BREATHING BAG - Aquarium accessories - Kordon
BREATHING BAG - Bags–plastic - Novalek, Inc.
BREATHING BRA, THE - Apparel stores–lingerie - Formfit Rogers
BREATHLESS - Calendars - Landmark General Corp.
BREATHLESS - Health care products ☆ - A.H. Robins Co. Inc.
BREATHLESS - Perfumes ☆ - Avon Products, Inc.
BREATHLESS - Toothpaste - Leonard J. Wong
BREATHPAC - Medical apparatus - Save-A-Life Kits Inc.
BREATHROUGH - Paints - Procos Group
BREATHSAVER - Health care products - Vector Products Inc.
BREATHSCAN - Chemical preparations - WNCK, Inc.
BREATHSCAN - Medical apparatus - U.S. Alcohol Testing of America Inc.
BREATHSTICK - Dental equipment - Sidekick Inc.
BREATHWASH - Mouthwashes ☆ - Noxell Corp.
BREAUX ARTS - Photographic equipment - Vincent Lippe Co.
BREAUX BRIDGE, LOUISIANA - Spices and extracts - All Cajun Food Co.
BREBBIA - Pipes–tobacco - Mastercraft Pipes Inc.
BRECK - Hair care products - Dial Corp.
BRECK SALON ESSENTIALS - Hair care products - Dial Corp.
BRECKENRIDGE - Apparel–women's - Leslie Fay Companies Inc.
BRECKENRIDGE - Beverages–malt - Breckenridge Brewery, Inc.
BRECKENRIDGE - Clocks - General Time Corp. (Westclox/Seth Thomas Div.)
BRECKENRIDGE - Floor coverings - Congoleum Corp.
BRECKENRIDGE - Furniture ☆ - Athens Furniture Industries Inc.
BRECKENRIDGE - Wallpaper - Koroseal Wallcoverings
BRECKENRIDGE CELLARS - Wines - Giumarra Vineyards
BRECKENRIDGE FARM - Fruit drinks–bottled or canned - John C. Meier Grape Juice Co.
BRECKENRIDGE FARMS - Fruits–dried - Pace Membership Warehouse, Inc.
BRECKENRIDGE FARMS - Juices - Meier's Wine Cellars Inc.
BRECKENWOOD - Floor coverings–carpet and rugs - Milliken & Co. Inc.
BRECKINRIDGE - Cabinets - Aristokraft, Inc.
BRECKINRIDGE - Furniture ☆ - Bassett Furniture Industries, Inc.
BRECKSET - Hair care products - Dial Corp.
BRECY - Glassware–household - Durand International
BREDE OLD FASHIONED - Horseradish - Brede Inc.

☆ = Now out of production

BREE BUNNY - Toys–stuffed - Dakin Inc.
BREECHER L-8 - Toys - Tonka Corp.
BREED BACK 10 - Veterinary pharmaceutical preparations - Boehringer Ingelheim Animal Health, Inc.
BREED 'N' SHOW - Aquariums–household - Penn-Plax, Inc.
BREEDBACK - Animal feeds - Bluebonnet Milling Co.
BREEDE RIVER VALLEY - Wines - Three Suns, Ltd.
BREEDER'S BLEND - Animal feeds - Milk Specialties Co.
BREEDER'S CHOICE - Pet products - Breeder's Choice Pet Foods, Inc.
BREEDERS CLASSICS - Glassware–household - West Virginia Breeders' Classics, Ltd.
BREEDLITE - Bicycles - Supracor Systems, Inc.
BREEDLOVE GUITAR CO. - Guitars - Breedlove Guitar Co.
BREESE BLUE - Cheese - Dairy Fresh Products Co.
BREETHER - Sporting goods ☆ - Dacon Manufacturing
BREEX - Crocheted and knitted items - Munsingwear, Inc.
BREEZ PROOF - Tablecloths - Straubel Paper Co.
BREEZAIRE - Housewares ☆ - Daily Dryer Co. Inc.
BREEZAIRE - Refrigerators - Breezaire Products Co.
BREEZE - Bicycles - Schwinn Cycling & Fitness Inc.
BREEZE - Cameras - Eastman Kodak Co.
BREEZE - Cheese ☆ - Safeway Stores Inc.
BREEZE - Cigarettes - Brown & Williamson Tobacco Corp.
BREEZE - Computer software - Quintero-Smith, Inc.
BREEZE - Computer software - SourceView Software International
BREEZE - Deodorizers - Airwick Industries
BREEZE - Detergents - Lever Brothers Co. Inc.
BREEZE - Exercising equipment - Pro-Tec Inc.
BREEZE - Motor vehicles–automobiles - Chrysler Corp. (Chrysler-Plymouth Div.)
BREEZE - Pens ☆ - Faber-Castell Corp.
BREEZE - Recording label - Jazz Composer's Orchestra Association Inc.
BREEZE - Trailers–travel ☆ - Hi-Lo Trailer Co. Inc.
BREEZE - Yarn - Brunswick Yarns
BREEZE 2000 - Computer software - Datasource
BREEZE BUSTER - Fishing tackle ☆ - Hypark Specialty Co., Inc.
BREEZE FREE - Vitamins and nutritional supplements - Planetary Formulas
BREEZE-KING - Housewares - Pro Hardware Inc.
BREEZE LOW PROFILE AIR STRIPPER - Water purification systems - Aeromix Systems, Inc.
BREEZE-PORT - Steel products - Kwik-Bilt Inc.
BREEZECORD - Fabrics - Crompton Co. Inc.
BREEZEE MIST - Health care products - Pedinol Pharmacal Inc.
BREEZEMETER - Meteorological instruments - R.A. Simerl (Instrument Div.)
BREEZER - Bicycles - Joe Breeze Cycles, Inc.
BREEZER - Confections - Colombo Inc. (Frozen Desserts Div.)
BREEZER - Health care products - Clairol Inc.
BREEZER - Housewares - Gretchen G. Walberg
BREEZER - Life preservers ☆ - Stearns Manufacturing Co.
BREEZERS - Underwear and nightwear - QVC, Inc.
BREEZETTES - Facial tissues - Clairol Inc.
BREEZEWAY - Awnings - Carefree of Colorado
BREEZEWOOD - Fencing–wood - Machalk Enterprises Inc.
BREEZEWOOD - Manufactured homes - Redman Industries, Inc.
BREEZIA - Flowers, plants, and seeds - Vans, Inc.
BREEZIE - Seafood products–fresh or frozen - Meridian Products
BREEZIES - Toys - Milton Bradley Co.
BREEZIES - Underwear and nightwear - QVC, Inc.
BREEZY - Apparel and accessories - Breton Industries
BREEZY - Petroleum - Allanco
BREEZY - Toys - Tonka Corp.
BREEZY - Wheelchairs - Quickie Designs Inc.
BREEZY BASIC BY QUICKIE - Wheelchairs - Quickie Designs Inc.
BREEZY MORNING - Teas–herbal - Nature's Design Ltd.
BREEZY POINT - Swimming pools - Lomart Industries
BREEZY RIDGE - Musical instruments - Breezy Ridge Instruments
BREEZY SINGERS - Bird cages - Takara USA Corp.
BREEZY SURFKILTS - Apparel and accessories - Breezy Surfkilts
BREEZY Z - Wheelchairs - Quickie Designs Inc.
BREIER OF AMSTERDAM - Apparel and accessories - Breier of Amsterdam Inc.
BREITENBACH - Wines - Breitenbach Wine Cellars
BREKOO - Musical instruments - Ardsley Musical Instrument Co.
BRELL-A-PLEX - Paints - Cowman-Campbell Paint Co.
BRELLA - Motor vehicle parts and accessories ☆ - Prince Lionheart, Inc.
BRELLA-SLING - Apparel and accessories - Brollys in Bondage Co., Ltd.

BREMA - See TONON
BREMA - Seafood products–fresh or frozen - C. & J. Willenborg Inc.
BREMEN - Glassware–household ☆ - Anchor Hocking Glass, Inc.
BREMNER - Snack foods - Bremner Inc.
BREMO PRESS - Publisher's imprints - Gerald C. Hammon
BREMSHEY - Casual furniture ☆ - International Products Trading Inc.
BREMSHEY SPORT - Sporting goods ☆ - International Products Trading Inc.
BREMWORTH - Floor coverings ☆ - Bellbridge Carpets
BRENARD - Clocks - Ridgeway Clock Co.
BRENATONE - Pharmaceutical preparations ☆ - C.O. Truxton Inc.
BRENDA - Frames–eyeglass - Rozin Optical Export Corp.
BRENDA - Ophthalmic goods - Vista Optical Corp.
BRENDA - Shampoos ☆ - Hunt Products Inc.
BRENDA STARR'S YELLOW ROOT TEA - Water–mineral - Brenda Trivett
BRENDA THOMAS' ONCE UPON A RHYME - Music boxes - Brenda Thomas Studio Inc.
BRENDENBURY - Floor coverings - Congoleum Corp.
BRENEMAN - Window shades - Kirsch Co.
BRENET - Watches ☆ - Meylan Corp.
BRENNA LOUISE - Hosiery - Clovermere Sales Corp.
BRENNAN'S - Coffee ☆ - Brennan's Restaurant
BRENNAN'S - Seasonings ☆ - McCormick & Co., Inc.
BRENNAN'S MARDI GRAS - Dairy products - Brennan's Restaurant
BRENNAN'S OF NEW ORLEANS - Food products ☆ - McCormick & Co., Inc.
BRENO - Watches ☆ - Meylan Corp.
BRENT - Bedding–linen - Dan River Inc.
BRENT - Pottery products - American Art Clay Co. Inc.
BRENT - Socks - Montgomery Ward & Co. Inc.
BRENT N SAMS - Cookies - Fancy Foods of Virginia Inc.
BRENTHAVEN - Bags–duffel - Fairhaven Group, Inc.
BRENTON - Floor coverings–carpet and rugs - Atlas Carpet Mills Inc.
BRENTON REEF - Apparel and accessories ☆ - North By Northeast
BRENTON SUPREME - Floor coverings–carpet and rugs - Atlas Carpet Mills Inc.
BRENTON WOOD - Compact discs–prerecorded - Original Sound Record Co. Inc.
BRENTWOOD - Apparel and accessories - Smith & Weber Co.
BRENTWOOD - Barometers ☆ - Airguide Instrument Co.
BRENTWOOD - Bicycles ☆ - Murray, Inc.
BRENTWOOD - Cabinets - Aristokraft, Inc.
BRENTWOOD - Cabinets - Dewils Industries Inc.
BRENTWOOD - Cabinets ☆ - American Woodmark Corp.
BRENTWOOD - Chests–wood - Service Merchandise Co. Inc.
BRENTWOOD - Cigarettes - R.J. Reynolds Tobacco Co.
BRENTWOOD - Clocks - General Time Corp. (Westclox/Seth Thomas Div.)
BRENTWOOD - Door frames - Canyon Creek Cabinet Co.
BRENTWOOD - Drapery hardware - Kirsch Co.
BRENTWOOD - Electrical equipment - Blusound Electronics, Inc.
BRENTWOOD - Floor coverings - Congoleum Corp.
BRENTWOOD - Floor coverings–carpet and rugs - Dorsett Carpet Mills Inc.
BRENTWOOD - Floor coverings–carpet and rugs - Glen Eden Wool Carpets
BRENTWOOD - Floor coverings–carpet and rugs - Richmond Carpet Mills
BRENTWOOD - Floor coverings–carpet and rugs ☆ - Downs Carpet Co. Inc.
BRENTWOOD - Glassware–household - May Department Stores Co.
BRENTWOOD - Housewares - Brown Stove Works Inc.
BRENTWOOD - Medical apparatus ☆ - Lumex, Inc.
BRENTWOOD - Shutters–wood - Ohline Corp.
BRENTWOOD - Siding - Aluminum Co. of America
BRENTWOOD - Tableware–china ☆ - Lenox, Inc.
BRENTWOOD ARCH - Door frames - Canyon Creek Cabinet Co.
BRENTWOOD HILL - Floor coverings–carpet and rugs - Karastan-Bigelow Inc.
BRENTWOOD JAZZ - Recording label - Brentwood Music, Inc.
BRENTWOOD KIDS COMPANY - Recording label - Brentwood Music, Inc.
BRENTWOOD MUSIC - Recording label ☆ - Brentwood Music, Inc.
BRENTWORTH PLAID - Bedding–linen - Dan River Inc.
BREONESIN - Pharmaceutical preparations - Sterling Winthrop Inc.
BRER RABBIT - Molasses - Nabisco Foods Group
BRESCIA - Cosmetics - Brescia Hair Salon
BRESCIA - Floor coverings–carpet and rugs - Cabin Crafts Carpets
BRESLER'S - Ice cream - Bresler's Industries Inc.
BRESSANT - Hair care products - William Marvy Co., Inc.
BRESSE BLEU - Cheese - Bresse Bleu Inc.
BREST DU JOUR - Meat products–poultry - Hester Industries, Inc.
BREST FORM - Prosthetic apparatus - Atco Truelife International
BREST-MIGNON - Meat products–poultry - Pierce Foods Corp.
BREST-NUGGETS - Meat products–poultry - Pierce Foods Corp.

☆ = Now out of production

BREST O'TURK'Y - Meat products–poultry ☆ - Pierce Foods Corp.
BREST-PARMESAN - Meat products–poultry - Pierce Foods Corp.
BREST-SUPREMES - Meat products–poultry - Pierce Foods Corp.
BREST TENDER - Meat products–poultry - Pierce Foods Corp.
BREST TREASURES - Meat products–poultry - Hester Industries, Inc.
BRESTARS - Meat products–poultry - Hester Industries, Inc.
BRESTEAK - Food products - Pierce Foods Corp.
BRESTIX - Meat products–poultry - Pierce Foods Corp.
BRESTSTRIPS - Meat products–poultry - Pierce Foods Corp.
BRETAGNE - Frames–picture - Terragrafics Inc.
BRETFORD - Furniture - Bretford Manufacturing, Inc.
BRETHAIRE - Pharmaceutical preparations - Ciba-Geigy Corp.
BRETHINE - Pharmaceutical preparations - Ciba-Geigy Corp.
BRETHREN PRESS - Video production - Church of the Brethren General
   Board
BRETLIN - Floor coverings–carpet and rugs - Carriage Industries, Inc.
BRETON - Bedding–linen - Dan River Inc.
BRETON - Floor coverings ☆ - Bruce Hardwood Floors
BRETON - Frames–eyeglass - Hudson Optical Corp.
BRETONNE - Furniture ☆ - Bassett Furniture Industries, Inc.
BRETON'S HAND & SEAL - Whiskey - Heublein, Inc.
BRETT - Ophthalmic goods ☆ - Luxottica
BRETT ALIXANDER - Apparel and accessories - Jamie Brooke Inc.
BRETT COLLECTION, THE - Greeting cards - Brett-Forer Greetings Inc.
BRETT FORER - Greeting cards - Royal Stationery Co.
BRETT GALLERIA - Greeting cards - Brett-Forer Greetings Inc.
BRETTANY PROFESSIONAL - Hair care products - Brettany Professional
   Beauty Corp.
BRETTLINE - Electronic equipment - Brett Aqualine Inc.
BRETUIL - Glassware–household - Durand International
BREUER/TORNADO - Battery chargers - Breuer Electric Manufacturing Co.
BREUER TORNADO - Battery chargers - Breuer/Tornado Corp.
BREUKELEU ABBEY - Beverages–alcohol - Brooklyn Brewery Ltd.
BREVA 100'S - Cigars - F.D. Grave & Son, Inc.
BREVA A LA CONSERVA - Cigars - Faber, Coe & Gregg Inc.
BREVAS - Cigar boxes–wood - Consolidated Cigar Corp.
BREVAS FINAS - Cigars - Faber, Coe & Gregg Inc.
BREVE - Handbags - Pacific Connections of California, Inc.
BREVEL - Motors–automotive - Howard Industries Inc.
BREVERRA - Infant product - Century Products Co.
BREVI-KATH - Catheters - Medical Evaluation Devices & Instruments Corp.
BREVICON - Pharmaceutical preparations - Syntex USA, Inc.
BREVIS - Computer software - Ai Data, Inc.
BREVITAL - Pharmaceutical preparations - Jones Medical Industries, Inc.
   (Medical Div.)
BREVITAL SODIUM - Pharmaceutical preparations - Eli Lilly and Co.
BREVITIES - Apparel and accessories - Strouse, Adler Co.
BREVITY - Frames–eyeglass - Liberty Optical Manufacturing Co.
BREVOXYL -4 GEL - Skin care products - Stiefel Laboratories, Inc.
BREVOXYL -5 GEL - Skin care products - Stiefel Laboratories, Inc.
BREVOXYL CLEANSING LOTION - Skin care products - Stiefel Laboratories,
   Inc.
BREW 66 - Beverages–malt - Rainier Brewing Co.
BREW 102 - Beverages–malt - S & P Co.
BREW FOR TWO - Coffee makers–electric - Hamilton Beach/Proctor-Silex Inc.
BREW HAHA! - Coffee - Brew-Haha! Inc.
BREW 'N SERV QUIK DRIP - Coffee makers–electric ☆ - West Bend Co.
BREW 'N SERVE - Coffee makers–electric ☆ - West Bend Co.
BREW RITE - Paper - Rockline Industries Inc.
BREW SAV'R - Coffee makers–electric ☆ - Sunbeam-Oster Household
   Products
BREW STARTER - Coffee makers–electric ☆ - Black & Decker Corp.
BREW-THRU - Coffee - Royal House Food Products Co.
BREW-THRU - Coffee makers–electric ☆ - Black & Decker Corp.
BREWBAR - Housewares - Santa Cruz Coffee Roasting Co.
BREWCELLAR, THE - Machinery - Piedmont Brewing Co.
BREWCO - Machinery - Nu-Tech Industries, Inc.
BREWED AWAKENINGS - Coffee - Todd Alan Gunderson
BREWED IN VERMONT LONG TRAIL - Beverages–malt - Long Trail Brewing
   Co.
BREWED WITH AN ATTITUDE - Apparel and accessories - Gambrinus Co.
BREWER - Boats–canoes - Fort Myers Yacht & Shipbuilding Inc.
BREWER - Cereal ☆ - Mr. Z's Fund Raising Corp.
BREWER COTE - Building materials - Brewer Co.
BREWER-TITCHENER - Tackle blocks, forged fittings ☆ - Cooper Industries,
   Inc.

BREWER'S - Pet products ☆ - BenePet Pet Care Products
BREWERS BONES - Animal feeds - Brewers Bones
BREWER'S BREA - Breads ☆ - Melaleuca, Inc.
BREWER'S CAVE - Beverages–malt - Minnesota Brewing Co.
BREWERS CHOICE - Coffee - Four-O-Coffee Co.
BREWERS' CHOICE - Coffee makers–electric - Salton/Maxim Housewares,
   Inc.
BREWERS GOLD PREMIUM - Beverages–alcohol ☆ - Falstaff Brewing Corp.
BREWERS PRIDE - Beverages–malt - Dover Vineyards Inc.
BREWERS YEAST SPECIALISTS - Pet products - Brewers Yeast Specialist
.BREWERY FRESH TASTE. GUARANTEED - Beverages–alcohol - Anheuser-
   Busch Companies Inc.
BREWERY HILL - Beverages–malt - Lion Brewery, Inc.
BREWERY HILL BLACK & TAN - Beverages–malt - Lion Brewery, Inc.
BREWERY HILL CENTENNIAL LAGER - Beverages–malt - Lion Brewery,
   Inc.
BREWERY HILL HONEY AMBER ALE - Beverages–malt - Lion Brewery, Inc.
BREWERY HILL PALE ALE - Beverages–malt - Lion Brewery, Inc.
BREWERY HILL RASPBERRY RED ALE - Beverages–malt - Lion Brewery,
   Inc.
BREWHOUND - Apparel and accessories - Madlock Corp.
BREWMASTER - Coffee makers–electric - Robert Krups North America
BREWMASTER JR. - Coffee makers–electric ☆ - Robert Krups North America
BREWMASTER T4 - Housewares ☆ - Robert Krups North America
BREWMASTER'S BOTTLE OPENER - Bottle openers - Franmara Co. Inc.
BREWMATE - Filters–water - Robert Lehrer Associates, Inc.
BREWMATES - Coffee makers–electric - Mr. Coffee, Inc.
BREW'N GO - Coffee makers–electric - Black & Decker Corp.
BREWRON - Pharmaceutical preparations ☆ - C.O. Truxton Inc.
BREWS BROTHERS, THE - Housewares - David Windt
BREWS FAST - Teas - Southern Tea Co.
BREWS IN YOUR FRIDGE - Teas - Celestial Seasonings, Inc.
BREWSKI PUB CLASSIC - Beverages–malt - Brewski Brewing Co.
BREWSKI PUB LIGHT - Beverages–malt - Brewski Brewing Co.
BREWSTER - Cheese - Brewster Dairy Inc.
BREWSTER - Clocks ☆ - Toastmaster Inc.
BREWSTER - Lenses–optical - Ditto Industries Inc.
BREWSTER - Shoes - Allen-Edmonds Shoe Corp.
BREWSTER - Vitamins and nutritional supplements - Test Laboratories Inc.
   (Brewster Foods Div.)
BREWSTER - Wallpaper ☆ - Budeke's Paint
BREWSTER BACKGROUNDS II - Wallpaper ☆ - Brewster Wallcovering Co.
BREWSTER BASICS II - Wallpaper ☆ - Brewster Wallcovering Co.
BREWSTER DAIRY - Milk - Brewster Dairy Inc.
BREWSTER HALL - Furniture - Harden Furniture Co. Inc.
BREWSTER ROOSTER - Toys–stuffed - Russ Berrie and Co., Inc.
BREWSTER VILLAGE - Furniture ☆ - Mersman Furniture Co.
BREWSTER'S - Coffee - Rair Systems, Inc.
BREWSTER'S COLORFUL INVENTION - Kaleidoscopes - Gemini
   Kaleidoscopes
BREXIN - Pharmaceutical preparations ☆ - Savage Laboratories Inc.
BREXIN L.A. - Pharmaceutical preparations - Savage Laboratories Inc.
BREYER - Toys - Reeves International, Inc.
BREYER ANIMAL CREATIONS - Toys–models - Reeves International, Inc.
BREYERS - Ice cream - Kraft Foods, Inc.
BREZZI - Food products - De Choix Specialty Foods Co.
BRG BROOKLYN - Apparel and accessories - Negro Leagues Baseball
   Museum, Inc.
BRI-LAC - Shellac - Briner Paint Manufacturing Co. Inc.
BRI SABOTED SLUG - Ammunition - Olin Corp. (Winchester Div.)
BRI-TEX - Spices and extracts ☆ - Cumberland-Swan, Inc.
BRI-TOP - Paints - Mar-Hyde Corp.
BRIAN - Frames–eyeglass ☆ - U.S. Optical Frame Co.
BRIAN - Toys - Tonka Corp.
BRIAN BAKER'S DEJA VU COLLECTION - Plaster–wallboard - Michael's
   Limited
BRIAN BEAR - Toys–stuffed - Dakin Inc.
BRIAN BROTHERS - Apparel and accessories - Brian Brothers, Inc.
BRIAN JARVI - Posters - Stanton & Lee
BRIAN MACNEIL - Apparel stores–sports - Gillman Knitwear Co.
BRIAN MAY - Guitars - Dimarzio, Inc.
BRIANA - Apparel–women's - Jonathan Logan Inc.
BRIANCON - Glassware–household - Durand International
BRIANNA - Toys - Tonka Corp.
BRIANNAS - Salad dressings–bottled - Del Sol Food Co. Inc.
BRIANNI'S - Salad dressings–bottled - Castle Food Products

☆ = Now out of production

BRIAR - Apparel and accessories - Briar Inc.
BRIAR - Apparel–men's - Hartmarx Corp.
BRIAR - Bedding–linen - Dan River Inc.
BRIAR - Flatware - Trend Pacific Inc.
BRIAR - Hosiery ☆ - Randa Corp.
BRIAR - Recording label ☆ - Sierra Records, Books & Home Video
BRIAR BOOKS - Publisher's imprint, now out of print - Scarborough House Publishing
BRIAR CLUB - Apparel and accessories - Breier of Amsterdam Inc.
BRIAR CREEK - Apparel and accessories ☆ - Lady Ester Lingerie Corp.
BRIAR CREEK NATURAL - Tobacco–chewing or smoking - 1776 Tobacco Co.
BRIAR-CUT - Hardware - Alside Div.
BRIAR-CUT SUPREME - Hardware - Alside Div.
BRIAR EDGE - Shovels - True Temper Hardware Co.
BRIARBROOK - Pencils - Gardner Rubber Stamp Co.
BRIARCLIFF - Cabinets ☆ - Aristokraft, Inc.
BRIARCLIFF - Floor coverings - Mannington Resilient Floors
BRIARCLIFF - Floor coverings–carpet and rugs - Collins & Aikman Corp.
BRIARCLIFF - Floor coverings–carpet and rugs - Patrick Carpet Mills
BRIARCLIFF - Floor coverings–carpet and rugs ☆ - Richmond Carpet Mills
BRIARCLIFF - Furniture - Bassett Furniture Industries, Inc.
BRIARCLIFF - Hardware ☆ - Masonite Corp.
BRIARCLIFF - Rings–jewelry ☆ - Artcarved Inc.
BRIARCLIFF INN - Wallpaper ☆ - Westchester Prints
BRIARCREST - Floor coverings–carpet and rugs - Evans-Black Carpet Mills
BRIARCREST - Mattresses - National Bedding & Furniture Industries Inc.
BRIARCREST - Wines - Clos du Bois Wines
BRIARE - Ceramic tile - Integrity Tile Co.
BRIARGATE - Food products - Aldi Inc.
BRIARGLASS - Shingles - Atlas Roofing Corp.
BRIARHILL - Cabinets ☆ - Medallion Kitchens of Minnesota Inc.
BRIARHURST - Floor coverings–carpet and rugs - Roxbury Carpet Co.
BRIARHURST PLACE - Floor coverings–carpet and rugs - Roxbury Carpet Co.
BRIARHURST SQUARE - Floor coverings–carpet and rugs - Roxbury Carpet Co.
BRIARLEE - Pipes–tobacco - Bradberry Briar Pipe Corp.
BRIARLEY - Floor coverings–carpet and rugs ☆ - Kelly Group Inc.
BRIARLEY PLUS - Floor coverings–carpet and rugs ☆ - Kelly Group Inc.
BRIARPATCH BUNNY - Candy ☆ - R.M. Palmer Co.
BRIAR'S ROOT BEER - Beverages–carbonated - Briar's USA Inc.
BRIAR'S SIX GUN - Soft drinks - Briar's USA Inc.
BRIARTONE - Frames–eyeglass ☆ - Universal/Univis Inc.
BRIARWOOD - Cabinets ☆ - Medallion Kitchens of Minnesota Inc.
BRIARWOOD - Cabinets ☆ - Yorktowne Inc.
BRIARWOOD - Desks - Orna-Metal Inc.
BRIARWOOD - Drapery hardware - Kirsch Co.
BRIARWOOD - Floor coverings - Tarkett, Inc.
BRIARWOOD - Floor coverings–carpet and rugs - Cabin Crafts Carpets
BRIARWOOD - Floor coverings–carpet and rugs - Collins & Aikman Corp.
BRIARWOOD - Frames–eyeglass ☆ - Universal/Univis Inc.
BRIARWOOD - Furniture ☆ - Lane Co. Inc.
BRIARWOOD - Leather goods ☆ - AR Accessories Group Inc.
BRIARWOOD - Rings–jewelry - Artcarved Inc.
BRIARWOOD - Shingles - Atlas Roofing Corp.
BRIARWOOD - Trailers–travel - Fleetwood Enterprises, Inc.
BRIARWOOD - Wines - Fenn Valley Vineyards
BRIARWOOD CASTLE - Games ☆ - Mayfair Games, Inc.
BRIARWOOD MANOR - House furnishings ☆ - Florida Furniture Industries Inc.
BRIC-BOND - Mortars–clay ☆ - Master Builders Inc.
BRIC-V-NEER - Bricks ☆ - Frederic Co. Inc.
BRICE'S - Yogurt–frozen - Brice Foods, Inc.
BRICK - Amplifiers–musical instrument - Video Accessory Corp.
BRICK 1 - Recording label - Slep-Tone Entertainment Corp.
BRICK BATH - Paints - Goldblatt Tool Co.
BRICK BOND - Cement - Riverton Corp.
BRICK BY BRICK - Puzzles - Binary Arts Corp.
BRICK CITY - Recording label - Brick City Records
BRICK HOUSE SPRING WATER - Water–bottled or canned - Brick House Farm Water Co.
BRICK/MASTER - Floor coverings - Wonderbrix Inc. (Brick/Master Div.)
BRICK-MIX - Cement - Riverton Corp.
BRICK-O-LATOR - Fireplace-heat converter ☆ - Boren Clay Products
BRICK OVEN - Food products - Weight Watchers International, Inc.
BRICK OVEN - Meats–luncheon - Farmland Foods, Inc.

BRICK-PACK CLIP - Beverage dispensing equipment - Tops Manufacturing Co. Inc.
BRICK-STICK - Mortars–clay ☆ - Applied Texture Inc.
BRICK, THE - Novelty items - Koplow Games
BRICKER MEGA POWER BAR - Pharmaceutical preparations - Bricker Laboratories
BRICKETTE - Floor coverings ☆ - Congoleum Corp.
BRICKETTE - Tiles–ceramic ☆ - Huntington/Pacific Ceramics Inc.
BRICKETTES - Bricks - Modern Methods Inc.
BRICKHEAD - Glassware–household - Brickhead Accessories, Llc.
BRICKOVEN - Dinnerware–glass - Tienshan, Inc.
BRICKSTOP - Bricks - BrickStop Corp. USA
BRICKTOWN BREWERY - Apparel and accessories - Bricktown Brewery
BRICKTOWN BREWERY, RESTAURANT, BILLIARDS & DIVERSIONS - Shirts - Bricktown Brewery
BRICKWALK - Floor coverings - Mannington Resilient Floors
BRICKYARD - Games - Mayfair Games, Inc.
BRICKYARD - Indoor-outdoor turf - Instant Turf Industries Inc.
BRICKYARD BLDG. BRICKS - Toys - Nickel Industries, Inc.
BRICKYARD SUPPLY - Toy bricks - James Industries, Inc.
BRICOUT - Wines - Buena Vista Winery, Inc.
BRICOVER - Bricks - Plastonics Inc.
BRID-A-LINE - Novelty items - A.F. Grenci Co. Inc.
BRIDAL - Food products - Comly-Flanigen Co. Inc.
BRIDAL & BOUDOIR - Wedding gowns ☆ - Floragraphics
BRIDAL BELLE'S - Hosiery - Crystal Creations
BRIDAL BLUSH - Roses - DeVor Nurseries Inc.
BRIDAL BOUQUET - Dinnerware–glass - Salem China Co.
BRIDAL BOUQUET - Dishes–china - Viletta China Co.
BRIDAL BOUQUET - Glassware–household ☆ - Lotus Glass Co.
BRIDAL ELEGANCE - Patterns–clothing - Fabric Fancies
BRIDAL GALLERY - Jewelry - Roman Co.
BRIDAL HEATHER - Novelty items–paper - Bloomin' Roses
BRIDAL JUST IN CASE - Bags–cosmetic - Renee Ambrose
BRIDAL LAVENDER - Novelty items - Bloomin' Roses
BRIDAL ORGANIZER, THE - Calendars - Pamela Cody Baer
BRIDAL ORIGINALS - Wedding gowns - Bridal Originals Inc.
BRIDAL PARTY - Dolls - Justin Products, Inc.
BRIDAL ROSE - Dinnerware–glass ☆ - Royal China & Porcelain Companies Inc.
BRIDAL STAR - Napkins–paper - Erving Paper Products Inc.
BRIDAL SUITE - Dolls ☆ - Effanbee Doll Corp.
BRIDAL TIARA - Glassware–household - Seneca Glass Co.
BRIDALETTE - Cash boxes - Lady Marlene
BRIDALLURE - Wedding gowns - Alfred Angelo Inc.
BRIDALVEIL ALE - Beverages–malt - Butterfield Brewing Co.
BRIDALWOOD - Wallpaper - Exeter Wallcoverings
BRIDE - Watches - Gruen Marketing Corp.
BRIDE & GROOM - Glassware–household - Rezler & Howell Co.
BRIDE & GROOM - Stationery - Taylor Corp.
BRIDE AND GROOM COLLECTION, THE - Jewelry - Sandberg & Sikorski Diamond Corp.
BRIDE HAS WHISPERED - Giftware - Bride Has Whispered Services
BRIDE'S - Audio tapes–blank - Advance Magazine Publishers Inc.
BRIDE'S CHOICE - Hobby kits - Stanislaus Imports, Inc.
BRIDE'S CHOICE - Invitations - Classic Thermographers Ltd.
BRIDE'S CHOICE, THE - Novelty items ☆ - Hortense B. Hewitt Inc.
BRIDE'S DELIGHT - Food products ☆ - Taormina Co.
BRIDE'S MATE - Wedding-planning computer software - KRP Inc.
BRIDES TIME - Publisher's imprints - Scott Publishing Co.
BRIDESBURG - Paints ☆ - Impervious Paint Industries Ltd.
BRIDESHEAD - Floor coverings–carpet and rugs - Daltonian Carpet & Cushion Inc.
BRIDESMAID, THE - Jewelry - Something Old, Something New, Inc.
BRIDESMAIDS BY PRISCILLA - Wedding gowns - Priscilla of Boston Inc.
BRIDESMART - Wedding gowns - Al's Formal Wear of Houston, Inc.
BRIDGE - Computer software - Vertex Industries Inc.
BRIDGE - Fertilizers and plant foods - Harmony Products, Inc.
BRIDGE - Medical apparatus - Wright Medical Technology, Inc.
BRIDGE - Recording label - Koch International
BRIDGE BLASTER - Toys–automobiles - Mattel, Inc.
BRIDGE BUDDY - Fishing tackle - Tuzee Associates, Inc.
BRIDGE BUILDER - Computer software - Bridge Builder Technologies, Inc.
BRIDGE CLUB - Giftware - Classic Cards and Games
BRIDGE-COR - Construction equipment - Contech Construction Products Inc.
BRIDGE FOR 4 - Games - Cardinal Inc.

☆ = Now out of production

BRIDGE FOR FRIENDS - Games - Cardinal Inc.
BRIDGE FOR JUNIORS - Games ✩ - Milton Bradley Co.
BRIDGE-JACK - Musical instrument accessories - M & M Distributing Co.
BRIDGE MASTER - Computer software - Capstone Software
BRIDGE MASTER - Windows–plastic - Denbarr Corp.
BRIDGE MIX - Paving materials–concrete - Sealwall Products Inc.
BRIDGE/MONITOR - Computer software - Bridge Technology Inc.
BRIDGE NET - See **RUN TIME**
BRIDGE-O-LITE - Lighting fixtures - RDM Sales
BRIDGE OF COMFORT - Footwear - Wolverine World Wide, Inc.
BRIDGE TENDER, THE - Games - George F. Scott
BRIDGE TIPS - Tablecloths ✩ - Bob Stone
BRIDGEAID - Dental compounds - Floss Aid Corp.
BRIDGEBUOY - Life preservers - Datrex Inc.
BRIDGEFORD - Furniture–upholstered ✩ - Henredon Furniture Industries Inc.
BRIDGEHAMPTON - Shower rods - Sufolla Industries Inc.
BRIDGEHAMPTON WINERY - Wines - Bridgehampton Winery Inc.
BRIDGEKOTE - Paints - Triangle Coatings Inc.
BRIDGEMOBILE - Racks - Jarke Corp.
BRIDGEPORT - Apparel and accessories ✩ - Morris Apparel Inc.
BRIDGEPORT - Automotive parts and accessories - Robertshaw Controls Co.
BRIDGEPORT - Beverages–alcohol - Bridgeport Brewing Co.
BRIDGEPORT - Cabinets - American Woodmark Corp.
BRIDGEPORT - Cabinets - Aristokraft, Inc.
BRIDGEPORT - Cabinets - Dewils Industries Inc.
BRIDGEPORT - Cabinets ✩ - Decora
BRIDGEPORT - Ceramic floor tile - Interceramic Inc.
BRIDGEPORT - Compressors–air - Bridge Products, Inc.
BRIDGEPORT - Eyeglasses - Eddie Bauer Inc.
BRIDGEPORT - Floor coverings–carpet and rugs ✩ - Catalina Carpet Mills
 Inc.
BRIDGEPORT - Furniture ✩ - Bassett Furniture Industries, Inc.
BRIDGEPORT - Wainscotting - Georgia-Pacific Corp.
BRIDGEPORT BLUE HERON - Draft ale - Bridgeport Brewing Co.
BRIDGEPORT II - Floor coverings–carpet and rugs ✩ - Royalweve Carpet
 Mills
BRIDGES - Perfumes ✩ - Tsumura International Inc.
BRIDGES IN MATHEMATICS - Textbooks - Math Learning Center
BRIDGES, SMITH - Paints - Bridges Smith & Co.
BRIDGES, THE - Real estate agencies - Bridges Owners Association, Inc.
BRIDGESONG MEDIA - Recording label - Bridgesong Media
BRIDGESTONE - Tires - Bridgestone/Firestone, Inc.
BRIDGESTONE-KABUKI - Sporting goods - C. Itoh & Co. America Inc.
BRIDGET - Calendars ✩ - American Publishing Co.
BRIDGETEK - Concrete products - Bridge Technologies, Ltd.
BRIDGETON - Shoes - Allen-Edmonds Shoe Corp.
BRIDGETTE - Games - Mayfair Games, Inc.
BRIDGEVIEW - Wines - Bridgeview Vineyards, Inc.
BRIDGEWATER - Furniture ✩ - Hickory Chair Co.
BRIDGEWATER - Paints ✩ - Empire State Varnish Co.
BRIDGEWATER BOOKS - Publisher's imprints - Troll Associates, Inc.
BRIDGEWOOD - Grinders - Wilke Machinery Co.
BRIDGEWOOD - Trailers–travel - Fleetwood Enterprises, Inc.
BRIDGEWORKS - Computer software - Solid Concepts, Inc.
BRIDGEWORKS SPEEDI - Computer software - Jesness Consulting Ltd., Inc.
BRIDGFORD - Food products - Bridgford Foods Corp.
BRIDGFORD FAST'N EASY - Breads - Bridgford Foods Corp.
BRIDGING THE GAP - Video production - Bridging the Gap
BRIDGING THE TECHNOLOGY GAP - Computer software - XDB Systems,
 Inc.
BRIDGIT - Computer program - Unelko Corp.
BRIDGIT - Toys–erector sets - Jolly U.S.A., Inc.
BRIDLE-HYDE - Travel accessories - American Guard-It Manufacturing Co. Inc.
BRIDLE TAN - Leather goods - Lefkowitz and Santangelo Co.
BRIDLEPATH - Wallpaper ✩ - Newmarket Designs Ltd.
BRIDLES 'N BOWS - Hair care products - Animal Lovers Pet Centre, Inc.
BRIDON CORDAGE - Twine - Bridon Cordage LLC
BRIE COUPIL - Food products - Crystal Food Import Corp.
BRIE ROYALE - Cheese - Bc-USA, Inc.
BRIEF - Bathing suits - Ocean Pool Co.
BRIEF ENCOUNTER - Floor coverings–carpet and rugs - Monticello Carpet
 Mills
BRIEF ENCOUNTER - Greeting cards ✩ - Gallant Greetings Corp.
BRIEF ENCOUNTER - Underwear and nightwear - Maidenform Inc.
BRIEF HOLDER - Office supplies ✩ - JM Co.
BRIEF-NITER - Luggage ✩ - Korchmar Case Co.

BRIEF-PAC - Luggage - Airway Industries, Inc.
BRIEF-PAK - Paper–thermoplastics coated - Champion International Corp.
BRIEF-RITE - Briefcases ✩ - Korchmar Case Co.
BRIEFCASE BUDDIES - Puzzles ✩ - International Playthings Inc.
BRIEFER WITH A BRAIN, THE - Apparel and accessories - Strouse, Adler Co.
BRIEFIES - Apparel–women's ✩ - Bali Co. Inc.
BRIEFLING - Underwear and nightwear - Maidenform Inc.
BRIEFOLIO - Binders - Colad Group Inc.
BRIEFTAPES - Recording label - American Cyanamid Co.
BRIEFX - Apparel–women's - Nuvogue Creations
BRIER ROSE - Floor coverings–carpet and rugs - Rugby Rugs Inc.
BRIER ROSE - Labels–gummed - Victorian Papers
BRIERCROFT - Statuary–wood - Briercroft, Inc.
BRIESE - Electronic equipment - Leedal Inc.
BRIESE GLACE - Hair care products - Peter Hantz Co.
BRIFF - Shaving preparations - Briff Products Ltd.
BRIGADE - Beverages–alcohol - Evansville Brewing Co.
BRIGADE - Floor coverings–carpet and rugs ✩ - Blue Ridge Carpet Mills
BRIGADE - Floor coverings–carpet and rugs ✩ - Customweave Carpets Inc.
BRIGADE - Luggage - Airway Industries, Inc.
BRIGADE - Ophthalmic goods - Foremost Optical Products
BRIGADE - Shingles–asphalt or tar ✩ - GS Roofing Products Co.
BRIGADE - Shirts - Phillips-Van Heusen Corp.
BRIGADE - Watches - Precise International/Wenger
BRIGADE II - Floor coverings–carpet and rugs ✩ - Blue Ridge Carpet Mills
BRIGADES - Furniture - Lane Co. Inc.
BRIGADE'S MRE - Apparel and accessories - Brigade Quartermasters Ltd.
BRIGADIER - Floor coverings - American Floor Products Co. Inc.
BRIGADIER - Floor coverings–carpet and rugs - Collins & Aikman Corp.
BRIGADIER - Floor coverings–carpet and rugs ✩ - Blue Ridge Carpet Mills
BRIGADIER - Floor coverings–carpet and rugs ✩ - Mannington Carpets, Inc.
BRIGADIER - Gin - Jim Beam Brands Co.
BRIGADIER - Hardware - Emhart Inc.
BRIGADIER - Jewelry - Jacoby-Bender Inc.
BRIGADIER - Mattresses and box springs - Ohio Mattress Co.
BRIGADIER - Padding–foam - Crain Industries Inc.
BRIGADIER - Tires - Reynolds Tire and Rubber Corp.
BRIGADIER - Watches - Bulova Corp.
BRIGADOON - Paper - Strathmore Paper Co.
BRIGANCE WATERCOLORS - Crocheted and knitted items - M and M Woolen
 Co. Inc.
BRIGANTINE - Coats–men's - Gallron
BRIGATA - Apparel and accessories ✩ - Brigata International, Inc.
BRIGATA SILK - Apparel and accessories ✩ - Brigata International, Inc.
BRIGGS - Candy ✩ - F.B. Washburn Candy Corp.
BRIGGS - Food products - Southland Corp.
BRIGGS - Paper products - Briggs Medical Services, Inc.
BRIGGS - Plumbing fixtures - Briggs Plumbing Products, Inc.
BRIGGS - Tobacco products - House of Windsor Inc.
BRIGGS & RILEY - Luggage - Mainland Marketing, Inc.
BRIGGS & STRATTON - Lawn mowers - Briggs & Stratton Corp.
BRIGHT - Chairs–wood - Bright Chair Co.
BRIGHT - Cigarettes - R.J. Reynolds Tobacco Co.
BRIGHT - Stationery ✩ - Diagraph Corp.
BRIGHT - Tiles–ceramic - Florida Tile Industries, Inc.
BRIGHT AND BEAUTIFUL - Floor coverings–carpet and rugs ✩ - Calladium &
 Marglen
BRIGHT & DEEP - Paints ✩ - Montgomery Ward & Co. Inc.
BRIGHT & EARLY - Juices–frozen - Coca-Cola Co.
BRIGHT & MATLE GLAZE - Tiles–ceramic - Porcelanite, Inc.
BRIGHT & MATTE - Tiles–ceramic ✩ - American Olean Tile Co.
BRIGHT & SHINE - Pet products - Vo-Toys Inc.
BRIGHT BALL - Toys–stuffed - Playskool, Inc.
BRIGHT BEAUTY - Paints - Krylon/Dupli-Color
BRIGHT BEGINNINGS - Health care products - Helene Curtis Industries Inc.
BRIGHT BLOCKS - Toys–blocks - BB Marketing Inc.
BRIGHT BOY - Abrasive products - Bright Boy Abrasives
BRIGHT BRONZE - Musical instrument accessories - GHS Strings
BRIGHT BUNNY - Toys–stuffed - Playskool, Inc.
BRIGHT CITRUS - Deodorizers - Claire Manufacturing Co.
BRIGHT CLOUD - Fabrics ✩ - Burlington House Fabrics Group
BRIGHT COAT - Veterinary pharmaceutical preparations - Sunbeam Corp.
BRIGHT DAY - Salad dressings–bottled - Martin Gillet and Co. Inc.
BRIGHT ENERGY - Vitamins and nutritional supplements - Omma Nutrition,
 Inc.
BRIGHT EYE - Teas - San Francisco Herb & Natural Food Co.

✩ = Now out of production

BRIGHT EYES - Cat food - Nestle USA

BRIGHT EYES - Lighting fixtures - Point Electric

BRIGHT EYES - Puzzles ☆ - Warren Industries Inc.

BRIGHT EYES - Vitamins and nutritional supplements - Richard Anderson and Avona L'carttier Both U.S. Citizens, AS Trustees of Visioninternational Trust

BRIGHT FUTURE - Apparel–children's - J.C. Penney Co., Inc.

BRIGHT FUTURE - Underwear and nightwear - Bestform Foundations, Inc.

BRIGHT GIRL - Skin care products ☆ - Avon Products, Inc.

BRIGHT GLAZE - Tiles–ceramic - United States Ceramic Tile Co.

BRIGHT GLAZE - Wall tile - Interceramic Inc.

BRIGHT HARVEST - Vegetables–frozen - Promark International, Inc.

BRIGHT HORIZONS - Lighting fixtures - Mercuries and Associates (USA), Ltd.

BRIGHT IDEA - Hair coloring preparations - Helene Curtis Industries Inc.

BRIGHT IDEA - Lighting fixtures - Liteway

BRIGHT IDEA - Perfumes - Aromatic Industries, Inc.

BRIGHT IDEAS - Pet products - ASPC Inc.

BRIGHT IDEAS FOR YOU, INC. - Apparel and accessories - Bright Ideas ™For You∫, Inc.

BRIGHT LACE - Brassieres (Bras) - Warnaco Inc.

BRIGHT LIFE - Lighting fixtures - Lights of America Inc.

BRIGHT LIFE - Paints - Martin-Senour Co.

BRIGHT LIGHTS - Bedding–linen - Dan River Inc.

BRIGHT LIGHTS - Paper–gift wrap - Stephen Lawrence Co.

BRIGHT LIGHTS - Wallpaper - Secrest Handprints Inc.

BRIGHT LINE - Shelving units–wood ☆ - Hirsh Co.

BRIGHT LINES - Brassieres (Bras) - Vanity Fair Mills Inc.

BRIGHT LITES - Girdles - H.F. Robbins

BRIGHT N' BOLD - Glassware–household - Owens-Illinois Inc. (Libbey Div.)

BRIGHT 'N BREEZY - Floor coverings ☆ - Congoleum Corp.

BRIGHT-N-DIM - Lighting equipment ☆ - Home Equipment Manufacturing Co.

BRIGHT 'N LIVELY - Cooking equipment–household ☆ - Imperial Schrade Corp.

BRIGHT N' SHINEY - Pet products - Best n' Show Pet Products Inc.

BRIGHT N SUNNY - Beverages - The Sqwincher Corp.

BRIGHT N. SUNNY - Toys - Lisco, Inc.

BRIGHT 'N WHITE - Bleach ☆ - Penn Champ Inc.

BRIGHT-NET - Sporting goods - Porter Athletic Equipment Co.

BRIGHT-ON - Interior paints - Insilco Corp.

BRIGHT ORANGE - Recording label - Cadet Records Inc.

BRIGHT PATH - Food products - Flexpac Foods

BRIGHT SEASONS - Floor coverings–carpet and rugs - Roxbury Carpet Co.

BRIGHT SHINE - Brassieres (Bras) - Warnaco Inc.

BRIGHT SIDE - Shampoos - Colgate-Palmolive Co.

BRIGHT SPIRIT - Floor coverings–carpet and rugs ☆ - Downs Carpet Co. Inc.

BRIGHT SPOTS - Paper products - Lisa Marie Arneson

BRIGHT SPRAY - Paints ☆ - Valspar Corp.

BRIGHT STAR - Batteries - Bright Star Industries Inc.

BRIGHT STAR - Computer software - Bright Star Technology Inc.

BRIGHT STAR - Electrical equipment - General Electric Co.

BRIGHT STAR - Floor coverings–carpet and rugs ☆ - Galaxy Carpet Mills Inc.

BRIGHT STAR - Rings–jewelry - Artcarved Inc.

BRIGHT STAR - Strollers–baby - Spectrum Juvenile Products Inc.

BRIGHT STARTERS - Playground equipment - Kenner Products

BRIGHT STARTS - Infant product - Pansy Ellen Products, Inc.

BRIGHT STARTS - Meat products–pork - Schwan's Sales Enterprises, Inc.

BRIGHT STICKS - Markers–felt-tip - Sanford Corp.

BRIGHT STIK - Lamp bulbs–incandescent - General Electric Co.

BRIGHT STRIPES - Bleach ☆ - Noxell Corp.

BRIGHT STRIPES! - Hobby kits - Murdock Webbing Co. Inc.

BRIGHT TABS - Office supplies - Avery Dennison Corp.

BRIGHT TEENS - Jewelry–costume - Selected Trading Corp.

BRIGHT TIGER - Inks - Flexible Products Co.

BRIGHT TIME - Clocks - General Time Corp. (Westclox/Seth Thomas Div.)

BRIGHT WATER - Cleaning preparations - Great Atlantic & Pacific Tea Co., Inc.

BRIGHT WATER ULTRA - Detergents ☆ - Blue Cross Laboratories Inc.

BRIGHT WHITE - Lighting fixtures - Progress Lighting Inc.

BRIGHT WHITE - Pet products - Vo-Toys Inc.

BRIGHTBEAM - Projectors–photographic ☆ - Keystone Camera Corp.

BRIGHTBELLS - Weightlifting equipment - Bollinger Industries

BRIGHTEN - Housewares ☆ - Shafford Co. Inc.

BRIGHTEN-UP - Floor waxers–household - Cello Chemical Co.

BRIGHTEN UP, TIGHTEN UP - Cosmetics - Charles Revson Inc.

BRIGHTER CHILD - Computer software - Landoll, Inc.

BRIGHTER CHILD - Educational materials - American Education Publishing Co.

BRIGHTER CHILD SERIES - Publisher's imprints - American Education Publishing Co.

BRIGHTER CHOICE, THE - Signs - Glo-Max Fiber Optics System, Inc.

BRIGHTER DAY, A - Televisions - Jan D. D'atri

BRIGHTER IMAGE GROUP - Display cases–wood - Replex Mirror Co.

BRIGHTLIFE - Floor coverings - Congoleum Corp.

BRIGHTLIGHT - Photographic equipment - Navitar, Inc.

BRIGHT'N EASY - Floor coverings - Congoleum Corp.

BRIGHTON - Cabinets - Western Cabinet & Millwork Inc.

BRIGHTON - Cabinets - Yorktowne Inc.

BRIGHTON - Cabinets ☆ - Karman Kitchens Inc.

BRIGHTON - Clocks - Ridgeway Clock Co.

BRIGHTON - Dishes–china ☆ - WMF/USA

BRIGHTON - Fencing–steel - Semmerling Fence and Supply Inc.

BRIGHTON - Flatware - Pfaltzgraff Investment Co.

BRIGHTON - Floor coverings - Mannington Resilient Floors

BRIGHTON - Furniture - American Furniture Co. Inc.

BRIGHTON - Furniture ☆ - Fancher Furniture Co. Inc.

BRIGHTON - Furniture ☆ - Hammary Furniture Co. Inc.

BRIGHTON - Furniture ☆ - Singer Furniture Co.

BRIGHTON - Glassware–household - Owens-Illinois Inc. (Libbey Div.)

BRIGHTON - Glassware–household ☆ - Lenox Crystal, Inc.

BRIGHTON - Hobby kits - Craft World International Inc.

BRIGHTON - Lamps - Turkart

BRIGHTON - Manufactured homes - Redman Industries, Inc.

BRIGHTON - Pool tables - Brunswick Corp.

BRIGHTON - Rings–jewelry - Artcarved Inc.

BRIGHTON - Watches ☆ - Longines-Wittnauer Watch Co.

BRIGHTON II - Floor coverings–carpet and rugs ☆ - Mannington Carpets, Inc.

BRIGHTON BAY - Leather goods - Enger-Kress Co.

BRIGHTON BEACH - Floor coverings - Mannington Resilient Floors

BRIGHTON CHOICE - Manufactured homes - Redman Industries, Inc.

BRIGHTON COURT - Floor coverings–carpet and rugs ☆ - Hollytex Carpet Mills Inc.

BRIGHTON MANOR - Luggage - Airway Industries, Inc.

BRIGHTON MANOR - Manufactured homes - Redman Industries, Inc.

BRIGHTON PLACE - Floor coverings ☆ - Congoleum Corp.

BRIGHTON'S - Food products - Eagle Crest Foods Inc.

BRIGHTS - Cases–eyeglass - California Optical Leather Inc.

BRIGHTS - Hair care products - Clairol Inc.

BRIGHTS - Paints–artists' - Tri-Chem Inc.

BRIGHTS - Toys - Maui Toys

BRIGHTS BY NICE 'N EASY - Hair care products - Clairol Inc.

BRIGHTSIDE - Polyurethane enamels - Interlux Yacht Finishes

BRIGHTSIDES - Greeting cards - Current, Inc.

BRIGHTWATER - Fish–canned or cured - Odom's Tennessee Pride Sausage Co.

BRIGHTWATER SCOTT - Apparel and accessories - Scott Powr-Ply Co.

BRIGHTWAY - Feather dusters ☆ - Texas Feathers Inc.

BRIGHTWEAR - Apparel and accessories - Head Lites Corp.

BRIGHTWORKS - Hair care products ☆ - Avon Products, Inc.

BRIGITTE - Dolls ☆ - Effanbee Doll Corp.

BRIGITTE - Floor coverings–carpet and rugs - Masland Corp.

BRIGITTE - Yarn - Brunswick Yarns

BRIK - Building blocks - BRIK Toy Co.

BRIK-BLOK - Floor coverings ☆ - Anderson Hardwood Floors Inc.

BRIK HAUZ - Pet products - Dogloo Inc.

BRIKARIER - Bricks - Fuller Manufacturing Co.

BRIKDECO - Silicon products - Vortex International Co., Inc.

BRIKSET - Cement - Medusa Corp.

BRILEY PARK - Floor coverings ☆ - Congoleum Corp.

BRILHART - Musical instrument accessories ☆ - Selmer Co. Inc.

BRILL - Food products - H.C. Brill Co., Inc.

BRILL - Food products - Venice Maid Co. Inc.

BRILL - Machinery - Oil Skimmers, Inc.

BRILL-FLEX - Abrasive products - Trademarks Holdings Inc.

BRILLANT LUMIERE - Cosmetics - Chanel Inc.

BRILLANT SOLEIL - Sulfuric acid - Chanel Inc.

BRILLANT SUPER PRO - Pet products - Tetra Sales USA

BRILLANTE - Floor coverings–carpet and rugs ☆ - J.L. Benson Co.

BRILLANTE - Glassware–household - Crystal Glass Tube & Cylinder Co.

BRILLANTE - Nail care products - Nat Robbins Ltd.

BRILLANTISSIMO - Lipstick, nail polish - Bourjois Ltd.

BRILLAT - Artichokes–canned - A. Sargenti Co. Inc.

BRILLAT SAVARIN - Beverages–alcohol - Niche Marketing Corp.

BRILLAT SAVARIN - Cheese - ULN America Inc.

BRILLIANCE - Audio equipment - Belden Wire & Cable Co.
BRILLIANCE - Cleaning preparations–carpet and rug - Ecolab Inc.
BRILLIANCE - Computer peripheral equipment - Phillips Electronics North America Corp.
BRILLIANCE - Cookware - Anchor Hocking Glass, Inc.
BRILLIANCE - Cosmetics - Honey & Spice Toiletries
BRILLIANCE - Doors–glass - Majestic Co.
BRILLIANCE - Fabrics - Greenwood Mills Inc.
BRILLIANCE - Faucets - Masco Corp. (Plumbing Products Div.)
BRILLIANCE - Floor coverings - Aladdin Mills, Inc.
BRILLIANCE - Metals - Masco Building Products Corp.
BRILLIANCE - Recording label - Brilliance Corp. Inc.
BRILLIANIZE - Cleaning preparations - Chemical Products Co.
BRILLIANSHEEN - Hay - Revlon Consumer Products Corp.
BRILLIANT - Apparel and accessories - Andmore Sportswear Corp.
BRILLIANT - Cosmetics - American International Industries
BRILLIANT - Fabrics - Guilford Mills, Inc.
BRILLIANT - Floor coverings–carpet and rugs - Stanton Carpet Corp.
BRILLIANT - Glassware–household - ACC
BRILLIANT - Hair care products - A-Veda Corp.
BRILLIANT - Thread - DMC Corp.
BRILLIANT - Thread ☆ - Coats and Clark Inc.
BRILLIANT - Toothpaste - Pacific Man Corp.
BRILLIANT - Water colors - M. Grumbacher Inc.
BRILLIANT ALTERNATIVE, THE - Jewelry - Swarogem Ltd.
BRILLIANT BEADS - Jewelry - QVC, Inc.
BRILLIANT BLONDE - Hair care products ☆ - Schwarzkopf Inc.
BRILLIANT COLOR CARDS - Paper–coated - Brilliant Color Cards, Inc.
BRILLIANT-CUT ROPE - Jewelry - Grando, Inc.
BRILLIANT HOMES - Mobile homes - Brilliant Homes Corp.
BRILLIANT ILLUSIONS - Jewelry - Aurafin Corp.
BRILLIANT MOMENT - Floor coverings–carpet and rugs - Monticello Carpet Mills
BRILLIANT NEW MUSIC - Recording label - Capitol Records, Inc.
BRILLIANT NITE SOFTWARE, INC. - Computer software - Brilliant Nite Software, Inc.
BRILLIANT THOUGHTS - Publisher's imprints - Brilliant Enterprises
BRILLIANT WATERCOLORS - Artists' materials - Winsor & Newton
BRILLIANTINE - Hair care products - Madame C.J. Walker Inc.
BRILLIANTS - Paints ☆ - Quartet Manufacturing Co.
BRILLIANTSHINE - Cleaning preparations - Guardsman Products, Inc.
BRILLIG - Sweaters - Watchung Resources, Inc.
BRILLION - Wallcoverings - Victorian Collectibles Ltd.
BRILLION COLLECTION I - Wallcoverings - Victorian Collectibles Ltd.
BRILLION COLLECTION II - Wallcoverings - Victorian Collectibles Ltd.
BRILLITE - Paints - Red Spot Paint & Varnish Co., Inc.
BRILLO - Cleaning preparations - Dial Corp.
BRILLO PADDY - Scouring pads - Dial Corp.
BRILLO SCRUBBERS - Scouring pads - Dial Corp.
BRILLO SYNDISC - Fabrics - Loren Products
BRILOK - Sealing devices - Millcreek Plastics Co.
BRIM - Computer peripheral equipment - Cabletron Systems, Inc.
BRIMAR - Trimmings–fabric - Brimar Inc.
BRIMFULL - Food products ☆ - Super Valu Inc.
BRIMMS - Denture cleaners - Brimms Inc.
BRIMSTONE - Ceramic cookware, bakeware, servingware ☆ - Corning Inc.
BRIMSTONE - Computer software ☆ - Broderbund Software, Inc.
BRIMSTONE - Toys - Tonka Corp.
BRIMSTONE HILL VINEYARD - Wines - Brimstone Hill Winery
BRIMWICK - Sweaters - Binghamton Knitting Co.
BRINDALL BERRY DIET - Health care products ☆ - Above All Health Inc.
BRINDALL TRIM - Vitamins and nutritional supplements - Nutriguard Research, Inc.
BRINDLEY'S - Tobacco products - Faber, Coe & Gregg Inc.
BRINDLY MANOR - Floor coverings–carpet and rugs - Lock Weave Carpet Mills Inc.
BRINE - Fish food - Artemia of Utah Inc.
BRINE - Soccer equipment - Brine Inc.
BRINE ALIVE - Pet products ☆ - Aquatronics-Filtronics
BRINE GUARD - Water purification systems - Wigen Companies, Inc.
BRINE SHRIMP PLUS - Pet products - Ocean Nutrition Corp.
BRING ALONG - Mayonnaise - CPC International Inc.
BRING ALONG A SONG - Toys - Tomy America, Inc.
BRING BACK - Data-retrieval software ☆ - Parsons Technology, Inc.
BRING BACK BAG - Bags - Roplast Industries Inc.

BRING IT ON - Apparel and accessories - Biowear, Inc.
BRING OUT THE BEST - Relishes - CPC International Inc.
BRING THE COUNTRY HOME - Sausages - Wamplers Farm Sausage
BRING UP THE REAR - Apparel–women's - Exquisite Form Industries
BRING YOUR OWN BALLS - Apparel–women's - Insana-Tee's
BRINGGOLD - Meat products–beef - Schumacher Wholesale Meats Inc.
BRINGING NEIGHBORHOODS TO LIFE - Real estate agencies - Rouse/Chamberlin, Ltd.
BRINGING THE PIECES TOGETHER AGAIN - T-shirts–men's - Tracking Project Inc.
BRINK - Air purification systems - Monsanto Co.
BRINK & COTTON - Clamps - Brink & Cotton
BRINK-FLOR - Floor coverings - L.D. Brinkman & Co. Inc.
BRINK VAN KEULEN - Lighting fixtures - Dutch Products & Supply Co.
BRINKLEY - Health care products - Fasco Industries Inc.
BRINLY - Lawn-care product - Brinly-Hardy Co.
BRINLY-HARDY - Lawn-care product - Brinly-Hardy Co.
BRINNCO - Housewares - Brinns China & Glassware Co. Inc.
BRINNS - Housewares - Brinns China & Glassware Co. Inc.
BRINSDON - Refrigerators - Kerner Industries
BRINTON - Housewares - Brinns China & Glassware Co. Inc.
BRINTONS - Pretzels - Vesper Corp.
BRINTONS PRETZELS - Pretzels - Vesper Corp.
BRINWOOD - Floor coverings ☆ - Congoleum Corp.
BRIO - Bedding–linen - Dan River Inc.
BRIO - Floor coverings - VPI
BRIO - Floor coverings–carpet and rugs - Karastan-Bigelow Inc.
BRIO - Glassware–household - Lancaster Colony Corp.
BRIO - Health care products - Samhall Rehab
BRIO - Toys - BRIO Corp.
BRIOLETTE - Piccolos - Kathy R. Gavigan
BRIONI - Girdles - Vanity Corset Co. Inc.
BRIOPUBLISH - Computer software - Brio Technology, Inc.
BRIOSCHI - Antacids - Brioschi Inc.
BRIOSO RECORDINGS - Recording label - Composers' & Musicians' Connection World Wide, Inc.
BRIPOLY - Thread ☆ - Perfect Thread Co. Inc.
BRIQ - Luggage - Tumi Luggage, Inc.
BRIQUE - Giftware - Sasaki
BRIQUE - Lipsticks - Cosmair Inc.
BRIQUE WARE - Cooking equipment–household ☆ - Nordic Ware
BRISA - Whirlpools - Americh Corp.
BRISAS DE PLATA - Wines ☆ - Admiral Wine Merchants
BRISBANE - Floor coverings - Mannington Resilient Floors
BRISBANE - Floor coverings–carpet and rugs - Collins & Aikman Corp.
BRISBANE - Floor coverings–carpet and rugs ☆ - Burtco Enterprises Inc.
BRISBANE - Occasional tables ☆ - JDI Group, Inc.
BRISBANE - Whirlpools - Lasco Products Group
BRISBANE KOALA - Toys–stuffed - Dakin Inc.
BRISBANE KOALA - Toys–stuffed - Russ Berrie and Co., Inc.
BRISK - Coffee - Brisk Coffee Co.
BRISK - Detergents - Stearns Packaging Corp.
BRISK - Iced tea–bottled or canned - Lipton Investments, Inc.
BRISK - Pharmaceutical preparations - Pharmex Inc.
BRISK-AIR - Air conditioning equipment - Dometic Corp.
BRISK-SET - Apparel and accessories - Brisk Set Rhinestone Co.
BRISKER - Kitchen appliances - Brisker Dry Food Crisper, Inc.
BRISS-L - Artists' materials - Stangren Co.
BRISSARC - Brandy - John Gross & Co.
BRISSON - Beverages–alcohol - R. Torre & Co.
BRISTACYCLINE - Antibiotics ☆ - Bristol-Myers Squibb Co.
BRISTAMYCIN - Antibiotics ☆ - Bristol-Myers Squibb Co.
BRISTEN - Cabinets - Merillat Industries, Inc.
BRISTLE BLOCKS - Toys ☆ - Playskool, Inc.
BRISTLE BLOCKS - Toys–blocks - Adica Pongo Inc.
BRISTLE BUDDIES - Toys ☆ - Playskool, Inc.
BRISTLE RIDGE VINEYARD - Wines - Bristle Ridge Vineyards & Winery
BRISTLENE - Brushes–paint - E-Z Paintr Corp.
BRISTLES - Computer software - First Star Software Inc.
BRISTLETTE - Artists' materials - M. Grumbacher Inc.
BRISTOIL - Oils–lubricating - Santex Corp.
BRISTOL - Cabinets - American Woodmark Corp.
BRISTOL - Cabinets ☆ - Medallion Kitchens of Minnesota Inc.
BRISTOL - Cordage and twine ☆ - Wonder Craft
BRISTOL - Dinnerware–glass ☆ - Gorham Inc.
BRISTOL - Dishes–earthenware ☆ - Homer Laughlin China Co.

☆ = Now out of production

BRISTOL - Glass products ☆ - Pittsburgh Corning Corp.
BRISTOL - Glassware–household ☆ - Crystal Clear Importing Co. Inc.
BRISTOL - Glassware–household ☆ - Lenox Crystal, Inc.
BRISTOL - Jewelry - Bristol Seamless Ring Corp.
BRISTOL - Meat products–beef - Western State Sales
BRISTOL - Medical apparatus - Bristoline Inc.
BRISTOL - Office furniture–wood ☆ - Haskell of Pittsburgh, Inc.
BRISTOL - Seafood products–fresh or frozen ☆ - Pocasset Seafoods Inc.
BRISTOL - Ships–sailing vessels - Bristol Yachts
BRISTOL - Shutters–wood - Catalina Shading Systems Inc.
BRISTOL - Signal flares - Sea Spike Marine Supply Co. Inc.
BRISTOL - Silver products - Poole Silver Co.
BRISTOL - Windows–storm - Winchester Industries Inc.
BRISTOL BABCOCK - Electrical equipment - Bristol Babcock Inc.
BRISTOL BAY - Floor coverings–carpet and rugs ☆ - Burtco Enterprises Inc.
BRISTOL BOULEVARD - Wallpaper ☆ - Imperial Wallcoverings, Inc.
BRISTOL CHANNEL - Furniture - Harden Furniture Co. Inc.
BRISTOL COUNTY - Furniture ☆ - Bassett Furniture Industries, Inc.
BRISTOL COURT - Floor coverings–carpet and rugs - Evans-Black Carpet Mills
BRISTOL CRAFTS - Giftware - Crisloid Inc.
BRISTOL DIAMOND - Glassware–household - Mayflower Glass Works
BRISTOL FARM COLLECTION - Dining room furniture ☆ - John Boos and Co. Inc.
BRISTOL FARMS - Baskets–wood - Bristol Farms
BRISTOL FARMS THE FOOD PLACE - Baskets–wood ☆ - Bristol Farms
BRISTOL FASHION - Varnishes - Marine Development & Research Corp.
BRISTOL FROST - Cabinets - Triangle Pacific Corp. (Cabinet Division)
BRISTOL GOLD - Cheese - Merkt Cheese Co., Inc.
BRISTOL HOUSE - Furniture - Bristol House
BRISTOL II - Pool tables - Brunswick Corp.
BRISTOL LANE - Underwear and nightwear - LANZ, Inc.
BRISTOL MANOR - Flatware - Utica Cutlery Co.
BRISTOL MANOR - Furniture - Conover Chair Co. Inc.
BRISTOL MOUNTAIN - Wines ☆ - Widmer's Wine Cellars Inc.
BRISTOL PARK - Furniture ☆ - Bassett Furniture Industries, Inc.
BRISTOL PARK - Glassware–household - Anchor Hocking Corp.
BRISTOL PEARL - Jewelry - Monopearl Inc.
BRISTOL PLACE - Floor coverings–carpet and rugs - Queen Carpet Corp.
BRISTOL/SUSSEX - Caulking compounds - Hooper Industries Inc.
BRISTOL, THE - Paint sets–hobby ☆ - Winsor & Newton
BRISTOL WALKER - Footwear–men's - Hagerstown Shoe Co.
BRISTOLETTE - Binders ☆ - Smead Manufacturing Co.
BRISTOLINE - Medical apparatus - Bristoline Inc.
BRISTOLINE - Microscopes - Graham-Field Inc.
BRISTOLITE - Skylights - Bristolite Skylights
BRISTOLPIPE - Drainage and waste pipes, etc. - Bristol Corp.
BRISTOLS - Paper–bond - Marvin Envelope & Paper Co.
BRISTOLSCOPE - Medical apparatus - Bristoline Inc.
BRISTOLSPHYG - Medical apparatus - Bristoline Inc.
BRISTOLWARE - Giftware - Tin Box Co. of America, Inc.
BRISTOW - Mechanical cable controls - Tuthill Corp.
BRIT/TEX - Nail care products - Sheila Brit Ltd.
BRITA - Water purification systems - Clorox Co.
BRITAINS - Toys - Reeves International, Inc.
BRITANIA - Yarn - William Unger & Co. Inc.
BRITANNI - Cutlery ☆ - Washington Forge Inc.
BRITANNIA - Beverages–alcohol ☆ - Montebello Brands, Inc.
BRITANNIA - Food products - Shore Lobster & Shrimp Corp.
BRITANNIA - Furniture - Ebenreiter Woodworking Co.
BRITANNIA - Gin - Charles Jacquin et Compagnie Inc.
BRITANNIA - Glassware–household - Durand International
BRITANNIA - Wallpaper ☆ - Mayfair Wallcoverings
BRITANNIA 10 - Wallpaper ☆ - Mayfair Wallcoverings
BRITANNIA LTD. - Food products ☆ - Stokes/Ellis Foods
BRITAX - See COLUMBIA
BRITAX - Health care products - Fabrication Enterprises
BRITCHES - Apparel–men's ☆ - Elder Manufacturing Co., Inc.
BRITCHES 'N THINGS - Apparel–women's - Joni Blair of California Inc.
BRITCHES 'N THINGS - Apparel–women's - Joni Blair of California
BRITCHES/VYMURA - Wallpaper - ICI Americas Inc.
BRITE - Cleaning preparations - Durawool Inc.
BRITE - Cleaning preparations–carpet and rug - S.C. Johnson & Son, Inc.
BRITE - Computer peripheral equipment - Adb-Alnaco, Inc.
BRITE - Cording - Pepperell Braiding Co. Inc.
BRITE & MATTE - Tiles–ceramic - Wenczel Tile Co.

BRITE BEAM - Floodlights - Electripak
BRITE BEAM - Lamps–sealed beam - Osram Sylvania Inc.
BRITE BEAMS - Footwear ☆ - E.S. Originals, Inc.
BRITE BITES - Cookies - Ripon Foods, Inc.
BRITE BLUE - Cleaning preparations - Senoret Chemical Co.
BRITE-BOND - Floor coverings - Tarkett, Inc.
BRITE BORE - Guns - Mill Run Products Co.
BRITE BOWL - Cleaning preparations - Senoret Chemical Co.
BRITE CHOICE - Floor coverings–tile - Tarkett, Inc.
BRITE DECK - Detergents - AmeriPlus Inc.
BRITE EYE - Eyedrops and eye lotion - American Laboratories Inc.
BRITE EYES - Lamps ☆ - Roxter Lighting
BRITE FLATS - Musical instrument accessories - GHS Strings
BRITE-GARD - Lighting fixtures - Carlon
BRITE GLAZE - Floor coverings–tile ☆ - VPI
BRITE GLAZE - Tiles–ceramic - Monarch Tile Inc.
BRITE-GLO PATCHES - Greeting cards ☆ - Best Emblem & Insignia Co. Inc.
BRITE-GLOW - Abrasive products - Park Metallurgical Corp.
BRITE HOUSE - Bleach - Brite-House Co.
BRITE HOUSE GLASS MAGIC - Cleaning preparations–household - Brite-House Co.
BRITE ICE - Ice - Coleman Co., Inc.
BRITE IDEAS - Ribbons - Pacific Balloon Co., Inc.
BRITE IMAGE - Floor coverings - Tarkett, Inc.
BRITE KOTE - Hardware - Phifer Wire Products Inc.
BRITE KOTE - Paints - Eaglo Paint & Varnish Corp.
BRITE LEGS - Hosiery - Mayer/Berkshire Corp.
BRITE LIFE - Product description unknown - Wright and Lato Inc.
BRITE LIFE - Detergents - Better Living Products Inc.
BRITE LIFE GUARD - Flashlights - Terry Lee Shaffer
BRITE LIGHT TASK LIGHTING TL - Lighting fixtures - International Lighting Manufacturing Co.
BRITE LINE - Thermometers - Liquid Crystal Sciences Inc.
BRITE-LITE - Kitchen appliances ☆ - Will & Baumer, Inc.
BRITE LITE - Lighting equipment–bicycles - Specialized Bicycle Components, Inc.
BRITE-LITE - Skylights - Bristol Fiberlite Industries
BRITE-LITES - Christmas tree lights - General Enterprises Inc.
BRITE LITES - Cosmetics ☆ - Hazel Bishop International
BRITE LITES - Jewelry - D. Chabbott Inc.
BRITE LITES - Pencils - National Pen & Pencil Co.
BRITE MAGIC - Adhesives and sealants - Miracle Adhesives
BRITE MAGIC - Adhesives and sealants - Pratt & Lambert, Inc. (Specialty Products Div.)
BRITE-MARK - Markers–felt-tip - Mark-Tex Corp.
BRITE-MITE - Lamps - Vantage Products Inc.
BRITE N' CLEAR - Aquariums–household - Mardel Laboratories, Inc.
BRITE N' SHINE - Pet products - Mardel Laboratories, Inc.
BRITE 'N SHINY - Floor waxes - Kentile Floors Inc.
BRITE 'N WHITE - Pet products - Richard Hanau Pet Foods Corp.
BRITE ORCHID - Cosmetics ☆ - Bonne Bell, Inc.
BRITE-POLY - File folders - Angler's Roslyn Group Ltd.
BRITE-PRIDE - Steel products - Parkersburg Steel Co.
BRITE SCREEN - Cleaning preparations - Standard Antiseptic Inc.
BRITE SCRIPT - Decals and transfers - Lion Ribbon Co. Inc.
BRITE SHOT - Guns - S/R Industries, Inc. (Marksman Products)
BRITE SIDE - Footwear ☆ - E.S. Originals, Inc.
BRITE SITES - Binoculars - Sake International Inc.
BRITE STAR - Christmas tree ornaments - J. Kinderman and Sons Brite Star Manufacturing Co.
BRITE STIK - Dental Concepts Inc.
BRITE-STROKES - Paints ☆ - DecoArt, Inc.
BRITE TOGS - Children's apparel - Colberts, Inc.
BRITE-TONE - Dental cream ☆ - Iodent Co.
BRITE-TONE - Paints–artists' - Brite-Tone Co.
BRITE-TOUCH - Lighting equipment - Carlon
BRITE TOUCH - Paints - Krylon/Dupli-Color
BRITE-TRIM - Christmas tree lights ☆ - General Enterprises Inc.
BRITE WALLETS - Stationery - Mead Corp.
BRITE WASH - Boats ☆ - Fibre Glass-Evercoat Co. Inc.
BRITE WAY - Cleaning preparations - Analab Inc.
BRITE WHITE - Artists' materials - Badger Air-Brush Co.
BRITE WHITES - Bowling balls - DBA Products Co.
BRITE WIRES - Musical instrument accessories - Gibson Strings & Accessories
BRITE WOOD - Finishing agents ☆ - Fibre Glass-Evercoat Co. Inc.
BRITE YEARS - Health care products - Brite Years Vitamins

BRITE YEARS FITNESS PAKS - Health care products - Brite Years Vitamins

BRITE YEARS PM PLUS - Health care products - Brite Years Vitamins

BRITEBORE - Cleaning preparations - Remington Arms Co., Inc.

BRITELINE - Hardware - St. Louis Screw and Bolt Co.

BRITELITE - Pet products - Aquarium Products Inc.

BRITELITES - Cups–plastic - WNA Comet

BRITEMARK - Chalk ☆ - Walbuck Crayon Co., Inc.

BRITEN-ALL - Cleaning preparations–household - Calgon Vestal Laboratories

BRITEN-ZIT - Cleaning preparations - Hillyard Enterprises, Inc.

BRITE'NUP SUNSHINE FROM THE GROUND - Plastics - Adcock Manufacturing Corp.

BRITEPAK - Lighting equipment - Fiberstars, Inc.

BRITEPOINT - Paints - St. Louis Paint Manufacturing Co.

BRITERWAY - Cleaning preparations - Henry Bresky & Sons Inc.

BRITES - Desk sets ☆ - Newell Office Products

BRITES - Office supplies ☆ - Esselte Corp.

BRITES - Rubber bands - Alliance Rubber Co.

BRITES CUPS - Cups–plastic - Nyman Manufacturing Co.

BRITESENSOR - Electronic equipment - Intelligent Controls, Inc.

BRITESET - Paper–writing - Champion International Corp.

BRITETONE - Paints - Cloverleaf Paint & Varnish

BRITEVIEW - Signs - Scott Sign Systems, Inc.

BRITEWEB - Paper–writing - Champion International Corp.

BRITEX - Aquatic pharmacuetical preparations ☆ - Aquatronics-Filtronics

BRITEX - Cleaning preparations - Brogdex Co.

BRITEX - Fabric stores - Britex Fabrics

BRITEX - Thread ☆ - American & Efird, Inc.

BRITISH 66 - Hosiery–women's - Fischer Hosiery Co.

BRITISH BRICK - Floor coverings ☆ - Azrock Commercial Flooring

BRITISH CLASSICS - Furniture - Ethan Allen Finance Corp.

BRITISH CLOCKMAKER, THE - Clocks - British Clockmaker Inc.

BRITISH CREW - Shirts - Munsingwear, Inc.

BRITISH CROWN - Colognes - Schnapp Enterprises Inc.

BRITISH DESIGN - Furniture - Loroman Co.

BRITISH GRENADIER - Tobacco–chewing or smoking - 1776 Tobacco Co.

BRITISH HERITAGE COLLECTION, THE - Seasonings - Chase Collection, Inc.

BRITISH ISLES COLLECTION - Crocheted and knitted items ☆ - Schuessler Knitting Mills Inc.

BRITISH KNIGHTS - Shoes–athletic - British Knights Inc.

BRITISH LION - Apparel and accessories - Kellwood Co.

BRITISH NATIONAL TRUST COLLECTION, THE - Furniture–wood ☆ - Century Furniture Co.

BRITISH NATIONAL TRUST, THE - Wallpaper - Payne Fabrics

BRITISH NAVY PUSSER'S RUM - Rum - Jim Beam Brands Co.

BRITISH OVERSEAS AIRWAYS MUSIC - Recording label - Trend Recording & Distributing Co., Inc.

BRITISH PIPER - Men's apparel - Tomen Apparel Group Inc.

BRITISH RAILS - Games ☆ - Mayfair Games, Inc.

BRITISH RED COAT - Nail care products - Cosmair Inc.

BRITISH RELIEF - Wallpaper - Blumenthal

BRITISH ROYAL - Health care products - Saxony Products Inc.

BRITISH ROYALTY - Crackers - Tree of Life, Inc.

BRITISH STERLING - Air purification systems ☆ - Medo Industries, Inc.

BRITISH STERLING - Skin care products ☆ - Hirsch Speidel Inc.

BRITISH TRAVELOGUE - Paper–newsprint - Cowles Magazines, Inc.

BRITISH TWEED - Dialing devices–telephone - Baltimore Luggage Co.

BRITMARK - Stationery ☆ - Diagraph Corp.

BRITO - Paints ☆ - Adelphi Coatings Co.

BRITOL - Cribs–wood ☆ - Welsh Co.

BRITONE - Musical instrument accessories ☆ - Herco Products

BRITOS - Snack foods - Conagra, Inc.

BRITTANIA - Apparel and accessories - Aberdeen Sportswear Inc.

BRITTANIA - Apparel and accessories - Wemco, Inc.

BRITTANIA - Apparel–children's ☆ - Health-Tex Inc.

BRITTANIA - Belts–apparel - Humphrey's Inc.

BRITTANIA - Games - Avalon Hill Game Co.

BRITTANIA - Neckties - Mallory and Church Corp.

BRITTANIA - Shoes - Sidney Rich Associates Inc.

BRITTANIA - Tiles–ceramic ☆ - Dal-Tile Corp.

BRITTANIA - Underwear and nightwear - Nantucket Industries Inc.

BRITTANIA - Watches - Genender International, Inc.

BRITTANY - Bicycles - Sears, Roebuck and Co.

BRITTANY - Cabinets - American Woodmark Corp.

BRITTANY - Cabinets - Major Line Products Co. Inc.

BRITTANY - Dolls - Uneeda Doll Co., Ltd.

BRITTANY - Eyeglasses - Willson/Dalloz Safety

BRITTANY - Fabrics - J.B. Martin Co. Inc.

BRITTANY - Floor coverings ☆ - Congoleum Corp.

BRITTANY - Floor coverings ☆ - Teak International

BRITTANY - Floor coverings–carpet and rugs - Atlas Carpet Mills Inc.

BRITTANY - Floor coverings–carpet and rugs - Kelly Group Inc.

BRITTANY - Floor coverings–carpet and rugs - Whitecrest Carpet Mills

BRITTANY - Glassware–household ☆ - Crisa Corp.

BRITTANY - Luggage - York Luggage Co.

BRITTANY - Office supplies ☆ - Faber-Castell Corp.

BRITTANY - Paper ☆ - Finch, Pruyn and Co.

BRITTANY - Rings–jewelry - Artcarved Inc.

BRITTANY - Watches - M.R.F. Resources Ltd.

BRITTANY - Wigs - Paula Young

BRITTANY BATISTE - Pajamas–men's - Knothe Corp.

BRITTANY BAY - Men's neckwear and sweaters - Specialty Department Stores, Inc.

BRITTANY COTTAGE - Furniture ☆ - Bassett Furniture Industries, Inc.

BRITTANY LANE - Cheese - Raskas Foods, Inc.

BRITTANY LANE - Childrens apparel - Pamida, Inc.

BRITTANY LEIGH - Apparel - QVC, Inc.

BRITTANY MANOR - Mobile homes - Fleetwood Enterprises, Inc.

BRITTANY OAK - Curtain rods - Newell Window Furnishing Co.

BRITTANY PARK - Trailers–travel ☆ - Fleetwood Enterprises, Inc.

BRITTANY WOODS - Furniture ☆ - Southern Furniture Co. of Conover

BRITTLE BUSINESS - Food products - Brittle Business

BRITTLE KITTLE - Bakery products - Brittle Kittle

BRITTSPORT - Neckties - Mallory and Church Corp.

BRIWAX - Furniture polish and wax - Henry Flack International, Inc.

BRIX - Charcoal - Royal Oak Enterprises, Inc.

BRIX 15 - Beverages–carbonated ☆ - Reggae Imports

BRIX STIX - Candy bar ☆ - Intersweet Candy Inc.

BRIXTON - Computer storage devices - CNT/Brixton Systems, Inc.

BRIXTON - Medical apparatus - Filmtech Inc.

BRK BRANDS - Smoke detectors - BRK Brands, Inc.

BRK ELECTRONICS - Electrical equipment - BRK Electronics Inc.

BRO-CUT - Rods–steel - J.S. Brower & Associates Inc.

BRO-EG - Eggs - Brokay Products Inc.

BRO-T - Pharmaceutical preparations - Brothers Pharmaceuticals Inc.

BRO-TISSERIE - Cooking equipment–commercial - Broaster Co.

BRO-TUSS - Pharmaceutical preparations - Brothers Pharmaceuticals Inc.

BROAD - Artists' materials - Robert Simmons Inc.

BROAD STREET - Coffee - Weyland Hayes Inc.

BROAD STREET BAKERY - Bakery products - Flowers Family Bakeries, Inc.

BROADBEAM - Fishing tackle - Lowrance Electronics, Inc.

BROADCARE - Milk - Broadacre Dairies Inc.

BROADCAST - Electronic equipment - Beyerdynamic Inc.

BROADCAST - Food products ☆ - John Morrell & Co.

BROADCAST - Meat products–canned - Nestle USA

BROADCAST - Paper - Butler Paper Co.

BROADCAST - Recording label - Jazz Composer's Orchestra Association Inc.

BROADCAST BOXING CLUB - T-shirts–men's - Broadcast Boxing Club, Inc.

BROADCAST GROUP - Electronic equipment - Beyerdynamic Inc.

BROADCAST INTERNATIONAL FAVORITES - Meat products–canned ☆ - John Morrell & Co.

BROADCAST ONE - Broadcasting stations–cable television - VDI

BROADCAST TURFLIME - Hardware - J.E. Baker Co.

BROADCASTER - Watches - Bulova Corp.

BROADCASTER III - Electronic equipment - P/H Electronics

BROADCASTER PENSION SERVICES - Consulting services - Pension Sciences Associates, Inc.

BROADCLOTH - Fabrics - Minnetonka Mills Inc.

BROADFIELD - Binoculars ☆ - Bausch & Lomb Inc.

BROADKASTER - Musical instruments ☆ - Fred Gretsch Enterprises

BROADLEAF - Wood products - Georgia-Pacific Corp.

BROADLEAF'S - Food products - Broadleaf Venison (USA) Inc.

BROADLUME - Lighting fixtures - Guth Lighting

BROADMAN & HOLMAN - Publisher's imprints - Broadman & Holman

BROADMOOR - Clocks - General Time Corp. (Westclox/Seth Thomas Div.)

BROADMOOR - Floor coverings–carpet and rugs - Sweetwater Carpet Corp.

BROADMOOR BAKER - Bakery products - Broadmoor Baker, Inc.

BROADMOOR BOOKS - Publisher's imprints ☆ - Zondervan Publishing House

BROADMORE - Trailers–travel - Fleetwood Enterprises, Inc.

BROADMORE COLLECTION - Floor coverings–carpet and rugs ☆ - Callaway Carpets

BROADRANGE - Herbicides - Wilbur-Ellis Co.

☆ = Now out of production

BROADSIDES - Filing cabinets–metal - Steelcase Inc.
BROADSIDES - Recording label ☆ - Rounder Records Corp.
BROADSTIX - Breads - Cathy, Inc.
BROADSTREET - Shoes - Allen-Edmonds Shoe Corp.
BROADSTREET'S - Apparel and accessories - McCrory Corp.
BROADSTRIKE - Herbicides - Dowelanco
BROADSWORD - Toys–models - Estes Industries
BROADVIEW DAIRY SINCE 1897 - Dairy products - Inland Northwest Dairies, Inc.
BROADWATER - Boats–motor - Broadwater Boat Co.
BROADWAY - Bicycles - Ross Bicycles USA, Ltd.
BROADWAY - Binders ☆ - Stationers Loose Leaf Co.
BROADWAY - Brushes–paint ☆ - Winsor & Newton
BROADWAY - Cabinets - Nutone Inc.
BROADWAY - Envelopes - Union Envelope Co.
BROADWAY - Finishing agents - Calgon Vestal Laboratories
BROADWAY - Floor coverings–carpet and rugs - Richmond Carpet Mills
BROADWAY - Floor coverings–carpet and rugs - Specialty Carpets
BROADWAY - Floor coverings–carpet and rugs - World Carpets, Inc.
BROADWAY - Food products - Hygrade Food Products Corp.
BROADWAY - Frames–eyeglass - U.S. Optical Frame Co.
BROADWAY - Fretted instruments ☆ - International Music Corp.
BROADWAY - Needles–sewing - Cascade Fibers Co.
BROADWAY - Pencils - Century Merchandising Corp.
BROADWAY - Photo albums - Holson Co.
BROADWAY - Pickles - M.A. Gedney Co.
BROADWAY - Recording label - Old Homestead Record Co.
BROADWAY - Wallpaper - Pickhardt & Siebert USA Inc.
BROADWAY - Wallpaper ☆ - Wolf-Gordon Inc.
BROADWAY - Watches - Bulova Corp.
BROADWAY BABE - Leotards - Hollywood Babe Inc.
BROADWAY BABY - Colognes ☆ - Key West Aloe Inc.
BROADWAY BETTY - Fireworks - Maryland Specialty Products, Inc.
BROADWAY BRASS - Hardware - Avondale Distributors Inc.
BROADWAY COLLECTION - Jewelry - Charles Lowe Productions Inc.
BROADWAY FOOTLIGHTS - Dolls ☆ - Effanbee Doll Corp.
BROADWAY GRADE - Office supplies - Esselte Corp.
BROADWAY NOP - Floor coverings–carpet and rugs - V & B Carpet
BROADWAY, USA! - Compact discs–prerecorded - Hard Hat Records
BROADWOOD - Floor coverings ☆ - Robbins Inc.
BROAN - Bathroom accessories - Monarch Metal Products Corp.
BROAN - Electronic equipment - Broan Manufacturing Co., Inc.
BROAN - Lighting fixtures - Rangaire
BROASTER - Cooking equipment–household - Alco Standard Corp.
BROASTER CHICKEN - Chickens - Broaster Co.
BROASTER FOODS - Fruits and vegetables - Broaster Co.
BROBELLA-P.B. - Pharmaceutical preparations - Brothers Pharmaceuticals Inc.
BROCA - Computer software - Cortex Medical Management Systems, Inc.
BROCADA - Floor coverings–carpet and rugs ☆ - Kelly Group Inc.
BROCADE - Cleaning preparations–household ☆ - Safeway Stores Inc.
BROCADE - Dishes–china - Pickard Inc.
BROCADE - Floor coverings–carpet and rugs - Barrett Carpet Mills Inc.
BROCADE - Furniture - Stanley Furniture Co. Inc.
BROCADE - Glassware–household ☆ - Lotus Glass Co.
BROCADE - Paper ☆ - Howard Paper Mills Inc.
BROCADE GOLD - Dinnerware–glass ☆ - Dansk International Designs, Ltd.
BROCADO - Glassware–household - Seneca Glass Co.
BROCATELLE - Dishes–china - Taylor, Smith & Taylor Co.
BROCATO - Hair care products - Brocato International
BROCCAMOLE - Dips–sour cream based - Mann Packing Co., Inc.
BROCCOLETTES - Food products - California & Washington Co.
BROCCOLI HEARTS - Fruits and vegetables - Mann Packing Co., Inc.
BROCCOLINI - Fruits and vegetables - Mann Packing Co., Inc.
BROCHURE 7 - Wallpaper ☆ - Winfield Design Associates, Inc.
BROCILLIN - Pharmaceutical preparations - Brothers Pharmaceuticals Inc.
BROCK - Cabinets ☆ - Marsh Furniture Co.
BROCK - Candy - Brock Candy Co. Inc.
BROCK - Rakes - California Flexrake Corp.
BROCK INTERNATIONAL - Computer software - Brock International, Inc.
BROCK LEE AND FRIENDS - Plastics - Brock Lee & Friends
BROCKER SIDES - Beds–metal ☆ - HARD Manufacturing Co. Inc.
BROCKLES - Food products - Brockles Food Co. Inc.
BROCKPORT - Floor coverings–carpet and rugs ☆ - Daltonian Carpet & Cushion Inc.
BROCK'S - Salads–prepackaged - J.C. Brock Corp.

BROCKTON - Cabinets - Imperial Cabinet Co. Inc.
BROCKTON - Floor coverings - Mannington Resilient Floors
BROCKTON - Wallpaper ☆ - Koroseal Wallcoverings
BROCKUM - Key rings - Brockum Co.
BROCKWAY - Toilets–enameled - Kohler Co.
BROCLICAPS - Vitamins and nutritional supplements - Amrion, Inc.
BROCO UNDERWATER - Welding equipment - Broco, Inc.
BROCON - Pharmaceutical preparations - Forest Laboratories, Inc.
BROCYCLINE - Pharmaceutical preparations - Brothers Pharmaceuticals Inc.
BRODERICK - Apparel and accessories - Broderick Co. Inc.
BRODICK CASTLE - Wallcoverings - Laura Ashley
BRODSPEC - Pharmaceutical preparations - C.O. Truxton Inc.
BRODY - Beverages–malt - Miller Brewing Co.
BRODY CIDER - Cider - Martlet Importing Co.
BROEKMAN'S & VAN POPPEL - Music–sheet - GSP
BROGAN - Tobacco–chewing or smoking - Amar Blends Co.
BROGDEX - Paints - Brogdex Co.
BROGESIC - Pharmaceutical preparations - Brothers Pharmaceuticals Inc.
BROGUE - Fabrics ☆ - Charter Fabrics Inc.
BROGUIERE - Milk - Broguiere's Farm Fresh Dairy, Inc.
BROGUIERE'S - Dairy products - Broguiere's Farm Fresh Dairy, Inc.
BROIL-AIR - Barbecues and grills ☆ - Buffalo Forge Co.
BROIL BEST - Charcoal - Royal Oak Enterprises, Inc.
BROIL-R-ANGE - Kitchen appliances - Capitol Products Co.
BROILED & BROWNED - Meat products–pork - Hormel Foods Corp.
BROILMASTER - Barbecues and grills - Locke Home Products Inc.
BROILMASTER - Barbecues and grills - Martin Industries, Inc.
BROILMATE - Barbecues and grills - Martin Industries, Inc.
BROKATY - T-shirts, stuffed toys, canisters, etc ☆ - American Greetings Corp.
BROKAW - Paper ☆ - Wausau Paper Mills Co.
BROKAY - Cookies - Brokay Products Inc.
BROKE & READEY - Egg substitutes - Papetti's Hygrade Egg Products, Inc.
BROKEN ARROW - Glass products - Big Pine Glass
BROKEN HELIX - Computer storage devices–optical - Konami (America) Inc.
BROKEN RECORD - Puzzles ☆ - Ben Cooper Inc.
BROKEN RECORDS - Recording label - Clay Pigeon Records
BROKEN SOUND - Floor coverings–carpet and rugs - Bloomsburg Carpet Industries
BROKEN WING COOKER FRYER GRILL - Barbecues and grills - R and D Sales, Inc.
BROKER - Luggage - Samsonite Corp.
BROKER - Watches - Bulova Corp.
BROKER, THE - Crocheted and knitted items - Reliable of Milwaukee
BROKER VISION - Computer software - A.G. Edwards Inc.
BROKERLINK - Computer software - Data-Connection, Inc.
BROKERS - Beverages–alcohol - Hood River Distillers Inc.
BROKSONIC - Electronic equipment - Hatzlachh Supply Inc.
BROLADE - Pharmaceutical preparations - Brothers Pharmaceuticals Inc.
BROLINE - Pharmaceutical preparations ☆ - Legere Pharmaceuticals Inc.
BROLIO - Wines - Seagram's Chateau & Estate Wines Co.
BROLOC - Hardware - Broderick & Bascom Rope Co.
BROM A SPA - Water treating compounds - Robarb Inc.
BROM-BLUE - Water treating compounds - Silco Pet Products
BROM-CORT - Prescription drug - IDE-Interstate Inc.
BROM-CORTANN - Prescription drug - IDE-Interstate Inc.
BROM QUICKMOUNT - Electrical testing instruments - Theodore R. Bromwell
BROMA - Paints ☆ - Dap Products Inc.
BROMA SILVER ROOF - Paints ☆ - Dap Products Inc.
BROMALATE - Cough medicines - Consolidated Midland Corp.
BROMALINE - Pharmaceutical preparations - Rugby Laboratories Inc.
BROMANATE - Pharmaceutical preparations - Barre-National, Inc.
BROMANYL - Pharmaceutical preparations - Barre-National, Inc.
BROMBAY - See **MYPHETANE**
BROME - Cosmetics - Comare Corp.
BROMEGRASS - Flowers, plants, and seeds - Jacklin Seed
BROMELAIN - Pharmaceutical preparations - Vita Plus Industries Inc.
BROMELAIN EXTRACT - Vitamins and nutritional supplements - Vitamin Research Products Inc.
BROMELAIN FORTE 550 TABS - Vitamins and nutritional supplements - Great Life Laboratories Inc.
BROMEPHEN - Cough medicines - Consolidated Midland Corp.
BROMEZYME - Vitamins and nutritional supplements - Amrion, Inc.
BROMFED - Pharmaceutical preparations - Muro Pharmaceuticals Inc.
BROMFED DM - Cold remedies - Muro Pharmaceuticals Inc.
BROMFED-PD - Pharmaceutical preparations - Muro Pharmaceuticals Inc.
BROMI-LOTION - Skin care products - Gordon Laboratories

BROMI-TALC - Skin care products - Gordon Laboratories

BROMI-TALC PLUS - Skin care products - Gordon Laboratories

BROMINIADS - Flowers, plants, and seeds - Kerry's Bromeliad Nursery, Inc.

BROMLEIGH - Bicycles - Columbia Manufacturing Inc.

BROMLEIGH RACER - Bicycles - Columbia Manufacturing Inc.

BROMLEIGH SPORTS - Bicycles - Columbia Manufacturing Inc.

BROMLEIGH TOURIST - Bicycles - Columbia Manufacturing Inc.

BROMLEY - Floor coverings–carpet and rugs - Karastan-Bigelow Inc.

BROMLEY - Teas - Eastern Tea Corp.

BROMLEY - Watches - Bulova Corp.

BROMO SELTZER - Antacids ☆ - Warner-Lambert Co.

BROMO-SHOCK - Chemical preparations ☆ - Aqua Clear Industries Inc.

BROMOCHEM - Chemical preparations - Robarb Inc.

BROMOPHEN - Paper–photographic - ILFORD Photo Corp.

BROMOPHEN - Pharmaceutical preparations - Rugby Laboratories Inc.

BROMOTUSS - Pharmaceutical preparations - Rugby Laboratories Inc.

BROMPHEN - Pharmaceutical preparations - Rugby Laboratories Inc.

BROMPHEN TAPP - Pharmaceutical preparations ☆ - Scrip-Physician Supply Co.

BROMPHENIRAMINE MALEATE - Pharmaceutical preparations - Forest Pharmaceuticals Inc.

BROMPTON - Tanks–water - Kohler Co.

BROMPTON COURT - Dinnerware–glass - Associated Merchandising Corp.

BROMTANE - Pharmaceutical preparations ☆ - Veratex Group

BROMTRINE - Chemical preparations ☆ - Applied Biochemists, Inc.

BRON-D-GEN - Pharmaceutical preparations ☆ - Goldline Laboratories, Inc.

BRON-EL - Automotive parts and accessories - K-Line Industries

BRONCARE - Health care products - Nature's Way Products, Inc.

BRONCHERBAL - Vitamins and nutritional supplements - McZand Herbal, Inc.

BRONCHI-LYPTUS - Cough medicines - Bronchi-Lyptus Laboratories, Inc.

BRONCHITIS AND ASTHMA AIDE - Pharmaceutical preparations - Boericke & Tafel

BRONCHLOFORM - Pharmaceutical preparations ☆ - JMI-Canton Pharmaceuticals

BRONCHO SALINE - Pharmaceutical preparations - Blairex Laboratories, Inc.

BRONCHOBID - Pharmaceutical preparations - Glaxo Wellcome Inc.

BRONCHOLATE - Pharmaceutical preparations - Bock Pharmacal Co.

BRONCHOLATE CS - Pharmaceutical preparations - Bock Pharmacal Co.

BRONCIDEX - Pharmaceutical preparations ☆ - Cumberland Pharmacal Co. Inc.

BRONCO - Apparel and accessories ☆ - Texas Boot Co.

BRONCO - Boats–motor - Century Boat Co.

BRONCO - Colognes - Frances Denney

BRONCO - Firearms, accessories, and parts - Welsh Sporting Goods Corp. (Boyt Div.)

BRONCO - Golfing equipment - Besco USA

BRONCO - Health care products - Farnam Cos. Inc.

BRONCO - Herbicides - Monsanto Co.

BRONCO - Meat products–poultry - Byron's Bar-B-Q

BRONCO - Motor vehicles–trucks - Ford Motor Co.

BRONCO - Thread - Threads USA Div.

BRONCO - Toys ☆ - Collier-Keyworth Inc.

BRONCO - Toys–stuffed - Dakin Inc.

BRONCO - Wheelbarrows - Ames Lawn & Garden Tool Co.

BRONCO - Wines - Pompei Winery Inc.

BRONCO - Wire–barbed - Thyssen-Bornemisza Inc.

BRONCO BLUE - Toys - Tonka Corp.

BRONCO BOB'S - Coffee - Lady Walton's Cookies, Inc.

BRONCO II - Motor vehicles–trucks ☆ - Ford Motor Co.

BRONCO TE - Teas–herbal - Jose M. Gonzalez-Blanco

BRONCO TENDER SWEET - Food products - Timmer Brothers

BRONCOFYLLINE - Pharmaceutical preparations ☆ - Jones Medical Industries, Inc. (Medical Div.)

BRONCOLOR - Lighting fixtures - Sinar-Bron Inc.

BRONCOMAR - Pharmaceutical preparations ☆ - Marlop Pharmaceuticals Inc.

BRONCOT - Pharmaceutical preparations - C.O. Truxton Inc.

BRONCRIN - Pharmaceutical preparations ☆ - Nature's Way Products, Inc.

BRONDECON - Pharmaceutical preparations ☆ - Parke-Davis

BRONDELATE - Pharmaceutical preparations - Barre-National, Inc.

BRONICA - Cameras - GMI Photographic Inc.

BRONICA - Photographic equipment - Tamron Industries Inc.

BRONITIN - Pharmaceutical preparations - Whitehall Laboratories

BRONJO MUSIC - Publisher's imprints - San Juan Music Group

BRONKAID - Cold remedies - Bayer Corp. (Consumer Care Div.)

BRONKEPHRINE - Pharmaceutical preparations - Sterling Winthrop Inc.

BRONKIE THE BRONCHIASAURUS - Computer software - Raya Systems, Inc.

BRONKOLATE - Pharmaceutical preparations - Parmed Pharmaceuticals, Inc.

BRONKOLIXIR - Antihistamine preparations - Sterling Winthrop Inc.

BRONKOMETER - Antihistamine preparations - Sterling Winthrop Inc.

BRONKOSOL - Antihistamine preparations - Sterling Winthrop Inc.

BRONKOTABS - Antihistamine preparations - Sterling Winthrop Inc.

BRONKOTUSS - Pharmaceutical preparations - Hyrex Pharmaceuticals

BRONNEROS - Christmas tree ornaments - Vincent Lippe Co.

BRONNER'S - Ornamental products–glass - Bronner's Christmas Decorations

BRONQUELL - Pharmaceutical preparations ☆ - Warner-Lambert Co.

BRONSON - Tobacco products - Quiktrip Corp.

BRONSON FORMULA, THE - Vitamins - Bronson Pharmaceuticals

BRONTE - Biscuits - Bri-AL, Inc.

BRONTEX - Cough medicines - Procter & Gamble Pharmaceuticals, Inc.

BRONTINI - Neckties - Salant/Manhattan Industries

BRONTO BABI - Candy ☆ - L.E.G. Inc.

BRONTO BONE - Pet products - Classic Products

BRONTOBONE - Pet food - Migatz & Migatz, Inc.

BRONTON - Coats - Bronton Apparel Ltd.

BRONZ-GLOW - Coatings - Bronz-Glow Technologies, Inc.

BRONZE ACE - Rackets–tennis - Pro Kennex, Inc.

BRONZE AGE - Apparel and accessories - Bronze Age, Inc.

BRONZE BRAID - Adhesives and sealants - Gemini Braids, Inc.

BRONZE-BULLET - Automotive parts and accessories - K-Line Industries

BRONZE BY RONL - Bronze sculpture ☆ - Corbell & Co.

BRONZE COIN - Nail care products - Cosmair Inc.

BRONZE DOUBLES - Cosmetics - Clinique Laboratories, Inc.

BRONZE FOX - Lighting equipment - Fox Lite Inc.

BRONZE FOX - Sporting goods - FTM Sports

BRONZE GALLERY - Figurines - Aus-Ben Studios

BRONZE-GARD - Weather stripping ☆ - Macklanburg-Duncan Co.

BRONZE GLAZE - Cosmetics ☆ - Honey & Spice Toiletries

BRONZE ICE - Lipsticks ☆ - Elysee Scientific Cosmetic Co.

BRONZE KNIGHT - Paints - Glidden Co.

BRONZE LTD. - Rackets–tennis - Pro Kennex, Inc.

BRONZE MEDAL - Mattress Pads - Pillowtex Corp.

BRONZE MENAGERIE, THE - Figurines ☆ - H & G Studio Inc.

BRONZE PERFECTION - Cosmetics - Noxell Corp.

BRONZE RUNNER - Footwear–athletic - KangaROOS USA Inc.

BRONZE STONE - Figurines - Living Stone, Inc.

BRONZE WINNER - Golfing equipment - John Rouzee Green Co., Inc.

BRONZEAL - Weather stripping - Zegers Inc.

BRONZEBERRY - Cosmetics - Elysee Scientific Cosmetic Co.

BRONZEE - Beauty shop equipment - Focus 21 International Inc.

BRONZEGOLD - Cosmetics - Elysee Scientific Cosmetic Co.

BRONZELLE - Panty hose - Bossong Hosiery Mills, Inc.

BRONZER - Suntanning product, makeup ☆ - Aubrey Organics, Inc.

BRONZERAL - Glass products - Glass Inc.

BRONZES OF FLEURIER, THE - Statuary - Actuelle Products Inc.

BRONZETTA - Cosmetics - European American Cosmetics Inc.

BRONZEVILLE - Apparel and accessories - Albert D. Cunningham

BRONZEWOOD LINE - Giftware ☆ - Bar & Barbeque Products Inc.

BRONZINI - Apparel and accessories ☆ - Host Apparel Inc.

BRONZINI - Apparel–athletic - Stage II Apparel Corp.

BRONZINI - Bronze products - Adhesive Products, Inc.

BRONZINI - Frames–eyeglass - Universal/Univis Inc.

BRONZOGRIT - Trimmings–metal - Wooster Products Inc.

BRONZTIQUE - Hardware - Alumax Aluminum Corp.

BRONZZER - Cosmetics - Pavion Ltd.

BROOD-ALL - Lamps - DriQuik, Inc.

BROODER-LITE - Lamps - Philips Lighting Co.

BROOHLYNER WEISSE - Beverages–alcohol - Brooklyn Brewery Ltd.

BROOK - Cabinets - Legeis Corp.

BROOK FARM - Floor coverings–carpet and rugs - Colonial Mills Inc.

BROOK FARMS - Food products - Gerawan Foods Inc.

BROOK HOLLOW - Footwear - JBI, Inc.

BROOK VALLEY - Furniture ☆ - Vaughan Furniture Co. Inc.

BROOKDALE - Floor coverings - Congoleum Corp.

BROOKDALE - Floor coverings–carpet and rugs ☆ - Evans-Black Carpet Mills

BROOKDALE - Glassware–household ☆ - Lenox Crystal, Inc.

BROOKDALE - Tableware–china ☆ - Lenox, Inc.

BROOKE - Floor coverings–carpet and rugs ☆ - Regal Rugs Inc.

BROOKFAIR - Rings–jewelry - Artcarved Inc.

BROOKFIELD - Apparel and accessories - Unitog Co.

BROOKFIELD - Cabinets - American Woodmark Corp.

☆ = Now out of production

BROOKFIELD - Cabinets - Dewils Industries Inc.
BROOKFIELD - Clocks - General Time Corp. (Westclox/Seth Thomas Div.)
BROOKFIELD - Fireplace equipment - Design Specialties Inc.
BROOKFIELD - Floor coverings–carpet and rugs - Criterion Mills Inc.
BROOKFIELD - Food products - Beatrice Cos. Inc.
BROOKFIELD - Furniture ✩ - U.S. Furniture Industries Inc.
BROOKFIELD - Sinks–metal - Kohler Co.
BROOKFIELD - Sporting goods - Brookfield Athletic Co. Inc.
BROOKFIELD - Trailers–travel - Fleetwood Enterprises, Inc.
BROOKFIELD - Wallpaper - Thomas Strahan Wallcoverings
BROOKFIELD 3 - Fabrics–tapestry - Comark Wallcoverings
BROOKFIELD BY HARTMANN - Luggage - Lenox, Inc.
BROOKFIELD CHEDDAR - Cheese ✩ - Swift Edible Oil Co.
BROOKFIELD HILLS - Floor coverings–carpet and rugs - Monticello Carpet Mills
BROOKFIELD ZOO - Jewelry - Chicago Zoological Society
BROOKHAVEN - Bathtubs–enameled - Kohler Co.
BROOKHAVEN - Cabinets - Wood-Mode Industries Inc.
BROOKHAVEN - Furniture ✩ - Vaughan Furniture Co. Inc.
BROOKHAVEN - Hair care products - Marietta Corp.
BROOKHAVEN - Motor vehicles–motor homes - Baron Motor Homes Inc.
BROOKHILL - Cabinets ✩ - Medallion Kitchens of Minnesota Inc.
BROOKHILL - Food products - Brookhill Frozen Meat Corp.
BROOKHOLLOW - Floor coverings - Bruce Hardwood Floors
BROOKHOLLOW - Manufactured homes - Redman Industries, Inc.
BROOKHOLLOW COLLECTION - Greeting cards ✩ - Drawing Board Greeting Cards Inc.
BROOKIES - Salad dressings–bottled - Brookies Inc.
BROOKINGS BOOKS - Publisher's imprints - Brookings Institution
BROOKLACE - Tablecloths - Brooklyn Lace Paper Works Inc.
BROOKLAWN 1895 - Apparel and accessories - Brooklawn Country Club Inc.
BROOKLEIGH - Furniture ✩ - Hooker Furniture Corp.
BROOKLINE - Fiberboard - Roxite Fiberglass
BROOKLINE - Shoes ✩ - Endicott Johnson Corp.
BROOKLINE - Toilets–enameled - Kohler Co.
BROOKLINE - Watches - Bulova Corp.
BROOKLITE - Food products - Brookside Deli Meats
BROOKLYN - Daters and numberers - Consolidated Stamp Manufacturing Co. Inc.
BROOKLYN - Shirts - Los Angeles Dodgers, Inc.
BROOKLYN BAGEL BOYS - Seafood - Brooklyn Bagel Boys
BROOKLYN BLACK CHOCOLATE STOUT - Beverages–alcohol - Brooklyn Brewery Ltd.
BROOKLYN BOW INTERNATIONAL - Ribbons - Brooklyn Bow & Ribbon Co., Inc.
BROOKLYN BROWN - Beverages–alcohol - Brooklyn Brewery Ltd.
BROOKLYN DRY STOUT - Beverages–alcohol - Brooklyn Brewery Ltd.
BROOKLYN EAST INDIA - Beverages–alcohol - Brooklyn Brewery Ltd.
BROOKLYN FLAVORED - Leather - Matthew & Co. of N.Y., Inc.
BROOKLYN GROOVE - Recording label - Echo Records Inc.
BROOKLYN JAVA - Coffee - Gillies Coffee Co.
BROOKLYN JEAN CO. - Apparel and accessories - Brooklyn Jean Co. Inc.
BROOKLYN LAGER - Beverages–alcohol - Brooklyn Brewery Ltd.
BROOKLYN MONSTER BARLEYWINE - Beverages–alcohol - Brooklyn Brewery Ltd.
BROOKLYN MUSEUM POSTCARDS (NEW YORK) - Postcards - Fotofolio Inc.
BROOKLYN OVERALL - Apparel and accessories - JLB Marketing, Inc.
BROOKLYN PENNANT - Beverages–alcohol - Brooklyn Brewery Ltd.
BROOKLYN PILSNER - Beverages–alcohol - Brooklyn Brewery Ltd.
BROOKLYN PROVISION - Meat products–beef - Emes Provisions, Inc.
BROOKMANOR - Cabinets ✩ - Mouser Kitchens Inc.
BROOKMERE - Flatware - Washington Forge Inc.
BROOKMONT - Floor coverings–carpet and rugs ✩ - Mannington Carpets, Inc.
BROOKPARK - Dinnerware–plastic - Brookpark Plastics Inc.
BROOKRIDGE - Bicycles - Western Auto Supply Co.
BROOKS - Brushes–hair - Traditional Products Inc.
BROOKS - Draperies - Brooks Window Coverings Inc.
BROOKS - Fishing lures ✩ - Harrison-Hoge Industries Inc.
BROOKS - Footwear - Brooks Shoe Inc.
BROOKS - Footwear - Wolverine World Wide, Inc.
BROOKS - Furniture ✩ - Brooks Furniture Manufacturing Inc.
BROOKS - Pet products - Jones Seed Co.
BROOKS - Shoes - Brooks Orthopedic & Custom Shoes
BROOKS - Surgical supplies - Brooks Appliance Co.
BROOK'S - Thread ✩ - Coats and Clark Inc.

BROOKS - Toys–stuffed - Eden LLC
BROOKS - Vegetables–canned - Curtice-Burns Foods, Inc.
BROOKS - Watches - Helbros International
BROOKS - Wheelchair - Frances Brooks Frame
BROOKS ADDITIONS - Apparel–women's ✩ - Bobbie Brooks Inc.
BROOKS AMORY - Pens ✩ - Anson Inc.
BROOKS & BENTLEY - Giftware - Lenox, Inc.
BROOKS & DUNN - Apparel and accessories - B & D, Inc.
BROOKS APEX - Footwear ✩ - Brooks Shoe Inc.
BROOKS BROTHERS - Apparel and accessories - Brooks Brothers, Inc.
BROOKS BROTHERS - Ophthalmic goods - Luxottica
BROOKS CHARIOT - Footwear ✩ - Brooks Shoe Inc.
BROOKS/COLE PUBLISHING CO. - Publisher's imprints - Brooks/Cole Publishing Co.
BROOKS COLLECTION, THE - Floor coverings–carpet and rugs - Karastan-Bigelow Inc.
BROOKS COUNTY - Meat products–pork - Sunnyland Foods Inc.
BROOKS FARMS - Sausages - Schwarz Sausage Co. Inc.
BROOKS GRANDE PRIMA - Cigars - T.E. Brooks & Co.
BROOKS PALMA DELUXE - Cigars - T.E. Brooks & Co.
BROOKS PUBLISHING CO. - Publisher's imprints ✩ - William Kaufmann, Inc.
BROOKS SENTRY - Footwear ✩ - Brooks Shoe Inc.
BROOKS TEMPO - Footwear ✩ - Brooks Shoe Inc.
BROOKS TRILOGY - Footwear ✩ - Brooks Shoe Inc.
BROOKS TROPICALS - Fruits and vegetables - Brooks Tropicals, Inc.
BROOKSCLOTH SHIRT COLLECTION - Shirts - Brooks Brothers, Inc.
BROOKSHIRE - Dishes–china - Waterford Wedgewood USA, Inc.
BROOKSHIRE - Floor coverings–carpet and rugs ✩ - Karastan-Bigelow Inc.
BROOKSHIRE - Milk - Dairy Fresh Corp.
BROOKSIDE - Crocheted and knitted items ✩ - Puritan Sportswear Corp.
BROOKSIDE - Floor coverings - Bruce Hardwood Floors
BROOKSIDE - Hair care products - Hunt Products Inc.
BROOKSIDE - Motor vehicles–motor homes ✩ - Georgie Boy Manufacturing, Inc.
BROOKSIDE - Shirts - Creighton Inc.
BROOKSIDE - Sporting goods ✩ - Maurice Sporting Goods, Inc.
BROOKSIDE - Wallpaper - Seabrook Wallcoverings, Inc.
BROOKSIDE - Whiskey - Paramount Distillers Inc.
BROOKSIDE - Wines - Brookside Enterprises Inc.
BROOKSONG - Christmas tree ornaments ✩ - Cracker Box Inc.
BROOKSONG - Pillows - Hoechst Celanese Corp.
BROOKSTILL - Liquors - Hughes Markets Inc.
BROOKSTONE - Beverages–alcohol - Sazerac Co. Inc.
BROOKSTONE - Floor coverings ✩ - Kentile Floors Inc.
BROOKSTONE - Floor coverings–carpet and rugs - Atlas Carpet Mills Inc.
BROOKSTONE - Floor coverings–carpet and rugs - Lotus Carpets
BROOKSTONE - Floor coverings–carpet and rugs - Patcraft Mills Inc.
BROOKSTONE - Paints ✩ - DecoArt, Inc.
BROOKSTONE NEUTRALS - Floor coverings–carpet and rugs - Atlas Carpet Mills Inc.
BROOKTROUT TECHNOLOGY - Computer hardware - Brooktrout Technology, Inc.
BROOKVIEW - Crocheted and knitted items ✩ - Puritan Sportswear Corp.
BROOKVILLE - Bedding–linen - Dan River Inc.
BROOKVILLE - Dishes–china - Viletta China Co.
BROOKVILLE - Food products - Staff Supermarket Associates, Inc.
BROOKVILLE - Furniture ✩ - Bassett Furniture Industries, Inc.
BROOKVILLE - Rings–jewelry - Artcarved Inc.
BROOKWOOD - Cabinets - Starmark, Inc.
BROOKWOOD - Furniture ✩ - Singer Furniture Co.
BROOKWOOD - Hardware - Alside Div.
BROOKWOOD - Mobile homes - Commodore Corp.
BROOKWOOD - Motor vehicles ✩ - General Motors Corp. (Chevrolet Motor Div.)
BROOKWOOD - Motor vehicles–motor homes - Baron Motor Homes Inc.
BROOKWOOD - Shoes ✩ - Allen-Edmonds Shoe Corp.
BROOKWOOD - Wallpaper ✩ - Advent Industries Inc.
BROOKWOOD FARMS - Food products - Brookwood Farms
BROOM BUDDY - Pans - Emsco Inc.
BROOM DESIGNS - Greeting cards - Broom Designs Inc.
BROOM SAVER - Brooms - B.O.B. Enterprises, Inc.
BROOM, THE - Brooms ✩ - Suburbanite Industries
BROOM VAC - Vacuum cleaners and accessories - Royal Appliance Manufacturing Co.
BROOMETTE - Carpet sweepers ✩ - Bissell Inc.
BROOMIES - Cakes ✩ - Crystal Food Import Corp.

✩ = Now out of production

BROOMSCRU, THE - Garment hangers - Rumsey Enterprise, Inc.
BROOMSKIRTS - Apparel and accessories - Lucia Lukken, Inc.
BROOMSTICKS - Slacks–men's - Glen Oaks Industries Inc.
BROPHENTAPP - Pharmaceutical preparations ☆ - Geneva Generics Inc.
BROPON - Glassware–household ☆ - Brookpark Plastics Inc.
BROS. - See also **BROTHERS**
BROS - Motorcycle parts and accessories - TBR, Inc.
BROSCO - Building materials–concrete - Brockway-Smith Co.
BROSEMA - Pharmaceutical preparations ☆ - Legere Pharmaceuticals Inc.
BROSERPINE - Pipes–tobacco - Brothers Pharmaceuticals Inc.
BROSET - Tools–hand-operated - Woodstock International, Inc.
BROTANE - Health care products - Halsey Drug Co. Inc.
BROTH BREAK - Broth - Wyler Foods/Borden Inc.
BROTHA MAN - Apparel and accessories - American Needle
BROTHER - Electrical equipment - Brother International Corp.
BROTHER - Toys - Tonka Corp.
BROTHER GRYM - Recording label - Rene Eiffert
BROTHER JIMMY'S - Apparel and accessories - National Themes, Ltd.
BROTHER JOHN - Computer software - Compudata, Inc.
BROTHER JUNIPERS - Bakery products - Neighborhood Baking Co.
BROTHER MATES - Crocheted and knitted items ☆ - Manchester Knitted Fashion Inc.
BROTHERHOOD - Gloves - Wells Lamont Corp.
BROTHERHOOD - Snowboards - Brotherhood, Inc.
BROTHERHOOD - Wines - Brotherhood America's Oldest Winery Ltd.
BROTHERS - See also **BROS.**
BROTHERS - Cream–canned or powdered - Brothers Gourmet Products, Inc.
BROTHERS AND SISTERS SPORTSWEAR - Apparel–children's - Ronald J. Margolis
BROTHERS & SONS - Vegetables–frozen - Seabrook Brothers & Sons Inc.
BROTHERS INTERNATIONAL DESSERTS - Snack foods - Brothers International Desserts
BROTHERS KEEPER - Containers - Brothers Gourmet Coffees, Inc.
BROTHERS SILVER DOLLAR ICE CREAM SANDWICH - Ice cream cones - Brothers International Desserts
BROUGHAM - Automotive parts and accessories ☆ - Lancaster Colony Automotive Group
BROUGHAM - Motor vehicles–automobiles - General Motors Corp. (Cadillac Motor Car Div.)
BROUGHAM - Pens ☆ - Pilot Pen Corp. of America
BROUGHAM - Recreational vehicle dealers - Brougham Industries Inc.
BROUGHAM D'ELEGANCE - Motor vehicles–automobiles - General Motors Corp. (Cadillac Motor Car Div.)
BROUSSARD - Perfumes - Difaya International, Inc.
BROUTHERS & KEEFE CHAMPION HOUSE - Trading cards and stamps - Tabloid, Inc.
BROVIRA - Paper–photographic - Miles Inc. (Agfa Div.)
BROW BEATERS - Cosmetics - Sassaby, Inc.
BROW BEAUTIFUL - Skin care products - Revlon Consumer Products Corp.
BROW SHAPERS - Skin care products - Ardell International Inc.
BROW TAMER - Cosmetics - Max Factor & Co.
BROWLINE - Cosmetics - Cici Cosmetic Co.
BROWN - Housewares - Brown Stove Works Inc.
BROWN - Jewelry - Brown Goldsmiths & Co. Inc.
BROWN - Musical instruments - Brown Distributing Co.
BROWN - Paper–toweling ☆ - Seventh Generation Wholesale Inc.
BROWN ADOBE, THE - Food products - Wagner Gourmet Foods, Inc.
BROWN & CRISP - Paper - American Direct Marketing, Inc.
BROWN & GRIST - Hardware - Blaine Window Hardware Inc.
BROWN & HALEY - Candy - Brown & Haley
BROWN & HALEY SELECTIONS - Candy - Brown & Haley
BROWN & SERVE BREAD STIX - Breadsticks - Meyer's Bakeries
BROWN & SHARPE - Locks–padlocks - Brown and Sharpe Manufacturing Co.
BROWN & SHARPE GRINDING MACHINE - Grinders - Devlieg-Bullard Services Group
BROWN BAG - Dog food - Lone Star Pet Foods
BROWN BAG BONANZA - Bags–paper - Ace Hardware Corp.
BROWN BAG COOKIE ART - Cooking utensils–china - Hill Design, Inc.
BROWN BAG PAPER ART - Cooking utensils–earthenware - Hill Design, Inc.
BROWN BEAR - Archery equipment ☆ - Bear Archery Inc.
BROWN BEAR - Beverages–malt - Golden Pacific Brewing Co., Inc.
BROWN BEAR - Candy - Rocky Mountain Chocolate Factory, Inc.
BROWN BEAR - Fishing lures - Brown Bear Bait Co.
BROWN BEARFOOT - Toys–stuffed ☆ - Dakin Inc.
BROWN BEAUTY - Brooms - Hanset Brothers Inc.
BROWN BEAUTY - Preserved foods–canned - Allen Canning Co.

BROWN BOUND - Binders - Homer B. Brown Co.
BROWN-BRIDGE - Paper–gummed - Brown-Bridge Industries
BROWN BROS. - Wines ☆ - Banfi Vintners
BROWN CLASSIC - Pelts - Kelly Mink Farm
BROWN COW - Confections - Mayfield Dairy Farms, Inc.
BROWN COW FARMS - Yogurt - Brown Cow West
BROWN CROWN - Shortening ☆ - CPC International Inc.
BROWN DERBY - Beverages–malt ☆ - The Stroh Brewery Co.
BROWN DERBY - Hotels and motels - Brown Derby, Inc.
BROWN DERMATOME - Surgical instruments - Zimmer, Inc.
BROWN DISC - Computer diskettes–blank - Brown Disc Products Co. Inc.
BROWN DOG - Recording label - Mainstream Records Inc.
BROWN E-BEAR - Toys–stuffed ☆ - Dakin Inc.
BROWN EDGE - Cookies - Nabisco Foods Group
BROWN-EX - Cleaning preparations–carpet and rug - Castex Industries Inc.
BROWN FLECK - Dishes–earthenware ☆ - Hadley Pottery Co. Inc.
BROWN FRUIT FARM - Food products - Betters International Food Corp.
BROWN GOLD - Coffee - Tetley Inc.
BROWN JORDAN - Furniture - Brown Jordan Co.
BROWN KRAFT - Envelopes - American Printing & Envelope Co.
BROWN KWIK - Food products - Bodin Foods Inc.
BROWN MACHINE BY SOLIS - Dryers–hair - Magic Distributing Ltd.
BROWN MULE - Confections - Land-O-Sun Dairies, Inc.
BROWN MULE - Ice cream - Pet Dairy
BROWN MULE - Tobacco–chewing or smoking - Swedish Math North America Inc.
BROWN 'N ROAST - Cooking equipment–household - E-Z-Por Corp.
BROWN N' SEASON - Seasonings ☆ - Adolph's Ltd.
BROWN 'N SERVE - Cooking equipment–household ☆ - Nordic Ware
BROWN 'N SERVE - Sausages - Armour Swift-Eckrich
BROWN OF BURLINGTON - Footwear - Brown Wooten Mills Inc.
BROWN OUT KIT - Lanterns–electric ☆ - Kaadan Ltd.
BROWN PELICAN - Boats–kayaks - Phoenix Products Inc.
BROWN RICE CHEWIES - Rice ☆ - Wehah Farm, Inc.
BROWN RICE CRISPS - Cereal - Barbara's Bakery, Inc.
BROWN RICE CRUNCHIES - Cereal ☆ - Wehah Farm, Inc.
BROWN RICE SNAPS - Crackers - Edward & Sons Trading Co., Inc.
BROWN SPOT OIL - Skin care products ☆ - Fanie International
BROWN SUGAR - Hosiery - Rice Juice Co.
BROWN SUGAR - Hosiery ☆ - Sheffield Industries Inc.
BROWNBERRY - Breads - Best Foods Baking Group
BROWNELL - Electronic equipment ☆ - Avnet, Inc.
BROWNELLS - Chemical preparations - Brownells, Inc.
BROWNIE - Beverages - Atlas Bottling Co.
BROWNIE - Brooms - Deshler Broom Factory Inc.
BROWNIE - Cameras - Eastman Kodak Co.
BROWNIE - Food products - Brownie Special Products Co.
BROWNIE - Sporting goods ☆ - Edwards Sports Products
BROWNIE BAR - Ice cream - Ben and Jerry's Homemade, Inc.
BROWNIE BASH - Ice cream - West Lynn Creamery, Inc.
BROWNIE BEAR - Toys–stuffed - Russ Berrie and Co., Inc.
BROWNIE BITES - Brownies - Interstate Brands Corp.
BROWNIE CHOCOLATE - Beverages - Seven-Up Brooklyn Bottling Co. Inc.
BROWNIE CRISP - Cookies - Pogens Family Bakery
BROWNIE IN THE ROUND - Pies–fresh - Sweet Street Desserts, Inc.
BROWNIE LIGHTS - Snack foods - McKee Foods Corp.
BROWNIE POINT - Cookies - Brownie Points Natural Bakers
BROWNIEPOP - Bakery products - Browniepop, Inc.
BROWNIEPOPPERS - Chocolate candy - Browniepop, Inc.
BROWNING - Radios - Maycom Communication
BROWNING - Sporting goods ☆ - Browning Manufacturing Co.
BROWNMOUSSE - Skin care products - Tweezerman Corp.
BROWNNOSE - Chocolate candy - Robert Mistretta
BROWN'S - Jackets - Omnisport Inc.
BROWN'S - Paper - L.L. Brown Paper Co.
BROWN'S - Pet products - Hummingbird Heaven
BROWNS 98S - Vegetables–dried - Kelley Bean Co., Inc.
BROWN'S BEST - Vegetables–dried - Kelley Bean Co., Inc.
BROWNS BRUSHWARE - Brushes - Pacific Resources International
BROWN'S MULE - Tobacco products - R.J. Reynolds Tobacco Co.
BROWNS SHAMROCK - Fabrics–linen ☆ - Ulster Weaving Co. Limited
BROWN'S SUPERCEDER - Pet products - George C. Brown & Co.
BROWN'S VELVET - Dairy products - Brown's Velvet Dairy
BROWNSTONE - Apparel–men's ☆ - Superba, Inc.
BROWNSTONE - Bicycles - Giant Bicycle, Inc.

☆ = Now out of production

BROWNSTONE - Cooking utensils–stoneware ☆ - Western Stoneware
BROWNSTONE BOOKS - Publisher's imprint - Borgo Press
BROWNSTONE COLLECTION - Furniture ☆ - Virginia House Furniture Corp.
BROWNSTONE OVENS - Cookies - President Baking Co., Inc.
BROWNSTONE RUSSET - Marble products ☆ - Carl Schilling Stoneworks
BROWNSTONE WEST - Recording label - Hallways to Fame Productions Inc.
BROWNSVILLE - Musical instrument accessories - Sam Ash Music Corp.
BROWNSWORD - Greeting cards ☆ - Recycled Paper Products, Inc.
BROWNULATED - Sugar–granulated, refined, or powdered - Domino Sugar Corp.
BROWNWOOD - Food products - Brownwood Acres Inc.
BROWSABOUTS - Footwear–women's - Oomphies Inc.
BROWSER - Computer software - Chicago One Stop/Browser Display
BROWSER - Crocheted and knitted items ☆ - Hercules-Carnation Knitwear Inc.
BROX - Toys ☆ - Tomy America, Inc.
BROXODENT - Toothbrushes - Bristol-Myers Squibb Co.
BROXTON - Floor coverings–carpet and rugs ☆ - Atlas Carpet Mills Inc.
BROYHAN - Beverages–malt - EFCO Importers
BROYHILL - Furniture–wood - Broyhill Furniture Industries, Inc.
BROZ - Apparel–men's - Big Boy Head Gear, Inc.
BROZ-O-PHONIC - Guitars - GRH Inc.
BRP - Skin care products - Shaklee Corp.
BRRR - Ice chests–metal - Divajex
BRRR - Sporting goods - Stearns Manufacturing Co.
BRRR BEAR - Toys–stuffed - Eden LLC
B.R.S. - Brushes–paint - Perfection Letz Paint Co.
BRSV-KV - Veterinary pharmaceutical preparations ☆ - Boehringer Ingelheim Animal Health, Inc.
BRT SMOKEY - Meat products–pork - Harker's, Inc.
BRU-NAMEL - Enamels ☆ - Waterlox Coatings Corp.
BRU-TECT - Paints ☆ - Bruning Paint Co.
BRU-TONE - Paints - Bruning Paint Co.
BRU-TOSS - Toys - Mattel, Inc.
BRUBOON - Recording label ☆ - Soul-Po-Tion Records
BRUCE - Anchors - Imtra Corp.
BRUCE - Cabinets ☆ - Triangle Pacific Corp. (Cabinet Division)
BRUCE - Floor coverings - Bruce Hardwood Floors
BRUCE - Floor waxes - Dial Corp.
BRUCE - Flooring–hardwood - Triangle Pacific Corp.
BRUCE - Food products - Bruce Foods Corp.
BRUCE - Lamps - Dibrell Brothers Inc.
BRUCE - Ophthalmic goods ☆ - Rozin Optical Export Corp.
BRUCE AMERICAN HOME SERIES - Flooring–hardwood - Triangle Pacific Corp. (Cabinet Division)
BRUCE CLEAN & WAX - Housewares ☆ - Bruce Hardwood Floors
BRUCE COLD-STIK - Floor coverings - Bruce Hardwood Floors
BRUCE DARK TONE - Housewares ☆ - Bruce Hardwood Floors
BRUCE FOX - Awards, plaques and medals - Bruce Fox, Inc.
BRUCE FOX DESIGN - Giftware - Wilton Co.
BRUCE LEE LIVES - Computer software - Software Toolworks, Inc.
BRUCE ONE STEP - Housewares ☆ - Bruce Hardwood Floors
BRUCE SATO - Toys - Tonka Corp.
BRUCE'S OLD TIME - Food products - Bruce Foods Corp.
BRUCHER - Wines ☆ - European Beverage Co., Inc.
BRUCIE BUNNY - Toys–stuffed - Russ Berrie and Co., Inc.
BRUCINE ALKALOID - Pharmaceutical preparations - City Chemical Corp.
BRUDDA SHARK - Apparel and accessories - Design Tees Hawaii Inc.
B.RUDE - Shirts - Gullwing Screenprint, Inc.
BRUDER - Dairy products - Bruder Dairy Products Co.
BRUDER - Health care products - Bruder Healthcare Co.
BRUDER - Toys - Importoys
BRUE - Statuary - Sandicast
BRUEBECK - Wines - Codera Wine Group
BRUECKENKELLEREI - Beverages–alcohol - Nor-Glo Import Co.
BRUEL & KJAER - Microphones - Bob White Associates
BRUFFIN - Breads - John Brophy
BRUGAL - Rum - Shaw-Ross International Importers
BRUGO - Wines - Blair Importers Ltd.
BRUGSE TRIPEL - Beverages–malt - Phoenix Imports Ltd.
BRUIN - Archery equipment - Bear Archery Inc.
BRUIN PALE ALE - Beverages–malt - Hudepohl-Schoenling Brewing Co.
BRUIN PALE ALE - Beverages–malt - Schoenling Brewing Co.
BRUISE BROTHER - Toys ☆ - Those Characters from Cleveland, Inc.
BRUISER - Containers–trash - Fesco Plastics Corp.
BRUISER - Metals - Hoover Universal
BRUISER BEAR - Toys–stuffed - Dakin Inc.

BRUISER II - Containers–trash - Fesco Plastics Corp.
BRUISER, THE - Locks–door - National Lock Hardware
BRUJITAS - Candy - Usher Products International, Inc.
BRULE - Vitamins and nutritional supplements - Vita Source, Inc.
BRUMBERGER - Photographic supply stores - Brumberger Co. Inc.
BRUMMEL - Hooks - Davis Instruments Corp.
BRUMMEL - Soap - So.De.Co (Usa)
BRUMMEL & BROWN - Sauces - Conopco, Inc.
BRUMMETT - Boats–motor - Brummett Marine
BRUMMI - Candy - Bahlsen Inc.
BRUMOL - Vitamins and nutritional supplements - Howard David Kass
BRUNA BOSSI - Footwear - Nouvo Design Inc.
BRUNCH - Candy ☆ - Leaf, Inc.
BRUNCH - Wallpaper - Motif Designs, Inc.
BRUNCH BREADS - Bakery products - Miss Kings Kitchen Inc.
BRUNCH TIME - Salads–prepackaged - Herman Miller, Inc.
BRUNDY - Chemical preparations - Brundy Corp.
BRUNELLAS' - Prepared food - Concept Foods, Inc.
BRUNELLO DI MONTALCINO - Wines - Banfi Vintners
BRUNER - Water purification systems - Bruner Corp.
BRUNER-MATIC - Water purification systems - Bruner Corp.
BRUNET - Cosmetics - Brunet International, Ltd.
BRUNGE - Cleaning equipment - Ekco Housewares, Inc.
BRUNO - Apparel–men's - Cote De France, Inc.
BRUNO - Musical instruments - C. Bruno & Son Inc.
BRUNO ARTIST - Musical instruments - C. Bruno & Son Inc.
BRUNO BEAR - Toys–stuffed - Dakin Inc.
+BRUNO +BERNINI - Eyeglasses - B.B. Frames
BRUNO LORELLI - Handbags - B.H. Smith, Inc.
BRUNO MAURIZIO - Apparel–men's - Reflex Manufacturing Inc.
BRUNO THE BAD DOG - Toys - Mattel, Inc.
BRUNO VALENTI - Footwear - Olem Shoe Corp.
BRUNO WALTER SOCIETY - Recording label - Music and Arts Programs of America Inc.
BRUNO'S BEST - Dog food - Hubbard Milling Co.
BRUNS - Cigars - Gesty Trading & Manufacturing Corp.
BRUNSANA - Yarn - Brunswick Yarns
BRUNSCHWIG & FILS - Lamps - Brunschwig and Fils Inc.
BRUNSCHWIG & FILS SARATOGA COLLECTION - Furniture - Brunschwig and Fils Inc.
BRUNSCO - Pool tables ☆ - Brunswick Corp.
BRUNSWICK - Bedding–linen - Dan River Inc.
BRUNSWICK - Furniture - Boling Co.
BRUNSWICK - Paint sets–hobby ☆ - Winsor & Newton
BRUNSWICK - Recording label - MCA Universal Studios
BRUNSWICK - Seafood products–fresh or frozen - Connors Brothers Inc.
BRUNSWICK - Shirts - Wilson Brothers
BRUNSWICK - Sporting goods - Brunswick Corp.
BRUNSWICK - Televisions - Projectapix-II
BRUNSWICK - Tires - Uniroyal Goodrich Tire Co.
BRUNSWICK - Watches - Bulova Corp.
BRUNSWICK - Yarn - Brunswick Yarns
BRUNTON - Compasses–gyroscopic - Rothco Inc.
BRUNVIL - Watches - Nicolet International Inc.
BRUSH-A-ROUND - Brushes–hair - I. Sekine Co. Inc.
BRUSH AND CLEAN - Floor coverings - Apache Mills Inc.
BRUSH-AWAY! - Cleaning preparations - Robarb Inc.
BRUSH-B-GON - Herbicides - Chevron Chemical Co.
BRUSH BABY - Fishing lures - Luhr Jensen & Sons, Inc.
BRUSH BAG - Bags - Busy Bee Manufacturing
BRUSH BASIN - Artists' materials - Plaid Enterprises, Inc.
BRUSH/BLUSH II - Cosmetics - Maybelline Co.
BRUSH BOX - Office supplies - Clearsnap, Inc.
BRUSH BUSTER - Lawn mowers - Harvey Equipment Center, Inc.
BRUSH BUSTERS - Apparel and accessories - Bob Allen Sportswear
BRUSH BUTTONS - Sporting goods ☆ - Trueflight Manufacturing Co. Inc.
BRUSH CLIP - Barrettes - Riviera Trading, Inc.
BRUSH CREEK - Automotive parts and accessories - Tremar U.S. Inc.
BRUSH CREEK - Furniture - Lexington Furniture Industries, Inc.
BRUSH DANCE - Greeting cards - Brush Dance, Inc.
BRUSH DELITE - Cleaning preparations - King Research, Inc.
BRUSH FLUSH - Paint thinners - American Art Clay Co. Inc.
BRUSH-HESS - Skin care products - Hess Hair Milk Laboratories Inc.
BRUSH IT! - Hair care products - Natural Glass
BRUSH-IT-AWAY - Skin care products - Victoria Vogue, Inc.
BRUSH-IT-ON - Cosmetics - Max Factor & Co.

BRUSH KIL - Pesticides–household - Bonide Products, Inc.

BRUSH KLEEN - Cleaning preparations - Phillips Brush Corp.

BRUSH KONTROL - Cleaning preparations ☆ - Mark Allen Co.

BRUSH-LESS - Cosmetics - Nino Originals

BRUSH LIFT II - Combs ☆ - Comare Corp.

BRUSH-LITER - Pens - Micro Pen of USA, Inc.

BRUSH LOOP - Floor coverings - Apache Mills Inc.

BRUSH MASTER - Herbicides - PBI/Gordon Corp.

BRUSH MATE - Artists' materials - Plaid Enterprises, Inc.

BRUSH ME DECORATIONS - Hobby kits - Mats Etc. Inc.

BRUSH 'N BLEND - Paints ☆ - DecoArt, Inc.

BRUSH 'N BLUSH - Skin care products - Schering-Plough Healthcare Products

BRUSH 'N BODY - Brushes - Windmere Corp.

BRUSH 'N' CURL - Brushes–hair - I. Sekine Co. Inc.

BRUSH 'N FILL - Automotive parts and accessories ☆ - Fibre Glass-Evercoat Co. Inc.

BRUSH-N'-GO! - Cosmetics - Brush-N'-Go!, Inc.

BRUSH 'N LEAF - Finishing agents - American Art Clay Co. Inc.

BRUSH-N-SCRAPE - See **RING LEADER**

BRUSH 'N SCRAPE - Housewares - Plumb Shop

BRUSH NOW - Toothbrushes - Sarcon International, Inc.

BRUSH OFF - Brushes - Selfix, Inc.

BRUSH OFF - Hair care products - Helene Curtis Industries Inc.

BRUSH-OFF - Rust removers ☆ - Kester Solder Co.

BRUSH OFFS - Archery equipment - Saunders Archery Co.

BRUSH-ON - Adhesives and sealants - Epoxy Coatings Co.

BRUSH-ON LIGHTS - Hair care products - Clairol Inc.

BRUSH ON NAILS - Manicure preparations - Gena Laboratories Inc.

BRUSH PLUS - Cleaning preparations - Plaid Enterprises, Inc.

BRUSH PLUS - Pharmaceutical preparations - Applied Microdontics

BRUSH PLUS - Shaving preparations - Gillette Co.

BRUSH POPPER - Sporting goods - James Heddon's Sons

BRUSH QUIVER - Brushes–paint - Masterson Art Products, Inc.

BRUSH SAVER - Containers - R & D Business Systems, Inc.

BRUSH-STEP - Mats - Matworks

BRUSH STROKE - Skin care products - Dorothy Gray Cosmetics Ltd.

BRUSH SYSTEM - Artists' materials - Pentech International Inc.

BRUSH SYSTEM 20 - Markers–felt-tip - Pentech International Inc.

BRUSH TIP - Soldering equipment - Electronics Soldering Toolnology Inc.

BRUSH TONES - Brushes–hair - Hilda Choy Wong

BRUSH TUB - Buckets–plastic - Loew-Cornell Inc.

BRUSH-UP - Artists' materials - Loew-Cornell Inc.

BRUSH UP - Vacuum cleaners and accessories - The Eureka Co.

BRUSH-UPS - Artists' materials - Duncan Enterprises

BRUSH UPS - Skin care products - Ardell International Inc.

BRUSH-VAC - Vacuum cleaners and accessories - The Hoover Co.

BRUSH WITH SUCCESS, A - Brushes–hair - Spornette International, Inc.

BRUSHCUT - Machinery - Langston Corp.

BRUSHED BLUE - Dishes–earthenware ☆ - Louisville Stoneware Co.

BRUSHED VELVET - Headphones - Westone Laboratories Inc.

BRUSHED WOOD - Siding–insulating - Aluminum Co. of America

BRUSHES BY BAKER - Brushes–paint - Baker Brush Co. Inc.

BRUSHES BY KAHANA - Skin care products - Phase One Distributing

BRUSHETTE - Saws–chain ☆ - Hoffco Inc.

BRUSHFLUSH - Cleaning preparations ☆ - Demert & Dougherty, Inc.

BRUSHING - Skin care products - Dynex International

BRUSHING BRUSH - Skin care products - La Coupe

BRUSHKEEPER - Turpentine - Reliable Finishing Products, Inc.

BRUSHLESS - Shaving preparations - Mennen Co.

BRUSHLON - Abrasive products - Minnesota Mining & Manufacturing Co.

BRUSHMARK - Hardware ☆ - United Manufacturers Supplies Inc.

BRUSHMASTER - Guns - Remington Arms Co., Inc.

BRUSHMASTER - Paints - KCI Coatings, Inc.

BRUSHMASTER - Paper - Hunt Manufacturing Co.

BRUSH'N BLUSH - Cosmetics - Viviane Woodard Industries, Ltd.

BRUSHOGRAPH - Pens–fountain ☆ - Koh-I-Noor, Inc.

BRUSHSAVERS - Housewares - Lynted Corp.

BRUSHSTROKE - Fabrics - Greenwood Mills Inc.

BRUSHSTROKE - Siding–insulating - Norandex, Inc.

BRUSHSTROKES - Floor coverings–carpet and rugs - Regal Rugs Inc.

BRUSHSTROKES - Kitchenware–earthenware ☆ - Arita Sales Co. Inc.

BRUSHSTROKES II - Wallpaper - Seabrook Wallcoverings, Inc.

BRUSHTECH - Brushes - Brushtech Inc.

BRUSHTIQUES - Cosmetics - SBS Beauty Systems

BRUSHWHITE - Cleaning preparations - Kafko International Ltd.

BRUSHWOOD - Floor coverings - Congoleum Corp.

BRUSHWORK - Dinnerware–glass ☆ - Lenox, Inc.

BRUSHWORKS - Brushes–hair - Wal-Mart Stores Inc.

BRUSHWORX - Housewares - Wilen Companies, Inc.

BRUSHY-BRUSHY - Toothbrushes - Shirley Leiser

BRUSSELS - Cookies - Pepperidge Farm Inc.

BRUSSELS - Floor coverings–carpet and rugs ☆ - LaVelle Textile Marketing Inc.

BRUSSELS - Luggage - Universal Trav-ler Inc.

BRUSSELS - Mattresses - Simmons USA

BRUSSELS - Wallcoverings - Stretchwall Fabrics Co.

BRUSTICK - Mallets - Mike Balter Mallets

BRUT - Cosmetics - Faberge Co.

BRUT - Jewelry - CPI Fab, Inc.

BRUT - Leather goods - RGA Accessories Inc.

BRUT - Leather–chamois - S.M. Arnold Inc.

BRUT - Manicure sets - London International U.S. Holdings

BRUT - Underwear and nightwear - Nantucket Industries Inc.

BRUT - Wines ☆ - Moyer Texas Champagne Co.

BRUT 33 - Cosmetics - Faberge Co.

BRUT ACTIF - Colognes - Chesebrough-Pond's USA Co.

BRUT ACTIF BLUE - Colognes - CPI Fab, Inc.

BRUT ACTIF BLUE - Deodorants–personal - Faberge Co.

BRUT ACTIF BLUE - Perfumes - Chesebrough-Pond's USA Co.

BRUT DARGENT - Wines - Palm Bay Imports, Inc.

BRUT ESPECIAL - Wines ☆ - Moyer Texas Champagne Co.

BRUT JR. - Cosmetics - Faberge Co.

BRUT L.D. - Iron Horse Vineyards

BRUT NATURALE - Wines ☆ - Moyer Texas Champagne Co.

BRUT PREMIER - Wines - IDV Wines (Beaulieu Vineyard)

BRUT ROYALE - Colognes - Faberge Co.

BRUTAL - Computer software - Gametek, Inc.

BRUTAL BEACH - T-shirts–women's - Sharky's Clothing Co.

BRUTAL YOUTH N.Y.C. - Apparel and accessories - John S. Pierce

BRUTALLY STRONG - Footwear ☆ - H.H. Brown Shoe Co., Inc.

BRUTE - Amplifiers–musical instrument - Westheimer Corp.

BRUTE - Apparel–athletic - Henson Manufacturing Co.

BRUTE - Bicycles - Ross Bicycles USA, Ltd.

BRUTE - Blocks–concrete - VERSA-LOK Retaining Wall Systems (Kiltie Corp.)

BRUTE - Buckets–plastic - Rubbermaid Commercial Products Inc.

BRUTE - Flashlights - Bridgeport Metal Goods Manufacturing Co.

BRUTE - Golfing equipment - Ram Golf Corp.

BRUTE - Hammers - S-B Power Tool Co.

BRUTE - Hardware - Trans-Atlantic Co.

BRUTE - Insecticides - Y-Tex Corp.

BRUTE - Ladders–metal - Davidson Ladders Inc.

BRUTE - Lawn mowers - Alamo Group

BRUTE - Office supplies - Ames Safety Envelope Co.

BRUTE - Rivets–metal - Creative Engineering

BRUTE - Tool boxes - Flambeau Products Corp.

BRUTE - Tools - Arrow Fastener Co. Inc.

BRUTE - Tools - Quick Cable Corp.

BRUTE - Vacuum cleaners and accessories - Shop Vac Corp.

BRUTE - Wet suits–rubber ☆ - Parkway Systems

BRUTE CRUSHER - Toys–automobiles - Buddy L Inc.

BRUTE FORCE - Cleaning preparations - Blue Coral, Inc.

BRUTE FORCE - Exercising equipment - Sport Supply Group, Inc.

BRUTE FORCE - Toys–automobiles - Buddy L Inc.

BRUTE FORCE - Vacuum cleaners and accessories–commercial - Breuer Electric Manufacturing Co.

BRUTE HAULERS - Toys–automobiles - Buddy L Inc.

BRUTE POWER - Automotive parts and accessories - Echlin Inc.

BRUTE, THE - Mail boxes - Steel City Corp.

BRUTEM - Building materials–concrete - Master Builders Inc.

BRUTES - Toys–automobiles - Buddy L Inc.

BRUTINI - Footwear–athletic - Mercury International Trading Corp.

BRUTON - Tobacco–chewing or smoking - United States Tobacco Co.

BRUTUS - Electrical equipment - GB Electrical Inc.

BRUTUS - Exercising equipment - Excel, The Exercise Co.

BRUTUS - Exercising equipment - Rocket Industries

BRUTUS - Vibrators - Dynamote Corp.

BRUTUS THE BARBER BEEFCAKE - Toys ☆ - Titan Sports, Inc.

BRUTUS TIGER - Toys–stuffed - Russ Berrie and Co., Inc.

BRUXELLE - Wallpaper - Marburg Wallcoverings Inc.

BRUXELLES - Glassware–household ☆ - Wallace International Silversmiths, Inc.

BRUXTON - Apparel–children's - Elder Manufacturing Co., Inc.

BRUYNZEEL - Artists' materials - International Playthings Inc.
BRUYNZEEL - Plywood - Harbor Sales Co.
BRYAN - Apparel–children's - Bryan Industries, Inc.
BRYAN - Food products - Saramar Corp.
BRYAN - Gravy - Sara Lee Corp.
BRYAN - Meat products–canned - Bryan Foods, Inc.
BRYAN EDWARDS - Apparel–children's - Montgomery Ward & Co. Inc.
BRYAN EXTRA LEAN - Sausages - Bryan Foods, Inc.
BRYAN FAMILY RECIPE - Hams - Bryan Foods, Inc.
BRYAN LONG - Footwear - J.B. Long Inc.
BRYAN MAID - Vegetables–canned - Bryan Canning Co.
BRYAN SMOKY HOLLOW - Meat products - Saramar Corp.
BRYAN TROTTIER - Hockey equipment ☆ - Right Gard Corp.
BRYANT - Air conditioning equipment - United Technologies Corp.
BRYANT - Heating equipment - Carrier Corp.
BRYANT - Luggage ☆ - Missouri Trunk & Case Co.
BRYANT - Machine parts - Bryant Grinder Corp.
BRYANT - Watches - Bulova Corp.
BRYANT - Wiring devices - Hubbell Electrical Products
BRYANT COLLEGE EXPANDING THE WORLD OF OPPORTUNITY 1863 - Educational materials - Bryant College
BRYANT COLLEGE EXPANDING THE WORLD OF OPPORTUNITY SINCE 1863 - Educational materials - Bryant College
BRYANT LIFE-CARE PRODUCTS - Medical apparatus - Sandra E. Petersen
BRYANT ORTHOPEDIC - Orthopedic belt - Boyce Ann Proctor
BRYANT PARK - Apparel–women's - Lane Bryant, Inc.
BRYANT PARK - Bicycles - Ross Bicycles USA, Ltd.
BRYCE - Computer software - HSC Software
BRYCE CANYON - Blankets - Pendleton
BRYCE CANYON BURGUNDY - Hardwood flooring - Harris-Tarkett, Inc.
BRYCEWOOD - Lighting fixtures ☆ - Hubbell Lighting, Inc. (Lighting Div.)
BRYCO - Automotive parts and accessories - Carfel Inc.
BRYCO - Pipe cleaners - Bryn Mawr Smokers Sundries Inc.
BRYLCREEM - Hair care products - J.B. Williams Co. Inc.
BRYN CONNELLY - Apparel–women's - Federated Department Stores, Inc.
BRYN MAWR - Apparel and accessories ☆ - Bobbie Brooks Inc.
BRYN MAWR - Floor coverings–carpet and rugs ☆ - Masland Corp.
BRYN MAWR - Furniture ☆ - Bassett Furniture Industries, Inc.
BRYN MAWR - Smokers accessories - Chenille Kraft Co.
BRYN MAWR - Tableware–china ☆ - Lenox, Inc.
BRYN MAWR - Watches - Bulova Corp.
BRYNDZA - Cheese - Tatra Sheep Cheese Co.
BRYTIN - Veterinary pharmaceutical preparations ☆ - Upjohn Co.
BRYTOL - Oils–lubricating - Pennsylvania Petroleum Products Co.
BRYTONE - Mirrors - Mechanical Mirror Works Inc.
BS - Apparel and accessories - Napa Valley Box Co. Inc.
BS - Chemical preparations - Bright Solutions, Inc.
B'S - Fabrics - Gretchen Bellinger Inc.
BS-2 - Saws–hand-operated ☆ - Emco-Maier Corp.
BS BAGS - Novelty items - Cal Themes Inc.
BS BRAND - Meat products - Baney Meats, Inc.
BSA - Motorcycles - Triumph Motorcycles America Inc.
BSAP - Computer software - Bechtel Group, Inc.
BSC - Footwear - Boston Strider Corp.
BSC-93 - Cleaning preparations - Ofna Environmental Products
BSC-2000 - Computer software - Management Information Technology Corp.
BSE - Footwear–athletic ☆ - Ken-Pin Inc.
BSF - Food products - Beaver Street Fisheries Inc.
BSF COMPONENTS - Construction equipment rental services - Bao Shing Trading, Inc.
BSG - Audio equipment - BSG Laboratories, Inc.
B.S.I. - Helmets–athletic - Bell Sports Corp.
BSI - Insulation board - Big Sky Insulations, Inc.
BSL - Helmets–athletic - Bell Sports Corp.
BSMART - Computer software - C.H. Robinson Co.
BSOLO DESIGNS - Apparel and accessories - B-Solo Designs, Inc.
BSQUEEZE - Computer software - Mesa Business Solutions
BSS - Audio equipment - AKG Acoustics Inc.
BSS - Chemical preparations - Alcon Laboratories, Inc.
BSS - Educational materials - Encyclopaedia Britannica Inc.
BSS PLUS - Surgical supplies - Alcon Laboratories, Inc.
BST - Explosives - Beston Chemical Corp.
BST DIRECT - Computer programming services - At&T Corp.
B.S.U.R. - Hats - Be AS You Are, Inc.
BSW - Recording label - BSW Records
BSW - Tea kettles–nonelectric ☆ - Herman Dodge & Son Inc.

BT - Computer integrated systems design services - Brooktree Corp.
BT - Cosmetics - Moore Beauty Inc.
BT - Pesticides–household - Bonide Products, Inc.
BT-8 - Fuel additives - Ferrous Corp.
B.T. BIOSPRAY - Insecticides - Chevron Chemical Co.
BT MASTERBRAND - Office supplies - BT USA, Inc.
BT20 - Tape–adhesive - Protecto Wrap Co.
BT20 XL - Tape–adhesive - Protecto Wrap Co.
BTB - Apparel - Perrier Inc.
BTC - Cleaning preparations ☆ - Jungle Laboratories Corp.
BTC - Golfing equipment - Ryobi-Toski Corp.
BTC - Wheelchairs - Labac Systems, Inc.
BTC: PRECISION CHUCK - Metal finishing equipment - Golden Lyon Investment, Inc.
B.T.D.T. - Apparel and accessories - Been There, Done That, Inc.
BTE CIC - Hearing aids - Rexton Inc.
BTF - Computer peripheral equipment - Before the Fact Management Systems, Inc.
BTG PHARMACEUTICALS - Pharmaceutical preparations - Bio-Technology General Corp.
BTI NUTRITEX - Agricultural products - Biorecycling Technologies, Inc.
BTJ - Onions - Bosgraaf Sales Co.
BTK - Apparel and accessories - Mcgregor Corp.
BTK-PLUS - Disinfectants - Geritrex Corp.
BTS - Buckles - BTS Solid Brass Specialties
BTSB CONNECTION - Computer software - Bound to Stay Bound Books, Inc.
BTU BUCKET - Solar energy collectors - Solar Usage Now Inc.
BTU STOKER - Apparel and accessories - BTU Stoker, Inc.
BTV - Televisions - Brooktree Corp.
BTVISION - Television equipment ☆ - Blonder-Tongue Laboratories Inc.
BTX - Apparel and accessories - Triumph of California Inc.
BU BAR - Pharmaceutical preparations ☆ - Cumberland Pharmacal Co. Inc.
BU-LAX - Pharmaceutical preparations ☆ - Ulmer Pharmacal Co.
BUAK - Food products - Buak Fruit Co.
BUB - Sporting goods - John B. Flaherty Co. Inc.
BUB-IT-ON - Stencils - P-T Templet Co. Inc.
BUBARBEL - Pharmaceutical preparations ☆ - C.O. Truxton Inc.
BUBB-A-LOONS - Toys - Imperial Toy Corp.
BUBBA - Beverages - Moran Foods, Inc.
BUBBA - Braces–orthopedic - Occumed International Inc.
BUBBA - Food products - Atlantis Coastal Foods
BUBBA - Food products - Charleston Catalog Co.
BUBBA BEAR - Candy - Gladstone Candies
BUBBA BEAR - Toys–stuffed - Dakin Inc.
BUBBA BRAND - Toys - Charleston Catalog Co.
BUBBA DOG - Beverages–alcohol - Yellow Rose Brewing Co
BUBBA GEAR - Tents - Myriad Licensing, Inc.
BUBBA TEDDY - Toys–stuffed - Russ Berrie and Co., Inc.
BUBBA U - Colognes - Charleston Catalog Co.
BUBBA'S - Candy - DiFranco Foods
BUBBE BESSIE - Greeting cards ☆ - Designer's Connection
BUBBETTE - Pharmaceutical preparations - Myriad Licensing, Inc.
BUBBETTE - Shirts - Charleston Catalog Co.
BUBBI - Greeting cards - Bubbi Creations
BUBBIE & ZAIDA'S - Bagels - Bubbie & Zaida's
BUBBIES RUGGIES - Confections - Bubbies Ruggies
BUBBL-EEZ - Chewing gum - Lotte USA Inc.
BUBBLATOR - Toys - Original Ideas
BUBBLE - Apparel and accessories ☆ - Alger Creations Inc.
BUBBLE - Furniture ☆ - Stow/Davis Furniture Co.
BUBBLE - Golfing equipment - Taylor Made Golf Co. Inc.
BUBBLE-A-GO-GO - Chewing gum ☆ - Leaf, Inc.
BUBBLE BALLET - Toys - Tonka Corp.
BUBBLE BALLS - Plastics ☆ - Fry Plastics International Inc. (O)
BUBBLE-BAR - Pet products - Penn-Plax, Inc.
BUBBLE BARS - Chewing gum - Philadelphia Chewing Gum Corp.
BUBBLE BEE - Shampoos - Arctic Pak, Inc.
BUBBLE BEEPER - Chewing gum - Amurol Confections Co.
BUBBLE BITS - Chewing gum - Amurol Confections Co.
BUBBLE BLASTER - Toys ☆ - Henry Gordy International Inc.
BUBBLE BLISS - Bathroom accessories - Homedics Inc.
BUBBLE BLOWIN' - Dolls - Mattel, Inc.
BUBBLE BOBBLE - Video games ☆ - Taito America Corp.
BUBBLE BOPPER - Toys - Tiger Electronics, Inc.
BUBBLE BOPPERS - Chewing gum - R.L. Albert & Son, Inc.
BUBBLE BOTTLE - Chewing gum - Amurol Confections Co.

☆ = Now out of production

BUBBLE BOULDERS - Chewing gum ☆ - Amurol Confections Co.
BUBBLE BRAIN - Chewing gum - Creative Confection Concepts, Inc.
BUBBLE BRIGADE - Cleaning preparation - Slipsafe Professional Products, Inc.
BUBBLE BUCKS - Chewing gum - Philadelphia Chewing Gum Corp.
BUBBLE BUG - Toys ☆ - Combi International Corp.
BUBBLE BURGER - Chewing gum - Fleer Corp.
BUBBLE BURST - Computer software - Spinnaker Software Corp.
BUBBLE BUSTER - Cleaning preparations - W.W. Grainger, Inc.
BUBBLE CANDY - Chewing gum - Tootsie Roll Industries, Inc.
BUBBLE-CAP - Pet products - Penn-Plax, Inc.
BUBBLE CARRIAGE - Toys - Mattel, Inc.
BUBBLE CLUB - Bath salts - Dial Corp.
BUBBLE-DISK - Pet products - Penn-Plax, Inc.
BUBBLE DOT - Fabrics - Gretchen Bellinger Inc.
BUBBLE EXTINGUISHER - Toys - Mattel, Inc.
BUBBLE FACTORY, THE - Skin care products - Northern Labs, Inc.
BUBBLE FAIRIES - Figurines - Rawcliffe Corp.
BUBBLE FLO - Plumbing fixtures–plastic ☆ - Waxman Industries Inc.
BUBBLE FLYER - Toys - Strombecker Corp.
BUBBLE FORCE - Toys - Strombecker Corp.
BUBBLE FUN - Toys - Jak-Pak Inc.
BUBBLE GEMS - Plastics ☆ - Fry Plastics International Inc. (O)
BUBBLE GHOST - Computer software ☆ - Accolade Inc.
BUBBLE GUM BY THE GALLON - Chewing gum - Food For Thought Inc.
BUBBLE GUM EGGS - Candy ☆ - Topps Co., Inc.
BUBBLE GUM GANG - Hobby kits ☆ - Bell Ceramics, Inc.
BUBBLE GUM MOONS - Chewing gum - Philadelphia Chewing Gum Corp.
BUBBLE GUM PIE - Chewing gum - Philadelphia Chewing Gum Corp.
BUBBLE GUM SHAKE - Candy ☆ - Topps Co., Inc.
BUBBLE GUM SMOKES - Chewing gum ☆ - Spangler Candy Co.
BUBBLE GUM STRIPS - Chewing gum ☆ - Leaf, Inc.
BUBBLE GUM SURF WAX - Apparel - Bubble Gum, Inc.
BUBBLE GUMMY BEARS - Chewing gum - Fleer Corp.
BUBBLE GUND - Toys–stuffed - Gund, Inc.
BUBBLE HEAD - Chewing gum - Philadelphia Chewing Gum Corp.
BUBBLE HEADS - Rubber–molded - Impact International Inc.
BUBBLE JET - Kites - Llumar Star Kites Inc.
BUBBLE-JET - Printers–computer - Canon USA, Inc.
BUBBLE JUG - Chewing gum - Amurol Confections Co.
BUBBLE JUMPER - Jump rope ☆ - Cap Toys, Inc.
BUBBLE KING - Candy - Colombina Candy Co., Inc.
BUBBLE KING - Chewing gum - Leaf, Inc.
BUBBLE KING POPS - Candy ☆ - Leaf, Inc.
BUBBLE KITE - Toys - Spectra Star Kites
BUBBLE LIGHTS - Glass–illuminating ☆ - Will & Baumer, Inc.
BUBBLE LITE - Novelty items ☆ - Fry Plastics International Inc. (O)
BUBBLE LOCKERS - Chewing gum ☆ - Amurol Confections Co.
BUBBLE MACHINE - Chewing gum - Philadelphia Chewing Gum Corp.
BUBBLE MAGIC - Soap ☆ - Strombecker Corp.
BUBBLE MASK - Packaging–paper - Sealed Air Corp.
BUBBLE MOWER - Toys - Fisher-Price, Inc.
BUBBLE NOSE - Chewing gum ☆ - Dorval Trading Co., Ltd.
BUBBLE-O - Skin care products - Frances Denney
BUBBLE O'BILL - Ice cream - Good Humor Corp.
BUBBLE PALACE - Dolls - Mattel, Inc.
BUBBLE PATTERN - Housewares ☆ - Doranne
BUBBLE PLAY - Confections - Good Humor Corp.
BUBBLE POPS - Chewing gum - Philadelphia Chewing Gum Corp.
BUBBLE PRINCESS - Dolls - Mattel, Inc.
BUBBLE RAKE - Tools–hand-operated - Melvin E. Acott
BUBBLE SAFE - Chewing gum ☆ - Amurol Confections Co.
BUBBLE SAX - Toys - Fisher-Price, Inc.
BUBBLE STAR - Health care products ☆ - Genki USA
BUBBLE STONE - Aquariums–household - Rotoco Inc.
BUBBLE STOP - Housewares - Blue Magic Products Inc.
BUBBLE-STREAM - Faucets - Moen Inc.
BUBBLE TANK - Bathing suits - Authentic Fitness Corp.
BUBBLE TANK - Pet products - Hawkeye Corp.
BUBBLE TAPE - Chewing gum - Amurol Confections Co.
BUBBLE THING, THE - Toys ☆ - Wham-O Manufacturing Co.
BUBBLE TOCO - Surgical instruments ☆ - Utah Medical Products, Inc.
BUBBLE TONGUE - Candy - Creative Confection Concepts, Inc.
BUBBLE TOYS - Toys - Hart Enterprises, Inc.
BUBBLE TOYS - Toys - Placo Products Co.
BUBBLE TROUBLE - Toys - Hirsch Co.

BUBBLE TUMBLER - Toy - Little Kids, Inc.
BUBBLE TUNES - Toys–musical - Cap Toys, Inc.
BUBBLE UP - Beverages–carbonated - Monarch Co., Inc.
BUBBLE-UP - Pet products - Rolf C. Hagen (USA) Corp.
BUBBLE-WALL - Air purification systems - Penn-Plax, Inc.
BUBBLE WAND - Garden-hose attachment ☆ - Invention Marketing Inc.
BUBBLE WHITE - Nail care products - E.O.H. Industries, Inc.
BUBBLE WRAP - Packaging–paper - Sealed Air Corp.
BUBBLE YO - Toys - Shure Products, Inc.
BUBBLE YUM - Chewing gum - Planters LifeSavers Co.
BUBBLEBACK - Bathing suits - Ocean Pool Co.
BUBBLEBAGS - Packaging–paper - Sealed Air Corp.
BUBBLEBUD BOOKS - Posters - Diana Malerba
BUBBLEBUDS, THE - Posters - Diana Malerba
BUBBLEGUM BECKY - Dolls - Mattel, Inc.
BUBBLEGUMMERS - Shoes–athletic - Bata Shoe Co. Inc.
BUBBLEHEAD - Posters - Michael Mcneilly
BUBBLELITE - Windows–plastic ☆ - O'Keeffe's, Inc.
BUBBLEMINT - Shampoos - Kim Laube & Co. Inc.
BUBBLEOOODLES - Toys - Gymboree Corp.
BUBBLEPAD - Health care products ☆ - HNE Healthcare
BUBBLER - Water purification systems - Penn-Plax, Inc.
BUBBLER HYDRANT - Irrigation equipment - Raindrip, Inc.
BUBBLEREX - Cold remedies - Johnson & Johnson
BUBBLERS - Toy vehicles - Cilius Lam Inc.
BUBBLES - Aquariums–household - Marine Metal Products
BUBBLES - Bakery products–frozen - Bubbles Baking Co.
BUBBLES! - Candy - Foreign Candy Co. Inc.
BUBBLES - Toys–banks - A.J. Renzi Plastic Corp.
BUBBLES - Yarn - Henry's Attic
BUBBLES & BATH - Window coverings ☆ - S. Morantz Inc.
BUBBLES FOR TWO - Cleaning preparations - Karen Mervine, Inc.
BUBBLES 'N PLAY - Dolls - Mattel, Inc.
BUBBLES THE WHALE - Hampers - Rubbermaid Inc.
BUBBLESAUROS - Apparel and accessories - Newport Soap Co.
BUBBLESHADE - Giftware - Creative Consumer Products Inc.
BUBBLETUB - Hot tubs–fiberglass - Novi American Inc.
BUBBLEWAND - Pet products - Marineland Aquarium Products
BUBBLICIOUS - Chewing gum - American Chicle Co.
BUBBLICIOUS ORANGE OUTBREAK - Chewing gum - Warner-Lambert Co.
BUBBLIN' MERMAID - Dolls - Mattel, Inc.
BUBBLING CATAWBA - Wines - Heritage Wine Cellars
BUBBLING CHAMPAGNE SAUCE - Seasonings ☆ - El Paso Chili Co.
BUBBLING CREEK - Jewelry - Bubbling Creek Co., Inc.
BUBBLING ISABELLA - Wines - Heritage Wine Cellars
BUBBLING NIAGRA - Wines - Heritage Wine Cellars
BUBBLING PRETTY - Dolls - Mattel, Inc.
BUBBLITE - Photographic equipment - Nu Arc Co. Inc.
BUBBLLOON - Decorations - A.J. Ganz Co. Inc.
BUBBLO THE CLOWN - Toys - Imperial Toy Corp.
BUBBLOPE - Stationery-type folders - Design Ideas Ltd.
BUBBY CARDS - Greeting cards - Recycled Paper Products, Inc.
BUBLEAK - Chemical preparations - Kano Laboratories Inc.
BUBLETS - Candy ☆ - Elmer Candy Corp.
BUBOOZLE - Candy - Wal-Mart Stores Inc.
BUBROMIDE - Pharmaceutical preparations ☆ - C.O. Truxton Inc.
BUB'S DADDY - Chewing gum - Leaf, Inc.
BUBSY - Video games - Accolade Inc.
BUC-PAK - Hardware - SDI Partners I, L.P.
BUC PLUS - Hunting equipment - Buck Stop Lure Co., Inc.
BUCALENI - Yarn - Glen Raven Mills Inc.
BUCANEER - Seafood products–canned or cured - Tampa Maid Seafoods, Inc.
BUCANNEER - Boats–motor ☆ - Bayliner Marine Corp.
BUCARONI - Yarn - Glen Raven Mills Inc.
BUCCANEER - Computer peripheral equipment - Strategic Simulations, Inc.
BUCCANEER - Cutlery ☆ - National Housewares
BUCCANEER - Floor coverings ☆ - Robbins Inc.
BUCCANEER - Food products - Southeast Packing Co.
BUCCANEER - Footwear–men's - L.B. Evans' Son Co.
BUCCANEER - Musical instrument accessories - Sottile Manufacturing Co.
BUCCANEER - Paints ☆ - Bruning Paint Co.
BUCCANEER - Sporting goods ☆ - Outdoor Technologies Group
BUCCANEER - Steering mechanisms–motor vehicle - Detroit Marine Engineering
BUCCANEER - Watches - Bulova Corp.

☆ = Now out of production

BUCCANEER I - Floor coverings–carpet and rugs ☆ - Ebsco Carpet Mills

BUCCANEER II - Floor coverings–carpet and rugs ☆ - Ebsco Carpet Mills

BUCCANEERS - Apparel and accessories - Greater Des Moines Ice Sports Association

BUCCANEERS - Candy ☆ - Leaf, Inc.

BUCCELLATI SILVER LTD. - Flatware - Buccellati Silver Ltd.

BUCCIA - Wines - Buccia Vineyards

BUCCINI - Footwear–men's - Atsco Footwear Inc.

BUCENTAUR GALLERY - Greeting cards - Kensington Cards

BUCET CAPSULES - Pharmaceutical preparations - Forest Pharmaceuticals Inc.

BUCGRUNTER - Hunting equipment - Hunter's Specialties, Inc.

BUCHANAN - Medical apparatus - Luminaud Inc.

BUCHANAN - Tableware–china - Lenox, Inc.

BUCHANAN'S - Whiskey ☆ - Sazerac Co. Inc.

BUCHER'S BROOM EXTRACT - Vitamins and nutritional supplements - Vitamin Research Products Inc.

BUCHY'S - Sausages ☆ - Chas. G. Buchy Packing Co.

BUCILLA - Yarn - Bucilla

BUCK - Knife sheaths - Buck Knives, Inc.

BUCK - Knives–hunting - Hard Hat Inc.

BUCK - Knives–hunting - Rothco Inc.

BUCK - Stoves–wood-burning - Buck Stove Corp.

BUCK-ALGONQUIN - Hardware - Buck-Algonquin Marine Hardware

BUCK BAGGER - Sporting goods - D & H Products Co.

BUCK-BALL - Pens - Universal Fountain Pen & Pencil Co.

BUCK BLASTER - Arrowheads - Buckblaster Broadhead Co.

BUCK-BOARD - Fishing tackle ☆ - Frabill Inc.

BUCK BROS. - Chisels - Buck Bros. Inc.

BUCK BROS. - Hand tools - Great Neck Saw Manufacturers, Inc.

BUCK BUCKET - Machinery - Joseph M. Bostick, Jr.

BUCK BUNNY - Candy ☆ - R.M. Palmer Co.

BUCK BUSTER - Sporting goods - Ole Time Woodsman

BUCK CREEK - Eyeglasses - Eddie Bauer Inc.

BUCK-FIRE - Deodorizers - Wildlife Research Center, Inc.

BUCK FORAGE FOOD PLOT SEED - Flowers, plants, and seeds - Arkansas County Seed Co., Inc.

BUCK-HORN BLEND - Animal feeds - Camp-Cap Products

BUCK HORSE - Furniture ☆ - Cosco, Inc.

BUCK HUSTLER - Sporting goods - Raymond S. Mattucci

BUCK LIGHT - Flashlights - Buck Knives, Inc.

BUCK MADNESS - Sporting goods - Wellington Leisure Products, Inc.

BUCK-MATE - Sporting goods ☆ - Kolpin Manufacturing, Inc.

BUCK NAKED - Recording label - Georgian Communications, Inc.

BUCK NAKED - Toys–stuffed - Barely, Inc.

BUCK-PRO - Apparel stores–sports - Buck-Pro Inc.

BUCK QUEST - Games - Buck Quest, Inc.

BUCK ROGERS - Games - Tsr, Inc.

BUCK ROGERS - Toys - Hasbro, Inc.

BUCK-RUB - Sporting goods - Camp-Cap Products

BUCK-SHOT - Fishing tackle - Northland Fishing Tackle, Inc.

BUCK SKEIN - Apparel–men's - Arnav Industries Inc.

BUCK SKINNER - Sporting goods - Buck Skinner, Inc.

BUCK STOPS HERE - Apparel and accessories - Buck Stop Lure Co., Inc.

BUCK STUMPER - Sporting goods - G & H Decoy, Inc.

BUCK THE SYSTEM USA - Apparel and accessories - Buck the System Foundation

BUCK-UP - Window frames - Sinclair Industries Inc.

BUCK WILDER - Publisher's imprints - Buck Wilder, Inc.

BUCKAROO - Bagels ☆ - Olympic Foods Inc.

BUCKAROO - Beverages–alcohol - All Saint's Brands, Inc.

BUCKAROO - Dinners–frozen - Conagra, Inc.

BUCKAROO - Musical instrument accessories - Sottile Manufacturing Co.

BUCKAROO - Sauces - Jardine Foods

BUCKAROO - Thread - Threads USA Div.

BUCKAROO BEER - Beverages–malt - All Saint's Brands, Inc.

BUCKAROO CHEW - Chewing gum ☆ - Amurol Confections Co.

BUCKBOARD - Boats - Glen-L Marine Designs

BUCKBOARD - Puppets - Dakin Inc.

BUCKBOX - Flower pots–earthenware - Forest Time Products Inc.

BUCKBRITE - Flashlights - Buck Knives, Inc.

BUCKBUSTER - Shotguns ☆ - Ithaca Gun Co. Inc.

BUCKBUSTER SHOTGUN BULLETS - Ammunition - Shotgun Bullets Manufacturing

BUCKEROO - Musical instrument accessories ☆ - Shadows Studio Strings

BUCKET - Apparel and accessories - Barrel Industries Inc.

BUCKET - Apparel–children's - Barrel-Marvin Apparel, Inc.

BUCKET - Games ☆ - Lakeside Games

BUCKET BENCH - Chairs–plastic - McGuire-Nicholas Co., Inc.

BUCKET BOY - Food products - Mille Lacs Maple Products Corp.

BUCKET BRIGADE - Ice buckets ☆ - Kraftware Corp. (Morgan Div.)

BUCKET HOLDER - Hardware - Aqua-Tainer Co.

BUCKET O BLOOD - Chewing gum - Fleer Corp.

BUCKET O RAWHIDE - Dog food - Canine's Choice

BUCKET OF FUN - Ice chests–plastic - Igloo Products Corp.

BUCKET OF FUN - Meat sauces - WSF L.P. of Michigan

BUCKET OF JUNK - Hobby kits - Lisa Frank, Inc.

BUCKET SEAT - Housewares - Portable Products, Inc.

BUCKET STACKER - Trays - Portable Products, Inc.

BUCKETEER - Bags ☆ - Gold Medal Inc.

BUCKETT & TUBBS - Food products - Walden Farms, Inc.

BUCKEYE - Bathing suits - Buckeye Apparel Inc.

BUCKEYE - Bicycles - Gordon Cycle & Supply Inc.

BUCKEYE - Brushes–paint - Wooster Brush Co.

BUCKEYE - Cereal - Quaker Oats Co.

BUCKEYE - Cookies - President Baking Co., Inc.

BUCKEYE - Cooking utensils–cast iron ☆ - Regal Ware, Inc.

BUCKEYE - Firearms, accessories, and parts - Welsh Sporting Goods Corp. (Boyt Div.)

BUCKEYE - Flowers, plants, and seeds - Hooven Allison

BUCKEYE - Garden equipment - Seymour Manufacturing Co.,Inc.

BUCKEYE - Music stands - Krauth & Benninghofen Inc.

BUCKEYE - Musical instrument accessories ☆ - Grossman Music Corp.

BUCKEYE - Paper–bond - Buckeye Business Products Inc.

BUCKEYE - Pasta - Buckeye Beans & Herbs, Inc.

BUCKEYE - Tools ☆ - Hartwell Brothers Handle Co.

BUCKEYE - Water–distilled ☆ - Magnetic Springs Water Co.

BUCKEYE - Wood products - Buckeye Cellulose Corp.

BUCKEYE BOND - Paper - Copco Papers Inc.

BUCKEYE BOND - Ribbons–inked - Buckeye Business Products Inc.

BUCKEYE CABLESYSTEM - Broadcasting stations–cable television - Buckeye Cablevision, Inc.

BUCKEYE CHUNKS - Dog food - Buckeye Feed Mills, Inc.

BUCKEYE FOAL AIDE - Animal feed supplements - Buckeye Feed Mills, Inc.

BUCKEYE HI-PERFORMANCE - Dog food - Buckeye Feed Mills, Inc.

BUCKEYE PROFESSIONAL FORMULA - Dog food - Buckeye Feed Mills, Inc.

BUCKEYE SALVE - Pharmaceutical preparations - Luyties Pharmacal Co.

BUCKEYE STICK - Sausages - Fred Usinger, Inc.

BUCKHEAD - Furniture - Universal Flooring

BUCKHEAD - Recording label - Score Productions, Inc.

BUCKHEAD BEER - Beverages–malt - H.K. Brewing Co., Ltd.

BUCKHEAD SOFTWARE - Computer software ☆ - B & N Companies, Inc.

BUCKHORN - Beverages–malt - Pabst Brewing Co.

BUCKHORN - Lenses - Bausch & Lomb Inc.

BUCKIES - Footwear - J. Bart Buckner

BUCKIN BAGEL WHERE THE EAST MEETS THE WILD WEST, THE - Bagels - Sawtooth Enterprises, Inc.

BUCKINGHAM - Cabinets - Imperial Cabinet Co. Inc.

BUCKINGHAM - Cabinets–wood - American Woodmark Corp.

BUCKINGHAM - Carriages–baby ☆ - Welsh Co.

BUCKINGHAM - Clocks ☆ - General Time Corp. (Westclox/Seth Thomas Div.)

BUCKINGHAM - Cutlery - Washington Forge Inc.

BUCKINGHAM - Draperies - Maharam Vertical Surfaces

BUCKINGHAM - Floor coverings–carpet and rugs - Cabin Crafts Carpets

BUCKINGHAM - Floor coverings–carpet and rugs - Edgecrest Carpet Mills

BUCKINGHAM - Glassware–household - Seneca Glass Co.

BUCKINGHAM - Harnesses - Buckingham Manufacturing Co.

BUCKINGHAM - Manufactured homes - Redman Industries, Inc.

BUCKINGHAM - Mobile homes - Western Homes Corp.

BUCKINGHAM - Musical instruments ☆ - Grossman Music Corp.

BUCKINGHAM - Office furniture–metal ☆ - Joyce International Inc.

BUCKINGHAM - Tables–wood - Riverside Furniture Corp.

BUCKINGHAM - Tiles–mosaic - Buckingham-Virginia Slate Corp.

BUCKINGHAM - Trailers–travel ☆ - Starcraft Corp.

BUCKINGHAM - Wallpaper - Capital Carousel Inc.

BUCKINGHAM - Watches - Bulova Corp.

BUCKINGHAM - Windows–storm - Duo-Temp

BUCKINGHAM - Wood products - Georgia-Pacific Corp.

BUCKINGHAM BEAR - Toys–stuffed ☆ - Dakin Inc.

BUCKINGHAM BROWN - Nail care products - Cosmair Inc.

BUCKINGHAM GALLERIES - Greeting cards - Sunshine Art Studios Inc.

BUCKINGHAM PALACE - Dolls ☆ - Effanbee Doll Corp.

BUCKINGHAM VALLEY VINEYARDS - Wines - Buckingham Valley Vineyards
BUCKINGHAM VELVET - Leather goods - Korchmar Case Co.
BUCKINGHAM-VIRGINIA - Tiles—mosaic - Buckingham-Virginia Slate Corp.
BUCKIT APRON - Aprons - Hometown Advantage, Inc.
BUCKIT BALL - Games - Craig Reese
BUCKLE BUNNY - Toys—stuffed - Russ Berrie and Co., Inc.
BUCKLE-IT - Jewelry - Feature Enterprises
BUCKLE UP - Games - Jo Ann E. Duncan
BUCKLE UP - Key rings - Syner-Mar, Inc.
BUCKLE UP FOR ME! - Frames—picture - Domino's Pizza Inc.
BUCKLE UP FOR SAFETY - Belts—apparel - Jack Gasnick, The Virtuous Locksmith
BUCKLE UP 'N DRIVE - Toys - Tyco Toys
BUCKLE UP! PALS - Automotive parts and accessories - HLM Sales, Inc.
BUCKLEIN - Washers—metal - JDC Manufacturing Co.
BUCKLER - Beverages—malt - Van Munching and Co. Inc.
BUCKLES OF AMERICA - Buckles - RKP Industries
BUCKLES THE BUCKLE-UP BUNNY - Costumes - Weiner/Seaman Productions
BUCKLEY'S - Confections - Emac International Inc.
BUCKMADE - Fiberboard ☆ - Buck Stove Corp.
BUCKMAN'S BEST - Sauces - Lendy's
BUCKMASTERS - Apparel and accessories - Buckmasters, Ltd.
BUCKMASTERS ELECTRONIC 3-D SPORT - Firearms, accessories, and parts - Buckmasters, Ltd.
BUCKNELL - Ophthalmic goods - Foremost Optical Products
BUCKO - Pipes—tobacco - Dr. Grabow Pre-Smoked Pipes Inc.
BUCKRAM - Machinery - S. Morantz Inc.
BUCK$ - Cigarettes - Philip Morris Companies Inc.
BUCK$ BAG - Bags - Domino's Pizza Inc.
BUCKS COUNTIAN - Crocheted and knitted items - Jacques De Loux Inc.
BUCKS COUNTRY VINEYARDS - Wines - Bucks Country Vineyards Inc.
BUCKS COUNTY - Floor coverings ☆ - Congoleum Corp.
BUCKS FIZZ - Wallpaper - BDH Two, Inc.
BUCK'S VALLEY - Dog food - MFA Inc.
BUCKSHOT - Bicycles - Columbia Manufacturing Inc.
BUCKSHOT - Candy - Austin, Nichols & Co., Inc.
BUCKSHOT - Food products - Jardine's Texas Foods
BUCKSHOT - Games - International Gamco, Inc.
BUCKSHOT - Recording label - Jeree Records
BUCKSHOT - Snuff - Brown & Williamson Tobacco Corp.
BUCKSHOT - Sporting goods ☆ - Bear Archery Inc.
BUCKSHOT - Toys - Tonka Corp.
BUCKSKIN - Bicycles ☆ - Hunt-Wilde Corp.
BUCKSKIN - Cigarette paper - James D. Kegley
BUCKSKIN - Fabrics - Dan River Inc.
BUCKSKIN - Paints - Sherwin-Williams Automotive Finishes Corp.
BUCKSKIN - Pencils - Blackfeet Writing Instruments Inc.
BUCKSKIN - Thread - Threads USA Div.
BUCKSKIN DEER - Toys—stuffed - Dakin Inc.
BUCKSKIN WILDLIFE MIX - Flowers, plants, and seeds ☆ - Barenbrug USA
BUCKSON - Food products - Joseph Buchwald & Sons Inc.
BUCKSON - Food products ☆ - All Fresh Products Inc.
BUCKSPORT GROUP - Shelving units—wood ☆ - Moosehead Manufacturing Co.
BUCKSTAG - Flatware - Utica Cutlery Co.
BUCKTAIL TONI - Sporting goods ☆ - James Heddon's Sons
BUCKTOOL - Pliers - Buck Knives, Inc.
BUCKY - Toys—stuffed - CBS Toys
BUCKY BRA - Apparel and accessories ☆ - Strouse, Adler Co.
BUCKY BRIEF - Apparel and accessories ☆ - Strouse, Adler Co.
BUCKY O'HARE - Puzzles - Milton Bradley Co.
BUCKY PANTS - Apparel and accessories ☆ - Strouse, Adler Co.
BUCKY'S CALAMITY JEANS - Apparel—women's - Bucky's Calamity Jeans Ltd.
BUCLADIN - Pharmaceutical preparations ☆ - Zeneca Inc.
BUCO - Clocks - American Buco Corp.
BUCOL - Pharmaceutical preparations ☆ - Barre-National, Inc.
BUCOTONE - Veterinary pharmaceutical preparations ☆ - Schering-Plough Animal Health
BUCRATTLER - Hunting equipment - Hunter's Specialties, Inc.
BUCRUT - Hunting equipment - Hunter's Specialties, Inc.
B.U.C.S. - Silos—farm - J-Star Industries, Inc.
BUD - Beverages—malt - Anheuser-Busch Companies Inc.
BUD - Cleaning preparations ☆ - Tessco Technologies Inc.
BUD BERMA - Shirts - Russ Togs Inc.

BUD BUBBLES - Bubble bath ☆ - Strombecker Corp.
BUD CASSETTE - Audio tapes—blank ☆ - Tessco Technologies Inc.
BUD CHILLING - Beverages—malt - Anheuser-Busch Companies Inc.
BUD DRY - Beverages—malt - Anheuser-Busch Companies Inc.
BUD ICE - Beverages—malt - Anheuser-Busch Companies Inc.
BUD ICE LIGHT - Beverages—malt - Anheuser-Busch Companies Inc.
BUD LIGHT - Beverages—malt - Anheuser-Busch Companies Inc.
BUD LIGHT I SAID - Beverages—malt - Anheuser-Busch Companies Inc.
BUD MUG - Giftware - Ricker Co.
BUD 'N BLOOM - Fertilizers - Thompson Manufacturing Co.
BUD NIP - Garden equipment - PPG Industries, Inc.
BUD OF CALIFORNIA - Food products - Dole Food Co., Inc.
BUD ONE - Beverages—malt ☆ - Anheuser-Busch Companies Inc.
BUD SKI - Beverages—malt - Anheuser-Busch Companies Inc.
BUD SPECIAL - Fruits and vegetables - Bud Antle Inc.
BUDADICKA - Hats - Budadicka, Inc.
BUDARI - Recording label - Vandor Motion Pictures, Phonorecords & Music Publishing Group
BUDAY BOOKS VINTAGE READING - Publisher's imprints - Buday Printers & Lithographers Inc.
BUDD - Leather goods - H.C. Meyers Co.
BUDD SWEET - Cigars - National Cigar Corp.
BUDDAH - Recording label - Essex Entertainment Inc.
BUDDEX - Tools - Jenrik Marketing Group Inc.
BUDDHA - Rice - Sung Ly International Corp.
BUDDIE - Pencils - National Pen & Pencil Co.
BUDDIE - Vegetables—canned - Stokely USA, Inc.
BUDDIES - Diapers—disposable - Mark One Healthcare Products Inc.
BUDDIG - Meat products—cured - Carl Buddig & Co.
BUDDING BEAUTY - Skin care products - Dorothy Gray Cosmetics Ltd.
BUDDING STRIPES - Bedding—linen - Dan River Inc.
BUDDING TULIP - Clocks - General Time Corp. (Westclox/Seth Thomas Div.)
BUDD'S - Cigars - National Cigar Corp.
BUDDY - Apparel and accessories ☆ - Palm Beach Co., Inc.
BUDDY - Brooms - Lighthouse Industries
BUDDY - Cleaning preparations - Puritan-Churchill Chemical Co.
BUDDY - Computer software - Jeffrey Mattox
BUDDY - Diaries ☆ - ACCO USA, Inc.
BUDDY - Mobile homes - Skyline Corp.
BUDDY - Stoves—wood-burning - Fatsco
BUDDY B - Tools—garden - Rugg Manufacturing Co. Inc.
BUDDY BAR - Candy - Bishop Baking Co.
BUDDY BASKET - Baskets—wood ☆ - Frem Corp.
BUDDY BOX - Containers—plastic - Frem Corp.
BUDDY BOYS - Sunglasses - Isaac Morris Ltd.
BUDDY BUCKET - Buckets—plastic - Frem Corp.
BUDDY BURRO - Greeting cards - Louis Richard Valasquez
BUDDY L - Barbecues and grills ☆ - Sunbeam Outdoor Products Inc.
BUDDY L - Swimming pools - SLM Inc.
BUDDY L - Toys - Buddy L Inc.
BUDDY SEAT - Swimming pools - Wexco Inc.
BUDDY START - Cables - Kaiser Electroprecision
BUDDY SYSTEM - Bathing suits - Authentic Fitness Corp.
BUDDY SYSTEM - Safety products - David S. Gray
BUDDY WALKERS - Exercising equipment - Sawyer Industries, Inc.
BUDDY'S - Beef - Waltham Beef & Provision Co.
BUDDY'S - Beverages—carbonated - August Schell Brewing Co.
BUDDY'S - Food products - Buddy's Kitchen Inc.
BUDEKE - Paints - Budeke's Paint
BUDFARI - Beverages—malt - Anheuser-Busch Companies Inc.
BUDGE - Covers—seat - Budge Industries, Inc.
BUDGE LITE - Motor vehicle parts and accessories - Budge Industries, Inc.
BUDGE NOT - Housewares - Mitchell Productions, Inc.
BUDGET - Desks - Vanguard Corp.
BUDGET - Fruits and vegetables - Johnston Farms
BUDGET - Pasta - Gooch Foods Inc.
BUDGET BAGS - Bags—trash - G P Plastics Corp.
BUDGET BRIDALS - Wedding gowns - Alfred Angelo Inc.
BUDGET BUDDY - Office supplies - Budget Buddy Co.
BUDGET BUDDY - Stationery - D & S Products
BUDGET BUY - Foil—aluminum - Arrow Industries, Inc.
BUDGET CITY - Games - Attainment Co., Inc.
BUDGET DELIGHT - Meat products—beef ☆ - Atalanta Corp.
BUDGET EXPRESS - Computer software - Symantec Corp.
BUDGET GOURMET - Dinners—frozen - H.J. Heinz Co.

☆ = Now out of production

BUDGET GOURMET HEARTY & HEALTHY - Dinners–frozen - H.J. Heinz Co.

BUDGET GOURMET ITALIAN ORIGINALS - Dinners–frozen - H.J. Heinz Co.

BUDGET GOURMET LIGHT & HEALTHY - Dinners–frozen - H.J. Heinz Co.

BUDGET INDY - Toys–electronic - Bird Bromiticous Inc.

BUDGET MAKER - Binders - Budgetmaker Corp.

BUDGET MASTER - Computer software - Comprehensive Video Supply Corp.

BUDGET MASTER - House furnishings ☆ - Florida Furniture Industries Inc.

BUDGET SAVER - Apparel and accessories - S and S Industries Inc. (Thermo Saver Div.)

BUDGET TOWN - Games - Attainment Co., Inc.

BUDGET WALLS - Wallpaper - Pantasote Inc. (Wallcovering Div.)

BUDGET-WISE - Meat products–poultry - Norbest Inc.

BUDGETBOARD - Paper - Sonoco-Rixie Coaster Division

BUDGETEER - Bathroom accessories - Franklin Brass Manufacturing Co.

BUDGETEER - Computer software - Security National Recovery and Insurance, Inc.

BUDGETER - File folders ☆ - Orna-Metal Inc.

BUDGETFOLD - Napkins–paper - Wisconsin Tissue Mills Inc.

BUDGETLINE - Office supplies - McBee Loose Leaf Binders

BUDGETOOL - Trowels - Goldblatt Tool Co.

BUDGETWARE - Plates–paper - Fonda Group, Inc.

BUDGETWIZ - Consulting services - Action Advocacy Law Offices, P.C.

BUDGIE - Pens - Micropoint Inc.

BUDGIE - Toys - F.J. Strauss Co. Inc.

BUDGIMINE - Pet products - Kellogg Inc.

BUDGIT - Boxes - Boxit Packaging Corp.

BUDGIT - Boxes–corrugated paperboard - Mason Box Co. Inc.

BUDGITRAC - Traction apparatus–medical ☆ - Lossing Orthopedic Co.

BUDLONG - Pickles - Green Bay Foods Co.

BUDS A BLOOMIN - House furnishings - Dan River Inc.

BUD'S BITES - Cookies - Bud's Best Cookies Inc.

BUDS 'N' BUTTERFLIES - Bakeware - Corning Inc.

BUD'S PREMIUM HEAT - Sporting goods - Bud's BuckLure Co.

BUDSTRAPS - Suspenders - Maid Rite Novelty Corp.

BUDTOOL - Computer software - Delta Microsystems, Inc.

BUDTURBO - Computer software - Delta Microsystems, Inc.

BUDWEISER - Beverages–malt - Anheuser-Busch Companies Inc.

BUDWEISER - Key rings - Gift Creations, Inc.

BUDWEISER - Playing cards - United States Playing Card Co.

BUDWEISER - Shoes ☆ - Brown Shoe Co.

BUDWINE - Beverages–carbonated - Southern Beverage Packers, Inc.

BUE - Olive oil - Pastene Companies Ltd.

BUECHE-GIROD - Sunglasses - JBM Venture Co., Inc.

BUECHE GIROD - Sunglasses - JBM Venture Co., Inc.

BUEHLER - Hams - Peer Food Products Co.

BUEHLER - Sights–gun - Buehler Scope Mounts (Maynard P. Buehler Inc.)

BUEHLER VINEYARDS - Wines - Buehler Vineyards

BUELL - Cleaning preparations - Polychem Corp.

BUELL - Horns–motor vehicle - Buell Manufacturing Co.

BUELL - Motorcycles - Buell Motorcycle Co.

BUELL IN - Electrical equipment - General Electric Co.

BUELL'S - Beeswax - Buell's Bee Haven Farms

BUELL'S BEEHAVEN FARMS - Honey - Buell's Bee Haven Farms

BUENA - Thread - Van Waters and Rogers Inc.

BUENA COCINA - Sauces - Buena Cocina

BUENA VIDA - Dairy products - Danco Cheese, Inc.

BUENA VIDA - Tortillas - Azteca Foods, Inc.

BUENA VISTA - Floor coverings - Mannington Resilient Floors

BUENA VISTA - Floor coverings–carpet and rugs ☆ - Cumberland Mills Inc.

BUENA VISTA - Furniture - O'Sullivan Industries, Inc.

BUENA VISTA - Motion picture distributors–prerecorded - Walt Disney Co.

BUENA VISTA - Wines - Buena Vista Winery, Inc.

BUENA VISTA CARNEROS GRAND RESERVE - Wines - Buena Vista Winery, Inc.

BUENDNERFLEISCH - Meat products - H.J. Gasser Specialty Foods

BUENO - Food products - Bueno Food Products

BUENOS - Tortillas - Nabisco Foods Group

BUENOS AIRES IMPORTS - Luggage - Buenos Aires Imports

BUESCHER - Musical instruments - Selmer Co. Inc.

BUESCHER TRUE-TONE - Musical instruments ☆ - Selmer Co. Inc.

BUESCHER'S CORN COBS - Pipes–tobacco - Buescher's Industries Inc.

BUF-FAT - Agricultural products - CS Animal Feeds, Inc.

BUF-PUF - Skin care products - Minnesota Mining & Manufacturing Co.

BUF-PUF SINGLES - Skin care products - Minnesota Mining & Manufacturing Co.

BUF-TEX - See **PERMALINED**

BUFALINI MARBLE - Ceramic tile ☆ - Integrity Tile Co.

BUFALO - Food products - American Pacific Pet

BUFETTE - Skin care products - Delby System

BUFF - Apparel–athletic - Stephen L. Binder

BUFF-A - Pharmaceutical preparations ☆ - Merz Inc.

BUFF-A-BALL - Bowling balls - Master Industries Inc.

BUFF-A COMP - Analgesic/antipyretic ☆ - Merz Inc.

BUFF BAR - Soap - Karlen Manufacturing, Inc.

BUFF-BELT - Machine parts - Buff Polish & Grind Industrial Supply Co., Inc.

BUFF BOSS - Tools–power-driven - Black & Decker Corp.

BUFF BRITE - Finishing agents ☆ - C.B. Dolge Co.

BUFF COTE - Floor waxes - Arcal Chemicals Inc.

BUFF-LO-MAID - Food products - J.G. Pieri Co. Inc.

BUFF N' CLEAN - Cleaning preparations ☆ - Hako Minuteman Inc.

BUFF-N-GLO - Floor waxes - Uncle Sam Chemical Co., Inc.

BUFF N' GLOW - Manicuring implements ☆ - London International U.S. Holdings

BUFF 'N PUFF - Greeting cards - American Greetings Corp.

BUFF 'N SHINE - Manicure preparations - Barristo Ltd.

BUFF NE'ER TEAR - Paper–writing - Champion International Corp.

BUFF RACCOON - Toys–stuffed - Russ Berrie and Co., Inc.

BUFF STUFF - Apparel and accessories - Wayne Davis

BUFF STUFF - Cleaning preparations–carpet and rug ☆ - Hillyard Enterprises, Inc.

BUFF-TABS - Health care products ☆ - Halsey Drug Co. Inc.

BUFF-UP - Furniture polish and wax - Amway Corp.

BUFFACETIN - Pharmaceutical preparations ☆ - Kay Pharmacal Co. Inc.

BUFFADYNE-LEMMON - Pharmaceutical preparations ☆ - Lemmon Co.

BUFFALINO B - Footwear - Buffalino U.S.A., Inc.

BUFFALO - Brushes ☆ - I. Sekine Co. Inc.

BUFFALO - Dinnerware–glass - Oneida Ltd.

BUFFALO - Gloves–work - Parade Distributors

BUFFALO - Markers–felt-tip - Dri Mark Products, Inc.

BUFFALO - Motorcycles - Central States Tool & Die Works

BUFFALO - Pens ☆ - K-9 Pen Co.

BUFFALO - Thread - Coats and Clark Inc.

BUFFALO - Tools - Buffalo Tool

BUFFALO - Vegetables–canned - Taormina Co.

BUFFALO ARTIST COLORS - Markers–felt-tip - Dri Mark Products, Inc.

BUFFALO BAG COMPANY - Luggage - Coastside Creations

BUFFALO BALL - Cakes - Great Cakes

BUFFALO BILL - Meat products - Daniel Weaver Co.

BUFFALO BILL - Toys–guns - Daisy Manufacturing Co.

BUFFALO BILL - Toys–stuffed - Dakin Inc.

BUFFALO BILLS - Apparel and accessories - Buffalo Bills, Inc.

BUFFALO BILLS - Tortillas - Great Western Tortilla Co.

BUFFALO BITES - Food products - Bojangles Restaurants Inc.

BUFFALO BOB'S - Barbecue sauce - Festive Foods, Inc.

BUFFALO BOLD PREMIUM ALE - Beverages–malt - Rockies Brewing Co.

BUFFALO BRAND - Barbecue sauce - Continental Distributors Inc.

BUFFALO BREATH - Barbecue sauce - Masterfoods Specialities, Inc.

BUFFALO BULL - Toys - R.E. Bee, Inc.

BUFFALO BUTT - Beverages–malt - American Food Classics, Inc.

BUFFALO CAR CARE KIT - Automotive cleaners - MFB Productions, Inc.

BUFFALO CARBINE - Rifles ☆ - Euroarms of America

BUFFALO CHIP COOKIE - Cookies - Cowboy Vittles & More

BUFFALO CHIP STIX - Beef - Walt's Meat Processing

BUFFALO CHIPS - Cookies - Quaker Bonnet

BUFFALO CHUNK HUMONGOUS - Bakery products - Codyco, Inc.

BUFFALO COACH - Coats - Dale W. Power

BUFFALO DON - Water–bottled or canned - Buffalo Don's Artesian Wells Ltd.

BUFFALO GOLD PREMIUM ALE - Beverages–malt - Walnut Brewery Inc.

BUFFALO JUNCTION - Jeans–women's - Jonbil Inc.

BUFFALO MILKE AUTOMOTIVE POLISHING PRODUCTS INC. - Waxes–sealing - Buffalo Milke Automotive Polishing Products, Inc.

BUFFALO NICKELS - Game machines - Infinity Group, Inc.

BUFFALO RECORDS - Recording label - TNT Productions & Management

BUFFALO ROBE - Footwear - H.S. Trask & Co.

BUFFALO ROLLER - Pens ☆ - Blackfeet Writing Instruments Inc.

BUFFALO SHRIMP - Sahlman Seafoods, Inc.

BUFFALO SNOW - Fabrics - Buffalo Batt and Felt Corp.

BUFFALO SOLDIERS - Apparel and accessories - Ruel E. Hampton

BUFFALO VALLEY - Wines - Buffalo Valley Winery

BUFFALO WINGS - Chickens - Pilgrim's Pride Corp.

BUFFAPRIN - Pharmaceutical preparations - Buffington

BUFFAPRIN EXTRA - Pharmaceutical preparations - Buffington

BUFFASAL - Pharmaceutical preparations - Dover Pharmaceutical Inc.

BUFFASAL MAX - Pharmaceutical preparations - Dover Pharmaceutical Inc.

BUFFATRON - Dolls - Mattel, Inc.

BUFFAY - Shrimp–canned or cured ☆ - Robinson Canning Co. Inc.

BUFFCO - Wood products - Buffelen Woodworking Co.

BUFFDOG - Frankfurters - Denver Buffalo Co.

BUFFED BISQUE - Cosmetics - Lancome

BUFFER HIGH - Pet products - Lake Products Co. Inc.

BUFFER LOW - Pet products - Lake Products Co. Inc.

BUFFER PLUS - Water treating compounds - Mardel Laboratories, Inc.

BUFFER SEAL - Rubber–molded - Macrotech Fluid Sealing, Inc.

BUFFER-UP - Aquarium accessories - Mardel Laboratories, Inc.

BUFFER WITH THE BEST - Veterinary pharmaceutical preparations - Church and Dwight Co. Inc.

BUFFEREZE - Photographic equipment - Eastman Kodak Co.

BUFFERFLY - Health care products - Madys Co.

BUFFERIN - Analgesics - Bristol-Myers Squibb Co.

BUFFERIN 1-S - Analgesics - Bristol-Myers Squibb Co.

BUFFERIN AF NITE TIME - Analgesics - Bristol-Myers Squibb Co.

BUFFET - Chili sauce - Henry J's Hashtime-USA

BUFFET - Clarinets - Boosey & Hawkes Buffet Crampon USA

BUFFET - Computer software - U.S. Internet Inc.

BUFFET - Dinnerware–glass ☆ - Trend Pacific Inc.

BUFFET - Musical instruments - Ardsley Musical Instrument Co.

BUFFET - Pet products - Nestle USA

BUFFET COLLECTION - Glassware–household - Lancaster Colony Corp.

BUFFET CRAMPON - Musical instruments - Boosey & Hawkes Buffet Crampon USA

BUFFET DICES - Food products - Lamb-Weston, Inc.

BUFFET SERVER II - Cooking equipment–commercial - West Bend Co.

BUFFETS - Pharmaceutical preparations ☆ - JMI-Canton Pharmaceuticals

BUFFETWARE - Glassware–household - Van Dow-Fenton Inc.

BUFFEX - Analgesics - Roberts/Hauck Pharmaceuticals Inc.

BUFFEX - Aquatic pharmacuetical preparations ☆ - Aquatronics-Filtronics

BUFFINGTON - Health care products - Buffington

BUFFINOL - Pharmaceutical preparations - Otis Clapp & Son Inc.

BUFFINOL EXTRA - Pharmaceutical preparations - Otis Clapp & Son Inc.

BUFFINOX - Pharmaceutical preparations - Afassco

BUFFLE - Toys–stuffed - Cozy's Inc.

BUFFLEX - Pipes - Bufflex Corp.

BUFFO - Locks–padlocks - Abus Lock Co.

BUFFS - Computer software - SourceView Software International

BUFFTONE CLASP - Envelopes–paper - Specialty Envelopes Inc.

BUFFY - Toys ☆ - South Bend Toy Manufacturing Co.

BUFFY BROWN - Paper–gift wrap ☆ - Plus Mark Inc.

BUFFY BUNNY - Toys–stuffed - Russ Berrie and Co., Inc.

BUFFY COCKER SPANIEL - Toys–stuffed - Dakin Inc.

BUFFY GLOVE - Gloves–work - Rich-Glo Products

BUFORD - Pet products - Pride 'N Joy Inc.

BUG - Pins–jewelry - Bug House

BUG A BOO - Candles ☆ - Candle-Lite Co.

BUG-A-BOO - Sprayers - Packaging Concepts Assoc. Inc.

BUG-A-DOOS - Toys - Tonka Corp.

BUG-A-WAY - Lamps - Philips Lighting Co.

BUG ADVENTURE - Computer software - Knowledge Adventure, Inc.

BUG-ALL - Flycatchers - Dars Met-All Industries Inc.

BUG BANISHER - Insect repellents - George Miller Dewberry II

BUG BARRIER - Insecticides - ARI

BUG BATTLER - Lamps–insect ☆ - Aladdin Industries, Inc.

BUG BIND - Adhesives and sealants - Troy Biosciences, Inc.

BUG BITE - Toys - Tonka Corp.

BUG BITES - Chocolate candy - Jon Stocking

BUG-BLOCK - Garden equipment - Dalen Products Inc.

BUG BLOCK - Skin care products - Duane Caraballo

BUG BLOCK - Skin care products - Solar Gear Inc.

BUG BONNET - Infant product - Two Little Girls Inc.

BUG BRIGADE - Toys - Toymax Inc.

BUG BUSTER - Insecticides - Klenatron Inc. Inc.

BUG BUSTER - Windows–screen - Williams Manufacturing Corp.

BUG CAP - Containers - Midland Chicago Corp.

BUG DART - Garden equipment ☆ - Scotts Co. (Organics Business Group)

BUG DART PLUS - Garden equipment ☆ - Scotts Co. (Organics Business Group)

BUG DEMON - Squeegees - Laitner Brush Co.

BUG-EYE - Fishing lures ☆ - Fred Arbogast Co. Inc.

BUG EYE - Kaleidoscopes - Gemini Kaleidoscopes

BUG-EYED BRIGADE - Toys - Toymax Inc.

BUG-EYED MONSTER - Candy - Uniconfis Corp.

BUG EYES - Costumes - McCain Ellio's Foods, Inc.

BUG FIGHTER - Insecticides ☆ - Flowtron Outdoor Products

BUG-GARD - Automotive parts and accessories - G.T. Styling Inc.

BUG-GETA - Chemical preparations - Chevron Chemical Co.

BUG-GLUE - Irons–electric - Roxide International, Inc.

BUG-GO - Insecticides - Beverly Manufacturing Corp.

BUG GUARD - Electronic equipment ☆ - Johnson Kart Manufacturing

BUG GUTS - Apparel and accessories - Bug Guts, Ltd.

BUG HOUSE - T-shirts–men's - Squint Design Inc.

BUG HOUSE, THE - Hobby kits - Tierney Specialties

BUG JUG - Toys ☆ - Uncle Milton Industries Inc.

BUG KILL - Housewares - Athena Products Corp.

BUG MAN - Pesticides–household ☆ - Woodstream Corp.

BUG ME NOT - Insecticides - Jesse H. Bidanset

BUG-N-BUFF - Sponges - JDR Enterprises Inc.

BUG-NIP - Insecticides ☆ - Roccorp, Inc.

BUG-O-BUCKET - Candles - Candle Corp. of America

BUG-O-SYSTEMS - Welding equipment - Weld Tooling Corp.

BUG-OFF - Insecticides - Carpet Products Co.

BUG-OFF - Pet products - Kevlex Products Co., Inc.

BUG-OFF - Toys - North Pacific Products Inc.

BUG OUT - Water treating compounds - Great Lakes Biochemical Co., Inc.

BUG PLUG - Fishing lures - Storm Manufacturing Co.

BUG POPPER - Hardware - Environmental Systems Corp.

BUG-PRUF! - Insecticides ☆ - Schering-Plough Healthcare Products

BUG SCOUT - Cleaning preparations - E.R. Squibb & Sons, Inc.

BUG SNAPPER - Insecticides ☆ - Sunbeam Outdoor Products Inc.

BUG STUFF - Insecticides - WPC Holdings, Inc.

BUG TRUCKS - Toys - Tyco Toys

BUG UP - Insecticides - Garon Products Inc.

BUG ZAPPER - Automotive parts and accessories - Optronics Inc.

BUGABOO - Coats ☆ - Columbia Sportswear Co.

BUGABOOT - Shoes ☆ - Columbia Sportswear Co.

BUGATTI - Luggage - Bugatti Inc.

BUGAWAY - Pesticides–household - Magnagard Inc.

BUGBASE - Computer software - Archimedes Software, Inc.

BUGFLECTOR - Automotive parts and accessories - Auto Ventshade Co.

BUGFLECTOR II - Motor vehicle parts and accessories - Auto Ventshade Co.

BUGGATI - Apparel–men's - Superba, Inc.

BUGGIE BUNS - Apparel–women's - Kransco Manufacturing Inc.

BUGGS - Computer peripheral equipment - CSI Systems Inc.

BUGGY BEAR - Toys - Tomy America, Inc.

BUGGY CAR - Candy ☆ - Pennsylvania Dutch Candies

BUGGY CHALLENGE - Video games - Taito America Corp.

BUGGY HUGGY - Infant product - Susan Hitchcock Turner

BUGGY, THE - Awnings ☆ - Alpha Productions Inc.

BUGGYMAN - Toys - Tonka Corp.

BUGHUNTERS - Fantasy role-playing games, boardgames, and game accessories - Tsr, Inc.

BUGKIL - Garden equipment - Vandermolen Corp.

BUGLE BEAR - Toys–stuffed - Bugle Boy Industries, Inc.

BUGLE BOY - Apparel and accessories - Bugle Boy Industries, Inc.

BUGLE BOY - Bags–duffel - A.D. Sutton & Sons Inc.

BUGLE BOY - Frames–eyeglass - Marine Optical, Inc.

BUGLE BOY AUTHENTICS - Apparel and accessories - Bugle Boy Industries, Inc.

BUGLE BOY BAGGIES - Apparel - Bugle Boy Industries, Inc.

BUGLE BOY BRIDGE - Apparel and accessories - Bugle Boy Industries, Inc.

BUGLE BOY CLASSICS - Apparel and accessories - Bugle Boy Industries, Inc.

BUGLE BOY CO. - Apparel and accessories - Bugle Boy Industries, Inc.

BUGLE BOY FOR HER - Apparel–women's - Bugle Boy Industries, Inc.

BUGLE BOY PREFERRED - Apparel and accessories - Bugle Boy Industries, Inc.

BUGLE BOY TRANSITION - Apparel and accessories - Bugle Boy Industries, Inc.

BUGLER - Cigarettes - Brown & Williamson Tobacco Corp.

BUGLES - Snack foods - General Mills, Inc.

BUGLETTES - Apparel and accessories - Bugle Boy Industries, Inc.

BUGMEN OF INSECTA - Toys - Multi Toys Corp.

BUGMUGGER - Insecticides ☆ - E-Z Sales & Manufacturing, Inc.

BUGNUTS - Animal feeds - Untethered Feathers

BUGONEX - Insecticides ☆ - Hydroponic Chemical Co. Inc.

BUGS AWAY - Insecticides - Coughlan Products Corp.

☆ = Now out of production

BUGS BE-GONE - Housewares - Athena Products Corp.
BUGS BUNNY - Air purification systems - Medo Industries, Inc.
BUGS BUNNY - Cookies - Nabisco Foods Group
BUGS BUNNY - Electronic equipment - Time Warner Entertainment Co., L.P.
BUGS BUNNY - Infant product ☆ - Reliance Products Corp.
BUGS BUNNY - Novelty items - Easter Unltd. Inc.
BUGS BUNNY - Vitamins and nutritional supplements - Bayer Corp. (Consumer Care Div.)
BUGS BUNNY - Watches ☆ - Genender International, Inc.
BUGS BUNNY & FRIENDS - Snack foods - General Mills, Inc.
BUGS BUNNY'S CRAZY CASTLE II - Video games - Nintendo of America Inc.
BUGS EAR - Apparel–children's - Bugs Ear
BUGS IN A BOX - Publisher's imprints - Intervisual Books, Inc.
BUGS-NO-MORE - Insecticides - Stinger Environmental Products
BUGS OFF - Windshield cleaner - Inter-City Manufacturing Co.
BUGS PLUS - Chemical preparations - Wik Biosystems, Inc.
BUGS R GONE - Insecticides - EnviroMan, Inc.
BUGSIE - Toys - Tonka Corp.
BUGSTERS - Recording label - Bugsters Co. Inc.
BUGSY BIGMOUTH - Toys ☆ - Uncle Milton Industries Inc.
BUGSY SIEGEL - Watches - Seth Levin
BUGVAC - Exterminating products - Bugvac USA, Inc.
BUGWISER - Insecticides - H.D. Hudson Manufacturing Co.
BUGZ - Writing instruments - Pentech International Inc.
BUGZY BROS. VOCAL ATHLETICS - Music–sheet - Jackman Music Corp.
BUHLER - Cookies - De Choix Specialty Foods Co.
BUHLFILM - Electronic equipment - Buhl Industries, Inc.
BUHLITE - Electronic equipment - Buhl Industries, Inc.
BUICK - Motor vehicles–automobiles - General Motors Corp. (Buick Motor Div.)
BUILD-A-BALL - Toys ☆ - Small World Toys
BUILD-A-BELT - Tool belts - McGuire-Nicholas Co., Inc.
BUILD A BOOK - Computer software - Mindscape Software Inc.
BUILD-A-BOOK - Computer software - Theatrix Interactive, Inc.
BUILD-A-BOOK - Photo albums - General Products
BUILD-A-BREAKFAST - Food products - Denny's Inc.
BUILD-A-HOUSE - Dolls - Mattel, Inc.
BUILD A NEW FAMILY TRADITION - Bakery products ☆ - McGlynn Bakeries Inc.
BUILD-A-SCENE - Toys–trains ☆ - Life-Like Products Inc.
BUILD-A-SET - Tools–machine - Black & Decker Corp.
BUILD-A-SKILL - Toys ☆ - Lauri Inc.
BUILD-ALL - Cleaning preparations - Build-All Corp.
BUILD-BY-NUMBER - Toys–airplanes - Paul K. Guillow Inc.
BUILD IT! - Apparel and accessories - Donnelly's U.S. 1, Inc.
BUILD-IT - Dental compounds - Jeneric/Pentron Inc.
BUILD-IT-YOURSELF - Wood products - Easi-Bild Directions Simplified Inc.
BUILD N PLAY - Toys - M.&S. Shillman Inc.
BUILD 'N PLAY - Toys–blocks - Mattel, Inc.
BUILD ON A SOLID FOUNDATION - Cash registers - Upper Midwest Industries, Inc.
BUILD TOUGH - Cleaning equipment - Contec, Inc.
BUILD-UP - Apparel stores–lingerie - H.F. Robbins
BUILD-UP REMOVERS - Cleaning preparations - Black Swan Manufacturing Co.
BUILD YOUR OWN - Calendars - Stuart Hall Co., Inc.
BUILDCOATE - Asphalt felts and coatings - Andek Corp.
BUILDCOATE - Pigments–paint - Building Protective Industries
BUILDER - Bathtubs–enameled - Pearl Baths Inc.
BUILDER - Chemical preparations - Rouse Rubber Industries, Inc.
BUILDER - Fireplaces ☆ - Superior Fireplace Co.
BUILDER - Garden equipment - Scotts Co. (Organics Business Group)
BUILDER GRIP - Exercising equipment - Trend Plastics II, Inc.
BUILDER PORTFOLIO - Whirlpools - Kohler Co.
BUILDER-TUB - Bathroom fixtures - Artesian Industries
BUILDERBOTS - Toys - Trendmasters, Inc.
BUILDERFLOR - Floor coverings - Congoleum Corp.
BUILDER+PLUS - Computer software - Xantel, Inc.
BUILDERS ADVANTAGE SERIES - Wood products - Simpson Timber Co.
BUILDER'S CHOICE - Adhesives and sealants - Macco Adhesives
BUILDERS CHOICE - Floor coverings–carpet and rugs - No-Muv Corp., Inc.
BUILDER'S CHOICE - Whirlpools - Lasco Products Group
BUILDER'S DREAM, THE - Computer software - T. Davis Software Engineering, Inc.
BUILDERS EDGE - Building materials–asbestos - Kingsford Building Products
BUILDER'S EDGE - Fireplaces - Preway Industries Inc.

BUILDERS EDGE - Hardware - Specialty Building Products International Corp.
BUILDERS EDGE - Shutters–plastic - Builders Edge, Inc.
BUILDERS EMPORIUM - Building materials–concrete - Collins & Aikman Corp.
BUILDER'S FINEST - Paints - Sherwin-Williams Automotive Finishes Corp.
BUILDER'S LUXURY - Bathroom fixtures ☆ - St. Thomas Creations
BUILDER'S MASTERPIECE - Paints - Duron, Inc.
BUILDER'S PREFERENCE - Building materials - Empire Co., Inc.
BUILDERS PRIDE - Siding–metal - Amerimark Building Products, Inc.
BUILDERS SAW - Saws–hand-operated - Delta International Machinery Corp.
BUILDERS SUPREME - Plumbing fixtures–metal - Our Own Hardware Co.
BUILDERS WAREHOUSE - Hardware stores - Builders Warehouse Association, Inc.
BUILDEX - Hardware - Illinois Tool Works Inc.
BUILDIN' MAGIC - Toys–blocks - Mattel, Inc.
BUILDING A HEALTHIER YOU - Publisher's imprints - Health Maintenance Programs Inc.
BUILDING A WORLD OF TRUST - Computer peripheral equipment - Trusted Information Systems, Inc.
BUILDING BETTER BODIES THROUGH SCIENCE - Vitamins and nutritional supplements - Natural Supplement Association, Inc.
BUILDING BLASTERS - Toys - Tonka Corp.
BUILDING BLOCKS - Hair care products - LMF Products Inc.
BUILDING BOX - Tool boxes - Flambeau Products Corp.
BUILDING CARE - Cleaning preparations - Midland Chicago Corp.
BUILDING COST PEOPLE, THE - Publisher's imprints - Marshall & Swift
BUILDING INNOVATIONS - Publisher's imprints - Aluminum Co. of America
BUILDING PRO - Floor waxes - Jad Corp. of America
BUILDING SYSTEMS ANALYSIS, INC. - Archery equipment - Building Systems Analysis, Inc.
BUILDING TEN STRATEGY - Computer software - Hartley Courseware Inc.
BUILDING THE AMERICAN DREAM - Bricks - General Shale Products Corp.
BUILDING THE SPIRIT - Lumber - Georgia-Pacific Corp.
BUILDSUPCO - Wire-fence product - BP & N Inc.
BUILT BY WENDY - Musical instrument accessories - Built by Wendy, Inc.
BUILT-FOR-LIFE - Furniture - Krueger International, Inc.
BUILT FOR SPEED - Sporting goods - Built for Speed, Inc.
BUILT FOR TWO - Bicycles ☆ - Roadmaster Corp.
BUILT-IN CIRCULATOR - Fireplaces ☆ - Majestic Co.
BUILT INVISIBLE - Audio equipment - Bose Corp.
BUILT LIKE A SKYSCRAPER - Furniture - Knoll Group
BUILT RITE - Puzzles ☆ - Warren Industries Inc.
BUILT-RITE DAIRY EQUIPMENT - Conveyors - C.J. Machine, Inc.
BUILT TRUE CLEAR THRU - Desks - Wood Design Inc.
BUILT-UP - Roofing materials–slate ☆ - GS Roofing Products Co.
BUILT-UP BASICS - Office supplies - Climax Paper Converters Inc.
BUITEMAN - Biscuits - Holland-American Importing Co. Inc.
BUITONI - Pasta - Nestle USA
BUKA - Balls - Oriam Sport Inc.
BUKARA - Dishes–earthenware ☆ - Denby USA Limited
BUKETS - Diuretics ☆ - Keller Co.
BUKI - Stationery - DGI/Buki
BUKO - Cheese - MD Foods USA Inc.
BUKTOG - Bookmarks - Buktog Inc.
BULA - Eyeglasses - Fiji Wear Inc.
BULA LOOPS - Eyeglasses - Fiji Wear Inc.
BULB BOPPER - Augers - Bulb Bopper, Inc.
BULB BOSS - Computer peripheral equipment - Angelo Brothers Co.
BULB DUST - Pesticides–household - Bonide Products, Inc.
BULB GARD - Chemical preparations - Unifinium Ltd.
BULB-MISER - Lamp bulbs ☆ - Waxman Industries Inc.
BULB-TONE - Flowers, plants, and seeds - Espoma Co.
BULBS ALIVE! - Plant growth regulators - Gardens Alive! Inc.
BULGARI - Cheese ☆ - Caltex Trading, Inc.
BULGARI - Jewelry - Bulgari Danaos Ltd.
BULGARI - Ophthalmic goods - Luxottica
BULGARIAN BURST - Vitamins and nutritional supplements - Strength & Conditioning Technologies
BULGARICUM I.B. - Health care products - Natren Inc.
BULGER, THE - Bats–baseball - Hillerich & Bradsby Co.
BULGOMME - Placemats - William Ewart & Son New York Ltd.
BULK - Toys - Saban Entertainment, Inc.
BULK FORCE 750 - Vitamins and nutritional supplements - American Body Building Products, Inc.
BULK LAX - Laxatives ☆ - Standard Homeopathic Co., Inc.
BULK-PAK - Glass products - Bellco Glass Inc.

☆ = Now out of production

BULKAN - Containers - Sealright Co., Inc.
BULKIEKNIT - Crocheted and knitted items - Garland Knitting Mills
BULKIES - Crocheted and knitted items - Le Roy Knitted Sportswear Inc.
BULKSCAN - X-ray apparatus - Eg&G Instruments
BULKY BOUCLE - Yarn ☆ - Caron International Inc.
BULKY HULK SKID STEER - Tires–automobile - Galaxy Tire & Wheel, Inc.
BULL - Vegetable sauces - Trappey's Fine Foods Inc.
BULL & BEAR - Office supplies - Seminole Paper & Printing Co.
BULL BASH - Athletic associations - United Sports of America
BULL BUSTIN' - Apparel and accessories - Time for Freedom, Inc.
BULL DENIM - Fabrics - Graniteville Co.
BULL DOG - Beverages - Atlas Bottling Co.
BULL DOG - Chains - Merchants Metals Inc.
BULL DOG - Fish–canned or cured - R.J. Peacock Canning Co.
BULL DOG - Handles–wood - Turner, Day and Woolworth Handle Corp.
BULL-DOG - Hot dogs - Southeast Food Systems, Inc.
BULL DOG - Insulating tape ☆ - American Biltrite Tape Products
BULL DOG - Oils–lubricating ☆ - Ashland Oil, Inc.
BULL DRIVER - Tools - Klein Tools Inc.
BULL DURHAM - Cigarettes, tobacco - American Tobacco Co.
BULL-ETTES - Meat products–beef ☆ - Reser's Fine Foods Inc.
BULL FROG - Apparel–children's - Bull Frog Knits/Brinlaw
BULL HORN - Electronic equipment - Brumberger Co. Inc.
BULL ICE - Beverages–malt - The Stroh Brewery Co.
BULL ICE ICE BREWED MALT LIQUOR - Beverages–malt ☆ - The Stroh Brewery Co.
BULL-IT - Paints - Adelphi Coatings Co.
BULL IT PROOF - Agricultural machinery - Bar F Manufacturing, Inc.
BULL LINE, THE - Novelty items ☆ - Rocky Mountain Cookware
BULL MOOSE - Shirts - Lands' End Inc.
BULL NOSE - Frames–picture - Framemica Co.
BULL OF THE WOODS - Tobacco - Conwood Co. L.P.
BULL PUP 12D - Toys–models - Estes Industries
BULL-RAGE - Hunting equipment - Wildlife Research Center, Inc.
BULL RUN - Games - Avalon Hill Game Co.
BULL SHOT - Cleaning preparations - Dash Sales Corp.
BULL TAIL PIZZA - Pizzas–frozen - Bull Tail Pizza Corp.
BULL TERRIER - Knives–hunting - James F. Parker Trust
BULL, THE - Wines - M.S. Walker Inc./Seacoast
BULL TIGER - Apparel and accessories - Mamiye Brothers, Inc.
BULLARD - Machine tools - Devlieg-Bullard Services Group
BULLDOG - Beverages–malt - Barton Brands, Ltd.
BULLDOG - Binders - Boorum & Pease Co.
BULLDOG - Binders ☆ - Esselte Corp.
BULLDOG - Chains - Hodell-Natco Industries, Inc.
BULLDOG - Firearms, accessories, and parts - Welsh Sporting Goods Corp. (Boyt Div.)
BULLDOG - Flags - Dettra Flag Co. Inc.
BULLDOG - Floor finishing machines–commercial - Mercury Floor Machines Inc.
BULLDOG - Guns - Charter Arms
BULLDOG - Hardware - Bulldog Home Hardware
BULLDOG - Musical instrument accessories - Stewart-MacDonald Manufacturing
BULLDOG - Paint removers ☆ - Klean-Strip
BULLDOG - Pencil sharpeners - Hunt Manufacturing Co.
BULLDOG - Rope ☆ - Waterbury Rope Mills
BULLDOG - Shovels - True Temper Hardware Co.
BULLDOG - Sporting goods - Sport Supply Group, Inc.
BULLDOG - Staplers - Arrow Fastener Co. Inc.
BULLDOG - Tools - O.P. Link Handle Co. Inc.
BULLDOG - Vacuum cleaners and accessories - Shop Vac Corp.
BULLDOG BACO - Wines - Bully Hill Vineyards, Inc.
BULLDOG BEER - Beverages–malt - Bulldog Brewing Co.
BULLDOG PUG - Guns - Charter Arms
BULLDOGS - Waterproof footwear - Kaysam Corp. of America
BULLDOZER - Brooms - Quickie Manufacturing Corp.
BULLDOZER - Paints - Sheffield Bronze Paint Corp.
BULLEIT KENTUCKY STRAIGHT BOURBON WHISKEY 45% ALC/VOL (90 PROOF) 750 ML - Whiskey - Kenagra, Inc.
BULLEIT THOROUGHBRED KENTUCKY STRAIGHT BOURBON WHISKEY 50% ALC/VOL (100 PROOF) 7 - Whiskey - Kenagra, Inc.
BULLET - Bicycles - Cycle Products Co.
BULLET - Bicycles ☆ - Huffy Corp.
BULLET - Cameras - Eastman Kodak Co.
BULLET - Drill bits - Black & Decker Corp.

BULLET - Herbicides - Monsanto Co.
BULLET - Kites - Llumar Star Kites Inc.
BULLET - Luggage - Lark Luggage Co. Inc.
BULLET - Recording label ☆ - Web IV Music Inc.
BULLET - Skateboards - Santa Cruz Skateboards
BULLET - Skates–roller - Chicago Roller Skate Co.
BULLET - Skates–roller - National Sporting Goods Corp.
BULLET - Tractors - HME Inc.
BULLET - Trading cards - ANCO Collector Supplies, Inc.
BULLET - Whiskey - Kenagra, Inc.
BULLET BAND - Firearms, accessories, and parts - Anderson Manufacturing Co.
BULLET BLOCK - Ships–sailing vessels - Harken Yacht Fittings
BULLET BOND - Adhesives and sealants - Laporte Construction Chemicals North America, Inc.
BULLET BROS. RACING EXTREME DOWNHILL PRODUCTS - Bicycle parts and accessories - Bullet USA
BULLET CHAIN - Chains - Thomas John Ruzich
BULLET PEN - Pens - Eversharp Pen Co.
BULLET PROOF - Sunglasses - Uvex Sports, Inc.
BULLET-PROOF SOFTWARE - Computer software - Software Bullet-Proof Inc.
BULLET SPORT - Pens - Eversharp Pen Co.
BULLET, THE - Telephone accessories - Fiber Plus International
BULLET, THE - Kitchen utensils–aluminum - Metrokane
BULLETIN - Pencils ☆ - Reliance Pen & Pencil Corp.
BULLETIN - Stencils - Heyer Inc.
BULLETIN BALL - Bulletin boards–cork ☆ - Park Sherman
BULLETIN BALL LAMP - Lamps–desk ☆ - Park Sherman
BULLETIN BAR - Bulletin boards–cork - Davson Inc.
BULLETIN BOARD CONSTRUCTION SET - Computer software - SourceView Software International
BULLETIN BOARD CORK - Corks - Forbo Industries, Inc.
BULLETIN BORDER - Bulletin boards–cork - Bemiss-Jason Corp.
BULLETIN BORDER - Bulletin boards–wood - Boone International, Inc.
BULLETIN COLOR - Paints - Radiant Color Div.
BULLETIN STROKE - Brushes–paint - M. Grumbacher Inc.
BULLETPROOF - Luggage - Stavros C. Aloizos
BULLETPROOF - Varnishes - Barrett Varnish Co.
BULLETRON - Computer software - IDK Computer Systems, Inc.
BULLFROG - Recording label ☆ - Roots and Rhythm
BULLFROG - Sporting goods - O'Brien International
BULLFROG - Suntan lotions - Chattem Inc.
BULLFROG LIGHT - Candles - Root Candle Co.
BULLHEAD - Apparel - Pacific Sunwear of California Inc.
BULLHEAD - Oysters–canned or cured - Star-Kist Foods, Inc.
BULLIARD'S - Food products - Acadiana Pepper Co.
BULLION - Beverages–malt - Mar
BULLISH - Lenses–optical - Ditto Industries Inc.
BULLMATE - Games - Majek Inc.
BULLMOOSE - Handlebars–bicycle - Fisher Mountain Bikes
BULLOCH LADE - Whiskey - Sazerac Co. Inc.
BULLOCK & JONES - Apparel–men's - Bullock and Jones, Inc.
BULLPEN CHEW - Nuts–candied - Nabisco Foods Group
BULLPEN, THE - Sporting goods - Pelican Design
BULLS - Apparel - Chicago Professional Sports LP
BULL'S CLUB JERKY - Meat products - Bull's Club
BULL'S-EYE - Barbecue sauce - Kraft Foods, Inc.
BULL'S EYE - Boats - Glen-L Marine Designs
BULL'S EYE - Chemical preparations - Farmland Industries Inc.
BULL'S-EYE - Cigars - Patrick Brooks
BULL'S EYE - Cleaning preparations - W.W. Grainger, Inc.
BULL'S EYE - Clocks - General Time Corp. (Westclox/Seth Thomas Div.)
BULLS EYE - Guns ☆ - Daisy Manufacturing Co.
BULLS EYE - Herbicides - Frank Miller and Sons Inc.
BULL'S EYE - Plugs–ear - Aearo Co.
BULL'S EYE - Plumbing fixtures - Fluidmaster, Inc.
BULLS EYE - Shellac - William Zinsser & Co. Inc.
BULL'S-EYE - Toys - Trend Enterprises, Inc.
BULLS EYE 1-2-3 - Primers - William Zinsser & Co. Inc.
BULLS-EYES - Candy - Goetze's Candy Co., Inc.
BULL'S HEAD - Cases–musical instrument - Harptone
BULLS ONE AND ONLY - Meat products - Knauss Snack Food Co.
BULLSEYE - Antennas–satellite - Recoton Corp.
BULLSEYE - Aquariums–household - Wardley Corp.
BULLSEYE - Automotive parts and accessories ☆ - Loctite Corp.
BULLSEYE - Bicycles - Bullseye Cycle Corp.

☆ = Now out of production

BULLSEYE - Bowling balls - Action Products, Inc.
BULLSEYE - Carpet-cleaning supplies - American Textile Products Co.
BULLSEYE - Dog food - Mardel Laboratories, Inc.
BULLSEYE - Flashlights - Zelco Industries, Inc.
BULLSEYE - Frames–eyeglass - Hudson Optical Corp.
BULLSEYE - Glass - D & L Stained Glass Supply, Inc.
BULLSEYE - Jewelry ☆ - Anson Inc.
BULLSEYE - Measuring and dispensing pumps - Apache Technologies, Inc.
BULLSEYE - Musical instrument accessories - D'Andrea Manufacturing Co. Inc.
BULLSEYE - Pet products - Harvest Industries, Inc.
BULLSEYE - Ships–sailing vessels - Cape Cod Shipbuilding Co.
BULLSEYE - Surgical instruments - Linvatec Corp.
BULLSEYE - Tools - Frederickseal, Inc.
BULLSEYE - Toys - Tonka Corp.
BULLSEYE BOOKS - Publisher's imprints - Alfred A. Knopf Inc.
BULLSEYE BOWIE - Knives ☆ - Tru-Balance Knife Co.
BULLSEYE BUSTER - Knives - Tru-Balance Knife Co.
BULLSHOT - Lubricants - Bullshot Systems Inc.
BULLSIEYE - Hardware - W.H. Maze Co.
BULLSKIN - Apparel and accessories - Custom Chrome, Inc.
BULLTILE - Floor coverings - Tek Stil Concepts Inc.
BULLTOP - Automotive parts and accessories - Aduco International, Inc.
BULLWHIP CANNON - Toys - Tonka Corp.
BULLWHIP SHAFT - Golfing equipment - Black Rock Golf Corp.
BULLWHIP SHAFT - Golfing equipment - Golfsmith International Inc.
BULLY - Apparel and accessories - No Fear, Inc.
BULLY - Cleaning preparations - R.T. French Co.
BULLY - Educational materials - St. Vrain Valley School District
BULLY - Ophthalmic goods - Embassy Creations Inc.
BULLY - Sporting goods - Schutt Manufacturing Co.
BULLY BLU BOY - Cleaning preparations - Airwick Industries
BULLY BROTHERS, THE - Publisher's imprints - Jared D. Lee Studio Inc.
BULLY HILL - Wines ☆ - Bully Hill Vineyards, Inc.
BULLY PLUS BLUE - Cleaning preparations - R.T. French Co.
BULLY PORTER - Beverages–malt - Boulevard Brewing Associates L.P.
BULLY POWER - Cleaning preparations - R.T. French Co.
BULLY, THE - Frames–picture - Framemica Co.
BULLYBOARD - Surfboards - Wahoo International Inc.
BULLYWORLD - Figurines - Bullyland Inc.
BULLZEYE - Skates–roller - Hyper Corp.
BULOVA - Watches - Bulova Corp.
BULWARK - Protective apparel - Bulwark Protective Apparel Inc.
BULWARK - Tobacco - American Tobacco Co.
BULY - Watches - Bulova Corp.
B.U.M. - Apparel–men's - BUM International Inc.
B.U.M. EQUIPMENT JEANSWEAR - Apparel and accessories - Chauvin International Ltd.
B.U.M. JEANSWEAR - Apparel–athletic - BUM International Inc.
B.U.M. RAP - Apparel and accessories - BUM International Inc.
B.U.M. RUNNER - Apparel–men's - Chauvin International Ltd.
BUM SHIRT, THE - Shirts ☆ - Manhattan International
B.U.M. SPORT - Sunglasses - BUM International Inc.
BUM WRAPS - Apparel and accessories - Chauvin International Ltd.
BUMBLE BALL - Toys - ERTL Co., Inc.
BUMBLE BALL BOLTERS - Vitamins and nutritional supplements - ERTL Co., Inc.
BUMBLE BALL BUDDY - Toys - ERTL Co., Inc.
BUMBLE BALL BUMBLEHEAD - Toys - ERTL Co., Inc.
BUMBLE BALL PUP - Toys - ERTL Co., Inc.
BUMBLE BALL VEHICLES - Toys–automobiles - ERTL Co., Inc.
BUMBLE BEE - Bicycles - Ross Bicycles USA, Ltd.
BUMBLE BEE - Engines - Caribbean Ventures Limited, Inc.
BUMBLE BEE - Frames–eyeglass ☆ - Universal/Univis Inc.
BUMBLE BEE - Soccer equipment ☆ - Brine Inc.
BUMBLE BEE - Toys - Tyco Toys
BUMBLE BEE - Tuna–canned - Bumble Bee Seafoods, Inc.
BUMBLE BEE TUNA EXTENDER SALAD & SANDWICH MIX - Food products - Bumble Bee Seafoods, Inc.
BUMBLE BRIGHT - Toys - ERTL Co., Inc.
BUMBLE PLOT - Computer software ☆ - Gessler Publishing Co., Inc.
BUMBLEBEE BALM - Skin care products - Old World Honey
BUMBLEBEEZ, THE - Recording label - Bumblebeez Partners
BUMBLES - Candy - Willy Wonka Brands
BUMBLES - Ice - Jack Frost Laboratories Inc.
BUMBLES BUNNY - Toys–stuffed - Russ Berrie and Co., Inc.

BUMBLING BOXING - Games - Tomy America, Inc.
BUMEX - Diuretics - Roche Laboratories
BUMMER - See SOFT SEAT
BUMMER BUNNY - Writing product - American Greetings Corp.
BUMP & ROAR - Toys - Trendmasters, Inc.
BUMP-AROUNDS - Bathroom accessories - Better Sleep, Inc.
BUMP AUTHENTIC STYLE - Apparel–women's - Tropic Tex International, Inc.
BUMP BILLIARDS - Games - C.G. Wood Co.
BUMP !EM - Toys - Tonka Corp.
BUMP FIGHTER - Razors - American Safety Razor Co.
BUMP GUARD - Razors–electric ☆ - American Safety Razor Co.
BUMP IN THE NIGHT - Shoes ☆ - S. Goldberg and Co. Inc.
BUMP IN THE NIGHT - Watches - Greengrass Productions, Inc.
BUMP-ME - Rubber–molded - W.T. Ayres & Associates
BUMP-ME - Trailers - Dale D. Devries
BUMP 'N' GO EGG-MOBILE - Toys–stuffed - Fun World Inc.
BUMP-N-TURN - Machinery - Dick Moll & Sons, Inc.
BUMP OFF - Shaving preparations - Valentine & Son Inc.
BUMP PATROL - Health care products - Therman McKenzie
BUMPA - Pool tables - American International Shuffleboard Corp.
BUMPAROUND - Infant product ☆ - Sandbox Industries
BUMPAS - Ratatouille - Bumpas Gourmet Foods
BUMPER - Curling irons–electric - Windmere Corp.
BUMPER - Dryers–hair - Belson Products
BUMPER - Fungicides - Makhteshim-Agan of North America Inc.
BUMPER BAND - Electronic equipment - Omega Engineering, Inc.
BUMPER BLACK - Paints - United Coatings, Inc.
BUMPER BOB - Motor vehicle parts and accessories - Robert L. Liland
BUMPER BUDDY - Novelty items - First Amendment Products, Inc.
BUMPER BUGGY - Toys - Tomy America, Inc.
BUMPER CHROME - Paints - Plasti-Kote Co. Inc.
BUMPER CROP - Fertilizers - Master Nurserymen's Association
BUMPER DUMPER - Toys ☆ - Montgomery Schoolhouse
BUMPER HARVEST - Gypsum products - Georgia-Pacific Corp.
BUMPER SCRIPTURES - Decals and transfers - Andrew G. Harris
BUMPER SHOT - Games ☆ - CBS Toys
BUMPER THUMPER - Toys–automobiles - Mattel, Inc.
BUMPER TO BUMPER - Games - A Work of Art, Inc.
BUMPERCROP - Staple foods - Nancy W. Turner
BUMPERMANIAS - Paper–gummed ☆ - Wry Idea Co.
BUMPERS - Bed linens and outdoor cushions - Intuition Inc.
BUMPERS - Footwear - International Seaway Trading Corp.
BUMPIN' BUSY BOX - Toys - Playskool, Inc.
BUMPKINS - Candy - R.M. Palmer Co.
BUMPKINS - Dolls - Uneeda Doll Co., Ltd.
BUMPKINS KIDS - Dolls - Uneeda Doll Co., Inc.
BUMPLES - Playground equipment - National Latex Products Co.
BUMPS - Candy ☆ - Maxfield Candy Co.
BUMPY BEER - Mustard - El Paso Chili Co.
BUMPY-LUMPY - Candy - American Chewing Gum Inc.
BUMS IN PARADISE - Shirts - Thomas J. Wittman
BUN - Candy ☆ - Storck USA L.P.
BUN - Ice cream - Good Humor Corp.
BUN-BRATZ - Sausages - Johnsonville Foods Co.
BUN-BUDDY - Cushions - Action Products Co.
BUN BUNS - Toys–stuffed - Dakin Inc.
BUN BUSTERS - Sausages - Fred Usinger, Inc.
BUN BUSTERS! - Video production - Goodtimes Home Video Corp.
BUN COZY - Kitchenware–earthenware - Ruby Whitney Manufacturing
BUN GEE BAG BAG IT & FLAG IT - Bags–storage - Murray E. Stanley, Jr.
BUN KEEPER - Containers - Products Resource Group, LLC
BUN N' BURGER - Restaurants–fast food - Bun n' Burger International
BUN SAV'R - Exercising equipment - Thomas R. Puckett
BUN-TALIAN - Sausages - Johnsonville Foods Co.
BUNBELIEVABLE! - Food products - Conagra, Inc.
BUNBUTTER - Skin care products - A.B. Firethorne & Co.
BUNCH 'O CRUNCH - Fish–fresh or frozen - Frionor USA Inc.
BUNCH O CRUNCH - Snack foods - Land-O-Sun Dairies, Inc.
BUNCH O' KRUNCH - Cereal - Gilster-Mary Lee Corp.
BUNCH-UMS - Pet products - A & C Designs, Inc.
BUNCHA CRUNCH - Chocolate candy - Nestle USA
BUNCHIE LEASH - Pet products - Aspen Pet Products
BUNCHY - Sporting goods ☆ - Unique Sports Products Inc.
BUNDANNA - Apparel and accessories - Bundanna
BUNDELI - Biscuits - Bundeli Foods, Inc.
BUNDLE BAND - Saw blades - Simonds Industries Inc.

BUNDLE OF BABIES - Dolls - Cap Toys, Inc.
BUNDLE OF COLORS - Crayons - Binney & Smith Inc.
BUNDLE OF JOY - Dolls - Goldberger Doll Manufacture Co.
BUNDLE OF JOY - Hobby kits - Stanislaus Imports, Inc.
BUNDLE OF LOVE - Dolls - Uneeda Doll Co., Inc.
BUNDLE O'JOY - Toys–stuffed ☆ - Fun World Inc.
BUNDLE PACK - Paper–tissue - Kimberly-Clark Corp.
BUNDLE UP BABY - Dolls - Fisher-Price, Inc.
BUNDLER, THE - Containers - Vinyl Art, Inc.
BUNDLES - Bedding–linen - Sterncraft/Mike Stern Co.
BUNDLES - Cigars - Lane Ltd.
BUNDLES OF CHOCOLATES - Candy ☆ - Brock Candy Co. Inc.
BUNDT-LETTE - Pans - Nordic Ware
BUNDT PAN - Cooking equipment–household - Nordic Ware
BUNDY - Musical instruments ☆ - Selmer Co. Inc.
BUNDY'S BEST - Food products - Bundy Foods Inc.
BUNGALOW - Furniture - Bassett Furniture Industries, Inc.
BUNGALOW - Paints - Schulte Paint & Lacquer Manufacturing Co., Inc.
BUNGALOW - Wainscotting - Georgia-Pacific Corp.
BUNGALOW BLONDE - Beverages - Viewpoint International, Inc.
BUNGALOW BRAND - Jams and jellies - Bungalow Brand Foods
BUNGALOW BREW - Beverages–malt - Viewpoint International, Inc.
BUNGE - Oils–edible - Bunge Corp.
BUNGE FOODS - Food products - Bunge Foods Corp.
BUNGEE BABY - Infant product - Cosco, Inc.
BUNGEE BETH - Laces–boot and shoe - Beth A. Sigren
BUNGEE BOUNCER - Infant product - Cosco, Inc.
BUNGEE COMBO - Infant product - Cosco, Inc.
BUNGEE JUMPING SYSTEMS - Novelty items - Bungee Jumping Systems Inc.
BUNGEE MAN - Toys - Gary David Piaget
BUNGEE TENNIS - Ballgames - Charles P. Yelton
BUNGI - Pet products - JT Industries
BUNGIE - Computer software - Bungie Software Products Corp.
BUNGLEBUG - Jewelry - Gale Bartlett Nemec
BUNGO GORILLA - Toys–stuffed - Russ Berrie and Co., Inc.
BUNGY BUNNY - Puppets - Russ Berrie and Co., Inc.
BUNICCI - Olive oil - Bunge Foods Corp.
BUNION RELIEF KIT - Manicure preparations - Professional Foot Care Products Inc.
BUNK BAGS - Luggage ☆ - Hartmann Luggage Co.
BUNK BIN - Containers–plastic - Romanoff Products Inc.
BUNK HOUSE - Trailers–travel - Trotwood Corp.
BUNK-IN-A-BOX - Furniture ☆ - Cosco, Inc.
BUNK JUNK - Stationery - Fran Mar Greeting cards Ltd.
BUNK SHOP - Furniture - Universal Flooring
BUNKA - Thread ☆ - Cronar Ltd.
BUNKER-BALL - Paddle ball game - Jack Mack, Inc.
BUNKER HILL - Floor coverings ☆ - Robbins Inc.
BUNKER HILL - Food products - Liberty Bell Wholesale Grocery Co.
BUNKER HILL - Meat products–canned - Bunker Hill Foods
BUNKER HILL - Thread - Blue Mountain Industries, Inc.
BUNKER HILL-18 - Floor coverings–carpet and rugs ☆ - Cumberland Mills Inc.
BUNKER HILL, THE - Pet products - R and B Wire Products Inc.
BUNKERNIT - Paints - Hempel Coatings USA Inc.
BUNKERS - Shirts - David Geoffrey & Associates
BUNKERS - Spirits - Paramount Distillers Inc.
BUNKHOUSE - Bacon ☆ - Dold Foods Inc.
BUNKHOUSE - Food products - Jardine's Texas Foods
BUNKHOUSE - Manufactured homes - Redman Industries, Inc.
BUNKHOUSE - Motor vehicles–motor homes ☆ - Honey Recreational Vehicles Inc.
BUNKHOUSE - Trailers–travel ☆ - Coachmen Industries, Inc.
BUNKIE - Lenses–optical - National Optical Co.
BUNKLES BUNNY - Toys–stuffed - Russ Berrie and Co., Inc.
BUNKO - Games - Bunko
BUNN - Coffee makers–electric - Bunn-O-Matic Corp.
BUNN - Coffee makers–electric - Gillies Coffee Co.
BUNN-O-MATIC - Coffee makers–electric - Bunn-O-Matic Corp.
BUNNETS - Pet products - Nutritional Research Associates Inc.
BUNNIE - Candy ☆ - Candymax, Inc.
BUNNIES - Candy - Rodda Candy Co.
BUNNIES - Footwear - Rod-Man Children's Footwear Corp.
BUNNY - Baked goods - Bost Bakery Inc.
BUNNY - Bicycles - Columbia Manufacturing Inc.

BUNNY - Bleach - Livingston Industries Inc.
BUNNY - Candy - Leaf, Inc.
BUNNY - Frames–eyeglass - Pathway Optical Prods.
BUNNY - Yarn ☆ - JCA, Inc.
BUNNY & ME - Infant product - S. Schwab Co., Inc.
BUNNY B - Ice - Bunny B Inc.
BUNNY BANK, THE - Toys–stuffed - Fun World Inc.
BUNNY BANKS - Candy - Leaf, Inc.
BUNNY BASKET - Flowers, plants, and seeds - Florists' Transworld Delivery Association, Inc.
BUNNY BATH - Rabbits - Four Paws Products Ltd.
BUNNY BATTS - Fibers–polyester - Putnam Co., Inc.
BUNNY BEANS - Dolls - Mattel, Inc.
BUNNY BIG WHEEL - Toys–stuffed - Fun World Inc.
BUNNY BINKS - Candy ☆ - R.M. Palmer Co.
BUNNY BLUE RIBBON - Candy ☆ - R.M. Palmer Co.
BUNNY BOTTOMS - Diapers–disposable - American Tissue
BUNNY BRUNCH - Animal feeds - Kellogg Inc.
BUNNY BUDDIES - Toys–stuffed ☆ - Fun World Inc.
BUNNY BUNCH - Toys–stuffed - Fun World Inc.
BUNNY BUNNY BUNNIES - Toys - Shoot the Moon Products, Inc.
BUNNY BUNTING - Dolls - Fun World Inc.
BUNNY BUTTERFLY - Candy ☆ - R.M. Palmer Co.
BUNNY CHOPPER - Toys–stuffed - Fun World Inc.
BUNNY COUSINS - Giftware - Russ Berrie and Co., Inc.
BUNNY CRISP - Candy - R.M. Palmer Co.
BUNNY CRUNCH - Food products - Louis Fishgold Inc.
BUNNY EGGS CHOCOLATE FILLED EGG SHELLS - Chocolate candy - Chariot Corp.
BUNNY ESMOND - Bedding–linen - Beacon Manufacturing Co.
BUNNY ESMOND - Blankets - Chatham Manufacturing Co.
BUNNY FAVORS - Toys–stuffed ☆ - Fun World Inc.
BUNNY FOLKS - Toys–stuffed - Paper Magic Group Inc.
BUNNY FOLKS - Toys–stuffed - Spearhead Industries Inc.
BUNNY FOUNTAIN - Pet products - Masters Gifts Inc.
BUNNY FRIENDS - Giftware - Russ Berrie and Co., Inc.
BUNNY HOLLOW - Paper products - Giordano Art, Ltd.
BUNNY HOP - Bath salts - GPS, Inc.
BUNNY HOP - Games - Smethport Specialty Co.
BUNNY HOPS - Toys–stuffed - Dakin Inc.
BUNNY HOUSE - Candy ☆ - Haviland Candy Inc.
BUNNY HOUSE - Candy ☆ - New England Confectionery Co.
BUNNY HUGS - Toys–stuffed - Fun World Inc.
BUNNY HUGS - Toys–stuffed - Russ Berrie and Co., Inc.
BUNNY-IN-AN-EGG - Hobby kits - Grizzlies
BUNNY JOY - Toys–stuffed - Dakin Inc.
BUNNY KINS - Toys–stuffed - Fun World Inc.
BUNNY-LUV CARROT SNAX - Fruits and vegetables - Mike Yurosek & Son, L.P.
BUNNY MATES - Toys–stuffed - Paper Magic Group Inc.
BUNNY MUNNY - Candy - R.M. Palmer Co.
BUNNY PARTY - Giftware - Russ Berrie and Co., Inc.
BUNNY PATCH - Candy - R.M. Palmer Co.
BUNNY PATCH - Novelty items - Paper Magic Group Inc.
BUNNY POP - Popcorn - National Oats Co. Inc.
BUNNY POPS - Candy - R.M. Palmer Co.
BUNNY PRINTS - Chocolate candy - Brach and Brock Confections Inc.
BUNNY ROBIN - Ice cream - Carvel Corp.
BUNNY ROSEBUD - Candy - R.M. Palmer Co.
BUNNY SKATES - Toys–stuffed ☆ - Fun World Inc.
BUNNY STICKY-FEET - Toys–stuffed ☆ - Fun World Inc.
BUNNY TAILS - Candy - Brach and Brock Confections Inc.
BUNNY TAILS - Paper products - Giordano Art, Ltd.
BUNNY WARMER - Underwear and nightwear - Meltzer Industries Corp.
BUNNYBEES - Toys - Original Appalachian Artworks, Inc.
BUNNYBELL - Toys–stuffed ☆ - Gund, Inc.
BUNNYETTES - Candy - R.M. Palmer Co.
BUNNYHUGS - Diapers–disposable - Paper Converting Industry, Inc.
BUNNYKINS - Dinnerware–glass - Royal Doulton-Somerset UK Ltd.
BUNNYLOONS - Dolls - Mattel, Inc.
BUNNYMALLOWS - Candy - Kraft Foods, Inc.
BUNNYTOWNE - Figurines - Flambro Imports, Inc.
BUNNYTRAIL TREAT - Bakery products - Tasty Baking Co.
BUNNYTUNES - Toys–stuffed ☆ - Fun World Inc.
BUNNYVILLE, USA - Candy ☆ - R.M. Palmer Co.

☆ = Now out of production

BUNRATTY IRISH POTCHEEN PRODUCT OF IRELAND 90 PROOF - Whiskey - Camelot Importing Co., Inc.

BUNS & THIGHS OF STEEL - Video production - Warner Steel Vision Inc.

BUNS OF STEEL - Pre-recorded video tapes - Maier Group Inc.

BUNS OF STEEL - Publisher's imprints - Warner Steel Vision Inc.

BUNS UP - Detachable vehicle step - Buns Up Inc.

BUNS WORKER - Exercising equipment - Fitness Quest Inc.

BUNSALATOR - Exercising equipment - Torso Technology, Inc.

BUNT-A-BOUT - Infant product - Dundee Mills, Inc.

BUNTE - Candy - American Candy Co.

BUNTE MI CHOICE - Candy ✰ - American Candy Co.

BUNTEES - Shoes - Stride Rite Corp.

BUNTING - Gloves - Patagonia, Inc.

BUNUELITOS - Cereal - General Mills, Inc.

BUNUELOS COOKIE CHIPS - Cookies - La Canasta Food Products

BUNYAN BUG - Apparel and accessories - Richard Rose

BUNYAN BUG - Fishing lures - Bunyan Bug

BUNYAN ONION - Food product - Edward P. Grace, III

BUNZLAUER - Kitchenware—earthenware - Zanger Co.

BUON - Pizzas—frozen - Dairy Fresh Products Co.

BUON APPETITO - Bakery products - Bon Appetit Danish Co., Inc.

BUON GUSTO - Food products - Dairy Fresh Products Co.

BUONA SALUTE - Pasta - Good Health Products, Inc.

BUOY - Infant product - A Better World Co.

BUOY BAG - Bags - Byer of Maine

BUOY BATH - Toys - Playskool, Inc.

BUOY-CLIPPER - Boats - RMC Marine Co.

BUOY SHELL - Diaper covers - A Better World Co.

BUOYANCY - Skin care products - Ilona, Inc.

BUOYANCY AND RESISTANCE CUFFS - Exercising equipment - Hydro-Fit, Inc.

BUOYANT BOATWEAR - Life preservers ✰ - Stearns Manufacturing Co.

BUOYWEAR - Life preservers - Buoywear, Inc.

BUPAP - Pharmaceutical preparations - ECR Pharmaceuticals

BUPH - Hair care products - Mahdeen Laboratory

BUPLEURUM CALMATIVE COMPOUND - Vitamins and nutritional supplements - Planetary Formulas

BUPRENEX - Pharmaceutical preparations - Norwich-Eaton Pharmaceuticals

BUQUETS - Pharmaceutical - American Laboratories Inc.

BUR-ACME - Tackers and staples - Automation Fastening Co. Inc.

BUR-M-ZINC - Skin care products - Syosset Laboratories Inc.

BUR-MIL - Fabrics - Burlington Industries, Inc.

BURAGO - Toys - DGI/Buki

BURAGO - Toys—models - Small World Toys

BURATI - Wines - Monsieur Henri Wines Ltd.

BURBANK - Clocks - Ridgeway Clock Co.

BURBANK - Lenses—optical - Ditto Industries Inc.

BURBATRON - Carpets, now out of production - Couristan Inc.

BURBER-COLOR - Carpets, now out of production - Couristan Inc.

BURBER-CORD - Carpets, now out of production - Couristan Inc.

BURBER-KNIT - Carpets, now out of production - Couristan Inc.

BURBERRY - Apparel and accessories - Burberry

BURBERRY - Ophthalmic goods - Swank Optical

BURBERRYS - Apparel and accessories - Cluett, Peabody & Co.

BURBERRYS - Beverages—alcohol - Barton Brands, Ltd.

BURBERRYS - Colognes - Faberge Co.

BURBERRYS - Sunglasses - L'Amy Inc.

BURBERRYS OF LONDON - Food products ✰ - De Medici Imports Ltd.

BURBERRY'S OF LONDON - Jewelry - Grosse Jewels N.Y. Inc.

BURBERTEX - Carpets, now out of production - Couristan Inc.

BURBERWEVE - Carpets, now out of production - Couristan Inc.

BURCANE - Wood products ✰ - Kinsman Co. Inc.

BURCO CEBORA - Welding equipment - Burco Welding & Cutting Products, Inc.

BURCOR - Corks - Burcor Inc.

BURDEO - Skin care products - Hill Dermaceuticals

BURDICK - Meat products—cured - Burdick Packing Co.

BURDICK - Office furniture—metal - Herman Miller, Inc.

BURDINES - Apparel and accessories - Burdines Inc.

BURDS, THE - Puppets - Toy Originators Inc.

BUREAU OF DANGEROUS GOODS LTD. - Computer software - Bureau of Dangerous Goods, Ltd.

BUREAU, THE - Circuit boards—printed - Bureau of Engraving, Inc.

BUREAUCRACY - Games ✰ - Avalon Hill Game Co.

BUREN - Pharmaceutical preparations ✰ - B.F. Ascher & Co. Inc.

BUREN - Watches ✰ - SMH (US) Inc.

BURFORD - Finishing agents - Baf Industries

BURGBRAU - Beverages—malt - Burgbrau

BURGER - Beverages—malt - Hudepohl-Schoenling Brewing Co.

BURGER BUILDER - Food products ✰ - General Mills, Inc.

BURGER BUNDLES - Doughs—frozen ✰ - Pillsbury Co.

BURGER CATCH - Games ✰ - Tomy America, Inc.

BURGER CHEESE - Cheese - Sargento Cheese Co. Inc.

BURGER CHEF - Restaurants—fast food - Hardee's Food Systems, Inc.

BURGER FRIES - Vegetables—frozen - Lamb-Weston, Inc.

BURGER KING - Restaurants—fast food - Burger King Corp.

BURGER KING - Telephones - Pierre Cardin Electronique

BURGER LIGHT - Beverages—malt - Hudepohl-Schoenling Brewing Co.

BURGER-LOVER - Meat products—beef - Irwin L. Gold & Assoc.

BURGER MAKER - Housewares - Continental/SiLite International Inc.

BURGER PLUS - Food products ✰ - Stevens Industries Inc.

BURGER-PRO - Beef - The Kroger Co.

BURGER VITTLES - Sandwiches—prepackaged - Zartic, Inc.

BURGERBITS - Dog food - Chenango Valley Pet Foods Inc

BURGERDIER GENERAL - Toys - Mattel, Inc.

BURGERMAKER - Food products ✰ - Wis-Pak Foods, Inc.

BURGERMEISTER - Beverages—malt ✰ - The Stroh Brewery Co.

BURGERMEISTER LIGHT - Beverages—malt ✰ - The Stroh Brewery Co.

BURGERS & FRIES - Dog food - Gimborn U.S., Inc.

BURGERS UP! - Toys - Tonka Corp.

BURGESS - Flashlights - Burgess Inc.

BURGESS - Housewares - The Fountainhead Group, Inc.

BURGESS & WICKIZER - Publisher's imprint - Borgo Press

BURGESS CELLARS - Wines - Burgess Cellars

BURGESS CELLARS - Wines - House of Burgundy Inc.

BURGESS LEIGH - Glassware—household - Crownford Giftware Co. Inc.

BURGHARDT'S - Breads - Burghardt's Bakery

BURGIE DRAFT - Beverages—malt ✰ - The Stroh Brewery Co.

BURGIN-ARDEN - Health care products ✰ - Physician Sales & Service

BURGLAR BARS - Locks—door - John Sterling Corp.

BURGLAR GUARD - Hardware - Windor Security Manufacturing Inc.

BURGLAR STOPPER - Alarm systems—burglar - Safety Technology International, Inc.

BURGOYN - Greeting cards - Timberline Artists Publishing Inc.

BURGOYNE - Floor coverings ✰ - Congoleum Corp.

BURGOYNE - Greeting cards - Burgoyne Inc./Curtis Swann

BURGOYNE BUSINESS BOOK - Greeting cards - Burgoyne Inc./Curtis Swann

BURGUND - Glassware—household ✰ - Oneida Ltd.

BURGUNDY - Crackers - Prepco

BURGUNDY - Dinnerware ✰ - Corning Inc.

BURGUNDY - Flatware - Reed and Barton Corp.

BURGUNDY - Food products ✰ - Goodmark Foods, Inc.

BURGUNDY BLAZE - Lipsticks ✰ - Honey & Spice Toiletries

BURGUNDY CAROUSEL - Flowers, plants, and seeds - Bailey Nurseries, Inc.

BURGUNDY CHERRY - Teas - Eastern Shore Tea Co.

BURGUNDY PARFAIT - Lipsticks - Honey & Spice Toiletries

BURGUS - Wines - BPW Holding, Ltd.

BURIED BLUEPRINTS - Puzzles - Largely Literary Designs, Inc.

BURIED IN TIME - Video games - Presto Studios, Inc.

BURIED TREASURE - Ice cream - Nestle USA

BURING'S COUNTRY BRAND - Processed meats - Saramar Corp.

BURINI - Accordions - Castiglione Accordion

BURK HALL - Paints - Burk Hall Paint Co.

BURKE - Chairs—folding - Boling Co.

BURKE - Fishing tackle - McClellan Industries Inc.

BURKE - Floor coverings—tile - Burke Flooring Products

BURKE - Meat products—cured - Burke Marketing Corp.

BURKE - Patching compounds, joint fillers, etc. - Burke Co.

BURKE - Tuxedos - Lord West Formals

BURKE & BARRY - Whiskey - David Sherman Corp.

BURKE & BURKE - Glassware—household - Burke & Burke USA Ltd.

BURKE DESIGN GROUP - Computer software - Burke Design Group, Inc.

BURKE FLOW TRUE - Cement - Burke Co.

BURKE ROULEAU - Wood products - Burke Flooring Products

BURKE STONE - Cement - Burke Co.

BURKE-WORTHINGTON - Golfing equipment - Tommy Armour Golf Co.

BURKEBASE - Floor coverings - Burke Flooring Products

BURKEBEINER - Sporting goods - A & T Ski Co. Inc.

BURKEEN - Machinery - Burkeen Construction Co.

BURKEPOXY - Adhesives and sealants - Burke Co.

BURKMANN FEEDS - Animal feeds - Burkmann Mills

BURKS - Pumps - Burks Pumps, Inc.

✰ = Now out of production

BURKSHIRE - Fabrics - Uniroyal Engineered Products

BURL - Desk sets - Micropoint Inc.

BURL REWINDZIT - Tools - Burl N Co.

BURLANA - Fabrics - Burlington Industries, Inc.

BURLAP - Wallpaper - Koroseal Wallcoverings

BURLAP PAC - Fabrics–burlap - Eaton Brothers Corp.

BURLAPLUS - Fabrics–polypropylene - Eaton Brothers Corp.

BURLEE - Yarn ☆ - National Spinning Co., Inc.

BURLEIGH WILLOW - Dinnerware–glass ☆ - Crownford Giftware Co. Inc.

BURLESON - Honey - T.W. Burleson & Son Inc.

BURLEY - Bicycles - Burley Design Cooperative

BURLEY - Frames–eyeglass ☆ - Universal/Univis Inc.

BURLEY - Pipes–tobacco - S.M. Frank & Co. Inc. (Kaywoodie-Yello-Bole-Medico)

BURLEY-CUB - Bicycle parts and accessories - Burley Design Cooperative

BURLEY D'LITE - Bicycle parts and accessories - Burley Design Cooperative

BURLEY DUET - Bicycles - Burley Design Cooperative

BURLEY LITE - Bicycles ☆ - Burley Design Cooperative

BURLEY-ROO - Bicycles ☆ - Burley Design Cooperative

BURLEY-SOLO - Bicycles - Burley Design Cooperative

BURLINGAME CO. - Consulting services - Burlingame Co.

BURLINGTON - Cabinets ☆ - Aristokraft, Inc.

BURLINGTON - Clocks - General Time Corp. (Westclox/Seth Thomas Div.)

BURLINGTON - Crackers - Vista Bakery, Inc.

BURLINGTON - Fabrics - Burlington Industries, Inc.

BURLINGTON - Hosiery - Kayser-Roth Corp.

BURLINGTON BASICS - Hosiery - Kayser-Roth Corp.

BURLINGTON BIO MED - Garden equipment - Lawn & Garden Supply Co.

BURLINGTON BULLET - Toys–trains ☆ - Life-Like Products Inc.

BURLINGTON HOUSE - Draperies - Burlington Industries, Inc.

BURLINGTON HOUSE LONG ON LOOKS - Floor coverings–carpet and rugs - Burlington House Carpets

BURLINGTON MAINSTAY - Skin care products ☆ - Major/Advance International

BURLINGTON MEDICAL - Apparel–rubberized - Burlington Medical Supplies Inc.

BURLITE - Siding–insulating ☆ - Forestex Co.

BURLON - Paints - Adelphi Coatings Co.

BURLON - Window shades - C-Mor Co.

BURLTON - Cabinets - Prestige Inc.

BURLUXE - Wood products - Weyerhaeuser Co.

BURLWOOD - Floor coverings - Congoleum Corp.

BURLWOOD - Wines - Ernest and Julio Gallo Winery

BURLY - Apparel and accessories - Cary Breeden

BURLY - Bags–trash - North American Plastics Corp.

BURLY - Frames–eyeglass ☆ - Universal/Univis Inc.

BURLY - Thread - Threads USA Div.

BURLY BEAR - Gloves - Brookville Glove Manufacturing Co.

BURLY BEAR NETWORK - Broadcasting stations–cable television - Burly Bear Network

BURMA - Furniture–wood - Chaircraft Div.

BURMA - Nuts–salted, roasted, cooked, or canned ☆ - Leavitt Corp.

BURMA - Spices - Consumers Vinegar and Spice Co.

BURMA - Wallpaper - Capital Carousel Inc.

BURMA - Window coverings - Levolor Inc.

BURMA BEY - Aftershave Now out of production ☆ - American Safety Razor Co.

BURMA BIBAS - Apparel–men's - Burma-Bibas, Inc.

BURMA BLOCKADE - Deodorant Now out of production ☆ - American Safety Razor Co.

BURMA ROUGE - Jewelry–precious - Val Casting, Inc.

BURMA SHAVE - Shaving preparations - American Safety Razor Co.

BURMAH, THE - Golfing equipment - Highlander Golf, Inc.

BURMAX - Hair care products - Burmax Co. Inc.

BURMESE - Glass products ☆ - Fenton Art Glass Co.

BURN-AID - Pharmaceutical preparations ☆ - Barre-National, Inc.

BURN AWAY - Lubricating oils - Conoco Inc.

BURN FAT PLUS - Vitamins and nutritional supplements - Amerifit, Inc.

BURN FREE - Pharmaceutical preparations - Golightly International Corp.

BURN JEL - Pharmaceutical preparations - Water-Jel Technologies, Inc.

BURN-N-BITE - Analgesics - Q. A. Laboratories Inc.

BURN-O-FENE - Health care products ☆ - Gena Laboratories Inc.

BURN-O-JEL - Analgesics - S.S.S. Co.

BURN-OFF - Suntan lotions ☆ - Aloe Gator Suncare Co.

BURN OUT - Cleaning preparations - Promaster

BURN OUT TIMER - Electronic equipment - John Elliott

BURN SEPTIC - Health care products - Afassco

BURN THAT FAT - Vitamins and nutritional supplements - Vitamin Classics, Inc.

BURNAM - Publisher's imprints - Willis Music Co.

BURNDOWN - Herbicides - Frank Miller and Sons Inc.

BURNER BUBBLE - Golfing equipment - Taylor Made Golf Co. Inc.

BURNES - Frames–picture - Holson Burnes Group

BURNES OF BOSTON - Frames–picture - Holson Burnes Group

BURNETTE FARMS - Food products - Burnette Foods Inc.

BURNETT'S - Food products - Doxsee Food Corp.

BURNETT'S - Gin - Heaven Hill Distilleries, Inc.

BURNETT'S - Vodka - Joseph E. Seagram & Sons, Inc.

BURNFREE - Skin care products - Nortrade International, Inc.

BURNHAM - Air conditioning equipment ☆ - Burnham Corp.

BURNHAM & BRADY - Candy - Burnham and Brady Inc.

BURNHAM BROS. - Sporting goods - Burnham Brothers

BURNHAM PARK - Floor coverings - Congoleum Corp.

BURNIN' KEY CARS - Toys–automobiles - Matchbox Toys USA

BURNIN' LAVA - Fireworks - Midwest Wholesale Manufacturing Co., Inc.

BURNING BUSH PRESS - Publisher's imprints - United Synagogue Book Service

BURNING DESIRE - Fireplace equipment - Pyro Industries, Inc.

BURNING DESIRE - Guitars - Zion Guitar Technology

BURNING DESIRES - Apparel and accessories - Sky's the Limit of Maryland, Inc.

BURNING EMBERS - Fireplace logs–electric - Majestic Co.

BURNING SKY - Fireworks - L. W. Loyd Co., Inc.

BURNING SOLDIER - Video games - Matsushita Electric Corp. of America

BURNING SUN - Barbecue sauce - Winn-Dixie Stores, Inc.

BURNING TREE - Furniture - Pilliod Co.

BURNISHED BORDEAUX - Cosmetics - Merle Norman Cosmetics

BURNISHINE - Finishing agents - Burnishine Products

BURNISHMATE - Fabrics - Veratec

BURNOUT - Posters - Aegis Entertainment, Inc.

BURNS - Coffee - Q & P Coffee Inc.

BURNS - Furniture ☆ - Union National Inc.

BURNS AEROSPACE - Aircraft parts - Burns Aerospace

BURNS & RICKER - Snack foods - Swissrose International Inc.

BURNS & RICKER FAT FREE - Snack foods - Burns and Ricker Inc.

BURNSIDE - Guitars ☆ - Guild Music Corp.

BURNSIDE PLANK - Floor coverings - Hartco Wood Flooring

BURNT CHIMNEYS - Furniture ☆ - Ridgeway Clock Co.

BURNT PINE - Matches ☆ - Cathay International

BURNTAME - Anesthetics - Buffington

BURNTAME - Skin care products - Otis Clapp & Son Inc.

BURNWORTH TESTER - Electrical testing instruments - Burnworth Tester Co.

BURNWYCK - Cabinets ☆ - Merillat Industries, Inc.

BURNY - Bakery products - Entenmann's Inc.

BURO-SOL - Astringents - Doak Dermatologics

BUROVELOUR - Floor coverings–carpet and rugs ☆ - Mohawk Industries Inc.

BURP-UMS - Baby supplies - Early Care Products Inc.

BURPABLES - Infant product - A Unique Beginning

BURPEE - Flowers, plants, and seeds - W. Atlee Burpee and Co.

BURPEE'S BIG BOY - Flowers, plants, and seeds - W. Atlee Burpee and Co.

BURPEE'S BIG GIRL - Flowers, plants, and seeds - W. Atlee Burpee and Co.

BURPERS - Infant product - Babee Burper Co.

BURPIES FOR BABIES - Infant product - Stork Stuff

BURR-PATT - Jewelry - Burr Patterson and Auld Co. Inc.

BURR RIDGE VALLEY - Meat products–beef - Hinsdale Farms Ltd.

BURRELL ORCHARDS - Food products - Burrell Orchards Inc.

BURREN - Bedding–linen - Dan River Inc.

BURRIS - Binoculars - Burris Co., Inc.

BURRIS - Chairs–upholstered - La-Z-Boy Chair Co.

BURRIS - Dog food - Burris Pet Food

BURRITO BROTHERS - Frozen foods - Festa Food Co.

BURRITO DOS MANOS - Sandwiches–prepackaged - Triune Corp.

BURRITO GRANDE - Food products ☆ - Hormel Foods Corp.

BURRITO RICO - Food products ☆ - Taco John's International Inc.

BURRITO SPECIALIST, THE - Mexican food products - International Multifoods Corp.

BURRO - Bicycles - Ross Bicycles USA, Ltd.

BURRO - Cleaning preparations–household - Gottschalk Metal Sponge Sales Corp.

BURRO CLIP - Paper clips - Labelon Corp.

BURRON - Health care products - Burron Medical Inc.

BURROUGHS - Office supplies - Unisys Corp.

☆ = Now out of production

BURROW PROBE - Cameras–video - Fuhrman Diversified

BURRUSS - Floor coverings - Burruss Co.

BURRY - Cookies - Sunshine/Salerno Inc.

BURRY BIGGIES - Candy - Sunshine/Salerno Inc.

BURRY-LU - Cookies - Sunshine/Salerno Inc.

BURRY'S BEST - Cookies - Sunshine/Salerno Inc.

BURSIMUNE - Veterinary pharmaceutical preparations - Biomune Co.

BURST - Detergents - Colgate-Palmolive Co.

BURST - Electronic equipment - Burst Electronics, Inc.

BURST - Vitamins and nutritional supplements - Leiner Health Products Inc.

BURST-ALERT - Electrical sensor - BS&B Safety Systems, Inc.

BURST O'BERRIES - Fruits–frozen - J.R. Wood Inc.

BURST OF BEAUTY - Candles ☆ - Avon Products, Inc.

BURST OF HEAT - Dryers–hair ☆ - Sunbeam-Oster Household Products

BURST OF MENTHOL - Cold remedies - Schiff Products, Inc.

BURST OF POWER - Food processors - Sunbeam-Oster Household Products

BURSTERS - Popcorn - Pepsico, Inc.

BURSTWARE - Computer software - Instant Video Technologies, Inc.

BURT - Apparel–men's - Zanella Ltd.

BURT - Ophthalmic goods ☆ - Luxottica

BURT - Ophthalmic goods ☆ - Rozin Optical Export Corp.

BURTEK - Motor vehicles–trucks - Burtek, Inc.

BURTON - Frames–eyeglass ☆ - Universal/Univis Inc.

BURTON - Stoves–gas - Max Burton Enterprises Inc.

BURTON BLACK LABEL - Whiskey - Four Roses Distillers Co.

BURTON GRILLS - Barbecues and grills - Max Burton Enterprises Inc.

BURTON RUG - Floor coverings–carpet and rugs - Mohawk Carpet Corp.

BURTON WHITE LABEL - Whiskey - Four Roses Distillers Co.

BURTONIQUE - Jewelry boxes - Leonard Burton

BURTONWARE - Dishes–earthenware - Max Burton Enterprises Inc.

BURTS - Shoes - Edison Brothers Stores, Inc.

BURT'S AUTHENTIC BAGELS - Bagels - McGlynn Bakeries Inc.

BURT'S BEES - Lip balms - Burt's Bees Inc.

BURWOOD - House furnishings - Burwood Products Co.

BURY-PAC - Glass products ☆ - Corning Inc.

BUS BOOTH - Tents - Larry P. Collins

BUS BOYS - Toys–automobiles - Mattel, Inc.

BUS DEPOT - Electronic equipment - Banner Engineering Corp.

BUS STOP - Shoes - New York Transit, Inc.

BUS STORY - Computer software - E. David & Associates

BUS-WATCH - Recording label - Radio Engineering Industries, Inc.

BUSAK SHAMBAN - Bearings–industrial - Busak & Shamban, Inc.

BUSBAR - Fasteners–snap - Penn Engineering and Manufacturing Corp.

BUSBOX - Computer software - Pro-Log Corp.

BUSBOY - Paper–toweling - IFC Disposables, Inc.

BUSCAM - Telephone apparatus - Metro-Tel Corp.

BUSCH - Beverages–malt - Anheuser-Busch Companies Inc.

BUSCH - Tools–hand-operated - PFingst & Co., Inc.

BUSCH BAVARIAN - Beverages–malt ☆ - Anheuser-Busch Companies Inc.

BUSCH ICE - Beverages–malt - Anheuser-Busch Companies Inc.

BUSCH-JAEGER - Wire - Helenor Industries

BUSCH LIGHT - Beverages–malt - Anheuser-Busch Companies Inc.

BUSCH LIGHT DRAFT - Beverages–malt ☆ - Anheuser-Busch Companies Inc.

BUSCH NA - Beverages–malt - Anheuser-Busch Companies Inc.

BUSCHMAN - Conveyors - Buschman Co.

BUSCHMAN A PINNACLE AUTOMATION COMPANY - Conveyors - Buschman Co.

BUSH - Audio cabinets–wood - Bush Industries, Inc.

BUSH - Fabrics - Greenwood Mills Inc.

BUSH - Food products - Hagen House

BUSH GEAR - Pens - Sheaffer Inc.

BUSH INDUSTRIES - Furniture - Bush Industries, Inc.

BUSH MASTERS - Holsters - Kane Products, Inc.

BUSH PILOT - Hats - Chums Ltd.

BUSH RECIPE - Skin care products - American Outback, Inc.

BUSHA BROWNE'S - Food products - Blue Mountain Imports Inc.

BUSHEL BOY - Fruits and vegetables - Vine Ripe Inc.

BUSHEL O FRAGRANCE - Candles - Candle Corp. of America

BUSHEL OF KISSES - Novelty items - Doc's Apothecary

BUSHER - Medical apparatus - Becton, Dickinson and Co.

BUSHIDO - Toys - Hasbro, Inc.

BUSHMASTER - Archery equipment - Martin Archery Inc.

BUSHMASTER - Bicycles - Columbia Manufacturing Inc.

BUSHMASTER - Firearms, accessories, and parts - Welsh Sporting Goods Corp. (Boyt Div.)

BUSHMASTER - Motor vehicles–motor homes - Munroe Machine Works Inc.

BUSHMILLS - Whiskey - Brown-Forman Corp.

BUSHNELL - Binoculars - Bausch & Lomb Inc.

BUSH'S - Food products - Bush Brothers and Co.

BUSH'S BEST - Baked beans–canned - Bush Brothers and Co.

BUSH'S CAMPFIRE - Food products - Bush Brothers and Co.

BUSH'S FIRESIDE - Food products - Bush Brothers and Co.

BUSHWACKER - Boats–motor ☆ - Ebbtide Corp.

BUSHWACKER - Firearms, accessories, and parts - Welsh Sporting Goods Corp. (Boyt Div.)

BUSHWHACKER - Glass–optical - Welling International

BUSHWHACKER - Meat products - Vernon County Meat Packers

BUSHWHACKER - Pesticides–household - Bethurum Research & Development Inc.

BUSHWHACKER, THE - Golfing equipment - Illah California, Inc.

BUSHWHACKERS - Novelty items - Titan Sports, Inc.

BUSHWHACKER'S - Sauces - Hudson Valley Homestead

BUSHWHACKERS, THE - Novelty items ☆ - Titan Sports, Inc.

BUSHY BUNCH - Toys - Tonka Corp.

BUSHY RIDGE - Fabrics–coated - Teledyne Industries Inc.

BUSHY TAIL - Animal feeds - Pine Tree Farms, Inc.

BUSICARD - Computer software - Advanced High Tech Corp.

BUSIN - Luggage - Rona Leather Inc.

BUSINESS ACCOUNTANT GOLD, THE - Computer software - Brilliant Nite Software, Inc.

BUSINESS ADVANTAGE - Computer software - Borland International, Inc.

BUSINESS ADVANTAGE - Computer software - Harte-Hanks Data Technologies

BUSINESS BAGS - Bags–trash - Carlisle Plastics, Inc.

BUSINESS BASICS - Clothing - Celebrating Excellence, Inc.

BUSINESS BASICS - Office accessories - Successories, Inc.

BUSINESS BEAR - Toys–stuffed - Dakin Inc.

BUSINESS BROWSER - Computer storage devices - One Source Information Services, Inc.

BUSINESS CARD - Pagers ☆ - NEC America, Inc.

BUSINESS CARD MAKER DELUXE - Computer software - Capstone Software

BUSINESS CARD STUDIO - Computer software - Bear Rock Technologies Corp.

BUSINESS CARDS - Computer software - Taligent, Inc.

BUSINESS CLASS - Luggage - Service Merchandise Co. Inc.

BUSINESS CLUB - Luggage - Travelers Club Luggage Inc.

BUSINESS EDGE - Calculators - Texas Instruments Inc.

BUSINESS ENGINE - Software - Micro-Frame Technologies, Inc.

BUSINESS EQUIPMENT - Luggage - American Tourister, Inc.

BUSINESS LETTER EXPERT - Computer software - Parsons Technology, Inc.

BUSINESS MAIL EXPRESS - Mailing machines - D.B. Acquisition, Inc.

BUSINESS MANAGER - Calculators - Texas Instruments Inc.

BUSINESS MATES - Apparel and accessories - H.I.T. Industries, Ltd.

BUSINESS ON THE GO - Office supplies - A.I.P. Products, Inc.

BUSINESS ONE IRWIN - Publisher's imprints - Richard D. Irwin Inc.

BUSINESS ORGANIZATIONS MATE - Publisher's imprints - Little, Brown and Co., Inc.

BUSINESS PARTNER - Computer software - American Custom Software, Inc.

BUSINESS PARTNER, THE - Audio equipment - General Electric Co.

BUSINESS PARTNERS - Attache cases - Ventura Travelware Inc.

BUSINESS PLAN WRITER - Computer software - Graphite Software, Inc.

BUSINESS PLAYGROUND - Paper products - Jeff Baird

BUSINESS-PRO - Attache cases - United States Luggage Co. L.P.

BUSINESS PROCESS IMPROVEMENT - Publisher's imprints - DPI Worldwide, Ltd.

BUSINESS RESOURCE FOR THE 90'S - Telephone directories - Southern New England Telephone Co.

BUSINESS SLEUTH - See **OPV SOFTWARE**

BUSINESS STRATEGY - Games ☆ - Avalon Hill Game Co.

BUSINESS TALK - Electrical equipment - General Electric Co.

BUSINESS TIES - Computer software - Computer Language Research Inc.

BUSINESS TIPS - Apparel trimmings - Career Footwear Corp.

BUSINESS TOUCH - Communications equipment - Touch 1 Communications, Inc.

BUSINESS TRAVELER - Computer peripheral equipment - Kensington Microware Ltd.

BUSINESS WEEK - Calendars - House of Doolittle

BUSINESS WEEK'S BUSINESS ADVANTAGE - Computer software - Reality Technologies

BUSINESSCAD - Computer software - Open Engineering Inc.

BUSINESSCOM - Telephones - TIE Communications Inc.

BUSINESSERVER ALR - Computer peripheral equipment - Advanced Logic Research Inc.
BUSINESSFORMS - Computer software - Manzanita Software Systems
BUSINESSMAN - Eyeglasses - Art-Craft Optical Co.
BUSINESSMAX - Computer software - Applied Information for Marketing, Inc.
BUSINESSVIEW - Computer software - Rolm Co.
BUSINESSWORKS - Computer software - Manzanita Software Systems
BUSKENS - Footwear—women's - Wohl Shoe Co.
BUSLOGIC - Circuit boards - Bus Logic Inc.
BUSNAV - Antennas—satellite - KVH Industries, Inc.
BUSNEL CALVADOS - Whiskey - Austin, Nichols & Co., Inc.
BUSODIUM - Pharmaceutical preparations ☆ - C.O. Truxton Inc.
BUSPAGE - Amplifiers—public address - Sound & Video Systems, Inc.
BUSPAR - Pharmaceutical preparations - Bristol-Myers Squibb Co.
BUSS - Fuses, plastic fuse holders - Cooper Industries, Inc.
BUSSE - Fabrics—wool - Zweigart/Joan Toggit Ltd.
BUSSE - Pallets—metal - Busse Bros., Inc.
BUSSMAN - Fuses - Cooper Industries, Inc.
BUST DESIGN - Skin care products - Thermo Trim USA Inc.
BUST IT UP - Bathing suits - Apparel Ventures, Inc.
BUST OUT! - Publisher's imprints - Mavety Media Group Ltd.
BUST-RUST - Oils—mineral - G-96 Products Co. Inc.
BUSTA GEAR - T-shirts—men's - Busta Gear Inc.
BUSTABUG - Veterinary pharmaceutical preparations - Carter-Wallace, Inc.
BUSTANUT - Apparel and accessories - Michael Beers
BUSTED! - Toys - Leaf, Inc.
BUSTED PUTTER - Golfing equipment - Harte Industries, Inc.
BUSTELO - Coffee - Bustelo Coffee Co.
BUSTELO ICED TEA - Teas - Bustelo Coffee Co.
BUSTER - Candy ☆ - Haviland Candy Inc.
BUSTER - Dog food - Agway Country Foods Inc.
BUSTER - File folders - Hedges Manufacturing Co.
BUSTER - Food products - Western Farmers Association
BUSTER - Frames—eyeglass - Zylo Ware Corp.
BUSTER - Toys—stuffed ☆ - Gund, Inc.
BUSTER BEAR - Toys—stuffed - Russ Berrie and Co., Inc.
BUSTER BEAR & COMPANY - Recording label - Buster Bear & Co.
BUSTER BROWN - Apparel—children's - Buster Brown Apparel Inc.
BUSTER BROWN - Shoes - Brown Shoe Co.
BUSTER BUSTS LOOSE - Computer software ☆ - Konami (America) Inc.
BUSTER CRABBE - Swimming pools - Cascade Pools
BUSTER MACBIRDIE - Golf sportswear - Sports Kiosks, Inc.
BUSTER THE BALANCING BEAR - Games ☆ - Tomy America, Inc.
BUSTER THE CRAB - Apparel and accessories - Incredible Inflatables, Inc.
BUSTER THE TORTOISE - Containers - Rubbermaid Inc.
BUSTERS - Apparel—children's - Buster Brown Apparel Inc.
BUSTERS - Cookies ☆ - Sunshine Biscuits, Inc.
BUSTER'S HIDDEN TREASURE - Computer software ☆ - Konami (America) Inc.
BUSTIN BUBBLES - Detergents - Promaster
BUSTOPHER - Toys—stuffed ☆ - Gund, Inc.
BUSTOPS - Computer software - Microanalytics
BUSTRUX - Oils—lubricating - Parr Products
BUSTY - Lubricants - Herdor's, Inc.
BUSTY BABES - Computer software - Douglas J. Zimmer
BUSY - Infant product - Playskool Baby Inc.
BUSY - Novelty items ☆ - All-Art Products Inc.
BUSY - Toys—stuffed - CBS Toys
BUSY BAGS - Handbags - American Angel Corp.
BUSY BAKER - Food products - Safeway Stores Inc.
BUSY BALLS - Infant product - Playskool Baby Inc.
BUSY BAND - Toys - Playskool, Inc.
BUSY BEA - Gloves - Knoxville Glove Co.
BUSY BEADS - Toys - Playskool, Inc.
BUSY BEAK BOARD - Pet products - Emerald Bird Caddy
BUSY BEAUTY - Cosmetics - Revlon Consumer Products Corp.
BUSY BEE - Handbags - Commercial Sewing, Inc.
BUSY BEE - Honey - Barkman Honey Co. Inc.
BUSY BEE - Honey - La Paz Products
BUSY BEE CANDLES - Candles - Busy Bee Candles Ltd.
BUSY BELT - Tool belts - Portable Products, Inc.
BUSY BIG BIRD - Toys - Playskool, Inc.
BUSY BODY - Toys - Tomy America, Inc.
BUSY BONES - Toys - Petcare Plus, Inc.
BUSY BOX - Craft supplies - June Tailor Inc.
BUSY BOX - Toys - Playskool, Inc.

BUSY BOYS - Clothing - Busy Boys
BUSY BUBBLE MAKER - Infant product - Playskool Baby Inc.
BUSY BUCKET - Infant product - Playskool Baby Inc.
BUSY BUNGALOW - Toys ☆ - Tomy America, Inc.
BUSY BUNNIES - Candy - R.M. Palmer Co.
BUSY CAMERA - Infant product - Playskool Baby Inc.
BUSY CLUTCH BALL - Toys—stuffed - CBS Toys
BUSY DAY - Food products - Supreme Foods Inc.
BUSY DRIVER - Infant product - Playskool Baby Inc.
BUSY DRIVER - Toys - Playskool, Inc.
BUSY ELEPHANT - Toys - Playskool, Inc.
BUSY FEET - Footwear—children's - Yachett Shoe Manufacturing Corp.
BUSY GARDEN - Toys—stuffed ☆ - CBS Toys
BUSY GEARS - Infant product - Playskool Baby Inc.
BUSY GUITAR - Toys - Playskool, Inc.
BUSY GYM - Toys—stuffed - CBS Toys
BUSY KIDS-BIRTHDAY - Toys - Tyco Toys
BUSY KIDS-FIRST GARDEN - Toys - Tyco Toys
BUSY KIDS-GET BETTER - Toys - Tyco Toys
BUSY KIDS-HAPPY TRAVELER - Toys - Tyco Toys
BUSY KIDS-SOMETHING TO DO - Toys - Tyco Toys
BUSY LI'L DOLLHOUSE - Infant product - Playskool Baby Inc.
BUSY-LIZ - Cooking equipment—household ☆ - Mirro Corp.
BUSY MIXER - Toys - Playskool, Inc.
BUSY POCKETS - Leather goods - Hometown Advantage, Inc.
BUSY POP UP BEAR - Infant product - Playskool Baby Inc.
BUSY POP UP PHONE - Toys - Playskool, Inc.
BUSY POPPIN PLANE - Toys - Playskool, Inc.
BUSY PUPPY - Toys - Playskool, Inc.
BUSY SOFT VEHICLES - Toys - Playskool, Inc.
BUSY SPLASH 'N PLAY - Infant product - Playskool Baby Inc.
BUSY STREET - Cleaning preparations—carpet and rug - Imperial Manufacturing Co. Inc.
BUSY WOMAN - Stationery - Current, Inc.
BUSY WORKSHOP - Infant product - Playskool Baby Inc.
BUSY WORLD OF RICHARD SCARRY, THE - Computer software - Paramount Pictures Corp.
BUSYBODY - Frames—eyeglass - Liberty Optical Manufacturing Co.
BUSYTOWN TALKER - Toys - Tomy America, Inc.
BUSYTOWN TALKING PICTURE PHONE - Toys - Tomy America, Inc.
B.U.T. BUTTON UP THINGS - Apparel and accessories - Bentley Lingerie, Inc.
BUT-ERALL - Food products - H.C. Brill Co., Inc.
BUT, GORDON - Women's apparel - Gordon Henderson
BUT-R-CREME - Frosting - Dawn Food Products Inc.
BUT-ROME - Food products ☆ - Lawrence Foods Inc.
BUTA-SPAS - Pharmaceutical preparations - Southern Pharmacal Co. Inc.
BUTABELL HMB - Pharmaceutical preparations - Saron Pharmacal Corp.
BUTAC - Adhesives and sealants - Sterling-Clark-Lurton Corp.
BUTACALM - Pharmaceutical preparations ☆ - Wesley Pharmacal Co. Inc.
BUTACE - Pharmaceutical preparations - American Urologicals Inc.
BUTADOR - Pharmaceutical preparations ☆ - Purdue Frederick Co.
BUTAFLAME - Candles - Tampus Gifts, Inc.
BUTAFORM - Plastic sheets - E.I. Dupont de Nemours and Co.
BUTAGEN - Pharmaceutical preparations - Goldline Laboratories, Inc.
BUTAGEN ALKA - Pharmaceutical preparations ☆ - Goldline Laboratories, Inc.
BUTAGESIC - Analgesics ☆ - Laser Inc.
BUTAKRAFT G.R. - Pharmaceutical preparations - Kraft Pharmaceutical Co.
BUTAL - Sedative ☆ - Blaine Co. Inc.
BUTALAN - Pharmaceutical preparations - Lannett Co. Inc.
BUTALBACET - Pharmaceutical preparations - Lannett Co. Inc.
BUTALIX - Pharmaceutical preparations ☆ - Pal-Pak Inc.
BUTANEDIONE MONIXIME - Pharmaceutical preparations - City Chemical Corp.
BUTAPHALT - Asphalt - Asphalt Technology and Consulting, Inc.
BUTAPHED - Pharmaceutical preparations ☆ - Wendt-Bristol Co.
BUTASED - Pharmaceutical preparations ☆ - C.O. Truxton Inc.
BUTATAB - Pharmaceutical preparations ☆ - Roberts/Hauck Pharmaceuticals Inc.
BUTATRAN - Pharmaceutical preparations ☆ - Roberts/Hauck Pharmaceuticals Inc.
BUTATRON - Veterinary pharmaceutical preparations - Sanofi Animal Health, Inc.
BUTAZOLIDIN - Pharmaceutical preparations - Ciba-Geigy Corp.
BUTCH - Dog food - Kitty Queen Pet Foods
BUTCH - Frames—eyeglass ☆ - Universal/Univis Inc.
BUTCH - Toys—stuffed ☆ - Gund, Inc.

☆ = Now out of production

BUTCH BULLDOG - Toys–stuffed - Dakin Inc.
BUTCH CASSIDY - Fabrics - Greenwood Mills Inc.
BUTCH CASSIDY - Worcestershire sauce - Frazier Extract Co.
BUTCH LONG'S STEAKS OF NEBRASKA - Meat products - Oren E. Long, Jr.
BUTCHER - Toys - Tonka Corp.
BUTCHER BILL'S - Barbecue sauce - William J. Roche
BUTCHER BLOCK - Clocks ☆ - General Time Corp. (Westclox/Seth Thomas Div.)
BUTCHER BLOCK - Cutlery ☆ - Regent Sheffield, Ltd.
BUTCHER BLOCK - Floor coverings–tile ☆ - National Floor Products Co., Inc.
BUTCHER BLOCK - Telephones - At&T Corp.
BUTCHER BLOCK WAREHOUSE - Furniture–wood ☆ - Pankratz Forest Industries
BUTCHER BONES - Dog food - Nabisco Foods Group
BUTCHER BOY - Food products - Multifoods Inc.
BUTCHER BOY - Hams ☆ - Dold Foods Inc.
BUTCHER BOY - Meat products–cured - Butcher Boy Meats Inc.
BUTCHER BOY - Oils–edible - Columbus Foods Co.
BUTCHER BOY BRAND CRAFTED SOLID OAK FURNITURE US MADE - Furniture - Brian L. Lyman
BUTCHER BUDDY - Food products machinery - M & E Manufacturing Co., Inc.
BUTCHER FRESH - Meat products - Saramar Corp.
BUTCHER FRESH - Pork - Bryan Foods, Inc.
BUTCHER PRO - Food products machinery - M & E Manufacturing Co., Inc.
BUTCHER SHOP - Food products - Chiquita Brands, Inc.
BUTCHER WAGON - Meat products - Hqm, Ltd.
BUTCHER WAGON - Sausages - Hatfield, Inc.
BUTCHER WRAP - Food products ☆ - Empire Kosher Poultry Inc.
BUTCHER'S BEST - Food products - Tyson Foods Inc.
BUTCHER'S BLEND - Pet products - Ralston Purina Co.
BUTCHER'S BLEND - Seasonings - Flavorbank
BUTCHER'S CHOICE - Meat products - Tav Brands Inc.
BUTCHER'S FINEST - Meat products - Quantum Foods, Inc.
BUTCHER'S GOT A BURGER YOUR DOG'LL FLIP FOR, THE - Dog food - Ralston Purina Co.
BUTCHER'S KITCHEN - Sausages - Saag's Products Inc.
BUTCHER'S QUALITY - Food products - Butcher's Quality Meat, Inc.
BUTCHER'S TRAY - Artists' materials - Arthur Brown and Bros. Inc.
BUTCHER'S WAX - Floor waxes - Butcher Co.
BUTE - Ophthalmic goods - Embassy Creations Inc.
BUTEN GEM - Paints - Buten Paint & Wallpaper
BUTERY CULTURE - Food products - Brokay Products Inc.
BUTESIN PICRATE - Analgesics - Abbott Laboratories
BUTI - Handbags - Magnum Fashions Inc.
BUTIBEL - Pharmaceutical preparations - Wallace Laboratories
BUTIBEL-ZYME - Pharmaceutical preparations ☆ - McNeil Pharmaceuticals
BUTICAPS - Health care products ☆ - McNeil Pharmaceuticals
BUTIGETIC - Pharmaceutical preparations ☆ - McNeil Pharmaceuticals
BUTIREX - Pharmaceutical preparations ☆ - Rex Research Laboratories
BUTISERPAZIDE - Pharmaceutical preparations ☆ - McNeil Pharmaceuticals
BUTISERPINE - Pharmaceutical preparations ☆ - McNeil Pharmaceuticals
BUTISOL - Pharmaceutical preparations - Wallace Laboratories
BUTIZIDE - Pharmaceutical preparations ☆ - McNeil Pharmaceuticals
BUTLER - Boats–dinghies ☆ - E.R. Butler & Sons
BUTLER - Carpet sweepers ☆ - Bissell Inc.
BUTLER - Denture cleaners - John O.Butler Co.
BUTLER - Furniture–wood - Butler Specialty Co.
BUTLER - Paper–writing - Butler Paper Co.
BUTLER - Wheelchairs - Flinchbaugh Co. Inc.
BUTLER - Window shades - Distinctive Cover-Ups
BUTLER ADVANTAGE - Computer software - Butler Manufacturing Co.
BUTLER-AID - Serving carts ☆ - Artex-Green Corp. of N.Y.
BUTLER CREEK - Photographic equipment - Butler Creek Corp.
BUTLER IN A BOX, THE - Remote control devices - MasterVoice Inc.
BUTLER, THE - Glassware–household ☆ - Anchor Hocking Glass, Inc.
BUTLER VIDEO PRODUCTIONS - Apparel and accessories - Butler Video Productions
BUTLER WEAVE - Dental equipment - John O.Butler Co.
BUTLERETTE - Tables–wood - Artex-Green Corp. of N.Y.
BUTLERS - Dust cloths - Suburbanite Industries
BUTLER'S CHOICE - Coffee - Coffee Butler Service Inc.
BUTLER'S PRIDE - Fruits–canned - Butler Trading Co. Inc.
BUTON - Beverages–alcohol - Blair Importers Ltd.
BUTONE - Vitamins and nutritional supplements - International Medical Research, Inc.
BUTSECO - Pharmaceutical preparations ☆ - JMI-Canton Pharmaceuticals

BUTT BALM - Pharmaceutical preparations - Comar, Inc.
BUTT BOOSTER - Apparel and accessories - Warnaco Inc.
BUTT BOOSTER THIGHSLIMMER - Apparel and accessories - Warnaco Inc.
BUTT CRACK PUTTY - Novelty items - Corine Knox
BUTT-CUTS - Bathing suits - Surf Line Hawaii, Ltd.
BUTT OUT DENIM WEAR - Apparel and accessories - Butt Out Denim Wear
BUTT UGLY - T-shirts–men's - Ja-Mar Apparel Manufacturing Co., Inc.
BUTTA - Fish–fresh or frozen - International Seafood Delicacies Corp.
BUTTA BANANA - Butter-banana flavor - American Flavor & Fragrance Corp.
BUTTE - Apparel–women's - Jonathan Logan Inc.
BUTTE - Bicycles - Giant Bicycle, Inc.
BUTTE - Pharmaceutical preparations ☆ - Scrip-Physician Supply Co.
BUTTE - Thread - Van Waters and Rogers Inc.
BUTTE KNIT - Apparel and accessories - Butte Knitting Mills
BUTTER - Cookies - Nikki's Cookies, Inc.
BUTTER - Frames–eyeglass - Zylo Ware Corp.
BUTTER - Skin care products - California Suncare, Inc.
BUTTER-AID - Food products ☆ - Wild Flavors, Inc.
BUTTER BALL - Dolls - Effanbee Doll Corp.
BUTTER BASTED - Food products - Land O'Lakes Inc.
BUTTER BETTER - Brushes - Warren E. Conley Corp.
BUTTER BUDS - Butter-flavor granules ☆ - American Home Food Products Inc.
BUTTER BUDS - Margarine - Cumberland Packing Corp.
BUTTER CHARM - Cookies - Parco Foods, Inc.
BUTTER-CREME - Spices and extracts - Ottens Flavors
BUTTER-CRUNCHERS - Cookies - Linden Cookies, Inc.
BUTTER CUP - Mayonnaise - Piknik Products Co. Inc.
BUTTER DAINTY - Can openers–electric - R.L. Albert & Son, Inc.
BUTTER-E-VANILLA KREAMEX - Doughs–frozen - Lyons-Magnus Inc.
BUTTER 'EM UP! - Pharmaceutical - American Hygienic Laboratories Inc.
BUTTER GOLD - Meat products–poultry - El Jay Poultry Corp.
BUTTER KERNAL - Vegetables–canned - Durand Canning Co.
BUTTER KERNEL - Vegetables–canned - Faribault Foods Inc.
BUTTER KIST - Food products - Waldman's Meats Inc.
BUTTER KNIFE TENDER - Food products - Land O'Lakes Inc.
BUTTER KRAK EGGS - Candy - S. Zitner Co.
BUTTER LOVER'S - Popcorn - Golden Valley Microwave Foods, Inc.
BUTTER MAGIC - Seasonings - Williams Foods Inc.
BUTTER-MATIC - Popcorn poppers - West Bend Co.
BUTTER MOIST - Food products - Land O'Lakes Inc.
BUTTER-NUT - Bakery products - Country Style Baking Co.
BUTTER-NUT - Coffee ☆ - Coca-Cola Co.
BUTTER OF COCOA - Cosmetics - Maynard Inc.
BUTTER STARLETT'S - Cookies - De Beukelaer Corp.
BUTTER THINS - Crackers ☆ - Keebler Co.
BUTTER TOFFEE - Candy - Idaho Candy Co.
BUTTER TOP CLASSICS - Bread - Interstate Brands Corp.
BUTTER-UP - Housewares - Tupperware Co.
BUTTER UP - Popcorn poppers - Hamilton Beach/Proctor-Silex Inc.
BUTTER UPPER - Housewares - Centsable Toys Inc.
BUTTERBALL - Turkeys - Armour Swift-Eckrich
BUTTERBALL BEAR - Toys–stuffed - Russ Berrie and Co., Inc.
BUTTERBLEND - Margarine - H.P. Hood & Sons Inc.
BUTTERCHURN - Vegetable sauces - Rogers Foods Inc.
BUTTERCOAT - Paints - Proko Industries Inc.
BUTTERCROWN - Bread - Interstate Brands Corp.
BUTTERCRUNCH SQUARES - Candy - Fanny Farmer Candy Shops Inc.
BUTTERCRUNCHIES - Candy - Cultural Survival, Inc.
BUTTERCUP - Bicycles ☆ - Murray, Inc.
BUTTERCUP - Breads - Strand Baking Co.
BUTTERCUP - Christmas tree ornaments ☆ - Cracker Box Inc.
BUTTERCUP - Dishes–china - Gorham Inc.
BUTTERCUP - Dishes–earthenware - Royal China & Porcelain Companies Inc.
BUTTERCUP - Dolls - Horsman
BUTTERCUP - Dolls ☆ - Effanbee Doll Corp.
BUTTERCUP - Food products - Ventura Foods
BUTTERCUP - Frames–eyeglass - Zylo Ware Corp.
BUTTERCUP - Glassware–household ☆ - Lenox Crystal, Inc.
BUTTERCUP - Glassware–household ☆ - Lotus Glass Co.
BUTTERCUP BEAR - Toys–stuffed - Dakin Inc.
BUTTERCUPS - Candy - Miss Saylor's Candies
BUTTERCUPS - Milk - Land O'Lakes Inc.
BUTTERCUPS ON BLUE - Dinnerware–glass ☆ - Lenox, Inc.
BUTTERCUT - Hair care products - Buttercut Shear Co.

BUTTERFIELD - Food products - Tony Downs Foods Co.
BUTTERFIELD - Vegetables–canned - Allen Canning Co.
BUTTERFIELD B - Food products - Allen Canning Co.
BUTTERFIELD BEAR - Novelty items - Current, Inc.
BUTTERFIELD STAGE - Wines - Filsinger Vineyards & Winery
BUTTERFIELDS - Candy - Wilson Candy Co.
BUTTERFINGER - Candy - Nestle USA
BUTTERFINGER BB'S - Chocolate candy - Nestle USA
BUTTERFLAKE - Popcorn - National Oats Co. Inc.
BUTTERFLIES - Floor coverings–carpet and rugs - Concepts International
BUTTERFLIES - Hair-cutting shears - B.W. Boyd Shears Inc.
BUTTERFLIES - Kaleidoscopes - Gemini Kaleidoscopes
BUTTERFLIES ARE FREE - Christmas tree ornaments ☆ - Cracker Box Inc.
BUTTERFLIES FOB - Glassware–household - Hillside House of Originals
BUTTERFLIES OF NORTH AMERICA - Computer software - Hopkins Technology LLC
BUTTERFLO - Margarine - Lumberland Packing Inc.
BUTTERFLY - Air purification systems ☆ - Medo Industries, Inc.
BUTTERFLY - Apparel and accessories - Ramco Arts
BUTTERFLY - Apparel and accessories - Wemco, Inc.
BUTTERFLY - Apparel–children's - H.R. Kaminsky & Sons Inc.
BUTTERFLY - Archery equipment - Martin Archery Inc.
BUTTERFLY - Awnings - Sunesta Products
BUTTERFLY - Brooms - Hamburg Broom Works Inc.
BUTTERFLY - Chairs–folding ☆ - Hedstrom Corp.
BUTTERFLY - Cheese - Beatrice Cheese Co.
BUTTERFLY - Housewares ☆ - Doranne
BUTTERFLY - Laces–boot and shoe ☆ - Pepperell Braiding Co. Inc.
BUTTERFLY - Mops - Royal Maid Association for the Blind Inc.
BUTTERFLY - Ophthalmic goods ☆ - Luxottica
BUTTERFLY - Pillows - Body Care Inc.
BUTTERFLY - Sporting goods - Barnett Boat Co. Inc.
BUTTERFLY - Sports rackets and accessories - Martin-Kilpatrick Table Tennis Co.
BUTTERFLY - Toys - Duncan Toys Co.
BUTTERFLY - Toys - Tyco Toys
BUTTERFLY - Watches - Bulova Corp.
BUTTERFLY BAR - Bicycles - Sears, Roebuck and Co.
BUTTERFLY BREST - Meat products–poultry - Whistlin' Dixie Fried Chicken Inc.
BUTTERFLY DELIGHT - Giftware ☆ - Fenton Art Glass Co.
BUTTERFLY FAIRY - Dolls - Mattel, Inc.
BUTTERFLY GOLD - Dinnerware - Corning Inc.
BUTTERFLY PAVILION - Hobby kits - Insect Lore Products, Inc.
BUTTERFLY PRINCESS - Dolls - Mattel, Inc.
BUTTERFLY SCREEN PATCH - Doors–screen - J.H. Wonderworks
BUTTERFLY SPECIAL - Hair-cutting shears ☆ - B.W. Boyd Shears Inc.
BUTTERFLY STEAK - Meat products–beef - Whistlin' Dixie Fried Chicken Inc.
BUTTERFLY WINGS - Cosmetics ☆ - Madeleine Mono Ltd.
BUTTERFLYBACK - Bathing suits - Ocean Pool Co.
BUTTERFLYER - Toys - Mattel, Inc.
BUTTERGOLD - Meat products–poultry - National Tea Co.
BUTTERHEAD - Food products - Campbell Soup Co.
BUTTERICK - Patterns–clothing - Butterick Co. Inc.
BUTTERICK FASHIONS - Housewares stores - Butterick Co. Inc.
BUTTERIN - Spices and extracts - Ottens Flavors
BUTTERINE - Sandwiches–prepackaged - Perino Foods, Inc.
BUTTERING - Flowers, plants, and seeds - D. Landreth Seed Co.
BUTTERKRUST - Bread and rolls - Cotton Bros. Baking Co. Inc.
BUTTERLETS - Candy - Brock Candy Co. Inc.
BUTTERLITE - Syrup - Quaker Oats Co.
BUTTERLOAF - Breads ☆ - Super Valu Inc.
BUTTERMAID - Bread - Interstate Brands Corp.
BUTTERMATCH - Food products - Van Den Bergh Foods Co.
BUTTERMATIC II - Popcorn poppers - West Bend Co.
BUTTERMILK/BATTERGOLD - Food products - Tyson Foods Inc.
BUTTERMILK CREEK - Wallpaper - Tattersalls
BUTTERMILK RECIPE - Food products - Kraft Food Ingredients Corp.
BUTTERNUT - Bread - Interstate Brands Corp.
BUTTERNUT - Candy - Leaf, Inc.
BUTTERNUT - Cookies - Richmond Baking Co.
BUTTERNUT CASTLE - Bagels - Interstate Brands Corp.
BUTTERNUT COUNTRY WHEAT - Bread - Interstate Brands Corp.
BUTTERNUT CREME - Nail care products - Cosmair Inc.
BUTTERNUT ROAD - Hobby kits - Marilyn Leavitt-Imblum
BUTTERNUT SWEET - Pet products - Carlson Speciality Seeds, Inc.

BUTTERSCOTCH - Apparel and accessories ☆ - Pandora Sportswear Industries
BUTTERSCOTCH - Christmas tree ornaments ☆ - Cracker Box Inc.
BUTTERSCOTCH - Dinnerware–glass ☆ - Nikko Ceramics Inc.
BUTTERSCOTCH - Toys–stuffed ☆ - Gund, Inc.
BUTTERSCOTCH ALMOND - Candy ☆ - Annabelle Candy Co. Inc.
BUTTERSCOTCH BUTTONS - Bakery products - Peerless Confection Co.
BUTTERSCOTCH DISKS - Candy - Brach and Brock Confections Inc.
BUTTERSCOTCH KITTY - Toys–stuffed - Dakin Inc.
BUTTERSCOTCH SENSATIONS - Candy - S.L. Kaye Co., Inc.
BUTTERSCOTCH SKIMMERS - Candy - Nabisco Foods Group
BUTTERSCOTCH STIX - Candy ☆ - Leaf, Inc.
BUTTERSCOTCH TOFFEE - Coffee - Cameron Coffee Co. Inc.
BUTTERSHOTS - Beverages–alcohol - Jim Beam Brands Co.
BUTTERSOFT - Ophthalmic goods ☆ - Fidelity Case Corp.
BUTTERSUEDE - Fabrics - Vanity Fair Mills Inc.
BUTTERSWEET - Food products - Crystal Farms Inc.
BUTTERWAX - Candles ☆ - Lamplight Farms, Inc.
BUTTERWELL - Kitchen appliances - National Presto Industries, Inc.
BUTTERWORTH - Cleaning equipment - Butterworth Tank Cleaning Machines, Inc.
BUTTERWORTH PUBLISHERS - Publisher's imprints - Butterworth Publishers Inc.
BUTTERY DELITE - Oils–edible - Par-Way Group
BUTTERY SOFT - Toys–stuffed - Dan-Dee International Ltd.
BUTTFLEX - Exercising equipment - Deanna L. Jones
BUTTHEAD - Caps–baseball ☆ - Laid Back Enterprises, Inc.
BUTTHEAD - Toys - Mattel, Inc.
BUTTILLA - Recording label - Rains Recording Co.
BUTTMASTER - Exercising equipment - Roadmaster Corp.
BUTTOCK'S - Health care products ☆ - Emerson Laboratories
BUTTON - Fishing lures - Den Manufacturing Co.
BUTTON - Toys ☆ - Playskool, Inc.
BUTTON & BOWS - Toys–stuffed - Bijou Enterprises Inc.
BUTTON BABIES - Hobby kits - Darrow Production Co., Inc.
BUTTON BANNER BEARS - Giftware - Securitag Corp.
BUTTON BANNERS - Novelty items - Securitag Corp.
BUTTON BOUTIQUE - Buttons - JHB International Inc.
BUTTON BOWS - Paper–gift wrap - Glitterwrap Inc.
BUTTON BOX KIDS - Figurines - Hal Payne
BUTTON BUDDIES - Jewelry - Russ Berrie and Co., Inc.
BUTTON CUFVERS - Apparel and accessories - Dazl, Inc.
BUTTON DECOR - Buttons - Caro Creations Inc.
BUTTON DOWN - Frames–eyeglass ☆ - Universal/Univis Inc.
BUTTON DOWNS - Fasteners–hook and eye - Baumgarten's
BUTTON EXPRESS - Buttons - Lamcom, Inc.
BUTTON EYES - Buttons - Blumenthal/Lansing Co.
BUTTON FACTORY - Hobby kits - Tyco Toys
BUTTON-HOLE - Metals - Morton Manufacturing Co.
BUTTON LADY - Buttons - JHB International Inc.
BUTTON MAGIC - Sewing machines–household ☆ - Singer Co.
BUTTON MEMORY - Computer peripheral equipment - Macsema, Inc.
BUTTON NOSE - Dolls - Effanbee Doll Corp.
BUTTON NOSE COLLECTION - Housewares - Franco Manufacturing Co., Inc.
BUTTON-ON - Racks - Jarke Corp.
BUTTON RITE - Buttons - Streamline Industries, Inc.
BUTTON SHOPPE, THE - Buttons - Streamline Industries, Inc.
BUTTON STUFFINS - Christmas tree ornaments - Hartland Traditions, Inc.
BUTTON, THE - Telephones - Martin Switch Corp.
BUTTON, THE - Cameras ☆ - Polaroid Corp.
BUTTON TOPPERS - Buttons - Happiness Express Inc.
BUTTON UP - Hair care products - Andre Fantasies Inc.
BUTTON-UPS - Shelving units–wood ☆ - Kirsch Co.
BUTTONFILE - Computer software - ButtonWare Inc.
BUTTONKAP - Hardware - Carolina Nail, Inc.
BUTTONMANIA - Buttons - Beach Co.
BUTTONMANIA - Hobby kits - Rose Art Industries, Inc.
BUTT*ONS - Notebooks and notepads ☆ - Butt*Ons Inc.
BUTTONS - Ophthalmic goods - Swank Optical
BUTTONS - Toys–stuffed ☆ - Gund, Inc.
BUTTONS - Wallpaper - United Wallcoverings
BUTTONS - Yarn ☆ - Tahki Imports Ltd.
BUTTONS 4 YOU - Badges–uniform - Buttons 4 You, Inc.
BUTTONS AND BOWS - Magnets - Franco Manufacturing Co., Inc.
BUTTONS & TOES - Toys - Fisher-Price, Inc.
BUTTONS, BOWS & BOXES - Hobby kits - Rose Art Industries, Inc.

☆ = Now out of production

BUTTON'S ELEPHANT - Toys–stuffed - Russ Berrie and Co., Inc.
BUTTONS N' BOWS - Bicycles - Roadmaster Corp.
BUTTONS N' BOWS - Dresses–women's - Carolina Maid Products Inc.
BUTTONS 'N BOWS - Flowers, plants, and seeds - Monrovia Nursery Co.
BUTTONS 'N BOWS - Toys–stuffed ☆ - Gund, Inc.
BUTTONS/NUTS 'N BOLTS - Toys - Playskool, Inc.
BUTTONS PLUS - Computer software - Wenzel Computer Services
BUTTONTALES - Dolls - Price Stern Sloan Inc.
BUTTONZ - Games - Florence Jones
BUTTS 'N STUFF - Wastebaskets - F.H. Lawson Co.
BUTTSAVER - Sporting goods - Southern Comfort Outdoors, Inc.
BUTYL BED - Adhesives and sealants - Dap Products Inc.
BUTYL-FLEX - Caulking compounds - Dap Products Inc.
BUTYLAIRE - Tires - Bridgestone/Firestone, Inc.
BUTYLGRIP - Sealing compounds - Biddle Co.
BUTYN - Analgesics - Abbott Laboratories
BUTYN SULFATE - Ophthalmic goods ☆ - Abbott Laboratories
BUX-KIN - Leather goods - Buxton Inc.
BUXTON - Eyeglasses - Martin-Copeland Eyewear Corp.
BUXTON - Floor coverings–carpet and rugs - Wunda Weve Carpet Co.
BUXTON - Leather goods - Buxton Inc.
BUXTON - Thread - Cincinnati Thread Co.
BUY 'N SAVE - Food products - Nash-Finch Co.
BUY RITE - Food products - Modern Foods Inc.
BUY-RITE - Hardware - Brown-Rogers-Dixson Co.
BUY SAM A DRINK AND GET HIS DOG ONE TOO!! - Apparel and accessories - Michael B. Lange
BUY THE BUNDLE - Paper - Marcal Paper Mills, Inc.
BUY THE HOUR - Computer software - Austin Computer Resources, Inc.
BUY THE MOUNTAIN - Syrup - J & J Snack Foods Corp.
BUY YOUR OWN - Cigarettes - G.A. Georgopulo & Co. Inc.
BUYER'S ADVANTAGE - Computer software - Lebhar-Friedman, Inc.
BUYER'S CHOICE - Advertising agencies - Thomas Nelson, Inc.
BUYERS' CHOICE - Cosmetics - Roundy's Inc.
BUYERS CHOICE - Food products - Midland Grocery Co.
BUYER'S CHOICE - Mattresses - Ther-A-Pedic Associates, Inc.
BUYERS DELIGHT - Food products - Mid-America Potato Co.
BUYER'S WORKMATE - Computer software - IT Resources Inc.
BUYERS WORKSHOP - Apparel–women's ☆ - Bobbie Brooks Inc.
BUYMATE - Computer software - Budgetext Corp.
BUZ-AWF - Insecticides - Stewart-Hall Chemical Corp.
BUZ-PLUZ - Candy bars - Special Preparations Co.
BUZBY - Toys–stuffed ☆ - Gund, Inc.
BUZZ - Coffee - Barrie House Coffee Co., Inc.
BUZZ - Food products - Herbs of China Ltd.
BUZZ - Guitars - M.V. Pedulla Guitars
BUZZ - Musical instruments - M V Pedulla Guitars, Inc.
BUZZ - Thread - New Bedford Thread Co. Inc.
BUZZ ABOUT - Apparel and accessories - Colonial Textile Manufacturing Corp.
BUZZ ALDRIN - Computer software - Buzz Aldrin
BUZZ AWAY - Insecticides - Quantum, Inc.
BUZZ BASS - Fishing lures ☆ - Joe's Flies
BUZZ BEAMER - Study kit - Bill Hinds
BUZZ BEANS CHOCOLATE COVERED ESPRESSO BEANS! - Coffee beans - Bruce/Jan Milletto Partnership
BUZZ BEE - Toys - Steven Manufacturing Co.
BUZZ BIKE - Bicycles - Western Auto Supply Co.
BUZZ BUZZ - Fabrics - Gretchen Bellinger Inc.
BUZZ MINNOW - Fishing tackle - Horizon Lure Co.
BUZZ OFF - Toys - Mattel, Inc.
BUZZ OFF - Veterinary pharmaceutical preparations - Boehringer Ingelheim Animal Health, Inc.
BUZZ OFF II - Insecticides - Boehringer Ingelheim Animal Health, Inc.
BUZZ RECORDS - Recording label - Buzz Records, Inc.
BUZZ-SAW - Toys - Mattel, Inc.
BUZZ, THE - Hardware - With Design in Mind
BUZZA-CARDOZO - Greeting cards - Gibson Greetings, Inc.
BUZZARDS BAY - Ships–sailing vessels - R & M Marine Products Inc.
BUZZ'S BOMBERS - Health care products - Herbs of China Ltd.
BUZZWORD - Toys–electronic ☆ - Philips Consumer Electronics Co.
BUZZY BEAVER - Toys - Tonka Corp.
BV - Handbags - Sirco International Corp.
BV - Leather goods - Bottega Veneta, Inc.
BV - Wines - Beaulieu Vineyard
BV BRITE VIEW TECHNOLOGIES - Computer hardware - Briteview Technologies, Inc.

BV PHEAP BOVOIR - Apparel and accessories - Chansopheap Chhim
B.V.D. - Underwear and nightwear - B.V.D. Co. Inc.
B.V.I. - Hair accessories, jewelry - MGZ Jewels
BVM - Recording label - BVM Records
BVM AARTS - Fruits–canned - Haddon House Food Products Inc.
BVMO - Veterinary pharmaceutical preparations ☆ - Schering-Plough Animal Health
BVPM - Microscopes - CRB, Inc.
BVS - Medical apparatus - Mentor O & O Inc.
BW - Computer software - Beame & Whiteside Software, Inc.
BW - Jewelry - Blue White Diamond Co. Inc.
BW - Jewelry–precious - Kobi Katz Inc.
BW/C 800 - Pharmaceutical preparations - Republic Drug Co. Inc.
BW JACKS - Cigarettes - Brown & Williamson Tobacco Corp.
BWANA - Frames–eyeglass - Hudson Optical Corp.
BWANA ELEPHANT - Toys–stuffed - Dakin Inc.
BWANGA - Drums–musical instruments ☆ - Solutions
BWC - Health care products - Beauty Without Cruelty
BWC - Watches - Bella Watch Corp.
BWD - Automotive parts and accessories - BWD Automotive Corp.
BWE - Recording label - Bonneville International Corp.
BWEAR OR B FASHIONED - Apparel and accessories - YCU Enterprises, Inc.
BWICK - Wicking - Hooper Industries Inc.
BWL - Recording label - Jazz Composer's Orchestra Association Inc.
BWMZIT - Chemical preparations - Challenger Manufacturing, Inc.
BX - Audio tapes–blank ☆ - Minnesota Mining & Manufacturing Co.
BX-50 - Automotive parts and accessories - BX Industries, Inc.
BX-100 - Brake parts - BX Industries, Inc.
BX-200 - Automotive parts and accessories - BX Industries, Inc.
BXR - Apparel and accessories - Brigata International, Inc.
BY APPOINTMENT - Shirts ☆ - Grunwald-Marx Inc.
BY APPOINTMENT - Wallpaper - Doshi Wallcoveringss Inc.
BY BARAD - Apparel and accessories - Barad & Co.
BY BELLINI - Apparel–athletic ☆ - Midstates Sportswear
BY BOSCA - Leather goods and gifts - Hugo Bosca Co., Inc.
BY BRANDT - Stationery - Pen-Tab Industries
BY CORBIN - Apparel and accessories - Corbin Ltd.
BY DESIGN - Clocks - By Design Corp.
BY DESIGN - Computer software - Streetwise Software
BY DESIGN RESOURCES - Publisher's imprints - Gruner Jahr Printing & Publishing Co.
BY DESIGN TIME - Clocks ☆ - By Design Corp.
BY FIRE AND SWORD - Games ☆ - Avalon Hill Game Co.
BY GADD - Apparel and accessories - Decorp Inc.
BY-GEORGE - Soap - Bethurum Research & Development Inc.
BY GEORGE II - Wallpaper - Sellers & Josephson
BY GEORGE III - Wallpaper - Sellers & Josephson
BY GILFORD - Furniture–upholstered - Gilford Corp.
BY GO PRO - Sporting goods - Geoffrey L. O'Connor
BY GOLLY LOLLY - Candy ☆ - Spangler Candy Co.
BY GRANDMA - Jackets - Angela Swanson
BY HOOK OR CROOK - Games - Avalon Hill Game Co.
BY INVITATION ONLY - Wallpaper - Imperial Wallcoverings, Inc.
BY JAMES - Hosiery–women's ☆ - Easton International
BY JASON - Cosmetics ☆ - Jason Natural Products, Inc.
BY KIMBERLY - Apparel and accessories - Mattson-Casey
BY-LINE - Frames–eyeglass - Liberty Optical Manufacturing Co.
BY LINES - Underwear and nightwear - Maidenform Inc.
BY-LO - Gasoline - By-Lo Oil Co.
BY MARSH - Jewelry - Marsh Industries Inc.
BY MAY - Frames–eyeglass - May Optical Co. Inc.
BY MOM - Jackets - Angela Swanson
BY-MYSELF - Diapers–disposable ☆ - Plainwell Tissue
BY-O-BOY - Apparel–children's - Happy Kids Ltd.
BY POPULAR DEMAND - Hair care products - Esirg's Manufacturing Co. Inc.
BY POPULAR DEMAND - Wallpaper - Essex Wallcoveringss
BY PRODUCT - Apparel–women's - Product Studio Inc.
BY RECOMMENDATION ONLY - Publisher's imprints - Johanna Kaestner
BY REQUEST - Floor coverings–carpet and rugs ☆ - Customweave Carpets Inc.
BY SPECIAL APPOINTMENT - Apparel stores–sports - Barrie House Coffee Co., Inc.
BY SPECIAL ARRANGEMENT - Product description unknown - Two's Co. Inc.
BY THE ARBOR - Giftware - N.S. Gustin Co.
BY THE BAGFUL - Novelty items - Squire Boone Caverns, Inc.

BY-THE-SEA - Seafood products–fresh or frozen ☆ - Arctic King Trading Corp.

BY THE SEASHORE - Christmas tree ornaments - Seasonal Specialties Electrics, Inc.

BY THE SHORE - Wallpaper - Andover Wallcovering

BY THE TOOL STUD - Apparel and accessories - Whiteside Manufacturing Co.

BY-WAY - Shoes - Hills Department Store Co.

BY WILLIAMHOUSE - Greeting cards - Pen-Tab Industries

BYBBLOS - Bubble-blowing toy - Toy Originators Inc.

BYBLOS - Colognes - Gary Farn Ltd.

BYBLOS - Ophthalmic goods ☆ - Luxottica

BYBLOS MEDITERRANEAN FOOD - Food products - Byblos Mediterranean Foods, Inc.

B.Y.C. - Apparel–athletic ☆ - Ramm Styles Inc.

BYCO - Vegetables–frozen - Bryd Harvest Inc.

BYE-BYE - Bags - Kracke International

BYE BYE - Toys ☆ - Peg Perego USA Inc.

BYE BYE BABY - Dolls ☆ - Effanbee Doll Corp.

BYE BYE BABY - Infant product - Pacesetter

BYE BYE BIRD - Toys - Gerber Products Co.

BYE BYE DECUBITI - Cushions - Ken McRight Supplies Inc.

BYE BYE DESIGNS - Scarves and neck warmers - Sandra L. Scannell

BYE-BYE DIAPERS - Dolls - Mattel, Inc.

BYE BYE TREK - Toys ☆ - Peg Perego USA Inc.

BYE GUM - Cleaning preparations–household - Imperial Manufacturing Co. Inc.

BYE LINES - Skin care products - Avon Products, Inc.

BYELO BABY - Dolls - Horsman

BYER OF MAINE - Bags–canvas - KMS Co.

BYERLY'S - Soups–canned - Byerly's

BYER'S BEST - Cookies - Charles Chips of Southern California

BYERS DATA BRIDGE - Computer software - Byers Engineering Co.

BYERS EWO - Computer software - Byers Engineering Co.

BYERS MAP VIEWER - Computer software - Byers Engineering Co.

BYF - Firearms - New Helvetia Trade Group

BYFIELD - Cutlery - Carvel Hall Inc.

BYFIELD - Snuff ☆ - Byfield Snuff Co.

BYFORD - Wallets - Enger-Kress Co.

BYGONE - Health care products - Lakon Herbals Inc.

BYGONE BUGS - Health care products - Lakon Herbals Inc.

BYINGTON - Wines ☆ - Shaw-Ross International Importers

BYJ - Figurines ☆ - Goebel of North America

BYK-TRAC - Sporting goods - All American Products Inc.

BYLINE - Apparel and accessories ☆ - Edison Brothers Stores, Inc.

BYN - Watches - Byn Watch Co. Inc.

BYN DE LUXE - Watches - Byn Watch Co. Inc.

BYN-O-SEAL - Hardware - Heliodyne Inc.

B.Y.O. - Perfumes - Frances Goldmark

BYOB - Apparel and accessories - B.Y.O.B. Clothing Co.

BYOGENIC - Skin care products ☆ - Christine Valmy, Inc.

BYOSAN - Pharmaceutical preparations - Biosante Distributors Inc.

BYPASS - Bags–duffel - Dan McHale

BYPASS - Fans–exhaust ☆ - Mercury Hi-Performance Group

BYRD - Cookies - Byrd Cookie Co.

BYRD - Vegetables–frozen - Bryd Harvest Inc.

BYRD - Wines - Byrd Vineyards

BYRD & HIS FLOCK - Barbecue sauce - Masterfoods Specialities, Inc.

BYRD CLOTH - Fabrics - Reeves Brothers Inc.

BYRD ESTATE - Beverages–malt - Byrd Vineyards

BYRD MILL - Food products - E.M. Todd Co. Inc.

BYRDE - Glassware–household ☆ - Miller Import Corp.

BYRD'S - Crab meat–canned or cured - Byrd's Inc.

BYRD'S - Food products - Byrd Foods Inc.

BYRNE - Dairy products - Byrne Dairy, Inc.

BYRO-JET - Toys–models - Midwest Industries Inc.

BYRON - Frames–eyeglass - Rozin Optical Export Corp.

BYRON - Ophthalmic goods ☆ - Luxottica

BYRON - Shoes - Allen-Edmonds Shoe Corp.

BYRON - Watches - Bulova Corp.

BYRON EAST - Tobacco–chewing or smoking - Brown & Williamson Tobacco Corp.

BYRON LARS - Apparel–women's - Byron Lars

BYRON NELSON ELEVEN STRAIGHT - Apparel–athletic - Byron Nelson

BYRON SMYRNIOTIS - Peanut oil - Mound City Shelled Nut

BYRON VINEYARDS & WINERY - Wines - Byron Vineyard and Winery

BYRON'S - Frozen foods - Byron's Bar-B-Q

BYRON'S BRONCO - Meat products–canned - Byron's Bar-B-Q

BYRON'S OLD FASHIONED - Sandwiches–prepackaged - Rich-Seapak Corp.

BYRRH - Beverages–alcohol - House of Burgundy Inc.

B.Y.'S - Cosmetics - Jim Griffith Co.

BYS - Pet products - Brewers Yeast Specialist

BYSON - Giftware - B. Yaffe & Sons, Inc.

BYTEPRO - Computer software - Bytepro, Inc.

BYTRECE - Fabrics–nylon - E.I. Dupont de Nemours and Co.

BYU - Apparel and accessories - Brigham Young University Press

BYWAYMAN - Toys–automobiles - Mattel, Inc.

BYZANTINE - Candy - Russell Stover Candies, Inc.

BYZANTINE - Dinnerware–glass - Cyclamen Studio

BYZANTINE - Floor coverings ☆ - Congoleum Corp.

BYZANTINE - Floor coverings–carpet and rugs ☆ - Regal Rugs Inc.

BYZANTINE - Tiles–ceramic - KPT Inc.

BYZANTINE - Wallpaper ☆ - Maya Romanoff Corp.

BYZANTINE COLLECTION - Giftware - Russ Berrie and Co., Inc.

BYZANTINE GOLD ACCENT - Flatware - Yamazaki Tableware Inc.

BYZANTIUM NIGHTS - Wallpaper - Kirk-Brummel

BZ PRO BOARDS - Bodyboards - Earth & Ocean Sports, Inc.

BZ SNOWBOARDS - Snowboards - Earth & Ocean Sports, Inc.

BZAR - Watches ☆ - I.D. Enterprises

BZNS - Apparel and accessories - Georges Marciano

BZZZ - Candles ☆ - Carolina Designs Ltd.

☆ = Now out of production

C

Addresses and phone numbers for the companies cited in the brands below
are available in the Company Listings section immediately following the brands listings.

C - Carhartt, Inc.

C - Air conditioning equipment - Champion Cooler Corp.

C - Apparel and accessories - Chicago National League Ball Club Inc.

C - Apparel and accessories - South Carolina Baseball Club, L.P.

C - Apparel–athletic ☆ - Cayman Sports Co.

C - Boats - Fiberglass Engineering Inc.

C - Cables–signal - Cewl Custom Connections

C - Computer storage devices–magnetic - Computer Products Center, Inc.

C - Computers–mainframe - A-Best International Inc.

C - Footwear - Justin Boot Co.

C - Jewelry - Cellini, Inc.

C - Jewelry - Cristiara International Inc.

C - Medical apparatus - Camtronics Medical Systems

C - Medical apparatus - Clarus Medical Systems, Inc.

C - Novelty items - Champion Eximport Enterprise Inc.

C - Rails–aluminum - Advantus, Corp.

C - Ski goggles - Optyl Eyewear Fashion International Corp.

C+ - Skin care products - Aesthe-Derm Inc.

C - Veterinary equipment - Corometrics Medical Systems Inc.

C-3 - Aquariums–household - Marine Environment/Aqua Craft

C-3PO - Apparel and accessories - Lucasfilm Ltd.

C-8 - Steel products - Consolidated Metal Products, Inc.

C-14 - Chemical preparations - Calgon Carbon Corp.

C-20 - Cleaning preparations–household - Mt. Hood Chemical Corp.

C-50 - Water purification systems - Pure Water Inc.

C-60 - Degreasing solvents - Sprayway Inc.

C-60 - Vitamins and nutritional supplements - Purdue Frederick Co.

C-100 - Water treating compounds - Aquarium Products Inc.

C-100+ - Vitamins and nutritional supplements - Fibertone Co.

C-101 - Electronic equipment - AudioControl

C-130 HERCULES - Toys–models - Estes Industries

C-131 - Electronic equipment - AudioControl

C-200 - Windows–storm ☆ - Caradco

C-310/315 - Printers–computer - C-TECH Electronics Inc.

C 350 - Agricultural products - North American Green, Inc.

C/400 - Computer software - International Business Machines Corp.

C-410/415 - Printers–computer - C-TECH Electronics Inc.

C-420/425 - Printers–computer - C-TECH Electronics Inc.

C-500 - Vitamin-C supplement - Bretney Corp.

C-520 - Water purification systems - Pure Water Inc.

C-610 - Printers–computer - C-TECH Electronics Inc.

C 610 II - Printers–computer - C-TECH Electronics Inc.

C-610 III - Printers–computer - C-TECH Electronics Inc.

C-615 II - Printers–computer - C-TECH Electronics Inc.

C-645 - Printers–computer - C-TECH Electronics Inc.

C-1500 - Motor vehicles–trucks - General Motors Corp. (Chevrolet Motor Div.)

C-2500 - Motor vehicles–trucks - General Motors Corp. (Chevrolet Motor Div.)

C-3500 - Motor vehicles–trucks - General Motors Corp. (Chevrolet Motor Div.)

C-68000 - Computer compiler program - Green Hills Software Inc.

C. A. COOPER - Guitars - Musician's Repair & Supply

C-A-R-E - Paper–tissue - Ashdun Inc.

C-A-Y-L - Vitamins and nutritional supplements - Amsoil, Inc.

C & B - See CROSSE & BLACKWELL

C & B - Wines - Wine World Inc.

C & B VINTAGE CELLARS - Wines - C & B Vintage Cellars

C & C - Beverages–carbonated - C & C Cola Co. Inc.

C & C - Cleaning preparations - W.W. Grainger, Inc.

C & C - Finishing agents - Cowman-Campbell Paint Co.

C & C - Pharmaceutical preparations ☆ - U.S. Ethicals Inc.

C & C RELIEF - Cough medicines ☆ - Upjohn Co.

C. & C. SELECTIONS - Cooking equipment–household - Clayson Co.

C & D - Desk sets - C and D Hit Inc.

C & D - Ducks - Maple Leaf Farms Inc.

C & D - Paints, etc. - Cook and Dunn Paint Corp.

C & D BRUSH SAVER - Brush cleaner ☆ - Cook and Dunn Paint Corp.

C & D HIT - Pens - C and D Hit Inc.

C & E - Catsup - C and E Canners Inc.

C & E - Pharmaceutical preparations - Nature's Bounty, Inc.

C & E COMBO - Pharmaceutical preparations - Republic Drug Co. Inc.

C & F - Wines - Leonard Kreusch Inc.

C & F FORMULA - Health care products - Alta Health Products

C & H - Sugar–granulated, refined, or powdered - California and Hawaiian Sugar Co.

C & H ADVANTAGE - Tools - Nielsen & Bainbridge

C & J - Boating equipment and accessories - C & J Marine, Inc.

C & L - Swimming pools - Clayton & Lambert Manufacturing Co.

C & LO ZOO ANIMALS - Toys ☆ - South Bend Toy Manufacturing Co.

C & M - Paints - Valspar Corp.

C & R - Apparel stores–men's - Men's Wearhouse

C & R - Musical instrument accessories - C & R Guitars

C & R CLOTHIERS - Apparel stores–men's - Men's Wearhouse

C & R CLOTHIERS - Apparel–men's - C & R Clothiers Inc.

C & R INDUSTRIES - Antifreeze - James R. Welsh

C & T - Pharmaceutical preparations ☆ - Hyrex Pharmaceuticals

C & W - Vegetables–frozen - California & Washington Co.

C & W VALENCIA - Juices ☆ - California & Washington Co.

C & Y - Furniture ☆ - Foley & Robinson Inc.

C-ASCORB - Vitamins and nutritional supplements - Natural Organics, Inc.

C/B - Corsets ☆ - Strouse, Adler Co.

C-B - Pharmaceutical preparations - C-B Drug Co.

C B SMOOTHE - Hair care products - Selected Chemical Products Co.

C-B VONE - Pharmaceutical preparations - Rhone-Poulenc Rorer Pharmaceuticals Inc.

C-BAC - Binders - The Union Group

C-BALL - Valves - Grinnell Corp.

C/BASE - Computer software - Conetic Software Systems, Inc.

C BEAM - Electrical equipment - International Business Machines Corp.

C-BELL - Cosmetics - Andre Corp.

C-BELT - Conveyors - Key Technology, Inc.

C-BERRY COMPLEX 125 - Vitamins and nutritional supplements - Great Life Laboratories Inc.

C-C 102 - Pharmaceutical preparations - Camall Co.

C-C 105 - Pharmaceutical preparations - Camall Co.

C/C ACCOMPLI - Apparel and accessories - Leonard Cagan

C/C CIGN - Publisher's imprints - C/C Cign Co., Inc.

C C HUGHES - Sunglasses - Meijer, Inc.

C CAMP CALIFORNIA - Paper - Camp California Inc.

C CAOUTCHOUC - Apparel and accessories - Kristan of Aspen

C CAP - Ophthalmic goods - Allergan, Inc.

C CARRERA - Ski goggles - Optyl Eyewear Fashion International Corp.

C CASPIAN - Firearms, accessories, and parts - Caspian Arms, Ltd.

C CAYMAN - Sports rackets and accessories - Cayman Sports Co.

☆ = Now out of production

C CENTON ELECTRONICS - Electronic equipment - Centon Electronics, Inc.
C CERAMI CONSTRUCTION COMPANY, LTD. - Cement–asphalt - Cerami Construction Co., Ltd.
C CHAMPION TECHNOLOGIES INC. - Chemical preparations - Champion Technologies Inc.
C CINEBASE - Computer software - Visual F/X, Inc.
C-CLASS - Motor vehicles–automobiles - Mercedes-Benz of North America Inc.
C CLASSIC - Cultured pearls - Daltron, Inc.
C COMFORTWEAR - Floor coverings–carpet and rugs - General Felt Industries, Inc.
C-CON - Seal connectors - Reflange, Inc.
C CONICAL - Targets - Johnson Matthey Electronics, Inc.
C CONNECTION - Furniture - A. Brandt Co. Inc.
C-COR CHAMP - Coaxial amplifiers - C-Cor Royalty Corp.
C-CORE - Bats–baseball - Easton Aluminum Inc.
C CORRECT - Recording label - Grind Stone Records
C-COVE - Moldings and trim - Kim Supply, Inc.
C COVEE - Caps–baseball - Covee Corp.
C CPAC - Marker buoys - Coastal & Offshore Pacific Corp.
C CROWNLINE - Boats–motor - Crownline Boats, Inc.
C CUP AND UP - Bathing suits - Patricia Byrnes Kane
C-CURE - Adhesives and sealants - C-Cure Corp.
C-D - Hardware - Amifast Corp.
C-D ANTITOXIN - Veterinary pharmaceutical preparations - Boehringer Ingelheim Animal Health, Inc.
C-D TOXOID - Veterinary pharmaceutical preparations - Boehringer Ingelheim Animal Health, Inc.
C DE CARAT - Jewelry - SBL, Inc.
C-DINOSAURS - Vitamins and nutritional supplements - Makers of Kal, Inc.
C. DREW - Tools - Universal Products International
C-DUCER - Microphones - C-T Audio Marketing Inc.
C. E. CLOWN & CO. - Clown figurines ☆ - Aus-Ben Studios
C. E. KAISER - Adhesives and sealants - Laticrete International Inc.
C-EAGLE - Boats–motor ☆ - Sport-Craft Inc.
C F - Convenience stores - Crystal Flash LP of Michigan
C. F. BURGER - Dairy products - C.F. Burger Creamery Co.
C. F. MARTIN - Guitars - C.F. Martin & Co., Inc.
C FILE - Filing cabinets–metal - Mayline/Hamilton
C. FILIPPONI - Leather goods ☆ - Leon Fleischer, International Marketing
C-FILM - Office supplies - C-Line Products, Inc.
C-FILM - X-ray apparatus - Apothecus, Inc.
C-FLAP - Sporting goods - Markwort Sporting Goods Co.
C-FLEX - Traction apparatus–medical - Shamrock Medical Inc.
C-FLEX - Vitamins and nutritional supplements - Inter-Cal Corp.
C-FLUX - Solder - Rectorseal Corp.
C-FOLD - Luggage - Group III International Ltd.
C-FOOD - Fertilizers - Plantabbs Products
C/FOOD SOFTWARE - Computer software - Southeastern Digital Images, Inc.
C-FREE - Paper–writing - Union Camp Corp. (Fine Paper Division)
C-GARD! - Cases–cigar - Bobby Lee Renfro
C-GEL - Vitamins and nutritional supplements - J.R. Carlson Laboratories Inc.
C-GEM - Giftware - Crystal Optics Research Inc.
C-GEM - Seafood products–fresh or frozen - Flag/Westbay Seafood Brokers
C-GLO - Pedestals–wood - Dap Products Inc.
C-GROOVE - Golfing equipment - Progear, Inc.
C-GULL - Boats–motor ☆ - Sport-Craft Inc.
C. H. ELLIS - Attache cases - C.H. Ellis Co. Inc.
C. H. HALE - Apparel–women's - Carter Hawley Hale Stores Inc.
C. H. OLIVER - Apparel–men's - Hartz & Co., Inc.
C. H. STUART - China cabinets–wood - C.H. Stuart & Co. Inc.
C-HAWK - Boats–motor ☆ - Sport-Craft Inc.
C HEADWATERS - Water transportation - Colorado Headwaters Inc.
C-HOOKS - Computer software - Procell, Inc.
C-I - Sporting goods - Edwards Sports Products
C ICE PILOTS PENSACOLA - Broadcasting stations–television - Pensacola Professional Hockey Club, Inc.
C-III - Artists' materials - Gilman Co. Inc.
C III - Floor coverings–carpet and rugs - Omalon
C. J. BONNET - Fabrics - Leimtex Corp.
C. JERE - Statuary - Artisan House Inc.
C. K. MONDAVI - Wines - Charles Krug Winery
C KNIGHTS - Posters - Charlotte Baseball, Inc.
C KNIT APPAREL - Apparel and accessories - Dixie Yarns, Inc.
C-KURE - Gloves - C & K Manufacturing & Sales LLC
C/L - Pumps - Cole-Parmer Instrument Co.

C. L. KIDS - Footwear–children's - Jumping-Jacks Shoes Inc.
C-L-TWO - Cleaning preparations - Lake Products Co. Inc.
C-LARK - Ships–sailing vessels - Clark Boat Co.
C-LECT - Dental laboratories - Keller Laboratories, Inc.
C-LECT-CHOKE - Firearms, accessories, and parts - O.F. Mossberg & Sons, Inc.
C-LETZ ELECTRODES - Medical apparatus - Utah Medical Products, Inc.
C-LEVEL - Pharmaceutical preparations ☆ - DDI Pharmaceuticals Inc.
C-LEXIN - Pharmaceutical preparations ☆ - Roberts/Hauck Pharmaceuticals Inc.
C-LIFE - Men and boys' apparel - C-Life Corp.
C LINE - Office furniture–metal ☆ - Joyce International Inc.
C-LITE - Optical machinery - Coburn Optical Industries Inc.
C-LITE - Plastics - Polysource, Inc.
C-LOC - Nuts and bolts - Lok-Mor, Inc.
C-LOCK - Health care products - Nellcor Inc.
C-LOGO - Sport socks - J.P. Manning Inc.
C. M. DEER - Apparel and accessories - Watch Em Fly, Inc.
C. M. LABS - Apparel and accessories - Watch Em Fly, Inc.
C-MARK - Audio equipment - George Technology
C MEC - Water purification systems - Whitmer Co.
C-MON - Razors - Peter J. Michels Inc.
C-MON CADILLAC - Scissors–hand-operated - Peter J. Michels Inc.
C-MON PETITE - Hair care products - Peter J. Michels Inc.
C MONSTER - Juices ☆ - Odwalla, Inc.
C-MOR COMPANY - Blinds–vertical - Amsterdam Fabricators
C-MORE - Lamps - Vantage Products Inc.
C-NOTE - Games - Douglas Press, Inc.
C-O - Lenses–optical - Colors in Optics
C-O-C - Deodorizers - Surco Products Inc.
C-O-TWO - Fire extinguishers - Fyr-Fyter Co. Inc.
C OAKITE - Chemical preparations - Oakite Products, Inc.
C-OPHEN - Analgesics - Alacer Co.
C P - Publisher's imprints - Candlewick Press, Inc.
C-PA - Veterinary pharmaceutical preparations - Vital Nutrition Products
C-PACK - Envelopes - Quality Park Products Co.
C-PAKS - Pharmaceutical preparations - Paks Drugs Inc.
C/PALABRAS & CONCEPTS - Computer software ☆ - Laureate Learning Systems Inc.
C PALM - Skin care products - Keratech Services, Inc.
C. PARKER WOOD'S - Mustard - C. Parker Wood Products, Inc.
C. PELEGRIN - Jewelry - Sazingg, Inc.
C-PHONE - Video equipment - C-Phone Corp.
C. PLATH - Navigation equipment - Weems & Plath, Inc.
C-PLEX - Balls - Lisco, Inc.
C-PLEX - Vitamins and nutritional supplements - Vita-Fore Products Co.
C PLUS - Juices - Paramount Citrus Association
C-PLUS - Pharmaceutical preparations - P. & S. Laboratories Inc.
C PLUS - Vitamins and nutritional supplements - Vitamin Research Products Inc.
C PLUS E - Pharmaceutical preparations - Nature's Bounty, Inc.
C POCKET - Linen - Morris A. Bedor
C-POST - Computer software - Management Science Associates, Inc.
C-POWER GUARDIAN - Computer hardware - C-Power Products, Inc.
C-Q - Boats–canoes - Noah Corp.
C-R - Tobacco products - Shepherd Tobacco Co.
C. R. BROOKES - Food products - ACB/Richard Watson
C-R-E-S - Apparel and accessories - Zoological Society of San Diego, Inc.
C. R. LAINE - Furniture - C.R. Laine Furniture Co. Inc.
C-RAM IT! - Adhesive - American Velodur Metal, Inc.
C. RANDALL BROOKS - Dresses–women's ☆ - Campus Casuals of California
C-RINGS - Toy - James Industries, Inc.
C-RON - Pharmaceutical preparations ☆ - Solvay Pharmaceuticals Inc.
C S CREATIVE STRUCTURES - Building materials - Creative Structures, Inc.
C. S. DENT - Pharmaceutical preparations - Grandpa Brands Co.
C/S DEVELOPER - Computer software - Object Group, Inc.
C SET++ - Computer software - International Business Machines Corp.
C. SHARPS ARMS - Firearms, accessories, and parts - John R. Schoffstall
C. SILVERA - Jewelry - Carolyn Silvera
C-SOLVE - Housewares - Midland Chicago Corp.
C-SOLVE - Pharmaceutical preparations - Syosset Laboratories Inc.
C-SPAN - Pharmaceutical preparations ☆ - Edwards Pharmaceuticals, Inc.
C-SPAS - Pharmaceutical preparations ☆ - Wesley Pharmacal Co. Inc.
C SPERIDIN - Vitamins and nutritional supplements ☆ - Marlyn Co. Inc.
C-SPORT - Caps–baseball - C-Sport, Inc.

☆ = Now out of production

C-SPORT - Motor vehicles–motor homes - Fleetwood Enterprises, Inc.

C SQUARED - Apparel–women's - Rohr Enterprises Inc.

C-STAT - Bandages - S. Jackson, Inc.

C. STONE - Floor coverings–tile - Finetex Co. Inc.

C/T/S - Pharmaceutical preparations - Hoechst-Roussel Pharmaceuticals Inc.

C-TAC - Telephones–cellular ☆ - ORA Electronics

C-TEC - Medical apparatus - Capintec, Inc.

C-TECH - Braces–orthopedic - Orthopedic Technology, Inc.

C-TECH - Computers - C-Tech Computer Systems Inc.

C-TECH - Veterinary nutritional supplements - Cuprem, Inc.

C-TEN - Pet products ☆ - Hess & Clark, Inc.

C TEST - Ophthalmic apparatus - Leica Inc.

C-THRU - Rulers–metal - C-Thru Ruler Co.

C-THRU - Thread - Gudebrod, Inc.

C/TNS - Computer software - DI/COM Ltd.

C-TOWN - Pizza - Continental Food Products Inc.

C-TRACT - Tools ☆ - Granberg International

C-TREC - Prerecorded audio tapes - Children's Television Resource and Education Center

C-TREE - Trees - Ben Haines Barteldes

C-TUSSIN - Pharmaceutical preparations - Century Pharmaceuticals Inc.

C-TYM - Vitamins and nutritional supplements - Econo Med Pharmaceuticals Inc.

C. U. LATER - Apparel–men's - Berkley Shirt Co. Inc.

C VALENTINO - Watches - Global Trading Industries Inc./Stelux

C-WATCH - Watches ☆ - Cronus Precision Products Inc.

C-WHITE - Packaging–paper - Chesapeake Corp.

C-ZONE - Slacks–men's ☆ - Haggar Corp.

C1 - CAPRI ONE - Lighting fixtures - Thomas Lighting (Accent Division)

C2 - Cardboard - Creative Communications International, Inc.

C2 - Computer peripheral equipment - C-2, Inc.

C2 HOMEWORKS UNLIMITED - Clocks - Sligh Furniture Co.

C2BGA - Computer peripheral equipment - Prolinx Labs Corp.

C2C - Electrical equipment - Tencor Instruments

C.2.C. - Footcare products - Galina Eakins

C2C - Footwear - Morse Shoe, Inc.

C2E - Prosthetic apparatus - Personal Performance Medical Corp.

C3 - Apparel–athletic - Cyrk Inc.

C3 - Cold remedies ☆ - SmithKline Beecham Consumer Healthcare

C3 - Electronic equipment - Gemstar Development Corp.

C3D - Cleaning preparations - Data Medical Associates Inc.

C4 CLEARFIRE - Golfing equipment - Clear Difference Co., Inc.

C4 EZPILOT - Computer software - C4 Network Inc.

C4I NEWS - Paper–newsprint - Montrose Publishing, Inc.

C5 - Educational materials - Performance Resources, Inc.

C6L - Nuts and bolts - Huck International, Inc.

C26 - Ships–sailing vessels - Offshore Sailing School Ltd.

C36 - Motor vehicles–automobiles - Mercedes-Benz of North America Inc.

C50L - Nuts and bolts - Huck International, Inc.

C90 SPOTTING SCOPES - Photographic equipment - Celestron International

C220 - Motor vehicles–automobiles - Mercedes-Benz of North America Inc.

C280 - Motor vehicles–automobiles - Mercedes-Benz of North America Inc.

C320 - Heat exchangers - ITT Corp. (Heat Transfer Div.)

C405 - Amalgamators - Aluminum Co. of America

C500 - Computer terminals - Nec Technologies, Inc.

CA - Abrasive products ☆ - Carborundum Abrasives North America

CA - Coffee - Coffee Associates, Inc.

CA - Jewelry - Aldridge Co.

CA - Metals - Golden West Baseball Co.

CA - Road construction machinery - United Dominion Industries, Inc.

CA-1 - Computer software - CA Management Inc.

CA-5 - Paints ☆ - Fry Plastics International Inc. (O)

CA-ADS - Computer software - Computer Associates International, Inc.

CA AUTOGUARD - Automotive parts and accessories - Akro Corp.

CA-CLIPPER/EXOSPACE - Computer software - Computer Associates International, Inc.

CA-COMMONVIEW - Computer software - Computer Associates International, Inc.

CA-COMPETE - Software - CA Management Inc.

CA D 'ESTE - Vinegar - De Choix Specialty Foods Co.

CA-DATACOM - Computer software - Computer Associates International, Inc.

CA-DBFAST - Computer software - Computer Associates International, Inc.

CA DE LA PASINA - Food products ☆ - De Medici Imports Ltd.

CA DEL SOLO - Wines - Bonny Doon Winery Inc.

CA DESK - Desks - Collapsible Auto Desk

CA-NETMAN - Computer software - Computer Associates International, Inc.

CA-OPENROAD - Computer software - Computer Associates International, Inc.

CA-PARADIGM SERVICE DESK - Computer software - Computer Associates International, Inc.

CA-REALIZER - Computer software - Computer Associates International, Inc.

C.A. REED - Plates–paper - Creative Expressions Group

CA-REZZ - Skin care products - FNC Medical Corp.

CA SA DE CARMEN - Food products - Abuelita Mexican Foods

CA-SESMAN - Computer software - Computer Associates International, Inc.

CA-SIMPLY FINANCE - Computer software - Computer Associates International, Inc.

CA-SIMPLY MONEY - Computer software - Computer Associates International, Inc.

C.A. SPORT - Apparel stores - Rousso Apparel Group, Inc.

CA-SYSTEM/MANAGER - Computer software - Computer Associates International, Inc.

CA-UNICENTER/SYSTEMS ALERT - Computer software - Computer Associates International, Inc.

CA-UNIPACK - Computer software - CA Management Inc.

CA VA BIEN - Apparel and accessories - Spelcor

CA VESCOVO - Wines - Francis A. Bonanno, Inc.

CA-VISUAL 20/20 - Computer software - Computer Associates International, Inc.

CA-VISUAL EXPRESS - Computer software - Computer Associates International, Inc.

CA-VISUAL OBJECTS - Computer software - Computer Associates International, Inc.

CA-VISUAL REALIA - Computer software - Computer Associates International, Inc.

CA-XCOM - Computer peripheral equipment - Computer Associates International, Inc.

CAAEALZER - Wallpaper ☆ - Capital Carousel Inc.

CAAPS - Computer software - United Insurance Co. of America

CAATS - Computer software - William H. Erskine

CAB - Cleaning preparations - Windsor Wax Co. Inc.

CAB-1 REMOTE CONTROLLER - Toys - Kughn Enterprises

CAB 3 - Electrical equipment - Pass & Seymour, Inc.

CAB CAD - Computer software - Zero Corp.

CAB CRUNCHER - Toys–automobiles - Mattel, Inc.

CAB DRIVER'S SECRET - Automotive parts and accessories - Lifestyle Resource

CAB-L-UBE - Lubricants - Manlee Industries Inc.

CAB MINDER - Locks–door - G & D Communications Corp.

CAB-O-JET - Dyes and pigments - Cabot Corp.

CABA WABA INTERNATIONAL - Suntan lotions - Sunal Enterprises, Inc.

CABACHONS - Jewelry ☆ - American Mineral Gift Co.

CABADON-M - Pharmaceutical preparations ☆ - Solvay Pharmaceuticals Inc.

CABAL - Computer software ☆ - Milton Bradley Co.

CABAL - Posters and comic magazines - Brandon Choi

CABALENE - Veterinary pharmaceutical preparations - Nutra-Vet Research Corp.

CABALLERO - Cigarettes - G.A. Georgopulo & Co. Inc.

CABALLERO - Eyeglasses - Art-Craft Optical Co.

CABALLERO - Footwear - Vans, Inc.

CABALLERO - Motor vehicle dealers ☆ - General Motors Corp.

CABALLERO - Sporting goods - Powell Skateboards

CABALLERO - Watches - Design Time USA Inc.

CABANA - Cigars - Gesty Trading & Manufacturing Corp.

CABANA - Floor coverings - Congoleum Corp.

CABANA - Floor coverings–carpet and rugs - Stanton Carpet Corp.

CABANA - Food products - Dole Food Co., Inc.

CABANA - Furniture–upholstered ☆ - Mersman Furniture Co.

CABANA - Seafood products–fresh or frozen - Gloucester Corp.

CABANA - Snack foods - Cabana Foods, Inc.

CABANA - Toilets–portable ☆ - Monogram Sanitation Co.

CABANA BANNERS - Banners - Randy Nash

CABANA DE CAMARONES - Food products - El Torito Restaurants Inc.

CABANA STRIPE - Floor coverings–carpet and rugs ☆ - Regal Rugs Inc.

CABANA STRIPE - Window shades - Joanna Western Mills Co.

CABANA SUN - Apparel and accessories ☆ - Africana Gifts & Shells Inc.

CABANAS - Cigar boxes–wood - Consolidated Cigar Corp.

CABARET - Apparel–women's - United States Shoe Corp.

CABARET - Cosmetics - Sornette International, Inc.

CABARET - Costumes - Lookingglass Inc.

CABARET - Dinnerware–glass - Nikko Ceramics Inc.

CABARET - Electronics equipment - JBL Inc.

CABARET - Floor coverings–carpet and rugs ☆ - Atlas Carpet Mills Inc.

CABARET - Frames—eyeglass - Zylo Ware Corp.
CABARET - Furniture - Bean Station Furniture Factory Inc.
CABARET - Glassware—household - Seneca Glass Co.
CABARET - Handwork supplies - Bernat Yarn & Craft Corp.
CABARET - House furnishings - Link-Taylor Corp.
CABARET - Pianos - Aeolian Pianos Inc.
CABARET - Recording label ☆ - DRG Records Inc.
CABARET - Wigs ☆ - Paula Young
CABASIL - Health care products - Dr. Stuart Kabnick
CABAWABA - Suntan lotions - Sunal Enterprises, Inc.
CABAZON - Apparel and accessories - Cheerful International Corp.
CABBAGE BUD - Novelty mirror ☆ - Cosrich Inc.
CABBAGE LEAF - Glassware—household - Dalzell-Viking
CABBAGE PATCH - Footwear ☆ - Pagoda Trading Co.
CABBAGE PATCH - Games - Tyco Toys
CABBAGE PATCH - Games ☆ - Ben Cooper Inc.
CABBAGE PATCH COLLECTION - Cosmetics for children ☆ - Cosrich Inc.
CABBAGE PATCH KIDS - Cereal - Ralston Purina Co.
CABBAGE PATCH KIDS - Cosmetic sets, toiletries - Cosrich Inc.
CABBAGE PATCH KIDS - Dolls - Hasbro, Inc.
CABBAGE PATCH KIDS - Dolls - Original Appalachian Artworks, Inc.
CABBAGE PATCH KIDS - Games ☆ - Parker Brothers
CABBAGE PATCH KIDS - Paper dolls, art sets, etc ☆ - Coloron Industries
CABBAGE PATCH KIDS - Puzzles - Milton Bradley Co.
CABBAGE PATCH KIDS - Skates—roller ☆ - National Sporting Goods Corp.
CABBAGE PATCH KIDS - Toys - American Toy & Furniture Co.
CABBAGE PATCH KIDS - Vitamins and nutritional supplements ☆ - Tishcon Corp.
CABBAGE PATCH KIDS BUSY BODIES - Games ☆ - Parker Brothers
CABBAGE PATCH KOOSAS - Toys—stuffed - Hasbro, Inc.
CABBIE COMPANION - Wheelchairs - Kareco International Inc.
CABCO - Cables - Cabco, Inc.
CABCOR - Particle board - Georgia-Pacific Corp.
CABELA'S - Sporting goods - Cabela's Inc.
CABELL'S - Food products - Southland Corp.
CABER - Sporting goods - Rossignol Ski Co., Inc.
CABERET - Floor coverings—carpet and rugs ☆ - World Carpets, Inc.
CABERNET - Floor coverings—carpet and rugs ☆ - Zenith Carpets
CABERNET - Furniture - Bassett Furniture Industries, Inc.
CABERNET - Glassware—household - Oneida Ltd.
CABERNET - Nail care products - Cosmair Inc.
CABERNET - Toilets—enameled - Kohler Co.
CABERNET - Underwear and nightwear - Dillard Department Stores Inc.
CABERNET - Vinegar ☆ - Liberty Richter Inc.
CABERNET CLASSICS - Furniture - Drexel Heritage Furnishings, Inc.
CABERNET FRANC - Wines - Fife Vineyards LLC
CABERNET POLYCARBONATE STEMWARE - Glassware—household - Carlisle Foodservice Products, Inc.
CABERNET PRINTS - Wallpaper ☆ - J.M. Lynne Co. Inc.
CABERNET SAUVIGNON - Wines - Fife Vineyards LLC
CABERNET SAUVIGNON - Wines - Merryvale Vineyards
CABERNET SAUVIGNON HILLSIDE - Wines - Merryvale Vineyards
CABERNET WINE - Salad dressings—bottled - Kozlowski Farms Inc.
CABEZON - Office supplies - Faber-Castell Corp.
CA'BIANCA - Wines ☆ - Prestige Wine Imports Corp.
CABIBE - Cigars - Cabibe, Inc.
CABIN - Cigarettes ☆ - Japan Tobacco Inc.
CABIN - Lighting equipment—boat and ship - Imtra Corp.
CABIN - Slippers ☆ - Acorn
CABIN COMFORT - Windshields—plastic - Tech-Tool Plastics, Inc.
CABIN CRAFT - Prefabricated buildings—wood ☆ - Log Cabin Homes Ltd.
CABIN CRAFTS - Floor coverings—carpet and rugs - Cabin Crafts Carpets
CABIN CREEK - Apparel—women's - J.C. Penney Co., Inc.
CABIN FEVER - Videos - UST Enterprises Inc.
CABIN FEVER CRAFTS, INC. - Christmas decorations - Cabin Fever Crafts, Inc.
CABIN KENNEL - Pet products - Doskocil Manufacturing Co., Inc.
CABIN LIGHT PANELS - Photographic equipment - Mamiya America Corp.
CABIN LOUPES - Photographic equipment - Mamiya America Corp.
CABIN MILD - Cigarettes - Japan Tobacco Inc.
CABIN SKIFF - Boats - Glen-L Marine Designs
CABIN-SOLE - Plywood - Harbor Sales Co.
CABIN STILL - Whiskey - United Distillers of North America
CABIN STRIP - Flooring—hardwood - Memphis Hardwood Flooring Co.
CABINART - Furniture - Cabinart Inc.
CABINET ACCENTS - Hardware ☆ - Amerock Corp.

CABINET CRAFTSMAN COLLECTION - Furniture - Pilliod Co.
CABINET JEWELRY - Hardware ☆ - Nutone Inc.
CABINET MAGIC - Furniture polish and wax - Magic American Corp.
CABINET MAID - Cabinets - Clairson International Corp.
CABINET MAKERS - Waxes—sealing - J. Goddard & Sons
CABINET WORLD - Advertising agencies - Door-Master Corp.
CABINETMAKER COLLECTION - Furniture - Lane Co. Inc.
CABINETMATE - Housewares - Lescoa Inc.
CABINETPAK - Cabinets - Homewood Industries Inc.
CABINWEAR - Fabrics - GPS, Inc.
CABIPOLE - Antennas - Unarco Industries UNR
CABIRIA - Coffee makers—electric - Zyliss USA Inc.
CABL-BUS - Hardware - Mphusky Corp.
CABLE - Bathing suits - Catalina
CABLE - Pianos - Aeolian Pianos Inc.
CABLE & CO. - Footwear—men's - Cable & Co.
CABLE & LABOR$AVER - Racks - DGW/RDP Manufacturing, Inc.
CABLE CADDY - Cables - Cable Design Technologies, Inc.
CABLE CAR - Bakery products - National Baking Div.
CABLE CAR - Beverages—malt - Golden Pacific Brewing Co., Inc.
CABLE CAR - Teas - San Francisco Herb & Natural Food Co.
CABLE CAR CANDIES - Candy - Core-Mark International, Inc.
CABLE CAR KNITS - Crocheted and knitted items ☆ - Saha-Union International USA Inc.
CABLE CLASSICS - Gloves - Aris Isotoner Inc.
CABLE CLEAN - Cleaning preparations - CRC Chemicals USA/Siloo
CABLE CLIP - Fasteners—snap - Silver St. Inc.
CABLE CORP - Cables—coaxial - Santa Rosa Folk Guitar Co.
CABLE CORP - Musical instrument accessories - Cable Corp.
CABLE-CRAFT - Musical instrument accessories - VMI Industries
CABLE DESIGN - Wire—insulated - General Cable Corp.
CABLE DUCK - Computer peripheral equipment - MicroComputer Accessories Inc.
CABLE-FLEX - Optical services ☆ - Universal/Univis Inc.
CABLE GLIDER - Scissors—hand-operated - Condux International Inc.
CABLE IN CABLE TV, THE - Cables—fiber optic - Comm/Scope Inc.
CABLE INNOVATIONS - Cable line products - Cable Innovations, Inc.
CABLE INNOVATIONS - Satellite receivers - Gerrold General Instrument Corp.
CABLE-LINE - Electronic equipment - Perma Power Electronics Inc.
CABLE-MATIC - Microphones - Hamilton Electronics Corp.
CABLE 'N CLAMP - Christmas tree stands - HMS Manufacturing Co.
CABLE-NELSON - Pianos ☆ - Everett Piano Co.
CABLE PHONE - Telephones - Genral Instrument Corp.
CABLE-POST - Binders - Dennison National Co.
CABLE PULLER - Scissors—hand-operated - Condux International Inc.
CABLE-Q - Audiocable tester - InterFax Inc.
CABLE RIGHT - Wiring devices - Siemon Co.
CABLE SAFE - Cables - Kirkhill Rubber Co.
CABLE SNAPPER - Scissors—hand-operated ☆ - Condux International Inc.
CABLE SPEC - Electronic equipment - Qintar, Inc.
CABLE SYSTEMS INTERNATIONAL - Communications equipment - Cable Systems International Inc.
CABLE TENSIOMETER - Ships—sailing vessels - Rudolph E. Krueger Co.
CABLE-TEX - Cables - Wolf Imports
CABLE TO-GO - Transmitting apparatus - Pro Brand International, Inc.
CABLE WORKS - Bathing suits ☆ - Jantzen Inc.
CABLECURE - Chemicals - Dow Corning Corp.
CABLEEYE - Electronic equipment - Cami Research Inc.
CABLELINK - Electronic equipment - Teltone Corp.
CABLEMAP - Computer software - 21st Century Innovations, Inc.
CABLEMETER - Electrical testing instruments - Fluke Corp.
CABLENET - Broadcasting stations—cable television - Cable Television Laboratories, Inc.
CABLESCAN - Measuring instruments - Eubanks Engineering Co.
CABLESPAN - Digital encoders - Tellabs Operations, Inc.
CABLETOWN - Recording label - Dagene/Cabletown Corp.
CABLETRON SYSTEMS - Computer hardware - Cabletron Systems, Inc.
CABLEUPS - Power transformers - Alpha Technologies Inc.
CABLEVIEW - Computer hardware - Adcom Information Services, Inc.
CABLEWARE - Hand tools - Loos & Co., Inc.
CABLEWORKS - Video equipment accessories - Recoton Corp.
CABLON - Varnishes - Pratt & Lambert, Inc. (Specialty Products Div.)
CABLON-FLEX - Medical apparatus - Cabot Development
CABMAN - Computer software - Corporate Connectivity Resources, Inc.
CABMATE - Automotive parts and accessories - Link Manufacturing, Ltd.
CABMATE - Motor vehicle parts and accessories - Leer Inc.

CABNETRIM - Wood products - Waddell Manufacturing Co.
CABO - Fruits and vegetables - Lakeview Farms
CABO - Sunglasses - Cat Harbor Boats Inc.
CABO DE HORNOS - Wines - Shaw-Ross International Importers
CABO RICO - Ships–sailing vessels - Cabo Rico Yachts Inc.
CABO RICO PILOT - Ships–sailing vessels - Cabo Rico Yachts Inc.
CABO WABO CANTINA - Apparel–athletic - Cabo Wabo Joint Venture
CABOCHARD - Colognes - Gary Farn Ltd.
CABOCHON - Dinnerware–glass - Nikko Ceramics Inc.
CABOFLEX - Plugs–ear - Aearo Co.
CABOODLES - Boxes - Plano Molding Co.
CABOODLES - Makeup brushes and manicure tools - London International U.S. Holdings
CABOODLES LIQUID METALLICS - Plastics - Plano Molding Co.
CABOOSE - Apparel and accessories - RHG Ltd.
CABOOSE - Trailers–travel - Coleman Co., Inc.
CABOOSE EXPRESS - Apparel–athletic - RHG Ltd.
CABOT - Cheese - Cabot Creamery Cooperative, Inc.
CABOT - Paint - Cabot Corp.
CABOT - Skin care products - Cabot Laboratories Inc.
CABOT - Thread - Threads USA Div.
CABOT BLEACHING OIL - Varnishes - Samuel Cabot Inc.
CABOT CASUALS - Knit goods - Coronet Casuals Inc.
CABOT COVE - Furniture - Virginia House Furniture Corp.
CABOT FACTORY FINISH - Paints - Samuel Cabot Inc.
CABOT FINISH - Paints - Samuel Cabot Inc.
CABOT JUNIOR - Recording label ☆ - Peter Pan Industries
CABOT SEMI-SOLID STAIN - Varnishes - Samuel Cabot Inc.
CABOT SQUARE - Floor coverings ☆ - Tarkett, Inc.
CABOT VERMONT - Cheese - Cabot Creamery Cooperative, Inc.
CABOTHANE - Finishing agents ☆ - Samuel Cabot Inc.
CABOTINE - Colognes - Gary Farn Ltd.
CABOT'S - Paints ☆ - Samuel Cabot Inc.
CABOT'S - Skin-care products, cosmetics - Cabot Laboratories Inc.
CABOT'S CREOSOTE - Pigments–paint ☆ - Samuel Cabot Inc.
CABOT'S PRESCRIPTION FOR NAILS - Nail-care products - Cabot Laboratories Inc.
CABOTSTAINS PREMIUM QUALITY - Paints - Samuel Cabot Inc.
CABOUCHON - Tableware–china - Pfaltzgraff Investment Co.
CABOVER - Recreational vehicle dealers - Space Craft Manufacturing Inc.
CABRAIL - Furniture - Larry G. Fox Group, Inc.
CABREA - Motorcycles - Suzuki of America Automotive Corp.
CABRELLI - Handbags - Ronay Inc.
CABRETTA - Golfing equipment - Lynx Golf, Inc.
CABRIATRAK, THE - Awnings - Alpha Productions Inc.
CABRIO - Bicycles - Corsaro Imports Inc.
CABRIO - Boats–motor - Larson Boat Div.
CABRIO - Motor vehicles–automobiles - Volkswagen of America Inc.
CABRIO - Occasional tables ☆ - JDI Group, Inc.
CABRIOLE - Furniture ☆ - Bassett Furniture Industries, Inc.
CABRIOLET - Motor vehicles–automobiles - Audi of America Inc.
CABRIOLET - Motor vehicles–automobiles - Volkswagen of America Inc.
CABRIOLET - Strollers–baby - Aprica Kassai USA Inc.
CABS AND CAPPS - Publisher's imprints - Robert P. Guay
CABSHA - Confections ☆ - R.L. Albert & Son, Inc.
CABX - Telephone apparatus - Teletronics International, Inc.
CAC - Adhesives, sealants, waterproofing product, etc. - Construction Adhesives Inc.
CAC - Apparel and accessories - Claude Apparel Co., Inc.
CACAO - Lipsticks - Cosmair Inc.
CACHAGUA CABERNET - Wines - Durney Winery Corp.
CACHAREL - Apparel and accessories - Phillips-Van Heusen Corp.
CACHAREL - Footwear - G.H. Bass and Co.
CACHAREL - Handbags - Senix Group
CACHAREL - Perfumes - Cosmair Inc.
CACHAREL - Watches - Natico Originals Inc.
CACHE - Computer peripheral equipment - Oxford Molecular Group
CACHE - Flatware ☆ - Yamazaki Tableware Inc.
CACHE - Floor coverings–carpet and rugs - Bloomsburg Carpet Industries
CACHE - Window coverings - Jencraft Corp.
CACHE 24 KARAT - Flatware - Yamazaki Tableware Inc.
CACHE CELLAR - Wines - Cache Cellars
CACHE COOKER - Barbecues and grills - Camp Chef
CACHE DROP - Safes - Armor Safe Technologies
CACHE GOLD ACCENT - Flatware - Yamazaki Tableware Inc.
CACHE PACK - Leather goods - AR Accessories Group Inc.

CACHE SCIENTIFIC - Computer peripheral equipment ☆ - Oxford Molecular Group
CACHE VALLEY - Cheese - Tony Ingoglia Salami and Cheese Co. Inc.
CACHE VALLEY - Cheese - Western Dairymen Cooperative, Inc.
CACHEMIRE - Floor coverings–carpet and rugs - J.L. Benson Co.
CACHEMIRE/KAT - Wallpaper ☆ - Wallquest, Inc.
CACHESYSTEM - Safes - Armor Safe Technologies
CACHET - Dinnerware–glass - Nikko Ceramics Inc.
CACHET - Floor coverings–carpet and rugs - Durkan Patterned Carpets
CACHET - Floor coverings–carpet and rugs - Karastan-Bigelow Inc.
CACHET - Floor coverings–carpet and rugs - Philadelphia Carpets
CACHET - Handbags - St. Thomas Inc.
CACHET - Perfumes - Prince Matchabelli
CACHET - Rubber stamps - Porelon, Inc.
CACHET - Stamps–hand - U.S. Stamp
CACHET - Tablecloths - Town & Country Linen Corp.
CACHET - Tiles–ceramic - Latco Products
CACHET - Tiles–ceramic - Los Angeles Tile Co., Inc.
CACHET - Trailers–travel ☆ - Carriage, Inc.
CACHET COORDINATES - Floor coverings–carpet and rugs ☆ - Callaway Carpets
CACHET NOIR - Perfumes - Prince Matchabelli
CACIQUE - Cheese - Cacique Cheese Co.
CACIQUE - Cigars - Tropical Tobacco, Inc.
CACIQUE RON ANEJO - Rum - Shaw-Ross International Importers
CACKLEBERRY - Eggs - Crystal Farms Inc.
CACOLIV - Veterinary nutritional supplements - Oralx Corp.
CACOTHELINE - Pharmaceutical preparations - City Chemical Corp.
CACTAS - Computer software - Ransco Industries
CACTI - Liquors - Black Prince Distillery, Inc.
CACTINA - Pharmaceutical preparations - Natcon Chemical Co. Inc.
CACTUS - Computer software - Information Builders, Inc.
CACTUS - Printers–computer - Cactus
CACTUS - Sauces - El Paso Chili Co.
CACTUS ANNIE'S - Food products - Crawford Group, Inc.
CACTUS BROTHERS, THE - Recording label - Cactus Brothers
CACTUS CATSUP - Food products - Desert Rose Corp.
CACTUS CEDAR-BERRY - Health care products - Bio-Research Laboratories
CACTUS CITY - Greeting cards - Kersten Bros. Studios
CACTUS CLOTH - Washcloths - Barbara Salomone & Associates, Inc.
CACTUS COLORS - Apparel and accessories - Durango Apparel Inc.
CACTUS COOLER - Beverages–carbonated - Canada Dry Corp.
CACTUS COWBOY - Mustard - Cowboy Vittles & More
CACTUS CUTTER - Toilets–enameled - Kohler Co.
CACTUS FLOWER - Apparel–men's ☆ - Jonbil Inc.
CACTUS FLOWER - Breaded onion - Sizzler International Inc.
CACTUS FLOWER - Cooking utensils–enameled ☆ - National Housewares
CACTUS FLOWER - Toys - Tonka Corp.
CACTUS JACK - Beverages–alcohol - Heaven Hill Distilleries, Inc.
CACTUS JACK'S - Detergents - Cactus Jack's Marketing Corp.
CACTUS JUICE - Beverages–alcohol - Jim Beam Brands Co.
CACTUS JUICE - Plant growth regulators - Security Products Co.
CACTUS JUICE - Shirts - Loco Wear
CACTUS KID - Mats–grass, reed, and jute ☆ - Cactus Mat Manufacturing Co.
CACTUS KID - Pens - Adventure Products, Inc.
CACTUS KID ALUMA-RACK - Mats - Cactus Mat Manufacturing Co.
CACTUS KID TIRE-TEX - Rubber–molded - Cactus Mat Manufacturing Co.
CACTUS MONTEREY - Mats - Cactus Mat Manufacturing Co.
CACTUS PUNCH - Computer peripheral equipment - Cactus Punch, Inc.
CACTUS QUEEN - Beverages–malt - Yellow Rose Brewing Co
CACTUS ROSE - Condiments - Hamilton Foods, Inc.
CACTUSTAT - Mats - Cactus Mat Manufacturing Co.
CAD - Audio equipment - C.T.I. Audio Inc.
CAD-100 - Amplifiers - Cary Audio Design Inc.
CAD-5500 - Compact disc players - Cary Audio Design Inc.
CAD ASSISTANT - Computer programs - Newport Corp.
CAD CANNONDALE - Bicycles - Cannondale Corp.
CAD CONSOLE - Computer software - 21st Century Innovations, Inc.
CAD-CUT - Adhesives and sealants - Stahls' Inc.
CAD-CUT THERMO-FILM - Film - Stahls' Inc.
CAD-CUT THERMO-FLOCK - Fabrics–flock - Stahls' Inc.
CAD/EM - Computer software - Blade Software, Inc.
CAD/IQ - Computer software - International TechneGroup Inc.
CAD LAC - Cosmetics ☆ - Divina Products Co.
CAD OVERLAY - Computer software - Image Systems Technology, Inc.
CAD-TAKEOFF - Computer software - Visual Information Access, Inc.

CAD-V - Lenses–optical ☆ - Capo, Inc.
CADABAG - Golfing equipment - Korex Corp.
CADALOG - Computer software - Daman Products Co.
CADBURY CREME EGGS - Chocolate candy - Peter Paul
CADBURY'S - Candy - Hershey Chocolate USA
CADBURY'S CREAM - Beverages–alcohol ☆ - Shaw-Ross International Importers
CADCO - Plastics film - Cadillac Plastic and Chemical Div.
CADCORNER - See VARITASK
CADD-1 PUMP - Health care products - Sims Deltec, Inc.
CADD-MICRO PUMP - Medical apparatus - Sims Deltec, Inc.
CADD-PCA PUMP - Medical apparatus - Sims Deltec, Inc.
CADD-PLUS PUMP - Health care products - Sims Deltec, Inc.
CADD-PRIZM PUMP - Health care products - Sims Deltec, Inc.
CADD-TPN PUMP - Health care products - Sims Deltec, Inc.
CADDIE - Electronic equipment ☆ - H. Wilson Co.
CADDIECOMMAND - Motorized golf cart ☆ - Kangaroo Golf Ltd.
CADDIESHACK - Flowers, plants, and seeds - Jacklin Seed
CADDIO - Portable radio - Garrett Gadgets Co.
CADDO VALLEY - Water–bottled or canned - Water House
CADDOFAB - Fabrics–nylon - Jaylee Manufacturing
CADDOHYDE - Fabrics–nylon - Jaylee Manufacturing
CADDOTEX - Fabrics–nylon - Jaylee Manufacturing
CADDVIEW - Computer software - Monumental Computer Applications, Inc.
CADDY - Artists' materials - Binney & Smith Inc.
CADDY - Food products machinery - Food Specialties Co. Inc.
CADDY - Golfing equipment - Caddy Co.
CADDY - Golfing equipment - D & M Products
CADDY-ALL - Carts - Carol Ann Wilson
CADDY BRUSH - Golf club brush - Chandler Enterprises
CADDY CORNER - Shelving units–wood - Sally Designs, Ltd.
CADDY CRITTERS - Housewares - Sunshine Industries Inc.
CADDY GOLFWEAR - Apparel and accessories ☆ - Caddy Co.
CADDY PACK - Video games ☆ - Playing Mantis
CADDY PAL - Golfing equipment - Dersley, Inc.
CADDY SACK - Bags - Dunn Manufacturing Corp.
CADDY SACK - Home-health-care products - Intromark Inc.
CADDY SHAFT - Golfing equipment - James F. Moyneur
CADDY WAGON - Golf carts - Korex Corp.
CADDYLAK - Bulletin boards–wood - Cornerstone Direct Corp.
CADDYMASTER - Golf carts - Moore or Les Inc.
CADDYTRAX - Golf bags - Douglas R. Fehan
CADE-GRAYSON - Vegetables–dried - Cade Grayson Co.
CADEAUX - Giftware ☆ - Milton Bradley Co.
CADEAUX - Wines - D. Wingfield Ltd.
CADEAUX DIFFUSION - Toys ☆ - Estus Export-Import
CADENASSO - Wines - Cadenasso Winery
CADENCE - Audio equipment - Cadence Sound Systems Inc.
CADENCE - Computer software - Cadence Design Systems, Inc.
CADENCE - Computer software - Elan Associates (GreenLight Software Division)
CADENCE - Desks ☆ - Domore/DO3
CADENCE - Floor coverings–carpet and rugs - Patrick Carpet Mills
CADENCE - Floor coverings–carpet and rugs ☆ - Playfield International Inc.
CADENCE - Furniture ☆ - Tropitone Furniture Co. Inc.
CADENCE - Furniture–wood ☆ - Century Furniture Co.
CADENCE - Medical apparatus - Camp, Inc.
CADENCE - Recording label - Cadence Communications Group, Inc.
CADENCE - Siding–insulating - Georgia-Pacific Corp.
CADENCE - Transmissions–motor vehicle - E.B.T. Inc.
CADENCE - Wallpaper ☆ - Gilford Corp.
CADENZA - Computer software - Voiceline Inc.
CADENZA - Medical apparatus - Camp, Inc.
CADES COVE - Furniture ☆ - Singer Furniture Co.
CADET - Air purification systems - Simco
CADET - Aircraft ☆ - New Piper Aircraft, Inc.
CADET - Bathroom fittings - American Standard Inc.
CADET - Batteries - Pep Boys Manny, Moe & Jack
CADET - Belts–apparel - Camp, Inc.
CADET - Bicycles - Columbia Manufacturing Inc.
CADET - Boats - Zodiac of North America
CADET - Boats–motor ☆ - Glassmaster Co.
CADET - Firearms, accessories, and parts - Pars International Corp.
CADET - Floor coverings–carpet and rugs ☆ - Customweave Carpets Inc.
CADET - Garden equipment - H.D. Hudson Manufacturing Co.
CADET - Headphones - Hamilton Electronics Corp.

CADET - Industrial machinery - Advantage Engineering, Inc.
CADET - Industrial machinery - Tuthill Corp.
CADET - Infant product - Graco Children's Products
CADET - Medical apparatus - Chase Ergonomics Inc.
CADET - Musical instruments - Ideal Musical Merchandise Co.
CADET - Paints, enamels ☆ - Cook and Dunn Paint Corp.
CADET - Pet products - Triumph Pet Industries, Inc.
CADET - Rackets–tennis - Dayton Racquet Co. Inc.
CADET - Recording label - Cadet Records Inc.
CADET - Shoe polish - Whittemore Polish Co.
CADET - Staplers - Ace Fastener
CADET - Toys–automobiles - Nylint Toy Corp.
CADET - Trailers–travel ☆ - Coachmen Industries, Inc.
CADET - Watches - Bulova Corp.
CADET GIT-R-STRAP - Musical instrument accessories - Sottile Manufacturing Co.
CADET LYTE - Firearms, accessories, and parts - Welsh Sporting Goods Corp. (Boyt Div.)
CADET PRESTIGE - Faucets - American Standard Inc.
CADET RACE TRAILERS - Trailers - Haulmark Industries, Inc.
CADET, THE - Awnings - Alpha Productions Inc.
CADETS - Cigar boxes–wood - Consolidated Cigar Corp.
CADETTE - Doors–garage ☆ - Raynor Manufacturing Co.
CADETTE - Headphones - Hamilton Electronics Corp.
CADETTE - Skin care products - International Cosmetics and Fragrances, Inc.
CADETTE U.S.A. - Cosmetics - International Cosmetics and Fragrances, Inc.
CADEX - Paints–artists' ☆ - Geo. Sproull Co. Inc.
CADEX - Tables–metal - Dearborn Gage Co.
CADFIX - Computer software - International TechneGroup Inc.
CADIE - Sponges - Cadie Products Corp.
CADILLAC - Apparel–men's ☆ - Carl Neckwear Co. Inc.
CADILLAC - Automotive parts and accessories - General Motors Corp.
CADILLAC - Cases–musical instrument ☆ - Herco Products
CADILLAC - Cigars - G.W. Van Slyke & Horton
CADILLAC - Coffee - Cadillac Coffee Co.
CADILLAC - Decals and transfers - Cadillac Co., Inc.
CADILLAC - Dog food - Menu Foods Inc. Cadillac Foods Div.
CADILLAC - Frames–picture - Frem Corp.
CADILLAC - Jewelry - Monet Jewelers
CADILLAC - Meters–electric - Claussen Engineering, Inc.
CADILLAC - Motor vehicles–automobiles - General Motors Corp. (Cadillac Motor Car Div.)
CADILLAC - Musical instrument accessories - Sottile Manufacturing Co.
CADILLAC - Paints - Talon Paint Inc.
CADILLAC - Shoe accessories - Speen & Co. Inc.
CADILLAC - Shoes - Cadillac Shoe Products Inc.
CADILLAC - Vacuum cleaners and accessories–commercial - Clements National Co.
CADILLAC CLUB - Sunglasses - Cadillac Club Fashions, Inc.
CADILLAC CLUB - Watches - General Motors Corp.
CADILLAC FAJITAS - Food products - Brinker Restaurant Corp.
CADILLAC FOR CATS - Cat food - Menu Foods Inc. Cadillac Foods Div.
CADILLAC ROYALEVEND SUPREME - Coffee - Cadillac Coffee Co.
CADILLAC SUPREME - Microscopes - Cadillac Optical Corp.
CADILLAC WHITE - Paints ☆ - United States Refining Co.
CADILLACS AND DINOSAURS - Books–comic - General Motors Corp.
CADIS-PMX - Computer software - Cadis, Inc.
CADIZ - Rings–jewelry - Artcarved Inc.
CADJET - Computer hardware - Encad, Inc.
CADKEY - Computer software - Cadkey, Inc.
CADMANVIEW - Computer software - Bara Inc.
CADMAX - Computer software - Cadmax Corp.
CADMOTION - Computer software - SimSoft Inc.
CADNET - Computer software - Cadnet Corp.
CADO FLO MASTER - Office supplies ☆ - Faber-Castell Corp.
CADON - Fibers–synthetic ☆ - Monsanto Co.
CADORE MODA - Ophthalmic goods - Cadore Moda, Inc.
CADPAK - Computer software - MTI Corp.
CADRE - Ceiling panels - USG Interiors, Inc.
CADRE - Sunglasses ☆ - Corning Inc.
CADRE D'OR - Coffee - Casino North America
CADSYS - Computer storage devices - Spectra-Physics Laserplane, Inc.
CADTASTIC - Computer software - Connally Consulting Inc.
CADTEX - Computer software - Cadtex Corp.
CADUM - Health care products ☆ - Block Drug Co., Inc.
CADUM - Soap - Colgate-Palmolive Co.

☆ = Now out of production

CADVANTAGE - Furniture - Haworth, Inc.
CADY LAKE - Wines - Seven Lakes Vineyard
CAEDMON - Recording label - Harper Audio
CAELIX - Recording label ☆ - Lorenz Creative Services Corp.
CAELYN - Recording label - Eucharist Films Distribution
CAEMINT - Food products - Belle Island International Inc.
CAENIS - Fishing lures - Thomas and Thomas Rodmakers Inc.
CAESAR - Bathroom fixtures - Crane Plumbing/Fiat Products
CAESAR - Computer software - Cycledata Corp.
CAESAR - Dinnerware–glass ☆ - Royal China & Porcelain Companies Inc.
CAESAR - Meat products–beef ☆ - Pierce Foods Corp.
CAESAR - Skin care products - Imperial Inc.
CAESAR - Wallets - Westport Corp.
CAESAR ALESIA - Games ☆ - Avalon Hill Game Co.
CAESAR CARDINI - Salad dressings–bottled - Caesar Cardini Foods
CAESAR CLASSIC KROUTONS - Bread crumbs ☆ - CPC International Inc.
CAESAR RODNEY - Vegetables–frozen - J.G. Townsend Jr. & Co. Inc.
CAESARS - Cigars ☆ - General Cigar Co., Inc.
CAESAR'S - Pasta - Fancy Foods of Virginia Inc.
CAESAR'S - Pasta products - Caesar's Pasta Products Inc.
CAESAR'S - Telephones ☆ - Sun Coast Merchandise Corp.
CAESAR'S BEST - Salad dressings - L. Carolyn Auerbach
CAESAR'S HEAD - Beverages–malt - Reedy River Brewery
CAESAR'S LEGIONS - Games ☆ - Avalon Hill Game Co.
CAESAR'S PALACE - Floor coverings - Mannington Resilient Floors
CAESARS RUGS - Floor coverings–carpet and rugs - Goldenrise Development, Inc.
CAESARS SANDWICHES - Sandwiches–prepackaged - Little Caesar Enterprises, Inc.
CAESARS SINGLES - Pizzas–frozen - Little Caesar Enterprises, Inc.
CAESARS WOMAN - Perfumes - Caesars World Inc.
CAESARUS - Beverages–malt ☆ - Phoenix Imports Ltd.
CAESY CLINICALLY ADVANCED EDUCATION SYSTEM - Computer software - Advanced Learning Technologies, LLC
CAF/XPRESS - Computer software - Relational Data Services Inc.
CAFACETIN - Pharmaceutical preparations ☆ - JMI-Canton Pharmaceuticals
CAFAMINE - Pharmaceutical preparations ☆ - Legere Pharmaceuticals Inc.
CAFAMINE 2X - Pharmaceutical preparations ☆ - Legere Pharmaceuticals Inc.
CAFE' - Apparel and accessories - Cafe Clothing, Inc.
CAFE - Broadcasting stations–radio - Southwest Suburban Broadcasting, Inc.
CAFE - Candy ☆ - Van Melle Inc.
CAFE - Colognes - Taramax U.S.A., Inc.
CAFE - Floor coverings - Congoleum Corp.
CAFE - Floor coverings–carpet and rugs ☆ - Trans-Ocean Import Co. Inc.
CAFE - Recording label ☆ - Mobile Fidelity Sound Lab
CAFE - Wines - Frick Winery
CAFE 085 - Leather - Classic Soft Trim Inc.
CAFE 1686 - Coffee - Kraft Foods, Inc.
CAFE ALTURA - Coffee - Clean Foods Inc.
CAFE APRICOT DREAM - Coffee ☆ - R.C. Bigelow, Inc.
CAFE ARRAY - Coffee - Geneva Industries, Inc.
CAFE ARTS - Pottery products - Henriksen Imports Inc.
CAFE AU CHOCOLAT - Coffee ☆ - R.C. Bigelow, Inc.
CAFE AU RHUM - Nail care products - Cosmair Inc.
CAFE BISCOTTI - Bakery products - Nonni's, Corp.
CAFE BISTROS - Food products - Tony's Pizza Service
CAFE BLUE - Apparel and accessories - AJ Brandon
CAFE BOEUF - Aprons ☆ - Garrison Keillor
CAFE BORDEAUX - Furniture ☆ - Bassett Furniture Industries, Inc.
CAFE BUSTELO - Coffee - Bustelo Coffee Co.
CAFE BUSTELO - Coffee - Tetley Inc.
CAFE BUSTELO CAPPUCCINO - Coffee - Bustelo Coffee Co.
CAFE CANTON - Food products ☆ - Multi-National Food Service
CAFE CARIBE - Coffee - Coffee Holding Co.
CAFE CARMEL - Coffee - Coffee Beanery Ltd.
CAFE CHECKS - Fabrics - Dan River Inc.
CAFE CHIC - Coffee - Alcacha Distribution
CAFE CHOICE - Coffee - Papy's Foods, Inc.
CAFE CINNAMON SWIRL - Coffee ☆ - R.C. Bigelow, Inc.
CAFE CLASSICS - Food products - Conagra, Inc.
CAFE COLA - Beverages–carbonated - Somojo, Inc.
CAFE COLLECTION - Dinnerware - Corning Inc.
CAFE CONCEPTS - Coffee - United Restaurant Equipment, Inc.
CAFE CONTINENTAL - Coffee - Continental Coffee Products Co.
CAFE COPACABANA - Coffee - Cafe Copacabana Enterprises Inc.
CAFE CUBANEY - Coffee - Nature's Finest Products Inc.

CAFE CUP - Coffee - Cafe Cup Corp.
CAFE DE TODD - Coffee - Cafe de Todd USA Inc.
CAFE DECARLO NATURAL - Coffee - Lehmann Farms, Inc.
CAFE DEL MUNDO - Coffee - Cafe Del Mundo
CAFE DIABLO - Coffee - Coffee Beanery Ltd.
CAFE D'ORO - Coffee ☆ - Tidelands Sales Co. Inc.
CAFE DU JOUR - Coffee - Fairwinds Gourmet Coffee Co. Inc.
CAFE EL MORRO - Coffee - Pan American Coffee Co., Inc.
CAFE EL PICO - Coffee - Bustelo Coffee Co.
CAFE EL PICO - Coffee - Tetley Inc.
CAFE ENCORE - Coffee ☆ - Tostino Coffee Roasters
CAFE ESPRESSO EL PARAISO - Coffee - Coffea Arabica, Inc.
CAFE FANNY - Granola - Chez Panisse
CAFE FLAVOUR - Coffee makers–electric ☆ - Philips Electronics North America Corp.
CAFE FRANCAIS VANILLE - Coffee - Western Family Foods, Inc.
CAFE GENEVA - Food products - John Christen Corp.
CAFE GLACE - Ice cream - Sunberry Farms
CAFE GODIVA - Coffee - Godiva Chocolatier
CAFE GODIVA - Syrup - Godiva Chocolatier, Inc.
CAFE GOURMET - Coffee makers–electric ☆ - Philips Electronics North America Corp.
CAFE GOYA - Coffee - Goya Foods, Inc.
CAFE GRIND - Spices and extracts ☆ - McCormick & Co., Inc.
CAFE HAG - Coffee - Gilway Co. Ltd.
CAFE JAVA - Coffee - Fountain Industries Co.
CAFE KONA - Coffee - Brothers Gourmet Products, Inc.
CAFE LATINO - Coffee - Roma Export Inc.
CAFE LATTE KRISPY - Candy - See's Candy Shops, Inc.
CAFE LE LLAVE ESPRESSO - Coffee - F. Gavina and Sons Inc.
CAFE LE SEMEUSE - Coffee - Trade Marc Group Inc.
CAFE LIBRE - Coffee - Equal Exchange Inc.
CAFE LICORICE STICK - Coffee ☆ - R.C. Bigelow, Inc.
CAFE MAGIC - Coffee-flavoring wafers - Advanced Food Technologies
CAFE MEXICANO - Coffee - Nature's Finest Products Inc.
CAFE MEXICO - Coffee - Equal Exchange Inc.
CAFE MEXICO - Food products - Multi-National Food Service
CAFE MEXICO - Food products - Tony's Pizza Service
CAFE MINT SUPREME - Coffee ☆ - R.C. Bigelow, Inc.
CAFE' MONA LISA - Coffee - Bag-Pak, Inc.
CAFE' NERVOSA - Apparel and accessories - Paramount Pictures Corp.
CAFE NICA - Coffee - Equal Exchange Inc.
CAFE NOEL - Coffee - East Indies Coffee & Tea Co.
CAFE OQUENDO - Coffee - Bustelo Coffee Co.
CAFE ORANGE DELIGHT - Coffee ☆ - R.C. Bigelow, Inc.
CAFE ORIFLAMA - Coffee - Flama De Oro, SA
CAFE ORLEANS - Food products ☆ - Multi-National Food Service
CAFE PARISIEN - Coffee - De Choix Specialty Foods Co.
CAFE PASQUAL'S - Coffee beans - Cafe Pasqual's
CAFE PEKING - Food products - Multi-National Food Service
CAFE PERU - Coffee - Equal Exchange Inc.
CAFE PIERRE - Sandwiches–prepackaged ☆ - Hudson Foods, Inc.
CAFE PRESSO - Coffee makers–electric - Robert Krups North America
CAFE QUICK - Vending machines - Cafe Quick Enterprises Inc.
CAFE RACER - Apparel–athletic - Dangerous Design
CAFE RECORDS - Recording label - Stephen Bruce
CAFE ROYAL - Dinnerware–glass - Franciscan by Johnson Brothers, USA, Inc.
CAFE ROYAL - Food products - Sara Lee Corp.
CAFE ROYALE - Coffee makers–electric ☆ - Philips Electronics North America Corp.
CAFE SABOR DE CUBA - Coffee - Timothy J. Sheehan
CAFE SALVADOR - Coffee - Cafe Salvador Inc.
CAFE SELECT - Coffee - Southland Corp.
CAFE SERRANOS AND CANTINA - Sauces - Serranos Cafe Services, Inc.
CAFE SOCIETY - Coffee - Convergence, Inc.
CAFE SOLE - Spices and extracts - Spice Hunter
CAFE SPECIAL - Coffee - Community Coffee Co., Inc.
CAFE SPERL - Coffee - Kraft Foods, Inc.
CAFE SUISSE - Coffee ☆ - Clean Foods Inc.
CAFE SUPREME - Coffee - Try Coffee Group Ltd.
CAFE SUPREME REX - See **THOMAS ESTATE BLEND**
CAFE SUPREMO ESPRESSO - Coffee - Coffee Holding Co.
CAFE SYSTEM 7 - Vending machines - Unidynamics Corp.
CAFE TIERRA - Coffee - Coffee Bean International, Inc.
CAFE TRAYS - Cookware - Carlisle Foodservice Products, Inc.

CAFE TU TU TANGO - Apparel - Cafe Tu Tu Tango
CAFE TWISTS - Pastries - Barry Yellen
CAFE VALU - Bakery products - Super Valu Inc.
CAFE VIENNA - Coffee - Western Family Foods, Inc.
CAFE VIVO - Coffee - Cowan & Fransman
CAFECON - Pharmaceutical preparations - Consolidated Midland Corp.
CAFERGOT - Pharmaceutical preparations - Sandoz Pharmaceuticals Corp.
CAFERLINE - Pharmaceutical preparations - Goldline Laboratories, Inc.
CAFE'S COLOMBIA - Beverages–alcohol - Blair Importers Ltd.
CAFESAN - Coffee makers–electric - Sanyo Fisher (USA) Corp.
CAFETERIA ADVENTURES - Food products ☆ - Pierre Frozen Foods Inc.
CAFETERIA STYLE - Rice ☆ - China Doll, Inc.
CAFETRATE - Pharmaceutical preparations ☆ - Schein Pharmaceutical Inc.
CAFF - Glass–flat - Dlubak Bending Studios
CAFFE ACORTO - Coffee makers–electric - Caffe Acorto Inc.
CAFFE APPASSIONATO - Coffee - Caffe Appassionato, Inc.
CAFFE BAR - Coffee makers–electric - Salton/Maxim Housewares, Inc.
CAFFE CLASSICO - Ice cream/yogurt shop franchise - Caffe Classico
CAFFE D'ARTE - Coffee - 1 Uno Espresso, Inc.
CAFFE DI TREVI - Liquors - Chatham Imports, Inc.
CAFFE D'VITA - Coffee - Brad Barry Co. Ltd.
CAFFE ESPRESS - Coffee - Caffe Espress Corp.
CAFFE ESPRESSO - Coffee makers–electric - Benjamin & Medwin Inc.
CAFFE FANTASTICO - Coffee - National Fruit Flavor Co.
CAFFE GEMMA - Coffee - Starbucks Corp.
CAFFE GIO - Coffee - Dayton Hudson Corp.
CAFFE-ITALIA - Cooking utensils–aluminum - Himark Enterprises Inc.
CAFFE LATTE CASCADE - Coffee - Coffee Beanery Ltd.
CAFFE LEONE - Coffee - Ellis Coffee Co.
CAFFE LOLITA - Beverages–alcohol - David Sherman Corp.
CAFFE PICOLO'S ESPRESSO - Coffee - C & C Coffee, Inc.
CAFFE RISTAURANTE - Coffee makers–electric - Mr. Coffee, Inc.
CAFFE SIGNORE - Coffee - Rowland Coffee Roasters, Inc.
CAFFE VENEZIA - Coffee - Oasis Coffee Co., Inc.
CAFFE VERONA - Coffee - Starbucks Corp.
CAFFE VERONA STARBUCKS COFFEE 80/20 BLEND - Coffee - Starbucks Corp.
CAFFECCINO - Coffee - Cafecc Tea & Sales Inc.
CAFFEDRINE - Pharmaceutical preparations - Thompson Medical Co., Inc.
CAFFEINDS - Coffee - Fiedler Romberg Partnership
CAFFEINE-FREE COCA-COLA CLASSIC - Beverages–carbonated - Coca-Cola Co.
CAFFEINE-FREE COKE LIGHT - Beverages–carbonated - Coca-Cola Co.
CAFFEINE-FREE DIET COKE - Beverages–carbonated - Coca-Cola Co.
CAFFEINE FREE DIET PEPSI-COLA - Beverages–carbonated - Pepsi-Cola Co.
CAFFEINE FREE DR. PEPPER - Beverages–carbonated - Dr. Pepper/Seven Up, Inc.
CAFFEINE FREE PEPSI-COLA - Beverages–carbonated - Pepsi-Cola Co.
CAFFEINE-FREE TAB - Beverages–carbonated - Coca-Cola Co.
CAFFEINE MACHINE - Coffee makers–electric - Mark M. Crawford
CAFFEINNATION - Coffee - Lemar Distribution Enterprises Inc.
CAFFETO - Beverages–alcohol - Paterno Imports, Ltd.
CAFFINO - Coffee - E.X.S. Inc.
CAFFREE - Toothpaste - Block Drug Co. Inc.
CAFI - Dairy products - Caldwell Farms Inc.
CAFI TODD - Coffee - Chase Collection, Inc.
CAFIX - Coffee substitutes - InterNatural Foods
CAFLISCH SCRIPT - Computer software - Adobe Systems Inc.
CAFLO 300 - Chemical preparations - United States Mineral Products Co.
CAFLO 400 - Chemical preparations - United States Mineral Products Co.
CAFLO 800 - Chemical preparations - United States Mineral Products Co.
CAFLO BLAZE SHIELD II - Chemical preparations - United States Mineral Products Co.
CAFLO BOND SEAL - Chemical preparations - United States Mineral Products Co.
CAFLO BOND SEAL X - Chemical preparations - United States Mineral Products Co.
CAFLO FENDOLITE II - Chemical preparations - United States Mineral Products Co.
CAFLO QWIK-SET - Chemical preparations - United States Mineral Products Co.
CAFLO SPRAYFILM - Chemical preparations - United States Mineral Products Co.
CAFLO SPRAYFILM WB - Chemical preparations - United States Mineral Products Co.

CAFLO TPS - Chemical preparations - United States Mineral Products Co.
CAG AMERICAN - Apparel and accessories - Negro Leagues Baseball Museum, Inc.
CAGE - Footwear - Fila USA, Inc.
CAGE CONNECTION - Pet products - Blue Ribbon Pet Products, Inc.
CAGE CRAFT - Pet products - Penn-Plax, Inc.
CAGE FREE MOARK'S HAPPY HENS - Eggs - Moark Productions, Inc.
CAGE FRESH - Pet products ☆ - Pets International, Ltd.
CAGE-KLENZ - Pet products - Merck & Co., Inc. (Merck Research Laboratories)
CAGE LITE - Floodlights - Galaxy Leasing Corp.
CAGE-MATE - Pet products - Next to Nature
CAGE NUT PUZZLE - Pet products - JungleTalk Inc.
CAGE RATTLER - Apparel and accessories - Gerald F. Jaynes
CAGE TOPPERS - Pet products - Emerald Bird Caddy
CAGEGUARD - Veterinary pharmaceutical preparations - Mardel Laboratories, Inc.
CAGEMASTER - Electromedical apparatus - Metropolitan Vacuum Cleaner Co. Inc.
CAGETAINER - Tanks–storage - Hoover Group, Inc.
CAGIVA - Motorcycles - Cagiva of North America
CAGLE'S - Meat products–poultry - Cagle's Inc.
CAGNASSO - Wines - Cagnasso Winery
CA$H - Chewing gum ☆ - Amurol Confections Co.
CA$H CARD$ - Greeting cards - Cash Cards Enterprises
CA$H GRAF - Computer software - R.J. Pearce, Inc.
CA$H KEEPER - Binders - Linda Hackett
CA$H STASHERS - Toys - Rebecca A. Smith
CAHABA - Floor coverings - Miller and Co. Inc.
CA$HGRAF CHECKS PLUS - Computer software - Ca$Hgraf Software Inc.
CA$HGRAF HOME OFFICE PLUS - Computer software - Ca$Hgraf Software Inc.
CA$HGRAF PERSONAL INVENTORY PLUS - Computer software - Ca$Hgraf Software Inc.
CAHILL - Confections - Sunset Food & Beverage Corp.
CAHILL - Fishing tackle - Maurice Sporting Goods, Inc.
CAHNERS MANUFACTURING MARKETPLACE - Computer hardware - Reed Elsevier Inc.
CAHOKIA - Flour–blended - Cahokia Flour Co.
CAHOKIA PRIDE - Food products - Cahokia Flour Co.
CAHOON FARMS - Fruits–frozen - Cahoon Farms Inc.
CAHUENGA - Guitars - European Crafts/USA
CAI - Figurines ☆ - Cast Art Industries, Inc.
CAICARA - Vegetables–canned ☆ - Liberty Richter Inc.
CAICE - Computer software - AGA Computer Services Inc.
CAICOS - Apparel–women's - Caicos Swimwear Corp.
CAIG - Chemical preparations - ARS Electronics
CAILEAN MOR - Floor coverings–carpet and rugs ☆ - Olympic Carpets Inc.
CAIN CELLARS - Wines - Cain Cellars Inc.
CAIN FIVE - Wines - Cain Cellars Inc.
CAINS - Coffee - Nestle Beverage Co.
CAIN'S - Salad dressings–bottled - John E. Cain Co.
CAIN'S COUNTRY - Salad dressings–bottled - John E. Cain Co.
CAINS COUNTRY - Salad dressings–bottled - Cains Foods, Inc.
CAIRN - Gnome figurines - Cairn Studio Ltd.
CAIRNS RS1 - Firefighting suits - Cairns Trademark Trust
CAIRNS SWIMMER - Fishing lures - Boone Bait Co. Inc.
CAIRO BEAUTIES - Pickles - W.B. Roddenbery Co., Inc.
CAIROPHONE - Recording label - Rashid Sales Co.
CAIS - Computer software - Danka Corp.
CAISE - Computer software - AGA Computer Services Inc.
CAITHNESS - Glass products - Caithness Glass, Inc.
CAITHNESS - Glassware–household ☆ - Leland Limited Inc.
CAITLYN SCOTT - Apparel–children's - Kids R Us Co.
CAJA-HOLLAND - Juvenile product - International Imports
CAJE - Figurines - Andre M. Lugo
CAJETA CELEYA - Confections - Rartar Corp.
CAJON T-SEAL - Couplings - Swagelok Co.
CAJUN - Accordions - Castiglione Accordion
CAJUN - Tarpaulins - Foster Corp.
CAJUN - Toys–models ☆ - Estes Industries
CAJUN AUJUS 7 - Spices and extracts - Trappey's Fine Foods Inc.
CAJUN BEGINNINGS - Soups–mixes ☆ - Bon Melange Inc.
CAJUN BITES - Food products - Bodin Foods Inc.
CAJUN BOY - Meat products - Baudin's Sausage Kitchen, Inc.
CAJUN CHEF - Pickles - Cajun Chef Products Inc.

CAJUN CLASSICS - Recording label - Master-Trak Sound Recorders
CAJUN COOKERS - Seafood products–fresh or frozen - Bryan Foods, Inc.
CAJUN COOKERY - Seasonings - Autin's Cajun Cookery
CAJUN COOKIN' - Dinners–frozen - Pet Inc.
CAJUN COUNTRY - Rice - Falcon Rice Mill Inc.
CAJUN CREATIONS - Seafood products–fresh or frozen - Cajun Creations Inc.
CAJUN CREOLE COFFEE - Coffee - Cajun Creole Products Inc.
CAJUN CREOLE COFFEE & CHICORY - Coffee - Cajun Creole Products Inc.
CAJUN CREOLE HOT NUTS - Nuts–salted, roasted, cooked, or canned - Cajun Creole Products Inc.
CAJUN GOLF - Towels - Cajun Sports Gear, Inc.
CAJUN HEARTLAND USA - Jewelry - Cajun Heartland USA Inc.
CAJUN HEAT - Vegetables–frozen - McCain Ellio's Foods, Inc.
CAJUN HOLLAR - Meat products - John Foshee
CAJUN HOLLER - Jams and jellies - J & B Sausage Co., Inc.
CAJUN HOUSE - Sausages - Savoie's Sausage & Food Products, Inc.
CAJUN JACK SAUCE - Food products - Frank Sbragia FGS Food Corp.
CAJUN KING - Seasonings - Bruce Foods Corp.
CAJUN KING - Seasonings ✰ - Louisiana Boyel Seafood, Inc.
CAJUN LADY - Food products - Vince's Seafood
CAJUN LAND - Seasonings - Deep South Blenders
CAJUN LITE - Meat products–poultry - BJ Acquisition Corp.
CAJUN MADE - Golfing equipment - Cajun Made Golf Products Inc.
CAJUN MARINADE INJECTOR - Kitchenware–plastic - Cajun Injector, Inc.
CAJUN! MEAN DEVIL WOMAN - Spices and extracts - R & H New Orleans Cajun Products Inc.
CAJUN MIX - Snack foods - Glico Harmony Foods Corp.
CAJUN ORIGINAL - Rice - Estherwood Rice Sales
CAJUN PRIZE - Food products - Manda Fine Meats
CAJUN QUEEN - Accordions ✰ - Southern Highland Dulcimers & Accordions Ltd.
CAJUN QUEEN - Meat products–beef - Thompson Packers Inc.
CAJUN QUICK - Seasonings - McCormick & Co., Inc.
CAJUN ROYAL - Food products ✰ - Bodin Foods Inc.
CAJUN SLICK WILDLIFE PRODUCTS, INC. - Fishing lures - Cajun Slick Wildlife Products, Inc.
CAJUN STYLE - Rice - Falcon Rice Mill Inc.
CAJUNITE - Bauxite - Kaiser Aluminum & Chemical Corp.
CAJUN'S NU GLASS - Stain removers - Cajun's NuGlass Inc.
CAJUPUT - Pharmaceutical preparations - City Chemical Corp.
CAK-A-PIPE - Pipe cleaners - Buescher's Industries Inc.
CAKAROME - Hair care products ✰ - Givaudan-Roure Corp.
CAKE BREAKER - Cutlery ✰ - C.J. Schneider Manufacturing Co. Inc.
CAKE CART - Cakes–frozen - Sara Lee Corp.
CAKE COOL - Novelty items ✰ - Sell-O Manufacturing Inc.
CAKE CRAFT - Craft supplies - Wilton Industries, Inc.
CAKE CRITTERS - Bakery products - Wetterau Inc.
CAKE DELIGHTS - Cakes - Interstate Brands Corp.
CAKE DOCTOR DOC, THE - Cakes - Coast Novelty Manufacturing Co.
CAKE KEEPER - Containers ✰ - Nordic Ware
CAKE-MATE - Candles - McCormick & Co., Inc.
CAKE MATE - Confections - Signature Brands, LLC
CAKE SENSATIONS - Cakes - Saramar Corp.
CAKE SUPREME - Cakes–frozen - Pepperidge Farm Inc.
CAKE TOWERS - Glassware–household - Van Horn Hayward
CAKE WALK - Candy - Hershey Foods Corp.
CAKEBREAD CELLARS - Wines - Cakebread Cellars, Inc.
CAKEBREAD CELLARS - Wines - Kobrand Corp.
CAKES TO GO - Bakery products - Interstate Brands Corp.
CAKETTS - Cakes - Vitafort International Corp.
CAKIES - Cookies - Mrs. Fields Development Corp.
CAL - Beverages–alcohol - White Rock Distilleries Inc.
CAL - Meat products–beef - Ranch Hand Foods Inc.
CAL - Mops - Piedmont Mop Co.
CAL-1000 - Audio equipment - Clarion Corp. of America
CAL-AID - Veterinary pharmaceutical preparations - Dr. Larson's Teat Tube Co.
CAL-ALOE - Juices - Real Aloe Co.
CAL ASCORBS - Vitamins and nutritional supplements - Alacer Co.
CAL BEST - Food products - Oh Boy Corp.
CAL-BID - Vitamins and nutritional supplements - Geriatric Pharmaceutical Corp.
CAL-BRAND - Steel springs–railroad - Needlecraft Industries
CAL-BRITE - Cleaning preparations - Nu-Calgon Wholesaler, Inc.
CAL-C-BATE - Health care products ✰ - Kay Pharmacal Co. Inc.
CAL-C-FRESH - Veterinary nutritional supplements - Vets Plus Inc.

CAL-C-VESCENCE - Vitamins and nutritional supplements - Triarco Industries, Inc.
CAL-CADDY - Cosmetics ✰ - Marianna Imports, Inc.
CAL-CAP - Fireplace equipment - Bernard Dalsin Manufacturing
CAL CHECK - Computer software - Hunter Engineering Co.
CAL CHLOR - Chemical preparations - Chem Lab Products, Inc.
CAL-CLUB - Food products ✰ - Kern Industries
CAL-CONTROL SLICES - Ice cream - Lipton Investments, Inc.
CAL-CORD - Extension cords - Pacific Electricord Co.
CAL-COTER - Paints - Touraine Paints Inc.
CAL-CRAFT - Apparel and accessories - California Manufacturing Co. Inc.
CAL-CREST - Apparel and accessories ✰ - California Manufacturing Co. Inc.
CAL CRU - Apparel and accessories - Granite Knitwear Inc.
CAL-CURL - Cosmetics - RBI Distributors
CAL-CUTTA - Dairy products - Sani-Dairy
CAL-D-MINT - Pharmaceutical preparations - Enzyme Process Co. Inc.
CAL-D-TRONS - Pet products - Lambert-Kay
CAL DATE - Dates - Dole Dried Fruit & Nut Co.
CAL-DEXTRO - Veterinary product - American Home Products Corp.
CAL DRENCH PLUS - Agricultural products - C & G Products, Inc.
CAL FAME - Juices - Paramount Citrus Association
CAL FIG - Fruits and vegetables - J. & R. Debenedetto Orchards, Inc.
CAL FLEX - Rakes - California Flexrake Corp.
CAL-FRUIT - Fruits–frozen - Cal-Fruit (Frozen Foods Div.)
CAL GLORY - Juices - Agrigold Juice Products
CAL-GRASS - Flowers, plants, and seeds - California Products Corp.
CAL-GRO - Fertilizers - Aluminum Co. of America
CAL-GROVE - Juices - Sunkist Growers Inc.
CAL-HAWK - Tools–power-driven - CTT Tools, Inc.
CAL HEMATINIC IMPROVED - Vitamins and nutritional supplements ✰ - Key Pharmaceuticals Inc.
CAL INDIA - Fruit juice - Cal India Foods International
CAL INK - Inks - Flint Ink Corp.
CAL INTERNATIONAL - Food products ✰ - Galaxy Food Brokers
CAL JET - Chemical preparations - Coastal Industries Inc.
CAL LOCK - Locks–door - Cal Lock, Inc.
CAL LOTTOMASTER - Computer software - SourceView Software International
CAL M - Pharmaceutical preparations - Legere Pharmaceuticals Inc.
CAL-MAG - Vitamins and nutritional supplements - Solaray
CAL-MAG - Vitamins and nutritional supplements ✰ - Ethical Nutrients
CAL MAG ZINC COMPLEX - Vitamins and nutritional supplements - M.M.R.C., Ltd. Co.
CAL-MAID - Juices - Ludford Fruit Products Inc.
CAL-MARK - Truck beds - Aubrey's Recreational Vehicle Center Inc.
CAL-MINT CHEWABLE - Vitamins and nutritional supplements - Freeda Vitamins Inc.
CAL-MOST - Vitamins and nutritional supplements - Reyman Drug Co., Inc.
CAL-NATE-K - Veterinary pharmaceutical preparations - Greever's
CAL-NOR - Pharmaceutical preparations ✰ - Vortech Pharmaceuticals
CAL-O-TAB - Vitamins and nutritional supplements - Alacer Co.
CAL-O-TINT - Wallpaper - Muralo Co. Inc.
CAL OAK - Fireplace equipment - Duraflame, Inc.
CAL-ORO - Fruits and vegetables - Villa Park Orchards Association
CAL-PAC - Skateboards - Cal-Pac, Triad Bicycle Corp.
CAL PAL - Measuring instruments - Thermo Electric Co., Inc.
CAL PAPERBACKS - Publisher's imprints - University of California Press
CAL-PLUS - Computer software - Transmation, Inc.
CAL-PLUS - Vitamins and nutritional supplements - Geriatric Pharmaceutical Corp.
CAL-POWER - Vitamins and nutritional supplements ✰ - Dietary Specialties
CAL-PRENAL - Pharmaceutical preparations ✰ - Vortech Pharmaceuticals
CAL-PRO - Cleaning preparations–household - Grow Group, Inc.
CAL PRO - Fruits–candied ✰ - Cal-Pro Sales
CAL-Q-CLUTCH - Calculators - Buxton Inc.
CAL-QUICK - Vitamins and nutritional supplements - Twinlab
CAL RIPKEN - Sporting goods - Franklin Sports, Inc.
CAL-SAN - Pharmaceutical preparations - Physician Sales & Service
CAL-SHIELD - Coatings - Nu-Calgon Wholesaler, Inc.
CAL-SILICA - Vitamins and nutritional supplements - Nature's Way Products, Inc.
CAL-SNACK - Calcium supplement - Country Life
CAL-SPAN - Pharmaceutical preparations - Alva-Amco Pharmacal Co.
CAL SPAS - Game tables - California Acrylic Industries Inc.
CAL STAR - Olives - Cal Star Olives
CAL-STRIPES - Automotive parts and accessories ✰ - Arlon, Inc.
CAL-STYLE - Furniture ✰ - Masco Corp.

CAL-SUL - Lime and gypsum ☆ - AMPEL Corp.

CAL-SUN - Vegetables–canned - Moody Dunbar Inc.

CAL-SUN - Vegetables–canned - Saticoy Foods Corp.

CAL-SUP - Vitamins and nutritional supplements - Minnesota Mining & Manufacturing Co.

CAL-TIE - Wire - CF and I Steel L.P.

CAL TOGS - Apparel and accessories - Breton Industries

CAL TOGS II - Apparel and accessories - Breton Industries

CAL-TONES - Automotive parts and accessories ☆ - Arlon, Inc.

CAL-TOP - Food products - Pet Inc.

CAL-TRACS - Automotive parts and accessories - John Calvert

CAL-TREAT - Fruits and vegetables ☆ - J.R. Simplot Co.

CAL-TRIM - Automotive parts and accessories ☆ - Arlon, Inc.

CAL-TROL - Pharmaceutical preparations - Lanpar Co.

CAL-TUF - Tempered glass - International Aluminum Corp.

CAL-VALLEY - Juices–frozen - Ludford Fruit Products Inc.

CAL VM - Vitamins and nutritional supplements ☆ - Fibertone Co.

CAL-ZO - Pharmaceutical preparations ☆ - Ulmer Pharmacal Co.

CALA - Recording label - Cala Records, Inc.

CALA-BAY - Wines ☆ - Lipton Investments, Inc.

CALA DI VOLPE - Fabrics–linen - Maytex Mills

CALABANA - Fabrics - Graniteville Co.

CALABANA CLOTH - Fabrics - Astrup Co.

CALABASH - Apparel–children's - Doe Spun Inc.

CALABASH - Seasonings - Calabash Seafood Co., Inc.

CALABATE - Vitamins and nutritional supplements - Oxford Laboratories Inc.

CALABRIA - Pasta - American Italian Pasta Co.

CALABRO - Cheese - Hommus Factory Inc.

CALAC - Varnishes - Perry & Derrick Co.

CALADINA - Wines ☆ - Bardenheier Wine Cellars

CALADIUM BOOSTER - Fertilizers - Pursell Industries, Inc.

CALADRYL - Pharmaceutical preparations - Warner-Wellcome

CALADRYL CLEAR - Pharmaceutical preparations - Warner-Wellcome

CALAFIA CELLARS - Wines - Calafia Wines

CALAHIST - Pharmaceutical preparations - Barre-National, Inc.

CALAIS - Bedding - Ohio Mattress Co.

CALAIS - Bicycles - Columbia Manufacturing Inc.

CALAIS - Blinds–vertical - Tontine/VyTech Industries Inc.

CALAIS - Cabinets ☆ - Aristokraft, Inc.

CALAIS - Carriages–baby - Evenflo Co.

CALAIS - Eyeglasses - Willson/Dalloz Safety

CALAIS - Fireplace equipment - Thermo-Rite Manufacturing Co.

CALAIS - Flatware - Gorham Inc.

CALAIS - Floor coverings–carpet and rugs ☆ - Criterion Mills Inc.

CALAIS - Furniture - Tropitone Furniture Co. Inc.

CALAIS - Furniture - Weiman Co.

CALAIS - Furniture ☆ - Broyhill Furniture Industries, Inc.

CALAIS - Furniture ☆ - Singer Furniture Co.

CALAIS - Wallpaper - Koroseal Wallcoverings

CALAIS RIPPLE - Stationery ☆ - Berkshire Stationery Inc.

CALAIS SPORTS - Bicycles - Columbia Manufacturing Inc.

CALAIS SUPREME - Motor vehicles–automobiles ☆ - General Motors Corp. (Oldsmobile Div.)

CALAIS TOURIST - Bicycles - Columbia Manufacturing Inc.

CALAMAR - Seafood products–fresh or frozen - State Fish Co., Inc.

CALAMARI CRISPS - Fish–canned or cured - Ecrevisse Acadienne USA

CALAMARI KING - Food products - U.S. Freezer Co.

CALAMARI OF CALIFORNIA - Seafood products–fresh or frozen - State Fish Co., Inc.

CALAMARI RINGERS - Seafood products–fresh or frozen - Fish King Processors Inc.

CALAMATA - Salad dressings–bottled - Santa Barbara Olive Co.

CALAMATUM - Pharmaceutical preparations - Blair Laboratories Inc.

CALAMED - Pharmaceutical preparations - Rugby Laboratories Inc.

CALAMITY JANE - Apparel–children's - Mcgregor Corp.

CALAMITY JANE - Watches - Hortex Inc.

CALAMITY JEANS - Apparel and accessories - Coleman Co.

CALAMITY JEANS - Apparel and accessories - Coleman-Frizzell, Inc.

CALAMO - Apparel and accessories - Calamo Silk, Inc.

CALAMO SILK - Fabrics–silk - Calamo Silk, Inc.

CALAMOX - Pharmaceutical preparations - Roberts/Hauck Pharmaceuticals Inc.

CALAMYCIN - Skin care products - Pfeiffer Pharmaceuticals Inc.

CALAN - Pharmaceutical preparations - G. D. Searle & Co.

CALAN IV - Pharmaceutical preparations - G. D. Searle & Co.

CALANDAR CATS - Giftware - Fenton Art Glass Co.

CALANDIA GUIDEBOOK - Games ☆ - Mayfair Games, Inc.

CALANDRE - Perfumes - Paco Rabanne Parfums

CALAPITTER CREATIONS - Playground equipment - Calapitter Creations, Inc.

CALAS - Pharmaceutical preparations - Meridian Diagnostics, Inc.

CALASEPT - Dental equipment - Js Dental Manufacturing, Inc.

CALATO - Drums–musical instruments - J.D. Calato Manufacturing Inc.

CALAVERAS - Olive oil - Calaveras Olive Oil and Land Co., Inc.

CALAVO - Dates - California Redi-Date Co.

CALAVO - Food products ☆ - Calavo Growers of California

CALAVO DIP FIXINS - Food products - Calavo Growers of California

CALAVO LITE - Food products - Calavo Growers of California

CALBA - Apparel and accessories - Eagle Button Inc.

CALBERI - Strawberries - Calberi Inc.

CALBON - Vitamins and nutritional supplements - Econo Med Pharmaceuticals Inc.

CALBONATE - Antacids - Schein Pharmaceutical Inc.

CALC-O-KNIT - Rulers–metal - Scandinavian House Imports Inc.

CALC-U-FOLIO - Notebooks and notepads - Design-A-Day, Inc.

CALCAIRE - Wines - Clos du Bois Wines

CALCEE - Pharmaceutical preparations ☆ - Pasadena Research Laboratories, Inc.

CALCET - Vitamins and nutritional supplements - Mission Pharmacal Co.

CALCET PLUS - Vitamins and nutritional supplements - Mission Pharmacal Co.

CALCI-CHEW - Vitamins and nutritional supplements - R & D Laboratories Inc.

CALCI-FREE - Chemical preparations - Aqua Enhance Inc.

CALCI-MIX - Pharmaceutical preparations - R & D Laboratories Inc.

CALCI-PHOS - Pharmaceutical preparations ☆ - Nutritional Research Associates Inc.

CALCI-SKIM - Milk - Cass-Clay Creamery Inc.

CALCI-SOLVE - Descaler - Nyco Products Co.

CALCIDAY-667 - Vitamins and nutritional supplements - Nature's Bounty, Inc.

CALCIDERM - Skin care products - Garcoa Labs/Vitamin Classics

CALCIDRINE - Cough drops - Abbott Laboratories

CALCIFEROL - Vitamins and nutritional supplements - Schwarz Pharma

CALCIGEST - Vitamins and nutritional supplements - Home Health Products, Inc.

CALCIGIZER - Dietary supplement - Natural Organics, Inc.

CALCIGUM - Vitamins and nutritional supplements - Schering-Plough Healthcare Products

CALCIHAB - Pharmaceutical preparations ☆ - JMI-Canton Pharmaceuticals

CALCIKIDS - Vitamins and nutritional supplements - Health Products Corp.

CALCILAC - Pharmaceutical preparations - Schein Pharmaceutical Inc.

CALCILIT E - Paints - Cloverleaf Paint & Varnish

CALCIMAX - Vitamins and nutritional supplements - Revlon Consumer Products Corp.

CALCIMILK - Milk - Lehigh Valley Dairies Inc.

CALCIMILK - Milk ☆ - Ryan Foods Co.

CALCINATOR - Incinerators–concrete ☆ - Magic Heat Corp.

CALCIOMAR - Vitamins and nutritional supplements - Marlop Pharmaceuticals Inc.

CALCIPET - Veterinary pharmaceutical preparations ☆ - Schering-Plough Animal Health

CALCISALIN - Vitamins and nutritional supplements ☆ - Warner-Lambert Co.

CALCITREL - Antacids - Sterling Winthrop Inc.

CALCIUM 2-AEP - Nutritional supplements ☆ - International Nutrition

CALCIUM 100 - Milk ☆ - Pevely Dairy Co.

CALCIUM 600 - Vitamins and nutritional supplements - Solgar Vitamin and Herb Co., Inc.

CALCIUM ALMOND BLITZ - Vitamins and nutritional supplements - Natural Organics, Inc.

CALCIUM & VITAMIN D3 SUPPLEMENT - Veterinary pharmaceutical preparations - Mardel Laboratories, Inc.

CALCIUM GEL - Nail care products - RTS Laboratories, Inc.

CALCIUM GUARD - Cosmetics - Orly International Inc.

CALCIUM HARDNESS UP - Chemical preparations - Great Lakes Biochemical Co., Inc.

CALCIUM NIGHT - Vitamins and nutritional supplements - Source Naturals

CALCIUM PELLETS - Veterinary pharmaceutical preparations - Mardel Laboratories, Inc.

CALCIUM PLUS - Calcium compounds - Bretney Corp.

CALCIUM RICH ROLAIDS - Antacids - Warner-Lambert Co.

CALCIUM SHIELD - Nail care products - Orly International Inc.

CALCIUM SUPER COMPLEX - Health care products - Futurebiotics

CALCIUM SUPPLEMENT - Veterinary pharmaceutical preparations - Mardel Laboratories, Inc.

CALCLEAN - Cleaning preparations - Nu-Calgon Wholesaler, Inc.

☆ = Now out of production

CALCPAC - Computer software - System Essentials, Inc.
CALCU-TAPE+ - Measuring instruments - Sonin Inc.
CALCU-TAPE - Measuring instruments - Sonin Inc.
CALCUFLOW - Computer software - Baker Hughes Inc.
CALCULATED INDUSTRIES - Calculators - Calculated Industries, Inc.
CALCULATED SKIN CARE - Cosmetics - Janet Sartin Inc.
CALCULATING CREW - Computer software - Edmark Corp.
CALCULATIONS - Floor coverings–carpet and rugs ✰ - Karastan-Bigelow Inc.
CALCULATOR - Pencils ✰ - Empire Berol USA
CALCULATOR COMPANIONS - Calculators - Stokes Publishing Co., Inc.
CALCULATOR TIME & FUN - Toys–electronic - Video Technology U.S. Inc.
CALCULIGHTER - Cigarette lighters - Park Lane Associates, Inc.
CALCULINC SYSTEMS - Computer software - CLS & Associates, Inc.
CALCULITE - Lighting fixtures - Lightolier Inc.
CALCUMETRIC - Metric converter - Success Business Industries, Inc.
CALCUTAPE - Calculators ✰ - Keson Industries Inc.
CALCUTRON - Watches - Bulova Corp.
CALCUTTA - Floor coverings - Congoleum Corp.
CALCUTTA - Floor coverings–carpet and rugs - Newport Carpet Mills Inc.
CALCUTTA - Floor coverings–carpet and rugs ✰ - Rugby Rugs Inc.
CALCUTTA - Golfing equipment - Components Plus, Inc.
CALCUTTA - Tobacco products - Shepherd Tobacco Co.
CALCUTTA - Window shades ✰ - Spring Window Fashions Division, Inc.
CALCUTTA 2 - Ceiling fans - Corbett Lighting, Inc.
CALCUTTA AMERICAN - Ceiling fans - Corbett Lighting, Inc.
CALCWARE - Calculators - da Vinci Technologies Group, Inc.
CALDECORT - Health care products - Fisons Corp.
CALDECORT LIGHT - Health care products - Fisons Corp.
CALDER - Faucets - Kohler Co.
CALDER CONTEMPORARY - Furniture–wood ✰ - Calder Manufacturing Co.
CALDER COUNTRY - Furniture–wood - Calder Manufacturing Co.
CALDER GREENWOOD - Furniture–wood - Calder Manufacturing Co.
CALDERA - Floor coverings–carpet and rugs - Mannington Carpets, Inc.
CALDEROL - Pharmaceutical preparations - Organon Inc.
CALDER'S - Dairy products - Calder Bros. Dairy
CALDESENE - Infant product - Fisons Corp.
CALDEX - Calendars - Gemaco Playing Card Co.
CALDO PRONTO - Soups–mixes - Sanwa Foods Inc.
CALDOR - Gasoline - Tenneco Oil Co.
CALDURA - Fabrics - Southern Mills Inc.
CALDWELL - Floor coverings - Congoleum Corp.
CALDWELL - Gin - Heublein, Inc.
CALDWELL - Hardware - Blaine Window Hardware Inc.
CALDWELL - Linen - FCC Canada, Inc.
CALDWELL - Watches - Bulova Corp.
CALE' COLLECTION OF FLORIDA - Apparel and accessories - Jumer Enterprise
CALE YARBOROUGH - Toys - ERTL Co., Inc.
CALEATE - Pharmaceutical preparations ✰ - ICN Pharmaceuticals Inc.
CALEB C - Jackets - JCE Hebron Corp.
CALEB'S - Cookie dough, cookies - Caleb's Gourmet Cookies
CALECA - Kitchen utensils–aluminum ✰ - Reston Lloyd Ltd.
CALECTRO - Toys–electronic ✰ - GC Thorsen, Inc.
CALEDON HILLS - Wallpaper - Seabrook Wallcoverings, Inc.
CALEDONIA - Apparel and accessories - Caledonia Knitwear Co.
CALEDONIA - Beverages–malt - European Beverage Co., Inc.
CALEDONIA, THE - Golfing equipment - Highlander Golf, Inc.
CALEDONIAN - Tobacco–chewing or smoking - James B. Russell Inc.
CALEM - Wines - Carradale Import Co.
CALEMONA - Juices - Sunkist Growers Inc.
CALENDAR - Apparel and accessories - Calendar, Inc.
CALENDAR - Pencils - General Pencil Co.
CALENDAR FOR SCIENTISTS - Novelty calendars - Instruments for Research and Industry, I2R Inc.
CALENDAR GIRLS - Dolls - Bradley Import Co.
CALENDAR OF MEMORIES - Calendars - American Greetings Corp.
CALENDAR PACK - Jams and jellies - Knott's Berry Farm
CALENDAR PAWS - Pet products - Barkleigh Productions, Inc.
CALENDAR, THE - Computer software - Gamco Industries Inc.
CALENDAR TRAK - Calendars - Cal-Trak, Inc.
CALENDAR WORKS - Computer software - Parsons Technology, Inc.
CALENDARCARDS - Greeting cards - Mac Art Direction
CALENDAREYE - Computer software - Elan Associates (GreenLight Software Division)
CALENDARIA - Calendars - Sormani Inc.
CALENDARMAKER - Computer software - CE Software, Inc.

CALENDARS AND MORE - Computer software - Mindscape Software Inc.
CALENDARS PLUS - Calendars - Graphic Information Systems, Inc.
CALENDARS UNLIMITED - Computer software - Timewise
CALENDATER - Calendars - Success Business Industries, Inc.
CALENDATER - Lighters - Colibri Inc.
CALENDE - Liquors ✰ - United States Distilled Products Co.
CALENDER GIRL - Footwear - Polly of California
CALENDERMETO - Watches - Movado Time Corp.
CALENDESK PAD - Desk sets - Sainberg and Co. Inc.
CALENDIAL - Watches - Bulova Corp.
CALENDOLUX - Watches - Movado Time Corp.
CALENDOMATIC - Watches - Movado Time Corp.
CALENDOODLES - Calendars - Jack Taylor
CALENDOPLAN - Watches - Movado Time Corp.
CALENDOSCOPE - Watches - Movado Time Corp.
CALENDULA - Skin care products ✰ - Nature's Answer (Bio Botanica)
CALENTIME - Watches - Bulova Corp.
CALERA - Wines - Calera Wine Co.
CALEX - Aquatic pharmacuetical preparations ✰ - Aquatronics-Filtronics
CALF BALANCE - Animal feeds - Cenex/Land O'Lakes AG Services
CALF CADDY - Farm machinery - Diamond Country
CALF CALM - Veterinary nutritional supplements - Oralx Corp.
CALF FORMULA SF - Veterinary pharmaceutical - Walco International, Inc.
CALF GLO - Veterinary nutritional supplements - Vita Plus Corp.
CALF-MANNA - Pet products - Manna Pro Corp.
CALF NEBRASKA - Leather - Amerian Premier Leather Co.
CALF PLAN - Animal feeds - Conagra, Inc.
CALF-TEK - Animal feeds ✰ - Pacer Technology
CALFOJECT - Pharmaceutical preparations - Wesley Pharmacal Co. Inc.
CALFORD - Apparel and accessories - Kellwood Co.
CALFOS-D - Pharmaceutical preparations ✰ - Pal-Pak Inc.
CALFS - Computer software ✰ - Iowa State Bar Association
CALFSCALE - Measuring instruments - Calfscale Co.
CALFWEENA - Pet products - Merrick's Inc.
CALGA SPRINGS - Water–bottled or canned - Beverage America, Inc.
CALGARY - Floor coverings–carpet and rugs ✰ - Blue Ridge Carpet Mills
CALGARY - Window coverings - Vertilux-Louverlux Inc.
CALGARY AMBER - Beverages–alcohol - Century Importers Inc.
CALGARY BRITL - Breads - Siljans of North America Inc.
CALGESIC - Vitamins and nutritional supplements ✰ - Whitby Pharmaceuticals, Inc.
CALGLO - Thread ✰ - SCT Yarns Inc.
CALGLYCINE - Pharmaceutical preparations - Rugby Laboratories Inc.
CALGON - Skin care products - Smithkline Beecham Corp.
CALGON ECLIPSE - Chemical preparations - Calgon Carbon Corp.
CALGONATE - Skin care products - Calgonate Corp.
CALGONITE - Dishwashing compounds ✰ - Smithkline Beecham Corp.
CALHEAD - Caps–baseball - California Headwear, Inc.
CALHOUN BURNS - Toys - Tonka Corp.
CALI-FAME - Hats - Cali-Fame of Los Angeles Inc.
CALI-GUARD - Laboratory apparatus - Calibrated Instruments, Inc.
CALIBER - Cleaning preparations–carpet and rug - Chemspec, Inc.
CALIBER - Computer hardware - Caliber Computer Corp.
CALIBER - Cooking equipment–household - Roshco, Inc.
CALIBER - Fishing tackle - Impecco, Ltd.
CALIBER - Floor coverings–carpet and rugs - Philadelphia Carpets
CALIBER - Flowers, plants, and seeds - Jacklin Seed
CALIBER - Freight cars–locomotive - Roadway Services, Inc.
CALIBER - Knives–pocket - W.R. Case & Sons Cutlery Co.
CALIBER - Medical apparatus - M.E. Sampson & Associates, Inc.
CALIBER - Ships–sailing vessels - Caliber Yacht Corp.
CALIBER - Skates–roller - Variflex, Inc.
CALIBER - Starch–laundry - Stevens Industries Inc.
CALIBER 21-8 - Dog food - Specialty Feeds Inc.
CALIBER 2000 - Bicycles - Huffy Corp.
CALIBER COMICS - Books–comic - Stabur Corp.
CALIBER ULTRA 26 - Dog food - Specialty Feeds Inc.
CALIBOGIE - Boats–motor - International Marine
CALIBRATE - Hair care products - Concentrics Inc.
CALIBRATOR - Firearms, accessories, and parts - Welsh Sporting Goods Corp. (Boyt Div.)
CALIBRE - Computer software - Mentor Graphics Corp.
CALIBRE - Fabrics - Greenwood Mills Inc.
CALIBRE - Pens ✰ - Faber-Castell Corp.
CALIBRE - Skin care products - Kenra Laboratories, Inc.
CALIBRE - Tires - Goodyear Tire & Rubber Co.

✰ = Now out of production

CALIBRE PLUS - Skin care products - Kenra Laboratories, Inc.
CALIBRON - Audio equipment - Recoton Corp.
CALIBRON PRO - Headphones - Recoton Corp.
CALICCHIO - Trumpets - Calicchio Trumpets
CALICO - Computer software - At&T Corp.
CALICO - Dinnerware–glass - Crownford Giftware Co. Inc.
CALICO - Dinnerware–glass ☆ - Nikko Ceramics Inc.
CALICO - Footwear - Fisher Camuto Corp.
CALICO - Fudge - Calico Cottage, Inc.
CALICO - Handwork supplies - Bernat Yarn & Craft Corp.
CALICO - Pet products - The Crab Connection
CALICO - Pet products - Sanex Corp.
CALICO - Pottery ☆ - Rubens Originals
CALICO - Publisher's imprint ☆ - Contemporary Books Inc.
CALICO - Recording label - Waltner Enterprises
CALICO - Toys - California Toytime Balloons Inc.
CALICO BETH - Doll-making kit ☆ - Coloron Industries
CALICO CAT - Clocks - General Time Corp. (Westclox/Seth Thomas Div.)
CALICO COLLECTION - Jams and jellies - Knott's Berry Farm
CALICO COTTAGE - Fudge - Calico Cottage, Inc.
CALICO COUNTY - Hobby kits ☆ - Design Works Crafts
CALICO CRITTERS OF CLOVERLEAF CORNERS - Dolls - Tomy America, Inc.
CALICO GAL - Golfing equipment - John Flouzee Green Co., Inc.
CALICO JACK - Rum - White Rock Distilleries Inc.
CALICO KIDS - Wallcovering ☆ - Colortree Designs
CALICO KITTENS - Figurines ☆ - Enesco Corp.
CALICO LACE - Deodorizers - Norpak Companies Ltd.
CALICO LITES - Footwear - Nine West Group Inc.
CALICO ROSE - Dinnerware and counter saver - Corning Inc.
CALICO ZOO - Flowers, plants, and seeds - Florists' Transworld Delivery Association, Inc.
CALICO ZOO - Greeting cards - Florists' Transworld Delivery, Inc.
CALICYLIC CREME - Skin care products - Gordon Laboratories
CALIDAD BRAND - Tortillas - Calidad Foods, Inc.
CALIDO CHILE TRADERS - Jams and jellies - Calido Chile Traders Systems, Inc.
CALIDO CHILE TRADERS HOT N' SPICY - Jackets–men's - Calido Chile Traders Systems, Inc.
CALIENTE - Bicycles - Schwinn Cycling & Fitness Inc.
CALIENTE - Boats–motor ☆ - Lund Boat Co.
CALIENTE - Cameras–video - Good Times Home Video Corp.
CALIENTE - Floor coverings - Congoleum Corp.
CALIENTE - Golfing equipment - Acushnet Co.
CALIENTE - Perfumes - Coty Inc.
CALIENTE - Roofing materials–clay - United States Tile Co.
CALIENTE - Tires - Bridgestone/Firestone, Inc.
CALIENTE CAB CO. - Tortillas - Caliente Cab Restaurant Co., Inc.
CALIENTE! NATURAL BEAUTY BY FIRE - Tiles–clay - United States Tile Co.
CALIENTITAS - Fruits and vegetables - Schwan's Sales Enterprises, Inc.
CALIERNIO SAURUGRION - Wines - Cilurzo Vineyard & Winery
CALIFLORA CALENDULA - Pharmaceutical preparations - Boericke & Tafel
CALIFONE - Audio equipment - Califone International Inc.
CALIFORMAED COASTERS - Footwear - Ambassador Shoe Corp.
CALIFORNEON - Lighting equipment–automotive - American International Pacific Industries Corp.
CALIFORNIA - Beverages–alcohol - White Rock Distilleries Inc.
CALIFORNIA - Blinds–venetian ☆ - Byteway's Manufacturing Inc.
CALIFORNIA - Brushes–paint ☆ - Winsor & Newton
CALIFORNIA - Caviar - Cowboy Caviar
CALIFORNIA - Cigarettes - Philip Morris Companies Inc.
CALIFORNIA - Colognes - Max Factor & Co.
CALIFORNIA - Floor coverings–carpet and rugs ☆ - Royalweve Carpet Mills
CALIFORNIA - Flooring–hardwood - Mannington Wood Floors
CALIFORNIA - Flower pots–plastic - Davids & Royston Bulb Co. Inc.
CALIFORNIA - Food products - Garlic Festival Foods
CALIFORNIA - Glass products - California Glass Bending Co.
CALIFORNIA - Guitars ☆ - Chandler Industries
CALIFORNIA - Musical instrument accessories - Max Roisman
CALIFORNIA - Oils–edible - California Olive Oil Corp.
CALIFORNIA - Paints - California Products Corp.
CALIFORNIA - Rice - Estus Gourmet
CALIFORNIA - Snack foods - Mexi-Snax Inc.
CALIFORNIA - Soft drinks - Corr's Natural Beverages Inc.
CALIFORNIA - Sporting goods - EMF Co. Inc.

CALIFORNIA - Toys - California Toytime Balloons Inc.
CALIFORNIA - Wallpaper - Studio IV Graphics Inc.
CALIFORNIA - Window shades - Castec Window Shading Inc.
CALIFORNIA - Yarn ☆ - Joseph Galler Inc.
CALIFORNIA 2GRG063 PASSENGER - Shirts - Balatbat Consolidated
CALIFORNIA AMPLIFIER - Amplifiers - California Amplifier
CALIFORNIA ANGELS - Apparel and accessories - Golden West Baseball Co.
CALIFORNIA APPLES - Boxes–corrugated paperboard - Mead Corp.
CALIFORNIA AUDIO LABS - Audio equipment - GNP Audio Video Inc.
CALIFORNIA BABY - Skin care products - Jessica Iclisoy
CALIFORNIA BASMATI - Rice - Wehah Farm, Inc.
CALIFORNIA BEACH CLUB - Apparel and accessories - Oxford Industries, Inc.
CALIFORNIA BEACH ROLL - Ice chests - Robert B. Gerard
CALIFORNIA BEAUTY BAR - Soap - Action Laboratories Inc.
CALIFORNIA BEBE BLOND - Apparel and accessories - Back2back Kidswear, Inc.
CALIFORNIA BLACK GOLD - Lubricants - California Black Gold International, Inc.
CALIFORNIA BODY - Apparel–athletic - Gilda Marx Inc.
CALIFORNIA BOMBER - Golfing equipment - Slotline Golf
CALIFORNIA BOUQUET - Wines ☆ - San Antonio Winery Inc.
CALIFORNIA BRONZE - Cosmetics - Max Factor & Co.
CALIFORNIA BUBBLES - Bubble bath - Cosmania, Inc.
CALIFORNIA BUTTERFLY - Skin care products - Nature's Paradise by Joanna International, Inc.
CALIFORNIA CAFE - Sauces - California Cafe Restaurant Corp.
CALIFORNIA CALLAS - Flowers, plants, and seeds - Golden State Bulb Growers
CALIFORNIA CAP FLAP - Apparel and accessories ☆ - G. Gary Holt Enterprises, Inc.
CALIFORNIA CASUAL - Furniture - Bassett Furniture Industries, Inc.
CALIFORNIA CAVIAR - Snack foods - Nasco Gourmet Foods, Inc.
CALIFORNIA CEDAR - Fireplace equipment ☆ - Duraflame, Inc.
CALIFORNIA CHARM - Paints - Pervo Paint Co.
CALIFORNIA CHOICE - Flowers, plants, and seeds - Ferry-Morse Seed Co.
CALIFORNIA CITRUS DELITE - Juices ☆ - Vita-Pakt Citrus Products Co.
CALIFORNIA CLASSIC - Floor coverings–carpet and rugs - World Carpets, Inc.
CALIFORNIA CLASSIC - Fruits and vegetables - San Joaquin Figs, Inc.
CALIFORNIA CLASSIC - Grass seed - Scotts Co. (Organics Business Group)
CALIFORNIA CLASSIC SKATEBOARDS - Skateboards ☆ - Watson Laminates, Inc.
CALIFORNIA CLOCK - Clocks - California Clock Co.
CALIFORNIA CLOTHING CO. - Apparel and accessories - Kathy of California, Inc.
CALIFORNIA COBBLERS - Footwear - Footwear Unlimited, Inc.
CALIFORNIA COLDWATER CARROTS - Fruits and vegetables - William Bolthouse Farms Inc.
CALIFORNIA COLLARS CC - Pet collars - Karen A. Doose
CALIFORNIA COLLECTION - Floor coverings–carpet and rugs ☆ - American Carpet Mills
CALIFORNIA COLLECTION - Toys - Imperial Toy Corp.
CALIFORNIA COLLECTION - Wallpaper ☆ - Wall-Pride Inc.
CALIFORNIA COLONY - Wines - The Beverage Source Inc.
CALIFORNIA COLORS - Frames–eyeglass - Spotlight Industries Inc.
CALIFORNIA COLORS - Paints - Morris Paint & Varnish Co.
CALIFORNIA COLORS - Pet collars - Leatherite-Nylorite Manufacturing Inc.
CALIFORNIA COLORS - Skin care products - Blue Cross Beauty Products Inc.
CALIFORNIA COLORS - Wigs - Eva Gabor International, Ltd.
CALIFORNIA CONCEPT - Hair care products - California Concept Corp.
CALIFORNIA CONCEPT FORMULA 37 - Hair care products - California Concept Corp.
CALIFORNIA CONNECTION - Hair care products - Rescue Marketing Group
CALIFORNIA CONNEXION - Motor vehicle parts and accessories ☆ - Target Motorsports
CALIFORNIA COOPERAGE - Hot tubs–plastic - Coleman Spas
CALIFORNIA COORDINATES - Wallpaper ☆ - Wall-Pride Inc.
CALIFORNIA CORDIALS L.A. - Liquors - Gaetano Specialties Ltd.
CALIFORNIA CORN - Health care products - Cal-Corn Inc.
CALIFORNIA CORN BRAND - Popcorn - Cal-Corn Inc.
CALIFORNIA COSMETICS - Skin care products - California Cosmetics, Inc.
CALIFORNIA COUNTRY - Hobby shops - Yarn Kits Inc.
CALIFORNIA COUNTRY - Wallpaper ☆ - Wall-Pride Inc.
CALIFORNIA COWBOYZ - Apparel and accessories - Westpac Products Co. Inc.

☆ = Now out of production

CALIFORNIA CRISP - Fruits and vegetables - Fresh Express Inc.

CALIFORNIA CRUISIN' - Bicycles - Columbia Manufacturing Inc.

CALIFORNIA CRUNCH - Bakery products - Pacific Coast Baking Co. Inc.

CALIFORNIA CRUNCHIES - Nuts–salted, roasted, cooked, or canned - Nunes Farms

CALIFORNIA CUISINE - Pasta - Gourmet's Fresh Pasta Inc.

CALIFORNIA CULINARY ACADEMY - Bags–canvas - California Culinary Academy

CALIFORNIA CULINARY CLASSICS - Spices and extracts ☆ - San Francisco Herb & Natural Food Co.

CALIFORNIA CURVES - Apparel and accessories - Bodylines Inc.

CALIFORNIA DAYS - Food products - Sacramento Foods

CALIFORNIA DEL SUR - Confections - California Del Sur

CALIFORNIA DELI - Meats–luncheon - Zacky Foods Co. (Los Angeles Div.)

CALIFORNIA DELI MIX - Mustard - Fusano California Valley

CALIFORNIA DIET - Vitamins and nutritional supplements - California Diet/Worldwide Inc.

CALIFORNIA DONS - Leather goods - S and S Leather Goods

CALIFORNIA DREAM - Dolls - Mattel, Inc.

CALIFORNIA DREAMER - Watches - California Dreamer Inc.

CALIFORNIA DREAMERS - Stationery - Recycled Paper Products, Inc.

CALIFORNIA DREAMIN' - Bicycles - Columbia Manufacturing Inc.

CALIFORNIA DREAMIN - Fireworks - Ingram Enterprises, Inc.

CALIFORNIA DREAMIN - Floor coverings–carpet and rugs - Mohawk Industries Inc.

CALIFORNIA DREAMIN' - Game machines - Bally Gaming International, Inc.

CALIFORNIA DYNASTY - Clothing - MGT Industries, Inc.

CALIFORNIA EARTHQUAKE - Golfing equipment - Frugal Golfer

CALIFORNIA EARTHQUAKE HELMET, THE - Construction hardhats - California Earthquake Helmets

CALIFORNIA EASIES - Footwear - Chesapeake Shoe Co. of California

CALIFORNIA EDGE - Apparel and accessories - Caribbean Apparel Network, Inc.

CALIFORNIA ENERGY BAR - Breads - New York Bagel Factory

CALIFORNIA ENVIRONMENTAL CUP - Containers - California Environmental Cup Inc.

CALIFORNIA EXOTIC - Skin care products - California Publishers and Liquidating Corp.

CALIFORNIA EYES - Frames–eyeglass - Spotlight Industries Inc.

CALIFORNIA FACIAL - Skin care products - Conair Corp.

CALIFORNIA FARM - Food products ☆ - California Farm Products Div.

CALIFORNIA FARMED STRIPED BASS - Fish–fresh or frozen - Kent Sea arms Corp.

CALIFORNIA FARMS - Vegetables–canned - California Farms and Canners, Inc.

CALIFORNIA FASHION - Frames–eyeglass - Spotlight Industries Inc.

CALIFORNIA FEELING - Apparel and accessories - Montgomery Ward & Co. Inc.

CALIFORNIA FINEST - Chocolate candy - Hooper's Chocolates

CALIFORNIA FITNESS - Vitamins and nutritional supplements - Sportelesis, Inc.

CALIFORNIA FITNESS EQUIPMENT - Exercising equipment - John Swete

CALIFORNIA FITNESS TPRODUCTS - Exercise equipment - Impex Inc.

CALIFORNIA FITNUTS - Nuts–salted, roasted, cooked, or canned - California Fitnuts, Inc.

CALIFORNIA FLAIR - Wallpaper ☆ - Gamrod-Harman

CALIFORNIA FLATS - Breads - Lavosh Hawaii

CALIFORNIA FORMALS - Apparel–women's - Bi-Flex International

CALIFORNIA FRAMER - Tools - Vaughan & Bushnell Manufacturing Co.

CALIFORNIA FRESH - Vitamins and nutritional supplements - Eckhart Corp.

CALIFORNIA FRESH - Yogurt–frozen - California Fresh Treats Inc.

CALIFORNIA FUNKY - Frames–eyeglass - Spotlight Industries Inc.

CALIFORNIA GAMES - Computer software ☆ - Milton Bradley Co.

CALIFORNIA GARDEN - Vegetables–canned - California Garden Products Inc.

CALIFORNIA GARDEN - Wallpaper - Pelican Prints

CALIFORNIA GARLIC CREME - Food products - Golden Whisk Pasta Partners

CALIFORNIA GEMS - Cosmetics - Cosmania, Inc.

CALIFORNIA GIRL - Bicycles ☆ - Hedstrom Corp.

CALIFORNIA GOLD - Agricultural seeds - Winsor Grain, Inc.

CALIFORNIA GOLD - Christmas tree ornaments - Cracker Box Inc.

CALIFORNIA GOLD - Dairy products - California Gold Dairy Products

CALIFORNIA GOLD - Exercising equipment - California Gym Equipment

CALIFORNIA GOLD - Frames–eyeglass - Spotlight Industries Inc.

CALIFORNIA GOLD - Hair-care products and personal-care products - J & J Jojoba

CALIFORNIA GOLD - Jewelry - The Crab Connection

CALIFORNIA GOLD - Jewelry - Rossi D'Italia

CALIFORNIA GOLD - Juices - Walker International

CALIFORNIA GOLD - Shampoos - Giovanni Cosmetics Inc.

CALIFORNIA GOLD GLASSWORKS - Doors–glass - Kohler Co.

CALIFORNIA GOLDEN - Nuts - Wedding Time Products

CALIFORNIA GREEN, THE - Chili sauce - Huy Fong Foods, Inc.

CALIFORNIA GT - Toys–electronic - Tyco Toys

CALIFORNIA HARVEST - Fruits–dried - Grapevine Trading Co., Inc.

CALIFORNIA HARVEST ALE - Beverages–malt - Wolfgang D. Morandell

CALIFORNIA HEALTH - Vitamins and nutritional supplements - Barnes Wholesale Inc.

CALIFORNIA HEAT - Pet collars - Leatherite-Nylorite Manufacturing Inc.

CALIFORNIA HERITAGE - Pottery - Freeman-McFarlin Potteries Inc.

CALIFORNIA HERITAGE - Wallpaper ☆ - Wall-Pride Inc.

CALIFORNIA HI-LITES - Fruits–dried - California Hi-Lites, Inc.

CALIFORNIA HOME FASHIONS - Window coverings - Glare-Con Inc.

CALIFORNIA HOTS - Apparel and accessories - Demco Group

CALIFORNIA I.D. ATHLETIC WEAR - Apparel and accessories - Innovation Health & Fitness Systems, Inc.

CALIFORNIA IMPERIAL - Apparel and accessories - California Manufacturing Co. Inc.

CALIFORNIA INFLUENCE - Apparel and accessories - Kellwood Co.

CALIFORNIA INTERNATIONAL - Recording label - Joseph Nicoletti Music Co.

CALIFORNIA IVY - Dinnerware–glass ☆ - Metlox Pottery Shoppe

CALIFORNIA JADE - Wallpaper ☆ - Wall-Pride Inc.

CALIFORNIA JAMMER - Sporting goods ☆ - Outdoor Technologies Group

CALIFORNIA-KADETTZ - Wines - Bestsky Industries, Inc.

CALIFORNIA KING SALMON - Fish–fresh or frozen - California Salmon Council

CALIFORNIA KWIKFIT II - Exercising equipment - California Gym Equipment

CALIFORNIA LEMON - Cookies ☆ - Barbara's Bakery, Inc.

CALIFORNIA LICORICE STICKS - Candy - American Licorice Co.

CALIFORNIA LIGHT - Beverages–carbonated - Original New York Seltzer

CALIFORNIA LIMITED - Liquors - United States Distilled Products Co.

CALIFORNIA LIPWORKS - Cosmetics - Cosmania, Inc.

CALIFORNIA LITE - See ONETIME LITE

CALIFORNIA LITE - Bicycles - Hunt-Wilde Corp.

CALIFORNIA LOOK - Hair care products - Jack Forcelledo

CALIFORNIA LOOK, THE - Floor coverings–carpet and rugs - West Point-Pepperell Mill Store

CALIFORNIA LOOKS - Dresses–girls' - Mailo Designs, Inc.

CALIFORNIA MAGDESIANS - Footwear - Magdesian Bros.

CALIFORNIA MANGO - Cosmetics - Rudy Lenzkes

CALIFORNIA MANGO - Skin care products - Beautiful Feet

CALIFORNIA MIST - Cosmetics - American International Industries

CALIFORNIA MOP SAUCE - Seasonings - Garlic Festival Foods

CALIFORNIA MUSCLE - Exercising equipment - California Gym Equipment

CALIFORNIA NAIL - Nail care products - Onyx Corp.

CALIFORNIA NATURAL - Beverages–carbonated ☆ - Vernors Inc.

CALIFORNIA NATURAL - Food products - Chiquita Brands, Inc.

CALIFORNIA NATURAL - Pet food - Natura Pet Products, Inc.

CALIFORNIA NATURAL FARMS - Fish–fresh or frozen - Solar Aquafarms Inc.

CALIFORNIA NATURALS - Oils–edible - California Olive Oil Corp.

CALIFORNIA NATURALS - Snack foods - California Super Naturals Inc.

CALIFORNIA NEON - Electronic equipment - Bob Bartlett & Associates Inc.

CALIFORNIA NORTH - Sunblocks - California North

CALIFORNIA ORANGE - Cookies ☆ - Barbara's Bakery, Inc.

CALIFORNIA ORCHARD - Dinnerware–glass ☆ - Metlox Pottery Shoppe

CALIFORNIA PADS - Calendars - House of Doolittle

CALIFORNIA PEARL - Fruits and vegetables - California Vegetable Specialties, Inc.

CALIFORNIA PET - Pet products - American Pacific Pet

CALIFORNIA PIZZA KITCHEN - Soups and salads - California Pizza Kitchen Inc.

CALIFORNIA PLASTICS - Garden equipment - Lawn & Garden Supply Co.

CALIFORNIA POPS - Candy - Luce Candy Co.

CALIFORNIA PRIDE U.S.A. - Apparel and accessories - Family & Fashions

CALIFORNIA PROFESSIONAL - Hair care products - Tu-K Industries Inc.

CALIFORNIA PURE - Water purification systems - Shanti S. Dewan

CALIFORNIA QUENCHER - Wines ☆ - Lost Hills Winery

CALIFORNIA QUIVERS - Juices - California Quivers

CALIFORNIA RAISINS - Games ☆ - Ben Cooper Inc.

☆ = Now out of production

CALIFORNIA RAISINS BOARD GAME, THE - Games ☆ - Decipher Inc.
CALIFORNIA RAISINS CARD GAME, THE - Games ☆ - Decipher Inc.
CALIFORNIA RANCHO - Siding–metal - GAF Corp.
CALIFORNIA RECIPE - Rice - Rice Growers of California
CALIFORNIA RED, THE - Chili sauce - Huy Fong Foods, Inc.
CALIFORNIA REV & RACE - Toys–automobiles - Mattel, Inc.
CALIFORNIA RIDGE - Wines ☆ - Canandaigua Wine Co. Inc.
CALIFORNIA ROAST SUNBEANS FOR THE WORLD - Coffee - California Coffee Co.
CALIFORNIA ROSES - Herbal products - William R. Crinklaw Inc.
CALIFORNIA SAFARI - Luggage - Holland Brothers
CALIFORNIA SANDS - Sweaters - Edan Products, Inc.
CALIFORNIA SCENTS - Deodorizers - California Scents
CALIFORNIA SEA SALT - Salt - Stevens Industries Inc.
CALIFORNIA SERIES - Glass–tempered - Southwall Technologies Inc.
CALIFORNIA SHINE - Hair care products - Conair Corp.
CALIFORNIA SIDECAR - Motor vehicles - California Sidecar
CALIFORNIA SKIN THERAPY - Skin-care products - California SunCare, Inc.
CALIFORNIA SLIM - Vitamins and nutritional supplements - California Slim Inc.
CALIFORNIA SOURCE - Beverages - Triple L Distributing Co., Inc.
CALIFORNIA SPACEPORT - Air transportation - Western Commercial Space Center, Inc.
CALIFORNIA SPECIAL - Flour–blended - Lacey Milling Co.
CALIFORNIA SPECIAL - Guitars - Alembic Inc.
CALIFORNIA SPEEDWAY, THE - Shirts - Speedway Development Corp.
CALIFORNIA SPLASH - Apparel–children's - Elder Manufacturing Co., Inc.
CALIFORNIA SPLASH - Water–mineral - L and A Juice Co. Inc.
CALIFORNIA SPORT - Skin care products ☆ - Spotlight Industries Inc.
CALIFORNIA SPORT UNLIMITED - Shirts - Communication & Trading Services, Inc.
CALIFORNIA SPRINGS - Bottles–plastic - AC International
CALIFORNIA SQUARE - Floor coverings - Mannington Resilient Floors
CALIFORNIA STRAWBERRY - Beverages–carbonated - Canada Dry Corp.
CALIFORNIA STRAWBERRY - Dinnerware–glass ☆ - Metlox Pottery Shoppe
CALIFORNIA SUN - Eyeglasses - Cable Car Eyeware
CALIFORNIA SUN DRY - Food products - California Sundry Foods
CALIFORNIA SUN-KICKS - Shoes - Edison Brothers Stores, Inc.
CALIFORNIA SUNSET - Jewelry - Rossana Oro Fashion, Inc.
CALIFORNIA SUNSET - Tuna–canned - Tri-Union International, LLC
CALIFORNIA SUNSHINE - Seafood products–canned or cured - Tsar Nicoulai Caviar
CALIFORNIA SUNSHINE VITAL - Whey - California Sunshine Ultra Fresh Dairy Products
CALIFORNIA SUNSHINE VITAL - Whey - Luberski, Inc.
CALIFORNIA TAN - Sun-care products - California SunCare, Inc.
CALIFORNIA TAN HELIOTHERAPY - Skin care products - California SunCare, Inc.
CALIFORNIA TEMPO - Dinnerware–glass ☆ - Metlox Pottery Shoppe
CALIFORNIA TERRA - Wallpaper ☆ - Wall-Pride Inc.
CALIFORNIA TOYTIME - Toys - California Toytime Balloons Inc.
CALIFORNIA TRAVELER - Games - World Traveler Ltd.
CALIFORNIA TREATS - Snack foods - ACB/Richard Watson
CALIFORNIA TWIST - Juices - Heinke's Inc.
CALIFORNIA VILLAGES - Wines - Gibson Wine Co.
CALIFORNIA WEAVE - Hair care products - American International Industries
CALIFORNIA WINERY, THE - Wines - Bronco Wine Co.
CALIFORNIAN - Bicycles - Ross Bicycles USA, Ltd.
CALIFORNIAN - Boats ☆ - Wellcraft Marine Corp.
CALIFORNIAN - Fishing tackle - Turner's Outdoorsman
CALIFORNIAN - Food products - Zacky Foods Co. (Los Angeles Div.)
CALIFORNIAN - Luggage ☆ - Maximillian Luggage Corp.
CALIFORNIAN - Vinyl floor covering - Congoleum Corp.
CALIFORNIAN SNOW FREEZE - Ice cream novelty - Cosmos International
CALIFORNIAPRO - Skates–roller - California Pro USA Corp.
CALIFORNIA'S BEST - Fertilizers - J.R. Simplot Co.
CALIFORNIA'S FINEST - Beverages - Mendocino Beverages International Inc.
CALIFORNIA'S FINEST - Food products - California Meat Seasonings
CALIFORNIA'S FIRST GROWTH - Wines - Buena Vista Winery, Inc.
CALIFORNIA'S NATURAL CHOICE - Beverages - California's Natural Choice, Inc.
CALIGARIS OF PARAGUAY - Handbags - Global Import-Export Inc.
CALIMERE - Crocheted and knitted items - Le Roy Knitted Sportswear Inc.
CALIMONT - Bananas - Calimont Capital Corp.
CALINATE-FA - Pharmaceutical preparations ☆ - Solvay Pharmaceuticals Inc.
CALINE - Perfumes - Jean Patou, Inc.
CALIOS - Vitamins and nutritional supplements - Heritage Store Inc.

CALIPH - Rings–jewelry - Artcarved Inc.
CALIPPO - Ice cream - Good Humor Corp.
CALIPRO - Electronic equipment - Silver Creek Nurseries, Inc.
CALIQUE - Footwear - Circle Shoe Co.
CALISSANO - Wines - Shaw-Ross International Importers
CALISTA - Seafood substitutes - Calista Sea Foods Inc.
CALISTOGA - Glassware–household - Crate and Barrel
CALISTOGA - Juices - Calistoga Mineral Water Co.
CALISTOGA - Occasional tables - JDI Group, Inc.
CALISTOGA - Water–bottled or canned - Perrier Group of America Inc.
CALISTOGA VINEYARDS - Wines ☆ - Cuvaison Inc.
CALIWEAR - Apparel and accessories - Caliway Trade International Corp.
CALIXTO LOPEZ - Cigars - Villco Imports Inc.
CALJACK - Dairy products - Churny Co., Inc.
CALK-IN - Screws - Rawlplug Co., Inc.
CALK-SCREW - Hardware - Maze Nails
CALKDZ - Apparel and accessories - Kellwood Co.
CALKE - Stamps–hand - Bycin Industries, Inc.
CALKELASTIC - Caulking compounds - Pecora Chemical Corp.
CALL - Publisher's imprints - Thomas A. Edison State College
CALL-A-NURSE - Electronic equipment - Rauland-Borg Corp.
CALL BACK PHONE - Toys - Mattel, Inc.
CALL CARRY-ALL - Sporting goods - Penn's Woods Products Inc.
CALL CATCHER - Telephone answering machines ☆ - Bogen Communications, Inc.
CALL CHECK - Telephone answering machines - Dictaphone Corp.
CALL COMMANDER - Telephone answering machines ☆ - Lanier Voice Products
CALL DIRECTOR - Telephones - At&T Corp.
CALL DOCTOR - Computer software - Tropper Technologies, Inc.
CALL-GARD - Novelty items - Seron Manufacturing Co.
CALL HOME PHONE BOOTH - Toys ☆ - Steven Manufacturing Co.
CALL IT COLOR - Wallpaper - Wallcoverings Unlimited Inc.
CALL IT SPICEY! - Barbecue sauce - Word of Mouth Foods, Inc.
CALL JAM - Computer software - AG Communication Systems Inc.
CALL-ME - Toys - Hasbro, Inc.
CALL ME BACK - Toys - Tonka Corp.
CALL-ME-CAMI - Apparel–women's ☆ - Lovable Co.
CALL OF CTHULHU - Games - Chaosium Inc.
CALL OF CTHULHU - Games - Grenadier Models
CALL OF CTHULHU FICTION - Publisher's imprints - Chaosium Inc.
CALL OF THE WILD - Animal feeds - Central Distributing Co.
CALL OF THE WILD - Cosmetics - Del Pharmaceuticals, Inc.
CALL OF THE WIND - Pager services - James Anthony Martin
CALL PORT - Audio tapes–blank - Coherent Communications Systems Corp.
CALL SAVER - Sporting goods ☆ - Penn's Woods Products Inc.
CALL THE PARROT - Computer software - Hartley Courseware Inc.
CALL TO COLORS - Housewares - Call to Colors, Inc.
CALL-UPS - Electronic equipment - American Power Conversion Corp.
CALL WHERE - Computer peripheral equipment - A & A Teledata Services, Inc.
CALLA - Tableware–china - Villeroy and Boch Tableware Ltd.
CALLA - Toys - Tonka Corp.
CALLA LILY - Giftware - Russ Berrie and Co., Inc.
CALLA LILY - Housewares - Himark Enterprises Inc.
CALLAGENT - Telephones - Centigram Communications Corp.
CALLAHAN'S ORIGINAL CALABASH - Seasonings - Calabash Seafood Co., Inc.
CALLARD & BOWSER - Confections - Callard & Bowser USA Inc.
CALLAWASSIE ISLAND - Apparel and accessories - Callawassie Development Corp.
CALLAWAY - Dinnerware - Corning Inc.
CALLAWAY - Floor coverings–carpet and rugs - Callaway Carpets
CALLAWAY - Food products - Caleb Haley and Co. Inc.
CALLAWAY - Furniture - Lowy Group Inc.
CALLAWAY - Golfing equipment - Callaway Golf Co.
CALLAWAY PATTERN COLLECTION - Floor coverings–carpet and rugs - Callaway Carpets
CALLAWAY VINEYARD & WINERY - Wines - Callaway Vineyard and Winery
CALLAWAY'S COLORADO - Beef - Callaway Packing, Inc.
CALLBASE - Computer software - Soffront Software
CALLBOOK - Communications equipment - Momentum, Inc.
CALLBRIDGE - Computer software - Rolm Co.
CALLEBAUT - Chocolate candy - Gourmet America
CALLEBAUT - Food products - De Choix Specialty Foods Co.
CALLEGAUD - Chocolate candy - Made in France

CALLEN - Photo albums - Callen Photo Mount Corp.

CALLEN - Trailers–travel - Callen Camper Co.

CALLER ID PLUS - Electronic equipment - Gemini Industries, Inc.

CALLER, THE - Paper–newsprint - National Wild Turkey Federation

CALLEY & CURRIER - Medical apparatus - Calley and Currier Co. Inc.

CALLFLOW - Computer software - Early, Cloud & Co.

CALLGUARD - Telephones–cellular - Clifford Electronics Inc.

CALLI - Cosmetics - Sunrider Corp.

CALLI - Inks - Steig Products

CALLIGA ROBOLLA - Wines - S & J Importing Co. Inc.

CALLIGRA-COTE - Artists' materials - Loctite Corp.

CALLIGRAPH DUO - Markers–felt-tip - Staedtler, Inc.

CALLIGRAPHIC - Pens - Sanford Corp.

CALLIGRAPHRASE - Housewares - Books of Love, Inc.

CALLIGRAPHY PRESENTATIONS - Greeting cards ☆ - Caravan Products Inc.

CALLIGRAPRINTS - Artists' materials - Ken Brown Studio of Calligraphic Art Inc.

CALLING ALL ANGELS - Skin care products - Keller Productions, Inc.

CALLING CARD - Wallpaper ☆ - Wiffle Hill Studio

CALLING CARTONS - Boxes–paperboard - Jubilee Promotional Co., Inc.

CALLINK - Electronic equipment - Spear Voice Systems, Inc.

CALLIOPE - Fabrics - Astrup Co.

CALLIOPE - Fabrics - Dan River Inc.

CALLIOPE - Fabrics ☆ - Greenwood Mills Inc.

CALLIOPE - Floor coverings–carpet and rugs - Masland Corp.

CALLIOPE - Furniture - Harter

CALLIOPE - Wallpaper - Camelot Design Studios

CALLIOPE - Yarn - William Unger & Co. Inc.

CALLIOPE BOUQUET - Flowers, plants, and seeds - Alphaflora Imports, Inc.

CALLIOPE-OF-COLOR - Wallpaper - Camelot Design Studios

CALLIPEN - Pens–fountain - Sakura of America

CALLIPYGIAN - Apparel–athletic - Ross D. Holcomb

CALLIROBICS - Health care products - Maddak Inc.

CALLISTA - Trailers–travel ☆ - Carriage, Inc.

CALLISTA COVE - Trailers–travel ☆ - Carriage, Inc.

CALLISTO - Computer software - Imagine Multimedia Inc.

CALLLAB - Computer software - Bard Technologies Inc.

CALLO-SAN - Pharmaceutical preparations - Vartex Pharmaceuticals Inc.

CALLOUS REMOVER CREME - Skin care products - Fanie International

CALLOWAY COTTAGE - Wallcovering - Colortree Designs

CALLPRO - Telephone accessories - Teltone Corp.

CALLPRODUCER - Computer software and hardware ☆ - Q.Sys International

CALLREPORTER II - Computer software - DPSC Software Inc.

CALLSET - Remote control devices - Gemstar Development Corp.

CALLSTAR - Computer software - Microlog Corp.

CALLSTAR FXD - Computer software - Microlog Corp.

CALLTRAX - Computer software - Kassing Investments, Inc.

CALLVISION - Computer software - DMD Technology, Inc.

CALLWISE - Computer software - Intecom Inc.

CALLWORX - Pagers - Pagenet

CALLWRITER - Pens - Distribuetl, Inc.

CALM - Deodorants–personal - Alberto-Culver Co.

CALM - Mattresses - E & S Vinyl Manufacturing Inc.

CALM 2 - Deodorants–personal - Alberto-Culver Co.

CALM-AID - Pharmaceutical preparations ☆ - Reese Chemical Co.

CALM-AID ELIXIR - Pharmaceutical preparations ☆ - Reese Chemical Co.

CALM AND COOL - Veterinary nutritional supplements - Oralx Corp.

CALM CHILD - Vitamins and nutritional supplements - Planetary Formulas

CALM DAYS-NIGHTS - Pharmaceutical preparations - Botanical Laboratories Inc.

CALM DOWN - Body wash - Matrix Essentials, Inc.

CALM 'N EASY - Veterinary pharmaceutical preparations - Farnam Cos. Inc.

CALM-R-REST - Vitamins and nutritional supplements - Highland Laboratories

CALM STRESS - Veterinary pharmaceutical preparations - Dr. Goodpet

C.A.L.M. SYSTEM - Publisher's imprints - Kay See Lasley Associates

CALM-X - Pharmaceutical preparations - Republic Drug Co. Inc.

CALMA - Footwear–athletic ☆ - Climb High Inc.

CALMA - Lubricants ☆ - Shell Oil Co.

CALMADOL - Analgesics - Grandall Distributing Co., Inc.

CALMAID - Vitamins and nutritional supplements - Nature's Way Products, Inc.

CALMANAC - Calendars - Success Business Industries, Inc.

CALMATI - Rice - Estus Gourmet

CALMAX - Vitamins and nutritional supplements - Nutrina

CALMAZINE - Pharmaceutical preparations ☆ - Wesley Pharmacal Co. Inc.

CALMAZING - Skin care products - Garcoa Labs/Vitamin Classics

CALMCAT - Bags - Vital Visions, Inc.

CALMCOF - Cough medicines ☆ - Cameron Medical Corp.

CALMERDAY - Vitamins and nutritional supplements - Nutrition Headquarters, Inc.

CALMETS - Food products - Barth's Nutra Products

CALMEX - Seafood products–fresh or frozen - Ocean Garden Products, Inc.

CALMEZE - Pharmaceutical preparations - Alva-Amco Pharmacal Co.

CALMICID - Antacids - Melaleuca, Inc.

CALMIES - Pharmaceutical preparations - Alva-Amco Pharmacal Co.

CALMING - Health care products - Lakon Herbals Inc.

CALMING ESSENCE - Pharmaceutical preparations - Ellon USA, Inc.

CALMITOL - Pharmaceutical preparations ☆ - Pfizer Inc.

CALMOL 4 - Health care products - Mentholatum Co.

CALMOSEPTINE - Pharmaceutical preparations - Perry Laboratories

CALMOSIN - Pharmaceutical preparations - G.O. Spanner Inc.

CALMPLEX - Pharmaceutical preparations - Sundown Vitamins, Inc.

CALMPLEX 2000 - Pharmaceutical preparations - Rexall Sundown, Inc.

CALMS - Tranquilizers - P. & S. Laboratories Inc.

CALMS FORTE - Tranquilizers - Standard Homeopathic Co., Inc.

CALMS KIDS - Vitamins and nutritional supplements - Natrol, Inc.

CALMTABS - Vitamins and nutritional supplements - Amrion, Inc.

CALNUT ORCHARDS - Nuts–salted, roasted, cooked, or canned - Zaloom Brothers Co. of New Jersey

CALOCIDE - Corn and callus medication ☆ - Benjamin Ansehl Co.

CALODEX - Pharmaceutical preparations ☆ - Wesley Pharmacal Co. Inc.

CALON - Tape–adhesive ☆ - Arlon, Inc.

CALOR 110 - Cooking equipment–household - Vita Craft Corp.

CALORA - Paints - Standard T Chemical Co. Inc.

CALORIC - Air conditioning equipment - Raytheon Co.

CALORIC - Kitchen appliances - Caloric Corp.

CALORIC-HERITAGE - Kitchen appliances - Caloric Corp.

CALORIC METER - Cottage cheese ☆ - Friendship Food Products Inc.

CALORIE COUNTER - Food products - Deering Ice Cream Corp.

CALORIE COUNTER - Yogurt–frozen - Frozen Desserts, Inc.

CALORIE CURVE CONTROL - Apparel and accessories ☆ - Playtex Apparel, Inc.

CALORIE EXPRESS - Nutritional supplements - Calorie Shop Weight Loss Centers Inc.

CALORIE GOURMET - Prepared food - Calorie Shop Weight Loss Centers Inc.

CALORIE WATCHERS - Meats–luncheon - Beatrice Cos. Inc.

CALORIEWATCH - Health care products - Elexis Corp.

CALORMATIC - Agricultural machinery - Sweet Manufacturing Co., Inc.

CALOXOL - Pharmaceutical preparations ☆ - JMI-Canton Pharmaceuticals

CALPAC - Fruits and vegetables - Dole Fresh Vegetables Inc.

CALPAC - Paper containers - Calpac Inc.

CALPAK - Computer peripheral equipment - CALPAK Corp.

CALPANATE - Vitamins and nutritional supplements - Oxford Laboratories Inc.

CALPHALON - Cooking utensils–aluminum - Commercial Aluminum Cookware Co.

CALPHOS - Fertilizers - Britz Fertilizers Inc.

CALPHOSAN - Health care products - Glenwood LLC

CALPLEX E.M. - Vitamins and nutritional supplements - Great Life Laboratories Inc.

CALPLUS - Pharmaceutical preparations ☆ - Mericon Industries Inc.

CALPRO - Cleaning preparations - Grow Group, Inc.

CALPROX - Skin care products - Epi Products USA, Inc.

CALREA - Fertilizers - Team Laboratory Chemical Corp.

CALROD - Heating equipment - General Electric Co.

CALRON PLUS - Pharmaceutical preparations ☆ - Geneva Generics Inc.

CALS - Footwear - Vans, Inc.

CALS AT WORK - Computer software - ArborText Inc.

CAL'S CHOICE - Milk - Robin W. Bissell

CAL'S CHOICE - Milk - Cal's Choice Marketing

CALSA - Pharmaceutical - American Laboratories Inc.

CALSCAN - Computer software and manuals - RBC Inc.

CALSCORBATE - Pharmaceutical preparations ☆ - Forest Pharmaceuticals Inc.

CALSIMAG - Insulating materials - American Premier, Inc.

CALSOL - Lubricant - Calgene Chemical

CALSORB - Vitamins and nutritional supplements - Amrion, Inc.

CALSORCIN - Pharmaceutical preparations - Ohio Valley-Clarksburg Inc.

CALSUL - Insecticides ☆ - Dexol Industries

CALSUXAPHEN - Analgesics - Lannett Co. Inc.

CALSUXYLATE - Pharmaceutical preparations ☆ - Dolgin Acme Foods

CALTAR - Lenses–photographic - Calumet Photographic Inc.

CALTECH - Decals and transfers - California Institute of Technology

CALTEX - Audio equipment - Caltex Manufacturing Distributing Inc.

CALTEX - Petroleum - Caltex Petroleum Corp.
CALTEX RECORDS - Recording label - Caltex Trading, Inc.
CALTIME - Calendars - Global Marketing (US) Inc.
CALTRAC - Electronic equipment - Muscle Dynamics Fitness Network, Inc.
CALTRATE - Vitamins and nutritional supplements - Lederle Laboratories
CALTRATE JR. - Vitamins and nutritional supplements - Lederle Laboratories
CALTRO - Pharmaceutical preparations - Geneva Generics Inc.
CALTROL - Pharmaceutical preparations ☆ - Murray Drug Corp.
CALTRON - Plastics - Douglas & Sturgess
CALUMET - Flowers, plants, and seeds - Calumet Growers
CALUMET - Furniture - Homecrest Industries Inc.
CALUMET - Lighting fixtures - Benjamin Electric Manufacturing Co.
CALUMET - Photographic equipment - Calumet Photographic Inc.
CALUMET - Thread - Threads USA Div.
CALUMET - Wines - Thompson Winery
CALURIN - Analgesics - Dorsey Laboratories
CALVADOS BOULARD - Beverages–alcohol - Sunbelt Beverage Corp.
CALVADOS DU PRIEURE - Brandy - Leonard Kreusch Inc.
CALVALCADE - Whirlpools - Lasco Products Group
CALVAR - Finishing agents ☆ - Dutch Boy Group
CALVARESI - Wines - Calvaresi Winery
CALVARY - Recording label - Calvary Records Inc.
CALVATE - Vitamins and nutritional supplements - Douglas R. Casey
CALVE - Food products - Holland-American Importing Co. Inc.
CALVEREZ - Floor coverings ☆ - Congoleum Corp.
CALVERT - Apparel–men's - Wm. B. Kessler Inc.
CALVERT - Candles - Calvert Candle
CALVERT - Fish–fresh or frozen - New England Fish Co.
CALVERT - Flatware ☆ - Kirk Stieff Co.
CALVERT - Nail care products - Spilo/Mehaz Worldwide
CALVERT - Paints ☆ - Dutch Boy Group
CALVERT - Skin care products - Calvert International
CALVERT - Whiskey - Joseph E. Seagram & Sons, Inc.
CALVERT CEDAR STREET - Mustard ☆ - El Paso Chili Co.
CALVERT EXTRA - Whiskey - Jim Beam Brands Co.
CALVERT EXTRA - Whiskey - Joseph E. Seagram & Sons, Inc.
CALVERT GIN - Gin - Jim Beam Brands Co.
CALVERT PARK - Flowers, plants, and seeds - Seaboard Seed Co.
CALVERT STREET - Recording label - Calvert Street Records Inc.
CALVERT'S - Food products - Wally Sea Products Corp.
CALVET - Wines - Hiram Walker & Sons, Inc.
CALVIN - Apparel and accessories - Crystal Brands Inc.
CALVIN COLLEGE - Recording label - Calvin College
CALVIN-FOR-MEN - Apparel–men's - Calvin Clothing Corp.
CALVIN KLEIN - Apparel and accessories - Calvin Klein Ltd.
CALVIN KLEIN - Underwear and nightwear - Calvin Klein Trademark Trust
CALVIN KLEIN CLASSIFICATIONS - Footwear - Calvin Klein Ltd.
CALVIN KLEIN COLLECTION - Footwear - Calvin Klein Ltd.
CALVIN RUFFIN CIRCA 1940 - Apparel–men's - Circa 1940, Inc.
CALWEB - Binding materials - California Webbing Industries, Inc.
CALYPSO - Automotive parts and accessories ☆ - Save-a-Life
CALYPSO - Boats - Glen-L Marine Designs
CALYPSO - Boats–motor ☆ - Bayliner Marine Corp.
CALYPSO - Computers - Calypso Software Corp.
CALYPSO - Cosmetics - Monaco Import/Export Inc.
CALYPSO - Dinnerware–glass - Nikko Ceramics Inc.
CALYPSO - Dinnerware–glass - WMF/USA
CALYPSO - Dinnerware–glass ☆ - Franciscan by Johnson Brothers, USA, Inc.
CALYPSO - Eyeglasses - Goat Eyewear
CALYPSO - Fabrics - Dan River Inc.
CALYPSO - Fabrics - Superior Shade & Blind Co. Inc.
CALYPSO - Floor coverings–carpet and rugs - Foreign Accents
CALYPSO - Furniture - Halcyon Inc.
CALYPSO - Glassware–household - Crisa Corp.
CALYPSO - Glassware–household - Owens-Illinois Inc. (Libbey Div.)
CALYPSO - High chairs ☆ - Welsh Co.
CALYPSO - Indoor-outdoor carpets and rugs - Instant Turf Industries Inc.
CALYPSO - Liquors - Canandaigua Wine Co. Inc.
CALYPSO - Mats - Matworks
CALYPSO - Mattresses - Richards Quality Bedding
CALYPSO - Mobile homes ☆ - Golden West Homes
CALYPSO - Shoes - Daniel Green Co.
CALYPSO - Skin diving equipment - U.S. Divers Co., Inc.
CALYPSO - Tableware–china ☆ - Villeroy and Boch Tableware Ltd.
CALYPSO - Tiles–ceramic ☆ - Monarch Tile Inc.
CALYPSO - Toys–models ☆ - Estes Industries

CALYPSO - Toys–stuffed ☆ - CBS Toys
CALYPSO - Vases - Durand International
CALYPSO BLUSH - Manicure preparations - Del Pharmaceuticals, Inc.
CALYPSO BREEZE - Food products - Chiquita Brands, Inc.
CALYPSO CAGES - Pet cages - Petporium Ltd.
CALYPSO COCONUT - Confections - Dreyer's Grand Ice Cream, Inc.
CALYPSO FRUITERIA - Juices - Brasa Distributors, Inc.
CALYPSO-GLO - Paper–writing - Rupaco Paper Corp.
CALYPSO MELODY - Floor coverings–carpet and rugs - Mohawk Carpet Corp.
CALYPSO PINDOT - Floor coverings–carpet and rugs - Ebsco Carpet Mills
CALYPSO WEAVE - Floor coverings–carpet and rugs - Ebsco Carpet Mills
CALYTES - Soft drink - R.W. Frookies Inc.
CALYX - Cosmetics - Estee Lauder Inc.
CALYX - Golfing equipment - Vardon Golf Co., Inc.
CALYXWARE - Earthenware ☆ - Waterford Wedgewood USA, Inc.
CALZALETAS - Sandals ☆ - Playazul International Inc.
CALZINO - Socks - Rudin & Roth Inc.
CALZONE - Cases–musical instrument - Calzone Case Co.
CALZONE RING - Pizzas–frozen - Mazzio's Corp.
CAM - Buckles ☆ - Erich M. Reich Inc.
CAM - Skin care products - Allergan Skin Care
CAM CAP - Motor vehicle parts and accessories - Temco Metal Products Co.
CAM-CARE - Computer software - Annika Systems Inc.
CAM-CASE - Cases–camera - Acme-Lite Manufacturing Co.
CAM COAT - Cases–camera - Camcoat
CAM COAT - Cases–plastic - Lisa M. Kleiger
CAM-CURE - Rubber–molded - Bridge Products, Inc.
CAM GEAR - Cameras–video - Jasco Products Co. Inc.
CAM JAMMER - Toys - Tonka Corp.
CAM-KLEEN - Bathroom accessories ☆ - Loctite Corp.
CAM-KOTE - Cleaning preparations ☆ - Loctite Corp.
CAM-LIFT - Forklifts - JH Industries Inc. (Copperloy Div.)
CAM-LINK - Tripods–photographic - QuickSet International Inc.
CAM LOC - Hardware - Central Boiler, Inc.
CAM LOC - Hardware - Sash Controls Inc.
CAM-LOCK - Concrete products - Gates & Sons Inc.
CAM-LOCK - Office supplies ☆ - Letterguide Inc.
CAM-MASTER - Brakes–motor vehicle - Rockwell International Corp.
CAM-MATIC - Ships–sailing vessels - Harken Yacht Fittings
CAM-O-FISH - Apparel and accessories - Cam-O-Fish Products, Inc.
CAM-O-FISH - T-shirts–children's - Wainwright-Corriher
CAM-O-FLAGE - Fishing lines - Cortland Line Co., Inc.
CAM POCKET - Cases–camera - Sima Products Corp.
CAM-POST - Computer software - Icam Technologies Corp. U.S.A.
CAM RAMMER - Toys - Tonka Corp.
CAM-RON - Pliers - Pro America Premium Tools
CAM-STAT - Controls–air conditioning systems - Cam-Stat Inc.
CAM-TITE - Sash locks - H.B. Ives
CAM TRAC - Circuit boards - Semco Machine Corp.
CAM-TRAK - Shelving units–metal - Phoenix Display & Manufacturing Corp.
CAM2 - Automotive parts and accessories - Cam2 Oil Products Co.
CAMA - Analgesics - Dorsey Laboratories
CAMA - Olives–canned - James P. Smith & Co., Inc.
CAMA GOLD - Fruit drinks–bottled or canned - Golden Valley Citrus Inc.
CAMADINE - Pharmaceutical preparations ☆ - Wesley Pharmacal Co. Inc.
CAMAIR - Machinery - Camair, Inc.
CAMALOX - Antacids - Rhone-Poulenc Rorer Pharmaceuticals Inc.
CAMANO - International Yachting Center
CAMARGO - Floor coverings - Mannington Resilient Floors
CAMARGO - Floor coverings–carpet and rugs ☆ - Regal Rugs Inc.
CAMARGO - Furniture–wood ☆ - Ficks Reed Co. Inc.
CAMARGUE - Motor vehicles–automobiles - Rolls-Royce Motors Inc.
CAMARGUE - Yarn ☆ - Joseph Galler Inc.
CAMARIBE - Seafood products–fresh or frozen - J.F. Clarke Corp.
CAMARILLO - Floor coverings ☆ - Congoleum Corp.
CAMARILLO - Housewares ☆ - Treasure Craft Co.
CAMARO - Motor vehicles - General Motors Corp. (Chevrolet Motor Div.)
CAMARO IROC-Z - Motor vehicles ☆ - General Motors Corp. (Chevrolet Motor Div.)
CAMARSA - Seafood products–fresh or frozen ☆ - Penguin Frozen Foods, Inc.
CAMAS - Computer software - Dana Corp.
CAMAX SYRINX - Flutes - Jack Spratt Woodwind Shop
CAMAY - Soap - Procter & Gamble Co.
CAMAYA - Beverages–alcohol - Black Prince Distillery, Inc.

☆ = Now out of production

CAMBER - Bags - Ace Product
CAMBER - Desks - Boling Co.
CAMBER - Furniture–wood ✩ - Century Furniture Co.
CAMBIASO - Wines - Cannon Wines Ltd.
CAMBIASO - Wines - Domaine St. George Winery & Vineyards
CAMBIO - Whirlpool spa ✩ - Jacuzzi Inc.
CAMBIO ITALIA - Apparel and accessories - Kennington Limited Inc.
CAMBIUM - Computer storage devices–optical - Cambium Development, Inc.
CAMBIUM - Office supplies ✩ - Heartwood Creations
CAMBLOCK - Toys - Tonka Corp.
CAMBO - Cameras - Calumet Photographic Inc.
CAMBOR - Playing cards - Cambor Enterprises Inc.
CAMBRIA - Barometers ✩ - Airguide Instrument Co.
CAMBRIA - Flatware - Washington Forge Inc.
CAMBRIA - Glassware–household ✩ - Anchor Hocking Glass, Inc.
CAMBRIA - Hardware - Simpson Timber Co.
CAMBRIA - Invitations - Classic Thermographers Ltd.
CAMBRIA - Ships–sailing vessels - Cabo Rico Yachts Inc.
CAMBRIA - Wines - Kendall Jackson Winery, Ltd.
CAMBRIAN COLLECTION - Faucets ✩ - U.S. Brass Corp.
CAMBRIC - Cabinets - Merillat Industries, Inc.
CAMBRIC - Office supplies - File-A-Dex Inc.
CAMBRIDGE - Dean Distributors, Inc.
CAMBRIDGE - Apparel–men's - Harper Shirt Co.
CAMBRIDGE - Artists' materials - Solo-Horton Brush Co.
CAMBRIDGE - Bathroom fixtures - Artesian Industries
CAMBRIDGE - Bathtubs - American Standard Inc.
CAMBRIDGE - Bicycles ✩ - Murray, Inc.
CAMBRIDGE - Cabinets - H.J. Scheirich Co.
CAMBRIDGE - Cabinets - Yorktowne Inc.
CAMBRIDGE - Cabinets–wood - Decora
CAMBRIDGE - Cabinets–wood - Parcraft Distinctive Cabinetry
CAMBRIDGE - Cabinets–wood ✩ - Kemper
CAMBRIDGE - Coffee - Cambridge/Wechsler Coffee
CAMBRIDGE - Colognes - Mem Co., Inc.
CAMBRIDGE - Compressors–refrigeration - Philip Morris Companies Inc.
CAMBRIDGE - Cordage and twine ✩ - Winchester-Auburn Mills Inc.
CAMBRIDGE - Craft supplies ✩ - Talisman of Georgia
CAMBRIDGE - Cutlery - Washington Forge Inc.
CAMBRIDGE - Dishes–china ✩ - Gorham Inc.
CAMBRIDGE - Doors–glass - Therma-Tru Corp.
CAMBRIDGE - Exercising equipment - Little River Marine Co.
CAMBRIDGE - Floor coverings - Bruce Hardwood Floors
CAMBRIDGE - Floor coverings - Congoleum Corp.
CAMBRIDGE - Floor coverings–carpet and rugs - Atlas Carpet Mills Inc.
CAMBRIDGE - Floor coverings–carpet and rugs ✩ - American Carpet Mills
CAMBRIDGE - Frames–eyeglass - Universal/Univis Inc.
CAMBRIDGE - Furniture ✩ - Hooker Furniture Corp.
CAMBRIDGE - Furniture ✩ - Lane Co. Inc.
CAMBRIDGE - Furniture ✩ - Stanley Furniture Co. Inc.
CAMBRIDGE - Furniture–upholstered ✩ - Mersman Furniture Co.
CAMBRIDGE - Giftware - Simon Golub & Sons Inc.
CAMBRIDGE - Glassware–household - Seneca Glass Co.
CAMBRIDGE - Glassware–household - Super Glass Corp.
CAMBRIDGE - Helmets–athletic - Libertyville Saddle Shop, Inc.
CAMBRIDGE - Hobby kits ✩ - Craft World International Inc.
CAMBRIDGE - Housewares - Baldwin Hardware Corp.
CAMBRIDGE - Lamps - Kaadan Ltd.
CAMBRIDGE - Mobile homes - Commodore Corp.
CAMBRIDGE - Motor vehicle parts and accessories - Lancaster Colony Automotive Group
CAMBRIDGE - Musical instruments - Trophy Music Co.
CAMBRIDGE - Occasional tables - JDI Group, Inc.
CAMBRIDGE - Office supplies - Da-Lite Screen Co. Inc.
CAMBRIDGE - Saddles - State Line Tack, Inc.
CAMBRIDGE - Shoes - Allen-Edmonds Shoe Corp.
CAMBRIDGE - Stationery - Mead Corp.
CAMBRIDGE - Storm doors - Cole Sewell Corp.
CAMBRIDGE - Strollers–baby - Combi International Corp.
CAMBRIDGE - Tires–automobile - Dunlap and Kyle Co. Inc.
CAMBRIDGE - Trailers–travel ✩ - Coachmen Industries, Inc.
CAMBRIDGE - Video equipment - Cambridge Educational
CAMBRIDGE - Wallpaper ✩ - Schooner Prints Inc.
CAMBRIDGE - Watches - Bulova Corp.
CAMBRIDGE - Yarn ✩ - Caron International Inc.
CAMBRIDGE 100S - Cigarettes - Philip Morris Companies Inc.

CAMBRIDGE BEADED - Siding - Norandex, Inc.
CAMBRIDGE BUSINESSWEAR - Office supplies - Mead Corp.
CAMBRIDGE CATHEDRAL - Cabinets–wood ✩ - Kemper
CAMBRIDGE CLASSICS - Cosmetics ✩ - Noxell Corp.
CAMBRIDGE COLLECTION - Furniture ✩ - Evenflo Juvenile Furniture Co.
CAMBRIDGE COLLECTION - Furniture ✩ - Hickory Chair Co.
CAMBRIDGE COLLECTION - Giftware - Lenox, Inc.
CAMBRIDGE COLLECTION - Neckties - Damon Creations Inc.
CAMBRIDGE COLLECTION - Women's apparel - Cambridge Dry Goods Co. Inc.
CAMBRIDGE COLLECTION, THE - Furniture - Stanley Furniture Co. Inc.
CAMBRIDGE COLONY - Cabinets - Master Woodworks Kitchen Studio
CAMBRIDGE COTTAGE - Sample books for wallcoverings - Seabrook Wallcoverings, Inc.
CAMBRIDGE COUNTRY STORE - Bags–duffel - Cambridge Dry Goods Co. Inc.
CAMBRIDGE COURT - Floor coverings - Mannington Resilient Floors
CAMBRIDGE EDUCATIONAL - Computer software - Cambridge Research Group, Ltd.
CAMBRIDGE HALL - Shirts - Wearever Shirt Co., Inc.
CAMBRIDGE MANOR - Furniture ✩ - Sumter Cabinet Co., Inc.
CAMBRIDGE PARENTING & FAMILY LIFE - Publisher's imprints - Cambridge Research Group, Ltd.
CAMBRIDGE PLACE - Floor coverings–carpet and rugs ✩ - Evans-Black Carpet Mills
CAMBRIDGE SPECIAL - Meat products–canned - Ninety-Six Canning Co.
CAMBRIDGE SUPREME - Meat products–canned ✩ - Ninety-Six Canning Co.
CAMBRIDGE TECHNOLOGY PARTNERS - Computer software - Cambridge Technology Partners (Massachusetts), Inc.
CAMBRIDGE TEDDY - Toys–stuffed - Russ Berrie and Co., Inc.
CAMBRIDGE, THE - Paint sets–hobby ✩ - Winsor & Newton
CAMBRIDGE TWEED - Seat covers - Saddleman, Inc.
CAMBRIDGE ULTRA - Pet products - State Line Tack, Inc.
CAMBRIX PUBLISHING - Computer software - Cambrix Publishing, Inc.
CAMBUCHION - Vitamins and nutritional supplements - Greenfield Home Care Ltd.
CAMCAD - Medical apparatus - Cobe Laboratories, Inc.
CAMCAL - Decals and transfers - Monterey Bay Corp.
CAMCARRIER - Food containers - Cambro Manufacturing Co.
CAMCART - Containers - Cambro Manufacturing Co.
CAMCO - Bookcases–metal ✩ - Lucas Products Corp.
CAMCO - Giftware - Cathedral Art Metal Co., Inc.
CAMCO - Knives–pocket - Camillus Cutlery Co.
CAMCO - Paints - Camco Paints Inc.
CAMCOMM - Computer software - Freese Enterprises, Inc.
CAMCRAFT - Hardware - Camcraft
CAMCRETE - Paints - Camco Paints Inc.
CAMCRUISER - Serving carts - Cambro Manufacturing Co.
CAMDEN - Blinds–vertical - Tontine/VyTech Industries Inc.
CAMDEN - Cabinets - Imperial Cabinet Co. Inc.
CAMDEN - Cabinets ✩ - American Woodmark Corp.
CAMDEN - Furniture - Boling Co.
CAMDEN - Furniture - Pilliod Co.
CAMDEN - Furniture - Singer Furniture Co.
CAMDEN - Furniture ✩ - Moosehead Manufacturing Co.
CAMDEN - Paper–kraft - International Paper Co.
CAMDEN - Photographic equipment - Eastman Kodak Co.
CAMDEN - Recording label - Essex Entertainment Inc.
CAMDEN - Shoes ✩ - Allen-Edmonds Shoe Corp.
CAMDEN - Tableware–china - Pfaltzgraff Investment Co.
CAMDEN - Wire–copper - Camden Wire Co., Inc.
CAMDEN BASKETS - Baskets–wood - Camden Basket Co. Inc.
CAMDEN CIRCLE - Floor coverings–carpet and rugs ✩ - Hollytex Carpet Mills Inc.
CAMDEN CREEK BAKERY - Cookies - Schwan's Sales Enterprises, Inc.
CAMDEN OAK - Furniture - Hammary Furniture Co. Inc.
CAMDEN PARK - Apparel–men's - N.W. Buyers & Jobbers Inc.
CAMDEN PASSAGE - Wallpaper ✩ - Sandpiper Studios
CAMDEN REACH - Bells - North Country Wind Bells Inc.
CAMDEN SOUL - Recording label - All Star Promotions
CAMDEN SQUARE - Floor coverings - Mannington Resilient Floors
CAMDEN YARDS - Apparel and accessories - Maryland Stadium Authority
CAMDITIONER - Battery chargers - Eveready Battery Co., Inc.
CAMDRIVER - Toys - Tonka Corp.
CAMDURA - Floor coverings ✩ - Cambridge Tile Manufacturing Co.
CAMECO - Food processing equipment - Cameco Industries, Inc.

✩ = Now out of production

CAMECO - Hams - Cameco Inc.
CAMEL - Cigarettes - R.J. Reynolds Tobacco Co.
CAMEL - Containers - Hormel Corp.
CAMEL - Fabrics - Gretchen Bellinger Inc.
CAMEL - Food products ☆ - Hommus Factory Inc.
CAMEL - Grinders - Solcoor Inc.
CAMEL - Yarn - Joseph Galler Inc.
CAMEL BAY - Floor coverings–carpet and rugs ☆ - Walter Carpet Mills
CAMEL BOCK - Beverages–malt - Camelback Ski Corp.
CAMEL LIGHTS - Cigarettes - R.J. Reynolds Tobacco Co.
CAMEL MOTORSPORTS - Shoes - R.J. Reynolds Tobacco Co.
CAMEL PINK - Nail care products - Cosmair Inc.
CAMEL TOES - Apparel and accessories - William O. Williams
CAMEL WIDES - Cigarettes - R.J. Reynolds Tobacco Co.
CAMELBACK - Notebooks and notepads - Norcom Inc.
CAMELBACK MOUNTAIN GOURMET - Preserved foods–canned - Sunset Food & Beverage Corp.
CAMELEON - Computer peripheral equipment - Oxford Molecular Group
CAMELIA - Food products ☆ - Mampeza International Inc.
CAMELIA - Furniture–wood ☆ - Century Furniture Co.
CAMELIA - Milk - Camellia Food Stores Inc.
CAMELIA - Wallpaper ☆ - Gamrod-Harman
CAMELLIA - Apparel and accessories ☆ - Strouse, Adler Co.
CAMELLIA - Flatware - Gorham Inc.
CAMELLIA - Rice - Producers Rice Mill, Inc.
CAMELLIA - Salad dressings–bottled - Hudson Industries, Inc.
CAMELLIA - Skin care products - Covermark Cosmetics
CAMELLIA - Vases–ceramic - Crisa Corp.
CAMELOT - Cabinets ☆ - Triangle Pacific Corp. (Cabinet Division)
CAMELOT - Cakes–mixes - Dawn Food Products Inc.
CAMELOT - Candles ☆ - W and F Products Inc.
CAMELOT - Cases–eyeglass ☆ - Camelot Laboratories
CAMELOT - Christmas tree ornaments ☆ - Cracker Box Inc.
CAMELOT - Cooking utensils–cast iron ☆ - Regal Ware, Inc.
CAMELOT - Cord tables - California Acrylic Industries Inc.
CAMELOT - Cutlery ☆ - Lifetime Hoan Corp.
CAMELOT - Dinnerware–glass - Franciscan by Johnson Brothers, USA, Inc.
CAMELOT - Dishes–earthenware ☆ - Denby USA Limited
CAMELOT - Fabrics ☆ - Greenwood Mills Inc.
CAMELOT - Floor coverings - Congoleum Corp.
CAMELOT - Floor coverings–carpet and rugs - Collins & Aikman Corp.
CAMELOT - Floor coverings–carpet and rugs ☆ - Interloom Ltd.
CAMELOT - Floor coverings–carpet and rugs ☆ - Regal Rugs Inc.
CAMELOT - Floor coverings–tile ☆ - Kepcor, Inc./SSI Tiles
CAMELOT - Health care products - Sunrise Medical
CAMELOT - Jewelry - TNJ Advertising Co., Inc.
CAMELOT - Luggage - Airway Industries, Inc.
CAMELOT - Relishes - Stache Foods
CAMELOT - Sinks–metal - Moen Inc.
CAMELOT - Trailers–travel ☆ - Starcraft Corp.
CAMELOT - Wallpaper - Pickhardt & Siebert USA Inc.
CAMELOT - Wines - Kendall Jackson Winery, Ltd.
CAMELOT BOOKS - Publisher's imprints - Hearst Corp.
CAMELOT CARVED - Jewelry - TNJ Advertising Co., Inc.
CAMELOT MEAD - Wines - Oliver Wine Co. Inc.
CAMELOT UNI - Cases–eyeglass ☆ - Camelot Laboratories
CAMELOT UNICORN - Toys–stuffed - Dakin Inc.
CAMELS - Candy ☆ - Crystal Pure Candy Co.
CAMEO - Accordions ☆ - Pacific Music Supply Co.
CAMEO - Apparel stores–lingerie ☆ - Century/Nazareth Mills
CAMEO - Artists' materials - Leisurecrafts
CAMEO - Bathroom fixtures ☆ - Showerlux USA
CAMEO - Bedding, comforters - CHF Industries, Inc.
CAMEO - Belts - Metro Fashions Ltd.
CAMEO - Bicycles ☆ - Murray, Inc.
CAMEO - Blinds–venetian - Cameo Products
CAMEO - Bottles–glass - Drug Plastic and Glass Co.
CAMEO - Brassieres (Bras) - Cameo Coutures
CAMEO - Cabinets - American Woodmark Corp.
CAMEO - Cameras - Eastman Kodak Co.
CAMEO - Candles - Glico Harmony Foods Corp.
CAMEO - Candles ☆ - Candle-Lite Co.
CAMEO - Candy - California Peanut Co.
CAMEO - Chairs–wood - Trendway Corp.
CAMEO - Cleaning preparations - Dial Corp.
CAMEO - Clocks - General Time Corp. (Westclox/Seth Thomas Div.)

CAMEO - Cookies - Nabisco Foods Group
CAMEO - Cosmetics - Cameo Cosmetics
CAMEO - Crocheted and knitted items - Broadway Knitting Mills Inc.
CAMEO - Dishes–china - Pickard Inc.
CAMEO - Dolls ☆ - Strombecker Corp.
CAMEO - Envelopes - Quality Park Products Co.
CAMEO - Fireplace equipment - Thermo-Rite Manufacturing Co.
CAMEO - Floor coverings - Congoleum Corp.
CAMEO - Floor coverings–carpet and rugs - American Carpet Mills
CAMEO - Floor coverings–carpet and rugs - Alexander Smith Carpets
CAMEO - Flowers, plants, and seeds - Hines Nurseries, Inc.
CAMEO - Furniture - Hammary Furniture Co. Inc.
CAMEO - Furniture - Universal Flooring
CAMEO - Glassware–household ☆ - Fenton Art Glass Co.
CAMEO - Greeting cards - Gibson Greetings, Inc.
CAMEO - Hair care products - Cameo Inc.
CAMEO - Health care products - Medco Lab Inc.
CAMEO - Hearing aids - Argosy Electronics, Inc.
CAMEO - Housewares - Cameo China, Inc.
CAMEO - Lamps - Philips Lighting Co.
CAMEO - Leather goods - Springfield Leather Products Co.
CAMEO - Luggage - Airway Industries, Inc.
CAMEO - Luggage - American Tourister, Inc.
CAMEO - Manicure preparations - Cameo Beauty Supply Co.
CAMEO - Mattresses ☆ - Kingsdown, Inc.
CAMEO - Packaging–paper - Bagcraft Corp. of America
CAMEO - Paints - Perry & Derrick Co.
CAMEO - Paper–gift wrap ☆ - Cleo Inc.
CAMEO - Plywood ☆ - Ply-Gem Manufacturing Corp.
CAMEO - Rings–jewelry - Artcarved Inc.
CAMEO - Sealing compounds - Craftmade International Inc.
CAMEO - Sinks–metal - Moen Inc.
CAMEO - Soap ☆ - Stahl Soap Corp.
CAMEO - Stationery - Burgoyne Inc./Curtis Swann
CAMEO - Telephones - Conair Corp.
CAMEO - Tiles–ceramic - Monarch Tile Inc.
CAMEO - Tiles–ceramic ☆ - H & R Johnson Inc.
CAMEO - Trailers–travel - Carriage, Inc.
CAMEO APPEARANCES - Wallpaper - Taylor Wallcoverings Inc.
CAMEO BLUE - Dinnerware–glass ☆ - Nikko Ceramics Inc.
CAMEO CAY - Furniture ☆ - Bassett Furniture Industries, Inc.
CAMEO CLASSICS - Recording label - Essex Entertainment Inc.
CAMEO CLASSICS - Recording label - Moss Music Group Inc.
CAMEO COLLECTION - Furniture ☆ - Evenflo Juvenile Furniture Co.
CAMEO COLLECTION - House furnishings - Greenwich Workshop, Inc.
CAMEO CREATIONS - Lamps - Harris Lamps Co.
CAMEO LIFT - Cosmetics ☆ - Spilo/Mehaz Worldwide
CAMEO LIQUID MAKEUP - Cosmetics - Viviane Woodard Industries, Ltd.
CAMEO PARIS WRAP - Plaster–wallboard - Leisurecrafts
CAMEO PARKWAY - Recording label - ABKCO Records
CAMEO PINK - Dinnerware–glass ☆ - Nikko Ceramics Inc.
CAMEO ROSE - Apparel and accessories - Miller Stockman Western Wear
CAMEO ROSE - Burial vaults–concrete - Wilbert, Inc.
CAMEO ROSE - Dinnerware–glass - Nikko Ceramics Inc.
CAMEO ROSE - Flatware - Utica Cutlery Co.
CAMEO ROSE - Wallpaper - Mirage Wallcovering Co.
CAMEO ROSE COLLECTION - Toys - Brass Key, Inc.
CAMEO SATIN - Paints - Perry & Derrick Co.
CAMEO SHORES - Floor coverings–carpet and rugs - Catalina Carpet Mills Inc.
CAMEO SUPREME - Enamels - Perry & Derrick Co.
CAMEO ZOOM PLUS - Cameras - Eastman Kodak Co.
CAMEOBRONZE - Figurines - Cameo Guild, Inc.
CAMEOLEFIN, TOO - Wallpaper ☆ - Gilford Corp.
CAMEOS - Shoes - El Greco Inc.
CAMER ROSE - Kitchen appliances ☆ - National Housewares
CAMERA - Colognes - Le Monde D.F.L., Inc.
CAMERA - Paper–photographic ☆ - Keuffel & Esser Co.
CAMERA COMMAND - Photographic equipment - SP Systems/Saratons
CAMERA CONFIGURATOR - Computer software - Imaging Technology Inc.
CAMERA GUARD 35 - Cameras - Montgomery Ward & Co. Inc.
CAMERAFLEX - Cameras - Team Products
CAMERALARM - Cases–camera - SP Systems/Saratons
CAMERALITE - Lighting equipment - Acme-Lite Manufacturing Co.
CAMERAMAN - Cameras - Parkervision Inc.
CAMERASHIELD - Cases–camera ☆ - Sima Products Corp.

☆ = Now out of production

CAMERASOUND - Electronic equipment - Radmar Inc.
CAMERINO - Furniture ☆ - Bernhardt Industries
CAMERO - Watches - Lean & Jones Inc.
CAMERON - Apparel and accessories ☆ - Sara Lee Knit Products Inc.
CAMERON - Coffee - Cameron Coffee Co. Inc.
CAMERON - Curtain rods - Newell Window Furnishing Co.
CAMERON - Floor coverings - Mannington Resilient Floors
CAMERON - Floor coverings—carpet and rugs ☆ - Mannington Carpets, Inc.
CAMERON - Furniture - Haworth, Inc.
CAMERON - Furniture ☆ - Stanley Furniture Co. Inc.
CAMERON - Glassware—household ☆ - Anchor Hocking Glass, Inc.
CAMERON - Jewelry - Cameron Ltd.
CAMERON - Shoes ☆ - Allen-Edmonds Shoe Corp.
CAMERON BEAR - Toys—stuffed - Dakin Inc.
CAMERON CATHEDRAL - Cabinets—wood - Kemper
CAMERON CREST - Stationery - Tuttle Law Print Inc.
CAMERON PARK - Apparel—men's - S & K Famous Brands, Inc.
CAMERON SQUARE - Cabinets—wood - Kemper
CAMERON'S KEEPING - Coffee - Cameron Coffee Co. Inc.
CAMEROUN - Floor coverings—carpet and rugs ☆ - Zenith Carpets
CAMERTON - Sinks—metal - Kohler Co.
CAMERZ - Cameras - Photo-Sonics Inc.
CAMET - Industrial machinery - W.R. Grace & Co.
CAMET - Metals - Chicago Powdered Metal Products Co.
CAMEX - Cameras—motion picture ☆ - Heitz Service Corp.
CAMI-LACE - Apparel and accessories - Brazabra Corp.
CAMI VIDEO - T-shirts—men's - Cami Video, Inc.
CAMIE - Cleaning preparations - Camie-Campbell Inc.
CAMILA - Frames—eyeglass - Rozin Optical Export Corp.
CAMILE - Frames—eyeglass ☆ - Universal/Univis Inc.
CAMILIA - Pharmaceutical preparations - Boiron Inc.
CAMILIO - Leather goods - Crown Handbags Ltd.
CAMILLA - Dinnerware—glass ☆ - Royal China & Porcelain Companies Inc.
CAMILLA'S GARDEN - Wallpaper - Greeff Fabrics Inc.
CAMILLE - Cosmetics - Lancome
CAMILLE - Floor coverings—carpet and rugs ☆ - Regal Rugs Inc.
CAMILLE - Furniture - Thomasville Furniture Industries Inc.
CAMILLE - House furnishings ☆ - Kellwood Co.
CAMILLE - Jewelry - Camille Jewelry Inc.
CAMILLE - Nail care products - Michigan Ceramic Sales & Engineering Inc.
CAMILLE - Photo albums - Camille Co. Inc.
CAMILLE - Recording label - Camille B. Harrison
CAMILLE - Rings—jewelry - Artcarved Inc.
CAMILLE - Sporting goods ☆ - O'Brien International
CAMILLE - Watches - Bulova Corp.
CAMILLE - Yarn - William Unger & Co. Inc.
CAMILLE FIERENZE - Apparel and accessories - Breton Industries
CAMILLE SEA WEES - Toys - Tonka Corp.
CAMILLE TROPICAL - Toys - Tonka Corp.
CAMILLUS - Cutlery - Camillus Cutlery Co.
CAMILLUS CLASSIC CARTRIDGE - Knives—pocket ☆ - Camillus Cutlery Co.
CAMINAL-S - Veterinary pharmaceutical preparations ☆ - Schering-Plough Animal Health
CAMINO - Beverages—alcohol - Carradale Import Co.
CAMINO - Bicycles - Ross Bicycles USA, Ltd.
CAMINO NEUROCARE - Medical apparatus - Heyer-Schulte Neurocare, LP
CAMINO REAL - Floor coverings ☆ - Azrock Commercial Flooring
CAMINO REAL - Food products - Camino Real Foods
CAMINOS - Cigar boxes—wood - Consolidated Cigar Corp.
CAMINTONN - Computer accessories - Camintonn Corp.
CAMIS - Computer software - Systemware, Inc.
CAMISA - Apparel—women's - Hairston Roberson
CAMISETTE - Underwear and nightwear - A. Brod, Inc.
CAMISO-BRA - Brassieres (Bras) ☆ - Lovable Co.
CAMKLEEN - Cleaning preparations—household - Cambridge Tile Manufacturing Co.
CAMLIGHT - Cameras—video - Sima Products Corp.
CAMLIGHT 3 - Cameras—video - Sima Products Corp.
CAMLIN - Doors - Simpson Timber Co.
CAMLOC - Fasteners ☆ - Rexnord Corp.
CAMLOK - Projection screens - Da-Lite Screen Co. Inc.
CAMLOK BINDING - Sporting goods - Wellington Leisure Products, Inc.
CAMMARATA CIGAR CO. - Cigars - James T. Tyre
CAMMIE'S - Candy - Dayton Hudson Corp.
CAMMIKE - Microphones - Sima Products Corp.
CAMO - Meat products—beef - Curtice-Burns Foods, Inc.

CAMO - Pens - Parker Pen USA
CAMO CAN - Meat products—beef - Curtice-Burns Foods, Inc.
CAMO-CAPS - Sporting goods - Camp-Cap Products
CAMO CARE - Health care products ☆ - Abkit, Inc.
CAMO-CLEAN - Sporting goods - Camp-Cap Products
CAMO-COMPAC - Cosmetics - Hunter's Specialties, Inc.
CAMO FORCE - Toys—automobiles - Mattel, Inc.
CAMO-HUNTER - Sporting goods - Easton Aluminum Inc.
CAMO LOUNGE - Pet products - O'Donnell Industries Inc.
CAMO-OFF - Cosmetics - Hunter's Specialties, Inc.
CAMO PAK - Meat products—beef - Curtice-Burns Foods, Inc.
CAMO-PATCH - Camouflage cloth patches - Big River Game Calls
CAMO ROPE - Cordage and twine - Wellington Leisure Products, Inc.
CAMO/SCENT - Sporting goods - Normark Corp.
CAMO-STICKS - Sporting goods - Camp-Cap Products
CAMO VAC - Jars—plastic ☆ - Rubbermaid Inc.
CAMOCARE - Skin care products - Abkit, Inc.
CAMOCO - Brooms - Carolina Mop Manufacturing Co.
CAMOFORCE - Pharmaceutical preparations - Murdock, Madaus, Schwabe, Inc.
CAMOLOT - Cabinets - Noble Cabinet Corp.
CAMOSKIN - Hunter camouflage - Jinxie's, Inc.
CAMOUFLAGE - Pens - Bic Corp.
CAMOUFLAGE CRAYON - Cosmetics - Covermark Cosmetics
CAMOX - Artists' materials ☆ - M. Grumbacher Inc.
CAMP - Chairs—folding - Heartwood Furniture
CAMP - Cleaning preparations—carpet and rug - Host/Racine Industries Inc.
CAMP - Computer software ☆ - Lowell Corp.
CAMP - Fabrics - Gretchen Bellinger Inc.
CAMP - Hosiery - Camp Hosiery
CAMP - Medical apparatus ☆ - Camp, Inc.
CAMP 7 - Apparel and accessories - Sport Chalet Inc.
CAMP AMERICA - Sporting goods ☆ - Maurice Sporting Goods, Inc.
CAMP ANDERSON - Apparel—women's - Carol Anderson, Inc.
CAMP BEBE - Apparel—children's - Jeanne W. Ruderman
CAMP BEVERLY HILLS - Apparel and accessories - Camp Beverly Hills Inc.
CAMP BEVERLY HILLS - Colognes - Frances Denney
CAMP BEVERLY HILLS - Sunglasses ☆ - International Tropic-Cal Inc. (I SKI Div.)
CAMP CALIFORNIA - Toys - Camp California Inc.
CAMP CALIFORNIA - Toys—stuffed ☆ - Mighty Star Inc. (Special Effects Div.)
CAMP-CAP - Sporting goods - Camp-Cap Products
CAMP CHEF - Barbecues and grills - Camp Chef
CAMP CHEF - Portable propane stove - Steelcore Plastics Co.
CAMP DAVID - Jackets - Camp David, Inc.
CAMP DRY - Waterproofing compounds - Kiwi Brands, Inc.
CAMP FIRE BOYS AND GIRLS - Playing cards - Camp Fire, Inc.
CAMP FROG HOLLOW - Computer software - Don Johnston Inc.
CAMP GIVES KIDS A WORLD OF GOOD - T-shirts—men's - American Camping Association, Inc.
CAMP GONE TO THE DOGS - Pet products - Gone to the Dogs
CAMP GRILL - Barbecues and grills - Camp Chef
CAMP-INN - Tents - Cerf Brothers Bag Co. Inc.
CAMP MUDPUDDLE - Paper products - Suzy's Zoo
CAMP 'N' COOK - Stoves ☆ - Ronson Consumer Products Corp.
CAMP 'N' GLO - Lanterns—kerosene ☆ - Ronson Consumer Products Corp.
CAMP POD - Barbecue and grill accessories - Camp-Pod Enterprises
CAMP SIMPLICITY - Patterns—clothing ☆ - Simplicity Pattern Co., Inc.
CAMP STEP AHEAD - Publisher's imprints ☆ - Western Publishing Co., Inc.
CAMP TRAILS - Sporting goods - Johnson Camping Inc.
CAMP TRAILS - Tents - Johnson Worldwide Associates, Inc.
CAMP TRAILS OUTDOOR GEAR SINCE 1946 - Backpacks ☆ - Johnson Worldwide Associates, Inc.
CAMP TV VIDEO - Video production - Camp TV Video Productions, Inc.
CAMPA-CHEM - Recreational vehicle dealers - Thetford Corp.
CAMPACK - Cameras—video - Sima Products Corp.
CAMPAGNE - Meats—luncheon - De Choix Specialty Foods Co.
CAMPAIGN - Floor coverings—carpet and rugs ☆ - Mannington Carpets, Inc.
CAMPAIGN - Golfing equipment - Sun Mountain Sports, Inc.
CAMPAIGN - Herbicides - Monsanto Co.
CAMPAIGN ALE - Beverages—malt - Chatham Imports, Inc.
CAMPAIGN MATH - Computer software - Mind Play
CAMPAIGNBALL - Balls—football - Concepts, Inc.
CAMPAIGNER - Floor coverings—carpet and rugs - Mohawk Carpet Corp.
CAMPAIGNER - House furnishings ☆ - Lexington Furniture Industries, Inc.
CAMPAIGNER - Tires - Dunlop Tire Corp.

☆ = Now out of production

CAMPAIGNERS - Safe deposit boxes - Boxes By Pandora Inc.
CAMPAN - Beverages–alcohol - Campari USA Inc.
CAMPANA - Accordions ☆ - Bell Duovox Corp.
CAMPANA - Whirlpools - Jason International, Inc.
CAMPANI - Tiles–ceramic - Federal Tile Imports Inc.
CAMPANIA - Dishes–china - Pasmantier Co. Inc.
CAMPANILE - Dinnerware–glass ☆ - WMF/USA
CAMPANILE II-D - Bells and chimes - Schulmerich Carillons Inc.
CAMPANINI - Rice - De Medici Imports Ltd.
CAMPANULA - Dinnerware–glass - Royal China & Porcelain Companies Inc.
CAMPARI - Fruits and vegetables - New Horizon
CAMPARI - Furniture ☆ - Stanley Furniture Co. Inc.
CAMPARI APERITIVO - Cordials - Campari USA Inc.
CAMPBELL - Boats–motor - London Bridge Boat Co.
CAMPBELL - Locks - Cooper Industries, Inc.
CAMPBELL - Publisher's imprints - Willis Music Co.
CAMPBELL - Skin care products - Hess Hair Milk Laboratories Inc.
CAMPBELL - Windows–storm - Thermal Technology Industries Inc.
CAMPBELL & COOPER - Beverages–alcohol - Frank-Lin Distillers Products
CAMPBELL CONTRACT - Furniture - R. Jones & Associates, Inc.
CAMPBELL EXPRESS - Snack foods - Campbell Soup Co.
CAMPBELL HANSFELD - Compressors–air - Campbell Group (Wayne Home Equipment Div.)
CAMPBELL KIDS - Apparel–children's - William Carter Co.
CAMPBELL KIDS - Toys ☆ - Knickerbocker Toy Co. Inc.
CAMPBELL KIDS FUN BOX - Book ends - CSC Brands, Inc.
CAMPBELL KIDS FUN BOX - Novelty items - Campbell Soup Co.
CAMPBELL QUALITY - Paints ☆ - M.L. Campbell Co.
CAMPBELL'S - Juices - CSC Brands, Inc.
CAMPBELL'S - Soups–canned - Campbell Soup Co.
CAMPBELL'S CUP - Soups–mixes - Campbell Soup Co.
CAMPBELL'S EARLY - Wines - Sax's Winery
CAMPBELL'S FINEST - Coffee - Thomas A. Campbell Co.
CAMPBELL'S FRESH - Food products ☆ - Campbell Soup Co.
CAMPBELL'S GRO-GREEN - Fertilizers - H.D. Campbell Co.
CAMPBELL'S KITCHEN - Dinners–frozen - Campbell Soup Co.
CAMPBELL'S SIMMER CHEF - Sauces - Campbell Soup Co.
CAMPCARD - Telephone apparatus - Rodger M. Popkin
CAMPDEN PARK - Furniture ☆ - Riverside Furniture Corp.
CAMPECHE - Food products - Wally Sea Products Corp.
CAMPECHE BAY - Seafood products–fresh or frozen ☆ - Penguin Frozen Foods, Inc.
CAMPECHE GULF - Food products - Wally Sea Products Corp.
CAMPECHE HARVEST - Seafood products–fresh or frozen - Penguin Frozen Foods, Inc.
CAMPECHE MARQUES - Seafood products–fresh or frozen ☆ - G.F. Higgins
CAMPECHE PEARL - Seafood products–fresh or frozen - Impex Shrimp & Fish Co.
CAMPECHE PRIDE - Seafood products–fresh or frozen - G.F. Higgins
CAMPECHE PRINCESS - Seafood products–canned or cured - Campeche Seafood Products, Inc.
CAMPECHE STAR - Seafood products–fresh or frozen - Zaloom Brothers Co. of New Jersey
CAMPECHE TREASURE - Seafood products–canned or cured - Campeche Seafood Products, Inc.
CAMPER - Axes - E-Z Sales & Manufacturing, Inc.
CAMPER - Boats–canoes - Old Town Canoe Co.
CAMPER - Boats–motor ☆ - Carver Boat Corp.
CAMPER - Lighting fixtures - Big Beam Emergency Systems Inc.
CAMPER - Office furniture ☆ - Inwood Office Furniture
CAMPER CLOTH - Tents - Colorado Tent Co.
CAMPER JOHNS - Tents ☆ - Plaza Enterprises Inc. (Magnador Div.)
CAMPER-KLOZER - Doors–screen - Carefree of Colorado
CAMPER SPECIALTIES - Hoses - Coast Distribution System
CAMPERCADDIE - Partitions–wood ☆ - Fleetwood Enterprises, Inc.
CAMPERS - Shoes ☆ - Edison Brothers Stores, Inc.
CAMPER'S AID - First aid kits - Camp-Cap Products
CAMPER'S BUDDY - Novelty items - Proseed (USA), Inc.
CAMPER'S CHOICE - Sporting goods - All-Luminum Products Inc.
CAMPERS COOLER - Ice chests ☆ - Poloron Products Inc.
CAMPETTE - Trailers–travel ☆ - Shasta Industries Inc.
CAMPFIRE - Coffee - Jardine's Texas Foods
CAMPFIRE - Marshmallows - Cracker Jack
CAMPFIRE - Meat products–beef - Armour Swift-Eckrich
CAMPFIRE CHICKEN AND WORMS - Meat products–poultry - Bugaboo Creek Steak House, Inc.

CAMPFIRE JELLY - Jams and jellies - Mountain Maid Gourmet Jelly
CAMPFIRE MEMORIES - Incense - Campfire Products, Inc.
CAMPFIRE SERIES - Stoves and lanterns - Coleman Co., Inc.
CAMPFIRE TO GO - Novelty items - Gold N' Silver Productions, Inc.
CAMPFIRE TOOTERS - Preserved foods–prepackaged - Philip R. Hagadorn
CAMPFIRES - Floor coverings–carpet and rugs - Sweetwater Carpet Corp.
CAMPHO-PHENIQUE - Antiseptics - Bayer Corp. (Consumer Care Div.)
CAMPHORCOL - Pharmaceutical preparations ☆ - Wendt-Bristol Co.
CAMPHOROLE - Cold remedies - Camphorole Inc.
CAMPIN' CUBS - Toys–stuffed - Fun World Inc.
CAMPINEIRA - Confections ☆ - R.L. Albert & Son, Inc.
CAMPING COMPANY, THE - Sporting goods - Kellwood Co.
CAMPING FUN - Toys - Mattel, Inc.
CAMPING GAZ - Camp furniture–metal - Suunto USA
CAMPINILE - Vegetables–canned - Lico Brands, Inc.
CAMPION BOOKS - Publisher's imprints - Loyola University Press
CAMPIONE - Boats–motor - Ebbtide Corp.
CAMPIONE D'ITALIA - Food products - Campione D'Italia Foods Inc.
CAMPIONI - Sausages - Fresh Mark, Inc.
CAMPISANO'S PRIDE - Fruits and vegetables - Al Campisano Fruit Co. Inc.
CAMPLAMP - Sporting goods - 49er Products Inc.
CAMPLITE - Footwear - Stride Rite Corp.
CAMPLITE - Trailers–travel - Damon Corp.
CAMPMOR - Apparel and accessories - Campmor Inc.
CAMP'N GRILL - Barbecues and grills - Arizona Enterprises, Industries & Opportunities Unlimited, Inc.
CAMPO - Balls ☆ - Mikasa Sports
CAMPO LEONADO - Wines - Leonard Kreusch Inc.
CAMPO PACK - Meat products–beef - Curtice-Burns Meat Snacks Inc.
CAMPOBELLO - Dinnerware–glass - Noritake Co. Inc.
CAMPOBELLO - Wines - Opici Wine Co.
CAMPOD - Tripods–photographic - Sima Products Corp.
CAMPOFRIO - Food products - Beatrice Cos. Inc.
CAMPOO - Cleaning preparations–carpet and rug - Multi-Care Corp.
CAMPOREE - Popcorn - The Fireworks Popcorn Co.
CAMPORT - Cameras - Silicon Vision, Inc.
CAMPOS SILHOF - Housewares ☆ - Crate and Barrel
CAMPOWER - Batteries - Sima Products Corp.
CAMPOXY C-800 - Epoxy - Cambridge Tile Manufacturing Co.
CAMPS - Meat products–beef - Camp Steak Co. Inc.
CAMP'S FIRE - Charcoal - Caldo International, Inc.
CAMPSIDES - Footwear - Sebago Inc.
CAMPSITE - Motor vehicles–motor homes - Winnebago Industries, Inc.
CAMPTON - Cabinets - Sunny Wood Products Co. Inc.
CAMPTON PLACE - Floor coverings–carpet and rugs - World Carpets, Inc.
CAMPTOWN - Apparel–children's - Camptown Togs Inc.
CAMPUS - Apparel and accessories - Campus Sportswear Co.
CAMPUS - Apparel and accessories - Donnkenny Inc.
CAMPUS - Floor coverings–carpet and rugs ☆ - Atlas Carpet Mills Inc.
CAMPUS - Luggage - Samsonite Corp.
CAMPUS - Pencils - Faber-Castell Corp.
CAMPUS - Pencils - Staedtler, Inc.
CAMPUS - Pipes–tobacco - S.M. Frank & Co. Inc. (Kaywoodie-Yello-Bole-Medico)
CAMPUS BOND - Paper - Southworth Co.
CAMPUS CASUALS - Apparel and accessories - Campus Casuals of California
CAMPUS CLOTH - Wallcoverings - Ben Rose Ltd.
CAMPUS CLUB - Luggage - Travelers Club Luggage Inc.
CAMPUS COLLECTION - Eyeglasses - Styl-Rite Optical Manufacturing Co., Inc.
CAMPUS COLLECTION - Notebooks and notepads - Norcom Inc.
CAMPUS COLORAY - Pencils - Faber-Castell Corp.
CAMPUS COMPACT - Bicycles ☆ - Murray, Inc.
CAMPUS-E1 - Transmission equipment–industrial - Pairgain Technologies, Inc.
CAMPUS ECOLOGY - Educational materials - National Wildlife Federation
CAMPUS GIRL - Apparel–women's ☆ - Movie Star Lingerie
CAMPUS MATES - Stationery ☆ - Mead Corp.
CAMPUS SHEETS - Linen - Comfort USA, Inc.
CAMPUS SPIRIT - Apparel and accessories - Tultex Corp.
CAMPUS STRIPE - House furnishings - Dan River Inc.
CAMPUS-T1 - Communications equipment - Pairgain Technologies, Inc.
CAMPUS TOGS - Apparel–men's - Kayser-Roth Corp.
CAMPUSPORT - Apparel and accessories - Campus Sportswear Co.
CAMPWARE - Computer software - David A. Lazuk
CAMPWEAR - Apparel - Thomaston Mills Inc.

☆ = Now out of production

CAMPY - Figurines - Antique Electronic Supply L.P.

CAMQUIP - Cameras–video - Gemini Industries, Inc.

CAMRAY - Skin care products - Veeco Manufacturing Co.

CAMRON - Frames–eyeglass - U.S. Optical Frame Co.

CAMRY - Motor vehicles–automobiles - Toyota Motor Sales USA Inc.

CAMS - Computer software and electronics equipment - Valmont Industries, Inc.

CAMS - Games - Dynamix, Inc.

CAMSCO - Mushrooms - Mushroom Growers Association Sales Co.

CAMSERVER - Beverage dispensing equipment - Cambro Manufacturing Co.

CAMSET - Adhesives and sealants - Cambridge Tile Manufacturing Co.

CAMSHAFTS - Product description unknown - Textron Inc.

CAMSIN - Vitamins and nutritional supplements - Tyson & Associates, Inc.

CAMSQUARES - Containers - Cambro Manufacturing Co.

CAMSTAND - Video camera support frame - Videovision Assemblers

CAMSTAR - Exercising equipment - Hoggan Health Industries Inc.

CAMTAINER - Insulating materials - Cambro Manufacturing Co.

CAMTRONIC - Metals - Textron Inc.

CAMTUT - Stationery - Tuttle Law Print Inc.

CAMUS - Chocolate candy ☆ - Liberty Richter Inc.

CAMUS - Computer software ☆ - CONDUIT

CAMVET - Veterinary pharmaceutical preparations ☆ - Merck & Co., Inc. (Merck Agvet Division)

CAMWEAR - Food containers - Cambro Manufacturing Co.

CAMWILL - Office supplies ☆ - Faber-Castell Corp.

CAN-AM - Fencing–wood - Canadian Cedar Products Inc.

CAN-AM - Motorcycles - Bombardier Corp.

CAN-AM - Toys ☆ - Strombecker Corp.

CAN AMS - Footwear - G.H. Bass and Co.

CAN CADDY - Containers - Creative Concepts Unlimited, Inc.

CAN-CAN - Brassieres (Bras) - Bi-Flex International

CAN-CAN - Cosmetics ☆ - Cassidy Inc.

CAN CAN - Fabrics - Gretchen Bellinger Inc.

CAN CAN - Greeting cards - Gallant Greetings Corp.

CAN-COASTER - Trays - Aqua-Tainer Co.

CAN COOLER - Insulating materials - Life-Link International, Inc.

CAN COOLR - Containers - Team Products

CAN CRUSHER - Electronic equipment - West Bend Co.

CAN-D-PAK - Food products ☆ - Stilwell Foods

CAN-D-STOR - Housewares - International Dyno Corp.

CAN-DO - Can openers–electric ☆ - Ronson Consumer Products Corp.

CAN-DO - Can openers–hand-operated ☆ - Marson Creative Fastener Group

CAN-DO - Enamels - Cowman-Campbell Paint Co.

CAN-DO KINDER GARDEN MODERN CURRICULUM PRESS - Audio tapes–blank - Modern Curriculum Press, Inc.

CAN-DUIT - Lighting equipment - Carlon

CAN-GEST - Health care products - Alta Health Products

CAN-GRABBER - Containers–insulated - Aladdin Industries, Inc.

CAN-GUN - Hardware - Safeworld International Inc.

CAN I SLIP YOU A BANANA - Beverages–alcohol - Barton Brands, Ltd.

CAN-IT - Games ☆ - Lakeside Games

CAN-O - Pet products - Lewis Food Co.

CAN-O-LITE - Paints - Spencer-Adams Paint Co. Inc.

CAN-O-MATIC - Can openers–electric - Rival Manufacturing Co.

CAN-O-PETS - Toys–stuffed ☆ - Commonwealth Toy and Novelty Co. Inc.

CAN-O-SCENT - Air purification systems - Medo Industries, Inc.

CAN-PAK - Trays - International Container Systems

CAN-PAN - Containers–trash ☆ - Compac Industries Inc.

CAN PIPE - Automotive parts and accessories - AAEN Performance Parts Inc.

CAN-RAP - Insulating materials - Reliable Plastics

CAN-SCORE - Recording label - Factory Beat Records Inc.

CAN SLIM - Diet-drink mix - True Quality Pharmacies Inc.

CAN-SWIPER - Cleaning preparations - Midwest Plastics Inc.

CAN TOO! - Video production - Bellman Girls, LLC

CAN-TOP - Marine-oil transfer pumps ☆ - ITT Jabsco

CAN U KEEP A SECRET - Apparel–children's - Barrel-Marvin Apparel, Inc.

CAN VAC - Vacuum cleaners and accessories - Royal Appliance Manufacturing Co.

CAN-VERTIBLE - Can openers–electric ☆ - Waring Products Div.

CAN-YAK - Boats - Glen-L Marine Designs

CAN YOU FIND - Apparel and accessories - Mister Vino's Enterprises, Inc.

CAN YOU SCORE? - Shirts - Albert J. Sokaitis Jr.

CAN YOU SEE IT? - Posters - Hidden Designs, Inc.

CANA-NUPTIAL - Rings–jewelry - Cana-Nuptial

CANA-SONIC - Drums–musical instruments - Ancris-Cana-Sonic Inc.

CANAAN - Recording label - Word, Inc.

CANADA - Recording label - Terock Records

CANADA BUSINESS PHONE - Compact discs–prerecorded - Procd, Inc.

CANADA DRY - Beverages–alcohol - United Distillers of North America

CANADA DRY - Beverages–carbonated - Canada Dry Corp.

CANADA DRY - Beverages–carbonated - Dr. Pepper/Seven Up, Inc.

CANADA DRY - Water–bottled or canned - Cadbury Beverages Inc.

CANADA DRY - Water–bottled or canned - Mountain Valley Spring Co.

CANADA GOOSE - Cigarettes - Commonwealth Brands, Inc.

CANADA HOUSE - Whiskey - Jim Beam Brands Co.

CANADA MINTS - Candy - New England Confectionery Co.

CANADA VIC - Hockey equipment ☆ - Life Industries Inc.

CANADAIGUA - Juices - Canandaigua Wine Co. Inc.

CANADANE - Cheese ☆ - Crystal Food Import Corp.

CANADA'S FAVOURITE - Food products - Tone Brothers, Inc.

CANADA'S NORTHLAND - Whiskey - United States Distilled Products Co.

CANADEL - Automotive parts and accessories - Rolls-Royce Motors Inc.

CANADELLE - Hosiery - Sara Lee Corp.

CANADIAN - Boats–canoes ☆ - Sawyer Composite Products

CANADIAN - Containers ☆ - Hormel Corp.

CANADIAN ACE - Beverages–malt ☆ - Eastern Brewing Corp.

CANADIAN AMERICAN - Recording label - Caprice International Records

CANADIAN BRASS - Musical instruments - Getzen Co.

CANADIAN CAVERN - Beverages - Merlen Foods, Inc.

CANADIAN CHAMP - Beverages–alcohol - Ammex Tax & Duty Free

CANADIAN CLOVER - Honey - Alveole Foods

CANADIAN CLUB - Beverages–alcohol - Hiram Walker & Sons, Inc.

CANADIAN CLUB CLASSIC - Beverages–alcohol - Hiram Walker & Sons, Inc.

CANADIAN CLUBS - Cigars - T.E. Brooks & Co.

CANADIAN COLA - Beverages–carbonated - International Trademarks Inc.

CANADIAN COOLER - Wines ☆ - Labatt Importers Inc.

CANADIAN CROWN - Hams - M.H. Greenebaum Inc.

CANADIAN DELUXE - Whiskey - David Sherman Corp.

CANADIAN DEW - Whiskey - Kentucky Brands of California Inc.

CANADIAN ELEGANCE - Wallpaper - Taylor Wallcoverings Inc.

CANADIAN EXPRESS - Cigarettes and tobacco - National Tobacco Corp.

CANADIAN FLYER - Shoes–athletic - Brookfield Athletic Co. Inc.

CANADIAN GOLD - Beverages–alcohol - Kasser Laird Distilling Co.

CANADIAN HOST - Liquors - Canandaigua Wine Co. Inc.

CANADIAN HOST - Whiskey - Barton Brands, Ltd.

CANADIAN HUNTER - Whiskey - House of Seagram

CANADIAN JIG - Fishing lures ☆ - Lindy Little Joe Inc.

CANADIAN LABEL - Beverages–alcohol - Alpha Industries, Inc.

CANADIAN LAKE - Whiskey - Majestic Distilling Co.

CANADIAN LEAF - Beverages–alcohol - Majestic Distilling Co.

CANADIAN LTD - Liquors - Canandaigua Wine Co. Inc.

CANADIAN MAJESTY - Beer, wine - Charles Jacquin et Compagnie Inc.

CANADIAN MIST - Whiskey - Brown-Forman Corp.

CANADIAN MUSIC - Water–bottled or canned - Today Products Inc.

CANADIAN PINE - Air purification systems - Medo Industries, Inc.

CANADIAN PINE - Deodorizers - Claire Manufacturing Co.

CANADIAN PRIDE - Meat products–pork ☆ - Safeway Stores Inc.

CANADIAN PROVINCE - Whiskey - Jenkins Spirits Corp., Ltd.

CANADIAN R & R - Beverages–alcohol - Sunbelt Beverage Corp.

CANADIAN RESERVE - Beverages–alcohol - Consolidated Distilled Products Inc.

CANADIAN SELECT - Beverages–alcohol - East-West Distributing Co.

CANADIAN SPRINGS - Whiskey - David Sherman Corp.

CANADIAN SUPREME - Whiskey - Barton Brands, Ltd.

CANADIAN WILD - Water–bottled or canned - Canadian Shield Spring Water Co., Ltd.

CANADIANA - Telescopes - Northern Telecom, Inc.

CANADIEN - Sporting goods - Ed Cumings Inc.

CANADIENE - Axes - E-Z Sales & Manufacturing, Inc.

CANADIENNE - Boats–canoes - Old Town Canoe Co.

CANAGE BEIGE - Tiles–ceramic ☆ - Monarch Tile Inc.

CANAGE BLANC - Tiles–ceramic ☆ - Monarch Tile Inc.

CANAL - Thread - New Bedford Thread Co. Inc.

CANAL CARE - Pet products - Toogood Laboratories

CANAL DRI - Pet products - Toogood Laboratories

CANAL DROPS - Pharmaceutical preparations ☆ - Bock Pharmacal Co.

CANAL MATE - Hearing aids - United Hearing Systems Inc.

CANAL PRESS - Publisher's imprints - Schiffer Publishing, Ltd.

CANAL STREET BLUES - Apparel–men's - Reed Manufacturing Co. Inc.

CANALWARE - Dinnerware–glass - Media Artists Inc.

CANALWEAR - Apparel and accessories - Media Artists Inc.

CANANDAIGUA - Wines ☆ - Canandaigua Wine Co. Inc.
CANANDAIGUA LAKE - Wines - Widmer's Wine Cellars Inc.
CANAPHIN - Furniture - Bassick Casters
CANARD DE BARBARIE - Ducks ☆ - Maple Leaf Farms Inc.
CANARD-DUCHENE - Wines ☆ - Bercut-Vandervoort & Co.
CANARE - Connectors–electrical ☆ - ARS Electronics
CANARI - Apparel and accessories - Canari Cycle Wear
CANARI - Apparel–athletic - Kassach Marketing, Inc.
CANARI - Tableware–china - Villeroy and Boch Tableware Ltd.
CANARIA D'ORO - Cigars - General Cigar Co., Inc.
CANARINO - Beverages–carbonated - Michael J. Verrochi
CANARY - Electronic equipment - Rangertone Research Inc.
CANARY - Measuring instruments - Bacharach, Inc.
CANARY CLOTHES - Apparel–women's - Doris Brundza
CANARY COMMUNICATIONS - Computer hardware - Canary Communications, Inc.
CANARY CRIB CHOIR - Toys ☆ - Tomy America, Inc.
CANARY SONG RATION - Pet products - Nutritional Research Associates Inc.
CANASONIC - Musical instruments ☆ - Meisel Music Inc.
CANASOY - Pasta - San Francisco Herb & Natural Food Co.
CANASTA - Thread - Threads USA Div.
CANATA - Window shades - John Miceli & Sons Inc.
CANATEX - Window coverings ☆ - Vertical Blind Factory
CANAVERAL - Luggage ☆ - American Tourister, Inc.
CANBERRA - Wallpaper ☆ - Koroseal Wallcoverings
CANBERRA PLAZA - Wallpaper ☆ - Koroseal Wallcoverings
CANCEL - Hair care products - Scruples Professional Salon Products, Inc.
CANCEL - Paints - Sophir Morris Paint
CANCEL STAT - Fabrics - Guilford Mills, Inc.
CANCELITE - Window shades ☆ - Spring Window Fashions Division, Inc.
CANCELYZER - Respirators - Cloud 9
CANCER - Teas–herbal - Calvin Thornton
CANCER - Wines - Unique Wines, Inc.
CANCUN - Bathing suits - Ocean Pool Co.
CANCUN - Housewares - Elon Inc.
CANCUN - Sandals ☆ - Playazul International Inc.
CANCUN - Spices and extracts - Finest Kind Spices
CANCUN BAY - Shrimp–fresh or frozen - Penguin Frozen Foods, Inc.
CANCUN GLASSWORKS - Bathroom accessories - Kohler Co.
CANCUN II - Doors–glass - Kohler Co.
CANDA - Weather stripping - Collins & Aikman Corp.
CANDABUILD - Computer software - Clinical Multiphase Research, Inc.
CANDACE - Flatware - Reed and Barton Corp.
CANDALON - Fabrics–broadcloth - Collins & Aikman Corp.
CANDAVIEW - Computer software - Clinical Multiphase Research, Inc.
C&C SPORTSWEAR AUTHENTIC STYLE GENUINE QUALITY - Apparel and accessories - C & C Textiles, Inc.
CANDCO - Flowers, plants, and seeds - C & C Florists Supplies Inc.
CANDELA - Computer software - Candela, Ltd.
CANDELABRA - Furniture - Koch Originals Inc.
CANDELABRA - Wines - Monarch Wine Co. of Georgia
CANDELABRA LIGHTS - Christmas tree lights ☆ - Mr. Christmas, Inc.
CANDELETTES - Candles - Columbia Wax Products Inc.
CANDELIGHT - Yarn - YLI Corp.
CANDELIGHTS - Novelty items - UniteDesign
CANDELITE - Greeting cards ☆ - Nu-Art Inc.
CANDELITE - Lighting equipment ☆ - Duro-Lite Lamps Inc.
CANDELRAMA - Candlesticks ☆ - Anchor Hocking Glass, Inc.
CANDEPTIN - Pharmaceutical preparations - Schmid Laboratories
CANDERMYL - Skin care products - Owen/Galderma Laboratories Inc.
CANDESA INTERACTIVE - Computer software - LC Candesa Interactive
CANDESCENCE - Floor coverings–carpet and rugs ☆ - Karastan-Bigelow Inc.
CANDEX - Skin care products ☆ - Miles Inc.
CANDI - Dolls ☆ - Mego Financial Corp.
CANDI APPLE MISS - Dolls - Mattel, Inc.
CANDI CANE - Sugar–granulated, refined, or powdered ☆ - Safeway Stores Inc.
CANDI CRYSTALS - Paints - Tulip Productions
CANDIA - Boats–motor - Four Winns Inc.
CANDIBEAR - Toys–stuffed ☆ - Gund, Inc.
CANDICAPS - Vitamins and nutritional supplements ☆ - Chase Laboratories Inc.
CANDICE - Wigs ☆ - Paula Young
CANDICIDAL - Vitamins and nutritional supplements - Source Naturals
CANDICIN - Vitamins and nutritional supplements - Metagenics, Inc.
CANDID - Clocks - General Time Corp. (Westclox/Seth Thomas Div.)

CANDID - Food products ☆ - Eaton Foods Inc.
CANDID - Paper ☆ - Wausau Paper Mills Co.
CANDID - Perfumes - Avon Products, Inc.
CANDIDA - Apparel and accessories - Bushnell Associates
CANDIDA - Cheese ☆ - Webeco Foods Inc.
CANDIDA - Floor coverings - Mannington Resilient Floors
CANDIDATE - Floor coverings–carpet and rugs ☆ - Mannington Carpets, Inc.
CANDIDATE - Furniture - Thomasville Furniture Industries Inc.
CANDIDATE Q - Clocks ☆ - SMH (US) Inc.
CANDIDE - Yarn ☆ - JCA, Inc.
CANDIE - Ophthalmic goods - Foremost Optical Products
CANDIES - Apparel and accessories - Tom Togs of Carolina, Inc.
CANDIES - Footwear - Americal Corp.
CANDIE'S - Shorts–women's - El Greco Inc.
CANDIES BY CANDACE - Chocolate candy - Boccone's Inc.
CANDIFLOR - Candy ☆ - Liberty Richter Inc.
CANDIFLOR - Food products - De Choix Specialty Foods Co.
CANDILICIOUS - Candy ☆ - American Chicle Co.
CANDIQUIK - Candy - Log House Foods Inc.
CANDITA - Candy - Bohemian Biscuit Co.
CANDITO - Giftware ☆ - Grainware Co.
CANDIZINE - Veterinary pharmaceutical preparations ☆ - SmithKline Beecham Animal Health Products
C&L TOOLS - Tools - Eaton Leonard, Inc.
CANDLE CRAFT CANDLE COMPANY - Candlesticks - Loomis Sales Co.
CANDLE CROCKS - Candles - Carolina Designs Ltd.
CANDLE-FLEX - Candles - Mann Lake, Ltd.
CANDLE-GLO - Lamps - Natalie Lamp and Shade Corp.
CANDLE GLOW - Candles ☆ - Kaadan Ltd.
CANDLE-GLOW - Cooking equipment–household ☆ - Anchor Hocking Glass, Inc.
CANDLE GLOW PILLARS - Candles - Muench-Kreuzer Candle Co.
CANDLE GLOWS - Candles - Russ Berrie and Co., Inc.
CANDLE-GRAMS - Greeting cards ☆ - Amberley Greeting Card Co.
CANDLE KRAZE - Candles - Hunt Holdings, Inc.
CANDLE LIGHT - Cabinets - Schrock
CANDLE-LITE - Candles - Lancaster Colony Corp.
CANDLE-LITE - Candles ☆ - Candle-Lite Co.
CANDLE LITE - Food products - Weight Watchers International, Inc.
CANDLE LUSTER - Chemical preparations - Mann Lake, Ltd.
CANDLE MAGIC - Candles - Gibson Greetings, Inc.
CANDLE MAGIC - Hobby kits - Distlefink Designs, Inc.
CANDLE MANAGEMENT WORKSTATION - Computer software - Candle Corp.
CANDLE MILL VILLAGE - Candles - Peterbrook Inc.
CANDLE OCCASIONS - Candles - Biedermann & Sons Inc.
CANDLE SENSATIONS - Craft supplies - Mangelsen's
CANDLE STAX - Candlesticks ☆ - Anchor Hocking Glass, Inc.
CANDLE STICKS - Ornamental products–glass - Candle-Sticks, Inc.
CANDLE TECHNOLOGIES - Computer software - Candle Corp.
CANDLEBOX - T-shirts–men's - Candlebox
CANDLECAKES THE PERFECT REFILL - Candles - Our Secret, Ltd.
CANDLECORN - Candles - Import Connections, Inc.
CANDLEGLOBE - Lamps - Candle Station, Ltd.
CANDLEGLOW - Glassware–household - Fenton Art Glass Co.
CANDLEJACK - Candlesticks - Peter Sears
CANDLELIGHT - Cabinets ☆ - Aristokraft, Inc.
CANDLELIGHT - Dishes–china ☆ - Pickard Inc.
CANDLELIGHT - Floor coverings–carpet and rugs - Barrett Carpet Mills Inc.
CANDLELIGHT - Glassware–household ☆ - Lenox Crystal, Inc.
CANDLELIGHT - Rings–jewelry - Artcarved Inc.
CANDLELIGHT - Thread - Sew-Art International
CANDLELIGHT - Tiles–ceramic ☆ - Monarch Tile Inc.
CANDLELIGHT EXPRESSIONS - Candles - Russ Berrie and Co., Inc.
CANDLELIGHT GREETINGS - Candles - Reed Candle Co.
CANDLELIGHT ROMANCES - Publisher's imprints - Bantam Doubleday Dell Publishing Group, Inc.
CANDLELIGHT WHITE - Dishes–china - Waterford Wedgewood USA, Inc.
CANDLELITE - Furniture ☆ - Bassett Furniture Industries, Inc.
CANDLELITE - Recording label - Candlelite Marketing Inc.
CANDLES BY WICK - Candles - Clinton Watkinson
CANDLES ET CETERA - Candles - Candles Et Cetera Inc.
CANDLES INTERNATIONAL - Candles - Biedermann & Sons Inc.
CANDLES 'N GLASS - Candlesticks - Modern Forge Manufacturing Co.
CANDLESTICK - Flower pots–plastic - Norse Co. Designers
CANDLESTICK PINE II - Furniture ☆ - Hooker Furniture Corp.

CANDLESTICK TELEPHONES - Personal telephones - American Telecommunications Corp.

CANDLESTICKS - Apparel–children's - Lawrence Children's Underwear Co. Inc.

CANDLETORCH - Torches - Gardner Marketing Services, Inc.

CANDLETREE COLLECTION, INC., THE - Pottery products - Candletree Collection, Inc.

CANDLEWARE - Candles ☆ - FMG/Tsumara Medical

CANDLEWICK - Comforters - American Home Ensembles, Inc.

CANDLEWICK - Furniture ☆ - Broyhill Furniture Industries, Inc.

CANDLEWICK COLLECTION - House furnishings ☆ - Lexington Furniture Industries, Inc.

CANDLEWICK PRESS - Publisher's imprints - Candlewick Press, Inc.

CANDLEWOOD - Crocheted and knitted items - M and M Woolen Co. Inc.

CANDLEWOOD - Furniture ☆ - Broyhill Furniture Industries, Inc.

CANDLEWOOD - Prefabricated buildings–wood - Champion Enterprises Inc.

CANDLEWYCK - Wallpaper ☆ - Ginger Tree Designs

CANDLEWYCK II - Wallpaper ☆ - Ginger Tree Designs

CANDO - Cleaning preparations–household ☆ - J.A. Wright & Co.

CANDOLFI - Jewelry - T & L Jewelry

CANDONI - Oils–essential - Dear, Inc.

CANDORA - Floor coverings–carpet and rugs ☆ - Evans-Black Carpet Mills

C&P - Telephones - Bell Atlantic Corp.

C&P PRESS - Computer software - C & P Press

CANDY - Electrical equipment - Futaba Corp. of America

CANDY - Food products - Southern Retailers Inc.

CANDY - Fruits and vegetables - Eakin Fruit Co.

CANDY - Recording label - Candy Records

CANDY - Recording label - Jeree Records

CANDY - Toys–stuffed - Dan-Dee International Ltd.

CANDY - Toys–stuffed ☆ - Gund, Inc.

CANDY APPLE - Candy ☆ - Topps Co., Inc.

CANDY APPLE - Christmas tree ornaments - Cracker Box Inc.

CANDY APPLE COOLER - Beverages–carbonated ☆ - Coca-Cola Co.

CANDY APPLES - Chewing gum ☆ - Leaf, Inc.

CANDY BAR - Beverages–alcohol - David Briggs Enterprises, Inc.

CANDY BARRELS - Candy ☆ - American Candy Co.

CANDY BARS - Game machines - IGT - North America

CANDY BLOSSOMS - Toys - Those Characters from Cleveland, Inc.

CANDY BOUQUET - Candy - Candy Bouquet International, Inc.

CANDY BOX KIDS - Dolls - Barbara A. Hock

CANDY BOX, THE - Candy - L. G. Foods Inc.

CANDY BRIGHTS - Barrettes - American Greetings Corp.

CANDY BULLETS - Candy ☆ - Ce De Candy Inc.

CANDY BY THE YARD - Candy - Price Candy Co. Inc.

CANDY-C - Vitamins and nutritional supplements - Vita-Fore Products Co.

CANDY CALLER - Candy - Kraft Food Ingredients Corp.

CANDY CANE - Food products - Beckman and Gast Co. Inc.

CANDY CANE - Pens - Micropoint Inc.

CANDY CANE HOLIDAY BALLS - Candy - Tootsie Roll Industries, Inc.

CANDY CANE JELLY - Jams and jellies - Mountain Maid Gourmet Jelly

CANDY CANE PIE - Pies–fresh - Vicorp Restaurants, Inc.

CANDY CHEF - Candy - Pangburn Candy Co.

CANDY CLASSICS - Candy - Campbell Soup Co.

CANDY CLUB - Candy - A.L. Bazzini Co. Inc.

CANDY CONE - Belts - Trenz Inc.

CANDY CORD - Fabrics - Greenwood Mills Inc.

CANDY CORN - Candy - Brach and Brock Confections Inc.

CANDY COTTAGE COMPANY, THE - Candy - Candy Cottage Co., Inc.

CANDY COUNTER - Ice cream - Oberweis Dairy Inc.

CANDY COUNTER - Ice cream ☆ - Roney-Oatman Inc.

CANDY CRANE - Game machines - Smart Industries Corp.

CANDY CREATIONS - Candy ☆ - Bissinger's Inc.

CANDY CRISP - Ice cream - H.P. Hood & Sons Inc.

CANDY CROWN - Chocolate candy - Kalva Corp.

CANDY CUPBOARD - Chocolate candy - New England Confectionery Co.

CANDY DISH - Candy - Brock Candy Co. Inc.

CANDY DOCTORS KIT - Candy ☆ - Grandpa Brand Co. (Par Beverage Co.)

CANDY DROPS - Tiles–ceramic - Latco Products

CANDY FLORA, INC. - Chocolate candy - Candy Flora, Inc.

CANDY GANG CHEWS - Candy ☆ - Sunline Brands

CANDY GIRLS - Dolls - Hamilton Toys Inc.

CANDY-GRAM - Greeting cards - Arnold S. Silling

CANDY HOUSE BUTTONS - Candy - New England Confectionery Co.

CANDY HQTRS - Candy - Candy Headquarters, Inc.

CANDY INTERNATIONAL - Candy ☆ - R.L. Albert & Son, Inc.

CANDY JAR CHOCOS - Candy ☆ - Russell Stover Candies, Inc.

CANDY JUG - Candy - Amurol Confections Co.

CANDY KANE - Apparel–children's - Jonathan Logan Inc.

CANDY KEYBOARD - Candy - Philip Morris Companies Inc.

CANDY KID'S - Shoes - MSF Corp.

CANDY KING - Candy ☆ - Trolli, Inc.

CANDY KISSES - Lipsticks - Beautycology Inc.

CANDY KISSES - Toys - Tonka Corp.

CANDY LAND - Dolls ☆ - Effanbee Doll Corp.

CANDY LAND - Games - Milton Bradley Co.

CANDY LAND BINGO - Games - Milton Bradley Co.

CANDY LIPSTICK KIT - Candy ☆ - Grandpa Brand Co. (Par Beverage Co.)

CANDY MACHINE - Candy - Fleer Corp.

CANDY MAGIC - Candy - Tootsie Roll Industries, Inc.

CANDY MANSION - Candy ☆ - Home of the Hebert Candies, Inc.

CANDY MAZES - Candy ☆ - Fleer Corp.

CANDY MELTS - Candy - Wilton Industries, Inc.

CANDY MONEY - Candy - Ce De Candy Inc.

CANDY MOUSE - Toys–stuffed - Russ Berrie and Co., Inc.

CANDY N COOKIES - Cookies - Bud's Best Cookies Inc.

CANDY NURSES KIT - Candy ☆ - Grandpa Brand Co. (Par Beverage Co.)

CANDY OF DISTINCTION - Candy - Laymon Candy Co. Inc.

CANDY OF THE FUTURE - Honey - Glenn Peters

CANDY PAGER - Candy - Kraft Food Ingredients Corp.

CANDY PAGER - Candy - Philip Morris Companies Inc.

CANDY PEBBLES - Candy - Sweet Candy Co.

CANDY PENNIES - Candy ☆ - Topps Co., Inc.

CANDY PENNYZ - Candy - Copper Kettle Candy, Inc.

CANDY POPPER - Candy - Cap Toys, Inc.

CANDY QUEEN - Candy ☆ - Square Shooter Candy Co.

CANDY SHOP, THE - Candy - MCS (USA) Marketing, Service & Commerce, Inc.

CANDY SHOPPE SUNDAE - Ice cream - Friendly Ice Cream Corp.

CANDY SHOTS - Candy ☆ - Sunline Brands

CANDY SO CHOCOLATEY.CAN WE EVER MAKE ENOUGH! - Candy - Nabisco Brands Co.

CANDY SPELLING - Dolls - Carol Gene Spelling

CANDY SPELLING - Dolls - Carole Gene Spelling

CANDY SPELLING ALPHABET DOLLS - Dolls - Carole Gene Spelling

CANDY SPELLING FANTASY DOLLS - Dolls - Carole Gene Spelling

CANDY SQUID - Confections - Sunmark Inc.

CANDY STICKS - Tiles–ceramic - Latco Products

CANDY STIX - Candy ☆ - New England Confectionery Co.

CANDY STORE - Ice cream - Borden, Inc.

CANDY-STRIPE - Candles - Columbia Wax Products Inc.

CANDY STRIPE - Fishing lures - Den Manufacturing Co.

CANDY STRIPE - Paint rollers - Wooster Brush Co.

CANDY-STRIPE - Pens - Micropoint Inc.

CANDY TABS - Candy ☆ - R.L. Albert & Son, Inc.

CANDY TOPS - Ice cream - Nestle USA

CANDY VILLAGE - Cordials ☆ - Brock Candy Co. Inc.

CANDY WORKS MELT-UMMS - Candy ☆ - Nestle USA

CANDYCALLER - Candy - BerZerk Candy Werks

CANDYDISH - Candy - Liss Brothers Inc.

CANDYKIND - Fudge - J. Hungerford Smith Co.

CANDYLAND - Chocolate candy - Dae Julie, Inc.

CANDYLAND - Floor coverings–carpet and rugs ☆ - World Carpets, Inc.

CANDYLAND - Lumber - Georgia-Pacific Corp.

CANDYLITE - Candles - Candle Corp. of America

CANDYLITE - Candles - Carolina Designs Ltd.

CANDYPANTS - Confection - California Novelties, Inc.

CANDYS PEP PATTIE - Wines - M.S. Walker Inc./Seacoast

CANDYSAURUS - Candy - Philadelphia Chewing Gum Corp.

CANDYSAURUS DINOSAUR TEETH - Candy - Philadelphia Chewing Gum Corp.

CANDYWRAP - Packaging–paper - Multifilm Packaging Corp.

CANE - Blinds–vertical - Kittrich Corp.

CANE - Glassware–household - Owens-Illinois Inc. (Libbey Div.)

CANE AND UN-ABLE - Canes - Just Enterprises

CANE COMPANY, THE - Candy - Spangler Candy Co.

CANE CREEK - Bicycle parts and accessories - Dia-Compe USA, Inc.

CANE DEER - Candy - Four Score Inc.

CANE DRIP - Food products - W.B. Roddenbery Co., Inc.

CANE ELEGANTE - Garden furniture–rattan - Samsonite Furniture Co. (Consumer Products Div.)

CANE PATCH - Syrup - W.B. Roddenbery Co., Inc.

CANE VALET - Health care products - Maddak Inc.
CANE VANE - Blinds–venetian ☆ - Hunter Douglas, Inc.
CANEASE - Medical apparatus - American Health Specialties Inc.
CANEDEER, THE - Books–comic - Sizzo-Link Productions
CANEDOR - Doors–wood - Panelfold Inc.
CANEEL BAY - Floor coverings–carpet and rugs - World Carpets, Inc.
CANEEL BAY SLING COLLECTION - Furniture - Telescope Casual Furniture Inc.
CANEEL CLASSICS - Cosmetics ☆ - Carr Products Co. Inc.
CANEI - Wines - Wine Shippers Import Co.
CANELITA - Herbal products - Jose M. Gonzalez-Blanco
CANELLI - Wines - Renwood Winery, Inc.
CANEPA - Fruits and vegetables - Marglo Products Corp.
CANEPA CELLARS - Wines - Diamond Wine Merchants
CANEPA'S RED CROSS - Macaroni ☆ - Red Cross Macaroni Co.
CANESTRATO PEPATO - Cheese - Park Cheese Co., Inc.
CANETTI - Luggage - Recyco
CANEY - Recording label - Guajiro Records Inc.
CANFIELD - Beverages - A.J. Canfield Co.
CANFIELD - Glass–stained - D & L Stained Glass Supply, Inc.
CANFIELD - Glassware–household - Anchor Hocking Glass, Inc.
CANFIELD - Wallpaper - Old Deerfield Fabrics Inc.
CANFIELD'S CLEAR - Water–bottled or canned - A.J. Canfield Co.
CANFORD AUDIO - Audio equipment - Connectronics Corp.
CANGURO - Footwear–athletic - KangaROOS USA Inc.
CANHANDLER - Can openers–electric - Hamilton Beach/Proctor-Silex Inc.
CANIDAE - Waterproof outerwear ☆ - Fox-Knapp Inc.
CANINE ADVANTAGE - Dog food - O.H. Kruse Grain and Milling Corp.
CANINE BAKER, THE - Dog food - DOCA USA, Inc.
CANINE BALANCE - Pet products - Biogenetics Food Corp.
CANINE BASIC - Animal feed supplements - Vita Bran
CANINE BIOTIC - Pet products - Wysong Corp.
CANINE BREEDER - Dog food - MFA Inc.
CANINE CANTEEN - Pet products - Osborne Industries Inc.
CANINE CASTLE - Pet products - Pet Castle Co.
CANINE CLASICS - Pet products - Pampered Pet
CANINE CLASSIC - Pet products - Maggie Mae's Gourmet Pet Products Inc.
CANINE CLEAN-UP - Bags–plastic - Barna Ltd.
CANINE CLUB - Animal feeds - Price Co.
CANINE COLLECTION - Novelty items - Papel Freelance, Inc.
CANINE CONES - Dog biscuits - Golden Barrel, Inc. (O)
CANINE CONSULTANT, THE - Pet products ☆ - Bardwyn Productions Inc.
CANINE COOKIES - Dog food ☆ - Gimborn U.S., Inc.
CANINE COOLER - Pet products - Maverick Marketing Ventures, Inc.
CANINE COT - Pet products - Canine Cushion Co.
CANINE COTTAGE - Pet products - Fort Wayne Plastics, Inc.
CANINE COUNTRY - Pet food - American Leather Specialties
CANINE COUTURE CUSTOM AND READY-MADE DOG COATS - Pet products - Liberty T. Rees
CANINE CROISSANTS - Dog food - Gimborn U.S., Inc.
CANINE DELIGHT - Dog food ☆ - Central Soya Co. Inc.
CANINE DIGESTIVE ENZYMES - Veterinary pharmaceutical preparations - Dr. Goodpet
CANINE-FARE - Pet products - Reliable Protein Products
CANINE/FELINE - Pet products - Wesley Pharmacal Co. Inc.
CANINE FLEX PROTECT - Vitamins and nutritional supplements - Earthrise Trading Co.
CANINE GOOD CITIZEN AMERICAN KENNEL CLUB INCORPORATED A K C - Educational materials - American Kennel Club Inc.
CANINE GOURMET - Pet product - American Leather Specialties
CANINE KISSES - Dog food ☆ - Gimborn U.S., Inc.
CANINE PRINCIPLE - Pet food - Nulaid Foods Inc.
CANINE SERVER - Pet products - Alco Industries, Inc.
CANINE WORM CAPS - Veterinary pharmaceutical preparations - K.C. Pharmacal Inc.
CANINE'S BEST - Pet products - Canine Specialties
CANINE'S CHOICE - Dog food - Canine's Choice
CANINO'S - Sausages - Canino's Sausage Co., Inc.
CANIS - Veterinary pharmaceutical preparations - NNQ Inc.
CANISTAR - Pet products - Penn-Plax, Inc.
CANISTER CONNECTION, THE - Jars–glass - Gemco Ware, Inc.
CANISY - Glassware–household - Durand International
CANJI C - Pharmaceutical preparations - Canji Inc.
CANKAID - Antiseptics - E.E. Dickinson Co.
CANKARE - Pharmaceutical preparations - James F. Lichon
CANKER CURE - Lip balms - Jerome Pharmaceutical Corp.

CANNABIS WORKS - Apparel and accessories - Pan World Traders
CANNED BEACH - Novelties - Robert P. Sowash
CANNED HEAT - Trays–warming - Colgate-Palmolive Co.
CANNEROS BIGHORN - Wines - Hill & Thoma Wines
CANNERY - Wines - Cannery Wine Cellar
CANNERY ROW - Salmon - Inn Foods, Inc.
CANNERY ROW - Seafood products–fresh or frozen - Sunshine Food Sales Inc.
CANNES - Dinnerware–glass - Crisa Corp.
CANNES - Flatware - Washington Forge Inc.
CANNES - Floor coverings–carpet and rugs - Karastan-Bigelow Inc.
CANNES - Furniture - Homecrest Industries Inc.
CANNIBAL - Perfumes - Candles Et Cetera Inc.
CANNOCK - Faucets - Kohler Co.
CANNOLI FACTORY - Bakery products - Michael V. Zucaro
CANNOLI FACTORY - Desserts - Fancy Foods of Virginia Inc.
CANNON - Bedding–linen - Fieldcrest Cannon, Inc.
CANNON - Bicycles - Hunt-Wilde Corp.
CANNON - Footwear - R.G. Barry Corp.
CANNON - Gasoline - Cannon Oil Corp.
CANNON - Golfing equipment - Lisco, Inc.
CANNON - Industrial chemicals - Puritan-Churchill Chemical Co.
CANNON - Posters - Wildstorm Productions
CANNON - Shoes - Cannon Shoe Co.
CANNON - Tools–masonry - Apla-Tech, Inc.
CANNON - Vegetables–canned - Moody Dunbar Inc.
CANNON ANVIL - Sporting goods - Crown Prince Inc.
CANNON BALL - Candy ☆ - Leaf, Inc.
CANNON BALL - Chewing tobacco - Conwood Co. L.P.
CANNON BALL - Door frames - Cannon Ball HNP
CANNON BRAND - Vegetables–canned - Moody Dunbar Inc.
CANNON KITCHEN CLASSICS - Towels - Fieldcrest Cannon, Inc.
CANNON, THE - Sporting goods - Lax World, Inc.
CANNON WHEELS - Toys - Saban Entertainment, Inc.
CANNONADE PRESS - Publisher's imprints - Konocti Books/Cannonade Press
CANNONBALL - Apparel–children's - Doe Spun Inc.
CANNONBALL - Cleaning preparations - Puritan-Churchill Chemical Co.
CANNONBALL - Lamps ☆ - Lamplight Farms, Inc.
CANNONBALL 88 - Toys–trains ☆ - Life-Like Products Inc.
CANNONBALL 484 - Barbecue sauce - Logos Group
CANNONBALLS - Meat products–poultry - Brakebush Brothers Inc.
CANNONBALLS - Percussion mallets - American Drum
CANNONDALE - Bicycles - Cannondale Corp.
CANNON'S SWEET HOTS - Vegetables–canned - Cannon Unlimited
CANNULA - Cushions - Innovative Support Group Inc.
CANNULOC - Surgical equipment - Linvatec Corp.
CANO - Dog food - Heinz Pet Products Co.
CANOAH - Boats–canoes - Noah Corp.
CANODE INKS - Inks - Starkey Chemical Process Co.
CANOE - Rice - Mille Lacs Wild Rice Co.
CANOE - Skin care products - Dana Perfumes Corp.
CANOE RIDGE - Wines - Chalone Wine Group Ltd.
CANOE SPORT - Toiletries - Les Parfums De Dana, Inc.
CANOGA - Counting devices - Minnesota Mining & Manufacturing Co.
CANOGA - Games - Pacific Game Co.
CANOGA - Machines and tools - Southeast Construction Products, Inc.
CANOGA PARK - Vitamins and nutritional supplements - Natural Food Supplements
CANOLA - Calculators ☆ - Canon USA, Inc.
CANOLA CHOICE - Oils–edible - Nabisco Foods Group
CANOLA GOLD - Vegetables–frozen - Lamb-Weston, Inc.
CANOLA QUICK - Vegetables–frozen - Lamb-Weston, Inc.
CANOLEO - Margarine - Spring Tree Corp.
CANOMAR - Recording label - Combo Records
CANON - Electronic equipment - Canon USA, Inc.
CANON - Herbicides - Monsanto Co.
CANON BALLS - Food products - Tom's Foods Inc.
CANONERO - Tobacco products - Stephen Hagan
CANONET - Cameras ☆ - Canon USA, Inc.
CANOPY - Awnings - Awnings by Sunair/Sunair Awnings
CANOPY - Cases–musical instrument ☆ - Protec International
CANOPY - Computer software - Natural Path Forestry Consultants, Inc.
CANOPY - Dinnerware ☆ - Corning Inc.
CANOPY - Herbicides - E.I. Dupont de Nemours and Co.
CANOPY CAP - Chimney caps - Improved Consumer Products Inc.
CANOPY CHIMES - Carson Industries, Inc.

☆ = Now out of production

CANOR PLAREX - Ships - Canor Plarex Inc.
CANOSAURUS - Bins - Home Recycling Products Inc.
CANOSOARUS - Toys - Aero Visions Group, Inc.
CANOVA - Furniture - Ethan Allen, Inc.
CANOVISION 8 - Cameras–video ✩ - Canon USA, Inc.
CANOVITE - Veterinary pharmaceutical preparations - Evsco Pharmaceuticals
CANPARTS - Brake drums - Abex Corp. (Friction Products Group)
CANPRO - Sporting goods - MacGregor Sport Products Inc.
CANSLER PHOTOGRAPHY - Photographic equipment - Bradley L. Cansler
CANSON & MONTGOLFIER - Paper–kraft ✩ - Canson-Talens Inc.
CANSON BEVERLY - Paper - Canson-Talens Inc.
CANSON BIGGIE - Paper–kraft - Canson-Talens Inc.
CANSON BLANK GREETING CARDS - Greeting cards - Canson-Talens Inc.
CANSON BLANK WATERCOLOR POSTCARDS - Postcards - Canson-Talens Inc.
CANSON C A GRAIN - Paper - Canson-Talens Inc.
CANSON CHARCOAL - Paper - Canson-Talens Inc.
CANSON FIELD SKATCH BOOKS - Notebooks and notepads - Canson-Talens Inc.
CANSON FIELD SKETCH JOURNALS - Notebooks and notepads - Canson-Talens Inc.
CANSON INGRES - Paper - Canson-Talens Inc.
CANSON MI-TEINTES - Paper–kraft - Canson-Talens Inc.
CANSON PAD-O-PALETTE - Palettes - Canson-Talens Inc.
CANSON RECYCLE CLASSIC DRAWING - Notebooks and notepads - Canson-Talens Inc.
CANSON TRACING - Paper - Canson-Talens Inc.
CANSON WATERCOLOR - Paper - Canson-Talens Inc.
CANSON WORTHY BRISTOL - Paper - Canson-Talens Inc.
CANSTRUT - Steel products - Thomas & Betts Holdings, Inc.
CAN'T BEAT 'EM - Sprinklers–lawn - L.R. Nelson Corp.
CANT BREAK EM - Tools - O.P. Link Handle Co. Inc.
CAN'T BUDGE FUDGE - Fudge - Budge Factory
CANT-CURL - Typewriters - Codo Manufacturing Corp.
CANTAB - Corn syrup - Penford Products Co.
CANTADA - Apparel–women's - La Strada Sportswear Inc.
CANTAINEOR - Sporting goods - Bag Co.
CANTAN - Cosmetics - Ray Drug Co.
CANTARA - Floor coverings–carpet and rugs ✩ - Columbus Mills, Inc.
CANTARE - Cheese - Cantare, Inc.
CANTARE FRITTATA - Dinners–frozen - Cantare, Inc.
CANTATA - Blinds–venetian ✩ - Hunter Douglas, Inc.
CANTATA - Computer software - Temair Software Corp.
CANTATA - Dishes–china - Waterford Wedgewood USA, Inc.
CANTATA - Floor coverings - Mannington Resilient Floors
CANTATA - Glassware–household ✩ - Oneida Ltd.
CANTATA - Rings–jewelry - Artcarved Inc.
CANTATA - Toilets–enameled - Kohler Co.
CANTEEN - Deodorizers - Quality of Life Associates
CANTEEN - Eyeglasses - Canteen Clothing, Inc.
CANTEEN - Salmon–smoked, salted, dried, or pickled - North Pacific Seafoods
CANTEEN - Sunglasses ✩ - International Tropic-Cal Inc. (I SKI Div.)
CANTEEN - Vending machines - Canteen Corp.
CANTERBURY - Barometers - Airguide Instrument Co.
CANTERBURY - Belts–apparel - Canterbury Belts Ltd.
CANTERBURY - Cabinets - Aristokraft, Inc.
CANTERBURY - Cabinets - Dewils Industries Inc.
CANTERBURY - Cabinets ✩ - Medallion Kitchens of Minnesota Inc.
CANTERBURY - Cabinets–wood - Parcraft Distinctive Cabinetry
CANTERBURY - Clocks - Canterbury Designs, Inc.
CANTERBURY - Crocheted and knitted items - Puritan Sportswear Corp.
CANTERBURY - Dinnerware–glass - Royal China & Porcelain Companies Inc.
CANTERBURY - Dishes–earthenware ✩ - Denby USA Limited
CANTERBURY - Floor coverings - Harris-Tarkett, Inc.
CANTERBURY - Floor coverings ✩ - Robbins Inc.
CANTERBURY - Floor coverings–carpet and rugs - Collins & Aikman Corp.
CANTERBURY - Floor coverings–carpet and rugs - Dan River Inc.
CANTERBURY - Floor coverings–carpet and rugs - Quaker Inc.
CANTERBURY - Floor coverings–carpet and rugs ✩ - Interloom Ltd.
CANTERBURY - Flowers, plants, and seeds - Jonathan Green, Inc.
CANTERBURY - Furniture - Arbek Furniture Manufacturing Inc.
CANTERBURY - Furniture - Ethan Allen, Inc.
CANTERBURY - Glassware–household ✩ - Colony Glass
CANTERBURY - Hardware - Baldwin Hardware Corp.
CANTERBURY - Mattresses - Stearns & Foster Bedding Co.

CANTERBURY - Moldings - ABT Co., Inc.
CANTERBURY - Office furniture–wood ✩ - Haskell of Pittsburgh, Inc.
CANTERBURY - Rings–jewelry - Artcarved Inc.
CANTERBURY - Snack foods ✩ - Marin Food Specialties
CANTERBURY - Teas ✩ - Safeway Stores Inc.
CANTERBURY - Trailers–travel ✩ - Starcraft Corp.
CANTERBURY - Vases–ceramic - Crisa Corp.
CANTERBURY - Vinyl ✩ - Reynolds Aluminum Supply Co.
CANTERBURY - Water–mineral - F & W Marketing, Inc.
CANTERBURY ANNOUNCEMENTS - Envelopes - Niagara Envelope Co., Inc.
CANTERBURY ART - Greeting cards - Sunshine Art Studios Inc.
CANTERBURY COBBLES - Tiles–ceramic ✩ - Latco Products
CANTERBURY COLLECTION - Cosmetics - Dial Corp.
CANTERBURY COLLECTION - Lighting fixtures - Fredrick Ramond Inc.
CANTERBURY COURT - Furniture ✩ - Bassett Furniture Industries, Inc.
CANTERBURY CUISINE - Food products - Canterbury Cuisine Inc.
CANTERBURY GARDENS - Wallpaper - Dekortex Inc.
CANTERBURY NITES - Underwear and nightwear - Berkliff Corp.
CANTERBURY PARK - Floor coverings–carpet and rugs - Lees Carpets
CANTERBURY SQUARE - Furniture - Hooker Furniture Corp.
CANTERBURY STATION - Toys - Toywrights Ltd.
CANTERBURY TALES - Candy ✩ - Brown & Haley
CANTERBURY WOODWORKS - Boxes - Canterbury Woodworks Inc.
CANTERBURY'S CRACK & PEEL - Housewares - Canterbury's Crack & Peel, Inc.
CANTESLOPE - Mining equipment - Baker Hughes Inc.
CANTHARONE - Health care products ✩ - Seres Laboratories Inc.
CANTHARONE PLUS - Health care products ✩ - Seres Laboratories Inc.
CANTICO - Floor coverings–carpet and rugs ✩ - Evans-Black Carpet Mills
CANTICO DELLA CROSIA - Wines - Kendall Jackson Winery, Ltd.
CANTIL - Pharmaceutical preparations - Marion Merrell Dow
CANTILEVER - Shoes - Drew Shoe Corp.
CANTILEVER BOOKS - Publisher's imprints ✩ - Zondervan Publishing House
CANTINA - Beverages–carbonated - Brazos Country Foods
CANTINA - Dinnerware - Syracuse China Co.
CANTINA - Floor coverings - Mannington Resilient Floors
CANTINA - Furniture - Tropitone Furniture Co. Inc.
CANTINA - Pet products - Novalek, Inc.
CANTINA - Sinks–metal - Kohler Co.
CANTINA CRUNCHIES - Snack food - Prepco
CANTINA MEXICANA - Food products - Columbus Distributing
CANTINE GEMMA - Wines - House of Burgundy Inc.
CANTINE GINI - Wines - Tempo Imports Ltd.
CANTINE MEZZACORONA - Wines - Prestige Wine Imports Corp.
CANTMUPL - Lighting equipment–boat and ship - Imtra Corp.
CANTO - Computer software - Canto Software, Inc.
CANTO - Musical instruments - International Music Corp.
CANTO - Office furniture–metal - Stow/Davis Furniture Co.
CANTO - Whirlpools - Jason International, Inc.
CANTOBELLA - Floor coverings - Mannington Resilient Floors
CANTON - Audio equipment - Canton North America
CANTON - Cabinets - Imperial Cabinet Co. Inc.
CANTON - Clothing - American Fashion Network, Inc.
CANTON - Floor coverings–carpet and rugs - Artistic Rugs Inc.
CANTON - Floor coverings–carpet and rugs - Trans-Ocean Import Co. Inc.
CANTON - Glassware–household - Canton Glass Co.
CANTON - House furnishings ✩ - Lexington Furniture Industries, Inc.
CANTON AKRON INDIANS - Trading cards and stamps - Cleveland Indians Baseball Co. L.P.
CANTON MING - Floor coverings–carpet and rugs ✩ - Capel, Inc.
CANTON SPICE - Teas - Eastern Shore Tea Co.
CANTON TILE - Floor coverings - Congoleum Corp.
CANTONI - Fabrics ✩ - Stylecrest Fabrics Ltd.
CANTRECE - Fabrics–nylon - E.I. Dupont de Nemours and Co.
CANTRELL & COCHRANE - Beverages - Tribev Corp.
CANTRI - Pharmaceutical preparations ✩ - Roberts/Hauck Pharmaceuticals Inc.
CANTROC - Roofing materials–slate - Cant Products Inc.
CANTROL - Tools–hand-operated - John P. Miley
CANTROL - Vitamins and nutritional supplements - Nature's Way Products, Inc.
CANTUCCI - Bakery products - La Tempesta Bakery Confections, Inc.
CANUSA CORPORATION FIBER GROUP - Paper products - Canusa Corp.
CANUTE WATER - Hair dye ✩ - Benjamin Ansehl Co.
CANVA-PAPER - Paper - Canson-Talens Inc.
CANVA-TEX - Paper–kraft - Canson-Talens Inc.
CANVALESCENT HOME - Pet products - Lee's Aquarium Products

CANVAS - Fabrics - Uniroyal Engineered Products
CANVAS - Paper ☆ - Permalin Products Co.
CANVAS BACK - Footwear ☆ - N Shasta Shoe
CANVAS CAPERS - Hobby kits ☆ - Leisure Arts, Inc.
CANVAS CITY - Games - Diana M. Calvin
CANVAS CLASSICS - Luggage ☆ - Jinwoong Inc.
CANVAS COSMETICS - Cosmetics - Barbara Guttenberg
CANVAS MASTER - Canvas–artists' - Master Woodcraft Inc.
CANVAS ONE - Handbags - Trade Am International, Inc.
CANVAS PACIFICA - Window shades - Castec Window Shading Inc.
CANVAS PACK - Bags–canvas - Canvas-Pack Inc.
CANVAS TOOL BOX - Bags–canvas - Portable Products, Inc.
CANVASBACK - Adhesives and sealants - Canvasback Coatings
CANVASBACK - Apparel–athletic - Red Head Brand Corp.
CANVASBACK OF IDAHO - Automotive parts and accessories - Canvasback, Inc.
CANVASBACKS - Paper - Mead Corp.
CANVASBACKS - Shirts - Canvasbacks, Inc.
CANVASEAL - Paints - Everseal International Sales Co. Inc.
CANVASETTE - Paper - Hunt Manufacturing Co.
CANVASKIN - Paper - Bee Paper Co. Inc.
CANVATEX - Artists' materials - Glenview Products Inc.
CANVATEX - Tarpaulins - Great American Marketing, Inc.
CANVAX - Hardware - Tufco Technologies Inc.
CANVERTER - Pumps - Nu-Calgon Wholesaler, Inc.
CANVERTIBLES - Hobby kits ☆ - Rapco
CANVEX - Hobby kits - Vogart Crafts Corp.
CANVEX - Plastics film - Raven Industries Inc.
CANYON - Bicycles ☆ - Huffy Corp.
CANYON - Colognes - Express, Inc.
CANYON - Electronic equipment - Titano Accordion Co. International
CANYON - Floor coverings–carpet and rugs ☆ - Regal Rugs Inc.
CANYON - Soups–canned - Canyon Specialties, Inc.
CANYON - Sporting goods - Lisco, Inc.
CANYON - Wallcoverings - Stretchwall Fabrics Co.
CANYON - Wines - Ste. Chapelle Inc.
CANYON BLEND - Coffee - Grand Canyon Theatre Venture
CANYON BOMBER - Video games - Atari Games Corp.
CANYON BOWLS - Pet products - Anchor Aquarium Products
CANYON CAPPUCCINO - Coffee - Grand Canyon Theatre Venture
CANYON CARVERS OF AMERICA - Apparel - Allen S. Guilmette
CANYON CLASSIC - Floor coverings–carpet and rugs ☆ - World Carpets, Inc.
CANYON CLIMBER - Tires - Dunlop Tire Corp.
CANYON CLOTH - Fabrics ☆ - Glen Raven Mills Inc.
CANYON COLORS - Floor coverings–tile - Robbins Interior Surface Inc.
CANYON COUGAR - Toys–stuffed - Dakin Inc.
CANYON COUNTRY - Food products - Silverado Foods, Inc.
CANYON COUNTRY - Footwear - Dynasty Footwear, Ltd.
CANYON CREEK BLUES - Jeans–men's - Salant/Manhattan Industries
CANYON CREEK RECORDS - Recording label - Canyon Creek Records Inc.
CANYON CREST - Wines - Joseph Victori Wines, Inc.
CANYON CRUISER - Footwear - L.A. Gear, Inc.
CANYON GROUP - Apparel and accessories - Damze Co., Inc.
CANYON GUIDE OUTFITTERS - Apparel and accessories - California Manufacturing Co. Inc.
CANYON HOME - Apparel and accessories - Damze Co., Inc.
CANYON KIDS - Apparel and accessories - Damze Co., Inc.
CANYON LAKE - Apparel and accessories - Fu Kong Inc.
CANYON LIGHTS - Floor coverings–carpet and rugs - Evans-Black Carpet Mills
CANYON MIST - Floor coverings–carpet and rugs ☆ - Galaxy Carpet Mills Inc.
CANYON RIVER BLUES - Apparel and accessories - Sears, Roebuck and Co.
CANYON ROAD - Floor coverings–carpet and rugs - Gulistan Carpet Inc.
CANYON ROAD - Wines - Geyser Peak Winery
CANYON RUN - Floor coverings - Mannington Resilient Floors
CANYON SCULPTURES - Pet products - Anchor Aquarium Products
CANYON SKY - Apparel–women's - El & El Novelty Co., Inc.
CANYON SPORT - Motor vehicles ☆ - DaimlerChrysler
CANYON STRATA - Floor coverings–carpet and rugs - Milliken & Co. Inc.
CANYON SUITE - Floor coverings–carpet and rugs ☆ - World Carpets, Inc.
CANYON TRAILS - Footwear - Fiorini Footwear Inc.
CANYON TUNNELS - Pet products - Anchor Aquarium Products
CANYON WOOD - Hardware - Alside Div.
CANYONSTONE - Floor coverings - Congoleum Corp.
CANYONSTONE - Tiles–ceramic - American Marazzi Tile, Inc.
CANYONSTONE PLUS - Tiles–ceramic - American Marazzi Tile, Inc.

CANZ - Pharmaceutical preparations ☆ - Forest Pharmaceuticals Inc.
CANZONE DEL MARE - Food products - Golden Whisk Pasta Partners
CAO - Cigars - C.A.O. International, Inc.
CAP - Cleaning preparations - State Chemical Manufacturing Co.
CAP - Computer software - Industrial Information Resources, Inc.
CAP - Controls–heating systems - Engineering & Research Associates, Inc.
CAP - Medical apparatus - Carolon Co.
CAP - Recording label - Cha-Cha Records
CAP 10 - Water–bottled or canned - Absopure Water Co.
CAP-A-DOODLE - Games - Arnie Goodman
CAP ACCOUNTANT - Computer software - CAP Automation
CAP BACKS - Scarves - Protec, Inc.
CAP BANGERS - Toys - Strombecker Corp.
CAP BLASTER - Toys - Tootsietoy
CAP BLASTIN' - Toys–automobiles - Mattel, Inc.
CAP CAPERS - Novelty items - Harry P. Capers, Jr.
CAP CHECK - Display cases–metal - Caps Plus, Inc.
CAP-IT-AL - Shingles–asphalt or tar - Celotex Corp.
CAP-IT-ALL - Hats - Pace/Cap-It-All
CAP-LITE - Flashlights - H.I.S. Associates
CAP-LOC - Nuts and bolts - Lok-Mor, Inc.
CAP-M-QUIK - Vitamins and nutritional supplements - Whole Herb Co.
CAP MASTER - Ventilation equipment - Mid-America Building Products Corp.
CAP N JAC - Apparel–athletic - Louisville Manufacturing
CAP-PAC - Containers–paper - Nimco Corp.
CAP POS - Computer software - CAP Automation
CAP-RIA - Medical apparatus - Capintec, Inc.
CAP ROCK WINERY - Wines - Cap Rock Winery, Inc.
CAP-SEAL - Converters–electric - Minnesota Mining & Manufacturing Co.
CAP SHADES - Hats - Keith H. Clement
CAP SPECIAL - Thread ☆ - Perfect Thread Co. Inc.
CAP SYSTEM - Building panels - Steelite Inc.
CAP-TURE! - Frames–picture - Kenneth Masaji Kudo
CAP WAVES - Novelty items - Kirby Knutson
CAPA - Pharmaceutical preparations ☆ - U.S. Ethicals Inc.
CAPABLE CABANA, THE - Portable bathrooms for the handicapped - Capable Cabana Corp.
CAPAC - Automotive parts and accessories ☆ - Wells Manufacturing Corp.
CAPAC CHIEF - Food products - Eastern Michigan Vegetable Marketing Co.
CAPAC PRIDE - Food products - Eastern Michigan Vegetable Marketing Co.
CAPACITY PLUS - Stoves - General Electric Co.
CAPADVANTAGE - Computer software - Informedics, Inc.
CAPALINO - Footwear - O & B Shoe Co.
CAPARONE - Wines - Caparone Vineyard
CAPARS - Computer software and hardware - Alphatrac, Inc.
CAPARZO - Wine - Palace Brands Co.
CAPASTAT SULFATE - Pharmaceutical preparations - Eli Lilly and Co.
CAPATTERY - Capacitors - Evans Findings Co., Inc.
CAPAZZANA - Wines ☆ - Pellegrini Bros. Wines Inc.
CAPBACKER - Brushes - Capbacker, Inc.
CAPCIL - Computer software - Simkin, Inc.
CAPCO - Almond pastes - Chicago Almond Inc.
CAPCO - Food products - W.B. Roddenbery Co., Inc.
CAPCO X-TRA MELT - Chemical preparations - Capitol Soap Corp.
CAPCOM - Computer software - Capcom USA Inc.
CAPDANA - Apparel and accessories - Tamami, Inc.
CAPE - Seafood products–canned or cured - Maloney Seafood Corp.
CAPE - Toothpaste ☆ - Noxell Corp.
CAPE ANN - Brooms - Lighthouse Industries
CAPE ANN - Floor coverings–carpet and rugs ☆ - Colonial Mills Inc.
CAPE ANN - Seafood products–fresh or frozen - F.J. O'Hara & Sons Inc.
CAPE BEND C - Lighting fixtures - Stephen F. Warner
CAPE BRITON - Furniture - Homecrest Industries Inc.
CAPE CHARLES - Floor coverings–carpet and rugs - Capel, Inc.
CAPE CHECKS - Fabrics - Dan River Inc.
CAPE CLASSIC - Women's footwear - Peebles Inc.
CAPE COD - Bells - North Country Wind Bells Inc.
CAPE COD - Beverages - The Atlantic Beverage Group, USA, Inc.
CAPE COD - Beverages–malt ☆ - Eastern Brewing Corp.
CAPE COD - Bicycles - Roadmaster Corp.
CAPE COD - Crab meat–fresh - Bay Trading Co.
CAPE COD - Door frames - Canyon Creek Cabinet Co.
CAPE COD - Food products - Eatmor Cranberries Inc.
CAPE COD - Glass–leaded ☆ - Vesta Glass Co.
CAPE COD - Lamps ☆ - Lamplight Farms, Inc.
CAPE COD - Lighting fixtures - Meyda Tiffany Inc.

☆ = Now out of production

CAPE COD - Pet products - Dogloo Inc.
CAPE COD - Polishing cloths - Cape Cod Polish Co., Inc.
CAPE COD - Potato chips - Cape Cod Potato Chips
CAPE COD - Seafood - Chincoteague Seafood Co.
CAPE COD - Shoes - Daniel Green Co.
CAPE COD - Tea kettles–nonelectric ☆ - Revere Ware Corp.
CAPE COD - Trailers–travel - Fleetwood Enterprises, Inc.
CAPE COD - Wines - Chicama Vineyards
CAPE COD - Yarn ☆ - Lion Brand Yarn Co.
CAPE COD ANGELS - Dolls - Cinnamon Stick, Inc.
CAPE COD CATBOAT - Ships–sailing vessels - Cape Cod Shipbuilding Co.
CAPE COD COOKER - Crock pots ☆ - West Bend Co.
CAPE COD COOLERS - Fruit drinks–bottled or canned - The Atlantic Beverage Group, USA, Inc.
CAPE COD COUNTRY CLUB - Apparel–women's - Cape Cod Cricket Lane
CAPE-COD CRANBERRY COOKIES - Cookies - Cape Cod Cranberry Cookie Co., Inc.
CAPE COD CRANBERRY DRY - Beverages–carbonated - Polar Corp.
CAPE COD CRANBERRY FLAVORS - Fruit drinks–bottled or canned - The Atlantic Beverage Group, USA, Inc.
CAPE COD II - Shower stalls–metal - Kohler Co.
CAPE COD MATCHMATES - Apparel and accessories ☆ - Kellwood Co.
CAPE COD MERCURY - Ships–sailing vessels - Cape Cod Shipbuilding Co.
CAPE COD PETITES - Apparel and accessories - Kellwood Co.
CAPE COD SPORTSWEAR - Apparel and accessories - Kellwood Co.
CAPE CORAL - Wainscotting - Georgia-Pacific Corp.
CAPE DORY - Boats - Newport Shipyards (Cape Dory Div.)
CAPE DORY TYPHOON - Ships–sailing vessels - Newport Shipyards (Cape Dory Div.)
CAPE FEAR - Boats - Lanness K. McKee & Co.
CAPE HATTERAS - Shower stalls–metal - Kohler Co.
CAPE HEIGHTS - Apparel–athletic - Cape Heights, Inc.
CAPE HORN - Brooms - Lighthouse Industries
CAPE HORN - Food products ☆ - Seaspan Products Corp.
CAPE ISLE - Apparel and accessories - Phillips-Van Heusen Corp.
CAPE MAY - Floor coverings–carpet and rugs - Monticello Carpet Mills
CAPE MAY - Wallpaper ☆ - Linden Street Gallery
CAPE MAY - Whirlpools - Kohler Co.
CAPE ROYALE - Furniture ☆ - Bassett Furniture Industries, Inc.
CAPE SHORE - Stationery - Cape Shore Inc.
CAPE SPRAY - Seafood - Cape Spray Fisheries
CAPE THONDER - Apparel–men's - Asher Co.
CAPE WELL PLANNING SYSTEM - Computer software - Antelope Engineering, Inc.
CAPEANS - Giftware - Exquisite China & Crystal Inc.
CAPEL PISCO - Beverages–alcohol - Shaw-Ross International Importers
CAPELANDS - Wines - Blair Importers Ltd.
CAPELLA - Apparel and accessories - Spornette International, Inc.
CAPELLA - Candlesticks ☆ - Lenox Crystal, Inc.
CAPELLA - Chairs–metal - Herman Miller, Inc.
CAPELLA - Liquors - Orion Imports Ltd.
CAPELLA - Pens - Capella America, Inc.
CAPELLA - Tables–wood - Riverside Furniture Corp.
CAPELLA - Violins - VMI Industries
CAPELLA - Whirlpools - Jacuzzi Inc.
CAPELLE - Drums–musical instruments ☆ - Paul A. Real Sales
CAPELON - Floor coverings–carpet and rugs - Capel, Inc.
CAPEL'S ORIGINAL - Floor coverings–carpet and rugs - Capel, Inc.
CAPER - Shoes ☆ - Daniel Green Co.
CAPER - Trailers–travel ☆ - Coachmen Industries, Inc.
CAPER XL - Trailers–travel ☆ - Coachmen Industries, Inc.
CAPERS - Candy ☆ - Pet Inc. (Whitman's Chocolates Div.)
CAPERS - Fabrics - Dan River Inc.
CAPERS - Gloves - Wells Lamont Corp.
CAPERS - Optical services ☆ - Universal/Univis Inc.
CAPE'S KITCHEN - Pasta sauces - Cape's Kitchen, Inc.
CAPETOWN - Floor coverings ☆ - Congoleum Corp.
CAPETOWN GROUP - Furniture ☆ - Bean Station Furniture Factory Inc.
CAPEWAY - Seafood products–fresh or frozen - Atlantic Coast Fisheries Corp.
CAPEWELL - Saws–power - Rule Industries, Inc.
CAPEWOOD - Mobile homes - Commodore Corp.
CAPEZIO - Apparel–athletic - Physical Fashions
CAPEZIO - Boots - Texas Boot Co.
CAPEZIO - Footwear–women's - United States Shoe Corp.
CAPEZIO - Handbags - Mischief Makers Inc.
CAPEZIO - Leather goods - A & L Seamon Inc.

CAPEZIO - Watches - Temlex/Jupiter Watch Corp.
CAPEZIO SPORT - Footwear - United States Shoe Corp.
CAPEZZANA - Beverages–alcohol - Palace Brands Co.
CAPEZZANA - Wines - Heublein, Inc.
CAPICO - Inks - Flint Ink Corp.
CAPIL PLACENTA - Hair care products ☆ - Nino Originals
CAPILENE - Underwear and nightwear - Patagonia, Inc.
CAPILIGHT - Candles - Vitro Dynamics Inc.
CAPILLARIS-X - Shampoos ☆ - J.H. Guild Co. Inc.
CAPISTRANO - Floor coverings - Mannington Resilient Floors
CAPISTRANO - Floor coverings–carpet and rugs - Cabin Crafts Carpets
CAPISTRANO - Liquors ☆ - SPAR Inc.
CAPISTRANO - Trailers–travel - Compact Equipment Co.
CAPISTRANO - Trailers–travel ☆ - Coachmen Industries, Inc.
CAPITAL - Apparel and accessories - Capital Plastics Awards & Gifts Co.
CAPITAL - Floor coverings–carpet and rugs - Eagle Carpets Inc.
CAPITAL - Ladders–metal - John S. Tilley Ladders Co. Inc.
CAPITAL - Macaroni - Pastamania
CAPITAL - Photographic equipment ☆ - Keystone Camera Corp.
CAPITAL - Sewing machines–household - Capital Automation, Inc.
CAPITAL - Watches - Hampden Corp.
CAPITAL - Wire ☆ - General Cable Corp.
CAPITAL AND CODEINE - Pharmaceutical preparations - Carnick Laboratories Inc.
CAPITAL BULLETS - Apparel and accessories - Capital Bullets Basketball Club, Inc.
CAPITAL CITY BOMBERS - Apparel and accessories - Columbia Professional Baseball, Inc.
CAPITAL CITY PRODUCTS - Edible fats - Karlshamns USA Inc.
CAPITAL COURT - Dinnerware–glass ☆ - Lenox, Inc.
CAPITAL DATA SYSTEMS - Computer software, manuals, and programs - Capital Data Systems, Inc.
CAPITAL E - Apparel - Levi Strauss & Co.
CAPITAL ELECTRO-CIRCUITS - Electrical equipment - Capital Electro-Circuits Inc.
CAPITAL FERMETE - Skin care products - Sothys USA Inc.
CAPITAL GAINS - Floor coverings–carpet and rugs - Karastan-Bigelow Inc.
CAPITAL IMAGING - Computer peripheral equipment - Capital Imaging Co. Inc.
CAPITAL PRIDE - Margarine - Karlshamns USA Inc.
CAPITAL PUFF - Margarine - Karlshamns USA Inc.
CAPITAL PUNISHMENT - Snowboards ☆ - Earth & Ocean Sports, Inc.
CAPITAL SQUARE - Floor coverings - Mannington Resilient Floors
CAPITALIST PIG - Computer software - Pluma, Inc.
CAPITALIZATION MACHINE, THE - Computer software - Southwest Edpsych Services Inc.
CAPITALIZATION PLUS - Computer software - CBS Software
CAPITAN DE TUEROS - Cigars ☆ - Consolidated Cigar Corp.
CAPITANO WAITER'S CORKSCREW - Corkscrews - Franmara Co. Inc.
CAPITELLO - Glassware–household ☆ - Oneida Ltd.
CAPITOL - Adhesives and sealants ☆ - Capitol Adhesives Inc.
CAPITOL - Floor coverings–carpet and rugs - Onthank Co.
CAPITOL - Flour–blended ☆ - North Dakota Mill and Elevator Association
CAPITOL - Hair care products - Capitol Novelty Co.
CAPITOL - Hotplates - Capitol Products Co.
CAPITOL - Musical instruments ☆ - Grossman Music Corp.
CAPITOL - Pencils ☆ - Empire Berol USA
CAPITOL - Recording label - Capitol-EMI Music Inc.
CAPITOL - Shoes - Manistee Inc.
CAPITOL - Tires - Aoyama International Inc.
CAPITOL - Water purification systems - Capital Controls Co.
CAPITOL - Wet mops ☆ - American Textile Products Co.
CAPITOL - Windows–storm - Capitol Products Corp.
CAPITOL ADHESIVES - Adhesives and sealants - Capitol Adhesives Inc.
CAPITOL BOND - Paper–bond - Fox River Paper Co.
CAPITOL BOND & COVER - Paper - Howard Paper Mills Inc.
CAPITOL CITY - Rebuilt engines - Automotive Rebuilders
CAPITOL CRITTERS - Kites - Hi-Flier Manufacturing Co.
CAPITOL DELUXE - Jackets - Horace Small Apparel Co.
CAPITOL ENQUIRY - Publisher's imprint - Cougar Books
CAPITOL FARMS - Food products - Hartford Provision Co.
CAPITOL FAVORS - Cosmetics - Capitol Novelty Co.
CAPITOL HILL - Furniture ☆ - Bassett Furniture Industries, Inc.
CAPITOL-OX - Brushes–paint - Elder & Jenks, Inc.
CAPITOL PUNISHMENT - Apparel and accessories - Shirt Xplosion Co. Inc.
CAPITOL RECORDS - Recording label - Capitol Records, Inc.

☆ = Now out of production

CAPITOL RUSTIC - Tiles–ceramic - Capitol Tile Import Co.
CAPITOL SHOP - Combs - Capitol Novelty Co.
CAPITOL TOOL AND DIE - Motor vehicles–trucks - Capitol Tool and Die Co.
CAPITOL VICTORIAN - Furniture reproductions - Victorian Classics
CAPITROL - Shampoos - Westwood-Squibb Pharmaceuticals, Inc.
CAPKEEPER - Cases–camera - Sima Products Corp.
CAPLET - Photographic equipment - Eastman Kodak Co.
CAPMAC-S - Medical apparatus - Capintec, Inc.
CAPMASTER - Firearms, accessories, and parts - Ox-Yoke Originals, Inc.
CAPMAT - Mats - Phytotronics, Inc.
CAP'N - Seafood products–fresh or frozen ☆ - Chuck's Seafoods
CAP'N CLEAN - Detergents ☆ - Blue Cross Laboratories Inc.
CAP'N CRUNCH - Cereal - Quaker Oats Co.
CAP'N CRUNCH CRUNCHBERRY - Cereal - Quaker Oats Co.
CAP'N CRUNCH DEEP SEA CRUNCH - Cereal ☆ - Quaker Oats Co.
CAP'N CRUNCHERS - Cookies ☆ - Quaker Oats Co.
CAP'N CRUNCH'S CRUNCH BERRIES - Cereal - Quaker Oats Co.
CAP'N CRUNCH'S HOMERUN CRUNCH - Cereal - Quaker Oats Co.
CAP'N DENNY'S SEAFOOD PLATE - Food products ☆ - Denny's Inc.
CAP'N HANKS - Seafood products–fresh or frozen - Hanks Seafood Co. Inc.
CAP'N JOE - Seafood products–fresh or frozen - Gorton Group
CAP'N JOE - Seafood products–fresh or frozen - Tampa Maid Seafoods, Inc.
CAP'N JOHN - Food products - A.M. Look Canning Co.
CAP'N KID - Peanut butter - Algood Food Co.
CAP'N PRIDE - Seafood products–fresh or frozen - Rich-Seapak Corp.
CAP'N SALTY - Seafood products–fresh or frozen - Raffield Fisheries, Inc.
CAP'N SHRIMPY - Food products - Treasure Isle Inc.
CAPNOGARD - Medical apparatus - Novametrix Medical Systems, Inc.
CAPO - Eyeglasses - Capo, Inc.
CAPO - Hats - George D. Donovan & Sons Inc.
CAPODIMOME CLASSICS COLLECTION - Giftware - Arnart Imports Inc.
CAPONE'S - Pizzas–frozen - Castle Lanes of Southeastern Wisconsin, Inc.
CAPOTE - Footwear - G & M Distributors
CAPOTEN - Pharmaceutical preparations - Bristol-Myers Squibb Co.
CAPPED HOLD-GUARD - Pet products - Novalek, Inc.
CAPPED T-SEAL - Rubber–molded - Macrotech Fluid Sealing, Inc.
CAPPEL - Apparel and accessories - Ride Snowboard Co.
CAPPELLA - Drums–musical instruments - Cappella Wood Enterprises
CAPPELLA PUBLISHING, A - Publisher's imprints - A Cappella Publishing
CAPPELLANO - Wines - Tempo Imports Ltd.
CAPPER - Pet products - United Pacific Mills
CAPPIE - Apparel - Bill Whitten
CAPPU DAVINCI - Beverages - Da Vinci Gourmet, Ltd.
CAPPU DAVINCI - Coffee - Coffee Beanery Ltd.
CAPPUCCINO AMERICANA - Coffee - Rolly's Convenient Foods, Inc.
CAPPUCCINO BLAST - Ice cream - Baskin-Robbins USA Co.
CAPPUCCINO CASCADE - Coffee - Coffee Beanery Ltd.
CAPPUCCINO CHIP - Ice cream - Neal's
CAPPUCCINO COOLER - Coffee - Fairwinds Gourmet Coffee Co. Inc.
CAPPUCCINO COOLERS - Coffee - Elkin Coffee, Inc.
CAPPUCCINO CREAMERS - Cream–canned or powdered ☆ - Spice Hunter
CAPPUCCINO ICER - Coffee - Granito Coffee Works, Inc.
CAPPUCCINO INSTANTANEO - Coffee - National Fruit Flavor Co.
CAPPUCCIO'S - Tomato pastes and sauces - C and E Canners Inc.
CAPPUCINO - Neckties - A. Schreter & Sons Co. Inc.
CAPPUCINO - Yarn ☆ - William Unger & Co. Inc.
CAPPY & SCRUFFY - Apparel and accessories - Back2back Kidswear, Inc.
CAPPY'S - Advertising agencies - Cappy Devlin International, Inc.
CAPQUELL - Capacitors - General Electric Co.
CAPRA - Recording label - CRS Inc.
CAPRA - Wines - Wine Imports Ltd.
CAPRA PRESS - Publisher's imprints - Capra Press Inc.
CAPRAC - Medical apparatus - Capintec, Inc.
CAPRALIN - Vitamins and nutritional supplements - Synergy Plus
CAPRE - Pharmaceutical preparations ☆ - Marion Merrell Dow
CAPREE - Depth charges ☆ - Datamarine International Inc.
CAPRI - Apparel–women's ☆ - Bobbie Brooks Inc.
CAPRI - Artists' materials ☆ - M. Grumbacher Inc.
CAPRI - Ashtrays–glass ☆ - Frank J. Curran-Esquire Chemical Co.
CAPRI - Bathroom accessories - Zenith Products Corp.
CAPRI - Bathroom fixtures - Crane Plumbing/Fiat Products
CAPRI - Bathtubs–enameled ☆ - Lasco Products Group
CAPRI - Blankets–electric ☆ - Sunbeam-Oster Household Products
CAPRI - Blinds–venetian - Draco Corp.
CAPRI - Boats - Catalina Yachts Inc.
CAPRI - Boats–motor - Bayliner Marine Corp.

CAPRI - Boats–motor - Glastex Co.
CAPRI - Boats–motor ☆ - Forester Boats Inc.
CAPRI - Boats–motor ☆ - Starcraft Corp.
CAPRI - Cabinets - Dewils Industries Inc.
CAPRI - Cabinets - Wellborn Cabinet, Inc.
CAPRI - Cabinets ☆ - Decora
CAPRI - Cameras ☆ - Keystone Camera Corp.
CAPRI - Candy - Perugina Chocolate & Confections Inc.
CAPRI - Carpets, now out of production - Couristan Inc.
CAPRI - Cheese - Imperia Foods Inc.
CAPRI - Cigarettes - Brown & Williamson Tobacco Corp.
CAPRI - Cookies - Pepperidge Farm Inc.
CAPRI - Cosmetics - Spornette International, Inc.
CAPRI - Cutlery - Latama Inc.
CAPRI - Dialing devices–telephone - Baltimore Luggage Co.
CAPRI - Dishes–china - Pasmantier Co. Inc.
CAPRI - Flatware - Lifetime Hoan Corp.
CAPRI - Floor coverings–carpet and rugs - Coronet Carpets Inc.
CAPRI - Floor coverings–carpet and rugs ☆ - Fieldturf & Carpet Inc.
CAPRI - Floor coverings–carpet and rugs ☆ - Foreign Accents
CAPRI - Floor coverings–carpet and rugs ☆ - Galaxy Carpet Mills Inc.
CAPRI - Floor coverings–carpet and rugs ☆ - Trans-Ocean Import Co. Inc.
CAPRI - Food products - Sara Lee Corp.
CAPRI - Furniture - Bean Station Furniture Factory Inc.
CAPRI - Furniture - Homecrest Industries Inc.
CAPRI - Furniture - Stanley Furniture Co. Inc.
CAPRI - Furniture - Suncast Corp.
CAPRI - Furniture - Universal Flooring
CAPRI - Furniture ☆ - Bassett Furniture Industries, Inc.
CAPRI - Giftware - Sasaki
CAPRI - Glassware–household - Federal Glass
CAPRI - Glassware–household - Owens-Illinois Inc. (Libbey Div.)
CAPRI - Glassware–household - Royal Crystal Rock Inc.
CAPRI - Glassware–household ☆ - AAA Glass Corp.
CAPRI - Greeting cards - John Henry Co.
CAPRI - Hair care products - S.C. Johnson & Son, Inc.
CAPRI - Hot tubs–fiberglass ☆ - Jacuzzi Brothers
CAPRI - Indoor-outdoor carpet - Instant Turf Industries Inc.
CAPRI - Life preservers ☆ - Alexander-Roberts Co.
CAPRI - Lighting fixtures - Swivelier Co. Inc.
CAPRI - Lighting fixtures - Thomas Industries Inc.
CAPRI - Lighting fixtures - Thomas Lighting (Accent Division)
CAPRI - Lipsticks - Maybelline Co.
CAPRI - Meat products–beef - Galileo-Capri Salami Inc.
CAPRI - Mobile homes ☆ - Wick Building Systems Inc. (Manufactured Home Div./North)
CAPRI - Motor vehicle parts and accessories - Cricket Camper Manufacturing Co.
CAPRI - Motor vehicles–automobiles - Ford Motor Co. (Lincoln-Mercury Div.)
CAPRI - Motor vehicles–motor homes ☆ - Beaver Coaches Inc.
CAPRI - Mushrooms - Giorgio Foods Inc.
CAPRI - Musical instruments - Getzen Co.
CAPRI - Office furniture–wood ☆ - Haskell of Pittsburgh, Inc.
CAPRI - Paper - Plainwell Tissue
CAPRI - Plastics–laminated ☆ - Plaskolite Inc.
CAPRI - Powerboat ☆ - Invader Marine Inc.
CAPRI - Ribbons–inked - Eaton Allen Ko-Rec-Type Corp.
CAPRI - Rings–jewelry ☆ - Artcarved Inc.
CAPRI - Salad dressings–bottled - Kraft Food Ingredients Corp.
CAPRI - Skin care products - Northern Labs, Inc.
CAPRI - Sleeping bags - Coleman Co., Inc.
CAPRI - Sunglasses - Capo, Inc.
CAPRI - Swimming pools - Lomart Industries
CAPRI - Tents - Johnson Camping Inc.
CAPRI - Tiles–ceramic - H & R Johnson Inc.
CAPRI - Trays ☆ - Knobler International Ltd.
CAPRI - Upholstery leather - American Leather Manufacturing Co.
CAPRI - Watches - Criterion Watch Co. Inc.
CAPRI - Wines - Batavia Wine Cellars Inc.
CAPRI - Yarn ☆ - JCA, Inc.
CAPRI ARCH - Cabinets - Wellborn Cabinet, Inc.
CAPRI BY ATS - Motor vehicles–all-terrain - American Travel Systems, Inc.
CAPRI OF CALIFORNIA - Glassware–scientific ☆ - AAA Glass Corp.
CAPRI PRINTS - Wallpaper - Coverwalls Inc.
CAPRI SCENTS - Deodorizers - Pavalor Merchandising, Inc.
CAPRI SQUARE - Cabinets - Wellborn Cabinet, Inc.

☆ = Now out of production

CAPRI WITH ESP - Lighting fixtures - Thomas Lighting (Accent Division)
CAPRICCIO - Floor coverings–carpet and rugs ☆ - Lees Carpets
CAPRICCIO - Housewares - Doranne
CAPRICCIO - Recording label - Delta Entertainment Corp.
CAPRICCIO - Wallpaper - Carlton-Metro Wallcoverings
CAPRICCIO - Wines ☆ - Warner Vineyards Inc.
CAPRICE - Apparel–women's ☆ - Maidenform Inc. (True Form Foundations Div.)
CAPRICE - Apparel–women's ☆ - Q-T Foundations Co. Inc.
CAPRICE - Aquatic pharmacuetical preparations - Superior Shade & Blind Co. Inc.
CAPRICE - Bathroom accessories - Century Shower Door, Inc.
CAPRICE - Bathroom accessories - Franklin Brass Manufacturing Co.
CAPRICE - Boats–houseboats ☆ - Harris-Kayot Inc.
CAPRICE - Boats–motor ☆ - Dolphin Boats Ltd.
CAPRICE - Boats–motor ☆ - Sport-Craft Inc.
CAPRICE - Brassieres (Bras) - Lady Marlene
CAPRICE - Cabinets - Aristokraft, Inc.
CAPRICE - Changeable earrings ☆ - Robert Rose
CAPRICE - Cheese ☆ - Bongrain Cheese USA
CAPRICE - Clocks - General Time Corp. (Westclox/Seth Thomas Div.)
CAPRICE - Cosmetics - Lancome
CAPRICE - Dinnerware–glass ☆ - Metlox Pottery Shoppe
CAPRICE - Dishes–china - Viletta China Co.
CAPRICE - Dishes–china ☆ - WMF/USA
CAPRICE - Floor coverings–carpet and rugs - Dan River Inc.
CAPRICE - Floor coverings–carpet and rugs ☆ - Karastan-Bigelow Inc.
CAPRICE - Glassware–household - Seneca Glass Co.
CAPRICE - Glassware–household ☆ - Crisa Corp.
CAPRICE - Glassware–household ☆ - Lenox Crystal, Inc.
CAPRICE - Jewelry - Jacoby-Bender Inc.
CAPRICE - Mattresses and box springs - Ohio Mattress Co.
CAPRICE - Motor vehicles - General Motors Corp. (Chevrolet Motor Div.)
CAPRICE - Rings–jewelry ☆ - Artcarved Inc.
CAPRICE - Wafer rolls - Inorex Inc.
CAPRICE - Watches - Bulova Corp.
CAPRICE - Watches - Time Products Corp.
CAPRICE - Yarn ☆ - William Unger & Co. Inc.
CAPRICE CLASSIC - Motor vehicles - General Motors Corp. (Chevrolet Motor Div.)
CAPRICE DESIGN - Handbags - Armand & Richard
CAPRICE DESIGN - Leather goods - Caprice Design
CAPRICE II - Wallpaper ☆ - Benchmark Preferred Wallcoverings
CAPRICE OF HOLLYWOOD - Girdles ☆ - Maidenform Inc. (True Form Foundations Div.)
CAPRICE ORIGINALS - Boxes - Albert E. Price, Inc.
CAPRICHO CANDIES - Candy - Sweet Systems Inc.
CAPRICHOS - Apparel and accessories - Armani Shoes Corp.
CAPRICORN - Cheese - Swiss American Import Co.
CAPRICORN - Coffee - Capricorn Coffees Inc.
CAPRICORN - Frames–eyeglass - May Optical Co. Inc.
CAPRICORN - Lawn mowers - Lambert Manufacturing Corp.
CAPRICORN - Recording label - Capricorn Records Inc.
CAPRICORN - Teas–herbal - Calvin Thornton
CAPRICORN - Tiles–ceramic - H & R Johnson Inc.
CAPRICORN - Wine - Unique Wines, Inc.
CAPRICORNE - See CHRISTOFLE
CAPRINELLE - Cheese ☆ - Swissrose International Inc.
CAPRINEX - Vitamins and nutritional supplements - Nature's Way Products, Inc.
CAPRINOL - Hardware - Sherwin-Williams Automotive Finishes Corp.
CAPRINUS - Lubricating oils - Shell Oil Co.
CAPRIO - Beverages–carbonated - Caprio Beverage Corp.
CAPRIOTTI'S - Pizzas–frozen - Cap's Italian Foods Inc.
CAPRIS FURNITURE - Furniture - Capris Furniture Industries, Inc.
CAPRISETA - Crocheted and knitted items ☆ - Puritan Sportswear Corp.
CAPRISUN - Fruit drinks–bottled or canned - Kraft Foods, Inc.
CAPRITARN - Cheese ☆ - Swissrose International Inc.
CAPRITAURUS - Musical instruments - Folkcraft Instruments
CAPRO - Electronic equipment - Teleflex Inc.
CAPRO RINGLITE - Photographic equipment ☆ - Nikon Inc.
CAPROCK - Tomato pastes and sauces ☆ - Diven Packing Co.
CAPROCK - Windows–screen - Caprock Developments Inc.
CAPRON - Pharmaceutical preparations ☆ - Vitarine Pharmaceuticals Inc.
CAPRS - Computer software - Compusist, Inc.
CAPRYL - Vitamins and nutritional supplements - Solaray

C.A.P.S. - Computer software - Automotive Rentals, Inc.
CAPS - Computer software - Credit Bureau of Connecticut, Inc.
CAPS - Computer software - Valens Business Machines
CAPS - Computer software - Xerox Corp.
CAP'S - Food products - Cap's Italian Foods Inc.
CAP'S - Puzzles - Classic Cards and Games
CAPS - Shoes ☆ - Edison Brothers Stores, Inc.
CAP'S BLEND - Tobacco–chewing or smoking - Amar Blends Co.
CAP'S CHOICE - Fruit drinks–bottled or canned ☆ - Natures Choice
CAPS LOGISTICS TOOLKIT - Computer software - CAPS Logistics, Inc.
CAPSAGEL - Topical analgesic - Iyata Pharmaceutical, Inc.
CAPSAGESIC - Analgesics - Stiefel Laboratories, Inc.
CAPSAGESIC - Dermatological preparations - Durham Pharmacal Corp.
CAPSAL - Office supplies ☆ - Faber-Castell Corp.
CAPSEEKID - Toys ☆ - Play-Tech, Inc.
CAPSELA - Toys - Play-Tech, Inc.
CAPSELA KID - Toys ☆ - Play-Tech, Inc.
CAPSELA POWERBOLT - Toys ☆ - Play-Tech, Inc.
CAPSELA POWERTRAM - Toys - Play-Tech, Inc.
CAPSELA SCIENCE CONSTRUCTION TOY SYSTEM - Toys - Play-Tech, Inc.
CAPSELA SPACELINK - Toys ☆ - Play-Tech, Inc.
CAPSICOOL - Vitamins and nutritional supplements - Nature's Way Products, Inc.
CAPSICRUMB - Bread crumbs - Newly Weds Foods, Inc.
CAPSICUM - Analgesics - Polam Wholesale Inc.
CAPSIDER - Toys–automobiles - Mattel, Inc.
CAPSIL - Plastics - Empak, Inc.
CAPSIM - Computer software - Xcad Corp.
CAPSIN - Pharmaceutical preparations - Richard H. Mann
CAPSIZER - Hoists - G.F. Equipment, Inc.
CAPSOLIN - Pharmaceutical preparations ☆ - Parke-Davis
CAPSPRAY - Paint sprayers - Wagner Spray Tech Corp.
CAPSTAC - Furniture - Robert C. Fitzgerald
CAPSTAN - Tobacco–chewing or smoking - James B. Russell Inc.
CAPSTAN NAVY CUT - Tobacco - American Tobacco Co.
CAPSTAND - Artists' materials - Flagship Group II, Inc.
CAPSTONE - Compact discs–prerecorded - Capstone Records, Inc.
CAPSU-PHOTOHELIC - Surgical supplies - Dwyer Instruments, Inc.
CAPSUL-BAN - Insecticide ☆ - Hess & Clark, Inc.
CAPSULE - Filters–air - Controls Corp. of America
CAPSULINK - Inks - A.B. Dick Co.
CAPSULORBLUE - Ophthalmic goods - Storz Instrument Co.
CAPSUR - Integrated Chemistries Inc.
CAPSUREFIX - Medical apparatus - Medtronic, Inc.
CAPSY ADVISOR - Computer software - Spectra-Physics Laserplane, Inc.
CAPSYN - Spices and extracts - Kalsec, Inc.
CAPT. - See also CAPTAIN
CAPT. ACE - Shrimp - International Seafood Traders
CAPT. BAIDAL - Shrimp–fresh or frozen - Darik Enterprises Inc.
CAPT. BASTARD'S OATMEAL STOUT - Beverages–malt - Salt Lake Brewing Co., L.C.
CAPT. BECK - Seafood products–fresh or frozen - Hopkins & Sons Seafood & Storage Inc.
CAPT COMET - Toys–airplanes - Comet Montrose Ltd.
CAPT. COURAGEOUS - Cleaning preparations - W.W. Grainger, Inc.
CAPT. CRANKY - Apparel and accessories - John D. White
CAP'T. DUKE - Food products - Channel Fish Co.
CAPT. ED - Seafood products–fresh or frozen - Hopkins & Sons Seafood & Storage Inc.
CAPT. FRED - Seafood products–canned or cured - Sea Watch International Ltd.
CAPT. GREGG - Seafood products–fresh or frozen - Hopkins & Sons Seafood & Storage Inc.
CAPT. HARRY'S - Fishing lures - Capt. Harry's Fishing Supply
CAPT. HENRY - Seafood products–fresh or frozen ☆ - Penguin Frozen Foods, Inc.
CAP'T J - Food products - Canal Marine Inc.
CAPT. JOHN - Food products - Seafood Enterprises Inc.
CAPT. LEE'S AUTO SPRA - Paint removers - Capt. Lee's Inc.
CAPT. LEE'S METAL PREP & CONDITIONER - Rust removers - Capt. Lee's Inc.
CAPT. LEE'S SPRAY RUST AWAY - Rust removers - Capt. Lee's Inc.
CAPT. LEE'S WOOD SPRA - Paint removers - Capt. Lee's Inc.
CAPT. WALKER'S - Teas - Eastern Shore Tea Co.
CAPTAIN - See also CAPT., CAPTN.
CAPTAIN - Batteries - Douglas Battery Manufacturing Co.

CAPTAIN - Boats–pontoons ☆ - Harris-Kayot Inc.
CAPTAIN - Computers - Cochran Undersea Technology Div.
CAPTAIN - Freezers - Frigibar Industries Inc.
CAPTAIN - Hooks - Weisner Steel Products Inc.
CAPTAIN - Machine tools - Okuma America
CAPTAIN - Paper–bond - Riverside Paper Corp.
CAPTAIN - Recording label - Sonic Arts Corp.
CAPTAIN - Skin care products - Collins Manufacturing Co.
CAPTAIN - Sunglasses - Command Marketing Corp.
CAPTAIN - Thread - Threads USA Div.
CAPTAIN - Watches - Nelson Industries
CAPTAIN - Wet mops - American Textile Products Co.
CAPTAIN ACTION - Books–comic - Karl Art Publishing
CAPTAIN ACTION - Dolls - Funtime Toys, Ltd.
CAPTAIN AMERICA - Toys - Marvel Entertainment Group, Inc.
CAPTAIN ANDY - Food products - Imperial Commodities Corp.
CAPTAIN APPLE - Wines - Laird and Co.
CAPTAIN BEAVER - Food products - Beaver Street Fisheries Inc.
CAPTAIN BLACK - Tobacco products - Lane Ltd.
CAPTAIN BLACK GOLD - Tobacco products - Lane Ltd.
CAPTAIN BLACK ROYAL - Tobacco products - Lane Ltd.
CAPTAIN BLACK SUPREME - Tobacco products - Lane Ltd.
CAPTAIN BLOOD - Computer software - Mindscape Software Inc.
CAPTAIN CAM - Toys - Tonka Corp.
CAPTAIN CAT - Pet products - Rich Health
CAPTAIN CATCH - Seafood products–canned or cured - Hanks Seafood Co. Inc.
CAPTAIN CHOCO'S - Cereal - Moran Foods, Inc.
CAPTAIN COOLER - Containers - BP Exploration & Oil Inc.
CAPTAIN COURAGE - Toys ☆ - Henry Gordy International Inc.
CAPTAIN D - Food products - Sea Harvest Packing Co.
CAPTAIN D'S - Restaurant franchise - Shoney's, Inc.
CAPTAIN FRESH - Meat products–poultry - Superior Seafoods Inc.
CAPTAIN GULL - Toys ☆ - Playskool, Inc.
CAPTAIN HOOK - Golf clubs - Austad Co.
CAPTAIN HOOK - Rum - M.S. Walker Inc./Seacoast
CAPTAIN JACK - Bathroom accessories - Better Living Products Inc.
CAPTAIN JACK - Pastries - Captain Jack Ltd.
CAPTAIN JAVA - Coffee - Fairwinds Gourmet Coffee Co. Inc.
CAPTAIN JOHN DERST'S GOOD OLD FASHIONEDBREAD - Bakery products - Derst Baking Co.
CAPTAIN KATHRYN JANEWAY - Game machines - Paramount Pictures Corp.
CAPTAIN KEN'S - Baked beans–canned - Captain Ken's Foods Inc.
CAPTAIN KEN'S FIREHOUSE - Food products - Captain Ken's Foods Inc.
CAPTAIN KEV - Food products - VS Tampa Inc.
CAPTAIN KIDD - Dolls ☆ - Effanbee Doll Corp.
CAPTAIN KIDS - Food products - Beatrice Cos. Inc.
CAPTAIN MIDNIGHT - Toy jewelry - Klutz Press
CAPTAIN MORGAN - Rum - House of Seagram
CAPTAIN NEMO - Watches - Gruen Marketing Corp.
CAPTAIN NEPTUNE - Shrimp–fresh or frozen - Neptune Sea Food Co.
CAPTAIN NERFULS - Toys - Tonka Corp.
CAPTAIN NICK - Seafood products–fresh or frozen - Aslanis Seafoods Inc.
CAPTAIN OSCAR - Seafood products–fresh or frozen - Kennerly Co.
CAPTAIN PADDLEWHEEL - Candy ☆ - R.M. Palmer Co.
CAPTAIN PLANET - Housewares - Tupperware Co.
CAPTAIN PLANET AND THE PLANETEERS - Apparel and accessories - TBS Productions, Inc.
CAPTAIN PUNCH - Fruit drinks–bottled or canned ☆ - Green Spot Packaging, Inc.
CAPTAIN SCOTT - Food products - Sea Tang Fisheries Inc.
CAPTAIN SEA - Seafood products–fresh or frozen - Milfico Foods Inc.
CAPTAIN SHINE - Cleaning preparations–household - USA Detergents Inc.
CAPTAIN SHIPLY - Toys - Mattel, Inc.
CAPTAIN SHRIMP - Seafood products–fresh or frozen - Gloucester Corp.
CAPTAIN SKYHAWK - Games ☆ - Milton Bradley Co.
CAPTAIN TOM - Shrimp - Alpha Seafood Enterprises Inc.
CAPTAIN TRAVEL - Hats - West Coast Novelty Corp.
CAPTAIN'S - Glassware–household - Crisa Corp.
CAPTAIN'S APPLEJACK - Beverages–alcohol - Laird and Co.
CAPTAIN'S CHOICE - Marine product - Inter-City Manufacturing Co.
CAPTAIN'S CHOICE - Seafood products–fresh or frozen - Sea Harvest Packing Co.
CAPTAINS CORD - Fabrics ☆ - Greenwood Mills Inc.
CAPTAINS CREST - Food products - Fadler Co. Inc.
CAPTAIN'S FINEST - Seafood - International Multifoods Corp.

CAPTAINS HARVEST - Seafood products–fresh or frozen - Deiss Sales Co., Inc.
CAPTAINS ISLAND TRADERS - Apparel and accessories - William P. Dynan
CAPTAIN'S LANDING - Floor coverings–carpet and rugs - Catalina Carpet Mills Inc.
CAPTAIN'S LOG - Computer software - Interactive Products, Inc.
CAPTAIN'S LOG - Information management software - Lighthouse Software Inc.
CAPTAIN'S MATE - Seafood products–fresh or frozen - Marcus Food Co.
CAPTAINS OF CRUSH - Exercising equipment - Ironmind Enterprises, Inc.
CAPTAIN'S RESERVE - Wines - Guild Wineries
CAPTAIN'S ROYALE - Seafood products–fresh or frozen - Aqua Royale Foods, Inc.
CAPTAINS' SHIP STORE, THE - Cleaning preparations - Autre Products, Ltd.
CAPTAN - Pesticides–household - Bonide Products, Inc.
CAPTAN SPRAY - Fungicides - Security Products Co.
CAPTEK - Dental equipment - Leach & Dillon, Inc.
CAPTIAN - Liquors - Canandaigua Wine Co. Inc.
CAPTIFF - Food products - International Flavors & Fragrances Inc.
CAPTION MAKER - Electronics equipment - Computer Prompting and Captioned Co.
CAPTION MASTER - Video-cassette recorder with caption decoder - Instant Replay, Inc.
CAPTION WRITER - Video equipment - Instant Replay, Inc.
CAPTIONMAKER - Computer software - Computer Prompting and Captioned Co.
CAPTIONS - Games - Jayne L.M. Griffith
CAPTIVA - Boats–motor - Rinker Boat Co. Inc.
CAPTIVA - Boats–motor ☆ - Ebbtide Corp.
CAPTIVA - Cameras - Polaroid Corp.
CAPTIVA - Eyeglasses - Martin-Copeland Eyewear Corp.
CAPTIVA - Floor coverings - Mannington Resilient Floors
CAPTIVA - Furniture ☆ - Halcyon Inc.
CAPTIVA - Iced tea–bottled or canned ☆ - The Stroh Brewery Co.
CAPTIVA - Jewelry - Gumuchdjian Fils Ltd.
CAPTIVA - Shower stalls–metal - Kohler Co.
CAPTIVA - Tents - SGI Inc.
CAPTIVA BEACH COLLECTION - Blankets - SGI Inc.
CAPTIVA DATE:+ - Computer software - Polaroid Corp.
CAPTIVA II - Floor coverings–carpet and rugs - Mannington Carpets, Inc.
CAPTIVATE - Fabrics ☆ - Greenwood Mills Inc.
CAPTIVATE - Floor coverings–carpet and rugs - Philadelphia Carpets
CAPTIVATING - Candy - Ethel M. Chocolates, Inc.
CAPTIVATING - Floor coverings–carpet and rugs - World Carpets, Inc.
CAPTIVATION - Floor coverings–carpet and rugs ☆ - Downs Carpet Co. Inc.
CAPTIVATOR - Frames–eyeglass ☆ - Universal/Univis Inc.
CAPTIVATOR - Kaleidoscopes - C. Bennett Scopes Inc.
CAPTIVATOR, THE - Garment racks - Strong Arm Creations
CAPTIVATORS - Shoes - Edison Brothers Stores, Inc.
CAPTIVE - American International Industries
CAPTIVE - Floor coverings–carpet and rugs - Galaxy Carpet Mills Inc.
CAPTIVE - Nuts and bolts - Captive Fasteners Corp.
CAPTIVE COLOR - Cosmetics - Noxell Corp.
CAPTIVE OPAL - Novelty items - E.H. Ashley & Co. Inc.
CAPTIVE RAINBOW, THE - Jewelry - Kabana Inc.
CAPTN. - See also CAPTAIN
CAPT'N BENNY - Sardines–canned - B.H. Wilson Fisheries
CAPT'N DON'S - Seafood - Chincoteague Seafood Co.
CAPTN. JACK'S - Publisher's imprints - Marine Trade Publications Inc.
CAPT'N PAT'S SHARK REPELLENT - Beds–wood - Waterworth
CAPTN'S BEST - Food products - O.F. Mossberg & Sons, Inc.
CAPTOR - Measuring instruments - Weber Sensors
CAPTRIX - Arthritis treatment - Biozone Laboratories
CAPTROL - Electronic equipment - Capital Controls Co.
CAPTURE - Apparel–women's ☆ - Carnival Creations
CAPTURE - Cleaning preparations–carpet and rug - Milliken & Co. Inc.
CAPTURE - Cosmetics - Parfums Christian Dior U.S. Corp.
CAPTURE - Frames–eyeglass ☆ - Universal/Univis Inc.
CAPTURE - Hair care products - Kenra Laboratories, Inc.
CAPTURE - Pumps–vacuum - Welch Vacuum Technology, Inc.
CAPTURE - Shampoos - S.C. Johnson & Son, Inc.
CAPTURE - Skin care products - Christian Dior Perfumes Corp.
CAPTURE-IT - Computer software - Chart-It, Inc.
CAPTURE LIFT - Skin-care products - LVMH Moet Hennesy Louis Vuitton Inc.
CAPTURE LOG STAIN - Stains - Sashco Inc.
CAPTURE PLUS - Hair care products - Kenra Laboratories, Inc.

CAPTURE RECOVERY - Computer software - Compusoft Consulting

CAPTURE THE CAMPGROUND - Sporting goods - Kellwood Co.

CAPTURE THE FUN! - Boats - Intex Recreation Corp.

CAPTURE THE MAGIC - Toys - Trendmasters, Inc.

CAPTURE YOUR MEMORIES - Calendars - Graphic Information Systems, Inc.

CAPTURED DREAMS - Glassware–household ☆ - Fenton Art Glass Co.

CAPTURED ELEGANCE - Floor coverings–carpet and rugs ☆ - Mohawk Carpet Corp.

CAPTUREPLUS - Computer software - Kinetic Systems Corp.

CAPTUS - Medical apparatus - Capintec, Inc.

CAPTYANE - Skin care products - Physicians Formula Cosmetics Inc.

CAPUAN - Furniture–wood - Century Furniture Co.

CAPUCCI DE CAPUCCI - Perfumes - Classic Fragrances Ltd.

CAPUCELLO - Liquors - Joseph E. Seagram & Sons, Inc.

CAPUCUI POUR HOMME - Perfumes - Classic Fragrances Ltd.

CAPUDINE - Analgesics - Oakhurst Co.

CAPUDINE HEADACHE REMEDY - Health care products - Woolfoam Corp.

CAPULETS - Pharmaceutical preparations ☆ - Vitarine Pharmaceuticals Inc.

CAPULIN JARABE - Pharmaceutical preparations - Vartex Pharmaceuticals Inc.

CAPUTO - Cheese - Wisconsin Corp.

CAPUTO - Pasta - Wisconsin Cheese

CAPVENT - Implants–surgical - Trebay Medical Corp.

CAPW - Electronic equipment - Moor Electronics Inc.

CAPZACIN-HP - Health care products - Thompson Medical Co., Inc.

CAPZACIN-P - Health care products - Thompson Medical Co., Inc.

CAR AND DRIVER - Antifreeze - Hachette Filipacchi Magazines, Inc.

CAR AND DRIVER - Apparel–women's - Allison Corp.

CAR & TRUCK MAGIC - Deodorizers - Huff Industries, Inc.

CAR ANTENNA LUBE-OIL - Lubricant - Ronald Henderson

CAR BLASTER - Toys - Tyco Toys

CAR/BOND - Paper–bond - Port Huron Paper Co.

CAR-BRITE - Cleaning preparations - National Chemsearch Corp.

CAR BUILDER - Computer software - Optimum Resource, Inc.

CAR BUYING PAIN RELIEF - Advertising agencies - Auto-By-Tel Corp.

CAR CADDY - Leather goods ☆ - AR Accessories Group Inc.

CAR-CARE - Cleaning preparations - Swiss-Tex Inc.

CAR CLINGS - Novelty items - Ogren Companies Inc.

CAR CLOTHES - Seat covers - Shelly D. Schonberger

CAR-COATE - Cleaning preparations–upholstery ☆ - Guardsman Products, Inc.

CAR-COME-BACK - Toys–automobiles - Buddy L Inc.

CAR CRUSH - Toys ☆ - Playskool, Inc.

CAR-CUSH - Orthopedic products - Kinetic Diversified Industries, Inc.

CAR DEL - Fabrics - Car Del

CAR FRESH - Deodorizers - Surco Products Inc.

CAR-FRESHENER - Deodorizers - Car-Freshner Corp.

CAR-FRESHENER GOLD - Deodorizers - Car-Freshner Corp.

CAR-GANIZER - Motor vehicle parts and accessories ☆ - Talus Corp.

CAR-GO - Deicing fluid - Home Safety Research Laboratories, Inc.

CAR/GO - Trailers–travel ☆ - Fruehauf Trailer Corp.

CAR HOP - Beverages - Creative Beverage Co.

CAR HOP - Shampoos - W.W. Grainger, Inc.

CAR INCENSE - Air purification systems ☆ - Medo Industries, Inc.

CAR-LOK - Wire - A.J. Gerrard & Co.

CAR-MAC - Garden equipment ☆ - Spring Window Fashions Division, Inc.

CAR-MATE - Automotive parts and accessories ☆ - Atlas Tool

CAR-MATE - Luggage - United States Luggage Corp.

CAR MOBILE - Toys - Wimmer-Ferguson Inc.

CAR-MOUNT - Audio equipment ☆ - Philips Electronics North America Corp.

CAR-PET - Air purification systems ☆ - Medo Industries, Inc.

CAR PETS - Motor vehicle parts and accessories ☆ - Cobbs Manufacturing Co.

CAR-PLATE - Carwashes - S.C. Johnson & Son, Inc.

CAR ROBE - Pet products - O'Donnell Industries Inc.

CAR-SAC - Luggage ☆ - Airway Industries, Inc.

CAR SEAL - Sealing compounds - Monsey Products Co.

CAR SEAT CIRCUS - Infant product - Summer Infant Products Inc.

CAR SEAT GALLERY - Toys - Wimmer-Ferguson Inc.

CAR-SECURE - Remote control devices - Car-Safe, Inc.

CAR SHOT - Cameras–television - Terry D. Scharton

CAR-SKIN - Coatings - American Grease Stick Co.

CAR STICKS - Automotive parts and accessories - Dar-Lin Products Inc.

CAR TOGS - Motor vehicle parts and accessories ☆ - Cobbs Manufacturing Co.

CAR-TOWN - Abrasive products ☆ - Park Metallurgical Corp.

CAR TOYS - Communications equipment - Car Toys, Inc.

CAR TRAILERS - Trailers–truck - U.S. Cargo, Inc.

CAR TRAVEL - Games ☆ - Milton Bradley Co.

CAR WARRIORS - Games - Steve Jackson Games Inc.

CAR WARS - Games - Steve Jackson Games Inc.

CAR WASH FIZZ TABS - Cleaning preparations - Coughlan Products Corp.

CARA - Cheese - Tatra Sheep Cheese Co.

CARA - Flatware - Mikasa Co.

CARA - Flatware - Yamazaki Tableware Inc.

CARA - Handbags ☆ - Mutterperl Group Inc.

CARA - Hot tubs–fiberglass ☆ - Jacuzzi Inc.

CARA - Luggage - Airway Industries, Inc.

CARA - Ophthalmic goods ☆ - Luxottica

CARA - Recording label - Sony Disco Inc.

CARA - Water bottles–rubber - Cara, Inc.

CARA BELLA - Cosmetics - Royal Laboratories Cosmetics

CARA BITES - Fresh carrots - Zellwin Farms Co.

CARA CRONINGER - Jewelry - Cara Croninger

CARA GOLD ACCENT - Flatware - Yamazaki Tableware Inc.

CARA-LITE - Candy ☆ - El Molino Mills

CARA LUCIA - Cheese - Tatra Sheep Cheese Co.

CARA MIA - Apparel–women's - NCC Industries, Inc.

CARA MIA - Food products - Artichoke Industries Inc.

CARA MIA - Rings–jewelry - Artcarved Inc.

CARA NONNA - Pasta - Victoria Packing Corp.

CARA TELLA - Candy ☆ - Van Melle Inc.

CARABACHOL - Pharmaceutical preparations - City Chemical Corp.

CARABANA - Cigars - National Cigar Corp.

CARABEEF - Buffalo meat - Carabeef Inc.

CARABELLA - Apparel and accessories - Carabella Corp.

CARABELLA - Cosmetics - Pentech International Inc.

CARABELLI - Hosiery - Kartex International Cos. Inc.

CARACAL - Sunglasses ☆ - Corning Inc.

CARACALLA - Shoes ☆ - Tessler Shoe Corp.

CARACAS - Floor coverings–carpet and rugs - Barrett Carpet Mills Inc.

CARACOA - Candy - El Molino Mills

CARACUL - Floor coverings–carpet and rugs - Philadelphia Carpets

CARADCO - Hardware - Blaine Window Hardware Inc.

CARADCO - Windows–storm - Caradco

CARAFE - Frames–eyeglass - Zylo Ware Corp.

CARAFECTION - Candy - American Natural Snacks

CARAGLAS ULTRA - Tape–adhesive - Carapace, Inc.

CARAGOL - Pharmaceutical preparations - Paraeusal Co.

CARALINDA - Soap ☆ - Hair Specialty Co.

CARALUX - Projectors–photographic - Eastman Kodak Co.

CARAMATE - Electronic equipment - Telex Communications, Inc.

CARAMBA - Floor coverings–carpet and rugs ☆ - Masland Corp.

CARAMBA - Frames–eyeglass - Hudson Optical Corp.

CARAMEL - Stoves–gas - Malm Fireplaces Inc.

CARAMEL APPLE WRAP - Food products - Concord Foods Inc.

CARAMEL BEAR - Toys–stuffed - Russ Berrie and Co., Inc.

CARAMEL CREAMS - Candy - Goetze's Candy Co., Inc.

CARAMEL KINGS - Candy - Nabisco Foods Group

CARAMEL NIP - Candy - Nabisco Foods Group

CARAMEL QWIK - Confections - Caravan Products Inc.

CARAMEL SPLENDOR - Candy - Ethel M. Chocolates, Inc.

CARAMEL WHIRLS - Candy - World's Finest Chocolate, Inc.

CARAMELCRISP - Popcorn - Caramelcrisp Corp.

CARAMELICIOUS - Bakery products - Caramelicious Co.

CARAMELLE - Health care products - Colora Henna

CARAMELLO - Candy bars - Peter Paul

CARAMELS - Shoes ☆ - Combine Group Division Inc.

CARAMIA - Floor coverings–carpet and rugs ☆ - Masland Corp.

CARAN D'ACHE - Pens - Caran D'Ache of Switzerland Inc.

CARANDO - Meat products–cured - Carando Inc.

CARANINA - Pasta - Beta Worldwide Trading, Inc.

CARANUTTA - Food products - Conagra, Inc.

CARASOFT - Yarn ☆ - Caron International Inc.

CARAT - Wallpaper - Surface Industries Inc.

CARAT - Yarn ☆ - Joseph Galler Inc.

CARAVAGGIO - Optical frames - Aptaker Co. Inc.

CARAVALI - Coffee and tea - Caravali Coffees, Inc.

CARAVALI COFFEE, INC. - Coffee - Java City

CARAVAN - Bathroom fixtures - Jack Nahon Import Corp.

CARAVAN - Beverages–carbonated - Carolina Beverage Inc.

CARAVAN - Bicycles ☆ - Roadmaster Corp.

CARAVAN - Cymbals - Grossman Music Corp.

CARAVAN - Dialing devices–telephone - Baltimore Luggage Co.
CARAVAN - Eyeglasses - Bausch & Lomb Inc.
CARAVAN - Fabrics - Gretchen Bellinger Inc.
CARAVAN - Floor coverings ☆ - Tarkett, Inc.
CARAVAN - Floor coverings–carpet and rugs - Bloomsburg Carpet Industries
CARAVAN - Floor coverings–carpet and rugs - Cabin Crafts Carpets
CARAVAN - Floor coverings–carpet and rugs - Foreign Accents
CARAVAN - Floor coverings–carpet and rugs - Quaker Inc.
CARAVAN - Golfing equipment - Sun Mountain Sports, Inc.
CARAVAN - Heating equipment - Slant/Fin Corp.
CARAVAN - Luggage - Shalam Imports Inc.
CARAVAN - Motor vehicles - Chrysler Corp. (Dodge Car Div.)
CARAVAN - Paper–bond ☆ - Saxon Paper Co.
CARAVAN - Strollers–baby ☆ - Welsh Co.
CARAVAN BEADS - Jewelers' findings - Caravan Beads, Inc.
CARAVAN BOOKS - Publisher's imprints - Scholars' Facsimiles & Reprints
CARAVAN CAROUSEL - Carousels ☆ - Bradley Import Co.
CARAVAN FLAGS - Flags - Flag Co., Inc.
CARAVANNER - Trailers–travel - Airstream Inc.
CARAVEL - Juvenile history books - American Heritage
CARAVEL - Toys ☆ - Peg Perego USA Inc.
CARAVELL FASHIONS - Coats–children's - MZL Fashions Corp.
CARAVELLA - Beverages–alcohol - Barton Brands, Ltd.
CARAVELLA - Liquors - Canandaigua Wine Co. Inc.
CARAVELLE - Bicycles ☆ - Murray, Inc.
CARAVELLE - Bidets - Kohler Co.
CARAVELLE - Boats ☆ - John G. Alden Inc.
CARAVELLE - Cabinets - Classic Bath Products
CARAVELLE - Candy bars ☆ - Peter Paul
CARAVELLE - Cooking utensils–enameled ☆ - National Housewares
CARAVELLE - Curtain rods - Newell Window Furnishing Co.
CARAVELLE - Cutlery ☆ - Regent Sheffield, Ltd.
CARAVELLE - Floor coverings - Mannington Resilient Floors
CARAVELLE - Floor coverings–carpet and rugs - Atlas Carpet Mills Inc.
CARAVELLE - Frames–eyeglass ☆ - Universal/Univis Inc.
CARAVELLE - Furniture - Weiman Co.
CARAVELLE - Giftware ☆ - W.M.F. of America Inc.
CARAVELLE - Motor vehicles–automobiles ☆ - Chrysler Corp. (Chrysler-Plymouth Div.)
CARAVELLE - Musical instruments ☆ - Deg Music Products Inc.
CARAVELLE - Rings–jewelry - Artcarved Inc.
CARAVELLE - Sporting goods ☆ - National Sporting Goods Corp.
CARAVELLE - Trailers–travel - Airstream Inc.
CARAVELLE - Wallcovering ☆ - Capital Carousel Inc.
CARAVELLE - Wallpaper - Advent Industries Inc.
CARAVELLE - Watches - Bulova Corp.
CARAVELLE PLACE - Floor coverings–carpet and rugs - Atlas Carpet Mills Inc.
CARAVELLE ROSE - Bakery products - Anhing Corp.
CARB AID - Cleaning preparations - Zecol Inc.
CARB AMINO DYNAMITE - Vitamins and nutritional supplements - Healthy 'N Fit Nutritionals
CARB-AMM - Water treating compounds - Silco Pet Products
CARB-BOOM - Vitamins and nutritional supplements - John Michael Cooney
CARB CLEAN - Cleaning preparations - Cyclo Industries, Inc.
CARB-MEDIC - Automotive parts and accessories - Radiator Specialty Co.
CARB-O-NATED - Candy ☆ - Nellson Candies Inc.
CARB XCELERATOR - Vitamins and nutritional supplements - Juice Pak
CARBAMIDE PEROXIDE - Pharmaceutical preparations - Raway Pharmacal Inc.
CARBAMINE - Antacids ☆ - Key Pharmaceuticals Inc.
CARBAMYL CHOLINE CHLORIDE - Pharmaceutical preparations - City Chemical Corp.
CARBATUSS - Cough medicines - GM Pharmaceuticals, Inc.
CARBAX - Vitamins and nutritional supplements ☆ - Diaprex Marketing Inc.
CARBEL - Electrodes - W.L. Gore & Associates, Inc.
CARBELITE - Gun stocks - Bell & Carlson Inc.
CARBETUSSIC - Pharmaceutical preparations - C.O. Truxton Inc.
CARBEX - Tools - Symmco HD, Inc.
CARBEX BELL - Pharmaceutical preparations - Hollings-Smith Co. Inc.
CARBI-TWIST - Drill bits ☆ - MKT Fastening, LLC
CARBICHAIN - Saws–chain - Hal E. Verble & Son Inc. (Veri Products Div.)
CARBICOTE - Paints - Carbit Paint Co.
CARBINE - Alarm systems - Magnadyne Corp.
CARBINE WORMER - Veterinary pharmaceutical preparations ☆ - Vineland Laboratories Inc.

CARBISET - Pharmaceutical preparations - Glenwood LLC
CARBIT - Paints - Carbit Paint Co.
CARBITE - Golfing equipment - Carbite, Inc.
CARBITHANE - Paints - Carbit Paint Co.
CARBO CHARGE - Vitamins and nutritional supplements ☆ - Nature's Way Products, Inc.
CARBO CLEAN - Vitamins and nutritional supplements - Royal Source, Inc.
CARBO COKE - Petroleum - Great Lakes Carbon Corp.
CARBO COOLER - Health care products - Ultimate Strength Systems Labs, Inc.
CARBO CUT - Paper–sand ☆ - Carborundum Abrasives North America
CARBO EDGE - Vitamins and nutritional supplements - Vita Life Products
CARBO ENERGIZER - Beverages - Weider Health and Fitness
CARBO ENERGY BAR - Vitamins and nutritional supplements - Body Wise International, Inc.
CARBO FIRE - Dietary powder and supplements - Weider Health and Fitness
CARBO-FLO - Aquarium product - Imi Cornelius Inc.
CARBO FORCE - Vitamins and nutritional supplements - American Body Building Products, Inc.
CARBO FUEL - Vitamins and nutritional supplements - Twinlab
CARBO-GOLD - Beverages - Nutri-West
CARBO GOLD - Paper–sand - Carborundum Abrasives North America
CARBO-LASTIC - Finishing agents - Fred A. Wilson Co.
CARBO LIGHT - Vitamins and nutritional supplements - American Body Building Products, Inc.
CARBO LOAD - Vitamins and nutritional supplements ☆ - ICN Pharmaceuticals Inc.
CARBO-MEX - Charcoal - V & V Food Products, Inc.
CARBO PLUS - Health care products - Nature Health
CARBO POWER - Vitamins and nutritional supplements - Nature's Best Inc.
CARBO-QUENCH - Health care products - Natural Organics, Inc.
CARBO QUICK - Vitamins and nutritional supplements - Royal Source, Inc.
CARBO-SEPTIC - Health care products ☆ - Mackwin Co.
CARBO-SURGE - Vitamins and nutritional supplements - Nutri-West
CARBO-WELD - Pencils - General Pencil Co.
CARBO-Z - Chemical preparations - Petcetera Inc.
CARBOCAINE - Pharmaceutical preparations - Sterling Winthrop Inc.
CARBODEC DM - Pharmaceutical preparations - Rugby Laboratories Inc.
CARBOGEN - Food supplement - Triarco Industries, Inc.
CARBOGRAF - Semiconductors - Carbone-Lorraine North America Corp.
CARBOLINE - Adhesives and sealants - Carboline Co.
CARBOMASK - Cosmetics - Hutton Labs, Inc.
CARBOMATIC - Cash registers - Standard Register Co.
CARBOMAX - Sunglasses - Nikon Inc.
CARBOMETPLUS - Brake parts - Hawkhead Automotive Inc.
CARBON - Frames–eyeglass ☆ - Universal/Univis Inc.
CARBON - Wallets - Samsonite Corp.
CARBON 95 - Pet products - Sandpoint Aquarium Products
CARBON BLASTER - Carburetors - Justice Brothers Inc.
CARBON BLUE - Fabrics–denim - Dan River Inc.
CARBON COMMANDO - Motor vehicles - BSI Technologies
CARBON COPIES - Apparel and accessories - J.C. Penney Co., Inc.
CARBON CYCLE ORGANIC - Fresh produce - Jimmy Domingos Produce
CARBON-IT - Pet products ☆ - Aquatronics-Filtronics
CARBON LITE - Archery equipment - Game Tracker, Inc.
CARBON MATE - Archery equipment - Saunders Archery Co.
CARBON METALLIC - Brake pads - Performance Friction Corp.
CARBON STICK - Golfing equipment - Golfsmith International Inc.
CARBON STICK OVB 86 - Golfing equipment - Golfsmith International Inc.
CARBON TECH SYSTEM - Golfing equipment - Golfsmith International Inc.
CARBON TOUR - Golfing equipment - Golfsmith International Inc.
CARBON WEAVE - Golfing equipment - Golfsmith International Inc.
CARBONA - Cleaning preparations - Carbona Products Co.
CARBONADO - Knives–carving ☆ - Martin Carbone Inc.
CARBONE CUTTER - Cutlery ☆ - Martin Carbone Inc.
CARBONELL - Olive oil - La Cena Fine Foods Inc.
CARBONEX - Sports rackets and accessories ☆ - Winn, Inc.
CARBONITE - Chemical preparations - Hill & Griffith Co.
CARBONOEL - Hair care products - Gold Medal Hair Products Inc.
CARBON'S - Waffles - Carbon's Frozen Products Inc.
CARBONSAVER 14 - Air purification systems - World Envirotech Services & Technologies, Inc.
CARBOPLAN - Paper–carbon - Kores Nordic USA Corp.
CARBOPLEX - Dietary supplements - Metagenics, Inc.
CARBOPLEX - Vitamins and nutritional supplements - Unipro Inc.
CARBOREST - Sporting goods - New Archery Products Corp.

☆ = Now out of production

CARBORUNDUM - Abrasive products - Carborundum Abrasives North America

CARBOSORB - Chemical preparations - Microwave Filter Co., Inc.

CARBRITAL - Pharmaceutical preparations ✩ - Parke-Davis

CARBROGESIC - Pharmaceutical preparations ✩ - JMI-Canton Pharmaceuticals

CARBURETOR - Pipes–tobacco ✩ - S.M. Frank & Co. Inc. (Kaywoodie-Yello-Bole-Medico)

CARBUTATOR - Cleaning preparations ✩ - Kleer Flo Co. Inc.

CARCAREDIARY - Log book - Harmony Productions

CARCASS COVERS - Apparel and accessories ✩ - Carcass Covers, Inc.

CARCASS COVERS - Men's and women's apparel - Marino Brothers Studio

CARCHALK - Artists' materials - Joseph Edward Daniel

CARCLAD - Doors–metal ✩ - Aluminum Co. of America

CARCLAD - Windows–storm - Caradco

CARCO - Health care products - Carr Products Co. Inc.

CARCOP - Alarm systems–burglar - Mobile Security Communications, Inc.

CARCROSS - Pens ✩ - Ad-a-Day Co. Inc.

CARD - Cigarette lighters - Park Lane Associates, Inc.

CARD - Computer software - S-Matrix Corp.

CARD ATTACK - Toys - Tonka Corp.

CARD-B-LOON - Novelty items - CTI Industries Corp.

CARD BY CURLY - Greeting cards - P.S. Greetings

CARD CAPER - Games - Twinson Co.

CARD-CAT - Computer software - Compu-Tations Inc.

CARD CATCHER - Cases–plastic - Russell Specialties Corp.

CARD CREATIONS - Greeting cards - Trost & Mueller, Inc.

CARD DICE - Games - Wheeler Games

CARD DYNAMICS - Trading cards and stamps - Source International Inc.

CARD FOR ALL AGES, A - Greeting cards - Designer Greetings Inc.

CARD GUARDIAN - Credit institutions - Andrew E. Weiss

CARD HOLDSTIR - Bar fixtures–plastic - Spir-it Inc.

CARD KEEPER - Office supplies - Light Impressions Corp.

CARD-MATE - Paper goods - Textmate Corp.

CARD-MATIC - Office machines - Mead-Hatcher, Inc.

CARD MINDER - Spring clip - Epco Design

CARD-O-MATIC - Business-card accessory - Intromark Inc.

CARD PARTS - Greeting cards - Luan Dinh Vv Pham

CARD PLAYER - Health care products - Maddak Inc.

CARD SHARKS - Computer software ✩ - Accolade Inc.

CARD STADIUM - Trading card collecting kit - ANCO Collector Supplies, Inc.

CARD STUFFER - Decals and transfers - Barbara Jean

CARD-TAINER - Wallets - Buxton Inc.

CARDABID - Pharmaceutical preparations - Saron Pharmacal Corp.

CARDACHROME - Greeting cards - Agent Andy Inc.

CARDAGEN - Vitamins and nutritional supplements - Great Life Laboratories Inc.

CARDAMON - Apparel–women's ✩ - Jez of California

CARDAMONDO - Liqueurs ✩ - Shaw-Ross International Importers

CARDAS AUDIO - Cables - GNP Audio Video Inc.

CARDASSIAN - Toys - Paramount Pictures Corp.

CARDCRAFT - Artists' materials - M. Grumbacher Inc.

CARDD - Electronic equipment - ImagineNation

CARDDOCK - Computer software - Greystone Peripherals, Inc.

CARDE MOUCHE - Hair accessories, jewelry - I.J. Grace Corp.

CARDEAL DAO - Wines - Admiral Wine Merchants

CARDEAUX - Cosmetics - Cardeaux Cosmetics

CARDEC - Pharmaceutical preparations - Barre-National, Inc.

CARDED - Plumbing fixtures–metal - Peerless Faucet Co. (Plumbing Products Div.)

CARDEF - Bricks - North American Refractories Co.

CARDEILHAC - See CHRISTOFLE

CARDEL - Boats–motor - Century Boat Co.

CARDELL - Floor coverings ✩ - Scottdel Inc.

CARDELLA - Furniture–wood - Century Furniture Co.

CARDENAL MENDOZA - Brandy - Shaw-Ross International Importers

CARDEROCK - Stone products - Tri-State Stone and Building Supply, Inc.

CARDEROCKS - Stone products - Tri-State Stone and Building Supply, Inc.

CARDETTE - Leather goods - AR Accessories Group Inc.

CARDETTE - Office supplies - Wescosa Inc.

CARDGRABBER - Computer software - Pacific Crest Technologies Inc.

CARDHU - Whiskey - United Distillers of North America

CARDI-OMEGA 3 - Vitamins and nutritional supplements ✩ - Thompson Medical Co., Inc.

CARDI-RITE - Vitamins and nutritional supplements - J.R. Carlson Laboratories Inc.

CARDIA - Spices and extracts - Ambi, Inc.

CARDIAC DIRECTIONS - Educational materials - Dialogue Co., Inc.

CARDIAC DIRECTIONS HEALTHY HABITS FOR YOUR HEART - Potash - Dialogue Co., Inc.

CARDIAC REPORTER, THE - Computer software - Dorne Medical Software, Inc.

CARDIAFORCE - Health care products - Bioforce of America Ltd.

CARDIC - Bricks - North American Refractories Co.

CARDIFF - Shutters–wood - Cardiff Industries Inc.

CARDIFF GATES - Floor coverings–carpet and rugs - Lock Weave Carpet Mills Inc.

CARDIFF GREEN - Floor coverings - Southern Aggregates

CARDIGAN - Eyeglasses - Art-Craft Optical Co.

CARDIGAN - Paper products - Georgia-Pacific Corp.

CARDIGAN CUT OUTS - Hobby kits - Daisy Kingdom, Inc.

CARDIGAN, THE - Apparel and accessories - Chums Ltd.

CARDILATE - Pharmaceutical preparations - Burroughs Wellcome Co.

CARDILINE - Microphones - Electro-Voice, Inc.

CARDILL - Floor coverings ✩ - Tarkett, Inc.

CARDIN RELAX - Apparel–men's ✩ - Crystal Brands Inc.

CARDINAL - Antifreeze - J.D. Streett & Co. Inc.

CARDINAL - Beverages–malt - Sibra Products

CARDINAL - Cabinets - Fixture Exchange Corp.

CARDINAL - Computer peripheral equipment - Cardinal Technologies, Inc.

CARDINAL - Envelopes - Unisource Converting (Envelope Div.)

CARDINAL - Erasers ✩ - Empire Berol USA

CARDINAL - Eyeglasses - Art-Craft Optical Co.

CARDINAL - Flatware - Couzon USA

CARDINAL - Food products - Betters International Food Corp.

CARDINAL - Fruits and vegetables - Southern Fruit Distributors Inc.

CARDINAL - Giftware - Cardinal Inc.

CARDINAL - Hair care products - Cardinal Comb & Brush

CARDINAL - Jewelry - Bauman-Massa Jewelry Co.

CARDINAL - Office supplies - Cardinal Products

CARDINAL - Paper–writing - Gilbert Paper Co.

CARDINAL - Pet products - Cardinal Laboratories, Inc.

CARDINAL - Scales–bathroom - Cardinal Scale Manufacturing Co.

CARDINAL - Seafood products–fresh or frozen - Hallmark Fisheries

CARDINAL - Trailers–travel - Adams Vacation Trailer Manufacturing Inc.

CARDINAL - Trailers–travel - Forest River, Inc.

CARDINAL - Wallpaper ✩ - Wolf-Gordon Inc.

CARDINAL CHINA - Furniture ✩ - Foley & Robinson Inc.

CARDINAL CHOICE - Agricultural products - Agway, Inc.

CARDINAL CLASSIC - Bird feeds - Duncraft, Inc.

CARDINAL CREST BIRDE BISTRO - Bird feeders - Deli, Inc.

CARDINAL CREST CHEEP CAFE - Bird feeders - Deli, Inc.

CARDINAL CREST WINDOW CAFE - Bird feeders - Deli, Inc.

CARDINAL FG - Glass–flat - Cardinal IG Co.

CARDINAL FRUIT TREAT - Pet products ✩ - Coicor

CARDINAL OF THE KREMLIN - Computer software ✩ - Capstone Software

CARDINAL QUALITY - Jewelry - Bauman-Massa Jewelry Co.

CARDINAL RED - Jams and jellies - Dawn Food Products Inc.

CARDINAL SPECIALE - Beverages–malt - White Rock Products Corp.

CARDINAL TEEN - Toys–stuffed - Cardinal Teen Toy Inc.

CARDINAL ZIN - Wines - Ahlgren Vineyard

CARDINALE - Wines - Kendall Jackson Winery, Ltd.

CARDINAL'S CREST - Wines ✩ - Biltmore Estate Wine Co.

CARDINEL - Seafood products–fresh or frozen - Route 11 Potato Chip Factory

CARDINI - Watches - D.P. Collection Inc.

CARDINI'S - Salad dressings–bottled - Dolefam Corp.

CARDIO-BASE - Computer software - Ergometrx Corp.

CARDIO-BASICS - Vitamins and nutritional supplements - Rexall Sundown, Inc.

CARDIO CARE - Vitamins and nutritional supplements - Vitamin Research Products Inc.

CARDIO COMPLETE - Vitamins and nutritional supplements - Earth's Resources, Inc.

CARDIO COUNTRY - Video production - Power Productions International, Inc.

CARDIO FACTORS - Vitamins - Country Life

CARDIO FACTORS - Vitamins and nutritional supplements - Consac Industries, Inc.

CARDIO FIT - Exercising equipment - Icon Health & Fitness, Inc.

CARDIO-ISLAND - Medical apparatus - Precision Air Products Co.

CARDIO-KEY - Computer storage devices - Ergometrx Corp.

CARDIO KICKBOXING - Video production - Sport Karate, Inc.

CARDIO LIFE - Health care products - Esteem Products Ltd.

CARDIO-TMG - Vitamins and nutritional supplements - Natural Balance, Inc.

CARDIO WISE - Vitamins and nutritional supplements - Body Wise International, Inc.

CARDIOBEAT - Medical apparatus - Medasonics, Inc.

CARDIOCHART - Medical apparatus - Del Mar Avionics

CARDIOCORDER - Medical apparatus - Del Mar Avionics

CARDIOCYCLE - Exercising equipment - Engineering Dynamics Corp.

CARDIOEXPRESS - Medical apparatus - Del Mar Avionics

CARDIOGLIDE - Exercising equipment - Icon Health & Fitness, Inc.

CARDIOGLIDE PLUS - Exercising equipment - Icon Health & Fitness, Inc.

CARDIOGRAFIN - Pharmaceutical preparations - Bristol-Myers Squibb Co.

CARDIOGUARD - Medical apparatus - Del Mar Avionics

CARDIOHEALTH - Vitamins and nutritional supplements - Enrich Corp.

CARDIOLAB - Medical apparatus - Arrhythmia Research Tech., Inc.

CARDIOLOGIST - Greeting cards - Susanne L. Rosen

CARDIOLOGIST, THE - Computer software - David A. Ness

CARDIOMAC - Computer software - Iowa Heart Institute

CARDIOMATE - Medical apparatus - Del Mar Avionics

CARDIOMINS - Vitamins and nutritional supplements - Amrion, Inc.

CARDIOPRIN - Pharmaceutical preparations - Univest Technologies Ltd.

CARDIOQUIN - Medical apparatus - Purdue Frederick Co.

CARDIORHYTHM - Medical apparatus - Medtronic, Inc.

CARDIOSCOPE - Medical apparatus - Del Mar Avionics

CARDIOSENS - Medical equipment - Siemens Burdick, Inc.

CARDIOSMART - Electrocardiographs - Marquette Medical Systems

CARDIOSMART - Vitamins and nutritional supplements - Amrion, Inc.

CARDIOTHORACIC SYSTEMS - Medical apparatus - Cardiothoracic Systems, Inc.

CARDIOTIC - Health care products - Nellcor Puritan Bennett

CARDIOTRACK - Sporting goods - Nordictrack, Inc.

CARDIOVASCULAR PROVIDER RESOURCES - Consulting services - Cardiovascular Provider Resources Holdings, Inc.

CARDIOXY - Health care products - Healthwatchers System

CARDIT - Computer terminals - Quiktrip Corp.

CARDIZEM - Pharmaceutical - Dow Chemical Co.

CARDKEEPER - Frames–picture - Rubicon Products Co.

CARDLETS - Greeting cards ☆ - Fran Mar Greeting cards Ltd.

CARDMAKER - Computer peripheral equipment - Sangamon Co.

CARDMAKERS - Greeting cards - Peter D. Diebold

CARDMASTER - Board games and accessories - Tsr, Inc.

CARDMASTER - Electronic equipment - Califone International Inc.

CARDMATE - Photographic equipment - Lucht Engineering Inc.

CARDO - Awnings - Cardo Industries

CARDO BROTHERS - Wines - Gibson Wine Co.

CARDOVICH PRONOUNCED CARDS OF EACH - Greeting cards - Marketing Systems of America, Inc.

CARDOX-1 - Pharmaceutical preparations ☆ - Wesley Pharmacal Co. Inc.

CARDOXIN - Veterinary pharmaceutical preparations - Evsco Pharmaceuticals

CARDPAK - Leather goods - St. Thomas Inc.

CARDPORT - Computer peripheral equipment - CNF Inc.

CARDPOWER - Computer software - American Express Travel Related Services Co., Inc.

CARDPRO - Computer software - Data I/O Corp.

CARDPRO - Identification tags - Cardpro Services, Inc.

CARDRASE - Pharmaceutical preparations ☆ - Upjohn Co.

CARDRUNNER - Fabrics - Spence Cole International

CARDS - Computer hardware - Proprietary Controls Systems Corp.

CARDS BY EMILY - Greeting cards ☆ - Shulsinger Sales Inc.

CARDS BY KRISTEN - Greeting cards - Burgoyne Inc./Curtis Swann

CARDS FOR CARDS - Greeting cards - Cards for Cards

CARDS N' IMAGES - Greeting cards - Cards N' Images Inc.

CARDS NOW - Computer software - Topitzes & Associates, Inc.

CARDS OF THE LIGHT - Publisher's imprints - Connie Norris Penney

CARDS QS - Diagnostic apparatus - Quidel Corp.

CARDS THAT GROW - Greeting cards - Cards That Grow, Inc.

CARDS TO BE TREASURED - Greeting cards - Matthew John Productions

CARDS TO KEEP - Greeting cards - Sunrise Publications, Inc.

CARDS WITH A CAUSE - Greeting cards - Tanager Place

CARDSAVER - Computer software - Kronos Inc.

CARDSETTES - Recording label - Sound Identity Corp. of America, Inc.

CARDSHARK - Eyeglasses - Art-Craft Optical Co.

CARDSHARKII - Computer hardware - Curtis, Inc.

CARDSTATION - Computer peripheral equipment - Axonix Corp.

CARDTOONS - Trading cards and stamps - Cardtoons L.C.

CARDTRACKER - Stationery - Card Tracker Enterprises

CARDTRAK - Automatic teller machines - Kathleen D. Hostert

CARDU - Beverages–alcohol - Guinness Import Co.

CARDVAULT - Display cases–metal - John Hoffman

CARDVELOPE - Scented greeting card - Greenleaf, Inc.

CARDVIEW - Computer software ☆ - Systemsoft Corp.

CARDWARE - Computer software - Award Software International, Inc.

CARDWATCH - Computer software - Cheetah Software Systems, Inc.

CARDWIZARD - Computer software - Systemsoft Corp.

CARDWRAPS - Envelopes - AGC, Inc.

CARDWRAPS - Envelopes - American Greetings Corp.

CARDY - Pens ☆ - Zebra Pen Corp.

CARDZ - Trading cards and stamps - Cardz Distribution, Inc.

CARDZILLION - Trading cards and stamps - Bandai America Inc.

CARE - Cleaning preparations - Conklin Co., Inc.

CARE - Hair care products ☆ - Aquamint Laboratories Inc.

C.A.R.E. - Health care products - Labeltape Meditect Inc.

CARE - Health care products ☆ - National Tea Co.

CARE - Lubricants - Care Laboratories Inc.

CARE - Video production - Mountain Lake Ventures, Inc.

CARE 1 - Skin care products - GOLDWELL Cosmetics (USA) Inc.

CARE-4 - Vitamins and nutritional supplements ☆ - Marlyn Co. Inc.

CARE-ALL - Health care products - Omron Healthcare, Inc.

CARE & COMFORT - Hair care products - Novatrend Inc.

CARE AND CONTROL FOR TODAY'S ENVIRONMENT - Housewares - Technical Concepts, L.P.

CARE BAND - Beads - Aso Corp.

CARE BEAR - Apparel–children's - Dobie Industries Inc.

CARE BEAR COUSINS - Dishes–plastic - Deka Plastics Inc.

CARE BEAR COUSINS - Stuffed toys, canisters ☆ - American Greetings Corp.

CARE BEAR COUSINS - Toys–stuffed - Kenner Products

CARE BEAR COUSINS BUSY BODIES - Games ☆ - Parker Brothers

CARE BEAR RAINBOW - Kites - Hi-Flier Manufacturing Co.

CARE BEARS - Bathroom accessories ☆ - Tsumura International Inc.

CARE BEARS - Candy - A & A Food Products Corp.

CARE BEARS - Games ☆ - Parker Brothers

CARE BEARS - Ice cream - Pierre's French Ice Cream Distributing Co. of Akron

CARE BEARS - Kites - Hi-Flier Manufacturing Co.

CARE BEARS - Novelty items - Those Characters from Cleveland, Inc.

CARE BEARS - Toys–stuffed - Kenner Products

CARE BEARS ON THE PATH TO CARE-A-LOT - Games ☆ - Parker Brothers

CARE BEARS PARADE - Kites - Hi-Flier Manufacturing Co.

CARE BEARS WARM FEELINGS - Games ☆ - Parker Brothers

CARE CAGES - Cages–wire - Ozark Honey-Dew Farms, Inc.

CARE CARD - Greeting cards - Creative Communications for the Parish

CARE CHAIR - Child restraint - Chicken Little Industries

CARE CHAIR - Health care products - Activeaid Inc.

CARE CHAIR - Medical apparatus - Modern Healthcare Products Inc.

CARE COAT - Paints - Suntec Paint Inc.

CARE COVERS - Hair-care products - Care Products Inc.

CARE-CREME - Skin care products - Care-Tech Laboratories Inc.

CARE CRITTER HOMES - Cages–wire - Pets International, Ltd.

CARE CUBES - Health care products - Bryant Specialties Inc.

CARE DECISIONS - Identification tags - Harrill & Harrill, Inc.

CARE EXPOSITION - Health care products - National Home Health Care Exposition

CAR'E-FLOW - Health care products - Neoterik Health Technologies Inc.

CARE FOR KIDS - Shampoos - Revlon Consumer Products Corp.

CARE-FOR-ME BABY - Doll - TCA Ground Inc.

CARE FREE - See **SNOW BOSS**

CARE FREE - See **SNOWBLAZER**

CARE-FREE - Chewing gum - Planters LifeSavers Co.

CARE-FREE - Rakes - Ames Lawn & Garden Tool Co.

CARE-FREE - Tape–adhesive - Lepage's, Inc.

CARE-FREE - Windows–storm - Care-Free Windows

CARE FREE CURL - Hair care products - Soft Sheen Products Co.

CARE-FREE KITTY - Pet products - American Colloid Co.

CARE FREE ME - Wigs - Revlon General Wig Manufacturers, Inc.

CARE FRESH - Pet products - Absorption Corp.

CARE LABEL - Pet products ☆ - Pets International, Ltd.

CARE 'N SHARE - Inflatable swimming pools ☆ - Intex Recreation Corp.

CARE-NET - Alarm systems - American Medical Alert Corp.

CARE PADS - Fabrics - David Leo Molitor

CARE PLUS - Shampoos - Beauty Brands Group

CARE-SEAT - Infant product ☆ - Evenflo Co.

CARE TAKER - Lighting fixture ☆ - Cooper Industries, Inc.

☆ = Now out of production

CARE-TECH ADULT CLEANSING WIPES - Skin care products - Care-Tech Laboratories Inc.
CAREACTERS - Toiletries - PMC, Inc.
CAREBORNE - Crutches - Careborne, Inc.
CARECLOCK - Medical apparatus - USMS, Inc.
CAREEN - Cleaning preparations - Douglas Products and Packaging Co.
CAREER - Clocks - General Time Corp. (Westclox/Seth Thomas Div.)
CAREER - Frames–eyeglass - May Optical Co. Inc.
CAREER - Office supplies - Paul R. Strauss
CAREER ACTION INVENTORY - Paper–book - Career Systems, Inc.
CAREER ALLIANCE - Publisher's imprints - Harcourt Brace & Co.
CAREER APPAREL - Fabrics - Dan River Inc.
CAREER ARCHITECT - Computer software - Lominger Limited, Inc.
CAREER AWARENESS PEOPLE - Toys–blocks - Guidecraft Inc.
CAREER CASES - Leather goods - Minnowhead & Co. Inc.
CAREER CLASSICS - Apparel and accessories - Phillips-Van Heusen Corp.
CAREER CLUB - Shirts - Career Club Shirt Co.
CAREER COMMENCEMENT - Computer software - Career Interactive, Inc.
CAREER CURE, THE - Educational materials - Career Dimensions, Inc.
CAREER DIRECTIONS - Computer software - Cambridge Educational
CAREER ESSENTIALS - Apparel and accessories - Nordstrom, Inc.
CAREER EXPLORERS - Games - Thomas Hoffman
CAREER FASHIONS - Uniforms–tailored - Angelica Uniform Group
CAREER GIRL - Frames–eyeglass ☆ - Universal/Univis Inc.
CAREER IMAGE - Apparel–women's - United States Shoe Corp.
CAREER INTERACTIVE - Computer peripheral equipment - Career Interactive, Inc.
CAREER LADY - Ophthalmic goods - Embassy Creations Inc.
CAREER MAN - Eyeglasses - Art-Craft Optical Co.
CAREER MANAGEMENT INTERNATIONAL - Video production - Career Management International Inc.
CAREER MATCH - Computer software - Cambridge Educational
CAREER MOVES - Apparel and accessories - Robert McCleave
CAREER ORIGINALS - Apparel–women's ☆ - Ramm Styles Inc.
CAREER PALS - Dolls - Linda Stackdale
CAREER QUEST - Computer software - Cambridge Educational
CAREER SET - Pet products - Classic Products
CAREER SHEER - Hosiery - Glendale Hosiery Co.
CAREER SMOCKS - Apparel–children's - Two's Co. Inc.
CAREER SUCCESS SYSTEM - Computer software - Career Advantage Resources Enterprises, LLC
CAREER TOES - Hosiery, toe portion - Ithaca Industries Inc.
CAREERMARX - Apparel–men's - Hartmarx Corp.
CAREERMATE - Computer software - Lois Ann Berkowitz
CAREERPOWER - Paper–book - Career Systems, Inc.
CAREERS - Toys - Tonka Corp.
CAREERSCOPE - Computer software - Vocational Research Inst.
CAREFOR - Diapers–cloth - Salk Co. Inc.
CAREFREE - Awnings - Carefree of Colorado
CAREFREE - Batteries - Eagle-Picher Industries Inc.
CAREFREE - Boats–motor - Glastex Co.
CAREFREE - Brassieres (Bras) - Jezebel-Renee of Hollywood
CAREFREE - Cleaning preparations–household - S.C. Johnson & Son, Inc.
CAREFREE - Cushions ☆ - Graham-Field Inc.
CAREFREE - Eyeglasses - Art-Craft Optical Co.
CAREFREE - Faucets ☆ - Universal-Rundle Corp.
CAREFREE - Floor coverings - Congoleum Corp.
CAREFREE - Floor coverings–carpet and rugs - Mattel Carpet & Rug Inc.
CAREFREE - Footwear - Orly Shoe Corp.
CAREFREE - Furniture - C.G. Wood Co.
CAREFREE - Housewares - Shelton-Ware Corp.
CAREFREE - Lawn mowers - Toro Co.
CAREFREE - Mats - Proffitt Manufacturing Co.
CAREFREE - Pumps ☆ - Simer Pump Co.
CAREFREE - Sanitary napkins - Johnson & Johnson
CAREFREE - Yarn ☆ - Caron International Inc.
CAREFREE COAL - Fuel additives - Genesis Research Corp.
CAREFREE COAT - Fibers–acrylic - Finnaren & Haley Inc.
CAREFREE COWGIRL - Toys - Tonka Corp.
CAREFREE ESSENTIALS - Health care products - Procter & Gamble Co.
CAREFREE FLOWER FARM - Garden equipment - Carefree Garden Products
CAREFREE GARDEN COLLECTION - Flowers–artificial - Country Floral Supply, Inc.
CAREFREE KIDS - Wallpaper ☆ - Imperial Wallcoverings, Inc.
CAREFREE KIDS III - Wallpaper - Imperial Wallcoverings, Inc.
CAREFREE ME - Wigs - Revlon General Wig Manufacturers, Inc.

CAREFREE PERENNIAL GARDEN - Garden equipment - Carefree Garden Products
CAREFREE PLUS - Prosthetic apparatus - Atco Truelife International
CAREFREE PLUS - Yarn ☆ - Caron International Inc.
CAREFREE RESORTS - Wines - Resorts L.P.
CAREFREE SOFTWARE - Computer software - Townsquare Title Services Corp.
CAREFREE VEGETABLE VILLAGE - Garden equipment - Carefree Garden Products
CAREGARD - Floor coverings–carpet and rugs ☆ - Fleetwood Enterprises, Inc.
CAREGIVER - Computer software - Sunquest Information Systems, Inc.
CAREL - Cookware - Dazey Corp.
CARELESS - Frames–eyeglass - Pathway Optical Prods.
CARELL - Recording label - Jazz Composer's Orchestra Association Inc.
CARELLE - Rings - Creations by Carelle, Ltd.
CAREMAIL - Tape–adhesive - Manco, Inc.
CAREMATE - Heart monitors - Guardian Products Inc.
CAREN CHARLES - Apparel–women's - Selby Shoe Co.
CAREN DESIREE - Apparel and accessories - Rampage Clothing Co.
CARENA - Cameras–video - Exakta Camera Co. Inc.
CARENE - Ophthalmic goods - Styl-Rite Optical Manufacturing Co., Inc.
CARENET - Computer software - Cerner Corp.
CAREPLUS - Health care products - Confab, Inc.
CAREQUILT - Blankets–electric - Mallinckrodt Medical, Inc.
CARESITE - Tubes–plastic - Care Medical Devices, Inc.
CARESS - Blankets - Mervyn's
CARESS - Carpets - Couristan Inc.
CARESS - Eyeglasses - Art-Craft Optical Co.
CARESS - Fabrics - Guilford Mills, Inc.
CARESS - Facial tissues ☆ - Scott Paper Co.
CARESS - Floor coverings–carpet and rugs ☆ - Regal Rugs Inc.
CARESS - Golfing equipment - Tagco, Inc.
CARESS - Paper–writing - Monadnock Paper Mills Inc.
CARESS - Rings–jewelry ☆ - Artcarved Inc.
CARESS - Sanitary napkins - Sterling USA, Inc.
CARESS - Skin care products - Conopco, Inc.
CARESS - Soap - Lever Brothers Co. Inc.
CARESS - Toys–stuffed - Russ Berrie and Co., Inc.
CARESS - Yarn - Melrose Yarn Co. Inc.
CARESS-A-NET - Hair care products - Andre Fantasies Inc.
CARESS MOISTURIZING BODY WASH - Skin care products - Lever Brothers Co. Inc.
CARESS OF WOOL - Mattresses - Spring Air Bedding Inc.
CARESSA - Eyeglasses - Martin-Copeland Eyewear Corp.
CARESSA - Shoes - Caressa Inc.
CARESSA - Upholstery leather - American Leather Manufacturing Co.
CARESSA - Whirlpool spa ☆ - Jacuzzi Inc.
CARESSABLE - Watches - Gruen Marketing Corp.
CARESSABLES - Greeting cards - Happiness Inc.
CARESSABLES - Puppets - Russ Berrie and Co., Inc.
CARESSABLES - Shoes - AmAsia International Ltd.
CARESSANT - Apparel and accessories ☆ - Vanity Fair Mills Inc.
CARESSE - Skin care products - Veeco Manufacturing Co.
CARESSE - Washcloths - Mark One Healthcare Products Inc.
CARESSE - Watches - Bulova Corp.
CARESSE OF ITALY - Skin care products - European Cosmetics Inc.
CARESSMA - Negligees - Gelmart Industries Inc.
CARESSO - Lenses–optical - Ditto Industries Inc.
CARETAKER - Leather goods - St. Thomas Inc.
CARETAKER - Mats - Ludlow Composites Corp.
CARETAKER - Vitamins and nutritional supplements - Bioenergy Nutrient's Inc.
CARETAPE - Tape–adhesive - Manco, Inc.
CARETEX - Irons–electric ☆ - Robert Krups North America
CARETOOLS - Computer software - Win2 Technologies, Inc.
CARETRENDS - Computer software - Medicode, Inc.
CAREVIEW FOR WINDOWS - CarePoint Analytics Inc.
CAREW - Tools - Universal Products International
CAREWARE - Linen - Perfect Fit Industries, Inc.
CAREWARE - Sponges - Acme Sponge & Chamois Co., Inc.
CAREX - Dyes–food - Nutritional Research Associates Inc.
CAREX - Health care products - Carex Health Products Inc.
CAREX - Soap - James River Corp.
CAREY - Salt - North American Salt Co.
CAREY CELLARS - Wines ☆ - Foley Estates Vineyard and Winery
CAREY DEVUONO'S HOLLYWOOD MOGUL - Video games - Carey Devuono

CAREY LIND KITCHENS & BATHS - Wallpaper ☆ - Carey Lind Designs
CAREY'S WINDER - Kites - Carey's Winders
CAREZZA - Alcoholic beverages - Capstone International, Inc.
CARFONE - Telephones–cellular - General Electric Co.
CARFUSIN - Antiseptics ☆ - Rhone-Poulenc Rorer Pharmaceuticals Inc.
CARGILL - Chemical preparations - Stevens Industries Inc.
CARGILL - Food products - Cargill Corp.
CARGILL QUALITY PLUS - Pet products ☆ - Stevens Industries Inc.
CARGO - Boxes - Wescosa Inc.
CARGO - Gasoline - Igloo Products Corp.
CARGO - Sportswear - Squire of California
CARGO - Thread ☆ - Perfect Thread Co. Inc.
CARGO CADDY - Toys - MTS Products
CARGO CARRIER - Toys–automobiles - Mattel, Inc.
CARGO CAT - Luggage ☆ - Blue Ridge International Products Co., Inc.
CARGO CLOTHING CONCEPT - Apparel and accessories - Sagi Inc.
CARGO COAT - Work clothes - Topps Manufacturing Co.
CARGO CYCLE - Tricycles ☆ - GT Bicycles Inc.
CARGO-GEL - Vitamins and nutritional supplements - Tishcon Corp.
CARGO HAULER - Toys–trains ☆ - Life-Like Products Inc.
CARGO HOUSTON - Giftware - Faroy Sales
CARGO MATES - Containers - Crawford Products Inc.
CARGO PASSPORT - Apparel and accessories - Newstar Group, Inc.
CARGO-RIDER - Vehicle suspensions products ☆ - Ridewell Corp.
CARGO WITH WALLY-MO - Trailers - Monroe Motors, Inc. Wally Mo Division
CARGODISK - Computer software - Reed Elsevier Properties Inc.
CARGOGUARD - Trailers–truck - Dorsey Trailers, Inc.
CARGOLOC - Cargo nets - Allied Wholesale Inc.
CARGOLOK - Industrial machinery - S & H Industries, Inc.
CARGOMASTER - Electronic equipment ☆ - Delta Consolidated Industries, Inc.
CARGOMASTER - Hoses - Willcox Engineered Products, Inc.
CARGOWAGON - Trailers–travel - Wells Cargo Inc.
CARGOYLE - Toys–automobiles - Mattel, Inc.
CARGROOM - Resins–acrylic - Alco Industries, Inc.
CARHARTT - Work clothes - Carhartt, Inc.
CARHARTT FOR CHILDREN - Apparel–children's - Carhartt, Inc.
CARHARTT FOR WOMEN - Work clothes - Carhartt, Inc.
CARI-LOC - Electrical equipment - Andon Electronics Corp.
CARIANI - Meat products–pork - Bob Ostrow Co.
CARIB - Frames–eyeglass - May Optical Co. Inc.
CARIBA - Beverages–carbonated - Pepsi-Cola Co.
CARIBAYA - Rum - Star Liquor Imports Inc.
CARIBBEAN - Bathtubs–enameled - Kohler Co.
CARIBBEAN - Bird feeds - Darrell W. Jones
CARIBBEAN - Boats ☆ - Correct Craft Inc.
CARIBBEAN - Boats–motor - Cobia Boat Co.
CARIBBEAN - Boats–motor - Glastex Co.
CARIBBEAN - Cigars - House of Windsor Inc.
CARIBBEAN - Eyeglasses - Bausch & Lomb Inc.
CARIBBEAN - Flatware - Wallace International Silversmiths, Inc.
CARIBBEAN - Floor coverings - Congoleum Corp.
CARIBBEAN - Floor coverings–tile - Interface, Inc.
CARIBBEAN - Furniture - Homecrest Industries Inc.
CARIBBEAN - Guitars ☆ - International Music Corp.
CARIBBEAN - Tiles–ceramic ☆ - American Olean Tile Co.
CARIBBEAN - Underwear and nightwear - Bestform Foundations, Inc.
CARIBBEAN - Watches - Bulova Corp.
CARIBBEAN - Wines ☆ - Bardenheier Wine Cellars
CARIBBEAN BALM - Skin care products - Michael Lutfey
CARIBBEAN BAY - Beverages–alcohol - Halland-St. John, Ltd.
CARIBBEAN BAY - Seafood products–fresh or frozen - Penguin Frozen Foods, Inc.
CARIBBEAN BLISS - Spices and extracts - Pluto's Caribbean Bliss
CARIBBEAN BLUE - Jewelry - Bijou Bebe
CARIBBEAN BREEZE - Air freshener - Drackett Co.
CARIBBEAN CALYPSO - Sauces - Culinary Canteen & Smokehouse
CARIBBEAN CHILL - Yogurt - Alta-Dena Certified Dairy, Inc.
CARIBBEAN CLASSIC - Luggage - Samsonite Corp.
CARIBBEAN CLASSICS - Fans–electric - Service Merchandise Co. Inc.
CARIBBEAN CLOTHING COMPANY - Apparel and accessories - Caribbean Jean Co., Inc.
CARIBBEAN COFFEE COMPANY - Coffee - Caribbean Coffee Co.
CARIBBEAN CONE - Frozen foods - Caribbean Cone
CARIBBEAN COOL - Hair care products - Mennen Co.
CARIBBEAN COOLER - Medical apparatus - Dominic O. Licausi
CARIBBEAN COOLER - Wines - Bardenheier Wine Cellars

CARIBBEAN CREME - Ice cream - Golden Ice Cream Churn of St. Louis, Inc.
CARIBBEAN CREME CAKE - Bakery products - Pollo Tropical, Inc.
CARIBBEAN CRUNCH - Snack foods - Planters LifeSavers Co.
CARIBBEAN FANTASY - Furniture - Tel-O-Post Co.
CARIBBEAN FLORA - Bedding–linen - Dan River Inc.
CARIBBEAN GEMS - Floor coverings–carpet and rugs - Lotus Carpets
CARIBBEAN GOURMET - Spices and extracts - Finest Kind Spices
CARIBBEAN HEART - Flooring–hardwood - Caribbean Lumber Co. Inc.
CARIBBEAN ICEBERG - Coffee - Coffee Beanery Ltd.
CARIBBEAN II - Fabrics - Interface, Inc.
CARIBBEAN II - Tiles–ceramic ☆ - American Olean Tile Co.
CARIBBEAN KNIGHTS - Apparel and accessories - Hard Hat Records
CARIBBEAN OASIS - Tea - Celestial Seasonings, Inc.
CARIBBEAN PACIFIC - Skin care products - Caribbean Pacific International, Inc.
CARIBBEAN REEF RUNNERS - Boats - Dean
CARIBBEAN ROMANCE - Teas - Rio-Vida Botanicals
CARIBBEAN SALSA - Seasonings - Cinnabar Specialty Foods, Inc./Neera's Products
CARIBBEAN SONG - Floor coverings–carpet and rugs - Milliken & Co. Inc.
CARIBBEAN SOUL - Note pads - J.B.'s Caribbean Soul Inc.
CARIBBEAN SUN - Sunblocks - Puretan International Inc.
CARIBBEAN, THE - Fencing–plastic - Nebraska Plastics, Inc.
CARIBBEAN WAY - Fruit drinks–bottled or canned - Smoothie King Franchises, Inc.
CARIBE - Boats ☆ - Correct Craft Inc.
CARIBE - Coffee - Coffee Holding Co.
CARIBE - Floor coverings - Mannington Resilient Floors
CARIBE - Fruit drinks–bottled or canned - V. Suarez and Co.
CARIBE - Sinks–porcelain ☆ - Artesian Industries
CARIBE - Steering mechanisms–motor vehicle - Detroit Marine Engineering
CARIBE - Wallpaper ☆ - Pickhardt & Siebert USA Inc.
CARIBE - Wallpaper ☆ - Southport
CARIBE - Watches - Bulova Corp.
CARIBEE - Soap - Lever Brothers Co. Inc.
CARIBENA - Food products - ICD Group Inc.
CARIBL - Recording label - Boddie Record Manufacturing & Recording Inc.
CARIBLU - Luggage - Universal Trav-ler Inc.
CARIBOO - Food products - Cariboo Growers Inc.
CARIBOU - Exercising equipment - National Barbell Supply, Inc.
CARIBOU - Hosiery - Wigwam Mills Inc.
CARIBOU - Seafood products–fresh or frozen - Fishery Products International USA
CARIBOU - Tape players–cassette - Sony Music Entertainment Inc.
CARIBOU - Trailers–travel - Fleetwood Enterprises, Inc.
CARIBOU FARMS - Onions - Fishery Products International USA
CARIBOU GOLD - Seafood products–canned or cured - Fishery Products International USA
CARIBSEA - Water treating compounds - Caribsea Inc.
CARICIA - Footwear - Olem Shoe Corp.
CARICIA CARE - Shampoos - Care-Tech Laboratories Inc.
CARICO - Carts - REC Enterprises Ltd.
CARICO - Dinnerware–glass - Carico International Inc.
CARIGNITE - Drill bits - Cleveland Twist Drill Co.
CARILLION - Lamps - Lamplight Farms, Inc.
CARILLON - Floor coverings - Congoleum Corp.
CARILLON - Footwear - Conjac Inc.
CARILLON - Furniture ☆ - Bernhardt Industries
CARILLON - Glass–window - Simpson Timber Co.
CARILLON - Paper - Strathmore Paper Co.
CARILLON - Rings–jewelry - Artcarved Inc.
CARILLON - Telephones–cellular - Carillon Corp.
CARILLONIC BELLS - Musical instrument accessories - Schulmerich Carillons Inc.
CARILOY - Chemical preparations - Shell Oil Co.
CARINA - Curtain rods - Newell Window Furnishing Co.
CARINA - Glassware–household - Waterford Wedgwood USA, Inc.
CARINA - Motor vehicles–automobiles ☆ - Toyota Motor Sales USA Inc.
CARINA - Shelving units–metal - Prairie Products Inc.
CARINA - Shoes - Caressa Inc.
CARINA - Yarn ☆ - Blumenthal/Lansing Co.
CARINA COLLECTION - Floor coverings–carpet and rugs - Nourison
CARINDA - Flowers, plants, and seeds - Messick Co.
CARINEAU - Floor coverings–carpet and rugs ☆ - Karastan-Bigelow Inc.
CARING - Breads - Perfection Bakeries, Inc.
CARING - Dermatological preparations - Medline, Industries, Inc.

☆ = Now out of production

CARING - Jewelry - R.N. Koch Inc.
CARING CANDID TREASURES - Paper products - Jeanie Troutt
CARING CAREERS - Dolls - Mattel, Inc.
CARING COLLECTION, THE - Novelty items–paper - Warner Press, Inc.
CARING COLOR COLLECT - Skin care products - Borlind of Germany
CARING STROKES - Greeting cards - Elizabeth A. Gorcey
CARING TOUCH - Wigs/ hair-care products - International Hairgoods Inc.
CARING WORDS - Greeting cards - Sangray Corp.
CARINHOSO - Shoes - Armani Shoes Corp.
CARINO - Cameras–video - Good Times Home Video Corp.
CARINO - Frames–eyeglass ✫ - Universal/Univis Inc.
CARINO - Window coverings - Vertilux-Louverlux Inc.
CARIOCA - Apparel and accessories ✫ - Glamorise Foundations Inc.
CARIOCA - Boats - Glen-L Marine Designs
CARIOCA - Eyeglasses - Art-Craft Optical Co.
CARIOCA - Rum - Schenley Industries Inc.
CARIOCA - Shoes ✫ - Daniel Green Co.
CARIOCA - Watches - Gruen Marketing Corp.
CARIOCA - Yarn - Bernat Yarn & Craft Corp.
CARIOLIER - Housewares - Tupperware Co.
CARISBROOK - Fabrics - Carisbrook Industries Inc.
CARISLE - Ophthalmic goods - Embassy Creations Inc.
CARISMA - Automotive parts and accessories - Turtle Wax, Inc.
CARISSIMA - Underwear and nightwear - Maidenform Inc.
CARITA - Rings–jewelry - Artcarved Inc.
CARITEL - Photographic equipment - Hudson Photographic Industries Inc.
CARITINE - Toys - Peg Perego USA Inc.
CARJEAN - Jewelry - T & L Jewelry
CARKEEPER - Publisher's imprints - Andrew Joseph Bedoian, Jr.
CARL - Glassware–household - Van Dow-Fenton Inc.
CARL - Ophthalmic goods ✫ - Luxottica
CARL BUDDIG - Food products - Pioneer Food Sales Inc.
CARL FISCHER - Music–sheet - Carl Fischer Music Distributors
CARL JUNG - Wines - Hilton Commercial Group Inc.
CARL JUNG - Wines ✫ - Haddon House Food Products Inc.
CARL LARSSON - Stationery ✫ - Merry Thoughts Inc.
CARL LINDER - Figurines - Matthew J. Reul
CARL MILLER - Candy - Williams & Randolph Inc.
CARL MONKHOUSE - Medical apparatus ✫ - Cutlery Associates Inc.
CARL POOL - Garden equipment - Athena Products Corp.
CARL SCHILLER - Musical instruments - Newark Musical Merchandise Co.
CARL SITTMAN - Wines - Joseph Gies Import
CARL-TEX - Wallpaper - Carlton-Metro Wallcoverings
CARL ZEISS - Lenses - Carl Zeiss Optical Inc.
CARLA - Bathroom fixtures - Crane Plumbing/Fiat Products
CARLA - Glassware–household ✫ - Dansk International Designs, Ltd.
CARLA - House furnishings - Dan River Inc.
CARLA - Shoes ✫ - Daniel Green Co.
CARLA - Watches - Bulova Corp.
CARLA BEROTTI - Footwear ✫ - Glamour Footwear
CARLA CRISTALDI - Footwear - J. Baker Inc.
CARLA LEIGH - Footwear - J. Baker Inc.
CARLA MANCINI - Handbags - Caprice Design
CARLA MUSK - Skin care products - Sara Lee Corp.
CARLANNA - Candy ✫ - De Soto Confectionary
CARLA'S - Food products - Carla's Pasta Inc.
CARLCO - Apparel–men's ✫ - Carl Neckwear Co. Inc.
CARLEE - Pillows - Carlee Corp.
CARLEN - Recording label - Ripete Music Group
CARLETON - Boats–canoes ✫ - Old Town Canoe Co.
CARLETON - Furniture - Drexel Heritage Furnishings, Inc.
CARLETON - Furniture ✫ - Bassett Furniture Industries, Inc.
CARLETON - Tires - Armtec Industries Inc.
CARLETON COLLECTION - Furniture - BDO Seidman
CARLETON GALLERY - Fabrics–tapestry - Comark Wallcoverings
CARLETON GALLERY II - Wallpaper - Mokena Mills Inc.
CARLEY - Skin care products - Vi-Jon Laboratories, Inc.
CARLI BALSAMIC - Vinegar - Crystal Food Import Corp.
CARLIN - Fabrics–linen - West Point-Pepperell Inc.
CARLIN - Music–sheet ✫ - TRF Production Music Libraries
CARLIN - Ophthalmic goods - Robin Optical
CARLING - Beverages–malt ✫ - The Stroh Brewery Co.
CARLING CANADA - Beverages–malt - G. Heileman Brewing Co., Inc.
CARLINK - Alarm systems - Adaptive Vehicle Systems, Inc.
CARLISLE - Bathroom fixtures - Artesian Industries

CARLISLE - Boating equipment and accessories - Johnson Worldwide Associates, Inc.
CARLISLE - Cabinets–wood - UltraCraft Co.
CARLISLE - Clocks - Ridgeway Clock Co.
CARLISLE - Computer peripheral equipment - Carlisle Corp.
CARLISLE - Doors–wood - Georgia-Pacific Corp.
CARLISLE - Floor coverings–carpet and rugs - Atlas Carpet Mills Inc.
CARLISLE - Furniture–children's ✫ - Child Craft Industries Inc.
CARLISLE - Glassware–household - Crisa Corp.
CARLISLE - Tires ✫ - Carlisle Tire & Rubber Co.
CARLISLE PLASTICS - Bags–trash - Carlisle Plastics, Inc.
CARLISLE VERSAPOUR PITCHERS - Kitchen appliances - Carlisle Foodservice Products, Inc.
CARLITE - Glass–safety - Ford Motor Co. (Glass Div.)
CARLITE - Lighting equipment–automotive - Black & Decker Corp.
CARLO ALBERTO - Eyeglasses - Guess Eyewear
CARLO CHERELI - Shoes ✫ - Ennesi Shoe Co. Inc.
CARLO CIATTI - Apparel–men's - Leon of Paris Co. Inc.
CARLO D'SANTI - Handbags - B.H. Smith, Inc.
CARLO GIANNINI - Housewares - Zyliss USA Inc.
CARLO MAGGIO DESIGN - Apparel–athletic - Carlo Maggio Design, L.C.
CARLO MICELLI - Musical instruments - Meisel Music Inc.
CARLO MORANDI - Footwear–men's - Harbor Footwear Group Ltd.
CARLO PELLEGRINO - Wines - Paterno Imports, Ltd.
CARLO ROBELLI - Musical instruments - Sam Ash Music Corp.
CARLO ROSSI - Apparel and accessories - Damon Creations Inc.
CARLO ROSSI - Wines - Ernest and Julio Gallo Winery
CARLO SUEDE - Wallpaper - Carlton-Metro Wallcoverings
CARLO SUEDE II - Wallpaper - Carlton-Metro Wallcoverings
CARLO URBANI - Food products - Paul A. Urbani
CARLO V - Jewelry - Benjamin E. Woomer
CARLON - Lubricants - Lamson & Sessions Co.
CARLOS - Guitars ✫ - Kaman Music Corp.
CARLOS - Ophthalmic goods - Styl-Rite Optical Manufacturing Co., Inc.
CARLOS - Wines - Old South Winery
CARLOS CAMPESINO - Electronic equipment - Radmar Inc.
CARLOS DRY - Wines - Old South Winery
CARLOS FALCHI - Gloves ✫ - Grandoe Corp.
CARLOS FALCHI - Scarves - Ashear Brothers
CARLOS I - Brandy - Domecq Importers Inc.
CARLOS IMPERIAL - Brandy - Domecq Importers Inc.
CARLOS MESH - Wire products - Carlos Designs
CARLOS O'BRIEN'S - Vegetable sauces - Sean O'Brien
CARLOS SERRAS - Beverages–alcohol ✫ - Connolly & Co. Inc.
CARLOTTA - Colognes - Eurostar Corp.
CARLOTTA - Floor coverings ✫ - Congoleum Corp.
CARLOTTA - Watches ✫ - Helbros International
CARL'S - Beef - Dallas Dress Beef
CARLSBAD - Bicycles ✫ - Raleigh USA Bicycle Co.
CARLSBAD - Fruits and vegetables - James Ukegawa
CARLSBAD - Occasional tables ✫ - JDI Group, Inc.
CARLSBAD - Wallpaper - BDH Two, Inc.
CARLSBERG - Beverages–malt - Anheuser-Busch Companies Inc.
CARLSBERG GOLD - Beverages–malt ✫ - Anheuser-Busch Companies Inc.
CARLSBERG LIGHT - Beverages–malt - Anheuser-Busch Companies Inc.
CARLSBRO - Amplifiers–musical instrument ✫ - Meisel Music Inc.
CARLSON - Vitamins and nutritional supplements - J.R. Carlson Laboratories Inc.
CARLSON-CRAFT - Greeting cards - Carlson Craft
CARLSON'S - Greeting cards - Ports of Scandinavia Inc.
CARLSSON - Musical instrument accessories - M & M Distributing Co.
CARLTON - Badminton equipment - Tide-Rider Inc.
CARLTON - Cigarettes - American Tobacco Co.
CARLTON - Dinnerware–glass - Sango Co. Ltd. (Sango USA Div.)
CARLTON - Fabrics - Dan River Inc.
CARLTON - Floor coverings–carpet and rugs ✫ - Blue Ridge Carpet Mills
CARLTON - Glass products - Mt. Clemens Pottery Co.
CARLTON - Greeting cards - American Greetings Corp.
CARLTON - Mops ✫ - Helen Keller Services for the Blind
CARLTON - Musical instruments - J.M. Sahlein Music Co. Inc.
CARLTON - Ophthalmic goods - Foremost Optical Products
CARLTON - Paper - Potlatch Corp.
CARLTON - Paper ✫ - Northwest Paper Co.
CARLTON - Razors - Aldi Inc.
CARLTON - Sparkling wine - Austin, Nichols & Co., Inc.
CARLTON - Sporting goods - Dunlop Maxfli Sports Corp.

✫ = Now out of production

CARLTON - Watches - Bulova Corp.
CARLTON - Watches - North American Watch Corp.
CARLTON - Watches ☆ - Swatch Watch USA
CARLTON B. RABBIT - Toys - American Greetings Corp.
CARLTON B. RABBIT JR. - Toys - American Greetings Corp.
CARLTON-BATH BAR - Lighting fixtures ☆ - Liteway
CARLTON CLUB - Tobacco - American Tobacco Co.
CARLTON HILL - Furniture - Taylor-Ramsey Corp.
CARLTON MANOR - Furniture ☆ - Hammary Furniture Co. Inc.
CARLTON MCLENDON - Furniture reproductions ☆ - Victorian Classics
CARLTON ORCHARD - Food products ☆ - Del Mar Food Products Corp.
CARLTON ROSE - Glassware–household ☆ - Lotus Glass Co.
CARLTON SLIMS - Cigarettes - American Tobacco Co.
CARLTON SLIMS DELUXE 100S - Cigarettes - American Tobacco Co.
CARLTON SLIMS ULTRA LOW TAR - Cigarettes - American Tobacco Co.
CARLTON T. BEAR, JR. - Toys - American Greetings Corp.
CARLTON T. BEAR, SR. - Toys - American Greetings Corp.
CARLTON TOWER - Floor coverings–carpet and rugs ☆ - Customweave Carpets Inc.
CARLTON VARNEY: FRENCH COUNTRY GARDEN - Wallpaper ☆ - Imperial Wallcoverings, Inc.
CARLY - Dolls - Hasbro, Inc.
CARLY ST. CLAIRE - Sweaters - Tiara International, Inc.
CARLYLE - Blankets–electric ☆ - Sunbeam-Oster Household Products
CARLYLE - Dialing devices–telephone - Baltimore Luggage Co.
CARLYLE - Frames–eyeglass ☆ - Universal/Univis Inc.
CARLYLE - Furniture ☆ - Hammary Furniture Co. Inc.
CARLYLE - Mail boxes - Steel City Corp.
CARLYLE - Rings–jewelry - Artcarved Inc.
CARLYLE - Sofas - Carlyle Custom Convertibles Ltd.
CARLYLE - Tableware–china ☆ - Lenox, Inc.
CARLYN - Plastics film - Carlisle Plastics, Inc.
CARMA - Computer software - Lor/Geske Bock Associates, Inc.
CARMAG - Bricks - North American Refractories Co.
CARMARK - Maps - Carmark Enterprises
CARME - Skin care products ☆ - Carme Inc.
CARMEL - Brushes–paint - Corona Brushes Inc.
CARMEL - Cabinets ☆ - American Woodmark Corp.
CARMEL - Desks ☆ - Haskell of Pittsburgh, Inc.
CARMEL - Dinnerware ☆ - Corning Inc.
CARMEL - Fabrics - Dan River Inc.
CARMEL - Flatware ☆ - Wallace International Silversmiths, Inc.
CARMEL - Floor coverings - Mannington Resilient Floors
CARMEL - Floor coverings–carpet and rugs ☆ - S and S Mills Inc.
CARMEL - Food products - Douglas Food Co., Inc.
CARMEL - Frames–eyeglass ☆ - U.S. Optical Frame Co.
CARMEL - Furniture - American Furniture Co. Inc.
CARMEL - Furniture - Homecrest Industries Inc.
CARMEL - Furniture - Lane Co. Inc.
CARMEL - Furniture–children's ☆ - Child Craft Industries Inc.
CARMEL - Glassware–household ☆ - Colony Glass
CARMEL - Lighting fixtures - LSI Industries, Inc.
CARMEL - Motor vehicles–motor homes ☆ - Beaver Coaches Inc.
CARMEL - Recording label - Carmel Records
CARMEL - Stoves–gas - Malm Fireplaces Inc.
CARMEL - Sweaters - Pine State Knitwear Co.
CARMEL - Wines - Blair Importers Ltd.
CARMEL - Wines - Parliament Import Co.
CARMEL - Yarn ☆ - Caron International Inc.
CARMEL ARTISTS - Giftware ☆ - Couroc of Monterey Inc.
CARMEL BAY - Floor coverings–carpet and rugs ☆ - Hollytex Carpet Mills Inc.
CARMEL C - Pens - Supertech Enterprises Int'l., Inc.
CARMEL COCKER SPANIEL - Toys–stuffed - Dakin Inc.
CARMEL STIX - Candy ☆ - Leaf, Inc.
CARMEL VALLEY - Tandem Imports Corp.
CARMEL VALLEY - Beverages–alcohol - Durney Vineyard
CARMELA - Ophthalmic goods ☆ - Luxottica
CARMELA COLLECTION - Dolls - Carmela Collection
CARMELA'S - Bakery products - Carmela's, Inc.
CARMELITA - Meat products–cured - Carmelita Provision Co. Inc.
CARMELITA - Vinegar ☆ - Salvati Foods, Inc.
CARMELL - Furniture–wood ☆ - Century Furniture Co.
CARMELLA - Tableware–china ☆ - Lenox, Inc.
CARMELLAS CHOICE - Coffee - Cadillac Coffee Co.
CARMELLE - Doors–wood - Masonite Corp.

CARMELLE - Floor coverings–carpet and rugs - Cabin Crafts Carpets
CARMELTAWAY - Candy - Gardners Candies
CARMEN - Brassieres (Bras) - Carmen Foundations Inc.
CARMEN - Fabrics ☆ - J.B. Martin Co. Inc.
CARMEN - Fruit and vegetable markets - Strohmeyer and Arpe Co.
CARMEN - Glassware–household ☆ - Oneida Ltd.
CARMEN - Harmonicas - Hohner Inc.
CARMEN - Jewelry - Hobe Cie. Ltd.
CARMEN - Watches - Bulova Corp.
CARMEN SANDIEGO JUNIOR DETECTIVE - Computer software - Broderbund Software, Inc.
CARMEN SANDIEGO JUNIOR DETECTIVE EDITION - Computer software - Broderbund Software, Inc.
CARMENET VINEYARD - Wines - Carmenet Vineyard
CARMEN'S - Food products - Bon Melange Inc.
CARMEN'S PRIDE - Seafood products–fresh or frozen ☆ - Impex Shrimp & Fish Co.
CARMEX - Lip balms - Carma Laboratories Inc.
CARMICHAEL AND JONES - Apparel and accessories ☆ - Vanderbilt Shirt Co.
CARMICHAEL'S - Cosmetics - Caswell-Massey Co. Ltd.
CARMINE - Food products - Carmine Foods Inc.
CARMINE - Jams and jellies - Carmine's Vintage Wine Jelly
CARMOL - Skin care products - Doak Dermatologics
CARMOL - Skin care products - Syntex USA, Inc.
CARMONT - Bathtubs–enameled - Kohler Co.
CARN-A-BABY - Dryers–hair ☆ - Dubl Duck/Jet Set Inc.
CARNABY - Hair care products - Dubl Duck/Jet Set Inc.
CARNABY - Watches - Hampden Corp.
CARNABY II - Hair curlers - Dubl Duck/Jet Set Inc.
CARNABY CLASSIC - Hair care products - Dubl Duck/Jet Set Inc.
CARNABY STREET - Apparel and accessories ☆ - Edison Brothers Stores, Inc.
CARNABY'S - Gin - Star Industries Inc.
CARNATE - Cosmetics - Caswell-Massey Co. Ltd.
CARNATION - Bacon - Dubuque Foods, Inc.
CARNATION - Dairy products - Nestle Beverage Co.
CARNATION - Food products - Mitsui & Co. Inc.
CARNATION - Food products ☆ - California-Omega Foods Inc.
CARNATION - Seafood products–fresh or frozen ☆ - King & Prince Seafood Corp.
CARNATION COFFEE-MATE - Dairy products - Ryan Foods Co.
CARNATION FOLLOW-UP FORMULA - Baby foods - Nestle Beverage Co.
CARNATION KIDS - Bakery products - Nestle USA
CARNAVAL - Drums–musical instruments - LP Music Group
CARNAVAL - Soap - Multi Care Products Co., Inc.
CARNEA - Lubricating oils - Shell Oil Co.
CARNEGIE - Floor coverings–carpet and rugs ☆ - Masland Corp.
CARNEGIE COMMERCIAL CARPETS - Floor coverings–carpet and rugs - Whitecrest-Dorsett Commercial, Inc.
CARNEGIE HALL - Dolls ☆ - Effanbee Doll Corp.
CARNEGIE HALL - Furniture ☆ - Mersman Furniture Co.
CARNEGIE HALL - Printed matter; namely, posters, paper bags, and paperweights - Carnegie Hall Corp.
CARNELIAN - Wines - European Beverage Co., Inc.
CARNEROS - Wines ☆ - Belvedere Winery
CARNEROS CREEK - Wines ☆ - Cannon Wines Ltd.
CARNEROS CREEK WINERY - Wines - Carneros Creek Winery
CARNET - Chemical preparations - Carnet Automotive
CARNET DE RENDEZ-VOUS - Women's watches - Jaeger-Le Coultre SA
CARNFORTH - Dishes–china - Viletta China Co.
CARNI FORM - Vitamins and nutritional supplements - Integrated Health, Inc.
CARNI FUEL - Vitamins and nutritional supplements - Twinlab
CARNITAS SUPREMAS DE MUY BUEN GUSTO. - Pork - Cal Western Beef Dist.
CARNIVAL - Apparel–women's - Carnival Creations
CARNIVAL - Artists' materials - Carnival Arts, Inc.
CARNIVAL - Bowls ☆ - National Housewares
CARNIVAL - Dinnerware–glass - Cyclamen Studio
CARNIVAL - Dinnerware–glass - Nikko Ceramics Inc.
CARNIVAL - Drums–musical instruments ☆ - Grossman Music Corp.
CARNIVAL - Envelopes - Champion International Corp.
CARNIVAL - Flatware ☆ - Washington Forge Inc.
CARNIVAL - Floor coverings–carpet and rugs - Lees Carpets
CARNIVAL - Floor coverings–carpet and rugs - Quaker Inc.
CARNIVAL - Floor coverings–carpet and rugs - Richmond Carpet Mills
CARNIVAL - Floor coverings–carpet and rugs ☆ - Capel, Inc.

☆ = Now out of production

CARNIVAL - Floor coverings–carpet and rugs ☆ - Trans-Ocean Import Co. Inc.
CARNIVAL - Garden equipment ☆ - Rubens Originals
CARNIVAL - Glassware ☆ - Indiana Glass Co.
CARNIVAL - Glassware–household - Fenton Art Glass Co.
CARNIVAL - Ice cream ☆ - Weis Markets Inc.
CARNIVAL - Seafood products–canned or cured - Ludwig Shrimp Co.
CARNIVAL - Seafood products–fresh or frozen - Carnival Brand Seafood Co.
CARNIVAL - Shortening ☆ - Hunt-Wesson, Inc.
CARNIVAL! - Shrimp–fresh or frozen - Hi-Seas of Dulac, Inc.
CARNIVAL - Straws–drinking - Clear Shield National Inc.
CARNIVAL - Toys - Hasbro, Inc.
CARNIVAL - Vases–ceramic - Crisa Corp.
CARNIVAL - Wallpaper - Blumenthal
CARNIVAL CASUAL FURNITURE - Furniture - Carnival Casual Furniture
CARNIVAL CRUISE BARBIE - Dolls - Carnival Corp.
CARNIVAL CRUISE LINES - Colognes ☆ - Carnival Corp.
CARNIVAL FOUNTAIN - Fireworks - China Pyrotechnics, Inc.
CARNIVAL OF COLORS - Office supplies - House of Doolittle
CARNIVAL STACKER - Toys - Fisher-Price, Inc.
CARNIVALE - Floor coverings–carpet and rugs - Patrick Carpet Mills
CARNIVALE - Skin care products - Ross Cosmetics Inc.
CARNIVORES - Toys - Matchbox Toys USA
CARNOUSTIE - Apparel–athletic - Mancillas Enterprises, Inc.
CARNU - Motor vehicle parts and accessories - S.C. Johnson & Son, Inc.
CARO - Candy ☆ - Y & S Candies Inc.
CARO - Furniture - Broyhill Furniture Industries, Inc.
CARO - Wallets - Westport Corp.
CARO-FORM - Apparel and accessories - Caro-Knit Inc.
CARO-GEL - Vitamins and nutritional supplements - Tishcon Corp.
CARO-KNIT - Apparel and accessories - Caro-Knit Inc.
CARO-NET - Sporting goods - Carron Net Co. Inc.
CARO-PLETE - Vitamins and nutritional supplements - J.R. Carlson Laboratories Inc.
CARO-SET - Apparel and accessories - Caro-Knit Inc.
CARO-SHEEN - Apparel and accessories - Caro-Knit Inc.
CAROB - Giftware - Doranne
CAROB SWIRL - Cookies ☆ - Barbara's Bakery, Inc.
CAROBA - Snack foods - Sunspire Foods
CAROBA INSTANT - Beverages - Sunspire Foods
CAROBY - Confections ☆ - Worthington Foods Inc.
CAROCAL - Vitamins and nutritional supplements - CBP Resources Inc.
CAROCELLE - Dishwashers–household - SES Industries Inc.
CARODAL - Floor coverings - Parquet de France Inc.
CAROGUARD PLUS - Vitamins and nutritional supplements ☆ - Pharmacaps Inc.
CAROID - Health care products ☆ - Winthrop Pharmaceuticals
CAROID - Laxatives - Mentholatum Co.
CAROIPLETE - Vitamins and nutritional supplements - J.R. Carlson Laboratories Inc.
CAROL - Cables - General Cable Corp.
CAROL - Cookies - Banner Biscuit Co. Inc.
CAROL - Dolls - Goldberger Doll Manufacture Co.
CAROL - Frames–eyeglass ☆ - Rozin Optical Export Corp.
CAROL - Greeting cards - Carol Cards Inc.
CAROL - Watches - Bulova Corp.
CAROL AND JANE - Handbags - Etra Handbags Inc.
CAROL ANDERSON - Apparel and accessories - Carol Anderson, Inc.
CAROL ANGELL'S - Relishes - Fresh Pasta Co.
CAROL ANTON FOR KAREN ALEXANDER - Hats - Shady Grove Inc.
CAROL BELT - Apparel–women's - Nuvogue Creations
CAROL D. - Jewelry - Jewelmont Corp.
CAROL DRYDEN - Seafood products–fresh or frozen - Carol Dryden & Co. Inc.
CAROL ESCRITOR - Apparel–women's - Carolyn Escritor
CAROL EVANS - Footwear–children's - J.C. Penney Co., Inc.
CAROL JANE - Housewares ☆ - All Power Manufacturing Co.
CAROL KITCHEN - Fruits and vegetables - Biggers Brothers Inc.
CAROL LAWN AND GARDEN - Extension cords - General Cable Corp.
CAROL LEONE - Fabrics - Dan River Inc.
CAROL LEWIS - Skin care products - Cosmetic Technologies
CAROL MALONY - Apparel and accessories - Breton Industries
CAROL MANN - Golfing equipment - Wilson Sporting Goods Co.
CAROL SUE - Food products - Pet Inc.
CAROL TANGLE PROOF - Cables - General Cable Corp.
CAROL WIOR - Bathing suits - Wior Corp.

CAROLANS - Beverages–alcohol - Hiram Walker & Sons, Inc.
CAROLANS FINEST - Liquors - C. & C. International
CAROLA'S - Cribs–metal - Evenflo Juvenile Furniture Co.
CAROLCO STUDIOS INC. - Novelty items - Carolco Studios Inc.
CAROLE - Apparel–women's - Carolina Underwear Co.
CAROLE - Frames–eyeglass - U.S. Optical Frame Co.
CAROLE FABRICS - Fabric - Carole Fabrics Corp.
CAROLE FRANCK - Skin care products - Carole Franck USA
CAROLE HOCHMAN - Underwear and nightwear - Carole Hochman Designs Inc.
CAROLE LITTLE - Apparel and accessories - Jonathan Logan Inc.
CAROLE LITTLE - Belts, jewelry, hair accessories - Honey Fashions Ltd.
CAROLE LITTLE II - Apparel–women's - Carole Leonard
CAROLE TALBOTT - Recording label - Visual Coordination by Carole Talbott, Inc.
CAROLEE - Floor coverings - Mannington Resilient Floors
CAROLEE - Watches - Carolee Designs Inc.
CAROLEE SIGNATURE FINE JEWELRY - Jewelry - Carolee Designs Inc.
CAROLEE'S STERLING SENTIMENTS - Jewelry - Carolee Designs Inc.
CAROLINA - Cotton–sterilized - Carolina Absorbent Cotton
CAROLINA - Desserts - Sweetery
CAROLINA - Fans–electric ☆ - Nutone Inc.
CAROLINA - Floor coverings ☆ - Anderson Hardwood Floors Inc.
CAROLINA - Floor coverings–carpet and rugs ☆ - Stanton Carpet Corp.
CAROLINA - Frames–picture - Terragrafics Inc.
CAROLINA - Furniture ☆ - Universal Flooring
CAROLINA - Glass products - HGP Industries Inc.
CAROLINA - Guitars ☆ - Fred Gretsch Enterprises
CAROLINA - Kitchen, vanity, and bathroom cabinets - IXL Furniture Co. Inc.
CAROLINA - Ladders–metal - Michigan Ladder Co. Inc.
CAROLINA - Mirrors - Carolina Mirror Co.
CAROLINA - Paper–bond - Weyerhaeuser Co.
CAROLINA - Rice - Riviana Foods Inc.
CAROLINA - Rocking chairs - P and P Chair Co.
CAROLINA - Sausages - Arnold's Meat Food Products Inc.
CAROLINA - Shoes - Carolina Shoe Co.
CAROLINA - Soap - Carolina Designs Ltd.
CAROLINA - Tableware–china ☆ - Lenox, Inc.
CAROLINA - Tack - B & B Leather Co.
CAROLINA - Thread - Elmore-Pisgah, Inc.
CAROLINA - Turkey - Carolina Turkeys
CAROLINA - Water–bottled or canned - Carolina Mountain Spring Water Co.
CAROLINA - Wines - Duplin Wine Cellars
CAROLINA ASH - Floor coverings–tile - ECC International
CAROLINA BEADED - Siding–insulating - Certainteed Corp. (Roofing Products Group)
CAROLINA BILL - Apparel and accessories - L.C. King Manufacturing Co.
CAROLINA BLUE TICK DRESSING - Salad dressings–bottled - Carolina Swamp Stuff, Inc.
CAROLINA BROWN RICE - Rice - Riviana Foods Inc.
CAROLINA CAJUN - Spices and extracts - Loy Dellinger
CAROLINA CAJUN BAR-B-QUE - Meat products–pork - BJ Acquisition Corp.
CAROLINA CARDINEL - Wines - Duplin Wine Cellars
CAROLINA CEDAR SPRAY - Seasonings - Carolina Swamp Stuff, Inc.
CAROLINA CHOICE - Fruit drinks–bottled or canned - Southern Beverage Packers, Inc.
CAROLINA CLACKER - Fishing tackle - Kalin Co.
CAROLINA CLIPPER - Furniture - CTH/Sherrill Occasional
CAROLINA CLUB - Pickles - Chas. F. Cates & Sons Inc.
CAROLINA COLA - Beverages–carbonated - Carolina Beverage Inc.
CAROLINA COLONY - Furniture ☆ - Universal Flooring
CAROLINA COLONY - Tiles–clay ☆ - Porcelanite, Inc.
CAROLINA COLOR - Inks–drawing - Carolina Color & Chemical Co.
CAROLINA COMPASS PORTFOLIO - Banks–commercial - Carolina First Bank
CAROLINA CONEY ROLLS - Bakery products - Southern Bakeries, Inc.
CAROLINA COOKOUT ROLLS - Bakery products - Southern Bakeries, Inc.
CAROLINA COUGARS - Apparel and accessories - John A. Busch
CAROLINA COUNTRY - Wines - Duplin Wine Cellars
CAROLINA CREMES - Cakes - B.D. Bundt, Inc.
CAROLINA CRUSHER - Athletic associations - Gary Douglas Porter
CAROLINA CUPBOARD - Jams and jellies - A Southern Season
CAROLINA DAIRIES - Milk - Carolina Dairies Corp.
CAROLINA DELUXE - Fishing tackle - Williamson & Co. Inc.
CAROLINA GEM - Flour–blended - Allen Bros. Milling Co./ADLUH Flour Mills
CAROLINA GOLD - Footwear - H.H. Brown Shoe Co., Inc.

CAROLINA GOLD - Juices - Carolina Products Inc.
CAROLINA GRILLE - Meat products–poultry - BJ Acquisition Corp.
CAROLINA KITCHEN INC. - Food products - Carolina Kitchen, Inc.
CAROLINA LEATHERCRAFTS - Belts–apparel - Gem-Dandy, Inc.
CAROLINA LIGHTNING - Beverages–alcohol - Elca Corp.
CAROLINA MAID - Dresses–women's - Carolina Maid Products Inc.
CAROLINA MODE - Furniture–factory ☆ - Clayton Marcus Co. Inc.
CAROLINA PINE TAR - Salad dressings–bottled - Carolina Swamp Stuff, Inc.
CAROLINA PINES - Wines - La Rocca Wine Co.
CAROLINA PURE - Water–bottled or canned - Hickory Springs Water Co. Inc.
CAROLINA RECIPE - Food products - Stannis Research International Inc.
CAROLINA RED TIDE - Salad dressings–bottled - Carolina Swamp Stuff, Inc.
CAROLINA RICE MIXES - Rice - Riviana Foods Inc.
CAROLINA SEAWEED SPLASH - Food products - Carolina Swamp Stuff, Inc.
CAROLINA SWAMP SAUCE - Salad dressings–bottled - Carolina Swamp Stuff, Inc.
CAROLINA SWAMP STUFF - Food products - Carolina Swamp Stuff, Inc.
CAROLINA SWAMP STUFF - Food products - Wagner Gourmet Foods, Inc.
CAROLINA TADPOLE TEA - Food products - Carolina Swamp Stuff, Inc.
CAROLINAS AGC ESP - Computer software - Carolinas AGC
CAROLINA'S FAVORITES - Deodorizers - Norpak Companies Ltd.
CAROLINA'S FINEST - Sausages - Neese Country Sausage, Inc.
CAROLINE - Computer hardware - Carolina Digital, Inc.
CAROLINE - Cosmetics - Carolina Designs Ltd.
CAROLINE - Dolls ☆ - Effanbee Doll Corp.
CAROLINE - Floor coverings–carpet and rugs ☆ - Regal Rugs Inc.
CAROLINE - Food products - Saulsbury Bros. Inc.
CAROLINE - Hair care products - Gloria Cabrera International Inc.
CAROLINE - Recording label - Caroline Records, Inc.
CAROLINE DE PARIS - Toys - Fine Art Pillow & Specialties Corp.
CAROLINE EMMONS - Jewelry - Emmons Jewelers Inc.
CAROLING - Ladders–wood - Michigan Ladder Co. Inc.
CAROLING KIDS, THE - Recording label - Someday Baby, Inc.
CAROLITE - Candles ☆ - Carolina Designs Ltd.
CAROLITE - Electrical equipment - General Cable Corp.
CAROLPRENE - Electrical equipment - General Cable Corp.
CAROLRHODA BOOKS - Publisher's imprints - Lerner Publishing Group
CAROL'S COLLECTION - Wallpaper - Storeys Wallcoverings
CAROL'S ROSE GARDEN - Greeting cards - Carol Wilson Fine Arts, Inc.
CAROLYN - Flatware - Washington Forge Inc.
CAROLYN - Watches - Bulova Corp.
CAROLYN CLOTH - Hobby kits - Craft World International Inc.
CAROLYN FORSMAN - Hair care products - Bead Weaver Ltd.
CAROLYN JEAN'S - Cocoa–powders or mixes - Gloria Jean's Gourmet Coffees Corp.
CAROLYN KINDER - Lamps - J.C. Penney Co., Inc.
CAROMAR - Recording label - Beatlefest Inc.
CAROMIX - Spices and extracts - Pharmachem Laboratories, Inc.
CARON - Jewelry - Victoria Creations Inc.
CARON - Sponges - National Sponge Corp.
CARON - Yarn ☆ - Caron International Inc.
CARON CHRISTMAS - Yarn ☆ - Caron International Inc.
CARON GOLD - Yarn ☆ - Caron International Inc.
CARON PREMIUM - Yarn ☆ - Caron International Inc.
CARON ULTRA - Yarn ☆ - Caron International Inc.
CARONEX - Charcoal ☆ - Hydroponic Chemical Co. Inc.
CAROPLEX - Vitamins and nutritional supplements - R.P. Scherer Corp.
CAROPLEX - Vitamins and nutritional supplements - Source Naturals
CAROTEAM - Vitamins and nutritional supplements - Vitamin Research Products Inc.
CAROTENE + - Vitamins and nutritional supplements ☆ - Vitamin Research Products Inc.
CAROTENE-7 - Pharmaceutical preparations - Light Force Inc.
CAROTENE BEADS - Spices and extracts - Pharmachem Laboratories, Inc.
CAROTENE-E - Health care products - Health Maintenance Programs Inc.
CAROTENE-E-FORTE - Vitamins and nutritional supplements - Health Maintenance Programs Inc.
CAROTENE FEEDING OIL - Pet products - Nutritional Research Associates Inc.
CAROTENE-HEALTH PACKS - Vitamins and nutritional supplements - Health Maintenance Programs Inc.
CAROTENE PLUS - Vitamins and nutritional supplements - Ethical Nutrients
CAROTENOID CAPS - Vitamins and nutritional supplements ☆ - Vitamin Research Products Inc.
CAROTHER'S - Olive oil - Carother's Research Laboratories
CAROUSEL - Bakery products - Shopper's Food Warehouse

CAROUSEL - Candy ☆ - American Candy Co.
CAROUSEL - Chewing gum - Ford Gum and Machine Co.
CAROUSEL - Christmas tree ornaments ☆ - Cracker Box Inc.
CAROUSEL - Diapers–cloth - SPH Inc.
CAROUSEL - Dolls ☆ - Effanbee Doll Corp.
CAROUSEL - Floor coverings - Mannington Resilient Floors
CAROUSEL - Floor coverings–carpet and rugs ☆ - Hollytex Carpet Mills Inc.
CAROUSEL - Flowers, plants, and seeds - Panamerican Seed
CAROUSEL - Food products - Benjamin Lipitz Co.
CAROUSEL - Furniture–wood - Ficks Reed Co. Inc.
CAROUSEL - Game machines - Universal Distributing of Nevada, Inc.
CAROUSEL - Glassware–household - Crisa Corp.
CAROUSEL - Glassware–household - Denby USA Limited
CAROUSEL - Greeting cards - Carousel Greeting cards Inc.
CAROUSEL - Home health care products - Arjo Manufacturing Co.
CAROUSEL - Ice cream - Carousel Ice Cream
CAROUSEL - Kitchen appliances ☆ - Sunbeam-Oster Household Products
CAROUSEL - Kitchen utensils–aluminum ☆ - Reston Lloyd Ltd.
CAROUSEL - Office supplies ☆ - Permacel
CAROUSEL - Photographic equipment - Eastman Kodak Co.
CAROUSEL - Puddings–mixes - Carousel Foods Inc.
CAROUSEL - Recording label - W.W. Associates Inc.
CAROUSEL - Rocking horses - Flexible Flyer Co.
CAROUSEL - Shoes - Craddock-Terry Inc.
CAROUSEL - Tablecloths - Artex International, Inc.
CAROUSEL - Tools - Frederickseal, Inc.
CAROUSEL - Trailers–travel ☆ - Coachmen Industries, Inc.
CAROUSEL - Wainscoting - Georgia-Pacific Corp.
CAROUSEL - Weather vanes - Vitos Products
CAROUSEL - Window shades - Vertical Blind Factory
CAROUSEL - Window treatments - Home Fashions Inc.
CAROUSEL - Windows–screen - Le Font USA
CAROUSEL - Wines - Bercut-Vandervoort & Co.
CAROUSEL CELLULAR - Window treatments - Home Fashions Inc.
CAROUSEL CLASSICS - Figurines - Willitts Design International, Inc.
CAROUSEL DESIGNS - Bedding–linen - Carousel Designs Ltd.
CAROUSEL II - Paneling - Georgia-Pacific Corp.
CAROUSEL KNITTER - Craft supplies - Milton Bradley Co.
CAROUSEL ORNAMENTS - Christmas tree ornaments - Mr. Christmas, Inc.
CAROUSEL PEGBOARD - Candy ☆ - American Candy Co.
CAROUSELLE - Flatware - Yamazaki Tableware Inc.
CAROUSELLE - Frames–picture - Intercraft Industries
CAROUSELLE GOLD ACCENT - Flatware - Yamazaki Tableware Inc.
CAROUSELS - Chains–industrial - Flexsteel Industries Inc.
CARPACHO - Toys - Cinnamuffs, Inc.
CARPAD - Dripmats - Evergreen Studio
CARPAL CARE - Exercising equipment - Repetitive Motion Trauma Corp.
CARPAL-LOCK - Apparel stores–sports - CMO Inc.
CARPAL-WATCH - Watches - Neurotron Inc.
CARPANO - Beverages–alcohol - Vinvino Wine Co. Inc.
CARPANO PUNT E MES - Beverages–alcohol - Carillon Importers Ltd.
CARPATHIA - Furniture - Romweber Co.
CARPATHIA COLLECTION - Furniture ☆ - Union National Inc.
CARPE DIEM - Computer software - Prosoft Corp.
CARPEDIEM INTERNATIONAL - Neckties - Impact Apparell, Inc.
CARPENE MALVOLTI - Wines - Orion Imports Ltd.
CARPENTER - Musical instrument accessories ☆ - Carpenter Co.
CARPENTER - Publisher's imprints ☆ - Harold Shaw Publishers
CARPENTERS' CHOICE - Hardware - ISM
CARPENTERS' CHOICE - Tools - Fi-Shock Inc.
CARPENTER'S GOOP - Adhesives and sealants - Eclectic Products Inc.
CARPENTER'S PRIDE - Tools - Vaughan & Bushnell Manufacturing Co.
CARPENTIER-EDWARDS PHYSIO - Medical apparatus - Baxter International Inc.
CARPENTREE - Posters - Carpentree, Inc.
CARPET - Flowers, plants, and seeds - Panamerican Seed
CARPET BUTLER - Carpet sweepers ☆ - Bissell Inc.
CARPET CARE - Deodorizers - Blue Cross Laboratories Inc.
CARPET-COATE - Cleaning preparations–upholstery ☆ - Guardsman Products, Inc.
CARPET COMPANION - Deodorizers - American Specialty Products Corp.
CARPET COMPANIONS - Floor mouldings - Johnsonite Flooring Products
CARPET COUNTRY - Floor coverings–carpet and rugs - Carpet Shop, Inc.
CARPET-COVER - Mats, matting, now out of production - American Floor Products Co. Inc.
CARPET-COVER - Mats ☆ - Ludlow Composites Corp.

☆ = Now out of production

CARPET-COVER II - Mats ☆ - Ludlow Composites Corp.

CARPET CREATIONS - Pet products - Carpet Creations

CARPET CRITIC - Cleaning preparations–carpet and rug - Hillyard Enterprises, Inc.

CARPET DETAILS - Cleaning preparations–carpet and rug - Doyle L. Timmons

CARPET FRESH - Cleaning preparations–carpet and rug - PLC

CARPET FRESH - Deodorizers - Airwick Industries

CARPET FRESH - Deodorizers - Reckitt & Colman, Inc.

CARPET GRABBER - Mats - U.S. Mat & Rubber Co. Inc.

CARPET GRIP - Cushion padding - Capel, Inc.

CARPET-GUARD - Cleaning preparations–upholstery - Guardsman Products, Inc.

CARPET GUN, THE - Stain removers - Fast Industries, Inc.

CARPET ICING - Cleaning preparations–carpet and rug - Blue Coral, Inc.

CARPET-KING - Cleaning preparations–carpet and rug - Malter International Corp.

CARPET-LOC - Antislip rug treatment ☆ - American Non-Slip Products

CARPET LOCK - Carpeting - Guilford Mills, Inc.

CARPET LUSTER - Shampoos ☆ - Klean-Strip

CARPET MACHINE PLUS - Cleaning preparations–carpet and rug - Bissell Inc.

CARPET MAGIC - Rug cleaning machines–commercial - Hartz Mountain Corp.

CARPET-MATE - Deodorizers ☆ - Great American Herb Co.

CARPET MATE - Floor coverings–carpet and rugs - Foamex LP

CARPET-MATE - Vacuum cleaners and accessories ☆ - General Floorcraft Inc.

CARPET MAX - Floor covering stores - Carpetmax, LP

CARPET PILE COVER - Paint rollers - Corona Brushes Inc.

CARPET-PLUS - Floor coverings - Belting Associates Inc.

CARPET POWER - Cleaning preparations–carpet and rug - Blue Coral, Inc.

CARPET RIDE - Motor vehicle parts and accessories - Talus Corp.

CARPET ROSE - Flower pots–plastic - Anthony Tesselaar USA Inc.

CARPET SCENT - Deodorizers - Blue Cross Laboratories Inc.

CARPET SCIENCE - Cleaning preparations–carpet and rug - Drackett Co.

CARPET SCIENCE - Cleaning preparations–carpet and rug - S.C. Johnson & Son, Inc.

CARPET SCULPTURE GALLERY - Floor coverings - Carpet Sculptures International Inc.

CARPET SHIELD - Mats - Aqua-Tainer Co.

CARPET SHOE - Footwear - 3-B & Associates

CARPET SKLEEN - Cleaning preparations–carpet and rug ☆ - Calgon Vestal Laboratories

CARPET SOLUTION, THE - Stain removers - KC Products, Inc. (Sharon D. Spence)

CARPET SPARKLE - Cleaning preparations–carpet and rug - Better Living Products Inc.

CARPET SPOTTER - Cleaning preparations - Uncle Sam Chemical Co., Inc.

CARPET SPOTTER - Cleaning preparations–carpet and rug - Hillyard Enterprises, Inc.

CARPET STAR - Carpet cleaning equipment - R.E. Whittaker Co., Inc.

CARPET STUDIO - Floor coverings–carpet and rugs - Shaw Industries Inc.

CARPET-TEX - Rubber matting - Ace Rubber Products Inc.

CARPET-TO-GO - Floor coverings–carpet and rugs - Habitat International Inc.

CARPET-TOP - Carpet mats ☆ - American Floor Products Co. Inc.

CARPET TOP - Floor coverings–tile ☆ - Pawling Corp. (Standard Products Div.)

CARPET VET - Deodorizers - Mcauley's, Inc.

CARPET VIEW - Mats - Roope Corp.

CARPETAID + - Cleaning preparations–carpet and rug - Heartland Corp.

CARPETBAGGER - Cases–musical instrument - Hybrid Cases

CARPETECH - Floor covering stores - Carpetech International, Inc.

CARPETMASTER - Hardware - Darnell Corp.

CARPETMASTER - Mats - Akro Corp.

CARPETMASTER - Vacuum cleaners and accessories - Clarke Industries, Inc.

CARPETMAX - Floor coverings–carpet and rugs - Maxim Group Inc.

CARPETRIEVER - Vacuum cleaners and accessories - Advance Machine Co.

CARPETRINSER/DRYER - Vacuum cleaners and accessories - Breuer Electric Manufacturing Co.

CARPETRON - Carpet-shampooing machine - Advance Machine Co.

CARPETS BY AMERICAN - Floor coverings ☆ - American Sales and Distribution Services, Inc.

CARPETSHEEN - Cleaning preparations–carpet and rug ☆ - Hillyard Enterprises, Inc.

CARPETWALL - Wallpaper - PCI Industries Inc.

CARPETWIN - Vacuum cleaners and accessories - Advance Machine Co.

CARPINETO - Beverages–alcohol - Rolar Imports Ltd.

CARPOL - Floor coverings - E.R. Carpenter Co.

CARR - Frames–picture - M.W. Carr & Co. Inc.

CARR INTERNATIONAL - Frames–picture - M.W. Carr & Co. Inc.

CARRA-BAN - Crocheted and knitted items ☆ - Puritan Sportswear Corp.

CARRAGAUZE - Bandages - Carrington Laboratories, Inc.

CARRANO - Footwear - Andrea Carrano

CARRARA - Envelopes - Western States Envelope Co.

CARRARA - Floor coverings - Mannington Resilient Floors

CARRARA - Floor coverings ☆ - Bellbridge Carpets

CARRARA - Floor coverings–carpet and rugs - J and J Industries Inc.

CARRARA - Food products - Vigo Importing Co. Inc.

CARRARA - Furniture ☆ - Henredon Furniture Industries Inc.

CARRARA - Marble products ☆ - Dryvit Systems, Inc.

CARRARA - Mat boards - Onyx Mat Board

CARRARA - Paper products - Georgia-Pacific Corp.

CARRARA - Stoneware dishes - Pfaltzgraff Investment Co.

CARRARA - Tiles–ceramic - KPT Inc.

CARRARA - Towels - Necessities

CARRARA - Wallpaper - Blumenthal

CARRASYN - Pharmaceutical preparations - Carrington Laboratories, Inc.

CARRAVELLE - Cutlery - Robeson Industries

CARRAVET - Veterinary pharmaceutical preparations - Carrington Laboratories, Inc.

CARRE - Artists' materials - Sakura of America

CARRE - Floor coverings–carpet and rugs ☆ - Masland Corp.

CARRE - Floor coverings–carpet and rugs ☆ - Regal Rugs Inc.

CARR'E - Neckties - Salant/Manhattan Industries

CARRE - Tiles–ceramic - WesekPalley Tile Inc.

CARRE - Watches - Gruen Marketing Corp.

CARREAU - Floor coverings–carpet and rugs ☆ - Mohawk Industries Inc.

CARRERA - Carpets, now out of production - Couristan Inc.

CARRERA - Floor coverings–carpet and rugs ☆ - Prestige Mills Inc.

CARRERA - Hairpins - Continental Accessory Corp.

CARRERA - Motor vehicles–automobiles - Porsche Cars North America Inc.

CARRERA - Ski boat ☆ - American Skier Boat Co.

CARRERA - Ski suits–men's ☆ - Authentic Fitness Corp.

CARRERA - Sunglasses - Carrera Eyewear Corp.

CARRERA - Wallpaper - Koroseal Wallcoverings

CARRERA - Watches - Nicolet International Inc.

CARRERA - Wheelchairs ☆ - Ortho-Kinetics, Inc.

CARRERA - Wines - Joseph Victori Wines Inc.

CARRERA PARK - Trailers–travel ☆ - Fleetwood Enterprises, Inc.

CARRERA PORSCHE - Sunglasses - Carrera Eyewear Corp.

CARRERA, THE SPIRIT OF POWER - Colognes - Frances Denney

CARRETTE - Wheelchairs ☆ - Everest and Jennings International Ltd.

CARRI-ALL - Trailers–industrial ☆ - Fleetwood Enterprises, Inc.

CARRI-BINDER - Binders - 20th Century Plastics

CARRI CRADLE - Strollers–baby - Kolcraft Enterprises, Inc.

CARRI-LITE - Trailers–travel - Carriage, Inc.

CARRI-ON - Recording label - Stephen Michal Berka

CARRIAGE - Cabinets ☆ - HomeCrest Corp.

CARRIAGE - Hams - Sugardale Foods Inc.

CARRIAGE - Trailers–travel - Carriage, Inc.

CARRIAGE CARPET - Motor vehicle parts and accessories - Bob Bartlett & Associates Inc.

CARRIAGE CLUB - Golfing equipment - Golfsmith International Inc.

CARRIAGE COLLECTION - Briefcases - H.I.T. Industries, Ltd.

CARRIAGE COLLECTION - Furniture–wood - Flexsteel Industries Inc.

CARRIAGE COLLECTION - Watches - Vogue Watch Strap Creations

CARRIAGE COURT - Apparel and accessories - Sears, Roebuck and Co.

CARRIAGE HILL - Trailers–travel - Fleetwood Enterprises, Inc.

CARRIAGE HOUSE - Candles - Colonial Candle of Cape Cod

CARRIAGE HOUSE - Cutlery ☆ - Washington Forge Inc.

CARRIAGE HOUSE - Floor coverings–carpet and rugs - Atlas Carpet Mills Inc.

CARRIAGE HOUSE - Floor coverings–carpet and rugs - Johnson's Carpets Inc.

CARRIAGE HOUSE - Floor coverings–carpet and rugs ☆ - Quaker Inc.

CARRIAGE HOUSE - Food products - Carriage House Foods

CARRIAGE HOUSE - Furniture ☆ - Bassett Furniture Industries, Inc.

CARRIAGE HOUSE - Furniture ☆ - Vaughan Furniture Co. Inc.

CARRIAGE HOUSE - Hardware - Amerock Corp.

CARRIAGE HOUSE - Meat products–beef - Carriage House Meat and Provision Co. Inc.

CARRIAGE HOUSE - Paints - Bruning Paint Co.

CARRIAGE HOUSE - Shingles–asphalt or tar - Certainteed Corp. (Roofing Products Group)

CARRIAGE HOUSE - Toys - M. Ginsburg & Co.

CARRIAGE HOUSE - Wines - C. Mondavi and Sons

CARRIAGE HOUSE COLLECTION, THE - Frames–picture - Fred M. Lawrence Co. Inc.

CARRIAGE LANE - Wallpaper ☆ - Mobile Paint Manufacturing Co.

CARRIAGE-LS - Trailers–travel - Carriage, Inc.

CARRIAGE PATH - Hardware ☆ - Alside Div.

CARRIAGE PETS - Toys–stuffed - Fun World Inc.

CARRIAGE PINE - Furniture ☆ - Bassett Furniture Industries, Inc.

CARRIAGE RUN - Furniture ☆ - Bassett Furniture Industries, Inc.

CARRIAGE TRADE - Bedding–linen - Springs Industries, Inc.

CARRIAGE TRADE - Cleaning preparations - Viking Manufacturing Co. Inc.

CARRIAGE TRADE - Fruits and vegetables - George F. Joseph Orchard Siding Inc.

CARRIAGE TRADE - Napkins–paper ☆ - Royal Imprints Corp.

CARRIAGE TRADE - Paper–writing ☆ - The Rytex Co.

CARRIAGE TRADE LTD. - Apparel and accessories - Cluett, Peabody & Co.

CARRIAGESTONE - Stone products - Pava, Inc.

CARRIAI-CORE - Drill bits - Hawera Inc.

CARRIBEAN COLLECTION - Shoes - Allen-Edmonds Shoe Corp.

CARRIE - Recording label - Carrie Records

CARRIE - Yarn ☆ - JCA, Inc.

CARRIE & HER LIL ONE - Dolls - Goldberger Doll Manufacture Co.

CARRIER - Air conditioning equipment - Carrier Corp.

CARRIER - Games - Avalon Hill Game Co.

CARRIER COMBAT - Computer software - Complete Computer Services

CARRIER COMMAND - Computer software ☆ - Microprose Software, Inc.

CARRIER-LIFT - Platform lift - Access Industries, Inc.

CARRIER MODE - Toys - Saban Entertainment, Inc.

CARRIER TRANSICOLD - Air conditioning equipment - Carrier Corp.

CARRIERS AT WAR - Computer software - Electronic Arts Inc.

CARRIFF CORPORATION INC. - Textiles - Carriff Corp. Inc.

CARRIGALINE - Pottery - Bewley Irish Imports

CARRIGDHOUN - Pottery ☆ - Bewley Irish Imports

CARRILLO - Housewares - Elon Inc.

CARRINGTON - Clocks and weather instruments - Indecor Inc.

CARRINGTON - Gun cases, luggage - Jameslee Corp.

CARRINGTON - Pharmaceutical preparations - Carrington Laboratories, Inc.

CARRINGTON HOUSE - Floor coverings–carpet and rugs ☆ - Mohawk Industries Inc.

CARRION - Jewelry - Carrion Jewelry Manufacturing Inc.

CARRISA - Floor coverings–carpet and rugs - Evans-Black Carpet Mills

CARRIVUE - Audio equipment - T.M. Visual Industries Inc.

CARROGEN - Skin care products - Fiske Industries Inc.

CARROKEEL - Salmon - Corman Foods

CARROLL - Health care products ☆ - Cumberland-Swan, Inc.

CARROLL REED OF NEW ENGLAND - Apparel and accessories - Carroll Reed Inc.

CARROLL SHELBY - Chili–canned - Wm. B. Reily & Co. Inc.

CARROLL SHELBY CHILI MIX - Food products - Reily Foods

CARROLL SHELBY'S ORIGINAL TEXAS BRAND - Seasonings - Carroll Shelby's Original Texas Chili Co.

CARROLL'S FARM - Meat products–poultry - Carolina Turkeys

CARROLLS NO. 1 - Cigarettes - G.A. Georgopulo & Co. Inc.

CARROLLS ORIGINAL VIRGINIA - Cigarettes - G.A. Georgopulo & Co. Inc.

CARROLLTON - Floor coverings–carpet and rugs ☆ - Evans-Black Carpet Mills

CARROM - Games - Carrom Co.

CARROT-BONE - Pet food - T.F.H. Publications, Inc.

CARROT CONCOCTION - Health care products - Old Amish Herbs

CARROT CRYSTALS - Juice extracting devices - Florida Food Products Inc.

CARROT CUTIES - Toys–stuffed ☆ - Fun World Inc.

CARROT DELIGHT - Beverages–carbonated - Futurebiotics

CARROT DOG CHEW - Pet food - T.F.H. Publications, Inc.

CARROT FRESH - Chemical preparations - Extended Product Life, Inc.

CARROT LITES - Snack foods - Health Valley Food

CARROT-PACK BUNNY - Toys–stuffed ☆ - Fun World Inc.

CARROT PATCH - Figurines - May Department Stores Co.

CARROT PATCH MUSICIANS - Chocolate candy - Superior Fruit & Confections

CARROT-TEIN - Vitamins and nutritional supplements - Natural Organics, Inc.

CARROT TOP - Paper products - Carrot Top, Inc.

CARROT TOP - Toys ☆ - Gerber Products Co.

CARROTS PLUS - Vitamins and nutritional supplements - Vital Food Sources, Inc.

CARROUSEL - Bathroom accessories - Wilardy Originals Inc.

CARROUSEL - Furniture - CTH/Sherrill Occasional

CARROUSEL - Party favors ☆ - Atkinson Sales Co.

CARROUSEL - Posters - Heartprint Inc.

CARROUSEL - Rings–jewelry ☆ - Artcarved Inc.

CARROUSHELF - Housewares - Lescoa Inc.

CARR'S - Crackers - Shaffer, Clark & Co. Inc.

CARRS CLEAN-OFF - Denture cleaners ☆ - Robinette Inc.

CARR'S MINI CROISSANT SNACKS - Crackers - Shaffer, Clark & Co. Inc.

CARRUADES DE LAFITE ROTHSCHILD - Wines ☆ - European Beverage Co., Inc.

CARRY-A-LONG - Toys - Little Tikes Co.

CARRY-AD - Bags–canvas - Amplaco Group Inc.

CARRY ALL - Bags–duffel - Ektelon

CARRY-ALL - Housewares - Tupperware Co.

CARRY-ALL - Infant product - Railnet Corp.

CARRY-ALL SUPREME - Cases–camera - SP Systems/Saratons

CARRY-ALL-WOOD - Footwear ☆ - Condar Co.

CARRY CASE - Leather goods - S and S Leather Goods

CARRY CLEAN - Toothbrushes - Brimms Inc.

CARRY COOL - Air conditioning equipment - General Electric Co.

CARRY COVERS - Bedding–linen - Carry Covers

CARRY GOAL - Soccer equipment - Sport Supply Group, Inc.

CARRY HOME - Plastics film - Warp Bros.

CARRY-IT - Trailers–travel - Chariot Manufacturing Co. Inc.

CARRY-LITE - Cases–musical instrument - M & M Distributing Co.

CARRY-LITE - Decoys - Carry-Lite, Inc.

CARRY ME BAG - Infant product - Carry Me Inc.

CARRY ME TRASH CANN - Toys ☆ - Sun Products Corp. (Wellington)

CARRY-ON - See **ALDER COVE**

CARRY-ON - Air conditioning equipment - Marine Development Corp.

CARRY PHONE - Leather goods - S and S Leather Goods

CARRY PHONE - Telephones - Carry Phone, Inc.

CARRY PRO - Cases–camera - Actad Corp. of America

CARRY RITE - Infant product - Pansy Ellen Products, Inc.

CARRY-RITE - Luggage - Carry-Rite Travelware Co.

CARRY STAR - Boxes - Star Case Manufacturing Co. Inc.

CARRYALL - Carts - Club Car, Inc.

CARRYALL - Cases–musical instrument - G. Leblanc Corp.

CARRYAWAYS - Luggage ☆ - Samsonite Corp.

CARRY'EM AQUARIUM - Toys - Philip B. Fleet

CARRYLIGHT2 - Golfing equipment - Wilson Sporting Goods Co.

CARRYLITE - Golfing equipment - All American Golf Sales, Inc.

CARRYLITE - Musical instrument accessories - Viking Cases

CARRYMATE - Buckets–plastic - Geerpres Wringer Co.

CARRYMATE - Cases–camera - Lenmar Enterprises, Inc.

CARRYON - Bags–duffel - Ektelon

CARRYPAK - Luggage - Samsonite Corp.

CARS - Computer program - James W. Kerr

CARS - Computer software - Daktronics Inc.

CARS FROM THE MOON - Posters - J. Paul Guyer

CARSMART - Computer software - A.I.N., Inc.

CARSON - Cigarettes - Brown & Williamson Tobacco Corp.

CARSON - Utensils and garden tools - Carson Industries, Inc.

CARSON COUNTRY - Metals ☆ - Carson Industries, Inc.

CARSTAIRS - Whiskey - Sazerac Co. Inc.

CARSTAIR'S WHITE SEAL - Whiskey - Sazerac Co. Inc.

CARSTENS - Medical office supplies - Carstens Health Industries, Inc.

CARSUALS - Apparel and accessories - Stanwood Corp.

CART-ALL - Bags - Craft Corp.

CART ALONG - Luggage racks–automotive - R.C. Steele Co.

CART BAG - Golfing equipment - Exim Manufacturers, Inc.

CART CAFFE - Espresso carts - Biega Limited

CART-MATIC - Pens–fountain ☆ - Faber-Castell Corp.

CART MULE - Carts - CDS Inc.

CART 'N' CARRY - Golfing equipment - Wilson Sporting Goods Co.

CART OASIS - Golfing equipment - Starline Products, Inc.

CART SMART - Golfing equipment - Wilson Sporting Goods Co.

CART WRIGHT SPORTSWEAR - Apparel–children's - M Hidary & Co., Inc.

CARTA BLANCA - Beverages–carbonated - Labatt Importers Inc.

CARTA GOLD - Food products - Osceola Fruit Distributors

CARTA-KID - Infant product - Rock-A-Bye Baby Inc.

CARTA NEVADA - Wines ☆ - Freixenet USA

CARTAGENA - Floor coverings ☆ - Azrock Commercial Flooring

☆ = Now out of production

CARTAGENA - Floor coverings–carpet and rugs - Cabin Crafts Carpets

CARTALL - Carts - Peco Manufacturing Co. Inc.

CARTAMEX - Courier services–air - Cartamex Inc.

CARTE BLANCHE - Floor coverings–carpet and rugs ☆ - Masland Corp.

CARTE BLANCHE - Furniture - Thomasville Furniture Industries Inc.

CARTE BLANCHE - Greeting cards - House of Oz

CARTE JEWEL, THE - Pearl jewelry - International Cultured Pearls

CARTECAY - Floor coverings–carpet and rugs - Atlas Carpet Mills Inc.

CARTELO - Apparel and accessories - James H. Feuling, Jr.

CARTER - Cheese - Dan Carter Inc.

CARTER - Fuel systems–motor vehicle - Federal-Mogul Corp.

CARTER - Work clothes - H.W. Carter & Sons Inc.

CARTER & HOLMES - Neckties - K and B International Silks Ltd.

CARTER BELL - Oils–vulcanized - Harwick Standard Distribution Corp.

CARTER-CRAFT - Electronic equipment - Carter Craft Co.

CARTER HALL - Tobacco products - John Middleton Inc.

CARTER-HOFFMANN QUICK SERVE - Serving carts - Carter-Hoffmann Corp.

CARTER RINGER - Apparel stores–sports ☆ - Gladding Braided Products Inc.

CARTER SHADES - Trailers awnings - Carter Shades, Inc.

CARTERRA - Computer software - Space Imaging, Inc.

CARTER'S - Apparel–children's - William Carter Co.

CARTER'S - Fruits and vegetables - Agway Country Foods Inc.

CARTERS - Health care products ☆ - Invacare Corp.

CARTERS - Infant product - Mount Vernon Mills Inc.

CARTERS - Infant product ☆ - La Rue International, Inc.

CARTERS - Lamps - Dolly, Inc.

CARTER'S - Office supplies - Avery Dennison Corp.

CARTER'S FOR WOMEN - Underwear and nightwear - Dwight-Johnson & Co. Inc.

CARTER'S GROWBODY - Apparel–children's - William Carter Co.

CARTER'S LITTLE PILLS - Laxatives - Carter-Wallace, Inc.

CARTER'S NATURAL - Baby foods - William Carter Co.

CARTER'S WATCH THE WEAR - Apparel and accessories - H.W. Carter & Sons Inc.

CARTES D'ART - Postcards - Fotofolio Inc.

CARTHAGE - Hardware - Blaine Window Hardware Inc.

CARTHAGE - Olive oil - $imex, USA, Inc.

CARTHAGE - Recording label - Rykodisc Inc.

CARTHAME - Skin care products - Rene Furterer

CARTIER - Floor coverings–carpet and rugs - Patcraft Mills Inc.

CARTIER - Floor coverings–carpet and rugs ☆ - Royalweve Carpet Mills

CARTIER - Jewelry - Cartier Inc.

CARTIER - Scarves - Jerry Kohn Inc.

CARTIER - Wallpaper ☆ - David & Dash

CARTIER VENDOME - Corn–flour or meal - Philip Morris Companies Inc.

CARTIME - Seafood products–canned or cured - Fishery Products International USA

CARTISTAT - Vitamins and nutritional supplements - Basic Organics, Inc.

CARTLOCK - Cording - Fla. Orthopedics, Inc.

CARTOMAKER - Stencils - Mason Marking Systems Corp.

CARTON CAP - Housewares - Hy Wald

CARTON MASTER - Paper–gummed - Tape Inc.

CARTONMATE - Paperboard - Gulf States Paper Corp.

CARTOON-A-PLATE - Hobby kits ☆ - Makit Products

CARTOON COOKIES - Cookies - Century Cookies

CARTOON FACTORY - Greeting cards - American Greetings Corp.

CARTOON IMAGES - Computer software - Parsons Technology, Inc.

CARTOON MAKER - Computer software - Capstone Software

CARTOON NETWORK - T-shirts–men's - Time Warner, Inc. (Cartoon Network)

CARTOON NETWORK WACKY RACING - Apparel and accessories - Cartoon Network, Inc.

CARTOONMEDIA - Publisher's imprints - Cartoonmedia, Inc.

CARTOPLEX II - Health care products - Helene Curtis Industries Inc.

CARTOPPER - Boats–motor ☆ - Marathon Boat Group, Inc.

CARTOPPERS - Boats–dinghies ☆ - C-G Industries Inc.

CARTOUCHE GOLD ACCENT - Flatware ☆ - Yamazaki Tableware Inc.

CARTOWEL - Motor vehicle parts and accessories - Talus Corp.

CARTRAX - Tranquilizers - J.B. Roerig & Co.

CARTRIDGE CADDY, THE - Cartridges–pen - Key Productions

CARTRIDGE EXPRESS - Swimming pools - Fountainhead Technologies, Inc.

CARTRIDGE MARK - Typewriters - Montgomery Ward & Co. Inc.

CARTRIDGE PLEAT - Window shades - Protech Shading Inc.

CARTRIDGEMATE - Printers–computer - Jetfill, Inc.

CARTRISEAL - Machine parts - Rexnord Corp.

CARTS VERMONT - Carts - Carts Vermont

CARTUNES - Toy vehicles - Intex Recreation Corp.

CARTWHEEL - Bicycles ☆ - Hedstrom Corp.

CARTWHEELS - Beads - Mangelsen's (VDI)

CARTWHEELS - LUCITE carts - Grainware Co.

CARTWHEELS - Luggage - Samsonite Corp.

CARTWHEELS USA - Apparel–children's - Cartwheels USA, Inc.

CARUSO - Cheese - Pollio Dairy Products Corp.

CARUSO - Cosmetics - Celeste Co. Inc.

CARUSO - Food products - Cudahy Co.

CARUSO - Olive oil - Food Oils Corp.

CARUST - Automotive parts and accessories - Turtle Wax, Inc.

CARUTHR PLANK - Floor coverings - Bruce Hardwood Floors

CARVAC - Vacuum cleaners and accessories - Black & Decker Corp.

CARVAC PLUS - Vacuum cleaners and accessories - Black & Decker Corp.

CARVE & CAST - Artists' materials - Dick Blick Co.

CARVE 'N' SLICE - Knives–electric ☆ - Ronson Consumer Products Corp.

CARVED CASUAL - Dinnerware–glass - Lenox, Inc.

CARVED ELEGANCE - Floor coverings–carpet and rugs - Ashley Commercial Carpets

CARVED GOLD - Frames–picture - A.P.F. Master Framemaker

CARVEDOR - Doors–wood - Panelfold Inc.

CARVEL - Doors–glass - Peachtree Doors and Windows Inc.

CARVEL HALL - Cutlery - Carvel Hall Inc.

CARVEL SINFUL LOVE BAR - Ice cream - Carvel Corp.

CARVER - Audio equipment - Carver Corp.

CARVER - Boats–motor - Carver Boat Corp.

CARVER - Chairs–wood - Gunlocke Co.

CARVER AID - Cutlery ☆ - Lifetime Hoan Corp.

CARVER CLUB - Food products - Boston Chicken, Inc.

CARVER TRIPP - Stains - Parks Corp.

CARVER TRIPP CONTEMPO - Paints ☆ - Parks Corp.

CARVER TRIPP SUPER SPAR - Varnishes - Parks Corp.

CARVER WINE CELLARS - Beverages–alcohol - Carver Wine Cellars

CARVERS COLLECTION - Drapery hardware ☆ - Kirsch Co.

CARVER'S MILL - Shutters–wood - ABT Co., Inc.

CARVER'S ORIGINAL - Beverages–carbonated ☆ - Coca-Cola Co.

CARVERS, THE - Recording label - Douglas B. McGaughyey

CARVESQUE - Floor coverings–carpet and rugs ☆ - Gulistan Carpet Inc.

CARVIN - Guitars - Carvin Manufacturing Co.

CARVING - Meat products–poultry - Perdue Farms Inc.

CARVING - Meat products–poultry - Perdue Holdings, Inc.

CARWOOD - Slacks–men's - Duck Head Apparel Co., Inc.

CARY - Apparel–athletic - Heritage Sportswear

CARY - Audio equipment - Cary Audio Design Inc.

CARY - Boats - Randall Enterprises

CARY - Food products - Doxsee Food Corp.

CARY - Frames–eyeglass - U.S. Optical Frame Co.

CARY - Musical instrument accessories ☆ - Fred Gretsch Enterprises

CARY-ETTE - Toilets–portable ☆ - Monogram Sanitation Co.

CARY MIDDLECOFF - Slacks–men's ☆ - Jaymar-Ruby Inc.

CARYL ADLER - Apparel–women's - Cape Cod Cricket Lane

CARYL PICKER - Jewelry - Caryl Picker, Inc.

CARYL RICHARDS - Hair care products - Faberge Co.

CARYOPHYLLINE - Pharmaceutical preparations - City Chemical Corp.

CARY'S - Syrup - Borden, Inc.

CARZILLAS - Toy - Tonka Corp.

CAS - Alarm systems - Crimestopper Security Products Inc.

CAS - Computer software - Crowell Systems

CAS - Cuffs–hand - Casco International Inc.

C.A.S. - Footwear - Freeman International, Inc.

CAS-CAR-ANS BELL - Pharmaceutical preparations - Hollings-Smith Co. Inc.

CAS-EVAC - Laxatives ☆ - Parke-Davis

CAS-KER - Clocks - Cas Ker Co.

CASA - Crackers - Vitarroz

CASA - Fans–electric - Lamps Plus Inc.

CASA - Processed foods - Casera Foods, Inc.

CASA BELLA - Fans–electric - Classic Concepts Inc.

CASA BELLA - Flatware ☆ - Lifetime Hoan Corp.

CASA BELLA - Floor coverings–carpet and rugs ☆ - Columbus Mills, Inc.

CASA BLANCA - Cigars - Casa Blanca Cigar Co. Inc.

CASA BLANCA - Floor coverings–carpet and rugs ☆ - American Carpet Mills

CASA BLANCA - Furniture ☆ - White Furniture Co.

CASA BRAVA - Dinners–frozen ☆ - Campbell Soup Co.

CASA BUENA - Food products - Southland Corp.

CASA DE BLANCO - Furniture ☆ - White Furniture Co.

CASA DE FRUTA - Fruits–dried - Casa De Fruta

CASA DE LA GUITARRA - Music–sheet - GSP
CASA DE LORENA - Coffee - Millstone Coffee, Inc.
CASA DE ORO 2 - Deodorizers - NHS, Inc.
CASA DE PANCAS - Wines - Admiral Wine Merchants
CASA DE PFAFFIA - Health care products - Top of the Line
CASA DE TOMAS - Food products - Casa de Thomas
CASA DEL GRANO - Pasta ☆ - Dean & Deluca Inc.
CASA DEL PUEBLO - Tortillas - Glencourt Products
CASA DEL SOL - Floor coverings–carpet and rugs ☆ - Kelly Group Inc.
CASA DEL SOL - Food products - Chelten House Products Inc.
CASA DEL SUR - Food products - Paramount Foods Inc.
CASA DI BERTACCHI - Food products - Casa Di Bertacchi Corp.
CASA DI LISIO - Sauces - Casa Di Lisio Products Inc.
CASA DI PESCATORI - Wines - William Grant & Sons, Inc.
CASA-DICOLE - Health care products - Halsey Drug Co. Inc.
CASA DONOSO - Wines - Parliament Import Co.
CASA FIESTA - Food products - Bruce Foods Corp.
CASA FINA - Housewares - Cecil Saydah Co.
CASA FLORES - Tortillas - Mission Foods Corp.
CASA FRANCESCO - Wines - Francis A. Bonanno, Inc.
CASA GRANDE - Bathtubs–enameled - Lyons Industries Inc.
CASA GRANDE - Floor coverings - Congoleum Corp.
CASA GRANDE - Floor coverings–carpet and rugs ☆ - Masland Corp.
CASA GRANDE - Garden furniture–rattan - Lloyd/Flanders Industries
CASA GRANDE - Housewares - Cecil Saydah Co.
CASA GRANDE - Pizzas–frozen - Perry County Foods, Inc.
CASA JOVAN - Liquors - United States Distilled Products Co.
CASA LANTE - Dishes–china - Viletta China Co.
CASA LARGA - Wines - Casa Larga Vineyards Inc.
CASA LOMA - Floor coverings–carpet and rugs ☆ - Masland Corp.
CASA LUPITA - Restaurants–fast food - Ponderosa Inc.
CASA MADRE - Floor coverings–carpet and rugs - Burlington House Carpets
CASA MAGLIA - Apparel–women's - Casa Maglia, Inc.
CASA MAID - Food products - Hanover Foods Corp.
CASA MAMITA - Food products - Aldi Inc.
CASA MARQUEZ TOPLESS - Mexican entrees - International Multifoods Corp.
CASA MARTIN - Cigars ☆ - Tropical Tobacco, Inc.
CASA MIA - Floor coverings - Mannington Resilient Floors
CASA MIA - Vegetable oil - Catania-Spagna Corp.
CASA NOVA - Fabrics–tapestry ☆ - Coloroll Inc.
CASA NOVA 3 - Fabrics–tapestry - Coloroll Inc.
CASA NUESTRA - Wines - Casa Nuestra Winery
CASA NUEVA - Tortillas - Joseph Patoskie
CASA PALMERO - Wines - Deinhard & Partners
CASA RAMOS - Salad dressings–bottled ☆ - Caesar Cardini Foods
CASA RICA - Tortillas - York Snacks Inc.
CASA RIO - Floor coverings–carpet and rugs - Mohawk Carpet Corp.
CASA RIO - Floor coverings–carpet and rugs - Alexander Smith Carpets
CASA ROMA - Floor coverings - Mannington Resilient Floors
CASA ROMA BURRITOS - Dinners–frozen - Dadco Food Products Inc.
CASA ROYAL - Floor coverings ☆ - Congoleum Corp.
CASA RUSTICA - Furniture - Casa Rustica, Inc.
CASA SAN LOUISA - Cheese dips - Diversified Foods, Inc.
CASA SOLANA - Food products - Sysco Corp.
CASA VELASQUEZ - Tortillas - Azteca Foods, Inc.
CASA VERDE - Coffee - Compact Industries, Inc.
CASA VICTORIA - Floor coverings ☆ - Tarkett, Inc.
CASA VIEJA - Dips–sour cream based - Conagra, Inc.
CASA VIEJA - Fans–electric - Lamps Plus Inc.
CASA VINO - Cooking wine - Inter-State Cider & Vinegar Co.
CASA VISCO - Spaghetti - Casa Visco Finer Foods
CASA VISTA - Floor coverings–tile - Kentile Floors Inc.
CASA VOGUE - Furniture ☆ - Lea Industries Inc.
CASABELLA - Wallpaper ☆ - Pickhardt & Siebert USA Inc.
CASABLANCA - Apparel–women's - Casablanca and Fundamental Things
CASABLANCA - Candles ☆ - Corning Inc.
CASABLANCA - Carpets, now out of production - Couristan Inc.
CASABLANCA - Fabrics ☆ - Charter Fabrics Inc.
CASABLANCA - Fans–electric - Casablanca Fan Co.
CASABLANCA - Floor coverings ☆ - Tarkett, Inc.
CASABLANCA - Floor coverings–carpet and rugs - Artistic Rugs Inc.
CASABLANCA - Floor coverings–carpet and rugs - Coronet Carpets Inc.
CASABLANCA - Floor coverings–carpet and rugs - Ebsco Carpet Mills
CASABLANCA - Floor coverings–carpet and rugs - Foreign Accents
CASABLANCA - Floor coverings–carpet and rugs - Regal Rugs Inc.
CASABLANCA - Floor coverings–carpet and rugs - V & B Carpet

CASABLANCA - Furniture ☆ - Evenflo Juvenile Furniture Co.
CASABLANCA - Furniture ☆ - Halcyon Inc.
CASABLANCA - Handbags - Hazan Imports Corp.
CASABLANCA - Lamps ☆ - Sperti Sunlamp
CASABLANCA - Motor vehicles–motor homes ☆ - Beaver Coaches Inc.
CASABLANCA - Recording label - Polygram Records, Inc.
CASABLANCA - Underwear and nightwear - Bestform Foundations, Inc.
CASABLANCA - Window shades ☆ - Colony Shade Co.
CASABLANCA - Wines ☆ - Franciscan Vineyards, Inc.
CASABLANCA - Yarn - Brunswick Yarns
CASABLANCA - Yarn - Henry's Attic
CASABLANCA - Yarn ☆ - Joseph Galler Inc.
CASABLANCA - Yarn ☆ - Tahki Imports Ltd.
CASACOA ISLANDS - Hair care products - Precious Times International, Inc.
CASADA - Shoes - Craddock-Terry Inc.
CASAFRU - Laxatives ☆ - Key Pharmaceuticals Inc.
CASAL - Lighting fixtures - Talon, Inc.
CASAL DE VALLE PRADINHOS - Wines - Admiral Wine Merchants
CASAL MENDES - Wines - Wine Merchants Ltd.
CASAL THAULERO - Wines - Palace Brands Co.
CASALEIRO - Wines - Admiral Wine Merchants
CASALINGA - Vegetables–canned - Lico Brands, Inc.
CASALINI - Beverages–alcohol - M.S. Walker Inc./Seacoast
CASALINO - Chairs–wood ☆ - Krueger International, Inc.
CASALON - Floor coverings–carpet and rugs - Milliken & Co. Inc.
CASAMITE - Adhesives and sealants - Harbor Sales Co.
CASANDRA - Dolls - Mattel, Inc.
CASANOVA - Candy - Casanova Chocolate Co.
CASANOVA - Cigars ☆ - General Cigar Co., Inc.
CASANOVA - Cigars ☆ - Tropical Tobacco, Inc.
CASANOVA - Toys–stuffed - Gund, Inc.
CASANOVA 2 - Wallpaper ☆ - Wallquest, Inc.
CASARA - Cabinets - Bomboy, Inc.
CASARINO - Floor coverings–carpet and rugs ☆ - Columbus Mills, Inc.
CASARO - Cheese - Park Cheese Co., Inc.
CASARO - Food products - Kold Kist Brands Inc.
CASARSA - Whirlpools - Jason International, Inc.
CASARSA - Wines - Transamerica Wine Corp.
CASBAH - Food products - Casbah/Sahara Natural Foods Inc.
CASBAH - Health care products ☆ - Avon Products, Inc.
CASBAH - Rice - Sahara Natural Foods, Inc.
CASBAH PASTRIES - Cake and cookies - Diamond Go Enterprises, Inc.
CASCABEL - Chili peppers–powdered ☆ - Frieda's, Inc.
CASCADA - Beverages–alcohol - Vinos Argentinos Imports USA
CASCADE - Air purification systems - Research Industries, Inc.
CASCADE - Apparel–men's ☆ - Michaels/Stern & Co. Inc.
CASCADE - Bathroom fixtures ☆ - Artesian Industries
CASCADE - Bicycles - Raleigh USA Bicycle Co.
CASCADE - Boats - Phoenix Products Inc.
CASCADE - Boats–canoes - Old Town Canoe Co.
CASCADE - Boats–motor - Cascade Yachts, Inc.
CASCADE - Boats–motor ☆ - Bayliner Marine Corp.
CASCADE - Cabinets - Aristokraft, Inc.
CASCADE - Cabinets - Trendlines Inc.
CASCADE - Cabinets ☆ - Karman Kitchens Inc.
CASCADE - Christmas tree ornaments - Cracker Box Inc.
CASCADE - Clocks - Sunbeam Precision Measurement
CASCADE - Computer software - Mantix Systems, Inc.
CASCADE - Dental equipment - A-Dec Inc.
CASCADE - Detergents - Procter & Gamble Co.
CASCADE - Dinnerware–glass ☆ - Nikko Ceramics Inc.
CASCADE - Fabrics - Thompson of California Inc.
CASCADE - Fabrics - Vertilux-Louverlux Inc.
CASCADE - Fans–electric ☆ - Nutone Inc.
CASCADE - Faucets - Neoperl Inc.
CASCADE - Fishing reels - American Import Co.
CASCADE - Floor coverings - Congoleum Corp.
CASCADE - Flowers, plants, and seeds - Cascade International Seed Co.
CASCADE - Food products ☆ - General Mills, Inc.
CASCADE - Footwear–athletic - New Balance Athletic Shoe, Inc.
CASCADE - Fruits–canned - Cashmere Fruit Exchange
CASCADE - Furniture - Bassett Furniture Industries, Inc.
CASCADE - Furniture - Weiman Co.
CASCADE - Furniture ☆ - Tropitone Furniture Co. Inc.
CASCADE - Giftware - Grainware Co.
CASCADE - Glassware–household - Owens-Illinois Inc. (Libbey Div.)

☆ = Now out of production

CASCADE - Glassware–household - Seneca Glass Co.
CASCADE - Integrated circuits - Lsi Logic Corp.
CASCADE - Jewelry - Orogem Corp.
CASCADE - Knives - Precise International/Wenger
CASCADE - Lighting equipment ☆ - Creative Concepts
CASCADE - Mattresses - Ohio Mattress Co.
CASCADE - Nozzles - Lakeshore Automatic Products Inc.
CASCADE - Paper - Boise Cascade Corp.
CASCADE - Paper–writing ☆ - Canson-Talens Inc.
CASCADE - Prefabricated buildings–wood - Champion Enterprises Inc.
CASCADE - Rings–jewelry ☆ - Artcarved Inc.
CASCADE - Stoves - Pyro Industries, Inc.
CASCADE - Swimming pools - Cascade Pools
CASCADE - Toilet seats ☆ - Ginsey Industries, Inc.
CASCADE - Toilets–porcelain - Armitage Shanks Inc.
CASCADE - Trailers–travel - Cascade Campers Ltd.
CASCADE - Vases ☆ - Lenox Crystal, Inc.
CASCADE - Water–bottled or canned - Cascade Bottled Water Co.
CASCADE - Window shades - Eli Custom Window Treatment, Ltd.
CASCADE - Windows–vinyl - Window Products, Inc.
CASCADE AUTO GLASS - Automotive repair shops–glass - Cascade Auto Glass, Inc.
CASCADE BAY TRADERS - Clothing - Krauss-Fels Co., Inc.
CASCADE BEAUTY - Flowers, plants, and seeds - Grimes Seed Co.
CASCADE BLACK - Yarn - Henry's Attic
CASCADE BLUES - Slacks–men's - Kellwood Co.
CASCADE BRAND - Flowers, plants, and seeds - Cascade International Seed Co.
CASCADE CONSERVES - Jams and jellies - Cascade Conserves
CASCADE COOKIE - Cookies - Cascade Cookie Co., Inc.
CASCADE CREST - Wood products - Boise Cascade Corp.
CASCADE DESIGNS - Bags–duffel ☆ - Cascade Designs, Inc.
CASCADE FALLS - Tandem Imports Corp.
CASCADE FLAP - Window shades - Protech Shading Inc.
CASCADE FRESH - Milk - Auburn Dairy Products, Inc.
CASCADE HEARTH - Food products - Associated Grocers, Inc.
CASCADE I - Floor coverings–carpet and rugs ☆ - Regal Rugs Inc.
CASCADE KIDS - Apparel–children's - Fred Meyer, Inc.
CASCADE LIQUIGEL - Detergents - Procter & Gamble Co.
CASCADE LOOP - Window shades - Protech Shading Inc.
CASCADE MASTER SERIES - Dental equipment - A-Dec Inc.
CASCADE MIST - Water–bottled or canned - Quality Food Centers, Inc.
CASCADE MOUNTAIN - Doors–storm - Weather Shield Manufacturing, Inc.
CASCADE MOUNTAIN VINEYARD - Wines - Cascade Mountain Winery
CASCADE NATURAL - Yarn - Henry's Attic
CASCADE PETITE - Yarn - Henry's Attic
CASCADE PETITE BLACK - Yarn - Henry's Attic
CASCADE-POLY-KOTE - Wood Kote Products, Inc.
CASCADE PREMIUM - Beverages–malt - Beverage America, Inc.
CASCADE SELECT - Food products - Unisea Foods Inc.
CASCADE SPORT - Apparel and accessories - Fred Meyer, Inc.
CASCADE TOY - Toys–stuffed - Cascade Toy, Ltd.
CASCADES - Floor coverings–carpet and rugs - Southern Carpet Mills
CASCADES - Footwear - Wolverine World Wide, Inc.
CASCADES - Sprinklers–lawn - Clearman Co. Inc.
CASCADES - Wallpaper ☆ - Capital Carousel Inc.
CASCADIA - Cabinets ☆ - Canyon Creek Cabinet Co.
CASCADIA - Water–bottled or canned - WinterBrook Beverage Group
CASCADIAN - Fruits–canned - Cascadian Fruit Shippers
CASCADIAN - Potato products - Cascadian Farm, Inc.
CASCADIAN FARM - Frozen fruits and vegetables - Cascadian Farm, Inc.
CASCANATE - Pharmaceutical preparations ☆ - Physician Sales & Service
CASCARA CPX - Health care products ☆ - Nature's Herbs
CASCARONES! - Novelty items - Eggspressions, Inc.
CASCO - Cigarette lighters - Casco Products Corp.
CASCO - Confections - Caspers Ice Cream Inc.
CASCO - Insulating materials–foam - Casco Mineral Wool
CASCO - Sporting goods - Casco USA
CASCO BAY - Beverages–malt - Casco Bay Brewing Co.
CASCO BAY - Food products ☆ - Ocean Beauty Seafood, Inc.
CASCOA - Food products ☆ - Leavenworth Fruit Co.
CASCODE - Amplifiers–musical instrument ☆ - Seymour Duncan Pickups
CASCURE - Adhesives and sealants - Caschem, Inc.
CASE - Audio cabinets–wood - Bush Industries, Inc.
CASE - Bulldozers - Case Corp.
CASE - Cutlery - W.R. Case & Sons Cutlery Co.

CASE - Stationery ☆ - Case Stationery Co. Inc.
CASE - Toys - ERTL Co., Inc.
CASE - Tractors ☆ - J.I. Case Co.
CASE-BASE - Attache cases - Elizabeth Leather Bags
CASE BOX - Medical apparatus - Ralph E. Jordan
CASE CALIBER - Knives–pocket - Case Acquisition Corp.
CASE CLASSICS - Knives–pocket - Case Acquisition Corp.
CASE COUNTER - Computer peripheral equipment - Software for Surgeons
CASE IH - Agricultural machinery - Case Corp.
CASE-LINKS - Computer software - CAT Links Inc.
CASE MASTER - Sporting goods - Blount International, Inc. (Sporting Equipment Group)
CASE-MATE - Mushroom spawn - Amycel Inc.
CASE-N-CORD - Cases–eyeglass - Notti, Inc.
CASE #1 - Computer software ☆ - Queue Inc.
CASE #2: THE DISAPPEARING DOLPHIN - Computer software ☆ - Queue Inc.
CASE OF COLORS - Artists' materials - Rose Art Industries, Inc.
CASE SLICK - Lubricants - Blount, Inc.
CASE SLICK - Sporting goods - Blount International, Inc. (Sporting Equipment Group)
CASE-SWAYNE - Vegetables–canned - Case-Swayne Co. Inc.
CASE TECHNOLOGY, INC. - Computer peripheral equipment - Case Technology, Inc.
CASE-TEK - Carrying cases - Jameslee Corp.
CASE THE MUSIC - Musical instrument accessories - Duro Finishing Corp.
CASE XX - Cutlery - W.R. Case & Sons Cutlery Co.
CASEBINDERS - File folders - Smead Manufacturing Co.
CASEBOOKS OF ACE HARDING, THE - Computer software - VNM Inc.
CASEC - Pharmaceutical preparations - Bristol-Myers Squibb Co.
CASECRAFT - Eyeglasses - Casecraft, Inc.
CASECRAFT - Leather goods - Casecraft Inc.
CASECRAFT - Luggage - Case Products, Inc.
CASED GLASS - Glass products - Pilgrim Glass Corp.
CASE*EXCHANGE - Computer software - Oracle Corp.
CASEGUARD - Alarm systems - System Innovations, Inc.
CASEINE - Pharmaceutical preparations - Spectrum Chemical Manufacturing Corp.
CASELITE - Lighting equipment - Acme-Lite Manufacturing Co.
CASEM - Sporting goods - Hocks Laboratories
CASEMAKER - Computer software - Casemaker, Inc.
CASEMAKER REW - Computer software - Casemaker, Inc.
CASEMAKER SCB - Computer software - Casemaker, Inc.
CASEMAKER SDW - Computer software - Casemaker, Inc.
CASEMASTER - Computer software - Gemini Systems, Inc.
CASEMASTER - Darts and dart games - Great Lakes Dart Distributors, Inc.
CASEMASTER - Windows–storm - Marvin Windows and Doors
CASEMATE - Controls–heating systems - Surface Combustion, Inc.
CASEMENT - Air conditioning equipment - Friedrich Air Conditioning Co.
CASENOTE - Publisher's imprints - Casenotes Publishing Co., Inc.
CASERA - Food products - La Paloma Foods
CASERA - Fruit drinks–bottled or canned - Campbell Soup Co.
CASERA - Meat products–canned - Caserita Enterprises Inc.
CASERA - Processed beans and peas - Casera Foods, Inc.
CASERO - Cheese - Marquez Brothers Mexican Imports, Inc.
CASERTA - Meat products–beef - Armour Swift-Eckrich
CASES THAT GO PLACES - Office supplies - Faber-Castell Corp.
CASESCRIPT - Computer software - Asset, Inc.
CASESERV - Computer software - Trego Systems
CASETRAK - Computer software - Carstensen Co.
CASETTA PIEMONTESE - Wines ☆ - Bercut-Vandervoort & Co.
CASEWATCH - Computer software - ACMS, Inc.
CASEWORKS - Attache cases - Caseworks of Chicago Inc.
CASEY - Nuts–salted, roasted, cooked, or canned - Casey's Food & Nut Processors
CASEY - Pitching machine - Grand Slam USA
CASEY - Tableware–china ☆ - Lenox, Inc.
CASEY - Tape recorders ☆ - Playskool, Inc.
CASEY - Toys–stuffed - Lisa Frank, Inc.
CASEY - Toys–stuffed ☆ - Gund, Inc.
CASEY & MAX - Apparel–women's - Oak Hill Sportswear Corp.
CASEY AND ME - Audio equipment ☆ - Playskool, Inc.
CASEY BIG LEAGUER - Pitching machine - Grand Slam USA
CASEY BROWN - Shoes - JBI, Inc.
CASEY JONES - Playground equipment - Hedstrom Corp.
CASEY JONES - Toys–electronic ☆ - Tyco Toys

☆ = Now out of production

CASEY QUINN - Apparel–children's - Carole Hochman Designs Inc.
CASEY'S CUFFS - Children's apparel - Rompco
CASEY'S FLOWER - Dinnerware ☆ - Corning Inc.
CASH - Computer software - Cornell Research Foundation, Inc.
C.A.S.H. - Machinery - Bradbury Co. Inc.
CASH - Recording label - Musimex Inc.
CASH ACCESS ATM - Banks–commercial - Cash Access, Inc.
CASH ACME - Valves–industrial - Imi Cash Valve, Inc.
CASH & STARS - Broadcasting stations–radio - Faircom Flint Inc.
CASH EXPRESS - Cash registers - Computer Sports Systems
CASH FLITE - Balls–golf - Pro Glow Sports Inc.
CASH FLOW MAXIMIZER - Computer software - Private Business, Inc.
CASH HATCHERY - Novelty items - Nest Egg Construction Co. Inc.
CASH MASTER - Electronic equipment - Village Car Wash, Inc.
CASH MINDER - Paper - Frischkorn Systems, Inc.
CASH 'N CARRY - Computer software - CAP Automation
CASH ROUTE - Banks–commercial - Ziegler Thrift Trading, Inc.
CASH-TO-CLOSE - Computer software - Cash to Close Corp.
CASH TORNADO - Games - Universal Manufacturing Co., Inc.
CASHAY - Trailers–travel ☆ - Carriage, Inc.
CASHBACK - Computer software - Massachusetts Co. Inc.
CASHCAN - Recycling machines - Cashcan, Inc.
CASHCO - Valves–industrial - Cashco Inc.
CASHE - Computer software - Business Matters Inc.
CASHE BARK - Candy - Cultural Survival, Inc.
CASHEL - Earthenware ☆ - Waterford Wedgewood USA, Inc.
CASHELL - Yarn ☆ - Coats and Clark Inc.
CASHELLE - Apparel–women's - Novelle Industries Inc.
CASHELLE - Floor coverings–carpet and rugs - Atlas Carpet Mills Inc.
CASHEW CARAMEL TORTOISES - Candy - Cultural Survival, Inc.
CASHEW CHEW - Food products - Honeypot Treats
CASHEW TORTOISE - Candy - Bari & Gail
CASHGARD - Safes - Diebold Inc.
CASHIER - Leather goods - St. Thomas Inc.
CASHMELLE - Hats - Aris Isotoner Inc.
CASHMELOUR - Underwear and nightwear - Henson-Kickernick Inc.
CASHMERE - Bedding–linen - Dan River Inc.
CASHMERE - Ceiling panels - Celotex Corp.
CASHMERE - Furniture–wood - Century Furniture Co.
CASHMERE - House furnishings ☆ - Lexington Furniture Industries, Inc.
CASHMERE - Wallpaper ☆ - Pickhardt & Siebert USA Inc.
CASHMERE BLUE - Cosmetics - Lancome
CASHMERE BOUQUET - Soap ☆ - Colgate-Palmolive Co.
CASHMERE CASHMERE - Apparel and accessories - Ballantyne Cashmere USA Inc.
CASHMERE COLLECTOR, THE - Cashmere apparel - Jeanne P. Atkinson
CASHMERE COLORS - Cosmetics ☆ - Noxell Corp.
CASHMERE CONCEPTS - Apparel and accessories - USA Peninsula, Inc.
CASHMERE PLUSH - Scarves - Charles S. Gelles & Son
CASHMERE SWISS - Yarn ☆ - Joseph Galler Inc.
CASHMERELLE - Sweaters - Nygard, Inc.
CASHMERIT - Crocheted and knitted items - Goulder Co. Inc.
CASHMINK - Scarves, neckwear - V. Fraas USA, Inc.
CASHMIST - Sweaters - Puritan Sportswear Corp.
CASHNEAR - Scarves, neckwear - Calzeat & Co. Ltd.
$CASHNET$ - Computer software - New Gaming Systems
CASHOP - Computer software - Aureus Corp.
CASH'S - Labels–fabric - Brett-Forer Greetings Inc.
CASHSAVER - Toilets–portable - Water Control International Inc.
CASHTRACKER - Computer software - Meridian Associates, Inc.
CASHTRAX - Computer software - Aulabaugh Consulting Group, Inc.
CASI - Computer storage devices - Computer Aided Systems, Inc.
CASIE RESIE - Adhesives - National Casein Sales
CASIE SWINGER - Sportswear - Casimir A. Swinger
CASILLA - Floor coverings–tile - Kentile Floors Inc.
CASIM - Computer software and hardware - Seer Technologies Inc.
CASIMIR - Glassware–household - Houston Art Glass Enterprises Inc.
CASINA - Floor coverings - Mannington Resilient Floors
CASINA ROSA - Sausages - Capitol Wholesale Meats
CASINO - Cigars ☆ - Avanti Cigar Co.
CASINO - Colognes - Brandy Harvest
CASINO - Floor coverings - Congoleum Corp.
CASINO - Floor coverings–carpet and rugs ☆ - Galaxy Carpet Mills Inc.
CASINO - Floor coverings–carpet and rugs ☆ - Len Dal Carpets
CASINO - Frames–eyeglass ☆ - Universal/Univis Inc.
CASINO - Games ☆ - Milton Bradley Co.

CASINO - Glassware–household - Owens-Illinois Inc. (Libbey Div.)
CASINO - Motor vehicles–motor homes ☆ - Beaver Coaches Inc.
CASINO - Pipes–tobacco ☆ - S.M. Frank & Co. Inc. (Kaywoodie-Yello-Bole-Medico)
CASINO II - Yarn - Henry's Attic
CASINO 21 - Computer software - Recreational Mathemagical Software
CASINO BLACKJACK - Computer software - Manhattan Software
CASINO CANDY - Candy - Mardi Gras Candies, Inc.
CASINO CAT - Boats - Rodney E. Lay Associates, Inc.
CASINO CHEF - Food products - Cohen's Famous Frozen Foods
CASINO CLASSICS - Computer software ☆ - DataPak Software Inc.
CASINO COLLECTION - Computer software - Capstone Software
CASINO COLLECTION - Greeting cards - Leanin' Tree Inc.
CASINO CRAPS - Computer software - Manhattan Software
CASINO DE FRANCE - Coffee - Casino North America
CASINO GEMS - Jewelry - Silver Fetish Co.
CASINO GRANDE - Games - Universal Manufacturing Co., Inc.
CASINO KENO - Game machines - International Technical Systems, Inc.
CASINO MANIA - Games - Brown and Bigelow Inc.
CASINO NIGHT - Game machines - IGT - North America
CASINO PERKS - Games - The Learning Experience Inc.
CASINO POKER - Computer software - Robert L. Nicolai
CASINO PRODUCTS - Game machines - Casino Products
CASINO ROYALE - Floor coverings - Mannington Resilient Floors
CASINO ROYALE - Floor coverings–carpet and rugs - Lees Carpets
CASINO ROYALE - Games - The Learning Experience Inc.
CASINO SLOT MACHINE - Toys–electronic ☆ - Philips Consumer Electronics Co.
CASINO VEGAS - Games ☆ - Western Publishing Co., Inc.
CASINO WAR - Games - Bet Technology, Inc.
CASINO YAHTZEE - Games ☆ - Milton Bradley Co.
CASINOLAND - Computer software - Imagination Network, Inc.
CASINOS OF THE WORLD - Computer software ☆ - Capstone Software
CASIO - Watches - Casio, Inc.
CASION COLLECTION - Floor coverings - Beaulieu of America, Inc.
CASIOTRON - Watches - Casio, Inc.
CASITA - Windows–screen ☆ - Care-Free Windows
CASITE - Automotive parts and accessories - Hastings Manufacturing Co.
CASITE BRAND - Fuel additives - Hastings Manufacturing Co.
CASK - Wines ☆ - Warner Vineyards Inc.
CASK 23 - Wines - Stag's Leap Wine Cellars
CASK GREAT LAKES - Wine coolers ☆ - Warner Vineyards Inc.
CASMA - Colognes - Caswell-Massey Co. Ltd.
CASORON - Herbicides - Uniroyal Chemical Co. Inc. (Crop Protection Div.)
CASPARI - Greeting cards - H. George Caspari Inc.
CASPECO - Cameras ☆ - Edixa Camera Co.
CASPER - Lunch boxes - Thermos Co.
CASPER - Seafood ☆ - Winter Harbor Fisheries
CASPER - Shirts - Harvey Comics Entertainment, Inc.
CASPER - Socks - High Point Knitting Inc.
CASPER - Toys - Tyco Industries, Inc.
CASPER THE FRIENDLY GHOST - Games - Tyco Toys
CASPER THE GHOST - Pet products - Precious Paws
CASPER XL - Trailers–travel ☆ - Coachmen Industries, Inc.
CASPIA - Wallpaper ☆ - Sandpiper Studios
CASPIAN - Bathtubs–enameled - Briggs Plumbing Products, Inc.
CASPIAN - Boats–motor - Forester Boats Inc.
CASPIAN - Firearms, accessories, and parts - Caspian Arms, Ltd.
CASPIAN - Floor coverings–carpet and rugs - Trans-Ocean Import Co. Inc.
CASPIAN - Furniture ☆ - Athens Furniture Industries Inc.
CASPIAN COLLECTION, THE - Wallpaper - Warner Co.
CASS - Audio equipment - Cass
CASS - Computer software - Cass Information Systems, Inc.
CASS-CLAY - Milk - Cass-Clay Creamery Inc.
CASSALLENI COLLI ALBANI - Wines - M.S. Walker Inc./Seacoast
CASSANDRA - Floor coverings–carpet and rugs ☆ - Walter Carpet Mills
CASSANDRA - Gas heaters - American Road Equipment Co.
CASSANDRA - Giftware - Anne Klein & Co.
CASSANDRA - Wigs - Helene Curtis Industries Inc.
CASSANDRA EDITIONS - Publisher's imprints - Academy Publications Ltd.
CASSANDRA STONE - Gowns - Creative Imports
CASSARO - Floor coverings–carpet and rugs - Evans-Black Carpet Mills
CASSARON - Lenses–photographic ☆ - Edixa Camera Co.
CASSCO - Ice - Cassco Ice and Cold Storage Inc.
CASSEIVER - Audio equipment - Emerson Radio Corp.
CASSEL - Fabrics - Greenwood Mills Inc.

CASSELBERRY - Flatware - Pfaltzgraff Investment Co.
CASSELL - Publisher's imprints - MacMillan Publishing Co. Inc.
CASSERETTE - Cookware, servingware - Corning Inc.
CASSEROLE - Vegetables–canned - Haney Seed/Bean Growers
CASSETTE - Fishing-reel spools - STH Reels USA Inc.
CASSETTE - Pencils–mechanical - Empire Berol USA
CASSETTE BOY - Cassette players - Nintendo of America Inc.
CASSETTE CRACKER - Sporting goods - Pamir Engineering
CASSETTE FINDER - Containers–metal - S.A. Richards, Inc.
CASSETTE 'N GAME - Electronics equipment - Innovative Concepts Inc.
CASSETTECORDER - Tape recorders–cassette ☆ - Marantz Co.
CASSETTER - Electronic equipment - Hamilton Electronics Corp.
CASSETTES - Ceiling panels - Armstrong World Industries, Inc.
CASSI - Window coverings ☆ - Vertical Blind Factory
CASSIA - Rings–jewelry - Artcarved Inc.
CASSIA DAINTIES - Candy ☆ - Just Born Inc.
CASSIDY - Apparel and accessories - Limited Inc.
CASSIDY - Cosmetics ☆ - Cassidy Inc.
CASSIDY - Machinery - Pacific Steamex Cleaning System Inc.
CASSIDY SPIRALS - Cosmetics ☆ - Cassidy Inc.
CASSIE - Apparel–children's - Cassie Cotillion Inc.
CASSIE - Dolls ☆ - Effanbee Doll Corp.
CASSIE CALICO CAT - Toys–stuffed - Dakin Inc.
CASSIE'S COLLECTION - Bedding–linen ☆ - Noel Joanna, Inc.
CASSIN - Sporting goods ☆ - Climb High Inc.
CASSINA - Furniture - Cassina, USA Inc.
CASSINO - Grocery stores - Joseph Fragola Inc.
CASSINO - Handwork supplies - Bernat Yarn & Craft Corp.
CASSINO - Tomato pastes and sauces - Salvati Foods, Inc.
CASSINO - Vinegar - Keller Food Products Co.
CASSIOPEIA E-11 PALM-SIZE PC - Computers - Casio, Inc.
CASSIS - Lubricating oils ☆ - Shell Oil Co.
CASSOULETS USA - Food products - Zursun Ltd.
CAST-ADE - Health care products - Halsey Drug Co. Inc.
CAST & CRAFT - Hobby kits ☆ - Deep Flex Plastic Molds Inc.
CAST & CREW - Apparel and accessories - Cast & Crew Clothing
CAST-CLIP - Veterinary medical equipment - K-Vet, Inc.
CAST COAT - Paints - Krylon/Dupli-Color
CAST CRAFT - Sporting goods - Cast Craft
CAST IRON - Thread ☆ - American & Efird, Inc.
CAST IRON SERIES - Pharmaceutical preparations - Charm-Tex, Inc.
CAST OFF - Cleaning preparations–carpet and rug - W.W. Grainger, Inc.
CAST-OFF - Skin care products - Travaco Laboratories Inc.
CAST PLUS - Cooking utensils–cast iron ☆ - Regal Ware, Inc.
CAST-RITE - Cooking utensils–cast iron - Jacksonville Manufacturing
CAST SHUS - Footwear - Mike Mennies & Son Inc.
CASTA CARBONOFF - Cleaning preparations - Castoleum Corp.
CASTA FILM - Oils–lubricating - Castoleum Corp.
CASTA LUBE - Fuel additives - Castoleum Corp.
CASTA LUBE D - Fuel additives - Castoleum Corp.
CASTADERM - Skin care products - Lannett Co. Inc.
CASTAGNA - Figurines - Jack Lucchesi
CASTAGNARI - Accordions - Castiglione Accordion
CASTALIA'S - Music–sheet - Castalia Publications
CASTANA - Sporting goods - Boone Bait Co. Inc.
CASTAND - Musical-instrument cases, music stands ☆ - D'Andrea Manufacturing Co. Inc.
CASTANET - Floor coverings - Mannington Resilient Floors
CASTAREDE ARMAGNACS - Brandy - Shaw-Ross International Importers
CASTASPELLA - Toys - Mattel, Inc.
CASTAWAY - Boats–motor - Lyn-Craft Boat Co.
CASTAWAY - Fishing tackle - South Bend Sporting Goods Inc.
CASTAWAY - Orthodontic equipment - United States Manufacturing Co.
CASTAWAY - Shoes - Daniel Green Co.
CASTAWAY - Wastebaskets ☆ - Witt Co.
CASTAWAY GRAPHITE RODS - Apparel and accessories - Castaway Fishing Products Inc.
CASTAWAY SOFTWARE - Computer software - Puuoa Software Development of Hawaii, Inc.
CASTAWAYS - Apparel and accessories - Workwear Corp. Inc.
CASTAWAYS - Candy and gum - Philadelphia Chewing Gum Corp.
CASTAWAY'S DILEMMA - Computer software - Southwest Edpsych Services Inc.
CASTCAL - Decals and transfers - CastCal
CASTCRAFT - Computer software - Transfertech Inc.
CASTEC - Window shades - Castec Window Shading Inc.

CASTEEL - Shelving units–metal - Clairson International Corp.
CASTEL - Glassware–household - Durand International
CASTEL LIMOGES - Dishes–china - Decora Imports Inc.
CASTEL MINUS - Skin care products - Syosset Laboratories Inc.
CASTEL-PLUS - Skin care products - Syosset Laboratories Inc.
CASTELAIN BLOND BIERE DE GARDE - Beverages–malt - Vanberg & Dewulf
CASTELAINE - Floor coverings–carpet and rugs - Alexander Smith Carpets
CASTELETS - Cookies - Stella D'Oro Biscuit Co. Inc.
CASTELL - Office supplies - Faber-Castell Corp.
CASTELLANA - Pasta - Gourmet America
CASTELLANI - Wines ☆ - European Beverage Co., Inc.
CASTELLANI FORMULA - Pharmaceutical preparations ☆ - Gordon Laboratories
CASTELLANI PAINT - Pharmaceutical preparations - Pedinol Pharmacal Inc.
CASTELLBLANCH - Wines ☆ - Freixenet USA
CASTELLE - Toilets–enameled - Kohler Co.
CASTELLI - Accordions - Fred Gretsch Enterprises
CASTELLINA - Olive oil - Brinker Restaurant Corp.
CASTELLINA EXTRA VIRGIN OLIVE OIL FIRSTGOLD PRESSED NATURALLY CHOLESTEROL FREE P - Olive oil - Brinker Restaurant Corp.
CASTELLINA OLIO EXTRA VERGINE DI OLIVA - Olive oil - Brinker Restaurant Corp.
CASTELLINO - Vegetables–canned - De Choix Specialty Foods Co.
CASTELLO - Dishes–china - Pasmantier Co.
CASTELLO - Tiles–ceramic - American Marazzi Tile, Inc.
CASTELLO - Wallcoverings - Worldwalls International Inc.
CASTELLO - Wines ☆ - European Beverage Co., Inc.
CASTELLO DEI RAMPOLA - Wines ☆ - Diamond Wine Merchants
CASTELLO DEL POGGIO - Wines - Francis A. Bonanno, Inc.
CASTELLO DI GABBIANO - Wines ☆ - Prestige Wine Imports Corp.
CASTELLO DI NEIVE - Wines - William Grant & Sons, Inc.
CASTELLO DI QUERCETO - Wines - Prestige Wine Imports Corp.
CASTELLO DI TASSAROLO - Wines - Paterno Imports, Ltd.
CASTELLO DI VERRAZZANO CHIANTI CLASSICO - Wines - Palm Bay Imports, Inc.
CASTELLO DI VOLPAIA - Wines - William Grant & Sons, Inc.
CASTELLO DI VOLPAIA - Wines ☆ - Diamond Wine Merchants
CASTELLO LEONE - Wines - Chateau De Leu Winery
CASTELLON - Floor coverings - Mannington Resilient Floors
CASTELLON - Tableware–china - Villeroy and Boch Tableware Ltd.
CASTELVANIA: THE BLOODLETTING - Computer storage devices–optical - Konami (America) Inc.
CASTER - Cigarettes ☆ - Japan Tobacco Inc.
CASTER MILD - Cigarettes - Japan Tobacco Inc.
CASTER PULLER - Office supplies - Master Caster Co.
CASTERJET - Nozzles - Spraying Systems Co.
CASTIGLIA - Sporting goods - Casco USA
CASTIGLIONE - Accordions - Castiglione Accordion
CASTILE - Dishes–earthenware ☆ - Denby USA Limited
CASTILE - Floor coverings–carpet and rugs ☆ - Eurotex Inc.
CASTILE - Jewelry ☆ - Hirsch Speidel Inc.
CASTILIAN - Rings–jewelry - Artcarved Inc.
CASTILLA - Glassware–household ☆ - Oneida Ltd.
CASTILLA - Guitars - Kaman Music Corp.
CASTILLA - Seafood products–canned or cured - Ludwig Shrimp Co.
CASTILLE - Floor coverings ☆ - Congoleum Corp.
CASTILLE - Floor coverings–carpet and rugs - Atlas Carpet Mills Inc.
CASTILLE - Floor coverings–carpet and rugs ☆ - Kelly Group Inc.
CASTILLE - Floor coverings–carpet and rugs ☆ - Mohawk Industries Inc.
CASTILLE COLLECTION - Plumbing fixtures–metal - Woodmark International, Inc.
CASTILLIAN - Cleaning preparations - W.W. Grainger, Inc.
CASTILLIAN COCOA - Beverages–carbonated - Castillian Cocoa
CASTILLIAN IV - Furniture ☆ - Lea Industries Inc.
CASTILLO - Floor coverings - Mannington Resilient Floors
CASTILLO - Rum - Bacardi Imports Inc.
CASTILLO DE JIJONA - Candy - La Cibeles Inc.
CASTILLO DE MOLINA - Wines - Shaw-Ross International Importers
CASTILLO DE PERELADA - Beverages–alcohol - World Shippers & Importers
CASTILLO INTERNATIONAL - Recording label - Castillo International Inc.
CASTILLO PERLADA - Wines - Admiral Wine Merchants
CASTIN - Video production - Castin Enterprises
CASTIN' CRAFT - Publisher's imprints - Environmental Technology, Inc.
CASTING - Fabrics - Gretchen Bellinger Inc.
CASTING - Hair coloring preparations - Cosmair Inc.

CASTING - Magazines - Pierre Jolys' French Imports
CASTING KING - Fishing lures - Hofmanns Lures
CASTIONI - Handbags ☆ - Gilt Import Co. Inc.
CASTIPLAST - Resins–epoxy - National Engineering Products, Inc.
CASTKLEEN - Filters–oil - Baker Hughes Inc.
CASTLE - Bakery products - National Baking Div.
CASTLE - Bedding–linen - Whiting Manufacturing Co. Inc.
CASTLE - Cooking equipment–commercial - Comstock Castle Stove Co.
CASTLE - Greeting cards - Regency Thermographers Inc.
CASTLE - Infant product - Dundee Mills, Inc.
CASTLE - Office supplies - Boorum & Pease Co.
CASTLE - Recording label - All Star Promotions
CASTLE - Siding–insulating ☆ - Champion International Corp.
CASTLE ART - Glassware–household - Neuwirth Co.
CASTLE BAGS - Bags–trash - Prince Castle Inc.
CASTLE BAY - Golfing equipment - Sinclair & Rush, Inc.
CASTLE BIN - Wastebaskets - Prince Castle Inc.
CASTLE BRIDGE - Floor coverings–carpet and rugs - Mohawk Carpet Corp.
CASTLE CAY - Furniture - Homecrest Industries Inc.
CASTLE CHAIR REBAR SUPPORTS - Plastics - Aztec Concrete Accessories, Inc.
CASTLE CLIMBER - Toys - Rainbow Play Systems, Inc.
CASTLE COMMUNICATIONS - Recording label - Fiesta Record Co. Inc.
CASTLE COURT - Floor coverings–carpet and rugs ☆ - Criterion Mills Inc.
CASTLE COVE - Floor coverings–carpet and rugs - Downs Carpet Co. Inc.
CASTLE CREEK - Wines - Price Co.
CASTLE CUT - Glassware–household - Neuwirth Co.
CASTLE DELITES - Wafers, cookies, cream puffs - Inorex Inc.
CASTLE GARDEN - Dolls ☆ - Effanbee Doll Corp.
CASTLE GARDEN - Floor coverings–carpet and rugs - Monticello Carpet Mills
CASTLE GARDEN - Glassware–household ☆ - Lenox Crystal, Inc.
CASTLE GARDEN - Tableware–china ☆ - Lenox, Inc.
CASTLE GATE - Floor coverings–carpet and rugs - Mohawk Carpet Corp.
CASTLE GATE - Floor coverings–carpet and rugs ☆ - Playfield International Inc.
CASTLE GRAND - Wines ☆ - Weibel Vineyards
CASTLE GRAYSKULL - Toys - Mattel, Inc.
CASTLE HARBOR - Floor coverings ☆ - Congoleum Corp.
CASTLE HARBOR - Floor coverings–carpet and rugs - Galaxy Carpet Mills Inc.
CASTLE HARBOR - Floor coverings–carpet and rugs ☆ - Catalina Carpet Mills Inc.
CASTLE HARBOUR - Furniture ☆ - Tropitone Furniture Co. Inc.
CASTLE HILL - Flatware - Towle Manufacturing Co.
CASTLE HILL - Flatware ☆ - Gorham Inc.
CASTLE INC. - Machinery - Castle Tool Machinery, Inc.
CASTLE INFINITY - Computer peripheral equipment - Starwave Corp.
CASTLE INTERNATIONAL - Alcoholic beverages - Inorex Inc.
CASTLE JEWELS - Jewelry - Norman T. Kanel Corp.
CASTLE KENO - Hotels and motels - Trump Castle Associates
CASTLE KIDS - Apparel–children's - New Castle Corp.
CASTLE KINGDOM - Toys - Discovery Toys, Inc.
CASTLE LODGE - Floor coverings–carpet and rugs - Gulistan Carpet Inc.
CASTLE MOTORCYCLES - Motorcycle parts and accessories - Castle Motorcycles Manufacturing, Inc.
CASTLE MURANO - Glassware–household - Neuwirth Co.
CASTLE OF DR. BRAIN - Computer software - Sierra On-Line, Inc.
CASTLE OF DRAGON - Electronic game - SETA USA Inc.
CASTLE OF FLAGS - Flags - Flags International Inc.
CASTLE OF GOLD - Deodorizers - NHS, Inc.
CASTLE ORANGE - Marmalade - H. Hamstra & Co.
CASTLE-PAK - Glassware–household - Federal Glass
CASTLE PEAK - Luggage - C.P.H. (U.S.) Corp.
CASTLE PINES CHAMPIONSHIP COURSE - Computer software ☆ - Access Software Inc.
CASTLE PLAY BLOCKS - Toys - Tomy America, Inc.
CASTLE PUFFS - Cream puffs - Inorex Inc.
CASTLE RIDGE - Siding–insulating - Georgia-Pacific Corp.
CASTLE RISK - Toys - Tonka Corp.
CASTLE ROCK - Floor coverings - Mannington Resilient Floors
CASTLE ROCK - Floor coverings–carpet and rugs - Queen Carpet Corp.
CASTLE ROCK - Mattresses - Ohio Mattress Co.
CASTLE ROCK ORCHIDS - Flowers, plants, and seeds - Castle Rock Orchids, Ltd.
CASTLE SKYE - Whiskey - Joseph E. Seagram & Sons, Inc.
CASTLE SUPER BLOCKS - Toys - Tyco Toys

CASTLE TOWER - Floor coverings–carpet and rugs - Mohawk Carpet Corp.
CASTLE VILLAGE - Food products ☆ - Liberty Richter Inc.
CASTLE VILLAGE - Pickles - Castle Food Products
CASTLE WISHSTAR - Dolls - Tonka Corp.
CASTLE WOLFENSTEIN - Computer software - Muse Software
CASTLEBERRY - Meat products–beef - Castleberry's Food Co.
CASTLEBERRY KNITS LTD. - Apparel and accessories - Leslie Fay Companies Inc.
CASTLEBORG - Cheese - Steuben Foods Inc.
CASTLEBRIDGE - Furniture ☆ - Bassett Furniture Industries, Inc.
CASTLEBROOK - Floor coverings–carpet and rugs - Gulistan Carpet Inc.
CASTLEBURY - Chessboards ☆ - Fort USA
CASTLEBURY'S - Yogurt - Quality Food Centers, Inc.
CASTLEFIELD - Dishes–china ☆ - Gorham Inc.
CASTLEGATE - Doors–metal - Castlegate Industries
CASTLEGATE - Furniture–wood ☆ - Century Furniture Co.
CASTLEMAINE XXXX - Beverages–malt - Adolph Coors Co.
CASTLEROC - Wallcovering ☆ - Parex, Inc.
CASTLES OF IRELAND - Christmas tree ornaments - Cracker Box Inc.
CASTLES OF SPAIN - Toys - F.A.O. Schwarz
CASTLETON - Cabinets ☆ - Decora
CASTLETON - Floor coverings ☆ - Congoleum Corp.
CASTLETON - Floor coverings–carpet and rugs - Collins & Aikman Corp.
CASTLETON - Wallpaper - Norwall Wallcoverings
CASTLETON COLLECTION, THE - Coffee - Jamaica Coffee Traders
CASTLETOWN - Earthenware ☆ - Waterford Wedgewood USA, Inc.
CASTLEVANIA BLOODLINES - Computer software ☆ - Konami (America) Inc.
CASTLEVANIA DRACULA X - Computer software - Konami (America) Inc.
CASTLEVEIL - Fabrics - Newcastle Fabrics Corp.
CASTLEVIEW - Wines - European Beverage Co., Inc.
CASTLEWOOD - Cabinets - H.J. Scheirich Co.
CASTLOC - Hitches–trailer - Amsted Industries Inc.
CASTMATE - Bandages–orthopedic - Kayser-Roth Corp.
CASTMATE - Chemical preparations - Dow Corning Corp.
CASTOCKINGS - Cast coverings - Castockings, Inc.
CASTOFLEX - Hobby kits - Castolite Inc.
CASTOGLAS - Hobby kits - Castolite Inc.
CASTOLITE - Hobby kits - Castolite Inc.
CASTOMOLD - Hobby kits - Castolite Inc.
CASTONE - Resins–epoxy - Deep Flex Plastic Molds Inc.
CASTOR - Motors–air - Thiokol Corp.
CASTOR 120 - Motors–air - Thiokol Corp.
CASTRO - Furniture–wood - Castro Convertibles
CASTRO CONVERTIBLES - Furniture–wood - Castro Convertibles
CASTRO-MATIC - Recliners - Castro Convertibles
CASTRO-PEDIC - Mattresses - Castro Convertibles
CASTROL - Oils–lubricating - Castrol Heavy Duty Lubricants Inc.
CASTROL - Oils–lubricating - Castrol, Inc.
CASTROL MULTI-GRADE - Oils–lubricating - Castrol, Inc.
CASTROL SUPER CLEAN - Cleaning preparations - Castrol, Inc.
CASTWARE - Cooking equipment–household - Jacksonville Manufacturing
CASTWOOD - Wood products ☆ - Smurfit Newsprint Corp. (Cladwood Div.)
CASUAL - Cups–paper - Sweetheart Plastics Inc.
CASUAL - Furniture - Keller Scroll/Casual
CASUAL - Garters - Custom Designs
CASUAL - Glassware–household - Canton Glass Co.
CASUAL - Greeting cards - Gibson Greetings, Inc.
CASUAL - Musical instrument accessories - Humes & Berg Manufacturing Co. Inc.
CASUAL - Perfumes - Paul Sebastian, Inc.
CASUAL - Pottery products - Western Stoneware
CASUAL ACCENTS - Floor coverings–carpet and rugs - Evans-Black Carpet Mills
CASUAL ATTITUDES - Apparel–athletic - Van Leunens, Inc.
CASUAL BLUES - Apparel–children's - Robin International (USA), Inc.
CASUAL BOTTOMS - Apparel–men's - Perry Lewis Ltd.
CASUAL BROWN - Housewares ☆ - Scio Pottery Co.
CASUAL CARE - Tablecloths and placemats - Decor Home Fashions, Inc.
CASUAL CERAM - Tableware–china ☆ - Lipper International Inc.
CASUAL CLASSICS - Apparel–men's - May Department Stores Co.
CASUAL CLASSICS - Floor coverings–carpet and rugs ☆ - Callaway Carpets
CASUAL CLEAN - Cleaning preparations - Patio Products, Inc.
CASUAL COMFORT - Footwear - Washington Shoe Co.
CASUAL COOL FASHIONS - Dolls - Mattel, Inc.
CASUAL CORNER - Apparel–women's - United States Shoe Corp.

☆ = Now out of production

CASUAL CRUISERS - Apparel and accessories - Diversified Fashion Group, Inc.

CASUAL CRUISERS - Apparel and accessories - Hay J, Inc.

CASUAL DAY - Apparel and accessories - Russell Specialties

CASUAL DECOR - Floor coverings—carpet and rugs ☆ - World Carpets, Inc.

CASUAL DELIGHT - Floor coverings—carpet and rugs ☆ - Whitecrest Carpet Mills

CASUAL ELEGANCE - Dinnerware—glass - Lenox, Inc.

CASUAL ELEGANCE - Floor coverings—carpet and rugs ☆ - Downs Carpet Co. Inc.

CASUAL ELEGANCE - Furniture - Alexvale Furniture, Inc.

CASUAL ELEGANCE - Furniture ☆ - Vaughan Furniture Co. Inc.

CASUAL ELEGANCE - Wallpaper - Wallcoverings Unlimited Inc.

CASUAL EVOLUTION - Apparel—men's ☆ - Randa Corp.

CASUAL FELT - Hats - GWB, Inc.

CASUAL FINE PARFUM - Perfumes - Paul Sebastian, Inc.

CASUAL FLAIR - Floor coverings—carpet and rugs ☆ - Karastan-Bigelow Inc.

CASUAL FOR MEN - Perfumes - Paul Sebastian, Inc.

CASUAL FRIDAY - Footwear - Univshoe Inc.

CASUAL IMAGES BY LENOX - Dinnerware - Lenox, Inc.

CASUAL KITCHEN & BATH - Wallcovering - Colortree Designs

CASUAL LIVING - Dinnerware - Gibson Overseas Inc.

CASUAL LIVING - Floor coverings—carpet and rugs ☆ - Gulistan Carpet Inc.

CASUAL MISS - Handbags - Regal Bag Corp.

CASUAL MOOD - Floor coverings—carpet and rugs - Philadelphia Carpets

CASUAL NEWS BY RONNIE - Apparel and accessories - House of Ronnie, Inc.

CASUAL RADIANCE - Apparel—athletic - Zillions Industrial Inc.

CASUAL SCENE - Floor coverings—carpet and rugs ☆ - Lees Carpets

CASUAL SHOPPE - Furniture - Universal Flooring

CASUAL SOLUTIONS - Apparel—women's - Warnaco Inc.

CASUAL SOPHISTICATES - Dinnerware—glass ☆ - Nikko Ceramics Inc.

CASUAL SPLENDOR - Floor coverings—carpet and rugs ☆ - Playfield International Inc.

CASUAL STUDIO - Apparel—women's - International Cotton Inc.

CASUAL TOUCH - Floor coverings—carpet and rugs ☆ - Blue Ridge Carpet Mills

CASUAL-WALKERS - Shoes - Titleist & Foot-Joy Worldwide

CASUALAIRE - Fabrics—broadcloth - Ely and Walker Co.

CASUALAIRE L'ESPRIT DE VIE - Apparel and accessories - Casualaire Sportswear, Inc.

CASUALAIRE, THE - Shoes - Bernie Mev Shoes Inc.

CASUALE - Floor coverings—carpet and rugs ☆ - Galaxy Carpet Mills Inc.

CASUALES - Socks ☆ - Sara Lee Corp.

CASUALETS - Shoes - Edison Brothers Stores, Inc.

CASUALON - Knitting machines - Peter Freund Knitting Mills

CASUALS - Paper—tissue - Kimberly-Clark Corp.

CASUALSTONE - Dishes—earthenware - JMP-Newcor International, Inc.

CASUALWARE - Cooking equipment—household ☆ - Imperial Schrade Corp.

CASUELLA - Furniture—metal - Telescope Casual Furniture Inc.

CASUELLA II - Furniture ☆ - Telescope Casual Furniture Inc.

CASUWOOL - Fabrics—wool - Forstmann and Co. Inc.

CASWELL - Furniture - Boling Co.

CASWELL-MASSEY - Soap - Caswell-Massey Co. Ltd.

CASWELL-MASSEY AMERICA'S OLDEST CHEMISTS AND PERFUMERS ESTABLISHED 1752 - Skin care products - Caswell-Massey Co. Ltd.

CASYLLIUM - Laxatives ☆ - Upjohn Co.

C.A.T. - Alarm systems - Cobra Systems, Inc.

CAT - Computer software - Computer Adaptive Technologies, Inc.

CAT - Footwear - Caterpillar Inc.

CAT - Hair care products - Redken Laboratories, Inc.

C.A.T. - Orthodontic equipment - Lancer Orthodontics, Inc.

CAT - Synthesizers—musical instrument ☆ - Syn-Cordion Musical Instruments Corp.

CAT-A-BALL - Pet products - Doskocil Manufacturing Co., Inc.

CAT-A-LOG - Lighting fixtures ☆ - Prestigeline Inc.

CAT-A-POLE - Pet products - American Cat Emporium

CAT A TRAIL - Pet products - Dogloo Inc.

CAT & MOUSE - Games ☆ - Parker Brothers

CAT & MOUSE - Publisher's imprints - Malibu Comics Entertainment, Inc.

CAT AWAY - Pet products - Farnam Cos. Inc.

CAT BEATS - Pet products ☆ - Petrapport, Inc.

CAT BED, THE - Beds—hospital - Sci-O-Tech Inc.

CAT BEDS - Pet products ☆ - Black Sheep Inc.

CAT CAFE - Cat food - American Pet Food Co.

CAT CAN - Pet products - Shippan Distributors Inc.

CAT CAY - Boats ☆ - Lanness K. McKee & Co.

CAT CAY - Fabrics ☆ - Greenwood Mills Inc.

CAT-CHA-MOUSE - Pet products - P.M. Pet Products

C.A.T. CHAMPIONSHIP ATHLETIC TURF - Floor coverings - Warren's Turf Nursery, Inc.

CAT CHARMER - Pet products - Cat Dancer Products, Inc.

CAT CHOVIES - Pet products - Lone Toy Tree Inc.

CAT CHOW - Pet products - Ralston Purina Co.

CAT CHOW MATURE - Cat food - Ralston Purina Co.

CAT COAT - Finishing agents - Permagile Industries Inc.

CAT CODEPENDENTS - Calendars - Ronnie Sellers Productions

CAT COLLECTORS - Recording label - Jazz Composer's Orchestra Association Inc.

CAT COMPANIONS - Novelty items - Papel Freelance, Inc.

CAT CORCILIUS - Giftware - Reco International Corp.

CAT COUNTRY - Pet products - Mountain Meadows Pet Products, Inc.

CAT CRAFT - Pet products - Cat Craft Co.

CAT DANCER - Pet products - Cat Dancer Products, Inc.

CAT DECO - Pet products - Gerard-Pellham Co.

CAT DOCTOR, THE - Cat food - Pet Products, Inc.

CAT DODGER - Toys ☆ - Tomy America, Inc.

CAT-ERTAINMENT - Video production - A & M Products Inc.

CAT-ETTE - Veterinary medical equipment - Lora Laboratories Inc.

CAT-EYES - Glass products - Vitro Agate Corp.

CAT FANCY - Apparel and accessories - Fancy Publications, Inc.

CAT FISHIN' - Pet products - Migatz & Migatz, Inc.

CAT FISHIN' POLE - Pet products ☆ - Gone to the Dogs

CAT FOREST - Pet products - Petmaster, Inc.

CAT FOUNTAIN - Pet products - Molor Products Co.

CAT FUN - Pet products - Europet Inc.

CAT GRASS PLUS - Agricultural products - Gimborn U.S., Inc.

CAT HABITAT - Pet products - Tree Play Inc.

CAT HOLE - Pet products - James L. Owens

CAT IN THE BAG - Games ☆ - Tyco Toys

CAT KETTLE - Tea kettles—nonelectric ☆ - Metrokane

CAT KNITS - Pet products - Tawn Chi & Associates Inc.

CAT LAX - Veterinary pharmaceutical preparations - Pharmaderm Inc.

CAT LEAGUE - Trading cards and stamps - Louis B. Schneiderman

CAT LIFE - Cat food ☆ - Pet Life Foods Inc.

CAT MAGIC - Pet products - Bentonite Corp.

CAT MAGIC - Pet products - Bluebonnet Milling Co.

CAT MAT - Pet products - Zerick Co.

CAT MATE - Pet products - Ani Mate Co.

CAT MUNCHIES - Cat food ☆ - Menu Foods Inc. Cadillac Foods Div.

CAT-'N-A-SACK - Toys—stuffed ☆ - Bradley Import Co.

CAT 'N KITTEN - Pet products - L/M Animal Farms, Inc.

CAT N MOUSE - Computer software - Mind Play

CAT NIP BLOSSOMS - Pet products ☆ - Pets International, Ltd.

CAT NIPS - Calendars ☆ - American Greetings Corp.

CAT NIPS - Cat food - E.J. Houle Inc.

CAT NIPS - Pet products - Judith Ann McCullough

CAT-O-DONTICS - Pet products - Canine Dental Health

CAT-OFF - Deodorizers - Thornell Corp.

CAT PAN ODORMUTE - Pet products - Ryter Corp.

CAT-PLEX - Vitamins and nutritional supplements - Revere Manufacturing

CAT RACKET TUNNEL - Pet products - Southern California Foam, Inc.

CAT REFLECTORIZED I.D. TAG - Pet products - Molor Products Co.

CAT RESIN - Pet products - Peptide Laboratory

CAT SACK - Pet products - JT Industries

CAT SNAPS - Pet products - Prime Pet Products

CAT SNAX - Pet products - Vo-Toys Inc.

CAT SOCIETY - Toys - Russ Berrie and Co., Inc.

CAT SORB - Pet products - P.M. Pet Products

CAT SPA JR - Cat-scratching pads - Alco Industries, Inc.

CAT STUF - Pet products - American Pet Products Inc.

CAT-SUP - Cat food ☆ - Central Soya Co. Inc.

CAT TAILS - Candy ☆ - Gilliam Candy Co. Inc. (Gilliam Candy Brands)

CAT TAILS - Pet products - American Colloid Co.

CAT TAILS PREMIUM - Pet products - American Colloid Co.

CAT TEASER - Pet products - P.M. Pet Products

CAT TEE PEE - Pet products - Dogloo Inc.

CAT TOYZ - Pet products - Dogloo Inc.

CAT TRACK - Pet products - Doskocil Manufacturing Co., Inc.

CAT TRACKER - Fishing tackle - Junnie's Lounge, Ltd.

CAT TRACKER WORM - Fishing lures - Junnie's Lounge, Ltd.

CAT TRACKS - Boots - Seirus Innovative Accessories, Inc.

☆ = Now out of production

CAT5 - Cables - BB Technologies, Inc.
CATAC - Pet products - Colony Pet Goods
CATACOMBS - Computer software - SourceView Software International
CATACOMBS - Publisher's imprints - Tsr, Inc.
CATALAN COLLECTION - Giftware - Lenox, Inc.
CATALASE - Pharmaceutical preparations - City Chemical Corp.
CATALAST - Lacquers - Rudd Co. Inc.
CATALIN CHECKERS - Games ☆ - Milton Bradley Co.
CATALIN DICE - Games ☆ - Milton Bradley Co.
CATALIN DOMINOES - Games ☆ - Milton Bradley Co.
CATALINA - Bathing suits - Authentic Fitness Corp.
CATALINA - Bathing suits - Catalina
CATALINA - Boats - Catalina Yachts Inc.
CATALINA - Boats–motor - Chris Craft Boats
CATALINA - Boats–motor - Ebbtide Corp.
CATALINA - Boats–motor - Thompson Boat Co.
CATALINA - Boats–motor ☆ - Four Winns Inc.
CATALINA - Boats–pontoons ☆ - Godfrey Marine Co.
CATALINA - Building materials - Texas Aluminum Industries Inc.
CATALINA - Cabinets - Schrock
CATALINA - Cribs–metal - Evenflo Juvenile Furniture Co.
CATALINA - Electronic equipment - Compco Photographic/Goldberg Bros.
CATALINA - Floor coverings - Congoleum Corp.
CATALINA - Floor coverings–carpet and rugs - Mohawk Industries Inc.
CATALINA - Floor coverings–carpet and rugs - Specialty Carpets
CATALINA - Floor coverings–carpet and rugs - Whitecrest Carpet Mills
CATALINA - Furniture ☆ - Broyhill Furniture Industries, Inc.
CATALINA - Furniture ☆ - Riverside Furniture Corp.
CATALINA - Furniture–children's ☆ - Child Craft Industries Inc.
CATALINA - Guitars ☆ - International Music Corp.
CATALINA - Hammocks - E-Z Sales & Manufacturing, Inc.
CATALINA - Jewelry ☆ - Hirsch Speidel Inc.
CATALINA - Kitchen appliances - White Stores Inc.
CATALINA - Lighting fixtures - Swivelier Co. Inc.
CATALINA - Mats - Cactus Mat Manufacturing Co.
CATALINA - Mobile homes - Wick Building Systems Inc. (Manufactured Home Div./North)
CATALINA - Motor vehicles–automobiles ☆ - General Motors Corp. (Pontiac/GMC Div.)
CATALINA - Motor vehicles–motor homes - Coachmen Industries, Inc.
CATALINA - Motor vehicles–motor homes ☆ - Beaver Coaches Inc.
CATALINA - Ophthalmic goods - Foremost Optical Products
CATALINA - Pet products - Catalina Water Co.
CATALINA - Pet products - Michelle International Ltd.
CATALINA - Salad dressings–bottled - Kraft Foods, Inc.
CATALINA - Seats–automobile ☆ - Cramer Inc.
CATALINA - Shutters–wood - Catalina Shading Systems Inc.
CATALINA - Siding–insulating ☆ - Champion International Corp.
CATALINA - Sporting goods ☆ - Gladding Braided Products Inc.
CATALINA - Strollers–baby - Kolcraft Enterprises, Inc.
CATALINA - Sunglasses - Viva Optique, Inc.
CATALINA - Tableware–china - Villeroy and Boch Tableware Ltd.
CATALINA - Wallpaper ☆ - Richard E. Thibaut, Inc.
CATALINA - Watches - Bulova Corp.
CATALINA - Window shades - Castec Window Shading Inc.
CATALINA - Window shades - Kirsch Co.
CATALINA BRAND - Beverages - Plus Marketing, Inc.
CATALINA CHILDREN - Bathing suits - Catalina
CATALINA EXPRESS - Boats - Glen-L Marine Designs
CATALINA GIRLS - Bathing suits - Catalina
CATALINA JRS. - Bathing suits - Catalina
CATALINA KIDS - Bathing suits - Catalina
CATALINA MENS - Bathing suits - Catalina
CATALINA SPORT - Motor vehicles–motor homes - Coachmen Industries, Inc.
CATALINK DIRECT! - Computer software - Catalink Direct, Inc.
CATALOG MAKER - Computer software - Integrated Software
CATALOG PLUS - Computer peripheral equipment - Follett Corp.
CATALOGUE TV - Recording label - Fashion Television Associates, L.P.
CATALPA PORK - Bait - Uncle Josh Bait Co.
CATALYST - Apparel and accessories - BMG Entertainment North America
CATALYST - Apparel and accessories - BMG Music
CATALYST - Colognes - Halston Borghese Inc. (North America Div.)
CATALYST - Computer software - BioCad Corp.
CATALYST - Computer software - Cisco Systems, Inc.
CATALYST - Computer software ☆ - Quark, Inc.

CATALYST - Floor coverings–carpet and rugs - Masland Corp.
CATALYST - Furniture - Haworth, Inc.
CATALYST - Games - Continuous Learning Group Limited Liability Co.
CATALYST - Games - Flying Buffalo Inc.
CATALYST - Golfing equipment - Ryobi-Toski Corp.
CATALYST - Jewelry - Fammi Industries Corp.
CATALYST - Plant growth regulators - Countrymark Cooperative, Inc.
CATALYSTE - Cosmetics - Revlon Consumer Products Corp.
CATALYTIC - Stoves–wood-burning - Russo Products Inc.
CATAMOUNT - Cookware and glassware ☆ - International Housewares Corp.
CATAMOUNT HOLLOW - Wines ☆ - Naked Mountain Vineyard
CATANIA - Carpets and rugs - Couristan Inc.
CATANIA - Floor coverings–carpet and rugs ☆ - Eligere Carpets
CATANIA - Soybean oil - Catania-Spagna Corp.
CATAPRES - Pharmaceutical preparations - Boehringer Ingelheim Pharmaceuticals Inc.
CATAPRES-TTS - Pharmaceutical preparations - Boehringer Ingelheim Pharmaceuticals Inc.
CATAPULT - Computer utility programs - Tangent Group Inc.
CATAPULT - Footwear - L.A. Gear, Inc.
CATAPULT - Golfing equipment - Focus Golf Systems, Inc.
CATAPULT - Motor vehicle parts and accessories - Packard Motor Car Co.
CATARACT - Sporting goods - Advanced Composites, Inc.
CATARASE - Prescription drug - Iolab Pharmaceuticals
CATARINA CAT - Toys–stuffed - Dakin Inc.
CATASCATCAN - Pet products - Michelle International Ltd.
CATASTROPHE - Pet products - Michelle International Ltd.
CATATONIC - Pet products - Michelle International Ltd.
CATAVITE - Vitamins and nutritional supplements - Vision Research Technologies Inc.
CATAWBA - Furniture ☆ - Lea Industries Inc.
CATAWBA - Hardware - Blaine Window Hardware Inc.
CATAWBA - Motor vehicles - Catawba Coach Co. Inc.
CATAWBA - Siding–insulating - Georgia-Pacific Corp.
CATAWBA - Twine - Blue Mountain Industries, Inc.
CATAWBA MANOR - Furniture–factory ☆ - Clayton Marcus Co. Inc.
CATAWBALITE - Lumber - Georgia-Pacific Corp.
CATAWISSA LUMBER & SPECIALTY CO., INC. - Wood products - Catawissa Lumber & Specialty Co., Inc.
CATBALL RECORDS - Records, cassette tapes, videotapes, and compact disc - Catball Records
CATCARDS - Greeting cards ☆ - Workman Publishing Co., Inc.
CATCH 5 - Chemical preparations - Sealy Inc.
CATCH 21 - Toys–stuffed - CBS Toys
CATCH 22 - Apparel and accessories - Sunset Products, Inc.
CATCH 40 - Toys–electronic - Bally Manufacturing Corp.
CATCH-A-FAX - Office supplies - Rubbermaid Office Products Inc.
CATCH-A-STAR - Games ☆ - Fun World Inc.
CATCH A STAR COLLECTIBLES INC. - Giftware - Catch A Star Collectibles Inc.
CATCH-A-WINK - Toys–models ☆ - Century Products Co.
CATCH-ALL - Containers - Myers Industries, Inc.
CATCH-ALL - Mats - Prince Lionheart, Inc.
CATCH & CARRY - Toys ☆ - Tomy America, Inc.
CATCH AND HOLD - Computer hardware - Advanced NMR Systems, Inc.
CATCH AND RELEASE - Cameras - Paul A. Carpenter
CATCH AND RELEASE - Pet products - Jungle Laboratories Corp.
CATCH AND RELEASE TROUT UNLIMITED - Labels–paper - Trout Unlimited, Inc.
CATCH BALL - Toy - Sportime
CATCH DISK - Computer hardware - YBM Technologies, Inc.
CATCH-IT - Sporting goods - Excel Sports Products
CATCH IT IF YOU CAN - Apparel–athletic - Anheuser-Busch Companies Inc.
CATCH-ME-PUPPY - Toys - Tonka Corp.
CATCH 'N CARRY - Garment hangers - Rubbermaid Inc.
CATCH 'N COOK - Food products - Bickford Flavors Inc.
CATCH 'N' COVER - Aquariums–household - Penn-Plax, Inc.
CATCH OF KINGFISHER - Shrimp–fresh or frozen - Darik Enterprises Inc.
CATCH OF THE DAY - Seafood products–canned or cured - Fishery Products International USA
CATCH ONE - Sunglasses - Wal-Mart Stores Inc.
CATCH THE BREEZE - Aerated water ☆ - Golden Brands Marketing
CATCH THE HATCH - Apparel and accessories - Catch the Hatch
CATCH-UP - Tomato pastes and sauces - Health Valley Food
CATCH UP CYCLE - Toys ☆ - Tomy America, Inc.
CATCH U.S.A. - Apparel and accessories - Seung Won Yu

☆ = Now out of production

CATCHALL - Housewares - Royal Paper Products Inc.
CATCH'ALL - Office supplies - Rubbermaid Office Products Inc.
CATCHER - Apparel–athletic - Scandia Trading Co. Inc.
CATCHER - Boats–motor - Glastex Co.
CATCHING ON II - Floor coverings–carpet and rugs ✩ - Regal Rugs Inc.
CATCHING ZZZS - Syrup - Origins Natural Resources Inc.
CATDOMINIUM - Pet products - Karen F. Hinkle
CATEGORY IV - Recliners - Action Industries Inc.
CATEGORY MANAGEMENT SYSTEMS - Computer software - Del Monte Corp.
CATER BLEND - Desserts - Presto Food Products, Inc.
CATER CAR - Ovens–bakery - Nelgo Manufacturing Corp.
CATER-S - Desserts - Presto Food Products, Inc.
CATERA - Motor vehicles–automobiles - General Motors Corp. (Cadillac Motor Car Div.)
CATERAID - Bakery products - Cateraid Inc.
CATERAIDE - Kitchen appliances - Carlisle Foodservice Products, Inc.
CATERCOOLER - Kitchen appliances - Carlisle Foodservice Products, Inc.
CATERED GOURMET - Bakery products - Cateraid Inc.
CATERER'S CHOICE - Cookware - Metal Foil Products Manufacturing Co.
CATERER'S SELECT - Tableware–plastic ✩ - Genpak Corp.
CATERINA - Wines - Caterina Winery
CATERINA - Wines - Spokane Winery, Inc.
CATERINA'S - Candy - Caterina's Franchise Co. Inc.
CATERING QUALITY - Meat products–poultry - Louis Rich Co.
CATERLINE - Flatware - Maultasch Enterprises, Inc.
CATERPEG TRACTOR - Scooters–children's - Peg Perego USA Inc.
CATERPILLAR - Artists' materials - Sooner Arts & Crafts Inc.
CATERPILLAR - Footwear - Caterpillar Inc.
CATERPILLAR - Footwear - Wolverine World Wide, Inc.
CATERPILLAR BOOKS - Publisher's imprints - Price Stern Sloan Inc.
CATERQUIP - Food processors - Camilo Pereira
CATERWHIP - Desserts - Presto Food Products, Inc.
CATEYE EC-1000 - Exercising equipment ✩ - Maximus Fitness Products
CATFISH - Beverages–malt - Fish Brewing Co.
CATFISH - Fishing lures - Brown Bear Bait Co.
CATFISH - Recording label - Antique-Catfish Records
CATFISH BITES - Fishing lures - Strike King Lure Co.
CATFISH CANDY - Fishing equipment - Garry Loyd Mathews
CATFISH CUISINE - Catfish entrees - Country Skillet Catfish Co.
CATFISH DESIGNS - Computer software - Catfish Designs, Inc.
CATFISH WITH CAPERS - Food products - Antique Mall & Crown
CATFORMATION - Pet products - Nutrisource Pet Products of Stewart, Inc.
CATH-CONTROL - Catheters - Anago Inc.
CATH GUARD - Health care products - Medical Industries America, Inc.
CATH MANAGER - Containers–metal - Innerspace Corp.
CATH-SECURE DUAL TAB - Medical apparatus - M.C. Johnson Co., Inc.
CATH-TRAC - Cables–armored - Datel, Inc.
CATHA-COAT - Paints - Grow Group, Inc.
CATHADIA - Giftware - Sasaki
CATHALIA - Apparel and accessories - Young Town Enterprises Inc.
CATHARSIS - Books–comic - Anthony Masino
CATHAY - Chinese foods - Cathay Foods Corp.
CATHAY - Clocks - Cathay International
CATHAY - Frames–picture - Terragrafics Inc.
CATHAY - Furniture - Lane Co. Inc.
CATHAY - Furniture ✩ - Hickory Chair Co.
CATHAY - Furniture - Vaughan Furniture Co. Inc.
CATHAY - Vases ✩ - Lenox Crystal, Inc.
CATHAY COLLECTION, THE - Jewelry - Catherine R. Butler
CATHEDRAL - Apparel and accessories - Kellwood Co.
CATHEDRAL - Cheese - Anco Foods Corp.
CATHEDRAL - Chimes - Maas-Rowe Carillons Inc.
CATHEDRAL - Christmas tree ornaments ✩ - Cracker Box Inc.
CATHEDRAL - Clocks ✩ - General Time Corp. (Westclox/Seth Thomas Div.)
CATHEDRAL - Floor coverings - Bruce Hardwood Floors
CATHEDRAL - Floor coverings–carpet and rugs - Customweave Carpets Inc.
CATHEDRAL - Floor coverings–carpet and rugs - Porter Carpet Mills Inc.
CATHEDRAL - Paper–writing ✩ - Kurtz Bros. Inc.
CATHEDRAL - Varnishes ✩ - Valspar Corp.
CATHEDRAL ART METAL - Jewelry - Cathedral Art Metal Co., Inc.
CATHEDRAL CHATHAM - Cabinets - Marsh Furniture Co.
CATHEDRAL CLASSICS - Greeting cards - Cathedral Art Metal Co., Inc.
CATHEDRAL DE MEAUX - Cheese - Anco Foods Corp.
CATHEDRAL HALL - Musical instruments - Lo Duca Bros. Musical Instruments Inc.

CATHEDRAL LEXINGTON - Cabinets - Marsh Furniture Co.
CATHEDRAL PINE - Furniture - Broyhill Furniture Industries, Inc.
CATHEDRAL WINCHESTER - Cabinets - Marsh Furniture Co.
CATHERINE - Molasses - J. Supple's Sons Planting
CATHERINE - Recording label - Catherine
CATHERINE CLARK - Breads ✩ - Best Foods Baking Group
CATHERINE DENEUVE - Jewelry - Nina Ricci Jewelry-Pierre Balmain
CATHERINE FORD - Jewelry - Bruce Lindsay
CATHERINE RYAN - Apparel and accessories - Rycam, Inc.
CATHERINE'S FINEST - Candy - Oceanside Sales & Marketing, Inc.
CATHOLIC YELLOW PAGES - Paper–book - Thurman & Jackson Design Associates, Inc.
CATHX - Disinfectants - Minntech Corp.
CATHY - Apparel and accessories - Guisewite Studio
CATHY - Greeting cards - Recycled Paper Products, Inc.
CATHY - House furnishings - Dan River Inc.
CATHY - Needlecraft kits ✩ - Janlynn Corp.
CATHY'S - Cookies ✩ - Bon Melange Inc.
CATHY'S FAVORITES - Chocolate bars - That's My Favorite Inc.
CATILLAC - Pet products - Michelle International Ltd.
CATIO/THERM - Health care products - Helene Curtis Industries Inc.
CATISFACTION - Cat food ✩ - Fromm Family Foods, Inc.
CATISFACTION - Pet products ✩ - Aquarium Products Inc.
CATLEY - Tiles–ceramic - Capitol Tile Import Co.
CATLIN - House furnishings - Dan River Inc.
CATMAN - Computer software ✩ - Zephyr Services
CATMAN - Recording label ✩ - Mirror Records Inc.
CATMANIA! - Games - Brooks C. Sackett
CATMAP - Computer software - Applied Insurance Research Inc.
CATMASTER - Apparel - Arctco, Inc.
CATNAPPER - Recliners - Cleveland Chair Co.
CATNIP! - Games - Hasbro, Inc.
CATNIP - Toys–stuffed - Dakin Inc.
CATNIP CAPERS - Pet products - Flexi-Mat Corp.
CATNIP CRAZIES - Pet products - Petrapport, Inc.
CATNIP FUZZIES - Pet products - Cosmic Cat Corp.
CATNIP TRADING COMPANY, THE - Pet products - De Facto, Inc.
CATNIP TWISTER - Pet products - Cosmic Cat Corp.
CATNOC - Pharmaceutical preparations ✩ - C.O. Truxton Inc.
CATO - Food products ✩ - Curtice-Burns Foods, Inc.
CATO - Oils–lubricating - Citgo Petroleum Corp.
CATO - Toys–models - Estes Industries
CATO KIDS - Apparel–children's - Cato Corp.
CATOCTIN VINEYARDS - Wines - Catoctin Vineyards
CATONE - Paints ✩ - Frazee Paint
CATONEX - Chemical preparations ✩ - Hydroponic Chemical Co. Inc.
CATOY - Pet products - Mapes Industries Inc.
CATPHRODESIAC - Pet products - Dirigo Corp.
CATPURE-ALL - Photographic equipment - Phoenix Corp. of America
CATRA - Toys - Mattel, Inc.
CATRINA MEOWFORD - File folders - Lisa Frank, Inc.
CATRIX - Vitamins and nutritional supplements - Econugenics, Inc.
CATRIX - Vitamins and nutritional supplements - Lescarden, Inc.
CATRON III - Veterinary pharmaceutical preparations ✩ - Boehringer Ingelheim Animal Health, Inc.
CATS - Candy - Rodda Candy Co.
CATS - Electronic equipment - Diamond Electronics Inc.
CATS AND DOGS - Kaleidoscopes - Gemini Kaleidoscopes
CATS & JAMMERS - Music–sheet - Ripete Music Group
CAT'S CLAW - Vitamins and nutritional supplements - Horizon Worldwide Export Corp.
CAT'S CLAW - Vitamins and nutritional supplements - Vitamin Research Products Inc.
CAT'S CLAW DEFENSE COMPLEX - Vitamins and nutritional supplements - Source Naturals
CATS COMING AND GOING - Apparel and accessories - Anna Grupke
CAT'S EYE - Games ✩ - Milton Bradley Co.
CAT'S EYE - Rubber stamp pads - Clearsnap, Inc.
CAT'S EYE - Toys–marbles - Al Sandberg
CAT'S EYE THE PRESSURE MAINTENANCE SYSTEM - Measuring instruments - Link Manufacturing, Ltd.
CAT'S EYE VIEW, A - Calendars - American Greetings Corp.
CAT'S MEOW - Artists' materials - Stangren Co.
CAT'S MEOW - Bicycles ✩ - Murray, Inc.
CAT'S MEOW - Cat food ✩ - Superior Brands Inc.
CAT'S MEOW - Pet supplies - Pillowtex Corp.

CAT'S MEOW, THE - Statuary - F.J. Designs Inc.
CATS MEOWSE, THE - Pet products ✩ - Flexi-Mat Corp.
CATS OF LESLEY ANN IVORY, THE - Calendars ✩ - Amcal Inc.
CATS PAW - Chairs–upholstered - Master Woodcraft Inc.
CATS PAW - Computers - Joel Michael Gibney
CAT'S PAW - Shoe repair shops - American Biltrite Inc.
CATS PAW - Sporting goods - Joel Gibney
CATS PAW - Tools - Mayhew Steel Products
CAT'S PAW - Tools - Universal Products International
CAT'S PRIDE - Pet products - Oil-Dri Corp. of America
CAT'S PRIDE NATURAL - Pet products - Oil-Dri Corp. of America
CATS TOWEL, THE - Pet products - Rabbit Foot, Inc.
CATS WITH AN ATTITUDE - Toys - Nip & Tuck Playtoys, Inc.
CATSCAM - Pet products - Michelle International Ltd.
CATSHELV - Pet products - R.A.F. Trading Inc.
CATSIP - Pet products - Akpharma Inc.
CATSKILL - Lumber - Georgia-Pacific Corp.
CATSKILL COOLER - Wine coolers - Walker Valley Vineyards
CATSKILL CRYSTAL WATER - Water–bottled or canned - Catskill Crystal Water, Inc.
CATSKILL GOOD WATER - Water–bottled or canned - Good Water Corp.
CATSKILL MOUNTAIN - Vitamins and nutritional supplements - Ginseng Plus
CATS...OF COURSE - Quilts - D.A. Brinkmann Designs
CATSPAW - Learning aid - American Visual Aids
CATTANEO BROS. BRAND - Food products - Cattaneo Brothers Inc.
CATTANI - Wines - Admiral Wine Merchants
CATTANI CALIFORNIA - Apparel–women's - Middendorf Enterprises Inc.
CATTARUGUS - Knives - A.G. Russell Knives Inc.
CATTITUDES - Toys–stuffed - John Zaboyan
CATTLE ADVANTAGE - Animal feed supplements - American Superior Feeds, Inc.
CATTLE CHARGE - Animal feeds - MFA Inc.
CATTLE MANAGER, THE - Computer software - Vertical Solutions, Inc.
CATTLE PRO - Computer software - Bowman Farm Systems, Inc.
CATTLEBARON - Spices and extracts - Cattlebaron Foods
CATTLEMAN - Food products - American Beef Packers Inc.
CATTLEMAN'S - Desks - National/Mt. Airy Furniture
CATTLEMAN'S BAR-B-Q - Beef - Dallas Dress Beef
CATTLEMAN'S CUT - Meat products–beef - Oh Boy! Oberto
CATTLEMAN'S CUT - Meat products–dried - Oberto Sausage Co.
CATTLEMAN'S RESERVE - Meat products–poultry - Stevens Industries Inc.
CATTLEMEN'S BEST - Meat products - Steak Specialists, Inc.
CATTLEMEN'S GOLD - Food products - Reckitt & Colman, Inc.
CATTLYST - Veterinary pharmaceutical preparations - Syntex USA, Inc.
CATTRAX - Computer software - DCS Corp.
CATTY SHACK - Cat food - Kelly Foods Corp.
CATTY SHACK - Pet products - E.J. Jordan Co.
CATTYLAC SIAMESE - Toys–stuffed - Dakin Inc.
CATVIAR - Cat food - Ralston Purina Co.
CATWALK - Wallpaper - Blumenthal
CATWALKERS - Sportswear - C.W. Surf & Sport Inc.
CATWARE - Computer software - Illumination Arts Inc.
CATWOMAN - Novelty items - DC Comics
CATWORKS - Pet products - Absorption Corp.
CATYAK - Boats–skiffs ✩ - Arbor Plastic Products Inc. (Dayton Marine Div.)
CATYOGA - Stationery - Mike Gabriel
CATZ - Video games - Pf. Magic, Inc.
CAU OUR D - Cheese - Land O'Lakes Inc.
CAUCAL LICOR DE CARDAMOMO - Beverages–alcohol - Massie Brands Ltd.
CAUGHT IN THE ACT - Glassware–household ✩ - Fenton Art Glass Co.
CAULDRON - Computer software ✩ - Broderbund Software, Inc.
CAULDRON POP-UPS - Toys–stuffed - Fun World Inc.
CAULIFLOWER HEARTS - Fruits and vegetables - Mann Packing Co., Inc.
CAULK-A-DOO - Caulking compounds - Sterling-Clark-Lurton Corp.
CAULK-BE-GONE - Solvents - Dap Products Inc.
CAULK-CRETE - Caulking compounds - Muralo Co. Inc.
CAULK DEVIL - Trowels - Red Devil Inc.
CAULK-IN-COLORS - Sealing compounds ✩ - Tec Inc.
CAULK MASTER - Caulking guns - Roean Industries, Inc.
CAULK-N-SEAL - Caulking compounds - Blue Ridge Talc Co. Inc.
CAULK ONE - Caulking compounds ✩ - Ohio Sealants Inc.
CAULK-TEX - Hardware - Travaco Laboratories Inc.
CAULKEEPER - Caulking guns - Myro, Inc.
CAULKER'S EDGE, THE - Tools - Pere Marquette Enterprises, Inc.
CAULKING STUFF - Now out of production ✩ - Insta-Foam Products, Inc.

CAULKINS INDIANTOWN - Juices - Caulkins Indiantown Citrus Co.
CAULKMASTER - Caulking compounds ✩ - Sashco Inc.
CAULKSAV'R - Caulking compounds - W.J. Dennis & Co.
CAULKSTRIP - Caulking compounds - Myro, Inc.
CAULKTRIM - Plastics - Manco, Inc.
CAULKWORKS - Caulking compounds - Master's Choice Inc.
CAULLET - Food products - De Choix Specialty Foods Co.
CAUSAL TRACING - Computer software - Ventana Systems, Inc.
CAUSE AND EFFECT - T-shirts–men's - Dogfish Productions
CAUSEWAY - Bicycles - Huffy Corp.
CAUSTIC FISH, THE - Recording label - Caustic Fish Co.
CAUTIER - Wines ✩ - Cannon Wines Ltd.
CAUTION - Sporting goods - Caution USA, Inc.
CAV - Computer software - Comprehensive Video Supply Corp.
CAV - Nuts and bolts - Cavalier Bolt & Nut, Inc.
CAV-SUEDE - Fabrics–broadcloth - Collins & Aikman Corp.
CAV-TWILL - Fabrics–nylon - King Group
CAVA CA - Leather - Nam Sup Han
CAVA D'ARTA - Wine ✩ - International Wine & Spirits Inc.
CAVAGNOLO - Accordions - Castiglione Accordion
CAVAL - Footwear - Cavort International Inc.
CAVALAIRE - Furniture ✩ - Hammary Furniture Co. Inc.
CAVALCADE - Cutlery ✩ - Carvel Hall Inc.
CAVALCADE - Mobile homes - Commodore Corp.
CAVALCADE - Motorcycles - Suzuki of America Automotive Corp.
CAVALCADE - Projectors–photographic - Eastman Kodak Co.
CAVALCADE - Recording label - Westwood Entertainment Group
CAVALCADE OF COLOR - Floor coverings–carpet and rugs ✩ - Callaway Carpets
CAVALETTI - Apparel stores–men's - Savi, Inc.
CAVALIER - Apparel and accessories - Adept Manufacturing Co.
CAVALIER - Boats–motor ✩ - Chris Craft Boats
CAVALIER - Briefcases - NSM Industries Inc.
CAVALIER - Chessboards - Pacific Game Co.
CAVALIER - Cigarettes - R.J. Reynolds Tobacco Co.
CAVALIER - Cooking utensils–enameled ✩ - National Housewares
CAVALIER - Cosmetics ✩ - Kresco
CAVALIER - Dinnerware–glass - Homer Laughlin China Co.
CAVALIER - Doors–metal ✩ - Remington Building Products
CAVALIER - Fabrics - Dan River Inc.
CAVALIER - Footwear–children's - Goodwear Shoe Co. Inc.
CAVALIER - Furniture - Pilliod Co.
CAVALIER - Glassware–household ✩ - Knobler International Ltd.
CAVALIER - Lumber - Georgia-Pacific Corp.
CAVALIER - Motor vehicles - General Motors Corp. (Chevrolet Motor Div.)
CAVALIER - Office supplies - Bates Manufacturing Co.
CAVALIER - Padding–foam - Crain Industries Inc.
CAVALIER - Paints ✩ - Atlantic Varnish & Paint Co. Inc.
CAVALIER - Pencils ✩ - Faber-Castell Corp.
CAVALIER - Pipes–tobacco - S.M. Frank & Co. Inc. (Kaywoodie-Yello-Bole-Medico)
CAVALIER - Shoe polish - Kiwi Brands, Inc.
CAVALIER - Tableware–china - Villeroy and Boch Tableware Ltd.
CAVALIER - Tires - Uniroyal Goodrich Tire Co.
CAVALIER - Tobacco–chewing or smoking - Sterling Tobacco Co.
CAVALIER - Tools - Smith Equipment
CAVALIER - Trailers–travel - Forest River, Inc.
CAVALIER - Watches - Bulova Corp.
CAVALIER ACCOLADE - Tires - Uniroyal Goodrich Licensing Services, Inc.
CAVALIER BULB COMPANY - Flowers, plants, and seeds - K. Van Bourgondien & Sons, Inc.
CAVALIER EVER-DRI - Waterproofing compounds - Kiwi Brands, Inc.
CAVALIER II - Pool tables - Brunswick Corp.
CAVALIER JRS. - Shoes ✩ - Consolidated Shoe Co., Inc.
CAVALIER SRX - Tires - Uniroyal Goodrich Licensing Services, Inc.
CAVALIERO - Apparel–men's - Cavaliero Cravats
CAVALIERS - Shoes - Consolidated Shoe Co., Inc.
CAVALLI - Vinegar - Dean & Deluca Inc.
CAVALLI BALSAMICO - Vinegar - De Medici Imports Ltd.
CAVALLINO - Cigars - Gesty Trading & Manufacturing Corp.
CAVALLINO - Tires - Bridgestone/Firestone, Inc.
CAVALLOTTO - Wines - Dreyfus Ashby Inc.
CAVALLUCCI - Food products - Bel Canto Fancy Foods Ltd.
CAVALRY - Hammers - NC Tool Co.
CAVALRY - Wallets - Enger-Kress Co.
CAVALRY - Watches ✩ - Swiss Army Brands, Ltd.

✩ = Now out of production

CAVATINA - Watches - Timex Corp.
CAVCO - Building materials - Cavco Industries, Inc.
CAVCOM - Radio communications equipment - Impact Health Services, Inc.
CAVE BASHER - Toys - Mattel, Inc.
CAVE CRAWLERS - Games ☆ - Tomy America, Inc.
CAVE CREEK CHILI BEER - Watches - Black Mountain Brewing Co., Inc.
CAVE KIDS - Apparel–children's - Hanna-Barbera Productions, Inc.
CAVE KIDS - Toys - Smethport Specialty Co.
CAVE KITS - Skin care products - Tweezerman Corp.
CAVE-NICK - Greeting cards ☆ - Fran Mar Greeting cards Ltd.
CAVE SPRING - Slacks–men's - Rome Manufacturing Co. Inc.
CAVE WARS - Computer software - Monarch Avalon, Inc.
CAVEL - Apparel and accessories - Collins & Aikman Corp.
CAVELLA - Crocheted and knitted items ☆ - Collins & Aikman Corp.
CAVELLI - Apparel–men's - Profile Menswear International Ltd.
CAVELOUR - Crocheted and knitted items - Collins & Aikman Corp.
CAVEMAN CREATIONS - Greeting cards - Lisa R. Beightol and Joseph B. Field Partnership
CAVEMAN JOE - Computer software - Tyke Studios, LLC
CAVENDER'S - Seasonings - Grace A. Rush Inc.
CAVENDER'S BOOT CITY WHERE TEXANS GET THEIR BOOTS - Apparel and accessories - Cavender's Boot City
CAVENDER'S WESTERN OUTFITTERS - Apparel and accessories - Cavender's Boot City
CAVENDISH - Dinnerware–glass - Royal China & Porcelain Companies Inc.
CAVENDISH - Frozen vegetables and potato products - Cavendish Farms
CAVENDISH - Furniture - Haworth, Inc.
CAVENDISH - Pillows - Pillowtex Corp.
CAVENDISH - Soap ☆ - Chase Collection, Inc.
CAVENDISH - Tobacco–chewing or smoking - Amar Blends Co.
CAVENDISH & HARVEY - Candy - Acme Food Specialties Inc.
CAVENDISH & HARVEY - Candy - Morris National Inc.
CAVENDISH SEASONED SELECT - Frozen vegetables and potato products - Cavendish Farms
CAVENDISH SELECT XLF - Frozen vegetables and potato products - Cavendish Farms
CAVENHAM - Lumber - Cavenham Forest Industries Inc.
CAVERJECT - Pharmaceutical preparations - Upjohn Co.
CAVERN BLEND - Coffee - Coffee Cavern Inc.
CAVERNS OF CALLISTO - Video games - Origin Systems, Inc.
CAVERNS OF MARS - Video games - Atari Games Corp.
CAVERSWALL - Dishes–china - Britannia Collection Inc.
CAVES CHANTEFLEUR - Wines - Parliament Import Co.
CAVES DES PAPES - Wines - Cannon Wines Ltd.
CAVES MOVENPICK - Wines ☆ - Seagram's Chateau & Estate Wines Co.
CAVES ST. PIERRE - Wines - World Wide Wine and Spirits Inc.
CAVEX - Tools–garden - Emsco Inc.
CAVI-SCRUB - Soap - E & D Dental Products, Inc.
CAVIAR - Apparel–athletic - Exclusive Imports
CAVIAR - Artists' materials - FM Brush Co., Inc.
CAVIAR - Belts–apparel - Leon Fleischer, International Marketing
CAVIAR - Cigars - General Cigar Co., Inc.
CAVIAR BEAD - Handbags ☆ - Lumured Corp.
CAVIAR COLLECTION - Frames–eyeglass - Palm Optical Co., Inc.
CAVIAR DE CHOCOLAT - Candy ☆ - Brown & Haley
CAVIAR DIRECT - Caviar - Caviar & Caviar Corp.
CAVIAR LOUISE - Caviar - Rite Foods, Inc.
CAVIARTERIA - Caviar - Caviarteria Inc.
CAVINESS - Boats - Caviness Woodworking Co.
CAVINO - Wine - Attiki Imports & Distributors
CAVISTE - Wines - Acacia Winery
CAVIT - Wines - Palm Bay Imports, Inc.
CAVIT NORTHERN ITALIAN WINES - Wines - Palm Bay Imports, Inc.
CAVITY COP - Novelty items - Sherman Specialty Co., Inc.
CAVITY FLOW SYSTEM - Golfing equipment - Dunlop Maxfli Sports Corp.
CAVITY-LOK - Building materials–concrete - AA Wire Products Co.
CAVS - Apparel–children's - Nationwide Advertising Service, Inc.
CAVS - Sporting goods - Gund Business Enterprises, Inc.
CAVYLETS - Pet products - Nutritional Research Associates Inc.
CAWCRAFT - Boats ☆ - Woolsey Marine Industries
CAWKING - Chemical preparations ☆ - Woolsey Marine Industries
CAWLAC - Paints ☆ - Woolsey Marine Industries
CAWLEY - Giftware - Contemporary Inc.
CAWLUX - Chemical preparations - Woolsey Marine Industries
CAWPACO - Paints ☆ - Woolsey Marine Industries
CAWSEAL - Chemical preparations - Woolsey Marine Industries

CAWSPAR - Chemical preparations - Woolsey Marine Industries
CAWSPRAY - Chemical preparations ☆ - Woolsey Marine Industries
CAWSTAIN - Chemical preparations - Woolsey Marine Industries
CAWSTON OSTRICH FARM, THE - Apparel and accessories - Dehylton Studio
CAWTHANE - Chemical preparations ☆ - Woolsey Marine Industries
CAWTITE - Chemical preparations ☆ - Woolsey Marine Industries
CAWY LEMON LIME - Beverages–carbonated - Cawy Bottling Co., Inc.
CAWY MALTA - Beverages–carbonated - Florida Brewing Co.
CAXTON - Office supplies ☆ - Esselte Corp.
CAXTON - Toilets–enameled - Kohler Co.
CAY - Ships–sailing vessels ☆ - Glander Boats Inc.
CAYENNE PEOPLE, THE - Vitamins and nutritional supplements - Heart Foods Co., Inc.
CAYENNE POWER CAPS - Vitamins and nutritional supplements - Heart Foods Co., Inc.
CAYENNE POWER PLUS - Vitamins and nutritional supplements - Heart Foods Co., Inc.
CAYL - Skin care products - Amsoil, Inc.
CAYMAN - Boats - Wood Manufacturing Co., Inc.
CAYMAN - Furniture - Tropitone Furniture Co. Inc.
CAYMAN - Life preservers ☆ - Parkway Systems
CAYMAN BAY - Furniture–wood ☆ - Flanders Industries Inc.
CAYMAN BAY II - Furniture–wood ☆ - Flanders Industries Inc.
CAYMAN COLLECTION - Wallcovering - Gencorp Inc.
CAYMAN ISLAND - Colognes - Vi-Jon Laboratories, Inc.
CAYMAN ISLE - Furniture - Homecrest Industries Inc.
CAYMAN KAI - Furniture–wood ☆ - Flanders Industries Inc.
CAYMUS - Wines - Caymus Vineyards
CAYO HUESO - Colognes - Key West Aloe Inc.
CAYTRONICS - Cameras–video - Good Times Home Video Corp.
CAYUGA - Concrete products - KBW Holding, Inc.
CAYUGA - Wines - Bully Hill Vineyards, Inc.
CAYUGA - Wines - Calvaresi Winery
CAYUGA-CHAMBOURGIN - Wines - Fink Winery
CAZAM - Tomato pastes and sauces - Caragol, Esformes & Phelan Corp.
CAZLOR - Housewares - USTI Inc.
CB - Drums–musical instruments - Kaman Music Corp.
C.B. - Frames–eyeglass ☆ - Universal/Univis Inc.
CB - Insecticides - Waterbury Companies, Inc.
CB - Toys–models ☆ - Reeves International, Inc.
CB 2 - Sporting goods - Voit Corp.
CB 3 - Electrical equipment - General Electric Co.
CB 34 - Footwear - BRS, Inc.
CB BLEND - Tobacco–chewing or smoking - Amar Blends Co.
CB BUNNY - Candy ☆ - R.M. Palmer Co.
CB CONVOY CODE STICKERS - Candy ☆ - Donruss Co.
CB EDUCATOR - Drums–musical instruments - Kaman Music Corp.
CB INTERNATIONALE - Drums–musical instruments ☆ - Kaman Music Corp.
CB SPORTS - Apparel stores–sports - CB North America Inc.
CB STICK - Golfing equipment - Mega Pro, Inc.
CB TALK PLATTER POPS - Candy ☆ - Spangler Candy Co.
CB TALK SUPER POPS - Candy ☆ - Spangler Candy Co.
CBA - Apparel and accessories - Sutton Shirt Corp.
CBAR C - Fruits and vegetables - Cecelia Packing Corp.
CBASIC - Computer software ☆ - Novell, Inc.
CBASIC COMPILER - Computer software ☆ - Novell, Inc.
C.B.C. - Burnishing compound - Vibe Records Inc.
CBC - Filters–water - Ametek, Inc., Plymouth Products Division
C.B.C. - Shotguns - Fie Corp.
CBC - Tools–power-driven - California Buff Co. Inc.
CBC-ACE - Computer software - CB Commercial Holdings, Inc.
CBC RE-TRACK - Computer software - CB Commercial Holdings, Inc.
CBC-THRUSTER - Tools - Dailey Petroleum Services Corp.
CBD CLOS.TAG - Chemical preparations - Novagen, Inc.
CBE 24/6 - Vitamins and nutritional supplements - Chemco Industries Inc.
C.B.F. - Recording label - Charlie Fields Productions
CBG - Garden equipment - Barco Manufacturing Co. Inc.
CBI - Jewelry - Claar Bros. Inc.
CBI PUBLISHING INC. - Publisher's imprints - Van Nostrand Reinhold Inc.
CBIS EDGE FAMILY OF PRODUCTS - Computer software - Cincinnati Bell Information Systems Inc.
CBK - Rackets–racquetball - Ektelon
CBM - Brass products - Century Brass Manufacturing, Inc.
C.B.M. - Water purification systems ☆ - Penn-Plax, Inc.
CBM RECORDS - Recording label - Gerald F. Cannan

CBNY - Apparel–women's - Carry Back Ltd.

CBO - Recording label - True Records Inc.

C'BONTE - Hair care products - Zotos International Inc.

CBP - Animal feeds - CBP Resources Inc.

CBR - Recording label - Rustron Music Productions

CBR - Vitamins and nutritional supplements - Source Naturals

CBS - Fixtures–plastic - Advanced Technology Inc.

CBS - Microphones ☆ - ERTL Co., Inc.

CBS - Pharmaceutical preparations ☆ - C.O. Truxton Inc.

CBS - Screws - CBS Fasteners, Inc.

CBS - Tape players–cassette - Sony Music Entertainment Inc.

CBS APPAREL - Apparel and accessories - CBS Apparel

CBS MASTERSOUND - Computer software - Sony Music Entertainment Inc.

CBS SPECIAL PRODUCTS - Tape players–cassette - Sony Music Entertainment Inc.

CBSLIDIA - Electronic equipment - CBS Inc.

CBT SYSTEMS - Computer software - Personal Training Systems

C.B.V. 2000 - Vitamins and nutritional supplements - Petland, Inc.

CBW - Hardware - Quaker City Manufacturing Co.

CBW - Malt - Briess Industries, Inc.

CC - Apparel and accessories - Texas Professional Baseball, Inc.

CC - Apparel and accessories - Thousand Stars Inc.

CC - Circuit boards–printed - Circo Caribe Corp.

CC - Computer software - Claflin and Clayton Inc.

CC - Computer software - Common Census Partnership

CC - Hats - Nationwide Advertising Service, Inc.

CC - Jewelry - C & C Clothing, Inc.

CC - Jewelry - Clover Chain Co.

CC - Jewelry - Crystaline North America, Inc.

CC - Packaging material - Alusuisse Flexible Packaging Inc.

CC - Perfumes - Chanel Inc.

C.C. - Petrolatums - United States Tobacco Co.

CC - Pharmaceutical preparations - Cytel Corp.

C.C. - Shrimp–canned or cured ☆ - C & C Office Supply Co. Inc.

CC - Skin care products - California Cosmetics, Inc.

CC-78 - Wire - Hudson International Conductors

CC-103 - Calcium compounds - ECC International

CC 107 - Pharmaceutical preparations - Camall Co.

CC 109 - Pharmaceutical preparations - Camall Co.

CC 0147 - Pharmaceutical preparations - Camall Co.

CC 37.5 - Pharmaceutical preparations - Camall Co.

CC-500 - Skin care products - Care-Tech Laboratories Inc.

CC 18.75 - Pharmaceutical preparations - Camall Co.

CC BATES - Apparel - Tux Companies, Inc.

CC BIG DIPPER - Kitchen utensils–aluminum - Bonny Products Inc.

CC BISCUIT - Shortening - Karlshamns USA Inc.

CC CLASSIC CLUB - Footwear–men's - Melville Corp.

CC COLOR CODE - Skin care products - Bet Direct, Inc.

CC DESIGNS - Fabrics–linen ☆ - Arthur Court Designs Inc.

CC:MAIL - Computer software - Lotus Development Corp.

C.C. OUTLAW - Apparel and accessories - Kymsta Corp.

CC PROFESSIONAL - Drums–musical instruments ☆ - Music Sales Corp.

C.C. PURDY - Glassware–household - C.C. Purdy Co.

CC RIBS - Meat products–pork - Custom Ribs Co.

C.C. RICERS - Crackers ☆ - Keebler Co.

CC RIDER - Exercising equipment - Mettler Electronics Corp.

C.C. RIDER - Motor vehicle parts and accessories - Custom Chrome, Inc.

C.C. SPORT - Apparel and accessories - Career Club Shirt Co.

CC VINEYARD - Wines - Bronco Wine Co.

CCA - Furniture - Beatrice Cos. Inc.

CCA - Lumber - PSR Co.

CCA MEDICAL - Computer software - Carolina Computer Associates, Inc.

CCAPTURE - Computer software - Dynatech Newstar, Inc.

CCAR - Optical products - Viratec Thin Films, Inc.

CCAST ZONES - Apparel and accessories - Roydon Wear Inc.

CCB - Brakes–locomotive - New York Air Brake Corp.

CCC - Computer software - Computer Concepts Corp.

CCC - Firearms, accessories, and parts - Canyon Cartridge Corp.

CCC - Paints ☆ - H. Behlen & Bro. Inc.

CCC - Stoves–gas - LazyMan, Inc.

CCC CONTINENTAL CAN COMPANY - Packaging machines - Continental Can Co., Inc.

CCCP - Apparel–athletic - Dao M. Phan

CCCPINS - Patches, insignia, and emblems ☆ - Best Emblem & Insignia Co. Inc.

CCD-100E FAMILY - Cameras - CCTV Corp./GBC

CCD-200 FAMILY - Cameras - CCTV Corp./GBC

CCD-400 - Cameras - CCTV Corp./GBC

CCD-500E - Cameras - CCTV Corp./GBC

CCD-835C FAMILY - Cameras - CCTV Corp./GBC

CCEL - Computer software - Churchill Livingstone Inc.

CCEX - Computer software ☆ - SR Research, Inc.

CCEX COLLECTION EXPERT - Computer software - SR Research, Inc.

CCEX CORPORATE - Computer software - SR Research, Inc.

CCEX LEASE EXPERT - Computer software - SR Research, Inc.

C.C.G. - Recording label - Jazz Composer's Orchestra Association Inc.

CCH - Chemical preparations - Olin Corp.

CCH - Computer software - CCH Inc. (Wolters Kluwer)

CCI - Computer software - Cooperative Computing, Inc.

CCI - Firearms, accessories, and parts - Blount International, Inc. (Sporting Equipment Group)

CCI - Jewelry - Carat Creation Inc.

CCI - Motorcycle parts and accessories - Custom Chrome, Inc.

CCI - Motorcycles - Suzuki of America Automotive Corp.

CCI CONTROLS - Alarm systems - CCI Controls

CCIOLI-CRISPS - Snack foods - Ali Karim A. Jaffer

CCJ - Jewelry–precious - Continental J.C. Inc.

CCL - Archery equipment - Wasp Archery Products, Inc.

CCL - Communications equipment - California Communications Lab, Inc.

CCM - Chemical preparations - CELLEX BIOSCIENCES Inc.

CCM - Sporting goods - Northland Sports Inc.

CCM-2 - Chemical preparations - CELLEX BIOSCIENCES Inc.

CCM CALCIUM - Vitamins and nutritional supplements - Source Naturals

CCMM DATA EXPRESS - Computer equipment - Computer Communications Inc.

C.C.M.P. - Pharmaceutical preparations - Balas Dental Supply Co.

CCP - Audio equipment - ADA Signal Processors Inc.

CCP - Plaster–wallboard - Centex Corp.

C.C.P. SUPER CAPS - Pharmaceutical preparations - Concord Chemists

CCQ - Publisher's imprints - Ibbotson Associates

CCRIDER - Pet products - Goodwinol Products Corp.

CCS - Computer software - Corp. Computer Systems Inc.

CCS CARDINAL CHEMICAL SYSTEMS - Cleaning preparations - Cardinal Chemical Systems, Inc.

CCT - Polishing cloths - Mothers Polishes Waxes Cleaners

CD - Audio equipment - Speakerkits Inc.

CD - Bicycle parts and accessories - GT Bicycles Inc.

CD - Computer hardware - Ceridian Corp.

CD - Electrical equipment - Control Devices, Inc.

CD - Gypsum products - Georgia-Pacific Corp.

CD-1 - Cleaning preparations - Recoton Corp.

CD-2 ENGINE WEAR PROTECTOR - Fuel additives - Stewart Warner Corp.

CD 200 - Cameras–video ☆ - Yashica Inc.

CD 1100 - Cameras–video ☆ - Yashica Inc.

CD 2000 - Cleaning preparations - CD Magic, Inc.

CD ANALYST - Computer storage devices–optical - Thomson Trading Services Inc.

CD ANYWHERE - Computer storage devices–optical - Kingston Technology Corp.

CD ART - Containers - Erling W. Johansen

CD BRANDER - Labels–gummed - Zebra Graphics

CD BROWSER PAKS - Fixtures - Chicago One Stop/Browser Display

CD BTSB COMPACT DISCOVERER - Computer software - Bound to Stay Bound Books, Inc.

CD CORE WORKS - Computer software - Roth Publishing Inc.

C.D. DENISON'S - Braces–orthopedic - C.D. Denison Orthopaedic Appliance Corp.

C.D. +DENISON'S - Medical apparatus - C.D. Denison Orthopaedic Appliance Corp.

CD DIGITAL GUM - Chewing gum - Zeebs Enterprises, Inc.

CD-DIRECT - Computer software - Lanshark Systems, Inc.

CD DOUBLER JEWEL CASE - Cases–compacts - Acco World Corp.

CD ESSENTIALS - Audio cabinets - Mactec Products

CD-EYE - Educational materials - Alcon Laboratories, Inc.

CD GALLERY - Racks - Quest Products, Inc.

CD GAME COLLECTION - Computer software - Capstone Software

CD GREENE - Apparel and accessories - CD Greene Inc.

CD GRIPPEE - Electronic equipment - Ingenious Designs, Inc.

CD HORIZON - Surgical supplies - Danek Medical, Inc.

CD HYDROBATH - Cleaning preparations - Recoton Corp.

CD HYMAL, THE - Recording label - Crossfire Productions, Inc.

CD-I - Electronic equipment - Philips Consumer Electronics Co.

CD/INSURANCE - Computer software - Lotus Development Corp.

CD-LINK - Computer software - Invzn Development Corp.

CD-MAKER - Computer peripheral equipment - Knowledge Access International, Inc.

CD MANAGEMENT SYSTEM - Compact disc players - Sanyo Fisher (USA) Corp.

CD MASTER LINX - Containers–plastic - Team Vision, Inc.

CD MATCH - Computer software - Interactive Multimedia Association

CD MATCH IT WORKS! - Computer software - Interactive Multimedia Association

CD MOM - Recording label - Wendy Dubit

CD/NOTES - Computer software - Lotus Development Corp.

CD-NOW! - Computer software - Microtest, Inc.

CD PAGES - Compact discs–prerecorded - Microsource, Inc.

CD PHOTO LIBRARY, THE - Computer storage devices–optical - Digital Vision, Inc.

CD-PREP INTERACTIVE - Recording label - Computerprep, Inc.

CD PROTECTION - Self-defense spray - Civilian Defense, Inc.

CD-QUICKSHARE - Computer software - Stac Electronics

CD-RAUNCH - Computer software - Phay Beau Productions

CD-ROM: 15 PHONICS LESSONS - Recording label - Learn Phonics/Will Read Co.

CD-ROM BROWSER PAKS - Fixtures - Chicago One Stop/Browser Display

CD ROM POWER - Magazines - HG Publications, Inc.

CD-RUNNER - Computer software - Beyond Software

CD SAFEGUARD - Computer storage devices–optical - Armron Corp.

CD SCAN CENTER - Computer software - Infolink Technologies, Inc.

CD SHARE - Computer software - Netpro Computing, Inc.

CD SHOWCASE - Computer peripheral equipment - International Business Machines Corp.

CD SLIDE - Video tapes–blank - Microplas Inc.

CD SOLUTIONS - Compact discs–prerecorded - International Data Group, Inc.

CD SPEEDWAY - Computer software ☆ - IMSI

CD STATION - Audio cabinets - Mactec Products

CD STEALTH - Cleaning preparations - Recoton Corp.

CD-TAGGING - Pharmaceutical preparations - Vyrex Corp.

CD TECHNOLOGY - Computers - CD Technology, Inc.

CD TIMESKETCH - Computer software ☆ - Electronic Courseware Systems Inc.

CD VISION - Computer software - Multicom Publishing, Inc.

CD WORLD - Compact discs–prerecorded - CD World Publishing Plus Corp.

CD-X DIGITAL AUDIO SYSTEM - Electronic transmitters and receivers - Scientific-Atlanta, Inc.

CD-X07 - Electrical equipment - Mas-Hamilton Group, Inc.

CD ZOOMING - Recording label - Capitol Records, Inc.

CDA - Pens - Caran D'Ache of Switzerland Inc.

CDARTS - Publisher's imprints - Software Productivity Consortium L.P.

CDB - Computer software - CDB Software, Inc.

CDC - Apparel–women's - Rampage Clothing Co.

CDC - Cardboard cutouts - Unicover Corp.

CDC - Jewelry–precious - Carat Diamond Corp.

CDCENTRAL - Computer hardware - CD Solutions, Inc.

CDEXTENDER - Computer software ☆ - OTG Software

CDF CULINARY DESIGN AND FIXTURE, INC. - Food products machinery - Culinary Design and Fixture, Inc.

CDF FIREFIGHTERS - Apparel and accessories - CDF Firefighters

CDG PLUS - Recording label - Slep-Tone Entertainment Corp.

CDH - Doors–metal - NKL Industries, Ltd.

CDI - Computer software ☆ - SRA/McGraw-Hill (Div. of The McGraw-Hill Companies)

CDI - Jewelry - Classique D'or Inc.

CDI - Lighting equipment - Northeast Robotics, Inc.

CDI - Steering mechanisms–boat - Edson Corp.

CDID - Computer software - Knowledge Access International, Inc.

CDIM - Computer software - Abbott Laboratories

CDIT - Audio tapes–blank - Sony Corp. of America

CDL - Computer software - BMC Software, Inc.

CDL - Jewelry - Carl D. Lindstrom & Sons Inc.

CDM - Building materials - Nanticoke Homes Inc.

CDM - Coffee - Wm. B. Reily & Co. Inc.

C.D.M. - Cold remedies - Lannett Co. Inc.

CDM - Compact discs–prerecorded - TRF Production Music Libraries

CDM - Distillation apparatus - Miles Inc. (Agfa Div.)

CDM - Furniture - Coastal Design Manufacturing Inc.

CDM BONING - Meat products–pork - Calumet Diversified Meats Inc.

C.D.M. CUIR DU MONDE - Coats–leather - MGRR, Inc.

CDMI - Advertising agencies - Coupon Data Marketing, Inc.

CDMS - Computer software - Motorola, Inc. (Land Mobile Products Sector)

CDP - Amplifiers - Electro-Voice, Inc.

CDP - Computer software - Calera Recognition Systems Inc.

CDPS - Pumps–cylinder - Camco International Inc.

CDQPRIMA - Audio equipment - Corporate Computer Systems, Inc.

CDR7 - Computer software - U.S. Intelco Networks, Inc.

CDS - Jewelry - Crystal Diamond Setters Ltd.

CDS - Motorcycles - Diversified Products Corp.

CDS CAPITAL DATA SYSTEMS - Computer software - Capital Data Systems, Inc.

CD'S DIGITAL GUM - Candy - Zeebs Enterprises, Inc.

C.D.'S STORY TIME - Computer storage devices–optical - Houghton Mifflin Co.

CDT CHOICE PRODUCTS, INC. - Stoves - Custom Design Technologies, Inc.

CDU - Electrical equipment - Phillips Electronics North America Corp.

CDX - Electronic equipment - Tandy Corp.

CDXPRT - Computer software ☆ - Aces Research, Inc.

CDXTENDER - Computer peripheral equipment - OTG Software

CE - Cosmetics - Charmelle Inc.

CE-1 CONTROL EXPANDER - Electrical apparatus - Bose Corp.

CE 22 - Guitars - Paul Reed Smith Guitars

CE CAROLINE ELLEN - Jewelry–precious - Caroline Ellen

CE COMMERCIAL ELECTRIC - Electric lighting equipment - M G Products, Inc.

CE-DOOX - Apparel and accessories - Carla Hilger

CE SOIR - Apparel–women's ☆ - Bali Co. Inc.

CE-VI-SOL - Vitamins and nutritional supplements - Bristol-Myers Squibb Co.

CEA - Hair care products - John Amico Expressive Hair Care Products

CEASAR - Cheese - Swissrose International Inc.

CEASARSTONE - Granite tile ☆ - Integrity Tile Co.

CEASE - Pet products - 8 in 1 Pet Products Inc.

CEASE-FIRE - Wastebaskets - Justrite Manufacturing Co.

CEASE FIRE CHILDREN'S DEFENSE FUND AND FRIENDS - Posters - Children's Defense Fund

CEASERS - Watches - Temlex/Jupiter Watch Corp.

CEBE - Sunglasses - Suunto USA

CEBECO - Shortening ☆ - Patrick Cudahy Inc.

CEBEFORTIS - Pharmaceutical preparations ☆ - Upjohn Co.

CEBELIA - Thread - DMC Corp.

CEBENASE - Pharmaceutical preparations ☆ - Upjohn Co.

CEBES - Vegetable oil - Aarhus Inc.

CEBETINIC - Pharmaceutical preparations ☆ - Upjohn Co.

CEBID - Pharmaceutical preparations ☆ - Roberts/Hauck Pharmaceuticals Inc.

CEBOCAP - Pharmaceutical preparations - Forest Pharmaceuticals Inc.

CEBRALAN - Vitamins and nutritional supplements - Lannett Co. Inc.

CEBU - Occasional tables ☆ - JDI Group, Inc.

CECCHI - Wines - Banfi Vintners

CECCHI AND CECCHI - Blankets - Molly Roberts & Co. Inc.

CECE KLESELSTEIN - Handbags - Ann Klein for Oroton

CECELIA'S GOLD - Fruits and vegetables - Cecelia Packing Corp.

CECELIAS PRIDE - Fruits and vegetables - Cecelia Packing Corp.

CECHIC - Shoes - Futura Shoe Corp.

CECIL - Watches - Prestige Enterprises, Inc.

CECIL B. DELION - Toys–stuffed - Gund, Inc.

CECILIA BERETTA - Wines - Parliament Import Co.

CECILIA SOH COLLECTION - Apparel and accessories - Cecilia Soh

CECILIA STAPLES - Greeting cards ☆ - American Artists Group Inc.

CECILLE - Watches - Bulova Corp.

CECILY KNITS - Apparel and accessories ☆ - Esprit De Corp.

CECLOR - Pharmaceutical preparations - Eli Lilly and Co.

CECO - Hardware - Blaine Window Hardware Inc.

CECO - Sporting goods - J.A. Cissel Manufacturing Co.

CECO - Steel products - Robertson-Ceco Corp.

CECOLOK - Roofing materials–slate - Robertson-Ceco Corp.

CECON - Vitamins and nutritional supplements - Abbott Laboratories

CECOROLL - Roofing materials–slate - Robertson-Ceco Corp.

CECRISA - Tiles–ceramic - Maxsam Sales, Inc.

CED - Condensers–electronic - ITT Industries, Inc.

CEDA-TONE - Siding–asphalt ☆ - GAF Corp.

CEDAB - Pharmaceutical preparations ☆ - Edom Laboratories Inc.

CEDALUX - Cleaning preparations - Cedalux, Inc.

CEDAR - Brushes–paint - Allpro Corp.

CEDAR - Closet organizers ☆ - Vermillion Inc.

CEDAR - Novelty items - J.B. Deere Cedar Craft Co.

CEDAR - Trailers–travel ☆ - Fleetwood Enterprises, Inc.

CEDAR-AL - Deodorizers - Cedar-Al Products
CEDAR ALL - All purpose cleaner - Great Northeast Corp.
CEDAR AUDIO LTD. - Audio equipment - G Prime Limited
CEDAR BLUE DRUM - Herbicides - Cedar Chemical Corp.
CEDAR BREATHER - Roofing materials - Benjamin Obdyke Inc.
CEDAR BREEZE - Perfumes - Carolina Designs Ltd.
CEDAR BROOK - Playground equipment - Cedar Brook Rustic Co.
CEDAR CANYON - Siding–metal - Aluminum Co. of America
CEDAR CHALET - Toys ☆ - Handy Home Products
CEDAR CHALET II - Toys - Handy Home Products
CEDAR CHEST - Fabrics–tapestry ☆ - Coloroll Inc.
CEDAR CHEST - Wallpaper - Madison Ave. Wallcoverings
CEDAR CHEST - Wallpaper ☆ - Imperial Wallcoverings, Inc.
CEDAR CHEST, THE - Containers - Whitmor Manufacturing Co. Inc.
CEDAR CLASSIC - Wood products - Weyerhaeuser Co.
CEDAR CLOSE-IT - Bags–plastic - Cedar Partners
CEDAR CLOSET SHOP COLLECTION - Luggage - Whitmor Manufacturing Co. Inc.
CEDAR CREEK - Lighting fixtures - Kirkland's, Inc.
CEDAR CREEK - Popcorn - Noble Distributors, Inc.
CEDAR CREEK - Siding–insulating - Weekes Forest Products Inc.
CEDAR CREEK - Vegetables–canned - McCall Farms Inc.
CEDAR CREEK - Wines - Cedar Creek Winery Inc.
CEDAR CREEK - Wines - House of Burgundy Inc.
CEDAR CREEK COLLECTION - Christmas tree ornaments - Kirkland's, Inc.
CEDAR CREEK WEST - Wines - Wollersheim Winery, Inc.
CEDAR CREST - Floor coverings - Tarkett, Inc.
CEDAR CREST - Footwear - Heartland Shoe Co.
CEDAR CREST - Shoes ☆ - Genesco Inc.
CEDAR CREST - Wood products - Champion International Corp.
CEDAR DECK - Fencing–wood - Gerber Industries Inc.
CEDAR DREAMS - Pet products - Cedarsack Pet Products, Inc.
CEDAR FARMS - Frozen foods - Pacific Valley Foods
CEDAR FRESH - Deodorizers - Surco Products Inc.
CEDAR FRESH - Pet products - Mid-Florida Mining Co.
CEDAR GLEN - Swimming pools ☆ - Doughboy Recreational Inc.
CEDAR GROVE - Floor coverings ☆ - Congoleum Corp.
CEDAR GROVE - Wood products - Champion International Corp.
CEDAR HILL - Swimming pools - Lomart Industries
CEDAR HILL - Wallpaper - Belmont Wallcoverings
CEDAR HOLLOW - Meat products - Arck Foods Inc.
CEDAR HOLLOW - Wainscotting - Georgia-Pacific Corp.
CEDAR ISLE - Floor coverings–carpet and rugs - Patcraft Mills Inc.
CEDAR-IZE - Cleaning preparations - Willert Home Products, Inc.
CEDAR JOE - Cigars - H.T.L., Inc.
CEDAR KEY - Food processors - Seasweet Crabmeat Co.
CEDAR-KING - Pencils - National Pen & Pencil Co.
CEDAR KOTE - Paints - Rodda Paint Co.
CEDAR LAKE - Food products - Cedar Lake MGM Foods
CEDAR LANE - Siding–insulating - Georgia-Pacific Corp.
CEDAR-LIFE - Paints ☆ - Adelphi Coatings Co.
CEDAR LITE - Pet products - Cedrus International Inc.
CEDAR-LOK - Wood products - Aspen Valley Lumber Co. Inc.
CEDAR PLUS - Deodorizers - Coughlan Products Corp.
CEDAR PLUS - Shingles–shakes - American Wood Treaters US, Inc.
CEDAR RAPIDS KERNELS - Apparel and accessories - Cedar Rapids Professional Baseball Club Inc.
CEDAR REZ - Adhesives and sealants ☆ - PPG Industries, Inc.
CEDAR RIDGE - Food products ☆ - Louis Rich Co.
CEDAR RIDGE - Furniture - Bart Williamson
CEDAR RIDGE - Swimming pools ☆ - Doughboy Recreational Inc.
CEDAR RIDGE - Vinyl siding - Reynolds Metals Co.
CEDAR SELECT - Vinyl ☆ - Variform, Inc.
CEDAR SENSE - Chests–cedar - Natural Products Corp.
CEDAR SENSE - Pencils - Musgrave Pencil Co. Inc.
CEDAR SLEEPERS - Pet products - Jen Cel Lite Corp.
CEDAR VALLEY - Log cabins–prefabricated - Ward Log Homes
CEDAR VALLEY - Wood products - Magla Products Inc.
CEDAR WOODS - Tandem Imports Corp.
CEDAR WORKS - Bird feeders - Cedar Works Inc.
CEDAR WORKS - Freezers - Dibrell Brothers Inc.
CEDAR WRAP - Cigar boxes–wood ☆ - Consolidated Cigar Corp.
CEDARAIRE - Deodorizers - Coughlan Products Corp.
CEDARAK - Garment hangers–wood - Ink-Rol Products, Inc.
CEDARBROOK - Floor coverings - Mannington Resilient Floors
CEDARBROOK - Saunas - Cedarbrook Sauna Inc.

CEDARBURG DAIRY - Milk - Cedarburg Dairy Inc.
CEDARCOOL - Lubricants - Cedar Lubricants Corp.
CEDARCUT - Lubricants - Cedar Lubricants Corp.
CEDARDALE - Prefabricated buildings–wood - Cedardale Homes Inc.
CEDARENE - Pet products - Black Sheep Inc.
CEDARFLAME - Fireplace equipment - Duraflame, Inc.
CEDARFLAME II - Fireplace equipment ☆ - Duraflame, Inc.
CEDARIFIC - Pet products - Northeastern Products Corp.
CEDARLAND - Tortillas - Cedarlane Foods
CEDARLINE - Wood products - Giles and Kendall Inc.
CEDARLITE - Roofing materials - Monierlifetile
CEDARLITE - Roofing materials–concrete - Monier Roof Tile Inc.
CEDARLOCK - Office supplies - McBee Loose Leaf Binders
CEDARMONT KIDS - Recording label - Cedarmont Music, LLC
CEDARMONT KIDS - Recording label - Mike and Sue Guy
CEDAROMA - Cigars ☆ - General Cigar Co., Inc.
CEDAROMA - Giftware - Blair Cedar and Novelty Works
CEDAROMA - Pet products ☆ - National Display Materials
CEDAROSE - Cosmetics - Lancome
CEDARPLY - Plywood - K-Ply Inc.
CEDARPRO - Wood products - Canton Lumber
CEDARPRO - Wood products - P & M Cedar Products, Inc.
CEDAR'S NATURALLY DELICIOUS - Vegetable sauces - Cedar's Mediterranean Foods, Inc.
CEDARSIDE - Siding–insulating - Masonite Corp.
CEDARSTRAIN - Wood products - George C. Brown & Co.
CEDARSWING - Swings–wood - CedarWorks
CEDARTONE - Wood products - Houston Woodtech Inc.
CEDARTOPS - Containers–plastic - Tucker Housewares Inc.
CEDARWOOD - Bird feeders - Cedar Works Inc.
CEDARWOOD - Siding–insulating ☆ - Masonite Corp.
CEDARWOOD - Siding–metal - Alcan Aluminum Corp. Alcan Building Products Div.
CEDATEX - Siding - GAF Corp.
CEDCO - Calendars - Cedco Publishing Co.
CEDE - Bird feeds - Sunshine Bird Supplies, Inc.
CEDELIA KILIMS - Giftware ☆ - Kuhn Concepts
CEDER CREEK ORCHARDS - Fruits and vegetables - Edward Pitsch Produce Inc.
CEDERGREEN - Fruits and vegetables ☆ - J.R. Simplot Co.
CEDERROTH - Bandages - Roberts/Hauck Pharmaceuticals Inc.
CEDILANID - Pharmaceutical preparations ☆ - Sandoz Pharmaceuticals Corp.
CEDIR - Floor coverings–tile - Federal Tile Imports Inc.
CEDON - Corkscrews - Franmara Co. Inc.
CEDRIC HARTMAN - Furniture - Jack Lenor Larsen, Inc.
CEDROS - Cigars - Cedros
CEE - Vitamins and nutritional supplements - Legere Pharmaceuticals Inc.
CEE-B-COMPLEX - Pharmaceutical preparations ☆ - Pasadena Research Laboratories, Inc.
CEE-BEES - Food products - Cap's Italian Foods Inc.
CEE COMPLETE - Vitamins and nutritional supplements - Natural Organics, Inc.
CEE CRYSTALS - Health care products - Above All Health Inc.
CEE KLEIN ACCESSORIES - Leather goods - RJK Enterprises, Ltd.
CEE-PLEX - Vitamins and nutritional supplements - Nutrition Enterprises
CEE-ROSE - Vitamins and nutritional supplements ☆ - J.R. Carlson Laboratories Inc.
CEE TEE CO - Tools ☆ - Crescent
CEE VEE - Envelopes - Connecticut Valley Paper & Envelope Co. Inc.
CEE W BEE - Pharmaceutical preparations - Wesley Pharmacal Co. Inc.
CEEJECT - Pharmaceutical preparations - Wesley Pharmacal Co. Inc.
CEELECT - Food products - Martha White Foods Inc.
CEENU - Pharmaceutical preparations - Bristol-Myers Squibb Co.
CEEPA - Pharmaceutical preparations - Armenpharm Ltd.
CEERON - Pharmaceutical preparations ☆ - Physician Sales & Service
CEESPAN - Pharmaceutical preparations - Wesley Pharmacal Co. Inc.
CEETOLAN - Mouthwashes - Lannett Co. Inc.
CEF PRESS - Publisher's imprints - Child Evangelism Fellowship Inc.
CEFA-TABS - Veterinary pharmaceutical preparations - Bristol-Myers Squibb Co.
CEFADYL - Antibiotics - Bristol-Myers Squibb Co.
CEFOBID - Pharmaceutical preparations - Pfizer Inc.
CEFOL - Pharmaceutical preparations - Abbott Laboratories
CEFOTAN - Pharmaceutical preparations - Zeneca Inc.
C.E.G. - Pharmaceutical preparations - Schering-Plough Healthcare Products
CEGAB - Computer hardware - Cegab Development Corp.

☆ = Now out of production

CEI PACER - Trailers–truck - Courtesy Enterprises, Inc.
CEIL-O-LITE - Paints - Cloverleaf Paint & Varnish
CEILCOTE - Sealing compounds - Master Builders Inc.
CEILCRETE - Sealing compounds - Master Builders Inc.
CEILFLOR - Floor coverings ☆ - Master Builders Inc.
CEILGARD - Adhesives and sealants - Master Builders Inc.
CEILHEAT - Heating equipment - ABB Power T&D Co. Inc.
CEILING ARMOR - Tiles–ceiling - Helvie Plastics Extrusions
CEILING CLOSET - Prefabricated buildings–metal - Stowitup Products
CEILING MASTER - Fastening tool ☆ - ITW Ramset/Red Head
CEILITE - Paints ☆ - Fuller-O'Brien Paints Inc.
CEILLINE - Adhesives and sealants - Master Builders Inc.
CEILTILE - Staples - Arrow Fastener Co. Inc.
CEISAR - Computer software - Ceisar Systems Inc.
CEJON - Hairpins - Cee Bee Manufacturing Inc.
CEL - Gasoline - Cel Oil Products Corp.
CEL-TON-SA - Health care products ☆ - CTS Laboratories Inc.
CEL-U-JEL - Pharmaceutical preparations - Roberts/Hauck Pharmaceuticals Inc.
CEL-U-ROL - Cellulose plastics materials ☆ - Johnson & Johnson
CELADON - Roofing materials–clay - Certainteed Corp. (Roofing Products Group)
CELADONIA - Giftware ☆ - European Imports of California Inc.
CELAN - Computer peripheral equipment - Celan Technology, Inc.
CELANDINE - Rings–jewelry - Artcarved Inc.
CELANEX - Pharmaceutical preparations - Hoechst-Roussel Pharmaceuticals Inc.
CELANO - Floor coverings–tile - Kentile Floors Inc.
CELATOM - Chemical preparations - Eagle-Picher Minerals, Inc.
CELCO - Lighting equipment - Celco Inc.
CELCON - Pharmaceutical preparations - Hoechst-Roussel Pharmaceuticals Inc.
CELCON ACETALK - Paper–newsprint - Hoechst Celanese Corp.
CELDYNE - Telephones–cellular - Tessco Technologies Inc.
CELEBRATE - Floor coverings–carpet and rugs - Olympic Carpets Inc.
CELEBRATE - Glassware–household - Anchor Hocking Glass, Inc.
CELEBRATE - Jewelry - Deborah West Accessory Art Collection
CELEBRATE - Novelty items - Kuepper Favor Co., Inc.
CELEBRATE POTTSVILLE - Beverages–alcohol ☆ - D.G. Yuengling & Son Inc.
CELEBRATE READING! - Computer software - HarperCollins Educational Publishers Inc.
CELEBRATING EXCELLENCE - Awards, plaques and medals - Successories, Inc.
CELEBRATING OREGON - Greeting cards - Willow Creek West
CELEBRATING WASHINGTON - Greeting cards - Willow Creek West
CELEBRATION - Apparel–children's - Federated Department Stores, Inc.
CELEBRATION - Bedding–linen - Dan River Inc.
CELEBRATION - Beverages–malt - Sierra Nevada Brewing Co.
CELEBRATION - Bicycles ☆ - Huffy Corp.
CELEBRATION - Cooking equipment–household - Jacksonville Manufacturing
CELEBRATION - Dinnerware–glass ☆ - Nikko Ceramics Inc.
CELEBRATION - Dolls - Mattel, Inc.
CELEBRATION - Easels - Anco Wood Specialties Inc.
CELEBRATION - Floor coverings - Congoleum Corp.
CELEBRATION - Furniture ☆ - Lane Co. Inc.
CELEBRATION - Giftware - Arnart Imports Inc.
CELEBRATION - Glassware–household - Crest Studios
CELEBRATION - Glassware–household - Oneida Ltd.
CELEBRATION - House furnishings ☆ - Lea Industries Inc.
CELEBRATION - Housewares - Mervyn's
CELEBRATION - Invitations - Celebration Wedding Stationery
CELEBRATION - Jewelry - Pakula & Co.
CELEBRATION - Kitchenware–earthenware ☆ - Arita Sales Co. Inc.
CELEBRATION - Napkins–paper - Erving Paper Products Inc.
CELEBRATION - Organs–musical instrument - Midi Music Center, Inc.
CELEBRATION - Rings–jewelry ☆ - Artcarved Inc.
CELEBRATION - Stationery - Taylor Corp.
CELEBRATION - Toilets–porcelain - Friendship Designs
CELEBRATION - Toys–stuffed ☆ - Gund, Inc.
CELEBRATION - Wines - Pliska Winery
CELEBRATION - Wines ☆ - Domecq Importers Inc.
CELEBRATION II - Floor coverings–carpet and rugs - Patrick Carpet Mills
CELEBRATION BLEND - Cookies - Parco Foods, Inc.
CELEBRATION/CABARET - Floor coverings–carpet and rugs - Johnson's Carpets Inc.

CELEBRATION DESIGNS - Trees–artificial - Celebration Designs
CELEBRATION FOR KIDS - Jewelry - Pakula & Co.
CELEBRATION OF SPIRIT! - Paper products - Kristen & Clayton Huntington
CELEBRATION PEOPLE, THE - Greeting cards - CUC Publishing, Inc.
CELEBRATION PEOPLE, THE - Paper–gift wrap - Sally Foster, Inc.
CELEBRATION SOFTWARE - Computer software - Pascal M. Kaplan
CELEBRATIONS - Candlesticks - Crystal Clear Industries, Inc.
CELEBRATIONS - Christmas tree lights - Ace Hardware Corp.
CELEBRATIONS - Furniture - Hammary Furniture Co. Inc.
CELEBRATIONS - Paper–gift wrap - American Greetings Corp.
CELEBRATIONS - Publisher's imprints - Heartland Samplers Inc.
CELEBRATIONS - Punch sets - Indiana Glass Co.
CELEBRATIONS ETC....WEDDING WHEEL - Paper–writing - Celebrations Etc....
CELEBRATIONS II - Luggage - American Tourister, Inc.
CELEBRATIONS OF FAITH - Greeting cards - American Greetings Corp.
CELEBRATIONS OF LIFE - Jewelry - CJC Holdings, Inc.
CELEBRATIONS OF THE HEART - Greeting cards - American Greetings Corp.
CELEBRATOR DOPPLEBOCK - Beverages–malt - Merchant du Vin Corp.
CELEBRET - Wines ☆ - Maison Jomere Ltd.
CELEBRIS - Computer software - Digital Equipment Corp.
CELEBRITE - Clocks - Ridgeway Clock Co.
CELEBRITY - Apparel and accessories - Crystal Brands Inc.
CELEBRITY - Blinds–venetian - Hunter Douglas, Inc.
CELEBRITY - Cabinets - Nutone Inc.
CELEBRITY - Cabinets ☆ - Haas Cabinet Co. Inc.
CELEBRITY - Clocks - General Time Corp. (Westclox/Seth Thomas Div.)
CELEBRITY - Combs - Burmax Co. Inc.
CELEBRITY - Compasses–magnetic ☆ - Dinsmore Instrument Co.
CELEBRITY - Cookies ☆ - Parco Foods, Inc.
CELEBRITY - Dinnerware - Genpak Corp.
CELEBRITY - Fireplace equipment - Thermo-Rite Manufacturing Co.
CELEBRITY - Floor coverings ☆ - Tarkett, Inc.
CELEBRITY - Floor coverings–carpet and rugs - Philadelphia Carpets
CELEBRITY - Floor coverings–carpet and rugs - Queen Carpet Corp.
CELEBRITY - Floor coverings–carpet and rugs - S and S Mills Inc.
CELEBRITY - Floor coverings–carpet and rugs ☆ - American Carpet Mills
CELEBRITY - Floor coverings–carpet and rugs ☆ - Regal Rugs Inc.
CELEBRITY - Footwear - Reebok International Ltd.
CELEBRITY - Fruits–canned - Atalanta Corp.
CELEBRITY - Furniture ☆ - Bassett Furniture Industries, Inc.
CELEBRITY - Furniture ☆ - Hooker Furniture Corp.
CELEBRITY - Furniture ☆ - Mersman Furniture Co.
CELEBRITY - Glassware–household - Crystal Clear Importing Co. Inc.
CELEBRITY - Glassware–household - Durand International
CELEBRITY - Guitars - Ovation Instruments
CELEBRITY - Hams - Bob Ostrow Co.
CELEBRITY - Hardware ☆ - Amerock Corp.
CELEBRITY - High chairs - Lisco, Inc.
CELEBRITY - Housewares - Pro Hardware Inc.
CELEBRITY - Motor vehicles - General Motors Corp. (Chevrolet Motor Div.)
CELEBRITY - Pens - Sanford Corp.
CELEBRITY - Scooters–motorized - Pride Health Care, Inc.
CELEBRITY - Seafood products–fresh or frozen - Southeast Foods Inc.
CELEBRITY - Sinks–metal - Elkay Manufacturing Co.
CELEBRITY - Sporting goods - Brunswick Corp.
CELEBRITY - Sporting goods - O'Brien International
CELEBRITY - Telephones - At&T Corp.
CELEBRITY - Toys–stuffed ☆ - Fun World Inc.
CELEBRITY - Trailers–travel - Travel Line Enterprises Inc.
CELEBRITY - Trailers–travel ☆ - Coachmen Industries, Inc.
CELEBRITY - Underwear and nightwear - Lovable Co.
CELEBRITY - Vacuum cleaners and accessories ☆ - The Hoover Co.
CELEBRITY - Wallpaper ☆ - Morton Jonap Co. Inc.
CELEBRITY - Wigs - Jean Paree Weegs Inc.
CELEBRITY - Window shades - Acme Window Coverings Ltd.
CELEBRITY BY LOVABLE - Underwear and nightwear - Lovable Co.
CELEBRITY CHOICE - Floor coverings–carpet and rugs - Burlington House Carpets
CELEBRITY CLASSIQUE BY ELKAY - Sinks - Elkay Manufacturing Co.
CELEBRITY EUROSPORT - Motor vehicles ☆ - General Motors Corp. (Chevrolet Motor Div.)
CELEBRITY GOLF ASSOCIATION - Bags–duffel - Celebrity Golf Association
CELEBRITY KIDS - Apparel–children's - Celebrity International, Inc.
CELEBRITY SCRAMBLR - Games - Scramb-L-Gram, Inc.

CELEBRITY SHADES - Eyeglasses - Cable Car Eyeware
CELEBRITY TABOO - Games - Milton Bradley Co.
CELECTRIC - Refrigerators - Caronel Enterprises, Inc.
CELENESE - Window coverings - Curtron Curtain Inc.
CELENTANO - Spaghetti sauces - Celentano Brothers Inc.
CELERE - Ships–sailing vessels - Sorensen Yachts
CELERITY - Boats - Glen-L Marine Designs
CELERITY - Computer software - Celerity Systems, Inc.
CELERO - Gelatin - Vyse Gelatin Co.
CELEST-EL - Lamps - Metro Mark, Inc.
CELESTA - Chimes ☆ - J.W. Stannard Co.
CELESTE - Floor coverings–carpet and rugs - Eligere Carpets
CELESTE - Floor coverings–carpet and rugs ☆ - Regal Rugs Inc.
CELESTE - Glassware–household - Seneca Glass Co.
CELESTE - Glassware–household ☆ - Gorham Inc.
CELESTE - Harps - Castiglione Accordion
CELESTE - Jewelry - Victoria Creations Inc.
CELESTE - Prosthetic apparatus - OTC Professional Appliances
CELESTE - Tape recorders - V-M Corp.
CELESTE - Toys–stuffed - Gund, Inc.
CELESTE - Whirlpool spa ☆ - Jacuzzi Inc.
CELESTE BLUE STRETCH - Giftware ☆ - Fenton Art Glass Co.
CELESTE PROFESSIONAL - Hair curlers - Caruso International, Inc.
CELESTIAL - Blinds–venetian ☆ - Hunter Douglas, Inc.
CELESTIAL - Dinnerware ☆ - Corning Inc.
CELESTIAL - Dinnerware–glass ☆ - Nikko Ceramics Inc.
CELESTIAL - Floor coverings - American Floor Products Co. Inc.
CELESTIAL - Floor coverings–carpet and rugs ☆ - Dorsett Carpet Mills Inc.
CELESTIAL - Floor coverings–carpet and rugs ☆ - Royalweve Carpet Mills
CELESTIAL - Giftware - Accessories International
CELESTIAL - Glassware–household - Federal Glass
CELESTIAL - Paints - Jones Blair Co.
CELESTIAL - Teas–herbal - Celestial Seasonings, Inc.
CELESTIAL ARTS - Publisher's imprints - Ten Speed Press
CELESTIAL BLUE - Dinnerware - Corning Inc.
CELESTIAL CAFE - Teas - Celestial Seasonings, Inc.
CELESTIAL CANDLE - Candles - Biedermann & Sons Inc.
CELESTIAL CATS - Vitamins and nutritional supplements - Celeste Yarnall & Associates
CELESTIAL CREATIONS - Garden furniture - Celeste Garvey
CELESTIAL DREAMS - Candles - Joel Wyman
CELESTIAL FARMS - Food products - Prestige American Foods
CELESTIAL GATE - Wines - Sokol Blosser Winery
CELESTIAL HARMONIES - Recording label - Celestial Harmonies
CELESTIAL INTERIORS - Wallpaper ☆ - Eisenhart Wallcoverings Co.
CELESTIAL SCENTS - Incense - Inno-Scents, Inc.
CELESTIAL SEASONINGS - Teas–herbal - Celestial Seasonings, Inc.
CELESTIAL SEASONINGS HERBAL THROAT DROPS - Cough drops - American Chicle Co.
CELESTIAL SEASONINGS SOOTHERS - Cough drops - American Chicle Co.
CELESTIAL STARS - Rings–jewelry - Artcarved Inc.
CELESTIAL SUNFLOWER - Puzzles - Warren Industries Inc.
CELESTIAL SYMPHONY - Giftware ☆ - Enesco Corp.
CELESTIALE - Perfumes - Revlon Consumer Products Corp.
CELESTIALS - Candy ☆ - Casanova Chocolate Co.
CELESTINO VEGA - Cigars - American Case and Luggage Co., Inc.
CELESTION - Audio equipment - Celestion Industries Inc.
CELESTIQUE - Fans–electric - Wal-Mart Stores Inc.
CELESTONE - Pharmaceutical preparations - Schering-Plough Healthcare Products
CELESTONE SOLUSPAN - Pharmaceutical preparations - Schering-Plough Healthcare Products
CELESTRA - Fabrics - BBA Nonwovens Simpsonville, Inc.
CELESTRA - Floor coverings–carpet and rugs - Milliken & Co. Inc.
CELESTRA - Toys ☆ - Placo Products Co.
CELESTRIAL STAR - Floor coverings–carpet and rugs - Mohawk Carpet Corp.
CELGARD - Pharmaceutical preparations - Hoechst-Roussel Pharmaceuticals Inc.
CELI - See **14 KT. CELI**
CELIA - Rings–jewelry - Artcarved Inc.
CELICA - Motor vehicles–automobiles - Toyota Motor Sales USA Inc.
CELIMA - Tiles–ceramic ☆ - Maxsam Sales, Inc.
CELINA - Housewares - Himark Enterprises Inc.
CELINE - Glassware–household - Crystal Clear Importing Co. Inc.
CELIO - Olive oil - Made in France

CELIS GOLDEN - Beverages–malt - Celis Brewery, Inc.
CELIS GRAND CRIL - Beverages–malt - Celis Brewery, Inc.
CELIS PALE BOCK - Beverages–malt - Celis Brewery, Inc.
CELIS RASPBERRY - Beverages–malt - Celis Brewery, Inc.
CELIS WHITE - Beverages–malt - Celis Brewery, Inc.
CELISSE - Perfumes ☆ - Dana Perfumes Corp.
CELL ACTIVATOR - Vitamins and nutritional supplements - Herbalife International, Inc.
CELL-AIRE - Packaging–paper - Sealed Air Corp.
CELL BLOCKS - Skateboards - Santa Cruz Skateboards
CELL BLOK - Electronic equipment - Douglas A. Taylor
CELL CHARGE - Vitamins and nutritional supplements - Bionutritional Research Group, Inc.
CELL DEFENSE - Vitamins and nutritional supplements - Makers of Kal, Inc.
CELL ENSEMBLE - Computer software - Cadence Design Systems, Inc.
CELL GARD - Electronic equipment - J.R. Hunt Ventures
CELL GUARD - Vitamins and nutritional supplements - Source Naturals
CELL-KLEEN - Cleaning preparations - Penetone Corp.
CELL-O-GEN - Pharmaceutical preparations - Gen-Cell Research
CELL-O-SEED - Flowers, plants, and seeds - North American Green, Inc.
CELL-O-WRAPT - Candy - Peerless Confection Co.
CELL PLEX - Vitamins and nutritional supplements - Natural Organics, Inc.
CELL PROTECTOR - Antitoxins - Foodscience Laboratories Inc.
CELL RENEWAL SYSTEMS - Skin care products - Cell Renewal Systems Inc.
CELL ROBOTICS INC. - Microscopes–corneal - Cell Robotics Inc.
CELL SAVER - Regulators–voltage - Exide Electronics Corp.
CELL-SELECTOR - Batteries - Matsushita Electric Corp. of America
CELL-SENTINEL - Cellular telecommunications package - Signal Crafters Inc.
CELL STRENGTH - Vitamins and nutritional supplements - Source Naturals
CELL THERAPY 7 - Skin care products - Arizona Natural Resources
CELL-THRU - Antennas - Electronics Research, Inc.
CELL TIME JAPAN - Batteries - Cellular Shop Corp.
CELL-U-CORE - Pipes–plastic - Shapco, Inc.
CELL-U-COTTON - Skin care products - Hess Hair Milk Laboratories Inc.
CELL-U-MEMO - Telephone answering machines - Salton/Maxim Housewares, Inc.
CELL-U-PHONE - Telephone apparatus ☆ - Allen Telecom Group, Inc.
CELL-U-WELD - File folders - Smead Manufacturing Co.
CELL-U-WETT - Fertilizers - Creative Services, Inc.
CELL-WISE - Vitamins and nutritional supplements - Melaleuca, Inc.
CELLA - Agendas ☆ - George R. Chaby, Inc.
CELLA - Cosmetics - Multisonic Corp.
CELLA BRELLA - Umbrellas ☆ - George R. Chaby, Inc.
CELLA WINES - Wines - Shaw-Ross International Importers
CELLADOORS - Building materials–asbestos - Gordon Corp.
CELLAL - Enamels ☆ - Woolsey Marine Industries
CELLAMINS - Vitamins and nutritional supplements - Twinlab
CELLAR - Food products ☆ - Morgan Pickle Co.
CELLAR DWELLERS - Books–comic - David James Harrison
CELLAR SAVER - Electronic equipment - Kenneth Zuchlewski
CELLARMASTER - Computer software - Grapevine Software Corp.
CELLARMASTER'S BOTTLE PEPPERMILL - Pepper mills - Franmara Co. Inc.
CELLA'S - Candy - Tootsie Roll Industries, Inc.
CELLBASE - Telephones–cellular - Hello Direct
CELLCO - Electrical equipment - Telewave, Inc.
CELLCORDER - Battery testers - Albercorp.
CELLCYCLE MINERALLS - Vitamins and dietary supplements - Naturally Vitamin Supplements Inc.
CELLEBOOST - Vitamins and nutritional supplements - Reliv' International, Inc.
CELLEBRATE - Vitamins and nutritional supplements - Reliv' International, Inc.
CELLECT - Printing trades machinery - Consolidated Group, Inc.
CELLERATION - Skin care products - Cut-Heal Animal Care Products, Inc.
CELLERITY - Communications equipment–mobile - Pacific Communication Sciences, Inc.
CELLGUARD - Radio communications equipment - Narda Microwave Corp.
CELLIER DES SAMSONS - Beverages–alcohol - Margus Co.
CELLIFE - Vitamins and nutritional supplements - Cell Life Corp.
CELLINI - Cosmetics - Faberge Co.
CELLINI - Lighters - Colibri Inc.
CELLINI - Pigments - Engelhard Corp.
CELLINI - Shoes - Globe Footwear Corp.
CELLINI - Watches - Rolex Watch USA, Inc.
CELLINI COLLECTION - Apparel and accessories ☆ - Edison Brothers Stores, Inc.
CELLINI SPORT - Apparel and accessories ☆ - Edison Brothers Stores, Inc.

☆ = Now out of production

CELLINI TAPESTRY - Luggage ☆ - Ventura Travelware Inc.
CELLINI'S - Breads - Grandma Emilie Brown, Inc.
CELLINO - Jewelry - Cellino Inc.
CELLITE - Antennas - Radio Frequency Systems, Inc.
CELLLINK - Telephones - Delaware Capital Formation Inc.
CELLMATE - Cases–plastic - Pioneer Marketing & Research, Inc.
CELLMATE - Computer peripheral equipment - Interactive Products Corp.
CELLO - Adhesives and sealants ☆ - Seal-O-Matic Corp.
CELLO - Audio equipment - Cello, Ltd.
CELLO - Cigars - Avanti Cigar Co.
CELLO - Cleaning preparations - Cello Chemical Co.
CELLO - Fruits and vegetables ☆ - Mann Packing Co., Inc.
CELLO BIG BAG - Snack foods - Planters LifeSavers Co.
CELLO BY ANNETTE - Perfumes - Aloe Vera Development Corp.
CELLO-FLOOR - Musical instrument accessories - M & M Distributing Co.
CELLO PLASTIC - Glue–household or industrial ☆ - Empire Blended Products Co.
CELLO RIBBON STICK - Candy ☆ - Bradley Candy Manufacturing Co.
CELLO-SHEEN - Housewares ☆ - American Textile Products Co.
CELLO SLITTER - Adhesives and sealants ☆ - Seal-O-Matic Corp.
CELLOBESE - Pharmaceutical preparations - Lanpar Co.
CELLOBUFFER - Hair care products - Sebastian International, Inc.
CELLOCK - Metals - Environmental Interiors, Inc.
CELLOCOUP - Cellulosic plastic sheets - John Henry Co.
CELLOFIX - Hair care products - Sebastian International, Inc.
CELLOFOAM - Insulating materials–foam - CelloFoam North America Inc.
CELLONE - Communications equipment - Cellular One Group
CELLONET - Mobile phone - Continental Telephone Corp.
CELLOPLAST - Bags–plastic - Rosenlew Inc.
CELLOROME - Skin care products - Aveda Corp.
CELLOTHANE - Floor waxers–household - Cello Chemical Co.
CELLOTHYL - Laxatives ☆ - Numark Laboratories Inc.
CELLOTYPE - Paper–stencil - A.B. Dick Co.
CELLOUETTE - Bath products - Cellouette Inc.
CELLPLEX - Computer peripheral equipment - 3Com Corp.
CELLSAVER - Paper products - Sonoco Products Co.
CELLSIGHT - Computer software - LCC Inc.
CELLSPARC 360 - Vitamins and nutritional supplements - Aim International, Inc.
CELLSTAR - Cellular telephones - National Auto Center, Inc.
CELLSTAR - Fish–fresh or frozen - Ocean Duke Corp.
CELLSTAR - Laboratory apparatus - Revco Scientific, Inc.
CELLSTAR - Telephone apparatus ☆ - RF Communications Div.
CELLTEC - Cables - Cable Design Technologies, Inc.
CELLU-CRAFT - Packaging–foam - Alusuisse Flexible Packaging Inc.
CELLU-CUSHION - Packaging–paper - Sealed Air Corp.
CELLU-MASK - Packaging–paper - Sealed Air Corp.
CELLU SOLVE - Hair care products - Gold Medal Hair Products Inc.
CELLU SPRAY - Insulating materials–foam - Thermoguard Co.
CELLU-TITE - Skin care products - Momentum Marketing Inc.
CELLU-TONE - Paints - Pratt & Lambert, Inc.
CELLU-VAR - Health care products - Enzymatic Therapy, Inc.
CELLUCLAY - Papier-mache articles - Activa Products Inc.
CELLUCLEAR - Rubber-stamp supplies - Consolidated Stamp Manufacturing Co. Inc.
CELLUCOTTON - Cotton–balls - Kimberly-Clark Corp.
CELLUFIRM - Skin care products - Elysee Scientific Cosmetic Co.
CELLUFRESH - Ophthalmic goods - Allergan, Inc.
CELLUGRAF - SIGNALS - Labels–gummed - Labelon Corp.
CELLUGREEN - Fabrics - K.D. Richards Inc.
CELLUGRO - Plant growth regulators - Atlantic Construction Fabrics, Inc.
CELLULAR - Chewing gum - Amurol Confections Co.
CELLULAR - Skin care products - T.R. International
CELLULAR BILLING MANAGER - Computer software - McCaw Cellular Communications, Inc.
CELLULAR DATA-PASSAGE - Radio communications equipment - Motorola, Inc. (Land Mobile Products Sector)
CELLULAR ESSENTIALS - Vitamins and nutritional supplements - Rexall Sundown, Inc.
CELLULAR FORCE - Batteries - Sakar International Inc.
CELLULAR NUTRITION - Vitamins and nutritional supplements - Herbalife International, Inc.
CELLULAR PROTECTION SYSTEM - Health care products - Enzymatic Therapy, Inc.
CELLULAR RECEPTION-IST, THE - Telephone accessories - Jasco, Inc.

CELLULAR RECOVERY COMPLEX - Skin care products - Viviane Woodard Industries, Ltd.
CELLULAR SHIELD - Telephone apparatus - RTI Inc.
CELLULAR SHIELD, THE - Telephone apparatus - RTI Inc.
CELLULAREADY - Modems - DATA RACE Inc.
CELLULARONE - Telephones–cellular - Cellular One Group
CELLULAX - Vitamins and nutritional supplements - Tishcon Corp.
CELLULAX BELL - Pharmaceutical preparations - Hollings-Smith Co. Inc.
CELLULENE - Enamels - Dozier & Gay Paint Co.
CELLULINER - Insulation board - Gilman Brothers Co.
CELLULITE - Flotation, insulation, and ceiling-panel foam - Gilman Brothers Co.
CELL*U*LITE ELIMINATOR - Vitamins and nutritional supplements - Head Start Vitamin Products
CELLULITE III - Artists' materials - Gilman Brothers Co.
CELLULOGEN FIBER - Bran–flour or meal - Green Foods
CELLULOID - Recording label - Celluloid Records
CELLULOID FANFARE - Recording label - Fifth Continent Music Corp.
CELLUPAC - Packaging–paper - Conwed Bonded Fiber
CELLUPHONE - Cellular telephones and accessories - Celluphone, Inc.
CELLUSPONGE - Sponges ☆ - Schroeder & Tremayne, Inc.
CELLUTECH - Cleaning preparations - Schaefer Associates Ltd.
CELLUTENNA - Antennas - Recoton Corp.
CELLUVISC - Ophthalmic goods - Allergan, Inc.
CELLVIEW - Computer hardware - RAM/BSE Communications, L.P.
CELLWOOD - Shutters–plastic - Aluminum Co. of America
CELLWOOD - Shutters–plastic - Cellwood Products
CELLXSHIELD - Telephone apparatus - Cellx Products
CELO-GUARD - Roofing materials - Celotex Corp.
CELO-VENT - Insulating materials–foam - Celotex Corp.
CELOID - Paints ☆ - Kyanize Paint Co.
CELOID - Pharmaceutical preparations ☆ - Xttrium Laboratories Inc.
CELONTIN - Pharmaceutical preparations - Parke-Davis
CELOTONE - Ceiling panels - Celotex Corp.
CELPREP - Diagnostic preparations - FMC Corp.
CELRAMIC - Glass products - Pittsburgh Corning Corp.
CELS - Footwear–women's - Cels Enterprises Inc.
CELSERINO - Fabrics–rayon - Infinite Textile, Inc.
CELSTAR - Faucets - Moen Inc.
CELSWITCH - Communications equipment–satellite - Telular Corp.
CELTECH - Loudspeakers - Stephen James Gertner, Jr.
CELTIC - Photographic equipment ☆ - Minolta Corp.
CELTIC - Vodka ☆ - White Rock Distilleries Inc.
CELTIC - Water heaters–household ☆ - Hydrotherm
CELTIC - Window coverings ☆ - Vertilux-Louverlux Inc.
CELTIC ADVERTISING - Advertising agencies - Celtic Advertising, Inc.
CELTIC BRAID - Tableware–china - Lenox, Inc.
CELTIC CLASSICS - Floor coverings–carpet and rugs - Masland Corp.
CELTIC KEY - Floor coverings–carpet and rugs - Milliken & Co. Inc.
CELTIC MILLS - Cosmetics - Sormani Inc.
CELTIC TALES: BALOR OF THE EVIL EYE - Computer software - Koei Corp.
CELTOID - Recording label - DNA Records
CELTRA - Medical apparatus - Cardiac Pacemakers Inc.
CELU-PAK - Sponges - Hydra Sponge Co., Inc.
CELUGRO - Vitamins and nutritional supplements - Celugro/Suprafoods Inc.
CELUKA - Construction equipment - Marley Mouldings Inc.
CELULEN - Skin care products - Lendan USA Co.
CELULON - Adhesives and sealants - Red Devil Inc.
CEM - Handbags - CEM Imports & Designs Ltd.
CEM-FLO - Lubricants - Maxi-Crete, Inc.
CEM-SEAL - Sealing compounds - Hillyard Enterprises, Inc.
CEMA - Computers - Advanced Technology Laboratories, Inc.
CEMA VISION - Video production - Capitol-EMI Music Inc.
CEMBALET - Musical instruments - Hohner Inc.
CEMBOND - Glue–household or industrial ☆ - Rock-Tred Corp.
CEMCO - Sporting goods - D.L.C. Fabricating Co. Inc.
CEMCON - Electronic equipment - Enviroplan, Inc.
CEMCOTE - Paints - Premix-Marbletite Manufacturing Co.
CEMENT - Apparel–women's - Wet Seal Inc.
CEMENT-COAT - Cement ☆ - Atlas Chemical Co.
CEMENT-O-FILM - Electronics equipment - RTI Research Technology International
CEMENT, PRIMERS - Cement - Black Swan Manufacturing Co.
CEMENT QUALITY RAIMENT - Apparel and accessories - Cement
CEMENT STAIN 2000 - Stains - Waterlox Coatings Corp.
CEMENTO PONCE - Cement - Puerto Rican Cement Co., Inc.

☆ = Now out of production

CEMENTO PUERTO RICO - Cement - Puerto Rican Cement Co., Inc.
CEMLINK - Computer software - Vim Technologies Inc.
CEMONSA - Tiles–ceramic ☆ - Federal Tile Imports Inc.
CEMSCAN - Computer software - Research-Cottrell Technologies, Inc.
CEM.SYS - Computer hardware - Automated Control Systems, Inc.
CEN PREM - Chemical preparations - CFI of Wisconsin, Inc.
CEN-PRODUCTS - Hot tubs–plastic - Arjo Manufacturing Co.
CENAC - Skin care products ☆ - Central Pharmaceutical Inc.
CENADEX - Pharmaceutical preparations ☆ - Central Pharmaceutical Inc.
CENAFED - Pharmaceutical preparations - Century Pharmaceuticals Inc.
CENAGESIC - Cold remedies ☆ - Central Pharmaceutical Inc.
CENAID - Pharmaceutical preparations - Century Pharmaceuticals Inc.
CENALAX - Pharmaceutical preparations - Century Pharmaceuticals Inc.
CENALENE - Pharmaceutical preparations ☆ - Central Pharmaceutical Inc.
CENCELL - Insulating materials–asbestos - Central Fiber Corp.
CENCON SYSTEM 2000 - Computer software - Mas-Hamilton Group, Inc.
CENCOR - Bathroom accessories - Vermax Inc.
CENDEVAX - Vaccines - Smithkline Beecham Corp.
CENEI - Slide viewer - Saul Bower Inc.
CENERE - Watches - Precision International Co. Inc.
CENEX - Oils–lubricating - Cenex/Land O'Lakes AG Services
CENOCORT A-40 - Pharmaceutical preparations - Central Pharmaceutical Inc.
CENOCORT FORTE - Pharmaceutical preparations - Central Pharmaceutical Inc.
CENOL - Insecticides - Cenol Co. Inc.
CENPRO - Food products - Central Soya Co. Inc.
CENPRO - Recording label - Century Productions Inc.
CENRESMASTER - Computer software - Reservation Technologies, Inc.
CENSEA - Seafood products–fresh or frozen - Central Seaway Co.
CENSORCHIP BACKDOORPROCESSORS - Apparel and accessories - Peter C. Schreiber
CENSUSSCAN - Computer software - Transamerica Corp.
CENSUSWATCH - Computer software - MCIS, Inc.
CENSYS - Computer software - Cincinnati Bell Information Systems Inc.
CENTAMETER - Computer software - Tally Systems Corp.
CENTANNI - Apparel and accessories - Barganza
CENTANNI - Wines - Wine World Inc.
CENTAR - Motor vehicles–vans - LCM, Inc.
CENTAUR - Bicycles - Ross Bicycles USA, Ltd.
CENTAUR - Boats–motor - Andrew Gemeny & Son
CENTAUR - Boats–motor ☆ - Cobia Boat Co.
CENTAUR - Floor coverings–tile - Daltonian Carpet & Cushion Inc.
CENTAUR - Recording label - Centaur Records
CENTAUR - Scientific apparatus - Ecolab Inc.
CENTAUR SIX - Synthesizers–musical instrument - Fender Musical Instruments
CENTAUR SYSTEMS - Computer software - Centaur Systems Ltd.
CENTAURI - Carpets, now out of production - Couristan Inc.
CENTAURI - Mattresses - Namaco Industries, Inc.
CENTAURI - Motor vehicles–vans - Winnebago Industries, Inc.
CENTAURI - Toys–stuffed ☆ - Gund, Inc.
CENTAURUS - Electronics equipment - ALTA Group
CENTAURUS - Floor coverings–carpet and rugs ☆ - Royalweve Carpet Mills
CENTAURUS - Furniture ☆ - Bassett Furniture Industries, Inc.
CENTAXARIN - Pharmaceutical preparations - Celsus, Inc.
CENTECH - Automotive accessories - Atlas Group
CENTELLA VEIN - Vitamins and nutritional supplements - Solaray
CENTELLIN - Nutritional supplement - Sabinsa Corp.
CENTENARIO - Brandy ☆ - Distillerie Stock USA Ltd.
CENTENARIO - Meat products–beef ☆ - Sampco Inc.
CENTENARY - Incense - Auroma International Inc.
CENTENIAL - Oysters–canned or cured ☆ - Coast Seafoods Co.
CENTENIAL OAK - Cash registers - Auer Register Co.
CENTENIUM - Computer peripheral equipment - Electronic Information Systems, Inc.
CENTENNIA - Computer software - Clockwork Software, Inc.
CENTENNIAL - Apparel and accessories - Adidas USA Inc.
CENTENNIAL - Apparel and accessories ☆ - Bausch & Lomb Inc.
CENTENNIAL - Balls–billiard - Brunswick Bowling & Billiards Corp.
CENTENNIAL - Balls–billiard ☆ - Brunswick Corp.
CENTENNIAL - Beds, mattresses, box springs, and sofabeds - King Koil Licensing Co., Inc.
CENTENNIAL - Bicycles - Columbia Manufacturing Inc.
CENTENNIAL - Cabinets - Nutone Inc.
CENTENNIAL - Cabinets - Scott Manufacturing, Inc.
CENTENNIAL - Candy - Sweet Candy Co.

CENTENNIAL - Candy ☆ - Wilbur Chocolate Co. Inc.
CENTENNIAL - Doors–storm - Canyon Creek Cabinet Co.
CENTENNIAL - Firearms, accessories, and parts - Centennial Arms Corp.
CENTENNIAL - Floor coverings - Congoleum Corp.
CENTENNIAL - Floor coverings–carpet and rugs ☆ - Regal Rugs Inc.
CENTENNIAL - Flowers, plants, and seeds - J.W. Abrell
CENTENNIAL - Fruits and vegetables - Limoneira Co.
CENTENNIAL - Furniture - Sumter Cabinet Co., Inc.
CENTENNIAL - Furniture - Universal Flooring
CENTENNIAL - Furniture ☆ - Hooker Furniture Corp.
CENTENNIAL - Hardware ☆ - Amerock Corp.
CENTENNIAL - Harmonicas - Hohner Inc.
CENTENNIAL - Headphones ☆ - Centennial Electric Sound Co. Ltd.
CENTENNIAL - Hobby kits ☆ - Craft World International Inc.
CENTENNIAL - Ice cream - H.P. Hood & Sons Inc.
CENTENNIAL - Office supplies - R.A. Stewart Superior
CENTENNIAL - Pork - AMK for Service
CENTENNIAL - Tableware–china ☆ - Lenox, Inc.
CENTENNIAL - Tiles–ceramic - Dal-Tile Corp.
CENTENNIAL - Tires - Dunlop Tire Corp.
CENTENNIAL - Wallpaper ☆ - Thomas Strahan Wallcoverings
CENTENNIAL - Watches - Bulova Corp.
CENTENNIAL 2 - Lumber - Georgia-Pacific Corp.
CENTENNIAL 25 - Floor waxes - Sanitek Products Inc.
CENTENNIAL CHANTILLY - Dishes–china ☆ - Gorham Inc.
CENTENNIAL COLLECTION - Clocks, lamps, etc. - IMS Corp.
CENTENNIAL COLLECTION, THE - Furniture ☆ - Bernhardt Industries
CENTENNIAL FARM - Wines ☆ - Montelle Winery
CENTENNIAL KNIVES, THE - Knives - Marble Arms Corp.
CENTENNIAL PEACH - Teas - Eastern Shore Tea Co.
CENTENNIAL PRESS - Publisher's imprints - Cliff's Notes, Inc.
CENTENNIALS - Candy ☆ - Miss Saylor's Candies
CENTER - Pharmaceutical preparations - EM Industries, Inc.
CENTER - Recording label - Biograph Records Inc.
CENTER CONSOLE - Boats–fishing - Donzi Marine Corp.
CENTER COURT - Apparel–men's ☆ - Jantzen Inc.
CENTER COURT - Finishing agents - Betco Corp.
CENTER COURT - Floor coverings–carpet and rugs ☆ - Burtco Enterprises Inc.
CENTER COURT - Games - Huffy Corp.
CENTER CUT - Bacon - Oscar Mayer Foods Corp.
CENTER CUT - Turkeys - Norbest Inc.
CENTER DEE - Pet collars - Leatherite-Nylorite Manufacturing Inc.
CENTER FIRE - Archery equipment - Pro Line Co.
CENTER FOR HOMEWARES DESIGNS - Ironing board pads - Pressing Supply Co.
CENTER FOR LOSS & LIFE TRANSITION - Educational materials - Alan D. Wolfelt
CENTER FOR MUSIC AND YOUNG CHILDREN - Recording label - Center for Music and Young Children
CENTER FOR THE QUEEN OF PEACE - Recording label - Cosmotone Records
CENTER OF ATTRACTION - Perfumes - Helene Curtis Industries Inc.
CENTER OF THE PLATE - Meat products–poultry - Acme Continental Foods Inc.
CENTER OF THE ROOM COLLECTION - Furniture ☆ - Lane Co. Inc.
CENTER OF THE UNIVERSE - Apparel and accessories - Center of the Universe
CENTER PIECE - Dinnerware–plastic - Sweetheart Cup Co. Inc.
CENTER PLY - False eyelashes ☆ - Cosrich Inc.
CENTER RITE - Tools - Gilbert and Bennett Manufacturing Co.
CENTER-SCORE - Golfing equipment - Echelon, Golf Inc.
CENTER-SHARP - Photographic equipment - SP Systems/Saratons
CENTER SIMMER - Stoves–gas ☆ - Harper-Wyman Co.
CENTER SQUARE - Furniture - Athens Furniture Industries Inc.
CENTER STAGE - Computer storage devices ☆ - Hunt Manufacturing Co.
CENTER STAGE - Glassware–household ☆ - Crystal Clear Importing Co. Inc.
CENTER STRUT - Sporting goods - Porter Athletic Equipment Co.
CENTER SUDRE - Sporting goods - Lindy Little Joe Inc.
CENTER-VANISH - Photographic equipment - SP Systems/Saratons
CENTERBROOK-MUSIC - Music–sheet - Centerstream Publications
CENTERFIGURE - Computer software - Target Software Inc.
CENTERFIRE - Archery equipment - Martin Archery Inc.
CENTERFOLD - Boats - Glen-L Marine Designs
CENTERFOLD COLLECTOR CARDS - Playing cards - Playboy Enterprises, Inc.

☆ = Now out of production

CENTERING - Health care products - East Earth Herb Inc.

CENTERING - Recording label - Jazz Composer's Orchestra Association Inc.

CENTERING/FOCUS - Pharmaceutical preparations - Natural Laboratories Corp.

CENTERLINE - Computer software - Centerline Software, Inc.

CENTERLINE - Furniture - Steelcase Inc.

CENTERLINE CIRCUIT BOARD PRODUCTS - Wood products - Standard Supply & Equipment Co., Inc.

CENTERLINE SPORTS - Sporting goods - Centerline Sports, Inc.

CENTERPIECE - Flower pots–plastic - Norse Co. Designers

CENTERPIECE - Furniture ☆ - Bassett Furniture Industries, Inc.

CENTERPIECE COLLECTION - Furniture - Dinaire Corp.

CENTERPOINTE - Floor coverings–carpet and rugs ☆ - Hollytex Carpet Mills Inc.

CENTERS OF ATTENTION - Novelty items - Score Board Holding Corp.

CENTERSCORE - Tiles–ceramic - Stark Ceramics Inc.

CENTERSTONE - Jewelry - Michael Beaudry, Inc.

CENTERSTREAM - Health care products - Marquest Medical Products Inc.

CENTERSTREAM - Music–sheet - Centerstream Publications

CENTERTON - Floor coverings - Mannington Resilient Floors

CENTEST - Computer peripheral equipment - Telecommunications Techniques Corp.

CENTET - Antibiotics ☆ - Central Pharmaceutical Inc.

CENTEX - Food products - Central Soya Co. Inc.

CENTEX 28 - Floor coverings–carpet and rugs - Whitecrest Carpet Mills

CENTEX MATERIALS, INC. - Concrete–mixture - Centex Corp.

CENTI-SEED - Flowers, plants, and seeds - Patten Seed Co.

CENTIGRADE - Hair care products - Redken Laboratories, Inc.

CENTIMIST - Health care products ☆ - Marquest Medical Products Inc.

CENTINA - Rings–jewelry - Artcarved Inc.

CENTINE - Wines - Banfi Vintners

CENTINE ROSSO DI MONTALCINO - Wines - Banfi Vintners

CENTIPEDE - Video games - Atari Games Corp.

CENTIUM - Lighting equipment - Philips Electronics North America Corp.

CENTO - Food products - Cento Fine Foods Inc.

CENTRA - Cribs–wood ☆ - Cosco, Inc.

CENTRA-CLEAN - Vacuum cleaners and accessories - George P. Crossman

CENTRABEST - Oils–edible - CS Oilseeds, Inc.

CENTRAC - Filing cabinets–metal - ACME Design Technology

CENTRAGEN - Pharmaceutical preparations - Goldline Laboratories, Inc.

CENTRAL - Canvas–artists' - New York Central Art Supply Co.

CENTRAL - Floor coverings–carpet and rugs ☆ - World Carpets, Inc.

CENTRAL - Labels–gummed - Paper Corp. of America

CENTRAL AMERICA - Games - Avalon Hill Game Co.

CENTRAL BLVD. - Floor coverings - Bellbridge Carpets

CENTRAL BOILER - Heating equipment - Central Boiler, Inc.

CENTRAL COAST - Wines - Calera Wine Co.

CENTRAL CT. - Apparel and accessories - Todd Number 1

CENTRAL FINE PACK - Food containers - Central Fine Pack, Inc.

CENTRAL MARKET - Meat products - Karn Meats Inc.

CENTRAL MARKET SPECIALTY MEATS - Deli meats - Karn Meats Inc.

CENTRAL PALACE - Vitamins and nutritional supplements - Ethical Nutrients

CENTRAL PARK - Apparel and accessories - Central Park

CENTRAL PARK - Bicycles - Ross Bicycles USA, Ltd.

CENTRAL PARK - Cabinets - Brammer Manufacturing Co.

CENTRAL PARK - Dolls ☆ - Effanbee Doll Corp.

CENTRAL PARK - Floor coverings–carpet and rugs - Lees Carpets

CENTRAL PARK - Floor coverings–carpet and rugs ☆ - Regal Rugs Inc.

CENTRAL PARK - Floor coverings–tile - Interface, Inc.

CENTRAL PARK - Furniture ☆ - Lane Co. Inc.

CENTRAL PARK - Glassware–household - Owens-Illinois Inc. (Libbey Div.)

CENTRAL PARK EAST - Furniture ☆ - Lane Co. Inc.

CENTRAL PARK II - Furniture ☆ - Lane Co. Inc.

CENTRAL PARK MEDIA - Video production - Central Park Media Corp.

CENTRAL PARK WEST - Furniture ☆ - Lane Co. Inc.

CENTRAL PARK ZOO - Apparel and accessories - Central Park

CENTRAL PERK - Earthenware - Time Warner Entertainment Co., L.P.

CENTRAL PK. SETTEE - Benches–public buildings - Central Park. Conservancy, Inc.

CENTRAL PLAZA - Floor coverings–carpet and rugs ☆ - Cumberland Mills Inc.

CENTRAL POINT BACKUP - Computer software - Central Point Software Inc.

CENTRAL SCIENTIFIC COMPANY - Laboratory apparatus - Central Scientific Co.

CENTRAL STATION - Computer hardware - Artisoft, Inc.

CENTRAL TALK - Computer software - Central Point Software Inc.

CENTRAL VALLEY - Toys–trains - Central Valley Model Works

CENTRAL-VITE - Vitamins and nutritional supplements - Leiner Health Products Inc.

CENTRALALERT - Computer program - Central Point Software Inc.

CENTRALGARD - Valves–industrial - Central Brass Manufacturing Co.

CENTRALIGN - Surgical instruments - Zimmer, Inc.

CENTRALIS DIRECT - Lenses - Volk Optical, Inc.

CENTRALITE - Medical apparatus - Diacor Inc.

CENTRALOGIC - Thermostats - Warren Manufacturing Co., Inc.

CENTRAMARK - Vending machines - Centramark Corp.

CENTRAPOUR - Vegetable oil - Central Soya Co. Inc.

CENTRAX - Pharmaceutical preparations ☆ - Parke-Davis

CENTRAX - Tires–automobile - Dunlop Tire Corp.

CENTRAX - Watches - Century Time

CENTRAY - Hardware - Mphusky Corp.

CENTRAZ - Detergents - Ceutnaz Industries, Inc.

CENTRAZ ULTRA - Detergents - Ceutnaz Industries, Inc.

CENTRE COURT - Balls–tennis - Gencorp Inc.

CENTRE COURT - Balls–tennis - Penn Athletic Products

CENTRE POINTE - Women's apparel - E. Benjamin, Inc.

CENTRE' SERIES - Air conditioning equipment - Structural Concepts Corp.

CENTRECOM - Computer hardware - Allied Telesis Inc.

CENTREDEC - Window coverings - Norman Lacoff & Associates Inc.

CENTREFUSE - Machinery - T.D. Williamson, Inc.

CENTRELLA - Food products - Central Grocers Co-op Inc.

CENTREX - Audio equipment ☆ - Pioneer Electronics USA Inc.

CENTREX - Sporting goods ☆ - Raichle Molitor USA, Inc.

CENTRI-MAX - Pumps–water - ITT Jabsco

CENTRI-VAC - Machinery - Centri-Vac, Inc.

CENTRICS - Floor coverings–carpet and rugs ☆ - Heuga USA

CENTRIFUSE - Automotive parts and accessories - Motor Wheel Corp.

CENTRINE - Veterinary pharmaceutical preparations - Bristol-Myers Squibb Co.

CENTRIX COMPUTER - Computers - Centrix Computer Inc.

CENTRO - Glassware–household - Dansk International Designs, Ltd.

CENTRO - Hardware - The Centro Co. Inc.

CENTRO - Tables–wood - Krueger International, Inc.

CENTRO STORICO - Wallpaper ☆ - Wolf-Gordon Inc.

CENTROBAKE - Food products - CS Oilseeds, Inc.

CENTROBULB - Insecticides - The Centro Co. Inc.

CENTROCAP - Health care products - Central Soya Co. Inc.

CENTROL - Food products - Central Soya Co. Inc.

CENTROLEX - Food products - Central Soya Co. Inc.

CENTRON - Pipes - Triple G Coatings Inc.

CENTRON - Thermostats - White Rogers Co.

CENTROSPRAY - Hardware - The Centro Co. Inc.

CENTROVITE - Pharmaceutical preparations - Rugby Laboratories Inc.

CENTRUM - Bicycles - Columbia Manufacturing Inc.

CENTRUM - Computer software - Centrum Business Systems, Inc.

CENTRUM - Floor coverings - Mannington Resilient Floors

CENTRUM - Furniture ☆ - Lane Co. Inc.

CENTRUM - Furniture–upholstered ☆ - Mersman Furniture Co.

CENTRUM - Vitamins and nutritional supplements - Lederle Laboratories

CENTRUM JR. - Vitamins and nutritional supplements - Lederle Laboratories

CENTRUM SINGLES - Vitamins and nutritional supplements - Lederle Laboratories

CENTRY - Doors–wood - Morgan Products Ltd.

CENTRY - Electrical equipment - Cummins Engine Co. Inc.

CENTRY-COVER - Bellows - Centryco Inc.

CENTRY-SPOUT - Air conditioning equipment ☆ - Centryco Inc.

CENTRY-TAP - Air conditioning equipment ☆ - Centryco Inc.

CENTRY-VENT III - Air conditioning equipment ☆ - Centryco Inc.

CENTSABLE - Eggs - Papetti's Hygrade Egg Products, Inc.

CENTSABLE - Games - Centsable Toys Inc.

CENTSABLE SOFTWARE - Computer software - Bill Lieberman

CENTSIBLE - Cleaning preparations - Apollo Industries Inc.

CENTUM - Brandy ☆ - Distillerie Stock USA Ltd.

CENTURA - Automotive parts and accessories - Lancaster Colony Automotive Group

CENTURA - Boats–motor ☆ - Dolphin Boats Ltd.

CENTURA - Cabinets ☆ - American Woodmark Corp.

CENTURA - Communications equipment - American Digital Switching, Inc.

CENTURA - Dinnerware ☆ - Corning Inc.

CENTURA - Faucets - Kohler Co.

CENTURA - Gelatin - Vyse Gelatin Co.

CENTURA - Hair care products - Scruples Professional Salon Products, Inc.

CENTURA - Housewares - Melard Manufacturing Corp.

CENTURA - Pipes–tobacco ☆ - S.M. Frank & Co. Inc. (Kaywoodie-Yello-Bole-Medico)
CENTURA - Switches–electric ☆ - Leviton Manufacturing Co., Inc.
CENTURA - Wallpaper ☆ - Wolf-Gordon Inc.
CENTURA GOLD - Auto storage batteries - Exide Corp.
CENTURIA - Wallpaper ☆ - Winfield Design Associates, Inc.
CENTURIAN - Clocks - Sligh Furniture Co.
CENTURIAN - Clocks ☆ - SMH (US) Inc.
CENTURIAN - Electronic equipment ☆ - H. Wilson Co.
CENTURIAN - Floor coverings ☆ - Congoleum Corp.
CENTURIAN - Furniture ☆ - Bassett Furniture Industries, Inc.
CENTURIES - Wallpaper - Capital Carousel Inc.
CENTURIO - Wines - Joseph Victori Wines Inc.
CENTURION - Bicycle parts and accessories ☆ - Diamondback
CENTURION - Boats - Warrior Fiberglass Products Inc.
CENTURION - Bricks - A.P. Green Industries Inc.
CENTURION - Cabinets - Saco Industries Inc.
CENTURION - Cutlery ☆ - Regent Sheffield, Ltd.
CENTURION - Doors–garage - Wayne-Dalton Corp.
CENTURION - Electric lighting equipment - Lutron Electronics Co., Inc.
CENTURION - Exercising equipment - Universal Gym Equipment, Inc.
CENTURION - Fabrics - Weblon Inc.
CENTURION - Filters–air - Controls Corp. of America
CENTURION - Firearms, accessories, and parts - Bausch & Lomb Inc.
CENTURION - Firearms, accessories, and parts - Welsh Sporting Goods Corp. (Boyt Div.)
CENTURION - Floor coverings–carpet and rugs - Dan River Inc.
CENTURION - Floor coverings–carpet and rugs ☆ - Kelly Group Inc.
CENTURION - Floor-scrubbing machine ☆ - Advance Machine Co.
CENTURION - Furniture–wood - Century Furniture Co.
CENTURION - Glassware–household - Lenox, Inc.
CENTURION - Guns ☆ - Weatherby Inc.
CENTURION - Lighting equipment - Standard-Keil Hardware Manufacturing Co.
CENTURION - Mattresses and box springs - Ohio Mattress Co.
CENTURION - Motor vehicles–automobiles ☆ - General Motors Corp. (Buick Motor Div.)
CENTURION - Motors–hydraulic - Magnetek Inc.
CENTURION - Musical instruments ☆ - Jupiter Band Inst. Inc.
CENTURION - Smoke detectors ☆ - Sunbeam-Oster Household Products
CENTURION - Telephones - Cortelco Systems Inc.
CENTURION - Thread - Imperial Threads Inc.
CENTURION - Valves - Mueller Co.
CENTURION - Vans–conversion - Centurion Vehicles, Inc.
CENTURION STONE - Stone products - Centurion Products, Inc.
CENTURIONS - Games ☆ - Ben Cooper Inc.
CENTURIONS - Toys–stuffed - Kenner Products
CENTURY - Accordions - Atlas Accordions Inc.
CENTURY - Air conditioning equipment - Heat Controller Inc.
CENTURY - Amplifiers–musical instrument - Peavey Electronics Corp.
CENTURY - Antiseptics - Century Pharmaceuticals Inc.
CENTURY - Apparel and accessories - Pandora Sportswear Industries
CENTURY - Apparel and accessories ☆ - Warnaco Inc.
CENTURY - Automotive parts and accessories ☆ - Echlin Inc.
CENTURY - Beverages–carbonated - Stars Beverage Co.
CENTURY - Bicycles - Raleigh USA Bicycle Co.
CENTURY - Boats–motor - Century Boat Co.
CENTURY - Cabinets - Classic Bath Products
CENTURY - Cabinets - Nutone Inc.
CENTURY - Cabinets–wood ☆ - Kemper
CENTURY - Cigarettes - R.J. Reynolds Tobacco Co.
CENTURY - Cookies - Century Cookies
CENTURY - Cooking equipment–household - Birmingham Stove & Range Co.
CENTURY - Dishes–earthenware ☆ - Homer Laughlin China Co.
CENTURY - Fabrics - Greenwood Mills Inc.
CENTURY - Flatware - Crate and Barrel
CENTURY - Floor coverings - American Floor Products Co. Inc.
CENTURY - Floor coverings–carpet and rugs - Criterion Mills Inc.
CENTURY - Floor coverings–carpet and rugs - Philadelphia Carpets
CENTURY - Food products - Northern Star Co.
CENTURY - Footwear - Century Shoe Corp.
CENTURY - Furniture - Equipto
CENTURY - Furniture–wood - Century Furniture Co.
CENTURY - Glassware–household - Federal Glass
CENTURY - Glass–window - Jeld-Wen, Inc.
CENTURY - Greeting cards - Century Engraving & Embossing Co.
CENTURY - Hardware - Alside Div.

CENTURY - Hardware ☆ - Mosler Inc.
CENTURY - Hot tubs–plastic - Arjo Manufacturing Co.
CENTURY - Infant product - Century Products Co.
CENTURY - Jewelry - Century Associates, Ltd.
CENTURY - Knives–pocket - Imperial Schrade Corp.
CENTURY - Labels–gummed - Century Marketing Corp.
CENTURY - Ladders–metal ☆ - John S. Tilley Ladders Co. Inc.
CENTURY - Lighting fixtures - Lava-Simplex Internationale
CENTURY - Mops - Lighthouse Industries
CENTURY - Motor vehicles–automobiles - General Motors Corp. (Buick Motor Div.)
CENTURY - Motors–hydraulic - Magnetek Inc.
CENTURY - Paints - Century Supply Co.
CENTURY - Paperboard - Pohlig Brothers, Inc.
CENTURY - Pens - A.T. Cross Co.
CENTURY - Pens ☆ - Alexander Manufacturing Co.
CENTURY - Pet products - Century Craft Industries
CENTURY - Photo albums - 20th Century Plastics
CENTURY - Pool tables - Brunswick Corp.
CENTURY - Projection screens ☆ - Draper Shade and Screen Co. Inc.
CENTURY - Projectors–photographic - Optical Radiation Corp.
CENTURY - Rings–jewelry - Artcarved Inc.
CENTURY - Scissors–hand-operated ☆ - Acme United Corp.
CENTURY - Skin care products - Hess Hair Milk Laboratories Inc.
CENTURY - Telephone directories - Park Sherman
CENTURY - Tools - Century Drill & Tool Co.
CENTURY - Toys–models - Magnuson Models Inc.
CENTURY - Toys–models - Wm. K. Walthers Inc.
CENTURY - Trailers–travel ☆ - Coachmen Industries, Inc.
CENTURY - Watches - Bulova Corp.
CENTURY - Window coverings - Levolor Inc.
CENTURY - Yarn ☆ - Caron International Inc.
CENTURY 21 - Recording label - Random Enterprises Inc.
CENTURY 100S - Cigarettes - R.J. Reynolds Tobacco Co.
CENTURY 1600 - High chairs - Century Products Co.
CENTURY 2000 - Cabinets - Triangle Pacific Corp. (Cabinet Division)
CENTURY 2000 - Pens - A.T. Cross Co.
CENTURY 2000 PUBLISHING - Video production - Omni 2000 Inc.
CENTURY 2100 TENS - Health care products - Wholesale Medical Import
CENTURY ACRES - Eggs ☆ - Century Acres Eggs
CENTURY BLONDE - Floor coverings–carpet and rugs - Glen Eden Wool Carpets
CENTURY BRASS MFG., INC. - Brass products - Century Brass Manufacturing, Inc.
CENTURY CATHEDRAL - Cabinets–wood ☆ - Kemper
CENTURY CC - Beds–hospital - Hill Rom, Inc.
CENTURY CITY - Furniture ☆ - Bassett Furniture Industries, Inc.
CENTURY CLASSICS - Lamps - Electrix Inc.
CENTURY COLLECTION - Clocks - Chelsea Clock Co. Inc.
CENTURY COLLECTION - Luggage - Welsh Sporting Goods Corp. (Boyt Div.)
CENTURY CUSTOM - Motor vehicles–automobiles - General Motors Corp. (Buick Motor Div.)
CENTURY ESTATE WAGON - Motor vehicles–automobiles - General Motors Corp. (Buick Motor Div.)
CENTURY FARMS - Food products - Packer Foods, Inc.
CENTURY FARMS - Fruit pie mixes - Buskirk Processing Inc.
CENTURY FILE CONVERSION - Computer software - Quintic Systems, Inc.
CENTURY II - Bicycles - Columbia Manufacturing Inc.
CENTURY II - Carpet sweepers ☆ - Bissell Inc.
CENTURY II - Floor coverings ☆ - National Floor Products Co., Inc.
CENTURY II - Poultry feeds - Standard Manufacturing Co.
CENTURY II - Refuse systems - McNeilus Truck and Manufacturing, Inc.
CENTURY III - Fireplaces ☆ - Roesch Inc.
CENTURY LIGHTS - Cigarettes - R.J. Reynolds Tobacco Co.
CENTURY LIMITED - Motor vehicles–automobiles - General Motors Corp. (Buick Motor Div.)
CENTURY LUXUS - Motor vehicles–automobiles ☆ - General Motors Corp. (Buick Motor Div.)
CENTURY MAINTENANCE - Cleaning preparations–carpet and rug ☆ - Hako Minuteman Inc.
CENTURY MARBLE - Floor coverings - Azrock Commercial Flooring
CENTURY NITE-LITE - Lighting fixtures - Solid Electric Corp.
CENTURY OF PROGRESS - Harmonicas - Hohner Inc.
CENTURY OVATION - Infant product - Century Products Co.
CENTURY PC - Machinery - AMF Bowling Worldwide
CENTURY-POLY - Office supplies - 20th Century Plastics

☆ = Now out of production

CENTURY PROPANE - Propylene - Century Propane Co., Inc.
CENTURY PROTECT ALL - Paints ☆ - Century Industries Corp.
CENTURY RECORDS INC. - Recording label - Century Records Inc.
CENTURY-SAFE - Office supplies - 20th Century Plastics
CENTURY SENIOR - Vitamins and nutritional supplements - L. Perrigo Co.
CENTURY SHOWPLACE - Furniture–wood - Century Furniture Co.
CENTURY SNACKTACULAR - Meat products - Century Resources, Inc.
CENTURY STEEL PIERS - Pier footings - William B. McCown, Sr.
CENTURY, THE - Recliners - Lane Co. Inc.
CENTURY TROJAN - Binders - 20th Century Plastics
CENTURY-VITE - Vitamins and nutritional supplements - Pharmavite Corp.
CENTURY WHITE WOVE - Envelopes - Quality Park Products Co.
CENTURYLON - Handlebars–bicycle - Pac Am International
CENTURYMUX - Digital encoders - Whitehall Corp.
CENTUS - Computer software - Edfel J. Rivera
CENTZ - Apparel–women's - Kellwood Co.
CENZA - Apparel and accessories - Knight Industries
C.E.O. - Apparel and accessories - Kellwood Co.
CEO - Automotive parts and accessories - RCI
C.E.O. - Floor coverings–carpet and rugs ☆ - Olympic Carpets Inc.
C.E.O. - Wallcoverings - Ben Rose Ltd.
C.E.O. CAREER EYEWEAR OPTIONS - Eyeglasses - Marchon and Marcolin Eyewear Inc.
C.E.O. CHIEF EXECUTIVE OFFICER - Apparel and accessories - Kellwood Co.
CEO COLLECTION - Giftware - Jonal Crystal Ltd.
CEO CREEPING BG BLEND - Flowers, plants, and seeds - Jacklin Seed
C.E.O. II - Leather goods ☆ - Prince Gardner Inc.
CEO SUMMIT - Consulting services - ABC Media, Inc.
CEO-TWO - Laxatives - Beutlich L.P. Pharmaceuticals
CEPAC - Packaging–paper - Controlled Environment Packaging, Inc.
CEPAC - Tiles–ceramic - Jun Ceramic Inc.
CEPACOL - Anesthetics - Marion Merrell Dow
CEPASTAT - Cough medicines - SmithKline Beecham Consumer Healthcare
CEPASTAT - Health care products - Marion Merrell Dow
CEPELIA - Apparel–athletic ☆ - United Knitwear Co. Inc.
CEPELIA - Giftware - Amceco International Corp.
CEPHULAC - Pharmaceutical preparations - Marion Merrell Dow
CEPIMAX - Antibiotics - Bristol-Myers Squibb Co.
CEPTCIDE - Skin care products - Rudolph International, Inc.
CER. 84 - Tiles–ceramic - United Ceramic Tile Corp.
CER-MAG - Toys–models - Polk's Model Craft Hobbies, Inc.
CER-THIN - Paints ☆ - Waterlox Coatings Corp.
CERA - Glassware–household - Ceraglass Inc.
CERA BALL - Pens - Yasutomo
CERA COLLECTION - Furniture ☆ - Lane Co. Inc.
CERA-GLASS - Dental products - New Image Dental Laboratory
CERA-ROD - Adhesives and sealants - W.R. Meadows Inc.
CERABEX T - Pharmaceutical preparations ☆ - Vitarine Pharmaceuticals Inc.
CERABLANKET - Insulating materials - Thermal Ceramics Inc.
CERACRYLIC - Glassware–household - Ceraglass Inc.
CERADERM - Skin care products - Naturecorp International, Inc.
CERAFOAM - Wallpaper - Glass Inc.
CERAGLASS - Glassware–household - Ceraglass Inc.
CERAGLAZE - Paints ☆ - Dunn Edwards Corp.
CERAGLAZE E.P. - Paints - Dunn Edwards Corp.
CERAGLOW - Floor coverings ☆ - Toli International
CERALAS - Medical apparatus - Ceramoptec, Inc.
CERALENE - Dinnerware–glass - Ceralene Inc.
CERALON - Lamps - Nolarec Industries, Inc.
CERALYTE - Vitamins and nutritional supplements - Cera Products, Inc.
CERAM-A-STAR - Coatings - Akzo Nobel Coatings Inc.
CERAM-A-STYLIST - Manicure preparations - Belle De St. Claire
CERAM ALLOY - Adhesives and sealants - Enecon Corp.
CERAM-KOTE 54 - Epoxy coatings - Freecom, Inc.
CERAMA - Floor coverings - Azrock Commercial Flooring
CERAMA-BOND - Adhesives and sealants - Continental Brands Inc.
CERAMA-CRAFT - Finishing agents - National Artcraft Co.
CERAMACOUPLE - Couplings - Stitt Spark Plug Co.
CERAMADEK II - Tiles–ceramic ☆ - Huntington/Pacific Ceramics Inc.
CERAMAFIBER - Insulating materials–foam - CelloFoam North America Inc.
CERAMALITE - Glass products - HGP Industries Inc.
CERAMALUX - Lamps - Philips Lighting Co.
CERAMAR - Building materials–concrete - W.R. Meadows Inc.
CERAMARTE LTD. - Glass products - Primex International Corp.
CERAMASEAL - Floor coatings, grout, etc. - Bostik Inc.

CERAMASET - Adhesives and sealants - Para-Chem Southern, Inc. (Parabond Adhesives Division)
CERAMASUEDE - Tiles–ceramic - Huntington/Pacific Ceramics Inc.
CERAMATEX - Building materials–concrete - Weyerhaeuser Co.
CERAMCOAT - Paints - Shiva Inc.
CERAMDIPITY - Tiles–ceramic - Latco Products
CERAMDIPITY - Tiles–ceramic - Los Angeles Tile Co., Inc.
CERAMEL - Enamels - Sampson Coatings Inc.
CERAMEX - Ceramic coating, now out of production - Activa Products Inc.
CERAMI-COTE - Paints ☆ - Devoe & Raynolds Co.
CERAMI-SEALS - Gaskets ☆ - DecoArt, Inc.
CERAMIC - Health care products - Melard Manufacturing Corp.
CERAMIC 6 - Epoxy anchor (chemical) - ITW Ramset/Red Head
CERAMIC A LA MODE - Tiles–ceramic ☆ - Huntington/Pacific Ceramics Inc.
CERAMIC & GLASS - Giftware - Concepts Plus
CERAMIC ART - Pottery - Brastoff Designs Inc.
CERAMIC CLASSICS - Tiles–ceramic ☆ - American Olean Tile Co.
CERAMIC EXCITEMENT - Tiles–ceramic ☆ - American Olean Tile Co.
CERAMIC FLOOR CLEANER - Cleaning preparations - Hertron International Inc.
CERAMIC GLAZE - Skin care products - Ceramic Glaze Inc.
CERAMIC GLAZE NAIL TREATMENTS - Manicure preparations - Roberts Research Laboratories, Inc.
CERAMIC GUARD - Paints - Nationwide Chemical Coating Manufacturers, Inc.
CERAMIC LITE - Chimes ☆ - Nutone Inc.
CERAMIC LTX - Paints - Mac-O-Lac Paints Inc.
CERAMIC MOSAICS - Tiles–ceramic - Monarch Tile Inc.
CERAMIC ON STEEL - Cooking utensils–enameled - General Housewares Corp.
CERAMIC POWER - Heaters–space - Holmes Products, Corp.
CERAMIC SHIELD - Paints - Nationwide Chemical Coating Manufacturers, Inc.
CERAMIC TILE NETWORK, THE - Tiles–ceramic - International Tile Exposition
CERAMIC TILES OF ITALY - Floor and wall tiles installation guides - Italian Trade Commission (Ceramic Tile Department)
CERAMIC WALL CLEANER GEL - Cleaning preparations - Hertron International Inc.
CERAMICA - Tiles–ceramic ☆ - Halstead International
CERAMICA - Wallpaper - Advance Wallcoverings
CERAMICA ADEX - Ceramic tile ☆ - Integrity Tile Co.
CERAMICA DECORATIVA - Plumbing fixtures - American Standard Inc.
CERAMICA EXCELSIS - Giftware - Roman, Inc.
CERAMICA FBV - Ceramic tile ☆ - Integrity Tile Co.
CERAMICA F.G. - Ceramic tile ☆ - Integrity Tile Co.
CERAMICA LA PERLA - Ceramic tile ☆ - Integrity Tile Co.
CERAMICA REX - Ceramic tile - Integrity Tile Co.
CERAMICA SAN LORENZO - Tiles–ceramic - Matrix Trading Co.
CERAMICA TERRA-MEX - Ceramic tile ☆ - Integrity Tile Co.
CERAMICA WEISS - Glass products - Primex International Corp.
CERAMICHROME - Tiles–ceramic ☆ - DecoArt, Inc.
CERAMICLEAN - Cleaning preparations - Stone Care International Inc.
CERAMICOAT - Signs - James L. Wyckoff
CERAMICOR - Dinnerware - Delco Tableware International, Inc.
CERAMICORE - Bowling balls - Columbia Industries, Inc.
CERAMICRAFT - Tiles–ceramic - American Marazzi Tile, Inc.
CERAMICRITTERS - Pottery - Duncan Enterprises
CERAMICRON - Pens - Pentel of America, Ltd.
CERAMICS - Lighting fixtures ☆ - Nutone Inc.
CERAMICS - Wallpaper - J.M. Lynne Co. Inc.
CERAMICS - Wallpaper - Winfield Design Associates, Inc.
CERAMIDE TIME - Skin care products - Elizabeth Arden Inc.
CERAMIFLEX - Floor coverings–tile - Mondo America Inc.
CERAMIGUARD - Cooking utensils–earthenware - Lincoln Foodservice Products, Inc.
CERAMIKE - Electronic equipment - Sonotone Corp.
CERAMIQUE - Floor coverings ☆ - Tarkett, Inc.
CERAMIQUE - Pens - Itoya of America, Ltd.
CERAMITAL - Tiles–ceramic ☆ - Huntington/Pacific Ceramics Inc.
CERAMIX - Faucets - American Standard Inc.
CERAMIX ELECTRONIX - Faucets - American Standard Inc.
CERAMO - Cleaning preparations–household - Mapei East Corp.
CERAMOGRAFIA - Tiles–ceramic - Federal Tile Imports Inc.
CERAMOPTEC - Cables–fiber optic - Ceramoptec, Inc.
CERAMTEK - Laboratory apparatus - Secure Medical
CERANOMATIC - Pens - Pentel of America, Ltd.
CERAPRISM - Tiles–ceramic - Huntington/Pacific Ceramics Inc.

☆ = Now out of production

CERASPAN - Dental equipment - Glasspan, Inc.
CERASTONE - Dishes–earthenware - Mikasa Co.
CERASTONE - Wallcovering - Parex, Inc.
CERATA - Sheet metal products - Hartson-Kennedy Cabinet Top Co., Inc.
CERATEMP - Tempered glass - Unique Industries
CERATEX - Corn–flour or meal - J.R. Short Milling Co.
CERATONES - Tiles–ceramic - Huntington/Pacific Ceramics Inc.
CERAUCO - Ceramic tile ☆ - Integrity Tile Co.
CERAVISION - Tiles–ceramic ☆ - Huntington/Pacific Ceramics Inc.
CERCA AGUARDENTE - Wines - Admiral Wine Merchants
CERCO CAP - Floor coverings–carpet and rugs - Mercer Products Co., Inc.
CERCOR - Heating equipment - Corning Inc.
CERDISA - Floor tile - Integrity Tile Co.
CERDISA - Tiles–ceramic - Federal Tile Imports Inc.
CERDOMUS - Ceramic tile - Integrity Tile Co.
CEREAL CLIP - Kitchenware–plastic - Guardsman Products, Inc.
CEREAL MATCH - Oils–edible - Paradise Valley Foods, Inc.
CEREAL 'N SNACK - Food products - Sovex Foods, Inc.
CEREAL NOT INCLUDED - Toys - N.S.G. Marketing Corp.
CEREALBOX - Computer software - BG Systems, Inc.
CEREBELLUM - Video production - Cerebellum Corp.
CEREBID - Pharmaceutical preparations - Saron Pharmacal Corp.
CEREBRAL - Recording label - Cerebral Records
CEREBRAL MANAGER - Computer software - Eastman Kodak Co.
CEREBYX - Pharmaceutical preparations - Parke-Davis
CEREDA - Sunglasses - Biba Optique Inc.
CEREGEN - Hair coloring preparations - Nu Skin International, Inc.
CEREMONY - Wines - Guild Wineries
CERENEX - Pharmaceutical preparations - Glaxo Wellcome Inc.
CERES - Antennas - Roadtrac Ltd.
CERES - Health care products - Guadalupe Natural Productions Inc.
CERES - Housewares - Ceres, Inc.
CERES - Ophthalmic goods ☆ - Luxottica
CERES - Pencils - Musgrave Pencil Co. Inc.
CERES - Wallpaper - Koroseal Wallcoverings
CERES SPIRULINA - Health care products - Guadalupe Natural Productions Inc.
CERESOTA - Flour–blended - Uhlmann Co.
CERESPAN - Pharmaceutical preparations - Rhone-Poulenc Rorer Pharmaceuticals Inc.
CERESTAT - Pharmaceutical preparations - Cambridge Neuroscience, Inc.
CERETEX - Pharmaceutical preparations - Enzyme Process Co. Inc.
CERETTO - Beverages–alcohol - Palace Brands Co.
CEREX - Pharmaceutical preparations - Vyrex Corp.
CEREZYME - Pharmaceutical preparations - Genzyme Corp.
CERFEX - Plaster–patching - United Gilsonite Laboratories
CERIANI - Motorcycle parts and accessories - Storz Performance, Inc.
CERIDIAN - Computer storage devices - Ceridian Corp.
CERIM - Floor tile - Integrity Tile Co.
CERISE - Manicure preparations ☆ - Orly International Inc.
CERISE - Maraschino cherries - Curtice-Burns Foods, Inc.
CERISE ARCH - Cabinets–wood - Kemper
CERISE DAWN - Flowers, plants, and seeds - DeVor Nurseries Inc.
CERISE SQUARE - Cabinets–wood - Kemper
CERISSA - Skin care products - Revlon Consumer Products Corp.
CERIUS - Computer software - Molecular Simulations Inc.
CERLINE - Pipes - Cerline Ceramic Corp.
CERMET 2000 - Golfing equipment - Golfsmith International Inc.
CERMET TOUR - Golfing equipment - Golfsmith International Inc.
CERMITATION - Enamels - Tivian Laboratories Inc.
CERNILTON - Vitamins and nutritional supplements - Cernitin America Inc.
CERNIT - Toys - Importoys
CEROGRAS - Animal feed supplements - Agri-Tech Inc.
CEROSE - Pharmaceutical preparations - Wyeth-Ayerst Laboratories
CEROSE-DM - Antihistamine preparations - Wyeth-Ayerst Laboratories
CERRETA - Candy - Cerreta Candy Co. Inc.
CERRO AZUL - Seafood products–fresh or frozen ☆ - Pocasset Seafoods Inc.
CERROBRAZE - Copper compounds - Marmon Group Inc.
CERROGROOVE - Tubes–copper - Marmon Group Inc.
CERROSPEC - Copper tubing - Marmon Group Inc.
CERRUTI - Men's apparel - Intercontinental Branded Apparel
CERRUTI 1881 - Handbags - Senix Group
CERT-I-SELECT - Pork - Wilson Foods Corp.
CERT-O-FIED - Health care products - Summa Pharmaceutical Laboratories Inc.
CERTA-LOK - Pipes - Certainteed Corp. (Roofing Products Group)

CERTAFLEX - Ducts–metal - Certainteed Corp. (Roofing Products Group)
CERTAIN - Paper–toilet - Procter & Gamble Co.
CERTAIN CURL - Hair care products ☆ - Framesi USA/Roffler Industries Inc.
CERTAIN-DRI - Deodorants–personal - Numark Laboratories Inc.
CERTAIN ELEGANCE - Floor coverings–carpet and rugs - Gulistan Carpet Inc.
CERTAIN FEELING - Floor coverings–carpet and rugs ☆ - Gulistan Carpet Inc.
CERTAIN PLEASURE - Floor coverings–carpet and rugs - World Carpets, Inc.
CERTAIN SEAL - Weather stripping - K.J. Miller Corp.
CERTAINLY RED - Lipsticks - Revlon Consumer Products Corp.
CERTAINTEED - Roofing materials–concrete - Certainteed Corp. (Roofing Products Group)
CERTAINTEED XT 25 - Roofing materials–concrete - Certainteed Corp. (Roofing Products Group)
CERTAINTEED XT-30 - Shingles–asphalt or tar - Certainteed Corp. (Roofing Products Group)
CERTAINTY - Vitamins and nutritional supplements - Bioenergy Nutrient's Inc.
CERTAVENT - Shingles–asphalt or tar - Certainteed Corp. (Roofing Products Group)
CERTI-CAL - Computer software - Johnson Yokogawa Corp.
CERTI-FOAM - Cleaning preparations–carpet and rug - Certified International
CERTI-FRESH - Seafood products–fresh or frozen - Certi-Fresh Foods Inc.
CERTI-PRIDE - Health care products ☆ - Certified Grocers Midwest Inc.
CERTI-SEAL - Tape–adhesive - Whitaker Corp.
CERTICOAT - Shellac - Bradshaw-Praeger & Co.
CERTIFIABLY YOURS - Greeting cards - American Greetings Corp.
CERTIFICARDS - Greeting cards - Vintage Images
CERTIFICATE - Floor coverings–carpet and rugs - J and J Industries Inc.
CERTIFICOIN - Giftware - Presentation Box Co.
CERTIFIED - Analgesics - A and S Pharmaceutical Corp.
CERTIFIED - Barbecues and grills - Char-Broil
CERTIFIED - Cleaning preparations–carpet and rug - Certified International
CERTIFIED - Doilies - U.S. Lace Paper Works Inc.
CERTIFIED - Dyes–food - McMormick Flavor Division
CERTIFIED - Food products - Blair Milling and Elevator Co. Inc.
CERTIFIED - Food products - Certified Grocers of California, Ltd.
CERTIFIED - Gasoline - Certified Oil Co.
CERTIFIED - Meat products–canned - Wilson Foods Corp.
CERTIFIED - Trading cards and stamps - Pinnacle Brands, Inc.
CERTIFIED 39 - Paints - North Jersey Paint Co. Inc.
CERTIFIED 2001 - Vacuum cleaners and accessories–commercial - Certified International
CERTIFIED ACTIVE - Beverages - Yerba Prima, Inc.
CERTIFIED ANTI-STAT - Cleaning preparations–carpet and rug - Certified International
CERTIFIED BISSC BAKING INDUSTRY SANITATION STANDARDS COMMITTEE - Bakery machines - Baking Industry Sanitation Standards Committee
CERTIFIED BOND - Cigars - Reiss Dabney Cigar Co.
CERTIFIED C SEG I INCINERABLE - Apparel and accessories - Scientific Ecology Group, Inc.
CERTIFIED CALIFORNIA GROWN CALIFORNIA POULTRY INDUSTRY FEDERATION - Meat products–poultry - California Poultry Industry Federation, Inc.
CERTIFIED HARVEST KING - Fertilizers - Vigoro Industries, Inc.
CERTIFIED HCC HEALTH CARE CARPETS - Floor coverings–carpet and rugs - Carpetland USA, Inc.
CERTIFIED HEREFORD BEEF - Beef - American Hereford Association, Inc.
CERTIFIED HOME PROTECTION - Alarm systems–burglar - Positive Response Television, Inc.
CERTIFIED INSTALLER - Cleaning preparations - Gold Eagle Co.
CERTIFIED MODEL S PILEBRUSH AND VACUUM - Vacuum cleaners and accessories–commercial - Certified International
CERTIFIED ORGANIC - Teas - Satori Fine Herbals
CERTIFIED PERFECT - Jewelry–precious - Helzbergs Diamond Shops Inc.
CERTIFIED POTENCY POWER-HERBS - Health care products ☆ - Nature's Herbs
CERTIFIED POTENCY STANDARDIZED LIQUID POWER HERBS - Health care products ☆ - Nature's Herbs
CERTIFIED RED LABEL - Fruits–canned ☆ - Certified Grocers Midwest Inc.
CERTIFIED ROCK - Salt - Gunther Salt Co.
CERTIFIED STREAKER - Flowers, plants, and seeds - Jacklin Seed
CERTIFIED USA BELGIAN BLUE BEEF - Beef - American Belgian Blue Assn.
CERTIFYD - Brushes - Morris-Flamingo Inc.
CERTILITE - Lighting fixtures ☆ - Hubbell Lighting, Inc. (Lighting Div.)

                 ☆ = Now out of production

CERTISEAL - Shellac - Bradshaw-Praeger & Co.
CERTROCK - Plaster–wallboard - Georgia-Pacific Corp.
CERTRON - Audio tapes–blank - Certron Corp.
CERTRONIX - Computer software - Certronix International Corp.
CERTS - Candy - American Chicle Co.
CERTS SUGAR FREE - Candy - American Chicle Co.
CERUBIDINE - Pharmaceutical preparations - Wyeth-Ayerst Laboratories
CERULEAN - Computer peripheral equipment - Cerulean Technology, Inc.
CERULEAN - Oils–lubricating - Ashland Oil, Inc.
CERUMENE - Veterinary pharmaceutical preparations - Evsco Pharmaceuticals
CERUMENEX - Pharmaceutical preparations - Purdue Frederick Co.
CERUMITE - Veterinary pharmaceutical preparations - Evsco Pharmaceuticals
CERV-EASE - Medical apparatus - Florida Manufacturing Corp.
CERV-O-CURVE - Health care products - Mor-Loc Corp.
CERV-O-CURVE PLUS - Health care products - Mor-Loc Corp.
CERVA - Olives–pickled or brined ☆ - Musco Olive Products Inc.
CERVALITE - Health care products - Camp, Inc.
CERVDIL - Pharmaceutical preparations - Forest Pharmaceuticals Inc.
CERVENE - Pharmaceutical preparations - Baker Norton Pharmaceuticals, Inc.
CERVENY - Tubas - Ideal Musical Merchandise Co.
CERVEZA CLARA - Beverages–malt - Montezuma Imports Inc.
CERVI-GARDE - Health care products - Bell-Horn
CERVI-SATIN - Pillowcases - Maxxim Medical Inc.
CERVIBRACE - Medical apparatus ☆ - Camp, Inc.
CERVIDIL - Medical apparatus - Forest Laboratories, Inc.
CERVISOFT - Medical apparatus - Hardwood Products Co.
CERVITAL - Antitoxins - Cernitin America Inc.
CERVITRAK - Health care products - Staodyn, Inc.
CERWIN - Footwear - Cerwin Shoes Corp.
CERWIN - Publisher's imprints - Pinnacle Books/Windsor Corp.
CERWIN-VEGA - Audio equipment - Cerwin-Vega Inc.
CERWIN VEGA - Audio equipment - Speakerkits Inc.
CES CHEVEUX - Hair care products - Cheveux Inc.
CES LINK - Computer software - Card Establishment Services Inc.
CESARANI - Apparel–men's - Hartmarx Corp.
CESARE POLI ORIGINALS - Glassware–household - Neuwirth Co.
CESCOWELD - Tools ☆ - U.S. Safety Corp.
CESHIRE - Floor coverings–carpet and rugs - Coronet Carpets Inc.
CESIBON - Combs - B.W. Boyd Shears Inc.
CESS-FLO - Detergents - Pequa Industries Inc.
CESS-TIC - Cleaning preparations - Ramco Chemical Inc.
CESSNA 150 AEROBAT - Toys–airplanes - Cox Products Inc.
CESSNA 182 SKYLANE - Vests–men's - Cox Products Inc.
CESSNA CENTURION - Vests–men's ☆ - Cox Products Inc.
CESSNA EAGLE - Vests–men's - Cox Products Inc.
C'EST BIEN - Jewelry - Rolyn, Inc.
C'EST BON - Food products ☆ - Nature's Pride Inc.
C'EST BON - Rice - Estherwood Rice Sales
C'EST BON CHOCOLAT - Confections - Mama Tish's Italian Specialties, Inc.
C'EST CITY - Apparel–women's - Bramead International, Inc.
C'EST DUO BY CASABLANCA - Apparel and accessories - Casablanca Group, LP
C'EST FRANCAIS - Skin care products ☆ - WES Publishing
C'EST JOLIE - Draperies - Arrow Textile Corp.
C'EST LA FORCE - Hair care products - KMS Research Inc.
C'EST LA VIE - Floor coverings–carpet and rugs - Customweave Carpets Inc.
C'EST MOI! - Perfumes - Avon Products, Inc.
C'EST OUI - Apparel–women's - Apparel Group, Ltd.
C'EST PAPIER - Invitations - C'est Papier Inc.
C'EST SI BON - Meat products - Fine French Foods, Inc.
C'EST SIMONE - Apparel–women's - Swan Industries Ltd.
CESTAD - Motorcycles - Central States Tool & Die Works
CESTO - Tableware–china ☆ - Villeroy and Boch Tableware Ltd.
C.E.T.A. - Computer software - Zenith Insurance Co.
CETA-TAR - Shampoos ☆ - Alcon Laboratories, Inc.
CETABUFF - Pharmaceutical preparations ☆ - Wesley Pharmacal Co. Inc.
CETACEA - Apparel and accessories - Cetacea Corp.
CETACET - Pharmaceutical preparations ☆ - Wesley Pharmacal Co. Inc.
CETACORT - Skin care products - Owen/Galderma Laboratories Inc.
CETAKLENZ - Skin care products - Geritrex Corp.
CETAMIDE - Ophthalmic goods - Alcon Laboratories, Inc.
CETANE - Vitamins and nutritional supplements ☆ - Forest Pharmaceuticals Inc.
CETAPHIL - Skin care products - Owen/Galderma Laboratories Inc.
CETAPRED - Ophthalmic goods - Alcon Laboratories, Inc.
CETASED - Pharmaceutical preparations ☆ - Wesley Pharmacal Co. Inc.

CETAZINE - Pharmaceutical preparations ☆ - JMI-Canton Pharmaceuticals
CETAZO - Pharmaceutical preparations ☆ - JMI-Canton Pharmaceuticals
CETI - Cabinets ☆ - Lane Co. Inc.
CETIME - Pharmaceutical preparations ☆ - Jones Medical Industries, Inc. (Medical Div.)
CETINA - Whirlpools - Lasco Products Group
CETRA - Whirlpools - Jacuzzi Inc.
CETRO - Cigars - Tropical Tobacco, Inc.
CETRO-CIROSE - Cough medicines - Wyeth-Ayerst Laboratories
CETRON - Gasoline ☆ - BP America Inc.
CETYLCIDE - Hearing aids - Hocks Laboratories
CEV - Valves - Provacon, Inc.
CEVALIN - Vitamins and nutritional supplements - Eli Lilly and Co.
CEVI - Ceramic tile ☆ - Integrity Tile Co.
CEVI-BID - Vitamins and nutritional supplements - Geriatric Pharmaceutical Corp.
CEVI-FER - Pharmaceutical preparations - Geriatric Pharmaceutical Corp.
CEVIM-T - Vitamins and nutritional supplements ☆ - Whitby Pharmaceuticals, Inc.
CEVIRON - Vitamins and nutritional supplements ☆ - U.S. Ethicals Inc.
CEVITA - Pharmaceutical preparations - Kay Pharmacal Co. Inc.
CEWL - Cables–signal - Ross Martin Anderson
CEWS - Medical apparatus - Del Mar Avionics
CEYLON - Cabinets - Del Mar Cabinets
CEYLON - Cooking utensils–enameled ☆ - National Housewares
CEYLON - Dinnerware–glass - Dansk International Designs, Ltd.
CEYLON - Floor coverings–carpet and rugs - Milliken & Co. Inc.
CEYLON - Teas - Royal Gardens Tea
CEYLON - Wallpaper - Capital Carousel Inc.
CEYLON - Wallpaper - Gloria Merrill Enterprises
C.E.Z. SPECS - Eyeglasses - Capo, Inc.
CEZAME - Recording label ☆ - Rounder Records Corp.
CEZANI - Apparel and accessories - Phillips-Van Heusen Corp.
CEZANNE - Artists' materials ☆ - Binney & Smith Inc.
CEZANNE - Computer software - Netlogic Inc.
CEZANNE - Floor coverings - Bellbridge Carpets
CEZANNE - Floor coverings–carpet and rugs - Patcraft Mills Inc.
CEZAR - Apparel–women's - Silk Icon Apparel, Inc.
CEZIN-S CAPSULES - Pharmaceutical preparations - Forest Pharmaceuticals Inc.
CEZLAN - Computer software - Cellsys, Inc.
CF - Agricultural products - JMK International, Inc.
CF - Cosmetics - Cosmetics Factory, Inc.
CF - Flags - Flags International Inc.
CF - Jewelry - JMK International, Inc.
CF - Nuts and bolts - Captive Fasteners Corp.
CF-20 - Chemical preparations - Comstar International Inc.
CF-20 - Cleaning preparations - Comstar International Inc. (IPC Div.)
C.F. HATHAWAY - Apparel and accessories - Warnaco Inc.
CF PRIMETIME AIR - Air transportation - Consolidated Freightways, Inc.
CF SCANSTATION - Computer software - Scangraphics, Inc.
CFD-ACE - Computer software - CFD Research Corp.
CFD-VIEW - Computer software - CFD Research Corp.
CFDESIGN - Computer software - Blue Ridge Numerics, Inc.
CFDESIGNTK - Computer software - Blue Ridge Numerics, Inc.
CFG - Eyeglasses - Marchon and Marcolin Eyewear Inc.
CFGMGR - Computer software - Bruce G. Jackson & Associates Inc.
CFI - Floor covering stores - Cooper Flooring International, Inc.
CFI - Fuel additives - Bell Additives, Inc.
CFI - Nuts and bolts - Capital Fasteners, Inc.
C.F.I. - Vitamins and nutritional supplements ☆ - Ethical Nutrients
CFJ - Food products ☆ - Hunt-Wesson, Inc.
CFJ - Jewelry - CFJ Manufacturing, Inc.
CFL - Lighting fixtures–stage - Lighttech Group, Inc.
CFLEXPRO - Cement - Custom Building Products
CFM - Computer software - Jon Goldman Associates, Inc.
CFM - Fabrics ☆ - Greenwood Mills Inc.
CFO VISION - Computer software - Sas Institute Inc.
CFP - Food products - Custom Food Products Inc.
CFP - Golfing equipment - Carbon Fiber Products, Inc.
CFPS - Computer software - Crowell Systems
CFS - Chemical preparations - Complex Fluid Systems, Inc.
CFS PACIFIC THEATRE - Computer software - Abacus Software, Inc.
CG - Computer hardware - Bayer Corp.
CG++ - Computer peripheral equipment - Belmont Research, Inc.
CG - Exercising equipment - California Gym Equipment

☆ = Now out of production

CG - Jewelry - Jewelry Works Inc.

CG 14K - Jewelry - Gabriel & Co.

CG-90 - Deicing fluid ☆ - Cargill Salt

CG CINEGUARD - Recording label - Macrovision Corp.

C.G. P.J.'S - Apparel and accessories - Damze Co., Inc.

CGA - Apparel–athletic - Celebrity Golf Association

CGB - Veterinary pharmaceutical preparations - Schering Corp.

CGC - Jewelry - Colormasters Gem Corp.

CGF - Pharmaceutical preparations - Bricker Laboratories

CGFS - Stationery - Cole, Grasso, Fencl & Skinner

CGI - Pharmaceutical preparations - Compare Generiks, Inc.

CGI - Recording label - CGI Records, Inc.

CGL REPORTER - Publisher's imprints - International Risk Management Institute

CGM 2 - Audio equipment ☆ - C.T.I. Audio Inc.

CGMAGE BUILDER - Computer software - Zeh Graphic Systems, Inc.

C.G.S. - Flatware - Excel Cutlery Inc.

CGS - Machinery parts - Corrugated Gear and Sprocket, Inc.

CH - Furniture–restaurant - Stainless Inc.

CH - Thread - Scandinavian House Imports Inc.

CH-AERO - Sporting goods - Ch-Aero, Inc.

CH. BEAUREGARD-DUCASSE - Wines - Bercut-Vandervoort & Co.

CH. BELLEGRAVE-VANDERVOORT - Wines - Bercut-Vandervoort & Co.

CH. MONBAZILLAC - Wines - Bercut-Vandervoort & Co.

CH RACING SYSTEM - Computer peripheral equipment - Joystick Technologies (CH Products Division)

CH THROTTLE - Computer peripheral equipment - Joystick Technologies (CH Products Division)

CH. TROCARD MONREBOS - Wines - Bercut-Vandervoort & Co.

CHA-CHA - Cookies - Sunshine/Salerno Inc.

CHA-CHA - Recording label - Cha-Cha Records

CHA CHA - Soups–mixes - Fantastic Foods Inc.

CHA CHA CHA - Bathing suits ☆ - Apparel Ventures, Inc.

CHA-CHA CHINESE - Salad dressings–bottled - Soy Vay Enterprises

CHA CHA ROUNDS - Candy ☆ - Casanova Chocolate Co.

CHA-CHING! - Games - International Gamco, Inc.

CHA-SEAL - Adhesives and sealants - Chase Instruments Corp.

CHA-SHEP-SKA - Animal feeds - Timothy Whiteagle

CHA-ZAH - Food products - Lo-An/Florida Inc.

CHAAVAE - Jewelry - Tilson Gem Designs Associates, L.P.

CHABANNEAU - Liquors - Crown Capital USA Inc.

CHABLIS - Cabinets ☆ - Aristokraft, Inc.

CHABLIS - Fabrics ☆ - Decorative Aides Co. Inc.

CHABLIS - Flatware - Wallace International Silversmiths, Inc.

CHABLIS - Floor coverings - Tarkett, Inc.

CHABLIS - Furniture - Stanley Furniture Co. Inc.

CHABLIS - Silverware - Imperial Schrade Corp.

CHABLIS - Toilets–enameled - Kohler Co.

CHABLIS - Wallpaper - Pickhardt & Siebert USA Inc.

CHABLIS III - Wallpaper - Pickhardt & Siebert USA Inc.

CHACE - Candles - Chace Candles, Inc.

CHACE LIFETIME - Candles - Chace Candles, Inc.

CHACHIES - Sauces - Chachies, Inc.

CHACHO'S - Potato chips ☆ - Keebler Co.

CHACO - Apparel and accessories - Mark Paigen

CHACOPA - Chocolate bars ☆ - California Natural Products

CHAD - Toys - Tonka Corp.

CHAD ENTERPRISES MORNING STRETCH - Fabrics - Chad Enterprises

CHADALEE FARMS - Food products - Chadalee Farms

CHADBOURN - Furniture - Haworth, Inc.

CHADBOURN - Hosiery ☆ - Stanwood Corp.

CHADDSFORD - Wines - Chaddsford Winery

CHADEAU - Doors–glass ☆ - Peachtree Doors and Windows Inc.

CHADFIELD GARDEN - Nurseries and garden stores - Chadfield Garden, Inc.

CHADMORE - Apparel–men's - Nulook Fashions Menswear Inc.

CHADMORE EXECUTIVE - Apparel–men's - Nulook Fashions Menswear Inc.

CHADO - Tea - Chado International Tea Trading, Inc.

CHAD'S - Food products ☆ - Chadalee Farms

CHADSFORD - Floor coverings–carpet and rugs ☆ - Evans-Black Carpet Mills

CHADSTON - Footwear - Dianne Coroneos

CHADSWORTH - Cabinets - Saco Industries Inc.

CHADWICK - Computer software - Knowware

CHADWICK - Dishes–china - Waterford Wedgewood USA, Inc.

CHADWICK - Floor coverings ☆ - Congoleum Corp.

CHADWICK - Frames–eyeglass - May Optical Co. Inc.

CHADWICK - Furniture - Bench Craft Inc.

CHADWICK - Lamps - Kaadan Ltd.

CHADWICK - Paper - Gilbert Paper Co.

CHADWICK - Trailers–travel - Fleetwood Enterprises, Inc.

CHADWICK MANOR - Wallpaper ☆ - Parkview Designs

CHADWOOD - Cabinets–wood - Kitchen Kompact Inc.

CHADWYCK - Floor coverings–carpet and rugs - Langhorne Carpet Co. Inc.

CHAFE-GARD - Marine rigging - W.H. Salisbury & Co.

CHAFE GUARD - Health care products ☆ - Kleinert's Inc.

CHAFE GUARD - Pharmaceutical preparations - Jess Clarke & Sons Inc.

CHAFE-GUARD - Pharmaceutical preparations - Winning Solutions Inc./Miracle of Aloe

CHAFE SAFE - Food warming equipment - Candle Corp. of America

CHAFE SHIELD - Skin care products - Q. A. Laboratories Inc.

CHAFEZE - Apparel and accessories - Warnaco Inc.

CHAGALL - Yarn ☆ - Tahki Imports Ltd.

CHAI - Food products - Barth's Nutra Products

CHAIN BRAKERS - Apparel and accessories - Mar-Mac Manufacturing Co. Inc.

CHAIN DRIVE - Drums–musical instruments - Drum Workshop, Inc.

CHAIN GANG - Key rings - Imagine

CHAIN GANG PLAYLINKS - Pet products - Blue Ribbon Pet Products, Inc.

CHAIN GANG WAR - Books–comic - DC Comics

CHAIN LEADER - Publisher's imprints - Reed Elsevier Properties Inc.

CHAIN LETTERS - Hobby kits - Creative Art Activities Inc.

CHAIN LIFE - Oils–lubricating - Champions Choice Inc.

CHAIN MATE - Lubricants - LPS Laboratories, Inc.

CHAIN OF LOVE - Rings–jewelry - Artcarved Inc.

CHAIN OF PRIDE - Jewelry ☆ - James Angelo Marino

CHAIN REACTION - Toys–automobiles - Tonka Corp.

CHAIN-RITER - Pens - Block and Co., Inc.

CHAIN SAW SHARPENER - Tools–power-driven - Dremel

CHAIN SHADE, THE - Window shades - Sol-R-Veil Inc.

CHAIN STORE GUIDE - Publisher's imprints - Business Guides, Inc.

CHAIN TALK - Educational materials - Crestwood Co.

CHAINART - Jewelry ☆ - James Angelo Marino

CHAINBLAZER - Toys–guns - Tonka Corp.

CHAINDEARS - Jewelry - Kaspar & Esh Inc.

CHAINDEX - Index cards - Victor Systems & Equipment Co.

CHAINGRIP - Pulleys–industrial - Steelgrip Tools Inc.

CHAINGUARD - Chemical preparations - Angus Chemical Co.

CHAINLIGHTNING - Shoe polish ☆ - George J. Kelly Div.

CHAINMAIL - Games - Tsr, Inc.

CHAINMASTER - Jewelry - Nera

CHAINS, CHARMS N' THINGS - Toys - Imperial Toy Corp.

CHAINSAW - Amusement rides - James H. Drew, III

CHAINSHARP - Tools ☆ - Granberg International

CHAINSTITCH - Floor coverings–carpet and rugs ☆ - Capel, Inc.

CHAINTAMER - Tools–hand-operated - GW Tools Corp.

CHAINTRACK - Computer software - Softechnics, Inc.

CHAINVIEW - Computer software - Efficient Marketing Systems

CHAIR & STAIR - Infant product - Lisco, Inc.

CHAIR BEAR - Infant product - Hugger Bugger Corp.

CHAIR-EEZ - Chairs–plastic - Aqua Buoyz, Inc.

CHAIR-LOC - Adhesives and sealants - Chair-Loc Co.

CHAIR MATES - Furniture - Hammary Furniture Co. Inc.

CHAIR-PERSON - Frames–eyeglass - Liberty Optical Manufacturing Co.

CHAIR RAILS OF AMERICA - Hardware - Palm Beach Plastics Inc.

CHAIR SHOPPE - Furniture - Broyhill Furniture Industries, Inc.

CHAIRLADY - Frames–eyeglass - Liberty Optical Manufacturing Co.

CHAIRMAN - Batteries - Concorde Battery Corp.

CHAIRMAN - Clocks - General Time Corp. (Westclox/Seth Thomas Div.)

CHAIRMAN - Floor coverings–carpet and rugs ☆ - Mannington Carpets, Inc.

CHAIRMAN - Floor coverings–carpet and rugs ☆ - Royalweve Carpet Mills

CHAIRMAN - Golfing equipment - Daiwa Corp.

CHAIRMAN - Knives - Precise International/Wenger

CHAIRMAN - Luggage - United States Luggage Corp.

CHAIRMAN 50 - Bowling centers - AMF Bowling Worldwide

CHAIRMAN OF THE BOARD - Cookies - Parco Foods, Inc.

CHAIRMAN OF THE BOARD - Eyeglasses - Martin-Copeland Eyewear Corp.

CHAIRMAN OF THE BOARD - Floor coverings–carpet and rugs - Barrett Carpet Mills Inc.

CHAIRMAN OF THE BOARD - Tobacco–chewing or smoking - Sterling Tobacco Co.

CHAIRMAN'S CLUB - Apparel–men's - S & K Famous Brands, Inc.

CHAIRMATE - Health care products - Maddak Inc.

CHAIRONE - Furniture - EAC Corp.

CHAIRS OF CHOICE - Office furniture–metal - Invincible Metal Furniture Co.

☆ = Now out of production

CHAIRS THAT MOVE - Chairs–folding - Franklin Corp.

CHAIRS TO GO - Furniture - Les Brown Chair Co.

CHAIRSIDE FILE - Filing cabinets–metal ☆ - Marvel Group Inc.

CHAIRWORLD - Office furniture–wood - Globe Business Furniture, Inc.

CHAIS BAUMIERE - Wines - House of Burgundy Inc.

CHAJARO - Shampoos - Chajaro, International

CHAKRA - Beverages - Fred G. Farago

CHALAIS - Furniture ☆ - Stanley Furniture Co. Inc.

CHALET - Apparel–athletic ☆ - Samco Sportswear Inc.

CHALET - Bird feeds - Duncraft, Inc.

CHALET - Cabinets - Alpine Cabinet Co.

CHALET - Cabinets - Quality Cabinets

CHALET - Cabinets ☆ - Merillat Industries, Inc.

CHALET - Cheese - International Marketing Services Inc.

CHALET - Dishes–china ☆ - Pickard Inc.

CHALET - Faucets ☆ - Moen Inc.

CHALET - Floor coverings - Congoleum Corp.

CHALET - Manufactured homes - Redman Industries, Inc.

CHALET - Motor vehicles–motor homes - Winnebago Industries, Inc.

CHALET - Motor vehicles–motor homes ☆ - Avco Aerostructures Inc.

CHALET - Roofing materials - Atlas Roofing Corp.

CHALET - Toys - Brumberger Co. Inc.

CHALET - Watches - Webster Watch Co. Associates

CHALET - Yogurt - La Corona Foods Inc.

CHALET 21 - Food products - Mike Hudson Distributing Inc.

CHALET '87 - Wallpaper ☆ - Pickhardt & Siebert USA Inc.

CHALET COLLECTION - Glassware–household - Crisa Corp.

CHALET DEBONNE VINEYARDS - Wines - Chalet Debonne Vineyards Inc.

CHALET DUPLEX - Weather vanes - Vitos Products

CHALET ROSE - Flatware ☆ - Kirk Stieff Co.

CHALET SUZANNE - Soups–canned - Chalet Suzanne Foods Inc.

CHALEUR ESTATE - Wines - Delille Cellars, Inc.

CHALICE - Dinnerware–glass - Block China Co.

CHALICE - Floor coverings–carpet and rugs ☆ - Interloom Ltd.

CHALICE - Frames–eyeglass ☆ - Universal/Univis Inc.

CHALICE - Paper–writing - Champion International Corp.

CHALICE - Recording label - MGM Inc.

CHALIF - Mustard ☆ - Cortina Corp.

CHALINI - Shorts–women's - El Greco Inc.

CHALK-A-DOODLE - Chalk - Ore Originals, Inc.

CHALK ART - Electronic equipment - Rite-Off, Inc.

CHALK BOARD - Computer software - Dunamis Inc.

CHALK GUARD - Chalk - Listo Pencil Corp.

CHALK HILL WINERY - Wines - Chalk Hill Winery

CHALK-LINE - Hardware - L.S. Starrett Co. Inc. (Consumer Products Div.)

CHALK MATE - School supplies - Stephanie A. Vlahos

CHALK-O-GRAPHIC - Toys - Bandai America Inc.

CHALK-OFF - Erasers ☆ - Coloron Industries

CHALK TALK - Chalk - Venture Stores, Inc.

CHALK TALK - Trading cards and stamps - Upper Deck Co.

CHALK-TITE - Engines–internal combustion ☆ - Foy-Johnston Inc.

CHALK WHITE MICA - Blackboards–slate ☆ - Anco Wood Specialties Inc.

CHALKBOARD - Pencils - Faber-Castell Corp.

CHALKBOARD CUTIES - Giftware - Russ Berrie and Co., Inc.

CHALKBOOK - Paints - Triangle Coatings Inc.

CHALKIE - Blackboards–slate ☆ - Kirste Screen Printing

CHALKLINE - Jackets ☆ - Innovo Inc.

CHALKLINE - Publisher's imprints - Roy K. Ellis

CHALKMASTER - Erasers - Quartet Manufacturing Co.

CHALK'S - Postcards, paperweights, and decals - Chalk's International Airlines

CHALKY CHUNKS - Chalk - Walbuck Crayon Co., Inc.

CHALLACET - Apparel–men's - Alps Sportswear Manufacturing Co.

CHALLANGER - Bathing suits - Ocean Pool Co.

CHALLEDON - Recording label - Challedon Record Co.

CHALLENGAIR - Pet products - Double K Industries, Inc.

CHALLENGE - Automotive parts and accessories - AP Parts

CHALLENGE - Binders - The Union Group

CHALLENGE - Binders ☆ - Hedges Manufacturing Co.

CHALLENGE - Cigarettes - Brown & Williamson Tobacco Corp.

CHALLENGE - Cleaning preparations - Dualle Products

CHALLENGE - Computer hardware - Silicon Graphics, Inc.

CHALLENGE - Dairy products - Challenge Dairy Co.

CHALLENGE - Degreasing solvents - Reliable Finishing Products, Inc.

CHALLENGE - Detergents - Colgate-Palmolive Co.

CHALLENGE - Eyeglasses - Martin-Copeland Eyewear Corp.

CHALLENGE - Fabrics - Greenwood Mills Inc.

CHALLENGE - Floor coverings–carpet and rugs - Philadelphia Carpets

CHALLENGE - Margarine ☆ - Swift Edible Oil Co.

CHALLENGE - Occasional tables ☆ - JDI Group, Inc.

CHALLENGE - Paper–carbon ☆ - Curtis-Young Corp.

CHALLENGE - Rackets–tennis - Slazengers

CHALLENGE - Tableware–plastic - Solo Cup Co.

CHALLENGE - Tools - Lufkin Rule Co.

CHALLENGE - Toys–models - Estes Industries

CHALLENGE - Wallpaper ☆ - Capital Carousel Inc.

CHALLENGE 100 - Toys–electronic - Tyco Toys

CHALLENGE AIR - Compressors–air - Curtis Toledo Inc.

CHALLENGE BAND - Exercise equipment - Hygenic Corp.

CHALLENGE COURT - Footwear–athletic ☆ - Nike, Inc.

CHALLENGE I - Rackets–tennis ☆ - Slazengers

CHALLENGE IS ON, THE - Games - Finger-Sports, Inc.

CHALLENGE JACQUARDS - Wallpaper ☆ - Capital Carousel Inc.

CHALLENGE MATH - Computer software ☆ - Sunburst Communications, Inc.

CHALLENGE OF FLIGHT, THE - Video production - U.S. Fighter Squadrons, Inc.

CHALLENGE OF FLIGHT, THE - Recording label - US Fighter Squadrons, Inc.

CHALLENGE PAC - Pet products - Kelly Foods Corp.

CHALLENGE PREMIUM - Mufflers–motor vehicle - AP Parts

CHALLENGE RACERS - Sporting goods - Aqua-Leisure Industries, Inc.

CHALLENGE SERIES - Automotive parts and accessories - D.A.S. Distributors, Inc.

CHALLENGE, THE - Hair care products ☆ - Redken Laboratories, Inc.

CHALLENGE THE CHIEF - Toys–stuffed ☆ - CBS Toys

CHALLENGE YAHTZEE - Games ☆ - Milton Bradley Co.

CHALLENGER - Air conditioning equipment - Friedrich Air Conditioning Co.

CHALLENGER - Apparel and accessories - Challenger Co.

CHALLENGER - Apparel stores–sports - Challenger-General

CHALLENGER - Apparel–women's - Rockaway Beach Surf Shop Inc.

CHALLENGER - Aquariums–household - Willinger Bros., Inc.

CHALLENGER - Archery equipment - High Country American

CHALLENGER - Archery equipment ☆ - Bear Archery Inc.

CHALLENGER - Automotive parts and accessories - Stant Corp.

CHALLENGER - Awnings–metal - Mapes Industries Inc.

CHALLENGER - Batteries - Exide Corp.

CHALLENGER - Beverages–carbonated - Laneco Inc.

CHALLENGER - Bicycles - Columbia Manufacturing Inc.

CHALLENGER - Boating equipment and accessories - Diversified Marine Products

CHALLENGER - Boats - Clark Craft Boat Co.

CHALLENGER - Boats ☆ - Falcon Safety Products, Inc.

CHALLENGER - Boats–canoes - Black River Canoes

CHALLENGER - Boats–motor ☆ - Commander Marine

CHALLENGER - Boats–motor ☆ - Cruisers

CHALLENGER - Boats–motor ☆ - Marathon Boat Group, Inc.

CHALLENGER - Boats–motor ☆ - Seajay Boats Inc.

CHALLENGER - Bodyboards - Foam Design Consumer Products Inc.

CHALLENGER - Cameras - Eastman Kodak Co.

CHALLENGER - Circuit breakers - Challenger Electrical Equipment Corp.

CHALLENGER - Cleaning preparations - Reliable Finishing Products, Inc.

CHALLENGER - Clocks - General Time Corp. (Westclox/Seth Thomas Div.)

CHALLENGER - Containers–insulated - Aladdin Industries, Inc.

CHALLENGER - Doors - Jeld-Wen, Inc.

CHALLENGER - Electronic equipment - Educational Insights, Inc.

CHALLENGER - Envelopes - Quality Park Products Co.

CHALLENGER - Fertilizers - Kemmer Agricultural Manufacturing Co. Inc.

CHALLENGER - Floor coverings–carpet and rugs ☆ - Royalweve Carpet Mills

CHALLENGER - Frames–eyeglass - Universal/Univis Inc.

CHALLENGER - Fruits and vegetables - Frank T. Almaguer Inc.

CHALLENGER - Games - Fidelity Electronics International Inc.

CHALLENGER - Gloves - Champion Glove Manufacturing Co.

CHALLENGER - Gloves - Ektelon

CHALLENGER - Inflatable boats - Intex Recreation Corp.

CHALLENGER - Kites ☆ - Airplane Kite Co.

CHALLENGER - Lawn mowers - Lambert Manufacturing Corp.

CHALLENGER - Motor vehicle parts and accessories - Leer Inc.

CHALLENGER - Motor vehicles - Chrysler Corp. (Dodge Car Div.)

CHALLENGER - Motor vehicles–motor homes ☆ - Mitchell & Sons Inc.

CHALLENGER - Musical instrument accessories - Sottile Manufacturing Co.

CHALLENGER - Nozzles - La Fayette Brass Co. Inc.

CHALLENGER - Paint sprayers - Speeflo Manufacturing Corp.

CHALLENGER - Paints - Nelson Paint Co., Inc.

CHALLENGER - Pens ☆ - Parker Pen USA
CHALLENGER - Pet products - Boomer Ball
CHALLENGER - Pet products - Tetra Sales USA
CHALLENGER - Pistols ☆ - Colt's Manufacturing Co. Inc.
CHALLENGER - Radios - E.F. Johnson Co.
CHALLENGER - Rifles ☆ - Crosman Corp.
CHALLENGER - Rug cleaning machines–commercial ☆ - Castex Industries Inc.
CHALLENGER - Saws–power - Disston Co.
CHALLENGER - Skates–roller ☆ - Steven Manufacturing Co.
CHALLENGER - Slacks - Horace Small Apparel Co.
CHALLENGER - Sleds - Lightning Group Inc.
CHALLENGER - Sleds - Standard Novelty Works
CHALLENGER - Snowmobiles - Camoplast Rockland, Ltd.
CHALLENGER - Sporting goods - Award Winner Corp.
CHALLENGER - Sporting goods - Blue Mountain Industries, Inc.
CHALLENGER - Sporting goods - Wellington Leisure Products, Inc.
CHALLENGER - Sporting goods ☆ - Wright & McGill Co.
CHALLENGER - Televisions ☆ - Philips Consumer Electronics Co.
CHALLENGER - Thread - United Thread Mills Corp.
CHALLENGER - Tires - Oliver Rubber Co.
CHALLENGER - Tools - Wilton Corp.
CHALLENGER - Tools ☆ - Fleischmann Handle Co.
CHALLENGER - Toys - American Toy & Furniture Co.
CHALLENGER - Toys - Creative Playthings Ltd.
CHALLENGER - Toys - Newco, Inc.
CHALLENGER - Toys–trains - Digitrax, Inc.
CHALLENGER - Trailers–travel - Damon Corp.
CHALLENGER - Trailers–travel ☆ - Coachmen Industries, Inc.
CHALLENGER - Vacuum cleaners and accessories ☆ - Sunbeam-Oster Household Products
CHALLENGER - Welding equipment - Controls Corp. of America
CHALLENGER - Window frames - Biltbest Windows
CHALLENGER - Wrench - Stanley-Proto Industrial Works
CHALLENGER 1 - Toys–models ☆ - Estes Industries
CHALLENGER II - Toys–models ☆ - Estes Industries
CHALLENGER FISH N SKI - Boats–motor - Seajay Boats Inc.
CHALLENGER HEATERS - Pet products - Tetra Sales USA
CHALLENGERS - Automotive parts and accessories ☆ - Arlon, Inc.
CHALLENGERS - Toy guns ☆ - Intex Recreation Corp.
CHALLENGIT - Computer software ☆ - Right on Programs
CHALLISSA - Floor coverings–carpet and rugs ☆ - Evans-Black Carpet Mills
CHALMETTE - Furniture ☆ - Bassett Furniture Industries, Inc.
CHALON - Furniture - Bassett Furniture Industries, Inc.
CHALONE VINEYARD - Wines - Chalone Wine Group Ltd.
CHALOUR - Fabrics - Guilford Mills, Inc.
CHALYCE COLLECTION - Bathroom accessories ☆ - Chicago Faucet Co.
CHAM-FOAM - Cleaning preparations ☆ - Kafko International Ltd.
CHAM-FORM - Paper–writing - Champion International Corp.
CHAM-IT - Towels - Easy Day Manufacturing Co.
CHAM ME - Cleaning preparations ☆ - Capo, Inc.
CHAM-O-SPUN - Mops - Zephyr Manufacturing Co.
CHAM-PAK - Sponges - Hydra Sponge Co., Inc.
CHAM-TEX - Wallpaper ☆ - Richard E. Thibaut, Inc.
CHAMACO - Shrimp–fresh or frozen ☆ - Darik Enterprises Inc.
CHAMADE - Floor coverings–carpet and rugs ☆ - Karastan-Bigelow Inc.
CHAMADE - Perfumes - Guerlain Inc.
CHAMALON - Underwear and nightwear ☆ - Henson-Kickernick Inc.
CHAMAY - Cider ☆ - Vintners International Co. Inc.
CHAMBARAMA - Recording label - Chambara Entertainment
CHAMBARRY - Mattresses - Ohio Mattress Co.
CHAMBER - Lamps - Lamplight Farms, Inc.
CHAMBER CHECK - Alarm systems–fire - Detection Systems, Inc.
CHAMBER SERIES, THE - Maps - Map Works, Inc.
CHAMBERLAIN - Dishes–china ☆ - Royal China & Porcelain Companies Inc.
CHAMBERLAIN - Electrical equipment - Chamberlain Group Inc.
CHAMBERLAIN - Floor coverings–carpet and rugs - Karastan-Bigelow Inc.
CHAMBERLAIN - Furniture ☆ - Bassett Furniture Industries, Inc.
CHAMBERLAIN - Skin care products - Weeks & Leo Co. Inc.
CHAMBERLAIN WAXMASTER - Waxes–sealing - Chamberlain Group Inc.
CHAMBERLIN - Furniture–upholstered ☆ - Mersman Furniture Co.
CHAMBERS - Baskets–wood - Kinsman Co. Inc.
CHAMBERS - Stoves ☆ - Kitchenaid
CHAMBERS BY REN ELLIS - Leather goods - Chambers Belt Co.
CHAMBERS CANDY CO. - Confections - Christopher Brookes Distinctive Foods

CHAMBERY - Earthenware ☆ - Shafford Co. Inc.
CHAMBERY - Furniture ☆ - Bassett Furniture Industries, Inc.
CHAMBERY - Furniture–wood - Century Furniture Co.
CHAMBORD - Bathroom fixtures - Showerlux USA
CHAMBORD - Flatware - Reed and Barton Corp.
CHAMBORD - Flatware ☆ - Couzon USA
CHAMBORD - Floor coverings–carpet and rugs - Capel, Inc.
CHAMBORD - Furniture ☆ - Bernhardt Industries
CHAMBORD - Ophthalmic goods - Foremost Optical Products
CHAMBORD - Preserved foods–canned - Castle Food Products
CHAMBORD - Tableware–china ☆ - Villeroy and Boch Tableware Ltd.
CHAMBORD PECANS - Food products - Mrs. Powell's Gourmet Pecans
CHAMBOUR - Furniture ☆ - Bassett Furniture Industries, Inc.
CHAMBOURCIN - Wines - Shenandoah Vineyards
CHAMBOURCIN - Wines - Ziem Vineyards
CHAMBOURCY - Desserts - Nestle USA
CHAMBRAY - Blinds–venetian ☆ - Hunter Douglas, Inc.
CHAMBRAY - Cording - M.W. Kasch Co.
CHAMBRAY - Floor coverings–carpet and rugs ☆ - Masland Corp.
CHAMBRAY - Frames–eyeglass ☆ - Universal/Univis Inc.
CHAMBRAY - Stationery - Georgia-Pacific Corp.
CHAMBRAY TEDDY - Toys - Kids II, Inc.
CHAMBRE D'AMI - Furniture - Debry-Pexton Inc.
CHAMBRIL - Paper–writing - Champion International Corp.
CHAMDEVILLE - Wines ☆ - Blair Importers Ltd.
CHAMELACOLORS - Inks - Poskudny Industries Inc.
CHAMELEON - Alarm systems - Valley Products & Design Inc.
CHAMELEON - Amplifiers–musical instrument - Rocktron Corp.
CHAMELEON - Furniture - Corry Hiebert
CHAMELEON - Interactive, motion-based virtual reality simulator ride for the amusement ind. - Chameleon Technologies, Inc.
CHAMELEON - Lipsticks - Preview Products
CHAMELEON - Medical apparatus - Camp, Inc.
CHAMELEON - Paint sprayers - Binks Manufacturing Co.
CHAMELEON - Paint stripper - Custom Hobbyist, Inc.
CHAMELEON - Recording label - Chameleon Music Group Inc.
CHAMELEON - Sunblocks - Michael Allwine
CHAMELEON - Sunglasses - Charmant Inc. USA
CHAMELEON - Sunglasses ☆ - Corning Inc.
CHAMELEON - Thread ☆ - SCT Yarns Inc.
CHAMELEON - Tiles–ceramic - Epro Inc.
CHAMELEON - Watches - Hampden Corp.
CHAMELEON - Watches - Rolex Watch USA, Inc.
CHAMELEON - Window coverings - Right Track
CHAMELEON 32+ - Computer peripheral equipment - Tekelec Inc.
CHAMELEON COLLECTION - Wallcovering - C/S Group/DecoGard Products
CHAMELEON METAL RESIN CEMENT - Dental compounds - Myron International Inc.
CHAMELEON OPEN - Computer peripheral equipment - Tekelec Inc.
CHAMELEON OPEN-X - Computer peripheral equipment - Tekelec Inc.
CHAMELEON REPUBLIC - Housewares - Safariland Imports
CHAMELEON, THE - Mailing machines - Park Sherman
CHAMELON - Frames–eyeglass ☆ - Universal/Univis Inc.
CHAMEX - Paper–writing - Champion International Corp.
CHAMFER - Floor coverings–carpet and rugs ☆ - Regal Rugs Inc.
CHAMFOLD - Paper–writing - Champion International Corp.
CHAMINADE - Floor coverings–carpet and rugs - Cabin Crafts Carpets
CHAMINADE-JULIENNE - Apparel and accessories - Chaminade-Julienne High School, Inc.
CHAMISAL VINEYARD - Wines - Chamisal Vineyard
CHAMISE - Apparel and accessories - Kirkwood International, Inc.
CHAMKOTE - Paper–writing - Champion International Corp.
CHAMOCONDITION - Hair care products - Kristine M. Schoenauer
CHAMODAN - Fabrics–chambray - Dan River Inc.
CHAMOIS CREME - Pharmaceutical preparations - Nutri-West
CHAMOIS SUEDE - Wallpaper - Lawrence Wallcoverings
CHAMOMILE - Shampoos - S.C. Johnson & Son, Inc.
CHAMOMILE CPX - Health care products ☆ - Nature's Herbs
CHAMOMILE OF THE COUNTRY - Skin care products - Jason Natural Products, Inc.
CHAMOMILE PH RECTIFIER - Hair-care products - Tri-Institute of Trichology
CHAMONETTE - Furniture - Knothe Corp.
CHAMONIX - Eyeglasses - Art-Craft Optical Co.
CHAMONIX - House furnishings ☆ - Lexington Furniture Industries, Inc.
CHAMONIX - Liqueurs - NWS, Inc.
CHAMONIX - Window coverings ☆ - Vertilux-Louverlux Inc.

☆ = Now out of production

CHAMONIX USA 1924 TEAM - Pins–jewelry - United States Olympic Committee

CHAMOPURE - Hair care products - Kristine M. Schoenauer

CHAMOVERA - Shampoos - Home Health Products, Inc.

CHAMOYADA - Syrup - Francisco Garcia

CHAMP - Automotive parts and accessories - Champion Laboratories, Inc.

CHAMP - Automotive parts and accessories - Standard Motor Products, Inc.

CHAMP - Bandages - Carolon Co.

CHAMP - Bandages - Cramer Products Inc.

CHAMP - Bicycles - Columbia Manufacturing Inc.

CHAMP - Binoculars - Pioneer Marketing & Research, Inc.

CHAMP - Boats–motor ☆ - Marathon Boat Group, Inc.

CHAMP - Buckets–plastic - Geerpres Wringer Co.

CHAMP - Cameras - Eastman Kodak Co.

CHAMP - Dog food - Sunshine Mills Inc.

CHAMP - Filing cabinets–metal - Joyce International Inc.

CHAMP - Food products - Universal Frozen Foods Co.

CHAMP - Frames–picture - Framemica Co.

CHAMP - Guitars - Fender Musical Instruments

CHAMP - Hats ☆ - Resistol Hats

CHAMP - Ice cream - Alpine Distribution Services

CHAMP - Motor vehicles–automobiles ☆ - Chrysler Corp. (Chrysler-Plymouth Div.)

CHAMP - Ophthalmic goods - Styl-Rite Optical Manufacturing Co., Inc.

CHAMP - Photocopy machines - Canon USA, Inc.

CHAMP - Prosthetic apparatus ☆ - Camp, Inc.

CHAMP - Scissors–hand-operated - Aaronco Grooming Products

CHAMP - Scissors–hand-operated - Aaronco Pet Products, Inc.

CHAMP - Shoes–athletic - MacNeill Engineering Co.

CHAMP - Toys - American Toy & Furniture Co.

CHAMP - Tripods–photographic ☆ - QuickSet International Inc.

CHAMP - Trophies–metal - Contemporary Inc.

CHAMP CHERRY - Beverages–carbonated - Amazing Beverages, Inc.

CHAMP CIV - Catheters - Carolon Co.

CHAMP EXCEL - Bandages - Carolon Co.

CHAMP-HEATER - Heaters–space - Lawn-Boy

CHAMP LAKE CHAMPLAIN CREATURE AMERICA'SOWN NEW YORK VERMONT - Shirts - Frank Soriano

CHAMP!, THE - Fruit pie mixes - Wells' Dairy, Inc.

CHAMPACA - Skin care products - Frances Denney

CHAMPAGNE - Apparel–women's - Jezebel-Renee of Hollywood

CHAMPAGNE - Bedding - Ohio Mattress Co.

CHAMPAGNE - Brushes - Corona Brushes Inc.

CHAMPAGNE - Cabinets ☆ - Aristokraft, Inc.

CHAMPAGNE - Candy - James P. Linette Inc.

CHAMPAGNE - Cigars - G.W. Van Slyke & Horton

CHAMPAGNE - Cigars ☆ - General Cigar Co., Inc.

CHAMPAGNE - Dishes–china - Pickard Inc.

CHAMPAGNE - Furniture ☆ - Halcyon Inc.

CHAMPAGNE - Furniture–children's - Child Craft Industries Inc.

CHAMPAGNE - Lipsticks - Lancome

CHAMPAGNE - Mustard ☆ - Cortina Corp.

CHAMPAGNE - Ophthalmic goods - Styl-Rite Optical Manufacturing Co., Inc.

CHAMPAGNE - Pet products - Gone to the Dogs

CHAMPAGNE - Rings–jewelry - Artcarved Inc.

CHAMPAGNE - Thread - Bond Products Inc.

CHAMPAGNE & ROSES - Dinnerware - Corning Inc.

CHAMPAGNE BEAR - Toys–stuffed - Effanbee Doll Corp.

CHAMPAGNE CLUTCH - Leather goods - St. Thomas Inc.

CHAMPAGNE COUNTRY - Wallpaper - Lin-Gor Wallcoverings

CHAMPAGNE DELAMOTTE - Wines - Wilson Daniels Ltd.

CHAMPAGNE DELIGHT - Food products - Giovanni's Appetizing Food Products

CHAMPAGNE DEUTZ - Wines - Wine World Inc.

CHAMPAGNE GLACE - Wallcoverings - Wallworks

CHAMPAGNE LADY - Dolls ☆ - Effanbee Doll Corp.

CHAMPAGNE LANSON - Beverages–alcohol ☆ - IDV Wines (Beaulieu Vineyard)

CHAMPAGNE MIX - Candy - Sathers Inc.

CHAMPAGNE MUMM - Wines - Seagram's Chateau & Estate Wines Co.

CHAMPAGNE NUT COMPANY, THE - Nuts–salted, roasted, cooked, or canned - Champagne Nut Co.

CHAMPAGNE ON ICE - Apparel and accessories ☆ - Warnaco Inc.

CHAMPAGNE SALON - Wines - Wilson Daniels Ltd.

CHAMPAGNE SUITE - Lighting fixtures - Angelo Brothers Co.

CHAMPAGNE TINKER - Novelty items ∑ - Norstar Enterprises

CHAMPAGNES POL ROGER - Wines - Frederick Wildman and Sons Ltd.

CHAMPALE - Beverages–malt - The Stroh Brewery Co.

CHAMPAYN - Beverages - Comfrey International Co.

CHAMPDECK - Wood products - Champion International Corp.

CHAMPIGNON - Cheese - Champignon N.A.

CHAMPIGNONS DE PARIS - Tableware–earthenware ☆ - Seymour Mann Inc.

CHAMPIGNY - Glassware–household - Durand International

CHAMPION - Adding machines ☆ - Victor Technology

CHAMPION - Air conditioning equipment - York International Corp.

CHAMPION - Ammunition - Federal Cartridge Co.

CHAMPION - Apparel and accessories - Oxford Industries, Inc.

CHAMPION - Apparel and accessories - Sara Lee Corp.

CHAMPION - Apparel and accessories - Texace Corp.

CHAMPION - Audio equipment - Pro-Co. Sound Co. Inc.

CHAMPION - Bags–duffel - Saramar Corp.

CHAMPION - Basketball footwear ☆ - Autry Industries Inc.

CHAMPION - Bathing suits - Ocean Pool Co.

CHAMPION - Batteries - Amglo-Kemlite

CHAMPION - Batteries - GNB Inc. (Automotive Battery Div.)

CHAMPION - Beverages–alcohol - Schenley Industries Inc.

CHAMPION - Blankets–horse - Smith-Worthington Saddlery Co. Inc.

CHAMPION - Boats–canoes ☆ - Sawyer Composite Products

CHAMPION - Brooms - F.M. Thorpe Manufacturing Co.

CHAMPION - Brushes - Wright-Bernet

CHAMPION - Brushes–paint - Corona Brushes Inc.

CHAMPION - Cakes - Interstate Brands Corp.

CHAMPION - Chemical preparations - Lowe Oil Co.

CHAMPION - Cleaning preparations - Chase Products Co.

CHAMPION - Cleaning preparations–window ☆ - Gold Eagle Co.

CHAMPION - Combs - Burmax Co. Inc.

CHAMPION - Dental equipment - American Dental Products Unlimited, Inc.

CHAMPION - Dishwashers–commercial - Champion Industries, Inc.

CHAMPION - Drywall screws - BP & N Inc.

CHAMPION - Electronic equipment - Bell Atlantic Network Services, Inc.

CHAMPION - Electronic equipment - Telex Communications, Inc.

CHAMPION - Envelopes - Quality Park Products Co.

CHAMPION - Extension ladders - W.W. Babcock Co. Inc.

CHAMPION - Fabrics–broadcloth - Desire Mills Co. Inc.

CHAMPION - Fertilizers - Chilean Nitrate Corp.

CHAMPION - Fertilizers - Reliance Plastic & Chemical Corp.

CHAMPION - Flags - Dettra Flag Co. Inc.

CHAMPION - Floor coverings–carpet and rugs - Calladium & Marglen

CHAMPION - Floor coverings–carpet and rugs - Conquest Carpet Mills Inc.

CHAMPION - Floor coverings–carpet and rugs ☆ - Playfield International Inc.

CHAMPION - Footwear - Distributors Service Corp.

CHAMPION - Footwear - Stride Rite Corp.

CHAMPION - Furniture ☆ - H. Wilson Co.

CHAMPION - Games - Stuart Entertainment, Inc.

CHAMPION - Glass products - Peltier Glass Co.

CHAMPION - Gloves - Champion Glove Manufacturing Co.

CHAMPION - Hammers - Numa

CHAMPION - Hardware - Associated Hardware Supply Co.

CHAMPION - Hardware - Tel-O-Post Co.

CHAMPION - Hardware, lawn and garden supplies - Bostwick-Braun Co.

CHAMPION - Hats - HYP

CHAMPION - Health care products - Everest & Jennings

CHAMPION - Heaters–space ☆ - Lawn-Boy

CHAMPION - Hoists - Century Wrecker Corp.

CHAMPION - Knives ☆ - Tru-Balance Knife Co.

CHAMPION - Ladders–wood - John S. Tilley Ladders Co. Inc.

CHAMPION - Lawn mowers - White Consolidated Industries, Inc.

CHAMPION - Lighting fixtures - Acme-Lite Manufacturing Co.

CHAMPION - Maps - Natural Color Cards Co.

CHAMPION - Mats - JCH International Inc.

CHAMPION - Musical instrument accessories - Grover/Trophy Musical Products Inc.

CHAMPION - Musical instruments - Fred Gretsch Enterprises

CHAMPION - Pasta ☆ - Nalley's Fine Foods

CHAMPION - Pencil sharpeners - Hunt Manufacturing Co.

CHAMPION - Pencils ☆ - Faber-Castell Corp.

CHAMPION - Pet products ☆ - Trophy Animal Health Care

CHAMPION - Pipes–tobacco ☆ - Lane Ltd.

CHAMPION - Pistols - Precise International/Wenger

CHAMPION - Plumbing fixtures - Jameco Industries, Inc.

CHAMPION - Prefabricated buildings–wood - Champion Enterprises Inc.

CHAMPION - Prosthetic apparatus - OTC Professional Appliances

☆ = Now out of production

CHAMPION - Raisins - National Raisin Co.
CHAMPION - Recording label - Stanley Schneider
CHAMPION - Rifles ☆ - Iver Johnson Arms Co.
CHAMPION - Rope ☆ - Tubbs Cordage Co.
CHAMPION - Safety glasses - Bilsom International Inc.
CHAMPION - Saw blades - Heinemann Saw Corp.
CHAMPION - Scoreboards - Daktronics Inc.
CHAMPION - Shoes–athletic - Phoenix Integrated Inc.
CHAMPION - Skates–roller ☆ - Lancaster Toy Co.
CHAMPION - Sleds - Paris Co. Inc.
CHAMPION - Socks - Kayser-Roth Corp.
CHAMPION - Spark plugs - Cooper Industries (Cooper Automotive)
CHAMPION - Sporting goods - Arnold Health Equipment Co.
CHAMPION - Sporting goods ☆ - Wright & McGill Co.
CHAMPION - Sports rackets and accessories - Winn, Inc.
CHAMPION - Sprinklers–lawn - La Fayette Brass Co. Inc.
CHAMPION - Sunglasses - Status Eyes Ltd.
CHAMPION - Sunglasses ☆ - International Tropic-Cal Inc. (I SKI Div.)
CHAMPION - Thread - Gudebrod, Inc.
CHAMPION - Tires - Bridgestone/Firestone, Inc.
CHAMPION - Tool boxes - Homak Manufacturing Co. Inc.
CHAMPION - Tools - Railway Handle Corp.
CHAMPION - Tools - Turner Industries Ltd.
CHAMPION - Toys - Creative Playthings Ltd.
CHAMPION - Vacuum cleaners and accessories - Kent Co.
CHAMPION - Watchbands - Jacoby-Bender Inc.
CHAMPION - Watches - Bulova Corp.
CHAMPION - Waterproofing compounds - Midland Chicago Corp.
CHAMPION - Wood products - Champion International Corp.
CHAMPION ARMOR - Jewelry - Jacoby-Bender Inc.
CHAMPION BORONAT - Fertilizers - Chilean Nitrate Corp.
CHAMPION BRAND - Vitamins and nutritional supplements - Holy Bible Gospel Ministry of The Body of Christ, Yeshua, of the Holy Land,
CHAMPION BROOMS - Brooms - Hamburg Broom Works Inc.
CHAMPION BULLY - Sponges - Hydra Sponge Co., Inc.
CHAMPION CHEW - Candy ☆ - Confex Inc.
CHAMPION EXT - Archery equipment - High Country American
CHAMPION FASTBACK - Sleds - Paris Co. Inc.
CHAMPION FAT FIGHTERS - Vitamins and nutritional supplements - Pharmics Inc.
CHAMPION-FLEX - Jewelry - Jacoby-Bender Inc.
CHAMPION GROOMER - Pet products - Chemilizer Products Inc.
CHAMPION GT - Archery equipment - High Country American
CHAMPION II - Skates–roller ☆ - Steven Manufacturing Co.
CHAMPION INTERNATIONAL - Paper–writing - Champion International Corp.
CHAMPION JUICER, THE - Juice extracting devices - Plastaket Manufacturing Co. Inc.
CHAMPION MARBLES - Toys–marbles - Imperial Toy Corp.
CHAMPION NOK-HOCKEY - Games - Carrom Co.
CHAMPION OXFORD - Shoes–athletic - Stride Rite Corp.
CHAMPION PAPERS - Paper–writing - Champion International Corp.
CHAMPION PET - Pet food - Doane Products Co.
CHAMPION PLANTER - Tires - Bridgestone/Firestone, Inc.
CHAMPION PROFLEX - Vitamins and nutritional supplements - Health Options, Inc.
CHAMPION SAFETY - Goggles–safety - Champion Safety, Inc.
CHAMPION SHOTGUN - Toys - Tonka Corp.
CHAMPION SPORTS T - Floor coverings–tile - JCH International Inc.
CHAMPION SPRAYON - Paints - Chase Products Co.
CHAMPION U.S.A. - Apparel and accessories - Champion Products Inc.
CHAMPION WRITINGS - Paper–writing - Champion International Corp.
CHAMPION XEROCOPY - Paper–writing - Champion International Corp.
CHAMPIONNAT - Toys–airplanes - Hobbico Inc.
CHAMPIONS - Bowling balls - Champions Bowling Products Corp.
CHAMPIONS - Computer software - Hero Games
CHAMPION'S CREAM COOLER - Beverages–carbonated - Olga's Kitchen Licensing, Inc.
CHAMPIONSHIP - Sporting goods - D & R Industries, Inc.
CHAMPIONSHIP - Sporting goods - Penn Athletic Products
CHAMPIONSHIP BASEBALL - Games ☆ - Milton Bradley Co.
CHAMPIONSHIP BLACKJACK - Computer software - PCSoftware
CHAMPIONSHIP BOXING - Computer software - Sierra On-Line, Inc.
CHAMPIONSHIP CRAPS - Computer software - PCSoftware
CHAMPIONSHIP GOAL - Sporting goods - Porter Athletic Equipment Co.
CHAMPIONSHIP JOYSTICK - Video games - C & L Performance and Controls
CHAMPIONSHIP RECIPE - Chili–canned ☆ - Stokes/Ellis Foods

CHAMPIONSHIP ROULETTE - Computer software - PCSoftware
CHAMPIONSHIP SERIES - Drums–musical instruments - Pearl Corp.
CHAMPIONSHIP SOCCER - Video games - Atari Games Corp.
CHAMPKNITS - Apparel and accessories - Champion Products Inc.
CHAMPLAIN - Eyeglasses - Martin-Copeland Eyewear Corp.
CHAMPLAIN - Musical instruments - Fred Gretsch Enterprises
CHAMPLAIN - Resins–synthetic - Champlain Cable Corp.
CHAMPLAIN - Thread - Threads USA Div.
CHAMPLAIN BLACK - Marble products - Carl Schilling Stoneworks
CHAMPLAIN CRYSTAL - Lighting fixtures - Schonbek Worldwide Lighting Inc.
CHAMPLAIN VALLEY - Fruits–canned - Champlain Valley Apple Storage Inc.
CHAMPLEVE - Copper products - Brastoff Designs Inc.
CHAMPLEVE - Toilets–enameled - Kohler Co.
CHAMPLIN - Floor coverings–carpet and rugs - Karastan-Bigelow Inc.
CHAMPLIN - Oils–lubricating - Union Pacific Corp.
CHAMPLIN CMO - Oils–lubricating - Union Pacific Corp.
CHAMPLIN GEO-XL - Oils–lubricating - Union Pacific Corp.
CHAMPLIN S-3 PLUS - Oils–lubricating - Union Pacific Corp.
CHAMPLIN TRANSEASON - Oils–lubricating - Union Pacific Corp.
CHAMPLITE - Frames–eyeglass ☆ - U.S. Optical Frame Co.
CHAMPON - Meat products–pork - Produce Trading Corp.
CHAMPPS - Apparel and accessories - Champps Entertainment, Inc.
CHAMPPS AMERICANA - Shirts - Champps Entertainment, Inc.
CHAMPS - Apparel stores–children's ☆ - D. Glasgow & Sons Inc.
CHAMPS - Candy - American Chewing Gum Inc.
CHAMP'S - Frozen pizza - Better Baked Pizza, Inc.
CHAMPS - Giftware - Cawley Co.
CHAMPS - Handbags - Fine International Footwear Inc.
CHAMP'S COLA - Beverages–carbonated - Cawy Bottling Co., Inc.
CHAMPS COLLEGE - Candy - Brach and Brock Confections Inc.
CHAMPS DE BRIONNE - Wines - Champs De Brionne Winery
CHAMPS ELYSEES - Glassware–household - Spiegelau Inc.
CHAMPS-ELYSEES - Recording label - Champs-Elysees Inc.
CHAMPTONE - Paints - Associated Hardware Supply Co.
CHAMPTONE DESIGNER - Paints - Associated Hardware Supply Co.
CHAMY - Apparel–men's - J. Schoeneman Inc.
CHAN-CHAN - Frames–eyeglass - Hudson Optical Corp.
CHAN HEE - Apparel and accessories - Jan-Wee Co., Inc.
CHAN-L-SLIDE - File folders ☆ - Smead Manufacturing Co.
CHAN-L-WIRE - Electrical equipment - Wiremold Co.
CHAN-TEL - Underwear and nightwear - LANZ, Inc.
CHAN THE PANDA - Toys–stuffed - Animal Fair Inc.
CHANA - Lenses–optical - National Optical Co.
CHANCE - Augers - Seymour Manufacturing Co.,Inc.
CHANCE - Frames–eyeglass - Zylo Ware Corp.
CHANCE - Games - Tonka Corp.
CHANCE CHALLENGER - Games - Leellen Corp.
CHANCE FOR SURVIVAL, A - Jewelry - Felley Inc.
CHANCE IT! - Computer software - Gamco Industries Inc.
CHANCE R - Frames–eyeglass - Zylo Ware Corp.
CHANCELLER - Cigarettes - R.J. Reynolds Tobacco Co.
CHANCELLOR - Burial vaults–stone - Cardinal/Embassy Group, Inc.
CHANCELLOR - Clocks - General Time Corp. (Westclox/Seth Thomas Div.)
CHANCELLOR - Dinnerware–glass - Royal China & Porcelain Companies Inc.
CHANCELLOR - Floor coverings–carpet and rugs ☆ - Royalweve Carpet Mills
CHANCELLOR - Frames–eyeglass ☆ - U.S. Optical Frame Co.
CHANCELLOR - Frames–eyeglass ☆ - Universal/Univis Inc.
CHANCELLOR - Giftware - World of Porcelain & Glassware
CHANCELLOR - Pool tables - AMF Bowling Worldwide
CHANCELLOR - Wines - Ziem Vineyards
CHANCELLORSVILLE - Games ☆ - Avalon Hill Game Co.
CHANCERY - Floor coverings–carpet and rugs - Roxbury Carpet Co.
CHANCY - Frames–eyeglass ☆ - U.S. Optical Frame Co.
CHANDELIER - Christmas tree ornaments - Cracker Box Inc.
CHANDELIER - Electronic equipment - Hamilton Electronics Corp.
CHANDELIER - Frames–eyeglass ☆ - Universal/Univis Inc.
CHANDELLE - Furniture - Weiman Co.
CHANDELLE - Jewelry - Imperial-Deltah Inc.
CHANDELLE - Jewelry - Imperial Pearl Syndicate Inc.
CHANDLER - Apparel–men's - Harper Shirt Co.
CHANDLER - Flatware - Gorham Inc.
CHANDLER - Guitars - Chandler Industries
CHANDLER - Ophthalmic goods - Styl-Rite Optical Manufacturing Co., Inc.
CHANDLER & SHARP PUBLISHERS, INC. - Publisher's imprints - Chandler & Sharp Publishers Inc.

☆ = Now out of production

CHANDLER ATTWOOD LTD. C A - Office furniture–wood - Chandler Attwood Ltd.

CHANDLER DIAMONDBACKS - Novelty items ☆ - Arizona Fall League, Inc.

CHANDLER HILL - Apparel–women's - Goody's Family Clothing, Inc.

CHANDLER'S - Shoes - Edison Brothers Stores, Inc.

CHANDLERS COURT - Furniture–wood ☆ - Century Furniture Co.

CHANDON - Wines - Domaine Chandon

CHANDON - Wines - Schieffelin & Co.

CHANDON CLUB - Wines - Schieffelin and Somerset Co.

CHANDON DLUB CUVEE - Wines - Schieffelin and Somerset Co.

CHANDOS - Recording label - Koch International

CHANDRIKA - Soap - Auroma International Inc.

CHANDRIKA - Soap - Auromere Inc.

CHANEL - Perfumes - Chanel Inc.

CHANEL BEAUTE - Cosmetics - Chanel Inc.

CHANEL BOUTIQUE - Apparel–women's - Chanel Inc.

CHANEL ENCHANTMENT - Perfumes - Chanel Inc.

CHANEL FOR MEN - Colognes - Chanel Inc.

CHANEL NO. 5 - Colognes - Chanel Inc.

CHANEL NO. 19 - Colognes - Chanel Inc.

CHANEL NO. 22 - Colognes - Chanel Inc.

CHANG COLLECTION - Floor coverings–carpet and rugs - Royal Ambassador Rugs

CHANG'BLE - Vinyl mats - Poly Enterprises

CHANGE-A-BOARD - Bulletin boards–wood - Timewise

CHANGE-A-LOCK - Hardware - Topper Hardware Inc.

CHANGE-A-PAD - Filters–air - Air Kontrol Inc.

CHANGE-A-PLEAT - Filters–air - Air Kontrol Inc.

CHANGE-A-TUNE CAROUSEL - Toys - Fisher-Price, Inc.

CHANGE CARD - Electronic equipment - Nynex Corp.

CHANGE! FOCUS! SPEED! - Chemical preparations - BASF Corp.

CHANGE FOR THE BUTTER, A - Margarine - Western Family Foods, Inc.

CHANGE INTEGRATION - Computer software - Price Waterhouse Llp

CHANGE IS AN INSIDE JOB - Recording label ☆ - Pacific Institute Inc.

CHANGE LANES - Video games - Taito America Corp.

CHANGE 'N GO - Infant product - D & M Products Group Inc.

CHANGE 'N MATCH - Toilet seats ☆ - Sanderson Plumbing Products, Inc.

CHANGE-O-LIFE - Vitamins and nutritional supplements - Nature's Way Products, Inc.

CHANGE-O-MATIC - Electronic equipment - Apollo Audiovisual Div.

CHANGE-O-MATIC - Jewelry - Jacoby-Bender Inc.

CHANGE O-PLATE - Stamps–hand - GB Products International Corp.

CHANGE OF LIFE FORMULA - Herbal products - 21st Century Manna

CHANGE THE GAME - Apparel and accessories - Fila USA, Inc.

CHANGE THE WORLD - Apparel and accessories - Farook I. Hameed

CHANGE-UP - Underwear and nightwear ☆ - Lovable Co.

CHANGEABLE - Apparel and accessories - New England Accessories Co.

CHANGEABLE CHARLIE - Toys ☆ - Playskool, Inc.

CHANGEABLES - Lenses - Bausch & Lomb Inc.

CHANGEBANK - Safes - Armor Safe Technologies

CHANGEMAKER - Candy ☆ - Brock Candy Co. Inc.

CHANGEMARKS - Computer software - Informative Graphics Corp.

CHANGEMASTER - Computer software - Industrial Strength Software Co.

CHANGE'N'MATCH - Toilet seats ☆ - Magnolia Products

CHANGEPOINT - Pens–fountain - Kerr-Changepoint

CHANGEPRO - Computer software - Price Waterhouse Llp

CHANGEPRO - Computer software - Solution1, Inc.

CHANGER-ETTES - Toys ☆ - Hedstrom Corp.

CHANGES - Beauty shop equipment - Focus 21 International Inc.

CHANGES - Computer software - Hartley Courseware Inc.

CHANGES - Vitamins and nutritional supplements - McZand Herbal, Inc.

CHANGES NATUREL - Cosmetics - Camilla Hepper

CHANGESUITE - Computer software - Price Waterhouse Llp

CHANGEVISION - Computer software - Hewlett-Packard Co.

CHANGING DIRECTIONS BY BREAKING BARRIERS - Recording label - Pacific Institute Inc.

CHANGING ELEMENTS - Shirts - Cluett, Peabody & Co.

CHANGING FACES - Toys–stuffed ☆ - Fun World Inc.

CHANGING MOODS - Floor coverings–carpet and rugs ☆ - Patcraft Mills Inc.

CHANGING PLACES - Fabrics–tapestry - Comark Wallcoverings

CHANGING PLACES - Wallpaper - Benchmark Preferred Wallcoverings

CHANGING SCENES - Frames–eyeglass ☆ - Universal/Univis Inc.

CHANGING TIME - Infant product - Sassy Inc.

CHANGING TIMES - Floor coverings–carpet and rugs ☆ - Walter Carpet Mills

CHANGING TIMES - Jewelry - Gruen Precision, Inc.

CHANGING TIMES - Toys - M.&S. Shillman Inc.

CHANGING TIMES - Vitamins and nutritional supplements - Natural Organics, Inc.

CHANGING WHIRL-D - Frames–eyeglass - May Optical Co. Inc.

CHANGING WOMAN'S HERBAL FORMULA - Vitamins and nutritional supplements - Matrix Health Products, Inc.

CHANGING WORLD - Computer software - New Paradigm Software Corp.

CHANGPAI MOUNTAIN - Teas - Superior Trading Co.

CHANG'S - Food products - Atlas Horn Food Service

CHANL TRIM - Frames–picture - Hy-Jo Picture Frames

CHANNEL - Containers–glass - Svend Jensen of Denmark Inc.

CHANNEL - Fish–fresh or frozen ☆ - Greentree Packing Inc.

CHANNEL - Food products - Channel Fish Co.

CHANNEL - Lighting fixtures - Liteway

CHANNEL - Ophthalmic goods - Embassy Creations Inc.

CHANNEL - Thread ☆ - Imperial Threads Inc.

CHANNEL 1000 - Recording label - Musicland Group, Inc.

CHANNEL ADVANTAGE - Television equipment - American Channel Systems, Inc.

CHANNEL-CAD - Computer software - Grinnell Corp.

CHANNEL CASE - Cases–eyeglass - California Optical Leather Inc.

CHANNEL CAT - Housewares ☆ - Blue Ridge International Products Co., Inc.

CHANNEL CAT - Novelty items - Item Co., Inc.

CHANNEL CATS HUNTSVILLE - Apparel and accessories - Huntsville Channel Cats, Inc.

CHANNEL CENSOR - Television equipment ☆ - Quasar Co.

CHANNEL-COVE - Waterproofing compounds - Richtech Industries, Inc.

CHANNEL EDGE - Blackboards–slate ☆ - Anco Wood Specialties Inc.

CHANNEL FLOW - Aquarium accessories - Willinger Bros., Inc.

CHANNEL FLOW - Pipes - Hancor Inc.

CHANNEL GARD - Luggage - Samsonite Corp.

CHANNEL ISLANDS WHEAT - Beverages–malt - Shields Brewing

CHANNEL ISLE - Floor coverings–carpet and rugs ☆ - Catalina Carpet Mills Inc.

CHANNEL MARK - Apparel stores–sports ☆ - Tultex Corp.

CHANNEL MASTER - Antennas–satellite - Avnet, Inc.

CHANNEL MASTER - Mats - Roope Corp.

CHANNEL MASTER - Office supplies ☆ - Esselte Corp.

CHANNEL-MATE - Hardware - Beckson Marine Inc.

CHANNEL ONE - Television equipment–cable - Channel One Communications Corp.

CHANNEL OPPORTUNITY ANALYSIS - Publisher's imprints - Channel Strategies, Inc.

CHANNEL PANEL - Cases–plastic - Merchandising Systems Manufacturing, Inc.

CHANNEL PLUS - Communications equipment - Multiplex Technology, Inc.

CHANNEL R.E.A.D. - Recording label - Houghton Mifflin Co.

CHANNEL RUSTIC - Building materials–concrete - Weyerhaeuser Co.

CHANNEL SURFING - Games - Milton Bradley Co.

CHANNEL SURFING - Toys–electronic - Hasbro, Inc.

CHANNEL SYSTEM - Computer software - Moore Business Forms, Inc.

CHANNEL TEX - Hair care products - Fromm Industries

CHANNELBIND - Machinery - Xerox Corp.

CHANNELED RESOURCES - Paper - Channeled Resources, Inc.

CHANNELITES - Lighting fixtures - Swivelier Co. Inc.

CHANNELL - Glass products - Channell Glass

CHANNELLOCK - Tools - Channellock, Inc.

CHANNELLOCK BLUE - Tools–hand-operated - Channellock, Inc.

CHANNELMAX - Television equipment ☆ - Avnet, Inc.

CHANNELON - Lubricant - Anchor Hocking Glass, Inc.

CHANNELS - Furniture - Weiman Co.

CHANNELS TWO - Wallcoverings - Coral of Chicago

CHANNELSCOPE - Computer peripheral equipment - McDATA Corp.

CHANNELSIDE - Siding–insulating - Masonite Corp.

CHANNELTRON - Electronic equipment - Galileo Corp.

CHANNELWAVE - Computer software - Channelwave

CHANNELWOOD - Wood products - Weyerhaeuser Co.

CHANNELWORKS - Computer hardware - Digital Equipment Corp.

CHANNING - Frames–eyeglass - May Optical Co. Inc.

CHANNING RUDD CELLARS - Wines - Channing Rudd Cellars

CHANO - Apparel and accessories ☆ - Edison Brothers Stores, Inc.

CHANS - Jeans–men's - N I G, Inc.

CHANSON - Dishes–china - Viletta China Co.

CHANSONETTE - Brassieres (Bras) - Maidenform Inc.

CHANSONETTE - Frames–eyeglass - Pathway Optical Prods.

CHANT - Buttons - Capitol Records, Inc.

CHANTAINE - Furniture–wood ☆ - Century Furniture Co.

CHANTAINE BRUT - Sparkling wine - Charles Jacquin et Compagnie Inc.
CHANTAL - Blinds–venetian ☆ - Hunter Douglas, Inc.
CHANTAL - Cooking equipment–household - Chantal Cookware Corp.
CHANTAL - Cosmetics - Glenn Matteson Co. Inc.
CHANTAL - Ophthalmic goods ☆ - Rozin Optical Export Corp.
CHANTAL - Wallpaper - Pickhardt & Siebert USA Inc.
CHANTAL - Wallpaper - Southport
CHANTAL MONROE - Cosmetics - U.S. Polo Club Inc.
CHANTAL MONROE PARIS - BEVERLY HILLS - MILAN - Skin care products - U.S. Polo Club Inc.
CHANTAY - Floor coverings–carpet and rugs - Evans-Black Carpet Mills
CHANTE - Furniture ☆ - Bassett Furniture Industries, Inc.
CHANTECLAIR - Floor coverings–carpet and rugs - Lock Weave Carpet Mills Inc.
CHANTECLAIR - Furniture - Weiman Co.
CHANTECLER - Cheese ☆ - Swissrose International Inc.
CHANTECLER - Furniture–wood ☆ - Century Furniture Co.
CHANTEFLEUR - Wines - Parliament Import Co.
CHANTELLE - Floor coverings–carpet and rugs ☆ - World Carpets, Inc.
CHANTERELLE - Wallpaper ☆ - Ashford House
CHANTERELLE II - Wallpaper ☆ - Ashford House
CHANTERRELLE - Music–sheet - GSP
CHANTEUSE - Floor coverings–carpet and rugs - Barrett Carpet Mills Inc.
CHANTICLAIR - Floor coverings–carpet and rugs - Prestige Mills Inc.
CHANTICLEER - Bowls ☆ - Lenox Crystal, Inc.
CHANTICLEER - Dinnerware–glass ☆ - Johnson Brothers, USA, Inc.
CHANTICLEER - Recording label - San Francisco Chanticleer, Inc.
CHANTICLEER - Teas - Eastern Shore Tea Co.
CHANTIFRAIS - Food products - Gourmet America
CHANTIK - Apparel–women's - Shakti Comix
CHANTILLY - Blinds–venetian ☆ - Hunter Douglas, Inc.
CHANTILLY - Cabinets ☆ - Merillat Industries, Inc.
CHANTILLY - Cookies - PF Brands, Inc.
CHANTILLY - Cosmetics - Houbigant, Inc.
CHANTILLY - Cutlery ☆ - Lifetime Hoan Corp.
CHANTILLY - Dinnerware–glass - Nikko Ceramics Inc.
CHANTILLY - Dinnerware–glass ☆ - Royal China & Porcelain Companies Inc.
CHANTILLY - Dishes–china - Gorham Inc.
CHANTILLY - Dolls ☆ - Effanbee Doll Corp.
CHANTILLY - Floor coverings - Parquet de France Inc.
CHANTILLY - Floor coverings–tile ☆ - Kentile Floors Inc.
CHANTILLY - Frames–eyeglass ☆ - Universal/Univis Inc.
CHANTILLY - Furniture ☆ - Universal Flooring
CHANTILLY - Glassware–household - Crystal Clear Importing Co. Inc.
CHANTILLY - Glassware–household - Oneida Ltd.
CHANTILLY - Glassware–household - Seneca Glass Co.
CHANTILLY - Hardware ☆ - Amerock Corp.
CHANTILLY - Plumbing fixtures - Universal-Rundle Corp.
CHANTILLY - Tables–wood - Riverside Furniture Corp.
CHANTILLY - Toys - Tonka Corp.
CHANTILLY - Underwear and nightwear - Maidenform Inc.
CHANTILLY - Wallpaper ☆ - Wallquest, Inc.
CHANTILLY CREATIONS - Draperies - Arrow Textile Corp.
CHANTILLY LACE - Christmas tree ornaments ☆ - Cracker Box Inc.
CHANTILLY LACE - Wallpaper - Maya Romanoff Corp.
CHANTILLY LADY - Frames–eyeglass ☆ - Universal/Univis Inc.
CHANTONNAY - Earthenware ☆ - Shafford Co. Inc.
CHANTUNG - Furniture - American Furniture Co. Inc.
CHANTYN - Hair and skincare products, fragrance, etc. - Benjamin Ansehl Co.
CHANZES-R - Games - Lowell Sandeen
CHAOS - Apparel and accessories - Mitchel D. Perlman
CHAOS - Bicycles - Giant Bicycle, Inc.
CHAOS - Games - IGT - North America
CHAOS - Games - Lakeside Games
CHAOS - Iced tea–bottled or canned ☆ - The Stroh Brewery Co.
CHAOS - Musical sound recordings - Sony Music Entertainment Inc.
CHAOS ICED TEA - Iced tea–bottled or canned ☆ - The Stroh Brewery Co.
CHAOS PIE - Pastries - Alden Merrell Corp.
CHAOS STRIKES BACK - Computer software - FTL Games
CHAOSOLV - Biochemicals - Biotecx Laboratories, Inc.
CHAP - Stationery - Camp Hill Art Press Inc.
CHAP - Video production - National League for Nursing
CHAP-ANS - Skin care products - Frances Denney
CHAP-ET - Lip balms - Stanback Co.
CHAP-ET PJ - Lip balms ☆ - Stanback Co.
CHAP-MATE - Lip balms - Thursday Plantation Ltd.

CHAP NO MORE - Skin care products - Senoret Chemical Co.
CHAP-PRUF - Lip balms - Frances Denney
CHAP STICK - Lip balms - A.H. Robins Co. Inc.
CHAP WRAP - Netting - Kane Products, Inc.
CHAPALA - Chili sauce - Chapala International Inc.
CHAPARAL - Luggage - American Tourister, Inc.
CHAPARRAL - Barbecue sauce - Diversified Foods, Inc.
CHAPARRAL - Bicycles - Ross Bicycles USA, Ltd.
CHAPARRAL - Dog food - Chaparral Sales Corp.
CHAPARRAL - Fabrics - Dan River Inc.
CHAPARRAL - Floor coverings - Congoleum Corp.
CHAPARRAL - Insulating materials ☆ - Owens Corning
CHAPARRAL - Sporting goods ☆ - Voit Corp.
CHAPARRAL - Trailers–travel ☆ - Coachmen Industries, Inc.
CHAPATI - Breads - Garden of Eatin', Inc.
CHAPCO - Adhesives and sealants - Chicago Adhesive Products Co.
CHAPEAU ROUGE BEAUJOLAIS VILLAGES - Wines - Bercut-Vandervoort & Co.
CHAPEL - Books–comic - Rob Liefeld, Inc.
CHAPEL - Flatware - Reed and Barton Corp.
CHAPEL - Floor coverings–carpet and rugs ☆ - Porter Carpet Mills Inc.
CHAPEL - Recording label - Bellaire Record Sales
CHAPEL ART - Wallpaper - Regency-Sonnell Greetings Inc.
CHAPEL/BRIDGE - Recording label - Pacific Press Publishing Association
CHAPEL CHAIR - Furniture - Boling Co.
CHAPEL HILL - Apparel–athletic - Heritage Sportswear
CHAPEL HILL - Cabinets - Prestige Inc.
CHAPEL HILL - Doors–wood - Georgia-Pacific Corp.
CHAPEL HILL - Trailers–travel - Fleetwood Enterprises, Inc.
CHAPEL HILL - Wines - Ste. Chapelle Inc.
CHAPEL LINE - Greeting cards - Regency Thermographers Inc.
CHAPELAIN - Musical instruments - J.M. Sahlein Music Co. Inc.
CHAPELLE - Cabinets ☆ - Yorktowne Inc.
CHAPELLE - Christmas tree ornaments - Cracker Box Inc.
CHAPELLE - Floor coverings–carpet and rugs - Milliken & Co. Inc.
CHAPELLE - Watches - Kruckemeyer & Cohn Inc.
CHAPERON - Infant product - Lisco, Inc.
CHAPERONE - See DETOUR
CHAPERONE - Health care products - Ray Drug Co.
CHAPERONE - Strollers–baby ☆ - Aprica Kassai USA Inc.
CHAPEX - Lip balms - Frances Denney
CHAPIN - Dusters - R.E. Chapin Manufacturing Works Inc.
CHAPIN-LANDIS - Wines ☆ - Kobrand Corp.
CHAPIN PLUS - Dusters - R.E. Chapin Manufacturing Works Inc.
CHAPIN PREMIER - Dusters - R.E. Chapin Manufacturing Works Inc.
CHAPITRE 3 - Luggage - Dynamic Classics Ltd.
CHAPLESS TEAT DIP - Veterinary pharmaceutical preparations - Boehringer Ingelheim Animal Health, Inc.
CHAPMAN - Furniture–wood - Chapman Manufacturing Co.
CHAPMAN & HALL - Publisher's imprints ☆ - Routledge
CHAPMAN STICK - Musical instruments - Stick Enterprises, Inc.
CHAPMAN STICK TOUCHBOARD, THE - Musical instruments - Stick Enterprises, Inc.
CHAPMAN'S - Publisher's imprints - Hearst Corp.
CHAPOLA - Skin care products - Frances Denney
CHAPOUTIER - Wines - Heublein, Inc.
CHAPPAQUA - Ophthalmic goods - Styl-Rite Optical Manufacturing Co., Inc.
CHAPPARAL - Leather goods - Enger-Kress Co.
CHAPPARAL - Wallets - Rewards Group Ltd.
CHAPPARAL COLLECTION - Leather goods - Enger-Kress Co.
CHAPPAREL - Glassware–household - Durand International
CHAPPAREL - Wallpaper - Tattersalls
CHAPPARRAL - Eyeglasses - Art-Craft Optical Co.
CHAPPELLET - Wines - Chappellet Vineyard
CHAPPELLET VINEYARD - Wines - House of Burgundy Inc.
CHAPPY - Toys–models - Yamaha Motor Corp. USA
CHAPS - Cigarettes - Brown & Williamson Tobacco Corp.
CHAPS - Colognes - Cosmair Inc.
CHAPS - Hosiery–men's - Hot Sox Co. Inc. Ralph Lauren Hosiery Div.
CHAPS - Lenses - Polo Ralph Lauren, LP
CHAPS BY RALPH LAUREN - Apparel and accessories - Warnaco Inc.
CHAPS BY RALPH LAUREN - Apparel–men's - Greif Cos.
CHAPTER TWO - Apparel and accessories - Oxford Industries, Inc.
CHAPTERS - Wallpaper - Gencorp Polymer Products
CHAQUERS - Liquors ☆ - Frank Sutton & Co.
CHAR & CO - Invitations ☆ - Signprint, Inc.

☆ = Now out of production

CHAR-B-QUE - Barbecue sauce - Harris & Mallow Products
CHAR-B-QUE - Indoor barbecue ☆ - Contempra Industries
CHAR BROIL - Barbecues and grills - Char-Broil
CHAR-BROIL - Barbecues and grills - Char-Broil
CHAR-BROIL FLAVORMASTER - Barbecues and grills - Char-Broil
CHAR-BROIL H2O SMOKER - Barbeque grills - Char-Broil
CHAR-BROIL MASTERFLAME - Barbecues and grills - Char-Broil
CHAR-BROIL PRECISION FLAME - Barbecues and grills - Char-Broil
CHAR-CARE - Vitamins and nutritional supplements - Char-Care Inc.
CHAR-DIAMONDS - Barbecue and grill accessories - W.C. Bradley Co., Inc.
CHAR-GLO - Barbecues and grills ☆ - Thermador
CHAR-KOLE - Paints - Quartet Manufacturing Co.
CHAR-ROCK - Barbecues and grills ☆ - Char-Broil
CHAR-TROL - Barbecues and grills - Coleman Co., Inc.
CHARACTER - Apparel stores–lingerie - Character Foundations Inc.
CHARACTER - Frames–eyeglass ☆ - Universal/Univis Inc.
CHARACTER - Liquors - Seagram's Chateau & Estate Wines Co.
CHARACTER COLLECTIBLES - Figurines - Home Decorator Dream Club
CHARACTER COOKIES - Cookies - Parco Foods, LLC
CHARACTER FACTORY, THE - Computer software - Seven Hills Software
CHARACTERSWAP - Typewriters - Smith Corona Corp.
CHARACTURES - Shirts - Lou M. Ruiz
CHARADE - Colognes - BC International Cosmetics & Image Services, Inc.
CHARADE - Floor coverings ☆ - National Floor Products Co., Inc.
CHARADE - Floor coverings–carpet and rugs - World Carpets, Inc.
CHARADE - Glass–plate - Sasaki
CHARADE - Glassware–household ☆ - Crisa Corp.
CHARADE - Jewelry–costume - Crystal Brands Inc.
CHARADE - Motor vehicles–automobiles ☆ - Daihatsu America Inc.
CHARADE GAME, THE - Games ☆ - Pressman Toy Corp.
CHARADES - Costumes - Masquerade International, Inc.
CHARADES FOR JUNIORS - Games ☆ - Milton Bradley Co.
CHARAIDS - Games - Learning Things Inc.
CHARAY - Recording label - Le Cam Records
CHARBLUM - Girdles - Character Foundations Inc.
CHARBON - Girdles - Character Foundations Inc.
CHARBONI - Apparel–children's - Fine Line, Inc.
CHARBONNEAU - Wines - Rick Small
CHARBONO - Wines ☆ - Fife Vineyards LLC
CHARBURN - Recording label - Charlie Fields Productions
CHARCO - Pencils ☆ - Empire Berol USA
CHARCOAID - Pharmaceutical preparations - Requa Manufacturing Co. Inc.
CHARCOAL - Apparel and accessories - Charcoal Apparel Group, Inc.
CHARCOAL - Handbags - Stuart Kern Fine Leather Goods
CHARCOAL CHEF - Lighter fluid - Midwest Polychem, Ltd.
CHARCOAL COMPANION - Cookware - The Companion Group
CHARCOAL COMPANION - Housewares - Companion Group
CHARCOAL GRAPHITE - Tiles–enamel - Kohler Co.
CHARCOAL MASTER CM - Charcoal - Charcoal Master International Inc.
CHARCOAL PIT OF LAKE PLACID - Salad dressings–bottled - Cold Brook Inn, Inc.
CHARCOAL R - Paper–photographic - Luminos Photo Corp.
CHARCOCAPS - Pharmaceutical preparations - Requa Manufacturing Co. Inc.
CHARCOIL - Fireplace equipment ☆ - Ray A. Martin
CHARCOL-IT' - Seasonings - Alberto-Culver Co.
CHARCOMB - Fabrics - Dan River Inc.
CHARCOMID - Charcoal - Leonard N. Swatkiewicz
CHARCON - Artificial floral arrangements - Charcon Florals
CHARD - Wine coolers - Luneau USA Inc.
CHARDEAU - Furniture–wood ☆ - Century Furniture Co.
CHARDON - Cabinets - Imperial Cabinet Co. Inc.
CHARDON - Toilets–enameled - Kohler Co.
CHARDON - Water treating compounds - Chardon Laboratories Inc.
CHARDONAY - House furnishings - Link-Taylor Corp.
CHARDONNA - Pharmaceutical preparations - Schwarz Pharma
CHARDONNA-2 - Barbituates - Rhone-Poulenc Rorer Pharmaceuticals Inc.
CHARDONNAY - Cabinets ☆ - Aristokraft, Inc.
CHARDONNAY - Fabrics–tapestry ☆ - Coloroll Inc.
CHARDONNAY - Flatware - Reed and Barton Corp.
CHARDONNAY - Floor coverings–carpet and rugs - Trend Carpet
CHARDONNAY - Glassware–household - Durand International
CHARDONNAY - Toilets–enameled - Kohler Co.
CHARDONNAY - Wallpaper - Somerville Designs
CHARDONNAY - Wines - Cilurzo Vineyard & Winery
CHARDONNAY ELISE - Wines - Bully Hill Vineyards, Inc.
CHARDONNAY, GRAVE DEL FRIULI - Wines - Kobrand Corp.

CHARDONNAY RESERVE - Wines - Merryvale Vineyards
CHARDONNAY STARMONT - Wines - Merryvale Vineyards
CHARGE - See HOT SHOT
CHARGE - Cleaning preparations–household - PYA/Monarch Inc.
CHARGE - Plant food - Kemmer Agricultural Manufacturing Co. Inc.
CHARGE ALL - Battery chargers - Goodall Manufacturing Co.
CHARGE & TALK - Telephones–cellular - ORA Electronics
CHARGE IT - Automotive parts and accessories - Unival Corp.
CHARGE IT - Games - Talicor Inc.
CHARGE-ITS - Film - School Stationers Corp.
CHARGE MATE - Battery chargers - Matsushita Electric Corp. of America
CHARGE-N-GO - Cables - SAFCO Corp.
CHARGE SAFE - Cables - General Cable Corp.
CHARGE WIZARD - Electrical equipment - Progressive Dynamics, Inc.
CHARGEAIR PRO - Compressors–air - Devilbiss Air Power Co.
CHARGEBACK - Sporting goods - Marty Gilman Inc.
CHARGEMASTER - Battery chargers ☆ - Japlar Acquisition Co. (Japlar/Schauer)
CHARGEMASTER - Static eliminator - Simco
CHARGER - Abrasive products - Norton Co.
CHARGER - Bicycles - Columbia Manufacturing Inc.
CHARGER - Boats - Charger Inc.
CHARGER - Boats–canoes ☆ - Sawyer Composite Products
CHARGER - Boats–motor ☆ - Cobia Boat Co.
CHARGER - Boats–motor ☆ - Glassmaster Co.
CHARGER - Brushes–hair - Wright-Bernet
CHARGER - Floor coverings–carpet and rugs ☆ - Barrett Carpet Mills Inc.
CHARGER - Floor coverings–carpet and rugs ☆ - Lees Carpets
CHARGER - Fruit and vegetable markets ☆ - Haas Fruit Co. Inc.
CHARGER - Golfing equipment - Arnold Palmer Golf Co.
CHARGER - Lanterns–electric - Coleman Co., Inc.
CHARGER - Luggage ☆ - Lark Luggage Co. Inc.
CHARGER - Motor vehicles ☆ - Chrysler Corp. (Dodge Car Div.)
CHARGER - Watches - Hampden Corp.
CHARGER 2.2 - Motor vehicles ☆ - Chrysler Corp. (Dodge Car Div.)
CHARGER BASSBOAT - Boats–motor - Charger Inc.
CHARGER DAYTONA - Motor vehicles ☆ - Chrysler Corp. (Dodge Car Div.)
CHARGER RT - Motor vehicles ☆ - Chrysler Corp. (Dodge Car Div.)
CHARGER SUPER BEE - Motor vehicles ☆ - Chrysler Corp. (Dodge Car Div.)
CHARGER, THE - Luggage ☆ - Samsonite Corp.
CHARGER V - Boats–motor ☆ - Cobia Boat Co.
CHARGETTE - Deodorizers - Airosol Co. Inc.
CHARGEUR - Frames–eyeglass - Hoya Corp. USA
CHARI - Glass–optical - Welling International
CHARING CROSS - Neckties - A. Schreter & Sons Co. Inc.
CHARINGTON MANOR - Furniture–wood ☆ - Century Furniture Co.
CHARIOT - Boats - Paul G. Schoen
CHARIOT - Candles - Merrill-West Publishing
CHARIOT - Trailers–travel - Chariot Manufacturing Co. Inc.
CHARIOT BOOKS - Publisher's imprint - David C. Cook Publishing Co.
CHARIOTEER - Floor coverings–carpet and rugs ☆ - Mohawk Carpet Corp.
CHARIOTS, COUGARS & KINGS - Computer software - Hartley Courseware Inc.
CHARISIS - Computer software - Mathematical Technologies Inc.
CHARISMA - Athletic shoes - Reebok International Ltd.
CHARISMA - Bedding–linen - Fieldcrest Cannon, Inc.
CHARISMA - Chairs–wood - Flexsteel Industries Inc.
CHARISMA - Computer software - KSH Systems, Inc.
CHARISMA - Computer software - Micrografx, Inc.
CHARISMA - Cosmetics - Ruckel Manufacturing Co. Inc.
CHARISMA - Floor coverings - Sponge-Cushion Inc.
CHARISMA - Floor coverings–carpet and rugs - Dan River Inc.
CHARISMA - Floor coverings–carpet and rugs ☆ - American Carpet Mills
CHARISMA - Frames–eyeglass - Pioneer Optical Co.
CHARISMA - Furniture - Henredon Furniture Industries Inc.
CHARISMA - Golfing equipment - Lynx Golf, Inc.
CHARISMA - Pens - Pentel of America, Ltd.
CHARISMA - Pens ☆ - Accutec Inc.
CHARISMA - Perfumes ☆ - Avon Products, Inc.
CHARISMA - Recording label - Atlantic Records
CHARISMA - Recording label - Virgin Records
CHARISMA - Wallpaper - Pickhardt & Siebert USA Inc.
CHARISMA - Watches - Wakmann Watch Co. Inc.
CHARISMA 12 - Wallpaper - Pantasote Inc. (Wallcovering Div.)
CHARISMA CHARM - Jewelry - Charisma Jewelers of Rochester Ltd.
CHARISMA II - Wallpaper - Pickhardt & Siebert USA Inc.

☆ = Now out of production

CHARISMA NITELITES - Hair care products - O.E. Clark Paper Box Co.

CHARISMA PRINTS - Paper–gift wrap ☆ - Stephen Lawrence Co.

CHARISMA VIDEO - Recording label - Plus Communications, Inc.

CHARISMATIC CATS - Figurines - Bronson Collectibles

CHARITY - Apparel - Surya, Inc.

CHARITY - Food products - Mark Owens

CHARITY - Ophthalmic goods - Swank Optical

CHARITY'S - Fruits and vegetables - Marianne Fong

CHARKATE - Apparel and accessories - Eastco Industrial Safety Corp.

CHARKOL - Pencils - National Pen & Pencil Co.

CHARL-MONT - Candy - Price Candy Co. Inc.

CHARLAINE - Floor coverings–carpet and rugs - Evans-Black Carpet Mills

CHARLAPS DAIRY - Milk - Charlaps Dairy Farms Inc.

CHARLEE BEAR - Dog food - Charlee Bear Farms, Inc.

CHARLEE BEAR DOG TREATS - Pet food - Charlee Bear Farms, Inc.

CHARLEMAGNE - Frames–picture - Terragrafics Inc.

CHARLEMAGNE - Glassware–household ☆ - ACC

CHARLEMONT PLANK - Floor coverings - Bruce Hardwood Floors

CHARLENE - Hair care products - Charlene Hair Products Inc.

CHARLENESILK - Artificial flowers - Charcon Florals

CHARLEROI - Floor coverings - Mannington Resilient Floors

CHARLES - See also **CHAS.**

CHARLES ALBRECHT - Pianos - American Piano Service and Supply Corp.

CHARLES ALEXANDER - Apparel–men's - Big & Tall Associates

CHARLES ANTELL - Hair care products ☆ - A.R. Winarick Inc.

CHARLES ANTHONY SIGNATURE - Belts - Parrish Inc.

CHARLES BAY - Musical instrument accessories - Bay Woodwind Mouthpieces

CHARLES CHIPS - Snack foods - Charles Chip Corp.

CHARLES DALY - Binoculars, pistol and rifle cases, luggage, and apparel - Outdoor Sports Headquarters Inc.

CHARLES DANA GIBSON - Posters - One-of-a-Kind Workshop

CHARLES DE GRANVILLE - Beverages–alcohol - European Beverage Co., Inc.

CHARLES DE TAHITI - Fabric - Janpro Products

CHARLES DENBY - Cigars - National Cigar Corp.

CHARLES DICKENS - Teas - Products-from-Sweden Inc.

CHARLES DUVEAUX - Wines - Regal Brewing, Inc.

CHARLES DYLAN - Apparel and accessories - Roy Smith Shoes, Inc.

CHARLES F. SHAW - Wines - Charles F. Shaw Vineyard & Winery

CHARLES FOSTER - Apparel–men's - Warnaco Inc.

CHARLES FOSTER C.F. HATHAWAY - Apparel and accessories - Warnaco Inc.

CHARLES FOURNIER - Wines - Gold Seal Vineyards Inc.

CHARLES G. SPILO - Skin care products - Spilo/Mehaz Worldwide

CHARLES GOODNIGHT - Apparel and accessories - Harwood Companies Inc.

CHARLES HEIDSIECK - Wines ☆ - Pellegrini Bros. Wines Inc.

CHARLES HILL - Food products - Lindsay Olive Growers

CHARLES J. WAHBA - Skin care products - Charles J. Wahba Co.

CHARLES JACQUIN'S - Food products ☆ - Castle Food Products

CHARLES JORDAN - Watches - Nicolet International Inc.

CHARLES JOURDAN - Footwear–women's - Charles Jourdan

CHARLES JOURDAN - Hosiery–women's ☆ - Hampshire Hosiery, Inc.

CHARLES JOURDAN - Sunglasses - Sunlovers

CHARLES JOURDAN MONSIEUR - Apparel–men's - Hartz & Co., Inc.

CHARLES KLEIN - Coats - Burlington Coat Factory Warehouse Corp.

CHARLES KRUG - Wines - Charles Krug Winery

CHARLES LARUCCI - Skin care products - European Cosmetics Inc.

CHARLES LAURENT BROTTE - Wines - Chrissa Imports Ltd.

CHARLES LE FRANC - Wines - Heublein, Inc.

CHARLES LESTERS - Candlesticks - Root Candle Co.

CHARLES LIGHT - Popcorn - Charles Chip Corp.

CHARLES LILES - Cheese - Galaxy Trading Co.

CHARLES OF THE RITZ - Cosmetics - Charles of the Ritz Group Ltd.

CHARLES OF THE RITZ ORIGINAL - Colognes - Charles of the Ritz Group Ltd.

CHARLES ORTMAN - Wines ☆ - St. Andrew's Winery

CHARLES PFISTER COLLECTION, THE - Furniture - Baker, Knapp & Tubbs

CHARLES PRESS INC. - Publisher's imprints - Prentice-Hall, Inc.

CHARLES R. SLIGH - Clocks - Sligh Furniture Co.

CHARLES R. WALTER - Pianos - Walter Piano Co.

CHARLES RIVER - Paper–looseleaf - Fay Paper Products Inc.

CHARLES RIVER APPAREL - Jackets - Charles River Apparel

CHARLES RIVER BOOKS INC. - Publisher's imprints - Charles River Books Inc.

CHARLES SADEK - Giftware - Charles Sadek and Jay Willfred Import Co.

CHARLES ST. CHARLES - Belts - Yamani of America

CHARLES SCHWAB - Computer software - Charles Schwab & Co., Inc.

CHARLES SCRIBNER'S SONS - Publisher's imprints - Charles Scribner's Sons

CHARLES SHAW - Wines ☆ - Kobrand Corp.

CHARLES SKINNY LIGHTS - Pretzels - Charles Chip Corp.

CHARLES SPIVANT - Carry-on bag sets - C.S.B. Commodities Inc.

CHARLES THE GREAT - Cigars - Finck Cigar Co.

CHARLES WEINSTEIN - Coats - Just Coats Inc.

CHARLES +WINSLOW - Food products - Charles Winslow International

CHARLES WYSOCKI - Music boxes ☆ - Schmid Inc.

CHARLES WYSOCKI'S AMERICANA - Puzzles - Milton Bradley Co.

CHARLES X - Furniture - Henredon Furniture Industries Inc.

CHARLESBANK - Wallpaper - Thomas Strahan Wallcoverings

CHARLESTON - Cabinets - Belwood Inc.

CHARLESTON - Cabinets - Imperial Cabinet Co. Inc.

CHARLESTON - Cabinets ☆ - Marsh Furniture Co.

CHARLESTON - Chimes ☆ - Nutone Inc.

CHARLESTON - Cigarettes - Brown & Williamson Tobacco Corp.

CHARLESTON - Clocks - General Time Corp. (Westclox/Seth Thomas Div.)

CHARLESTON - Clocks ☆ - Ridgeway Clock Co.

CHARLESTON - Cookies - PF Brands, Inc.

CHARLESTON - Dishes–china - Viletta China Co.

CHARLESTON - Dolls ☆ - Effanbee Doll Corp.

CHARLESTOWN - Fireplace equipment - Design Specialties Inc.

CHARLESTON - Flatware - Washington Forge Inc.

CHARLESTON - Floor coverings–carpet and rugs ☆ - Mannington Carpets, Inc.

CHARLESTON - Flooring–hardwood - Mannington Wood Floors

CHARLESTON - Furniture - Samsonite Furniture Co. (Consumer Products Div.)

CHARLESTON - Glassware–household ☆ - Lenox Crystal, Inc.

CHARLESTON - Luggage - York Luggage Co.

CHARLESTON - Tableware–china - Lenox, Inc.

CHARLESTON - Tableware–china ☆ - Villeroy and Boch Tableware Ltd.

CHARLESTON - Tiles–ceramic ☆ - Laufen Ceramic Tile

CHARLESTON - Wallpaper ☆ - Schooner Prints Inc.

CHARLESTON BAY - Apparel–men's - Montgomery Ward & Co. Inc.

CHARLESTON CHEW - Candy - Tootsie Roll Industries, Inc.

CHARLESTON CHOCOLATE CHIP PIE - Pies–fresh - Gilbert-Robinson Inc.

CHARLESTON COLLECTION - Paints - Valspar Corp.

CHARLESTON FAN, THE - Fans–ceiling - Fasco Industries Inc. (Consumer Products Div.)

CHARLESTON FOLLIES - Liqueurs - Marie Brizard Et Roger, Inc.

CHARLESTON FORGE - Furniture–wood - Charleston Forge Inc.

CHARLESTON GOLD - Glassware–household - Lenox, Inc.

CHARLESTON HARBOR - Dolls ☆ - Effanbee Doll Corp.

CHARLESTON HOUSE - Fabrics–tapestry ☆ - Coloroll Inc.

CHARLESTON MANOR - Furniture ☆ - Kincaid Furniture Co. Inc.

CHARLESTON PAPERS, THE - Wallpaper - Scalamandre Silks Inc.

CHARLESTON SOAP AND CANDLE CO. - Soap - Yancy Co., Inc.

CHARLESTON TRELLIS - Bedding–linen - Dan River Inc.

CHARLESTON WAY - Wallcoverings - Wall Visions

CHARLESTON WHARF - Floor coverings - Mannington Resilient Floors

CHARLESTOWN - Furniture ☆ - Hammary Furniture Co. Inc.

CHARLESWOOD - Audio equipment - Charleswood Furniture Corp.

CHARLEVOIX - Boating equipment and accessories - Martone Marine Products, Inc.

CHARLEVOIX FLAG CLIPS - Clamps - Martone Marine Products, Inc.

CHARLEY - Pens - National Pen & Pencil Co.

CHARLEY - Toys - Tyco Toys

CHARLEY'S - Salad dressing - Arnie's

CHARLEY'S - Spices and extracts - Charley's Specialty Foods Co., Inc.

CHARLEY'S CHOICE - Pet products - Liss Brothers Inc.

CHARLEY'S TOYS - Toys ☆ - Swiss Plywood Corp.

CHARLIE - Electronic equipment - Educational Insights, Inc.

CHARLIE - Jewelry–costume - Revlon Consumer Products Corp.

CHARLIE - Tableware–earthenware - Metro/Thebe, Inc.

CHARLIE - Wheelchairs ☆ - Ventura Enterprises, Inc.

CHARLIE 1 HORSE - Clothing - Charlie 1 Horse Hat Co.

CHARLIE BEAR - Toys–stuffed - Dakin Inc.

CHARLIE BEIGG'S - Salad dressings–bottled - Horsefeathers of North Windham, Inc.

CHARLIE BROWN - Nuts–salted, roasted, cooked, or canned ☆ - Casey's Food & Nut Processors

CHARLIE BROWN - Shirts - Pennshire Shirt Corp.

CHARLIE BROWN'S ABC'S - Computer software - Random House, Inc.

☆ = Now out of production

CHARLIE BROWN'S ALL-STAR BASEBALL - Games ☆ - Parker Brothers

CHARLIE CLOWN - Dolls - Russ Berrie and Co., Inc.

CHARLIE DANIELS VOLUNTEER - Jams and jellies - Volunteer Ventures

CHARLIE GO LIGHTLY - Perfumes - Revlon Consumer Products Corp.

CHARLIE MCCARTHY - Dolls - Goldberger Doll Manufacture Co.

CHARLIE MY PHONE - Toys ☆ - Steven Manufacturing Co.

CHARLIE NATURALS - Perfumes - Revlon Consumer Products Corp.

CHARLIE RED - Perfumes - Revlon Consumer Products Corp.

CHARLIE SLAB - Fishing lures - Shirley P. Davis

CHARLIE STRINGER'S...UNPLUGGED - Musical instrument accessories - Stringer Industries Inc.

CHARLIE THE CANDYMAN - Candy ☆ - Pennsylvania Dutch Candies

CHARLIES - Candy - Rebecca Ruth Candy Inc.

CHARLIE'S - Fishing lures - Yakima Bait Co.

CHARLIE'S - Pet food - Federal Foods Corp.

CHARLIE'S CAFE - Pizzas–frozen - Sabatasso Foods Inc.

CHARLIE'S CHOICE - Spices and extracts - To Market to Market

CHARLIE'S GOLDEN CHOICE - Oats–rolled or meal - Purity Foods, Inc.

CHARLIE'S LUNCH KIT - Food products - Star-Kist Foods, Inc.

CHARLIE'S LUNCH KIT - Tuna–canned - Star-Kist Foods, Inc.

CHARLIE'S PRIDE - Grapes - Delano Farms Co.

CHARLIE'S PRIDE - Meat products–beef - Charlie's Pride Meats

CHARLOIN - Food products - K-Bob's USA, Inc.

CHARLOK - Wire - Avco Corp.

CHARLOT BYJ - Figurines ☆ - Goebel of North America

CHARLOTTE - Brushes–paint - Corona Brushes Inc.

CHARLOTTE - Dinnerware–glass ☆ - Crownford Giftware Co. Inc.

CHARLOTTE - Dishes–china - Waterford Wedgewood USA, Inc.

CHARLOTTE - Furniture - Falcon Products Inc.

CHARLOTTE - Glassware–household ☆ - Lenox Crystal, Inc.

CHARLOTTE - Stationery ☆ - Chase Collection, Inc.

CHARLOTTE CHARLES - Mushrooms - American Specialty Foods Inc.

CHARLOTTE GOOSE - Toys–stuffed ☆ - Gund, Inc.

CHARLOTTE HORNETS - Trading cards and stamps - Charlotte NBA Limited

CHARLOTTELUND - Dishes–china - Viletta China Co.

CHARLOTTE'S KITCHEN - Food products - Sierra Sunset Inc.

CHARLOTTESVILLE - Floor coverings–carpet and rugs ☆ - Capel, Inc.

CHARLSPROD - Novelty items - Charles Products Inc.

CHARLY - Bicycle parts and accessories ☆ - Windstream Power Systems Inc.

CHARM - Brushes–paint - Wright-Bernet

CHARM - Clocks - General Time Corp. (Westclox/Seth Thomas Div.)

CHARM - Dishes–earthenware ☆ - Denby USA Limited

CHARM - Flatware - Washington Forge Inc.

CHARM - Floor coverings - Aladdin Mills Inc.

CHARM - Rings–jewelry - Artcarved Inc.

CHARM - Skin care products - Gaylord Products Inc.

CHARM - Skin care products - Northern Labs, Inc.

CHARM - Wigs - Paula Young

CHARM-CRAFT - House furnishings - C-Mor Co.

CHARM FARM - Apparel and accessories - Dennis White

CHARM GEMS - Jewelry - F & F Creations Inc.

CHARM GIRL - Hairpins - Sta-Rite Ginnie Lou Inc.

CHARM-GLO - Lamp shades–fabric - Natalie Lamp and Shade Corp.

CHARM HOUSE - Paints - Commercial Chemical Co. Inc.

CHARM PEDERMA - Health care products - Charm Pederma Inc.

CHARM STEP - Shoes ☆ - Charm Step Shoes

CHARM-SWEETHEART - Scissors–hand-operated - F.W. Engels Inc.

CHARM-TEX INSTITUTIONAL TEXTILES QUALITY VALUE SERVICE - Linen - Charm-Tex, Inc.

CHARMADE - Corsets - Sears, Roebuck and Co.

CHARMAINE - Hair care products - Charmaine Inc.

CHARMAINE - Rings–jewelry - Artcarved Inc.

CHARMALADES - Candy - Tootsie Roll Industries, Inc.

CHARMANT - Cabinets - Actua

CHARMANT - Cigars - Gesty Trading & Manufacturing Corp.

CHARMANT - Furniture ☆ - Broyhill Furniture Industries, Inc.

CHARMANT - Underwear and nightwear ☆ - Jobst Institute Inc.

CHARMANTE - Floor coverings–carpet and rugs - J.L. Benson Co.

CHARMANTE - Floor coverings–carpet and rugs ☆ - World Carpets, Inc.

CHARMANTE - Furniture - Key City Furniture Co.

CHARMANTE - Jewelry–costume - B.B. Greenberg Co.

CHARMCYCLE - Bicycles ☆ - Hedstrom Corp.

CHARME - Floor coverings–carpet and rugs ☆ - Regal Rugs Inc.

CHARME - Wallpaper - Bayview Wallcoverings

CHARME II - Wallpaper - Bayview Wallcoverings

CHARMED - Candles - Tops Malibu

CHARMED CIRCLE - Apparel–women's - Wacoal America Inc.

CHARMED CIRCLE - Underwear and nightwear - Bestform Foundations, Inc.

CHARMED CIRCLES - Apparel–women's ☆ - Carnival Creations

CHARMED LAND - Food products ☆ - J.R. Simplot Co.

CHARMED LIFE - Hosiery - Virginia Maid Hosiery Mills Inc.

CHARMED LIFE - Rings–jewelry - Artcarved Inc.

CHARMEL - Food products ☆ - Allen Bros., Inc.

CHARMER GIRL - Footwear - SRL, Inc.

CHARMERS - Figurines - Heartprint Inc.

CHARMERS - Greeting cards - Hallmark Cards Inc.

CHARMER'S CEREAL HELPER - Marshmallows - Taylor Trading Inc.

CHARMETTE - Jewelry - Jacoby-Bender Inc.

CHARMETTE - Lamps - Natalie Lamp and Shade Corp.

CHARMETTE - Yarn ☆ - Lion Brand Yarn Co.

CHARMETTES - Deodorizers ☆ - Car-Freshner Corp.

CHARMETTES - Jewelry - Charmettes Inc.

CHARMEUR - Floor coverings–carpet and rugs ☆ - Karastan-Bigelow Inc.

CHARMGLOW - Barbecues and grills - Sunbeam Outdoor Products Inc.

CHARMGLOW PREMIER - Barbecues and grills - Sunbeam Outdoor Products Inc.

CHARMIN - Needlecraft kits ☆ - Janlynn Corp.

CHARMIN - Paper–toilet - Procter & Gamble Co.

CHARMIN CARE - Paper–toilet - Procter & Gamble Co.

CHARMIN' FARM FRIENDS - Dolls - Meritus Industries, Inc.

CHARMIN FREE - Paper–toilet - Procter & Gamble Co.

CHARMIN PLUS - Paper–toilet - Procter & Gamble Co.

CHARMIN ULTRA - Paper–toilet - Procter & Gamble Co.

CHARMINAIRE - Perfumes - Ritornelle Inc.

CHARMINAR - Rice - Ghais Shenouda

CHARMING ANGLES - Quilts - Extra Special Products Corp.

CHARMING CHECKS - Dolls ☆ - Effanbee Doll Corp.

CHARMING CHUMS - Toys–stuffed - Centsable Toys Inc.

CHARMING KITTENS WITH FUNTIME HOUSE - Toys–stuffed - Tonka Corp.

CHARMING NANCY - Wines - Breitenbach Wine Cellars

CHARMING TAILS - Figurines - FFSC, Inc.

CHARMING TOUCH - Floor coverings–carpet and rugs - Barrett Carpet Mills Inc.

CHARMINGLY DIFFERENT - Wallpaper - Westhill Wallcoverings Inc.

CHARMKINS - Candy - Philadelphia Chewing Gum Corp.

CHARMO - Glass–window - Surface Combustion, Inc.

CHARMONT - Furniture - Lane Co. Inc.

CHARMONT - Furniture ☆ - Singer Furniture Co.

CHARMONY COLORS - Paints - United Hardware

CHARMRINGS - Jewelry - Charmettes Inc.

CHARMS - Beverages–carbonated - Charms Co.

CHARMS - Candy - Tootsie Roll Industries, Inc.

CHARMS - Food products - DCA Food Industries, Inc.

CHARMS & THINGS - Toys - Imperial Toy Corp.

CHARMS-ON-A-RING - Toys - Gerber Products Co.

CHARMS POPS - Candy - Tootsie Roll Industries, Inc.

CHARMS THE WORLD - Games - Mattel, Inc.

CHARMSTONE - Figurines ☆ - Lakeshore Artisans

CHARNA - Shoes ☆ - D'Rossana Associates LLC

CHARNOFF - Gin - David Sherman Corp.

CHARNWOOD - Wallpaper - Seabrook Wallcoverings, Inc.

CHARON - Lighting fixtures ☆ - Hubbell Lighting, Inc. (Lighting Div.)

CHARPEN ACOUSTIC-O - Musical instruments - Enzo Pizzi

CHARQUI BRAND - Beef - Overseas Food Imports Corp. (USA)

CHARRED KEG - Whiskey - Majestic Distilling Co.

CHARRITO - Food products - Arden International Kitchens Inc.

CHARRO - Recording label - TMC Productions

CHAR'S - Soups–mixes - Mt Lizzie Beans

CHARSPAST - Pharmaceutical preparations ☆ - C.O. Truxton Inc.

CHART - Computer software - Educational Testing Service

CHART - Computer software - Microsoft Corp.

CHART A LABEL - Labels–gummed - Nurseplus, Inc.

CHART-A-MATIC - Paper - Ampad Corp.

CHART ADVISOR - Computer software - DeltaPoint Inc.

CHART EQUIPMENT - Apparel - Hub Distributing Inc.

CHART LITER - Marine rigging - N.A. Taylor Co. Inc.

CHART N STITCH - Hobby kits - Serendipity Designs Inc.

CHART ROOM, THE - Wallpaper - Chapters Wallcoverings

CHART SAVER - Briefcases ☆ - Rod Caddy Industries

CHART SMART - Computer software - College of Dupage

CHARTA - Recording label - Charta Records

CHARTAPE - Tape–adhesive ☆ - Artist Aid Transfer Lettering Co.

☆ = Now out of production

CHARTBOOK - Computer software - Technical Tools Inc.
CHARTEK - Chemical preparations - Textron Systems Corp.
CHARTER - Automotive parts and accessories - Gates Rubber Co. (Automotive Aftermarket/Hardware Sales Div.)
CHARTER - Floor coverings–carpet and rugs - Lees Carpets
CHARTER - Flooring–hardwood - Biwood Flooring
CHARTER - Markers–felt-tip - Faber-Castell Corp.
CHARTER - Pencils - Reliance Pen & Pencil Corp.
CHARTER - Plywood - Georgia-Pacific Corp.
CHARTER - Publisher's imprints - Berkley Publishing Corp.
CHARTER - Steel - Charter Manufacturing Co. Inc.
CHARTER - Tables–wood ☆ - Ridgeway Clock Co.
CHARTER - Tobacco products - Faber, Coe & Gregg Inc.
CHARTER - Watches ☆ - Littman Jewelers
CHARTER - Yarn - Dixie Yarns, Inc.
CHARTER ARMS - Guns - Charter Arms
CHARTER-BOAT - Fishing tackle - Yakima Bait Co.
CHARTER CAY - Wallpaper ☆ - Linden Street Gallery
CHARTER CLUB - Watches - Bulova Corp.
CHARTER CLUB BY JANE JUSTIN - Apparel and accessories - R.H. Macy & Co.
CHARTER COLLECTION - Hardware ☆ - Amerock Corp.
CHARTER COMMUNICATIONS - Broadcasting stations–cable television - Charter Communications, Inc.
CHARTER HOUSE - Floor coverings - Mannington Resilient Floors
CHARTER MAPLE - Furniture ☆ - Broyhill Furniture Industries, Inc.
CHARTER MASTER - Apparel and accessories - Meijer, Inc.
CHARTER OAK - Artists' materials ☆ - Andrews/Nelson/Whitehead
CHARTER OAK - Craft supplies - Superior Knitting Co.
CHARTER OAK - Saddles - Smith-Worthington Saddlery Co. Inc.
CHARTER OAK PRESS - Publisher's imprints - Charter Oak Press
CHARTERHALL - Furniture–wood ☆ - Century Furniture Co.
CHARTEX - Electronic equipment - Seal Products Inc.
CHARTIER - Musical instrument accessories - Chartier Reeds
CHARTING COACH - Computer software - Mercedes Arzu Wilson
CHARTIST - Computer software - Novagraph, Inc.
CHARTLEY - Dishes–china - Waterford Wedgewood USA, Inc.
CHARTLINK - Nautical instruments - Datamarine International Inc.
CHARTLITE - Lighting equipment–boat and ship - Soderberg Manufacturing Co. Inc.
CHARTMASTER - Computer software - Spacelabs Medical, Inc.
CHARTMATE - Navigational instruments - Magellan Corp.
CHARTMATS - Place mats - Convergence Corp.
CHARTONE - Seasonings - Dean Distributors, Inc.
CHARTPAK - Markers–felt-tip - Chartpak
CHARTPARTS - Computer software - Dakota Technologies, Inc.
CHARTPATH - Computer software - Erisco Inc.
CHARTPLUS - Computer software - Erisco Inc.
CHARTQ - Computer software - Softmed Systems, Inc.
CHARTRES - Christmas tree ornaments ☆ - Cracker Box Inc.
CHARTRES - Dinnerware–glass - Block China Co.
CHARTREUSE - Dinnerware–glass ☆ - Nikko Ceramics Inc.
CHARTS & CHARMS - Hobby kits - Dimensions, Inc.
CHARTS, GRIDS & FORMS - Computer software - Ventura Educational Systems
CHARTS NOW - Computer software - Foundation Microsystems, Inc.
CHARTS NOW ! - Computer software - Foundation Microsystems, Inc.
CHARTSCAN - Optical scanners–computer - Quartet Manufacturing Co.
CHARTSMITH - Computer software - Blacksmith, Inc.
CHARTVIEW - Computer software - Softmed Systems, Inc.
CHARTWELL - Audio equipment ☆ - Kevek Speaker Technology
CHARTWELL OAK - Furniture - Stanley Furniture Co. Inc.
CHARTWHEELS - Computer software - Astrolabe Software
CHARTWISE VERY INTELLIGENT - Computer software - Datatron Technical Services, Inc.
CHARTWRITER - Computer software - Prism Data Systems, Inc.
CHARVAL - Wines - Tarara
CHARVEL - Guitars - Jackson/Charvel
CHARVEL - Shirts–polo - Sunrise Apparel, Inc.
CHARVOZ - Seats–automobile - Charvoz
CHARYSMA - Paints ☆ - Gulf States Paint Co.
CHAS. - See also CHARLES
CHAS C STADDEN - Figurines - Britannia Collection Inc.
CHAS. COLIN PUBLICATIONS - Educational materials - Charles Colin Music Publishers
CHAS. M. STIEFF - Pianos ☆ - Cunningham Piano Co.

CHAS. SWEETSER & SONS - Snuff ☆ - Byfield Snuff Co.
CHASE - Amplifiers - Chase Technologies, Inc.
CHASE - Boats–motor - Grady-White Boats, Inc.
CHASE - Thermometers ☆ - Chase Instruments Corp.
CHASE A BUG - Lighting fixtures - Satco Products, Inc.
CHASE-A-WAY - Housewares - Centsable Toys Inc.
CHASE-A-WAY - Repellent - Chase-A-Way Inc.
CHASE & SANBORN - Coffee - Nestle Beverage Co.
CHASE AUTHENTICS - Apparel and accessories - Chase Racewear, LLC
CHASE CARS - Toys–automobiles - Racing Champions Inc.
CHASE COLLECTION-COCOA TIME - Cocoa–powders or mixes ☆ - Chase Collection, Inc.
CHASE CREEK - Wines - Shafer Vineyards Inc.
CHASE FARMS - Food products - Chase Farms Inc.
CHASE-LIMOGERE - Beverages–alcohol - Canandaigua Wine Co. Inc.
CHASE-LIMOGERE - Wines - Guild Wineries
CHASE MANHATTAN - Floor coverings–carpet and rugs - Miles Carpets Inc.
CHASE ME - Apparel–children's - Julie Hopkins Johnson
CHASE-MM - Paints - Chase Products Co.
CHASE MUSIC GROUP - Recording label - Chase Music Group
CHASE NET - Bags - Chase Bag Co.
CHASE ORCHARDS - Food products - Chase Farms Inc.
CHASE RACEWEAR - Apparel and accessories - Chase Racewear, LLC
CHASE RUN - Jeans–men's - Jonbil Inc.
CHASE THE RAINBOW - Game machines - Purple Star, Inc.
CHASE TOYS - Toys - Chase Toys, Inc.
CHASELLE - Paints–artists' - Chaselle Inc.
CHASEN'S CHILI - Food products - Chasen Food Specialties, Inc.
CHASER - Beverages–carbonated - Double Cola Co.-USA
CHASER - Chemical preparations - Terra International, Inc.
CHASER PALE - Beverages–malt - Kent C. Taylor
CHASERS - Shoes ☆ - Combine Group Division Inc.
CHASE'S - Paints - Chase Products Co.
CHASIBEX - Vitamins and nutritional supplements ☆ - Chase Laboratories Inc.
CHASKA - Vodka - Marie Brizard Wines & Spirits, USA
CHASM GRAPHICS - Computer software - Chasm Graphics
CHASOPHEN - Laxatives ☆ - Chase Laboratories Inc.
CHASQUI INTERNATIONAL - Advertising agencies - Severino Czapski
CHASS - Clocks - Hinpo-Chass International Inc.
CHASSE - Apparel–women's - Althuser Co.
CHASSIS - Trailers–travel - Callen Camper Co.
CHASSIS BLACK - Paints - Easthill Group, Inc.
CHASSIS CLASSIC - Automotive parts and accessories - S.J. Miller Co.
CHASSIS STACKER - Transportation vehicles and equipment - Chassis Systems, Inc.
CHASTAIN PARK - Floor coverings–carpet and rugs - Eagle Carpets Inc.
CHASTE BERRY EXTRACT - Vitamins and nutritional supplements - Vitamin Research Products Inc.
CHASTEBERRY-POWER - Vitamins and nutritional supplements - Natur-Pharma, Inc.
CHASTENET - Liquors - Crestfield Importers Ltd.
CHASTITY RINGS - Jewelry - Stuller Settings, Inc.
CHASUBLE - Glass products - Durand International
CHASY - Computer software - Pythia Corp.
CHAT - Computer software - Netscape Communications Corp.
CHAT ST. - Apparel and accessories - Chat St., Inc.
CHATA - Desserts - Mina International Services
CHATA - Food products - Yolean
CHATEAU - Bedding–linen - Whiting Manufacturing Co. Inc.
CHATEAU - Bedroom furniture - American Furniture Co. Inc.
CHATEAU - Cabinets–wood - Parcraft Distinctive Cabinetry
CHATEAU - Chandeliers ☆ - Crystal Clear Importing Co. Inc.
CHATEAU - Christmas tree ornaments - Cracker Box Inc.
CHATEAU - Clocks ☆ - Ridgeway Clock Co.
CHATEAU - Dinnerware–glass - Crisa Corp.
CHATEAU - Dishes–china - Tidemark Co.
CHATEAU - Doors–screen ☆ - Taylor Building Products Co.
CHATEAU - Drapery hardware - Kirsch Co.
CHATEAU - Faucets - Moen Inc.
CHATEAU - Floor coverings–carpet and rugs - S and S Mills Inc.
CHATEAU - Food products - Chateau Food Products Co.
CHATEAU - Fragrance ☆ - Coty Inc.
CHATEAU - Furniture ☆ - Singer Furniture Co.
CHATEAU - Furniture ☆ - Southern Furniture Co. of Conover
CHATEAU - Glassware–household - Lancaster Colony Corp.
CHATEAU - Housewares - Super Valu Inc.

☆ = Now out of production

CHATEAU - Lighting fixtures - Angelo Brothers Co.
CHATEAU - Locks–padlocks - Chateau Products, Inc.
CHATEAU - Mobile homes - Wick Building Systems Inc. (Manufactured Home Div./North)
CHATEAU - Mobile homes ☆ - Kit Manufacturing Co.
CHATEAU - Napkins–paper - Wisconsin Tissue Mills Inc.
CHATEAU - Padding–foam ☆ - Foamex LP
CHATEAU - Pharmaceutical preparations - Pfizer Inc.
CHATEAU - Rings–jewelry - Artcarved Inc.
CHATEAU - Tableware–china ☆ - Lenox, Inc.
CHATEAU - Trailers–travel - Chateau RV Inc.
CHATEAU - Wallpaper ☆ - S.M. Hexter Co.
CHATEAU - Wallpaper ☆ - Pickhardt & Siebert USA Inc.
CHATEAU 2000 - Motor vehicles - Thor Tech, Inc.
CHATEAU ANTOINETTE - Wines - Lembo Vineyards
CHATEAU AUSONE - Wines - Seagram's Chateau & Estate Wines Co.
CHATEAU AUSONE - Wines ☆ - European Beverage Co., Inc.
CHATEAU BARON DU BORDEAUX - Wines - Richard Adlai Corp.
CHATEAU BARON PHILIPPE DE ROTHSCHILD - Wines - Paterno Imports, Ltd.
CHATEAU BARON SEGUR - Wines - Seagram's Chateau & Estate Wines Co.
CHATEAU BASTOR LAMONTAGNE - Wines - Admiral Wine Merchants
CHATEAU BAYERETTE - Wines - World Wide Wine and Spirits Inc.
CHATEAU BEAREGARD - Wines - Admiral Wine Merchants
CHATEAU BEAU VALLON - Wines - House of Burgundy Inc.
CHATEAU BEAUSEJOUR DUFFAU-LAGARROSSE - Wines - Kobrand Corp.
CHATEAU BEL AIR - Wines - Seagram's Chateau & Estate Wines Co.
CHATEAU BENOIT - Wines - Chateau Benoit Winery
CHATEAU BEYCHEVELLE - Wines - Seagram's Chateau & Estate Wines Co.
CHATEAU BILTMORE - Wines - Biltmore Co.
CHATEAU BILTMORE - Wines - Biltmore Estate Wine Co.
CHATEAU BLANC - Dinnerware–glass - Block China Co.
CHATEAU BON PASTEUR - Wines - Wine House Ltd.
CHATEAU BOUCHAINE - Wines - Bouchaine Vineyards
CHATEAU BOUQUET - Dinnerware–glass ☆ - Block China Co.
CHATEAU BOURDILEY - Wines - European Beverage Co., Inc.
CHATEAU BOURGNEUF - Wines - Seagram's Chateau & Estate Wines Co.
CHATEAU BOUSCAUT - Wines - Seagram's Chateau & Estate Wines Co.
CHATEAU BOUSQUETTE - Wines - Chartrand Imports
CHATEAU BRANE CANTENAC - Wines - Seagram's Chateau & Estate Wines Co.
CHATEAU BRANE-CANTENAC - Wines ☆ - European Beverage Co., Inc.
CHATEAU BRONZE - Dinnerware–glass ☆ - Block China Co.
CHATEAU BROWN PESSAC LEOGMAN - Wines ☆ - European Beverage Co., Inc.
CHATEAU BUFFET - Dishes–earthenware - Taylor, Smith & Taylor Co.
CHATEAU CALIFA - Wines - Chamisal Vineyard
CHATEAU CALON SEGUR - Wines - Seagram's Chateau & Estate Wines Co.
CHATEAU CAMBON LE PELOUSE - Wines - Leonard Kreusch Inc.
CHATEAU CAMENSAC - Wines - Seagram's Chateau & Estate Wines Co.
CHATEAU CANON LA GAFFELIERE - Wines - Seagram's Chateau & Estate Wines Co.
CHATEAU CANON-MOUEIX - Wines - Seagram's Chateau & Estate Wines Co.
CHATEAU CANTEMERLE - Wines - Seagram's Chateau & Estate Wines Co.
CHATEAU CANTERAINE - Wines - European Beverage Co., Inc.
CHATEAU CARBONNIEUX - Wines - Seagram's Chateau & Estate Wines Co.
CHATEAU CERTAN DE MAY - Wines - Seagram's Chateau & Estate Wines Co.
CHATEAU CHABOT - Wines - Gibson Wine Co.
CHATEAU CHANTEGRIVE - Wines - Seagram's Chateau & Estate Wines Co.
CHATEAU CHARDON - Wines - Gibson Wine Co.
CHATEAU CHARMAIL - Wines ☆ - Admiral Wine Merchants
CHATEAU CHAUVIN - Wines - Wine House Ltd.
CHATEAU CHEVAL BLANC - Wines - Seagram's Chateau & Estate Wines Co.
CHATEAU CHEVALIER - Wines - Chateau Chevalier Winery
CHATEAU CHEVRE - Wines - Chateau Chevre Winery
CHATEAU CLARKE WINES - Wines - Marie Brizard Wines & Spirits, USA
CHATEAU CLOS FOURTET - Wines - Seagram's Chateau & Estate Wines Co.
CHATEAU COLLECTION - Floor coverings–carpet and rugs ☆ - Karastan-Bigelow Inc.
CHATEAU COLLECTIONS - Fabrics - Ian Crawford Ltd.
CHATEAU CORONA - Cigars - General Cigar Co., Inc.
CHATEAU COS D'ESTOURNEL - Wines - Seagram's Chateau & Estate Wines Co.

CHATEAU COUFRAN - Wines - Kobrand Corp.
CHATEAU COUTET BARSAC - Wines - European Beverage Co., Inc.
CHATEAU D'AIGUEVILLE - Wines - Seagram's Chateau & Estate Wines Co.
CHATEAU D'AQUERIA - Wines - Kobrand Corp.
CHATEAU D'ARGENT - Dinnerware–glass ☆ - Block China Co.
CHATEAU DASSAULT - Wines - Seagram's Chateau & Estate Wines Co.
CHATEAU D'AUVERNIER - Wines - Dreyfus Ashby Inc.
CHATEAU DAUZAC - Wines ☆ - European Beverage Co., Inc.
CHATEAU D'AZUR - Dinnerware–glass ☆ - Block China Co.
CHATEAU DE BARBE BLANCHE - Wines ☆ - Admiral Wine Merchants
CHATEAU DE BEAUREGARD - Wines - Bercut-Vandervoort & Co.
CHATEAU DE BOISFRANC BEAUJOLAIS - Wines - Chartrand Imports
CHATEAU DE CHAMPS - House furnishings - Lea Industries Inc.
CHATEAU DE CHANTEGRIVE - Wines - Seagram's Chateau & Estate Wines Co.
CHATEAU DE FONTPINOT - Wines - William Grant & Sons, Inc.
CHATEAU DE GARGUILLE - Wines - World Wide Wine and Spirits Inc.
CHATEAU DE LA CHAIZE - Wines - Seagram's Chateau & Estate Wines Co.
CHATEAU DE LA GARDINE - Wines - Bercut-Vandervoort & Co.
CHATEAU DE LA TOUR CLOS VOUGEOT - Wines ☆ - Kobrand Corp.
CHATEAU DE LACARELLE - Wines - Seagram's Chateau & Estate Wines Co.
CHATEAU DE LEU - Wines - Chateau De Leu Winery
CHATEAU DE MALIGNY - Wines - Parliament Import Co.
CHATEAU DE MARBUZET - Wines - Kobrand Corp.
CHATEAU DE MONTE - Wines - Wiederkehr Wine Cellars Inc.
CHATEAU DE MONTFORT - Wines - Seagram's Chateau & Estate Wines Co.
CHATEAU DE PARIS - Candy bars - Morris National Inc.
CHATEAU DE PEZ - Wines - Remy Martin Amerique Inc.
CHATEAU DE POMMARD - Wines - Kobrand Corp.
CHATEAU DE RIBEBON - Wines - World Wide Wine and Spirits Inc.
CHATEAU DE SALES - Wines - Seagram's Chateau & Estate Wines Co.
CHATEAU DE TIGNE - Wines - Seagram's Chateau & Estate Wines Co.
CHATEAU DE VEAU - Veal - Atlantic Veal & Lamb
CHATEAU D'ERMO - Food products - Amway Corp.
CHATEAU DES HERBEUX - Wines ☆ - Parliament Import Co.
CHATEAU DES VERGNES - Wines - World Wide Wine and Spirits Inc.
CHATEAU DIANA - Wines - Chateau Diana
CHATEAU DU CHENE - Wines ☆ - Oak Knoll Winery Inc.
CHATEAU DU GOLF - T-shirts–men's - G & S Co.
CHATEAU DU LAC - Wines ☆ - Admiral Wine Merchants
CHATEAU DU MAYNE - Wines - Kobrand Corp.
CHATEAU DU PIN - Wines - European Beverage Co., Inc.
CHATEAU DUCRU BEAUCAILLOU - Wines - Seagram's Chateau & Estate Wines Co.
CHATEAU DUHART-MILON ROTHSCHILD - Wines - Seagram's Chateau & Estate Wines Co.
CHATEAU D'YQUEM - Wines - Seagram's Chateau & Estate Wines Co.
CHATEAU ELAN - Beverages–alcohol - Chateau Elan Ltd.
CHATEAU ELAN - Floor coverings–carpet and rugs ☆ - Karastan-Bigelow Inc.
CHATEAU ELEGANTE - Floor coverings–carpet and rugs ☆ - Karastan-Bigelow Inc.
CHATEAU ELYSSES - Wines - Weibel Vineyards
CHATEAU EMPIRE - Dinnerware–glass ☆ - Block China Co.
CHATEAU ESPIRIT - Floor coverings–carpet and rugs ☆ - Karastan-Bigelow Inc.
CHATEAU FAIZEAU - Wines ☆ - Admiral Wine Merchants
CHATEAU FARGUES - Wines - Seagram's Chateau & Estate Wines Co.
CHATEAU FAURES BELLVUE - Wines - European Beverage Co., Inc.
CHATEAU FERBOS - Wines ☆ - Kobrand Corp.
CHATEAU FIGEAC - Wines - Seagram's Chateau & Estate Wines Co.
CHATEAU FILIPPI - Wines - J. Filippi Vintage Co.
CHATEAU FLEURI - Dinnerware–glass ☆ - Block China Co.
CHATEAU FONTELOUP - Wines ☆ - Admiral Wine Merchants
CHATEAU FORTIA - Wines ☆ - Banfi Vintners
CHATEAU FOURCAS HOSTEN - Wines - Frederick Wildman and Sons Ltd.
CHATEAU FROMBRAUGE - Wines - Kobrand Corp.
CHATEAU FUISSE - Wines - Frederick Wildman and Sons Ltd.
CHATEAU GARDENS - Mustard ☆ - Estus Export-Import
CHATEAU GAZIN - Wines - Kobrand Corp.
CHATEAU GAZIN - Wines - Seagram's Chateau & Estate Wines Co.
CHATEAU GISCOURS - Wines - Remy Martin Amerique Inc.
CHATEAU GISCOURS - Wines - Seagram's Chateau & Estate Wines Co.
CHATEAU GISCOURS - Wines ☆ - European Beverage Co., Inc.
CHATEAU GLORIA - Wines - Seagram's Chateau & Estate Wines Co.
CHATEAU GRAND CHEMIN - Wines ☆ - House of Burgundy Inc.
CHATEAU GRAND JOUR - Wines - European Beverage Co., Inc.

☆ = Now out of production

CHATEAU GRAND PUY LACOSTE - Wines - Seagram's Chateau & Estate Wines Co.

CHATEAU GRAND TEYSSERE - Wines ☆ - Admiral Wine Merchants

CHATEAU GRAND TRAVERSE - Wines - Chateau Grand Traverse Ltd.

CHATEAU GRAND VILLAGE - Wines ☆ - Admiral Wine Merchants

CHATEAU GRAVES DE LA VALADE - Wines - European Beverage Co., Inc.

CHATEAU GREC - Dinnerware–glass ☆ - Block China Co.

CHATEAU GREYSAC - Wines - Seagram's Chateau & Estate Wines Co.

CHATEAU GRUAUD-LAROSE - Wines - Seagram's Chateau & Estate Wines Co.

CHATEAU GUEYROSSE - Beverages–alcohol - Margus Co.

CHATEAU GUIRAUD CHEVAL BLANC - Wines - Seagram's Chateau & Estate Wines Co.

CHATEAU HAUT BATAILLEY - Wines - Seagram's Chateau & Estate Wines Co.

CHATEAU HAUT-BRION - Wines - Seagram's Chateau & Estate Wines Co.

CHATEAU HAUT BRION - Wines ☆ - European Beverage Co., Inc.

CHATEAU HAUT BRISSON ST. EMILION GRAND CRU - Wines - Admiral Wine Merchants

CHATEAU HAUT-CAILLOU - Wines ☆ - Kobrand Corp.

CHATEAU HAUT GROS BONET - Wines - Margus Co.

CHATEAU HAUT PEYRAGUE - Wines ☆ - Palm Bay Imports, Inc.

CHATEAU HIP - Furniture - Gregory G. Smith

CHATEAU IMPERIAL - Floor coverings–carpet and rugs ☆ - Karastan-Bigelow Inc.

CHATEAU INTERNATIONAL - Bread crumbs - Prepared Products Co., Inc.

CHATEAU JERO - Food products ☆ - Sunstar Foods Inc.

CHATEAU JIMBEAUX - Wines - James Garner

CHATEAU JOANNA - Wine - R. & J. Cook

CHATEAU JULIEN - Wines - Chateau Julien

CHATEAU JULIEN - Wines - House of Burgundy Inc.

CHATEAU KYANAC - Wines - European Beverage Co., Inc.

CHATEAU LA CARDONNE - Wines - Seagram's Chateau & Estate Wines Co.

CHATEAU LA CROIX MILLORIT - Wines - Parliament Import Co.

CHATEAU LA CROIX ST. VINCENT - Wines ☆ - European Beverage Co., Inc.

CHATEAU LA FAYETTE - Wines - Weibel Vineyards

CHATEAU LA FLEUR PETRUS - Wines ☆ - Bercut-Vandervoort & Co.

CHATEAU LA GAFFELIERE - Wines - Seagram's Chateau & Estate Wines Co.

CHATEAU LA GRAVIERE - Wines - European Beverage Co., Inc.

CHATEAU LA LAGUNE - Wines - Seagram's Chateau & Estate Wines Co.

CHATEAU LA LOUVIERE - Wines - Seagram's Chateau & Estate Wines Co.

CHATEAU LA MISSION-HAUT-BRION - Wines - Seagram's Chateau & Estate Wines Co.

CHATEAU LA PIC - Wines - Lapic Winery Ltd.

CHATEAU LA TOUR PRADOTS - Wines - World Wide Wine and Spirits Inc.

CHATEAU LACHESNAYE - Wines ☆ - European Beverage Co., Inc.

CHATEAU LAFAURIE-PEYRAGUEY - Wines - Seagram's Chateau & Estate Wines Co.

CHATEAU LAFITE-ROTHSCHILD - Wines - Seagram's Chateau & Estate Wines Co.

CHATEAU LAFITE ROTHSCHILD - Wines ☆ - European Beverage Co., Inc.

CHATEAU LAFLEUR - Wines - Kobrand Corp.

CHATEAU LAGNIAPPE - Wines ☆ - Cedar Hill Wine Co.

CHATEAU LAGRANGE - Wines - Seagram's Chateau & Estate Wines Co.

CHATEAU LANESSAN - Wines ☆ - European Beverage Co., Inc.

CHATEAU L'ANGELUS - Wines - Seagram's Chateau & Estate Wines Co.

CHATEAU LARCHEVAL - Wines - Admiral Wine Merchants

CHATEAU LARMANDE - Wines - Wine House Ltd.

CHATEAU LAROQUE - Wines ☆ - European Beverage Co., Inc.

CHATEAU LAROSE-TRINTAUDON - Wines - Seagram's Chateau & Estate Wines Co.

CHATEAU LARTENAC - Wines - European Beverage Co., Inc.

CHATEAU LASCOMBES - Wines ☆ - European Beverage Co., Inc.

CHATEAU LATOUR - House furnishings ☆ - Lexington Furniture Industries, Inc.

CHATEAU LATOUR - Wines - Seagram's Chateau & Estate Wines Co.

CHATEAU LATOUR - Wines ☆ - European Beverage Co., Inc.

CHATEAU LATOUR FIGEAC - Wines - Seagram's Chateau & Estate Wines Co.

CHATEAU LATOUR HAUT BRION - Wines - Seagram's Chateau & Estate Wines Co.

CHATEAU LAURENT - Beverages–alcohol - Monarch Wine Co.

CHATEAU LAURETTE - Wines - Seagram's Chateau & Estate Wines Co.

CHATEAU LAVILLE-HAUT-BRION - Wines - Seagram's Chateau & Estate Wines Co.

CHATEAU LE REYSSAC - Wines ☆ - Admiral Wine Merchants

CHATEAU LE SARTRE - Wines - Paterno Imports, Ltd.

CHATEAU LEGRAND - Floor coverings–carpet and rugs - Karastan-Bigelow Inc.

CHATEAU LEOVILLE-BARTON - Wines - Seagram's Chateau & Estate Wines Co.

CHATEAU LEOVILLE LAS CASES - Wines - Seagram's Chateau & Estate Wines Co.

CHATEAU LEOVILLE POYFERRE - Wines - Seagram's Chateau & Estate Wines Co.

CHATEAU LES DONATS - Wines ☆ - House of Burgundy Inc.

CHATEAU LES GRANDS JAYE - Wines ☆ - Palm Bay Imports, Inc.

CHATEAU LES PARRE - Wines - Pellegrini Bros. Wines Inc.

CHATEAU LICHINE - Wines - European Beverage Co., Inc.

CHATEAU LORRAINE - Furniture ☆ - Hammary Furniture Co. Inc.

CHATEAU LORRAINE - Wines ☆ - Batavia Wine Cellars Inc.

CHATEAU LOUDENNE - Wines - Dreyfus Ashby Inc.

CHATEAU LOUIS XVI COLLECTION - Tables–wood - Wells Furniture Co.

CHATEAU LUZERNE - Wines - Laird and Co.

CHATEAU LYNCH BAGES - Wines - Seagram's Chateau & Estate Wines Co.

CHATEAU MADELEINE - Beverages–carbonated - Chateau Madeleine

CHATEAU MAGDELAINE - Wines - Bercut-Vandervoort & Co.

CHATEAU MAGNOL - Wines - Seagram's Chateau & Estate Wines Co.

CHATEAU MAJA - Wines ☆ - Stimson Lane Vineyards & Estates

CHATEAU MALESCOT - Wines - Kobrand Corp.

CHATEAU MALROME - Wines - Jose Collazo

CHATEAU MAMOU - Wines - European Beverage Co., Inc.

CHATEAU MARGAUX - Wines - Seagram's Chateau & Estate Wines Co.

CHATEAU MARQUIS - Coffee - Wechsler Coffee Corp.

CHATEAU MARTIN - Beverages–alcohol - Canandaigua Wine Co. Inc.

CHATEAU MARTIN - Wines - Martin's Wines Inc.

CHATEAU MARTIN - Wines ☆ - Admiral Wine Merchants

CHATEAU MARTINET - Wines - Seagram's Chateau & Estate Wines Co.

CHATEAU MERIC - Wines - Chartrand Imports

CHATEAU MERVILLE - Wines ☆ - Admiral Wine Merchants

CHATEAU MEYNEY - Wines - Seagram's Chateau & Estate Wines Co.

CHATEAU MIEL'S COCOA NUGGETS CHOCOLATE FOR BEVERAGES AND DESSERTS - Chocolate candy - Chateau Miel Inc.

CHATEAU MIEL'S ICE CAP FROSTY CAPPUCCINO - Coffee - Chateau Miel Inc.

CHATEAU MILLET - Beverages–alcohol - World Shippers & Importers

CHATEAU MONBOUSQUET - Wines - Excelsior Wine & Spirits Corp.

CHATEAU MONCONTOUR - Wines ☆ - Bercut-Vandervoort & Co.

CHATEAU MONET - Liquer - White Rock Distilleries Inc.

CHATEAU MONTELENA - Wines - Chateau Montelena

CHATEAU MONTGOLFIER VINEYARDS - Wines - Chateau Mongolfier Vineyards

CHATEAU MONTROSE - Wines - Seagram's Chateau & Estate Wines Co.

CHATEAU MORRISETTE - Wines - Chateau Morrisette, Inc.

CHATEAU MOUTON ROTHSCHILD - Wines - Seagram's Chateau & Estate Wines Co.

CHATEAU MOUTON ROTHSCHILD - Wines ☆ - European Beverage Co., Inc.

CHATEAU NAPOLEON - Wines - Weibel Vineyards

CHATEAU NAPPY - Dinnerware–glass - Crisa Corp.

CHATEAU NENIN - Wines - Seagram's Chateau & Estate Wines Co.

CHATEAU NICOLE - Wallpaper ☆ - Somerville Designs

CHATEAU NOIR - Dinnerware–glass ☆ - Block China Co.

CHATEAU NORMANDY - Floor coverings–carpet and rugs ☆ - Karastan-Bigelow Inc.

CHATEAU NORMANDY - Furniture - Ethan Allen, Inc.

CHATEAU NOTTON - Wines - Seagram's Chateau & Estate Wines Co.

CHATEAU PASTORAL - Dinnerware–glass ☆ - Block China Co.

CHATEAU PAVIE - Wines - Seagram's Chateau & Estate Wines Co.

CHATEAU PERRON LA GRAVIERE - Wines ☆ - Palm Bay Imports, Inc.

CHATEAU PETRUS - Wines - Seagram's Chateau & Estate Wines Co.

CHATEAU PEYMARTIN - Wines - Seagram's Chateau & Estate Wines Co.

CHATEAU PICHON LALANDE - Wines - Seagram's Chateau & Estate Wines Co.

CHATEAU PICHON LONGUEVILLE BARON - Wines - Seagram's Chateau & Estate Wines Co.

CHATEAU PICHON LONGVILLE BARON - Wines ☆ - European Beverage Co., Inc.

CHATEAU PLAGNAC - Wines - Seagram's Chateau & Estate Wines Co.

CHATEAU PONTET CANET - Wines - Seagram's Chateau & Estate Wines Co.

CHATEAU PONTUS - Beverages–alcohol - Margus Co.

CHATEAU POTENSAC - Brands - Seagram's Chateau & Estate Wines Co.

☆ = Now out of production

CHATEAU PRIEURE LICHINE - Wines - Seagram's Chateau & Estate Wines Co.

CHATEAU PUY BLANQUET - Wines - Seagram's Chateau & Estate Wines Co.

CHATEAU RANIER - Wines - Tomasello Winery

CHATEAU RAUSAN SEGLA - Wines - Seagram's Chateau & Estate Wines Co.

CHATEAU RAYNALDY - Wines - European Beverage Co., Inc.

CHATEAU RAYNE-VIGNEAU - Wines - Seagram's Chateau & Estate Wines Co.

CHATEAU REGE - Wines - Diamond Oaks Vineyard

CHATEAU REIEM - Wines - Meier's Wine Cellars Inc.

CHATEAU REYNELLA - Wines - House of Burgundy Inc.

CHATEAU RICHON - Wines - Seagram's Chateau & Estate Wines Co.

CHATEAU RIEUSSEC - Wines - Seagram's Chateau & Estate Wines Co.

CHATEAU ROCHER BELLEVUE FIGEAC - Wines - Seagram's Chateau & Estate Wines Co.

CHATEAU ROMER - Wines - Seagram's Chateau & Estate Wines Co.

CHATEAU ROSE - Dinnerware–glass ✩ - Block China Co.

CHATEAU ROUGE - Dinnerware–glass ✩ - Block China Co.

CHATEAU ROYALE - Floor coverings–carpet and rugs - Karastan-Bigelow Inc.

CHATEAU ROYALE - Wallpaper - Brewster Wallcovering Co.

CHATEAU RUTHERFORD - Wines - Rutherford Vintners Inc.

CHATEAU ST. CYR - Beverages–alcohol - Chatam Imports Inc.

CHATEAU STE. GENEVIEVE - Beverages–alcohol - Carver Wine Cellars

CHATEAU ST. GEORGES - Wines - House of Burgundy Inc.

CHATEAU ST. GEORGES - Wines - Pellegrini Bros. Wines Inc.

CHATEAU ST. JEAN - Wines - Chateau St. Jean

CHATEAU ST. JEAN LA PETITE ETOILE - Beverages–alcohol - Beringer Wine Estates Co.

CHATEAU ST. JULIAN - Wines ✩ - St. Julian Wine Co.

CHATEAU SAINT LOUIE - Wines - Bardenheier Wine Cellars

CHATEAU ST. MARTIN - Brandy - Martin's Wines Inc.

CHATEAU STE. MICHELLE - Wines - Stimson Lane Vineyards & Estates

CHATEAU ST. NICHOLAS - Wines - R.H. Phillips Vineyard Inc.

CHATEAU ST. PIERRE - Wines - Seagram's Chateau & Estate Wines Co.

CHATEAU ST. ROBERT - Wines ✩ - Admiral Wine Merchants

CHATEAU SENEJAC - Wines - Frederick Wildman and Sons Ltd.

CHATEAU SERIES, THE - Cabinets - Vinotemp International

CHATEAU SIMARD - Wines - Seagram's Chateau & Estate Wines Co.

CHATEAU SMITH HAUT LAFITTE - Wines - Seagram's Chateau & Estate Wines Co.

CHATEAU SOCIANDO MALLET - Wines - Seagram's Chateau & Estate Wines Co.

CHATEAU SOUVERAIN - Wines - Chateau Souverain

CHATEAU SPRINGS - Water–bottled or canned - D.R. Doerflein, Inc.

CHATEAU SUDUIRAUT - Wines ✩ - Kobrand Corp.

CHATEAU T-SHIRT - Novelty items - G & S Co.

CHATEAU TALBOT - Wines - Seagram's Chateau & Estate Wines Co.

CHATEAU TERREFORT LE CALVAIRE - Wines ✩ - Palm Bay Imports, Inc.

CHATEAU THAYER - Wines ✩ - Bardenheier Wine Cellars

CHATEAU TOUR CALON - Wines - House of Burgundy Inc.

CHATEAU TROTANOY - Wines - Seagram's Chateau & Estate Wines Co.

CHATEAU VEE - Boats–motor ✩ - Cruisers

CHATEAU VERT - Dinnerware–glass ✩ - Block China Co.

CHATEAU VIDASSE - Wines - World Wide Wine and Spirits Inc.

CHATEAU VILLARD - Wines ✩ - Admiral Wine Merchants

CHATEAU WHITE - Tableware–china - Villeroy and Boch Tableware Ltd.

CHATEAU WOLTNER - Wines - Parliament Import Co.

CHATEAU WOLTNER - Wines - Woltner & Co.

CHATEAU Y - Wines ✩ - Seagram's Chateau & Estate Wines Co.

CHATEAUGAY - Cheese - Dean Foods Co.

CHATEAULET - Wines - Gibson Wine Co.

CHATEAUNEUF - Glassware–household - Durand International

CHATEAUNEUF-DU-PAPE - Wines - Kobrand Corp.

CHATEAUROUX - Wallpaper - Greeff Fabrics Inc.

CHATEAUX - Beverages–alcohol - Jim Beam Brands Co.

CHATEAUX COUNTRY - Wallpaper - Surface Industries Inc.

CHATELAINE - Clocks ✩ - Ridgeway Clock Co.

CHATELAINE - Floor coverings ✩ - Tarkett, Inc.

CHATELAINE - Floor coverings–carpet and rugs ✩ - Karastan-Bigelow Inc.

CHATELET - Glassware–household - Durand International

CHATELLE - Brandy - Crown Capital USA Inc.

CHATEU DU MALTROYE - Wines - Wine House Ltd.

CHATEU VAL JOANIS WINES - Wines - Marie Brizard Wines & Spirits, USA

CHATFIELD - Furniture - Thomasville Furniture Industries Inc.

CHATFIELDS BAKING - Carob and cocoa products - American Natural Snacks

CHATFIELD'S CAROB & COMPLIMENTS - Carob and cocoa products - American Natural Snacks

CHATHAM - Bathroom accessories - Chatham Brass Co. Inc.

CHATHAM - Blankets - Chatham Manufacturing Co.

CHATHAM - Cabinets - Del Mar Cabinets

CHATHAM - Cabinets - Marsh Furniture Co.

CHATHAM - Dinnerware–glass ✩ - Royal China & Porcelain Companies Inc.

CHATHAM - Dishes–earthenware ✩ - Gorham Inc.

CHATHAM - Floor coverings ✩ - Bruce Hardwood Floors

CHATHAM - Floor coverings–carpet and rugs ✩ - Atlas Carpet Mills Inc.

CHATHAM - Flowers, plants, and seeds - Jonathan Green, Inc.

CHATHAM - Food products - Liberty Fish Co.

CHATHAM - Furniture ✩ - Drexel Heritage Furnishings, Inc.

CHATHAM - Gin - Peerless Importers Inc.

CHATHAM - Luggage - American Tourister, Inc.

CHATHAM - Pet products - Sunshine Mills Inc.

CHATHAM - Prefabricated buildings–wood - All American Homes Inc.

CHATHAM - Thread - Threads USA Div.

CHATHAM BRICK - Floor coverings–tile - Kentile Floors Inc.

CHATHAM COLLECTION - Desks - Boling Co.

CHATHAM COUNTY - Furniture - U.S. Furniture Industries Inc.

CHATHAM CREATED - Jewelry - Chatham Created Gems Inc.

CHATHAM GATE - Dinnerware–glass ✩ - Lenox, Inc.

CHATHAM HALL - Furniture ✩ - Bassett Furniture Industries, Inc.

CHATHAM HALL - Furniture–upholstered ✩ - Webb Furniture Enterprises Inc.

CHATHAM HILL - Wallpaper - Sanitas Wallcoverings

CHATHAM OAK - Cabinets - Del Mar Cabinets

CHATHAM PRESS, THE - Publisher's imprints - Chatham Press

CHATHAM RIDGE - Siding–insulating - Georgia-Pacific Corp.

CHATHAM SQUARE - Furniture ✩ - Riverside Furniture Corp.

CHATHAM SQUARE - Recording label - Jazz Composer's Orchestra Association Inc.

CHATHAM STATION - Wallpaper ✩ - Stonebridge Co.

CHATILAN - Yarn - Hohenberg Co. Inc.

CHATKA - Crab meat–canned or cured - Amtorg Trading Corp.

CHATKA - Seafood products–fresh or frozen - New England Fish Co.

CHATMOSS - Furniture - Pilliod Co.

CHATONET - Wines - Admiral Wine Merchants

CHATSWORTH - Clocks ✩ - General Time Corp. (Westclox/Seth Thomas Div.)

CHATSWORTH - Furniture - Haworth, Inc.

CHATSWORTH - Furniture ✩ - Harden Furniture Co. Inc.

CHATSWORTH - Hardware ✩ - Amerock Corp.

CHATSWORTH - Wood products - Georgia-Pacific Corp.

CHATSWORTH OAK - Furniture - Broyhill Furniture Industries, Inc.

CHATTAHOOCHEE - Paints–artists' - MCI Quality Coatings

CHATTAHOOCHEE CHOCOLATE - Ice cream - Kinnett Dairies, Inc.

CHATTAHOOCHEE VALLEY TRADING CO. - Apparel–men's - West Point-Pepperell Inc.

CHATTANOOGA CHEW - Chewing tobacco - American Maize-Products Co.

CHATTANOOGA CHOO CHOO - Candy - Brock Candy Co. Inc.

CHATTANOOGA CHOO-CHOO - Toys–electronic - Tyco Toys

CHATTANOOGA LOOKOUTS - Clothing - Engel Stadium Corp.

CHATTER ANIMALS - Toys–stuffed - Dakin Inc.

CHATTER CHUMS - Toys - Mattel, Inc.

CHATTER CLOCK - Toys - Mattel, Inc.

CHATTER PAL - Toys - Mattel, Inc.

CHATTER PLATTERS - Cooking utensils–earthenware - Heritage Mint, Ltd.

CHATTER TELEPHONE - Toys - Fisher-Price, Inc.

CHATTERBOX - Electronic equipment - Westcode Inc.

CHATTERBOX - Mobile communicators - Hong Jin Crown America, Inc.

CHATTERBOX - Novelty items ✩ - Jobar International Inc./Bibi Products

CHATTERGUARD - Lighting fixtures ✩ - Teledyne Laars

CHATTSWORTH - Dinnerware–glass ✩ - Denby USA Limited

CHATTY - Dolls - Mattel, Inc.

CHATTY PATTY - Dolls - Mattel, Inc.

CHATZ ROASTING COMPANY COFFEES & TEAS - Coffee - Artamus Roasting Co.

CHAUCER - Floor coverings - Harris-Tarkett, Inc.

CHAUCER - Floor coverings ✩ - Robbins Inc.

CHAUCER - Floor coverings–carpet and rugs - Atlas Carpet Mills Inc.

CHAUCER'S MEAD - Wines - Bargetto's Santa Cruz Winery

CHAULER - Air conditioning equipment - Selkirk Metalbestos

CHAUMES - Cheese ✩ - Bongrain Cheese USA

CHAUMIERE - Furniture - Romweber Co.

CHAUMONT - Floor coverings–carpet and rugs - Masland Corp.
CHAUMONT - Floor coverings–carpet and rugs ☆ - Evans-Black Carpet Mills
CHAUNCEY PUPPY - Puppets - Dakin Inc.
CHAUNCEY THE UNICORN - Toys ☆ - Mego Financial Corp.
CHAUNCH GEAR - Apparel and accessories - Abel Hernandez
CHAUTAUQUA - Tools - Keeler Hardware Group
CHAUTAUQUABLOOMCHEN - Wines - Schloss Doepken Winery
CHAUVET - Musical instruments - Custom Music Co.
CHAUVET - Musical instruments ☆ - Midco International
CHAUVIN - Apparel–men's - Chauvin International Ltd.
CHAUVIN - Shrimp - International Seafood Traders
CHAUVIN ARNOUX - Measuring instruments - Chauvin Arnoux Holdings, Inc.
CHAUVIN ELLE - Apparel–women's ☆ - Chauvin International Ltd.
CHAUVINIST PIGS - Games - Tiger Electronics, Inc.
CHAVEZ - Pasta ☆ - Food City USA Inc.
CHAVON - Skin-care products - Cotton House, Inc.
CHAVRIE - Cheese - Bongrain Cheese USA
CHAYA - Apparel–women's - En Chante
CHAZ - Colognes - Revlon Consumer Products Corp.
CHAZY ORCHARDS - Fruits and vegetables - Chazy Orchards Inc.
CHAZZZ BY CHARLES GHAILIAN - Apparel–athletic - CMS Inc.
CHB - Paints - Sherwin-Williams Automotive Finishes Corp.
CHC - Computer software - Community Health Computing, Inc.
CHC - Garment hanger ☆ - Cleaners Hanger Co.
CHE BELLA - Apparel–women's - Jacobson Stores Inc.
CHE-CHE - Cosmetics ☆ - Cassidy Inc.
CHE-CRI - Crackers ☆ - Liberty Richter Inc.
CHEA - Footwear ☆ - Trico International Inc.
CHEAHA VALLEY - Cakes - Margaret Van Der Blom Sapp
CHEALAMIDE - Pharmaceutical preparations ☆ - Vortech Pharmaceuticals
CHEAP BAG O FOOD - Animal feed supplements - Vita Bran
CHEAP QUICKIE - Polishing cloths ☆ - Music Accessories Manufacturing Co. Inc.
CHEAP SHOT - Deodorizers - Unit Chemical Corp.
CHEAP SHOTS - Greeting cards - American Greetings Corp.
CHEAP TRICKS WARE - Computer peripheral equipment - Shu Associates, Inc.
CHEAPER BUY THE DOZEN - Towels - Franco Manufacturing Co., Inc.
CHEAPER THAN DIRT - Fibers–synthetic - Central Fiber Corp.
CHEAPSCAPE - Free-standing screens ☆ - Yates Furniture Systems Corp.
¢HEAPWARE - Computer software - Robert L. Nicolai
CHEAPWARE WORD SLEUTH - Computer software - Robert L. Nicolai
CHEASEL - Easels - Fredrix Artist Canvas Inc.
CHEAT SEAT - Cushions - Al Bolser Tire Stores Inc.
CHEATER - Fathometers - Rule Industries, Inc.
CHEATER - Fuel systems–motor vehicle - Nitrous Oxide Systems, Inc.
CHEATER-BEATER - Chemical preparations - Rectorseal Corp.
CHEATER'S DELIGHT - Pharmaceutical preparations - Emutech International, Inc.
CHEBACHE - Games - Scott D. Pardee
CHECK - Brake fluids - Pep Boys Manny, Moe & Jack
CHECK - Veterinary pharmaceutical preparations ☆ - Upjohn Co.
CHECK BOOK - Chewing gum - Amurol Confections Co.
CHECK-FOLD - Leather goods - St. Thomas Inc.
CHECK GALLERY - Checkbooks - Check Gallery, Inc.
CHECK IN THE BOX - Advertising agencies - Paul A. Baker
CHECK-INN - Computer software - Innsoft LP
CHECK IT - Oxygen - Caire
CHECK IT OUT - Video tapes–blank - Inphomation, Inc.
CHECK IT PRO ADVANCED DIAGNOSTIC SOFTWARE - Computer software - Touchstone Software Corp.
CHECK-LITE - Office supplies - Avery Label Systems
CHECK MATE - Electronic equipment - Phase 72, Inc.
CHECK-MATE - Envelopes - Pen-Tab Industries
CHECK MATE - Fabrics - Rosebar Textile Co.
CHECK MATE - Hair care products - Andre Fantasies Inc.
CHECK MATE - Medical apparatus - Bristoline Inc.
CHECK MATES - Wallpaper ☆ - Benchmark Preferred Wallcoverings
CHECK-MATIC - Office supplies - Ameriforms Inc.
CHECK-O-LITE - Chandeliers - Check-O-Lite Inc.
CHECK-OUT - Stain removers ☆ - Bramton Co.
CHECK OUT - Toys - Tomy America, Inc.
CHECK POINT - Apparel and accessories - Flywear International Inc.
CHECK POINT - Bicycles - Roadmaster Corp.
CHECK POINT - Floor coverings - Mannington Resilient Floors
CHECK STORE, THE - Checkbooks - John H. Harland Co.

CHECK-UP - Toothpaste - Lion Corp. of America
CHECK + UP CHARLIE - Games - Hasbro, Inc.
CHECK WRITER - Check writing templates - Liberty Share Draft & Check Printers, Inc.
CHECK YOUR TEAM - Stationery - Check Your Team, Inc.
CHECKART - Computer software - Intuit Inc.
CHECKED - Food products - A. Levy & J. Zentner Co.
CHECKER - Cereal ☆ - Malt-O-Meal Co.
CHECKER - Garment racks - Vogel Peterson Furniture Co.
CHECKER - Grass seed ☆ - International Seeds, Inc.
CHECKER - Motor vehicles - Checker Motors Corp.
CHECKER - Pipes–tobacco - S.M. Frank & Co. Inc. (Kaywoodie-Yello-Bole-Medico)
CHECKER - Recording label - MCA Records, Inc.
CHECKER RECORD CO. - Recording label - MCA Records, Inc.
CHECKERBOARD - Floor coverings–carpet and rugs ☆ - Ebsco Carpet Mills
CHECKERBOARD - Floor coverings–carpet and rugs ☆ - Quaker Inc.
CHECKERBOARD - Floor coverings–carpet and rugs ☆ - Trans-Ocean Import Co. Inc.
CHECKERBOARD - Floor coverings–tile - Kentile Floors Inc.
CHECKERBOARD - Musical instrument accessories - Hamer Guitars
CHECKERBOARD - Uniforms–tailored - Chef Revival USA Inc.
CHECKERBOARD-15 - Games - Milton Bradley Co.
CHECKERBOARD TEDDY - Toys–stuffed - Dakin Inc.
CHECKERED FLAG - Trading cards and stamps - ANCO Collector Supplies, Inc.
CHECKERETTE - Garment racks - Vogel Peterson Furniture Co.
CHECKERMINT - Chewing gum - Nabisco Foods Group
CHECKERS - Bathing suits - Catalina
CHECKERS - Cigars ☆ - Swisher International, Inc.
CHECKERS - Fast-food franchise - Checkers Drive-In Restaurants Inc.
CHECKERS - Floor coverings–carpet and rugs - Quaker Inc.
CHECKERS - Floor coverings–carpet and rugs ☆ - LaVelle Textile Marketing Inc.
CHECKERS - Toys–stuffed ☆ - Fun World Inc.
CHECKERS 2000 - Games - Rex Games, Inc.
CHECKERS4 - Games - Wow Toys, Inc.
CHECKERTURF - Synthetic turf - Instant Turf Industries Inc.
CHECKFIRE - Alarm systems–fire - Ansul, Inc.
CHECKGARD - Computer software - Bottomline Technologies, Inc.
CHECKING - Crayons - Dixon Ticonderoga Co.
CHECKING - Pencils - Faber-Castell Corp.
CHECKLASER - Paper products - Georgia-Pacific Corp.
CHECKLESS - Computer software - Payment Systems Technology, Inc.
CHECKLINE - Games ☆ - Crestline Manufacturing Co.
CHECKLINK - Computer software - Cascade Medical, Inc.
CHECKLINK - Computer storage devices - J.D. Carreker & Associates, Inc.
CHECKLOAD - Computer software - Checkmate Electronics, Inc.
CHECKLOGIC - Computer software - Checklogic Systems, Inc.
CHECKMAATE - Computer software - Servidyne Systems, Inc.
CHECKMARK - Paper–carbon ☆ - Buckeye Business Products Inc.
CHECKMARK BOOKS - Publisher's imprints ☆ - Facts on File Inc.
CHECKMASTER - Calculators - Bedol International Group, Inc.
CHECKMATE - Automotive parts and accessories - Karnig Devices Inc.
CHECKMATE - Blankets - Tuf-Tex, Inc.
CHECKMATE - Computer software - Interplay Productions
CHECKMATE - Computer software - Texas Commerce Bank National Association
CHECKMATE - Cushions - E.R. Carpenter Co.
CHECKMATE - Diagnostic instruments - Cascade Medical, Inc.
CHECKMATE - Dishwashing compounds - PYA/Monarch Inc.
CHECKMATE - Fabrics - Tara Handcrafts
CHECKMATE - Floor coverings - Mannington Resilient Floors
CHECKMATE - Floor coverings–carpet and rugs - Philadelphia Carpets
CHECKMATE - Floor coverings–carpet and rugs ☆ - Downs Carpet Co. Inc.
CHECKMATE - Game machines - IGT - North America
CHECKMATE - Guitars - WMI Corp.
CHECKMATE - Hardware - Rixson Firemark Inc.
CHECKMATE - Lime products - Pioneer Manufacturing Co.
CHECKMATE - Office supplies ☆ - Enger-Kress Co.
CHECKMATE - Pet products - National Display Materials
CHECKMATE - Salt and pepper mills - William Bounds, Ltd.
CHECKMATE - Tablecloths - Cascade Fibers Co.
CHECKMATE - Toothbrushes - Veritech Inc.
CHECKMATE - Veterinary pharmaceutical preparations ☆ - Upjohn Co.
CHECKMATE - Wood products - Artistry In Veneers, Inc.

☆ = Now out of production

CHECKMATES - Dishes—earthenware - Mikasa Co.

CHECKO - Stationery ✩ - Superior Marking Equipment Co.

CHECKOFFS - Stationery ✩ - Joli Greeting Card Co.

CHECKOUT - Soap - Ecolab Inc.

CHECKPLOT - Imaging material - Graphic Technology Inc.

CHECKPOINT - Pencils - Faber-Castell Corp.

CHECKPRINT - Computer software - Aatrix Software Inc.

CHECKSERVER/400 - Computer software - Digital Designs, Inc.

CHECKSUM - Software - Sirius Solutions, Inc.

CHECKUP - Cleaning preparations - RTW International Corp.

CHECKWEAVE - Floor coverings—carpet and rugs ✩ - Karastan-Bigelow Inc.

CHECKWEAVE II - Floor coverings—carpet and rugs ✩ - Regal Rugs Inc.

CHECKWRITER - Calculators - Texas Instruments Inc.

CHECKWRITER - Computer software - Aatrix Software Inc.

CHECO - Meat products - Cibao Meat Products, Inc.

CHED - Apparel—athletic - McCrory Corp.

CHED-R-LO - Cheese - Alpine Lace Brands, Inc.

CHEDA-RINGS - Food products - McCormick & Co., Inc.

CHEDABLANCA - Cheese - Cabot Creamery Cooperative, Inc.

CHEDDABUENA - Cheese - SSQ, Inc.

CHEDDAR BROWNS - Vegetables—frozen - Ore-Ida Foods, Inc.

CHEDDAR CHEESE EXPLOSION - Dog food - Howard M. Cohen

CHEDDAR CHEEZ-ZER - Snack foods - Zappe Endeavors Inc.

CHEDDAR CLASSICS - Potato flakes - General Mills, Inc.

CHEDDAR FLINGS - Cheese puffs - Nabisco Foods Group

CHEDDAR HOTS - Sausages - Hillshire Farm Co.

CHEDDAR HOTS - Sausages - Saramar Corp.

CHEDDAR MELT - Cheese - Old Fashioned Foods, Inc.

CHEDDAR TATERS - Snack foods ✩ - General Mills, Inc.

CHEDDAR TRIPLE - Food products - Mcdonald's Corp.

CHEDDAR VALLEY - Snack foods ✩ - Frito-Lay, Inc.

CHEDDAR WEDGES - Crackers - Nabisco Foods Group

CHEDDARCRUNCH - Popcorn - Naturestar Foods, Inc.

CHEDDARWURST - Sausages - Flint Hills Foods Inc.

CHEDDEASE - Cheese - Land O'Lakes Inc.

CHEDDI-DOGS - Frankfurters - Cher-Make Sausage Co.

CHEDDI-LINKS - Sausages - Cher-Make Sausage Co.

CHED'R'PEPPERS - Snack foods - Janice C. George

CHEE CHEE GORILLA - Toys—stuffed - Russ Berrie and Co., Inc.

CHEE CHEE THE CHATTERING CHIMP - Toys - Trendmasters, Inc.

CHEE WEES - Snack foods ✩ - Elmer Candy Corp.

CHEE-ZEE BREAD - Bakery products - Joe Corbi's Wholesale Pizza Inc.

CHEEBLERS - Cheese puffs ✩ - Keebler Co.

CHEEGLES - Snack foods - Eagle Snacks, Inc.

CHEEK CHALK - Cosmetics - Chanel Inc.

CHEEK CHARMS - Toys - Mattel, Inc.

CHEEK COLOR - Skin care products - Almay Inc.

CHEEK SHADOW - Cosmetics - Estee Lauder Inc.

CHEEK TO CHEEK - Apparel and accessories - Breton Industries

CHEEKERS - Cosmetics - Noxell Corp.

CHEEKIE - Apparel and accessories - Bendigo International Inc.

CHEEKTOWAGA - Wines - Schloss Doepken Winery

CHEEKY KNITS - Apparel and accessories - Salant/Manhattan Industries

CHEEP CAFE - Pet products - Deli, Inc.

CHEER - Computer game - Charlotte-Mecklenburg Hospital Authority

CHEER - Detergents - Procter & Gamble Co.

CHEER - Paints - Synkoloid Co.

CHEER BEAR - Toys - Those Characters from Cleveland, Inc.

CHEER CHARTS PLUS - Toys - Trend Enterprises, Inc.

CHEER-FREE - Detergents - Procter & Gamble Co.

CHEER LEADERS - Shoes - Interco Inc.

CHEER UP - Beverages - Atlas Bottling Co.

CHEER WITH COLOR GUARD - Detergents - Procter & Gamble Co.

CHEERING CHERRY - Beverages ✩ - Gossner Foods, Inc.

CHEERING IS THIRSTY WORK - Cups—plastic - Coca-Cola Co.

CHEERIO - Ice cream ✩ - Good Humor Corp.

CHEERIO SINCE 1933 - Fruits and vegetables - Merrill Farms

CHEERIOS - Cereal - General Mills, Inc.

CHEERIOS SNACK MIX - Snack foods - General Mills, Inc.

CHEERIOS X AND OS - Cereal - General Mills, Inc.

CHEERLEADER - Apparel—athletic - Ruse Rouge Inc.

CHEERLEADER - Floor coverings—carpet and rugs ✩ - Calladium & Marglen

CHEERLEADER - Food products - United Apple Sales Inc.

CHEERLEADERS - Dolls - Russ Berrie and Co., Inc.

CHEERLEADERS - Publisher's imprints - Scholastic Inc.

CHEERS - Beverages—carbonated - Paramount Pictures Corp.

CHEERS - Cups—paper - Tri-Par Corp.

CHEERS - Floor coverings—carpet and rugs ✩ - Columbus Mills, Inc.

CHEERS - Floor coverings—carpet and rugs ✩ - Cumberland Mills Inc.

CHEERS - Footwear - Olem Shoe Corp.

CHEERS - Greeting cards - Freedom Greeting Card Co. Inc.

CHEERS! - Greeting cards - Woodbridge Press Publishing Co.

CHEERS - Greeting cards, note cards - American Needlework Co. Inc.

CHEERS - Tablecloths - Kimberly-Clark Corp.

CHEERS - Toys—stuffed ✩ - Gund, Inc.

CHEERS TO YOU - Food products - Wildwood Creations

CHEERUPS - Hobby kits ✩ - Blumenthal/Lansing Co.

CHEERWINE - Beverages—carbonated - Carolina Beverage Inc.

CHEERY PAPER - Wallpaper - Maya Romanoff Corp.

CHEERY-TEARY CLOWN - Dolls - Dakin Inc.

CHEERY TRACINGS - Wallpaper - Maya Romanoff Corp.

CHEES-TREME - Seasonings - Beatreme Foods, Inc.

CHEESE-A-ROOS - Snack foods - Variety Foods, Inc.

CHEESE BITES - Crackers - Barbara's Bakery, Inc.

CHEESE BONES - Pet food - T.F.H. Publications, Inc.

CHEESE BOREKAS - Snack foods ✩ - Empire Kosher Poultry Inc.

CHEESE BROGIES - Snack foods - Swiss Village Cheese

CHEESE CAKE IN THE ROUND - Food products ✩ - Just Desserts Inc.

CHEESE CHOOSERS - Snack foods - Pepsico, Inc.

CHEESE CRISP - Food products - Tom's Foods Inc.

CHEESE DAWGS - Dog food - Ralston Purina Co.

CHEESE EGG FLY - Fishing lures - Joe's Flies

CHEESE EXPRESS - Food products ✩ - Hernke Foods Inc.

CHEESE FACTORY - Cheese - Minerva Dairy Inc.

CHEESE FESTIVAL - Cheese - Lactoprot USA, Inc.

CHEESE KING - Food products - A. Camacho Inc.

CHEESE KURLS - Food products - Cheese Kurls Inc.

CHEESE KURLS CHICAGO STYLE TRIPLE MIX - Food products - Cheese Kurls Inc.

CHEESE LOVERS - Cheese - Land O'Lakes Inc.

CHEESE MAGIC - Cheese - Armour Dairy Co.

CHEESE MANIA! - Food products - Little Caesar Enterprises, Inc.

CHEESE MASTERS, THE - Cheese - Bruder Dairy Products Co.

CHEESE MINNOWS - Fishing lures ✩ - Day Bait Co.

CHEESE 'N BACON - Cheese ✩ - Borden, Inc.

CHEESE N' SEASON - Cheese ✩ - M.H. Greenebaum Inc.

CHEESE NIPS - Crackers - Nabisco Foods Group

CHEESE PIXIES - Potato sticks - Wise Foods

CHEESE PLEASE - Cheese ✩ - Idahoan Foods Inc.

CHEESE ROUSETTES - Snack foods - Gerber Cheese Co., Inc.

CHEESE SHOP - Food-store franchise - Cheese Shop International Inc.

CHEESE SHUFFLES - Crackers ✩ - Sunshine Biscuits, Inc.

CHEESE SMOKERS - Cheese - Cheese Smokers Inc.

CHEESE TORTELLINI - Food products - My Own Meals Inc.

CHEESE TORTELLINI IN SAUCE - Food products - My Own Meals Inc.

CHEESE TWIRLS - Snack foods ✩ - Curtice-Burns Foods, Inc.

CHEESE WACKIES - Cheese - Fromageries Bel, Inc.

CHEESE WHEELS - Crackers - Health Valley Food

CHEESE WORLD - Cheese - Olfisco Inc.

CHEESEBURGER IN PARADISE - T-shirts—men's - Jimmy Buffett

CHEESECAKE FACTORY - Apparel and accessories - Cheesecake Factory Inc.

CHEESECAKE FACTORY - Bakery products - Dee's Cheesecake Factory

CHEESECAKE KAPOP - Food products ✩ - International Provisions

CHEESEHEADS - Cheese - Lynchburg Merchantile

CHEESEMAKERS CHOICE - Cheese - Scott's, Inc.

CHEESER - Sandwiches—prepackaged - Little Caesar Enterprises, Inc.

CHEESEREPLEX - Seasonings - Ingretec Ltd.

CHEESESTICKS - Snack foods - John Macy's Cheesesticks

CHEESEWICH - Crackers - Old London Foods Inc.

CHEESLICERS - Cutlery ✩ - C.J. Schneider Manufacturing Co. Inc.

CHEESTIX - Snack foods ✩ - A.V. Olsson Trading Co., Inc.

CHEESY BEER 'N BRATWURST - Sausages - Johnsonville Sausage, Inc.

CHEESY CHECKERS - Snack foods - Frito-Lay, Inc.

CHEESY JUMBOS - Frankfurters - Saramar Corp.

CHEETAH - Antacids - Lafayette Pharmaceuticals Inc.

CHEETAH - Archery equipment ✩ - High Country American

CHEETAH - Archery equipment ✩ - Martin Archery Inc.

CHEETAH - Bicycles - Columbia Manufacturing Inc.

CHEETAH - Bicycles - Corsaro Imports Inc.

CHEETAH - Bowling balls - Christopher C. Keller

CHEETAH - Computer peripheral equipment - Seagate Technology, Inc.

CHEETAH - Footwear–athletic - American Athletic Shoe Co.
CHEETAH - Health care products ☆ - Invacare Corp.
CHEETAH - Printers–computer - Fargo Electronics Inc.
CHEETAH - Recording label - Cheetah Records Inc.
CHEETAH - Toys - Lakeside Games
CHEETAH - Tripods–photographic - Phoenix Corp. of America
CHEETAH - Yarn ☆ - William Unger & Co. Inc.
CHEETAH CLUB - Recording label - Toddilin' Town Recording Studio
CHEETAH HUNTER - Archery equipment ☆ - High Country American
CHEETAH RACING BUBBLE - Windshield frames–motor vehicle ☆ - National Cycle Inc.
CHEETAH VALLEY - Beverages–alcohol - Rafiki and Associates, Inc.
CHEETER - Tools–hand-operated - Becker Industries
CHEETERS - Bathing suits - Surf Line Hawaii, Ltd.
CHEETOS - Snack foods - Frito-Lay, Inc.
CHEEZ BAIT - Fishing lures - Brown Bear Bait Co.
CHEEZ BAIT STIK - Fishing lures ☆ - Brown Bear Bait Co.
CHEEZ DOODLES - Cheese puffs - Old London Foods Inc.
CHEEZ-IT - Crackers - Sunshine Biscuits, Inc.
CHEEZ-IT HOT & SPICY - Crackers - Sunshine Biscuits, Inc.
CHEEZ KISSES - Cheese ☆ - Borden, Inc.
CHEEZ 'N CHIPS - Potato chips ☆ - Keebler Co.
CHEEZ-PIX - Snack foods ☆ - Sunshine Biscuits, Inc.
CHEEZ PRESTO - Cheese - Beatrice Cheese Co.
CHEEZ WAFFIES - Snack foods - Borden, Inc.
CHEEZ WAFFLES - Sandwiches–prepackaged - Old London Foods Inc.
CHEEZ WHIZ - Cheese - Kraft Foods, Inc.
CHEEZ-WILLIKERS - Snack foods ☆ - General Mills, Inc.
CHEEZBITS - Cheese - Fromageries Bel, Inc.
CHEEZE CRISP - Candy ☆ - Holland American Wafer Co.
CHEEZE PLEEZERS - Snack foods - Curtice-Burns Foods, Inc.
CHEEZECAKE - Cakes - Creative Bakers Inc.
CHEEZELETS - Snack foods - Jays Foods LLC
CHEEZELS - Pretzels - Toad-Ally Snax Inc.
CHEEZER - Cheese - Tom's Foods Inc.
CHEEZERS - Crackers - Tom's Foods Inc.
CHEEZETTE - Bait ☆ - Siberian Salmon Egg Co.
CHEEZFILM - Plastics film - Huntsman Chemical Corp.
CHEEZOIDS - Food products - Crystal Farms Inc.
CHEEZTONE - Seasonings - Dean Distributors, Inc.
CHEEZ'UMS - Potato chips - Procter & Gamble Co.
CHEEZWICHS - Snack foods ☆ - Miller's Cheese Corp.
CHEEZY CRUNCHERS - Vegetables–frozen - Ore-Ida Foods, Inc.
CHEEZY DOES IT - Dairy products - Topco Associates, Inc.
CHEEZY SPRED - Cheese - Old Fashioned Foods, Inc.
CHEF - Cooking equipment–household - Nordic Ware
CHEF - Jewelry - Chef Revival USA Inc.
CHEF - Pepper - Chef Specialties Co.
CHEF ALFREDO - Seasonings ☆ - Orval Kent Food Co., Inc.
CHEF ANDRIU - Pet products - Chef Andriu Inc.
CHEF ANTONIO - Pizzas–frozen - Willow Foods Inc.
CHEF ASIA - Allied Marketing, Inc.
CHEF ATSA NICE - Food products ☆ - Gourmet Confections Inc.
CHEF BAILEY'S - Butter - Mid-America Dairymen Inc. Southern Div.
CHEF BERNEA - Pies–fresh - Bernea Food Service
CHEF BOY-AR-DEE - Italian-style prepared foods, sauces, soups - American Home Food Products Inc.
CHEF BOYARDEE DINOSAURS - Pasta - American Home Food Products Inc.
CHEF BOYARDEE SHARKS - Pasta - American Home Food Products Inc.
CHEF BRAND - Bacon - John Morrell & Co.
CHEF BUBBA - Meat products - Chef Bubba Fine Foods, Inc.
CHEF BUBBA'S SEA MART SEAFOOD - Seafood products–fresh or frozen - Chef Bubba Fine Foods, Inc.
CHEF BUD'S BODACIOUS - Spices and extracts - Worldwide Management and Technical Service, Inc.
CHEF CARE - Uniforms–tailored - Chef Revival USA Inc.
CHEF CARLO - Pizzas–frozen - Profera, Inc.
CHEF CARLO BODACIOUS BAGELS - Bagels - Profera, Inc.
CHEF CENTO - Pizzas–frozen - Patrick M. Ciccotelli
CHEF CERTIFIED - Food products - Pilot Trading Co., Inc.
CHEF CHEDDAR - Crackers - American Natural Snacks
CHEF CHEDDAR - Crackers - Tree of Life, Inc.
CHEF CONTE - Food products - Conte Inc.
CHEF CUT - Food products - Jewel Food Stores Inc.
CHEF DAN'S - Wines - Pliska Winery
CHEF DOG - Clocks - General Time Corp. (Westclox/Seth Thomas Div.)

CHEF D'ORSAY - Food products ☆ - Vincent Food Industries Inc.
CHEF DU JOUR - Frozen foods - Agripac, Inc.
CHEF FAIRGROVE - Housewares ☆ - Aluminum Housewares Co. Inc.
CHEF FAROLDI'S - Gravy - Stage Door Cafe, Inc.
CHEF FRANCISCO - Food products - John Labatt Foods
CHEF FRITZ ORIGINAL - Food products - Gulf Fresh Seafood, Inc.
CHEF GARDEN - Vegetables–frozen - Twin City Foods
CHEF GIACOMO - Food products - Ravioli Kitchen Inc.
CHEF GIUSEPPE - Food products - Topco Associates, Inc.
CHEF GOLD - Poultry feeds - Sweet Sue Kitchens
CHEF HELPER - Milk–canned or powdered - Associated Milk Producers Inc.
CHEF HUBEE'S - Bakery products - Odom Foods Inc.
CHEF ITALIA - Meat products–beef - Chef Italia Inc.
CHEF JOE HYDES - Seafood products–fresh or frozen ☆ - Poole's Fish Inc.
CHEF JOSEF'S - Food products - St. Gallen Enterprises
CHEF KING - Griddles–electric - Rocky Mountain Cookware
CHEF KITCHEN - Food products - Jewel Food Stores Inc.
CHEF KITTY - Publisher's imprints - Joan Akkerman
CHEF LUIGI - Vinegar - Bargetto's Santa Cruz Winery
CHEF LUIS - Food products - Hartford Provision Co.
CHEF MAGIC - Food products - Trappey's Fine Foods Inc.
CHEF MAGNUM - Cooking equipment–household - International Technology, Inc.
CHEF MARIO - Food products - Rotanelli Foods Inc.
CHEF MARTIN - Sauces - Mission Valley Foods LLC
CHEF MASTER - Cookware ☆ - Corning Inc.
CHEF MAXLOTTE - Food products - Aspen Foods, a division of Koch Poultry
CHEF MICHAEL - Seafood products–fresh or frozen - Sealand Foods, Inc.
CHEF MILANO - Food products - A.M. Gilardi and Sons, Inc.
CHEF M.J. BRANDO - Preserved foods–prepackaged - Bran-Zan, Inc.
CHEF N.T. BEAR - Toys–stuffed - Nantucket Cobblestones, Ltd.
CHEF-PAK - Plates–paper ☆ - Potlatch Corp.
CHEF PAPY'S SEASONINGS - Catsup - Chef Papy's Foods
CHEF PAUL PRUDHOMME'S MAGIC PEPPER SAUCE - Seasonings - Magic Seasoning Blends
CHEF PIERRE - Pies–frozen - Chef Pierre Inc.
CHEF PLEASER - Bacon - Hatfield, Inc.
CHEF PREPARED GOURMET BUTTERS - Butter - Vermont Back Home, Inc.
CHEF PRIDE - Food products - Old Home Foods Inc.
CHEF REDDY - Food products - McCain Foods Inc.
CHEF REDDY BLUE - Vegetables–frozen - McCain Foods Inc.
CHEF REDDY GREEN - Vegetables–frozen - McCain Foods Inc.
CHEF REDDY RED - Vegetables–frozen - McCain Foods Inc.
CHEF RENE - Sauce - Continental Food Products Inc.
CHEF REVIVAL - Uniforms–tailored - Chef Revival USA Inc.
CHEF SAUTE - Condiments - NewLand Foods
CHEF SCHY'S ORIGINAL TOMATO KETCHAPENO - Seasonings - Hat Dance Restaurants
CHEF SELECT - Tools–hand-operated - Surmont Enterprises, Inc.
CHEF SHAIKH'S - Sauces - Mahtab Uddin Shaikh
CHEF SHOP - Cooking equipment–household - GSW Jackes-Evans Manufacturing Co.
CHEF SHOP - Cooking equipment–household ☆ - Cardinal Inc.
CHEF SLUGGER - Pepper mills - Chef Specialties Co.
CHEF SPARES - Buttons - Chef Revival USA Inc.
CHEF SPECIAL - Mayonnaise - Kennedy Mayonnaise Products
CHEF STARTER - Food products - Mrs. Giles Country Kitchens Inc.
CHEF TO CHEF - Food kits - Chef to Chef Inc.
CHEF-TO-CHEF - Food products - Sanderson Farms Inc.
CHEF TOM'S - Seasonings - Eckroth Foods
CHEF WALLY - Kitchen utensils–aluminum - Wallace C. Keene
CHEF-WAY - Cooking utensils–aluminum - Wisconsin Aluminum Foundry Co.
CHEF-WAY BEGINNINGS - Rice - Riceland Foods, Inc.
CHEF WERNER'S - Vegetables–dried - Malibu Farms Co.
CHEF WILLEY'S - Seasonings - Rite Foods, Inc.
CHEF WILLIAMS' ORIGINAL 5 MINUTE SHOOTER - Cooking equipment–household - Cajun Injector, Inc.
CHEFMASTER - Bakery products - Chefmaster Products
CHEFMASTER - Dinners–frozen - Design Foods
CHEFMATE - Stoves–gas - Keromate Products Inc.
CHEF'S - Food products - De Choix Specialty Foods Co.
CHEF'S - Turkeys - Foster Poultry Farms
CHEF'S AWARD - Can openers–electric - Windmere Corp.
CHEF'S AWARD - Food products - Tony Downs Foods Co.
CHEF'S BASICS - Cooking utensils–enameled - Federated Department Stores, Inc.

☆ = Now out of production

CHEF'S BEST - Mats - U.S. Mat & Rubber Co. Inc.
CHEF'S BEST - Vegetables–canned - Stokely USA, Inc.
CHEF'S BLEND - Cat food - Nestle USA
CHEF'S BUTTER - Butter - Cabot Creamery Cooperative, Inc.
CHEF'S CERTIFIED - Food products - Northwest Cold Pack Co.
CHEF'S CHOICE - Barbecues and grills - M.E. Heuck Co. Inc.
CHEF'S CHOICE - Barbecues and grills - Sunbeam-Oster Household Products
CHEF'S CHOICE - Charcoal - Arrow Industries, Inc.
CHEF'S CHOICE - Chickens - Perdue Holdings, Inc.
CHEF'S CHOICE - Cooking equipment–household ☆ - Cardinal Inc.
CHEF'S CHOICE - Cooking utensils–cast iron - Lodge Manufacturing Co.
CHEF'S CHOICE - Cutting boards - Edgecraft Corp.
CHEF'S CHOICE - Doughs–frozen - Athens Pastries & Frozen Foods Inc.
CHEF'S CHOICE - Food containers - Purity Products Inc.
CHEF'S CHOICE - Frozen foods - Ocean to Ocean Seafood
CHEF'S CHOICE - Fruits and vegetables - Conagra, Inc.
CHEF'S CHOICE - Meat products–beef - Waltham Beef & Provision Co.
CHEFS CLUB - Housewares - Notra Trading, Inc.
CHEFS COLLECTION - Soups–mixes ☆ - CPC International Inc.
CHEF'S COMPANION - Food products - North American Laboratory Co.
CHEF'S COMPANION - Puddings–mixes - Menu Magic Foods Inc.
CHEFS CREAM - Dairy products - Chefs Cream
CHEF'S CREATIONS - Soups - Diversified Foods, Inc.
CHEF'S CUT TOMATOES - Vegetables–canned - Patrick M. Ciccotelli
CHEF'S DELIGHT - Food products - DCA Food Industries, Inc.
CHEF'S DELIGHT - Housewares - Doranne
CHEF'S DELIGHT - Seafood - Boja's Foods Inc.
CHEF'S DESIGN - Cooking utensils–aluminum - Wisconsin Aluminum Foundry Co.
CHEF'S DREAM - Cooking equipment–household - Noh Foods International
CHEF'S EDGE - Cutlery ☆ - Towle Silversmiths
CHEF'S EDGE - Cutting boards - C & K Manufacturing & Sales LLC
CHEF'S EGGS - Egg substitutes - Pureggs Brands, Inc.
CHEFS FANCY - Coffee - Hansen Good Coffee
CHEF'S FAVORITE - Cookies - Parco Foods, Inc.
CHEF'S FINEST - Food products - Emil Lerch Inc.
CHEF'S FRY - Cooking equipment–household - Dazey Corp.
CHEF'S GALLERY - Cookware - Regal Ware, Inc.
CHEF'S GARDEN - Fruits and vegetables - Interfrost, Inc.
CHEF'S GRIDDLE - Cooking equipment–household - Dazey Corp.
CHEF'S HELPER - Cooking utensils - Action Industries Inc.
CHEFS IDEAL - Food products - Girard's Fine Foods Inc.
CHEF'S INN, THE - Preserved foods–prepackaged - Maurice Mayer
CHEF'S JUICER - Juice extracting devices - Metrokane
CHEF'S NUTRI-BLEND - Nutritional supplements - New Vita-Life Inc.
CHEF'S ORIGINALS - Rice - Ricetec, Inc.
CHEF'S OVEN - Cooking equipment–household ☆ - Dazey Corp.
CHEF'S OWN - Sauces - Custom Food Products Inc.
CHEF'S PANTRY - Food products - Oscar Mayer Foods Corp.
CHEF'S PET - Kitchen accessories - Toby Sales Inc.
CHEF'S POT - Cooking equipment–household - Dazey Corp.
CHEF'S POT JR. - Cooking equipment–household ☆ - Dazey Corp.
CHEF'S PREFERENCE, THE - Food products - Southern Foods, Inc.
CHEFS' PRIDE - Cooking equipment–household - Estia Corp.
CHEF'S PRIDE - Food products - Valley Foods
CHEF'S PRIDE - Food products ☆ - Papetti's Hygrade Egg Products, Inc.
CHEF'S PRIDE - Meat products - Loewenstein Poultry and Game Co.
CHEF'S PRIDE - Paper products - Conagra, Inc.
CHEF'S PRIDE - Plates–paper - Arrow Industries, Inc.
CHEF'S PRIDE - Shortening - Wilsey Foods, Inc.
CHEF'S PRIME ANY WAY YOU SLICE IT! - Food products - Muir-Roberts Co. Inc.
CHEFS PRIVATE RESERVE - Wines - Winequest
CHEF'S QUALITY - Food products - Wampler Foods Inc.
CHEF'S RECIPE RANCHHOUSE - Salad dressings–bottled - Henri's Food Products Co. Inc.
CHEF'S REQUEST - Meat products–canned - Dial Corp.
CHEF'S SEASONERS - Kitchen utensils–enameled ☆ - National Housewares
CHEFS' SECRET - Seasonings - Meat Seasonings Inc.
CHEF'S SELECT - Cutting boards - Vermillion Inc.
CHEF'S SELECT - Food products - Wampler Foods Inc.
CHEF'S SELECT - Prepared foods - Chef's Select
CHEF'S SERIES - Soups–mixes ☆ - CPC International Inc.
CHEF'S SPECIAL - Coffee - American Ace LLC
CHEF'S SPECIAL - Food products - Bush Brothers and Co.
CHEF'S SPECIAL - Ravioli - American Home Food Products Inc.

CHEF'S SUCCESS - Kitchen utensils–aluminum - Nordic Products Inc.
CHEF'S TABLE - Meat products–canned - Tupman Thurlow Co. Inc.
CHEF'S TASTE - Spices - Tone Brothers, Inc.
CHEFS, THE - Seasonings - Pepper Mill
CHEF'S TOTE - Food containers - Frye International Corp.
CHEF'S ULTIMATE - Beef - Atlantic Food Services, Inc.
CHEF'S VARIETY - Fruits–canned - JP Foodservice, Inc.
CHEF'S WOOD - Charcoal - S & W Fine Foods, Inc.
CHEF'SCHOICE - Slicing machines - Edgecraft Corp.
CHEFTENDER - Barbecue and grill accessories - M.E. Heuck Co. Inc.
CHEFWARE - Cooking utensils–aluminum - Harold Leonard & Co. Inc.
CHEFWAY - Rice - Riceland Foods, Inc.
CHEHALIS - Vegetables–frozen - National Frozen Foods Corp.
CHEK - Paints - Vanex Inc.
CHEK-CHART - Publisher's imprints - Simon & Schuster, Inc.
CHEK-GARD - Hardware - Sherwin-Williams Automotive Finishes Corp.
CHEK-RUST - Paints - M.A.B. Paints
CHEKA BOOTS - Boots - Imxco Sales Inc.
CHEKINK - Security tags - Checkpoint Systems Inc.
CHEKOV - Toys - Paramount Pictures Corp.
CHEL-AID - Vitamins and nutritional supplements - Vita-Vista
CHEL-LIV-IR - Veterinary pharmaceutical preparations - Traileze Veterinary Products Inc.
CHELA - Recording label - Wan Star Entertainment Group
CHELADRATE - Pharmaceutical preparations ☆ - Pharmex Inc.
CHELAN BEAUTY - Fruits–canned - Cascadian Fruit Shippers
CHELAN CLASSIC - Fruits–canned - Cascadian Fruit Shippers
CHELAN RED - Fruits and vegetables - Northern Fruit Co.
CHELAPLEX - Health care products - Desert Health Products, Inc.
CHELATOR - Hair care products - Trionics Systems Corp.
CHELAVITE - Vitamins and nutritional supplements - Albion Laboratories, Inc.
CHELCO - Televisions - Chelco Sound Inc.
CHELITAS - Vegetables–canned - Dairy Fresh Products Co.
CHELLY - Cosmetics - Chelly Cosmetics Manufacturing, Inc.
CHELMSFORD - Clocks ☆ - General Time Corp. (Westclox/Seth Thomas Div.)
CHELMSFORD - Fabrics ☆ - Freudenberg Nonwovens Apparel Division
CHELOIS - Wines - Ziem Vineyards
CHELSEA - Apparel and accessories ☆ - Host Apparel Inc.
CHELSEA - Bathroom fixtures - Crane Plumbing/Fiat Products
CHELSEA - Blinds–venetian ☆ - Hunter Douglas, Inc.
CHELSEA - Boxes ☆ - Tannery Lane Co. Inc.
CHELSEA - Cabinets - Imperial Cabinet Co. Inc.
CHELSEA - Chairs–wood ☆ - Loewenstein Inc.
CHELSEA - Cigarettes - R.J. Reynolds Tobacco Co.
CHELSEA - Clocks - Chelsea Clock Co. Inc.
CHELSEA - Dinnerware–glass - Nikko Ceramics Inc.
CHELSEA - Dishes–china ☆ - Gorham Inc.
CHELSEA - Dolls - Mattel, Inc.
CHELSEA - Electronic equipment - Argraph Corp. (Samigon Div.)
CHELSEA - Facial tissues - Price Co.
CHELSEA - Flatware - Yamazaki Tableware Inc.
CHELSEA - Floor coverings–carpet and rugs - Collins & Aikman Corp.
CHELSEA - Floor coverings–carpet and rugs ☆ - Atlas Carpet Mills Inc.
CHELSEA - Floor coverings–carpet and rugs ☆ - World Carpets, Inc.
CHELSEA - Flooring–hardwood - Memphis Hardwood Flooring Co.
CHELSEA - Furniture ☆ - Hammary Furniture Co. Inc.
CHELSEA - Furniture–children's ☆ - Child Craft Industries Inc.
CHELSEA - Plumbing fixtures–metal - Sterline Manufacturing Corp.
CHELSEA - Shower rods - Sufolla Industries Inc.
CHELSEA - Stationery ☆ - American Artists Group Inc.
CHELSEA - Teas - Coffee Masters, Inc.
CHELSEA - Trailers–travel ☆ - Starcraft Corp.
CHELSEA - Window coverings - Joanna Western Mills Co.
CHELSEA - Yarn ☆ - Tahki Imports Ltd.
CHELSEA BIRD - Dinnerware–glass - Royal China & Porcelain Companies Inc.
CHELSEA BRICK - Floor coverings ☆ - Congoleum Corp.
CHELSEA CIRCLE - Furniture ☆ - Bassett Furniture Industries, Inc.
CHELSEA COURT - Wallpaper - Parkview Designs
CHELSEA DOWNS - Wallpaper - Design Directions
CHELSEA FLOWERS - Dishes–china - Viletta China Co.
CHELSEA GARDENS - Dinnerware–glass ☆ - Royal China & Porcelain Companies Inc.
CHELSEA GOLD ACCENT - Flatware - Yamazaki Tableware Inc.
CHELSEA HALL - House furnishings - Safegard Corp.

CHELSEA HOUSE PUBLISHERS - Publisher's imprints - Chelsea House Publishers

CHELSEA II - Furniture ☆ - Hammary Furniture Co. Inc.

CHELSEA PINK - Frames–picture - Terragrafics Inc.

CHELSEA PLACE - Floor coverings–carpet and rugs ☆ - Regal Rugs Inc.

CHELSEA PUBLISHING CO. INC. - Publisher's imprints - Chelsea Publishing Co. Inc.

CHELSEA ROW CLASSICS - Underwear and nightwear - Specialty Department Stores, Inc.

CHELSEA SHIP'S BELL - Clocks - Chelsea Clock Co. Inc.

CHELSEA SQUARE - Floor coverings–carpet and rugs ☆ - Evans-Black Carpet Mills

CHELSEA SQUARE - Wallpaper - Exeter Wallcoverings

CHELSEA VILLAGE - Wallpaper ☆ - Thomas Strahan Wallcoverings

CHELSEA WICKER - Dishes–earthenware - Royal China & Porcelain Companies Inc.

CHELSEY BY JOSEPH - Neckties - Chelsey Imports Ltd.

CHELSIE - Dolls - Mattel, Inc.

CHELTEN HOUSE - Salad dressings–bottled - Chelten House Products Inc.

CHELTENHAM - Clocks - Ridgeway Clock Co.

CHELTENHAM BOX - Artists' materials - Winsor & Newton

CHEM-8 - Lubricants - Fluoramics Inc.

CHEM-BOARD - Storage files - Convoy Inc.

CHEM-BOND - Paints - Chemex Paint & Coatings Inc.

CHEM-CAL - Computer software - Inject-O-Meter Manufacturing Co., Inc.

CHEM CALK - Sealants - Bostik Inc.

CHEM-CLEAN - Franchised furniture-care process - Seneca Research Inc.

CHEM-COTE - Varnishes - Graham Paint and Varnish Co.

CHEM-DEFENSE - Vitamins and nutritional supplements - Source Naturals

CHEM-DRI - Paints - Chemex Paint & Coatings Inc.

CHEM-DRY - Cleaning preparations–carpet and rug - Harris Research, Inc.

CHEM-DRY EXTINGUISHER - Cleaning preparations–carpet and rug - Harris Research, Inc.

CHEM-FAST - Building materials–concrete - Rawlplug Co., Inc.

CHEM-FLO - Paints - Paragon Paint & Varnish Corp.

CHEM-GARD - Paints - Chemex Paint & Coatings Inc.

CHEM-GUARD - Cleaning preparations - National Chemsearch Corp.

CHEM GUARD PIG - Chemical preparations - New Pendulum Corp.

CHEM-KILL - Water purification systems - Pro-Flo Products

CHEM-KOTE - Chemical preparations - Colonial Refining and Chemical Co.

CHEM-LUSTRE - Varnishes - Paragon Paint & Varnish Corp.

CHEM-LUX - Paints - Chemex Paint & Coatings Inc.

CHEM MASTERS - Cleaning preparations - Chem-Masters, Inc.

CHEM-O-CONE - Paints - Jones Blair Co.

CHEM-O-GEL - Paints - Jones Blair Co.

CHEM-O-HIDE - Enamels - Jones Blair Co.

CHEM-O-LITE - Paints - Jones Blair Co.

CHEM-O-MASTIC - Epoxy coatings ☆ - Standard Paint Co.

CHEM-O-PLEX - Paints - Jones Blair Co.

CHEM-O-PON - Paints - Jones Blair Co.

CHEM-O-THIX - Paints - Jones Blair Co.

CHEM-O-Z - Paints - Jones Blair Co.

CHEM-PATCH - Paints - Chemex Paint & Coatings Inc.

CHEM-PRO - Paints - Chemex Paint & Coatings Inc.

CHEM PURE - Aquarium products - Richard Boyd Enterprises, Inc.

CHEM-PURE - Pipes–plastic - Nibco Inc.

CHEM-R - Adhesives and sealants - Induron Coatings Inc.

CHEM REPAIR - Hair care products - All Ways Natural Industries Inc.

CHEM-SEAL - Electronic equipment - ITT Corp.

CHEM-SHIELD - Plywood - Ply-Gem Manufacturing Corp.

CHEM-SKID - Epoxy coatings - Pratt & Lambert, Inc.

CHEM-STOR - Containers–metal - Ken Anderson

CHEM STRONG - Glass products ☆ - Laminated Glass Corp.

CHEM-STUD - Adhesives and sealants - Rawlplug Co., Inc.

CHEM-TAPE - Tape–adhesive - Kappler Safety Group

CHEM-TEK - Toys - Maryland Toy Corp.

CHEM TEM - Glass–tempered - Globe-Amerada Glass Co.

CHEM-TEX - Paints - Chemex Paint & Coatings Inc.

CHEM THREAD - Fittings–cast iron - Smith Fiberglass Products Inc.

CHEM-TOX - Chemical preparations - Paxon Manufacturing Co.

CHEM-TRAK - Computer software - Research Information Associates, Inc.

CHEM TV - Computer educational software - Betty A. Luceigh

CHEM-VAC - Soot cleaner - Comstar International Inc. (IPC Div.)

CHEM VELVET - Paints - Paragon Paint & Varnish Corp.

CHEM-WIK - Solder - Chemtronics Inc.

CHEM X - Vitamins and nutritional supplements - Kroeger Herb Products Co. Inc.

CHEM3D - Computer software - Cambridge Soft Corp.

CHEMACCT XL - Computer software - Conpro Corp.

CHEMACOIL - Oils–lubricating - McWhorter Technologies

CHEMAGRO - Insecticides ☆ - Bayer Corp. (Agriculture Div.)

CHEMAID - Computer software - Ventura Educational Systems

CHEMAID - Computer software - Ventura Educational Systems

CHEMAIR - Air purification systems - Gilian Environmental Corp.

CHEMAIRE - Artists' materials - LogEtronics Corp.

CHEMALOY - Oils–lubricating - Ashland Oil, Inc.

CHEMASK - Boats–kayaks - Chemtronics Inc.

CHEMASSIST - Computer peripheral equipment - Hewlett-Packard Co.

CHEMASTIC - Adhesives and sealants - Pratt & Lambert United, Inc.

CHEMBOOK - Computers - 5d Technology Inc.

CHEMCARD - Health care products - Chematics Inc.

CHEMCARE - Containers - Van Waters and Rogers Inc.

CHEMCLAD - Coatings - Enecon Corp.

CHEMCO - Paper products - Chemco Manufacturing Co., Inc.

CHEMCO - Pigments - Environmental Technology, Inc.

CHEMCO WATER TECHNOLOGY - Water treating compounds - Chemco Water Technology, Inc.

CHEMCOMP - Cement ☆ - Medusa Corp.

CHEMCOPY - Office supplies - F-P Label Co.

CHEMCOR - Glass sheet - Corning Inc.

CHEMCRAFT - Bathroom accessories - Chemcraft

CHEMCRAFT - Toys–erector sets - CBS Toys

CHEMCRETE - Concrete products - Gulf Coast Concrete and Stabilized Materials

CHEMDRAW - Computer software - Cambridge Soft Corp.

CHEMEATH - Apparel–women's ☆ - Bali Co. Inc.

CHEMEC - Fertilizers - Plant Marvel Laboratories

CHEMERE - Pharmaceutical preparations ☆ - Rexall Nutritional Products Inc.

CHEMETRON - Oxygen tents - Allied Healthcare Products Inc.

CHEMETS - Pet products - CHEMetrics Inc.

CHEMEX - Coffee makers–electric - International Housewares Corp.

CHEMEX - Paints - Chemex Paint & Coatings Inc.

CHEMEX-BONDED - Coffee-filter paper - International Housewares Corp.

CHEMEX COFFEE CLIQUE - Coffee - International Housewares Corp.

CHEMEX WARMER - Coffee makers–electric - International Housewares Corp.

CHEMFINDER - Computer software - Cambridge Soft Corp.

CHEMFINISH - Paints - Wattyl Paint Corp.

CHEMFLEX - Chemical preparations - Hosokawa Micron International Inc.

CHEMFLEX - Filters–air - Porous Media Corp.

CHEMFORM - Coatings - PPG Industries, Inc.

CHEMFREE - Cleaning preparations - Chemfree Corp.

CHEMGLAZE - Paints - Lord Corp. (Chemical Products Div.)

CHEMGRATE - Building materials - Fibergrate Composite Structures

CHEMGRID - Floor coverings ☆ - Fibergrate Composite Structures

CHEMGROUT - Machinery - Chemgrout, Inc.

CHEMGUARD - Chemical preparations - Chemguard, Inc.

CHEMHOE - Herbicides ☆ - PPG Industries, Inc.

CHEMI-COTE - Electronic equipment ☆ - Da-Lite Screen Co. Inc.

CHEMI-DRAIN - Clay products ☆ - Logan Clay Products Co.

CHEMI-MAT - Aquarian filters and filter pads - Richard Boyd Enterprises, Inc.

CHEMIC - Enamels ☆ - PPG Industries, Inc.

CHEMICAL ACTION - Apparel–women's - Nisha Sportswear Inc.

CHEMICAL ADVISOR, THE - Computer software - Chemadvisor, Inc.

CHEMICAL FENCE - Chemical preparations - Unifinium Ltd.

CHEMICAL LIGHTSTICK ALTERNATIVE, THE - Safety products - Tektite Industries, Inc. (Tektite Manufacturing Division)

CHEMICAL MACE - Chemical preparations - Smith & Wesson Corp.

CHEMICAL PRODUCTS TECHNOLOGIES - Chemical preparations - Chemical Products Technologies

CHEMICALC - Computer software - Zephyr Services

CHEMICALLY PERFECT COLORS - Artists' materials ☆ - Rich Art Color Co., Inc.

CHEMICRAFT - Ribbons–inked - Chemicraft International, Inc.

CHEMIGATOR - Garden equipment - Performance Products Inc.

CHEMIGUM - Hoses - Goodyear Tire & Rubber Co.

CHEMINILLE - Fabrics - Guilford Mills, Inc.

CHEMINK - Ink - United States Printing Ink Corp.

CHEMINTOSH - Computer software - Softshell International Ltd.

CHEMIQUE PREMIUM BRAND PRODUCTS - Cleaning preparations - Chemique Inc.

☆ = Now out of production

CHEMISE BY KENNINGTON - Shirts - Kennington Limited Inc.

CHEMISE LACOSTE - Apparel and accessories - Crystal Brands Inc.

CHEMISTRY - Colognes - Clinique Laboratories, Inc.

CHEMISTRY CLINIQUE - Colognes - Clinique Laboratories, Inc.

CHEMISTRY FACTS - Computer software - Electronic Courseware Systems Inc.

CHEMISTRY FILMS - Film–motion picture - Harmoney Holdings Inc.

CHEMISTRY OF LOVE - Jewelry ☆ - Anson Inc.

CHEMKARE - Toilets–portable ☆ - Monogram Sanitation Co.

CHEMLAB - Toys ☆ - Revell-Monogram, Inc.

CHEMLINE - Hair care products ☆ - California Concept Corp.

CHEMLINE - Industrial machinery - Parker Coatings Inc.

CHEMLOK - Adhesives and sealants - Lord Corp. (Chemical Products Div.)

CHEMMAIL - Computer software - Chemmist LP

CHEMMASTER - Apparel and accessories - Standard Safety Equipment Co.

CHEMMASTER - Photographic equipment - Houston Fearless 76 Inc.

CHEMODRUM - Containers–trash - BioSafety Systems, Inc.

CHEMOLEE - Hair care products - Chemolee Laboratories Corp.

CHEMOLOY - Boats–kayaks - Chemtronics Inc.

CHEMONITE - Lumber - PSR Co.

CHEMONITE ACZA - Lumber - PSR Co.

CHEMOPROTECT - Medical apparatus - Codan Medlon Inc.

CHEMOTHERAPY - Medical apparatus - Bemiss-Jason Corp.

CHEMOTX SYSTEM - Medical apparatus - Neuro Probe, Inc.

CHEMOX - Paints ☆ - Valspar Corp.

CHEMPA-ADD - Chemical preparations - Chem-Pak Inc.

CHEMPACLEAN - Cleaning preparations - Chem-Pak Inc.

CHEMPAGARD - Adhesives and sealants - Chem-Pak Inc.

CHEMPAGREAZ - Lubricants - Chem-Pak Inc.

CHEMPAKOOL - Lubricants - Chem-Pak Inc.

CHEMPAKUT - Lubricants - Chem-Pak Inc.

CHEMPALUBE - Lubricants - Chem-Pak Inc.

CHEMPASYN - Lubricants - Chem-Pak Inc.

CHEMPATACK - Adhesives and sealants - Chem-Pak Inc.

CHEMPAVAN - Oils–lubricating - Chem-Pak Inc.

CHEMPLATE - Building materials - Fibergrate Composite Structures

CHEMPLEX - Medical chemicals - Chemplex Industries, Inc.

CHEMQUEST - Science kits - Nasco International, Inc.

CHEMRAY - Paints - Chemray Coatings Corp.

CHEMRAZ - Gaskets - Greene & Co.

CHEMRAZ - Gaskets - Greene, Tweed of Delaware, Inc.

CHEMREL - Fabrics - Kappler Safety Group

CHEMREX - Sealant - ChemRex Inc.

CHEMRITE - Paints - Utex Industries, Inc.

CHEMRON - Apparel and accessories - Kappler Safety Group

CHEMSAVER - Valves–industrial - Spraying Systems Co.

CHEMSCAN - Measuring and dispensing pumps - Biotronics Technologies Inc.

CHEMSDS+ - Computer software - Chemadvisor, Inc.

CHEMSEAL - Industrial machinery - Parker Coatings Inc.

CHEMSEARCH CONSENTRATE - Cleaning preparations - National Chemsearch Corp.

CHEMSECO - Caulking compounds - Sika Corp.

CHEMSET - Epoxy anchors ☆ - ITW Ramset/Red Head

CHEMSHIELD - Fuel additives - Berryman Products Inc.

CHEMSHIELD RUST-TUFF - Rust removers - Coatings Lab

CHEMSMART - Computer software ☆ - ISI Software

CHEMSPEC - Cleaning preparations–carpet and rug - Chemspec, Inc.

CHEMSPEC - Measuring instruments - Rupprecht & Patashnick Co., Inc.

CHEMSTAR - Cleaning preparations–carpet and rug ☆ - Habitat International Inc.

CHEMSTAR - Pumps–vacuum - Welch Vacuum Technology, Inc.

CHEMSTITCH - Fabrics ☆ - Guilford Mills, Inc.

CHEMSTONE - Stones–synthetic - Clock Motors Inc.

CHEMSTOP - Wood products - Tamms Industries Co.

CHEMSTOR - Containers–atomic waste ☆ - Falcon Safety Products, Inc.

CHEMSTRAND - Fibers–synthetic ☆ - Monsanto Co.

CHEMSTRIP - Health care products - Boehringer Mannheim Corp.

CHEMSTRIP VET - Veterinary pharmaceutical preparations - Boehringer Mannheim Corp.

CHEMTAPE - Gauging instruments - Metritape, Inc.

CHEMTEC - Paints - Pratt & Lambert United, Inc.

CHEMTOOL - Automotive parts and accessories - Berryman Products Inc.

CHEMTOY - Games - Strombecker Corp.

CHEMTRACK - Computer software - ChemTreat, Inc.

CHEMTRAVELLER - Pumps - Tuthill Corp.

CHEMTRED - Building materials - Fibergrate Composite Structures

CHEMTRONICS - Cleaning preparations - Chemtronics Inc.

CHEMTUFF - Fabrics - Kappler Safety Group

CHEMUNG - Water–bottled or canned - Chemung Spring Water Co.

CHEMWARE - Computer software - JFM Management, Inc.

CHEMWAY - Leak detector fluid - ChemWay Inc.

CHEMWELD - Chemical preparations - Minstar Inc.

CHEN - Electronic equipment - Kremona Music Co.

CHEN HOLON - Brass religious articles - Israeli Accents

CHENANGO - Sauerkraut - Rea-D-Pack Foods Inc.

CHENAULT - Floor coverings–carpet and rugs - Evans-Black Carpet Mills

CHENEN BLANC - Wines - Cilurzo Vineyard & Winery

CHENEY - Health care products - Cheney Co. Inc.

CHENG BENG - Apparel and accessories - Young Town Enterprises Inc.

CHENG CHU - Floor coverings–carpet and rugs - Trans-Ocean Import Co. Inc.

CHENICE - Cosmetics - Chenice Beverly Hills

CHENICE SUPER DRY - Nail care products - Chenice Beverly Hills

CHENILLE - Area rugs, now out of production - Couristan Inc.

CHENILLE - Toilets–enameled - Kohler Co.

CHENILLE-A-POINT - Hobby kits ☆ - Mangelsen's (VDI)

CHENILLE KRAFT - Pipe cleaners - Barry Products Co.

CHENILLE KRAFT - Toy and hobby kits - Chenille Kraft Co.

CHENILLE LUSTER - Blinds–venetian ☆ - Hunter Douglas, Inc.

CHENILLE SATIN - Blinds–venetian ☆ - Hunter Douglas, Inc.

CHENILLE SENSATIONS - Yarn - Lion Brand Yarn Co.

CHENIN BLANC - Crackers - Prepco

CHENIX - Pharmaceutical preparations - Solvay Pharmaceuticals Inc.

CHENNESEN - Skin care products - Takara Belmont USA, Inc.

CHENONCEAU - Floor coverings - Parquet de France Inc.

CHENONCEAUX - Glassware–household - Durand International

CHENTI - Hair care products - Chenti Products Inc.

CHEONG CHAN - Food products - Cheong Chan (Hup Kee) Inc.

CHEOY LEE - Ships–sailing vessels - Lion Yachts

CHEP BLUE - Pallets–wood - Chep USA

CHEPPU - Apparel–women's - Cheppu Himal

CHEQUE - Veterinary pharmaceutical preparations ☆ - Upjohn Co.

CHEQUEMATE - Floor coverings–carpet and rugs ☆ - Blue Ridge Carpet Mills

CHEQUERS - Fabrics ☆ - Gretchen Bellinger Inc.

CHEQUERS - Floor coverings–carpet and rugs - Milliken & Co. Inc.

CHEQUERS - Paper - Norcom Inc.

CHEQUERS PREMIUM - Paper - Norcom Inc.

CHER - Perfumes ☆ - Avon Products, Inc.

CHER - Shoes - Conaway-Winter Inc.

CHER - Wigs - Jean Paree Weegs Inc.

CHER-AMINO - Vitamins and nutritional supplements - Twinlab

CHER FITNESS - Prerecorded audio cassettes - Cher

CHERACOL - Cough medicines ☆ - Upjohn Co.

CHERACOL D - Cough medicines ☆ - Upjohn Co.

CHERACOL PLUS - Cough medicines ☆ - Upjohn Co.

CHERAGAN - Pharmaceutical preparations - H.R. Cenci Laboratories Inc.

CHERALIN - Cough medicines - Lannett Co. Inc.

CHERAPAS - Health care products - Kay Pharmacal Co. Inc.

CHERASYL NN - Cough syrup ☆ - Iodent Co.

CHERATUSSIN - Cough syrup - Iodent Co.

CHERAW - Vegetables–canned ☆ - McCall Farms Inc.

CHERBORG - Furniture ☆ - Broyhill Furniture Industries, Inc.

CHERBOURG - Earthenware ☆ - Shafford Co. Inc.

CHERBOURG - Floor coverings–carpet and rugs - Masland Corp.

CHERBOURG - Furniture - Drexel Heritage Furnishings, Inc.

CHERBOURG - Furniture ☆ - Stanley Furniture Co. Inc.

CHERBOURNE - Furniture - Hooker Furniture Corp.

CHERBROOK - Furniture ☆ - Mersman Furniture Co.

CHERCHEZ LA FEMME - Ophthalmic goods - Foremost Optical Products

CHEREFRESH - Juices - Krier Foods Inc.

CHEREUX - Floor coverings–carpet and rugs - Dixie Manufacturing Co. Inc.

CHERI - Flowers, plants, and seeds - Jacklin Seed

CHERI - Toys–stuffed - Russ Berrie and Co., Inc.

CHERI POODLE - Toys–stuffed - Russ Berrie and Co., Inc.

CHERI-SUISSE - Beverages–alcohol - Joseph E. Seagram & Sons, Inc.

CHERIE - Hair care products ☆ - N.B. Cohen Co.

CHERIE - House furnishings - Link-Taylor Corp.

CHERIE - Jewelry - Jacoby-Bender Inc.

CHERIE - Shoes ☆ - Canter Shoe Co.

CHERIE CHERRY - Nail care products - Cosmair Inc.

CHERIE II - House furnishings - Lea Industries Inc.

CHERIMOYA - Hair care products - Peter Hantz Co.

CHERIMOYA CLENZ - Hair care products - Image Laboratories, Inc.

CHERIMOYA RINSE - Hair care products - Image Laboratories, Inc.
CHERISA - Apparel–children's - Shane Hunter Inc.
CHERISH - Clocks - General Time Corp. (Westclox/Seth Thomas Div.)
CHERISH - Diapers–disposable - Weyerhaeuser Co.
CHERISH - Fertilizers - Cherish Co.
CHERISH - Floor coverings–carpet and rugs - Coronet Carpets Inc.
CHERISH - Glassware–household - Durand International
CHERISH - Occasional tables - JDI Group, Inc.
CHERISH - Prosthetic apparatus - OTC Professional Appliances
CHERISH - Wallpaper - Bob Mitchell Designs
CHERISH AMERICA - Dolls - Susan Wakeen Doll Co., Inc.
CHERISHABLE CHERUB - Figurines - Sparkleberry Faire
CHERISHABLES - Novelty items - Bradford Novelty Co., Inc.
CHERISHED-HEIRLOOMING - Display cases–metal - Judy Folk
CHERISHED LINE - Craft supplies - Western Trimming Corp.
CHERISHED LINE, THE - Scrapbooks - Westrim Crafts
CHERISHED MOMENTS - Apparel and accessories ☆ - L.V. Myles
CHERISHED SENTIMENTS - Key rings - C.M. Paula Co.
CHERISHED TEDDIES - Apparel–children's - Quiltex
CHERISHED TEDDIES - Blankets - Manual Woodworkers & Weavers, Inc.
CHERISHED TEDDIES - Giftware ☆ - Enesco Corp.
CHERISHED TRADITIONS - Fabrics–tapestry - Comark Wallcoverings
CHERISHES - Cat food - Gimborn U.S., Inc.
CHERISS - Cheese - Noon Hour Food Products
CHERMONT - Furniture–wood ☆ - Century Furniture Co.
CHERMONT - Wines - Chermont Winery
CHERNER - Tables–wood ☆ - Howe Furniture Corp.
CHERO-TRISULFA-V - Pharmaceutical preparations - Vita Elixir Co. Inc.
CHEROKEE - Aircraft ☆ - New Piper Aircraft, Inc.
CHEROKEE - Belts - Crown Pacific Accessories
CHEROKEE - Bicycles ☆ - Huffy Corp.
CHEROKEE - Boats - McKenzie Boat Manufacturing Co.
CHEROKEE - Floor coverings - American Floor Products Co. Inc.
CHEROKEE - Floor coverings–carpet and rugs ☆ - Len Dal Carpets
CHEROKEE - Footwear–men's - L.B. Evans' Son Co.
CHEROKEE - Footwear–women's - Cherokee Group
CHEROKEE - Frames–eyeglass - Creative Optiks
CHEROKEE - Fruits–pickled or brined - R.C. McAteer Co.
CHEROKEE - Handles–wood - Sequatchie Handle Works Inc.
CHEROKEE - Leather goods - Sirco International Corp.
CHEROKEE - Motor vehicles–jeeps - DaimlerChrysler
CHEROKEE - Pianos - Mapes Piano String Co.
CHEROKEE - Rifles ☆ - Thompson/Center Arms
CHEROKEE - Seafood products–fresh or frozen - Didi Seafood Corp.
CHEROKEE - Sunglasses - Outlook Eyewear Co.
CHEROKEE - Trailers–travel - Forest River, Inc.
CHEROKEE - Travelware - Action Travelware
CHEROKEE CHIEF - Motor vehicles ☆ - DaimlerChrysler
CHEROKEE D - Toys–models ☆ - Estes Industries
CHEROKEE GUIDE - Boats–motor ☆ - Lund Boat Co.
CHEROKEE KID, THE - Statuary - Sandra Van Zandt
CHEROKEE LITE - Apparel and accessories - Cherokee Group
CHEROKEE MAID - Jams and jellies ☆ - EasTex Farms
CHEROKEE PINE - Furniture ☆ - Broyhill Furniture Industries, Inc.
CHEROKEE RED - Carbonated beverage - Cotton Club Bottling Co.
CHEROKEES - T-shirts–men's - Knoxville Cherokees Hockey, Inc.
CHEROKEES, THE - Novelty items - Cherokees
CHEROSAN - Cough medicines ☆ - Chase Laboratories Inc.
CHEROSPECT - Pharmaceutical preparations ☆ - C.O. Truxton Inc.
CHERRA - Candy - Gerrit J. Verburg Co.
CHERRACON - Pharmaceutical preparations - Consolidated Midland Corp.
CHERRALEX - Pharmaceutical preparations - Barre-National, Inc.
CHERRI AND BUBB - Candy - Just Born Inc.
CHERRI-B - Pharmaceutical preparations ☆ - Vortech Pharmaceuticals
CHERRI-LYNN - Apparel–women's ☆ - Craftex Creations Inc.
CHERRI-LYNN JRS. - Apparel–women's ☆ - Craftex Creations Inc.
CHERRI PON - Hair care products ☆ - Gena Laboratories Inc.
CHERRIE TWINS - Candy ☆ - Melster Candies Inc.
CHERRIES - Footwear–women's - Cherries Footwear Inc.
CHERRIES - Fruits–frozen - Northern Michigan Fruit Co.
CHERRIES AND STRAWBERRIES - Candy ☆ - Bohemian Biscuit Co.
CHERRIES IN THE SNOW - Christmas tree ornaments - Cracker Box Inc.
CHERRIES JUBILEE - Christmas tree ornaments - Cracker Box Inc.
CHERRIES JUBILEE - Dolls ☆ - Effanbee Doll Corp.
CHERRIES R WILD - Game machines - Sigma Game Inc.
CHERRISTOCK - Beverages–alcohol - Distillerie Stock USA Ltd.

CHERRY - Brushes–paint - Allpro Corp.
CHERRY - Glassware–household - Durand International
CHERRY - Recording label - Soundmasters Studio
CHERRY - Tableware–china ☆ - Villeroy and Boch Tableware Ltd.
CHERRY 7-UP - Beverages–carbonated - Dr. Pepper/Seven Up, Inc.
CHERRY 7-UP '57 T-BIRD - Toys–electronic - Bird Bromiticous Inc.
CHERRY 7UP - Chewing gum ☆ - Amurol Confections Co.
CHERRY-A-LET - Candy - Adams & Brooks, Inc.
CHERRY ANTIGUA - Tiles–ceramic ☆ - Wenczel Tile Co.
CHERRY/APPLE SPLITS - Candy - Nabisco Holdings Corp.
CHERRY BEAR - Toys–stuffed - Russ Berrie and Co., Inc.
CHERRY BERRY BLEND - Fruits–frozen ☆ - VIP Sales Co. Inc.
CHERRY BLAST - Candy ☆ - Fleer Corp.
CHERRY BLEND - Tobacco products - John Middleton Inc.
CHERRY BLOSSOM - Candy ☆ - Glade Taffy Town, Inc.
CHERRY BLOSSOM - Crackers - Prepco
CHERRY BOMB - Beverages–carbonated - Richard D. Bristow
CHERRY BOMB - Chewing gum - Philadelphia Chewing Gum Corp.
CHERRY BOMB - Insecticides - Puritan-Churchill Chemical Co.
CHERRY BOMB - Mufflers–motor vehicle - Maremont Exhaust Products Inc.
CHERRY BOMB - Toys - Mattel, Inc.
CHERRY BOMB TURBO - Mufflers–motor vehicle - Maremont Exhaust Products Inc.
CHERRY BOMBE - Perfumes - Shiara Holdings, Inc.
CHERRY BOOM - Fireworks - L. W. Loyd Co., Inc.
CHERRY-BURRELL - Remote control devices - United Dominion Industries, Inc.
CHERRY CALIFORNIA - Handbags - West Unity
CHERRY CENTRAL - Fruits–canned - Cherry Central Cooperative Inc.
CHERRY CHEST RUB FOR KIDS - Pharmaceutical preparations - Mentholatum Co.
CHERRY CLAN - Candy - Ferrara Pan Candy Co., Inc.
CHERRY CLASSICS - Furniture ☆ - Hooker Furniture Corp.
CHERRY COCKTAIL - Candy - Idaho Candy Co.
CHERRY COKE - Beverages–carbonated - Coca-Cola Co.
CHERRY COOLERS - Cookies ☆ - Sunshine Biscuits, Inc.
CHERRY CORDIAL - Ice cream - United Dairy Farmers Inc.
CHERRY COURT - Furniture ☆ - Lexington Furniture Industries, Inc.
CHERRY CREAM - Beverages - Logret Import & Export Co.
CHERRY CREEK - Furniture - Singer Furniture Co.
CHERRY CREEK COLLECTION, THE - Office furniture–wood - Riverside Furniture Corp.
CHERRY CROSSINGS - Furniture ☆ - Kincaid Furniture Co. Inc.
CHERRY DALE - Furniture - Universal Flooring
CHERRY ESTATE - Furniture - CTH/Sherrill Occasional
CHERRY FLIP - Candy ☆ - Storck USA L.P.
CHERRY GARCIA - Ice cream - Ben and Jerry's Homemade, Inc.
CHERRY-GO-ROUND - Toys - Mattel, Inc.
CHERRY GROVE - Furniture - American Drew
CHERRY GROVE - Pet products - Pacwest Resources
CHERRY HILL - Chimes - Nutone Inc.
CHERRY HILL - Flatware - Washington Forge Inc.
CHERRY HILL - Furniture - Broyhill Furniture Industries, Inc.
CHERRY HILL COLLECTION, THE - Furniture - Hickory Manufacturing Co.
CHERRY HUMPS - Candy ☆ - Brock Candy Co. Inc.
CHERRY HUT - Fruits–canned - Cherry Hut Products
CHERRY-ITS - Candy ☆ - Donruss Co.
CHERRY JUBILEE - Pottery ☆ - Doranne
CHERRY JUBILEE - Skin care products - Paula Payne Products Co. Inc.
CHERRY JUBILEE - Tobacco–chewing or smoking - Amar Blends Co.
CHERRY JUBILEE THINS - Candy - Andes Candies Inc.
CHERRY JULEP - Wines ☆ - Jack Poust & Co. Inc.
CHERRY KARISE - Liquors ☆ - House of Seagram
CHERRY KIJAFA - Wine beverage - Austin, Nichols & Co., Inc.
CHERRY KNOLL - Cosmetics - C. K. Products Inc.
CHERRY LANE - Furniture ☆ - Lane Co. Inc.
CHERRY-LIME RICKEY - Beverages–carbonated - Snapple Beverage Corp.
CHERRY LOCK - Rivets–metal - Textron Aerospace Fasteners
CHERRY-LOK - Wood products ☆ - Aspen Valley Lumber Co. Inc.
CHERRY MANOR - Furniture - Lineage Home Furnishings, Inc.
CHERRY MANOR - Furniture ☆ - Vaughan Furniture Co. Inc.
CHERRY MASH BARS - Candy - Chase & Poe Candy Co.
CHERRY MASTER - Games - International Gamco, Inc.
CHERRY MAX - Rivets–metal - Textron Aerospace Fasteners
CHERRY MERRY MUFFIN - Toys - Mattel, Inc.
CHERRY MOON - Teas - Eastern Shore Tea Co.

☆ = Now out of production

CHERRY MOONS - Chewing gum - Philadelphia Chewing Gum Corp.
CHERRY MOUNTAIN - Furniture ☆ - Kincaid Furniture Co. Inc.
CHERRY MOUNTAIN BAR - Candy - Brown & Haley
CHERRY MOUNTAIN II - Furniture - Kincaid Furniture Co. Inc.
CHERRY MOUNTAIN III - Furniture - Kincaid Furniture Co. Inc.
CHERRY MUNCH - Candy ☆ - Holland American Wafer Co.
CHERRY NEWTONS - Cookies - Nabisco Foods Group
CHERRY NUBBINS - Licorice - Brach and Brock Confections Inc.
CHERRY-OLA - Beverages–carbonated - A.J. Canfield Co.
CHERRY ORGANIC - Cosmetics - Nutrine Ltd.
CHERRY PARK - Furniture ☆ - Brooks Furniture Manufacturing Inc.
CHERRY PETAL - Dolls - Mattel, Inc.
CHERRY PICKER - Tobacco products - Sterling Tobacco Corp.
CHERRY PIE - Apparel and accessories - George K. Setka
CHERRY PIE - Toys - Milton Bradley Co.
CHERRY-PIT-PAC - Medical apparatus - Darcy Shawver
CHERRY RAINBOW CANES - Candy - Bobs Candies Inc.
CHERRY RC - Beverages–carbonated - Royal Crown Cola Co.
CHERRY RE-MO PLUS - Pet products - Hansen's Pet Products Co.
CHERRY RED STIX - Licorice - Leaf, Inc.
CHERRY RED WHIPS - Licorice ☆ - Leaf, Inc.
CHERRY RIDGE - Wines - Pommeraie Winery
CHERRY RIVER - Furniture ☆ - Kincaid Furniture Co. Inc.
CHERRY RIVET - Tools - Textron Aerospace Fasteners
CHERRY ROCHER - Brandied fruit - International Marketing Services Inc.
CHERRY SHAKE - Candy ☆ - Topps Co., Inc.
CHERRY SOURS - Candy - Judson-Atkinson Candies
CHERRY STIX - Candy - Leaf, Inc.
CHERRY SURPRISE - Toys - Mattel, Inc.
CHERRY SWEET - Dolls - Mattel, Inc.
CHERRY TART - Christmas tree ornaments ☆ - Cracker Box Inc.
CHERRY TART - Juices - Knudsen & Sons Inc.
CHERRY TIME - Candy - Beacon Sweets, Inc.
CHERRY TREAT WASHINGTON CHERRIES - Fruits and vegetables - Valley Fruit
CHERRY TREE - Apparel–children's - Cherry Tree
CHERRY VALE - Cabinets - Schrock
CHERRY VALLEY - Apparel and accessories - Worcester Knitting Co.
CHERRY VALLEY - Furniture - Jamestown Sterling
CHERRY VALLEY FARMS - Poultry feeds ☆ - Showell Co.
CHERRY VALLEY INN - Furniture - Jamestown Sterling
CHERRY VANILLA - Tobacco products - John Middleton Inc.
CHERRY VILLAGE COLLECTION - Cabinets ☆ - Gragg Cabinet Industries
CHERRYBELL - Underwear and nightwear - Cherrybell Manufacturing Corp.
CHERRYBLOCK CABERNET - Wines - Sebastiani Vineyards, Inc.
CHERRYBROOK MANOR - Furniture - Harden Furniture Co. Inc.
CHERRYBUCK - Hardware - Textron Aerospace Fasteners
CHERRYDALE FARMS - Chocolate candy - Cherrydale Farms Inc.
CHERRYDILLS - Fruits–canned ☆ - Harry and David Inc.
CHERRYFIELD - Clocks - General Time Corp. (Westclox/Seth Thomas Div.)
CHERRYHEAD - Candy - Ferrara Pan Candy Co., Inc.
CHERRYMAN - Maraschino cherries - Gray & Co.
CHERRY'S - Apparel–women's - CWT Specialty Stores Inc.
CHERRY'S - Cough medicines ☆ - Polamer Drug Co. Inc.
CHERRYVALE - Furniture - Sumter Cabinet Co., Inc.
CHERRYWOOD - Cutlery - General Housewares Corp.
CHERRYWOOD - Giftware - Gorham Inc.
CHERRYWOOD - Leather goods - Lefkowitz and Santangelo Co.
CHERRYWOOD - Sporting goods - Outdoor Technologies Group
CHERRYWOOD GOLD - Glassware–household - Gorham Inc.
CHERUB - Recording label - Vincent F. Taylor
CHERUB COLLECTION, THE - Jewelry - Zale Corp.
CHERUBINI - Boats–motor - Cherubini Boat Co.
CHERUBINI - Infant product - Cherubini Inc.
CHERUBS - Infant product - Playtex Beauty Care, Inc.
CHERVLA - Skin care products - La Lueur International Inc.
CHERY WILLIAMS HEIRLOOM - Patterns–clothing - McCarn Enterprises Inc.
CHERYL - Flatware ☆ - Kirk Stieff Co.
CHERYL - Glassware–household ☆ - Lotus Glass Co.
CHERYL - Wigs ☆ - Jean Paree Weegs Inc.
CHERYL KAYE - Apparel and accessories - Breton Industries
CHERYL LYN - Bakery products - Progressive Foods Inc.
CHERYL LYN - Food containers - Purity Products Inc.
CHERYL TIEGS - Apparel–women's - Sears, Roebuck and Co.
CHERYL TIEGS - Jewelry - Cheryl Tiegs
CHERYLA - Cosmetics - La Lueur International Inc.

CHESAPEAK VALLEY FARMS - Sausages - Hatfield, Inc.
CHESAPEAKE - Apparel–men's - J. Schoeneman Inc.
CHESAPEAKE - Bells - North Country Wind Bells Inc.
CHESAPEAKE - Bicycles - Huffy Corp.
CHESAPEAKE - Boats - McKenzie Boat Manufacturing Co.
CHESAPEAKE - Boats–motor - Glastex Co.
CHESAPEAKE - Cabinets - Riviera Cabinets Inc.
CHESAPEAKE - Cabinets - H.J. Scheirich Co.
CHESAPEAKE - Clocks - General Time Corp. (Westclox/Seth Thomas Div.)
CHESAPEAKE - Fabrics–canvas - C.R. Daniels Inc.
CHESAPEAKE - Flatware - Royal Silver Manufacturing Co. Inc.
CHESAPEAKE - Floor coverings - American Floor Products Co. Inc.
CHESAPEAKE - Floor coverings–carpet and rugs - Kelly Group Inc.
CHESAPEAKE - Floor coverings–carpet and rugs - Masland Corp.
CHESAPEAKE - Furniture - Bean Station Furniture Factory Inc.
CHESAPEAKE - Furniture - Broyhill Furniture Industries, Inc.
CHESAPEAKE - Furniture - Cochrane Furniture Co. Inc.
CHESAPEAKE - Furniture ☆ - Athens Furniture Industries Inc.
CHESAPEAKE - Furniture–children's ☆ - Child Craft Industries Inc.
CHESAPEAKE - Garden furniture–metal - Samsonite Furniture Co. (Consumer Products Div.)
CHESAPEAKE - Giftware ☆ - Lenox Crystal, Inc.
CHESAPEAKE - Housewares - Himark Enterprises Inc.
CHESAPEAKE - Occasional tables - JDI Group, Inc.
CHESAPEAKE - Seafood products–fresh or frozen - Larkin's Seafood
CHESAPEAKE - Shelving units–metal - Baldwin Hardware Corp.
CHESAPEAKE - Siding–insulating ☆ - Certainteed Corp. (Roofing Products Group)
CHESAPEAKE - Tableware–china - Lenox, Inc.
CHESAPEAKE - Toilets–enameled - Kohler Co.
CHESAPEAKE - Trailers–travel ☆ - Fleetwood Enterprises, Inc.
CHESAPEAKE - Wood products ☆ - Masonite Corp.
CHESAPEAKE - Yarn ☆ - JCA, Inc.
CHESAPEAKE BAY - Apparel and accessories - Commander Garment Co.
CHESAPEAKE BAY - Furniture–children's - Child Craft Industries Inc.
CHESAPEAKE BAY - Garden furniture–rattan ☆ - Lloyd/Flanders Industries
CHESAPEAKE BAY - Wallpaper - Pickhardt & Siebert USA Inc.
CHESAPEAKE BAY DELIGHTS - Seafood products–fresh or frozen - Shore Seafood, Inc.
CHESAPEAKE BAY LTD. SUPERB SEASONINGS, THE - Seasonings - Cherubini Inc.
CHESAPEAKE BAY SHIRT CO. - Apparel and accessories - Altuf Corp., Inc.
CHESAPEAKE BAY STYLE - Seasonings - McCormick & Co., Inc.
CHESAPEAKE BREEZE - T-shirts–men's - Ron Free
CHESAPEAKE BREEZE, THE - Apparel and accessories - Ron Free
CHESAPEAKE FARM - Seafood products–fresh or frozen - Larkin's Seafood
CHESAPEAKE PRIDE - Fish–fresh or frozen - Chesapeake Oyster Marketing Co.
CHESAPEAKE PRIDE - Oysters–fresh - B.G. Smith and Sons Oyster Co. Inc.
CHESCO - Tools - American Tool Companies Inc.
CHESHIRE - Dinnerware–glass - Nikko Ceramics Inc.
CHESHIRE - Knit goods - Coronet Casuals Inc.
CHESHIRE BAY - Furniture - Homecrest Industries Inc.
CHESHIRE LINEN - Binders - Fiber Mark, Inc.
CHESHIRE LINEN COVER - Binders - Fiber Mark, Inc.
CHESIRE - Cabinets - Riviera Cabinets Inc.
CHESIRE - Clocks - General Time Corp. (Westclox/Seth Thomas Div.)
CHESS - Bags–canvas - The Chess Set
CHESS CHALLENGER - Games - Fidelity Electronics International Inc.
CHESS CHAMP - Computer software ☆ - Zephyr Services
CHESS ERA - Games - Risto Inc.
CHESS FOR JUNIORS - Chessboards ☆ - Milton Bradley Co.
CHESS INTERNATIONAL - Games - Alex Cramer Co.
CHESS IS NO LONGER JUST A BATTLE, NOW IT'S WAR! - Chessboards - Wow Toys, Inc.
CHESS MASTER - Video games - Nintendo of America Inc.
CHESS MENTOR - Computer software - Ricorso
CHESS THE FOURTH DIMENSION - Games - Jonathan Peter Bilowus
CHESS TUTOR - Chessboards ☆ - Milton Bradley Co.
CHESS3 - Games - Classic Games Co. Inc.
CHESSBOARDS OF DISTINCTION - Chessboards - Wood Expressions Inc.
CHESSETTE - Chessboards - Pacific Game Co.
CHESSIE - Toys–stuffed - Clare Creations Inc.
CHESSIE FLYER - Boats - Glen-L Marine Designs
CHESSINGTON - Floor coverings ☆ - Congoleum Corp.
CHESSMAN - Wallpaper - Warner Co.

☆ = Now out of production

CHESSMASTER - Floor coverings–carpet and rugs ☆ - Karastan-Bigelow Inc.
CHESSMASTER, THE - Computer software - Software Toolworks, Inc.
CHESSMEN - Chessboards - Milton Bradley Co.
CHEST-LOCKE - Golfing equipment - Willard A. Steele
CHEST-PAK - Electronic equipment - Compco Photographic/Goldberg Bros.
CHEST STRIPES - Fabrics–broadcloth - Desire Mills Co. Inc.
CHEST VEST - Pharmaceutical preparations - Exu-Dry Wound Care Products, Inc.
CHESTAL - Pharmaceutical preparations - Boiron Inc.
CHESTER - Cooking equipment–commercial - Giles Enterprises, Inc.
CHESTER - Hobby kits - Craft World International Inc.
CHESTER - Music–sheet - MMB Music Inc.
CHESTER - Recording label - Electricity Enterprises Inc.
CHESTER - Shoes - Allen-Edmonds Shoe Corp.
CHESTER - Thread - Threads USA Div.
CHESTER - Toys–stuffed - Russ Berrie and Co., Inc.
CHESTER - Toys–stuffed ☆ - Gund, Inc.
CHESTER BAY - Furniture–wood ☆ - Century Furniture Co.
CHESTER CHEETAH - Kites - Hi-Flier Manufacturing Co.
CHESTER CHEETAH - Snack foods - Frito-Lay, Inc.
CHESTER CHIPMUNK - Toys–stuffed - Dakin Inc.
CHESTER DAIRY - Milk - Chester Dairy Co.
CHESTER FREDERICK - Apparel and accessories - KGR, Inc.
CHESTER MUSIC - Musical instrument accessories - Music Sales Corp.
CHESTER RIDGE - Floor coverings ☆ - Congoleum Corp.
CHESTER ROAST - Cooking equipment–household ☆ - Giles Enterprises, Inc.
CHESTERFIELD - Apparel and accessories - Chesterfield Manufacturing Corp.
CHESTERFIELD - Beverages–malt ☆ - D.G. Yuengling & Son Inc.
CHESTERFIELD - Cabinets - Imperial Cabinet Co. Inc.
CHESTERFIELD - Cases–musical instrument ☆ - Selmer Co. Inc.
CHESTERFIELD - Cigarettes - Liggett Group Inc.
CHESTERFIELD - Floor coverings ☆ - Congoleum Corp.
CHESTERFIELD - Furniture ☆ - Singer Furniture Co.
CHESTERFIELD - Jewelry - Jacoby-Bender Inc.
CHESTERFIELD - Occasional furniture ☆ - JDI Group, Inc.
CHESTERFIELD - Pipes–tobacco ☆ - S.M. Frank & Co. Inc. (Kaywoodie-Yello-Bole-Medico)
CHESTERFIELD - Watches - Bulova Corp.
CHESTERFIELD C U.S.A. - Shirts - Chesterfield Manufacturing Corp.
CHESTER'S - Popcorn - Frito-Lay, Inc.
CHESTER'S - Popcorn - Recot, Inc.
CHESTERTON - Floor coverings - Mannington Resilient Floors
CHESTERTOWN - Teas - Eastern Shore Tea Co.
CHESTNUT - Brushes–paint - Allpro Corp.
CHESTNUT - Dinnerware ☆ - Corning Inc.
CHESTNUT - Dinnerware–glass ☆ - Nikko Ceramics Inc.
CHESTNUT CREEK - Furniture - Keller Manufacturing Co.
CHESTNUT CREEK - Paneling - Georgia-Pacific Corp.
CHESTNUT FIELD - Fabrics - Lee Jofa Inc.
CHESTNUT HILL - Floor coverings–carpet and rugs ☆ - Mohawk Carpet Corp.
CHESTNUT HILL - Food products - Betters International Food Corp.
CHESTNUT HILL - Sinks–porcelain - Mansfield Plumbing Products, Inc.
CHESTNUT HILL - Wallpaper ☆ - Mokena Mills Inc.
CHESTNUT HILL FARMS - Onions and squash - Seaboard Corp.
CHESTNUT HILL FARMS - Shrimp - Chestnut Hill Farms Inc.
CHESTNUT HILL II - Wallpaper ☆ - Mokena Mills Inc.
CHESTNUT KNOLL - Floor coverings–carpet and rugs - Colonial Mills Inc.
CHESTNUT RIDGE - Socks - Preger & Wertenteil, Inc.
CHESTNUT STREET - Candy - Salem's Old Fashioned Candies Inc.
CHESTNUT VALLEY FARMS - Pastries - Park 100 Foods Inc.
CHESTNUT WEAVE - Dinnerware–glass ☆ - Franciscan by Johnson Brothers, USA, Inc.
CHESTPHONES - Personal telephones ☆ - American Telecommunications Corp.
CHESTY - Snack foods - Borden, Inc.
CHESUN - Wines - Door Peninsula Winery
CHET ATKIN - Musical instrument accessories - Gibson Strings & Accessories
CHET'S - Food products ☆ - John Labatt Foods
CHETWYND - Floor coverings–carpet and rugs ☆ - Evans-Black Carpet Mills
CHEVAL - Apparel and accessories - Lee Thomas Inc.
CHEVAL - Handbags - Bobtron International Inc.
CHEVAL BLANC - Chocolate candy ☆ - Bell'amore Imports Inc.
CHEVAL BOOKS - Publisher's imprints - Stanyan Record Co.
CHEVAL QUANCARD - Wines - Chrissa Imports Ltd.
CHEVALIER - Cheese - Tour Eiffel
CHEVALIER LICHINE - Wines ☆ - European Beverage Co., Inc.

CHEVALLE - Floor coverings–carpet and rugs - Evans-Black Carpet Mills
CHEVELLE - Floor coverings–carpet and rugs ☆ - Masland Corp.
CHEVELLE - Motor vehicles ☆ - General Motors Corp. (Chevrolet Motor Div.)
CHEVELLE LAGUNA - Motor vehicles ☆ - General Motors Corp. (Chevrolet Motor Div.)
CHEVERE - Recording label - Kubaney Publishing Corp.
CHEVERLY - Floor coverings - Mannington Resilient Floors
CHEVERNAY - Sparkling cider ☆ - Charles Jacquin et Compagnie Inc.
CHEVERNY - Glassware–household - Durand International
CHEVET - Musical instruments and accessories - Atlas Accordions Inc.
CHEVETTE - Motor vehicles ☆ - General Motors Corp. (Chevrolet Motor Div.)
CHEVETTO - Apparel–men's - UFO Contemporary, Inc.
CHEVILLY - Glassware–household - Durand International
CHEVIOT - Paper - Smurfit Newsprint Corp. (Cladwood Div.)
CHEVRE BLANC - Cheese - Swissrose International Inc.
CHEVRECHAUD - Cheese - Fromark
CHEVRIGOTTE - Cheese - Swissrose International Inc.
CHEVRION - Cheese - Swissrose International Inc.
CHEVRO - Shoes - Chevro America, Inc.
CHEVROLET - Motor vehicles - General Motors Corp. (Chevrolet Motor Div.)
CHEVROLLE - Cheese - Anco Foods Corp.
CHEVROLLE - Cheese - Churny Co., Inc.
CHEVRON - Electronic equipment - Galileo Corp.
CHEVRON - Floor coverings ☆ - Congoleum Corp.
CHEVRON - Floor coverings–carpet and rugs - Ludlow Composites Corp.
CHEVRON - Floor coverings–carpet and rugs ☆ - Bellbridge Carpets
CHEVRON - Floor coverings–carpet and rugs ☆ - Foreign Accents
CHEVRON - Furniture–wood ☆ - Century Furniture Co.
CHEVRON - Gasoline - Chevron Corp.
CHEVRON - Jewelry - Jacoby-Bender Inc.
CHEVRON - Medical apparatus - Sroufe Manufacturing Inc.
CHEVRON - Projectors–photographic - Eastman Kodak Co.
CHEVRON - Underwear and nightwear - Rago Foundations Inc. LLC
CHEVRON ECO - Lubricants - Chevron Corp.
CHEVRONE EYEGEAR - Sunglasses - Sungold Enterprises Ltd.
CHEVY - Motor vehicles–trucks - General Motors Corp. (Chevrolet Motor Div.)
CHEVY CHASE - Floor coverings–carpet and rugs - Barrett Carpet Mills Inc.
CHEVY ROAD REBEL 4X4 - Toys - Fisher-Price, Inc.
CHEVYVAN - Motor vehicles - General Motors Corp. (Chevrolet Motor Div.)
CHEW-C - Vitamins and nutritional supplements - J.R. Carlson Laboratories Inc.
CHEW CHEW - Garden equipment - Lambert Manufacturing Corp.
CHEW CHEW VITES HONEY VITA - BEAR - Vitamins and nutritional supplements - M.K. Health Food Distributors, Inc.
CHEW-EEZ - Dog food - Superior Brands Inc.
CHEW-ETS - Candy - Goldenberg Candy Co.
CHEW LACES - Chewing gum ☆ - Amurol Confections Co.
CHEW LOGS - Pet products - Pyramid Bird Toys
CHEW-NOT - Chemical preparations - Nott Manufacturing Co. Inc.
CHEW-ON - Chewing gum ☆ - Leaf, Inc.
CHEW Q'S - Pet products - Gimborn U.S., Inc.
CHEW-RITE - Denture materials - Chew-rite Co.
CHEW-SOME TWO-SOME - Chewing gum - Leaf, Inc.
CHEW STIK - Candy - Adams & Brooks, Inc.
CHEW-STOP - Pet products - Nala Barry Laboratories
CHEW STOP - Veterinary pharmaceutical preparations - Farnam Cos. Inc.
CHEW-TABS - Vitamins and nutritional supplements ☆ - Fibertone Co.
CHEW THE FAT AWAY - Chewing gum - Health Products Corp.
CHEW TUNNEL - Pet products - Cheryl Brodka
CHEW-VI-TABS - Health care products - Halsey Drug Co. Inc.
CHEWABLES - Pharmaceutical preparations - Nature's Bounty, Inc.
CHEWBACCA - Toys–stuffed - Kenner Products
CHEWBILEE TEXAS TWISTERS - Candy ☆ - American Licorice Co.
CHEWBILEE TWISTS - Licorice ☆ - American Licorice Co.
CHEWELS - Candy - Nature's Best Inc.
CHEWELS - Candy ☆ - American Chicle Co.
CHEWEY KISSES - Candy - Hooper's Chocolates
CHEWIE NEWGETT - Toys–stuffed - Dakin Inc.
CHEWIES - Infant product - Admar International, Inc.
CHEWLOO - Pet products - Dogloo Inc.
CHEW'M - Dog food - Hartz Mountain Corp.
CHEW'M HOOVES - Dog food - Hartz Mountain Corp.
CHEWMAN - Toys–stuffed - Willoughby's Finest, Inc.
CHEWOLA - Chewing gum - Philadelphia Chewing Gum Corp.
CHEWRITE - Denture cleaners ☆ - Chew-rite Co.
CHEWSIES - Vitamins and nutritional supplements ☆ - Marlyn Co. Inc.

☆ = Now out of production

CHEWY - Snack foods - Quaker Oats Co.
CHEWY BEARS - Vitamins and nutritional supplements - American Health, Inc.
CHEWY BONE - Pet products - Phydeaux Enterprises Inc.
CHEWY CHALK - Candy ☆ - Leaf, Inc.
CHEWY FRUIT - Snack foods ☆ - Knudsen & Sons Inc.
CHEWY GOOEY BROWNIE MIX - Cakes–mixes - Mixed Co. Inc.
CHEWY HUEY - Candy ☆ - Sunline Brands
CHEWY MORSELS - Dog food - Ralston Purina Co.
CHEWY PALS - Infant product - Summer Infant Products Inc.
CHEWY PLUS - Pet food - Cotter & Co.
CHEWY PRALINES - Candy ☆ - Judson-Atkinson Candies
CHEWY SWEETARTS - Candy - Sunline Brands
CHEWY SWIRL - Cookies ☆ - Pepsico, Inc.
CHEWY....THE FRIENDLY BEAR - Toys–stuffed - Sound Improvement, Inc.
CHEX - Candy ☆ - Chex Co.
CHEX - Cereal - Ralston Purina Co.
CHEX - Floor coverings–carpet and rugs ☆ - Daltonian Carpet & Cushion Inc.
CHEX - Hardware ☆ - Bondex International Inc.
CHEX-FLAME - Sealing compounds - Champion Products Inc.
CHEX JUNIORS - Cereal - Ralston Purina Co.
CHEX SNACK MIX - Snack foods - Ralston Purina Co.
CHEX-TEX - Hardware ☆ - Bondex International Inc.
CHEX-WEAR - Paints - Benjamin Moore & Co.
CHEXCHEX - Paints ☆ - Akron Paint and Varnish, Inc.
CHEXIT - Pharmaceutical preparations - Dorsey Laboratories
CHEYBOYGAN - Paints - Cheyboygan Paint
CHEYENE - Trailers–travel - Fleetwood Enterprises, Inc.
CHEYENNE - Bicycles - Columbia Manufacturing Inc.
CHEYENNE - Cabinets - Wellborn Cabinet, Inc.
CHEYENNE - Fabrics - Dan River Inc.
CHEYENNE - Flatware - Wallace International Silversmiths, Inc.
CHEYENNE - Floor coverings - American Floor Products Co. Inc.
CHEYENNE - Flowers, plants, and seeds - Jacklin Seed
CHEYENNE - Lawn mowers - WW Grinder Corp.
CHEYENNE - Motor vehicles–motor homes ☆ - Mitchell & Sons Inc.
CHEYENNE - Recording label - Homeland Recording & Publishing
CHEYENNE - Seat covers - Saddleman, Inc.
CHEYENNE - Sunglasses - Bausch & Lomb Inc.
CHEYENNE - Tableware–china - Villeroy and Boch Tableware Ltd.
CHEYENNE - Thread - Van Waters and Rogers Inc.
CHEYENNE - Trailers–travel ☆ - Marathon Homes Corp.
CHEYENNE 400LS - Aircraft ☆ - New Piper Aircraft, Inc.
CHEYENNE IA - Aircraft ☆ - New Piper Aircraft, Inc.
CHEYENNE IIIA - Aircraft ☆ - New Piper Aircraft, Inc.
CHEYENNE IIXL - Aircraft ☆ - New Piper Aircraft, Inc.
CHEYENNE KID - Jeans–children's ☆ - Jonbil Inc.
CHEYENNE RIDING CLUB - Apparel and accessories - George Morris
CHEYENNE SUEDE - Wallpaper - Wall Fashion Inc.
CHEZ BON - Candy - Kitchen Fresh Foods, Inc.
CHEZ BON - Custard–frozen - Kozy Shack Inc.
CHEZ BONNE - Beverages - Bonne Foods, Inc.
CHEZ CHOCOLAT - Chocolate candy - Candy Candy Inc.
CHEZ JOSE - Salsa - Chez Jose, Inc.
CHEZ L'AUTRUCHE HOME OF THE OSTRICH - Meat products - Specialty Seafoods, Ltd.
CHEZ MAITRE - Cigars - Gesty Trading & Manufacturing Corp.
CHEZ MICHELLE - House furnishings - Lexington Furniture Industries, Inc.
CHEZ MONTPELLIER - Salads–prepackaged - Chez Alberto Food Inc.
CHEZ ROBERE - Hairpins ☆ - Karina Inc.
CHEZ SHAY - Apparel and accessories - Marilyn Stein
CHEZ SOIE - Apparel and accessories - Tai-Yu Wang Tao
CHEZ SOLEIL - Tanning agents - Olympic Mountain Products
CHEZDE PREZ DESSERTS - Bakery products–frozen - Deprez Enterprises, Inc.
CHEZOOM - Motor vehicles–automobiles - Hot Rods by Boyds
CHGWRITER - Computer software - Bruce G. Jackson & Associates Inc.
CHI - Computers - Computer Hut International Corp.
CHI - Health care products - Nature's Plus
CHI BLOCKS - Novelty items - Theodore Davis and Willie Cole Jr. Partnership
CHI CHEETAH - Toys–stuffed - Dakin Inc.
CHI-CHI - Chinese fortune teller - Pacifico
CHI CHI - Food products - Chi-Chi Foods Ltd.
CHI-CHI - Frames–eyeglass - Hudson Optical Corp.
CHI CHI - Golfing equipment - Juan A. Rodriguez
CHI-CHI RODRIGUEZ HEADWEAR - Hats - Bollman Hat Co.
CHI-CHI'S - Food products - Hormel Foods Corp.

CHI-CHI'S COCKTAILS - Liquors - Canandaigua Wine Co. Inc.
CHI-CHI'S RESTAURANT STYLE - Chili–canned - Hormel Foods Corp.
CHI ENERGY - Health care products - Natural Laboratories Corp.
CHI-LOC - Electrical equipment - Chi-Loc
CHI POWER - Vitamins and nutritional supplements - Threshold Enterprises Ltd.
CHI POWER - Vitamins and nutritional supplements ☆ - Source Naturals
CHI-RHO - Rings–jewelry - Cana-Nuptial
CHI SING - Food products - Chi Sing Enterprises (Usa), Inc.
CHI-SOUND - Recording label - MGM Inc.
CHIA - Fertilizers ☆ - Joseph Enterprises Inc.
CHIA BRAND - Seeds - Joseph Enterprises Inc.
CHIA HERB GARDEN - Flowers, plants, and seeds - Joseph Enterprises Inc.
CHIA PET - Flowers, plants, and seeds - Joseph Enterprises Inc.
CHIAKI - Apparel and accessories - Tempo Sportswear
CHIANG - Bedding–linen - Dan River Inc.
CHIANGO - Coats - Fleet Street Ltd.
CHIANTI - Floor coverings–carpet and rugs ☆ - Playfield International Inc.
CHIANTI - Plumbing fixtures–metal - Barclay Products Ltd.
CHIANTI ITALICA - Wines ☆ - Delicato Vineyards
CHIARO - Glass products ☆ - Pittsburgh Corning Corp.
CHIAVARI - Apparel stores–men's - R.S. Lords, Inc.
CHIAVARIO VINEYARDS - Wines - Chiavario Vineyards
CHIBICRON - Toys - Hirsch Co.
CHIC - Apparel–athletic - H.I.S. Sportswear
CHIC - Apparel–women's - Bi-Flex International
CHIC - Apparel–women's - Chic by H.I.S. Inc.
CHIC - Apparel–women's - Henry I. Siegel Co. Inc.
CHIC - Belts–apparel - Chic by H.I.S. Inc.
CHIC - Floor coverings–carpet and rugs - Mohawk Industries Inc.
CHIC - Floor coverings–carpet and rugs - Patcraft Mills Inc.
CHIC - Footwear–athletic - Mercury International Trading Corp.
CHIC - Frames–eyeglass - Marine Optical, Inc.
CHIC - Razors ☆ - Philips Electronics North America Corp.
CHIC - Wallpaper - Pageant Wallpaper Corp.
CHIC-A-DEE - Fruits and vegetables - Chick Orchards Inc.
CHIC BOUTIQUE - Apparel and accessories ☆ - Greene Plastics Corp.
CHIC-E - Pet products ☆ - Strongheart Products, Inc.
CHIC-KETTS - Food products - Worthington Foods Inc.
CHIC LIT - Watches - H.I.S. Licensing Corp.
CHIC MODES - Girdles - Bi-Flex International
CHIC 'N' TIME - Meat products–poultry - B.C. Rogers Food Service, Inc.
CHIC-O-STEAK - Meat products–poultry - Maid-Rite Steak Co. Inc.
CHIC PIX - Postcards - Fotofolio Inc.
CHIC-SHIELD - Medical apparatus - PFB Inter-Apparel Corp.
CHIC SPORTSWEAR - Apparel - Chic by H.I.S. Inc.
CHIC STYLE - Wallpaper - Pageant Wallpaper Corp.
CHICAGO - Abrasive products - Sandusky-Chicago Abrasive Wheel Co.
CHICAGO - Almond pastes - Chicago Almond Inc.
CHICAGO - Apparel and accessories - Chicago White Sox, Ltd.
CHICAGO - Banjos ☆ - Fred Gretsch Enterprises
CHICAGO - Boxes - Dehler Manufacturing Co. Inc.
CHICAGO - Cutlery - General Housewares Corp.
CHICAGO - Floor coverings–tile - Interface, Inc.
CHICAGO - Flowers, plants, and seeds - Jacklin Seed
CHICAGO - Glass products - D & L Stained Glass Supply, Inc.
CHICAGO - Hand daters - Consolidated Stamp Manufacturing Co. Inc.
CHICAGO - Hardware - Sea Spike Marine Supply Co. Inc.
CHICAGO - Musical instrument accessories - Sottile Manufacturing Co.
CHICAGO - Pencil sharpeners - Empire Berol USA
CHICAGO - Plumbing fixtures–metal - Moen Inc.
CHICAGO - Sausages - Aries Prepared Beef Co.
CHICAGO - Skates–roller - Chicago Roller Skate Co.
CHICAGO - Skates–roller - National Sporting Goods Corp.
CHICAGO - Skin care products ☆ - FMG/Tsumara Medical
CHICAGO - Snack foods - Ultima Foods
CHICAGO - Thread ☆ - Perfect Thread Co. Inc.
CHICAGO - Tools - Klein Tools Inc.
CHICAGO - Trading cards and stamps - 23 Food, Inc.
CHICAGO 5 - Housewares - Impressions Handprinters Inc.
CHICAGO AND NORTH WESTERN SYSTEM - Calendars - Chicago and North Western Railway Co.
CHICAGO ART INSTITUTE - Wallpaper - Warner Co.
CHICAGO BICYCLE CO., THE - Bicycles - Chicago Bicycle Co.
CHICAGO BLUE - Cutlery - General Housewares Corp.
CHICAGO BLUES - Musical instrument accessories - Adder Plus Corp.

☆ = Now out of production

CHICAGO BROTHERS - Pizzas–frozen - Chicago Brothers, Inc.
CHICAGO BROTHERS LITE - Pizzas–frozen - Chicago Brothers, Inc.
CHICAGO CAPER, THE - Games - Decipher Inc.
CHICAGO CASE CO. - Tool boxes - Chicago Case Co.
CHICAGO CLASSIC - Hot dogs - Carousel Snack Bars of Minnesota Inc.
CHICAGO COFFEE COMPANY - Coffee - Harvel Corp.
CHICAGO COFFEE ROASTERY INC. - Coffee - Chicago Coffee Roastery, Inc.
CHICAGO COW - Beverages–carbonated - A.J. Canfield Co.
CHICAGO CUTLERY - Cutlery - Chicago Cutlery Manufacturing Inc.
CHICAGO CUTLERY - Cutlery - General Housewares Corp.
CHICAGO CUTLERY INTERNATIONAL - Cutlery - General Housewares Corp.
CHICAGO EXPRESS - Toys–automobiles - Toy Truck Lines, Inc.
CHICAGO FIRE - Flowers, plants, and seeds - Chicagoland Grows, Inc.
CHICAGO FIRE - Housewares - Impressions Handprinters Inc.
CHICAGO FIRE - Mustard ☆ - Plochman, Inc.
CHICAGO FIRE - Wallpaper - Capital Carousel Inc.
CHICAGO GOLD - Glass–plate - Sasaki
CHICAGO GOLF & SPORTS - Golfing equipment - Chicago Golf & Sports, Inc.
CHICAGO HAIR GOODS - Hair care products - Chicago Hair Good Inc.
CHICAGO HEARTH - Breads - Metz Baking Co.
CHICAGO INDUSTRIAL - Tools - Bass & Sons Inc.
CHICAGO KID - Beverages–carbonated - Chicago Kid Inc.
CHICAGO LOCK - Metals - Chicago Lock Co.
CHICAGO LOOP - Paintbrushes - Corona Brushes Inc.
CHICAGO MEAT HOUSE, THE - Meat products–poultry - Cherry Meat Packers Inc.
CHICAGO METALLIC - Ceiling panels - Chicago Metallic Corp.
CHICAGO MUSCLE - Apparel and accessories - Thomas Lee Hickman
CHICAGO MUSIC MART AT DEPAUL CENTER, THE - Stationery - Depaul University
CHICAGO NOW - Greeting cards - Remigraphics, State of the Heart
CHICAGO NOW AND THEN - Greeting cards - Remigraphics, State of the Heart
CHICAGO ORIGINALS - Publisher's imprints - University of Chicago Press
CHICAGO PAJAMA DEPT. C.P.D. - Underwear and nightwear - Bentley Lingerie, Inc.
CHICAGO PNEUMATIC - Wrenches - Chicago Pneumatic Tool Co. Inc.
CHICAGO RAWHIDE - Automotive parts and accessories - Chicago Rawhide
CHICAGO SPEAKER STANDS - Furniture–public buildings - GNP Audio Video Inc.
CHICAGO SPECIALTY - Plumbing fixtures–metal - Moen Inc.
CHICAGO STAR - Wines ☆ - Wine Group Inc.
CHICAGO STYLE - Popcorn - Hopewell Enterprises
CHICAGO SYNDICATE, THE - Jewelry - Imperial Pearl Syndicate Inc.
CHICAGO TOOL CRIB - Computer software - Landgrebe Development Corp.
CHICAGO TRAVELWEAR - Luggage ☆ - NSC Corp. (Johnson Tent Div.)
CHICAGO V.V - Wallpaper - Capital Carousel Inc.
CHICAGO WHEELERS - Games - Chicago Wheelers, Inc.
CHICAGO WINDOWS - Computer software - Microsoft Corp.
CHICAGOLAND GREEN - Flowers, plants, and seeds - Chicagoland Grows, Inc.
CHICAGO'S HOT DOG - Frankfurters - Vienna Sausage Manufacturing Co.
CHICAGO'S ORIGINAL - Pizza - Pizzeria Uno Corp.
CHICAGO'S OWN - Wigs - Chicago Hair Good Inc.
CHICAMA VINEYARDS - Wines - Chicama Vineyards
CHICANERY - Floor coverings–carpet and rugs - Sweetwater Carpet Corp.
CHICCA - Footwear - Magnes Sales Co. Inc.
CHICCO - Games - Small World Toys
CHICCO - Toys - Artsana of America Inc.
CHICK - Egg stamps, markers - Consolidated Stamp Manufacturing Co. Inc.
CHICK A BOOM - Games - Pressman Toy Corp.
CHICK-A-DEES - Frankfurters ☆ - Shelton's Poultry, Inc.
CHICK-A-DOODLE - Soups–canned - Buckeye Beans & Herbs, Inc.
CHICK-CHICK - Dyes–food ☆ - Doxsee Food Corp.
CHICK-CHICK - Incubators–veterinary - Vegetable Factory, Inc. (Sunbeam Structures Div.)
CHICK DIPPERS - Chickens - Olga's Kitchen Licensing, Inc.
CHICK-FIL-A.M. - Preserved foods–prepackaged - Chick-Fil-A, Inc.
CHICK-N-SHELL - Toys–stuffed - Fun World Inc.
CHICK-O-STICK - Candy - Atkinson Candy Co.
CHICK PEASO - Food products - American Miso Co.
CHICKA CHICKA BOOM BOOM - Computer software ☆ - Knowledge Adventure
CHICKADEES - Diapers–disposable - Paragon Trade Brands, Inc.
CHICKASAW - Flooring–hardwood - Memphis Hardwood Flooring Co.
CHICKEN - Games - Gary Dixson

CHICKEN ALL-WAYS! - Food products - Lyle Foods, Inc.
CHICKEN & BLACK BEAN - Meat products–poultry - My Own Meals Inc.
CHICKEN & CHEDDAR - Food products ☆ - Cheese Kurls Inc.
CHICKEN & NOODLES - Meat products–poultry - My Own Meals Inc.
CHICKEN & TURKEY CAT TREATS - Cat food - Mardel Laboratories, Inc.
CHICKEN APPLAUSE! - Food products - Kraft Foods, Inc.
CHICKEN BALL - Balls–rubber - Llumar Star Kites Inc.
CHICKEN BALLOTINE - Chickens - Elwell Farms
CHICKEN BONES - Candy - Sweet Candy Co.
CHICKEN BREST-CORDON - Meat products–poultry ☆ - Pierce Foods Corp.
CHICKEN BY GEORGE - Meat products–poultry - Hormel Foods Corp.
CHICKEN CARVER - Food products - Boston Chicken, Inc.
CHICKEN CHUNKS - Meat products–poultry - A and W Restaurants, Inc.
CHICKEN CRISPERS - Meat products–poultry - Brinker International Inc.
CHICKEN CROSSING - Toys - Mattel, Inc.
CHICKEN DASH - Video production - Konami (America) Inc.
CHICKEN DINOBITES - Food products - Discovery Zone L.P.
CHICKEN DIPSTERS - Meat products–poultry ☆ - Campbell Soup Co.
CHICKEN DOG TREATS - Dog food - Mardel Laboratories, Inc.
CHICKEN DRAW - Video production - Merit Industries
CHICKEN DUETS - Dinners–frozen ☆ - Campbell Soup Co.
CHICKEN EASY - Seasonings - Burns Philp Food Inc.
CHICKEN EASY - Seasonings - Specialty Brands Inc.
CHICKEN FEED - Candy ☆ - Leaf, Inc.
CHICKEN-FNEE - Food products - Health is Wealth
CHICKEN FOR DIPPIN' - Food products - Del Monte Corp.
CHICKEN GEMS - Prepared chicken pieces ☆ - Cooking Masters
CHICKEN GRANDE - Chili–canned - Stagg Foods, Inc.
CHICKEN HELPER - Food products - General Mills, Inc.
CHICKEN HOLIDAY - Restaurants–fast food - Chicken Holiday
CHICKEN IN A BISKIT - Crackers - Nabisco Foods Group
CHICKEN IN A POCKET - Food products - GDF, Inc.
CHICKEN INTERNATIONAL - Food products - Gold Kist Inc.
CHICKEN-LIKE - Food products ☆ - Worthington Foods Inc.
CHICKEN LIMBO - Games - Hasbro, Inc.
CHICKEN LIVERWURST - Food products ☆ - Tyson Foods Inc.
CHICKEN-LOVER - Meat products–poultry - Irwin L. Gold & Assoc.
CHICKEN MAGIC - Vegetable sauces ☆ - Chelten House Products Inc.
CHICKEN MCNUGGETS - Meat products–poultry - Mcdonald's Corp.
CHICKEN MEDITERRANEAN - Meat products–poultry - My Own Meals Inc.
CHICKEN MEXICANA - Food products - Valley Fresh Inc.
CHICKEN MINI-DRUMS - Food products - Tyson Foods Inc.
CHICKEN 'N' RIBS - Barbecue sauce - Torbitt & Castleman Co.
CHICKEN N'CHIPS - Pet products - Gimborn U.S., Inc.
CHICKEN NIBBLES - Meat products–poultry - Campbell Soup Co.
CHICKEN, NOODLES, CARROTS, & GREEN BEANS - Meat products–poultry - My Own Meals Inc.
CHICKEN (NOT!) - Meat extracts - Dixie, USA, Inc.
CHICKEN OF THE SEA - Food products - Van Camp Seafood Co. Inc.
CHICKEN ORIGINALS - Food products - Tyson Foods Inc.
CHICKEN OUT - Games - Tonka Corp.
CHICKEN PHILADELPHIA - Sandwiches–prepackaged - Nicar Enterprises
CHICKEN, PLEASE - Meat products–poultry - My Own Meals Inc.
CHICKEN PLUS - Food products - General Mills, Inc.
CHICKEN POPS - Meat products–poultry - Continental Grain Co.
CHICKEN QUEEN - Rotisserie-cooked meat - Chicken Queen Inc.
CHICKEN RICE & SAUCE - Meat products–poultry - My Own Meals Inc.
CHICKEN ROMANOFF ROY'ELL - Food products - Acme Continental Foods Inc.
CHICKEN RONDELETS - Food products - Tyson Foods Inc.
CHICKEN SENSATIONS - Meat sauces ☆ - Hunt-Wesson, Inc.
CHICKEN SHIFT - Video game - Bally Sente Inc.
CHICKEN SOUP VITAMINS - Vitamins and nutritional supplements - Health Products Corp.
CHICKEN STOP - Chickens - Conagra, Inc.
CHICKEN TO GO - Games - Tomy America, Inc.
CHICKEN TRADITIONS - Food products - McCarty Foods Inc.
CHICKEN VITTLES - Sandwiches–prepackaged - Zartic, Inc.
CHICKEN WRAP - Sandwiches–prepackaged - Gyro Wrap, Inc.
CHICKEN ZONE, THE - Food products - Chicken Zone, Inc.
CHICKENETTES - Food products - Eat-All Frozen Food Co.
CHICKENFOOT - Musical instrument accessories - Farrell Morris
CHICKENLINK - Sausages ☆ - Fircrest Farms
CHICKERING - Pianos - Aeolian Pianos Inc.
CHICKERS - Board games - Colleen Grimm
CHICKERY - Food products - Lunds, Inc.

☆ = Now out of production

CHICKIE CARDS - Greeting cards ☆ - Fran Mar Greeting cards Ltd.

CHICKLETTE - Ophthalmic goods - Foremost Optical Products

CHICK'N BISCUIT - Meat products–poultry - Rymer Chicken Inc.

CHICK'N BISCUIT - Meat products–poultry ☆ - Simmons Foods

CHICK'N CHUNKS - Food products - Tyson Foods Inc.

CHICK'N DIPPERS - Food products - Tyson Foods Inc.

CHICK'N EASY - Meat products–poultry - Rymer Chicken Inc.

CHICK'N EASY - Meat products–poultry ☆ - Simmons Foods

CHICK'N PASTA - Soups–mixes ☆ - CPC International Inc.

CHICK'N QUICK - Food products - Tyson Foods Inc.

CHICK'N ROAST-UMMS - Meat products–poultry - Designer Foods, Inc.

CHICK'N SPUDS - Seasonings - Chick'n Spuds Inc.

CHICKNFRYER - Pressure cookers ☆ - National Presto Industries, Inc.

CHICKS - Candy - American Chewing Gum Inc.

CHICKS DIG ME - Apparel and accessories - J & J Graphics, Inc.

CHICLE - Greeting cards ☆ - Fran Mar Greeting cards Ltd.

CHICLE CHEWS - Chewing gum - Ford Gum and Machine Co.

CHICLETS - Candy - American Chicle Co.

CHICO - Beverages–carbonated ☆ - Knudsen & Sons Inc.

CHICO - Food products - Chiquita Brands, Inc.

CHICO - Milk - Chico Dairy Co. Inc.

CHICO - Musical instrument accessories ☆ - Hershman Musical Instrument

CHICO - Recording label ☆ - Kubaney Publishing Corp.

CHICO - Spices and extracts - Ralph's Foods Co.

CHICO - Tape–adhesive - A. Meyers & Sons Corp.

CHICO NUT CO. - Nuts–salted, roasted, cooked, or canned - Chico Nut Co.

CHICO-SAN - Rice - H.J. Heinz Co.

CHICOMETRICS - Video production - Chico Caldwell

CHICOPEE - Windows–screen - Chicopee

CHICOR - Apparel and accessories - Chicor Apparel & Specialty Products

CHICORY SPORT - Apparel and accessories - Meijer, Inc.

CHICSET - Hair care products - Helene Curtis Industries Inc.

CHIEF - Apparel and accessories - Jays Industries Inc.

CHIEF - Apparel–women's - Albee Collection, Inc.

CHIEF - Ashtrays–glass - Ashtray Specialty Co./Marion Products Co.

CHIEF - Boats–canoes - Black River Canoes

CHIEF - Boats–motor ☆ - Caddo Boat Manufacturing Co.

CHIEF - Boats–motor ☆ - Glassmaster Co.

CHIEF - Cylinders–hydraulic - Bailey Sales Corp.

CHIEF - Drums–musical instruments ☆ - Grossman Music Corp.

CHIEF - Erasers ☆ - Bright Boy Abrasives

CHIEF - Housewares - Central Notion Co. Inc.

CHIEF - Paper - Mead Corp.

CHIEF - Saws–chain ☆ - Clinton Engines Corp.

CHIEF - Tools - Chickasaw Handle Co. Inc.

CHIEF - Toys–trains - Digitrax, Inc.

CHIEF - Trailers–travel - Rancho Trailers Inc.

CHIEF - Wet mops ☆ - American Textile Products Co.

CHIEF AUTO PARTS - Batteries - Chief Auto Parts Inc.

CHIEF BUSINESS OPERATING SYSTEM - Computer software - Unitrendix Corp.

CHIEF BY ROTHSCHILD - Coats - S. Rothschild & Co., Inc.

CHIEF CAHAP - Fruits and vegetables - Occanneechi Inc.

CHIEF CHELAN - Fruits–canned - Chief Wenatchee

CHIEF CHIRPA - Toys - Lucasfilm Ltd.

CHIEF ENGINEER B'ELANNA TORRES - Toys - Paramount Pictures Corp.

CHIEF EXECUTIVE PONY - Toys ☆ - Hartco Inc.

CHIEF JOSEPH - Apparel and accessories - Tropical Sportswear International Corp.

CHIEF OF STAFF - Mattresses - Ohio Mattress Co.

CHIEF OF THE MOULDINGS - Moldings and trim - Jeld-Wen, Inc.

CHIEF POLICE DOG - Toys–stuffed - Dakin Inc.

CHIEF SEATTLE - Bait - Siberian Salmon Egg Co.

CHIEF, THE - Golfing equipment - Northwestern Golf Co.

CHIEF, THE - Luggage ☆ - Samsonite Corp.

CHIEF TONASKET - Fruits–canned - Chief Tonasket Growers

CHIEF WAHOO - Fruits and vegetables - Westin Inc.

CHIEF WENATCHEE - Fruits–canned - Chief Wenatchee

CHIEFEL - Watches - Natico Originals Inc.

CHIEFMATE - Computer software - Advanced Marine Enterprises, Inc.

CHIEF'S CHOICE - Popcorn - Star Manufacturing International Inc.

CHIEFS SPECIAL - Revolvers - Smith & Wesson Corp.

CHIEFTAIN - Aircraft ☆ - New Piper Aircraft, Inc.

CHIEFTAIN - Boats–motor - Starcraft Corp.

CHIEFTAIN - Jewelry - Jacoby-Bender Inc.

CHIEFTAIN - Motor vehicles–motor homes - Winnebago Industries, Inc.

CHIEFTAIN - Paper–bond - Kimberly-Clark Corp.

CHIEFTAIN - Rice ☆ - Chief Industries Inc.

CHIFFOJEL - Gelatin - Vyse Gelatin Co.

CHIFFOM - Apparel–women's - Blue Bay Inc.

CHIFFON - Margarine - Nabisco Foods Group

CHIFFON - Paper–tissue - James River Paper Co., Inc.

CHIFFON - Paper–toilet - James River Corp.

CHIFFON - Wigs - Helene Curtis Industries Inc.

CHIFFON DE LYS - Fabric stores - Jaunty Textile Div.

CHIFFON DELIGHT - Hair care products - Andre Fantasies Inc.

CHIFFON FINISH - Cosmetics - Madeleine Mono Ltd.

CHIFFON SEASON - Oils–edible - Kraft Food Ingredients Corp.

CHIFFON VELVET - Jams and jellies ☆ - Mallet and Co.

CHIFS FINTES - Food products - Acme Foods

CHIGG AWAY - Pharmaceutical preparations ☆ - Reese Chemical Co.

CHIGGER MAGIK - Pharmaceutical preparations ☆ - Reese Chemical Co.

CHIGGEREX - Pharmaceutical preparations - Schering-Plough Healthcare Products

CHIGGERTOX - Pharmaceutical preparations - Schering-Plough Healthcare Products

CHIGIRI - Beef - Tengu Co., Inc.

CHIGNON - Skin care products - Henry Beauty Imports Inc.

CHIHUAHUA - Beverages–carbonated - Labatt Importers Inc.

CHIK-NACHOS - Meat products–poultry - Pierce Foods Corp.

CHIK PATTIES - Food products - Specialty Foods Investment Co.

CHIK STIKS - Food products - Worthington Foods Inc.

CHIK-TAC-TOE - Meat products–poultry - Perdue Holdings, Inc.

CHIK-WICH - Food products - Whistlin' Dixie Fried Chicken Inc.

CHIKKA - Shoes ☆ - Allen-Edmonds Shoe Corp.

CHIK'N G'RILLA BREST - Meat products–poultry - Pierce Foods Corp.

CHIK'N G'RILLAS - Meat products–poultry - Pierce Foods Corp.

CHIK'N LIK'N - Food products - Texxstar Resources (USA), Inc.

CHIK'N PIZZAZ - Chickens - Hester Industries, Inc.

CHIK'N'ZIPS - Meat products–poultry - Brakebush Brothers Inc.

CHIKYU - Greeting cards - Darwell Import Co. Inc.

CHIL-A-PAIR - Sporting goods - Chesal Golf

CHIL-A-PAK - Sporting goods - Chesal Golf

CHIL-CHOKE - Fruits and vegetables ☆ - Marglo Products Corp.

CHIL-D-LITE - Vitamins and nutritional supplements - Nutritional Research Associates Inc.

CHILA - Beverages–alcohol - Consolidated Distilled Products Inc.

CHILACA - Chili peppers–powdered ☆ - Frieda's, Inc.

CHILADA - Tortillas ☆ - Frito-Lay, Inc.

CHILD - Perfumes - Jessden Co.

CHILD CRAFT - Furniture–children's - Child Craft Industries Inc.

CHILD DEVELOPMENT SERIES, THE - Playground equipment - Rainbow Play Systems, Inc.

CHILD GUARD - Lighters - Bic Corp.

CHILD-GUARD - Play swings - Par Industries, Inc.

CHILD GUARD - Safety products - American Mineral Gift Co.

CHILD GUIDANCE - Infant product - Azrak-Hamway International, Inc.

CHILD HORIZONS - Publisher's imprints - Standard Educational Corp.

CHILD LIFE - Figurines - Arnart Imports Inc.

CHILD LIFE - Footwear - Osaga Footwear, Inc.

CHILD LIFE - Shoes - Osage Footwear, Inc.

CHILD LINE - Furniture–children's - Child Craft Industries Inc.

CHILD LOVE - Vitamins and nutritional supplements - Synergy Plus

CHILD MATTERS - Educational materials - Child Matters

CHILD MILD - Sausages - Dean Sausage Co. Inc.

CHILD-O-LAX - Health care products ☆ - CTS Laboratories Inc.

CHILD OF GOD - Dolls - Angel Spirit, Inc.

CHILD OF GOD BROADCASTING NETWORK - Broadcasting stations–radio - Holy Bible Gospel Ministry of The Body of Christ, Yeshua, of the Holy Land,

CHILD O'MINE IRISH CREAM - Coffee - Frontier Cooperative Herbs

CHILD-PLAY - Toys - Placo Products Co.

CHILD PRODIGY - Toys ☆ - Decipher Inc.

CHILD PROTECTOR TOP - Housewares ☆ - Shell Oil Co.

CHILD SAFE - Exercising equipment - Columbia Medical Manufacturing

CHILD SAFE - Furniture - Directions East

CHILD SAFEOCKS - Infant product - BB Marketing Inc.

CHILD STRIDE - Shoes - Ephrata Shoe Co. Inc.

CHILD WORLD - Recording label ☆ - Peter Pan Industries

CHILD WORLD - Watches - Univex Licensing Group, Inc.

CHILDCHURCH - Publisher's imprints - Ronald B. Mierzwa

CHILDESIGNS - Furniture–children's - Generation 2 Worldwide LLC

CHILDEX - Cough medicines - Rogers' Drug Co.

CHILDGUARD - Coatings - Fiberlock Technologies, Inc.
CHILDHOOD - Containers - Phoenix Closures, Inc.
CHILDHOOD ENCHANTMENT - Apparel–children's - Kathleen May Godwin
CHILDHOOD EXPERIENCE READER - Publisher's imprints - Perfection Form Co.
CHILDHOOD MEMORIES - Paper–gift wrap - Gift Wrap Co.
CHILDHOOD STICKS - Candy ☆ - Bobs Candies Inc.
CHILDHOOD TREATS - Candy - Fritz Co., Inc.
CHILDLIFE - Playground equipment - Child Life Inc.
CHILDLIFE - Vitamins and nutritional supplements - Lifessence Labs
CHILDMASTER - Infant product ☆ - Graco Children's Products
CHILDREN FOR THE EARTH - Wallpaper - Royson's Corp.
CHILDREN OF DIVORCE - Publisher's imprints - Children of Divorce, Inc.
CHILDREN OF THE EARTH - Wallpaper - Capital Carousel Inc.
CHILDREN OF THE GREAT SPIRIT - Dolls - Georgetown Collection, Inc.
CHILDREN OF THE WORLD - Dolls - Nellie Ruth Ingram
CHILDREN OF THE WORLD - Jewelry - Wieck Family L.P.
CHILDREN OF THE WORLD TRAVEL CLUB - Boxes - Photopals
CHILDREN OF YESTERYEAR - Dolls ☆ - Kish & Co.
CHILDREN SHOULD BE SEEN AND NOT HURT - Safety products - Mericon Corp.
CHILDREN'S ALPHA 98.6 - Pharmaceutical preparations - Boericke & Tafel
CHILDREN'S ALPHA CF - Pharmaceutical preparations - Boericke & Tafel
CHILDREN'S ALPHA TLC - Pharmaceutical preparations - Boericke & Tafel
CHILDREN'S ART FOR CHILDREN'S SCHOOLS - Calendars - Hannelore Engelman
CHILDREN'S B&B - Pharmaceutical preparations - Boericke & Tafel
CHILDREN'S BEDTIME - Pillows - Pacific Coast Feather Co.
CHILDREN'S BEST SOFTWARE - Computer software - Learning Curve Toys, LLC
CHILDREN'S BIBLE TRIVIA - Games - Cadaco Div.
CHILDREN'S BOOK TRUST - Publisher's imprint - Auromere Inc.
CHILDREN'S CARROUSEL - Computer software - Dynacomp Inc.
CHILDREN'S CLASSICS - Puzzles - Warren Industries Inc.
CHILDREN'S CLASSICS PUZZLES - Puzzles - Warren Industries Inc.
CHILDREN'S CORNER - Frames–picture - Fetco International Corp.
CHILDREN'S CULTURAL COLLECTION - Video production - V.I.E.W. Video Inc.
CHILDREN'S DAY - Novelty items - Nurserymen's Exchange, Inc.
CHILDREN'S GARDEN OF CRITTERS - Figurines - United Design Corp.
CHILDREN'S HEALTH - Pillows - Pacific Coast Feather Co.
CHILDREN'S HOUR - Games ☆ - Parker Brothers
CHILDREN'S HOUR, THE - Apparel–children's - Children's Hour, Inc.
CHILDREN'S MOTRIN - Analgesics - McNeil Consumer Products Co.
CHILDREN'S NEWSPAPER MAK - Computer software - Orange Cherry Software
CHILDREN'S OUTREACH - Publisher's imprints - Elaine Cole
CHILDREN'S SEAFARER - Publisher's imprints - Penguin Books USA Inc.
CHILDREN'S SUDAFED - Cold remedies - Warner-Lambert Co.
CHILDREN'S TELEVISION RESOURCE & EDUCATION CENTER - Educational materials - Children's Television Resource and Education Center
CHILDREN'S TREASURES - Figurines - Fort USA
CHILDREN'S TYLENOL - Analgesics - McNeil Consumer Products Co.
CHILDREN'S VIDEO LIBARY - Recording label - LIVE Entertainment Inc.
CHILDREN'S VIDEO THEATER - Vests–women's - Jacoby Entertainment, Ltd.
CHILDREN'S WEAR - Apparel–children's - Laid Back Enterprises, Inc.
CHILDRENS WORLD - Figurines - Arnart Imports Inc.
CHILDREN'S WRITING AND PUBLISHING CENTER, THE - Computer software - Learning Co.
CHILDREN'S WRITING & PUBLISHING CENTER, THE - Computer software - The Learning Co., Inc.
CHILDS - Antennas - Childs Corp.
CHILDS - Pharmaceutical preparations ☆ - Childs Co.
CHILD'S GIFT OF BEDTIME STORIES, A - Recording label - Someday Baby, Inc.
CHILD'S GIFT OF LULLABYES, A - Recording label - Child's Gift of Lullabyes
CHILD'S GIFT OF LULLABYES, A - Frames–picture - Someday Baby, Inc.
CHILD'S PLAY - Candy - Tootsie Roll Industries, Inc.
CHILD'S PLAY - Crayons ☆ - Coloron Industries
CHILD'S PLAY - Paints - Valspar Corp.
CHILD'S PLAY I - Computer software - Dynacomp Inc.
CHILD'S PLAYTIME CANDY - Candy - Tootsie Roll Industries, Inc.
CHILDSHOP - Grafix Plastics
CHILD*STAR - Computer software - Matrix Software, Inc.
CHILDVIEW - Mirrors - Prince Lionheart, Inc.

CHILE ADDICT - Peppers - Fran's Enterprises
CHILE CAFE - Racks - Mexisource, Inc.
CHILE CHEWS - Candy - Ash Enterprises, Inc.
CHILE DE ARBOL - Chili peppers–powdered ☆ - Frieda's, Inc.
CHILE DOGS - Toys–stuffed - Daniel L. Clavio
CHILE EXPRESS - Chili–canned - Drew-More Inc.
CHILE HEAD - Coffee - Southwest Specialty Foods
CHILE TODAY - HOT TAMALE - Spices and extracts - Chile Today-Hot Tamale, Inc.
CHILE WEAR - Apparel and accessories - Chile Wear
CHILI - Hair care products - Cosmair Inc.
CHILI CHOMPERS - Apparel and accessories - Chili Chompers, Inc.
CHILI CON TOFU - Chili–canned ☆ - San Diego Soy Dairy
CHILI DOG - Chili–canned - Curtice-Burns Foods, Inc.
CHILI DOG CHILI - Chili–canned - Curtice-Burns Foods, Inc.
CHILI-ETS - Food products ☆ - Shurfine International, Inc.
CHILI FAJITAS - Olive oil - Santa Barbara Olive Co.
CHILI FIXIN'S - Chili sauce - Stubb's Legendary Kitchen
CHILI FIXIN'S - Seasonings - Hell on the Red Inc.
CHILI GOURMET - Chili–canned - Claude Marshall
CHILI LINE FLAVORED - Tortillas - Guiltless Gourmet, Inc.
CHILI LINKS - Sausages - Pittsburg Hot Link Packers, Inc.
CHILI MAC - Chili–canned - Hormel Foods Corp.
CHILI MAGIC REGIONAL FAVORITES - Seasonings - Bush Brothers,LP
CHILI MAKIN'S - Seasonings - S & W Fine Foods, Inc.
CHILI MASTER - Chili sauce - Hormel Foods Corp.
CHILI PARLOR - Food products - Stegner Food Products Co.
CHILI PEPPER - Apparel and accessories - Toppe California Inc.
CHILI-QUIK - Seasonings ☆ - Hunt-Wesson, Inc.
CHILICIN - Skin care products - Sabinsa Corp.
CHILIO - Chili sauce - R.T. French Co.
CHILI'S MELTDOWN - Beverages–alcohol - Brinker Restaurant Corp.
CHILIWARE - Bowls ☆ - Chili Plastics Inc.
CHILKOOT-CHARLIE'S - Beverages–alcohol - Jadon Inc.
CHILL - Beauty aids - Paul Sebastian, Inc.
CHILL - Games - Mayfair Games, Inc.
CHILL - Housewares - SGI Inc.
CHILL - Ice cream - Moore Enterprises, Inc.
CHILL-A-CCINO - Beverages - Brad Barry Co. Ltd.
CHILL-A-TRON - Toys - Mattel, Inc.
CHILL-A-TRON LAB - Toys - Mattel, Inc.
CHILL AWAY - Heating equipment - Pollenex Corp.
CHILL BLUE CREME - Beverages–carbonated - Clark Distributing Co., Inc.
CHILL CAN - Beverage dispensing equipment - Joseph Co.
CHILL CHASER - Heating equipment - Coleman Co., Inc.
CHILL CHASER - Jackets ☆ - Horace Small Apparel Co.
CHILL CHASER - Lamps - General Electric Co.
CHILL CHICK - Chickens - Conagra, Inc.
CHILL CITRUS - Beverages - Clark Distributing Co., Inc.
CHILL COLA - Beverages - Clark Distributing Co., Inc.
CHILL COMPANION - Games - Mayfair Games, Inc.
CHILL DIET COLA - Beverages–carbonated - Clark Distributing Co., Inc.
CHILL EXPRESS - Beverages - Atlantic Refining & Marketing Corp.
CHILL-EZ - Neckties - Headlinerz, Inc.
CHILL FRUIT PUNCH - Beverages - Clark Distributing Co., Inc.
CHILL GRIP - Beverages–malt - Anheuser-Busch Companies Inc.
CHILL ISLE - Iced tea–bottled or canned - Pepsico, Inc.
CHILL-IT - Health care products - Sunbeam-Oster Household Products
CHILL N' GRILL - Housewares ☆ - SGI Inc.
CHILL-O-MINTS - Candy - Nabisco Foods Group
CHILL OUT - Cologne - Coty Inc.
CHILL OUT - Insulating materials - Sierra Housewares, Inc.
CHILL PILLS - Herbal products - Hit Products, Inc.
CHILL-RIPE - Food products - Curtice-Burns Foods, Inc.
CHILL-RIPE - Fruits and vegetables - Southern Frozen Foods Inc.
CHILL RITE 32 - Beverage dispensing equipment - Desco, Inc.
CHILL ROOT BEER - Beverages - Clark Distributing Co., Inc.
CHILL-THERM - Cooking equipment–household ☆ - Anchor Hocking Glass, Inc.
CHILLBUSTER - Fireplace equipment - Rasmussen Iron Works Inc.
CHILLED OR GRILLED - Salad dressings–bottled - CPC Best Foods
CHILLED SELECTIONS - Fruits–dried - Orval Kent Food Co., Inc.
CHILLED TO THE BONE - Games - Mayfair Games, Inc.
CHILLER - Ice ☆ - Coleman Co., Inc.
CHILLER - Juice novelties - Daily Juice Products Inc.
CHILLERS - Confections - Canada Dry Corp.

☆ = Now out of production

CHILLERY - Salads–prepackaged - Kraft Foods, Inc.
CHILLETS - Pet products - Nutritional Research Associates Inc.
CHILLGUARD - Underwear and nightwear - Hot Chillys Inc.
CHILLI HEADS - Apparel and accessories - Susan Bryant
CHILLI MAN - Chili peppers–powdered - Milnot Co.
CHILLI-O - Meat products–beef - Chilli-O Frozen Foods Inc.
CHILLIE WILLIE - Apparel–men's - A.H.M./Streetline Inc.
CHILLIN' CHERRY - Food products - Jel Sert Co.
CHILLIT - Ice chests–plastic ☆ - Glacier Ware Inc.
CHILLMETER - Thermometers ☆ - Maximum Inc.
CHILL'N - Apparel and accessories - Personal Comfort Corp.
CHILLON - Floor coverings–carpet and rugs - Cabin Crafts Carpets
CHILLON - Floor coverings–carpet and rugs - Walter Carpet Mills
CHILLOW - Pillows - Maverick Marketing Ventures, Inc.
CHILLPAX - Medical apparatus - Abanda Inc.
CHILLPLUS - Ice chests–plastic - Chesal Golf
CHILLS - Apparel and accessories - Hill Industries USA, Inc.
CHILLS - Footwear - JBI, Inc.
CHILLS - Sunglasses - Face 2 Face Corp.
CHILLS AND CHATTER - Toys - Russ Berrie and Co., Inc.
CHILLS AND THRILL - Games ☆ - Mego Financial Corp.
CHILLY BEAN - Fans–electric - Circulair, Inc.
CHILLY BEARS - Ice cream - Steve's Homemade Ice Cream Inc.
CHILLY DILLY - Pickles - Dean Pickle & Specialty Products Co.
CHILLY DOG - Pet products - Biological Engineering/High Tech Pet Products
CHILLY THINGS - Dairy products - Vroman Foods Inc.
CHILLY WILLEE SOFT ICE - Beverages - Chilly Willee, Inc.
CHILLZONNE - Insulating materials - Sierra Housewares, Inc.
CHILMAR - Pet products - Chilmar Inc.
CHILMARK - Figurines - Lance Corp.
CHILMARK CHOCOLATES - Candy - Jan Campbell
CHILORIO - Meat products - Jorge Aviles
CHILTERN SQUARE - Wallpaper - Doshi Wallcoveringss Inc.
CHILTON - Clocks ☆ - Robertshaw Controls Co.
CHILTON - Floor coverings–carpet and rugs - Monticello Carpet Mills
CHILTON - Giftware - Therm-O-Ware Electric
CHILTON - Paints - Chilton Paint Co.
CHILTON-GLOBE - Toys - Chilton-Globe, Inc.
CHILTON'S - Publisher's imprints - Chilton Co.
CHIM - Computer software - AT/Scan Ltd.
CHIM-A-LATOR - Fireplace equipment - Bernard Dalsin Manufacturing
CHIM-CLEEN - Cleaning preparations ☆ - Stewart-Hall Chemical Corp.
CHIM RAM - Fire extinguishing compositions - N.A. Taylor Co. Inc.
CHIMACOS - Food products - Chimacos Food Products, Inc.
CHIMAL - Skin care products - Mil-Tex Corp.
CHIMALONG - Musical instruments - Woodstock Percussion, Inc.
CHIMAY - Beverages–malt - Mannekin-Brussel Imports
CHIMAY GRANDE RESERVE - Beverages–alcohol - Mannekin-Brussel Imports
CHIMAY RED TRAPPIST - Beverages–alcohol - Mannekin-Brussel Imports
CHIMAYO - Beverages–alcohol - Nicholas Enterprises
CHIME - Recording label - QCA Inc.
CHIME - Toys - Gerber Products Co.
CHIME ALERT - Hardware - Morris Industries Inc.
CHIME ALERT - Pet product - Audio Alert Systems
CHIME BABY - Toys–stuffed ☆ - Gund, Inc.
CHIME BALL - Toys - Fisher-Price, Inc.
CHIME BALL - Toys–stuffed - Dakin Inc.
CHIME BIRD - Toys - Playskool, Inc.
CHIME CHUMS - Toys - Tomy America, Inc.
CHIME COM - Door openers–electronic - Aiphone Corp.
CHIME-O-MATIC - Housewares ☆ - Hitachi Home Electronics America Inc.
CHIME WORKS - Chimes - Chime Works
CHIMEARA - Jewelry and glassware - Wilkinson Enterprises
CHIMEATRON - Bells and chimes - Schulmerich Carillons Inc.
CHIMECRAFT - Chimes - Chimetime, Inc.
CHIMELITE - Clocks ☆ - Toastmaster Inc.
CHIMERE - Perfumes - Prince Matchabelli
CHIMES - Decorative items - Seville Industries Dark's Silk Flowers
CHIMES - Guitars - Goodman Music Corp.
CHIMES OF WESTMINSTER - Chimes - Woodstock Percussion, Inc.
CHIMESCAPES - Chimes - ChimeScapes
CHIMESCAPES - Chimes - J.W. Stannard Co.
CHIMEX - Chimes - Maple Chase Co.
CHIMFEX - Fire extinguishing compositions - Orion Safety Products (Signal Products Operation)

CHIMGARD - Thermometers - Condar Co.
CHIMI - Tortillas - Southwest Specialty Foods
CHIMIN-EEZ - Fireplace equipment - Hy-C Co. Inc.
CHIMING BIG BIRD - Toys - Playskool, Inc.
CHIMNEY CORNERS II - Furniture - Bassett Furniture Industries, Inc.
CHIMNEY DOOR BRICK - Floor coverings ☆ - Tarkett, Inc.
CHIMNEY GUARD - Fireplace equipment ☆ - American Building Components Co.
CHIMNEY GUARD II - Fireplace equipment - American Building Components Co.
CHIMNEY KING - Blocks–chimney - Chimney King, Ltd.
CHIMNEY-LITE - Lamp bulbs–fluorescent - Duro-Test Corp.
CHIMNEY QUICK - Lighter fluid - GSW Jackes-Evans Manufacturing Co.
CHIMNEY SWEEP - Chimney cleaner ☆ - Coughlan Products Corp.
CHIMNEY SWEEPS - Cleaning preparations ☆ - Johnson Kart Manufacturing
CHIMNEYVILLE - Recording label - Malaco Records Inc.
CHIMP SHOTS - Greeting cards - Sangamon Co.
CHIMP WRITER - Computer software - Edward A. Katzenberg
CHIN BONE - Sporting goods - Powell Skateboards
CHIN CHIN - Furniture - Chinese Native Products
CHIN CHIN - Toys–stuffed ☆ - Gund, Inc.
CHIN CHU - Teas - Eastern Tea Corp.
CH'IN COLLECTION - Fabrics–tapestry ☆ - Combeau Industries
CHIN GYM - Exercising equipment - Eugene P. Shaffer
CHIN HUA - Furniture–wood - Century Furniture Co.
CHIN UP - Crocheted and knitted items ☆ - Puritan Sportswear Corp.
CHIN-UPS - Infant product ☆ - Dolly, Inc.
CHINA - Coffee ☆ - Thanksgiving Coffee Co.
CHINA - Games - S. Alden Inc.
CHINA - Shoes - Green Market Services Co.
CHINA - Skin care products - Takara Belmont USA, Inc.
CHINA-AMERICA - Pharmaceutical preparations - China-America Herb Co.
CHINA BEARS HEIRLOOM COLLECTION - Giftware - Lenox, Inc.
CHINA BLACK - Tobacco pouches - Consolidated Cigar Corp.
CHINA BLACK - Tobacco pouches - Sutliff Tobacco Co.
CHINA BLOSSOM - Dinnerware ☆ - Corning Inc.
CHINA BLUE - Tableware–china ☆ - Villeroy and Boch Tableware Ltd.
CHINA BOWL - Food products - China Bowl Trading Co.
CHINA BOY - Food products - China Doll, Inc.
CHINA BOY - Food products - Everfresh Foods Corp.
CHINA BOY FINEST QUALITY AMERICAN LONG GRAIN RICE - Rice - China Doll, Inc.
CHINA-BRITE - Cleaning preparations–household - Peerless Chemical Co. Inc.
CHINA CHLORELLA - Flowers, plants, and seeds - Natrol, Inc.
CHINA COAST - Furniture ☆ - Bassett Furniture Industries, Inc.
CHINA COLA - Beverages–carbonated - Tianfu Cola
CHINA CONNECTION - Cooking utensils–enameled - Westminster International Co., Inc.
CHINA COURT - Wallpaper - Milbrook Wallcoverings
CHINA DOLL - Food products - China Doll, Inc.
CHINA DOLL DRIED BEANS - Food products - China Doll, Inc.
CHINA DOLL PARBOILED - Food products - China Doll, Inc.
CHINA DOLL POPCORN - Food products - China Doll, Inc.
CHINA DOLL WHITE RICE - Food products - China Doll, Inc.
CHINA DOLL YELLOW & BROWN RICE - Food products - China Doll, Inc.
CHINA DRIP - Coffee makers–electric - Westerlo House Inc. of Albany
CHINA DUST - Spices and extracts - Cajun Dust, LLC
CHINA EXPORT - Wallpaper - Sterling Prints
CHINA FARM - Rice - Comet American Marketing
CHINA FLEET - Brushes–paint - Corona Brushes Inc.
CHINA FLOWER - Handcrafted rugs, now out of production - Couristan Inc.
CHINA FOAM - Housewares ☆ - Amoco Fabrics and Fibers Co.
CHINA GARDEN - Food products - Chung's Gourmet Foods
CHINA GARDEN - Food products - Health Jet, Inc.
CHINA GIRL - Brushes–paint ☆ - Wooster Brush Co.
CHINA GIRL - Food products - Chinese Maid Inc.
CHINA GLAZE - Nail care products - Worldwide Cosmetics
CHINA HARN SOUP MIX BEANS - Food products - China Doll, Inc.
CHINA-KOTE - Enamels - Commercial Chemical Co. Inc.
CHINA LANDSCAPE - Wallpaper ☆ - Maya Romanoff Corp.
CHINA LILY - Colognes - A.K.A. Saunders, Inc.
CHINA LUXE - Paints–artists' - MCI Quality Coatings
CHINA MAGIC - Ceramic coating, now out of production - Activa Products Inc.
CHINA MAID - Food products - Perk-Up, Inc.
CHINA MIST - Teas - China Mist Tea Co.

CHINA MULTICOLOR - Building materials–concrete - Eurocal Trading Inc.
CHINA MUSK - Colognes - A.K.A. Saunders, Inc.
CHINA NATIONAL - Beverages–malt - Nan Yang Trading Co.
CHINA NIGHT - Skin care products - Uncommon Scents, Inc.
CHINA PACK - Food products - Perk-Up, Inc.
CHINA PASSAGE - Baskets–wood ☆ - Knobler International Ltd.
CHINA PEARL - Dinnerware–glass - C.C.A. International Inc.
CHINA PEARL - Nail care products - Cosmair Inc.
CHINA PRIDE - Food products - Allied Old English, Inc.
CHINA RAIN - Colognes - A.K.A. Saunders, Inc.
CHINA SEAS - Wallpaper - China Seas Inc.
CHINA SEAS CLASSIC COLLECTION - Wallpaper - China Seas Inc.
CHINA SILK KIT - Cosmetics - American International Industries
CHINA SLIM TEA - Teas–herbal - Fec Ginseng & Marine Products
CHINA SNOW - Flowers, plants, and seeds - Chicagoland Grows, Inc.
CHINA! THE GRAND TOUR - Computer software - Hopkins Technology LLC
CHINA TODAY 7 - Wallpaper - Pantasote Inc. (Wallcovering Div.)
CHINA TOWN - Food products - Health Jet, Inc.
CHINA TRADE - Clocks ☆ - General Time Corp. (Westclox/Seth Thomas Div.)
CHINA TREASURES - Giftware - Lenox, Inc.
CHINA VILLAGE - Kitchenware–china - Keilen Ltd.
CHINA YUNNAN SILVER TIP CHOICE - Teas - Grace Tea Co. Ltd.
CHINACO - Liquors - Jim Beam Brands Co.
CHINAFIRM - Plates–paper - Alfred Bleyer and Co. Inc.
CHINALIKE - Plates–paper - Alfred Bleyer and Co. Inc.
CHINAMERICA - Ornamental products–metal - Hugh Rose
CHINA'S SECRET - Vinegar - Europa Foods Ltd.
CHINA'S SECRET - Vinegar - L.T. Longevity Foods, Inc.
CHINASTONE - Dinnerware–glass - Lenox, Inc.
CHINATOWN - Meats–luncheon - Silver Palate Kitchen
CHINATOWN - Wallcovering ☆ - Fashon Wallcoverings
CHINCHILLA - Cosmetics - Lancome
CHINCOTEAGUE - Seafood - Chincoteague Seafood Co.
CHINDI - Floor coverings–carpet and rugs ☆ - Foreign Accents
CHINE D'AMOUR - Dinnerware–glass ☆ - Arita Sales Co. Inc.
CHINEMEL - Containers–metal - Bill Yee Associates, Inc.
CHINESE AND AMERICAN SALES COMPANY - Food products - Perk-Up, Inc.
CHINESE BASKET - Dinnerware–glass ☆ - Royal China & Porcelain Companies Inc.
CHINESE BASKET - Floor coverings–carpet and rugs - Quaker Inc.
CHINESE BOUQUET - Dishes–china - Martin's Herend Imports Inc.
CHINESE CHECKERS - Glass products - Vitro Agate Corp.
CHINESE CHECKERS - Snack foods - Everfresh Foods Corp.
CHINESE CHECKERS - Toys–marbles - Al Sandberg
CHINESE CLASSICS - Vitamins and nutritional supplements - McZand Herbal, Inc.
CHINESE DESSERT COOKIES - Cookies - Stella D'Oro Biscuit Co. Inc.
CHINESE DRAGON - Analgesics - Superior Trading Co.
CHINESE DRAGON - Kites ☆ - Hi-Flier Manufacturing Co.
CHINESE ENERGETICS YANG - Vitamins and nutritional supplements - Planetary Formulas
CHINESE ENERGETICS YIN - Vitamins and nutritional supplements - Planetary Formulas
CHINESE FLOWERS - Dishes–china - Waterford Wedgewood USA, Inc.
CHINESE FLOWERS - Perfumes - Kiehl's Since 1851, Inc.
CHINESE FORTUNE - Teas - R.C. Bigelow, Inc.
CHINESE GARDEN - Dinnerware–glass - Royal China & Porcelain Companies Inc.
CHINESE GARDEN - Housewares ☆ - Shafford Co. Inc.
CHINESE HERBAL DEFENDER - Health care products - Futurebiotics
CHINESE JUNK FOOD - Food products ☆ - Delbert E. Esche
CHINESE KEY - Floor coverings–carpet and rugs ☆ - Capel, Inc.
CHINESE LAUNDRY - Footwear - Robert L. Goldman
CHINESE LAUNDRY - Footwear–women's - Cels Enterprises Inc.
CHINESE MAID - Food products - Chinese Maid Inc.
CHINESE MELLOW MAGIC - Pharmaceutical preparations - Twin Laboratories, Inc.
CHINESE RIBBON DANCE - Educational materials - Twinson Co.
CHINESE ROSE - Dishes–earthenware - Royal China & Porcelain Companies Inc.
CHINESE SPLENDOR - Area rugs - Couristan Inc.
CHINESE WILLOW - Dinnerware–glass - Franciscan by Johnson Brothers, USA, Inc.
CHINESE YELLOW PAGES - Publisher's imprints - Asia System Media, Inc.
CHINET - Peroxides–inorganic - Keyes Fibre Co.

CHING - Floor coverings–carpet and rugs ☆ - Capel, Inc.
CHING CHEW-AN - Beverages–malt - Ching Chew-An Group
CHING CHOK - Drums–musical instruments - LP Music Group
CHING CHOW - Toys–stuffed - Dakin Inc.
CH'ING DYNASTY - Floor coverings–carpet and rugs - Trans-Ocean Import Co. Inc.
CHING SHIN - Health care products - Tip Wholesaler Distributing
CHING-T'AI-LAN ARTISTS WORKSHOP, THE - Art objects - CHLC Ltd.
CHINGON - Apparel and accessories - Chingon Wear & Accessories
CHININ - Apparel and accessories - Chinin USA, Inc.
CHINIOFON - Pharmaceutical preparations ☆ - City Chemical Corp.
CHINMI - Fish–canned or cured - RGR Network, Inc.
CHINO VINO - Fabrics - Burlington House Fabrics Group
CHINOGRAPH - Pens–fountain ☆ - Canson-Talens Inc.
CHINOISERIE - Wallpaper - Charles Barone Inc.
CHINON - Glassware–household - Durand International
CHINON - Photographic equipment and supplies - Chinon America Inc.
CHINOOK - Wheels–motor vehicle - Sun Metal Products, Inc.
CHINOOK CUDDY CABIN - Boats–motor ☆ - Yar-Craft, Inc.
CHINOOK OUTFITTERS - Shirts - Chinook Trading Co.
CHINOSOL - Fungicides - Vernon Laboratories Inc.
CHINOTTO - Beverages - San Pellegrino USA
CHINTA - Flowers, plants, and seeds ☆ - Coe & Dru Inc.
CHINTZ - Frames–picture - Terragrafics Inc.
CHINTZ - Paper product - Two's Co. Inc.
CHINTZ - Tableware–china - Villeroy and Boch Tableware Ltd.
CHINZEI - Artists' materials - Andrews/Nelson/Whitehead
CHIO - Toys - William J. Embro
CHIODO - Candy - Chiodo Candy Co.
CHIONANTHUS - Pharmaceutical preparations - Sherwood Laboratories Inc.
CHIP - Brushes–paint - Corona Brushes Inc.
CHIP - Brushes–paint - Wooster Brush Co.
CHIP - Frames–eyeglass - Hudson Optical Corp.
CHIP - Toys - Mattel, Inc.
CHIP-A-ROOS - Cookies - Sunshine Biscuits, Inc.
CHIP & EDDY'S - Pet products - Howard M. Cohen
CHIP & PUTT - Golfing equipment - Brandell Products, Inc.
CHIP-AWAY - Golf flags - Chip-Away Products, Inc.
CHIP AWAY - Toy figures - Toymax Inc.
CHIP CITY - Snack foods - Recot, Inc.
CHIP CLIP - Housewares - Guardsman Products, Inc.
CHIP CONNECTION, THE - Food products - Moran Foods, Inc.
CHIP CONTROL - Nail care products - Salon Sciences Inc.
CHIP CUT - Clippers–barber - Marianna Imports, Inc.
CHIP DELIGHTS - Cookies - Springwater Cookie
CHIP FACTORY - Cooking equipment–household ☆ - West Bend Co.
CHIP FIX - Paints - Ziebart International Corp.
CHIP FLIP - Snack cakes ☆ - Interstate Brands Corp.
CHIP GUARD - Cosmetics ☆ - Orly International Inc.
CHIP HILTON - Publisher's imprints - Proserv Television
CHIP-IN - Golfing equipment - Golfsmith International Inc.
CHIP N CHEW - Pet products - Emerald Bird Caddy
CHIP 'N DALE RESCUE RANGERS - Ice cream - Good Humor Corp.
CHIP-N-DRIVE - Golfing equipment - Wittek Golf Supply Co., Inc.
CHIP NO MORE - Skin care products - Ardell International Inc.
CHIP-O-LOTOMUS - Cookies ☆ - Sunshine Biscuits, Inc.
CHIP-O-MATIC - Games ☆ - Milton Bradley Co.
CHIP-O-RACKS - Games - Pacific Game Co.
CHIP-O-SPENSER - Games - Pacific Game Co.
CHIP ON A STICK - Health care products - Baxter International Inc.
CHIP-PIK - Tools–hand-operated - Virtual Industries, Inc.
CHIP SHOTS - Greeting cards - Duck Press
CHIP STEAKS - Meat products–beef - Chip Steak Co. of Buffalo
CHIP THAT IS NOT OFF THE SAME BLOCK, THE - Computer peripheral equipment - Onyx Computer Inc.
CHIP-THE-RIPPER - Toys - Mattel, Inc.
CHIP, THE TALKING TEDDY - Plush toys - Tele-Bear
CHIP TREETOT - Toys - Tonka Corp.
CHIP-WELD - Tools ☆ - Willson/Dalloz Safety
CHIP-ZIP - Bags–plastic - Nabisco Foods Group
CHIPAMOLES - Snack foods - Hofert Trading Co.
CHIPAWAY - Candy - Hershey Chocolate USA
CHIPBONDER 345 - Adhesives and sealants - Loctite Corp.
CHIPBONDER 346 - Adhesives and sealants - Loctite Corp.
CHIPBONDER 347 - Adhesives and sealants - Loctite Corp.
CHIPBONDER 348 - Adhesives and sealants - Loctite Corp.

☆ = Now out of production

CHIPBONDER 360 - Adhesives and sealants - Loctite Corp.
CHIPBONDER 368 - Adhesives and sealants - Loctite Corp.
CHIPBONDER 3603 - Adhesives and sealants - Loctite Corp.
CHIPBURGERS - Food products - Chip Steak Co. of Buffalo
CHIPCOM - Computer software - Chipcom Corp.
CHIPCORDER - Integrated circuits - Information Storage Devices, Inc.
CHIPEE'S - Cookies - Advanced Marketing & Sales
CHIPFRAME - Integrated circuits - Micromodule Systems, Inc.
CHIPICO - Pickles - Chicago Pickle Co. Inc.
CHIPICO - Pickles - Vienna Sausage Manufacturing Co.
CHIPITIN - Golfing equipment - Pinseeker Golf Corp.
CHIPITOS - Snack foods - Bachman Co.
CHIPITS - Cookies - Nabisco Foods Group
CHIPKAN - Containers - Sealright Co., Inc.
CHIPLAB - Computer hardware - Data I/O Corp.
CHIPLESS REMARK-ABLE BINGO SYSTEM - Toys - Spectacular Bingo Designs, Ltd.
CHIPMASTER - Electronic equipment - Amistar Corp.
CHIPMASTER - Electronic equipment - Scheu and Scheu, Inc.
CHIPMUNK - Electronic equipment ☆ - AVL
CHIPMUNK - Rifles - James G. Thompson
CHIPMUNKS - Wallpaper ☆ - Priss Prints Inc.
CHIPMUNKS, THE - Toys–stuffed - CBS Toys
CHIPMUNKS, THE - Shampoos - RC International
CHIP'N SCORE - Games - William L. Shewry
CHIPOS - Snack foods ☆ - General Mills, Inc.
CHIPOTLE - Chili peppers–powdered ☆ - Frieda's, Inc.
CHIPOTLE - Food products - Festin Foods
CHIPOTLE CHA CHA CHA - Sauces - El Paso Chili Co.
CHIPPED AND CONQUERED - Novelty items–paper - Karl M. Kudenchak
CHIPPED BARK - Knives–hunting - Queen Cutlery Co.
CHIPPENDALE - Dishes–china - Waterford Wedgewood USA, Inc.
CHIPPENDALE - Dishes–earthenware ☆ - Gorham Inc.
CHIPPENDALE - Fans–electric - Homestead Products
CHIPPENDALE - Flatware ☆ - Towle Silversmiths
CHIPPENDALE - Floor coverings–carpet and rugs ☆ - Calladium & Marglen
CHIPPENDALE - Furniture - Drexel Heritage Furnishings, Inc.
CHIPPENDALE - Furniture–wood ☆ - Ficks Reed Co. Inc.
CHIPPENDALE - Health care products ☆ - Sunrise Medical
CHIPPENDALE MANOR - Furniture ☆ - Hooker Furniture Corp.
CHIPPENDALES - Air purification systems - Medo Industries, Inc.
CHIPPENDALES - Underwear and nightwear ☆ - Nantucket Industries Inc.
CHIPPENHOOK - Artichokes–canned - Chippenhook Corp.
CHIPPER - Clocks ☆ - General Time Corp. (Westclox/Seth Thomas Div.)
CHIPPER - Dolls ☆ - Effanbee Doll Corp.
CHIPPER - Food products - Ranch Hand Foods Inc.
CHIPPER - Meat products–dried - Chipper Products, Inc.
CHIPPER BY THE DOZEN - Cookies - Chipper by the Dozen, Inc.
CHIPPER CHEW - Meat products–dried - Chipper Products, Inc.
CHIPPER COLT - Rocking horses - Dawn 'til Dusk Inc.
CHIPPER STAX - Meat products–dried - Chipper Products, Inc.
CHIPPER STUFF - Meat products–dried - Chipper Products, Inc.
CHIPPERS - Crackers - Nabisco Foods Group
CHIPPEWA - Boats - Glen-L Marine Designs
CHIPPEWA - Fishing lures - Worth Co.
CHIPPEWA - Footwear - Chippewa Shoe Co.
CHIPPEWA - Lawn mowers - WW Grinder Corp.
CHIPPEWA - Rice - Hicks Wild Rice Co.
CHIPPEWA - Shoes - Justin Cos.
CHIPPEWA - Water–bottled or canned - Chippewa Springs, Ltd.
CHIPPEWA CHARLIE - Fishing lures - Lake Country Products
CHIPPEWA PRIDE - Beverages–malt ☆ - Jacob Leinenkugel Brewing Co., Inc.
CHIPPEWA SPRINGS - Water–bottled or canned - Chippewa Springs, Ltd.
CHIPPIEST CHIPS AROUND - Potato chips ☆ - Hiland Potato Chip Co.
CHIPPLES - Food products ☆ - Breadshop's Natural Foods
CHIPPY - Cookies - Interbake Foods Inc.
CHIPPY - Fishing lures ☆ - Fred Arbogast Co. Inc.
CHIPPY - Scissors–hand-operated - Diane Products Inc.
CHIPPY CHEWS - Cookies ☆ - Sunshine Biscuits, Inc.
CHIPS - Beverages - Vincent M. Cipollone
CHIPS - Candy - Chipurnoi Inc.
CHIPS - Hats ☆ - Arlington Hat Co. Inc.
CHIPS - Paper products - Bonanza Press, Inc.
CHIPS - Soft drinks - Bottlers International Ltd.
CHIPS 1000 - Cookies - Sunshine/Salerno Inc.

CHIPS A PLENTY - Cookies - Ripon Foods, Inc.
CHIPS AHOY! - Cakes–mixes - Nabisco Holdings Corp.
CHIPS AHOY! - Cookies - Nabisco Foods Group
CHIPS AHOY ROCKERS - Cookies - Nabisco Foods Group
CHIPS & CONTRACTS - Games - Psychological Associates, Inc.
CHIPS & TWISTS - Snack foods - Gardetto's
CHIP'S BEST - Dog food - Arkat Feeds Inc.
CHIPS CHOCOLAT - Cookies - Sunshine/Salerno Inc.
CHIPS CHOCOLATE FUDGE SODA - Soft drink - Bottlers International Ltd.
CHIPS CLOWN - Dolls - Russ Berrie and Co., Inc.
CHIPS DELUXE - Cookies - Keebler Co.
CHIPS DELUXE BAKERY CRISP - Cookies - Keebler Co.
CHIPS GLACIAL MINTS - Candy - Chipurnoi Inc.
CHIPS-IT - Ice cream - Jamal's Enterprises, Inc.
CHIPS N CHEWS - Candy - Peerless Confection Co.
CHIPS 'N' CHUNKS - Candy - Comet Confectionery Inc.
CHIPS 'N MORE - Cookies - Nabisco Foods Group
CHIPS 'N TWIGS - Apparel–men's - Fishman and Tobin Inc.
CHIPS OFF THE OLD BLOCK - Figurines - Barnard Enterprises, Inc.
CHIPS O'GOLD - Potato chips - Colorado Gold Chips Inc.
CHIP'S SCOOP 'N FLUSH - Pet products - Chip's Pet Products
CHIPS TELLOS - Cigarettes ☆ - Nat Sherman, Inc.
CHIPSAWAY - Paints - ChipsAway Inc.
CHIPSET - Games - Set Enterprises, Inc.
CHIPSHOT - Kitchen appliances - National Presto Industries, Inc.
CHIPSIES - Cookies ☆ - Keebler Co.
CHIPS'N MIDDLES - Cookies ☆ - Sunshine Biscuits, Inc.
CHIPSTERS - Confections - Carvel Corp.
CHIPSTERS - Snack foods - Nabisco Foods Group
CHIPSTICK - Tools–hand-operated - Service Excellence Organization Inc.
CHIPSTONE - Floor coverings–tile ☆ - Kentile Floors Inc.
CHIPWICH - Ice cream - Chipwich Inc. (Chipwich Div.)
CHIPWICH - Milk - Farmland Dairies Inc.
CHIPWRECKS - Potato chips - Bedre Nut Co., Inc.
CHIQUITA - Cameras - Eastman Kodak Co.
CHIQUITA - Food products - Chiquita Brands, Inc.
CHIQUITA - Fruit drinks–bottled or canned - Naked Juice
CHIQUITA - Toys–stuffed ☆ - Gund, Inc.
CHIQUITA BABY - Baby foods - Chiquita Brands, Inc.
CHIQUITA BREAKFAST BREADS - Bakery products - Chiquita Brands, Inc.
CHIQUITA JUNIOR - Food products - Chiquita Brands, Inc.
CHIQUITA POPS - Food products - Chiquita Brands, Inc.
CHIQUITA TROPICALS - Iced tea–bottled or canned - Chiquita Brands, Inc.
CHIRI - Artists' materials - Andrews/Nelson/Whitehead
CHIRO-COMFORT - Mattresses - Spring Air Bedding Inc.
CHIRO CUSHION - Automotive parts and accessories - Universal Bead Cushion Inc.
CHIRO-KINETICS - Health care products - Promatek Medical Systems Inc.
CHIRO MAGIC - Mattresses - Richards Quality Bedding
CHIRO MINS - Vitamins and nutritional supplements - Natural Organics, Inc.
CHIRO-PEDIC - Mattresses - Schubert Industries, Inc.
CHIRO-PILLOW - Pillows - Regency Products
CHIRO POSTURE - Mattresses - Bemco Associates, Inc.
CHIRO-PROTECTOR - Mattresses - W.S. Manufacturing Corp.
CHIRO-REST - Mattresses - Namaco Industries, Inc.
CHIRO-RUB - Analgesics - Cox Chiro-Manis, Inc.
CHIRO STRESS - Vitamins and nutritional supplements - Natural Organics, Inc.
CHIRO TONIC - Mattresses - U.S. Mattress Corp.
CHIRO VITE - Vitamins and nutritional supplements - Natural Organics, Inc.
CHIRO-ZYME - Vitamins and nutritional supplements - Enzyme Formulations Inc.
CHIROBEDIC - Mattresses and box springs - Spine Align, Inc.
CHIRO.CARE - Vitamins and nutritional supplements - Medical Weight Management Inc.
CHIROMATIC - Medical apparatus ☆ - General Physiotherapy, Inc.
CHIRON - Pharmaceutical preparations - Chiron Corp.
CHIRON OPTIONALLY PILOTED AIRCRAFT - Aircraft - Aurora Flight Sciences Corp.
CHIROPODINE - Foot plasters ☆ - Benjamin Ansehl Co.
CHIROPRACTIC CARING FOR YOU - Apparel and accessories - Semantodontics, Inc.
CHIROPRACTORS CARE - Mattresses - Chittenden & Eastman Co.
CHIROPRO - Juices - Chiro Pro, Inc.
CHIROSSAGE - Medical apparatus ☆ - General Physiotherapy, Inc.
CHIROVISION - Computer software - Multi Sensory Systems, Inc.
CHIRP - Bird feeds ☆ - Agway Country Foods Inc.

☆ = Now out of production

CHIRP - Pet products - Lambert-Kay
CHIRP - Toys–stuffed ☆ - Gund, Inc.
CHIRPIN' CHARLIE - Toys–stuffed - Fun World Inc.
CHIRPIN' CHUMS - Toys–stuffed - Fun World Inc.
CHIRPING CHICKEN - Shirts - Chirping Chicken USA Inc.
CHIRPY HERBY - Toys–stuffed ☆ - Russ Berrie and Co., Inc.
CHIRPY SONGBIRD - Toys–stuffed - Dakin Inc.
CHISANDRA ADAPTOGEN - Herbal products - Swedish Herbal Institute, Ltd.
CHISEL - Adhesives and sealants - Loctite Corp.
CHISEL - Apparel–men's - Sigallo Ltd.
CHISEL TOP - Chemical preparations - Chemproof Polymers, Inc.
CHISHOLM - Lumber - Georgia-Pacific Corp.
CHISLER - Cleaning preparations - N.A. Taylor Co. Inc.
CHISPA CELLARS - Wines - Chispa Cellars
CHISTU - Mushrooms - Joseph Caragol Inc.
CHIT BRAND - Apparel and accessories - Chit Products Co.
CHIT CHAT - Apparel–children's - Isfel Co. Inc.
CHIT CHAT - Crackers - Nabisco Foods Group
CHIT CHAT - Dresses–girls' - Micronaut Industries Inc.
CHIT-CHAT - Teas - Royal House Food Products Co.
CHIT RODRIGUEZ - Apparel and accessories - Stanton Ward
CHIT RODRIGUEZ NO PROFANITY - T-shirts–men's - Stanton Ward
CHITI-MAXX - Vitamins and nutritional supplements - Body Wise International, Inc.
CHITOLEAN - Vitamins and nutritional supplements - Foodscience Laboratories Inc.
CHITOSAN CAPS - Vitamins and nutritional supplements - Vitamin Research Products Inc.
CHITTY CHAT BEARS - Infant product - Playskool Baby Inc.
CHIU CHIU RABBIT - Toys–stuffed ☆ - Fun World Inc.
CHIVALRY - Computer software - Optimum Resource, Inc.
CHIVALRY - Floor coverings–carpet and rugs ☆ - Interloom Ltd.
CHIVALRY - Floor coverings–carpet and rugs ☆ - Robertex Associates Inc.
CHIVALRY - Floor coverings–carpet and rugs ☆ - Royalweve Carpet Mills
CHIVALRY - Glassware–household - Owens-Illinois Inc. (Libbey Div.)
CHIVAS REGAL - Liquors - House of Seagram
CHIVAS ROYAL-SALUTE - Liquors - House of Seagram
CHIVIER - Cottage cheese ☆ - H.P. Hood & Sons Inc.
CHIX - Fabrics–broadcloth - Chicopee
CHIX-B-Q - Food products - Pierre Frozen Foods Inc.
CHIX-STIX - Meat products–poultry - Pierce Foods Corp.
CHIX THE CHICKEN STATION - Food products - Orion Enterprises, Inc.
CHIXTEX - Fabrics–broadcloth - Chicopee
CHIYODA - Wines ☆ - Suntory International Corp.
CHIZ'L - Markers–felt-tip ☆ - Chartpak
CHIZZEL - Artists' materials - Stangren Co.
CHLO-AMINE - Pharmaceutical preparations - Bayer Corp. (Pharmaceutical Division)
CHLOE - Apparel and accessories ☆ - Jerry Kohn Inc.
CHLOE - Perfumes - Parfums International Ltd.
CHLOE - Toys - Tonka Corp.
CHLOE FLEURON - Dinnerware–glass - WMF/USA
CHLOE NARCISSE - Colognes - Elizabeth Arden Inc.
CHLOR-10 - Pharmaceutical preparations ☆ - Vortech Pharmaceuticals
CHLOR-100 - Pharmaceutical preparations ☆ - Vortech Pharmaceuticals
CHLOR-A-VAC - Pumps–water - Gas Induction, Inc.
CHLOR-FREE - Water purification systems - Aqua-Pure International
CHLOR-HYDRO - Pharmaceutical preparations ☆ - Vortech Pharmaceuticals
CHLOR-KIL - Pesticides–agricultural ☆ - Durham's Products Co.
CHLOR-MAL - Pharmaceutical preparations ☆ - Rugby Laboratories Inc.
CHLOR-O-FILL - Pet products - Alfa-Pet Inc.
CHLOR-OFF - Hair care products - William B. Hugg, Inc.
CHLOR-OUT - Water treating compounds - Silco Pet Products
CHLOR-PHEN - Pharmaceutical preparations - C.O. Truxton Inc.
CHLOR-PZ - Tranquilizers ☆ - Rhone-Poulenc Rorer Pharmaceuticals Inc.
CHLOR-REST - Pharmaceutical preparations - Rugby Laboratories Inc.
CHLOR-TERGENT - Detergents - Oakite Products, Inc.
CHLOR-THANE - Insecticides ☆ - Security Product Co.
CHLOR TRIMETON - Antihistamine - Schering Corp.
CHLOR-TRIMETON - Antihistamine preparations - Schering-Plough Healthcare Products
CHLORA-TABS - Veterinary pharmaceutical preparations ☆ - Evsco Pharmaceuticals
CHLORADERM - Soap - Sporicidin International
CHLORADONNA - Pharmaceutical preparations ☆ - Ulmer Pharmacal Co.

CHLORAL-METHYLOL - Pharmaceutical preparations ☆ - Ulmer Pharmacal Co.
CHLORALERT - Gastroscopes - Fischer & Porter Co.
CHLORALOY - Sheet waterproofing - Noble Co.
CHLORAM-X - Water purification systems - Aquascience Research Group Inc.
CHLORAMINE BUSTER - Pet products - Aquatic Biotechnologies Inc.
CHLORAPAP - Pharmaceutical preparations - C.S. Ruckstuhl Co. Inc.
CHLORAPREP - Pharmaceutical preparations - Medi-Flex Hospital Products
CHLORASAN - Veterinary product - American Home Products Corp.
CHLORASEPTIC - Health care products - Procter & Gamble Co.
CHLORASONE - Veterinary pharmaceutical preparations - Evsco Pharmaceuticals
CHLORATE - Pharmaceutical preparations ☆ - Physician Sales & Service
CHLORAZONE - Chemical preparations - Lavelle Industries Inc.
CHLORCAPS - Pharmaceutical preparations ☆ - Pharmex Inc.
CHLORDEX - Vitamins and nutritional supplements - Health Care Industries Inc.
CHLORDINUM SEALERS - Pharmaceutical preparations ☆ - Lemmon Co.
CHLORELLA - Vitamins and nutritional supplements - Vitamin Research Products Inc.
CHLORESIN - Pharmaceutical preparations - Afassco
CHLORESIUM - Toothpaste - Rystan Co. Inc.
CHLORETONE - Pharmaceutical preparations ☆ - Parke-Davis
CHLOREX - Pharmaceutical preparations - C.S. Ruckstuhl Co. Inc.
CHLORFOS - Insecticides - Griffin Corp.
CHLORI-BOUY - Water purification systems - Chem Lab Products, Inc.
CHLORIDAMINE - Pharmaceutical preparations - Barre-National, Inc.
CHLORIMED - Hair care products - John Amico Expressive Hair Care Products
CHLORINE FREE PROCESS - Paper–writing - Cross Pointe Paper Corp.
CHLORISTAMINE - Pharmaceutical preparations ☆ - Keene Pharmaceuticals Inc.
CHLORITON - Pharmaceutical preparations - C.S. Ruckstuhl Co. Inc.
CHLORO-SOLV - Degreasing solvents - State Chemical Manufacturing Co.
CHLOROBALM - Health care products ☆ - JMI-Canton Pharmaceuticals
CHLOROFON-F - Pharmaceutical preparations - Rugby Laboratories Inc.
CHLOROFRESH - Deodorants–personal - Nature's Way Products, Inc.
CHLOROMATIC - Deodorizers - Coughlan Products Corp.
CHLOROMINE - Health care products - Kay Pharmacal Co. Inc.
CHLOROMYCETIN - Antibiotics - Parke-Davis
CHLOROMYXIN - Pharmaceutical preparations ☆ - Parke-Davis
CHLORON - Enamels - Pratt & Lambert United, Inc.
CHLOROPTIC - Ophthalmic goods - Allergan, Inc.
CHLOROPTIC SOP - Ophthalmic goods - Allergan, Inc.
CHLOROSTAT - Pharmaceutical preparations - Jones Medical Industries, Inc. (Medical Div.)
CHLOROTHEOPHYLLINE - Pharmaceutical preparations - City Chemical Corp.
CHLOROZYME FRESH - Vitamins and nutritional supplements - Great Life Laboratories Inc.
CHLORPHED - Pharmaceutical preparations - Roberts/Hauck Pharmaceuticals Inc.
CHLORPHEDRIN - Pharmaceutical preparations ☆ - Scrip-Physician Supply Co.
CHLORPHENIST - Pharmaceutical preparations - Bio-Factor Laboratories
CHLORPOX - Pharmaceutical preparations ☆ - Kenyon Drug Co. Inc.
CHLORSERP-250 - Pharmaceutical preparations ☆ - Veratex Group
CHLORTAB - Pharmaceutical preparations ☆ - Vortech Pharmaceuticals
CHLORTRINE - Chemical preparations ☆ - Applied Biochemists, Inc.
CHLORTRINE SPOT-KIL - Herbicides ☆ - Applied Biochemists, Inc.
CHLORULAN - Pharmaceutical preparations - Lannett Co. Inc.
CHO-CHOSAN - Pottery ☆ - Rubens Originals
CHO-LICS - Candy ☆ - E. Rosen Co.
CHO PET - Sporting goods - Mueller Sports Medicine Inc.
CHOATE - Pharmaceutical preparations - Bickmore Inc.
CHOC - Beverages–malt - Pete's Place of Krebs, Inc.
CHOC - Cosmetics - Lancome
CHOC-AU-LAIT - Baking chocolate - Guittard Chocolate Corp.
CHOC FUL O FRUIT - Frosting - Brokay Products Inc.
CHOC FULL O'CHIPS - Cookies ☆ - Natural Nectar Corp.
CHOC-O-BAR - Pet products ☆ - Gimborn U.S., Inc.
CHOC-O-DOUGH - Food products - Donutland Inc.
CHOC-O-FLOSS - Candy - Gold Medal Products Co.
CHOC-O-LANTERNS - Candy - R.M. Palmer Co.
CHOC-O-LETS - Animal feeds - Black Industries Inc.
CHOC-O-LICIOUS - Chocolate syrup ☆ - Pet Dairy
CHOC-O-MALT - Ice cream - Nestle USA
CHOC-O-PUP - Pet products - Gilpa

☆ = Now out of production

CHOC-O-TACO - Ice cream - Jack & Jill Ice Cream Co.
CHOC 'OH'S - Chocolate bars - Saco Foods, Inc.
CHOC-OLA - Beverages ☆ - Pokka, Inc.
CHOC-QUILIZER - Vitamins and nutritional supplements - Tinos, LLC
CHOC' SAUCE - Chocolate syrup - Casino North America
CHOC-SHOP - Candy - Adams & Brooks, Inc.
CHOCAID - Novelty items - Lemberger Candy Corp.
CHOCALATY PAYDAY - Candy ☆ - Leaf, Inc.
CHOCANAT - Food products - Nutracane, Inc.
CHOCANET - Chocolate candy - Immunopath Profile, Inc.
CHOCK FULL O' BEANS - Coffee - Chock Full O'Nuts Corp.
CHOCK FULL O' NUTS - Apparel and accessories - Chock Full O'Nuts Corp.
CHOCK FULL O'NUTS - Coffee - Chock Full O'Nuts Corp.
CHOCK O'CCINO - Coffee - Chock Full O'Nuts Corp.
CHOCKS - Vitamins and nutritional supplements - Miles Inc.
CHOCKS PLUS IRON - Vitamins and nutritional supplements - Miles Inc.
CHOC'LA CREME - Yogurt - Cultured Foods Inc.
CHOCLAIRS - Candy ☆ - American Chicle Co.
CHOC'LATE LOVIN' SPOON CAKE - Bakery products - Sweet Street Desserts, Inc.
CHOCO - Food products - Peter Paul
CHOCO - Ice cream cones - Sweetheart Cup Co. Inc.
CHOCO-BAKE - Baking chocolate - Nestle USA
CHOCO BLEND - Tobacco products ☆ - Lane Ltd.
CHOCO-BLISS - Snack cakes - Interstate Brands Corp.
CHOCO-BLOCKS - Candy ☆ - Chex Co.
CHOCO CHILL - Beverages ☆ - Nestle Beverage Co.
CHOCO-CHIPS - Candy ☆ - Chex Co.
CHOCO CHUPS - Candy ☆ - Uniconfis Corp.
CHOCO DADDY POP - Candy - Nabisco Foods Group
CHOCO-DELIGHTS - Cakes - Interstate Brands Corp.
CHOCO-DILES - Snack cakes - Interstate Brands Corp.
CHOCO D'LITE - Food products - Paradise Valley Foods, Inc.
CHOCO DOOS - Cereal - Amway Corp.
CHOCO LEIBNIZ - Biscuits - Bahlsen Inc.
CHOCO-LICIOUS - Snack cakes - Interstate Brands Corp.
CHOCO' LITE - Candy ☆ - Nestle USA
CHOCO-LOTTO - Chocolate candy - Lanco Corp.
CHOCO LUMPS - Candy - Doug Johnson, Inc.
CHOCO MANIA - Cereal - General Mills, Inc.
CHOCO-MINT - Tobacco–chewing or smoking - Amar Blends Co.
CHOCO POPPO - Popcorn - Panache Chocolatier
CHOCO POPS - Popcorn - Popcorn Explosion Inc.
CHOCO SHREDS - Cakes - Cocoline Chocolate Co.
CHOCO-STAR - Cookies - Bahlsen Inc.
CHOCO TACO - Ice cream - Choco Taco Co.
CHOCO VITA D'LITE - Beverages - Paradise Valley Foods, Inc.
CHOCO-ZABA - Candy ☆ - Annabelle Candy Co. Inc.
CHOCOA - Cocoa–powders or mixes - Bradway Chocolate Co.
CHOCOBAREN - Candy ☆ - Storck USA L.P.
CHOCOCHIP - Toys–stuffed ☆ - Gund, Inc.
CHOCOCO - Cordials ☆ - David Sherman Corp.
CHOCOHOLICS SURVIVAL KIT - Candy - Green County of Wisconsin
CHOCOLA - Chocolate bars - Food For Thought Inc.
CHOCOLANTERNS - Candy ☆ - R.M. Palmer Co.
CHOCOLAT NOUVEAU - Chocolate candy - Marie Ford
CHOCOLAT SWIRLS - Chocolate syrup - Michel et Mere, Inc.
CHOCOLATE - Dishes–earthenware ☆ - Denby USA Limited
CHOCOLATE - Lipsticks - Tinkerbell
CHOCOLATE - Puzzles - Joslin Photo Puzzle Co.
CHOCOLATE - Skates–roller - Rollerblade, Inc.
CHOCOLATE - Toys–stuffed - Ty, Inc.
CHOCOLATE AGGIES - Candy - Dearborn
CHOCOLATE ANATOMY KIT - Candy - Hearts & Flowers Candy Co.
CHOCOLATE BAR - Liquors ☆ - Paramount Distillers Inc.
CHOCOLATE BEAR - Toys–stuffed ☆ - Gund, Inc.
CHOCOLATE BLASTER - Chocolate syrup - Inagra
CHOCOLATE BODY PAINT - Novelty items - Tom and Sally's Handmade Chocolates, Inc.
CHOCOLATE BUDDIES - Candy ☆ - Sweet Candy Co.
CHOCOLATE CANDI - Dolls - Mattel, Inc.
CHOCOLATE CANDY CANE - Coffee - Saramar Corp.
CHOCOLATE CARAMEL CREAMS - Candy - Goetze's Candy Co., Inc.
CHOCOLATE CARTOON FUNNIES - Candy ☆ - Casanova Chocolate Co.
CHOCOLATE CHANTILLY - Cookies - Pepperidge Farm Inc.
CHOCOLATE CHARLIE - Candy - Claeys Candy Inc.

CHOCOLATE CHECKERS - Candy - World's Finest Chocolate, Inc.
CHOCOLATE CHERRY KISS - Coffee - Saramar Corp.
CHOCOLATE CHESS - Puddings–mixes - Charles Freihofer Baking Co.
CHOCOLATE CHIP FAMILY, THE - Dolls - Freda Kimbrew
CHOCOLATE CHIP MINT - Lipsticks - Tinkerbell
CHOCOLATE CHIP PARADE - Cookies - Mother's Cake & Cookie Co.
CHOCOLATE CHIPLETS - Ice cream - Vroman Foods Inc.
CHOCOLATE CHOICE, THE - Cakes - Tasty Baking Co.
CHOCOLATE CHOPPERS - Candy - R.M. Palmer Co.
CHOCOLATE CLASSICS - Candy - Fanny Farmer Candy Shops Inc.
CHOCOLATE CLOUDS - Pastries - PF Brands, Inc.
CHOCOLATE COINS - Chocolate candy - Tom and Sally's Handmade Chocolates, Inc.
CHOCOLATE COOKIESAURUS - Cookies ☆ - Sunshine Biscuits, Inc.
CHOCOLATE CORKS - Food products - Universal Foods Corp.
CHOCOLATE COTTAGE - Candy ☆ - Eddyleon Chocolate Co. Inc.
CHOCOLATE COW - Beverages - Yoo-Hoo Chocolate Beverage Corp.
CHOCOLATE COW TALES - Candy - Goetze's Candy Co., Inc.
CHOCOLATE CRATER CONE MIX - Bakery products - Dawn Food Products Inc.
CHOCOLATE CRAYONS - Chocolate candy - Lemberger Candy Corp.
CHOCOLATE DECADENCE - Bakery products - Nonni's, Corp.
CHOCOLATE DECADENCE - Confections - Famous Pacific Dessert Co.
CHOCOLATE DELIGHT - Beverages - White Rock Products Corp.
CHOCOLATE DELIGHT - Chocolate milk - Givaudan Rare Flavors
CHOCOLATE DELIGHT - Snack foods - Red Chip Investment Group
CHOCOLATE DREAM BABYCAKES - Food products - Baby Watson Cheesecake Inc.
CHOCOLATE DROP - Dolls - Mattel, Inc.
CHOCOLATE DUET - Cheese - Love at First Bite
CHOCOLATE DUTCH MINTS - Candy - Herman Goelitz Candy Co., Inc.
CHOCOLATE EDITIONS, INC. - Chocolate candy - The Planning Factory, Inc.
CHOCOLATE FACTORY - Candy - Superior Fruit & Confections
CHOCOLATE FANTASIES - Chocolate candy ☆ - Latham Studios
CHOCOLATE FILM - Chocolate candy - Lemberger Candy Corp.
CHOCOLATE FINGER PAINT - Chocolate syrup - Soft Wear Corp.
CHOCOLATE FLAVOR BABIES - Candy ☆ - Henry Heide, Inc.
CHOCOLATE FLAVOR MINT TEES - Candy ☆ - Henry Heide, Inc.
CHOCOLATE FUNK - Toys - Michael Wilkerson Jones
CHOCOLATE GOLD INGOTS - Chocolate candy - Lemberger Candy Corp.
CHOCOLATE GRAHAMS - Cereal - New Morn, Inc.
CHOCOLATE HOUSE - Candy - Chocolate House, Inc.
CHOCOLATE ICE 'N BASE - Frosting - Dawn Food Products Inc.
CHOCOLATE JOLLIES - Chocolate candy - Hooper's Chocolates
CHOCOLATE KISS - Cosmetics - Hard Candy, Inc.
CHOCOLATE LOVERS CHIPS DELUXE - Cookies - Keebler Co.
CHOCOLATE MACADAMIA MONET - Candy - Hearts & Flowers Candy Co.
CHOCOLATE MANIA - Food products - International Multifoods Corp.
CHOCOLATE MAVEN - Candy - Edible Arts Inc.
CHOCOLATE MINTS - Candy - Judson-Atkinson Candies
CHOCOLATE MOOSE - Apparel–children's - Johnston Inc.
CHOCOLATE MOOSE - Ice cream - Emack & Bolio's
CHOCOLATE MOOSE, THE - Toys–stuffed ☆ - Dakin Inc.
CHOCOLATE MOUSSE - Lipsticks - Honey & Spice Toiletries
CHOCOLATE MOUSSE BALLS, THE - Candy - David Glass
CHOCOLATE MOUSSE CAKE, THE - Candy - David Glass
CHOCOLATE N' VANILLA - Toys–stuffed ☆ - Dakin Inc.
CHOCOLATE NUGGET - Cookies ☆ - Sunshine Biscuits, Inc.
CHOCOLATE NUGGETS - Candy - S.L. Kaye Co., Inc.
CHOCOLATE ORANGE STICKS - Candy - Sweet Candy Co.
CHOCOLATE PARFAIT - Candy - Nabisco Foods Group
CHOCOLATE PATCH, THE - Chocolate candy ☆ - Urban Imports
CHOCOLATE PEANUT PERFECTION! - Candy - Promotion in Motion, Inc.
CHOCOLATE PEOPLE, THE - Candy - Hershey Foods Corp.
CHOCOLATE PETALS - Cookies - De Beukelaer Corp.
CHOCOLATE PETTICOAT TAILS - Cookies - Simmers Products
CHOCOLATE PIX - Cooking equipment–household - Chocolate Pix Inc.
CHOCOLATE POPS - Candy - Home of the Hebert Candies, Inc.
CHOCOLATE PRETZEL BARK BAR - Chocolate bars - Alan E. King
CHOCOLATE RASPBERRY STICKS - Candy - Sweet Candy Co.
CHOCOLATE RASPBERRY TRUFFLE - Bakery products - Cheesecake Factory Inc.
CHOCOLATE REEF - Candy - Hearts & Flowers Candy Co.
CHOCOLATE ROCKERS - Candy - Frankford Candy & Chocolate Co. Inc.
CHOCOLATE ROYALE - Bakery products - Tasty Baking Co.
CHOCOLATE ROYALE - Beverages–carbonated ☆ - Monarch Co., Inc.

CHOCOLATE ROYALE - Cakes - Godiva Chocolatier
CHOCOLATE SANDWICH - Confections - Sara Lee Corp.
CHOCOLATE SHOP - Dolls - Mattel, Inc.
CHOCOLATE SHOPPE - Confections - Hershey Foods Corp.
CHOCOLATE SMOOTHIES - Candy - Hooper's Chocolates
CHOCOLATE SNAPS - Cookies - Nabisco Foods Group
CHOCOLATE SOLDIER - Beverages–carbonated ☆ - Monarch Co., Inc.
CHOCOLATE SOY 50 - Vitamins and nutritional supplements - Re-Vita Manufacturing Co., Inc.
CHOCOLATE SPECIALTIES - Candy - Gertrude Hawks Chocolate Inc.
CHOCOLATE SPOONS - Novelty items - Tom and Sally's Handmade Chocolates, Inc.
CHOCOLATE STREET, USA - Chocolate candy - Beth M. Barton
CHOCOLATE SUICIDE - Cakes - Heidi's Pastry, Inc.
CHOCOLATE SUPREME - Food products - Bread and Chocolate
CHOCOLATE SUPREME - Yogurts - Whitney Foods, Inc.
CHOCOLATE SWIRL - Cookies ☆ - Barbara's Bakery, Inc.
CHOCOLATE TEENS - Bakery products ☆ - Tasty Baking Co.
CHOCOLATE THUNDER/WHITE LIGHTNING - Confections - Famous Pacific Dessert Co.
CHOCOLATE TIME - Beverages - White Rock Products Corp.
CHOCOLATE TREAT - Food products - Weight Watchers International, Inc.
CHOCOLATE TRIO - Candy - Ferrara Pan Candy Co., Inc.
CHOCOLATE TRUFFLE - Toys–stuffed ☆ - Gund, Inc.
CHOCOLATE TRUFFLE, THE - Candy - Ternus & Co., Inc.
CHOCOLATE TWINS - Cakes - McKee Foods Corp.
CHOCOLATE VELVET - Food products ☆ - Cal-Gar Corp.
CHOCOLATE WHIP - Candy - Chocolate House, Inc.
CHOCOLATE WONDER - Candy - Alberto-Culver Co.
CHOCOLATES OF DISTINCTION - Candy - Laymon Candy Co. Inc.
CHOCOLATIER - Cookies - Pepperidge Farm Inc.
CHOCOLATROL - Novelty items - Didi Goldmark
CHOCOLATTE BARS - Confections - Famous Pacific Dessert Co.
CHOCOLATY FORTUNE - Candy - Lanco Corp.
CHOCOLINCHEN - Chocolate candy ☆ - Storck USA L.P.
CHOCOLOTTIE - Dolls - Mattel, Inc.
CHOCOMEL - Milk - Nutricia Inc.
CHOCOMETZ - Chocolate candy - Morris National Inc.
CHOCONANA - Dairy products - Concord Foods Inc.
CHOCORAMA - Spices and extracts - David Michael & Co.
CHOCOVIVA! - Bakery products - International Multifoods Corp.
CHOCTAW - Paper–bond - Weyerhaeuser Co.
CHOCTAW CHIEF - Archery equipment - Rollin Wilson Co. Inc.
CHOCTAW MAID - Meat products–poultry - Choctaw Maid Farms Inc.
CHOCZELS - Chocolate candy - Toad-Ally Snax Inc.
CHODI - Apparel and accessories - Dexter Knitting Mills Inc.
CHOICE - Apparel–women's ☆ - Jonathan Logan Inc.
CHOICE - Bottles–plastic - Kiddie Products, Inc.
CHOICE - Brushes–hair - Helen of Troy Corp.
CHOICE - Cigarettes - Brown & Williamson Tobacco Corp.
CHOICE - Fabrics - Capital Carousel Inc.
CHOICE - Fireplace equipment ☆ - Schaefer Co.
CHOICE - Glass products - D & L Stained Glass Supply, Inc.
CHOICE - Hearing aids - Magnatone Hearing Aid Corp.
CHOICE - Meat products–poultry ☆ - Choice One Foods
CHOICE - Pipes–tobacco - S.M. Frank & Co. Inc. (Kaywoodie-Yello-Bole-Medico)
CHOICE - Recording label ☆ - MMO Music Group Inc.
CHOICE - Seafood products–canned or cured ☆ - Arista Industries Inc.
CHOICE - Snowboards - Choice Snowboard Co.
CHOICE - Soap - Colgate-Palmolive Co.
CHOICE - Tools–machine - Choice Corp.
CHOICE - Toothbrushes - NutraMax Products Inc.
CHOICE - Trading cards and stamps - Malibu Comics Entertainment, Inc.
CHOICE - Watches - K & H Time Inc.
CHOICE BY MATT'S - Beverages–malt ☆ - F.X. Matt Brewing Co.
CHOICE CROP - Fruit drinks–bottled or canned - Golden Gem Growers Inc.
CHOICE CUTS - Dog food ☆ - Kal Kan Foods, Inc.
CHOICE CUTS - Seafood products–fresh or frozen - Aquastar Inc.
CHOICE DECALS - Decals and transfers - Choice Decals
CHOICE HOTELS - Vitamins and nutritional supplements - Choice Hotels International Inc.
CHOICE IS CANOLA!, THE - Food products - Nabisco Foods Group
CHOICE IS CLEAR, THE - Gasoline ☆ - Custom Design Technologies, Inc.
CHOICE-KUT - Kitchen appliances - Sunbeam-Oster Household Products
CHOICE MEAT COMPANY, INC. - Meat products ☆ - Choice One Foods

CHOICE OF CHAMPIONS - Golfing equipment ☆ - Northwestern Golf Co.
CHOICE OF NORWAY - Seafood products–fresh or frozen ☆ - King Oscar Inc.
CHOICE OF THE WEST - Food products - Western Family Foods, Inc.
CHOICE ONE - Lumber - Scotty's Inc.
CHOICE ONE FOODS - Food products - Choice One Foods
CHOICE ORGANIC TEAS - Teas–herbal - Granum Inc.
CHOICE PRODUCTS - Lamps ☆ - Custom Design Technologies, Inc.
CHOICE SEATS - Chairs - American Furniture Co. Inc.
CHOICE SELECTION - Candy - William's Candy Co.
CHOICE, THE - Pumps - Georgia Power Co.
CHOICE TIME - Floor coverings–carpet and rugs - Barrett Carpet Mills Inc.
CHOICE WORDS - Toys - Michael D. Hitt
CHOICELINK - Computer storage devices–magnetic - Choice Hotels International Inc.
CHOICES - Apparel–women's - Bugle Boy Industries, Inc.
CHOICES - Floor coverings - Congoleum Corp.
CHOICES - Furniture - Trendway Corp.
CHOICES - Games - Rainfall Inc.
CHOICES - Wallpaper ☆ - Camelot Design Studios
CHOICES - Window coverings ☆ - Verosol
CHOICES & DECISIONS - Educational materials - Visa International Service Association
CHOICES, CHOICES - Computer software - Tom Snyder Productions, Inc.
CHOICEWOOD - Wood products - Weyerhaeuser Co.
CHOIR PUBLISHING CO. - Music–sheet - Jackman Music Corp.
CHOIR THE NATIONAL CHRISTIAN - Recording label - National Christian Choir, Inc.
CHOKIN - Artists' materials - Dynasty Import Co.
CHOKO BUTTER - Food products - Goya Foods, Inc.
CHOKOS - Cereal ☆ - Kellogg Co.
CHOL-FREE - Cheese - Swissrose International Inc.
CHOLAC - Pharmaceutical preparations - Alra Laboratories, Inc.
CHOLAN HMB - Pharmaceutical preparations - Fisons Corp.
CHOLEDOM - Pharmaceutical preparations ☆ - Edom Laboratories Inc.
CHOLEDYL - Pharmaceutical preparations - Parke-Davis
CHOLERVAC-PM-1 - Pharmaceutical preparations - Intervet, Inc.
CHOLES GENIC - Health care products - Pacific Genesis Inc.
CHOLESEN - Pharmaceutical preparations - Bios
CHOLESSTEROL - Vitamins and nutritional supplements - Williams Marketing Group International, Inc.
CHOLEST-ARREST - Vitamins and nutritional supplements - Great Life Laboratories, Inc.
CHOLEST CONTROL - Pharmaceuticals - Advantage Life Products Inc.
CHOLEST-U-LOW - Teas - Vegetarian Health Inc.
CHOLESTA-LO - Health care products - Futurebiotics
CHOLESTAGEL - Pharmaceutical preparations - Geltex, Inc.
CHOLESTAID - Health care products ☆ - Performance Labs Inc.
CHOLESTATIN - Health care products - Traco Laboratories Inc.
CHOLESTATIN - Vitamins and nutritional supplements - Traco Labs, Inc.
CHOLESTCONTROL - Health care products - Advantage Life Products Inc.
CHOLESTERADE - Vitamins and nutritional supplements - Phoenix Advanced Technology, Inc.
CHOLESTEROL BLOCKER - Health care products - Nature Health
CHOLESTEROL COUNTER - Dietary and nutritional supplements - Great Earth Distribution Inc.
CHOLESTEROL COUNTERS - Milk ☆ - Smith's Dairy Products Co.
CHOLESTEROL SUPPORT - Vitamins and nutritional supplements - Reese Chemical Co.
CHOLESTEROUT - Pharmaceutical preparations - Golden West Medical Supply Co.
CHOLESTIN - Vitamins and nutritional supplements - Pharmanex, Inc.
CHOLESTREX - Vitamins and nutritional supplements - Source Natural, Inc.
CHOLESTREX - Vitamins and nutritional supplements - Source Naturals
CHOLESTROL - Hair care products - Master Chemical Co.
CHOLESTROL HAIR CARE PRODUCTS - Hair care products - Para Laboratories Inc.
CHOLEX - Health care products - Healthwatchers System
CHOLINE CAPS - Vitamins and nutritional supplements - Vitamin Research Products Inc.
CHOLINE COCKTAIL - Vitamins and nutritional supplements - Twinlab
CHOLINOID - Pharmaceutical preparations - Goldline Laboratories, Inc.
CHOLLA CHAIN - Pet products - JungleTalk Inc.
CHOLLA CHEWS - Pet products - JungleTalk Inc.
CHOLLA CITY - Giftware - The Crab Connection
CHOLLY - Toys–stuffed ☆ - Russ Berrie and Co., Inc.

☆ = Now out of production

CHOLLY DOLL - Dolls - Fisher-Price, Inc.
CHOLMONDLEY'S - Food products - Orth Co. (Bruce)
CHOLNIXX - Health care products - Pharma Botanixx
CHOLO-PAK - Vitamins and nutritional supplements - Better Health Products
CHOLOGRAFIN MEGLUMINE - Pharmaceutical preparations - Bristol-Myers Squibb Co.
CHOLOREX - Pharmaceutical preparations - C.S. Ruckstuhl Co. Inc.
CHOLOXIN - Pharmaceutical preparations - Boots Pharmaceuticals Inc.
CHOLPHYTIN VMH - Health care products - Pacific BioLogic Inc.
CHOLYBAR - Pharmaceutical preparations ☆ - Parke-Davis
CHOMBERT BOUTIQUE - Apparel–women's - Chombert Inc.
CHOMBREY - Floor coverings–carpet and rugs - Evans-Black Carpet Mills
CHOMEY CHEWS - Pet products - Hill Top Enterprises
CHOMOCHA CHILLER - Coffee - Coffee Beanery Ltd.
CHOMP! - Computer software - Cosmi Corp.
CHOMP STIX - Pet products - Mason Distributing
CHOMPERS - Apparel and accessories - David Nelems
CHOMPERS - Dog food - Hubbard Milling Co. (Landon Div.)
CHOMPERS - Fishing lures - Table Rock Bait and Tackle Co.
CHOMPERS - Tools - Zenith Cutter Co.
CHOMPS - Candy - Sunmark Inc.
CHONDROITIN SULFATE CAPS - Vitamins and nutritional supplements - Vitamin Research Products Inc.
CHONDROPROTEC - Pharmaceutical preparations - Hymed Group Corp.
CHONDROYTAMINE - Vitamins and nutritional supplements - Olympian Labs, Inc.
CHONE AUX LOUPS - Floor coverings - Parquet de France Inc.
CHONES! - Underwear and nightwear - Chones Inc.
CHOO-B-DOOS - Candy - Murray-Allen International Inc.
CHOO CHOO - Beverages - B & M Products, Inc.
CHOO CHOO BONES - Dog food - J. Narby Inc.
CHOO CHOO CHARLIE - Toys - Tomy America, Inc.
CHOO CHOO CHEWIES - Food products - National Railroad Passenger Corp.
CHOO CHOO CHIPS - Dog food - J. Narby Inc.
CHOO CHOO GRAHAMS - Cookies - Happiness Express Inc.
CHOO-CHOO NURSERY - Fabrics - VIP/VIP Crafts
CHOO-CHOO PATRICK - Candy - Zachary Confections Inc.
CHOO-CHOO PETS - Toys–stuffed - Fun World Inc.
CHOO CHOO STICKS - Dog food - J. Narby Inc.
CHOO CHOO TEDDY - Toys–stuffed - Dakin Inc.
CHOO CHOO TRAIN - Crib mirrors - Pansy Ellen Products, Inc.
CHOO CHOO TRAIN - Toys - Kids II, Inc.
CHOO-HOOVES - Pet products - Products Carousel Inc.
CHOO-HOOVES ROPER - Dog food - Products Carousel Inc.
CHOOBLES - Pet products - Petstuff, Inc.
CHOOGO - Apparel–children's - Choozie Wear Corp.
CHOOKERS - Apparel and accessories ☆ - Toy-Tex, Inc.
CHOOKIES - Candy - Brach Van Houten Holding Inc.
CHOOKIES - Cookies - Bedre Nut Co., Inc.
CHOOSE-A-CHAIN - Jewelry - Lasting Impressions Inc.
CHOOSE & USE - Paints - Warren Paint & Color
CHOOSE CHANGE BK - Apparel–men's - Jack Schwartz Shoes, Inc.
CHOOSE OR LOSE - Posters - Viacom International Inc.
CHOOSE THE RIGHT - Apparel and accessories - Love Works
CHOOSE WISELY. LIVE WELL. - Broadcasting stations–cable television - National Media Corp.
CHOOSE YOUR OWN ADVENTURE - Publisher's imprints - Bantam Doubleday Dell Publishing Group, Inc.
CHOOSE YOUR SHOT CAREFULLY - Ammunition - Federal-Hoffman, Inc.
CHOOSESMART! - Computer software - Expert Buying Systems, Inc.
CHOOZ - Antacids - Schering-Plough Healthcare Products
CHOOZ - Pet products - Nylabone Products
CHOOZ CHEESE CHEW - Pet food - T.F.H. Publications, Inc.
CHOOZIE - Apparel–children's - Choozie Wear Corp.
CHOP & CHOP - Cutting boards - New Age Products, Inc.
CHOP-CHOP - Food processors - Collins Products Co.
CHOP N' BLOCK - Food products - AMK for Service
CHOP-O-MATIC - Housewares - RonCo Inc.
CHOP RIGHT - Frames–picture - Chop Right, Inc.
CHOP SUEY - Quilts - Extra Special Products Corp.
CHOP TO THE TOP - Clothing - Tomahawk Press
CHOPARD - Watches - Chopard Watch Corp.
CHOPARD GENEVE - Watches - Chopard Watch Corp.
CHOPIN - Floor coverings–carpet and rugs - Columbus Mills, Inc.
CHOPIN - Glassware–household ☆ - Avitra Corp.
CHOPIN - Hearing aids - Magnatone Hearing Aid Corp.

CHOPLETS - Food products - Worthington Foods Inc.
CHOPMEN - Publisher's imprints - Advent Books Inc.
CHOPPER - Bicycles - Columbia Manufacturing Inc.
CHOPPER - Toys - Tonka Corp.
CHOPPER T - Musical instrument accessories - Dimarzio, Inc.
CHOPPER, THE - Musical instrument accessories - Dimarzio, Inc.
CHOPPERS - Candy - Glenn Confections Inc.
CHOPPERS - Garden equipment - Emsco Inc.
CHOPPERS - Jeans–men's - Jacksol Trading Co., Inc.
CHOPPERS ALLIGATOR - Toys–stuffed ☆ - Dakin Inc.
CHOPPER'S CHOICE - Kitchen utensils–aluminum - Bonny Products Inc.
CHOPPER'S CHOICE - Wood products - EMC Co.
CHOPPIN BLOCK - Cheese - American Cheeseman Inc.
CHOPS - Toys–stuffed - Ty, Inc.
CHOPS THE BEAVER - Toys - Tonka Corp.
CHORAEGUS SHAREMUSIC - Music–sheet - Choraegus ShareMusic
CHORAL-H - Pharmaceutical preparations ☆ - Rex Research Laboratories
CHORALE - Dishes–china - Waterford Wedgewood USA, Inc.
CHORALE - Rings–jewelry - Artcarved Inc.
CHORD-O-MATIC - Musical instrument accessories - Trebb Sales
CHORD OF NATURE - Chimes - J.W. Stannard Co.
CHORDAL - Veterinary pharmaceutical preparations ☆ - Zirin Laboratories International
CHORDEASY - Computer software - Infogrip, Inc.
CHORDETTE - Musical instruments - Excelsior Accordions Inc.
CHORDIANA - Musical instruments - Excelsior Accordions Inc.
CHORDOMONICA - Harmonicas - Hohner Inc.
CHORE BOY - Scouring pads - Airwick Industries
CHORE MASTER - Washers–metal - Mi-T-M Corp.
CHOREMASTER - Housewares - Arden Corp.
CHOREMASTER - Paper–toweling - Georgia-Pacific Corp.
CHOREMINDER - Publisher's imprints - Kids for Chores
CHOREOGRAPHER! - Computer software - Motorola, Inc. (Land Mobile Products Sector)
CHOREOGRAPHICS - Electronic equipment - Laser Images, Inc.
CHOREOGRAPHY - Underwear and nightwear ☆ - Maidenform Inc.
CHOREX - Pharmaceutical preparations - Hyrex Pharmaceuticals
CHORIGON - Pharmaceutical preparations - Dunhall Pharmaceuticals Inc.
CHORIO - Olive oil - Krinos Foods, Inc.
CHORION PLUS - Pharmaceutical preparations - Pharmex Inc.
CHORIPAN - Breads ☆ - Corte & Co.
CHORIPAN - Sandwiches–prepackaged - Edgardo Carballo
CHORON - Pharmaceutical preparations ☆ - Forest Pharmaceuticals Inc.
CHORTLES CHOCOLATE CHIP COOKIE NUGGETS - Cookies - Chortles
CHORTS - Shorts–men's - Dennis Harris
CHORUS - Electronic signal receivers - Audiological Engineering Corp.
CHORUS - Floor coverings–carpet and rugs - Karastan-Bigelow Inc.
CHORUS BLUES - Apparel–women's - Chorus Line Corp.
CHORUS CLASSIC - Musical instrument accessories ☆ - GSP
CHORUS LINE - Apparel–women's - Chorus Line Corp.
CHORUS LINE - Cosmetics - Spencer Gifts, Inc.
CHORUS LINE - Floor coverings–carpet and rugs ☆ - Hollytex Carpet Mills Inc.
CHORUS OF CULTURES, A - Recording label - Hampton-Brown Co., Inc.
CHORUS PUBLICATIONS - Music–sheet ☆ - GSP
CHOTCH-KEES - Hobby kits - Craftics Inc.
CHOUINARD - Coats - Patagonia, Inc.
CHOUTEAU - Water–bottled or canned - QuickSilver Water Co.
CHOW - Cosmetics - Yao Industries
CHOW - Furniture - CTH/Sherrill Occasional
CHOW SUN - Jewelry - Nancy Givens and Richard Crook Partnership
CHOWHOUND CHARLIE - Cement - Rectorseal Corp.
CHOWINING'S - Nuts–salted, roasted, cooked, or canned - Whitley Peanut Factory
C.H.R. - Cosmetics - Revlon Consumer Products Corp.
CHR. HANSEN - Food products - Chris Hansen, Inc.
CHRIS - Candy - Chris Candies Inc.
CHRIS' & PITT'S - Barbecue sauce - Durkee French Foods
CHRIS CAKES - Pancakes–mixes - Mason Marketing
CHRIS CHEE - Snack foods - Parisien
CHRIS-CRAFT - Boats–motor - Chris Craft Boats
CHRIS-CRAFT - Sporting goods ☆ - Hedstrom Corp.
CHRIS CRINGLE - Candy - Bobs Candies Inc.
CHRIS CROSS - Sauces - Chris Cross Products Inc.
CHRIS CROSS CHOWDERS & BASES - Chowders–frozen - Chris Cross Products Inc.

CHRIS CRUNCH - Cereal - Ralston Purina Co.
CHRIS C'S - Recording label - 3 G's Industries Inc.
CHRIS EVERT - Cosmetics - Seasons Inc.
CHRIS EVERT - Rackets–tennis - Wilson Sporting Goods Co.
CHRIS EVERT - Sporting goods - Converse Inc.
CHRIS EVERT CALYPSO - Athletic footwear - Converse Inc.
CHRIS HOLLY - Fertilizers - Teufel Nursery Inc.
CHRIS KING - Bicycle parts and accessories - Christopher D. King
CHRIS-KISS - Chocolate candy - Haram-Christensen Corp.
CHRIS LOCKE - Decals and transfers - Chase Collection, Inc.
CHRIS MCLAUGHLIN - Clothes - Three R's, Inc.
CHRIS-SWISS - Cheese ☆ - Haram-Christensen Corp.
CHRIS-TOL CLEAN - Iron products - Christensen Boyles Corp.
CHRISEED - Flowers, plants, and seeds - Alf Christianson Seed Co.
CHRISHAWN - Novelty items - Chrishawn Associates Inc.
CHRISKIT - First aid kits - Savalif, Inc.
CHRISMOOSE - Toys–stuffed - Michael Wahl
CHRISSY AEROBIC - Dolls - Russ Berrie and Co., Inc.
CHRISSY-LEE - Dolls - Cap Toys, Inc.
CHRISTABEL - Dishes–china - Waterford Wedgewood USA, Inc.
CHRISTALI - Shoes - Christali International Inc.
CHRISTEN - Fireplace equipment ☆ - GSW Jackes-Evans Manufacturing Co.
CHRISTENING MEMORIES - Dolls - Doll Factory, Inc.
CHRISTENSEN - Breads ☆ - Haram-Christensen Corp.
CHRISTENSEN - Fruits and vegetables - Christensen Farms
CHRISTENSEN - Saw blades - Norton Construction Products
CHRISTI - Computer software - Anser
CHRISTI - Recording label - Le Cam Records
CHRISTIAN - Candles ☆ - Lancaster Colony Corp.
CHRISTIAN A. - Hockey equipment - Christian Brothers, Inc.
CHRISTIAN A. - Apparel–women's - A. Christian Inc.
CHRISTIAN ART - Artists' materials - Warner Press, Inc.
CHRISTIAN AUJARD - Hosiery–women's - Magnolia Hosiery Mill Inc.
CHRISTIAN BERNARD - Watches - Holzerwatch Co. Inc.
CHRISTIAN BROTHERS - Brandy - IDV Wines (Beaulieu Vineyard)
CHRISTIAN CLASSICS - Recording label - Thomas York Concert Marketing Inc.
CHRISTIAN CRITTERS, THE - Computer software - Shaddai Software, Inc.
CHRISTIAN DE ROZ - Ophthalmic goods - Rozin Optical Export Corp.
CHRISTIAN DIOR - Apparel and accessories - Jaymar-Ruby Inc.
CHRISTIAN DIOR - Apparel and accessories - Warnaco Inc.
CHRISTIAN DIOR - Apparel–children's - William Carter Co.
CHRISTIAN DIOR - Apparel–women's - Jones Apparel Group Inc.
CHRISTIAN DIOR - Bathing suits ☆ - Milady Brassiere & Corset Co., Inc.
CHRISTIAN DIOR - Belts–apparel - Speyer-Milor
CHRISTIAN DIOR - Frames–eyeglass ☆ - Carrera Eyewear Corp.
CHRISTIAN DIOR - Gloves - Aris Isotoner Inc.
CHRISTIAN DIOR - Hosiery - Vision Hosiery
CHRISTIAN DIOR - Hosiery–men's - Camp Hosiery
CHRISTIAN DIOR - Jewelry - Grosse Jewels N.Y. Inc.
CHRISTIAN DIOR - Luggage - York Luggage Co.
CHRISTIAN DIOR - Robes ☆ - Periphery Loungewear Inc.
CHRISTIAN DIOR - Skin care products - Christian Dior Perfumes Corp.
CHRISTIAN DIOR - Umbrellas - Liberty Umbrella Inc.
CHRISTIAN DIOR - Underwear and nightwear - Carole Hochman Designs Inc.
CHRISTIAN DIOR - Underwear and nightwear - Slumbertogs Inc.
CHRISTIAN DIOR - Watches - Memox
CHRISTIAN DIOR JEUNE HOMME - Apparel and accessories - Esskay Manufacturing Co.
CHRISTIAN DIOR SACS DE BEAUTE - Cosmetics - Trina/Genie
CHRISTIAN FAITH - Greeting cards ☆ - Warner Press, Inc.
CHRISTIAN FAITH - Recording label - Skylite-Sing Inc.
CHRISTIAN FOLK - Recording label - Skylite-Sing Inc.
CHRISTIAN HERITAGE - Jewelry - Uncas Manufacturing Co.
CHRISTIAN KEY, THE - Jewelry - Mark J. Davis
CHRISTIAN KROPF - Fruits and vegetables - Kropf Fruit Co.
CHRISTIAN LACROIX - Sunglasses ☆ - Carrera Eyewear Corp.
CHRISTIAN LEAGUE ATHLETIC WEAR - Apparel stores–sports - Everlasting Gospel Productions
CHRISTIAN MOERLEIN - Beverages–malt - Hudepohl-Schoenling Brewing Co.
CHRISTIAN MOUEIX MERLOT - Wines - Kobrand Corp.
CHRISTIAN ROTH - Colognes - Optical Affairs, Inc.
CHRISTIAN SCHMIDT - Beverages–malt ☆ - The Stroh Brewery Co.
CHRISTIAN STANDARD - Publisher's imprints - Standex International Corp.
CHRISTIAN, THE - Giftware - Anthony Dembski

CHRISTIAN ULBRICHT - Nutcrackers - Rolf Wallach Inc.
CHRISTIAN UNIVERSITY PRESS - Publisher's imprints ☆ - Wm. B. Eerdmans Publishing Co.
CHRISTIAN WITNESS - Giftware ☆ - Warner Press, Inc.
CHRISTIANA BY BONNIE J. - Jewelry - Sanoy Inc.
CHRISTIE - Dolls - Mattel, Inc.
CHRISTIE - Frames–eyeglass - U.S. Optical Frame Co.
CHRISTIE - Tableware–china ☆ - Lenox, Inc.
CHRISTIE & JILL - Blouses–women's - J.C. Penney Co., Inc.
CHRISTIE BRINKLEY - Patterns–clothing ☆ - Simplicity Pattern Co., Inc.
CHRISTIE BRINKLEY PERSPECTIVES - Eyeglasses - Aptaker Co. Inc.
CHRISTIE'S - Crab meat–canned or cured - Byrd's Inc.
CHRISTIE'S - Footwear–women's - World Import Co. Inc.
CHRISTIES - Gin - Barton Brands, Ltd.
CHRISTIE'S CLOSET - Apparel and accessories - Toll-Gate Garment Co.
CHRISTINA - Bathing suits - Christina USA Inc.
CHRISTINA - Dolls - Russ Berrie and Co., Inc.
CHRISTINA - Food products - Escalon Frozen Foods
CHRISTINA - Glassware–household ☆ - Dansk International Designs, Ltd.
CHRISTINA - Oils–edible - California Olive Oil Corp.
CHRISTINA COLLECTION - Jewelry - E.N.S. Inc.
CHRISTINA DANI - Footwear - Nordstrom, Inc.
CHRISTINA LUCCI - Frames–eyeglass - Unilan Fashion Group, Inc.
CHRISTINA'S - Dolls ☆ - Christina's Dolls & Crafts
CHRISTINE - Dinnerware–glass ☆ - Svend Jensen of Denmark Inc.
CHRISTINE - Floor coverings–carpet and rugs ☆ - Regal Rugs Inc.
CHRISTINE - Glassware–household ☆ - Oneida Ltd.
CHRISTINE - Jewelry - Lawrence Jewelry Co.
CHRISTINE - Toys–automobiles - Thomas Lowe Ventures, Inc.
CHRISTINE'S - Watches - Bulova Corp.
CHRISTINE - Wigs - Jean Paree Weegs Inc.
CHRISTINE ASHLEY - Nail care products - Marianna Imports, Inc.
CHRISTINE ASHLEY NAILS - Cosmetics - Marianna Imports, Inc.
CHRISTINE B. - Wallpaper ☆ - Sunwall of America
CHRISTINE HODEN - Apparel–children's ☆ - Ajanta Enterprises
CHRISTINE JORDAN - Wigs - Paula Young
CHRISTINE MARJON - Apparel–women's - Silks & Silhouettes Inc.
CHRISTINE PHILLIPE - Apparel and accessories - Christine Phillipe Co.
CHRISTINE VICTORIA - Glassware–household - Christine Victoria Designs Inc.
CHRISTINEN BRUNNEN - Water–mineral - Kreiner Imports
CHRISTINENHUTTE - Glassware–household - Oneida Ltd.
CHRISTKIND GLUHWEIN - Wines - HDT Importers Inc.
CHRISTKINDLMARKT BETHLEHEM - T-shirts–men's ☆ - Bethlehem Musikfest Association
CHRISTMAS - Dishes–earthenware - Hadley Pottery Co. Inc.
CHRISTMAS - Dolls ☆ - Gorham Inc.
CHRISTMAS - Recording label ☆ - Prince/SF Productions
CHRISTMAS - Rice - Wehah Farm, Inc.
CHRISTMAS - Sauces - Cowan & Fransman
CHRISTMAS A LA CARTE - Greeting cards - Renaissance Greeting Cards Inc.
CHRISTMAS ADVENT INC. - Candles - Biedermann & Sons Inc.
CHRISTMAS AT HOME - Glassware–household ☆ - Fenton Art Glass Co.
CHRISTMAS AT HOME - Recording label - Soundtastic, Inc.
CHRISTMAS AVENUE - Novelty items - Eckerd Corp.
CHRISTMAS BLEND - Coffee - Starbucks Corp.
CHRISTMAS BOX, THE - Greeting cards - Richard Paul Evans
CHRISTMAS BOXES - Giftware - Waterford Wedgewood USA, Inc.
CHRISTMAS BREW - Beverages–malt - Anheuser-Busch Companies Inc.
CHRISTMAS BUBBLE - Ornamental products–glass - Visionary Products, Inc.
CHRISTMAS BUBBLE BEARS - Toys–stuffed ☆ - Fun World Inc.
CHRISTMAS CANDLE SAKS - Candles - Candle Corp. of America
CHRISTMAS CARDS - Playing cards - Novelti Playing Cards
CHRISTMAS CARESS - Toys - Russ Berrie and Co., Inc.
CHRISTMAS CAROL - Toys–stuffed ☆ - Gund, Inc.
CHRISTMAS CAROUSEL - Coffee - First Colony Coffee and Tea Co. Inc.
CHRISTMAS CASH - Games - Store Marketing
CHRISTMAS CHARMERS - Christmas tree ornaments - Santa's Best
CHRISTMAS CHEER - Christmas tree ornaments - Cracker Box Inc.
CHRISTMAS CHEERS - Giftware - Russ Berrie and Co., Inc.
CHRISTMAS CHOIR - Christmas tree ornaments - Cracker Box Inc.
CHRISTMAS CLASSICS - Giftware - Enesco Corp.
CHRISTMAS CLASSICS - Giftware - Fort USA
CHRISTMAS CLASSICS - Greeting cards - Hampton Greeting Card Co.
CHRISTMAS CLASSICS - Greeting cards ☆ - Brett-Forer Greetings Inc.
CHRISTMAS CLASSICS - Paper–gift wrap ☆ - CPS Corp.

☆ = Now out of production

CHRISTMAS CLICS - Pens - Bic Corp.
CHRISTMAS COLLECTIBLES - Christmas tree ornaments - Campus Originals Inc.
CHRISTMAS COLLECTIBLES - Giftware - Seymour Mann Inc.
CHRISTMAS COLLECTION - Fabrics - Dan River Inc.
CHRISTMAS COLLECTION - Glassware–household - Magicsilk
CHRISTMAS COLLECTION, THE - Figurines ☆ - E.M.I. Inc.
CHRISTMAS COLLECTION, THE - Paper–gift wrap - Gift Wrap Co.
CHRISTMAS COLLECTION, THE - Flowers–artificial - Magicsilk
CHRISTMAS COMPANIONS - Giftware - Russ Berrie and Co., Inc.
CHRISTMAS CONCEPTS - Paper–gift wrap ☆ - CPS Corp.
CHRISTMAS CORNER - Christmas tree ornaments - Christmas Corner
CHRISTMAS CORNER - Christmas tree ornaments - Vincent Lippe Co.
CHRISTMAS COTTAGE MOUSE - Toys–stuffed - Dan-Dee International Ltd.
CHRISTMAS COVER - Fabrics - Union Wadding Co.
CHRISTMAS CRATE - Containers - Maidware Products, Inc.
CHRISTMAS CREATIONS - Christmas tree ornaments ☆ - Mr. Christmas, Inc.
CHRISTMAS CREME - Coffee - Executive Coffee Service Co.
CHRISTMAS CRITTERS - Candy - Brock Candy Co. Inc.
CHRISTMAS CRITTERS - Toys–stuffed - Fun World Inc.
CHRISTMAS CRUNCH - Cereal - Quaker Oats Co.
CHRISTMAS CUTIES - Christmas tree ornaments - Seasonal Specialties Electrics, Inc.
CHRISTMAS CUTIES - Ornamental products–glass - Fun World Inc.
CHRISTMAS DANCERS - Toys–stuffed ☆ - Fun World Inc.
CHRISTMAS DELIGHTS - Lamps - Russ Berrie and Co., Inc.
CHRISTMAS DREAM, A - Christmas tree ornaments ☆ - Roman, Inc.
CHRISTMAS DREAMERS - Toys–stuffed - Trendmasters, Inc.
CHRISTMAS ELEGANCIES - Greeting cards - Masterpiece Studios Inc.
CHRISTMAS EVE - Dinnerware–glass - Salem China Co.
CHRISTMAS EVE TOGETHER - Dolls - Effanbee Doll Corp.
CHRISTMAS FAIRY...MAKING CHRISTMAS MAGIC, THE - Christmas tree ornaments - James M. Reid
CHRISTMAS FAMILY, THE - Toys–stuffed - Fun World Inc.
CHRISTMAS FANTASIES - Greeting cards ☆ - Stephen Lawrence Co.
CHRISTMAS FANTASY - Figurines - International Silver Co.
CHRISTMAS FAVORITES - Greeting cards - Masterpiece Studios Inc.
CHRISTMAS FLUFFIES - Toys–stuffed ☆ - Fun World Inc.
CHRISTMAS FOLLIES - Novelty items - International Silver Co.
CHRISTMAS GALLERY - Greeting cards - Masterpiece Studios Inc.
CHRISTMAS GARDEN COLLECTION - Christmas tree ornaments - Lenox, Inc.
CHRISTMAS GEMS - Greeting cards - Nu-Art Inc.
CHRISTMAS GIFT BAGS - Rice - Estherwood Rice Sales
CHRISTMAS GLITTER - Yarn - Caron International Inc.
CHRISTMAS GOLD COLLECTION - Christmas tree ornaments - Lenox, Inc.
CHRISTMAS GOOSE - Glassware–household - Ceraglass Inc.
CHRISTMAS GREETINGS - Potpourri - Countryside Fragrances Inc.
CHRISTMAS G.S. - Giftware - U.S. Fiberglass Inc.
CHRISTMAS HANG-EM UPS - Toys–stuffed ☆ - Fun World Inc.
CHRISTMAS HEIRLOOM - Tableware–china ☆ - Pfaltzgraff Investment Co.
CHRISTMAS HEIRLOOMS - Hobby kits - Heirloom Shop Inc.
CHRISTMAS HERITAGE BY PFALTZGRAFF - Tableware–china - Pfaltzgraff Investment Co.
CHRISTMAS HUGGLES - Toys - Russ Berrie and Co., Inc.
CHRISTMAS IMPRESSIONS - Greeting cards - Manhattan Greeting
CHRISTMAS IN ALABAMA - Christmas tree ornaments - Dot Miazza
CHRISTMAS IN CROSS-STITCH - Hobby kits - Oxmoor House Inc.
CHRISTMAS IN JULY - Skin care products - Monico Inc.
CHRISTMAS IN MOTION - Ornaments - Bradford Novelty Co., Inc.
CHRISTMAS IN THE AIR - Deodorizers - Spice Market, Inc.
CHRISTMAS IN THE CITY - Figurines - Department 56 Inc.
CHRISTMAS IN VAIL - Decorations - Santa's Best
CHRISTMAS IN VERMONT - Christmas tree ornaments - Santa's Best
CHRISTMAS IS LOVE - Toys - Russ Berrie and Co., Inc.
CHRISTMAS ITTY BITTYS - Erasers - Diener Industries Inc.
CHRISTMAS JOY - Dinnerware ☆ - Corning Inc.
CHRISTMAS JUNIORS - Greeting cards - American Artists Group Inc.
CHRISTMAS LEGENDS - Dolls - Lawton Doll Co.
CHRISTMAS LIGHTS - Candy - Sathers Inc.
CHRISTMAS MAGIC - Toys - Trendmasters, Inc.
CHRISTMAS MELODY BEAR - Toys–stuffed ☆ - Gund, Inc.
CHRISTMAS MEMORIES - Catalogs - Lillian Vernon Corp.
CHRISTMAS MEMORIES - Christmas tree ornaments - General Foam Plastics Corp.
CHRISTMAS MEMORIES - Giftware - Arnart Imports Inc.

CHRISTMAS MEMORIES - Giftware ☆ - Giordano Art, Ltd.
CHRISTMAS MEMORIES - Perfumes - FMG/Tsumara Medical
CHRISTMAS MINT - Teas - Eastern Shore Tea Co.
CHRISTMAS MOOD - Greeting cards ☆ - Papercraft Corp.
CHRISTMAS MORNIN' - Flowers–artificial - Hanford's Inc.
CHRISTMAS MUSICAL BELLS - Giftware - Lenox, Inc.
CHRISTMAS NAIL, THE - Hardware - Ton Communications, Inc.
CHRISTMAS OIL NOVELLO - Olive oil - Crate and Barrel
CHRISTMAS OMNIBUS - Greeting cards - American Artists Group Inc.
CHRISTMAS ORIGINALS - Greeting cards ☆ - Paper Magic Group Inc.
CHRISTMAS PEANUT BUDDY - Candy - R.M. Palmer Co.
CHRISTMAS PEN-PALS - Pens - Fun World Inc.
CHRISTMAS PRESENT - Craft supplies ☆ - VIP/VIP Crafts
CHRISTMAS PRESENT AND PAST - Christmas tree ornaments - Danny Udell, Inc.
CHRISTMAS REMEMBERED - Educational materials - Leisure Arts, Inc.
CHRISTMAS REPORT CARD - Novelty items - Russ Berrie and Co., Inc.
CHRISTMAS REVERENCE - Greeting cards - Hampton Greeting Card Co.
CHRISTMAS SAMPLER, A - Computer software ☆ - Cross Educational Software Inc.
CHRISTMAS SAVERS - Novelty items ☆ - Steven Manufacturing Co.
CHRISTMAS SNOW - Craft supplies - Morning Glory Products
CHRISTMAS SNUFF - Toys–stuffed - Gund, Inc.
CHRISTMAS SPLENDOR - Greeting cards - Cleo Inc.
CHRISTMAS STAR SERIES - Giftware - Fenton Art Glass Co.
CHRISTMAS STORIES SERIES - Christmas tree ornaments - Lenox, Inc.
CHRISTMAS TINYTALES - Toys–stuffed ☆ - Gund, Inc.
CHRISTMAS TODAY - Greeting cards ☆ - Regency Thermographers Inc.
CHRISTMAS TRADITIONALS - Greeting cards - Hampton Greeting Card Co.
CHRISTMAS TRADITIONS - Novelty items - Aldik Artificial Flower Co. Inc.
CHRISTMAS TRADITIONS - Syrup - Saramar Corp.
CHRISTMAS TREASURES - Greeting cards - Nu-Art Inc.
CHRISTMAS TREE - Dishes–earthenware - Royal China & Porcelain Companies Inc.
CHRISTMAS TREE - Games ☆ - Koplow Games
CHRISTMAS TREE - Lamps ☆ - Lamplight Farms, Inc.
CHRISTMAS TREE - Pasta - Buckeye Beans & Herbs, Inc.
CHRISTMAS TREE BEARS, THE - Toys–stuffed - Dan-Dee International Ltd.
CHRISTMAS TREE CAKES - Cakes - McKee Foods Corp.
CHRISTMAS TWISTS - Chocolate novelties - Bortz Chocolate Co.
CHRISTMAS WOWEE - Candy - Glenn Confections Inc.
CHRISTMAS WREATH - Christmas tree ornaments - Cracker Box Inc.
CHRISTMASTIME - Dinnerware–glass - Nikko Ceramics Inc.
CHRISTOBELLA - Floor coverings - Mannington Resilient Floors
CHRISTOFF - Cigars - Christoff Cigar Co.
CHRISTOFF'S - Salad dressings and cooking oils - Christoff's Gourmet Foods, Ltd.
CHRISTOFLE - Silver products - Christofle Silver Inc.
CHRISTOL - Bathroom accessories - Leo Products Co.
CHRISTON INTERNATIONAL - Frames–picture - Schildkraut Giftware Corp.
CHRISTOPHER - Apparel and accessories - Salant/Manhattan Industries
CHRISTOPHER & HOLLY - Toys–stuffed - Geoffrey Inc.
CHRISTOPHER BEAR - Toys–stuffed - Dakin Inc.
CHRISTOPHER COLUMBUS - Glassware–household ☆ - Fenton Art Glass Co.
CHRISTOPHER COLUMBUS VOYAGE TO AMERICA - Games - Cardinal Industries, Inc.
CHRISTOPHER COMPASS - Toys - Rudell Design
CHRISTOPHER CRACKER - Novelty items - Nancy Chupp
CHRISTOPHER CREEK - Wines - Christopher Creek Winery
CHRISTOPHER DAVID III - Recording label - Sand Hand Records Inc.
CHRISTOPHER EDWARDS - Food products - Edwards Baking Co.
CHRISTOPHER HART - Apparel–men's - Big & Tall Associates
CHRISTOPHER HAYES - Apparel and accessories - R.H. Macy & Co.
CHRISTOPHER KENT - Apparel–women's - Zachar Ltd.
CHRISTOPHER PRINTS - Fabrics–tapestry ☆ - Christopher Prints
CHRISTOPHER RADKO - Christmas tree ornaments - Christopher Radko
CHRISTOPHER RANCH - Food products - Christopher Ranch
CHRISTOPHER SCOTT - Apparel and accessories - Elder Manufacturing Co., Inc.
CHRISTOPHER STUART - Frames–picture - Mikasa Licensing, Inc.
CHRISTOPHER WINKLE - Furniture - Christopher Winkle Products
CHRISTOPHER'S - Beverages–malt ☆ - Barbara's Bakery, Inc.
CHRISTOPHER'S - Candy - Ben Myerson Candy Co.
CHRISTOPHER'S CHEWIES - Snack foods - Christopher's Chewies
CHRISTOS - Food products - A. Camacho Inc.

☆ = Now out of production

CHRISTY - Dinnerware–glass ☆ - Brigitte Pottery
CHRISTY - Guitars - Arthur H. Christiansen
CHRISTY - Knives–pocket - Christy Co.
CHRISTY - Recording label - Christy Records International
CHRISTY - Recording label - Leonard E. Lesourd
CHRISTYANN - Trees - J. Frank Schmidt & Son Co.
CHRO-MOR - Animal feed supplements - Nutribasics L.P.
CHROM & GRAV - Tools - Contemporary Inc.
CHROM PICO PLUS - Vitamins and nutritional supplements - Ethical Nutrients
CHROM-X - Sunglasses - Bausch & Lomb Inc.
CHROMA - Audio equipment - Telesensory Systems Inc.
CHROMA - Computer software - Interspec Inc.
CHROMA - Floor coverings–carpet and rugs ☆ - J and J Industries Inc.
CHROMA - Floor coverings–carpet and rugs ☆ - Regal Rugs Inc.
CHROMA - Paper ☆ - Strathmore Paper Co.
CHROMA - Tiles–ceramic - Buchtal USA
CHROMA - Tiles–ceramic - Dal-Tile Corp.
CHROMA 3 - Window coverings ☆ - Hunter Douglas, Inc.
CHROMA AIRBRUSH COLORS - Paints–artists' - Chroma Acrylics Inc.
CHROMA-BURN - Vitamins and nutritional supplements - Action Labs, Inc.
CHROMA-CAL 828 - Vitamins and nutritional supplements - Vita Source, Inc.
CHROMA-CALC - Spectrometers - Applied Color Systems, Inc.
CHROMA GAR-D - Vitamins and nutritional supplements - Creative Nutritional Concepts, Inc.
CHROMA-GLIDE - Drafting supplies - Koh-I-Noor, Inc.
CHROMA GRAPHICS - Decals and transfers - Chroma Graphics Corp.
CHROMA GUM - Vitamins and nutritional supplements - Bros USA Inc.
CHROMA-LOCK - Hair care products - Wella Corp. (Consumer Products Div.)
CHROMA MOUSE - Computer peripheral equipment - Logitech, Inc.
CHROMA POSTER COLOURS - Paints–artists' - Chroma Acrylics Inc.
CHROMA RACERS - Toys–automobiles - Mattel, Inc.
CHROMA-SENSOR - Spectrometers - Applied Color Systems, Inc.
CHROMA SLIM - Vitamins and nutritional supplements - Richardson Labs, Inc.
CHROMA SLIM PLUS - Vitamins and nutritional supplements - Richardson Labs, Inc.
CHROMA-SPEC - Building materials - MM Systems Corp.
CHROMA TINTS - Wallpaper - RDH Two Inc.
CHROMA TRIM - Chewing gum - Gum Tech International
CHROMA VISION - Kaleidoscopes - Gemini Kaleidoscopes
CHROMA-ZONES - Apparel and accessories - Kristine Bercot, Inc.
CHROMABOND - Floor coverings - Congoleum Corp.
CHROMABRITE - Television tubes ☆ - J.C. Penney Co., Inc.
CHROMACLEAN - Cleaning preparations–window - Spectrum Chemical Manufacturing Corp.
CHROMACLONE - Pharmaceutical - Ultradent Products, Inc.
CHROMACOLOR - Television equipment - Zenith Electronics Corp.
CHROMACRYL - Artists' supply stores ☆ - Chroma Acrylics Inc.
CHROMACRYL JUNIOUR STUDENT ACRYLICS - Paints–artists' - Chroma Acrylics Inc.
CHROMAFLAIR - Pigments–paint - Flex Products, Inc.
CHROMAFLOW - Chromatographs - Chromaflow, Inc.
CHROMAGEN - Pharmaceutical preparations - Savage Laboratories Inc.
CHROMAGEN OB - Pharmaceutical preparations ☆ - Savage Laboratories Inc.
CHROMAGLO - Watches - Golden State Imports International, Inc.
CHROMAGRAM - Photographic equipment - Eastman Kodak Co.
CHROMAGRAPHICS - Floor coverings–carpet and rugs - Mohawk Carpet Corp.
CHROMAHARP - String instruments - International Music Corp.
CHROMAIR - Electronic equipment - Gilian Environmental Corp.
CHROMALEX - Lighting fixtures - Perko Inc.
CHROMALINE - Lamps - General Electric Co.
CHROMALITE - Automotive parts and accessories - Fibre Glass-Evercoat Co. Inc.
CHROMALITE - Packaging material - Composite Concepts, Inc.
CHROMALON - Floor coverings–carpet and rugs - Mohawk Carpet Corp.
CHROMALOX - Heating pads–electric - Chromalox
CHROMALUX - Pet products - M. Pencar Associates
CHROMAPOINT - Floor coverings–carpet and rugs - Collins & Aikman Corp.
CHROMAPRO - Electronics equipment - Chromapro International
CHROMARAMA - Office supplies - Prestype Inc.
CHROMASCREEN - Architectural graphic glass windows - Claudio Cesar
CHROMASOY - Inks - Ron Ink Co. Inc.
CHROMATEK - Floor coverings–carpet and rugs - Chembond
CHROMATEMP LIQUID TEMPERA - Paints–artists' - Chroma Acrylics Inc.
CHROMATIC - Desk sets - Souvenir Inc.
CHROMATIC - Floor coverings–carpet and rugs - Whitecrest Carpet Mills

CHROMATIC - Frames–eyeglass - Zylo Ware Corp.
CHROMATIC - Paints - Hempel Coatings USA Inc.
CHROMATIC - Pens - Ritepoint Inc.
CHROMATIC RESEARCH - Computer hardware - Chromatic Research, Inc.
CHROMATIC TECHNOLOGIES, INC. - Cables–fiber optic - Draka USA Corp.
CHROMATIC V-8 - Toys–automobiles - Mattel, Inc.
CHROMATICS - Dinnerware - JMP-Newcor International, Inc.
CHROMATICS - Dinnerware–glass ☆ - Block China Co.
CHROMATICS - Floor coverings–carpet and rugs - World Carpets, Inc.
CHROMATICS - Floor coverings–carpet and rugs ☆ - J and J Industries Inc.
CHROMATICS - Footwear - Totes, Inc.
CHROMATIKS - Floor coverings–carpet and rugs ☆ - Customweave Carpets Inc.
CHROMATINA - Musical instrument accessories - JTG of Nashville
CHROMATIQUE - Floor coverings–carpet and rugs - J.L. Benson Co.
CHROMATIX - Office furniture–metal - Hon Co.
CHROMATO-VUE - Cabinets - UVP Inc.
CHROMATONE - Hair care products - Vapon, Inc.
CHROMATONE - Metallic paint - Crescent Bronze Powder
CHROMATRIM 100 - Chewing gum - Gum Tech International
CHROMAX - Printers–computer - NewGen Imaging Systems Corp.
CHROMAX - Sunglasses - Bausch & Lomb Inc.
CHROMAX - Veterinary nutritional supplements - Prince Agri Products, Inc.
CHROMAX - Vitamins and nutritional supplements - Nutrition 21
CHROMAZONE - Computer software - Gibson Research Corp.
CHROMCRAFT - Furniture - Chromcraft Corp.
CHROMDIOXID - Audio equipment ☆ - BASF Corp.
CHROMDIOXID EXTRA II - Audio equipment ☆ - BASF Corp.
CHROMDIOXID MAXIMA II - Audio equipment ☆ - BASF Corp.
CHROME CARE - Furniture polish and wax - Apple Polishes Inc.
CHROME CLAD - Tools - Lufkin Rule Co.
CHROME CLASSICS - Lamps ☆ - Electrix Inc.
CHROME COAT - Paint sprayers ☆ - Marson Creative Fastener Group
CHROME DOME - Bar fixtures–metal ☆ - Spill-Stop Manufacturing LLC
CHROME-DOME - Musical instruments - GRH Inc.
CHROME EXTRA II - Audio equipment - BASF Corp.
CHROME GEAR - Apparel and accessories - Custom Chrome, Inc.
CHROME HEARTS - Leather goods - Chrome Hearts, Inc.
CHROME KOAT - Epoxy coatings ☆ - Star Bronze Co. Inc.
CHROME-LOCK - Hardware ☆ - Courtaulds Aerospace Inc.
CHROME MAXIMA II - Audio equipment - BASF Corp.
CHROME MIDNIGHT - Toys–automobiles - Hasbro, Inc.
CHROME-PRO - Video tapes–blank - Swire Magnetics Co.
CHROME SAVER - Wrenches - Chrome Saver Inc.
CHROME-SEAL - Hardware - Trim-Lok Inc.
CHROME SERIES - Shelving units–plastic - Better Sleep, Inc.
CHROME SPECIALTIES - Motorcycles - Chrome Specialties, Inc.
CHROME STAR - Window shades - Protech Shading Inc.
CHROME-TEK - Chemical preparations - Graphic Technologies, Inc.
CHROME THINGS - Hardware - Rensen Products
CHROME TOTAL - Exercising equipment - Universal Gym Equipment, Inc.
CHROME-TRIM - Rubber–synthetic - Trim-Lok Inc.
CHROME-UP - Vitamins and nutritional supplements - JBN Enterprises, Inc.
CHROME WISE - Motor vehicle parts and accessories - Bob Bartlett & Associates Inc.
CHROMED CRUSADER, THE - Toy robots - Diversified Specialists, Inc.
CHROMEFLEX - Metals - Metal Film Co. Inc.
CHROMEGA - Photographic equipment ☆ - Omega/Arkay
CHROMEGATROL - Photographic equipment ☆ - Omega/Arkay
CHROMEGUIDE - Film - Sun Chemical Corp.
CHROMELIN - Blenders - Summers Laboratories Inc.
CHROMEMATE - Health care products - Interhealth Co.
CHROMEMATE - Vitamins and nutritional supplements - Natrol, Inc.
CHROMEMATE PLUS - Vitamins and nutritional supplements - Natrol, Inc.
CHROMES - Musical instrument accessories - J. D'Addario & Co. Inc.
CHROMETTA - Harmonicas - Hohner Inc.
CHROMETTE - Pet collars - Leatherite-Nylorite Manufacturing Inc.
CHROMETUBE - Motor vehicle parts and accessories ☆ - Products for Power
CHROMEX 500 - Cleaning preparation - CME Plastics, Inc.
CHROMEXCEL - Leather - Horween Leather Co.
CHROMIACIN - Vitamins and nutritional supplements - Solaray
CHROMIC BALANCE + SIL-X - Health care products - Alta Health Products
CHROMIUM - Trading cards - Signs & Glassworks, Inc.
CHROMIUM DEXTRATE - Richard A. Deer
CHROMIUM K6 - Vitamins and nutritional supplements - Rexall Sundown, Inc.

☆ = Now out of production

CHROMIUM PICOLINATE - Pharmaceutical preparations - Mericon Industries Inc.

CHROMIUM PICOLINATE - Pharmaceutical preparations - Reese Chemical Co.

CHROMIUM PICOLINATE - Vitamins and nutritional supplements - M.M.R.C., Ltd. Co.

CHROMIUM PICOLINATE - Vitamins and nutritional supplements - Vitamin Research Products Inc.

CHROMIUM PLUS - Vitamins and nutritional supplements - B & H Distributors, Inc.

CHROMIUM POWER - Vitamins and nutritional supplements - Desert Star Management, Inc.

CHROMOACRYL STUDENT ACRYLICS - Paints–artists' - Chroma Acrylics Inc.

CHROMOCORE - Artists' materials ☆ - Hunt Manufacturing Co.

CHROMONICA - Harmonicas - Hohner Inc.

CHROMOS IMAGER SYSTEM - Medical apparatus - Chromos Imaging, Inc.

CHROMOSOME XX XY - Skin care products - Parfums Visions International, Ltd.

CHROMOTECH - Floor coverings–carpet and rugs - Bentley Mills, Inc.

CHROMOUT - Water treating compounds - Kentucky Water Treatment

CHROMSPUN - Shoes - Eastman Kodak Co. (Eastman Chemicals Div.)

CHROMSTAR II - Antennas - Winegard Co.

CHROMSTAR II PREAMPS - Amplifiers - Winegard Co.

CHROMSTAR 2000 - Electronic equipment - Winegard Co.

CHROMTEC - Wheels–motor vehicle - Lacks Industries, Inc.

CHROMTRIM - Trimmings–metal ☆ - Werner Co.

CHROMULIN - Vitamins and nutritional supplements - Natural Balance, Inc.

CHRONATRON - Watches - Bulova Corp.

CHRONAUTIC - Watches - Rolex Watch USA, Inc.

CHRONDAC - Circuit boards - Chrontel, Inc.

CHRONIC - Apparel and accessories - Pamela Lyster

CHRONICLE-DATE - Clocks ☆ - General Time Corp. (Westclox/Seth Thomas Div.)

CHRONICLE STREET - Hosiery - Belmont Hosiery Mills Inc.

CHRONICLER - Eyeglasses - Martin-Copeland Eyewear Corp.

CHRONICLES - Recording label - Polygram Records, Inc.

CHRONICURE - Pharmaceutical preparations - ABS Lifesciences, Inc.

CHRONO DYNAMICS - Medical equipment - Chrono Dynamics, Ltd.

CHRONO-MATIC - Watches ☆ - SMH (US) Inc.

CHRONO-TIMER - Watches - Gruen Marketing Corp.

CHRONOBELL - Timers–appliance - Maas-Rowe Carillons Inc.

CHRONODATE - Radios - Tandy Corp.

CHRONODIVER - Watches - Movado Time Corp.

CHRONOLOGIST - Eyeglasses - Martin-Copeland Eyewear Corp.

CHRONOMASTER - Watches - Croton Watch Co., Inc.

CHRONOMAT - Watches ☆ - Wakmann Watch Co. Inc.

CHRONOMATH - Electronic equipment - Tandy Corp.

CHRONOMATIC - Radios - Tandy Corp.

CHRONOMIX - Sporting goods - Chronomix Corp.

CHRONON - Clocks - Clock Motors Inc.

CHRONOS - Wallpaper - Sellers & Josephson

CHRONOS 3 - Wallpaper - Sellers & Josephson

CHRONOS 4 - Wallpaper - Sellers & Josephson

CHRONOS VI - Wallpaper - Wall Fashion Inc.

CHRONOSPHERE - Computer software - Now What Software

CHRONOSPORT - Watches - Chronosport Inc.

CHRONOSTROKE - Sporting goods - Nielsen-Kellerman Co.

CHRONOTECH - Computer software - Chronotech

CHRONOTHERM III - Thermostats - Honeywell Residential & Building Controls

CHRONSET - Medical apparatus - Alza Corp.

CHRONULAC - Pharmaceutical preparations - Marion Merrell Dow

CHRYSALIS - Office furniture - Chrysalis Inc.

CHRYSALIS - Recording label - Chrysalis Records

CHRYSALIS BAY - Wallpaper - Seabrook Wallcoverings, Inc.

CHRYSANTHEME - Sweaters - Dress Barn, Inc.

CHRYSANTHEMUM - Glassware–household ☆ - Spiegelau Inc.

CHRYSLER - Motor vehicles–automobiles - DaimlerChrysler

CHRYSLER 300 - Motor vehicles–automobiles ☆ - Chrysler Corp. (Chrysler-Plymouth Div.)

CHRYSNBON - Craft supplies ☆ - Midwest Products Co. Inc.

CHRYSOS - Jewelry - Zale Corp.

CHRYSOS - Jewelry - Zale Delaware, Inc.

CHRYSTAR - Plastics film - Samsill Corp.

CHRYSTIE - Wallpaper ☆ - Ginger Tree Designs

C.H.S. - Corsets - Sears, Roebuck and Co.

CHS - Medical apparatus - Techmedica Inc.

CHS CERTIFIED HYDRAULIC SPECIALISTS - Motors - Donahue Enterprises, Inc.

C.H.S. SPORTSWEAR - Apparel and accessories - Esskay Manufacturing Co.

CHU - Apparel and accessories - Kellwood Co.

CHU AND DESIGN - Apparel and accessories - Kellwood Co.

CHU-BOPS - Chewing gum ☆ - Amurol Confections Co.

CHU CHU - Costumes - McCain Ellio's Foods, Inc.

CHU KIANG BRAND - Pharmaceutical preparations - So's USA Co., Inc.

CHU-MAN-CHU - Candy ☆ - Leaf, Inc.

CHU MOR - Candy - American Chewing Gum Inc.

CHU-STICKS - Candy ☆ - Atkinson Candy Co.

CHUB - Candles ☆ - Candle-Lite Co.

CHUBB - Safes - Fire King International, Inc.

CHUBB - Skis - Volant Ski Corp.

CHUBBE - Sweatshirts - Landon Chance Allred

CHUBBIES - Sausages - Foodbrands America, Inc.

CHUBBIES - Toys - Classic Coachworks Toys Inc.

CHUBBLES - Candy - Gerrit J. Verburg Co.

CHUBBMUSE - Computer software - Chubb Corp.

CHUBBS - Infant product - Sterling Winthrop Inc.

CHUBB'S BRO'S - Apparel and accessories - Leslie Taylor

CHUBBY - Dolls ☆ - Uneeda Doll Co., Inc.

CHUBBY - Eyeglasses - Art-Craft Optical Co.

CHUBBY - Pencil sharpeners - Dahle USA

CHUBBY BLOCS - Toys ☆ - Placo Products Co.

CHUBBY BOY - Crocheted and knitted items ☆ - Schuessler Knitting Mills Inc.

CHUBBY CAPER - Crocheted and knitted items ☆ - Schuessler Knitting Mills Inc.

CHUBBY CHASERS - Dog food - Harlmen, Inc.

CHUBBY CHECKS - Toys–stuffed ☆ - Fun World Inc.

CHUBBY CHEEKS - Toys - Dan-Dee International Ltd.

CHUBBY-CHERUBS - Toys–stuffed - Heaven Sent Distributing, Inc.

CHUBBY CHICK - Footwear - Americal Corp.

CHUBBY CHICKEN - Meat products–poultry - A and W Restaurants, Inc.

CHUBBY CHIMES - Toys–stuffed - Dakin Inc.

CHUBBY CHOPPER - Toys - Tomy America, Inc.

CHUBBY DUCKLING - Toys–stuffed - Dakin Inc.

CHUBBY GIRL - Crocheted and knitted items ☆ - Schuessler Knitting Mills Inc.

CHUBBY HUBBY - Ice cream - Ben and Jerry's Homemade, Inc.

CHUBBY PUZZLES - Puzzles - Lauri Inc.

CHUBBY SANTA - Candy - Brock Candy Co. Inc.

CHUBBY TUB-A-TOT - Dolls - Uneeda Doll Co., Ltd.

CHUBBY WOOD - Apparel–men's - Kimberleigh Wood and Steven Wood Partnership

CHUBBYKINS - Stamps–hand - Stampendous, Inc.

CHUBBYKINS - Toys - Eugene Doll & Novelty Co. Inc.

CHUBEI - Plaything - C. Itoh & Co. America Inc.

CHUBMASTER - Packaging machines - BWI Kartridgpak Co.

CHUBS PACKABLES - Cleaning preparations - Linden Corp.

CHUBS STACKABLES - Infant product - L & F Consumer Products

CHUBSTER - Pens - Staedtler, Inc.

CHUCK - Ophthalmic goods - Swank Optical

CHUCK-A-LUCK - Ophthalmic goods - Foremost Optical Products

CHUCK A LUCK DARTS - Games - Arachnid, Inc.

CHUCK-A-MATIC - Pencils - Universal Fountain Pen & Pencil Co.

CHUCK BEAR - Toys–stuffed ☆ - At the Zoo

CHUCK-EEZ - Lubricating oils - Specialty Lubricants Corp.

CHUCK-FIL - Asphalt - Garon Products Inc.

CHUCK FULL OF NUTS - Games - Smethport Specialty Co.

CHUCK NORRIS - Games ☆ - Ben Cooper Inc.

CHUCK NORRIS - Toys–stuffed - Kenner Products

CHUCK PILL - Ornamental products–glass - Charles L. Divelbiss

CHUCK TAYLOR - Sports apparel - Converse Inc.

CHUCK WAGON - Bakery products - Bouyea-Fassetts Inc.

CHUCK WAGON - Dog food - Ralston Purina Co.

CHUCK WAGON - Food products - Bar S Food Co. Inc.

CHUCK WAGON JUJU - Candy - Sweet Candy Co.

CHUCK WAGON STAMPEDE - Dog food - Ralston Purina Co.

CHUCK YEAGER'S ADVANCED FLIGHT TRAINER - Computer software - Electronic Arts Inc.

CHUCKIE - Labels–paper - LRJ Records

CHUCKIE - Toys–stuffed ☆ - Russ Berrie and Co., Inc.

CHUCKLE - Recording label - K-Tel International, Inc.

CHUCKLE A DAY..., A - Calendars - E.P. Publishing

CHUCKLE HOUSE - Recording label - Chuckle House Tapes Inc.

CHUCKLE POPS - Computer software - Enlighten Co.
CHUCKLEBERRY - Puppets - Yummy Designs
CHUCKLES - Candy - Leaf, Inc.
CHUCKLES! - Greeting cards - G. Neil Companies
CHUCKLES - Shoes ☆ - Harbor Footwear Group Ltd.
CHUCKLES & CO. - Infant product - Eden LLC
CHUCKLES NEW ARRIVALS - Infant product - Eden LLC
CHUCKLET - Fishing lures - Eppinger Manufacturing Co.
CHUCKLIN' CHERRY - Juices - General Mills, Inc.
CHUCK'R - Toys–airplanes - North Pacific Products Inc.
CHUCK'S - Confections - Parco Foods, Inc.
CHUCKS - Footwear–athletic ☆ - C.O. Lynch Enterprises, Inc.
CHUCK'S BEST - Seafood products–canned or cured - Chuck's Seafoods
CHUCKSTER - Rifles - O.F. Mossberg & Sons, Inc.
CHUCKWAGON - Candy - Sweet Candy Co.
CHUCKY - Ophthalmic goods - Styl-Rite Optical Manufacturing Co., Inc.
CHUFFA PUFFA - Toys - Tomy America, Inc.
CHUG-A-CHOO - Dinnerware–plastic ☆ - WMF/USA
CHUG-A-POP RAILROAD - Toys - Tomy America, Inc.
CHUG BUG - Fishing lures - Storm Manufacturing Co.
CHUGGA BUG - Dolls - Mattel, Inc.
CHUGGA-CHUGGA CHOO-CHOO - Toys–trains - Little Tikes Co.
CHUGGA CHUGGA DING DING CHOO CHOO - Toys - Tomy America, Inc.
CHUGGER - Bicycles - Murray, Inc.
CHUGGER - Juices - Tropicana Products, Inc.
CHUGGER SPOOK - Sporting goods - James Heddon's Sons
CHUGIAK - Backpacks - Outside Design Corp.
CHUG'N CHERRY - Beverages - Premiere Innovations, Inc.
CHUGO - Dresses–women's - Chugo International Corp.
CHUGUM - Candy - American Chewing Gum Inc.
CHUKAR CHERRY - Snack foods - Chukar Cherry
CHUKKER - Boots - McCrory Corp.
CHUKKER COLLECTION - Trading cards and stamps - Chukker Co.
CHUKKIES - Stationery - Giordano Art, Ltd.
CHULA - Ophthalmic goods - Styl-Rite Optical Manufacturing Co., Inc.
CHUM GUM - Candy ☆ - Fleer Corp.
CHUMFORTERS - Ophthalmic goods - Chums Ltd.
CHUMMY - Stoves–gas - Fatsco
CHUMP - Apparel and accessories - Ogio International, Inc.
CHUMPIES - Potato chips - Home Boys Inc.
CHUMTHING? - Key rings - Chums Ltd.
CHUN KING - Chow mein - Hunt-Wesson, Inc.
CHUN KING - Dinners–frozen - Conagra, Inc.
CHUN KING - Food products - Nabisco Foods Group
CHUN KING PREMIUM - Food products - Nabisco Foods Group
CHUNG HAA - Paints - Oriental Trading Co., Inc.
CHUNG HWA - Floor coverings–carpet and rugs ☆ - Rugby Rugs Inc.
CHUNGA - Toys–stuffed - Trendmasters, Inc.
CHUNG'S - Food products - Health Jet, Inc.
CHUNG'S DELIGHT - Food products - Health Jet, Inc.
CHUNG'S EXPRESS - Chickens - Health Jet, Inc.
CHUNK - Bacon ☆ - Dold Foods Inc.
CHUNK-O-CRAYON - Crayons - Scratch-Art Co., Inc.
CHUNKEE - Food products machinery - Chunkee Food Co.
CHUNKERO - Chili–canned - Stagg Foods, Inc.
CHUNKS - Dog food - Iams Co.
CHUNKS 'N NUTS - Cookies ☆ - Pepsico, Inc.
CHUNK'S O' FRUTI - Desserts - Natural Fruit
CHUNKSTER - Ice cream - Simco Sales Service of Pennsylvania, Inc.
CHUNKY - Candy - Nestle USA
CHUNKY - Fruits–frozen ☆ - VIP Sales Co. Inc.
CHUNKY - Soups–canned - Campbell Soup Co.
CHUNKY - Toys–automobiles - Processed Plastic Co.
CHUNKY - Toys–automobiles - Tyco Toys
CHUNKY APPLE - Fruit butters - Sarabeth's Kitchen
CHUNKY FOR COOKING - Seasonings ☆ - Campbell Soup Co.
CHUNKY INTERNATIONAL - Soups–canned - Campbell Soup Co.
CHUNKY MONKEY - Ice cream - Ben and Jerry's Homemade, Inc.
CHUNKY RED CHILI - Frozen foods - Dewey's Foods Inc.
CHUNKY TRUCK - Toys–automobiles - Processed Plastic Co.
CHUNX - Dog food - Jim Dandy Co.
CHUNX N' GRAVY - Dog food - Jim Dandy Co.
CHUPPLEE - Shoes ☆ - Clarks of England Inc.
CHURCH - Toilet seats - Bemis Manufacturing Co.
CHURCH ART PLUS ON DISK - Computer software - Communication Resources, Inc.

CHURCH MUSIC FOR CHILDREN - Recording label - United Methodist Publishing House
CHURCH OF SKATAN - Video production - Shorty's, Inc.
CHURCH TACKLE - Fishing lures ☆ - Church Tackle Co.
CHURCHILL - Apparel and accessories ☆ - Genesco Inc.
CHURCHILL - Beverages–malt - Rouseabout International
CHURCHILL - Cigars - Tropical Tobacco, Inc.
CHURCHILL - Clocks ☆ - General Time Corp. (Westclox/Seth Thomas Div.)
CHURCHILL - Coffee - Church Point Wholesale Groceries Inc.
CHURCHILL - Glassware–household - Crisa Corp.
CHURCHILL - Hats - Resistol Hats
CHURCHILL - Snuff - Gesty Trading & Manufacturing Corp.
CHURCHILL - Whirlpools - Lasco Products Group
CHURCHILL TABLEWARE - Dinnerware - Cuthbertson Imports Inc.
CHURCH'S - Restaurants–fast food - Church's Fried Chicken Inc.
CHURCH'S FAMOUS ENGLISH SHOES - Shoes - Church's English Shoes Ltd.
CHURN PROPHET - Computer software - Lightbridge, Inc.
CHURN SPREAD - Butter - Harvest States Cooperatives
CHURNY - Cheese - Churny Co., Inc.
CHURNY GARDEN - Cheese - Churny Co., Inc.
CHURNY LITE - Cheese - Kraft Foods, Inc.
CHURROS BY MANNY - Food products - Manuel Suarez
CHU'S - Novelty items - Importoys
CHUSEI - Chemical preparations - Chusei USA Inc.
CHUTE 5 - Games ☆ - Milton Bradley Co.
CHUTE, THE - Skis - Golconda Industries
CHUTES - Pet products - Hamilton Products Inc.
CHUTES - Sandals - Wolverine World Wide, Inc.
CHUTES - Tool boxes - Portable Products, Inc.
CHUTES AND LADDERS - Games - Milton Bradley Co.
CHUTESCOOP - Marine rigging - V.F. Shaw Co., Inc.
CHUTNEY - Marble products - Kohler Co.
CHUTZPAH - Games - CFC Games
CHUX - Diapers–disposable - Johnson & Johnson
CHX - Exchangers–heat - Babcock & Wilcox Co.
CHX - Pet products - St. Jon Pet Care Products Inc.
CHYMOSTAR - Enzyme preparation - Rhone-Poulenc Specialty Chemicals Co.
CHYNA - Dinnerware–plastic - Ullman Co. Inc.
CHYNOZYME - Vitamins and nutritional supplements - Ethical Nutrients
CHYPRE - Fragrance ☆ - Coty Inc.
CHYTOWNS - Recording label - Jerma Records Co. (Div. of Jerma Productions)
CI - Braces–orthopedic - Smith & Nephew DonJoy Inc.
CI - Exercising equipment - Schwinn Cycling & Fitness Inc.
CI - Handbags - Carteras Italianas Handbags and Designs Inc.
CI - Identification tags - Card Imaging Inc.
CI - Jewelry - Cache' International
CI - Jewelry - Color International, Inc.
CI - Tools - Bass & Sons Inc.
CI-4 - Printers–computer - C-TECH Electronics Inc.
CI-8 - Printers–computer - C-TECH Electronics Inc.
CI-8E - Printers–computer - C-TECH Electronics Inc.
CI BELLA - Pasta - Westbrae Natural Foods, Inc.
CI BON - Frames–eyeglass - Hudson Optical Corp.
CI CRANDALL INTERNATIONAL - Machinery - Crandall International, Inc.
CI DESIGN - Computer peripheral equipment - Commercial and Industrial Design Co. Inc.
CIA - Cosmetics - Cia Facial Products, Inc.
CIA - Electromedical apparatus - Waters Investments Limited
CIA - Flatware ☆ - Trend Pacific Inc.
CIA - Medical apparatus - Chiron Corp.
CIA - Tools - Tool and Equipment Distributors Associates, Inc.
CIA - Tools–hand-operated - Tool and Equipment Distributors Associates, Inc.
CIAA - Sunglasses - Central Intercollegiate Athletic Association
CIABATTA - Breads - Orlando Baking Co. Inc.
CIAMPI - Footwear - Samuels Shoe Co.
CIANI - Jewelry ☆ - Monet Jewelers
CIAO - Fabrics–canvas ☆ - Crown Textile Co.
CIAO - Floor coverings–carpet and rugs - Customweave Carpets Inc.
CIAO! - Luggage - Lifestyle International, Inc.
CIAO - Office supplies - Between You & Me
CIAO - Perfumes - Houbigant, Inc.
CIAO - Wines - Richard Adlai Corp.
CIAO BELLA - Dairy products - Ciao Bella Gelato Co. Inc.
CIAO ITALIA - Glassware–household - Mary Ann Esposito, Inc.

☆ = Now out of production

CIAPESC - Seafood products–fresh or frozen ☆ - J.F. Clarke Corp.

CIARA - Frames–eyeglass ☆ - U.S. Optical Frame Co.

CIARA - Perfumes - Revlon Consumer Products Corp.

CIARO - Apparel–men's - UFO Contemporary, Inc.

CIATTI - Apparel–men's - Leon of Paris Co. Inc.

CIB COLLECTORS' INFORMATION BUREAU - Publisher's imprints - Collectors' Information Bureau

CIBA VISION - Contact lenses - Ciba-Geigy Corp.

CIBACALCIN - Pharmaceutical preparations - Ciba-Geigy Corp.

CIBACEL - Chemical preparations - Ciba-Geigy Corp.

CIBACHROME II & CTD F7 - See **ILFOCHROME CLASSIC**

CIBAFIX - Chemical preparations - Ciba-Geigy Corp.

CIBAFLOW - Chemical preparations - Ciba-Geigy Corp.

CIBAFLUID - Chemical preparations - Ciba-Geigy Corp.

CIBARI - Beverages–alcohol - Canandaigua Wine Co. Inc.

CIBEL - Colognes - Darling Corp.

CIBIE - Lighting equipment–automotive - Aardvark International

CIBO DI LIDIA - Food products - Tanjoe Enterprises, Inc.

CIBONEY CARPET MILLS - Floor coverings–carpet and rugs - Aladdin Mills, Inc.

CIBREO - Apparel–athletic - Arnold Goldberg Enterprises Inc.

CIC - Balls–baseball - Lisco, Inc.

CICA-CARE - Elastomers - Smith & Nephew Inc. (Rehabilitation Div.)

CICA FOR WINDOWS - Computer software - Walnut Creek CD ROMs, Inc.

CICCARELLI - Toothpaste ☆ - Dean & Deluca Inc.

CICELY M. BARKER COLLECTION - Giftware - Roman, Inc.

CICERO - Frames–eyeglass - Pathway Optical Prods.

CICHLID BIO-GOLD FOOD - Pet products - Hikari Sales USA Inc.

CICHLID EXCEL FOOD - Pet products - Hikari Sales USA Inc.

CICHLID GOLD FOOD - Pet products - Hikari Sales USA Inc.

CICHLID LAKE SALT - Pet products - Seachem Laboratories

CICHLID-PROTEIN SUPREME - Pet products ☆ - Aquatrol, Inc.

CICHLID STAPLE FOOD - Pet products - Hikari Sales USA Inc.

CICHLID T.E.N. - Fish food - Wardley Corp.

CICI - Cosmetics - Cici Cosmetic Co.

CICO - Food products - Conway Import Co. Inc.

CICRON - Fabrics ☆ - Bacon Felt Co. Inc.

CICS/400 - Computer software - International Business Machines Corp.

CICS/6000 - Computer peripheral equipment - International Business Machines Corp.

CICSPLEX - Computer software - International Business Machines Corp.

CID - Jewelry - Clyde Duneier Inc.

C.I.D. - Ventilation equipment - L.D. Sterns Corp.

CIDAL'S - Skin care products - East Village Soap Co. Ltd.

CIDCO INCORPORATED - Telephone apparatus - Cidco, Inc.

CIDER 84 - Beverages - Mott's Inc.

CIDER JACK - Beverages–alcohol - American Hard Cider Co., Inc.

CIDER MATE - Spices and extracts - Frontier Products

CIDER 'N SPICE - Juices - Johanna Foods, Inc.

CIDER SPICER - Spices and extracts ☆ - Alltrista Corp.

CIDER TYME - Fruit drinks–bottled or canned - Natural Country Juice Products, Inc.

CIDETRAK - Insect repellents - Trece, Inc.

CIDEW - Computer software - Aegis Computer Enterprise Systems, Inc.

CIDEX - Disinfectants - Johnson & Johnson

CIDEX 7 - Disinfectants - Johnson & Johnson

CIDEX FORMULA 7 - Cleaning preparations - Johnson & Johnson

CIDICOL - Pharmaceutical preparations ☆ - Upjohn Co.

CIE DES CRISTALLERIES DE BACCARAT - Glassware–household - Haviland Limoges

CIEL DE BLEU - Spices and extracts - Michael Berlin

CIEL GRIS - Cosmetics - Lancome

CIELO ABIERTO - Publisher's imprints - Harcourt Brace & Co.

CIEMMEMODULE - Tiles–enamel - Federal Tile Imports Inc.

CIEN - Glassware–household - Crisa Corp.

CIENA OPTICAL COMMUNICATIONS - Optical machinery - Ciena Corp.

CIENCIAS Y MAS - Publisher's imprints - Harcourt Brace & Co.

CIENEGA GLASS - Glassware–household - Alchemy Glass & Light, Inc.

CIENTOS - Lighters - Colibri Inc.

CIENTRA - Tires - Uniroyal Goodrich Licensing Services, Inc.

CIERA - Boats–motor - Bayliner Marine Corp.

CIERA - Floor coverings–carpet and rugs ☆ - Criterion Mills Inc.

CIERA - Motor vehicles–minivans - General Motors Corp. (Oldsmobile Div.)

CIERRA - Golf clubs - Austad Co.

CIERRA - Windows - Louisiana-Pacific Corp.

CIERRA CLAD - Window frames ☆ - Louisiana-Pacific Corp.

CIERRA GRANDE - Window frames - Louisiana-Pacific Corp.

CIERVA - Rings–jewelry - Artcarved Inc.

CIESIN - Publisher's imprints - Consortium for International Earth Science Information Network

CIF - Sportswear, jewelry, key chains, etc. - California Interscholastic Federation

CIG - Lighters - Young's Association Inc.

CIG-A-RID - Cigarettes - More Direct Response Inc.

CIGANA - Beverages–carbonated - Marcos A. Fernandes

CIGANY - Jewelry - Linda Virgilio

CIGAR-ETTE - Deodorizers - Surco Products Inc.

CIGAR FRIENDLY - Apparel and accessories - Cigar Friendly, Inc.

CIGAR PHD - Apparel and accessories - Arangold Corp.

CIGAR POPPER - Fishing lures - Boone Bait Co. Inc.

CIGAR TASTER'S COMPANION - Tobacco products - Reid G. Wientge

CIGAR USA - Apparel and accessories - Arangold Corp.

CIGARE VOLANT - Wines - Bonny Doon Winery Inc.

CIGARETTE - Boats–motor - Cigarette Racing Team Inc.

CIGARETTELLOS - Cigarettes - Nat Sherman, Inc.

CIGARETTELLOS SLIMS - Cigarettes ☆ - Nat Sherman, Inc.

CIGARGOYLES - Apparel–men's - Steven Furlet

CIGARIAN - Ashtrays–glass - Holmes & Holmes

CIGARLET - Cigar boxes–wood ☆ - Consolidated Cigar Corp.

CIGARWARE - Jewelry–costume - Cigars by Santa Clara N.A. Inc.

CIGLIANO - Apparel and accessories - MGRR, Inc.

CIGNA PROFILES - Computer storage devices - Cigna Corp.

CIGNAL - Apparel and accessories - MGRR, Inc.

CIGNAL SPORT - Apparel–women's - MGRR, Inc.

CII - Jewelry - Contrast Imports, Inc.

C.I.L. - Lighting fixtures - Light Inc.

CILAX - Artists' materials ☆ - Artoptic International Corp.

CILINDRO COLLECTION, THE - Artists' materials - Artisan House Inc.

CILKI II - Yarn - Roselon Industries, Inc.

CILL - Floor coverings - E.R. Carpenter Co.

CILOXAN - Health care products - Alcon Laboratories, Inc.

CILS LUMIERE - Cosmetics - Chanel Inc.

CILS MAGIQUE - Cosmetics - Chanel Inc.

CILURZO - Wines - Cilurzo Vineyard & Winery

CIM - Adhesives and sealants - C.I.M. Industries, Inc.

CIM - Coatings - C.I.M. Industries, Inc.

CIM-DEX - Computer software - Cimtek-Thomas

CIMA - Coffee makers–electric - Star Manufacturing International Inc.

CIMA RED - Beverages–carbonated ☆ - Coca-Cola Co.

C.IMAGING - Computer software - Compix Inc.

CIMARRON - Bicycles - Schwinn Cycling & Fitness Inc.

CIMARRON - Cigarettes - R.J. Reynolds Tobacco Co.

CIMARRON - Clocks - Ridgeway Clock Co.

CIMARRON - Cut stone - Cold Spring Granite Co.

CIMARRON - Dialing devices–telephone - Baltimore Luggage Co.

CIMARRON - Firearms, accessories, and parts - Old West Co. of Texas, Inc.

CIMARRON - Floor coverings - Congoleum Corp.

CIMARRON - Furniture - Bean Station Furniture Factory Inc.

CIMARRON - Furniture ☆ - Stanley Furniture Co. Inc.

CIMARRON - Motor vehicles–automobiles ☆ - General Motors Corp. (Cadillac Motor Car Div.)

CIMARRON - Shoes - Genesco Inc.

CIMARRON - Trailers–travel - Apache

CIMARRON - Wallpaper ☆ - David Merritt Handprints Inc.

CIMARRON BONDED LEATHER - Leather - Permalin Products Co.

CIMARRON CITY - Apparel - Sheplers, Inc.

CIMASTAT - Computer software - Construction Industry Manufacturers Association

CIMFILM - Concrete products - Axim Concrete Technologies Inc.

CIMIRRON - Recording label - Cimirron/Rainbird Records

CIMMARON - Boats–motor - Ebko Industries Inc.

CIMMARON - Chili - American Fine Foods Inc.

CIMMARON - Deodorizers - Eurostar Corp.

CIMMARON - Meat products–canned - Chiquita Processed Food, LLC

CIMMARON - Wallpaper - Gloria Merrill Enterprises

CIMMARON GROUP, THE - Furniture - Bean Station Furniture Factory Inc.

CIMMARRON - Fabrics - Dan River Inc.

CIMONE - Tiles–ceramic - Mediterranean Exports

CIMOS - Computer software - Gas Research Institute

CIMPACT - Chemical preparations - Luzenac America Inc.

CIMPITER - Computer software - Cimpiter Corp.

CIMPLICITY - Electronic equipment - General Electric Co.

CIMPOL - Computer software - Harridan Corp.
CIMTEK THOMAS - Computer software - Cimtek-Thomas
CIMWORKS - Computer software - Gagetalker Corp.
CIN QUIN - Pharmaceutical preparations ☆ - Solvay Pharmaceuticals Inc.
CIN-TEC - Computer software - Cincinnati Gear Co.
CINA - Carpets and rugs - Vista Corp.
CINA - Floor coverings–carpet and rugs - Princeton Carpets
CINAACTION - Computer software - Formosa USA, Inc.
CINACOA - Flour–blended ☆ - Traders Protein
CINAGRO - Garden equipment ☆ - Organic Conversion Corp.
CINAHL - Computer storage devices–optical - Western Adventist Health Services
CINALOG - Pharmaceutical preparations - Econo Med Pharmaceuticals Inc.
CINALONE - Pharmaceutical preparations - Legere Pharmaceuticals Inc.
CINCH - Apparel–men's - Miller International Inc.
CINCH - Chemical preparations - Klein Tools Inc.
CINCH - Cleaning preparations–household - Procter & Gamble Co.
CINCH - Fencing–steel - CF and I Steel L.P.
CINCH - Food products - H.J. Heinz Co.
CINCH - Ophthalmic goods - Capo, Inc.
CINCH - Tools–hand-operated - Labinal Components & Systems, Inc.–Cinch Connectors Div.
CINCH - Veterinary medical equipment ☆ - Franklin Laboratories
CINCH 2 TO 1 - Sporting goods - O'Brien International
CINCH-ALL - Girdles - Vanity Corset Co. Inc.
CINCH BRA - Underwear and nightwear - Bestform Foundations, Inc.
CINCH-CUFF - Law enforcement restraints - Tri-Tech Inc.
CINCH-IT - Medical apparatus - Freeman Manufacturing Co.
CINCH LOCK - Hardware - Lightware, Inc.
CINCH SAK - Bags–plastic - Mobil Chemical Co. Plastics Div.
CINCHLOCK - Metals - Rovac Corp.
CINCHO - Cheese - Los Altos Food Products, Inc.
CINCI CREAM - Beverages–alcohol ☆ - Century Importers Inc.
CINCINNATI - Printing presses - Cincinnati Screen Printing Equipment Co.
CINCINNATI - Radar systems and equipment - Cincinnati Microwave, Inc.
CINCINNATI BEARCATS - Apparel and accessories - University of Cincinnati
CINCINNATI BENGALS - Trading cards and stamps - Cincinnati Bengals, Inc.
CINCINNATI RECIPE - Chili–canned - Skytime, Inc.
CINCINNATI SHOE - Shoe stores - United States Shoe Corp.
CINCINNATIAN - Furnaces–electric - McClain & Sons, Inc.
CINCINNATUS - Ophthalmic goods ☆ - Universal/Univis Inc.
CINCO - Bird feeders - Cinco Plastics, Inc.
CINCO - Cigars ☆ - Phillies Cigar Co.
CINCO DE MAYO - Beverages–alcohol - Shaw-Ross International Importers
CINCORITA - Beverages–alcohol - Chi-Chi's, Inc.
CINCRON - Tools–machine - Cincinnati Machine
CINCY - Brushes - Wright-Bernet
CINDAMY - Rings–jewelry - Artcarved Inc.
CINDER CLAUS - Dolls - Rhonda Brennan
CINDER SUDS - Soap - Cramer Products Inc.
CINDERELLA - Apparel–women's - International Licensing Corp.
CINDERELLA - Cakes - Cinderella Cheese Cake Co.
CINDERELLA - Fabrics - Gretchen Bellinger Inc.
CINDERELLA - Footwear - S. Goldberg and Co. Inc.
CINDERELLA - Games - Cadaco Div.
CINDERELLA - Glassware ☆ - Corning Inc.
CINDERELLA - Glassware–household ☆ - Oneida Ltd.
CINDERELLA - Hair care products - Faberge Co.
CINDERELLA - Manicure preparations - W.R. Rayson Co., Inc.
CINDERELLA - Paper dolls - Coloron Industries
CINDERELLA - Peanut butter - Stevens Industries Inc.
CINDERELLA - Skin care products ☆ - Robinette Inc.
CINDERELLA - Slippers ☆ - Daniel Green Co.
CINDERELLA - Tableware–china - Lenox, Inc.
CINDERELLA - Tinsel - Kaminow Bros. Inc.
CINDERELLA - Underwear and nightwear - Reeves Brothers Inc.
CINDERELLA - Yarn ☆ - Joseph Galler Inc.
CINDERELLA FROZEN IN TIME - Recording label - Dorothy Hamill International, Inc.
CINDERELLA LITE - Cakes - Cinderella Cheese Cake Co.
CINDERELLA'S COACH - Christmas tree ornaments - Cracker Box Inc.
CINDERELLA'S TREASURE CHEST - Toys - Natural Science Industries, Ltd.
CINDET - Cleaning preparations - C.B. Dolge Co.
CINDET ALL PURPOSE - Finishing agents - C.B. Dolge Co.
CINDI MUFSON'S CONTEMPORARY COUNTRY CLASSICS - Wallpaper - B. Berger Co.

CINDOL - Lubricants - E.F. Houghton & Co.
CINDRA - Pet products - DeYoannes Inc.
CINDY - Aerobics footwear ☆ - Autry Industries Inc.
CINDY - Fabric softeners - Sinclair Manufacturing Co.
CINDY - Floor coverings–carpet and rugs - Alexander Smith Carpets
CINDY - Frames–eyeglass ☆ - Rozin Optical Export Corp.
CINDY - Grass seed - International Seeds, Inc.
CINDY - Mops ☆ - Helen Keller Services for the Blind
CINDY - Shoes–athletic - Coast Shoes Inc.
CINDY CURL - Wigs ☆ - Jean Paree Weegs Inc.
CINDY JORDAN - Apparel and accessories - Regent International Corp.
CINDY SUE - Dolls - Jolly U.S.A., Inc.
CINDY SUE COW - Novelty items–stitched - A + A
CINDY WB - Glass–optical - Welling International
CINDYANN - Eyeglasses - Martin-Copeland Eyewear Corp.
CINDY'S BOWS - Novelty items - Cindy's Bows
CINE - Apparel–women's - Jezebel-Renee of Hollywood
CINE 15 - Projection screens - Draper Shade and Screen Co. Inc.
CINE EXTENAR - Lenses–photographic ☆ - Edixa Camera Co.
CINE JOUR - Apparel and accessories - Sanmark-Stardust Inc.
CINE KING - Electronic equipment ☆ - Da-Lite Screen Co. Inc.
CINE-KODAK - Photographic equipment - Eastman Kodak Co.
CINE NAVITAR - Lenses–projection ☆ - Navitar, Inc.
CINE NIKKOR - Electronic equipment - Nikon Inc.
CINE STAR - Apparel–women's - Sanmark-Stardust Inc.
CINE-SUN - Photographic equipment ☆ - Hudson Photographic Industries Inc.
CINE-TWIN - Watches ☆ - Longines-Wittnauer Watch Co.
CINEBOOKS - Publisher's imprints - News America Publishing Inc.
CINEDEX - Computer software - Jeffrey Aaron Goldstein
CINEFLECTOR - Lighting equipment - Acme-Lite Manufacturing Co.
CINEFLEX - Projection screens - Draper Shade and Screen Co. Inc.
CINEFOLD - Projection screens - Draper Shade and Screen Co. Inc.
CINEFRAME - Projection screens - Draper Shade and Screen Co. Inc.
CINEFUSION - Computer software - Ultimatte Corp.
CINEGEL - Electronic equipment - Rosco Laboratories Inc.
CINEGLASS - Projection screens - Draper Shade and Screen Co. Inc.
CINEGON-SCHNEIDER - Lenses–photographic - Schneider Optics, Inc.
CINELARGER - Film ☆ - Testrite Instrument Co. Inc.
CINELLI - Bicycles - Corso Bicycle Distributor Inc.
CINELOUNGER - Furniture - First Impressions Design and Management, Inc.
CINELUX - Lenses–photographic - Schneider Optics, Inc.
CINELUX-ULTRA - Lenses–optical - Schneider Optics, Inc.
CINEMA - Floor coverings–carpet and rugs ☆ - Criterion Mills Inc.
CINEMA - Lighting fixtures - Swivelier Co. Inc.
CINEMA - Ophthalmic goods - Embassy Creations Inc.
CINEMA - Recording label - Cinema Records Inc.
CINEMA ETOILE - Apparel–women's - Cinema Etoile
CINEMA KOSHER - Lipsticks - Cinema Beaute
CINEMA MASTER - Computer software - SourceView Software International
CINEMA ONE - Loudspeakers - Ameriwood Industries International Corp.
CINEMA RIDE - Apparel and accessories - Cinema Ride, Inc.
CINEMA SECRETS - Cosmetics - Cinema Secrets Inc.
CINEMA SERIES - Televisions - Toshiba America Consumer Products, Inc. (Consumer Products Business Sector)
CINEMAC - Computer software - Jim Roberts
CINEMAGE - Photographic equipment ☆ - Hudson Photographic Industries Inc.
CINEMAGIC - Computer hardware - IPC Technologies, Inc.
CINEMAGIC SIX HOME THEATER - Televisions - DCM Corp.
CINEMANIA - Computer software - Microsoft Corp.
CINEMASCOPE - Electronic equipment - Bausch & Lomb Inc.
CINEMASOUND - Projectors–photographic - Creatron Inc.
CINEMASTER - Electronic equipment - Telex Communications, Inc.
CINEMAT - Vending machines - Cinemat Corp.
CINEMATAR - Electronic equipment ☆ - Navitar, Inc.
CINEMATIC MULTIMEDIA - Computer software - Interplay Productions
CINEMATRIX INTERACTIVE ENTERTAINMENT SYSTEMS - Computer hardware - Rachel Carpenter
CINEMATRONICS - Computer software - Cinematronics, LLC
CINEMAVISION - Projectors–photographic - Matsushita Consumer Electronics Co.
CINEMAX - Flashlights - Time Warner Entertainment Co., L.P.
CINEMEASURE - Medical apparatus - Infimed, Inc.
CINEMECCANICA - Electronic equipment - Xetron
CINEMODE - Apparel and accessories - Joujou Designs Inc.
CINEMORPH - Computer software - ASDG, Inc.
CINEON - Photographic equipment - Eastman Kodak Co.

☆ = Now out of production

CINEPAK - Computer software - Supermac Technology
CINEPERM - Projection screens - Draper Shade and Screen Co. Inc.
CINEPHONIC EIGHT - Cameras - Sentry Test Systems
CINEPHOR - Electronic equipment - Bausch & Lomb Inc.
CINEPLEX - Projection screens - Draper Shade and Screen Co. Inc.
CINER - Jewelry - Ciner Manufacturing Inc.
CINERAMA - Video production - Cinerama, Inc.
CINERAMA - Wallpaper - Bayview Wallcoverings
CINERAMA II - Wallpaper - Bayview Wallcoverings
CINERATOR - Liqueurs - Heaven Hill Distilleries, Inc.
CINESCAN - Electronics equipment - RTI Research Technology International
CINESCREEN - Projection screens - Draper Shade and Screen Co. Inc.
CINESOUND - Electronic equipment - Apollo Audiovisual Div.
C.I.NES.Y.S. - Educational materials - National Research Group, Inc.
CINEVISION - Electronic equipment ✰ - H. Wilson Co.
CINEWIDE - Electronic equipment ✰ - Buhl Optical Co.
CINEWORLD - Computer software - Min Yee
CINFUL - Seasoned bread topping - Frank J. Italiano Inc.
CINN-A-QUICK - Cakes—mixes - Cereal Ingredients, Inc.
CINN-THETICS - Bakeries - Bush, Boake, Allan Inc.
CINNA-COLA - Beverages—carbonated - Nick G. Gatchis
CINNABAR - Apparel - Cinnabar Traders Ltd.
CINNABAR - Apparel and accessories - Kellwood Co.
CINNABAR - Dishes—china - Pickard Inc.
CINNABAR - Floor coverings—carpet and rugs ✰ - Masland Corp.
CINNABAR - Perfumes - Estee Lauder Inc.
CINNABON - Dairy products - Cinnabon, Inc.
CINNAMAGIC - Cereal - Quaker Oats Co.
CINNAMAZE - Bakery products - Chicago Pretzel Co.
CINNAMINT - Chewing gum - Clark Gum Co.
CINNAMON - Dinnerware—glass ✰ - Nikko Ceramics Inc.
CINNAMON - Toys—stuffed ✰ - CBS Toys
CINNAMON & RAISIN BAGELS - Bagels - Natural Ovens of Manitowoc Inc.
CINNAMON BABIES - Dolls - Trinette Chase
CINNAMON BAY - Floor coverings—carpet and rugs ✰ - Lees Carpets
CINNAMON BEAR, THE - Toys—stuffed - Stiles-Bishop Productions Inc.
CINNAMON BEARS - Candy - Sweet Candy Co.
CINNAMON BEARS - Candy ✰ - New England Confectionery Co.
CINNAMON BUN - Candles - Village Candle, Inc.
CINNAMON CELEBRATION - Coffee - Saramar Corp.
CINNAMON CIDER - Deodorizers - Aromatique, Inc.
CINNAMON CRISP - Crackers - Keebler Co.
CINNAMON CRISP - Food products - Antique Mall & Crown
CINNAMON CRUMBLE APPLE CRISP - Bakery products - Sweet Street Desserts, Inc.
CINNAMON CRUNCHIES - Snack foods ✰ - Sathers Inc.
CINNAMON DISKS - Candy - Brach and Brock Confections Inc.
CINNAMON DROPS - Underwear and nightwear - Maidenform Inc.
CINNAMON GIRL - Apparel and accessories - Jonelle Okamura
CINNAMON GRAHAM MINI-BITES - Cereal - New Morn, Inc.
CINNAMON GRAHAMS - Cereal - New Morn, Inc.
CINNAMON GRINS - Cereal - Breadshop's Natural Foods
CINNAMON HILL - Furniture - Tell City Chair Co.
CINNAMON HONEY GEMS - Cookies ✰ - Archway Cookie Inc.
CINNAMON HOTHEADS - See AIRHEADS
CINNAMON IMPERIALS - Candy - Brach and Brock Confections Inc.
CINNAMON IMPERIALS - Candy ✰ - Judson-Atkinson Candies
CINNAMON JIM'S - Bakery products - Mendy, Inc.
CINNAMON JOE - Cereal ✰ - General Mills, Inc.
CINNAMON KISS - Jams and jellies - Mountain Maid Gourmet Jelly
CINNAMON MAID - Crackers - Nabisco Foods Group
CINNAMON, MON - Yogurt—frozen - Alta-Dena Certified Dairy, Inc.
CINNAMON ROSE - Teas—herbal - Celestial Seasonings, Inc.
CINNAMON SENSATION - Teas—herbal - Farmer Bros. Co.
CINNAMON SIAMESE - Toys—stuffed - Dakin Inc.
CINNAMON SPICE - Teas - Traditional Medicinals, Inc.
CINNAMON STICK - Christmas tree ornaments - Cracker Box Inc.
CINNAMON STICK - Sportswear - Benditel, Inc.
CINNAMON STICK - Teas - R.C. Bigelow, Inc.
CINNAMON STICKS - Wallpaper - Glidden Co.
CINNAMON STIX - Breads ✰ - A and W Restaurants, Inc.
CINNAMON STIX - Perfumes - Lumi-Lite Candle Co. Inc.
CINNAMON STREET - Bakery products - Orion Enterprises, Inc.
CINNAMON STREET BAKERY - Coffee - Hot Stuff Food Systems, Inc.
CINNAMON-SWIRL - Cleaning preparations - Georgia-Pacific Corp.
CINNAMON TOAST CRUNCH - Cereal - General Mills, Inc.

CINNAMON TREATS - Cereal - Nabisco Foods Group
CINNAMON VIENNA - Teas—herbal - Celestial Seasonings, Inc.
CINNAMONEY - Computer software - Thought Inc.
CINNAMONSTER - Cinnamon rolls - Cinnamonster Inc.
CINNANUT CREAM - Coffee - Brothers Gourmet Coffees, Inc.
CINNAPADS - Footwear - Atlas Trading Associates, Inc.
CINNAPPLE SPICE - Food products - Breadshop's Natural Foods
CINNAROMA - Biscuits - YZ Enterprises, Inc.
CINNFULLY DELICIOUS - Pretzels - Pretzelmaker, Inc.
CINN'MON POLE - Candy ✰ - Gilliam Candy Co. Inc. (Gilliam Candy Brands)
CINNSATION - Suntan lotions - Most Products
CINO - Food products ✰ - Wild Flavors, Inc.
CINO - Thread - Cincinnati Thread Co.
CINO-40 - Pharmaceutical preparations ✰ - Solvay Pharmaceuticals Inc.
CINOKAP - Health care products ✰ - Kay Pharmacal Co. Inc.
CINONIDE - Pharmaceutical preparations - Legere Pharmaceuticals Inc.
CINQUE TERRE - Wines - Tyfield Importers
CINTRIDE - Tools—hand-operated - Anglo American Enterprises Corp.
CINTURA - Frames—eyeglass - Pathway Optical Prods.
CINZANO - Beverages—alcohol - Palace Brands Co.
CINZIA - Dishes—china - Pasmantier Co. Inc.
CIOCCO' VILLA - Bakery products - Log House Foods Inc.
CIOCCOLATO PARADISO - Bakery products - Nonni's, Corp.
CIOCCOLOTTI - Bakery goods - La Tempesta Bakery Confections, Inc.
CIOVANE - Wines - Hilton Commercial Group Inc.
C.I.P. - Paints - P.S.AM.S., Inc.
CIP-100 - Cleaning preparations - E.R. Squibb & Sons, Inc.
CIP 200 - Cleaning preparations - E.R. Squibb & Sons, Inc.
CIP 220 - Cleaning preparations - E.R. Squibb & Sons, Inc.
CIP 300 - Detergents - E.R. Squibb & Sons, Inc.
CIPANGO - Beverages—malt ✰ - Kirin USA, Inc.
CIPOLLETTI GALLERY - Giftware - Roman, Inc.
CIPREA - Whirlpools - Jacuzzi Inc.
CIPRIANI - Floor coverings ✰ - Tarkett, Inc.
CIPRIANI - Floor coverings—carpet and rugs - Atlas Carpet Mills Inc.
CIPRO - Computer peripheral equipment - Computer Identics Corp.
CIR-O - Welding equipment ✰ - Weld Tooling Corp.
CIR-Q - Teas—herbal - Health Concerns
CIRAGE - Dinnerware—glass - Arita Sales Co. Inc.
CIRBO - Tools—power-driven - Rogers Tool Works, Inc.
CIRC-L-CUT - Tools - Hepp Industries Inc.
CIRCA - Housewares - Shepherd Products U.S. Inc.
CIRCA - Lighting fixtures - Swivelier Co. Inc.
CIRCA - Recording label - Virgin Records
CIRCA - Sunglasses - F.G.G. Investments, Inc.
CIRCA - Trading cards and stamps - Fleer Corp.
CIRCA 35 - Furniture - Lyon-Shaw Inc.
CIRCA 38 - Floor coverings—carpet and rugs ✰ - World Carpets, Inc.
CIRCA '83 - Paper ✰ - Fox River Paper Co.
CIRCA 90 - Furniture ✰ - Bassett Furniture Industries, Inc.
CIRCA 1776 - Furniture - Ethan Allen, Inc.
CIRCA 1900 - Jewelry - Mel Bernie and Co., Inc.
CIRCA 1990 - Furniture ✰ - Henredon Furniture Industries Inc.
CIRCA 2000 - Wallpaper - Textile Wallcoverings International Ltd.
CIRCA LINEN - Paper ✰ - Fox River Paper Co.
CIRCA-LITE - Frames—eyeglass ✰ - Universal/Univis Inc.
CIRCA SELECT - Paper ✰ - Fox River Paper Co.
CIRCADIAN - Clocks - Wavemaster Technology Inc.
CIRCATROL - Paint sprayers ✰ - Speeflo Manufacturing Corp.
CIRCAVITE T - Vitamins and nutritional supplements - Circle Pharmaceuticals Inc.
CIRCE - Fabrics—spandex - Dan River Inc.
CIRCE - Rings—jewelry - Artcarved Inc.
CIRCL-HEAT - Heat pumps ✰ - Schaefer Co.
CIRCLE - Convenience stores - Circle K Corp.
CIRCLE - Glassware—household - Svend Jensen of Denmark Inc.
CIRCLE - Jewelry - Circle Jewelry Products Inc.
CIRCLE - Recording label - Jazzology-GHB Records
CIRCLE - Thread - Threads USA Div.
CIRCLE 54 - Ophthalmic goods - Benson Optical Co., Inc.
CIRCLE A - Food products - Patrick Cudahy Inc.
CIRCLE A, A - Saddles - American Saddlery, Inc.
CIRCLE AIR - Hair care products ✰ - Fromm Industries
CIRCLE & STAR - Recording label - Rustron Music Productions
CIRCLE AW - Electrical equipment - B-Line Systems, Inc.
CIRCLE B - Food products - Sara Lee Corp.

CIRCLE C - Glassware–household - Chattanooga Glass Co.
CIRCLE C BRAND - Saddles - James Cox Saddlery
CIRCLE 'C' SADDLERY - Saddles - James Cox Saddlery
CIRCLE CITY - Recording label - Tyscot Records Inc.
CIRCLE-CRAFT - Underwear and nightwear - Circle Manufacturing Co.
CIRCLE D - Paper - Zellerbach
CIRCLE D LIGHTS - Lighting equipment - Natale Machine & Tool Co.
CIRCLE DIAMONDS - Games - International Gamco, Inc.
CIRCLE E - Beef - Excel Corp.
CIRCLE EIGHT DIAMONDS - Games - International Gamco, Inc.
CIRCLE-GLIDE PROTRACTOR - Drafting supplies - Guthrie-Ergino
   Enterprises, Inc.
CIRCLE H - Crocheted and knitted items - Heritage Sportswear
CIRCLE III - Apparel and accessories - Triangle Lingerie Corp.
CIRCLE K - Food products ✩ - Hygrade Food Products Corp.
CIRCLE LAYJETKORE - Rope - American Manufacturing Co. Inc.
CIRCLE-M - Apparel–athletic - Campus Designs Inc.
CIRCLE MATE - Product description unknown - Fletcher-Terry Co.
CIRCLE MINTS - Candy ✩ - Henry Heide, Inc.
CIRCLE MISER - Lamps - General Electric Co.
CIRCLE MISER - Lighting fixtures - Kenall Manufacturing Co.
CIRCLE-O-COMFORT - Shoes - Endicott Johnson Corp.
CIRCLE-O-FORM - Apparel–women's - Exquisite Form Industries
CIRCLE O' LOVE - Jewelry - Helzbergs Diamond Shops Inc.
CIRCLE OF BEAUTY - Cosmetics - Sears, Roebuck and Co.
CIRCLE OF CARING - Infant product - Ameda/Egnell Corp.
CIRCLE OF FIRE - Jewelry ✩ - Hirsch Speidel Inc.
CIRCLE OF FRIENDS - Statuary - Home Interiors & Gifts, Inc.
CIRCLE OF HEALTH - Vitamins and nutritional supplements - Alacer Co.
CIRCLE OF LIFE - Analgesics - Euphoria Cosmetics, Inc.
CIRCLE OF LIFE - Greeting cards - Blue Mountain Arts Inc.
CIRCLE OF LOVE - Paperback books ✩ - Bantam Doubleday Dell Publishing
   Group, Inc.
CIRCLE OF TRANQUILITY - Fabrics - Adelle Weiss
CIRCLE R CLASSICS - Apparel and accessories - Ruddock Manufacturing Co.
CIRCLE R INC. SIDE DUMP - Trailers - Circle R, Inc.
CIRCLE S - Apparel and accessories - Sidran, Inc.
CIRCLE S - Hams - Armour Swift-Eckrich
CIRCLE SASH - Windows–storm - Thermal Industries Inc.
CIRCLE SEA - Fishing tackle - Wright & McGill Co.
CIRCLE SHUTTER - Shutters–wood - Faircloth Woodworking
CIRCLE SPEC - Tiles–ceiling - Artcrest Products Co. Inc.
CIRCLE STITCH - Underwear and nightwear ✩ - Lovable Co.
CIRCLE SURROUND - Audio equipment - Rocktron Corp.
CIRCLE T - Apparel–women's - Circle T Western Wear
CIRCLE T - Food products ✩ - State Fair Foods, Inc.
CIRCLE T - Pet products - Coastal Pet Products, Inc.
CIRCLE TOP - Window frames - Quaker Window Products Co.
CIRCLE USA - Fertilizers - Circle One International, Inc.
CIRCLE Z - Sandwiches–prepackaged - Zartic, Inc.
CIRCLE Z PLUS - Sandwiches–prepackaged - Zartic, Inc.
CIRCLEMATIC 2000 - Sporting goods - Wright & McGill Co.
CIRCLES - Frames–eyeglass - May Optical Co. Inc.
CIRCLES - Paper - Bonanza Press, Inc.
CIRCLES 'N' SAND - Apparel–women's - Wal-Mart Stores Inc.
CIRCLES N SQUARES - Pottery ✩ - Rubens Originals
CIRCLES O' YOUTH - Brassieres (Bras) ✩ - Milady Brassiere & Corset Co.,
   Inc.
CIRCLES OF GOLD - Nuts–salted, roasted, cooked, or canned - Di Mare
   Bros.
CIRCLES OF LIFE - Jewelry - OroAmerica Inc.
CIRCLES OF LOVE - Jewelry–precious - Oscar Heyman & Brothers, Inc.
CIRCLETIME TALES - Computer software - Don Johnston Inc.
CIRCLETS - Jewelry - Sandberg & Sikorski Diamond Corp.
CIRCLETTE - Hair care products ✩ - Willat Co.
CIRCLINE - Lamp bulbs–fluorescent - GTE Corp.
CIRCLING SUNS - Calendars - Green Tiger Press
CIRCLITE - Lamps - General Electric Co.
CIRCLOAD - Projectors–photographic - Rangertone Research Inc.
CIRCLON - Needles–sewing ✩ - Coats and Clark Inc.
CIRCLON - Needlework supplies ✩ - Susan Bates Inc.
CIRCO - Apparel and accessories - Target
CIRCO - Gasoline - Sun Co. Inc.
CIRCO - Nail care products ✩ - Spilo/Mehaz Worldwide
CIRCO MIRROTACH - Photographic equipment - SP Systems/Saratons
CIRCOIL - Engine oil test kit - Herguth Laboratories Inc.

CIRCOLO MODA - Apparel–men's - Webster Clothes Inc.
CIRCU-CARE - Dietary supplement - Natur-Pharma, Inc.
CIRCU FLOW - Vitamins and nutritional supplements - Kroeger Herb Products
   Co. Inc.
CIRCUIT - Bicycles - Schwinn Cycling & Fitness Inc.
CIRCUIT - Floor coverings–carpet and rugs ✩ - Regal Rugs Inc.
CIRCUIT - Furniture - Davis Furniture Industries, Inc.
CIRCUIT BAR - Valves - Mac Valves, Inc.
CIRCUIT BREAKER - Toys - Tonka Corp.
CIRCUIT CARD STOR - Computer storage devices - L.O. Drake Inc.
CIRCUIT GUARD - Mats - Matworks
CIRCUIT MASTER - Automotive-circuit tester - M. Eagles Tool Warehouse Inc.
CIRCUIT SAVER - Electronic equipment - Unitek Miyachi Corp.
CIRCUIT TRAINER - Apparel–athletic - Fila USA, Inc.
CIRCUITEER II - Pet products - Electric Cleaner Co.
CIRCUITRACER - Regulators–voltage - Desco Industries Inc.
CIRCUITSENTRY - Computer-based telecommunications equipment - Sotas,
   Inc.
CIRCUITTUTOR - Computer software - TutorWare Inc.
CIRCULAFORCE - Pharmaceutical preparations - Bioforce of America Ltd.
CIRCULAIRE - Air conditioning equipment - General Electric Co.
CIRCULAR PROPULSION UNITS - Apparel and accessories - Kryptonics, Inc.
CIRCULARSCENT - Labels–paper - Uarco Inc.
CIRCULATE - Health care products - Healthwatchers System
CIRCULATION - Games - Teaching Concepts Inc.
CIRCULATION CONTROL - Computer software ✩ - Right on Programs
CIRCULATOR - Fireplace equipment - Majestic Co.
CIRCUMFLOW - Air purification systems - Bio-Logical Controls, Inc.
CIRCUS - Bandages - American White Cross, Inc.
CIRCUS - Candy - Spangler Candy Co.
CIRCUS - Dinnerware–glass ✩ - Cyclamen Studio
CIRCUS - Fruit drinks–bottled or canned ✩ - Southern Fruit Distributors Inc.
CIRCUS - Garment hangers–wood ✩ - Reliance Products Corp.
CIRCUS - Giftware - Sasaki
CIRCUS - Toys ✩ - Brunswick Corp.
CIRCUS - Toys ✩ - Rollin Wilson Co. Inc.
CIRCUS & RODEO - Toys - Educational Products Co.
CIRCUS ATARI - Video games - Atari Games Corp.
CIRCUS BABIES - Toys–stuffed ✩ - Gund, Inc.
CIRCUS BEARS - Toys–models ✩ - Century Products Co.
CIRCUS CHEWS - Vitamins and nutritional supplements - Rexall Sundown, Inc.
CIRCUS FUN - Cereal - General Mills, Inc.
CIRCUS FUN - Novelty items - Morris House of Drane
CIRCUS MAXIMUS - Apparel and accessories - Salant/Manhattan Industries
CIRCUS MAXIMUS - Games - Avalon Hill Game Co.
CIRCUS MAXIMUS - Pottery ✩ - Rubens Originals
CIRCUS O'S - Cereal - Moran Group Inc.
CIRCUS O'S - Pasta - Campbell Soup Co.
CIRCUS PEANUTS - Candy - Brach and Brock Confections Inc.
CIRCUS RINGS - Cereal - Ralston Purina Co.
CIRCUS SEALS - Game machines - Mattel, Inc.
CIRCUS SEALS - Games - Smethport Specialty Co.
CIRCUS STICKS - Candy ✩ - Bobs Candies Inc.
CIRCUS THROWER - Knives ✩ - Tru-Balance Knife Co.
CIRCUS TIME - Figurines - Arnart Imports Inc.
CIRCUS TIME - Musical instruments - Trophy Music Co.
CIRCUS TURF - Floor coverings–carpet and rugs - Conquest Carpet Mills Inc.
CIRCUSWORKS - Paper products - Ringling Bros.-Barnum & Bailey Combined
   Shows, Inc.
CIREPIL - Skin care products - Genesis II USA
CIRGEOS - Paper products - John S. Hicks
CIRIO - Food products - New Horizon
CIRKIDS - Footwear - J. Baker Inc.
CIRMOSA - Drapery hardware - Kirsch Co.
CIRO - Computer software - Colonnade Technologies, Inc.
CIRO - Frames–eyeglass - Hudson Optical Corp.
CIRO - Tape recorders - Compco Photographic/Goldberg Bros.
CIROLITE - Stones–synthetic - Ciro of Bond Street Inc.
CIRQUE - Apparel and accessories - Gerry Sportswear Corp.
CIRQUE - Goggles–safety - David Milo Myers
CIRQUE - Tea kettles–nonelectric - Metro/Thebe, Inc.
CIRQUE OPTICS - Sunglasses - Cirque Optics
CIRQUEL - Lenses–optical - Kelley & Hueber
CIRRUS - Aircraft parts - Cirrus Design Corp.
CIRRUS - Apparel–athletic - Sun Mountain Sports, Inc.
CIRRUS - Bicycles - Ross Bicycles USA, Ltd.

✩ = Now out of production

CIRRUS - Blinds–vertical ☆ - Kittrich Corp.
CIRRUS - Cabinets - Merillat Industries, Inc.
CIRRUS - Faucets - Kohler Co.
CIRRUS - Fishing tackle - Shakespeare Fishing Tackle
CIRRUS - Floor coverings–carpet and rugs - Regal Rugs Inc.
CIRRUS - Footwear–athletic - Puma Inc.
CIRRUS - Furniture ☆ - Bernhardt Industries
CIRRUS - Glass products - Pittsburgh Corning Corp.
CIRRUS - Lenses–optical ☆ - Outlook Eyewear Co.
CIRRUS - Medical apparatus - Medonics LLC
CIRRUS - Motor vehicles–automobiles - DaimlerChrysler
CIRRUS - Seats–automobile - Cramer Inc.
CIRRUS - Tiles–ceiling ☆ - Florida Tile Industries, Inc.
CIRRUS - Tobacco products - Quiktrip Corp.
CIRRUS COLLECTION - Wallpaper - I. Gottlieb & Associates
CIRRUS LOGIC - Circuit boards - Cirrus Logic, Inc.
CIRVIBE - Computer software - John E. Starr
CIS MYELOCATH - Catheters - Catheter Imaging Systems
CISA - Tiles–mosaic - TJ Imports
CISAL ARCANA - Plumbing fixtures–metal ☆ - Barclay Products Ltd.
CISAL BLITZ - Plumbing fixtures–metal ☆ - Barclay Products Ltd.
CISCO - Food products - Multifoods Inc.
CISCO - Milk - Associated Milk Producers Inc.
CISCO - Wines - Canandaigua Wine Co. Inc.
CISCO IOS - Computer software - Cisco Systems, Inc.
CISCO KID'S - Food products - Jardine's Texas Foods
CISCO POUR HOMME - Perfume - Jean Philippe Fragrances, Inc.
CISM - Electronic equipment - Sunquest Information Systems, Inc.
CISPIANO - Beverages–alcohol - Alseca Corp.
CISSO - Cigars - M & M Tobacco Products
CISTERCIAN - Publisher's imprints - Cistercian Publications Inc.
CISTINOL - Skin care products - Lendan USA Co.
CISUM - Recording label - Antique-Catfish Records
CIT - Hair care products - John Amico Expressive Hair Care Products
CITAC - Computers - Citac Computer, Inc.
CITADEL - Cabinets ☆ - Medallion Kitchens of Minnesota Inc.
CITADEL - Candles - Carolina Designs Ltd.
CITADEL - Doors–glass - Peachtree Doors and Windows Inc.
CITADEL - Filing cabinets–metal - Kardex Systems, Inc.
CITADEL - Floor coverings - Congoleum Corp.
CITADEL - Floor coverings–carpet and rugs - Patrick Carpet Mills
CITADEL - Floor coverings–carpet and rugs ☆ - World Carpets, Inc.
CITADEL - Hardware - Harloc, Inc.
CITADEL - Heaters–kerosene - Sunbeam-Oster Household Products
CITADEL - Helmets–athletic - Bell Sports Corp.
CITADEL - Paper–looseleaf - Ampad Corp.
CITADEL - Plumbing fixtures–metal - Crane Plumbing/Fiat Products
CITADEL - Shingles–asphalt or tar ☆ - Globe Building Materials Inc.
CITADEL - Tableware–china ☆ - Lenox, Inc.
CITADELLE - Beverages–carbonated - Chemaly & Sons
CITADELLE - Recording label - Art Records Manufacturing Co.
CITATION - Bicycles - Murray, Inc.
CITATION - Boats - Sea-Pro Boats, Inc.
CITATION - Boats–motor - Midwestern Industries Corp.
CITATION - Boats–motor ☆ - Commander Marine
CITATION - Boats–motor ☆ - Glassmaster Co.
CITATION - Boats–motor ☆ - Larson Boat Div.
CITATION - Cabinets ☆ - H.J. Scheirich Co.
CITATION - Cabinets–wood - Parcraft Distinctive Cabinetry
CITATION - Doors–glass - Peachtree Doors and Windows Inc.
CITATION - Electronic equipment - Hamilton Electronics Corp.
CITATION - Firearms, accessories, and parts - High Standard Manufacturing Corp.
CITATION - Floor coverings–carpet and rugs - Karastan-Bigelow Inc.
CITATION - Floor coverings–carpet and rugs ☆ - Ebsco Carpet Mills
CITATION - Floor coverings–carpet and rugs ☆ - Walter Carpet Mills
CITATION - Food products - Debruyn Co.
CITATION - Frames–eyeglass ☆ - Bausch & Lomb Inc.
CITATION - Furniture–wood - Century Furniture Co.
CITATION - Glassware–household - Owens-Illinois Inc. (Libbey Div.)
CITATION - Golfing equipment - Hillerich & Bradsby Co.
CITATION - Guitars ☆ - Grossman Music Corp.
CITATION - Housewares - Western Auto Supply Co.
CITATION - Kitchen appliances ☆ - Hamilton Beach/Proctor-Silex Inc.
CITATION - Loudspeakers - Harman Kardon, Inc.
CITATION - Luggage - United States Luggage Corp.

CITATION - Medical apparatus - Howmedica Inc.
CITATION - Motor vehicles ☆ - General Motors Corp. (Chevrolet Motor Div.)
CITATION - Pencils - National Pen & Pencil Co.
CITATION - Pet products ☆ - Marianna Imports, Inc.
CITATION - Recreational vehicle dealers ☆ - Commodore Corp.
CITATION - Shoes - Somersworth Shoe Co. Inc.
CITATION - Sporting goods ☆ - Lob-Ster Inc.
CITATION - Trailers–travel ☆ - Coachmen Industries, Inc.
CITATION - Typewriters - Smith Corona Corp.
CITATION - Watches - Hampden Corp.
CITATION - Wet suits–rubber ☆ - Parkway Systems
CITATION - Window shades - Newell Window Furnishing Co.
CITATION II - Floor coverings–carpet and rugs ☆ - Blue Ridge Carpet Mills
CITATION 2000 - Motor vehicles - Thor Tech, Inc.
CITATION GOLD - Flatware - Kirk Stieff Co.
CITATION GOLD - Tableware–china - Lenox, Inc.
CITATION GOLD COMPLEMENTS - Glassware–household - Lenox, Inc.
CITATION II - Mobile homes - Commodore Corp.
CITATION LACE - Tableware–china - Lenox, Inc.
CITATION PLATINUM - Dinnerware–glass - Lenox, Inc.
CITATION STICKS - Candy ☆ - Just Born Inc.
CITATION VILLA - Motor vehicles–motor homes - Thor Industries West
CITATIONS - Furniture - Broyhill Furniture Industries, Inc.
CITE MATE - Educational materials - Little, Brown and Co., Inc.
CITEK - Televisions ☆ - Fujitsu General America Inc.
CITGO - Gasoline - Citgo Petroleum Corp.
CITGO SAYS GO! - Gasoline - Citgo Petroleum Corp.
CITGO T-BIRD - Toys–electronic - Bird Bromiticous Inc.
CITI BY YANSI FUGEL - Apparel–women's - Apparel Resources, Inc.
CITI-COM - Telephones–cellular ☆ - RELM Communications Inc.
CITI COMFORTS - Apparel–women's - Nordstrom, Inc.
CITI DESIGN GROUP - Apparel–women's - Apparel Resources, Inc.
CITIBAG - Bags–trash - AEP Industries, Inc.
CITIBUS - Communications equipment - Baker Hughes Inc.
CITIES - Shoes - New Retail Concepts Inc.
CITIES - Shorts–women's - El Greco Inc.
CITILAMPS - Lamps–desk - Art Specialty Co. Inc.
CITIMINI - Strollers–baby - Aprica Kassai USA Inc.
CITINETTING - Computer software - Citicorp
CITISPORT - Luggage - Shalam Imports Inc.
CITITECH - Computer software - Computoservice, Inc.
CITIWEAR - Apparel–women's - Kellwood Co.
CITIZEN - Calculators - Citizen America Corp.
CITIZEN - Frames–eyeglass ☆ - Universal/Univis Inc.
CITIZEN - Watches - Citizen Watch Co. of America Inc.
CITIZEN PROLASER - Printers–computer - Citizen America Corp.
CITIZEN VCP - Televisions ☆ - Citizen America Corp.
CITM - Checkbooks - Checks in the Mail, Inc.
CITORI - Rackets–racquetball - Ektelon
CITRA - Beverages–alcohol ☆ - Peppinella Import Co.
CITRA - Beverages–carbonated ☆ - Dr. Pepper/Seven Up, Inc.
CITRA - Cough medicines - Boyle & Co.
CITRA - Wines - Palm Bay Imports, Inc.
CITRA CARE - Hair care products ☆ - Peter Hantz Co.
CITRA-CLEAR - Food products - Givaudan Roure
CITRA FOAM-BATH - Cleaning preparations - Analab Inc.
CITRA GLAZE - Hair care products - Mane Street Products USA
CITRA-GOLD - Juices - Agrigold Juice Products
CITRA JINX - Cleaning preparations - Claire Manufacturing Co.
CITRA-MAID - Cleaning preparations - Slipsafe Professional Products, Inc.
CITRA ORANGE - Cleaning preparations - Vin-Dotco Inc.
CITRA SIPPER - Juice extracting devices ☆ - Citra Products of Florida, Inc.
CITRA-SOLV - Cleaning preparations ☆ - Seventh Generation Wholesale Inc.
CITRACAL CALCIUM CITRATE - Vitamins and nutritional supplements - Mission Pharmacal Co.
CITRACAL CALCIUM CITRATE CAPLETS +D - Vitamins and nutritional supplements - Mission Pharmacal Co.
CITRACAL CALCIUM CITRATE LIQUITAB - Vitamins and nutritional supplements - Mission Pharmacal Co.
CITRADERM - Health care products ☆ - Pedinol Pharmacal Inc.
CITRAHIST - Cold remedies ☆ - Republic Drug Co. Inc.
CITRALAX - Laxatives ☆ - Purdue Frederick Co.
CITRALKA - Pharmaceutical preparations ☆ - Parke-Davis
CITRALL - Cleaning preparations–carpet and rug - Ecolab Inc.
CITRAMINO - Vitamins and nutritional supplements - Twinlab
CITRANOX - Detergents - Alconox Inc.

☆ = Now out of production

CITRAPLEX - Fertilizers - Balcom Chemicals, Inc.
CITRASEAL - Hair care products - Mane Street Products USA
CITRASPECT - Pharmaceutical preparations ☆ - C.O. Truxton Inc.
CITRE SHINE - Hair care products - Advanced Research Laboratories
CITRENE - Cosmetics - Cosmair Inc.
CITRESHINE FOAM BRILLIANCE - Hair care products ☆ - Advanced Research Laboratories
CITRESSENCE - Pet products - Wysong Corp.
CITRI BEAST - Cleaning preparations - Bailey Equip. & Supply of Texas
CITRI-BURN - Vitamins and nutritional supplements - Action Labs, Inc.
CITRI FRESH - Deodorizers - Nutrition Headquarters, Inc.
CITRI-GLOW - Cleaning preparations–household - Mia Rose Products Inc.
CITRI-LIFE - Vitamins and nutritional supplements - Windmill Marketing Services, Inc.
CITRI-PLEX - Vitamins and nutritional supplements - Hillestad International, Inc.
CITRI-SNACKS - Vitamins and nutritional supplements ☆ - Hillestad International, Inc.
CITRI-THIN - Vitamins and nutritional supplements - International Health Products, Inc.
CITRI-THIN - Vitamins and nutritional supplements - International Health Products, Inc.
CITRI TONE - Vitamins and nutritional supplements - National Nutritional Network
CITRICIDAL - Vitamins and nutritional supplements - NutriBiotic
CITRICIDEX - Vitamins and nutritional supplements - Source Naturals
CITRIDUCE - Vitamins and nutritional supplements - Barth-Spencer Corp.
CITRIFIER - Hair care products - Redmond Products, Inc.
CITRIKLEEN - Degreasing solvents - Penetone Corp.
CITRIMAX - Vitamins and nutritional supplements - Source Naturals
CITRISLIM - Vitamins and nutritional supplements - Vaxa International, Inc.
CITRISTRIP - Paint removers - Klean-Strip
CITRISTRIP - Paint removers - Specialty Environmental Technologies, Inc.
CITRITAN - Suntan lotions - D'Lanerg Ltd.
CITRIUM - Vitamins and nutritional supplements - Houston International, LLC
CITRO-BLAST - Pumice - State Chemical Manufacturing Co.
CITRO-FLAV 200 - Pharmaceutical preparations - Goldline Laboratories, Inc.
CITROCARBONATE - Pharmaceutical preparations ☆ - Upjohn Co.
CITROCORB - Health care products ☆ - Halsey Drug Co. Inc.
CITRODYNE - Cold remedies ☆ - Chase Laboratories Inc.
CITROFLEX - Insect repellents - Morflex, Inc.
CITROL - Vitamins and nutritional supplements - Healthscan Products Inc.
CITROLITH - Pharmaceutical preparations - Beach Pharmaceuticals, Inc.
CITRON - Christmas tree ornaments - Cracker Box Inc.
CITRON - Cleaning preparations - Analab Inc.
CITRONELLA - Candles - Candle Corp. of America
CITRONELLA SUMMER - Lamps - Lamplight Farms, Inc.
CITRONET - Wines - Nabisco Foods Group
CITRONEX - Cleaning preparations - Walter G. Legge Co., Inc.
CITRONGE - Liquors - St. Maarten Spirits, Ltd.
CITRONS - Dishes–china - Waterford Wedgwood USA, Inc.
CITROTEIN - Vitamins and nutritional supplements - Novartis Nutrition Corp.
CITROXAIN - Toothpaste - Den-Mat Corp.
CITRU-BOR - Pet products ☆ - Glo-Marr Products Inc.
CITRU-MELA PLUS - Pet products - Mary Grossman Meeks
CITRU SIP - Beverages - Quaker Oats Co.
CITRU SLIM - Pharmaceutical preparations ☆ - Barth's Nutra Products
CITRUCEL - Health care products - SmithKline Beecham Consumer Healthcare
CITRUCEL - Laxatives - Marion Merrell Dow
CITRUE - Oils–essential - International Flavors & Fragrances Inc.
CITRUM - Clay products - Green Mountain Products Inc.
CITRUS - Bathing suits - Apparel Ventures, Inc.
CITRUS - Detergents - Huish Detergents, Inc.
CITRUS - Dinnerware ☆ - Corning Inc.
CITRUS - Floor coverings–carpet and rugs ☆ - Regal Rugs Inc.
CITRUS 7 - Beverages–carbonated ☆ - Dr. Pepper/Seven Up, Inc.
CITRUS AIR - Deodorizers - Sterling Teal, Inc.
CITRUS BELLE - Juices–frozen - Citrus Belle
CITRUS BITES - Confections - Good Humor Corp.
CITRUS BLAST - Beverages - BCB USA Corp.
CITRUS BLOSSOM - Deodorizers - Mcauley's, Inc.
CITRUS BLOSSOM - Housewares ☆ - Shell Oil Co.
CITRUS BLUE - Cleaning preparations - Kleen Products, Inc.
CITRUS BOY - Food products ☆ - Estus Export-Import
CITRUS BREEZE - Deodorizers - S.C. Johnson & Son, Inc.
CITRUS CENTRAL - Juices - Crown, Cork & Seal
CITRUS CIRCLE - Juices - Nabisco Foods Group

CITRUS COMBO - Juices ☆ - Treesweet Products Co.
CITRUS CONSCIOUSNESS - Juices - Coca-Cola Co.
CITRUS ESSENCE - Water–bottled or canned - Nanco, Inc.
CITRUS ESSENCE LASSIE - Pesticides–household - Carter-Wallace, Inc.
CITRUS EVERSCENT - Deodorizers - Creative Products Inc. of Rossville
CITRUS FLUSH - Juices - Haarmann & Reimer Corp.
CITRUS FRESH - Deodorizers - Church and Dwight Co. Inc.
CITRUS GEL - Cleaning preparations - Gent-L-Kleen Products Inc.
CITRUS GLASS - Cleaning preparations - Pre-Vent Laboratories, Inc.
CITRUS GROVE - Jewelry–costume ☆ - Safari Ltd.
CITRUS GROVE - Juices - Juice Services Inc.
CITRUS HILL - Juices - Procter & Gamble Co.
CITRUS HILL SELECT - Juices - Procter & Gamble Co.
CITRUS ICE - Candy - Ragold Inc.
CITRUS JELLY - Shampoos ☆ - Dobre Products Inc.
CITRUS LITES - Confections - Wells' Dairy, Inc.
CITRUS LOTION - Cleaning preparations - Gent-L-Kleen Products Inc.
CITRUS MAGIC - Cosmetics - Beaumont Products, Inc.
CITRUS MIST - Deodorizers - Beaumont Products, Inc.
CITRUS NATURAL - Pet products - Revere Manufacturing
CITRUS NIGHT TIME REVERSAL - Skin care products - Zia Cosmetics Inc.
CITRUS PLUS - See **MANDARIN MAGIC**
CITRUS PLUS - Cleaning preparations–household - Turtle Wax, Inc.
CITRUS PLUS - Vitamins and nutritional supplements - Smithkline Beecham Corp.
CITRUS-POWER - Cleaning preparations - Hocking International Chemical Corp.
CITRUS PRO - Juice extracting devices - Metrokane
CITRUS QUEEN - Juices ☆ - Minute Maid Foodservice Group
CITRUS ROSE - Wine coolers ☆ - Canandaigua Wine Co. Inc.
CITRUS ROYALE - Fruit drinks–bottled or canned - Green Spot Packaging, Inc.
CITRUS SCRUB - Cleaning preparations–carpet and rug - Hillyard Enterprises, Inc.
CITRUS SECRET - Hair care products - Beaumont Products, Inc.
CITRUS SENSATIONS - Fruits and vegetables - Orval Kent Food Co., Inc.
CITRUS SNACKS - Fruit pops–frozen - Wells' Dairy, Inc.
CITRUS SPRINGS JUICE CONCENTRATES - Beverages–carbonated - Citrus Springs, Inc.
CITRUS SQUEEZE - Beverages - Juice Club, Inc.
CITRUS SUNSET - Teas–herbal - Lipton Investments, Inc.
CITRUS SUNSHINE - Fruit drinks–bottled or canned - Olympic Foods Inc.
CITRUS TROPICALE - Beverages - Logret Import & Export Co.
CITRUS TWIST - Wines - Diamond Island Cellars Inc.
CITRUS VALLEY - Juices - Coastlog Industries Ltd.
CITRUS WET ONES - Cleaning preparations - L & F Consumer Products
CITRUS WORLD - Fruit drinks–bottled or canned - Citrus World Inc.
CITRUS XL - Cleaning preparations - Gulf States Chemical Co., Inc.
CITRUSAL - Pet products - Best Friend Products
CITRUSCENT - Deodorizers - Spilo/Mehaz Worldwide
CITRUSCENT - Health care products - Medical Science Products Inc.
CITRUSCENT 100% PURE CITRUS - Air fresheners - Beaumont Products, Inc.
CITRUSILK - Detergents - Beaumont Products, Inc.
CITRUSOLV'IT - Cleaning preparations - DCS Distributing Inc.
CITS - Telephone apparatus - Harris Corp.
CITTERIO USA - Food products - Dairy Fresh Products Co.
CITY - Cigarettes - R.J. Reynolds Tobacco Co.
CITY - Dinnerware–glass - WMF/USA
CITY - Floor coverings–carpet and rugs ☆ - Capel, Inc.
CITY - Thread - Quality Thread Co.
CITY - Tiles–ceramic - Federal Tile Imports Inc.
CITY - Toys–automobiles - Mattel, Inc.
CITY-ART - Artists' materials - Classic Oils & Portraits
CITY AT PEACE - Publisher's imprints - Creative Response, Inc.
CITY BAG - Cases–camera ☆ - Innovative Manufacturing Corp.
CITY BALL - Balls–baseball - Lisco, Inc.
CITY BASE - Cosmetics - Clinique Laboratories, Inc.
CITY BEAN - Coffee - City Bean Inc.
CITY BIKE - Bicycles - Roadmaster Corp.
CITY BIRD - Recording label - Gail Garfield
CITY BLOCKS - Play mat - City Blocks
CITY BLOCKS - Wallpaper - Blumenthal
CITY BOUND - Floor coverings–carpet and rugs ☆ - Masland Corp.
CITY CHEF - Dinnerware–glass - S & C International Inc.
CITY CHIC - Dinnerware–glass - Lenox, Inc.
CITY CLUB - Cigars ☆ - House of Windsor Inc.

☆ = Now out of production

CITY CLUB - Eyeglasses - Art-Craft Optical Co.
CITY CLUB - Faucets - Kohler Co.
CITY CLUB - Floor coverings—carpet and rugs - Dan River Inc.
CITY CLUB - Shoes - Interco Inc.
CITY COWBOY - Dolls - Mattel, Inc.
CITY CRUISER - Bicycles - Kent International Inc.
CITY CYCLES - Toy bicycles ☆ - Intex Recreation Corp.
CITY DAIRY - Dairy products - City Dairy
CITY DOG DESIGNED - Pet products - City Dog Designed Co., Inc.
CITY EYES - Eyeglasses - Mitchel Glanzbergh
CITY FILE - Office supplies - Metro Files Inc. (Rolodex Corp.)
CITY GAL - Frames—eyeglass - Liberty Optical Manufacturing Co.
CITY GEAR - Sporting goods - Rollerblade, Inc.
CITY GIRL - Beverages - Lite Whippes Corp.
CITY GIRL - Jewelry - California Swimwear Co., Inc.
CITY GREEN - Computer software - American Forestry Association
CITY GRIS - Floor coverings—carpet and rugs ☆ - Regal Rugs Inc.
CITY HALL - Frames—eyeglass - Liberty Optical Manufacturing Co.
CITY ICE - Ice - City Ice Co.
CITY JAM - Footwear - Reebok International Ltd.
CITY JEANS - Apparel and accessories - City Jeans
CITY LIGHTS - Bicycles - Columbia Manufacturing Inc.
CITY LIGHTS - Candles - D'Adant and Sons Inc.
CITY LIGHTS - Dinnerware—glass - Nikko Ceramics Inc.
CITY LIGHTS - Fabrics - Uniroyal Engineered Products
CITY LIGHTS - Floor coverings—carpet and rugs - Lotus Carpets
CITY LIGHTS - Floor coverings—carpet and rugs ☆ - Atlas Carpet Mills Inc.
CITY LIGHTS - Floor coverings—carpet and rugs ☆ - Blue Ridge Carpet Mills
CITY LIGHTS - Floor coverings—carpet and rugs ☆ - Burtco Enterprises Inc.
CITY LIGHTS - Floor coverings—carpet and rugs ☆ - Galaxy Carpet Mills Inc.
CITY LIGHTS - Floor coverings—carpet and rugs ☆ - Quaker Inc.
CITY LIGHTS - Footwear - Ambassador Shoe Corp.
CITY LIGHTS - Frames—eyeglass - Liberty Optical Manufacturing Co.
CITY LIGHTS - Jeans—men's - Klayman Pants Co.
CITY LIGHTS - Wallpaper - Royson's Corp.
CITY LIPS - Apparel and accessories - Top Promotions Inc.
CITY LITES - Glass—window - Taylor Building Products Co.
CITY LITES AUTOSHOW - Giftware - Agent Andy Inc.
CITY LITES COMPANY STORES - Giftware - Agent Andy Inc.
CITY LOOKS SALONS INTERNATIONAL - Hair care products - City Looks International
CITY MACHINE - Automotive parts and accessories ☆ - Sea Spike Marine Supply Co. Inc.
CITY MAGIC - Bicycles - Columbia Manufacturing Inc.
CITY MAN - Frames—eyeglass - Liberty Optical Manufacturing Co.
CITY MARKET - Milk - Western Dairymen Cooperative, Inc.
CITY MISS - Frames—eyeglass ☆ - U.S. Optical Frame Co.
CITY MIX - Furniture ☆ - Kaylyn Inc.
CITY NEWZ - Apparel—children's - City Newz
CITY NIGHTS - Dolls - Mattel, Inc.
CITY NIGHTS - Floor coverings—carpet and rugs ☆ - Karastan-Bigelow Inc.
CITY OF FEAR-WELCOME TO NY - Games ☆ - Mayfair Games, Inc.
CITY OF LOUISVILLE - Recording label - Slamdek/Scramdown
CITY OF LOVE - Greeting cards - City of Love Industries
CITY OF LOVE INDUSTRIES - T-shirts—children's - City of Love Industries
CITY OF TAMPA - Cigars - V. Guerrieri Cigar Co. Inc.
CITY PARK - Floor coverings—carpet and rugs ☆ - Ebsco Carpet Mills
CITY PLANNING - Shoes - AmAsia International Ltd.
CITY PRIDE - Bakery products - City Pride Bakery Inc.
CITY RAP - Apparel and accessories - Jolem Imports, Inc.
CITY ROAST - Apparel stores—sports - Barrie House Coffee Co., Inc.
CITY SERVICE - Toys - Majorette Toys (U.S.) Inc.
CITY SHADES - Boots ☆ - Georgia Boot Inc.
CITY SHIRTS - Shirts - Great Lakes Apparel LLC
CITY SHOPPER - Dolls - Mattel, Inc.
CITY SIGNS - Signs - City Signs Inc.
CITY SLICKER - Decals and transfers ☆ - Creative Teaching Press
CITY SLICKER - Maps - American Map Corp.
CITY SLICKER - Pet products - Coastal Pet Products, Inc.
CITY SMART GUIDEBOOKS - Publisher's imprints - John Muir Publications
CITY SNAPPERS - Shoes - J & L Footwear, Inc.
CITY SOPHISTICATE - Dolls - Mattel, Inc.
CITY SPECTRUM - Apparel and accessories ☆ - Jantzen Inc.
CITY SQUARE - Apparel—women's - Winsome Togs Inc.
CITY-SQUARE - Blocks—concrete - Paver Systems, Inc.

CITY-STATE OF THE INVINCIBLE OVERLORD - Games ☆ - Mayfair Games, Inc.
CITY STEPS - Footwear - J. Baker Inc.
CITY STREETS - Apparel and accessories - J.C. Penney Co., Inc.
CITY STREETS - Balls—baseball - Voit Corp.
CITY STREETS - Computer software - Road Scholar, Inc.
CITY STREETS - Floor coverings—tile - Interface, Inc.
CITY, THE - Floor coverings—carpet and rugs ☆ - Regal Rugs Inc.
CITY TRIVIA - Games - Stan K. Delzell
CITY VICE - Toys—guns ☆ - Ray Plastic Inc.
CITY VIEW COLLECTION - Frames—eyeglass ☆ - Luxottica
CITY VISIONS - Games - TLI Games
CITY-VITES - Vitamins and nutritional supplements - Tishcon Corp.
CITY WOMAN - Apparel and accessories - M. Serman & Co. Inc.
CITY WOMAN - Cosmetics - Forsythe Cosmetic Group
CITY ZEN CANE - Jewelry - City Zen Cane
CITYBLUEPRINT - Computer storage devices—magnetic - Payne Loving Trust
CITYBOOK - Games - Flying Buffalo Inc.
CITYCELL - Transceivers - Kentrox Industries, Inc.
CITYFARM - Nuts—salted, roasted, cooked, or canned - Rocky Peanut Co., Inc.
CITYKEY - Computer software - U.S. West Marketing Resources Group, Inc.
CITYLIGHTS - Clocks ☆ - General Time Corp. (Westclox/Seth Thomas Div.)
CITYLIGHTS - Markers—felt-tip - Staedtler, Inc.
CITYLIGHTS - Posters - Collector Series Inc.
CITYSAC - Luggage - Le Sportsac, Inc.
CITYSCAPES - Fabrics - Interface, Inc.
CITYSCENE - Glass-block sculpture - Ostrom & Co. Inc.
CITYSCOPE - Games - Education Development Center, Inc.
CITYSOURCE - Computer software - Citysource Inc.
CITYSPORT - Bicycles ☆ - Raleigh USA Bicycle Co.
CITYSTICKERS - Decals and transfers - X-Industries, LLC
CITYSTYLE - Dolls - Mattel, Inc.
CITYWIDE - Apparel and accessories ☆ - Citywide Garments
CIV/E - Computer software - Algor, Inc.
CIVA - Whirlpools - Jacuzzi Inc.
CIVE - Glassware—household ☆ - Penco Industries Inc.
CIVIC - Bathroom fixtures - Crane Plumbing/Fiat Products
CIVIC - Motor vehicles—automobiles - American Honda Motor Co. Inc. (Acura Div.)
CIVIC 1300 FE - Motor vehicles—automobiles - American Honda Motor Co. Inc. (Acura Div.)
CIVIC DEL SOL - Motor vehicles—automobiles - American Honda Motor Co. Inc. (Acura Div.)
CIVIC DOODYS - Paperboard—corrugated - Dirty Business Deals Inc.
CIVICROSS - Bicycles - Miyata Bicycle of America Inc.
CIVICS CORNER - Publisher's imprints - Dennis Andrews
CIVIL PROCEDURE MATE - Publisher's imprints - Little, Brown and Co., Inc.
CIVIL WAR - Games - Avalon Hill Game Co.
CIVIL WAR LADY - Dolls ☆ - Effanbee Doll Corp.
CIVIL WAR SOCIETY, THE - Publisher's imprint, calendars, etc. - Cool Spring Associates Inc.
CIVIL WAR, THE - Computer software - Hartley Courseware Inc.
CIVILIAN JAN - Electronic equipment - Bell & Howell Co.
CIVILIZATION - Games - Avalon Hill Game Co.
CIVITAN INTERNATIONAL - Jewelry - Civitan International
CIVONA - Yarn - E.I. Dupont de Nemours and Co.
CIW - Computer peripheral equipment - Medcam USA, Inc.
CIZI - Apparel—women's - F & J Designs, Inc.
CJ-300 - Printers—computer - C-TECH Electronics Inc.
CJ ADAMS - Women's apparel - Phyllis Sportswear Inc.
CJ BIS - Footwear—women's ☆ - Charles Jourdan
C.J. COTTON COMPANY - Apparel and accessories - J. Chandler & Co., Inc.
C.J. LEWIS PORTRAIT COLLECTION - Posters - TM Group Graphic Services, Inc.
C.J. MOFFETT'S TEETHINA - Health care products - Woolfoam Corp.
C.J. OLSON CHERRIES - Fruits and vegetables - Olson's Cherries
CJ5 - Motor vehicles—jeeps ☆ - DaimlerChrysler
CJ7 - Motor vehicles—jeeps ☆ - DaimlerChrysler
CJ7 LIMITED - Motor vehicles ☆ - DaimlerChrysler
CJ10 - Photocopy machines - Canon USA, Inc.
CJO - Jewelry - C.J. Ostalkiewicz & Co., Inc.
CJS - Jewelry - Mark Gronlund
CJT/KOOLCARB - Drills—electric - CJT/Koolcarb, Inc.
CK - Apparel and accessories - Calvin Klein Ltd.
CK - Apparel—athletic - Cliff Keen Wrestling Products, Inc.

☆ = Now out of production

CK - Chemical preparations - Crompton and Knowles Corp.
CK - Jewelry - Monte Carlo Designs
CK - Wines - C. Mondavi and Sons
CK CALVIN KLEIN - Apparel and accessories - Calvin Klein Trademark Trust
CK CURLS - Food products - Cheese Kurls Inc.
C.K. KIDS - Bakery products - Lepage Bakeries Inc.
CK ONE - Colognes - Calvin Klein Ltd.
CKA - Leather goods - CKA Group, Inc.
CKA - Pharmaceutical preparations - Pannett Products Inc.
CKE FOODS - Food products - Carl Karcher Enterprises Inc.
CK'S JUST GREAT CHILI - Chili sauce - Carolina Kitchen, Inc.
CL - Bottles–plastic - Chester Labs, Inc.
CL - Epoxy coatings - Sterling-Clark-Lurton Corp.
CL - Lighting equipment - Cordelia Lighting Inc.
CL - Publisher's imprints - Center for Learning
CL - Recording label - Christopher Lowell's, Inc.
CL 10 - See 1200 DEGREES
CL-450 PLUS - Lubricants - Envir-O-Lube, Inc.
CL 500 - Sports rackets and accessories ✩ - Victor Sports
CL COLLECTION - Shoes - Munro & Co., Inc.
CL GROUP - Office furniture–metal ✩ - Metier Furniture Corp.
CL GUINAND - Watches ✩ - Smith Time Inc.
CL II - Apparel–women's - Carole Leonard
CL-O-VE - Candy ✩ - Planters LifeSavers Co.
CL STUDIO - Apparel and accessories - At Last Sportswear Inc.
CL WATCH - Computer software - Clam Associates, Inc.
CL-X - Epoxy coatings - Sterling-Clark-Lurton Corp.
CLA-VAL - Valves–industrial - Cla-Val Co.
CLAAR - Jewelry - Clear Brothers Inc.
CLABBER GIRL - Food products - Hulman and Co.
CLABOURNE - Floor coverings ✩ - Congoleum Corp.
CLACK - Chairs–folding ✩ - Fixtures Furniture
CLACKER - Fishing lures ✩ - Lindy Little Joe Inc.
CLACKERS - Cereal ✩ - General Mills, Inc.
CLACTON & FRINTON - Apparel and accessories - Takapuna Inc.
CLAD CHALLENGER - Window frames ✩ - Biltbest Windows
CLAD FOAM - Fiberboard ✩ - Kemlite Co., Inc.
CLAD PLUS - Windows - East Coast Millwork Distributors, Inc.
CLAD TUFF - Fiberboard - Kemlite Co., Inc.
CLAD TUFF FRP - Insulating materials - Dyrotech Industries, Inc.
CLADDAGH HOUSE LTD. - Jewelry - Fragrances of Ireland Accent on Irish Wares Ltd.
CLADWOOD - Wood products - Smurfit Newsprint Corp. (Cladwood Div.)
CLAESSENS - Canvas–artists' ✩ - Canson-Talens Inc.
CLAFORAN - Antibiotics - Hoechst-Roussel Pharmaceuticals Inc.
CLAIBORNE - Apparel–men's - Liz Claiborne Inc.
CLAIBORNE - Sunglasses - International Tropic-Cal Inc. (I SKI Div.)
CLAIBORNE FOR MEN - Perfumes - Liz Claiborne Inc.
CLAIBORNE FOR MEN - Sunglasses - International Tropic-Cal Inc. (I SKI Div.)
CLAIM-EXEC - Computer software - Data Systems Northwest, Inc.
CLAIM TO FAME - Games ✩ - Parker Brothers
CLAIMING RACE - Recording label - Claiming Race Records
CLAIMIX - Computer software - Tis Software, Inc.
CLAIMPOWER - Computer software - Myrtle Holdings Inc.
CLAIMS*WIZARD - Computer software - Integra Software, Inc.
CLAIMTRACK - Computer software - HDS
CLAIR - Floor coverings–carpet and rugs ✩ - Customweave Carpets Inc.
CLAIR DE LUNE - Christmas tree ornaments - Cracker Box Inc.
CLAIR DE LUNE - Wallpaper ✩ - Wallquest, Inc.
CLAIR-FILL - Hair care products - Clairol Inc.
CLAIR-PAK - Food products ✩ - Eau Claire Packing Co.
CLAIRCOM - Telephones–cellular - Claircom Communications Group, Inc.
CLAIRE - Disinfectants - Claire Manufacturing Co.
CLAIRE - Watches - Bulova Corp.
CLAIRE BURKE HOME - Perfumes - FMG/Tsumara Medical
CLAIRE BURKE WISTERIA - Air purification systems - Tsumura International Inc.
CLAIRE DES BECKER - Dinnerware–plastic - Claire Des Becker Ceramics
CLAIRE FONTAINE - Notebooks and notepads - Exaclair Inc.
CLAIRE MURRAY - Floor coverings–carpet and rugs - ANB International, Inc.
CLAIRE SANDRA - Underwear and nightwear ✩ - Lucie Ann Inc.
CLAIRE STEWART - Jewelry - W.R. Cobb Co.
CLAIRE TOPPER - Nail care products - Claire Topper Enterprises
CLAIRE'S - Jewelry - CSL, Inc.
CLAIRE'S CLOSET - Dolls - The Berry Patch
CLAIRE'S COLLECTION - Jewelry - CSL, Inc.

CLAIRE'S DIAPER CAKE - Glassware–household - Im-Ex Around The World
CLAIRE'S ROSE - Toys - TJX Companies, Inc.
CLAIRESSE - Hair coloring preparations - Clairol Inc.
CLAIREX - Electronic equipment - Clairex Technologies, Inc.
CLAIRITEX - Garden furniture ✩ - Rubbermaid-Allibert Inc.
CLAIRMIST - Hair care products - Clairol Inc.
CLAIRMONT - Brushes–hair - The Montclair Co.
CLAIRMONT - Jewelry - Clairmont Trading Corp.
CLAIRMONT ELEGANCE - Floor coverings - Bruce Hardwood Floors
CLAIROL - Hair care products - Clairol Inc.
CLAIROL-BLUE - Shampoos - Clairol Inc.
CLAIROL-GREEN - Shampoos - Clairol Inc.
CLAIROLITE - Hair care products ✩ - Clairol Inc.
CLAIROXIDE - Hair care products - Clairol Inc.
CLAM - Chairs–folding - Heartwood Furniture
CLAM - Watches - Bulova Corp.
CLAM BIVALVE CASES - Bags–duffel - Susan Bush
CLAM MANNA FLAKE - Pet products ✩ - Aquatronics-Filtronics
CLAM RAM - Food products - C.J.R. Co.
CLAM, THE - Portable ice fishing shelter - U.S. Lawn Products, Inc.
CLAMATO - Beverages - Mott's Inc.
CLAMATO CAESAR - Beverages - Cadbury Beverages Inc.
CLAMATO PICANTE - Beverages - Mott's Inc.
CLAMBAKE - Seafood products–fresh or frozen - Eat-All Frozen Food Co.
CLAMBOAT - Seafood products–fresh or frozen - Hershey Foods Corp.
CLAMETTES - Seafood products–fresh or frozen - Eat-All Frozen Food Co.
CLAMMASTER - Telephone apparatus - Gamber-Johnson Inc.
CLAMP-ALL - Pipes - Clamp-All Corp.
CLAMP-FIT - Marine rigging - Walter Machine Co. Inc.
CLAMP-IT - Binders - Dennison National Co.
CLAMP-IT - Clamps - Brink & Cotton
CLAMP-IT - Clamps - Deco Products Co. (Fast-Lok Div.)
CLAMP-IT - Photographic equipment - SP Systems/Saratons
CLAMP-MATE - Tools - Adjustable Clamp Co. Inc.
CLAMP N GO - Clamps - Macrodyne, Inc.
CLAMP NAILS - Fasteners–snap - Clamp Nail Co.
CLAMP-ON - Lighting fixtures - Swivelier Co. Inc.
CLAMP, THE - Television equipment - H. Wilson Co.
CLAMPIPE - Electrical equipment ✩ - Mueller Electric Co.
CLAMPLITES - Lighting fixtures - Acme-Lite Manufacturing Co.
CLAMPLOCK - Tubes–steel - Tripac International, Inc.
CLAMPSCOPE - Electronic equipment - Core Industries Inc.
CLAMS CASINO - Novelty items ✩ - EMM Enterprises
CLAMSHELL - Lamps ✩ - Lamplight Farms, Inc.
CLAMSHELL - Sponges ✩ - Armaly Sponge Co.
CLAMSHELL BUCKETS - Cable Arm Clamshell
CLAN CAMPBELL - Floor coverings–carpet and rugs ✩ - Olympic Carpets Inc.
CLAN MACGREGOR - Liquors - William Grant & Sons, Inc.
CLAN, THE - Computer software ✩ - Sir-Tech Software, Inc.
CLANCY - Toys–stuffed - Silent Sentiments
CLANDESTINO - Apparel and accessories - Carlos E. Cuellar
CLANKIN' HORSESHOES - Toys - Playskool, Inc.
CLAPPER - Games - Carrom Co.
CLAPPER, THE - Switches–electric - Joseph Enterprises Inc.
CLAPPERS - Recording label - Relativity/Combat/In-Effect
CLAPTRAP - Drums–musical instruments - Simmons Group Centre Inc.
CLAR-AQUA - Chemical preparations - Brothers Three Inc.
CLAR-VU - Doors–screen - Weather Shield Manufacturing, Inc.
CLARA - Food products - Sansone Food Products Co. Inc.
CLARA BARTON - Watches - Bulova Corp.
CLARA BEE - Paints - Sooner Arts & Crafts Inc.
CLARA'S PLACE - Apparel–women's - Tae Young Yoon
CLARE - Beverages - Georgia Mountain Water Inc.
CLARE - Glassware–household - Waterford Wedgwood USA, Inc.
CLARE CREATIONS - Apparel–children's - Friemanit Corp.
CLAREBLEND - Medical equipment - Clareblend, Inc.
CLAREMONT - Cabinets - American Woodmark Corp.
CLAREMONT - Cabinets - Imperial Cabinet Co. Inc.
CLAREMONT - Dinnerware–glass - Nikko Ceramics Inc.
CLAREMONT - Dishes–china ✩ - WMF/USA
CLAREMONT - Floor coverings - Congoleum Corp.
CLAREMONT - Floor coverings–carpet and rugs ✩ - Rugby Rugs Inc.
CLAREMONT - Furniture ✩ - Lane Co. Inc.
CLAREMONT - Trailers–travel - Fleetwood Enterprises, Inc.
CLAREMONT - Watches - Golden State Imports International, Inc.

✩ = Now out of production

CLAREMONT - Windows–storm - Norandex, Inc.

CLARENCE CLOWN - Dolls ☆ - Effanbee Doll Corp.

CLARENCE HOUSE - Window coverings - Award Fabrics Inc.

CLARENCE HOUSE II - Wallpaper ☆ - Imperial Wallcoverings, Inc.

CLARENCE HOUSE: JUBILEE - Wallpaper ☆ - Imperial Wallcoverings, Inc.

CLARENCE HOUSE WORLD CRUISE - Wallpaper - Imperial Wallcoverings, Inc.

CLARENDON - Artists' materials - Solo-Horton Brush Co.

CLARENDON - Clocks ☆ - General Time Corp. (Westclox/Seth Thomas Div.)

CLARENDON - Flatware ☆ - Rogers, Lunt and Bowlen Co.

CLARENDON - Furniture ☆ - White Furniture Co.

CLARENDON PARK - Wallpaper - Textile Wallcoverings International Ltd.

CLARIDGE - Bicycles - Kent International Inc.

CLARIDGE - Fabrics–crepe - Rosebar Textile Co.

CLARIDGE - Floor coverings–carpet and rugs - Karastan-Bigelow Inc.

CLARIDGE - Floor coverings–carpet and rugs - Whitecrest Carpet Mills

CLARIDGE - Floor coverings–carpet and rugs ☆ - Atlas Carpet Mills Inc.

CLARIDGE - Floor coverings–carpet and rugs ☆ - Patrick Carpet Mills

CLARIDGE - Furniture ☆ - Hooker Furniture Corp.

CLARIDGE - Furniture–wood - Century Furniture Co.

CLARIDGE - Tableware–china - Pfaltzgraff Investment Co.

CLARIDGE - Weather tracking equipment ☆ - Bausch & Lomb Inc.

CLARIDGE CORK - Bulletin boards–cork - Claridge Products and Equipment Inc.

CLARIDGE DELUXE - Bulletin boards–wood - Claridge Products and Equipment Inc.

CLARIDGE HALL COLLECTION - Furniture ☆ - Harden Furniture Co. Inc.

CLARIDGE HI-TEC - Firearms, accessories, and parts - Claridge Hi-Tec Inc.

CLARIDGE MANOR - Furniture - Hammary Furniture Co. Inc.

CLARIDGE WOOD - Floor coverings ☆ - Tarkett, Inc.

CLARIDGE'S - Chocolate candy - Monica's Best Foods Ltd.

CLARIDON - Floor coverings ☆ - Azrock Commercial Flooring

CLARIFIER, THE - Glare reduction device - Less Gauss Inc.

CLARIFYE - Computer software - Claret Software, Inc.

CLARIFYING COOLERS - Cosmetics - Max Factor & Co.

CLARIMAGE - Skin care products - Cosmeceutical Research Institute, Inc.

CLARINA - Harmonicas - Hohner Inc.

CLARINETTE I - Phonographs - Tandy Corp.

CLARINETTE II - Phonographs - Tandy Corp.

CLARINETTE III - Phonographs - Tandy Corp.

CLARINO - Footwear - Marubeni America Corp.

CLARINS COLOUR - Cosmetics - Clarins USA Inc.

CLARINS U.S.A. - Cosmetics - Clarins USA Inc.

CLARION - Advertising agencies - Gery Kotthoff

CLARION - Cabinets - Triangle Pacific Corp. (Cabinet Division)

CLAR+ION - Chemical preparations - General Chemical Corp.

CLARION - Christmas tree ornaments - Cracker Box Inc.

CLARION - Computer hardware - Data General Corp.

CLARION - Cosmetics - Noxell Corp.

CLARION - Fans–electric - Hunter Fan Co.

CLARION - Floor coverings - Aladdin Mills, Inc.

CLARION - Floor coverings - Congoleum Corp.

CLARION - Floor coverings–carpet and rugs - Karastan-Bigelow Inc.

CLARION - Floor coverings–carpet and rugs - Kelly Group Inc.

CLARION - Fruits and vegetables ☆ - Midland Grocery Co.

CLARION - Furniture - Lane Co. Inc.

CLARION - Furniture ☆ - Tropitone Furniture Co. Inc.

CLARION - Glassware–household ☆ - Crisa Corp.

CLARION - Glassware–household ☆ - Lenox Crystal, Inc.

CLARION - Hardware - Baldwin Hardware Corp.

CLARION - Hotels and motels - Choice Hotels International Inc.

CLARION - Lubricating oils - Citgo Petroleum Corp.

CLARION - Luggage - Airway Industries, Inc.

CLARION - Motor vehicles–motor homes - Coachmen Industries, Inc.

CLARION - Musical instruments ☆ - Selmer Co. Inc.

CLARION - Projection screens - Draper Shade and Screen Co. Inc.

CLARION - Recording label - Calvary Records Inc.

CLARION - Tape recorders–cassette - Kaman Music Corp.

CLARION - Telephones–cellular - Clarion Corp. of America

CLARION BOOKS - Publisher's imprints - Houghton Mifflin Co.

CLARION CLASSICS - Publisher's imprints ☆ - Zondervan Publishing House

CLARION INFINITE LENGTHS - Cosmetics - Noxell Corp.

CLARION SUDDEN LASH - Cosmetics - Noxell Corp.

CLARIOS - Wallpaper - Fidelity Industries, Inc.

CLARIS HOME PAGE - Computer software - Claris Corp.

CLARISDRAW - Computer storage devices - Claris Corp.

CLARISIMPACT - Computer software - Claris Corp.

CLARISSA - Dinnerware–glass - Nikko Ceramics Inc.

CLARISSA - Furniture - Homecrest Industries Inc.

CLARISSA - Paper–tissue - Aldi Inc.

CLARISSA - Tableware–china - Villeroy and Boch Tableware Ltd.

CLARISSA EXPLAINS IT ALL - Greeting cards - Viacom International Inc.

CLARISSE - Wallpaper - Tony Putnam Inc.

CLARISTINE - Liquors ☆ - House of Seagram

CLARIT - Computer software - Carnegie Mellon University

CLARITA - Hardware - Contractors Wardrobe, Inc.

CLARITABS - Chemical preparations - Aqua Clear Industries Inc.

CLARITEC - Water purification systems - Fountainhead Technologies, Inc.

CLARITECH - Computer software - Claritech Corp.

CLARITIN - Antihistamine preparations - Schering Corp.

CLARITIN - Antihistamine preparations - Schering-Plough Healthcare Products

CLARITIN-D - Antihistamine preparations - Schering Corp.

CLARITY - Clocks - General Time Corp. (Westclox/Seth Thomas Div.)

CLARITY - Eyeglasses - Cable Car Eyeware

CLARITY - Floor coverings–carpet and rugs - J and J Industries Inc.

CLARITY - Glass–stained - D & L Stained Glass Supply, Inc.

CLARITY - Glassware–household - Lenox, Inc.

CLARITY - Hair care products - Peter Hantz Co.

CLARITY - Vegetable oil - Karlshamns USA Inc.

CLARITY CUBE - Filters–industrial - Omni Corp.

CLARITY GOLD - Glassware–household - Lenox, Inc.

CLARITY MULTIMEDIA - Computer storage devices–optical - Coastal Video Communications Corp.

CLARITY PLASTICS - Giftware ☆ - Bar & Barbeque Products Inc.

CLARITY PLUS - Caning–rattan - Hunt Holdings, Inc.

CLARITY PLUS - Pet product - Innovate Corp.

CLARK - Audio equipment ☆ - David Clark Co. Inc.

CLARK - Candy - D.L. Clark Candy Co.

CLARK - Chemical preparations - Clark Refining & Marketing, Inc.

CLARK - Musical instrument accessories - Roberto Ciarfella Inc.

CLARK - Musical instrument accessories ☆ - American Way Marketing Inc.

CLARK - Petroleum - Clark Oil & Refining Corp.

CLARK - Sporting goods ☆ - FNT Industries Inc.

CLARK - Tiles–ceiling - Clark Tile Co.

CLARK - Water–mineral - Clark Spring Water Co.

CLARK AMERICA - See **THE DESIGNER TOUCH**

CLARK & BURCHFIELD - Wallpaper - K.M.L. Industries

CLARK BROTHERS - Construction equipment - Federal Aluminum Products

CLARK CANDY BAR - Ice cream - Tri Point Ice Cream

CLARK CHANG - Footwear–women's ☆ - Margaret Gerald

CLARK GUM - Chewing gum - Clark Gum Co.

CLARK IMPORTS - Fabrics–tapestry - Clark Imports Inc.

CLARK JUNIOR - Candy ☆ - Leaf, Inc.

CLARK-RELIANCE - Humidifiers - Clark-Reliance Corp.

CLARK TERRY - Trumpets - Wolf Imports

CLARKBURGERS - Meat products–beef - Clark Meat Co.

CLARKCRAFT - Boats - Clark Craft Boat Co.

CLARKE - Washing machine parts - Alto U.S. Inc.

CLARKE AMERICAN - Business cards - Clarke American Corp.

CLARKE THE ODD-VARK - Toys - L'hats of Cheer, Inc.

CLARKS - Meat products–beef - Clark Meat Co.

CLARKS - Pet products - Mr. Mutt Pet Products Inc.

CLARK'S - Trees - Walter E. Clark & Son

CLARKS CABLES - Bicycles - Torelli Imports

CLARKS DESERT - Shoes - Clarks of England Inc.

CLARKS OF ENGLAND - Shoes ☆ - Clarks of England Inc.

CLARK'S O.N.T. - Zippers ☆ - Coats and Clark Inc.

CLARKSBURG - Fireplace equipment - Majestic Co.

CLARKSBURG BREAD CO. - Bakery products - Clarksburg Bread Co., Inc.

CLARKSON - Floor coverings–carpet and rugs ☆ - Daltonian Carpet & Cushion Inc.

CLARKSON N. POTTER - Publisher's imprints - Crown Publishers Inc.

CLARO - Electrical equipment - Lutron Electronics Co., Inc.

CLARO - Health care products ☆ - DBA Products Co.

CLARO CAST - Plastics ☆ - Fry Plastics International Inc. (O)

CLARON - Furniture ☆ - Broyhill Furniture Industries, Inc.

CLAROS - Cigar boxes–wood - Consolidated Cigar Corp.

CLARTE - Shampoos - Mastey De Paris

CLARUS - Medical unit - Medilase, Inc.

CLARUS - Recording label - Clarus Music Ltd.

CLARUS - Vegetables–pickled or brined - Pacific Resources International

CLAS - Computer software - Stockholder Systems, Inc.

☆ = Now out of production

CLAS - Medical apparatus - Kera-Metrics, Inc.
CLASH - Beverages–malt ☆ - The Stroh Brewery Co.
CLASH - Games ☆ - Pressman Toy Corp.
CLASH - Rackets–racquetball - Lisco, Inc.
CLASH BEAST - Dolls - Trendmasters, Inc.
CLASH SAN JOSE - Paper products - Major League Soccer, LLC
CLASICO - Coffee - Nestle Beverage Co.
CLASICO - Meat products–canned - Sampco Inc.
CLASICO - Wines - Codorniu USA Inc.
CLASP WRAP - Jewelry - Sandberg & Sikorski Diamond Corp.
CLASPIT - Hairpins ☆ - Perfecto Products Co.
CLASS - Computer software - Microtique, Inc.
CLASS - Dishwashing compounds - Blue Cross Laboratories Inc.
CLASS - Pencils - Reliance Pen & Pencil Corp.
CLASS - Publisher's imprints - Harcourt Brace & Co.
CLASS - Watches - ETA Industries Inc.
CLASS 1 - Auto parts - Class 1, Inc.
CLASS 5 - Footwear - John W. Schelling
CLASS A - Cigarettes - Liggett Group Inc.
CLASS A CIGARETTES - Cigarettes - Eve Holdings Inc.
CLASS AB - Boats - Glen-L Marine Designs
CLASS ACT - Computer software - David Everson
CLASS ACT - Dairy products - Smith's Dairy Products Co.
CLASS ACT - Footwear - Pro-Joggs International Inc.
CLASS ACT - Herbicides - Cenex/Land O'Lakes AG Services
CLASS ACT - Hosiery - Handcraft Manufacturing Corp.
CLASS ACT - Stain removers - Petro-Tech Services Inc.
CLASS ACT - Wallpaper - Unique Wall Fashions Inc.
CLASS ACTS - Wallcovering - Gilford Corp.
CLASS ANTIQUE - Dinnerware–glass ☆ - Metlox Pottery Shoppe
CLASS CD - Boats - Glen-L Marine Designs
C.L.A.S.S. CLINICAL ANATOMY STUDY SYSTEM - Recording label - Mosby-Year Book, Inc.
CLASS CLUB - Apparel–children's - Dillard Department Stores Inc.
CLASS DECKER - Boats - H & H Molded Products
CLASS I - Adhesives and sealants - Geocel Corp.
CLASS-IN-A-BOX - Paints–artists' - JSA Inc.
CLASS J - Boats - Glen-L Marine Designs
CLASS MATE - Stationery - Mead Corp.
CLASS MATES - Chewing gum - Amurol Confections Co.
CLASS OF '54, THE - Games - Decipher Inc.
CLASS OF '55 - Guitars - Dimarzio, Inc.
CLASS OF '60 SOMETHIN' - Recording label - Leash & Associates Inc.
CLASS OF '88 - Publisher's imprints - Scholastic Inc.
CLASS OF '89 - Publisher's imprints - Scholastic Inc.
CLASS OF 2000 - Apparel and accessories - Demetriadi Odysseus
CLASS OF 2000 - Apparel–athletic - Pacific Sportswear and Emblem Co.
CLASS ONE - Pillow stuffing - American Fiber Industries Corp.
CLASS ONE - Uniforms–tailored ☆ - Horace Small Apparel Co.
CLASS PACK - Toys - Tonka Corp.
CLASS POPS - Candy - Maredy Corp.
CLASS RINGS - Shower rods - Associated Products Inc.
CLASS-RITE - Electronic equipment - Da-Lite Screen Co. Inc.
CLASS STRUGGLE - Games - Avalon Hill Game Co.
CLASS THOUGHTS - Rings–jewelry - CJC Holdings, Inc.
CLASSACT - Computer software - L.J. Technical Systems
CLASSACT - Scissors–hand-operated - Aaronco Grooming Products
CLASSACT - Scissors–hand-operated - Aaronco Pet Products, Inc.
CLASSAIRE - Air conditioning equipment - Suburban Manufacturing Co.
CLASSEN - Railings–metal - Classen Enterprises, Inc.
CLASSETTE - Tape recorder - L & M Auto Supply
CLASSI-FILE - File folders ☆ - Kardex Systems, Inc.
CLASSI NAIL - Cosmetics - American International Industries
CLASSIC - Naturally Fresh
CLASSIC - Aluminum products - Remington Building Products
CLASSIC - Amplifiers - Peavey Electronics Corp.
CLASSIC - Amplifiers–musical instrument ☆ - Seymour Duncan Pickups
CLASSIC - Apparel and accessories - Classic Rope Manufacturing, Inc.
CLASSIC - Apparel and accessories - Jantzen Inc.
CLASSIC - Apparel and accessories - Winona Camo System, Inc.
CLASSIC - Aquariums–household - O'Dell Industries
CLASSIC - Archery equipment ☆ - Martin Archery Inc.
CLASSIC - Artists' materials - Classic Oils & Portraits
CLASSIC - Artists' materials ☆ - Logan Graphic Products Inc.
CLASSIC - Automotive parts and accessories - Wright-Bernet
CLASSIC - Backpacks - Royal Cushion Co. Inc.

CLASSIC - Bags - Porox International Co., Inc.
CLASSIC - Bathroom accessories - Franklin Brass Manufacturing Co.
CLASSIC - Bathroom accessories - Watkins Manufacturing Corp.
CLASSIC - Bathtubs–enameled - Novi American Inc.
CLASSIC - Bathtubs–enameled - Pearl Baths Inc.
CLASSIC - Batteries - Eveready Battery Co., Inc.
CLASSIC - Beauty aids ☆ - S.R. Droescher Inc.
CLASSIC - Beds–wood - Classic Corp.
CLASSIC - Benches–metal - Victor Stanley, Inc.
CLASSIC - Beverages–alcohol - Consolidated Distilled Products Inc.
CLASSIC - Beverages–alcohol - United States Distilled Products Co.
CLASSIC - Beverages–malt ☆ - Anheuser-Busch Companies Inc.
CLASSIC - Bicycles - Columbia Manufacturing Inc.
CLASSIC - Bicycles - Ross Bicycles USA, Ltd.
CLASSIC - Blankets–electric ☆ - Sunbeam-Oster Household Products
CLASSIC - Blinds–venetian - Mark Window Products
CLASSIC - Boats–canoes ☆ - Sawyer Composite Products
CLASSIC - Boats–motor - Alumacraft Boat Co.
CLASSIC - Boats–motor - Harris-Kayot Inc.
CLASSIC - Boats–pontoons - Forester Boats Inc.
CLASSIC - Books–blank - Sun Graphix
CLASSIC - Bowls ☆ - Denby USA Limited
CLASSIC - Brassieres (Bras) - Goddess Bra
CLASSIC - Brushes–hair ☆ - Phillips Brush Corp.
CLASSIC - Cabinets - Gragg Cabinet Industries
CLASSIC - Cabinets - Kabom Kitchen & Bath Manufacturing
CLASSIC - Cabinets - Quality Cabinets
CLASSIC - Cabinets - Scott Manufacturing, Inc.
CLASSIC - Cabinets–metal - Par Metal Products Inc.
CLASSIC - Cameras - Bell & Howell Co.
CLASSIC - Candy - Pangburn Candy Co.
CLASSIC - Candy - Rebecca Ruth Candy Inc.
CLASSIC - Carpet sweepers ☆ - Bissell Inc.
CLASSIC - Cases–vanity - Triangle Pacific Corp. (Cabinet Division)
CLASSIC - Chairs–wood - Gold Medal Inc.
CLASSIC - Chili–canned - Stagg Foods, Inc.
CLASSIC - Cigarettes - Nat Sherman, Inc.
CLASSIC - Clay–modeling - J.F. McCaughin Co.
CLASSIC - Clocks, giftware - American Intercontinental Trade Group Inc.
CLASSIC - Coffee - Nestle Beverage Co.
CLASSIC - Combs - Lawndale Products Inc.
CLASSIC - Computer software - McGraw-Hill Companies, Inc.
CLASSIC - Cookies - Allied Marketing, Inc.
CLASSIC - Cookies ☆ - Sunshine Biscuits, Inc.
CLASSIC - Cosmetics - Classic Laboratories Inc.
CLASSIC - Cosmetics - Revlon Consumer Products Corp.
CLASSIC - Cotton–sterilized - U.S. Cotton, LLC
CLASSIC - Desk sets - Rosa Pen Co.
CLASSIC - Dining room furniture - Lexington Furniture Industries, Inc.
CLASSIC - Dinners–frozen ☆ - Pillsbury Co.
CLASSIC - Dishes–wood - Dansk International Designs, Ltd.
CLASSIC - Doors–metal - Raynor Manufacturing Co.
CLASSIC - Doors–storm - Gerkin Windows & Doors
CLASSIC - Drapery hardware - Kenney Manufacturing Co.
CLASSIC - Drinkware - Corbell & Co.
CLASSIC - Drums–musical instruments - Selmer Co. Inc.
CLASSIC - Electrical equipment - Challenger Circle F Inc.
CLASSIC - Enamels - Frazee Paint
CLASSIC - Exercising equipment ☆ - World Famous Trading Co., Ltd.
CLASSIC - Eyeglasses - Uvex Safety LLC
CLASSIC - Fans–electric - Nutone Inc.
CLASSIC - Faucets ☆ - Webstone Co. Inc.
CLASSIC - Fencing–wood - ADPI Enterprises Inc.
CLASSIC - Filing cabinets ☆ - Corry Hiebert
CLASSIC - Finishing agents ☆ - Flintkote Co.
CLASSIC - Fireplace equipment - Hearth Craft
CLASSIC - Fireplace equipment - Thermo-Rite Manufacturing Co.
CLASSIC - Flatware ☆ - National Housewares
CLASSIC - Floor coverings - Beaulieu of America, Inc.
CLASSIC - Floor coverings - Bruce Hardwood Floors
CLASSIC - Floor coverings–carpet and rugs - Aldon Industries Inc.
CLASSIC - Floor coverings–carpet and rugs - Daltonian Carpet & Cushion Inc.
CLASSIC - Floor coverings–carpet and rugs - Johnson's Carpets Inc.
CLASSIC - Floor coverings–carpet and rugs - Lotus Carpets
CLASSIC - Floor coverings–carpet and rugs ☆ - American Carpet Mills
CLASSIC - Floor coverings–carpet and rugs ☆ - Atlas Carpet Mills Inc.

☆ = Now out of production

CLASSIC - Floor coverings–carpet and rugs ☆ - Capel, Inc.
CLASSIC - Floor coverings–carpet and rugs ☆ - Patrick Carpet Mills
CLASSIC - Floor coverings–carpet and rugs ☆ - Regal Rugs Inc.
CLASSIC - Floor coverings–tile - Classic Concepts Inc.
CLASSIC - Flowers, plants, and seeds - Jacklin Seed
CLASSIC - Footwear–athletic - Head Sports USA
CLASSIC - Frames–picture - Howell Mouldings Inc.
CLASSIC - Furniture - Halcyon Inc.
CLASSIC - Furniture - Southern Furniture Co. of Conover
CLASSIC - Furniture - Virco Manufacturing Corp.
CLASSIC - Furniture ☆ - A.A. Laun Furniture Co.
CLASSIC - Furniture–children's ☆ - Child Craft Industries Inc.
CLASSIC - Furniture–wood ☆ - Flanders Industries Inc.
CLASSIC - Giftware - Gessner Products Co. Inc.
CLASSIC - Giftware ☆ - Lenox Crystal, Inc.
CLASSIC - Glassware–household - Crisa Corp.
CLASSIC - Glassware–household - Federal Glass
CLASSIC - Glassware–household - Oneida Ltd.
CLASSIC - Glassware–household - Owens-Illinois Inc. (Libbey Div.)
CLASSIC - Gloves - Ektelon
CLASSIC - Gloves–rubber - Cross Country Paper Products, Inc.
CLASSIC - Golfing equipment - Allied Golf Co.
CLASSIC - Golfing equipment - Creative Products Inc.
CLASSIC - Golfing equipment - Datrek Professional Bags, Inc.
CLASSIC - Golfing equipment - Eaton Corp.
CLASSIC - Greeting cards ☆ - Doehla Greeting Cards Inc.
CLASSIC - Guns - Remington Arms Co., Inc.
CLASSIC - Hair care products - Fromm Industries
CLASSIC - Hardware - Worthy Works Inc.
CLASSIC - Health care products - Rx Rocker Corp.
CLASSIC - Hearing aids - Magnatone Hearing Aid Corp.
CLASSIC - Herbicides - E.I. Dupont de Nemours and Co.
CLASSIC - High chairs - Century Products Co.
CLASSIC - Hosiery - Classic Hosiery Inc.
CLASSIC - Housewares ☆ - Doranne
CLASSIC - Identification jewelry - Jacoby-Bender Inc.
CLASSIC - Infant product - Inglesina Baby Ltd.
CLASSIC - Lamps - Luxo Corp.
CLASSIC - Lamps - Tensor Corp.
CLASSIC - Leather goods - Korchmar Case Co.
CLASSIC - Luggage - Samsonite Corp.
CLASSIC - Luggage - Service Manufacturing Corp.
CLASSIC - Luggage - SGI Inc.
CLASSIC - Mats - Majestic Mat Co.
CLASSIC - Meats–luncheon - Oscar Mayer Foods Corp.
CLASSIC - Medical apparatus - Uni-Patch
CLASSIC - Mirrors ☆ - Bassett Furniture Industries, Inc.
CLASSIC - Mobile homes - Oakwood Homes Corp.
CLASSIC - Mops - M.B. Walton, Inc.
CLASSIC - Motor vehicle parts and accessories - Cards for Cards
CLASSIC - Motor vehicles - Metrotrans Corp.
CLASSIC - Motor vehicles–motor homes - Coachmen Industries, Inc.
CLASSIC - Motor vehicles–motor homes ☆ - Beaver Coaches Inc.
CLASSIC - Musical instrument accessories - J. D'Addario & Co. Inc.
CLASSIC - Musical instrument accessories - Micro Musical Products Corp.
CLASSIC - Musical instruments ☆ - Deg Music Products Inc.
CLASSIC - Notebooks and notepads - Alvin and Co. Inc.
CLASSIC - Notebooks and notepads - Amplaco Group Inc.
CLASSIC - Office supplies - Bates Manufacturing Co.
CLASSIC - Office supplies - Vanguard Corp.
CLASSIC - Paints - Plasti-Kote Co. Inc.
CLASSIC - Paints ☆ - GS Roofing Products Co.
CLASSIC - Paints–artists' - Triangle Coatings Inc.
CLASSIC - Paper–writing - Kimberly-Clark Corp.
CLASSIC - Paper–writing - Neenah Paper Co.
CLASSIC - Peanut butter - Federated Group, Inc.
CLASSIC - Pencils–mechanical - Scripto-Tokai Corp.
CLASSIC - Pens - Gillette Co.
CLASSIC - Pens - Parker Pen USA
CLASSIC - Pens–fountain ☆ - Faber-Castell Corp.
CLASSIC - Personal-care shower - Interbath, Inc.
CLASSIC - Pet products - Grah & Plumacher USA
CLASSIC - Pet products - Manna Pro Corp.
CLASSIC - Pet products - Merion Station Mail Order Co.
CLASSIC - Pet products - SPI
CLASSIC - Pet products - Valhoma Industries Inc.

CLASSIC - Pianos - Classic Player Pianos Inc.
CLASSIC - Pillows - Encore Products Inc.
CLASSIC - Pipes - National Briar Pipe Co.
CLASSIC - Placemats - Cascade Fibers Co.
CLASSIC - Plaques - Classic Plaques Inc.
CLASSIC - Plates–paper - Fonda Group, Inc.
CLASSIC - Plumbing fixtures–metal - Barclay Products Ltd.
CLASSIC - Pool tables ☆ - Brunswick Corp.
CLASSIC - Popcorn ☆ - Wyandot, Inc.
CLASSIC - Portable partition - Brewster Corp.
CLASSIC - Rails–iron - Leslie-Locke, Inc.
CLASSIC - Recording label - Terock Records
CLASSIC - Ribbons–inked - Distinguished Brands Inc.
CLASSIC - Rifles - Crosman Corp.
CLASSIC - Sauces - Eastern Foods, Inc.
CLASSIC - Saws–power - S-B Power Tool Co.
CLASSIC - Seats–automobile ☆ - Cramer Inc.
CLASSIC - Shelving units–wood - Clairson International Corp.
CLASSIC - Shelving units–wood ☆ - Hirsh Co.
CLASSIC - Shingles - Owens Corning
CLASSIC - Ships–sailing vessels - Classic Sailing Vessels
CLASSIC - Sporting goods - Outdoor Technologies Group
CLASSIC - Sporting goods - Prince Manufacturing Inc.
CLASSIC - Sporting goods - Wellington Leisure Products, Inc.
CLASSIC - Sporting goods ☆ - Wright & McGill Co.
CLASSIC - Sports rackets and accessories - Victor Sports
CLASSIC - Stamps–hand - Louis Melind Co.
CLASSIC - Statuary - Hillside House of Originals
CLASSIC - Teas–herbal ☆ - Traditional Medicinals, Inc.
CLASSIC - Tents - Coleman Co., Inc.
CLASSIC - Tiles–ceramic - Franciscan by Johnson Brothers, USA, Inc.
CLASSIC - Tiles–ceramic ☆ - Huntington/Pacific Ceramics Inc.
CLASSIC - Tools - Red Devil Inc.
CLASSIC - Tools–garden - Gilmour Manufacturing Co.
CLASSIC - Toothbrushes - Colgate-Palmolive Co.
CLASSIC - Toys - Creative Playthings Ltd.
CLASSIC - Toys–musical - Kazoo Co. Inc.
CLASSIC - Trailers–travel ☆ - Classic Manufacturing Inc.
CLASSIC - Umbrellas - Haas-Jordan Co.
CLASSIC - Uniforms–tailored - Classic Uniform Co.
CLASSIC - Vitamins and nutritional supplements - Reliv' International, Inc.
CLASSIC - Watches - Bulova Corp.
CLASSIC - Wet-mop handles - American Textile Products Co.
CLASSIC - Wigs - New Image
CLASSIC - Windows–storm - Caradco
CLASSIC - Wines ☆ - The Monterey Vineyard
CLASSIC II - Clarinets ☆ - G. Leblanc Corp.
CLASSIC II - Trailers–travel ☆ - Turtle Top Specialty Products
CLASSIC 5 - Games ☆ - Pacific Game Co.
CLASSIC 7 - Window shades - Allied Extrusions
CLASSIC 35 - Lamps - Duro-Test Corp.
CLASSIC-42 - Lamp bulbs–fluorescent - Duro-Test Corp.
CLASSIC 50 - Musical instrument accessories - Wenger Corp.
CLASSIC 50'S - Golfing equipment - Louisville Golf Club Co. Inc.
CLASSIC 99 - Paints - Sherwin-Williams Automotive Finishes Corp.
CLASSIC 100 - Beverage dispensing equipment - American Business Computers Corp.
CLASSIC 106 - Siding–insulating - Ashland-Davis Co.
CLASSIC 150 - Food products - Kraft Food Ingredients Corp.
CLASSIC 165 - Inks–letterpress - Heritage Inks International Corp.
CLASSIC 200 - Milk - Kraft Food Ingredients Corp.
CLASSIC 500 TR-X - Toys–electronic - Tyco Toys
CLASSIC 707 - Trailers–travel ☆ - Seven O Seven Industries Inc.
CLASSIC 727 - Trailers–travel ☆ - Seven O Seven Industries Inc.
CLASSIC 1000 - Beverage dispensing equipment - American Business Computers Corp.
CLASSIC 1800 - Dryers–hair - JRC Products Inc.
CLASSIC 2000 - Beverage dispensing equipment - American Business Computers Corp.
CLASSIC ACCENTS - Drapery hardware - Newell Operating Co.
CLASSIC-ADA - Computer software - Software Productivity Solutions, Inc.
CLASSIC ADVANTAGE - Mirrors - Holiday Classics
CLASSIC AIRE - Air conditioning equipment - Mark Durrell
CLASSIC AMARETTO - Cakes - Dinkel's Bakery
CLASSIC AMERICAN CHILI - Seasonings - McCormick & Co., Inc.

☆ = Now out of production

CLASSIC AMERICAN SPORTS CAR - Toys–automobiles - Kingsbury Mini Motors of America Inc.

CLASSIC APPEAL - Floor coverings–carpet and rugs - Alexander Smith Carpets

CLASSIC ARTIST OILS - Paints - Triangle Coatings Inc.

CLASSIC ARTISTS - Greeting cards - Hampton Greeting Card Co.

CLASSIC ARTISTS RECORDINGS - Recording label - Voss Music Inc.

CLASSIC BAGELS - Bagels - G.M. Marketing Co.

CLASSIC BASKET - Candy - Home of the Hebert Candies, Inc.

CLASSIC BEAUTY COLLECTION - Dolls - Totsy Manufacturing Co., Inc.

CLASSIC BEST - Trading cards and stamps - Classic Games Co. Inc.

CLASSIC BLACK - Dinnerware - Corning Inc.

CLASSIC-BLEND - Grouting material - Custom Building Products

CLASSIC BOOK COLLECTION - Computer storage devices–optical ☆ - World Library, Inc.

CLASSIC BRASSWARE - Hardware - Stanley Hardware Div.

CLASSIC BREED - Toys - Imperial Toy Corp.

CLASSIC BRIDES OF THE CENTURY - Giftware - Roman, Inc.

CLASSIC BUTTER-SCOTCH - Candy - Callard & Bowser-Suchard, Inc.

CLASSIC BUTTERFLY - Chairs–folding - Algoma Net Co.

CLASSIC CALIPER - Archery equipment - Tru-Fire Corp.

CLASSIC CAMPER - Trailers–travel ☆ - Turtle Top Specialty Products

CLASSIC CANVAS - Canvas–artists' ☆ - E-Z Industries Inc.

CLASSIC CARE - Paints - Krylon/Dupli-Color

CLASSIC CARRIAGE CLOCK - Clocks - Avon Products, Inc.

CLASSIC CARRY-OUT - Containers - Packaging Corp. of America

CLASSIC CARS - Erasers - Diener Industries Inc.

CLASSIC CARTERS - Containers–metal - Carter-Hoffmann Corp.

CLASSIC CASE, THE - Musical instrument accessories - Fenton Music

CLASSIC CASSEROLE - Food products ☆ - Pillsbury Co.

CLASSIC CENTER, THE - Stationery - Unified Government of Athens-Clarke County, Georgia

CLASSIC CHARACTERS - Toys–stuffed - Eden LLC

CLASSIC CHARM - Flatware - Utica Cutlery Co.

CLASSIC CHEF - Cutlery - Chicago Cutlery Manufacturing Inc.

CLASSIC CHEF - Cutlery - General Housewares Corp.

CLASSIC CHEF - Meat products–beef - Foodbrands America, Inc.

CLASSIC CHEFWARE - Cooking equipment–household ☆ - Mirro Corp.

CLASSIC CHESS - Chessboards ☆ - Pacific Game Co.

CLASSIC CHESTS - Dressers–wood ☆ - Welsh Co.

CLASSIC CHILD - Apparel–children's - Classic Child, Inc.

CLASSIC CHIP - Pet products - Howard M. Cohen

CLASSIC CHOICE - Beverages - Orange-Co, Inc.

CLASSIC CHOICE - Floor coverings–carpet and rugs - Evans-Black Carpet Mills

CLASSIC CHOICE - Floor coverings–carpet and rugs - World Carpets, Inc.

CLASSIC CHOICE - Pillows - Pillowtex Corp.

CLASSIC CHORUS - Amplifiers–musical instrument - Peavey Electronics Corp.

CLASSIC CHRISTMAS - Potpourri - Countryside Fragrances Inc.

CLASSIC CLASSIC GOLD - Rope - Classic Rope Manufacturing, Inc.

CLASSIC CLEAN - Antiperspirant/deodorants - Carter-Wallace, Inc.

CLASSIC CLEAN LINE - Furniture–upholstered - Classic Leather, Inc.

CLASSIC CLEAR - Drums–musical instruments - Aquarian Accessories Corp.

CLASSIC CLEAR - Toys - Gerber Products Co.

CLASSIC CLIPS - Paper clips - Scott L. Brotzman

CLASSIC CLOISONNE - Dishes–china - Pickard Inc.

CLASSIC CLOTH - Musical instrument accessories - Fenton Music

CLASSIC CLUB - Beverages–alcohol - Majestic Distilling Co.

CLASSIC CLUB - Beverages–carbonated - Natick Corp.

CLASSIC CLUB - Luggage - Atchison Products, Inc.

CLASSIC COBRA A/C FLUSH SYSTEM - Machinery - Classic Tool Design, Inc.

CLASSIC COFFEE CONCEPTS - Sweeteners–artificial - Mr. Coffee Concepts, Inc.

CLASSIC COINS - Candy - Ethel M. Chocolates, Inc.

CLASSIC COLLECTIBLES - Figurines - Emrad Ltd.

CLASSIC COLLECTIBLES - Furniture - Lane Co. Inc.

CLASSIC COLLECTION - Cabinets - Yorktowne Inc.

CLASSIC COLLECTION - Dinnerware–glass - Nikko Ceramics Inc.

CLASSIC COLLECTION - Greeting cards - Hampton Greeting Card Co.

CLASSIC COLLECTION - Invitations - Classic Thermographers Ltd.

CLASSIC COLLECTION - Office supplies - Samsill Corp.

CLASSIC COLLECTION, THE - Office supplies - Samsill Corp.

CLASSIC COLLECTIONS - Food products - John Labatt Foods

CLASSIC COLONIAL - Candles ☆ - Colonial Candle of Cape Cod

CLASSIC COLORS - Paper–gift wrap - Paper & Film Converting Corp.

CLASSIC COLUMNS - Paper–writing - Kimberly-Clark Corp.

CLASSIC COLUMNS - Paper–writing - Neenah Paper Co.

CLASSIC COLUMNS - Tables–wood ☆ - Artisan House Inc.

CLASSIC COMBINATIONS - Spaghetti sauces - Van Den Bergh Foods Co.

CLASSIC COMFORT - Footwear ☆ - Avanti Shoe

CLASSIC COMFORT - Furniture - Bean Station Furniture Factory Inc.

CLASSIC COMFORT - Hosiery - Sara Lee Corp.

CLASSIC COMFORT - Mattresses - Spring Air Bedding Inc.

CLASSIC COMMUTER - Motor vehicles–ambulances - Metrotrans Corp.

CLASSIC CONCENTRATION - Games ☆ - Pressman Toy Corp.

CLASSIC CONTEMPORARY - Clocks - General Time Corp. (Westclox/Seth Thomas Div.)

CLASSIC CONVERTABLE - Wheels ☆ - Faultless Caster Co.

CLASSIC COOLIE - Containers–insulated - Elgin Kristinik

CLASSIC CORE - Furniture - Columbia Forest Products, Inc.

CLASSIC CORE II - Furniture - Columbia Forest Products, Inc.

CLASSIC CORELLE - Dinnerware - Corning Inc.

CLASSIC CORK - Blinds–vertical ☆ - Kittrich Corp.

CLASSIC COTE - Paints - Perry & Derrick Co.

CLASSIC COTE PLUS - Paints - Perry & Derrick Co.

CLASSIC COTTON - Blankets - MTC

CLASSIC COUNTRY - Breads - Giant Food Stores, Inc.

CLASSIC COUNTRY - Furniture–wood ☆ - Century Furniture Co.

CLASSIC COUNTRY INTERIORS - Wallpaper - Old Stone Mill

CLASSIC COVER - File folders ☆ - Anthes Universal

CLASSIC COVER - Musical instrument accessories - Seymour Duncan Pickups

CLASSIC COVER-UP, THE - Wallpaper - Decor International Wallcovering Inc.

CLASSIC-CRAFT - Doors - Therma-Tru Corp.

CLASSIC CREATION - Floor coverings–carpet and rugs ☆ - Mohawk Carpet Corp.

CLASSIC CREATION - Floor coverings–carpet and rugs ☆ - World Carpets, Inc.

CLASSIC CREATIONS - Giftware - Atlas Enterprises

CLASSIC CREATIONS & ELEGANCE BY BRADLEY - Dolls ☆ - Bradley Import Co.

CLASSIC CREST - Paper–writing - Kimberly-Clark Corp.

CLASSIC CREST - Paper–writing - Neenah Paper Co.

CLASSIC CRISP - Cookies - McKee Foods Corp.

CLASSIC CRUISER - Boats–motor ☆ - Trojan Yacht

CLASSIC CRYSTAL - Cups–plastic - WNA Comet

CLASSIC CUISINE - Food products - El Chico Foods

CLASSIC CUT - Clippers–barber - Sunbeam Corp.

CLASSIC CUT - Trees - W.D. Young & Sons

CLASSIC DANSK - Flatware ☆ - Dansk International Designs, Ltd.

CLASSIC DARK - Beverages–malt - Anheuser-Busch Companies Inc.

CLASSIC DECOR - Hardware ☆ - Grove Products Inc.

CLASSIC DELIGHT - Sandwiches–prepackaged - Pioneer Food Sales Inc.

CLASSIC DELIGHTS! - Sandwiches–prepackaged - Classic Delight Inc.

CLASSIC DESIGN - Floor coverings–carpet and rugs - Olympic Carpets Inc.

CLASSIC DESIGN - Floor coverings–carpet and rugs - Sears, Roebuck and Co.

CLASSIC DESIGNS - Hosiery–women's - Steven R. Corns

CLASSIC DIARY SYSTEM - Diaries - Global Sales Corp.

CLASSIC DIMENSIONS - Apparel–women's - Broadway Stores, Inc.

CLASSIC DIMENSIONS - Stencils - Creative Holdings, Inc.

CLASSIC DIP-ON NAILSILK - Cosmetics - Classic Laboratories Inc.

CLASSIC DIRECTIONS - Suits–men's - J.C. Penney Co., Inc.

CLASSIC DISTORTION - Amplifiers–musical instrument - Seymour Duncan Pickups

CLASSIC DOWNLIGHTS - Lighting fixtures ☆ - Nutone Inc.

CLASSIC EDITION - Calendars - Day Runner, Inc.

CLASSIC EDITION - Soap - Hewitt Soap Co., Inc.

CLASSIC EDITION - Tableware–china - Lenox, Inc.

CLASSIC ELEGANCE - Coffee - Brad Barry Co. Ltd.

CLASSIC ELEGANCE - Floor coverings - Congoleum Corp.

CLASSIC ELEGANCE - Floor coverings–carpet and rugs - Ashley Commercial Carpets

CLASSIC ELEGANCE - Greeting cards - American Greetings Corp.

CLASSIC ELEGANCE - Tableware–china - Lenox, Inc.

CLASSIC ENGLISH BREAKFAST - Teas–herbal - Celestial Seasonings, Inc.

CLASSIC E.Q. - Amplifiers–musical instrument ☆ - Seymour Duncan Pickups

CLASSIC EQUINE COLLECTION - Sporting goods - Classic Rope Manufacturing, Inc.

CLASSIC ERA - Wallpaper - Pantasote Inc. (Wallcovering Div.)

CLASSIC ESTATES - Doors - Addison Corp.

☆ = Now out of production

CLASSIC FAIRY TALES - Computer software - Tele-Story
CLASSIC FEDERAL GOLD - Glassware–household - Lenox, Inc.
CLASSIC FLAME - Fireplaces - Desa International, Inc.
CLASSIC FLAVORS - Yogurt - Dannon Co., Inc.
CLASSIC FLINTSTONES - Apparel and accessories - Hanna-Barbera Productions, Inc.
CLASSIC-FLITE - Balls–golf - Lisco, Inc.
CLASSIC FLOWER - Dinnerware–glass ☆ - Metlox Pottery Shoppe
CLASSIC FLUTES - Flatware ☆ - Kirk Stieff Co.
CLASSIC FLUTES - Silver products - Wallace International Silversmiths, Inc.
CLASSIC FLUTES COLLECTION - Silverware - Wallace International Silversmiths, Inc.
CLASSIC FORM - Colognes - Mem Co., Inc.
CLASSIC FOUR SPORT - Trading cards and stamps - Score Board Holding Corp.
CLASSIC FRESH - Deodorants–personal - Church and Dwight Co. Inc.
CLASSIC GALLERY - Wallpaper - Stroheim & Romann, Inc.
CLASSIC GALLERY II - Wallpaper - Stroheim & Romann, Inc.
CLASSIC GARDEN - Fruits and vegetables - Cafeteria Operators, L.P.
CLASSIC GARDENIA - Colognes - Dana Perfumes Corp.
CLASSIC GOLD - Potato chips - Shearer's Foods, Inc.
CLASSIC GOLD - Rope - Classic Rope Manufacturing, Inc.
CLASSIC GOLD DUCK - Glassware–household - Ceraglass Inc.
CLASSIC GOLF - Glassware–household - Crest Studios
CLASSIC GOURMET - Fruits–canned - Oregon Fruit Products Co., Inc.
CLASSIC GOURMET - Salad dressings–bottled - Wilsey Foods, Inc.
CLASSIC GOURMET - Salads–prepackaged - Blue Ridge Farms, Inc.
CLASSIC GOURMET - Sauces - Wilsey Foods, Inc.
CLASSIC GOURMET SMALL BALE - Animal feeds - Agri-Products, Inc.
CLASSIC GRANITE - Floor coverings - Azrock Commercial Flooring
CLASSIC GREENBACK - Rope - Classic Rope Manufacturing, Inc.
CLASSIC GREY - Tableware ☆ - Corning Inc.
CLASSIC GRILLS - Seafood products–fresh or frozen - Iceland Seafood Corp.
CLASSIC GUARD - Bedding–linen ☆ - Classic Corp.
CLASSIC GUARD CHAIR - Swimming pools - Recreonics, Inc.
CLASSIC GUIDES TO THE VISUAL ARTS - Publisher's imprint - American Life Foundation & Study Institute
CLASSIC HARVEST - Cabinets ☆ - Haas Cabinet Co. Inc.
CLASSIC HEART - Jewelry - National Chain Co.
CLASSIC HEARTH - Bakery products - Continental Mills, Inc.
CLASSIC HEARTH - Fireplaces - Desa International, Inc.
CLASSIC HERITAGE - Floor coverings–carpet and rugs ☆ - Walter Carpet Mills
CLASSIC HOAGIES - Sandwiches–prepackaged - Wawa Inc.
CLASSIC HOLDERS - Candlesticks ☆ - Candles Et Cetera Inc.
CLASSIC HOME - Wallpaper - Beachwood Wallcoverings
CLASSIC HOME - Wallpaper - Eisenhart Wallcoverings Co.
CLASSIC IDAHO BEAN BLEND - Vegetables–frozen - J.R. Simplot Co.
CLASSIC IDEA IN COFFEE CONCEPTS, A - Sweeteners–artificial - Mr. Coffee Concepts, Inc.
CLASSIC II - Fishing tackle ☆ - South Bend Sporting Goods Inc.
CLASSIC II - Sports rackets and accessories - Victor Sports
CLASSIC III - Sports rackets and accessories - Victor Sports
CLASSIC IMAGES - Cutting boards - Vermillion Inc.
CLASSIC IMAGES - Wallpaper - Hoyne Industries Inc.
CLASSIC IMPRESSIONS - Candles - Classic Impressions & Co.
CLASSIC IMPRESSIONS - Tableware–plastic - Amoco Fabrics and Fibers Co.
CLASSIC IMPRESSIONS - Toys–stuffed - Kellytoy (USA), Inc.
CLASSIC INNS - Hotels and motels - Coventry Hotels
CLASSIC INTERIORS: DESIGNER EDITION I - Wallpaper ☆ - Imperial Wallcoverings, Inc.
CLASSIC INTERIORS: DESIGNER EDITION II - Wallpaper ☆ - Imperial Wallcoverings, Inc.
CLASSIC INTERIORS II - Wallpaper ☆ - Imperial Wallcoverings, Inc.
CLASSIC INTERIORS III - Wallpaper ☆ - Imperial Wallcoverings, Inc.
CLASSIC INTRASCAPES - Window treatments ☆ - Intrascapes
CLASSIC IRON - Lighters–cigarette - Adams Apple Distributing L.P.
CLASSIC JAZZ - Recording label ☆ - MMO Music Group Inc.
CLASSIC JET CRAFT - Boats - Norgroup Industries, Inc.
CLASSIC JUNIOR - Cosmetics ☆ - S.R. Droescher Inc.
CLASSIC KEYS - Synthesizers–musical instrument - E-Mu Systems, Inc.
CLASSIC KIDS - Wallpaper ☆ - Eisenhart Wallcoverings Co.
CLASSIC KNITS - Apparel–men's - Sara Lee Knit Products Inc.
CLASSIC LAB - Electronics equipment ☆ - Educational Media Inc.
CLASSIC LADY - Golfing equipment - Square Two Golf
CLASSIC LADY - Panty hose - Rice Hosiery Corp.

CLASSIC LAM - Furniture - Columbia Forest Products, Inc.
CLASSIC LAUREL - Glassware–household - Lenox Crystal, Inc.
CLASSIC LEAF - Floor coverings–carpet and rugs ☆ - Capel, Inc.
CLASSIC LIGHT - Cigarettes - Nat Sherman, Inc.
CLASSIC LIGHT - Dairy products ☆ - Welsh Farms Inc.
CLASSIC LIGHTS - Lamps - General Electric Co.
CLASSIC LINE - Mattresses - Simmons USA
CLASSIC LINE, THE - Frames–picture - MCS Industries Inc.
CLASSIC LINEN - Paper–writing - Neenah Paper Co.
CLASSIC LITE - Chimes ☆ - Nutone Inc.
CLASSIC LITE - Food products - Conagra, Inc.
CLASSIC LIVING - Floor coverings–carpet and rugs - Ashley Commercial Carpets
CLASSIC LIVING - Housewares - Ames Department Stores, Inc.
CLASSIC LOOK, THE - Publisher's imprints - Pen-Tab Industries
CLASSIC M-7000 - Doors–wood - Wells Aluminum
CLASSIC MAIL - Computer software - At&T Corp.
CLASSIC MALT, THE - Whiskey - Schenley Industries Inc.
CLASSIC MANOR - Floor coverings–carpet and rugs ☆ - Columbus Mills, Inc.
CLASSIC MANOR - Furniture - Ethan Allen, Inc.
CLASSIC MARBLE - Housewares ☆ - Treasure Craft Co.
CLASSIC MARINE - Shirts - Nautica Enterprises Inc.
CLASSIC MARINE BY DATCON - Nautical instruments ☆ - Datcon Instrument Co.
CLASSIC MARK - Guns - Weatherby Inc.
CLASSIC MASTERPIECE - Toys - Tonka Corp.
CLASSIC MATCH - Colognes - Delagar
CLASSIC MATE - Mats - Cactus Mat Manufacturing Co.
CLASSIC MEILLANDINA - Flowers, plants, and seeds - J. Benjamin Williams
CLASSIC MEMORIES - Furniture - Stanley Furniture Co. Inc.
CLASSIC MILWAUKEE - Bratwurst sauce - Milwaukee Marketing Associates Inc.
CLASSIC MINIATURES - Bronze and pewter miniatures - Classic Miniatures
CLASSIC MINT - Cigarettes - Nat Sherman, Inc.
CLASSIC MODERN - Tableware–china - Lenox, Inc.
CLASSIC MOMENT - Floor coverings–carpet and rugs - Ashley Commercial Carpets
CLASSIC MOMENTS - Watches - Bulova Corp.
CLASSIC MONEYMAKER - Rope - Classic Rope Manufacturing, Inc.
CLASSIC MUNCHIE - Cakes - Boulder Brownie Co.
CLASSIC MUPPETS - Puzzles - Milton Bradley Co.
CLASSIC NAVY - Cosmetics - Noxell Corp.
CLASSIC NORTHERN FOX - Lighting equipment - Fox Lite Inc.
CLASSIC NUT QUARTET - Nuts–salted, roasted, cooked, or canned - Ross Nut Co.
CLASSIC OAK - Aquariums–household - All Glass Aquarium Co. Inc.
CLASSIC OAK - Dining room furniture - The Davis Co.
CLASSIC OAK AGED ALE - Beverages–malt - Brown-Forman Corp.
CLASSIC OVALTINE - Vitamins and nutritional supplements - Himmel Nutrition Inc.
CLASSIC P - Bags - Porox International Co., Inc.
CLASSIC PAINTER - Brushes–paint - Wooster Brush Co.
CLASSIC PERFORMANCE - Skin care products - Classic Care Cosmetics, Inc.
CLASSIC PILASTER - Shelving units–wood - Naomi Gale Wall Systems
CLASSIC PLATINUM - Rope - Classic Rope Manufacturing, Inc.
CLASSIC PLAYTHINGS - Dolls - Lawton Doll Co.
CLASSIC PLISSE - Blinds–venetian ☆ - Hunter Douglas, Inc.
CLASSIC PLUS - Giftware - Gessner Products Co. Inc.
CLASSIC PLUS - Golf putters - Ray Cook Co.
CLASSIC PLUS - High chairs - Century Products Co.
CLASSIC PLUS - Lawn and garden tools - True Temper Hardware Inc.
CLASSIC PLUS - Tools–hand-operated ☆ - Duro Metal Products Inc.
CLASSIC PLUSH - Seat covers - Saddleman, Inc.
CLASSIC POOH - Stamps–hand - All Night Media, Inc.
CLASSIC POP - Popcorn - Sysco Corp.
CLASSIC PORCELON - Cosmetics - Classic Laboratories Inc.
CLASSIC PREMIUMS - Diapers - Classic Premiums
CLASSIC PRESTIGE - Cosmetics ☆ - S.R. Droescher Inc.
CLASSIC PYRAMID - Floor coverings - American Floor Products Co. Inc.
CLASSIC QUARTERS - Floor coverings–carpet and rugs - Evans-Black Carpet Mills
CLASSIC QUARTERS - Margarine - Van Den Bergh Foods Co.
CLASSIC RACER - Sleds - Flexible Flyer Co.
CLASSIC RAGE - Skin care products - California SunCare, Inc.
CLASSIC RECIPE - Seafood products–canned or cured ☆ - Hernke Foods Inc.

☆ = Now out of production

CLASSIC RECIPE - Seasonings - H.J. Heinz Co.
CLASSIC REEL - Sporting goods ☆ - Gladding Braided Products Inc.
CLASSIC REFLECTIONS - Glass products - Taylor Building Products Co.
CLASSIC REGENCY - Glassware–household ☆ - Lenox Crystal, Inc.
CLASSIC REIGN - Furniture ☆ - Bassett Furniture Industries, Inc.
CLASSIC REMEMBRANCE - Figurines - Value City of Michigan, Inc.
CLASSIC REST - Mattresses ☆ - Classic Corp.
CLASSIC REVIVAL - Fabrics - Capital Carousel Inc.
CLASSIC RIB - Siding–metal - Metal Sales Manufacturing Corp.
CLASSIC RINGS - Candlesticks ☆ - Candles Et Cetera Inc.
CLASSIC ROSE - Dinnerware–glass ☆ - Rosenthal USA Ltd.
CLASSIC ROYALE - Finishing agents ☆ - Flintkote Co.
CLASSIC ROYALE - Paints ☆ - GS Roofing Products Co.
CLASSIC SANTA - Chocolate candy - Superior Fruit & Confections
CLASSIC SAVER - Shingles - Owens Corning
CLASSIC SCENT - Deodorizers - Surco Products Inc.
CLASSIC SCOT - Floor coverings–carpet and rugs ☆ - Daltonian Carpet & Cushion Inc.
CLASSIC SEASONS - Food products - Pierre Frozen Foods Inc.
CLASSIC SEASONS - Meat products–poultry - Hudson Foods, Inc.
CLASSIC SENIOR - Fireplace equipment ☆ - Schaefer Co.
CLASSIC SERIES - Computer software - EDCON Publishing
CLASSIC SERIES - Pens - Rolamech Inc.
CLASSIC SERIES - Skylights - Sun-Tek Industries Inc.
CLASSIC SERPENTINE - Calendars - Cullman Ventures Inc.
CLASSIC SERVINGS - Trays - Farberware Inc.
CLASSIC SHEER - Housewares - Tupperware Co.
CLASSIC SHELL - Glassware–household - Lenox Crystal, Inc.
CLASSIC SHIELD - Building-insulation sheathing board - Atlas Roofing Corp.
CLASSIC SHOW RABBIT - Animal feeds - Manna Pro Corp.
CLASSIC SHOWCASE - Floor coverings–carpet and rugs - Masterpiece Finishing Co.
CLASSIC SIGNATURE - Salad dressings - Georgia International Foods, Inc.
CLASSIC SIGNATURES - Wallpaper ☆ - Capital Carousel Inc.
CLASSIC SILVER - Shampoos - KMS Research Inc.
CLASSIC SILVER DOLLAR - Rope - Classic Rope Manufacturing, Inc.
CLASSIC SINGLE - Flowers - Southern Rainbow Corp.
CLASSIC SLEEPER - Beds–wood ☆ - Classic Corp.
CLASSIC SLY FOX - Machinery - Classic Tool Design, Inc.
CLASSIC SMOOTHER - Brushes–paint - Corona Brushes Inc.
CLASSIC SOLE - Socks - Synergy Enterprises Inc.
CLASSIC SOLUTIONS - Kitchenware–earthenware - Jay Import Co., Inc.
CLASSIC SPA - Toiletries - Albert Nichols
CLASSIC SPICE - Computer software - Vamp Inc.
CLASSIC STAR - Flatware - Washington Forge Inc.
CLASSIC STAR - Sporting goods - Star Line Baton Co. Inc.
CLASSIC STATIS PRO BASEBALL - Games ☆ - Avalon Hill Game Co.
CLASSIC STRIPE - House furnishings - Dan River Inc.
CLASSIC STRIPES - Caps–baseball - AJD Cap Corp.
CLASSIC STYLE - Curling irons–electric - Conair Corp.
CLASSIC STYLE - Wallpaper - Sanitas Wallcoverings
CLASSIC SUITE - Wallpaper - Newmarket Designs Ltd.
CLASSIC SUPERFECTION - Scissors–hand-operated - J.A. Henckels Zwillingswerk Inc.
CLASSIC SUPREME - Cheese - Sargento Cheese Co. Inc.
CLASSIC SWIRL - Drinking glasses and dinnerware - C.S.B. Commodities Inc.
CLASSIC TEDDY - Toys–stuffed - Russ Berrie and Co., Inc.
CLASSIC TEMPTATIONS - Cardboard cartons - Field Container Corp.
CLASSIC TEXTURES - Floor coverings–carpet and rugs - Columbus Mills, Inc.
CLASSIC TEXTURES - Wallpaper - Warner Co.
CLASSIC, THE - Footwear - Award Dance Footwear Corp.
CLASSIC TILE - Tiles–ceramic - Classic International Ceramics, Inc.
CLASSIC TITLED - File folders - Jesse Jones Box Corp.
CLASSIC TOE - Socks - Synergy Enterprises Inc.
CLASSIC TONES - Paper–toweling ☆ - Orchids Paper Products, Inc.
CLASSIC TORPEDO - Lighting fixtures - Swivelier Co. Inc.
CLASSIC TOUCH - Barrettes - American Greetings Corp.
CLASSIC TOUCH - Deodorant and soap - International Distribution Systems, Inc.
CLASSIC TOUCH - Drapery hardware - Ralph Friedland and Brothers Inc.
CLASSIC TOUCH - Floor coverings - Congoleum Corp.
CLASSIC TOUCH - Floor coverings–carpet and rugs - Philadelphia Carpets
CLASSIC TOUCH - Frames–eyeglass - U.S. Optical Frame Co.
CLASSIC TOUCH - Hosiery - Classic Hosiery Inc.
CLASSIC TOUCH - Tiles–ceramic - Wenczel Tile Co.

CLASSIC TOWEL SET - Infant product - Rock-A-Bye Baby Inc.
CLASSIC TRADITION - Floor coverings–carpet and rugs - Mohawk Industries Inc.
CLASSIC TRADITIONS - Seasonings - Robert C. Carl
CLASSIC TRADITIONS - Wallpaper - Seabrook Wallcoverings, Inc.
CLASSIC TREASURES - Jewelry boxes - Wal-Mart Stores Inc.
CLASSIC TREASURES - Meat products–poultry - Hester Industries, Inc.
CLASSIC TRIMS - Christmas tree ornaments - J. Kinderman and Sons Brite Star Manufacturing Co.
CLASSIC TUB - Containers - Ultra Pac, Inc.
CLASSIC TURF - Floor coverings–carpet and rugs ☆ - Proffitt Manufacturing Co.
CLASSIC TURF - Mats - Tumer H. Eren
CLASSIC TWIST - Floor coverings–carpet and rugs - Regal Rugs Inc.
CLASSIC U - Apparel - Harvard Research Group, Inc.
CLASSIC ULTRA-BOND - Cosmetics - Classic Laboratories Inc.
CLASSIC VALUES - Wallcovering - BDH Two, Inc.
CLASSIC VICTORIAN STEARINE - Candles - Lumi-Lite Candle Co. Inc.
CLASSIC VINES - Candy - American Licorice Co.
CLASSIC WALLS - Wallcoverings - Designtex Fabrics Inc.
CLASSIC WALLS 2 - Wallpaper ☆ - H & S Sales Inc.
CLASSIC WALLS 3 - Wallpaper - H & S Sales Inc.
CLASSIC WALLS 4 - Wallpaper - H & S Sales Inc.
CLASSIC WALLS 4 - Wallpaper - Wall Fashion Inc.
CLASSIC WALLS 5 - Wallpaper - H & S Sales Inc.
CLASSIC WALLS 5 - Wallpaper - Wall Fashion Inc.
CLASSIC WALLS 6 - Wallpaper - H & S Sales Inc.
CLASSIC WALLS I - Wallpaper ☆ - Capital Carousel Inc.
CLASSIC WALLS II - Wallcoverings - Designtex Fabrics Inc.
CLASSIC WALLS II - Wallpaper ☆ - Capital Carousel Inc.
CLASSIC WALNUT - Cutlery - Gerber Legendary Blades
CLASSIC WEAR BY GCA - Uniforms–tailored - Garment Corp. of America
CLASSIC WEAVERS - Floor coverings–carpet and rugs - Options Tai Ping Carpets Inc.
CLASSIC WHITE - Dinnerware–glass - Nikko Ceramics Inc.
CLASSIC WOMAN - Apparel–women's - Palm Beach Co., Inc.
CLASSIC WOOLRICH - Apparel and accessories - John Rich & Sons Investment Holding Co.
CLASSIC WRITERS - Pens - Tops Pen Co.
CLASSIC XI - Air conditioning equipment - Rheem Manufacturing Co.
CLASSIC XIII - Air conditioning equipment - Rheem Manufacturing Co.
CLASSIC YELLOW - Spices and extracts - Reckitt & Colman, Inc.
CLASSICA - Floor coverings - Tarkett, Inc.
CLASSICA - Furniture - Hickory Manufacturing Co.
CLASSICA - Health care products - Melard Manufacturing Corp.
CLASSICA - Wallpaper - K.M.L. Industries
CLASSICAL - Floor coverings–carpet and rugs - Burtco Enterprises Inc.
CLASSICAL - Musical instrument accessories - Gibson Strings & Accessories
CLASSICAL - Wallpaper - Koroseal Wallcoverings
CLASSICAL 24 - Broadcasting stations–radio - Public Radio International, Inc.
CLASSICAL ARTS - Boxes - Wilton Co.
CLASSICAL CATS - Recording label - Zanicorn Entertainment, Ltd.
CLASSICAL CLIPS - Computer software - Mil Kered Inc.
CLASSICAL COOKIE COLLECTION - Cookies - Parco Foods, Inc.
CLASSICAL ELEGANCE - Wallpaper - Studio Designs
CLASSICAL GRACE - Floor coverings–carpet and rugs ☆ - Cabin Crafts Carpets
CLASSICAL ILLUSTRATIONS - Wallpaper - Seabrook Wallcoverings, Inc.
CLASSICAL JAZZ - Floor coverings–carpet and rugs - Alexander Smith Carpets
CLASSICAL KEEPSAKES - Dolls - Spiegel, Inc.
CLASSICAL NOTES - Computer software - Hopkins Technology LLC
CLASSICAL STRINGS - Wallcoverings - Cork Products Co. Inc.
CLASSICAL STYLE, A - Wallpaper ☆ - Sanitas Wallcoverings
CLASSICAL TEXTILE - Wallpaper - Blumenthal
CLASSICAL TEXTURES - Wallpaper - I. Gottlieb & Associates
CLASSICARVINGS - Wood products - M.I.M. Architecturals
CLASSICASTINGS - Wood products - M.I.M. Architecturals
CLASSICLEAN - Cleaning preparations–household - Farberware Inc.
CLASSICLINE - Seats–automobile - Charvoz
CLASSICO - Candles - Candle-Lite Co.
CLASSICO - Chocolate candy ☆ - Liberty Richter Inc.
CLASSICO - Furniture ☆ - Bassett Furniture Industries, Inc.
CLASSICO - Glass–plate - Sasaki
CLASSICO - Juice extracting devices - Angel Life Corp.
CLASSICO - Paper - Fabriano America Inc.

☆ = Now out of production

CLASSICO - Pasta - BDH Two, Inc.
CLASSICO - Pasta - Borden, Inc.
CLASSICO - Sauces - Borden/Prince Foods (Canning Div.)
CLASSICO BOLD - Desk sets ☆ - Park Sherman
CLASSICO LINE KITS - Paints - Leather Factory Inc.
CLASSICO TRIM - Desk sets ☆ - Park Sherman
CLASSICON - Floor coverings - Mannington Resilient Floors
CLASSICPDA - Measuring instruments ☆ - Dantec Measurement Technology Inc.
CLASSICREPE - Paper–crepe ☆ - Cindus Corp.
CLASSICS - Area rugs - Couristan Inc.
CLASSICS - Bathing suits - Bendigo International Inc.
CLASSICS - Bird feeds - Duncraft, Inc.
CLASSICS - Boats ☆ - Wellcraft Marine Corp.
CLASSICS - Boots - KangaROOS USA Inc.
CLASSICS - Catalogs - Sears, Roebuck and Co.
CLASSICS - Cigar boxes–wood - Consolidated Cigar Corp.
CLASSICS - Cigarettes - Nat Sherman, Inc.
CLASSICS - Fasteners–hook and eye - Boye Needle
CLASSICS - Food products - General Mills, Inc.
CLASSICS - Footwear - Sebago Inc.
CLASSICS - Furniture ☆ - Bernhardt Industries
CLASSICS - Garden furniture–rattan - Lloyd/Flanders Industries
CLASSICS - Golfing equipment - Slotline Golf
CLASSICS - Greeting cards - Specialty Sales Inc.
CLASSICS - Hardware - Baldwin Hardware Corp.
CLASSICS - Health care products - Sunrise Medical
CLASSICS - Hosiery - Sara Lee Corp.
CLASSICS - Knives–pocket - Queen Cutlery Co.
CLASSICS - Pet products - Penn-Plax, Inc.
CLASSICS - Ribbons - Berwick Industries, Inc.
CLASSICS - Scales - Counselor Co.
CLASSICS - Shoes - Cadillac Shoe Products Inc.
CLASSICS - Shoes–athletic - Titleist & Foot-Joy Worldwide
CLASSICS - Tableware–china - Lenox, Inc.
CLASSICS - Tiles–ceramic - Dal-Tile Corp.
CLASSICS - Toys ☆ - Intex Recreation Corp.
CLASSICS - Toys–models - ERTL Co., Inc.
CLASSICS - Wallcoverings - Laura Ashley
CLASSICS - Wallpaper - Queens Decorative Wallcoverings Inc.
CLASSICS - Wallpaper ☆ - Capital Carousel Inc.
CLASSICS - Wallpaper ☆ - Imperial Wallcoverings, Inc.
CLASSICS 2-GO! - Toys - Mattel, Inc.
CLASSICS ACCENTS - Candles - Lumi-Lite Candle Co. Inc.
CLASSICS: BEYOND THE LOOK OF SILK - Wallpaper - Bolta Wallcoverings
CLASSICS BY CAROLINA COLOURS - Apparel and accessories - Cato Corp.
CLASSICS BY ESSKAY - Apparel and accessories - Esskay Manufacturing Co.
CLASSICS BY HAGGAR - Apparel–women's ☆ - Haggar Corp.
CLASSICS CLUB - Publisher's imprints - Walter J. Black Inc.
CLASSICS-DRY - Shoes–athletic - Foot-Joy, Inc.
CLASSICS HMC - Hosiery - Handcraft Manufacturing Corp.
CLASSICS I - Furniture–wood - Empire Furniture Co.
CLASSICS II BY CAROLINA COLOURS - Apparel and accessories - Cato Corp.
CLASSICS ILLUSTRATED - Publisher's imprints - Frawley Corp.
CLASSICS-LITES - Shoes–athletic - Titleist & Foot-Joy Worldwide
CLASSICS MADE CLEAR - Recording label - MCA Universal Studios
CLASSICS O G - Apparel and accessories - Officer Gentleman, Inc.
CLASSICS OF THE COURTROOM - Educational materials - Professional Education Group, Inc.
CLASSICS, THE - Dinnerware–glass - Franciscan by Johnson Brothers, USA, Inc.
CLASSICS, THE - Furniture–upholstered - HTB Contemporary Designs
CLASSICS TO KEEP - Recording label - Stanyan Record Co.
CLASSICTONE - Giftware - Atlas Enterprises
CLASSICU - Dinnerware–glass - Cyclamen Studio
CLASSICURL - Hair curlers - Magic Distributing Ltd.
CLASSICVIEWS - Recording label - Newvisions, Inc.
CLASSICWARE - Plates–plastic - WNA Comet
CLASSIE LASSIE - Fruits and vegetables - Van Buren County Fruit Exchange
CLASSIFIED LOVE - Giftware - Alaska Momma
CLASSIFIED WIZARD - Computer software - Oz Software Inc.
CLASSIFIER - Air purification systems - Air Conveying Corp.
CLASSIFILER, THE - Office supplies - Mead Corp.
CLASSIFLEX - Wood products - M.I.M. Architecturals

CLASSIFOLDER - Office supplies - Universal Paper Goods Co.
CLASSIKA - Cheese - Cucina Classica Italiana, Inc.
CLASSILACE - Wood products - M.I.M. Architecturals
CLASSIQUE - Apparel and accessories - Strouse, Adler Co.
CLASSIQUE - Bicycles - Ross Bicycles USA, Ltd.
CLASSIQUE - Doors–wood - Masonite Corp.
CLASSIQUE - Flatware - Dansk International Designs, Ltd.
CLASSIQUE - Floor coverings–carpet and rugs ☆ - Karastan-Bigelow Inc.
CLASSIQUE - Floor coverings–tile - Kentile Floors Inc.
CLASSIQUE - Food products - Greentree Packing Inc.
CLASSIQUE - Furniture - CTH/Sherrill Occasional
CLASSIQUE - Glassware–household - Durand International
CLASSIQUE - Greeting cards - Gibson Greetings, Inc.
CLASSIQUE - Hair care products - Conair Corp.
CLASSIQUE - Health care products - Cheney Co. Inc.
CLASSIQUE - Leather goods - St. Thomas Inc.
CLASSIQUE - Padding–foam - Image Carpets Inc.
CLASSIQUE - Paints ☆ - Hampton Paint Manufacturing Co.
CLASSIQUE - Recording label ☆ - Mystic Records
CLASSIQUE - Strollers–baby ☆ - Cosco, Inc.
CLASSIQUE - Telephone accessories - Rest-a-Phone Corp.
CLASSIQUE - Toilet seats - Ginsey Industries, Inc.
CLASSIQUE - Toys–stuffed - Dakin Inc.
CLASSIQUE - Wallets - Enger-Kress Co.
CLASSIQUE - Wallpaper - Doshi Wallcoveringss Inc.
CLASSIQUE - Wallpaper - Glidden Co.
CLASSIQUE - Window coverings - Del Mar Window Coverings
CLASSIQUE ACCENTS - Floor coverings–carpet and rugs ☆ - Karastan-Bigelow Inc.
CLASSIQUE COLLECTION - Floor coverings–carpet and rugs - Mannington Carpets, Inc.
CLASSIQUE COLLECTION - Furniture - Basic Furniture Styles
CLASSIQUE COLLECTION - Jewelry–costume - H.K. Schaeffer & Co.
CLASSIQUE FASHION - Toilet seats - Ginsey Industries, Inc.
CLASSIQUE GOLD - Giftware ☆ - Gorham Inc.
CLASSIQUE NOIR - Luggage - French Co.
CLASSIQUE WORKS - Skirts–women's - J.C. Penney Co., Inc.
CLASSIQUES - Greeting cards - Fravessi Greetings, Inc.
CLASSIQUES ENTIER - Leather goods - Nordstrom, Inc.
CLASSIX - Pottery - Austram, Inc.
CLASSKNIT - Fabrics - E.R. Moore Co.
CLASSMAKER - Furniture - Virco Manufacturing Corp.
CLASSMAN - Wood desks ☆ - Inwood Office Furniture
CLASSMASTER - Stationery - Star Industries Inc.
CLASSMATE - Adding machines ☆ - Monroe Systems for Business Inc.
CLASSMATE - Audio equipment - Telex Communications, Inc.
CLASSMATE - Clocks - General Time Corp. (Westclox/Seth Thomas Div.)
CLASSMATE - Computer software ☆ - Knowledge Adventure
CLASSMATE - Drums–musical instruments ☆ - Grossman Music Corp.
CLASSMATE - Electronic equipment - Da-Lite Screen Co. Inc.
CLASSMATE - Headsets–telephone - Hamilton Electronics Corp.
CLASSMATES - Computer software - Franklin Electronic Publishers, Inc.
CLASSMATES - Toys–stuffed ☆ - Fun World Inc.
CLASSNET - Computer hardware - Yudan, Ltd.
CLASSNOTES - Computer software - Oxymoron Corp.
CLASSROOM - Electronic equipment - AVAS Corp.
CLASSROOM BEAUTIFUL - Publisher's imprints - Education Center, Inc.
CLASSROOM BROADCASTER - Electronic equipment - P/H Electronics
CLASSROOM CHALLENGER - Electronic equipment - Nasco International, Inc.
CLASSROOM CUBBY - Office supplies - Bemiss-Jason Corp.
CLASSROOM IN A BOOK - Educational materials - Adobe Systems Inc.
CLASSROOM MANAGER - Computer software - Baldwin Piano & Organ Co.
CLASSROOM ON THE GO - Toys - Mattel, Inc.
CLASSSPEED - Computer software - Digital Technology International
CLASSTIME - Clocks - General Time Corp. (Westclox/Seth Thomas Div.)
CLASSTRAK - Computer software - Trisec Associates, Inc.
CLASSY - Apparel–women's - Wacoal America Inc.
CLASSY - Bags–trash - Effa Manufacturing, Inc.
CLASSY - Caps–baseball - California Headwear, Inc.
CLASSY - Flowers, plants, and seeds - E.G. Hill Co. Inc.
CLASSY - Fruits and vegetables - Mills Distributing Co.
CLASSY - Hair care products - William Marvy Co., Inc.
CLASSY & SASSY - Bicycles - Roadmaster Corp.
CLASSY BANDANAS - Pet products - P.M. Pet Products
CLASSY BRACKETS - Hardware - G.H. Meiser & Co.

CLASSY CAT - Pet collars - Little Giant Products
CLASSY CHASSIS - Calendars - Landmark General Corp.
CLASSY CHASSIS - Computers–personal - Gimix Inc.
CLASSY CHICKEN NOODLE - Soups–canned - Buckeye Beans & Herbs, Inc.
CLASSY COW - Plates–paper - Dairy Mart Convenience Stores, Inc.
CLASSY CREATIONS - Pet products - P.M. Pet Products
CLASSY CREW - Bicycles ☆ - Huffy Corp.
CLASSY CRISPS - Snack foods - Beatrice Cheese Co.
CLASSY CURL - Hair care products - Johnson Products Co., Inc.
CLASSY CUTS - Mat boards - Callen Photo Mount Corp.
CLASSY GLASSYS - Glassware–household ☆ - Oak Hill Industries Corp.
CLASSY GLASSYS - Greeting cards ☆ - Hambly Studios
CLASSY K - Fruits and vegetables - Mills Distributing Co.
CLASSY LADY - Key rings - Russ Berrie and Co., Inc.
CLASSY LADY - Nail care products ☆ - Gena Laboratories Inc.
CLASSY PACK - Toys - Tonka Corp.
CLASSY POTS - Flower pots–earthenware ☆ - Oak Hill Industries Corp.
CLASSYGRASS - Floor coverings–carpet and rugs - Playfield International Inc.
CLATTER TAD - Sporting goods - James Heddon's Sons
CLAUDE - Apparel and accessories - Smith & Weber Co.
CLAUDE BERNARD - Watches - Viva Time Corp.
CLAUDE CARBONEL - Figurines - Estus Export-Import
CLAUDE GORDON - Trumpets ☆ - Selmer Co. Inc.
CLAUDE LAKEY - Musical instruments - Claude Lakey Mouthpieces
CLAUDE LUCIEN - Apparel–women's ☆ - Young Stuff Apparel Group
CLAUDE MERCIER - Wines - Jack Poust & Co. Inc.
CLAUDE MONET MUSEUM GIVERNY - Wallcoverings - Versailles Foundation, Inc.
CLAUDE MONTANA - Apparel and accessories - Jerry Kohn Inc.
CLAUDE MONTANA - Apparel–men's - Superba, Inc.
CLAUDE RENE - Apparel and accessories - Ben Elias Industries Corp.
CLAUDEL - Cheese - Besnier USA, Inc.
CLAUDEL - Flutes ☆ - Deg Music Products Inc.
CLAUDIA CUDDLETAIL - Candy - Frankford Candy & Chocolate Co. Inc.
CLAUDIA SLOAN - Apparel and accessories - Sloan Apparel, Inc.
CLAUDIO DELORENA - Footwear - De La Rentis Imports Inc.
CLAUDIO LA VIOLA - Eyeglasses ☆ - Private Eyes Sunglass Corp.
CLAUDIO MAURICIO - Footwear - CMA Marketing Corp.
CLAURITO - Handbags - Claurito, Inc.
CLAUS VINEYARDS - Wines ☆ - Mill Creek Vineyards
CLAUSS - Cutlery - Clauss Cutlery Co.
CLAUSS AMERICANA USA - Scissors–hand-operated ☆ - Clauss Cutlery Co.
CLAUSSEN - Pickles - Claussen Pickle Co. Inc.
CLAUSSEN - Pickles - Oscar Mayer Foods Corp.
CLAUSTHALER - Beverages–alcohol - Labatt Importers Inc.
CLAUSTROPHOBIA - Toys - Skyline Toys Inc.
CLAVE - Medical apparatus - ICU Medical Inc.
CLAVE SAFE - Lubricants - DCI International, Inc.
CLAVINET - Musical instruments - Hohner Inc.
CLAVO - Toilets–enameled - Mansfield Plumbing Products, Inc.
CLAVUS - Lubricants - Shell Oil Co.
CLAW - Clamps ☆ - Brewster Corp.
CLAW - Musical instrument accessories - LP Music Group
C.L.A.W. - Toys - Tonka Corp.
CLAW D'OEUVRES - Seafood products–fresh or frozen ☆ - Nichirei Foods America
CLAW ISLAND - Seafood products–fresh or frozen - Claw Island Foods Inc.
CLAW, THE - Golfing equipment - Irvine L. Dubow
CLAW, THE - Stainless steel - Ecolab Inc.
CLAW, THE - Toys - Rory Healy
CLAW, THE - Novelty items - Merle A. Mikell
CLAW, THE - Drill bits - Vermont American Corp.
CLAWBER - Toys - Mattel, Inc.
CLAWDEEN - Toys - Mattel, Inc.
CLAWFUL - Toys - Mattel, Inc.
CLAWGUT - Toys - Tomy America, Inc.
CLAWLOCK - Finishing agents - Pratt & Lambert, Inc.
CLAWS - Nail care products - Nature's Bounty, Inc.
CLAWS - Tools - Penn-Plax, Inc.
CLAWSBY - Toys–stuffed ☆ - Gund, Inc.
CLAWSON - Food products - Clawson Co.
CLAWSON ROCKER - Orthopedic products - Curtis Clawson
CLAXTON - Apparel–women's - Sanmark-Stardust Inc.
CLAY - Brushes–paint - Corona Brushes Inc.
CLAY CARVE - Tiles–ceramic ☆ - DecoArt, Inc.

CLAY CUTTER - Compost - Betty's Azalea Ranch, Inc.
CLAY FERRY - Luggage - Universal Trav-ler Inc.
CLAY FIGHTER - Computer programs - Interplay Productions
CLAY-GLO - Artists' materials - Binney & Smith Inc.
CLAY KIDS - Toys ☆ - Henry Gordy International Inc.
CLAY MACHE - Novelty items ☆ - Western Pulp Products Co.
CLAY-MAGIC - Cleaning equipment - Auto Wax Co., Inc.
CLAY PIGEON - Recording label - Clay Pigeon Records
CLAY POT COOKBOOKS - Cooking utensils–earthenware - Reco International Corp.
CLAY POT, THE - Agricultural products - Gourmet Bouquet, Inc.
CLAY REX - Adhesives and sealants ☆ - PPG Industries, Inc.
CLAY THERAPY - Hair care products - Cabot Laboratories Inc.
CLAYBAKE - Cooking equipment–household ☆ - Liberty Ridge
CLAYBOURNE - Cigars - General Cigar Co., Inc.
CLAYBOURNE - Food products - Clayco Foods Inc.
CLAYCASTLE - Recording label ☆ - Torrid Records
CLAYCRETE - Papier-mache articles - American Art Clay Co. Inc.
CLAYLITE - Roofing materials ☆ - Monierlifetile
CLAYMAN - Hair care products - Clayman Co.
CLAYMANIA - Games - Peachtree Products, Inc.
CLAYMASTER - Artists' materials ☆ - Dick Blick Co.
CLAYMATES - Computer software - Interplay Productions
CLAYMATION - Clay–modeling - Will Vinton Studios, Inc.
CLAYMATOR - Clay–modeling - Van Aken International
CLAYMAX - Roofing materials - United States Tile Co.
CLAYMONT - Floor coverings ☆ - Congoleum Corp.
CLAYMORE - Beverages–alcohol - Jim Beam Brands Co.
CLAYMORE - Books–comic - Aegis Entertainment, Inc.
CLAYOLA - Artists' materials - Binney & Smith Inc.
CLAYPAC CLAYONS - Hair care products - Altobella Hair Products Inc.
CLAYPACO - Paperboard - Rupaco Paper Corp.
CLAYPOOL CLASSICS - Health care products - Claypool Classics
CLAYSEAL - Chemical preparations - Baroid Technology, Inc.
CLAYSTONE - Artists' materials - Sculpture House Inc.
CLAYTHINGS - Tiles–ceramic - Los Angeles Tile Co., Inc.
CLAYTON - Guitars - Steve Clayton Inc.
CLAYTON - Mobile homes - Clayton Homes, Inc.
CLAYTON - Stoves–gas - Clayton Manufacturing Inc.
CLAYTON & LAMBERT - Swimming pools - Clayton & Lambert Manufacturing Co.
CLAYTON HOMES - Mobile homes - Clayton Homes, Inc.
CLAYTON SQUARE - Floor coverings - Congoleum Corp.
CLAYTONS - Wallpaper - Koroseal Wallcoverings
CLAYTOWN COLLECTION - Statuary - Claytown Collection, Inc.
CLAYWOOD - Display cases–wood ☆ - Anco Wood Specialties Inc.
CLAYWOOD - Giftware - Doranne
CLAYZEE PEOPLE - Toys ☆ - Henry Gordy International Inc.
CLC - Belts–industrial - Custom Leathercraft Manufacturing
CLC - Chemical preparations - Midwest Industrial Supply, Inc.
CLC - Tennis footwear ☆ - Autry Industries Inc.
CLE-BIDE - Tools - Cleveland Twist Drill Co.
CLE. DES DUCS - Beverages–alcohol - Remy Martin Amerique Inc.
CLE-FORGE - Tools - Cleveland Twist Drill Co.
CLE SOURCE, THE - Educational materials - Professional Education Group, Inc.
CLEAN - Insulating materials - Central Fiber Corp.
CLEAN-2 - Air purification systems - Airflow Systems, Inc.
CLEAN-A-FINISH - Cleaning preparations–carpet and rug ☆ - Howard Products
CLEAN-A-PIPE - Pipe cleaners - Buescher's Industries Inc.
CLEAN-A-PLATEN - Cleaning preparations - Lee Products Co.
CLEAN-A-PRINTER - Cleaning preparations ☆ - Lee Products Co.
CLEAN-A-SCREEN - Cleaning preparations ☆ - Lee Products Co.
CLEAN-A-WAY - Cleaning preparations - Robarb Inc.
CLEAN-ACT - Cylinders - Compact Air Products, Inc.
CLEAN ACTION - Cleaning preparations–carpet and rug - Hillyard Enterprises, Inc.
CLEAN ADVANTAGE - Cleaning preparations - ChemPlus
CLEAN-AID - Hearing aids - Hocks Laboratories
CLEAN AIR - Bedding–linen - Gotham Industries II
CLEAN AIR - Candles - Carolina Designs Ltd.
CLEAN AIR - Duplicating machines - Heyer Inc.
CLEAN AIR - Linen - J. Lamb, Inc.
CLEAN AIR-A GLOBAL AFFAIR - Apparel and accessories - American Lung Association of California

☆ = Now out of production

CLEAN AIR PAINTS - Paints - Standard Paints Inc.
CLEAN ALL - Washers–metal - Goodall Manufacturing Co.
CLEAN & CART - Containers–trash - Igloo Products Corp.
CLEAN & CLEAR - Hair care products - Revlon Consumer Products Corp.
CLEAN & CLEAR - Skin care products - Johnson & Johnson
CLEAN & CLEAR AND UNDER CONTROL - Skin care products - Johnson & Johnson
CLEAN & CONDITION - China and glassware cleaner - Corning Inc.
CLEAN & CURL - Shampoos - Fleetwood Co.
CLEAN & EASY - Beauty aids - Inverness Corp.
CLEAN & ETCH - Epoxy coatings - Steelcote Manufacturing Corp.
CLEAN & FEED - Fertilizers - Botanical Science
CLEAN AND FRESH - Cleaning preparations - Brondow Inc.
CLEAN AND FRESH - Mattress pads - Perfect Fit Industries, Inc.
CLEAN AND FRESH - Skin care products - Freeman Cosmetics Corp.
CLEAN & GENTLE - Shampoos - Almay Inc.
CLEAN AND GLEAM - Shoe accessories - Kiwi Brands, Inc.
CLEAN & LIGHT - Shampoos - Clairol Inc.
CLEAN & LIGHT SHAMPOO PLUS - Hair care products - Clairol Inc.
CLEAN & RINSE - Cleaning preparations - Super-Tek Products Inc.
CLEAN & SEXY - Skin care products - Waverly Beauty Products
CLEAN & SHEEN - Wigs ☆ - Cassidy Inc.
CLEAN & SHIELD - Skin care products - Gentell, Inc.
CLEAN & SHINE - Cleaning preparations - Super-Tek Products Inc.
CLEAN & SMOOTH - Soap - Benckiser Consumer Products Inc.
CLEAN BOWL - Cleaning preparations ☆ - Senoret Chemical Co.
CLEAN BOWL CONTROL - Cleaning preparations–household - Clean Control Corp.
CLEAN BREATH - Mouthwashes - Ranir Corp.
CLEAN BREEZE - Skin care products - Gillette Co.
CLEAN CALL - Telephone accessories - Elizabeth Wilkes
CLEAN CANTEEN - Pet products - Penn-Plax, Inc.
CLEAN CAT - Motor vehicle parts and accessories - Robert Marino
CLEAN CATH - Health care products - C.R. Bard, Inc.
CLEAN CHANGE - Automotive parts and accessories - Perf-form Products Inc.
CLEAN CHOICE - Gasoline - Thermogas Co.
CLEAN CLOTHES - Knit, woven apparel - Frederick Atkins, Inc.
CLEAN COAT - Cleaning preparations - Ziebart International Corp.
CLEAN COLOR - Cosmetics ☆ - Bonne Bell, Inc.
CLEAN COLORS - Paints - Rich Art Color Co., Inc.
CLEAN COMFORT - Cosmetics - Origins Natural Resources Inc.
CLEAN CONTROL - Cleaning preparations - Clean Control Corp.
CLEAN CRETE - Concrete products - Pioneer Manufacturing Co.
CLEAN CUFF - Gloves–rubber - Wilshire Technologies, Inc.
CLEAN CURLS HOODED BIBS - Apparel–children's - Access Wear Plus, Inc.
CLEAN CUT - Cleaning preparations - Pioneer Manufacturing Co.
CLEAN CUT - Glassware–household ☆ - East Hampton Industries Inc.
CLEAN-CUT - Machine parts - Robert Laflamme
CLEAN CUT - Nail care products - Tweezerman Corp.
CLEAN CUT - Toys - Hasbro, Inc.
CLEAN CUT FOIL REMOVER - Housewares - Franmara Co. Inc.
CLEAN CUT PLUS - Cutting boards - Pacific International Group Inc.
CLEAN CUTS - Recording label - Clean Cuts Inc.
CLEAN DRI - Sweeping compounds - Excel-Mineral Co. Inc.
CLEAN DRIVE KIT - Cleaning preparations - Curtis Manufacturing Co., Inc.
CLEAN EARS - Pet products - Novalek, Inc.
CLEAN-EASE - Cushions - Samsonite Furniture Co. (Consumer Products Div.)
CLEAN-EASY - Erasers ☆ - Faber-Castell Corp.
CLEAN EDGE TECHNOLOGY - Labels–paper - Pinnacle Label, Inc.
CLEAN ENCOUNTERS - Cleaning preparations - Stone Care International Inc.
CLEAN ETCH - Cleaning preparations - Sealwall Products Inc.
CLEAN-EZE - Skin care products - Concept Communications Co.
CLEAN FAX - Cleaning preparations - Curtis Manufacturing Co., Inc.
CLEAN FINISH - Skin-care products - Estee Lauder Inc.
CLEAN FIRE AMMUNITION - Ammunition - Blount International, Inc. (Sporting Equipment Group)
CLEAN-FIT - Brushes - Mill Rose Co.
CLEAN FLAME - Wood fuel pellets - Arends and Sons Inc.
CLEAN-FLO - Marine rigging - Walter Machine Co. Inc.
CLEAN GETAWAY - Toiletries - Stephan Co.
CLEAN GREENS - Cleaning preparations ☆ - Seventh Generation Wholesale Inc.
CLEAN HEALTH - Health care products - Earthnet
CLEAN-IT - Cleaning preparations ☆ - Clayton Corp.
CLEAN-IT - Water treating compounds ☆ - Aquatronics-Filtronics
CLEAN-IT-ALL - Cleaning comparations - Solvit Inc.

CLEAN JOB - Cleaning preparations–household - Publicker Industries Inc.
CLEAN KING - Cleaning preparations - Comstar International Inc. (IPC Div.)
CLEAN KING - Gloves–work - Magid Manufacturing Co. Inc.
CLEAN LASH - Cosmetics - Noxell Corp.
CLEAN LIFE - Shampoos - Noxell Corp.
CLEAN LIKE A WASHCLOTH - Washboards - Kimberly-Clark Corp.
CLEAN LIVIN' - Fish food - Aquaculture Technologies Inc.
CLEAN LUBE - Lubricants - Raleigh USA Bicycle Co.
CLEAN MACHINE - Automotive parts and accessories - Turtle Wax, Inc.
CLEAN MACHINE, THE - Faucets ☆ - Moen Inc.
CLEAN MATES - Audio equipment ☆ - Recoton Corp.
CLEAN MOUSE - Cleaning preparations - Curtis Manufacturing Co., Inc.
CLEAN MOVE - Housewares - Dial Industries Inc.
CLEAN N BRITE - Eyeglasses - Clear-Sight Inc.
CLEAN 'N' CARRY - Polishing cloths - DBA Products Co.
CLEAN 'N CLEAR - Cleaning preparations–carpet and rug - S.C. Johnson & Son, Inc.
CLEAN-N-COMFY - Pet products - Green Pet Products, Inc.
CLEAN-N-DRY - Floor coverings - Durable Corp.
CLEAN N FRESH - Cosmetics - Power
CLEAN 'N GENTLE - Cleaning preparations - Alberto-Culver Co.
CLEAN-N-GLEAM - Cleaning preparations - Uncle Sam Chemical Co., Inc.
CLEAN 'N' LUBE - Pet products - Best n' Show Pet Products Inc.
CLEAN N' NATURAL - Detergents - Garcoa, Inc.
CLEAN 'N SIT - Toiletries - Practical Answers, Inc.
CLEAN-N-SOAK - Ophthalmic goods - Allergan, Inc.
CLEAN-N-STOW - Ophthalmic goods ☆ - Allergan, Inc.
CLEAN 'N STRIP - Building materials - Minnesota Mining & Manufacturing Co.
CLEAN 'N' STRIP - Cleaning preparations - Bruce Hardwood Floors
CLEAN NAIL - Nail care products - E.O.H. Industries, Inc.
CLEAN NAIL - Nail care products ☆ - Orly International Inc.
CLEAN NATE - Skin care products - Revlon Consumer Products Corp.
CLEAN-O-CATOR - Filters–water ☆ - Doughboy Recreational Inc.
CLEAN-O-LITE II - Cleaning preparations - Hillyard Enterprises, Inc.
CLEAN-O-SHINE - Floor treatment - Continental Chemical Corp.
CLEAN ONE, THE - Furnaces–electric - Central Boiler, Inc.
CLEAN OPENER - Housewares - Waring Products Div.
CLEAN PACK - Charcoal - Bradford Marketing Group, Inc.
CLEAN PAK - Cleaning preparations - Fire-Tech, Ltd.
CLEAN-PAK - Labor organizations - Lawson Mardon Wheaton Inc.
CLEAN PINE - Cleaning preparations - Brondow Inc.
CLEAN PINE - Cleaning preparations - White Cap Inc.
CLEAN PRIDE - Cleaning preparations - USFTM, Inc.
CLEAN QUICK - Cleaning preparations - Procter & Gamble Co.
CLEAN-R-CARB - Cleaning preparations - CRC Chemicals USA/Siloo
CLEAN RAY - Cosmetics - Morris-Flamingo Inc.
CLEAN RELEASE - Cleaning preparations–carpet and rug - Hillyard Enterprises, Inc.
CLEAN RELEASE - Tape–adhesive - Manco, Inc.
CLEAN RESULTS - Brooms - Ekco Housewares, Inc.
CLEAN RITE - Cleaning accessories - Clean-Rite Products Co.
CLEAN-RITE - Inks ☆ - Formulabs, Inc.
CLEAN ROOM - Floor coverings - American Floor Products Co. Inc.
CLEAN RUNNER - Cleaning preparations ☆ - Recoton Corp.
CLEAN-SAFE - Floor cleaner - American Home Products Corp.
CLEAN + SANITIZED - Cleaning preparations - Samlo
CLEAN SCALP - Hair care products - La Coupe
CLEAN SCENE - Paper - Stuart Hall Co., Inc.
CLEAN-SCREEN - Building materials - Brod & McClung - Pace Co.
CLEAN SCREEN KIT - Cleaning preparations - Curtis Manufacturing Co., Inc.
CLEAN SCRUB - Cleaning preparations - Hillyard Enterprises, Inc.
CLEAN-SEAL - Plumbing fixtures–metal - Cherne Industries Inc.
CLEAN SEAS - Electronic equipment - Clean Seas Co.
CLEAN SEAT - Paper–toilet - Lenaco Corp.
CLEAN-SHEEN - Hair coloring preparations - Sparkle Sheen Co.
CLEAN SHEETS - Paper–writing - G. Gary Holt Enterprises, Inc.
CLEAN SHIELD - Cleaning preparations - Barcolene Inc.
CLEAN-SIGHT - Windows–storm - Wyssmont Co. Inc.
CLEAN SIGHTS - Ophthalmic goods - Blairex Laboratories, Inc.
CLEAN SIGHTS SPRAY - Cleaning preparations - Blairex Laboratories, Inc.
CLEAN SKIN TO GO - Skin care products - Clairol Inc.
CLEAN SLATE CLOTHING - Apparel–women's - Lilli Group, Inc.
CLEAN SLATES - Toys - Samuel Lowe Co.
CLEAN SLEEP - Pillows ☆ - American Fiber Industries Corp.
CLEAN-SLOT - Wire products - Buffalo Wire Works Co., Inc.

CLEAN SOL - Cleaning preparations–household - Imperial Manufacturing Co. Inc.

CLEAN START - Antiseptics - Ladyfingers

CLEAN START - Cleaning preparations ☆ - Armor All Products Corp.

CLEAN START - Skin care products - Jason Natural Products, Inc.

CLEAN START - Wax removers - Sterling Winthrop Inc.

CLEAN STEAM - Dri-Steem Humidifier Co.

CLEAN STEP - Automotive parts and accessories - S & S Clean Step, Inc.

CLEAN-STEP - Floor coverings–carpet and rugs - Daltonian Carpet & Cushion Inc.

CLEAN-STEP - Mats ☆ - Superior Manufacturing Group/Notrax Floor Matting

CLEAN STREAM - Toothbrushes - Carewell Industries, Inc.

CLEAN STREAMS - Water pruification units - Lanois-Walrus Air Co.

CLEAN STRIP - Concrete products - Dayton Superior Corp.

CLEAN SWEEP - Aquariums–household - Wardley Corp.

CLEAN SWEEP - Automotive parts and accessories - Cleartec Corp.

CLEAN SWEEP - Brooms - Wilen Companies, Inc.

CLEAN SWEEP - Carpet sweepers ☆ - Bissell Inc.

CLEAN SWEEP - Cleaning preparations - Stempel Manufacturing Co.

CLEAN SWEEP - Deodorizers - Selig Co. Inc.

CLEAN SWEEP - Game machines - Smart Industries Corp.

CLEAN SWEEP - Machinery - JBL Co.

CLEAN SWEEP - Mirrors - Armament Systems and Procedures, Inc.

CLEAN TEAM - Skin care products - Charles Revson Inc.

CLEAN TEAM, THE - Automotive parts and accessories - Penreco

CLEAN-TEX - Sponges - National Sponge Corp.

CLEAN TOUCH - Cosmetics - Roux Laboratories, Inc.

CLEAN TOUCH - Gloves–work - Magla Products Inc.

CLEAN TOUCH PLUS - Washcloths - Pacific International Group Inc.

CLEAN-UP - Cleaning preparations - Clorox Co.

CLEAN-UP - Cleaning preparations - Stewart-Hall Chemical Corp.

CLEAN UP! - Hardware - Excel-Mineral Co. Inc.

CLEAN UP! - Household cleaner ☆ - Aubrey Organics, Inc.

CLEAN UP AMERICA - Cleaning preparations - Mirachem Corp.

CLEAN UP TIME - Watches - Troma, Inc.

CLEAN-UPS - Cleaning preparations - Lee Products Co.

CLEAN WHEEL - Conveyors - Speedways Conveyors, Inc.

CLEAN/WISE - Degreasing solvents - John W. Bell

CLEAN WRAP - Foil–tin - Hyundai Food America

CLEAN XPRESS - Soap - Spartan Chemical Co., Inc.

CLEANAIRE - Air purification systems - Adams Manufacturing Co.

CLEANAMEL - Cleaning preparations - J.N.T. Manufacturing Co. Inc.

CLEANAROUND - Cleaning preparations - Max C's Ceramic & Craft

CLEANAWAY - Dusters - 1 Mark Consumer Products, Inc.

CLEANBURN - Fuel additives - Turner Industries Ltd.

CLEANCOTE - Wood products - Weyerhaeuser Co.

CLEANCUFF - Health care products - Vital Signs, Inc.

CLEANDUSTER - Cleaning preparations - Recoton Corp.

CLEANE - Shampoos - Sorbie Acquisition Co.

CLEANEARTH - Household products - OneEarth

CLEANEE - Scouring pads - Arden Corp.

CLEANER PAINTS FOR A CLEANER TOMORROW - Paints - OEM Paints, Inc.

CLEANESSENCE - Beauty aids - Costec 20 Inc.

CLEANGUARD - Fire extinguishers - Ansul, Inc.

CLEANING DETAIL - Cleaning preparations - Marikate Ship Shape, Inc.

CLEANING KITS - Rifle-cleaning compounds - Armsport Inc.

CLEANING SPECIALTY COMPANY - Mops - The Lassen Companies

CLEANKEY - Cleaning preparations - Recoton Corp.

CLEANLET - Medical apparatus - Gainor Medical U.S.A. Inc.

CLEANLINE - Garden equipment - Permaloc Aluminum Edging

CLEANLINE - Tables–metal ☆ - Cramer Inc.

CLEANLINE - Tape–masking - Polyken Technologies

CLEANLINE - Windows - Vega Industries, Inc.

CLEANMACHINE - Electronic equipment - Stripping Technologies, Inc.

CLEANMACHINE - Pumps - Adobeair, Inc.

CLEANMASTER - Aquariums–household - Ginger, Inc.

CLEANMASTER - Cleaning preparations - Kleer Flo Co. Inc.

CLEANMASTER - Floor finishing machines–commercial - Mercury Floor Machines Inc.

CLEANMIST - Hair care products - Dowbrands L.P.

CLEAN'N TREAT - Paper–toweling ☆ - Schering-Plough Healthcare Products

CLEANOL - Cleaning preparations - Garon Products Inc.

CLEANPOWER - Cleaning preparations - Sellco International, Ltd.

CLEANRAP - Paper - Smurfit Newsprint Corp. (Cladwood Div.)

CLEANROOMS - Pennwell Publishing Co.

CLEANSAFER - Cleaning preparations - Savogran Co.

CLEANSAHERB - Vitamins and nutritional supplements ☆ - J.R. Carlson Laboratories Inc.

CLEANSE-A-GEL - Cosmetics - Max Factor & Co.

CLEANSE-PHREE - Shampoos - KMS Research Inc.

CLEANSOIL - Medical apparatus - SRE, Inc.

CLEANSOURCE - Water purification systems - Clack Corp.

CLEANSTREAM - Vacuum cleaners and accessories - W.L. Gore & Associates, Inc.

CLEANSWEEP - Computer software - Quarterdeck Corp.

CLEANSWEET - See MEANER CLEANER

CLEANSYSTEM3 - Gasoline - Texaco, Inc.

CLEANSYSTEM3 - Gasoline - Texaco Lubricants Co.

CLEANTAC - Labels - Moore Business Forms, Inc.

CLEANTALKER - Labels–paper - Moore Business Forms, Inc.

CLEANTERP - Cleaning preparations - Texwipe Co. LLC

CLEANTEX - Cleaning preparations - Texwipe Co. LLC

CLEANTEXX - Containers–plastic ☆ - Latex Partners, Inc.

CLEANTOOLS - Brushes - Emgee CleanTools

CLEANTOP - Domestic cooking units - Whirlpool Properties, Inc.

CLEANTRAC - Electronic equipment - Illinois Tool Works Inc.

CLEANTRAX - Cleaning preparations - Equine Technologies, Inc.

CLEANWOODE - Cleaning preparations - Wilson Imperial Co.

CLEANWORKS - Bags - Scott Paper Co.

CLEANZ-EFX - Laxatives - Natural Efx, Inc.

CLEAR - Optical services - W.R. Grace & Co.

CLEAR - Pharmaceutical preparations - Care Technologies Inc.

CLEAR-10 - Skin care products - Western Family Foods, Inc.

CLEAR A BASEMENT - Chemical preparations - Enviro-Dynamics Inc.

CLEAR-A-SLIDE - Electronic equipment ☆ - Charles Beseler Co.

CLEAR-A-WAY - Drain cleaner - Comstar International Inc. (IPC Div.)

CLEAR ACT - Skin care products - Standard Homeopathic Co., Inc.

CLEAR-AD - Signs - Catalina Coating and Plastics, Inc.

CLEAR ADVANTAGE - Bakeware - Corning Inc.

CLEAR ADVANTAGE - Labels–paper - Avery Dennison Corp.

CLEAR ADVANTAGE - Paints - Vanex Inc.

CLEAR ADVANTAGE - Plastics–laminated - TCC Enterprises, Inc.

CLEAR ADVANTAGE - Windshield wiper - Libbey-Owens-Ford Co.

CLEAR & CLEAN - Clear wood finish - Wood Kote Products, Inc.

CLEAR & DRY - Pharmaceutical preparations - Whitehall Laboratories

CLEAR & NATURAL - Water–bottled or canned - Schooner's International, Inc.

CLEAR AND SOFT - Nipples–rubber - Gerber Products Co.

CLEAR & WHITE - Toothpaste and rinses - MDR Fitness Corp.

CLEAR ASSETS - Trading cards and stamps - Score Board Holding Corp.

CLEAR AWAY - Pharmaceutical preparations - Schering-Plough Healthcare Products

CLEAR-BANDS - Bandages - American White Cross Laboratories

CLEAR BENEFIT - Hair care products - Gillette Co.

CLEAR BLUE - Water treating compounds - Great Lakes Biochemical Co., Inc.

CLEAR BOND - Glue–household or industrial - H.B. Fuller Co. (North American Adhesives, Sealants and Coatings Group)

CLEAR-BREW - Coffee makers–electric ☆ - Sunbeam-Oster Household Products

CLEAR BY DESIGN - Pharmaceutical preparations - SmithKline Beecham Consumer Healthcare

CLEAR CARE - Cleaning preparations ☆ - Mothers Polishes Waxes Cleaners

CLEAR CATCH - Fishing tackle - David A. Brundage

CLEAR CHLOR - Chlorine - Locey Swim Pool Co.

CLEAR CHOICE - Beverages–carbonated - Strategic Brands, Inc.

CLEAR CHOICE - Cleaning preparations - Mission Kleensweep Products, Inc.

CLEAR CHOICE - Containers - Primex International Corp.

CLEAR CHOICE - Dinnerware–plastic - Nyman Manufacturing Co.

CLEAR CHOICE - Hair care products - Hawkins Pro-Cuts, Inc.

CLEAR CHOICE - Hearing aids - John J. Haupt III

CLEAR CHOICE - Lamp bulbs–incandescent - Kmart Properties, Inc.

CLEAR CHOICE - Oils–edible - Bunge Foods Corp.

CLEAR CHOICE - Skin care products - Plasto Tech Co. International

CLEAR CHOICE - Transparency films - American Transparency Resources

CLEAR CHOICE - Water treating compounds - SCP Holding Corp.

CLEAR CHOICE - Water–bottled or canned - Premium Beverage Packers Inc.

CLEAR CHOICE - Window coverings - Three Day Blinds, Inc.

CLEAR CHOICE, THE - Windows–plastic ☆ - Aluminum Co. of America

CLEAR CHROME - Trading cards and stamps - Signs & Glassworks, Inc.

CLEAR, CLEAN, SOAK - Contact-lens cleaner - Contex, Inc.

CLEAR CLEAN SYSTEMS - Filters–industrial - Clear Clean Systems Inc.

CLEAR CLEANER - Cleaning preparations - Hartco Inc.
CLEAR CLICS - Pens - Bic Corp.
CLEAR COAT - Automotive parts and accessories - Turtle Wax, Inc.
CLEAR/COLOREDGE - Frames–picture - Ammak Manufacturing Corp.
CLEAR COMFORT - Face masks - Gibeck-Dryden Corp.
CLEAR COMPLEXION - Skin care products - Helga Van Dyke Skin Care
CLEAR COMPLEXION - Soap - Andrew Jergens Co.
CLEAR CONTROL - Skin care products - Christine International, Inc.
CLEAR COPY - Plastics–laminated - Edwards Aviator
CLEAR COUGH - Cough medicines - Vetco, Inc.
CLEAR COUGH NIGHTTIME - Pharmaceutical preparations - Vetco, Inc.
CLEAR COUNT 30 - Health care products - Apothecary Products, Inc.
CLEAR COVER - Plastics film - Kittrich Corp.
CLEAR CREEK - Bicycle parts and accessories - Schwinn Cycling & Fitness Inc.
CLEAR CREEK - Garden furniture - Wikco Industries Inc.
CLEAR CREEK - Hosiery - Preger & Wertenteil, Inc.
CLEAR CRISP - Food products - Kerry Ingredients Inc.
CLEAR CT. - Balls–basketball - Huffy Corp.
CLEAR-CUTS - Fish–fresh or frozen - Clear Springs Trout Co.
CLEAR DAY - Fabrics - Dan River Inc.
CLEAR DAY - Wines - Pliska Winery
CLEAR DECK - Adhesives and sealants - Coronado Paint Co.
CLEAR DESK - Desk accessories ☆ - Newell Office Products
CLEAR DIFFERENCE - Hair care products - Gillette Co.
CLEAR DRAIN - Inks - Formulabs, Inc.
CLEAR DRY - Deodorizers - Procter & Gamble Co.
CLEAR-EASE - Chemical preparations - Mydor Industries Inc.
CLEAR EDGE LOUVER GROOVER - Window coverings ☆ - Hunter Douglas, Inc.
CLEAR EDGE, THE - Tools - Creative Concepts, Inc.
CLEAR ELASTOMERIC - Caulking compounds - Dap Products Inc.
CLEAR ELEGANCE - Bakeware ☆ - Corning Inc.
CLEAR ENERGY - Tape–adhesive - Manco, Inc.
CLEAR EYES - Pharmaceutical preparations - Ross Laboratories
CLEAR EYES - Veterinary pharmaceutical preparations - Farnam Cos. Inc.
CLEAR-FIELD - Paper–writing - Kurtz Bros. Inc.
CLEAR FIT - Hardware - Mill Rose Co.
CLEAR-FLO - Varnishes ☆ - Valspar Corp.
CLEAR FOR ACTION - Games ☆ - Avalon Hill Game Co.
CLEAR-FREE - Water purification systems - Penn-Plax, Inc.
CLEAR GEL - Deodorants–personal - Gillette Co.
CLEAR-GLO - Paints - California Products Corp.
CLEAR-GRAIN - Paints - Vanguard Paints & Finishes Inc.
CLEAR GRIP - Adhesives and sealants ☆ - Loctite Corp.
CLEAR GRIP - Containers - Carlysle Plastics
CLEAR GRIP - Footwear - Skechers USA, Inc.
CLEAR-GRIP - Medical apparatus - Innovative Medical Design Corp.
CLEAR GUARD - Automotive parts and accessories - Turtle Wax, Inc.
CLEAR GUARD - Plastic wrap - Hunt Holdings, Inc.
CLEAR-GUARD - Tape–adhesive - Gexco Enterprises
CLEAR-HANG - Wallpaper - Allpro Corp.
CLEAR HEAD - Shampoos - Origins Natural Resources Inc.
CLEAR HOLD - Photo albums - Light Impressions Corp.
CLEAR HOLDEX - Aquariums–household - Jungle Laboratories Corp.
CLEAR ICE - Colognes - Eurostar Corp.
CLEAR-ICH - Aquatic pharmacuetical preparations ☆ - Aquatronics-Filtronics
CLEAR-ICH TETRID - Pet products - Aquatronics-Filtronics
CLEAR IMAGE SERIES - Cleaning preparations ☆ - Mothers Polishes Waxes Cleaners
CLEAR IMPACT - Computer software - Impact Development Inc.
CLEAR-LAY - Plastics film - Grafix Plastics
CLEAR LIGHT - Audio-video products - Cornerstone/Clearlight
CLEAR LINE FILL - Skin care products - Alfin Inc. Adrien Arpel
CLEAR LITE - Paints - Payson Corp.
CLEAR LITES - Hair care products - Matrix Essentials, Inc.
CLEAR LOGIX - Skin care products - Advanced Research Laboratories
CLEAR-LUX - Lighting equipment ☆ - Penn-Plax, Inc.
CLEAR MAGIC - Chemical preparations - Hydrotech Chemical Corp.
CLEAR MAGIC - Paints ☆ - Valspar Corp.
CLEAR MIND - Vitamins and nutritional supplements - Planetary Formulas
CLEAR MOUNTAIN - Honey - E.F. Lane & Son
CLEAR MOUNTAIN NATURAL SPRING WATER THE QUALITY IS CLEAR - Water–bottled or canned - Raleigh Spring Water Co.
CLEAR 'N' CLEAN - Cleaning preparations ☆ - Spontex, Inc.
CLEAR N' NATURAL - Skin care products - Garcoa Labs/Vitamin Classics

CLEAR-N-TUF - Hardware ☆ - Boatlife Inc.
CLEAR NO. 61 - Cosmetics - Revlon Consumer Products Corp.
CLEAR-O-STAT - Fabrics - Master Woodcraft Inc.
CLEAR-OUT - Chemical preparations - Aqua Clear Industries Inc.
CLEAR OXILY - Skin care products - IT&LY Hairfashion NA Inc.
CLEAR PAK - Plastics film - Daubert Coated Products, Inc.
CLEAR-PAK - Plastics film - General Cable Corp.
CLEAR PATH - Electronic equipment - AAMP of Florida, Inc.
CLEAR PERCEPTION - Publisher's imprints - Marcia R. Kurtze
CLEAR PERFECTION - Cosmetics - Cabot Laboratories Inc.
CLEAR PERFORMANCE - Hair care products - All American Hart Inc.
CLEAR PLAN - Pharmaceutical preparations - Whitehall Laboratories
CLEAR PLASTIC DETAILER - Polishes - Meguiar's, Inc.
CLEAR-POND - Pet products - Aquatic Biotechnologies Inc.
CLEAR PRINT - Office supplies - Phillips Process Co. Inc.
CLEAR REFLECTIONS - Cleaning preparations–window - Dymon, Inc.
CLEAR REFLECTIONS - Cosmetics ☆ - Spilo/Mehaz Worldwide
CLEAR RESULT - Chemical preparations - Haviland Consumer Products, Inc.
CLEAR SAILING - Vegetables–canned - Allen Canning Co.
CLEAR-SCAN - Labels–paper - Trion Industries Inc.
CLEAR SCRIPT - Stationery ☆ - Mead Corp.
CLEAR SEAS - Seafood products–fresh or frozen - Consolidated Seafood Enterprises, Inc.
CLEAR-SELE - Finishing agents - Rust-Oleum Corp.
CLEAR SET - Finishing agents - Flintkote Co.
CLEAR SET - Paints ☆ - GS Roofing Products Co.
CLEAR SHIELD - Finishing agents ☆ - Zegers Inc.
CLEAR SHOCK - Chlorine - Locey Swim Pool Co.
CLEAR SHOT - Toys–guns - Imperial Toy Corp.
CLEAR SIGHT - Ophthalmic goods - Karlen Manufacturing, Inc.
CLEAR SIGHTS - Ophthalmic goods - Apex Medical Corp.
CLEAR SITE ADVANCED GEL TECHNOLOGY - Wound dressings - NDM Acquisition Corp.
CLEAR SKIN - Cosmetics - Maybelline Co.
CLEAR SKIN II - Skin care products - Avon Products, Inc.
CLEAR SMEAR - Automotive parts and accessories - Turtle Wax, Inc.
CLEAR SOLUTION - Varnishes - Samuel Cabot Inc.
CLEAR SOLUTIONS - Calculators ☆ - Zelco Industries, Inc.
CLEAR SOUND - Musical instrument accessories - Actodyne General, Inc.
CLEAR SPAR - Varnishes - Pettit Paint Co. Inc.
CLEAR SPRAY - Adhesives and sealants - W.J. Ruscoe Co.
CLEAR SPRING - Beverages–alcohol - Jim Beam Brands Co.
CLEAR SPRINGS - Fish–fresh or frozen - Clear Springs Trout Co.
CLEAR SPRINGS - Water–bottled or canned - Clear Springs, Inc.
CLEAR-STAT - Mats - United Technical Products Inc.
CLEAR SUN - Cosmetics ☆ - Elysee Scientific Cosmetic Co.
CLEAR TAC - Medical apparatus - Uni-Patch
CLEAR-TEX - Paints ☆ - DecoArt, Inc.
CLEAR TEX - Thread - Signal Thread Co. Inc.
CLEAR THANE - Coatings - W.P. Hickman Systems
CLEAR THOUGHTS - Office supplies - Wald Designs Acrylic Idea Factory
CLEAR THOUGHTS - Vitamins and nutritional supplements - Rexall Sundown, Inc.
CLEAR THROUGH - Skin care products - Ilona, Inc.
CLEAR-THRU - Frames–picture ☆ - Tom Kedzie Projects
CLEAR TIP - Sporting goods - Shakespeare Fishing Tackle
CLEAR-TITE - Adhesives and sealants - R-H Products Co.
CLEAR-TITE - Tape–adhesive - Manco, Inc.
CLEAR TO SEND - Electronic equipment - Clear to Send Electronics, Inc.
CLEAR-TONE - Music boxes ☆ - National Artcraft Co.
CLEAR TOUCH - Paints - Servistar Corp.
CLEAR TRAK - Vacuum cleaners and accessories - Amway Corp.
CLEAR TRAN - Decals and transfers ☆ - Sangray Corp.
CLEAR-TRAX - Mats ☆ - Superior Manufacturing Group/Notrax Floor Matting
CLEAR TROPIQUARIUM - Pet products - Rolf C. Hagen (USA) Corp.
CLEAR-TUSSIN - Cough medicines - Atlantic Licensing Corp.
CLEAR-UPS - Skin care products - Richardson-Vicks USA
CLEAR VALLEY - Wines - Gibson Wine Co.
CLEAR-VAR - Varnishes ☆ - Valspar Corp.
CLEAR VIDEO - Computer software - Iterated Systems, Inc.
CLEAR VIEW - Bags–cosmetic - Capitol Novelty Co.
CLEAR-VIEW - Bath Packaging - Sterling Plumbing Group Inc.
CLEAR-VIEW - Chairs–plastic - Regal Plastic Co.
CLEAR VIEW - Cleaning preparations - Nu Arc Co. Inc.
CLEAR VIEW - Dairy products ☆ - Sommer Maid Creamery Inc.
CLEAR VIEW - Housewares - Shuford Mills Inc. (Diversified Products Division)

CLEAR VIEW - Skin care products - Plasto Tech Co. International
CLEAR-VIEW - Window coverings - Clear-View Shade Inc.
CLEAR VIEW PEEP - Archery equipment - Saunders Archery Co.
CLEAR VISION - Cleaning preparations ☆ - K & W Products
CLEAR VISION - Cleaning preparations–window - Kafko International Ltd.
CLEAR VISION - Hobby kits - Constance Y. Marine
CLEAR-VIZ - Safety products - Conspicuity Inc.
CLEAR VOICE - Computer software - Interactive Products, Inc.
CLEAR-VU - Housewares - Taylor Environmental Instruments
CLEAR-VU - Nutrition product - Welcon
CLEAR VU - Tools–garden - WCI Outdoor Products, Inc.
CLEAR-VU BY ELO - Leather goods - Oppenheim Products Co.
CLEAR-VUE - Decals and transfers - Richards Distributing, Inc.
CLEAR-VUE - Lighters ☆ - S.M. Frank & Co. Inc. (Kaywoodie-Yello-Bole-Medico)
CLEAR-VUE - Office supplies ☆ - Mayer Manufacturing Corp.
CLEAR-VUE - Pencils ☆ - Dixon Ticonderoga Co.
CLEAR WATER - Aquariums–household - Jungle Laboratories Corp.
CLEAR WATERS - Finishing agents - Valspar Corp.
CLEAR WAVE - Water purification systems - Field Controls Co.
CLEAR WINDEX - Cleaning preparations–window - S.C. Johnson & Son, Inc.
CLEAR YOUR POND - Filters–water - Pond Filtration Inc.
CLEARAC - Pharmaceutical preparations - P. & S. Laboratories Inc.
CLEARAC - Skin care products - Standard Homeopathic Co., Inc.
CLEARADINE - Iodinated diagnostic agents - Clinipad Corp.
CLEARADON - Water purification systems - North East Environmental Products, Inc.
CLEARADVANTAGE - Swimming pools - FMC Corp.
CLEARAIRE - Air purification systems - Amcor Group Ltd.
CLEARASIL - Pharmaceutical preparations - Richardson-Vicks USA
CLEARASIL CLEARSTICK - Acne treatment - Procter & Gamble Co.
CLEARATHANE - Paints - Royal Lustre Brands
CLEARAX - Trays - Millrock Inc.
CLEARBLUE EASY - Pregnancy test kits - Whitehall Laboratories
CLEARBORN - Seafood products–fresh or frozen - Gloucester Corp.
CLEARBROOK - Dinnerware–glass - Durand International
CLEARBROOK FARMS - Jams and jellies - Cincinnati Preserving Co.
CLEARCHANNEL LTR - Radios - E.F. Johnson Co.
CLEARCO - Paper–writing - Kurtz Bros. Inc.
CLEARCOAT - Paints - Hirshfield's Paint Manufacturing
CLEARCOLLAR - Pet products - Blair Campbell
CLEARCOLOR - Computer hardware - Cornerstone Imaging, Inc.
CLEARCOPY - Paper - Esleeck Manufacturing Co., Inc.
CLEARCRIMP - Scientific apparatus - E.I. Dupont de Nemours and Co.
CLEARCUSHION - Floor coverings ☆ - Congoleum Corp.
CLEARDIAL - Telephones - Infosystems Resources, Inc.
CLEARDOME - Thread - Threads USA Div.
CLEARER THAN CLEAR - Veterinary pharmaceutical preparations - Farnam Cos. Inc.
CLEARERASE - Paper - Esleeck Manufacturing Co., Inc.
CLEARET - Skin care products ☆ - Scruples Professional Salon Products, Inc.
CLEAREX - Cleaning preparations–household ☆ - Graham-Field Inc.
CLEAREYE BEAM - Automotive parts and accessories - Optronics Inc.
CLEARFAX - Electronic equipment - Buhl Industries, Inc.
CLEARFIELD - Tomato pastes and sauces - Woods Cross Canning Co.
CLEARFIRE DE-LITE - Candles - Lancaster Colony Corp.
CLEARFIX - Cleaning preparations - Clearfix, Corp.
CLEARFLEX - Paints - Triangle Coatings Inc.
CLEARFLEX - Wire - General Cable Corp.
CLEARFLO - Bathroom accessories ☆ - Selfix, Inc.
CLEARFLO - Chemicals - Sybron Chemical Holdings Inc.
CLEARFLO - Drains - Kohler Co.
CLEARFLOW - Cleaning preparations - International Biosystems, Inc.
CLEARFLOW - Filters–industrial - Waxman Industries Inc.
CLEARFORM - Glass products - Corning Inc.
CLEARFRUIT - Fruit drinks–bottled or canned - Everfresh Beverages, Inc.
CLEARFRYE - Fireplace equipment - Thomas Industries Inc. (Portland Willamette Div.)
CLEARGARD - Hoses - Sanitary Couplers, Inc.
CLEARGLASS - Musical instrument accessories - Dunlop Manufacturing, Inc.
CLEARGLAZE - Adhesives and sealants ☆ - Plastics & Resins Ltd.
CLEARGLOW - Fireplace screens - Jack-Post Corp.
CLEARGUARD - Water filters and softening units - Atlantic Filter Corp.
CLEARIGATE - Herbicides - Great Lakes Biochemical Co., Inc.
CLEARIMAGE - Identification tags - Precision Dynamics Corp.
CLEARING 21 - Computer hardware - Chicago Mercantile Exchange

CLEARING EXPRESS - Saws–power - Johnson Technologies
CLEARLINE - Calculators - Clearline Concepts Corp.
CLEARLINE - Tiles–ceramic ☆ - American Olean Tile Co.
CLEARLITE - Lacquers ☆ - H. Behlen & Bro. Inc.
CLEARLITE - Polishes - Mike Gejeian
CLEARLITE - Salad and cooking oils - Life Services Supplements, Inc.
CLEARLITE - Ventilation equipment - Double L Group, Ltd.
CLEARLOGISTICS - Computer software - Clarify Inc.
CLEARLON - Thread - Threads USA Div.
CLEARLY - Glassware–household - Crisa Corp.
CLEARLY A MATTER OF TASTE - Beef - American Angus Association
CLEARLY ACRYLIC - Glassware–household - Anacapa Corp.
CLEARLY BETTER - Cleaning preparations - No Touch North America Corp.
CLEARLY CALA-GEL - Health care products - Tec Laboratories, Inc.
CLEARLY CANFIELD'S - Water–bottled or canned - A.J. Canfield Co.
CLEARLY CLEAN - Cleaning preparations - Sunshine Quality Products, Inc.
CLEARLY DIGITAL - Audio equipment - Harris Corp.
CLEARLY ME - Underwear and nightwear - Maidenform Inc.
CLEARLY MINT - Candy - Farley Candy Co.
CLEARLY NATURAL - Soap - Clearly Natural Products
CLEARLY PERFECTION - Aquariums–household - Advanced Aquatic Technologies Inc.
CLEARLY PINE - Cleaning preparations - Gulf States Chemical Co., Inc.
CLEARLY POWERFUL SOFTWARE - Computer software - Lucid Corp.
CLEARLY REMARKABLE - Beverages–carbonated - BCB USA Corp.
CLEARLY SENSATIONAL - Beverages - BCB USA Corp.
CLEARLY THE BEST - Cleaning preparations - Blake Schwartzman
CLEARLY THE BEST - Floor coverings–carpet and rugs ☆ - Calladium & Marglen
CLEARLY VISIBLE - Cleaning preparations - Chem Lab Products, Inc.
CLEARLYTE - Decorative plating - Enthone-OMI
CLEARMAN'S - Food products - Dairy Fresh Products Co.
CLEARMASK - Paper - Ivex Coated Products Corp.
CLEARMASK - Paper–writing - Cavert Wire Co. Inc.
CLEARMASTER - Paper - Fox River Paper Co.
CLEARMASTER - Paper - Howard Paper Mills Inc.
CLEARO-TABS - Pet products - Lake Products Co. Inc.
CLEAROC - Varnishes - Olympic Paint & Varnish Co.
CLEARON - Fishing tackle ☆ - Gladding Braided Products Inc.
CLEARON - Varnishes - Lasting Paints Inc.
CLEAROSCOPE - Stencils - Heyer Inc.
CLEARPAC - Plastic food containers - Dart Container Corp.
CLEARPASS - Drains - Kohler Co.
CLEARPATH - Computer software - Unisys Corp.
CLEARPHANE - Gift wrap - Highland Supply Corp.
CLEARPRINT - Glycerine rubber-stamp inks - Irwin-Hodson Co.
CLEARPRINT - Paper - Clearprint Paper Co.
CLEARQUALITY - Publisher's imprints - Clarify Inc.
CLEARR CC - Signs - Clearr Corp.
CLEARSEAL - Adhesives and sealants - Avery Dennison Corp.
CLEARSEAL-150 - Sealing compounds - A.C. Horn Co.
CLEARSET - Telephone accessories - Clearvox Communications, Inc.
CLEARSHIELD - Shutters–plastic - Clearshield, Inc.
CLEARSHIELD - Window coverings - Solar-Gard International, Inc.
CLEARSHIELD - Windows - Lindgren RF Enclosures, Inc.
CLEARSHOT - Cameras - RICOH Corp.
CLEARSIGHT - Coatings - U.S. Coatings, Inc.
CLEARSOUNDS - Electronic equipment - Hitec Group International, Inc.
CLEARSPAN - Radio modem - Comptek Telecommunications Inc.
CLEARSTEEL - Prefabricated buildings–wood - Matrix Technical Engineering Corp.
CLEARSTICK - Pharmaceutical preparations - Richardson-Vicks USA
CLEARSTREAM - Water purification systems - Reynolds Water Conditioning Co.
CLEARSTRIP - Stripping solvents - Abatron, Inc.
CLEARSTRIP - Wallpaper - Nicolaus Paper Inc.
CLEARSUPPORT - Computer software - Clarify Inc.
CLEARSWITCH - Electronic equipment - Jayco Interface Technology Inc.
CLEARTAP - Electrical equipment - KSCO Corp.
CLEARTECH CT-II - Telephones - U.S. West Enterprises Inc.
CLEARTEX - Plastics–laminated - Maytex Mills
CLEARTEX - Typewriters ☆ - Codo Manufacturing Corp.
CLEARTONE - Thread - Bond Products Inc.
CLEARTONES - Tiles–ceramic ☆ - American Olean Tile Co.
CLEARTOX - Wood products ☆ - Miller Purcell Co.
CLEARTOY - Candy - Gladstone Candies

☆ = Now out of production

CLEARTREAT - Clay mix - Wyo-Ben Inc.

CLEARTRINE - Herbicides ☆ - Applied Biochemists, Inc.

CLEARTYPE - Maps - American Map Corp.

CLEARVAN - Food products - Adams Extract Co. Inc.

CLEARVEIL - Air purification systems - Pacific Spirit Corp.

CLEARVIEW - Computer peripheral equipment - Denton Vacuum, Inc.

CLEARVIEW - Contact lenses - Pilkington Barnes Hind, Inc.

CLEARVIEW - Cribs—wood ☆ - Welsh Co.

CLEARVIEW - Easels ☆ - Anco Wood Specialties Inc.

CLEARVIEW - Measuring instruments ☆ - Martingale & Co.

CLEARVIEW - Paper - Smurfit Newsprint Corp. (Cladwood Div.)

CLEARVIEW CHLAMYDIA - Pharmaceutical preparations - Wampole Laboratories Div.

CLEARVIEW HCG II & HCG DUO - Pharmaceutical preparations - Wampole Laboratories Div.

CLEARVIEW STREP A - Pharmaceutical preparations - Wampole Laboratories Div.

CLEARVISION - Water purification systems - Fountainhead Technologies, Inc.

CLEARVISN - Computer software - Digital Equipment Corp.

CLEARVOICE - Hearing aids - Beltone Electronics Corp.

CLEARVOICE - Microphones - Shure Brothers, Inc.

CLEARVUE - Brushes - Wooster Brush Co.

CLEARVUE - Novelty items - Sports Memories Inc.

CLEARVUE - Office supplies - Samuel Ward Manufacturing Inc.

CLEARVUE/EAV - Educational materials - Clearvue/EAV, Inc.

CLEARWARE DECORATING SYSTEM - Plastic decorating device - HFDC, Inc.

CLEARWATER - Faucets - Kohler Co.

CLEARWATER - Ships—sailing vessels - Holby Marine Co.

CLEARWATER - Wallpaper - Belmont Wallcoverings

CLEARWATER CHOICE - Filters—water - Innova Pure Water, Inc.

CLEARWATER COLON HYDROTHERAPY - Medical apparatus - Clearwater Colon Hydrotherapy, Inc.

CLEARWATER PRO - Sporting goods - Zercom Corp.

CLEARWATER WOODS - Shutters—wood - Clearwater Woods Inc.

CLEARWAY - Automotive parts and accessories - Ricon Corp.

CLEARWOOD - Hardware - Marley Mouldings Inc.

CLEARWOOD PS - Hardware - Marley Mouldings Inc.

CLEARY'S CRITTERS - Greeting cards - Hourglass Editions

CLEASE CONTROL - Hair care products - Pro Design International, Inc.

CLEAT CHEATER - Paperboard - Anderson & Middleton Co.

CLEAT SEAT - Sporting goods - Randy C. Rattenberger

CLEAT STAT - Mats - Rubbermaid Commercial Products Inc.

CLEATMAT - Seat covers - Rubbermaid Inc.

CLEATSTAT - Mats - Rubbermaid Office Products Inc.

CLEATSTAT PLUS - Office furniture—plastic - Rubbermaid Office Products Inc.

CLEAVER - Propellers - Brunswick Corp.

CLEAVER - Thread - Cincinnati Thread Co.

CLEAVER BEAVER - Toys—stuffed - Dakin Inc.

CLEAVER BROOKS HIGH EFFICIENCY EXL - Lawn mowers - Aqua-Chem

CLECO - Tools—power-driven - Indresco Inc.

CLEEN - Finishing agents - Red Spot Paint & Varnish Co., Inc.

CLEEN-SEAL - Paper—carbon - A.B. Dick Co.

CLEEN TRAC - Air purification systems - Simco

CLEENEST - Ribbons—inked ☆ - Eaton Allen Ko-Rec-Type Corp.

CLEENIT - Musical instrument accessories - M & M Distributing Co.

CLEENY - Eyeglass-cleaning kit - MacKenzie-Koch

CLEER - Health care products ☆ - Mackwin Co.

CLEER-ADHEER - Adhesives and sealants - C-Line Products, Inc.

CLEER BEER - Beer - Miller Brewing Co.

CLEER-POCKETS - Office supplies - C-Line Products, Inc.

CLEERSPAN - Fibers—synthetic - Globe Manufacturing Co.

CLEF - Computer software - Gessler Publishing Co., Inc.

CLEF - Recording label ☆ - Aztec Corp.

CLEF NOTES - Computer software - Electronic Courseware Systems Inc.

CLEGG'S CATCH - Fish—fresh or frozen - Clegg Shrimp Co. Inc.

CLEI - Decorative soaps - Country Lane Enterprises Inc.

CLEM - Toys - Russ Berrie and Co., Inc.

CLEM MARKER - Pens ☆ - Ben Clements & Sons Inc.

CLEMATIS - Salmon—smoked, salted, dried, or pickled - Trident Seafoods Corp.

CLEMATITE - Tiles—ceramic ☆ - Monarch Tile Inc.

CLEMENS - Clocks ☆ - Ridgeway Clock Co.

CLEMENS - Fasteners—snap - J. & E. McLane Co. Inc.

CLEMENS MARKETS HOMESTYLE PRIVATE COLLECTION RECIPES - Food products - Clemens Markets Inc.

CLEMENT - Crackers ☆ - Liberty Richter Inc.

CLEMENT FAUGIER - Food products ☆ - Liberty Richter Inc.

CLEMENTE - Handbags - Secreta

CLEMENTE GUASTI - Wines - Francis A. Bonanno, Inc.

CLEMENTE MICARELLI - Giftware - Reco International Corp.

CLEMENTINE - Toys—stuffed - Silent Sentiments

CLEMINTINE - Kitchen appliances ☆ - National Housewares

CLEM'S - Meat sauces - Clemco, Inc.

CLEN DENT - Chewing gum - Advantage Marketing, Inc.

CLENCH - Epoxy ☆ - Hartline Products Co. Inc.

CLENCHER - Mops - Golden Star Inc.

CLENE-N-GLO - Cleaning preparations ☆ - Flo-Pac Corp.

CLENS - Ophthalmic goods ☆ - Alcon Laboratories, Inc.

CLENSATRON, THE - Cleaning preparations - Lifestyle Resource

CLENZOIL - Cleaning preparations - Clenzoil Corp.

CLEO - Bathtubs—enameled - Kohler Co.

CLEO - Chocolate candy ☆ - Liberty Richter Inc.

CLEO - Footwear—athletic - Vans, Inc.

CLEO - Glassware—household ☆ - Crystal Clear Importing Co. Inc.

CLEO - Greeting cards - Gibson Greetings, Inc.

CLEO - Machine parts - Buff Polish & Grind Industrial Supply Co., Inc.

CLEO - Pet product - Interwood Corp.

CLEO - Recording label - Jazz Composer's Orchestra Association Inc.

CLEO - Skin care products - Troika International Inc.

CLEO - Yarn ☆ - Plymouth Yarn Co.

CLEO CARES - Paper—gift wrap ☆ - Cleo Inc.

CLEO EARTH FRIENDLY - Greeting cards, gift wrap, etc. - Sepralash Co.

CLEO EARTH FRIENDLY - Paper ☆ - Cleo Inc.

CLEO POMKOTCHNEY - Jewelry - Dianne Moseley

CLEO WRAP - Paper—gift wrap - Cleo Inc.

CLEOCIN - Antibiotics - Upjohn Co.

CLEOCIN HCI - Pharmaceutical preparations - Upjohn Co.

CLEOCIN PEDIATRIC - Pharmaceutical preparations - Upjohn Co.

CLEOCIN PHOSPHATE - Antibiotics - Upjohn Co.

CLEOCIN T - Antibiotics - Upjohn Co.

CLEOPATRA - Artists' materials - Stangren Co.

CLEOPATRA - Bathroom fixtures - Crane Plumbing/Fiat Products

CLEOPATRA - Brassieres (Bras) - Goddess Bra

CLEOPATRA - Combs - Krest Products Corp.

CLEOPATRA - Glass—plate - Sasaki

CLEOPATRA - Jewelry - Jacoby-Bender Inc.

CLEOPATRA - Soap - Colgate-Palmolive Co.

CLEOPATRA - Thread ☆ - Susan Bates Inc.

CLEOPATRA - Tiles—ceramic - H & R Johnson Inc.

CLEOPATRA'S - Pasta - Gabriele Macaroni

CLEOPATRA'S NEEDLES - Hobby kits ☆ - Chase Collection, Inc.

CLEOPATRA'S SECRET - Flowers, plants, and seeds - Silhouettes of the Desert

CLEOPATRA'S SECRET - Seasonings - Nile Spice Foods Inc.

CLEOTRA - Candy ☆ - Andre Prost Inc.

CLER GEAR - Luggage - Shalam Imports Inc.

CLERA - Ophthalmic goods ☆ - Alcon Laboratories, Inc.

CLERATON - Pharmaceutical preparations - H.R. Cenci Laboratories Inc.

CLERET - Housewares - Bel-Aire Sales Corp.

CLERET BATH SQUEEGEE - House furnishings - Cleret, Inc.

CLERGY - Floor coverings—carpet and rugs - Porter Carpet Mills Inc.

CLERGY JOURNAL, THE - Video production - Logos Productions Inc.

CLERICO - Wine - European Beverage Co., Inc.

CLERMOND - Furniture ☆ - Hooker Furniture Corp.

CLERMONT - Doors—wood - Masonite Corp.

CLERMONT - Giftware ☆ - Gorham Inc.

CLERMONT - Juices - Clermont Fruit Processers, Inc.

CLERMONT - Perfumes - Anjac Inc.

CLERMONT - Wallpaper ☆ - Eisenhart Wallcoverings Co.

CLERMONT OAK - Cabinets - Del Mar Cabinets

CLERZ - Ophthalmic goods - Alcon Laboratories, Inc.

CLES DES DUC ARMAGNA - Beverages—alcohol - Cointreau America Inc.

CLESOL - Cleaning preparations - BASF Corp.

CLETIS - Apparel and accessories - Scratch Golf Inc.

CLEUGH'S - Fruits—frozen - Cleugh's Rhubarb Co.

CLEVE - Apparel and accessories - Cleve Shirtmakers Inc.

CLEVELAND - Bicycles - Columbia Manufacturing Inc.

CLEVELAND - Daters and numberers - Consolidated Stamp Manufacturing Co. Inc.

CLEVELAND - Dog food - Eagle Roller Mill Co.
CLEVELAND - Musical instruments ☆ - King Musical Instruments
CLEVELAND - Toys–automobiles - 1992 Mathre Family Trust
CLEVELAND - Wines - Dover Vineyards Inc.
CLEVELAND BROWNS - Trading cards and stamps - Cleveland Browns, Inc.
CLEVELAND CLASSIC - Golfing equipment - Roger Cleveland Golf Co.
CLEVELAND DORNBACK - Thermostats - Dornback Furnace Division
CLEVENGER OLD SOUTH JERSEY - Glassware–household - Charles Zahn-
   Import Merchant
CLEVER CATCHER COLLECTION, THE - Games - Frank & Klein Associates
   Inc.
CLEVER CLOCK - Computer software - Non-Inc., Inc.
CLEVER COOKIE - Cookies - Clever Cookie Corp.
CLEVER ENDEAVOR - Games - Gameplan
CLEVER LEVER - Paper–toilet ☆ - Fort Howard Corp.
CLEVER TOTS - Diapers–disposable - J.J. Newberry Co.
CLEVERWEAR - Jewelry–costume - Cleverwear
CLEVITE - Automotive parts and accessories - AE Clevite Inc.
CLEVITE 77 - Bearings–industrial - AE Clevite Inc.
CLEVITETION - Bearings–motor vehicle - AE Clevite Inc.
CLEVLOK - Hooks - Columbus Mckinnon Corp.
CLEVO - Paints ☆ - Kyanize Paint Co.
CLI - Coatings - Coastal Labs, Inc.
CLI - Computer software - Canary Labs, Inc.
CLI INTERNATIONAL SOCRATES - Computer software - Cli International, Inc.
CLIC - Erasers - Pentel of America, Ltd.
CLIC STIC - Pencils–mechanical - Bic Corp.
CLICHADES - Games - R & R Fun Factory, Inc.
CLICHE - Apparel and accessories - Breton Industries
CLICK - Chairs–cane - Stylex Inc.
CLICK - Hair care products - Helene Curtis Industries Inc.
CLICK - Naphthalene chips - Coughlan Products Corp.
CLICK ALONG RIDERS - Toys - Fisher-Price, Inc.
CLICK & CREATE - Computer software - Corel USA
CLICK! & TREAT - Pet products - Michele Wilkes
CLICK AND TREAT - Recording label - Jon M. Lindbergh
CLICK CLACK - Food containers ☆ - Le Creuset of America, Inc.
CLICK-CLIP - Novelty items - Euroconcepts Inc.
CLICK EFFECTS - Computer software - Sound Creations, Inc.
CLICK LINK - Machine parts - Ryobi America Corp.
CLICK N CATCH - Toys ☆ - Henry Gordy International Inc.
CLICK 'N CLATTER CAR - Toys - Fisher-Price, Inc.
CLICK 'N CLEAN - Can openers–electric - Rival Manufacturing Co.
CLICK-ON - Bicycle carrier - Automaxi Inc.
CLICK-ON - Wiring devices - Academy Electrical Products Corp.
CLICK RACK - Bicycle parts and accessories - American Recreation Co., Inc.
CLICK SET - Watches - Elgin Watch Co.
CLICK-STOP - Blood-pressure monitors - Propper Manufacturing Co., Inc.
CLICK TRICK - Toys–stuffed - Fun World Inc.
CLICKART - Computer software - T/Maker Co.
CLICKART CHRISTIAN IMAGES - Computer software - T/Maker Co.
CLICKBOOK - Computer software - Bookmaker Corp.
CLICKER - Pet collars - Nancy J. Harris
CLICKER REPLACEMENT TRANSMITTER FOR GARAGE DOOR & GATE
   OPENERS MODEL #100 - Electrical equipment - Clicker Corp.
CLICKER REPLACEMENT TRANSMITTER FOR GARAGE DOOR & GATE
   OPENERS MODEL #200 - Electrical equipment - Clicker Corp.
CLICKER REPLACEMENT TRANSMITTER FOR GARAGE DOOR & GATE
   OPENERS MODEL #300 - Electrical equipment - Clicker Corp.
CLICKLINE - Fishing lures - Southern Lure Co.
CLICKS - Apparel and accessories - Edison Brothers Stores, Inc.
CLICKS CLASSIC - Shoes - Edison Brothers Stores, Inc.
CLICKSEARCH - Computer software - Raxsoft, Inc.
CLICKTOONS - Computer peripheral equipment - Music Pen Inc.
CLICKTRACKS - Computer software - Passport Designs Inc.
CLICROLLER - Pens - Pentel of America, Ltd.
CLICSHARP - Pencils - Pentel of America, Ltd.
CLIEN TRAK - Computer software - Curtin Matheson Scientific, Inc.
CLIENT ACCESS - Insurance agencies–life - New York Life Insurance Co.
CLIENT DATA SYSTEM - Computer software - E-Z Data, Inc.
CLIENT EDUCATOR, THE - Computer peripheral equipment - Visuale Corp.
CLIENT PORTRAIT - Computer software - Elan Associates (GreenLight
   Software Division)
CLIENT PROJECT - Computer software - Micro Billing Systems, Inc.
CLIENT REPO - Computer software - Federated Investors, Inc.
CLIENT SELECT COTTON - Fabrics–cotton - Dunavant Enterprises Inc.

CLIENTEL - Communications equipment–satellite - Business Telecom, Inc.
CLIENTLINK - Computer software - Raider Software, Inc.
CLIENT'S CHOICE - Floor coverings–carpet and rugs - Milliken & Co. Inc.
CLIFF - Toys - Tonka Corp.
CLIFF CLIMBER - Toys - Mattel, Inc.
CLIFF HANGER - Bicycles - Roadmaster Corp.
CLIFF HANGERS - Toys–electronic - Tyco Toys
CLIFF KEEN - Sporting goods - Nichols Wrestling Products Inc.
CLIFF SOUNDS & FILMS - Recording label - Vision Records Inc.
CLIFFHANGER - Pens - Sheaffer Holdings Inc.
CLIFFHANGER - Wood products - Weyerhaeuser Co.
CLIFFORD - Alarm systems - Clifford Electronics Inc.
CLIFFORD - Publisher's imprints - Scholastic Inc.
CLIFFORD - Towels - Norman Bridwell
CLIFFORD & WILLS - Apparel - Clifford & Wills, Inc.
CLIFFORD CUDDLETAIL - Candy - Frankford Candy & Chocolate Co. Inc.
CLIFFORD THE BIG RED DOG - Toys - Norman Bridwell
CLIFFORD THE BIG RED DOG - Toys–stuffed - Eden LLC
CLIFFS & CAVES - Pet products - Penn-Plax, Inc.
CLIFFS NOTES - Publisher's imprints - Cliff's Notes, Inc.
CLIFFSTAR - Food products - Cliffstar Corp.
CLIF'S - Food products - Matador Processors Inc.
CLIFTEX - Apparel–men's - Cliftex Corp.
CLIFTON - Floor coverings - Mannington Resilient Floors
CLIFTON - Recording label - Relic Record Productions Inc.
CLIFTON - Thread - Cincinnati Thread Co.
CLIFTON - Toilets–porcelain - Sterline Manufacturing Corp.
CLIFTON'S - Vegetables–canned - Clifton Canning Co.
CLIK-CLAK BUNNY - Toys ☆ - Playskool, Inc.
CLIK-CLAK DUCK - Toys ☆ - Playskool, Inc.
CLIK-CLAK PUPPY - Toys ☆ - Playskool, Inc.
CLIK CLOK - Computer software - Sundial Systems Corp.
CLIK-STIK - Pencils ☆ - Faber-Castell Corp.
CLIKIT THE CRIKIT - Toys - Sky-Way Products
CLIMA-F.I.T. - Footwear–athletic - Nike, Inc.
CLIMA-RADIATE - Heating equipment ☆ - Halstead Industries Inc.
CLIMACTIC - Pharmaceutical preparations ☆ - Physician Sales & Service
CLIMADRY - Heat pumps - Climate Master, Inc.
CLIMAGARD - Cleaning preparations–window ☆ - BP America Inc.
CLIMAGEN - Pharmaceutical preparations - Berlex Laboratories, Inc.
CLIMALENE - Detergents - Malco Products, Inc.
CLIMASEAL - Coatings - Illinois Tool Works Inc.
CLIMAT - Perfumes - Lancome
CLIMATE CARE - Air purification systems - Holmes Products, Corp.
CLIMATE CONTROL - Weather stripping - KEL-EEZ
CLIMATE GUARD - Batteries - Exide Corp.
CLIMATE KOTE - Polishes - Auto Wax Co., Inc.
CLIMATE MASTER - Heat pumps - Climate Master, Inc.
CLIMATE PRO - Insulating materials - Schuller International, Inc.
CLIMATECH - Cases–cigar - Vigilant Inc.
CLIMATECH - Fibers - Pacific Trail, Inc.
CLIMATECH - Motor vehicle parts and accessories - Paccar Inc.
CLIMATEMASTER - Air conditioning equipment - Climate Master, Inc.
CLIMATEST - Paints - Pioneer Paint of Arizona
CLIMATIC - Skin care products - Freeman Cosmetics Corp.
CLIMATIC CLOTH - Coats–women's - Target Licensing Corp.
CLIMATICE - Thermal storage heating - American Standard Inc.
CLIMATRESS - Hair care products - Redken Laboratories, Inc.
CLIMATROL - Air conditioning equipment - Fedders North America Inc.
CLIMATRON - Jewelry - Sterling Inc.
CLIMATUBE - Insulating materials - Halstead Industries Inc.
CLIMAX - Audio equipment ☆ - M & G Electronics
CLIMAX - Colognes - Plast-O-Matic Valves Inc.
CLIMAX - Flour–blended ☆ - Climax Mills Inc.
CLIMAX - Machine tools - Climax Portable Machine Tools Inc.
CLIMAX - Paper - Fay Paper Products Inc.
CLIMAX - Shoes - R. Josephs Sportswear, Inc.
CLIMAX - Skin care products - California SunCare, Inc.
CLIMAX - Wicking ☆ - Hooper Industries Inc.
CLIMAX FRAGRANCE - Colognes - Select Brands
CLIMAX SPINNER - Sporting goods ☆ - James Heddon's Sons
CLIMAXX - Vitamins and nutritional supplements - Hit Products, Inc.
CLIMB HIGH - Sporting goods - Climb High Inc.
CLIMB-IT! - Wallpaper - Climb-It Inc.
CLIMB 'N SLIDE - Playground equipment - Little Tikes Co.
CLIMB 'N SWING - Toys - Creative Playthings Ltd.

☆ = Now out of production

CLIMB TO THE TOP - Recording label - Coulter Legal Products, Inc.
CLIMBASAURUS - Exercising equipment - Flexible Flyer Co.
CLIMBER - Bicycles - Kent International Inc.
CLIMBER - Fruits and vegetables - Comstock Michigan Fruit
CLIMBING IRIS - Floor coverings–carpet and rugs ☆ - Capel, Inc.
CLIMBING ROSES - Christmas tree ornaments - Cracker Box Inc.
CLIMBING TO SUCCESS CHILDREN'S SERIES BOOKS - Publisher's imprints - Megakinetics Inc.
CLIMBING TOWER - Playground equipment - Wonderline
CLIMBMASTER - Exercising equipment - Heart Rate Inc.
CLIMMAXX - Audio equipment - Elm Street Industries, Inc.
CLIN D'OEIL - Fragrance - Bourjois Ltd.
CLINASEPT - Plastic envelopes - Eastman Kodak Co.
CLINCALOGIC - Computer software - Medicalogic, Inc.
CLINCH - Hair care products - Paul Mazzotta Inc.
CLINCH EDGE - Tools–hand-operated - Simonds Industries Inc.
CLINCH FAST - Hobby kits - Time Saver Tool Corp.
CLINCH-ON - Hardware - Continuous Coating Corp.
CLINCH RIVER - Food products - Bush Brothers and Co.
CLINCHED-ON-HEAD - Housewares ☆ - W.E. Kautenberg Co.
CLINCHER - Balls–baseball - J. De Beer & Son Inc.
CLINCHER - Fabrics - Burlington House Fabrics Group
CLINCHER - Hardware ☆ - Cole Consumer Products Inc.
CLINCHER - Shoes - Interco Inc.
CLINCHER - Weather stripping - W.J. Dennis & Co.
CLINCHER, THE - Conveyors - Wire Belt Co. of America
CLINCOR - Adhesives and sealants - Clinton Corn Starch Co.
CLINDA-DERM - Pharmaceutical preparations - Paddock Laboratories Inc.
CLINDETS - Pharmaceutical preparations - Stiefel Laboratories, Inc.
CLINDEX - Pharmaceutical preparations - Rugby Laboratories Inc.
CLINDO - Cleaning preparations - Demert & Dougherty, Inc.
CLINDOXYL - Pharmaceutical preparations - Stiefel Laboratories, Inc.
CLINE-BUCKNER - Pet products - Morton Jones Co.
CLINE SINCE 1889 - Pianos - Music Investments
CLING - Cleaning preparations–household - L & F Consumer Products
CLING - Vinyl ☆ - Columbus Coated Fabrics Co.
CLING-A-WING - Bird feeds - Duncraft, Inc.
CLING-ALON - Hosiery - Sears, Roebuck and Co.
CLING-EVER - Apparel and accessories ☆ - Playtex Apparel, Inc.
CLING FREE - Fabric softeners - Smithkline Beecham Corp.
CLING FREE ULTRA - Fabric softeners - Benckiser Consumer Products Inc.
CLING-N - Stencils - Mason Marking Systems Corp.
CLING-ON - Bathroom accessories - Kace Products, Inc.
CLING-ON AFFIRMATIONS - Decals and transfers - Janice G. Jones
CLING SHIELD - Health care products - Palmero Health Care
CLING-SURFACE - Lubricants - ITW Fluid Products
CLINGCOTE - Paints - Kyanize Paint Co.
CLINGEES - Novelty items - Betta Products, Inc.
CLINGER - Office supplies - Staver Westport Inc.
CLINGFAST - Paints - Colony Paints Div.
CLINGGEL - Protective gel coating - Dorsey Industries Inc.
CLINGING CRITTERS - Toys–stuffed - Russ Berrie and Co., Inc.
CLINGMASTER - Plastics film - AEP Industries, Inc.
CLING'N SEAL RTV - Adhesives and sealants - ITW Fluid Products
CLINGTEX - Girdles - Sears, Roebuck and Co.
CLINI-CLIP - Clippers–barber - Wahl Clipper Corp.
CLINI-COST - Computer software ☆ - Management Prescriptives, Inc.
CLINI SWAB - Sanitary napkins - Clinipad Corp.
CLINIC - Bandages ☆ - Spenco Medical Corp.
CLINIC - Footwear - Clinic Shoe Co.
CLINIC - Vitamins and nutritional supplements - Vitech America Corp.
CLINIC - Watches - Croton Watch Co., Inc.
CLINIC DROPPER - Health care products - Medi Inc.
CLINIC I - Electronic equipment ☆ - AMI Medical Electronics Inc.
CLINICAINE - Anesthetics - Johnson & Johnson
CLINICAL ASSISTANT - Computer software - Psychological Corp., Inc.
CLINICAL MASTER - Computer software - Clinical Networx, Inc.
CLINICAL MASTER - Computer software - RTJ Corp.
CLINICAL NETWORX - Computer software - Clinical Networx, Inc.
CLINICAL REFORMER - Medical apparatus - Current Concepts Corp.
CLINICAL RESPONSE - See **SKIN RESPONSE**
CLINICAL SYSTEMS, INC. - Labels–paper - Clinical Systems, Inc.
CLINICARE - Veterinary pharmaceutical preparations - Pet-Ag, Inc.
CLINICATH - Catheters - Sims Deltec, Inc.
CLINICOL - Cold remedies ☆ - Republic Drug Co. Inc.
CLINICORT - Health care products - Johnson & Johnson

CLINICYDIN - Antibiotics - Johnson & Johnson
CLINIDAN - Hair care products - KMS Research Inc.
CLINIDAS - Computer software - North American Drager
CLINIDINE - Iodinated diagnostic agents - Clinipad Corp.
CLINILOG - Diaries - Miles Inc.
CLINIPAD - Cosmetics - Clinipad Corp.
CLINIQUE - Cosmetics - Estee Lauder Inc.
CLINISAFE - Health care products ☆ - Ulster Scientific Inc.
CLINISOL - Soybean oil - Clintec Nutrition Co.
CLINISPHERE - Computer software - Facts and Comparisons
CLINISTIX - Chemical preparations - Miles Inc.
CLINITEMP - Thermometers ☆ - Parmed Pharmaceuticals, Inc.
CLINITEST - Chemical preparations - Miles Inc.
CLINITOUCH - Computer software - Outreach Health Services, Inc.
CLINITRAC - Health care products ☆ - Lossing Orthopedic Co.
CLINITRON AT HOME - Medical apparatus - Hill Rom, Inc.
CLINKY TOP - Recording label - Ron-Dom Productions Inc.
CLINOMINT - Toothpaste - Church and Dwight Co.
CLINORIL - Pharmaceutical preparations - Merck & Co., Inc. (Merck Research Laboratories)
CLINOXIDE - Pharmaceutical preparations - Geneva Generics Inc.
CLINPEN - Computer software - Housecall Medical Resources, Inc.
CLINSTEEL - Tools - Sands Level & Tool
CLINT - Colognes ☆ - Avon Products, Inc.
CLINTAGONISTS - Housewares - Clintagonists, Inc.
CLINTEX - Sponges - National Sponge Corp.
CLINTON - Brushes–paint - Corona Brushes Inc.
CLINTON - Corn starch - Clinton Corn Starch Co.
CLINTON - Engines ☆ - Clinton Engines Corp.
CLINTON - Food products ☆ - Bush Brothers and Co.
CLINTON - Locks–padlocks ☆ - Fort Lock Corp.
CLINTON - Milk - Clinton Milk Co.
CLINTON - Watches ☆ - Hampden Corp.
CLINTON COURT - Floor coverings - Tarkett, Inc.
CLINTON PRINTS - Stationery - C.R. Gibson Co.
CLINTON VINEYARDS - Wines - Clinton Vineyards Inc.
CLINTOSE - Sugar–granulated, refined, or powdered - Clinton Corn Starch Co.
CLINTOY - Toys–airplanes - Clinton Toy Corp.
CLIO - Footwear–women's - P.H. Volk Co.
CLIO - Furniture - Harter
CLIO - Giftware - Waterford Wedgewood USA, Inc.
CLIO - Olive oil - L. Lacagnina & Sons
CLIO 2 SUIT - Apparel–women's - HBS Ltd.
CLIP - Binders - The Union Group
CLIP 2 VO - Computer software - Sofdesign International, Inc.
CLIP-A-LONGS - Giftware ☆ - Quality Artworks Inc.
CLIP-A-LONGS - Toys - Tonka Corp.
CLIP-A-NOTE - Hardware ☆ - Miller Studio
CLIP-A-TAPE - Office supplies ☆ - Ideal Stencil Machine and Tape Co.
CLIP & CLAP - Chewing gum - Dandy Confectionery
CLIP & CLEAN SHRUB AND GARDEN GROOMER - Tools–garden - Jackson Enterprises
CLIP & FLIPS - Eyeglasses - Foster Grant Co. Inc.
CLIP & GRIP - Bags–plastic - Compac Industries Inc.
CLIP-ART CONNECTION - Computer software - Adonis Corp.
CLIP-ART FOR MATH TEACHERS - Computer software - Ventura Educational Systems
CLIP ART FOR SCIENCE TEACHERS - Computer software - Ventura Educational Systems
CLIP CABINET - Water purification systems - Aquathin Corp.
CLIP-CASE - Cases–plastic - Form/Tec Plastics, Inc.
CLIP CHIPS - Pet products - Mass-Appeal Inc.
CLIP CLOP CONESTOGA CLUBHOUSE - Playground equipment ☆ - Wonderline
CLIP CREATOR - Computer software - AABACA Inc.
CLIP-DESK - Briefcases - Korchmar Case Co.
CLIP-EYELET - Nozzles - Spraying Systems Co.
CLIP-EZE - Pet products - Crowne Royale, Ltd.
CLIP-EZE - Signs - Scott Sign Systems, Inc.
CLIP FILE - File folders - Clip File, Inc.
CLIP FRAME - Frames–picture - Ammak Manufacturing Corp.
CLIP GUN - Staplers - Wescosa Inc.
CLIP HANGERS - Hardware - Miller Studio
CLIP HANGERS - Hardware - Moore Push-Pin Co.
CLIP-IN-COLOR - Clip-in hair extensions - International Hairgoods Inc.

CLIP IT - Hardware - Moore Push-Pin Co.
CLIP IT - Notebooks and notepads ☆ - Willert Home Products, Inc.
CLIP IT CLAMP IT GRIP IT HANG IT - Heaters–gas - Holmes Products, Corp.
CLIP-LITE - Lamps ☆ - Park Sherman
CLIP-LOCK - File folders - K & M Co.
CLIP-LOK - Motor vehicle parts and accessories - York Products, Inc.
CLIP-MATE - Hardware - Beckson Marine Inc.
CLIP 'N CARRY - Boxes - Wescosa Inc.
CLIP 'N CARRY BAGS - Bags–canvas - Horizon Designs Inc.
CLIP N' COUNT - Office supplies ☆ - Rediform
CLIP 'N HOOK - Fasteners - Baumgarten's
CLIP 'N HOOK - Partitions–wood - Exclusive Imports
CLIP N' SIP - Housewares - Allied Plastics
CLIP 'N SPREAD - Housewares - Pampered Chef, Ltd.
CLIP 'N TAILS - Toys - Tonka Corp.
CLIP-N-TRIM - Tools - Granberg International
CLIP-O-MATIC - Jewelry - Jacoby-Bender Inc.
CLIP-ON - Cosmetics - Capitol Novelty Co.
CLIP-ON - Mops - Perfex Corp.
CLIP-ON - Watchbands–base metal ☆ - Hirsch Speidel Inc.
CLIP ON CONNECTION - Sunglasses - Sungold Enterprises Ltd.
CLIP-ON CRITTERS - Novelty animals with fragrance ☆ - Cosrich Inc.
CLIP-ON CUTIES - Toys–stuffed - Fun World Inc.
CLIP-ON DIALRITER - Office supplies ☆ - Park Sherman
CLIP-ON EMULATION - Electrical and electronic instrumentation - Orion Instruments, Inc.
CLIP-ONS - Skates–roller ☆ - Steven Manufacturing Co.
CLIP PEN - Pens ☆ - Park Sherman
CLIP-PET - Clippers–barber - Wahl Clipper Corp.
CLIP-POC - Pencils - Lanir Trading Co., Inc.
CLIP-PUR - Fastening tool - ITW Ramset/Red Head
CLIP-RITE - Nail clippers - London International U.S. Holdings
CLIP SHOT CLIPSHOT - Novelty items - Sports Novelties Co.
CLIP STICK - Office supplies ☆ - Park Sherman
CLIP-STRIP - Clamps–metal - CTB, Inc.
CLIP-STRIP - Plastics - C-Line Products, Inc.
CLIP TOGETHER - Dinnerware–plastic - Plastics Manufacturing Co.
CLIP-UP - Sunglasses - Dioptics Medical Products, Inc.
CLIP-UPS - Plastics - Dinsmore Instrument Co.
CLIPAD - Office supplies - The Union Group
CLIPAMATIC - Desk sets - Sainberg and Co. Inc.
CLIPART - Stationery - Marketing Innovations International, Inc.
CLIPBOARD INHERITANCE - Computer software - Microedge Inc.
CLIPBOARD, THE - Office supplies ☆ - Globe-Weis
CLIPBOX - School supplies - Cornell Concepts Corp.
CLIPENGLYDE TUBULAR TRACKING SYSTEMS - Doors–garage - Anozira Door Systems, Inc.
CLIPETTE - Health care products ☆ - Apothecary Products, Inc.
CLIPEX - Photographic equipment - Richard Manufacturing Co.
CLIPFINDER - Computer software - DHA/USA, Inc.
CLIPHANGER - Knives–pocket - Imperial Schrade Corp.
CLIPHANGERS - Dolls - Mattel, Inc.
CLIPHOLDER - Paint rollers - Mr. Paintshield Inc.
CLIPION - Wigs - Louis Ferre, Inc.
CLIPIT - Pet products - Mardel Laboratories, Inc.
CLIPIT - Wigs - Revlon General Wig Manufacturers, Inc.
CLIPLITE - Electrical equipment - Wonder Corp. of America
CLIPLOADER - File folders ☆ - Angler's Roslyn Group Ltd.
CLIPLOCK - Musical instrument accessories - Dimarzio, Inc.
CLIPMASTER - Clippers–barber - Sunbeam-Oster Household Products
CLIPMATE - Electrical equipment - Clipmate Corp.
CLIPMATE - Office supplies - Mead Corp.
CLIPMOUNT - Electronics equipment - Visual Communications Co., Inc.
CLIPODEX - Stick files - Insilco Corp.
CLIPOUTS - Computer software - Frontier Graphics Co.
CLIPPER - Aprons - Lois Noyes California Unusuals
CLIPPER - Artists' materials - Dynamic Graphics Inc.
CLIPPER - Bars–aluminum - Susquehanna Glass Co.
CLIPPER - Bicycles - Columbia Manufacturing Inc.
CLIPPER - Boats–houseboats ☆ - Cron Houseboats
CLIPPER - Brushes–paint - Wooster Brush Co.
CLIPPER - Dusters - Majestic Industries Inc.
CLIPPER - Floor coverings–carpet and rugs ☆ - Evans-Black Carpet Mills
CLIPPER - Furniture ☆ - Bean Station Furniture Factory Inc.
CLIPPER - Garden equipment ☆ - H.D. Hudson Manufacturing Co.
CLIPPER - Glassware–household - Oneida Ltd.

CLIPPER - Hardware - Beckson Marine Inc.
CLIPPER - Kites - Gayla Industries Inc.
CLIPPER - Lawn mowers - Lambert Manufacturing Corp.
CLIPPER - Medical instruments - Merit Medical Systems Inc.
CLIPPER - Medical measuring device - Cybermedic Inc.
CLIPPER - Nutcrackers - H.M. Quackenbush Inc.
CLIPPER - Office supplies - Ace Fastener
CLIPPER - Paper–kraft ☆ - Canson-Talens Inc.
CLIPPER - Pens ☆ - Faber-Castell Corp.
CLIPPER - Rackets–tennis - Dayton Racquet Co. Inc.
CLIPPER - Saw blades - Norton Construction Products
CLIPPER - Seafood products–fresh or frozen ☆ - Gorton Group
CLIPPER - Shelving units–wood - Penco Products Div.
CLIPPER - Ships–sailing vessels - Ray Greene Industries
CLIPPER - Ships–sailing vessels ☆ - Lion Yachts
CLIPPER - Tobacco–chewing or smoking ☆ - Swedish Math North America Inc.
CLIPPER - Toys–models ☆ - Estes Industries
CLIPPER - Trailers–travel - Coachmen Industries, Inc.
CLIPPER - Wicker product - Clipper Industries Inc.
CLIPPER AID - Lubricants - Evsco Pharmaceuticals
CLIPPER BOOSTER - Pet products - Rapid Electric/R & R Manufacturing
CLIPPER CITY - Beverages–alcohol - Sisson Management, Inc.
CLIPPER CLEAN - Pet products ☆ - Roccorp, Inc.
CLIPPER CLEAR - Polyurethane varnish - Interlux Yacht Finishes
CLIPPER CRAFT - Apparel–men's - Cliftex Corp.
CLIPPER CRAFT - Boats–motor - Clipper Craft Manufacturers Co. Inc.
CLIPPER CRAFT - Corks - Rebel Industries Inc.
CLIPPER FLAVORS - Fruit drinks–bottled or canned - Foote & Jenks Corp.
CLIPPER II - Floor coverings - American Floor Products Co. Inc.
CLIPPER II - Photographic equipment - Yankee Photo Products Inc.
CLIPPER KING - Firearms, accessories, and parts ☆ - Marlin Firearms Co.
CLIPPER MATE - Pet products ☆ - Fromm Industries
CLIPPER MISS - Bicycles - Columbia Manufacturing Inc.
CLIPPER MIST - Men's apparel - Interco Inc.
CLIPPER SHIP - House furnishings ☆ - Lexington Furniture Industries, Inc.
CLIPPER SHIP - Seafood products–fresh or frozen - Deals Seafood Co. Inc.
CLIPPER STAR - Bicycles - Columbia Manufacturing Inc.
CLIPPER TECH - Hair care products - Windmere Corp.
CLIPPER TRAVELLER - Exercising equipment - Pro Advantage Inc.
CLIPPER VAC - Pet products - M.D.C. Romani Inc.
CLIPPERCIDE - Disinfectants - King Research, Inc.
CLIPPERCRAFT - Boats–motor - Glasco Marine
CLIPPING CATCHER, THE - Cardboard - Genesis Products, Inc.
CLIPPING PATHS - Photographic equipment - Photodisc, Inc.
CLIPPIT - Bird cages ☆ - Pet Supply Imports Inc.
CLIPPITY CLOCK - Clocks - Fantasma
CLIPPITY STRIPS - Framing supplies - Tom Kedzie Projects
CLIPPO THE CLOWN - Puppets ☆ - Fagan International
CLIPPOR - Binoculars ☆ - Bausch & Lomb Inc.
CLIPPOT - Giftware - Stewart Co. Inc.
CLIPQUIK - Lawn mowers - White Consolidated Industries, Inc.
CLIPS - Stationery - Clips, Inc.
CLIPSER - Housewares ☆ - Simer Pump Co.
CLIPSMART - Computer software - Stahls' Inc.
CLIPSTIX - Hardware - Jon M. Blumenaus
CLIPSTORE - Computer terminals - Carlton International Corp.
CLIPTIMER - Timers–appliance ☆ - Healthometer
CLIPTITE - Film - Testrite Instrument Co. Inc.
CLIPZIT - Paper products - Larson Design & Manufacturing
CLIQUE - Golf clubs - Cunningham Golf Co. Inc.
CLISTANAL - Pharmaceutical preparations ☆ - McNeil Pharmaceuticals
CLISTIN - Health care products - McNeil Pharmaceuticals
CLIVIA - Recording label - Kevin B. Eastman
CLIX - Candy - Banner Candy Manufacturing Corp.
CLIX - Paper clips - Clix Products, Inc.
CLM - Laundry machines–commercial - Rosco Machinery Co., Inc.
CLMS - Computer software - Mitratech Inc.
CLO - Pet products - Thomas Veterinary Drug
CLO WHITE - Cleaning preparations - Clo White Co.
CLO*2 - Computer software - CMS/DATA Corp.
CLOAK SPECIAL - Thread ☆ - Perfect Thread Co. Inc.
CLOAKING - Computer software - Helix Software Co., Inc.
CLOBBER - Drain pipe cleaners - Hercules Chemical Co. Inc.
CLOCK - Computer software - Hartley Courseware Inc.
CLOCK-A-DOODLE-DOO - Toys–stuffed - Direct Connect International Inc.

☆ = Now out of production

CLOCK ART - Clocks - Sunbeam Precision Measurement
CLOCK COAT - Epoxy - Environmental Technology, Inc.
CLOCK E - Vitamins and nutritional supplements ☆ - Marlyn Co. Inc.
CLOCK-IN! - Computer software - Dean L. Hiller
CLOCK IN A BOX - Electronic equipment - Jason Data Systems, Inc.
CLOCK MAKER - Clocks - Innovation Specialties, Inc.
CLOCK MOVEMENTS - Clocks - American Mineral Gift Co.
CLOCK SAYS, THE - Toys - Mattel, Inc.
CLOCK SHOP - Computer software - Nordic Software, Inc.
CLOCK-TABS - Pharmaceutical preparations - Alva-Amco Pharmacal Co.
CLOCK TICKING - Fabrics - Dan River Inc.
CLOCK TIMER II - Timers–appliance - West Bend Co.
CLOCK USA - Recording label - Mystic Records
CLOCK-WATCHER - Calculators - Seminole Paper & Printing Co.
CLOCK WISE - Skin care products - Ilona, Inc.
CLOCKCHIP - Generators - MF Electronics Corp.
CLOCKER - Fabrics - Dan River Inc.
CLOCKER - Watches - Dejuno Watch Corp.
CLOCKS - Giftware - Sasaki
CLOCKWERX - Computer software - Spectrum Holobyte, Inc.
CLOCKWORK - Apparel–athletic - Roland O. Hobart
CLOCKWORK - Computer software - Compu-Tations Inc.
CLOCKWORK MAGE - Games - Mayfair Games, Inc.
CLOCREAM - Skin care products ☆ - Upjohn Co.
CLOD-HOPPERS - Apparel and accessories - Gym Rat, Inc.
CLODERM - Pharmaceutical preparations - Center Laboratories/Hermal Dermatology Group
CLOETTA PEPS - Candy ☆ - Andre Prost Inc.
CLOG - Sporting goods - Climb High Inc.
CLOG-AWAY - Containers - Eagle Industries Inc.
CLOG BLASTER - Drain pipe cleaners ☆ - Dynatec International Inc.
CLOG BUSTER - Drain pipe cleaners - Durst Industries Inc.
CLOG SHOOTER - Tools–plumbing ☆ - Faultless Starch/Bon Ami Co.
CLOGMASTER - Drain pipe cleaners - Cobra Products Inc.
CLOGS BY ESKIL'S - Footwear–women's - Eskil's Clog Shop
CLOISART - Jewelry - Klitzner Industries Inc.
CLOISENAMEL - Lighters - Park Lane Associates, Inc.
CLOISONEE UNUSUALS - Key rings - Lois Noyes California Unusuals
CLOISONNE - Wallpaper - Warner Co.
CLOISONNE EMBASSY - Flatware - Kirk Stieff Co.
CLOISONNE ROYALE - Flatware - Kirk Stieff Co.
CLOISTER - Furs–artificial ☆ - Porter Carpet Mills Inc.
CLOISTER - Water–distilled - Cloister Pure Spring Water Co.
CLOMID - Pharmaceutical preparations - Marion Merrell Dow
CLONE - Recording label - Clone Records
CLONE-A-BONE - Games - Donald Gitlitz
CLONE CARD - Office supplies - Patrick S. Fahey
CLONEDETECTOR - Electronic equipment - GTE Telecommunications Services Inc.
CLONEGUARD - Computer software - Electronic Data Systems Corp.
CLONEHEADS - Costumes ☆ - Spearhead Industries Inc.
CLONERWATCH - Computer software ☆ - Cellular Technical Services Inc.
CLONEX - Agricultural products - Superior Growers Supply, Inc.
CLONICEL - Pharmaceutical preparations - H. Joseph Horace
CLOPANE - Cold remedies ☆ - Eli Lilly and Co.
CLOPAY - Doors–garage - Clopay Millwork
CLOPAY - Window shades ☆ - Kirsch Co.
CLOPAY CONFIDENCE SYSTEM, THE - Doors–garage - Clopay Building Products Co., Inc.
CLOPETY CLOP - Rocking horses - Volcano Woodworks
CLOQUE - Floor coverings–carpet and rugs - Masland Corp.
CLORAZINE - Pharmaceutical preparations ☆ - Pasadena Research Laboratories, Inc.
CLORETS - Candy - American Chicle Co.
CLOROMAT - Bleach - Ionics, Inc.
CLOROX - Cleaning preparations–household - Clorox Co.
CLOROX 2 - Bleach - Clorox Co.
CLOROX CLEAN-UP - Cleaning preparations - Clorox Co.
CLOROX HOUSEHOLD - Cleaning preparations ☆ - Clorox Co.
CLOROX PREWASH - Stain removers ☆ - Clorox Co.
CLOROX STAIN-OUT - Stain removers ☆ - Clorox Co.
CLOROX SUPER DETERGENT - Detergents ☆ - Clorox Co.
CLOS BAUDOIN - Beverages–alcohol - Wine Imports Ltd.
CLOS DANIELLE - Wines ☆ - European Beverage Co., Inc.
CLOS D'ARCY - Cheese - Anco Foods Corp.
CLOS DE ROBLES - Wines - Quorum Properties

CLOS DES JACOBINS - Wines - Seagram's Chateau & Estate Wines Co.
CLOS DU BOIS - Wines - Clos du Bois Wines
CLOS DU LION - Wines - Monsieur Touton Selection Ltd.
CLOS DU MARQUIS - Wines - Seagram's Chateau & Estate Wines Co.
CLOS DU MERLE - Wines ☆ - Pellegrini Bros. Wines Inc.
CLOS DU VAL - Wines - Clos du Val Wine Co. Ltd.
CLOS FONTAINE - Wines - Hill & Thoma Wines
CLOS JULIEN - Wines - Petit Pois Corp.
CLOS PEGASE - Wines - Wilson Daniels Ltd.
CLOS REISSIER - Wines - Seagram's Chateau & Estate Wines Co.
CLOS ROBERT - Wines - Remy Martin Amerique Inc.
CLOS. STE. MARIE - Wines ☆ - Coastal Wine Merchants
CLOS STE. NICOLE - Wines ☆ - Domaine St. George Winery & Vineyards
CLOS TRIGUEDINA CAHORS - Wines ☆ - Dreyfus Ashby Inc.
CLOSCO - Varnishes - McCloskey Corp.
CLOSE - Colognes ☆ - Remington Products Co.
CLOSE - Hair care products - Tomar Enterprises, Inc.
CLOSE ASSAULT - Games ☆ - Avalon Hill Game Co.
CLOSE CONTACT - Gloves - New York, Inc.
CLOSE KOTE - Paper–sand - Norton Co.
CLOSE 'N PLAY - Phonographs ☆ - Kenner Products
CLOSE QUARTER - Hand saw - American Saw & Manufacturing Co.
CLOSE QUARTERS - Vitamins and nutritional supplements - MDR Fitness Corp.
CLOSE-SURE - Paper - Mactac Inc. (Packaging Closures Systems Div.)
CLOSE UP - Ceiling fans - Design House, Inc.
CLOSE-UP - Toothpaste - Chesebrough-Pond's USA Co.
CLOSE-UP PELLET - Livestock vitamins - Dawe's, Inc.
CLOSESURE - Locks–door - Blue Ribbon Pet Products, Inc.
CLOSET BOLTS - Nuts and bolts - Black Swan Manufacturing Co.
CLOSET CADDY - Closet organizers - Mega Organizers, Inc.
CLOSET CLASSICS - Closet organizers - Windquest Companies, Inc.
CLOSET CLEAR - Deodorizers - Enviro-Dynamics Inc.
CLOSET CONTROLLER - Crates - Spectrum International, Inc.
CLOSET COORDINATORS - Racks - Debbie G Inc.
CLOSET EXPANDER - Shelving units–wood ☆ - Hirsh Co.
CLOSET GUARD - Deodorizers ☆ - Frank J. Curran-Esquire Chemical Co.
CLOSET LADY, THE - Closet organizers - Ellyn G. Elstein
CLOSET MAID - Shelving units–plastic - Clairson International Corp.
CLOSET PEOPLE, THE - Closet organizers - MGR Industries, Inc.
CLOSET SCENTS - Cleaning preparations - Scentex Inc.
CLOSET TRAK - Hardware - Vogel Peterson Furniture Co.
CLOSETSOFT - Computer software - Pro Technologies, Inc.
CLOSETTE - Underwear and nightwear - Rago Foundations Inc. LLC
CLOSETVAULT - Vaults - Remagen Corp.
CLOSING THOUGHTS - Recording label - Norwest Mortgage, Inc.
CLOSTROID - Veterinary product - American Home Products Corp.
CLOSURE - Accounting services - Charles T. Almond, III
CLOSURE - Tape–adhesive - Central Products Co.
CLOT POPPER - Toys - Mattel, Inc.
CLOTH-COTE - Fabrics–coated ☆ - Afco Products Inc.
CLOTH OF GOLD - Fabrics - Cloth of Gold, Inc.
CLOTHES AND EFFECT - Apparel–women's - MGRR, Inc.
CLOTHES FOR YOUR HAIR - Hair care products - Hair Apparel, Inc.
CLOTHES FRESH - Deodorizers - Coughlan Products Corp.
CLOTHES LOOK SMOOTH-YOU LOOK SUPER - Apparel and accessories - Playtex Apparel, Inc.
CLOTHES ONLY - Insecticides - Langer Caribbean Corp.
CLOTHES QUARTERS - Shelving units–metal - Test-Rite Products Corp.
CLOTHES SHAVER - Fabrics - Windmere Corp.
CLOTHES THAT COMMUNICATE - Apparel and accessories - Raymond Robinson
CLOTHES TO SLEEP IN - Pajamas–women's - San Francisco Necessities
CLOTHESLINE - Pottery ☆ - Rubens Originals
CLOTHESTIME - Apparel–women's - Clothestime Inc.
CLOTHING CREATOR - Sewing machines–industrial - Symagery Productions Inc.
CLOTHINGCARE - Hooks - Nina Enterprises, Inc.
CLOTHSTOK - File folders - National Fiberstok Corp.
CLOTRIMAZOLE - Pharmaceutical preparations - NutraMax Products Inc.
CLOUD - Cribs–metal ☆ - Cosco, Inc.
CLOUD - Dinnerware–glass ☆ - WMF/USA
CLOUD - Housewares - H.D. Hudson Manufacturing Co.
CLOUD 9 - Bicycles - Columbia Manufacturing Inc.
CLOUD 9 - Finishing agents - Byrne Ceramic Supply Co. Inc.
CLOUD 9 STERILE-AIRE - Air purification systems - Cloud 9

☆ = Now out of production

CLOUD-10 - Mats - Ludlow Composites Corp.
CLOUD 17 - Girdles ☆ - Playtex Apparel, Inc.
CLOUD 28 - Sporting goods - Kellwood Co.
CLOUD BANDS - Floor coverings–carpet and rugs ☆ - Regal Rugs Inc.
CLOUD BURSTS - Candy - Uniconfis Corp.
CLOUD CHART - Weather tracking equipment - Cloud Chart Inc.
CLOUD CITY - Toys - Lucasfilm Ltd.
CLOUD COUNTRY - Colognes ☆ - Avon Products, Inc.
CLOUD CRIB & DRESSING TABLE - Furniture–children's ☆ - Cosco, Inc.
CLOUD CUTIES BORN IN HEAVEN ABOVE, TO BRING YOU LOVE AND A LIL' PEACE OF HEAVEN - Dolls - Bethann Shannon
CLOUD FLANNEL - Fabrics–flannel - Collins & Aikman Corp.
CLOUD FLEECE - Crocheted and knitted items - Collins & Aikman Corp.
CLOUD FOAM - Slippers - Sara Lee Corp.
CLOUD KIST - Food products - Draper-King Cole Inc.
CLOUD MASTER - Gasoline - Maxus Energy Corp.
CLOUD NINE - Candy - Leaf, Inc.
CLOUD NINE - Cleaning preparations - Barcolene Inc.
CLOUD NINE - Dolls - Mae T. Rossiter
CLOUD NINE - Floor coverings–carpet and rugs ☆ - Southern Carpet Mills
CLOUD NINE - Giftware ☆ - World of Porcelain & Glassware
CLOUD NINE - Popcorn ☆ - Seventh Generation Wholesale Inc.
CLOUD-NINE HERBAL DIP - Homeopathic remedies - Andrea Brown
CLOUD NINETEEN - Wallcovering - Wall Trends, Inc.
CLOUD PUFF - Fabrics–cotton - Collins & Aikman Corp.
CLOUD SOFT - Bathroom accessories - World Wide Manufacturing Inc.
CLOUD SOFT - Bedding products - Piedmont Quilting Corp.
CLOUD, THE - Cushions - Genesis Composites, Inc.
CLOUDBURST - Apparel and accessories - Abel Industries Inc.
CLOUDEES - Footwear–women's - E.S. Originals, Inc.
CLOUDHOPPERS - Shoes - Oomphies Inc.
CLOUDLAND - Dinnerware–glass ☆ - Nikko Ceramics Inc.
CLOUDRIFT - Floor coverings–carpet and rugs - Queen Carpet Corp.
CLOUDS - Eyeglasses - Tropic-Cal Inc.
CLOUDS - Floor coverings–carpet and rugs ☆ - Regal Rugs Inc.
CLOUDS - Lumber - Georgia-Pacific Corp.
CLOUDS ACROSS THE MOON - Christmas tree ornaments - Cracker Box Inc.
CLOUDS OF HERBAL ESSENCE - Soap ☆ - Clairol Inc.
CLOUDSCAPE - Computer software - Visidyne, Inc.
CLOUDSPUN - Handwork supplies - Bernat Yarn & Craft Corp.
CLOUDSTER - Shoes–athletic - Ektelon
CLOUDTEX - Christmas tree ornaments - Santa's Best
CLOUDY SOFT - Paper–toilet - International Products Trade Corp.
CLOUT - Computer software ☆ - Microrim Inc.
CLOUT - Detergents - Price Co.
CLOUT - Garden equipment ☆ - Scotts Co. (Organics Business Group)
CLOUT - Water treating compounds - Aquarium Products Inc.
CLOVAINE - Health care products ☆ - Suppositoria Laboratories
CLOVE-A-DAY - Vitamins and nutritional supplements - Pure-Gar
CLOVE & BABY PARSLEY - Toys–stuffed ☆ - Gund, Inc.
CLOVE ENCOUNTER - Salad dressings–bottled - Johnny's Enterprises Inc.
CLOVE ENCOUNTERS - Seasonings - Garlic Festival Foods
CLOVER - Abrasive products - Fel-Pro Inc.
CLOVER - Cheese - F.M. Van Tol
CLOVER - Dog food - MFC Services
CLOVER - Dolls - Uneeda Doll Co., Inc.
CLOVER - Food products - Chiquita Brands, Inc.
CLOVER - Greeting cards ☆ - Fran Mar Greeting cards Ltd.
CLOVER - Jewelry - Clover Chain Co.
CLOVER - Milk - Clover Farms Dairy Co.
CLOVER - Needles–sewing ☆ - JCA, Inc.
CLOVER - Pet products - SF Services, Inc.
CLOVER - Skin care products - Lado Co. of America
CLOVER - Toys–stuffed ☆ - Russ Berrie and Co., Inc.
CLOVER BLOOM TWIST - Tobacco products - Scott Tobacco Co.
CLOVER BLOSSOM - Cheese ☆ - Farmers Cheese Co.
CLOVER CEIL - Paints - Seagraves Coatings
CLOVER CLUB - Apparel and accessories - Breton Industries
CLOVER CLUB - Snack foods - Granny Goose Foods, Inc.
CLOVER FARM - Food products - Scrivner, Inc.
CLOVER HILL - Candy - Clover Hill Candies
CLOVER LEAF - Barbecues and grills ☆ - Rasmussen Iron Works Inc.
CLOVER LEAF - Milk - Clover Leaf Jersey Dairy
CLOVER LEAF - Paints - Seagraves Coatings
CLOVER LEAF - Seafood products–canned or cured - Bumble Bee Seafoods, Inc.

CLOVER ORCHARD - Food products ☆ - Seneca Foods Corp.
CLOVER SEAL - Paints - Seagraves Coatings
CLOVER SWEET - Milk - Wild Goose Holding Co., Inc.
CLOVER TONE - Paints - Seagraves Coatings
CLOVER TRADING CO. - Apparel trimmings - Big Bear Stores Co.
CLOVER VALLEY - Food products - The Kroger Co.
CLOVERBLOOM - Dairy products - Armour Dairy Co.
CLOVERDALE PRIDE - Ice cream - Cloverdale Farms Dairy Inc.
CLOVERFIELD - Milk - Cumberland Farms Inc.
CLOVERFILL - Fibers–polyester - Leslie Blok
CLOVERINE - Cough drops - Wilson Products Co. Inc.
CLOVERINE - Pharmaceutical preparations - Medtech Laboratories Inc.
CLOVERLAND - Meat products - Moran Foods, Inc.
CLOVERLAND - Milk - Cloverland Farms Dairy
CLOVERLEAF - Computers - Eventide Inc.
CLOVERLEAF - Glassware–household ☆ - Anchor Hocking Glass, Inc.
CLOVERLEAF - Paperboard ☆ - A.I. Friedman Inc.
CLOVERLEAF LANE - Greeting cards - American Greetings Corp.
CLOVERLY - Giftware - Instar Enterprises International Inc.
CLOVERTREE SPRING WATER SINCE 1982 - Water–bottled or canned - Clovertree, Inc.
CLOVERVALE FOODS - Frozen foods - Clovervale Foods, Inc.
CLOVIS - Vinegar ☆ - Spruce Foods Inc.
CLOVIS RUFFAY - Product description unknown - Boutique Loungewear Inc.
CLOVIS RUFFIN - Apparel–women's - Famous Designers Ltd.
CLOVITE - Veterinary product - American Home Products Corp.
CLOVOCAINE - Pharmaceutical preparations - Vita Elixir Co. Inc.
CLOWN - Flowers, plants, and seeds - Geo. J. Ball, Inc.
CLOWN - Flowers, plants, and seeds - Panamerican Seed
CLOWN - Kites ☆ - Hi-Flier Manufacturing Co.
CLOWN - Recording label - Clown
CLOWN A ROUN - Toys - Marlin Toy Products Inc.
CLOWN-A-ROUND - Toys–stuffed - Fun World Inc.
CLOWN-A-ROUNDS - Candy ☆ - Dorval Trading Co., Ltd.
CLOWN ALLEY - Figurines ☆ - E.M.I. Inc.
CLOWN & CIRCUS PLAY KIT - Puzzles ☆ - Warren Industries Inc.
CLOWN AROUND - Dolls ☆ - Dakin Inc.
CLOWN AROUND - Games - Pressman Toy Corp.
CLOWN AROUND BEAR - Toys–stuffed ☆ - Dakin Inc.
CLOWN BABY - Dolls - Uneeda Doll Co., Inc.
CLOWN COLLEGE - Paper products - Ringling Bros.-Barnum & Bailey Combined Shows, Inc.
CLOWN FACES - Cosmetics - Paper Magic Group Inc.
CLOWN GO'ROUND - Toys ☆ - Steven Manufacturing Co.
CLOWN MOUTH - Candy - Glenn Confections Inc.
CLOWN STACK - Toys - Playskool, Inc.
CLOWN WALKER - Toys - Steven Manufacturing Co.
CLOWNAROUND - House furnishings - Gear Holdings, Inc.
CLOWNIN' AROUND - Figurines - Delfino Products Inc.
CLOWNING AROUND RABBIT - Toys–stuffed - Dakin Inc.
CLOWNS, THE - Greeting cards ☆ - Kersten Bros. Studios
CLOWNY - Dolls - Just Clowns
CLOXAPEN - Pharmaceutical preparations - Smithkline Beecham Corp.
CLOYNE COURT - Floor coverings ☆ - Tarkett, Inc.
CLOZE: FAMOUS FABLES - Computer software - Orange Cherry Software
CLOZE-PLUS - Computer software - Instructional/Communications Technology Inc.
CLOZE: READING IN CONTEXT - Computer software - Orange Cherry Software
CLP WIZARD - Computer software - Chemsoft, Inc.
CLP(BNR) - Computer software - Applied Logic Systems, Inc.
CLPR - Computer peripheral equipment - Computational Engineering International, Inc.
CLR - Cleaning preparations - Jamie Industries, Inc.
CLSR - Publisher's imprints - Robert P. Bigelow
CLT - Safety products - Uvex Safety LLC
CLUB - Apparel and accessories - Crystal Brands Inc.
CLUB - Beverages–alcohol - Heublein, Inc.
CLUB - Beverages–malt ☆ - Labatt Importers Inc.
CLUB - Candy - Thos. D. Richardson Co.
CLUB - Cooking utensils–aluminum - Jacksonville Manufacturing
CLUB - Cooking utensils–aluminum - Regal Ware, Inc.
CLUB - Crackers - Keebler Co.
CLUB - Floor coverings–carpet and rugs ☆ - Regal Rugs Inc.
CLUB - Metals - Winner International Royalty Corp.
CLUB - Musical instrument accessories - Davitt and Hanser Music Co.

CLUB - Office supplies - R.A. Stewart Superior
CLUB - Paper–cigarette - Robert Burton Associates Ltd.
CLUB - Sprayers - Winner International Corp.
CLUB 40 - Apparel–children's - Names, Inc.
CLUB 99 - Recording label - Custom Duplication, Inc.
CLUB 273 - Leather goods - Fred Hayman Beverly Hills Inc.
CLUB 400 - Whiskey - Majestic Distilling Co.
CLUB 900 - Sporting goods - Nordictrack, Inc.
CLUB AMERICA - Footwear - Dynasty Footwear, Ltd.
CLUB ART CRAFT - Coffee makers–electric - Jacksonville Manufacturing
CLUB BABY - Recording label - New Reality Productions, Ltd.
CLUB BAGS - Luggage - Mercury Luggage Manufacturing Co.
CLUB BARON - Pizzas–frozen ☆ - Schwan's Sales Enterprises, Inc.
CLUB BEVERLY HILLS INTERNATIONAL 2001 - Apparel and accessories - Beverly Hills Products, Inc.
CLUB BINGO - Games - Pacific Game Co.
CLUB-BIRD - Meat products–poultry - Pierce Foods Corp.
CLUB BRONZE - Suntan lotions - Fruit of the Earth, Inc.
CLUB CALIFORNIA - Eyeglasses - Cable Car Eyeware
CLUB CANDLE - Candles ☆ - Candle-Lite Co.
CLUB CAPRI - Luggage - Travelers Club Luggage Inc.
CLUB CAROUSEL - Furniture - Prodesign, Inc.
CLUB CASINO - Playing cards - United States Playing Card Co.
CLUB CHAMPION - Floor coverings–carpet and rugs ☆ - Mannington Carpets, Inc.
CLUB CHAMPION - Games ☆ - Pacific Game Co.
CLUB CHEESE - Cheese - Old Tavern Food Products Inc.
CLUB CHEF - Fruits and vegetables - Club Chef
CLUB CHINESE CHECKERS - Games ☆ - Milton Bradley Co.
CLUB CLASSIC - Housewares - Jacksonville Manufacturing
CLUB CLASSIC - Ophthalmic goods - Foremost Optical Products
CLUB CLASSIC - Shoe polish - Fore Supply Co.
CLUB/COLLEGIATE 420 - Boats - Vanguard Racing Sailboats
CLUB COLORS - Clothing - Club Colors, Inc.
CLUB COOKERS - Barbecues and grills ☆ - Jacksonville Manufacturing
CLUB DANCE - Apparel and accessories - Opryland USA Inc.
CLUB DISNEY - Socks ☆ - High Point Knitting Inc.
CLUB DU DISQUES ARABE - Recording label - Rashid Sales Co.
CLUB DU FAISAN - Food products - De Medici Imports Ltd.
CLUB ELITE - Apparel and accessories - Brooks Leather Sportswear Inc.
CLUB EXCLUSIF - Colognes - Tristar Corp.
CLUB FITNESS GYM & PERSONAL TRAINING - Apparel and accessories - Club Fitness Inc.
CLUB GARD - Golfing equipment - Ajay Leisure Products Inc.
CLUB GLOVE - Golfing equipment - West Coast Trends Inc.
CLUB GREEN - Fertilizers - Lange-Stegmann Co.
CLUB GUARANTEED QUALITY - Exercising equipment - Hoist Fitness Systems
CLUB HOUSE - Wallpaper - Longmeadow Studio
CLUB/JUNIOR - Boats - Vanguard Racing Sailboats
CLUB KIEL CENTER, THE - Apparel and accessories - Kiel Center Partners
CLUB-KIT - Golfing equipment - Club Kit Inc.
CLUB KUAII - Jewelry - Music City Marketing, Inc.
CLUB L.A. - Frames–eyeglass - Euro-Frames Inc.
CLUB LA JOLLA CALIFORNIA - Apparel and accessories - CLJ Designs, Inc.
CLUB LA MER - Sunglasses - Optica Italee
CLUB LOCKER - Golf accessories - Summit Industries, Inc.
CLUB LONDON - Tobacco products - Shepherd Tobacco Co.
CLUB LOUNGE - Apparel and accessories - Knothe Corp.
CLUB-MAID - Golfing equipment - Ultrasonics International Corp.
CLUB MASTER - Rackets–tennis - Head Sports USA
CLUB MATE - Golf clips - Ronald L. Strahan
CLUB MATES - Crocheted and knitted items ☆ - Goodman Knitting Co. Inc.
CLUB MEDLEY - Fruits and vegetables - Harry and David Inc.
CLUB MIRAGE - Hotels and motels - Mirage Resorts, Inc.
CLUB MODA - Shoes - Chainson Footwear, Inc.
CLUB MONTANA - Handbags - Mischief Makers Inc.
CLUB MOO - Beverages - The Kroger Co.
CLUB NAUTICO - Apparel and accessories - Adventurent, Inc.
CLUB NET INTERNATIONAL - Nutritional supplements - Club Net International, Inc.
CLUB NEWPORT - Apparel and accessories - Chadwick's of Boston, Ltd.
CLUB OASIS - Games - International Gamco, Inc.
CLUB OF SPADE - Recording label - Longhorn Records
CLUB ONE - Golfing equipment - TourEdge Golf Manufacturing Inc.
CLUB OPUS - Luggage and travel accessories - Jameslee Corp.

CLUB ORGANIZER - Golfing equipment - Exim Manufacturers, Inc.
CLUB PACK - Golfing equipment - Wilson Sporting Goods Co.
CLUB PARCHMENT - Stationery - Samuel Ward Manufacturing Inc.
CLUB PARK - Furniture - Collingwood Furniture
CLUB PC - Computer peripheral equipment - Pacific Business Systems, Inc.
CLUB PORPOISE - Air mattresses - Porpoise Pool & Patio, Inc.
CLUB PRESIDENT - Floor coverings–carpet and rugs - Barrett Carpet Mills Inc.
CLUB PRO - Floor coverings–carpet and rugs - Johnson's Carpets Inc.
CLUB PRO - Games - Precise Exercise Equipment, Inc.
CLUB PROFESSIONAL - Rackets–tennis - Head Sports USA
CLUB QT - Bicycles ☆ - Hedstrom Corp.
CLUB R - Frames–eyeglass - Barbara Kauz & Associates
CLUB RENO - Playing cards ☆ - United States Playing Card Co.
CLUB RIVIERA - Luggage - Travelers Club Luggage Inc.
CLUB ROOM - Apparel–men's - R.H. Macy & Co.
CLUB ROOST - Sporting goods - Mady International Inc.
CLUB ROYAL - Floor coverings–carpet and rugs ☆ - Kelly Group Inc.
CLUB ROYALE - American International Industries
CLUB SABATASSO - Breads–frozen - Sabatasso Foods Inc.
CLUB SANDWICH - Food products - York Barbell Co., Inc.
CLUB SHRED - Eyeglasses - Cable Car Eyeware
CLUB SHRED - Sunglasses - Lifeforms International, Inc.
CLUB SMARTY CATS - Jewelry - Lawrence Jewelry Co.
CLUB SODA - Recording label - Jazz Composer's Orchestra Association Inc.
CLUB SOX - Crocheted and knitted items - Reliable of Milwaukee
CLUB SPECIAL - Popcorn poppers - Original Designs/Famor Inc.
CLUB SPECIAL - Whiskey - Standard Distillers Products Inc.
CLUB SPORTSWEAR - Apparel–athletic - Club Sportswear Inc.
CLUB SQUARE - Luggage - Travelers Club Luggage Inc.
CLUB SURFNIKS - Sportswear - Squire of California
CLUB T, THE - Golfing equipment - Ragusin, Dianna
CLUB TAHITI - Beverages - Romanoff International Inc.
CLUB, THE - Alarm systems - Winner International Corp.
CLUB TIES - Wallpaper - Surface Industries Inc.
CLUB TOWEL, THE - Towels - West Point-Pepperell Inc.
CLUB TRAINER - Exercising equipment ☆ - Trotter Inc.
CLUB TRANS ATLANTIQUE - Waterproof outerwear - Fox-Knapp Inc.
CLUB TROPICANA - Luggage - Travelers Club Luggage Inc.
CLUB TUB BY ELLIS - Golfing equipment - Howard F. Ellis
CLUB VELLUM - Stationery - Samuel Ward Manufacturing Inc.
CLUB VOGUE - Jewelry - William Feldman and Co. Inc.
CLUB WAGON - Motor vehicles–automobiles - Ford Motor Co.
CLUBFAST - Cosmetics - Morris-Flamingo Inc.
CLUBHOUSE - Floor coverings - American Floor Products Co. Inc.
CLUBHOUSE - Floor coverings–carpet and rugs - Conquest Carpet Mills Inc.
CLUBHOUSE - Floor coverings–carpet and rugs - Mohawk Carpet Corp.
CLUBHOUSE - Luggage - Airway Industries, Inc.
CLUBHOUSE - Trading cards - ANCO Collector Supplies, Inc.
CLUBHOUSE CHOPS - Toys - Charlie and the Chops Warnervision Entertainment
CLUBHOUSE DIAMONDS SERIES - Trading cards and stamps - Clubhouse Diamonds Ltd.
CLUBHOUSE SPORTS - Computer software - Mindscape Software Inc.
CLUBLINKS - Computer software - Hudson Consulting Co.
CLUBMAC - Computers - Pacific Business Systems, Inc.
CLUBMAN - American International Industries
CLUBMAN - Audio equipment ☆ - Meteor Light & Sound Co.
CLUBMAN SPORT - American International Industries
CLUBMAN SUPREME - American International Industries
CLUBMAN TOP COVER - American International Industries
CLUBPRO - Computer software - Soma Software
CLUBSTER II - Golf carts ☆ - Bag Boy Inc.
CLUBTRACK PLUS - Exercising equipment - Quinton Instrument Co.
CLUBWARE - Cooking equipment–household - Jacksonville Manufacturing
CLUBWEIGHT SCALE, THE - Golfing equipment - Golfsmith International Inc.
CLUCK WAGON CHICKEN - Food products - Brinker Restaurant Corp.
C.L.U.E. - Apparel–men's - World Source, Inc.
CLUE - Frames–eyeglass - Zylo Ware Corp.
CLUE - Games - Parker Brothers
CLUE FOR KIDS - Puzzles - Hasbro, Inc.
CLUE IN ON PHONICS - Computer software - Gamco Industries Inc.
CLUE JUNIOR - Games - Parker Brothers
CLUE MASTER DETECTIVE - Games ☆ - Parker Brothers
CLUELESS - Cosmetics - Sassaby Inc.
CLUELESS - Paper products - Paramount Pictures Corp.

☆ = Now out of production

CLUJ-NAPOCA - Dinnerware–glass - M & M Associates Ltd.
CLUM MANUFACTURING CO., INC. - Electrical equipment - Camdec Corp.
CLUMSY CLAUS - Giftware - Roman, Inc.
CLUNY - Beverages–alcohol ☆ - Scottish & Newcastle Importers Co.
CLUNY - Floor coverings–carpet and rugs ☆ - Regal Rugs Inc.
CLUNY - Rings–jewelry - Artcarved Inc.
CLUPAK - Paper - Clupak Inc.
CLUPS, THE - Computer software - Clever Software Solutions, Inc.
CLUSIVAL - Vitamins and nutritional supplements - Whitehall Laboratories
CLUSTER - Aquariums–household - Northwest Aquarium Supply Ltd.
CLUSTER - Fruits and vegetables - Upland Lemon Co.
CLUSTER - Jewelry - Cluster Jewelry Co. Inc.
CLUSTER 120 - Furniture ☆ - Esselte Corp.
CLUSTER BOMB - Fireworks - American Promotional Events, Inc.
CLUSTER BOX - Candy - Fanny Farmer Candy Shops Inc.
CLUSTER-COMB - Furniture - Hamilton Sorter Co. Inc.
CLUSTER-CORE - Furniture - Hamilton Sorter Co. Inc.
CLUSTER HOLDER - Fishing tackle - Hawie Manufacturing Co.
CLUSTERPICK - Computer software - Hans A. Nijkamp
CLUSTERS - Cereal - General Mills, Inc.
CLUSTERS - Fishing lures ☆ - Brown Bear Bait Co.
CLUSTERSCAN - Electronics equipment - Rappaport Exhibits Inc.
CLUSTERSWITCH - Computer hardware - Netstar, Inc.
CLUTCH - Toys - Tonka Corp.
CLUTCH BRUSH - Hair curlers - Sunbeam-Oster Household Products
CLUTCH CITY - Trading cards and stamps - Rocket Ball, Ltd.
CLUTCH POPPERS - Toys - Tonka Corp.
CLUTCHESS - Cases–eyeglass ☆ - California Optical Leather Inc.
CLUTTER BUSTER - Garment hangers - A & S Gutterman
CLUTTER CATCHER - Automotive parts and accessories - Texas Saddlebags, Inc.
CLUTTER CUTTER - Desk sets - Artistic Office Products
CLUTTER CUTTER - Housewares - Quick Order Systems
CLUTTER CUTTER - Paneling - Georgia-Pacific Corp.
CLUTTER-PROOF - Desks ☆ - Knoll Group
CLYBOURN CANDLE CRAFTS PURVEYORS OF FINE CANDLES - Candles - Artmark-Chicago, Ltd.
CLYDE - Frames–eyeglass - Zylo Ware Corp.
CLYDE - Guns - Charter Arms
CLYDE MCCOY - Musical instrument accessories ☆ - Micro Musical Products Corp.
CLYDE O SCOPE - Kaleidoscopes - Gemini Kaleidoscopes
CLYDESDALE - Fountains - Anheuser-Busch Companies Inc.
CLYDESDALE - Hardware ☆ - Amerock Corp.
CLYDESDALE - Watches - Bulova Corp.
CLYDESENTRY - Computer software - Raxco Software Inc.
CLYNELISH - Beverages–malt - European Beverage Co., Inc.
CLYO - Colognes - Chesebrough-Pond's USA Co.
CM - Computer software - Codemaster Corp.
CM - Electrical equipment - Coin Mechanisms, Inc.
CM - Microphones - Crown International, Inc.
CM - Paper - Crunden Martin Manufacturing Co.
CM - Surgical instruments - Cross Medical Products, Inc.
CM - Yarn - ANB International, Inc.
CM/1 - Computer software - Corporate Memory Systems, Inc.
CM-21 - Vitamins and nutritional supplements - Australian Bodycare Enterprises, Inc.
CM-88 - Chemical preparations - Georgia-Pacific Corp.
CM-100 - Exercising equipment - Empi Inc.
C.M. ALMY & SON - Apparel and accessories - C.M. Almy & Son Inc.
CM BIG ORANGE - Hooks - Columbus Mckinnon Corp.
CM CASTLE MOTORCYCLES - Motorcycle parts and accessories - Castle Motorcycles Manufacturing, Inc.
CM CRITICAL MASS - Bowling balls - Track, Inc.
CM CRYSTAL MILLS - Shirts - Manis & Singer, Inc.
C.M. GEESE - Apparel and accessories - Wayne L. Phillips
CM III - Microscopes - Mentor O & O Inc.
CM IV - Microscopes - Mentor O & O Inc.
CM-L LIFTER - Forklifts - Custom Metalcraft, Inc.
CM LABS - Audio equipment ☆ - Meteor Light & Sound Co.
CM MAX - Industrial machinery - Columbus Mckinnon Corp.
CM/P - Computer software - BMC Software, Inc.
CM/PILOT - Computer software - BMC Software, Inc.
CM PLUS - Health care products - Klabin Computer and Marketing Consultants Ltd., Inc.
CM/PROSONIX - Audio equipment ☆ - Meteor Light & Sound Co.

CM PULLER - Tools - Columbus Mckinnon Corp.
C.M. SHAPES - Apparel and accessories - Lawrence Stevens Fashions, Ltd.
C.M. SHAPES - Apparel–women's - Lawrence Stevens Inc.
C.M. WANGS - Apparel–athletic - Talbot Street Pier, Inc.
CM2 - Computer software - Hampton Systems Group, Inc.
CM3 - Ice making machinery - Scotsman Group, Inc.
CM4 - Vitamins and nutritional supplements - Omega Pharmaceutical, Inc.
CM5 - Computers - Thinking Machines Corp.
C.M.A. - Paints ☆ - C.M. Athey Paint Co.
CMA - Vitamins and nutritional supplements - Alacer Co.
CMA STANDARDS COOKWARE MANUFACTURERS ASSOCIATION - Cookware - Cookware Manufacturers Association
CMATH - Computer software - Life Science Associates
CMB - Recording label - CM Productions, Inc.
CMC - Ceiling panels - Chicago Metallic Corp.
CMC - Drums–musical instruments - Chesbro Music Co.
CMC - Flag poles ☆ - Dap Products Inc.
CMC - Food products ☆ - Cumberland-Swan, Inc.
CMC - Machine parts - Cleveland Motion Controls, Inc.
C.M.C. - Motor vehicles–trucks - C.M.C. Trailer Distributors, Inc.
CMC 2000 - Golfing equipment - Golfsmith International Inc.
CMC 5000 - Golfing equipment - Golfsmith International Inc.
CMCD - Computer software - Clement Mok Design Inc.
CMCV - Wines - CM/CV Society
CMDS - Electronic equipment - Paso Sound Products Inc.
CME INFORMATION SERVICES - Video production - CME Conference Video, Inc.
CMEE - Textbooks - National Computer Systems, Inc.
CMEVIDEO - Recording label - CME Conference Video, Inc.
CMG - Jewelry - Carlson Marketing Group, Inc.
CMG - Paper mills - Conflict Management Group
CMG CENTURY MARKETING GROUP - Labels–paper - Century Marketing Corp.
CMI - Concrete–mixture - WL & Associates
CMI - Fruits and vegetables - Columbia Fruit Packers Inc.
CMI - Sporting goods - Climb High Inc.
C.M.I. - Sweaters - Manning Trading Co., Inc.
CMIF - Recording label - Jazz Composer's Orchestra Association Inc.
CMJ - Jewelry - Cordova Inc.
CML - Jewelry - Carl Messler Ltd.
CML - Tools - Witco Corp.
CML DUO - Medical apparatus - Cobe Laboratories, Inc.
CML MACARR - Nautical instruments - Marine Electric Systems Inc.
CMM LIVE - Computer software - Process Focus Software, Inc.
CMMS - Computer software - Horizon Systems, Inc.
C.M.N. OF ITALY - Hosiery - Kartex International Cos. Inc.
CMOS-CBA - Integrated circuits - Siarc
CMP - Chemical preparations - Edwin W. Albers
CMR-8 - Adhesives and sealants - Loctite Corp.
CMR-MAX - Computer software - Schlumberger Industries, Inc.
C.M.S. - Antacids ☆ - Vernon Laboratories Inc.
CMS - Desks - Herman Miller, Inc.
CMS - Medical apparatus - Computerized Medical Systems, Inc.
CMS 1000 - Cleaning preparations–carpet and rug - Amway Corp.
CMS CAMPAIGN MANAGEMENT SYSTEM - Computer software - Drake Beam Morin, Inc.
C.M.S. CLIPART SKETCHBOOK - Artwork - Creative Media Services
CMS DATA - Computer software - CMS/DATA Corp.
CMS MARKETRACK - Computer software - Computerized Mailing Systems, Inc.
CMS PROTOCOL - Dyes and pigments - Curtin Matheson Scientific, Inc.
CMS RELI-A-BILT - Cranes - Crane Manufacturing & Service Corp.
CMW - Motor vehicles - New York Sidecar Connection
CMX - Mufflers–motor vehicle - Engelhard Corp.
CMX AEGIS - Computer peripheral equipment - Chyron Corp.
CMX OMNI - Computer peripheral equipment - Chyron Corp.
CN - Bathroom accessories - Venturi, Inc.
CN - Floor coverings ☆ - Congoleum Corp.
CNA - Jewelry - Crystaline North America, Inc.
CNB - Boilers–hot water - Combustion Service & Equipment Co.
CNB - Nuts and bolts - Chicago Nut and Bolt, Inc.
CNB TRI-FUEL - Boilers–hot water - Combustion Service & Equipment Co.
CNC VISUALIZER - Computer software - Fadal Engineering Co., Inc.
CNF - Vitamins and nutritional supplements - Natural Balance, Inc.
CNG - Natural gas - Shell Oil Co.
CNI - Binders - Circuit Network Inc.

☆ = Now out of production

CNIKKO - Product description unknown ☆ - E. Chaput Inc.

CNLAB 3202 CYANIDE ANALYZER - Analyzers–industrial - O.I. Corp.

CNS - Medical apparatus - CNS, Inc.

CNS - Wood preservative - Continental Products Co.

CNS/LINK - Electronic equipment ☆ - Arinc, Inc.

CNSOLUTION 3000 CYANIDE ANALYZER - Analyzers–industrial - O.I. Corp.

CNTZ - Apparel–women's - Kellwood Co.

CNX - Glass lanterns, globes ☆ - Corning Inc.

CO-A - Hair care products - Dowbrands L.P.

CO-A KINETICS - Hair care products - Dowbrands L.P.

CO ACCESS - Communications equipment - Boston Technology Inc.

CO-ACH - Computer software - Applied Communications, Inc.

CO-BACIL - Agricultural products - CCT Corp.

CO-BILE - Pharmaceutical preparations - Western Research Laboratories

CO-BOY - Figurines ☆ - Goebel of North America

CO-CA NAMEL - Enamels - Cowman-Campbell Paint Co.

CO CO - Pet products - Rolf C. Hagen (USA) Corp.

CO-CO-RA - Liqueurs - Lawrence Foods Inc.

CO-ED - Frames–eyeglass ☆ - Universal/Univis Inc.

CO-ED - Girdles - Sears, Roebuck and Co.

CO-ED - Watches - Bulova Corp.

CO-EEZ - Cough medicines ☆ - Coast Laboratories Inc.

CO-ENTERO - Pharmaceutical preparations ☆ - Coast Laboratories Inc.

CO ENZYME Q - Vitamins and nutritional supplements - Great Life Laboratories Inc.

CO-EXYLENE - Bags–plastic - Winpak Films Inc.

CO-FLEX - Bandages - Andover Coated Products Inc.

CO-FLEX - Bandages–orthopedic - Cramer Products Inc.

CO-GEL - Pharmaceutical preparations ☆ - Ulmer Pharmacal Co.

CO-GESIC - Analgesics - Central Pharmaceutical Inc.

CO-HISTINE - Health care products ☆ - Kay Pharmacal Co. Inc.

CO-HOST - Frames–eyeglass - Liberty Optical Manufacturing Co.

CO-LOUR - Hair care products ☆ - IFM Group, Inc.

CO-LU-GEL - Pharmaceutical preparations ☆ - Ulmer Pharmacal Co.

CO-MO - Artists' materials - Bee Paper Co. Inc.

CO-NIB - Health care products - J.H. Guild Co. Inc.

CO-OP - Food products - Universal Cooperative Inc.

CO-OP EASY - Computer software - JNS Technologies, LLC

CO-OP SUPER DIESELEX-4 - Gasoline - Countrymark Cooperative, Inc.

CO-ORDINATES - Carpets, now out of production - Couristan Inc.

CO-PERAZINE - Prescription drug ☆ - IDE-Interstate Inc.

CO PILOT - Frames–eyeglass - Pathway Optical Prods.

CO-PILOT - Girdles - Custom Maid Brassiere Co.

CO-PILOT - Marine rigging - Outboard Marine Corp.

CO-PILOT - Seats–automobile ☆ - Collier-Keyworth Inc.

CO PLANAR WING - Golf clubs - DeLuca Sports

CO-POLY - Caulking compounds - Nu Puttie Corp.

CO-PRODUCTS - Chemical preparations - Castlebar Industries Corp.

CO-PYRONIL - Pharmaceutical preparations - Dista Products Co.

CO Q - Vitamins and nutritional supplements ☆ - Ethical Nutrients

CO-Q-1O - Vitamins and nutritional supplements - Horizon Worldwide Export Corp.

CO Q-10 - Health care products - Above All Health Inc.

CO-Q-10 - Pharmaceutical preparations - Hillestad International, Inc.

CO-SCENTRY - Housewares stores - Rule Industries, Inc.

CO SNIFFER - Measuring instruments - Bacharach, Inc.

CO-ST CUTTERS - Tools - LRH Enterprises Inc.

CO STAR - Apparel–children's - Softwear Co. for Kids Inc.

CO STAR - Apparel–women's - Exquisite Form Industries

CO-STAR - Cleaning preparations - W.W. Grainger, Inc.

CO-STAR - Computer storage devices - Alpha Pacific

CO-STAR - Eyeglasses - Art-Craft Optical Co.

CO-STAR - Recording label - American Railroad Corp.

CO-STAR - Recording label ☆ - Nationwide Sound Distributors

CO-TAR-OX - Pharmaceutical preparations ☆ - Ulmer Pharmacal Co.

CO-TINIC - Pharmaceutical preparations ☆ - Vortech Pharmaceuticals

CO-VA-CO - Food products - Del Monte Corp.

CO-VAL-U - Paints ☆ - Valspar Corp.

CO: WRITER - Computer software - Don Johnston Inc.

CO-XAN - Cold remedies ☆ - Central Pharmaceutical Inc.

CO2SMO - Medical apparatus - Novametrix Medical Systems, Inc.

CO2X - Alarm systems - Dickson/Unigage, Inc.

COACH - Bandages - Johnson & Johnson

COACH - Computer software - Phase 2 Consulting Inc.

COACH - Frames–eyeglass ☆ - Universal/Univis Inc.

COACH - Health care products - Elexis Corp.

COACH - Leather goods - Coach Leatherware

COACH - Outerwear - Saramar Corp.

COACH - Sporting goods - Hoag-Co.

COACH - Sporting goods - Jim Viola Co.

COACH ARMOR - Motor vehicle parts and accessories - Mills Manufacturing, Inc.

COACH COLLECTION - Golfing equipment - Daiwa Corp.

COACH CRAFT - Travel trailers - American Travel Systems, Inc.

COACH GUARD - Motor vehicle parts and accessories - Universal Coach Parts, Inc.

COACH HOUSE - Candy ☆ - Home of the Hebert Candies, Inc.

COACH HOUSE - Fabrics - Decorative Coverings Inc.

COACH HOUSE - Seasonings - Silver Foods Corp.

COACH HOUSE - Trailers–travel ☆ - Coachmen Industries, Inc.

COACH HOUSE COLLECTIBLES - Cooking equipment–household ☆ - Anchor Hocking Glass, Inc.

COACH HYDE - Ophthalmic goods - Fidelity Case Corp.

COACH LAMP - Candles ☆ - Empire Manufacturing Co.

COACH LANTERN - Lighting fixtures - Lava-Simplex Internationale

COACH LEATHERWEAR - Eyeglass cases - Saramar Corp.

COACH, THE - Jackets - Howe K. Sipes Co.

COACHELLA - Recording label - Accent Records

COACHELLA JOE - Fruits and vegetables - Sun World, Inc.

COACHES CHOICE - Soccer equipment ☆ - Brine Inc.

COACHMAN - Fishing rods - Maurice Sporting Goods, Inc.

COACHMAN - Frames–eyeglass - May Optical Co. Inc.

COACHMAN - Toys–guns - Parris Manufacturing Co.

COACHMAN - Varnishes - Barrett Varnish Co.

COACHMAN - Waterproof outerwear - Seaway Importing Co.

COACHMASTER - Archery equipment - Range-O-Matic Archery Co.

COACHMEN - Trailers–travel - Coachmen Industries, Inc.

COACHMEN'S - Tobacco–chewing or smoking - 1776 Tobacco Co.

COACHOUSE - Floor coverings–carpet and rugs - Atlas Carpet Mills Inc.

COACH'S ASSISTANT SOCCER EDITION - Computer software - Logical Solutions, Inc.

COACH'S COLLECTION - Apparel and accessories - Vicki Lea Enterprises, Inc.

COACH'S REPORT - Trading cards and stamps - Upper Deck Co.

COACHWAXX - Cleaning preparations - North American

COACTIN - Antibiotics ☆ - Roche Laboratories

COACTIVE - Software - Coactive Computing Corp.

COACTIVE CONNECTOR - Computer system software - Coactive Computing Corp.

COAG-U-LOID - Dairy products - T.H. Angermeier & Co.

COAL BLUE - Fabrics–denim - Dan River Inc.

COAL IS BLACK GOLD - Paper products - Black Gold Committee, Inc.

COAL MINE COMPANY, THE - Apparel and accessories - Tropical Sportswear International Corp.

COAL PAK - Bricks ☆ - Pasvalco

COAL TAR - Pet products - Tomlyn Products

COALITION - Computer software - Marketplace Systems Group, Inc.

COALMASTER - Heating equipment - Suburban Manufacturing Co.

COALPORT - Earthenware ☆ - Waterford Wedgwood USA, Inc.

COARSE & SASSY - Mustard - Cortina Corp.

COARSEGOLD WINE CELLARS - Wines - Coarsegold Wine Cellar

COAST - Kites - Coast Kites Inc.

COAST - Novelty items - Coast Novelty Manufacturing Co.

COAST - Oils–lubricating ☆ - Kerr-McGee Chemical Corp.

COAST - Shoes–athletic - Coast Shoes Inc.

COAST - Soap - Procter & Gamble Co.

COAST-AIRE - Hardware - Servistar Corp.

COAST BICYCLES USA - Bicycles - Servistar Corp.

COAST COLLECTION - Hats - West Coast Novelty Corp.

COAST CREATIONS - Shoes - D & E Accessories Inc.

COAST EAST - Shirts - Heritage Sportswear

COAST GARD HARDWARE - Hardware - Truth Hardware Corp.

COAST GUARD - Fabrics - Dickson Elberton Mills, Inc.

COAST PAD & TRIM - Shoulder pads - Coast Pad & Trim Corp.

COAST RANGE - Beverages–malt - Coast Range Brewing Co.

COAST RANGE - Wines - Ridge Vineyards Inc.

COAST RUNNER - Boats - Coast Distribution System

COAST TELECOURSES - Video production - Coast Community College District

COAST TO COAST - Balls–basketball - Voit Corp.

COAST TO COAST - Floor coverings–carpet and rugs ☆ - Regal Rugs Inc.

COAST TO COAST - Recording label ☆ - Roadshow Music Corp.

COAST TO COAST - Wallpaper - Hunting Valley Prints
COAST TO COAST'RS - Paper - Florence Paper Co., Inc.
COASTAL - Chemical preparations - Coastal Industries Inc.
COASTAL - Floor coverings—carpet and rugs - Customweave Carpets Inc.
COASTAL - Food products - Connors Brothers Inc.
COASTAL - Pet products - Coastal Pet Products, Inc.
COASTAL AMUSEMENT - Video games - Coastal Amusement, Inc.
COASTAL BLUES - Apparel - Donmoor, Inc.
COASTAL BREEZE - Fans—electric - Hunter Fan Co.
COASTAL CLASSIC - Wine - Corbett Canyon Vineyards
COASTAL COLLECTION - Greeting cards - Leanin' Tree Inc.
COASTAL COLLECTION - Window coverings - Blind Design Inc.
COASTAL COMMANDER - Boats—motor - Holiday Mansion
COASTAL CREST - Wines - Joseph Victori Wines, Inc.
COASTAL GUARD - Colognes - Brandy Harvest
COASTAL OAKS - Wines ☆ - Caymus Vineyards
COASTAL VALLEY - Wines - Louis Glunz Inc.
COASTAL VINTERS - Beverages—alcohol - Canandaigua Wine Co. Inc.
COASTALS - Boats - Wellcraft Marine Corp.
COASTCAST - Golfing equipment - Coastcast Corp.
COASTCOM - Electrical equipment - Coastcom
COASTER - Boats - Glen-L Marine Designs
COASTER - Boats—motor - North East Wind Yacht Group
COASTER - Frames—eyeglass - Zylo Ware Corp.
COASTER - Toys - Kransco Manufacturing Inc.
COASTER-BUOY - Housewares - Orbex Inc.
COASTER DUDE - Apparel and accessories - Six Flags Theme Parks Inc.
COASTERS BY DESIGN - Placemats - EgoArts Inc.
COASTERSTONE - Stone products - Hindostone Products Inc.
COASTGARD - Brackets - Truth Hardware Corp.
COASTLINE - Floor coverings—carpet and rugs ☆ - Catalina Carpet Mills Inc.
COASTLINE - Fruits and vegetables - Sunridge Farms, Inc.
COASTLINE - Wood products - States Industries Inc.
COASTLINE PLUS - Fabrics - Astrup Co.
COASTLINE PLUS - Fabrics - Weblon Inc.
COASTLINE WHITE - Paints - Hancock Paint & Varnish Co.
COASTLOG - Fruits—canned - Coastlog Industries Ltd.
COAT-A-COLOR - Paints ☆ - Valspar Corp.
COAT CLIP - Hooks - Artistic Office Products
COAT COLLECTIBLES - Apparel—women's - Colberts, Inc.
COAT-EM - Epoxy coatings - Stoner Inc.
COAT GUARD - Pet products - Pro-Tec Pet Health
COAT HANDLER - Pet products - Senproco Inc.
COAT-IT - Epoxy coatings - Titan Corp.
COAT NATURALS - Pet products - Clifford W. Estes Co. Inc.
COAT OF ARMS - Christmas tree ornaments - Cracker Box Inc.
COAT OF ARMS - Colognes - Frances Denney
COAT OF ARMS - Paper—carbon ☆ - Buckeye Business Products Inc.
COAT-SEAL - Paints - Steelcote Manufacturing Corp.
COAT-SO-SOFT - Pet products - Rio Vista Marketing Associates, Inc.
COAT TAILS - Apparel—men's - Cross Country Clothes
COATASHEEN - Pet products ☆ - St. Aubrey
COATASTONE - Paints ☆ - Foy-Johnston Inc.
COATED KA-RUNCH - Candy ☆ - Holland American Wafer Co.
COATED MINTY MUNCH - Candy ☆ - Holland American Wafer Co.
COATIDES - Paints - KCI Coatings, Inc.
COATS - Thread - Coats and Clark Inc.
COATS & CLARK - Zippers - Coats and Clark Inc.
COATS N TAILS - Pet products - Shawnee Milling Co.
COATSTONE - Paints - Perry & Derrick Co.
COAUTHOR - Computer software - Oracle Corp.
COAX - Laxatives ☆ - Nature's Way Products, Inc.
COAX-CHECK - Computer peripheral equipment - Weidmuller Inc.
COAX-U - Apparel—women's ☆ - Advance Biofactures Corp.
COAXESS - Medical apparatus - Conceptus, Inc.
COAXIALBIMODE - Medical apparatus - Del Mar Avionics
COAXMAX - Electrical surge protectors - Panamax
COB CORN SHORTIES - Vegetables—frozen - Norpac Services, Inc.
COB DRY - Agricultural products - Composition Materials Co., Inc.
COBALAMED - Pharmaceutical preparations ☆ - U.S. Pharmaceutical Corp.
COBALASINE - Pharmaceutical preparations ☆ - Keene Pharmaceuticals Inc.
COBALDROX 12 - Pharmaceutical preparations - Wesley Pharmacal Co. Inc.
COBALIN - Pharmaceutical preparations ☆ - Ulmer Pharmacal Co.
COBALM - Electronic equipment - Enthone-OMI
COBALOY - Adhesives and sealants - John L. Armitage & Co.
COBALPLEX - Pharmaceutical preparations ☆ - C.O. Truxton Inc.

COBALT - Amplifiers—musical instrument - Orion Industries
COBALT - Boats—motor - Cobalt Boats
COBALT - Dinnerware—glass ☆ - Nikko Ceramics Inc.
COBALT - Giftware ☆ - Fenton Art Glass Co.
COBALT - Glass products - Blenko Glass Co. Inc.
COBALT - Luggage - Airway Industries, Inc.
COBALT - Manicure preparations - Antoine de Paris
COBALT CONTESSA - Dishes—china ☆ - Gorham Inc.
COBALT CURE - Water treating compounds - United Chemical Corp.
COBALT ENHANCEMENTS - Dinnerware ☆ - Corning Inc.
COBALT MARIGOLD - Glassware—household ☆ - Fenton Art Glass Co.
COBAYA - Veterinary pharmaceutical preparations - Nutra-Vet Research Corp.
COBB - Pipes - Missouri Meerschaum Co.
COBB MOUNTAIN - Water—bottled or canned - Cobb Mountain Spring Water Co.
COBB-V - Chickens - Cobb-Vantress Inc.
COBB-VANTRESS - Chickens - Cobb-Vantress Inc.
COBBETTES - Vegetables—frozen - Norpac Services, Inc.
COBBIE - Footwear—women's - United States Shoe Corp.
COBBIE - Pipes - Missouri Meerschaum Co.
COBBIE CUDDLERS - Footwear—women's - United States Shoe Corp.
COBBIES - Vegetables—frozen - Norpac Services, Inc.
COBBIES BY COS COB - Apparel—women's - Oxford Industries, Inc.
COBBLE - Floor coverings—carpet and rugs - Daltonian Carpet & Cushion Inc.
COBBLE - Floor coverings—carpet and rugs - Regal Rugs Inc.
COBBLE - Wallcoverings - Coral of Chicago
COBBLE CUT - Breads - Willow Foods Inc.
COBBLE HILL - Fabrics - Dan River Inc.
COBBLE HILL - Floor coverings—carpet and rugs - Karastan-Bigelow Inc.
COBBLE LANE - Blouses—women's ☆ - J.C. Penney Co., Inc.
COBBLE POINT - Floor coverings—carpet and rugs ☆ - Patrick Carpet Mills
COBBLE ROAD - Floor coverings—carpet and rugs - Karastan-Bigelow Inc.
COBBLECRETE - Concrete products - Stepstone, Inc.
COBBLEHILL - Floor coverings—carpet and rugs - Atlas Carpet Mills Inc.
COBBLEHILL BOOKS - Publisher's imprints - E.P. Dutton Inc.
COBBLELOCK - Limestone products - Medusa Minerals Co.
COBBLER - Fabrics—cotton ☆ - Dan River Inc.
COBBLER - Wines ☆ - Laird and Co.
COBBLER'S - Shoe polish - George J. Kelly Div.
COBBLER'S BENCH - Toys - Playskool, Inc.
COBBLESQUE - Floor coverings ☆ - Kentile Floors Inc.
COBBLESTONE - Blinds—venetian ☆ - Hunter Douglas, Inc.
COBBLESTONE - Cosmetics - Madeleine Mono Ltd.
COBBLESTONE - Floor coverings - Congoleum Corp.
COBBLESTONE - Floor coverings—carpet and rugs - Cabin Crafts Carpets
COBBLESTONE - Floor coverings—carpet and rugs - Innovative Flooring Systems Inc.
COBBLESTONE - Floor coverings—carpet and rugs - Patcraft Mills Inc.
COBBLESTONE - Floor coverings—carpet and rugs - Regal Rugs Inc.
COBBLESTONE - Floor coverings—carpet and rugs - Robertex Associates Inc.
COBBLESTONE - Furniture - Pilliod Co.
COBBLESTONE - Mats—rattan - Golden Star Inc.
COBBLESTONE - Spices and extracts - Scentex Inc.
COBBLESTONE - Tiles—ceramic ☆ - Quarry Tile Co.
COBBLESTONE - Tiles—mosaic - Capitol Tile Import Co.
COBBLESTONE CROSSING - Toys—stuffed - CTI Industries Corp.
COBBLESTONE FARM - Breads - Flowers Industries Inc.
COBBLESTONE LANE - Floor coverings—carpet and rugs ☆ - Galaxy Carpet Mills Inc.
COBBLESTONE MILL - Breads - Flowers Bakeries
COBBLESTONE MILL HEALTHY 'N HEARTY - Bread - Flowers Family Bakeries, Inc.
COBBLESTONE WAY - Calendars - Amcal Inc.
COBBLESTONES - Floor coverings—carpet and rugs - Burtco Enterprises Inc.
COBBLESTONES - Footwear - E.S. Originals, Inc.
COBBLETEX - Floor coverings—carpet and rugs - Atlas Carpet Mills Inc.
COBBLETONE - Floor coverings - Congoleum Corp.
COBBLEWEVE - Carpets, now out of production - Couristan Inc.
COBBS - Novelty items - Cobbs Manufacturing Co.
COBBS CREEK - Floor coverings - Mannington Resilient Floors
COBE RENAL INTENSIVE CARE - Pharmaceutical preparations - Cobe Laboratories.
COBEX - Pharmaceutical preparations - Pasadena Research Laboratories, Inc.
COBIA - Boats—motor - Cobia Boat Co.
COBIOZIN - Vitamins and nutritional supplements - Great Life Laboratories Inc.
COBIWE - Projectors—photographic ☆ - Heitz Service Corp.

☆ = Now out of production

COBLE - Dairy products - Coble Dairy Products Cooperative
COBMANIAC - Pet products - Judee K. Creations, Inc. (Crazy Corn Division)
COBOL FERRET - Computer software - Ferret Technology
COBOLAID - Computer software - Casemaker, Inc.
COBOLIN-M - Pharmaceutical preparations - Legere Pharmaceuticals Inc.
COBRA - Air purification systems - Simco
COBRA - Archery equipment - Archer Sports Inc.
COBRA - Automotive parts and accessories - Mitech
COBRA - Bags–duffel - SGI Inc.
COBRA - Bicycles - Lawee Inc.
COBRA - Bicycles ☆ - Roadmaster Corp.
COBRA - Boats–motor - Bayliner Marine Corp.
COBRA - Catheters - Scimed Life Systems, Inc.
COBRA - Chemical preparations - Midwest Industrial Supply, Inc.
COBRA - Cleaning preparations - Top Brass Metal, Inc.
COBRA - Colognes - Renee Distributors
COBRA - Computer peripheral equipment - Mouse Systems Corp.
COBRA - Computer peripheral equipment - TranSwitch Corp.
COBRA - Computer peripheral equipment - Welcom
COBRA - Darts and dart games - Dart Mart Inc.
COBRA - Exercising equipment - American Athletic Inc.
COBRA - Filters–water ☆ - Sta-Rite Industries Inc.
COBRA - Firearms, accessories, and parts ☆ - Colt's Manufacturing Co. Inc.
COBRA - Fishing lines - Cortland Line Co., Inc.
COBRA - Furniture ☆ - Boling Co.
COBRA - Golfing equipment - Cobra Golf Inc.
COBRA - Grass seed - International Seeds, Inc.
COBRA - Guitars - Silver St. Inc.
COBRA - Herbicides ☆ - Chevron Corp.
COBRA - Jewelry ☆ - Hirsch Speidel Inc.
COBRA - Ophthalmic apparatus - Surgical Design Corp.
COBRA - Patches, insignia, and emblems - Ford Motor Co.
COBRA - Pool-cue sticks - Cobra Cues & Billiard Supplies Inc.
COBRA - Projectors–photographic - Apollo Audiovisual Div.
COBRA - Single-strand barbed wire ☆ - Atlantic Steel Co.
COBRA - Telephone apparatus - Cobra Electronics Corp.
COBRA - Tools - Railway Handle Corp.
COBRA - Tools–hand-operated - Cobra Tools Inc.
COBRA - Toys - Hasbro, Inc.
COBRA - Toys–models - Cox Products Inc.
COBRA - Twine - Blue Mountain Industries, Inc.
COBRA - Ventilation equipment - GAF Corp.
COBRA - Video production - Stephen J. Cannell Productions, Inc.
COBRA - Vitamins and nutritional supplements - Natural Balance, Inc.
COBRA 2-10 COMBO - Audio equipment - ADA Signal Processors Inc.
COBRA-1500 - Toys–models ☆ - Estes Industries
COBRA COUNTRY - Recording label - Bradley Brothers Records & Tapes
COBRA E.S.P. - Automotive parts and accessories ☆ - Se-Kure Controls Inc.
COBRA FASCIA VENT - Building materials - Cobra Ventilation Co., Inc.
COBRA FORCE - Gloves ☆ - Swany America Corp.
COBRA KAYAKS - Boats–kayaks - Warren Aitken
COBRA LAWN EDGING - Garden equipment - Cobraco Manufacturing, Inc.
COBRA OUTBACK - Golfing equipment - Cobra Golf Inc.
COBRA PLUS - Radios–citizens' band - Cobra Electronics Corp.
COBRA RT - Computers - Robotech, Inc.
COBRA SAFETY ALERT - Transmitting apparatus–radio - Cobra Electronics Corp.
COBRA SPORT - Footwear - Dabsan Shoe Corp.
COBRA, THE - Pens - Alexander Manufacturing Co.
COBRA TRAP - Boats–pontoons - Lakes Manufacturing Inc.
COBRA VENOM - Cement - Building Materials Corp. of America
COBRA WB - Glass–optical - Welling International
COBRALINKS - Bicycles - Cobralinks-J.J. Tourek Manufacturing Co.
COBRALINKS JR. - Bicycles - Cobralinks-J.J. Tourek Manufacturing Co.
COBRALINKS SL - Bicycles - Cobralinks-J.J. Tourek Manufacturing Co.
COBRAMIG - Welding equipment - M.K. Products, Inc.
COBRAPHONE - Telephones - Cobra Electronics Corp.
COBRASCAN - Optical scanners–computer - Radiographic Digital Imaging
COBRATIG - Welding equipment - M.K. Products, Inc.
COBRONZE - Steel products - Cobronze Technologies, Ltd.
COBURG - Dinnerware–glass - WMF/USA
COBURG - Milk - Coburg Dairy Inc.
COBURN - Health care products - Revlon Consumer Products Corp.
COBURN DESIGNS - Puzzles - Coburn Designs
COBURNE SQUARE - Apparel and accessories - J.C. Penney Co., Inc.
COC - Apparel and accessories - Thomas Jee Kyu Byun

COCA COLA - Apparel stores–sports - Bay 1 Swimwear Inc.
COCA-COLA - Hosiery ☆ - Keepers International
COCA COLA - Key rings - Gift Creations, Inc.
COCA-COLA - Leather goods - RGA Accessories Inc.
COCA-COLA - Playing cards - United States Playing Card Co.
COCA-COLA - Telephones - Pierre Cardin Electronique
COCA COLA - Watches - SMH Corp.
COCA-COLA CLASSIC - Beverages–carbonated - Coca-Cola Co.
COCADAS - Cookies - Mother's Cake & Cookie Co.
COCCA - Greeting cards ☆ - Kersten Bros. Studios
COCHRANE - Furniture - Cochrane Furniture Co. Inc.
COCIMIENTO BLANCO - Health care products ☆ - D'Franssia Corp.
COCINA DEL SOL - Jellies and jams - Red Hot Creations
COCK O' THE WALK - Food products - Tri Valley Growers, Inc.
COCKATEIL NESTING BOX - Pet products - R.A.F. Trading Inc.
COCKBURN - Wines - Hiram Walker & Sons, Inc.
COCKERELL MARBLES - Artists' materials - Andrews/Nelson/Whitehead
COCKLESHELLS - Wallpaper - Seabrook Wallcoverings, Inc.
COCKNEY ACCENT - Tables–wood ☆ - Ridgeway Clock Co.
COCKPIT MOTORYACHT - Boats - Wellcraft Marine Corp.
COCKPIT, THE - Apparel and accessories - Avirex Ltd.
COCKSPUR - Rum - Sazerac Co. Inc.
COCKTAIL - Watches - Borel Watch Co.
COCKTAIL CLUB - Glassware–household - Villeroy and Boch Tableware Ltd.
COCKTAIL COLLECTION - Furniture - CTH/Sherrill Occasional
COCKTAIL DEVILS - Nuts–salted, roasted, cooked, or canned - Dearborn
COCKTAIL TIME - Seafood products–fresh or frozen ☆ - Eat-All Frozen Food Co.
COCKTAILLETTES - Food products ☆ - Chef Italia Inc.
COCKTAILS - Cigarettes - James B. Russell Inc.
COCKTAILS FOR TWO LIGHT - Beverages–alcohol - Heublein, Inc.
COCKTAILS NATURALLY - Beverages - N & N International Ltd.
COCLIANA - Candy ☆ - Tootsie Roll Industries, Inc.
COCO - Fabrics - Dan River Inc.
COCO - Perfumes - Chanel Inc.
COCO - Yarn ☆ - JCA, Inc.
COCO BAY SCHNAPPS - Beverages–alcohol ☆ - Sazerac Co. Inc.
COCO BEADS - Cleaning preparations - Knight Marketing Corp.
COCO BIANCO - Apparel–women's - Betsy's Things Sportswear Inc.
COCO CABARET - Coffee - Executive Coffee Service Co.
COCO CASA - Coconut–shredded - Mott's Inc.
COCO CHIP RINGS - Cookies - Sunshine/Salerno Inc.
COCO COLA - Watches - Fada Industries Inc.
COCO DOLL - Dolls - Ballena Studio, Inc.
COCO D'OR - Candy - Sterling Candy Corp.
COCO E COCOA - Skin care products - Pro-Capa Products Inc.
COCO-FRIO - Beverages - Colita Beverage Corp.
COCO GOYA - Food products - Goya Foods, Inc.
COCO LITES - Candles ☆ - Aloha Candle Manufacturing Co. Inc.
COCO LOTO - Juices - First World International
COCO MALTLETS - Candy ☆ - Brock Candy Co. Inc.
COCO MAR - Coconut liqueur - International Wine & Spirits Inc.
COCO MIST - Beverages–alcohol - Black Prince Distillery, Inc.
COCO-NOTES - Computer software - CBS Software
COCO OLE - Beverages - Young's Market Co.
COCO PINA - Beverages–carbonated - Canada Dry Corp.
COCO POP - Vegetable oil - Ventura Foods LLC (Lou Ana Division)
COCO RICO - Beverages–carbonated - Coco Rico, Inc.
COCO-ROOS - Cereal - Malt-O-Meal Co.
COCO SCRUB - Soap - Knight Marketing Corp.
COCO SOL - Suntan lotions - Caribia, Cosmetic Research Laboratories Inc.
COCO SOLO - Beverages–carbonated - Cawy Bottling Co., Inc.
COCO SUPREME - Cocoa–powders or mixes - Nestle Beverage Co.
COCO TROPICAL - Confections - Commerce Foods Inc.
COCO-WHEATS - Cereal - Little Crow Foods
COCO WILLY - Skin care products - Kija
COCOA - Mats - JCH International Inc.
COCOA AMORE - Cocoa–powders or mixes - Coffee Masters, Inc.
COCOA BEACH COFFEE CO. - Cups–plastic - Thomas A. Maschhoff
COCOA BUTTER - Skin care products - Cococare Products Inc.
COCOA BUTTER CREME - Skin care products - Para Laboratories Inc.
COCOA BUTTER LOTION - Skin care products - Para Laboratories Inc.
COCOA CASCADE - Coffee - Coffee Beanery Ltd.
COCOA CLASSICS - Cocoa–powders or mixes - Land O'Lakes Inc.
COCOA COMETS - Cereal - Malt-O-Meal Co.
COCOA CRAZY - Cocoa–powders or mixes - Pinnacle Food Products, Inc.

COCOA CRISP RICE - Cereal - New Morning
COCOA CRISPY RICE - Cereal - New Morn, Inc.
COCOA CRUNCH STARS - Cereal - Barbara's Bakery, Inc.
COCOA-DEPENDENT - Chocolate candy - Julie Simon
COCOA DRESS - Fertilizers ☆ - MacAndrews and Forbes Corp.
COCOA FACTORY - Chocolate candy - Webb's Gourmet Brands, Inc.
COCOA FROST - Lipsticks ☆ - Honey & Spice Toiletries
COCOA GODIVA - Cocoa–powders or mixes - Godiva Chocolatier
COCOA JUMBIE - Cookies - Original Caribbean Cookie Co., Inc.
COCOA LEAF - Tobacco–chewing or smoking - Amar Blends Co.
COCOA MAGIC - Skin care products - John G. Kyles Inc.
COCOA MARSH - Chocolate syrup - Frank Foods Co.
COCOA-NOLA - Cereal ☆ - Organic Milling
COCOA OATIES - Cereal - New Morning
COCOA OATIOS - Cereal - New Morn, Inc.
COCOA PLEASURES - Cocoa–powders or mixes - Wagner Gourmet Foods, Inc.
COCOA PLUS - Food products - Robertet Flavors Inc.
COCOA PUFFS - Cereal - General Mills, Inc.
COCOA RICH - Skin care products - Woltra Corp.
COCOA ROSE - Lipsticks ☆ - Honey & Spice Toiletries
COCOA ROYAL - Food products - Robertet Flavors Inc.
COCOA ROYALE - Cocoa–powders or mixes - Chicago Coffee Roastery, Inc.
COCOA TEDDY - Toys–stuffed - Russ Berrie and Co., Inc.
COCOA TIME - Cocoa–powders or mixes ☆ - Chase Collection, Inc.
COCOANUT - Skin care products - Master Chemical Co.
COCOANUT CLOUDS - Candy - Miss Chocolate Co. Inc.
COCOCARE - Skin care products - Cococare Products Inc.
COCOCHERRI - Candy - Koppers Chocolate Specialty Co. Inc.
COCOFECTION - Candy - American Natural Snacks
COCOGRO - Garden equipment - Austram, Inc.
COCOLADA - Juices - Stevens Tropical Plantation Inc.
COCOLINER - Coconut–shredded - Austram, Inc.
COCOMAC - Cookies - Mrs. Fields Development Corp.
COCOMALT - Chocolate milk - Nabisco Foods Group
COCOMO JOE - Shoes - Tohkutsu America Corp.
COCOMOSS - Garden equipment - Austram, Inc.
COCONETTOS - Candy - Peter Paul
COCONUT ALOHA - Beverages - Tourelle
COCONUT CARNATION - Toys - Those Characters from Cleveland, Inc.
COCONUT CHARLIE'S - Beverages–alcohol - Black Prince Distillery, Inc.
COCONUT CHARLIE'S - Cordials - Ginger Spirits, Inc.
COCONUT CHIPS - Candy ☆ - Chex Co.
COCONUT CODE - Computer software - Coconut Code, Inc.
COCONUT CRUNCH - Candy - Tom's Foods Inc.
COCONUT GROVE - Candy - Nabisco Foods Group
COCONUT GROVE - Hammocks - Handmade Creations Inc.
COCONUT GROVE - Wallpaper - Frankford Wallcoverings Inc.
COCONUT GROVE SHRIMP - Food products - Brinker Restaurant Corp.
COCONUT GROVES - Juices - Florida Bottling Inc.
COCONUT HUTS - Candy - Tom's Foods Inc.
COCONUT ISLAND - Syrup - Flavors of Hawaii Inc.
COCONUT KANDY KAKES - Cakes - Tasty Baking Co.
COCONUT OIL - Vitamins and nutritional supplements - Vitamin Research Products Inc.
COCONUT OIL SHAMPOO - Shampoos - Analab Inc.
COCONUT RAINBOW BARS - Candy - Keppel's Inc.
COCONUT SLICE - Candy - Tom's Foods Inc.
COCONUT SNOW - Beverages - Mele-Koi Farms
COCONUT SOAP 220 - Soap - Hillyard Enterprises, Inc.
COCONUT-T GALLERY - Apparel and accessories - Coconut Triangle, Co. Ltd.
COCONUT WATER - Apparel and accessories - Richard Druz
COCONUT ZIPPERS - Candy - Squirrel Brand Co.
COCONUTHEADS, THE - Apparel and accessories - Gregory H. Istock
COCOON - Bathtubs–enameled - Kohler Co.
COCOON IMPRINTS LIFESTYLE COLLECTION - Apparel and accessories - Cocoon Inc.
COCORIBE RUM SPECIALTY - Beverages–alcohol - Jim Beam Brands Co.
COCREMA - Skin care products ☆ - Blistex Inc.
COCYNTAL - Pharmaceutical preparations - Boiron Inc.
C.O.D. - Shirts - Georges Marciano
COD BOATS - Seafood products–fresh or frozen - Golden Platter Foods
CODA - Apparel and accessories - Edison Brothers Stores, Inc.
CODA - Bicycle parts and accessories - Cannondale Corp.
CODA - Publisher's imprints - Auto Book Press

CODA FREESTYLE - Boats–canoes ☆ - Sawyer Composite Products
CODA PUBLICATIONS - Publisher's imprints - Coda Publications
CODACOLOR - Office supplies - Southern Folder & Index Co.
CODAFED - Pharmaceutical preparations ☆ - Roberts/Hauck Pharmaceuticals Inc.
CODAFOAM - Photographic equipment - CODA Inc.
CODAL - Pepper - Gourmet Club Corp.
CODALAN - Analgesics - Lannett Co. Inc.
CODAMINE - Pharmaceutical preparations - Barre-National, Inc.
CODAN - Olive oil - Gerard J. Danco International Corp.
CODANOL - Vitamin ointment - American Pharmaceutical Co.
CODAR TECHNOLOGY INC. - Computers - Codar Technology Inc.
CODASOL - Pharmaceutical preparations ☆ - Wesley Pharmacal Co. Inc.
CODDINGTON SQUARE - Furniture–wood - Century Furniture Co.
CODDO - Boats–motor ☆ - Caddo Boat Manufacturing Co.
CODE - Food products - Park Corp.
CODE - Frames–eyeglass - Zylo Ware Corp.
CODE - Turkeys - Watson Quality Foods Inc.
CODE 1 - Lighting fixtures - Lamplight Farms, Inc.
CODE-1 CANADA - Computer software - Group 1 Software Financial Services Corp.
CODE 4 - Goggles–safety - Outdoor Optics, Inc.
CODE 7 - Pet products - Gerard-Pellham Co.
CODE 10 - Cables - Whitaker Corp.
CODE 10 - Hair care products - Colgate-Palmolive Co.
CODE-A-COLOR - Binders - Samsill Corp.
CODE-A-MODULE - Furniture ☆ - Triangle Pacific Corp. (Cabinet Division)
CODE-A-PHONE - Telephones - Code-a-Phone Corp.
CODE-A-PHONE INTREPID - Telephones ☆ - Code-a-Phone Corp.
CODE-A-PHONE SEQUENCE V - Telephones ☆ - Code-a-Phone Corp.
CODE-A-PHONE TEL-A-MODEM - Modems ☆ - Code-a-Phone Corp.
C.O.D.E. B.C. - Apparel and accessories - I. Samson Rubin
CODE BLEU - Jeans–women's - Sun Apparel, Inc.
CODE BLUE - Alarm systems - Genzink Steel Supply and Welding Co.
CODE BLUE - Books–comic ☆ - Marvel Entertainment Group, Inc.
CODE BLUE - First aid kits ☆ - Woodstream Corp.
CODE BLUE - Games - St. Luke's Episcopal Hospital
CODE BLUE - Health care products - Vital Signs, Inc.
CODE-COM - Telephones - At&T Corp.
CODE COURIER - Office machines - Cognitive Solutions, Inc.
CODE ELITE - Fruits–canned - Emco Foodservice Systems, Inc.
CODE-EMBASSY - Food products - Chef Italia Inc.
CODE GENESIS - Computer software - Scientific and Engineering Software, Inc.
CODE I SPORT - Apparel–athletic - Stevens Sportwear
CODE KEEPER - Electrical equipment - L.E. Mason Co.
CODE NAME: SECTOR - Games ☆ - Parker Brothers
CODE OF BUSHIDO - Games - Avalon Hill Game Co.
CODE ONE - Portable smoke detectors ☆ - Jameson Home Products Inc.
CODE ONE 2000 - Smoke and fire alarms - Jameson Home Products Inc.
CODE QUEST - Computer software - Frontier Software Inc.
CODE QUEST - Computer software ☆ - Sunburst Communications, Inc.
CODE RED - Alarms–personal - Arvis Corp.
CODE RED - Foam rubber - Hickory Springs Manufacturing Co.
CODE THE BOOK - Directories - Castalia Publications
CODE WEST - Boots - Genesco Inc.
CODEBANK - Computer software - Visual Components, Inc.
CODEBREAKER - Computer software - Almedica Services Corp.
CODEBREAKER - Video games - Atari Games Corp.
CODECENTER - Computer software - Centerline Software, Inc.
CODEDODGER - Alarm systems - Overhead Door Corp.
CODEHIST - Pharmaceutical preparations - Geneva Generics Inc.
CODEL - Pharmaceutical preparations ☆ - ICN Pharmaceuticals Inc.
CODEMASTER - Computer software - Hewlett-Packard Co.
CODEMASTER - Electronic equipment - Brumberger Co. Inc.
CODEMASTER - Inkwells - Mark Master Inc.
CODEMASTER - Video production - Boy Scouts of America
CODEMPIRAL - Analgesics ☆ - Burroughs Wellcome Co.
CODENAME: STRYKE FORCE - Books–comic - Top Cow Productions, Inc.
CODEP - Fans–electric - Codep International Inc.
CODES & CYPHERS - Computer software ☆ - Optimum Resource, Inc.
CODETAPER - Office supplies - Better Packages
CODETITE - Lighting fixtures - Guth Lighting
CODETRON - Health care products - Codetron Inc.
CODEWATCH - Medical apparatus - American Clicical Industries
CODEWORDS - Apparel–athletic - Montgomery Ward & Co. Inc.

☆ = Now out of production

CODEWORKS - Computer software - Glyphic Technology

CODEX - Electronic equipment - Codex Corp.

CODEXIN - Pharmaceutical preparations - Nature's Bounty, Inc.

CODI - Containers - Codi, Inc.

CODI - Electronic equipment - Chyron Corp.

CODI - Jewelry - Diaco International Corp.

CODICLEAR DH - Cold remedies - Central Pharmaceutical Inc.

CODIFA - Iron - French & Pacific Trading Corp.

CODIMAL - Analgesics - Central Pharmaceutical Inc.

CODIMAL-A - Pharmaceutical preparations - Central Pharmaceutical Inc.

CODIMAL DH - Antihistamine preparations - Central Pharmaceutical Inc.

CODIMAL DM - Antihistamine preparations - Central Pharmaceutical Inc.

CODIMAL-LA - Antihistamine preparations - Central Pharmaceutical Inc.

CODIMAL-LA HALF - Antihistamine preparations - Central Pharmaceutical Inc.

CODIMAL PH - Antihistamine preparations - Central Pharmaceutical Inc.

CODINETS - Pharmaceutical preparations ☆ - Wesley Pharmacal Co. Inc.

CODISCOS - Recording label - Sonotone Corp.

CODISTAN - Pharmaceutical preparations ☆ - Vortech Pharmaceuticals

CODO - International Violin Co. Ltd.

CODOCET - Health care products - Halsey Drug Co. Inc.

CODOCIDE-F - Pharmaceutical preparations - Deleon Laboratories Inc.

CODOLON - Ribbons–inked ☆ - Codo Manufacturing Corp.

CODOLON 22 - Cleaning preparations - Codo Manufacturing Corp.

CODORNIU - Wines - Codorniu USA Inc.

CODORUS - Building materials–concrete - Cavert Wire Co. Inc.

CODOXY - Health care products - Halsey Drug Co. Inc.

CODROXOMIN - Pharmaceutical preparations ☆ - Forest Pharmaceuticals Inc.

CODUREX - Pharmaceutical preparations ☆ - Rexall Nutritional Products Inc.

CODY - Brushes–paint - Corona Brushes Inc.

CODY - Ophthalmic goods ☆ - Rozin Optical Export Corp.

CODY - Toys–stuffed ☆ - Gund, Inc.

CODY BISON - Toys–stuffed - Russ Berrie and Co., Inc.

CODY JAMES - Shirts for men, women, and children - Coopers, Inc.

CODY'S CHOICE - Meat and poultry - Cody Distribution, Inc.

COE - Disinfectants - GC America Inc.

COE-CRAFT - Furniture–wood - David H. Coe

COED - Bicycles - Columbia Manufacturing Inc.

COED - Soap ☆ - Comfort Manufacturing Co.

COEFFICIENT - Tires - Michelin Tire Corp.

COENTRANT - Audio equipment - Renkus-Heinz Inc.

COENZ-B - Vitamins and nutritional supplements - Integrated Health, Inc.

COENZYMATED B - Vitamins and nutritional supplements - Source Naturals

COENZYME Q-10 - Vitamins and nutritional supplements - Vitamin Research Products Inc.

COENZYME Q10+ - Vitamins and nutritional supplements - Body Wise International, Inc.

COENZYME Q10 - Vitamins and nutritional supplements - Integrated Health, Inc.

COENZYME Q10 - Vitamins and nutritional supplements - Natrol, Inc.

COER DE LION - Beverages–alcohol - Blair Importers Ltd.

COETS - Skin care products - Johnson & Johnson

COEUR DE CHEVRE - Dairy products - Rykoff-Sexton, Inc.

COEUR DE LION - Beverages–alcohol ☆ - Twelve Stone Flagons Ltd.

COEXCELL - Containers–plastic - U.S. Coexcell, Inc.

COEXIST - Computer software ☆ - CONDUIT

COF - Cough medicines - Pfeiffer Pharmaceuticals Inc.

COFCO - Seafood products–fresh or frozen ☆ - Coast to Coast Seafood Inc.

COFFALAR - Pharmaceutical preparations - Lardon Laboratories

COFFARDON - Cold remedies - Lardon Laboratories

COFFEE - Lenses–optical - Kelley & Hueber

COFFEE ACCENTS - Cream–canned or powdered - Xcell International Corp.

COFFEE AROMA - Coffee makers–electric - Robert Krups North America

COFFEE AROMA PLUS - Coffee makers–electric - Robert Krups North America

COFFEE ASSOCIATES - Coffee - Coffee Associates, Inc.

COFFEE BEAN, THE - Coffee - International Coffee & Tea, Inc.

COFFEE BREAK - Candy ☆ - Holland American Wafer Co.

COFFEE BREAK - Doughnuts - R.S. Prewitt Co.

COFFEE BREAK - Pharmaceutical preparations ☆ - Columbia Laboratories Inc.

COFFEE BREAK BAR - Candy - Gayle's Chocolates, Ltd.

COFFEE BUTLER - Coffee - Coffee Butler Service Inc.

COFFEE BUTLER - Food containers - Thermos Co.

COFFEE BUTLER SUPER 50 - Food containers - Thermos Co.

COFFEE BUTTONS - Candy - Peerless Confection Co.

COFFEE CAKE JR. - Cakes - Drake Bakeries, Inc.

COFFEE CAT - Coffee - Coffee Cat, Inc.

COFFEE CAVERN - Coffee - Coffee Cavern Inc.

COFFEE CLASSICS SPECIALTY - Coffee - Coffee Classics Inc.

COFFEE CLIP - Housewares - Guardsman Products, Inc.

COFFEE COMBO - Coffee makers–electric ☆ - Metal Ware Corp.

COFFEE CONNECTIONS - Syrup - Coffee Connection, Inc.

COFFEE CORNER - Housewares ☆ - Black & Decker Corp.

COFFEE COURIER, THE - Automotive parts and accessories - Coffee Courier, Inc.

COFFEE CROWN - Cream - Farmer Bros. Co.

COFFEE DELIGHT - Candy - Colombina Candy Co., Inc.

COFFEE ECONOMIZER - Coffee maker accessories - Coffee Economizer, Inc.

COFFEE ESSENTIALS - Grinders - William Bounds, Ltd.

COFFEE-ETS - Candy - Miss Saylor's Candies

COFFEE EXPRESS - Coffee - Coffee Express Co.

COFFEE FIZZ - Coffee - Coffee Creations

COFFEE GRIND - Restaurants–coffee shops - Cynmar, Inc.

COFFEE HIGH - Nondairy coffee creamer - Cream Products Co. Inc.

COFFEE HOUSE - Greeting cards - American Greetings Corp.

COFFEE HOUSE PRESS - Publisher's imprints - Coffee House Press

COFFEE IS A BEAR ESSENTIAL - Kitchenware–china - Marjorie Sarnat & Associates, Inc.

COFFEE KIDS BLEND - Coffee - Frontier Cooperative Herbs

COFFEE-LITE - Cream–canned or powdered - I. Rokeach and Sons Inc.

COFFEE LOVERS - Coffee - Savon/Coffee Lovers Coffee

COFFEE-MATE - Milk–canned or powdered - Nestle Beverage Co.

COFFEE-MATE LITE - Milk–canned or powdered - Nestle Beverage Co.

COFFEE MISER - Coffee makers–electric ☆ - Regal Ware, Inc.

COFFEE NIPS - Candy - Nabisco Foods Group

COFFEE OCCASIONS - Coffee - Saramar Corp.

COFFEE O'LEI - Novelty items - William M. Harrison

COFFEE-ON-DEMAND - Nonelectric beverage maker and carafe - Corning Inc.

COFFEE PAL - Specialty foods–canned - Ryan Foods Co.

COFFEE PASSION EXPRESS-O - Coffee - Coffee Passion Express-O

COFFEE PLEASURES - Food products - Wagner Gourmet Foods, Inc.

COFFEE PLUS - Dairy products - Hormel Foods Corp.

COFFEE PLUS - Housewares ☆ - Robert Krups North America

COFFEE POT SINGLES - Coffee - Millstone Coffee, Inc.

COFFEE POT, THE - Beverages - Berardi's Fresh Roast, Inc.

COFFEE RICH - Cream - Rich Products Corp.

COFFEE RICH LIGHT - Food products - Rich Products Corp.

COFFEE RIO - Candy - Adams & Brooks, Inc.

COFFEE ROASTER - Coffee - Coffee Roasters Inc.

COFFEE SINGLES - Coffee - Folger Coffee Co.

COFFEE SOUTHERN - Beverages–alcohol ☆ - Brown-Forman Corp.

COFFEE, TEA & THEE - Coffee - Candy Candy Inc.

COFFEE, THE - Coffee - Pokka, Inc.

COFFEE-TIME - Beverages–carbonated - Canada Dry Corp.

COFFEE TIME - Clocks - Quick Point, Inc.

COFFEE TIME - Coffee makers–electric ☆ - Metal Ware Corp.

COFFEE TIME - Housewares - Robert Krups North America

COFFEE TIME - Pajamas–women's - J.C. Penney Co., Inc.

COFFEE TIME PLUS - Coffee makers–electric - Robert Krups North America

COFFEE TOFFEE - Candy - Hooper's Chocolates

COFFEE TOPPERS - Syrup - David Michael & Co.

COFFEEHOUSE - Greeting cards - AGC, Inc.

COFFEEHOUSE MURDER, THE - Games ☆ - Milton Bradley Co.

COFFEEMAKER KLEEN - Cleaning preparations - G.G. Bean Inc.

COFFEEMASTER - Coffee makers–electric - Sunbeam-Oster Household Products

COFFEEMATIC - Coffee makers–electric - Black & Decker Corp.

COFFEES OF HAWAII - Coffee - Coffees of Hawaii Inc.

COFFEES OF THE OLD WEST - Coffee - First Colony Coffee and Tea Co. Inc.

COFFEE'S ON - Wallpaper - Gencorp Inc.

COFFEESCOPE - Coffee makers–electric ☆ - Hamilton Beach/Proctor-Silex Inc.

COFFEETEENS - Candy ☆ - Price Candy Co. Inc.

COFFEETIME - Syrup ☆ - Globe Extracts Inc.

COFFEETREE - Coffee - Coffeetree Ltd.

COFFERETTE - Lighting fixtures ☆ - Hubbell Lighting, Inc. (Lighting Div.)

COFFEYVILLE - Boots - Centerville Co., Inc.

COFFEYVILLE BOOTS - Boots - Centerville Co., Inc.

COFFIN - Pumps - Coffin Turbo Pump Inc.

COFFINA SUPER - Grinders ☆ - Robert Krups North America

COFFINETTE - Cigarettes - Idea Group

COFFIN'S - Salmon–smoked, salted, dried, or pickled - Tidewater Packing Co.

COFFIOCA - Candy - Nabisco Foods Group

☆ = Now out of production

COFFMAN - Wood products - Visador Co.
COFFMAN SPIRAL - Staircases—wood - Visador Co.
COFI BEAN - Apparel and accessories - Cofi Bean, Inc.
COFIMA - Apparel and accessories - Rahmey International Inc.
COFISH - Apparel and accessories - Cofish International Inc.
COFRIPESCA - Seafood products—fresh or frozen ☆ - J.F. Clarke Corp.
COFRON - Vitamins and nutritional supplements ☆ - Abbott Laboratories
COFRUSA - Food products - Joseph Caragol Inc.
COG HILL - Golf courses - Cog Hill Golf and Country Club, Inc.
COGEN - Pharmaceutical preparations - Vista Laboratories Inc.
COGENT LIGHT - Surgical instruments - Cogent Light Technologies, Inc.
COGENTIN - Pharmaceutical preparations - Merck & Co., Inc. (Merck Research Laboratories)
COGENTVISION - Lighting equipment - Cogent Light Technologies, Inc.
COGITO - Computer software - Cogito Learning Media, Inc.
COGITO - Computer software - Coqito Software
COGITO-VIA - Computer software - Cogito Economic Systems, Inc.
COGNAC - Chimes - Nutone Inc.
COGNAC - Furniture ☆ - Stanley Furniture Co. Inc.
COGNAC PERFECTION - Beverages—alcohol - Paterno Imports, Ltd.
COGNAC PRUNIER - Beverages—alcohol - Deinhard & Partners
COGNAC PUMPKIN CHEESECAKE - Cakes - Plaza Sweets Bakery
COGNEX - Pharmaceutical preparations - Parke-Davis
COGNITECH - Computer software - Cognitech Corp.
COGNITIVE PROCESSOR - Computer software - Bruce G. Molloy
COGO BEAR - Children's books - Chycogo and Co., Ltd.
COGSCREEN - Computer software - Psychological Assessment Resources, Inc.
COHAMA - Fabrics—cotton ☆ - Cohn-Hall-Marx Co.
COHAMA RIVERDALE - Fabrics - United Merchants and Manufacturers Inc.
COHANSEY - Vegetables—frozen - Seabrook Brothers & Sons Inc.
COHARDITE - Wrenches - Stevens Walden Inc.
COHEN'S - Hors d'oeuvres, entrees, knishes - Cohen's Famous Frozen Foods
COHEN'S OPTICAL - Eyeglasses - Cohen Fashion Optical, Inc.
COHERENT - Telephones - Teleconferencing Systems International Inc.
COHESION - Hair care products - Scruples Professional Salon Products, Inc.
COHI - Fruits and vegetables ☆ - Stanley Orchards Sales Inc.
COHINI - Luggage - Melissa Designs Inc.
COHN-STONE - Giftware - N.S. Gustin Co.
COHO - Boats—fishing - Glasstream Boats Inc.
COHO - Boats—motor - O.M.C. Aluminum Boat Group
COHO - Boats—motor - Sea Nymph Boats
COHO - Fresh apples - Trout, Inc.
COHO LAKER TAKERS - Fishing lures - Bay De Noc Lure Co.
COHORT - Fruits and vegetables - Snokist Growers
COHOSH TWO - Health care products - Old Amish Herbs
COHOST - Computer software - Geac Computer Systems, Inc.
COICOR-REHAB - Pet products ☆ - Coicor
COIDOCORT - Pharmaceutical preparations ☆ - Coast Laboratories Inc.
COIFFEUR - Dryers—hair ☆ - Ronson Consumer Products Corp.
COIFFURE - Brushes—hair - Nino Originals
COIFFURE CUSHION - Cushions ☆ - Better Sleep, Inc.
COIFFURE Q - Hair care products - Intra-America Beauty Network
COIL-A-MATIC - Bicycles - Weil Service Products Corp.
COIL-CORD - Electric-guitar connecting cords - International Music Corp.
COIL CRADLE - Tools - Van Mark Products Corp.
COIL CUTS - Food products - Sysco Food Services
COIL GUARD - Chemical preparations - Clayton Industries
COIL KING - Cleaning preparations - Comstar International Inc. (IPC Div.)
COIL ON COIL - Mattresses - Kingsdown, Inc.
COIL-PEN - Desk sets - Slencil Co.
COIL-RITE - Cleaning preparations - Stewart-Hall Chemical Corp.
COIL SAFE - Cleaning preparations - Comstar International Inc. (IPC Div.)
COIL-SCRU - Screws - Quick Drive USA Inc.
COIL-SERT - Tools—hand-operated - Inserts and Kits, Ltd.
COIL STRIP - Weather stripping - KEL-EEZ
COILBOIL - Cleaning preparations - Stewart-Hall Chemical Corp.
COILEASH - Pet products - Premier Pet Products Inc.
COILED RIG - Sporting goods ☆ - Lindy Little Joe Inc.
COILFIELD - Tubes—steel - Precision Tube Technology, Inc.
COILFLOW - Automotive parts and accessories - Coilhose Pneumatics Inc.
COILGARD - Racks - Jarke Corp.
COILHOSE PNEUMATICS - Automotive parts and accessories - Coilhose Pneumatics Inc.
COILMASTER - Sporting goods - R.M. & G. Products, Inc.
COILPLATE - Machine parts - Tippins Inc.

COILTRONICS - Electrical equipment - Coiltronics, Inc.
COILZAK - Sheet metal products - Aluminum Co. of America
COILZIT - Cordage and twine - Guco-Plastron Industries
COIMBRA - Confections ☆ - Ferrero U.S.A Inc.
COIMBRA - Recording label ☆ - Penco Industries Inc.
COIN A TUNE - Figurines ☆ - Ohio Ceramic Supply Inc.
COIN CRITTERS - Computer software - Nordic Software, Inc.
COIN CUBE - Toys—banks - Boxes By Pandora Inc.
COIN-DEX - Counting devices - Metal Products Engineering Inc.
COIN DOT - Glassware—household ☆ - Fenton Art Glass Co.
COIN EXCHANGE - Toys—banks - Mag-Nif Inc.
COIN-GATES - Component part of a coin-holder - Block and Co., Inc.
COIN IN THE CRYPT - Toys - Hasbro, Inc.
COIN JAMMERS - Toys - Fisher-Price, Inc.
COIN MAGIC - Jewelry - SASCO Inc.
COIN PAK - Leather goods - St. Thomas Inc.
COIN-THIN - Watches - Gruen Marketing Corp.
COINAGE - Tiles—ceramic ☆ - Latco Products
COINAGER - Vending machines - General Signal Corp.
COINDISPLAY - Hobby kits - Unicover Corp.
COINFAX - Duplicating machines ☆ - Olivetti North America Inc. (Consumer Products Div.)
COINFONE - Telephones - Coinfone USA, Inc.
COINGOLD - Glassware—household ☆ - Crest Studios
COINMASTER - Electronic equipment - White's Electronics, Inc.
COINOLA - Musical instrument accessories - Player Piano Co. Inc.
COINPAK - Commemorative-coin protectors - Unicover Corp.
COINS - Cigarettes - Brown & Williamson Tobacco Corp.
C-O-I-N-S - Computer software - Compu-Quote Software
COINS - Computer software - INSCI Corp.
COINS OF ALL NATIONS - Candy - R.M. Palmer Co.
COINS UNIQUE - Jewelry - Coins Unique Co.
COINTAINER - Containers—paper - Data-Link Corp.
COINTENDER - Coin holder - Block and Co., Inc.
COINTREAU - Liquors - Cointreau America Inc.
COINTREAU PERE ET FILS - Liquors - Cointreau America Inc.
COINVERTER - Electronic equipment - Ace USA, Inc.
COIRONAL - Pharmaceutical preparations ☆ - Coast Laboratories Inc.
COIT - Cleaning preparations - Coit Services Inc.
COIT SMOOTH STROKE - Pens - Coit Calligraphics Inc.
COIT'S - Pens - Coit Calligraphics Inc.
COJACK - Tables—metal - Schroer Manufacturing Co.
COK-L-BUR - Weather tracking equipment - Davis Instruments Corp.
COKE CLASSIC CORVETTE - Toys—electronic - Bird Bromiticous Inc.
COKE CORVETTE - Toys—electronic - Bird Bromiticous Inc.
COKE II - Beverages—carbonated ☆ - Coca-Cola Co.
COKE LIGHT - Beverages—carbonated - Coca-Cola Co.
COKER - Tires - Coker Tire Inc.
COKER CLASSIC - Tires - Coker Tire Inc.
COKI'S - Perfumes - Sara Lee Corp.
COKO BLOCKS - Toys - Larami Limited, Inc.
COL. - See also COLONEL
COL. CRUMB'S ANIMAL CRACKERS - Games - Warren Industries Inc.
COL-ERASE - Pencils - Faber-Castell Corp.
COL-MAN - Fruits and vegetables - Salem Fruit Growers Coop. Association
COL-O-FOAM - Fabrics—tapestry ☆ - Columbus Coated Fabrics Co.
COL-O-VAR - Varnishes ☆ - Valspar Corp.
COL-PARBENEM - Pharmaceutical preparations - Parmed Pharmaceuticals, Inc.
COL-R-CORN - Popcorn - National Oats Co. Inc.
COL-R-FIRE - Fireplace equipment - Empire Manufacturing Co.
COL-R-TONE - Hardware stores - Epmar Corp.
COL-TEC - Markers—felt-tip - Fluorographic Services Inc.
COL-VI-NOL - Pharmaceutical preparations ☆ - Ulmer Pharmacal Co.
COLA - Chewing gum - Leaf, Inc.
COLA - Frames—eyeglass ☆ - Universal/Univis Inc.
COLA CANDLE - Candles ☆ - American Candle Co. Inc.
COLA-CHU - Chewing gum - Philadelphia Chewing Gum Corp.
COLA COOLER - Ice chests ☆ - Poloron Products Inc.
COLA SYRUP - Pharmaceutical preparations - Reese Chemical Co.
COLACE - Laxatives - Bristol-Myers Squibb Co.
COLAGE - Floor coverings—carpet and rugs - V & B Carpet
COLANI - Pens - Pelikan, Inc.
COLANI - Robes ☆ - Spirite Industries Inc.
COLARART - Pencils - Dixon Ticonderoga Co.
COLAROMA - Paints - Wattyl Paint Corp.

☆ = Now out of production

COLAVITA - Food products - Colavita USA, Inc.

COLAVITA - Pasta ☆ - De Choix Specialty Foods Co.

COLAVITA - Spaghetti sauces ☆ - S.J. Paris & Co.

COLAVITA - Vegetable oil - Castle Food Products

COLBENEMID - Pharmaceutical preparations - Merck & Co., Inc. (Merck Research Laboratories)

COLBENI-MOR - Pharmaceutical preparations ☆ - Moore Medical Corp.

COLBERT - Flatware - Dansk International Designs, Ltd.

COLBI-LO - Cheese - Alpine Lace Brands, Inc.

COLBY - Eyeglasses - Martin-Copeland Eyewear Corp.

COLBY OXFORD - Fabrics - Dan River Inc.

COLBY ROAD - Floor coverings–carpet and rugs ☆ - Hollytex Carpet Mills Inc.

COLCHESTER - Flatware ☆ - Towle Silversmiths

COLCHESTER - Glassware–household ☆ - WMF/USA

COLCHESTER BRICK - Floor coverings - Tarkett, Inc.

COLD - Filters–industrial - Memtec America Corp.

COLD AGED AT 29° - Beverages–malt - Miller Brewing Co.

COLD AIR - Apparel - Cold Air

COLD & FLU - Health care products - Herbs of China Ltd.

COLD BATTERY - Batteries - O.E.M. Products Inc.

COLD BEAR - Wines ☆ - Wine Group Inc.

COLD BLOODED - T-shirts–men's - Cold Blooded Design

COLD BLUE - Recording label - Jazz Composer's Orchestra Association Inc.

COLD BUTLER, THE - Ice chests–plastic - Glacier Ware Inc.

COLD CAPS - Cold remedies - Rexall Nutritional Products Inc.

COLD CARE P.M. - Teas–herbal - Traditional Medicinals, Inc.

COLD CASE, THE - Containers–insulated - Robert Billet Promotions, Inc.

COLD-CHEX - Automotive parts and accessories - Thexton Manufacturing Inc.

COLD CLAD - Swimming pools ☆ - Doughboy Recreational Inc.

COLD COMFORT - Ice - Minnesota Mining & Manufacturing Co.

COLD CONTROL - Cold remedies - Nature's Herbs

COLD CONTROL + - Pharmaceutical preparations - Reese Chemical Co.

COLD CREEK DELI STYLE - Hams - CKF Foods, Inc.

COLD DUCK - Fabrics - Graniteville Co.

COLD DUCK BLIND - Wine coolers ☆ - Glacier Ware Inc.

COLD EARTH - Apparel and accessories - Lawrence Arin

COLD EARTH WEAR - Clothing - Cold Earth Wear

COLD-EEZE - Cold remedies - Quigley Corp.

COLD FACTS - Vitamins and nutritional supplements - Highland Laboratories

COLD FIRE - Fire extinguishers - Firefreeze Worldwide, Inc.

COLD-FLEX - Health care products - Workwear Corp. Inc.

COLD FLO - Fuel additives - Hammonds Fuel Additives, Inc.

COLD FLOW - Roofing materials–clay - L.D. Sterns Corp.

COLD FREE - Health care products - Pacific BioLogic Inc.

COLD FRONT - Containers - Chevron Corp.

COLD FRONT - Labels–paper - K-Tel International, Inc.

COLD FROST - Frames–eyeglass ☆ - U.S. Optical Frame Co.

COLD FUSION - Computer software - Allaire, LLC

COLD FUSION - Converters–rotary - QQC, Inc.

COLD FUSION - Novelty items - Equidex Inc.

COLD GOLD - Juices - Vita-Pakt Citrus Products Co.

COLD GOOSE - Wines - Heritage Wine Cellars

COLD-GUARD - Refrigerators - White Consolidated Industries, Inc.

COLD HAT - Health care products - Mason & Mason Engineering Inc.

COLD-HOLD - Paints - Triangle Coatings Inc.

COLD ICE - Health care products - Cold Ice Corp.

COLD KING - Antifreeze - Coastal Unilube, Inc.

COLD KING - Food products - Stilwell Foods

COLD-LITE - Photographic equipment - Aristo Grid Lamp Products Inc.

COLD MACHINE - Refrigerators - Kenyon Marine, Inc. (Adler/Barbour Div.)

COLD MAX - Cold remedies - Reese Chemical Co.

COLD-MOUNT - Adhesives and sealants - CODA Inc.

COLD MOUNTAIN - Food products - Miyako Oriental Foods Inc.

COLD MOUNTAIN - Recording label - Jazz Composer's Orchestra Association Inc.

COLD-NOSE - Office machines - Design Technology Corp.

COLD ONE, THE - Cups–plastic ☆ - Nyman Manufacturing Co.

COLD PACK - Ice chests ☆ - Poloron Products Inc.

COLD PLATTER - Food products machinery - Elmar Manufacturing Co.

COLD POUR - Artists' materials - Sculpture House Inc.

COLD POWER - Detergents - Colgate-Palmolive Co.

COLD PRO - Asphalt roofing cement - Henry Co.

COLD RIVER - Food products - Idaho Trout Processors Co.

COLD S. T. E. P. - Orthopedic products - Step Orthopaedics, LLC

COLD SEAL - Packaging–paper - Sealed Air Corp.

COLD SEASON PLUS - Cold remedies - Quantum, Inc.

COLD SHIELD - Insulating materials - Metallized Products Inc.

COLD SHOWER - Novelty items - Shane Kennedy

COLD SHRINK - Electrical equipment - Minnesota Mining & Manufacturing Co.

COLD SPRING - Beverages–carbonated - Cold Spring Brewing Co.

COLD SPRING - Wallpaper - Hudson Valley Handprints

COLD SPRING EXPORT - Beverages–malt - Cold Spring Brewing Co.

COLD SPRING II - Wallpaper - Hudson Valley Handprints

COLD SPRING LIGHT - Beverages–malt - Cold Spring Brewing Co.

COLD STANDARD - Seafood products–fresh or frozen - New England Fish Co.

COLD-STAR - Motor vehicle parts and accessories - Morgan Trailer Manufacturing. Co.

COLD-STEAM - Air purification systems - Walton Laboratories

COLD-STER - Chemical preparations - First Materials & Technology, Inc.

COLD STERILOG - Health care products ☆ - Trimline Medical Products Corp.

COLD STOPPER - Windows–storm - Tyz-All Plastics Inc.

COLD STORAGE - Jackets - Outrageous Inc.

COLD STREAM PREMIUM NATURAL SPRING WATER - Water–bottled or canned - Cold Stream Water Co.

COLD TERM - Electronic equipment - Plymouth Rubber Co., Inc.

COLD THERAPY - Ice bags - Bruder Healthcare Co.

COLD TURKEY - Candy ☆ - Brock Candy Co. Inc.

COLD WAR - Games - Avalon Hill Game Co.

COLD WAR - Syrup - Origins Natural Resources Inc.

COLD WATER - Food products - Union Fish Co.

COLD WATER GEYSER - Water–bottled or canned - Christopher Michael Vance

COLD WATER WASHED - Fruits and vegetables - Dole Fresh Vegetables Inc.

COLD WAVE - Apparel and accessories - Specialty Sports Ltd.

COLD WAVE - Liqueurs - Heaven Hill Distilleries, Inc.

COLD-X - Pharmaceutical ☆ - Iodent Co.

COLDATE - Pharmaceutical preparations ☆ - ICN Pharmaceuticals Inc.

COLDBROOK - Margarine - Safeway Stores Inc.

COLDCALM - Pharmaceutical preparations - Boiron Inc.

COLDCARE - Paper–tissue - Kimberly-Clark Corp.

COLDCAST - Coatings, etc. - Abatron, Inc.

COLDEN - Latex - Columbia Paint Inc.

COLDERS 29 - Beer - Miller Brewing Co.

COLDEXTENDER - Computer software ☆ - OTG Software

COLDFRONT - Crocheted and knitted items - Puritan Sportswear Corp.

COLDIRON LIGHT-A-BAG - Wood products - Coldiron Wood Products

COLDIST - Pharmaceutical preparations ☆ - U.S. Ethicals Inc.

COLDLOC - Pharmaceutical preparations - Flemming Pharmaceuticals, Inc.

COLDMASTER - Thermal underwear - Indera Mills Co.

COLDMASTER WINE & JUICE COOLER - Kitchen appliances - Carlisle Foodservice Products, Inc.

COLDONYL - Pharmaceutical preparations - Dover Pharmaceutical Inc.

COLDPRUF - Thermal underwear - Indera Mills Co.

COLDPUMP - Refrigerators ☆ - Kenyon Marine, Inc. (Adler/Barbour Div.)

COLDRAN - Health care products - Halsey Drug Co. Inc.

COLDRINE - Analgesics - Roberts/Hauck Pharmaceuticals Inc.

COLDRINK - Spoons - Spir-it Inc.

COLDSPOT - Housewares - Sears, Roebuck and Co.

COLDTERM - Cables - Plymouth Rubber Co., Inc.

COLDWATER - Seafood products–fresh or frozen - Fadler Co. Inc.

COLDWATER CREEK - Jewelry - Coldwater Creek Inc.

COLDWELD CONNECTION - Resins - Coldweld Corp.

COLDXTENDER - Computer peripheral equipment - OTG Software

COLE - Bathing suits - Cole of California Inc.

COLE - Giftware - James A. Cole Co. Inc.

COLE - Keys - Cole Consumer Products Inc.

COLE - Machinery - Axxess Technologies Inc.

COLE - Office furniture–metal - Joyce International Inc.

COLE - Pottery ☆ - Cole Ceramic Laboratories

COLE & SONS - Fabrics–tapestry ☆ - Clarence House Imports Ltd.

COLE BOSTON - Switches–electric - Cole Hersee Co.

COLE FARMS OLD-FASHIONED DRESSING - Salad dressings–bottled - Cole Farms Dressing Inc.

COLE FOR KIDS - Bathing suits - Cole of California Inc.

COLE HAAN - Shoes - Cole-Haan

COLE-HAAN RESORT - Footwear - Cole-Haan

COLE HERSEE - Switches–electric - Cole Hersee Co.

COLE JRS. - Bathing suits - Cole of California Inc.

COLE MINORS - Bathing suits - Cole of California Inc.

COLE OF CALIFORNIA - Bathing suits - Authentic Fitness Corp.

COLE OF CALIFORNIA - Bathing suits - Cole of California Inc.

COLE STOVE - Heating equipment ☆ - Ratelco, Inc.

COLEBROOK - Apparel and accessories - G-III Apparel Group, Ltd.

COLEBROOK - Clocks ☆ - General Time Corp. (Westclox/Seth Thomas Div.)

COLEBROOK KIDS - Apparel and accessories - G-III Apparel Group Ltd.

COLECO - Toys–electronic - Hasbro, Inc.

COLECOVISION - Computers - Hasbro, Inc.

COLEMA - Health care products - Peterson's Health Products

COLEMA BOARDS - Medical apparatus - Colema Boards of California

COLEMAN - Camping equipment - Coleman Co., Inc.

COLEMAN - Footwear - Coleman

COLEMAN - Furniture - The Coleman Co.

COLEMAN - Hosiery–men's ☆ - Keepers International

COLEMAN - Hot tubs–plastic ☆ - Coleman Spas

COLEMAN - Milk - Coleman Dairy Inc.

COLEMAN FOLDING TRAILERS - Trailers–travel - Fleetwood Enterprises, Inc.

COLEMAN NATURAL - Beef - Coleman Natural Meats Inc.

COLEMAN RANGER - Toys - Coleman Co., Inc.

COLEMAN'S - Confections - Coleman's Ice Cream Inc.

COLEMAN'S - Salad dressings–bottled - R.T. French Co.

COLENE - Ophthalmic goods ☆ - Luxottica

COLEO - Cosmetics - Colgate-Palmolive Co.

COLE'S - Bird feeds - Cole's Wild Bird Products Co.

COLE'S - Candy - Jane B. Brockenbrough

COLE'S - Food products - Cole's Quality Foods, Inc.

COLES - Puddings–canned - Christopher Brookes Distinctive Foods

COLE'S BAKING COMPANY - Bakery products - Cole's Quality Foods, Inc.

COLE'S QUALITY FOODS, INC. - Bakery products–frozen - Cole's Quality Foods, Inc.

COLES SHADOWS & REFLECTIONS - Fabrics–tapestry ☆ - Clarence House Imports Ltd.

COLES SPECIAL EFFECTS COLLECTION - Fabrics–tapestry ☆ - Clarence House Imports Ltd.

COLESCE COUTURE - Apparel and accessories - Cameo Coutures

COLESTID - Pharmaceutical preparations - Upjohn Co.

COLETTE - Darts and dart games - Dart World Inc.

COLEUR - Floor coverings–carpet and rugs ☆ - Mannington Carpets, Inc.

COLEX - Lantern globes–glass - Coleman Co., Inc.

COLEYWARE - Glassware–household - Coley Industries

COLFAX - Giftware - Gorham Inc.

COLFAX - Shoes - Allen-Edmonds Shoe Corp.

COLFAX OMEGA 3 - Shortening - Colfax Inc.

COLFLEX - Insulating materials - Noco Co.

COLGATE - Ophthalmic goods - Foremost Optical Products

COLGATE - Soap - Domestic Exports Inc.

COLGATE - Toothpaste - Colgate-Palmolive Co.

COLGATE 100 - Mouthwashes - Colgate-Palmolive Co.

COLGATE BAKING SODA & PEROXIDE WITH TARTAR CONTROL - Toothpaste - Colgate-Palmolive Co.

COLGATE-PALMOLIVE READY-TO-CLEAN - Cleaning preparations– household - Colgate-Palmolive Co.

COLGATE PLATINUM - Toothpaste - Colgate-Palmolive Co.

COLGATE PLUS - Toothbrushes - Colgate-Palmolive Co.

COLGATE PRECISION - Dental floss - Colgate-Palmolive Co.

COLGATE PREMIER - Mattresses - Colgate Mattress Co.

COLGATE TOTAL - Toothpaste - Colgate-Palmolive Co.

COLGATE TOTAL DESIGNS - Toothbrushes - Colgate-Palmolive Co.

COLGATE TRADITIONAL - Mattresses - Colgate Mattress Co.

COLGATE ULTRA FIT - Toothbrushes - Colgate-Palmolive Co.

COLGINS - Hickory liquid smoke - Richard E. Colgin Co. Inc.

COLIBRI - Bathroom accessories - Kohler Co.

COLIBRI - Lighters - Park Lane Associates, Inc.

COLIBRI - Medical apparatus - Bernafon Inc.

COLIBRI - Toys - Peg Perego USA Inc.

COLICON - Pharmaceutical preparations - Reese Chemical Co.

COLICON - Pharmaceutical preparations ☆ - U.S. Ethicals Inc.

COLICON DROPS - Pharmaceutical preparations ☆ - Reese Chemical Co.

COLIDROPS - Pharmaceutical preparations - Marin Pharmaceuticals

COLIGON - Lenses–photographic - Aetna Optix Inc.

COLIN - Musical instrument accessories - Charles Colin Music Publishers

COLIN MOUTHPIECE - Musical instrument accessories ☆ - Charles Colin Music Publishers

COLIN STUART - Footwear - Victoria's Secret Stores, Inc.

COLINA - Pharmaceutical preparations - Luyties Pharmacal Co.

COLISEUM - Amplifiers–musical instrument - Fender Musical Instruments

COLISEUM - Apparel–men's - Cami'z, Inc.

COLL-AGE - Mat boards - Callen Photo Mount Corp.

COLL-TEX - Sporting goods - Climb High Inc.

COLL363 GR4DUAT3 - Apparel and accessories - Lloyd M. Hughes Enterprises, Inc.

COLLABORATIONS - Apparel and accessories - Zee International, Inc.

COLLABORATIVE - Computer peripheral equipment - Photonics Corp.

COLLABORATIVE TECHNOLOGIES CORPORATION - Computer software - Collaborative Technologies Corp.

COLLABRA - Computer software - Collabra Software, Inc.

COLLABRA SHARE - Computer software - Collabra Software, Inc.

COLLADERM - Skin care products - C&M Pharmacal, Inc.

COLLAFOAM - Health care products - Tecnol Medical Products, Inc.

COLLAGE - Computer software - Fotodyne Inc.

COLLAGE - Cosmetics ☆ - Bonne Bell, Inc.

COLLAGE - Floor coverings–carpet and rugs - Regal Rugs Inc.

COLLAGE - Floor coverings–carpet and rugs ☆ - Columbus Mills, Inc.

COLLAGE - Frames–eyeglass - Zylo Ware Corp.

COLLAGE - Furniture ☆ - Mersman Furniture Co.

COLLAGE - Furniture–wood - Ficks Reed Co. Inc.

COLLAGE - Paper - Union Camp Corp. (Fine Paper Division)

COLLAGE - Soap - Dawson Home Fashions, Inc.

COLLAGE - Tableware–china ☆ - Villeroy and Boch Tableware Ltd.

COLLAGE - Wallpaper - Glidden Co.

COLLAGE - Wallpaper - Royson's Corp.

COLLAGE - Wallpaper ☆ - Motif Designs, Inc.

COLLAGE ART CREATIONS - Craft supplies - Lisa Frank, Inc.

COLLAGEN CARE - Lipsticks - Honey & Spice Toiletries

COLLAGEN CARE - Skin care products - Roberts Research Laboratories, Inc.

COLLAGEN CREME - Skin care products - Fanie International

COLLAGEN PLUS - Skin care products - Palm Beach Beauty Products

COLLAGENASE ABC - Skin care products - Advance Biofactures Corp.

COLLAGENE - Skin care products - Nailtex Inc.

COLLAGES OF THE GREATS - House furnishings - Thomas A. Salomon

COLLAMORE EDUCATIONAL PUBLISHING - Publisher's imprints - D.C. Heath & Co.

COLLANCO - Cough medicines - Claflin Co.

COLLANO - Floor coverings ☆ - Azrock Commercial Flooring

COLLAPS-O! CATERPILLARS - Games - Tomy America, Inc.

COLLAPSIBLE CLASSICS - Furniture - Bower Studios Corp.

COLLAPSIBLE CRADLE - Music stands - LP Music Group

COLLAR - Files–tools - Anglo American Enterprises Corp.

COLLAR BAR - Apparel and accessories ☆ - Edison Brothers Stores, Inc.

COLLAR CHAINS - Pet products - Pet Concepts

COLLAR CHARMS - Pet products - Pet Concepts

COLLAR CRAFT - Pet products - Collar Craft/Petite Originals

COLLAR 'N' CUFF - Health care products - Tecnol Medical Products, Inc.

COLLAR, THE - Pet products - Fletcher Products Corp.

COLLAR WEAR - Apparel–men's - Apparel Group, Ltd.

COLLARD CRITTERS - Toys–stuffed - Jeri Collard

COLLARLOK - Nuts and bolts ☆ - MacLean-ESNA

COLLARSET - Television equipment - Television Equipment Associates

COLLATERAL - Paper–bond - Esleeck Manufacturing Co., Inc.

COLLATERALTRAK - Computer software - Vintek, Inc.

COLLAVINI - Wines - Blair Importers Ltd.

COLLE - Apparel and accessories ☆ - Skea Ltd.

COLLEAGUE - Eyeglasses - Art-Craft Optical Co.

COLLEAGUE - Floor coverings–carpet and rugs - Milliken & Co. Inc.

COLLEAGUE - Furniture - Harter

COLLEAGUE - Infant product - Lisco, Inc.

COLLEAGUE - Office furniture–wood - Harter Corp.

COLLECT A BEAR BY 1928 - Jewelry - Mel Bernie and Co., Inc.

COLLECT-A-BOX - Boxes - Deluxe Craft Manufacturing Co.

COLLECT-A-CUBE RECYCLING CONTAINERS - Wastebaskets - United Receptacle Inc.

COLLECT-A-MUG - Novelty items ☆ - Papel Freelance, Inc.

COLLECT-A-ROOM - Craft supplies ☆ - Western Trimming Corp.

COLLECT & COLOR WITH STAMPS - Toys - ZOE Arts

COLLECT CALL - Computer software - Steven J. Cohen

COLLECT DUST - Sweeping compounds - Paxon Manufacturing Co.

COLLECTA - Photo albums - JM Co.

COLLECTABLE - Frames–picture - Structural Industries

COLLECTABLES - Cutlery ☆ - Imperial Schrade Corp.

COLLECTABLES - Furniture - Weiman Co.

COLLECTABLES - Greeting cards ☆ - Small World

COLLECTABLES - Recording label - Collectables Record Corp.

☆ = Now out of production

COLLECTIBLE COUNTERS - Toys - Lauri Inc.
COLLECTIBLE ELECTRONICS - Electronic equipment - Kash N' Gold, Ltd.
COLLECTIBLE TELEPHONES - Telephones - Kash N' Gold, Ltd.
COLLECTIBLE TREASURES - Giftware - Campus Originals Inc.
COLLECTIBLE VILLAGE - Novelty items - Biedermann & Sons Inc.
COLLECTIBLES - Checkbooks - Clarke American Corp.
COLLECTIBLES - Frames–eyeglass ☆ - Universal/Univis Inc.
COLLECTIBLES - Furniture - Hammary Furniture Co. Inc.
COLLECTIBLES - Leather goods - AR Accessories Group Inc.
COLLECTIBLES - Window coverings - Norman's of Salisbury
COLLECTIBLES BY ARIS - Hats - Saramar Corp.
COLLECTIBLES CATALOGER - Computer software - Right on Programs
COLLECTING CONSORT - Audio tapes–blank - Collecting Consort
COLLECTION - Furniture - Weiman Co.
COLLECTION - Quilts - D.A. Brinkmann Designs
COLLECTION '76 - Floor coverings–carpet and rugs ☆ - Concepts International
COLLECTION 1991 - Leather goods - Holiday Fair, Inc.
COLLECTION CANADA - Housewares ☆ - Grainware Co.
COLLECTION CARTOONS - Office supplies - Action Cartoons
COLLECTION DE LUXE - Jewelry ☆ - Hirsch Speidel Inc.
COLLECTION D'ORIENT - Wallpaper - Dondares
COLLECTION GENEVE - Pens - Caran D'Ache of Switzerland Inc.
COLLECTION, THE - Eyeglasses - Art-Craft Optical Co.
COLLECTION, THE - Wallpaper - Wall Fabrics Inc.
COLLECTIONS - Apparel and accessories - Montgomery Ward & Co. Inc.
COLLECTIONS BY JOYCE - Apparel stores–children's - Frog Pond Kids Inc.
COLLECTIONS FOR YOUNG SCHOLARS - Educational materials - Open Court Publishing Co.
COLLECTOR - Cabinets - Tannery Lane Co. Inc.
COLLECTOR PRO+ - Computer peripheral equipment - Wind Associates, Inc.
COLLECTOR PROTECTOR - Office supplies - Tamerica Products Inc.
COLLECTOR SAFE - Display cases–plastic - Berco Products, Inc.
COLLECTOR SERIES - Greeting cards ☆ - Blue Mountain Arts Inc.
COLLECTOR SERIES, THE - Publisher's imprints ☆ - Martingale & Co.
COLLECTOR, THE - Games ☆ - Avalon Hill Game Co.
COLLECTOR, THE - Vacuum cleaners and accessories - Black & Decker Corp.
COLLECTOR, THE - Chimes ☆ - Nutone Inc.
COLLECTOR, THE - Toys - Tonka Corp.
COLLECTORS - Furniture ☆ - Athens Furniture Industries Inc.
COLLECTOR'S - Furniture ☆ - Broyhill Furniture Industries, Inc.
COLLECTORS ALBUM - Greeting cards - American Artists Group Inc.
COLLECTOR'S BEST INVENTORY SYSTEMS - Publisher's imprints - Paul K. Beaver
COLLECTOR'S BOTTLES - Candy - Glenn Confections Inc.
COLLECTOR'S BOUTIQUE, THE - Jewelry - Mel Bernie and Co., Inc.
COLLECTOR'S CHERRY - Furniture - Thomasville Furniture Industries Inc.
COLLECTOR'S CHOICE - Corn–flour or meal - Philip Morris Companies Inc.
COLLECTOR'S CHOICE - Floor coverings–carpet and rugs ☆ - Calladium & Marglen
COLLECTOR'S CHOICE - Wallcovering ☆ - Colortree Designs
COLLECTOR'S CLASSIC - Golfing equipment - Nassau Precision Casting Co., Inc.
COLLECTORS CLASSICS - Furniture - Ethan Allen, Inc.
COLLECTORS CLASSICS - Furniture ☆ - Ridgeway Clock Co.
COLLECTORS CLASSICS - Furniture ☆ - White Furniture Co.
COLLECTOR'S CLUB, THE - Toys - Trinkets-N-Things, Ltd.
COLLECTORS CORNER - Greeting cards - American Artists Group Inc.
COLLECTORS CORNER - Housewares - Knobler International Ltd.
COLLECTOR'S EDGE - Decals and transfers - Collector's Edge, L.P.
COLLECTOR'S EDITION - Containers ☆ - Arrow Group Industries
COLLECTOR'S EDITION - Furniture ☆ - Baker, Knapp & Tubbs
COLLECTOR'S EDITION - Wallpaper - United Wallcoverings
COLLECTORS EDITION RAFFLE - Metals - Silver Creek Minting
COLLECTOR'S GALLERY, THE - Giftware - J.C. Penney Co., Inc.
COLLECTORS GROUP - Floor coverings–carpet and rugs - Cabin Crafts Carpets
COLLECTORS HOLD! - Adhesives and sealants - Trevco
COLLECTORS INTERNATIONAL - Giftware - Royal Doulton-Somerset UK Ltd.
COLLECTORS ITEM - Floor coverings–carpet and rugs - Monticello Carpet Mills
COLLECTOR'S ITEMS - Frames–eyeglass - May Optical Co. Inc.
COLLECTORS' LEAGUE - Pottery - Score Board Holding Corp.
COLLECTOR'S MIX - Furniture ☆ - Hickory Chair Co.
COLLECTOR'S PLATES - Hobby kits - Craft House Corp.
COLLECTORS SERIES - Calendars - Collector Series Inc.

COLLECTORS' SERIES - Tape players–cassette - Sony Music Entertainment Inc.
COLLECTOR'S SERIES, THE - Publisher's imprints - American Cooking Guild
COLLECTOR'S SERIES, THE - Cabinets - Vinotemp International
COLLECTORS STUDIO INC., THE - Jewelry - Franklin Mint
COLLECTRAMATIC - Pressure cookers - Winston Products Inc.
COLLEEN - Blinds–venetian ☆ - Hunter Douglas, Inc.
COLLEEN - Brooms - Hofmann Broom Works Inc.
COLLEEN - Earthenware ☆ - Waterford Wedgewood USA, Inc.
COLLEEN - Eyeglasses - Art-Craft Optical Co.
COLLEEN - Furniture ☆ - Stanley Furniture Co. Inc.
COLLEEN - Recording label - Rego Irish Records, Tapes & Videos
COLLEEN MICHAELS - Apparel and accessories - Breton Industries
COLLEEN'S - Candy - Bewley Irish Imports
COLLEGE - Darts and dart games ☆ - Dart World Inc.
COLLEGE - Footwear - Olem Shoe Corp.
COLLEGE - Milk - College Dairy
COLLEGE - Thread - Threads USA Div.
COLLEGE AID CALCULATOR - Computer software - Think Ahead, Inc.
COLLEGE APPLICATION PLANNER - Computer software - Peterson's Guides, Inc.
COLLEGE AUTHENTICS - Apparel and accessories - Larry Haughey
COLLEGE BOY - Pencils - National Pen & Pencil Co.
COLLEGE CASH - Coupons - Interactive Networks Inc.
COLLEGE CLUB - Hats - Grass-Grossinger Cap Manufacturing Co.
COLLEGE COST EXPLORER/FUND FINDER - Computer software - College Entrance Examination Board
COLLEGE DOLLARS - Computer software - Systems Organization Services, Inc.
COLLEGE EXPLORER, THE - Computer software ☆ - Knowledge Access International, Inc.
COLLEGE FINDER - Computer software - Wintergreen Software, Inc.
COLLEGE FOOTBALL TRIVIA - Computer software - Half-Time Enterprises, Inc.
COLLEGE FORMALS - Apparel stores - Mark Young, Inc.
COLLEGE HOOPS ILLUSTRATED - Sporting goods - Professional Sports Publications, Inc.
COLLEGE HOUSE - Apparel–athletic - College House Inc.
COLLEGE HYPE - T-shirts–men's - College Hype Athletic Attire
COLLEGE INN - Chickens - Nabisco Foods Group
COLLEGE IS JUST A GAME - Apparel and accessories - College is Just a Game, Inc.
COLLEGE KEEPSAKES - Posters - College Keepsakes
COLLEGE LINEBACKER HALL OF FAME - Athletic associations - Downtown Athletic Club of Orlando, Inc.
COLLEGE MEMORIES AT CHRISTMAS - Christmas tree ornaments - Campus Originals Inc.
COLLEGE MINIATURES - Apparel and accessories ☆ - Imperial Knitting Co. Inc.
COLLEGE PARK - Furniture ☆ - Bassett Furniture Industries, Inc.
COLLEGE PROF - Eyeglasses - Martin-Copeland Eyewear Corp.
COLLEGE STRIPE - House furnishings - Dan River Inc.
COLLEGE-TOWN - Apparel–women's - College-Town Inc.
COLLEGE VISIONS - Greeting cards ☆ - Blue Mountain Arts Inc.
COLLEGE WHERE - Computer software - McCabe Software, Inc.
COLLEGENT - Novelty items - Pence Industries
COLLEGEVIEW - Apparel–children's - Collegeview Partnership
COLLEGEVILLE - Flags - Flags International Inc.
COLLEGIAN - Exercising equipment ☆ - American Athletic Inc.
COLLEGIANA - Bulletin boards–wood ☆ - Quartet Manufacturing Co.
COLLEGIATE - Apparel and accessories - Wemco, Inc.
COLLEGIATE - Apparel and accessories ☆ - Campus Sportswear Co.
COLLEGIATE - Artists' materials - Bee Paper Co. Inc.
COLLEGIATE - Bicycles - Schwinn Cycling & Fitness Inc.
COLLEGIATE - Electronic equipment ☆ - Hamilton Electronics Corp.
COLLEGIATE - Musical instrument accessories - G. Leblanc Corp.
COLLEGIATE - Musical instruments - Hyer Percussion Products
COLLEGIATE - Pens - Quill Co. Inc.
COLLEGIATE - Pipes–tobacco ☆ - S.M. Frank & Co. Inc. (Kaywoodie-Yello-Bole-Medico)
COLLEGIATE - Sporting goods - Gared Sports, Inc.
COLLEGIATE - Sporting goods ☆ - Nichols Wrestling Products Inc.
COLLEGIATE - Sporting goods ☆ - Soccer Sport Supply Co. Inc.
COLLEGIATE - Telephones - Collegiate Telephones, Inc.
COLLEGIATE - Watches - Bloomfield International Inc.
COLLEGIATE CAPS - Games - Major League Music

COLLEGIATE CHAMPION - Scoreboards - Daktronics Inc.
COLLEGIATE CRITTERS - Statuary - Collegiate Critters
COLLEGIATE CRUNCHIES - Novelty items–stitched - A + A
COLLEGIATE GEAR - Apparel–athletic - Caicos Swimwear Corp.
COLLEGIATE SPORT NUTRITION - Vitamins and nutritional supplements - Natural Alternatives International, Inc.
COLLEGIATE, THE - Cakes - Tasty Baking Co.
COLLEGIATE TRADITIONS - Sweaters - Collegiate Traditions, Inc.
COLLEGIUM - Furniture–wood - Steelcase Inc.
COLLEGIUM - Recording label - Collegium Sound Inc.
COLLEGIUM GRAPHICUM - Publisher's imprints - Alan Wofsy Fine Arts
COLLETTE - Rings–jewelry - Artcarved Inc.
COLLETTE BY MISS ELAINE - Apparel–women's ☆ - Miss Elaine, Inc.
COLLETTS - Furniture - Colletts Inc.
COLLEX - Motor vehicle parts and accessories - Collex Collision Experts
COLLEZIO - Watches - Nelson Industries
COLLI DI CATONE - Wines - William Grant & Sons, Inc.
COLLI DI TUSCOLO - Wines - Blair Importers Ltd.
COLLIDESCAPE-MATHEMATICAL - Games - Kadon Enterprises Inc.
COLLIE - Hot-dog sandwiches - Southeast Food Systems, Inc.
COLLIEFLOWERS - Dog food - Three Dog Bakery, Inc.
COLLIER - Infant product ☆ - Collier-Keyworth Inc.
COLLIER - Publisher's imprints - MacMillan Publishing Co. Inc.
COLLIER CAMPBELL - Wallpaper ☆ - Manuscreens
COLLIER FAST FICTION - Publisher's imprints - MacMillan Publishing Co. Inc.
COLLIER MACMILLAN INTERNATIONAL - Publisher's imprints - MacMillan Publishing Co. Inc.
COLLIERS - Tobacco–chewing or smoking - Gesty Trading & Manufacturing Corp.
COLLIN COUNTY - Beverages–malt - Reinheitsgebot Brewing Co.
COLLIN CREEK - Apparel–women's - Althuser Co.
COLLINES D'OR - Beverages–alcohol - Holmbru, Ltd.
COLLINGDALE - Floor coverings - Congoleum Corp.
COLLINGSWOOD - Floor coverings - Mannington Resilient Floors
COLLINGWOOD - Posters - Graphic Arts Unltd. Inc.
COLLINITE - Cleaning preparations - Collinite Corp.
COLLINS - Fishing tackle - Truline Glass Rod Manufacturing Co.
COLLINS - Handbags - Collin's of Texas
COLLINS - Sporting goods - Collins Ski Products Inc.
COLLINS & AIKMAN - Fabrics–broadcloth - Collins & Aikman Corp.
COLLINS BLACK - Beverages–alcohol - Hy-Vee Food Stores Inc.
COLLINS CAVIAR - Caviar and caviar products - Carolyn Collins Caviar Co.
COLLINS DEBDEN - Calendars - Sormani Inc.
COLLINS FIELDS - Nuts–salted, roasted, cooked, or canned - Brans Nut Co.
COLLINS VINEYARD - Wine - Limerick Lane Cellars
COLLINSWOOD - Wood products - Collins Pine Co.
COLLINSWORTH - Giftware ☆ - Anchor Hocking Glass, Inc.
COLLIO ATTEMS - Wines - Blair Importers Ltd.
COLLIS - Tool boxes - Collis Inc.
COLLIS CURVE - Toothbrushes - Nylander's Vantage Products
COLLISIONFREE - Computers - Grand Junction Networks, Inc.
COLLO-MIN - Pet products - Natural Animal Nutrition Inc.
COLLOGEN - Beauty aids ☆ - Cellouette Inc.
COLLOID OSMOMETER - Diagnostic apparatus - Wescor, Inc.
COLLOIDAL SILVER - Vitamins and nutritional supplements - Matrix Health Products, Inc.
COLLOIDAL SUPREME - Vitamins and nutritional supplements - Bit International Ltd.
COLLOIDALIFE - Vitamins and nutritional supplements - Source Naturals
COLLONNADE - Glass–plate - Sasaki
COLLOPAKE - Paints ☆ - Samuel Cabot Inc.
COLLORAL - Pharmaceutical preparations - Autoimmune, Inc.
COLLUM - Splints - Smith & Nephew Inc. (Rehabilitation Div.)
COLLUSION - Fabrics–polyethylene - American Trading and Production Corp.
COLLYRIUM - Skin care products ☆ - Wyeth-Ayerst Laboratories
COLMAR - Mats - Colmar Industries, Inc.
COLMAR - Rings–jewelry - Artcarved Inc.
COLMCILLE - Computer software - Monotype Corp.
COLO ZONE - Pharmaceutical preparations - En Garde Health Products, Inc.
COLOBUNNIES - Toys–banks - Ralphco, Inc.
COLOCTYL - Pharmaceutical preparations ☆ - Vitarine Pharmaceuticals Inc.
COLOFILE - Office supplies - Reynolds and Reynolds Co.
COLOGEL - Pharmaceutical preparations - Eli Lilly and Co.
COLOGNE - Frames–eyeglass - Liberty Optical Manufacturing Co.
COLOGNE 73 - Perfumes - Kiehl's Since 1851, Inc.
COLOGNE CRITTERS - Animal figurines with cologne ☆ - Cosrich Inc.

COLOGNE MERVEILLEUSE - Colognes - FMG/Tsumara Medical
COLOGNE MIST FOR HER - Cosmetics - Viviane Woodard Industries, Ltd.
COLOGNE O' THE WILD - Pet products - Professional Pet Products
COLOMA - Food products - Coloma Frozen Foods Inc.
COLOMBIA - Shrimp–canned or cured ☆ - Darik Enterprises Inc.
COLOMBIA CREST - Food products ☆ - Ocean Beauty Seafood, Inc.
COLOMBIAN HAYLLI - Coffee - Atlanta Coffee Roastery, Inc.
COLOMBINA - Candy - Colombina Candy Co., Inc.
COLOMBINA - Candy - Dorval Trading Co., Ltd.
COLOMBINE - Flatware ☆ - Couzon USA
COLOMBO - Accordions - Colombo & Sons Accordion Co.
COLOMBO - Prepared foods - San Francisco French Bread Co.
COLOMBO - Wines - William Grant & Sons, Inc.
COLOMBO - Yogurt–frozen - Colombo Inc. (Frozen Desserts Div.)
COLOMBO NEW GOURMET FROZEN YOGURT - Yogurt–frozen - CMHC, Inc.
COLOMBO SHOPPE STYLE - Yogurt–frozen - CMHC, Inc.
COLOMBO SHOPPE STYLE - Yogurt–frozen - Colombo Inc. (Frozen Desserts Div.)
COLOMBO SLIM - Yogurt - Colombo Inc. (Frozen Desserts Div.)
COLOMBO TOFREE - Tofu–frozen ☆ - Colombo Inc. (Frozen Desserts Div.)
COLOMBO'S - Pizzas–frozen - Jeno's Inc.
COLON 8 - Health care products - Ion Laboratories Inc.
COLON-AID - Health care products - Healthwatchers System
COLON CLEANSE - Herbal products - 21st Century Manna
COLON CLENZ - Vitamins and nutritional supplements - Natural Balance, Inc.
COLON CLN - Vitamins and nutritional supplements - Momentum Marketing Inc.
COLON COMPLEMENTS - Health care products - Holistic Laboratories Inc.
COLON CONDITIONER - Health care products - Naturade Inc.
COLON CONDITIONER - Vitamins and nutritional supplements - Matrix Health Products, Inc.
COLON DETOXIFIER - Health care products - Holistic Laboratories Inc.
COLON GREEN - Health care products - Futurebiotics
COLON-TIME - Vitamins and nutritional supplements - Nutrition Headquarters, Inc.
COLONADE - Clocks ☆ - General Time Corp. (Westclox/Seth Thomas Div.)
COLONADE - Clocks ☆ - Ridgeway Clock Co.
COLONADE - Floor coverings ☆ - Congoleum Corp.
COLONADE - Floor coverings–carpet and rugs - Sweetwater Carpet Corp.
COLONADE - Furniture ☆ - Mersman Furniture Co.
COLONEL - See also **COL.**
COLONEL - Ophthalmic goods - Embassy Creations Inc.
COLONEL - Thread ☆ - American & Efird, Inc.
COLONEL - Trailers–travel ☆ - Coachmen Industries, Inc.
COLONEL BLUE - Dinnerware–glass - Royal China & Porcelain Companies Inc.
COLONEL CANINE - Dog food - Famous Fido's Specialty Foods
COLONEL CARVER - Cutlery - Niblack
COLONEL HICKORY - Cabinets–wood - Haas Cabinet Co. Inc.
COLONEL K'S PASTIES - Pies–fresh - Sandra Bayerl
COLONEL LEE - Beverages–alcohol - Barton Brands, Ltd.
COLONEL LEE - Liquors - Canandaigua Wine Co. Inc.
COL. LITTLETON - Knives–pocket - Col. Littleton Ltd., Inc.
COLONEL LOGAN - Staircases–metal - Logan Inc.
COLONEL'S CRISPY STRIPS - Chickens - KFC Corp.
COLONEL'S ROTISSERIE GOLD - Food products - KFC Corp.
COLONEL'S, THE - Puddings–canned - KFC Corp.
COLONIA - Floor coverings - Mannington Resilient Floors
COLONIA ART PUBLICATIONS - Greeting cards - Colonia Art Publications
COLONIAL - Adhesives and sealants ☆ - Induron Coatings Inc.
COLONIAL - Bakery products - Campbell Taggart Inc.
COLONIAL - Books–blank - Colonial Co.
COLONIAL - Brooms - Royal Maid Association for the Blind Inc.
COLONIAL - Candles - Colonial Candle of Cape Cod
COLONIAL - Candy ☆ - Helms Candy Manufacturing Co. Inc.
COLONIAL - Candy ☆ - Johnson Candy Co.
COLONIAL - Candy ☆ - Melster Candies Inc.
COLONIAL - Coffee - C.B. Ragland Co.
COLONIAL - Dinnerware–glass ☆ - Nikko Ceramics Inc.
COLONIAL - Dishes–earthenware ☆ - Gorham Inc.
COLONIAL - Dishes–earthenware ☆ - Homer Laughlin China Co.
COLONIAL - Fans–electric - Hunter Fan Co.
COLONIAL - Fireplace equipment - Seymour Manufacturing Co.,Inc.
COLONIAL - Floor coverings ☆ - Harris-Tarkett, Inc.
COLONIAL - Flowers, plants, and seeds - Continental Farms, Inc.

COLONIAL - Flowers, plants, and seeds - D. Landreth Seed Co.
COLONIAL - Food products - AMK for Service
COLONIAL - Frames–picture - Colonial Moulding & Frame Co. Inc.
COLONIAL - Frames–picture - Terragrafics Inc.
COLONIAL - Furniture ☆ - Evenflo Juvenile Furniture Co.
COLONIAL - Gasoline - Colonial Oil Industries Inc.
COLONIAL - Glass products - Westmoreland Glass Co.
COLONIAL - Glassware–household ☆ - Lotus Glass Co.
COLONIAL - Glassware–scientific - Federal Glass
COLONIAL - Hardware - Hy-Ko Products Co.
COLONIAL - Hardware ☆ - Amerock Corp.
COLONIAL - Hobby kits ☆ - Craft World International Inc.
COLONIAL - Knitting machines - Colonial Corp. of America
COLONIAL - Knives–pocket - Colonial Knife Co. Inc.
COLONIAL - Lamps - General Electric Co.
COLONIAL - Lamps ☆ - Roxter Lighting
COLONIAL - Mail boxes - Gordon Associates
COLONIAL - Meat products - Tav Brands Inc.
COLONIAL - Meat products–cured - Colonial Provision Co.
COLONIAL - Molasses - Crompton & Knowles Corp.
COLONIAL - Paints ☆ - Hampton Paint Manufacturing Co.
COLONIAL - Pottery products - Western Stoneware
COLONIAL - Recording label - Lamon Records
COLONIAL - Recording label - The Pegasus Group, Inc.
COLONIAL - Recording label - Stark Records & Tape Co.
COLONIAL - Salt - Akzo America Inc.
COLONIAL - Siding–insulating - Bird Inc.
COLONIAL - Sugar–granulated, refined, or powdered - Savannah Foods and Industries Inc.
COLONIAL - Tiles–ceramic - Monarch Tile Inc.
COLONIAL - Trailers–travel - Coleman Co., Inc.
COLONIAL - Watches - Elgin Watch Co.
COLONIAL '76 - Furniture - Conover Chair Co. Inc.
COLONIAL ALUMINUM RESIDENTIAL PICKET FENCING A MEMBER OF THE ANCHOR GROUP - Fencing–gates and posts - Anchor Fence, Inc.
COLONIAL AMBER - Glassware–household ☆ - Fenton Art Glass Co.
COLONIAL AMERICAN - Varnishes - Barrett Varnish Co.
COLONIAL BENNINGTON - Cutlery ☆ - Lifetime Hoan Corp.
COLONIAL BLUE - Dinnerware ☆ - Corning Inc.
COLONIAL BREWERY COMPANY - Beverages–malt - Old European Brewery Co.
COLONIAL BRICK - Floor coverings - Congoleum Corp.
COLONIAL BRICK - Floor coverings–tile - Kentile Floors Inc.
COLONIAL CAMEOS - Stationery - Burgoyne Inc./Curtis Swann
COLONIAL CANDLE OF CAPE COD - Candles - Colonial Candle of Cape Cod
COLONIAL CHARM - Floor coverings ☆ - Congoleum Corp.
COLONIAL CHARM - Furniture ☆ - Bassett Furniture Industries, Inc.
COLONIAL CLASSIC - Hardware ☆ - Amerock Corp.
COLONIAL CLUB - Cordials - Paramount Distillers Inc.
COLONIAL COLLECTION - Fans–electric ☆ - Hunter Fan Co.
COLONIAL COLLECTION, THE - Giftware - Russ Berrie and Co., Inc.
COLONIAL COLLECTION, THE - Wallpaper - Shelbourne Wallcoverings
COLONIAL COUNTRY - Furniture - Virginia House Furniture Corp.
COLONIAL CRAFT - Frames–picture - Colonial Craft
COLONIAL CRAFT - Window coverings - Mid-America Custom Inc.
COLONIAL CRAFTSMAN - Wallpaper - Imperial Wallcoverings, Inc.
COLONIAL CRAFTSMEN - Pewter miniatures ☆ - Colonial Craftsmen Industries
COLONIAL CROCK - Crock pots ☆ - West Bend Co.
COLONIAL CUSTOM - Wood products - Dale John Amborski
COLONIAL DAYS - Giftware ☆ - Doranne
COLONIAL DIGEST - Furniture - Lane Co. Inc.
COLONIAL DOLLAR - Candy - Sweet Candy Co.
COLONIAL FARMS - Confectioneries - American Maple Products Corp.
COLONIAL FARMS - Food products - Oxford Corp.
COLONIAL FIGURE - Stationery - American Greetings Corp.
COLONIAL FOODS - Meat products–beef - Colonial Beef Co.
COLONIAL FORGE - Cutlery - Ontario Knife Co.
COLONIAL GARDEN - Dinnerware–glass ☆ - Metlox Pottery Shoppe
COLONIAL GINGHAM - Cooking utensils–enameled ☆ - National Housewares
COLONIAL GRAIN COUNTRY - Breads - Original Oatmeal Baking Co.
COLONIAL GRAND - Real estate agencies - Colonial Realty LP
COLONIAL HANDY HORSE - Hardware - Centrum Products Co.
COLONIAL HARVEST OAK - Furniture ☆ - Gerry Wood Products
COLONIAL HEARTH - Cakes - World's Best Cheesecake
COLONIAL HEIGHTS - Furniture - Bean Station Furniture Factory Inc.

COLONIAL HEIRLOOM - Furniture - Keller Manufacturing Co.
COLONIAL HOMES - Publisher's imprints - Hearst Corp.
COLONIAL HOMES - Wallpaper ☆ - Lifestyle Studios
COLONIAL HOUSE - Candy - Fine Products Co. Inc.
COLONIAL HOUSE - Candy - Gilliam Candy Brands
COLONIAL HOUSE - Candy - Gilliam Candy Co. Inc. (Gilliam Candy Brands)
COLONIAL HOUSE - Floor coverings–carpet and rugs - Mohawk Carpet Corp.
COLONIAL HOUSE - Floor coverings–carpet and rugs ☆ - Evans-Black Carpet Mills
COLONIAL INTERNATIONAL COFFEE - Coffee makers–electric - Roma Export Inc.
COLONIAL KITCHEN - Cutting boards ☆ - Bemis Manufacturing Co.
COLONIAL LADY - Dolls ☆ - Effanbee Doll Corp.
COLONIAL LINEN - Yarn - Henry's Attic
COLONIAL MASTER - Meat products–cured - Colonial Provision Co.
COLONIAL MIST - Dinnerware, bakeware, servingware, etc ☆ - Corning Inc.
COLONIAL NYL-GLO - Flags - Annin and Co.
COLONIAL PARCHMENT - Stationery ☆ - Mead Corp.
COLONIAL PEPPER JELLY - Jams and jellies - Lollipop Tree
COLONIAL PLANK - Floor coverings–carpet and rugs - Roxbury Carpet Co.
COLONIAL POINT - Floor coverings–carpet and rugs - Downs Carpet Co. Inc.
COLONIAL PORTFOLIO - Wallpaper ☆ - Thomas Strahan Wallcoverings
COLONIAL PREFERENCE - Siding–insulating - Variform, Inc.
COLONIAL-PREMIER - Lamps - Rembrandt Lamps
COLONIAL REPRODUCTIONS - Vases - S.A. Leart Co.
COLONIAL SAMPLER - Wallpaper - Norwall Wallcoverings
COLONIAL SAMPLER VI - Wallpaper - Norwall Wallcoverings
COLONIAL SCENE - Furniture ☆ - Bassett Furniture Industries, Inc.
COLONIAL SHELL - Flatware - Reed and Barton Corp.
COLONIAL SKIRMISH - Games ☆ - Gamescience
COLONIAL SPIRALITE - Candles ☆ - Colonial Candle of Cape Cod
COLONIAL STREET SCENES - Patterns–clothing - Ann's Cottage
COLONIAL TIPT - Flatware - Gorham Inc.
COLONIAL TRADITION - Food products - Pocahontas Foods USA Inc.
COLONIAL TRUST - House furnishings - Custom House Industries, Inc.
COLONIAL VILLAGE - Figurines - George Zolton Lefton Co.
COLONIAL VILLAGE - Real estate agencies - Colonial Realty LP
COLONIAL VINEYARDS - Wines - Colonial Vineyards
COLONIAL VINTAGE - Tobacco–chewing or smoking - 1776 Tobacco Co.
COLONIAL VIRGINIA - Patterns–clothing - Ann's Cottage
COLONIAL VIRGINIA BRASS - Giftware - Hampton Roads Manufacturing Corp.
COLONIAL WILLIAMSBURG - Food products - Rowena's Gourmet Foods Inc.
COLONIAL WILLIAMSBURG - Lighting fixtures - Virginia Metalcrafters Inc.
COLONIAL WILLIAMSBURG - Towels - Stevens Linen Associates Inc.
COLONIAL WILLIAMSBURG REPRODUCTIONS - Dinnerware - Eastern Shore Trading Co.
COLONIAL WOOD - Floor coverings ☆ - Tarkett, Inc.
COLONIAL WOODWORKERS - Candlesticks - Biedermann & Sons Inc.
COLONIALS - Tiles–ceramic - Dal-Tile Corp.
COLONIST - Doors–wood - Masonite Corp.
COLONNA - Food products - Colonna Brothers Inc.
COLONNA - Glassware–household ☆ - Rosenthal USA Ltd.
COLONNA - Stones–synthetic - Colonna & Co. Inc.
COLONNA ITALIAN KITCHEN - Cheese - Colonna Brothers Inc.
COLONNADE - Blinds–vertical - Tontine/VyTech Industries Inc.
COLONNADE - Dishes–china - Waterford Wedgewood USA, Inc.
COLONNADE - Floor coverings - Collins & Aikman Corp.
COLONNADE - Floor coverings - Congoleum Corp.
COLONNADE - Floor coverings–carpet and rugs ☆ - American Carpet Mills
COLONNADE - Furniture - Councill Craftsmen Inc.
COLONNADE - Glassware–household - Villeroy and Boch Tableware Ltd.
COLONNADE - Hardware ☆ - Amerock Corp.
COLONNADE COLLECTION - Upholstered furniture - Jamestown Lounge Co.
COLONNADE GLOSS - Paper–bond - Weyerhaeuser Co.
COLONNAIDE - Mats - Matworks
COLONY - Automotive parts and accessories ☆ - Lancaster Colony Automotive Group
COLONY - Bathing suits - Water Club Too, Inc.
COLONY - Cabinets - Imperial Cabinet Co. Inc.
COLONY - Candles ☆ - Candle-Lite Co.
COLONY - Coffee makers–electric - Lancaster Colony Commercial Products, Inc.
COLONY - Computer software - Mindscape Software Inc.
COLONY - Floor coverings - Mannington Resilient Floors
COLONY - Flooring–hardwood - Memphis Hardwood Flooring Co.

☆ = Now out of production

COLONY - Furniture ☆ - Evenflo Juvenile Furniture Co.
COLONY - Furniture ☆ - Tropitone Furniture Co. Inc.
COLONY - Glassware–household - Lancaster Colony Corp.
COLONY - Hams - Dairy Fresh Products Co.
COLONY - Jewelry - Nat Klarsfeld Inc.
COLONY - Meat products–canned - R.W. Zant Co.
COLONY - Nuts–salted, roasted, cooked, or canned - Old Dominion Foods Inc.
COLONY - Paints - Colony Paints Div.
COLONY - Paints - Valspar Corp.
COLONY - Seasonings ☆ - T. Marzetti Co.
COLONY - Window shades - Colony Corp.
COLONY - Window shades - Colony Shade Co.
COLONY - Window shades - Draper Shade and Screen Co. Inc.
COLONY - Wines ☆ - The Beverage Source Inc.
COLONY 7 - Video games - Taito America Corp.
COLONY '76 - Cabinets ☆ - Triangle Pacific Corp. (Cabinet Division)
COLONY BAY - Apparel and accessories - Apparel Management Inc.
COLONY CITY - Sausages - Lowell Packing Co.
COLONY CLUB - Frames–eyeglass - May Optical Co. Inc.
COLONY CRAFTS - Housewares - Lancaster Colony Corp.
COLONY GARDEN - Seafood products–canned or cured - Taylor's Frozen Foods & Cold Storage Inc.
COLONY HEARTH, THE - Stoves–wood-burning ☆ - Earth Stove Inc.
COLONY HOUSE - Hosiery - Hole-in-None Hosiery
COLONY HOUSE - Mobile homes ☆ - Wick Building Systems Inc. (Manufactured Home Div./North)
COLONY II - Floor coverings–carpet and rugs ☆ - Kelly Group Inc.
COLONY II - Furniture - Bassett Furniture Industries, Inc.
COLONY IMAGES - Chemical preparations - United States Biochemical Corp.
COLONY OAK - Furniture ☆ - Bassett Furniture Industries, Inc.
COLONY PARK - Cabinets ☆ - Aristokraft, Inc.
COLONY PARK - Motor vehicles–automobiles - Ford Motor Co. (Lincoln-Mercury Div.)
COLONY PAVERS - Stone products - Oldcastle, Inc.
COLONY POINT II - Floor coverings–carpet and rugs ☆ - Playfield International Inc.
COLONY SQUARE - Floor coverings - Congoleum Corp.
COLONY SQUARE - Floor coverings–carpet and rugs - Criterion Mills Inc.
COLONY TAVERN COLLECTION - Furniture–factory ☆ - Clayton Marcus Co. Inc.
COLONY TRAIL - Floor coverings - Congoleum Corp.
COLONY VILLAGE - Wines - Colony Village Winery
COLONY*COUNTER - Computer software - Apogee Systems, Inc.
COLONYFINDER - Chemical preparations - Novagen, Inc.
COLOPHON BOOKS - Publisher's imprints - Harper & Row Publishers Inc.
COLOR 2 COLOR - Nail care products - Kent & Spiegel Direct, Inc.
COLOR A MAT - Placemats - Straight Edge Inc.
COLOR ACCENT - Dinnerware–glass ☆ - Kenro Inc.
COLOR ACCENTS - Floor coverings–carpet and rugs - Mohawk Carpet Corp.
COLOR ACCENTS - Hair coloring preparations - Soft Sheen Products Co.
COLOR ACCENTS - Ophthalmic goods - Foremost Optical Products
COLOR-ACT - Chemical preparations - Hoechst Celanese Corp.
COLOR-AID - Artists' materials - Geller Artist Materials Inc.
COLOR AIRE - Dyes and pigments - Tandy Leather Co.
COLOR ALL - Enamels - Krylon/Dupli-Color
COLOR ALLIANCE - Cosmetics - Beauty for All Seasons Inc.
COLOR AMERICA - Apparel and accessories - Garan Services Corp.
COLOR AND APPLIQUE - Craft supplies - Price Stern Sloan Inc.
COLOR & CLARITY - Stationery - Kimball Concepts Ltd.
COLOR & CO. - Apparel and accessories - Geoffrey Inc.
COLOR & HERBAL - Pet food - Color & Herbal Co.
COLOR AND LIGHT - Cosmetics - Max Factor & Co.
COLOR AND PUZZLE - Craft supplies - Price Stern Sloan Inc.
COLOR & SEW - Hobby kits ☆ - Craft House Corp.
COLOR & SHINE - Lipsticks ☆ - Honey & Spice Toiletries
COLOR AND STITCH - Craft supplies - Price Stern Sloan Inc.
COLOR-ARMOR - Floor coverings–carpet and rugs - Mohawk Carpet Corp.
COLOR-ART - Paper–gummed ☆ - Park Sherman
COLOR ART - School supplies - Dixon Ticonderoga Co.
COLOR ART - Watercolors ☆ - Coloron Industries
COLOR BANDS - Novelty items - Paper Magic Group Inc.
COLOR BAR, THE - Manicure preparations - Nail Gems by Cara
COLOR BARS - Fabrics–cotton - E Z International, Inc.
COLOR BASICS - Cosmetics - Margaret L. Rowe
COLOR BEAR - Toys - Brass Key, Inc.

COLOR BLIND - Apparel and accessories - C & G, Ltd.
COLOR BLOC - Paper - Nocopi Technologies, Inc.
COLOR BLUSH - Ophthalmic goods - Foremost Optical Products
COLOR-BOUND - Notebooks and notepads - Dennison National Co.
COLOR BOX - Rubber stamp inkpad - Clearsnap, Inc.
COLOR-BREAK - Glass products - Owens-Illinois Inc. (Libbey Div.)
COLOR BREEZE - Ophthalmic goods - Foremost Optical Products
COLOR BRIGHTS - Flatware ☆ - Lifetime Hoan Corp.
COLOR BRIGHTS - Telephones - Conair Corp.
COLOR BRILLIANCE - Hair care products - Marianna Imports, Inc.
COLOR BRITE - Decals and transfers - National Artcraft Co.
COLOR-BRITE - Ironing board pads - Magla Products Inc.
COLOR-BRITES - Eyeglasses - Sellstrom Manufacturing Co.
COLOR BRITES - Window treatments - Jencraft Corp.
COLOR BRUSHERS - Felt-tip markers - All Night Media, Inc.
COLOR BUBBLE - Chewing gum - Leaf, Inc.
COLOR BUNCH - Card game - International Games
COLOR BURST - Faucets - U.S. Brass Corp.
COLOR BURST - Paper–gift wrap - American Greetings Corp.
COLOR BURSTS - Pens ☆ - Bic Corp.
COLOR BY DESIGN - Novelty items–paper ☆ - Amscan Inc.
COLOR-BY-PHYSICS - Pigments–paint ☆ - Flex Products, Inc.
COLOR BY THE FOOT - Snack foods - General Mills, Inc.
COLOR CAFE STUDIOS - Artists' materials - Duncan Enterprises
COLOR CAN MAKE A DIFFERENCE - Hair care products - Clairol Inc.
COLOR CAP - Inks - ADT Security Systems, Inc.
COLOR CARE - Cleaning preparations - FSP Research, Inc.
COLOR CARE - Cosmetics ☆ - Bonne Bell, Inc.
COLOR CART - Tricycles ☆ - Hedstrom Corp.
COLOR CASE - Artists' materials - Rose Art Industries, Inc.
COLOR CASSETTE - Cosmetics - Revlon Consumer Products Corp.
COLOR CATALYST - Hair coloring preparations - A-Veda Corp.
COLOR CENTRAL - Computer software - Compumation Inc.
COLOR CEPTOR - Antennas ☆ - Winegard Co.
COLOR CHANGE - Dolls - Mattel, Inc.
COLOR CHANGE PLASTI-GOOP - Toys - Toymax Inc.
COLOR CHARM - Hair care products - Wella Corp. (Consumer Products Div.)
COLOR CHARMS - Flatware ☆ - Lifetime Hoan Corp.
COLOR CHOICE - Cosmetics - Diamond Co.
COLOR-CLAD - Cooking equipment–household ☆ - Imperial Schrade Corp.
COLOR CLAD - Curtain rods - Newell Window Furnishing Co.
COLOR CLAD - Hardware - Babcock Industries Inc. (Babcock Control Group)
COLOR-CLAD - Paints - Missouri Paint & Varnish Co.
COLOR CLASSICS - Cosmetics - Flori Roberts Inc.
COLOR CLASSICS - Floor coverings–carpet and rugs ☆ - Callaway Carpets
COLOR CLASSICS - Linen - Kmart Properties, Inc.
COLOR CLASSICS - Paints - KCI Coatings, Inc.
COLOR CLASSICS - Wallpaper - Wallcoverings Unlimited Inc.
COLOR CLEAN - Chemical preparations - Graphic Technologies, Inc.
COLOR CLEAR - Automotive parts and accessories - Philips Electronics North America Corp.
COLOR CLICKS - Toys - Mattel, Inc.
COLOR CLINCH - Sprinklers–lawn - L.R. Nelson Corp.
COLOR-CLINGS - Window shades - Ogren Companies Inc.
COLOR CLIPPER - Electronic equipment - GAF Corp.
COLOR CLIPS - Computer software - Wizard Ware Group Inc.
COLOR CLOUD - Bathroom accessories - Kohler Co.
COLOR CODE - Skin care products - Bet Direct, Inc.
COLOR CODE CALENDARS - Calendars ☆ - Color Code, Inc.
COLOR CODE COMPATIBLES - Office supplies ☆ - Barkley Filing Supplies
COLOR-CODED ROLL LABELS - Labels–paper - Southern Folder & Index Co.
COLOR CODER - Computer peripheral equipment - SRW Computer Components, Inc.
COLOR CODES - Fabrics - Valley Forge Fabrics Inc.
COLOR COIL - Binders - General Binding Corp.
COLOR COILS - Toys ☆ - Lewis-Frank Corp.
COLOR COLLECTION - Artists' materials - Xonex International, Inc.
COLOR COLLECTION - Frames–eyeglass ☆ - Universal/Univis Inc.
COLOR COMB - Hair care products - Alvin Last Inc.
COLOR COMBO - Wet suits–rubber ☆ - Parkway Systems
COLOR COMBOS - Pens - Bic Corp.
COLOR COMMANDER - Electronic equipment - Perma Power Electronics Inc.
COLOR COMPASS - Artists' materials - M. Grumbacher Inc.
COLOR COMPASS - Computer software - Praxis Innovations, Inc.
COLOR COMPUTER - Artists' materials - M. Grumbacher Inc.

☆ = Now out of production

COLOR CONCEPT - Toys–blocks ☆ - Learning Materials Workshop
COLOR CONCEPT - Wallpaper - Wallcoverings Unlimited Inc.
COLOR CONCEPTS - Fabrics - Valley Forge Fabrics Inc.
COLOR CONCEPTS - Flowers–artificial - Celebrity, Inc.
COLOR CONCEPTS - Jewelry - SPAF Enterprises Inc.
COLOR CONFIDENCE - Cosmetics - Chanel Inc.
COLOR CONNECTION - Window shades - Montgomery Ward & Co. Inc.
COLOR CONNECTORS - Labels–gummed ☆ - Pelikan, Inc.
COLOR CONNECTORS - Plugs–electric - Anthes Universal
COLOR COORDINATOR - Frames–eyeglass ☆ - Universal/Univis Inc.
COLOR COPY - Lipsticks - Markwins International Corp.
COLOR CORE - Pigmented middlebrand - Nielsen & Bainbridge
COLOR CORRECT - Sunglasses - Command Marketing Corp.
COLOR-COTE - Housewares - Magla Products Inc.
COLOR COUTURE - Cosmetics - Elizabeth Arden Inc.
COLOR CRAFT - Awnings - Florida Rock Industries Inc.
COLOR CRAFT - Cooking utensils–enameled ☆ - Flambeau Products Corp.
COLOR CRAFT - Novelty items–glass - GRK Manufacturing
COLOR CRAFT - Paints, crayons ☆ - Coloron Industries
COLOR CREATIONS - Paints - United Coatings, Inc.
COLOR CREATIONS - Wallpaper - Wallcoverings Unlimited Inc.
COLOR-CRETE - Paints ☆ - Waterlox Coatings Corp.
COLOR CRITTERS - Dolls - Imagi-Toy Group Inc.
COLOR CROWN - Glassware–household - Lancaster Colony Corp.
COLOR-CROWN - Paints - Color-Crown Corp.
COLOR CUE CUSTOM - Musical instrument accessories ☆ - GHS Strings
COLOR CURE - Chemical preparations - R & M Chemical Technologies Inc.
COLOR CURLS - Toys ☆ - Henry Gordy International Inc.
COLOR CUTS - Scissors–hand-operated - Acme United Corp.
COLOR DANCE - Floor coverings–carpet and rugs - Coronet Carpets Inc.
COLOR DEEP - Concrete products - Blue Ridge Talc Co. Inc.
COLOR DESIGN - Hair care products - Wella Corp. (Consumer Products Div.)
COLOR DESIGNER - Cosmetics - Almay Inc.
COLOR-DEX - Plastics film - C-Line Products, Inc.
COLOR DIET - Vitamins and nutritional supplements - Medical Nutrition Inc.
COLOR-DIP - Brushes–hair - Goody Products, Inc.
COLOR DISCOVERY COORDINATOR - Novelty items–paper - Matrix Essentials, Inc.
COLOR DISK SCRIPSIT - Computer software ☆ - Tandy Corp.
COLOR-DOODLE - Hobby kits - Creatnetics
COLOR DOODLER - Toys - Tyco Industries, Inc.
COLOR DOT DOMINOES - Games - Cardinal Industries, Inc.
COLOR DOUGH - Clay–modeling ☆ - Craft House Corp.
COLOR DROPPER - Measuring and dispensing pumps - Fluid Management
COLOR DUKE - Pipes–tobacco - Dr. Grabow Pre-Smoked Pipes Inc.
COLOR DUST - Frames–picture - Framemica Co.
COLOR DYNAMICS - Floor coverings–carpet and rugs - Burlington Industries, Inc.
COLOR EASY - Dyes and pigments ☆ - Norma Dharma Trading Co.
COLOR EDITION - Shirts - Capital Mercury Shirt Corp.
COLOR ENBASIC - Computer software ☆ - Queue Inc.
COLOR EXCHANGE - Apparel and accessories - Renee's Manufacturing, Inc.
COLOR EXPERT!, THE - Detergents - Procter & Gamble Co.
COLOR EXPLOSION - Stationery - Diffraction Co.
COLOR EXPRESS - Artists' materials ☆ - Western Publishing Co., Inc.
COLOR-EZ - Adhesives and sealants - Chemray Coatings Corp.
COLOR FALL - Candles ☆ - Muench-Kreuzer Candle Co.
COLOR FAN, THE - Cosmetics - Gloria Munde International
COLOR FASHIONS - Planters - Diversified Recycling Systems
COLOR-FAST - Pencils ☆ - Empire Berol USA
COLOR-FIL - Adhesives and sealants - Bavinger, Inc.
COLOR FIX - Cosmetics - Chesebrough-Pond's USA Co.
COLOR FLAIR - Floor coverings–carpet and rugs - Downs Carpet Co. Inc.
COLOR FLAME KINDLERS - Fireplace equipment ☆ - Fox Run Craftsmen
COLOR FLASHES - Hosiery–women's - Glen Raven Mills Inc.
COLOR-FLO - Varnishes - Harrison Paint Corp.
COLOR FLOW - Floor coverings–carpet and rugs - Mohawk Carpet Corp.
COLOR FOAMS - Paints - Carnival Arts, Inc.
COLOR FRAMES - Toys - Learning Materials Workshop
COLOR-FULL - Pet collars - Combe Inc.
COLOR-FULLS - Cabinets - Akro-Mils Inc.
COLOR-FULLS - Containers - Myers Industries, Inc.
COLOR FUN - Crayons - Oceanside Sales & Marketing, Inc.
COLOR FUSION - Computer hardware - P.G. Design Electronics, Inc.
COLOR FUSIONS - Cosmetics - Chesebrough-Pond's USA Co.
COLOR FX - Toys–automobiles - Mattel, Inc.

COLOR GARD - Automotive cleaner - Automotive International, Inc.
COLOR GARD - Hair coloring preparations - Graham Medical Products
COLOR GARDEN - Baskets–steel - Color Garden Inc.
COLOR GEAR - Artists' materials - Roseart Industries, Inc.
COLOR GIRL - Ophthalmic goods - Foremost Optical Products
COLOR GLAZE - Dinnerware–plastic - Taylor, Smith & Taylor Co.
COLOR-GLAZE - Enamels - Reed and Barton Corp.
COLOR GLEAM - Ophthalmic goods - Foremost Optical Products
COLOR GLO - Eyeglasses - Art-Craft Optical Co.
COLOR GLOSS - Ophthalmic goods - Foremost Optical Products
COLOR GLOVE - Publisher's imprints - Bruce Blitz
COLOR-GRAD - Photographic equipment - Tiffen Manufacturing Corp.
COLOR GRAPHICS - Markers–felt-tip - Dri Mark Products, Inc.
COLOR GROW - Soil–potting - Evergreen Products Corp.
COLOR-GUARD - Garden equipment - Northwestern Steel and Wire Co.
COLOR GUARD - Pet collars - Lambert-Kay
COLOR GUARD - Sealer coatings - Southern Grouts & Mortars Inc.
COLOR GUARD - Wigs - Monte Carlo Hairpiece Co.
COLOR HARMONY - Floor coverings–carpet and rugs - Mohawk Carpet Corp.
COLOR HOLD - Hair care products - Clairol Inc.
COLOR IMAGES - Paper–gift wrap - Gift Wrap Co.
COLOR IMPACT - Cosmetics - Intercon Merchandising Source, Inc.
COLOR IMPRESSIONS - Floor coverings–carpet and rugs - Mohawk Carpet Corp.
COLOR INK - Publisher's imprints - Color Ink, Inc.
COLOR-INOS - Games ☆ - Teaching Concepts Inc.
COLOR INSTANTANE - Hair coloring preparations - Mastey De Paris
COLOR INSTITUTE - Cosmetics - Markwins International Corp.
COLOR INSTITUTE, THE - Cosmetics - Markwins International Corp.
COLOR INTENSE 24 - Cosmetics - Great American Cosmetics, Inc.
COLOR INTENSIFIED - Rings–jewelry - Hammerman Bros., Inc.
COLOR-IT - Computer software - MicroFrontier Inc.
COLOR IT - Inks - Ranger Industries
COLOR-IT! - Paints - Neyra Industries, Inc.
COLOR IT SUNSHINE - Wallpaper ☆ - Artisan Handprints Inc.
COLOR IT WITH DOUGLASS - Fabrics - Douglass Industries, Inc.
COLOR-KATCH - Chemical preparations - Kem-Tron, Inc.
COLOR-KEEPER - Chemical preparations - Heartland Building Products Inc.
COLOR KEY - Keys ☆ - Jobar International Inc./Bibi Products
COLOR KEY SYSTEM, THE - Cleaning preparations–household - Grow Group, Inc.
COLOR-KEYED INDEXING - Binders - Oblique Filing Systems
COLOR KEYS - Computer software ☆ - Sunburst Communications, Inc.
COLOR KIDS - Dolls - Imagi-Toy Group Inc.
COLOR KINESIS - Ultrasonic scanning devices - Hewlett-Packard Co.
COLOR KING - Printing presses - King Press Corp.
COLOR KINGDOM - Toys - E.K. Success Ltd.
COLOR LASER COPIER 700 - Photocopy machines - Canon USA, Inc.
COLOR LASER COPIER 800 - Photocopy machines - Canon USA, Inc.
COLOR LAWN - Floor coverings–carpet and rugs - Conquest Carpet Mills Inc.
COLOR LIFE - File folders - ACCO USA, Inc.
COLOR LIFE - Paints - Royal Lustre Brands
COLOR LIFT - Photographic equipment ☆ - C-Line Products, Inc.
COLOR LINE - Office supplies - McBee Loose Leaf Binders
COLOR LINE - Paper - Stuart Hall Co., Inc.
COLOR-LITE - Hardware ☆ - Cole Consumer Products Inc.
COLOR-LITES - Candles - Columbia Wax Products Inc.
COLOR LITES - Scissors–hand-operated ☆ - Acme United Corp.
COLOR LOCK - Cosmetics - Revlon Consumer Products Corp.
COLOR LOCK - Hair care products - Le Kair Scientific Research Products Inc.
COLOR-LUX - Lighting equipment - Penn-Plax, Inc.
COLOR LYTES - Lamp bulbs - Intermatic Inc.
COLOR MAC - Boxes–corrugated paperboard - MacMillan Bloedel Packaging Inc.
COLOR MACHINE - Housewares - Hiac/Royco Co.
COLOR MAGIC - Automotive parts and accessories - Turtle Wax, Inc.
COLOR MAGIC - Paper–gift wrap - Gibson Greetings, Inc.
COLOR MANAGEMENT - Measuring and dispensing pumps - Fluid Management
COLOR MAP - Artists' materials - Binney & Smith Inc.
COLOR MARKS - Crayons ☆ - Bemiss-Jason Corp.
COLOR MARKS - Markers–felt-tip - Dri Mark Products, Inc.
COLOR MASTER - Computer software - KCI Coatings, Inc.
COLOR MASTER - Darts and dart games - Dart World Inc.
COLOR MASTER - Electronic equipment - Telex Communications, Inc.
COLOR MASTER - Hair coloring preparations - Helene Curtis Industries Inc.

COLOR MASTER - Television equipment - Lance Industries
COLOR MASTERS - Trading cards and stamps - Megacards, Inc.
COLOR MATCH - Games - CBS Toys
COLOR MATCH - Games - International Gamco, Inc.
COLOR MATCH - Paper - Vogart Crafts Corp.
COLOR MATCH - Toys - Montgomery Schoolhouse
COLOR MATCH MATES - Floor coverings ☆ - Azrock Commercial Flooring
COLOR-MATE - Ophthalmic goods - Karlen Manufacturing, Inc.
COLOR-MATE - Pens - Salis International, Inc.
COLOR MATES - Floor coverings–tile - Robbins Interior Surface Inc.
COLOR-MATES - Nail care products - SRA Industries Inc.
COLOR MATES - Ophthalmic goods - Originalities
COLOR MATES - Paper–gift wrap ☆ - CPS Corp.
COLOR ME - Artists' materials - Bee Paper Co. Inc.
COLOR-ME - Beverages - Teledyne Mecca
COLOR ME - Placemats - Hoffmaster
COLOR ME BEAUTIFUL - Apparel–women's - Hartmarx Corp.
COLOR ME BEAUTIFUL - Cosmetics - Color Me Beautiful, Inc.
COLOR ME CARD - Greeting cards - Babcock Publishing Co.
COLOR ME FUN - Apparel and accessories - Wal-Mart Stores Inc.
COLOR ME FUN - Computer software - Imagery Studios, Inc.
COLOR-ME-HAPPY - Shampoos - Panco Ltd.
COLOR ME HOME - Real estate agencies - Bluesky Unlimited, Inc.
COLOR ME-IN - Magnets - Distinctive Design
COLOR ME KENTE KENYA - Dolls - Tyco Industries, Inc.
COLOR ME KIDS - Apparel–children's - Kids to Parents
COLOR ME NATURAL - Panty hose - Rice Hosiery Corp.
COLOR ME PRETTY - Lipstick, nail polish, etc. - Cosrich Inc.
COLOR ME PRETTY - Underwear and nightwear - Maidenform Inc.
COLOR ME QUICK - Nail care products - Color Me Quick Inc.
COLOR ME SMART - Educational materials - Robert W. Carey
COLOR-ME-SOFT - Cosmetics - Panco Ltd.
COLOR-ME TRANSFERS - Crayons ☆ - Binney & Smith Inc.
COLOR MEMORY - Lipsticks - Revlon Consumer Products Corp.
COLOR MINDER - Computer software - Valis Group
COLOR MOMENT - Hair coloring preparations - King Research, Inc.
COLOR MUSIC - Floor coverings–carpet and rugs ☆ - Alexander Smith Carpets
COLOR MY CLASS - Balls - Sport Supply Group, Inc.
COLOR MY TOWN - Markers–felt-tip - B. Dazzle, Inc.
COLOR MY WORLD - Floor coverings–carpet and rugs ☆ - Gulistan Carpet Inc.
COLOR MYSTIQUE - Cosmetics ☆ - Lachine Inc.
COLOR 'N CARE - Markers–felt-tip - Tonka Corp.
COLOR 'N CARRY - Art-materials tote case - Coloron Industries
COLOR 'N CONTRAST - Toys - Playskool, Inc.
COLOR 'N CUDDLE - Toys - IBTT
COLOR 'N GROOM - American International Industries
COLOR N' PLAY - Games ☆ - Colorforms
COLOR 'N PLAY - Toys - BH & H Industries, LLC
COLOR 'N RECOLOR - Coloring toys - Coloron Industries
COLOR N' RICH - Hair care products - Dena Corp.
COLOR-N-ROLL - Toys - Hall Co. (Scrollcraft Div.)
COLOR 'N SEND - Artists' materials - Life Lines, Inc.
COLOR NATURALS - Paints - Glidden Co.
COLOR NEGATIVE - Dyes and pigments - Retouch Methods Co. Inc.
COLOR NEW - Paints - Hartco Wood Flooring
COLOR OF CHRISTMAS - Christmas lights and decorations - Minami International Corp.
COLOR OF MURDER, THE - Puzzles - Hasbro, Inc.
COLOR OF QUALITY, THE - Flowers, plants, and seeds - Sunrise Growers
COLOR-OFF - Cosmetics - Coty US Inc.
COLOR ON COLOR - Cosmetics - Frances Denney
COLOR ON COLOR - House furnishings - Dan River Inc.
COLOR OPTICS - Hair care products - Redken Laboratories, Inc.
COLOR OUT - Hair care products - American International Industries
COLOR PAINT - Computer software - International Business Machines Corp.
COLOR PALACE II - Floor coverings–carpet and rugs - Milliken & Co. Inc.
COLOR PALETTE - Wallpaper - Capital Carousel Inc.
COLOR PALETTE, THE - Wallpaper - Wall Fabrics Inc.
COLOR PALS - Toys - Mattel, Inc.
COLOR-PEN - Pens ☆ - Faber-Castell Corp.
COLOR PERFECT - Cosmetics - Yves St. Laurent Parfum Corp.
COLOR PERFECT - Hair care products - Wella Corp. (Consumer Products Div.)
COLOR PERFECT - Lenses–optical - Capo, Inc.

COLOR PERFECT GENTLE CARE - Hair care products - Wella Corp. (Consumer Products Div.)
COLOR PERFECT LIGHTS - Hair care products - Wella Corp. (Consumer Products Div.)
COLOR PERFECT PERFORMANCE PLUS - Hair care products - Wella Corp. (Consumer Products Div.)
COLOR PERFORMANCE - Cosmetics - Les Parfums De Dana, Inc.
COLOR PINK, THE - Insulating materials - Owens Corning
COLOR PLACE - Brushes–paint - United Coatings Inc.
COLOR PLAY - Cosmetics - Estee Lauder Inc.
COLOR PLAY - Hair care products ☆ - Clairol Inc.
COLOR PLUS - Detergents - Colgate-Palmolive Co.
COLOR PLUS - Electronic equipment ☆ - Kroy, Inc.
COLOR PLUS - Hair care products - Framesi USA/Roffler Industries Inc.
COLOR PLUS - Hardware - Cole Consumer Products Inc.
COLOR PLUS - Lipsticks - Madeleine Mono Ltd.
COLOR PLUS - Transparency film - American Coated Products Inc.
COLOR PLUS INK SYSTEM - Writing product - Coates Bros. Inks USA Inc.
COLOR POINT - Floor coverings–carpet and rugs - Mohawk Carpet Corp.
COLOR POPS - Toys ☆ - Merchants Publishing Co.
COLOR PORTFOLIO & COLORCORE - Adhesives and sealants - Formica Corp.
COLOR-POXY - Bostik Inc.
COLOR PRESERVER - Sporting goods - Weber Industries Inc.
COLOR-PRIME - Coatings - Sherwin-Williams Automotive Finishes Corp.
COLOR PRO - Lighting fixtures - High End Systems, Inc.
COLOR-PROBE - Artists' materials - HunterLab
COLOR PROCESS - Cosmetics - Research Council of Make-Up Artists Inc.
COLOR PROMPTER - Dyes–cosmetic - Clairol Inc.
COLOR PROTECTIVE - Lipsticks - Almay Inc.
COLOR-QC - Computer software - Altana, Inc. (Savage Laboratories, Div.)
COLOR QUARTERBACK - Computer software - Valspar Corp.
COLOR QUEST - Antennas - TDP Electronics
COLOR QUEST - Cosmetics - Color Quest
COLOR RACERS - Toys–automobiles - Mattel, Inc.
COLOR RED - Veterinary pharmaceutical preparations - Dyna Pet Inc.
COLOR REFRESHER - Skin care products - GOLDWELL Cosmetics (USA) Inc.
COLOR RESPONSE - Hair care products - KMS Research Inc.
COLOR REVERSE - Stain removers - Cadie Products Corp.
COLOR RHYTHMS - Floor coverings–carpet and rugs - Karastan-Bigelow Inc.
COLOR RICH - Cosmetics - Avon Products, Inc.
COLOR RIFICS - Shelving units–wood - Hirsh Co.
COLOR RINGS - Novelty items - Paper Magic Group Inc.
COLOR RITE - Caulking compounds - Color Rite Inc.
COLOR RITE - Ribbons–inked - Ribbons Unltd.
COLOR-RULE - Office supplies - Bemiss-Jason Corp.
COLOR SATIN - Paints ☆ - United States Refining Co.
COLOR SCENES - Decals and transfers - Chartpak
COLOR-SCENTS - Construction and art paper - Riverside Paper Corp.
COLOR SCENTS - Deodorizers ☆ - Natural Products Corp.
COLOR SCRIPSIT - Computer software - Tandy Corp.
COLOR-SEAL - Paints - Sherwin-Williams Automotive Finishes Corp.
COLOR SENTRY - Television equipment - Zenith Electronics Corp.
COLOR SHADES - Bags–trash - Reynolds Consumer Products, Inc.
COLOR-SHEEN - Adhesives and sealants - Missouri Paint & Varnish Co.
COLOR SHELF - Shelving units–wood ☆ - Home Equipment Manufacturing Co.
COLOR SHIELD - Manicure preparations - Mary Kay Cosmetics Inc.
COLOR-SHIELD - Paints - Kelly-Moore/Preservative Paints
COLOR SHINE - Lipsticks - Revlon Consumer Products Corp.
COLOR SHINE - Sprayers - Chase Industries, Inc.
COLOR SHINE FOAMING ARCH - Sprayers - Chase Industries, Inc.
COLOR SHOWER - Candles ☆ - Will & Baumer, Inc.
COLOR SIGNAL - Paper products - Georgia-Pacific Corp.
COLOR SIGNALS - Electrical equipment - Conair Corp.
COLOR SKETCH - Artists' materials - Valu-Plus, Inc.
COLOR-SNAPS - Fasteners–snap - Scovill Inc.
COLOR SOLUTIONS - Hair care products - Helene Curtis Industries Inc.
COLOR SOUND - Cymbals - Paiste America, Inc.
COLOR SOURCE - Educational materials - Clairol Inc.
COLOR SOURCE - Electric lighting equipment - Wybron, Inc.
COLOR SPECTRUM - Electrical equipment - Finney Co.
COLOR SPECTRUM - Fabrics - Valley Forge Fabrics Inc.
COLOR SPECTRUM - Fabrics–cotton - P & B Fabrics, Inc.

☆ = Now out of production

COLOR SPHERE, THE - Measuring instruments - Altana, Inc. (Savage Laboratories, Div.)

COLOR SPIN - Toys - Mattel, Inc.

COLOR SPRAY - Paints - Chase Products Co.

COLOR-SPREE - Paints - Kyanize Paint Co.

COLOR SQUARES - Floor coverings ✩ - Azrock Commercial Flooring

COLOR STICK - Paints - Panelmatch

COLOR STICKS - Cosmetics ✩ - Redken Laboratories, Inc.

COLOR STICKS - Printers–computer - Teckton Innovations Inc.

COLOR-STIK - Electronic equipment ✩ - Charles Beseler Co.

COLOR STITCH - Hobby kits - Carilorz Corp.

COLOR STITCH - Hobby kits - JCA, Inc.

COLOR STIX - Cosmetics - Maybelline Co.

COLOR STIX PEN - Nail care products - Nailtex Inc.

COLOR STUDIO - Floor coverings–carpet and rugs ✩ - Callaway Carpets

COLOR STUDIO - Paints - Valspar Corp.

COLOR STYLE - Cosmetics - Revlon Consumer Products Corp.

COLOR SURPRISE - Lipsticks ✩ - Noxell Corp.

COLOR SWIPES - Nail care products - Rm Distribution, Inc.

COLOR SYSTEM, THE - Apparel and accessories - Go On Sportswear USA Ltd.

COLOR TECH - Furniture - Wilburn Co. Inc.

COLOR TECH SYSTEMS - Automotive paint kits - Color Tech Systems

COLOR-TEX - Cases–plastic - Venture 703, Inc.

COLOR-TEX - Pencils - General Pencil Co.

COLOR-TEX - Photographic equipment - CODA Inc.

COLOR THANE - Coatings - W.P. Hickman Systems

COLOR THEME - Floor coverings–carpet and rugs - Mohawk Carpet Corp.

COLOR THRU - Floor coverings–tile - American Biltrite Inc.

COLOR TILE - Tiles–ceramic - Color Tile Ceramic Manufacturing Co.

COLOR-TIME - Games - Little Harbor Corp.

COLOR TINT - Eyeglasses - Art-Craft Optical Co.

COLOR TIPS - Sprayer nozzles - Hardi Inc.

COLOR TO GO - Hair coloring preparations - Home Hair Color, Inc.

COLOR-TONE - Musical instrument accessories - Humes & Berg Manufacturing Co. Inc.

COLOR TONES - Pigments - Georgia-Pacific Corp.

COLOR TOUCH - Electronics equipment - Technidyne Corp.

COLOR-TOUCH - Paints - United Coatings Inc.

COLOR TRACK - Publisher's imprints - Direct Business Technologies, Inc.

COLOR TRANSITION - Handbags - Jaclyn, Inc.

COLOR TREATMENT, THE - Cleaning preparations–upholstery - Treatment Products, Ltd.

COLOR TRED - Paints - Suntec Paint Inc.

COLOR TREE - Wallcovering - Eisenhart Wallcoverings Co.

COLOR TREE DESIGNS - Fabrics - Eisenhart Wallcoverings Co.

COLOR-TREME - Food products - Beatrice Cos. Inc.

COLOR TREND - Office supplies ✩ - Samsill Corp.

COLOR TRENDS - Plastics–laminated ✩ - Formica Corp.

COLOR TRIM - Frames–eyeglass - Hoya Corp. USA

COLOR TUNES - Toys–electronic - Binney & Smith Inc.

COLOR TWIST - Ophthalmic goods - Foremost Optical Products

COLOR UNLIMITED - Cosmetics - Revlon Consumer Products Corp.

COLOR-UP - Apparel - Color-Up Kids, Inc.

COLOR-UP STICKS - Cosmetics - Revlon Consumer Products Corp.

COLOR-UPS - Cosmetics - Libby Lee Toys Inc.

COLOR UPS - Markers–felt-tip - Dri Mark Products, Inc.

COLOR VEILS - Cosmetics - Sebastian International, Inc.

COLOR VELVET - Floor coverings–carpet and rugs - LaVelle Textile Marketing Inc.

COLOR VIBES - Cosmetics ✩ - Noxell Corp.

COLOR-VISION - Markers–felt-tip ✩ - Empire Berol USA

COLOR VISTA - Fabrics - Valley Forge Fabrics Inc.

COLOR-VU - Dry-mounting sheet - Color-Vu Corp.

COLOR WAND - Cosmetics - Maybelline Co.

COLOR WARE - Pans - E-Z-Por Corp.

COLOR WASH - Cosmetic - Estee Lauder Inc.

COLOR WAVES - Bicycles - Huffy Corp.

COLOR WHIRL CAR - Toys - Mattel, Inc.

COLOR WHIZ - Educational materials - Vtech Industries, Inc.

COLOR WITH PLANTS - Live plants - Bailey Nurseries, Inc.

COLOR WITH YARN - Toys - Fisher-Price, Inc.

COLOR WORK - Wallpaper - Wallcoverings Unlimited Inc.

COLOR WORKS TWO - Wallpaper - Wallcoverings Unlimited Inc.

COLOR WOVEN - Bedding–linen - Dan River Inc.

COLOR WRITER - Toys - Mattel, Inc.

COLOR YOUR GARDEN - Flowers, plants, and seeds - White Swan, Ltd.

COLOR YOUR OWN - Placemats - Anacapa Corp.

COLORA - Skin care products - Colora Henna

COLORA HENNA - Hair care products - Colora Henna

COLORABLE KIDS - Toys - Rainbow Village

COLORACTIVE - Paper products - Georgia-Pacific Corp.

COLORADO - Bicycles - Raleigh USA Bicycle Co.

COLORADO - Camp furniture–metal ✩ - Carefree of Colorado

COLORADO - Fireplace equipment - Design Specialties Inc.

COLORADO - Floor coverings–carpet and rugs - V & B Carpet

COLORADO - Florists - Denver Wholesale Florists

COLORADO - Hobby kits - Craft World International Inc.

COLORADO - Jewelry–precious - Diamond Co. N.L.

COLORADO - Photographic equipment - Eastman Kodak Co.

COLORADO - Printers–computer - Alliant Techsystems Inc.

COLORADO - Shoes–athletic - Kinney Shoe Corp.

COLORADO - Sporting goods - Cut 'n Jump Ski Corp.

COLORADO - Sporting goods - Weber Industries Inc.

COLORADO - Surgical instruments - Colorado Biomedical, Inc.

COLORADO - Tiles–ceramic ✩ - American Olean Tile Co.

COLORADO - Trailers–travel ✩ - Fleetwood Enterprises, Inc.

COLORADO - Wallpaper ✩ - Brewster Wallcovering Co.

COLORADO - Wallpaper ✩ - Mirage Wallcovering Co.

COLORADO BOOMERANGS - Boomerangs - Windsports, Inc.

COLORADO BRONZE GLASSWORKS - Doors–glass - Kohler Co.

COLORADO BROWN - Cooking utensils–stoneware - Western Stoneware

COLORADO CHILLER - Beverages–alcohol ✩ - Adolph Coors Co.

COLORADO CITY CREAMERY - Ice cream - Colorado City Creamery

COLORADO CLASSICS - Apparel and accessories ✩ - Gerry Sportswear Corp.

COLORADO COMBO - Sandwiches–prepackaged - Southland Corp.

COLORADO COUNTRY - Footwear - Kinney Shoe Corp.

COLORADO CRYSTAL - Water–bottled or canned - Hinckley & Schmitt (Bottled Water Group)

COLORADO CUT - Apparel–women's - Colorado Contract Cut and Sew

COLORADO FRESH - Dairy products - Sinton Dairy Foods Co. Inc.

COLORADO GOLD - Meat products - Colorado Boxed Beef Co.

COLORADO GOLDEN BEAUTY - Onions - Delta Potato Growers Cooperative Association

COLORADO GREENHOUSE - Fruits and vegetables - Colorado Greenhouse, LLC

COLORADO KINDLE CONES - Fireplace equipment - Colorado Kindle Cones

COLORADO MUD - Bakery products - Our Name is Mud, Inc.

COLORADO PEAKS - Tiles–ceramic - American Olean Tile Co.

COLORADO PRIME - Meat products–beef - Colorado Prime Corp.

COLORADO PRIME FOODS - Seafood products–fresh or frozen - Colorado Prime Corp.

COLORADO ROCKIES - Apparel and accessories - Colorado Rockies Baseball Club, Ltd.

COLORADO ROCKIES - Key chains, money clips, and trophies - Colorado Baseball Partnership 1993, Ltd.

COLORADO SAGE - Colognes ✩ - Bonne Bell, Inc.

COLORADO SPORT - Exercising equipment - Saratoga Access & Fitness Inc.

COLORADO SPORT - Trailers–travel ✩ - Fleetwood Enterprises, Inc.

COLORADO SPRINGS - Floor coverings–carpet and rugs ✩ - Walter Carpet Mills

COLORADO SUPREME - Meat products - Colorado Boxed Beef Co.

COLORADO TRAIL NUT BROWN ALE - Beverages–malt - Carver Brewing Co.

COLORADO'S FAVORITE - Apparel–athletic - Winter Park Recreational Association

COLORADO'S FAVORITE SKI RESORT - Apparel and accessories - Winter Park Recreational Association

COLORAIL - Hardware - Julius Blum & Co. Inc.

COLORAK - Needles–sewing ✩ - Coats and Clark Inc.

COLORALL - Motor vehicle dealers - Colorall Technologies, Inc.

COLORALL TECHNOLOGIES - Motor vehicle dealers - Colorall Technologies, Inc.

COLORALLS - Hosiery - Sara Lee Corp.

COLORAM - Lighting equipment - Wybron, Inc.

COLORAMA - Accordions - Pancordion Inc.

COLORAMA - Candy - Leaf, Inc.

COLORAMA - Cooking utensils–cast iron ✩ - Regal Ware, Inc.

COLORAMA - Felt - Aetna Felt Corp.

COLORAMA - File folders - File-A-Dex Inc.

COLORAMA - Paint sets–hobby ✩ - Canson-Talens Inc.

✩ = Now out of production

COLORAMA - Paints - Pervo Paint Co.
COLORAMA - Paper - School Stationers Corp.
COLORAMA - Paper–gift wrap - Gibson Greetings, Inc.
COLORAMA - Pencils ☆ - Faber-Castell Corp.
COLORAMA - Pottery ☆ - Rubens Originals
COLORAMA - String instruments - International Music Corp.
COLORAMA - Watches - Croton Watch Co., Inc.
COLORAMA CONTRACT - Floor coverings ☆ - Tek Stil Concepts Inc.
COLORANCE - Hair care products - GOLDWELL Cosmetics (USA) Inc.
COLORARC - Lighting equipment - GTE Corp.
COLORART - Paper–construction - Pen-Tab Industries
COLORATIONS - Cosmetics - Prince Matchabelli
COLORAY - Fabrics–rayon - Courtaulds Fibres Inc.
COLORAY - Pencils - Faber-Castell Corp.
COLORBAND - Color-separation filters - Optical Coating Laboratory Inc.–Santa Rosa Div.
COLORBAR - Computer software - Document Control Systems, Inc.
COLORBESTOS - Shingles ☆ - Manville/Schuller
COLORBLASTER - Toy craft kits - Tonka Corp.
COLORBLASTER - Toys–electronic - Kenner Products
COLORBOLT - Paints - Carnival Arts, Inc.
COLORBOLT ANTIQUITY STEIN - Paints - Carnival Arts, Inc.
COLORBOLT CRACKLE - Sponges - Carnival Arts, Inc.
COLORBOLT NATURAL PEARL - Paints - Carnival Arts, Inc.
COLORBOLT VELVET - Varnishes - Carnival Arts, Inc.
COLORBOND - Carpets and rugs - Milliken & Co.
COLORBOND - Fencing–steel ☆ - Semmerling Fence and Supply Inc.
COLORBOND - Lipsticks - Maybelline Intermediate Co.
COLORBOOK - Computers - Gateway 2000, Inc.
COLORBOX - Inkpad - All Night Media, Inc.
COLORBRE - Hair care products - Wella Corp. (Consumer Products Div.)
COLORBRETOR - Hair care products - Wella Corp. (Consumer Products Div.)
COLORBRITE - Pencils ☆ - Faber-Castell Corp.
COLORBURST - Cameras - Eastman Kodak Co.
COLORBURST - Floor coverings–carpet and rugs ☆ - Gulistan Carpet Inc.
COLORBURST - Hair care products - Cosmair Inc.
COLORBURST - Novelty items - Paper Magic Group Inc.
COLORBUS CYCLONE IMAGING SYSTEM - Computer imaging software - Colorbus
COLORCAL - Paper products - Champion International Corp.
COLORCAPTURE - Computers ☆ - Data Translation, Inc.
COLORCARE - Cosmetics - Revlon-Realistic Professional Products Inc.
COLORCASE WOVENS - Bedding–linen - Pillowtex Corp.
COLORCAST - Cooking utensils–cast iron - Jacksonville Manufacturing
COLORCAST - Jewelry - Cosmopolitan Gem Corp.
COLORCAST - Paper–writing - Champion International Corp.
COLORCELL - Window shades - Colorel Corp.
COLORCHECK - Computer software - Synex
COLORCHECKER - Photographic equipment - Kollmorgen Instruments Corp.
COLORCLAD - Beds–metal - Wonderline
COLORCLIPS - Clothespins ☆ - L.K. Hecht Co. Inc.
COLORCOAT - Floor coverings - Andek Corp.
COLORCODES - Housewares - Amoco Fabrics and Fibers Co.
COLORCORE - Artists' materials - Formica Corp.
COLORCOTE - Paints - Farrell-Calhoun Inc.
COLORCOTE - Waxes–mineral - Lombard Management, Inc.
COLORCRAFT - Dishes–earthenware - Taylor, Smith & Taylor Co.
COLORCREME COLLECTION - Hair coloring preparations ☆ - Clairol Inc.
COLORCRETE SEALER - Paints - Reliance Supply Co.
COLORCRON - Concrete products - Master Builders Inc.
COLORCROSS - Games - Scramb-L-Gram, Inc.
COLORCUBE - Computer software - Colorcube Corp.
COLORCUED - Hair care products - Amethyst Investment Group, Inc.
COLORCUSHION - Strollers–baby - MTS Products
COLORDESK - Computers - Colordesk, Inc.
COLORDRIVE - Computer software ☆ - Pantone, Inc.
COLORE - Hair coloring preparations - Sebastian International, Inc.
COLOREADY - Nail care products - Pacific World Corp.
COLOREASE - Computer printers - Eastman Kodak Co.
COLOREDGE - Photocopy machines - Eastman Kodak Co.
COLOREDGE PLUS - Frames–picture - Ammak Manufacturing Corp.
COLORES INTERNATIONAL - Novelty items - Flags International Inc.
COLORES PARA TI - Cosmetics - Flori Roberts Inc.
COLORESSENCE - Hair coloring preparations - Helene Curtis Industries Inc.
COLORETTES - Cosmetics - Delby System
COLORETTES - Dolls - Mattel, Inc.

COLOREX - Chalk ☆ - Faber-Castell Corp.
COLOREX - Floor coverings - Forbo Industries, Inc.
COLOREX AS2000 - Floor coverings - Forbo Industries, Inc.
COLOREX EL 5000 - Vinyl tile - Forbo Industries, Inc.
COLOREX EL5000 - Floor coverings - Forbo Industries, Inc.
COLORFACTS - Hair care products - Clairol Inc.
COLORFAX - Floor coverings–carpet and rugs - Burlington Industries, Inc.
COLORFIL - Fabrics ☆ - Veratec
COLORFILL - Inks - Sentinel Imaging
COLORFINDER - Electrical equipment - Gavin Electronics
COLORFLARE - Computers - Advanced Hi-Tech Corp. (User Friendly Operating Systems Division)
COLORFLECT - Self-adhesive letters and numbers ☆ - Cole Consumer Products Inc.
COLORFLEX - Artists' materials - Steig Products
COLORFLOW - Photographic equipment - SP Systems/Saratons
COLORFLOW - Pigments - Miles Inc.
COLORFOAM - Artists' materials - Notions Marketing Corp.
COLORFOAMS - Toys–blocks - Colorforms
COLORFORMS - Ophthalmic goods - Foremost Optical Products
COLORFORMS BOARD BOOKS - Publisher's imprints - Scholastic Inc.
COLORFREE - Medical apparatus - Freeman Manufacturing Co.
COLORFRESH - Lipsticks - Maybelline Co.
COLORFROST - Fabrics - Dan River Inc.
COLORFUL 10 - Nail care products - ATM America Corp.
COLORFUL ANIMAL BALL - Balls - Oliver Sporting Goods, Inc.
COLORFUL CONSTRUCTION - Paper–book - Colorful Publishing
COLORFUL DINOSAUR BALL - Balls - Oliver Sporting Goods, Inc.
COLORFUL GOLF - Paper products - Colorful Publishing
COLORFUL NAILS SALON EDITION NAIL LACQUE; R - Nail care products - Lal Rewachand
COLORFUL PHRE-PERM - Cosmetics ☆ - Colorful Products Corp.
COLORFUL PROTEIN FILLERS - Hair care products - Colorful Products Corp.
COLORFUL SECRET - Dolls - Mattel, Inc.
COLORFUL SHINE - Hair care products ☆ - Colorful Products Corp.
COLORFUN - Toys - Kool Pak
COLORFUN BALL - Toys–stuffed - Gund, Inc.
COLORGARD - Medical apparatus - Abbott Laboratories
COLORGELS - Projectors–photographic - SP Systems/Saratons
COLORGEMS - Flatware ☆ - Lifetime Hoan Corp.
COLORGIZE - Dyes–cosmetic - Susan R. McCarthy
COLORGLAZE - Flower pots–earthenware - Reubens's Originals Corp.
COLORGLAZE - Pottery - Rubens Originals
COLORGLAZED CLOSETCARE - Boxes–corrugated paperboard - MSA Designs
COLORGLIDE 3 - Refrigerators - Ardco Inc.
COLORGLO - Paints - Hirshfield's Paint Manufacturing
COLORGRAFX TONER - Toners - Xerox Corp.
COLORGRAIN - Veneer - Veneer Technologies Ltd.
COLORGRAM - Educational materials - Phyllis J. Grumney
COLORGRAPHIC - Computer hardware - Voyager VGA
COLORGRAPHICS - Hair coloring preparations - Matrix Essentials, Inc.
COLORGRIP - Electrical equipment - Arlington Industries Inc.
COLORGUARD - Bumpers–motor vehicle - Boston Metal Products Corp.
COLORGUARD - Eyeglasses - Surgical Laser Products Inc.
COLORGUARD - Lamps–ultraviolet - Aquafine Corp.
COLORGUARD - Office supplies ☆ - Globe-Weis
COLORIBBONS - Cosmetics - Maybelline Co.
COLORIFFICS - Shoes - Speen & Co. Inc.
COLORIFIC - Computer software - Sonnetech, Ltd.
COLORIFIC - Finishing agents - Red Spot Paint & Varnish Co., Inc.
COLORIFIC - Hair care products - Vidal Sassoon Inc.
COLORIFIC - House furnishings - Dan River Inc.
COLORIFIC - Markers–felt-tip - Empire Berol USA
COLORIFIC - Markers–felt-tip - Sanford Corp.
COLORIFIC - Office supplies - P.A. Plymouth, Inc.
COLORIFICS - Floor coverings–carpet and rugs ☆ - Burtco Enterprises Inc.
COLORIFICS - Ophthalmic goods - Foremost Optical Products
COLORIMETRIC - Caulking compounds - Cast Products Corp.
COLORING BALL - Balls - Oliver Sporting Goods, Inc.
COLORING BOOK - Floor coverings–carpet and rugs - Mohawk Industries Inc.
COLORING BOOK, THE - Cosmetics - Cosmedic Concepts, Inc.
COLORING BOOK, THE - Wallpaper - Wall Fabrics Inc.
COLORING CASTLE - Markers–felt-tip - Lisa Frank, Inc.
COLORING KIDS - Greeting cards - Wemarc Co., Inc.

☆ = Now out of production

COLORING SERIES I - Computer software - Koala Technologies Corp.

COLORINGS - Cosmetics - Forsythe Cosmetic Group

COLORINGS - Dinnerware–plastic - Plastics Manufacturing Co.

COLORINGS - Dyes–food - Spearhead Industries Inc.

COLORISSIMO - Cosmetics - Renbow International Ltd. USA

COLORISSIMO - Lipstick - Bourjois Ltd.

COLORIT - Floor coverings–carpet and rugs - V & B Carpet

COLORITE - Computer software - W.R. Grace & Co.

COLORITE - Hoses - Colorite Plastic Co.

COLORITE - Office supplies ☆ - Faber-Castell Corp.

COLORITE - Paper–construction - Cascade School Supplies

COLORITE - Photographic equipment - GTE Corp.

COLORITE WATERWORKS - Hoses - Colorite Plastic Co.

COLORIX - Graphics software for personal computers - RIX SoftWorks Inc.

COLORIZER - Dental compounds - Dentsply International Inc.

COLORIZER - Paints ☆ - Colorizer Associates

COLORKING - Electrical equipment - Gavin Electronics

COLORKIT - Computer software - Data Translation, Inc.

COLORLASTEC - Grouting material - Tec Inc.

COLORLEUM - Floor coverings–linoleum - Lucky America Inc.

COLORLIGHTS - Signs - Geographics Inc.

COLORLINE - Coatings - Sherwin-Williams Automotive Finishes Corp.

COLORLINE - Desk sets - Staver Westport Inc.

COLORLINE - Paper - Canson-Talens Inc.

COLORLINK - Printing supplies - Hoechst Celanese Corp.

COLORLITE BY CLUB - Cooking equipment–household - Jacksonville Manufacturing

COLORLOGIC - Cosmetics - Mary Kay Cosmetics Inc.

COLORLOK - Siding–insulating - Masonite Corp.

COLORLON - Floor coverings–linoleum - Lucky America Inc.

COLORLOOM - Placemats - Dansk International Designs, Ltd.

COLORLUXE - Linen - Springs Industries, Inc.

COLORLY - Hair care products - Hairtech International Inc.

COLORMAGIC - Paints - Magicolor Co.

COLORMARK - Inks - Mason Marking Systems Corp.

COLORMARK - Medical apparatus - Echocath, Inc.

COLORMARVL - Coatings, etc. - Cook and Dunn Paint Corp.

COLORMASTER - Electronic equipment - Ed-Tech Service Co.

COLORMASTER - Paints - Evans Paint

COLORMASTER - Photographic equipment - Houston Fearless 76 Inc.

COLORMASTER PLUS - Computer printers - Calcomp Inc.

COLORMAT - Skin care products - GOLDWELL Cosmetics (USA) Inc.

COLORMATCH - Floor coverings - Johnsonite Flooring Products

COLORMATCH - Hooks - Vogel Peterson Furniture Co.

COLORMATCH APPLICATOR - Brushes–paint - Corcoran Manufacturing Co., Inc.

COLORMATES - Dinnerware–plastic - JMP-Newcor International, Inc.

COLORMATES - Dishes–china - Mikasa Co.

COLORMATES - Hobby kits ☆ - Blumenthal/Lansing Co.

COLORMATES - Soap - Twinscents

COLORMATIC - Hair care products - Wella Corp. (Consumer Products Div.)

COLORMATICS - Fabric appliques and embroidery - Joseph C. Gilardone and Son Inc.

COLORMATICS - Pencils–mechanical - Faber-Castell Corp.

COLORMATRIX - Floor coverings–carpet and rugs - Karastan-Bigelow Inc.

COLORMATTE - Cosmetics - Nat Robbins Ltd.

COLORMAX - Food products - Chr. Hansen, Inc.

COLORMAZE - Games - Kadon Enterprises Inc.

COLORMERIC ELASTOMERIC COATING - Adhesives and sealants - Consolidated Coatings Corp.

COLORMINE - Pharmaceutical preparations - Gail A. Leicher

COLORMODE - Cooking utensils–aluminum ☆ - Mirro Corp.

COLORMOUNT - Electronic equipment - Seal Products Inc.

COLOR'N DIAL - Toys - Rainfall Inc.

COLOR'N MOTION - Computer software - Rose Studios, Inc.

COLOR'N SCENT - Dyes–food ☆ - Schering-Plough Healthcare Products

COLOR'N TURN - Toys - Rainfall Inc.

COLORNET - Lighting equipment - Colortran Inc.

COLOROCK - Garden equipment - Far West Forests

COLORON - Crayons, chalk - Coloron Industries

COLOROO ZOO - Dolls - Mattel, Inc.

COLOROOS - Shoes - KangaROOS USA Inc.

COLORPACK - Cameras - Polaroid Corp.

COLORPADDLES - Toys - Childcraft Education Corp.

COLORPERFECT - Film - E.I. Dupont de Nemours and Co.

COLORPLAN - Photographic equipment - Leica USA Inc.

COLORPLAYS - Cosmetics - Elizabeth Arden Inc.

COLORPOINT - Paints - Tulip Productions

COLORPOINT BEAD - Paints - Tulip Productions

COLORPOINT IRON-ON COLOR DESIGNS - Decals and transfers - Tulip Productions

COLORPOINT SINGLE DESIGNS - Decals and transfers - Tulip Productions

COLORPOINT STITCH - Paints - Tulip Productions

COLORPORT - Cement - Riverton Corp.

COLORPRINT - Dyes and pigments - Retouch Methods Co. Inc.

COLORPRINT - Maps - American Map Corp.

COLORPRINTS - Decals and transfers - Stahls' Inc.

COLORQUARTZ - Floor coverings - Minnesota Mining & Manufacturing Co.

COLORQUEST - Artists' materials - HunterLab

COLORQUEST - Floor coverings–carpet and rugs ☆ - Burtco Enterprises Inc.

COLORRIGHT - Electronic printer - Prime Option Inc.

COLORRINGS - Dyes–food - Spearhead Industries Inc.

COLORS - Candy ☆ - Sathers Inc.

COLORS - Cups–plastic - WNA Comet

COLORS - Hardware - Amerock Corp.

COLORS - Infant product - Prince Lionheart, Inc.

COLORS - Nail-care products, cosmetics ☆ - London International U.S. Holdings

COLORS - Skin care products - Benetton

COLORS - Wallpaper - Bayview Wallcoverings

COLORS BY DESIGN - Greeting cards - David M & Co.

COLORS BY KASEN - Dinnerware–glass ☆ - Peter Pan Industries

COLORS BY KOHLER - Bathroom accessories - Kohler Co.

COLORS BY MUSTANG - Pet products - Mustang Products, Inc.

COLORS BY P.F.I. - Footwear–women's - Diesse Shoes Inc.

COLORS, COLORS - Stationery - Stuart Hall Co., Inc.

COLORS DE BENETTON - Colognes - Benetton

COLORS FOR U - Hosiery–women's - Glen Raven Mills Inc.

COLORS II - Wallpaper - Bayview Wallcoverings

COLORS III - Wallpaper - Madison Wallcoverings

COLORS IN BLOOM - Wallpaper ☆ - Sandpiper Studios

COLORS IN BLOOM II - Wallpaper ☆ - Sandpiper Studios

COLORS IN MOTION - Ophthalmic goods - Foremost Optical Products

COLORS IN OIL - Paints - Sheffield Bronze Paint Corp.

COLORS IN THE SUN - Wallpaper ☆ - Sandpiper Studios

COLORS IN THE SUN II - Wallpaper - Sandpiper Studios

COLORS IN WHITE - Paper products - Color Guild Associates, Inc.

COLORS N KISSES - Children's play cosmetics - Cosrich Inc.

COLORS PLUS - Bathroom fixtures - Shower-Rite Corp.

COLORS PROVENCE - Wallpaper ☆ - Sandpiper Studios

COLORS PROVENCE II - Wallpaper ☆ - Sandpiper Studios

COLORSAURUS - Publisher's imprints - Jerry Haines Sales Corp.

COLORSAVER - Veterinary pharmaceutical preparations - Susan R. McCarthy

COLORSCAN - File folders - Kardex Systems, Inc.

COLORSCAPE - Floor coverings–carpet and rugs ☆ - World Carpets, Inc.

COLORSCAPE SEED CANS - Flowers, plants, and seeds - Applewood Seed & Garden Group

COLORSCAPES - Paints - Benjamin Moore & Co.

COLORSCOPE - Floor coverings–carpet and rugs - LaVelle Textile Marketing Inc.

COLORSCOPE - Postcards - Scope Enterprises

COLORSEAL - Paint, roofing materials - Innovative Formulations Corp.

COLORSENSE - Computer software - Eastman Kodak Co.

COLORSERVE SYSTEM - Hair care products - Clairol Inc.

COLORSET - Floor coverings - Mannington Resilient Floors

COLORSET - Stencils ☆ - Letraset USA Inc.

COLORSHAKERS - Hair care products - Image Laboratories, Inc.

COLORSHAPES - Toys - Childcraft Education Corp.

COLORSHARE - Computer software - Apple Computer Inc.

COLORSHIELD - Electronic equipment ☆ - Harcourt General, Inc.

COLORSHINE - Cosmetics - Revlon-Realistic Professional Products Inc.

COLORSHOW - Video equipment - Sayett Technology Inc.

COLORSILK - Hair care products - Revlon Consumer Products Corp.

COLORSIN - Pens ☆ - Sanford Corp.

COLORSPERSE - Chemical preparations - Gayson Specialty Dispersions, Inc.

COLORSPOC - Paints - Multicolor Specialties Inc.

COLORSTAR - Markers–felt-tip - Staedtler, Inc.

COLORSTAR - Mats - Andersen Brothers Holding Co., Inc.

COLORSTAR - Mats - Andersen Co.

COLORSTAX - Dinnerware–glass - Metlox Pottery Shoppe

COLORSTAY - Cosmetics - Revlon Consumer Products Corp.

COLORSTAY - Yarn - BASF Corp.

☆ = Now out of production

COLORSTAY LIPCOLOR - Lipsticks - Revlon Consumer Products Corp.
COLORSTIK - Dyes and pigments - Colorstik Ltd.
COLORSTIX - Inks - Tektronix, Inc.
COLORSTIX - Lipsticks - Markham, Susan Mcgovert
COLORSTONE - Dinnerware–glass ☆ - Nikko Ceramics Inc.
COLORSTYLE - Cosmetics - Revlon Consumer Products Corp.
COLORSTYLE - Doors–metal - Robertson-Ceco Corp.
COLORSTYLE - Floor coverings ☆ - Forbo Industries, Inc.
COLORSUITE - Publisher's imprints - Pantone, Inc.
COLORSWEPT - Floor coverings–carpet and rugs ☆ - Galaxy Carpet Mills Inc.
COLORSYNC C - Computer software - Apple Computer Inc.
COLORSYNERGY - Computer software - Candela, Ltd.
COLORTAC - Lany Fax of America Inc.
COLORTAG - Copy coloring system ☆ - Esselte Corp.
COLORTEC - Tufting machines - Spencer Wright Industries, Inc.
COLORTECH - Furniture ☆ - Quaker Industries Ltd.
COLORTECH - Watches - David L. Pakter
COLORTEK - Photocopy machines - LogEtronics Corp.
COLORTEX - Craft supplies ☆ - Sax Arts & Crafts
COLORTEX - Needles–sewing - Colortex Co.
COLORTEX - Paper–crepe ☆ - Bemiss-Jason Corp.
COLORTEX - Paper–toweling - Orchids Paper Products, Inc.
COLORTEX - Window coverings - Arquati Inc.
COLORTHRU - Cushions - Polar Manufacturing Co.
COLORTONE - Bulletin boards–cork - K & M Co.
COLORTONE - Drapery hardware - Newell Window Furnishing Co.
COLORTONE - Finishing agents - Hillyard Enterprises, Inc.
COLORTONE - Lamps - Philips Lighting Co.
COLORTONE - Posters ☆ - Milton Bradley Co.
COLORTONERS - Photographic equipment ☆ - Edwal Scientific Products Corp.
COLORTONES - Sealing compounds - Gloucester Co., Inc.
COLORTONES - Wallpaper - Stroheim & Romann, Inc.
COLORTOUCH - Protective keypad overlay - Pittway Corp.
COLORTRACK - Apparel–children's - Doe Spun Inc.
COLORTRAK - Televisions - Thomson Consumer Electronics, Inc.
COLORTRAP - Plastics–laminated - Redound Industries, Inc.
COLORTREAD - Paints ☆ - Tremco Inc.
COLORTREE - Wallcovering ☆ - Colortree Designs
COLORTRENDS - Lipsticks - Revlon Consumer Products Corp.
COLORTROL - Photographic equipment - Lektra Service Corp.
COLORTRON - Floor coverings–carpet and rugs - Maples Industries, Inc.
COLORTRON - Video games - Hasbro, Inc.
COLORTRUE - Computer peripheral equipment ☆ - Epson America, Inc.
COLORTRUE - Shampoos - Clairol Inc.
COLORTUFF - Finishing agents - Sterling Plumbing Group Inc.
COLORTUNES - Books–comic - Dri Mark Products, Inc.
COLORTURA - Tea kettles–nonelectric ☆ - Robinson Knife & Fiddlers Plastics
COLORTURA - Wallpaper - S.R. Wood Inc.
COLORTYME - Furniture - ColorTyme Inc.
COLORUP - Computer software - Pantone, Inc.
COLORUP - Plastics–laminated - Beaumont G. Lyons
COLORVISION - Eyeglasses - Blublocker Corp.
COLORVISION - Floor coverings–carpet and rugs - Distributor Buying Associates Inc.
COLORVISION - Lasers - Corp. for Laser Optics Research
COLORVIVE TECHNICARE - Hair care products - Cosmair Inc.
COLORWAND - Cosmetics - Nat Robbins Ltd.
COLORWARE - Computer hardware - Sys-Lan, Inc.
COLORWARE - Cooking utensils–enameled - Jacksonville Manufacturing
COLORWASH - Skin-care products - McGlynn Bakeries Inc.
COLORWATCH - Photographic equipment - Eastman Kodak Co.
COLORWAVE - Frames–picture - Nielsen & Bainbridge
COLORWAVE - Paper–kraft - Pacon Corp.
COLORWAVES - Wallpaper ☆ - Imperial Wallcoverings, Inc.
COLORWAX - Candy ☆ - Fox Run Craftsmen
COLORWAYS - Housewares - Treasure Craft Co.
COLORWAYS II - Wallpaper - B. Berger Co.
COLORWEB - Computer software - Pantone, Inc.
COLORWEB - Fabrics–broadcloth - American Cord & Webbing Co., Inc.
COLORWELL - Diagnostic test kits - Aquila Biopharmaceuticals, Inc.
COLORWHIZZ - Toys ☆ - Play-Tech, Inc.
COLORWIZ - Print software - C4 Network Inc.
COLORWOOD - Paints - Wattyl Paint Corp.
COLORWORKS - Candy - Mars, Inc.
COLORWORKS - Cosmetics - Circle of Beauty, Inc.

COLORWORKS - Cosmetics - Sears, Roebuck and Co.
COLORWORKS - Crayons - Binney & Smith Inc.
COLORWORKS - Enamels - Krylon/Dupli-Color
COLORWORKS - Flatware - JMP-Newcor International, Inc.
COLORWORKS - Floor coverings–carpet and rugs - Hartford Carpet Mills
COLORWORKS - Furniture - Walt Disney Co.
COLORWORKS - Manicure sets ☆ - London International U.S. Holdings
COLORWORKS - Ophthalmic goods - Foremost Optical Products
COLORWORKS - Watches - Medana Watch Corp.
COLORWORKS - Watches - Webster Watch Co. Associates
COLORYOURBATH - Housewares - Dawson Home Fashions, Inc.
COLORYOURKITCHEN - Tablecloths - Dawson Home Fashions, Inc.
COLOSSAL - Candy ☆ - Annabelle Candy Co. Inc.
COLOSSAL - Floor coverings–carpet and rugs - World Carpets, Inc.
COLOSSAL - Ice chests–plastic - Coleman Co., Inc.
COLOSSAL - Pillows - Pillowtex Corp.
COLOSSAL - Recording label - New Renaissance Records
COLOSSAL - Soft drink - Creative Beverage Co.
COLOSSAL COOKER - Cooking utensils–aluminum - West Bend Co.
COLOSSAL CRAWLERS - Toy figure molds and accessories - Toymax Inc.
COLOSSAL CURL - Curling irons–electric - Windmere Corp.
COLOSSAL DOG - Frankfurters - Atlantic Richfield Co.
COLOSSAL DONUTS - Doughnuts - SFW Licensing Corp.
COLOSSAL POPS - Candy - Rosemary Candy Co.
COLOSSAL TUBE - Sporting goods - O'Brien International
COLOSSEO - Dishes–china - Pasmantier Co. Inc.
COLOSSEUM - Floor coverings ☆ - Congoleum Corp.
COLOSSEUM ONE - Furniture–public buildings - Dant Clayton Corp.
COLOSSO - Food products - Ace Baking Co. L.P.
COLOSSO-CONE - Ice cream cones ☆ - Ace Baking Co. L.P.
COLOSSO CRUMBS - Snack foods - Ace Baking Co. L.P.
COLOSSUS - Bicycles - Huffy Corp.
COLOSSUS - Toys–models ☆ - Estes Industries
COLOSSUS, THE - Pizzas–frozen - Pizza Pipeline, Inc.
COLOTRYM - Hardware - Colotrym
COLOUR CHANGE - Frames–eyeglass ☆ - Ambassador Eyewear Group
COLOUR COLLECTIONS, THE - Office supplies - Esselte Corp.
COLOUR CONFIDENCE - Cosmetics - Chanel Inc.
COLOUR DESTINY - Floor coverings–carpet and rugs - Ashley Commercial Carpets
COLOUR DUO - Cosmetics - Revlon Consumer Products Corp.
COLOUR ENDURE - Cosmetics - Cosmair Inc.
COLOUR FLAVORS - Floor coverings–carpet and rugs - Ashley Commercial Carpets
COLOUR FOLK - Giftware - N.S. Gustin Co.
COLOUR MAJESTY - Floor coverings–carpet and rugs - Ashley Commercial Carpets
COLOUR MILL USA, THE - Apparel and accessories - Knitex, Inc.
COLOUR OF MONEY - Toys–electronic ☆ - WMS Gaming Inc.
COLOUR REFRESHING SHAMPOO - Shampoos - Mastey De Paris
COLOUR RICHE - Lipsticks - Cosmair Inc.
COLOUR RUB - Cosmetics - Clinique Laboratories, Inc.
COLOUR SCENTS - Perfumes - Revlon Consumer Products Corp.
COLOUR SHAPER - Artists' materials - Forsline & Starr, Ltd.
COLOUR SUPREME - Cosmetics - Cosmair Inc.
COLOUR SYMPHONY - Floor coverings–carpet and rugs - Ashley Commercial Carpets
COLOUR WEAVES - Cosmetics - Yves St. Laurent Parfum Corp.
COLOUR YOUR WORLD - Socks - Moretz Hosiery Mills Inc.
COLOURA - Health care products - Sunrise Medical
COLOURAGE - Hair care products - Tressa, Inc.
COLOURANT - Hair care products - Clairol Inc.
COLOURCOMP - Computer software - Colourcomp Corp.
COLOURCOMP CORPORATION - Computer storage devices - Colourcomp Corp.
COLOURINGS - Cosmetics - The Body Shop
COLOURLINE - Blinds–venetian ☆ - Kenney Manufacturing Co.
COLOURS - Blinds–venetian ☆ - Hunter Douglas, Inc.
COLOURS - Cosmetics - Morris-Flamingo Inc.
COLOURS - Faucets - Gerber Plumbing Fixtures Corp.
COLOURS - Floor coverings - Congoleum Corp.
COLOURS - Floor coverings–carpet and rugs ☆ - Mannington Carpets, Inc.
COLOURS - Floor coverings–tile ☆ - Robbins Interior Surface Inc.
COLOURS - Furniture - A. Brandt Co. Inc.
COLOURS - Perfumes, colognes, and aftershave lotion - Alexander Julian Inc.
COLOURS - Puzzles - Warren Industries Inc.

☆ = Now out of production

COLOURS - Shaving preparations - Schick/Wilkinson

COLOURS AND CONTOURS - Wallpaper ☆ - Capital Carousel Inc.

COLOURS BY ALEXANDER JULIAN - Apparel–men's - Alexander Julian Inc.

COLOURS BY ALEXANDER JULIAN - Apparel–men's - Swank Inc.

COLOURS BY ALEXANDER JULIAN - Apparel–men's ☆ - Greif Cos.

COLOURS BY ALEXANDER JULIAN - Eyeglasses - Marchon and Marcolin Eyewear Inc.

COLOURS BY ALEXANDER JULIAN - Hosiery - Silver Knit

COLOURS BY ALEXANDER JULIAN - Hosiery–men's - Paul Lavitt Mills, Inc.

COLOURS BY ALEXANDER JULIAN - Luggage - Verdi Travelware

COLOURS BY ALEXANDER JULIAN - Watches - Alexander Julian, Inc.

COLOURS II - Floor coverings–carpet and rugs ☆ - J and J Industries Inc.

COLOURS SUPREME - Floor coverings–carpet and rugs - J and J Industries Inc.

COLOURSPORT - Apparel–men's - Alexander Julian, Inc.

COLOURSPORT ALEXANDER JULIAN - Apparel–men's - Alexander Julian Inc.

COLOURSTEP - Floor coverings - Forbo Industries, Inc.

COLOURSTIKS - Neckties - Dunleigh Tuxton Inc.

COLOVE - Games - Fitness Games, Inc.

COLOWEAR - Apparel–men's - Royce Apparel, Inc.

COLPAC - Health care products - Chattanooga Group, Inc.

COLREX - Pharmaceutical preparations ☆ - Solvay Pharmaceuticals Inc.

COLRING - Wire - Pass & Seymour, Inc.

COLSALIDE - Pharmaceutical preparations ☆ - Vortech Pharmaceuticals

COLSIN - Cold remedies ☆ - Harvey Laboratories Inc.

COLSOLVE - Rubber cement - Columbia Cement Co. Inc.

COLSON - Hardware - Colson Caster Corp.

COLSON - Wire - Pass & Seymour, Inc.

COLSPAN - Pharmaceutical preparations ☆ - Murray Drug Corp.

COLT - Bicycles - Ross Bicycles USA, Ltd.

COLT - Brushes–paint - Corona Brushes Inc.

COLT - Brushes–paint ☆ - Linzer Products Corp.

COLT - Cameras ☆ - Edixa Camera Co.

COLT - Clocks ☆ - General Time Corp. (Westclox/Seth Thomas Div.)

COLT - Firearms, accessories, and parts - Colt's Manufacturing Co. Inc.

COLT - Glassware–household - Rezler & Howell Co.

COLT - Knives - United Cutlery Corp.

COLT - Motor vehicles ☆ - Chrysler Corp. (Dodge Car Div.)

COLT - Motorcycles ☆ - Suzuki of America Automotive Corp.

COLT - Motors–outboard ☆ - Outboard Marine Corp.

COLT - Office supplies ☆ - Bates Manufacturing Co.

COLT - Pipes–tobacco ☆ - S.M. Frank & Co. Inc. (Kaywoodie-Yello-Bole-Medico)

COLT - Shoes–athletic ☆ - Brookfield Athletic Co. Inc.

COLT - Skis - Wellington Leisure Products, Inc.

COLT - Sunglasses - New Colt Holding Corp.

COLT 45 - Beverages–malt - The Stroh Brewery Co.

COLT 45 DOUBLE MALT - Beverages–malt - The Stroh Brewery Co.

COLT 45 DRY - Beverages–malt ☆ - The Stroh Brewery Co.

COLT 45 PREMIUM - Beverages–malt ☆ - The Stroh Brewery Co.

COLT BOLTS - Candy - Colt Candy Inc.

COLT ICE - Beverages–malt - The Stroh Brewery Co.

COLT VISTA - Motor vehicles ☆ - Chrysler Corp. (Dodge Car Div.)

COLTAB - Pharmaceutical preparations - Roberts/Hauck Pharmaceuticals Inc.

COLTEC INDUSTRIES - Electrical power distribution transformers - Coltec Industries Inc.

COLTEER 1-22, THE - Rifles ☆ - Colt's Manufacturing Co. Inc.

COLTER BAY - Apparel and accessories - Colter Bay International Ltd.

COLTERYAHN - Milk - Carl Colteryahn Dairy Inc.

COLTIVA - Wines - Shaw-Ross International Importers

COLTON - Brushes–paint ☆ - PPG Industries, Inc.

COLTON'S - Spices and extracts - McCormick & Co., Inc.

COLTS NECK - Sweaters ☆ - Logo Knits Inc.

COLTURA - See SIGMAGUARD

COLTURIET - See SIGMACOVER

COLUMBIA - Antiseptics - F.C. Sturtevant Co.

COLUMBIA - Artists' materials ☆ - M. Grumbacher Inc.

COLUMBIA - Artists' materials ☆ - Hamilton Industries

COLUMBIA - Bicycles - Columbia Manufacturing Inc.

COLUMBIA - Boats–canoes ☆ - Old Town Canoe Co.

COLUMBIA - Boats–motor - Hampton Shipyards/Hampton Boat Sales Ltd.

COLUMBIA - Books–blank - Boorum & Pease Co.

COLUMBIA - Brooms - Wright-Bernet

COLUMBIA - Cabinets - Imperial Cabinet Co. Inc.

COLUMBIA - Cabinets ☆ - Aristokraft, Inc.

COLUMBIA - Candles - Columbia Wax Products Inc.

COLUMBIA - Cases–camera ☆ - Edixa Camera Co.

COLUMBIA - Clocks - Ridgeway Clock Co.

COLUMBIA - Cribs–wood ☆ - Welsh Co.

COLUMBIA - Doors–screen - Columbia Manufacturing Corp.

COLUMBIA - Floor coverings–carpet and rugs ☆ - Mannington Carpets, Inc.

COLUMBIA - Food products - James Ferrera and Sons Inc.

COLUMBIA - Fruits and vegetables ☆ - J.R. Simplot Co.

COLUMBIA - Glassware–household - Oneida Ltd.

COLUMBIA - Handles–wood - Turner, Day and Woolworth Handle Corp.

COLUMBIA - Lawn mowers ☆ - MTD Products Inc.

COLUMBIA - Lighting equipment - Hanson Lighting Group

COLUMBIA - Mattresses - Namaco Industries, Inc.

COLUMBIA - Music–sheet - Theodore Presser Co.

COLUMBIA - Office supplies - Globe-Weis

COLUMBIA - Orthopedic products - Columbia Medical Manufacturing

COLUMBIA - Paints - Columbia Paint Inc.

COLUMBIA - Paper–photographic ☆ - Keuffel & Esser Co.

COLUMBIA - Pasta - Liberty Richter Inc.

COLUMBIA - Rings–jewelry - Columbia Diamond Ring Co. Inc.

COLUMBIA - Rubber cement - Columbia Cement Co. Inc.

COLUMBIA - Sauces - Curtice-Burns Foods, Inc.

COLUMBIA - Sauerkraut - Nalley's Fine Foods

COLUMBIA - Stepladders - W.W. Babcock Co. Inc.

COLUMBIA - Tableware–china - Lenox, Inc.

COLUMBIA - Tape players–cassette - Sony Music Entertainment Inc.

COLUMBIA - Window shades - Spring Window Fashions Division, Inc.

COLUMBIA - Wood products ☆ - The Coleman Co.

COLUMBIA - Yarn ☆ - Lees Carpets

COLUMBIA 300 - Sporting goods - Columbia Industries, Inc.

COLUMBIA CELEBRITY - Ships–sailing vessels - Hampton Shipyards/Hampton Boat Sales Ltd.

COLUMBIA CREST - Wines - Stimson Lane Vineyards & Estates

COLUMBIA CROWN - Fruits and vegetables - Columbia Crown Brand Inc.

COLUMBIA DELUXE III - Bicycles - Columbia Manufacturing Inc.

COLUMBIA DELUXE TOURIST III - Bicycles - Columbia Manufacturing Inc.

COLUMBIA FLOORING - Flooring–hardwood - Columbia Forest Products, Inc.

COLUMBIA KNIT - Knitting machines - Columbia Knit Inc.

COLUMBIA-MATIC - Window shades - Berkshire Industries Inc.

COLUMBIA MEDICAL SOFT TOUCH CUPS - Medical apparatus - Utah Medical Products, Inc.

COLUMBIA MEDICAL TENDER TOUCH FLEX CUPS - Medical apparatus - Utah Medical Products, Inc.

COLUMBIA MEDICAL TENDER TOUCH ULTRA CUPS - Medical apparatus - Utah Medical Products, Inc.

COLUMBIA MEDICAL VACUUM PUMPS - Medical apparatus - Utah Medical Products, Inc.

COLUMBIA MEDICAL VELVET TOUCH CUPS - Medical apparatus - Utah Medical Products, Inc.

COLUMBIA PRIDE - Fruits and vegetables - Grigg and Sons

COLUMBIA RACER X - Bicycles - Columbia Manufacturing Inc.

COLUMBIA REACH APPLES - Agricultural products - Columbia Reach Pack

COLUMBIA RIVER CELLARS - Wines ☆ - Preston Premium Wines

COLUMBIA ROADSTER - Bicycles - Columbia Manufacturing Inc.

COLUMBIA RX-5 - Toys - Xonex International, Inc.

COLUMBIA SPORTS - Bicycles - Columbia Manufacturing Inc.

COLUMBIA SPORTS TOURIST III JR. - Bicycles - Columbia Manufacturing Inc.

COLUMBIA SPORTSWEAR COMPANY - Apparel and accessories - Columbia Sportswear Co.

COLUMBIA SUPER III - Bicycles - Columbia Manufacturing Inc.

COLUMBIA SUPER X - Bicycles - Columbia Manufacturing Inc.

COLUMBIA TENDER - Boats–dinghies - Edey & Duff, Ltd.

COLUMBIA TOURIST V - Bicycles - Columbia Manufacturing Inc.

COLUMBIA VISTA - Manufactured homes - Redman Industries, Inc.

COLUMBIA WINERY - Wines - Columbia Winery

COLUMBIAKNIT - Apparel and accessories - Columbia Knit Inc.

COLUMBIAKNIT - Apparel and accessories - Columbiaknit, Inc.

COLUMBIAN - Calendars - Success Business Industries, Inc.

COLUMBIAN - Clamps - Warren Tool Group

COLUMBIAN - Envelopes - Westvaco Corp.

COLUMBIAN - Floor coverings–carpet and rugs ☆ - Concord/Aldon Industries Inc.

COLUMBIAN - Glassware–household - Owens-Illinois Inc. (Libbey Div.)

COLUMBIAN - Hardware - Brink & Cotton

COLUMBIAN - Housewares ☆ - General Housewares Corp.

COLUMBIAN - Rope - Geo. B. Carpenter Co.
COLUMBIAN - Tools–garden - Columbian Cutlery Co.
COLUMBIAN - Trailers–travel ☆ - Coachmen Industries, Inc.
COLUMBIAN SELECT - Coffee - Nestle Beverage Co.
COLUMBIANA - Tires - Bridgestone/Firestone, Inc.
COLUMBIANO - Liquors ☆ - Frank Sutton & Co.
COLUMBINE - Banjos - OME Co. Inc.
COLUMBINE - Iced tea–bottled or canned - Columbine Beverage
COLUMBINE - Paper–carbon ☆ - Ner Data Products, Inc.
COLUMBINE - Spinning machines - Columbine Products
COLUMBINE - Tableware–china ☆ - Lenox, Inc.
COLUMBINE - Watches - Bulova Corp.
COLUMBINE - Wines - Minnesota Winegrowers Cooperative
COLUMBUS - Alarm systems ☆ - Philips Communication & Security Systems Inc.
COLUMBUS - Bathroom accessories - KLR Products, Inc.
COLUMBUS - Bicycles - Columbia Manufacturing Inc.
COLUMBUS - Canvas–artists' ☆ - Columbus Coated Fabrics Co.
COLUMBUS - Floor coverings–carpet and rugs ☆ - Columbus Mills, Inc.
COLUMBUS - Pencils ☆ - Faber-Castell Corp.
COLUMBUS - Puzzles - Milton Bradley Co.
COLUMBUS - Sausages - Dairy Fresh Products Co.
COLUMBUS - Washboards - Columbus Washboard Co.
COLUMBUS 92 - T-shirts and sweatshirts - 1992 Corp.
COLUMBUS 1492 LAGER - Beverages–malt ☆ - Columbus Brewing Co.
COLUMBUS CIRCLE - Jewelry - Jacoby-Bender Inc.
COLUMBUS CLIPPERS - Key rings - Columbus Baseball Team, Inc.
COLUMBUS CREAM - Hazelnut liqueur ☆ - Euromark Inc.
COLUMBUS EGG, THE - Toys - Hirsch Co.
COLUMBUS MCKINNIN - Chains - Sea Spike Marine Supply Co. Inc.
COLUMELA - Vinegar - Gourmet America
COLUMN - Glassware–household - Svend Jensen of Denmark Inc.
COLUMN GOLD - Flatware - Gorham Inc.
COLUMN WRITE - Office supplies - ACCO USA, Inc.
COLUMNLIFT - Automotive parts and accessories - Maxon Industries, Inc.
COLURA - Hosiery - Kayser-Roth Corp.
COLUSSI - Cookies - Bell'amore Imports Inc.
COLY-MYCIN - Antibiotics - Parke-Davis
COLYTE - Health care products - Reed & Carnrick
COM - Blinds–vertical - Custom Laminations Inc.
COM - Radiotelephones - Intech Inc.
COM-5 - Computer peripheral equipment - Mouse Systems Corp.
COM 21 - Communications equipment - Com 21, Inc.
COM-BAC - Cushions - Commander-Omni Co. Inc.
COM-CALL - Telephone apparatus - TT Systems Corp.
COM CHECK - Computer software - Boca Research, Inc.
COM-ETTES - Candy ☆ - Raymond Foods Inc.
COM-FIT - Apparel–women's - Wacoal America Inc.
COM FITT - Weightlifting equipment - Com Fitt, LLC
COM-FREE - Vitamins and nutritional supplements - Joe Bassett
COM KEY - Telephones - At&T Corp.
COM KOIL - Cleaning preparations - Comstar International Inc. (IPC Div.)
COM-PAC - Ships–sailing vessels - Hutchins Co. Inc.
COM-PAC - Ships–sailing vessels - Nord Yachts
COM-PAC CLOTHING MARKING KIT - Apparel trimmings - F.R. Bean Manufacturing
COM-PAK - Electronic equipment ☆ - E.F. Johnson Co.
COM-PAK'S - Sporting goods - Lafayette Instrument Co. Inc.
COM-PLEET - Insecticides - Green Light Co.
COM-PLETE MODIFER - Hair care products - Mahdeen Laboratory
COM PLEX SKIN FITNESS CLINICS - Skin care products - Colorado Skin Care Clinic, Inc.
COM SYS - Communications equipment - Stanton Magnetics Inc.
COM-TRUK - Tires - Oliver Rubber Co.
COM-VI-FORTE - Pharmaceutical preparations ☆ - Murray Drug Corp.
COM-WELD - Chemical preparation - Tarkett, Inc.
COMAL - Animal feed supplements - Nutramax Laboratories, Inc.
COMANCHE - Bicycles - Ross Bicycles USA, Ltd.
COMANCHE - Boats–motor ☆ - Thunderbird Products
COMANCHE - Brushes–paint ☆ - Linzer Products Corp.
COMANCHE - Computer software - Novalogic, Inc.
COMANCHE - Motor vehicles–jeeps ☆ - DaimlerChrysler
COMANCHE - Powerboat - American Skier Boat Co.
COMANCHE - Radio communications equipment - Motorola, Inc. (Land Mobile Products Sector)
COMANCHE-3 - Toys–models - Estes Industries

COMANCHE BUFFALO - Toys–stuffed - Dakin Inc.
COMANCHE CHIEF - Nuts–salted, roasted, cooked, or canned - Golden Peanut Co.
COM&DIA - Computer software - Com&Dia, LLC
COMANDER - Electronic equipment - Valley Audio Products, Inc.
COMAR - Health care products - Gilliar Pharmacy Co.
COMAR - Paints - Allentown Paint Manufacturing Co. Inc.
COMARE - Brushes–hair - Spilo/Mehaz Worldwide
COMARE - Combs - Comare Corp.
COMARE ELITE COLLECTION - Hair brushes - Windmere Corp.
COMARK - Fabrics–tapestry - Comark Wallcoverings
COMART - Photographic equipment - Camera Mart Inc.
COMAS - Food products ☆ - Borden, Inc.
COMASEC - Gloves - Comasec Safety, Inc.
COMAX Q10 - Vitamins and nutritional supplements - Nutramax Laboratories, Inc.
COMB-A-LASH - Mascara ☆ - Cosrich Inc.
COMB GRAY AWAY - Hair care products ☆ - Helmac Products Corp.
COMB-INATION - Hair care products - K.B. Marketing Inc.
COMB-O-CYCLE - Medical apparatus - American Walker Inc.
COMB-ON MASCARA - Cosmetics - Maybelline Co.
COMB-PREP - Hair-replacement product - International Hairgoods Inc.
COMB-THRU - Hair care products - Nexxus Products Co.
COMB-THRU - Hair care products - Pro-Line Corp.
COMBAGEN - Pharmaceutical preparations - Goldline Laboratories, Inc.
COMBAT - Insecticides - Clorox Co.
COMBAT - Insecticides - Kingsford Co.
COMBAT - Motorcycles ☆ - Pabatco
COMBAT - Polyester film sheets - Hurricane Window Protection International, Inc.
COMBAT - Recording label - Relativity/Combat/In-Effect
COMBAT - Sandals - ALP Sport Sandals
COMBAT BATTLE TANK - Toys - Tyco Toys
COMBAT CALCULATOR - Games ☆ - Gamescience
COMBAT CARTON - Toys–automobiles - Mattel, Inc.
COMBAT CHESS - Games ☆ - Avalon Hill Game Co.
COMBAT CLOTH - Apparel and accessories - Brigade Quartermasters Ltd.
COMBAT COMMAND - Figurines - GHQ
COMBAT COMMAND - Toys - Tyco Toys
COMBAT COMMANDER - Pistols - Colt's Manufacturing Co. Inc.
COMBAT COMMANDO CANNON - Toys–guns - Trendmasters, Inc.
COMBAT COMMANDO RIDERS - Toys - Trendmasters, Inc.
COMBAT COMMANDOES - Toys–airplanes - Comet Montrose Ltd.
COMBAT CRAWLERS - Toys - Trendmasters, Inc.
COMBAT ELITE - Pistols - Colt's Manufacturing Co. Inc.
COMBAT ELITE - Pistols - New Colt Holding Corp.
COMBAT EXCHANGE - Gun stocks - Combat Exchange Inc.
COMBAT FORTRESS - Toys - Tyco Toys
COMBAT GOVERNMENT - Pistols ☆ - Colt's Manufacturing Co. Inc.
COMBAT LABS - Insecticides - Kingsford Products Co.
COMBAT MAGNUM - Revolvers - Smith & Wesson Corp.
COMBAT MASTERPIECE - Revolvers - Smith & Wesson Corp.
COMBAT MEDIC - Toys–automobiles - Mattel, Inc.
COMBAT OUTDOOR ANT KILLING STAKES/GRANULES - Insecticides - Kingsford Co.
COMBAT RATIONS - Chewing gum - Leaf, Inc.
COMBAT TEAM - Toys - Tyco Toys
COMBAT THROWER - Knives - Tru-Balance Knife Co.
COMBAT THUNDER - Toys - Mattel, Inc.
COMBAT ZOOKA - Toys–guns - Trendmasters, Inc.
COMBATIT - Rust removers - California Products Corp.
COMBATRIBES, THE - Computer software - American Technos Inc.
COMBATSTICK - Computer peripheral equipment - Joystick Technologies (CH Products Division)
COMBATT - Machinery - Donald P. Deitesfeld
COMBED COLLECTION, THE - Fabrics–tapestry ☆ - Clarence House Imports Ltd.
COMBI - Apparel and accessories - Freudenberg Nonwovens Apparel Division
COMBI - Awnings - Awnings by Sunair/Sunair Awnings
COMBI - Paperboard packaging materials - SIG Combibloc Inc.
COMBI - Safety glasses - Bilsom International Inc.
COMBI - Toys ☆ - Combi International Corp.
COMBI CHAIR - High chairs ☆ - Combi International Corp.
COMBI COLD - Refrigerators ☆ - Kenyon Marine, Inc. (Adler/Barbour Div.)
COMBI CUSHION - Cushions - Jay Medical Ltd.
COMBI-CUT - Hardware - Mitek Industries Inc.

☆ = Now out of production

COMBI-DISC - Machine tools - Pferd Inc.
COMBI DRIVE - Toys ☆ - Combi International Corp.
COMBI-DRY - Bathroom accessories - R-Z Co. of America Inc.
COMBI-FOLD - Cabinets - Fort Howard Corp.
COMBI-IC - Antigens - Caltag Laboratories, Inc.
COMBI-PACT - Conveyors - Richwood Industries, Inc.
COMBI-PAN - Griddles–electric - Legion Industries, Inc.
COMBI-QUICK - Electronic equipment - Hudson Photographic Industries Inc.
COMBI-SET - Tools–power-driven - Mitek Industries Inc.
COMBI-TWIST - Containers–metal - White Cap, Inc.
COMBIBLOC - Containers–paper - SIG Combibloc Inc.
COMBIBLOT - Diagnostic substances - Epitope Inc.
COMBID - Pharmaceutical preparations - Smithkline Beecham Corp.
COMBIE - Paints - Hempel Coatings USA Inc.
COMBINATION - Projectors–photographic - Rollei of America Inc.
COMBINATION - Wigs - New Image
COMBINATION BAND - Medical apparatus - Physicians Appliance Co.
COMBINATION BELT - Archery equipment - Martin Archery Inc.
COMBINATION PERM - Hair care products - Helene Curtis Industries Inc.
COMBINATIONS - Apparel–women's - Oxford Industries, Inc.
COMBINATIONS - Dinnerware–glass ☆ - Dansk International Designs, Ltd.
COMBINATIONS - Tiles–ceramic - American Olean Tile Co.
COMBINATIONS - Wallpaper ☆ - J. Josephson, Inc.
COMBINATORIX - Games - Kadon Enterprises Inc.
COMBINE - Apparel and accessories - NHS, Inc.
COMBINE - Snowboards - NBS, Inc.
COMBIOTIC - Veterinary pharmaceutical preparations - Pfizer Inc.
COMBIPRES - Pharmaceutical preparations - Boehringer Ingelheim
  Pharmaceuticals Inc.
COMBISCOPE - Measuring instruments - Fluke Corp.
COMBIVENT - Pharmaceutical preparations - Boehringer Ingelheim
  Pharmaceuticals Inc.
COMBO - Brooms - O-Cedar/Vining Household Products Co.
COMBO - Corn–flour or meal - Philip Morris Companies Inc.
COMBO - Detergents - Hydrite Chemical Co.
COMBO - Fuel additives ☆ - Demert & Dougherty, Inc.
COMBO - Furniture ☆ - Brunswick Corp.
COMBO - Lamps - Luxo Corp.
COMBO - Locks–padlocks - Weiser Lock Corp.
COMBO - Microphones - G & G Music Accessories
COMBO - Musical instruments - Selmer Co. Inc.
COMBO - Pet products ☆ - Lazy Pet Products
COMBO - Recording label - Combo Records
COMBO - Refrigerators ☆ - Raritan Engineering Co. Inc.
COMBO - Sausages ☆ - Mr. Dell Foods
COMBO - Saw blades - Sandvik Saws & Tools
COMBO - Shampoos - Mennen Co.
COMBO - Thread ☆ - Perfect Thread Co. Inc.
COMBO 300 - Amplifiers–musical instrument - Peavey Electronics Corp.
COMBO-BLADE - Saw blades - M.K. Morse Co.
COMBO-CARTS - Dollies–industrial - Richard A. Taylor
COMBO-COMB - Huff & Co.
COMBO COOLERS - Desserts - Paradise Fat Free Italian Ice, Inc.
COMBO CRIB - Cribs–metal ☆ - Evenflo Juvenile Furniture Co.
COMBO GRILLE - Stoves - Amana Refrigeration Inc.
COMBO-GUARD-6-K - Pet products - Thomas Veterinary Drug
COMBO II - Locks–padlocks - Weiser Lock Corp.
COMBO KEYS - Musical instrument accessories ☆ - D & F Products Inc.
COMBO KILLER - Fishing lures - Sheldons', Inc.
COMBO KIT - First aid kits - Physicians & Nurses Manufacturing Corp.
COMBO KIT - Musical instrument accessories ☆ - Rico International
COMBO-LITE - Lighting fixtures - Swivelier Co. Inc.
COMBO-LON - Thread ☆ - Perfect Thread Co. Inc.
COMBO-PAC - Headphones - Avid Corp.
COMBO PACK A - Toys–airplanes - Paul K. Guillow Inc.
COMBO-PAK - Paper products - Georgia-Pacific Corp.
COMBO-PENCILS - Cosmetics - Cici Cosmetic Co.
COMBO PLUS - Printers–computer - Lucht Engineering Inc.
COMBO POINTS - Archery equipment - Saunders Archery Co.
COMBO ROCKER - Infant product ☆ - Century Products Co.
COMBO SEAT - Health care products - Temco Health Care
COMBO SILL - Window coverings - Combo Aluminum Products
COMBO-TIP - Dental equipment - Cross Country Paper Products, Inc.
COMBO-TWIST - Thread ☆ - Perfect Thread Co. Inc.
COMBOS - Snack foods - Mars, Inc.
COMBOTS - Games - Avalon Hill Game Co.

COMBOURG - Glassware–household - Durand International
COMBOW HUNTER - Hunting equipment - JRH Sport Industries, Inc.
COMBRUSH - Brushes–hair ☆ - Phillips Brush Corp.
COMBS-TO-GO! - Combs - Bravo International Corp.
COMBUSTION - Health care products ☆ - East Earth Herb Inc.
COMBUSTIONEER - Furnaces–electric ☆ - Will-Burt Co.
COMBYTE - Computer peripheral equipment - Combyte, Inc.
COMCAB - Tools–hand-operated - Wakefield Electronics Group Inc.
COMCARE - Hearing aids - Comcare International, Inc.
COMCENTER - Electrical equipment - Overhead Door Corp.
COMCO - Cleaning preparations–window - Commercial Plastics and Supply
  Inc.
COMCO - Electronic equipment ☆ - E.F. Johnson Co.
COMCOR - Dinnerware - Corning Inc.
COME ALIVE - Floor coverings–carpet and rugs ☆ - Cabin Crafts Carpets
COME ALIVE - Skin care products - Alacer Co.
COME ALIVE GRAY - Hair coloring preparations ☆ - Clairol Inc.
COME-ALONG - Construction equipment - J.E. Shaffer Co.
COME ALONG - Floor coverings–carpet and rugs ☆ - Cabin Crafts Carpets
COME BACK - Apparel and accessories ☆ - Glamorise Foundations Inc.
COME BACK BAG - Luggage - A. Rifkin Co.
COME CLEAN - Skin care products - Beaute, Inc.
COME CORRECT! - Apparel and accessories - James D. Young
COME FLY WITH ME SERIES - Video production - Jean A. Pogue
COME ON DOWN - Games - Mayfair Games, Inc.
COME OUT OF THE STONE AGE - Dental equipment - Silva Group
COME OUT SMILING - Underwear and nightwear ☆ - Lovable Co.
COME SUMMER - Colognes - Avon Products, Inc.
COME TO THE FAIR - Wallpaper ☆ - Sanitas Wallcoverings
COME TOGETHER - Greeting cards - Stanyan Record Co.
COMEAU - Food products - Wally Sea Products Corp.
COMEAUTION - Footwear - Agita Footwear, Inc.
COMEAUX CAPS - Caps–baseball - Comeaux Marketing, Inc.
COMEBACK CUP - Cups–plastic - Pepsico, Inc.
COMEDONE SOLUTION - Health care products - Dr. Babor Natural Cosmetics
COMEDOSTAT - Skin care products - P.P.R.L., Inc.
COMEDY CENTRAL - Games - Comedy Partners
COMEDY IS KING - Greeting cards - Gallant Greetings Corp.
COMEDY LABEL, THE - Recording label - Score Productions, Inc.
COMEGA - Food products ☆ - Upsher-Smith Laboratories, Inc.
COME'N GET IT - Dog food - Nestle USA
COMERAGH - Earthenware ☆ - Waterford Wedgewood USA, Inc.
COMERRICO - Food products ☆ - Nokota Foods Corp.
COMES TO LIFE - Audio equipment - Yes! Entertainment Corp.
COMET - Balls - Star Sports, Inc.
COMET - Bathroom fixtures - Shower-Rite Corp.
COMET - Bicycles - Hunt-Wilde Corp.
COMET - Boats–canoes - Formula Yachts
COMET - Brushes–paint - Corona Brushes Inc.
COMET - Chocolate candy - C. J. Van Houten & Zoon, Inc.
COMET - Cleaning preparations - Procter & Gamble Co.
COMET - Computer software - Heart Watchers International Inc.
COMET - Computer software - University Corp. for Atmospheric Research
COMET - Cups–plastic - WNA Comet
COMET - Electronic equipment - Eaton Corp.
COMET - Electronic equipment ☆ - Da-Lite Screen Co. Inc.
COMET - Erasers ☆ - Faber-Castell Corp.
COMET - Fishing lures - Sheldons', Inc.
COMET - Floor coverings - American Floor Products Co. Inc.
COMET - Floor coverings - Congoleum Corp.
COMET - Floor coverings–carpet and rugs ☆ - Galaxy Carpet Mills Inc.
COMET - Food products - De Choix Specialty Foods Co.
COMET - Garden equipment - H.D. Hudson Manufacturing Co.
COMET - Gasoline - Ashland Oil, Inc.
COMET - Glassware–household - Rezler & Howell Co.
COMET - Hardware - Alumatic Corp. of America
COMET - Harmonicas - Hohner Inc.
COMET - Housewares ☆ - Shepherd Products U.S. Inc.
COMET - Ice cream cones - Nabisco Foods Group
COMET - Indoor-outdoor carpet, synthetic turf - Instant Turf Industries Inc.
COMET - Jewelry ☆ - Barr Enterprises Inc.
COMET - Key rings - Ford Motor Co.
COMET - Lanterns–kerosene ☆ - R.E. Dietz Co.
COMET - Locks–door - Arrow Lock Manufacturing Co.
COMET - Measuring tapes, tools - U.S. Tape Co.
COMET - Mobile homes - Commodore Corp.

☆ = Now out of production

COMET - Mops - Golden Star Inc.

COMET - Motor vehicles–automobiles ☆ - Ford Motor Co. (Lincoln-Mercury Div.)

COMET - Paving materials–stone - Hessit Works, Inc.

COMET - Ribbons–inked - Eaton Allen Ko-Rec-Type Corp.

COMET - Rice - Comet American Marketing

COMET - Self-inking daters, numberers, time stamps - Consolidated Stamp Manufacturing Co. Inc.

COMET - Sporting goods - Star Line Baton Co. Inc.

COMET - Sporting goods ☆ - Ronson Consumer Products Corp.

COMET - Toys–airplanes - Comet Montrose Ltd.

COMET - Toys–models ☆ - Estes Industries

COMET - Trailers–travel - Starcraft Corp.

COMET - Turpentine ☆ - Reliable Finishing Products, Inc.

COMET ACOUSTICS - Computer software - Automated Analysis Corp.

COMET CAT - Toys - Mattel, Inc.

COMET CHOCOLATE - Candy - Comet Confectionery Inc.

COMET FLYER - Toys - Strombecker Corp.

COMET HEAVY DUTY - Cleaning preparations–household - Procter & Gamble Co.

COMET II - Lawn mowers - Actava Group Inc.

COMET LIQUID GEL BLEACH + CLEANER - Cleaning preparations - Procter & Gamble Co.

COMET-NORTH PACIFIC - Toys–airplanes - Comet Montrose Ltd.

COMET/VISION - Computer software - Automated Analysis Corp.

COMET WARRIORS - Toys - Mattel, Inc.

COMET WATCH - Computer software ☆ - Zephyr Services

COMETROID - Toys - Mattel, Inc.

COMETY - Bedding–linen - Dan River Inc.

COMEX SYSTEMS - Radio communications equipment - Comex Systems Co.

COMFAB - Fabrics - Russell Athletic Div.

COMFALOFT - Pillows - Pillowtex Corp.

COMFALOFT PLUS - Pillows - Pillowtex Corp.

COMFALOFT SLEEP SYSTEM - Pillows - Pillowtex Corp.

COMFAPEDIC - Mattresses - Bemco Associates, Inc.

COMFEE CASUALS - Health care products ☆ - Betty Dain Creations Inc.

COMFEES+ - Paper–tissue - Al Nyman and Son

COMFEES BY MAGNIVISION - Eyeglasses - Al Nyman and Son

COMFEET - Health care products - Total Medical Systems Inc.

COMFEX 2000 - Footwear ☆ - Home Court International, Ltd.

COMFIDERM - Hair care products - Amethyst Investment Group, Inc.

COMFIT - Footwear - New Balance Athletic Shoe, Inc.

COMFITABLES - Underwear and nightwear - Sara Lee Corp.

COMFLO - Apparel and accessories - Abel Industries Inc.

COMFO CLASSIC - Respirators - Mine Safety Appliances Co.

COMFO-FLEX - Medical apparatus - Nelkin/Piper Health Products

COMFO LOUNGER - Recliners - Norwalk Furniture Corp.

COMFO-SEAT - Chairs–plastic ☆ - Plasticoid Manufacturing Inc.

COMFO-TEX - Pharmaceutical preparations - Tetra Medical Supply Corp.

COMFO TOPS - Hosiery - Allstate Hosiery Sales Inc.

COMFOLAX - Laxatives - G. D. Searle & Co.

COMFOLETTE - Girdles ☆ - Playtex Apparel, Inc.

COMFOOT - Podiatric product - Aetna Felt Corp.

COMFOR-TEEN - Apparel–women's - Wacoal America Inc.

COMFOR-TIP - Hair care products - Goody Products, Inc.

COMFOR-TOES - Socks - Viking Technology Inc.

COMFORCE - Computer software - Snickelways, Inc.

COMFORCLEERS - Medical apparatus - Smithers Medical Products, Inc.

COMFORDENT - Denture cleaners - Comfordent

COMFORDOME - Tools - Klein Tools Inc.

COMFOREL - Foam rubber - E.I. Dupont de Nemours and Co.

COMFORETTE - Hair care products ☆ - Wella Corp. (Consumer Products Div.)

COMFORLON - Fabrics–broadcloth - Collins & Aikman Corp.

COMFORMAX - Fabrics - E.I. Dupont de Nemours and Co.

COMFORSHEAR - Knives–carving - Ernestn Beltrami

COMFORSORB - Fabrics - E.I. Dupont de Nemours and Co.

COMFORSPAN - Fabrics - E.I. Dupont de Nemours and Co.

COMFORT - Apparel–athletic - Walking Co.

COMFORT - Blinds–venetian - Custom Shade Co.

COMFORT - Boating equipment and accessories - Ocean Kayak, Inc.

COMFORT - Contact lenses ☆ - Camelot Laboratories

COMFORT - Diapers–disposable ☆ - Mount Vernon Mills Inc.

COMFORT - Furniture - Alvin and Co. Inc.

COMFORT - Irons–electric - Sunbeam-Oster Household Products

COMFORT - Mattresses - Kingsdown, Inc.

COMFORT - Medical apparatus - Guards Corp.

COMFORT - Pencils ☆ - Empire Berol USA

COMFORT - Pharmaceutical preparations - Gynetech Laboratories, Ltd.

COMFORT - Slippers ☆ - Okawa Trading

COMFORT - Teas–herbal ☆ - Oakmont Investments Co.

COMFORT - Veterinary nutritional supplements - Landco

COMFORT - Vitamins and nutritional supplements - Lander Corp.

COMFORT - Vitamins and nutritional supplements - Solaray

COMFORT 12 - Yarn ☆ - Caron International Inc.

COMFORT 88 - Hair care products - Fromm Industries

COMFORT ADVANTAGE WINDOW, THE - Windows - Comfort Window & Door Corp.

COMFORT/AID - Medical apparatus - Durango Sport and Travel, Inc.

COMFORT AIDS - Foundation accessories - Nuvogue Creations

COMFORT-AIR - Respirators - U.S. Safety Corp.

COMFORT-AIRE - Air conditioning equipment - Heat Controller Inc.

COMFORT-AIRE - Pet products - Kennel-Aire Inc.

COMFORT AIRE - Skin care products - Collins Manufacturing Co.

COMFORT-AIRE-PAC - Air conditioning equipment ☆ - Heat Controller Inc.

COMFORT-AIRE TWIN-PAC - Air conditioning equipment ☆ - Heat Controller Inc.

COMFORT BAND - Apparel and accessories - Playtex Apparel, Inc.

COMFORT BAND - Apparel stores–lingerie - Formflex Foundations Inc.

COMFORT BASE - Floor coverings - Homasote Co.

COMFORT BLEND - Fabrics - Standard Textile Co., Inc.

COMFORT BLEND - Pillows - American Fiber Industries Corp.

COMFORT BLEND - Underwear and nightwear - Sara Lee Corp.

COMFORT BOUNCER SEAT - Infant product - Summer Infant Products Inc.

COMFORT BREEZE - Fans–electric - Hunter Fan Co.

COMFORT CAB - Trucks - Capacity of Texas, Inc.

COMFORT CALCULATOR - Computer software - Blade Software, Inc.

COMFORT CARE - Diapers–disposable - Paper-Pak Products, Inc.

COMFORT CARE - Mattresses - Cosco, Inc.

COMFORT CARE - Medical apparatus - CH Administration, Inc.

COMFORT CARE - Ophthalmic goods - Allergan, Inc.

COMFORT CATH - Health care products - Sierra Laboratories Inc.

COMFORT CENTRAL - Comforters - Pacific Coast Feather Co.

COMFORT CHAIR - Medical apparatus - Modern Healthcare Products Inc.

COMFORT CHOICE - Mattresses - Cosco, Inc.

COMFORT CLEAN - Cleaning equipment - Contec, Inc.

COMFORT CLINIC - Cushions - Bio Clinic Corp.

COMFORT CLIP - Seat belts - Century Products Co.

COMFORT CLOUD - Health care products - Med Foam

COMFORT CLUSTER - Pillows - American Fiber Industries Corp.

COMFORT COCKTAILS - Fruit-flavored cordial ☆ - Brown-Forman Corp.

COMFORT COLLECTION, THE - Gowns–hospital - Salk Co. Inc.

COMFORT COLORS - Underwear and nightwear - Sara Lee Knit Products Inc.

COMFORT CONDITIONER - Air purification systems - Toastmaster Inc.

COMFORT CONSTRUCTION - Footwear - AmAsia International Ltd.

COMFORT CONTACTS - Pet products - Perimeter Technologies, Inc.

COMFORT CONTROL - Health care products - Electropedic Manufacturing Corp.

COMFORT CONTROL - Heating equipment ☆ - Sealy Inc.

COMFORT CONTROL II - Product description unknown - Somfy Systems Inc.

COMFORT COOLER - Fans–electric - Triangle Engineering

COMFORT CORE - Pillows - Pacific Coast Feather Co.

COMFORT CORNER - Bathtubs–enameled - Pearl Baths Inc.

COMFORT COVER - Infant product - Pansy Ellen Products, Inc.

COMFORT CRAFTED - Footwear - Wolverine World Wide, Inc.

COMFORT CRAFTED - Thermostats - Conservation Services Group, Inc.

COMFORT CRATERS - Mattress pads ☆ - All-Foam Products Co.

COMFORT CREATIONS - Pillows - Carpenter Co.

COMFORT CREST - Furnaces–electric ☆ - White Outdoor Products Inc.

COMFORT CRIMP - Tools - Thomas & Betts Holdings, Inc.

COMFORT CROWN - Health care products ☆ - Bodyline Comfort Systems

COMFORT CRUTCH - Crutches - Tubular Fabricators Industry, Inc.

COMFORT CUISINE - Bakery products - Lasting Impression, Inc.

COMFORT-CURVE - Apparel and accessories ☆ - Warnaco Inc.

COMFORT CURVE - Drums–musical instruments - LP Music Group

COMFORT CURVE - Footwear - Wolverine World Wide, Inc.

COMFORT CURVE - Medical apparatus - Wahl Clipper Corp.

COMFORT CUSHION - Cushions - The Family Care Co.

COMFORT CUSHION - Infant product - Tailored Baby Inc.

COMFORT CUSHION - Paper products - Crosstex

COMFORT CUT - Hair care products - Dubl Duck/Jet Set Inc.

COMFORT-DESIGN - Tampons - Kimberly-Clark Corp.

COMFORT-DRIV - Screw drivers - A.T. & G. Co., Inc.

COMFORT DROPS - Ophthalmic goods - Barnes-Hind Inc.
COMFORT E - Glass products - AFG Industries Inc. (Glass Group Div.)
COMFORT E2 - Glass products - AFG Industries Inc. (Glass Group Div.)
COMFORT EAR - Plugs–ear - All American Mold Laboratories Inc.
COMFORT EAR - Telephone accessories - Hitec Group International, Inc.
COMFORT-EASE - Respirators - Parmelee Industries, Inc.
COMFORT-EASE - Respirators - U.S. Safety Corp.
COMFORT EASE - Shoes - Blair Corp.
COMFORT-ENGINEERED FOR YOUR FEET - Footwear - Saramar Corp.
COMFORT ENHANCER - Mattresses - Spring Air Bedding Inc.
COMFORT EYE DROPS - Pharmaceutical preparations ☆ - Akorn Inc.
COMFORT-EZE - Mats - Superior Manufacturing Group/Notrax Floor Matting
COMFORT-EZE - Sanitary paper - Maurice H. Cornellier
COMFORT-EZE - Wheelchairs - Control Products
COMFORT FIT - Apparel–women's - Eddie Haggar Ltd., Inc.
COMFORT FIT - Health care products - Geri-Care Products, LLC
COMFORT-FIT - Medical apparatus - Professional's Choice Sports Medicine Products, Inc.
COMFORT FLAME - Heaters–gas - Desa International, Inc.
COMFORT FLEX - Footwear - Wolverine World Wide, Inc.
COMFORT FLEX - Frames–eyeglass - Kenmark Optical Co.
COMFORT FLEX - Mattresses - Spring Air Bedding Inc.
COMFORT-FLOAT - Furniture–upholstered ☆ - Mersman Furniture Co.
COMFORT FLOW - Fans–electric - Homestead Products
COMFORT FORCE - Shoe insoles - Red Wing Shoe Co. Inc.
COMFORT FORM - Bicycles - Schwinn Cycling & Fitness Inc.
COMFORT FORMULA - Footwear - Tohkutsu America Corp.
COMFORT FRAME - Brassieres (Bras) - S & S Industries, Inc.
COMFORT-GARD - Apparel and accessories - Durafab Inc.
COMFORT-GLIDE - Medical apparatus - American Ergonomics Corp.
COMFORT GLOW - Electronic equipment - Century Products Co.
COMFORT GLOW - Heaters–space - Desa International, Inc.
COMFORT GLOW PLUS - Infant product - Century Products Co.
COMFORT GRIP - Brushes–hair ☆ - Belson Products
COMFORT-GRIP - Denture materials - Sentage Corp.
COMFORT GRIP - Hair care products - Fromm Industries
COMFORT GRIP - Health care products - Maddak Inc.
COMFORT GUARD - Apparel and accessories - Scott Paper Co.
COMFORT GUARD - Mattresses - Kingsdown, Inc.
COMFORT HOURS - Apparel and accessories - Playtex Apparel, Inc.
COMFORT HOURS - Tampons - Johnson & Johnson
COMFORT I ULTRA - Athletic shoes - Reebok International Ltd.
COMFORT INNS - Housewares stores - Choice Hotels International Inc.
COMFORT KEY - Remote-control automobile starter - Comfort Key Corp.
COMFORT KEY - Tools - L. Lawrence Products Inc.
COMFORT KIT - Ophthalmic goods - Karlen Manufacturing, Inc.
COMFORT LENSES - Eyeglasses - Transitions Optical, Inc.
COMFORT-LINE - Furniture - Birmingham Stove & Range Co.
COMFORT LINK - Motor vehicle parts and accessories - Lin-Bil Products, Inc.
COMFORT LITES - Footwear–men's - Melville Corp.
COMFORT LOCK - Comforters - Pacific Coast Feather Co.
COMFORT LOUNGER - Mattresses - HMI Industries Inc.
COMFORT-LUME - Lighting fixtures - Legion Lighting Co., Inc.
COMFORT MAKER - Heating and cooling systems - Inter-City Products Corp. (USA)
COMFORT MAKERS, THE - Cushions - Master Manufacturing Co., Inc.
COMFORT MASTER - Uniforms–tailored - Topps Manufacturing Co.
COMFORT MATE - Bedding–linen - Dynamic Development
COMFORT MATE - Cushions - Encore Products Inc.
COMFORT-MATE - Health care products - Equi-Tron Inc.
COMFORT MATE - Health care products - Sierra Laboratories Inc.
COMFORT-ME - Skin care products - Grandpa Brands Co.
COMFORT MED - Health care products - Comfort Med
COMFORT MIST - Thermostats ☆ - Field Controls Co.
COMFORT NET - Radios - Motorola, Inc. (Land Mobile Products Sector)
COMFORT PADS - Medical apparatus - Ventura Enterprises, Inc.
COMFORT PAGE - Pagers - McCaw Cellular Communications, Inc.
COMFORT PERCH - Pet products - Pets International, Ltd.
COMFORT PERSONAL LUBRICANT - Skin-care products - Dynamic Concepts, Inc.
COMFORT PLACE - Pet products - Pets International, Ltd.
COMFORT PLUS - Bicycle parts and accessories - Diamondback
COMFORT PLUS - Constrictor seal - Osbon Medical Systems, Ltd.
COMFORT PLUS - Electric heaters - Cotter & Co.
COMFORT PLUS - Floor coverings–carpet and rugs - Milliken & Co.
COMFORT PLUS - Garden equipment - Ames Lawn & Garden Tool Co.

COMFORT PLUS - Gloves - Granet Inc.
COMFORT-PLUS - Health care products - Biotech Ltd.
COMFORT PLUS - Health care products - Omron Healthcare, Inc.
COMFORT PLUS - Orthopedic support devices ☆ - Invacare Corp.
COMFORT PLUS - Shoes - Kobacker Co.
COMFORT PLUS - Shoes - Premier Brands of America
COMFORT PLUS - Skin care products - Collins Manufacturing Co.
COMFORT POINT - Computer peripheral equipment - GBM Design
COMFORT PORTS - Footwear - United States Shoe Corp.
COMFORT PRINT - Publisher's imprints - Thomas Nelson, Inc.
COMFORT PRO - Health care products - Biotech Ltd.
COMFORT PROMISE - Laxatives - Purdue Frederick Co.
COMFORT QUILT - Health care products - Geri-Care Products, LLC
COMFORT-RATED - Fabrics - Guilford Mills, Inc.
COMFORT-REST - Air beds - Intex Recreation Corp.
COMFORT REST - Bathroom accessories - Better Sleep, Inc.
COMFORT RIBS - Underwear and nightwear - Jockey International, Inc.
COMFORT RIDE - Seats–automobile ☆ - Cosco, Inc.
COMFORT RIDE SLEEVE - Seat belts - Indiana Mills & Manufacturing, Inc.
COMFORT RITE - Footwear - Redwood Sportswear Ltd.
COMFORT SCIENCE - Footwear - James L. Throneburg
COMFORT SEAL - Glass products - AFG Industries Inc. (Glass Group Div.)
COMFORT SEAL - Health care products - Sierra Laboratories Inc.
COMFORT SEAT - Seat covers - Gold Inc.
COMFORT SEAT - Toilet seats - Astro Nautics Co. Inc.
COMFORT SENSATION - Apparel–women's - Cupid Foundations Inc.
COMFORT SENSOR - Heaters–gas - Toastmaster Inc.
COMFORT SERIES - Doors–vinyl - Gerkin Windows & Doors
COMFORT SERIES - Furniture - Ohio Mattress Co.
COMFORT SERIES - Portable lamps - Pacific Trends Lamp & Lighting Products, Inc.
COMFORT SERIES VINYL - Windows–vinyl - Gerkin Windows & Doors
COMFORT SHADE - Fabrics–linen - West Point-Pepperell Inc.
COMFORT SHAPER - Foundation garments–women's - Saramar Corp.
COMFORT SHOE SPECIALISTS - Shoes - Comfort Shoe Specialists, Inc.
COMFORT SHOWCASE - Chairs–upholstered - Lane Co. Inc.
COMFORT SILKIE - Bedding–linen - Comfort Silkie Co. Inc.
COMFORT SLEEPER - Pillows - Bio Clinic Corp.
COMFORT SOUND - Hearing aids - Telex Communications, Inc.
COMFORT SPECTRUM - Pillows ☆ - Lumex, Inc.
COMFORT SPIRAL - Pillows - American Fiber Industries Corp.
COMFORT SPOON - Shoes - Howard Davis
COMFORT SPRING TEMPLES - Sunglasses - Riviera Trading, Inc.
COMFORT-STAT - Thermostats - Desa International, Inc.
COMFORT STATION - Pet products - Pets International, Ltd.
COMFORT STRIDE - Panty hose - No Nonsense Fashions Inc.
COMFORT SUITES - Hotels and motels - Choice Hotels International Inc.
COMFORT SYSTEM - Footwear - Thom McAn Shoe Co.
COMFORT SYSTEM - Shoes - Melville Corp.
COMFORT TEARS - Pharmaceutical preparations ☆ - Akorn Inc.
COMFORT-TEMP - Bathroom fixtures - Universal-Rundle Corp.
COMFORT TI - Glass products - AFG Industries Inc. (Glass Group Div.)
COMFORT TIPS - Pet collars - Coastal Pet Products, Inc.
COMFORT TOO! - Footwear - Pic 'n Pay Stores, Inc.
COMFORT TOUCH - Bedding–linen - J.C. Penney Co., Inc.
COMFORT-TOUCH - Fans–electric - Casablanca Fan Co.
COMFORT TOUCH - Footwear–women's ☆ - E.S. Originals, Inc.
COMFORT TOUCH - Health care products - Geri-Care Products, LLC
COMFORT TOUCH - Health care products - Omron Healthcare, Inc.
COMFORT-TRAC - Pillows - Banyan Research, Inc.
COMFORT TRAP - Furniture - Homecrest Industries Inc.
COMFORT TREAD - Furniture - Rubbermaid Office Products Inc.
COMFORT TUFF - Apparel and accessories - Tingley Rubber Corp.
COMFORT WALK - Exercising equipment - Fitness Solutions, Inc.
COMFORT WEAVE - Sanitary napkins - Paragon Trade Brands, Inc.
COMFORT WRAP - Medical apparatus - Nature's Spa, Inc.
COMFORT WRITER - Pens–fountain - A.T.X. International, Inc.
COMFORT ZONE - Aluminum products - Reynolds Metals Co.
COMFORT ZONE - Bedding–linen - E.R. Carpenter Co.
COMFORT ZONE - Beverages–alcohol - Brown-Forman Corp.
COMFORT ZONE - Cushions - ACCO USA, Inc.
COMFORT ZONE - Eyeglasses - Magnivision, Inc.
COMFORT ZONE - Fuel additives - Index Industries Inc.
COMFORT ZONE - Hosiery - Alba-Waldensian, Inc.
COMFORT ZONE - Mats - Cactus Mat Manufacturing Co.
COMFORT ZONE - Paints ☆ - Evans Paint

COMFORT ZONE - Skin care products - Body Comfort Inc.
COMFORT ZONE - Underwear and nightwear - Exquisite Form Industries
COMFORT ZONE PALM PAD - Sporting goods - Lisco, Inc.
COMFORTABLES - Furniture ☆ - Mersman Furniture Co.
COMFORTABLY CLEAN - Cleaning preparations–household - Empire Brushes, Inc.
COMFORTAGE INDUSTRIES - Stationary - Simex International, Inc.
COMFORTAIRE - Air mattresses - Park Place Corp.
COMFORTASK - Chairs–metal - Hon Co.
COMFORTCAINE - Skin care products - Key West Aloe Inc.
COMFORTCALE - Bedding–linen - Fieldcrest Cannon, Inc.
COMFORTCARE - Beds–metal - HARD Manufacturing Co. Inc.
COMFORTEASE - Health care products - Medtronic Nortech
COMFORTEC - Medical apparatus - Sandhill Scientific, Inc.
COMFORTECH - Floor coverings - Duramax, Inc.
COMFORTECH - Footwear - Interco Inc.
COMFORTEDGE - Windows - Louisiana-Pacific Corp.
COMFORTER - Controls–heating systems - Comforter Stove Works
COMFORTER CLOTHES - Bedspreads - Dan River Inc.
COMFORTER SACK - Bedding–linen - Perfect Fit Industries, Inc.
COMFORTERCUSHION - Pillows - Pacific Coast Feather Co.
COMFORTERRY - Bedding–linen - Fieldcrest Cannon, Inc.
COMFORTERS - Apparel–women's - Jockey International, Inc.
COMFORTEX - Cushions and mattresses - Comfortex Inc.
COMFORTEX - Draperies - Comfortex Corp.
COMFORTEX - Fabrics–spandex - Nfa Corp.
COMFORTEX - Window coverings - Vertical Blind Factory
COMFORTFLEX - Apparel and accessories - Playtex Apparel, Inc.
COMFORTFLOR - Floor coverings - Congoleum Corp.
COMFORTFLOW - Infant product - Playtex Beauty Care, Inc.
COMFORTGUIDE - Thermometers - Taylor Environmental Instruments
COMFORTHOLD - Comforters - Pacific Coast Feather Co.
COMFORTIME - Apparel and accessories - Playtex Apparel, Inc.
COMFORTINE - Pharmaceutical preparations ☆ - Dermik Laboratories Inc.
COMFORTING MOMENTS - Pillows - Pacific Coast Feather Co.
COMFORTING SOLUTION - Cosmetics - Origins Natural Resources Inc.
COMFORTIP - Health care products - C.B. Fleet Co. Inc.
COMFORTKNIT - Hosiery - Alba-Waldensian, Inc.
COMFORTLINE - Furniture - Stenograph Corp.
COMFORTLINE - Heaters–space - Emerson Electric Co.
COMFORTLINE - Mattresses - Hill Rom, Inc.
COMFORTLITE - Comforters - Pacific Coast Feather Co.
COMFORTMAKER - Office supplies - Master Caster Co.
COMFORTMASTER - Apparel–men's - Edmonton Manufacturing Co.
COMFORTMATE - Bed linens - Pillowtex Corp.
COMFORTMATES - Furniture - Lane Co. Inc.
COMFORTMETER - Thermometers - Taylor Environmental Instruments
COMFORTO - Furniture - Haworth, Inc.
COMFORTONE - Hearing aids - Professional Hearing Aid Service
COMFORTOUCH - Health care products - Borda Products Inc.
COMFORTPAK - Pharmaceutical preparations - Comfortpak, Inc.
COMFORTROL - Windows ☆ - Louisiana-Pacific Corp.
COMFORTRON - Beds–hospital - Sci-O-Tech Inc.
COMFORTS - Footwear - Rockport Co. Inc.
COMFORTS BY SHADOWLINE - Apparel–women's - ShadowLine Inc.
COMFORTS OF HOME - Wallpaper - Taylor Wallcoverings Inc.
COMFORTSOFT - Fabric - Sara Lee Corp.
COMFORTSTEPS - Footwear - Home Shopping Club, Inc.
COMFORTSTITCH - Thread ☆ - Perfect Thread Co. Inc.
COMFORTSUEDE - Bedding–linen - Fieldcrest Cannon, Inc.
COMFORTTECH - Floor coverings - Johnsonite Flooring Products
COMFORTUB - Bathroom fixtures - Artesian Industries
COMFORTWEAR - Apparel and accessories - Comfortwear, Inc.
COMFORTWEAR - Floor coverings–carpet and rugs - General Felt Industries, Inc.
COMFORTWORKS - Computer software ☆ - Carrier Corp.
COMFORTWORKS - Shoes - R. Josephs Sportswear, Inc.
COMFORTYPE - Braces–orthopedic - William H. Terbrack
COMFREE - Vitamins and nutritional supplements - Solaray
COMFREL - Medical apparatus - Schering-Plough Healthcare Products, Inc.
COMFREY - Health care products - Country Comfort
COMFREY FARMS - Health care products - Comfrey International Co.
COMFY - Apparel and accessories - Raven Industries Inc.
COMFY - Infant product - Judkins Co.
COMFY - Pet products - Fashion Pet Accessories Inc.
COMFY - Pet products - J & M Stuart Co.

COMFY - Shoes - Daniel Green Co.
COMFY - Slip covers - Reeves Brothers Inc.
COMFY-BACK - Health care products - Comfy-Back/E.J. Evans
COMFY-BACK - Health care products - Scott Specialties, Inc.
COMFY BEDS - Pet products ☆ - American Cat Emporium
COMFY CARE - Breast shields - International Design Manufacturing Inc.
COMFY COZY - Linen - Margaret V. Schafer
COMFY CUP - Insulating materials - Kitchen Klothware Co.
COMFY CUSHION - Infant product - Stork Stuff
COMFY CUSHION - Infant product ☆ - Century Products Co.
COMFY CUSHIONS - Pet products ☆ - American Cat Emporium
COMFY-DRY - Bra pads - International Design Manufacturing Inc.
COMFY-EYES - Eyeglasses - Cynthia L. Sadowsky
COMFY-FIT CAR-NAP PILLOW - Infant product - TL Care Inc.
COMFY-FIT CUSHION - Infant product - TL Care Inc.
COMFY READYMADE - Slip covers - Reeves Brothers Inc.
COMFY SEAT - Infant product - Pansy Ellen Products, Inc.
COMFY SKI - Apparel–athletic - Raven Industries Inc.
COMFY SPLINT - Orthopedic products - Lenjoy Engineering, Inc.
COMFY TALK - Telephone accessories ☆ - Blue Ridge International Products Co., Inc.
COMFY WIPE WARMER - Infant product - Rock-A-Bye Baby Inc.
COMHIST - Pharmaceutical preparations - Norwich-Eaton Pharmaceuticals
COMIC CARD GAME - Games ☆ - Milton Bradley Co.
COMIC CHARACTERS - Computer software ☆ - Broderbund Software, Inc.
COMIC DEFENSE SYSTEM CD - Binders - Capital City Distribution, Inc.
COMIC DOMINOES - Games ☆ - Warren Industries Inc.
COMIC FACE POPS - Candy - Murray-Allen International Inc.
COMIC HERO PLAY CASES - Games ☆ - CBS Toys
COMIC PACK - Beverages - Kraft Food Ingredients Corp.
COMIC SHELL - Plastic holders - Collectors Products Corp.
COMIC STOR - Novelty items - Rembrandt Photo Services
COMIC STRIPS - Apparel and accessories - Barbara Thomas Enterprises Inc.
COMIC STRIPS - Bandages - Futuro Inc.
COMIC TRUTH - Apparel–athletic - J.C. Penney Co., Inc.
COMIC WORKS - Computer software - Mindscape Software Inc.
COMICASE - Plastics - Collectors Products Corp.
COMICOVERS - Bags - Moondog's Inc.
COMINA - Floor coverings ☆ - Azrock Commercial Flooring
COMING ATTRACTION - Skin care products - Ritornelle Inc.
COMING ATTRACTIONS - Sporting goods - Coming Attractions
COMING HOME - Wallpaper - Lin-Gor Wallcoverings
COMING TO THE RESCUE OF SHY PEOPLE EVERYWHERE - Dolls - Direct Connect International Inc.
COMING UP ROSES - Wallpaper ☆ - Wiffle Hill Studio
COMIT - Computer software - Professional Computing Resources, Inc.
COMITE - Insecticides - Uniroyal Chemical Co. Inc. (Crop Protection Div.)
COMITROL - Food products machinery - Urschel Laboratories Inc.
COMIX - Animal feeds - Farmland Industries Inc.
COMIX - Toys - Jak-Pak Inc.
COMIX ZONE - Computer software - Sega of America, Inc.
COMLINEAR - Electronic equipment - Comlinear Corp.
COMLINK - Communications equipment–mobile - Telex Communications, Inc.
COMM DESK - Computer software - MCI International
COMM MASTER - Office machines - Diebold Inc.
COMM QUEST TECHNOLOGIES, INC. - Computers - CommQuest Technologies, Inc.
COMMANCHE - Apparel and accessories - Tropical Garment Manufacturing Co.
COMMANCHE - Furniture - Bean Station Furniture Factory Inc.
COMMAND - Cleaning preparations - Uncle Sam Chemical Co., Inc.
COMMAND - Computer software ☆ - Pinpoint Publishing
COMMAND - Detergents - Kimberly-Clark Corp.
COMMAND - Doors–metal - Caradon Doors and Windows, Inc.
COMMAND - Engines–marine - Kohler Co.
COMMAND - Fabrics–tapestry ☆ - Coloroll Inc.
COMMAND - Furniture - Command Products Co.
COMMAND - Golfing equipment - TT Sports Inc.
COMMAND - Motor vehicle parts and accessories - Morse Controls
COMMAND - Recording label - Command Records
COMMAND - Skin care products - Alberto-Culver Co.
COMMAND 54 - Fabrics–tapestry ☆ - Coloroll Inc.
COMMAND ACOUSTICALS - Fabrics–tapestry ☆ - Coloroll Inc.
COMMAND ADVENTURES - Video games - Future Visionary, Inc.
COMMAND ADVENTURES: STARSHIP - Video games - Future Vision
COMMAND-AIRE - Heat pumps - American Standard Inc.

☆ = Now out of production

COMMAND AND CONQUER - Computer peripheral equipment - Westwood Studios, Inc.

COMMAND ANTIVIRUS - Computer software - Command Software Systems, Inc.

COMMAND/BUTTON LUMENATOR - Flashlights ☆ - Bridgeport Metal Goods Manufacturing Co.

COMMAND CENTER - Desks - Studio RTA, Inc.

COMMAND CENTER - Electronics equipment - Crestron Electronics Inc.

COMMAND CENTER - Housewares - Butcher Co.

COMMAND CENTER - Marine rigging - Outboard Marine Corp.

COMMAND CENTER - Toys - Tonka Corp.

COMMAND CENTRAL - Computers ☆ - Evans International Inc.

COMMAND CLASSICS - Fabrics–tapestry ☆ - Coloroll Inc.

COMMAND COMMUNICATIONS INC. - Electronic equipment - Command Communications, Inc.

COMMAND CONSOLE - Electrical equipment - Trippe Manufacturing Co. Inc.

COMMAND CONTROL - Games - Hasbro, Inc.

COMMAND CONTROL - Toys–models - Estes Industries

COMMAND CONTROL CENTER - Computer peripheral equipment - Interactive Products Corp.

COMMAND COORDINATES - Fabrics–tapestry ☆ - Coloroll Inc.

COMMAND EXPRESS - Fabrics–tapestry ☆ - Coloroll Inc.

COMMAND HQ - Computer software ☆ - Microprose Software, Inc.

COMMAND LOUNGER - Furniture - Rojan Manufacturing Co.

COMMAND MODULE - Remote control devices - Eiki International Inc.

COMMAND-PAK - Electronic equipment - Apollo Audiovisual Div.

COMMAND PERFORMANCE - Cigars - General Cigar Co., Inc.

COMMAND PERFORMANCE - Finishing agents - Calgon Vestal Laboratories

COMMAND PERFORMANCE - Floor coverings - Beaulieu of America, Inc.

COMMAND PERFORMANCE - Televisions - General Electric Co.

COMMAND PERFORMER - Electronic equipment - Arion Corp.

COMMAND/POST - Computer software - Boole & Babbage, Inc.

COMMAND POST - Radio communications equipment - Gamber-Johnson Inc.

COMMAND POST - Telephones–cellular - Braley Communication Systems Inc.

COMMAND PRO - Communications equipment - Remtron, Inc.

COMMAND RECORDER - Electronic equipment - Arion Corp.

COMMAND SHIP INVASION - Games - McJay Game Co.

COMMAND SPANISH - Computer software - Command Spanish

COMMAND TANK - Toys–automobiles - Mattel, Inc.

COMMAND TECHNOLOGIES - Amplifiers - Command Technologies Inc.

COMMAND-TEX - Fabrics–tapestry ☆ - Coloroll Inc.

COMMAND-TEX AMBASSADOR - Fabrics–tapestry ☆ - Coloroll Inc.

COMMAND, THE - Uniforms–tailored - Fechheimer Brothers Co.

COMMAND-TRAC - Computer software - Whitaker Corp.

COMMAND-TRAC - Motor vehicles–jeeps - DaimlerChrysler

COMMANDAIRE - Actuators–hydraulic - ITT Industries, Inc.

COMMANDANT - Boats–motor ☆ - Larson Boat Div.

COMMANDE - Electronic equipment - Kaman Music Corp.

COMMANDER - Apparel and accessories - Walls Industries, Inc.

COMMANDER - Audio equipment - Pro-Co. Sound Co. Inc.

COMMANDER - Audio equipment - Valley Audio Products, Inc.

COMMANDER - Binoculars - Pioneer Marketing & Research, Inc.

COMMANDER - Binoculars ☆ - Bausch & Lomb Inc.

COMMANDER - Boats - Clark Craft Boat Co.

COMMANDER - Boats - O.M.C. Aluminum Boat Group

COMMANDER - Boats–motor - Commander Marine

COMMANDER - Boats–motor ☆ - Black River Canoes

COMMANDER - Boats–motor ☆ - Chris Craft Boats

COMMANDER - Boats–motor ☆ - Lund Boat Co.

COMMANDER - Boats–pontoons ☆ - Harris-Kayot Inc.

COMMANDER - Brushes–paint ☆ - PPG Industries, Inc.

COMMANDER - Caulking guns - Great American Marketing, Inc.

COMMANDER - Computers - Cochran Undersea Technology Div.

COMMANDER - Electrical equipment - Interstitial Systems

COMMANDER - Electronic equipment - Diversey Corp.

COMMANDER - Fabrics - Dan River Inc.

COMMANDER - Firearms, accessories, and parts - Colt's Manufacturing Co. Inc.

COMMANDER - Fishing tackle - Trophy Products Inc.

COMMANDER - Floor coverings - Aladdin Mills, Inc.

COMMANDER - Floor coverings - American Floor Products Co. Inc.

COMMANDER - Floor coverings–carpet and rugs ☆ - American Carpet Mills

COMMANDER - Footwear - Brown Wooten Mills Inc.

COMMANDER - Furniture–wood - Gold Medal Inc.

COMMANDER - Glassware–household ☆ - Svend Jensen of Denmark Inc.

COMMANDER - Hardware ☆ - King Cotton Cordage Co.

COMMANDER - Health care products - Commander-Omni Co. Inc.

COMMANDER - Holsters - Welsh Sporting Goods Corp. (Boyt Div.)

COMMANDER - Horns–motor vehicle - Falcon Safety Products, Inc.

COMMANDER - Infant product - Century Products Co.

COMMANDER - Knives - Precise International/Wenger

COMMANDER - Leather goods ☆ - AR Accessories Group Inc.

COMMANDER - Lighting equipment - Federal Signal Corp.

COMMANDER - Motor vehicles - Carlin Manufacturing Inc.

COMMANDER - Musical instruments ☆ - Fred Gretsch Enterprises

COMMANDER - Paint sprayers - Speeflo Manufacturing Corp.

COMMANDER - Plumbing fixtures–metal - Speakman Co. (Manufacturing Div.)

COMMANDER - Projectors–photographic ☆ - Dukane Corp.

COMMANDER - Pumps - Flint & Walling Industries, Inc.

COMMANDER - Rocking chairs - Imperial of Morristown Inc.

COMMANDER - Sardines–canned ☆ - Stinson Seafood Co.

COMMANDER - Sporting goods - Gear 2000, Ltd.

COMMANDER - Sporting goods - Sea Mate Products Co.

COMMANDER - Sporting goods ☆ - Brunswick Corp.

COMMANDER - Tires - Coker Tire Inc.

COMMANDER - Tobacco products - Philip Morris Companies Inc.

COMMANDER - Trailers - Classic Manufacturing Inc.

COMMANDER - Trailers–travel ☆ - Carriage, Inc.

COMMANDER - Vacuum cleaners and accessories - Babson Bros. Co.

COMMANDER - Vacuum cleaners and accessories - Yard Vac Products, Inc.

COMMANDER - Watches - Bulova Corp.

COMMANDER-3 - Horns–motor vehicle ☆ - Falcon Safety Products, Inc.

COMMANDER 701 - Leather goods - Leather Sophisticates

COMMANDER 2000 - Alarm systems - Interactive Technologies, Inc.

COMMANDER BLOOD - Computer software - Mindscape Software Inc.

COMMANDER CLASSICS - Fabrics–tapestry ☆ - Coloroll Inc.

COMMANDER DOGSTAR - Toys - Continuity Graphic Associates, Inc.

COMMANDER FOR CONTROLWARE - Computer software - Controlware Technologies Corp.

COMMANDER GUL DUKAT - Toys–models - Paramount Pictures Corp.

COMMANDER II - Bicycles - Ross Bicycles USA, Ltd.

COMMANDER II - Paper–toilet - Fort Howard Corp.

COMMANDER L.W. - Pistols - Colt's Manufacturing Co. Inc.

COMMANDER SELA - Toys - Paramount Pictures Corp.

COMMANDERS CHOICE - Furniture ☆ - Henredon Furniture Industries Inc.

COMMANDER'S PALACE CREOLE CRAVINGS - Food products ☆ - McCormick & Co., Inc.

COMMANDER'S TOWER - Toys - Newco, Inc.

COMMANDO - Electronic equipment - Perma Power Electronics Inc.

COMMANDO - Envelopes - Westvaco Corp.

COMMANDO - Lenses–projection ☆ - Swift Instruments, Inc.

COMMANDO - Lighting equipment–railroad - Koehler Manufacturing Co.

COMMANDO - Motor vehicles–jeeps ☆ - DaimlerChrysler

COMMANDO - Office supplies - Alvin and Co. Inc.

COMMANDO - Office supplies - Wescosa Inc.

COMMANDO - Revolvers ☆ - Colt's Manufacturing Co. Inc.

COMMANDO - Sporting goods - Brigade Quartermasters Ltd.

COMMANDO - Sweaters - Jack Young Associates Inc.

COMMANDO - Tents - Cerf Brothers Bag Co. Inc.

COMMANDO - Toys - Park Plastics Co.

COMMANDO - Vitamins - Natural Organics, Inc.

COMMANDO - Wastebaskets ☆ - F.H. Lawson Co.

COMMANDO SPAWN - Toys - TMP International, Inc.

COMMANDO SPECIAL - Revolvers ☆ - Colt's Manufacturing Co. Inc.

COMMANDWRITER 2 - Computer software ☆ - Command Software Systems, Inc.

COMME LES CHAPEAUX - Apparel–athletic ☆ - Skea Ltd.

COMMEMORATIVE COLTS - Sporting goods - Colt's Manufacturing Co. Inc.

COMMENCE - Computer software - Jensen-Jones, Inc.

COMMENCE - Herbicides - FMC Corp.

COMMEND - Pet food - Ralston Purina Co.

COMMENDABLE - Floor coverings–carpet and rugs - World Carpets, Inc.

COMMENTARY - Furniture - Thomasville Furniture Industries Inc.

COMMENTATOR - Floor coverings–tile ☆ - Mannington Carpets, Inc.

COMMENTATOR - Pens ☆ - Alexander Manufacturing Co.

COMMERCE - Floor coverings - Congoleum Corp.

COMMERCE - Floor coverings–carpet and rugs - Karastan-Bigelow Inc.

COMMERCE - Floor coverings–carpet and rugs ☆ - Hollytex Carpet Mills Inc.

COMMERCE - Food products ☆ - Bumble Bee Seafoods, Inc.

COMMERCE BOND - Paper–looseleaf ☆ - Ampad Corp.

COMMERCE:CONNECTION - Computer software - Sterling Software, Inc.

☆ = Now out of production

COMMERCE:FORMS - Computer software - Sterling Software, Inc.
COMMERCE:LIBRARY - Computer software - Sterling Software, Inc.
COMMERCE:MAIL - Computer software - Sterling Software, Inc.
COMMERCIAL - Electronic equipment - Seal Products Inc.
COMMERCIAL - Tools ☆ - Vaughan & Bushnell Manufacturing Co.
COMMERCIAL ADVANCE - Electronic equipment - Thomson Consumer Electronics, Inc.
COMMERCIAL BAY - Boats–motor - Duracraft Boats Inc.
COMMERCIAL BRAKE - Electronic equipment - Arista Enterprises Inc.
COMMERCIAL BRAKE - Television equipment - Arista Technologies, Inc.
COMMERCIAL CLASSIFY-PLUS - Computer peripheral equipment - Electric Power Research Institute Inc.
COMMERCIAL COILS, INC. - Heating equipment - Commercial Coils, Inc.
COMMERCIAL FLOOR SEALER - Coatings - Seal-Krete Inc.
COMMERCIAL ICE - Agricultural machinery - Environmental Instruments Co.
COMMERCIAL PAPER MATE - Publisher's imprints - Little, Brown and Co., Inc.
COMMERCIAL REAL ESTATE SOUTH - Paper–newsprint - Intertec Publishing Corp.
COMMERCIAL SALES - Hardware stores - Servistar Corp.
COMMERCIAL SERIES - Locks–door - Emhart Inc.
COMMERCIAL SERVICE - Lamps - Angelo Brothers Co.
COMMERCIAL TECHNOLOGIES, INC. - Electronic equipment - Commercial Technologies, Inc.
COMMERICAL - Vacuum cleaners and accessories - Yard Vac Products, Inc.
COMMETREX - Computer software - Commetrex Corp.
COMMISION ADVANTAGE - Computer software - Data Directions
COMMISSARY - Vitamins and nutritional supplements - Rebos Distributing Co., Inc.
COMMISSARY BRAND - Cough medicines - Rebos Distributing Co., Inc.
COMMISSARY FRESH - Pizzas–frozen - Crestar Food Products, Inc.
COMMISSION PLUS - Computer software - Integration Systems
COMMITMENT - Floor coverings–carpet and rugs - Gulistan Carpet Inc.
COMMITMENT - Floor coverings–carpet and rugs - Karastan-Bigelow Inc.
COMMITMENT TO CHARACTER - Paper products - Warner Press, Inc.
COMMITMENTS - Computer software - Carl E. Hewitt
COMMITTEE - Trumpets - G. Leblanc Corp.
COMMLINK - Computer peripheral equipment - Shape Inc.
COMMNET PAGING - Pagers - Commnet Cellular Inc.
COMMODITY MAGIC - Food products - Pierre Frozen Foods Inc.
COMMODOR - Shoes–athletic - Ektelon
COMMODORE - Boats–motor - Regal Marine Industries Inc.
COMMODORE - Boats–motor - Carver Boat Corp.
COMMODORE - Boats–motor ☆ - Crestliner Boats Inc.
COMMODORE - Boats–motor ☆ - Cruisers
COMMODORE - Boats–motor ☆ - Larson Boat Div.
COMMODORE - Boats–pontoons - Harris-Kayot Inc.
COMMODORE - Clocks ☆ - Ridgeway Clock Co.
COMMODORE - Computers–personal - Commodore Business Machines Inc.
COMMODORE - Flag stands - Annin and Co.
COMMODORE - Floor coverings–carpet and rugs - Coronet Carpets Inc.
COMMODORE - Floor coverings–carpet and rugs ☆ - Mannington Carpets, Inc.
COMMODORE - Freezers - Frigibar Industries Inc.
COMMODORE - Hardware ☆ - Alside Div.
COMMODORE - Hats - Bollman Hat Co.
COMMODORE - Liquors - Hughes Markets Inc.
COMMODORE - Mobile homes - Commodore Corp.
COMMODORE - Motor vehicles–buses - Champion Motor Coach Inc.
COMMODORE - Pencils ☆ - Faber-Castell Corp.
COMMODORE - Pipes–tobacco ☆ - Dr. Grabow Pre-Smoked Pipes Inc.
COMMODORE - Recording label - Essex Entertainment Inc.
COMMODORE - Seafood products–fresh or frozen - Nordic Fisheries
COMMODORE - Seafood products–fresh or frozen ☆ - National Sea Products U.S. Corp.
COMMODORE - Sporting goods ☆ - Hedstrom Corp.
COMMODORE - Watches - Bulova Corp.
COMMODORE 16 - Computers–personal ☆ - Commodore Business Machines Inc.
COMMODORE 64 - Computers–personal - Commodore Business Machines Inc.
COMMODORE BY ROSALCO - Furniture - Rosalco Inc.
COMMODORE PLUS/4 - Computers–personal ☆ - Commodore Business Machines Inc.
COMMODORE VIC 20 - Computers–personal ☆ - Commodore Business Machines Inc.

COMMODORE'S POINT - Floor coverings–carpet and rugs - Catalina Carpet Mills Inc.
COMMON CANADA BLUEGRASS - Flowers, plants, and seeds - Jacklin Seed
COMMON CENTS - Fuel additives - Bardahl Manufacturing Corp.
COMMON CENTS - Paper–toweling - Laurel Hill Paper Co.
COMMON CHORD - Recording label - Sony Music Entertainment Inc.
COMMON COLORS - Apparel and accessories - Rich & Me, Inc.
COMMON GROUND - Apparel and accessories - Sedona Clothing Co., LLC
COMMON GROUND - Computer software - No Hands Software, Inc.
COMMON HULLED - Flowers, plants, and seeds - Jacklin Seed
COMMON KNOWLEDGE - Computer software - On Technology Corp.
COMMON KNOWLEDGE - Games - Christina H. Lutz
COMMON REDTOPS - Flowers, plants, and seeds - Jacklin Seed
COMMON SCENTS - Apparel–children's - Ann C. Greenberg
COMMON SENSE - Cereal - Kellogg Co.
COMMON SENSE - Electronic equipment - Common Sense
COMMON SENSE - Fencing–chain link - Common Sense Fence
COMMON SENSE - File folders and binders - Asa L. Shipman's Sons, Ltd.
COMMON SENSE - Health care products - Lotus Brands Inc.
COMMON SENSE - Ledgers - Beach Publishing Co.
COMMON SENSE - Soap - Robert H. Racine
COMMON SENSE - Sporting goods ☆ - Carron Net Co. Inc.
COMMON SENSE - Uniforms–academic - Ottenheimer and Co. Inc.
COMMON SENSE CONSERVATION - Apparel and accessories - David Earl Miller
COMMON SHEEP FESCUES - Flowers, plants, and seeds - Jacklin Seed
COMMON STOCK RED-FLAGS TEMPLATE, THE - Publisher's imprints - Bankers Common Stock Analysis, Inc.
COMMON THREAD, A - Apparel and accessories - Bugle Boy Industries, Inc.
COMMON THREADS - Apparel and accessories - Common Threads
COMMON THREADS - Greeting cards - Hallmark Cards Inc.
COMMON UNHULLED - Flowers, plants, and seeds - Jacklin Seed
COMMONSCENTS - Pharmaceutical preparations - Aroma Therapies and Technologies, Inc.
COMMONSENSE - Office furniture–wood - Marvel Group Inc.
COMMONSENSE FINANCIAL PROCESS - Computer software - JML Industries, Inc.
COMMONSPACE - Computer software - Houghton Mifflin Co.
COMMONWEALTH - Cases–musical instrument - Mechanical Music Corp.
COMMONWEALTH - Cigarettes - Commonwealth Brands, Inc.
COMMONWEALTH - Dishes–china - Wilton Co.
COMMONWEALTH - Floor coverings–carpet and rugs - Milliken & Co. Inc.
COMMONWEALTH - Furniture - Kincaid Furniture Co. Inc.
COMMONWEALTH - Furniture ☆ - Bassett Furniture Industries, Inc.
COMMONWEALTH - Furniture ☆ - Bernhardt Industries
COMMONWEALTH - Paints ☆ - Sherwin-Williams Automotive Finishes Corp.
COMMONWEALTH - Paints–artists' - Chaselle Inc.
COMMONWEALTH - Pencils ☆ - Faber-Castell Corp.
COMMONWEALTH HEALTH ALLIANCE - Insurance agencies–health - Commonwealth Health Alliance, Inc.
COMMONWEALTH MAHOGANY - Furniture ☆ - Hooker Furniture Corp.
COMMONWEALTH MANOR - Furniture ☆ - Hooker Furniture Corp.
COMMPLETE - Computer hardware - Multi-Tech Systems, Inc.
COMMPOINT - Computer software - Telephone Response Technologies
COMMSCOPE - Cables–fiber optic - Gerrold General Instrument Corp.
COMMSENSE - Computer software - Focas, Inc.
COMMSERV-2010 - Computer software - Datamaxx Applied Technologies, Inc.
COMMTRANS - Computer software - On Line Solutions, Inc.
COMMTRON - Videocassette tapes - Ingram Entertainment
COMMUNI-COM - Electronic equipment - P/H Electronics
COMMUNICARDS - Textbooks ☆ - Communication Skill Builders, Inc.
COMMUNICARE - Hearing aids - Oticon Corp.
COMMUNICATION 2000 - Video production - Susan Peterson Productions Inc.
COMMUNICATION CARDS - Stationery - Wilton Herbert Hasty Jr.
COMMUNICATIONS MADE EASY - Computer peripheral equipment - PSI Integration, Inc.
COMMUNICATIONS TECHNOLOGY - Communications equipment - Communications Technology Corp.
COMMUNICATOR - Audio equipment - Pro-Co. Sound Co. Inc.
COMMUNICATOR - Cooling systems–cryogenic - Graphic Communications Corp.
COMMUNICATOR - Hearing aids - Electone Inc.
COMMUNICATOR - Markers–felt-tip - Dri Mark Products, Inc.
COMMUNICATOR, THE - Novelty items - J.L. Harper Inc.
COMMUNICENTER - Telephone answering machines - Nutone Inc.
COMMUNICOM - Humphrey Systems

☆ = Now out of production

COMMUNICORE - Computer hardware - At&T Corp.
COMMUNICORE - Computer storage devices ☆ - Hunt Manufacturing Co.
COMMUNIQUE - Computer software - Electronic Courseware Systems Inc.
COMMUNIQUE - Telephones–cellular - NovAtel Carcom Inc.
COMMUNITEL - Electronic equipment ☆ - Bogen Communications, Inc.
COMMUNITY - Bakery products - Community Bakeries
COMMUNITY - Beverages - Community Coffee Co., Inc.
COMMUNITY - Flatware - Oneida Ltd.
COMMUNITY - Paints ☆ - Waterlox Coatings Corp.
COMMUNITY 3 - Recording label - Jazz Composer's Orchestra Association Inc.
COMMUNITY CASH FOR SCHOOLS - Cream–canned or powdered - Community Coffee Co., Inc.
COMMUNITY CHIPS - Pet products - Nippon Pet Food
COMMUNITY CLASSICS - Beverages - Community Coffee Co., Inc.
COMMUNITY FOODS - Food products - Community Coffee Co., Inc.
COMMUNITY FOODS - Mayonnaise - Spectrum Naturals, Inc.
COMMUNITY KITCHENS - Snack foods - Community Coffee Co., Inc.
COMMUNITY MILL AND BEAN - Flower pots–earthenware - Community Mill & Bean Crusoe Island Natural Foods
COMMUNITY T.E.N. - Fish food - Wardley Corp.
COMMUNITY WORKERS - Toys–blocks - Guidecraft Inc.
COMMUNO-PHONE - Electronic equipment - Bogen Communications, Inc.
COMMUTE-TACHE - Luggage ☆ - Hartmann Luggage Co.
COMMUTER - Health care products ☆ - Smith and Davis Manufacturing Co.
COMMUTER - Luggage - Samsonite Corp.
COMMUTER - Microfiche equipment - Bell & Howell Co.
COMMUTER - Mopeds - Columbia Manufacturing Inc.
COMMUTER - Seats–automobile ☆ - Cosco, Inc.
COMMUTER - Tires - Bridgestone/Firestone, Inc.
COMMUTER - Wheelchairs - Fortress Inc.
COMMUTER CLASSICS - Automotive parts and accessories - Allied Plastics
COMMUTER DESK - Desks ☆ - Flambeau Products Corp.
COMMUTER, THE - Cribs–wood - Newborne Co.
COMMUTER'S LIBRARY - Recording label - Sound Room Publishers
COMMWORKS - Computer software - Traveling Software, Inc.
COMO - Canned tomatoes - Tri Valley Growers, Inc.
COMO - Floor coverings ☆ - Congoleum Corp.
COMO - Food products - Clement Pappas and Co.
COMO - Furniture ☆ - Lane Co. Inc.
COMO - Paper–tissue ☆ - Plainwell Tissue
COMO - Recording label - CA-Song Music
COMO - Shoes ☆ - Allen-Edmonds Shoe Corp.
COMO - Spices and extracts ☆ - Cumberland-Swan, Inc.
COMOBAR - Coffee makers–electric - Comobar Inc.
COMONITOR - Valves–industrial - Westlock Controls Corp.
COMORO - Boats–motor ☆ - Larson Boat Div.
COMORO - Floor coverings–carpet and rugs - Danube Carpet Mills Inc.
COMOTEXTILE - Wallpaper - Blumenthal
COMOTION, THE - Fans–electric - Davoil, Inc.
COMOY'S OF LONDON - Giftware - H.C. Meyers Co.
COMP - Goggles–sun - Totes-Isotoner Corp.
COMP - Skis - Wellington Leisure Products, Inc.
COMP 1 - Footwear–athletic - Leo's Dancewear, Inc.
COMP 950 - Golfing equipment - TourEdge Golf Manufacturing Inc.
COMP ACE - Rackets–tennis - Pro Kennex, Inc.
COMP CAMS - Motor vehicle parts and accessories - Competition Cams, Inc.
COMP COMMANDER - Computer software - Blue Moon Software, Inc.
COMP DECOR - Computer peripheral equipment - Comp Decor
COMP EQUIPE - Golfing equipment - Sean Toulon
COMP IV - Games ☆ - Milton Bradley Co.
COMP. JR. - Rackets–racquetball - Ektelon
COMP PRO 20 - Rackets–tennis - Spalding Sports Worldwide
COMP-SEALOR - Gaskets - Newcourt, Inc.
COMP-U-HIKE - Exercising equipment - Precise International/Wenger
COMP-U-STEP - Exercising equipment ☆ - Precise International/Wenger
COMP U STEP II - Exercising equipment - Precise International/Wenger
COMP-U-STITCH - Needles–sewing - Comp-U-Stitch, Inc.
COMP WARE - Computer peripheral equipment - L.I. Industries, Inc.
COMPA-Z - Pharmaceutical preparations ☆ - Roberts/Hauck Pharmaceuticals Inc.
COMPAC - Salt - United Salt Corp.
COMPAC - Staplers - ACCO USA, Inc.
COMPAC-TABLE - Ironing boards - Seymour Housewares Corp.
COMPACK'R - Trash compactors–household - Equity Industries Corp.
COMPACT - Artists' materials - Logan Graphic Products Inc.
COMPACT - Bicycles - Ross Bicycles USA, Ltd.

COMPACT - Boats–pontoons - Kennedy Inc.
COMPACT - Cylinders–pneumatic - Compact Air Products, Inc.
COMPACT - Electronic equipment - Motorola, Inc. (Land Mobile Products Sector)
COMPACT - Embossing tool - International Rotex Inc.
COMPACT - Hearing aids - Widex Hearing Aid Co., Inc.
COMPACT - Housewares - Endicott-Seymour of Ann Arbor
COMPACT - Housewares ☆ - Beverage-Air
COMPACT - Industrial machinery - Federal-Hoffman, Inc.
COMPACT - Paper products - James River Paper Co., Inc.
COMPACT - Toilets–porcelain - Raritan Engineering Co. Inc.
COMPACT 5 - Lathes ☆ - Emco-Maier Corp.
COMPACT 20 - Electronic equipment ☆ - Paso Sound Products Inc.
COMPACT 38 - Lighting fixtures - Swivelier Co. Inc.
COMPACT 100 - Balls ☆ - Mikasa Sports
COMPACT 110 - Balls - Mikasa Sports
COMPACT 1000 - Balls - Mikasa Sports
COMPACT-AIRE - Air conditioning equipment - Heat Controller Inc.
COMPACT CHECK-OUT - Toys - Mattel, Inc.
COMPACT COMFORT - Medical apparatus - Wahl Clipper Corp.
COMPACT CUBE - Lighting fixtures - Legion Lighting Co., Inc.
COMPACT CURE - Adhesives and sealants - Dymax Corp.
COMPACT D - Computer storage devices–optical - Disclosure Inc.
COMPACT DISH - Cook books - Sally L. Owens
COMPACT EASI - Computer software - Compact Software, Inc.
COMPACT ELECTROL - Projection screens - Da-Lite Screen Co. Inc.
COMPACT FINISH - Cosmetics - Estee Lauder Inc.
COMPACT FLOOD - Lighting equipment - Kim Lighting Inc.
COMPACT FOR SUEDE, THE - Cleaning preparations - Colorstik Ltd.
COMPACT POWER - Audio equipment - Royal Sound Co. Inc.
COMPACT PRO - Computer program - William Goodman
COMPACTA-STAK - Shelving units–metal - Stacor Corp.
COMPACTO - Cases–musical instrument ☆ - Selmer Co. Inc.
COMPACTO-MIRROR - Mirrors - Electro-Optix Inc.
COMPACTVENDOR - Machinery - Coin Acceptors, Inc.
COMPACVAN - Trailers–travel - Wells Cargo Inc.
COMPAD - Cushions - Mark One Healthcare Products Inc.
COMPADRE - Computer peripheral equipment - Three D Graphics
COMPADRE - Herbicides - Monsanto Co.
COMPAGNIE DU ROY - Kitchenware–earthenware - Sabine, Inc.
COMPAGNIE INTERNATIONALE EXPRESS TAILLEUR - Apparel and accessories - Expressco, Inc.
COMPAK - Computer software - Georgia-Pacific Corp.
COMPAK - Metal goods - Getz Enterprises
COMPAK - Photographic equipment - Kalart Victor Corp.
COMPAL - Pharmaceutical preparations ☆ - Solvay Pharmaceuticals Inc.
COMPANDER - Plugs–ear - MXR Innovations Inc.
COMPANION - Audio equipment - Bose Corp.
COMPANION - Bicycles - Ross Bicycles USA, Ltd.
COMPANION - Cat food - Bench & Field
COMPANION - Cigars ☆ - Havatampa Inc.
COMPANION - Cleaning preparations - Unit Chemical Corp.
COMPANION - Computer terminals - Random Corp.
COMPANION - Dog food - Martin's Feed Mills, Inc.
COMPANION - Fabrics - Greenwood Mills Inc.
COMPANION - Health care products - Innovative Medical Engineering Inc.
COMPANION - Health care products - Medisense, Inc.
COMPANION - Health care products - Puritan-Bennett Corp.
COMPANION - Paper - L.L. Brown Paper Co.
COMPANION - Photo albums ☆ - JM Co.
COMPANION - Prosthetic apparatus - OTC Professional Appliances
COMPANION - Pumps - Gaymar Industries, Inc.
COMPANION - Rings–jewelry - Artcarved Inc.
COMPANION - Strollers–baby ☆ - Welsh Co.
COMPANION - Telescopes - Northern Telecom, Inc.
COMPANION - Trailers–travel - Kit Manufacturing Co.
COMPANION - Wallpaper - Taylor Wallcoverings Inc.
COMPANION BAG - Leather goods - AR Accessories Group Inc.
COMPANION CALAY - Motor vehicles–motor homes ☆ - Kit Manufacturing Co.
COMPANION CARE - First-aid slide rules for pet care - Intromark Inc.
COMPANION CHAIR LOUNGE - Furniture - Shepher Corp.
COMPANION CLASSIC - Motor vehicles–motor homes ☆ - Kit Manufacturing Co.
COMPANION COLLECTIONS - Wallpaper ☆ - Wall Fabrics Inc.
COMPANION GUIDES - Publisher's imprints - Simon & Schuster, Inc.

COMPANION LOUNGE - Toys - Aqua-Leisure Industries, Inc.

COMPANION MUSIC - Recording label - Kitty L. Milligan

COMPANION PORTRAIT - Prosthetic apparatus - OTC Professional Appliances

COMPANION, THE - Luggage - Insell Co.

COMPANIONS - Tiles–ceramic - Wenczel Tile Co.

COMPANIONS - Wallpaper ☆ - Marburg Wallcoverings Inc.

COMPANIONS 2 - See **COMPANIONS**

COMPANY 5 - Dresses–women's - Anne Klein & Co.

COMPANY 2000 - Tableware–china - CBK Ltd. Inc.

COMPANY B - Floor coverings–carpet and rugs - Masland Corp.

COMPANY CLASSICS - Hosiery - Paul Lavitt Mills, Inc.

COMPANY COFFEE FINE COFFEES AND TEAS, THE - Coffee - Co. Coffee, Inc.

COMPANY COLLECTION - Apparel–women's - Hamrick's, Inc.

COMPANY HASH BROWNS - Potato sticks - Byerly's

COMPANY MESSENGER - Computer software - Eclipse Computer Solutions Inc.

COMPANY OF FRIENDS, A - Giftware - Determined Productions, Inc.

COMPANY OF NOTE, THE - Music boxes - Ardleigh Elliot & Sons Ltd.

COMPANY STORE'S EUROPEAN GOOSE DOWN, THE - Comforters - Co. Store

COMPANY STORE'S WHITE EUROPEAN DOWN, THE - Comforters - Co. Store

COMPANY WAR, THE - Games ☆ - Mayfair Games, Inc.

CO. X - Apparel–athletic - Spring Ford Knitting Co., Inc.

COMPAQ - Computers–personal - Compaq Computer Corp.

COMPAQ DESKPRO - Computers–personal ☆ - Compaq Computer Corp.

COMPAQ LTE - Computers–personal - Compaq Computer Corp.

COMPAQ PC CARD SOLUTION - Computer peripheral equipment - Compaq Computer Corp.

COMPAQ SLT/286 - Computers–personal - Compaq Computer Corp.

COMPAR-A-BOARD - Hardware - Star Key & Lock Manufacturing Co. Inc.

COMPARABLES - Apparel–women's - Montgomery Ward & Co. Inc.

COMPARATOR - Electronic equipment - Hamilton Electronics Corp.

COMPARE - Cleaning preparations - Barcolene Inc.

COMPARE AND SAVE - Diapers–disposable - Weyerhaeuser Co.

COMPARE BEARS - Toys - Learning Resources, Inc.

COMPAREWARE - Computer software - Dave Edson

COMPARI - Jewelry–costume ☆ - Anne Klein Jewelry

COMPARISON KITCHEN - Computer software - SRA/McGraw-Hill (Div. of The McGraw-Hill Companies)

COMPARON - Lenses–photographic - Schneider Optics, Inc.

COMPARTMENT TUBES - Tubes–plastic - VisiPak

COMPARTMENTS - Apparel and accessories - Judy Ann of California

COMPARTMENTS - Cabinets - A-Bee Syndicate Inc.

COMPARTMENTS - File folders ☆ - Newell Office Products

COMPASITE - Compasses–magnetic - Rebel Industries Inc.

COMPASS - Apparel–men's - J.C. Penney Co., Inc.

COMPASS - Computer software - Copeland Corp.

COMPASS - Computer software - Dearborn Financial Publishing, Inc.

COMPASS - Floor coverings–carpet and rugs - Trend Carpet

COMPASS - Mailing machines - Total Mailroom Support Inc.

COMPASS - Office furniture–wood - Meridian, Inc.

COMPASS - Tires - Goodyear Tire & Rubber Co.

COMPASS - Watches - Compass Industries, Inc.

COMPASS COMBS - Combs - Randy M. Henry

COMPASS COMPANION - Drafting supplies ☆ - Sakura of America

COMPASS COMPUTER - Computers–personal - Grid Systems Corp.

COMPASS CONTRACT - Computer software - Western Data Systems, Inc.

COMPASS GOLD - Coffee ☆ - Compass Foods Inc.

COMPASS KING - Compasses–magnetic ☆ - Precise International/Wenger

COMPASS LINE - Marine rigging - NWTX Controls Inc.

COMPASS RECORDS - Recording label - Small World Music, Inc.

COMPASSENTERPRISE - Computer software - Western Data Systems, Inc.

COMPASSIONATE SAGE - Health care products - East Earth Herb Inc.

COMPASSPOINT - Computer software - Northpoint Software

COMPAT - Cement - Hartline Products Co. Inc.

COMPAT-A-PILLOW - Bathroom accessories - Better Sleep, Inc.

COMPATABLES - Tables–wood - La-Z-Boy Chair Co.

COMPATH-ES - Computer software - APL-Synetics, Inc.

COMPATIBILITY PLUS - Computers - Laptop Solutions, Inc.

COMPATIBLE - Floor coverings–carpet and rugs - Trend Carpet

COMPATIBLE - Hair care products - Revlon Consumer Products Corp.

COMPATIBLE - Tableware ☆ - Corning Inc.

COMPATIBLE - Tiles–ceramic ☆ - Huntington/Pacific Ceramics Inc.

COMPATIBLES - Apparel and accessories - Colonial Textile Manufacturing Corp.

COMPATIBLES - Fabrics–tapestry ☆ - Coloroll Inc.

COMPAX - Electronic equipment - General Electric Co.

COMPAX - Filters–industrial - Porous Media Corp.

COMPAX - Tampons - Tambrands Inc.

COMPAX - Watches ☆ - Holzerwatch Co. Inc.

COMPAX 17C - Wheelchairs ☆ - Convaid Inc.

COMPAZINE - Pharmaceutical preparations - Smithkline Beecham Corp.

COMPCO - Film - Compco Photographic/Goldberg Bros.

COMPCORDER - Del Mar Avionics

COMPCORE - Sporting goods - Glassmaster Co.

COMPEAN - Spices and extracts - Herbert Marmorek & Son, Inc.

COMPEL - Laxatives ☆ - Nature's Way Products, Inc.

COMPENSATE - Apparel–women's ☆ - Bali Co. Inc.

COMPENSATE - Computer software - Laforest Systems, Inc.

COMPENSATOR - Wood products - Hanover Architectural Products Businesstrust

COMPETE - Computer software ☆ - CONDUIT

COMPETE - Skin care products - Mennen Co.

COMPETE - Vitamins and nutritional supplements - Mission Pharmacal Co.

COMPETENCY ARCHITECT - Computer software - Lominger Limited, Inc.

COMPETENCY COACH - Computer software - Coopercomm, Inc.

COMPETENT KIDS - Educational materials - Three Bears Books, Inc.

COMPETER RABBIT - Computer software ☆ - Gessler Publishing Co., Inc.

COMPETIDORA - Cigars - Dosal Tobacco Corp.

COMPETITAR - Fishing tackle - South Bend Sporting Goods Inc.

COMPETITION - Animal feeds - TDI, Inc.

COMPETITION - Bicycles - Murray, Inc.

COMPETITION - Fishing tackle - Zebco Corp.

COMPETITION - Health care products - Gold's Gym Enterprises Inc.

COMPETITION - Ships–sailing vessels - The Hinckley Co.

COMPETITION - Sporting goods - Voit Corp.

COMPETITION - Traps–animal - Remington Arms Co., Inc.

COMPETITION - Watches - Hampden Corp.

COMPETITION 100 - Balls–basketball - Mikasa Sports

COMPETITION 110 - Balls - Mikasa Sports

COMPETITION 200 - Balls ☆ - Mikasa Sports

COMPETITION 1000 - Balls - Mikasa Sports

COMPETITION 1500 - Balls - Mikasa Sports

COMPETITION 2000 - Balls - Mikasa Sports

COMPETITION AUTO TINT - Polyester film sheets - Enpro Distributing, Inc.

COMPETITION CLEAVER - Propellers - Mercury Hi-Performance Group

COMPETITION CONNEXION - Motor vehicle parts and accessories - Target Motorsports

COMPETITION G.S. - Bicycles ☆ - Raleigh USA Bicycle Co.

COMPETITION PLUS - Automotive parts and accessories - Hurst Performance Inc.

COMPETITION PLUS - Floor coverings–carpet and rugs ☆ - Olympic Carpets Inc.

COMPETITION SCRAMBLER SX1000 - Bicycles - Schwinn Cycling & Fitness Inc.

COMPETITION SERIES - Golf club shafts - United Sports Technologies Inc.

COMPETITION SET - Hair care products ☆ - Summit Laboratories

COMPETITION TAN - Skin care products - Jan Tana, Inc.

COMPETITIVE CLASS - Balls - Mikasa Sports

COMPETITIVE EDGE - Automotive parts and accessories - Explorer Competition Products, Inc.

COMPETITIVE EDGE - Health care products ☆ - Foodscience Laboratories Inc.

COMPETITIVE EDGE - Lenses–optical - Competitive Edge, Inc.

COMPETITOR - Bicycles ☆ - Raleigh USA Bicycle Co.

COMPETITOR - Boats–motor - Alumacraft Boat Co.

COMPETITOR - Boats–pontoons - Riviera Cruiser

COMPETITOR - Fabrics–twill ☆ - Greenwood Mills Inc.

COMPETITOR - Fishing tackle - Skyline Industries Inc.

COMPETITOR - Floor coverings–carpet and rugs - Value Carpets Inc.

COMPETITOR - Frames–eyeglass ☆ - Universal/Univis Inc.

COMPETITOR - Golfing equipment - Wild Hawk Apparel

COMPETITOR - Mufflers–motor vehicle - Goerlich's

COMPETITOR - Playground equipment - Newco, Inc.

COMPETITOR - Telescopes - Bausch & Lomb Inc.

COMPETITOR - Vitamins and nutritional supplements - Tishcon Corp.

COMPETITOR GT - Sporting goods ☆ - O'Brien International

COMPETITOR PLUS SLING - Firearms, accessories, and parts - Brownells, Inc.

COMPETITOR SERIES - Drums–musical instruments - Pearl Corp.

☆ = Now out of production

COMPETITOR, THE - Valves - B & K Industries, Inc.

COMPETITOR, THE - Bullets - Detroit Armor Corp.

COMPETITOR, THE - Firearms, accessories, and parts - Welsh Sporting Goods Corp. (Boyt Div.)

COMPETITOR X - Sporting goods ☆ - O'Brien International

COMPETITORS - Toys ☆ - Intex Recreation Corp.

COMPETITORS VIEW - Apparel and accessories - Chase Racewear, LLC

COMPILE/QGF - Computer software - Platinum Technology, Inc.

COMPILER + - Computer software ☆ - Spinnaker Software Corp.

COMPL-FIT - Apparel and accessories ☆ - Warnaco Inc.

COMPLAST - Windows–plastic - Complast, Inc.

COMPLAVITES - Vitamins and nutritional supplements - Tishcon Corp.

COMPLEAT - Vitamins and nutritional supplements - Novartis Nutrition Corp.

COMPLEAT ANGLER - Earthenware - Portmeirion USA

COMPLEAT-B - Vitamins and nutritional supplements - Novartis Nutrition Corp.

COMPLEMENT - Computer software - Ciba Corning Diagnostics Corp.

COMPLEMENT - Film - E.I. Dupont de Nemours and Co.

COMPLEMENT - Floor coverings–carpet and rugs ☆ - J and J Industries Inc.

COMPLEMENTARY CARE - Computer software - Healthcare Computer Corp.

COMPLEMENTS - Beverage ware - Indiana Glass Co.

COMPLEMENTS - Contact lenses - Wesley-Jessen Co.

COMPLEMENTS - Floor coverings–carpet and rugs ☆ - Mohawk Carpet Corp.

COMPLEMENTS - Furniture–wood - Century Furniture Co.

COMPLEMENTS - Hair coloring preparations - Clairol Inc.

COMPLEMENTS - Hardware - Marley Mouldings Inc.

COMPLEMENTS - Spices and extracts - Flavor Station Corp.

COMPLEMENTS - Wallpaper ☆ - Mayfair Wallcoverings

COMPLETABS - Pharmaceutical preparations - Morton Pharmaceuticals Inc.

COMPLETE - Beverages - Save Mart Supermarkets

COMPLETE - Cigarettes - All Service, Inc.

COMPLETE - Cleaning preparations - S.C. Johnson & Son, Inc.

COMPLETE - Denture cleaners - Richardson-Vicks USA

COMPLETE - Dog food - Iams Co.

COMPLETE - Hair care products - ABBA Products Inc.

COMPLETE - Ophthalmic goods - Allergan, Inc.

COMPLETE - Pet products - Breeder's Choice Pet Foods, Inc.

COMPLETE - Vitamins and nutritional supplements ☆ - Great Life Laboratories Inc.

COMPLETE 1, THE - Bags–plastic - Ag-Bag International Limited

COMPLETE ACUPUNCTURE, THE - Computer software - Hopkins Technology LLC

COMPLETE ADVANTAGE - Pet food - Purina Mills, Inc.

COMPLETE BAR-B-Q, THE - Barbecue and grill accessories - Caldo International, Inc.

COMPLETE BEDROOM BOOK - Wallpaper - Kingfisher Wallcoverings

COMPLETE BREED BOOK, THE - Publisher's imprints - Howell Book House Inc.

COMPLETE BURGER, THE - Food products ☆ - Pierre Frozen Foods Inc.

COMPLETE CONTROL - Hair care products - Chesebrough-Pond's USA Co.

COMPLETE COVER - Cosmetics - Charles of the Ritz Group Ltd.

COMPLETE CREATIVE COLLECTION - Computer software - Parsons Technology, Inc.

COMPLETE ELECTRONIC TAX WORKPLACE, THE - Computer software - Computer Language Research Inc.

COMPLETE FEEDING SYSTEM DRY CANNED BISCUITS - Pet food - Iams Co.

COMPLETE FRESH & SOFTWATER - Chemical preparations ☆ - Mydor Industries Inc.

COMPLETE FRESHWATER - Chemical preparations ☆ - Mydor Industries Inc.

COMPLETE HEALTH - Health care products - Apothecary Products, Inc.

COMPLETE HOG FINISHER - Animal feeds - Bluebonnet Milling Co.

COMPLETE KITCHEN I, THE - Wallpaper ☆ - Imperial Wallcoverings, Inc.

COMPLETE KITCHEN II, THE - Wallpaper ☆ - Imperial Wallcoverings, Inc.

COMPLETE MEAL DEAL, THE - Games - Addison-Wesley Publishing Co.

COMPLETE MICRO-BLEND - Fertilizers - Coston Consolidated Industries, Inc.

COMPLETE MILK DIGESTANT, THE - Pharmaceutical preparations - Malabar Formulas

COMPLETE MILK PROTEIN - Milk protein concentrate - American Casein Co.

COMPLETE PACKAGE, THE - Hearing aids - Earmold Design Inc.

COMPLETE REAL ESTATE SOFTWARE CATALOG, THE - Computer storage devices - Z-Law Software, Inc.

COMPLETE TEACHER, THE - Computer software - Compu-Tations Inc.

COMPLETE WARLOCK - Games ☆ - War House

COMPLETE WEB AUTHORING AND PUBLISHING SOLUTION, THE - Computer software - Blue Sky Software Corp.

COMPLETEHEAT - Heaters–space - Lennox Industries Inc.

COMPLETELY RECYCLABLE NYLON, THE - Yarn - BASF Corp.

COMPLETESHOP - Computer software - Complete Computer Consultants, Inc.

COMPLEX - Floor coverings–carpet and rugs ☆ - Walter Carpet Mills

COMPLEX - Skin care products - Lendan USA Co.

COMPLEX 15 - Skin care products - Key Pharmaceuticals Inc.

COMPLEX BLUE - Air purification systems - Jefferey Eden

COMPLEX BLUE - Cleaning preparations - CRC Chemicals USA/Siloo

COMPLEX-C - Vitamins and nutritional supplements - J.R. Carlson Laboratories Inc.

COMPLEX CONIC WAVEGUIDES - Audio equipment - Renkus-Heinz Inc.

COMPLEX II - Floor coverings–carpet and rugs ☆ - Walter Carpet Mills

COMPLEXE 5 - Skin care products - Rene Furterer

COMPLEXE EYE BEAUTE - Skin care products - Gary E. Loest

COMPLEXE EYE FERME - Skin care products - Gary E. Loest

COMPLEXION FRESH - Skin care products ☆ - Philips Electronics North America Corp.

COMPLEXION PERFECT - Cosmetics - Honey & Spice Toiletries

COMPLEXION PERFECTION - Vitamins and nutritional supplements - Earth's Resources, Inc.

COMPLEXION PERFECTOR - Skin care products - Ardell International Inc.

COMPLEXION PLUS - Skin care products ☆ - Philips Electronics North America Corp.

COMPLEXION PUFF - American International Industries

COMPLEXION THERAPY - Skin care products ☆ - Noxell Corp.

COMPLEYE - Computer software - Axiom Software Laboratories, Inc.

COMPLIANCE - Boilers–hot water - Bryan Steam Corp.

COMPLIANCE ADVISOR - Computer software - Decisis Corp.

COMPLIANCE PLUS - Electrical testing instruments - Compliance Plus

COMPLIANCE PLUS - Vitamins and nutritional supplements - M. Erickson Corp.

COMPLIANT CHIP - Semiconductors - Tessera, Inc.

COMPLIERS - Tools–hand-operated - Steven Visser and Ashok Midha Partnership

COMPLIMENT - Meat sauces - Pet Inc.

COMPLIMENT - Shower stalls–metal - Kohler Co.

COMPLIMENTS - Cosmetics - Al Nyman and Son

COMPLIMENTS - Dinnerware–glass - Arita Sales Co. Inc.

COMPLIMENTS - Furniture–factory ☆ - Clayton Marcus Co. Inc.

COMPLIMENTS - Window coverings - Norman's of Salisbury

COMPLOT - Electronic equipment ☆ - Houston Instrument

COMPLY - Floor coverings - Standard Textile Co., Inc.

COMPLY - Health care products - Dura Tex

COMPLY - Health care products - Sherwood Medical Co.

COMPLY - Insecticides - Ciba-Geigy Corp.

COMPLY - Paper products - National Sanitary Supply Co.

COMPLY - Pet products - Lynco Pet Products Inc.

COMPMASTER - Computer software - William M. Mercer, Inc.

COMPO - Paints - Dunn Edwards Corp.

COMPO BIN - Bins - Gilbert and Bennett Manufacturing Co.

COMPO-BOND - Mortars–clay ☆ - Master Builders Inc.

COMPO-FIBRE - Brushes–paint ☆ - Linzer Products Corp.

COMPOBELL - Hobby kits - Bell Ceramics, Inc.

COMPOCILLIN-V - Antibiotics ☆ - Abbott Laboratories

COMPOCILLIN-VK - Antibiotics ☆ - Abbott Laboratories

COMPONAR - Lenses–photographic - Schneider Optics, Inc.

COMPONAR-C - Lenses–photographic - Schneider Optics, Inc.

COMPONENT CUTTER - Tools - LRH Enterprises Inc.

COMPONENT FILE, THE - Furniture - Gusdorf Corp.

COMPONENT PLAY GROUNDS - Playground equipment - Swings & Things

COMPONENT TECHNOLOGIES - Metals - Component Technologies, Inc.

COMPONENTFACTORY - Computer software - I-Kinetics, Inc.

COMPONENTPACK - Computer software - Powersoft Corp.

COMPONENTS - Wallpaper ☆ - Manuscreens

COMPONENTS & MILLWORK INC. - Cabinets - Components & Millwork Inc.

COMPONETICS - Containers - W. Braun Co. Inc.

COMPONON - Lenses–photographic - Schneider Optics, Inc.

COMPONON-S - Lenses–photographic - Schneider Optics, Inc.

COMPORT - Computer hardware - Com21, Inc.

COMPOSE - Recording label ☆ - Peter Pan Industries

COMPOSER - Electronics equipment - Multivision Systems Inc.

COMPOSER - Lighting fixtures ☆ - Hubbell Lighting, Inc. (Lighting Div.)

COMPOSER 2000 - Hearing aids ☆ - Beltone Electronics Corp.

COMPOSI-TIGHT - Dental equipment - Garrison Dental Solutions, LLC

COMPOSIPAC - Packaging–paper - Graphic Packaging Corp.

COMPOSITE - Fishing tackle - Ashaway Line & Twine Manufacturing Co.

COMPOSITE - Furniture - Broyhill Furniture Industries, Inc.

☆ = Now out of production

COMPOSITE - Skis - Ski Accessories Co.
COMPOSITE - Thread - Belding Heminway Co. Inc.
COMPOSITE EDGE - Gas tanks–motor vehicle - Pressed Steel Tank Co., Inc.
COMPOSITE MASTER - Rackets–tennis - Head Sports USA
COMPOSITE PROFESSIONAL - Rackets–tennis - Head Sports USA
COMPOSITES - Furniture - Haworth, Inc.
COMPOSITION - Flatware ☆ - Kirk Stieff Co.
COMPOSITION - Floor coverings–carpet and rugs - Mannington Carpets, Inc.
COMPOSITION - Floor coverings–carpet and rugs - Regal Rugs Inc.
COMPOSITION - Floor coverings–carpet and rugs - Trend Carpet
COMPOSITION 1000 - Balls–basketball - Mikasa Sports
COMPOSITIONS - Fabrics–linen - Associated Merchandising Corp.
COMPOSITIONS - Floor coverings–tile - Interface, Inc.
COMPOSITIONS - Furniture–wood - Ficks Reed Co. Inc.
COMPOSITIONS - Wallpaper - Wall Fashion Inc.
COMPOSITOR - Electronics equipment - Broadcast Television Systems
COMPOSITOR I - Electronics equipment - Broadcast Television Systems
COMPOSITZ - Insulating materials - MacLean-Fogg Co.
COMPOST AID - Garden equipment - Mackwin Co.
COMPOST CORRAL - Prefabricated buildings–wood - Gear Up Technologies Corp.
COMPOST CRANK - Tools–hand-operated - Lotech Products
COMPOST FIX - Deodorizers - Bernard E. Ryan
COMPOST MAKER - Compost - Security Products Co.
COMPOUND - Ladders–wood - John S. Tilley Ladders Co. Inc.
COMPOUND SEMICONDUCTOR MATERIALS INC. - Semiconductors - Compound Semiconductor Materials Inc.
COMPOUND W - Pharmaceutical preparations - Whitehall Laboratories
COMPOZ - Pharmaceutical preparations - Medtech Laboratories Inc.
COMPOZ-A-PUZZLE - Puzzles - Compoz-A-Puzzle Inc.
COMPPOWER - Computer software - Myrtle and Co.
COMPREHENSION CONNECTION - Computer software - Milliken Publishing Co. (Computer Software Div.)
COMPREHENSION POWER - Computer software - Instructional/Communications Technology Inc.
COMPREHENSIVE - Audio equipment - Comprehensive Video Supply Corp.
COMPREHENSIVE - Wallpaper - Textile Wallcoverings International Ltd.
COMPRENDING - Computer software - Duck Corp.
COMPRESS - Apparel–children's - School Apparel, Inc.
COMPRESS-ALIGEN - Thermostats - Brass Products
COMPRESS-O-MATIC - Sealing devices - Zero International Inc.
COMPRESS PAC - Pet products - Sunshine Bird Supplies, Inc.
COMPRESSAIRE - Compressors–air ☆ - Raritan Engineering Co. Inc.
COMPRESSION - Hosiery - Cluett, Peabody & Co.
COMPRESSION 1 - Apparel and accessories - Top Performance
COMPRESSION ST. - Electrical equipment - Berger Industries Inc.
COMPRESSIONETTE - Bandages - Cramer Products Inc.
COMPRESSOR, THE - Racks - Artstyle Printing, Inc.
COMPREXX - Fabrics - Darlington Fabrics Corp.
COMPRI - Tiles–ceramic ☆ - American Olean Tile Co.
COMPRI NOUVEAU - Tiles–ceramic ☆ - American Olean Tile Co.
COMPRIBAND - Asphalt felts and coatings - Phoenix Building Products, Inc.
COMPRO - Windows–plastic - Vistawall
COMPROL - Bandages - Johnson & Johnson
COMPS - Banks–commercial - J.P. Morgan & Co. Inc.
COMPSAVE - Insurance agencies–health - Compdent Corp.
COMPSITE - Computer peripheral equipment - Simon & Schuster, Inc.
COMPSUPPORT - Computer software - Support Systems International, Inc.
COMPTECH - Golfing equipment - Knight Golf, Inc.
COMPTEX - Computer furniture - Atlantic Furniture Systems
COMPTOMETER - Calculators ☆ - Victor Technology
COMPTON - Musical instrument accessories - LP Music Group
COMPTON COURT - Floor coverings - Mannington Resilient Floors
COMPTON II - Cabinets - Dewils Industries Inc.
COMPTONE - Eyeglasses - Del Pharmaceuticals, Inc.
COMPTOWN - Recording label - MCA Universal Studios
COMPTRONIC - Safes - Sargent & Greenleaf, Inc.
COMPU-BINDER - Computers - Compu-Binder Inc.
COMPU-CARPET - Floor coverings–carpet and rugs - United Technical Products Inc.
COMPU-CARREL - Electronics equipment ☆ - Huff & Co.
COMPU-CENTRE - Computer furniture ☆ - JDI Group, Inc.
COMPU-CHEF - Computer software - Micro System Design Inc.
COMPU-CLIP - File folders - Angler's Roslyn Group Ltd.
COMPU CODE - Computer software - Kaden Arnone, Inc.
COMPU-COOK - Calculators - Sharp Electronics Corp.

COMPU-FIRE - Electronics equipment - Engine Electronics, Inc.
COMPU-FLOR - Floor coverings - Mannington Resilient Floors
COMPU-FLOW - Transmissions–motor vehicle - Ati Performance Products, Inc.
COMPU KIT - Computer hardware - Delmar International, Inc.
COMPU-LENZ - Computers - Florida New Concepts Marketing Inc.
COMPU-LOCK - Locks–padlocks - Compu-Lock, Inc.
COMPU-LOK - Electronic equipment - American Locker Security Systems
COMPU-LOOP - Floor coverings–carpet and rugs - Olympic Carpets Inc.
COMPU-MAT - Mats - United Technical Products Inc.
COMPU-MATIC - Television equipment ☆ - Quasar Co.
COMPU-RELEASE - Adhesives and sealants - United Technical Products Inc.
COMPU-ROUTE - Computer software - SGL Data Systems
COMPU-SCAN - Digital encoders - Digital Descriptor Systems Inc.
COMPU-SEARCH - Television equipment ☆ - Quasar Co.
COMPU-SKETCH - Digital encoders - Digital Descriptor Systems Inc.
COMPU-SPELL - Computer software - Encyclopaedia Britannica Inc.
COMPU-SQUIRT - Toys–guns ☆ - Imperial Toy Corp.
COMPU-STAT + - Floor coverings–carpet and rugs ☆ - Porter Carpet Mills Inc.
COMPU-TABLE - Computer peripheral equipment - Gusdorf Corp.
COMPU-THERM - Food processors - Oliver Products Co.
COMPU-TILE - Floor coverings–tile - United Technical Products Inc.
COMPU-TUTOR - Computer software - Chris B. Royal
COMPUBUILD - Computer software - Xerox Corp.
COMPUCAL II - Adhesive backed films - Flexcon Co. Inc.
COMPUCALLER - Pet products - Burnham Brothers
COMPUCAMPUS - Computers - David M. Mezzapelle
COMPUCAP - Computer software - Janet Vohariwatt
COMPUCARD - Office supplies ☆ - Rolodex Corp.
COMPUCARDS - Electronic equipment ☆ - McGraw-Hill Companies, Inc.
COMPUCARRIER - Cases–plastic - TJC, Inc.
COMPUCASE - Luggage - Incom America Inc.
COMPUCHAIR - Office furniture–wood - Compuchair, Inc.
COMPUCHASE - Circuit boards–printed - Walter Polan
COMPUCHOICE - Computer peripheral equipment - Compuchoice, Inc.
COMPUCHROME - Computer software - Absolute Data Solutions
COMPUCHRON - Clocks ☆ - Unisonic Products Corp.
COMPUCLEAN - Cleaning preparations - Super Soap Co. Inc.
COMPUCLIP - Optical services - Opsales, Inc.
COMPUCOLOR - Computer paper, envelopes ☆ - Coronet General Corp.
COMPUCOLOR - Computers - Interplastic Corp.
COMPUCOLOR - Photographic equipment - Electronic Systems Engineering Co.
COMPUCOLOR - Stationery - Tab Products Co.
COMPUCOM - Telephone apparatus - Paso Sound Products Inc.
COMPUCORDER - Computer storage devices - Science Instruments Co.
COMPUCOUNT - Computer software - Setra Systems, Inc.
COMPUCOURT - Computer software - Quest Computer Product, Inc.
COMPUCROSTICS - Computer software - E. David & Associates
COMPUCUSH - Orthopedic products - Kinetic Diversified Industries, Inc.
COMPUDYNE - Computers - Soft Warehouse Inc.
COMPUFET - Medical apparatus - Hoggan Health Industries Inc.
COMPUFORM - Forms–preprinted - Appleson Press Inc.
COMPUFRAMES - Electronics equipment - Lake Compuframes
COMPUGARDEN - Computer software - Compugarden
COMPUGOLF - Golfing equipment - Precise International/Wenger
COMPUHOUSE - Computer hardware - Pan West, Inc.
COMPUJET, A - Office supplies - American Ink Jet Corp.
COMPULABEL - Labels–paper - Continental Dataforms
COMPULAW - Computer software - Compulaw, Inc.
COMPULERT - Computer programming services - At&T Corp.
COMPULINER - Computer peripheral equipment - Avenues in Leather, Inc.
COMPUMASTER - Photographic equipment - Electronic Systems Engineering Co.
COMPUMERGE - Computer software - Xerox Corp.
COMPUMIST - Computer peripheral equipment - Microcomputer Controls Inc.
COMPUNOTE - Computer software - Ritter
COMPUNOTES - Notebooks and notepads - Compu-Notes, Inc.
COMPUPAC - Computer storage devices - Salt River Designs Ltd.
COMPUPHONE 2000 - Computer input peripherals - Integrated Technology Inc.
COMPUPLANTS - Computer software - Compuplants
COMPUPREP - Computer software - American Academy of Pediatrics
COMPUPREP - Computer software - Xerox Corp.
COMPUPULSE - Exercising equipment - Precise International/Wenger
COMPUQUIP - Computer hardware - Compuquip Inc.

☆ = Now out of production

COMPUR - Photographic equipment - Berkey Marketing Cos.

COMPUSELL THE MISSING LINK - Computer software - Furniture/Appliance Operations Group, Inc.

COMPUSERIES - Computer peripheral equipment - Xerox Corp.

COMPUSET - Jewelry - Jesse Bands, Inc.

COMPUSIGHT - Computer software - Kuau Technology Ltd.

COMPUSIGN - Hardware - Showcard Sign Systems

COMPUSPORT - Sporting goods ☆ - Chronomix Corp.

COMPUSUN - Computer software - Sun Industries, Inc.

COMPUSWITCH - Computer software - Raritan Computer, Inc.

COMPUTA-FIT - Hosiery–men's ☆ - Edison Brothers Stores, Inc.

COMPUTAGRID - Artists' materials - Graphic Products Corp.

COMPUTALK WITH TOM KING - Broadcasting stations–radio - Computalk Radio & Television, Inc.

COMPUTASTAT - Mats - U.S. Mat & Rubber Co. Inc.

COMPUTE ROW - Exercising equipment - Universal Gym Equipment, Inc.

COMPUTE-U-CLEAN - Cleaning preparations - Industrial Optical

COMPUTECH - Office furniture–wood - Krueger International, Inc.

COMPUTECT - Alarm systems - Holmes Protection Group, Inc.

COMPUTEMP - Dryers–hair - Helene Curtis Industries Inc.

COMPUTEMP - Thermometers - Premiere Products

COMPUTER - Hearing aids - Computer Hearing Aid Corp.

COMPUTER AIDED LABOR MEASUREMENT - Computer software - Gagnon & Associates

COMPUTER ATHLETE - Computer hardware and software - Computer Athlete Inc.

COMPUTER BASE - Health care products - Tennis Elbow Corp.

COMPUTER CARNIVAL - Computer software ☆ - Nordic Software, Inc.

COMPUTER CHEF - Computer software ☆ - Software Toolworks, Inc.

COMPUTER CHEF, THE - Computer peripheral equipment - ESHA Research Inc.

COMPUTER CITY KIDS - Apparel–children's - Tandy Corp.

COMPUTER CITY SUPERCENTER - Electronic equipment - Computer SuperCenters International Inc.

COMPUTER CLASSICS - Computer software - Edward R. Arnold

COMPUTER CLOTHES - Computers - Dallco Industries Inc.

COMPUTER CONCEPTS - Computer software - Ventura Educational Systems

COMPUTER CROSSWORDS - Computer software - Price Stern Sloan Inc.

COMPUTER DIMENSIONS - Educational materials - ITP Licensing Corp.

COMPUTER DISCOVERY - Computer software ☆ - SRA/McGraw-Hill (Div. of The McGraw-Hill Companies)

COMPUTER DOT - Fabric binding - Freudenberg Nonwovens Apparel Division

COMPUTER EYES - Optical scanners–computer - Stuart C. Grant

COMPUTER FUN - Electronic equipment - Texas Instruments Inc.

COMPUTER FUN NOTEBOOK - Computer software - Tiger Electronics, Inc.

COMPUTER HEALTH BREAK - Exercising equipment - Escape Ergonomics Inc.

COMPUTER HOWSE - Computer peripheral equipment ☆ - Ikon Office Solutions

COMPUTER IDIOT TAPES - Video production - International Art Galleries, Inc.

COMPUTER INDUSTRY YELLOW PAGES, THE - Publisher's imprints - Business Interactive, Inc.

COMPUTER INTELLIGENCE - Computer software - Ziff Communications Co.

COMPUTER KARAOKE - Computer storage devices–optical - Computer Karaoke Corp.

COMPUTER KNOW-HOW NOW! - Publisher's imprints - International Data Group, Inc.

COM'PU'73R LANGU46E - Apparel and accessories - Lloyd M. Hughes Enterprises, Inc.

COMPUTER LAW SERVICE REPORTER - Publisher's imprints - Robert P. Bigelow

COMPUTER LINKS - Computer software - Harcourt Brace & Co.

COMPUTER LOGIC LAB - Toys ☆ - Natural Science Industries, Ltd.

COMPUTER-MADE - Golfing equipment - Lawrence Y. Igarashi

COMPUTER-MATE - Electronic equipment - Arion Corp.

COMPUTER MODE - Floor coverings–carpet and rugs ☆ - Karastan-Bigelow Inc.

COMPUTER ONE - Computers - Computer One, Inc.

COMPUTER OUTDOORS, THE - Computers - Group Technologies Corp.

COMPUTER-PAK - Envelopes - Mail-Well Envelope

COMPUTER PAL - Games - Vtech Industries, Inc.

COMPUTER PALACE - Computers–mainframe - Los Angeles Computer Corp.

COMPUTER PERFECTION - Games ☆ - Lakeside Games

COMPUTER PERFORMANCE - Computer peripheral equipment - Computer Performance, Inc.

COMPUTER PERSONALS - Computer peripheral equipment - Mead-Hatcher, Inc.

COMPUTER PLUS - Computer peripheral equipment ☆ - AVAS Corp.

COMPUTER RENAISSANCE - Computer hardware - Grow Biz International, Inc.

COMPUTER REPAIR AND UTILITY DEVICE - Novelty items - Williams Resource Group

COMPUTER SMARTS - Toys - Connor Toy Corp.

COMPUTER-START - Audio equipment ☆ - Matsuzaka Co. America

COMPUTER SYSTEMS UNLIMITED - Computer memory devices - Computer Systems Unlimited

COMPUTER TRAC - Washing machines–household - Maytag Corp.

COMPUTER TUTOR - Computer software - Computer Tutor, Inc.

COMPUTER USER'S BEST FRIEND, A - Computer storage devices–optical - Kris Jamsa Software, Inc.

COMPUTER WARRIORS - Toys - Mattel, Inc.

COMPUTER WIZ - Knives–pocket - Precise International/Wenger

COMPUTER WORKS - Computers - Apaq Technology, Inc.

COMPUTERADIO - Electronic equipment - Thomson Consumer Electronics, Inc.

COMPUTERAID - Cases–compacts - Karen Anne Manufacturing Inc.

COMPUTERCOACH - Computer software - Golf Training Systems, Inc.

COMPUTERCRAFTS - Hobby kits - Janlynn Corp.

COMPUTEREASY - Computer software - Computer Easy International, Inc.

COMPUTERGUY - Computer software - Martin D. Thorne

COMPUTERIZED SECURITY SYSTEMS - Electrical equipment - Masco Corp.

COMPUTERLAND - Computer franchise - Computerland Corp.

COMPUTERMATE - Electronic equipment - A.L.S. Industries Inc.

COMPUTERMATE - Furniture - Beatrice Cos. Inc.

COMPUTEROBICS - Toys - Tonka Corp.

COMPUTER'S EDGE - Computers - A/T Enterprises

COMPUTERWALL - Computer peripheral equipment - RGB Spectrum

COMPUTERWORLD - Video production - International Data Group, Inc.

COMPUTHINK - Computer software - Computhink, Inc.

COMPUTIME - Computer software - Timemed Labeling Systems, Inc.

COMPUTIME - Computers - Computime, Inc.

COMPUTING DEVICES INTERNATIONAL - Computers and communication products - Computing Devices International, Inc.

COMPUTING FOR THE LONG RUN - Computer software - Marathon Technologies Corp.

COMPUTING IS FUN - Computer diskettes–blank - Sterling Plastics Co.

COMPUTRAINER - Bicycles - Racer-Mate, Inc.

COMPUTRIBE - Statuary - Joan Blue

COMPUTRIM - Exercising equipment ☆ - Roadmaster Corp.

COMPUTROL - Pumps - ITT Corp.

COMPUTRON - Computer software - Computron Technologies Corp.

COMPUTRON - Watches - Bulova Corp.

COMPUTRON 2000 - Watches - Bulova Corp.

COMPUTYMP 300 - Hearing aids - Beltone Electronics Corp.

COMPUTYPE - Labeling machinery - Computype, Inc.

COMPUWINE - Computer software - Comp-U-Wine

COMPUWINNER - Bething selection sheets - Compuwinner Computerized System, Inc.

COMPUZONE - Computer peripheral equipment - Compuzone, Inc.

COMPY - Apparel–athletic - Hind, Inc.

COMRAD WIRELESS DATA LINK - Computer peripheral equipment - PSQ Scientific, Inc.

COMRADAR - Computers–personal - Fox Electronics

COMRADE - Medical apparatus - Ventura Enterprises, Inc.

COMSCAN - Telephone apparatus - Command Communications, Inc.

COMSCIRE - Computer hardware - Quantum World Corp.

COMSERTER - Electrical equipment - Texscan Corp.

COMSOCK - Computer software - Stahura-Brenner Group, Inc.

COMSOURCE - Paper products - Unipro Food Service, Inc.

COMSOURCE - Preserved foods–prepackaged - Anchor Food Products, Inc.

COMSPACE - Electronic equipment - Comspace Corp.

COMSPEC - Amplifiers - Eden Electronics Inc.

COMSTAX - Computer hardware - Arnet Corp.

COMSTOC - Pens - Keuffel & Esser Co.

COMSTOCK - Cabinets - Imperial Cabinet Co. Inc.

COMSTOCK - Food products - Curtice-Burns Foods, Inc.

COMSTOCK - Recording label - Comstock Records Ltd.

COMSTOCK CARDS - Trading cards and stamps - Comstock Cards Inc.

COMSTOCK PUBLISHING ASSOCIATES - Publisher's imprint - Cornell University Press

COMSTOCK SHUTTERS - Shutters–wood - San Benito Shutter Co.

☆ = Now out of production

COMSUEDES - Wallpaper - Stamford Wall Paper Co. Inc.
COMTE - Cheese - Food & Wines From France
COMTE DE ROFFIGNAC - Beverages–alcohol - Moquet Ltd.
COMTE DE SANSAC - Wines - World Wide Wine and Spirits Inc.
COMTE DE VOGUE - Wines - Dreyfus Ashby Inc.
COMTE JOSEPH - Beverages–alcohol - Alimar & Cie. Inc.
COMTECH - Electronic equipment ☆ - Fairchild Data Corp.
COMTECH MICRO SYSTEM - Computers - Comtech Micro System Inc.
COMTEMPORARY - Mallets - Mike Balter Mallets
COMTEMPORARY CLEARS - Mats - Tenex Corp.
COMTES DE CHAMPAGNE BLANC DE BLANCS - Wines - Kobrand Corp.
COMTES DE CHAMPAGNE ROSE - Wines - Kobrand Corp.
COMTESSE - Corsets - R.H. Macy & Co.
COMTESSE - Glassware–household ☆ - WMF/USA
COMTESSE BLANCHE - Dinnerware–glass ☆ - WMF/USA
COMTESSE CATHERINE - Dinnerware–glass ☆ - WMF/USA
COMTESSE MARIE-CLAIRE - Dinnerware–glass ☆ - WMF/USA
COMTESSE MARIE-HELENE - Dinnerware–glass ☆ - WMF/USA
COMTEX - Floor coverings - Comtex Industries Inc.
COMTEX - Wallpaper ☆ - Capital Carousel Inc.
COMTEXT - Computer software - Budgetext Corp.
COMTOR-DIGITAL - Electrical testing instruments - Comtorgage Corp.
COMTREX - Cold remedies - Bristol-Myers Squibb Co.
COMTREX A/S - Pharmaceutical preparations - Bristol-Myers Squibb Co.
COMTREX CF - Cold remedies - Bristol-Myers Squibb Co.
COMTREX LIQUI-GELS - Analgesics - Bristol-Myers Squibb Co.
COMTREX MAXIMUM STRENGTH - Analgesics - Bristol-Myers Squibb Co.
COMTRON - Floor coverings–carpet and rugs - Western Carpet Mills
COMTRONIC - Electronic equipment - Compact Air Products, Inc.
COMUITA - Skin care products - Teaco International
COMUNITY ACCESS - Computer hardware - Com21, Inc.
COMVITA - Health care products - Pacific Resources International
COMWALL - Wallpaper - Stamford Wall Paper Co. Inc.
COMWALL - Wallpaper ☆ - Capital Carousel Inc.
COMWALL BASICS - Wallpaper - Stamford Wall Paper Co. Inc.
COMWALL CHALLENGE - Wallpaper ☆ - Capital Carousel Inc.
COMWALL LITES - Wallpaper ☆ - Capital Carousel Inc.
COMWALL STRAND - Wallpaper ☆ - Capital Carousel Inc.
COMYCIN - Pharmaceutical preparations ☆ - Keene Pharmaceuticals Inc.
CON-BOND - Rubber cement - Columbia Cement Co. Inc.
CON BRIO - Recording label - Con Brio Records
CON-COIL - Cleaning preparations - Stewart-Hall Chemical Corp.
CON-CRAX - Crack filler - Pioneer Manufacturing Co.
CON-CRE-COTE - Paints - Morris Paint & Varnish Co.
CON DEC - Furniture - Lowy Group Inc.
CON-DONE - Bags - Pro Hygiene
CON DOOR - Doors–wood - F.P.G. Wholesale, Inc.
CON-DOR - Floor coverings–tile - Pawling Corp. (Standard Products Div.)
CON-ETTE - Sound-responsive lights - Control Research Inc.
CON EX - Braces–orthopedic - Geoffrey G. Glidden
CON-GLO - Detergents ☆ - Care-Tech Laboratories Inc.
CON-GLOSS - Floor waxes ☆ - Care-Tech Laboratories Inc.
CON-KWICK - Nuts and bolts - Emhart Industries Inc.
CON-O - Welding equipment ☆ - Weld Tooling Corp.
CON-PAK - Trash compactor - International Baler Corp.
CON TA FLORA - Bedding–linen - Dan River Inc.
CON-TACT - Decals and transfers - Rubbermaid Inc.
CON-TECH - Lighting equipment - Conservation Technology Ltd.
CON-TEMPO-TRAY - Office supplies - Stempel Manufacturing Co.
CON-TEXT - Wallcoverings - Sherman & Associates International
CON-TEXT - Wallpaper - Aresda Design Associates
CON-TOOL CURE - Machinery - UV Process Supply, Inc.
CON-TORQ - Hardware - North and Judd Inc.
CON-TREET - Adhesives and sealants - Rooto Corp.
CON-TROL - Apparel–women's - Cupid Foundations Inc.
CON-X - Telephone apparatus - Con-X Corp.
CONAC - Fixtures–plastic - Concrete Accessories, Inc.
CONACETOL - Pharmaceutical preparations - Consolidated Midland Corp.
CONAGA - Food products - Semple Co.
CONAGRA - Seafood products–fresh or frozen - Conagra, Inc.
CONAGRA BAKERS - Flour–blended - Conagra, Inc.
CONAGRA CLUB - Chickens - Conagra, Inc.
CONAIR - Health care products - Conair Corp.
CONAIR GRAPHIX - Mirrors - Conair Corp.
CONAIR REFLECTIONS - Mirrors - Conair Corp.
CONAIR SENSATION - Hair care products - Conair Corp.

CONAIR SUPREME - Hair care products - Conair Corp.
CONAIR SWIRL-A-CURL - Hair curlers - Conair Corp.
CONAN - Electronics equipment - Berg Technology, Inc.
CONAN - Posters - Fairfax Prints Ltd.
CONAP - Adhesives and sealants - Phoenix Oil Co.
CONAR - Pharmaceutical preparations - Smithkline Beecham Corp.
CONARCH - Recording label - Conarch Productions
CONART - Apparel and accessories - Conart, Inc.
CONASAUR COLLECTION - Children's footwear and apparel - Converse Inc.
CONATAL - Pharmaceutical preparations ☆ - Coast Laboratories Inc.
CONATE - Pharmaceutical preparations - H.R. Cenci Laboratories Inc.
CONBASE - Roofing materials - Consolidated Fiber Glass Products Co.
CONBASE MB25 - Roofing materials - Consolidated Fiber Glass Products Co.
CONBASE MB40 - Roofing materials - Consolidated Fiber Glass Products Co.
CONBASE W-1 IV - Roofing materials - Consolidated Fiber Glass Products Co.
CONBEXTRA - Concrete products - Fosroc Inc.
CONBRIO - Cooking equipment–household - Birmingham Stove & Range Co.
CONBRIO - Tomato pastes and sauces - John N. Wright Jr. Inc.
CONCANNON - Wines - Parrott & Co.
CONCANNON VINEYARD - Wines - Concannon Vineyard
CONCANNON VINEYARDS - Wines - Shaw-Ross International Importers
CONCAP - Roofing materials - Consolidated Fiber Glass Products Co.
CONCEAL - Sporting goods - Camp-Cap Products
CONCEAL - Zippers - YKK USA Inc.
CONCEAL-IT - Firearms, accessories, and parts - Doctor Ctr.
CONCEALING SYSTEM - Cosmetics - Lasting Impression I Inc.
CONCEDE NOTHING - Rackets–tennis - Pro Kennex, Inc.
CONCEIVE - Pregnancy test kits - Ansell Inc. (Personal Products Div.)
CONCENSUS - Furniture ☆ - Bassett Furniture Industries, Inc.
CONCENSYS - Office furniture–metal - Hon Co.
CONCENTRA - Computer software - Concentra Corp.
CONCENTRATE - Apparel and accessories ☆ - Warnaco Inc.
CONCENTRATE! - Computer software ☆ - PCSoftware
CONCENTRATE 7 - Soap - Crystal Chemical Co.
CONCENTRATE 50 - Chemical preparations - Coastal Industries Inc.
CONCENTRATE! ON WORDS & CONCEPTS - Computer software - Laureate Learning Systems Inc.
CONCENTRE - Skin care products - Face Up Professional Skin Centers Inc.
CONCENTRIC AIR - Pans - Anchor Hocking Glass, Inc.
CONCENTRIC PROJECT MANAGEMENT - Computer software - Primavera Systems, Inc.
CONCENTRICS - Furniture - Stanley Furniture Co. Inc.
CONCENTRICS - Giftware - Sasaki
CONCENTRIN - Cough medicines ☆ - Warner-Lambert Co.
CONCENTRIX - Drill bits - Ingersoll-Rand Co.
CONCENTRIX - Furniture ☆ - Bassett Furniture Industries, Inc.
CONCEPT - Bathroom accessories - Ransburg Accessories Inc.
CONCEPT - Bicycles - Kent International Inc.
CONCEPT - Blankets–electric - Sunbeam-Oster Household Products
CONCEPT - Boats–motor - Chris Craft Boats
CONCEPT - Building materials - Hoffman
CONCEPT - Cabinets - HomeCrest Corp.
CONCEPT - Clocks - General Time Corp. (Westclox/Seth Thomas Div.)
CONCEPT - Computer peripheral equipment ☆ - QMS, Inc.
CONCEPT - Doors–glass ☆ - Pease Industries, Inc.
CONCEPT - Fabrics - Burlington House Fabrics Group
CONCEPT - Fishing tackle - Minnesota Mining & Manufacturing Co.
CONCEPT - Floor coverings–carpet and rugs - Ashley Commercial Carpets
CONCEPT - Floor coverings–carpet and rugs - Coronet Carpets Inc.
CONCEPT - Floor coverings–carpet and rugs ☆ - Mannington Carpets, Inc.
CONCEPT - Furniture ☆ - Bassett Furniture Industries, Inc.
CONCEPT - Glassware ☆ - Indiana Glass Co.
CONCEPT - Glassware–scientific - Federal Glass
CONCEPT - Hair care products - Wella Corp. (Consumer Products Div.)
CONCEPT - Household cleaner - Intex Chemical Inc.
CONCEPT - Luggage - Airway Industries, Inc.
CONCEPT - Markers–felt-tip ☆ - Faber-Castell Corp.
CONCEPT - Metals - Federal-Hoffman, Inc.
CONCEPT - Motor vehicle parts and accessories - Deflecta-Shield
CONCEPT - Paints - PPG Industries, Inc.
CONCEPT - Paperboard - International Paper Co.
CONCEPT - Recording label - Jazz Composer's Orchestra Association Inc.
CONCEPT - Refrigerators ☆ - White Consolidated Industries, Inc.
CONCEPT - Tires - Bridgestone/Firestone, Inc.
CONCEPT - Toothbrush - Concept Dental Inc.
CONCEPT - Toothbrushes - Tess Corp.

☆ = Now out of production

CONCEPT - Trailers–travel - Ohio Bus Sales, Inc.
CONCEPT - Water bottles–rubber - Connelly Skis, Inc.
CONCEPT 1 - Dinnerware–glass - Noritake Co. Inc.
CONCEPT II - Sporting goods - Schutt Manufacturing Co.
CONCEPT 5 - Games - Small World Toys
CONCEPT 10 - Air conditioning equipment - Armstrong Air Conditioning Inc.
CONCEPT 10 - Water purification systems ☆ - Penn-Plax, Inc.
CONCEPT 21 - Heating equipment - Slant/Fin Corp.
CONCEPT 21 - Kitchen appliances - T.J. Gundlach Machine Co.
CONCEPT 32 - Lumber - Georgia-Pacific Corp.
CONCEPT 35 - Furniture ☆ - Brill Manufacturing Co.
CONCEPT '70 - Floor coverings ☆ - Congoleum Corp.
CONCEPT 80'S - Apparel and accessories ☆ - Swirl II Ltd.
CONCEPT '90 - Floor coverings - Congoleum Corp.
CONCEPT 2000 - Flooring–hardwood - Biwood Flooring
CONCEPT 2000 - Sports rackets and accessories - Wilson Hunt International, Ltd.
CONCEPT BOOKS - Publisher's imprints - Albert Whitman and Co.
CONCEPT BY COUNTRY COACH - Motor vehicles–buses - Country Coach, Inc.
CONCEPT COOKER - Cooking equipment–commercial ☆ - West Bend Co.
CONCEPT EIGHTY - Furniture - Jackson of Danville Inc.
CONCEPT II - Cologne - Concept II Cosmetics, Inc.
CONCEPT II - Tables - Impact Furniture
CONCEPT II - Tables–wood - Quaker Industries Ltd.
CONCEPT INDUSTRIES - Packaging–paper - Concept Industries, Inc.
CONCEPT N NEEPER - Automotive parts and accessories - Mobile Hi-Tech Wheels
CONCEPT ONE - Vacuum cleaners and accessories - The Hoover Co.
CONCEPT ONE MAXUS - Reactor containment vessels - Novellus Systems, Inc.
CONCEPT PLUS - Electronic equipment - Concept Plus
CONCEPT/RYA - Floor coverings–carpet and rugs ☆ - Concepts International
CONCEPT STORES - Shoe stores - United States Shoe Corp.
CONCEPT SYSTEM, THE - Computer software - Concept Systems
CONCEPT TWO - Vacuum cleaners and accessories - The Hoover Co.
CONCEPT V - Furniture–upholstered ☆ - Mersman Furniture Co.
CONCEPT XXI - Tires - Bridgestone/Firestone, Inc.
CONCEPTION - Medical apparatus - Princeton Biomeditech Corp.
CONCEPTION ONE - Medical apparatus - Princeton Biomeditech Corp.
CONCEPTION PLUS - Medical apparatus - Princeton Biomeditech Corp.
CONCEPTIONS - Floor coverings–carpet and rugs ☆ - Callaway Carpets
CONCEPTROL - Pharmaceutical preparations - Ortho Pharmaceutical Corp.
CONCEPTS - Cabinets - Saco Industries Inc.
CONCEPTS - Floor coverings–carpet and rugs - Criterion Mills Inc.
CONCEPTS - Furniture ☆ - Bassett Furniture Industries, Inc.
CONCEPTS - Jewelry - Concept Marketing Inc.
CONCEPTS - Paneling - Georgia-Pacific Corp.
CONCEPTS - Wallpaper ☆ - Glidden Co.
CONCEPTS - Wallpaper ☆ - Manuscreens
CONCEPTS BY CAREN - Apparel and accessories - A.I.J.J. Enterprises, Inc.
CONCEPTS BY CENTURY - Furniture–wood ☆ - Century Furniture Co.
CONCEPTS BY MALCOLM - Apparel–women's - San Simeon, Inc.
CONCEPTS BY MIDMARK - Cabinets - Midmark Corp.
CONCEPTS DYNAMIC - Computer software - Concepts Dynamic, Inc.
CONCEPTS-EARRINGS FOR SENSITIVE EARS - Jewelry - Concept Marketing Inc.
CONCEPTS II - Wallpaper - Manuscreens
CONCEPTS IN COLOR - Wallpaper - Warner Co.
CONCEPTS IN COLOR III - Wallpaper - Warner Co.
CONCEPTS INTERNATIONAL - Floor coverings–carpet and rugs - Concepts International
CONCEPTS ONE - Furniture ☆ - The Coleman Co.
CONCEPTS PLUS - Giftware - Concepts Plus
CONCEPTUAL EFFECTS TYPING METHOD - Computer software - Joseph Delphonse
CONCEPTUS - Medical apparatus - Conceptus, Inc.
CONCERN - Insecticides - Stern's Miracle-Gro Products, Inc.
CONCERN COMPOST BIOACTIVATOR - Compost - Necessary Organics Inc.
CONCERN DIATOMACEOUS EARTH - Insecticides - Necessary Organics Inc.
CONCERN INSECT KILLING SOAP - Insecticides - Necessary Organics Inc.
CONCERN MULT-PURPOSE INSECT KILLER - Insecticides - Necessary Organics Inc.
CONCERN ROSE & FLOWER INSECT KILLER - Insecticides - Necessary Organics Inc.
CONCERN SLUG STOP - Insecticides ∑ Necessary Organics Inc.

CONCERN TOMATO & VEGETABLE INSECT KILLER - Insecticides - Necessary Organics Inc.
CONCERN VITALIZE - Fertilizers - Necessary Organics Inc.
CONCERN WEED PREVENTION PLUS - Fertilizers - Necessary Organics Inc.
CONCERT - Amplifiers–musical instrument - Fender Musical Instruments
CONCERT - Binoculars - Bausch & Lomb Inc.
CONCERT - Floor coverings - Tarkett, Inc.
CONCERT - Furniture - CTH/Sherrill Occasional
CONCERT - Furniture - JSJ Seating Corp.
CONCERT-DISC - Recording label - Everest Record Group
CONCERT GRAND - Drums–musical instruments ☆ - Selmer Co. Inc.
CONCERT HOUSE - Audio equipment - M and S Systems Inc.
CONCERT MACHINE - Audio equipment - Sound Concepts Inc.
CONCERT MASTER - Accordions - Italo-American Accordion Manufacturing Co.
CONCERT MASTER - Violins - Fender Musical Instruments
CONCERT MULTI-GRAND - Musical instruments - Excelsior Accordions Inc.
CONCERT STAR - Musical instruments ☆ - Fred Gretsch Enterprises
CONCERT TOUR - Dolls - Mattel, Inc.
CONCERT WARBLER - Harmonicas - William Kratt Co.
CONCERTAPE - Electronic equipment - Tandy Corp.
CONCERTINAS - Vegetables–frozen - Lamb-Weston, Inc.
CONCERTISTE - Musical instrument stores ☆ - Meisel Music Inc.
CONCERTLINE.COM - Advertising agencies - Sunshine Promotions, Inc.
CONCERTMASTER - Computer peripheral equipment - NMB Technologies Inc. (Hi-Tek Div.)
CONCERTMASTER - Computer software - Brio Technology, Inc.
CONCERTMATE - Electronic equipment - Tandy Corp.
CONCERTO - Accordions - Atlas Accordions Inc.
CONCERTO - Bathroom fixtures - Crane Plumbing/Fiat Products
CONCERTO - Blinds–venetian ☆ - Hunter Douglas, Inc.
CONCERTO - Chimes - Nutone Inc.
CONCERTO - Christmas tree ornaments - Cracker Box Inc.
CONCERTO - Clarinets - G. Leblanc Corp.
CONCERTO - Computer terminals - Compaq Computer Corp.
CONCERTO - Deodorizers - Willert Home Products, Inc.
CONCERTO - Dinnerware–glass - Dansk International Designs, Ltd.
CONCERTO - Fabrics - Vertilux-Louverlux Inc.
CONCERTO - Floor coverings–carpet and rugs - Patrick Carpet Mills
CONCERTO - Floor coverings–carpet and rugs - Regal Rugs Inc.
CONCERTO - Floor coverings–carpet and rugs ☆ - Galaxy Carpet Mills Inc.
CONCERTO - Footwear ☆ - Asics Tiger Corp.
CONCERTO - Furniture ☆ - Broyhill Furniture Industries, Inc.
CONCERTO - Glassware–household - Svend Jensen of Denmark Inc.
CONCERTO - Glassware–household - Royal Crystal Rock Inc.
CONCERTO - Glassware–household ☆ - National Housewares
CONCERTO - Hearing aids - Beltone Electronics Corp.
CONCERTO - Musical instrument accessories - GRK Manufacturing
CONCERTO - Occasional tables ☆ - JDI Group, Inc.
CONCERTO - Rings–jewelry - Artcarved Inc.
CONCERTO - Stadium seating - Krueger International, Inc.
CONCERTO - Wallpaper - K.M.L. Industries
CONCERTO - Wallpaper - Textile Wallcoverings International Ltd.
CONCERTO - Watches - Bulova Corp.
CONCERTO COLLECTION - Furniture ☆ - Bassett Furniture Industries, Inc.
CONCH - Dinnerware–glass - Franciscan by Johnson Brothers, USA, Inc.
CONCH 27 - Boats - Edey & Duff, Ltd.
CONCHA - Health care products - Hudson Respiratory Care Inc.
CONCHA - Hearing aids - G.N. Danavox Inc.
CONCHA Y TORO - Wines - Banfi Vintners
CONCHATERM - Health care products - Hudson Respiratory Care Inc.
CONCHITA - Handbags - Melbourne Manufacturing Co. Inc.
CONCHITAS - Cigars - Gesty Trading & Manufacturing Corp.
CONCHO - Flowers, plants, and seeds - White Swan, Ltd.
CONCHO - Garden equipment - Lindig Manufacturing Corp.
CONCHOCOVERS - Belts–apparel - Bell Group, Inc.
CONCHORD, THE - Musical instruments - Conchord Expert Technologies, Inc.
CONCISE - Dental compounds - Minnesota Mining & Manufacturing Co.
CONCISE - Floor coverings–carpet and rugs ☆ - Walter Carpet Mills
CONCISE - Medical apparatus - Wright Medical Technology, Inc.
CONCISE VISION - Computer software - Professional Alliance, Inc.
CONCLORGE - Mats - Matworks
CONCLUDE - Herbicides - BASF Corp.
CONCO - Paints - Smiland Paint Co.
CONCO-COTE - Coatings, etc. - Continental Products Co.
CONCO-PLEX - Paints - Conco Paint Co.

CONCO PRO - Paints - Conco Paint Co.

CONCOA - Welding equipment - Controls Corp. of America

CONCOA KITS - Welding equipment - Controls Corp. of America

CONCOAT - Roofing materials - Consolidated Fiber Glass Products Co.

CONCOL - Computer software - Concol Inc.

CONCOLOR STAIN - Concrete products ☆ - Consolidated Coatings Corp.

CONCORD - Adhesives and sealants - Garon Products Inc.

CONCORD - Air conditioning equipment - Armstrong Air Conditioning Inc.

CONCORD - Aquatic pharmacuetical preparations - Superior Shade & Blind Co. Inc.

CONCORD - Ashtrays–metal ☆ - Willert Home Products, Inc.

CONCORD - Bathroom accessories - F.H. Lawson Co.

CONCORD - Bathroom accessories ☆ - Kirsch Co.

CONCORD - Cabinets - Imperial Cabinet Co. Inc.

CONCORD - Cabinets - Western Cabinet & Millwork Inc.

CONCORD - Cabinets ☆ - Mouser Kitchens Inc.

CONCORD - Cabinets–wood ☆ - Kemper

CONCORD - Candles - Empire Manufacturing Co.

CONCORD - Candlesticks ☆ - Lenox Crystal, Inc.

CONCORD - Chimes - Nutone Inc.

CONCORD - Cigarettes - Philip Morris Companies Inc.

CONCORD - Computer storage devices - Concord Data Media, Inc.

CONCORD - Cooking utensils–stoneware ☆ - National Housewares

CONCORD - Drapery hardware - Kenney Manufacturing Co.

CONCORD - Fabrics ☆ - Wall-Pride Inc.

CONCORD - Flag poles - Concord Industries Inc.

CONCORD - Flag poles - Flags International Inc.

CONCORD - Flags - Valley Forge Flag

CONCORD - Floor coverings ☆ - Robbins Inc.

CONCORD - Floor coverings–carpet and rugs - Bellbridge Carpets

CONCORD - Floor coverings–carpet and rugs - Concord/Aldon Industries Inc.

CONCORD - Floor coverings–carpet and rugs - Trans-Ocean Import Co. Inc.

CONCORD - Footwear ☆ - Nozaki America Inc.

CONCORD - Furniture - Haworth, Inc.

CONCORD - Jewelry - Excell Manufacturing Co.

CONCORD - Lighting fixtures ☆ - Liteway

CONCORD - Luggage ☆ - Samsonite Corp.

CONCORD - Manicure preparations - Concord Shear Co.

CONCORD - Musical instruments - Ideal Musical Merchandise Co.

CONCORD - Office supplies - Da-Lite Screen Co. Inc.

CONCORD - Prefabricated buildings–wood - Champion Enterprises Inc.

CONCORD - Self-inking daters and numberers ☆ - Consolidated Stamp Manufacturing Co. Inc.

CONCORD - Stereos - Harman Consumer Group

CONCORD - Watches - North American Watch Corp.

CONCORD - Wood products ☆ - Gossen Corp.

CONCORD BAR CRYSTAL - Giftware - Lenox Crystal, Inc.

CONCORD CONCERTO - Recording label - Concord Records Inc.

CONCORD FARMS - Poultry feeds ☆ - Showell Co.

CONCORD FERMUS - Paper–carbon - Kores Nordic USA Corp.

CONCORD HALL - Furniture ☆ - Bassett Furniture Industries, Inc.

CONCORD HOUSE - Buttons - Concord Fabrics Inc.

CONCORD II - Wallpaper - Glidden Co.

CONCORD LITE - Chimes - Nutone Inc.

CONCORD MANOR - Furniture ☆ - Bassett Furniture Industries, Inc.

CONCORD MILLS - Bakery products - Concord Foods Inc.

CONCORD MINIATURES - Dolls - Cardinal Inc.

CONCORD MIXES - Desserts - Concord Foods Inc.

CONCORD PICANTE - Recording label - Concord Records Inc.

CONCORD SERIES - Siding - Alcan Aluminum Corp.

CONCORD SHEAR - Giftware - H.C. Meyers Co.

CONCORD SLING COLLECTION - Furniture - Telescope Casual Furniture Inc.

CONCORD, THE - Sinks–porcelain - Jameco Industries, Inc.

CONCORD WOODS - Floor coverings ☆ - Azrock Commercial Flooring

CONCORDA - Housewares - Cornwall Industries Inc.

CONCORDANCE - Computer software - Dataflight Software, Inc.

CONCORDE - Antennas - Valor Enterprises, Inc.

CONCORDE - Batteries - Concorde Battery Corp.

CONCORDE - Bedroom furniture - American Furniture Co. Inc.

CONCORDE - Bicycles - Veltec Sports, Inc.

CONCORDE - Boats–motor ☆ - Larson Boat Div.

CONCORDE - Containers–insulated - Premier Industries, Inc.

CONCORDE - Doors–glass - Therma-Tru Corp.

CONCORDE - Dryers–hair - Marianna Imports, Inc.

CONCORDE - Fishing rods - Maurice Sporting Goods, Inc.

CONCORDE - Floor coverings - American Floor Products Co. Inc.

CONCORDE - Floor coverings–carpet and rugs - Patcraft Mills Inc.

CONCORDE - Floor coverings–carpet and rugs ☆ - S and S Mills Inc.

CONCORDE - Flowers, plants, and seeds ☆ - Bodger Seeds, Ltd.

CONCORDE - Furniture - Weiman Co.

CONCORDE - Furniture ☆ - Halcyon Inc.

CONCORDE - Glass–plate - Sasaki

CONCORDE - Golfing equipment - Northwestern Golf Co.

CONCORDE - Guitars - Zon Guitars

CONCORDE - Mallets - Mike Balter Mallets

CONCORDE - Manufactured homes - Redman Industries, Inc.

CONCORDE - Motor vehicles–automobiles - Chrysler Corp. (Chrysler-Plymouth Div.)

CONCORDE - Office supplies ☆ - Ace Fastener

CONCORDE - Rackets–racquetball - Ektelon

CONCORDE - Rings–jewelry - Artcarved Inc.

CONCORDE - Rug cleaning machines–commercial - Castex Industries Inc.

CONCORDE - Strollers–baby - Century Products Co.

CONCORDE - Tables–metal ☆ - Howe Furniture Corp.

CONCORDE - Thread ☆ - Coats and Clark Inc.

CONCORDE - Wallpaper - Jolie Papier

CONCORDE 180 - Water purification systems - Penn-Plax, Inc.

CONCORDE 500, THE - Exercising equipment ☆ - California Gym Equipment

CONCORDE COLLECTION - Furniture–upholstered - Hickory Hill Furniture Corp.

CONCORDE I - Housewares ☆ - Lamplight Farms, Inc.

CONCORDE INTERNATIONAL - Recording label - Concorde International Records

CONCORDIA - Bicycles - Kent International Inc.

CONCORDIA - Food products - Rio Del Mar Food Inc.

CONCORDIA - Rings–jewelry - Artcarved Inc.

CONCORDIA YAWL - Boat dealers - Concordia Custom Yachts Inc.

CONCOTE - Computer peripheral equipment - Denton Vacuum, Inc.

CONCOURS - Floor coverings ☆ - Azrock Commercial Flooring

CONCOURS - Floor coverings–tile - Monarch Tile Inc.

CONCOURS - Motor vehicles ☆ - General Motors Corp. (Chevrolet Motor Div.)

CONCOURSE - Exercise treadmills - Diversified Products Corp.

CONCOURSE - Floor coverings–carpet and rugs - Eurotex Inc.

CONCOURSE - Floor coverings–carpet and rugs ☆ - Kelly Group Inc.

CONCOURSE - Floor coverings–carpet and rugs ☆ - Walter Carpet Mills

CONCOURSE - Mats - Cactus Mat Manufacturing Co.

CONCOURSE - Tiles–clay ☆ - Porcelanite, Inc.

CONCOURSE - Wallpaper - Winfield Design Associates, Inc.

CONCOURSE - Wallpaper ☆ - Pickhardt & Siebert USA Inc.

CONCREDAMP - Chemical preparations - Endslip Products Co.

CONCRELOK - Adhesives and sealants ☆ - Calgon Vestal Laboratories

CONCRESEAL - Concrete products - Perry & Derrick Co.

CONCRESIVE - Concrete repair products - Master Builders Inc.

CONCRETE - Concrete products ☆ - Midland Chicago Corp.

CONCRETE ARMOR - Adhesives and sealants - Absolute Coatings Inc.

CONCRETE-AUGER - Drill bits - Hawera Inc.

CONCRETE CHUTER - Machine parts - Glenmac Inc.

CONCRETE CLASSICS TEXTURE COATING SYSTEMS - Concrete products - John F. Patti

CONCRETE CLINIC INC. - Hardware stores - Concrete Clinic, Inc.

CONCRETE EXPRESS - Motor vehicle parts and accessories - Johnson Technologies

CONCRETE FINISHER - Waterproofing compounds - Tamms Industries Co.

CONCRETE FIXALL - Concrete repair products - Custom Building Products

CONCRETE MAGIC - Concrete products - Concrete Magic

CONCRETE 'N PATIO - Paints - Atlas Chemical Co.

CONCRETE PATCH - Concrete repair products - Custom Building Products

CONCRETE REPAIR SYSTEM - Concrete repair products - Custom Building Products

CONCRETE SAVER - Finishing agents - Rust-Oleum Corp.

CONCRETE SEALER - Sealing compounds - Permagile Industries Inc.

CONCRETE STABILIZATION TECHNOLOGIES - Concrete repair products - Concrete Stabilization Technologies, Inc.

CONCRETE STATEMENT - Cleaning preparations - Pioneer/Eclipse Corp.

CONCRETE-TERMITE - Drill bits - Relton Corp.

CONCRETELIFE - Waterproofing compounds - Dap Products Inc.

CONCRETEWORKS - Concrete products - Master's Choice Inc.

CONCUR - Floor coverings–carpet and rugs ☆ - Karastan-Bigelow Inc.

CONCURRENT COMPUTER - Computer hardware - Concurrent Computer Corp.

CONCURRENT DOS - Computer software ☆ - Novell, Inc.

CONCURTRAK - Computer software - Curtin Matheson Scientific, Inc.

☆ = Now out of production

CONCURV - Lenses–optical - Allergan Elite, Inc.
CONCURVE - Watches - Hampden Corp.
CONCUT - Saws–power - Concut, Inc.
CONDAR TEMP - Thermometers ☆ - Condar Co.
CONDE - Dairy equipment - Westmoor Ltd.
CONDE DE AMARANTE - Wines - Admiral Wine Merchants
CONDECAL COMPOUND - Pharmaceutical preparations ☆ - Geneva Generics Inc.
CONDENSTOP - Pipe-coating spray ☆ - Vibe Records Inc.
CONDESA - Boats–motor ☆ - Cobalt Boats
CONDESA - Fabric stores - Amoco Fabrics and Fibers Co.
CONDESA - Floor coverings - Mannington Resilient Floors
CONDIMEATS - Meat products–canned - Hansel 'n Gretel Brand, Inc.
CONDIMENT SYSTEM - Tables–wood ☆ - Krueger International, Inc.
CONDIMENTI SAN REMO - Sauces ☆ - Europa Foods Ltd.
CONDISHEEN - Hair care products - Keystone Laboratories Inc.
CONDITION - Hair care products - Clairol Inc.
CONDITION-IT-OUT - Hair care products ☆ - Cheveux Inc.
CONDITION PLUS - Animal feed - Cenex/Land O'Lakes AG Services
CONDITION: RED - Games - Avalon Hill Game Co.
CONDITION SET - Hair care products - Jheri Redding Products Inc.
CONDITIONAIR - Dryers–hair - P.S. Pibbs Inc.
CONDITIONED CURL, THE - Hair care products - Redken Laboratories, Inc.
CONDITIONER - Athletic footwear ☆ - Autry Industries Inc.
CONDITIONER - Bicycles - Columbia Manufacturing Inc.
CONDITIONER - Shampoos - Kim Laube & Co. Inc.
CONDITIONING FIXX - Hair care products - KMS Research Inc.
CONDITIONING LIPCOLOR - Cosmetics - Viviane Woodard Industries, Ltd.
CONDITIONING PLUS - Pet products - Wardley Corp.
CONDO - Cabinets - Nutone Inc.
CONDO - Floor coverings–carpet and rugs ☆ - Hollytex Carpet Mills Inc.
CONDO - Padding–foam - Foamex LP
CONDO - Pet products - The Crab Connection
CONDO COTE - Paints - Buten Paint & Wallpaper
CONDOGUARD - Household appliance hoses - Condoguard, Inc.
CONDOM CADDY - Containers - E. Lossini Co. Inc.
CONDOM COLLECTABLES-COLLECT WHILE YOU PROTECT - Prophylactics - Big Star Concepts Inc.
CONDOM COMMUNICATION - Prophylactics - James L. Casale
CONDOM LOC - Medical apparatus - Wetoo, Inc.
CONDOM POCKET - Apparel and accessories - William Nash Priestley
CONDOM REVOLUTION - Specialty stores - Dean Charter
CONDOMANIA - Prophylactics - Addazi, Inc.
CONDOR - Antenna - Checkpoint Systems Inc.
CONDOR - Balls–golf - Bost Enterprises, Inc.
CONDOR - Bicycles - Columbia Manufacturing Inc.
CONDOR - Binoculars ☆ - Swift Instruments, Inc.
CONDOR - Boats - Seaway Importing Co.
CONDOR - Boats–motor ☆ - Cobia Boat Co.
CONDOR - Brushes - Condor USA, Inc.
CONDOR - Brushes–paint - Allpro Corp.
CONDOR - Cabinets - Sequoia Mill
CONDOR - Computer software - Phoenix Computer Corp.
CONDOR - Fencing–steel ☆ - Bekaert Corp. (Wire & Wire Products Div.)
CONDOR - Fishing tackle - South Bend Sporting Goods Inc.
CONDOR - Frames–eyeglass - U.S. Optical Frame Co.
CONDOR - Plumbing fixtures–metal - Pro-Flo Products
CONDOR - Refractory bricks and shapes - General Refractories Co.
CONDOR - Sliding door control - Condor Marine, Inc.
CONDOR - Soccer balls ☆ - Audero Sports Supply
CONDOR - Thread - Threads USA Div.
CONDOR - Toys - Tonka Corp.
CONDOR - Trailers–travel ☆ - Sun-Lite Inc.
CONDOR - Wheelchairs - AM Scooters
CONDOR CLASSIX - Recording label - Azra International
CONDOR CRUNCHER - Golfing equipment - Bost Enterprises, Inc.
CONDOR GSM - Synthesizers–musical instrument - Gullickson Co.
CONDOR LIGHTING - Lighting fixtures - Basic Source, Inc.
CONDOR LONG CUT - Tobacco products - Faber, Coe & Gregg Inc.
CONDOR OF OIL - Insecticides - Ecogen Inc.
CONDOR RSM - Synthesizers–musical instrument - Gullickson Co.
CONDOR TRAV-L-GOLF - Bags - Bost Enterprises, Inc.
CONDOR WP - Insecticides - Ecogen Inc.
CONDOR XL - Insecticides - Ecogen Inc.
CONDRIN-LA - Pharmaceutical preparations - Roberts/Hauck Pharmaceuticals Inc.

CONDRIVE - Fastening tool for masonry screws - ITW Ramset/Red Head
CONDRIVE 2000 - Tools–power-driven - Illinois Tool Works Inc.
CONDU-LOCK - Nuts and bolts - Production Products, Inc.
CONDU-MATE - Building materials - Banner Sales Co., Inc.
CONDUCT-A-MARK - Pencils ☆ - Empire Berol USA
CONDUCT-MOR - Cables - S & J Products, Ltd.
CONDUCTIFLOR - Floor coverings ☆ - Tarkett, Inc.
CONDUCTILE - Floor coverings–tile - VPI
CONDUCTIVE - Floor coverings–tile - Kentile Floors Inc.
CONDUCTOR - Batteries - Eveready Battery Co., Inc.
CONDUCTOR - Clocks - General Time Corp. (Westclox/Seth Thomas Div.)
CONDUCTOR - Electronics equipment - Multivision Systems Inc.
CONDUCTOR - Health care products - Medical Science Products Inc.
CONDUCTOR, THE - Watches - General Time Corp. (Westclox/Seth Thomas Div.)
CONDURRE - Boats–motor - Cobalt Boats
CONDUSIVE - Prophylactics - Out Front, Inc.
CONDUTRED - Floor coverings - Rock-Tred Corp.
CONDYNE DIVISION - Recording label ☆ - Oceana Publications Inc.
CONE - Cosmetics - Capitol Novelty Co.
CONE - Lighting fixtures - Thomas Lighting (Accent Division)
CONE - Machinery - Kewtema, Inc.
CONE - Sporting goods - Macon Manufacturing
CONE CUT - Fish hooks - VMC, Inc.
CONE LITE - Automotive parts and accessories - Optronics Inc.
CONE MUSIC CO. - Publisher's imprints - The Keene Music Group
CONE-POURRI - Deodorizers - Aromax Inc.
CONE STACORD - Fabrics ☆ - Cone Mills Corp.
CONECT-A-KIT - Construction equipment - L.J. Smith Co., Inc.
CONECT-A-KIT - Handrail fittings - Lynn H. Smith
CONEHEADS - Apparel and accessories - National Broadcasting Co., Inc.
CONEHEADS HOMEMADE ICE CREAM - Ice cream - Dorothy Lum
CONEJET - Nozzles - Spraying Systems Co.
CONELLO - Confections - Good Humor Corp.
CONEPREST - Fabrics ☆ - Cone Mills Corp.
CONESET - Fabrics ☆ - Cone Mills Corp.
CONESPHERE - Lighting equipment - Trimble House Corp.
CONESTOGA - Bags–duffel - Akona Adventure Gear, Inc.
CONESTOGA - Corn–flour or meal - Pioneer Flour Mills
CONESTOGA - Doors–wood - Conestoga Wood Specialties, Inc.
CONESTOGA - Garden equipment ☆ - Parker Sweeper Co.
CONESTOGA - Housewares ☆ - Lamplight Farms, Inc.
CONESTOGA BERBERS - Floor coverings–carpet and rugs ☆ - Downs Carpet Co. Inc.
CONESTOGA BY PIONEER - Corn–flour or meal - Pioneer Flour Mills
CONESTOGA NATURALS - Floor coverings–carpet and rugs - Downs Carpet Co. Inc.
CONESTOGA WAGON WORKS, LTD. - Wagons–children's - Conestoga Wagon Works, Ltd.
CONESTRONE - Pharmaceutical preparations ☆ - Wyeth-Ayerst Laboratories
CONETROL - Rifles - Conetrol Scope Mounts
CONEWICH - Bakery products - Ward J. Goldstein
CONEX - Pharmaceutical preparations ☆ - Forest Pharmaceuticals Inc.
CONEXPORT - Wines - Prestige Wine Corp.
CONEXUS - Computer hardware - Leadership 2000, Inc.
CONEXUS - Video production - Conexus, Inc.
CONEY ISLAND - Food products ☆ - Agway Country Foods Inc.
CONFEC - Milk–canned or powdered - Express Foods Co. Inc.
CONFECTION ART - Candy - Alter Enterprises, Inc.
CONFECTION COLLECTION - Ribbons ☆ - Design Circle Ltd.
CONFECTIONARY EXPRESSIONS - Candy - Marsyl Inc. (Marsyl Enterprises, Inc.)
CONFECTIONS - Giftware - Indiana Glass Co.
CONFECTIONS - Giftware ☆ - Lenox Crystal, Inc.
CONFECTIONS - Tiles–ceramic ☆ - Huntington/Pacific Ceramics Inc.
CONFECTIONS - Underwear and nightwear - Maidenform Inc.
CONFEDERATE - Flowers, plants, and seeds - Turf-Seed, Inc.
CONFEREASE - Computer hardware - Communication Systems Technology, Inc.
CONFERENCE LINK - Computer software - Forrest Keith Blair
CONFERENCE MANAGER - Computer software - Ram Dynamics Inc.
CONFERENCE MASTER - Tables–metal ☆ - Howe Furniture Corp.
CONFERENCER - Telephones - Teleconferencing Systems International Inc.
CONFERMAIL - Computer software - Confertech International, Inc.
CONFETTI - Audio equipment - Telequest Inc.
CONFETTI - Bedding–linen - Dan River Inc.

CONFETTI - Bird feeds - Petland, Inc.
CONFETTI - Brushes–hair - Marianna Imports, Inc.
CONFETTI - Candles - Signature Brands, LLC
CONFETTI - Carpets and rugs - Couristan Inc.
CONFETTI - Cases–eyeglass ☆ - Fidelity Case Corp.
CONFETTI - Christmas tree ornaments - Cracker Box Inc.
CONFETTI - Dinnerware–glass - Nikko Ceramics Inc.
CONFETTI - Dolls - Windsor Toys, Inc.
CONFETTI - Flatware ☆ - Towle Silversmiths
CONFETTI - Floor coverings - Mannington Resilient Floors
CONFETTI - Floor coverings–carpet and rugs ☆ - LaVelle Textile Marketing Inc.
CONFETTI - Flowers, plants, and seeds - Flowerwood Nursery, Inc.
CONFETTI - Food products - Taco Time International, Inc.
CONFETTI - Footwear–women's - JBI, Inc.
CONFETTI - Glassware–household - Owens-Illinois Inc. (Libbey Div.)
CONFETTI - Glassware–household ☆ - Crisa Corp.
CONFETTI - Glassware–household ☆ - Mesa International
CONFETTI - Hairpins - Fit-All Sportswear Inc.
CONFETTI - Paper - Fox River Paper Co.
CONFETTI - Pasta ☆ - Kozy Shack Inc.
CONFETTI - Ribbons - Ribbon Magic, Inc.
CONFETTI - Safety products - Aearo Co.
CONFETTI - School bags, back packs, diaper bags - Bag Bazaar Ltd.
CONFETTI - Teas - Eastern Shore Tea Co.
CONFETTI - Tiles–ceramic - Florida Tile Industries, Inc.
CONFETTI BALLS - Candy - Leaf, Inc.
CONFETTI FELT - Fabrics–broadcloth - Foss Manufacturing Co., Inc.
CONFETTI FRUIT LOOPS - Cereal ☆ - Kellogg Co.
CONFETTI LIGHTS - Lamps - Lamplight Farms, Inc.
CONFETTI STRING - Games - Fun World Inc.
CONFEZIONI - Men's suits and sportcoats - Intercontinental Branded Apparel
CONFI-DENSE - Stationery ☆ - Tab Products Co.
CONFI-DENTURE A PINNACLE OF EXCELLENCE - Denture materials - Confi-Denture
CONFIBER - Roofing materials - Consolidated Fiber Glass Products Co.
CONFIDANT - Computer software and manuals - Ensuing Technologies Inc.
CONFIDANT - Generators–electric - Kohler Co.
CONFIDANTE - Brassieres (Bras) - Camp, Inc.
CONFIDE - Pharmaceutical preparations - Johnson & Johnson
CONFIDENCE - Diapers–disposable - Paper-Pak Products, Inc.
CONFIDENCE - Handbags - Alison International Co.
CONFIDENCE - Health care products - Geri-Care Products, LLC
CONFIDENCE IN CLEANING - Cleaning preparations - Linden Corp.
CONFIDENT - Health care products - Block Drug Co., Inc.
CONFIDENT - Paints - Dutch Boy Group
CONFIDENT - Paints - Sherwin-Williams Automotive Finishes Corp.
CONFIDENT CARE - Hair care products - Rhonda Rand M.D., Inc.
CONFIDENT COLLECTOR, THE - Publisher's imprints - Hearst Corp.
CONFIDENT CORAL - Lipsticks - Estee Lauder Inc.
CONFIDENTIAL - Colognes - Brandy Harvest
CONFIDETS - Sanitary napkins ☆ - Scott Paper Co.
CONFIGSAFE - Computer software - Imagine Lan, Inc.
CONFIGURATIONS - Games - Wff'n Proof Learning Games Associates
CONFIGURE - Hair care products - KMS Research Inc.
CONFIL - Fabrics - Veratec
CONFILM - Concrete repair products - Master Builders Inc.
CONFIRM - Insecticides - Rohm and Haas Co.
CONFIRM - Photographic equipment - Eastman Kodak Co.
CONFIRM - Pregnancy and ovulation kits - LRC North America, Inc.
CONFIRM - Pregnancy test kits - Durex Consumer Products
CONFIRM - Pregnancy test kits - London International U.S. Holdings
CONFIRMED RELEASE - Vitamins and nutritional supplements - L. Perrigo Co.
CONFISERIE DU CYGNE D' OR - Candy - International Gourmet
CONFIXOR - Hair care products - Aveda Corp.
CONFLICT - Perfumes - Del Pharmaceuticals, Inc.
CONFLICT - Toys - Tonka Corp.
CONFLICT 2500 - Games ☆ - Avalon Hill Game Co.
CONFLICT IN VIETNAM - Computer software ☆ - Microprose Software, Inc.
CONFLOR - Floor coverings–carpet and rugs - Eurotex Inc.
CONFLUENT - Computer software - Confluent, Inc.
CONFOCO - Fruits–dried - Confoco, Inc.
CONFOR - Health care products - E-A-R Specialty Composites
CONFORM - Sporting goods - Bike Athletic Co.
CONFORM-A-SPHERIC - Contact lenses - Conforma Contact Lenses
CONFORM-A-TUBE - Electrical equipment - Daburn Electronics & Cable Corp.

CONFORM II - Sporting goods - Bike Athletic Co.
CONFORM SBS - Roofing materials - Consolidated Fiber Glass Products Co.
CONFORMA - Apparel stores–lingerie - Formflex Foundations Inc.
CONFORMA - Mattresses - Spring Air Bedding Inc.
CONFORMA - Veneer - Haskell of Pittsburgh, Inc.
CONFORMA FOAM - Mattresses - Spring Air Co.
CONFORMAL - Shoes - Interco Inc.
CONFORMALITE - Contact lenses - Conforma Contact Lenses
CONFORMANCE - Comforters - Pacific Coast Feather Co.
CONFRIO - Food products - Shore Lobster & Shrimp Corp.
CONFRONTATIONAL CONTINUUM - Educational materials - Armament Systems and Procedures, Inc.
CONFURTI - Food products - Bel Canto Fancy Foods Ltd.
CONFUSABLES - Computer software - Franklin Electronic Publishers, Inc.
CONGA - Food products - Atalanta Corp.
CONGA - Pet products ☆ - Con Gor Inc.
CONGA BRAVA - Computer software - Adobe Systems Inc.
CONGAROC - Pet products - Con Gor Inc.
CONGDON - Fruits–canned - Congdon Orchards Inc.
CONGELADORA SAN FRANCISQUITO - Fruits and vegetables - Productores Agricolas
CONGENIAL - Floor coverings–carpet and rugs ☆ - Karastan-Bigelow Inc.
CONGENS - Prescription drug ☆ - Blaine Co. Inc.
CONGER LABEL - Milk ☆ - Conger Coop. Creamery Co.
CONGESPIRIN - Cold remedies - Bristol-Myers Squibb Co.
CONGESS - Pharmaceutical preparations - Fleming & Co.
CONGEST-EASE - Health care products - Natural Laboratories Corp.
CONGESTAC - Cold remedies - Smithkline Beecham Corp.
CONGESTAID - Pharmaceutical preparations - Colgate-Palmolive Co.
CONGESTAIDE - Pharmaceutical preparations - Boericke & Tafel
CONGESTEZE - Health care products - Hall Laboratories, Inc.
CONGESTRIN - Homeopathic remedies - Amrion, Inc.
CONGESTROGEN - Pharmaceutical preparations - Medical Chemical Corp.
CONGO - Computer software - Advanced Computer Communications
CONGO - Computer software - Paramount Pictures Corp.
CONGO - Repellent ☆ - Eagle Creek, Inc.
CONGO - Wallpaper - Carlton-Metro Wallcoverings
CONGO BEASTS - Toys - Trendmasters, Inc.
CONGO MONKEY - Toys–stuffed ☆ - Dakin Inc.
CONGO; THE MOVIE - Lunch boxes - Thermos Co.
CONGO TRADER - Jeans–men's - Kentogs Corp.
CONGOFLOR - Floor coverings ☆ - Congoleum Corp.
CONGOFOAM - Floor coverings ☆ - Congoleum Corp.
CONGOLEUM - Floor coverings - Congoleum Corp.
CONGOMATIC - Floor coverings ☆ - Congoleum Corp.
CONGOTREAD - Floor coverings ☆ - Congoleum Corp.
CONGOWALL - Floor coverings ☆ - Congoleum Corp.
CONGRATULATION - Furniture ☆ - Mersman Furniture Co.
CONGRATULATIONS! - Chocolate bars - Celebration Chocolates, Inc.
CONGRATULATIONS - Giftware - Roman, Inc.
CONGRESS - Guns ☆ - Armsport Inc.
CONGRESS - Playing cards - United States Playing Card Co.
CONGRESS - Sardines–canned ☆ - Strohmeyer and Arpe Co.
CONGRESS FESTIVAL - Hair care products - Aveda Corp.
CONGRESS SPRINGS - Wines - Anglo American Agriculture (USA)
CONGRESS SPRINGS VINEYARDS - Wines - Congress Springs Vineyards Inc.
CONGRESSIONAL - Watches - Bulova Corp.
CONGRESSIONAL DISTRICT - Knives–pocket - Camillus Cutlery Co.
CONGUETE DU SOLEIL BARRIERE SOLAIRE - Suntan lotions - Lancome
CONHESIVE - Roofing materials - Consolidated Fiber Glass Products Co.
CONIBEAR - Traps–animal - Woodstream Corp.
CONIC - Apparel and accessories - Conic Enterprises Ltd.
CONIFER LANE FARMS - Food products - Conifer Lane Farms
CONIMBRIGA - Statuary ☆ - Eastern Shore Trading Co.
CONIMEX - Rice - Holland-American Importing Co. Inc.
CONJENS - Health care products ☆ - Halsey Drug Co. Inc.
CONJURE - Computer software - Libera, Inc.
CONJUTRONE - Pharmaceutical preparations - Medical Chemical Corp.
CONKER TRADING - Towels - Conker Trading Corp.
CONKRETE CORE - Tools - Tilden-Rocket Tool Co.
CONLON COLLECTION - Baseball trading cards - Sporting News Publishing Co.
CONLYN - Paints - Impervious Paint Industries Ltd.
CONMAR - Marble tile - Continental Creative Sales Inc.
CONMARK - Measuring instruments - Conmark, Inc.

☆ = Now out of production

CONMASTIC - Roofing materials - Consolidated Fiber Glass Products Co.
CONMATIC - Zippers ☆ - Scovill Inc.
CONMEMORATIVO - Beverages–alcohol ☆ - Domecq Importers Inc.
CONN - Musical instruments - United Musical Instruments USA Inc.
CONN CREEK - Wines - Stimson Lane Vineyards & Estates
CONN STAR - Musical instrument accessories ☆ - United Musical Instruments USA Inc.
CONNAIRE - Air purification systems - Tomkins Industries Inc.
CONNAISSANCE - Floor coverings–carpet and rugs ☆ - Cabin Crafts Carpets
CONNAUGHT - Dinnerware–glass - Franciscan by Johnson Brothers, USA, Inc.
CONNEAUT CELLAR - Wines - Conneaut Cellars Winery
CONNECT - Computer software - Connect Computer Co.
CONNECT - Fabrics–cotton - Leucadia, Inc.
CONNECT-0-FOAM - Toys - Poof Toy Products, Inc.
CONNECT 3 - Computer software - Trend Offset Printing
CONNECT 4 - Games - Milton Bradley Co.
CONNECT-ALL - Vitamins and nutritional supplements - Natural Organics, Inc.
CONNECT:FIREWALL - Computer software - Sterling Software, Inc.
CONNECT FOUR - Toys–electronic - Hasbro, Inc.
CONNECT-OR-SEAL - Ventilating ducts - Harrow Products Inc.
CONNECT PLUS - Power switching equipment - Jo-Dan International, Inc.
CONNECT THE DOTS - Children's toys ☆ - Coloron Industries
CONNECT-UPS - Hosiery - 21st Century Hosiery Inc.
CONNECT WITH A LEADER - Batteries - Douglas Battery Manufacturing Co.
CONNECTED - Computer software - Bottom Line Software, Inc.
CONNECTICAT - Pet products - Mid-West Metal Products Co. Inc.
CONNECTICUT - Brakes–motor vehicle - Roper Whitney Co.
CONNECTICUT - Brakes–motor vehicle - Roper Whitney of Rockford, Inc.
CONNECTICUT ELECTRIC & SWITCH - Electrical equipment - American Circuit Breaker Corp.
CONNECTICUT PRIDE - T-shirts–men's - Hartford, Hellcats Inc.
CONNECTICUT SWITCH - Electrical equipment - American Circuit Breaker Corp.
CONNECTING HUMANITY - Jewelry - Zan Design, Inc.
CONNECTION - Games ☆ - Western Publishing Co., Inc.
CONNECTION - Heating equipment - Slant/Fin Corp.
CONNECTION MACHINE - Computers - Thinking Machines Corp.
CONNECTION PACK - Computer software - Persoft, Inc.
CONNECTIONS - Yamazaki Tableware Inc.
CONNECTIONS - Computer software ☆ - Electronic Arts Inc.
CONNECTIONS - Desks - GF Office Furniture Ltd.
CONNECTIONS - Fabrics - Piedmont Collections
CONNECTIONS - Furniture - Bretford Manufacturing, Inc.
CONNECTIONS - Wallpaper - Old Deerfield Fabrics Inc.
CONNECTIONS BETWEEN CULTURES - Educational materials - Lynda E. Plummer
CONNECTIONS IN TIME - Computer software ☆ - Krell Software Corp.
CONNECTIONS TELEMARKETING - Computer software - General Software Solutions, Inc.
CONNECTIONS WITH QUALITY - Electrical equipment - Northeastern Plastics, Inc.
CONNECTIX PHOTOBADGE - Computer software - Connectix Corp.
CONNECTIX PHOTOMATE - Computer hardware - Connectix Corp.
CONNECTLINK - Computer software - Intervoice, Inc.
CONNECTOR - Drinking straws - Sansom, Inc.
CONNECTOR - Novelty items - Fun-Time International, Inc.
CONNECTOR - Toys - Childcraft Education Corp.
CONNECTOR BOATS - Boating equipment and accessories - Anthony P. Lumpkin
CONNECTOR CENTER - Audio equipment - Pro-Co. Sound Co. Inc.
CONNECTOR PROTECTOR - Electronic equipment - Cami Research Inc.
CONNECTOR, THE - Connectors–electrical - Pulsetech Products Corp.
CONNECTORAIL - Hardware - Julius Blum & Co. Inc.
CONNECTORS - Bicycle parts and accessories - Serfus, Inc.
CONNECTPRESS - Computer software - Connectpress, Ltd.
CONNECT'R WARE - Fasteners–snap - Penn Engineering and Manufacturing Corp.
CONNECTRA - Building materials - Technical Exhibits Corp.
CONNECTRONICS - Cables - Bob White Associates
CONNECTRONIX - Computer software - Connectronix Corp.
CONNECTS 16 - Computers ☆ - Western Telematic Inc.
CONNELLA - Toiletries - Connella Inc.
CONNELL'S - Rice - Connell Co.
CONNELL'S 333 - Food products - Connell Co.
CONNELLY - Water bottles–rubber - Connelly Skis, Inc.

CONNEMARA FLEECE - Floor coverings–carpet and rugs ☆ - Navan Carpets Inc.
CONNER - Computer storage devices–magnetic - Conner Peripherals, Inc.
CONNEX - Liquid crystal displays - Curtin Matheson Scientific, Inc.
CONNEX-ALL - Air purification systems ☆ - Moen Inc.
CONNEXION - Tools - CVC
CONNEXIONS - Dictating machines - Dictaphone Corp.
CONNI GORDON - Artists' materials - Conni Gordon Art Method Inc.
CONNI GORDON ART METHOD - Artists' materials - Conni Gordon Art Method Inc.
CONNIE - Dolls - Uneeda Doll Co., Inc.
CONNIE - Footwear - Brown Shoe Co.
CONNIE - Footwear–women's - Wohl Shoe Co.
CONNIES BY P'NENA - Underwear and nightwear - P'nena Group, Inc.
CONNIE'S CHICAGO-STYLE PIZZA - Pizzas–mixes - Connie's Pizza
CONNIE'S KIDS - Apparel–children's - C.B. Wear Inc.
CONNOISSEAUR - Floor coverings–carpet and rugs ☆ - Patrick Carpet Mills
CONNOISSERVE - Containers - Hormel Corp.
CONNOISSEUR - Audio equipment ☆ - Teledyne Acoustic Research
CONNOISSEUR - Colognes - AZ Product Co.
CONNOISSEUR - Cutlery - Carvel Hall Inc.
CONNOISSEUR - Cutlery - Russell Harrington Cutlery, Inc.
CONNOISSEUR - Dinnerware–glass - Franciscan by Johnson Brothers, USA, Inc.
CONNOISSEUR - Dolls - Seymour Mann Inc.
CONNOISSEUR - Dryers–hair - Helen of Troy Corp.
CONNOISSEUR - Floor coverings–carpet and rugs - Coronet Carpets Inc.
CONNOISSEUR - Food products - John Sexton and Co.
CONNOISSEUR - Frames–picture - Intercraft Industries
CONNOISSEUR - Furniture - Drexel Heritage Furnishings, Inc.
CONNOISSEUR - Glassware–household - Owens-Illinois Inc. (Libbey Div.)
CONNOISSEUR - Glassware–household - Seneca Glass Co.
CONNOISSEUR - Greeting cards ☆ - American Artists Group Inc.
CONNOISSEUR - Pipes–tobacco - S.M. Frank & Co. Inc. (Kaywoodie-Yello-Bole-Medico)
CONNOISSEUR - Stationery - Sheaffer Inc.
CONNOISSEUR - Upholstery leather ☆ - American Leather Manufacturing Co.
CONNOISSEUR - Wallpaper - Kingfisher Wallcoverings
CONNOISSEUR - Water–bottled or canned - Connoisseur Beverage
CONNOISSEUR - Wood products ☆ - Knobler International Ltd.
CONNOISSEUR 5 - Wallpaper ☆ - Kingfisher Wallcoverings
CONNOISSEUR COLLECTION - Desks - National/Mt. Airy Furniture
CONNOISSEUR COLLECTION - Mattresses - Simmons USA
CONNOISSEUR COLLECTION - Patterns–clothing ☆ - Simplicity Pattern Co., Inc.
CONNOISSEUR GALLERY - Furniture–upholstered - Statesville Chair Co. Inc.
CONNOISSEUR IV - Wallpaper ☆ - Kingfisher Wallcoverings
CONNOISSEUR MASTER BLEND - Teas - Grace Tea Co. Ltd.
CONNOISSEUR PREMIUM - Coffee - Canteen Corp.
CONNOISSEUR SOCIETY - Recording label - Connoisseur Society Inc.
CONNOISSEUR, THE - Giftware - Seymour Mann Inc.
CONNOISSEURS - Jewelry - Connoisseurs Products Corp.
CONNOISSEUR'S CHOICE - Cleaning preparations - Liquid Glass Enterprises Inc.
CONNOISSEURS GALLERY - Furniture - Henredon Furniture Industries Inc.
CONNOLLY - Men's footwear ☆ - Bostonian Shoe Co.
CONNOR - Kitchen cabinets, wood floor covering, juvenile furniture ☆ - Continental Hardwood Floor Distributors Inc.
CONNOR - Toys - Bemiss-Jason Corp.
CONNOR - Toys - Connor Toy Corp.
CONNORS/BRUNSWICK - Seafood products–fresh or frozen - Connors Brothers Inc.
CONNOTATIONS III - Wallcovering ☆ - Capital Carousel Inc.
CONNOTATIONS III - Wallpaper - Academy Handprints Ltd.
CONNQUEROR - Musical instruments - United Musical Instruments USA Inc.
CONNQUEST - Musical instruments - United Musical Instruments USA Inc.
CONNSTELLATION - Musical instruments - United Musical Instruments USA Inc.
CONNXTION - Apparel–athletic - Jay Wolf
CONNY - Yarn - Nomis Yarn Co.
CONO - Apparel and accessories - Cono, Inc.
CONO-FLEX - Pharmaceutical preparations - Tetra Medical Supply Corp.
CONOCO - Automotive parts and accessories ☆ - Conoco Inc.
CONOFITE - Veterinary pharmaceutical preparations - Schering-Plough Animal Health
CONOFLEX - Plastics–laminated - Conolite

CONOFLOW - Machinery - ITT Corp.
CONOLAC - Coatings, etc. - Continental Products Co.
CONOLAM - Plastic laminated sheets ☆ - Pionite Decorative Surfaces
CONOLITE - Plastics–laminated - Conolite
CONOMICS - Books–comic - AccuServe Corp.
CONOSOL - Chemical preparations - Conoco Inc.
CONOVER - Pianos - Aeolian Pianos Inc.
CONOVER CLASSICS - Furniture - Conover Chair Co. Inc.
CONOVER COURT - Furniture - Conover Chair Co. Inc.
CONOVER GALLERIES - Furniture - Conover Chair Co. Inc.
CONPACT - Cleaning preparations–household - L & F Consumer Products
CONPERL - Roofing materials - Consolidated Fiber Glass Products Co.
CONPLATE - Concrete-surface hardener - Conspec Marketing & Manufacturing Co. Inc.
CONPLY - Roofing materials - Consolidated Fiber Glass Products Co.
CONPLY A-IV - Roofing materials - Consolidated Fiber Glass Products Co.
CONPLY HT60 - Roofing materials - Consolidated Fiber Glass Products Co.
CONPRIME - Roofing materials - Consolidated Fiber Glass Products Co.
CONPRO COAT - Adhesives and sealants - Conproco Corp.
CONQUER - Audio equipment - Raminton International, Inc.
CONQUER - Computer software - Trilogy Development Group
CONQUERER - Musical instruments - C. Bruno & Son Inc.
CONQUERER - Thread - Threads USA Div.
CONQUEROR - Bicycles - Union Cycle Co.
CONQUEROR - Cables - Conquest Sound Inc.
CONQUEROR - Chessboards - Pacific Game Co.
CONQUEROR - Duplicating machines - Heyer Inc.
CONQUEROR - Floor coverings–carpet and rugs ☆ - Downs Carpet Co. Inc.
CONQUEROR - Pipes–tobacco - S.M. Frank & Co. Inc. (Kaywoodie-Yello-Bole-Medico)
CONQUEROR SERIES BY FORMULA - Exercising equipment - Formula Ventures
CONQUERORS - Cigar boxes–wood - Consolidated Cigar Corp.
CONQUERS RAZOR BURN - Skin care products - Rumson Laboratories
CONQUEST - Air purification systems - Tomco, Inc.
CONQUEST - Air system controllers - Condyne Technology Inc.
CONQUEST - Boats - Boston Whaler, Inc.
CONQUEST - Boats–motor ☆ - Bayliner Marine Corp.
CONQUEST - Dehumidifiers - R.K. International Inc.
CONQUEST - Exercising equipment - Titan Exercise Equipment Inc.
CONQUEST - Fabrics - Greenwood Mills Inc.
CONQUEST - Fans–electric - Emerson Electric Co.
CONQUEST - Floor coverings–carpet and rugs - Philadelphia Carpets
CONQUEST - Floor coverings–carpet and rugs - Queen Carpet Corp.
CONQUEST - Floor coverings–carpet and rugs - Regal Rugs Inc.
CONQUEST - Fructose - J.R. Simplot Co.
CONQUEST - Heating equipment - Heat Controller Inc.
CONQUEST - Helmets–athletic ☆ - E.D. Bullard Co.
CONQUEST - Insecticides - Green Light Co.
CONQUEST - Labels–gummed - Morgan Adhesives Co.
CONQUEST - Motor vehicles–automobiles ☆ - DaimlerChrysler
CONQUEST - Occasional tables and wall units ☆ - JDI Group, Inc.
CONQUEST - Pipes - Dow Chemical Co.
CONQUEST - Recording label - Ichiban Records, Inc.
CONQUEST - Siding - Alside Div.
CONQUEST - Sporting goods - Wellington Leisure Products, Inc.
CONQUEST - Tires–automobile - Goodyear Tire & Rubber Co.
CONQUEST - Tobacco–chewing or smoking - P.T.C. Brands, Inc.
CONQUEST - Tools–power-driven - Hardinge Brothers, Inc.
CONQUEST - Vacuum cleaners and accessories - The Hoover Co.
CONQUEST - Vitamins and nutritional supplements - Primequest International, Inc.
CONQUEST - Watches - Hampden Corp.
CONQUEST CHRONOGRAPH - Watches - Longines-Wittnauer Watch Co.
CONQUEST MASS AIR FLOW SENSORS - Automotive parts and accessories - Tomco, Inc.
CONQUEST OF SPACE - Games ☆ - Gamescience
CONQUEST OF THE NEW WORLD - Computer software - Interplay Productions
CONQUEST OF THE WORLD - Toys–electronic ☆ - Philips Consumer Electronics Co.
CONQUEST PLUS - Fabrics - Greenwood Mills Inc.
CONQUEST SQUARE - Floor coverings–tile - Philadelphia Carpets
CONQUEST TSI - Motor vehicles–automobiles ☆ - DaimlerChrysler
CONQUETE DU SOLEIL - Cosmetics - Cosmair Inc.
CONQUIP - Tools - Goldblatt Tool Co.

CONQUISTA - Food products - Pet Inc.
CONQUISTA MUNDIAL - Apparel and accessories - Beyne Development, Inc.
CONQUISTADOR - Beverages–alcohol - Heaven Hill Distilleries, Inc.
CONQUISTADOR - Games ☆ - Avalon Hill Game Co.
CONQUISTADOR - Glassware–household - Benner Glassware Inc.
CONQUISTADOR - Watches - Borel Watch Co.
CONQUISTADORES - Cigars ☆ - General Cigar Co., Inc.
CONRAD - Brushes–paint ☆ - PPG Industries, Inc.
CONRAD - Musical instrument accessories - David Wexler & Co.
CONRAD - Window shades - Conrad Imports, Inc.
CONRAD II - Window shades - Conrad Imports, Inc.
CONRAD CUTTER - Knives - Seal-O-Matic Corp.
CONRAD-JOHNSON - Audio equipment - Conrad-Johnson
CONRAD ORIGINAL SUNSHADES - Window shades - Conrad Imports, Inc.
CONRAIL ACCESS - Computer programs - Consolidated Rail Corp.
CONRAN'S - Furniture - Conran's Habitat
CONRAY - Pharmaceutical preparations ☆ - Mallinckrodt Medical, Inc.
CONROTTO - Wines - Conrotto Winery Inc.
CONROY - Fruits–frozen - Conroy Packing Co.
CONROY - Gloves - Conroy Gloves
CONS - Balls - Converse Inc.
CONS REACT - Apparel - Converse Inc.
CONSAC - Construction equipment - W.W. Henry Co.
CONSEALTAB - Insulating materials - Therm-All Inc.
CONSEC - Lenses–optical - Younger Manufacturing Co.
CONSECUFOCAL - Lenses–optical - Younger Manufacturing Co.
CONSECULENS - Lenses–optical - Younger Manufacturing Co.
CONSECUTIVE - Lenses–optical - Younger Manufacturing Co.
CONSEIL - Watches - Gruen Marketing Corp.
CONSELLE - Publisher's imprints - Conselle L.C.
CONSELLTATION - Computer software - Learning Alliance, Inc.
CONSENSUS - Audioteleconferencing systems - Shure Brothers, Inc.
CONSENSUS - Floor coverings–carpet and rugs - Patcraft Mills Inc.
CONSENSUS - Furniture - American Furniture Co. Inc.
CONSENSUS - Prosthetic apparatus - U.S. Medical Products, Inc.
CONSENSUS BUILDER - Computer software - Chandler Associates Inc.
CONSENSYS - Computer software - North Mountain Software, Inc.
CONSENSYS SOFTWARE CORPORATION - Computer software - Consensys Software Corp.
CONSENT - Frames–eyeglass - May Optical Co. Inc.
CONSEP MEMBRANES - Pesticides–agricultural - Santa Cruz Horticultural Supply
CONSEPSIS - Pharmaceutical preparations - Ultradent Products, Inc.
CONSEPT - Ophthalmic goods - Allergan, Inc.
CONSEPT - Skin care products - Care-Tech Laboratories Inc.
CONSERV - Insulating materials - Halstead Industries Inc.
CONSERV-A-FILE - File folders - Supreme Equipment & Systems Corp.
CONSERV-ART - Varnishes - Winsor & Newton
CONSERV-N-AISLE - File folders ☆ - Supreme Equipment & Systems Corp.
CONSERVA - Lighting equipment - General Electric Co.
CONSERVA-DOR - Hardware ☆ - Alumatic Corp. of America
CONSERVADOR - Vinyl - Randall Industries Inc.
CONSERVAMAT - Paperboard ☆ - Rising Paper, Division of Fox River Paper Co.
CONSERVARATOR - Faucets - WPM Inc.
CONSERVARTE - Guitars ☆ - Kaman Music Corp.
CONSERVATION COUNTS - Sporting goods - K & M International, Inc.
CONSERVATION INTERNATIONAL - Greeting cards - Sunrise Publications, Inc.
CONSERVATION SERIES - Greeting cards - Renaissance Greeting Cards Inc.
CONSERVATIONIST - Apparel and accessories - Tracker Marine Corp.
CONSERVATIONIST - Fishing rods - Bass Pro Shops Inc.
CONSERVATIONIST - Water heaters–household - A.O. Smith Corp.
CONSERVATIONIST CHIP - Cookies ☆ - Michael D's Cookies
CONSERVATIVE - Wigs - New Image
CONSERVATOR - Computer software - Lachman Technology, Inc.
CONSERVATOR - Heaters–gas - Lennox Industries Inc.
CONSERVATOR - Oxygen tents ☆ - Penox Technologies Inc.
CONSERVATOR - Paper - Moore Business Forms, Inc.
CONSERVATORY - Furniture ☆ - Bernhardt Industries
CONSERVE - Water heaters–household ☆ - Dometic Corp.
CONSERVE SPRINKLER - Tree and shrub sprinkler - Conserve Sprinkler Co.
CONSERVE TO PRESERVE - Apparel and accessories - David B. Bonkovich
CONSERVERIES DU VELAY - Mushrooms ☆ - Liberty Richter Inc.
CONSERVO - Wood products ☆ - Samuel Cabot Inc.
CONSHELF - Skin diving equipment - U.S. Divers Co., Inc.

☆ = Now out of production

CONSIDER IT DONE - Furniture - Trendway Corp.

CONSIGNEASE - Computer software - B.C.T. Custom Databases

CONSIL - Medical apparatus - Nutramax Laboratories, Inc.

CONSIN - Pharmaceutical preparations ☆ - Wisconsin Pharmacal Co. Inc.

CONSIST - Apparel - Consist International Inc.

CONSIST FR - Consist International Inc.

CONSIST INTERNATIONAL - Computer software - Consist International Inc.

CONSISTCF - Computer programs ☆ - Consist International Inc.

CONSISTENCY - Thread ☆ - Perfect Thread Co. Inc.

CONSISTENTEE - Golfing equipment ☆ - GNU Innovations Inc.

CONSO - Window shades - Florida Shades Inc.

CONSO-FLEX SEALANT - Waterproofing compounds - Consolidated Coatings Corp.

CONSO PRODUCTS - Fringe - Endisco Supply Co.

CONSOCRAFT - Hobby kits ☆ - Conso Products Co.

CONSOL - Enamels - Lasting Paints Inc.

CONSOL - Skin care products - Care-Tech Laboratories Inc.

CONSOLAB - Electronic equipment - Artograph Inc.

CONSOLE - Hardware - Emerson Electric Co.

CONSOLE CLASSICS - Automotive parts and accessories - Allied Plastics

CONSOLE COLLECTION - Occasional furniture - American Furniture Co. Inc.

CONSOLE SKIFF - Boats - Glen-L Marine Designs

CONSOLETTE - Automotive parts and accessories - Lancaster Colony Automotive Group

CONSOLID-8 - Motor vehicle parts and accessories - Consolidated Metal Products, Inc.

CONSOLIDATE! - Computer software - Barry D. Needham

CONSOLIDATE DUTCHWEST - Stoves–wood-burning - Vermont Castings, Inc.

CONSOLIDATED - Gasoline - Emro Marketing

CONSOLIDATED - Laundry machines–household - Rosco Machinery Co., Inc.

CONSOLIDATED ARTISTS - Recording label - Jazz Composer's Orchestra Association Inc.

CONSOLIDATED BUSINESS SOLUTION - Computer software - Usable Systems, Inc.

CONSOLIDATED ELECTRIC - Electronic equipment - Consolidated Electric Co.

CONSOLIDATED OPERATING & REPORTING ENVIRONMENT CORE - Computer software - McGettigan Corporate Planning Services

CONSOLIDATED PLASTICS COMPANY, INC. - Bags–trash - Consolidated Plastics Co., Inc.

CONSOLIDATED SECURITY MANAGER/ISM - Computer software ☆ - Utimaco Mergent

CONSOLIDATOR - Searchlights - Havis-Shields Equipment Corp.

CONSOLINE - Bathroom accessories ☆ - Consolidated Looseleaf Inc.

CONSOLITE - Concrete products - Consolidated Coatings Corp.

CONSOLITE EPO FLOOR SEALER - Adhesives and sealants - Consolidated Coatings Corp.

CONSOLITE GEO-CRETE - Concrete products - Consolidated Coatings Corp.

CONSORB - Eggs ☆ - Sanovo-Seymour USA, Inc.

CONSORT - Artists' materials ☆ - Artoptic International Corp.

CONSORT - Fabrics - West Point-Pepperell Inc.

CONSORT - Floor coverings–carpet and rugs - Dan River Inc.

CONSORT - Floor coverings–carpet and rugs - Queen Carpet Corp.

CONSORT - Hair care products - Alberto-Culver Co.

CONSORT - Musical instruments ☆ - Oscar Schmidt International Inc.

CONSORT - Watches - Genender International, Inc.

CONSORTIUM - Communications equipment - Coherent Communications Systems Corp.

CONSORTIUM DATABASE, THE - Advertising agencies - D.L. Ryan Companies, Ltd.

CONSORZIO - Olive oil - De Medici Imports Ltd.

CONSORZIO - Olive oil - Napa Valley Kitchens

CONSORZIO VIGNETTE - Vinegar - Napa Valley Kitchens

CONSOTEX - Fabric stores - Conso Products Co.

CONSOTUSS - Pharmaceutical preparations ☆ - Marion Merrell Dow

CONSPAN - Roofing materials–concrete ☆ - Consolidated Fiber Glass Products Co.

CONSPEC - Concrete products - Conspec Marketing & Manufacturing Co. Inc.

CONSPEC - Mattresses - Simmons USA

CONSPEC 100 - Concrete products - Conspec Marketing & Manufacturing Co. Inc.

CONSPICUITY - Safety products - Conspicuity Inc.

CONSPICUOUS CONSUMER - Publisher's imprints - International Data Group, Inc.

CONSPIRACY - Apparel and accessories - Edison Brothers Stores, Inc.

CONSPIRACY - Frames–eyeglass - May Optical Co. Inc.

CONSTA-VU - Ophthalmic goods - Salvatori Ophthalmics Inc.

CONSTABLE HALL - Furniture ☆ - Harden Furniture Co. Inc.

CONSTABS - Pharmaceutical preparations - Barrows Pharmacal Inc.

CONSTANCE - Rings–jewelry - Artcarved Inc.

CONSTANCE - Tableware–china - Lenox, Inc.

CONSTANCE COLLECTION, THE - Figurines - Constance Collection

CONSTANCE HELPER - Ladders–metal ☆ - Werner Co.

CONSTANCE LEITER - Bedding–linen - Seville Industries Dark's Silk Flowers

CONSTANCE SPRY - Flowers–artificial - C & C Florists Supplies Inc.

CONSTANT - Product description unknown - Wright and Lato Inc.

CONSTANT - Hosiery - Jack Constant Inc.

CONSTANT-COMFORT CONVERTIBLES - Sofabeds - Imperial of Morristown Inc.

CONSTANT COMMENT - Teas - R.C. Bigelow, Inc.

CONSTANT FLOW - Chemical preparations - A.R. Wood Manufacturing Co.

CONSTANT PLEASURE - Floor coverings–carpet and rugs - Lees Carpets

CONSTANT-RANGE - Audio equipment ☆ - Electro-Voice, Inc.

CONSTANT T - Pharmaceutical preparations - Ciba-Geigy Corp.

CONSTANT-TORQUE - Clamps–hose - Breeze Industrial Products

CONSTANT TOUCH - Telephone apparatus - Glenayre Electronics, Inc.

CONSTANT WATCH - Water bottles–rubber - Charleswater

CONSTANTCOLOR - Lamps - General Electric Co.

CONSTANTINE - Butter - Michigan Milk Producers Association

CONSTANTINE - Dishes–china - Waterford Wedgewood USA, Inc.

CONSTANTINE - Rings–jewelry - Artcarved Inc.

CONSTANTINE'S - Hair care products - Professional Laboratories Inc.

CONSTANTINE'S EMPIRE - Hair care products - Professional Laboratories Inc.

CONSTANTLY - Frames–eyeglass - May Optical Co. Inc.

CONSTANZA - Cigarettes and cigars - Dominican Tobacco Imports, Inc.

CONSTAR - Bottles–plastic - Constar International Inc.

CONSTAVOLT - Battery chargers - La Marche Manufacturing Co.

CONSTAY - Health care products - Urocare Products Inc.

CONSTELLATION - Boats–motor ☆ - Chris Craft Boats

CONSTELLATION - Ceiling tile ☆ - Conwed Plastics

CONSTELLATION - Compasses–gyroscopic ☆ - Rule Industries, Inc.

CONSTELLATION - Electronic equipment - Telex Communications, Inc.

CONSTELLATION - Floor coverings - American Floor Products Co. Inc.

CONSTELLATION - Floor coverings–carpet and rugs - Burtco Enterprises Inc.

CONSTELLATION - Floor coverings–carpet and rugs ☆ - Regal Rugs Inc.

CONSTELLATION - Floor coverings–carpet and rugs ☆ - Royalweve Carpet Mills

CONSTELLATION - Furniture - Weiman Co.

CONSTELLATION - Furniture ☆ - Bassett Furniture Industries, Inc.

CONSTELLATION - Guitars - Fred Gretsch Enterprises

CONSTELLATION - Housewares ☆ - Shepherd Products U.S. Inc.

CONSTELLATION - Organs–musical instrument ☆ - Kimball International, Inc.

CONSTELLATION - Paper–book - Mont Blanc Entertainment

CONSTELLATION - Rings–jewelry - Artcarved Inc.

CONSTELLATION - Tents - Coleman Co., Inc.

CONSTELLATION - Tires - Bridgestone/Firestone, Inc.

CONSTELLATION - Trailers–travel - Starcraft Corp.

CONSTELLATION - Vacuum cleaners and accessories - The Hoover Co.

CONSTELLATION - Watches - Gruen Marketing Corp.

CONSTELLATION - Window shades - Hunter Corp.

CONSTELLATION BAROMETER - Nautical instruments - Swift Instruments, Inc.

CONSTELLATION CAFE - Coffee - Christy's Market, Inc.

CONSTELLATION STATION - Games - Aristoplay, Ltd.

CONSTELLATIONS - Computer software - Teach Yourself By Computer Software Inc.

CONSTELLATIONS - Floor coverings - Mannington Resilient Floors

CONSTILAC - Pharmaceutical preparations - Alra Laboratories, Inc.

CONSTITUENCY - Floor coverings–carpet and rugs ☆ - Lees Carpets

CONSTITUTION - Clocks - Ridgeway Clock Co.

CONSTITUTION - Cooking utensils–aluminum ☆ - General Housewares Corp.

CONSTITUTION - Floor coverings–carpet and rugs - Mohawk Carpet Corp.

CONSTITUTION - Pencils - National Pen & Pencil Co.

CONSTITUTION - Plywood - Georgia-Pacific Corp.

CONSTITUTION CLOCK - Nautical instruments - Swift Instruments, Inc.

CONSTITUTION CLOTHING COMPANY - Apparel and accessories - Edward G. O'Brien

CONSTITUTIONAL LAW MATE - Publisher's imprints - Little, Brown and Co., Inc.

CONSTIX - Cleaning equipment - Contec, Inc.

CONSTOLEIN - Pharmaceutical preparations - Bio-Factor Laboratories

CONSTONATE 60 - Pharmaceutical preparations - Bio-Factor Laboratories

CONSTOTABS - Pharmaceutical preparations - Bio-Factor Laboratories

CONSTRUCT - Footwear - Bee-Gee Shoe Corp

CONSTRUCT-A-WORD - Computer software - SRA/McGraw-Hill (Div. of The McGraw-Hill Companies)

CONSTRUCT-IT - Hardware - National Manufacturing Co.

CONSTRUCT-O-STRAWS - Toys - Tonka Corp.

CONSTRUCTA - Foam rubber - Alimed, Inc.

CONSTRUCTEX - Wire products - Bridon American Corp.

CONSTRUCTION - Paper–construction - French Paper Co.

CONSTRUCTION CASH FLOW MASTER - Computer software - SourceView Software International

CONSTRUCTION COMPANY, THE - Toys–erector sets ☆ - Parker Brothers

CONSTRUCTION GAME, THE - Games - David R. Zimmerman

CONSTRUCTION GOOP - Adhesives and sealants - Eclectic Products Inc.

CONSTRUCTION JILL - Apparel and accessories - Peter Zichelle

CONSTRUCTION JOE - Shirts - Peter Zichelle

CONSTRUCTION MASTER - Calculators - Calculated Industries, Inc.

CONSTRUCTION ZONE - Games - Treat Entertainment, Inc.

CONSTRUCTIVES - Toys - Inventure Development Corp.

CONSTRUCTOGONS - Toys ☆ - Lauri Inc.

CONSTRUCTOR - Hair care products - Brocato International

CONSTRUX - Hair care products - Paul Mazzotta Inc.

CONSTRUX - Toys - Fisher-Price, Inc.

CONSUELO - Floor coverings - Mannington Resilient Floors

CONSUELO'S - Tortillas - El Aguila Food Products, Inc.

CONSUL - Briefcases - United States Luggage Corp.

CONSUL - Dinnerware–glass - Royal China & Porcelain Companies Inc.

CONSUL - Flatware - Couzon USA

CONSUL - Food products - Vega Trading Co. Inc.

CONSUL - Projection screens - Draper Shade and Screen Co. Inc.

CONSUL - Trailers–travel - Royals International

CONSULATE - Furniture ☆ - Broyhill Furniture Industries, Inc.

CONSULATE - Liquors - William Grant & Sons, Inc.

CONSULEX BASE.COAT - Computer software - Consulex Corp.

CONSULTANT - Eyeglasses - Art-Craft Optical Co.

CONSULTATIONS - Uniforms–tailored - J.C. Penney Co., Inc.

CONSULTING - Magazines - Kennedy Information

CONSUMER - Eyeglasses - Art-Craft Optical Co.

CONSUMER - Garden equipment ☆ - Parker Sweeper Co.

CONSUMER CASKET USA - Funeral services - Consumer Casket USA, Inc.

CONSUMER COPY - Paper–bond - Georgia-Pacific Corp.

CONSUMER HEALTH ADVANTAGE - Consulting services - United Network Ventures, LLC

CONSUMER REPORTS BOOKS - Publisher's imprint - Consumer Reports Books

CONSUMERS - Brushes–paint ☆ - PPG Industries, Inc.

CONSUMERS - Food products - Universal Foods Corp.

CONSUMERS - Vegetables–frozen - Hanover Foods Corp.

CONSUMERS - Vinegar - Consumers Vinegar and Spice Co.

CONSUMERS AUTO CHOICE - Motor vehicles - Consumers Auto Choice

CONSUMERS BLUE - Vegetables–frozen - Hanover Foods Corp.

CONSUMERS RED - Vegetables–frozen - Hanover Foods Corp.

CONSUMMATE CONSUMER, THE - Boxes–hat - Marti Ann Schwartz

CONSUMNES RIVER VINEYARD - Wines ☆ - Story Vineyard

CONSYS - Computer software - THORN Automated Systems Inc.

CONT - Food products - Acme Foods

CONTAC - Cold remedies - SmithKline Beecham Consumer Healthcare

CONTAC - Pharmaceutical preparations - Smithkline Beecham Corp.

CONTAC C - Cold remedies ☆ - SmithKline Beecham Consumer Healthcare

CONTAC DAY & NIGHT - Pharmaceutical preparations - SmithKline Beecham Consumer Healthcare

CONTAC-DRI - Inks–duplicating - A.B. Dick Co.

CONTAC JR. - Cold remedies ☆ - SmithKline Beecham Consumer Healthcare

CONTAC SEVERE COLD FORMULA - Cold remedies - SmithKline Beecham Consumer Healthcare

CONTACLARIFIER - Water filters - Roberts Filter Manufacturing Co.

CONTACT - Apparel and accessories - USA Enterprises/Fifth Ave.

CONTACT - Apparel and accessories ☆ - Miller Bros. Industries Inc.

CONTACT - Automotive parts and accessories ☆ - Turtle Wax, Inc.

CONTACT - Herbicides ☆ - Dexol Industries

CONTACT - Paints - Lasting Paints Inc.

CONTACT - Spray adhesive - Contact Industries Inc.

CONTACT ACTIVITY PLANNER - Computer software - Industrial Information Resources, Inc.

CONTACT CLEANER - Electrical cleaner - Comstar International Inc. (IPC Div.)

CONTACT EDGE - Furniture - LUI Corp.

CONTACT-LENS! - Computer software - Kruse Control Software

CONTACT-PRO - Computer software - Disk-Count Software, Inc.

CONTACT WALL RIB - Wallpaper - V & B Carpet

CONTACTISOL - Contact-lens wetting solution ☆ - CooperVision Inc.

CONTACTLESS SAFETY EDGE - Roll-up garage doors - Albany International Corp.

CONTACTONE - Paper–photographic - Rollei of America Inc.

CONTACTOR, THE - Computer hardware - It Research, Inc.

CONTADINA - Meat products–canned - Nestle USA

CONTADINA DALLA CASA BUITONI - Pasta - Nestle USA

CONTADINA FRESH - Pasta - Nestle USA

CONTADINA HALF & HALF - Food products - Nestle USA

CONTADO - Wines ☆ - Frank Sutton & Co.

CONTAGE'US - Recording label - Freko Records

CONTAINED READER - Electronic equipment ☆ - EDCON Publishing

CONTAINERAMP - Ramps - JH Industries Inc. (Copperloy Div.)

CONTAINMENT - Underwear and nightwear - NCC Industries, Inc.

CONTAINMOBILE - Racks - Jarke Corp.

CONTAINS - Medical apparatus ☆ - INRAD, Inc.

CONTAK - Pencils - Faber-Castell Corp.

CONTAQ - Measuring instruments - Contaq Technologies Corp.

CONTARID - Mats–grass, reed, and jute - Bonterra America, Inc.

CONTAT - Sporting goods - Climb High Inc.

CONTAX - Cameras - Yashica Inc.

CONTAX - Computer software - Kelly H. Gross

CONTAX - Electrical equipment - Stewart-Hall Chemical Corp.

CONTAX - Herbicides ☆ - Chevron Chemical Co.

CONTAX 159 - Cameras ☆ - Yashica Inc.

CONTAX 167MT - Cameras - Yashica Inc.

CONTAX PREVIEW - Cameras ☆ - Yashica Inc.

CONTAX RTF - Photographic equipment - Yashica Inc.

CONTAX RTS-II - Cameras ☆ - Yashica Inc.

CONTAX RTS-III - Cameras - Yashica Inc.

CONTAX T2 - Cameras - Yashica Inc.

CONTAX TLA - Photographic equipment - Yashica Inc.

CONTE - Beverages–alcohol - Consolidated Distilled Products Inc.

CONTE - Food products - Furman Foods, Inc.

CONTE - Glassware–household - Oneida Ltd.

CONTE - Ophthalmic goods - Swank Optical

CONTE - Pencils - Hunt Manufacturing Co.

CONTE DI PANZANO - Wines - European Beverage Co., Inc.

CONTE LUNA - Macaroni, spaghetti, etc. - Conte Luna Foods Inc.

CONTE ZANDOTTI - Wines - Pellegrini Bros. Wines Inc.

CONTECH - Adhesives and sealants - Chemray Coatings Corp.

CONTECH - Pipes–aluminum - Pomona Pipe Products Co.

CONTECH - Pipes–plastic - Contech Construction Products Inc.

CONTEMPERA - Cosmetics - Revlon Consumer Products Corp.

CONTEMPLATES - Quilts - Extra Special Products Corp.

CONTEMPO - Blinds–venetian ☆ - Hunter Douglas, Inc.

CONTEMPO - Cabinets–metal - Par Metal Products Inc.

CONTEMPO - Cooking equipment–household ☆ - National Housewares

CONTEMPO - Cosmetics - Delta Industries International, Inc.

CONTEMPO - Dinnerware–glass - Sango Co. Ltd. (Sango USA Div.)

CONTEMPO - Eyeglasses - Martin-Copeland Eyewear Corp.

CONTEMPO - Floor coverings–carpet and rugs - Milliken & Co. Inc.

CONTEMPO - Frames–picture - North American Enclosures Inc.

CONTEMPO - Furniture - Lane Upholstery (Venture Furniture Div.)

CONTEMPO - Furniture ☆ - Bassett Furniture Industries, Inc.

CONTEMPO - Furniture ☆ - Broyhill Furniture Industries, Inc.

CONTEMPO - Giftware ☆ - Sangray Corp.

CONTEMPO - Guitars ☆ - Polytone Musical Instruments Inc.

CONTEMPO - Lamps–plastic - Creative Lighting Co.

CONTEMPO - Paints - Major Paint Co.

CONTEMPO - Plates–paper - Beach Products

CONTEMPO - Rails–iron - Leslie-Locke, Inc.

CONTEMPO - Scissors–hand-operated - Helene Curtis Industries Inc.

CONTEMPO - Shelving units–wood ☆ - Kirsch Co.

CONTEMPO - Stationery ☆ - Cranbrook Designs Inc.

CONTEMPO - Toilets–porcelain - Universal-Rundle Corp.

CONTEMPO - Wallcoverings - Flexcell Wallcoverings

CONTEMPO - Wallpaper - K.M.L. Industries

CONTEMPO - Wallpaper - Southland Wallcoverings

CONTEMPO - Watches - Hampden Corp.

☆ = Now out of production

CONTEMPO - Window shades ☆ - Spring Window Fashions Division, Inc.
CONTEMPO CANVAS - Canvas—artists' - Wolsey Co.
CONTEMPO CASUALS - Apparel—women's - Neiman-Marcus Group, Inc.
CONTEMPO EAST - Furniture - Tomlinson of High Point Inc.
CONTEMPO-I - Blinds—venetian - Custom Shade Co.
CONTEMPO I - Furniture ☆ - Athens Furniture Industries Inc.
CONTEMPO III - Dining room furniture ☆ - John Boos and Co. Inc.
CONTEMPO MASTERPIECES - Florists - Amlings Flowerland
CONTEMPO MATE - Washing machines—household ☆ - Speed Queen Co.
CONTEMPO-PRINTS - Artists' materials - Jeppson Galleries Inc.
CONTEMPO WHITE - Cooking equipment—household - Otagiri Mercantile Co. Inc.
CONTEMPOGRAPHICS - Thread - Graphic Prints Inc.
CONTEMPORA - Cabinets—wood - Parcraft Distinctive Cabinetry
CONTEMPORA - Cooking utensils—glass ☆ - Revere Ware Corp.
CONTEMPORA - Floor coverings ☆ - Congoleum Corp.
CONTEMPORA - Floor coverings—carpet and rugs - Carpet Crafts Inc.
CONTEMPORA - Floor coverings—carpet and rugs - Kelly Group Inc.
CONTEMPORA - Floor coverings—carpet and rugs - Monticello Carpet Mills
CONTEMPORA - Greeting cards ☆ - Nu-Art Inc.
CONTEMPORA - Rings—jewelry ☆ - Artcarved Inc.
CONTEMPORAGE - Wallpaper - Manhattan Creations Ltd.
CONTEMPORAGE - Wallpaper - Michele Wallpaper Inc.
CONTEMPORAMA - Cooking equipment—household ☆ - Anchor Hocking Glass, Inc.
CONTEMPORAMA - Furniture—wood - Flexsteel Industries Inc.
CONTEMPORARIES - Apparel and accessories ☆ - Manhattan International
CONTEMPORARY - Cabinets - Kent Moore Cabinets Inc.
CONTEMPORARY - Door mats - Royal Floor Mats
CONTEMPORARY - Doors—glass - Therma-Tru Corp.
CONTEMPORARY - Drapery hardware - Kenney Manufacturing Co.
CONTEMPORARY - Eyeglasses - Art-Craft Optical Co.
CONTEMPORARY - Fireplace equipment - Seymour Manufacturing Co.,Inc.
CONTEMPORARY - Floor coverings ☆ - Robbins Inc.
CONTEMPORARY - Floor coverings—carpet and rugs ☆ - Walter Carpet Mills
CONTEMPORARY - Glass—window - Crestline
CONTEMPORARY - Greeting cards - Ambassador Cards
CONTEMPORARY - Guitars ☆ - E.S.P. Guitar Co. Inc.
CONTEMPORARY - Hardware ☆ - Amerock Corp.
CONTEMPORARY - Ice buckets ☆ - Flambeau Products Corp.
CONTEMPORARY - Mats ☆ - Royal Rubber & Manufacturing Co.
CONTEMPORARY - Mats—rattan - Golden Star Inc.
CONTEMPORARY - Paper—gummed ☆ - Park Sherman
CONTEMPORARY - Recording label - CRS Inc.
CONTEMPORARY - Vases—ceramic - GraphiGallery
CONTEMPORARY - Wallpaper - Imperial Wallcoverings, Inc.
CONTEMPORARY - Wallpaper ☆ - Fidelity Industries, Inc.
CONTEMPORARY - Wigs - New Image
CONTEMPORARY AUTHORS - Computer software - The Gale Group
CONTEMPORARY AVENUES - Wallpaper ☆ - Bob Mitchell Designs
CONTEMPORARY BY PRISCILLA - Wedding gowns - Priscilla of Boston Inc.
CONTEMPORARY CAPRI - Greeting cards ☆ - John Henry Co.
CONTEMPORARY CLASSICS - Blenders - Sunbeam-Oster Household Products
CONTEMPORARY CLASSICS - Furniture - Keller Manufacturing Co.
CONTEMPORARY CLASSICS - Wallpaper - Thybony Wallcoverings Co.
CONTEMPORARY COLLECTION - Furniture - Evenflo Juvenile Furniture Co.
CONTEMPORARY COLORTONES - Wallpaper ☆ - Imperial Wallcoverings, Inc.
CONTEMPORARY CONCEPTS - Wallpaper - Academy Handprints Ltd.
CONTEMPORARY COORDINATES - Wallpaper ☆ - Parkview Designs
CONTEMPORARY COUNTRY - Fabrics—tapestry - Coloroll Inc.
CONTEMPORARY CRAFT - Artists' materials - Loew-Cornell Inc.
CONTEMPORARY CRYSTAL - Glassware—household ☆ - Anchor Hocking Glass, Inc.
CONTEMPORARY ELEGANCE - Wallpaper - Advent Industries Inc.
CONTEMPORARY ELEGANCE - Wallpaper ☆ - Capital Carousel Inc.
CONTEMPORARY EXPRESSIONS - Wallpaper - Dekortex Inc.
CONTEMPORARY FOCUS PAPERBACKS - Publisher's imprints - Dushkin Publishing Group Inc.
CONTEMPORARY HOUSE - Fabrics—tapestry ☆ - Coloroll Inc.
CONTEMPORARY ILLUSIONS - Fabrics—tapestry ☆ - Coloroll Inc.
CONTEMPORARY INNERWEAR - Apparel and accessories - Vanity Fair, Inc.
CONTEMPORARY ISSUES IN THE MIDDLE EAST - Publisher's imprints - Syracuse University Press
CONTEMPORARY LETTERS - Stationery - Stuart Hall Co., Inc.

CONTEMPORARY LINE - File folders - Hedges Manufacturing Co.
CONTEMPORARY LITE - Chimes ☆ - Nutone Inc.
CONTEMPORARY-LITES - Shoes—athletic - Titleist & Foot-Joy Worldwide
CONTEMPORARY LIVING - Fabrics—tapestry ☆ - Columbus Coated Fabrics Co.
CONTEMPORARY LIVING - Wallpaper - Galaxie Handprints
CONTEMPORARY LIVING TOO! - Wallpaper - Galaxie Handprints
CONTEMPORARY MAPLE - Floor coverings ☆ - Robbins Inc.
CONTEMPORARY MATRIX - Furniture ☆ - Virginia House Furniture Corp.
CONTEMPORARY MUSIC TEACHING GOD'S WORD - Music—sheet - Integrity Music, Inc.
CONTEMPORARY OAK II - Hardware ☆ - Amerock Corp.
CONTEMPORARY OAK I - Hardware ☆ - Amerock Corp.
CONTEMPORARY PINE - Clocks - General Time Corp. (Westclox/Seth Thomas Div.)
CONTEMPORARY PRINTS - Posters - C.M. Paula Co.
CONTEMPORARY REFLECTIONS - Mirrors - Hoyne Industries Inc.
CONTEMPORARY ROMANCE - Wallpaper ☆ - Camelot Design Studios
CONTEMPORARY ROSE - Bedding—linen - Dan River Inc.
CONTEMPORARY SERVER - Giftware - Artex-Green Corp. of N.Y.
CONTEMPORARY STORY I - Wallpaper - J. Josephson, Inc.
CONTEMPORARY STORY, THE - Wallpaper - K.M.L. Industries
CONTEMPORARY STRIP - Floor coverings ☆ - Robbins Inc.
CONTEMPORARY TOUCH - Wallpaper ☆ - Mayfair Wallcoverings
CONTEMPORARY TOUCH, A - Fabrics—tapestry ☆ - Coloroll Inc.
CONTEMPORARY WAYS - Wallpaper ☆ - Bob Mitchell Designs
CONTEMPORARY WOMAN - Hair care products - Helene Curtis Industries Inc.
CONTEMPOS - Shoes - Craddock-Terry Inc.
CONTEMPRA - Barbecues and grills - Harris & Mallow Products
CONTEMPRA - Cabinets ☆ - Medallion Kitchens of Minnesota Inc.
CONTEMPRA - Floor coverings—carpet and rugs - Masland Corp.
CONTEMPRA - Hardware ☆ - Amerock Corp.
CONTEMPRA - Pens - Empire Berol USA
CONTEMPRA - Stone products - Concrete Stone & Tile Corp.
CONTEMPRA - Telescopes - Northern Telecom, Inc.
CONTEMPRA - Wall clocks ☆ - Contempra Industries
CONTEMPRA 6000 SERIES - Filters—water - Lomart Industries
CONTEMPRA CHARBEQUE - Barbecues and grills - Harris & Mallow Products
CONTEMPRA DIMENSIONAL - Wallcoverings - Worldwalls International Inc.
CONTEMPRA SPORTCRUISER - Boats—motor ☆ - Larson Boat Div.
CONTEMPRA/TALIA - Telescopes - Northern Telecom, Inc.
CONTEMPRETTE - Telescopes - Northern Telecom, Inc.
CONTEMPRO - Sporting goods - Contemporary Products, Inc.
CONTEMP'TRY - Windows—screen ☆ - Laurco Fabrics Inc.
CONTEMPURA - Wallpaper - Aresda Design Associates
CONTENDER - Aquatic pharmacuetical preparations - Superior Shade & Blind Co. Inc.
CONTENDER - Boats - Dynamic Plastics Inc.
CONTENDER - Boats—pontoons ☆ - Kennedy Inc.
CONTENDER - Braces—orthopedic - Orthopedic Technology, Inc.
CONTENDER - Calculators ☆ - Casio, Inc.
CONTENDER - Electronic equipment - Appleton Electric Co.
CONTENDER - Finishing agents - Hillyard Enterprises, Inc.
CONTENDER - Floor coverings—carpet and rugs - Barrett Carpet Mills Inc.
CONTENDER - Floor coverings—carpet and rugs - Criterion Mills Inc.
CONTENDER - Floor coverings—carpet and rugs - West Point-Pepperell Mill Store
CONTENDER - Footwear - Summit Footwear Inc.
CONTENDER - Gloves - Ektelon
CONTENDER - Golfing equipment - Robert J. Williams
CONTENDER - Mattresses - Simmons USA
CONTENDER - Motor vehicles—buses - Champion Motor Coach Inc.
CONTENDER - Office supplies - Stempel Manufacturing Co.
CONTENDER - Pistols - Thompson/Center Arms
CONTENDER - Sporting goods - Shakespeare Fishing Tackle
CONTENDER - Wheelchairs ☆ - Penox Technologies Inc.
CONTENDER SECURITY SYSTEMS - Alarm systems - Samson Security Inc.
CONTENDERS - Sporting goods ☆ - O'Brien International
CONTENT - Diapers—disposable - Weyerhaeuser Co.
CONTENTA - Pillows - Hollander Home Fashions Inc.
CONTENTIONS - Apparel—athletic - Alyssa Carr Inc.
CONTENTS - Containers - Rubbermaid Inc.
CONTENTS TAB COMPOSER - Computer software - Blue Sky Software Corp.
CONTENTS UNDER PRESSURE - Clothes - Contents Under Pressure Inc.
CONTENTWARE - Computer software - Contentware, Inc.
CONTESSA - Apparel—women's - L & M Cultured Marble Co.

☆ = Now out of production

CONTESSA - Blinds–vertical - Ultra Vertical Blinds Inc.
CONTESSA - Boats–motor - Bayliner Marine Corp.
CONTESSA - Boats–motor - Lyn-Craft Boat Co.
CONTESSA - Boats–motor ☆ - Seajay Boats Inc.
CONTESSA - Candy ☆ - Perugina Chocolate & Confections Inc.
CONTESSA - Carpet sweepers ☆ - Bissell Inc.
CONTESSA - Dinnerware–glass - Royal China & Porcelain Companies Inc.
CONTESSA - Dolls ☆ - Effanbee Doll Corp.
CONTESSA - Fabrics - Charter Fabrics Inc.
CONTESSA - Floor coverings - Mannington Resilient Floors
CONTESSA - Floor coverings ☆ - Congoleum Corp.
CONTESSA - Floor coverings–carpet and rugs - Burtco Enterprises Inc.
CONTESSA - Floor coverings–carpet and rugs - Eligere Carpets
CONTESSA - Floor coverings–carpet and rugs - Trans-Ocean Import Co. Inc.
CONTESSA - Floor coverings–carpet and rugs - World Carpets, Inc.
CONTESSA - Floor coverings–carpet and rugs ☆ - Regal Rugs Inc.
CONTESSA - Frames–eyeglass - U.S. Optical Frame Co.
CONTESSA - Frames–eyeglass ☆ - Vanity Optical Manufacturing Co. Inc.
CONTESSA - Furniture ☆ - Bassett Furniture Industries, Inc.
CONTESSA - Handbags - Contessa Accessories Corp.
CONTESSA - Health care products ☆ - Abbott Laboratories
CONTESSA - Housewares ☆ - American Tack & Hardware Co., Inc.
CONTESSA - Housewares ☆ - Scio Pottery Co.
CONTESSA - Motor vehicles–motor homes - Beaver Coaches Inc.
CONTESSA - Musical instruments - Hohner Inc.
CONTESSA - Pens - Yafa Pen Co.
CONTESSA - Rings–jewelry - Artcarved Inc.
CONTESSA - Seafood products–fresh or frozen - Zb Industries, Inc.
CONTESSA - Shoes–athletic - Brooks Orthopedic & Custom Shoes
CONTESSA - Telescopes - Northern Telecom, Inc.
CONTESSA - Thimbles - JHB International Inc.
CONTESSA - Watches - Design Time USA Inc.
CONTESSA - Window coverings - Joanna Western Mills Co.
CONTESSA AZZURA - Colognes - J. Palazzolo Son Inc.
CONTESSA BRONZINI - Frames–eyeglass ☆ - Universal/Univis Inc.
CONTESSA COLLECTION - Fabric stores - Conso Products Co.
CONTESSA COLLECTION, THE - Bathroom accessories ☆ - American Tack & Hardware Co., Inc.
CONTESSINA - Floor coverings–carpet and rugs - Barrett Carpet Mills Inc.
CONTEST RUBBER - Craft supplies - Sig Manufacturing Inc.
CONTESTANT - Mattresses - Simmons USA
CONTESTOR, THE - Power tool blades - American Saw & Manufacturing Co.
CONTEX - Contact-lens cleaner - Contex, Inc.
CONTEXT - Apparel - Spiegel, Inc.
CONTEXT - Computer software - Oracle Corp.
CONTEXT - Nonwoven fabric - Irving Textile Products Inc.
CONTEXT - Recording label - Jazz Composer's Orchestra Association Inc.
CONTEXT CARDS - Postcards - Fotofolio Inc.
CONTI - Coffee - John Conti Coffee Co.
CONTI - Shampoos - Smithkline Beecham Corp.
CONTI ROYAL - Wines ☆ - Oak Ridge Vineyards
CONTI WEAVE - Floor coverings–carpet and rugs - Milliken & Co. Inc.
CONTICATH - Catheters - Contimed, Inc.
CONTICO - Plastic utility boxes ☆ - Contico International Inc.
CONTICO TUFF - Motor vehicle parts and accessories ☆ - Contico International Inc.
CONTIDRAIN - Medical apparatus - Contimed, Inc.
CONTIMA - Women's apparel - Country Miss Inc.
CONTIN-U-WEB - Labels–paper - Service Business Forms, Ltd.
CONTINENT EXPLORER II - Computer software - Pierian Spring L.P.
CONTINENTAL - Audio and video accessories, calculators - Continental Electronics Corp.
CONTINENTAL - Automotive parts and accessories - Toppertown Inc.
CONTINENTAL - Awnings - Anchor Industries Inc.
CONTINENTAL - Bathroom accessories - Melard Manufacturing Corp.
CONTINENTAL - Bicycles - Schwinn Cycling & Fitness Inc.
CONTINENTAL - Bicycles - XLM Corp.
CONTINENTAL - Bicycles ☆ - Graber Products, Inc.
CONTINENTAL - Boats–motor ☆ - Stamas Yacht Inc.
CONTINENTAL - Breads - A. Angonoa Inc.
CONTINENTAL - Brushes–hair - Spornette International, Inc.
CONTINENTAL - Cabinets - Nutone Inc.
CONTINENTAL - Cabinets–wood - Decora
CONTINENTAL - Cases–eyeglass - California Optical Leather Inc.
CONTINENTAL - Cases–musical instrument - M & M Distributing Co.
CONTINENTAL - Cash registers - Continental Industries Inc.

CONTINENTAL - Chocolate candy ☆ - Price Candy Co. Inc.
CONTINENTAL - Clocks - Ridgeway Clock Co.
CONTINENTAL - Coffee - Continental Coffee Co.
CONTINENTAL - Containers - Continental Wholesale Florists, Inc.
CONTINENTAL - Cultured food products, etc. - Continental Culture Specialists Inc.
CONTINENTAL - Curtain rods - Kirsch Co.
CONTINENTAL - Cutlery - Washington Forge Inc.
CONTINENTAL - Dental equipment - A-Dec Inc.
CONTINENTAL - Dressings, sauces, soup bases, etc. - Continental Food Products Inc.
CONTINENTAL - Dryers–hair - Helene Curtis Industries Inc.
CONTINENTAL - Electrical equipment - MacLean-Fogg Co.
CONTINENTAL - Felt typewriter and chair pads - Aetna Felt Corp.
CONTINENTAL - Fireplace equipment - Seymour Manufacturing Co.,Inc.
CONTINENTAL - Fireplace equipment - Vogelzang International Corp.
CONTINENTAL - Flag poles - Concord Industries Inc.
CONTINENTAL - Floor coverings - American Floor Products Co. Inc.
CONTINENTAL - Floor coverings–carpet and rugs - Mattel Carpet & Rug Inc.
CONTINENTAL - Floor coverings–carpet and rugs - Mohawk Carpet Corp.
CONTINENTAL - Floor wax - Continental Chemical Corp.
CONTINENTAL - Food products - SPADA enterprise, ltd.
CONTINENTAL - Furniture - American Furniture Co. Inc.
CONTINENTAL - Furniture - Bangkok International Inc.
CONTINENTAL - Furniture - Bean Station Furniture Factory Inc.
CONTINENTAL - Furniture - Stanley Furniture Co. Inc.
CONTINENTAL - Giftware ☆ - Bar & Barbeque Products Inc.
CONTINENTAL - Glassware–household - Federal Glass
CONTINENTAL - Glassware–household - Knobler International Ltd.
CONTINENTAL - Glassware–household - Seneca Glass Co.
CONTINENTAL - Glassware–household ☆ - Avitra Corp.
CONTINENTAL - Glassware–household ☆ - Crisa Corp.
CONTINENTAL - Greeting cards - Paramount Cards Inc.
CONTINENTAL - Health care products - Conair Corp.
CONTINENTAL - Luggage - Pantos Canvas Corp.
CONTINENTAL - Luggage ☆ - Hartmann Luggage Co.
CONTINENTAL - Mattresses ☆ - California Concepts
CONTINENTAL - Measuring instruments - Rite Autotronics Corp.
CONTINENTAL - Mobile homes - Oakwood Homes Corp.
CONTINENTAL - Motor vehicles–automobiles - Bentley Motors Inc.
CONTINENTAL - Motor vehicles–automobiles - Ford Motor Co. (Lincoln-Mercury Div.)
CONTINENTAL - Motor vehicles–motor homes - Baron Motor Homes Inc.
CONTINENTAL - Motor vehicles–motor homes ☆ - Beaver Coaches Inc.
CONTINENTAL - Nails, welded wire fabric, barbed wire - Continental Steel Corp.
CONTINENTAL - Occasional tables ☆ - JDI Group, Inc.
CONTINENTAL - Office supplies ☆ - Hedges Manufacturing Co.
CONTINENTAL - Pencil sharpeners - Wescosa Inc.
CONTINENTAL - Pencils ☆ - Empire Berol USA
CONTINENTAL - Pet products - Flexi-Mat Corp.
CONTINENTAL - Pipes–tobacco ☆ - Dr. Grabow Pre-Smoked Pipes Inc.
CONTINENTAL - Powerboat ☆ - Invader Marine Inc.
CONTINENTAL - Racks - A & T Ski Co. Inc.
CONTINENTAL - Recording label - Ernie Cash Enterprises
CONTINENTAL - Recording label - Cash Productions
CONTINENTAL - Rifles and shotguns - Continental Arms Corp.
CONTINENTAL - Shoes–athletic - Adidas USA Inc.
CONTINENTAL - Shutters–wood ☆ - Maywood Inc.
CONTINENTAL - Sinks–metal - Just Manufacturing Co.
CONTINENTAL - Soap ☆ - Stahl Soap Corp.
CONTINENTAL - Soups–mixes - Lipton Investments, Inc.
CONTINENTAL - Steel products - Salem China Co.
CONTINENTAL - Strollers–baby ☆ - Welsh Co.
CONTINENTAL - Toffee - Nabisco Foods Group
CONTINENTAL - Trailers–travel ☆ - Coachmen Industries, Inc.
CONTINENTAL - Watches - Gruen Marketing Corp.
CONTINENTAL - Water - Continental Water
CONTINENTAL - Water heaters–household - A.O. Smith Corp.
CONTINENTAL - Wet suits–rubber ☆ - Parkway Systems
CONTINENTAL - Wheelchairs - Ventura Enterprises, Inc.
CONTINENTAL - Wigs - Paula Young
CONTINENTAL 500 - Measuring instruments - Rite Autotronics Corp.
CONTINENTAL ART-CRAFT - Jewelry, giftware, folk art, crystal - Continental Art-Craft

☆ = Now out of production

CONTINENTAL AUDIOPHILE - Audio blank tapes - Continental Electronics Corp.

CONTINENTAL BUYING GROUP - Consulting services - Continental Buying Group, Inc.

CONTINENTAL CAFE - Pizzas–frozen ☆ - Mr. Z's Fund Raising Corp.

CONTINENTAL CAN COMPANY - Machine parts - Continental Can Co., Inc.

CONTINENTAL CHEF - Spaghetti sauces - Pastorelli Food Products Inc.

CONTINENTAL CLASSICS - Furniture - Hammary Furniture Co. Inc.

CONTINENTAL CLASSICS - Wallcoverings - James F. White & Co. Inc.

CONTINENTAL CLUTH - Ophthalmic goods ☆ - Fidelity Case Corp.

CONTINENTAL COFFEE - Coffee - Quaker Oats Co.

CONTINENTAL COLLECTION - Apparel stores–lingerie - Goddess Bra

CONTINENTAL COLLECTION - Flatware - Poole Silver Co.

CONTINENTAL COLLECTION - Floor coverings - Beaulieu of America, Inc.

CONTINENTAL COLLECTION - Furniture ☆ - Hooker Furniture Corp.

CONTINENTAL COLLECTION - Hobby kits - Craft World International Inc.

CONTINENTAL COLLECTION - Needles–sewing - Heritage Designs Inc.

CONTINENTAL COLLECTION - Tiles–mosaic - WesekPalley Tile Inc.

CONTINENTAL COUNTRY - Lighting fixtures - Fredrick Ramond Inc.

CONTINENTAL CREATIVE SALES - Marble tile, furniture, tables bases - Continental Creative Sales Inc.

CONTINENTAL CUISINE - Cooking equipment–household - May Department Stores Co.

CONTINENTAL DELI - Meat products–beef - Foodbrands America, Inc.

CONTINENTAL DESIGNS - Wood products ☆ - Gilbert Stone Enterprises Inc.

CONTINENTAL DIJONNAISE - Food products - Golden Whisk Pasta Partners

CONTINENTAL ELECTRIC - Kitchen appliances - Cargil International Corp.

CONTINENTAL ELECTRONICS - Communications equipment - Continental Electronics Corp.

CONTINENTAL FLAIR - Wallpaper - Gagne Wallcovering, Inc.

CONTINENTAL FLORAL GREENS - Containers - Continental Wholesale Florists, Inc.

CONTINENTAL GOURMET - Tools–hand-operated - Westminster International Co., Inc.

CONTINENTAL LEATHER FASHIONS - Leather goods - Continental Leather Fashions, Inc.

CONTINENTAL MICRONESIA - Air transportation - Continental Micronesia, Inc.

CONTINENTAL NO. 1 - Cleaning preparations - Stewart-Hall Chemical Corp.

CONTINENTAL PLUS - Curtain rods - Kirsch Co.

CONTINENTAL PRIDE - Pans - F.W. Woolworth Co.

CONTINENTAL SERIES - Kitchen appliances - Nutone Inc.

CONTINENTAL SETS - Glassware–household ☆ - Kraftware Corp. (Morgan Div.)

CONTINENTAL SINGERS - Records, CDs, and cassettes - Cameron D. Floria

CONTINENTAL STUDIOS - Plaster and fiberglass figurines, planters, etc. - Continental Accents Ltd.

CONTINENTAL TAPERS - Candles - Columbia Wax Products Inc.

CONTINENTAL TEXTILES - Wallpaper - Durawall Inc.

CONTINENTAL TEXTURES - Wallpaper - Durawall Inc.

CONTINENTAL, THE - Awnings - Alpha Productions Inc.

CONTINENTAL, THE - Jewelry - Helzbergs Diamond Shops Inc.

CONTINENTAL TOOLS - Stainless steel - Le Creuset of America, Inc.

CONTINENTAL TRADING - Cases–eyeglass - Continental Trading Co. Inc.

CONTINENTAL TRUNK - Luggage, etc. - Continental Vogue Luggage Co.

CONTINENTAL WALLCOVERING COLLECTION, THE - Wallpaper - Patterson Piazza

CONTINENTALS - Chocolate candy - World's Finest Chocolate, Inc.

CONTINENTALS - Shoes ☆ - Clarks of England Inc.

CONTINENTALS, THE - Records, cassettes, compact discs, and video tapes - Cameron D. Floria

CONTINENTALS, THE - Apparel stores–lingerie - Formfit Rogers

CONTINENTIAL - Brooms - Wright-Bernet

CONTINEX - Biological products - Polychem Corp.

CONTINNUUS - Housewares - Continnuus

CONTINU-MATIC - Forklifts - Pettibone Corp.

CONTINUATIONS - Dining room furniture - Hickory Manufacturing Co.

CONTINUELLE - Comforters - Carpenter Co.

CONTINUELLE - Pillows - E.R. Carpenter Co.

CONTINUO - Stationery - Samuel Ward Manufacturing Inc.

CONTINUOUS ACTION FORMULA - Deodorants–personal - Gillette Co.

CONTINUOUS COLOR - Lipsticks - Noxell Corp.

CONTINUOUS COLOR - Paints - Surface Protection Industries, Inc.

CONTINUOUS CURVE - Contact lenses - Revlon Consumer Products Corp.

CONTINUOUS ELEGANCE - Wallcovering - Wall Trends, Inc.

CONTINUOUS ELEGANCE III - Wallcovering - Wall Trends, Inc.

CONTINUOUS MONITOR - Laboratory apparatus - Kaye Instruments Inc.

CONTINUOUS PLAY - Ophthalmic goods - Foremost Optical Products

CONTINUOUS PROTECTION - Skin care products ☆ - Noxell Corp.

CONTINUOUS VISION - Ophthalmic goods ☆ - Vision Ease

CONTINUOUS WEAR - Cosmetics - Noxell Corp.

CONTINUTYPE-N - Stencils ☆ - Mason Marking Systems Corp.

CONTINUUM - Comforters - Pacific Coast Feather Co.

CONTINUUM - Computer peripheral equipment - Stratus Computer, Inc.

CONTINUUM - Computer software - Stenograph Corp.

CONTINUUM - Furniture - Bernhardt Industries

CONTINUUM - Hair care products - Helene Curtis Industries Inc.

CONTINUUM - Laser systems - Quantel International Inc.

CONTINUUM - Mattresses - Evenflo Juvenile Furniture Co.

CONTINUUM - Office furniture–metal - Stow/Davis Furniture Co.

CONTINUUM - Paper products - Crane & Co. Inc.

CONTINUUM - Pencils–mechanical - Empire Berol USA

CONTINUUM - Wallpaper ☆ - Bolta Wallcoverings

CONTINUUM 2000 - Computer peripheral equipment - Emtek Health Care Systems, Inc.

CONTINUUM II - Wallpaper - Bolta Wallcoverings

CONTIQUE - Floor coverings–carpet and rugs ☆ - Callaway Carpets

CONTIQUE - Ophthalmic goods ☆ - Alcon Laboratories, Inc.

CONTITECH - Belts–automotive - CRP Industries, Inc.

CONTITHERM - Electronic equipment - Heraeus Electro-Nite Co.

CONTOUR - Blinds–venetian ☆ - Kenney Manufacturing Co.

CONTOUR - Breads ☆ - Campbell Taggart Inc.

CONTOUR - Bumpers–motor vehicle - Wedgestone Automotive Corp.

CONTOUR - Cardboard - Chesapeake Fiber Packaging Corp.

CONTOUR - Chimes - Nutone Inc.

CONTOUR - Clocks - General Time Corp. (Westclox/Seth Thomas Div.)

CONTOUR - Dinnerware–glass ☆ - Nikko Ceramics Inc.

CONTOUR - Dry erase boards - Quartet Manufacturing Co.

CONTOUR - Eyeglasses - Art-Craft Optical Co.

CONTOUR - Fabrics - Greenwood Mills Inc.

CONTOUR - Fibers–synthetic - Georgia-Bonded Fibers, Inc.

CONTOUR - Floor coverings–carpet and rugs ☆ - Walter Carpet Mills

CONTOUR - Floor coverings–tile - Kentile Floors Inc.

CONTOUR - Furniture - Craftmatic/Contour Industries Inc.

CONTOUR - Furniture - Universal Flooring

CONTOUR - Furniture ☆ - Bassett Furniture Industries, Inc.

CONTOUR - Glassware–household - Oneida Ltd.

CONTOUR - Hair care products - Goody Products, Inc.

CONTOUR - Hair care products - Redken Laboratories, Inc.

CONTOUR - Herbicides - American Cyanamid Co.

CONTOUR - Medical apparatus - Bennett X-Ray Corp.

CONTOUR - Medical apparatus - Interventional Therapeutics Corp.

CONTOUR - Medical apparatus - Ventritex, Inc.

CONTOUR - Medical products - American West Medical Co., Inc.

CONTOUR - Motor vehicles–automobiles - Ford Motor Co.

CONTOUR - Office supplies - Vanguard Corp.

CONTOUR - Paint sprayers - International Marketings, Inc.

CONTOUR - Shaving preparations - Gillette Co.

CONTOUR - Siding–insulating ☆ - Aluminum Co. of America

CONTOUR - Silverware - Towle Manufacturing Co.

CONTOUR - Tiles–ceramic - Monarch Tile Inc.

CONTOUR - Truck caps - Jackson Enterprises Inc.

CONTOUR - Underwear and nightwear ☆ - Alba-Waldensian, Inc.

CONTOUR - Vibrator/massage chairs - Contour Chair Lounge Co. Inc.

CONTOUR - Wallets - Buxton Inc.

CONTOUR-BEST THERMOGUARD - Sporting goods - Stearns Manufacturing Co.

CONTOUR BOTTLE STABILIZER - Merchandise racks–plastic - Paul Flum Ideas, Inc.

CONTOUR BY ALIVE - Skin and hair-care products - Alive Skin Care Corp.

CONTOUR CARE - Mattresses ☆ - Classic Corp.

CONTOUR COLLECTION - Jewelry - Sandberg & Sikorski Diamond Corp.

CONTOUR COLLECTION - Shelving units–wood - Naomi Gale Wall Systems

CONTOUR CREME - Skin care products - Fanie International

CONTOUR DU CORPS - Skin care products - Naissance, Inc.

CONTOUR-FLEX - Medical apparatus - Wahl Clipper Corp.

CONTOUR FOAM - Weightlifting equipment - All Pro Exercise Products, Inc.

CONTOUR FRESH LOOKS - Wallpaper ☆ - Kingfisher Wallcoverings

CONTOUR-GRIP - Pens - Paper Mate Co.

CONTOUR II - Furniture - Universal Flooring

CONTOUR JOGGER - Treadmills - Battle Creek Equipment Co.

CONTOUR-KNIT - Fabrics - Guilford Mills, Inc.

☆ = Now out of production

CONTOUR-LASTIK - Girdles - H.F. Robbins

CONTOUR MAX - Sporting goods - Unique Sports Products Inc.

CONTOUR ONE - Wheelchairs - Adaptive Engineering Lab Inc.

CONTOUR-PAK - Containers - Owens-Illinois Inc.

CONTOUR-PEDIC - Mattresses - Sleepwell Mattress Co. Inc.

CONTOUR PLP - Golfing equipment - Golfsmith International Inc.

CONTOUR PROJECTOR - Electronic equipment - Optical Gaging Products, Inc.

CONTOUR SERIES - Golfing equipment - Golfsmith International Inc.

CONTOUR SLEEP SYSTEM - Bedspreads - Banyan Research, Inc.

CONTOUR STICK - Cosmetics - Viviane Woodard Industries, Ltd.

CONTOUR T-LOK - Siding–insulating ☆ - Aluminum Co. of America

CONTOUR TAPER TILE - Insulating materials - NPS

CONTOUR TILING-ON-A-ROLL - Wallpaper - Kingfisher Wallcoverings

CONTOUR TRAC - Golfing equipment - Golfsmith International Inc.

CONTOUR-U - Wheelchairs - Pin Dot Products

CONTOUR ULTRA - Pillows - Banyan Research, Inc.

CONTOUR WAVE - Exercising equipment - Tunturi, Inc.

CONTOUR WITCHERY - Apparel–women's - Exquisite Form Industries

CONTOURA - Fabrics - Malden Mills Industries, Inc.

CONTOURA - Hair care products - Modafini Inc.

CONTOURA - Rings–jewelry - Feature Enterprises

CONTOURE - Jewelry - Jacoby-Bender Inc.

CONTOURING BODY TREATMENT - Skin care products - Viviane Woodard Industries, Ltd.

CONTOURIST - Musical instrument accessories - Carpenter Co.

CONTOURKORE - Balsa wood for boat-building - Baltek Corp.

CONTOURLINE - Seats–automobile - Charvoz

CONTOURS - Apparel–women's - ShadowLine Inc.

CONTOURS - Dinnerware–glass - Arita Sales Co. Inc.

CONTOURS - Furniture - Broyhill Furniture Industries, Inc.

CONTOURS - Manicure preparations - Creative Nail Design, Inc.

CONTOURS - Wallpaper ☆ - Flexible Materials Inc.

CONTOURS - Wallpaper ☆ - Wall Fashion Inc.

CONTRA - Rackets–racquetball - Ektelon

CONTRA BASS - Loudspeakers - Intersonics Inc.

CONTRA-BOMBARDE - Audio equipment ☆ - Shahinian Acoustics Ltd.

CONTRA-EMPACHO - Pharmaceutical preparations - Vartex Pharmaceuticals Inc.

CONTRA-FLAME - Chemical preparations - Anscott Chemical Industries, Inc.

CONTRA FORCE - Sporting goods ☆ - Konami (America) Inc.

CONTRA-GLARE - Optical scanners–computer - Titmus Optical, Inc.

CONTRA III - THE ALIEN WARS - Games ☆ - Konami (America) Inc.

CONTRA-LATIDO - Pharmaceutical preparations - Vartex Pharmaceuticals Inc.

CONTRA: LEGACY OF WAR - Computer storage devices–optical - Konami (America) Inc.

CONTRABLEM - Skin care products - Texas Pharmacal Co.

CONTRAC - Office supplies - McDonald Products

CONTRACFLOOR - Floor coverings ☆ - Tarkett, Inc.

CONTRACT - Clocks - General Time Corp. (Westclox/Seth Thomas Div.)

CONTRACT - Padding–foam ☆ - Foamex LP

CONTRACT 16 - Floor coverings ☆ - Tarkett, Inc.

CONTRACT 30 - Floor coverings–carpet and rugs ☆ - S and S Mills Inc.

CONTRACT 40 - Floor coverings–carpet and rugs - S and S Mills Inc.

CONTRACT 2000 - Floor coverings–carpet and rugs ☆ - Proffitt Manufacturing Co.

CONTRACT 2200 - Floor coverings–carpet and rugs - Kelly Group Inc.

CONTRACT 2276 - Floor coverings–carpet and rugs - Kelly Group Inc.

CONTRACT 7000 - Office supplies - McDonald Products

CONTRACT ATLANTIS - Blinds–venetian - Hunter Douglas, Inc.

CONTRACT COLORWAYS - Tiles–ceramic - American Olean Tile Co.

CONTRACT CONCEPTS - Wallpaper ☆ - Walldesigns

CONTRACT CONCEPTS I - Wallpaper - Royson's Corp.

CONTRACT CONSTRUCTOR - Computer software - Alpine Press, Inc.

CONTRACT EXPRESS - Computer software - Learned-Mahn, Inc.

CONTRACT EXPRESS - Wallpaper - Capital Carousel Inc.

CONTRACT EXPRESS II - Wallpaper - Capital Carousel Inc.

CONTRACT EXPRESS III - Wallpaper - Capital Carousel Inc.

CONTRACT, INC. - Lighting fixtures - Contract, Inc.

CONTRACT LIGHTLINES DESIGNER SERIES - Blinds–venetian - Hunter Douglas, Inc.

CONTRACT MARBLE - Floor coverings–tile - Robbins Interior Surface Inc.

CONTRACT MASTER - Computer software ☆ - Sherikon, Inc.

CONTRACT PLUS - Floor coverings–carpet and rugs ☆ - American Excelsior Co.

CONTRACT PRINTS - Wallpaper - Durawall Inc.

CONTRACT SELECTOR - Wallpaper ☆ - Walldesigns

CONTRACT TEAM - Computer Software - Scopus Technology, Inc.

CONTRACT TEXTURES - Wallpaper - Len-Tex Inc.

CONTRACT TEXTURES - Wallpaper ☆ - Walldesigns

CONTRACT TEXTURES II - Wallpaper - Len-Tex Inc.

CONTRACT, THE - Games ☆ - Mayfair Games, Inc.

CONTRACT V - Floor coverings–tile - Flexco Co.

CONTRACT VISCOUNT - Blinds–venetian - Hunter Douglas, Inc.

CONTRACTOR - Generators–electric - Coleman Powermate, Inc.

CONTRACTOR - Insecticide - Contact Industries Inc.

CONTRACTOR - Ladders–metal - Rich Ladder Co.

CONTRACTOR - Safety glasses - Crews, Inc.

CONTRACTOR - Saw blades - Oldham Saw Co., Inc.

CONTRACTOR & MAINTENENCE COVERS - Paint rollers - Corona Brushes Inc.

CONTRACTOR BUDDY - Ladders–metal - Werner Co.

CONTRACTOR FRIENDLY - Lighting fixtures - Genlyte Group Inc.

CONTRACTOR GRADE - Cleaning preparations - Empire Brushes, Inc.

CONTRACTOR GUN - Paint sprayers - Graco Inc.

CONTRACTOR PLUS - Gloves–work - Adams Global Industries, Inc.

CONTRACTOR POWER - Electronic equipment ☆ - Triangle Wire & Cable, Inc.

CONTRACTOR SERIES - Locks–door - Schlage Lock Co.

CONTRACTOR SERIES - Paint rollers - DIMC, Inc.

CONTRACTOR STRENGTH - Tools–hand-operated - Fiskars Inc.

CONTRACTOR TOUGH AND DESIGN - Electrical equipment - General Cable Corp.

CONTRACTOR'S - Footwear–women's - Salvatrice Shoe Inc.

CONTRACTOR'S BRIEFCASE - Briefcases - Portable Products, Inc.

CONTRACTOR'S CHOICE - Locks–door - Harbor Sales Co.

CONTRACTORS CHOICE - Paints - Major Paint Co.

CONTRACTOR'S CHOICE - Tape–adhesive - Manco, Inc.

CONTRACTORS EDGE, THE - Computer software - Pro-Mation, Inc.

CONTRACTOR'S GRADE A - Paints - Major Paint Co.

CONTRACTOR'S PLUS - Paints - Smiland Paint Co.

CONTRACTOR'S SAW - Saws–hand-operated - Delta International Machinery Corp.

CONTRACTOR'S VINYL ADHESIVE - Wallpaper - Allpro Corp.

CONTRACTS MATE - Publisher's imprints - Little, Brown and Co., Inc.

CONTRACTWARE - Computer software - Linda Keckler

CONTRAFLOW - Kilns - Ped Technologies, Inc.

CONTRALOG - Speedometers - Airguide Instrument Co.

CONTRAPTION - Games - Lakeside Games

CONTRASPOT - Pet products - Tetra Sales USA

CONTRAST - Floor coverings - Congoleum Corp.

CONTRAST - Perfumes - Avon Products, Inc.

CONTRAST - Recording label ☆ - Ray Lawrence Ltd.

CONTRAST - Thread ☆ - American & Efird, Inc.

CONTRAST BLUE - Dishes–china ☆ - WMF/USA

CONTRAST-O - Artists' materials - Scratch-Art Co., Inc.

CONTRAST P.M. - Dental compounds - Discus Dental, Inc.

CONTRATTO - Wines - Blair Importers Ltd.

CONTRESS - Hair care products - Key West Aloe Inc.

CONTREX - Electronic equipment - Contrex, Inc.

CONTREX - Floor coverings–carpet and rugs - Roxbury Carpet Co.

CONTRIN - Pharmaceutical preparations - Geneva Generics Inc.

CONTROFLEX PHOSPHORATED - Pharmaceutical preparations ☆ - JMI-Canton Pharmaceuticals

CONTROL - Adhesives and sealants ☆ - Frazee Paint

CONTROL - Computer software - Phase One Systems

CONTROL - Cosmetics - Revlon-Realistic Professional Products Inc.

CONTROL - Hair spray - Tri-Institute of Trichology

CONTROL - Pencils - Reliance Pen & Pencil Corp.

CONTROL - Pet products - Clorox Co.

CONTROL - Pharmaceutical preparations - Republic Drug Co. Inc.

CONTROL - Sporting goods - Lisco, Inc.

CONTROL - Vitamins and nutritional supplements ☆ - Thompson Medical Co., Inc.

CONTROL 1 - Health care products - Prentke Romich Co.

CONTROL 19 - Cooking utensils–aluminum ☆ - Mirro Corp.

CONTROL-35 - Cleaning preparations - Pioneer Manufacturing Co.

CONTROL 5000 - Animal feeds - Bluebonnet Milling Co.

CONTROL-A-SHOW - Electronic equipment - Hudson Photographic Industries Inc.

CONTROL-ACE - Girdles - Vanity Corset Co. Inc.

CONTROL AIR - Fans–electric - Tensor Corp.

CONTROL BRUSH - Toothbrushes ☆ - Teledyne Water Pik

☆ = Now out of production

CONTROL CENTER - Golfing equipment - Robsan Corp.

CONTROL CENTRAL - Electrical equipment - General Electric Co.

CONTROL CLEANETTE - Cleaning preparations - Geritrex Corp.

CONTROL COAT - Machine parts - Nordson Corp.

CONTROL EASE - Pet products - Coastal Pet Products, Inc.

CONTROL-EZE - Apparel and accessories - Vanity Corset Co. Inc.

CONTROL FIVE - Electronics equipment - JBL Inc.

CONTROL-FLO - Stationery - Diagraph Corp.

CONTROL FREAKS - Electronic equipment - Control Freaks

CONTROL FROM A TO Z - Computer software - Elan Associates (GreenLight Software Division)

CONTROL GRIP - Bowling balls - Master Industries Inc.

CONTROL III - Disinfectants - Maril Products Inc.

CONTROL-JET - Printers–computer - Avery Dennison Corp.

CONTROL-L - Pharmaceutical preparations - Schein Pharmaceutical Inc.

CONTROL LABEL - Dairy products - Dutch Farms, Inc.

CONTROL LINE - Toys - Centuri Corp.

CONTROL LINK - Transmitters ☆ - Pro-Mark Corp.

CONTROL-LITE - Portable light dimmers - Control Research Inc.

CONTROL MASTER - Thermostats - National Presto Industries, Inc.

CONTROL MAX - Electronics equipment - Ecolab Inc.

CONTROL-O-FAX - Computer hardware and software - Control-O-Fax Corp.

CONTROL ONE - Electronics equipment - JBL Inc.

CONTROL PAK - Containers–paper - Stone Container Corp.

CONTROL PET CARE SYSTEM - Repellent - HTZ Investment Corp.

CONTROL PHORMULA DIET - Dog food - Kal Kan Foods, Inc.

CONTROL PILLS - Candy - Marsyl Inc. (Marsyl Enterprises, Inc.)

CONTROL PLUS - Artists' materials - M. Grumbacher Inc.

CONTROL PLUS - Computer software - Phase One Systems

CONTROL/PLUS - Hair care products - Helene Curtis Industries Inc.

CONTROL PLUS+ - Remote control devices - Gemstar Development Corp.

CONTROL POLE - Pet products - Fuhrman Diversified

CONTROL STIX - Bicycles - Samac and Samac

CONTROL TECH - Bicycles - Control Tech Northwest, Inc.

CONTROL TIP - Saws–chain - White Consolidated Industries, Inc.

CONTROL TOP PLUS - Hosiery–women's - Mayer/Berkshire Corp.

CONTROL TOWER - Remote control devices - Gemstar Development Corp.

CONTROL TRAC - Automotive parts and accessories - Ford Motor Co.

CONTROL WATER - Beverages - Big Beans, Inc.

CONTROL WIRE - Catheter products - Scimed Life Systems, Inc.

CONTROLD - Vitamins and nutritional supplements ☆ - Rexall Nutritional Products Inc.

CONTROLE - Skin care products - Lancome

CONTROLEDIT - Electronics equipment - York Controls

CONTROLENS - Lighting fixtures - Holophane Corp.

CONTROLEUR - Apparel and accessories - Strouse, Adler Co.

CONTROLFIRST - Computer software - Repository Technologies, Inc.

CONTROLINE - Thermostats - Barber-Colman Co.

CONTROLL - Medical apparatus - Mcgaw, Inc.

CONTROLLABLE PRODUCT, THE - Screws - Research Engineering & Manufacturing Inc.

CONTROLLED EXPANSION PERFORMANCE - Ammunition - Olin Corp. (Winchester Div.)

CONTROLLED FINISHING SYSTEM - Tools–power-driven - Black & Decker Corp.

CONTROLLED MAGNETIC - Electronic equipment - Shure Brothers, Inc.

CONTROLLED SUBSTANCES - Publisher's imprints ☆ - Ronin Publishing, Inc.

CONTROLLED VOLUME - Hair care products ☆ - Redken Laboratories, Inc.

CONTROLLER - Combs - Sta-Rite Ginnie Lou Inc.

CONTROLLER - Eyeglasses - Art-Craft Optical Co.

CONTROLLER - Games ☆ - Avalon Hill Game Co.

CONTROLLER - Gloves - Ektelon

CONTROLLER - Golfing equipment - Bost Enterprises, Inc.

CONTROLMATIC - Teleprinters–computer - At&T Corp.

CONTROLOCK - Locks–door - SecurityLink from Ameritech

CONTROLOK - Tape measures - L.S. Starrett Co.

CONTROLSHELL - Computer software - Real-Time Innovations, Inc.

CONTROLUX - Heating equipment ☆ - Sealy Inc.

CONTROLUX - Lighting fixtures - Hubbell Lighting, Inc. (Lighting Div.)

CONTROLWARE - Computer software - Controlware Technologies Corp.

CONTROLYTE - Vitamins and nutritional supplements ☆ - Novartis Nutrition Corp.

CONTRUA - Office supplies ☆ - Faber-Castell Corp.

CONTUR - Drapery hardware ☆ - Spring Window Fashions Division, Inc.

CONTUR - Mats - Tenex Corp.

CONTURA - Drapery rods - J.C. Penney Co., Inc.

CONTURA - Fabrics - Burlington House Fabrics Group

CONTURA - Furniture ☆ - Cosco, Inc.

CONTURA - Health care products - Helmac Products Corp.

CONTURA - Wood products ☆ - Penn Wood Products, Inc.

CONTURA-LITE - Scissors–hand-operated ☆ - Wiss-Cooper Tools

CONTURE - Prophylactics ☆ - Ansell Inc. (Personal Products Div.)

CONTUREDGE - Foil–copper ☆ - Lamps Ltd.

CONTURES - Bathing suits - Catalina

CONUNDRUM - Wines - Caymus Vineyards

CONVA - Fruit drinks–bottled or canned - Joseph Caragol Inc.

CONVA LUX - Mattresses - Angel Echevarria Co. Inc.

CONVACARE - Skin care products - E.R. Squibb & Sons, Inc.

CONVAIR - Ophthalmic goods - Styl-Rite Optical Manufacturing Co., Inc.

CONVALCO - Tools–woodworking - Connecticut Valley Manufacturing Co. of NB Inc.

CONVAQUIP - Home-health-care product - Convaquip Industries Inc.

CONVE - Medical apparatus - Alimed, Inc.

CONVECT-AIRE - Air conditioning equipment ☆ - Tjernlund Products Inc.

CONVECTISSERIÉ - Portable ovens - Hudson Standard Corp.

CONVELOPES - Envelopes - Uarco Inc.

CONVENE - Computer software - Peyton Capital Partners, Inc.

CONVENE - Fabrics - Veratec

CONVENIENCE - Strollers–baby - Combi International Corp.

CONVENIENCE-6100 - Strollers–baby - Combi International Corp.

CONVENIENCE-6300 - Strollers–baby - Combi International Corp.

CONVENIENCE-6400 - Strollers–baby - Combi International Corp.

CONVENIENCE WEAR - Apparel and accessories - Workwear Corp. Inc.

CONVENIENCECALL - Electrical equipment - Health Watch, Inc.

CONVENIENS - Recording label - Jazz Composer's Orchestra Association Inc.

CONVENIENT - Gasoline - Remote Services Inc.

CONVENIENT LIVING - Publisher's imprints - Home Planners Inc.

CONVENIENTLY CLOSE - Underwear and nightwear - P'nena Group, Inc.

CONVENTION - Floor coverings–carpet and rugs - Quaker Inc.

CONVENTION PLANN'R - Diaries - Arno Cahn Consulting Services, Inc.

CONVENTIONAL - Wheelchairs - Quickie Designs Inc.

CONVERGENCE - Office furniture–wood - Hunt Holdings, Inc.

CONVERIBLE - Locks–padlocks - ILCO Unican Corp.

CONVERSA-PHONE - Recording label - Conversa-Phone Institute Inc.

CONVERSANT INTRO - Computer software - At&T Corp.

CONVERSATION COASTERS - Housewares ☆ - Grandpa Brand Co. (Par Beverage Co.)

CONVERSATION PIECES - Games - Talicor Inc.

CONVERSATION PIECES - Jewelry - Letty Browdy

CONVERSATION PIECES - Neckties - A. Schreter & Sons Co. Inc.

CONVERSATION SHIRTS - Underwear and nightwear ☆ - Henson-Kickernick Inc.

CONVERSATIONAL COMPUTER, THE - Computer software - Recreational Mathemagical Software

CONVERSATIONAL INFLUENCE - Educational materials - Neuro Concepts Institute

CONVERSATIONS - Apparel–women's - Sallco, Inc.

CONVERSATIONS - Periodicals - CAS Graphics, Inc.

CONVERSE - Apparel and accessories - Converse Inc.

CONVERSE - Sporting goods - I.J.K. Sales Corp.

CONVERSE - Watches - Fada Industries Inc.

CONVERSE ALL STAR CHUCK TAYLOR - T-shirts–men's - Converse Inc.

CONVERSE ONE STAR - Canvas footwear - Converse Inc.

CONVERSESSIONS - Computer software - Van Cura Medical Computing, Inc.

CONVERSION - Golfing equipment ☆ - Focus Golf Systems, Inc. (Dunlop Golf)

CONVERSION 2 - Exercising equipment - Stamina Products, Inc.

CONVERSION PLUS - Musical instrument accessories ☆ - Voyetra Technologies Inc.

CONVERSION TUFSEAL - Adhesives and sealants - Gilbert Spruance Co.

CONVERSIONS PLUS - Computer software - Dataviz, Inc.

CONVERSPAZ - Pharmaceutical preparations ☆ - B.F. Ascher & Co. Inc.

CONVERT - Apparel–athletic - Columbia Sportswear Co.

CONVERT - Computer software - DataWare Development, Inc.

CONVERT - Computer software - Digital Marketing Corp.

CONVERT-A-BOTS - Toys - Village Toys

CONVERT-A-BULB - Electrical equipment - Miracle Products

CONVERT-A-CASE - Hardware - Presto Lock Co. Inc.

CONVERT-A-CYCLE - Sporting goods - All American Products Inc.

CONVERT-A-DECK - Tape recorders–cassette ☆ - Akai America Ltd.

CONVERT-A-FAN - Fans–electric - Schaefer Fan Co., Inc.

CONVERT-A-FLUE - Stoves–wood-burning - Russo Products Inc.

CONVERT A GRILL - Barbecues and grills - Natural Grilling & Fuel Systems, Inc.

CONVERT-A-LITE - Lighting fixtures - Swivelier Co. Inc.

CONVERT-A-LOCK - Locks–door - Abloy Security Inc.

CONVERT A PLUG - Electrical equipment - Gem Electric Manufacturing Co. Inc.

CONVERT-A SPACE - Tables–metal - Phoenix Manufacturing, Inc.

CONVERT-A-TRACK - Lighting fixtures - Swivelier Co. Inc.

CONVERT-A-VAC - Food containers ☆ - Thermos Co.

CONVERT-ABLES - Cups–plastic - K.I. Industries, Inc.

CONVERT-ABLES - Toys ☆ - Imperial Toy Corp.

CONVERTA CARTS - Serving carts ☆ - Quaker Industries Ltd.

CONVERTA-COOK - Stoves - White Consolidated Industries, Inc.

CONVERTA-CORD - Cord connectors–electric - Arbogast, Inc.

CONVERTA CRADLE - Infant product - Graco Children's Products

CONVERTA-CRIB - Infant product ☆ - Barden & Robeson Corp.

CONVERTA-PAK - Sporting goods - Bear Archery Inc.

CONVERTA-POINT - Archery equipment - Bear Archery Inc.

CONVERTA PUMP - Firearms, accessories, and parts - High Standard Manufacturing Corp.

CONVERTA-ROD - Sporting goods - Bear Archery Inc.

CONVERTA-SOUND - Electronic equipment ☆ - Fleetwood Furniture Co.

CONVERTA-TRAY - Electronic equipment - Lab Safety Supply, Inc.

CONVERTABLE - Tables–metal - N.A. Taylor Co. Inc.

CONVERTAMATIC - Tools - Advance Machine Co.

CONVERTER - Calculators ☆ - Texas Instruments Inc.

CONVERTER CONTROL CENTER - Converters–electric - Progressive Dynamics, Inc.

CONVERTERS - Electrical equipment - Franzus Co. Inc.

CONVERTER'S CHOICE - Paper products - Release International Inc.

CONVERTI-CYCLE - Bicycles - Columbia Manufacturing Inc.

CONVERTIBLE - Amplifiers–musical instrument - Seymour Duncan Pickups

CONVERTIBLE - Backpacks - Richard Jones Convertible Backpacks

CONVERTIBLE - Frames–eyeglass - May Optical Co. Inc.

CONVERTIBLE - Ice chests–plastic - Coleman Co., Inc.

CONVERTIBLE - Pet products - Tri-Tronics Inc.

CONVERTIBLE - Vacuum cleaners and accessories - The Hoover Co.

CONVERTIBLE - Wallets - Buxton Inc.

CONVERTIBLE-INVERTIBLE - Medical apparatus - Freeman Manufacturing Co.

CONVERTIBLE MICROBOTS - Toys - Imperial Toy Corp.

CONVERTIBLE STAND - Golfing equipment - Lisco, Inc.

CONVERTIBLES - Apparel–athletic ☆ - J.C. Penney Co., Inc.

CONVERTICOUPE - Automotive parts and accessories - Auto Accessories of America

CONVERTIN - Pharmaceutical preparations ☆ - B.F. Ascher & Co. Inc.

CONVERTISOR - Rulers–metal ☆ - C-Thru Ruler Co.

CONVERTO-KIT - Dryers–hair - Postcraft Co.

CONVERTO-ROCKER - Furniture–upholstered ☆ - Mersman Furniture Co.

CONVERTOR - Accordions - Titano Accordion Co. International

CONVERZYME - Pharmaceutical preparations ☆ - B.F. Ascher & Co. Inc.

CONVEX KICK - Golfing equipment - Wayne Products, Inc.

CONVEY - Computer software - Systems Techniques, Inc.

CONVEY 'OR DUMP - Truck bodies - Air-Flo Manufacturing Co., Inc.

CONVEYOSTAT - Static eliminator - Simco

CONVINCOR - Boats–motor ☆ - Checkmate Boats Inc.

CONVIS - Oils–lubricating - Davis-Howland Oil Corp.

CONVIVIAL WARE - Paints - Harry E. Howard Co.

CONVOCAN - Containers - Sealright Co., Inc.

CONVOLVOTRON - Computer peripheral equipment - Crystal River Engineering Inc.

CONVOY - Cases–musical instrument - Calzone Case Co.

CONVOY - Enamels - Kelley Technical Coatings Inc.

CONVOY - Oils–lubricating - Conklin Co., Inc.

CONVOY - Paper–gummed - Tape Inc.

CONVOY - Tires - Bridgestone/Firestone, Inc.

CONVOY - Toys–automobiles - Matchbox Toys USA

CONVOY - Watches - Bulova Corp.

CONVOY COMMAND - Antennas - D.A.S. Distributors, Inc.

CONVOY KING - Automotive parts and accessories ☆ - Gladding Corp. (Pearce-Simpson Div.)

CONVOYS - Prophylactics ☆ - Patrician Products Inc.

CONWAY - Brushes–paint ☆ - PPG Industries, Inc.

CONWAY - Food products - Minot Food Packers Inc.

CONWAY - Recreational vehicle dealers ☆ - Jayco Inc.

CONWAY CLASSICS - Handbags - Leather Loft Stores, Inc.

CONWAY SPRINGS - Water - Conway Springs Water

CONWED - Ceiling boards and tiles, insulation, office furnishings - Conwed Plastics

CONWOOD - Chewing tobacco - Conwood Co. L.P.

CONXN - Pharmaceutical preparations - Connective Therapeutics, Inc.

CONXN - Pharmaceutical preparations - Connetics Corp.

CONXPRT - Computer software - American Institute of Steel Construction Inc.

CONY - Seafood products–fresh or frozen ☆ - Southeast Foods Inc.

COO-COO - Frames–eyeglass - Zylo Ware Corp.

COOCHY COO - Dolls - ERTL Co., Inc.

COOCHY COO BABY - Dolls - ERTL Co., Inc.

COOEY - Guns ☆ - Olin Corp. (Winchester Div.)

COOK - Candy ☆ - Cook Chocolate Co.

COOK - Sailboat - William E. Cook

COOK - Worcestershire sauce ☆ - Frazier Extract Co.

COOK 3.0 SOFTWARE FOR FOOD LOVERS - Computer software ☆ - East Hampton Industries Inc.

COOK-A-ROUND - Ovens–microwave - Matsushita Consumer Electronics Co.

COOK & BROTHER - Rifles - Euroarms of America

COOK & CLEAN - Kitchen appliances ☆ - Sunbeam-Oster Household Products

COOK & SERVE - Toys ☆ - Playskool, Inc.

COOK & TOTE - Electrical equipment - West Bend Co.

COOK BATES - Manicure and pedicure instruments - LRC North America, Inc.

COOK BOOK - Breads - American Bakeries Co.

COOK DO - Vegetable sauces - Ajinomoto USA, Inc.

COOK-EASE - Housewares ☆ - Utica Cutlery Co.

COOK-ETTS - Cake decorations - Cook Chocolate Co.

COOK IT-STORE IT - Cooking equipment–household - E-Z-Por Corp.

COOK-KING - Housewares - Ironees Co.

COOK MASTER - Mats - Matworks

COOK 'N - Packaging films - Teepak, Inc.

COOK-N-BAKE - Cooking utensils–aluminum ☆ - General Housewares Corp.

COOK 'N' BREW - Cookware ☆ - Corning Inc.

COOK 'N CARRY - Cookware - Corning Inc.

COOK 'N CLEAN - Gloves–safety - Hand Care, Inc.

COOK-N-CLEAN CENTER - Stoves - Amana Refrigeration Inc.

COOK 'N' FOIL - Housewares - Progressus Co.

COOK N' HEAT - Fuel additives - Alco-Brite, Inc.

COOK 'N KEEP - Toys ☆ - Sun Products Corp. (Wellington)

COOK 'N LOOK - Cooking utensils–enameled - Jacksonville Manufacturing

COOK 'N' POUR - Cookware ☆ - Corning Inc.

COOK 'N SERVE - Cooking equipment–commercial - West Bend Co.

COOK 'N SERVE - Cooking utensils–aluminum ☆ - Revere Ware Corp.

COOK 'N' SERVE - Glass cookware ☆ - Corning Inc.

COOK 'N STIR - Housewares - Salton/Maxim Housewares, Inc.

COOK OB/GYN - Medical apparatus - Cook Imaging Corp.

COOK-OFF - Chili - American Home Food Products Inc.

COOK-OUT - Food products - Glenmark Industries, Ltd.

COOK-OUT - Seasonings - Silver Foods Corp.

COOK PROCAR - Medical equipment - Cook Imaging Corp.

COOK-RITE - Cooking utensils–aluminum - Himark Enterprises Inc.

COOK-RITE - Thermometers - Sunbeam Precision Measurement

COOK THINGS - Kitchen gadgets, cutlery - Cook Things

COOK THINGS CUSTOM - Cutlery - Cook Things

COOK THINGS PROFESSIONAL - Cutlery - Cook Things

COOK-TITE - Bags–plastic - Viskase Corp.

COOK VETERINARY PRODUCTS - Veterinary medical equipment - Cook Imaging Corp.

COOK-WELL - Cooking utensils–aluminum ☆ - General Housewares Corp.

COOKBEST - Cooking utensils–aluminum - West Bend Co.

COOKBOOK - Food products - Nestle USA

COOKBOOK - Tools ☆ - Regent Sheffield, Ltd.

COOKBOOK CLASSICS - Soups–canned ☆ - Campbell Soup Co.

COOKBOOK COMPANION - Greeting cards - Starmark Ltd.

COOKBOOK RECIPE - Food products - KFC Corp.

COOKBOOK SPICE - Tools ☆ - Regent Sheffield, Ltd.

COOKE - Garden equipment - Chas H. Lilly Co.

COOKE - Rotary daters, time stamps, etc. - Cooke Time Stamp Co.

COOKE & COBB - File folders ☆ - ACCO USA, Inc.

COOKERY, THE - Housewares - Doranne

COOKIE - Dolls ☆ - Effanbee Doll Corp.

COOKIE - Food products - W.B. Roddenbery Co., Inc.

COOKIE BAG GREETINGS - Bags - Continnuus

COOKIE BARON - Cookies - Cookie Baron

COOKIE BITES - Cookies - McGlynn Bakeries Inc.

COOKIE BONBONS - Candy - Premier Gourmet Products Inc.

☆ = Now out of production

COOKIE BREAK - Cookies - Nabisco Foods Group
COOKIE CELEBRATIONS - Cookies - Captain Jack Ltd.
COOKIE CHEF - Housewares - Vital Products Inc.
COOKIE CHIP - Chocolate candy - Paron Chocolatier
COOKIE CLASSICS - Bakery products ☆ - Boyer Printing Co.
COOKIE CLASSICS - Giftware - Mor-Fleur Enterprises, Ltd.
COOKIE CLAUS - Candy ☆ - R.M. Palmer Co.
COOKIE CONNECTION, THE - Cookies - The Cookie Connection
COOKIE COTTAGES - Pottery ☆ - Hartstone Inc.
COOKIE CRAFT - Hobby kits - Educational Products Co.
COOKIE CREATIONS - Pans - Ekco Housewares, Inc.
COOKIE CRISP - Cereal - Ralston Purina Co.
COOKIE CRUNCH - Cookies - Nikki's Cookies, Inc.
COOKIE CRUNCHERS - Apparel–children's - Charles Castro Manufacturing Co., Inc.
COOKIE CUTTER - Candles - Candle Station, Ltd.
COOKIE CUTTER CAPERS - Cooking equipment–household - Lone Toy Tree Inc.
COOKIE DAY - Cookies ☆ - Kettle Foods
COOKIE DELITES - Bakery products - Brach Van Houten Holding Inc.
COOKIE DELITES - Candy - Brach and Brock Confections Inc.
COOKIE DIPPERS - Candy - R.M. Palmer Co.
COOKIE DOUGH CRAZE - Confections - Weight Watchers International, Inc.
COOKIE DOUGH DYNAMO - Ice cream - Haagen-Dazs Co. Inc.
COOKIE DROP - Chocolate chips - Cook Chocolate Co.
COOKIE FACTORY - Bakery franchise - Cookie Factory of America
COOKIE FACTORY - Electric cookie maker - Rival Manufacturing Co.
COOKIE FRUIT EAST HAMPTON - Cookies - Cookie FruitEast Hampton
COOKIE HEAVEN - Doughs–frozen ☆ - Lightlife Foods, Inc.
COOKIE IMPRESSIONS - Bakery products - Cookie Impressions, Inc.
COOKIE ISLAND - Bakery products - Cookie Island Inc.
COOKIE JAR - Cookies - Century Cookies
COOKIE JAR - Tobacco products - Lane Ltd.
COOKIE JAR - Wallpaper ☆ - Imperial Wallcoverings, Inc.
COOKIE JAR III - Wallpaper ☆ - Imperial Wallcoverings, Inc.
COOKIE JARS - Giftware - Doranne
COOKIE JOYS - Snack foods - Harry London's Candies Inc.
COOKIE KING - Cooking utensils–aluminum ☆ - Nordic Ware
COOKIE KING - Flour–blended - Acme-Evans/A.D.M. Milling Co.
COOKIE KIT, THE - Cooking utensils–stoneware - Hartstone Inc.
COOKIE LEGENDS - Snack foods - Delicious Cookies
COOKIE LITTLE - Cookies - Nabisco Foods Group
COOKIE LOVER'S - Cookies - Tree of Life, Inc.
COOKIE LOVERS - Ice cream - Mother's Cake & Cookie Co.
COOKIE LOVIN' OVEN - Toys - Tonka Corp.
COOKIE MAN - Cookies - American Products Co. Inc.
COOKIE MONSTER - Furniture - Brite-Tone Co.
COOKIE MONSTER - Toys - Jim Henson Productions, Inc.
COOKIE MONSTER SHAPE MONSTER - Toys - Playskool, Inc.
COOKIE MONSTER SLIDE 'N POOL - Swimming pools - Wonderline
COOKIE NUT! GOURMET ORIGINAL, THE - Pastries - Cookie Nut Co., Inc.
COOKIE PARTY, THE - Cookies ☆ - Bon Melange Inc.
COOKIE PUZZLERS - Housewares - Mark Blosil
COOKIE STORE, THE - Cookies - Candy Candy Inc.
COOKIE TEDDY BEAR - Toys–stuffed - Russ Berrie and Co., Inc.
COOKIE, THE - Cookies - Attivo
COOKIEMANIA - Baked goods - Cookiemania
COOKIES - Barbecue sauce - Cookies Food Products Inc.
COOKIES & CREAM - Coffee - First Colony Coffee and Tea Co. Inc.
COOKIES & CREME - Cookies - Barbara's Bakery, Inc.
COOKIES & CREME SANDWICH COOKIES - Cookies ☆ - Barbara's Bakery, Inc.
COOKIES BY DESIGN - Cookies - Cookie Bouquet Franchising Corp.
COOKIES BY J. J. NISSEN - Cookies - John J. Nissen Bakeries
COOKIES FOR SANTA - Breads–mixes - Knott's Berry Farm
COOKIES FROM HOME - Cookies - Cookies from Home, Inc.
COOKIES FROM KANSAS - Cookies - Cookies from Kansas
COOKIES 'N CREAM - Dolls - Mattel, Inc.
COOKIES N' CREAM HAPPY HEARTS - Candy novelties - Bortz Chocolate Co.
COOKIES N' CREAM SNOWBALLS - Candy novelties - Bortz Chocolate Co.
COOKIES 'N FUDGE - Cookies - Nabisco Foods Group
COOKIES N' MILK - Snack foods - Pride of the Farm
COOKIES WINGS N THINGS - Barbecue sauce - Cookies Food Products Inc.
COOKIES WITH A BUZZ - Cookies - Lori Palmer
COOKIETREE BAKERIES - Cookies - Cookietree Bakeries

COOKIN' - Recording label - Boddie Record Manufacturing & Recording Inc.
COOKIN' CAT - Toys - Tonka Corp.
COOKIN' CHEAP - Publisher's imprints ☆ - System 4 Advertising
COOKIN' GOOD - Food products - Showell Farms Inc.
COOKIN GOOD - Poultry feeds - Showell Co.
COOKIN' KITCHEN - Dolls - Mattel, Inc.
COOKIN' MACHINE - Barbecues and grills - Coleman Co., Inc.
COOKIN' OUT - Toys - Tonka Corp.
COOKIN WITH CLASS - Magnets - Russ Berrie and Co., Inc.
COOKING COMPANION - Seasonings ☆ - R.C. Bigelow, Inc.
COOKING MAGIC - Oils–edible - Par-Way Group
COOKING MASTERS - Food products - Aspen Foods, a division of Koch Poultry
COOKING MASTERS - Food products - Cooking Masters
COOKING PUZZLE, THE - Puzzles ☆ - International Polygonics Ltd.
COOKING STICK - Blenders - Mr. Coffee, Inc.
COOKING WITH KIDS - Food products - Oohs n Ahs
COOKING ZONE - Barbecues and grills - Char-Broil
COOKMASTER - Kitchen appliances ☆ - Sunbeam-Oster Household Products
COOKMATES - Cookware, accessories, and utensils ☆ - Corning Inc.
COOKMATIC - Ovens–microwave - Amana Refrigeration Inc.
COOK'N SAVE - Meat products–poultry - Hardee's Food Systems, Inc.
COOK'N VENT - Cooking equipment–commercial - Thermador
COOKOUT - Food products - Knapp-Sherrill Co.
COOKOUT BURGERS - Meat products–beef - Glenmark Industries, Ltd.
COOKQUIK - Food products - Trinidad/Benham Holding Co.
COOK'S - Beverages–alcohol - Evansville Brewing Co.
COOK'S - Citrus product - B.C. Cook & Sons Enterprises Inc.
COOK'S - Food products - Hillshire Farm Co.
COOK'S - Food products - Liberty Richter Inc.
COOKS - Food products - Sugar Foods Corp.
COOK'S - Honey - Palm Apiaries
COOKS - Seasonings - Sigma Quality Foods Corp.
COOK'S - Spices and extracts - Europa Foods Ltd.
COOK'S - Wines - Canandaigua Wine Co. Inc.
COOK'S - Wines - Guild Wineries
COOK'S BAKERY - Honey - Palm Apiaries
COOK'S CHOICE - Fruits and vegetables ☆ - Ogden Services Corp.
COOK'S CHOICE - Honey - Palm Apiaries
COOKS CIRCLE C - Food products - Cooks Processed Foods Inc.
COOK'S CLASSICS - Salad dressings, sauces, marinades - Cook's Classics Ltd.
COOKS CLUB - Ladles - Cooks Club, Inc.
COOK'S COOKIE VANILLA - Spices and extracts - Cook Flavoring Co.
COOK'S DELITE - Hams ☆ - Prestige Foods Corp.
COOKS DINNER DIPS - Seasonings - Sigma Quality Foods Corp.
COOKS FAMILY PRIDE - Ice cream - Cook's Markets Inc.
COOKS GARDEN FRESH - Canned vegetables - Cook's Markets Inc.
COOK'S GARDEN, THE - Flowers, plants, and seeds - Cook's Garden
COOK'S GOLD - Chocolate syrup - World's Finest Chocolate, Inc.
COOKS KNOW HOW - Kitchen utensils–aluminum - Cooks Know How Inc.
COOK'S ORANGE - Honey - Palm Apiaries
COOK'S PALM - Honey - Palm Apiaries
COOK'S PANTRY - Publisher's imprints - Graphic Promotions Inc.
COOK'S SECRET - Vegetable oil ☆ - Ventura Foods LLC (Lou Ana Division)
COOKSOFT - Computer software - Zangsoft, Inc.
COOKTEK - Stoves - Cooktek, Inc.
COOKTOPS KITCHENWARE - Cookware - Tabletops Unlimited
COOKWEARS - Apparel - Loretta Forer
COOKWORKS - Computer software - Pinpoint Publishing
COOKY BOX - Dolls, clothing, and accessories - Gata Box Ltd.
COOKY CUDDLIES - Toys–stuffed - Fun World Inc.
COOL - Beverages–carbonated - Cool Cola
COOL-A-COO - Ice-cream sandwich - Cool-A-Coo Ice Cream
COOL-A-TRAY - Trays - Coleman Co., Inc.
COOL-AH - Beverages - I.C. Refreshment Co., Inc.
COOL AIDS - Ophthalmic goods - Foremost Optical Products
COOL AIR - Fans–electric ☆ - Robert Krups North America
COOL ALOE PLUS - Skin care products - Tanning Research Laboratories Inc.
COOL & DELICIOUS - Beverages - C & D Foods Co.
COOL & FRESH - Fruits and vegetables - Premium Valley Produce, Inc.
COOL ATTIC - Ventilators, fans, etc. - Cool Attic
COOL BALL - Ice chests - Polyset Products, Inc.
COOL BALL - Video games - Takara USA Corp.
COOL BAND - Health care products - Anodyne Inc.
COOL BEAMS - Flashlights - Garrity Industries

COOL BEAN - Coffee coolers - Original Coffeehouse Creations
COOL BEANS - Coffee - Brian Robert Rusden
COOL BLENDS - Beverages - Ephrata Diamond Spring Water Co., Inc.
COOL BLUE - Candy - Brach and Brock Confections Inc.
COOL BLUE - Gloves–rubber - West Coast Beauty Supply Co.
COOL BLUE - Nail care products - Creative Nail Design, Inc.
COOL BOTTLE - Bottles–plastic - AC International
COOL BRAKE - Brakes–motor vehicle - William L. Love
COOL BREEZE - Apparel - Cool Breeze Sportswear, Inc.
COOL BREEZE - Deodorants–personal - Bristol-Myers Squibb Co.
COOL BREEZE - Wines - Canandaigua Wine Co. Inc.
COOL BRIGHT - Lamp bulbs–incandescent - General Electric Co.
COOL CALCS - Calculators - Douglas E. Franco
COOL CAP - Coolers–electric - Foam America, Inc.
COOL CAPS - Containers–metal - Plastmold Inc.
COOL CAR - Ice chests - Super Ice Corp.
COOL CAREER FASHIONS - Dolls - Mattel, Inc.
COOL CASCADES - Deodorizers - Reckitt & Colman, Inc.
COOL CAT - Amplifiers - Evets Corp.
COOL CAT - Games - Universal Manufacturing Co., Inc.
COOL CAT - Pet products - Rabbit Foot, Inc.
COOL CATS - Seafood products–fresh or frozen - Iceland Seafood Corp.
COOL CAYENNE - Vitamins and nutritional supplements - Solaray
COOL CHIK - Ophthalmic goods - Foremost Optical Products
COOL CHOICE - Beverages - Lykes Services Co.
COOL CHOICE - Fruits and vegetables - Premium Valley Produce, Inc.
COOL, CLEAR GEMS - Toys - Binney & Smith Inc.
COOL COCONUT - Skin care products - Smithkline Beecham Corp.
COOL COFFEE BREAK - Ice cream - H.P. Hood & Sons Inc.
COOL-COIL - Motor vehicle parts and accessories ☆ - Dunham Bush, Inc.
COOL COLT - Beverages–malt ☆ - The Stroh Brewery Co.
COOL COMFORT - Apparel and accessories - Sara Lee Corp.
COOL COMPUTING - Computer peripheral equipment - Kryotech, Inc.
COOL-COOL-CANDLES - Hobby kits ☆ - Natural Science Industries, Ltd.
COOL COTE - Paints - Mobile Paint Manufacturing Co.
COOL COVER - Air conditioning equipment - Govmark Organization, Inc.
COOL COVER - Roofing materials–clay - Fulton Co.
COOL COVERS - Backpacks and tote bags - Kidcepts, Corp.
COOL COW - Apparel and accessories - Milk Made Inc.
COOL COW - Milk - Jersey Farms Corp.
COOL COYOTE - Snack foods - Saguaro Food Products
COOL CREATIONS - Dolls - Mattel, Inc.
COOL CRIMP - Dolls - Mattel, Inc.
COOL CRISP - Pickles - Gielow Pickles Inc.
COOL CUISINE - Lunch boxes ☆ - Trend Pacific Inc.
COOL CUPS - Containers - Carthage Cup Co.
COOL CUPS - Cups–plastic - WNA Comet
COOL CUT CARROTS - Dips–sour cream based - Tanimura & Antle, Inc.
COOL CUT CELERY - Fruits and vegetables - Tanimura & Antle, Inc.
COOL CUTS - Clippers–barber - Wahl Clipper Corp.
COOL CUTTERS - Scissors–hand-operated - Acme United Corp.
COOL D-LITE - Beverages - American Rags, Inc.
COOL-DANA - Medical apparatus - Personal Comfort Corp.
COOL DATE - Dolls - Mattel, Inc.
COOL DESIGNS - Bags–plastic - Reynolds Consumer Products, Inc.
COOL DESSERTS - Ice cream - Dessert Innovations, Inc.
COOL DOG - Dog food - Bradley Horn
COOL DOWN - Fruit drinks–bottled or canned - Everfresh Beverages, Inc.
COOL DOWN - Soap - Aramis Inc.
COOL DOWN AFTER EXERCISE REFRESHER - Fruit drinks–bottled or canned - Everfresh Beverages, Inc.
COOL DUCK - Toys - Assurance Industries Co. Inc.
COOL DUDE - Sunglasses - Echo, Inc.
COOL DUEL - Toys–automobiles - Mattel, Inc.
COOL-E-POPS - Candy - Helms Candy Manufacturing Co. Inc.
COOL-ETTE - Apparel–women's - Crown Foundations Inc.
COOL FEET - Footwear - Cool Feet Inc.
COOL FISH - Apparel and accessories - William J. Keach
COOL FLEX - Fabrics - GFD Fabrics, Inc.
COOL FLO - Splints - Smith & Nephew Inc. (Rehabilitation Div.)
COOL FLUE - Flues - Majestic Inc.
COOL FROM NESTEA - Iced tea–bottled or canned - Coca-Cola Co.
COOL FRUITS - Snack food - R.W. Frookies Inc.
COOL FRUITS FREEZE 'N SQUEEZE - Frozen snack - R.W. Frookies Inc.
COOL GEAR - Cycling apparel and accessories - Dionysian Inc. (Jacobs Div.)
COOL GHOUL - Apparel and accessories - Russ Berrie and Co., Inc.

COOL GLIDE 20 STABILIZER - Display units - Paul Flum Ideas, Inc.
COOL-GLO - Lighting fixtures - Swivelier Co. Inc.
COOL GRAPEFRUIT - Beverages–carbonated - Cool Natural Beverages
COOL GRIP - Housewares - SGI Inc.
COOL GRIP - Pet products - Edemco Dryers Inc.
COOL GRIP - Sporting goods ☆ - Gexco Enterprises
COOL HEAT - Skin care products - Solar Gear Inc.
COOL ISLAND - Juices - Coca-Cola Co.
COOL IT! - Coolers - Plastican, Inc.
COOL IT - Frames–eyeglass - Hudson Optical Corp.
COOL-IT - Glass froster - William Bounds, Ltd.
COOL-IT - Ice chests–plastic - Elmar Manufacturing Co.
COOL IT - Skin care products - Sogo Inc.
COOL-IT - Skin care products ☆ - Pharm-A-Lab
COOL IT FREEZE-A-SHELF - Ice chests–plastic ☆ - Life-Like Products Inc.
COOL-JACK - Thermostats - Ivy Group, Inc.
COOL JEANS - Dolls - Mattel, Inc.
COOL JESUS BODYWEAR - T-shirts–men's - Cool Jesus Bodywear, Inc.
COOL JET SYSTEMS - Machine parts - MKT Innovations
COOL JEWELS - Jewelry–costume - Phillips International Jewelry & Souvenirs Inc.
COOL JOCK - Apparel and accessories ☆ - Playtex Apparel, Inc.
COOL-JOCK - Apparel–athletic - Saramar Corp.
COOL JOURNEY - Clothing - Hossein S. Shoar
COOL KEYS - Toys–musical - Diversified Specialists, Inc.
COOL KIDS - Candy ☆ - Just Born Inc.
COOL-KING - Ice chests–plastic - General Foam Plastics Corp.
COOL KONG - Pet products - Kong Co.
COOL-LIFE - Paints - Fredericks/Hansen Paint Manufacturing Co.
COOL LIGHT - Electronics equipment - Burgess Inc.
COOL LIME - Shampoos ☆ - Duart Industries Ltd.
COOL-LINER - Underwear and nightwear - Saramar Corp.
COOL-LITE - Eyeglasses - Art-Craft Optical Co.
COOL LITE - Lighting fixtures - Thomas Lighting (Accent Division)
COOL LOOKS - Dolls - Mattel, Inc.
COOL MASCOT - Apparel and accessories - Apogee International, Inc.
COOL MELT - Tools - Stanley-Parker Inc.
COOL MICKEY - Wallpaper ☆ - Priss Prints Inc.
COOL MILLION - Eyeglasses - Martin-Copeland Eyewear Corp.
COOL MILLIONS - Game machines - Casino Data Systems
COOL MILLIONS - Game machines - IGT - North America
COOL MINT LISTERINE - Mouthwashes - Warner-Wellcome
COOL MINT LISTERINE - Toothpaste - Warner-Lambert Co.
COOL MIST - Dehumidifiers ☆ - Sunrise Medical (Respiratory Products Division)
COOL MIST - Hair care products ☆ - Joico Laboratories, Inc.
COOL MIST - Health care products ☆ - Sunbeam-Oster Household Products
COOL MIX - Dolls - Mattel, Inc.
COOL MOON - Beverages–carbonated - Carolina Beverage Inc.
COOL MOVES - Apparel–women's - Sara Lee Casualwear
COOL MOVES - Apparel–women's - SM Acquisition Sub, Inc.
COOL MOVES - Bicycles - Roadmaster Corp.
COOL N' CARE - Pet products - Best n' Show Pet Products Inc.
COOL 'N FRESH - Deodorants–personal - Bertsherm Products Inc.
COOL 'N FRUITY - Juices - McCormick & Co., Inc.
COOL N' LITE - Wigs ☆ - Paula Young
COOL 'N SASSY - Dolls - Mattel, Inc.
COOL NATURAL - Lipsticks ☆ - Elysee Scientific Cosmetic Co.
COOL NOUGAT - Candy ☆ - Leaf, Inc.
COOL N'SOFT - Apparel–women's - Bi-Flex International
COOL OFF - Cleaning preparations - Cleaners's Supply, Inc.
COOL ONE, THE - Toasters - Eastern Electric Appliance Co., Inc.
COOL ONE, THE - Apparel and accessories - Performance Contracting, Inc.
COOL ONES - Pens - Pentech International Inc.
COOL-PACK - Medical apparatus ☆ - Apothecary Products, Inc.
COOL PACK GREEN JELLY - Veterinary pharmaceutical preparations - Farnam Cos. Inc.
COOL PAK - Product description unknown - Meyer Furnace Co.
COOL PLATES - Dinnerware - WNA Carthage, Inc.
COOL PLAZ - Pumps - E/G Electro-Graph, Inc.
COOL POOL - Toys - North American Marketing Corp.
COOL PURE - Medical apparatus - Purepulse Technologies, Inc.
COOL QUACKERS - Toys–stuffed - Fun World Inc.
COOL QUENCHER - Beverages - Cool Natural Beverages
COOL RAILS FOR STRAT - Musical instrument accessories - Seymour Duncan Pickups

☆ = Now out of production

COOL RANCH - Snack foods - Frito-Lay, Inc.

COOL RAP TIE - Headbands - Karlen Manufacturing, Inc.

COOL-RAY - Sunglasses - Cool-Ray Inc.

COOL REVOLUTIONS - Fans–electric - Hunter Fan Co.

COOL RIB - Glass products - BP Chemicals Inc. (Filon Products Div.)

COOL RIDER DELUXE - Cushions - Saddleman, Inc.

COOL RODS - Musical instrument accessories - Pro-Mark Corp.

COOL-ROOF - Paints - Frazee Paint

COOL ROOT BEER - Beverages–carbonated - Cool Cola

COOL ROTORS - Brake parts - Vellios Motorsports Inc.

COOL SACK - Ice chests–plastic - Igloo Products Corp.

COOL-SAFE - Chests–wood - Cramer Products Co.

COOL SENSATION - Teas - Topco Associates, Inc.

COOL SET - Frames–eyeglass - May Optical Co. Inc.

COOL SHADES - Automotive parts and accessories - Volkswagen of America Inc.

COOL SHADES - Eyeglasses - Mattel, Inc.

COOL SHOE - Shoe accessories - Fast Industries, Inc.

COOL SHOTS FOR KIDS - Paints–artists' - Family Photo, Inc.

COOL SIDE SALAD DISHES - Dishes–china - Lipton Investments, Inc.

COOL SMOKE - Cigars ☆ - Havatampa Inc.

COOL SMOKES - Candy ☆ - Spangler Candy Co.

COOL SOLUTION - Fans–electric - Holmes Products, Corp.

COOL SOUNDS - Radios - Sakar International Inc.

COOL SPECS - Frames–eyeglass - Pathway Optical Prods.

COOL SPELL - Cologne ☆ - Coty Inc.

COOL SPELL - Pharmaceutical preparations - Pfizer Inc.

COOL SPIRIT - Floor coverings–carpet and rugs - Barrett Carpet Mills Inc.

COOL SPOT - Computer software - Dr Pepper/Seven-Up Corp.

COOL SPOT - Pet products - City Dog Designed Co., Inc.

COOL SPOT - Pet products - Zoecon Corp.

COOL SPOT - Video games ☆ - Dr. Pepper/Seven Up, Inc.

COOL SPRAY - Health care products - Sunbeam-Oster Household Products

COOL SPRING - Beverages–malt ☆ - Labatt Importers Inc.

COOL SPRING - Cheese - S.M. Flickinger Co. Inc.

COOL SPRING - Skin care products - Bath & Body Works, Inc.

COOL STICK - Insulating materials - Sierra Housewares, Inc.

COOL STOP - Dental equipment - Weissman Technology International Inc.

COOL STREAM - Vaporizers - Pollenex Corp.

COOL STUFF - Ice chests - Cool Stuff Corp.

COOL SUIT - Apparel and accessories - Cool Suit, Inc.

COOL-TEMP - Dryers–hair - Helene Curtis Industries Inc.

COOL-TEMP/PLUS - Dryers–hair - Helene Curtis Industries Inc.

COOL TEMPTATIONS - Shelving units–plastic - Brown-Forman Corp.

COOL TIMES - Dolls - Mattel, Inc.

COOL-TIP - Surgical instruments - Radionics Software Applications, Inc.

COOL-TONE - Frames–eyeglass - Pathway Optical Prods.

COOL TONY - Candy - Sunkist Growers Inc.

COOL TOOL - Hardware - Dexter Corp.

COOL TOOL - Tools - Fiskars Inc.

COOL TOOLS - Pens, note pads, etc. - Geoffrey Inc.

COOL TOOLS - Toys - Playskool, Inc.

COOL TOP - Paints ☆ - Bruning Paint Co.

COOL TOPS - Dolls - Mattel, Inc.

COOL-TOTE - Air conditioning equipment - J.C. Penney Co., Inc.

COOL-TOUCH - Cooking equipment–commercial - West Bend Co.

COOL TOUCH - Dryers–hair - Helen of Troy Corp.

COOL-TOUCH - Lamps - UVP Inc.

COOL TRAC - Industrial tires and rollers - Monarch Industrial Tire Corp.

COOL TROPICAL SPLASH - Beverages ☆ - Golden Brands Marketing

COOL TUBES - Ice cream - Wells' Dairy, Inc.

COOL-UPS - Fruit pops–frozen ☆ - Leaf, Inc.

COOL VIBES - Health care products ☆ - Dubl Duck/Jet Set Inc.

COOL WAVE - Insulating materials - Sierra Housewares, Inc.

COOL WAVE - Shaving preparations - Gillette Co.

COOL WEAVE - Apparel and accessories - L.L. Bean Inc.

COOL WOOL - Apparel - Wool Bureau, Inc.

COOL-X-SORB - Apparel and accessories - Ronald D. Taylor

COOL ZONE - Apparel and accessories - Cool Zone Products & Promotions, Inc.

COOLAIR - Fans and power roof ventilators - American Coolair Corp.

COOLAIRE - Apparel–women's - Maidenform Inc. (True Form Foundations Div.)

COOLANT - Medical apparatus - Sebra

COOLANT GUARD - Filters–industrial - Parker-Hannifin Corp.

COOLANT MANAGER - Generators - Hyde Products Inc.

COOLBLADE - Skates–roller - Rollerblade, Inc.

COOLBROOK - Fountains–drinking - Crane Plumbing/Fiat Products

COOLCARDS - Computer software - Network Sound & Light, Inc.

COOLDATE - Food containers - Thermos Co.

COOLED LILAC - Cosmetics - Lancome

COOLER - Colognes ☆ - Noxell Corp.

COOLER - Flowers, plants, and seeds - Panamerican Seed

COOLER - Frames–eyeglass - May Optical Co. Inc.

COOLER & MORE - Containers–insulated - Outer Circle Products, Ltd.

COOLER CADDIE - Coolers–electric ☆ - Flambeau Products Corp.

COOLER COLORS - Water cooler parts - Oasis Corp.

COOLER-FRESH - Deodorizers - Enviro-Dynamics Inc.

COOLER KING - Humidifiers - Humidity Control Systems, Inc.

COOLER RANCH - Snack foods - Frito-Lay, Inc.

COOLER TIMES - Beverages ☆ - The Beverage Source Inc.

COOLERS PLUS - Ice chests–plastic - Coolers Plus Corp.

COOLESSENCE - Ice chests–plastic - Coleman Co., Inc.

COOLESSENCE - Lotions - Rickey Lauren and Mark N. Kaplan

COOLEST ONES UNDER THE SUN - Windshields–glass - Libbey-Owens-Ford Co.

COOLEST T-SHIRTS ON THE PLANET LOGOTEL, THE - Consulting services - Logotel Properties, Inc.

COOLEST ULTRA TINY INDIVIDUALS ON EARTH - Toys - Mattel, Inc.

COOLETTE - Waterproof and canvas footwear - Converse Inc.

COOLEY-BRITE - Fabrics - Astrup Co.

COOLEY-LITE - Motor vehicle parts and accessories - Cooley, Inc.

COOLFLEX - Slacks ☆ - Horace Small Apparel Co.

COOLFLO - Saws–chain - WCI Outdoor Products, Inc.

COOLFRONT V - Crocheted and knitted items - Puritan Sportswear Corp.

COOLFUT - Shoes - Clinic Shoe Co.

COOLGLIDE 2000 - Display cases–plastic - Paul Flum Ideas, Inc.

COOLGLO - Furniture - Bishop Graphics Inc.

COOLHEADLUKE, THE - Wigs - Penthouse for Men

COOLHEAT - Exchangers–heat - Stein, Inc.

COOLHOOP - Toys - Kenneth Eugene Albert

COOLIDGE - Frames–eyeglass - May Optical Co. Inc.

COOLIDGE COLLECTION, THE - Apparel and accessories - Vincent J. Demarco

COOLIE - Frames–eyeglass - May Optical Co. Inc.

COOLING BLUE - Shaving preparations - Mennen Co.

COOLING TEETHER - Infant product - Mattel, Inc.

COOLISSA - Toys - Those Characters from Cleveland, Inc.

COOLIT - Candy - Ferrara Pan Candy Co., Inc.

COOLITE - Lighting fixtures - Swivelier Co. Inc.

COOLJAX - Telephone accessories - Multi-Tech Systems, Inc.

COOLMAX - Fabrics - E.I. Dupont de Nemours and Co.

COOL'N DRY - Apparel and accessories ☆ - Playtex Apparel, Inc.

COOLPACK - Luggage - Shalam Imports Inc.

COOLPAD - Coolers–electric - Research Products Corp.

COOLPAK - Coolers–electric ☆ - Research Products Corp.

COOLPLOT - Computer software - Daat Research Corp.

COOLPURE - Computer software - Maxwell Technologies, Inc.

COOLS - Shoes ☆ - Mother Goose Co.

COOLSCAN - Film scanners - Nikon Inc.

COOLSHAPES - Computer software - Micrografx, Inc.

COOLSIP - Water–bottled or canned - Sga Corp.

COOLSKIN - Skin care products ☆ - Solar Gear Inc.

COOLSNAK - Food containers ☆ - Thermos Co.

COOLSPEC - Eyeglasses - Uvex Safety LLC

COOLSPRING - Farm machinery - Ahrens Agricultural Industries, Inc.

COOLTIPT - Tobacco products - Philip Morris Companies Inc.

COOLTITE - Paints - Suntec Paint Inc.

COOLTRAK - Paper - Environmental Test Systems Inc.

COOLWICH - Candy - Homestead, Inc.

COOLWORKS - Heating equipment - Coolworks, Inc.

COOLWRAP - Footwear - Onyx Medical Corp.

COOLY-SAURUS - Fruit drinks–bottled or canned - Cliffstar Corp.

COON CREEK - Meat products–pork - Houchens Industries, Inc.

COON HUNTER - Footwear - Coon Den

COON HUNTERS PRIDE - Dog food - Hyland Co.

COON SQUALL - Pet products - Mr. Mutt Pet Products Inc.

COOOLIGAN - Greeting cards - David A. Salvato

COOP - Pasta - Holland-American Importing Co. Inc.

COOP 2000 - Computer software - Critical Skills Group, Ltd.

COOPER - Contact lenses - Cooper Companies Inc.

COOPER - Greeting cards - Ports of Scandinavia Inc.

COOPER - Household thermometers - Cooper Instrument Corp.
COOPER - Lighting - Cooper Industries, Inc.
COOPER - Pitch coatings - Coopers Creek Chemical Corp.
COOPER - Sporting goods - Canstar Sports USA
COOPER - Tires - Cooper Tire & Rubber Co.
COOPER - Tobacco—chewing or smoking - Swisher International, Inc.
COOPER 38 - Contact lenses - Cooper Companies Inc.
COOPER BAND - Toys - Dye-namic Movement Products, Inc.
COOPER BLANKET - Toys - Dye-namic Movement Products, Inc.
COOPER C - Oil machinery - Cooper Manufacturing Corp.
COOPER CLASSIC - Contact lenses - Cooper Companies Inc.
COOPER CLEAR - Contact lenses - Cooper Companies Inc.
COOPER COLLECTIONS - Apparel—athletic ☆ - Cooper Sportswear
    Manufacturing Co., Inc.
COOPER EDENS - Greeting cards - Green Tiger Press
COOPER FARMS - Food products - Southland Corp.
COOPER FARMS - Ice cream - Deering Ice Cream Corp.
COOPER FARMS V.H. COOPER FARMS 1938 - Meat products—poultry -
    Cooper Hatchery Inc.
COOPER-HEWITT - Lamps - Sperti Sunlamp
COOPER-JARRETT, INC. - Toys - Toy Truck Lines, Inc.
COOPER KIDS ADVENTURE SERIES, THE - Children's novels - Good News
    Publishers
COOPER OUTERWEAR COMPANY - Apparel—athletic - Cooper Sportswear
    Manufacturing Co., Inc.
COOPER-RAND - Medical apparatus - Luminaud Inc.
COOPER-SEAL - Waterproofing material - Coopers Creek Chemical Corp.
COOPER SPREADIN' SOFT - Cheese - H.P. Hood & Sons Inc.
COOPER SQUARE - Furniture ☆ - Harden Furniture Co. Inc.
COOPER-STANLEY - Paint stripper ☆ - Construction Technology, Inc.
COOPER SURGICAL - Smoke evacuator - Cooper Companies Inc.
COOPER THIN - Contact lenses - Cooper Companies Inc.
COOPER THORNHILL - Cheese ☆ - Swissrose International Inc.
COOPER VAC - Smoke evacuator - Cooper Companies Inc.
COOPER VISION - Contact lenses-cleaning solution - Cooper Companies Inc.
COOPERATIVE DEVELOPMENT ENVIRONMENT - Computer software -
    Oracle Corp.
COOPERATIVE MEDIA GROUP - Computer software - C Media Group
COOPERATIVE SERVER TECHNOLOGY - Computer storage devices - Oracle
    Corp.
COOPERCARE CUSTOM TORIC - Contact lenses - Coopervision, Inc.
COOPERS - Marmalade - Cornwall Group Inc.
COOPERS - Underwear and nightwear - Jockey International, Inc.
COOPER'S COMBO DINNER - Meat products—poultry - Cooper's Turkey
    Place, Inc.
COOPERS CREEK - Wines - Wines of the World Inc.
COOPERSBURG CLUBBER - Miniature baseball bats - Coopersburg Handle
    Works Inc.
COOPERSOTE - Brown creosote - Coopers Creek Chemical Corp.
COOPERSTOWN ASH - Lumber - Georgia-Pacific Corp.
COOPERSTOWN BEARS - Toys—stuffed - Cooperstown Bears L.P.
COOPERSTOWN CARD - Trading cards and stamps - Pinnacle Brands, Inc.
COOPERSURGICAL - Astringents - Coopersurgical, Inc.
COOPEXIM - Giftware - Amceco International Corp.
COOR LIGHT 16 OZ POUND - Beverages—malt - Adolph Coors Co.
COOR RED LIGHT - Beverages—malt - Adolph Coors Co.
COORDI-KNITS - Crocheted and knitted items - Winston Manufacturing Corp.
COORDINATE - Floor coverings—carpet and rugs ☆ - Customweave Carpets
    Inc.
COORDINATE - Stationery - Moore Business Forms, Inc.
COORDINATE - Tables—metal ☆ - Cramer Inc.
COORDINATE GEOMETRY - Computer software - Ventura Educational
    Systems
COORDINATE II - Tables—wood - Stacor Corp.
COORDINATED CONCEPTS - Wallpaper ☆ - Royson's Corp.
COORDINATED CONCEPTS II - Wallpaper - Royson's Corp.
COORDINATED CONCEPTS III - Wallpaper - Royson's Corp.
COORDINATED COPPER - Lipstick and nail polish ☆ - Cosrich Inc.
COORDINATED INTERIORS - Wallpaper - Andover Wallcovering
COORDINATED RETIREMENT INCOME SOLUTIONS - Computer software -
    MDW Software, Ltd.
COORDINATES - Luggage ☆ - Hartmann Luggage Co.
COORDINATES ETCETERA - Blinds—venetian - Hunter Douglas, Inc.
COORDINATION GRAPH PAPER - Paper—graph - Judy Lynn Schwimmer
COORS - Beverages—malt - Adolph Coors Co.
COORS ARCTIC ICE - Beverages—malt - Adolph Coors Co.

COORS ARTIC ICE - Shirts - Coors Brewing Co.
COORS CUTTER - Beverages—malt - Adolph Coors Co.
COORS DAIRY - Milk - Coors Brothers Co.
COORS DRY - Beverages—malt - Adolph Coors Co.
COORS EXTRA GOLD - Beverages—malt - Adolph Coors Co.
COORS EXTRA GOLD LIGHT - Beverages—malt - Adolph Coors Co.
COORS FIELD - Apparel and accessories - Adolph Coors Co.
COORS FIELD - Glassware—household - Coors Brewing Co.
COORS GOLD - Beverages—malt - Adolph Coors Co.
COORS LIGHT - Beverages—malt - Adolph Coors Co.
COOSA - Slacks—men's - Rome Manufacturing Co. Inc.
COOSEMANS - Fruits and vegetables - Coosemans Worldwide, Inc.
COOTIE - Games - Milton Bradley Co.
COOTS AND CRITTER - Placemats - Charles Don Hill
COP - Environmental testing equipment - Ransco Industries
COP - File folders - Collis Inc.
COP-A-BOND - Copper products - Afco Products Inc.
COP-A-BOND DUPLEX - Copper products - Afco Products Inc.
COP-A-LEAD - Asphalt felts and coatings - Afco Products Inc.
COP-A-WAY - Pet products ☆ - Aquatronics-Filtronics
COP COLLECTIBLES - Trading cards and stamps - Proimage Publishing Co.,
    Inc.
COP CUP - Containers—insulated - Armament Systems and Procedures, Inc.
COP-E-CAT - Fishing lures - Eppinger Manufacturing Co.
COP-E-EEZ - Duplicating machines - R. Funk and Co. Inc.
COP-E-ETT - Duplicating machines ☆ - R. Funk and Co. Inc.
COP-R-CHEF - Pans - All-Clad Metalcrafters Inc.
COP-R-DIP - Wood fillers - Sterling-Clark-Lurton Corp.
COP-R-TOX - Varnishes - Mobile Paint Manufacturing Co.
COP-TUR - Toys - Tonka Corp.
COP5 - Pumps - Beckett Corp.
COPA DE ORO - Liquors - Heaven Hill Distilleries, Inc.
COPACABANA - Dinnerware—glass ☆ - Nikko Ceramics Inc.
COPACABANA - Frames—eyeglass - May Optical Co. Inc.
COPACABANA - Underwear and nightwear - Russell-Newman, Inc.
COPAL - Brushes—paint - Rubberset Co.
COPAL - Photographic equipment ☆ - R.T.S. Inc.
COPALINER - Dental compounds - Harry J. Bosworth Co.
COPALOY - Tools - Diamond/Triangle Tool Group Inc.
COPALTITE - Caulking compounds - National Engineering Products, Inc.
COPAN - Pharmaceutical preparations ☆ - Roberts/Hauck Pharmaceuticals Inc.
COPAN TRADING - Apparel and accessories - Copan Trading L.C.
COPASCO - Glue—household or industrial ☆ - Evans Adhesive Corp.
COPASTETIC - Recording label - Ernest Walters, III
COPATE - See SEBASTE
COPAVIN - Pharmaceutical preparations - Eli Lilly and Co.
COPCO - Cookware, food storage containers, etc. - Copco Inc.
COPCO - Hardware - Blaine Window Hardware Inc.
COPE - Analgesics - Sterling Winthrop Inc.
COPE - Cleaning preparations ☆ - Mione Manufacturing Co.
COPED - Fishing lures - Lindy Little Joe Inc.
COPEFRUT - Fruits and vegetables ☆ - Marglo Products Corp.
COPEN - Kitchen and bathroom cabinets - IXL Furniture Co. Inc.
COPENCAST - Cooking utensils—cast iron ☆ - National Housewares
COPENHAGEN - Candy ☆ - R.L. Albert & Son, Inc.
COPENHAGEN - Coffee - White Coffee Corp.
COPENHAGEN - Cribs—wood ☆ - Welsh Co.
COPENHAGEN - Door frames - Canyon Creek Cabinet Co.
COPENHAGEN - Furniture ☆ - Lane Co. Inc.
COPENHAGEN - Furniture—children's ☆ - Child Craft Industries Inc.
COPENHAGEN - Tobacco products - United States Tobacco Co.
COPENHAGEN CRUISER - Bicycles - Jensen and Reitzel
COPENHAGEN DANISH BRAND - Meat products—pork - CKF Foods, Inc.
COPERNICUS - Computer software - New Paradigm Software Corp.
COPEROYD - Adhesives and sealants ☆ - James B. Day and Co.
COPE'S - Fruits and vegetables - John Cope's Food Products, Inc.
COPE'S ESCUDO - Tobacco products - Faber, Coe & Gregg Inc.
COPESCOL - Shrimp—fresh or frozen - Southeast Foods Inc.
COPHENE - Pharmaceutical preparations - Dunhall Pharmaceuticals Inc.
COPI-MATE - Paper—carbon - Leedall Products Manufacturing Co.
COPIA - Duplicating machines - Olivetti North America Inc. (Consumer
    Products Div.)
COPICONTROL - Paper—transfer - Nocopi International Inc.
COPIERXCEL - Office supplies - Georgia-Pacific Corp.
COPILOT - Ophthalmic goods - Foremost Optical Products
COPILOT-VERSION 2 - Computer software - Abacus Software, Inc.

☆ = Now out of production

COPIMARK - Printing inks - Nocopi Technologies, Inc.
COPING AWARD - Dolls ☆ - Mighty Star Inc. (Special Effects Div.)
COPING WITH - Publisher's imprints - Rosen Publishing Group & Pelion Press
COPION - Cosmetics - Cameo Beauty Supply Co.
COPISAFE - Paper–looseleaf - Nocopi International Inc.
COPLEY - Crayons ☆ - Milton Bradley Co.
COPLEY - Flatware - Reed and Barton Corp.
COPLEY - Frames–eyeglass ☆ - Universal/Univis Inc.
COPLEY ARCH - Cabinets–wood - Kemper
COPLEY HALL - Floor coverings ☆ - Tarkett, Inc.
COPLEY SQUARE - Cabinets–wood - Kemper
COPLEY SQUARE - Fabrics–tapestry ☆ - Coloroll Inc.
COPLEY SQUARE - Floor coverings–tile - Kentile Floors Inc.
COPLEY SQUARE - Footwear ☆ - Thom McAn Shoe Co.
COPLEY SQUARE - Plates–plastic - Sweetheart Plastics Inc.
COPOL - Chemical preparations ☆ - Woolsey Marine Industries
COPONYL - Brushes–paint - Adams Brush Manufacturing Co., Inc.
COPPA GLO - Brushes–paint ☆ - Linzer Products Corp.
COPPA MISTA - Ice cream - Caffe Classico
COPPELIA - Fabrics - Gretchen Bellinger Inc.
COPPER - Floor coverings–carpet and rugs - Textile Concepts
COPPER ACE - Rackets–tennis - Pro Kennex, Inc.
COPPER BEACH - Apparel and accessories - Dillard Department Stores Inc.
COPPER BOWL TUCSON - Apparel and accessories - Copper Bowl Foundation
COPPER BRAID - Adhesives and sealants - Gemini Braids, Inc.
COPPER-BRITE - Cleaning preparations - Copper Brite, Inc.
COPPER BRITE - Insecticides - Lawn & Garden Supply Co.
COPPER BRONZE - Adhesives and sealants ☆ - Pettit Paint Co. Inc.
COPPER CANYON CYCLING - Bicycle parts and accessories - American Recreation Co., Inc.
COPPER CARE LIQUID - Cleaning preparations - Blitz Manufacturing Co., Inc.
COPPER CHIEF - Office supplies ☆ - Ames Supply Co.
COPPER CLAD - Gloves - Brookville Glove Manufacturing Co.
COPPER CLASSIC - Golfing equipment - Golfsmith International Inc.
COPPER CLASSICS - Novelty items - Houston International Trading
COPPER COAT - Coatings ☆ - K & W Products
COPPER CRAFT - Giftware - Copper Craft
COPPER CURE - Pet products - Aquatrol, Inc.
COPPER CUTIE - Toys - Tonka Corp.
COPPER DOC - Cleaning preparations - X-I-M Products Inc.
COPPER DRAGON - Insecticides - Dragon Chemical Corp.
COPPER FORMALIN COMPLEX - Pet products - Marine Enterprises International, Inc.
COPPER GLO - Cleaning preparations - Servaas Laboratories Inc.
COPPER GLOW - Hair coloring preparations - Sebastian International, Inc.
COPPER-GREEN - Adhesives and sealants - Green Products Co.
COPPER GREEN - Pet products - Endich Inc.
COPPER HEAD - Toys–automobiles - Tonka Corp.
COPPER-K - Veterinary pharmaceutical preparations - Vineland Laboratories Inc.
COPPER KEY - Apparel and accessories - Dillard Department Stores Inc.
COPPER KEY CLOTHING COMPANY - Jeans–men's - Dillard Department Stores Inc.
COPPER LTD. - Rackets–tennis - Pro Kennex, Inc.
COPPER LITE - Brooms - O-Cedar/Vining Household Products Co.
COPPER-LOKT - Ammunition - Remington Arms Co., Inc.
COPPER-LUX - Boat-bottom coating ☆ - Interlux Yacht Finishes
COPPER MAID - Kitchen utensils–aluminum ☆ - Revere Ware Corp.
COPPER MATE - Kitchen utensils–enameled ☆ - Revere Ware Corp.
COPPER 'N BRASS JELLY - Cleaning preparations - Loctite Corp.
COPPER-NU - Cleaning preparations - Kester Solder Co.
COPPER PENNY - Coffee-shop franchise - Copper Penny Family Restaurants
COPPER POWER - Pet products - Endich Inc.
COPPER POWER - Veterinary pharmaceutical preparations ☆ - ICM Inc. (Gilcraft Div.)
COPPER POWER GREEN - Veterinary pharmaceutical preparations ☆ - ICM Inc. (Gilcraft Div.)
COPPER-QUICK - Automotive parts and accessories ☆ - Household Research Corp.
COPPER-RICH - Lubricants - Rectorseal Corp.
COPPER RIVER GREETINGS - Greeting cards - Sue Zajac
COPPER ROSE ON BLACK - Glassware–household ☆ - Fenton Art Glass Co.
COPPER SALICYLATE CAPS - Vitamins and nutritional supplements - Vitamin Research Products Inc.

COPPER SHOP, THE - Recording label - Phelps Dodge Industries, Inc.
COPPER SHOPPE - Housewares - Himark Enterprises Inc.
COPPER SKILLET - Food products - Russell Foods Co.
COPPER SPRAY - Adhesives and sealants - Loctite Corp.
COPPER-TINT - Cooking equipment–household ☆ - Anchor Hocking Glass, Inc.
COPPER TOP - Batteries - Duracell Co. USA
COPPER TOP - Electrical equipment - Duraname Corp.
COPPER TRU - Aquarium accessories - Kordon
COPPER XS - Silicon products - Pro Seal Products
COPPERBOY - Thermostats - Western Wire Products Co.
COPPERESSENCE - Dishes–china - Viletta China Co.
COPPERFIELD - Bakeware, servingware ☆ - Corning Inc.
COPPERFIELD - Toys–stuffed - Gund, Inc.
COPPERFIELDS - Meats–luncheon - Wilson Foods Corp.
COPPERHEAD - Ammunition - Crosman Corp.
COPPERHEAD - Bats–baseball - Worth Inc.
COPPERHEAD - Connectors–electrical - E & J Demark, Inc.
COPPERHOOD - Soups–mixes - Alberto-Culver Co.
COPPERIDGE - Wines - Ernest and Julio Gallo Winery
COPPERIZED - Electrical equipment - Electripak
COPPERLITE - Cooking utensils–earthenware ☆ - National Housewares
COPPERLITE INTERLUSION - Wigs - Taylormade Hair Replacement
COPPERLOY - Forklifts - JH Industries Inc. (Copperloy Div.)
COPPERPLATE - Artists' materials - Andrews/Nelson/Whitehead
COPPERSAFE - Pet products - Mardel Laboratories, Inc.
COPPERSOURCE - Glassware–household - Coppersource/Halves Inc.
COPPERTONE - Footwear–athletic ☆ - E.S. Originals, Inc.
COPPERTONE - Suntan lotions - Schering-Plough Healthcare Products
COPPERTONE 25 - Sunblocks - Schering-Plough Healthcare Products
COPPERTONE 30+ - Sunblocks - Schering-Plough Healthcare Products
COPPERTONE KIDS - Skin care products - Schering-Plough Healthcare Products
COPPERTONE PROTECT & TAN - Suntan lotions - Schering-Plough Healthcare Products
COPPERTONE SPORT - Sunblocks - Schering-Plough Healthcare Products
COPPERTRU - Water treating compounds - Novalek, Inc.
COPPERTRUNK - Computer peripheral equipment - Orckit Communications, Inc.
COPPES NAPANEE - Hardwood kitchen cabinets and furniture - Coppes Napanee Co.
COPPINI - Floor coverings ☆ - Tarkett, Inc.
COPPO - Floor waxes ☆ - Klean-Strip
COPPO EXTRA - Floor waxes ☆ - Klean-Strip
COPPO-W - Floor waxes ☆ - Klean-Strip
COPPOLA - Cosmetics ☆ - Cassidy Inc.
COPPUS POWER PLUS - Fans–electric - Tuthill Corp.
COPRA TRADING POST - Apparel and accessories - Tropical Joe, Inc.
COPRIN - Pharmaceutical preparations - Lunsco Inc.
COPRINE - Lipsticks - Lancome
COPRINE - Pharmaceutical, now out of production - IDE-Interstate Inc.
COPRO MEGA-GRO 10,000 - Vitamins and nutritional supplements ☆ - Titan Sports, Inc.
COPROX - Paints - Atlas Chemical Co.
COPS - Computer software - Harold S. Haller & Co.
COPS & CROOKS - Toys - Hasbro, Inc.
COPTER - Toys–airplanes ☆ - Victor Stanzel and Co.
COPTEX - Music boxes - Coehler-Coptex Co.
COPWARE SOFTWARE FOR PEACE OFFICERS - Computer software - Zax Electronic Publications, Inc.
COPY BAN + - Office supplies - Standard Register Co.
COPY CADDY - Office supplies - Esselte Corp.
COPY CAPS - Apparel and accessories - Bruce Einhorn
COPY CAPS CLOTHES TATTOO CREATE-A-CAP - Apparel and accessories - Bruce Einhorn
COPY-CARE - Cleaning preparations - James L. Harris
COPY CAST - Hobby kits - Creative Art Activities Inc.
COPY CAT - Markers–felt-tip - Dri Mark Products, Inc.
COPY CAT - Tools - Disston Co.
COPY CAT - Toys - Tiger Electronics, Inc.
COPY CATS - Candy - Sconza Candy Co.
COPY CLAW - Paper clips - Smead Manufacturing Co.
COPY COTE - Paper–bond ☆ - Mead Corp.
COPY DB - Computer software - Integrated Software
COPY-FAX - Pens - Micropoint Inc.
COPY FILM II - Film - Codo Manufacturing Corp.

☆ = Now out of production

COPY FIRST - Paper–bond - HOPR Inc.
COPY II - Computer software - Central Point Software Inc.
COPY MAGIC - Inks–duplicating - Angler's Roslyn Group Ltd.
COPY-NOT - Office supplies - Faber-Castell Corp.
COPY-RIGHT - Copyholders ☆ - Curtis-Young Corp.
COPY SAFE - Computer software - Infosafe Systems, Inc.
COPY SAFE - Office supplies - Esselte Corp.
COPY STAND - Easels - Gibson Holders, Inc.
COPY/VIEW - Electronic equipment - Arkwright Manufacturing Inc.
COPY-WRITE - Pencils ☆ - Faber-Castell Corp.
COPY WRITER - Photographic equipment ☆ - R.T.S. Inc.
COPYALL - Duplicating machines ☆ - Dietzgen Corp.
COPYBLOC - Business forms - Moore Business Forms, Inc.
COPYCATS - Toys–stuffed - Gund, Inc.
COPYCORDER - Photocopy machines - Hecon Corp.
COPYETTE - Electronic equipment - Telex Communications, Inc.
COPYFAST - Leather–vellum - National Printfast
COPYFRAME - Frames–picture - Fellowes Manufacturing Co.
COPYGAL - Paper–carbon ☆ - Eaton Allen Ko-Rec-Type Corp.
COPYGARD - Office supplies - JM Co.
COPYGUARD - Computers - Copyguard, Inc.
COPYIST, THE - Computer software - Dr. T's Music Software Inc.
COPYJET - Printers–computer - Hewlett-Packard Co.
COPYKIT - Video production - Sima Products Corp.
COPYLUX - Film - Joseph F. Barrett Jr.
COPYMATE - Photocopy machines - Access Control Devices, Inc.
COPYNEAT - Carbon and graphite products - Kores Nordic USA Corp.
COPYNET - Computer software - Xerox Corp.
COPYRIGHT WIZARD - Computer software - Transcender Corp.
COPYRIGHTPRO - Computer storage devices - Management Science Associates, Inc.
COPYRITE - Paper–bond - Badger Paper Mills, Inc.
COPYRUN - Paper–bond - Georgia-Pacific Corp.
COPYSAVER - Paper - Saxon Paper Co.
COPYSCREEN - Duplicating machines - Graphic Products Corp.
COPYSOURCE - Paper - Saxon Paper Co.
COPYTRAN - Photographic equipment ☆ - Bogen Photo Corp.
COPYWORKS - Computer software - Citizen Publishing Co. of Wisconsin, Inc.
COPYWRITER - Recording label - KK Microboards
COQ BLANC - Food products - George C. Brown's Biscuits & Confections
COQ PLEX 1000 - Vitamins and nutritional supplements - Highland Laboratories
COQUEREL - Brandy ☆ - David Sherman Corp.
COQUEREZ CALVADOS - Beverages–alcohol - Niche Marketing Corp.
COQUETTE - Brushes–hair - Phillips Brush Corp.
COQUETTE - Dolls ☆ - Effanbee Doll Corp.
COQUETTE - Floor coverings–carpet and rugs - Regal Rugs Inc.
COQUETTE - Hair care products ☆ - Alger Creations Inc.
COQUETTE - Handbags - IMA Fashions Inc.
COQUETTE - Lipsticks - Lancome
COQUETTE - Pencils ☆ - Empire Berol USA
COQUETTE - Rings–jewelry - Artcarved Inc.
COQUETTE - Wedding gowns - Alfred Angelo Inc.
COQUI - Knives - Akona Adventure Gear, Inc.
COQUI EGGS - Chewing gum - Lenny's Sales, Inc.
COQUI MALT LIQUOR - Beverages–malt - The Stroh Brewery Co.
COQUILLE - Floor coverings–carpet and rugs ☆ - Karastan-Bigelow Inc.
COQUILLE - Furniture ☆ - Bassett Furniture Industries, Inc.
COQUILLE DE MER - Jewelry - Richelieu Corp.
COQUILLE IMPERIAL - Floor coverings–carpet and rugs - Karastan-Bigelow Inc.
COQUILLE NOUVEAU - Floor coverings–carpet and rugs ☆ - Karastan-Bigelow Inc.
COQUILLE ROSE - Cosmetics - Lancome
COQUILLES - Prepared foods - City Bites
COQUILLES SUCRES - Candy - Koppers Chocolate Specialty Co. Inc.
COQUINA - Floor coverings - Mannington Resilient Floors
COQUINA - Furniture - Halcyon Inc.
COR-AL-GESIC - Pharmaceutical preparations ☆ - Ulmer Pharmacal Co.
COR-DRAWER - Boxes - Kole Industries Inc.
COR-GON - Pharmaceutical preparations ☆ - Merz Inc.
COR-KEY - Magnetic key - Corkey Control Systems Inc.
COR-KIT - Lockset - Corkey Control Systems Inc.
COR LES - Fishing tackle ☆ - Gladding Braided Products Inc.
COR-LUBE - Rustproofing compounds - Cortec Corp.
COR-MASTIC - Rustproofing compounds - Cortec Corp.

COR-O-FECT - Paints - Coronado Paint Co.
COR-O-FECT II - Coatings - Coronado Paint Co.
COR-O-FECT III - Coatings - Coronado Paint Co.
COR-OTICIN - Pharmaceutical preparations - Maurry Biological Co. Inc.
COR-PAK - Plastics - Cortec Corp.
COR-TAR-QUIN - Chemical preparations ☆ - Miles Inc.
COR TEMP - Thermometers - Steridyne Corp.
CORA - Food products - Casa Imports Inc.
CORA - Hardware - Cora International, Inc.
CORA - Ophthalmic goods ☆ - Rozin Optical Export Corp.
CORA - Wines ☆ - Palm Bay Imports, Inc.
CORA-CAINE - Denture ointment - Harry J. Bosworth Co.
CORA-NADO - Footwear - Circle Shoe Co.
CORACIN - Pharmaceutical preparations - Roberts/Hauck Pharmaceuticals Inc.
CORADO - Wines - Heublein, Inc.
CORAIL - Lipsticks - Cosmair Inc.
CORAL - Beverages–alcohol - Chi-Chi's, Inc.
CORAL - Brushes–paint ☆ - PPG Industries, Inc.
CORAL - Detergents - Sinclair Manufacturing Co.
CORAL - Erasers ☆ - Bright Boy Abrasives
CORAL - Margarine ☆ - Swift Edible Oil Co.
CORAL - Recording label - MCA Universal Studios
CORAL - Seafood products–canned or cured - Bumble Bee Seafoods, Inc.
CORAL - Sporting goods - Hedstrom Corp.
CORAL - Toys - Tonka Corp.
CORAL - Window coverings - Covoc Corp.
CORAL-AIR - Pet products - Penn-Plax, Inc.
CORAL ART - Aquariums–household - Oceanic Systems, Inc.
CORAL BAY - Floor coverings–carpet and rugs ☆ - Lees Carpets
CORAL BAY - Food products - Marx Brothers Inc.
CORAL BAY - Furniture ☆ - Bassett Furniture Industries, Inc.
CORAL BEACH - Aquarium accessories - Kordon
CORAL BEACH - Aquarium accessories - Novalek, Inc.
CORAL BEACH CLUB - Women's apparel - Home Shopping Club, Inc.
CORAL BLOSSOMS - Dinnerware–glass ☆ - Lenox, Inc.
CORAL CREATIONS - Pet products ☆ - Tetra Sales USA
CORAL GABLES - Fabrics - Dan River Inc.
CORAL GABLES - Underwear and nightwear ☆ - Alba-Waldensian, Inc.
CORAL ICE - Lipsticks ☆ - Elysee Scientific Cosmetic Co.
CORAL KEY - Apparel–women's ☆ - Apparel Ventures, Inc.
CORAL KEY - Floor coverings–carpet and rugs ☆ - Catalina Carpet Mills Inc.
CORAL LILY - Dinnerware–glass ☆ - Nikko Ceramics Inc.
CORAL LITE - Pet products - Tetra Sales USA
CORAL NACRE - Cosmetics - Lancome
CORAL PINK - Erasers ☆ - Bright Boy Abrasives
CORAL PLUS - Floor coverings - Pawling Corp. (Standard Products Div.)
CORAL REEF - Blinds–venetian ☆ - Hunter Douglas, Inc.
CORAL REEF - Cocktail mixes - Koala Koncepts, Inc.
CORAL REEF - Floor coverings–carpet and rugs - Catalina Carpet Mills Inc.
CORAL REEF - Housewares - Enterprise Trading Co.
CORAL REEF - Watches ☆ - Swatch Watch USA
CORAL SAND - Cosmetics - Lancome
CORAL SEA - Aquarium accessories - Kordon
CORAL SEA - Aquarium accessories - Novalek, Inc.
CORAL SEA - Furniture - Lane Upholstery (Venture Furniture Div.)
CORAL SEA - Wallpaper - Textile Wallcoverings International Ltd.
CORAL SEA WEE - Toys - Tonka Corp.
CORAL SEAS - Cleaning preparations - Coral International, Inc.
CORAL SILK - Fabrics–silk - Scalamandre Silks Inc.
CORAL SOL - Cosmetics - Caribbean Pacific International, Inc.
CORAL SPRINGS - Floor coverings ☆ - Congoleum Corp.
CORAL SPRINGS - Tableware–china ☆ - Lenox, Inc.
CORAL STAR - Seafood products–fresh or frozen - Crest International Corp.
CORAL WINDS - Flatware ☆ - Regent Sheffield, Ltd.
CORALAIR - Transmitting apparatus–radio - Tadiran Electronic Industries, Inc.
CORALAIS - Faucets - Kohler Co.
CORALART MOSAICS - Hobby kits - Paul Marshall Products L.P.
CORALAY CLASSICS - Reproductions of antiques and wall decor ☆ - Corbell & Co.
CORALETTE - Brushes–hair ☆ - Korex Corp.
CORALIFE - Pet products - Energy Savers Unlimited Inc.
CORALINE - Erasers ☆ - Bright Boy Abrasives
CORALTONE - Floor coverings - Congoleum Corp.
CORALURE - Boxes - Georgia-Pacific Corp.
CORAMINE - Pharmaceutical preparations - Ciba-Geigy Corp.
CORASHIELD - Paints - PPG Industries, Inc.

☆ = Now out of production

CORAZON - Vegetables–canned - J.M. Rodriguez & Co. Inc.
CORBAC - Transmissions–motor vehicle - Andantex USA Inc.
CORBANS - Wines - Dreyfus Ashby Inc.
CORBEE - Cushions - Supracor Systems, Inc.
CORBEL - Floor coverings–carpet and rugs ☆ - World Carpets, Inc.
CORBEL PLUS - Floor coverings–carpet and rugs ☆ - World Carpets, Inc.
CORBELL - Crystal, silver, jewelry, etc. - Corbell & Co.
CORBELL - Silver products - Vincent Lippe Co.
CORBETT - Brushes–paint ☆ - PPG Industries, Inc.
CORBETT - Lighting equipment - Corbett Lighting, Inc.
CORBETT - Lighting fixtures - Light Inc.
CORBETT CANYON - Wines - Corbett Canyon Vineyards
CORBIN - Apparel - Corbin Ltd.
CORBIN - Brushes–paint - Corona Brushes Inc.
CORBIN - Brushes–paint ☆ - PPG Industries, Inc.
CORBIN - Motorcycle parts and accessories - Corbin Pacific, Inc.
CORBIN RUSSWIN - Locks–door - Emhart Inc.
CORBIN RUSSWIN - Locks–padlocks - Corbin Russwin, Inc.
CORBY HALL DUDSON - Dishes–china - British American Imports
CORBY'S - Beverages–alcohol - Sunbelt Beverage Corp.
CORBY'S - Liquors - Canandaigua Wine Co. Inc.
CORCAAT - Computer software - Cortet, Inc.
CORCAM - Cosmetics ☆ - Jason Natural Products, Inc.
CORCILATE - Pharmaceutical preparations ☆ - Morton Pharmaceuticals Inc.
CORCILUX - Paints - Tenax Finishing Product
CORCO - Bulletin boards–cork - Design House, Inc.
CORCO - Cheese - Corte & Co.
CORCORAN - Footwear - Acme Boot Co., Inc.
CORCORAN FORLE - Footwear - Acme Boot Co., Inc.
CORCORAN MARAUDER - Footwear - H.H. Brown Shoe Co., Inc.
CORD - Motor vehicle parts and accessories - Auburn-Cord-Duesenberg Co.
CORD - Watches ☆ - Design Time USA Inc.
CORD BAG - Bags–storage - Benjamin R. Groeser
CORD COUPLER - Electrical equipment ☆ - BPE Inc.
CORD GRIPS - Hardware - Miller Studio
CORD KING - Cord connectors–electric - Cord King
CORD-LESS - Glue–household or industrial - Loctite Corp.
CORD-LOCK - Extension cords - Pacific Electricord Co.
CORD-MINDER - Telephone apparatus - Preco New Products Corp.
CORD-PEN - Desk sets - Slencil Co.
CORD-STICK - Extension cords - Pacific Electricord Co.
CORD TAMER - Electrical equipment - Michael S. Yocom
CORD WINDER - Electrical equipment - Black & Decker Corp.
CORDA - House furnishings ☆ - Lexington Furniture Industries, Inc.
CORDA - Sporting goods - Dacor Corp.
CORDABELLO - Apparel - Gentry Clothiers, Inc.
CORDAGE SOURCE, THE - Cordage and twine - Winchester-Auburn Mills Inc.
CORDAIR GLOSS - Paper–coated - Cincinnati Cordage and Paper Co.
CORDANA - Fabrics–cotton - Dan River Inc.
CORDARONE - Pharmaceutical preparations - Wyeth-Ayerst Laboratories
CORDAVEL - Floor coverings–carpet and rugs ☆ - Gulistan Carpet Inc.
CORDAWAY - Vacuum cleaners and accessories - The Eureka Co.
CORDAY - Floor coverings–carpet and rugs ☆ - Kelly Group Inc.
CORDE - Luggage ☆ - York Luggage Co.
CORDE BEAD - Handbags ☆ - Lumured Corp.
CORDE DU - Fabrics - Gretchen Bellinger Inc.
CORDE DU ROI - Mats - Majestic Mat Co.
CORDEA - Rackets–racquetball - Ektelon
CORDELIA - Clocks - Ridgeway Clock Co.
CORDELIA LIGHTING - Lighting equipment - Cordelia Lighting Inc.
CORDELL CC RATTLER - Fishing lures - EBSCO Industries Inc.
CORDELL HIGH-RES - Photographic processing equipment - Cordell Engineering Inc.
CORDELLE - Rope ☆ - Wellington Leisure Products, Inc.
CORDEMEX - Rope - Geo. B. Carpenter Co.
CORDENIM - Fabrics - Graniteville Co.
CORDERO - Dog food - Valley Feed and Supply, Inc.
CORDETTE - Fabrics - Greenwood Mills Inc.
CORDEX - Pharmaceutical preparations ☆ - Upjohn Co.
CORDGARD - Electrical equipment - SL Waber Inc.
CORDGUARD - Medical apparatus - Utah Medical Products, Inc.
CORDIA - Motor vehicles–automobiles - Mitsubishi Motor Sales of America Inc.
CORDIA - Wallcovering ☆ - Technique Textiles Inc.
CORDIA - Wallpaper - PCI Industries Inc.
CORDIAL - Cakes - Miss Kings Kitchen Inc.

CORDIAL - Vases ☆ - Lenox Crystal, Inc.
CORDIAL CAMPARI - Cordials - Campari USA Inc.
CORDIAL MEDOC - Liquors - Crestfield Importers Ltd.
CORDIALITES - Candles ☆ - Will & Baumer, Inc.
CORDIALLY YOURS - Candy - Brock Candy Co. Inc.
CORDIALS - Ice cream - Haagen-Dazs Co. Inc.
CORDIALS NOUVEAU - Beverages - Cumberland Farms Inc.
CORDIER - Musical instrument accessories ☆ - American Way Marketing Inc.
CORDINO - Shirts - Cluett, Peabody & Co.
CORDIP - Glass products ☆ - Corning Inc.
CORDLESS COMFORT - Medical apparatus - Wahl Clipper Corp.
CORDLESS CURLS - Hair curlers - Conair Corp.
CORDLESS MOUSEMAN - Computer peripheral equipment - Logitech, Inc.
CORDLESS PAINTER - Paint rollers - Wagner Spray Tech Corp.
CORDLESS ROLLER - Paint rollers - Wagner Spray Tech Corp.
CORDLEY - Coolers–electric - Elkay Manufacturing Co.
CORDLEY - Water–bottled or canned - Ozark Water Co.
CORDMATE - Electrical equipment - Wiremold Co.
CORDOBA - Floor coverings - Mannington Resilient Floors
CORDOBA - Guitars ☆ - Guild Music Corp.
CORDOBA - Luggage ☆ - Samsonite Corp.
CORDOBA - Motor vehicles–automobiles ☆ - Chrysler Corp. (Chrysler-Plymouth Div.)
CORDOBA - Motor vehicles–motor homes - Forest River, Inc.
CORDOBA - Motor vehicles–motor homes ☆ - Honey Recreational Vehicles Inc.
CORDOBA - Occasional tables ☆ - JDI Group, Inc.
CORDOBA LITE - Chimes - Nutone Inc.
CORDOHA - Beverages–alcohol - Mannekin-Brussel Imports
CORDOKINETIC - Bathing suits ☆ - Beach Patrol, Inc.
CORDON - Flatware ☆ - Dansk International Designs, Ltd.
CORDON - Thread ☆ - Perfect Thread Co. Inc.
CORDON BLEU - Cooking utensils–cast iron ☆ - Regal Ware, Inc.
CORDON BLEU - Cutlery ☆ - Lifetime Hoan Corp.
CORDON BLEU - Food products - Acme Continental Foods Inc.
CORDON BLEU - Furniture ☆ - Bassett Furniture Industries, Inc.
CORDON BLEU - Housewares stores - B.I.A. Cordon Bleu, Inc.
CORDON BLEU - Invitations - Bess Tyle Wedding Stationery Co.
CORDON BLUE - Dishes–china - Mikasa Co.
CORDON CRUZ - Wines - Arizona Vineyards
CORDON NEGRO - Wines ☆ - Freixenet USA
CORDON RICHE - Cheese ☆ - Raskas Foods, Inc.
CORDON ROUGE - Beverages–alcohol - Seagram's Chateau & Estate Wines Co.
CORDONNET - Thread - DMC Corp.
CORDOVA - Boats–motor ☆ - Four Winns Inc.
CORDOVA - Dinnerware–glass ☆ - Johnson Brothers, USA, Inc.
CORDOVA - Gloves - International Sourcing Co., Inc.
CORDOVA - Luggage ☆ - Universal Trav-ler Inc.
CORDOVA - Musical instruments - David Wexler & Co.
CORDOVA - Paper towels and toilet tissue - Laurel Hill Paper Co.
CORDOVA - Shelving units–wood ☆ - Hirsh Co.
CORDOVA - Upholstery leather ☆ - American Leather Manufacturing Co.
CORDOVAN - Tires - TBC Corp.
CORDRAN - Pharmaceutical preparations - Dista Products Co.
CORDROL - Pharmaceutical preparations - Vita Elixir Co. Inc.
CORDSPUN - Fabrics–cotton - Dan River Inc.
CORDUCT - Cordage and twine - Wiremold Co.
CORDULON - Robes - Henson-Kickernick Inc.
CORDURA - Fabrics ☆ - Eagle Creek, Inc.
CORDURA - Yarn - E.I. Dupont de Nemours and Co.
CORDURA PACKCLOTH - Fabrics - Minnetonka Mills Inc.
CORDURA PLUS - Fabrics ☆ - Eagle Creek, Inc.
CORDURO - Office supplies - JM Co.
CORDUROY - Aquatic pharmacuetical preparations ☆ - Superior Shade & Blind Co. Inc.
CORDUROY - Jewelry - Segal Collection, Ltd.
CORDUROY - Toys–stuffed - Eden LLC
CORDUROY - Wallpaper - Robert Crowder & Co.
CORDUROY BEAR - Toys ☆ - Trudy Corp.
CORDUROY-PLUS - Fabrics ☆ - Cone Mills Corp.
CORDWAINER SHOP, THE - Shoes - Cordwainer Shop
CORDWALL - Wallpaper - PCI Industries Inc.
CORDWHEEL - Hardware - Doskocil Manufacturing Co., Inc.
CORDWRAP - Hardware - Doskocil Manufacturing Co., Inc.

☆ = Now out of production

CORDY-GEN - Vitamins and nutritional supplements - Gourmet Mushrooms Inc.

CORDYMAX - Vitamins and nutritional supplements - Pharmanex, Inc.

CORE - Cleaning equipment - Core Products Co., Inc.

CORE - Computer software - Vitech Corp.

CORE - Decals and transfers - Huntsman Chemical Corp.

CORE - Electronic equipment - Broadcast Electronics, Inc.

CORE 2000 FOUNDATION SOFTWARE - Computer software - American Management Systems, Inc.

CORE-A-GATOR - Furniture - Virco Manufacturing Corp.

CORE-BOND - Adhesives and sealants - Sig Manufacturing Inc.

CORE C 500 - Vitamins and nutritional supplements - Miles Inc.

CORE COLLECTION MICROPUBLICATIONS - Publisher's imprints - Roth Publishing Inc.

CORE CONCEPTS - Apparel and accessories - Gregg Jones

CORE CONSERVE RESOURCES - Printed materials - Huntsman Chemical Corp.

CORE CRAFT - Canoe - Core Craft Inc.

CORE DISCOVERY - Computer peripheral equipment - McGettigan Corporate Planning Services

CORE GALAXY AUDIO - Sound equipment - Galaxy Audio

CORE-GUARD - Life preservers - Stearns Manufacturing Co.

CORE HARVESTER - Agricultural machinery - Ransomes-Cushman-Ryan

CORE-LEVEL - Vitamins and nutritional supplements - Nutri-West

CORE LEVEL - Vitamins and nutritional supplements - Nutrition Center, Inc.

CORE-LOCKED - Cables–fiber optic - Optical Cable Corp.

CORE-LOKT - Ammunition - E.I. Dupont de Nemours and Co.

CORE PROPERTIES - Real estate agencies - Core Properties, Inc.

CORE-SAFE - Safes - True Value Locksmith

CORE TEMP - Apparel trimmings - Patagonia, Inc.

CORE TRANSFORMATION - Recording label - NLP Comprehensive, Inc.

CORE WING - Flatware ☆ - Anchor Hocking Glass, Inc.

COREC - Mats - Ludlow Composites Corp.

CORECARE - Hair care products - Wella Corp. (Consumer Products Div.)

CORECHANGE BRIDGE - Computer software - Corechange, LLC

CORECHANGE GLOBE - Computer software - Corechange, LLC

COREDOSSIER - Computer software - Electronic Submission Publishing Systems, Inc.

COREEN - Apparel–women's - Goodview Enterprises, Ltd.

COREEN SIMPSON REGAL BEAUTY COLLECTION - Jewelry - Avon Products, Inc.

COREFAST - Concrete products - NPC Inc.

COREFICHE - Publisher's imprints - Roth Publishing Inc.

COREFUSE - Thread ☆ - United Thread Mills Corp.

COREGA - Health care products - Block Drug Co., Inc.

COREL - Computer software - Corel USA

CORELDRAW - Computer software - Corel USA

CORELESS - Thread - Perfect Thread Co. Inc.

CORELFLOW - Computer software - Corel USA

CORELIB - Computer software ☆ - Data Translation, Inc.

CORELINK - Electrical equipment - Whitaker Corp.

CORELLE - Dinnerware - Corning Inc.

CORELLE CASUALS - Dinnerware - Corning Inc.

CORELLE COORDINATES - Flatware - Regent Sheffield, Ltd.

CORELLE IMPRESSIONS - Dinnerware - Corning Inc.

CORELLE LIVINGWARE - Tableware - Corning Inc.

CORELLI - Footwear–women's - Wohl Shoe Co.

CORELXARA - Computer software - Corel USA

COREMAT - Boat building materials - Baltek Corp.

COREMAX - Hardware - FasTest Inc.

COREMOBILE - Racks - Jarke Corp.

CORENA - Lubricants - Shell Oil Co.

CORESA - Skin care products - Coresa Ltd.

CORESEW - Thread ☆ - United Thread Mills Corp.

CORESOFT - Thread - United Thread Mills Corp.

CORESPUN - Yarn - Dixie Yarns, Inc.

CORET - Apparel and accessories - Richton International Corp.

CORETACK - Insulating materials - Quiet Core Inc.

CORETEK - Animal feeds - CS Animal Feeds, Inc.

CORETTE - Underwear and nightwear - Spencer Supports Ltd.

COREWARE - Electronic equipment - Lsi Logic Corp.

COREX - Glass products - Corning Inc.

COREXIN FORTE - Pharmaceutical preparations ☆ - U.S. Ethicals Inc.

COREY - Educational materials - American Kennel Club Inc.

COREY & PATCHES - Apparel and accessories - Pamela R. Freeman

COREY OF CALIFORNIA - Apparel–women's - Middendorf Enterprises Inc.

COREY STEEL COMPANY - Metals - Corey Steel Co.

CORFI SISALANA - Twine - Malow Corp.

CORFLEX - Medical apparatus - Corflex Inc.

CORFORM - Paperboard - Westvaco Corp.

CORFOU - Vases - Durand International

CORFU - Carpets, now out of production - Couristan Inc.

CORFU - Glassware–household - Smyers Glass

CORGARD - Pharmaceutical preparations - Bristol-Myers Squibb Co.

CORGARD UNIMATIC - Pharmaceutical preparations - Bristol-Myers Squibb Co.

CORGI - Toys–models - Reeves International, Inc.

CORGONJECT-5 - Prescription drug ☆ - Merz Inc.

CORGRIP - Fencing–wood - Harsco Corp.

CORHAM - Artificial flowers and foliage - Corham Artificial Flower Co.

CORI - Recording label ☆ - Continental Recordings Inc.

CORIAN - Artists' materials - E.I. Dupont de Nemours and Co.

CORIANDRE - Perfumes - Classic Fragrances Ltd.

CORICIDIN - Cold remedies - Schering-Plough Healthcare Products

CORICIDIN D - Cold remedies - Schering-Plough Healthcare Products

CORICIDIN DEMILETS - Cold remedies - Schering-Plough Healthcare Products

CORICIDIN MEDILETS - Cold remedies - Schering-Plough Healthcare Products

CORICO - Seafood products–fresh or frozen - Southeast Foods Inc.

CORICONE 600 - Paints ☆ - Coricone Corp.

CORICONE 800 - Paints ☆ - Coricone Corp.

CORID - Veterinary pharmaceutical preparations - Merck & Co., Inc. (Merck Agvet Division)

CORIFORTE - Antihistamine preparations - Schering-Plough Healthcare Products

CORILIN - Antihistamine preparations - Schering-Plough Healthcare Products

CORIM COFFEE INTERNATIONAL - Coffee - International Coffee Imports & Exports 2INC

CORINA - Computer peripheral equipment - Oxford Molecular Group

CORINA - Food products - Tri Valley Growers, Inc.

CORINNA PLUS - Audio equipment ☆ - Telequest Inc.

CORINNE - Glassware–household ☆ - ACC

CORINNE MCCORMACK - Cases–eyeglass - Corinne McCormack, Inc.

CORINNE'S - Dips–sour cream based - Corinne's Gourmet Selections, Inc.

CORINTH - Cabinets - Imperial Cabinet Co. Inc.

CORINTH - Dinnerware–glass ☆ - Royal China & Porcelain Companies Inc.

CORINTH - Rings–jewelry - Artcarved Inc.

CORINTH - Tables–wood - Riverside Furniture Corp.

CORINTH DOWNS - Wallpaper - Surface Industries Inc.

CORINTHIA - Furniture - Stanley Furniture Co. Inc.

CORINTHIA - Glassware–household ☆ - Lotus Glass Co.

CORINTHIAN - Boats - Glen-L Marine Designs

CORINTHIAN - Boats–motor ☆ - Dolphin Boats Ltd.

CORINTHIAN - Dinnerware–glass - Nikko Ceramics Inc.

CORINTHIAN - Dishes–china - Pickard Inc.

CORINTHIAN - Dishes–china - Taylor, Smith & Taylor Co.

CORINTHIAN - Draperies - Maharam Fabric Corp.

CORINTHIAN - Floor coverings - Congoleum Corp.

CORINTHIAN - Floor coverings–carpet and rugs ☆ - Bellbridge Carpets

CORINTHIAN - Furniture - American Furniture Co. Inc.

CORINTHIAN - Furniture - Drexel Heritage Furnishings, Inc.

CORINTHIAN - Glassware–household - Seneca Glass Co.

CORINTHIAN - Hardware - National Lock Hardware

CORINTHIAN - Nautical instruments - Datamarine International Inc.

CORINTHIAN - Organizing accessories - Cobbs Manufacturing Co.

CORINTHIAN - Seafood products–fresh or frozen - R.B. & C.G. Stevens Co.

CORINTHIAN - Tobacco–chewing or smoking - Amar Blends Co.

CORINTHIAN COLLECTION 101 - Wallpaper - Scalamandre Silks Inc.

CORINTHIAN CROCKS AND PLATTERS - Cookware - Carlisle Foodservice Products, Inc.

CORINTHIAN GOLD - Hardware - Alumax Aluminum Corp.

CORINTHIAN INTERNATIONAL - Saddles - Miller Harness Co., Inc.

CORINTHIAN LEATHER CRAFTS - Luggage - United States Luggage Corp.

CORINTHIAN SUITE - Lighting fixtures - Angelo Brothers Co.

CORITA - Greeting cards ☆ - American Artists Group Inc.

CORK - Wallcoverings - Coral of Chicago

CORK BARK - Pet products - Tetra Sales USA

CORK-IT - Cork place mats and hot pads, coasters, etc. - Cork Products Manufacturing Co.

CORK-O-PLAST - Floor coverings–tile ☆ - Expanko Cork Co.

CORK PINE - Pickles - Dykhouse Pickle Co.

CORKBALL - Games - Markwort Sporting Goods Co.

CORKDECOR - Wallcoverings - Cork Products Co. Inc.

☆ = Now out of production

CORKEE - Toys - Park Plastics Co.
CORKER - Balls–baseball - J. De Beer & Son Inc.
CORKER - Brushes–paint ✩ - Linzer Products Corp.
CORKER - Fabrics–chambray - Dan River Inc.
CORKER SPRUCER - Gloves - Brookville Glove Manufacturing Co.
CORKER, THE - Golfing equipment - Wood Brothers Golf, Inc.
CORKERS - Women's shoes - International Seaway Trading Corp.
CORKETTE - Floor coverings ✩ - Congoleum Corp.
CORKEX - Corkscrews ✩ - Franmara Co. Inc.
CORKEZE - Floor coverings ✩ - Congoleum Corp.
CORKNET - Computer software - Manufacturing Technology Strategies, Inc.
CORKOPODGE JEWELRY - Craft supplies - Milton Bradley Co.
CORKSCAR - Corkscrews - Autoputter
CORKSCREW - Toys–automobiles - Mattel, Inc.
CORKSCREW - Toys–models - Estes Industries
CORKSCREWS - Pasta - Maxfor Foods Inc.
CORKTONE - Floor coverings–tile ✩ - Kentile Floors Inc.
CORKY - Cooking equipment–household - Kraftware Corp. (Morgan Div.)
CORKY - Pet products ✩ - Staff Supermarket Associates, Inc.
CORKY - Toys–stuffed - Russ Berrie and Co., Inc.
CORKY & COMPANY - Apparel stores–children's - Corky & Co.
CORKY'S - Apparel and accessories - Corky's Partners, LP
CORKY'S - Pork rinds ✩ - Savory Foods Inc.
CORLAP - Corks ✩ - Claridge Products and Equipment Inc.
CORLETTO - Jewelry - T & L Jewelry
CORLITE - Lighting components - Corning Inc.
CORLON - Metals - Coatings Lab
CORMACK - Apparel stores–sports ✩ - Gillman Knitwear Co.
CORMAN LIGHT BUTTER - Butter - Schratter Import
CORMATIC - Paper–toilet - Georgia-Pacific Corp.
CORMATIC AIRE - Cleaning preparations - Georgia-Pacific Corp.
CORMAX - Pharmaceutical preparations - Oclassen Pharmaceuticals, Inc.
CORMEDICA - Medical apparatus - Cormedica Corp.
CORN-AID - Skin care products - Halsey Drug Co. Inc.
CORN & CALLUS REDUCING CREAM - Pharmaceutical preparations - Jess Clarke & Sons Inc.
CORN-BONE - Pet food - T.F.H. Publications, Inc.
CORN BURSTS - Cereal - Malt-O-Meal Co.
CORN CHAMPS - Corn chips - Nabisco Foods Group
CORN CHEX - Cereal - Ralston Purina Co.
CORN COB - Pipes–tobacco - S.M. Frank & Co. Inc. (Kaywoodie-Yello-Bole-Medico)
CORN COB - Welding equipment - Controls Corp. of America
CORN COUNTRY - Dairy products ✩ - Sommer Maid Creamery Inc.
CORN CRIB - Pans ✩ - General Housewares Corp.
CORN DANCE CAFE - Shirts - Little Big Pie, Inc.
CORN DIGGERS - Popcorn - Nabisco Foods Group
CORN DOG CHEW - Pet food - T.F.H. Publications, Inc.
CORN-ER - Brooms - Lighthouse Industries
CORN FIX - Cosmetics - Alvin Last Inc.
CORN FLAKES -
CORN FLAKES-FLAX/OMEGA3 - Cereal - New Morn, Inc.
CORN FLOWER - Shampoos - S.C. Johnson & Son, Inc.
CORN HUSKERS LOTION - Skin care products - Warner-Wellcome
CORN KING - Meat products–canned - Wilson Foods Corp.
CORN-KITS - Breads–mixes - Morrison Milling Co.
CORN-LIK-R POPS - Candy - Gladstone Candies
CORN MOTHER - Corn chips ✩ - Col. Sanchez Foods
CORN MOTHER - Food products - Kachina Foods, Inc.
CORN OF PLENTY - Popcorn - Adobe Milling
CORN OFF THE COB - Toasted corn ✩ - Cornnuts Inc.
CORN PEARLS - Jewelry - Honora Jewelry Corp.
CORN PONE - Food products - Pierce Foods Corp.
CORN POPPER - Toys - Fisher-Price, Inc.
CORN SHUCKIN'S - Apparel and accessories - Edward C. Stevens
CORN SQUARES - Cereal - Quaker Oats Co.
CORN TARTS - Food products ✩ - 21st Century Foods Inc.
CORNALON - Skin care products ✩ - Cornrows & Co.
CORNATE - Bathroom fixtures - Crane Plumbing/Fiat Products
CORNBELT - Food products - Marketing Services Inc.
CORNE DE LA TOISON DOR - Chocolate candy ✩ - Grace A. Rush Inc.
CORNELIA - Watches - Bulova Corp.
CORNELIUS - Cereal ✩ - Kellogg Co.
CORNELL - Brushes–paint - Rubberset Co.
CORNELL - Floor coverings–carpet and rugs - Barrett Carpet Mills Inc.
CORNELL - Frames–eyeglass - U.S. Optical Frame Co.

CORNELL - Lamps, lampshades - Cornell Industries
CORNELL - Tires–automobile - Pep Boys Manny, Moe & Jack
CORNELL - Tobacco–chewing or smoking - Cornell & Diehl Inc.
CORNELL - Veterinary medical equipment - Popper & Sons Inc.
CORNELL II - Floor coverings–carpet and rugs - Patrick Carpet Mills
CORNELL IMPORTER - Glassware–household - H.C. Meyers Co.
CORNELL MARITIME PRESS INC. - Publisher's imprints - Cornell Maritime Press Inc.
CORNELLOKI - Bags - ACC Enterprises, LLC
CORNER-22 - Bathtubs–enameled - Pearl Baths Inc.
CORNER BUDDY - Ladders–metal - Kennett Corp.
CORNER CLEANER - Brushes - Wooster Brush Co.
CORNER-CLIP - File folders - Ameriforms Inc.
CORNER CUPBOARD - Craft supplies - Corner Cupboard Crafts Inc.
CORNER CUTTER - Knives–putty ✩ - Padco Companies, Inc.
CORNER DELI - Bakery products - DCB, Inc.
CORNER DELI CUISINE - Food products - American Stores Co.
CORNER ENFORCER - Plastics - Michael J. Watson
CORNER FORMER - Hardware ✩ - United Steel Products Co.
CORNER-GUARD - Pet products - Novalek, Inc.
CORNER GUARDS OF AMERICA - Hardware - Palm Beach Plastics Inc.
CORNER JACKETS - Frames–picture - Framemica Co.
CORNER-LOK - Building materials–concrete - AA Wire Products Co.
CORNER MARX-IT, THE - Giftware - Betty Rose Shelton
CORNER MASTER - Drills–electric - Matsushita Electric Corp. of America
CORNER OFFICE - Office supplies - Office Depot, Inc.
CORNER POCKET - Billiard-lounge franchise, pool tables, chairs, etc. - Corner Pockets of America Inc.
CORNER POCKETS - Vinyl - Sign-Up Corp.
CORNER SAVERS - Hardware - K.J. Miller Corp.
CORNER SHIELD - Paint rollers - Mr. Paintshield Inc.
CORNER STACKER - Shelving units–wood ✩ - Hirsh Co.
CORNER STONE - Handbags - Meijer, Inc.
CORNER TAPER - Tape–adhesive - Wall Tool & Tape Corp
CORNER-VISTA - Cabinets - Nutone Inc.
CORNER WELD - Glue–household or industrial - Framemica Co.
CORNERAMIC - Fireplaces ✩ - Superior Fireplace Co.
CORNERGARDS - Packaging–paper - Western Pulp Products Co.
CORNERITS - Brackets - Oldowan Co., LLC
CORNERSTONE - Animal feed - Purina Mills, Inc.
CORNERSTONE - Bread mixes - International Multifoods Corp.
CORNERSTONE - Building materials - Mutual Materials Co.
CORNERSTONE - Computer software - Activision, Inc.
CORNERSTONE - Dinnerware - Corning Inc.
CORNERSTONE - Drapery hardware ✩ - Spring Window Fashions Division, Inc.
CORNERSTONE - Floor coverings - B.F. Goodrich Co.
CORNERSTONE - Floor coverings - Mannington Resilient Floors
CORNERSTONE - Floor coverings–carpet and rugs - Ashley Commercial Carpets
CORNERSTONE - Floor coverings–carpet and rugs - Criterion Mills Inc.
CORNERSTONE - Floor coverings–carpet and rugs - Quaker Inc.
CORNERSTONE - Furniture ✩ - Bassett Furniture Industries, Inc.
CORNERSTONE - Hosiery - Meijer, Inc.
CORNERSTONE - Toys–models - Wm. K. Walthers Inc.
CORNERSTONE - Wallpaper - Koroseal Wallcoverings
CORNERSTONE CARDS - Greeting cards - McBeth Corp.
CORNERSTONE CELLARS - Wines - Cornerstone Cellars, Inc.
CORNERSTONE COMMENTARIES - Publisher's imprints ✩ - Harold Shaw Publishers
CORNERSTONE LIBRARY INC. - Publisher's imprints - Fireside Books
CORNERSTONE OAK - Furniture - Athens Furniture Industries Inc.
CORNET - Tables–metal ✩ - Cramer Inc.
CORNETS - Pet products - Nutritional Research Associates Inc.
CORNETTS - Toasted corn ✩ - Cornnuts Inc.
CORNEX - Pharmaceutical preparations - Premier Brands of America
CORNEY & BARROW - Beverages–alcohol ✩ - Sazerac Co. Inc.
CORNFETTI - Popcorn - National Oats Co. Inc.
CORNFLOWER - Cutlery ✩ - Lifetime Hoan Corp.
CORNFLOWER - Glass products - Corning Inc.
CORNFLOWER - Tools ✩ - Regent Sheffield, Ltd.
CORNFUCIUS SAY - Posters - Cross at the Green...Not in Between Enterprises
CORNHUSKER - Breads - Serv-Rite Meat Co.
CORNHUSKER - Food products - Nash-Finch Co.
CORNHUSKER LAGER - Beverages–malt - Heartland Brewery, Inc.

CORNICE - Brushes - Wright-Bernet
CORNICE - Dinnerware–glass ☆ - Nikko Ceramics Inc.
CORNICE - Ski apparel - Inside Edge
CORNICE BOARDS - Artists' materials - Plaid Enterprises, Inc.
CORNICHE - Apparel and accessories - Lyns Corp.
CORNICHE - Floor coverings–carpet and rugs - Masland Corp.
CORNICHE - Motor vehicles–automobiles - Rolls-Royce Motors Inc.
CORNICHE - Tables–wood - Henredon Furniture Industries Inc.
CORNICI MILANO COLLECTION - Frames–picture - Fetco International Corp.
CORNIES - Snack foods - Borden, Inc.
CORNING - Glass products - Corning Inc.
CORNING - Kitchen utensils–aluminum - Reston Lloyd Ltd.
CORNING COLLECTION - Sunglasses - Corning Inc.
CORNING DESIGNS - Dinnerware - Corning Inc.
CORNING LIFESTYLES - Dinnerware - Corning Inc.
CORNING WARE - Cookware - Corning Inc.
CORNINGWEAR - Apparel and accessories - Corning Inc.
CORNISH ROYAL FARMS - Meat products - Cornish Royal Farms Ltd.
CORNMALE - Food products - A Natural Harvest Inc.
CORNMASTER - Health care products - Fleetwood Co.
CORNMATES - Health care products - A Natural Harvest Inc.
CORNNUTS - Toasted corn - Cornnuts Inc.
CORNO - Dog food ☆ - Stevens Industries Inc.
CORNOLA - Corn oil - Food Oils Corp.
CORNPAK - Packaging–paper - Innovative Packaging Corp.
CORNPRIDE - Recording label - Jazz Composer's Orchestra Association Inc.
CORNQUISTOS - Snack foods - Mars, Inc.
CORNSILK - Cosmetics - Chattem Inc.
CORNSILK - Dinnerware ☆ - Corning Inc.
CORNSTALK - Fabrics - Dan River Inc.
CORNSTALKERS - Footwear - Rocky Shoes & Boots, Inc.
CORNSWEET - Corn syrup - Clinton Corn Starch Co.
CORNTILLAS - Snack foods - Garden of Eatin', Inc.
CORNTOP - Bakery products ☆ - Gardener Baking Co.
CORNUCOPIA - Clocks - General Time Corp. (Westclox/Seth Thomas Div.)
CORNUCOPIA - Cookware - Metro/Thebe, Inc.
CORNUCOPIA - Dishes–china - Waterford Wedgewood USA, Inc.
CORNUCOPIA - Fruit, cider - Cornucopia Farms
CORNUCOPIA - Incense - Hanna's Potpourri Specialties, Inc.
CORNUCOPIA - Pet products - Cornucopia Express
CORNUCOPIA ADVANTAGE - Animal feeds - Cornucopia Natural Pet Foods
CORNUCOPIA SUPER START - Dog food - Cornucopia Natural Pet Foods
CORNUCRESCINE - Veterinary pharmaceutical preparations - St. Lawrence Sales Inc.
CORNWALL - Clocks ☆ - General Time Corp. (Westclox/Seth Thomas Div.)
CORNWALL - Early American woodenware - Cornwall Industries Inc.
CORNWALL - Flatware - Utica Cutlery Co.
CORNWALL - Medical apparatus - Becton, Dickinson and Co.
CORNWALL - Wood products - Himark Enterprises Inc.
CORNWALL ARMS - Cigars - A.J. Golden Inc.
CORNWALL CLASSICS - Clocks - Cornwall Industries Inc.
CORNWALL COLLECTION - Furniture ☆ - Kaylyn Inc.
CORNWALL COTTAGE COLLECTION, THE - Collectible miniature homes - International Resourcing Services, Inc.
CORNWALL ORCHARDS - Fruits and vegetables - Mike Norinsberg Manufacturing Inc.
CORNWICH - Sandwiches–prepackaged - American Ethnic Foods Corp.
CORNY BAGS - Popcorn - Matrixx Marketing, Inc.
CORNY CREATIONS - Cooking utensils–aluminum ☆ - Regal Ware, Inc.
CORNY PIPFIELDS - Popcorn - Ellison Bakery Inc.
CORNY SUCKERS - Candy - Gladstone Candies
CORO - Cigars - Gesty Trading & Manufacturing Corp.
CORO - Costume jewelry ☆ - Robert Rose
CORO-FUEL - Compressors - Corken, Inc.
CORO-GRAPHICS - Maps - Bemiss-Jason Corp.
CORO-KLAD - Apparel and accessories - Richton International Corp.
CORO U.S.A. - Jewelry–costume ☆ - Jewelry Fashions Inc.
COROBELLA - Cigars - Gesty Trading & Manufacturing Corp.
COROBOND - Mortars–clay ☆ - Master Builders Inc.
COROBUFF - Paper - Bemiss-Jason Corp.
COROCRAFT - Costume jewelry ☆ - Robert Rose
COROCRETE - Floor coverings - Master Builders Inc.
CORODEL - Trees - Brandt's Fruit Trees, Inc.
CORODYL FORTE - Pharmaceutical preparations ☆ - Bock Pharmacal Co.
COROLAC - Sporting goods - Franklin Sports, Inc.
COROLINE - Sealing compounds - Master Builders Inc.

COROLLA - Cosmetics - Vina Cosmetics Inc.
COROLLA - Motor vehicles–automobiles - Toyota Motor Sales USA Inc.
COROLLA - Tableware–china - Villeroy and Boch Tableware Ltd.
COROLLA FX16 - Motor vehicles–automobiles - Toyota Motor Sales USA Inc.
COROLLA SPORT - Motor vehicles–automobiles - Toyota Motor Sales USA Inc.
COROLLARY - Computer peripheral equipment - Corollary, Inc.
COROLLE - Glassware–household - Durand International
COROLLE - Toys ☆ - BRIO Corp.
COROLUX - Paints - Davis Paint Co.
COROMACON - Circuit boards–printed - Smith Corona Corp.
COROMETRICS - Medical equipment - Corometrics Medical Systems Inc.
CORON PERE & FILS - Wines ☆ - Pellegrini Bros. Wines Inc.
CORONA - Beverages–malt - Canandaigua Wine Co. Inc.
CORONA - Beverages–malt - Joseph Victori Wines Inc.
CORONA - Brushes–paint ☆ - PPG Industries, Inc.
CORONA - Cheese - Golden Cheese Co. of California
CORONA - Floor coverings - American Floor Products Co. Inc.
CORONA - Floor coverings - Mannington Resilient Floors
CORONA - Food processors - Nabisco Foods Group
CORONA - Food products - Chiquita Brands, Inc.
CORONA - Furniture ☆ - Mersman Furniture Co.
CORONA - Gardening tools - Harrow Products Inc.
CORONA - Glassware–household ☆ - National Housewares
CORONA - Housewares - Doranne
CORONA - Kitchen utensils–enameled ☆ - R & R Mill Co. Inc.
CORONA - Meat products–beef - Nathan Schweitzer & Co.
CORONA - Motor vehicles–automobiles ☆ - Toyota Motor Sales USA Inc.
CORONA - Pepper mills - Franmara Co. Inc.
CORONA - Projection screens - Claridge Products and Equipment Inc.
CORONA - Rings–jewelry - Artcarved Inc.
CORONA - Sinks–porcelain - Artesian Industries
CORONA - Stationery - Ginn Card & Paper Co. Inc.
CORONA - Tables–wood - Riverside Furniture Corp.
CORONA - Tiles–ceramic - Federal Tile Imports Inc.
CORONA - Tiles–ceramic ☆ - Dal-Tile Corp.
CORONA - Tools–garden - Lawn & Garden Supply Co.
CORONA - Typewriters - Smith Corona Corp.
CORONA - Veterinary pharmaceutical preparations - Summit Industries, Inc.
CORONA II - Accordions - Hohner Inc.
CORONA BRASIL - Cigars - Gesty Trading & Manufacturing Corp.
CORONA CLIPPER - Tools–pruning - Harrow Products Inc.
CORONA DECO - Giftware - Corona Decor Co.
CORONA DEL MAR - Seafood products–fresh or frozen - Demerico Corp.
CORONA D'ORO - Wines - Wine Imports Ltd.
CORONA EXTRA - Beverages–malt - Barton Brands, Ltd.
CORONA IMMENSAS - Cigars - G.W. Van Slyke & Horton
CORONA PROFESSIONAL - Tools–pruning - Harrow Products Inc.
CORONACALC - Computer software - Smith Corona Corp.
CORONADO - Apparel–men's - J. Schoeneman Inc.
CORONADO - Bathroom accessories - Nutone Inc.
CORONADO - Bicycles - Raleigh USA Bicycle Co.
CORONADO - Boats - Catalina Yachts Inc.
CORONADO - Boats–motor - Century Boat Co.
CORONADO - Building materials - Coronado Stone Co.
CORONADO - Chairs–upholstered - United Chair Co., Inc.
CORONADO - Cooking utensils–cast iron ☆ - National Housewares
CORONADO - Fireplaces - Dyna Corp.
CORONADO - Floor coverings - American Floor Products Co. Inc.
CORONADO - Floor coverings–carpet and rugs - Mandate-Dawn Carpet Mills
CORONADO - Floor coverings–carpet and rugs ☆ - Catalina Carpet Mills Inc.
CORONADO - Furniture - Lane Co. Inc.
CORONADO - Glassware–household - Federal Glass
CORONADO - Golfing equipment - Acushnet Co.
CORONADO - Jewelry - Uncas Manufacturing Co.
CORONADO - Kitchen appliances - Gamble-Skogmo Inc.
CORONADO - Manufactured homes - Redman Industries, Inc.
CORONADO - Motor vehicles–motor homes ☆ - Beaver Coaches Inc.
CORONADO - Motor vehicles–motor homes ☆ - Honey Recreational Vehicles Inc.
CORONADO - Paints - Budeke's Paint
CORONADO - Paper–writing ☆ - Canson-Talens Inc.
CORONADO - Shrimp–canned or cured - Darik Enterprises Inc.
CORONADO - Stone veneer, tiles - Coronado Products Inc.
CORONADO - Trailers–travel - Fleetwood Enterprises, Inc.
CORONADO - Trailers–travel ☆ - Hop-Cap Inc.

☆ = Now out of production

CORONADO - Weather tracking equipment - Airguide Instrument Co.
CORONADO - Window shades - Castec Window Shading Inc.
CORONADO - Window shades - Protech Shading Inc.
CORONADO 6 - Bicycles ☆ - Raleigh USA Bicycle Co.
CORONADO 15 - Boats - Catalina Yachts Inc.
CORONADO BEACH - Floor coverings—carpet and rugs - Catalina Carpet Mills Inc.
CORONADO DUALS - Boats ☆ - Raritan Engineering Co. Inc.
CORONADO PRODUCTS - Stone products - Melton L. Bacon
CORONADO SST - Paper—bond - Fox River Paper Co.
CORONADOS - Cereal ☆ - General Mills, Inc.
CORONAFAX - Facsimile equipment - Smith Corona Corp.
CORONAFONT - Computer software - Smith Corona Corp.
CORONAJET - Printers—computer - Smith Corona Corp.
CORONAPRINT - Office supplies - Smith Corona Corp.
CORONAS - Cigars - G.A. Georgopulo & Co. Inc.
CORONAS CHICAS - Cigar boxes—wood - Consolidated Cigar Corp.
CORONAS QUEENS - Cigar boxes—wood - Consolidated Cigar Corp.
CORONATION - Christmas tree ornaments - Cracker Box Inc.
CORONATION - Cooking utensils—aluminum ☆ - Regal Ware, Inc.
CORONATION - Dinnerware—glass - Sango Co. Ltd. (Sango USA Div.)
CORONATION - Floor coverings—carpet and rugs - Calladium & Marglen
CORONATION - Furniture ☆ - Hammary Furniture Co. Inc.
CORONATION - Furniture ☆ - Keller Manufacturing Co.
CORONATION - Greeting cards ☆ - Doehla Greeting Cards Inc.
CORONATION - Watches - Longines-Wittnauer Watch Co.
CORONATION CHESS - Chessboards ☆ - Milton Bradley Co.
CORONATION II-D - Bells and chimes - Schulmerich Carillons Inc.
CORONELLA - Cigar boxes—wood - Consolidated Cigar Corp.
CORONET - Barometers - Airguide Instrument Co.
CORONET - Brushes—paint ☆ - PPG Industries, Inc.
CORONET - Cigarettes - Brown & Williamson Tobacco Corp.
CORONET - Cooking equipment—household - Regal Ware, Inc.
CORONET - Cooking utensils—enameled - Jacksonville Manufacturing
CORONET - Cosmetics - Coronet International
CORONET - Dishes—china ☆ - Royal China & Porcelain Companies Inc.
CORONET - Dishwashing compounds - PYA/Monarch Inc.
CORONET - Fabrics - Guilford Mills, Inc.
CORONET - Filing cabinets ☆ - Corry Hiebert
CORONET - Floor coverings - Mannington Resilient Floors
CORONET - Floor coverings—carpet and rugs - Coronet Carpets Inc.
CORONET - Footwear—athletic - Vans, Inc.
CORONET - Footwear—men's - L.B. Evans' Son Co.
CORONET - Fruits and vegetables - Dole Citrus
CORONET - Furniture - Weiman Co.
CORONET - Furniture ☆ - Hammary Furniture Co. Inc.
CORONET - Glassware—household - Federal Glass
CORONET - Hardware ☆ - TurnaSure LLC
CORONET - Holloware ☆ - Corbell & Co.
CORONET - Housewares - Doranne
CORONET - Ice cream - H.P. Hood & Sons Inc.
CORONET - Lawn mowers - Teknor Apex Co.
CORONET - Luggage ☆ - Maximillian Luggage Corp.
CORONET - Motor vehicles ☆ - Chrysler Corp. (Dodge Car Div.)
CORONET - Office supplies ☆ - Bates Manufacturing Co.
CORONET - Paper—toilet - Georgia-Pacific Corp.
CORONET - Pet products - Excel-Mineral Co. Inc.
CORONET - Photo albums - Holson Co.
CORONET - Printing trades machinery - Vidac
CORONET - Projectors—photographic - Rollei of America Inc.
CORONET - Sports rackets and accessories ☆ - Victor Sports
CORONET - Stationery ☆ - Mead Corp.
CORONET - Stationery ☆ - Nu-Art Inc.
CORONET - Tires - Armtec Industries Inc.
CORONET - Wallets ☆ - Enger-Kress Co.
CORONET - Watches - Bulova Corp.
CORONET - Wheels - Faultless Caster Co.
CORONET BIG 'N PRETTY - Napkins—paper - Georgia-Pacific Corp.
CORONET BOND - Envelopes ☆ - Quality Park Products Co.
CORONET BRAID - Yarn - Rainbow Gallery, Inc.
CORONET CRESTWOOD - Motor vehicles ☆ - Chrysler Corp. (Dodge Car Div.)
CORONET MICROWAVE - Paper towels - Georgia-Pacific Corp.
CORONET PRESS - Music—sheet - Theodore Presser Co.
CORONET SOFT ON SOFT - Paper—toilet - Georgia-Pacific Corp.
CORONET THIRSTY - Paper—toweling - Georgia-Pacific Corp.

CORONET ULTRA - Cooking equipment—household - Regal Ware, Inc.
CORONETTES - Boxed invitations - Coronet General Corp.
CORONETTI BY STEFANO - Footwear - Circle Shoe Co.
CORONIUM - Tools—pruning - Harrow Products Inc.
CORONOTES - Boxed stationery ☆ - Coronet General Corp.
COROPAK - Polyethylene panels - Coroplast Inc.
COROPLAST - Panels - Harbor Sales Co.
COROPLAST - Sheet plastic - Coroplast Inc.
COROPLAST+PLUS - Sheet plastic - Coroplast Inc.
COROSHELL - Paints - Davis Paint Co.
COROX - Heating equipment - Robertshaw Controls Co.
CORPA.D.S. - Computer software - Financial Decision Systems, Inc.
CORPFACT - Computer software - Financial Decision Systems, Inc.
CORPINTERNATIONAL - Computer software - Financial Decision Systems, Inc.
CORPORANT - Skin care products - Lendan USA Co.
CORPORATE - Floor coverings—carpet and rugs - Patrick Carpet Mills
CORPORATE CASE - Ledgers - Carolina Marking Devices, Inc.
CORPORATE CENTRE - Floor coverings—carpet and rugs - Lees Carpets
CORPORATE CENTRE - Floor coverings—carpet and rugs ☆ - Mannington Carpets, Inc.
CORPORATE CHALLENGE - Apparel and accessories - Chemical Bank
CORPORATE CIRCLE - Floor coverings - Matworks
CORPORATE COLLECTION - Binders ☆ - ACCO USA, Inc.
CORPORATE CONCEPTS - Floor coverings—carpet and rugs - Sheridan Carpet Mills
CORPORATE COURTESIES - Stationery - Corporate Courtesies Inc.
CORPORATE ELEGANCE - Floor coverings—carpet and rugs - J and J Industries Inc.
CORPORATE FRAMEWORK - Computer software - Financial Executives Institute
CORPORATE IMAGE - Cleaning preparations - Pioneer/Eclipse Corp.
CORPORATE IMAGE - Floor coverings—carpet and rugs - Lotus Carpets
CORPORATE IMAGE - Floor coverings—carpet and rugs ☆ - J and J Industries Inc.
CORPORATE IMAGE - Floor coverings—carpet and rugs ☆ - Whitecrest Carpet Mills
CORPORATE IMAGE - Novelty items - Pence Industries
CORPORATE IMAGES - Office supplies - Artistic Office Products
CORPORATE IMPRESSIONS - Posters - Successories, Inc.
CORPORATE LADDER - Computer software ☆ - IMSI
CORPORATE MEMORY SYSTEMS - Computer software - Corporate Memory Systems, Inc.
CORPORATE NETWORK - Computer software - UAI Technology Inc.
CORPORATE PRIDE - Floor coverings—carpet and rugs ☆ - Callaway Carpets
CORPORATE SOLUTIONS - Glass products - Kusak Cut Glass Works
CORPORATE SQUARE II - Floor coverings—carpet and rugs - Milliken & Co. Inc.
CORPORATE SUITE - Floor coverings—carpet and rugs ☆ - Customweave Carpets Inc.
CORPORATE SYSTEMS - Computer software - Corporate Systems, Ltd.
CORPORATE SYSTEMS THE RISK MANAGEMENT EDGE - Computer software - Corporate Systems, Ltd.
CORPORATE TALKRADIO FROM SCHORR COMMUNICATIONS - Broadcasting stations—radio - Schorr Communications, Inc.
CORPORATE TWILL - Floor coverings—carpet and rugs ☆ - J and J Industries Inc.
CORPORATE VISION - Computer software - IntelligenceWare Inc.
CORPORATION JOB GAME, THE - Computer software - Career Development Software
CORPS DIPLOMATIQUE - Cigars - Lane Ltd.
CORPSALES - Computer software - Financial Decision Systems, Inc.
CORPSMASTER - Musical instruments - Vic Firth Inc.
CORQUE - Pharmaceutical preparations - Geneva Generics Inc.
CORR-A-FLEX - Health care products - Hudson Respiratory Care Inc.
CORR-A-TUBE - Health care products - Hudson Respiratory Care Inc.
CORRADO - Motor vehicles—automobiles - Volkswagen of America Inc.
CORRADO - Occasional tables ☆ - JDI Group, Inc.
CORRADO'S - Cheese - Corrado's Specialty Goods, Inc.
CORRAL - Agricultural products - Countrymark Cooperative, Inc.
CORRAL - Meat products—poultry - Pfizer Inc.
CORRAL CRITTERS - Toys—stuffed - Dakin Inc.
CORRAL DE PIEDRA - Wines ☆ - Chamisal Vineyard
CORRDATA - Corrosion measurement instruments - Rohrback Cosasco Systems, Inc.
CORRDELIV - Machine tools - Geo. M. Martin Co.

CORRECT - Envelopes–paper - Cavert Wire Co. Inc.

CORRECT - Skin care products - Elementals Skin Care, LLC

CORRECT-A-CHROME - Photographic equipment ☆ - Edwal Scientific Products Corp.

CORRECT BITE - Dental compounds - Jeneric/Pentron Inc.

CORRECT-N-COPY - Ribbons–inked ☆ - Leedall Products Manufacturing Co.

CORRECT-O - Ribbons–inked ☆ - Eaton Allen Ko-Rec-Type Corp.

CORRECT PAC - Detergents - PortionPac Chemical Corp.

CORRECT PH 7.0 - Aquariums–household - Jungle Laboratories Corp.

CORRECT PROPORTION - Vitamins and nutritional supplements - Healthy 'N Fit Nutritionals

CORRECT SEATING - Furniture ☆ - Knoll Group

CORRECTEMP - Refrigeration system - Elliott-Williams Co. Inc.

CORRECTETTE - Correction fluid - Wirth International Inc.

CORRECTEURSTEINT - Cosmetics - Sothys USA Inc.

CORRECTEX - Hair care products - PCG Hair Products

CORRECTION KEY - Ribbons–inked - Leedall Products Manufacturing Co.

CORRECTIVE - Skin care products - Sacha International

CORRECTIVES - Face powder and makeup - Coty Inc.

CORRECTLY SIZING TABLECLOTHS - Paper products - At Work Sales Corp.

CORRECTOL - Laxatives - Schering-Plough Healthcare Products

CORRECTOL - Teas–herbal - Schering-Plough Healthcare Products, Inc.

CORRECTORS, THE - Hair care products - Wella Corp. (Consumer Products Div.)

CORRECTRONIC - Typewriters - Brother International Corp.

CORRECTSTAR - Computer software ☆ - WordStar International Inc.

CORRELATE - Computer software - General Electric Co.

CORRELATE CORNERS - Furniture - Universal Flooring

CORRELATION - Furniture–upholstered - Maharam Vertical Surfaces

CORRELATION - Steel modular furniture ☆ - Corry Hiebert

CORRELATIONAL - Computer software - Concord Communications Inc.

CORRELATIONS - Skin care products - Correlations Inc.

CORRELITES - Lamps - La-Z-Boy Chair Co.

CORRER CON LOS TOROS - Apparel and accessories - Edward A. Suska

CORRERE - Office furniture–wood - Sligh Furniture Co.

CORRESPOND - Paper - Mead Corp.

CORRESPONDENT - Binders ☆ - 20th Century Plastics

CORRETORA - Fish–fresh or frozen - J. Moniz Co.

CORRIDOR - Games - Flying Buffalo Inc.

CORRIDOR - Office furniture–wood - Sligh Furniture Co.

CORRIDOR 7 - Computer software - Capstone Software

CORRIDOR BASE - Floor coverings–carpet and rugs - Milliken & Co. Inc.

CORRIDOR CONNECTION - Floor coverings–carpet and rugs - Milliken & Co. Inc.

CORRIGANS - Jewelry - Zale Corp.

CORRINA - Floor coverings–carpet and rugs - Evans-Black Carpet Mills

CORRINNE - Toys - Tonka Corp.

CORRITRONICS - Lighting fixtures ☆ - Guth Lighting

CORRMATE - Plastics film - Superior Tape Corp.

CORRMATE PPS - Tape–masking - Superior Tape Corp.

CORRO PRIME - Paints - Sinclair Paint Co.

CORRO-PRIME - Primers - Kelly-Moore Paint Co., Inc.

CORRO-STOP - Paints - Frazee Paint

CORROBAR - Paints - Dunn Edwards Corp.

CORROPLAS - Adhesives and sealants ☆ - Plastics & Resins Ltd.

CORROSEAL - Paints - Corroseal, Inc.

CORROSION BUSTER PEN - Rust removers - Star Brite

CORROSION CAT - Paints - Triangle Coatings Inc.

CORROSION GARD - Hardware - Truth Hardware Corp.

CORROSION PROTECTION SYSTEM, THE - Paints - Plasti-Kote Co. Inc.

CORROSION SHIELD - Coatings - Sherwin-Williams Automotive Finishes Corp.

CORROSIONX - Rustproofing compounds - Corrosion Technologies, Corp.

CORROSITE - Paints - Reliance Paint Co. Inc.

CORROSORBERS - Rustproofing compounds - Cortec Corp.

CORROTONE - Paints - Reliance Paint Co. Inc.

CORR'S - Soft drinks - Corr's Natural Beverages Inc.

CORRSYS - Electrical equipment - Datron Technology, Inc.

CORRU-CARPET - Mats–rattan - Samuel Furiness Mat Co.

CORRU-FILL - Packaging material - Bio-Grade, Inc.

CORRU KOTE - Paperboard - Mead Corp.

CORRUGATED RUBBER - Floor coverings - Ludlow Composites Corp.

CORRUGATED SWITCHBOARD - Floor coverings - Ludlow Composites Corp.

CORRULUX - Hardware ☆ - Sequentia Inc. (Reinforced Plastics Div.)

CORRY JAMESTOWN - Furniture ☆ - Corry Hiebert

CORSA - Floor coverings–carpet and rugs - Providence Rug Co.

CORSA-GIRDLE - Girdles - Vanity Corset Co. Inc.

CORSA GT - Tires - Goodyear Tire & Rubber Co.

CORSABELT - Girdles - Vanity Corset Co. Inc.

CORSAGE - Dishes–china ☆ - WMF/USA

CORSAGE - Floor coverings–carpet and rugs - Glen Eden Wool Carpets

CORSAGE - Furniture–upholstered ☆ - Mersman Furniture Co.

CORSAGE - Rings–jewelry - Artcarved Inc.

CORSAIR - Boats - Wellcraft Marine Corp.

CORSAIR - Boats–motor - Seaswirl Boats Inc.

CORSAIR - Boats–motor ☆ - Lund Boat Co.

CORSAIR - Clocks - General Time Corp. (Westclox/Seth Thomas Div.)

CORSAIR - Compasses–gyroscopic ☆ - Rule Industries, Inc.

CORSAIR - Floor coverings–carpet and rugs - Patcraft Mills Inc.

CORSAIR - Frames–eyeglass - Universal/Univis Inc.

CORSAIR - Furniture–wood - Empire Furniture Co.

CORSAIR - Guitars - Fred Gretsch Enterprises

CORSAIR - Luggage ☆ - Samsonite Corp.

CORSAIR - Mats - Matworks

CORSAIR - Motor vehicles–motor homes - Thor Industries West

CORSAIR - Paint sprayers - Wagner Spray Tech Corp.

CORSAIR - Pencils - National Pen & Pencil Co.

CORSAIR - Tools - Great Neck Saw Manufacturers, Inc.

CORSAIR - Toys–models - Cox Products Inc.

CORSAIR - Toys–models ☆ - Estes Industries

CORSAIR - Trailers–travel ☆ - Commodore Corp.

CORSAIRE - Furnaces–electric - Rheem Manufacturing Co.

CORSAK - Thread ☆ - American & Efird, Inc.

CORSARA SPORT - Scooters–children's - Peg Perego USA Inc.

CORSARO - Bicycles and accessories - Corsaro Imports Inc.

CORSENDONK MONK'S BROWN ALE - Beverages–malt - Phoenix Imports Ltd.

CORSENDONK MONK'S PALE ALE - Beverages–malt - Phoenix Imports Ltd.

CORSETTA - Thread - United Thread Mills Corp.

CORSICA - Area rugs - Couristan Inc.

CORSICA - Boats - Wellcraft Marine Corp.

CORSICA - Coffee - La Colombe Torrefaction, Inc.

CORSICA - Flatware - Wallace International Silversmiths, Inc.

CORSICA - Floor coverings–carpet and rugs ☆ - Kelly Group Inc.

CORSICA - Furniture ☆ - Hammary Furniture Co. Inc.

CORSICA - Hot tubs–fiberglass ☆ - Jacuzzi Inc.

CORSICA - Housewares - Himark Enterprises Inc.

CORSICA - Motor vehicles - General Motors Corp. (Chevrolet Motor Div.)

CORSICA - Trailers–travel - Forest River, Inc.

CORSICA LTZ - Motor vehicles - General Motors Corp. (Chevrolet Motor Div.)

CORSICAN - Rings–jewelry - Artcarved Inc.

CORSICANA - Floor coverings - Congoleum Corp.

CORSINI - Jewelry - Uncas Manufacturing Co.

CORSO - Accordions - Hohner Inc.

CORSO - Bicycles - Corso Bicycle Distributor Inc.

CORSO - Dinnerware–glass - WMF/USA

CORSO - Sardines–canned - M.H. Greenebaum Inc.

CORSTAR - Glass products ☆ - Corning Inc.

CORSTONE - Sinks–plastic - Corstone

CORSTREAM - Computer software - Artisoft, Inc.

CORSYM - Antihistamine preparations ☆ - Fisons Corp.

CORT - Guitars - Westheimer Corp.

CORT BLOC - Pharmaceutical preparations - Robert Fritz

CORT-QUIN - Pharmaceutical preparations ☆ - Miles Inc.

CORTA-FLEX - Combs - Stylors Inc.

CORTABA - Pharmaceutical preparations - Upjohn Co.

CORTAGEL - Hydrocortisone - Norstar Consumer Products Co., Inc.

CORTAID - Pharmaceutical preparations - Upjohn Co.

CORTALOG - Pharmaceutical preparations ☆ - R.A. McNeil Co.

CORTAS - Dips–sour cream based - Mira International Foods Inc.

CORTAS - Marmalade - Cortas Canning and Refrigerating Co.

CORTATRIAGEN - Health care products - Goldline Laboratories, Inc.

CORTECH - Pharmaceutical preparations - Cortech, Inc.

CORTEF - Pharmaceutical preparations - Upjohn Co.

CORTEL BRANDY - Brandy - Marie Brizard Wines & Spirits, USA

CORTENEMA - Health care products - Solvay Pharmaceuticals Inc.

CORTE'S SPECIALS - Sausages - Corte & Co.

CORTESIA - Floor coverings–carpet and rugs ☆ - Evans-Black Carpet Mills

CORTET - Computer software - Cortet, Inc.

CORTEX - Bulletin boards–cork ☆ - Claridge Products and Equipment Inc.

CORTEX - Computer software - Cortex Corp.

CORTEX - Hair coloring preparations - Stylors Inc.

CORTEX - Health care products - Medical World Inc.

CORTEXPROTEIN - Chemical preparations - Brooks Industries, Inc.
CORTEXX - Hair care products - Alberto-Culver Co.
CORTEZ - Bicycles - Huffy Corp.
CORTEZ - Boats–motor ✫ - Century Boat Co.
CORTEZ - Brushes - Corona Brushes Inc.
CORTEZ - Footwear–athletic - Nike, Inc.
CORTEZ - Guitars - Westheimer Corp.
CORTEZ - Hardware - Emhart Inc.
CORTEZ - Motor vehicle parts and accessories ✫ - Krantz Building Systems
CORTEZ CORONITAS - Cigars - House of Bland
CORTIC - Pharmaceutical preparations - Everett Laboratories Inc.
CORTICAINE - Laxatives - Glaxo Wellcome Inc.
CORTICALM - Pharmaceutical preparations - DVM Pharmaceuticals, Inc.
CORTICELLI - Thread ✫ - Lily Craft Products
CORTICON-C - Pharmaceutical preparations - G.O. Spanner Inc.
CORTICREME - Pharmaceutical - American Pharmaceutical Co.
CORTICURE - Lotions - BC International Cosmetics & Image Services, Inc.
CORTIFOAM - Health care products - Reed & Carnrick
CORTIGEL - Pharmaceutical preparations ✫ - Savage Laboratories Inc.
CORTIKAY - Health care products ✫ - Kay Pharmacal Co. Inc.
CORTIN 1% - Pharmaceutical preparations ✫ - C&M Pharmacal, Inc.
CORTINA - Candy - Nabisco Foods Group
CORTINA - Food products ✫ - Westdale Foods Co.
CORTINA - Frames–eyeglass - Zylo Ware Corp.
CORTINA - Furniture - Broyhill Furniture Industries, Inc.
CORTINA - Furniture–children's ✫ - Child Craft Industries Inc.
CORTINA - Handwork supplies - Bernat Yarn & Craft Corp.
CORTINA - Hardware ✫ - Amerock Corp.
CORTINA - Mattresses and box springs - Ohio Mattress Co.
CORTINA - Recording label - R.D. Cortina Co.
CORTINA - Sporting goods - Mel Pinto Imports Inc.
CORTINA - Sports apparel and accessories - Cortina Ski Co. Inc.
CORTINA - Whirlpools - Jacuzzi Inc.
CORTINA - Window blinds - Cortina Shade Manufacturing Inc.
CORTINA - Yarn ✫ - Tahki Imports Ltd.
CORTINA CHERRIES - Candy - Nabisco Foods Group
CORTINA LEATHER - Wallcoverings - Ben Rose Ltd.
CORTINI - Accordions - David Wexler & Co.
CORTINI - Apparel and accessories - Wilson Brothers
CORTISOOTHE - Pet products - Virbac, Inc.
CORTISPORIN - Pharmaceutical preparations - Burroughs Wellcome Co.
CORTISTAT-PS - Vitamins and nutritional supplements - Champion Nutrition
CORTIVA - Clothing - E. Benjamin, Inc.
CORTIZONE-5 - Vitamins and nutritional supplements ✫ - Thompson Medical Co., Inc.
CORTIZONE 10 - Vitamins and nutritional supplements ✫ - Thompson Medical Co., Inc.
CORTIZONE FOR KIDS - Vitamins and nutritional supplements ✫ - Thompson Medical Co., Inc.
CORTLAND - Brushes–paint ✫ - PPG Industries, Inc.
CORTLAND - Cabinets - Yorktowne Inc.
CORTLAND - Fishing lines - Cortland Line Co., Inc.
CORTLAND - Floor coverings–carpet and rugs - Alexander Smith Carpets
CORTLAND - Manufactured homes ✫ - Bonnavilla Homes
CORTLAND - Plumbing fixtures - Harrington Brass Works Ltd. Inc.
CORTLAND - Watches - Concord Watches
CORTLAND BRICK - Floor coverings–tile ✫ - Kentile Floors Inc.
CORTLAND LAZER LINE - Fishing equipment - Cortland Line Co., Inc.
CORTLAND LTD. - Fishing rods and reels - Cortland Line Co., Inc.
CORTLAND VALLEY - Sauerkraut - Curtice-Burns Foods, Inc.
CORTLEY - Apparel–athletic ✫ - United Knitwear Co. Inc.
CORTLEY - Draperies - Decorator Industries Inc.
CORTONE - Pharmaceutical preparations - Merck & Co., Inc. (Merck Research Laboratories)
CORTOPLEX - Hair care products - Helene Curtis Industries Inc.
CORTOXIDE - Pharmaceutical preparations - Syosset Laboratories Inc.
CORTRAK - Computer software - First Class Solutions, Inc.
CORTRON - Floor coverings–carpet and rugs - Coronet Carpets Inc.
CORTROPHIN-GEL - Pharmaceutical preparations ✫ - Organon Inc.
CORTROPHIN-ZINC - Pharmaceutical preparations ✫ - Organon Inc.
CORTROSYN - Pharmaceutical preparations - Organon Inc.
CORUBEEN - Pharmaceutical preparations - G.O. Spanner Inc.
CORUM - Apparel and accessories - Phillips-Van Heusen Corp.
CORUM - Watches - North American Watch Corp.
CORUM BY VAN HEUSEN - Neckties ✫ - Randa Corp.
CORUM YACHT LINE - Pens - North American Watch Corp.

CORUS - Electronic equipment - Navico, Inc.
CORVA - Recording label - Jazz Composer's Orchestra Association Inc.
CORVAIR - Floor coverings–carpet and rugs - Queen Carpet Corp.
CORVAIR - Motor vehicles ✫ - General Motors Corp. (Chevrolet Motor Div.)
CORVAIR MONZA - Motor vehicles ✫ - General Motors Corp. (Chevrolet Motor Div.)
CORVALLIS - Floor coverings ✫ - Congoleum Corp.
CORVALLIS - Food products - Corvallis Packing Co.
CORVETTE - Bicycles - Schwinn Cycling & Fitness Inc.
CORVETTE - Eyeglasses ✫ - Cable Car Eyeware
CORVETTE - Food products - Union Fish Co.
CORVETTE - Game machines - General Motors Corp.
CORVETTE - Guitars ✫ - Fred Gretsch Enterprises
CORVETTE - Motor vehicles - General Motors Corp. (Chevrolet Motor Div.)
CORVETTE ZR-1 - Motor vehicles - General Motors Corp. (Chevrolet Motor Div.)
CORVETTE ZR-1 CHALLENGE - Games ✫ - Milton Bradley Co.
CORVINUS - Rings–jewelry - Artcarved Inc.
CORVIS - Pet products - Farnam Cos. Inc.
CORVO - Wines - Paterno Imports, Ltd.
CORVUS - Bicycles - Ross Bicycles USA, Ltd.
CORVUS - Desk calculator - Corvus Corp.
CORVUS - Recording label - Corvus
CORVUS TIME SQUARE - Digital clock - Corvus Corp.
CORWIPE - Rust removers - Cortec Corp.
CORWRTH - Floor coverings–carpet and rugs ✫ - Atlas Carpet Mills Inc.
CORX - Games - Corx, Inc.
CORY - Coffee - ARA Services
CORY - Recording label - 3 G's Industries Inc.
CORY EVERSON'S - Apparel–athletic - Cory Everson Fitness, Inc.
CORY-EZE - Pharmaceutical preparations - Bio-Factor Laboratories
CORY PRODUCTS - Musical instrument accessories - GRK Manufacturing
CORYBAN - Cough medicines - Pfizer Inc.
CORYBAN-D - Cough medicines - Pfizer Inc.
CORYELL'S - Mustard - Berry Best Farm
CORYELL'S CROSSING - Jams and jellies - Berry Best Farm
CORYELL'S CROSSING GOLD - Jams and jellies - Berry Best Farm
CORYZA BRENGLE - Cold remedies ✫ - Roberts/Hauck Pharmaceuticals Inc.
CORYZAID - Pharmaceutical preparations ✫ - ICN Pharmaceuticals Inc.
CORYZOL - Veterinary pharmaceutical preparations ✫ - Vineland Laboratories Inc.
CORYZTIME - Pharmaceutical preparations ✫ - ICN Pharmaceuticals Inc.
CORZIDE - Pharmaceutical preparations - Bristol-Myers Squibb Co.
COS - Computer software - Crowell Systems
COS COB - Apparel–women's - Oxford Industries, Inc.
COS COB BRICK - Floor coverings ✫ - Tarkett, Inc.
COS-NAPA VALLEY - Wine - Cosentino Wine Co.
COS-TAR - Epoxy coatings ✫ - Sigma Coatings USA BV.
COSA-HYDRATE - Cold remedies - Rex Research Laboratories
COSADEIN - Cough medicines ✫ - Parke-Davis
COSANT - Floor coverings–carpet and rugs ✫ - Evans-Black Carpet Mills
COSANYL - Pharmaceutical preparations - Health Care Industries Inc.
COSCI - Leather accessories - International Accessories Corp.
COSCO - Beverages - Cosco International Inc.
COSCO - Chemical preparations - Wexco Inc.
COSCO - Furniture - Cosco, Inc.
COSCO - Marking devices - Consolidated Stamp Manufacturing Co. Inc.
COSCO - Water transportation–freight - China Ocean Shipping Co. Americas, Inc.
COSCO BEDS - Furniture - Cosco, Inc.
COSELLE - Cosmetics - Weckerle Sales Corp.
COSEM - Pharmaceutical preparations - Johnson Laboratories, Inc.
COSENTINO SELECT - Wine - Cosentino Wine Co.
COSENTINO WINERY - Wines - Cosentino Wine Co.
COSENZA - Cheese - Atlantic Food Services, Inc.
COSESSION REMOTE - Computer software - Artisoft, Inc.
COSETTE - Dolls - Effanbee Doll Corp.
COSEX - Food products - Caragol, Esformes & Phelan Corp.
COSI - Apparel and accessories - Edison Brothers Stores, Inc.
COSI L'UOMO - Apparel and accessories - Edison Brothers Stores, Inc.
COSICOL - Pharmaceutical preparations ✫ - U.S. Ethicals Inc.
COSILINCO - Pharmaceutical preparations ✫ - Dixon-Shane Inc.
COSINBID - Cough medicines - Johnson Laboratories, Inc.
COSINILCO - Pharmaceutical preparations ✫ - Richie Pharmacal Co. Inc.
COSKI'S - Pet treats - Coski's Choice Inc.
COSMA KLEEN - Ophthalmic goods - Amcon Laboratories, Inc.

COSME PUF - Cosmetic applicators - American White Cross, Inc.

COSME-TEMP - Dental compounds - Scrimpshire Dental Studio, Inc.

COSMECAPS - Cosmetics - R.P. Scherer Corp.

COSMECOL - Cosmetics - Organics Corp. of America (Ambix Laboratories Div.)

COSMEDICAL TECHNOLOGIES - Cosmetics - Cosmedical Technologies, Inc.

COSMEGEN - Pharmaceutical preparations - Merck & Co., Inc. (Merck Research Laboratories)

COSMEPUF - Skin care products - Temco USA Inc.

COSMESTICK - Detergents - Edwards Creative Products, Inc.

COSMETCO - Manicure sets and manicure implements ✩ - London International U.S. Holdings

COSMETIC ARTS - Cosmetics - Cosmetic Arts Inc.

COSMETIC BAZAAR - Cosmetics ✩ - Cosrich Inc.

COSMETIC DISCS - Cosmetics - Jean Philippe Fragrances, Inc.

COSMETIC FACTORY, INC., THE - Cosmetics - Cosmetics Factory, Inc.

COSMETIC FIRST - Cosmetics ✩ - Cosmetic Firsts Ltd.

COSMETIC-LITE - Lighting equipment ✩ - Duro-Lite Lamps Inc.

COSMETIC SAQ - Bags - Curator

COSMETIC SHAVE, THE - Razors ✩ - Schick/Wilkinson

COSMETIC SOLUTIONS - Toothpaste - Life-Like Cosmetics, Inc.

COSMETIQUE - Cosmetics - ADY Chemical International Inc.

COSMETIQUE CE'LE'BRE - Cosmetics - Alo Pro of Chicago Inc.

COSMIC - Colognes ✩ - FMG/Tsumara Medical

COSMIC - Floor coverings - American Floor Products Co. Inc.

COSMIC - Floor coverings–carpet and rugs - Mohawk Industries Inc.

COSMIC - Jewelry - House of Commans Inc.

COSMIC - Microscopes - Gravely Research Corp.

COSMIC - Nail care products - Cosmic Nail International, Inc.

COSMIC - Pet products - Cosmic Cat Corp.

COSMIC AVENGER - Toys–electronic - Hasbro, Inc.

COSMIC BURST - Kites ✩ - Hi-Flier Manufacturing Co.

COSMIC CALF - Diagnostic product - Hyclone Laboratories, Inc.

COSMIC CAP - Containers–plastic ✩ - K & W Products

COSMIC CHICKEN NUGGETS - Preserved foods–prepackaged - Conagra, Inc.

COSMIC CLUSTERS - Snack foods ✩ - Natural Nectar Corp.

COSMIC COIL - Novelty items - Ideas in Motion

COSMIC CONFLICT - Toys–electronic ✩ - Philips Consumer Electronics Co.

COSMIC COOLERS - Beverages - Indian Summer, Inc.

COSMIC COWBOYS - Toys ✩ - Spearhead Industries Inc.

COSMIC CREATIONS - Sporting goods - Ron Jon Surf Shop

COSMIC CRITTERS - Toy figures - Russ Berrie and Co., Inc.

COSMIC CRUISER - Kites ✩ - Gayla Industries Inc.

COSMIC CRUNCH - Candy - Gayle's Chocolates, Ltd.

COSMIC CRUNCHERS - Toys - Mattel, Inc.

COSMIC CRYSTALS - Pens - Moon Products, Inc.

COSMIC CUSHION - Cushions - Pacific Spirit Corp.

COSMIC DESK ACCESSORIES - Office accessories - A.I.P. Products, Inc.

COSMIC FIRE - Recording label - Black Fire Records

COSMIC FLYER - Bicycles - Western Auto Supply Co.

COSMIC FROG - Bags–duffel - Frog's Pajamas, Inc.

COSMIC KATIE SOUL SEARCH - Computer software - Katherine M. Vickers

COSMIC KIDS - Pasta - American Home Food Products Inc.

COSMIC KOOSH - Toys ✩ - Oddzon Products, Inc.

COSMIC PERCUSSION - Musical instruments - LP Music Group

COSMIC POWERS - Books–comic ✩ - Marvel Entertainment Group, Inc.

COSMIC SHOWDOWN - Toys - Mattel, Inc.

COSMIC VOICE - Plaything - Cosmic Voice Inc.

COSMIC WAVE - Hair care products - Waverly Beauty Products

COSMIC WHIRL - Toys - Molor Products Co.

COSMIC WIND - Toys–airplanes ✩ - Cox Products Inc.

COSMICS - Shoes - Edison Brothers Stores, Inc.

COSMIK EYE - Recording label - Hallways to Fame Productions Inc.

COSMO - Advertising agencies - Antista Fairclough Design, Ltd. II

COSMO - Display cases–wood - Rocket Jewelry Box, Inc.

COSMO - Enamels - Masury Paint Co.

COSMO - Timeclocks–office - A.D. Joslin Manufacturing Co.

COSMO 58 - Eyeglasses - Eastern Safety Equipment Co. Inc.

COSMO LTD. - Candy - Wilkinson-Spitz Ltd.

COSMO-LITE - Mirrors - Monaco Import/Export Inc.

COSMO MOPEDS - Recreational vehicles, now out of production - Cosmopolitan Motors Inc.

COSMO-SPAR - Varnishes - Masury Paint Co.

COSMO-THANE - Varnishes - Masury Paint Co.

COSMO.58 - Goggles–safety - Aearo Co.

COSMOCALC - Computer software - Kuzmich Development

COSMOGRAPH - Watches - Rolex Watch USA, Inc.

COSMOLINE - Lubricants - E.F. Houghton & Co.

COSMOLON - Fasteners–hook and eye - YKK USA Inc.

COSMONAUT - Watches - Movado Time Corp.

COSMOOSE - Apparel–children's - Lifeforms International, Inc.

COSMOPOLITAN - Beds–wood ✩ - California Concepts

COSMOPOLITAN - Cages–wire - Ameriguard Corp.

COSMOPOLITAN - Clocks - General Time Corp. (Westclox/Seth Thomas Div.)

COSMOPOLITAN - Electronic equipment ✩ - Da-Lite Screen Co. Inc.

COSMOPOLITAN - Floor coverings - Congoleum Corp.

COSMOPOLITAN - Frames–eyeglass - Marine Optical, Inc.

COSMOPOLITAN - Furniture ✩ - Bassett Furniture Industries, Inc.

COSMOPOLITAN - Furniture–upholstered ✩ - Mersman Furniture Co.

COSMOPOLITAN - Glassware–household - Seneca Glass Co.

COSMOPOLITAN - Greeting cards ✩ - American Artists Group Inc.

COSMOPOLITAN - Hosiery - Virginia Maid Hosiery Mills Inc.

COSMOPOLITAN - Paints - Valspar Corp.

COSMOPOLITAN - Publisher's imprints - Hearst Corp.

COSMOPOLITAN - Tableware–china - Lenox, Inc.

COSMOPOLITAN - Underwear and nightwear - Bestform Foundations, Inc.

COSMOPOLITAN - Wallpaper - Fine Art Wallcoverings Ltd.

COSMOPOLITAN - Watches - Longines-Wittnauer Watch Co.

COSMOPOLITAN COFFEE CREMES - Cream–canned or powdered - Mrs. Adler's Foods Inc.

COSMOPOLITAN COUNTRY - Recording label - Metal Magic Records

COSMOPOLITAN GLASS - Nail care products - Nailco, Inc.

COSMOPOLITAN II - Furniture ✩ - White Furniture Co.

COSMOPOLITAN THEMES - Floor coverings–carpet and rugs - Philadelphia Carpets

COSMOPOWER - Lighting equipment - Cosmedico Light, Inc.

COSMOS - Brushes–paint - Corona Brushes Inc.

COSMOS - Computer software - Gaylord Bros. Inc.

COSMOS - Dinnerware–glass ✩ - Nikko Ceramics Inc.

COSMOS - Film - Eastman Kodak Co.

COSMOS - Fish–fresh or frozen - Cosmos Import Export Inc.

COSMOS - Floor coverings - B.F. Goodrich Co.

COSMOS - Floor coverings–carpet and rugs ✩ - Mannington Carpets, Inc.

COSMOS - Floor coverings–carpet and rugs ✩ - Royalweve Carpet Mills

COSMOS - Food products ✩ - Amberwave Foods

COSMOS - Furniture - Haworth, Inc.

COSMOS - Glassware–household ✩ - Crisa Corp.

COSMOS - Pliers - ACCO USA, Inc.

COSMOS - Tiles–ceramic ✩ - Latco Products

COSMOS - Vegetable oil ✩ - Catania-Spagna Corp.

COSMOS - Wallpaper ✩ - Koroseal Wallcoverings

COSMOTHERM - Bathtubs–enameled - Cosmopro Inc.

COSMOTONE - Recording label - Cosmotone Records

COSMOTRONIC - Lighting equipment - Cosmedico Light, Inc.

COSMOTS - Hair care products - Nature Clean, Inc.

COSMYK - Posters - Greeneman, Inc.

COSMYL SUNBEACH - Skin care products - Cosmyl, Inc.

COSO - Skin care products - Magick Mud

COSOM - Sporting goods - Mantua/Cosom Sporting Goods

COSPAINT - Adhesives and sealants - ISK Biosciences Corp.

COSPORT - Footwear–athletic - Cooperative Sports, Inc.

COSSACK - Beverages - Juice Bowl Products Inc.

COSSACK - Vodka - M.S. Walker Inc./Seacoast

COSSAP - Computer storage devices - Cadis, Inc.

COSSARTS - Wines ✩ - Kobrand Corp.

COST CONTAINMENT THROUGH TECHNOLOGICAL ADVANCEMENT. - Medical apparatus - Mercury Enterprises, Inc.

COST CUTTER - Beverages–alcohol ✩ - Falstaff Brewing Corp.

COST CUTTER - Dust mops - American Textile Products Co.

COST CUTTER - Food products - The Kroger Co.

COST CUTTERS FAMILY - Beauty shops - City Looks International

COST GUARD - Computer software - At-Your-Service Software, Inc.

COST OF INTOLERANCE - Publisher's imprints - Professional Development Group, Inc.

COSTA BELLA - Floor coverings - Mannington Resilient Floors

COSTA DEANO'S - Spaghetti sauces - Costa Deano's Gourmet Foods

COSTA DEL SOL - Cooking utensils–earthenware ✩ - Seymour Mann Inc.

COSTA DEL SOL - Floor coverings - Mannington Resilient Floors

COSTA DEL SOL - Footwear - De Osu Inc.

COSTA DO SOL - Wines - M.S. Walker Inc./Seacoast

COSTA PALM - Food products - Gourmet America

✩ = Now out of production

COSTA RICAN GOLD - Coffee - Costa Rican Gold Coffee Co.

COSTA RICAN TRIO'S - Coffee - Organic Coffee Co., Inc.

COSTA ROSADA - Wines - Joseph E. Seagram & Sons, Inc.

COSTA ROTARY GRILL, THE - Barbecues and grills - Rotary Grill Manufacturing, Inc.

COSTADEANO'S - Sauces - Dean Bacopoulos

COSTAMAR - Food products - American Roland Food Corp.

COSTAMAR - Food products - Costamar Corp.

COSTAPUR - Pet products ☆ - Sera Aquaristik USA Inc.

COSTAR - Measuring instruments - Quantum Group, Inc.

COSTCOMPARE - Computer software - Healthdemographics

COSTEC 20 - Beauty aids - Costec 20 Inc.

COSTELLANO - Tea kettles–nonelectric ☆ - National Housewares

COSTELLO - Erasers - Quartet Manufacturing Co.

COSTELLO - Food products machinery ☆ - Frozen Specialties, Inc.

COSTELLO'S - Vitamins and nutritional supplements - Juice Pak

COSTI - Tiles–terrazzo - Imperial Tile and Marble Corp.

COSTILLA - Floor coverings ☆ - National Floor Products Co., Inc.

COSTUMAKERS - Hobby kits - Blumenthal/Lansing Co.

COSTUME BALL - Dolls - Mattel, Inc.

COSTUME CREATIONS - Costumes - Topstone Industries Inc.

COSTUME WORKSHOP, THE - Video production - Bonnie Holt Ambrose

COSTUMES FOR WINNERS - Costumes - Art Stone Theatrical Corp.

COSTUMES ONLY A DOG WOULD WEAR - Pet products - Petcetera Originals Inc.

COSY - Fabrics - Burlington House Fabrics Group

COSY - Portable kerosene heaters ☆ - Consort Products Corp.

COT-1 DNA - Chemical reagents - Life Technologies, Inc.

COT-GARD - Medical apparatus - Karlen Manufacturing, Inc.

COT-N-TAIL - Socks - Leininger Mills Inc.

COTACORT - Pharmaceutical preparations - C.O. Truxton Inc.

CO'TAGE - Apparel and accessories - Cotton Age, Inc.

COTALAX - Pharmaceutical preparations - C.O. Truxton Inc.

COTAMETH - Pharmaceutical preparations - C.O. Truxton Inc.

COTANAL-65 - Pharmaceutical preparations - C.O. Truxton Inc.

COTAZYM - Pharmaceutical preparations - Organon Inc.

COTAZYM-S - Pharmaceutical preparations - Organon Inc.

COTE ALL - Enamels - Vogel Paint and Wax Co., Inc.

COTE BASQUE - Giftware - Seymour Mann Inc.

COTE D'AZUR - Incense - GPS, Inc.

COTE D'AZUR - Jewelry and accessories - Louis M. Schukar and Associates

COTE D'AZUR - Skin care products ☆ - Avon Products, Inc.

COTE DE ROBLES - Wines - Quorum Properties

COTE D'OR - Chocolate candy ☆ - Holland-American Importing Co. Inc.

COTE SANS DESSEINS - Wines - Green Valley Vineyards

COTEE - Fishing lures - Cotee Industries Inc.

COTERIE - Jewelry - Coterie Inc.

COTES DE SONOMA - Wines - Pellegrini Bros. Wines Inc.

COTES DU RHONE - Wines - Kobrand Corp.

COTHENE - Plastics film - LSH Materials, Ltd.

COTHERA - Antihistamine preparations ☆ - Wyeth-Ayerst Laboratories

COTHRAN COLLECTION, THE - Juvenile product - Cothran & Co. Inc.

COTIER - Floor coverings–carpet and rugs ☆ - Customweave Carpets Inc.

COTIERA - Scarves - V. Fraas USA, Inc.

COTIJA - Cheese - Cotija Cheese Co., Inc.

COTILLION - Apparel–women's - Mercantile Stores Co., Inc.

COTILLION - Colognes - Avon Products, Inc.

COTILLION - Dinnerware–glass - Nikko Ceramics Inc.

COTILLION - Floor coverings–carpet and rugs - Philadelphia Carpets

COTILLION - Furniture ☆ - Tropitone Furniture Co. Inc.

COTILLION - Ice cream cones ☆ - Safeway Stores Inc.

COTILLION - Lamps ☆ - Lamplight Farms, Inc.

COTILLION - Paper–gift wrap ☆ - Papercraft Corp.

COTILLION - Recording label - Atlantic Records

COTILLION - Wallpaper ☆ - Newmarket Designs Ltd.

COTLER - Apparel and accessories - Cotler Licensing Corp.

COTLETS - Candy - Liberty Orchards Co., Inc.

COTLON - Yarn - Pharr Yarns Inc.

COTMAN - Artists' materials - Winsor & Newton

COT'N WASH - Detergents - Conshohocken Cotton Co.

COTOFED - Pharmaceutical preparations ☆ - C.O. Truxton Inc.

COTOL-240 - Automotive parts and accessories - McNett Corp.

COTOLONE - Pharmaceutical preparations - C.O. Truxton Inc.

COTON - Floor coverings–carpet and rugs - Eligere Carpets

COTONEVE - Skin care products - Spilo/Mehaz Worldwide

COTONIA - Thread ☆ - DMC Corp.

COTRAN - Electronic equipment - BRK Brands, Inc.

COTRANZINE - Pharmaceutical preparations ☆ - Coast Laboratories Inc.

COTREL - Fabrics - Dan River Inc.

COTRIM - Pharmaceutical preparations - Lemmon Co.

COTRINO - Cotton–balls - Chesebrough-Pond's USA Inc.

COTROL-D - Pharmaceutical preparations - Smithkline Beecham Corp.

COTSWOLD - Dishes–earthenware ☆ - Denby USA Limited

COTSWOLD - Furniture - Bassett Furniture Industries, Inc.

COTT - Beverages - Cadbury Beverages Inc.

COTT - Beverages–carbonated - Dr. Pepper/Seven Up, Inc.

COTTAGE - Cabinets ☆ - Medallion Kitchens of Minnesota Inc.

COTTAGE - Floor coverings ☆ - Kentile Floors Inc.

COTTAGE - Floor coverings–carpet and rugs - Capel, Inc.

COTTAGE - Flowers, plants, and seeds - Sweeney Seed Co.

COTTAGE - Food products - Western Family Foods, Inc.

COTTAGE - Furniture ☆ - Universal Flooring

COTTAGE - Manufactured homes - Redman Industries, Inc.

COTTAGE - Mobile homes - Western Homes Corp.

COTTAGE - Plywood - Georgia-Pacific Corp.

COTTAGE - Tableware–china ☆ - Pfaltzgraff Investment Co.

COTTAGE - Tiles–ceramic - P D S Associates, Inc.

COTTAGE - Vinyl playhouses ☆ - Intex Recreation Corp.

COTTAGE - Wood products - Weyerhaeuser Co.

COTTAGE & CASTLE - Fabrics–tapestry ☆ - Columbus Coated Fabrics Co.

COTTAGE & CASTLE II - Fabrics–tapestry ☆ - Columbus Coated Fabrics Co.

COTTAGE BOUQUET - Furniture - Stanley Furniture Co. Inc.

COTTAGE BRICK - Floor coverings–tile ☆ - Kentile Floors Inc.

COTTAGE CHARM - Wallpaper - Hunting Valley Prints

COTTAGE CHARM II - Wallpaper - Hunting Valley Prints

COTTAGE COMBOS - Cottage cheese - H.P. Hood & Sons Inc.

COTTAGE CORNERS - House furnishings ☆ - Lea Industries Inc.

COTTAGE CRAFT - Floor coverings–carpet and rugs - Whitecrest Carpet Mills

COTTAGE CRAFT - Furniture ☆ - Bassett Furniture Industries, Inc.

COTTAGE CRAFTED - Bathroom accessories - Liette International Ltd.

COTTAGE DOOR - Giftware - N.S. Gustin Co.

COTTAGE FLOWERS - Dinnerware–glass ☆ - Royal China & Porcelain Companies Inc.

COTTAGE FRIES - Potato chips - Borden, Inc.

COTTAGE GARDEN - Cosmetics ☆ - Chase Collection, Inc.

COTTAGE GROVE - Furniture - Athens Furniture Industries Inc.

COTTAGE HEARTH - Breads - Certified Grocers of California, Ltd.

COTTAGE HEDDLES - Floor coverings–carpet and rugs - Eurotex Inc.

COTTAGE IN THE COUNTRY - Craft supplies ☆ - VIP/VIP Crafts

COTTAGE KETTLE - Soups–mixes - Sanwa Foods Inc.

COTTAGE LAKE - Furniture ☆ - Hammary Furniture Co. Inc.

COTTAGE OAK - Furniture - Hammary Furniture Co. Inc.

COTTAGE PINE - Furniture ☆ - Bassett Furniture Industries, Inc.

COTTAGE PRINTS - Wallpaper - Taylor Wallcoverings Inc.

COTTAGE PRINTS 3 - Wallpaper - Taylor Wallcoverings Inc.

COTTAGE QUILTS - Floor coverings–carpet and rugs - Eurotex Inc.

COTTAGE ROSE - Flatware - Reed and Barton Corp.

COTTAGE SALAD - Dips–sour cream based ☆ - Rose International

COTTAGE SALAD - Salads–prepackaged - Rella Good Cheese Co.

COTTAGE STONE - Tiles–ceramic - Porcelanite, Inc.

COTTAGE TREASURES - Furniture - Stanley Furniture Co. Inc.

COTTAGE TRELLIS - Floor coverings–carpet and rugs - Regal Rugs Inc.

COTTAGE VINEYARDS - Wines - Cottage Vineyards

COTTAGORA - Fabrics - Tabor Trading Co.

COTTILION - Clocks ☆ - Ridgeway Clock Co.

COTTINGHAM - Wallpaper - Seabrook Wallcoverings, Inc.

COTT'N SILK - Yarn - Bernat Yarn & Craft Corp.

COTTON - Detergents - Cotton Inc.

COTTON 2 WEAR - Apparel–athletic - Action Gear, Inc.

COTTON 100 - Apparel–men's - Phillips-Van Heusen Corp.

COTTON-AIDE HC - Chemical preparations - Monterey Chemical Co.

COTTON-AIRE - Underwear and nightwear ☆ - Alba-Waldensian, Inc.

COTTON AMERICA - Apparel and accessories - Cotton America Co., Inc.

COTTON ARMOR ACTIVEWEAR CLASSICS - Sweatshirts, sweatpants, t-shirts, etc. - Burt F. Paul & Associates Inc.

COTTON BED, THE - Beds–metal - M. Craig Cabinetmaker

COTTON BELLE - Brassieres (Bras) ☆ - Lovable Co.

COTTON BI-LINE - Underwear and nightwear - Maidenform Inc.

COTTON BOLE - Handkerchiefs ☆ - Carolina Manufacturing Inc.

COTTON BOLL - Chewing tobacco - Conwood Co. L.P.

COTTON BOLL - Tobacco - American Tobacco Co.

☆ = Now out of production

COTTON BROTHERS - Apparel and accessories - Warren Sewell Clothing Co. Inc.

COTTON CABOODLE - Apparel–children's - Cotton Caboodle Co.

COTTON CANDY - Apparel–women's - Jacob Boltz Knitting Mill Inc.

COTTON CANDY - Bicycles ☆ - Hedstrom Corp.

COTTON CANDY - Chewing gum ☆ - Amurol Confections Co.

COTTON CANDY - Christmas tree ornaments - Cracker Box Inc.

COTTON CANDY - Craft supplies - VIP/VIP Crafts

COTTON CANDY - Dolls ☆ - Effanbee Doll Corp.

COTTON CANDY - Toys ☆ - Those Characters from Cleveland, Inc.

COTTON CANDY - Yarn - Brunswick Yarns

COTTON CASUALS - Footwear - Brown Wooten Mills Inc.

COTTON CHENILLE 500 - Yarn - Henry's Attic

COTTON CHENILLE 900 - Yarn - Henry's Attic

COTTON CHOICE - Apparel and accessories - Playtex Apparel, Inc.

COTTON CLASSIC - Fabrics - Fairfield Processing Corp.

COTTON CLASSIC - Floor coverings–carpet and rugs ☆ - Regal Rugs Inc.

COTTON CLASSIC - Yarn ☆ - Tahki Imports Ltd.

COTTON CLASSIC II - Yarn ☆ - Tahki Imports Ltd.

COTTON CLASSICS - Apparel and accessories - Munsingwear, Inc.

COTTON CLASSICS - Towels - Barth-Dreyfuss of California

COTTON CLOUDS - Skin care products ☆ - B & B Distributors

COTTON CLOUDS - Yarn ☆ - Caron International Inc.

COTTON CLUB - Apparel and accessories - Uniflair Inc.

COTTON CLUB - Carbonated beverage - Cotton Club Bottling Co.

COTTON CLUB, THE - Floor coverings–carpet and rugs - Masland Corp.

COTTON COLLECTABLES - Apparel–children's - Haddad Apparel Group Ltd.

COTTON COLLECTION FOR KIDS, THE - Apparel–women's - Cotton Collection for Kids

COTTON COLLECTION, THE - Sweaters - Martin D. Zucker

COTTON COMFORT - Apparel–women's - Exquisite Form Industries

COTTON CONFECTIONS - Underwear and nightwear - Maidenform Inc.

COTTON CONTINENTALS, THE - Underwear and nightwear - Maidenform Inc.

COTTON COOLERS - Apparel and accessories ☆ - Jantzen Inc.

COTTON COUNTRY - Pies–frozen - Antique Mall & Crown

COTTON COUNTY - Socks - Renfro Corp.

COTTON COUTURE - Underwear and nightwear - Maidenform Inc.

COTTON COVE - Shirts - Premier Wear, Inc.

COTTON CREPE - Yarn ☆ - William Unger & Co. Inc.

COTTON CRUNCH - Hosiery - Moretz Hosiery Mills Inc.

COTTON DOT - Yarn ☆ - Tahki Imports Ltd.

COTTON DUOS - Underwear and nightwear - Maidenform Inc.

COTTON ELEGANCE - Brassieres (Bras) - Sara Lee Corp.

COTTON EXCHANGE - Sweaters - Puritan Sportswear Corp.

COTTON EXPRESS - Yarn ☆ - Joseph Galler Inc.

COTTON FEELS - Apparel and accessories - Strouse, Adler Co.

COTTON FOREVER - Apparel–women's - P.S. Knits Inc.

COTTON FRESH - Underwear and nightwear ☆ - Lovable Co.

COTTON GENERATION - Apparel and accessories - QVC, Inc.

COTTON HAPPYS - Apparel stores–lingerie ☆ - Formfit Rogers

COTTON IN ACTION - Shirts–polo - Sanfatex, Inc.

COTTON KING - Ribbons–inked - Leedall Products Manufacturing Co.

COTTON LACINGS - Underwear and nightwear - Warnaco Inc.

COTTON LIGHT - Underwear and nightwear - Henson-Kickernick Inc.

COTTON LOOK - Yarn ☆ - Lion Brand Yarn Co.

COTTON LUXE - Apparel and accessories - Playtex Apparel, Inc.

COTTON MAGIC - Apparel–women's - Exquisite Form Industries

COTTON MAGIC - Fabrics - Dan River Inc.

COTTON MAID - Starch–laundry - Gem Inc.

COTTON MILL - Shirts - Supreme International Corp.

COTTON MILL SHIRT CO. - Apparel and accessories - Publix Group Ltd.

COTTON MINE - Apparel–men's - Cotton Mine Group Inc.

COTTON MOON MUSIC - Recording label - Wizard & Feather Brown Productions

COTTON MOVING PARTS - Apparel and accessories - Danskin, Inc.

COTTON-N-COMFORT - Apparel and accessories - F. J.& M., Inc.

COTTON, NATURALLY - Underwear and nightwear - Lovable Co.

COTTON PALACE - Towels - Monarch Towel Co.

COTTON PARK COTTAGE - Tablecloths - Lintex Linens, Inc.

COTTON PATCH - Craft supplies ☆ - VIP/VIP Crafts

COTTON PATCH - Pet products - Radford Manufacturing

COTTON PICKER - Bicycles - Schwinn Cycling & Fitness Inc.

COTTON PICKINS - Fabrics - Hi-Fashion Fabrics Inc.

COTTON PLUS - Computer software - Mind Play

COTTON PLUS - Sanitary napkins ☆ - Tranzonic Cos.

COTTON POPPY - Men's and women's apparel - India Garments Inc.

COTTON PRESS - Artists' materials - American Art Clay Co. Inc.

COTTON PRETTY - Brassieres (Bras) - Playtex Apparel, Inc.

COTTON QUEEN - Apparel and accessories ☆ - Glamorise Foundations Inc.

COTTON QUEEN - Mops - Carolina Mop Manufacturing Co.

COTTON RAGG - Slippers - Acorn

COTTON REPUBLIC PRIME HARVEST - Clothing - Cotton Republic, Inc.

COTTON ROW - Apparel–men's - Edison Brothers Stores, Inc.

COTTON SKAMP - Underwear and nightwear - Henson-Kickernick Inc.

COTTON SMOOTHER, THE - Apparel and accessories - Strouse, Adler Co.

COTTON SMOOTHIE - Apparel and accessories - Strouse, Adler Co.

COTTON SOFT - Fabrics–denim - Lee Apparel Co. Inc.

COTTON SOURCE - T-shirts–men's ☆ - T-Shirts & More, Inc.

COTTON STUDIO - Apparel and accessories - Marc Wear

COTTON SUPPLY CO. - Apparel and accessories - Empire Manufacturing Co.

COTTON TAILOR, THE - Apparel–women's - Poseiden, Inc.

COTTON TAILS - Health care products - Rockline Industries Inc.

COTTON TALES - Computer software - Mind Play

COTTON-TEE - Linen - Notra Trading, Inc.

COTTON THAT DEFIES TIME, THE - Fabrics–cotton - Burlington Industries, Inc.

COTTON TOP - Thread ☆ - American & Efird, Inc.

COTTON TOPPER - Plastics–laminated - A.J. Gerrard & Co.

COTTON TOTS - Apparel–children's - Cotton Tots, Inc.

COTTON TOUCH - Jeans and shirts - Blue Bell, Inc.

COTTON TRADERS - Apparel and accessories - Gillman Knitwear Co.

COTTON TRADERS SPORT - Slacks–men's - Gillman Knitwear Co.

COTTON TREATS - Underwear and nightwear - Maidenform Inc.

COTTON TRUFFLES SKAMP - Underwear and nightwear ☆ - Henson-Kickernick Inc.

COTTON UN-LTD. - Underwear and nightwear - Maidenform Inc.

COTTON VALLEY - Towels - Cotton Valley Textiles Corp.

COTTON WAVE - Apparel and accessories - Goldenwood International, Inc.

COTTON WAYS - Apparel and accessories - Goldenwood International, Inc.

COTTON WEAR - Apparel and accessories - T/J Knit Enterprises, Inc.

COTTON WHITE - Flour–blended ☆ - Stevens Industries Inc.

COTTON WORKS - Apparel–athletic - Bassett-Walker Inc.

COTTON WORKS - Computer software - Mind Play

COTTONAIRE - Fabrics–cotton - Greenwood Mills Inc.

COTTONBLOSSOM - Blankets ☆ - Southern Mills Inc.

COTTONCALE - Fabrics–linen - West Point-Pepperell Inc.

COTTONDRY - Diapers–disposable - Brenda Schenk

COTTONELLA - Yarn - Melrose Yarn Co. Inc.

COTTONELLE - Paper–toilet - Scott Paper Co.

COTTONELLE WITH BAKING SODA - Paper–toilet - Scott Paper Co.

COTTONETTES - Cotton–balls - National Patent Medical

COTTONFARM CO-OP - Apparel and accessories - Tropical Garment Manufacturing Co.

COTTONQUIK - Chemical preparations - Entek Corp.

COTTON'S - Bread and rolls - Cotton Bros. Baking Co. Inc.

COTTON'S FIRST FILES - Computer software - Mind Play

COTTONSCRUBS - Mops - Suburbanite Industries

COTTONTAIL - Candy - R.M. Palmer Co.

COTTONTAIL CORNER - Craft supplies ☆ - VIP/VIP Crafts

COTTONTAIL LANE - Figurines ☆ - Midwest of Cannon Falls Inc.

COTTONTAIL TRAIL - Toys–stuffed - Sterling Inc.

COTTONTAILS - Baked good - Flowers Family Bakeries, Inc.

COTTONTAILS - Diapers–disposable - Cottontails International

COTTONTAILS - Diapers–disposable - Weyerhaeuser Co.

COTTONTALE - Yarn - Net Works, Inc.

COTTONTOPS - Apparel and accessories - Tom Togs of Carolina, Inc.

COTTONUITY - Apparel - Knight Industries

COTTONWOOD - Dinnerware–glass ☆ - Lenox, Inc.

COTTONWOOD - Fabrics–cotton - Greenwood Mills Inc.

COTTONWOOD - Trailers–travel - Fleetwood Enterprises, Inc.

COTTONWOOD CREEK - Dips–sour cream based - Laci Le Beau Corp.

COTTOVENETO - Tiles–ceramic - Amsterdam Corp.

COTTRELL & HAYES - Apparel and accessories ☆ - Edison Brothers Stores, Inc.

COTTTAGESTONE - Blocks–concrete - Mutual Materials Co.

COTURRI - Wine - H. Coturri & Son Ltd.

COTUSSIS - Pharmaceutical preparations ☆ - Marion Merrell Dow

COTY - Toiletries - Coty Inc.

COTY 24 - Lipstick - Coty Inc.

COTY MINIS - Makeup - Coty Inc.

COTYLENOL - Health care products ☆ - McNeil Consumer Products Co.

COU COU - Apparel and accessories - Comme-Ci Comme-Ca Ltd.

☆ = Now out of production

COUCH CONDOM - Housewares - Holly Haltner
COUCH CRITTERS - Wood products - David A. Christensen
COUCH CROISSANT - Pillows - Camp Kazoo, Ltd.
COUCH GUARD - Craft supplies - M.E. Keogh
COUCH KANGAROO - Novelty items–stitched - Maidens Home Accessories
COUCH POTATO - Furniture - Couch Potato Inc.
COUCH POTATO - Pillows - Daniel Hammer
COUCH POTATO CROSS-TRAINER - Novelty items - Couch Potato Cross-Trainer, Inc.
COUCH'S ORIGINAL SAUCE - Sauces - Couch's Corner Bar-B-Q Franchising Systems, Inc.
COUGAR - Archery equipment ☆ - Martin Archery Inc.
COUGAR - Bicycles - Ross Bicycles USA, Ltd.
COUGAR - Binoculars - Swift Instruments, Inc.
COUGAR - Cigarettes - Brown & Williamson Tobacco Corp.
COUGAR - Footwear–athletic - American Athletic Shoe Co.
COUGAR - Generators - Clarke Mosquito Equipment, Inc.
COUGAR - Golfing equipment - Roger Dunn Golf Shops Inc.
COUGAR - Lawn care equipment - Cougar Power Products Inc.
COUGAR - Machinery - Flow International Corp.
COUGAR - Motor vehicles–automobiles - Ford Motor Co. (Lincoln-Mercury Div.)
COUGAR - Neckties - Salant/Manhattan Industries
COUGAR - Paper–bond - Weyerhaeuser Co.
COUGAR - Toys–models ☆ - Estes Industries
COUGAR - Trailers–truck ☆ - Sun-Lite Inc.
COUGAR - Watches - Cartier Inc.
COUGAR - Watches - Hampden Corp.
COUGAR 2 - Tripods–photographic - Phoenix Corp. of America
COUGAR BOOKS - Publisher's imprint - Cougar Books
COUGAROO - Luggage - Ventura Travelware Inc.
COUGH-AID - Cough drops - Zee Medical Inc.
COUGH-ARREST - Cough medicines ☆ - Vita-Fore Products Co.
COUGH BUDDY - Pillows - Teddy-Tech Inc.
COUGH CALM - Veterinary nutritional supplements - Oralx Corp.
COUGH CALMERS - Cough medicines - A.H. Robins Co. Inc.
COUGH-CONTROL - Veterinary pharmaceutical preparations ☆ - Farnam Cos. Inc.
COUGH-EEZ - Health care products ☆ - Kay Pharmacal Co. Inc.
COUGH 'N' ASH TRAY - Novelty items ☆ - Jobar International Inc./Bibi Products
COUGH POPS - Cough drops - Merica Fooks Johnson
COUGH SILENCERS - Cough medicines - Richardson-Vicks USA
COUGH SOLUTION - Pharmaceutical preparations - Dolisos America, Inc.
COUGH SOOTHE - Veterinary pharmaceutical preparations ☆ - Farnam Cos. Inc.
COUGH-X - Pharmaceutical preparations - B.F. Ascher & Co. Inc.
COUGHAIDE - Pharmaceutical preparations - Boericke & Tafel
COUGHCARE - Vitamins and nutritional supplements - Ayurvedic Concepts Ltd.
COUGHINE - Cough medicines ☆ - JMI-Canton Pharmaceuticals
COUGHITALIA - Tiles–terrazzo - Imperial Tile and Marble Corp.
COUGHMASTERS - Hair care products - Henry Thayer Co.
COULEUR - Floor coverings–carpet and rugs - J.L. Benson Co.
COULEUR COULEUR - Cosmetics - Cosmair Inc.
COULEURELLE - Cosmetics - Cosmair Inc.
COULISSE - Furniture - Tomlinson of High Point Inc.
COULOURPRINTS - Skin care products - Christian Dior Perfumes Corp.
COUMADIN - Pharmaceutical preparations - Du Pont Pharmaceuticals
COUNCIL - Tables–wood - Krueger International, Inc.
COUNCIL PRO - Computer software - Vicom Systems Co.
COUNSELLOR - Pencils - National Pen & Pencil Co.
COUNSELLOR LINEN - Paper–writing - All-State Legal Supply Co.
COUNSELOR - Bath scales - Counselor Co.
COUNSELOR - Floor coverings–carpet and rugs ☆ - Callaway Carpets
COUNSELOR - Scales - Sunbeam Corp.
COUNSELOR BORG - Scales–bathroom - Sunbeam Corp.
COUNSELOR DEANNA TROI - Toys - Paramount Pictures Corp.
COUNSELRX - Computer software - Richard A. Foote
COUNT - Brushes–paint ☆ - PPG Industries, Inc.
COUNT - Footwear - Angel-Etts of California, Inc.
COUNT-A-SPACE - Toys - Lauri Inc.
COUNT & SQUEEZE - Toys ☆ - Shield Manufacturing Inc.
COUNT ARCO'S - Beverages–malt - Count Arco's
COUNT-AWAY - Games - Moon Products, Inc.
COUNT CHOCULA - Cereal - General Mills, Inc.

COUNT CREEPYHEAD - Toys - Tonka Corp.
COUNT DOWN - Games ☆ - Milton Bradley Co.
COUNT DOWN - Underwear and nightwear ☆ - Lovable Co.
COUNT DOWN 200 - Vitamins and nutritional supplements - Royal Products, Inc.
COUNT DRACULA - Candy ☆ - Alma-Leo USA Inc.
COUNT DREGON - Toys - Saban Entertainment, Inc.
COUNT DUCKULA - Candy - Alma-Leo USA Inc.
COUNT 'EM - Apparel and accessories - Count 'em
COUNT-MY-FINGERS - Puzzles - Lauri Inc.
COUNT 'N KEY HOUSE - Toys - Mattel, Inc.
COUNT 'N SORT - Games ☆ - Steven Manufacturing Co.
COUNT ON BARNEY - Computer software ☆ - SRA/McGraw-Hill (Div. of The McGraw-Hill Companies)
COUNT ON COACH MICKEY - Wallpaper ☆ - Priss Prints Inc.
COUNT-R-CLEAR - Can openers–electric - Sunbeam-Oster Household Products
COUNT-TO-10 - Toys–musical - Mattel, Inc.
COUNT TWISTS - Food products - Good Time Charlie's
COUNTACH - Motor vehicles–automobiles - DaimlerChrysler
COUNTACH 5000S - Motor vehicles–automobiles - DaimlerChrysler
COUNTCARD - Electrical equipment - Nu-Metrics, Inc.
COUNTDOWN - Computer software ☆ - Access Software Inc.
COUNTDOWN - Game ☆ - Tah Dah Inc.
COUNTDOWN - Health care products ☆ - Teledyne Water Pik
COUNTDOWN - Watches - Helbros International
COUNTDOWN 2000 ECONOLOGY - Shirts - Philippe Caland
COUNTDOWN POKER - Game machines - Universal Distributing of Nevada, Inc.
COUNTDOWN TO ARMAGEDDON - Games ☆ - Mayfair Games, Inc.
COUNTDOWN TO SHUTDOWN - Computer software - Activision, Inc.
COUNTER ACT - Electronic equipment - Impact Manufacturing, Inc.
COUNTER ASSAULT - Research–chemical - Bushwacker Backpack & Supply Co.
COUNTER ATTACK - Electric lighting equipment - CSL Lighting Manufacturing, Inc.
COUNTER ATTACK - Skin care products - Rudolph International, Inc.
COUNTER BRIGHT - Can openers–electric - Black & Decker Corp.
COUNTER 'CAP - Containers–plastic - West Co., Inc.
COUNTER-CARRIAGE - Cabinets–wood - JGS Ventures, Inc.
COUNTER-CHEM - Paints ☆ - Adelphi Coatings Co.
COUNTER CLASSICS - Can openers–electric - Windmere Corp.
COUNTER CULTURE - Apparel and accessories - Counter Culture
COUNTER CULTURE - Compact discs–prerecorded - Counter Culture
COUNTER DISPLAY - Spices and extracts - Jodie's Kitchen Inc.
COUNTER FIT - Apparel–women's - Counterparts Sportswear, Inc.
COUNTER-FLAME - Paints ☆ - Adelphi Coatings Co.
COUNTER KEEPERS - Glass storage jars ☆ - Corning Inc.
COUNTER PEN - Pens - Micropoint Inc.
COUNTER POINT - Furniture - JSJ Corp.
COUNTER-POINT - Lighting fixtures - Swivelier Co. Inc.
COUNTER PRO - Counter tops–laminated - Counter Pro, Inc.
COUNTER-RUST - Paints ☆ - Adelphi Coatings Co.
COUNTER SAFE - Shutters–metal - Qualitas Manufacturing, Inc.
COUNTER-SAVER - Glass products - Eagle Glass Products
COUNTER SAVER - Ovens–microwave - General Electric Co.
COUNTER SNAP - Screws - O'Berry Enterprises, Inc.
COUNTER THAT COOKS, THE - Electric cooktops ☆ - Corning Inc.
COUNTER TOPS - Wallpaper - Taylor Wallcoverings Inc.
COUNTER TRED - Mats - JCH International Inc.
COUNTER VIBE - Saws–chain - White Consolidated Industries, Inc.
COUNTER VISION - Doors–metal - Alpine Overhead Doors Inc.
COUNTERACT - Pharmaceutical preparations - Melaleuca, Inc.
COUNTERACT - Skin care products - Dana Perfumes Corp.
COUNTERANGE - Electric ranges ☆ - Corning Inc.
COUNTERANS - Pharmaceutical preparations ☆ - P.J. Noyes Co., Inc.
COUNTERBOY - Office supplies - Better Packages
COUNTERFEET - Audio equipment ☆ - Sumiko Inc.
COUNTERFITTER - Display cases–plastic - Paul Flum Ideas, Inc.
COUNTERFLOW - Heat pumps - T/M Industrial Supply, Inc.
COUNTERFORCE - Furniture–public buildings - Westinghoue Electric Corp.
COUNTERLINE - Health care products - Omron Healthcare, Inc.
COUNTERMATES - Stools–metal ☆ - Samsonite Furniture Co. (Consumer Products Div.)
COUNTERPAIN RUB - Analgesics - Bristol-Myers Squibb Co.
COUNTERPART - Furniture ☆ - Bernhardt Industries

☆ = Now out of production

COUNTERPARTS - Audio equipment ☆ - Sumiko Inc.
COUNTERPARTS - Furniture—wood ☆ - Ficks Reed Co. Inc.
COUNTERPOINT - Brassieres (Bras) - Maidenform Inc.
COUNTERPOINT - Floor coverings - Congoleum Corp.
COUNTERPOINT - Floor coverings—carpet and rugs - Mohawk Industries Inc.
COUNTERPOINT - Floor coverings—carpet and rugs ☆ - Kelly Group Inc.
COUNTERPOINT - Floor coverings—carpet and rugs ☆ - Mannington Carpets, Inc.
COUNTERPOINT - Furniture - Stanley Furniture Co. Inc.
COUNTERPOINT - Giftware - Van Dow-Fenton Inc.
COUNTERPOINT - Golfing equipment - Golfsmith International Inc.
COUNTERPOINT - Office equipment - HLF Furniture, Inc.
COUNTERPOINT - Recording label - Everest Record Group
COUNTERPOINT - Rings—jewelry - Artcarved Inc.
COUNTERPOINT - Wallpaper ☆ - Bolta Wallcoverings
COUNTERPOINTS - Furniture—upholstered - Maharam Vertical Surfaces
COUNTERPRINTS - Greeting cards ☆ - Stephen Lawrence Co.
COUNTERSTRIKE - Personal safety equipment - Kenneth E. Washington
COUNTERTAP - Water purification systems - Culligan International Co.
COUNTERTOP MAGIC - Furniture polish and wax - Magic American Corp.
COUNTESS - Bathroom fixtures - Crane Plumbing/Fiat Products
COUNTESS - Boats—motor ☆ - Regal Marine Industries Inc.
COUNTESS - Boats—motor ☆ - Seajay Boats Inc.
COUNTESS - Brushes—hair - Spornette International, Inc.
COUNTESS - Footwear - Angel-Etts of California, Inc.
COUNTESS - Furniture ☆ - Hammary Furniture Co. Inc.
COUNTESS - Glassware—household - Owens-Illinois Inc. (Libbey Div.)
COUNTESS - Glassware—household ☆ - Colony Glass
COUNTESS - Golfing equipment - Hillerich & Bradsby Co.
COUNTESS - Hair care products - Helene Curtis Industries Inc.
COUNTESS - Nail care products - Nailtex Inc.
COUNTESS - Opera glasses - Swift Instruments, Inc.
COUNTESS - Ships—sailing vessels - Sunfish Laser Inc.
COUNTESS - Vans—conversion - Coachmen Industries, Inc.
COUNTESS - Watches - Bulova Corp.
COUNTESS CHANTILLY - Dishes—earthenware ☆ - Gorham Inc.
COUNTESS CREEPYHEAD - Toys - Tonka Corp.
COUNTESS II - Postage meters - Pelouze Scale Co.
COUNTESS ISSERLYN - Cosmetics - Alexandra De Markoff, Ltd.
COUNTESS MARA - Neckties - Randa Corp.
COUNTESS MARA - Perfumes - Countess Mara Inc.
COUNTESS MARA - Umbrellas ☆ - Schertz Umbrellas Inc.
COUNTESS MARA - Watches - Hampden Corp.
COUNTING ANIMALS - Toys - Lauri Inc.
COUNTING CHEF, THE - Games - Tuxedo Toys
COUNTING CROWS - Posters - Counting Crows
COUNTING EGGS - Toys - Playskool, Inc.
COUNTING PLUS - Computer software - Professor Corp.
COUNTING READ ALONG - Computer programming services - Berta-Max Inc.
COUNTRY - Bacon - Agar Food Products Co.
COUNTRY - Candles - Country Candle Co., Inc.
COUNTRY - Candy - Miss Saylor's Candies
COUNTRY - Copper products ☆ - Burkart Bros. Inc.
COUNTRY - Dishes—earthenware - Hadley Pottery Co. Inc.
COUNTRY - Fabrics ☆ - Gretchen Bellinger Inc.
COUNTRY - Floor coverings—carpet and rugs - Barrett Carpet Mills Inc.
COUNTRY - Food products - Prosperity Farms
COUNTRY - Furniture - Thomasville Furniture Industries Inc.
COUNTRY - Glassware—household - Svend Jensen of Denmark Inc.
COUNTRY - Motor vehicles—jeeps - DaimlerChrysler
COUNTRY - Musical instruments - Southern Highland Dulcimers & Accordions Ltd.
COUNTRY - Mustard - Nabisco Foods Group
COUNTRY - Skin care products - Aramis Inc.
COUNTRY - Tiles—ceramic - Franciscan by Johnson Brothers, USA, Inc.
COUNTRY - Yarn ☆ - Lion Brand Yarn Co.
COUNTRY 105 - Siding—insulating - Bird Inc.
COUNTRY ACCENT - Furniture ☆ - Gerry Wood Products
COUNTRY ACCENTS - Area rugs - Couristan Inc.
COUNTRY ACCENTS - Furniture ☆ - Bassett Furniture Industries, Inc.
COUNTRY ACCENTS - Glassware—household - Anchor Hocking Glass, Inc.
COUNTRY ACCESSORIES - Boxes - Tinscapes
COUNTRY AIRE - Housewares ☆ - Himark Enterprises Inc.
COUNTRY AIRS - Giftware ☆ - Pfaltzgraff Investment Co.
COUNTRY ALBUM - Wallpaper - Planox
COUNTRY AMERICA - Bags—duffel - Country America Corp.

COUNTRY AMERICAN - House furnishings ☆ - Lexington Furniture Industries, Inc.
COUNTRY AMERICANA - Furniture ☆ - Keller Manufacturing Co.
COUNTRY AND WESTERN COMPANY - Wallets - Westport Corp.
COUNTRY ANIMALS ALMANAC - Calendars ☆ - American Greetings Corp.
COUNTRY ARTIST - Figurines ☆ - Gorham Inc.
COUNTRY ARTISTS - Frames—picture - Gift Link Inc.
COUNTRY ATTITUDE - Apparel and accessories - Mall Promotions Inc.
COUNTRY BABY - Towels - Terry Products, Inc.
COUNTRY BAKER - Bakery products - Specialty Bakers Inc.
COUNTRY BAZAAR - Publisher's imprints - Country Bazaar-Publishing
COUNTRY BEAR - Cutlery - Fingerhut Companies Inc.
COUNTRY BEST - Fruits and vegetables - Agway Country Foods Inc.
COUNTRY BIBLE - Recording label - Prescott Entertainment, Inc.
COUNTRY BLEND - Cat food - Ralston Purina Co.
COUNTRY BLEND - Cereal - Homestead Mills
COUNTRY BLEND - Cheese - Wisconsin Cheese
COUNTRY BLEND - Chewing tobacco - American Maize-Products Co.
COUNTRY BLEND - Deodorizers - Norpak Companies Ltd.
COUNTRY BLEND - Dog food ☆ - Central Soya Co. Inc.
COUNTRY BLEND - Tobacco—chewing or smoking - Swisher International, Inc.
COUNTRY BLOSSOM - Dishes—china ☆ - Denby USA Limited
COUNTRY BLUE - Cooking utensils—stoneware - Western Stoneware
COUNTRY BLUE - Dinnerware—glass ☆ - Lenox, Inc.
COUNTRY BOOGIE BABY - Games - Universal Manufacturing Co., Inc.
COUNTRY BOUQUET - Area rugs, now out of production - Couristan Inc.
COUNTRY BOY - Egg substitutes ☆ - Hansen Egg Co.
COUNTRY BOY - Food containers - Faribault Foods Inc.
COUNTRY BOY - Jeans—men's - City Boy Inc.
COUNTRY BOY - Paints - Schulte Paint & Lacquer Manufacturing Co., Inc.
COUNTRY BOY - Rice - Southwest Rice Mill Co. Inc.
COUNTRY BOY - Sandwich - Country Hospitality Corp.
COUNTRY BOY CAGES - Bird cages - Ronald P. Wright, Sr.
COUNTRY BRAID - Floor coverings—carpet and rugs ☆ - Regal Rugs Inc.
COUNTRY BREEZE - Deodorizers - S.C. Johnson & Son, Inc.
COUNTRY BREEZE - Perfumes ☆ - Avon Products, Inc.
COUNTRY BRICK - Floor coverings ☆ - Tarkett, Inc.
COUNTRY BRITCHES - Men's suits, sportcoats - Country Britches
COUNTRY BROWN - Cooking utensils—stoneware - Western Stoneware
COUNTRY BUBBA - Apparel and accessories - Myriad Licensing, Inc.
COUNTRY BUMP - Recording label - Ric Rac Records
COUNTRY BUMPKIN - Dolls ☆ - Effanbee Doll Corp.
COUNTRY BUNNIES - Toys—stuffed ☆ - Fun World Inc.
COUNTRY BUY - Turkey product - Iowa Turkey Products, Inc.
COUNTRY CALICO - Dishes—china - Mikasa Co.
COUNTRY CALICO - Wallpaper - Quality House Wallcoverings
COUNTRY CAMPER - Toys—automobiles - Mattel, Inc.
COUNTRY CANDLE - Candles - Laurence Candle Co., Inc.
COUNTRY CARAVAN - Floor coverings—carpet and rugs ☆ - Trans-Ocean Import Co. Inc.
COUNTRY CARVINGS - Deodorizers - S.C. Johnson & Son, Inc.
COUNTRY CASSEROLE - Cheese - Sargento Inc.
COUNTRY CASSEROLES - Cooking equipment—household ☆ - Anchor Hocking Glass, Inc.
COUNTRY CASUAL - Floor coverings—carpet and rugs - Downs Carpet Co. Inc.
COUNTRY CASUAL - Furniture - Bean Station Furniture Factory Inc.
COUNTRY CASUAL - Furniture—wood - Ficks Reed Co. Inc.
COUNTRY CASUAL PLANK - Floor coverings - Robbins Inc.
COUNTRY CAT - Cat food - Insta Pro International
COUNTRY CAT - Cat food ☆ - Central Soya Co. Inc.
COUNTRY CHARM - Cabinets ☆ - Aristokraft, Inc.
COUNTRY CHARM - Craft supplies - Piccadilly
COUNTRY CHARM - Drapery hardware - Kenney Manufacturing Co.
COUNTRY CHARM - Flatware - Reed and Barton Corp.
COUNTRY CHARM - Floor coverings—carpet and rugs ☆ - Cabin Crafts Carpets
COUNTRY CHARM - Floor coverings—carpet and rugs ☆ - Calladium & Marglen
COUNTRY CHARM - Furniture - Stanley Furniture Co. Inc.
COUNTRY CHARM - House furnishings - L.E. Smith Glass Co.
COUNTRY CHARM - Ice cream - Dean Foods Co.
COUNTRY CHARM - Paper—gift wrap - Papercraft Corp.
COUNTRY CHARM - Pet products - Teddy Pets
COUNTRY CHARM - Trailers—travel - Travel Line Enterprises Inc.

☆ = Now out of production

COUNTRY CHARMER - Furniture - LTD Commodities, Inc.
COUNTRY CHARMERS - Apparel–women's - Ely and Walker Co.
COUNTRY CHATEAU - Floor coverings ☆ - Tarkett, Inc.
COUNTRY CHATEAU - Floor coverings–carpet and rugs ☆ - Playfield International Inc.
COUNTRY CHECK - Floor coverings–carpet and rugs - Regal Rugs Inc.
COUNTRY CHEDDAR - Crackers - Nabisco Foods Group
COUNTRY CHEDDAR'N SESAME - Crackers - Nabisco Foods Group
COUNTRY CHEF - Food products - Country Chef Foods Inc.
COUNTRY CHERRY DE-LITE - Cherries and cranberry products - Country Ovens
COUNTRY CHIPS - Snack foods - Health Valley Food
COUNTRY CHOICE - Cereal - American Cereals Corp.
COUNTRY CHRISTMAS - Cutlery ☆ - Lifetime Hoan Corp.
COUNTRY CHRISTMAS - Ornamental products–glass - Natural Products Corp.
COUNTRY CHUNKS - Food products - Mr. Dell Foods
COUNTRY CLASSIC - Apparel and accessories - Berkshire Fashions, Inc.
COUNTRY CLASSIC - Bacon - Dinner Bell Foods Inc.
COUNTRY CLASSIC - Cheese - Merkt Cheese Co., Inc.
COUNTRY CLASSIC - Furniture - Dinaire Corp.
COUNTRY CLASSIC - Ice cream - Sani-Dairy
COUNTRY CLASSIC - Meat products - Wis-Pak Foods, Inc.
COUNTRY CLASSIC - Meat products–canned - Wilson Foods Corp.
COUNTRY CLASSIC - Milk - Auburn Dairy Products, Inc.
COUNTRY CLASSIC - Paints - Distribution America, Inc.
COUNTRY CLASSIC - Pancakes–mixes - Lollipop Tree
COUNTRY CLASSIC - Spices and extracts - Jodie's Kitchen Inc.
COUNTRY CLASSIC DINNERS - Rice–flour or meal - Farmhouse Foods Co.
COUNTRY CLASSIC, THE - Archery equipment ☆ - Bear Archery Inc.
COUNTRY CLASSICS - Food products - Maple Leaf Farms Inc.
COUNTRY CLASSICS - Furniture - Weiman Co.
COUNTRY CLASSICS - Furniture ☆ - Norwalk Furniture Corp.
COUNTRY CLASSICS - Furniture–wood ☆ - Century Furniture Co.
COUNTRY CLASSICS - Ice cream ☆ - Pevely Dairy Co.
COUNTRY CLASSICS - Paints–artists' - United Gilsonite Laboratories
COUNTRY CLASSICS - Paper–tissue - Fort Howard Corp.
COUNTRY CLASSICS - Pillows - American Pacific Enterprises, Inc.
COUNTRY CLASSICS - Tableware–china - Susquehanna Glass Co.
COUNTRY CLASSICS - Telephones - Conair Corp.
COUNTRY CLASSICS - Tiles–ceramic - Summitville Tiles, Inc.
COUNTRY CLASSICS - Wallpaper ☆ - Thomas Strahan Wallcoverings
COUNTRY CLEAN - Health care products - Barcolene Inc.
COUNTRY CLOTHES - Apparel and accessories ☆ - Pendleton
COUNTRY CLOVER - Wallpaper - Warner Co.
COUNTRY CLOVER II - Wallpaper - Warner Co.
COUNTRY CLUB - American International Industries
COUNTRY CLUB - Baked goods - Country Club Food Industries Inc.
COUNTRY CLUB - Beverages–alcohol - Kasser Laird Distilling Co.
COUNTRY CLUB - Beverages–carbonated - Brooklyn Bottling Corp.
COUNTRY CLUB - Beverages–malt - Pearl Brewing Co.
COUNTRY CLUB - Beverages–malt ☆ - Labatt Importers Inc.
COUNTRY CLUB - Fertilizers - Lebanon Seaboard Corp.
COUNTRY CLUB - Floor coverings–carpet and rugs - Porter Carpet Mills Inc.
COUNTRY CLUB - Floor coverings–carpet and rugs - Quaker Inc.
COUNTRY CLUB - Floor coverings–carpet and rugs - Sheridan Carpet Mills
COUNTRY CLUB - Guitars ☆ - Fred Gretsch Enterprises
COUNTRY CLUB - Housewares ☆ - Shafford Co. Inc.
COUNTRY CLUB - Infant product - Country Club Industries (U.S.A) Corp.
COUNTRY CLUB - Liquors - David Sherman Corp.
COUNTRY CLUB - Paint ☆ - Iowa Paint Manufacturing Co. Inc.
COUNTRY CLUB - Paints - Morris Paint & Varnish Co.
COUNTRY CLUB - Plumbing fixtures–metal - Bel-Aire Sales Corp.
COUNTRY CLUB - Printed ticket sets - World Wide Press, Inc.
COUNTRY CLUB - Shrimp - Continental Seafoods Inc.
COUNTRY CLUB - Tobacco products - Sterling Tobacco Co.
COUNTRY CLUB AT WAIKIKI, THE - Apparel - Ultimate Sports Inc.
COUNTRY CLUB CASUALS - Shoes - Jay-Bee Trading Co. Inc.
COUNTRY CLUB CLASSICS - Calendars - Tri-Marketing Group
COUNTRY CLUB COLLECTION - Lighting fixtures - Angelo Brothers Co.
COUNTRY CLUB DRIVE - Wallpaper ☆ - Pantasote Inc. (Wallcovering Div.)
COUNTRY CLUB OPEN HEARTH BROILER - Cooking equipment–household - LazyMan, Inc.
COUNTRY CLUB-PAK - Salad dressings–mixes - Tucker Food Products, Inc.
COUNTRY CLUB SALON PRO - Brushes–hair - Country Club Industries (U.S.A) Corp.

COUNTRY CLUBHOUSE - Playground equipment - Hedstrom Corp.
COUNTRY COACH CONVERSION BY COUNTRY COACH - Motor vehicles–buses - Country Coach, Inc.
COUNTRY COCKTAILS - Beverages–alcohol - Jack Daniel's Distillery
COUNTRY COLLECTIBLES - Cookies - Parco Foods, Inc.
COUNTRY COLLECTIBLES - Cooking equipment–household ☆ - General Housewares Corp.
COUNTRY COLLECTION - Frames–picture - Terragrafics Inc.
COUNTRY COLLECTION - Stencils ☆ - Slomons Laboratories Inc.
COUNTRY COLLECTION, THE - Apparel and accessories ☆ - Martingale & Co.
COUNTRY COLLECTIONS - Deodorizers - Spice Market, Inc.
COUNTRY COLORS - Furniture - Ethan Allen, Inc.
COUNTRY COMFORT - Skin care products - Country Comfort
COUNTRY COMFORT IV - Wallpaper ☆ - Imperial Wallcoverings, Inc.
COUNTRY COMFORT V - Wallpaper ☆ - Imperial Wallcoverings, Inc.
COUNTRY COMFORTS - Novelty items - Papel Freelance, Inc.
COUNTRY COMFORTS - Slippers ☆ - Tru-Stitch Footwear (Div. of Wolverine World Wide)
COUNTRY CONTEMPORARY - Dining room furniture ☆ - Richardson Brothers
COUNTRY COOKERY - Barbecues and grills ☆ - Colgate-Palmolive Co.
COUNTRY COOKHOUSE - Food products - Belle Island International Inc.
COUNTRY COOKIN' - Plates–paper - Packaging Corp. of America
COUNTRY CORDOVANS - Cosmetics - Yves St. Laurent Parfum Corp.
COUNTRY CORN FLAKES - Cereal - General Mills, Inc.
COUNTRY CORNER - Hair-care and bath product - Iodent Co.
COUNTRY CORNER - Housewares - Syroco
COUNTRY CORNER - Wallpaper ☆ - Parkview Designs
COUNTRY CORNERS - Furniture - Universal Flooring
COUNTRY CORNERS - Furniture ☆ - Bassett Furniture Industries, Inc.
COUNTRY CORNFLOWER - Dinnerware ☆ - Corning Inc.
COUNTRY CORNFLOWER - Kitchen utensils–aluminum ☆ - Reston Lloyd Ltd.
COUNTRY COTA - Flower pots–earthenware ☆ - Rubens Originals
COUNTRY COTTAGE - Bakery products - Rewco, Inc.
COUNTRY COTTAGE - Cooking utensils–enameled ☆ - Reston Lloyd Ltd.
COUNTRY COTTAGE - Dinnerware–glass ☆ - Lenox, Inc.
COUNTRY COTTAGE - Furniture ☆ - Bassett Furniture Industries, Inc.
COUNTRY COTTAGE - Furniture ☆ - Lane Co. Inc.
COUNTRY COTTAGE - House furnishings - Lexington Furniture Industries, Inc.
COUNTRY COTTAGE - Housewares - Washington Forge Inc.
COUNTRY COTTAGE - Paints ☆ - Cowman-Campbell Paint Co.
COUNTRY COTTAGE - Playground equipment - Little Tikes Co.
COUNTRY COTTAGE - Soil–potting - A.H. Hoffman Inc.
COUNTRY COTTAGE BLOSSOMS - Dinnerware–glass ☆ - Lenox, Inc.
COUNTRY COTTAGE COLLECTION - Furniture ☆ - Southern Furniture Co. of Conover
COUNTRY COTTAGE COURTYARD - Dinnerware–glass ☆ - Lenox, Inc.
COUNTRY COTTAGE ORCHARD - Dinnerware–glass ☆ - Lenox, Inc.
COUNTRY COTTON - Floor coverings–carpet and rugs - Regal Rugs Inc.
COUNTRY COTTON - Yarn - Elmore-Pisgah, Inc.
COUNTRY COTTONS - Shirts - Cross Creek Apparel Inc.
COUNTRY COURT - Floor coverings - Mannington Resilient Floors
COUNTRY COURT - Furniture–wood - Ficks Reed Co. Inc.
COUNTRY COUSIN - Meat products–beef - Foodbrands America, Inc.
COUNTRY COUSINS - Dolls ☆ - Effanbee Doll Corp.
COUNTRY COUSINS - Giftware ☆ - Enesco Corp.
COUNTRY COW - Cocoa–powders or mixes - The Herb Patch
COUNTRY CRAFT - Dinnerware–glass - Franciscan by Johnson Brothers, USA, Inc.
COUNTRY CRAFT - Dishes–china - Waterford Wedgewood USA, Inc.
COUNTRY CRAFTS - Furniture ☆ - Lane Co. Inc.
COUNTRY CRAFTS - Housewares - Barth-Dreyfuss of California
COUNTRY CRAFTSMAN - Furniture - Ethan Allen, Inc.
COUNTRY CRANBERRY - Glassware–household ☆ - Fenton Art Glass Co.
COUNTRY CREAM - Candles ☆ - Carolina Designs Ltd.
COUNTRY CREAM - Skin care products - Protex
COUNTRY CREAMERY - Ice cream - Land O'Lakes Inc.
COUNTRY CREAMS - Candy - Sathers Inc.
COUNTRY CREEK FARM - Honey - Glorybee Food Inc.
COUNTRY CREEK WINERY - Wines - Country Creek Winery
COUNTRY CREST - Fruits and vegetables - FreshWorld Farms Inc.
COUNTRY CRISP - Snack foods - Granny Goose Foods, Inc.
COUNTRY CRISPS - Food products - Worthington Foods Inc.
COUNTRY CRITTERS - Candy - Superior Fruit & Confections
COUNTRY CRITTERS - Housewares ☆ - Treasure Craft Co.

☆ = Now out of production

COUNTRY CROSSINGS - Cheese - Moran Foods, Inc.
COUNTRY CROSSINGS - Furniture - Ethan Allen Finance Corp.
COUNTRY CUDDLERS - Toys - Fisher-Price, Inc.
COUNTRY CUISINE - Dishes–earthenware - Denby USA Limited
COUNTRY CUISINE - Housewares - Ernest Sohn Creations
COUNTRY CUISINE - Spaghetti sauces ☆ - Romanoff International Inc.
COUNTRY CUPBOARD - Breads–mixes - Biringer Farm
COUNTRY CUPBOARD - Colognes ☆ - Avon Products, Inc.
COUNTRY CUPBOARD - Food products - Dairy Fresh Products Co.
COUNTRY CUPBOARD - Hardware ☆ - Amerock Corp.
COUNTRY CUPBOARD - Spices and extracts ☆ - Scentex Inc.
COUNTRY CUPBOARD COLLECTION - Jams and jellies - Knott's Berry Farm
COUNTRY CUSTOMS - Women's apparel - Country Miss Inc.
COUNTRY CUT - Beef - Excel Corp.
COUNTRY CUT - Meat products–poultry - Stevens Industries Inc.
COUNTRY CUT-OUTS - House furnishings ☆ - Miller Studio
COUNTRY CUTIE - Toys - Tonka Corp.
COUNTRY CUTIES - Dolls - Bradley Import Co.
COUNTRY CUTS - Food products ☆ - General Mills, Inc.
COUNTRY CUZINS STUFF - Product description unknown - Upstate Teaching Materials
COUNTRY DAY - Turkey product - Iowa Turkey Products, Inc.
COUNTRY DECORATING WITH LAURA ASHLEY - Wallpaper ☆ - Raintree Designs Inc.
COUNTRY DELIGHT - Floor coverings–carpet and rugs ☆ - Blue Ridge Carpet Mills
COUNTRY DELIGHT - Pet products ☆ - Carlson Speciality Seeds, Inc.
COUNTRY DIARY COLLECTION - Perfumes - FMG/Tsumara Medical
COUNTRY DINING - Wallpaper - Longwood Wallcovering
COUNTRY DOCTOR - Tobacco products - House of Windsor Inc.
COUNTRY DOCTOR - Tobacco products - Philip Morris Companies Inc.
COUNTRY DOTS - Fabrics ☆ - Greenwood Mills Inc.
COUNTRY DOVE - Dinnerware ☆ - Corning Inc.
COUNTRY DUCK - Clocks ☆ - General Time Corp. (Westclox/Seth Thomas Div.)
COUNTRY DUTCH - Tools ☆ - Regent Sheffield, Ltd.
COUNTRY ELEGANCE - Floor coverings–carpet and rugs ☆ - Columbus Mills, Inc.
COUNTRY ELEGANCE - Furniture–factory - Clayton Marcus Co. Inc.
COUNTRY ELEGANCE - Wallpaper - Scalamandre Silks Inc.
COUNTRY ENGLISH - Furniture ☆ - Virginia House Furniture Corp.
COUNTRY ENGLISH COLLECTION - Furniture - Southern Furniture Co. of Conover
COUNTRY EPICURE - Cakes - Vie De France Corp.
COUNTRY ESSENCE - Paints - Chase Products Co.
COUNTRY ESTATE - Fencing–plastic - Nebraska Plastics, Inc.
COUNTRY ESTATE - Floor coverings ☆ - Robbins Inc.
COUNTRY ESTATE - Furniture ☆ - Bassett Furniture Industries, Inc.
COUNTRY ESTATE - Hardware ☆ - Alside Div.
COUNTRY ESTATE - Mobile homes - Golden West Homes
COUNTRY ESTATE - Paints - Harrison Paint Corp.
COUNTRY ESTATE - Wallpaper - Stroheim & Romann, Inc.
COUNTRY ESTATES - Meat products–canned - Design Foods
COUNTRY FAIR - Butter - Lipton Investments, Inc.
COUNTRY FAIR - Craft supplies ☆ - VIP/VIP Crafts
COUNTRY FAIR - Floor coverings–carpet and rugs ☆ - Len Dal Carpets
COUNTRY FAIR - Furniture ☆ - Stanley Furniture Co. Inc.
COUNTRY FAIR - Melamine product - Boonton Molding Co. Inc.
COUNTRY FAIR - Tableware–china ☆ - Pfaltzgraff Investment Co.
COUNTRY FAIR - Vegetables–frozen - J.G. Townsend Jr. & Co. Inc.
COUNTRY FAIR FARM - Toys - Brumberger Co. Inc.
COUNTRY FAIRE - Wallpaper - Bayview Wallcoverings
COUNTRY FAIRE - Wallpaper - Madison Wallcoverings
COUNTRY FANCIES - Wallpaper - Warner Co.
COUNTRY FANCIES II - Wallpaper - Warner Co.
COUNTRY FARE - Furniture–wood - Ficks Reed Co. Inc.
COUNTRY FARE - Griddle-cake mix - American Maple Products Corp.
COUNTRY FARM - Juices - Cadbury Beverages Inc.
COUNTRY FARMS LTD. - Meat products–beef - Taylor Country Farms Ltd.
COUNTRY FASHION - Floor coverings–carpet and rugs ☆ - Zenith Carpets
COUNTRY FASHIONS - Dishes–china - Mikasa Co.
COUNTRY FAWN - Cosmetics - Lancome
COUNTRY FAYRE - Dinnerware–glass - Franciscan by Johnson Brothers, USA, Inc.
COUNTRY FIELDS - Wallpaper - Warner Co.
COUNTRY FIELDS II - Wallpaper - Warner Co.

COUNTRY FIXINS COOKING - Deodorizers - Lumi-Lite Candle Co. Inc.
COUNTRY FLAIRE - Fabrics–tapestry ☆ - Comark Wallcoverings
COUNTRY FLOORS - Floor coverings–tile - Country Floors Inc.
COUNTRY FLORAL - Dinnerware–glass ☆ - Lenox, Inc.
COUNTRY FLORAL - Glassware–household - Crest Studios
COUNTRY FLORALS - Fabrics - Concord Fabrics Inc.
COUNTRY FLOWERS - Dishes–china ☆ - Gorham Inc.
COUNTRY FOLKS - Wallpaper ☆ - Quality House Wallcoverings
COUNTRY FOODS - All natural salad dressings - Country Foods Distributing, Ltd.
COUNTRY FRENCH - Fabrics - Concord Fabrics Inc.
COUNTRY FRENCH - Flatware - Reed and Barton Corp.
COUNTRY FRENCH - Floor coverings ☆ - Tarkett, Inc.
COUNTRY FRENCH - Wallpaper - Old Stone Mill
COUNTRY FRENCH COLLECTION FINE ANTIQUE FURNITURE, THE - Furniture - The Country French Collection
COUNTRY FRESH - Candles ☆ - Carolina Designs Ltd.
COUNTRY FRESH - Dairy products - Country Fresh Dairy
COUNTRY FRESH - Food products - Tyson Foods Inc.
COUNTRY FRESH - Insecticides - Enforcer Products Inc.
COUNTRY FRESH - Milk - Los Dairies, Inc.
COUNTRY FRESH - Mushrooms - Wilson Mushroom
COUNTRY FRESH CLASSICS - Food products - Hanover Direct Inc.
COUNTRY FRESH FARMS - Meat products–poultry - Tops Markets Inc.
COUNTRY FRESH LITE - Sour cream - Country Fresh Dairy
COUNTRY FRESH RAID - Pesticides–household - S.C. Johnson & Son, Inc.
COUNTRY FRIENDS - Wood products ☆ - Spaulding & Frost Co. Inc.
COUNTRY FRUIT - Dinnerware–glass ☆ - Lenox, Inc.
COUNTRY FUN PETS - Toys - Hasbro, Inc.
COUNTRY GARDEN - Area rugs - Couristan Inc.
COUNTRY GARDEN - Candles - Keepsake Candles
COUNTRY GARDEN - Cleaning preparations - S.C. Johnson & Son, Inc.
COUNTRY GARDEN - Floor coverings - Mannington Resilient Floors
COUNTRY GARDEN - Floor coverings–carpet and rugs - Capel, Inc.
COUNTRY GARDEN - Garden furniture - Jack-Post Corp.
COUNTRY GARDEN - Glassware–household - Owens-Illinois Inc. (Libbey Div.)
COUNTRY GARDEN - Glassware–household ☆ - Fenton Art Glass Co.
COUNTRY GARDEN - Housewares - Himark Enterprises Inc.
COUNTRY GARDEN - Wallpaper ☆ - Decor International Wallcovering Inc.
COUNTRY GARDEN NURSERY - Toys - Hasbro, Inc.
COUNTRY GARDENS - Bedding–linen ☆ - Treasure Masters
COUNTRY GARDENS - House furnishings - Lea Industries Inc.
COUNTRY GARDENS - Wallpaper - Charles Barone Inc.
COUNTRY GEESE - Floor coverings ☆ - Tarkett, Inc.
COUNTRY GENTLEMAN - Clocks ☆ - General Time Corp. (Westclox/Seth Thomas Div.)
COUNTRY GENTLEMAN - Guitars ☆ - Fred Gretsch Enterprises
COUNTRY GENTLEMAN - Housewares - Shafford Co. Inc.
COUNTRY GENTLEMAN - Paints - Passonno Paints
COUNTRY GINGHAM - Dishes–china - Mikasa Co.
COUNTRY GIRL - Food containers - Faribault Foods Inc.
COUNTRY GIRL - Food products - Golden Pantry West Inc.
COUNTRY GIRL - Sandwich ☆ - Country Hospitality Corp.
COUNTRY GIRL - Toys ☆ - Mego Financial Corp.
COUNTRY GLOW - Cosmetics - Country Glow Cosmetics Inc.
COUNTRY GOLD - Food containers - Farmhouse Foods
COUNTRY GOLD - Fruits and vegetables - Gold Digger Apple Inc.
COUNTRY GOLD - Pet products - Sunshine Mills Inc.
COUNTRY GOOD - Food products - Brakebush Brothers Inc.
COUNTRY GOODNESS - Syrup - Sunset Food & Beverage Corp.
COUNTRY GOODNESS - Vegetables–frozen - Pacific Valley Foods
COUNTRY GOURMET - Coffee flavoring - Country Gourmet International Inc.
COUNTRY GOURMET COLLECTION - Glassware–household - Owens-Illinois Inc. (Libbey Div.)
COUNTRY GRAIN - Baked goods - Bost Bakery Inc.
COUNTRY GRAIN - Breads - Earthgrains/Waldensian Bakerie
COUNTRY GRIDDLE - Batter and bakery mixes - DCA Food Industries, Inc.
COUNTRY GROVE - Beverages - Price Co.
COUNTRY GROVE - Juices ☆ - Green Spot Packaging, Inc.
COUNTRY GROWN - Food products - Country Grown Foods
COUNTRY HAMLET - Statuary ☆ - Brennan Studio Inc.
COUNTRY HANG-UPS - Candles - Keepsake Candles
COUNTRY HARVEST - Candles - Paul Hoge Creations
COUNTRY HARVEST - Cleaning preparations - Sara Lee Corp.
COUNTRY HARVEST - Fruits–dried - California Hi-Lites, Inc.

☆ = Now out of production

COUNTRY HARVEST - Nuts–salted, roasted, cooked, or canned - Ann's House of Nuts, Inc.
COUNTRY HARVEST - Popcorn - National Oats Co. Inc.
COUNTRY HARVEST - Rice ☆ - AC Humko Rice Specialties
COUNTRY HARVEST - Soup mix - Betty J. Wolfrum
COUNTRY HEARTH - Baked goods - Interstate Brands Corp.
COUNTRY HEARTH - Bread crumbs - Metz Baking Co.
COUNTRY HEARTH - Breads - Perfection Bakery
COUNTRY HEARTH - Dinnerware ☆ - Corning Inc.
COUNTRY HEARTH - Floor coverings - Congoleum Corp.
COUNTRY HEARTH - Wallpaper - Warner Co.
COUNTRY HEARTH II - Wallpaper - Warner Co.
COUNTRY HEARTH LITE - Crackers - President Baking Co., Inc.
COUNTRY HEARTS - Dinnerware ☆ - Corning Inc.
COUNTRY HEATHERS - Apparel and accessories - Thomson Co.
COUNTRY HERB LOAF - Bakery products - Southern Roots
COUNTRY HERBALS BY ANDREA - Skin care products - Andrea's Country Herbals
COUNTRY HERITAGE - Fabrics–tapestry - Comark Wallcoverings
COUNTRY HERITAGE - Furniture - Stanley Furniture Co. Inc.
COUNTRY HERITAGE - Wallpaper ☆ - Thomas Strahan Wallcoverings
COUNTRY HERITAGE COLLECTION - Rugs - Nourison
COUNTRY HERITAGE COOPER - Meat products–poultry - Cooper Hatchery Inc.
COUNTRY HILLS - Footwear ☆ - E.S. Originals, Inc.
COUNTRY HITS - Food products - Saramar Corp.
COUNTRY HOLLY - Dinnerware–glass - Lenox, Inc.
COUNTRY HOME - Baked goods - Country Home Bakers, Inc.
COUNTRY HOME - Floor coverings–carpet and rugs - Evans-Black Carpet Mills
COUNTRY HOME - Mail boxes - Cedar Works Inc.
COUNTRY HOMES - Wood products - Paneling Instructions (Paneling Div.)
COUNTRY HOSPITALITY INN - Hotel franchise - Country Hospitality Corp.
COUNTRY HOSPITALITY SUITES - Hotel franchise - Country Hospitality Corp.
COUNTRY HOUSE - Bath salts - Chase Collection, Inc.
COUNTRY HOUSE - Biscuits ☆ - C. & J. Willenborg Inc.
COUNTRY HOUSE - Doughs–frozen ☆ - Fromm Family Foods, Inc.
COUNTRY HOUSE - Tents - Gale Group Inc.
COUNTRY HOUSE - Wallpaper - Greeff Fabrics Inc.
COUNTRY HUMOR NETWORK - Recording label - Bonita June Belshan
COUNTRY HUTCH - Night clubs - Aquathin Corp.
COUNTRY IMAGES - Furniture–wood ☆ - Ficks Reed Co. Inc.
COUNTRY IMAGES - Mail boxes - Steel City Corp.
COUNTRY IMPRESSIONS - Wallpaper - Warner Co.
COUNTRY IMPRESSIONS II - Wallpaper - Warner Co.
COUNTRY INN - Fabrics - Uniroyal Engineered Products
COUNTRY INN - Floor coverings–carpet and rugs ☆ - Evans-Black Carpet Mills
COUNTRY INN - Food products - Lipton Investments, Inc.
COUNTRY INN - Food products - Uncle Ben's, Inc.
COUNTRY INN - Furniture - Mersman Furniture Co.
COUNTRY INN - Furniture ☆ - Bassett Furniture Industries, Inc.
COUNTRY INN - Hams - Sugardale Foods Inc.
COUNTRY INN - Kitchen appliances ☆ - National Housewares
COUNTRY INN - Seasonings - Fresh Mark, Inc.
COUNTRY INN ALE - Beverages–malt - Rose's Restaurants, Inc.
COUNTRY INSPIRATIONS - Greeting cards - Country Inspirations
COUNTRY ITALIAN COOKING - Vegetable sauces - Nestle USA
COUNTRY JAM, USA - Posters - Country Jam USA, Inc.
COUNTRY JUBILEE - Recording label - Scorpio Enterprises Inc.
COUNTRY JUNCTION - Telephones - At&T Corp.
COUNTRY JUNIOR - Women's apparel - Country Miss Inc.
COUNTRY KEEPER - Containers - Rainfall Inc.
COUNTRY KEEPERS - Glassware–household - Owens-Illinois Inc. (Libbey Div.)
COUNTRY KENNEL - Dog food - Darigold, Inc.
COUNTRY KENNEL - Dog food - Insta Pro International
COUNTRY KETTLE - Cooking utensils–aluminum ☆ - West Bend Co.
COUNTRY KETTLE - Potato chips ☆ - State Line Potato Chip Co.
COUNTRY-KING - Labels–paper - Five Star Entertainment
COUNTRY-KINS - Dolls - Russ Berrie and Co., Inc.
COUNTRY KITCHEN - Air freshener - Dial Corp.
COUNTRY KITCHEN - Bakery products - F.R. Le Page Bakery
COUNTRY KITCHEN - Cookies - Parco Foods, Inc.
COUNTRY KITCHEN - Dinnerware–glass ☆ - Royal China & Porcelain Companies Inc.

COUNTRY KITCHEN - Dishes–china - Taylor, Smith & Taylor Co.
COUNTRY KITCHEN - Fabrics–tapestry ☆ - Coloroll Inc.
COUNTRY KITCHEN - Food products ☆ - Mrs. Giles Country Kitchens Inc.
COUNTRY KITCHEN - Fruits and vegetables - Wapato Fruit Products Inc.
COUNTRY KITCHEN - Giftware ☆ - Doranne
COUNTRY KITCHEN - Glassware–household - Anchor Hocking Glass, Inc.
COUNTRY KITCHEN - Kitchenware–earthenware ☆ - Arita Sales Co. Inc.
COUNTRY KITCHEN - Restaurant franchise - Country Hospitality Corp.
COUNTRY KITCHEN - Trays - Knobler International Ltd.
COUNTRY KITCHEN COUNTRY INN - Hotel franchise, no longer in use - Country Hospitality Corp.
COUNTRY KITCHENS - Wallpaper - Old Stone Mill
COUNTRY KRISP - Food products - Brakebush Brothers Inc.
COUNTRY KWENCHER - Wines - Ernest and Julio Gallo Winery
COUNTRY LACE - Artists' materials - Syroco
COUNTRY LACE - Floor coverings - Mannington Resilient Floors
COUNTRY LACE - House furnishings - Lea Industries Inc.
COUNTRY LACE - Wallpaper - Warner Co.
COUNTRY LANDINGS - Linen - Fingerhut Companies Inc.
COUNTRY LANE - Dairy products - Country Fresh Dairy
COUNTRY LANE - Floor coverings ☆ - Congoleum Corp.
COUNTRY LANE - Floor coverings–carpet and rugs ☆ - Playfield International Inc.
COUNTRY LANE - Floor coverings–carpet and rugs ☆ - Regal Rugs Inc.
COUNTRY LANE - Giftware - Russ Berrie and Co., Inc.
COUNTRY LANE - Meat product - Country Lane Foods Inc.
COUNTRY LANE - Shoes - Dentex Shoe Corp.
COUNTRY LANE - Tables–wood - Riverside Furniture Corp.
COUNTRY LANE - Tableware–china ☆ - Lenox, Inc.
COUNTRY LANE - Toiletries, decorated soaps and sachets - Country Lane Enterprises Inc.
COUNTRY LASS - Socks - Renfro Corp.
COUNTRY LEGEND - Clocks - Ridgeway Clock Co.
COUNTRY LEGEND - Shampoos - South Texas Pet Products, Inc.
COUNTRY LIFE - Furniture - Tomlinson of High Point Inc.
COUNTRY LIFE - Granola, fruit and nut mixes - Country Life Natural Foods
COUNTRY LIFE - Recording label - McLain Family Band
COUNTRY LIFE - Toiletries - Country Life
COUNTRY LIFE - Wallcoverings, carpets and rugs, etc. - Courtney Corp.
COUNTRY LIFE - Wallpaper - J. Josephson, Inc.
COUNTRY LIFE - Wallpaper ☆ - Charles Barone Inc.
COUNTRY LIFESTYLES - Furniture ☆ - Broyhill Furniture Industries, Inc.
COUNTRY LIGHT - Popcorn ☆ - McCormick & Co., Inc.
COUNTRY LITE - Dairy products - Country Fresh Dairy
COUNTRY LITE - Eggnog - Guida's Seibert Dairy
COUNTRY LIVING - Furniture ☆ - Bassett Furniture Industries, Inc.
COUNTRY LIVING - Publisher's imprints - Hearst Corp.
COUNTRY LODGE - Dinnerware–glass - Lenox, Inc.
COUNTRY LODGE - Furniture ☆ - Lane Co. Inc.
COUNTRY LOOKS - Dolls - Mattel, Inc.
COUNTRY LORE - Wallpaper - Warner Co.
COUNTRY LORE II - Wallpaper - Warner Co.
COUNTRY MAGIC - Flowers, plants, and seeds - Willamette Seed Co.
COUNTRY MAGIC - Wallpaper - Warner Co.
COUNTRY MAGIC II - Wallpaper - Warner Co.
COUNTRY MAID - Pickles - W.B. Roddenbery Co., Inc.
COUNTRY MAID - Pork - Dubuque Foods, Inc.
COUNTRY MANNERS - Wallpaper - Charles Barone Inc.
COUNTRY MANOR - See IMPRESSIONS
COUNTRY MANOR - Cabinets - Scott Manufacturing, Inc.
COUNTRY MANOR - Floor coverings - Mannington Resilient Floors
COUNTRY MANOR - Food products - P and C Food Markets Inc.
COUNTRY MANOR - Furniture - Stanley Furniture Co. Inc.
COUNTRY MANOR - Furniture ☆ - Bassett Furniture Industries, Inc.
COUNTRY MANOR - Garden furniture - Nebraska Plastics, Inc.
COUNTRY MANOR - Hardware ☆ - Amerock Corp.
COUNTRY MANOR - Linen - Notra Trading, Inc.
COUNTRY MANOR - Motor vehicle parts and accessories - Cricket Camper Manufacturing Co.
COUNTRY MANOR - Wallpaper - Frankford Wallcoverings Inc.
COUNTRY MANOR COLLECTION - Cosmetics - Estee Lauder Inc.
COUNTRY MANSION BY STEPHEN - Wallpaper - Westhill Wallcoverings Inc.
COUNTRY MART - Food products - Associated Wholesale Grocers, Inc.
COUNTRY MEADOWS - Skin care products - Energen Products Inc.
COUNTRY MEAL - Breads - Campbell Taggart Inc.
COUNTRY MEMORIES - Dinnerware ☆ - Corning Inc.

☆ = Now out of production

COUNTRY MEMORY - Giftware - Russ Berrie and Co., Inc.
COUNTRY MINIATURES - Wallpaper ☆ - Newmarket Designs Ltd.
COUNTRY MISS - Women's apparel - Country Miss Inc.
COUNTRY MOOD - Floor coverings–carpet and rugs ☆ - Galaxy Carpet Mills Inc.
COUNTRY MOODS - Furniture ☆ - Bassett Furniture Industries, Inc.
COUNTRY MORNING - Giftware ☆ - L.E. Smith Glass Co.
COUNTRY MORNING - Hobby kits - Design Works Crafts
COUNTRY MORNING - Margarine - Land O'Lakes Inc.
COUNTRY MOUSE - Paper - Beach Products
COUNTRY NATURAL - Hair care products - Willat Co.
COUNTRY NATURAL - Lipsticks ☆ - Avon Products, Inc.
COUNTRY NATURALS - Furniture - American Moulding & Millwork Co.
COUNTRY NIGHTS - Deodorizers - S.C. Johnson & Son, Inc.
COUNTRY NUGGETS - Food products - Pierce Foods Corp.
COUNTRY OAK - Cabinets - Del Mar Cabinets
COUNTRY OAK - Dining room furniture - Richardson Brothers
COUNTRY OAK - Floor coverings - Bruce Hardwood Floors
COUNTRY OAK - Furniture - Pennsylvania House
COUNTRY OAK - Knives - Imperial Schrade Corp.
COUNTRY OAK - Siding–metal - Aluminum Co. of America
COUNTRY OAK COLLECTION - Furniture - Brady Furniture Co. Inc.
COUNTRY OAKS - Furniture - Thomasville Furniture Industries Inc.
COUNTRY ONLINE - Computer software - Nashville Music Connection, Inc.
COUNTRY ORCHARD - Frames–picture - Terragrafics Inc.
COUNTRY ORIGINALS, INC. - Giftware - Country Originals Inc.
COUNTRY OVEN - Food products - The Kroger Co.
COUNTRY PAL - Dog food ☆ - Central Soya Co. Inc.
COUNTRY PARQUET - Floor coverings - Congoleum Corp.
COUNTRY PASTA - Pasta - Country Foods, Inc.
COUNTRY PEA PATCHWORK - Soups–canned - Buckeye Beans & Herbs, Inc.
COUNTRY PEACH - Glassware–household ☆ - Fenton Art Glass Co.
COUNTRY PEACH PASSION - Teas–herbal - Celestial Seasonings, Inc.
COUNTRY PEACH SPICE - Teas–herbal - Celestial Seasonings, Inc.
COUNTRY PEDDLER - Cooking utensils–glass - Cardinal Inc.
COUNTRY PEDDLER - Lamps - Kaadan Ltd.
COUNTRY PERFECTION - Dog food - O.H. Kruse Grain and Milling Corp.
COUNTRY PINE COLLECTION - Furniture - Brady Furniture Co. Inc.
COUNTRY PINE TRADITIONS - Unfinished and prefinished furniture - American Moulding & Millwork Co.
COUNTRY PLACE - Floor coverings–carpet and rugs - Galaxy Carpet Mills Inc.
COUNTRY PLACE - Lumber - Georgia-Pacific Corp.
COUNTRY PLEASURE - Wallpaper - K.M.L. Industries
COUNTRY PRIDE - Dinnerware ☆ - Corning Inc.
COUNTRY PRIDE - Floor coverings–carpet and rugs - Alexander Smith Carpets
COUNTRY PRIDE - Food products - Conagra, Inc.
COUNTRY PRIDE - Potato chips - State Line Potato Chip Co.
COUNTRY PRIME - Dog food - Hubbard Milling Co.
COUNTRY PRIME MOIST & TASTY - Pet food - Hubbard Milling Co.
COUNTRY PROMENADE - Dinnerware ☆ - Corning Inc.
COUNTRY PURE - Iced tea–bottled or canned - Alysia Inc.
COUNTRY PURE - Peanut butter ☆ - Safeway Stores Inc.
COUNTRY QUEEN - Egg product - Country Queen Foods Inc.
COUNTRY QUEST GOURMET SEASONING - Seasonings - John W. Ridings, Jr.
COUNTRY QUILT - Floor coverings - Mannington Resilient Floors
COUNTRY QUILT - Housewares ☆ - Vermillion Inc.
COUNTRY QUILTS & BASKETS - Wallpaper ☆ - Quality House Wallcoverings
COUNTRY RAMBLERS - Shoes - Manistee Inc.
COUNTRY RECIPE - Food products - Uncle Ben's, Inc.
COUNTRY REFLECTIONS - Fabrics - Greenwood Mills Inc.
COUNTRY REFLECTIONS - Furniture ☆ - Stanley Furniture Co. Inc.
COUNTRY RIPPLES - Snack foods - Health Valley Food
COUNTRY ROAD - Automotive parts and accessories - Lancaster Colony Automotive Group
COUNTRY ROAD - Floor coverings ☆ - Congoleum Corp.
COUNTRY ROAD - Recording label - Scene Productions/Purple Haze Music
COUNTRY ROAD PLUSH - Automotive parts and accessories - Lancaster Colony Automotive Group
COUNTRY ROADS - Apparel–women's - Creighton Inc.
COUNTRY ROADS - Furniture ☆ - Brooks Furniture Manufacturing Inc.
COUNTRY ROADS - Furniture ☆ - Kincaid Furniture Co. Inc.
COUNTRY ROADS - Skin care products ☆ - Carme Inc.

COUNTRY ROADS - Wood products - Weyerhaeuser Co.
COUNTRY ROMANCE - Dinnerware–glass - Lenox, Inc.
COUNTRY ROMANCE - Fabrics–tapestry - Comark Wallcoverings
COUNTRY ROSE - Floor coverings–carpet and rugs ☆ - Regal Rugs Inc.
COUNTRY ROSE - Nail care products - Cosmair Inc.
COUNTRY ROUNDS - Giftware - Walnut Hollow Farm, Inc.
COUNTRY RUFFLE - Curtains - Croscill Curtain Co. Inc.
COUNTRY SCENE - Furniture ☆ - Bassett Furniture Industries, Inc.
COUNTRY SCENE - Glassware–household ☆ - Fenton Art Glass Co.
COUNTRY SCENT - Cleaning preparations - Linden Corp.
COUNTRY SCENTS - Giftware - Natural Products Corp.
COUNTRY SCRAMBLE - Food products - Denny's Inc.
COUNTRY SEASONED - Food products ☆ - Pillsbury Co.
COUNTRY SEASON'S - Apparel and accessories - Farwest Garments Inc.
COUNTRY SECRET - Meat products–poultry - Hudson Foods, Inc.
COUNTRY SEDAN - Motor vehicles–automobiles ☆ - Ford Motor Co.
COUNTRY SELECT - Animal feeds - Kwik Trip, Inc.
COUNTRY SELECTIONS - Breakfast entrees - Saramar Corp.
COUNTRY SET - Apparel and accessories - Palm Beach Co., Inc.
COUNTRY SHOP - Furniture ☆ - Bernhardt Industries
COUNTRY SHOWCASE - Wallpaper ☆ - Eisenhart Wallcoverings Co.
COUNTRY SIDE - Floor coverings–carpet and rugs ☆ - Customweave Carpets Inc.
COUNTRY SIDE - Furniture–wood - Design Line Cabinets
COUNTRY SKILLET - Catfish - Country Skillet Catfish Co.
COUNTRY SKILLET - Food products - Conagra, Inc.
COUNTRY SKILLET CHEDDARS - Sausages - Johnsonville Foods Co.
COUNTRY SLIM - Dairy products - Zinal, Inc.
COUNTRY SOPHISTICATES - Apparel–women's ☆ - Pendleton
COUNTRY SPECIAL - Harmonicas - Hohner Inc.
COUNTRY SPECTRUM - Floor coverings–carpet and rugs - Regal Rugs Inc.
COUNTRY SPICE - Perfumes ☆ - Carolina Designs Ltd.
COUNTRY SPICE - Tea - Coffee Bean International, Inc.
COUNTRY SPICE TEA - Teas - Coffee Bean International, Inc.
COUNTRY SPOON - Jams and jellies - Rowley's South Ridge Farms, Inc.
COUNTRY SPORT - Apparel–women's - David Smith
COUNTRY SPRING, THE - Water–bottled or canned - Spring Water Vending Co. Inc.
COUNTRY SPRINGS - Beverages - Country Springs Beverage Co.
COUNTRY SPRINGS - Beverages–carbonated - Mountain Meadows Springs
COUNTRY SPRINGS - Dairy products ☆ - Country Fresh Dairy
COUNTRY SPRINGS - Water–bottled or canned - North American Beverages
COUNTRY SQUIRE - Apparel and accessories ☆ - Jantzen Inc.
COUNTRY SQUIRE - Astringents - GTA Feeds
COUNTRY SQUIRE - Cabinets - Riviera Cabinets Inc.
COUNTRY SQUIRE - Clocks ☆ - Sunbeam Precision Measurement
COUNTRY SQUIRE - Frames–eyeglass ☆ - Universal/Univis Inc.
COUNTRY SQUIRE - Furniture ☆ - Riverside Furniture Corp.
COUNTRY SQUIRE - Glassware–household ☆ - Owens-Illinois Inc. (Libbey Div.)
COUNTRY SQUIRE - Gloves - Boss Manufacturing Co.
COUNTRY SQUIRE - Hardware - National Lock Cabinet Hardware
COUNTRY SQUIRE - Mail boxes - Steel City Corp.
COUNTRY SQUIRE - Motor vehicles–automobiles ☆ - Ford Motor Co.
COUNTRY SQUIRE - Paints ☆ - Adelphi Coatings Co.
COUNTRY SQUIRE - Tables - Impact Furniture
COUNTRY SQUIRE - Telephones - At&T Corp.
COUNTRY SQUIRE - Tires - Universal Cooperative Inc.
COUNTRY SQUIRE - Wines - Fruit Wines of Florida Inc.
COUNTRY STAND - Fruits and vegetables - Ralston Purina Co.
COUNTRY STAR - Bicycles ☆ - J.C. Penney Co., Inc.
COUNTRY STAR - Jewelry - Country Star Restaurants, Inc.
COUNTRY STAR - Meat products–beef - Armour Swift-Eckrich
COUNTRY STAR INTERNATIONAL - Recording label - Country Star International
COUNTRY STENCIL - Clocks - General Time Corp. (Westclox/Seth Thomas Div.)
COUNTRY STENCIL - Floor coverings ☆ - Tarkett, Inc.
COUNTRY STITCHERY III - Wallpaper ☆ - Imperial Wallcoverings, Inc.
COUNTRY STITCHERY: SAMPLER EDITION - Wallpaper ☆ - Imperial Wallcoverings, Inc.
COUNTRY STORE - Candy ☆ - Good Taste Products, Inc.
COUNTRY STORE - Hair- and skin-care products, fragrance, etc. - Benjamin Ansehl Co.
COUNTRY STORE - Meats–luncheon - Dinner Bell Foods Inc.
COUNTRY STORE - Snack foods - Borden, Inc.
COUNTRY STORE - Tobacco products - 1776 Tobacco Co.

☆ = Now out of production

COUNTRY STORE - Wallpaper - Andover Wallcovering
COUNTRY STORE II - Wallpaper - J. Josephson, Inc.
COUNTRY STORE, THE - Wallpaper - Tattersalls
COUNTRY STORY I - Wallpaper - J. Josephson, Inc.
COUNTRY STORY II, THE - Wallpaper - J. Josephson, Inc.
COUNTRY STREAM - Snack foods ☆ - Golden Stream Quality Foods
COUNTRY STRIPES - Wallpaper - Warner Co.
COUNTRY STUFFER - Sandwich ☆ - Country Hospitality Corp.
COUNTRY STYLE - Breads - Country Style Baking Co.
COUNTRY STYLE - Chili, pork and beans - American Home Food Products Inc.
COUNTRY STYLE - Cookies - Sunshine Biscuits, Inc.
COUNTRY STYLE - Donut-shop franchise - Country Style Donuts
COUNTRY STYLE - Food products - Tom's Foods Inc.
COUNTRY STYLE - Potato sticks ☆ - Ore-Ida Foods, Inc.
COUNTRY STYLE - Soups–mixes - Lipton Investments, Inc.
COUNTRY STYLE - Wallpaper - Sanitas Wallcoverings
COUNTRY STYLE - Wallpaper - Surface Industries Inc.
COUNTRY STYLE BREAD - Breads - Cookie FruitEast Hampton
COUNTRY STYLE KRISSPY - Potato chips - M.C. Snack Inc.
COUNTRY SUBURBANS - Women's apparel - Country Miss Inc.
COUNTRY SUNSHINE - Giftware ☆ - Sangray Corp.
COUNTRY SUNSHINE - Infant product - Dundee Mills, Inc.
COUNTRY SWEET - Sauces - Country Sweet Food Products
COUNTRY SWEETS - Wallpaper ☆ - Imperial Wallcoverings, Inc.
COUNTRY SWEETS III - Wallpaper ☆ - Imperial Wallcoverings, Inc.
COUNTRY SWING - Flower pots–earthenware ☆ - Liberty Ridge
COUNTRY TABLE - Dinners–frozen - Conagra, Inc.
COUNTRY THEMES COLLECTION - Floor coverings–carpet and rugs - Trend Carpet
COUNTRY TILE - Plastics–laminated ☆ - Plaskolite Inc.
COUNTRY TILES - Floor coverings - Country Floors Inc.
COUNTRY TIME - Beverages–carbonated - Dr. Pepper/Seven Up, Inc.
COUNTRY TIME - Fabrics - Dan River Inc.
COUNTRY TIME - Sausages - Miller Sausage Co. Inc.
COUNTRY TIME RACING - Jewelry - Kraft Food Ingredients Corp.
COUNTRY TOUCH - Apparel–men's - Harper Shirt Co.
COUNTRY TOUR - Wallcoverings - Scancelli Prints, Inc.
COUNTRY TRADITIONAL KITCHEN & BATH - Wallpaper - Madison Wallcoverings
COUNTRY TRADITIONALS - Apparel–men's ☆ - Pendleton
COUNTRY TRADITIONALS - Fabrics–tapestry ☆ - Columbus Coated Fabrics Co.
COUNTRY TRADITIONALS COLLECTION - Fabrics–tapestry ☆ - Coloroll Inc.
COUNTRY TRADITIONS - Furniture ☆ - Bassett Furniture Industries, Inc.
COUNTRY TRADITIONS - Furniture–upholstered - Statesville Chair Co. Inc.
COUNTRY TRADITIONS COLLECTION - Giftware - Russ Berrie and Co., Inc.
COUNTRY TRAIL - Floor coverings ☆ - Congoleum Corp.
COUNTRY TRAIL - Snack foods - Farley Candy Co.
COUNTRY TRANSITIONS - Furniture ☆ - Kincaid Furniture Co. Inc.
COUNTRY TREASURE - Figurines - Decorator and Craft Corp.
COUNTRY TREASURE - Floor coverings–carpet and rugs - Downs Carpet Co. Inc.
COUNTRY TREASURES - Furniture - Athens Furniture Industries Inc.
COUNTRY TREASURES - Housewares ☆ - Vermillion Inc.
COUNTRY TREASURES - Meat products–poultry - Hester Industries, Inc.
COUNTRY TREASURES - Paints - Dap Products Inc.
COUNTRY TREASURES - Wallpaper - Warner Co.
COUNTRY TREASURES III - Wallpaper - Warner Co.
COUNTRY TWEED - Slippers - Acorn
COUNTRY VALLEY BAKERS - Cookies - Silver Lake Cookie Co., Inc.
COUNTRY VANILLA - Deodorizers - Reckitt & Colman, Inc.
COUNTRY VILLAGE - Clocks ☆ - General Time Corp. (Westclox/Seth Thomas Div.)
COUNTRY VILLAGE - Fabrics–tapestry ☆ - Coloroll Inc.
COUNTRY VILLAGE - Games ☆ - Milton Bradley Co.
COUNTRY VILLAGE - Popcorn - National Oats Co. Inc.
COUNTRY VIOLETS - Dinnerware - Corning Inc.
COUNTRY VOGUE II - Wallcovering ☆ - Colortree Designs
COUNTRY WALK - Furniture - Weiman Co.
COUNTRY WALK II - Furniture - Weiman Co.
COUNTRY WARE - Giftware - Wilton Co.
COUNTRY WAY - Wallpaper - Norwall Wallcoverings
COUNTRY WEAVE - Floor coverings–carpet and rugs ☆ - Carpet Crafts Inc.
COUNTRY WEDDING - Dolls - Seymour Mann Inc.
COUNTRY WELCOME, A - Wallcovering - Fashon Wallcoverings

COUNTRY WESTERN STAR - Dolls - Mattel, Inc.
COUNTRY WHITE - Breads ☆ - Schmidt Baking Co., Inc.
COUNTRY WOOD - Floor coverings - Congoleum Corp.
COUNTRY WOODS - Blinds–venetian - Hunter Douglas, Inc.
COUNTRY WOODS - Cleaning preparations - S.C. Johnson & Son, Inc.
COUNTRY WOODS - Window coverings - Hunter Douglas Intermountain Fabrication Co.
COUNTRY WOODWORKS - Furniture - Hills Department Store Co.
COUNTRYBLUEPRINT - Computer software - Philip B. Payne and Nancy C. Payne
COUNTRYMAN PRESS - Publisher's imprints - Countryman Press Inc.
COUNTRYMARK CO-OP - Fertilizers - Countrymark Cooperative, Inc.
COUNTRY'S DELIGHT - Food products - Certified Grocers Midwest Inc.
COUNTRYSIDE - Bedding–linen - Dan River Inc.
COUNTRYSIDE - Cooking equipment–household ☆ - Mirro Corp.
COUNTRYSIDE - Dairy products - Land-O-Sun Dairies, Inc.
COUNTRYSIDE - Dinnerware–glass ☆ - Lenox, Inc.
COUNTRYSIDE - Floor coverings–tile - VPI
COUNTRYSIDE - Flooring–hardwood ☆ - Memphis Hardwood Flooring Co.
COUNTRYSIDE - Food products - Home Canning Co.
COUNTRYSIDE - Food products - Hormel Foods Corp.
COUNTRYSIDE - House furnishings ☆ - Lexington Furniture Industries, Inc.
COUNTRYSIDE - Siding–insulating ☆ - Masonite Corp.
COUNTRYSIDE - Soap - Countryside Fragrances Inc.
COUNTRYSIDE - Wallpaper - S.M. Hexter Co.
COUNTRYSIDE CLASSICS - Apparel and accessories - Kellwood Co.
COUNTRYSIDE COLLECTION - Furniture - Brady Furniture Co. Inc.
COUNTRYSIDE FARMS - Meat products–cured - Butcher Boy Meats Inc.
COUNTRYSIDE FROM GREENFIELD VILLAGE - Wallpaper ☆ - S.M. Hexter Co.
COUNTRYSIDE HERB FARM - Potpourri - Countryside Fragrances Inc.
COUNTRYSIDE ORIGINALS - Frames–picture - Russ Berrie and Co., Inc.
COUNTRYSIDE ORIGINALS - Bicycles ☆ - Raleigh USA Bicycle Co.
COUNTRYSIDE OUTFITTERS - Apparel and accessories - DRL, Inc.
COUNTRYSIDE OUTFITTERS - Shirts - DRL Inc.
COUNTRYSIDE PLANTERS - Pottery products - Novelty Manufacturing Co.
COUNTRYSIDE PLANTERS PLANTER TUBS & FLOWER BOXES - Flower pots–earthenware - Novelty Manufacturing Co.
COUNTRYSIDE STENCILS - Wallpaper - Sellers & Josephson
COUNTRYSIDES - Stationery - Current, Inc.
COUNTRYTIME - Furniture ☆ - Bassett Furniture Industries, Inc.
COUNTRYTYME - Clocks ☆ - General Time Corp. (Westclox/Seth Thomas Div.)
COUNTRYWARE - Dinnerware–glass - Franciscan by Johnson Brothers, USA, Inc.
COUNTRYWARE - Giftware - Waterford Wedgewood USA, Inc.
COUNTRYWILD - Rice - Lundberg Family Farms
COUNTRYWOOD - Siding–metal - Alcan Aluminum Corp. Alcan Building Products Div.
COUNTY - Recording label - County Records
COUNTY BRITCHES - Apparel and accessories - Phillips-Van Heusen Corp.
COUNTY CLARE - Wallpaper - Newmarket Designs Ltd.
COUNTY FAIR - Beverages - Creative Beverage Co.
COUNTY FAIR - Bread - Interstate Brands Corp.
COUNTY FAIR - Floor coverings - Mannington Resilient Floors
COUNTY FAIR - Fruits–canned - Stapleton-Spence Packing Co.
COUNTY FAIR - Lumber - Georgia-Pacific Corp.
COUNTY FARE - Food products - Amendt Milling Co.
COUNTY FB - Apparel and accessories - Frisco County Inc.
COUNTY LIFE - Furniture - Universal Flooring
COUNTY LIFE II - Furniture - Universal Flooring
COUNTY LINE - Cheese ☆ - Hunt-Wesson, Inc.
COUNTY LINE - Furniture ☆ - Bassett Furniture Industries, Inc.
COUNTY LINE - Meat products–pork - County Line, Inc.
COUNTY LINE LIMITED - Bird feeders - County Line Limited LLC
COUNTY MARKET - Food products - Super Valu Inc.
COUNTY OF LOS ANGELES DEPARTMENT OF PARKS & RECREATION - Publisher's imprints - County of Los Angeles Department of Parks & Recreation
COUNTY PAVERS - Concrete products - County Concrete Corp.
COUNTY PRIZE - Beverages - Wyler Foods/Borden Inc.
COUNTY SEAT - Furniture ☆ - Vaughan Furniture Co. Inc.
COUNTY SQUARE - Floor coverings–carpet and rugs - Regal Rugs Inc.
COUNTY STONE - Stone products - County Concrete Corp.
COUNTY WAREHOUSE - Apparel and accessories - Charlotte Shops, Ltd.
COUNTYLINE PUBLISHING - Publisher's imprints - Vintage Images

COUP D' ECLAT - Skin care products - Nailtex Inc.
COUP D'ARGENT - Cosmetics - Lancome
COUPE - Shoes–athletic - Ektelon
COUPE - Sporting goods - Skis Dynastar, Inc.
COUPE BOURSIN - Cheese ☆ - Schratter Import
COUPE DE VILLE - Fabrics - Burlington House Fabrics Group
COUPE DE VILLE - Motor vehicles–automobiles - General Motors Corp. (Cadillac Motor Car Div.)
COUPE GT - Motor vehicles–automobiles ☆ - Audi of America Inc.
COUPE ROYAL - Fabrics - Dan River Inc.
COUPIE-UP - Toys - Concept Products Inc.
COUPLE POWER - Video production - Peter Sheras
COUPLER PEOPLE, THE - Toys–trains - Kadee Quality Products
COUPLES - Greeting cards - American Greetings Corp.
COUPLES - Novelty items ☆ - Papel Freelance, Inc.
COUPLES - Publisher's imprints - Scholastic Inc.
COUPLES COACH - Motor vehicles–motor homes ☆ - Avco Aerostructures Inc.
COUPLOX - Fittings–cast iron - Ward Manufacturing Inc.
COUPON - Paper–bond ☆ - Fox River Paper Co.
COUPONS ALA CART - Boxes - Joseph R. Gregoire
COUPONS GALORE - Coupons - Saul Lerner
COUPTITE - Fittings–cast iron - Ward Manufacturing Inc.
COUPY - Drafting supplies ☆ - Sakura of America
COUQUETTE POODLE - Toys–stuffed - Russ Berrie and Co., Inc.
COURACADO - Footwear ☆ - Conjac Inc.
COURAGE - Apparel–men's - Crystal Brands Inc.
COURAGE FOR YOUR HEAD - Safety products - Bell Sports, Inc.
COURAGEOUS - Floor coverings–carpet and rugs - Dorsett Carpet Mills Inc.
COURAGEOUS - Floor coverings–carpet and rugs - Philadelphia Carpets
COURAGEOUS - Toys - Tonka Corp.
COURAGEOUS BLEND - Coffee - Frontier Cooperative Herbs
COURAGEOUS CAPTAINS - Fish–fresh or frozen - North Atlantic Fish Co.
COURCEL - Fabrics–rayon ☆ - Courtaulds Fibres Inc.
COURCELLES - Glassware–household - Durand International
COURCHEVAL - Brandy - Chatam International Inc.
COURCHEVEL - Apparel–men's - Damon Creations Inc.
COURIER - Bicycles ☆ - Roadmaster Corp.
COURIER - Chimes - Friedland, Inc.
COURIER - Clocks ☆ - General Time Corp. (Westclox/Seth Thomas Div.)
COURIER - Computer software - U.S. Robotics Access Corp.
COURIER - Doors–wood ☆ - Peachtree Doors and Windows Inc.
COURIER - Electronic-data carrier cards - Datakey Inc.
COURIER - Floor coverings–carpet and rugs ☆ - Customweave Carpets Inc.
COURIER - Floor coverings–carpet and rugs ☆ - Mannington Carpets, Inc.
COURIER - Lamps ☆ - Lamplight Farms, Inc.
COURIER - Leather goods - AR Accessories Group Inc.
COURIER - Leather goods - St. Thomas Inc.
COURIER - Luggage - Sears, Roebuck and Co.
COURIER - Menswear ☆ - Michaels/Stern & Co. Inc.
COURIER - Motor vehicles–automobiles ☆ - Ford Motor Co.
COURIER - Paper–bond - Strathmore Paper Co.
COURIER - Pens ☆ - Anson Inc.
COURIER - Recording label - Conarch Productions
COURIER - Shoes–athletic - Ektelon
COURIER - Tires - Bridgestone/Firestone, Inc.
COURIER - Toys–models ☆ - Estes Industries
COURIER - Trailers–travel - Royals International
COURIER PLUS - Floor coverings–carpet and rugs ☆ - Customweave Carpets Inc.
COURIER, THE - Binders ☆ - 20th Century Plastics
COURIER, THE - Personal-grooming sets ☆ - London International U.S. Holdings
COURISTAN - Rugs, broadloom - Couristan Inc.
COURMAYEUR - Mattresses and box springs - Ohio Mattress Co.
COUROC OF MONTEREY - Giftware - Couroc of Monterey Inc.
COURONNE - Beverages - Fine Financial, Ltd.
COURREGE - Sunglasses - Sunlovers
COURREGES - Scarves, neckwear and umbrellas - Sprague & Coultas
COURREGES - Watches - Andre Victor America Ltd.
COURREGES HOMME - Apparel–men's - Leon of Paris Co. Inc.
COURREGES PARIS - Eyeglasses ☆ - Windsor Optical Inc.
COURRIERE - Beverages–alcohol - Cameron Craig Ltd.
COURRIERE - Brandy - Nicholas Enterprises
COURRIOR - Recording label ☆ - Ozark Opry Records
COURSE ENCOUNTERS - Computer software ☆ - Eugene F. Dente

COURSE, THE - Apparel and accessories - American Crest & Emblem, Inc.
COURSELINK - Computer software - Cygnus Multimedia Group, Inc.
COURSEPAK - Pesticides–household - Ciba-Geigy Corp.
COURT - Floor coverings–tile ☆ - National Floor Products Co., Inc.
COURT 1 - Balls–tennis - Penn Athletic Products
COURT AIDS - Sporting goods - Gexco Enterprises
COURT CABINET - Office accessories - Office Resources & Design, Inc.
COURT CASUALS - Apparel–athletic - United Merchandising Corp.
COURT CAT - Footwear–athletic - Puma Inc.
COURT CHAMPION - Bags–duffel - Ektelon
COURT CLASSIC - Shoes - Price Co.
COURT COMFORT - Footwear - Frelonic/Division of Dertek Corp.
COURT COURIER - Bags–duffel - Ektelon
COURT COUTURE - Apparel–women's - Court Couture Inc.
COURT-DOME - Pharmaceutical preparations - Miles Inc.
COURT FLARE - Footwear–athletic ☆ - Nike, Inc.
COURT GOGGLES - Goggles–safety - Ektelon
COURT JESTER SPORTSWEAR - Apparel–athletic - Court Jester Sportswear
COURT KING - Sporting goods ☆ - Pacifico Co.
COURT LEVEL - Apparel and accessories - Horn & Associates
COURT LINEN - Paper - Byron Weston Div.
COURT-LITER - Lighting fixtures - Hubbell Lighting, Inc. (Lighting Div.)
COURT LORD - Basketball shoes ☆ - Jaclar
COURT MASTER II - Adhesives and sealants - Huntington Laboratories Inc.
COURT OF JEWELS, THE - Jewelry - Harry Winston, Inc.
COURT/ORDER - Sporting goods - Patterson-Williams Manufacturing Co. Inc.
COURT PLAYER - Footwear - L.A. Gear, Inc.
COURT PLAZA - Floor coverings–carpet and rugs - Coronet Carpets Inc.
COURT PRO - Athletic footwear - International Seaway Trading Corp.
COURT QUARRY - Floor coverings - National Floor Products Co., Inc.
COURT QUEST - Footwear - L.A. Gear, Inc.
COURT SERVE - Sporting goods - John D. Henderson
COURT SILK - Apparel and accessories - Intercontinental Branded Apparel
COURT SILK - Coats–men's - M. Wile & Co., Inc.
COURT SPECS - Goggles–safety - Ektelon
COURT STONE - Floor coverings - Congoleum Corp.
COURT TECH - Footwear–athletic - Wilson Sporting Goods Co.
COURT TIME - Sporting goods - Lifetime Products, Inc.
COURTCRUISER - Shoes–athletic - Ektelon
COURTENAY - Tableware–china - Pfaltzgraff Investment Co.
COURTESY - Ashtrays–glass - Pap-R Products Co. Inc.
COURTESY CARRIAGE - Motor vehicles - Ransomes-Cushman-Ryan
COURTESY SR - Fabrics - Springs Industries, Inc.
COURTING - Bicycles - Rideable Bicycle Replicas Inc.
COURTING - Fabrics - Gretchen Bellinger Inc.
COURTLAND - Clocks ☆ - General Time Corp. (Westclox/Seth Thomas Div.)
COURTLAND - Floor coverings ☆ - Congoleum Corp.
COURTLAND - Stationery - Champion International Corp.
COURTLAND - Tableware–china ☆ - Lenox, Inc.
COURTLAND INN - Furniture–upholstered ☆ - Webb Furniture Enterprises Inc.
COURTLY - Giftware - Swiss Harmony Inc.
COURTLY SUEDE - Floor coverings–carpet and rugs ☆ - Mohawk Carpet Corp.
COURTMASTER - Sporting goods - J.A. Cissel Manufacturing Co.
COURTNEY - Dolls - Mattel, Inc.
COURTNEY - Frames–eyeglass - U.S. Optical Frame Co.
COURTNEY - Glassware–household - Anchor Hocking Glass, Inc.
COURTNEY - Pharmaceutical preparations ☆ - Pharmavite Corp.
COURTNEY & CO. - Apparel–women's - Federated Department Stores, Inc.
COURTNEY BROOKE - Cosmetics - Courtney Brooke, Inc.
COURTNEY COLLECTION - Food products - Golden Whisk Pasta Partners
COURTNEY SQUARE - Floor coverings - Mannington Resilient Floors
COURTNEY TAYLOR - Footwear - JBI, Inc.
COURTNEY WAY - Floor coverings–carpet and rugs - Lock Weave Carpet Mills Inc.
COURTOIS - Musical instruments - G. Leblanc Corp.
COURTOIS - Wines - Peaceful Bend Vineyard
COURTSCREEN - Sporting goods - Sport Supply Group, Inc.
COURTSHIP - Floor coverings–carpet and rugs - Barrett Carpet Mills Inc.
COURTSHORTS - Clothing - Gerda Osward
COURTSIDE - Apparel–athletic ☆ - J.C. Penney Co., Inc.
COURTSIDE - Floor coverings - Mannington Resilient Floors
COURTYARD - Dinnerware–glass - Arita Sales Co. Inc.
COURTYARD - Dinnerware–glass - Lenox, Inc.
COURTYARD - Fencing–chain link - Harbor Towne Fence Inc.

☆ = Now out of production

COURTYARD - Floor coverings - Compass Concepts
COURTYARD - Floor coverings - Congoleum Corp.
COURTYARD - Floor coverings–carpet and rugs - Colonial Mills Inc.
COURTYARD - Furniture ☆ - Bassett Furniture Industries, Inc.
COURTYARD - Wallpaper - United Wallcoverings
COURTYARD CLASSICS - Wallpaper ☆ - Wall-Pride Inc.
COURTYARD COLLECTION - Apparel–men's - Woolf Brothers Inc.
COURTYARD LIGHTING - Electric lighting equipment - Ampac Industries Inc.
COURTYARD OF LEARNING - Computer software - Open Court Publishing Co.
COURVOISIER - Beverages–alcohol - Domecq Importers Inc.
COURVOISIER - Beverages–alcohol - Hiram Walker & Sons, Inc.
COURVOISIER XO - Beverages–alcohol - Hiram Walker & Sons, Inc.
COUSCOUS CUP - Food products ☆ - Casbah/Sahara Natural Foods Inc.
COUSCOUS EXPRESS - Food products - Tipiak
COUSIN JEREMY - Dolls ☆ - Effanbee Doll Corp.
COUSIN JOHNNY - Apparel and accessories - Cousin Johnny Inc.
COUSIN RACHEL'S - Pretzels - Tom Sturgis Pretzels Inc.
COUSIN SUZY'S SWEETS - Candy - Clover Hill Candies
COUSIN WILLIE - Popcorn - Ramsey Popcorn
COUSINE - Giftware ☆ - Akko Inc.
COUSINS - Croutons - Krutons
COUSINS SUBS - Apparel and accessories - Cousins Submarines, Inc.
COUSTIC - Audio equipment - Concept Enterprises, Inc.
COUTUME - Floor coverings–carpet and rugs - J.L. Benson Co.
COUTURE - Cosmetics - Lord & Berry, Ltd.
COUTURE - Dishes–china - Mikasa Co.
COUTURE - Furniture–wood ☆ - Century Furniture Co.
COUTURE - Luggage ☆ - Hartmann Luggage Co.
COUTURE - Nail care products - Revlon Consumer Products Corp.
COUTURE - Toilets–enameled - Kohler Co.
COUTURE - Wallpaper ☆ - Capital Carousel Inc.
COUTURE - Wallpaper ☆ - Jolie Papier
COUTURE AVEC L' ATTITUDE - Apparel–children's - S and P Imports Inc.
COUTURE LADY - Apparel–women's - Colberts, Inc.
COUTURE LITE - Toilets–enameled - Kohler Co.
COUTURE SPECIALTIES - Women's apparel - Country Miss Inc.
COUTUTIER - Cheese - Made in France
COV A CLOTHES - Garment storage bags - Viator Products Corp.
COV-A-ROLLS - Paint rollers - Hansteck Corp.
COV-R-GUARD - Lamps - General Electric Co.
COVA - Paints - Tandy Leather Co.
COVAC - Antihistamine preparations - Brown Manufacturing Co.
COVADERM - Wound dressing - Deroyal Industries, Inc.
COVADERM PLUS - Bandages - Deroyal Industries, Inc.
COVALDA - Food products - Covaldo Inc.
COVALDA RANCH - Food products - Covaldo Inc.
COVANAMINE - Antihistamine preparations ☆ - Wallace Laboratories
COVANGESIC - Antihistamine preparations - Wallace Laboratories
COVE - Fireplaces - Majestic Co.
COVE - Flatware - Yamazaki Tableware Inc.
COVE - Footwear - H.H. Brown Shoe Co., Inc.
COVE - Thread - New Bedford Thread Co. Inc.
COVE BOND - Adhesives and sealants - Continental Brands Inc.
COVE CREEK - Apparel–women's - Saul International
COVE GOLD - Food products - Gillette Citrus Co.
COVE KLEEN - Housewares - Amaza Laboratories Inc.
COVE STICK - Cove sheeting product - Dexter Corp. (Mercer Plastics Div.)
COVEE - Apparel and accessories - Covee Corp.
COVEL - Boats–canoes - Coleman Co., Inc.
COVEMASTER - Building materials - Mid-America Building Products Corp.
COVEN 13 - Publisher's imprints - No Mercy Comics, Inc.
COVENANT - Compact discs–prerecorded - Bellaire Record Sales
COVENANT - Thread ☆ - SCT Yarns Inc.
COVENGTON - Motor vehicles–motor homes - Forest River, Inc.
COVENT GARDEN - Dinnerware–glass ☆ - Wallace International Silversmiths, Inc.
COVENT GARDEN - Dishes–earthenware ☆ - Gorham Inc.
COVENT GARDEN - Dolls ☆ - Effanbee Doll Corp.
COVENT GARDEN - Wallpaper ☆ - Stonebridge Co.
COVENT GARDEN BOX - Artists' materials - Winsor & Newton
COVENTRY - Cabinets - Imperial Cabinet Co. Inc.
COVENTRY - Cabinets ☆ - Medallion Kitchens of Minnesota Inc.
COVENTRY - Cabinets–wood - Parcraft Distinctive Cabinetry
COVENTRY - Candy ☆ - Brock Candy Co. Inc.
COVENTRY - Clocks - General Time Corp. (Westclox/Seth Thomas Div.)

COVENTRY - Doors–wood - Masonite Corp.
COVENTRY - Eyeglasses - Art-Craft Optical Co.
COVENTRY - Fireplace equipment - Majestic Co.
COVENTRY - Floor coverings ☆ - Congoleum Corp.
COVENTRY - Floor coverings–carpet and rugs - Atlas Carpet Mills Inc.
COVENTRY - Floor coverings–carpet and rugs - Kelly Group Inc.
COVENTRY - Floor coverings–carpet and rugs - Trans-Ocean Import Co. Inc.
COVENTRY - Floor coverings–carpet and rugs ☆ - Colonial Mills Inc.
COVENTRY - Footwear ☆ - Allen-Edmonds Shoe Corp.
COVENTRY - Furniture - Triangle Pacific Corp. (Cabinet Division)
COVENTRY - Furniture ☆ - Lane Co. Inc.
COVENTRY - Furniture–children's ☆ - Child Craft Industries Inc.
COVENTRY - Furniture–wood - Century Furniture Co.
COVENTRY - Glassware–household - Owens-Illinois Inc. (Libbey Div.)
COVENTRY - Glassware–household - Seneca Glass Co.
COVENTRY - Jewelry–costume - Sarah Coventry Fashion Jewelry
COVENTRY - Liquors - Hughes Markets Inc.
COVENTRY - Mattresses - Stearns & Foster Bedding Co.
COVENTRY - Paints - Mobile Paint Manufacturing Co.
COVENTRY - Paper - Willmann Paper Co., Inc.
COVENTRY - Stationery - Royal Imprints Corp.
COVENTRY - Trailers–travel ☆ - Coachmen Industries, Inc.
COVENTRY & CASE - Cabinets–wood - American Woodmark Corp.
COVENTRY ART - Greeting cards - Sunshine Art Studios Inc.
COVENTRY BRICK - Floor coverings - Azrock Commercial Flooring
COVENTRY COLLECTION - Furniture–wood - Flexsteel Industries Inc.
COVENTRY COLLECTION - Lamps - Beatrice Cos. Inc.
COVENTRY COURT - Furniture - CTH/Sherrill Occasional
COVENTRY FLYER - Bicycles - Western Auto Supply Co.
COVENTRY FORGE - Flatware ☆ - Wallace International Silversmiths, Inc.
COVENTRY FORGE - Floor coverings–carpet and rugs ☆ - Downs Carpet Co. Inc.
COVENTRY GARDENS - Garden equipment - Chas H. Lilly Co.
COVENTRY LANE - Fabrics–tapestry ☆ - Coloroll Inc.
COVENTRY LITE - Chimes - Nutone Inc.
COVENTRY MANOR - Furniture - Tropitone Furniture Co. Inc.
COVENTRY MANOR - Furniture ☆ - Drexel Heritage Furnishings, Inc.
COVENTRY MANOR - Wallpaper - Planox
COVENTRY PARQUET - Floor coverings ☆ - Robbins Inc.
COVENTRY RAG - Paper–lithograph - ANW-Crestwood Paper Co.
COVENTRY ROSE - Cosmetics - David Reynolds
COVENTRY SQUARE - Apparel–men's - Asher Co.
COVENTRY STRIPE - House furnishings - Dan River Inc.
COVEPLATE - Paneling - Ohio State Waterproofing, Inc.
COVEPOXY - Coatings - Garon Products Inc.
COVER - Paper–bond - Marvin Envelope & Paper Co.
COVER - Trailers–travel - Rancho Trailers Inc.
COVER ALL - Aluminum compounds - Regal Ware, Inc.
COVER ALL - Fabrics–tapestry ☆ - Comark Wallcoverings
COVER ALL - Microwave components ☆ - Anchor Hocking Glass, Inc.
COVER-ALL - Paint rollers - Bestt-Liebco
COVER-ALL CAPER - Hair care products - Andre Fantasies Inc.
COVER CARE - Cleaning preparations - Great Lakes Biochemical Co., Inc.
COVER CAT - Pet products - Golden Cat Corp.
COVER CHARGE - Envelopes - Sandra E. Levenson
COVER-CLEAR - Varnishes - Jones Blair Co.
COVER-COAT - Pottery products - Duncan Enterprises
COVER CRAFT - Computer storage devices - Amherst International Enterprises Co.
COVER-EZ - Tools–hand-operated - Cover-Ez Inc.
COVER-FLOR - Paints ☆ - Valspar Corp.
COVER GIRL - Boots - Genesco Inc.
COVER GIRL - Cosmetics - Noxell Corp.
COVER GIRL - Frames–eyeglass ☆ - Universal/Univis Inc.
COVER GIRL CLEAN - Skin care products - Noxell Corp.
COVER GIRL SANDI - Dolls ☆ - Totsy Manufacturing Co., Inc.
COVER-IT - Air conditioning equipment - Ameriguard Corp.
COVER-IT! - Skin care products - Joe Blasco Enterprises, Inc.
COVER-KOTE - Paints - Dunn Edwards Corp.
COVER M' PERFECT - Cosmetics - CCA Industries, Inc.
COVER MAGIC - Cases–plastic - Anthes Universal
COVER ME - Blankets–electric - Under Cover, Inc.
COVER 'N SPOUT - Automotive parts and accessories ☆ - Yale Engineering Co.
COVER-NOTE - Calendars ☆ - Success Business Industries, Inc.
COVER-PAD - Bandages - Beiersdorf Inc.

☆ = Now out of production

COVER POOLS - Swimming pool covers - Cover Pools Inc.
COVER-RITE - Paints ☆ - Farwest Paint Manufacturing Co. Inc.
COVER ROLL - Bandages - Beiersdorf Inc.
COVER SEAL - Primer - American Paints
COVER-STAIN - Paints - William Zinsser & Co. Inc.
COVER-STAIN - Shellac - Bradshaw-Praeger & Co.
COVER STICK - Cosmetics ☆ - Noxell Corp.
COVER STORY - Apparel and accessories ☆ - Edison Brothers Stores, Inc.
COVER STORY - Crocheted and knitted items ☆ - High Point Knitting Inc.
COVER STORY - Floor coverings–carpet and rugs - Calladium & Marglen
COVER STORY - Folders - American Loose Leaf Business Products Inc.
COVER STORY LTD. - Apparel–athletic ☆ - High Point Knitting Inc.
COVER-STRIP - Bandages - Beiersdorf Inc.
COVER THAT BIRD! - Bird cages - Cover That Bird!
COVER THE EARTH - Paints - Sherwin-Williams Automotive Finishes Corp.
COVER TO COVER - Golfing equipment ☆ - Square Two Golf
COVER TO COVER - Wallpaper - J. Josephson, Inc.
COVER-UP - Door frames - Dynatec International Inc.
COVER UP - Frames–eyeglass - May Optical Co. Inc.
COVER-UP - Mathematical game - Crisloid Inc.
COVER UP - Medical apparatus - Luminaud Inc.
COVER-UP - Paints - Growco Aerosol
COVER UP - Paints - Hirshfield's Paint Manufacturing
COVER-UP - Paints ☆ - Devoe & Raynolds Co.
COVER-UP - Stencils - Richards Distributing, Inc.
COVER-UP - Tarpaulins - Shur-Co Inc.
COVER-UP - Wallpaper - Lamvin Inc.
COVER-UP - Waterproof outerwear - Diane Products Inc.
COVER-UP SO NATURAL - Cosmetics - Hazel Bishop International
COVER UP, THE - Labels–paper - Lisa Morlas
COVER UPS - Pet products - Lone Toy Tree Inc.
COVER YOUR OWN - Buttons - Prym Dritz Corp.
COVERA-HS - Pharmaceutical preparations - G. D. Searle & Co.
COVERAGE - Wallpaper - Advance Wallcoverings
COVERAGE 256 - Detergents - Calgon Vestal Laboratories
COVERAGE PLUS - Disinfectants - E.R. Squibb & Sons, Inc.
COVERAGEQUEST - Computer software - American Bar Association
COVERALL - Bags–plastic - Flex-O-Glass, Inc.
COVERALL - Plastics film - Warp Bros.
COVERALLS - Pet products - Pupperwear Inc.
COVERAMA - Photo albums - Classic Album, LLC
COVERBIND ENVIRONMENTAL PRODUCTS - Lotions - Coverbind Corp.
COVERBOND 4 - Motor vehicle parts and accessories - Gupta Family LP
COVERCOAT - Paints - Valspar Corp.
COVERCRAFT - Blankets–horse - Covercraft Industries, Inc.
COVERCUT - Paper–coated - REXAM DSI
COVERDERM - Cosmetics - Dr. Babor Natural Cosmetics
COVERED BRIDGE - Wines - Markko Vineyard
COVERED WAGON - Breads - American Bakeries Co.
COVERED WAGON - Cigars - A.J. Golden Inc.
COVERED WAGON - Pancakes–mixes ☆ - Safeway Stores Inc.
COVERED WAGON - Toys - Newco, Inc.
COVERETTS - Cakes - Cocoline Chocolate Co.
COVEREX - Paints - Spencer-Adams Paint Co. Inc.
COVERGARD - Insulating materials - Southern Manufacturing, Inc.
COVERIT - Correction fluid - Bic Corp.
COVERITE - Bottle caps ☆ - Sealright Co., Inc.
COVERITE - Brushes–paint ☆ - Linzer Products Corp.
COVERITE - Paints - Chilton Paint Co.
COVERITE BODYSHOP, THE - Paint sets–hobby - Coverite
COVERKING - Automotive parts and accessories - Gupta Family LP
COVERKING - Car covers - Gupta Family L.P.
COVERLETS - Bandages–surgical - Beiersdorf Inc.
COVERLIGHT - Tarpaulins - Reeves Brothers Inc.
COVERLOVER - Boats - Coverlover Industries
COVERLUXE - Paper–coated - Flock Tex, Inc.
COVERMARK - Cosmetics - Covermark Cosmetics
COVERMATE - Laminator - Bind-It Corp.
COVERONCE - Paint sprayers - E-Z Paintr Corp.
COVERPLEX - Paints - Clement Coverall Co.
COVERPLY - Housewares - Ironees Co.
COVERS - Sunglasses - Bausch & Lomb Inc.
COVERS ALL - Paints - Tulip Productions
COVERS OVER BLACK - Paints ☆ - Paris Paint & Varnish Co.
COVERSOL - Enamels ☆ - James B. Day and Co.
COVERSTIK - Cosmetics - Covermark Cosmetics

COVERSTUF - Landscaping and mulch film ☆ - Rexam Flexible Packaging
COVERT - Hair spray - Tri-Institute of Trichology
COVERT - Snaps, fasteners, etc. - Cooper Industries, Inc.
COVERT - Transmitting apparatus - Schell Electronics
COVERT ACTION - Games - Microprose Software, Inc.
COVERT CARRIER - Sporting goods - Double Eagle Financial Systems
COVERTEERS - Covers–seat - Covercraft Co. Inc.
COVERTEX II - Paper products - REXAM DSI
COVERTONE - Cosmetics - Viviane Woodard Industries, Ltd.
COVERTONE - Paints ☆ - Clement Coverall Co.
COVERVAC - Sporting goods ☆ - Odyssey Systems
COVERWELL - Thread - Lewis Threads Inc.
COVERWORKS - Linen - U.T.C. Holdings
COVERX - Flowers, plants, and seeds - Germain's, Inc.
COVET - Frames–eyeglass - Liberty Optical Manufacturing Co.
COVETED - Floor coverings–carpet and rugs - Mohawk Industries Inc.
COVEWOOD - Floor coverings–carpet and rugs ☆ - Evans-Black Carpet Mills
COVEY RUN - Wines - Covey Run Winery
COVEY RUN - Wines - Quail Run Cellars & Vintners
COVI-OX - Vitamins and nutritional supplements - Henkel Corp. (Fine Chemicals Div.)
COVICONE - Skin care products - Abbott Laboratories
COVIL - Tools–power-driven - Covil Products, Inc.
COVINA - Occasional tables ☆ - JDI Group, Inc.
COVINGTON - Bathroom fixtures ☆ - Artesian Industries
COVINGTON - Cleaning preparations–window - Dixie Textile & Supply Co.
COVINGTON - Fabrics–tapestry ☆ - Coloroll Inc.
COVINGTON - Floor coverings - Anderson Hardwood Floors Inc.
COVINGTON - Floor coverings - Congoleum Corp.
COVINGTON - Floor coverings ☆ - Bruce Hardwood Floors
COVINGTON - Floor coverings–carpet and rugs - Philadelphia Carpets
COVINGTON - Floor coverings–carpet and rugs - Pretty Products, Inc.
COVINGTON - Floor coverings–carpet and rugs - Trend Carpet
COVINGTON - Frames–eyeglass ☆ - Universal/Univis Inc.
COVINGTON - Giftware ☆ - Gorham Inc.
COVINGTON - Plumbing fixtures - Harrington Brass Works Ltd. Inc.
COVINGTON COVE - Furniture - Singer Furniture Co.
COVINGTON FARMS - Meat products–poultry - Sanderson Farms Inc.
COVINGTON FILTERS 100'S - Cigarettes - Eve Holdings Inc.
COVINGTON PLANK - Wood flooring - Standard Plywood Inc.
COVIRO - Wines - Pastene Companies Ltd.
COVITOL - Vitamins and nutritional supplements - Henkel Corp. (Fine Chemicals Div.)
COVO - Shortening - Van Den Bergh Foods Co.
COVON - Colorant dispersions - Huls America Inc.
COVOX - Computer software - Covox, Inc.
COVRUP - Lenses–optical - Kelley & Hueber
COVWRAP - Lenses–optical - Kelley & Hueber
C.O.W. - Toys - Hasbro, Inc.
COW-A-LICIOUS! - Milk–flavored - Genesis Leverage Development Corp.
COW & CANCE - Greeting cards - Cow & Cance Greetings
COW & MILL - Milk–canned or powdered - Sun Hing Foods, Inc.
COW BABY CHINA - Toys - Pipestone
COW-BOY - Health care products ☆ - CTS Laboratories Inc.
COW BOY JO'S - Food products - Beatrice Cos. Inc.
COW BRAND - Baking powder ☆ - Church and Dwight Co. Inc.
COW CAMP - Dinnerware–glass - Pipestone
COW CHIP CREW, THE - Greeting cards - A + A
COW CHIPS - Novelty items - Tom and Sally's Handmade Chocolates, Inc.
COW COLLECTIBLES - Novelty items - A + A
COW CREAMS - Chocolate bars - Linda Grishman Chocolates, Inc.
COW CRUNCH - Chocolate bars - Linda Grishman Chocolates, Inc.
COW EGGS - Chewing gum - Lenny's Sales, Inc.
COW KISSES - Figurines - Brennan Studio Inc.
COW LIPS - Cosmetics - Vermont Skin Care Products, Inc.
COW-MOO-FLAGE - Jewelry - Papel Freelance, Inc.
COW OF A DIFFERENT COLOR, THE - Milk–flavored - Genesis Leverage Development Corp.
COW PIE - Candy - Baraboo Candy Co., Inc.
COW POWER - Dairy products - H.E.A., Inc.
COW PRINT - Seat covers - Saddleman, Inc.
COW TALES - Candy - Goetze's Candy Co., Inc.
COW-VAC - Veterinary pharmaceutical preparations - Oxford Veterinary Laboratories, Inc.
COWARDLY LION - Dolls - Effanbee Doll Corp.
COWAY - Filters–water - Coway, Inc.

         ☆ = Now out of production

COWBONES - Dog food - Pet Center, Inc.
COWBOY - Cakes - Grandma Pfeiffer's
COWBOY - Catsup - El Paso Chili Co.
COWBOY - Dishes–earthenware - Hadley Pottery Co. Inc.
COWBOY - Eyeglasses - Martin-Copeland Eyewear Corp.
COWBOY - Floor coverings - American Floor Products Co. Inc.
COWBOY - Food products - Cowboy Vittles & More
COWBOY - Frames–eyeglass - Blublocker Corp.
COWBOY - Fruits and vegetables - Hansen Fruit & Cold Storage Co., Inc.
COWBOY - Nail care products - Hard Candy, Inc.
COWBOY - Prophylactics - Boston Medical Corp.
COWBOY - Tobacco products - Philip Morris Companies Inc.
COWBOY & INDIAN PIN-UPS - Posters ✫ - Dolly, Inc.
COWBOY BEAR - Toys–stuffed - Russ Berrie and Co., Inc.
COWBOY BEAUTS - Boots - B.B. Walker Co.
COWBOY BOB'S - Apparel and accessories - Lindley & Co., Inc.
COWBOY CANDY - Meat products–dried - Beaver Creek Smokehouse, Inc.
COWBOY CAP - Hats–straw - Tinkertunes Music
COWBOY CASINO - Computer software ✫ - Intellimedia Sports, Inc.
COWBOY CAVIAR - Caviar - Cowboy Caviar
COWBOY CHIPPERS - Snack foods - Cowboy Vittles & More
COWBOY CLASSICS - Skin care products - Robert James Lovato
COWBOY COCKTAIL - Candy - Beverage Marketing USA, Inc.
COWBOY COLLECTION - Wallpaper - Kirk-Brummel
COWBOY COLORS - Apparel and accessories - Miller International Inc.
COWBOY COOKIES - Cookies - Cowboy Cookie Co., LLC
COWBOY CRUSHABLES - Hats - GWB, Inc.
COWBOY DECADENCE - Confections - Cowboy Vittles & More
COWBOY GE-TAR - Toys–musical - Mattel, Inc.
COWBOY HAT - Glass products - Blenko Glass Co. Inc.
COWBOY JUNCTION - Recording label - Cowboy Junction Flea Market
COWBOY QUILTIE - Meat products–beef - Cowboy Vittles & More
COWBOY RED - Chili peppers–powdered - Cowboy Vittles & More
COWBOY ROPIN - Gloves - Plenge Trading Co.
COWBOY TRAPPINGS OF THE AMERICAN WEST -SPIRIT OF THE COWBOY - Leather goods - Cowboy Trappings of the American West
COWBOY UP - Housewares - Super Bull Series, Inc.
COWBOYS - Shirts - Westmoor Manufacturing Co. Inc.
COWBOYS & ALIENS - Publisher's imprints - Platinum Studios
COWBOYS & INDIANS - Games - Universal Manufacturing Co., Inc.
COWBOY'S CHOICE - Seasonings - Byron's Bar-B-Q
COWBOYS HAVE IT TOGETHER - Shirts - Chit Products Co.
COWBOY'S ONLY - Apparel and accessories - Bacca Sportswear Inc.
COWDEN - Men's apparel - Interco Inc.
COWDY - Glass products ✫ - Westminster Trading Corp.
COWEN CABLE CORPORATION - Cables ✫ - Alpha Wire Co.
COWGIRL - Eyeglasses - Art-Craft Optical Co.
COWGIRL - Food products - Bootlegger Food
COWGIRL - Recording label - Cowgirl Records
COWGIRL - Sauces - Jardine Foods
COWGIRLS - Footwear–women's - Diesse Shoes Inc.
COWGIRLS' RODEO ASSOCIATION BY ROPER - Apparel and accessories - Karman Western Apparel
COWHAND - Frames–eyeglass - Zylo Ware Corp.
COWHANDS - Towels - Barth-Dreyfuss of California
COWHIDES - Candy - Glade Taffy Town, Inc.
COWKIES - Cookies - Venus Wafers, Inc.
COWLES - Epworth Morehouse-Cowles
COWLICKS - Novelty items - Tom and Sally's Handmade Chocolates, Inc.
COWLITZ - Lumber - Woodex Lumber Corp.
COWLITZ RIVER SOFTWARE - Computer software - Cowlitz River Software, Inc.
COWLORADO KID, THE - Toys - R.E. Bee, Inc.
COWLOVER - Flowers, plants, and seeds - Missouri Southern Seed Corp.
COWMOOFLAUGE - Apparel and accessories - Lisa Kimberly Schnee
COWPOKES - Candy - Sherwood Brands, Inc.
COWS - Candy - Sherwood Brands, Inc.
COW'S PRIDE - Cheese - Lactoprot USA, Inc.
COWSLIP - Dishes–earthenware ✫ - Royal China & Porcelain Companies Inc.
COWSMOPOLITANS - Toys–stuffed ✫ - Commonwealth Toy and Novelty Co. Inc.
COWTOWN - Boots - Cowtown Boot Co. Inc.
COWTOWN - Fabrics - Greenwood Mills Inc.
COX - Apparel and accessories - Parke Cox Trucking Co., Inc.
COX - Caulking guns - C.M.C.C. Inc.
COX - Toys - Centuri Corp.

COX - Toys–airplanes - Cox Products Inc.
COX & HAWKENS - Apparel–men's - Joseph and Feiss Co.
COX-BOX - Sporting goods - Nielsen-Kellerman Co.
COX/COLLIER & CO. WESTERN - Apparel and accessories - Cox/Collier Ltd.
COX/SANWA - Electrical equipment - Cox Products Inc.
COXMOORE OF ENGLAND - Apparel–athletic - Frank L. Savage Imports Inc.
COXSWAIN - Fabrics - Dan River Inc.
COY - Frames–eyeglass - Liberty Optical Manufacturing Co.
COY INTERNATIONAL - Beverages–malt ✫ - Dixie Brewing Co.
COY LIGHT MARATHON - Beverages–malt ✫ - Dixie Brewing Co.
COYOTE - Antennas ✫ - Firestik Antenna Co.
COYOTE - Apparel and accessories - American Argo Corp.
COYOTE - Audio equipment - Preformed Line Products Co.
COYOTE - Beverages–alcohol - Joseph E. Seagram & Sons, Inc.
COYOTE - Bicycles - Columbia Manufacturing Inc.
COYOTE - Dinnerware - Coyote Holdings, Inc.
COYOTE - Electronic equipment ✫ - AVL
COYOTE - Gocarts - Manco Products, Inc.
COYOTE - Knives–hunting - Colonial Knife Co. Inc.
COYOTE - Motor vehicles ✫ - Sunline Coach Co.
COYOTE - Recording label - Twin/Tone Records Inc.
COYOTE - Tires - Denman Tire Corp.
COYOTE - Tripods–photographic - Phoenix Corp. of America
COYOTE AND FOX - Apparel and accessories - Wendy Posey
COYOTE CAFE - Catsup - Coyote Cocina
COYOTE COCINA - Catsup - Coyote Cocina
COYOTE COCINA - Food products - Coyote Cafe L.P.
COYOTE CREEK - Apparel and accessories - Wrangler Apparel Co.
COYOTE GRILL - Frozen foods - Sabatasso Foods Inc.
COYOTE GRILL - Frozen foods - SSE Foods, Inc.
COYOTE NUTS - Nuts–salted, roasted, cooked, or canned - El Paso Chili Co.
COYOTE ROSE - Jewelry - Jody Coyote, Inc.
COYOTE SIX - Shirts - Keith A. Mcdowell
COYOTE TRAILS - Food products - Silverado Foods, Inc.
COYOTE'S CAPOTES - Coats - Ear Puller's Crafts and Goods
COYUCHI - Linen - Coyuchi Inc.
COZ - Nail care products - Nailco, Inc.
COZAAREX - Pharmaceutical preparations - E.I. Dupont de Nemours and Co.
COZEEZ - Slippers - S. Goldberg and Co. Inc.
COZETTE - Recording label ✫ - Soul-Po-Tion Records
COZI-CRIBS - Bassinets - Cramer Products Co.
COZIE COVER - Mattresses - Cozie Cover, Inc.
COZIES - Diapers–disposable - Ultra Care Products Inc.
COZMO - Thread - United Thread Mills Corp.
COZMO CLAM - Toys–automobiles - Mattel, Inc.
COZUMEL - Boats ✫ - Wellcraft Marine Corp.
COZUMEL - Floor coverings–carpet and rugs - Design Materials, Inc.
COZUMEL - Housewares - Elon Inc.
COZY - Chairs–upholstered ✫ - Small World Toys
COZY - Cups–paper - Solo Cup Co.
COZY - Eyeglasses - Art-Craft Optical Co.
COZY - Fabric softeners - Conklin Co., Inc.
COZY - Fabrics–broadcloth - Desire Mills Co. Inc.
COZY - Heaters–gas - Louisville Tin and Stove
COZY - Pet products - Dallas Manufacturing Inc.
COZY - Underwear - J.E. Morgan Knitting Mills
COZY - Yarn ✫ - William Unger & Co. Inc.
COZY CARRIERS - Infant product - Cozy Carriers
COZY CHAMOMILE - Teas–herbal - R.C. Bigelow, Inc.
COZY CHUMS - Greeting cards ✫ - American Greetings Corp.
COZY CONDO - Toys - Flexible Flyer Co.
COZY CONTOURS - Apparel–women's - ShadowLine Inc.
COZY CORNER - Toys–stuffed - Gund, Inc.
COZY CORNERS - Dining room furniture ✫ - Daystrom Furniture Inc.
COZY COTTAGE - Furniture - Little Tikes Co.
COZY COTTAGE - Syrup - Maple Grove Farms of Vermont, Inc.
COZY COUPE - Toys - Little Tikes Co.
COZY COVER - Carriages–baby - Entrepreneur Venture Capital, Inc.
COZY CRAFT - Wheelchairs - Quickie Designs Inc.
COZY CRIB - Cribs–metal - HARD Manufacturing Co. Inc.
COZY CRITTERS - Clocks ✫ - General Time Corp. (Westclox/Seth Thomas Div.)
COZY CUFFS - Apparel stores–children's - Dundee Mills, Inc.
COZY GRATE - Fireplace equipment - Thermo-Rite Manufacturing Co.
COZY HOT POT - Tea kettles–electric - Forman Family Inc.
COZY KITCHENS - Fabrics–tapestry - Comark Wallcoverings

✫ = Now out of production

COZY KITCHENS - Wallpaper ☆ - Decorative Coverings Inc.
COZY KITTENS - Greeting cards - American Greetings Corp.
COZY KITTY - Pet products - Teddy Pets
COZY-LITE - Lighting fixtures - Swivelier Co. Inc.
COZY-LITTER - Pet products - Novalek, Inc.
COZY N' CAREFREE - Fabrics-silk - Charles Komar and Sons Inc.
COZY NEST - Pet products - Lixit Animal Care Products
COZY NIGHTS - Underwear and nightwear - Herman Associates Inc.
COZY PET - Pet products - Dallas Manufacturing Inc.
COZY SOLES - Slippers - Solely Ours Inc.
COZY SPA - Hot tubs-fiberglass - Sunbeam-Oster Household Products
COZY SWING - Toys - Today's Kids Inc.
COZY-TIME - Slippers - Mel Shoe Corp.
COZY-TOP - Apparel-women's - Olga Co.
COZY TOUCH - Pillows - Unique Fibers Inc.
COZY TREADS - Slippers - Kentucky Derby Hosiery Co. Inc.
COZY-TROL - Electrical testing instruments - Telaire Systems, Inc.
COZY'S - Bakery products - Oregon Fruit Products Co., Inc.
COZZ E. BEAR - Toys-stuffed ☆ - Dakin Inc.
COZZOLI'S - Restaurants-coffee shops - Cozzoli's Restaurant-Pizzeria
COZZZY COMFORT - Furniture-children's ☆ - Child Craft Industries Inc.
CP - Bags-plastic - Carlisle Plastics, Inc.
CP - Brake parts - Raybestos/Brake Parts Inc.
CP - Chairs-cane - Stylex Inc.
CP - Drums-musical instruments - LP Music Group
C.P. - Ice cream - Carvel Corp.
CP - Jewelry - Caryl Picker, Inc.
CP - Publisher's imprints - Candlewick Press, Inc.
CP - Water colors ☆ - Rich Art Color Co., Inc.
CP 1 - Food products - Sea Harvest Packing Co.
CP-2 - Pharmaceutical preparations ☆ - Century Pharmaceuticals Inc.
CP 40 - Cream-canned or powdered ☆ - Cream Products Co. Inc.
CP-60 - Electronic equipment - Polaroid Corp.
CP-66 - Housewares - Shurtape Div.
CP-80 - Electronic equipment - Polaroid Corp.
CP BAR - Tools ☆ - Paratech Inc.
CP CANDLEWICK PRESS - Publisher's imprints - Candlewick Press, Inc.
CP FILLER - Calcium compounds - ECC International
CP LOCK - Medical apparatus - Sensor Devices Inc.
CP-VUE - Computer peripheral equipment - Quad-G Electronics, Inc.
CP2 - Health care products - P.I. Medical
CP2 - Recording label - Jazz Composer's Orchestra Association Inc.
CP90 - Coatings - Carwell Products, Inc.
CPA - Pharmaceutical preparations - Schein Pharmaceutical Inc.
CPA BUDDY - Computer software - Bailey Family Corp.
CPA CHECK PRINTING ACCOUNTANT - Electronic equipment - Matsushita Electric Corp. of America
CPB - Video production - Corp. for Public Broadcasting
CPB CONTRACTORS PUMP BUREAU - Pumps - Construction Industry Manufacturers Association
CPBA - Pool-base material - W.R. Grace & Co.
CPC - Bicycles - Cycle Products Co.
CPC - Buckets-plastic ☆ - Century Industries Corp.
CPC - Computer software - Computer Prompting and Captioned Co.
CPC - Giftware - Chinese Products Co.
CPC BIKEXTRAS CYCLE PRODUCTS CO. - Bicycles - American Recreation Co., Inc.
CPC STAIZ - Cardboard - Chesapeake Fiber Packaging Corp.
CPC2000 - Digital encoders - Digital Descriptor Systems Inc.
CPCMS - Computer software - Integrated Technologies of America, Inc.
CPCR - Publisher's imprints - C &,P Press
CPD - Jewelry - Carolyn Peters Designs, Inc.
CPD - Pharmaceutical preparations - Cytosol Laboratories, Inc.
CPDI CALL-CONTROL - Computer software - Communications Product Development, Inc.
CPE - Recording label - Christian P. Elliott
CPE TUTOR - Computer software - Irvine Co.
CPEX - Computer software - Continental Power Exchange, Inc.
CPF - Ophthalmic lenses, frames, etc. - Corning Inc.
CPF-44 - Veterinary product - American Home Products Corp.
CPF POWERFLOOD - Floodlights - General Electric Co.
CPF2D - Insecticides - Enviro-Chem Inc.
CPG - Fruits and vegetables - Colorado Potato Growers Exchange
CPH - Heat exchangers - ITT Corp. (Heat Transfer Div.)
CPH - Paper products - Concordia Publishing House

CPI - Cables - Ivolex
CPI - License plates-automotive - Creative Products Inc.
CPI - Telephones-cellular - Cellular Products Inc.
CPI COLOR PRINT FILM - Film - CPI Brands, Inc.
CPIC - Computer software - Raxsoft, Inc.
CPIM - Computer software - Servantis Systems, Inc.
CPKIDS - Food products - California Pizza Kitchen Inc.
CPK'SADILLAS - Tortillas - California Pizza Kitchen Inc.
CPL - Faucets - Emhart Inc.
CPLIB - Computer software ☆ - Data Translation, Inc.
CPM - Photo albums - Holson Co.
CPM 500 - Monitors-electronic - BHA Group, Inc.
CPM 1000 - Monitors-electronic - BHA Group, Inc.
CPM 2000 - Electronic equipment - BHA Group, Inc.
CPM 3000 - Filters-industrial - BHA Group, Inc.
CPMS - Electronic equipment - Joseph W. Kozora
C.P.O. - Apparel and accessories - International News, Inc.
CPO - Recording label - Koch International
C'PORTS - Statuary - C'ports Inc.
CPP - Vitamins and nutritional supplements - Carol Bond Health Foods, Inc.
C.P.Q. - Fabric - Coral of Chicago
C.P.R. - Adhesives and sealants - Nowstar
CPR - Cleaning preparations - La-Co Industries, Inc.
C.P.R. - Cleaning preparations - Recoton Corp.
C.P.R. - Dental equipment - Spartan Marketing Group
CPR MICROSHIELD - Health care products - Medical Devices International
CPREVIVER - Health care products - Winspan Inc.
CPRO - Computer software - Robert Haynie & Co.
CPRSERVER - Computer software - Digital Medical Systems, Inc.
CPS - Air conditioning equipment - CPS Products, Inc.
CPS - Antennas-satellite - KVH Industries, Inc.
CPS - Apparel-athletic - Made in the Shade by Prime Time
CPS - Boats-motor ☆ - Starcraft Corp.
C.P.S. - Lenses-optical - Younger Manufacturing Co.
CPS - Paper-gift wrap ☆ - CPS Corp.
CPS - Publisher's imprints - Critical Path Strategies, Inc.
CPS - Sporting goods - Bike Athletic Co.
CPS 2000 - Toys-guns - Larami Limited, Inc.
CPTO - Sportswear - Cpto Industries, Inc.
CPU PRODUCTS - Computer peripheral equipment - CPU Products Corp.
CPVC CEMENT - Cement - Comstar International Inc. (IPC Div.)
CPW - Apparel and accessories - Huntington Hampton Corp.
CPX - Telephones-cellular - Telular Corp.
CQ PRESS - Textbooks - Congressional Quarterly Inc.
CQCS - Computer software - Cyberscience Corp.
CR - Automotive parts and accessories - Chicago Rawhide
CR - Coatings - Nelsonite, Inc.
CR - Cylinders - American Cylinder Co., Inc.
CR - Jewelry - Cindy Royce Creations Inc.
CR - Wine - Quail Run Cellars & Vintners
CR-3 - Infant product - Century Products Co.
CR-95 - Paints ☆ - Dunn Edwards Corp.
C.R. & F. - Wines - Admiral Wine Merchants
CR CHERRY RIVET - Rivets-metal - Textron Aerospace Fasteners
CR/MX - Respirators ☆ - Glendale Protective Technologies Inc.
CR/PL - Plumbing fixtures-metal - CR-PL L.P.
C.R. SMITH MUSEUM - Pencils - American Airlines Inc.
C.R. SMITH MUSEUM AMERICANAIRLINES - Apparel-men's - American Airlines Inc.
CR SPECIAL - Vegetables-frozen - McCain Foods Inc.
CRA-ZEE ARROW - Toys - Maryland Toy Corp.
CRA-ZEE FACES - Toys - Maryland Toy Corp.
C.R.A.B. - Toys - Tonka Corp.
CRAB ALERT - Traps-animal - Cuba Specialty Manufacturing Co.
CRAB APPLE - Pet products ☆ - Petland, Inc.
CRAB BOMB, THE - Food products - Jerry's Seafood
CRAB CONNECTION - Giftware - The Crab Connection
CRAB CONTINENTAL - Seafood products-fresh or frozen - Fishery Products International USA
CRAB KING - Food products ☆ - Louisiana Boyel Seafood, Inc.
CRAB-N-WEED - Herbicides - J. & L. Adikes Inc.
CRAB-NAPPER - Traps-animal ☆ - Cuba Specialty Manufacturing Co.
CRAB NET - Computer software - Mid-Atlantic Real Estate Information Technologies, Inc.
CRAB NEWPORT - Seafood products-fresh or frozen - Fishery Products International USA

☆ = Now out of production

CRAB ORCHARD STONE CO., INC. - Stone products - Crab Orchard Stone Co., Inc.

CRAB STOPPER - Fertilizers - Seacoast Laboratories Inc.

CRABAPPLE COVE - Wallpaper - York Wall Coverings Inc.

CRABBY - Giftware - The Crab Connection

CRABBY ROAD - Publisher's imprints - Hallmark Cards Inc.

CRABETTES - Seafood products–fresh or frozen - Eat-All Frozen Food Co.

CRABICIDE - Fertilizers - Greenview Lawn & Garden Products

CRABICIDE GREEN - Fertilizers - Greenview Lawn & Garden Products

CRABLE SPORTSWEAR - Apparel stores–sports - CS Crable Sportswear, Inc.

CRABTREE & EVELYN SONG DE CHINE - Soap - Crabtree & Evelyn, Ltd.

CRACK-ATTACK - Epoxy - Sandstrom Products Co.

CRACK ATTACKER - Nail care products - D & L Industries, Inc.

CRACK CRETE - Concrete products ☆ - Gibson-Homans Co.

CRACK-FIL - Adhesives and sealants - Garon Products Inc.

CRACK FINDER - Adhesives and sealants - Chem-Pak Inc.

CRACK HEAD - Toys ☆ - Those Characters from Cleveland, Inc.

CRACK 'N PATCH - Adhesives and sealants - Rock-Tred Corp.

CRACK POTS - Pottery ☆ - Kersten Bros. Studios

CRACK SHOT - Rifles ☆ - Savage Arms Inc.

CRACK THE CASE - Games - Hasbro, Inc.

CRACK-UP - Sweatshirts - T.E.E. Inc.

CRACK-UPS - Toys–automobiles - Mattel, Inc.

CRACKAJACK - Ophthalmic goods - Embassy Creations Inc.

CRACKARM - Toys - Tonka Corp.

CRACKBOND - Chemical preparations - U.S. Anchor Corp.

CRACKED DICE - Games - Lakeside Games

CRACKED ICE - Christmas tree ornaments - Cracker Box Inc.

CRACKED ICE - Furniture - McGuire Furniture Co.

CRACKED ICE - Sporting goods ☆ - Duro Finishing Corp.

CRACKED SEED - Games - Yick Lung Co., Inc.

CRACKED WHEAT - Breads - Natural Ovens of Manitowoc Inc.

CRACKER BACKERS - Cheese - Beatrice Cheese Co.

CRACKER BARREL - Cheese - Kraft Foods, Inc.

CRACKER BARREL - Recording label ☆ - Ray Lawrence Ltd.

CRACKER BARREL - Signs - Corona Brushes Inc.

CRACKER BOX - Boats - Glen-L Marine Designs

CRACKER CRISPS - Tortillas ☆ - Frito-Lay, Inc.

CRACKER JACK - Cereal - Ralston Purina Co.

CRACKER JACK - Floor coverings–carpet and rugs ☆ - American Carpet Mills

CRACKER JACK - Flour–blended - Mennel Milling Co.

CRACKER JACK - Ice cream - Borden, Inc.

CRACKER JACK - Popcorn - Cracker Jack

CRACKER JACK - Wines - Laird and Co.

CRACKER JACK NUTTY DELUXE - Snack foods - Borden, Inc.

CRACKER KING - Flour–blended - Acme-Evans/A.D.M. Milling Co.

CRACKER PACKER - Toys - Tonka Corp.

CRACKER PAKS - Crackers - Keebler Co.

CRACKER SNAX - Snack foods ☆ - Frito-Lay, Inc.

CRACKER, THE - Nutcrackers - H.M. Quackenbush Inc.

CRACKER, THE - Chemical preparations - U.S. Anchor Corp.

CRACKER TOAST - Food products ☆ - Commerce Foods Inc.

CRACKERBALLS - Crackers ☆ - Edward & Sons Trading Co., Inc.

CRACKERJACK - Floor coverings–carpet and rugs - Southern Carpet Mills

CRACKERJACK - Wallpaper - Jack Foley Associates Inc.

CRACKERJACK - Wallpaper ☆ - W.H.S. Lloyd

CRACKERJACK - Yarn ☆ - William Unger & Co. Inc.

CRACKERS - Candles - Carolina Designs Ltd.

CRACKERS IN MY BED - Games - Tonka Corp.

CRACKERS PARROT - Puppets - Dakin Inc.

CRACKERS THAT CRUNCH LIKE CHIPS - Crackers - Keebler Co.

CRACKFINDER - Electronic equipment - Krautkramer-Branson Inc.

CRACKIN' GOOD - Food products - Jewel Food Stores Inc.

CRACKLE - Floor coverings–carpet and rugs - Calladium & Marglen

CRACKLE - Frames–picture - Russ Berrie and Co., Inc.

CRACKLE - Publisher's imprints ☆ - Kellogg Co.

CRACKLE BUD - Crackers - Umeya Rice Cake Co.

CRACKLE CHEWS - Candy ☆ - Swizzels Matlow (USA) Ltd.

CRACKLE EGG - Giftware - Russ Berrie and Co., Inc.

CRACKLE-IT - Finishing agents - Plaid Enterprises, Inc.

CRACKLED - Glassware ☆ - H.S. Blayman Inc.

CRACKLER - Fireplace equipment - Consumer Electronics Inc.

CRACKLESNAX - Crackers - Original Parisian Bakery Inc.

CRACKLETONE - Pottery products - Duncan Enterprises

CRACKLIN' CRISP - Confectionery - Bortz Chocolate Co.

CRACKLIN' OAT BRAN - Cereal - Kellogg Co.

CRACKLING - Colognes - Aramis Inc.

CRACKLING COBRA - Fireworks - Neptune Wholesale, Inc.

CRACKONTROL - Caulking compounds - Edison Coatings, Inc.

CRACKPOT - Toys - Tonka Corp.

CRACKPOTS - Computer software - Activision, Inc.

CRACKSTERS, THE - Apparel and accessories - Randle and Randle Visual Communications

CRACKUPS - Crackers - Nabisco Foods Group

CRACO - Pickling salt ☆ - Fairmont Snacks Group Inc.

CRADLE ART - Toys - Tot Inc.

CRADLE BABY - Dolls - Uneeda Doll Co., Inc.

CRADLE BATH - Infant product - Gerry Baby Products Co.

CRADLE CLUB - Infants' apparel and accessories, flannel sheeting - Infant Items Inc.

CRADLE DAYS - Apparel–athletic ☆ - Pine Hosiery Mills, Inc.

CRADLE FOAM - Cradles - Colgate Mattress Co.

CRADLE GEMS - Toys–stuffed - Dakin Inc.

CRADLE GRAB - Hooks - Columbus Mckinnon Corp.

CRADLE KICKS - Footwear–children's - Darling Baby Shoe Co.

CRADLE 'N SWING - High chairs ☆ - Century Products Co.

CRADLE SLEEP - Pillows - Mastex Industries, Inc.

CRADLE STEPPERS - Shoes - Clinic Shoe Co.

CRADLE TO CRAYONS - Wallpaper - Longwood Wallcovering

CRADLE TO HI - Knit goods - Infant-to-Teen Headwear Co.

CRADLEPHONES - Personal telephones - American Telecommunications Corp.

CRADLES - Medical apparatus - Bird & Cronin, Inc.

CRADLETTE - Infant product ☆ - Cosco, Inc.

CRADLETYME - Cradles - Colgate Mattress Co.

CRADLEVISION - Computer terminals - Terry K. Holdredge

CRAELY - Apparel–women's - Evan-Picone Inc.

CRAF-TONE - Artists' materials - Vogart Crafts Corp.

CRAF-TYPE - Decals and transfers - Vogart Crafts Corp.

CRAFT 100 - Fabrics–felt - Felters Co.

CRAFT 2001 - Fabrics–felt - Felters Co.

CRAFT AMERICA - Compressors–air ☆ - Thomas Industries Inc. (Power Air Div.)

CRAFT ART - Hobby kits - Vogart Crafts Corp.

CRAFT BARREL - Craft supplies ☆ - Tulip Productions

CRAFT BASICS - Hobby kits - Forster Inc.

CRAFT BREWED - Beverages–alcohol - Chatam Imports Inc.

CRAFT CARRIAGE - Carts ☆ - Leelo Industries, Inc.

CRAFT CAST - See POLYFOAM

CRAFT COLOR - Hobby kits - Vogart Crafts Corp.

CRAFT DOH - Toys - Tonka Corp.

CRAFT GALLERY, THE - Artists' materials - Har-Man Importing Group

CRAFT HAIR JIGS - Sporting goods - Charles E. Nuckols

CRAFT HOLD - Glue–household or industrial - National Artcraft Co.

CRAFT HOUSE - Hobby kits - Craft House Corp.

CRAFT HOUSE STITCHIN' FUN - Hobby kits ☆ - Craft House Corp.

CRAFT KING - Garbage disposal units–commercial - Geo. A. Morlan Plumbing & Appliance Co.

CRAFT KOTE - Paints - Duron, Inc.

CRAFT MARK - Office supplies ☆ - JM Co.

CRAFT-MASTER - Ladders–metal - Werner Co.

CRAFT MASTERS SINCE 1888, THE - Pork - Patcud Investments, Inc.

CRAFT MASTERS, THE - Sausages - Patcud Investments, Inc.

CRAFT-MATE - Frames–picture ☆ - Frank A. Edmunds and Co.

CRAFT MATE - Furniture - Ideal Creations Products, Inc.

CRAFT 'N NEEDLEWORK - Craft supplies ☆ - June Tailor Inc.

CRAFT PAINTER - Artists' materials - Robert Simmons Inc.

CRAFT PATTERNS - Publisher's imprints - National Plan Service

CRAFT PRO - Hobby kits - Mangelsen's (VDI)

CRAFT PUNCH - Hobby kits - Uchida of America Corp.

CRAFT SPUN - Yarn - Henry's Attic

CRAFT STAR - Golfing equipment - Dallas Golf Co., Inc.

CRAFT-TEX COUNTRY - Hobby kits - Craft-Tex Inc.

CRAFT TWINKLES - Paints ☆ - DecoArt, Inc.

CRAFT VILLAGE - Baskets–wood - Makoto Inc.

CRAFT WARES - Hobby kits - Janlynn Corp.

CRAFT WORLD - Hobby kits - Craft World International Inc.

CRAFT YOUR WORLD - Leather goods - Tandy Leather Co.

CRAFTAIDS - Leather goods - Tandy Leather Co.

CRAFTAMERICA - Paints - Thomas Paint Applicators

CRAFTASTIC - Hobby kits - Rose Art Industries, Inc.
CRAFTED ARTISTRY - Wallpaper - Andover Wallcovering
CRAFTED CLASSICS - Games ☆ - Pacific Game Co.
CRAFTED CRYSTAL - Glassware—household - Louie Glass Co. Inc.
CRAFTED WITH LOVE - Glue—household or industrial - Kmart Corp.
CRAFTERS ACRYLIC - Paints - DecoArt, Inc.
CRAFTERS CABIN - Pillow stuffing, forms, and batting - American Fiber
    Industries Corp.
CRAFTER'S CHOICE - Appliques - Blumenthal/Lansing Co.
CRAFTERS CHOICE - Pillows - Fairfield Processing Corp.
CRAFTER'S CHOICE - Steel wool ☆ - International Steel Wool Corp.
CRAFTER'S COLLECTION DALLAS, TEXAS - Apparel and accessories -
    Gary Daryanani
CRAFTERS CORNER - Craft supplies - VIP/VIP Crafts
CRAFTER'S GARDEN - Flowers, plants, and seeds - W. Atlee Burpee and Co.
CRAFTER'S PRIDE - Needlework products - Daniel Enterprises
CRAFTEX - Photo albums - Craftmount Co.
CRAFTGARD - Coatings - Burow Group, Inc.
CRAFTICS - Tools - Craftics Inc.
CRAFTIME - Hobby kits - Playtime Corp.
CRAFTING A TRADITION - Furniture - Thomasville Furniture Industries Inc.
CRAFTINT - Artists' materials - Vogart Crafts Corp.
CRAFTIP - Medical apparatus - Bio-Pak Associates
CRAFTIQUE - Floor coverings—carpet and rugs ☆ - Mohawk Industries Inc.
CRAFTIQUE - Furniture - Craftique Inc.
CRAFTIVITY - Hobby kits - Creative Art Activities Inc.
CRAFTIVITY - Paper—kraft - Pacon Corp.
CRAFTKIDS - Scissors—hand-operated - Acme United Corp.
CRAFTLAWN - Paperboard - Craftmount Co.
CRAFTLINE - Craft supplies - VWS Inc.
CRAFTMADE - Ceiling fans - Craftmade International Inc.
CRAFTMARK - Pens - Sakura of America
CRAFTMARK - Tools - Wall Lenk Corp.
CRAFTMARK - Wallets - Buxton Inc.
CRAFTMARK 21 - Siding—metal ☆ - Reynolds Aluminum Supply Co.
CRAFTMASTER - Doors—wood - Masonite Corp.
CRAFTMASTER - Scissors—hand-operated - Acme United Corp.
CRAFTMASTER - Water heaters—household - Mor-Flo Industries Inc.
CRAFTMASTER HARVEST - Building materials - Masonite Corp.
CRAFTMASTER NATURAL - Doors - Masonite Corp.
CRAFTMATE - Heating equipment - Heaters Engineering, Inc.
CRAFTMATIC - Furniture - Craftmatic/Contour Industries Inc.
CRAFTMERE - Jewelry - Ansul-Craft Inc.
CRAFTMIST PAINT - Hobby kits ☆ - Mangelsen's (VDI)
CRAFT'N'GO - Furniture - Ideal Creations Products, Inc.
CRAFTON - Floor coverings—carpet and rugs ☆ - Evans-Black Carpet Mills
CRAFTONE - Dinnerware—glass - Noritake Co. Inc.
CRAFTONE - Photo albums - Craftmount Co.
CRAFTOOLS - Leather goods - Tandy Leather Co.
CRAFTPLANS - Hobby kits - Craftplans
CRAFTS KIDS CAN DO - Craft supplies - Craft House Corp.
CRAFTS-MAID - Hobby kits - St. Louis Crafts Inc.
CRAFTSBURY - Floor coverings—carpet and rugs ☆ - Mohawk Carpet Corp.
CRAFTSBURY - Furniture—wood ☆ - Century Furniture Co.
CRAFTSMAN - Adhesives and sealants - Tandy Leather Co.
CRAFTSMAN - Apparel and accessories - Sears, Roebuck and Co.
CRAFTSMAN - Cooking equipment—household ☆ - West Bend Co.
CRAFTSMAN - Eyeglasses - Art-Craft Optical Co.
CRAFTSMAN - Furniture ☆ - Hooker Furniture Corp.
CRAFTSMAN - Furniture—public buildings - Craftsman Office Furniture Corp.
CRAFTSMAN - Handwork supplies - Bernat Yarn & Craft Corp.
CRAFTSMAN - Manufactured homes ☆ - Redman Industries, Inc.
CRAFTSMAN - Plywood - Georgia-Pacific Corp.
CRAFTSMAN - Tiles—ceramic ☆ - Terra Green Ceramics, Inc.
CRAFTSMAN - Watches - Bulova Corp.
CRAFTSMAN - Wood products ☆ - Champion International Corp.
CRAFTSMAN COLLECTION - Furniture - Statesville Chair Co. Inc.
CRAFTSMAN HOUSE - Publisher's imprints - Rizzoli International Publications
    Inc.
CRAFTSMAN II - Lumber - Georgia-Pacific Corp.
CRAFTSMAN LTX - Paints - Mac-O-Lac Paints Inc.
CRAFTSMAN OAK - Leather goods - Tandy Leather Co.
CRAFTSMAN PED - Paints - Mac-O-Lac Paints Inc.
CRAFTSMAN SHOPPE CS - Furniture—wood - Collins International Co., Ltd.
CRAFTSMAN, THE - Binders ☆ - 20th Century Plastics
CRAFTSMANS PRIDE - Apparel and accessories - Lady Squire Colors

CRAFTSMEN IN OPTICS - Ophthalmic goods - Benson Optical Co., Inc.
CRAFTSMEN IN STAINLESS - See LIFETIME
CRAFTSMEN'S CORNER - Dolls ☆ - Effanbee Doll Corp.
CRAFTSPACE - Hobby kits - Eagle Affiliates, Inc.
CRAFTSTONE - Artists' materials ☆ - Sculpture House Inc.
CRAFTSTONE - Kitchenware—earthenware ☆ - Arita Sales Co. Inc.
CRAFTSTOR - Craft supplies - Eagle Affiliates, Inc.
CRAFTSTORABLES - Housewares stores - Eagle Affiliates, Inc.
CRAFTWASH - Detergents - Burow Group, Inc.
CRAFTWEAR - Hats - Kraft Hat Manufacturers Inc.
CRAFTWEAVE - Photo albums - Craftmount Co.
CRAFTWOOD - Veneer ☆ - Ralph Wilson Plastics Co.
CRAFTWOOD PADDLES - Hobby kits - Farmdale Creamery Inc.
CRAFTWORKS - Scissors—hand-operated - Acme United Corp.
CRAFTWRAP - Paper—photographic - Craftmount Co.
CRAFTY - Glue—household or industrial ☆ - Tulip Productions
CRAFTY CADDY - Craft supplies - June Tailor Inc.
CRAFTY COCKNEY - Darts and dart games - Dart World Inc.
CRAFTY CORD - Fabrics ☆ - Hickory Industries, Inc.
CRAFTY CREATIONS - Artists' materials - Rose Art Industries, Inc.
CRAFTY CUTTERS - Scissors—hand-operated - Lisa Frank, Inc.
CRAFTY DECOR - Craft supplies - Fairfield Processing Corp.
CRAFTY MAGIC MELT - Glue—household or industrial - Adhesive
    Technologies Inc.
CRAFTY'S DAUB-ON - Dolls ☆ - Mangelsen's (VDI)
CRAFTY'S FEATHERWORKS - Hobby kits - Trueflight Manufacturing Co. Inc.
CRAGAR LITE - Wheels - Cragar Industries, Inc.
CRAGMONT - Beverages—carbonated - Safeway Stores Inc.
CRAIG - Apparel—men's - Palm Beach Co., Inc.
CRAIG - Photographic equipment - Kalart Victor Corp.
CRAIG - Stereos - Craig Consumer Electronics
CRAIG CRAELY - Apparel—women's - Palm Beach Co., Inc.
CRAIG-MARTIN - Shaving preparations - Comfort Manufacturing Co.
CRAIG TAYLOR - Waterproof outerwear - Craig Taylor Shirtmaker, Inc.
CRAIGLAM - Adhesives and sealants - Craig Adhesives & Coatings Co.
CRAIN BOOKS - Publisher's imprints ☆ - NTC Contemporary Publishing Group
CRAISINS - Fruits and vegetables - Ocean Spray Cranberries Inc.
CRAK-STOP - Adhesives and sealants - Camp Co. Inc.
CRAM-O-LUXE - Globes ☆ - Geo. F. Cram Co.
CRAMARC - Cabinets - Cramer Products Co.
CRAMER - Chairs—metal - Cramer Inc.
CRAMER TRANSPORTER - Bags - Cramer Products Inc.
CRAMERGESIC - Lotions - Cramer Products Inc.
CRAMEROL - Bandages - Cramer Products Inc.
CRAMMED - Recording label - Jazz Composer's Orchestra Association Inc.
CRAMORE - Beverages - Romanoff International Inc.
CRAMORTON - Fabrics - Burlington House Fabrics Group
CRAMP GUARD - Pharmaceutical preparations - Jess Clarke & Sons Inc.
CRAMP-GUARD - Pharmaceutical preparations - Winning Solutions Inc./Miracle
    of Aloe
CRAN - Fruit drinks—bottled or canned - Ocean Spray Cranberries Inc.
CRAN BARRY - Sporting goods - Cran Barry Inc.
CRAN-BLUEBERRY - Fruit drinks—bottled or canned - Ocean Spray
    Cranberries Inc.
CRAN-CHERRY - Fruit drinks—bottled or canned - Ocean Spray Cranberries
    Inc.
CRAN-CLEANSE - Vitamins and nutritional supplements - Nature's Products
    Inc.
CRAN-FRUIT - Fruits—canned - Ocean Spray Cranberries Inc.
CRAN-GRAPE - Fruit drinks—bottled or canned - Ocean Spray Cranberries
    Inc.
CRAN-MIX - Fruit drinks—bottled or canned - Ocean Spray Cranberries Inc.
CRAN-STRAWBERRY - Fruit drinks—bottled or canned - Ocean Spray
    Cranberries Inc.
CRAN TABS - Vitamins and nutritional supplements - Re-Vita Manufacturing
    Co., Inc.
CRANACTIN - Vitamins and nutritional supplements - Solaray
CRANAPPLE - Fruit drinks—bottled or canned - Ocean Spray Cranberries Inc.
CRANBARRY - Sporting goods - Cran Barry Inc.
CRANBERRA - See GRANDE CRANBERRY
CRANBERRIE RUMMIE - Jams and jellies - Chittenden Kitchens, Inc.
CRANBERRIE YUMMIE - Jams and jellies - Chittenden Kitchens, Inc.
CRANBERRY - Beverages—carbonated ☆ - The Atlantic Beverage Group,
    USA, Inc.
CRANBERRY - Glassware—household - Fenton Art Glass Co.
CRANBERRY - Jewelry—costume ☆ - Safari Ltd.

☆ = Now out of production

CRANBERRY - Teas - Eastern Shore Tea Co.
CRANBERRY ALMOND CRUNCH - Cereal - Kraft Foods, Inc.
CRANBERRY BLOSSOM - Dinnerware ☆ - Corning Inc.
CRANBERRY BOGS, ESQ. - Cakes ☆ - Christopher's Chewies
CRANBERRY CAFE - Teas - Seelect, Inc.
CRANBERRY CARNIVAL - Juices - Wagner Excello Foods Inc.
CRANBERRY CINAMMON - Deodorizers - Gilbertie's Herb Gardens, Inc.
CRANBERRY CLASSICS - Jams and jellies - Cranberry Products Inc.
CRANBERRY CONCENTRATE - Vitamins and nutritional supplements - Vitamin Research Products Inc.
CRANBERRY COVE - Teas–herbal - Celestial Seasonings, Inc.
CRANBERRY CUTIE - Toys - Tonka Corp.
CRANBERRY DEW - Perfumes - Fragranhaus
CRANBERRY FROST - Lipsticks ☆ - Honey & Spice Toiletries
CRANBERRY ICE - Christmas tree ornaments - Cracker Box Inc.
CRANBERRY LAKE - Leather goods - Vaughn Communications, Inc.
CRANBERRY LANE - Wallpaper ☆ - Sanitas Wallcoverings
CRANBERRY LEMONADE VISION - Juices - Coca-Cola Co.
CRANBERRY NEWTONS - Cookies - Nabisco Foods Group
CRANBERRY-POWER - Vitamins and nutritional supplements - Twin Laboratories Inc. (Nature's Herbs)
CRANBERRY RAZZ - Tea - Celestial Seasonings, Inc.
CRANBERRY RELISH - Food products - Mrs. Powell's Gourmet Pecans
CRANBERRY RELISH - Jams and jellies - Sarabeth's Kitchen
CRANBERRY ROYALE - Juices - Snapple Beverage Corp.
CRANBERRY SATIN - Wines - Chicama Vineyards
CRANBERRY SCROLL - Glassware–household ☆ - Culver Glass Inc.
CRANBERRY STUDIOS - Fabrics - International Textile Corp.
CRANBERRY TAP - Fruit juice - Noel Corp.
CRANBROOK CLASSICS - Wallpaper - Seabrook Wallcoverings, Inc.
CRANBROOK COLLECTION - Furniture - Sligh Furniture Co.
CRANBROOKE - Trailers–travel ☆ - Coachmen Industries, Inc.
CRANBURY - Bowls ☆ - Lenox Crystal, Inc.
CRANBURY SQUARE - Clocks - Papel Freelance, Inc.
CRANCKY GIRLS CLUB - Apparel–women's - Rich & Me, Inc.
CRANE - Bathroom fixtures - Crane Plumbing/Fiat Products
CRANE - Fruits and vegetables - Nuchief Sales Inc.
CRANE - Motor vehicle parts and accessories - Rivera Engineering, Inc.
CRANE - Potato chips - BDH Two, Inc.
CRANE CHIEF - Remote control devices - Control Chief Corp.
CRANE-FOIL - Gasket and packing material - John Crane Inc.
CRANE LAKE - Wines - Advantage Wine Group
CRANE NINJAZORD - Toys–automobiles - Saban Entertainment, Inc.
CRANE PLUMBING - Plumbing fixtures–metal - CR-PL L.P.
CRANE WALNUT ORCHARDS - Walnuts - Crane Cattle Co.
CRANECO - Apparel–women's - Craneco
CRANE'S - Food products - Crane & Crane
CRANES - Paper - Paper Co.
CRANE'S - Stationery - Crane & Co. Inc.
CRANES - Tool boxes - Rawson-Koenig, Inc.
CRANGEL - Vitamins and nutritional supplements - Banner-Pharmacaps Inc. (Advanced Nutritional Technology Division)
CRANHAM PUBLICATIONS - Puzzles - Kingdom Puzzles
CRANICOT - Fruit drinks–bottled or canned - Ocean Spray Cranberries Inc.
CRANIO KIDS - Dolls - Patricia A. Brechlin
CRANK - Helmets–athletic - Michael Wilkerson Jones
CRANK-DRIVE - Machinery - Dry-Tab Package Sealer Co.
CRANK IT UP - Sporting goods - Proform Fitness Products, Inc.
CRANK MASTER - Sporting goods - Gapen Co.
CRANK SHAFT - Golfing equipment - Nicklaus Golf Equipment Co.
CRANKBAIT - Fishing lures - Highland Group
CRANKCASE - Loudspeakers - International Jensen Inc.
CRANKE BOY - Apparel and accessories - Anderle Graphics
CRANKMISSION - Lubricants ☆ - Hertron International Inc.
CRANKSTERS - Sporting goods - Boone Bait Co. Inc.
CRANKY FRANKY - Candy ☆ - Sunline Brands
CRANMERE - Shelving units–wood ☆ - Kirsch Co.
CRANORANGE - Juices - Ocean Spray Cranberries Inc.
CRANPRUNE - Fruit drinks–bottled or canned - Ocean Spray Cranberries Inc.
CRANRASPBERRY - Fruit drinks–bottled or canned - Ocean Spray Cranberries Inc.
CRANSKA - Thread - Belding Heminway Co. Inc.
CRANSTON - Frames–eyeglass ☆ - Universal/Univis Inc.
CRANSTON CUT-OUTS - Appliques - Cranston Print Works Co.
CRANSTON FARMS - Seasonings - Broaster Co.
CRANSTON HOME FASHIONS - Fabrics - Cranston Print Works Co.

CRANSTON MANOR - Furniture ☆ - Bassett Furniture Industries, Inc.
CRANSWEETS - Food products ☆ - Cranberry Products Inc.
CRANTASIA - Beverages–alcohol - Jim Beam Brands Co.
CRANTASTIC - Fruit drinks–bottled or canned - Ocean Spray Cranberries Inc.
CRAOKER COUNTY - Figurines - Brennan Studio Inc.
C.R.A.P. CHILDREN REBELLING AGAINST PARENTS - Apparel - Simmons Hearing Aid Service Co.
CRAP SHOOT MINI CRAPS - Game machines - Tomarry, Inc.
CRAPAL - Wire products - Trefilarbed Inc.
CRAPJACK - Games - Wichita Brown Enterprises, Inc.
CRAPPIE DELUXE - Boats–motor - Alumacraft Boat Co.
CRAPPIE PRO - Boats–motor - Alumacraft Boat Co.
CRAPPIE QUEEN - Fishing lures - Lindy Little Joe Inc.
CRAPPIE RATTLER - Generators - Gammill's Fishing Tackle, Inc.
CRAPPIEMATIC - Fishing tackle ☆ - Martin Reel Co.
CRAPSHOOTER - Fishing lures ☆ - Plastics Research and Development Co.
CRAQUELE - Fabrics–tapestry ☆ - Clarence House Imports Ltd.
CRASH - Apparel and accessories - Hot Spices, Inc.
CRASH - Draperies - Maya Romanoff Corp.
CRASH & SMASH - Toys–automobiles - Mattel, Inc.
CRASH CANYON - Games - Milton Bradley Co.
CRASH CAVALRY - Toys - Mattel, Inc.
CRASH CITY - Games - Steve Jackson Games Inc.
CRASH CONTROL - Computer peripheral equipment - Software Cafe, Inc.
CRASH MASTER - Toys–automobiles - Mattel, Inc.
CRASH PACK - First aid kits - Jody R. Wayne
CRASH PAD - Pet products ☆ - Doskocil Manufacturing Co., Inc.
CRASH PADS - Apparel–athletic - Crash Pads, Inc.
CRASH PATROL - Toys–automobiles - Mattel, Inc.
CRASH VISION - Paper products - Rvision, Inc.
CRASHBACK - Toys - Hasbro, Inc.
CRASHER - Toys - Tonka Corp.
CRASHMOBILE - Toys - Lakeside Games
CRASHPILE - Toys–automobiles - Mattel, Inc.
CRASTO - Wines - W.J. Deutsch & Sons Ltd.
CRATAEGISAN - Health care products - Bioforce of America Ltd.
CRATCHIT - Computer software - PC Designs, Inc.
CRATE - Audio equipment - St. Louis Music Supply Co.
CRATE-A-FILE - File folders - Newell Office Products
CRATE ART - Hobby kits ☆ - Martin Universal Design Inc.
CRATE ESCAPE - Novelty items - Hasbro, Inc.
CRATE OF EIGHT - Recording label - Smarty Pants Audio and Video Inc.
CRATE O'RECIPES - Boxes - Reiman Publications, LP
CRATE PAD - Pet products - O'Donnell Industries Inc.
CRATE TIVITY PLUS - Giftware - Crate-Tivity Plus
CRATEC - Glass–ground - Owens Corning Fiberglass Technology Inc.
CRATEC - Insulating materials - Owens Corning
CRATER - Backpacks - Bianchi International
CRATER - Computer programming services - Berta-Max Inc.
CRATER CONE - Ice cream cones - Dawn Food Products Inc.
CRATER LAKE - Fruits–canned - Rogue River Packing Corp.
CRATERS - Syrup - Craters Pure Maple Syrup
CRAVANETTE - Waterproofing compounds - Cravanette Co. USA
CRAVAT - Blinds–venetian ☆ - Hunter Douglas, Inc.
CRAVATE - Wallpaper - Charterhouse Ltd.
CRAVE - Cat food ☆ - Kal Kan Foods, Inc.
CRAVE QUENCHER, THE - Beverages - White Castle System, Inc.
CRAVEN A - Cigarettes - G.A. Georgopulo & Co. Inc.
CRAVEN A - Cigarettes - Tobacco Exporters International (USA) Ltd.
CRAVEN MIXTURE - Tobacco products ☆ - House of Edgeworth
CRAVENELLA - Yarn - Melrose Yarn Co. Inc.
CRAVENS - Confections - Dae Julie, Inc.
CRAVEN'S - Confections ☆ - R.L. Albert & Son, Inc.
CRAVEX - Aquatic pharmacuetical preparations ☆ - Aquatronics-Filtronics
CRAVEX - Health care products - Healthwatchers System
CRAVIN'CREOLE - Spices and extracts - To Market to Market
CRAVING CAPSULES - Paper products - Theresa McKenney
CRAVING CONTROL - Potato chips ☆ - Nutri/System L.P.
CRAW-TAIL - Fishing lures - National Media Corp.
CRAW-TATORS - Potato chips - Zapp's Chips
CRAWDAD - Boats–fishing - Coleman Co., Inc.
CRAWDAD COUNTY - Housewares - Sara Anderson
CRAWDADDY - Greeting cards - Paul Williams
CRAWDADS - Apparel and accessories - Hickory Baseball, Inc.
CRAWDADS - Shoes ☆ - Interco Inc.
CRAWFISH TYME - Food products - Burger Tyme of America Inc.

☆ = Now out of production

CRAWFORD - Bicycles - Columbia Manufacturing Inc.
CRAWFORD - Doors–garage - Wayne-Dalton Corp.
CRAWFORD - Floor coverings - Tarkett, Inc.
CRAWFORD - Skin care products - Crawford Group, Inc.
CRAWFORD - Watches - Crawford Watch Co. Inc.
CRAWFORD - Whiskey - Schenley Industries Inc.
CRAWFORD & WILLIAMS - Skin care products - United Air Lines, Inc.
CRAWFORD'S FREE - Glue–household or industrial - Crawford Products Co., Inc.
CRAWL SPACE - Infant product ☆ - Century Products Co.
CRAWL-UP-TOOB - Pet products - Penn-Plax, Inc.
CRAWLER CALLER - Fishing lures - Natural Chemicals, Inc.
CRAWLER HARNESSES - Fishing tackle - Schumann's Fly Fish Kit Co.
CRAWLER HAULER - Sporting goods ☆ - Brown Bear Bait Co.
CRAWLIE CRAB - Toys ☆ - Creative Playthings Ltd.
CRAWLIGATOR - Toys ☆ - Creative Playthings Ltd.
CRAWLING CRITTER - Toys ☆ - Steven Manufacturing Co.
CRAWLING CRITTER PUPPETS - Toys - Lauri Inc.
CRAY-N-LICIOUS - Toys–banks - Ralphco, Inc.
CRAY-PAS - Artists' materials - Sakura of America
CRAY-PAS EXPRESSIONIST - Artists' materials - Sakura of America
CRAY-PAS JUNIOR ARTIST - Artists' materials - Sakura of America
CRAY-PAS JUNIOR ARTIST - Crayons - Sakura Color Products of America, Inc.
CRAY-PAS SPECIALIST - Artists' materials - Sakura of America
CRAY-SCRAPER - Artists' materials - Scratch-Art Co., Inc.
CRAYMARK - Pencils - Universal Fountain Pen & Pencil Co.
CRAYNELLA - Yarn - Melrose Yarn Co. Inc.
CRAYOGRAPH - Crayons - Dixon Ticonderoga Co.
CRAYOLA - Crayons - Binney & Smith Inc.
CRAYOLA - Infant product - Mount Vernon Mills Inc.
CRAYOLA - Mats ☆ - The Coleman Co.
CRAYOLA - Watches - E. Gluck Corp.
CRAYOLA BRAND - Lunch boxes - Thermos Co.
CRAYOLA CHANGEABLE - Crayons - Binney & Smith Inc.
CRAYOLA CRAFT - Hobby kits - Binney & Smith Inc.
CRAYOLA MAGIC SCENT - Crayons - Binney & Smith Inc.
CRAYOLA-ROLA - Markers–felt-tip ☆ - Binney & Smith Inc.
CRAYOLET - Crayons ☆ - Binney & Smith Inc.
CRAYON - Fabrics - Dan River Inc.
CRAYON - Toys - Remco Baby Inc.
CRAYON-BY-NUMBER - Crayons - Brite-Tone Co.
CRAYON COLORS - Paper–gift wrap - Stephen Lawrence Co.
CRAYON CREME - Cosmetics - Sothys USA Inc.
CRAYON DESIGNS - Greeting cards ☆ - Chase Collection, Inc.
CRAYON MULTIMEDIA - Computer software - Byron Preiss Multimedia Co., Inc.
CRAYON SOURCILS - Cosmetics ☆ - Sothys USA Inc.
CRAYON WEAR - Coloring kits - Foto-Wear Inc.
CRAYONFOIL KITES - Kites - New Tech Sports
CRAYONS - Apparel and accessories - Tom Togs of Carolina, Inc.
CRAYONS - Floor coverings–carpet and rugs ☆ - Porter Carpet Mills Inc.
CRAYONS - Hosiery–women's ☆ - Nantucket Industries Inc.
CRAYONS - Shorts–women's - El Greco Inc.
CRAYONS - Tiles–ceramic ☆ - American Marazzi Tile, Inc.
CRAYONS ANTICERNES - Cosmetics ☆ - Sothys USA Inc.
CRAYONS COUNTOUR DES LEVRES - Lipsticks - Sothys USA Inc.
CRAYONS KHOL-KAJAL - Cosmetics - Sothys USA Inc.
CRAYRITE - Crayons ☆ - Milton Bradley Co.
CRAYSOFT - Computer software - Cray Research, Inc.
CRAYTONS BREAKFAST BELL SAUSAGE - Sausages - Grover C. Crayton II, Grover C. Crayton, Leroy Crayton Jr. and John H. Lenear Partnership
CRAYTUFF - Crayons - Rose Art Industries, Inc.
CRAYZEE PUNCH BALL - Exercising equipment - Allen C. Sueirio
CRAZ-EYES - Frames–eyeglass - May Optical Co. Inc.
CRAZE - Ophthalmic goods - Embassy Creations Inc.
CRAZE E. PUMPKIN - Novelty items - Paper Magic Group Inc.
CRAZHUGS - Toys - Puppet Masters, Inc.
CRAZY - Beverages–alcohol - Heaven Hill Distilleries, Inc.
CRAZY ADMISSION TICKETS - Novelty items - BRC Corp.
CRAZY BABY - Hair care products ☆ - Clairol Inc.
CRAZY BALLOON - Video games - Taito America Corp.
CRAZY BALLS - Pet products - R.A.F. Trading Inc.
CRAZY-BITS - Candy ☆ - Chex Co.
CRAZY BONE - Pet chews - Items Inc.
CRAZY BONES - Cakes ☆ - Drake Bakeries, Inc.

CRAZY BREAD - Breads - Little Caesar Enterprises, Inc.
CRAZY BREAD DIPPERS - Food products - Little Caesar Enterprises, Inc.
CRAZY CAJUN - Barbecue sauce - Crazy Cajun Enterprises, Inc.
CRAZY CAJUN - Recording label - Music Enterprises Inc.
CRAZY CALYPSO - Potato chips - BDH Two, Inc.
CRAZY CALYPSO - Potato chips - Borden, Inc.
CRAZY CAMERA - Toys - Fisher-Price, Inc.
CRAZY CAN - Candy - Fleer Corp.
CRAZY CART - Toys–automobiles - Mattel, Inc.
CRAZY CAT - Pet products - Cardinal Laboratories, Inc.
CRAZY CAT - Toys - Tonka Corp.
CRAZY CAVALIER - Toys - Tonka Corp.
CRAZY CHARLEY - Barbecue sauce - Crazy Cajun Enterprises, Inc.
CRAZY CHEESE - Cheese spread - Little Caesar Enterprises, Inc.
CRAZY CIRCLE - Pet products - Doskocil Manufacturing Co., Inc.
CRAZY CLAY CHARACTERS - Toys - Fisher-Price, Inc.
CRAZY CLEAN - Cleaning preparations - Sprayway Inc.
CRAZY CLEAVER - Novelty items - Cal Themes Inc.
CRAZY CLIMBERS - Candy - Murray-Allen International Inc.
CRAZY CLOWN FIRE BRIGADE - Toys - Fisher-Price, Inc.
CRAZY CLUBHOUSE - Toys - Tiger Electronics, Inc.
CRAZY COLORS - Pencils ☆ - Faber-Castell Corp.
CRAZY COLORS - Pens - Pentech International Inc.
CRAZY COMB - Cosmetics - Nino Originals
CRAZY COMBINATION - Apparel–women's - Wacoal America Inc.
CRAZY COMBO - Toys - Fisher-Price, Inc.
CRAZY COMICS - Chewing gum - Philadelphia Chewing Gum Corp.
CRAZY COMMANDO - Toys - Mattel, Inc.
CRAZY CORDS - Toys - Hart Enterprises, Inc.
CRAZY CORN - Bird feeds - Judee K. Creations, Inc. (Crazy Corn Division)
CRAZY COVERS - Chewing gum ☆ - Fleer Corp.
CRAZY COW - Cereal ☆ - General Mills, Inc.
CRAZY CRAB - Games - Meyer/Glass Design L.P.
CRAZY-CRABS - Food products ☆ - Transcience Corp.
CRAZY CRAWLER - Sporting goods - James Heddon's Sons
CRAZY CREDIT CARDS - Novelty items–paper - Kalan Inc.
CRAZY CRITTERS - Toys - Tonka Corp.
CRAZY CRITTERS - Toys–stuffed - CPG Products Corp.
CRAZY CRUST - Breads - Little Caesar Enterprises, Inc.
CRAZY CUKES - Pickles - Green Bay Foods Co.
CRAZY CUSHION - Pillows - Centsable Toys Inc.
CRAZY DAISY - Toys - Fisher-Price, Inc.
CRAZY DANCERS - Toys - Sawyer Industries, Inc.
CRAZY DIPS - Candy - Pennsylvania Dutch Candies
CRAZY DIPS - Candy - Uniconfis Corp.
CRAZY DOG - Pet products - Cardinal Laboratories, Inc.
CRAZY EGGS - Fishing lures - Magic Products, Inc.
CRAZY EIGHTS - Restaurants–pizzerias - Little Caesar Enterprises, Inc.
CRAZY FEET - Figurines - Cal Themes Inc.
CRAZY FENCERS - Toys - Sawyer Industries, Inc.
CRAZY FLAG - Flags - National Banner Co., Inc.
CRAZY FLAVOR - Beverages–carbonated - Pepsico, Inc.
CRAZY FLICKERS - Lighting equipment ☆ - Duro-Lite Lamps Inc.
CRAZY FOAM - Soap - L & F Consumer Products
CRAZY FOR YOU - Housewares - Crazy for You Enterprises
CRAZY FRUIT - Candy - American Chewing Gum Inc.
CRAZY GIRL - Frames–eyeglass - Zylo Ware Corp.
CRAZY GLASSES - Novelty item - Sansom, Inc.
CRAZY GLASSES - Novelty items - Fun-Time International, Inc.
CRAZY GRAPE - Lipsticks - Honey & Spice Toiletries
CRAZY HORSE - Apparel and accessories - Russ Togs Inc.
CRAZY HORSE - Beverages–malt - Hornell Brewing Co. Inc.
CRAZY HORSE GIRL - Apparel–children's - Russ Togs Inc.
CRAZY HORSE II - Apparel and accessories - Russ Togs Inc.
CRAZY HORSE LEGENDS - Apparel - L.C. Licensing, Inc.
CRAZY HYPE! - Recording label - Avatar Productions
CRAZY J - Toys - Tonka Corp.
CRAZY JIM'S - Barbecue sauces - James Igo
CRAZY KEEPER - Toys - Discovery Toys, Inc.
CRAZY LABEL CANDY - Candy - BRC Corp.
CRAZY LEGS - Apparel–women's - Wacoal America Inc.
CRAZY LEGS - Exercising equipment - Sawyer Industries, Inc.
CRAZY LEGS - Fishing lures - Scovill Industries, Inc.
CRAZY LEGS - Hosiery ☆ - Liberty Hosiery Mills Inc.
CRAZY LEGS - Sleeping bags - Mountain Hardwear, Inc.
CRAZY LETTERS - Games - Meyers List Inc.

☆ = Now out of production

CRAZY MIXED-UP KIDS - Candy ☆ - Stark Candy Co.

CRAZY MOUNTAIN OUTFITTERS - Coats - Liberty Industries, Inc.

CRAZY PAK - Chewing gum ☆ - Fleer Corp.

CRAZY PET - Pet products - Cardinal Laboratories, Inc.

CRAZY PRICES EVERYDAY - Tools–hand-operated - T.U.I. Tools & Machinery Co. Ltd.

CRAZY PUZZLE PAPER - Paper–gummed - Puzzle Paper Co.

CRAZY QUARTERS - Electronic gaming devices - President Riverboat Casino

CRAZY ROACH CHALK - Cleaning preparations - ABA-tron Industries Inc. (ABA-tron Consumer and Household Products Div.)

CRAZY ROBOT - Fireworks - American Promotional Events, Inc.

CRAZY SAUCE - Sauces - Little Caesar Enterprises, Inc.

CRAZY SCRUBS - Medical apparatus - Crazy Scrubs, Inc.

CRAZY SHIRTS - Bags - Crazy Shirts, Inc.

CRAZY SLATE - Toys - Landoll, Inc.

CRAZY SPRAY - Chewing gum - Fleer Corp.

CRAZY STAMPS - Stamps–hand - Mattel, Inc.

CRAZY SWIRL - Curling irons–electric - Remington Products Co.

CRAZY TWIRL - Curling irons–electric - Remington Products Co.

CRAZY VIDEO - Candy - Fleer Corp.

CRAZY WRENCH - Toys - Mattel, Inc.

CRAZY!CRAZY! - Food products - Little Caesar Enterprises, Inc.

CRAZYHORSE LEGEND 1964 - Apparel and accessories - L.C. Licensing, Inc.

CRAZYLEGS - Skin care products ☆ - S.C. Johnson & Son, Inc.

CRAZYWORLD - Greeting cards - American Greetings Corp.

CRB - Cement - W.R. Grace & Co.

CRB 42-2 - Fabrics - Land Fabric Co.

CRB INFOTECH - Computer storage devices–magnetic - Commodity News Services Inc.

CRC - Cleaning preparations ☆ - CRC Chemicals USA/Siloo

CRC - Medical apparatus - Capintec, Inc.

CRC - Thermostats - Flair International Corp.

CRC PRESS DATABASE - Computer software - CRC Press, Inc.

CRCC - Coal - Carter-ROAG Coal Co. Inc.

CRE-MEL - Food products - Morningstar Group Inc.

CRE8 HAVOC - Apparel and accessories - Lee Thomas Inc.

CREA/MAX - Vitamins and nutritional supplements - Victor Rubino

CREA-STONE - Artists' materials - American Art Clay Co. Inc.

CREACIONES TROPICALES - Figurines - Handmade Creations Inc.

CREACIONS GRAU - Electronic equipment - Tano Inc.

CREAGLUTIDE - Vitamins and nutritional supplements - Bodyonics, Ltd.

CREALINE - Glassware–household ☆ - St. Gobain International Glassware

CREALOCK - Boats - Pacific Seacraft Corp.

CREAM AT THE TOP - Milk - Anbrook Associates

CREAM CARE - Hair care products - Stanley Fay Co.

CREAM CHEESE CLASSIC - Cakes - Edwards Baking Co.

CREAM CITY - Twine - John Rauschenberger Co.

CREAM CORN - Candy - Herman Goelitz Candy Co., Inc.

CREAM DE NOISETTE - Coffee - White Coffee Corp.

CREAM FLAKE - Bakery products ☆ - Wilsey Foods, Inc.

CREAM FLUFF - Shampoos - Ampro Industries, Inc.

CREAM GINGERIDE - Health care products - P-Bee Products

CREAM GLOW - Cosmetics ☆ - Elysee Scientific Cosmetic Co.

CREAM HAVARTI SAGA - Cheese - Tholstrup Cheese USA Inc.

CREAM KING - Smoke detectors ☆ - Kidde Safety

CREAM-NUT - Peanut butter ☆ - Koeze Co.

CREAM O CHOCOLATE SODA - Beverages–carbonated ☆ - American 76 Co.

CREAM O CROP - Eggs ☆ - Safeway Stores Inc.

CREAM-O-LAND - Food products - Midtown Provision Co. Inc.

CREAM-O-MATIC - Whipping machines ☆ - Kidde Safety

CREAM-O-WEBER - Butter, margerine, milk - Cream O' Weber

CREAM OF OATS - Food products - National Oats Co. Inc.

CREAM OF RICE - Cereal - Nabisco Foods Group

CREAM OF RYE - Cereal - Conagra, Inc.

CREAM OF THE CROP - Coffee ☆ - White Coffee Corp.

CREAM OF THE VALLEY - Tomato pastes and sauces - Diven Packing Co.

CREAM OF VANILLA - Spices and extracts - Marion-Kay-Reidco Inc.

CREAM OF WHEAT - Cereal - Nabisco Foods Group

CREAM PUFF - Bicycles - Columbia Manufacturing Inc.

CREAM PUFF - Dolls ☆ - Effanbee Doll Corp.

CREAM PUFF - Fabrics - Dan River Inc.

CREAM ROAST - Coffee - Hansen Good Coffee

CREAM ROSE - Lotions - St. Ives Laboratories, Inc.

CREAM SUDS - Cleaning preparations - Procter & Gamble Co.

CREAM-TO-POWDER - Cosmetics - Almay Inc.

CREAM WHITE - Food products - Kraft Food Ingredients Corp.

CREAMALIN - Antacids - Lee Pharmaceuticals

CREAMALIN - Antacids - Winthrop Pharmaceuticals

CREAMEDIC - Soap - Harley Chemicals

CREAMERIE TRIPLE CREAM - Food products - Kraft Foods, Inc.

CREAMETTE SPAGHETTI AND ALFREDO SAUCE MIX - Sauces - Williams Foods Inc.

CREAMETTES - Pasta - Creamette Co.

CREAMIES - Bakery products - Tasty Baking Co.

CREAMIES - Ice cream - Premium Leasing Limited Liability Co.

CREAMIES SPARKLING JUICE - Beverages - After the Fall Products Inc.

CREAMLAND - Dairy products - Dean Foods Co.

CREAMLINE - Milk - Ronnybrook Farm Dairy

CREAMPUFF - Furniture–upholstered ☆ - Mersman Furniture Co.

CREAMSICLE - Ice cream - Good Humor Corp.

CREAMSICLE - Lipsticks ☆ - Elysee Scientific Cosmetic Co.

CREAMSTIX - Ice cream - Heart to Heart Foods Inc.

CREAMWARE - Housewares - Shafford Co. Inc.

CREAMY BRILLIANCE - Butter - Pocahontas Foods USA Inc.

CREAMY CARAMEL CRUNCHY NUT - Ice cream - H.P. Hood & Sons Inc.

CREAMY CAROB - Teas ☆ - Traditional Medicinals, Inc.

CREAMY CLUSTER - Candy - Palmer Candy Co.

CREAMY COLLECTIONS - Food products - Brothers Gourmet Products, Inc.

CREAMY DELUXE - Frosting - General Mills, Inc.

CREAMY HOMESTYLE - Frosting - Procter & Gamble Co.

CREAMY LIME - Skin care products - House of Lowell Inc.

CREAMY 'MASH - Food products - Winnemucca Farms

CREAMY 'N DREAMY - Frosting ☆ - General Mills, Inc.

CREAMY SCALLOPED POTATOES EXPRESS - Food products - General Mills, Inc.

CREAMY SPREAD - Spices and extracts - Reckitt & Colman, Inc.

CREAMY SUPREME - Frosting - Pillsbury Co.

CREAMY TREAT - Ice cream - Melody Foods Lansing Dairy Inc.

CREAMY WHIP - Cottage cheese - Leehi Dally Dairies

CREAMY WHITE - Candy ☆ - Brocks Candy Co.

CREART - Figurines - Joy Zee Enterprises

CREASE GLO - Paints - Burley's Rink Supply, Inc.

CREASE 'N FUSE - Fabrics - Facemate Corp.

CREATABASE - Computer software ☆ - PCSoftware

CREATAFORM - See PACKMASTER

CREATE - Hobby kits - Wood World

CREATE-A-BAG - Hobby kits - A + A

CREATE-A-CAKE - Computer software - Responsive Retail Solutions

CREATE A CAPTION - Novelty items - Tawn Chi & Associates Inc.

CREATE-A-CARD - Greeting cards - A + A

CREATE-A-CHECK - Computer software - Create-A-Check, Inc.

CREATE-A-CLING - Decorations - Ogren Companies Inc.

CREATE-A-CLOCK - Clocks - ARW Distributor, Inc.

CREATE-A-CLOCK - Clocks - Jordak

CREATE-A-COLLAR - Pet products - Wee Waggers

CREATE A COSTUME - Costumes - Rubie's Costume Co., Inc.

CREATE A CRAFT - Craft supplies - Wal-Mart Stores Inc.

CREATE-A-CRAFT - Publisher's imprints - A + A

CREATE-A-CRATE - Containers - International Products Co., Inc.

CREATE A CREATURE - Toys - Toymax Inc.

CREATE-A-CUBE - Paper products - Paper Conversions Inc.

CREATE-A-DECK - Hardware - Cardinal Home Products

CREATE-A-DEX - Ring-binder index sets - Dennison Stationery Products Co.

CREATE-A-ENAMEL - Hobby kits - A + A

CREATE-A-FACE - Cosmetics - Rubie's Costume Co., Inc.

CREATE-A-FACE - Hobby kits - A + A

CREATE A FAVOR - Giftware - Party City Corp.

CREATE-A-FINISH - Paints - Prestype Inc.

CREATE-A-JEWEL - Hobby kits - A + A

CREATE A LAMP SHADE - Hobby kits - Wood World

CREATE A LOOK - Lamps - Mastercraft Lamp Co. Inc.

CREATE A MEAL! - Food products - Pillsbury Co.

CREATE-A-PICTURE - Hobby kits - A + A

CREATE-A-PLANTER - Hobby kits - A + A

CREATE-A-PLATE - Electrical equipment - Pass & Seymour, Inc.

CREATE-A-POND - Fountains - Henri Studio, Inc.

CREATE-A-POND KIT - Water treating compounds - Mardel Laboratories, Inc.

CREATE-A-POSTER - Hobby kits - A + A

CREATE-A-PRINT - Photographic equipment - Eastman Kodak Co.

CREATE-A-PUZZLE - Puzzles - A + A

CREATE-A-PUZZLE - Puzzles - Callen Photo Mount Corp.

CREATE-A-RUG - Hobby kits - A + A
CREATE-A-SAURUS - Playground equipment - Create-A-Saurus Inc.
CREATE A SCENE - Toys - Smethport Specialty Co.
CREATE-A-SHAPE - Stencils - Helix USA Ltd.
CREATE-A-SHELF - Hardware ☆ - Tel-O-Post Co.
CREATE A STORY - Computer software - Orange Cherry Software
CREATE-A-TAB - Index cards - Cel-U-Dex Corp.
CREATE-A-TAPE - Tape–adhesive - Ben Clements & Sons Inc.
CREATE-A-TEST - Computer software - Cross Educational Software Inc.
CREATE-A-TIE - Hobby kits - Rohde Royce, Inc.
CREATE-A-VIEW - Aquariums–household - St. Jon Pet Care Products Inc.
CREATE-AN-IMAGE - Kaleidoscopes - Gemini Kaleidoscopes
CREATE AN OFFICE - Office furniture–wood - BPI Inc.
CREATE & PLAY - Toys - Strombecker Corp.
CREATE HAVOC - Apparel and accessories - Lee Thomas Inc.
CREATE-IT - Cylinders - Walnut Hill Enterprises Inc.
CREATE ME - Craft supplies ☆ - ME Enterprises
CREATE 'N COLOR - Activity set - International Games
CREATE-N-FRAME - Toys - Axxent Corp.
CREATE WITH GARFIELD DELUXE - Computer software ☆ - SRA/McGraw-Hill (Div. of The McGraw-Hill Companies)
CREATE YOUR LOOK - Drapery hardware - Kenney Manufacturing Co.
CREATE YOUR OWN - Computer software - Hartley Courseware Inc.
CREATEABLE - Frames–picture - Structural Industries
CREATED BY MICHAEL FINELLI - Apparel - Elder-Beerman Stores Corp.
CREATED BY PARTICIPATION CLOTHING - Apparel and accessories - Roberta D. Boyajian
CREATED FOR THE SUN SET - Frames–eyeglass - May Optical Co. Inc.
CREATED FROM NATURE - Hair care products - Leiner Health Products Inc.
CREATED WONDERS - Jewelry - Samuel Aaron Inc.
CREATEX - Paints - United Coatings Inc.
CREATIA CLOTHING CREATIONS - Hats - Creatia
CREATIF - Hair care products - Redken Laboratories, Inc.
CREATIFICS - Hobby kits ☆ - Blumenthal/Lansing Co.
CREATINE 1000 - Vitamins and nutritional supplements - Natural Balance, Inc.
CREATINE 1000 - Vitamins and nutritional supplements - Caroline Owens
CREATINE DRINK - Vitamins and nutritional supplements ☆ - Vitamin Research Products Inc.
CREATINE FUEL - Vitamins and nutritional supplements - Twinlab
CREATING MEASURABLE RESULTS - Advertising agencies - Manlove Advertising, Inc.
CREATING THE FUTURE OF OVENABLE PACKAGING - Trays - Packaging Corp. of America
CREATING WITH STYLE - Apparel and accessories - Brigance Contractors, Inc.
CREATION - Automotive parts and accessories - Toppertown Inc.
CREATION - Dinnerware–glass ☆ - Block China Co.
CREATION - Floor covering, now out of production - Azrock Commercial Flooring
CREATION - Floor coverings–carpet and rugs ☆ - World Carpets, Inc.
CREATION - Perfumes ☆ - Fragrance Group
CREATION - Toys - Ibssl, Inc.
CREATION COMPANY - Recording label - Jazz Composer's Orchestra Association Inc.
CREATION CONSTANZE - Christmas tree ornaments - Salzburg Creations Inc.
CREATION GROSSE - Jewelry - Grosse Jewels N.Y. Inc.
CREATION STATION - Hobby kits - Rose Art Industries, Inc.
CREATION STATION - Photographic equipment - Eastman Kodak Co.
CREATION STATION - Restaurants–pizzerias - Little Caesar Enterprises, Inc.
CREATIONS - Cosmetics ☆ - Gefden International Inc.
CREATIONS - Floor coverings–carpet and rugs - Trend Carpet
CREATIONS - Lamps - Kaadan Ltd.
CREATIONS - Toys–stuffed - Dakin Inc.
CREATIONS - Wallpaper - Textile Wallcoverings International Ltd.
CREATIONS A.M. - Apparel–athletic - Pedigree USA Inc.
CREATIONS ARTISANALES - Wallpaper ☆ - Wallquest, Inc.
CREATIONS AT DALLAS - Furniture - Alexander Plastics
CREATIONS BY ALAN STUART - Novelty items - Creations by Alan Stuart Inc.
CREATIONS BY MAURICE - Footwear - M & H Shoes Inc.
CREATIONS OF TIMELESS ELEGANCE - Jewelry–precious - Peter J. Malnekoff
CREATIVE - Cooking equipment–household ☆ - Mirro Corp.
CREATIVE - Fabrics–nylon - Creative Coatings Corp.
CREATIVE - Food products - Creative Foods of America
CREATIVE - Labels–paper - May Tag and Label Co.

CREATIVE - Ophthalmic goods - Foremost Optical Products
CREATIVE - Toys - DGI/Buki
CREATIVE 1471 - Sewing machines–industrial - Pfaff American Sales Corp.
CREATIVE ACCENTS - Electric lighting equipment - Jackson Deerfield Manufacturing Corp.
CREATIVE ACCENTS - Giftware - Himark Enterprises Inc.
CREATIVE AMERICAN - Publisher's imprints - Hazel Pearson Handicrafts
CREATIVE AUDIO - Audio equipment - William J. Ray & Associates
CREATIVE BAKERS - Cakes - Fancy Foods of Virginia Inc.
CREATIVE BASICS - Apparel and accessories - F.C.F. Industries Inc.
CREATIVE BLOCKS - Toys - Fisher-Price, Inc.
CREATIVE BOOK CO. - Publisher's imprints ☆ - Creative Book Co.
CREATIVE CENTER - Artists' materials ☆ - Dahle USA
CREATIVE CHEF - Can openers–electric - Windmere Corp.
CREATIVE CHILD PRESS - Publisher's imprints - Playmore Inc. Publishers
CREATIVE CIRCLES - Apparel and accessories - Creative Circles, Inc.
CREATIVE CLASSICS - Floor coverings–carpet and rugs - Galaxy Carpet Mills Inc.
CREATIVE CLASSICS - Window frames - Simonton Building Products, Inc.
CREATIVE CLASSICS DELI CRISPS - Crackers - Creative Foods Corp.
CREATIVE COASTER - Infant product - Fisher-Price, Inc.
CREATIVE COLORS - Manicure preparations - Creative Nail Design, Inc.
CREATIVE COMMUNICATIONS INTERNATIONAL - Cardboard - Equalnet Corp.
CREATIVE CONCEPTS - Apparel and accessories - Frederick Atkins, Inc.
CREATIVE CONSTRUCTION FOR KIDS - Toys - Connector Set L.P.
CREATIVE CONTROLS - Video production - Nalpak Video Sales, Inc.
CREATIVE COUNTRY - Wallpaper ☆ - J. Josephson, Inc.
CREATIVE CRAFTS - Flowers–artificial - Frank's Nursery & Crafts, Inc.
CREATIVE CRAVATS - Apparel and accessories - Audrey A. Ing
CREATIVE CREAMERY - Ice cream - Creative Creamery
CREATIVE CREATIONS - Apparel–women's - Creative Imports
CREATIVE CRYSTAL - Jewelry - Creative Crystal Co., LLC
CREATIVE CRYSTALS - Jewelry - Creative Crystal Co.
CREATIVE CUISINE - Cooking utensils–earthenware ☆ - Anchor Hocking Glass, Inc.
CREATIVE CURL - Hair care products - Redken Laboratories, Inc.
CREATIVE CURLER - Hair care products - Major International Inc.
CREATIVE DECOR - Hobby kits - Gibson Greetings, Inc.
CREATIVE DESIGN SURFBOARDS - Apparel and accessories - Rockaway Beach Surf Shop Inc.
CREATIVE DESIGNS - Wallpaper ☆ - Brewster Wallcovering Co.
CREATIVE DIGITAL RESEARCH - Computer software - Creative Digital Research
CREATIVE DISKS - Toys - Go Images Inc.
CREATIVE DISKS-FUN PACK - Puzzles - Go Images Inc.
CREATIVE DISKS JR. - Puzzles - Go Images Inc.
CREATIVE EDGE - Apparel and accessories - Tex Venture Holding Ltd.
CREATIVE EDUCATION - Crayons ☆ - Mangelsen's (VDI)
CREATIVE ELEVATIONS - Door frames - Weathervane Window, Inc.
CREATIVE ENTERPRISES - Wood products - Creative Enterprises
CREATIVE EVOLUTION CNC - Computer software - Creative Technology Corp.
CREATIVE FLOORS - Floor coverings–carpet and rugs - Milliken & Co. Inc.
CREATIVE FOAM - Hobby kits - Flora Craft Inc.
CREATIVE FOIL - Hair coloring preparations - Concentrics Inc.
CREATIVE FOODS - Food products - Adam Starchild
CREATIVE FUEL - Computer software - T/Maker Co.
CREATIVE FUNMATS - Publisher's imprints - Highlights for Children, Inc.
CREATIVE FUR - Hobby kits - Craft World International Inc.
CREATIVE GALLERY - Computer software - Graphic Products Corp.
CREATIVE GLASS BY CORNING - Giftware ☆ - Corning Inc.
CREATIVE GOLDSMITHS - Jewelry - Irwin Gross Gemologist, Inc.
CREATIVE GOURMET - Giftware - E. Rosen Co.
CREATIVE GUIDANCE - Publisher's imprints ☆ - Playmore Inc. Publishers
CREATIVE HANDS - Publisher's imprints - Davis Publications Inc.
CREATIVE HEARTS - Machine parts - Creative Hearts LLC
CREATIVE HEIRLOOMS - Dolls - Creative Heirlooms
CREATIVE HOME COLLECTIONS - House furnishings - Creative Home Collections Inc.
CREATIVE HOMEOWNER PRESS - Publisher's imprints - Creative Homeowner Press
CREATIVE HORIZONS - Paper - Creative Horizons, LLC
CREATIVE IMPRESSIONS - Paper - Rediform
CREATIVE IMPRESSIONS - Posters - Greenwich Workshop, Inc.
CREATIVE IMPRESSIONS - Stationery - Moore Business Forms, Inc.

☆ = Now out of production

CREATIVE INDUSTRIES - Kilns - Creative Industries
CREATIVE INTERPLAY - Wallpaper - Wallcoverings Unlimited Inc.
CREATIVE KIDS - Artists' materials - Martin F. Weber Co.
CREATIVE KRAFTY - Hobby kits - Lady Squire Colors
CREATIVE LEARNER - Educational product - Bemiss-Jason Corp.
CREATIVE LICENSE - Computer software - Time Arts Inc.
CREATIVE LICENSE - Identification tags - Image Group Inc.
CREATIVE MANAGEMENT RESOURCES - Office supplies - Creative Management Resources, Inc.
CREATIVE MASTERS - Toys–models - Revell-Monogram, Inc.
CREATIVE MATTER - Hobby kits - Cascade Fibers Co.
CREATIVE MIND PROFILE - Paper–book - Career Systems, Inc.
CREATIVE MUSIC MAKER - Toys - Fisher-Price, Inc.
CREATIVE NAIL DESIGN - Cosmetics - Creative Nail Design, Inc.
CREATIVE NAIL DESIGN SYSTEMS - Nail care products - Creative Nail Design, Inc.
CREATIVE NEEDLES - Hobby kits - A + A
CREATIVE NETWORK CO. - Recording label - Joseph Nicoletti Music Co.
CREATIVE NOTES - Stationery - C.R. Gibson Co.
CREATIVE OUTDOOR DESIGNS - Playground equipment - Creative Outdoor Designs, Inc.
CREATIVE PAPERS - Paper–writing - School Stationers Corp.
CREATIVE PAPERS - Stationery - C.R. Gibson Co.
CREATIVE PHYSICS - Computer software - Stewart Software
CREATIVE PLAYTHINGS - Toys - Creative Playthings Ltd.
CREATIVE PULTRUSIONS - Building materials - Creative Pultrusion Inc.
CREATIVE PUNCHES - Hobby kits - A + A
CREATIVE PURSUITS - Computer software - Creative Pursuits
CREATIVE REAL ESTATE - Video production - Jaclyn S. McNary
CREATIVE RECIPES - Food products - Stouffer Foods Corp.
CREATIVE RIBBON - Ribbons ☆ - Mats Etc. Inc.
CREATIVE SHAPES PEGBOARD - Toys - Playskool, Inc.
CREATIVE STATIONERY - Stationery - C.R. Gibson Co.
CREATIVE STYLOR - Hair care products - Major International Inc.
CREATIVE SURROUNDINGS - Wallpaper - Bayview Wallcoverings
CREATIVE TAPES - Tape–adhesive ☆ - Gould Packaging Inc.
CREATIVE TEXTURES - Floor coverings–carpet and rugs ☆ - Callaway Carpets
CREATIVE TEXTURES III - Wallpaper ☆ - Gagne Wallcovering, Inc.
CREATIVE TEXTWOOD - Window coverings - Limb Corp.
CREATIVE THERAPY - Publisher's imprints - MMB Music Inc.
CREATIVE TOUCH - Paints–artists' - Palmer Paint Products, Inc.
CREATIVE TOUCH - Toasters - Windmere Corp.
CREATIVE TOUCH FASHION - Sewing machines–household ☆ - Singer Co.
CREATIVE TRADITIONALS - Wallpaper ☆ - J. Josephson, Inc.
CREATIVE VIDEO - Broadcasting stations–television - Creative Video of Washington, Inc.
CREATIVE VIDEO PRODUCTIONS - Video production - Waltner Enterprises
CREATIVE WHACK PACK - Computer software - Creative Think
CREATIVE WOOD PRODUCTS - Crates - Pastime Industries Inc.
CREATIVE WOODBURNER - Pens - Walnut Hollow Farm, Inc.
CREATIVE WORLD - Giftware - H & G Studio Inc.
CREATIVE WORLD - Recording label - GNP Crescendo Record Co. Inc.
CREATIVEBIZ BUSINESS - Stationery - Kelly W. Chenault
CREATIVELY YOURS - Adhesives and sealants - Loctite Corp.
CREATIVELY YOURS - Apparel and accessories - Uniflair Inc.
CREATIVELY YOURS INC. - Statuary - Creatively Yours, Inc.
CREATIVES - Hair care products - John Paul Mitchell Systems
CREATIVES MOISTURE & SHINE SHAMPOO - Hair care products - John Paul Mitchell Systems
CREATIVISION - Computer software ☆ - Harden Industries Inc.
CREATIVISION - Toys–electronic - Video Technology U.S. Inc.
CREATIVITY CASE - Hobby kits - Pastime Industries, Inc.
CREATIVITY FOR KIDS - Hobby shops - Creative Art Activities Inc.
CREATIVITY TOOLBOX, THE - Educational materials - Create-It! Inc.
CREATIVITY UNLIMITED - Computer software ☆ - Sunburst Communications, Inc.
CREATIVITY ZONE - Publisher's imprints - Scholastic Inc.
CREATOR - Ophthalmic goods - Embassy Creations Inc.
CREATOR PAK - Toys–models - Toymax Inc.
CREATOR, THE - Computer software - TNT Software Inc.
CREATORE - Apparel and accessories - Castle Apparel Group, Inc.
CREATORS UNIVERSE - Trading cards and stamps - Dynamic Entertainment, Inc.
CREATRON - Trays–photographic - Creatron Inc.
CREATURE - Sporting goods - NHS, Inc.

CREATURE ANTICS - Computer software - Laureate Learning Systems Inc.
CREATURE CAPERS - Computer software - Laureate Learning Systems Inc.
CREATURE CARTOONS - Computer software - Laureate Learning Systems Inc.
CREATURE CASTLE - Games ☆ - Western Publishing Co., Inc.
CREATURE CHORUS - Computer software - Laureate Learning Systems Inc.
CREATURE COMFORTS - Books–comic - Mystic Productions, Inc.
CREATURE COMFORTS - Needles–sewing - It's Polite to Point, Inc.
CREATURE CREATOR - Computer software - Compton's NewMedia
CREATURE CREATOR - Toys - Toymax Inc.
CREATURE FEATURES - Computer software - Laureate Learning Systems Inc.
CREATURE FEATURES - Rubber stamps - All Night Media, Inc.
CREATURE MAGIC - Computer software - Laureate Learning Systems Inc.
CREATURE SHOCK - Computer software - Virgin Interactive Entertainment, Inc.
CREATURECAPS - Trading cards and stamps - Western Publishing Co., Inc.
CREATURES OF THE DREAMLAND - Games - Chaosium Inc.
CREATURES OF THE NICE AGE - Toys - J.S. English Co.
CREATURES OF THE SEA - Toys - Imperial Toy Corp.
CREATURES OF THE WORLD - Toys - Imperial Toy Corp.
CREAZZO - Wines - Creazzo Imports Inc.
CREBEL - Skin-care products - Crebel International Corp.
CREBEL SPA - Skin care products - Crebel International Corp.
CRECIENDO CON MATEMATICAS - Recording label - Mimosa Publications, Inc.
CRECO CAST - Hardware - Creco Corp.
CREDENTIAL - Leather goods - AR Accessories Group Inc.
CREDENTIALS - Coats–children's - J.C. Penney Co., Inc.
CREDENTIALS - Cosmetics - CBI Laboratories, Inc.
CREDENTIALS - Trading cards and stamps - Pinnacle Brands, Inc.
CREDENZA - Calendars - House of Doolittle
CREDENZA - Electric lighting equipment - Lutron Electronics Co., Inc.
CREDIT CARD - Toys - Maryland Toy Corp.
CREDIT CARD COMB - Combs - Duck Engineering Inc.
CREDIT CARD COMPANION, THE - Tools–hand-operated - Tool Logic, Inc.
CREDIT CERTIFICATE - Paper - American Bank Note Co.
CREDIT FOLD - Leather goods - St. Thomas Inc.
CREDIT GUARD - Leather goods - AR Accessories Group Inc.
CREDIT MANAGER - Paper - E-Z Legal Forms, Inc.
CREDIT-PAC - Leather goods and gifts - Hugo Bosca Co., Inc.
CREDITCARD - Keys ☆ - Cole Consumer Products Inc.
CREDITEER - Leather goods - Hugo Bosca Co., Inc.
CREDITGUARD - Computer software - Electronic Data Systems Corp.
CREDITMETRICS - Banks–commercial - J.P. Morgan & Co. Inc.
CREDITOR 121-3 - Calculators ☆ - Citizen America Corp.
CREDITUNION2000 - Computer software - Electronic Recordkeeping Services, Inc.
CREDITWATCH - Computer software - Cellular Technical Services Inc.
CREDITWISE - Computer software - Mary Y. Shubert
CREDITWIZ - Consulting services - Action Advocacy Law Offices, P.C.
CREDO - Beauty shop equipment - F.W. Engels Inc.
CREDO - Cigars ☆ - Swisher International, Inc.
CREDO - Frames–eyeglass ☆ - Universal/Univis Inc.
CREDO - Hair care products - Fromm Industries
CREDO - Razors - Spilo/Mehaz Worldwide
CREDO - Recording label - Pathways of Sound Inc.
CREDO - Tools–power-driven - Credo Co.
CREE - Trailers–travel - Creative RV Corp.
CREE-EAGLE - Trailers–travel - Creative RV Corp.
CREE-PRINCESS - Trailers–travel - Creative RV Corp.
CREE TOURNAMENT - Motor vehicles–motor homes ☆ - Creative RV Corp.
CREE TRAPPER - Motor vehicles–motor homes ☆ - Creative RV Corp.
CREED - Jewelry - Creed Manufacturing Co.
CREED - Snowboards - Thomas Gage Tarrant
CREEDMORE - Sights–gun - Armsport Inc.
CREEK - Brushes–paint - Corona Brushes Inc.
CREEK-O-NITE - Clay products ☆ - Golden Cat Corp.
CREEK TOWN TACKLE - Fishing lures - Southern Plastics, Inc.
CREEK-TURN - Clay products - Creek-Turn Inc. (Ceramic Supply Div.)
CREEKMORE - Boats–pontoons - Creekmore Boats
CREEKSBRIDGE - Shoes - Wal-Mart Stores Inc.
CREEKSTONES - Tiles–ceramic ☆ - American Olean Tile Co.
CREEKVIEW - Bakery products - Smith's Food & Drug Centers, Inc.
CREEKWOOD - Apparel–men's - River Valley Mills Inc. (Creekwood Inc.)
CREEP - Oils–lubricating - Castoleum Corp.

☆ = Now out of production

CREEP-OVER - Work bench ☆ - Michael R. Hansen
CREEP SHOW - Novelty items - Russ Berrie and Co., Inc.
CREEP STOPPER - Motor vehicle parts and accessories - Bop & Pop Custom Cases
CREEPEES - Candy - Pangburn Candy Co.
CREEPER - Fireworks - American Promotional Events, Inc.
CREEPER - Lubricants - ITW Fluid Products
CREEPER KEEPER - Traps–animal - Today's Kids Inc.
CREEPERS - Footwear - NaNa Trading Co.
CREEPERS - Frames–eyeglass - Zylo Ware Corp.
CREEPERS - Shoes - Na Na Trading Co., Inc.
CREEPIES - Toys–stuffed - Fun World Inc.
CREEPING CREATURES - Toys–stuffed - Fun World Inc.
CREEPLE PEEPLE - Toy figures - Toymax Inc.
CREEPO - Toys–stuffed ☆ - Fun World Inc.
CREEPS - Candy ☆ - Leaf, Inc.
CREEPY - Toys - Tonka Corp.
CREEPY CASTLE - Computer software - Reactor Inc.
CREEPY COFFINS - Candy - R.M. Palmer Co.
CREEPY CORNERS - Candy ☆ - R.M. Palmer Co.
CREEPY CRAWLER SPIDER - Novelty items - Russ Berrie and Co., Inc.
CREEPY CRAWLERS - Candy - Toymax Inc.
CREEPY CREATURE - Toys - Spearhead Industries Inc.
CREEPY CREATURES - Novelty items - Paper Magic Group Inc.
CREEPY CRITTERS - Costumes - Spearhead Industries Inc.
CREEPY CRITTERS - Giftware - Russ Berrie and Co., Inc.
CREEPY HOLLOW - Figurines - Midwest of Cannon Falls Inc.
CREEPY KIDS - Toys ☆ - Spearhead Industries Inc.
CREIGHTON - Apparel–women's - Creighton Inc.
CREMA DANIA - Cheese - Swissrose International Inc.
CREMA DE ARROZ - Cereal - Nabisco Brands Co.
CREMACOAT - Cough medicines - Richardson-Vicks USA
CREMANDE - Chocolate bars - Nestle USA
CREMAS CREMAS UNLIMITED SYMBOL OF EXCELLENCE THE ORIGINAL - Liqueurs - Donald Cols
CREMASK - Skin care products - Mastey De Paris
CREMAVERA - Cheese ☆ - Swissrose International Inc.
CREMAZOLA - Cheese - Swissrose International Inc.
CREME - Fishing lures - Creme Lure Co.
CREME ANTIRIDES POUR LE COU - Skin care products - Ella Bache Inc.
CREME BIACTIVE - Skin care products - Ella Bache Inc.
CREME BLANC - Paper - French Paper Co.
CREME BOATS - Breads - American Bakeries Co.
CREME COLLAGENE - Skin care products - Ella Bache Inc.
CREME COLOURS - Paints–artists' - Plaid Enterprises, Inc.
CREME CONTOUR - Cosmetics - Lancome
CREME COPRA - Lipsticks - Cosmair Inc.
CREME COTE - Cleaning preparations - James Varley & Sons, Inc.
CREME D'CHOCOLATE - Beverages–carbonated ☆ - Snapple Beverage Corp.
CREME DE ALOE - Skin care products - Chasalco Inc.
CREME DE BLEU - Cheese - Bc-USA, Inc.
CREME DE BRIE - Cheese - Bongrain Cheese USA
CREME DE BRIE - Cheese - Bresse Bleu Inc.
CREME DE CHINE - Dinnerware–glass ☆ - Tienshan, Inc.
CREME DE COCOA - Cocoa–powders or mixes - Executive Coffee Service Co.
CREME DE FROMAGE - Cheese ☆ - Bongrain Cheese USA
CREME DE JAMAICA - Cigars - Faber, Coe & Gregg Inc.
CREME DE JOUR - Skin care products ☆ - Karin Herzog USA Ltd.
CREME DE JOUR A LA MILLE DE REQUIN - Skin care products - Ella Bache Inc.
CREME DE JOUR HYDRATANTE - Skin care products - Ella Bache Inc.
CREME DE LA CREME - Apparel and accessories - Memorial Creme De La Creme, Inc.
CREME DE LA CREME - Apparel–children's - N.I.T. Fashions, Inc.
CREME DE LA CREME - Cream–canned or powdered ☆ - Reily Foods
CREME DE LA CREME - Tiles–ceramic ☆ - Huntington/Pacific Ceramics Inc.
CREME DE LA CREME - Wallpaper ☆ - Advance Wallcoverings
CREME DE LA MOUSSE - Hair care products - KMS Research Inc.
CREME DE LEMON - Cheese ☆ - Bongrain Cheese USA
CREME DE LITE - Yogurt - Nestle USA
CREME DE MENTHE - Christmas tree ornaments - Cracker Box Inc.
CREME DE MINT - Skin care products - La Femme Cosmetics Inc.
CREME DE NUIT RICHE - Skin care products ☆ - Karin Herzog USA Ltd.

CREME DE ROSE - Hair- and skin-care products, fragrance, etc. - Benjamin Ansehl Co.
CREME DE SILK - Cosmetics - Isla Cosmetique
CREME D'IVOIRE - Floor coverings–tile - ECC International
CREME D'OR - Cheese ☆ - Swissrose International Inc.
CREME D'OR - Floor coverings–tile - ECC International
CREME D'ORANGE - Skin care products - Fanie International
CREME D'VANILLA - Beverages–carbonated - Snapple Beverage Corp.
CREME GLOSS - Furniture polish and wax - Uncle Sam Chemical Co., Inc.
CREME-ICE - Food products - Moorhead and Co. Inc.
CREME INTEX - Skin care products - Ella Bache Inc.
CREME INTEX NO.2 - Skin care products - Ella Bache Inc.
CREME JOJOBA - Skin care products - Ella Bache Inc.
CREME MAGIC - Skin care products - Care-Tech Laboratories Inc.
CREME-MOIST - Hair care products - ABBA Products Inc.
CREME-MOIST - Shampoos - U.K. Abba Products, Inc.
CREME OF BEAUTY - Skin care products - Maji Nail Inc.
CREME OF NATURE - Hair care products - Roux Laboratories, Inc.
CREME PARFAIT - Hair care products - Scruples Professional Salon Products, Inc.
CREME PARFAITE - Skin care products - Chanel Inc.
CREME PUFF - Cosmetics - Max Factor & Co.
CREME-PUFF - Girdles - Wacoal America Inc.
CREME REDUCTOR - Hair care products - Amethyst Investment Group, Inc.
CREME RICHE - Lipsticks - Cosmair Inc.
CREME ROSEE DU MATIN - Skin care products - Ella Bache Inc.
CREME ROYALE - Butter flavor - American Flavor & Fragrance Corp.
CREME ROYALE - Skin care products - Ella Bache Inc.
CREME SALMON - Lipsticks - Cosmair Inc.
CREME SUPEROXIDE - Hair coloring preparations - Roux Laboratories, Inc.
CREME SUPREME - Cheese - Swissrose International Inc.
CREME SUPREME - Cosmetics - Nino Originals
CREME SUPREMES - Snack foods - Lipton Investments, Inc.
CREME TEINT PUR - Skin care products - Ella Bache Inc.
CREME TEINTEE - Cosmetics - Sothys USA Inc.
CREME TONER - Hair coloring preparations - Clairol Inc.
CREME TREASURES - Cakes - Meijer, Inc.
CREME WAVES - Hair care products - Paula Payne Products Co. Inc.
CREME YOGURT - Yogurt ☆ - Crowley Foods, Inc.
CREMELADO - Food products - Chiquita Brands, Inc.
CREMELITE 21 - Fish–fresh or frozen - Trident Seafoods Corp.
CREMERICA - Skin care products - Ambrosia Cosmetics Inc.
CREMETASTIC - Whipped topping–frozen - Instantwhip Foods Inc.
CREMETOPS - Confections - Homestyle Foods
CREMEUX - Cheese ☆ - Bongrain Cheese USA
CREMEVAN - Food products - V. & E. Kohnstamm Inc.
CREMEY 8 - Cosmetics - Revlon Consumer Products Corp.
CREMEY BUMPERS - Vegetables - Flowers Family Bakeries, Inc.
CREMINO BRESKA - Jams and jellies - Triton International
CREMO - Cheese ☆ - Swissrose International Inc.
CREMO - Thread - Cincinnati Thread Co.
CREMOLAND - Butter - Zenith-Godley Co. Inc.
CREMOLINA - Cereal - Sahara Natural Foods, Inc.
CREMOLINA - Cereal ☆ - Casbah/Sahara Natural Foods Inc.
CREMOLINE - Skin care products - Luyties Pharmacal Co.
CREMONA - Doors - Masonite Corp.
CREMORA - Food products - Borden, Inc.
CREMOZZO - Hair care products - Modafini Inc.
CREO-TECH - Adhesives and sealants - Gibraltar National Corp.
CREO-TERPIN - Cough medicines - Medtech Laboratories Inc.
CREOLE - Frames–eyeglass - Pathway Optical Prods.
CREOLE CRAVINGS - Soups–canned ☆ - Commander's Palace Restaurant
CREOLE CRISCUITS - Food products - Bon Melange Inc.
CREOLE CUISINE - Food products - Vince's Seafood
CREOLE KING - Food products - Louisiana Boyel Seafood, Inc.
CREOLE NUVO - Yarn ☆ - Tahki Imports Ltd.
CREOLE QUEEN - Food products - Louisiana Boyel Seafood, Inc.
CREOLE TILE - Floor coverings ☆ - Tarkett, Inc.
CREOLE'S STUFFED BREAD - Food products - M & R Creole Enterprises Inc.
CREOLIN - Disinfectants - Oakhurst Co.
CREOLIN DEODORANT CLEANSER - Health care products - Woolfoam Corp.
CREOMULSION - Cough medicines - Creomulsion Lantiseptic
CREOMULSION COMPLETE - Cough medicines - Summit Industries, Inc.
CREOMULSION FOR CHILDREN - Cough medicines - Creomulsion Lantiseptic
CREON - Pharmaceutical preparations - Solvay Pharmaceuticals Inc.
CREOSOAP - Pharmaceutical preparations ☆ - Ulmer Pharmacal Co.

☆ = Now out of production

CREP-ETTE - Kitchen appliances ☆ - Nordic Ware
CREPAURA - Apparel–women's - Bichon Apparel Ltd.
CREPE CHIFFON - Fabrics–crepe - Collins & Aikman Corp.
CREPE CONTOUR - Fabrics–crepe - Jaunty Textile Div.
CREPE D'ARCI - Fabrics - Dan River Inc.
CREPE DE CHINE - Colognes - New Projects Group Ltd.
CREPE DE LYS - Fabrics–crepe - Jaunty Textile Div.
CREPE MEMOIR - Fabrics–crepe - Jaunty Textile Div.
CREPE PRIMAVERA PLUS - Crocheted and knitted items - Collins & Aikman Corp.
CREPE REMARQUE - Fabrics–crepe - Jaunty Textile Div.
CREPE SUZETTE - Apparel–children's - Andover Togs, Inc.
CREPE SUZETTE - Draperies - Maya Romanoff Corp.
CREPE SUZETTES - Apparel stores–lingerie - Formfit Rogers
CREPERIE - Kitchen appliances ☆ - Sunbeam-Oster Household Products
CREPES - Footwear ☆ - Rockport Co. Inc.
CREPES 'N THINGS - Kitchen appliances ☆ - Nordic Ware
CREPESET - Fabrics–nylon - BASF Corp.
CREPESOFT - Fibers–synthetic - BASF Corp.
CREPETRIQUE - Fabrics ☆ - Dan River Inc.
CREPETTES - Crackers ☆ - Liberty Richter Inc.
CREPUSCULE - Recording label - Jazz Composer's Orchestra Association Inc.
CRES FLEX - Apparel–women's - NCC Industries, Inc.
CRES-LITE - Paints - Crescent Bronze Powder
CRESCA - Food products ☆ - Liberty Richter Inc.
CRESCENDO - Artists' materials - Badger Air-Brush Co.
CRESCENDO - Cabinets - Aristokraft, Inc.
CRESCENDO - Candy - Leaf, Inc.
CRESCENDO - Dinnerware–glass ☆ - Wallace International Silversmiths, Inc.
CRESCENDO - Fertilizers - Biogenesis Systems, Inc.
CRESCENDO - Flatware - Reed and Barton Corp.
CRESCENDO - Floor coverings–carpet and rugs ☆ - Gulistan Carpet Inc.
CRESCENDO - Frames–eyeglass - Pathway Optical Prods.
CRESCENDO - Furniture ☆ - Boling Co.
CRESCENDO - Furniture ☆ - Lane Co. Inc.
CRESCENDO - Glassware–household ☆ - National Housewares
CRESCENDO - Hair coloring preparations - Cosmair Inc.
CRESCENDO - Wallpaper - Koroseal Wallcoverings
CRESCENDO - Watches - Bulova Corp.
CRESCENDO - Window shades - Verosol
CRESCENDO BOOKS - Publisher's imprints - Parkwest Publications Inc.
CRESCENDO CHESS - Games - Strato-Various Products Inc.
CRESCENDO OF DOOM - Games - Avalon Hill Game Co.
CRESCENDOE - Gloves - Gates Gloves
CRESCENT - Automotive parts and accessories - General Cable Corp.
CRESCENT - Bathroom fixtures - Kohler Co.
CRESCENT - Bicycles - Columbia Manufacturing Inc.
CRESCENT - Cabinets - Imperial Cabinet Co. Inc.
CRESCENT - Chemical preparations ☆ - Milex Products Inc.
CRESCENT - Cleaning preparations - Crescent Dental Manufacturing Co.
CRESCENT - Corkscrews - Franmara Co. Inc.
CRESCENT - Dishes–china - Pickard Inc.
CRESCENT - Drums–musical instruments ☆ - Grossman Music Corp.
CRESCENT - Erasers - Claridge Products and Equipment Inc.
CRESCENT - Fabrics ☆ - Greenwood Mills Inc.
CRESCENT - Floor coverings - Compass Concepts
CRESCENT - Floor coverings - Congoleum Corp.
CRESCENT - Food products - Crescent Duck Farm, Inc.
CRESCENT - Food products - Sea Products Co.
CRESCENT - Frames–eyeglass ☆ - Universal/Univis Inc.
CRESCENT - Furniture - Bassett Furniture Industries, Inc.
CRESCENT - Hair care products ☆ - Hunt Products Inc.
CRESCENT - Hardware - Crescent & Sprague Supply Co. Inc.
CRESCENT - Manufactured homes - Redman Industries, Inc.
CRESCENT - Mat boards - Crescent Cardboard Co.
CRESCENT - Office supplies - R.A. Stewart Superior
CRESCENT - Pickles - Green Bay Foods Co.
CRESCENT - Pillows - Body Care Inc.
CRESCENT - Seasonings - McCormick & Co., Inc.
CRESCENT - Seasonings - Pacific Foods Inc.
CRESCENT - Sewing machines–industrial - Crescent Manufacturing Co.
CRESCENT - Shrimp–canned or cured ☆ - Robinson Canning Co. Inc.
CRESCENT - Tools - Crescent
CRESCENT - Tools - O.P. Link Handle Co. Inc.
CRESCENT-AIRE - Cushions - Better Sleep, Inc.
CRESCENT BAY - Furniture - Homecrest Industries Inc.

CRESCENT BEACH - Aquarium accessories - Kordon
CRESCENT BEACH - Aquarium accessories - Novalek, Inc.
CRESCENT FARMS - Candy - Hills Department Store Co.
CRESCENT GUARDIAN - Computer software - Crescent Computer Corp.
CRESCENT HEIGHTS - Floor coverings–carpet and rugs - Gulistan Carpet Inc.
CRESCENT HILL - Furniture ☆ - Athens Furniture Industries Inc.
CRESCENT HILL II - Furniture - Athens Furniture Industries Inc.
CRESCENT HILL FM - Food products - Dutch Farms, Inc.
CRESCENT ISLE II - Furniture ☆ - Halcyon Inc.
CRESCENT MOON RECORDS - Recording label - Estefan Enterprises, Inc.
CRESCENT ST. - Watches - Elgin Watch Co.
CRESCENT SOX - Hosiery - Wigwam Mills Inc.
CRESCENT SPRINGS FARM - Meat products–poultry ☆ - Aunt Dee's Sausage Co.
CRESCENT VASES - Vases ☆ - Denby USA Limited
CRESCINI - Wines - Crescini Wines
CRESCORMON - Pharmaceutical preparations - Kabi Pharmacia Inc.
CRESCORT INTIMATES - Underwear and nightwear - NCC Industries, Inc.
CRESDECK - Mobile homes - Hambro Forest Products Inc.
CRESFORM - Particle board - Hambro Forest Products Inc.
CRESL-400 - Veterinary pharmaceutical preparations ☆ - Vineland Laboratories Inc.
CRESLAN - Fibers–acrylic - American Cyanamid Co.
CRESLAY - Wood products - Hambro Forest Products Inc.
CRESLINE - Pipes–plastic - Cresline & Wabash
CRESLITE - Electronics equipment - Crestron Electronics Inc.
CRESNET - Electronics equipment - Crestron Electronics Inc.
CRESOSOTE - Finishing agents - PSR Co.
CRESPI - Food products - Dean & Deluca Inc.
CRESPI SAN REMO - Food products - Bri-AL, Inc.
CRESSIDA - Motor vehicles–automobiles - Toyota Motor Sales USA Inc.
CRESSITE - Pet products - Pet Supply Imports Inc.
CREST - Antifreeze - Illinois Oil Products Inc.
CREST - Apparel and accessories - Cit Group/Business Credit, Inc.
CREST - Brushes–paint - Corona Brushes Inc.
CREST - Cabinets ☆ - Brandom Manufacturing Inc.
CREST - Candles - Signature Brands, LLC
CREST - Cigars - House of Edgeworth
CREST - Drums–musical instruments - J.M. Sahlein Music Co. Inc.
CREST - Fruits–canned - J.W. Allen & Co.
CREST - Hair care products - Helene Curtis Industries Inc.
CREST - Hardware ☆ - Vance Industries Inc.
CREST - Paper–gummed ☆ - Park Sherman
CREST - Pens - Sheaffer Holdings Inc.
CREST - Pipes–tobacco ☆ - S.M. Frank & Co. Inc. (Kaywoodie-Yello-Bole-Medico)
CREST - Sporting goods - J-S Sales Co. Inc.
CREST - Toothpaste - Procter & Gamble Co.
CREST - Uniforms–academic - White Rock Uniform
CREST - Wines - Fink Winery
CREST AUDIO - Amplifiers - Crest Audio Inc.
CREST CLASSIC - Apparel and accessories - Munsingwear, Inc.
CREST COMPLETE - Toothbrushes - Procter & Gamble Co.
CREST CONSOLES - Audio equipment - Crest Audio Inc.
CREST CORK - Bulletin boards–cork - Arcana Products Co.
CREST CRAFT - Giftware - Crest Craft Co.
CREST DEBONAIR - Pipes–tobacco ☆ - S.M. Frank & Co. Inc. (Kaywoodie-Yello-Bole-Medico)
CREST GODET - Pipes–tobacco ☆ - S.M. Frank & Co. Inc. (Kaywoodie-Yello-Bole-Medico)
CREST GOTHIC - Pipes–tobacco ☆ - S.M. Frank & Co. Inc. (Kaywoodie-Yello-Bole-Medico)
CREST GUM CARE - Toothpaste - Procter & Gamble Co.
CREST HOMES - Cabinets - Schult Homes Corp.
CREST-LINE - Bulletin boards–wood - Marsh Chalkboard Co.
CREST MARK BY CRICKETEER - Apparel–men's ☆ - Joseph and Feiss Co.
CREST MEAD - Wines - Fink Winery
CREST-O-GOLD - Dinnerware–glass - Mt. Clemens Pottery Co.
CREST-O-GOLD - Oils–edible ☆ - Mallet and Co.
CREST-O-MINT - Deodorizers - Ocean Coffee Co. Inc.
CREST-O-PINE - Disinfectants - Ocean Coffee Co. Inc.
CREST-PAC - Food products - Willman Cookie & Nut Co.
CREST ROSE N' HONEY - Wines - Fink Winery
CREST SUPER COOL FOR KIDS - Toothpaste - Procter & Gamble Co.

CREST TARTAR CONTROL BAKING SODA - Toothpaste - Procter & Gamble Co.
CREST-TO-CREST - Hardware - Smalley Steel Ring Co.
CREST TOP - Vegetables–canned - Allen Canning Co.
CREST WHITE NECTAR - Wines - Fink Winery
CRESTA - Bicycles ☆ - Raleigh USA Bicycle Co.
CRESTA - Dinnerware–glass ☆ - Johnson Brothers, USA, Inc.
CRESTA - Furniture ☆ - Bassett Furniture Industries, Inc.
CRESTA - Handbags - Collin's of Texas
CRESTA BELLA - Wines - Pompei Winery Inc.
CRESTA BLANCA - Wines - Guild Wineries
CRESTA D'ORO - Yarn - Rainbow Gallery, Inc.
CRESTABOLIC - Pharmaceutical preparations ☆ - Nutrition Control Products
CRESTCLAD - Glass–window - Crestline
CRESTEC - Floor coverings–carpet and rugs - Whitecrest Carpet Mills
CRESTED BUTTE - Beverages–malt - Crested Butte Brewery & Pub
CRESTEK - Cleaning preparations - Crestek International Inc.
CRESTITE - Limestone products - Medusa Minerals Co.
CRESTLEY COLLECTION, THE - Novelty items - Crestley Collection, Ltd.
CRESTLINE - Bathroom fixtures - Artesian Industries
CRESTLINE - Candy - McDonald Candy Co. Inc.
CRESTLINE - Drums–musical instruments - Grossman Music Corp.
CRESTLINE - Easels - Crestline Manufacturing Co.
CRESTLINE - Glass–window - Crestline
CRESTLINE - Musical instrument accessories - Trophy Music Co.
CRESTLINE - Napkins–paper - Wisconsin Tissue Mills Inc.
CRESTLINE - Pipes - National Briar Pipe Co.
CRESTLINE - Publisher's imprints - Motorbooks International
CRESTLINE - Trailers–travel ☆ - Coachmen Industries, Inc.
CRESTLINE - Window frames - SNE Enterprises Inc.
CRESTLINE EXPRESS - Furniture–upholstered - Hickory Hill Furniture Corp.
CRESTLINER - Boats–motor - Crestliner Boats Inc.
CRESTMARK - Clocks - Heritage International
CRESTMONT - Bathroom fixtures - Crane Plumbing/Fiat Products
CRESTMONT - Floor coverings ☆ - Congoleum Corp.
CRESTMONT - Ophthalmic goods - Styl-Rite Optical Manufacturing Co., Inc.
CRESTMORE - Boots ☆ - Genesco Inc.
CRESTOLOR - Blinds–venetian - Crestline
CRESTOLOY - Tools ☆ - Crescent
CRESTON - Floor coverings–carpet and rugs - Mannington Carpets, Inc.
CRESTON - Furniture ☆ - Bassett Furniture Industries, Inc.
CRESTON MANOR - Floor coverings–carpet and rugs - Gulistan Carpet Inc.
CRESTON MANOR - Wines ☆ - Creston Vineyards
CRESTON VINEYARDS - Wines - Creston Vineyards
CRESTONE - Amplifiers–musical instrument - LPD Music International
CRESTPOINT - Manufactured homes - Redman Industries, Inc.
CRESTRAND - Drapery hardware ☆ - Spring Crest Co.
CRESTRON RESPOND - Machinery - Crestron Electronics Inc.
CRESTRON VIDEOTOUCH - Computers - Crestron Electronics Inc.
CRESTRON VISIONPC - Computer software - Crestron Electronics Inc.
CRESTRON VISIONVGA - Computers - Crestron Electronics Inc.
CRESTVIEW - Floor coverings–carpet and rugs - Barrett Carpet Mills Inc.
CRESTVIEW - Furniture - Thomasville Furniture Industries Inc.
CRESTVUE - Frames–eyeglass ☆ - Universal/Univis Inc.
CRESTWALL - Wood products ☆ - Masonite Corp.
CRESTWARE - Housewares - Crest Manufacturing, Inc.
CRESTWAY - Furniture ☆ - Athens Furniture Industries Inc.
CRESTWOOD - Aquariums–household ☆ - O'Dell Industries
CRESTWOOD - Cabinets - American Woodmark Corp.
CRESTWOOD - Coffee - Earl Gill Coffee Co. Inc.
CRESTWOOD - Easels - Anco Wood Specialties Inc.
CRESTWOOD - Fabrics ☆ - Greenwood Mills Inc.
CRESTWOOD - Floor coverings–tile ☆ - Kentile Floors Inc.
CRESTWOOD - Food products - Godfrey Co.
CRESTWOOD - Frames–eyeglass - Hudson Optical Corp.
CRESTWOOD - Furniture ☆ - Athens Furniture Industries Inc.
CRESTWOOD - Furniture ☆ - Bassett Furniture Industries, Inc.
CRESTWOOD - Furniture ☆ - Cosco, Inc.
CRESTWOOD - Lighting fixtures - Holophane Corp.
CRESTWOOD - Motor vehicles–motor homes - Baron Motor Homes Inc.
CRESTWOOD - Musical instruments - LPD Music International
CRESTWOOD - Rings–jewelry - Artcarved Inc.
CRESTWOOD - Trailers–travel ☆ - Coachmen Industries, Inc.
CRESTWOOD CONSERVATION - Paperboard - ANW-Crestwood Paper Co.
CRESTWOOD II - Floor coverings–carpet and rugs ☆ - Alexander Smith Carpets

CRESTWOOD MUSEUM - Paperboard - ANW-Crestwood Paper Co.
CRESTWOOD SAVER - Insulating materials ☆ - Owens Corning
CRESWELL - Vegetables–canned - Agripac, Inc.
CRESYLATE - Health care products - Recsei Laboratories
CRETACEOUS CRUNCH - Granola bars - John & Elaine's Vermont Bakery, Inc.
CRETAN - Tableware–china ☆ - Lenox, Inc.
CRETE - Dinnerware–glass ☆ - Johnson Brothers, USA, Inc.
CRETE - Frames–eyeglass - Pathway Optical Prods.
CRETE-HARD - Concrete products - Dayton Superior Corp.
CRETE-LOK - Paints - Nu-Brite Chemical Co. Inc.
CRETE-MIX - Mortars–clay - Custom Building Products
CRETE-NU - Cleaning preparations - Savogran Co.
CRETER CRANE - Machinery - Rotec Industries, Inc.
CRETZEL - Cookies - Continental Cookies
CREVATONE - Tiles–ceiling ☆ - Flintkote Co.
CREVATONE - Tiles–ceiling ☆ - GS Roofing Products Co.
CREVICE - Recording label - Jazz Composer's Orchestra Association Inc.
CREW - Washboards - Kimberly-Clark Corp.
CREW CHIEF - Frames–eyeglass - Liberty Optical Manufacturing Co.
CREW KING - Lawn mowers - Textron Inc.
CREW-LA POO - Recording label - Luke Records Inc.
CREW LINE - Hand tools - Northern Automotive Corp.
CREW MATE - Eyeglasses - Art-Craft Optical Co.
CREW MATE - Marine accessories - Peterson Manufacturing Co.
CREW ONE - Computer software - Advanced Marine Enterprises, Inc.
CREW QUARTERS - House furnishings - Fournier Furniture, Inc.
CREWCUTS - Apparel–children's - J. Crew Inc.
CREW'S QUARTERS - Furniture - Brill Manufacturing Co.
CREZON - Plywood overlay - James River Corp.
CRG - Glass products - Globe-Amerada Glass Co.
CRG PLUS - Diagnostic apparatus - Marquette Electronics, Inc.
CRI - Recording label - Jazz Composer's Orchestra Association Inc.
CRI - Skin care products - Cosmeceutical Research Institute, Inc.
CRI D'AMOUR - Skin care products ☆ - Aloe Creme Laboratories
CRIADA - Tomato pastes and sauces - Empresas La Famosa, Inc.
CRIB B-GONE - Games - Jeffrey D. Brewer
CRIB BIB - Bedding–linen - Sandbox Industries
CRIB BLOX - Infant product - Prince Lionheart, Inc.
CRIB CARNIVAL - Toys - Welcome to the World Inc.
CRIB CLASSIC - Footwear - K-Swiss Inc.
CRIB CLINGERS - Toys ☆ - Those Characters from Cleveland, Inc.
CRIB CRUISER - Toys - Welcome to the World Inc.
CRIB CUDDLE II - Infant product ☆ - Century Products Co.
CRIB MATES - Bedding–linen - Michael Friedman Corp.
CRIB N CARRIAGE - Toys - Marlon Creations
CRIB 'N' MORE - Furniture - Simmons Juvenile Products Co., Inc.
CRIB-POKER - Games - Becton Enterprises, Inc.
CRIB RAIL BARNYARD - Toys–models - Century Products Co.
CRIB SNUGGLER - Dolls - Mattel, Inc.
CRIB TO COLLEGE - Furniture - Crib to College Furniture Co.
CRIBANIMALS - Toys–stuffed ☆ - Century Products Co.
CRIBARI - Wines - B. Cribari & Sons Winery
CRIBBAGE KING - Computer software - Software Toolworks, Inc.
CRIBBAGE MASTER II - Computer software - Manhattan Software
CRIBBAGEMASTER - Games - Carrom Co.
CRIBBLE - Games - Becton Enterprises, Inc.
CRIBESSENTIALS - Infant product - Pansy Ellen Products, Inc.
CRIBETTE - CRIBS - Cribs–metal - HARD Manufacturing Co. Inc.
CRIBEYE COVER - Cribs–metal - HARD Manufacturing Co. Inc.
CRIBMASTER - Cribs–wood ☆ - Evenflo Juvenile Furniture Co.
CRIB'N'BED - Furniture–children's - Child Craft Industries Inc.
CRIBSACK - Mattress pads - Perfect Fit Industries, Inc.
CRIBSY POPPLE - Toys–stuffed ☆ - Mattel, Inc.
C'RICH - Beverages - The Sqwincher Corp.
CRICKET - Audio equipment - Galaxy Audio
CRICKET - Bicycles - Columbia Manufacturing Inc.
CRICKET - Cribs–wood ☆ - Welsh Co.
CRICKET - Eyeglasses - Uvex Safety LLC
CRICKET - Furniture - Homecrest Industries Inc.
CRICKET - Gas analyzers - Mine Safety Appliances Co.
CRICKET - Golf bags - Voit Corp.
CRICKET - Lamps ☆ - Tensor Corp.
CRICKET - Luggage - Airway Industries, Inc.
CRICKET - Medical apparatus - Respironics, Inc.
CRICKET - Medical apparatus ☆ - Ortho-Kinetics, Inc.

☆ = Now out of production

CRICKET - Motor vehicle parts and accessories - Cricket Camper Manufacturing Co.

CRICKET - Motor vehicles–automobiles ☆ - Chrysler Corp. (Chrysler-Plymouth Div.)

CRICKET - Sprinklers–lawn - L.R. Nelson Corp.

CRICKET - Toilets–porcelain - Raritan Engineering Co. Inc.

CRICKET BLUES - Women's apparel - Guntersville Outlet Inc.

CRICKET BOX - Wallpaper - York Wall Coverings Inc.

CRICKET CLUB BY CRICKETEER - Apparel–men's - Joseph and Feiss Co.

CRICKET CORRAL - Containers - Pet-Tech Products

CRICKET COUNTER - Pet products - Armstrong's Cricket Farm

CRICKET DUST - Veterinary pharmaceutical preparations - Mardel Laboratories, Inc.

CRICKET II - Water purification systems - Water Soft Inc.

CRICKET LANE - Apparel and accessories - Kellwood Co.

CRICKET LANE PETITES - Apparel and accessories - Kellwood Co.

CRICKET MACHINE, THE - Pet products - Clyde Peeling's Reptiland Ltd.

CRICKET SHOP - Apparel–women's - Cricket Shop Corp., Inc.

CRICKETEER - Apparel and accessories - Phillips-Van Heusen Corp.

CRICKETEER - Apparel–women's - Joseph and Feiss Co.

CRICKETEER - Frames–eyeglass - Hudson Optical Corp.

CRICKETEER WOMAN - Apparel–women's - Joseph and Feiss Co.

CRICKLE - Candy - De Soto Confectionary

CRIEGIAU - Copper products ☆ - Charles Zahn-Import Merchant

CRIKET - Recording label - Sunny Day Productions Inc.

CRILLON - Bathtubs–enameled - Americh Corp.

CRILLON - Furniture–wood - Century Furniture Co.

CRIME BLOCKER - Alarm systems - Crime Blocker, Inc.

CRIME BUSTER LABELS - Labels–gummed - Stadia Colorado Corp.

CRIME BUSTERS - Games ☆ - Brown and Bigelow Inc.

CRIME LINE - Publisher's imprints - Bantam Doubleday Dell Publishing Group, Inc.

CRIME PATROL - Video games - Icat, Inc.

CRIME PAYS - Insurance agencies–life - Directed Electronics, Inc.

CRIME SCENE - Alarm systems - Rex L. Houston, Jr.

CRIME STOPPERS - Toys - Jak-Pak Inc.

CRIME WAVE - Computer software ☆ - Access Software Inc.

CRIMEBUSTERS - Games - Smethport Specialty Co.

CRIMEFIGHTER - Chains ☆ - Master Lock Co.

C.R.I.M.E.S. - Computer software - Imageware Software, Inc.

CRIMESHIELD - Alarm systems - Kobishi America, Inc.

CRIMESTAR - Computer software - Alec Jay Gagne

CRIMESTOPPER - Alarm systems - Crimestopper Security Products Inc.

CRIMEWATCH - Lighting fixtures - Consumer Engineering, Inc.

CRIMINAL PROCEDURE MATE - Publisher's imprints - Little, Brown and Co., Inc.

CRIMP-CLOSED TAGS & HOLDERS - Hardware - Premax L.P.

CRIMP N SEAL - Electrical equipment - KSCO Corp.

CRIMPLESS SYSTEM, THE - Pumps - Risdon Corp.

CRIMPNSONOFAGUN - Tools - Hydraulic Tool Engineering, Inc.

CRIMSON - Flowers, plants, and seeds - Carlton Fruit Trees, Inc.

CRIMSON CRYSTAL - Games - Tsr, Inc.

CRIMSON GLORY - Christmas tree ornaments - Cracker Box Inc.

CRIMSON JEWEL - Flowers, plants, and seeds - Monrovia Nursery Co.

CRIMSON JEWELL - Agricultural products - Black Jewell Popcorn, Inc.

CRIMSON KING - Agricultural products - Vanguard Trading Services, Inc.

CRIMSON SELECT - Food products - Oakes Packers, Inc.

CRIN-DU-FIRM - Fabrics–crinoline - Meyer Drapery Services Inc.

CRIN-O-FINE - Fabrics–crinoline - Meyer Drapery Services Inc.

CRINGE - Recording label - Cringe

CRINKLE - Bedding–linen - Thomaston Mills Inc.

CRINKLE - Cosmetics - Andre Fantasies Inc.

CRINKLE ART - Craft supplies - Milton Bradley Co.

CRINKLE CLAUS - Figurines - Possible Dreams, Ltd.

CRINKLE CREPE - Underwear and nightwear - Bestform Foundations, Inc.

CRINKLE PUFFS - Pet products - Classic Products

CRINKLE-TIE - Paper–gift wrap ☆ - CPS Corp.

CRINKLER - Clay–modeling - Tonka Corp.

CRINKLES - Cookies - Nabisco Foods Group

CRINKLES - Pet products - Petland, Inc.

CRINOLINE - Colognes ☆ - Avon Products, Inc.

CRIPPLE CREEK - Apparel and accessories - Sidran, Inc.

CRIPPLE CREEK - Frozen foods - Windsor Quality Food Co. Ltd.

CRIPPLE CREEK - Hats - Cripple Creek Hat Co., Inc.

CRIS - Computer software - Software AG of North America, Inc.

CRIS - Computer software - Tracking Technologies Inc.

CRIS KRINGLE CREATIONS - Toys–stuffed ☆ - Spearhead Industries Inc.

CRIS MINTS - Candy - Falcon Candy Co.

CRIS P. SALADMANDER - Salads–prepackaged - Tanimura & Antle, Inc.

CRIS-PIC - Electronic equipment - Kalart Victor Corp.

CRISA GLASS - Vases–glass - Syndicate Sales, Inc.

CRISAL - Dinnerware–glass - Block China Co.

CRISBRO - Food products - United Food Service Inc.

CRISBROOK - Paper–kraft ☆ - Canson-Talens Inc.

CRISCIONE - Perfumes - Criscione Designs, Ltd.

CRISCO - Food products - Procter & Gamble Co.

CRISCO BUTTER FLAVOR STICKS - Food products - Procter & Gamble Co.

CRISCO NATURAL BLEND - Food products - Procter & Gamble Co.

CRISCO SAVORY SEASONINGS - Oils–edible - Procter & Gamble Co.

CRISFIELD - Furniture ☆ - Bassett Furniture Industries, Inc.

CRISINI - Apparel and accessories - Crisini Ltd.

CRISIS - Pens - Pentech International Inc.

CRISIS ALERT - Personal-safety alarm - Plastics Technology Inc.

CRISIS CONTROLLER - Alarms–personal - Pactall Corp.

CRISIS KIT - Housewares - Grodin Enterprises, Inc.

CRISLOID - Games - Crisloid Inc.

CRISLU CAST - Jewelry - Crislu Corp.

CRISNET - Computer software - Megg Associates Inc.

CRISP BAKED BUGLES - Snack foods - General Mills, Inc.

CRISP CINNAMON - Lipstick ☆ - Cosrich Inc.

CRISP/COMMUNITY BANKER - Computer software - Palladium Interactive

CRISP COOKIES - Cookies - Barbara's Bakery, Inc.

CRISP CRUST - Pans - E-Z-Por Corp.

CRISP-I-TATERS - Snack foods ☆ - General Mills, Inc.

CRISP KRINGLE - Candy - R.M. Palmer Co.

CRISP MOUNTAIN - Cleaning preparations - Martin A. Kahn

CRISP 'N CRACKLING - Rice - Malt-O-Meal Co.

CRISP 'N SWEET - Vegetables–canned - Crookham Co.

CRISP 'N SWEET - Vegetables–frozen - Stokely USA, Inc.

CRISP 'N TASTY - Pizzas–frozen - Jeno's Inc.

CRISP 'N TENDER - Food products ☆ - General Mills, Inc.

CRISP-P-CRISP - Chocolate candy - Wolfgang Candy Co., Inc.

CRISP PLUS - Onions - McCormick & Co., Inc.

CRISPERS - Frozen french fries - Ore-Ida Foods, Inc.

CRISPEY CRUNCH - Candy - Peter Paul

CRISPHEART - Food products - Crispheart Produce Inc.

CRISPINI - Crackers - Burns and Ricker Inc.

CRISPIX - Cereal - Kellogg Co.

CRISP'N SPICY - Food products - Crisp 'n Spicy Growers Inc.

CRISPURA - Food products - Universal Frozen Foods Co.

CRISPWAVE - Ovens–microwave - Whirlpool Properties, Inc.

CRISPY - Candy ☆ - Leaf, Inc.

CRISPY APPLE & CINNAMON - Teas - Seelect, Inc.

CRISPY BROWN RICE - Cereal - New Morn, Inc.

CRISPY BROWNS - Vegetables–frozen - Lamb-Weston, Inc.

CRISPY CAKES - Snack foods ☆ - Pacific Grain Products, Inc.

CRISPY CHIK - Food products - Worthington Foods Inc.

CRISPY CLIP - Novelty items ☆ - Jobar International Inc./Bibi Products

CRISPY CROWNS - Potato sticks - Ore-Ida Foods, Inc.

CRISPY CRUNCHERS - Vegetables–frozen - Ore-Ida Foods, Inc.

CRISPY CRUNCHIES - Potato sticks - Ore-Ida Foods, Inc.

CRISPY CUBES - Vegetables–frozen - Lamb-Weston, Inc.

CRISPY DIGINS - Snack foods - Barrel O' Fun Inc.

CRISPY LIGHT - Food products - Tyson Foods Inc.

CRISPY LIGHTS - Crackers ☆ - Keebler Co.

CRISPY MINI GRAHAMS - Cereal - Ralston Purina Co.

CRISPY OATS - Cereal ☆ - Edward & Sons Trading Co., Inc.

CRISPY PLUS - Fried chicken - Shoney's, Inc.

CRISPY Q'S - Food products - Universal Frozen Foods Co.

CRISPY SANDWICH CUTS - Pickles - Cains Foods, Inc.

CRISPY STEAK - Meat products–canned - Zartic, Inc.

CRISPY THINS - Potato chips ☆ - Anheuser-Busch Companies Inc.

CRISPY WHEATS 'N RAISINS - Cereal - General Mills, Inc.

CRISPY WHIPS! - Potato sticks - H.J. Heinz Co.

CRISPY!CRISPY! - Pizzas–mixes - Little Caesar Enterprises, Inc.

CRISS CROSS - Floor coverings–carpet and rugs - Carpet Crafts Inc.

CRISS CROSS - Flowers, plants, and seeds - D. Landreth Seed Co.

CRISS CROSS - Games - International Gamco, Inc.

CRISS CROSS - Games ☆ - CBS Toys

CRISS-CROSS - Pencils ☆ - Empire Berol USA

CRISS CROSS - Snack foods - Deep Foods, Inc.

CRISS-CROSS - Underwear and nightwear - Bestform Foundations, Inc.

CRISS CROSS CRASH - Toys–automobiles - Mattel, Inc.

CRISSCROSS - Dinnerware–glass ☆ - Nikko Ceramics Inc.

CRISSCUT - Food products - Lamb-Weston, Inc.

CRISSCUT FRIES - Vegetables–frozen - Lamb-Weston, Inc.

CRISSMILK - Candy bars - Brocks Candy Co.

CRISSY - Frames–eyeglass - Pathway Optical Prods.

CRISSY - Toys–stuffed - CBS Toys

CRISSY'S COUNTRY FLOWERS - Toys–stuffed ☆ - CBS Toys

CRISSY'S FRAGRANT FROCKS - Toys–stuffed ☆ - CBS Toys

CRIST COSMOS - Tableware–earthenware - Durand International

CRISTAL - Beverages–alcohol - Shaw-Ross International Importers

CRISTAL - Ophthalmic goods ☆ - Luxottica

CRISTAL - Tiles–ceramic - H & R Johnson Inc.

CRISTAL BRITES - Tiles–ceramic - H & R Johnson Inc.

CRISTAL D'ARQUES - Glassware–household - Durand International

CRISTAL DE FLANDRE - Glassware–household - Durand International

CRISTAL-FLO - Filters–water - Sta-Rite Industries Inc.

CRISTAL GOLD PREMIUM - Brandy ☆ - Shaw-Ross International Importers

CRISTAL J. G. DURAND - Glassware–household - Durand International

CRISTAL ST. GEORGES - Wines - Parliament Import Co.

CRISTALDI - Frames–eyeglass - May Optical Co. Inc.

CRISTALES - Cigar boxes–wood - Consolidated Cigar Corp.

CRISTALIQUE, THE - Crystal Clear Importing Co. Inc.

CRISTALLE - Cosmetics - Chanel Inc.

CRISTALLE - Furniture ☆ - Bassett Furniture Industries, Inc.

CRISTALLERIES DE LORRAINE - Glassware–household - Lalique North America

CRISTALLINA - Beverages–carbonated ☆ - Ferrero U.S.A Inc.

CRISTALLO - Floor coverings - Congoleum Corp.

CRISTEL - Beverages–alcohol - Nor-Glo Import Co.

CRISTELLE - Dinnerware–glass - Durand International

CRISTIAN GENEVE - Watches - Brokoe Manufacturing Co. Inc.

CRISTIAN GENEVE II - Watches - Brokoe Manufacturing Co. Inc.

CRISTINA - Cigars - Tampa Sweetheart Cigar Co.

CRISTINA - Dolls ☆ - Effanbee Doll Corp.

CRISTINA - Hats - Spartan Brands, Inc.

CRISTINA - Ophthalmic goods ☆ - Rozin Optical Export Corp.

CRISTINA - Wallpaper ☆ - Wolf-Gordon Inc.

CRISTOFORO COLOMBO - Food products - Escalon Frozen Foods

CRISTOM - Wines - Cristom Vineyards, Inc.

CRIT CENTER FOR RESEARCH IN INSTRUCTIONAL TECHNOLOGY - Computer storage devices–magnetic - Carl A. Schuetz

CRITCHFIELD - Meat products - Critchfield Meats, Inc.

CRITERIA - Luggage - American Tourister, Inc.

CRITERIA BROMATRESS - Hair care products - Madame C.J. Walker Inc.

CRITERION - Bedding–linen - Marcus Bros. Crib Products Inc.

CRITERION - Cameras–motion picture ☆ - Keystone Camera Corp.

CRITERION - Casters - Young's

CRITERION - Cement - Api Technologies, Inc.

CRITERION - Computer software - Creditor Resources, Inc.

CRITERION - Copper products - Criterion Metals, Inc.

CRITERION - Decals and transfers ☆ - Criterion Decalcomania Co.

CRITERION - Doors–vinyl - Panelfold Inc.

CRITERION - Drums–musical instruments ☆ - Pearl Corp.

CRITERION - Fabrics - Dan River Inc.

CRITERION - Fishing tackle - Shakespeare Fishing Tackle

CRITERION - Floor coverings–carpet and rugs ☆ - Karastan-Bigelow Inc.

CRITERION - Floor coverings–tile - Kentile Floors Inc.

CRITERION - Furnaces–electric - Rheem Manufacturing Co.

CRITERION - Medical apparatus - Veratex Group

CRITERION - Musical instrument accessories - E. & O. Mari Inc.

CRITERION - Musical instruments - Kansas Music Co. Inc.

CRITERION - Notebooks and notepads - Roaring Spring Blank Book Co.

CRITERION - Recording label - Criterion Music Corp.

CRITERION - Thermometers - Maximum Inc.

CRITERION - Watches - Criterion Watch Co. Inc.

CRITERION - Weightlifting equipment - Criterion Bodybuilding Equipment, Inc.

CRITERION/ADVOCATE - Floor coverings–carpet and rugs - Johnson's Carpets Inc.

CRITERION & FONNELI - Musical instrument accessories - Kansas Music Co. Inc.

CRITERION TEETH - Dental equipment - Uni Lac Corp.

CRITERIUM - Bicycles - Klein Bicycle Corp.

CRITERIUM DECISIONPLUS - Computer software - Sygenex Inc.

CRITIC-AID - Skin care products - Sween Corp.

CRITICAL - Recording label - Urgent! Records

CRITICAL CARE FOR DAMAGED HAIR - Hair care products - Nature's Design Ltd.

CRITICAL CARVE - Shoe insoles - Northwest Podiatric Laboratory, Inc.

CRITICAL MASS - Food products - Anthony Bonviso

CRITICAL MASS - Vitamins and nutritional supplements ☆ - Nature's Way Products, Inc.

CRITICAL MASS POST WORKOUT - Vitamins and nutritional supplements - American Body Building Products, Inc.

CRITICAL PATH - Computer software - Media Vision Technology Inc.

CRITICAL PERSPECTIVE - Publisher's imprints - Three Continents Press

CRITICARE - Pharmaceutical preparations - Bristol-Myers Squibb Co.

CRITICOLOR - Lamps - Philips Lighting Co.

CRITIC'S CHOICE - Cutlery - Amway Corp.

CRITICS' CHOICE - Entertainment guide - New York Times Co.

CRITIC'S CHOICE - Fabrics–tapestry ☆ - Comark Wallcoverings

CRITIC'S CHOICE - Floor coverings–carpet and rugs - Coronet Carpets Inc.

CRITIC'S CHOICE - Lighting equipment - Marketing Insights, Inc.-Frank Luppino Jr., and Associates

CRITIC'S CHOICE - Popcorn - California Treats

CRITTER - Electrical testing instruments - Adobe Systems Inc.

CRITTER - Hair care products - Western Neckwear Manufacturing Co. Inc.

CRITTER - Key rings - U.S. Fiberglass Inc.

CRITTER - Lawn mowers ☆ - Hoffco Inc.

CRITTER & COVERS - Pet products - O'Dell Industries

CRITTER & LITTER SPRAY - Deodorizers - Krueger Enterprises

CRITTER BARN - Pet products - Next to Nature

CRITTER BEDDING - Pet products - Tetra Sales USA

CRITTER CAGE - Pet products ☆ - Armstrong's Cricket Farm

CRITTER CAKES - Bakery products - G & S Metal Products Co., Inc.

CRITTER CARE - Pet products - Mardel Laboratories, Inc.

CRITTER CARNIVAL - Toys - Educational Insights, Inc.

CRITTER CASTLES - Pet products - M.I.L.D. Kingdom

CRITTER CHEWS - Pet products - Mardel Laboratories, Inc.

CRITTER CHIPS - Toys - Southdale Kay-Bee Toy, Inc.

CRITTER CITY - Toys - Uncle Milton Industries Inc.

CRITTER COMFORT - Pet products - Werner Co.

CRITTER CONDO - Pet products - Educational Insights, Inc.

CRITTER CORN - Animal feeds - Critter Corn

CRITTER CORRAL - Pet products ☆ - Doskocil Manufacturing Co., Inc.

CRITTER COTTAGE - Pet products - Lee-Mar Pet Supplies

CRITTER COUCH COMPANY - Pet products - Alice Sakamoto

CRITTER COUNTRY - Giftware - Piccadilly

CRITTER COUNTRY - Pet products - Mountain Meadows Pet Products, Inc.

CRITTER CRAZI - Pet products - Caren Mellman

CRITTER CREATIONS - Mats ☆ - Colmar Industries, Inc.

CRITTER CUDDLERS - Toys - Fisher-Price, Inc.

CRITTER DINNER - Animal feeds - Agway Country Foods Inc.

CRITTER FACTORY, THE - Statuary - Kathleen Kelly

CRITTER FRESH - Cleaning preparations - Mardel Laboratories, Inc.

CRITTER FRESH CAGE CLEANER - Deodorizers - Mardel Laboratories, Inc.

CRITTER FRITTERS - Dog food - Petcetera Inc.

CRITTER GETTER GAME CALLS - Sporting goods - Robert Craig Schultz

CRITTER GITTER - Alarm systems - Amtek Pet Behavior Products

CRITTER HUT - Boxes - Charles L. Vanalstine

CRITTER LOG - Pet products - Tetra Sales USA

CRITTER MOUNTAIN WEAR - Apparel and accessories - Critter Mountain Wear, Inc.

CRITTER NEST - Pet products ☆ - Mardel Laboratories, Inc.

CRITTER NIPS - Animal feeds - Rowland Family Farms, Inc.

CRITTER NOTES - Greeting cards - Kersten Bros. Studios

CRITTER OASIS - Pet products - Tetra Sales USA

CRITTER PACS - Pet products - Custom Marketing

CRITTER PEN - Pet products - Rolf C. Hagen (USA) Corp.

CRITTER SEEDS - Pet products - Dynamic Development

CRITTER SITTERS - Giftware - Brushcreek Creative Co.

CRITTER SITTERS - Toys–stuffed - Animal Fair Inc.

CRITTER STUMP - Pet products ☆ - Tetra Sales USA

CRITTER TAILS - Apparel–children's - Oneita Industries Inc.

CRITTER TALES - Greeting cards - Kersten Bros. Studios

CRITTER TERRACE - Pet products - Tetra Sales USA

CRITTER TREATS YOGURT - Pet food - Mardel Laboratories, Inc.

CRITTER TUNES - Tape players–cassette - Creative Critters International

CRITTER VITES - Veterinary nutritional supplements - Mardel Laboratories, Inc.

CRITTER VITES-PLUS - Pet products - Mardel Laboratories, Inc.

CRITTERS - Apparel and accessories - Dennis Harris

CRITTERS - Chewing gum - Richardson Brands

☆ = Now out of production

CRITTERS - Toothbrushes - John O.Butler Co.
CRITTER'S CHOICE - Pet products - Werner Co.
CRITTER'S DELIGHT - Pet products - Werner Co.
CRITTERS ON CRYSTALS - Figurines - Jewel Tunnel
CRITTERS WITH A HEART - Jewelry - Waldeck Jewelers, Inc.
CRITTERTRAIL - Pet products - Pets International, Ltd.
CRIXILINE - Bandages - C.R. Bard, Inc.
CRIXIVAN - Pharmaceutical preparations - Merck & Co., Inc. (Merck Research Laboratories)
CRL - Cleaning preparations - C.R. Laurence Co. Inc.
CRM - Computer software - Womens Care Resources, Inc.
CRM & ME - Invitations - Editions Ltd.
CRMP - Vitamins and nutritional supplements - Vital Energy
CRO - Fruits–canned - CRO Fruit Co.
CRO-BAR - Electrical surge protectors - Polaroid Corp.
CRO-K - Games ✩ - A.J. Renzi Plastic Corp.
CRO-MAN-ZIN - Vitamins and nutritional supplements - Freeda Vitamins Inc.
CRO-NEL - Packaging–foam - Crowell Corp.
CROAKER FROG - Toys–stuffed - Dakin Inc.
CROAKIE BELT - Apparel and accessories ✩ - Life-Link International, Inc.
CROAKIES - Eyeglasses - Life-Link International, Inc.
CROAKS - Insecticides - Puritan-Churchill Chemical Co.
CROC-A-DOC - Health care products - Physician Engineered Products
CROC-A-RIDE - Toys - Aqua-Leisure Industries, Inc.
CROC-O-DIAL - Soap - Dial Corp.
CROCCANTELLA - Breads - Dean & Deluca Inc.
CROCCANTINA - Breads - Crystal Food Import Corp.
CROCHET CLASSICS - Dolls ✩ - Effanbee Doll Corp.
CROCHET MASTER - Crochet hooks - Boye Needle
CROCHET N' FUN - Hobby kits ✩ - Craft House Corp.
CROCHET-NIP - Pet products ✩ - Pets International, Ltd.
CROCK - Apparel and accessories - Daryl K. Crawford
CROCK-A-DILLY CROCODILE - Stuffed animals - Russ Berrie and Co., Inc.
CROCK-ETTE - Kitchen appliances - Rival Manufacturing Co.
CROCK LOC - Pet products - JV Products
CROCK O'TOOLS - Kitchen utensils–aluminum - Robinson Knife & Fiddlers Plastics
CROCK-PLATE - Kitchen appliances ✩ - Rival Manufacturing Co.
CROCK-POT - Kitchen appliances - Rival Manufacturing Co.
CROCK STICK - Kitchen appliances - Lansky Sharpeners
CROCK WATCHER - Crock pots - Hamilton Beach/Proctor-Silex Inc.
CROCKERY GOURMET - Seasonings - Superior Quality Foods, Inc.
CROCKERY LOOK, THE - Housewares - Tucker Housewares Inc.
CROCKERY, THE - Cookware - West Bend Co.
CROCKETT & RENALDE - Horse bits - Libertyville Saddle Shop, Inc.
CROCKETT COLLECTION, THE - Greeting cards - Crockett Collection
CROCKETT FARMS - Food products - Chiquita Brands, Inc.
CROCKETT LOG & TIMBER HOMES - Timers–appliance - Natural Building Systems, Inc.
CROCKETT TAVERN - Furniture - Bean Station Furniture Factory Inc.
CROCKETTS CROSSING - Furniture ✩ - Bassett Furniture Industries, Inc.
CROCO - Footwear ✩ - Conjac Inc.
CROCOBITE - Toys - Mattel, Inc.
CROCODILE - Cleaning preparations - Holtco, Inc.
CROCODILE - Electronic equipment - Mueller Electric Co.
CROCODILE - Office supplies ✩ - Samsill Corp.
CROCODILE CREEK - Toys - Melvin A. Brown
CROCODILE CREEK - Toys - European Toy Collection/Crocodile Creek
CROCODILE DENTIST - Games - Milton Bradley Co.
CROCODILE DUNDEE - Apparel - Paramount Pictures Corp.
CROCODILE DUNDEE II - Apparel and accessories - Paramount Pictures Corp.
CROCODILE ROCK - Rocking chairs - Flexible Flyer Co.
CROCODILES - Sporting goods - Outdoor Research, Inc.
CROCUS - Greeting cards ✩ - Brett-Forer Greetings Inc.
CROCUS - Rope - Geo. B. Carpenter Co.
CROCUS - Yarn - William Unger & Co. Inc.
CRODA APEX - Adhesives and sealants - Croda Apex Adhesives Inc.
CROFT - Beverages–alcohol - Palace Brands Co.
CROFT - Food products - C-Corp.
CROFT - Ladders–metal - Croft Metals Inc.
CROFT - Wines ✩ - European Beverage Co., Inc.
CROFT & BARROW - Leather goods - Kohl's Department Stores, Inc.
CROFT & CA. - Wines - Heublein, Inc.
CROFT JEREZ - Wines - Heublein, Inc.
CROFTERCRAFT - Wallpaper - Hamilton Adams Imports Ltd.

CROFTON - Cabinets - American Woodmark Corp.
CROFTON - Dolls - Mattel, Inc.
CROFTON - Hardware ✩ - Amerock Corp.
CROFTS CLASSICS - Publisher's imprints - Harlan Davidson Inc.
CROISADE - Flatware - Couzon USA
CROISSANT - Crackers - Shaffer, Clark & Co. Inc.
CROISSANT POCKETS - Frozen foods - Chef America, Inc.
CROIX DE SAVOIE - Corn–flour or meal - Gourmet America
CROIX SAVOIE - Food products - Newmarket
CROKINOLE - Games - China Creek, LLC
CROLON - Cleaning preparations ✩ - Flo-Pac Corp.
CROLYN - Tape recorders ✩ - E.I. Dupont de Nemours and Co.
CROMABON - Floor coverings ✩ - Congoleum Corp.
CROMAC - Gloves ✩ - Jomac Products Inc.
CROMARGAN - Flatware ✩ - W.M.F. of America Inc.
CROMATIC - Projectors–photographic - Rollei of America Inc.
CROMAX A-T - Paints - E.I. Dupont de Nemours and Co.
CROMAX-LTC - Paints - E.I. Dupont de Nemours and Co.
CROMAX WBC - Paints - E.I. Dupont de Nemours and Co.
CROMOSENE II - Pharmaceutical preparations - Pasadena Research Laboratories, Inc.
CROMPTON - Fabrics - Crompton Co. Inc.
CROMWELL - Bathroom fixtures - Crane Plumbing/Fiat Products
CROMWELL - Desks - Hon Co.
CROMWELL - Pencils - Reliance Pen & Pencil Corp.
CROMWELL - Silverware - Ellis Barker Silver Co.
CROMWELL - Watches - Bulova Corp.
CROMWELL - Watches - Hampden Corp.
CROMWELL & WORTH - Apparel - Gentry Clothiers, Inc.
CRON - Boats–houseboats ✩ - Cron Houseboats
CRONAFLEX - Photographic equipment - E.I. Dupont de Nemours and Co.
CRONALITH - Photographic equipment - E.I. Dupont de Nemours and Co.
CRONASCAN - Photographic equipment - E.I. Dupont de Nemours and Co.
CRONCO - Refrigerators - CMI Architectural Products
CRONCO-LITE - Doors–metal - CMI Architectural Products
CRONIN - Wines - Cronin Vineyards
CRONOS - Watches - Kix Athletic Corp.
CRONUS - Watches - Cronus Precision Products Inc.
CRONWELL - Floor coverings–carpet and rugs - Patcraft Mills Inc.
CROOKED BROOK - Apparel–women's - Syndicate Sales, Inc.
CROOKED DOGS - Cigars - G.A. Georgopulo & Co. Inc.
CROOKED ISLAND ALE - Beverages–malt ✩ - Sazerac Co. Inc.
CROOKED MOUNTAIN SPORTS - Apparel and accessories - Matthew W. Dockstader
CROOKED RIVER - Beverages–malt - CRB Co.
CROOKETTES - Cigars - House of Windsor Inc.
CROOKLYN - Apparel and accessories - Forty Acres and a Mule Filmworks, Inc.
CROOKS - Cigars - House of Windsor Inc.
CROOKSTICKS - Antennas ✩ - Wintenna Inc.
CROP GARD - Electrical equipment - Weitech Inc.
CROP-IT - Photographic equipment - SP Systems/Saratons
CROPPER HOPPER - Artists' materials - Leelo Industries, Inc.
CROQUET - Fabrics - Gretchen Bellinger Inc.
CROQUET - Placemats - Now Designs
CROQUET CLUB - Apparel–women's - Tropic Tex International, Inc.
CROQUET CONCEPTS - Games - Croquet International Ltd.
CROQUET INTERNATIONAL LTD - Games - Croquet International Ltd.
CROQUILLE - Pastries ✩ - Liberty Richter Inc.
CROSBY - Paper–bond - Geo. W. Millar & Co. Inc.
CROSBY - Refrigerators - Kenyon Marine, Inc. (Adler/Barbour Div.)
CROSBY SQUARE - Footwear - Hills Department Store Co.
CROSBY'S - Juices - Crosby Fruit Products Co. Inc.
CROSCI - Pipes–tobacco - Mastercraft Pipes Inc.
CROSCILL - Wallpaper - Imperial Wallcoverings, Inc.
CROSCILL HOME FASHIONS - Blinds–vertical - Croscill Curtain Co. Inc.
CROSETTI - Vegetables–frozen - Crosetti Frozen Foods Inc.
CROSFILLEX - Furniture–wood ✩ - Grosfillex Inc.
CROSLEY - Electronic equipment - Brown-Rogers-Dixson Co.
CROSMAN - Guns - Crosman Corp.
CROSMAN CLIMBERS - Sporting goods ✩ - Crosman Corp.
CROSMAN'S - Flowers, plants, and seeds - Crosman Corp.
CROSPETE - Golfing equipment - Cal Malibu, Inc.
CROSS - Bicycles - Raleigh USA Bicycle Co.
CROSS - Garden equipment - Cross Seed Co. Inc.
CROSS - Hardware - Black & Decker Corp.

✩ = Now out of production

CROSS - Harmonicas - Hohner Inc.

CROSS - Pens - A.T.X. International, Inc.

CROSS - Pens - A.T. Cross Co.

CROSS - Spaghetti machine - Cook Things

CROSS & WINSOR - Apparel and accessories - BDS Investment Corp.

CROSS AT THE GREEN...NOT IN BETWEEN - Posters - Cross at the Green...Not in Between Enterprises

CROSS-BAND - Girdles - Vanity Corset Co. Inc.

CROSS BASICS - Apparel and accessories - Manhattan Trade International Inc.

CROSS BLOCK - Board games - Star One Game Co.

CROSS BONES - Games - Smethport Specialty Co.

CROSS BONES - Sporting goods - Powell Skateboards

CROSS-BRACES - Clamps–metal - Sign-Up Corp.

CROSS CANYON - Apparel and accessories - Vazha Erenfrid

CROSS CLUES - Computer software ☆ - SRA/McGraw-Hill (Div. of The McGraw-Hill Companies)

CROSS COLOURS - Apparel and accessories - Solo Joint Inc.

CROSS COMFORT - Footwear - Wolverine World Wide, Inc.

CROSS CONDITIONING SYSTEMS - Exercising equipment - Cross Conditioning Systems, Ltd.

CROSS CONNECT - Computer software - Smith Micro Software, Inc.

CROSS-COOL - Chemical preparations - Cross Chemical Co. Inc.

CROSS COUNTREE - Furniture ☆ - White Furniture Co.

CROSS COUNTRY - Bags - SGI Inc.

CROSS COUNTRY - Bicycles - Kent International Inc.

CROSS COUNTRY - Bicycles - Murray, Inc.

CROSS COUNTRY - Crocheted and knitted items - Schuessler Knitting Mills Inc.

CROSS COUNTRY - Floor coverings–carpet and rugs ☆ - Regal Rugs Inc.

CROSS COUNTRY - Luggage ☆ - American Tourister, Inc.

CROSS COUNTRY - Oils–lubricating - Finish Line Technologies, Inc.

CROSS COUNTRY - Shoes - Tohkutsu America Corp.

CROSS COUNTRY SHOPPING - Catalogs - Jeremiah Junction, Inc.

CROSS COUNTRY STITCHING - Periodicals - Jeremiah Junction, Inc.

CROSS COUNTRY, THE - Apparel–athletic - Howe K. Sipes Co.

CROSS CREEK - Apparel–athletic - Russell Athletic Div.

CROSS CREEK - Furniture ☆ - Stanley Furniture Co. Inc.

CROSS CREEK CLASSICS - Sweaters - Cross Creek Apparel Inc.

CROSS CREEK PRO COLLECTION - Apparel–athletic - Cross Creek Apparel Inc.

CROSS CUBE 3D - Crossword puzzles - Nicholas Ralph Dalessandro

CROSS CURRENT - Bicycles - Huffy Corp.

CROSS CURRENT - Fabrics - Greenwood Mills Inc.

CROSS CURRENTS - Wallcovering ☆ - Colortree Designs

CROSS CUT BY MAJESTIC - Apparel–athletic - Majestic Athletic Wear, Ltd.

CROSS FIRE - Archery equipment - Spencer's Inc.

CROSS FIRE - Audio equipment - Caltek Electronics, Inc.

CROSS-FIRE - Deodorizers - Promaster

CROSS-GRID - Tiles–ceramic - Crossville Ceramics Co.

CROSS KEYS - Floor coverings - Mannington Resilient Floors

CROSS-KUTT - Siding–insulating - Aluminum Co. of America

CROSS LINK 3 - Resins–polyethylene - Old Town Canoe Co.

CROSS-LOK - Sporting goods - Outdoor Technologies Group

CROSS-MATRIX - Bricks - Southern Brick Co.

CROSS MEDICAL - Surgical supplies - Cross Medical Products, Inc.

CROSS N BLACKWELL - Seasonings - Fancy Foods of Virginia Inc.

CROSS 'N CLING - Apparel and accessories - Playtex Apparel, Inc.

CROSS OF DESTINY, THE - Jewelry - Robert P. Mirando

CROSS OF IRON - Games - Avalon Hill Game Co.

CROSS ORCHARDS - Food products - Cross Orchards & Storage Co.

CROSS PICK - Musical instrument accessories - Raul De La Rosa

CROSS PLAY - Sports rackets and accessories - Wilson Sporting Goods Co.

CROSS-PLUS - Tiles–ceramic - Crossville Ceramics Co.

CROSS POINTE - Paper - Cross Pointe Paper Corp.

CROSS PRO - Computer software - Aspen Gold Software

CROSS RIB - Mats - JCH International Inc.

CROSS-RIB - Mats - Wear Proof Mat Co.

CROSS RIB RUNNER - Mats - Superior Manufacturing Group, Inc.

CROSS RIB RUNNER II - Motor vehicle parts and accessories - Superior Manufacturing Group, Inc.

CROSS RIB RUNNER II - Floor coverings - Superior Manufacturing Group/ Notrax Floor Matting

CROSS ROAD COLLECTION - Furniture - Brady Furniture Co. Inc.

CROSS ROADS - Floor coverings - Tarkett, Inc.

CROSS ROADS COUNTRY FRESH QUALITY PORK - Pork - Houchens Industries, Inc.

CROSS-RUNNER - Footwear–athletic - L.A. Gear, Inc.

CROSS RUNNER - Mats - JCH International Inc.

CROSS SEARCH - Puzzles ☆ - Med-Comm Associates

CROSS-SLATE - Tiles–ceramic - Crossville Ceramics Co.

CROSS SPORT - Beverages - Pure Power Sports Nutrition

CROSS SPORT - Shoes - R. Josephs Sportswear, Inc.

CROSS SPORT - Vitamins and nutritional supplements - Nature's Way Products, Inc.

CROSS STICH - Fabrics - Interface, Inc.

CROSS STITCH - Clocks - General Time Corp. (Westclox/Seth Thomas Div.)

CROSS STRETCH - Brassieres (Bras) ☆ - Carnival Creations

CROSS-TOP - Drill bits - Relton Corp.

CROSS TOURING - Sporting goods - Alpina Sports Corp.

CROSS TOWNSEND - Pens - A.T.X. International, Inc.

CROSS TOWNSEND - Pens - A.T. Cross Co.

CROSS TRAINER - Bicycles ☆ - Huffy Corp.

CROSS TRAINER - Footwear–athletic - Nike, Inc.

CROSS TRAINING - Educational materials - Plus Communications, Inc.

CROSS TRAX - Food products - McCain Foods Inc.

CROSS TRAXER - Tires - Carlisle Tire & Rubber Co.

CROSS TREAD - Motor vehicle parts and accessories - Cross Tread Industries, Inc.

CROSS-TREAD - Tiles–ceramic - Crossville Ceramics Co.

CROSS UP - Games ☆ - Milton Bradley Co.

CROSS WALK - Exercising equipment - Proform Fitness Products, Inc.

CROSS YOUR HEART - Apparel and accessories - Playtex Apparel, Inc.

CROSS YOUR HEART BEAUTIFUL ONES - Brassieres (Bras) - Playtex Apparel, Inc.

CROSSACCESS - Computer software - DB Access, Inc.

CROSSACTION - Fabrics ☆ - Burlington House Fabrics Group

CROSSBAR - Golfing equipment ☆ - Bost Enterprises, Inc.

CROSSBARS - Games - Crossbars, Inc.

CROSSBARS SAMMY - Games - Crossbars, Inc.

CROSSBOLT - Toys - Tonka Corp.

CROSSBOW - Boats–motor - Donzi Marine Corp.

CROSSBOW - Communications equipment - Fibermux Corp.

CROSSBOW - Electronic equipment - Tandy Corp.

CROSSBOW - Golfing equipment - Tourshot Golf Co. Inc.

CROSSBOW - Toys ☆ - Wham-O Manufacturing Co.

CROSSBOWS AND CATAPULTS - Sporting goods - Link Group International

CROSSBREED - Apparel–men's - Giant Revolution Records

CROSSBUCK - Doors–storm - Quaker Window Products Co.

CROSSCHECK - Games ☆ - Tsr, Inc.

CROSSCHECK - Wallpaper ☆ - Koroseal Wallcoverings

CROSSCHECKER - Sportswear - Crosschecker

CROSSCLIME - Fabrics - Gretchen Bellinger Inc.

CROSSCORD - Fabrics–cotton - Dan River Inc.

CROSSCOUNTRY - Motor vehicles–motor homes ☆ - Coachmen Recreational Vehicle Co.

CROSSCREEK - Floor coverings–carpet and rugs ☆ - Callaway Carpets

CROSSCURRENTS - Rings–jewelry - Artcarved Inc.

CROSSCUT - Bicycles - Schwinn Cycling & Fitness Inc.

CROSSCUT ADVANTAGE - Plywood - Simpson Timber Co.

CROSSCUTS - Food products - Universal Frozen Foods Co.

CROSSCUTTER - Hardware - Black & Decker Corp.

CROSSE & BLACKWELL - Soups–frozen - Nestle USA

CROSSED LEAVES - Tobacco–chewing or smoking - Campbell Tobacco Rehandling Co. Inc.

CROSSFAX - Computer software - Digital Communications Associates, Inc.

CROSSFIRE - Alarm systems - Alarmex

CROSSFIRE - Audio equipment - Paramount Audio, Inc.

CROSSFIRE - Automotive exhaust system components - Randolph S. Barth

CROSSFIRE - Bicycles ☆ - Hedstrom Corp.

CROSSFIRE - Commercial dishwashing machines - Insinger Machine Co.

CROSSFIRE - Computer software ☆ - Sierra On-Line, Inc.

CROSSFIRE - Darts and dart games - Dart World Inc.

CROSSFIRE - Floor coverings–carpet and rugs - Calladium & Marglen

CROSSFIRE - Floor coverings–carpet and rugs - Quaker Inc.

CROSSFIRE - Footwear - E.S. Originals, Inc.

CROSSFIRE - Games - Milton Bradley Co.

CROSSFIRE - Games ☆ - CBS Toys

CROSSFIRE - Golfing equipment - King Par Corp.

CROSSFIRE - Jewelry - Donald Bruce & Co.

CROSSFIRE - Recording label - Oakridge Music Recording Service

☆ = Now out of production

CROSSFIRE - Scientific apparatus - Task Force Tips, Inc.
CROSSFIRE - Wood products - Georgia-Pacific Corp.
CROSSFLIGHT - Helmets–athletic - Schwinn Cycling & Fitness Inc.
CROSSHATCH - Blinds–venetian ☆ - Hunter Douglas, Inc.
CROSSHATCH - Floor coverings–carpet and rugs - J and J Industries Inc.
CROSSINGGUARD - Electrical industrial apparatus - Nestor, Inc.
CROSSINGS - Apparel–women's - Geneco Inc.
CROSSINGS - Cabinets - Fieldstone Cabinetry
CROSSINGS - Computer software - Steck-Vaughn Publishing Corp.
CROSSINGS - Floor coverings–carpet and rugs - Burtco Enterprises Inc.
CROSSINGS - Furniture - Haworth, Inc.
CROSSINGS FINE LINE - Sweaters - Geneco Inc.
CROSSIT - Caps, socks, shirts, swearters - Christopher Alan Edge
CROSSLANDS - Computers–personal - Marcraft International Corp.
CROSSLEY - Hardware - Blaine Window Hardware Inc.
CROSSLINK - Adhesives and sealants - Crosslink Technologies, Inc.
CROSSLINK - Belts–industrial - Cross Conditioning Systems, Ltd.
CROSSLINK - Chemical preparations - Rouse Rubber Industries, Inc.
CROSSLINK 3 - Boats–canoes - Old Town Canoe Co.
CROSSLOCK - Knives–pocket - Buck Knives, Inc.
CROSSMAIL - Computer software - System Development Co. of New Hampshire, Inc.
CROSSMANN COMMUNITIES - Construction equipment rental services - Crossmann Communities, Inc.
CROSSOVER - Apparel stores–sports ☆ - Tultex Corp.
CROSSOVER - Medical apparatus - Schneider (USA) Inc.
CROSSOVER - Recording label ☆ - Concord Records Inc.
CROSSOVER - Wallpaper - B. Berger Co.
CROSSOVER CREATIVE GROUP - Advertising agencies - Steve Climons
CROSSOVER KING - Apparel and accessories - Gary Sidney
CROSSPLEX - Computer peripheral equipment - Softouch Systems, Inc.
CROSSPOINT - Electronic equipment - Crosspoint Corp.
CROSSPOINT - Floor coverings–carpet and rugs - Patrick Carpet Mills
CROSSROAD - Recording label ☆ - Voyager Recordings & Publications
CROSSROADS - Bicycles ☆ - Roadmaster Corp.
CROSSROADS - Computer software - KOHOL Systems, Inc.
CROSSROADS - Educational materials - National Curriculum & Training Institute, Inc.
CROSSROADS - Flatware - Pfaltzgraff Investment Co.
CROSSROADS - Floor coverings - Mannington Resilient Floors
CROSSROADS - Floor coverings–carpet and rugs ☆ - Masland Corp.
CROSSROADS - Floor coverings–carpet and rugs ☆ - Regal Rugs Inc.
CROSSROADS - Furniture ☆ - Bassett Furniture Industries, Inc.
CROSSROADS - Signs - Imagine
CROSSROADS - Wallpaper - Gencorp Inc.
CROSSROADS II - Floor coverings–carpet and rugs - Trend Carpet
CROSSROBICS - Exercising equipment - Stairmaster Sports/Medical Products, Inc.
CROSSRUFF TAKE-HOME TOURNAMENT - Games - Royal T Enterprises
CROSSTARGET - Computer software ☆ - Dimensional Insight, Inc.
CROSSTECH - Apparel and accessories - W.L. Gore & Associates, Inc.
CROSSTECH - Life preservers - Stearns Manufacturing Co.
CROSSTITCH - Glassware–household - Owens-Illinois Inc. (Libbey Div.)
CROSSTONES - Floor coverings–carpet and rugs - Mohawk Carpet Corp.
CROSSTOWN - Bicycles ☆ - Raleigh USA Bicycle Co.
CROSSTOWN - Musical instrument accessories - Viking Cases
CROSSTRAIL - Bicycles - Schwinn Cycling & Fitness Inc.
CROSSTRAINER - Vitamins and nutritional supplements - 206 Macopin Corp.
CROSSTRAINERS - Hats - Crosstrainer Ministries, Inc.
CROSSTYLE - Tiles–ceramic - Crossville Ceramics Co.
CROSSWAY BOOKS - Publisher's imprints - Good News Publishers
CROSSWEAVE - Floor coverings–carpet and rugs - Lotus Carpets
CROSSWEVE - Floor coverings–carpet and rugs - Patrick Carpet Mills
CROSSWIND - Apparel and accessories - Eddie Bauer Inc.
CROSSWINDS - Floor coverings–carpet and rugs - Richmond Carpet Mills
CROSSWINDS - Wallpaper - S.M. Hexter Co.
CROSSWINDS - Wallpaper ☆ - Fairwinds Studio
CROSSWINDS II - Wallpaper ☆ - Fairwinds Studio
CROSSWINDS III - Wallpaper - Fairwinds Studio
CROSSWING - Fishing tackle - Wright & McGill Co.
CROSSWIRE - Computer software - Silversun, Inc.
CROSSWISE - Computer software - Groupware Authors
CROSSWORD - Toys - Tonka Corp.
CROSSWORD COMMUTER - See **CROSSWORDS-TO-GO**
CROSSWORD MAGIC - Computer software - Mindscape Software Inc.
CROSSWORD MAGIC - Computer software - Steven R. Sherman

CROSSWORD STUDIO - Computer software - Nordic Software, Inc.
CROSSWORDS PLUS - Computer software - Parsons Technology, Inc.
CROSSWORDS-TO-GO - Puzzles - Xtrax Corp.
CROSTAR - Photographic equipment - SP Systems/Saratons
CROSTINI - Breads - Nicole Inc.
CROSTINI - Crackers - Crystal Food Import Corp.
CROTON - Watches - Croton Watch Co., Inc.
CROUSE-HINDS - Lighting fixtures - Cooper Industries, Inc.
CROUTETTES - Breads - Kellogg Co.
CROVEX - Photographic equipment - E.I. Dupont de Nemours and Co.
CROW - Brushes–paint - Allpro Corp.
CROW MAGNUM - Firearms, accessories, and parts - Beeman Precision Airguns
CROW RIVER - Wheelchairs - Crow River Industries Inc.
CROWATT - Electric lighting equipment - Lutron Electronics Co., Inc.
CROWDBUSTER - Pizza - Mazzio's Corp.
CROWDPLEASER - Cigars - John T's Pipes & Fine Tobaccos
CROWELL BIOGRAPHIES - Publisher's imprints ☆ - Harper Junior Books Group
CROWELL-COLLIER PRESS - Publisher's imprints - MacMillan Publishing Co. Inc.
CROWELL CROCODILES - Publisher's imprints ☆ - Harper Junior Books Group
CROWELL HOLIDAY BOOKS - Publisher's imprints ☆ - Harper Junior Books Group
CROWELL JUNIOR BOOKS - Publisher's imprints - Harper Junior Books Group
CROWELL LET'S-READ-AND-FIND-OUT SCIENCE BOOKS - Publisher's imprints - Harper Junior Books Group
CROWELL POETS, THE - Publisher's imprints ☆ - Harper Junior Books Group
CROWELL YOUNG MATH - Publisher's imprints ☆ - Harper Junior Books Group
CROWLEY - Yogurt - Crowley Foods, Inc.
CROWLEY'S RIDGE - Wallpaper - Seabrook Wallcoverings, Inc.
CROWLOK - Tape–adhesive - Crowell Corp.
CROWN - Apparel–men's - Crown Clothing Corp.
CROWN - Artists' materials - Crown Art Products
CROWN - Artists' materials - Glenview Products Inc.
CROWN - Bicycles - Columbia Manufacturing Inc.
CROWN - Boats - Clark Craft Boat Co.
CROWN - Boxes - Packaging Service Co. Inc.
CROWN - Cabinets - Cabinet Craft
CROWN - Cabinets - Imperial Marble Corp.
CROWN - Cages–wire - Crown Products Co.
CROWN - Candy - Crown Candy Corp.
CROWN - Chocolate candy - Chocolate Packaging & Manufacturing, Corp.
CROWN - Cigars ☆ - National Cigar Corp.
CROWN - Cleaning preparations - Durawool Inc.
CROWN - Computer software - QMS, Inc.
CROWN - Cordage and twine - Wellington Leisure Products, Inc.
CROWN - Doors–metal - Crown Door Co. Inc.
CROWN - Electronic equipment - Crown International, Inc.
CROWN - Fabrics–canvas - Crown Textile Co.
CROWN - Fishing tackle - Cortland Line Co., Inc.
CROWN - Floor coverings–carpet and rugs - Johnson's Carpets Inc.
CROWN - Food products - Vlasic Foods Inc.
CROWN - Fruits and vegetables - Wapato Fruit Products Inc.
CROWN - Furniture - Hillside House of Originals
CROWN - Furniture–upholstered - Imperial of Morristown Inc.
CROWN - Glassware–household - Svend Jensen of Denmark Inc.
CROWN - Glassware–household - Riedel Crystal of America Inc.
CROWN - Greeting cards - Hallmark Cards Inc.
CROWN - Guitars ☆ - Castiglione Accordion
CROWN - Guitars ☆ - Sierra Instrument Co.
CROWN - Hair care products - Crown Cosmetics
CROWN - Hair care products - Crown Distributing Co. Inc.
CROWN - Hardware - Wal-Rich Corp.
CROWN - Kitchenware–earthenware - Robinson-Ransbottom Pottery Inc.
CROWN - Lighting fixtures - Hubbell Lighting, Inc. (Lighting Div.)
CROWN - Margarine - Ventura Foods
CROWN - Mats - Ludlow Composites Corp.
CROWN - Mattresses - Kingsdown, Inc.
CROWN - Meat products–beef - Schumacher Wholesale Meats Inc.
CROWN - Motor vehicle parts and accessories - Leer Inc.
CROWN - Music stands ☆ - Micro Musical Products Corp.
CROWN - Office supplies - Phillips Ribbon & Carbon Co.

CROWN - Paints ☆ - Devoe & Raynolds Co.
CROWN - Petroleum - Crown Central Petroleum Corp.
CROWN - Polishing cloths - Crown Manufacturing
CROWN - Projectors–photographic - Toshiba America Medical Systems Inc.
CROWN - Publisher's imprints - Crown Publishers Inc.
CROWN - Recording label - Cadet Records Inc.
CROWN - Rings–jewelry ☆ - Artcarved Inc.
CROWN - Rope - A & A Line & Wire Corp.
CROWN - Sardines–canned - King Oscar Inc.
CROWN - Scissors–hand-operated - Aaronco Grooming Products
CROWN - Scissors–hand-operated - Aaronco Pet Products, Inc.
CROWN - Skin care products - Crown Health Equipment Co.
CROWN - Stationery - Superior Marking Equipment Co.
CROWN - Steering mechanisms–motor vehicle - Superior Industries International, Inc.
CROWN - Tortillas ☆ - Bachman Co.
CROWN - Trailers–travel ☆ - Coachmen Industries, Inc.
CROWN - Vitamins and nutritional supplements - Crown Laboratories
CROWN - Vitamins and nutritional supplements - Nima Products Inc.
CROWN - Wines ☆ - Laird and Co.
CROWN II - Battery chargers - Raritan Engineering Co. Inc.
CROWN ACHIEVEMENT - Tobacco products - Lane Ltd.
CROWN AIR-TITE - Stoves ☆ - Malm Fireplaces Inc.
CROWN & ANCHOR - Games ☆ - Milton Bradley Co.
CROWN & CHASSIS - Lubricants - Texas Refinery Corp. (Lubricants Div.)
CROWN & SHIELD - Food products - Roberts Bros. Inc.
CROWN AQUATICS, INC. - Swimming pools - Crown Aquatics, Inc.
CROWN BULB - Lighting fixtures - Swivelier Co. Inc.
CROWN CLASSIC - Cigars - H.T.L., Inc.
CROWN COAT - Finishing agents - O'Brien Corp.
CROWN COLLECTION - Briefcases - Crown Handbags Ltd.
CROWN COLLECTION - Cutlery ☆ - Regent Sheffield, Ltd.
CROWN COLLECTION - Floor coverings - Beaulieu of America, Inc.
CROWN COLLECTION - Glassware–household - Owens-Illinois Inc. (Libbey Div.)
CROWN COLLECTION - Watches - Rolex Watch USA, Inc.
CROWN COLONY - Seafood products–fresh or frozen ☆ - Impex Shrimp & Fish Co.
CROWN COLONY - Spices and extracts - Safeway Stores Inc.
CROWN COLONY 2 PLY - Yarn - Henry's Attic
CROWN COLONY 3 PLY - Yarn - Henry's Attic
CROWN COLONY 4 PLY - Yarn - Henry's Attic
CROWN COMFORT - Mattresses ☆ - Kingsdown, Inc.
CROWN COMMERICAL SYSTEMS - Floor coverings - Royalty Carpet Mills, Inc.
CROWN CORNING - Glassware - Corning Inc.
CROWN-CRAFTED - Wigs - Crowning Creations Importers
CROWN CRAFTS - Bedding–linen - Crown Crafts, Inc.
CROWN CUT - Jewelry–precious - J & H Flyer, Inc.
CROWN CZAR - Liquors - Frank-Lin Distillers Products
CROWN DANCER - Floor coverings–carpet and rugs - Pacific Crest Carpets
CROWN DELUXE - Battery chargers - Raritan Engineering Co. Inc.
CROWN DELUXE - Pies–frozen - Chef Pierre Inc.
CROWN DESIGN - Cooking utensils–aluminum - West Bend Co.
CROWN DESIGN - Watches - Rolex Watch USA, Inc.
CROWN DESIGNE - Furniture ☆ - Harden Furniture Co. Inc.
CROWN DEVON - Dinnerware–glass - Ellis Barker Silver Co.
CROWN DORSET - Dishes–china - Heirloom Editions Ltd.
CROWN DUKE - Pipes–tobacco ☆ - Dr. Grabow Pre-Smoked Pipes Inc.
CROWN DUTCHESS - Rings–jewelry - Artcarved Inc.
CROWN EBONY - Dishes–china - Waterford Wedgewood USA, Inc.
CROWN EDITION - Backpacks ☆ - Zepter Sports International
CROWN ELITE - Pillows - American Fiber Industries Corp.
CROWN EMERALD - Dishes–china - Waterford Wedgewood USA, Inc.
CROWN EMPIRE - Dinnerware–glass ☆ - Tienshan, Inc.
CROWN EMPIRIA - Cheese - Imperia Foods Inc.
CROWN ESTATE - Floor coverings–carpet and rugs ☆ - Zenith Carpets
CROWN-ETTE - Apparel–women's - Crown Foundations Inc.
CROWN FIBERS - Yarn - Fibres South Inc.
CROWN-FLEXXX - Fabrics–canvas - Crown Textile Co.
CROWN GEM - Tobacco–chewing or smoking - Amar Blends Co.
CROWN GOLD - Dishes–china - Waterford Wedgewood USA, Inc.
CROWN HEAD - Toilets–porcelain - Raritan Engineering Co. Inc.
CROWN HEAD II - Toilets–porcelain - Raritan Engineering Co. Inc.
CROWN HILL STONE - Veneer - Crown Hill Stone Inc.

CROWN IMPERIAL - Mattresses - Kingsdown, Inc.
CROWN JEWEL - Cheese - Crystal Food Import Corp.
CROWN JEWEL - Floor coverings–carpet and rugs - Barrett Carpet Mills Inc.
CROWN JEWEL - Floor coverings–carpet and rugs - Columbus Mills, Inc.
CROWN JEWEL - Floor coverings–carpet and rugs - Galaxy Carpet Mills Inc.
CROWN JEWEL - Floor coverings–carpet and rugs ☆ - Karastan-Bigelow Inc.
CROWN JEWEL - Popcorn - Black Shield Inc.
CROWN JEWEL - Wallpaper ☆ - S.R. Wood Inc.
CROWN JEWELS - Christmas tree ornaments - Cracker Box Inc.
CROWN JEWELS - Floor coverings - Mannington Resilient Floors
CROWN JEWELS - Floor coverings–carpet and rugs - Navan Carpets Inc.
CROWN JEWELS - Rings–jewelry - Artcarved Inc.
CROWN JEWELS - Trading cards and stamps - Wheels Racing, Inc.
CROWN JEWELS - Wallpaper - Morton Jonap Co. Inc.
CROWN JEWELS OF CRYSTAL - Glassware–household - Queen Lace Co.
CROWN KENSINGTON - Dishes–china - Heirloom Editions Ltd.
CROWN MADURO - Cigars ☆ - General Cigar Co., Inc.
CROWN MARK - Furniture - CM International, Inc.
CROWN MARK - Wood products - Stewart Co. Inc.
CROWN MING - Dinnerware–glass - Tienshan, Inc.
CROWN MINT, THE - Jewelry - I.W. Searcy & Co. Inc.
CROWN/NAVAL - Plumbing fixtures - Sloan Valve Co.
CROWN OF DOWN - Pillows - Pacific Coast Feather Co.
CROWN OF ENGLAND - Wallpaper - Sunwall of America
CROWN ONE - Silverware - Imperial Schrade Corp.
CROWN PIK - Fresh vegetables - ABC Farms, Inc.
CROWN PILOT - Crackers - Nabisco Foods Group
CROWN PLACE - Furniture ☆ - Bassett Furniture Industries, Inc.
CROWN PLAZA - Floor coverings–carpet and rugs - Gulistan Carpet Inc.
CROWN POINT - Brooms - Lighthouse Industries
CROWN POINT - Floor coverings–carpet and rugs - Galaxy Carpet Mills Inc.
CROWN POINT - Glassware–household ☆ - Anchor Hocking Glass, Inc.
CROWN POINT - Mushrooms - Crown Point Ltd.
CROWN POINT GRAPHICS - Greeting cards - Michael Bursaw
CROWN POINT PRESS - Recording label - Jazz Composer's Orchestra Association Inc.
CROWN POINTE - Coffee - Coffee Beanery Ltd.
CROWN POINTE - Vans and pickup trucks - Tiara Motor Coach Inc.
CROWN PORCELAIN - Dinnerware–glass - Stanley Roberts, Inc.
CROWN PRINCE - Christmas tree ornaments - Cracker Box Inc.
CROWN PRINCE - Dog food - Continental Grain Co.
CROWN PRINCE - Dog food ☆ - Central Nebraska Packing Inc.
CROWN PRINCE - Firearms, accessories, and parts ☆ - Marlin Firearms Co.
CROWN PRINCE - Flatware - Richard-Stephen Co.
CROWN PRINCE - Seafood products–fresh or frozen - Crown Prince Inc.
CROWN PRINCE - Towels - Crown Prince Inc.
CROWN PRINCE INTERNATIONAL - Puzzles - Crown Prince International
CROWN PRINCESS - Rings–jewelry - Artcarved Inc.
CROWN PRINTS - Floor coverings–carpet and rugs - Roxbury Carpet Co.
CROWN PRINTS GALLERY, THE - Publisher's imprints - Lambert, Inc.
CROWN PUFF - Inks ☆ - Crown Art Products
CROWN REGAL - Rings–jewelry - Artcarved Inc.
CROWN REGENCY - Brandy ☆ - Oak Ridge Vineyards
CROWN REGENCY - Rings–jewelry - Artcarved Inc.
CROWN ROYAL - Bird cages - Crown Products Co.
CROWN ROYAL - Boats–motor ☆ - Holiday Mansion
CROWN ROYAL - Dolls ☆ - Cardinal Inc.
CROWN ROYAL - Hair care products - Republic Drug Co. Inc.
CROWN ROYAL - Whiskey - House of Seagram
CROWN ROYALE - Mats - Ludlow Composites Corp.
CROWN ROYALE - Rings–jewelry - Artcarved Inc.
CROWN ROYALE LTD. - Cleaning preparations - Crowne Royale, Ltd.
CROWN RUBY - Dishes–china - Waterford Wedgewood USA, Inc.
CROWN RUSSE - Vodka - Sazerac Co. Inc.
CROWN ST. OLIVIAN - Health care products - Hair Doc Co.
CROWN SAPPHIRE - Dishes–china - Waterford Wedgewood USA, Inc.
CROWN SELECT - Food products - Dairy Queen Operators Cooperative
CROWN SPAS - Physical fitness centers - National Equipment Manufacturing Corp.
CROWN SPOT - Lighting fixtures - Swivelier Co. Inc.
CROWN STERLING - Beverages–alcohol - Peerless Importers Inc.
CROWN SUPREME - Bicycles - Western Auto Supply Co.
CROWN SURPRISE - Toys - Mattel, Inc.
CROWN SWEDISH - Cosmetics - Morris-Flamingo Inc.
CROWN TAVERN - Snack foods ☆ - Bachman Co.
CROWN, THE - Food products - Antique Mall & Crown

☆ = Now out of production

CROWN TIP - Index cards - Cel-U-Dex Corp.

CROWN TOUCH - Floor coverings–carpet and rugs - Gulistan Carpet Inc.

CROWN TRUFFLES - Chocolate candy - Chocolate Packaging & Manufacturing, Corp.

CROWN-TURF - Mats - Ludlow Composites Corp.

CROWN VII - Pens - Alexander Manufacturing Co.

CROWN VANTAGE - Paper - Crown Paper Co.

CROWN VELOUR - Fabrics–velvet - Kellwood Co.

CROWN VICTORIA - Motor vehicles–automobiles - Ford Motor Co.

CROWN WARE - Copper compounds ✩ - Regal Ware, Inc.

CROWNCOPY - Computer hardware - QMS, Inc.

CROWNDALE - Paper - Freund-Mayer & Co. Inc.

CROWNE - Boats - Outboard Marine Corp.

CROWNE - Floor coverings–carpet and rugs - Patrick Carpet Mills

CROWNE - Floor coverings–tile ✩ - Monarch Tile Inc.

CROWNE COLONY - Furniture ✩ - Hammary Furniture Co. Inc.

CROWNE POINT - Furniture ✩ - Hammary Furniture Co. Inc.

CROWNE ROYAL - Furniture ✩ - Hammary Furniture Co. Inc.

CROWNE SERIES - Tiles–ceramic ✩ - Monarch Tile Inc.

CROWNFORD - Glassware–household ✩ - Crownford Giftware Co. Inc.

CROWNING COMFORT - Pillows - American Fiber Industries Corp.

CROWNING GLORY - Christmas tree ornaments - Cracker Box Inc.

CROWNING GLORY - Flowers, plants, and seeds - John Henry Co.

CROWNING LABEL FOR ALL YOUR LAWN AND GARDEN NEEDS, THE - Chemical preparations - Conrad Fafard, Inc.

CROWNING TOUCH - Floor coverings–carpet and rugs - Barrett Carpet Mills Inc.

CROWNING TOUCH - Floor coverings–carpet and rugs ✩ - Masland Corp.

CROWNING TOUCH - Food products - Woeber Mustard Manufacturing Co.

CROWNING TOUCH - Moldings–plaster of paris - Surface Industries Inc.

CROWNING TOUCH - Wigs - Paula Young

CROWNING TOUCH, THE - Metal chimney shrouds - Chimney King, Ltd.

CROWNING TOUCH, THE - Flowers, plants, and seeds - Van der Have, Oregon Inc.

CROWNLEY - Apparel and accessories ✩ - Modern Jacket Co. Inc.

CROWNLITE - Lamps–desk ✩ - Luxo Corp.

CROWNMARK - Motor vehicle parts and accessories - Crownmark Corp.

CROWNMASTER - Moldings and trim - Mid-America Building Products Corp.

CROWNNET - Computer hardware - QMS, Inc.

CROWNPOINTE - Trailers–travel - Fleetwood Enterprises, Inc.

CROWN'S OF LONDON - Cigarettes - American Tobacco Co.

CROWNSITE - Erasers ✩ - Quartet Manufacturing Co.

CROWNSPORT BACKPACKS - Bags ✩ - Zepter Sports International

CROWNSPORT DUFFELS - Bags ✩ - Zepter Sports International

CROWNSPORT MINI-PACK PACKS - Bags ✩ - Zepter Sports International

CROWNSTAFF - Dishes–china - Mikasa Co.

CROWNTUFT - Robes - Kellwood Co.

CROWNWEAR - Apparel–men's - Crown Clothing Corp.

CROWNWEST - Giftware ✩ - Papel Freelance, Inc.

CROWNWOOD - Lamps - Crown Creative Industries Inc.

CROWNY - Cakes–mixes - Holland-American Importing Co. Inc.

CROWS NEST - Playground equipment ✩ - Wonderline

CROXLEY - Puzzles - Milton Bradley Co.

CROYDON - Apparel and accessories - Warnaco Inc.

CROYDON - Floor coverings–carpet and rugs - Glen Eden Wool Carpets

CROYDON - Jewelry - Jacoby-Bender Inc.

CROYDON - Lighting fixtures ✩ - Liteway

CROYDON - Watches - Helbros International

CROZZZWORDS - Computer software - Mind Play

CRP - Automotive parts and accessories - Cadillac Rubber & Plastics, Inc.

C.R.P. - Guns ✩ - Crosman Corp.

CRP - Hoses - Radiator Specialty Co.

CRS - Medical apparatus - National Patient Care Systems, Inc.

CRS - Recording label - CRS Inc.

CRS - Recording label - Jazz Composer's Orchestra Association Inc.

CRS - Skates–roller - Chicago Roller Skate Co.

CRS SCREEN HIGHLIGHTER - Computer software - Travel Technologies Group, L.P.

C.R.T. - Cleaning preparations - Rite-Off Inc.

CRT - Computer peripheral equipment - Conductive Rubber Technology, Inc.

CRT - Ribbons ✩ - Eaton Allen Ko-Rec-Type Corp.

CRU - Humidifiers - Dri-Steem Humidifier Co.

CRUCIAL - Vitamins and nutritional supplements - Clintec Nutrition Co.

CRUCIANELLI - Accordions - Pancordion Inc.

CRUCIBLE - Computer software - Crucible Materials Corp.

CRUCIBLE - Pipes–tobacco - Bradberry Briar Pipe Co.

CRUD BUSTER - Guns - G-96 Products Co. Inc.

CRUDEX - Fire extinguishers - Environmental Science International Inc.

CRUDOLEUM - Hair care products - Heritage Store Inc.

CRUEL DUEL - Toys–automobiles - Mattel, Inc.

CRUEL TIMOTHY - Musical instruments - David Mandel

CRUEL WORLD - Crocheted and knitted items ✩ - Gillman Knitwear Co.

CRUISAIR - Air conditioning equipment - Marine Development Corp.

CRUISAIRE - Ships–sailing vessels ✩ - Lion Yachts

CRUISE - Musical instruments - VMI Industries

CRUISE - Ophthalmic goods ✩ - Rozin Optical Export Corp.

CRUISE - Recording label - Art Records Manufacturing Co.

CRUISE - Scuba diving equipment - U.S. Divers Co., Inc.

CRUISE - Yarn - William Unger & Co. Inc.

CRUISE-ABOUT - Infant product ✩ - Welsh Co.

CRUISE AIR - Motor vehicles–motor homes ✩ - Georgie Boy Manufacturing, Inc.

CRUISE AIR MINI - Motor vehicles–motor homes ✩ - Georgie Boy Manufacturing, Inc.

CRUISE ARROW - Sporting goods - Solar Survivor Shop

CRUISE CARDS - Postcards - Graham D. Wilson

CRUISE FOR MEN - Toiletries - Fragrance Unlimited Network, Inc.

CRUISE MASTER - Motor vehicles–motor homes - Georgie Boy Manufacturing, Inc.

CRUISE-MATIC - Tractors–lawn - White Outdoor Products Inc.

CRUISE MISSILE - Toys–models ✩ - Estes Industries

CRUISE N CAST - Boats–pontoons - Kennedy Inc.

CRUISE 'N CUSHION - Pillows - Rally Oil Inc.

CRUISE/VIEW - Computer software - George Pior

CRUISEBASS - Guitars - Hamer Guitars

CRUISELAN - Computer peripheral equipment - Zenith Data Systems Corp.

CRUISEMASTER - Ships–sailing vessels ✩ - Lion Yachts

CRUISER - Boats–canoes - Sawyer Composite Products

CRUISER - Compasses–gyroscopic - Rule Industries, Inc.

CRUISER - Fishing tackle - Trophy Products Inc.

CRUISER - Furniture–upholstered ✩ - Mersman Furniture Co.

CRUISER - Insecticides - Ecogen Inc.

CRUISER - Musical instrument accessories - Dimarzio, Inc.

CRUISER - Toys - Arne Dixon Entertainment, Inc.

CRUISER - Toys - Tonka Corp.

CRUISER - Wheelchairs - Convaid Inc.

CRUISER 5 - Bicycles - Schwinn Cycling & Fitness Inc.

CRUISER BRUISER - Toys - Tonka Corp.

CRUISER CLASSIC - Bicycles - Trek Bicycle Corp.

CRUISER COASTER - Bicycles - Schwinn Cycling & Fitness Inc.

CRUISER DUALS - Boats ✩ - Raritan Engineering Co. Inc.

CRUISER LITES - Automotive parts and accessories - DFM Corp.

CRUISER MATE - Office supplies - Saunders Manufacturing Co. Inc.

CRUISER SUPREME - Bicycles - Schwinn Cycling & Fitness Inc.

CRUISER, THE - Batteries - Battery Associates Inc.

CRUISER, THE - Swimming pools - Doughboy Recreational Inc.

CRUISER, THE - Golfing equipment - Izzo Systems, Inc.

CRUISER'S - Pet products - Pohina Inc.

CRUISERS - Skates–roller ✩ - Nash Manufacturing Inc.

CRUISER'S CHOICE - Heat pumps - Cruiser's Choice

CRUISETTE - Boats - Clark Craft Boat Co.

CRUISETTE - Boats - Glen-L Marine Designs

CRUISIN' - Compact discs–prerecorded - Increase Inc.

CRUISIN' CAPS - Hats - Warner-Hinke Group Inc.

CRUISIN' CAR - Toys–automobiles - Mattel, Inc.

CRUISIN' CHOCOLATE - Milk ✩ - Gossner Foods, Inc.

CRUISIN DUDE - Bicycles - Roadmaster Corp.

CRUISIN THE COAST SANDI - Dolls ✩ - Totsy Manufacturing Co., Inc.

CRUIS'N USA - Video games - Nintendo of America Inc.

CRUMAR - Accordions - Castiglione Accordion

CRUMB CATCHER BIB - Health care products ✩ - Sammons Preston

CRUMBLIES - Cookies - Bahlsen Inc.

CRUMBS - Consulting services - Rich Products Corp.

CRUMMLES & CO - Enameled ware - Britannia Collection Inc.

CRUMMLES ENAMELS - Enameled ware - British American Imports

CRUMPETS - Apparel–children's - Tumble Togs, Inc.

CRUMPLES - Infant product - Crumples Products, Inc.

CRUMPLES - Toys–stuffed - Dakin Inc.

CRUMPY - Chocolate candy - Tidelands Sales Co. Inc.

CRUNCH - Apparel and accessories - Crunch World, Inc.

CRUNCH - Chocolate bars - Nestle USA

CRUNCH - Food products ✩ - Pierre Frozen Foods Inc.

CRUNCH-A-BUNCH - Snack foods - Mister Snacks Inc.
CRUNCH AMINOS - Vitamins and nutritional supplements - Freeda Vitamins Inc.
CRUNCH & BLOW - Candy ☆ - Bobs Candies Inc.
CRUNCH ARENA - Toys–automobiles - Mattel, Inc.
CRUNCH BERRIES - Cereal - Quaker Oats Co.
CRUNCH BOMB - Confections - Merritt Foods Co.
CRUNCH BOMB - Frozen food products - Wells' Dairy, Inc.
CRUNCH CANYON - Games - CBS Toys
CRUNCH CHIEF - Toys–automobiles - Mattel, Inc.
CRUNCH CREAMS - Cookies - Pogens Family Bakery
CRUNCH GEAR - Apparel - Crunch World, Inc.
CRUNCH-MASTER - Exercise equipment - Flex Care Industries
CRUNCH MUESLI - Cereal - Breadshop's Natural Foods
CRUNCH 'N MUNCH - Popcorn/peanut candy - American Home Food Products Inc.
CRUNCH 'N MUNCH REDUCED FAT - Snack foods - American Home Food Products Inc.
CRUNCH 'N YOGURT LIGHT - Cereal - General Mills, Inc.
CRUNCH-STER - Sporting goods - Novel Products, Inc.
CRUNCH TATORS - Potato chips - Frito-Lay, Inc.
CRUNCH TIME - Candy - Nestle USA
CRUNCH TIME - Snack foods - Herman Miller, Inc.
CRUNCH TWISTS - Crackers ☆ - Keebler Co.
CRUNCHBOARD - Exercising equipment - Excel, The Exercise Co.
CRUNCHBOARD - Exercising equipment - Fitness Quest Inc.
CRUNCHEE SNACKS - Food products - Bake-Line Products Inc.
CRUNCHER, THE - Computer software - Knowledge Adventure
CRUNCHEROOS - Cereal ☆ - Kellogg Co.
CRUNCHERS - Candy - Leaf, Inc.
CRUNCHI-O'S - Snack foods ☆ - Curtice-Burns Foods, Inc.
CRUNCHIE MUNCHIE - Cookies - Splurge
CRUNCHIE PUFFS - Pet products - L/M Animal Farms, Inc.
CRUNCHIES - Pretzels - Sunlight Foods, Inc.
CRUNCHIPS - Snack foods - Pepsico, Inc.
CRUNCHY CARROT SQUARE CUTS - Pickled carrots - International Marketing Services Inc.
CRUNCHY COOKIE CUPS - Candy - Homestead, Inc.
CRUNCHY CRUST - Breads - HSF Enterprises Inc.
CRUNCHY CUBS - Cookies - Ralston Purina Co.
CRUNCHY CUP - Candy - Maramor Candy Co.
CRUNCHY DELIGHT - Cereal - Weetabix Co., Inc.
CRUNCHY FISHCUTS - Seafood products–fresh or frozen - Royal Seafoods Inc.
CRUNCHY LUNCH - Candy ☆ - Topps Co., Inc.
CRUNCHY MUNCHY APPLE SNACKS - Food products - Weight Watchers International, Inc.
CRUNCHY OAT BRAN CEREAL - Food products - Breadshop's Natural Foods
CRUNCHY TRIO - Snack foods - Nabisco Foods Group
CRUNCHYDUNKER - Cookies - Award Baking International
CRUSADER - Audio equipment - Pro-Co. Sound Co. Inc.
CRUSADER - Bicycles - Murray, Inc.
CRUSADER - Boats–motor - Crestliner Boats Inc.
CRUSADER - Boats–motor ☆ - Cruisers
CRUSADER - Boats–motor ☆ - Harris-Kayot Inc.
CRUSADER - Centrifuges–industrial - F.E. Myers Co.
CRUSADER - Cooking utensils–aluminum - Dura-Ware of America Inc.
CRUSADER - Electronic equipment ☆ - Overhead Door Corp.
CRUSADER - Engines - Crusader Engines
CRUSADER - Fishing tackle ☆ - Outdoor Technologies Group
CRUSADER - Floor coverings–carpet and rugs ☆ - Interloom Ltd.
CRUSADER - Handles–wood - Hartwell Brothers Handle Co.
CRUSADER - Kilns ☆ - American Art Clay Co. Inc.
CRUSADER - Paper - CST Office Products, Inc.
CRUSADER - Projectors–photographic - Radmar Inc.
CRUSADER - Ships–sailing vessels ☆ - Lewmar Marine Inc.
CRUSADER - Sporting goods - Rawlings Sporting Goods Co., Inc.
CRUSADER - Tool handles - IXL Manufacturing Co., Inc.
CRUSADER - Trailers–travel ☆ - Coachmen Industries, Inc.
CRUSADER - Waterproof outerwear - Distributors Service Corp.
CRUSADER SWING-WING - Toys–models ☆ - Estes Industries
CRUSADERS - Cigar boxes–wood - Consolidated Cigar Corp.
CRUSADERS, THE - Electronic equipment - Crusader Productions, Inc.
CRUSE - Wine - Austin, Nichols & Co., Inc.
CRUSH - Beverages–carbonated - Cadbury Beverages Inc.
CRUSH - Beverages–carbonated - Dr. Pepper/Seven Up, Inc.

CRUSH - Recording label - Jazz Composer's Orchestra Association Inc.
C.R.U.S.H. - Stationery ☆ - Scentex Inc.
CRUSH & STORE - Can compactory - Pacific Fabrication, Inc.
CRUSH-CLINCH - Fasteners–snap - Penn Engineering and Manufacturing Corp.
CRUSH MUSIC - Labels–paper - K-Tel International, Inc.
CRUSH-PAK - Paperboard cartons - Champion International Corp.
CRUSH-PROOF - Combs - Accessories International
CRUSH ZONE - Golfing equipment - Ken Linkfield
CRUSHABLES - Soap - Go-Jo Industries Inc.
CRUSHED LEAF - Paper - Howard Paper Mills Inc.
CRUSHED LEAF - Paper–bond - Fox River Paper Co.
CRUSHED PAPER - Wallpaper - Capital Carousel Inc.
CRUSHED PEARL - Cosmetics - Lancome
CRUSHED PEARL - Wallpaper - Maya Romanoff Corp.
CRUSHED ROSE - Lipsticks - Lancome
CRUSHED WALLPAPERS - Wallpaper - Wallpaper Imports Inc.
CRUSHER - Golf clubs - Austad Co.
CRUSHER - Toys–automobiles - Processed Plastic Co.
CRUSHERS - Toys–blocks - Lewis Galoob Toys, Inc.
CRUSHTANK - Containers–plastic - Adverse Adventure, Inc.
CRUSIN' CLASSICS - Toys - Imperial Toy Corp.
CRUSO - Shot–lead ☆ - C & C Office Supply Co. Inc.
CRUST BUSTER - Lime products - Conklin Co., Inc.
CRUSTAL KINGDOM - Giftware - Iris Arc Crystal Inc.
CRUSTY HOME BAKE - Bakery products - David Neville
CRUSTY'S - Food products - Dino's USA Inc.
CRUTCH SNEAKER - Crutches ☆ - Ambulatory Products International
CRUTCH TOTE - Medical apparatus - Crutch Tote, Inc.
CRUTCHFIELD - Flour–blended - Wilkins-Rogers Inc.
CRUTCHWEAR - Medical apparatus - Jak Design
CRUZ - Tortillas - La Canasta of Minnesota, Inc.
CRUZ - Tortillas - Sparta Foods, Inc.
CRUZ GARCIA SPANISH - Wines - Shaw-Ross International Importers
CRUZ VERDE - Health care products - Sara Lee Corp.
CRUZAN - Perfumes - Paradise Fragrance Ltd.
CRUZAN FOR MEN - Perfumes - Paradise Fragrance Ltd.
CRUZAN PUNCH - Soft drink - Bottlers International Ltd.
CRUZAN VIRGIN ISLANDS - Rum - Blair Importers Ltd.
CRX - Motor vehicles–automobiles - American Honda Motor Co. Inc. (Acura Div.)
CRX-115 - Tires - Oliver Rubber Co.
CRY BABY - Chewing gum - Philadelphia Chewing Gum Corp.
CRY BABY - Dolls - Horsman
CRY BABY - Fruits and vegetables - Tony Guerriero Fruit Co.
CRY BABY - Fruits and vegetables - Westin Inc.
CRY BABY MAGIC BOTTLE - Toys - South Bend Toy Manufacturing Co.
CRYIN' OVER CAYENNE - Spices and extracts - To Market to Market
CRYING CRISSIE - Toys–stuffed ☆ - Fun World Inc.
CRYING GAME - Apparel and accessories - Miramax Films
CRYING TIKI - Candles - Aloha Candle Manufacturing Co. Inc.
CRYLICOTE - Paints - Coronado Paint Co.
CRYLICOVER - Paints - Coronado Paint Co.
CRYMAX - Insecticides - Ecogen Inc.
CRYO CAPS - Health care products - Cramer Products Inc.
CRYO-CLEANER - Machinery - Drumbeaters of America Inc.
CRYO PUMP - Toys - Mattel, Inc.
CRYO-SECURE - Laboratory apparatus - USA/Scientific Plastics, Inc.
CRYO-SPICE - Food products - Tone Brothers, Inc.
CRYO-TEK - Antifreeze - Hercules Chemical Co. Inc.
CRYO-TEK AG - Antifreeze - Hercules Chemical Co. Inc.
CRYOCIDE - Disinfectants - Pettibone Laboratories Inc.
CRYOCUP - Health care products - Anodyne Inc.
CRYOGUN - Electronic equipment - Brymill Corp.
CRYOLASE - Spices and extracts ☆ - Sanofi Bio-Industries Inc.
CRYOLOGIC - Medical apparatus - Orthopedic Technology, Inc.
CRYONIC - Recording label - Jazz Composer's Orchestra Association Inc.
CRYOSCAN - Measuring instruments - ITT Fluid Technology Corp.
CRYOTECH - Seafood - Bayport Restaurant Group Inc.
CRYOTHERM - Window coverings - Levolor Inc.
CRYPT KICKER - Recording label - Ready to Rock Records
CRYPT KILLER - Computer storage devices–optical - Konami (America) Inc.
CRYPT OF MEDEA - Computer software ☆ - Sir-Tech Software, Inc.
CRYPTA PLUS - Computer peripheral equipment - Telequip Corp.
CRYPTEK - Facsimile equipment - General Kinetics Inc.
CRYPTKEEPER - Games - Tales from the Crypt Holdings

☆ = Now out of production

CRYPTKEEPER TALES FROM THE CRYPT - Candy - Bee International
CRYPTLINER - Burial vaults—concrete - Flexseal Packaging Corp.
CRYPTO BLOCK - Filters—water - Sterling Air & Water, Inc.
CRYPTO CUBE - Computer software - Compton's NewMedia
CRYPTO-FLEX - Construction equipment - AWMCO Inc.
CRYPTO-LA TEST - Pharmaceutical preparations - Wampole Laboratories Div.
CRYPTO-LOGIC - Toys—electronic ✫ - Philips Consumer Electronics Co.
CRYPTOCELL - Water purification systems - WTC Industries Inc.
CRYPTOGAM - Pharmaceutical preparations - Univax Biologics Inc.
CRYPTON - Fabrics - Hi-Tex, Inc.
CRYST-L-CRAZE - Paints - Fry Plastics International Inc. (O)
CRYST-O-LIKE - Paints - United States Refining Co.
CRYST-O-MINT - Candy - Planters LifeSavers Co.
CRYSTA-LUX - Lighting equipment - Penn-Plax, Inc.
CRYSTAAL - Glassware—household ✫ - Dansk International Designs, Ltd.
CRYSTACLEAR - Lacquers - Dunn Edwards Corp.
CRYSTACRYLIC - Fans—electric - Davoil, Inc.
CRYSTADOS - Food products - Crystal Farms Inc.
CRYSTADOS - Snack foods - Sparta Foods, Inc.
CRYSTAL - Audio equipment - J. R. Speaker Co.
CRYSTAL - Beverages—carbonated ✫ - Snapple Beverage Corp.
CRYSTAL - Beverages—malt ✫ - Labatt Importers Inc.
CRYSTAL - Cabinets - Crystal Cabinet Works Inc.
CRYSTAL - Cheese - Crystal Food Import Corp.
CRYSTAL - Cigars ✫ - General Cigar Co., Inc.
CRYSTAL - Cleaning preparations - Fabulon Products
CRYSTAL - Dog food - Crystal Springs Inc.
CRYSTAL - Dolls ✫ - Effanbee Doll Corp.
CRYSTAL - Fabrics—cheesecloth - Bond Chemical Products Co.
CRYSTAL - Floor coverings - American Floor Products Co. Inc.
CRYSTAL - Floor coverings - Congoleum Corp.
CRYSTAL - Floor coverings—carpet and rugs ✫ - Columbus Mills, Inc.
CRYSTAL - Floor coverings—carpet and rugs ✫ - Playfield International Inc.
CRYSTAL - Flowers, plants, and seeds - American Crystal Sugar Co.
CRYSTAL - Food products - Baumer Foods, Inc.
CRYSTAL - Food products - Kern Industries
CRYSTAL - Furniture ✫ - Bassett Furniture Industries, Inc.
CRYSTAL - Giftware - Doranne
CRYSTAL - Housewares - Amoco Fabrics and Fibers Co.
CRYSTAL - Paper—gift wrap - Crystal Tissue Co. Inc.
CRYSTAL - Petroleum - Crystal Oil Co.
CRYSTAL - Plates—plastic - Sweetheart Plastics Inc.
CRYSTAL - Recording label - Crystal Records Inc.
CRYSTAL - Ribbons—inked - Eaton Allen Ko-Rec-Type Corp.
CRYSTAL - Seafood products—fresh or frozen - Pocasset Seafoods Inc.
CRYSTAL - Sugar - United Sugars Corp.
CRYSTAL - Tiles—ceramic - Florida Tile Industries, Inc.
CRYSTAL - Upholstery leather - American Leather Manufacturing Co.
CRYSTAL - Varnishes - Pratt & Lambert, Inc. (Specialty Products Div.)
CRYSTAL - Water—bottled or canned - Crystal Bottled Waters
CRYSTAL - Water—bottled or canned ✫ - Ozark Water Co.
CRYSTAL - Wigs - Paula Young
CRYSTAL 3D DESIGNER - Computer software - CrystalGraphics Inc.
CRYSTAL 3D IMPACT! PRO - Computer software - CrystalGraphics Inc.
CRYSTAL 73 - Glass products - AFG Industries Inc. (Glass Group Div.)
CRYSTAL ACCENTS - Novelty items - Iris Arc Crystal Inc.
CRYSTAL AIR - Candles - Arizona Natural Resources
CRYSTAL ART - Glass products - Mechanical Mirror Works Inc.
CRYSTAL AVENUE - Floor coverings—carpet and rugs - Burlington House Carpets
CRYSTAL BALL - Magnifiers - 4sight Unltd.
CRYSTAL BALL - Recording label - Relic Record Productions Inc.
CRYSTAL BALLS - Candy - Zeebs Enterprises, Inc.
CRYSTAL BAR - Glassware—household ✫ - Oneida Ltd.
CRYSTAL BARRIER - Games - Mayfair Games, Inc.
CRYSTAL BAY - Beverages - Beverage Canners International Corp.
CRYSTAL BAY - Fireplace screens - Jack-Post Corp.
CRYSTAL BAY - Floor coverings—carpet and rugs - Catalina Carpet Mills Inc.
CRYSTAL BAY - Floor coverings—carpet and rugs - Criterion Mills Inc.
CRYSTAL BAY - Floor coverings—carpet and rugs ✫ - Mohawk Carpet Corp.
CRYSTAL BAY - Food products - Matlaw's Food Products Inc.
CRYSTAL BAY - Oysters—canned or cured - L.P. Maggioni & Co.
CRYSTAL BAY - Vegetables—canned ✫ - McCall Farms Inc.
CRYSTAL BEACH - Floor coverings—carpet and rugs - Karastan-Bigelow Inc.
CRYSTAL BLUE - Chemical preparations - Brothers Three Inc.
CRYSTAL BLUE - Lamp bulbs - American Auto Accessories, Inc.

CRYSTAL BOATS - Boats and boating accessories - Sherry Troiani
CRYSTAL BOUTIQUE - Glassware—household - Oneida Ltd.
CRYSTAL BREATH - Health care products - Crystal Breath, Inc.
CRYSTAL BREEZE - Water purification systems - Dr. Mainz U.S.A., Inc.
CRYSTAL BRIGHT - Bathroom accessories ✫ - Nutone Inc.
CRYSTAL BRIGHT - Dishwashing compounds - Amway Corp.
CRYSTAL BRITE - Electronic equipment - Amcam International, Inc.
CRYSTAL BRITE - Floor waxes - Arcal Chemicals Inc.
CRYSTAL BUFFET - Housewares - L.E. Smith Glass Co.
CRYSTAL C - Veterinary nutritional supplements - Dr. Goodpet
CRYSTAL CARE - Cleaning preparations - Athea Laboratories, Inc.
CRYSTAL CARE - Cleaning preparations - W.J. Hagerty & Sons Ltd. Inc.
CRYSTAL CASCADE - Washboards - Columbus Washboard Co.
CRYSTAL CASTLE - Toys - Mattel, Inc.
CRYSTAL CASUALS - Giftware - Princess House, Inc.
CRYSTAL CHARMERS - Figurines ✫ - Iris Arc Crystal Inc.
CRYSTAL CHRISTMAS - Christmas tree ornaments - Cracker Box Inc.
CRYSTAL CLAD - Glass products - Lasco Products Group
CRYSTAL CLASSIC - Barbecue sauce - Baumer Foods, Inc.
CRYSTAL CLEAN III - Pet products - Longlife Pet Products
CRYSTAL CLEAR - Adhesives and sealants - Epoxy Coatings Co.
CRYSTAL CLEAR - Adhesives and sealants ✫ - Roman Adhesives, Inc.
CRYSTAL CLEAR - Batteries - Star Struck Inc.
CRYSTAL CLEAR - Cleaning preparations - Photographic Solutions, Inc.
CRYSTAL CLEAR - Cups—plastic - WNA Comet
CRYSTAL CLEAR - Drapery hardware ✫ - Spring Window Fashions Division, Inc.
CRYSTAL CLEAR - Food containers - Farmhouse Foods
CRYSTAL CLEAR - Fruits—dried - California Hi-Lites, Inc.
CRYSTAL CLEAR - Glass products - Loctite Corp.
CRYSTAL CLEAR - Glassware—household - Crystal Clear Industries, Inc.
CRYSTAL CLEAR - Hair care products - Alberto-Culver Co.
CRYSTAL CLEAR - Hair care products - Rajoc International
CRYSTAL CLEAR - Nail care products - Cosmair Inc.
CRYSTAL CLEAR - Pet products - Novalek, Inc.
CRYSTAL CLEAR - Seasonings - Diamond Crystal Specialty Foods Inc.
CRYSTAL CLEAR - Tape—adhesive - Moore Push-Pin Co.
CRYSTAL CLEAR - Telephones—cellular - Thomson Consumer Electronics, Inc.
CRYSTAL CLEAR - Tubes—porcelain - Atlantic Ultraviolet Corp.
CRYSTAL-CLEAR - Water treating compounds - Aquarium Products Inc.
CRYSTAL CLEAVER - Novelty items - Hasbro, Inc.
CRYSTAL CLOUD - Christmas tree ornaments - Cracker Box Inc.
CRYSTAL COAST GOURMET - Seafood - Cryotech Industries Inc.
CRYSTAL COAT - Dinnerware—plastic - Mobil Oil Corp.
CRYSTAL COAT - Glass products - Lasco Products Group
CRYSTAL COLLECTABLES BY KUSAK - Glass products - Kusak Cut Glass Works
CRYSTAL COLLECTIONS - Apparel and accessories - Crystal Brands Inc.
CRYSTAL COMET - Fireworks - American Promotional Events, Inc.
CRYSTAL COMPUTER CORPORATION - Circuit boards—printed - Crystal Computer Corp.
CRYSTAL CORNER - Vases—glass ✫ - Schmid Inc.
CRYSTAL-COTE - Paints - Floquil-Polly S Color Corp.
CRYSTAL COVE - Floor coverings—carpet and rugs ✫ - Downs Carpet Co. Inc.
CRYSTAL COVE - Water—bottled or canned - Aqua-Pac, Inc.
CRYSTAL COVE SEAFOOD - Seafood products—fresh or frozen - Crystal Cove Seafood Corp.
CRYSTAL CRAFT - Paper—tissue - Crystal Tissue Co. Inc.
CRYSTAL-CREAM - Cosmetics - Circle of Beauty, Inc.
CRYSTAL CREATIONS - Figurines - Crystal World, Inc.
CRYSTAL CREATIONS - Figurines - Dalzell-Viking
CRYSTAL CREEK - Wines - Chateau Benoit Winery
CRYSTAL CREEK - Wines ✫ - San Martin Winery Inc.
CRYSTAL-CREST - Tiles—ceiling - Artcrest Products Co. Inc.
CRYSTAL CURRENTS - Water purification systems - Water-Right, Inc.
CRYSTAL DE LITES - Figurines - Manon
CRYSTAL DEEP SEAL - Waterproofing chemical compsition - Crystal Deep Seal Corp.
CRYSTAL DESIGN - Glass products - Corning Inc.
CRYSTAL DESKTOP ANIMATOR - Computer software - CrystalGraphics Inc.
CRYSTAL DEW - Pet shampoo - B-Elegant Products
CRYSTAL DIALOGUE - Audio equipment ✫ - Mitsubishi Electronics America Inc.
CRYSTAL DIAMONDS - Doors—glass - Therma-Tru Corp.

CRYSTAL-DINO - Flowers–artificial - New Tomorrow Inc.

CRYSTAL DRANO - Cleaning preparations–household - S.C. Johnson & Son, Inc.

CRYSTAL DROP - Water–bottled or canned - Crystal Drop Water

CRYSTAL DYNAMICS - Computer software - Crystal Dynamics, Inc.

CRYSTAL EAR - Hearing aids - Crystal Care International, Inc.

CRYSTAL ELEGANCE - Hobby kits - Greene Plastics Corp.

CRYSTAL-EX - Chemical preparations - Dryit Carpet Cleaning Inc.

CRYSTAL EYE - Pet products - Four Paws Products Ltd.

CRYSTAL EZE - Paints - Sophir Morris Paint

CRYSTAL FACETS SKIN BRIGHTENING POWDER - Cosmetics - Signature Club a Ltd.

CRYSTAL FALLS - Floor coverings–carpet and rugs - Evans-Black Carpet Mills

CRYSTAL FALLS - Publisher's imprints - Scholastic Inc.

CRYSTAL FALLS - Seafood products–fresh or frozen - Crystal Falls Seafoods, Inc.

CRYSTAL FALLS - Toys - Mattel, Inc.

CRYSTAL FALLS - Water–bottled or canned - P & P Marketing Inc.

CRYSTAL FANTASY - Floor coverings–carpet and rugs ✰ - Galaxy Carpet Mills Inc.

CRYSTAL FANTASY - Glassware–household ✰ - Lenox Crystal, Inc.

CRYSTAL FARMS - Food products - Crystal Farms Inc.

CRYSTAL-FIBER - Plywood - Sider-Oxydro

CRYSTAL FIN - Finishing agents - Daly's Inc.

CRYSTAL FINISH - Paints - Happy Painter Products

CRYSTAL FIRE-KING - Cooking utensils–earthenware - Anchor Hocking Glass, Inc.

CRYSTAL FLAME - Tiles–ceramic - American Olean Tile Co.

CRYSTAL-FLEX - Cups–plastic - WNA Comet

CRYSTAL-FLO - Filters–oil ✰ - Petcetera Inc.

CRYSTAL FLUID - Water purification systems - Crystal Fluid Filter Co.

CRYSTAL FOODS - Juices - Crystal Foods Inc.

CRYSTAL-FRESH - Sweeteners–artificial - Sweetener Products Co.

CRYSTAL FRESH LAVORIS - Mouth wash - Dep Corp.

CRYSTAL FROST - Beverages–carbonated - Bunge Foods Corp.

CRYSTAL FRUIT - Beverages - Metro Beverage Co. Inc.

CRYSTAL GARDEN - Glassware–household - Lancaster Colony Corp.

CRYSTAL GEMS - Apparel and accessories - Natural Products Corp.

CRYSTAL GEYSER - Water–mineral - Crystal Geyser Water Co.

CRYSTAL GLAZE - Floor coverings–carpet and rugs - Roxbury Carpet Co.

CRYSTAL GLAZE - Floor coverings–tile - Kentile Floors Inc.

CRYSTAL GLAZE - Manicure preparations - Faberge Co.

CRYSTAL GLAZE - Tiles–ceramic - Porcelanite, Inc.

CRYSTAL GLEN - Water–bottled or canned - Chippewa Springs, Ltd.

CRYSTAL GLOW - Meat products–poultry - Snowball Foods, Inc.

CRYSTAL GROOVED SERIES - Doors–metal - ODL, Inc.

CRYSTAL HAPPENINGS - Servingware ✰ - Indiana Glass Co.

CRYSTAL HILL - Cabinets ✰ - Aristokraft, Inc.

CRYSTAL HOUSE - Vases–glass ✰ - Schmid Inc.

CRYSTAL ICE - Beverages - Slender Delight, Inc.

CRYSTAL ICE - Christmas tree ornaments - Cracker Box Inc.

CRYSTAL ICE - Pressed glassware ✰ - Indiana Glass Co.

CRYSTAL-ICE - Sugar–granulated, refined, or powdered - Sweetener Products Co.

CRYSTAL ICING - Sugar–granulated, refined, or powdered - Edna H. Pagel Inc.

CRYSTAL II - Water purification systems - Camomile Enterprises, Inc.

CRYSTAL IMAGE - Doors - Addison Corp.

CRYSTAL IMAGE - Polishes - Auto Industrial Marine Chemicals, Inc.

CRYSTAL IMAGES - Mirrors - Conair Corp.

CRYSTAL ISLE - Fish–fresh or frozen - Tai Foong USA Inc.

CRYSTAL KING - Cigars ✰ - General Cigar Co., Inc.

CRYSTAL KINGDOM - Figurines - Iris Arc Crystal Inc.

CRYSTAL KISS - Figurines - Jonal Crystal Ltd.

CRYSTAL KLIPS - Fasteners - Baumgarten's

CRYSTAL-KOTC-LACQUER - Lacquers - Wood Kote Products, Inc.

CRYSTAL LAGER BEER - Beverages–malt - Stanley Stawski Distributing Co.

CRYSTAL LAKE - Floor coverings–carpet and rugs ✰ - World Carpets, Inc.

CRYSTAL LAKE - Fruits and vegetables - Per-Clin Orchards Inc.

CRYSTAL LAKE - Meat products–poultry - Crystal Lake Foods Inc.

CRYSTAL LAKE - Wines - Americana Vineyards Estate Winery

CRYSTAL LEAF - Tea - R.K. Gamage

CRYSTAL LEGENDS - Giftware - Godinger Silver Art Ltd.

CRYSTAL LIGHT - Beverages–carbonated - Dr. Pepper/Seven Up, Inc.

CRYSTAL LIGHTING MASTERPIECES - Chandeliers - Crystal Clear Importing Co. Inc.

CRYSTAL LIGHTS - Floor coverings–carpet and rugs - Patcraft Mills Inc.

CRYSTAL LIGHTS - Floor coverings–carpet and rugs ✰ - Bellbridge Carpets

CRYSTAL LIGHTS - Wallpaper - Cherry Hill Studio

CRYSTAL LIGHTS 2 - Wallpaper ✰ - Cherry Hill Studio

CRYSTAL-MAGIC - Cleaning preparations - R & R Manufacturing

CRYSTAL MAGIC - Deicing fluid - Paris & Sons, Inc.

CRYSTAL MAGIC - Flavored water - Citrico

CRYSTAL MAGIC - Jewelry - Sun Sales

CRYSTAL MANOR - Floor coverings - Congoleum Corp.

CRYSTAL MIRAGE - Bathroom fixtures - American Shower Door Co.

CRYSTAL MIST - Wallpaper ✰ - Imperial Wallcoverings, Inc.

CRYSTAL MOONBEAM - Toys - Mattel, Inc.

CRYSTAL MOUNT - Adhesives and sealants - ANCO Collector Supplies, Inc.

CRYSTAL MOUNT - Adhesives and sealants ✰ - H.E. Harris & Co.

CRYSTAL MULBERRY - Cosmetics ✰ - Honey & Spice Toiletries

CRYSTAL 'N BLUE - Display racks - Paul Flum Ideas, Inc.

CRYSTAL NAIL BUILDER - Nail care products - Beauty Selectives, Inc.

CRYSTAL NET - Hair care products ✰ - Gem Inc.

CRYSTAL NOVA - Floor coverings - Congoleum Corp.

CRYSTAL-PAK - Meat products–poultry ✰ - Cagle's Inc.

CRYSTAL PALACE - Beverages–alcohol - Hiram Walker & Sons, Inc.

CRYSTAL PALACE - Christmas tree ornaments - Cracker Box Inc.

CRYSTAL PALACE - Dolls ✰ - Effanbee Doll Corp.

CRYSTAL PALACE - Floor coverings - Tarkett, Inc.

CRYSTAL PALACE - Liquors - Canandaigua Wine Co. Inc.

CRYSTAL PEAK - Bottled drinking water - Curt Grob Jr.

CRYSTAL PEAK - Food products - Gilbert Orchards Inc.

CRYSTAL PEPSI - Beverages–carbonated - Pepsi-Cola Co.

CRYSTAL PERSUASION - Hair accessories, jewelry - Bead Shoppe

CRYSTAL PLEAT - Window shades - Spring Window Fashions Division, Inc.

CRYSTAL PLUS - Detergents - USA Detergents Inc.

CRYSTAL POINT - Floor coverings–carpet and rugs - Mohawk Carpet Corp.

CRYSTAL POINT - Water–bottled or canned - Spring Valley Water Co. of Abilene

CRYSTAL POLYMER - Cleaning preparations - Turtle Wax, Inc.

CRYSTAL POWER - Games - Mattel, Inc.

CRYSTAL POWER - Hair care products - Raymac Corp. Hair & Skin Technology

CRYSTAL POWER - Nail care products - Salon Sciences Inc.

CRYSTAL PRISM - Bedding–linen - Dan River Inc.

CRYSTAL PURE - Candy - Crystal Pure Candy Co.

CRYSTAL PURE - Nail care products - Pavion Ltd.

CRYSTAL RADIANCE - Skin care products - Aroma Vera Inc.

CRYSTAL RAINMAKER - Drums–musical instruments - LP Music Group

CRYSTAL RANGE - Wines - Madrona Vineyards

CRYSTAL RAYS - Yarn - Rainbow Gallery, Inc.

CRYSTAL REFLECTIONS - Craft supplies - Mangelsen's

CRYSTAL REFLECTIONS - Plastics - Mangelsen's (VDI)

CRYSTAL RESERVE - Wines ✰ - Bully Hill Vineyards, Inc.

CRYSTAL RHAPSODY - Dolls - Mattel, Inc.

CRYSTAL RIDGE - Food products ✰ - Gilbert Orchards Inc.

CRYSTAL RIDGE - Water–bottled or canned - Moran Foods, Inc.

CRYSTAL RIVER - Fishing rods - Maurice Sporting Goods, Inc.

CRYSTAL RIVER - Fishing rods - South Bend Sporting Goods Inc.

CRYSTAL ROCK - Water–bottled or canned - Crystal Rock Water Co.

CRYSTAL SANDS - Floor coverings–carpet and rugs - Queen Carpet Corp.

CRYSTAL SAVER - Tools - Diamond Machining Technology Inc.

CRYSTAL SCENTIMENTS - Housewares - MCI Products Group, Inc.

CRYSTAL SEA - Aquarium accessories - Marine Enterprises International, Inc.

CRYSTAL SEA - Recording label ✰ - Nazarene Publishing House

CRYSTAL SELECT - Vinegar - Burns Philp Food Inc.

CRYSTAL SENTIMINTS - Housewares - AZ Product Co.

CRYSTAL SHADOWS - Floor coverings–carpet and rugs ✰ - Karastan-Bigelow Inc.

CRYSTAL-SHEEN - Craft supplies - Environmental Technology, Inc.

CRYSTAL SIGNATURES - Figurines - Pynn Corp.

CRYSTAL SIMPLE GREEN - Cleaning preparations - Sunshine Makers, Inc.

CRYSTAL SNOWFLAKES - Christmas tree ornaments - Cracker Box Inc.

CRYSTAL SPLENDOR - Dolls - Mattel, Inc.

CRYSTAL SPRING - Food products - Weaver Brothers Inc.

CRYSTAL SPRING - Hair care products - Thompson and Formby

CRYSTAL SPRINGS - Apparel–athletic - Midstates Sportswear

CRYSTAL SPRINGS - Floor coverings–carpet and rugs - Barrett Carpet Mills Inc.

✰ = Now out of production

CRYSTAL SPRINGS - Furniture ☆ - Bassett Furniture Industries, Inc.
CRYSTAL SPRINGS - Pharmaceutical preparations - Summa Pharmaceutical Laboratories Inc.
CRYSTAL SPRINGS - Water–bottled or canned - Suntory Water Group. Inc.
CRYSTAL SPRINGS - Water–distilled - Howe Water Corp.
CRYSTAL SPRINGS - Wines - Pedrizzetti Winery
CRYSTAL STIRSTIC - Bar fixtures–plastic - Spir-it Inc.
CRYSTAL STRATUS DANBY - Marble products - Carl Schilling Stoneworks
CRYSTAL SUGAR - Sugar–granulated, refined, or powdered - United Sugars Corp.
CRYSTAL SUN DANCER - Toys - Mattel, Inc.
CRYSTAL SUNFLOWER - Apparel and accessories - Crystal Brands Inc.
CRYSTAL SUPREME - Seafood products–fresh or frozen - Pocasset Seafoods Inc.
CRYSTAL SWAN - Pet products ☆ - For the Birds
CRYSTAL SWEET - Spices and extracts - Crystal Sweet
CRYSTAL SWIFT WIND - Toys - Mattel, Inc.
CRYSTAL SYMPHONY - Giftware - S.S. Sarna Inc.
CRYSTAL-THANE - Craft supplies ☆ - Environmental Technology, Inc.
CRYSTAL TONES - Tiles–ceramic - United States Ceramic Tile Co.
CRYSTAL TREASURES - Glassware–household - Princess House, Inc.
CRYSTAL TULIP COLLECTION, THE - Giftware - Gorham Inc.
CRYSTAL TWIST - Hobby kits - Greene Plastics Corp.
CRYSTAL VALLEY - Floor coverings–carpet and rugs - World Carpets, Inc.
CRYSTAL VALLEY - Food products - Gilbert Orchards Inc.
CRYSTAL VALLEY - Shutters–wood - ABT Co., Inc.
CRYSTAL VALLEY - Wine - Cosentino Wine Co.
CRYSTAL VALLEY FOODS - Fruits and vegetables - Southern Distributing Enterprises, Inc.
CRYSTAL VANISH - Cleaning preparations–household - S.C. Johnson & Son, Inc.
CRYSTAL VAULT - Vaults - Matrix Technical Engineering Corp.
CRYSTAL VELVET - Glassware–household ☆ - Fenton Art Glass Co.
CRYSTAL VISION - Electronics equipment - Audio Visual Promotion Aids Inc.
CRYSTAL VISION - Lenses–magnifying - C. Bennett Scopes Inc.
CRYSTAL WALLS - Computer software - Domain Virtual Worlds, Inc.
CRYSTAL WASH - Hair care products - Chenice Beverly Hills
CRYSTAL WATERS - Water purification systems ☆ - King Technology, Inc.
CRYSTAL WEDDING - Oats–rolled or meal - Quaker Oats Co.
CRYSTAL WHITE - Cleaning preparations–household - Colgate-Palmolive Co.
CRYSTAL WHITE - Food products - A.M. Todd Co.
CRYSTAL WORKS - Glassware–household - Nachtmann USA Inc.
CRYSTAL WRITERS - Giftware - Iris Arc Crystal Inc.
CRYSTAL ZOO - Figurines - Silver Deer Ltd.
CRYSTALAC - Paints - Becker Labs
CRYSTALACE - Tiles–ceramic - Wenczel Tile Co.
CRYSTALAIRE - Deodorizers - Airwick Industries
CRYSTALCLEAR - Chemical preparations - General Electric Co.
CRYSTALCOOL - Hats - Steve Crisafi
CRYSTALCUT - Lubricants - Gard Corp.
CRYSTALEDGE - Novelty items - Curran Art Glass
CRYSTALENE - Paper–transfer - Keuffel & Esser Co.
CRYSTALETS - Candy ☆ - Crystal Pure Candy Co.
CRYSTALETTE - Foil–aluminum - The Eureka Co.
CRYSTALETTE - Lighting fixtures ☆ - Prestigeline Inc.
CRYSTALEX - Finishing agents - Kyanize Paint Co.
CRYSTALEX - Nail care products - Kristy Wells Inc.
CRYSTALEYES - Electronics equipment - Stereographics Corp.
CRYSTALIC - Nail care products - 7-11 Sales Inc.
CRYSTALIER - Lighting equipment ☆ - Duro-Lite Lamps Inc.
CRYSTALIKE - Tableware–plastic - Berman Industries
CRYSTALIN - Furniture–wood ☆ - Century Furniture Co.
CRYSTALIN SUNCATCHERS - Hobby kits - Craft House Corp.
CRYSTALINE - Faucet handles - Gerber Plumbing Fixtures Corp.
CRYSTALINE - Hobby kits ☆ - Accento Plastic Manufacturing Inc.
CRYSTALINE - Jewelry - East Bay Traders Inc.
CRYSTALIS - Toys - Naturalis, Inc.
CRYSTALITE - Candlesticks ☆ - Dansk International Designs, Ltd.
CRYSTALITE - Construction equipment - Domtar Gypsum Inc.
CRYSTALITE - Finishing agents - Joli Plastics & Chemical Corp.
CRYSTALITE - Floor coverings ☆ - Kentile Floors Inc.
CRYSTALITE - Glass products - Lasco Products Group
CRYSTALITE - Hair care products ☆ - Redken Laboratories, Inc.
CRYSTALITE - Handles–wood - Gerber Plumbing Fixtures Corp.
CRYSTALITE - Lamps - Lamplight Farms, Inc.
CRYSTALITES - Giftware ☆ - Gorham Inc.

CRYSTALIZED - Paper–tissue - Crystal Tissue Co. Inc.
CRYSTALIZER - Circuit boards - Crystal Computer Corp.
CRYSTALIZER - Skin care products - Sogo Inc.
CRYSTALLINE - Cleaning preparations - Crystal Magic, Inc.
CRYSTALLINE - Cosmetics - Lancome
CRYSTALLINE - Doors–glass - Therma-Tru Corp.
CRYSTALLINE - Floor coverings–carpet and rugs - Trend Carpet
CRYSTALLINE - Tiles–ceramic - American Olean Tile Co.
CRYSTALLINE CARVINGS - Giftware - Wald Designs Acrylic Idea Factory
CRYSTALLINE GOLD - Arthritis ointment - Jackson Enterprises
CRYSTALLINE SHINE - Hair care products - Lori Davis Hair, Inc.
CRYSTALLUME - Electrical and X-ray equipment - Crystallume, Inc.
CRYSTALMATE - Cleaning preparations - Ecolab Inc.
CRYSTALOCK - Batteries - Palos Verdes Building Corp.
CRYSTALON - Fabrics ☆ - Crystal Tissue Co. Inc.
CRYSTALON - Giftware - Incolay Studios Inc.
CRYSTALON - Ophthalmic goods - Hilsinger Corp.
CRYSTALON STACK-ALL TUMBLERS - Glassware–household - Carlisle Foodservice Products, Inc.
CRYSTALS - Cigars - National Cigar Corp.
CRYSTALS - Floor coverings–carpet and rugs - Heuga USA
CRYSTALS - Paints - Tulip Productions
CRYSTALS - Shoes - Crystal Shoe Co. Inc.
CRYSTALS - Skin care products - R & R International Corp.
CRYSTALSCAN - Monitors–electronic - Gateway 2000, Inc.
CRYSTALTALK - Clocks ☆ - Citizen Watch Co. of America Inc.
CRYSTALTAP - Water purification systems - McKesson Home Health Care
CRYSTALTEX - Tiles–ceramic - Dal-Tile Corp.
CRYSTALTONE - Floor coverings - Congoleum Corp.
CRYSTALTONE - Pottery products - Duncan Enterprises
CRYSTALUX - Paper–photographic ☆ - Luminos Photo Corp.
CRYSTALYTE - Cylinders–acetylene - Candle Corp. of America
CRYSTALZONE - Water purification systems - Spa Centers, Inc.
CRYSTALZYME - Chemical preparations - Valley Research, Inc.
CRYSTAMINE - Pharmaceutical preparations - Dunhall Pharmaceuticals Inc.
CRYSTAR - Ceramic products - Norton Co.
CRYSTAR - Toys - Azrak-Hamway International, Inc.
CRYSTELLE - Rouges ☆ - Avonite Inc.
CRYSTELLES - Jewelry - Ears-R-In Inc.
CRYSTI-12 - Pharmaceutical preparations - Roberts/Hauck Pharmaceuticals Inc.
CRYSTI-LIVER - Pharmaceutical preparations - Roberts/Hauck Pharmaceuticals Inc.
CRYSTICILLIN - Pharmaceutical preparations - Bristol-Myers Squibb Co.
CRYSTILLED - Water–bottled or canned - Absopure Water Co.
CRYSTIMIN - Pharmaceutical preparations ☆ - Solvay Pharmaceuticals Inc.
CRYSTINA - Floor coverings - Mannington Resilient Floors
CRYSTODIGIN - Digitalis - Eli Lilly and Co.
CRYSTOLON - Abrasive products - Norton Co.
CRYSTOREX - Pharmaceutical preparations ☆ - Rex Research Laboratories
CS - Aircraft parts - California Screw Products
CS - Amplifiers - Peavey Electronics Corp.
CS - Computer software - Cadsoft Computer, Inc.
CS - Drums–musical instruments - Remo, Inc.
CS - Footwear–athletic ☆ - Avia Athletic Footwear
CS - Jewelry - Kaprielian Enterprises Inc.
CS - Molding compounds–plastics - Gossen Corp.
CS - Recording label - Victori Promotions & Marketing Inc.
CS - Sporting goods - Continental Sports Supply Inc.
CS - Staircases–wood - Challis Stairways Inc.
CS - Steel products - Carolina Steel Corp.
CS-1 - Electronic equipment - J.L. Cooper Electronics
CS/2 - Computer software - Puget Sound Power & Light Co.
CS-2 - Labeling machinery - Timemed Labeling Systems, Inc.
CS-10X - Electronic equipment - J.L. Cooper Electronics
CS-22 - Chemical preparations - Chemtec Co. of Illinois, Inc.
CS-102 - Electronic equipment - J.L. Cooper Electronics
CS-232 - Computers - Celadon Inc.
CS-309 - Concrete–mixture - W.R. Meadows Inc.
CS 3000 - Adhesives and sealants - Creteseal Contract Services Inc.
CS-EDIT - Electronic equipment - J.L. Cooper Electronics
CS GEAR - Apparel–children's - Liberty Childrenswear Co., LLC
CS KNOWLEDGE - Computer software - Corporate Systems, Ltd.
C.S. RICHMOND - Guns - Euroarms of America
CS SYSTEMS - Computer software - International Business Machines Corp.
CS1 - Jewelry - C & G Jewelers

☆ = Now out of production

CSA - Swords - Atlanta Cutlery Corp.

CSA COMPREHENSIVE SURVIVAL ARTS - Apparel and accessories - CSA, Ltd.

CSC - Electronic equipment - Commonwealth Sprague Capacitor, Inc.

CSC - Oils–edible - Catania-Spagna Corp.

CSC CARGO SERVICE CENTER - Transportation vehicles and equipment - Gateway Freight Services

CSCI - Capacitors - Commonwealth Sprague Capacitor, Inc.

CSEP - Chromatographs - Advanced Separation Technologies Inc.

CSG - Diamond powder - General Electric Co.

CSG IMAGESOFT - T-shirts - Sony Imagesoft Inc.

CSI - Audio equipment - CSI/Speco

CSI - Cables - Conquest Sound Inc.

CSI - Communications equipment - Cable Systems International Inc.

CSI - Computer software - CSI of New Jersey, Inc.

CSI - Contact lenses - Pilkington Visioncare, Inc.

CSI - Golfing equipment - Steven Mark Verrette

CSI - Publisher's imprints - Christian Schools International

CSI - Radio communications equipment - Connect Systems, Inc.

CSI - Recording label - Country Star International

CSI CLARITY - Contact lenses - Pilkington Visioncare, Inc.

CSIMON - Computer software - US Software

CSL - Amplifiers - Crown International, Inc.

CSL - Computer hardware - Compuspeak Laboratories, Inc.

CSL - Jewelry–precious - Catherine S. Linville

CSL - Medical apparatus - Daig Corp.

CSL 1500 - Machinery - Morton International Inc. (Morton Salt Div.)

CSL AIRITE IC - Lighting fixtures - CSL Lighting Manufacturing, Inc.

CSL/ALTA ENERGY SAVINGS - Lighting fixtures - CSL Lighting Manufacturing, Inc.

CSL BAIN DE SORBE - Lighting fixtures ☆ - CSL Lighting Manufacturing, Inc.

CSL BREEZE - Lighting fixtures ☆ - CSL Lighting Manufacturing, Inc.

CSL CSL - Lighting fixtures - CSL Lighting Manufacturing, Inc.

CSL DINK - Lighting fixtures ☆ - CSL Lighting Manufacturing, Inc.

CSL ECHO-21 - Lighting fixtures ☆ - CSL Lighting Manufacturing, Inc.

CSL ESSENCE - Lighting fixtures ☆ - CSL Lighting Manufacturing, Inc.

CSL INTIMACEE - Lighting fixtures ☆ - CSL Lighting Manufacturing, Inc.

CSL INVIZILITE - Lighting fixtures - CSL Lighting Manufacturing, Inc.

CSL JEWELLIGHT - Lighting fixtures - CSL Lighting Manufacturing, Inc.

CSL MICRO-TRAC/MINIATURA - Lighting fixtures ☆ - CSL Lighting Manufacturing, Inc.

CSL MITELITE - Lighting fixtures ☆ - CSL Lighting Manufacturing, Inc.

CSL MULTIPLES - Lighting fixtures ☆ - CSL Lighting Manufacturing, Inc.

CSL PERGIEE - Lighting fixtures ☆ - CSL Lighting Manufacturing, Inc.

CSL PICTURA - Lighting fixtures - CSL Lighting Manufacturing, Inc.

CSL SAMOVAR - Lighting fixtures ☆ - CSL Lighting Manufacturing, Inc.

CSL SAN MIRO - Lighting fixtures ☆ - CSL Lighting Manufacturing, Inc.

CSL SIMES - Lighting fixtures ☆ - CSL Lighting Manufacturing, Inc.

CSL STONEHENGE - Lighting fixtures - CSL Lighting Manufacturing, Inc.

CSL SURETASK - Lighting fixtures - CSL Lighting Manufacturing, Inc.

CSL SURFACE SYSTEMS - Lighting fixtures - CSL Lighting Manufacturing, Inc.

CSL SURLOC - Lighting fixtures ☆ - CSL Lighting Manufacturing, Inc.

CSL TERRALUNA - Lighting fixtures ☆ - CSL Lighting Manufacturing, Inc.

CSL TINY TRACK - Lighting fixtures ☆ - CSL Lighting Manufacturing, Inc.

CSL TINY TUBE - Lighting fixtures ☆ - CSL Lighting Manufacturing, Inc.

CSL VALCO - Lighting fixtures ☆ - CSL Lighting Manufacturing, Inc.

CSM - Pumps–water - ITT Industries, Inc.

CSNAV - Computer software - Compuserve Inc.

CSOUND - Computer software - Massachusetts Institute of Technology

C.S.P. - Cleaning preparations - Hillyard Enterprises, Inc.

CSP - Goggles - Richey Industries, Inc.

CSP - Golfing equipment - Wilson Sporting Goods Co.

C.S.P. - Recording label - Jazz Composer's Orchestra Association Inc.

CSP INC. - Computer peripheral equipment - Computer System Products, Inc.

CSPOWER - Computer software - Client Server Computing, Inc.

CSS - Boats–motor - Starcraft Corp.

CSS - Computer peripheral equipment - Computer Support Systems Inc.

CSS POWER - Electronic equipment - CSS Power, Inc.

CST - Automotive parts and accessories - CST, Inc.

CST - Measuring instruments - Chicago Steel Tape Co.

CST - Recording label - National Council of State Boards of Nursing, Inc.

CST - Toilets–enameled - Toto Kiki USA Inc.

C.S.T. COBBLE - Paving materials–stone - Concrete Stone & Tile Corp.

CSU, LONG BEACH - Notebooks and stationery - 49er Shops, Inc.

CSUS - Jewelry - California State University, Sacramento

CSUS - License plates–automotive - California State University

CSX - Loudspeakers - Community Light & Sound, Inc.

CT - Containers - CT Consolidated Technology Corp.

CT - Electronic equipment - Clifford E. Mohs

CT - Furniture - Haworth, Inc.

CT - Jewelry - Cheever Tweedy Co. Inc.

CT - Locks–door - Powerbrace Corp.

CT - Lumber - Coastal Timbers Inc.

CT - Ships–sailing vessels - Tanton

CT/2 - Computer software - International Business Machines Corp.

CT 200 - Optical machinery - Dicon

CT ADVANTAGE - Computer software - C T Corp. System

CT ADVANTAGE - Computer software - CT Corp. System

CT CLASSICS - Glass–optical - Welling International

CT COMPU-TODO - Computer peripheral equipment - Compu-Todo, Inc.

CT CORPORATE PROFILE - Computer software - CT Corp. System

CT/DATA SERVER - Computer software - Candle Corp.

C.T. EXPRESS - Apparel and accessories - Breton Industries

CT MARINE BAND - Harmonicas - Hohner Inc.

CT-TOWER - Cabinets - CT Consolidated Technology Corp.

CT-Z-RIVET IT - Pliers - ACCO USA, Inc.

CT2-ADC - Water–bottled or canned - Everpure Inc.

CTA - Apparel and accessories - Karman Western Apparel

CTA ACOUSTICS - Insulating materials - CTA Acoustics, Inc.

CTA METRO - Waterproof outerwear - Fox-Knapp Inc.

CTAC - Motors - C-Tac Inc.

CTB - Textbooks - MacMillan/McGraw-Hill School Publishing Co.

CTC - Watches - Creation Time Corp.

CTC/CLC - Coal liquid - Coal Technology Corp.

CTC ORIGINAL BLEND - Coffee - CTC Food International

CTCW MAX - Electrical equipment - Baker Motion Control Systems Inc.

CTD - Saws–power - CTD Machines Inc.

CTEST++ - Computer software - Plum Hall Inc.

CTF BRAND - Packaged fruits and vegetables - N.A. Trading Co.

CTG COMPLEX - Tableware–earthenware - Quorum International, Ltd.

CTH GUARD - Hair care products - Helene Curtis Industries Inc.

CTH/SHERRILL - Furniture - Sherrill Furniture Co.

C.THERAPY - Nail care products - Creative Nail Design, Inc.

CTHULHU MONSTERS - Games - Chaosium Inc.

CTI - Cleaning preparations - Caravan Technologies, Inc.

CTI - Computers - Control Technology, Inc.

CTI - Jewelry - Coast Diamond Distributors

C.T.I. - Medical apparatus - Innovation Sports, Inc.

CTI - Pregnancy test kits ☆ - Carlsbad Technology

CTI - Safety products - Custom Tapes, Inc.

CTI - Trophies–precious metal - Continental Trophies, Inc.

CTI COMMAND SET - Computer software - Rochelle Communications, Inc.

CTI EDGE - Medical apparatus - Innovation Sports, Inc.

CTI HOLLOW GRAMS - Novelty items - CTI Industries Corp.

CTI-NH - Locks–door - Powerbrace Corp.

C.TI.2 - Braces–orthopedic - Innovation Sports, Inc.

CTJR - Footwear–athletic - New Balance Athletic Shoe, Inc.

CTM - Agricultural machinery - C & M Baling Systems, Inc.

CTM - Beauty aids, hair-care products, skin-care products - Sunny More International Inc.

CTM - Microphones ☆ - C.T.I. Audio Inc.

CTME - Apparel and accessories - Clothestime Inc.

CTP - Decals and transfers - Creative Teaching Press

CTR - Finishing agents - Camp-Cap Products

CTR - Health care products - Bioenergy Inc.

CTR - Recording label - Hallways to Fame Productions Inc.

CTR - Thread - Signal Thread Co. Inc.

CTR - Wines - Corp. of the President of the Church of Jesus Christ of Latter-Day Saints

CTR SYSTEMS - Computer software - CTR Systems, Inc.

CTRAX - Computer software - Times Mirror Multimedia Corp.

CTS - Boats–motor - Century Boat Co.

CTS - Window coverings - CMI Architectural Products

CTS APPROACH - Sporting goods - Prince Manufacturing Inc.

CTS LIGHTNING - Sporting goods - Prince Manufacturing Inc.

CTS RELIEF KIT - Surgical supplies - Linvatec Corp.

CTS THUNDERSTICK - Sporting goods - Prince Manufacturing Inc.

CTSC - Computer software - Computer Training & Support Corp.

CTT - Cleaning preparations - Stewart-Hall Chemical Corp.

CTT CARDS THAT TEACH - Greeting cards - Matas R & S Inc.

CTT-SM - Water treating compounds - Stewart-Hall Chemical Corp.

☆ = Now out of production

CTW SESAME STREET - Spaghetti–canned - Children's Television Workshop
CTX - Exercising equipment - Nordictrack, Inc.
CT.YARD DESIGNS - Furniture - Doskocil Manufacturing Co., Inc.
CU - Apparel–athletic - Regents of the University of Colorado
CU - Heating equipment - ITT Industries, Inc.
CU - Jewelry - Charms Unlimited Inc.
CU - Publisher's imprint - Consumer Reports Books
CU-7 - Pharmaceutical preparations - G. D. Searle & Co.
CU BASE - Computer software - West Michigan Computer Cooperative, Inc.
CU-LINK - Chemical preparations - Atotech USA Inc.
CU-PO-VENT - Cupolas ☆ - Aluminum Co. of America
CU31 - Amalgamators - Aluminum Co. of America
CU92 - Bidets - Aluminum Co. of America
CU95 - Bicycles - Aluminum Co. of America
CUADROS - Floor coverings–carpet and rugs ☆ - Eurotex Inc.
CUAN CLOISONNE - Vases - Oriental Trading Co., Inc.
CUATRERO MUSICAL - Recording label - Luna Music Corp.
CUAUHTEMOC - Sausages - Trevino Enterprises
CUB - Bags - Interstate Packaging Corp.
CUB - Bags–canvas - Stephen Lawrence Co.
CUB - Bicycles - Columbia Manufacturing Inc.
CUB - Blow torches - Microflame Inc.
CUB - Drums–musical instruments ☆ - Grossman Music Corp.
CUB - Fruits and vegetables - Upland Lemon Co.
CUB - Fruits–canned ☆ - Harry and David Inc.
CUB - Health care products - Bruno Independent Living Aids Inc.
CUB - Loudspeakers - Wilson Audio Specialties, Inc.
CUB - Recording label - MCP Davisound
CUB - Staplers - ACCO USA, Inc.
CUB CADET - Garden equipment - Cub Cadet Corp.
CUB FOODS - Food products - Super Valu Inc.
CUB HUNTER - Knives–pocket ☆ - Colonial Knife Co. Inc.
CUB-TO-KING - Puppets - Mattel, Inc.
CUBA-FRANKLIN - Fishing tackle - Cuba Specialty Manufacturing Co.
CUBA LIBRE - Caps–baseball - Karen Lynn Egozi & Luis Egozi
CUBAN CLUB RUM - Rum - Compania De Licores Internacionales, Inc.
CUBAN CUT - Bathing suits - Catalina
CUBASE - Computer software - Steinberg/Jones Corp.
CUBBERLEY - Food products ☆ - Cubberley Packing Co.
CUBBIHUGS - Toys–stuffed ☆ - Gund, Inc.
CUBBINS - Toys–stuffed ☆ - Gund, Inc.
CUBBY - Candy - Euro-American Brands Inc.
CUBBY - Pet products ☆ - Coleman Co., Inc.
CUBBY BEAR - Apparel and accessories - Loukas, Inc.
CUBBY BEAR - Candy - Euro-American Brands Inc.
CUBBY BEAR - Dinnerware–plastic - General Mills, Inc.
CUBBY BEAR - Toys–stuffed - Russ Berrie and Co., Inc.
CUBBY BEAR - Toys–stuffed - Santa's Best
CUBCAKES - Apparel and accessories - Albert E. Price, Inc.
CUBE - Computer hardware - Cube Computer Corp.
CUBE - Office furniture–metal - Stow/Davis Furniture Co.
CUBE 12 - Office furniture–metal ☆ - Joyce International Inc.
CUBE ART - Notebooks and notepads - Crayon Cube, Inc.
CUBE LINE - Office furniture–metal - Invincible Metal Furniture Co.
CUBE MASTER - Water treating compounds ☆ - Aquatronics-Filtronics
CUBE MATES - Containers - Steelworks, Inc.
CUBE SAVER - Shelving units–metal - Lozier Store Fixtures
CUBE, THE - Paper cutters - Dahle USA
CUBE, THE - Beverages–carbonated - Pepsico, Inc.
CUBE WEST - Paper products - Paper Conversions Inc.
CUBEAT - Computer software - Steinberg/Jones Corp.
CUBEITES - Salt ☆ - United Salt Corp.
CUBELETS - Sugar–granulated, refined, or powdered - California and Hawaiian Sugar Co.
CUBEPAK - Aquarium accessories - Kordon
CUBEPAK - Aquarium accessories - Novalek, Inc.
CUBEPUBLISHER - Computer software - Anzen Corp.
CUBES BOBBINS & BEAMS - Toys - Learning Materials Workshop
CUBESAVER - Cups–plastic - Solo Cup Co.
CUBESCAN 100 - Scales–industrial - Quantronix, Inc.
CUBETECH - Computer software - Anzen Corp.
CUBIC - Transmission equipment–industrial - Fairchild Industrial Products Co.
CUBIC III - Sporting goods ☆ - Powell Skateboards
CUBIC 10 - Uniforms–tailored - Angelica Uniform Group
CUBICLE CONCEPTS - Posters - Sharon's Imagination Inc.
CUBICS - Floor coverings–carpet and rugs ☆ - Regal Rugs Inc.

CUBIE - Ice - Central Ice Co.
CUBIES - Ice chests - Reliable Plastics
CUBIPAD - Bandages–surgical - Heelbo Inc.
CUBISM - Paper products - Paper Conversions Inc.
CUBITA - Cigars - Urbis Corp.
CUBITS - Food products - Hester Industries, Inc.
CUBITS - Meat products–poultry - Pierce Foods Corp.
CUBITS - Puzzles - Binary Arts Corp.
CUBITS - Puzzles - Kadon Enterprises Inc.
CUBIX - Cabinets–metal - Sycamore Systems, Inc.
CUBIZM PORTRAITS - Toys - Zolo Inc.
CUBO - Digital alarm clock - Corvus Corp.
CUBREMAX - Paints - Major Paint Co.
CUCA - Recording label - American Music Co.
CUCAMONGA - Honey - Western Commerce Corp.
CUCAMONGA COOLER WINE SPRITZERS - Wines - J. Filippi Vintage Co.
CUCAMONGA CRANKS - Bicycle parts and accessories - William M. Young
CUCCINI - Apparel and accessories - Turbo Sportswear, Inc.
CUCCINI TURBO CLUB - Apparel and accessories - Turbo Sportswear, Inc.
CUCHINA - Pasta - Schwan's Sales Enterprises, Inc.
CUCINA - Kitchen appliances ☆ - National Housewares
CUCINA CLASSICA ITALIANA - Cheese - Cucina Classica Italiana, Inc.
CUCINA! CUCINA! - Food products - Cucina! Cucina!, Inc.
CUCINA DELLA REGINA - Food products - Golden Whisk Pasta Partners
CUCINA D'ORO - Bakery products - Italian and American Bakery, Inc.
CUCINA ROYALE - Food products - Mivila Corp.
CUCKOO - Brushes–paint - Wooster Brush Co.
CUCKOO - Dishes–china - Waterford Wedgewood USA, Inc.
CUCKOO EGGS - Candy - Leaf, Inc.
CUCUMBER & ELDER FLOWER - Toiletries - Caswell-Massey Co. Ltd.
CUCUMBER ICE - Skin lotion ☆ - London International U.S. Holdings
CUCUMBRE FROST - Skin care products - Ana Maher, Inc.
CUCUMBRE MIST - Skin care products - Ana Maher, Inc.
CUDA - Bicycles - MRI, Inc.
CUDA - Bicycles ☆ - Roadmaster Corp.
CUDA - Industrial machinery - Cuda Corp.
CUDA - Motor vehicles–automobiles ☆ - Chrysler Corp. (Chrysler-Plymouth Div.)
CUDA - Saw blades - Credo Co.
CUDA CAY LINE - Beverages - Earth Ade Beverages Inc.
CUDAHY - Food products - Cudahy Co.
CUDAS - Apparel and accessories - A.G.S. of Hanover Inc.
CUDDL DUDS - Apparel and accessories - Duck Head Apparel Co., Inc.
CUDDL KIDS - Jackets–children's - O'Bryan Brothers, Inc.
CUDDL SILKS - Apparel–women's - O'Bryan Brothers, Inc.
CUDDLE ALERT - Apparel and accessories - Greg Smith
CUDDLE BAGS - Sleeping bags - A. Brandt Sleepworks
CUDDLE BEAR - Apparel–children's - Bon-Ton Trade Corp.
CUDDLE BED - Mattress pads - Hollander Home Fashions Inc.
CUDDLE BUDDY - Toys–stuffed - HC & E Inc.
CUDDLE BUNNIES - Candy - R.M. Palmer Co.
CUDDLE BUNNIES - Greeting cards - American Greetings Corp.
CUDDLE BUNNIES - Toys–stuffed - Russ Berrie and Co., Inc.
CUDDLE CAP - Hair care products - N. Seligman Co.
CUDDLE CAPS - Infant product - Comfort Silkie Co. Inc.
CUDDLE CARRIER - Infant product ☆ - Century Products Co.
CUDDLE COVERS - Diaper covers - TL Care Inc.
CUDDLE CUMFY - Infant product ☆ - Century Products Co.
CUDDLE FLEECE - Fabrics - Guilford Mills, Inc.
CUDDLE KIDS - Dolls - Goldberger Doll Manufacture Co.
CUDDLE KING - Dolls - Mattel, Inc.
CUDDLE KNIT - Crocheted and knitted items - Cuddle Knit Inc.
CUDDLE ME - Infant product - Noel Joanna, Inc.
CUDDLE ME - Tights–stockings - Kayser-Roth Corp.
CUDDLE ME - Toys–stuffed - Eden LLC
CUDDLE N' WATCH - Games ☆ - Royal Sound Co. Inc.
CUDDLE NET - Infant product - Century Products Co.
CUDDLE PACK - Infant product ☆ - Gerry Baby Products Co.
CUDDLE PAD - Infant product ☆ - Century Products Co.
CUDDLE TIME - Pillows - Triboro Quilt Manufacturing Corp.
CUDDLE TOUCH - Fabrics - Guilford Mills, Inc.
CUDDLE TOYS - Toys–stuffed - Douglas Co. Inc.
CUDDLE TUB - Infant product - Century Products Co.
CUDDLE UP - Blankets–electric - Sunbeam Corp.
CUDDLE-UP - Fabrics ☆ - Dan River Inc.
CUDDLE-UP - Infant product ☆ - Welsh Co.

☆ = Now out of production

CUDDLE-UPS - Dolls - Effanbee Doll Corp.
CUDDLE UPS - Hobby kits - JCA, Inc.
CUDDLE UP'S - Toys–stuffed - Fun World Inc.
CUDDLE WARMER - Blankets - Triboro Quilt Manufacturing Corp.
CUDDLE WIT - Toys–stuffed - C.W. International, Inc.
CUDDLE WRAP - Blankets - Biederlack of America
CUDDLE YOUR SPIRITS - Bags–paper - Cuddle Yours Spirits
CUDDLEBUNCH BY MARK ROWEN & CO. NEW YORK - Sleeping bags -
   Mark Rowen & Co., Inc.
CUDDLEDOWN - Crocheted and knitted items - Garland Knitting Mills
CUDDLEDOWN - Yarn - Bernat Yarn & Craft Corp.
CUDDLEE FUR - Hobby kits - Flora Craft Inc.
CUDDLEFLEECE - Blankets - Dakotah, Inc.
CUDDLEHEART - Infant product - Pauline V. Shakas
CUDDLEKINS - Dolls - Goldberger Doll Manufacture Co.
CUDDLEMERE - Apparel and accessories - ShadowLine Inc.
CUDDLENE - Skin care products - Hygeia Products Inc.
CUDDLER - Apparel–children's - Doe Spun Inc.
CUDDLER - Infant product - Gerry Baby Products Co.
CUDDLER - Pet products - Flexi-Mat Corp.
CUDDLER - Pet products - R.C. Steele Co.
CUDDLER COMPANIONS - Toys - Fisher-Price, Inc.
CUDDLER CUTIES - Toys - Fisher-Price, Inc.
CUDDLERS AT HOME - Toys - Fisher-Price, Inc.
CUDDLERS ON THE GO - Toys - Fisher-Price, Inc.
CUDDLES - Diapers–disposable - VMG Products Inc.
CUDDLES - Toys–stuffed ☆ - Fun World Inc.
CUDDLES BEAR - Toys–stuffed - Dakin Inc.
CUDDLES ELEPHANT - Toys–stuffed - Dakin Inc.
CUDDLES MOUSE - Toys–stuffed - Dakin Inc.
CUDDLES PANDA - Toys–stuffed - Dakin Inc.
CUDDLESILK - Apparel and accessories ☆ - Terramar Sports Worldwide, Ltd.
CUDDLESKIN - Underwear and nightwear - Barbizon Lingerie
CUDDLESOFT - Yarn - Caron International Inc.
CUDDLESOME - Toys - Eugene Doll & Novelty Co. Inc.
CUDDLESOMES - Figurines ☆ - Cast Art Industries, Inc.
CUDDLEY KINGDOM - Dolls - Mattel, Inc.
CUDDLIES - Toys–stuffed - Gerber Products Co.
CUDDLY - Puzzles ☆ - Milton Bradley Co.
CUDDLY BEASTIES, THE - Publisher's imprints - Ottenheimer Publishers, Inc.
CUDDLY CARE KIT - Toys - Bear Care Co.
CUDDLY CAT - Toys–stuffed - Gerber Products Co.
CUDDLY CHARACTERS - Toys–stuffed - Centsable Toys Inc.
CUDDLY CHUM - Toys–stuffed ☆ - Gerber Products Co.
CUDDLY CLASSICS - Toys–stuffed - Eckerd Corp.
CUDDLY CRAWLER - Toys–stuffed ☆ - Gerber Products Co.
CUDDLY CRITTERS - Stationery - Sangamon Co.
CUDDLY KINGDOM - Toys–stuffed - Dan-Dee International Ltd.
CUDDLY WORM - Toys–stuffed - Gerber Products Co.
CUDDY NAUTIQUE - Boats ☆ - Correct Craft Inc.
CUDDY'S - Meat products–poultry - Cuddy Farms, Inc.
CUDE & PICKENS PUBLISHING - Music–sheet - Hard Hat Records
CUDGEL - Computer software - Elan Associates (GreenLight Software Division)
CUDLIE - School bags, back packs, diaper bags - Bag Bazaar Ltd.
CUDO - Glass products - Crystal International Corp.
CUDSTER AND SADDLE SORE - Toys - Hasbro, Inc.
CUE - Food products - V. & E. Kohnstamm Inc.
CUE - Pagers - Cue Paging Corp.
CUE - Toothpaste - Colgate-Palmolive Co.
CUE BALL KELLY - Sporting goods ☆ - J-S Sales Co. Inc.
CUE-CARD - Musical instrument accessories ☆ - Herco Products
CUE CART - Cooking equipment–household - Birmingham Stove & Range Co.
CUE CRAFT - Craft supplies - Allied-Mayork Corp.
CUE-LOK - Audio equipment - Telex Communications, Inc.
CUE MASTER - Spas - Zenith Technologies, Inc.
CUE SENTRY - Lighting equipment - Cornerstone/Clearlight
CUE SILK - Sporting goods - Cue Silk, Inc.
CUE SPOT - Theatrical lights - Morpheus Lights Inc.
CUE STIX - Fishing tackle ☆ - South Bend Sporting Goods Inc.
CUE-WRITE - Computer software - Communication Skill Builders, Inc.
CUECHART - Computer software - Computer Associates International, Inc.
CUELITE - Flashlights - Vistalite Inc.
CUEMASTER - Audio equipment - Light Wave Systems
CUENTOS DE COQUI - Computer software - Jostens Learning Corp.
CUEPOINT - Electronic equipment - J.L. Cooper Electronics
CUERVO 1800 - Rum - Heublein, Inc.

CUERVO ALMONDRADO - Liquors - Heublein, Inc.
CUERVO ESPECIAL - Liquors - Heublein, Inc.
CUESTA-REY - Cigars - J.C. Newman Cigar Co.
CUESTARIDGE - Apparel and accessories - Copelands' Enterprises, Inc.
CUETARA - Cookies - Crispy Snacks
CUETEC USA - J-S Sales Co. Inc.
CUETO - Tobacco products - F.D. Grave & Son, Inc.
CUEVAS - Food products ☆ - Dean & Deluca Inc.
CUFF AND COMPANY - Jewelry - Prosperity at Royal, Inc.
CUFF-ETTES - Apparel and accessories - Angler's Roslyn Group Ltd.
CUFF IT - Paper products - Stephen E. Berglund
CUFF-ITS - Slippers ☆ - R.G. Barry Corp.
CUFF, THE - Sporting goods - Fabrication Enterprises
CUFF, THE - Alarm systems - MPI, Inc.
CUI - Oils–lubricating - Coastal Unilube Inc.
CUIDANDO SU SALUD - Broadcasting stations–radio - Prevencion, Inc.
CUISENAIRE - Games - Learning Games Inc.
CUISINART - Kitchen appliances - Cuisinart Inc.
CUISINE - Cooking utensils–stoneware - Estia Corp.
CUISINE - Dinnerware–plastic - Plastics Manufacturing Co.
CUISINE - Flatware - Reed and Barton Corp.
CUISINE - Floor coverings–carpet and rugs - Regal Rugs Inc.
CUISINE AIDS - Tools ☆ - Regent Sheffield, Ltd.
CUISINE CLASSIQUE - Frozen foods - D'artagnan
CUISINE COLLECTION - Cookware - Allied IMEX Inc.
CUISINE DE FRANCE SABATIER - Cutlery ☆ - Swiss Army Brands, Ltd.
CUISINE-MASTER - Ovens–microwave - Sanyo Fisher (USA) Corp.
CUISINE PEREL - Food products - Cuisine Perel Corp.
CUISINE QUEEN - Food products machinery - SCI Scandicrafts Inc.
CUISINE ROYALE - Cutlery ☆ - Lifetime Hoan Corp.
CUISINIER'S CHOICE - Coffee - Aroma Coffee Co. Inc.
CUIVRE - Lipsticks - Cosmair Inc.
CUIVREPLUS - Cooking utensils–aluminum - Harold Leonard & Co. Inc.
CUJO - Hockey equipment - Hillerich & Bradsby Co.
CUKETTE - Seeds–salted, roasted, cooked, or canned - Asgrow Seed Co.
CUKONVERTER - Power converter - Optimum Power Conversion, Inc. (Tesla
   Co., Div.)
CUL M RITE - Scales–industrial - Advanced Fishing Technologies
CULBERTSON - Beverages–alcohol - Thornton Winery
CULINAIRE FLAIR - Bakery products - Southern Foods, Inc.
CULINARIA - Bakeware ☆ - Corning Inc.
CULINARY ALCHEMY - Spices and extracts - Culinary Alchemy, Inc.
CULINARY ARTS - Dinnerware–glass - Tienshan, Inc.
CULINARY CLASSICS - Apparel and accessories - Peco, Inc.
CULINARY CLASSIQUES - Housewares - Herman Dodge & Son Inc.
CULINARY COLLECTIONS - Cutlery ☆ - Ontario Knife Co.
CULINARY CONCEPTS - Dishes–china - Reco International Corp.
CULINARY COURT - Novelty items–stitched - A + A
CULINARY CREATIONS - Breads–mixes - New Orleans Spice Co. Inc.
CULINARY CREATIONS - Vegetables–frozen - California & Washington Co.
CULINARY CRITTERS - Novelty items–stitched - A + A
CULINARY ENSEMBLE - Cooking equipment–household ☆ - Mirro Corp.
CULINARY HERBS - Flowers, plants, and seeds - Applewood Seed & Garden
   Group
CULINARY PUREE - Cooking equipment–household - Culinary Puree, Inc.
CULLIGAN - Water purification systems - Culligan International Co.
CULLIGAN PRESS, THE - Embossing plates ☆ - Devin-Adair Co. Inc.
CULLIGAN WATER - Water–bottled or canned - Plains Dairy Products
CULLIN HILLS CASHMERE - Apparel and accessories - Twin Star
   International, Ltd.
CULLMAN TRIPODS - Photographic equipment - Charles Beseler Co.
CULLMANN - Photographic equipment - GMI Photographic Inc.
CULLODEN - Knives - Cold Steel Inc.
CULLYSPRING - Water–bottled or canned - Cullyspring Water Co.
CULMINATION - Floor coverings–carpet and rugs - Monticello Carpet Mills
CULPEPPER MILL - Furniture ☆ - Bassett Furniture Industries, Inc.
CULT-A-EZE - Garden equipment ☆ - Earthway Products Inc.
CULTI-FIBRE - Gardening products - H.C. Helmut Aurenz
CULTIVA - Skin care products - The Wilkes Group
CULTIVATED GARDEN - Housewares - Shafford Co. Inc.
CULTRA - Giftware - Mike Mendelson & Associates Inc.
CULTURAL CONCEPTS - Stationery - Imani S. Newsome-McLaughlin
CULTURAL DESIGNS - Recording label - Cultural Designs
CULTURAL ICONS - Postcards - Cultural Icons, Inc.
CULTURAL SURVIVAL - Greeting cards - Cultural Survival, Inc.
CULTURAL TOYS - Toys - Cultural Exchange Corp.

CULTURE BOOSTER - Cushions - Ellen Pickler Harris
CULTURE CARE - Hair care products - Culture Connection, Inc.
CULTURE CATS - Toys–stuffed - Cultural Exchange Corp.
CULTURE JAM - Apparel and accessories - Apollo Overseas International Inc.
CULTURE KITS - Pet shops - Florida Aqua Farms Inc.
CULTURE OF NYC, THE - Maps - Vandam Inc.
CULTURE POKER - Computer software ☆ - Gessler Publishing Co., Inc.
CULTURE POWDER - Laxatives ☆ - Fibertone Co.
CULTURE STUDIO - Apparel–men's - Federated Department Stores, Inc.
CULTUREFIT - Computer software - Limra International, Inc.
CULTURES OF MAN - Neckties ☆ - A. Schreter & Sons Co. Inc.
CULTUREX - Chemical preparation - Louisiana Remediation Co., Inc.
CULTURIA - Health care products - Medical Monitoring Systems Inc.
CULVER - Glassware–household - Culver Glass Inc.
CULVERNEER - Boats - Water Street Yachts Service
CULVER'S KIDZ - Preserved foods–prepackaged - Culver Enterprises, Inc.
CULVERT-RENEW - Pipes–plastic - Poly Systems Inc.
CUM CUM, INC. - Apparel–men's - Carlos Gomes
CUMAR BEST - Shrimp - Chestnut Hill Farms Inc.
CUMBERLAND - Air conditioners and furnaces - American Standard Inc.
CUMBERLAND - Bicycles - Columbia Manufacturing Inc.
CUMBERLAND - Cabinets - Aristokraft, Inc.
CUMBERLAND - Cabinets - Del Mar Cabinets
CUMBERLAND - Cabinets ☆ - Nutone Inc.
CUMBERLAND - Cheese - State of Maine Cheese
CUMBERLAND - Floor coverings ☆ - Bruce Hardwood Floors
CUMBERLAND - Floor coverings–carpet and rugs - Cumberland Mills Inc.
CUMBERLAND - Fruits–canned - Charles H. Jones Co.
CUMBERLAND - Furniture - Boling Co.
CUMBERLAND - Furniture ☆ - Athens Furniture Industries Inc.
CUMBERLAND - Furniture ☆ - Bassett Furniture Industries, Inc.
CUMBERLAND - Handles–wood - Turner, Day and Woolworth Handle Corp.
CUMBERLAND - Insulating materials ☆ - Owens Corning
CUMBERLAND - Locks–door - Pease Industries, Inc.
CUMBERLAND - Shoes ☆ - Allen-Edmonds Shoe Corp.
CUMBERLAND - Tobacco products - Scott Tobacco Co.
CUMBERLAND - Tobacco–chewing or smoking - Conwood Co. L.P.
CUMBERLAND - Wallpaper ☆ - Wall-Pride Inc.
CUMBERLAND OUTFITTERS - Apparel–men's - Oxford Industries, Inc.
CUMBERLAND RIDGE - Candy - Standard Candy Co. Inc.
CUMBERLAND T & G - Floor coverings ☆ - Bruce Hardwood Floors
CUMBERLAND VALLEY - Furniture - Davis Cabinet Co.
CUMBRES & TOLTEC - Boots - Expasa Florida Inc.
CUMFY DESIGNER - Pet products - Cumfy Designer Pet Products Inc.
CUMFY DUMFY - Dolls - Plakie Inc.
CUMMINS - Calculators - Cummins-Allison Corp.
CUMMINS EAGLE V - Bakery machines - Donald L. Cummins
CUMQUAT - Postcards - Fotofolio Inc.
CUMULOFT - Fibers–nylon - Monsanto Polymer Products
CUMULUS - Apparel and accessories - Sun Mountain Sports, Inc.
CUMULUS - Blinds–venetian ☆ - Hunter Douglas, Inc.
CUMULUS - Floor coverings–carpet and rugs - Matworks
CUMULUS - Floor coverings–carpet and rugs ☆ - Regal Rugs Inc.
CUMULUS - Floor coverings–tile - ECC International
CUMULUS - Skin care products - Highland Laboratories
CUMULUS - Wallpaper - Koroseal Wallcoverings
CUNAPSOL - Waterproofing compounds - ISK Biosciences Corp.
CUNE - Wines - C & B Vintage Cellars
CUNEIFORM - Recording label - Cuneiform Records
CUNNINGHAM'S - Teas - J.B.R, Inc.
CUNOOCS - Coffee - Cuno Inc.
CUO2 - Skin care products - California Suncare, Inc.
CUONG NHU ORIENTAL MARTIAL ARTS - Apparel–athletic - Cuong Nhu Oriental Martial Arts Association, Inc.
CUORE DI LA FATTORIA - Soap - Meehan, Gary E.
CUORE DI POMODORO - Canned tomatoes ☆ - Delicato Foods, Inc.
CUORE D'ORO - Vegetables–canned - C & F Foods Inc.
CUP - Tobacco products - R.J. Reynolds Tobacco Co.
CUP - Tobacco–chewing or smoking - Swedish Math North America Inc.
CUP-A-FRUIT - Fruit drinks–bottled or canned ☆ - Coca-Cola Co.
CUP-A-FRUIT - Fruits and vegetables - Big Valley Marketing Corp.
CUP-A-MINIT - Coffee makers–electric ☆ - Mirro Corp.
CUP-A-RAMEN - Soups–mixes - Campbell Soup Co.
CUP-A-SOUP - Soups–mixes - Lipton Investments, Inc.
CUP ABOVE, A - Coffee - Saramar Corp.
CUP & SAUCER - Pajamas–women's ☆ - J.C. Penney Co., Inc.

CUP-AT-A-TIME - Coffee makers–electric - Black & Decker Corp.
CUP CLOTH - Fabrics–sailcloth ☆ - John Boyle & Co., Inc.
CUP CUSTARD - Cookies ☆ - Sunshine Biscuits, Inc.
CUP MAID - Bird feeder - Sun Glitz Corp.
CUP N CAKE - Bakery products - Savont Foods Inc.
CUP-N-STUFF - Automotive parts and accessories - Lancaster Colony Automotive Group
CUP-O-CLIPS - Office supplies ☆ - IDL Manufacturing & Sales Corp.
CUP O' CRITTERS - Puppets - Poppets, Inc.
CUP-O-DAY - Coffee - Four-O-Coffee Co.
CUP-O-GOLD - Candy - Adams & Brooks, Inc.
CUP O JOE - Coffee - Todd J. Appelbaum
CUP-O-JOY - Food products - Turnbull Cone Baking Co.
CUP O'NOODLES - Soups–canned - Nissin Foods USA Co. Inc.
CUP THAT CHEERS, THE - Glassware–household - Woolson Spice Co., Inc.
C.U.P., THE - Signs - National Banner Co., Inc.
CUPAL - Electrodes - Nippert Co.
CUPBAKES - Bakery products - Sunset Paper Products Inc.
CUPBOARD - Perfumes ☆ - Karen Carson Creations
CUPCAKE - Bicycles ☆ - Raleigh USA Bicycle Co.
CUPCAKE - Chewing gum ☆ - Fleer Corp.
CUPCAKE CAFE - Toys - Mattel, Inc.
CUPCAKE CAT - Toys–stuffed ☆ - Dakin Inc.
CUPCAKE CLASSICS - Desserts ☆ - Boyer Printing Co.
CUPCAKE CUTIES - Toys–stuffed - Russ Berrie and Co., Inc.
CUPCAKE, THE - Containers–insulated ☆ - Teledyne Water Pik
CUPCAKELAND - Dolls - Tonka Corp.
CUPCAKES - Dolls - Hasbro, Inc.
CUPID - Apparel–women's - Cupid Foundations Inc.
CUPID - Novelty items - UniteDesign
CUPID - Recording label - Sound Inc.
CUPID - Shoes - Shoe Masters Inc.
CUPID CHASER - Insecticides - Pierpont Products Co.
CUPID POPS - Candy - Square Shooter Candy Co.
CUPID TEDDY - Toys–stuffed - Russ Berrie and Co., Inc.
CUPIDO - Cigars - Gilfranco Cigar Co.
CUPIDS - Candy - Sunline Brands
CUPID'S ARROW - Teas - Eastern Shore Tea Co.
CUPID'S CANDLE - Candles - Mayflower Glass Works
CUPID'S CANDLE - Candles - National Treasure Productions, Inc.
CUPID'S CLIP-ON - Toys–stuffed ☆ - Fun World Inc.
CUPID'S KISSES - Candy - Sathers Inc.
CUPID'S MUSICAL HEART - Toys–stuffed ☆ - Fun World Inc.
CUPID'S QUIVER - Health care products - Tawn Ltd.
CUPIE DO'S - Dolls - Mangelsen's (VDI)
CUPKIN - Paper - Sonoco-Rixie Coaster Division
CUPL-UP - Racks - Jarke Corp.
CUPLETS - Cheese ☆ - Zausner Foods Corp.
CUPMATE - Specialty foods–canned - S & D Coffee, Inc.
CUPOLA-MATIC - Fans–attic - Kool-O-Matic Corp.
CUPPA - Dishes–earthenware - Stephen D. Redden
CUPPERS FRESHLY ROASTED SPECIALTY COFFEE AND TEAS FROM AROUND THE WORLD - Coffee - General Food Supply Corp.
CUPPLES - Hardware - Blaine Window Hardware Inc.
CUPRAMINE - Pet products - Seachem Laboratories
CUPRASHAN - Fabrics - Thompson of California Inc.
CUPREX - Aquatic pharmacuetical preparations ☆ - Aquatronics-Filtronics
CUPREX II - Pet products ☆ - Aquatronics-Filtronics
CUPRIMINE - Pharmaceutical preparations - Merck & Co., Inc. (Merck Research Laboratories)
CUPRIPLEX - Pet products ☆ - Seachem Laboratories
CUPRIQUANT - Pet products ☆ - Seachem Laboratories
CUPRISORB - Pet products ☆ - Seachem Laboratories
CUPROLIGNUM - Chemical preparations - Rudd Co. Inc.
CUPROTEX - Cleaning preparations ☆ - Woolsey Marine Industries
CUPRUM - Ladders–metal - Watling Ladder Co.
CUPSTACK - Games - Karango Enterprises
CUPUASSU - Fruits and vegetables - Cultural Survival, Inc.
CUR-NON - Recording label ☆ - Rounder Records Corp.
CUR-TAIL - Vitamins and nutritional supplements - Akpharma Inc.
CURAD - Bandages - Colgate-Palmolive Co.
CURAD FOR KIDS - Bandages - Kendall Co.
CURAD NEON STRIPS - Bandages - Kendall Co.
CURAD SENSITIVE SKIN - Bandages - Kendall Co.
CURADERM - Beads - Kendall Co.
CURAFIL - Bandages - Kendall Co.

CURAFORTE - Skin-care products - Borghese Cosmetics Inc.

CURAFUS - Antiseptics - Curafas

CURAGEL - Bandages - Kendall Co.

CURAKLENSE - Pharmaceutical preparations - Kendall Co.

CURALATE - Health care products ☆ - Halsey Drug Co. Inc.

CURAMESSAGE - Computer software - Curasoft Systems, Inc.

CURARE - Sporting goods - Mitsushiba International, Inc.

CURASALT - Bandages - Kendall Co.

CURASEAL - Adhesives and sealants - Testworth Laboratories Inc.

CURASORB - Bandages–surgical - Kendall Co.

CURATEK - Pharmaceutical preparations - Curatek Pharmaceutical L.P.

CURATIVE TECHNOLOGIES - Antibiotics - Curative Technologies Inc.

CURATOR - Coatings - Preferred Products, Inc.

CURAY - Dental compounds - Scientific Pharmaceuticals, Inc.

CURB - Chemical preparations - Kemin Industries, Inc.

CURB - Recording label - Capitol-EMI Music Inc.

CURB - Recording label - MCA Universal Studios

CURB CRUISER - Scooters–motorized - Cycle Products Co.

CURB SERVICE - Soft drinks - Creative Beverage Co.

CURB SIDE - Bags–plastic - Carlisle Plastics, Inc.

CURB SIDE - Bags–trash - Carlysle Plastics

CURB-SIDER - Health care products - Bruno Independent Living Aids Inc.

CURB-SMOKE - Pharmaceutical preparations - Quaker City Pharmacal Co.

CURBMATE - Carts - Cascade Enviromental Systems Inc.

CURBSIDE - Wire products - Kaspar Wire Works, Inc.

CURCU-GEL - Vitamins and nutritional supplements - Tishcon Corp.

CURE - Apparel and accessories - Technidyne LLC

CURE - Detergents - Malco Products, Inc.

CURE 81 - Meat products–pork - Hormel Foods Corp.

CURE ALL - Concrete products - Set Consumer Products Inc.

CURE AND HARD - Concrete products - Symons Corp.

CURE AND SEAL - Concrete products - Sealwall Products Inc.

CURE-DENTS - Toothpicks - Sanex North America

CURE FOR THE COMMON MEAL, THE - Cheese - Stella Foods, Inc.

CURE-HARD - Concrete–mixture - W.R. Meadows Inc.

CURE-IT - Concrete products ☆ - Fosroc Inc.

CURE-O-BOND - Concrete products ☆ - Grace Construction Products

CURE-TEX - Machinery - Sussman-Automatic Corp.

CURE, THE - Archery equipment - Golden Key Futura, Inc.

CURE, THE - Golfing equipment - Louisville Golf Club Co. Inc.

CUREBOND - Latex - C-Cure Corp.

CURECRETE - Mortars–clay - C-Cure Corp.

CURECRYLIC - Latex - C-Cure Corp.

CUREFAST - Chemical preparations - C-Cure Corp.

CUREL - Skin care products - S.C. Johnson & Son, Inc.

CUREL DERMATOLOGIST RECOMMENDED - Skin care products - Bausch & Lomb Inc.

CURELASTIC - Adhesives and sealants - C-Cure Corp.

CURELOCK - Adhesives and sealants - Federal Process Co.

CUREMASTER - Meat products–pork - Hormel Foods Corp.

CUREMIX - Latex - C-Cure Corp.

CUREPAK - Lighting equipment - Fusion Systems Corp.

CURES - Shirts - Vicki L. Lewis

CURES YOUR PLANT'S ACID INDIGESTION - Agricultural products - Wommack's Hardwood Farms

CURESSENCE - Hair care products - Aveda Corp.

CURETAGE - Skin care products - Ageless Products, Inc.

CURETEC - Lamps - S.Y. Technologies, Inc.

CUREX - Surgical instruments - Kendall Co.

CURI-O-LITES - Lighting equipment - Hobby Hill Inc.

CURI-STRIP - Bandages - Kendall Co.

CURIDAN - Shampoos - Head Shampoo, Inc.

CURIE - Watches - Bulova Corp.

CURING MUDDY - Hair care products - Redmond Products, Inc.

CURIO - Apparel and accessories - Michael J. Napoli

CURIO - Bathroom accessories - Kohler Co.

CURIO - Hardware - Sash Controls Inc.

CURIOSITIES? - Greeting cards - Charles R. Donner

CURIOSITY - Perfumes - Steve Dworman Enterprises, Inc.

CURIOSITY KITS - Hobby kits - Curiosity Development, Inc.

CURIOUS GEORGE - Toys–stuffed - Eden LLC

CURIOUS GEORGE COLLECTION - Toys - Toy Works, Inc.

CURIOUS GEORGE GOES SHOPPING - Computer software ☆ - SRA/McGraw-Hill (Div. of The McGraw-Hill Companies)

CURIOUS GEORGE IN OUTERSPACE - Computer software ☆ - SRA/McGraw-Hill (Div. of The McGraw-Hill Companies)

CURIOUS GEORGE VISITS THE LIBRARY - Computer software ☆ - SRA/McGraw-Hill (Div. of The McGraw-Hill Companies)

CURIOUS PICTURES - Broadcasting stations–television - Harmoney Holdings Inc.

CURITY - Diapers–cloth - Gerber Products Co.

CURITY - First aid kits - Colgate-Palmolive Co.

CURITY - Skin care products - Kendall Co.

CURL 2000 - Hair care products - Sabra Hair Products Inc.

CURL ACTIVATOR GEL - Hair care products - Keystone Laboratories Inc.

CURL & CONDITION - Hair care products - Redken Laboratories, Inc.

CURL & GO - Shampoos - Dowbrands L.P.

CURL CRAZY - Kitchen utensils–aluminum ☆ - West Bend Co.

CURL ENHANCER - Hair care products - Helene Curtis Industries Inc.

CURL EQUALITY - Hair care products - Helene Curtis Industries Inc.

CURL EVENT - Hair care products - Helene Curtis Industries Inc.

CURL FIX - Hair care products - Naturelle, Inc.

CURL FIX MAXI - Hair curlers - Naturelle, Inc.

CURL FIX MINI - Hair curlers - Naturelle, Inc.

CURL FREE - Hair care products - Gillette Co.

CURL FREE - Plastics–laminated - D & K International, Inc.

CURL FRIEND - Hair curlers ☆ - Philips Electronics North America Corp.

CURL JUICE - Hair care products - Image Laboratories, Inc.

CURL MEMORY - Shampoos - Dowbrands L.P.

CURL MIST - Hair curlers ☆ - Dazey Corp.

CURL 'N' CADDY - Cosmetics ☆ - Spilo/Mehaz Worldwide

CURL 'N' SET - Hair care products - All Clubman

CURL RELAXER - Hair care products - Revlon Consumer Products Corp.

CURL RELEASE - Hair care products - Revlon Consumer Products Corp.

CURL REPAIR - Hair care products - Samlo

CURL SAVER - Hair care products - Gold Medal Hair Products Inc.

CURL SAVER - Hair care products ☆ - Palm Beach Beauty Products

CURL SET - Floor coverings–carpet and rugs - Newport Carpet Mills Inc.

CURL SHEEN - Ribbons - Hallmark Cards Inc.

CURL SOFTLY - Hair care products ☆ - Roux Laboratories, Inc.

CURL SOURCE - Hair care products - Redken Laboratories, Inc.

CURL-STICK - Hair curlers ☆ - Sunbeam-Oster Household Products

CURL-TECHNICS - Curling irons–electric - Remington Products Co.

CURL TO BODY - Hair care products - Modafini Inc.

CURL UP - Curling irons–electric - Helene Curtis Industries Inc.

CURL-UP - Hair care products - For Perms Only Inc.

CURLAX - Hair care products - Dena Corp.

CURLE CURL - Hair care products - Ampro Industries, Inc.

CURLEASY - Skin care products - Curleasy Manufacturing

CURLEE - Apparel–men's - Palm Beach Co., Inc.

CURLEE WALKER - Dolls - Uneeda Doll Co., Inc.

CURLER CADDY - Bags–cosmetic - JRC Products Inc.

CURLER CONSOLE - Hair curlers ☆ - Sunbeam-Oster Household Products

CURLETTES - Chocolate candy - Charles Chocolate Corp.

CURLEX - Blankets - American Excelsior Co.

CURLEY - See **CUSTOM**

CURLEY CORDS - Telephones - Curley Cords

CURLEY QQQS - Food products - Universal Frozen Foods Co.

CURLEY'S - Barbecue sauce - PMS Foods

CURLEY'S - Milk - Curly's Dairy Inc.

CURLIER FRERES - Wines ☆ - Frederick Wildman and Sons Ltd.

CURLING COMBO - Hair curlers ☆ - Sunbeam-Oster Household Products

CURLING RIBBON EGGS - Novelty items–paper - Sopp America Inc.

CURLMASTER - Dryers–hair - Belson Products

CURLMASTER - Hair care appliance - Windmere Corp.

CURLMASTER - Machine parts - Innovative Closures, Inc.

CURLOC - Hair rollers - Michelangelo Systems Inc.

CURLS & COLOR - Cosmetics - L'anza Research International

CURLS AND CURVES - Hair care products - Redmond Products, Inc.

CURLS FOR A CHANGE - Hair care products - Dep Corp.

CURLS TO GO - Hair curlers ☆ - Sunbeam-Oster Household Products

CURLSETTE - Hair curlers ☆ - Sunbeam-Oster Household Products

CURLY - Cosmetics - Max Factor & Co.

CURLY - Toys–stuffed ☆ - Gund, Inc.

CURLY BAA-BAA - Toys–stuffed ☆ - Gund, Inc.

CURLY BOMBER - Hats - Mad Bomber Co.

CURLY CLAUS - Housewares - Great American Fun Corp.

CURLY CRISPS - Snack foods ☆ - General Mills, Inc.

CURLY CRYSTAL - Christmas tree ornaments - Santa's Best

CURLY CUES - Cake decorations - Cook Chocolate Co.

CURLY DOG - Stuffed animals - Russ Berrie and Co., Inc.

CURLY LAMB - Toys–stuffed ☆ - Commonwealth Toy and Novelty Co. Inc.

☆ = Now out of production

CURLY LOCKS - Hobby kits - Stanislaus Imports, Inc.
CURLY MOO-MOO - Toys–stuffed ☆ - Gund, Inc.
CURLY PIGGLE - Toys–stuffed ☆ - Gund, Inc.
CURLY PLUS - Hair curlers ☆ - Philips Electronics North America Corp.
CURLY Q - Hair curlers ☆ - Philips Electronics North America Corp.
CURLY Q - Yarn - Henry's Attic
CURLY SHREDS - Giftware - Natural Products Corp.
CURLY SQUIRLY - Dolls - Mattel, Inc.
CURLY STYLE - Hair care products - Gillette Co.
CURLY TOP - Dryers–hair - Windmere Corp.
CURLY TOP - Toys - Eugene Doll & Novelty Co. Inc.
CURLY TOPS LAMB - Toys–stuffed - Dakin Inc.
CURLY TROOPER - Hats - Mad Bomber Co.
CURLY-TWIST - Christmas tree ornaments - Union Wadding Co.
CURLY VELVET - Christmas tree ornaments - Santa's Best
CURLY WURLY - Candy ☆ - Peter Paul
CURLYTOPS - Dolls - Russ Berrie and Co., Inc.
CURMED - Film - Curwood, Inc.
CURMEGA - Film - Curwood, Inc.
CURO - Computer software - Mosaic Technology Inc.
CURON - Adhesives and sealants - Maintenance Inc.
CURRAGHMORE - Earthenware ☆ - Waterford Wedgewood USA, Inc.
CURRAN - Deodorizers ☆ - Frank J. Curran-Esquire Chemical Co.
CURRANT - Cosmetics - Lancome
CURRANT & SAGE - Wallcovering ☆ - Colortree Designs
CURRANT & SAGE II - Wallcovering ☆ - Colortree Designs
CURRANTS - Apparel–women's - Jeri-Jo Knitwear Inc.
CURRENCY GUARD - U.S. Currency Protection Corp.
CURRENT - Computer software - International Business Machines Corp.
CURRENT - Giftware - Sasaki
CURRENT - Stationery - Current, Inc.
CURRENT AFFAIRS - Apparel and accessories - Current Affairs, Inc.
CURRENT ATTRACTION - Floor coverings–carpet and rugs ☆ - Walter
    Carpet Mills
CURRENT ATTRACTIONS - Footwear–women's - Livermore-Farmington
    Shoe Co.
CURRENT CHECKS PLUS - Checkbooks - Current, Inc.
CURRENT CLINICAL TRIALS ONCOLOGY - Directories - Pyros Educational
    Group Limited
CURRENT CONTENTS CONNECTION - Computer software ☆ - ISI Software
CURRENT CONTROLS ON DISK - Computer software - ISI Software
CURRENT CRITTERS - Greeting cards - Current, Inc.
CURRENT EFFECTS - Hair care products - Windmere Corp.
CURRENT EVENT - Floor coverings–carpet and rugs ☆ - Columbus Mills, Inc.
CURRENT EVENT, A - Apparel stores–women's - Lady Ester Lingerie Corp.
CURRENT ISSUE - Cleaning preparations - State Chemical Manufacturing Co.
CURRENT NEWS ON FILE - Publisher's imprints - Facts on File Inc.
CURRENT POOL, THE - Exercising equipment - Swimex Systems Inc.
CURRENT SEEN - Apparel and accessories - Amerex of California Corp.
CURRENTMAKER - Computer software - John M. Eubanks
CURRENTS - Curling irons–electric - Remington Products Co.
CURRETAB - Pharmaceutical preparations - Solvay Pharmaceuticals Inc.
CURRICULUM - Floor coverings–carpet and rugs - Sweetwater Carpet Corp.
CURRICULUM BUILDER - Computer software - McGraw-Hill Companies, Inc.
CURRICULUM NAVIGATOR - Computer software - Dale Seymour
    Publications, Inc.
CURRICULUM NAVIGATOR, THE - Computer software - Dale Seymour
    Publications/Alternative Publishing Group
CURRIE-BONNER - Apparel and accessories - Currie-Bonner Inc.
CURRIER - File folders - Winthrop Metal Products Corp.
CURRIER & BRANCH - Apparel and accessories - Filene's Basement Corp.
CURRIER & IVES - Craft supplies - Marketing Action Group Inc. (American
    Family Crafts Div.)
CURRIER & IVES - Deodorizers - Spice Market, Inc.
CURRIER AND IVES - Dolls - Effanbee Doll Corp.
CURRIER & IVES - Giftware - Enesco Corp.
CURRIER & IVES - Housewares ☆ - Scio Pottery Co.
CURRIER & IVES - Paper–gift wrap - Papercraft Corp.
CURRITUCK - Powerboat ☆ - Boston Whaler, Inc.
CURRY - Fabrics - Dan River Inc.
CURRY - Toys–stuffed ☆ - Gund, Inc.
CURRY KING - Food products - Curry King Inc.
CURRY MASALA - Spices and extracts - Cinnabar Specialty Foods, Inc./
    Neera's Products
CURSE, THE - Toys - TMP International, Inc.
CURSOR - Toys - Mattel, Inc.

CURSORAMA PLUS - Computer software - IMSI
CURTAIN CALL - Apparel–athletic - Tighe Industries Inc.
CURTAIN CALL - Chocolate candy ☆ - Chipurnoi Inc.
CURTAIN CALL - Christmas tree ornaments - Cracker Box Inc.
CURTAIN CALL - Floor coverings–carpet and rugs ☆ - Atlas Carpet Mills Inc.
CURTAIN CALL - Floor coverings–carpet and rugs ☆ - Calladium & Marglen
CURTAIN CALL - Recording label - Music and Arts Programs of America Inc.
CURTAIN CALL COSTUMES - Costumes - Tighe Industries Inc.
CURTAIN CALL THEATRE - Games - CBS Toys
CURTAIN GRIPS - Caulking compounds - Myro, Inc.
CURTAIN JEWELRY - Novelty items - Green Mountain Vista
CURTAIN SPECIAL - Thread ☆ - Perfect Thread Co. Inc.
CURTICE - Food products ☆ - Curtice-Burns Foods, Inc.
CURTIS - Bologna - Curtis Packing Co.
CURTIS - Coffee makers–electric ☆ - Gillies Coffee Co.
CURTIS - Computer peripheral equipment - Curtis Manufacturing Co., Inc.
CURTIS - Gauging instruments - Curtis Instruments Inc.
CURTIS - Hardware - Blaine Window Hardware Inc.
CURTIS - Health care products - A.W. Curtis Laboratories, Inc.
CURTIS - Health care products - MK Battery
CURTIS - Locks–padlocks - Curtis Industries Inc.
CURTIS - Paper - Curtis Paper
CURTIS - Scissors–hand-operated - Helene Curtis Industries Inc.
CURTIS - Sealing devices - Curtis Industries, Inc.
CURTIS 900W - Gauging instruments - Curtis Instruments Inc.
CURTIS CARE - Hair care products - Helene Curtis Industries Inc.
CURTIS CLIP - Computer diskettes–blank - Curtis Manufacturing Co., Inc.
CURTIS COMMAND CENTER - Electrical equipment - Curtis Manufacturing
    Co., Inc.
CURTIS CORDUROY - Paper - Crown Paper Co.
CURTIS CREATIONS - Jewelry ☆ - Uncas Manufacturing Co.
CURTIS DIAMOND - Electrical equipment ☆ - Curtis Manufacturing Co., Inc.
CURTIS DIAMOND-PLUS - Electrical equipment ☆ - Curtis Manufacturing Co.,
    Inc.
CURTIS EMERALD - Electrical equipment ☆ - Curtis Manufacturing Co., Inc.
CURTIS JEWEL - Paper products - Crown Vantage Inc.
CURTIS-LOCTITE - Tape–adhesive - Curtis Industries Inc.
CURTIS MARBLE - Paper - Crown Vantage Inc.
CURTIS-MATHES - Stereos - Curtis-Mathes Corp.
CURTIS MUSIC PRESS - Publisher's imprints - Neil A. Kjos Music Co.
CURTIS PMC - Motor vehicle parts and accessories - Curtis Instruments Inc.
CURTIS REMOTE EMERALD - Electrical equipment ☆ - Curtis Manufacturing
    Co., Inc.
CURTIS REMOTE RUBY - Electrical equipment ☆ - Curtis Manufacturing Co.,
    Inc.
CURTIS RUBY - Electrical equipment ☆ - Curtis Manufacturing Co., Inc.
CURTIS RUBY-PLUS - Electrical equipment ☆ - Curtis Manufacturing Co., Inc.
CURTIS SAPPHIRE - Electrical equipment ☆ - Curtis Manufacturing Co., Inc.
CURTIS SWANN - Greeting cards - Burgoyne Inc./Curtis Swann
CURTIS THE CHOICE OF PROFESSIONALS - Adhesives and sealants -
    Curtis Industries, Inc.
CURTIS-TOLEDO - Compressors–air - Curtis Toledo Inc.
CURTISOL - Resins–polypropylene - Curtis Industries Inc.
CURTISS - Candy - Nabisco Foods Group
CURTISS - Recording label - Terock Records
CURTMAN - Jewelry - Uncas Manufacturing Co.
CURT'S - Gasoline - Curt's Oil Co. Inc.
CURTSY - Coats–children's - Brand & Puritz
CURV - Hair care products - Revlon-Realistic Professional Products Inc.
CURV-CLEAN - Denture cleaners - Brimms Inc.
CURV FLO - Counter tops–laminated - V.T. Industries
CURV N COMB - Curling irons–electric ☆ - Moro Beauty College
CURVALLURE - Apparel–women's ☆ - Jantzen Inc.
CURVALON - Apparel and accessories - Vanity Fair Mills Inc.
CURVAMATIC - Watches - Gruen Marketing Corp.
CURVATAR - Photographic equipment - SP Systems/Saratons
CURVCORK - Wallcoverings - Wallcovering Industries Inc.
CURVE - Skin care products - L.C. Licensing, Inc.
CURVE-FIT - Musical instrument accessories ☆ - Selmer Co. Inc.
CURVE-FLO - Belts–rubber - Goodyear Tire & Rubber Co.
CURVE-FOR-CURVE - Apparel and accessories ☆ - Playtex Apparel, Inc.
CURVE-GARD - Medical apparatus - Karlen Manufacturing, Inc.
CURVE SNUGGER - Medical apparatus - Roloke Co.
CURVE, THE - Frames–picture - Dynamic Plastics
CURVED FOR COMFORT - Apparel and accessories - Glamorise Foundations
    Inc.

CURVEDWARE - Cutlery - Curvedware, Inc.
CURVEMASTER - Chains–industrial - Rexnord Corp.
CURVEMASTER - Hair care products ☆ - Dubl Duck/Jet Set Inc.
CURVES - Prosthetic apparatus - Bodylines Inc.
CURVES - Vitamins and nutritional supplements - Jenny Craig, Inc.
CURVES AHEAD - Underwear and nightwear ☆ - Lovable Co.
CURVES BY RICHARD SIMMONS - Apparel and accessories - Breton Industries
CURVESHAPER - Exercising equipment ☆ - Precise International/Wenger
CURVET - Building materials - Behlen Manufacturing Co.
CURVETTE - Watches - Gruen Marketing Corp.
CURVEX - Watches - Gruen Marketing Corp.
CURVFIT - Furniture - Larry Shaw Co.
CURVI - Scissors–hand-operated - F.W. Engels Inc.
CURVILINEAL - Shutters–wood - Pinecrest, Inc.
CURVILINEAR - Sporting goods - Kellwood Co.
CURVILINEAR - Steel products - Clayton & Lambert Manufacturing Co.
CURVIPLAN - Watches - Movado Time Corp.
CURVLITE - Canes - Curvlite Surgical Products
CURV'N SHEAR - Hair care products ☆ - Moro Beauty College
CURVWALL - Wallcoverings - Wallcovering Industries Inc.
CURVWOOD - Wallcoverings - Wallcovering Industries Inc.
CURVY CUT - Seafood - Kraft Foodservice Holding Corp.
CURY Q - Extension cords - General Cable Corp.
CURZON - Dishes–china - Waterford Wedgewood USA, Inc.
CURZON DESIGNS - Giftware - Curzon Designs Ltd.
CUSA CREDIT UNION SYSTEMS FOR AMERICA - Computer software - Cusa
CUSANO ROMANI - Cigars - Michael J. Chiusano
CUSDUM FOODS, FOOD PRODUCTS - Food products - Bellegem Waffle Corp.
CUSENIER - Wines ☆ - Frank Sutton & Co.
CUSH - Bicycles - Hunt-Wilde Corp.
CUSH-EEZ - Apparel and accessories - Brazabra Corp.
CUSH GRIP - Bicycles - Hunt-Wilde Corp.
CUSH-MAT - Wooden slat mats, now out of production - American Floor Products Co. Inc.
CUSH-N-AIR - Footwear–men's - L.B. Evans' Son Co.
CUSH-N-AIRE - Padding–foam - Bondafoam Inc.
CUSH-N-AIRE - Wheels - Hamilton Caster & Manufacturing Co.
CUSH-N-BOND - Padding–foam - Bondafoam Inc.
CUSH N CUBES - Playground equipment - Miracle Recreation Equipment Co.
CUSH-N-FLEX - Fibers–synthetic - L & P Property Management Co.
CUSH-N-FLEX - Wheels - Hamilton Caster & Manufacturing Co.
CUSH-N-GRIP II - Vinyl matting with tips ☆ - American Floor Products Co. Inc.
CUSH-N-LYTE - Footwear–men's - L.B. Evans' Son Co.
CUSH-N-MOC - Footwear–men's - L.B. Evans' Son Co.
CUSH-N-TUF - Wheels - Hamilton Caster & Manufacturing Co.
CUSHABLES - Shoes - CSD Footgear, Inc.
CUSHEES - Sporting goods - Comfort Cushion Mills, Inc.
CUSHI-HEEL - Shoe soles - Calderon Products Inc.
CUSHIBEDS - Pet products ☆ - Flexi-Mat Corp.
CUSHIES - Facial tissues - Sterling Winthrop Inc.
CUSHIN - Golfing equipment - Karsten Manufacturing Corp.
CUSHING - Food products - Speaco Foods Inc.
CUSHINS - Footwear–men's - Jarman Shoe Co.
CUSHION - Denture materials - Oakhurst Co.
CUSHION - Hitches–trailer - Schuck Industries, Inc.
CUSHION - Mops - O-Cedar/Vining Household Products Co.
CUSHION AIR - Padding–foam - Carpet Co-Op of America Association
CUSHION-AIR - Saddles - Libertyville Saddle Shop, Inc.
CUSHION AIRE - Health care products ☆ - Camp, Inc.
CUSHION-AIRE SPONGE - Sporting goods - Wilson Sporting Goods Co.
CUSHION CONTROL SYSTEM - Sporting goods - Lisco, Inc.
CUSHION CUT - Saw blades - Cushion Cut, Inc.
CUSHION DECK - Exercising equipment - Proform Fitness Products, Inc.
CUSHION-DEK - Mats - Superior Manufacturing Group/Notrax Floor Matting
CUSHION-DRI - Socks - Sears, Roebuck and Co.
CUSHION-EASE - Furniture - Velsco Inc.
CUSHION FACTORY, THE - Floor coverings - Cushion Factory
CUSHION FIRM - Mattresses - Ohio Mattress Co.
CUSHION-GRID - Floor coverings - Durable Corp.
CUSHION GRIP - Denture materials - Schering-Plough Healthcare Products
CUSHION GRIP - Sporting goods ☆ - Outdoor Technologies Group
CUSHION JOY - Floor coverings - Cushion Factory
CUSHION LIFT - Orthopedic products - Ortho-Kinetics, Inc.
CUSHION LITE - Socks - Marilyn Werner

CUSHION-LITE SOLING - Sandals - ALP Sport Sandals
CUSHION-LOCK REGLETS - Moldings–plaster of paris - Dayton Superior Corp.
CUSHION-LOK - Mats - Superior Manufacturing Group/Notrax Floor Matting
CUSHION-MAILER - Bags - Pen-Tab Industries
CUSHION MAX - Sporting goods - Unique Sports Products Inc.
CUSHION NOK - Archery equipment - Tru-Fire Corp.
CUSHION-NU - Cleaning preparations - Keromate Products Inc.
CUSHION PLUS - Socks - Russell National Sport Socks
CUSHION POINT - Office supplies - Scripto-Tokai Corp.
CUSHION-REST - Frames–eyeglass - J.I. Morris Co.
CUSHION-RIDE III - Hardware - Darnell Corp.
CUSHION ROLL - Hosiery - Wigwam Mills Inc.
CUSHION SEAL - Lubricating oils - Power Punch Distributors
CUSHION SEAL - Weather stripping - Kessler Products Ltd.
CUSHION SLEEVE - Office supplies - Scripto-Tokai Corp.
CUSHION SOFT - Decals and transfers - Rubbermaid Inc.
CUSHION STAT - Mats - Superior Manufacturing Group/Notrax Floor Matting
CUSHION STEP - Mats - Ludlow Composites Corp.
CUSHION TILE - Floor coverings - Ludlow Composites Corp.
CUSHION-TOP - Hosiery - Wigwam Mills Inc.
CUSHION TRAX - Floor coverings–linoleum - Superior Manufacturing Group, Inc.
CUSHION WALK - Mats - Cactus Mat Manufacturing Co.
CUSHIONAIR - Mattresses - Paramount Industrial Companies Inc.
CUSHIONAIRE - Apparel–women's ☆ - Maidenform Inc. (True Form Foundations Div.)
CUSHIONAIRE - Garden furniture–metal ☆ - Samsonite Furniture Co. (Consumer Products Div.)
CUSHIONEASE - Medical apparatus - Lumex, Inc.
CUSHIONERA - Furniture–metal ☆ - Telescope Casual Furniture Inc.
CUSHIONERA II - Furniture ☆ - Telescope Casual Furniture Inc.
CUSHIONFALL - Fertilizers - Becker-Underwood, Inc.
CUSHIONFLOR - Floor coverings - Congoleum Corp.
CUSHIONFLOR SUPREME - Floor coverings - Congoleum Corp.
CUSHIONLITE - Plastics–laminated - Free-Flow Packaging Corp.
CUSHIONMASTER - Cushions - Master Woodcraft Inc.
CUSHIONVINYL - Floor coverings - Congoleum Corp.
CUSHIONWALL - Floor coverings - Congoleum Corp.
CUSHLIN - Medical apparatus - Schering-Plough Healthcare Products
CUSHMAN - Motor vehicles - Ransomes-Cushman-Ryan
CUSHMAN SCOTSMAN - Motor vehicles ☆ - Ransomes-Cushman-Ryan
CUSH'N STEP - Insoles - Safety Supply America Corp.
CUSH'N TOTE - Cushions - Timely Enterprises, Inc.
CUSHY - Cases–musical instrument - M & M Distributing Co.
CUSHY CORNERS - Hardware - Marka Industries Inc.
CUSHY FLOAT - Boating equipment and accessories - Evolution Co., Inc.
CUSHYWRAP - Packaging–blisterwrap - Reo Associates Inc.
CUSLON WRAP - Paper–gift wrap ☆ - Hallmark Cards Inc.
CUSTARD - Glassware–household ☆ - Fenton Art Glass Co.
CUSTER - Thread - Van Waters and Rogers Inc.
CUSTODY LOUNGE - Furniture - Norix Group, Inc.
CUSTOM - Aquariums–household - California Aquarium Supply Corp.
CUSTOM - Audio tapes–blank - Hamilton Electronics Corp.
CUSTOM - Binoculars - Bausch & Lomb Inc.
CUSTOM - Brushes–paint - A. Flohr Co. Inc.
CUSTOM - Cabinets - Fieldstone Cabinetry
CUSTOM - Cosmetics - Custom Cosmetics Co.
CUSTOM - Electronic equipment - Daktronics Inc.
CUSTOM - Flatware ☆ - Lifetime Hoan Corp.
CUSTOM - Flooring–hardwood - Memphis Hardwood Flooring Co.
CUSTOM - Food products - Custom Apple Packers Inc.
CUSTOM - Food products - Custom Food Products Inc.
CUSTOM - Furniture–upholstered - Woodland Furniture Manufacturing Co.
CUSTOM - Guitars - Paul Reed Smith Guitars
CUSTOM - Health care products - Fortress Inc.
CUSTOM - Machinery ☆ - Victor Technology
CUSTOM - Moldings and trim - Custom-Pak Inc.
CUSTOM - Motor vehicles–motor homes - Winnebago Industries, Inc.
CUSTOM - Musical instruments - Hyer Percussion Products
CUSTOM - Pizzas–frozen - Dairy Fresh Products Co.
CUSTOM - Recording label - Cadet Records Inc.
CUSTOM - Spirit duplicators ☆ - Copy Plus Inc.
CUSTOM - Sporting goods - Outdoor Technologies Group
CUSTOM - Stationery - Superior Marking Equipment Co.
CUSTOM - Tools ☆ - Russell Harrington Cutlery, Inc.

☆ = Now out of production

CUSTOM - Work benches - Shure Manufacturing Corp.
CUSTOM 100 - Golfing equipment - Northwestern Golf Co.
CUSTOM 400 - Cutlery ☆ - Lifetime Hoan Corp.
CUSTOM 500 - Motor vehicles–automobiles ☆ - Ford Motor Co.
CUSTOM-2000 - Adhesives and sealants ☆ - Custom Building Products
CUSTOM 2500 - Lighting fixtures ☆ - Brinkmann Lighting Products
CUSTOM 4500 - Firefighting apparatus - Mine Safety Appliances Co.
CUSTOM 8000 - Motors–hydraulic - General Electric Co.
CUSTOM ADVANTAGE - Furniture - Alexvale Furniture, Inc.
CUSTOM AIR V - Respirators - Mine Safety Appliances Co.
CUSTOM-AIRE - Sweaters - Pine State Knitwear Co.
CUSTOM ANGLER - Fishing rods - Gunarama Wholesale, Inc.
CUSTOM BALL - Balls–golf - Lisco, Inc.
CUSTOM BELT - Tires - Bridgestone/Firestone, Inc.
CUSTOM-BLEND - Cement - Custom Building Products
CUSTOM BLEND - Cosmetics - Posner Laboratories Inc.
CUSTOM-BLENZ - Paints ☆ - Standard Paints Inc.
CUSTOM-BOND - Adhesives and sealants - Custom Building Products
CUSTOM BREAK - Chemicals - Betz Energy Chemicals Inc.
CUSTOM-BUILT - Office supplies - Alvin and Co. Inc.
CUSTOM-BUILT COFFEES - Apparel - Speeder & Earl's, Inc.
CUSTOM CABINET - Racks - Hirsh Co.
CUSTOM CAR CENTER - Toys–automobiles - Mattel, Inc.
CUSTOM CARE - Curling irons–electric - Remington Products Co.
CUSTOM CARE - Dog food - Hill's Pet Nutrition Inc.
CUSTOM CARE - Medical apparatus - Span-America Medical Systems, Inc.
CUSTOM CARE - Pet products - Colgate-Palmolive Co.
CUSTOM-CAST - Belts–apparel - Valleau Brass Foundry
CUSTOM CASUALS - Apparel and accessories - Wilson Brothers
CUSTOM CAT - Bicycles - Murray, Inc.
CUSTOM CCI CHROME - Motorcycle parts and accessories - Custom Chrome, Inc.
CUSTOM CD-ROM PRODUCTIONS - Compact discs–prerecorded - Myriad Entertainment
CUSTOM CHOICE - Apparel and accessories - Simon's Copley Square
CUSTOM CLASSIC - Drapery hardware - Window Imagination
CUSTOM CLASSICS - Floor coverings - Kentucky Wood Floors Inc.
CUSTOM CLEANER - Cleaning equipment - Creative Products Resource, Inc.
CUSTOM CLOSET - Racks - Hirsh Co.
CUSTOM CLUB INTERNATIONAL - Apparel and accessories - Phillips-Van Heusen Corp.
CUSTOM COLLECTION, THE - Blinds–venetian ☆ - Hunter Douglas, Inc.
CUSTOM COLORS - Pencils - Dixon Ticonderoga Co.
CUSTOM COMFORT - Bicycles ☆ - Troxel Co. Cycling and Fitness
CUSTOM CONNECTION - Sockets–electric - Woods Industries, Inc.
CUSTOM CONTOUR GRIP - Golfing equipment - John Rouzee Green Co., Inc.
CUSTOM CORK - Floor coverings–tile ☆ - National Floor Products Co., Inc.
CUSTOM CORNER - Mattress pads - Perfect Fit Industries, Inc.
CUSTOM CORTINA - Floor coverings - Azrock Commercial Flooring
CUSTOM COUPE - Infant product - Century Products Co.
CUSTOM COVE - Bathroom fixtures - Artesian Industries
CUSTOM-CRAFT - Notebooks and notepads ☆ - Webway, Inc.
CUSTOM-CRAFT - Wallets - Accurate Leather & Novelty Co. Inc.
CUSTOM/CRAFT LINE - Cabinets–metal - Horizon Steel Products Inc.
CUSTOM-CRAFTED - Binders - General Loose Leaf Bindery Co.
CUSTOM-CRETE - Latex - Custom Building Products
CUSTOM CRUISER - Motor vehicles–automobiles ☆ - General Motors Corp. (Oldsmobile Div.)
CUSTOM CUFF - Mannequins - Roger Laviale, Ltd.
CUSTOM CURL - Hair care products - Windmere Corp.
CUSTOM CURVES - Hardware - Seal Rite Windows
CUSTOM CUSTOM - Musical instrument accessories - Seymour Duncan Pickups
CUSTOM CUT - Hair care products - Vapon, Inc.
CUSTOM CUT TAPE - Hair care products - Vapon, Inc.
CUSTOM DECAL FACTORY - Decals and transfers - American Art Clay Co. Inc.
CUSTOM DECOR - Floor coverings–carpet and rugs - Southern Carpet Mills
CUSTOM DELI - Sandwiches–prepackaged - E.A. Sween Co.
CUSTOM DELUXE - Boats ☆ - Lanness K. McKee & Co.
CUSTOM DELUXE - Cabinets - Diamond Cabinets
CUSTOM DELUXE II SERIES - Cabinets - Diamond Cabinets
CUSTOM DESIGNER COLLECTION - Floor coverings–carpet and rugs - Milliken & Co. Inc.
CUSTOM DESIGNS - Bedding–linen - Custom Designs
CUSTOM EYES - Cosmetics - Revlon Consumer Products Corp.

CUSTOM FIREBIRD - Musical instrument accessories - Seymour Duncan Pickups
CUSTOM FIT - Footwear - Northwest Podiatric Laboratory, Inc.
CUSTOM FIT - Golfing equipment - Henry-Griffitts, Inc.
CUSTOM FIT - Golfing equipment - Nassau Precision Casting Co., Inc.
CUSTOM FIT - Jewelry - Reese Corp.
CUSTOM FIT - Vitamins and nutritional supplements - Pdk Labs, Inc.
CUSTOM FIT - Window shades - Newell Window Furnishing Co.
CUSTOM FLEX - Hair care products - Fromm Industries
CUSTOM-FLEX - Latex - Custom Building Products
CUSTOM-FLOAT - Mortars–clay - Custom Building Products
CUSTOM FOLIO BY HENREDON - Furniture - Henredon Furniture Industries Inc.
CUSTOM FOOT, THE - Footwear - Measurably Better Corp.
CUSTOM FORMULA - Musical instrument accessories ☆ - GHS Strings
CUSTOM FRAMES - Trailers–boat - EZ Loader Boat Trailers Inc.
CUSTOM FUTURA - Cosmetics - Revlon-Realistic Professional Products Inc.
CUSTOM GOLD - Meat products–beef - Thompson Packers Inc.
CUSTOM GRADE - Pipes ☆ - Missouri Meerschaum Co.
CUSTOM GRAPHICS - Floor coverings–carpet and rugs - Hartford Carpet Mills
CUSTOM HOME - Fans–electric - Hunter Fan Co.
CUSTOM HOOD PROTECTOR - Motor vehicle parts and accessories - Saddleman, Inc.
CUSTOM HOUSE - Floor coverings - Mannington Resilient Floors
CUSTOM HOUSE - Furniture and mattresses - Edward Hostmann, Inc.
CUSTOM HOUSE - Wigs - Custom House International
CUSTOM IMAGE - Blinds–venetian - Craftsman Window Coverings Inc.
CUSTOM IMPACT - Vitamins and nutritional supplements - Purina Mills, Inc.
CUSTOM KEY - Keys - Armament Systems and Procedures, Inc.
CUSTOM KNIT - Apparel and accessories ☆ - Leininger Mills Inc.
CUSTOM KNIT - Prosthetic apparatus - Accurate Knitting Mills Inc.
CUSTOM KOTE - Paperboard - Mead Corp.
CUSTOM L-5 - Musical instruments - Gibson Guitar Corp.
CUSTOM LADIES - Hair care products - Chicago Hair Good Inc.
CUSTOM LIMITED - Apparel and accessories - Manhattan International
CUSTOM LOGO BY CAPPUCCINO - Neckties - A. Schreter & Sons Co. Inc.
CUSTOM LONG MILER - Tires - Uniroyal Goodrich Tire Co.
CUSTOM-LOOK - Floor coverings - Tarkett, Inc.
CUSTOM LOOMS - Floor coverings–carpet and rugs - Custom Looms Rug Mills Inc.
CUSTOM MAID - Brassieres (Bras) - Custom Maid Brassiere Co.
CUSTOM MANUFACTURE - Botanical extracts - Bio-Botanica
CUSTOM MATCH - Cosmetics - Revlon Consumer Products Corp.
CUSTOM-MATIC - Television equipment ☆ - Quasar Co.
CUSTOM MEDICAL PRODUCTS - Medical apparatus - Custom Medical Products, Inc.
CUSTOM NEB - Health care products - Medical Industries America, Inc.
CUSTOM OIL - Finishing agents - Chem-Pak Inc.
CUSTOM PACKER - Frozen vegetables - Columbia Foods Inc.
CUSTOM PAGE - Pagers - Custom Page, Inc.
CUSTOM-PAK - Cases–plastic - Custom-Pak Inc.
CUSTOM PATCH - Mortars–clay - Custom Building Products
CUSTOM PLEATS - Trimmings–fabric ☆ - Decorative Aides Co. Inc.
CUSTOM-PLUG - Cement - Custom Building Products
CUSTOM POPS - Candy - Rosemary Candy Co.
CUSTOM POWER 1700 - Toys–trains - Atlas Model Railroad Co., Inc.
CUSTOM-PRIME - Adhesives and sealants ☆ - Custom Building Products
CUSTOM-QUALITY - Frames–picture - Art Publishers
CUSTOM QUARRY - Floor coverings - National Floor Products Co., Inc.
CUSTOM-REDI - Doors–metal - Pioneer Industries
CUSTOM REGAL - Fireplace equipment - Thermo-Rite Manufacturing Co.
CUSTOM-RITE - Chairs–upholstered - Harold E. Martin
CUSTOM ROCK - Concrete products - Custom Rock International
CUSTOM ROCK INTERNATIONAL - Building materials–concrete - Concrete Design Specialties, Inc.
CUSTOM ROYALE - Floor coverings–tile - VPI
CUSTOM ROYALE - Slacks and tuxedos - Mcgregor Corp.
CUSTOM SEAL - Resins–acrylic - Custom Laminations Inc.
CUSTOM-SEAL - Resins–acrylic ☆ - Custom Building Products
CUSTOM SEAL - Windows–storm - Thermal Technology Industries Inc.
CUSTOM SEALDON 30 - Shingles–asphalt or tar - Certainteed Corp. (Roofing Products Group)
CUSTOM SERIES - Garbage disposers - Masco Building Products Corp.
CUSTOM SERIES - Musical instruments - Getzen Co.
CUSTOM-SHADE - Garden equipment ☆ - Custom Building Products

CUSTOM SHAPES - Pillows - Hollander Home Fashions Inc.
CUSTOM SHAVE SYSTEM - Electric shaver - Wahl Clipper Corp.
CUSTOM SHOP - Windows–storm ☆ - Remington Building Products
CUSTOM SHOWCASE - Floor coverings - Congoleum Corp.
CUSTOM SHOWER SYSTEM - Whirlpools - Jacuzzi Inc.
CUSTOM SIGNATURE - Floor coverings - Bangkok International Inc.
CUSTOM SNAP & BODY - Cosmetics - Revlon-Realistic Professional Products Inc.
CUSTOM SOUND - Stereos - Custom Sound Corp.
CUSTOM SPEC II - Floor coverings - Mannington Resilient Floors
CUSTOM SPORT - Bicycles ☆ - Raleigh USA Bicycle Co.
CUSTOM SQUARE - Floor coverings ☆ - Anderson Hardwood Floors Inc.
CUSTOM SQUARES - Floor coverings–carpet and rugs - Milliken & Co. Inc.
CUSTOM STRAPPER - Hobby kits - State Chemical Manufacturing Co.
CUSTOM SUPPORT - Apparel–women's - NCC Industries, Inc.
CUSTOM SYSTEM 45 - Cement - Edison Coatings, Inc.
CUSTOM TERRACE - Floor coverings - Congoleum Corp.
CUSTOM-TONES - Paints ☆ - Devoe & Raynolds Co.
CUSTOM TRAVERTINE - Floor coverings ☆ - Azrock Commercial Flooring
CUSTOM TSP SUBSTITUTE - Cleaning preparations - Custom Building Products
CUSTOM-TUNE - Firearms, accessories, and parts - Wilson's Gun Shop, Inc.
CUSTOM ULTRA GRAPHICS II - Floor coverings–carpet and rugs ☆ - Mannington Carpets, Inc.
CUSTOM-VAL - Draperies ☆ - United Merchants and Manufacturers Inc.
CUSTOM WALKER - Walking footwear ☆ - Autry Industries Inc.
CUSTOM WEAVING - Floor coverings–carpet and rugs - Langhorne Carpet Co. Inc.
CUSTOM WEDGE SYSTEMS - Golfing equipment - Golfsmith International Inc.
CUSTOM WRAP - Packaging–paper - Sealed Air Corp.
CUSTOM WROUGHT - Fireplace equipment ☆ - Reichman Inc.
CUSTOM X - Bodyboards - Superior Foam Products, Inc.
CUSTOMAGIC - Paints - Morwear Paint Co.
CUSTOMAIRE - Furniture ☆ - Samsonite Furniture Co. (Consumer Products Div.)
CUSTOMATIC - Duplicators and supplies ☆ - Copy Plus Inc.
CUSTOMATICS - Floor coverings–carpet and rugs ☆ - Mannington Carpets, Inc.
CUSTOMBILT - Floor coverings - Congoleum Corp.
CUSTOMBLEN - Fertilizers - Scotts-Sierra Horticultural Products Co.
CUSTOMBRITE - Floor coverings - Domco Industries Ltd.
CUSTOMBUILT - Musical instrument accessories - Humes & Berg Manufacturing Co. Inc.
CUSTOMCASE 7000 - Office furniture–metal ☆ - Simon Corp.
CUSTOMCRAFT - Manicure preparations - Customcraft Nails Inc.
CUSTOMCRAFT - Shoes ☆ - Schwartz & Benjamin Inc.
CUSTOMCRAFT - Weightlifting equipment - Crown Novelty Works
CUSTOMEASE - Computer software - Coastal Video Communications Corp.
CUSTOMER - Fruits–frozen - Cal-Fruit (Frozen Foods Div.)
CUSTOMER CONEXION - Computer peripheral equipment - Leadership 2000, Inc.
CUSTOMER PERSONAL EAR - Hearing aids - Qualitone
CUSTOMER STAR - Computer software - Electronic Data Systems Corp.
CUSTOMER VISION - Office supplies - Lanier Worldwide Inc.
CUSTOMERQ - Computer software - Quintus Corp.
CUSTOMERS CHOICE - Pretzels - Bez Enterprises, Inc.
CUSTOMFLEX - Flashlights - Rollei of America Inc.
CUSTOMFLOR - Floor coverings - Domco Industries Ltd.
CUSTOMFOAM - Hobby kits ☆ - Craft House Corp.
CUSTOMFOLD - Folding doors - American Fold Doors Inc.
CUSTOMIN - Cattle feed - Agway Country Foods Inc.
CUSTOMISER - Blinds–venetian ☆ - Spring Window Fashions Division, Inc.
CUSTOMIZED VISION PROGRAM - Ophthalmic goods - Pilkington Visioncare, Inc.
CUSTOMIZER - Binders - McBee Loose Leaf Binders
CUSTOMIZER - Fireplace equipment - Design Specialties Inc.
CUSTOMIZER - Photographic equipment - SP Systems/Saratons
CUSTOMIZERS - Toys–automobiles - Mattel, Inc.
CUSTOMLINE - Electrical equipment - Customline Inc.
CUSTOMLINE - Garment racks - Vogel Peterson Furniture Co.
CUSTOMLINE - Toys–trains - Atlas Model Railroad Co., Inc.
CUSTOMLINER - Motor vehicle parts and accessories - James P. Wright
CUSTOMPAY - Banks–commercial - SPS Payment Systems, Inc.
CUSTOMPLUS - Prosthetic apparatus - Tecnol Medical Products, Inc.
CUSTOMPLUS - Razors - Gillette Co.
CUSTOMPREP - Computer storage devices–optical - Computerprep, Inc.

CUSTOMSPEC - Floor coverings - Mannington Resilient Floors
CUSTOMSPEC II - Floor coverings - Mannington Mills, Inc.
CUSTOMWARE - Computer software - Random House, Inc.
CUSTOMWEAVE - Floor coverings–carpet and rugs - World Carpets, Inc.
CUSTON DECORATING - Floor coverings–carpet and rugs - Custom Decor Inc.
CUSTUM - Rifles - Conetrol Scope Mounts
CUT-A-DRAPE - Machinery - S. Morantz Inc.
CUT ABOVE - Floor coverings–carpet and rugs - Calladium & Marglen
CUT ABOVE - Floor coverings–carpet and rugs - Roxbury Carpet Co.
CUT ABOVE, A - Knives - A & W Products Co., Inc.
CUT ABOVE, A - Seasonings - A Cut Above Foods, Inc.
CUT ABOVE, A - Apparel stores–lingerie - Formfit Rogers
CUT ABOVE AT ANY ANGLE, A - Motor vehicles–all-terrain - UST Corp.
CUT ABOVE THE CROWD, A - Wallpaper - K.M.L. Industries
CUT ABOVE THE REST, A - Cabinets–wood - Coastal Wood Products, Inc.
CUT ABOVE THE REST, A - Apparel–women's - HCS International Inc.
CUT-ALL - Knives–hunting ☆ - Hunt Manufacturing Co.
CUT & DRY - Apparel–men's - Woodhouse Apparel, Inc.
CUT AND PASTE - Computer software - Electronic Arts Inc.
CUT & SCRAPE - Knives - L.S. Starrett Co. Inc. (Consumer Products Div.)
CUT & SERVE - Housewares - Willow Molded Plastics
CUT-AWAY - Skin care products - Opi Products, Inc.
CUT BERLIN - Glassware–household - Kusak Cut Glass Works
CUT BY GAUGE - Jewelry–precious - Ernest Slotar, Inc.
CUT CORONET WREATH - Glassware–household - Kusak Cut Glass Works
CUT CRYSTAL - Cups–plastic - Nyman Manufacturing Co.
CUT DEVIL - Tools - Warren Tool Group
CUT-EASE - Lubricants - American Grease Stick Co.
CUT-ELEC - Hardware - Atlas Copco Electric Tools Inc.
CUT GUARD - Shaving preparations - Faberge Co.
CUT-HEAL - Pet products - Cut-Heal Animal Care Products, Inc.
CUT-IT-OUT - Craft supplies ☆ - VIP/VIP Crafts
CUT-IT-UP - Recording label - Pandisc Records
CUT JASMINE - Glassware–household - Kusak Cut Glass Works
CUT KUSAK ROSE - Glassware–household - Kusak Cut Glass Works
CUT/LAP - Electronics equipment - Convergence Corp.
CUT LINE - Apparel and accessories - K & S Fashions
CUT-LOOSE CORAL - Nail care products - Maybelline Co.
CUT LUBE - Lubricating oils - Enterprise Oil Co.
CUT N CLIP - Housewares ☆ - London International U.S. Holdings
CUT N CRUNCH - Toys ☆ - Today's Kids Inc.
CUT-N-DRILL - Tools - Goldblatt Tool Co.
CUT 'N' FIT - Filters–air - American Air Filter International (Replacement Filter Products)
CUT 'N JUMP - Skis - Wellington Leisure Products, Inc.
CUT-N-SAUCER - Abrasive products ☆ - Norton Co.
CUT 'N SHINE - Steel wool - Meguiar's, Inc.
CUT N SHRED - Garden equipment - Roto-Hoe Co.
CUT 'N STICK - Hobby kits - Bemiss-Jason Corp.
CUT-N-TAP - Oils–lubricating - R.G. Shannon Co.
CUT-R-MATIC - Garden equipment - Olympia Industrial Inc.
CUT RITE - Paper–waxed - Reynolds Metals Co.
CUT-RITE - Scissors–hand-operated - Fiskars Inc.
CUT SALZBURG - Glassware–household ☆ - Kusak Cut Glass Works
CUT-SAW - Hardware - Black & Decker Corp.
CUT STOP - Pet products - Custom Cable Co.
CUT-TEC - Gears–bicycle - Marmon Holdings, Inc.
A CUT, THE - Jewelry - Harry Winston, Inc.
CUT-THRU - Recording label - The HeartMath System
CUT-TO-FIT - Patterns–clothing - Mccall Pattern Co.
CUT UP - Chewing gum - Gum Tech International
CUT-UP - Pharmaceutical preparations - Bricker Laboratories
CUT, WET N HANG - Wallpaper ☆ - E-Z Paintr Corp.
CUTABOVE - Can openers–electric - Rival Manufacturing Co.
CUTAR - Bathroom accessories - Summers Laboratories Inc.
CUTAWL - Saws–hand-operated - Foredom Electric Co.
CUTCO - Knives - Cutco/Vector Marketing Co.
CUTE AND CUDDLY - Calendars - American Greetings Corp.
CUTE AS A BUTTON - Barrettes - JHB International Inc.
CUTE AS A BUTTON - Doll with cologne ☆ - Cosrich Inc.
CUTE AS THE DICKENS - Paper–gift wrap - Papercraft Corp.
CUTE COUPLES - Toys–stuffed - Fun World Inc.
CUTE E NUFF - Toys - Etna Products Co. Inc.
CUTE LITTLE THINGS - Glassware–household - Delfino Products Inc.
CUTE 'N COOL - Dolls - Mattel, Inc.

☆ = Now out of production

CUTE 'N CUDDLY - Toys - Eugene Doll & Novelty Co. Inc.
CUTE N' SMART - Toys - Russ Berrie and Co., Inc.
CUTE OPTIONS - Apparel–women's - Harminder Kohli
C.U.T.E. ORIGINALS - Underwear and nightwear - Glencraft Lingerie
CUTE STUFF - Footwear - Somerset Footwear
CUTE TEEN - Apparel–women's - Wacoal America Inc.
CUTE TOGS - Coats–children's - MZL Fashions Corp.
CUTECUMBER - Apparel–children's - Evolutions, Inc.
CUTECUMBER - Apparel–children's - Mark Trouser Inc.
CUTEMOL - Bathroom accessories - Summers Laboratories Inc.
CUTERZ - Nail care products - Rudolph International, Inc.
CUTESLUMBER - Apparel–children's - Sanmark-Stardust Inc.
CUTESY - Footwear–children's - Norwich Shoe Co. Inc.
CUTEX - Cosmetics - Chesebrough-Pond's USA Co.
CUTEX COLOR-QUICK - Clippers–nail - Chesebrough-Pond's USA Co.
CUTEX COLOR SPLASH - Lip balms - Conopco, Inc.
CUTEX QUICK AND GENTLE - Nail care products - Conopco, Inc.
CUTHBERTSON HOUSE - Dinnerware–glass - Cuthbertson Imports Inc.
CUTHBERTSON IMPERIAL COLLECTION - Glassware–household ☆ - Cuthbertson Imports Inc.
CUTHEE - Towels - Mariana Thee and Ferry Thee Partnership
CUTI-CARE - Tools–hand-operated - Howard Eldon Ltd.
CUTI CAT - Candy ☆ - L.E.G. Inc.
CUTI-CLEAN - Manicure preparations - Customcraft Nails Inc.
CUTI-CLEAR - Cosmetics - Worldwide Cosmetics
CUTI-PUP - Deodorizers ☆ - Car-Freshner Corp.
CUTICIN - Hair care products - Wella Corp. (Consumer Products Div.)
CUTICLE BEAUTIFUL - Nail care products - Mennen Co.
CUTICLE CRAYONS - Skin care products - Fruit of the Earth, Inc.
CUTICLE CURE - Nail care product - Art of Beauty, Inc.
CUTICLE HAIR - Wigs - His & Her Hair Goods Co.
CUTICLE KEEPER - Nail care products - Revlon Consumer Products Corp.
CUTICLE SOLUTION - Nail care products - Naturally Beautiful Nails, Inc.
CUTICLE T.L.C. - Nail care products - Revlon Consumer Products Corp.
CUTICLE TREAT - Manicure preparations - Delore International
CUTICURA - Pharmaceutical preparations - Dep Corp.
CUTICURE + - Manicure preparations - Winning Solutions Inc./Miracle of Aloe
CUTIE - Key rings - Russ Berrie and Co., Inc.
CUTIE - Ophthalmic goods ☆ - Rozin Optical Export Corp.
C.U.T.I.E. - Toys - Mattel, Inc.
CUTIE - Toys - Village Toys
CUTIE CAR - Toys - Steven Manufacturing Co.
CUTIE CHICK - Candy ☆ - Keppel's Inc.
CUTIE CLIPS - Barrettes - Russ Berrie and Co., Inc.
CUTIE CLIPS - Greeting cards ☆ - Brett-Forer Greetings Inc.
CUTIE FACE - Candy ☆ - Rosemary Candy Co.
CUTIE FRUITI - Dolls - Tonka Corp.
CUTIE FRUITIE - Dolls and accessories, now out of production - American Greetings Corp.
CUTIE PIE - Dolls ☆ - Effanbee Doll Corp.
CUTIE PIE - Food products - Cutie Pie Corp.
CUTIE PIE - Toys–stuffed - Jolly U.S.A., Inc.
CUTIE PIES - Greeting cards ☆ - Brett-Forer Greetings Inc.
CUTIE POM POM - Toys - Village Toys
CUTIE SHORTIE - Apparel and accessories ☆ - Leininger Mills Inc.
CUTIES - Food products - Tofutti Brands Inc.
CUTIES - Giftware - Russ Berrie and Co., Inc.
CUTIES - Giftware - Terrace Ceramics Inc.
CUTIES BY JUDY - Clothing - Judy-Philippine, Inc.
CUTINOVA - Health care products - Beiersdorf Inc.
CUTIQUE - Nail care products - Orly International Inc.
CUTISEAL - Hair care products - Helene Curtis Industries Inc.
CUTLASS - Boats–motor ☆ - Cobia Boat Co.
CUTLASS - Brushes–paint - Corona Brushes Inc.
CUTLASS - Insecticides - Ecogen Inc.
CUTLASS - Motor vehicles–automobiles ☆ - General Motors Corp. (Oldsmobile Div.)
CUTLASS - Pens ☆ - Sheaffer Inc.
CUTLASS - Stencils - Wall Lenk Corp.
CUTLASS 4-4-2 - Motor vehicles–automobiles ☆ - General Motors Corp. (Oldsmobile Div.)
CUTLASS ASSOCIATES - Computer software - Cutlass Associates, Inc.
CUTLASS CALAIS - Motor vehicles–automobiles ☆ - General Motors Corp. (Oldsmobile Div.)
CUTLASS CIERA - Motor vehicles–automobiles - General Motors Corp. (Oldsmobile Div.)

CUTLASS CIERA BROUGHAM - Motor vehicles–automobiles ☆ - General Motors Corp. (Oldsmobile Div.)
CUTLASS CIERA ES - Motor vehicles–automobiles ☆ - General Motors Corp. (Oldsmobile Div.)
CUTLASS CIERA S - Motor vehicles–automobiles - General Motors Corp. (Oldsmobile Div.)
CUTLASS CIERA SL - Motor vehicles–automobiles - General Motors Corp. (Oldsmobile Div.)
CUTLASS CRUISER - Motor vehicles–automobiles ☆ - General Motors Corp. (Oldsmobile Div.)
CUTLASS CRUISER BROUGHAM - Motor vehicles–automobiles ☆ - General Motors Corp. (Oldsmobile Div.)
CUTLASS CRUISER S - Motor vehicles–automobiles - General Motors Corp. (Oldsmobile Div.)
CUTLASS CRUISER SL - Motor vehicles–automobiles - General Motors Corp. (Oldsmobile Div.)
CUTLASS SALON - Motor vehicles–automobiles ☆ - General Motors Corp. (Oldsmobile Div.)
CUTLASS SUPREME - Motor vehicles–automobiles ☆ - General Motors Corp. (Oldsmobile Div.)
CUTLASS SUPREME INTERNATIONAL - Motor vehicles–automobiles - General Motors Corp. (Oldsmobile Div.)
CUTLASS SUPREME S - Motor vehicles–automobiles - General Motors Corp. (Oldsmobile Div.)
CUTLER - Mail boxes - Cutler Manufacturing Corp.
CUTLER SPORTS APPAREL - Clothing - H.H. Cutler Co.
CUTLER'S - Apparel–children's - H.H. Cutler Co.
CUTLER'S - Egg substitutes - Cutler Egg Products, Inc.
CUTLER'S - Food products - Cutler-Magner Co.
CUTLERY CENTER - Kitchen appliances ☆ - Sunbeam-Oster Household Products
CUTLESS - Gloves–rubber - Granet Inc.
CUT'N COOK - Knives–carving - K & I Products
CUT'N PRESS - Craft supplies - June Tailor Inc.
CUTN'SERVE - Cutting boards - Evlo Plastics Inc.
CUTQUIK - Saws–power - Stihl Inc.
CUTRINE-PLUS - Herbicides - Applied Biochemists, Inc.
CUTRITE - Hair care products - A. Eickert Co., Inc.
CUTRITE - Scissors–hand-operated - Arius-Eickert Co. Inc.
CUTS - Food products - Hormel Foods Corp.
CUTS-A-LOT - Knives ☆ - K.J. Miller Corp.
CUTS ALL - Office supplies - IDL Manufacturing & Sales Corp.
CUTSALI - Artists' materials ☆ - Max C's Ceramic & Craft
CUTSTART - Vitamins and nutritional supplements - Vitamin Institute
CUTTER - Bicycles - Ross Bicycles USA, Ltd.
CUTTER - Brushes–paint - Wooster Brush Co.
CUTTER - First aid kits - Cutter Laboratories
CUTTER & BUCK C B - Leather goods - Jones-Rodolfo Corp.
CUTTER COLLECTION - Shirts - Westmoor Manufacturing Co. Inc.
CUTTER GARD - Cardboard - Reynolds Metals Co.
CUTTER GOLD - Insecticide preparation - Miles Inc.
CUTTER PASTE WORMER - Veterinary pharmaceutical preparations - Miles Inc. (Animal Health Div.)
CUTTER PASTE WORMER - Veterinary pharmaceutical preparations - Miles Inc.
CUTTER PLEASANT PROTECTION - Insect repellents - Miles Inc.
CUTTER SPORT-PACK - Insecticides - Miles Inc. (Agriculture Div.)
CUTTER, THE - Kitchen utensils–aluminum - Bonny Products Inc.
CUTTERS CREEK - Apparel and accessories - Skip's Cutting, Inc.
CUTTERS EDGE - Tools - Hirsh Co.
CUTTERS-UP - Housewares - Plasticoid Manufacturing Inc.
CUTTHROAT HEARTS - Computer software - Manhattan Software
CUTTHROAT PINOCHLE - Computer software - Manhattan Software
CUTTHROAT PORTER - Beverages–malt - Odell Brewing Co., Inc.
CUTTHROATS - Computer software - Activision, Inc.
CUTTING - Recording label - Cutting Records
CUTTING BOARD - Pasta ☆ - The Pasta Fresca Co. Inc.
CUTTING BOARDS - Cutting boards - Solid Surface Acrylics, Inc.
CUTTING CORNER, THE - Paper–die-cut - Cutting Corner
CUTTING EDGE - Computer software - Armstrong Blum Manufacturing Co.
CUTTING EDGE - Conduits–electrical - Georgia-Pacific Corp.
CUTTING EDGE - Cutlery - SMK Marketing
CUTTING EDGE - Eyeglasses - Barbara Creations, Inc.
CUTTING EDGE - Machinery - Cutting Edge, Inc.
CUTTING EDGE - Publisher's imprints - Bantam Doubleday Dell Publishing Group, Inc.

CUTTING EDGE - Toys - Tonka Corp.

CUTTING EDGE - Vitamins and nutritional supplements - Nutri Science Inc.

CUTTING EDGE PRODUCTS - Alarms–personal - Cutting Edge Products, Inc

CUTTING EDGE, THE - Batteries - Exide Corp.

CUTTING EDGE TOOLS - Hand tools - Cutting Edge Tools, Inc.

CUTTING ETCH, THE - Alarm systems–burglar - Global Automotive Systems, Inc.

CUTTING FLUID - Oils–lubricating - Castoleum Corp.

CUTTING FORCE - Beverages - Weider Nutrition Group, Inc.

CUTTING FORCE - Vitamins and nutritional supplements - American Body Building Products, Inc.

CUTTING OIL - Chemical preparations - Black Swan Manufacturing Co.

CUTTING OIL - Oils–lubricating - Castoleum Corp.

CUTTS - Sporting goods - Lyman Products Corp.

CUTTY 12 - Beverages–alcohol - Hiram Walker & Sons, Inc.

CUTTY PIPE - Tobacco - American Tobacco Co.

CUTTY SARK - Beverages–alcohol - Hiram Walker & Sons, Inc.

CUTUP, THE - Knives–electric ☆ - National Presto Industries, Inc.

CUTWATER - Fabrics - Gretchen Bellinger Inc.

CUTY CLUB - Floor coverings–carpet and rugs - Wunda Weve Carpet Co.

CUVAISON - Wines - Cuvaison Inc.

CUVEE BELLEROSE - Wines - Bellerose Vineyard

CUVEE DE FRONTIGNAN - Beverages–alcohol - Thornton Winery

CUVEE DE FUME - Wines - Preston Vineyards

CUVEE DU VIGNERON - Wines - Benmarl Wine Co. Ltd.

CUVEE HENRI IV DE CHATEAU DE BARBE BLANCHE - Wines ☆ - Admiral Wine Merchants

CUVEE MONTAGNE - Wines - L.M.A.V.G. Vineyard & Winery Inc.

CUVEE MONTINORE - Wines - Montinore Vineyards Ltd.

CUVEE PRESTIGE - Beverages–alcohol ☆ - Prestige Wine Corp.

CUVEE SAINT-JEAN DES CORDELIERS - Beverages–carbonated - Crown Capital USA Inc.

CUWE - Pet products - Shakespeare Fishing Tackle

CUZCO - Beverages–malt ☆ - Markstein Importers

CV - Boats–motor ☆ - Glastron Boats

CV BOOT - Clamps - Murray Corp.

CV CLASSIC - Contact lenses - Cooper Companies Inc.

CV-D - Microphones ☆ - Electro-Voice, Inc.

CV/ICEING - Computer program - Periscope Computing Co., Inc.

CV NUTRIENTS - Vitamins and nutritional supplements - J.R. Carlson Laboratories Inc.

CV STANDARD - Contact lenses - Cooper Companies Inc.

CV SUPERTHIN - Contact lenses - Cooper Companies Inc.

CVAP - Cooking equipment–household - Winston Products Inc.

CVC - Food products - Basic Vegetable Products Inc.

CVC CHRONISTER VALVE CO. - Valves–industrial - Diversified Energy Products, Inc.

CVJ AXLES INC - Motor vehicle parts and accessories - CVJ Axles, Inc.

CVL - Sporting goods - Hillerich & Bradsby Co.

CVLKB-6 - Pharmaceutical preparations ☆ - Dixon-Shane Inc.

CVM - Chemicals - Ciba Corning Diagnostics Corp.

CVM - Coffee - Wm. B. Reily & Co. Inc.

CVM - Computer software - Information Retrieval Companies Inc.

CVMOS - Computer software - Computervision Corp.

CVN - Computer software - Holly Franking

C.V.O. - Footwear - Autry Industries Inc.

CVP - Detergents - McLane Co., Inc.

C.V.P. - Pharmaceutical preparations - Rhone-Poulenc Rorer Pharmaceuticals Inc.

CVP SYSTEMS - Packaging machines - CVP Systems, Inc.

CVS - Audio tapes–blank - CVS, H.C., Inc.

CVS - Hair coloring preparations - CVS H.C., Inc.

CVS - Machinery - Constant Velocity Systems, Inc.

CVSCAN - Medical apparatus - Spacelabs Medical, Inc.

CVT - Toys–trains - Central Valley Model Works

CW - Apparel–children's - Clifford & Wills, Inc.

CW 6000 - Golfing equipment - FM Precision Golf Corp.

CW 8000 - Golfing equipment - FM Precision Golf Corp.

C.W. BLISS SIGNATURE COLLECTION - Frames–eyeglass - Kenmark Optical Co.

CW CO - Wire–copper - Camden Wire Co., Inc.

C.W. KIRSCH SIGNATURE - Drapery hardware - Kirsch Co.

CW PHOENIX - Apparel–men's - Greif Cos.

C.W. ROSE - Apparel–women's - Rosemead Boulevard Corp.

CW STARCLAMP - Bathroom fixtures - Contractors Wardrobe, Inc.

CW3 CONVERTER WELDING AND OVERHAUL SYSTEM - Motor vehicle parts and accessories - Ati Performance Products, Inc.

CWC - Computer software - Clear with Computers, Inc.

CWC - Watches - North American Watch Corp.

CWD - Furniture–public buildings - GNP Audio Video Inc.

CWE CENTER FOR WORKFORCE EDUCATION - Educational materials - Laubach Literacy International

CWF - Finishing agents - Flood Co.

CWF-UV - Finishing agents - Flood Co.

CWI BRAND - Frozen food productss - Charles Winslow International

CWIP - Computer software - Wheeling Hospital, Inc.

CWP - Brushes - Scott Fetzer Co.

CWP - Vitamins and nutritional supplements ☆ - DMV USA Inc.

C.W.S. - Recording label - Terock Records

CX - Audio equipment - DCM Corp.

CX - Audio tapes–blank ☆ - Minnesota Mining & Manufacturing Co.

CX - Computer software - Convex Computer Corp.

CX - Jewelry - Comex Jewelry

CX-2P - Mirrors - Electro-Optix Inc.

CX-3 - Musical instrument accessories - Alembic Inc.

CX 12 - Harmonicas - Hohner Inc.

CX 111 - Pet products ☆ - Nala Barry Laboratories

CX 1250 - Hoists - Sky Climber, Inc.

CX SPORT - Bicycles - Cycle Express, Inc.

CXP - Ammunition - Olin Corp. (Winchester Div.)

CXSOFT - Computer software - Convex Computer Corp.

CY 110 - Paper–carbon ☆ - Curtis-Young Corp.

CY-BAR SLOTS - Publisher's imprints - Douglas Press, Inc.

CY-CHROME - Diagnostic preparations - Pharmingen

CY COL O GY - Apparel and accessories - Stafford Blaine Designs Ltd.

CY-KILL - Toys - Tonka Corp.

CY-STAINER - Laboratory apparatus - Innovation Instruments, Inc.

CYADE-GEL - Pharmaceutical preparations - Medical Chemical Corp.

CYALUME - Chemical preparations - American Cyanamid Co.

CYALUME - Light reconnaissance and surveillance equipment ☆ - Rothco Inc.

CYAMINE - Pharmaceutical preparations ☆ - Keene Pharmaceuticals Inc.

CYANNE VERRE - Lamps - Kaadan Ltd.

CYANO - Pharmaceutical preparations - Keene Pharmaceuticals Inc.

CYANO-GEL - Pharmaceutical preparations - Maurry Biological Co. Inc.

CYANOJECT - Pharmaceutical preparations - Merz Inc.

CYBER - Hearing aids - Qualitone

CYBER 3D INTERACTIVE - Computer software - Cyber Scientific Inc.

CYBER CANNON - Toy gun - Trendmasters, Inc.

CYBER CARREL - Tables–wood - Hal Sandy

CYBER CELLAR - Computer software - E-8 Publications, Inc.

CYBER CITY FURNITURE WAREHOUSE - Apparel and accessories - DMI Management, Inc.

CYBER CLIMBER - Toys - Mattel, Inc.

CYBER-DOME - Tanning agents - Sun Industries, Inc.

CYBER FORCE - Books–comic - Top Cow Productions, Inc.

CYBER GEIST - Computer software ☆ - B & N Companies, Inc.

CYBER-GENETIC DINOSAURS - Toys - Trendmasters, Inc.

CYBER GRAFX - Computer peripheral equipment - Computer Tools Inc.

CYBER-GRIP - Footwear ☆ - La Crosse Footwear, Inc.

CYBER KNIGHTS - Computer software - Ferris Productions, Inc.

CYBER-LIP - Video games - Snk Corp. of America

CYBER OCTAVE - Recording label - Higher Octave Music, Inc.

CYBER PARK - Games - Imagination Network, Inc.

CYBER PITCH - Sporting goods - Boulder Product Development Corp.

CYBER POWER - Toys - Sky Kids Inc.

CYBER-RELLA BY ALDAN - Apparel and accessories - Lewis Samuel Widoff

CYBER SENTRY - Computer software - Microsystems Software Inc.

CYBER SPIN - Computer software - Takara USA Corp.

CYBER SQUIRTER - Toys - Henry Gordy International Inc.

CYBER STADIUM SERIES - Toys–electronic - Ultra Software Corp.

CYBER SWORD - Toys - Henry Gordy International Inc.

CYBER-SYSTEM - Footwear ☆ - La Crosse Footwear, Inc.

CYBER2000 - Computer hardware - Cybertech, Inc.

CYBERACTIVE - Apparel–women's - Jodi Lindley

CYBERADE - Beverages - L & S Research Corp.

CYBERAGENZ - Computer software - Cyberagenz, Inc.

CYBERBAR - Computer peripheral equipment - Francis L. Pugh

CYBERBARTER - Computer software - Cyberbarter, Inc.

CYBERBASS - Audio equipment - Peavey Electronics Corp.

CYBERBOOGIE - Recording label - Emm IIAcquistition Corp.

CYBERBROKER - Computer software - Cybersafe, Inc.

☆ = Now out of production

CYBERBYKES SHADOW RACER VR - Computer software - Gametek, Inc.

CYBERBYTE - Desserts - Wells' Dairy, Inc.

CYBERCAD - Computers - Virtual Technologies

CYBERCALL - Computer software - ATIO Corp.

CYBERCASE - Cases–camera - TKL Products Corp.

CYBERCAST SYSTEMS - Computer hardware - En Technology Corp.

CYBERCELL - Plastic pellets - Colorite Plastic Co.

CYBERCELLS - Computer peripheral equipment - Black Sun Interactive, Inc.

CYBERCHARGE - Beverages - L & S Research Corp.

CYBERCHART - Computer software - Cyberscience Corp.

CYBERCHIP - Electrical industrial apparatus - Dynasys Technologies Inc.

CYBERCITIZEN - Publisher's imprints - Yankelovich Partners Inc.

CYBERCRUISER - Toys–automobiles - Mattel, Inc.

CYBERDOC - Computer software - Jay R. Freeman

CYBERDREAMS - Computer software - Cyberdreams, Inc.

CYBERDROME - Computer games - Rhea-FX

CYBEREX - Plastic industrial material - Colorite Plastic Co.

CYBERFEST - Dance studios - Creative Artists Network, Inc.

CYBERFLIX - Computer software - Cyberflix, Inc.

CYBERFOAM - Foam rubber - Mastex Industries, Inc.

CYBERGEAR - Exercise equipment - Cybergear, Inc.

CYBERGENICS CYBERGRAIN - Beverages - L & S Research Corp.

CYBERGENICS FOR HARD GAINERS - Vitamin and food supplements - L & S Research Corp.

CYBERGENICS INFINITY - Beverages - L & S Research Corp.

CYBERGENICS PHASE I - Beverages - L & S Research Corp.

CYBERGENICS QUICK TRIM - Pharmaceutical preparations - L & S Research Corp.

CYBERGENICS QUICKMEAL - Vitamins and nutritional supplements - L & S Research Corp.

CYBERGENICS SUPER FAT-LOSS - Vitamin and food supplements - L & S Research Corp.

CYBERGLOVE - Electronic equipment - James F. Kramer

CYBERGUARD - Alarm systems–burglar - Cybermotion, Inc.

CYBERGUARD - Computer software - Harris Computer Systems Corp.

CYBERHAIR - Hair care products - International Hairgoods Inc.

CYBERIA - Computer software - Xatrix Interactive Design, Inc.

CYBERIMPACT - Computer peripheral equipment - Cybernet Systems Corp.

CYBERJACK - Computer software - Delrina

CYBERJUMP - Computer peripheral equipment - Logitech, Inc.

CYBERJUNCTION - Computer software - Frontier Technologies Corp.

CYBERKIDS - Toy figures - Virustatic Inc.

CYBERLABII - Computer software - Creative Computer Applications, Inc.

CYBERLAST - Plastic industrial material - Colorite Plastic Co.

CYBERLIGHT - Lighting fixtures - High End Systems, Inc.

CYBERLUXE - Computer peripheral equipment - N. Franklin Behrens

CYBERLYNX - Computer software - Cyberlynx, Inc.

CYBERMAN - Computer hardware - Logitech, Inc.

CYBERMANAGER - Computer software - Cyber Interactive, Inc.

CYBERMAT - Cutting boards - Verne Geidl

CYBERMED - Computer software - Creative Computer Applications, Inc.

CYBERMEM - Electrical industrial apparatus - Dynasys Technologies Inc.

CYBERMETRICS - Computer software - Jay Curtis Williams

CYBERMOLD - Plastic industrial material - Colorite Plastic Co.

CYBERMORPH - Video games - Atari Games Corp.

CYBERMOUSE - Computer software - World Information Networks Corp.

CYBERNARY - Posters - Wildstorm Productions

CYBERNATOR - Computer software ☆ - Konami (America) Inc.

CYBERNET - Stereos ☆ - Kyocera America Inc.

CYBERNOTES - Computer software - Affinity Computer Applications, Inc.

CYBERPAGE - Computer software - Strategic Open Solutions Group

CYBERPRESS - Computer software - Extensis Corp.

CYBERPRINT - Toners - Toner Cartridge Co.

CYBERPROPS - Computer storage devices–optical - Yglesias Wallock Divekar Inc.

CYBERPUPPY - Computer software - Cyberpuppy Software, Inc.

CYBERQUERY - Radio communications equipment - Cyberscience Corp.

CYBERRAD - Computer software - Creative Computer Applications, Inc.

CYBERRAX - Shelving units–metal - Hal Sandy

CYBERSAFE - Computer software - Cybersafe Corp.

CYBERSCAPE - Computer software - Richard Rommel

CYBERSCOPE - Computer peripheral - Simsalabim Systems Inc.

CYBERSEARCH - Computer software - Frontier Technologies Corp.

CYBERSHARK - Toys - Hasbro, Inc.

CYBERSHARK BRI - Computer hardware - Patriot Scientific Corp. (Communications Product Div.)

CYBERSHIELD - Plastic pellets - Colorite Plastic Co.

CYBERSIGHT - Computer software - Cybersight Software

CYBERSITES - Computer software - Cybersites, Inc.

CYBERSOFT - Computer software - Gametek, Inc.

CYBERSOUND - Computer hardware - Invision Interactive, Inc.

CYBERSPEED - Video games - Mindscape Software Inc.

CYBERSPELL - Computer software - INSO Corp.

CYBERSTAMP - Stamps–hand - Copestone, Inc.

CYBERSTAR - Computers–micro - Northern Computer Systems Inc.

CYBERSTOCK - Computer peripheral equipment - Digital Stock Corp.

CYBERSTORAGE - Computer storage devices - Cyberstorage Systems, Inc.

CYBERSUGGESTION - Recording label - Tomi Kent Silver

CYBERSWING - Golfing equipment - A. Clinton Ober

CYBERTABLE - Furniture - Via, Inc.

CYBERTAG - Video games - Virtual Reality Entertainment Corp.

CYBERTAROT - Computer software - Axismundi

CYBERTECH - Plastic pellets - Colorite Plastic Co.

CYBERTEK - Computer hardware - Cybertek Corp.

CYBERTERM - Computer software - Creative Computer Applications, Inc.

CYBERTEST - Wire - Motorola, Inc. (Land Mobile Products Sector)

CYBERTHERM - Controls–heating systems - Cybertherm, Inc.

CYBERTOOLS - Computer software - Cybertools

CYBERTOUCH - Computer peripheral equipment - Transparent Devices, Inc.

CYBERTOYS - Computer software - Cybertoys, Inc.

CYBERTRUST - Computer software - GTE Government Systems Corp.

CYBERTUFF - Plastic industrial material - Colorite Plastic Co.

CYBERTWIN - Computer peripheral equipment - Black Sun Interactive, Inc.

CYBERWARE - Computer hardware - Cyberware Laboratory Inc.

CYBERWEAR - Computer hardware - Virtual Technologies

CYBERX - Computer software - CyberTools Inc.

CYBEX - Computer hardware - Cybex Corp.

CYBIS - Computer software - CYBIS Medical Systems, Inc.

CYBIS - Glassware–household - Cybis Porcelains

CYBLADE - Books–comic - Top Cow Productions, Inc.

CYBOARS - Toys - Kenneth M. Smith

CYBORG - Sporting goods - Variflex, Inc.

CYBRID - Books–comic - Rob Liefeld, Inc.

CYBRON - Lubricants ☆ - Proton Engineering Inc.

CYBROS - Breads - Cybros Inc.

CYBURLESQUE - Computer software - Andover Productions, Inc.

CYC-O-LINE - Exercising equipment ☆ - National Sporting Goods Corp.

CYCL-A-VITES - Vitamins and nutritional supplements - Natural Organics, Inc.

CYCLADES - Computer peripheral equipment - Cyclades Corp.

CYCLAFEM - Pharmaceutical preparations - Dolisos America, Inc.

CYCLAINE - Anesthetics ☆ - Merck & Co., Inc. (Merck Research Laboratories)

CYCLAMATIC - Refrigerators - White Consolidated Industries, Inc.

CYCLAMENTRY - Bedding–linen - Dan River Inc.

CYCLAMYCIN - Pharmaceutical preparations ☆ - Wyeth-Ayerst Laboratories

CYCLAPEN-W - Pharmaceutical preparations - Wyeth-Ayerst Laboratories

CYCLARAC - Sporting goods - All American Products Inc.

CYCLART - Decals and transfers - Cyclart Inc.

CYCLE - Bicycles - Cycle Products Co.

CYCLE - Fruits and vegetables - Fillmore-Piru Citrus Association

CYCLE - Pet products - Rolf C. Hagen (USA) Corp.

CYCLE II - Paints - Major Paint Co.

CYCLE 4 - Air purification systems - Printmaster Products (Medical Div.)

CYCLE ALERT - Alarm systems - Brio Corp.

CYCLE-AM - Motor vehicle parts and accessories - Maier Manufacturing

CYCLE BALANCE - Skin care products - Wise Essentials Inc.

CYCLE-BLEND - Blenders - Sunbeam-Oster Household Products

CYCLE BUDDY - Portable insulated coolers - Janko USA, Inc.

CYCLE B.U.M. - Apparel–men's - Chauvin International Ltd.

CYCLE CHAIR - Motor vehicles–personnel carriers ☆ - Electric Mobility Corp.

CYCLE COMM - Motor vehicle parts and accessories - Cycle-Comm

CYCLE CRAFT - Motor vehicle parts and accessories - Carfel Inc.

CYCLE DESIGN - Bicycle parts and accessories - GT Bicycles Inc.

CYCLE EARS - Radio communications equipment - Alert Industries, Inc.

CYCLE EXPRESS - Bicycle parts and accessories - Cycle Express, Inc.

CYCLE-GEAR - Bathing suits - Catalina

CYCLE GUARD - Alarm systems - Anes Electronics Burglar Alarm Systems

CYCLE HERBS FORMULA - Health care products - Alta Health Products

CYCLE-LITE - Motor vehicle parts and accessories - Cycle-Comm

CYCLE-MATES - Bathing suits - Catalina

CYCLE MATES - Bicycles - Weil Service Products Corp.

CYCLE PETS - Toys–stuffed ☆ - Fun World Inc.

CYCLE RIDER - Toys - Steven Manufacturing Co.

CYCLE-SAFE - Bottles–plastic ☆ - Monsanto Co.
CYCLE SENTRY - Lighting equipment - Cornerstone/Clearlight
CYCLE SHOOTING - Video games - Taito America Corp.
CYCLE SHUTTLE - Trailers–travel - Chariot Manufacturing Co. Inc.
CYCLE SLED - Trailers–travel - Chariot Manufacturing Co. Inc.
CYCLE SPORT - Bicycles - Columbia Manufacturing Inc.
CYCLE-TAINER - Chemical preparations - Mallinckroot Baker, Inc.
CYCLE, THE - Trading cards and stamps - Pinnacle Brands, Inc.
CYCLE THERAPY - Apparel and accessories - Wolverine World Wide, Inc.
CYCLE THERAPY - Cleaning preparation - Michael J. Grivet
CYCLE TRUCK - Bicycles - Schwinn Cycling & Fitness Inc.
CYCLEASE - Pharmaceutical preparations - Boiron Inc.
CYCLEBINDING - Sporting goods - Cyclebinding
CYCLECOACH I - Health care products - Elexis Corp.
CYCLECOACH II - Health care products - Elexis Corp.
CYCLEHORN DBX - Bicycle horns - Cycleaware, Inc.
CYCLELINE - Bicycles - District Cycle Supply Co.
CYCLEMASTER - Valves - Mueller Industries, Inc.
CYCLEPRO - Bicycles ☆ - Raleigh USA Bicycle Co.
CYCLERITE - Bicycle parts and accessories - G. Joannou Cycle Co., Inc.
CYCLES - Floor coverings–carpet and rugs ☆ - Regal Rugs Inc.
CYCLESMITH - Backpacks - Mountainsmith Inc.
CYCLESTARS - Sporting goods - Cyclestars Inc.
CYCLESTIM - Electromedical apparatus - TH Charters, Inc.
CYCLETRAK - Electronic equipment - AVL
CYCLETRON - Sporting goods - CSA, Inc.
CYCLINE-250 - Antibiotics ☆ - Scrip-Physician Supply Co.
CYCLIST REPUBLIC - Helmets–athletic - Pac Am International
CYCLO-A-DAPTA - Tools ☆ - New England Carbide
CYCLO-CORE - Tools - New England Carbide
CYCLO-IMPAK - Tools - New England Carbide
CYCLO-MASSAGE - Furniture - Niagara Therapy Manufacturing Corp.
CYCLO PANEL - Wood products ☆ - Cyclops Industries (Empire-Detroit Steel Div.)
CYCLO-PROVERA - Pharmaceutical preparations - Upjohn Co.
CYCLO-TWIST - Tools - New England Carbide
CYCLOCEN - Pharmaceutical preparations ☆ - Central Pharmaceutical Inc.
CYCLOCKER - Lockers–metal - Columbia Cascade Co.
CYCLOD - Computer software - Sirius Software Development Inc.
CYCLOGRAPH - Toys–models - CPG Products Corp.
CYCLOGYL - Ophthalmic goods - Alcon Laboratories, Inc.
CYCLOHM - Fans–electric ☆ - Howard Industries Inc.
CYCLOHM FHP - Motors–automotive ☆ - Howard Industries Inc.
CYCLOID - Tire inflators - Grant J. Renier
CYCLOM - Computer equipment - Cyclades Corp.
CYCLOMATIC - Blenders ☆ - Sunbeam-Oster Household Products
CYCLOMATIC - Watches - Elgin Watch Co.
CYCLOMYDRIL - Ophthalmic goods - Alcon Laboratories, Inc.
CYCLOMYRAL - Chemical preparations - Hercules Inc.
CYCLONE - Bats–baseball - Lisco, Inc.
CYCLONE - Bicycles - Huffy Corp.
CYCLONE - Boats ☆ - Catalina Yachts Inc.
CYCLONE - Brushes - Anderson Products, Inc.
CYCLONE - Colognes ☆ - Avon Products, Inc.
CYCLONE - Connectors–electrical - Thomas & Betts Holdings, Inc.
CYCLONE - Darts and dart games - Dart World Inc.
CYCLONE - Electrical equipment - GB Electrical Inc.
CYCLONE - Fans–exhaust ☆ - Mercury Hi-Performance Group
CYCLONE - Fencing–gates and posts - Cyclone Fence Sales
CYCLONE - Firearms, accessories, and parts - Welsh Sporting Goods Corp. (Boyt Div.)
CYCLONE - Floor coverings–carpet and rugs ☆ - Regal Rugs Inc.
CYCLONE - Food products - Cyclone Enterprises Inc.
CYCLONE - Garden equipment - True Temper Hardware Co.
CYCLONE - Guns - Ox-Yoke Originals, Inc.
CYCLONE - Hardware - Black & Decker Corp.
CYCLONE - Hoists - Columbus Mckinnon Corp.
CYCLONE - Hoses - Gates Rubber Co. (Automotive Aftermarket/Hardware Sales Div.)
CYCLONE - Laboratory apparatus - Cytomation, Inc.
CYCLONE - Machinery - Castex Industries Inc.
CYCLONE - Matches - P.T.C. Brands, Inc.
CYCLONE - Mats - Ford Motor Co.
CYCLONE - Meters–electric - Emerson Electric Co.
CYCLONE - Paint removers ☆ - Dutch Boy Group
CYCLONE - Photographic equipment ☆ - Leedal Inc.

CYCLONE - Pumps - Sta-Rite Industries Inc.
CYCLONE - Saw blades - Credo Co.
CYCLONE - Sports apparel - Reebok International Ltd.
CYCLONE - Tables - Impact Furniture
CYCLONE - Toys–models - Estes Industries
CYCLONE - Welding equipment - Smith Equipment
CYCLONE - Yarns - Dixie Yarns, Inc.
CYCLONE CIP - Cleaning preparations - Ecolab Inc.
CYCLONE COARSE BUBBLE DIFFUSER - Water purification systems - Aeromix Systems, Inc.
CYCLONE FURIOUS FROZEN BEVERAGE TREAT - Beverages - Van Tone Co., Inc.
CYCLONE II - Archery equipment - Pro Line Co.
CYCLONE PRODUCTIONS - Recording label - Cyclone Entertainment Group
CYCLONE RC - Skates–ice - SLM Inc.
CYCLONE SLIDE - Playground equipment - Miracle Recreation Equipment Co.
CYCLONIL - Pharmaceutical preparations - Seatrace Co.
CYCLOP - Watches - Rolex Watch USA, Inc.
CYCLOPAR - See WARNER-CHILCOTT
CYCLOPAR - Antibiotics ☆ - Parke-Davis
CYCLOPS - Apparel and accessories ☆ - Edison Brothers Stores, Inc.
CYCLOPS - Hardware ☆ - M.A.G. Engineering & Manufacturing Co. Inc.
CYCLOPS - Musical instruments - LP Music Group
CYCLOPS - Sprayers - Alan Fann
CYCLOPS - Toys–models - Clark Manufacturing Co. Inc.
CYCLOPTOR - Toys - Saban Entertainment, Inc.
CYCLOSILENCER - Machine parts - Gardner Denver Machinery Inc.
CYCLOSPASMOL - Pharmaceutical preparations - Wyeth-Ayerst Laboratories
CYCLOTECH - Sporting goods - Service Cycle Supply Co.
CYCLOTROL-EIGHT - Blenders ☆ - Sunbeam-Oster Household Products
CYCLOVANTAGE - Heart monitors ☆ - Polar Electro Inc.
CYCLUS - Furniture - Harter
CYCOLAC - Resins–synthetic - General Electric Co.
CYCOLOY - Resins–synthetic - General Electric Co.
CYCOOL BIKE COOLER - Bicycle parts and accessories - Liquid Assets Enterprises Inc.
CYCRIN - Pharmaceutical preparations - Wyeth-Ayerst Laboratories
CYCRON - Water purification systems - Stephen M. Rollins
CYCUBE - Computers - Gustav Pedersen
CYDE WEIGHT - Glassware–household - Nourot Glass Studio
CYDEL - Pharmaceutical preparations ☆ - Roberts/Hauck Pharmaceuticals Inc.
CYDONIA - Golfing equipment - Mars Golf Supply
CYDONOL - Skin care products - Gordon Laboratories
CYDROTHANE - Adhesives and sealants - American Cyanamid Co.
CYGANY KEZ - Jewelry - Patricia L. C Henderson
CYGNE NEW YORK - apparel - Cygne Designs Inc.
CYGNET - Faucets - Kohler Co.
CYGNET - Flowers, plants, and seeds - White Swan, Ltd.
CYGNET - Wallcoverings - Swan Hill Studios
CYGNET - Wines - Swanson Vineyards and Winery
CYGNET - Yarn - Knitting Fever Inc.
CYGNET CELLARS - Wines - Cygnet Cellars
CYGNIA COLLECTION, THE - Office furniture–wood ☆ - Haworth, Inc.
CYGNUS - Electronics equipment - ALTA Group
CYGNUS - Furniture ☆ - Bassett Furniture Industries, Inc.
CYGOMATIC - Bicycle parts and accessories ☆ - Windstream Power Systems Inc.
CYGON - Security Products Co.
CYKLOKAPRON - Pharmaceutical preparations - Kabi Pharmacia Inc.
CYKLOP - Corkscrews - Franmara Co. Inc.
CYKX - Recording label - Jazz Composer's Orchestra Association Inc.
CYLERT - Pharmaceutical preparations - Abbott Laboratories
CYLINDA-LINE - Housewares - IDG-International Designers Group Inc.
CYLINDER BEAM - Lighting fixtures - Swivelier Co. Inc.
CYLINDER HEAD - Juices - Bully Hill Vineyards, Inc.
CYLINDRALUX - Lighting fixtures ☆ - Hubbell Lighting, Inc. (Lighting Div.)
CYLINK - Resins–urea and melamine - Cytec Technology Corp.
CYLOK - Adhesives and sealants - Lord Corp. (Chemical Products Div.)
CYLOPAK - Storage tubes ☆ - Intromark Inc.
CYLUMINE - Pharmaceutical preparations ☆ - Legere Pharmaceuticals Inc.
CYMA - Plywood - Harbor Sales Co.
CYMA - Watches - Glenn Corp.
CYMA IV - Computer software - Cyma Systems, Inc.
CYMALTEX - Vitamins and nutritional supplements - Fitness Systems Manufacturing Corp.
CYMAX - Printers–computer - Datametrics

☆ = Now out of production

CYMBAL-BRITE - Cleaning preparations ☆ - Herco Products
CYMBAL CROWN - Drums–musical instruments - Big Bang Distribution/A.P.I.
CYMBAL LIFE - Cymbals - Musician's Repair & Supply
CYMBAL SAFE - Cases–musical instrument - Avedis Zildjian Co.
CYMBAL SPRINGS - Cymbals ☆ - Aquarian Music
CYMBRION - Apparel - Cymbrion International Inc.
CYMTEC - Music stands - Super Star Products
CYNAR - Artichokes–canned - Cynar-A. C. Castelli Associates
CYNAY - Cosmetics ☆ - Nat Robbins Ltd.
CYNDER SEAL - Masonry-block filler - Commercial Chemical Co. Inc.
CYNDI LAUPER - Candy ☆ - Topps Co., Inc.
CYNOSURE - Lighting fixtures ☆ - Hubbell Lighting, Inc. (Lighting Div.)
CYNOTINIC - Pharmaceutical preparations ☆ - Jones Medical Industries, Inc.
   (Medical Div.)
CYNOX - Health care products - Omron Healthcare, Inc.
CYNTHEX - Varnishes - Morris Paint & Varnish Co.
CYNTHIA - Apparel–women's ☆ - Bali Co. Inc.
CYNTHIA - Dolls - Mattel, Inc.
CYNTHIA - Fabrics–tapestry - Comark Wallcoverings
CYNTHIA - Watches - Bulova Corp.
CYNTHIA GIBSON - Wallpaper - Cynthia Gibson Inc.
CYNTHIA GIBSON - Wallpaper - Goffle Warehouse & Distribution Co. Inc.
CYNTHIA HART - Greeting cards - Cynthia Hart
CYNTHIA J - Apparel and accessories - Kellwood Co.
CYNTHIA J. SPORT - Apparel and accessories - Kellwood Co.
CYNTHIA J SPORT - Women's Apparel - A.J. Brandon, Inc.
CYNTHIA LOCKHART - Leather goods - Accessories to the Fact
CYNTHIA ROWLEY - Apparel and accessories - Cynthia Rowley
CYNTHIAN - Faucets - Sterling Plumbing Group Inc.
CYNTHIANA - Wines - Sax's Winery
CYNTHIA'S - Bakery products - Svenhard's Swedish Bakery Inc.
CYOMIN - Pharmaceutical preparations - Forest Pharmaceuticals Inc.
CYPERMIST - Insecticides - Clarke Mosquito Equipment, Inc.
CYPHER - Aircraft - United Technologies Corp.
CYPHER - Recording label ☆ - Lucifer Records Inc.
CYPHER RECORDS - Recording label - Shay Kostiner
CYPHERNITIC - Sound-responsive lights - Control Research Inc.
CYPHERSCAN - Optical scanners–computer - Cyphertech, Inc.
CYPHOON - Water–bottled or canned - Aqua-Pac, Inc.
CYPKIT - Pharmaceutical preparations - Dorn C. Cook
CYPRES - Candles - FMG/Tsumara Medical
CYPRESS - Brushes–paint - Allpro Corp.
CYPRESS - Cabinets - Classic Bath Products
CYPRESS - Computer peripheral equipment - Information Systems Corp.
CYPRESS - Floor coverings–carpet and rugs - Cabin Crafts Carpets
CYPRESS - Footwear–women's - Hawaii Shoe Co.
CYPRESS - Fruit - Florida Fresh
CYPRESS - Furniture ☆ - Bassett Furniture Industries, Inc.
CYPRESS - Seat covers - Saddleman, Inc.
CYPRESS - Shampoos - S.C. Johnson & Son, Inc.
CYPRESS - Shrimp - Central Coast Seafood Inc.
CYPRESS - Tiles–ceramic ☆ - Metropolitan Ceramics
CYPRESS - Trailers–travel ☆ - Kit Manufacturing Co.
CYPRESS - Underwear and nightwear - Russell-Newman, Inc.
CYPRESS - Wallpaper ☆ - Wolf-Gordon Inc.
CYPRESS BAY - Furniture - Broyhill Furniture Industries, Inc.
CYPRESS GARDENS - Floor coverings–carpet and rugs ☆ - Hollytex Carpet
   Mills Inc.
CYPRESS GARDENS - Fruit drinks–bottled or canned - Orange-Co, Inc.
CYPRESS GARDENS - Indoor-outdoor carpets and rugs - Instant Turf
   Industries Inc.
CYPRESS GARDENS - Sporting goods ☆ - Hedstrom Corp.
CYPRESS GOLD - Compost - Mulch Manufacturing, Inc.
CYPRESS HILL - Apparel and accessories - Cypress Hill
CYPRESS LANE - Wines ☆ - Landmark Vineyards
CYPRESS LINKS - Sweaters - Pine State Knitwear Co.
CYPRESS PACKAGING & SUPPLY CORP. - Tape–adhesive - Cypress
   Packaging & Supply Corp.
CYPRESS POINT - Floor coverings–carpet and rugs ☆ - Catalina Carpet Mills
   Inc.
CYPRESS POINT - Floor coverings–carpet and rugs ☆ - Dorsett Carpet Mills
   Inc.
CYPRESS POINT - Synthetic turf - Instant Turf Industries Inc.
CYPRESS WOODS - Tandem Imports Corp.
CYPRESSIDE - Siding–insulating - Masonite Corp.
CYPRINA - Lubricants - Shell Oil Co.

CYPRINOPUR - Pet products ☆ - Sera Aquaristik USA Inc.
CYPROMAR - Cough medicines ☆ - Marlop Pharmaceuticals Inc.
CYPRUS - Floor coverings–carpet and rugs - Mannington Carpets, Inc.
CYPRUS - Floor coverings–carpet and rugs - Patcraft Mills Inc.
CYPRUS - Furniture - Homecrest Industries Inc.
CYQUANT - Chemical preparations - Molecular Probes, Inc.
CYQUEST - Apparel and accessories - M Hidary & Co., Inc.
CYRANO CHENTPACK - Computer software - Cyrano, Inc.
CYRANO MILENNIUMTEST - Computer software - Cyrano, Inc.
CYRANO SERVERTRACK - Computer software - Cyrano, Inc.
CYRANO VTPACK - Computer software - Cyrano, Inc.
CYRANOTEST - Computer software - Cyrano, Inc.
CYRANOTIMER - Computer software - Cyrano, Inc.
CYRILLA - Tobacco products - Arangold Corp.
CYRIX INSTEAD - Computer peripheral equipment - Cyrix Corp.
CYRK - Apparel and accessories - Cyrk Inc.
CYROFLEX - Molding compounds–plastics - Cyro Industries
CYROLITE - Molding compounds–plastics - Cyro Industries
CYROLON-ZX - Molding compounds–plastics - Cyro Industries
CYRUN - Computer software - Glen Haimovitz and John Roevekamp
   Partnership
CYRUS - Apparel and accessories - Cyrus Hakakian
CYRUS ALEXANDER ESTATE - Wines - Field Stone Winery
CYRUS NOBLE - Whiskey - Haas Bros.
CYRUS O'LEARY'S - Pies–fresh - Fresh Foods Corp. of America
CYSTAGON - Pharmaceutical preparations - Mylan Pharmaceuticals Inc.
CYSTAUR - Pharmaceutical preparations - C.S. Ruckstuhl Co. Inc.
CYSTEMMS-V - Pharmaceutical preparations - C.O. Truxton Inc.
CYSTEX - Analgesics - Numark Laboratories Inc.
CYSTO-CONRAY - Pharmaceutical preparations ☆ - Mallinckrodt Medical, Inc.
CYSTOGRAFIN - Pharmaceutical preparations - Bristol-Myers Squibb Co.
CYTADREN - Pharmaceutical preparations - Ciba-Geigy Corp.
CYTAL - Irrigation equipment - Cutter Laboratories
CYTEC - Computer equipment - Information Integration Inc.
CYTEC - Rubber–molded - Cytec Technology Corp.
CYTELLIN - Pharmaceutical preparations ☆ - Eli Lilly and Co.
CYTETTE - Diagnostic apparatus - Birchwood Laboratories, Inc.
CYTHERE - Candles - FMG/Tsumara Medical
CYTOBAR - Vitamins and nutritional supplements ☆ - Champion Nutrition
CYTOBUDDIES - Vitamins and nutritional supplements - Achievers Unlimited,
   Inc.
CYTOFLUOR - Scientific apparatus - Millipore Corp.
CYTOFUGE CENTRIFUGE - Medical apparatus - Statspin Technologies
CYTOGEN - Medical apparatus - Cytogen Corp.
CYTOGUARD - Vitamins and nutritional supplements - Celmark International,
   Inc.
CYTOLIFE - Vitamins and nutritional supplements - Achievers Unlimited, Inc.
CYTOMAX - Vitamins and nutritional supplements - Champion Nutrition
CYTOMED - Pharmaceutical preparations - Cytomed, Inc.
CYTOMEL - Pharmaceutical preparations - Jones Medical Industries, Inc.
   (Medical Div.)
CYTOMEL - Thyroid preparations - Smithkline Beecham Corp.
CYTOMEL - Vitamins and nutritional supplements - Jones Pharma Inc.
CYTONUTRIENT PAK - Vitamins and nutritional supplements - Achievers
   Unlimited, Inc.
CYTOPRO - Laboratory apparatus - Wescor, Inc.
CYTOPURE - Vitamins and nutritional supplements - Achievers Unlimited, Inc.
CYTOSAR-U - Pharmaceutical preparations - Upjohn Co.
CYTOSET - Diagnostic apparatus ☆ - Birchwood Laboratories, Inc.
CYTOSOL - Pharmaceutical preparations - Cytosol Laboratories, Inc.
CYTOTEC - Pharmaceutical preparations - Monsanto Co.
CYTOTOX 96 - Enzyme detection supplies - Promega Corp.
CYTOX - Pharmaceutical preparations - Bennett Pharmaceutical Corp.
CYTOXAN - Pharmaceutical preparations - Bristol-Myers Squibb Co.
CYTRAN - Pharmaceutical preparations ☆ - Upjohn Co.
CYTRON - Fixtures–plastic - Bromante Corp.
C.Z. GROW - Plant growth regulators - C.Z. Guest Ltd.
CZ PATCH - Computer software ☆ - Dr. T's Music Software Inc.
CZ RIDER - Computer software ☆ - Dr. T's Music Software Inc.
CZAR - Candy - Dilettante Chocolates, Inc.
CZAR - Colognes - Redken Laboratories, Inc.
CZAR, THE - Apparel and accessories - Sports America, Inc.
CZARINA - Christmas tree ornaments - Cracker Box Inc.
CZARINA - Liquors - Canandaigua Wine Co. Inc.
CZECH GLASSWORKS - Glass products - Nunnally International Trade, Inc.
CZECHOSLOVAKIA - Hockey equipment - Superior Fabricators Inc.

CZECHOSLOVAKIAN ORIGINAL LAGER BEER - Beverages–malt - Hornell Brewing Co. Inc.

CZEGGS - Giftware - Eggspressions, Inc.

CZELA - Novelty items ☆ - Cathay International

CZIMERS - Food products - Czimer Foods Inc.

CZO - Pharmaceutical preparations ☆ - ICN Pharmaceuticals Inc.

CZ'S - Jewelry - Nason Trading Co. Inc.

CZX CUSTOM - Drums–musical instruments - Pearl Corp.

CZX STUDIO - Drums–musical instruments - Pearl Corp.

D

Addresses and phone numbers for the companies cited in the brands below
are available in the Company Listings section immediately following the brands listings.

D - Boots ☆ - Miura Sports Inc.
D - Computer hardware - Daewoo International (America) Corp.
D - Computer peripheral equipment - Dynamic Circuits Inc.
D - Digital encoders - Texas Instruments Inc.
D - Ice cream - TMR Group, Inc.
D - Lighting fixtures - Craftmade International Inc.
D - Measuring instruments - Dantec Measurement Technology Inc.
D - Metals - Daniel Bolt & Gasket Inc.
D - Recording label - Paid Records
D-1 - Pet products - Vortex Innerspace Products Inc.
D-2 KOZY - Heating pads–electric ☆ - Electrozot Corp.
D III - Trading cards and stamps - Topps Co., Inc.
D-11 - Locks–padlocks - Medeco Security Locks, Inc.
D-32 - Cleaning preparations - Senoret Chemical Co.
D 41 - Paints ☆ - Monsanto Co.
D 50 - Pens–fountain ☆ - Universal Fountain Pen & Pencil Co.
D-100 - Balsa wood for lamininating - Baltek Corp.
D-148 - Lubricants - C.P. Hall Co.
D-300 - Printers–computer - Smith Corona Corp.
+ D, A - Pharmaceutical preparations - Schering Corp.
D-ALPHA-E - Pharmaceutical preparations - Alto Pharmaceuticals Inc.
D-ALPHA GEMS - Vitamins and nutritional supplements - J.R. Carlson Laboratories Inc.
D-AMP - Pharmaceutical preparations - Dunhall Pharmaceuticals Inc.
D & B - Jewelry - Dolan and Bullock Co.
D & C - Jewelry - Herff Jones Inc.
D & D - Games - Tsr, Inc.
D AND D - Paints ☆ - Demert & Dougherty, Inc.
D & E - Automotive parts and accessories - D & E Automotive Products, Inc.
D & E - Cleaning preparations - Transworld Business Services
D & E - Pharmaceutical preparations - D & E Pharmaceuticals, Inc.
D & E VIDEO HEAD CLEANER - Chemical preparations - Transworld Business Services
D & F SYN - Vitamins and nutritional supplements ☆ - Great Life Laboratories Inc.
D & G - Beverages–carbonated - Brooklyn Bottling Corp.
D & G - Dog food - Price-Wilhoite Co.
D & H - Sporting goods - D & H Products Co.
D & J - Electronic equipment - D & J Electronics Inc.
D & J - Jewelry - D & J Creation Inc.
D & J - Violins - Peter Redstone Harpsichords
D & L - Fruits and vegetables - Lionel M. Serimian
D & M - Ships–sailing vessels ☆ - Douglass & McLeod Inc.
D & P - Candy - Dryden & Palmer Inc.
D-ASMA - Pharmaceutical preparations - Dunhall Pharmaceuticals Inc.
D. B. SMITH - Garden equipment - The Fountainhead Group, Inc.
D. B. WALDO - Apparel and accessories - D.B. Waldo Inc.
D-BAN - Insecticides - Rite-Off Inc.
D-BEST - Juices - 4 Star Brands, Inc.
D BEST BY LIZ STUDIO - Apparel and accessories - Liz Studio, Inc.
D BETS - Vitamins and nutritional supplements - Kroeger Herb Products Co. Inc.
D BOND - Skin care products - Monaco Import/Export Inc.
D. +BOUZAN - Jewelry–precious - D. Bouzan Inc.
D-BOX - Cameras - George Paddock, Inc.
D-BUG - Computer software ☆ - Electronic Arts Inc.

D-C - Toys–automobiles - Toy Truck Lines, Inc.
D. C. HEATH & CO. - Publisher's imprints - D.C. Heath & Co.
D-C-P - Food products - Davis-Cleaver Foods Inc.
D-CAINE - Pharmaceutical preparations ☆ - Century Pharmaceuticals Inc.
D-CALCI-D - Pharmaceutical preparations ☆ - C.O. Truxton Inc.
D-CAPTIVA - Floor coverings–carpet and rugs ☆ - Regal Rugs Inc.
D-CEASE - Pesticides–household - Security Products Co.
D CHAIR - Chairs–stacking - Fixtures Furniture
D CIRCLE GROVE SEEDS, INC. - Flowers, plants, and seeds - Circle Grove Seeds, Inc.
D. CITY - Recording label - Black Diamond Records, Inc.
D-CLOG - Skin care products - Jason Natural Products, Inc.
D-CON - Insecticides - Linden Corp.
D-CON - Rodenticides - D-Con Co. Inc.
D-CON BROAD SPECTRUM CRAWLING BUG KILLER - Insecticides - Linden Corp.
D-CON D-STROY - Insecticides - Sterling Winthrop Inc.
D-CON LOGIC - Insecticides ☆ - D-Con Co. Inc.
D-CORE - Thread - American & Efird, Inc.
D-COT - Thread - United Thread Mills Corp.
D. D. COOPER - Apparel and accessories - Coopers, Inc.
D-DAY - Games - Avalon Hill Game Co.
D-DAY: OPERATION OVERLORD - Computer software - Virgin Interactive Entertainment, Inc.
D DECORA CLOSETS - Closet organizers - MGR Industries, Inc.
D DEFIANCE - Tools–machine - Defiance Machine & Tool Co., Inc.
D DEREK ANDREW - Anvils - Derek A. Federman
D DEXTER - Packaging–paper - Dexter Corp.
D-DIOL 50-2 - Pharmaceutical preparations - Physician Sales & Service
D DOANE SYSTEM - Computer software - Doane Agricultural Services Co.
D DRAG-IT - Computer peripheral equipment - Proformix, Inc.
D-D'S - Cinnamon rolls - D-D's Country Bakery
D DURASOL AWNINGS - Awnings - Durasol Systems, Inc.
D-E - Rings–jewelry - Dunn & Ewbank Inc.
D-EST - Pharmaceutical preparations - Physician Sales & Service
D. EVANS - Footwear–women's - B. Levy & Son
D-FEDA - Pharmaceutical preparations ☆ - Rhone-Poulenc Rorer Pharmaceuticals Inc.
D-FILM - Cleaner for hard contact lenses - CooperVision Inc.
D-FLATER STIK - Tubes–plastic - Pioneering Concepts Inc.
D-FLEA - Shampoos - Natra Pet Inc.
D/FLEX - Medical apparatus - Puritan-Bennett Corp.
D-FLOSS - Thread - United Thread Mills Corp.
D-FOAM - Health care products - Pharmaceutical Innovations
D-FUSE - Thread - United Thread Mills Corp.
D-FUZZ-IT - Combs - Oak Hill Industries Corp.
D. G. GARRISON - Apparel and accessories ☆ - Edison Brothers Stores, Inc.
D GENE - Laboratory apparatus - Bio-Rad Laboratories, Inc.
D-GERM - Cleaning preparations - Solomon J. Ruth
D. GHIRARDELLI - Chocolate candy - Ghirardelli Chocolate Co.
D GHIRARDELLI CHOCOLATE CO. - Chocolate candy - Ghirardelli Chocolate Co.
D-GLOSS - Cleaning preparations - United Gilsonite Laboratories
D-GUARD - Gasoline - Amoco Oil Co.
D H 12 FORMULA - Hair care products - Gold Medal Hair Products Inc.
D-H-D - Pharmaceutical preparations ☆ - Lexis Laboratories Inc.

D. HARRINGTON - Cutlery - Russell Harrington Cutlery, Inc.
D-HAZE - Cleaning preparations - Franmar Chemical, Inc.
D-HILL - Fruits and vegetables - Sadoian Brothers Inc.
D-I DIATOM - Pet products - Vortex Innerspace Products Inc.
D-ICER - Automotive product - Clean-Rite Products Co.
D-INKY - Cleaning preparations ☆ - Bic Corp.
D. J. HARRISON - Footwear - Bee-Gee Shoe Corp
D-L - Stamps–hand - Data-Link Corp.
D-L - Winches - Dutton-Lainson Co.
D. L. JARDINE'S - Food products - Jardine's Texas Foods
D-L-M - Pharmaceutical preparations ☆ - Mill-Mark Pharmaceuticals Inc.
D-LETE - Office supplies - Molecudyne Inc.
D-LIGHTS - Health care products - Omron Healthcare, Inc.
D-LITE - Breads–mixes - J.W. Allen & Co.
D-LITE - Craft supplies ☆ - Yaley Enterprises
D-LITE - Lamps - Cal-AV Labs Inc.
D-LUX - Adhesives and sealants - At&T Corp.
D/MENSION - Binders - Dennison National Co.
D. MILHADE - Wines - Classic Wine Imports Inc.
D. MORGAN - Posters - Dorris Messer
D-PLUS - Binders - General Loose Leaf Bindery Co.
D POST - Highway product - Poly Enterprises
D PRINTZ - Fabrics - Valley Forge Fabrics Inc.
D-R CINCH SYSTEM - Footwear - K-Swiss Inc.
D R DAVID RICKEY - Apparel–men's - David Rickey and Co.
D-REGION TOMAHAWK - Toys–models ☆ - Estes Industries
D-REX - Pharmaceutical preparations - C.S. Ruckstuhl Co. Inc.
D-RUST/7 - Paint removers - Dumond Chemicals Inc.
D-S-C - Apparel–women's - Cupid Foundations Inc.
D-S-S - Pharmaceutical preparations ☆ - Parke-Davis
D-SCENT - Hunting equipment - 3-J Inc.
D-SERV - Radio communications equipment - Kentrox Industries, Inc.
D-SHIELD - Cables - General Cable Corp.
D-SINUS - Pharmaceutical preparations ☆ - Laser Inc.
D SOLV - Skin care products - Monaco Import/Export Inc.
D SPARKY - Cleaning preparations - Takeo Enterprises Corp.
D-SPOZ-R - Containers–plastic - Euro Design, Inc.
D-STROY - Cleaning preparations - State Chemical Manufacturing Co.
D-STROY - Insecticides - L & F Consumer Products
D-TAM - Skin care products - Colormetric Laboratories, Inc.
D TECH - Chemical preparations - EM Industries, Inc.
D-TECH COLLECTION, THE - House furnishings ☆ - Recyco
D TECH ENVIRONMENTAL DETECTION SYSTEM - Chemical preparations - EM Industries, Inc.
D TECT AVISION - Video production - Detect-A-Vision, Inc.
D-TEST - Pharmaceutical preparations - Physician Sales & Service
D-THATCH - Lawn mowers ☆ - Security Products Co.
D THE DUMBELL MAN - Shirts - Dumbell Man
D-TIME - Computer software - Ballard Synergy Corp.
D-TIPPER - Machinery - Marcus Tate Wallace
D TOLEDO NEW YORK - Jewelry - D. Toledo New York, Ltd.
D-TOOL - Musical instrument accessories - C & R Guitars
D-TRANS - Insecticides - Uncle Sam Chemical Co., Inc.
D-TUSSIN - Cough medicines ☆ - Pharm-A-Lab
D-UV LITE - Lamps - Sperti Sunlamp
D-VAC-6 - Veterinary pharmaceutical preparations ☆ - Boehringer Ingelheim Animal Health, Inc.
D-VAC-7 - Veterinary pharmaceutical preparations - Boehringer Ingelheim Animal Health, Inc.
D-VAC-M - Veterinary pharmaceutical preparations ☆ - Boehringer Ingelheim Animal Health, Inc.
D-VASO - Pharmaceutical preparations - Dunhall Pharmaceuticals Inc.
D-VERT - Pharmaceutical preparations - Roberts/Hauck Pharmaceuticals Inc.
D-VISE - Clamps - Philadelphia Ceramics Inc.
D-VOUR - Cleaning preparations - Big D Industries Inc.
D-WORM - Pet products - Farnam Cos. Inc.
D WRAP - Skin care products - Monaco Import/Export Inc.
D-Y-N-A-STRENGTH - Bandages - Dyna-Strength Medical Inc.
D ZINER - Blinds–venetian ☆ - Bytheway's Manufacturing Inc.
D1 - Floor coverings–carpet and rugs - Omalon
D2 - Photographic equipment - Eastman Kodak Co.
D2 - Wines - Delille Cellars, Inc.
D2 ADVANTAGE - Medical apparatus - Western Enterprises
D2 COTTON - Fabrics–cotton - Doran Textiles, Inc.
D2 FAX - Facsimile equipment - Seponix Corp.
D2 + PLUS - Fuel additives - Fuels Plus Inc.

D2 SOL - Vitamins and nutritional supplements - Freeman Industries LLC
D2E GEAR - Apparel and accessories - Down 2 Earth Gear
D2MS - Computer peripheral equipment - Automated Technology Associates, Inc.
D3 - Footwear - L.A. Gear, Inc.
D3 - Lasers - Coherent, Inc.
D3 SOL - Vitamins and nutritional supplements - Freeman Industries LLC
D4+ - Cleaning preparations - Recoton Corp.
D40 M2 - Tires - Dunlop Tire Corp.
D60 A2 - Tires - Dunlop Tire Corp.
D65 - Tires - Dunlop Tire Corp.
D99 - Cleaning preparations - Tiodize Co. Inc.
+D'A - Musical instrument accessories ☆ - Dampp-Chaser Electronics Corp.
DA-30 - Computer hardware - Wandel & Goltermann Technologies, Inc.
D.A.-34 - Vitamins and nutritional supplements ☆ - J.R. Carlson Laboratories Inc.
DA 5800 - Alarm systems - X-10 Inc.
DA BOMB RECORDS - Recording label - Da Bomb Entertainment Group, Inc.
DA-BON - Vitamins and nutritional supplements - Barrows Pharmacal Inc.
DA CAPO - Musical instruments - Sweet Pipes, Inc.
DA-COR - Finishing agents - Davis Paint Co.
DA-CURVE SCREEN - Projection screens - Da-Lite Screen Co. Inc.
DA D'ANGELO - Hair care products - D'angelo Internationale
DA-DREAM - Enamels - Davis Paint Co.
DA DUDICALS - Apparel and accessories - Clyde W. Ching
DA-GLAS - Electronic equipment ☆ - Da-Lite Screen Co. Inc.
DA HUI NORTH SHORE O'AHU - Bathing suits - Da Hui, Inc.
DA-LI-KAPS - Vitamins and nutritional supplements ☆ - Ulmer Pharmacal Co.
DA-LITE - Projection screens - Da-Lite Screen Co. Inc.
DA-LITE - Window coverings - Covoc Corp.
DA-LUXE - Paints - Davis Paint Co.
DA-LY DROPS - Pharmaceutical preparations - Unique Products Co.
DA-MAN RECORDS - Recording label - Michael J. Mayberry, Sr.
DA-MAT - Electronic equipment - Da-Lite Screen Co. Inc.
DA MUSIC - Recording label - DA Music USA
DA-N-ITE - Hardware ☆ - Premax L.P.
DA-NITE - Signs - SEMTORQ Inc.
DA NOTTE - Underwear and nightwear - Russell-Newman, Inc.
DA-PLEX - Electronic equipment ☆ - Da-Lite Screen Co. Inc.
DA-POWER - Projection screens ☆ - Da-Lite Screen Co. Inc.
DA-PRO - Rope - New England Ropes Inc.
DA REF' - Apparel–athletic - Rimball Marketing and Development, Inc.
DA ROCK ZONE - Apparel and accessories - David Cole
DA SCHNOZOLA - Hardware - Sanitary-Dash Manufacturing Co. Inc.
DA-SHEEN - Enamels - Davis Paint Co.
DA-SNAP - Projection screens - Da-Lite Screen Co. Inc.
DA STUMPF - Toys–musical ☆ - Fiddle Factory Inc.
DA-TA-DAY - Calendars - Dennison National Co.
DA-TEX - Electronic equipment - Da-Lite Screen Co. Inc.
DA-TEX - Paints - Davis Paint Co.
DA TUNG - Soups–canned - Hong Kong Inc.
DA-VIEW - Projection screens - Da-Lite Screen Co. Inc.
DA VINCI - Colognes - Ritornelle Inc.
DA VINCI - Food products - World Finer Foods, Inc.
DA VINCI - Glassware–household ☆ - Crystal Clear Importing Co. Inc.
DA VINCI - Lighters - Colibri Inc.
DA VINCI - Paints–artists' - Da Vinci Paint Co. Inc.
DA VINCI - Sunglasses - Sunglass Originals Inc.
DA VINCI DESIGN COLLECTION, THE - Tiles–ceramic - VMC Corp.
DA WURST HAUS - Mustard - Norsland Kitchens
DAA - Handbags - Joseph Ames
DAAGNIM - Recording label - Jazz Composer's Orchestra Association Inc.
DAB - Cement - R.M. Hollingshead Corp.
DAB - Hair care products ☆ - J. Strickland & Co.
DAB - Office supplies ☆ - Faber-Castell Corp.
DAB A DOT - Inks - Clarence J. Venne Inc.
DAB-ALL-75 - Paper - Arrow International, Inc.
DAB-BIT - Brushes - Stangren Co.
DAB ENGINEERING, INC. - Computer software - DAB Engineering, Inc.
DAB-EZ - Games - Stuart Entertainment, Inc.
DAB LIGHT - Beverages–malt - Dab Marketing Services USA
DAB-O - Vegetable oil - Melvin F. Sawyer
DABAWAYS - Washcloths ☆ - Pfizer Inc.
DABBERS - Pens - Staedtler, Inc.
DABBLES - Skin care products - M.J. Woods, Inc.
DABETTE - Belts–apparel - Dan Dee Belt and Bag Co. Inc.

☆ = Now out of production

DABLER - Pens - Gillette Co.
DABL'S PUBLISHING - Greeting cards ☆ - Jokha Gallery
DABOND - Thread - Belding Heminway Co. Inc.
DABS - Cleaning preparations ☆ - Whitestone Products Inc.
DABURN CRT - Wire - Daburn Electronics & Cable Corp.
DABY - Nail care products - Carisen, Inc.
+D'AC - Electric lighting equipment - Nessen Lighting, Inc.
DAC - Electronic equipment - Honeywell-Measurex DMC Corp.
DAC - Fungicides ☆ - Noble Pine Products Co.
D.A.C. - Posters - Donald Art Co.
DAC FLOC - Chemical preparations - Dacar Chemical Co.
DAC TECHNOLOGIES - Alarm systems - DAC Technologies of America, Inc.
DACAR-GLO - Cleaning preparations ☆ - Dacar Chemical Co.
DACARCOTE - Rustproofing compounds - Dacar Chemical Co.
DACEASY - Computer software - DacEasy Inc.
DACEASY BASE - Computer software ☆ - DacEasy Inc.
DACEASY INSTANT - Computer software - DacEasy Inc.
DACEASY LIGHT - Computer software - DacEasy Inc.
DACEASY PAYROLL - Computer software - DacEasy Inc.
DACEASY WORD - Computer software ☆ - DacEasy Inc.
DACEY BROS. - Dairy products - Dacey Bros. Dairy Inc.
DACFUSE - Thread - United Thread Mills Corp.
DACH RANCH - Baskets–wood - Dach Ranch
DACHE - Apparel - Suzanne Dache Gauld
DACHSTEIN - Skis - Total Sports Ltd.
DACIA - Motor vehicles–automobiles - North American Import/Export Inc.
DACIS - Software - Dacis Systems, Inc.
DACM DISTRIBUTED ACCESS CONTROL MANAGER - Computer software - Atrium Technologies Inc.
DACO - File folders - Dur-A-Flex Inc.
DACOLAC - Adhesives and sealants ☆ - James B. Day and Co.
DACOMATIC - Photographic equipment - Eastman Kodak Co.
DACONIL - Fungicides - ISK Biosciences Corp.
DACONIL 2787 ZN - Fungicides - ISK Biosciences Corp.
DACONIL ULTREX - Fungicides - ISK Biosciences Corp.
DACONIL WEATHERSTIK - Fungicides - ISK Biosciences Corp.
DACONITE - Lacquers - James B. Day and Co.
DACOPA - Coffee substitutes - California Natural Products
DACOR - Air purification systems - Barnebey and Sutcliffe Corp.
DACOR - Backpacks - Dacor Corp.
DACOR - Floor coverings - Stanson Inc. (Dacor Brick Div.)
DACORA - Photographic equipment - AIC International Inc.
DACOTHANE - Enamels - James B. Day and Co.
DACOTHERM - Insulating materials ☆ - Occidental Chemical Corp.
DACPRO - Computer software - Resources Engineering Systems, Inc.
DACRIOSE - Ophthalmic irrigating solution - Iolab Pharmaceuticals
DACRON - Fibers–synthetic - E.I. Dupont de Nemours and Co.
DACSMATE - Computer software - At&T Corp.
DACSOFT - Thread - United Thread Mills Corp.
DACTIL - Pharmaceutical preparations ☆ - Marion Merrell Dow
DAD - Radio control equipment - Dave Abbe Development Co.
DAD & LAD - Adhesives and sealants - Miller Purcell Co.
DAD BAG, THE - Infant product ☆ - Newborne Co.
DAD RAGS - Sportswear - Stanley A. Levine, Inc.
DADANT - Candles - D'Adant and Sons Inc.
DADCO FASHIONS - Apparel–men's - Garward Associates Inc.
DADCO-LOK - Machine parts - Diebolt International, Inc.
DADCO ROMA - Food products - Dadco Food Products Inc.
D'ADDARIO - Musical instrument accessories - J. D'Addario & Co. Inc.
+D'ADDARIO - Musical instrument accessories - International Violin Co. Ltd.
DADDY BINKS - Candy ☆ - R.M. Palmer Co.
DADDY DOLLAR - Flour–blended - Acme-Evans/A.D.M. Milling Co.
DADDY DUCK - Candy ☆ - Keppel's Inc.
DADDY HINKLE'S INSTANT MEAT MARINATES - Spices and extracts - Daddy Hinkle's LLC
DADDY 'N ME - Toys - Natural Science Industries, Ltd.
DADDY-O - Puppets - Dakin Inc.
DADDY-STRAP - Infant product ☆ - Century Products Co.
DADDY'S - Dolls - KVK Inc.
DADDY'S - Sauces - Daddy's Original Recipes, Inc.
DADDYS GIRL - Bicycles - Roadmaster Corp.
DADDY'S LONG LEGS - Toys - KVK Inc.
DADDY'S TOOL BOX - Toys - Tonka Corp.
DADIMA - Snack foods - Abhay K. Sinha
DADIRU - Frozen foods - Pulpas Florida, Inc.
DAD'S - Beverages–carbonated - Monarch Co., Inc.

DADS - Courier services–land - Direct Access Delivery Service
DAD'S - Pet products - Dad's Products Co. Inc.
DAD'S BITE SIZE MEAL - Dog food - Dad's Products Co. Inc.
DAD'S BONES - Pet products - Dad's Products Co. Inc.
DAD'S CHUNX - Dog food - Dad's Products Co. Inc.
DAD'S DRIP STRIP - Paint removers - Sansher Corp.
DAD'S DUTY - Stationery - Dad's Duty, Inc.
DAD'S EASY SPRAY - Paint removers - Sansher Corp.
DAD'S FAVORITE - Dolls - Mary M. Anderson
DAD'S GOURMET BLEND - Cat food - Dad's Products Co. Inc.
DAD'S HAT RACK - Racks - Legreg Co.
DADS JEWELS - Jewelry - Wideband Jewelry Corp.
DAD'S LEAN-N-FIT - Dog food - Dad's Products Co. Inc.
DAD'S ORIGINAL - Cat food - Dad's Products Co. Inc.
DAD'S OWN - Sauces - Dad's Own Foods, LLC
DAD'S SPECIAL MIX - Cat food - Dad's Products Co. Inc.
DAD'S TRAIL MIX - Dog food - Dad's Products Co. Inc.
DAE-JULIE - Confections - Dae Julie, Inc.
DAE WON - Glass products ☆ - Glass Inc.
DAEDALUS - Computer software - Daedalus Group, Inc.
DAEDALUS ENCOUNTER, THE - Computer software - Virgin Interactive Entertainment, Inc.
DAEDOO - Food products - Korean Ginseng Products Co., Ltd.
DAEMONITE - Posters - Aegis Entertainment, Inc.
DAENONG - Rice - Oriental Farmers Food Corp.
DAF - Artists' materials - Diffraction Co.
DAF - Computer software - Aetna Life Insurance Co.
DAFFNEY DOG - Toys–stuffed ☆ - Dakin Inc.
DAFFODIL - Glassware–household - Crisa Corp.
DAFFODIL DUCK - Toys–stuffed - Russ Berrie and Co., Inc.
DAFFODIL FARM - Bread ☆ - Interstate Brands Corp.
DAFFY - Apparel–women's - Daffy Waterwear
DAFFY DINOSAURS - Toys–models ☆ - Reliance Products Corp.
DAFFY DOLLS - Deodorizers ☆ - Car-Freshner Corp.
DAFFY DOT DOLLS - Dolls ☆ - Effanbee Doll Corp.
DAFFY DUCK - T-shirts–men's - Time Warner Entertainment Co., L.P.
DAFIF - Computer software - Defense Mapping Agency
DAFLEX - Tubes–plastic - Daburn Electronics & Cable Corp.
DAFLON - Tubes–plastic - Daburn Electronics & Cable Corp.
DAFNE - Olive oil - RJV Marketing Corp.
DAFODIL - Pottery ☆ - Rubens Originals
DAG - Jewelry–precious - Da Gold Products Corp.
D'AG NYC - Apparel and accessories - D'agostino's Supermarkets, Inc.
DAGENE - Recording label - Dagene/Cabletown Corp.
DAGESTAN - Floor coverings–carpet and rugs - Milliken & Co. Inc.
DAGGER - Toys–models - Estes Industries
DAGGETT & RAMSDELL - Cosmetics - RH Cosmetics Corp.
DAGMAR - Apparel–women's - Fancee Free Manufacturing Co.
DAGNUTS - Apparel and accessories - Dagnuts
DAGO A.T.A. - Cases–plastic ☆ - PowerMark Case Corp.
DAGO BAGS - Cases–musical instrument ☆ - PowerMark Case Corp.
DAGS - Frames–eyeglass - RMA Sun Optics Inc.
DAGWOOD - Mustard - Beaverton Foods
DAHERWARE - Giftware - Tin Box Co. of America, Inc.
DAHLBERG - Hearing aids ☆ - Dahlberg, Inc.
DAHLE - Photographic equipment - Dahle USA
DAHLIA - Dinnerware–glass ☆ - Nikko Ceramics Inc.
DAHLIA - Electronic equipment - Weingrod Electronics
DAHLIA - Housewares - Himark Enterprises Inc.
DAHLIA - Kitchenware–earthenware - Pfaltzgraff Investment Co.
DAHLING - Toys–stuffed - Gund, Inc.
DAHLING COLLECTION - Wigs - Eva Gabor International, Ltd.
DAHLQUIST - Amplifiers - Dahlquist Inc.
DAHLUMAXX - Vitamins and nutritional supplements - JBN Enterprises, Inc.
DAI DAY - Food products - Allied Old English, Inc.
DAILEY - Pickles, relish, peppers - Aunt Jane's Foods
DAILEY - Vegetables–pickled or brined - Dean Pickle & Specialty Products Co.
DAILUAINE - Beverages–malt - European Beverage Co., Inc.
DAILY - Hair care products - Gelle-International Ltd.
DAILY BASICS - Vitamin supplements - Weight Watchers International, Inc.
DAILY BLEND - Nutritional supplements ☆ - Intracell Nutrition Inc.
DAILY BURN - Vitamins and nutritional supplements - Weider Nutrition Group, Inc.
DAILY C - Candy - F & F Laboratories, Inc.
DAILY-CAL - Health care products ☆ - F & F Laboratories, Inc.

DAILY CARE - Skin care products - Pfizer Inc.
DAILY CARE FROM DESTIN - Toiletries - Pfizer Inc.
DAILY CLASS MANAGER - Office paper products - Wallace Computer Services, Inc.
DAILY COMBO - Vitamins and nutritional supplements - Pharmavite Corp.
DAILY CONTROL - Hair care products - Hayashi for Hair Inc.
DAILY DELIGHT - Nuts–salted, roasted, cooked, or canned - Geo. J. Howe Co. Inc.
DAILY DETOX - Vitamins and nutritional supplements - Houston Enterprises
DAILY DIET - Pharmaceutical preparations - Michigan Pharmaceutical
DAILY DIET - Teas - Seelect, Inc.
DAILY DIGIT - Games - Creative Games, Inc.
DAILY DINING - Dinnerware–glass - Nikko Ceramics Inc.
DAILY DOSE - Vitamins - American Pharmaceutical Co.
DAILY DOUBLE - Candy ☆ - Palmer Candy Co.
DAILY DOUBLE - Floor coverings–carpet and rugs ☆ - Len Dal Carpets
DAILY-DOUBLE - Pet products - Penn-Plax, Inc.
DAILY DOUBLE - Toothbrushes ☆ - Ranir Corp.
DAILY DUBBLE - Gloves - Good Luck Glove Co.
DAILY DUTIES - Notebooks and notepads - Sun Sales, Inc.
DAILY EXPRESS - Shampoos - Cosmair Inc.
DAILY EXTRA - Vitamins and nutritional supplements - Georgia Bariatrics Pc
DAILY GOLD PACK - Vitamins and nutritional supplements - Solgar Vitamin and Herb Co., Inc.
DAILY GREENS - Vitamins and nutritional supplements - Nature's Way Products, Inc.
DAILY GRIND - Flour–blended - Michigan Milling Co-Op, Ltd.
DAILY GRINDER, THE - Grinders - McCormick & Co., Inc.
DAILY GUIDEPOSTS - Publisher's imprints - Guideposts Associates, Inc.
DAILY HEALTH NUGGETS - Pet products - Earth Animal
DAILY HELPERS - Medical apparatus - McKesson Home Health Care
DAILY JOURNAL - Computer software - Parsons Technology, Inc.
DAILY-KEY - Vitamins and nutritional supplements - J.R. Carlson Laboratories Inc.
DAILY KLEAN - Vitamins and nutritional supplements - Houston Enterprises
DAILY LIGHT GUARD - Skin care products - Aveda Corp.
DAILY-M - Vitamins and nutritional supplements ☆ - Vita-Fore Products Co.
DAILY MIRACLE - Educational materials - Twila Shakespeare Enterprises, Inc.
DAILY NEW - Underwear and nightwear ☆ - Lovable Co.
DAILY-PAK - Vitamins and nutritional supplements ☆ - J.R. Carlson Laboratories Inc.
DAILY PAK SELECT - Vitamins and nutritional supplements - Leiner Health Products Inc.
DAILY PAK SELECT - Vitamins and nutritional supplements - Lenmar Enterprises, Inc.
DAILY PAKS - Health care products - Leiner Health Products Inc.
DAILY PROTECTION - Pet products - Tomlyn Products
DAILY QUOTA - Vitamins and nutritional supplements - Republic Drug Co. Inc.
DAILY RATION - Vitamins and nutritional supplements - Pharmex Inc.
DAILY REMINDER - Diaries ☆ - Keith Clark Inc.
DAILY REMINDER - Paper–writing - Ampad Corp.
DAILY REVIVAL - Cosmetics - Avon Products, Inc.
DAILY RITUALS - Skin care products - CBI Laboratories, Inc.
DAILY SOLUTION - Vitamins and nutritional supplements - Earth's Resources, Inc.
DAILY-SOY - Vitamins and nutritional supplements - Tishcon Corp.
DAILY SPECTACLES - Ophthalmic goods - Riviera Trading, Inc.
DAILY START - Vitamins and nutritional supplements - Pdk Labs, Inc.
DAILY SUCCESS - Vitamins and nutritional supplements - Natural Alternatives International, Inc.
DAILY SUN - Fruit drinks–bottled or canned - Citrus World Inc.
DAILY TAB - Vitamins and nutritional supplements ☆ - Montgomery Ward & Co. Inc.
DAILY TREAT - Food products - Watsonville Exchange Inc.
DAILY TUNE-UPS - Publisher's imprints - Ideal School Supply Corp.
DAILY VM CAPS - Vitamins and nutritional supplements - Vitamin Shoppe Industries Inc.
DAILY WELLNESS COMPANY, THE - Vitamins and nutritional supplements - Wellness Beverage Co.
DAILYHIST-D - Antihistamine preparations - L. Perrigo Co.
DAILY'S - Beverages - Daily Juice Products Inc.
DAILY'S - Fruit drinks–bottled or canned - Ohio Pure Foods Inc.
DAILY'S BAKERY & CAFE - Bakery products - Daily's Bakery Inc.
DAIMOND SNAP-FORM - Insulating materials - AFM Corp.
DAINITE - Pharmaceutical preparations ☆ - Wallace Laboratories
DAINTEE - Brooms - Lighthouse Industries

DAINTEE - Candy - Sterling Candy Corp.
DAINTEX - Deodorants–personal ☆ - Demert & Dougherty, Inc.
DAINTI-TEEN - Brassieres (Bras) - Wacoal America Inc.
DAINTIFOLD - Napkins–paper - Wisconsin Tissue Mills Inc.
DAINTY - Cookies - Dainty Cookies Inc.
DAINTY - Pet products - Best Feeds and Farm Supplies Inc.
DAINTY DELL - Milk–canned or powdered - Defiance Milk Products Co.
DAINTY DON - Fabrics - Dan River Inc.
DAINTY MAID - House furnishings - Liberty Distributors Group
DAINTY MISS - Vegetables–canned - Durand Canning Co.
DAINTY-PAK - Vegetables–canned - Veronica Foods Co.
DAINTYPRINT - Paper–tissue - Crystal Tissue Co. Inc.
DAINTYTINT - Paper–tissue - Crystal Tissue Co. Inc.
DAIOHS FIRST CHOICE - Coffee - Daiohs First Choice Services
DAIQUIRI - Ophthalmic goods - Foremost Optical Products
DAIQUIRI SHOPPE - Beverages–alcohol - Daiquiri Shoppe, Inc.
DAIQUIRIS - Beverages - David Briggs Enterprises, Inc.
DAIQUIRIS A NEW ORLEANS ORIGINAL - Apparel - David Briggs Enterprises, Inc.
DAIR-E LITE - Lemonade - Purity Dairies, Inc.
DAIRA - Pressure gauges - Michelin Tire Corp.
D'AIRELLE - Hosiery - Aire Hosiery Inc.
DAIRI-BRITE - Detergents - Malco Products, Inc.
DAIRI-FRESH - Dairy products - Publix Super Markets, Inc.
DAIRY AID - Vitamins and nutritional supplements - Pharmavite Corp.
DAIRY BAKE - Dairy products - Foremost Farms USA
DAIRY BELT - Cheese - Land O'Lakes Inc.
DAIRY CAT - Pet products - ALPO Petfoods Inc.
DAIRY CHAIN - Milk ☆ - Maplehurst Farms Inc.
DAIRY CHARM - Ice cream - Maplehurst Farms Inc.
DAIRY CHARM - Milk - Flav-O-Rich, Inc.
DAIRY CHEER - Restaurants–fast food - Dairy Cheer Stores
DAIRY CREST - Cheese - Swissrose International Inc.
DAIRY CRISP - Cereal ☆ - Pet Inc.
DAIRY DINNER - Pet products - Ralston Purina Co.
DAIRY EASE - Pharmaceutical preparations - Bayer Corp. (Consumer Care Div.)
DAIRY EASE 100 - Dairy products - Ryan Foods Co.
DAIRY FAIR - Dairy products - Circle K Corp.
DAIRY FINEST - Dairy products - Wisconsin Milk Marketing Board, Inc.
DAIRY FREE - Food products - Carr Products Co. Inc.
DAIRY FRESH - Beverages - Dairy Fresh Corp.
DAIRY FRESH - Cheese - Detroit City Dairy Inc.
DAIRY FRESH - Desserts - Crowley Frozen Desserts Inc.
DAIRY FRESH - Food products - Avoset Food Corp.
DAIRY FRESH - Pizzas–frozen - Dairy Fresh Products Co.
DAIRY GIRL - Milk–canned or powdered - Sun Hing Foods, Inc.
DAIRY GLEN - Butter - Safeway Stores Inc.
DAIRY GOLD - Milk - B & G Distributing
DAIRY GUARD II - Livestock feed - Walco International, Inc.
DAIRY-HI - Juices - Home Juice Co.
DAIRY IN THE COUNTRY, THE - Dairy products - Smith's Dairy Products Co.
DAIRY KING - Restaurants–fast food - Dairy King Distributors
DAIRY LASS - Dairy products - Guth Dairy Inc.
DAIRY LEAN - Milk - Chico Dairy Co. Inc.
DAIRY LEE - Milk - Malone Dairy Inc.
DAIRY-LO - Dairy products - Pfizer Inc.
DAIRY-LYX - Animal feed supplements - Hubbard Milling Co.
DAIRY MAID - Animal feeds - Blue Seal Feeds Inc.
DAIRY MAID - Butter - Milk Marketing Inc.
DAIRY MAID - Dairy products - Valley Lea Dairies Inc.
DAIRY MAID - Food products - Cutler-Magner Co.
DAIRY MART - Food products - Alta-Dena Certified Dairy, Inc.
DAIRY MART - Ice cream - Dairy Mart Convenience Stores, Inc.
DAIRY MULTI-FACTORS - Animal feed supplements - Agri-King Inc.
DAIRY PURE - Milk - Ryan Foods Co.
DAIRY QUALITY & FRESHNESS SINCE 1929 - Cottage cheese - Land-O-Sun Dairies, Inc.
DAIRY QUEEN - Fast-food franchise - International Dairy Queen Inc.
DAIRY RECIPE - Soups–mixes - Norpac Services, Inc.
DAIRY RICH - Milk - KDK Inc.
DAIRY SURE - Vitamins and nutritional supplements - Barth-Spencer Corp.
DAIRY SWEET - Milk–canned or powdered - Milnot Co.
DAIRYFOOD USA - Cheese - Stauffer Cheese, Inc.
DAIRYLAC - Animal feeds - International Ingredient Corp.
DAIRYLAND - Cheese ☆ - Sargento Cheese Co. Inc.

☆ = Now out of production

DAIRYLAND - Ice cream - Clover Leaf Jersey Dairy
DAIRYLAND BRAND - Chemical preparations - Stearns Packaging Corp.
DAIRYLEA - Dairy products - H.P. Hood & Sons Inc.
DAIRYLITE - Paints ☆ - Everseal International Sales Co. Inc.
DAIRYMAID AIELLO'S ORIGINAL - Cheese - Aiello Bros. Cheese Co. Inc.
DAIRYMAN BRAND - Alfalfa - Michigan State Seed Co.
DAIRYMASTER - Electronic equipment - Remote AG Data, Inc.
DAIRYMATE - Dietary food supplement - Earthmade Natural Vitamins Inc.
DAIRYMATE - Milk–canned or powdered - Pet Inc.
DAIRYMENS - Dairymens
DAIRYMENS - Dairy products - Dairigold Inc.
DAIRYMENS - Milk - Oberlin Farms Dairy Inc.
DAIRYMEN'S EDGE - Animal feed supplements - LBJ Pakke, Inc.
DAIRYPRO - Detergents - Babson Bros. Co.
DAIRYQUICK - Food products - Daniel D. Conolly
DAIRYVILLE - Popcorn - American Specialty Foods, Inc.
DAISEY - Toys–stuffed ☆ - Gund, Inc.
DAISIES - Dinnerware–glass ☆ - Nikko Ceramics Inc.
DAISIES - Glass products - Westmoreland Glass Co.
DAISIES ON CUSTARD - Glassware–household ☆ - Fenton Art Glass Co.
DAISY - Baskets–steel ☆ - Dorco Manufacturing Inc.
DAISY - Bicycles ☆ - Roadmaster Corp.
DAISY - Carpet sweepers ☆ - Bissell Inc.
DAISY - Clocks - General Time Corp. (Westclox/Seth Thomas Div.)
DAISY - Correction fluid ☆ - Wirth International Inc.
DAISY - Drums–musical instruments ☆ - Grossman Music Corp.
DAISY - Glassware–household - Rezler & Howell Co.
DAISY - Glassware–household ☆ - Crystal Clear Importing Co. Inc.
DAISY - Guns - Daisy Manufacturing Co.
DAISY - Housewares - Griffith Rubber
DAISY - Laundry tubs–plastic - Loma/Rubberqueen
DAISY - Mops - Lighthouse Industries
DAISY - Polyethylene film sheets ☆ - Poly-America, Inc.
DAISY - Recording label - Cousins Music
DAISY - Scissors–hand-operated - Cutlery Associates Inc.
DAISY - Shaving preparations - Gillette Co.
DAISY - Sprinklers–lawn - L.R. Nelson Corp.
DAISY - Thread - Belding Heminway Co. Inc.
DAISY - Toys - Milton Bradley Co.
DAISY - Yarn - Lily Craft Products
DAISY - Yarn ☆ - William Unger & Co. Inc.
DAISY 2 - Pregnancy test kits - Ortho Pharmaceutical Corp.
DAISY & BUTTON - Glassware–household ☆ - Fenton Art Glass Co.
DAISY BASKET - Dinnerware–glass ☆ - Lenox, Inc.
DAISY BOUQUET - Glassware–household - Owens-Illinois Inc. (Libbey Div.)
DAISY CHARM - Glassware–household - Owens-Illinois Inc. (Libbey Div.)
DAISY CONE - Traffic marker - Poly Enterprises
DAISY CRAZY - Pottery ☆ - Rubens Originals
DAISY DISC - Deodorizers - Surco Products Inc.
DAISY DREAM - Housewares - Brinns China & Glassware Co. Inc.
DAISY DUCK - Candy ☆ - R.M. Palmer Co.
DAISY DUCK - Toys–stuffed - Russ Berrie and Co., Inc.
DAISY FLIP - Games - Poly Enterprises
DAISY FRESH - Apparel and accessories - Sara Lee Corp.
DAISY FRESH - Food products - Bowman Apple Products Co. Inc.
DAISY FRESH - Starch–laundry ☆ - Demert & Dougherty, Inc.
DAISY HILL PUPPIES - Apparel–children's - United Feature Syndicate, Inc.
DAISY KINGDOM - Fabrics - Daisy Kingdom, Inc.
DAISY KINGDOM - Patterns–clothing ☆ - Simplicity Pattern Co., Inc.
DAISY LANE - Dairy products ☆ - Wetterau Inc.
DAISY MAID - Bacon ☆ - Dold Foods Inc.
DAISY MAID - Candy - Wetterau Inc.
DAISY PATCH - Bathing suits ☆ - Jantzen Inc.
DAISY PATCH - Flowers, plants, and seeds - Ampro Industries, Inc.
DAISY PATCH - Musical instruments - Roberto Ciarfella Inc.
DAISY PLUS - Shaving preparations - Gillette Co.
DAISY ROLL - Meat products - Tav Brands Inc.
DAISY'S - Snack foods ☆ - General Mills, Inc.
DAISYSLIM - Shaving preparations - Gillette Co.
DAISYWORDPRO - Computer software - Daisywriter
DAITCH - Dairy products - Shopwell Inc.
DAITUCCI - Apparel–women's - Union Trading Co.
DAIZY - Apparel–women's - Knits-Cord Ltd.
DAIZY N'LIME - Pottery ☆ - Rubens Originals
DAJER - Meat products–cured - Leonard M. Esposito
DAK - Cookies - Prestige Foods Corp.

DAK-LINK 1000 - Electronic equipment - Daktronics Inc.
DAKA - Stoves–wood-burning - Daka Corp.
DAKA DOCK - Docks - Daka Corp.
DAKAR - Floor coverings–carpet and rugs ☆ - Trans-Ocean Import Co. Inc.
DAKAR - Recording label - Brunswick Record Corp.
DAKAR CARD - Office supplies - Data Visible Corp.
DAKAWARE - Fixtures–plastic - Davies Molding Co.
DAKIL - Pet products - Davis Manufacturing
DAKIN - Toys–stuffed - Dakin Inc.
DAKINI - Apparel and accessories - Dakini, Inc.
DAKINS - Antiseptics - Century Pharmaceuticals Inc.
DAKON - Photographic equipment - Eastman Kodak Co.
DAKON WHIRLPOOL - Health care products - Thermo-Electric Co.
DAKOT SEASONINGS - Seasonings - Harvey Bakery
DAKOTA - Aircraft ☆ - New Piper Aircraft, Inc.
DAKOTA - Beer - Miller Brewing Co.
DAKOTA - Cabinets - Marsh Furniture Co.
DAKOTA - Computer software - Dakota Software Corp.
DAKOTA - Dinnerware–glass ☆ - Lenox, Inc.
DAKOTA - Fireplace equipment - Design Specialties Inc.
DAKOTA - Floor coverings - Congoleum Corp.
DAKOTA - Floor coverings–carpet and rugs - Matworks
DAKOTA - Floor coverings–carpet and rugs ☆ - Mannington Carpets, Inc.
DAKOTA - Furniture - Dinaire Corp.
DAKOTA - Furniture–children's ☆ - Child Craft Industries Inc.
DAKOTA - Glassware–household - Libbey Glass Inc.
DAKOTA - Guns - Dakota Arms, Inc.
DAKOTA - Hats ☆ - Bee Hat Co.
DAKOTA - Jewelry - Wheeler Manufacturing Co. Inc.
DAKOTA - Luggage - Tumi Luggage, Inc.
DAKOTA - Motor vehicles–trucks - Chrysler Corp. (Dodge Truck Div.)
DAKOTA - Pet collars - Leatherite-Nylorite Manufacturing Inc.
DAKOTA - Playground equipment - Hedstrom Corp.
DAKOTA - Watches - Cooper & Co., Inc.
DAKOTA BELT - Belts–apparel - Tom G. Muller
DAKOTA BEST - Flour–blended - Tri-State Milling Co.
DAKOTA BLUES - Eyeglasses - California Design Studio Inc.
DAKOTA BRANDS INTERNATIONAL, INC. - Bakery products - Dakota Brands International, Inc.
DAKOTA BRAVE - Flour–blended - North Dakota Mill and Elevator Association
DAKOTA CAPITOL - Flour–blended - North Dakota Mill and Elevator Association
DAKOTA CENTENNIAL - Trees - NDSU Research Foundation
DAKOTA CHAMPION - Flour–blended - North Dakota Mill and Elevator Association
DAKOTA CHIEF - Flour–blended - North Dakota Mill and Elevator Association
DAKOTA DUDE, THE - Toys - R.E. Bee, Inc.
DAKOTA FARMS - Cheese - Alpine Lace Brands, Inc.
DAKOTA FRONTIER - Cookies - R.D. Offutt Co.
DAKOTA GIANT - Flour–blended - Tri-State Milling Co.
DAKOTA GOLDCHARM - Plants - NDSU Research Foundation
DAKOTA GOLDRUSH - Flowers, plants, and seeds - NDSU Research Foundation
DAKOTA GOURMET - Seeds–salted, roasted, cooked, or canned - Dakota Gourmet
DAKOTA GOURMET AMAZING CORN - Nuts–salted, roasted, cooked, or canned - Sonne Laboratories
DAKOTA GOURMET HEART SMART TRAIL MIX - Nuts–salted, roasted, cooked, or canned - Sonne Laboratories
DAKOTA GOURMETS - Seasonings ☆ - Sonne Laboratories
DAKOTA HEARTH - Breads–frozen - Rhodes International, Inc.
DAKOTA KING - Flour–blended - North Dakota Mill and Elevator Association
DAKOTA MAID - Flour–blended - North Dakota Mill and Elevator Association
DAKOTA MINN-DAK YEAST CO. - Yeast - Minn-Dak Yeast Co. Inc.
DAKOTA PRIDE - Flour–blended - North Dakota Mill and Elevator Association
DAKOTA QUEEN - Flour–blended - North Dakota Mill and Elevator Association
DAKOTA ROSE - Jewelry–precious - Coleman-Frizzell, Inc.
DAKOTA SIOUX - Flour–blended ☆ - North Dakota Mill and Elevator Association
DAKOTA SMITH - Eyeglasses - California Design Studio Inc.
DAKOTA SMITH - Shoes - California Design Studio Inc.
DAKOTA SMOOTH - Leather goods - Korchmar Case Co.
DAKOTA STATE - Flour–blended - North Dakota Mill and Elevator Association

☆ = Now out of production

DAKOTA STERLING SILVER BY WHEELER - Jewelry--precious - Wheeler Manufacturing Co. Inc.

DAKOTA SUNBURST - Plants - NDSU Research Foundation

DAKOTA SUNSPOT - Plants - NDSU Research Foundation

DAKOTA TERRITORY - Beef - Dakota Foods Inc.

DAKOTA TERRITORY PIONEER - Soups--canned - Frontier Soups

DAKOTA TRAIL - Meat products--dried - Dakota Trail, Inc.

DAKOTA WRAPAROUNDS - Goggles - Glendale Protective Technologies Inc.

DAKOTAH - Recording label - The SOAR Corp.

DAKOTAH PRAIRIE PRODUCTS - Honey - Hair by Stewarts, Inc.

DAKOVA NUTRITIONALS - Vitamins and nutritional supplements - Dakova Nutritionals, Inc.

DAKS - Apparel--men's - H. Freeman and Son Inc.

DAKS - Umbrellas ☆ - Shaw Creations Inc.

DAKSTATS - Computer software - Daktronics Inc.

DAKTRONICS - Scoreboards - Daktronics Inc.

DAL - Apparel and accessories - M & T Bank

DAL - Spices and extracts - Cinnabar Specialty Foods, Inc./Neera's Products

DAL - Tiles--ceramic - Amsterdam Corp.

DAL BELLO - Boots ☆ - Miura Sports Inc.

DAL-DRAINS - Drains - Dallas Specialty & Manufacturing Co.

DAL-FLEX - Sporting goods - Dalco Athletic Lettering Inc.

DAL-KEYSTONE - Tiles--mosaic - Dal-Tile Corp.

DAL-MOSAICS - Tiles--ceramic - Dal-Tile Corp.

DAL-PAVERS - Tiles--ceramic - Dal-Tile Corp.

DAL RACCOLTA - Olive oil - Fred Montesi Super Markets

DAL RACCOLTO - Oils--edible - Colavita USA, Inc.

DAL-TILE - Tiles--ceramic - Dal-Tile Corp.

DALA - Fabrics - Dan River Inc.

DALA PLASTMATTA - Floor coverings--carpet and rugs - Ports of Scandinavia Inc.

DALALONE - Pharmaceutical preparations - Forest Pharmaceuticals Inc.

DALALONE D.P. - Pharmaceutical preparations - Forest Pharmaceuticals Inc.

DALAVERA - Tiles--ceramic - Dal-Tile Corp.

DALAX - Paints - Williams-Hayward Protective Coatings Inc.

DALBEY - Musical instrument accessories - Ed Myers Co.

DALBI - Wigs - Louis Ferre, Inc.

DALCAINE - Pharmaceutical preparations ☆ - Forest Pharmaceuticals Inc.

DALCO - Audio equipment - Dalco Speaker Works

DALCON - Thread - Sebro Thread Corp.

DALE - Deodorants--personal ☆ - Willert Home Products, Inc.

DALE - Food products - Dale Foods Inc.

DALE - Food products - Vincent Food Industries Inc.

DALE - Greeting cards - Recycled Paper Products, Inc.

DALE - Medical apparatus - Dale Medical Products Inc.

DALE - Thread - Threads USA Div.

DALE - Watches - Bulova Corp.

DALE ACTIVE LIFE - Medical apparatus - Dale Medical Products Inc.

DALE ALEXANDER - Vitamins and nutritional supplements - Twinlab

DALE EARNHARDT - Toys - ERTL Co., Inc.

DALE FREDRICKS - Saddles - Donald Marshall Motsenbocker

DALEBOOT - Skis - Daleboot USA

DALEN - Garden equipment - Dalen Products Inc.

DALER - Paper--kraft ☆ - Canson-Talens Inc.

DALES - Diuretics ☆ - Robinette Inc.

DALE'S - Food containers - Farmhouse Foods

DALESPUN - Yarn - Bernat Yarn & Craft Corp.

DALEWOOD - Margarine ☆ - Safeway Stores Inc.

DALEYWEAR - Apparel--women's - Seattle Gear, Inc.

DALFOUR - Jams and jellies - Holland-American Importing Co. Inc.

DALI - Recording label - Chameleon Music Group Inc.

DALI DEE - Hobby kits - Morehead, Inc.

DALIA - Flatware ☆ - Wilton Co.

DALIDOME - Deodorants--personal ☆ - Miles Inc.

DALIDYNE - Antiseptics - Ion Laboratories Inc.

DALIN - Apparel and accessories - Mevisions International Inc.

DALISO WOOD - Wood products - Cutlers Owens

DALITE - Boating equipment and accessories - Datrex Inc.

DALITE - Projection screens - Nelson Beck of Washington

DALITE - Wire - Daburn Electronics & Cable Corp.

DALKON - Health care products ☆ - A.H. Robins Co. Inc.

DALLA COSTA, A - Postcards ☆ - Classico San Francisco Inc.

DALLA DECOR - Tiles--ceramic - La France

DALLA VALLE - Wines - Wilson Daniels Ltd.

DALLA VILLA - Tiles--ceramic - La France

DALLAGE CHATEAU - Marble products - La France

DALLAGE JARDIN - Tiles--ceramic - La France

DALLAGE PROVENCE - Tiles--ceramic - La France

DALLARI - Pasta ☆ - Liberty Richter Inc.

DALLAS - See **TRINITY CROSS**

DALLAS - Aquatic pharmacuetical preparations - Superior Shade & Blind Co. Inc.

DALLAS - Audio equipment - Robert Bosch Corp.

DALLAS - Colognes - Frances Denney

DALLAS - Dolls ☆ - Effanbee Doll Corp.

DALLAS - Doors--metal ☆ - General Aluminum Co.

DALLAS - Floor coverings--carpet and rugs - Kelly Group Inc.

DALLAS - Floor coverings--carpet and rugs ☆ - Len Dal Carpets

DALLAS - Floor coverings--carpet and rugs ☆ - World Carpets, Inc.

DALLAS - Suits--women's - Leslie Fay Companies Inc.

DALLAS - Trailers--travel ☆ - Marathon Homes Corp.

DALLAS CHAPARRALS - Apparel and accessories - John A. Busch

DALLAS COLLECTION - Juices - Dallas Collection Skin Care, Inc.

DALLAS DYNASTY - Apparel and accessories - Inger Canady

DALLAS GOLD - Beverages--malt - Dallas Brewing Co. Inc.

DALLAS HEAT - Massage products - Sarah Aloe Essence Cosmetics & Accessories, Inc.

DALLAS MAVERICKS - Balls - Dallas Basketball Limited

DALLAS ON THE GO - Telephone directories - Directories on the Go, Inc.

DALLAS PAJAMA DEPARTMENT D.P.D. - Apparel and accessories - Bentley Lingerie, Inc.

DALLAS Q - Floor coverings--carpet and rugs - Kelly Group Inc.

DALLAS STARS - Apparel and accessories - Dallas Hockey Club, Inc.

DALLAS WARE - Dinnerware--plastic - Plastics Manufacturing Co.

DALLAS WARE DINNERWARE - Dinnerware - Carlisle Foodservice Products, Inc.

DALLASTAT - Electronic equipment - Dallas Semiconductor Corp.

DALLE DE VERRE - Glass products - Blenko Glass Co. Inc.

DALLERGY - Pharmaceutical preparations - Laser Inc.

DALLERGY-D - Pharmaceutical preparations ☆ - Laser Inc.

DALLERGY-JR. - Pharmaceutical preparations - Laser Inc.

DALLES CHERRY GROWERS, THE - Fruits--frozen - Oregon Cherry Growers, Inc.

DALLIS - Coffee - Dallis Brothers Inc.

DALLO DECOR - Tiles--ceramic - La France

DALMACJIA - Wines - Stanley Stawski Distributing Co.

DALMANE - Pharmaceutical preparations - Roche Laboratories

DALMANIA - Games - John Daniel McLaughlin

DALMARKO - Flowers--artificial - Dalmarko Designs Inc.

DALMASSO - Cheese - J.G. Pieri Co. Inc.

DALMAZIN - Pharmaceutical preparations ☆ - Ulmer Pharmacal Co.

DALMO - Hardware ☆ - Vincent Whitney Co.

DALMORE - Beverages--malt - European Beverage Co., Inc.

DALMORE, THE - Beverages--alcohol - Jim Beam Brands Co.

DALO - Markers--felt-tip - Mark-Tex Corp.

+D'ALOE - Deodorants--personal - Key West Aloe Inc.

DALON - Electrical equipment - Acme Battery Manufacturing Co.

DALROC SYSTEM, THE - Building materials--concrete - Dal-Har Construction, Inc.

DALSIN LINE - Ventilation equipment - Bernard Dalsin Manufacturing

DALSPERSE - Water treating compounds - Dacar Chemical Co.

DALTEK QUICK KILL - Insect repellents - Landco

DALTON - Cigarettes - Brown & Williamson Tobacco Corp.

DALTON - Eyeglasses - Art-Craft Optical Co.

DALTON - Hardware - Fulton Corp.

DALTON - Meat products--beef - Penthouse Meat Co.

DALTON - Refrigerators - Dalton Holdings Inc.

DALTON - Shoes ☆ - Allen-Edmonds Shoe Corp.

DALTON ADMASTER - Paper ☆ - Hunt Manufacturing Co.

DALTON BOND - Paper - National Printfast

DALTON, THE - Fencing--plastic - Nebraska Plastics, Inc.

DALTONIAN - Floor coverings--carpet and rugs - Daltonian Carpet & Cushion Inc.

DALTOX C & D - Veterinary pharmaceutical preparations ☆ - Fermenta Animal Health

DALTRON - Fabrics--coated - Dalco Athletic Lettering Inc.

DALY & WOLCOTT - Computer software - Daly & Wolcott, Inc.

DALY'S - Finishing agents - Daly's Inc.

DALZOFOAM - Health care products - Tecnol Medical Products, Inc.

DAM - Computer software - Cabletron Systems, Inc.

DAM - Jewelry - Devon Ainsworth Mullen

DAM-LITE - Frames--eyeglass - May Optical Co. Inc.

☆ = Now out of production

DAMABI - Recording label - TSR Records
DAMACO - Wheelchairs - Damaco Inc.
DAMAGE IS DONE, THE - Skin care products - Cosmedic Concepts, Inc.
DAMAGE REPAIR - Hair care products - Vancar Research Inc.
DAMALUX - Lamp bulbs - Damar Worldwide, Inc.
DAMAR-LAC - Paints - Talon Paint Inc.
DAMARA - Ophthalmic goods - Foremost Optical Products
DAMARIS - Floor coverings–carpet and rugs ☆ - Regal Rugs Inc.
DAMARIS - Footwear - Argyris Inc.
DAMARLO - Cribs–wood ☆ - Welsh Co.
DAMART THERMAWEAR - Gloves - Damart
DAMAS - Frames–eyeglass - Hoya Corp. USA
DAMASCENE - Jewelry - Reed and Barton Corp.
DAMASCO - Wallpaper - Blumenthal
DAMASCO WHITE - Tableware–china - Villeroy and Boch Tableware Ltd.
DAMASCUS - Breads - Allied Bakers Co.
DAMASCUS - Floor coverings ☆ - Congoleum Corp.
DAMASCUS - Floor coverings–carpet and rugs ☆ - Regal Rugs Inc.
DAMASCUS - Gloves - Dakota Corp.
DAMASCUS - Lenses–optical - Kelley & Hueber
DAMASCUS ROAD - Recording label - Promise Concert Ministries
DAMASK - Dishes–china ☆ - Pickard Inc.
DAMASK - Floor coverings ☆ - Bellbridge Carpets
DAMASK - Rings–jewelry ☆ - Artcarved Inc.
DAMASK - Tiles–ceramic - American Olean Tile Co.
DAMASK ROSE - Toiletries - Crabtree & Evelyn, Ltd.
DAMASSE - Floor coverings–carpet and rugs ☆ - Regal Rugs Inc.
DAMCO - Jewelry - Golden Jewels Ltd.
DAME - Leather goods - Dame Belt Co. Inc.
DAME - Ophthalmic goods ☆ - Luxottica
D'AMELIA - Pasta ☆ - Mr. Coffee, Inc.
DAMIAN CHRISTOPHER - Hair care products - Damian Christopher Inc.
DAMIAN MUSIC - Recording label - Eyes Enterprises, Inc.
DAMIANA - Beverages–alcohol - Paddington Corp.
DAMIANA - Pharmaceutical preparations - Vartex Pharmaceuticals Inc.
DAMIANA - Recording label - Jazz Composer's Orchestra Association Inc.
D'AMICO - Sausages - Johnsonville Sausage, Inc.
DAMIEN'S - Sauces - LDN Marketing
+D'AMIGO - Handbags - Edison Brothers Stores, Inc.
DAMIXA - Faucets ☆ - Peerless Faucet Co. (Plumbing Products Div.)
DAMM - Beverages–malt - Anthony R. Holbrook
DAMMANN - Paper–condenser - Gourmet Club Corp.
DAMMAR VARNISH - Varnishes - Winsor & Newton
DAMME - Cheese ☆ - Swissrose International Inc.
DAMMER DIKER - Agricultural machinery - AG Engineering & Development Co., Inc.
DAMMIT - Toys–stuffed ☆ - Gund, Inc.
DAMOCLES - Computer software - International Business Machines Corp.
DAMON - Apparel–men's - Damon Creations Inc.
DAMON - Ophthalmic goods - Foremost Optical Products
DAMON INTERNATIONAL - Apparel–men's - Damon Creations Inc.
DAMON SPORT - Apparel–women's - Damon Creations Inc.
DAMP AWAY - Waterproofing compounds - Marine Development & Research Corp.
DAMP CHECK - Cleaning preparations - Check Corp.
DAMP-DEK - Roofing materials–clay - L.D. Sterns Corp.
DAMP/GRIP - Paints - Valspar Corp.
DAMP RID - Cleaning preparations - Vapor Products
DAMPCHEX - Paints - Klee Chemical Coatings
DAMPIT - Musical instrument accessories - Dampits Inc.
DAMPNEY - Paints - Dampney Co., Inc.
DAMPP-CHASER - Dehumidifiers - GRK Manufacturing
DAMPP-CHASER - Musical instrument accessories - Dampp-Chaser Electronics Corp.
DAMPPROOF - Primers - Waterlox Coatings Corp.
DAMPRUF - Paints - Lasting Paints Inc.
DAMPTEX - Epoxy coatings - Steelcote Manufacturing Corp.
DAMPWALL - Enamels ☆ - Waterlox Coatings Corp.
DAMSEL - Clocks - General Time Corp. (Westclox/Seth Thomas Div.)
DAMTITE - Waterproofing compounds - Thomas Waterproof Coatings Co.
DAMTITE PATCH - Adhesives and sealants - Thomas Waterproof Coatings Co.
DAMZOL - Floor coverings–carpet and rugs - Masland Corp.
DAN - Fabrics - Dan River Inc.
DAN - Ophthalmic goods - Rozin Optical Export Corp.
DAN BOONE - Cans–metal - Spraz Co.
DAN CLASSICS - Fabrics - Dan River Inc.

DAN-D - Doors–wood - Wahlfeld Manufacturing Co.
DAN D BIRD - Pet products - CBS Products
DAN DARE - Computer software ☆ - Electronic Arts Inc.
DAN DEE - Apparel and accessories ☆ - Dan Dee Belt and Bag Co. Inc.
DAN DEE - Food products - Troyer Potato Products, Inc.
DAN-DEE - Jams and jellies - Owen & Mowrey Inc.
DAN-DEE - Novelty items–paper - Dan-Dee International Ltd.
DAN DEE - Stencils - Ideal Stencil Machine and Tape Co.
DAN-DEE-O - Fruits and vegetables - Chris Sorensen Packing Co.
DAN-DI PAN - Film - Rollei of America Inc.
DAN FITZGERALD - Video production - Fitzgerald Hunting Enterprises, Inc.
DAN FRESH - Fabrics - Dan River Inc.
DAN GABLE - Sporting goods - Universal Gym Equipment, Inc.
DAN GAP - Fabrics - Dan River Inc.
DAN GO - Fabrics - Dan River Inc.
DAN GUARD - Fabrics - Dan River Inc.
DAN GURNEY - Motor vehicles–automobiles - All American Racers, Inc.
DAN HARVEY CASUALS - Crocheted and knitted items - Towne & King Inc.
DAN HEATHER - Fabrics - Dan River Inc.
DAN ILD 64 - Dinnerware–glass ☆ - Svend Jensen of Denmark Inc.
DAN-LOC - Nuts and bolts - Dan-Loc Bolt & Gasket, Inc.
DAN LURIE - Exercising equipment - Dan Lurie Barbell Co., Inc.
DAN LUSTRE - Fabrics–cotton - Dan River Inc.
DAN MARINER - Sporting goods - Franklin Sports, Inc.
DAN MATES - Apparel–children's - Dan River Inc.
DAN PATCH - Whiskey - Jim Beam Brands Co.
DAN PHREE - Shampoos - KMS Research Inc.
DAN POST - Boots - Acme Boot Co., Inc.
DAN POST EL PASO - Boots - Acme Boot Co., Inc.
DAN POST GOLD ADVANTAGE - Socks - Acme Boot Co., Inc.
DAN-PRESS - Fabric softeners - Dan River Inc.
DAN QUAYLE - Novelty items - Voodoo To You Inc.
DAN RESIST - Fabrics - Dan River Inc.
DAN RIPPLE - Fabrics - Dan River Inc.
DAN RIVER - Fabrics - Dan River Inc.
DAN RIVER KINDERCOTTON - Bedding–linen - Dan River Inc.
DAN RIVER LITES - House furnishings - Dan River Inc.
DAN RIVER SHEER BLISS - Hosiery - Dan River Inc.
DAN RIVER TARTAN WORKSHOP - Bedding–linen - Dan River Inc.
DAN RIVER U.S.A. - Bedding–linen - Dan River Inc.
DAN RIVER'S BOUTIQUE - Bedding–linen - Dan River Inc.
DAN ROYAL - Fabrics–corduroy - Dan River Inc.
DAN STAR - Hardware - Daniel Industries Inc.
DAN SUEDE - Fabrics - Dan River Inc.
DAN SWETT'S - Cleaning preparations - Star 10, Inc.
DAN-TEX DT - Paints - Dan-Tex Paint & Coating Manufacturing Co. Inc.
DAN THE SAUSAGEMAN - Meat products–pork - Dan the Sausageman
DAN WESSON - Guns - Wesson Firearms Co. Inc.
DANA - Boats - Pacific Seacraft Corp.
DANA - Cheese - Syrian Bakery Co., Inc.
DANA - Dairy products - Ziyad Brothers Importing
DANA - Dolls - Mattel, Inc.
DANA - Lamps, halogen bulbs, etc. - Dana Lighting Inc.
DANA - Ophthalmic goods - Styl-Rite Optical Manufacturing Co., Inc.
DANA BLAKE - Apparel–women's - Montgomery Ward & Co. Inc.
DANA-BROWN - Teas - Southern Tea Co.
DANA BUCHMAN - Perfumes - Liz Claiborne Inc.
DANA CARESS - Jewelry ☆ - Concept Marketing Inc.
DANA DESIGN - Backpacks - Dana Design Ltd.
DANA DESIGN - Backpacks - K2 Inc.
DANA LABELS - Labels–paper - Dana Labels, Inc.
DANA, NY - Wigs - It's a Wig!
DANA PIERCE - Apparel and accessories - CMT Enterprises, Inc.
DANA PUBLISHING - Music–sheet - Dana Publishing Co.
DANACOLORS - Artists' materials - Triangle Coatings Inc.
DANAE - Flatware ☆ - Kirk Stieff Co.
DANAE - Frames–eyeglass - Hoya Corp. USA
DANAI - Floor coverings–carpet and rugs ☆ - Regal Rugs Inc.
DANAIR - Fabrics - Dan River Inc.
DANAIR - Tools - Danair, Inc.
DANALOY - Copper products - Ultram International
DANALYST - Computer software - Buzzwords International Inc.
DANAR - Neckties - Danar Ties Inc.
DANARA DOCTORS CHOICE - Infant product - Danara International, Ltd.
DANARA SAFE-GUARD - Infant product - Danara International, Ltd.
DANARASAURS - Housewares - Danara International, Ltd.

DANAVOX - Hearing aids - G.N. Danavox Inc.
DANBADE - Pharmaceutical preparations ☆ - Danbury Pharmacal Inc.
DANBANNA - Hats - Capsmith, Inc.
DANBLEND - Fabrics - Dan River Inc.
DANBRIDGE - Furniture ☆ - Athens Furniture Industries Inc.
DANBURY - Belts–apparel - Gem-Dandy, Inc.
DANBURY - Cabinets - Imperial Cabinet Co. Inc.
DANBURY - Cabinets - Western Cabinet & Millwork Inc.
DANBURY - Eyeglasses - Art-Craft Optical Co.
DANBURY - Floor coverings–carpet and rugs ☆ - J and J Industries Inc.
DANBURY - Furniture polish and wax ☆ - Talisman of Georgia
DANBURY - Mattresses - Stearns & Foster Bedding Co.
DANBURY APPAREL - Apparel and accessories - Gem-Dandy, Inc.
DANBURY CATHEDRAL - Cabinets–wood - Kemper
DANBURY FAIR - Floor coverings - Tarkett, Inc.
DANBURY MILL - Furniture–upholstered ☆ - Webb Furniture Enterprises Inc.
DANBURY MINT - collectibles - MBI Inc.
DANBURY SQUARE - Cabinets–wood - Kemper
DANBURY, USA - Apparel and accessories - Gem-Dandy, Inc.
DANBY - Machinery - Danby of North America
DANCALE - Bedding–linen - Dan River Inc.
DANCATS - Footwear ☆ - Danner Shoe Manufacturing Co.
DANCE-A-THON - Recording label ☆ - Hottrax Records
DANCE-ALLURE - Wedding gowns - Alfred Angelo Inc.
DANCE & DRESS - Dolls - Mattel, Inc.
DANCE & PRANCE - Apparel–children's - Roget Industries Ltd.
DANCE BALLERINA DANCE - Dolls ☆ - Effanbee Doll Corp.
DANCE CLUB - Dolls - Mattel, Inc.
DANCE-DUET - Underwear and nightwear ☆ - Lovable Co.
DANCE FLOOR - Recording label - Echo Records Inc.
DANCE HORIZONS - Publisher's imprints - Princeton Book Co., Publishers
DANCE MAGIC - Dolls - Mattel, Inc.
DANCE MASTERS - Shoes–athletic - Jon Farbman
DANCE 'N PLAY - Dolls - Mattel, Inc.
DANCE 'N TWIRL - Dolls - Mattel, Inc.
DANCE OF FIRE - Christmas tree ornaments - Cracker Box Inc.
DANCE OF SHIVA, THE - Computer software ☆ - Krell Software Corp.
DANCE OF THE PLANETS - Computer software - Applied Research and Consulting Inc.
DANCE PARTY FAVORITES - Recording label - Turn Up the Music, Inc.
DANCE POOL - Recording label - Sony Music Entertainment Inc.
DANCE SENSATION - Dolls - Mattel, Inc.
DANCE THERE - Shoes - Famolare Inc.
DANCE TIME - Brassieres (Bras) ☆ - Lovable Co.
DANCE TIME - Shoes - Wal-Mart Stores Inc.
DANCE TRAINING - Footwear - L.A. Gear, Inc.
DANCE TRANCE - Vitamins and nutritional supplements - Hit Products, Inc.
DANCE VISION USA - Video production - W.D. Eng Inc.
DANCE WITH ME BALLERINA - Toys - Samet & Wells Inc.
DANCEATRONICS - Electronic show sets - Aaron Fechter
DANCEOUT - Video production - Phillip Alan Martin
DANCER - Artists' materials - Stangren Co.
DANCER - Frames–eyeglass ☆ - Universal/Univis Inc.
DANCERCIZE - Athletic shoes - International Seaway Trading Corp.
DANCER'S COLLECTION - Greeting cards ☆ - Princeton Book Co., Publishers
DANCESPORTS - Footwear–women's ☆ - Rockport Co. Inc.
DANCETIME SHOP - Toys - Mattel, Inc.
DANCHEK - Fabrics - Dan River Inc.
DANCHROMATIC - Fabrics - Dan River Inc.
DANCIN - Handbags - Edison Brothers Stores, Inc.
DANCIN' - Wallpaper - Essex Wallcoveringss
DANCIN' BABIES - Toys - Mattel, Inc.
DANCIN' DARLIN' - Novelty items ☆ - Cobbs Manufacturing Co.
DANCING ANIMALS - Music boxes - Fisher-Price, Inc.
DANCING BEARS - Toys–stuffed - Kamar International Inc.
DANCING BUDDIES - Toys–stuffed - Fun World Inc.
DANCING CAKES PRESS - Publisher's imprints - Annette Ooyevaar
DANCING CAT - Recording label - Windham Hill Productions Inc.
DANCING COLORS - Hardware ☆ - Danco Industries Inc. (Glenlo Products Div.)
DANCING DEVIL - Fireworks - American Promotional Events, Inc.
DANCING DEVIL - Fireworks - China Pyrotechnics, Inc.
DANCING DOLPHINS - Stationery - Lisa Frank, Inc.
DANCING EGGHEADS - Toys–stuffed - Fun World Inc.
DANCING GATOR - Seasonings - Robert M. James
DANCING GIRL - Eyeglasses - Art-Craft Optical Co.

DANCING GOATS - Coffee - Challain Inc.
DANCING GOATS ESPRESSO CO. - Coffee - Challain Inc.
DANCING HAIR - Hair care products - La Coupe
DANCING HOURS COLLECTION - Giftware - Waterford Wedgewood USA, Inc.
DANCING LIGHTS - Toys ☆ - Steven Manufacturing Co.
DANCING LITES - Christmas tree lights - General Enterprises Inc.
DANCING PARTNER - Apparel–women's - Jezebel-Renee of Hollywood
DANCING PRETTY - Dolls - Mattel, Inc.
DANCING SHADOWS - Carpet ☆ - Mohawk Carpet Corp.
DANCING SKELETON - Costumes - Spearhead Industries Inc.
DANCING SURF - Flatware - Kirk Stieff Co.
DANCING TARANTULA - Recording label - Darksilver Records & Filmworks Inc.
DANCLEAN - Fabrics - Dan River Inc.
DANCLOUD - Fabrics - Dan River Inc.
D'ANCO - Cheese - Anco Foods Corp.
DANCO EBONEE - Cables - Danco
DANCO NYLON - Cables - Danco
DANCOMB - Fabrics - Dan River Inc.
DANCOOL - Fabrics ☆ - Dan River Inc.
DANCORD - Fabrics - Dan River Inc.
DANCORT - Pharmaceutical preparations ☆ - Jones Medical Industries, Inc. (Medical Div.)
DANCRAFT - Bedding–linen ☆ - Dan River Inc.
DANCREPE - Fabrics - Dan River Inc.
DANCREST - Fabrics - Dan River Inc.
DANCRUISE - Fabrics - Dan River Inc.
DAND-A - Hair care products ☆ - Johnson Products Co., Inc.
DAND-O-LINE - Rope - Anchor Wire Corp.
DAND-R-OFF - Hair care products ☆ - Majestic Drug Co., Inc.
DANDARREST - Shampoos - Nexxus Products Co.
D&D - Figurines - Tsr, Inc.
DANDEE - Apparel and accessories - Stahl-Urban Co.
DANDEE FRY - Food products - Northern Star Co.
DANDEEN - Fabrics–cotton - Dan River Inc.
DANDELION - Ophthalmic goods - Embassy Creations Inc.
DANDERLION - Filters–air - Alan W. Jordan
DANDIGRAM - Musical instrument accessories - D'Andrea Manufacturing Co. Inc.
DANDILUX - Cases–musical instrument ☆ - D'Andrea Manufacturing Co. Inc.
DANDRASOLV - Hair care products - Moore Beauty Inc.
D'ANDREA - Musical instrument accessories - D'Andrea Manufacturing Co. Inc.
DANDRICIDE - Hair care products - King Research, Inc.
DANDRIDGE HOUSE - Food products ☆ - Wine & Schulz Inc.
DANDROFF - Shampoos ☆ - Demert & Dougherty, Inc.
DANDUX - Tarpaulins - C.R. Daniels Inc.
DANDY - Crackers - Holland-American Importing Co. Inc.
DANDY - Crackers - Nabisco Foods Group
DANDY - File folders - Hedges Manufacturing Co.
DANDY - Flowers, plants, and seeds - Jacklin Seed
DANDY - Frames–eyeglass ☆ - Universal/Univis Inc.
DANDY - Fruits and vegetables - A. Duda & Sons, Inc.
DANDY - Gliders–metal - Turner and Seymour Manufacturing Co.
DANDY - Ice cream cones - Dandy Baking Co.
DANDY - Nuts–salted, roasted, cooked, or canned ☆ - Southern Frozen Foods Inc.
DANDY - Paper cutters ☆ - Milton Bradley Co.
DANDY - Pencil sharpeners ☆ - Empire Berol USA
DANDY - Pet products - Dandy Products Inc.
DANDY - Pickles ☆ - Aunt Jane's Foods
DANDY - Projection screens ☆ - Da-Lite Screen Co. Inc.
DANDY - Sporting goods ☆ - Mill Run Products Co.
DANDY - Thread ☆ - Coats and Clark Inc.
DANDY - Tools–hand-operated ☆ - Durall-Eagle Tools
DANDY - Underwear and nightwear - Youthcraft-Charmfit
DANDY - Wallpaper ☆ - Wallquest, Inc.
DANDY BAG - Filters–water - Dandy Enterprises Limited
DANDY BRA - Brassieres (Bras) - Lady Marlene
DANDY BRITE - Bleach - Moran Foods, Inc.
DANDY DAUBER - Finishing agents - Deft Inc.
DANDY DIAMOND - Garden equipment - Valley View Specialties Co.
DANDY EDGE - Sheeting and tile - Dexter Corp. (Mercer Plastics Div.)
DANDY FORM - Brassieres (Bras) - Lady Marlene
DANDY GOURMET - Food products ☆ - A. Duda & Sons, Inc.
DANDY HANDY CHAIR, THE - Infant product - Handy Chair Corp.

☆ = Now out of production

DANDY JUMBO POODLE - Deodorizers ☆ - Car-Freshner Corp.
DANDY LION - Puppets - Dakin Inc.
DANDY MIX - Candy - Bradley Candy Manufacturing Co.
DANDYRUB - Erasers ☆ - Faber-Castell Corp.
DANDY'S - Chewing gum - Dandy Confectionery
DANDY'S EXOTIC - Chewing gum - Dandy Confectionery
DANE - Boats–motor - Crestliner Boats Inc.
DANE - Locks–door - Weiser Lock Corp.
DANE - Posters - Aegis Entertainment, Inc.
DANE - Recording label - Jazz Composer's Orchestra Association Inc.
DANE WEAR - Men's coats - Cosmopolitan Manufacturing Co.
DANECRAFT - Jewelry - Danecraft, Inc.
DANEKSCOPE - Endoscopic equipment - Danek Medical, Inc.
DANELECTRO - Amplifiers–musical instrument - Evets Corp.
DANELLI USA - Attache cases - Group III International Ltd.
DANERO - Glassware–household ☆ - Svend Jensen of Denmark Inc.
DANET - Food products - Orth Co. (Bruce)
DANEX - Shampoos - Allergan, Inc.
DANFAIR - Fabrics - Dan River Inc.
DANFIELD - Thread - Needlecraft Industries
DANFIT - Bedding–linen - Dan River Inc.
DANFLAIR - Fabrics - Dan River Inc.
DANFLOW - Fabrics - Dan River Inc.
DANFOODS - Food products - Danfoods Corp.
DANFORM OF AMERICA - Shoes - Bay Corp.
DANFORTH - Navigational instruments - Rule Industries, Inc.
DANFORTH - Ophthalmic goods - Styl-Rite Optical Manufacturing Co., Inc.
DANFORTH - Shoes ☆ - Allen-Edmonds Shoe Corp.
DANFOSS - Pumps - Danfoss, Inc. (Danfoss Fluid Power)
DANFROST - Fabrics - Dan River Inc.
DANG GOOD STUFF - Deodorizers - Carl Loughren
DANGARD - Fabrics - Dan River Inc.
D'ANGELICO - Musical instruments - G.H.S. Corp.
D'ANGELO NATURAL SPRING - Water–bottled or canned - D'Angelo Natural Spring
DANGER-CHANGER - Toys - Mattel, Inc.
DANGER UNLIMITED - Books–comic - John Byrne, Inc.
DANGER ZONE - Lighting fixtures - Big Beam Emergency Systems Inc.
DANGER ZONE - Toys - Playskool, Inc.
DANGERBOYS - Apparel–men's - Thomas Terrill
DANGERINE - Candy - Bobs Candies Inc.
DANGEROUS AIRPORTS - Computer software - Abacus Software, Inc.
DANGEROUS DINO - Recording label - Intermission Productions
DANGEROUS DINOS - Ice cream - Intermission Productions
DANGEROUS GIRL - Notebooks and notepads - Julie A. Crane
DANGEROUS OCHELTREE DRUMS - Musical instruments - Dangerous Ocheltree Drums
DANGEROUS SPORTS CLUB - Apparel–athletic - Dangerous Sports Wear, Inc.
DANGEROUS SPORTS GEAR - Apparel and accessories - No Fear, Inc.
DANGEROUS WILLIE - Apparel–men's - Y.M.L.A., Inc.
DANGLE - Pet products - Cosmic Cat Corp.
DANGLER - Fishing lures - Paul Warner Industries
DANGLERS - Ophthalmic goods - Al Nyman and Son
DANGLES - Manicure preparations ☆ - Nail Gems by Cara
DANGLIES - Stuffed animals with cologne ☆ - Cosrich Inc.
DANGLIN' ST. NICK-KNACKS - Toys–stuffed ☆ - Fun World Inc.
DANGLO - Fabrics - Dan River Inc.
DANI FIT-KIT-CUISINE...IT'S ABOUT TIME - Food products - Dani Group Inc.
DANIA - Dining room furniture ☆ - Daystrom Furniture Inc.
DANIA 2 - Dining room furniture - Daystrom Furniture Inc.
DANIBEN - Computer storage devices - Daniben Systems, Inc.
DANICA - Glassware–household ☆ - Svend Jensen of Denmark Inc.
DANICAS DESIGN - Candles - Danica Design Inc.
DANIEL - Dolls - Goldberger Doll Manufacture Co.
DANIEL - Frames–eyeglass - U.S. Optical Frame Co.
DANIEL A - Apparel and accessories - Daniel A Inc.
DANIEL AMES - Handbags - Aig/Ames International Group, Inc.
DANIEL & REBECCA - Women's dresses and suits - Mothers Work Inc.
DANIEL BOONE - Handles–wood - Turner, Day and Woolworth Handle Corp.
DANIEL BOONE - Novelty items - Adam Starchild
DANIEL BOONE - Playground equipment - Hedstrom Corp.
DANIEL BOONE - Popcorn - National Oats Co. Inc.
DANIEL BOONE - Toys–guns ☆ - Esquire Novelty Corp.
DANIEL CHAPTER ONE - Vitamins and nutritional supplements - World Sports Nutrition, Inc.

DANIEL DRESCOTT - Apparel–men's - Alexandre of England, Inc.
DANIEL DUCK - Dolls - Russ Berrie and Co., Inc.
DANIEL FIELD - Apparel–women's - Smooth Industries, Inc.
DANIEL GREEN - Apparel and accessories - Daniel Green Co.
DANIEL HAYS - Gloves - Gates Gloves
DANIEL HECHHER - Coats–men's - Gallron
DANIEL HECHTER - Neckties - Randa Corp.
DANIEL HECTOR - Hosiery, socks - J.P. Manning Inc.
DANIEL JOSEPH - Housewares - Daniel Joseph Fink
DANIEL LAURENT - Apparel–women's - Kenar Enterprises, Ltd.
DANIEL PERES - Clippers–barber ☆ - Marianna Imports, Inc.
DANIEL RION - Beverages–alcohol ☆ - Diamond Wine Merchants
DANIEL RIZZARDI - Hair care products - Daniel Rizzardi
DANIEL SMITH FINE ARTISTS' MATERIALS - Artists' materials - Daniel Smith Inc.
DANIEL WEBSTER - Clocks ☆ - Ridgeway Clock Co.
DANIELA - Cosmetics - Royal Laboratories Cosmetics
DANIELE - Wines - C. Daniele & Co., Inc.
DANIELE & ADAMI - Handbags - Gilt Import Co. Inc.
DANIELI - Sweaters - Gillman Knitwear Co.
DANIELLE - Cosmetic applicators - Teka Fine Line Brushes Inc. (Div. of Danielle Cosmetic)
DANIELLE - Cosmetics - Brescia Hair Salon
DANIELLE - Dolls - Goldberger Doll Manufacture Co.
DANIELLE - Dolls - Mattel, Inc.
DANIELLE - Manicure preparations - ESI Industries Inc.
DANIELLE ALLEN - Apparel–women's - American Fashion Group, Ltd.
DANIELLE BY LAURA - Apparel–women's - Laura Knit Collection, Inc.
DANIELLE CASEY - Apparel–women's - M.S. Apparel, Inc.
DANIELLE DANE - Skin care products - Dane Group
DANIELLE PAIGE - Apparel–women's - Norton Mcnaughton of Squire, Inc.
DANIELS - Novelty items - M.B. Daniels & Co. Inc.
DANIELS PULL PLOW - Snow plows - Greg Daniels & Co.
DANIELSON DESIGNS - Frames–picture - Danielson Designs Ltd.
DANILONE - Pharmaceutical preparations - Schieffelin & Co. (Pharmaceutical Laboratories Div.)
DANIMALS - Yogurt - Dannon Co., Inc.
DANIMS - Fabrics–denim - Dan River Inc.
DANIROCA - Glassware–household ☆ - Svend Jensen of Denmark Inc.
DANISH - Cabinets ☆ - Canyon Creek Cabinet Co.
DANISH - Furniture - Ever-Ready Co.
DANISH - Hosiery - Aire Hosiery Inc.
DANISH/AMERICAN - Eggs - Designer American
DANISH BAKERY - Bakery products - Publix Super Markets, Inc.
DANISH BAROQUE - Flatware - Towle Manufacturing Co.
DANISH BULKY - Handwork supplies - Bernat Yarn & Craft Corp.
DANISH COBBS - Pipes - Missouri Meerschaum Co.
DANISH CREAMERY - Milk ☆ - Danish Creamery Association
DANISH CROWN - Hams - M.H. Greenebaum Inc.
DANISH DANISH, THE - Bakery products ☆ - Allied Bakers Co.
DANISH DELIGHT - Cookies ☆ - Vincent Food Industries Inc.
DANISH DELUXE - Pastries - Interstate Brands Corp.
DANISH FLAG - Hams - M.H. Greenebaum Inc.
DANISH GIRL - Frames–eyeglass ☆ - Universal/Univis Inc.
DANISH HANDCRAFT GUILD - Craft supplies - Ginnie Thompson Originals Inc.
DANISH INN GLASS - Glassware–household ☆ - Svend Jensen of Denmark Inc.
DANISH KRINGLER - Cakes - Norsland Kitchens
DANISH LADY - Frames–eyeglass ☆ - Universal/Univis Inc.
DANISH MILL - Bakery products - Pride of the Farm
DANISH MILL - Cookies - J & J Snack Foods Corp.
DANISH MODERN - Glassware–household - Federal Glass
DANISH ORCHARDS - Food products - Acme Food Sales Inc.
DANISH ORCHARDS - Fruits–pickled or brined - Festival Food Corp.
DANISH SHIPGLASS - Glassware–household ☆ - Svend Jensen of Denmark Inc.
DANITALIA SUNGLASSES - Eyewear - Danitalia, Inc.
DANK - Apparel and accessories - Jason Hilbert
DANKER - Ophthalmic goods ☆ - Whitby Pharmaceuticals, Inc.
DANKERCHIEF - Fabrics - Dan River Inc.
DANKLIED DESIGN - Pet products - Danklied Laboratories Ltd.
DANKOFF SOLAR PUMBS - Pumps - Dankoff Solar Products, Inc.
DANLAWN - Bedding–linen - Dan River Inc.
DANLIN - Fabrics - Dan River Inc.
DANLOK - Valves - Danfoss Inc.

DANLYS - Cigars - Mark Goldman
DANMASTER - Fabrics - Dan River Inc.
DANNA LEE - Cheese - Paul's Popular Foods
DANNEMANN - Cigars ☆ - Swisher International, Inc.
DANNEMANN - Food products ☆ - Tower Brokerage Inc.
DANNER - Electronic equipment - G Prime Limited
DANNER - Footwear - Danner Shoe Manufacturing Co.
DANNER CROSSHIKERS - Boots - Danner Shoe Manufacturing Co.
DANNER LITES - Boots - Danner Shoe Manufacturing Co.
DANNI - Eyeglasses - Art-Craft Optical Co.
DANNICH - Apparel and accessories - Dannich, Inc.
DANNIFLEX - Medical apparatus - Danninger Medical Technology Inc.
DANNINGER - Health care products - Home Care Instruments Inc.
DANNON - Yogurt - Dannon Co., Inc.
DANNON DOUBLE DELIGHTS - Yogurt - Dannon Co., Inc.
DANNON INSTEAD - Yogurt ☆ - Dannon Co., Inc.
DANNON LIGHT - Yogurt - Dannon Co., Inc.
DANNON LIGHT 'N CRUNCHY - Yogurt–frozen - Dannon Co., Inc.
DANNON PREMIUM - Yogurts - Dannon Co., Inc.
DANNON SUPREME - Yogurt - Dannon Co., Inc.
DANNY - Candy ☆ - Chris Candies Inc.
DANNY - Food products - Beatrice Cos. Inc.
DANNY - Ophthalmic goods ☆ - Rozin Optical Export Corp.
DANNY BLUE - Apparel and accessories - Daniel Lewis Ltd.
DANNY BOY - Popcorn ☆ - TV Time Foods Inc.
DANNY DINOSAUR - Fishing tackle - South Bend Sporting Goods Inc.
DANNY DOO MUSIC - Publisher's imprints - San Juan Music Group
DANNY DUZIT - Sponges - Springfield Wire Inc.
DANNY FIRST - Apparel and accessories - Danny First Inc.
DANNY HODGE - Apparel–athletic - Logan Knitting Mills, Inc.
DANNY O'DAY - Dolls - Goldberger Doll Manufacture Co.
DANNY SAUR'S ART STUDIO - Paints–artists' - Teng International, Inc.
DANNY WILSON ORIGINAL - Glassware–household - Wilson Specialties Co. Inc.
DANNY-YO - Yogurt ☆ - Dannon Co., Inc.
DANNY-YOGURT ON A STICK - Confections ☆ - Dannon Co., Inc.
DANOCRINE - Pharmaceutical preparations - Winthrop Pharmaceuticals
DANOLA - Food products - East Asiatic Co. Inc. (Danola Foods Div.)
DANO'S - Pizzas–mixes - Winn-Dixie Stores, Inc.
DANPEL - Fabrics - Dan River Inc.
DANPEPPER - Fabrics ☆ - Dan River Inc.
DANPRIX GALLERY - Fabrics - Dan River Inc.
DANRAY - Fabrics - Dan River Inc.
DANRICH OF CALIFORNIA - Footwear–women's - Argyris Inc.
DANRISE - Fabrics - Dan River Inc.
DAN'S PRIZE - Meat products–beef - Dan's Prize, Inc.
DAN'S PRIZE 1 QUALITY CONSISTENCY VALUE - Beef - Dan's Prize, Inc.
DAN'S SUPERMARKET - Bakery products - Dan's Super Market, Inc.
DANSAN - Recording label ☆ - Telemark Dance Records
DANSE - Glassware–household ☆ - Crisa Corp.
DANSE FORM - Leotards - Leo's Dancewear, Inc.
DANSELP - Recording label ☆ - Telemark Dance Records
DANSEN CONTEMPORARY - Furniture–upholstered - Woodmark Originals
DANSET - Fabrics - Dan River Inc.
DANSETTE - Fabrics ☆ - Dan River Inc.
DANSEUSE - Eyeglasses - Art-Craft Optical Co.
DANSHEEN - Fabrics ☆ - Dan River Inc.
DANSHEER - Fabrics - Dan River Inc.
DANSHRUNK - Fabrics–cotton - Dan River Inc.
DANSK - Housewares - Dansk International Designs, Ltd.
DANSK - Paper ☆ - Rising Paper, Division of Fox River Paper Co.
DANSK DESIGNS - Dishes–wood - Dansk International Designs, Ltd.
DANSK-DISK - Recording label - Lindberg Records
DANSK ENTERTAINERS - Kitchen utensils–aluminum ☆ - Dansk International Designs, Ltd.
DANSK FOR KIDS - Housewares - Dansk International Designs, Ltd.
DANSK LIGHTS - Lighting fixtures - Dansk Lights Inc.
DANSKIN - Apparel and accessories - Danskin, Inc.
DANSKIN - Leotards - Victoria's Dance-Theatrical Supply
DANSKIN FOOTWEAR - Shoes–athletic - Danskin, Inc.
DANSKORD - Cordage and twine - Julius Koch USA Inc.
DANSNEAKER - Footwear–athletic - Ballet Makers, Inc.
DANSPORT - Fabrics ☆ - Dan River Inc.
DANSPUN - Bedding–linen - Dan River Inc.
DANSTAR - Fabrics - Dan River Inc.
DANSTORM - Fabrics–cotton - Dan River Inc.

DANSURE - Fabrics - Dan River Inc.
DANSYL - Fabrics - Dan River Inc.
DANTAG - Scuba diving equipment - Divers Alert Network, Inc.
DANTAY - Floor coverings–carpet and rugs - Evans-Black Carpet Mills
DANTE - Belts–apparel - Humphrey's Inc.
DANTE - Fireplace equipment - Joe Leighton & Associates, Inc.
DANTE - Giftware ☆ - Crisa Corp.
DANTE - Hair care products ☆ - P.S. Pibbs Inc.
DANTE - Mushrooms ☆ - Four H. Corp.
DANTE DE FIRENZE - Sweaters ☆ - Midstates Sportswear
DANTE UNIVERSITY PRESS - Publisher's imprints - Branden Publishing Co., Inc.
DANTEC - Electronic equipment - Dantec Measurement Technology Inc.
DANTELLO - Wines - Admiral Wine Merchants
DANTEX - Eggs - Milton G. Waldbaum Co.
DANTEX - Fabrics - C.R. Daniels Inc.
DANTHANE - Pharmaceutical preparations - C.S. Ruckstuhl Co. Inc.
DANTHROSS - Pharmaceutical preparations ☆ - ICN Pharmaceuticals Inc.
DANTITE CLEARSHIELD - Waterproofing compounds - Thomas Waterproof Coatings Co.
+D'ANTON - Pens ☆ - Chase Collection, Inc.
DANTONE - Fabrics–cotton - Dan River Inc.
DANTONE - Pharmaceutical preparations - Blair Pharmacal
DANTREL - Fabrics - Dan River Inc.
DANTRIS SIGNATURE SKIN CARE - Skin care products - Dantris Corp.
DANTRIUM - Pharmaceutical preparations - Norwich-Eaton Pharmaceuticals
DANTUFF - Fabrics–cotton - Dan River Inc.
DANTWEED - Fabrics - Dan River Inc.
DANTWILL - Fabrics - Dan River Inc.
DANUBE - Bathing suits - Ocean Pool Co.
DANUBE - Bathroom accessories - KLR Products, Inc.
DANUBE - Bathtubs–enameled - Briggs Plumbing Products, Inc.
DANUBE - Cheese ☆ - Crystal Food Import Corp.
DANUBE - Computer software - Advanced Computer Communications
DANUBE - Frames–eyeglass ☆ - Universal/Univis Inc.
DANUBE - Glassware–household - Durand International
DANUBE - Motor vehicle parts and accessories ☆ - Bob Bartlett & Associates Inc.
DANUBE - Rings–jewelry - Artcarved Inc.
DANUBE E.S.P. - Carpeting - Danube Carpet Mills Inc.
DAN'UP - Yogurt ☆ - Dannon Co., Inc.
DANVELLA - Fabrics - Dan River Inc.
DANVERS - Cabinets ☆ - American Woodmark Corp.
DANVERS - Shoes - Osceola Shoe Co. Inc.
DANVIK - Saw blades - Danish Import Inc.
DANVILLE - Cabinets - Karman Kitchens Inc.
DANVILLE - Manufactured homes - Redman Industries, Inc.
DANVILLE - Optical scanners–computer - Titmus Optical, Inc.
DANVILLE COLLECTION - House furnishings - Dan River Inc.
DANWEAR - Fabrics–cotton - Dan River Inc.
DANY - Frames–eyeglass - Felix M. Mendelson Co.
DANY - Frames–picture - Oak Hill Industries Corp.
DANYA - Pipes ☆ - Rayex Corp.
DANYON - Vinyl - Daburn Electronics & Cable Corp.
DANZIG - Meat products - Patrick Cudahy Inc.
DANZIG - Sausages - Patcud Investments, Inc.
DANZKA - Vodka - Leonard Kreusch Inc.
DAOIST MOON - Teas–herbal - Larry Lee Johnson
DAOIST SHIELD - Teas–herbal - Larry Lee Johnson
DAP - Adhesives and sealants - Dap Products Inc.
DAP ENERGY SAVER - Caulking compounds - Dap Products Inc.
DAP READY TO CAULK - Caulking compounds ☆ - Dap Products Inc.
DAP/WELDWOOD - Flag poles - Dap Products Inc.
DAPA - Analgesics - Ferndale Laboratories, Inc.
DAPA - Antennas - Dapa Communications, Inc.
DAPASE - Analgesics ☆ - Ferndale Laboratories, Inc.
DAPAWAY - Dental equipment - Crescent Dental Manufacturing Co.
DAPCO - Pharmaceutical preparations ☆ - Mericon Industries Inc.
DAPHINE - Leather - A & A Sales
DAPHNE - Dolls ☆ - Effanbee Doll Corp.
DAPHNE - Glass–optical - Welling International
DAPHNE - House furnishings ☆ - Kellwood Co.
DAPHNE - Watches - Bulova Corp.
DAPHNE DUCK - Toys–stuffed - Russ Berrie and Co., Inc.
DAPHNI - Vases - Durand International
DAPPER - Brushes - Wright-Bernet

☆ = Now out of production

DAPPER - Clocks ☆ - Toastmaster Inc.
DAPPER DAN - Dolls - Playskool, Inc.
DAPPER DAN - Fabrics - Dan River Inc.
DAPPER DAN - Toys - Smethport Specialty Co.
DAPPER DICE - Novelty items - S.J. Miller Co.
DAPPER DOG - Candy ☆ - Keppel's Inc.
DAPPER DOG - Pet collars - Little Giant Products
DAPPER DOG DUDS - Sweaters - Binghamton Knitting Co.
DAPPER DOUBLING CUBE - Novelty items - S.J. Miller Co.
DAPPER DOZEN - Frames–eyeglass - Liberty Optical Manufacturing Co.
DAPPER DUCK - Rocking horses - Dawn 'til Dusk Inc.
DAPPI - Diaper covers - TL Care Inc.
DAPPI BABI - Apparel and accessories - TL Care Inc.
DAPPI COMFY-FIT - Diapers–cloth - TL Care Inc.
DAPPI DIAPER DOUBLERS - Diaper covers - TL Care Inc.
DAPPI EARLY TRAINER - Apparel–children's - TL Care Inc.
DAPPI-LITE - Diaper covers - TL Care Inc.
DAPPI VELCRO-FIT - Diapers–cloth - TL Care Inc.
DAPPLE - Floor coverings ☆ - Congoleum Corp.
DAPPLE - Tiles–ceiling ☆ - Florida Tile Industries, Inc.
DAPPLE - Tiles–ceramic - Huntington/Pacific Ceramics Inc.
DAPPLE YELLOW - Dinnerware–glass ☆ - Nikko Ceramics Inc.
DAPPS - Apparel and accessories - Dapps
DAPRENE - Electronic equipment - Daburn Electronics & Cable Corp.
DAPSONE - Prescription drug - Jacobus Pharmaceutical Co., Inc.
DAPT-A-FILE - File folders ☆ - Cel-U-Dex Corp.
DAPTAR - Rifles - Conetrol Scope Mounts
DAQBOOK - Computers - Iotech Inc.
DAQCARD - Computer hardware - National Instruments Corp.
DAQDRIVE - Computer hardware - Quatech, Inc.
DAQPAD - Computer software - National Instruments Corp.
DAR FOODS - Meats - Dar Foods Corp.
DAR-HIST - Pharmaceutical preparations - David A. Rosow Inc.
DAR NALD - Pharmaceutical preparations - David A. Rosow Inc.
DAR-RAN - Furniture - Dar-Ran Furniture Industries, Inc.
DAR-VIDA - Crackers ☆ - Liberty Richter Inc.
DARA - Ophthalmic goods - Foremost Optical Products
DARA - Shampoos - Owen/Galderma Laboratories Inc.
DARA - Toys - Tonka Corp.
DARA2 - Computer software - National Metal Fabricators
DARACLAR - Chemicals - W.R. Grace & Co.
DARACODYL - Pharmaceutical preparations - David A. Rosow Inc.
DARACONE - Waterproofing compounds ☆ - A.C. Horn Co.
DARACOTE - Chemical preparations - W.R. Grace & Co.
DARAD II - Computer software - SourceView Software International
DARAFILL - Concrete additives - W.R. Grace & Co.
DARAFLOC - Chemical preparations - W.R. Grace & Co.
DARAFORM - Chemicals - W.R. Grace & Co.
DARAGEN - Shampoos - Owen/Galderma Laboratories Inc.
DARANIDE - Pharmaceutical preparations - Merck & Co., Inc. (Merck Research Laboratories)
DARAPLUS - Chemical preparations - W.R. Grace & Co.
DARAPRIM - Pharmaceutical preparations - Burroughs Wellcome Co.
DARASEAL U - Sealing compounds ☆ - A.C. Horn Co.
DARASOL - Chemical preparations - W.R. Grace & Co.
DARAWELD-C - Concrete repair products - Grace Construction Products
DARBEE - Plastics - Darbee Products, Inc.
DARBIB - Pharmaceutical preparations - Smithkline Beecham Corp.
DARBO - Jams and jellies - Steiner Foods
DARBO-JAM - Jams and jellies - Haram-Christensen Corp.
DARBY - Ophthalmic goods - Styl-Rite Optical Manufacturing Co., Inc.
DARBY - Wallets ☆ - Enger-Kress Co.
DARBY GREEN - Coats - London Fog Industries, Inc.
DARBY THE DINOSAUR - Publisher's imprints - Ray Bentley
DARBY'S DESIGNS - Apparel and accessories - Carron C. Willis
DARC CURE - Adhesives and sealants - Dymax Corp.
DARCEYLON - Teas - Lalith D. Paranavitana
D'ARCHES - Artists' materials - Andrews/Nelson/Whitehead
DARCI - Toys - Tonka Corp.
DARCIE - Ophthalmic goods ☆ - Luxottica
DARCO - Footwear–athletic - Meiller Co.
DARCO - Musical instrument accessories - C.F. Martin & Co., Inc.
D'ARCY - Cosmetics - D'Arcy Labs
DARCY - Ophthalmic goods - Swank Optical
+D'ARCY - Tools–machine - John D'arcy
DARCY - Watches - Bulova Corp.

DARCY CREEK - Hats - Hat Brands, Inc.
DARD HUNTER COLLECTION, THE - Floor coverings–carpet and rugs - Jaxco, Inc.
DARDA - Toys–automobiles - Darda Inc. USA
DARDANELLA - Thread - Cincinnati Thread Co.
DARDEN - Key rings - University of Virginia, Darden School Foundation
DARDEN COURT - Floor coverings - Tarkett, Inc.
DARDENELLA - Wines - Breitenbach Wine Cellars
DARDENELLES PILLOW PETS - Toys–stuffed ☆ - Dakin Inc.
DARDEVLE - Fishing lures - Eppinger Manufacturing Co.
DARDEVLE KLICKER - Fishing lures - Eppinger Manufacturing Co.
DARDINELLA - Frames–eyeglass - May Optical Co. Inc.
DARE - Frames–eyeglass - May Optical Co. Inc.
D.A.R.E. - Greeting cards - Evel Knievel
D.A.R.E. - Key rings - D.A.R.E. America
DARE - Perfumes - Quintessence Inc.
DARE - Toys - Tonka Corp.
DARE - Turpentine ☆ - Reliable Finishing Products, Inc.
DARE DEVIL - Books–comic - Marvel Entertainment Group, Inc.
DARE-DEVIL - Frames–eyeglass - Zylo Ware Corp.
DARE-O-MATIC - Valves - Dare Products Inc.
DARE TO BE A JUICER - Juices ☆ - Pokka, Inc.
DARE TO BE YOU - Apparel and accessories - Glamorise Foundations Inc.
DARE TO COMPARE PANASONIC SOUND - Electronic equipment - Matsushita Electric Corp. of America
DARE TO DANCE - Apparel and accessories - Christy Lane
DARE TO DREAM - Apparel and accessories - Dare to Dream
DARE TO DRESS - Kellwood Co.
DARE TO DRESS KIDS - Apparel–children's - Kellwood Co.
DARE-U - Colognes - Old 97 Co.
DAREDEVIL - Kites ☆ - Hi-Flier Manufacturing Co.
DAREDEVIL 500 - Toys - Tyco Toys
DAREDEVIL CLIFF HANGERS - Toys–electronic - Tyco Toys
DAREDEVIL SKYDIVER - Toys - Fisher-Price, Inc.
DAREDEVIL SPORT VAN - Toys - Fisher-Price, Inc.
DAREDEVILS - Candy ☆ - Willy Wonka Brands
DAREN L.A. KID - Children's apparel - Daren L.A. Kid Inc.
DARENTH - Marine rigging - Hyde Products Inc.
DAREPLANE - Toys–airplanes - Mattel, Inc.
DAREXSORDIL - Pharmaceutical preparations - David A. Rosow Inc.
DARFIELD - Urinals–enameled - Kohler Co.
DARGEL FISHERMAN - Boats–fishing - Dargel Boat Works
DARGEL SKOOTER - Boats–fishing - Dargel Boat Works
DARGEL SKOUTS - Boats–fishing - Dargel Boat Works
DARI-BEST - Food products - V. & E. Kohnstamm Inc.
DARI-DRI - Paper–toilet - Fort Howard Corp.
DARI-LEAN - Dairy products - H.P. Hood & Sons Inc.
DARI-TOWLS - Paper–toweling - Mosinee Paper Corp.
DARI-VALLEY - Dairy products ☆ - Knudsen Dairy Products
DARIA - Apparel and accessories - Viacom International Inc.
DARIA - Dolls - Mattel, Inc.
DARIAN - Frames–eyeglass - Pathway Optical Prods.
DARICON - Pharmaceutical preparations - Smithkline Beecham Corp.
DARICRAFT - Milk–canned or powdered - Mid-America Dairymen Inc. Southern Div.
DARIEN - Clocks ☆ - General Time Corp. (Westclox/Seth Thomas Div.)
DARIFAIR - Ice cream - Darifair Foods, Inc.
DARIGOLD - Dairy products - Darigold, Inc.
DARIGOLD CLASSIC - Ice cream - Darigold, Inc.
DARIGOLD-LITE - Dairy products - Darigold, Inc.
DARIK - Food products - Darik Enterprises Inc.
DARINA - Lubricants - Shell Oil Co.
DARINAMEL - Enamel ☆ - Bostik Inc.
DARING - Bicycles - Roadmaster Corp.
DARING - Frames–eyeglass - Zylo Ware Corp.
DARING - Recording label - Rounder Records Corp.
DARING DANGLES - Jewelry - Feature Enterprises
DARING DICE - Games - M.J. Moran Co.
DARING DINOS - Dolls - Meritus Industries, Inc.
DARING PASSAGES - Games - M.J. Moran Co.
DARING PUZZLES - Puzzles - M.J. Moran Co.
DARINGLY BARE - Apparel stores–lingerie - Daringly Bare, Inc.
DARINGLY BARE INCORPORATED - Apparel–women's - Daringly Bare, Inc.
DARITEK - Dairy products - Foremost Farms USA
DARIUS - Video games ☆ - Taito America Corp.
DARJEELING - Teas - Eastern Shore Tea Co.

☆ = Now out of production

DARJEELING GARDENS - Teas–herbal ☆ - Celestial Seasonings, Inc.
DARK & LOVELY - Hair care products - Carson Products Co.
DARK & LOVELY 24 HR THERAPY - Hair care products - Carson Products Co.
DARK & LOVELY COLOR CARE - Hair care products - Aminco Inc.
DARK & LOVELY PLUS - Cosmetics - Carson Products Co.
DARK & LOVELY QUIK FREEZE - Hair care products - Aminco Inc.
DARK & LOVELY RESTORE & REPAIR - Hair care products - Carson Products Co.
DARK & LOVELY ULTRA NOURISH - Hair care products - Carson Products Co.
DARK & NATURAL - Hair care products - Aminco Inc.
DARK BLAZER - Lanterns–electric - Brinkmann Lighting Products
DARK BREWED PORTER - Beverages–malt - D.G. Yuengling & Son Inc.
DARK CARAMEL - Tobacco–chewing or smoking - Amar Blends Co.
DARK CHASER - Lanterns–electric - Brinkmann Lighting Products
DARK COAT - Pet products - Lambert-Kay
DARK COLORS RUBBER STAMP INK - Inks ☆ - Ranger Industries
DARK CONSPIRACY - Games - Game Designers' Workshop, Inc.
DARK CRYSTAL, THE - Toys–models ☆ - Grenadier Models
DARK CRYSTAL, THE - Toys–electronic ☆ - Jim Henson Productions, Inc.
DARK DELIGHT - Candy ☆ - Peter Paul
DARK DELUXE - Candy - World's Finest Chocolate, Inc.
DARK EMBERS - Hosiery–women's - ETC. Hosiery, Inc.
DARK EYES - Frames–eyeglass - Liberty Optical Manufacturing Co.
DARK EYES - Vodka - Jim Beam Brands Co.
DARK FOLK - Games - Mayfair Games, Inc.
DARK FORCES - Publisher's imprints ☆ - Bantam Doubleday Dell Publishing Group, Inc.
DARK FORCES - Video games - Lucasfilm Ltd.
DARK HALF, THE - Computer software - Capstone Software
DARK HARBOR - Bags - Byer of Maine
DARK HEART - Toys - Saban Entertainment, Inc.
DARK HOLLOW - Floor coverings–carpet and rugs ☆ - Hollytex Carpet Mills Inc.
DARK LORD - Computer software ☆ - Electronic Arts Inc.
DARK MAGUS - Game - Dark Magus Productions, Inc.
DARK MOUNTAIN - Beverages–malt - R.W. Webb Winery
DARK 'N' RICH - Cleaning preparations - Bruce Hardwood Floors
DARK OXFORD - Cabinets–wood ☆ - Kemper
DARK RAGE - Toys - Walter J. McGivney
DARK RIDER SERIES - Toys–automobiles - Mattel, Inc.
DARK SEMI-SWEET - Snack foods - Keller's Crunch
DARK SHIELD - Toys–automobiles - Mattel, Inc.
DARK SIDE - Recording label - More Music Records Inc.
DARK STAR - Mordants - Rent-A-Mark
DARK STAR - Skates–ice ☆ - Built for Speed, Inc.
DARK STAR - Toys–models ☆ - Estes Industries
DARK STAR LAGER - Beverages–malt - Rose's Restaurants, Inc.
DARK SUN - Games - Tsr, Inc.
DARK, THE - Games - Wizards of the Coast, Inc.
DARK WIND FANTASIES - Computer software - Dark Wind Fantasies
DARK WORLD - Games - Mattel, Inc.
DARKAY - Hair coloring preparations ☆ - Majestic Drug Co., Inc.
DARKENING, THE - Computer software - Origin Systems, Inc.
DARKER IMAGE, THE - Calendars - Darker Image
DARKHORN - Games - Avalon Hill Game Co.
DARKLANDS - Computer software - Microprose Software, Inc.
DARKLITE - Lighting fixtures - Edison Price Lighting
DARKLITE - Microscopes - AZI Atlantex & Zieler Instrument Corp.
DARKO'S AFRICAN - Sauces - Darko Foods
DARKROOM COMFORTER - Fans–exhaust - SP Systems/Saratons
DARKROOM DIRECTOR - Photographic equipment - SP Systems/Saratons
DARKSEED - Computer software - Cyberdreams Inc.
DARKSIDE CUSTOMS - Motor vehicles - Pamela L. Brill
DARKSILVER - Recording label - Bainbridge Entertainment Co. Inc.
DARKSTAR - Postcards - Fotofolio Inc.
DARKSTAR - Tools–hand-operated ☆ - Built for Speed, Inc.
DARKWATER - Kites ☆ - Hi-Flier Manufacturing Co.
DARKWAVE - Books–comic - Malibu Comics Entertainment, Inc.
DARKWING DUCK - Apparel and accessories - Walt Disney Co.
DARLACE - Fabrics - Darlington Fabrics Corp.
DARLAHOOD - Apparel and accessories - Joe Magistro
DARLAN - Cabinets - Merillat Industries, Inc.
DARLEEN - Fabrics - Darlington Fabrics Corp.
DARLENE - Jewelry - Darlene Jewelry Manufacturing Co., Inc.

DARLENE'S - Compact discs–prerecorded - Darlene's Production Co.
DARLENO - Fabrics - Darlington Fabrics Corp.
DARLEY - Computer software - Orly Rachel Sharaby
DARLIN' DAISY - Giftware - Brushcreek Creative Co.
DARLIN' DEVILS - Novelty items ☆ - Lemberger Candy Corp.
DARLIN-DINO - Toys–stuffed ☆ - Gund, Inc.
DARLIN' DINOS - Playthings - Meritus Industries, Inc.
DARLING - Footwear–children's - Darling Baby Shoe Co.
DARLING - Frames–eyeglass - Zylo Ware Corp.
DARLING - Strollers–baby - Darling White Plains Inc.
DARLING - Yarn ☆ - William Unger & Co. Inc.
DARLING DALMATIANS - Toys - Trendmasters, Inc.
DARLING DUCKIE - Toys ☆ - Gerber Products Co.
DARLING KITTIES - Toys–stuffed - Trendmasters, Inc.
DARLING PONIES - Toys - Trendmasters, Inc.
DARLING SEA FRIENDS - Toys - Trendmasters, Inc.
DARLING ZOO TROOP - Toys - Trendmasters, Inc.
DARLINGTON - Clocks ☆ - General Time Corp. (Westclox/Seth Thomas Div.)
DARLINGTON - Dinnerware–glass - Crystal Clear Importing Co. Inc.
DARLINGTON - Dinnerware–glass ☆ - Royal China & Porcelain Companies Inc.
DARLINGTON - Housewares - International Speedway Corp.
DARLINGTON - Tires - Bridgestone/Firestone, Inc.
DARLIN'S OF THE MONTH - Dolls - Bradley Import Co.
DARLITE - Pharmaceutical preparations - Rugby Laboratories Inc.
DARLSPAN - Fabrics - Darlington Fabrics Corp.
DARN - Fabric binding - Loctite Corp.
DARN-E-Z - Drain pipe cleaners - Flow-Eze Co.
DARNELL - Casters - Young's
DARNETTE - Apparel–children's - Buster Brown Apparel Inc.
DARNIT - Thread ☆ - Pepperell Braiding Co. Inc.
DARNKNIT - Apparel and accessories ☆ - Vanderbilt Shirt Co.
DARNLESS - Apparel–children's - Buster Brown Apparel Inc.
DAROLENE - Water purification systems ☆ - Dacar Chemical Co.
DARPIEL - Small leather goods - American Angel Corp.
DARRA CALIFORNIA - Towels - Darra of California, Inc.
DARRELL WALTRIP - Toys ☆ - ERTL Co., Inc.
DARRICK - Colognes ☆ - Avon Products, Inc.
DARRIN - Dolls - Mattel, Inc.
DARRY - Biscuits ☆ - Purepak Foods Inc.
DARRYL'S - Beverages–malt - Gilbert-Robinson Inc.
DARRYL'S ORIGINAL PREMIUM LAGER BEER - Beverages–malt - Gilbert-Robinson Inc.
DARSHAN - Recording label - Syda Foundation
DARSOL - Cleaning preparations - Dacar Chemical Co.
D.A.R.T. - Apparel and accessories - Kellwood Co.
D.A.R.T. - Aquariums–household ☆ - Wardley Corp.
DART - Bicycles - Ross Bicycles USA, Ltd.
DART - Boats–motor - Lund Boat Co.
DART - Brushes - Wright-Bernet
DART - Cases–musical instrument - M & M Distributing Co.
DART - Computer hardware - Digital Audio Reconstruction Technology, Llc
DART - Computer software - Nikon Inc.
DART - Computer software - Wiseman Computer Group, Inc.
DART - Cooking utensils–stoneware ☆ - Westminster Trading Corp.
DART - Electrical testing instruments - Biddle Instruments
DART - Footwear - Angel-Etts of California, Inc.
DART - Frames–eyeglass - Zylo Ware Corp.
DART - Golfing equipment - Dart Golf Co.
DART - Hair care products - Summit Laboratories
DART - Health care products - Seamless
DART - Motor vehicles ☆ - Chrysler Corp. (Dodge Car Div.)
DART - Navigational instruments - Datamarine International Inc.
DART - Nozzles - H.B. Sherman Manufacturing Co.
DART - Office supplies - Dart Manufacturing Co.
DART - Office supplies ☆ - Ace Fastener
DART - Projection screens ☆ - Da-Lite Screen Co. Inc.
DART - Ships–sailing vessels - Sail Sports Ltd.
DART - Shirts - Cluett, Peabody & Co.
DART - Toys - Tonka Corp.
D.A.R.T. - Toys–models ☆ - Estes Industries
DART - Watches - Criterion Watch Co. Inc.
DART ABOUT RACER - Toys–automobiles - Learning Products Inc.
DART BAITER - Fishing lures - Classic Manufacturing Co., Inc.
DART DEMON - Motor vehicles ☆ - Chrysler Corp. (Dodge Car Div.)
DART GAFF - Fishing tackle - Hawie Manufacturing Co.

☆ = Now out of production

DART II - Pencils ☆ - Faber-Castell Corp.
DART MART INC. - Darts and dart games - Dart Mart Inc.
DART-N-POP - Fishing lures ☆ - Lindy Little Joe Inc.
DART RESPIRATORY - Air purification systems - Professional Medical Products, Inc.
DART SCAN - Medical apparatus ☆ - Del Mar Avionics
DART STAR - Darts and dart games - Medalist Marketing Corp.
DART SWINGER - Motor vehicles ☆ - Chrysler Corp. (Dodge Car Div.)
DART TARGET SYSTEM - Archery equipment - Dart Intl., Inc.
DARTAGE - Skin care products ☆ - T.N. Dickinson Co.
D'ARTAGNAN - Meat products - D'artagnan
D'ARTAGNAN - Meat products–poultry - Made in France
D'ARTAGNON - Perfumes - Estee Lauder Inc.
DARTANE - Pharmaceutical preparations - David A. Rosow Inc.
DARTAPP - Pharmaceutical preparations - David A. Rosow Inc.
DARTBALL - Toys - Apex Manufacturing Co.
DARTH VADER - Toys–stuffed - Kenner Products
DARTH VADER - Watches - Lucasfilm Ltd.
DARTH VADER VINYL FIGURE - Toys - ERTL Co., Inc.
D'ARTIGNY - Nonalcoholic aperitifs - RSD Marketing
DARTING TOUCH - Floor coverings–carpet and rugs - Milliken & Co. Inc.
DARTINGTON - Candles ☆ - Crate and Barrel
DARTINIC - Pharmaceutical preparations ☆ - Rugby Laboratories Inc.
DARTMASTER - Darts and dart games - Placo Products Co.
DARTMOOR - Footwear ☆ - Allen-Edmonds Shoe Corp.
DARTMOUTH - Clocks ☆ - General Time Corp. (Westclox/Seth Thomas Div.)
DARTMOUTH - Floor coverings–carpet and rugs - Atlas Carpet Mills Inc.
DARTMOUTH - Floor coverings–carpet and rugs ☆ - Barrett Carpet Mills Inc.
DARTMOUTH - Frames–eyeglass - U.S. Optical Frame Co.
DARTMOUTH - Mattresses - Stearns & Foster Bedding Co.
DARTMOUTH - Ophthalmic goods - Foremost Optical Products
DARTMOUTH - Prefabricated buildings–wood - Champion Enterprises Inc.
DARTMOUTH COLLEGE - Publisher's imprints - University Press of New England
DARTMOUTH HOUSE - Yarn - Robert Joseph Co.
DARTRONIX - Darts and dart games - Dart World Inc.
DARTS - Cigar boxes–wood ☆ - Consolidated Cigar Corp.
DARTS EYE - Games - Custom Manufacturing, Inc.
DARV-COLOR - Paints ☆ - Park Metallurgical Corp.
DARVEAUX - Candy - Sweet Street
DARVOCET-N - Analgesics - Eli Lilly and Co.
DARVON - Analgesics - Eli Lilly and Co.
DARVON-N - Analgesics - Eli Lilly and Co.
DARWIN - Computer software - Ameritrade, Inc.
DARWIN - Decorations - Evolution Design, Inc.
DARWIN - Fabrics - Dan River Inc.
DARWIN - Ophthalmic goods - Embassy Creations Inc.
DARWIN - Seafood products–fresh or frozen - ICD Group Inc.
DARWIN - Shrimp–fresh or frozen - Southeast Foods Inc.
DARWIN BOOKS - Publisher's imprints - Darwin Press Inc.
DARYL - Hardware - Blaine Window Hardware Inc.
DARYL - Ophthalmic goods ☆ - Luxottica
DARYL K. - Apparel and accessories - Daryl K. Inc.
DAS - Clay–modeling - Adica Pongo Inc.
DAS - Pharmaceutical preparations - Rugby Laboratories Inc.
DASANIT - Insecticides ☆ - Bayer Corp. (Agriculture Div.)
DASCARD - Computer peripheral equipment - Keithley Instruments, Inc.
DASCO - Electronic equipment - Amcam International, Inc.
DASEW - Thread - Belding Heminway Co. Inc.
DASH - See **RAINBOW**
DASH - Clocks - General Time Corp. (Westclox/Seth Thomas Div.)
DASH - Detergents - Procter & Gamble Co.
DASH - Dog food - Dial Corp.
DASH - Electronic equipment - Dixon Ticonderoga Co.
DASH - Frames–eyeglass - May Optical Co. Inc.
DASH - Gloves–safety - Dash Medical Gloves, Inc.
DASH - Markers–felt-tip ☆ - K-9 Pen Co.
DASH - Wallpaper - David & Dash
DASH - Wigs - Jean Paree Weegs Inc.
DASH-80 - Floor coverings–carpet and rugs ☆ - Quaker Inc.
DASH DESIGNS - Motor vehicle parts and accessories - Dash Designs, Inc.
DASH FLASHER - Automotive parts and accessories - Big Beam Emergency Systems Inc.
DASH GEAR - Motor vehicle parts and accessories - Dash Plus Co.
DASH HOUNDS - Games ☆ - Cadaco Div.
DASH LINK - Computer software - Astro-Med Inc.

DASH O LEMON - Food products - McCormick & Co., Inc.
DASH OF L.A. - Hair care products - Giovanni Cosmetics Inc.
DASH PATCH - Adhesives and sealants - Allied Compositions
DASH PATCH - Adhesives and sealants - L & F Products Inc.
DASH SAVER - Motor vehicle parts and accessories - Covercraft Industries Inc.
DASHEE - Toys–stuffed ☆ - Mego Financial Corp.
DASHELL - Shirts–polo - Dashell International Inc.
DASHER - Fishing lures - Fred Arbogast Co. Inc.
DASHER - Frames–eyeglass ☆ - Vanity Optical Manufacturing Co. Inc.
DASHER - Motor vehicles–automobiles ☆ - Volkswagen of America Inc.
DASHER - Toys–models ☆ - Estes Industries
DASHIKI - Hair care products - Frances Denney
DASHLITE - Flashlights - LHI Inc.
DASHLY - Stationery - Lisa Frank, Inc.
DASHMATE - Automotive parts and accessories - Sears, Roebuck and Co.
DASHMATE - Containers - Alpha Products, Inc.
DASHPRO - Dashboard covers - Gupta Family L.P.
DASHTAPE - Tape–adhesive - RND Co.
DASHU - Thread - Belding Heminway Co. Inc.
DASHWEAR - Scarves, neckwear - Dash Designs
DASHWRAP - Motor vehicle parts and accessories - Gupta Family LP
DASIKON - Pharmaceutical preparations ☆ - Smithkline Beecham Corp.
DASIN - Pharmaceutical preparations - Smithkline Beecham Corp.
DASI'S BEST - Milk - DASI Inc.
DASPORT - Computer peripheral equipment - Intelligent Instrumentation, Inc.
DASPUN - Thread - Belding Heminway Co. Inc.
DASSANT - Bakery products - Northwest Specialty Bakers Ltd.
DASUL - Oils–lubricating - Davis-Howland Oil Corp.
DAT - Audio tapes–blank ☆ - Minnesota Mining & Manufacturing Co.
DAT - Computer software - Psychological Corp.
D'AT - Recording label - Big Time Records Inc.
DAT-A-FILE - Office supplies - Boorum & Pease Co.
DAT-GLOW - Lighting equipment - Datcon Instrument Co.
DAT-LINK - Computer software - Datcon Instrument Co.
DATA - Eyeglasses - Art-Craft Optical Co.
DATA - Golfing equipment - Paramount Pictures Corp.
DATA/7 - Computer software - Mimetics Corp.
DATA/11 - Computer software - Mimetics Corp.
DATA 2000 - Computer software - Data 2000, Inc.
DATA ACQUISITION - Computer software - Pentek Inc.
DATA AMERICA - Paper - Ashlyn Corp.
DATA BANK - Floor coverings–carpet and rugs ☆ - Karastan-Bigelow Inc.
DATA BANK - Watches - Casio, Inc.
DATA-BASE - Communications equipment–mobile - Gamber-Johnson Inc.
DATA BASE - Floor coverings–carpet and rugs ☆ - Karastan-Bigelow Inc.
DATA BASED ADVISOR - Computer software - Data Based Solutions Inc.
DATA BASS - Amplifiers–musical instrument - Peavey Electronics Corp.
DATA-CABINET - Cabinets ☆ - ACCO USA, Inc.
DATA-CACHE - Computer software - Data-CACHE Corp.
DATA CADDY - Artists' materials - Artistic Office Products
DATA CART - Office supplies - Rubbermaid Office Products Inc.
DATA CASE - Computer-disk-storage system ☆ - Innovative Concepts Inc.
DATA CENTER - Office supplies - Mead Corp.
DATA CHECKER - Markers–felt-tip - Pentel of America, Ltd.
DATA CLIPS - Paper clips - Moore Push-Pin Co.
DATA CODE INCORPORATED - Computer software - Data Code, Inc.
DATA CODE INCORPORATED PROSPECT MANAGEMENT SYSTEM - Computer software - Data Code, Inc.
DATA COMMUTER - Electronic equipment - Kingston Technology Corp.
DATA CONNECTION, THE - Computer software - Computer Associates International, Inc.
DATA CONTROL BOARD - Bulletin boards–wood - Timewise
DATA COURIER - Computer peripheral equipment - Kingston Technology Corp.
DATA DEFENDER - Containers - Ring King Visibles, Inc.
DATA DIARIES - Diaries and journals - Coronet General Corp.
DATA DISPLAY - Computers–personal - Computer Accessories Corp.
DATA DOCK - Computer peripheral equipment - Micronet Technology, Inc.
DATA-DOT - Rubber tile, now out of production - American Floor Products Co. Inc.
DATA EAST - Video games - Data East USA Inc.
DATA EXPORT/DLL - Computer software - Spalding Software, Inc.
DATA FILE - Office supplies - Datacom Inc.
DATA FILES - Office supplies - Mead Corp.
DATA-FILM - Electronics equipment - RTI Research Technology International

DATA FIXX - Computer peripheral equipment - LAST Factory

DATA FLAG - Office supplies - Monarch Industries Inc.

DATA-FOLLOW-ME - Computer software - Wygant Scientific, Inc.

DATA GENERAL/ONE - Computers–personal - Data General Corp.

DATA GLOVE - Intercontinental Enterprises Ltd.

DATA-GRAPH - Computer software - Systems Management Inc.

DATA HI-LITER - Markers–felt-tip - Avery Dennison Corp.

DATA HUB - Electronic equipment - Detroit Diesel Corp.

DATA HUNTER - Telephone apparatus - Tempo Research Corp.

DATA INDUSTRIAL - Scientific apparatus - Data Industrial Corp.

DATA INSIGHTS - Computer software ☆ - Pavilion Technologies, Inc.

DATA LABEL - Labels–paper - Continental Dataforms

DATA LINK - Watches - Timex Corp.

DATA-LIT - Lighting equipment ☆ - Siemens Components Inc. (Optoelectronics Div.)

DATA-LOG - Binders ☆ - Master-Craft Corp.

DATA-MAILER - Mailing machines - Uarco Inc.

DATA MANAGER PC - Computer software - Timeworks International Inc.

DATA-MARKER - Pens ☆ - Pelikan, Inc.

DATA MASTER - Computer hardware - Kingston Technology Corp.

DATA MASTER CLASSICS - Office supplies - Datacom Inc.

DATA MATE - Connectors–electrical - Methode Electronics, Inc.

DATA-MATE - Furniture - Data-MATE Inc.

DATA MATRIX - Data loggers - National Systems Corp.

DATA MEDIA - Stationery - Tab Products Co.

DATA MORPH - Computer software - Advantageware, Inc.

DATA ON THE GO - Computer software - Qualcomm Inc.

DATA-PAC - Ledgers - Master-Craft Corp.

DATA PACKER - Computer software - BMC Software, Inc.

DATA-PAK - Printers–computer - Fellowes Manufacturing Co.

DATA PARTNER - Computer software - Icons International Inc.

DATA PAX - Labels–gummed - Maco Tag and Label Inc.

DATA PIGMENT - Markers–felt-tip ☆ - Sakura of America

DATA PLUS PRODUCTS - Computer peripheral equipment - Jo-Dan International, Inc.

DATA PORTER - Computers - The Tiffen Co.

DATA PRIVACY FACILITY - Computer software - Network Systems Corp.

DATA PRO - Electrical equipment - West Associates

DATA-RACK - Racks ☆ - ACCO USA, Inc.

DATA RANCH - Computer software - Virtual Reality Laboratories, Inc.

DATA-REF - Easels ☆ - ACCO USA, Inc.

DATA RESCUE - Computer software - Polaroid Corp.

DATA-SHAPER - Computer software - Axsys Technology Ltd.

DATA SHIELD - Electronic equipment - Corning Inc.

DATA SILO - Computer peripheral equipment - Kingston Technology Corp.

DATA SLIDES - Informational slide charts - Intromark Inc.

DATA STAND - Office supplies - Rubbermaid Office Products Inc.

DATA STAR - Telephones - TIE Communications Inc.

DATA STAR HYBRID - Telephones - TIE Communications Inc.

DATA-STOR - Storage system ☆ - Atlantic Furniture Systems

DATA STRIP - Signs - Fasteners for Retail, Inc.

DATA SYSTEMS & MANAGEMENT INC. - Computer software - Data Systems & Management, Inc.

DATA TILE - Games - Joiner Associates Inc.

DATA-TOTE - Cases–plastic ☆ - Anthes Universal

DATA TRANSLATION - Computers–micro - Data Translation, Inc.

DATA TRANSPORT - Computer software - Platinum Technology, Inc.

DATA-VAC MICROSWEEP - Vacuum cleaners and accessories - Metropolitan Vacuum Cleaner Co. Inc.

DATA VAULT - Boxes - Plastic Reel Corp. of America

DATA/VIEW - Electronic equipment - Arkwright Manufacturing Inc.

DATA VISIBLE - File folders - Data Visible Corp.

DATA WAITER - Furniture - Mead-Hatcher, Inc.

DATA WAREHOUSE COMPANY, THE - Computer software - Red Brick Systems

DATA WHEEL - Office supplies - Rubbermaid Office Products Inc.

DATABAG - Cases–plastic - Samsonite Corp.

DATABANK - Safes - Wright Line Inc.

DATABASE - Binders ☆ - Union Camp Corp. (Fine Paper Division)

DATABASE EXPLORER - Computer peripheral equipment - Blue Sky Software Corp.

DATABASE FARMING - Computer software - Earl W. Good

DATABASE ILLUSTRATOR - Computer software - Ray Ontko & Co.

DATABASE POWER WITHOUT PROGRAMMING - Computer software - Claris Corp.

DATABASE UTILITES - Computer storage devices - Bradmark Technologies, Inc.

DATABINDERS - Office supplies ☆ - Cardinal Products

DATABLADE - Computer software - Illustra Information Technologies, Inc.

DATABLASTER - Electronic equipment - Tiger Electronics, Inc.

DATABLASTER - Radio communications equipment - Grayson Electronics Co.

DATABOND - Computer software - Blade Software, Inc.

DATABORD - Tables–wood - Krueger International, Inc.

DATABRICK - Computer software - Datalux Corp.

DATABRITE - Cables - Belden Wire & Cable Co.

DATABROKER - Computer software - I-Kinetics, Inc.

DATABUILDER - Computer software - Dataplex, Inc.

DATACAPTURE - Photographic equipment - Eastman Kodak Co.

DATACASE - Digital encoders - ENSCO Inc.

DATACAST - Electronic equipment - Heraeus Electro-Nite Co.

DATACELL - Telephones–cellular - Steinbrecher Corp.

DATACENTRAL - Computer software - Unisys Corp.

DATACHECKER - Calculators ☆ - National Semiconductor Corp.

DATACHIP - Computer software - Datachip Corp.

DATACHRON - Watches - Movado Time Corp.

DATACLEANER - Computer software - Geoaccess, Inc.

DATACLEAR POWER SUM - Cables - Champlain Cable Corp.

DATACLUTCH - Handbags - Jack Georges Inc.

DATACOM - Office supplies - Datacom Inc.

DATACOR - Electrical equipment ☆ - Datron Technology, Inc.

DATADAY - Office supplies - Blue Star Leather Inc.

DATADIRECT - Computer software - Intersolv, Inc.

DATADRY - Chemical preparations - Safe Supplies

DATAEDIT - Computer software - Brio Technology, Inc.

DATAEXPERT - Computer hardware - Dataexpert Corp.

DATAFIELDER - Measuring instruments ☆ - Kaye Instruments Inc.

DATAFILE - Filing cabinets–metal ☆ - Wright Line Inc.

DATAFIRE - Computer hardware - Digi International Inc.

DATAFLASH - Computer software - GTE Telecommunications Services Inc.

DATAFLEX - Office supplies - Data Visible Corp.

DATAFOLIO - Binders - K & M Co.

DATAFUND SYSTEM, THE - Computer software - Annetta Freeman

DATAGARD - Electric lighting equipment - SL Waber Inc.

DATAGENDA - Handbags - Stuart Kern Fine Leather Goods

DATAGENIE - Computers - Data General Corp.

DATAGLIDE - Printers–computer - ETC Peripherals Inc.

DATAGLOVE - Intercontinental Enterprises Ltd.

DATAGLYPH - Computer software - Xerox Corp.

DATAGRAF - Electronic equipment - GNB Inc. (Automotive Battery Div.)

DATAGUARD 100 - Floor coverings–carpet and rugs - Lees Carpets

DATAGUARD I - Floor coverings–carpet and rugs ☆ - Lees Carpets

DATAGUIDE - Photographic equipment - Eastman Kodak Co.

DATAHOLD - Computer diskettes–blank - Eastman Kodak Co.

DATAHOST - Computer software - Howard W. Sams & Co.

DATAHUB - Computer software - International Business Machines Corp.

DATAIMPORT - Computer software - Spalding Software, Inc.

DATAJOINER - Computer software - International Business Machines Corp.

DATAK - Circuit boards–printed - Carter Craft Co.

DATAKEEPER - Notebooks and notepads ☆ - Union Camp Corp. (Fine Paper Division)

DATAKODE - Photographic equipment - Eastman Kodak Co.

DATALABS - Computer software - Viewpoint Animation Engineering, Inc.

DATALIFE - Computer diskettes–blank - Eastman Kodak Co.

DATALIFE - Computer diskettes–blank - Verbatim Corp.

DATALIFE COLORS - Computer diskettes–blank - Verbatim Corp.

DATALIFE PLUS - Computer diskettes–blank - Eastman Kodak Co.

DATALIFE PLUS - Computer diskettes–blank - Verbatim Corp.

DATALIGHTER - Pens - Schwan-STABILO USA Inc.

DATALITE - Ophthalmic goods - Vision Ease

DATALLIANCE - Computer software - Lincoln National Risk Management, Inc.

DATALUX - Computer peripheral equipment - Datalux Corp.

DATAMAGIC - Computer software - Dynamic Controls, Inc.

DATAMAIL - Computer software - Systore Companies, Inc.

DATAMAIL XPRESS - Computer software - Safeguard Business Systems, Inc.

DATAMAN - Electronic equipment - Cognex Corp.

DATAMAN - Electronic equipment ☆ - Texas Instruments Inc.

DATAMARINE - Nautical instruments - Datamarine International Inc.

DATAMARK FLIPPER - Electronic equipment - International Totalizator Systems Inc.

DATAMASTER - Computer software - Applied Color Systems, Inc.

DATAMASTER - Computer software - Autometric, Inc.

                                ☆ = Now out of production

DATAMASTER - Electronic equipment - J.L. Cooper Electronics
DATAMASTER - Sporting goods - Oceanic
DATAMATCH - Computer software - Applied Color Systems, Inc.
DATAMATE - Labels–gummed - Precision Dynamics Corp.
DATAMATE - Notebooks and notepads - Zellerbach
DATAMAX - Cables - Quabbin Wire & Cable
DATAMAX - Computer hardware - R.C. Electronics Inc.
DATAMAX - Sporting goods - Oceanic
DATAMAXX MESSAGEPROCESSING PROTOCOL - Computer software - Datamaxx Applied Technologies, Inc.
DATAMETRICS - Computer software - Datametrics Systems Corp.
DATAMETRICS - Computer software - Edison Price Lighting
DATAMETRICS - Paper - ESH Inc.
DATAMILL - Computer software - Nycoware, LLC
DATAMONITOR - Computer storage devices - UAI Technology Inc.
DATAMOST - Computer software - Datamost Corp.
DATAMOTION/MOI - Computer software - International TechneGroup Inc.
DATAMOVER - Radio communications equipment - Bydatel Corp.
DATANODE - Electronic equipment - Telxon Corp.
DATAPAK - Computer hardware - Kingston Technology Corp.
DATAPAK - Photographic equipment - Eastman Kodak Co.
DATAPERFECT - Computer software - Novell, Inc.
DATAPERFECT - Computer software - Wordperfect Corp.
DATAPHILE - Database software - Stone Design Corp.
DATAPHONE - Transmission equipment–industrial - At&T Corp.
DATAPHONE - Watches - Movado Time Corp.
DATAPLATES - Computer software - RTJ Associates
DATAPORT - Modems - At&T Corp.
DATAPRESS - Computer peripheral equipment - ETC Peripherals Inc.
DATAPRINT - Business forms - Dataprint, Inc.
DATAPRINT - Business forms - Standard Register Co.
DATAPRISM - Computer software - Brio Technology, Inc.
DATAPRODUCTS - Printers–computer - Dataproducts Corp.
DATAQ INSTRUMENTS - Computers - Dataq Instruments Inc.
DATAQUEST - Computer software - Data Sciences International, Inc.
DATARAID - Computer peripheral equipment - Dataram Corp.
DATARANGER - Computer peripheral equipment - Media Recovery Inc.
DATARIGHT - Computer software - i.d. Centric
DATARIGHT - Computer software - Postalsoft, a Firstlogic Technology
DATASAVE PLUS - Computer software - Clary Corp.
DATASAVER - Computer peripheral equipment - Cuesta Systems Corp.
DATASCOPE - Antennas–satellite - KVH Industries, Inc.
DATASCOPE - Computer software - Clifford Konold
DATASCRIBE - Electronic equipment - Avatel, Inc.
DATASET - Desks ☆ - Cramer Inc.
DATASET - Electrical equipment - Hunter Engineering Co.
DATASHOP - Computer software - Viewpoint Animation Engineering, Inc.
DATASHOW - Photographic equipment - Eastman Kodak Co.
DATASOFT PC - Computer software - Avatel, Inc.
DATASONDE 3 - Computer software - Hydrolab Corp.
DATASONDE 4 - Computer software - Hydrolab Corp.
DATASOURCE - Computer software - Datasource
DATASPEAKER - Electrical equipment - Berkeley Speech Technologies Inc.
DATASPEED - Teleprinters–computer - At&T Corp.
DATASPLIT - Communications equipment - Carrier Access Corp.
DATASTAGE - Computer software - Vmark Software Inc.
DATASTAR - Computer software ☆ - WordStar International Inc.
DATASTOR - Trade journals - Pennwell Publishing Co.
DATASYNC - Computer software - Syware, Inc.
DATASYNC - Electronic equipment - J.L. Cooper Electronics
DATASYNC2 - Electronic equipment - J.L. Cooper Electronics
DATASYS - Computer software - B & W Nuclear Technologies, Inc.
DATATAC - Radio communications equipment - Motorola, Inc. (Land Mobile Products Sector)
DATATAG - Hardware - Litton Industrial Automation Systems
DATATAG - Plumbing valves - B & K Industries, Inc.
DATATALKER - Computer hardware - Multi-Tech Systems, Inc.
DATATAPE - Tape recorders - Eastman Kodak Co.
DATATECH - Paper–bond - Weyerhaeuser Co.
DATATEL - Furniture - Datatel Corp.
DATATEX - Office furniture - Atlantic Furniture Systems
DATATIME - Electronic equipment - Daktronics Inc.
DATATIPS - Computer programming services - Microsoft Corp.
DATATOTE - Containers - Base-Line, Inc.
DATATOTE - Office supplies ☆ - Esselte Corp.
DATATRAC - Electronic equipment - B.F. Goodrich Co.

DATATRAC - Electronic equipment - Daktronics Inc.
DATATRAC - Office supplies ☆ - Esselte Corp.
DATATRACKER - Computers - Datatran Corp.
DATATRADE - Computer software - International Business Machines Corp.
DATATRAY - Cables - Belden Wire & Cable Co.
DATATREK COMCARD - Facsimile equipment - DataTrek Corp.
DATATREND - Computer peripheral equipment - Wabash Metal Products. Inc.
DATAVAC - Controls–heating systems - Surface Combustion, Inc.
DATAVERSE - Computer peripheral equipment - Virtual Data, LLC
DATAVIEW - Computer software - Newage Industries, Inc.
DATAVISOR - Electronic equipment - Advanced Technology Systems, Inc.
DATAVUE 25 - Computers–personal - Quadram Corp.
DATAWATCH - Computer software - Datawatch Corp.
DATAWINDOW - Computer peripheral equipment - Powersoft Corp.
DATAWONDER - Computer software - Addison-Wesley Publishing Co.
DATAWORLD - Computer software - Dataworld, Inc.
DATE-A-PRINT - Cameras - Vivitar Corp.
DATE & DOODLE - Calendars ☆ - Park Sherman
DATE KEEPER - Calendars - Myron Manufacturing Corp.
DATE KEEPERS - Calendars - Design House Inc.
DATE KING - Watches - Bulova Corp.
DATE MATES - Cosmetics - Pavcom, Inc.
DATE MATES - Towels - Stevens Linen Associates Inc.
DATE N TIME - Watches - Bulova Corp.
DATE PECAN SURPRISE - Confections - Arlin Dulin
DATE QUEEN - Watches - Bulova Corp.
DATE WATCHER - Watchbands–base metal ☆ - Newell Office Products
DATEBOOK II - Computer software ☆ - Digital Marketing Corp.
DATEFINDER - Calendars - Ad-a-Day Co. Inc.
DATEFRAME - Frames–picture - Richard D. Harroch
DATEJUST - Watches - Rolex Watch USA, Inc.
DATELINE - Calendars - Success Business Industries, Inc.
DATELINE - Floor coverings–carpet and rugs ☆ - Walter Carpet Mills
DATELINE - Paper - Crunden Martin Manufacturing Co.
DATELINE - Toys - Tonka Corp.
DATELINE - Watches ☆ - SMH (US) Inc.
DATEMATE - Brassieres (Bras) - Wacoal America Inc.
DATEMATE - Watches ☆ - Associated Stationers
DATERM - Computer peripheral equipment - APS Technologies
DATEVER - Computer software - John Bernard Dougherty
DATEX - Computer software - Risk Management Solutions, Inc.
DATEX - Thread ☆ - Belding Heminway Co. Inc.
DATEXX - Calculators - Teledex, Inc.
DATHON - Toys - Paramount Pictures Corp.
DATHROID - Pharmaceutical preparations ☆ - Scrip-Physician Supply Co.
DAT'L DO-IT - Hot pepper relish - Dat'l Do-It, Inc.
DATO - Computer software - Seth R. McCloud
DATOKA PLANK - Floor coverings - Bruce Hardwood Floors
DATON - Underwear and nightwear ☆ - Lovable Co.
DATONE - Recording label ☆ - San Juan Music Group
DATONO REGAL - Labels–gummed - Dayton Stencil Works Co.
DATOR - Computer peripheral equipment - Dator Corp.
DATREX - Boating equipment and accessories - Datrex Inc.
DATRIL - Analgesics - Bristol-Myers Squibb Co.
DATROAL - Electronic equipment - Datron Technology, Inc.
DATRON - Electronic equipment - Datron Technology, Inc.
DATRON - Radios - Datron Systems Inc.
DATRON - Watches - Movado Time Corp.
DATSPLUS - Communications equipment - Wiltron Co.
DATSUN - Motor vehicles–automobiles ☆ - Nissan Motor Corp. USA
DATWYLER - Floor coverings - Tek Stil Concepts Inc.
DAUB-N-WIPE - Publisher's imprints - Daub-N-Wipe
DAUBER BUOS - Stamps–hand - Tsukineko, Inc.
DAUFUSKI - Smoked oysters - Liberty Gold Fruit Co.
DAUGHTER EARTH - Pharmaceutical preparations - Daughter Earth, Ltd.
DAUGHTER'S PENDANT, THE - Jewelry - Kirchner Corp.
DAUNA - Watches - Wilcox-Mitchell Enterprises
DAUNOXOME - Prescription drug - Vestar, Inc.
DAUNTLESS - Boats - Glen-L Marine Designs
DAUNTLESS - Floor coverings–carpet and rugs - Mohawk Industries Inc.
DAUNTLESS - Floor coverings–carpet and rugs ☆ - Kelly Group Inc.
DAUNTLESS - Games - Avalon Hill Game Co.
DAUNTLESS - Thread - Threads USA Div.
DAUPHIN - Flatware - Gorham Inc.
DAUPHIN - Floor coverings–carpet and rugs ☆ - Gulistan Carpet Inc.
DAUPHIN - Furniture–wood ☆ - Charvoz

☆ = Now out of production

DAUPHIN - Guitars - Dauphin Co.
DAUPHINE - Dinnerware–glass - Nikko Ceramics Inc.
DAUPHINE - Drapery hardware ✩ - Spring Window Fashions Division, Inc.
DAUPHINE - Furniture ✩ - Hammary Furniture Co. Inc.
DAUPHINE - Glassware–household - Durand International
DAUPHINE - Watches - Bulova Corp.
DAUPHINE - Watches ✩ - SMH (US) Inc.
DAUPHNE - Recording label - Dellwood Music Co. Inc.
DAURELLE - Skin care products ✩ - T.N. Dickinson Co.
DAV DIGITAL AUDIO VIDEO - Computer software - Follett Corp.
DAVANCI - Sandals - Davis Sales
DAVANTI - Furniture ✩ - Lane Co. Inc.
DAVANTI - Socks - Garment Group of California
DAVCO - Apparel - Davco Fashion Accessories, Inc.
DAVCO - Bags–plastic - Webster Industries
DAVCO - Chemical preparations - Davis Petroleum
DAVE GROSSMAN - Stamps–hand - Dave Grossman Creations Inc.
DAVE GUARDALA - Musical-instrument mouthpieces and reeds - Dave Guardala Inc.
DAVE MARR GOLF COLLECTION - Apparel and accessories ✩ - Jantzen Inc.
DAVE SCOTT - Bicycling apparel ✩ - InSport International Inc.
DAVEGA - Golfing equipment - Nassau Precision Casting Co., Inc.
DAVENPORT - Cement - Lafarge Corp.
DAVENPORT - Dinnerware–glass - Cuthbertson Imports Inc.
DAVENPORT - Fans–electric - Marietta Hardware Co.
DAVENPORT - Floor coverings–carpet and rugs - Cameron Pande and Co. of New York, Inc.
DAVENPORT-TREACY - Pianos - Kohler & Campbell Inc.
DAVENTRY - Finishing agents ✩ - Flintkote Co.
DAVENTRY - Paints ✩ - GS Roofing Products Co.
DAVEY ALLISON'S WINNER'S CIRCLE - Chili–canned - Bunker Hill Foods
DAVEY DOG - Puppets - Dakin Inc.
DAVEY EST. 1842 SOLID BOARD GREEN LABEL - Binders - Davey Co.
DAVEY SOCKET-T - T-shirts–men's - Chums Ltd.
DAVEY SOLID BOARD RED LABEL EST. 1842 - Binders - Davey Co.
DAVI - Food products - Universal Packers Corp.
DAVID - Food products ✩ - Empire Kosher Poultry Inc.
DAVID - Veterinary pharmaceutical preparations - Microware Systems Corp.
DAVID - Violins - Selmer Co. Inc.
DAVID AARON - Apparel and accessories - David Aaron Inc.
DAVID ADAMS - Apparel–men's - Montage International Importing, Inc.
DAVID ALAN CHOCOLATIER - Candy - Lebanon Corp., Inc.
DAVID ALEXANDER - Apparel and accessories - B.S.D. Industries, Ltd.
DAVID & DASH - Fabrics - Cone Mills Corp.
DAVID & DASH - Fabrics - David & Dash
DAVID & DASH - Wallpaper - Imperial Wallcoverings, Inc.
DAVID & SONS - Snack foods - David and Sons Inc.
DAVID AULD ORIGINALS - Flatware ✩ - Reco International Corp.
DAVID BEARDS - Food products - Great American Foods
DAVID BROOKS - Apparel and accessories - Kellwood Co.
DAVID BROOKS - Apparel–women's - Robert Scott Ltd. Inc.
DAVID BROWN - Intimate apparel - I. Appel Corp.
DAVID BROWN BOUTIQUE - Bathing suits - Wior Corp.
DAVID BRUCE - Wines - David Bruce Winery
DAVID BRUCE WINERY - Wines - House of Burgundy Inc.
DAVID COMFORTS - Apparel and accessories - David Comforts Inc.
DAVID CRYSTAL - Apparel and accessories - Crystal Brands Inc.
DAVID DAINES MADISON AVENUE COLLECTION - Hair care products - David Daines Madison Avenue Collection Ltd.
DAVID DART - Apparel and accessories - Kellwood Co.
DAVID DART COLLECTION - Apparel and accessories - Kellwood Co.
DAVID DART DRESS - Apparel and accessories - Kellwood Co.
DAVID DART EMPORIUM - Apparel and accessories - Kellwood Co.
DAVID DART EMPORIUM - Dyes–household - Force One, Inc.
DAVID DART SPORT - Apparel and accessories - Kellwood Co.
DAVID EDEN D - Shoes - Fort Walker, Inc.
DAVID EVINS - Shoes - United States Shoe Corp.
DAVID GEOFFREY - Hair accessories jewelry - Imperial Jewelry Corp.
DAVID HARRISON - Apparel–men's - Harper Shirt Co.
DAVID JORDAN - Apparel and accessories - Howard R. Mash
DAVID KAPLAN STUDIO - Lithographic plates - David Kaplan Studio
DAVID KOPEL - Handbags - David Kopel
DAVID LAU - Food products - Beatrice Cos. Inc.
DAVID LAWRENCE - Apparel–men's - L.D.M. Enterprises, Inc.
DAVID MARSHALL DESIGNS - Lighting fixtures - Harris Industries
DAVID MEHLER FOR DAME - Belts–apparel ✩ - Dame Belt Co. Inc.

DAVID PAGE - Apparel–athletic - Ambiance Clothing Co. USA Ltd.
DAVID PALTERER - Flatware - Reed and Barton Corp.
DAVID PEYSER - Apparel–women's - JPM Co.
DAVID ROBINSON - Sporting goods - Franklin Sports, Inc.
DAVID ROSOW - Pharmaceutical preparations - David A. Rosow Inc.
DAVID S. DIAMONDS - Jewelry–precious - David S. Diamonds, Inc.
DAVID SMITH - Apparel–women's - David Smith
DAVID SOROKIN - Canes - David Sorokin
DAVID STERN - Jewelry - Jewelry Buyers International Inc.
DAVID URSO - Hair accessories, jewelry - Loom Co.
DAVID VARSANO - Jewelry - Silver for Less Inc.
DAVID WEBB - Jewelry - David Webb Inc.
DAVID YELLOWHORSE - Cutlery - David Yellowhorse
DAVID YELLOWHORSE - Knives - United Cutlery Corp.
DAVID YURMAN - Watches - Yurman Designs, Inc.
DAVID ZACHARY - Apparel - David Zachary, Ltd.
DAVIDOFF - Beverages–alcohol - Shaw-Ross International Importers
DAVIDOFF - Cigarettes - West Park Tobacco Inc.
DAVIDOFF - Perfumes - Coty Inc.
DAVID'S AMAIZ'N POPCORN - Popcorn - Popcorn Explosion Inc.
DAVID'S DELI - Food products - Crystal Farms Inc.
DAVID'S GOODBATTER - Food products - David's Goodbatter
DAVID'S SUNSNAX - Seeds–salted, roasted, cooked, or canned ✩ - David and Sons Inc.
DAVIDSON WINERY - Wines - Davidson Winery
DAVIDSON'S KID WORKS - Computer software ✩ - Knowledge Adventure
DAVIDSON'S ZOOKEEPER - Computer software ✩ - Knowledge Adventure
DAVIE - Furniture - Boling Co.
DAVIES - Chairs–folding - Harvester Co. Inc. (Davies Designed Products Div.)
DAVIES - Respirators - Regional Respotary
DAVIES - Television equipment - Television Equipment Associates
DAVIES-BLACK - Educational materials - Consulting Psychologists Press, Inc.
DAVILLA - Musical instrument accessories ✩ - Willis Music Co.
DAVINCI - Fireplaces - Martin Industries, Inc.
DAVINCI - Handkerchiefs - Carolina Manufacturing Inc.
DAVINCI - Luggage - Atchison Products, Inc.
DAVINCI - Tiles–ceramic - Kowa Texas Inc.
DAVINCI - Tiles–ceramic - KPT Inc.
DAVINCI BOUTIQUE - Frames–eyeglass - Windsor Optical Inc.
DAVINCI BUILDINGS - Computer software - Spinnaker Software Corp.
DAVINCI INTERIORS - Computer software - Spinnaker Software Corp.
DAVINCI LANDSCAPES - Computer software - Spinnaker Software Corp.
DAVINCI ROMA - Eyeglasses ✩ - Windsor Optical Inc.
DAVIS - Bakery products - Nabisco Foods Group
DAVIS - Fabrics - Sidney Davis Fabrics
DAVIS - Floor coverings–carpet and rugs - Concepts International
DAVIS - Furniture - Davis Cabinet Co.
DAVIS - Nautical instruments - Davis Instruments Corp.
DAVIS - Paints ✩ - Wescon Products Co.
DAVIS - Pet products - Davis Manufacturing
DAVIS - Sports rackets and accessories - Victor Sports
DAVIS & SANFORD - Tripods–photographic - Davis & Sanford Co. Inc.
DAVIS AND SMALL - Signs ✩ - H.C. Meyers Co.
DAVIS & SQUIRE - Suits–men's - TJX Companies, Inc.
DAVIS BYNUM - Wines - Davis Bynum Winery
DAVIS CLEAVER - Meat products–poultry - Davis-Cleaver Foods Inc.
DAVIS CUP - Balls–tennis - Penn Athletic Products
DAVIS CUP - Footwear–athletic ✩ - Puma Inc.
DAVIS RANGER - Nautical instruments - Davis Instruments Corp.
DAVIS TAD - Apparel and accessories - Craig Torruella
DAVIS VIRGINIA - Sausages - Potok Packing Co.
DAVIS-WALKER - Wire - Davis-Wire
DAVIS WELD - Insulating materials - Perma Flake Corp.
DAVIS/YACHTING - Nautical instruments ✩ - Davis Instruments Corp.
DAVISONGS - Recording label - Church of God
DAVISOUND - Audio equipment - MCP Davisound
DAVIT - Computer software - Datron Technology, Inc.
DAVITEST - Battery chargers ✩ - Storage Battery Systems
DAVKA - Computer software - Davka Corp.
DAVLIN - Paints - Davlin Coatings Inc.
DAVLIN - Trailers–travel ✩ - Davlin Campers
DAVOL - Surgical supplies - Davol Inc.
DAVOS - Footwear - K-Swiss Inc.
DAVRABLEND - Underwear and nightwear - Henson-Kickernick Inc.
DAVSC - Electronics equipment ✩ - AVBluebook
DAVSIGN - Bulletin boards–cork - Davson Inc.

✩ = Now out of production

DAVSON - Bulletin boards–cork - Davson Inc.
DAVSON - Office supplies ☆ - Rubbermaid Office Products Inc.
DAVY CROCKETT - Bedding–linen - Geronimo Productions Inc.
DAVY CROCKETT - Cans–metal - Spraz Co.
DAW BOOKS - Publisher's imprints - Daw Books Inc.
DAW SONATA - Cosmetics ☆ - RH Cosmetics Corp.
DAWCO - Novelty items - Dawson Co. Manufacturing
DAWG - Toys–stuffed - Russ Berrie and Co., Inc.
DAWG GONE COUNTRY - Pet products - Pedigrees
DAWHIDE - Laces–boot and shoe - Rochester Shoe Tree Co. Inc.
DAWLEEN'S D'LIGHTS - Candy - Peabody Products, Inc.
DAWLS - Apparel–women's - Drawls
DAWN - Bedding–linen - Dan River Inc.
DAWN - Brassieres (Bras) - Wacoal America Inc.
DAWN - Cabinets ☆ - Merillat Industries, Inc.
DAWN - Cakes–mixes - Dawn Food Products Inc.
DAWN - Detergents - Procter & Gamble Co.
DAWN - Dolls - Breslow, Morrison, Terzian & Associates, Inc.
DAWN - Electrical equipment ☆ - Leviton Manufacturing Co., Inc.
DAWN - Floor coverings–carpet and rugs ☆ - Regal Rugs Inc.
DAWN - Flowers, plants, and seeds - Jacklin Seed
DAWN - Glassware–household ☆ - Crisa Corp.
DAWN - Occasional tables ☆ - JDI Group, Inc.
DAWN - Office furniture–wood ☆ - Haskell of Pittsburgh, Inc.
DAWN - Paper–tissue - Kimberly-Clark Corp.
DAWN - Recording label - Biograph Records Inc.
DAWN - Tableware–china ☆ - Lenox, Inc.
DAWN - Telescopes - Northern Telecom, Inc.
DAWN/400 - Computer software - Sungard Investment Ventures, Inc.
DAWN/BAKER BOY - Food products ☆ - Dawn Food Products Inc.
DAWN/BESCO - Food products ☆ - Dawn Food Products Inc.
DAWN BLOSSOMS - Glassware–household - Lenox, Inc.
DAWN FAWN - Toys–stuffed ☆ - Dakin Inc.
DAWN FRESH - Mushrooms - Giorgio Foods Inc.
DAWN FRESH - Mushrooms - Green Giant Co.
DAWN FRESH - Sauces - Giorgifred Co.
DAWN GLO - Food products - Hanover Foods Corp.
DAWN-KIST - Food products - Union Sea Foods Inc.
DAWN LAKE - Floor coverings–carpet and rugs ☆ - Masland Corp.
DAWN MASTER BLEND - Frosting - Dawn Food Products Inc.
DAWN MIST - Dishes–china ☆ - Denby USA Limited
DAWN MIST - Flatware ☆ - Wallace International Silversmiths, Inc.
DAWN ODYSSEY - Yarn ☆ - Caron International Inc.
DAWN OF AQUARIUS - Apparel and accessories - Dawn Breeze
DAWN OF CIVILIZATION COLLECTION, THE - Jewelry - Michael Monahan
DAWN SURE SHOT - Detergents - Procter & Gamble Co.
DAWN, THE - Video production - Brocato International
DAWN TRAKKER - Boats–kayaks - Ocean Kayak, Inc.
DAWNEX - Medical apparatus - Dawnex Industries, Inc.
DAWNEX INDUSTRIES INC. - Medical apparatus - Dawnex Industries, Inc.
DAWNMIST - Cosmetics - Donovan Industries, Inc.
DAWN'S - Candy - D.E. Manufacturing Co.
DAWNS - Food products - Dawn's Foods, Inc.
DAWNS - Gloves–work ☆ - Pioneer Industrial Products Co.
DAWN'S RAINBOW - Bedding–linen - Dan River Inc.
DAWSON - Beverages–malt ☆ - Eastern Brewing Corp.
DAWSON - Food products - Dorothy Dawson Food Products Inc.
DAWSON - Hooks - Dawson Home Fashions, Inc.
DAWSON BATH & BODY COLLECTION - Skin care products - Dawson Home Fashions, Inc.
DAWSON CREEK - Footwear - JBI, Inc.
DAWSON ENERGETIC BATH - Deodorizers - Dawson Home Fashions, Inc.
DAWSON HOME FASHIONS - Housewares - Dawson Home Fashions, Inc.
DAWSON LUXURIANT BATH - Skin care products - Dawson Home Fashions, Inc.
DAWSON ROMANTIC BATH - Skin care products - Dawson Home Fashions, Inc.
DAWSON SENSUAL BATH - Skin care products - Dawson Home Fashions, Inc.
DAWSON SERENE BATH - Candles - Dawson Home Fashions, Inc.
DAWSONS - Apparel and accessories - J.D. Dawson Co.
DAWSTIK - Novelty items - Dawson Co. Manufacturing
DAX - Audio equipment - Dax
DAX - Foam rubber - Advanced Foam Products, Inc.
DAX - Frames–picture - Ammak Manufacturing Corp.
DAX - Hair care products - Imperial Dax Co.

DAX - Watches - General Time Corp. (Westclox/Seth Thomas Div.)
DAX 100 - Frames–picture - Ammak Manufacturing Corp.
DAX ARTPRINT - Frames–picture ☆ - Ammak Manufacturing Corp.
DAX CLEAR - Frames–picture - Ammak Manufacturing Corp.
DAX FUN WAVE - Hair care products - Imperial Dax Co.
DAX INTERNATIONAL - Frames–picture - Ammak Manufacturing Corp.
DAX LIGHT SHEEN - Hair care products - Imperial Dax Co.
DAXALEN - Skin care products ☆ - Miles Inc.
DAXCEL - Adhesives and sealants ☆ - Dacar Chemical Co.
DAXOLIN - Pharmaceutical preparations ☆ - Miles Inc.
D.A.Y. - Apparel–children's - D.A.Y. Kids Sportswear Inc.
DAY - Cosmetics - Dr. Babor Natural Cosmetics
DAY - Toiletries - GPS, Inc.
DAY 2 DAY - Apparel and accessories - Clothestime Inc.
DAY & NIGHT - Air conditioning equipment - United Technologies Corp.
DAY & NIGHT - Air conditioning equipment - Carrier Corp.
DAY & NIGHT BARBER POLE - Signs - Donald D. Ring
DAY-AT-A-GLANCE - Diaries ☆ - Keith Clark Inc.
DAY-AT-A-TIME - Office supplies - Dome Publishing Co., Inc.
DAY AT PLAY, A - Computer software - Don Johnston Inc.
DAY AT THE PARK, A - Trading cards and stamps - ANCO Collector Supplies, Inc.
DAY AT THE PARK, A - Games - Treat Entertainment, Inc.
DAY AT THE SLOPES, A - Health care products - Production Plus Inc.
DAY BOX - Boxes - Impel, Inc.
DAY BREAK - Dinnerware–glass - Block China Co.
DAY BREAK - Dinnerware–glass - Salem China Co.
DAY BREAK - Fruit drinks–bottled or canned - Presto Food Products, Inc.
DAY BREEZE - Apparel–women's - Morning Sun, Inc.
DAY-BRITE - Lighting equipment - Emerson Electric Co.
DAY-BRITE - Lighting fixtures - Thomas Industries Inc.
DAY-BY-DAY - Calendars ☆ - Verona Calendar Co.
DAY BY DAY - Diaries - Samuel Ward Manufacturing Inc.
DAY BY DAY - Dolls ☆ - Effanbee Doll Corp.
DAY BY DAY - Food products - Lodi Canning Inc.
DAY BY DAY - Magazines - Facts on File Inc.
DAY-CARE - Cold remedies - Richardson-Vicks USA
DAY CARE - Exercising equipment - Flexible Flyer Co.
DAY CARE PETS - Toys–stuffed ☆ - Century Products Co.
DAY-CHEM - Chemical preparations - Dayton Superior Corp.
DAY CRADLE - Furniture ☆ - Cosco, Inc.
DAY-DATE - Watches - Rolex Watch USA, Inc.
DAY DREAM - Floor coverings–carpet and rugs ☆ - Quaker Inc.
DAY DREAMER HAMMOCKS - Hammocks - Gleason Corp.
DAY DREAMERS - Apparel–children's - Daydreamers Inc.
DAY DREAMS - Toys - Meritus Industries, Inc.
DAY DREAMS - Underwear and nightwear - Maidenform Inc.
DAY-GLO - Paints - Day-Glo Color Corp.
DAY IN THE SUN, A - Suntan lotions - Matrix Essentials, Inc.
DAY INTO NIGHT - Hair care products - Redken Laboratories, Inc.
DAY ISLAND - Apparel - Morning Sun, Inc.
DAY-KARE - Water colors - Rich Art Color Co., Inc.
DAY KEEPER - Calendars - Better Office Products, Inc.
DAY KIDS - Apparel–children's - Kahn Lucas Lancaster Inc.
DAY LEE - Snack foods - Dennis J. Alba & Co.
DAY LIFE - Floor coverings–carpet and rugs ☆ - Hollytex Carpet Mills Inc.
DAY LIFT - Hair care products - Chanel Inc.
DAY LILY - Tableware–china ☆ - Seymour Mann Inc.
DAY LITES - Footwear–women's - Lowell Shoe, Inc.
DAY-LONG SADDLES - Motor vehicle parts and accessories - Russell Cycle Products
DAY MANAGER - Diaries - S J B Enterprises, Inc.
DAY MAX - Office supplies - Easter Seal Society of Western Pennsylvania
DAY MINDER - Calendars ☆ - Keith Clark Inc.
DAY MOIST - Skin care products - Key West Aloe Inc.
DAY N DATE - Watches ☆ - SMH (US) Inc.
DAY-N-NIGHT - Nameplates–engraved - Spear Engineering Co.
DAY-NITE - Auto supply stores ☆ - Courtaulds Performance Plus
DAY OF THE TENTACLE - Computer software - Lucasarts Entertainment Co.
DAY OF THE WEEK - Dolls ☆ - Fun World Inc.
DAY ONE - Computer software - Commonwealth Land Title Insurance Co.
DAY-ONE - Suntan lotions - Alba Products Group Inc.
DAY RELIEF - Pharmaceutical preparations - Sterling Winthrop Inc.
DAY RUNNER - Books–blank - Harper House
DAY RUNNER - Calendars - Day Runner, Inc.
DAY RUNNER - Office supplies - Day Runner, Inc.

☆ = Now out of production

DAY-SAVOR - Computer software - Day Savor, Inc.
DAY SHIFT - Apparel–women's - Richard Leeds International, Inc.
DAY SIX - Apparel and accessories - Augusta Sportswear, Inc.
DAY SPA - Skin care products - RTS Laboratories, Inc.
DAY-SPAN - Pharmaceutical preparations - Alva-Amco Pharmacal Co.
DAY-TIMERS - Diaries - Beatrice Cos. Inc.
DAY-TO-DAY - Brassières (Bras) - Lovable Co.
DAY TO FIND OUT, A - Computer software ☆ - Orange Cherry Software
DAY-TO-NIGHT - Dolls - Mattel, Inc.
DAY-TONE - Finishing agents ☆ - James B. Day and Co.
DAY TRIM - Pharmaceutical preparations - Quantum, Inc.
DAYALETS - Vitamins and nutritional supplements - Abbott Laboratories
DAYBOOK - Computer software - Asymetrix Corp.
DAYBOX - Toy box - Impel, Inc.
DAYBREAK - Clocks - General Time Corp. (Westclox/Seth Thomas Div.)
DAYBREAK - Coffee - Daybreak Coffee Roasters, Inc.
DAYBREAK - Dinnerware–glass ☆ - Lenox, Inc.
DAYBREAK - Dishes–earthenware - Denby USA Limited
DAYBREAK - Floor coverings–carpet and rugs - Colonial Mills Inc.
DAYBREAK - Flowers, plants, and seeds - Panamerican Seed
DAYBREAK - Gravy - Bost Distributing Co., Inc.
DAYBREAK - Meat products–beef - Fletcher's Fine Foods Inc.
DAYBREAK - Motor vehicles–motor homes - Damon Corp.
DAYBREAK - Vitamins and nutritional supplements - Natural Dietary Products, Inc.
DAYBREAK - Wallpaper - Imperial Wallcoverings, Inc.
DAYBREAK BOOKS - Publisher's imprints ☆ - Zondervan Publishing House
DAYBREAKS - Calendars - Zondervan Publishing House
DAYBREAKS - Footwear–women's - Nina Footwear Co., Inc.
DAYCO - Adhesives and sealants - James B. Day and Co.
DAYCO - Floor coverings–carpet and rugs ☆ - Dayco Products, Inc.
DAYCRAFT ORIGINALS - Toy stores - Forestcraft Inc.
DAYCYCLE - Pet products - Tetra Sales USA
DAYDOTS - Stationery - Daydots Label Co., Inc.
DAYDREAM - Fabrics - Spring Window Fashions Division, Inc.
DAYDREAM - Rings–jewelry - Artcarved Inc.
DAYDREAMER - Hammocks - Algoma Net Co.
DAYDREAMER - Sofabeds - Kinder Manufacturing Corp.
DAYDREAMS - Christmas tree ornaments - Cracker Box Inc.
DAYDREAMS - Colognes - Maybelline Co.
DAYDREAMS - Floor coverings–carpet and rugs - Patcraft Mills Inc.
DAYDREAMS - Perfumes - A & B Sales Unlimited, Inc.
DAYDREAMS - Wallpaper - Academy Handprints Ltd.
DAYFARER II - Crocheted and knitted items ☆ - Hampshire Hosiery, Inc.
DAYFLEX - Tubes–vacuum - Dayco Products, Inc.
DAYHIST - Antihistamine preparations - L. Perrigo Co.
DAYHIST-1 - Antihistamine preparations - L. Perrigo Co.
DAYHIST-D - Antihistamine preparations - L. Perrigo Co.
DAYHOFF - Perfumes - Richard Dayhoff Designs Inc.
DAYLIFT - Window coverings ☆ - Hunter Douglas Intermountain Fabrication Co.
DAYLIGHT - Artists' materials - Vogart Crafts Corp.
DAYLIGHT - Floor coverings–carpet and rugs ☆ - Colonial Mills Inc.
DAYLIGHT STAT - Cameras ☆ - Star Parts Inc.
DAYLIGHT TRACKER - Electronic equipment - Unenco Services, Inc.
DAYLIGHTER - Cameras ☆ - Graphline, Inc.
DAYLITE - Balls–golf - Pick Point Sports
DAYLITE - Health care products - Healthwatchers System
DAYLITE - Motor vehicle parts and accessories - Paccar Inc.
DAYLITE BLUE - Lamp bulbs–infrared - Duro-Test Corp.
DAYLITER - Windows–storm - APC Corp.
DAYLITES - Window coverings - Alberto-Culver Co.
DAYLON - Electrical equipment - Wonder Corp. of America
DAYLONG - Sun tanning oil - Fountain Pharmaceuticals Inc.
DAYLUX - Hardware ☆ - Leslie-Locke, Inc.
DAYMARK - Apparel and accessories - Melody, Inc.
DAYMINDER - Diaries - Cullman Ventures Inc.
DAYNE DUVALL - Jewelry - Dayne Duvall, Inc.
DAYO - Computer software - TJS Lab, Inc.
DAYPA - Dolls - Victor M. Bulgarelli Associates Inc.
DAYPAGE - Pagers - Daypage of America, Inc.
DAYPLANNER - Medical apparatus - Apex Medical Corp.
DAYPRO - Analgesics - G. D. Searle & Co.
DAYQUIL - Cold remedies - Richardson-Vicks USA
DAY'S END - Slipper socks - Medalist Apparel Inc.

DAYS OF CHRISTMAS COLLECTION - Christmas tree ornaments - Lenox, Inc.
DAYS OF OUR LIVES - Apparel and accessories - Sony Music Entertainment Inc.
DAY'S WORK - Tobacco products - R.J. Reynolds Tobacco Co.
DAY'S WORK - Tobacco–chewing or smoking - Swedish Math North America Inc.
DAYSAILOR - Boats - Catalina Yachts Inc.
DAYSAN - Pharmaceutical preparations - Daywell Laboratories Corp.
DAYSCAN - Books–blank - New England Business Service, Inc.
DAYSPLOSH - Hair care products - Tressa, Inc.
DAYSPRING - Recording label - Word, Inc.
DAYSPRING - Stationery - David C. Cook Publishing Co.
DAYSPRING - Stationery - Outreach Publications Inc.
DAYSQUARES - Labels–paper - Century Marketing Corp.
DAYSTAR - Building materials - Texas Aluminum Industries Inc.
DAYSTAR - Food products - Daystar International Inc.
DAYSTROM - Furniture–metal - Daystrom Furniture Inc.
DAYTAR - Electronic equipment - Apollo Audiovisual Div.
DAYTEC - Motorcycle parts and accessories - Daytec
DAYTEENS - Vitamins and nutritional supplements ☆ - Abbott Laboratories
DAYTEK - Computer hardware - Daewoo International (America) Corp.
DAYTIME - Dolls - Mattel, Inc.
DAYTIME BEN-GAY - Analgesics - Pfizer Inc.
DAYTIMERS - Footwear - J. Baker Inc.
DAYTO HIMBIN - Pharmaceutical preparations - Dayton Laboratories, Inc.
DAYTON - Glass–leaded - Seneca Glass Co.
DAYTON - Ladders–metal - Michigan Ladder Co. Inc.
DAYTON - Locks–door ☆ - SecurityLink from Ameritech
DAYTON - Motors–air - Grainger Division
DAYTON - Rackets–tennis - Dayton Racquet Co. Inc.
DAYTON - Sinks–metal - Elkay Manufacturing Co.
DAYTON - Tires - Bridgestone/Firestone, Inc.
DAYTON BOMBERS - Apparel and accessories - Dayton Hockey Club, Inc.
DAYTON LOUDSPEAKER CO. - Amplifiers - Parts Express International, Inc.
DAYTONA - Automotive parts and accessories - Echlin Inc.
DAYTONA - Boats–motor ☆ - Glassmaster Co.
DAYTONA - Cigarettes - Brown & Williamson Tobacco Corp.
DAYTONA - Gasoline - Major Oil Co.
DAYTONA - Jet skis - Arctco, Inc.
DAYTONA - License plates–automotive - International Speedway Corp.
DAYTONA - Motor vehicles ☆ - Chrysler Corp. (Dodge Car Div.)
DAYTONA - Motor vehicles–motor homes - Baron Motor Homes Inc.
DAYTONA - Shoes - Daniel Green Co.
DAYTONA - Skin care products - Kiehl's Since 1851, Inc.
DAYTONA - Tires - Bridgestone/Firestone, Inc.
DAYTONA - Toys ☆ - Strombecker Corp.
DAYTONA - Watches - Rolex Watch USA, Inc.
DAYTONA - Window coverings ☆ - Vertilux-Louverlux Inc.
DAYTONA 500 - Games - Milton Bradley Co.
DAYTONA 500 - Novelty license plates - International Speedway Corp.
DAYTONA ATP - Bicycles - Huffy Corp.
DAYTONA FOR MEN - Connectors–electrical - Kiehl's Since 1851, Inc.
DAYTONA GT - Tires - Bridgestone/Firestone, Inc.
DAYTONA INTERNATIONAL SPEEDWAY - Apparel and accessories - International Speedway Corp.
DAYTONA PACIFICA - Motor vehicles ☆ - Chrysler Corp. (Dodge Car Div.)
DAYTONA SHELBY Z - Motor vehicles ☆ - Chrysler Corp. (Dodge Car Div.)
DAYTONA SPEEDWAY - Toys–automobiles - Life-Like Products Inc.
DAYTONA SPEEDWEAR - Apparel and accessories - International Speedway Corp.
DAYTONA SPEEDWEEKS - Apparel and accessories - International Speedway Corp.
DAYTONA SPORT - Tires - Bridgestone/Firestone, Inc.
DAYTONA SPORT GRANDE - Tires - Bridgestone/Firestone, Inc.
DAYTONA SUPER STAG - Tires - Bridgestone/Firestone, Inc.
DAYTONA USA - Apparel - International Speedway Corp.
DAYTONA USA THE ULTIMATE MOTORSPORTS ATTRACTION - Amusement parks - International Speedway Corp.
DAYTONIAN - Tires - Bridgestone/Firestone, Inc.
DAYTRON - Televisions - Daewoo International (America) Corp.
DAYVA - Garden furniture - Dayva International, Inc.
DAYVA INDUSTRIES - Garden furniture - Dayva International, Inc.
DAYWEAR - Skin care products - Estee Lauder Inc.
DAYWIND - Recording label - Daywind, Inc.
DAZ-ZLE - Computer programs - Envelope Manager Software

☆ = Now out of production

DAZALON - Apparel and accessories ☆ - Vanity Fair Mills Inc.
DAZE MORTENSON - Dolls ☆ - Applause, Inc.
DAZE OF ISSUE - Artists' materials - Steve Smith
DAZEL - Computer software - Atrium Technologies Inc.
DAZER - Pet products - K-II Enterprises
DAZEY - Kitchen appliances - Dazey Corp.
DAZEY CHEF'S GRILL - Cooking equipment–household - Dazey Corp.
DAZEY CHEF'S PAN - Cooking equipment–household - Dazey Corp.
DAZEY HAMBURGER HEAVEN - Kitchen appliances - Dazey Corp.
DAZEY MELTING POT - Cooking equipment–household - Dazey Corp.
DAZEY MICRO-SEAL - Kitchen appliances - Dazey Corp.
DAZEY SIZZLING CHEF - Electric cooking appliance - Dazey Corp.
DAZEY STRIPPER - Cookware - Dazey Corp.
DAZIP - Thread - Belding Heminway Co. Inc.
DAZITE - Coating materials - Dazey Corp.
DAZITE II - Coating materials - Dazey Corp.
DAZOR - Lighting fixtures - Dazor Manufacturing Corp.
DAZOR - Skin care products - Guaranty Hair Removal
DAZZELINE - Sporting goods - Beacon Ballfields
DAZZELOONS - Toys - CTI Industries Corp.
DAZZEY DUKS - Novelty items - Isbell Records, Inc.
DAZZLE - Bleach - Kmart Corp.
DAZZLE - Brooms - Sunshine Industries Inc.
DAZZLE - Cleaning preparations - Zep Manufacturing Co.
DAZZLE - Glue–household or industrial - Hero Arts Rubber Stamps Inc.
DAZZLE - Paper–gift wrap - CPS Corp.
DAZZLE - Pet products - Farnam Cos. Inc.
DAZZLE - Pet products ☆ - Dexol (Ringer Corp.)
DAZZLE - Wallpaper ☆ - David & Dash
DAZZLE - Wigs ☆ - Jean Paree Weegs Inc.
DAZZLE BRIGHT - Christmas tree lights - Meijer, Inc.
DAZZLE-BRITE - Artists' materials ☆ - Dick Blick Co.
DAZZLE BRITE - Cosmetics - Posner Laboratories Inc.
DAZZLE DESIGNER - Toys - Discovery Toys, Inc.
DAZZLE DOOZIE - Toys–automobiles - Mattel, Inc.
DAZZLE DOT - Mirrors - Hills Industries
DAZZLE DOTS - Trimmings–fabric - Meadowbrook Inventions Inc.
DAZZLE SPORTS - Yarn ☆ - Caron International Inc.
DAZZLEAIRE - Yarn ☆ - Caron International Inc.
DAZZLEAIRE BRIGHTS - Yarn ☆ - Caron International Inc.
DAZZLEDRAW - Computer software ☆ - Broderbund Software, Inc.
DAZZLER - Clarinets - G. Leblanc Corp.
DAZZLER - Decorations - A.J. Ganz Co. Inc.
DAZZLER - Dental products - Robert P. Stoll
DAZZLER - Deodorizers - Roberta's, Inc.
DAZZLER - Floor coverings–carpet and rugs ☆ - Lees Carpets
DAZZLER - Furniture ☆ - Bassett Furniture Industries, Inc.
DAZZLER - Lamps - Public Service Lamp Corp.
DAZZLER - Underwear and nightwear - Bestform Foundations, Inc.
DAZZLERS - Chimes ☆ - Carson Industries, Inc.
DAZZLERS - Christmas tree ornaments - Empire Manufacturing Co.
DAZZLERS - Floor coverings ☆ - Kentile Floors Inc.
DAZZLERS - Stationery - Diffraction Co.
DAZZLES I FEEL GOOD ABOUT ME - Apparel and accessories - Charles E. Alexander
DAZZLIN' DATE - Dolls - Mattel, Inc.
DAZZLIN' EGGS - Dyes–food - Spearhead Industries Inc.
DAZZLING - Floor coverings - Aladdin Mills, Inc.
DAZZLING - Floor coverings–carpet and rugs - Mohawk Industries Inc.
DAZZLING - Floor coverings–carpet and rugs ☆ - Calladium & Marglen
DAZZLING - Floor coverings–carpet and rugs ☆ - Columbus Mills, Inc.
DAZZLING CRYSTALRAMA - Jewelry - Norman T. Kanel Corp.
DAZZLING DAISY - Toys–stuffed - Dakin Inc.
DAZZLING DANCER - Dolls - Mattel, Inc.
DAZZLING DIAMONDS - Hair care products - Andre Fantasies Inc.
DAZZLING HAIR PETS - Toys - Tonka Corp.
DAZZLING METALLICS - Paints ☆ - DecoArt, Inc.
DAZZLIT - Cleaning preparations - Dazzlit, Inc.
DB - Apparel and accessories - Drummer Boy Sportswear, Inc.
DB - Guitar pickups, now out of production - Jan-Mar Industries
DB - Tools–power-driven - DB Control
DB-60 - Valves–industrial - Knorr Brake Holding Corp.
DB-ABLE - Computer software - Utility Graphics Consultants Corp.
DB-ARCHITECT - Computer software - DBE Software, Inc.
DB BUDDY - Security locks - Locky Corp.
DB/CATALOG - Computer software - Relay Technology, Inc.

DB/CENTER - Computer software - VM Systems Group Inc.
DB DATAFUND SYSTEMS INC. - Computer software - Annetta Freeman
DB DEMAND - Apparel and accessories - Drummer Boy Sportswear, Inc.
DB DIRECTOR - Antennas–satellite - Allen Telecom Group, Inc.
DB DOUBLE BARREL - Insecticides - Mallinckrodt Veterinary, Inc.
DB-EXAMINER - Computer software - DBE Software, Inc.
D.B. EXPRESS - Computer software - Computer Concepts Corp.
DB GRAPHICS - Computer software ☆ - Microrim Inc.
DB/LD - Hearing aids - Magnatone Hearing Aid Corp.
DB-LINK - Computer software - Softstream Technologies Inc.
DB METIC - Compressors - Dunham Bush, Inc.
DB MOBILE - Antennas - Alliance Telecommunications Corp.
DB-PRO STEEL - Chromatographs - Curtin Matheson Scientific, Inc.
DB PRODUCTS - Antennas - Allen Telecom Group, Inc.
DB/RESTORE - Computer software - Relay Technology, Inc.
D.B. SIGNER - Computer peripheral equipment - RAMM Information Technologies, Inc.
DB-SPELL - Computer software - Alpha Software Corp.
DBA - Computer software - Information Retrieval Companies Inc.
DBA WHITE GLOVE - Cleaning preparations–household - DBA Products Co.
DBAGENT - Computer software - Cheyenne Software, Inc.
D.B.AMF - Jewelry - Designs by AMF Ltd.
DBANYWHERE - Computer peripheral equipment - Symantec Corp.
DBAR - Windows–storm - Southwall Technologies Inc.
DBARTISAN - Computer software - Embarcadero Technologies, Inc.
DB.BAS - Computer software - SourceView Software International
DBCOMPLETE - Computer peripheral equipment - Visual Components, Inc.
DBE - Computer software - DBE Software, Inc.
DBE SOFTWARE DATA BASE EXCELLENCE - Computer software - DBE Software, Inc.
DBELLCO SPRING IRRIGATION - Agricultural machinery - DBellco, Inc.
D'BELLO - Footwear - D'Bello Shoe Corp.
DBENCH - Computer software - Stanford Management Group, Inc.
DBEST - Pharmaceutical preparations - Ameritek, Inc.
DBI FINGER PRINTER CMS - Computer peripheral equipment - Digital Biometrics, Inc.
DBK - Clay products - Dry Branch Kaolin Co.
DBL-LOC - Nuts and bolts - Lok-Mor, Inc.
DBM - Recording label - Drake Beam Morin, Inc.
DBM DRAKE BEAM MORIN - Audio tapes–blank - Drake Beam Morin, Inc.
DBM PREMIER SERVICE - Educational materials - Drake Beam Morin, Inc.
DBM PUBLISHING - Publisher's imprints - Drake Beam Morin, Inc.
DBMAKER - Computer software - Casemaker, Inc.
D'BRIT - Apparel and accessories - Iverson Technology Corp.
DBRUNNER - Computer software - Platinum Technology, Inc.
D.B.S. - Florists - Dorothy Biddle Service
DBS - Sporting goods - Dr. Bone Savers Inc.
DBS-3000 - Broadcasting equipment - Datron Transco Inc.
DBS-4000 - Broadcasting equipment - Datron Transco Inc.
DBS TO-GO - Cables–signal - Pro Brand International, Inc.
DBSA - Computer software - DBSA, Inc.
DBSI INFORMATION SYSTEMS - Computer software - DBSI Information Systems, Inc.
DBTEXT - Computer software - Inmagic, Inc.
DBVAULT - Computer software - At&T Corp.
DBWEB - Computer software - Aspect Software Engineering, Inc.
DBX - Audio equipment - Dod Electronics
DC - Colognes - Dick Clark Productions Inc.
DC - Jewelry - Diane Creations Inc.
D.C. - Paint rollers - Elder & Jenks, Inc.
DC - Trading cards and stamps - DC Comics
DC-200 - Electrical equipment - General Electric Co.
DC-300 - Electrical equipment - General Electric Co.
D.C. AMERICA - Garden equipment - Dragon Claw USA Inc.
D.C. CAZIMI - Apparel and accessories - Gabar Inc.
DC DECONSTRUCTION - Recording label - BMG Music
DC DURA CRAFT - Boats - Noah Corp.
DC EIGHT - Sporting goods - Diversified Products Corp.
DC HANDLERS - Drumsticks - Deven Chase Drumsticks
DC HEROES - Games ☆ - Mayfair Games, Inc.
DC NIKKOR - Cameras - Nikon Inc.
DC OVEN, THE - Cooking equipment–household - Pacific Cornetta, Inc.
DC PLUS - Golfing equipment - Knight Golf, Inc.
DC SCORE - Compact discs–prerecorded - Bright Gray Productions, Inc.
D.C. SHADOW - Ships–sailing vessels - Howmar Boat Corp.
DC SOUND - Recording label - DC Sound Enterprises

☆ = Now out of production

DC SOUND COUNTRY - Recording label - DC Sound Enterprises

DCA - Audio equipment - Oxmoor Corp.

DCA FREE - Perfumes ☆ - Tristar Corp.

D'CASA - Meat products–pork - Caserita Enterprises Inc.

DCC - Connectors for circuits and cables - Miraco, Inc.

DCC - Recording label - DCC Compact Classics, Inc.

DCC - Tools–power-driven - Crystallume, Inc.

DCC COMPACT CLASSICS - Recording label - DCC Compact Classics, Inc.

DCE - Hearing aids - G.N. Danavox Inc.

DCF - Binoculars - Pentax Corp.

DCH - Computer software - D.C. Heath & Co.

DCI - Computer hardware - Dynamic Circuits Inc.

DCI - Credit institutions - Dynamic Controls, Inc.

DCI - Golfing equipment - Acushnet Co.

DCI - Golfing equipment - Titleist & Foot-Joy Worldwide

DCI - Lamps - Leonard Pincus

DCI - Radio communications equipment - Differential Corrections, Inc.

DCI - Reflectors–optical - Dielectric Coating Industries

DCI - Video production - Warner Bros. Publications

D.C.I. INC. - Recording label - Black Diamond Records, Inc.

DCI KIDS - Apparel and accessories - Durlacher & Co., Inc.

DCI MUSIC VIDEO - Video games - DCI Music Video

D.C.I.F. (DRESS CASUAL, IT'S FRIDAY) - Shirts - Cluett, Peabody & Co.

D.C.L. - Recording label - Jazz Composer's Orchestra Association Inc.

DCM - Audio equipment - DCM Corp.

DCM - Electronic equipment - Corning Inc.

DCMS - Computer software - Vertex Industries Inc.

DCMS*PLUS - Computer hardware - Ace*Comm Corp.

DCP - Lasers - Lightwave Electronics Corp.

DC.PRO - Photographic equipment - HTN Photo, Inc.

DCR - Computer software - Microtek Lab Inc.

DCR - Vending machines - Lottery Enterprises, Inc.

DCR II - Electrical equipment - Fostec, Inc.

DCS - Computer software - Computer Concepts Corp.

DCS - Concrete repair products - Dynamic Color Solutions, Inc.

DCS - Floor cleaning equipment - Bonakemi USA, Inc.

D.C.S. - Health care products - Kay Pharmacal Co. Inc.

DCS 200 - Cameras - Eastman Kodak Co.

DCS - DIGITAL CODE SYSTEM - Microphones - Lectrosonics Inc.

DCS PLUS - Electrical equipment - Azonix Corp.

DCSERV - Computer hardware - Falk Integrated Technologies, Inc.

DCTRUE - Computer software - Dreams C.T., Ltd.

D.C.U. - Truck cabs - A.R.E. Inc.

DCV BIOLOGICS - Veterinary nutritional supplements - DCV Biologics

DCW - Computer storage devices–optical - Defense Mapping Agency

DCW DRESS CASUAL WEAR - Belts–apparel - Swank, Inc.

DCX - Computers–mainframe - Imo Industries Inc.

DCX-11 - Hair care products - Hair Institute

DD - Watches - Aaron Minkowitz

D.D. COOPER - Apparel–women's - Coopers, Inc.

DDA - Sound mixers - EVI Pro Audio Group

DDA-7 - Chemical preparations - W.R. Grace & Co.

DDC - Jewelry - Diagold Designs Corp.

DDC - Transmission equipment–motor vehicle - Daikin Drivetrain Components Corp.

DDD - Apparel and accessories - Designers Direct Ltd.

DDDOMINICK - Apparel–women's - D.D. Dominick

DDEC - Electronic equipment - Detroit Diesel Corp.

DDF - Fittings–cast iron - Ward Manufacturing Inc.

DDF DOCTOR'S DERMATOLOGIC FORMULA - Skin care products - HDS Cosmetic Lab, Inc.

DDG - Jewelry - Dynasty Diamond & Gold Inc.

D.D.G. S. - Veterinary pharmaceutical preparations - K.C. Pharmacal Inc.

DDH - Balls–golf - Dunlop Maxfli Sports Corp.

DDH ACCURACY - Balls–golf - Dunlop Slazenger Corp.

DDH DISTANCE - Balls–golf - Dunlop Slazenger Corp.

DDH II - Golfing equipment - Dunlop Maxfli Sports Corp.

DDH III - Golfing equipment - Dunlop Maxfli Sports Corp.

D.D.I. - Garment hangers - Different Dimensions Inc.

DDI - Infant product - Dan-Dee International Ltd.

DDI - Telephone apparatus - Metro-Tel Corp.

DDM - Computer hardware - Perceptron, Inc.

DDM - Computer software - Magnetek Inc.

DDP - Home-health-care products - Infomed

DDS - Pharmaceutical preparations - UAS Laboratories

DDS - Skin care products ☆ - Hess Hair Milk Laboratories Inc.

DDS POWERTRAK - Computer software - DDS, Inc.

DDSI - Computer software - Softmed Systems, Inc.

DDT - Boats–motor ☆ - Seajay Boats Inc.

DDT/400 - Computer software - Systems & Programming Solutions, Inc.

DDTS - Computer software - Pure Acquisition Corp.

DDU - Apparel and accessories - Dunkin' Donuts of America Inc.

DDV - Valves - HR Textron Inc.

DDV - Varnishes - Hobsco Inc.

DDV - Varnishes - Wm. K. Walthers Inc.

DE - Hearing aids - Magnatone Hearing Aid Corp.

DE-AQUA LUBE - Lubricants ☆ - Hertron International Inc.

DE-BAC-N-KLEEN - Disinfectants ☆ - Uncle Sam Chemical Co., Inc.

DE BELLAY - Cheese - Besnier USA, Inc.

DE BETUWE - Juices - Holland-American Importing Co. Inc.

DE BLEM - Chemicals–photographic - Max Concepts Inc.

DE BOULLE - Watches - Deboulle Diamond & Jewelry, Inc.

DE BRAYE - Aprons - Michelle De Braye Clothing Co.

DE BUG-SHIELD - Motor vehicle parts and accessories - Deflecta-Shield

DE-CAL - Pharmaceutical preparations ☆ - Vortech Pharmaceuticals

DE-CAT-LON - Playing cards ☆ - Golden Cat Corp.

DE CECCO - Tomato pastes and sauces - De Cecco Inc.

DE CHAUNAC - Wines - Meredyth Vineyard

DE CHOIX - Food products - De Choix Specialty Foods Co.

DE CLEVES - Containers - Bottlemate Inc.

DE CLEVES - Cosmetics - De Cleves Corp.

DE COIR - Mats - USCOA International Corp.

DE-COLOR B - Hair care products - Framesi USA/Roffler Industries Inc.

DE COSTA'S OLD NEW ENGLAND - Sausages - Joseph Decosta Inc.

DE CRISTOFARO - Furniture - Lexington Furniture Industries, Inc.

D.E. DIGESTIVE ENZYME - Vitamins and nutritional supplements - Kroeger Herb Products Co. Inc.

DE FELICE - Tools–machine - De Felice Engineering Inc.

DE-FEND - Disinfectants - Fendall Co.

DE-FENDERS - Boots - Safety Center Inc.

DE FLEA - Pet products - Mr. Mutt Pet Products Inc.

DE-FOAM - Cleaning preparations–carpet and rug - Sanitek Products Inc.

DE-FOG - Hardware - Travaco Laboratories Inc.

DE FRANCO - Nuts–salted, roasted, cooked, or canned - D. DeFranco and Sons Inc.

DE FUSSIGNY - Beverages–alcohol - Jim Beam Brands Co.

DE GIORGI - Vegetables–canned ☆ - Dean & Deluca Inc.

DE-GROOVIE - Lip balms - Benefit Cosmetics

DE-HESIVE - Health care products - Cramer Products Inc.

DE-HUMMER - Fans–electric - Power Controls Corp.

DE ICE - Chemical preparations - Miller Purcell Co.

DE-ICER - Hardware - Klee Chemical Coatings

DE-INC - Cleaning preparations - Bic Corp.

DE JAY - Carts - Dejay Corp.

DE KENT - Lubricants - Pep Boys Manny, Moe & Jack

DE-KLOG - Plumbing fixtures–enameled - G & G Chemical Manufacturing Corp.

DE KONINCK - Beverages–malt - Victor Sales & Marketing

DE-KOTE - Paint removers ☆ - Wood Kote Products, Inc.

DE KROON - Hair care products - De Kroon, Inc.

DE KUYPER - Beverages–alcohol - Jim Beam Brands Co.

DE LA CASA - Cheese - Cacique Cheese Co.

DE LA CASA - Corn–flour or meal - Cacique, Inc.

DE LA COASTA - Wines - Louis Glunz Inc.

DE LA CUISINE - Cooking equipment–household ☆ - Old Dutch International Ltd.

DE LA FONTAINE - Cheese - Besnier USA, Inc.

DE LA HAYE - Cooking equipment–household ☆ - Old Dutch International Ltd.

DE LA RENTIS - Footwear - De La Rentis Imports Inc.

DE LA ROSE - Apparel–women's - Lady Ester Lingerie Corp.

DE LA TERRE - Floor coverings - Mannington Resilient Floors

DE LAROCHE - Liquors - European Beverage Co., Inc.

DE LAURENTI - Food products - De Laurenti Specialty Food Market

DE LEON - Juice extracting devices - Angel Life Corp.

DE LILLO - Jewelry - William O. DeLillo and Robert F. Clark Partnership

DE-LISH-US - Food products - Dejean Packing Co.

DE-LISH-US - Snack foods - Delicious Popcorn & Distributors Co. Inc.

DE-LITE - Furniture - Globe Business Furniture, Inc.

DE-LITE - Perfumes ☆ - Candle-Lite Co.

DE-LITE - Recording label - Polygram Records, Inc.

DE LITE - Relishes - Korbro Oil Corp.

DE-LITES - Candy ☆ - Sathers Inc.

☆ = Now out of production

DE LOACH VINEYARDS - Wines - De Loach Vineyards Inc.
DE LOACH'S - Water–bottled or canned - De Loach's Water Inc.
DE LOUX - Crocheted and knitted items - Jacques De Loux Inc.
DE LUXE - Ammunition - Fiocchi of America, Inc.
DE LUXE - Cigars - Gesty Trading & Manufacturing Corp.
DE LUXE - Enamels - Diamond/Kuhn Paint Co.
DE LUXE KWIK DRY - Towels - Northwestern Wiping Cloth Co.
DE LUZE CHATEAU - Wines - Remy Martin Amerique Inc.
DE LYS - Apparel–women's ✰ - Barbizon Lingerie
DE MAISON - Furniture - Singer Furniture Co.
DE MARNE - Mustard - Holland-American Importing Co. Inc.
DE MARTINO - CHILE - Wines ✰ - Winesellers Ltd.
DE MARZI - Oboes ✰ - John M. Connolly & Co. Inc.
DE-MAT SPRAY - Pet products - Kim Laube & Co. Inc.
DE MEDICI - Wallpaper - Pickhardt & Siebert USA Inc.
DE-MOIST - Chemical dehumidifier ✰ - Coughlan Products Corp.
DE MOOR - Wines - De Moor Winery
DE-MOTH-IT - Paints - Morris Paint & Varnish Co.
DE NIMES - Jeans - MGRR, Inc.
DE OSU - Footwear - De Osu Inc.
DE PEE-S - Racks - De Pee-s Ltd.
DE PORCELEYNE FLES - Decorative accessories - Royal Delft
DE POURSAC - Liquors - European Beverage Co., Inc.
DE PUFF - Cosmetics - Circle of Beauty, Inc.
DE-RUST - Rust removers ✰ - Elcal Enterprises Ltd.
DE RUYTER - Cakes - Holland-American Importing Co. Inc.
DE-SIGN-IT - Hobby kits ✰ - Bemiss-Jason Corp.
DE-SOIL - Detergents - Uncle Sam Chemical Co., Inc.
DE-SOLV-IT - Cleaning preparations - Orange-Sol Inc.
DE SOLVO - Automotive parts and accessories ✰ - Stoner Inc.
DE SOTA - Plumbing fixtures–metal ✰ - Orgill Brothers and Co.
DE SOTO - Candy - De Soto Confectionary
DE SOTO - Food products - Armour Dairy Co.
DE SOTO - Jewelry - Jacoby-Bender Inc.
DE SOTO - Motor vehicles–automobiles ✰ - Chrysler Corp. (De Soto Div.)
DE-STAIN - Stain removers - Marinize Products Corp.
DE-STAT 3 - Health care products - Sherman Pharmaceuticals, Inc.
DE-STAT 4 - Health care products - Sherman Pharmaceuticals, Inc.
DE-STINK-TIVE-PET - Pet products - Pets Smellfree Inc.
DE TAL - Pharmaceutical preparations - Deleon Laboratories Inc.
DE THERA - Pharmaceutical preparations - Deleon Laboratories Inc.
DE-TICKER - Medical apparatus - MACOR Industries, Inc.
DE TOLOMEI - Cookies ✰ - Liberty Richter Inc.
DE TOMASO GUARA - Motor vehicles–automobiles - De Tomaso Industries Inc.
DE-TONE - Plugs–ear ✰ - Sellstrom Manufacturing Co.
DE-TOX - Water treating compounds - Silco Pet Products
DE VENAGE - Wines ✰ - Palm Bay Imports, Inc.
DE VENOGE - Chocolate candy ✰ - Liberty Richter Inc.
DE VILLE - Bicycles - Columbia Manufacturing Inc.
DE VILLE - Furniture - National Service Industries, Inc.
DE VILLE - Lamps–ultraviolet ✰ - Atlantic Ultraviolet Corp.
DE VILLE - Lighters - Colibri Inc.
DE VILLE - Musical instruments ✰ - Selmer Co. Inc.
DE VILLIER - Trumpets - Castiglione Accordion
DE-VO-KO - Paints - Devoe & Raynolds Co.
DE-VO-PRO - Paints - Devoe & Raynolds Co.
DE-VO-TEX - Paints - Devoe & Raynolds Co.
DE-WAX - Wax remover - Continental Chemical Corp.
DE-WAX-ER - Wax removers - Uncle Sam Chemical Co., Inc.
DE WINT - Artists' materials ✰ - Andrews/Nelson/Whitehead
DE WITT'S - Analgesics - Church and Dwight Co. Inc.
DE WITT'S MAXI STRENGTH - Analgesics - Church and Dwight Co. Inc.
DE WRISTER - Golfing equipment ✰ - John Rouzee Green Co., Inc.
DE YARMAN - Shampoos - De Yarman Medical Group
DE ZAAN - Food products - ADM Cocoa
DEA - Food products ✰ - Europa Foods Ltd.
DEA - Housewares ✰ - Berarducci Bros. Manufacturing Co. Inc.
DEACON, THE - Golfing equipment ✰ - Arnold Palmer Golf Co.
DEAD AIM - Insecticide - American Home Products Corp.
DEAD AND GONE, TWICE AS LONG - Insecticides - United Industries Corp.
DEAD BOLT - Fishing rods - Silstar Corp. of America, Inc.
DEAD CENTER - Golfing equipment - Titleist & Foot-Joy Worldwide
DEAD COW - Beef jerky - Caldaho Bros. Inc.
DEAD END - Traps–animal - Atlantic Paste & Glue Co., Inc.
DEAD-EYE DUCK - Toys - Continuity Graphic Associates, Inc.

DEAD HEAT SCRAMBLE - Computer game - Electro Brain Corp.
DEAD-KOTE - Varnishes - True-Tagg Paint Co.
DEAD-N-GONE VEGETATION KILLER - Pesticides–household - Bonide Products, Inc.
DEAD POOL - Books–comic - Marvel Entertainment Group, Inc.
DEAD ROCKERS SOCIETY - Apparel and accessories - Inmemoribilia, Inc.
DEAD SEA - Apparel and accessories - Joseph William Kniseley
DEAD SEA - Bath salts - Lotus Brands Inc.
DEAD STOP - Golfing equipment - Golfsmith International Inc.
DEAD TREAD - Footwear - Landmark, U.S.A., Ltd.
DEAD ZONEELIMINATOR - Telephone accessories - Fiber Plus International
DEADBALL, THE - Sporting goods - Geoffrey L. O'Connor
DEADBOLT, THE - Hardware - National Lock Hardware
DEADEYE - Video production - Konami (America) Inc.
DEADHEAD - Tools–hand-operated - Estwing Manufacturing Co.
DEADHOOLIE - Recording label - Jazz Composer's Orchestra Association Inc.
DEADLINE - Computer software - Atex Publishing Systems Corp.
DEADLINE - Computer software ✰ - Activision, Inc.
DEADLINE - Fishing lures - Pace National Corp.
DEADLINE - Pencils ✰ - Staedtler, Inc.
DEADLY - Perfumes - Saxony Products Inc.
DEADLY NIGHTSHADE - Cosmetics - Tish & Snooky's N.Y.C. Inc.
DEADLY QUIET - Archery equipment - Saunders Archery Co.
DEADRINGER - Drums–musical instruments - Silver St. Inc.
DEADSHOT - Sporting goods ✰ - Bear Archery Inc.
DEADWHITE - Paints - Prince Agri Products, Inc.
DEADWOOD - Toys - Bandai America Inc.
DEADWOOD RED - Beverages–malt - Sodak Distributing Co.
DEAF SMITH - Food products - Arrowhead Mills, Inc.
DEAL A MILLION - Games - Deal a Million
DEAL APPEAL - Games - Casino Data Systems
DEAL ME IN - Paper–book - Career Systems, Inc.
DEAL WITH IT - Apparel and accessories - Michael Keith Mewborn
DEALBUILDER - Computer software - Arnold Dublin & Co.
DEALER PRIDE - Machinery - S.N.M. Manufacturing, Inc.
DEALERMASTER - Computer software - Livestock Marketing Services Corp.
DEALERS CHOICE - Ashtrays–glass - Gessner Products Co. Inc.
DEALER'S CHOICE - Floor coverings–carpet and rugs - Galaxy Carpet Mills Inc.
DEALER'S CHOICE - Games ✰ - S.J. Miller Co.
DEALERS CHOICE - Games ✰ - Parker Brothers
DEALER'S CHOICE - Motor vehicle parts and accessories - St. Cloud Industrial Products, Inc.
DEALERS CHOICE - Wines - Foxwood Wine Cellars
DEALERS MANUFACTURING - Motors–automotive - Dealers Manufacturing Co.
DEALER'S PRIDE - Dog food - Ralston Purina Co.
DEAL'S - Seafood products–fresh or frozen - Deals Seafood Co. Inc.
DEAN - Food products ✰ - Empire Kosher Poultry Inc.
DEAN - Footwear–athletic - Vans, Inc.
DEAN - Guitars - Dean Guitars
DEAN - Musical instruments - Tropical Music and Pro Audio
DEAN - Ophthalmic goods ✰ - Rozin Optical Export Corp.
DEAN - Prophylactics - Dean Rubber Co.
DEAN - Tires - Dean Tire & Rubber Co.
DEAN & DELUCA - Food products - Dean & Deluca Inc.
DEAN FAT FREE - Ice cream - Dean Foods Co.
DEAN FLORENTINO - Coffee - Pro-Team International, Inc.
DEAN FOODS ULTRA - Dairy products - Dean Foods Co.
DEAN FOODS ULTRA ULTRA-PASTEURIZED - Dairy products - Dean Foods Co.
DEAN JACOB'S - Seasonings - Xcell International Corp.
DEAN JACOB'S 4 B-B-Q - Seasonings - Xcell International Corp.
DEAN LIGHT - Ice cream - Dean Foods Co.
DEAN MARKLEY - Amplifiers–musical instrument - Kaman Music Corp.
DEAN MARKLEY - Amplifiers–musical instrument - Dean Markley Strings, Inc.
DEAN MARKLEY BLUE STEEL - Guitars - Dean Markley Strings, Inc.
DEAN PREMIUM - Ice cream - Dean Foods Co.
DEAN RAINSTAR - Tires - Dean Tire & Rubber Co.
DEAN SANTNER - Furniture - Dean Santner Design
DEAN UTILITIES - Computer software - SourceView Software International
DEANA - House furnishings - Dan River Inc.
DEANO - Sporting goods ✰ - Powell Skateboards
DEANO'S ORIGINAL GOURMET BRAND - Seasonings - Deano's, Inc.
DEAN'S - Converters–electric - Flavorite Laboratories Inc.
DEAN'S - Cream - Ryan Foods Co.

DEAN'S - Dairy products - Dean Foods Co.
DEAN'S - Food products - Dean Distributors, Inc.
DEAN'S - Food products - Willman Cookie & Nut Co.
DEANS - Insecticides - SSM Corp.
DEAN'S - Toys - Brittoys
DEANS EASY - Dairy products - Ryan Foods Co.
DEANS LIST - Pencils ☆ - Panda Inc.
DEAN'S MC CADAM - Cheese - Dean Foods Co.
DEAN'S SOUR DELITE - Dairy products - Dean Foods Co.
DEANSGATE - Apparel and accessories - Deansgate Inc.
DEAPRIL-ST - Pharmaceutical preparations - Bristol-Myers Squibb Co.
DEAR - Jewelry - Something Old, Something New, Inc.
DEAR & DARE - Apparel and accessories - China Trade & Research, Inc.
DEAR DIANE - Jewelry ☆ - Key Novelty Manufacturing Co.
DEAR DIARY - Computer software - Interactive Products, Inc.
DEAR DIARY - Electronic equipment - Tiger Electronics, Inc.
DEAR GOD KIDS - Desk sets - Samuel Ward Manufacturing Inc.
DEAR GOD KIDS - Giftware ☆ - Treasure Masters
DEAR HEARTS - Candy ☆ - Beacon Sweets, Inc.
DEAR HUNTER - Outerwear - Blue Wing, Inc.
DEAR JOHNS - Hobby kits - JCA, Inc.
DEAR LADY - Fruits and vegetables - Snokist Growers
DEAR LITTLE ME - Toys - Giordano Art, Ltd.
DEAR MOM - Apparel—women's - Jamknits Associates, Ltd.
DEAR SANTA - Christmas tree ornaments - Giordano Art, Ltd.
DEARBORN - Brass products - Dearborn Brass Co.
DEARBORN - Desks - Steelcase Inc.
DEARBORN - Floor coverings - Tarkett, Inc.
DEARBORN - Floor coverings—carpet and rugs - Atlas Carpet Mills Inc.
DEARBORN - Heaters—gas ☆ - Martin Industries, Inc.
DEARBORN - Heaters—space - Dearborn Stove
DEARBORN - Recording label - MSK Productions Inc.
DEARBORN - Vans—conversion - Coachmen Industries, Inc.
DEARBORN BRASS - Plumbing products - Moen Inc.
DEARBORN MONEYMAKER KIT - Computer software - Dearborn Financial Publishing, Inc.
DEARBORN SAUSAGE - Food products - Dearborn Sausage Co.
DEARDORFF - Cameras - L.F. Deardorff & Sons Inc.
DEARFOAMS - Footwear - R.G. Barry Corp.
DEARFOAMS - Slippers - Dearfoams
DEARLY - Toys - Playskool, Inc.
DEARMAN - Hand tools - Cogsdill Tool Products, Inc.
DEARMOND - Musical instrument accessories ☆ - Tosh Electronics Corp.
DEATH - Recording label - Metal Blade Records Inc.
DEATH BY CHOCOLATE - Desserts - Stache Foods
DEATH DICE - Novelty items - Flying Buffalo Inc.
DEATH FORETOLD - Puzzles - Hasbro, Inc.
DEATH GRIP - Tires—bicycles - Klein Bicycle Corp.
DEATH RAIN - Spices and extracts - Gardner Resources, Inc.
DEATH RAY - Lighting equipment—automotive - Paul W. Skjerven
DEATH STAR - Toys—airplanes ☆ - Kenner Products
DEATH STAR BATTLE - Video games - Lucasfilm Ltd.
DEATH STICK - Apparel and accessories - Paul E. Stevenson, Jr.
DEATH STICK - Golf clubs - Paul E. Stevenson, Jr.
DEATH TAN - Sunblocks - Steven James Lynn
DEATH TRAP - Games ☆ - Avalon Hill Game Co.
DEATHBLOW - Printed material - Brandon Choi
DEATHTRAP - Trading cards and stamps - Aegis Entertainment, Inc.
DEAUVILLE - Apparel trimmings - Minnesota Knitting Mills Inc.
DEAUVILLE - Boats—pontoons ☆ - Riviera Cruiser
DEAUVILLE - Cabinets - Nutone Inc.
DEAUVILLE - Floor coverings - Mannington Resilient Floors
DEAUVILLE - Furniture - Lyon-Shaw Inc.
DEAUVILLE - Luggage ☆ - Amerock Corp.
DEAUVILLE - Vases - Durand International
DEAUVILLE - Whirlpools - Lasco Products Group
DEAVANA - Pens - Stonegate International Corp.
DEB - Hobby kits ☆ - Barker Enterprises Inc.
DEB & KENS - Cookies - HSF Enterprises Inc.
DEB DON - Slippers - C. & M. Srery Co. Inc.
DEB DUDS - Apparel—children's - Kid Duds
DEB-TEEN - Dolls ☆ - Uneeda Doll Co., Inc.
DEBACTEROL - Pharmaceutical preparations - Northern Research Laboratories Inc.
DEBAGGER - Machinery - First Brands Properties Inc.
DEBAGIT - Tools - Superior Tech, Inc.

DEBBIE - Bags—paper - Interstate Packaging Corp.
DEBBIE - Bicycles - Schwinn Cycling & Fitness Inc.
DEBBIE - Detergents - Sinclair Manufacturing Co.
DEBBIE - Dolls - Uneeda Doll Co., Inc.
DEBBIE - Footwear ☆ - Wolverine World Wide, Inc.
DEBBIE - Garter belts ☆ - Fancee Free Manufacturing Co.
DEBBIE - Ribbons - Princess Ribbon Corp.
DEBBIE - Shoes—athletic ☆ - Coast Shoes Inc.
DEBBIE MUMM - Publisher's imprints - Mumm's the Word, Inc.
DEBBIES - Children's toys - Coloron Industries
DEBBIE'S DESIGN - Apparel and accessories - Mike Stewart Inc.
DEBBY - Recording label - Cha-Cha Records
DEBBY DEAR - Dolls ☆ - Fun World Inc.
DEBBY STEVENS - Jewelry - DS Imports Inc.
DEBCO - Food products - Debruyn Co.
DEBDEN - Publisher's imprints - Phoenix Stationery Products, Inc.
DEBEER - Balls—baseball - J. De Beer & Son Inc.
DEBENEDETTO FARMS - Fruits and vegetables - Debenedetto Farms, Inc.
DEBENTURE - Floor coverings—carpet and rugs - Eagle Carpets Inc.
DEBETTE - Apparel—women's - Wacoal America Inc.
DEBEVC VINEYARDS - Wines - Chalet Debonne Vineyards Inc.
DEBEZT - Electronic equipment - Malaysia Trading Inc.
DEBIT PEN - Pens - Distributel, Inc.
DEBLOOMS - Flowers, plants, and seeds - Turf-Seed, Inc.
DEBOLES - Food products - Deboles Nutritional Foods Inc.
DEBONAIR - Aircraft—airplanes ☆ - Beech Aircraft Corp.
DEBONAIR - Children's shoes - Interco Inc.
DEBONAIR - Cigars ☆ - Havatampa Inc.
DEBONAIR - Dishes—china ☆ - Pickard Inc.
DEBONAIR - Floor coverings—carpet and rugs - Dan River Inc.
DEBONAIR - Floor coverings—carpet and rugs ☆ - Regal Rugs Inc.
DEBONAIR - Glass—leaded - Seneca Glass Co.
DEBONAIR - Pencils - Reliance Pen & Pencil Corp.
DEBONAIR - Pens—fountain - Universal Fountain Pen & Pencil Co.
DEBONAIR - Wallpaper - Marburg Wallcoverings Inc.
DEBONAIRE - Dinnerware—glass - Kenro Inc.
DEBONAIRE - Floor coverings—carpet and rugs ☆ - Columbus Mills, Inc.
DEBONAIRE - Rings—jewelry ☆ - Artcarved Inc.
DEBONETTE - Pens—fountain ☆ - Universal Fountain Pen & Pencil Co.
DEBOR'AH - Apparel and accessories - Debor'ah Designs Inc.
DEBORAH - Floor coverings—carpet and rugs ☆ - Regal Rugs Inc.
DEBORAH AMANI - Belts - Yamani of America
DEBOR'AH BOUTIQUE - Apparel—women's - Debor'ah Designs Inc.
DEBOR'AH COLLECTION - Apparel—women's - Debor'ah Designs Inc.
DEBORAH ROBERTS - Jewelry - Deborah Roberts
DEBORAH SILVER - Wallcoverings - Beverly Stevens Ltd.
DEBOR'AH SPORT - Apparel—women's ☆ - Debor'ah Designs Inc.
DEBRA - Glassware—household ☆ - Lotus Glass Co.
DEBRA LUBELL - Apparel and accessories - Apparel Group, Ltd.
DEBRA LYNN - Cosmetics - Burmax Co. Inc.
DEBRA LYNNE - Handbags ☆ - Mutterperl Group Inc.
DEBRA'S PREMIUM - Granola bars - Natural Gourmet
DEBRA'S SPECIAL - Cookies - Mrs. Fields Development Corp.
DEBRIS - Apparel and accessories - Joshua J. Krause
DEBROX - Pharmaceutical preparations - Marion Merrell Dow
DEBROX - Pharmaceutical preparations - SmithKline Beecham Consumer Healthcare
DEBRY-PEXTON - Frames—picture - Debry-Pexton Inc.
DEBS - Shoes ☆ - World Import Co. Inc.
DEBT BREAKER - Computer software - Von Services Corp.
DEBT FREE - Jewelry - Steve Hale Evangelistic Association
DEBTDESK - Computer software - Commscan, Inc.
DEBUGG - Toys - Mattel, Inc.
DEBURR MASTER - Machine parts - Reynolds Tool Products, Inc.
DEBUS - Skin care products - SBS Products, Inc.
DEBUT - Coffee - Melitta North America Inc.
DEBUT - Fabrics—tapestry - Coloroll Inc.
DEBUT - Flatware - Kirk Stieff Co.
DEBUT - Floor coverings - Bruce Hardwood Floors
DEBUT - Floor coverings—carpet and rugs - Regal Rugs Inc.
DEBUT - Floor coverings—carpet and rugs ☆ - Gulistan Carpet Inc.
DEBUT - Floor coverings—carpet and rugs ☆ - Mannington Carpets, Inc.
DEBUT - Flooring—hardwood - Triangle Pacific Corp. (Cabinet Division)
DEBUT - Herbicides - E.I. Dupont de Nemours and Co.
DEBUT - Organs—musical instrument - Lowrey Organ Co.
DEBUT - Phonographs - Fantasy Inc.

☆ = Now out of production

DEBUT - Pottery - Duncan Enterprises
DEBUT - Recording label - Debut Records
DEBUT - Sanitary napkins - Amway Corp.
DEBUT - Strollers–baby ✩ - Combi International Corp.
DEBUT - Tables–wood - La-Z-Boy Chair Co.
DEBUT - Tableware–china - Lenox, Inc.
DEBUT - Yarn ✩ - JCA, Inc.
DEBUT COLLECTION, THE - Cooking equipment–household ✩ - Mirro Corp.
DEBUT ELEGANCE - Fabrics–tapestry - Coloroll Inc.
DEBUT GOLD - Glassware–household - Lenox, Inc.
DEBUT MUSIC SYSTEMS - Computer peripheral equipment - Baldwin Piano & Organ Co.
DEBUT REFLECTIONS - Fabrics–tapestry - Coloroll Inc.
DEBUTANTE - Bedding–linen - Dan River Inc.
DEBUTANTE - Bicycles - Roadmaster Corp.
DEBUTANTE - Christmas tree ornaments - Cracker Box Inc.
DEBUTANTE - Floor coverings–carpet and rugs ✩ - Callaway Carpets
DEBUTANTE - Floor coverings–carpet and rugs ✩ - Karastan-Bigelow Inc.
DEBUTANTE - Furniture - A. Brandt Co. Inc.
DEBUTANTE - Glassware–household ✩ - Wallace International Silversmiths, Inc.
DEBUTANTE - Gloves–rubber - Duracraft Corp.
DEBUTANTE - Watches - Bulova Corp.
DEBUTANTE LORRAINE - Fireplace inserts - American Road Equipment Co.
DEBUTEEN - Apparel–women's - Wacoal America Inc.
DEC-A-CAKE - Cakes - Durkee French Foods
DEC-A-PAK - Novelty items - Beistle Co.
DEC ART - Bathroom accessories - Dec-Art Co.
DEC-EAR-ATIONS - Jewelry–costume - Product Designs International Inc.
DEC-GROW - Flower pots–plastic - Nursery Supplies, Inc.
DEC-KING - Hardware - Illinois Tool Works Inc.
DEC KING - Waterproof coatings - Advanced Waterproof Coatings
DEC-KOR - Brackets - Dec-Kor, Inc.
DEC-N-ICE - Frosting - J.W. Allen & Co.
DEC-O-TRIM - Trimmings–fabric ✩ - Decorative Aides Co. Inc.
DEC-ONS - Cakes - Lucks Co.
DECA - Amplifiers ✩ - Peavey Electronics Corp.
DECA - Jewelry - Distributive Education Clubs of America, Inc.
DECA - Jewelry - Distributive Education Clubs of America, Inc.
DECA - Tiles–ceramic - Dal-Tile Corp.
DECA-BON - Pharmaceutical preparations - Barrows Pharmacal Inc.
DECA-DURABOLIN - Pharmaceutical preparations - Organon Inc.
DECA-GEN - Vitamins and nutritional supplements - Gourmet Mushrooms Inc.
DECA HIGHLITER - Felt-tip markers ✩ - Itoya of America, Ltd.
DECA-VI-SOL - Vitamins and nutritional supplements ✩ - Bristol-Myers Squibb Co.
DECA-VITE - Vitamins and nutritional supplements - Nutritional Research Associates Inc.
DECAB - Vitamins and nutritional supplements ✩ - U.S. Ethicals Inc.
DECABEAM - Lighting equipment - Dole Associates, Inc.
DECADE - Braces–orthopedic - Chase Ergonomics Inc.
DECADE - Cigarettes ✩ - Liggett Group Inc.
DECADE - Doors–wood - Raynor Manufacturing Co.
DECADE - Floor coverings–carpet and rugs - Mohawk Industries Inc.
DECADE - Furniture - Haworth, Inc.
DECADE - Paints - Standard Brands Paint Co.
DECADE - Photographic equipment - Lektra Service Corp.
DECADE - Vacuum cleaners and accessories - The Hoover Co.
DECADE - Vitamins and nutritional supplements - Nature's Best Inc.
DECADE 80 - Vacuum cleaners and accessories ✩ - The Hoover Co.
DECADE 90 - Cleaning preparations - Minuteman International, Inc.
DECADE 800 - Vacuum cleaners and accessories - The Hoover Co.
DECADE SHOWCASE - Doors–metal - Raynor Manufacturing Co.
DECADENCE - Perfumes - Parfums International Ltd.
DECADENCE - Wallpaper - Bayview Wallcoverings
DECADENT TEMPTATIONS - Ice cream - Alta-Dena Certified Dairy, Inc.
DECADERM - Pharmaceutical preparations - Merck & Co., Inc. (Merck Research Laboratories)
DECADES - Automotive–audio equipment - Delco Electronics Corp.
DECADES - Vitamins and nutritional supplements - Nature's Best Inc.
DECADRON - Pharmaceutical preparations - Merck & Co., Inc. (Merck Research Laboratories)
DECAF GAZEBO BLEND - Coffee - Starbucks Corp.
DECAJECT - Pharmaceutical preparations - Merz Inc.
DECAL-EASE - Automotive parts and accessories - Cal-West Automotive Products

DECAL-IT - Decals and transfers - Plaid Enterprises, Inc.
DECALC - Computer software - Digital Equipment Corp.
DECALENDAR - Calendars - People Systems Inc.
DECALON - Decals and transfers ✩ - Sangray Corp.
DECAPAVE - Concrete repair products - W.R. Grace & Co.
DECAPRYN - Antihistamine preparations ✩ - Marion Merrell Dow
DECAREX - Pharmaceutical preparations - C.S. Ruckstuhl Co. Inc.
DECARLITE - Furniture ✩ - Simon Corp.
DECARLO - Vases - Vincent Lippe Co.
DECASHIELD - Lighting equipment - General Electric Co.
DECASPRAY - Pharmaceutical preparations - Merck & Co., Inc. (Merck Research Laboratories)
DECATHLON - Bicycles ✩ - Roadmaster Corp.
DECATHLON - Cookware - Farberware Inc.
DECATHLON - Fabrics - Dan River Inc.
DECATHLON - Floor coverings - Congoleum Corp.
DECATHLON - Floor coverings–carpet and rugs - Wunda Weve Carpet Co.
DECATHLON - Flowers, plants, and seeds - Michael-Leonard Inc.
DECATHLON - Games - Avalon Hill Game Co.
DECATHLON - Health care products - D'Franssia Corp.
DECATHLON - Jewelry ✩ - Hirsch Speidel Inc.
DECATHLON - Skates–roller - National Sporting Goods Corp.
DECATHLON - Zippers - YKK USA Inc.
DECATHLON ARENA - Floor coverings - American Floor Products Co. Inc.
DECATUR - Cigarette lighters - Blue Ridge Mountain Woodcrafts
DECATUR - Toys–musical - Decatur Instruments Co.
DECAYS-NOT - Wood preservative ✩ - Coopers Creek Chemical Corp.
DECCA - Recording label - MCA Records, Inc.
DECCA - Recording label - MCA Universal Studios
DECCA LONDON - Stereo equipment - Audiophile Imports
DECCAPINOL - Skin care products ✩ - Warner-Lambert Co.
DECCAWALL - Wallpaper ✩ - Design Materials, Inc.
DECCO-CORK - Corks - Deccofelt Corp.
DECCO-FELT - Fabrics–felt - Deccofelt Corp.
DECCO-FOAM - Foam rubber - Deccofelt Corp.
DECCO-PUTTY - Putties ✩ - Deccofelt Corp.
DECCO-SPONGE - Sponges - Deccofelt Corp.
DECDECISION - Computer software - Digital Equipment Corp.
DECECCO - Pasta ✩ - Borden, Inc.
DECECCO - Pasta ✩ - Fancy Foods of Virginia Inc.
DECECCO - Tomato pastes and sauces - Williamsburg Canning Co.
DECEIVE - Skin care products - Ray Hayes Inc.
DECELERATOR - Firearms, accessories, and parts - Pachmayr Ltd.
DECEMBER 25TH - Giftware - Country Christmas, Inc.
DECENT EXPOSURE - Apparel and accessories - Decent Exposure
DECEPTION AT DASA - Games ✩ - Mayfair Games, Inc.
DECEPTOR - Computer software ✩ - Accolade Inc.
DECGRAPH - Computer software - Digital Equipment Corp.
DECHAUNAC - Wines - Ziem Vineyards
DECHLOR-EASE - Chemical preparations - Mydor Industries Inc.
DECHOLIN - Chemical preparations ✩ - Miles Inc.
DECI-MATE - Pesticides–household - El Mar Corp.
DECI-PACK - Nuts and bolts - Elco Industries, Inc.
DECIDEDLY DELECTABLE - Christmas tree ornaments - Cracker Box Inc.
DECIMAL DISCOVERY - Computer software - SRA/McGraw-Hill (Div. of The McGraw-Hill Companies)
DECIMAL DUNGEON - Computer software - Unicorn Software
DECIMATOR, THE - Toys - Saban Entertainment, Inc.
DECIPHER III - Puzzles ✩ - Decipher Inc.
DECISION ADVISOR - Computer software - IDS Partners
DECISION DATA - Computers–personal - IIS, Inc.
DECISION DESIGN - Computer peripheral equipment - Crg Group, Inc.
DECISION DICE - Desk sets ✩ - Postamatic Co. Inc.
DECISION DRIVERS - Computer software - Decision Drivers, Inc.
DECISION-MAKER 3 - Controls–heating systems - Kohler Co.
DECISION MONITOR - Controls–heating systems - Kohler Co.
DECISION PERT - Computer software ✩ - Everex Systems, Inc.
DECISION POINT - Computer software - R.L. Polk & Co.
DECISION POINT - Video production - 3-D Ventures
DECISION QUALITY CIGAR - Cigars - M & N Cigar Manufacturing Inc.
DECISIONPRO - Computer software - DecisionPro, Inc.
DECISIONQUEST - Computer peripheral equipment - Health Care Pharmacy Providers, Inc.
DECISIONS, DECISIONS - Computer software - Tom Snyder Productions, Inc.
DECISIONTOOLS - Computer software - Palisade Corp.
DECISIONVISION - Computer software - Telephonics Corp.

DECISIONVUE - Computer software - GRC International, Inc.
DECISIS - Computer software - Decisis Corp.
DECISPLIT - Computer peripheral equipment - Communications Specialties, Inc.
DECK-70 - Waterproofing compounds - Universal Protective Coatings
DECK A PELL - Adhesives and sealants - Chemprobe Technologies, Inc.
DECK & CABIN - Marine brushes - Corona Brushes Inc.
DECK ARE - Building materials - Deck Care of Iowa, Inc.
DECK BLADE - Saws–power - Disston Co.
DECK EASE - Hardware - Predator Industries, Inc.
DECK EASE - Screws - Abbott-Interfast Corp.
DECK-GARD - Nuts and bolts - A & I Bolt and Nut, Inc.
DECK-GARD - Rubber–molded - W.H. Salisbury & Co.
DECK HAILER - Communications equipment–marine ☆ - Andrea Electronics Corp.
DECK HAND SPECIAL - Fishing tackle - Truline Glass Rod Manufacturing Co.
DECK HANDS - Footwear - Wolverine World Wide, Inc.
DECK HANDS - Planter brackets - Novelty Manufacturing Co.
DECK HOUSE - Mobile homes - Deck House, Inc.
DECK-LOCK - Screws - Georgia-Pacific Corp.
DECK MASTER - Containers - Igloo Products Corp.
DECK MATE - Metals - Phillips Screw Co.
DECK MATES - Garden equipment - Cobraco Manufacturing, Inc.
DECK NECESSITIES - Lumber - Universal Forest Products Inc.
DECK NECESSITIES - Wood products - Universal Forest Products, Inc.
DECK-O-JOINT - Building materials–concrete - W.R. Meadows Inc.
DECK-O-SEAL - Adhesives and sealants - W.R. Meadows Inc.
DECK PLUS - Paints - Behr Process Corp.
DECK RENEW - Cleaning preparations - Ace MW Inc.
DECK-SAFE - Finishing agents - Farwest Paint Manufacturing Co. Inc.
DECK SEAL - Concrete products ☆ - Grace Construction Products
DECK SHIELD - Adhesives and sealants - FLR Paints Inc.
DECK SHIRT - Shirts - Jockey International, Inc.
DECK SLIDER - Automotive parts and accessories - Jon N. Nelson
DECK THE HALLS - Dinnerware–glass - Tienshan, Inc.
DECK-TIE - Hardware - Simpson Strong-Tie Co., Inc.
DECK WELD - Adhesives and sealants - Dap Products Inc.
DECKAIDER - Games - Gamescience
DECKBOAT PRO - Boats–fishing - Anchor Industries Inc.
DECKBUOY - Life preservers - Datrex Inc.
DECKCARE - Waterproofing compounds - ISK Biosciences Corp.
DECKEM - Insecticides - Fearing Manufacturing Co. Inc.
DECKER - Meat products–beef - Armour Swift-Eckrich
DECKER - Sausage - Decker Food Co.
DECKER GRID SYSTEM - Publisher's imprints - Decker Communications, Inc.
DECKERS - Footwear - Deckers Outdoor Corp.
DECKETTE - Boats–fishing - Anchor Industries Inc.
DECKETTE PRO - Boats–fishing ☆ - Anchor Industries Inc.
DECKFAST - Metals - Starborn Industries Inc.
DECKGARD - Coatings - Nelsonite, Inc.
DECKGARD PLUS - Coatings - Nelsonite, Inc.
DECKGRATES - Ventilation equipment ☆ - Cape Cod Air Grilles
DECKHAND - Cleaning preparations - Yale Engineering Co.
DECKLIFE - Waterproofing compounds - Dap Products Inc.
DECKMASTER - Paints - Amteco, Inc.
DECKMASTER - Trading cards and stamps - Wizards of the Coast, Inc.
DECKMATE - Fabrics - Greenwood Mills Inc.
DECKMATE - Marinas–prefabricated ☆ - Delta Consolidated Industries, Inc.
DECKMATES - Cord connectors–electric - Woods Wire Products, Inc.
DECKO PRODUCTS INC. - Confections - Decko Products, Inc.
DECKPRO - Screws - Rockford Products Corp. (International Group)
DECKS ON DISK - Computer software - Simon Direct, Inc.
DECKSKINS - Sporting goods - Neese Industries, Inc.
DECKTERGENT - Cleaning preparations - Duckback Products, Inc.
DECKWORKS - Floor coverings ☆ - Master's Choice Inc.
DECKWORKS - Hardware - Black & Decker Corp.
DECLARATION - Cutlery - Imperial Schrade Corp.
DECLARATION - Floor coverings–carpet and rugs - Coronet Carpets Inc.
DECLARATION - Furniture - Vaughan Furniture Co. Inc.
DECLARATION - Paper–bond ☆ - Marvin Envelope & Paper Co.
DECLARATION AMERICANA - Furniture - Nichols and Stone Co. Inc.
DECLARATION I - Furniture - Nichols and Stone Co. Inc.
DECLARATION OF INTERDEPENDENCE - Giftware ☆ - Wry Idea Co.
DECLOFEN - Pharmaceutical preparations ☆ - U.S. Ethicals Inc.
DECLOR-IT - Water treating compounds ☆ - Aquatronics-Filtronics
DECMAT - Computers - Digital Equipment Corp.

DECMATE II - Computers–personal - Digital Equipment Corp.
DECMATE III - Computers–personal - Digital Equipment Corp.
DECO - Artists' materials - Timeplanner Calendars, Inc.
DECO - Finishing agents ☆ - Dunn Edwards Corp.
DECO - Fixtures - Ideation Inc.
DECO - Floor coverings–carpet and rugs ☆ - Regal Rugs Inc.
DECO - Floor coverings–carpet and rugs ☆ - World Carpets, Inc.
DECO - Flowers, plants, and seeds - Panamerican Seed
DECO - Frames–picture - Structural Industries
DECO - Frames–picture ☆ - ME Enterprises
DECO - Marble products - Georgia Marble Co.
DECO - Pet collars ☆ - Leatherite-Nylorite Manufacturing Inc.
DECO - Plates–paper - Beach Products
DECO - Posters ☆ - Classic Plaques Inc.
DECO - Skin care products ☆ - B & B Distributors
DECO 160 - Office furniture–wood - Anderson Desk Inc.
DECO ACCENTS - Hardware - H.B. Ives
DECO-ARTS - Statuary ☆ - Fabulous Forgeries Ltd.
DECO BANDS - Dinnerware ☆ - Corning Inc.
DECO-BASE - Floor coverings - American Floor Products Co. Inc.
DECO-BRITE - Artists' materials - Pro Hardware Inc.
DECO CAMEOS - Jewelry - Stanislaus Imports, Inc.
DECO-CASTLES - Pet products - Penn-Plax, Inc.
DECO CELL - Lighting fixtures - Kenall Manufacturing Co.
DECO COLOR - Pens - Uchida of America Corp.
DECO-CORAL - Pet products - Penn-Plax, Inc.
DECO CRAFT - Electric lighting equipment - Waxman Industries Inc.
DECO DECO - Wallpaper - Judscott Handprints Ltd.
DECO-DECO-DECO - Wallpaper - Judscott Handprints Ltd.
DECO-DESIGN - Garden equipment - Home & Garden Industries Inc.
DECO DISC - Pharmaceutical preparations ☆ - Wesley Pharmacal Co. Inc.
DECO DOG - Pet products - Century Craft Industries
DECO ENDS - Book ends ☆ - Esselte Corp.
DECO-FABS - Wallpaper - Wall Fabrics Inc.
DECO GARD - Plastics film - MSC Specialty Films Inc.
DECO GLASS - Glass–stained - O & J Enterprises
DECO-GLAZE - Adhesives and sealants - Loctite Corp.
DECO GRID - Bars–steel ☆ - Alcan Aluminum Corp. Alcan Building Products Div.
DECO-GRIP - Building materials - Michael T. Abbaticchio
DECO LAWNLIME - Lime products - Georgia Marble Co.
DECO LITES - Candles ☆ - Emkay Candles
DECO-LOG - Pet products - Tetra Sales USA
DECO MARBLE - Marble products - Georgia Marble Co.
DECO MATE - Marble products - Vitro Agate Corp.
DECO NOUGAT FLUFFS - Candy - Miss Saylor's Candies
DECO-PAK - Hobby kits - Vogart Crafts Corp.
DECO-PAQUES - Paints ☆ - DecoArt, Inc.
DECO PEA PEBBLES - Stone products - Georgia Marble Co.
DECO PEBBLES - Stone products - Georgia Marble Co.
DECO PET - Pet products - Century Craft Industries
DECO-PLAQUE - Photo frame - Hardwood Frames of America
DECO PLEAT - Fabrics - Guilford Mills, Inc.
DECO-PUFFS - Paper–tissue - Bemiss-Jason Corp.
DECO-RAIL - Fencing–wood - Aire-Lite Industries Inc.
DECO-RATORS - Pet products - Penn-Plax, Inc.
DECO-REPLICAS - Aquarium accessories - Penn-Plax, Inc.
DECO-ROOM - Switch plates, hooks, and bath accessories ☆ - American Tack & Hardware Co., Inc.
DECO-SAND - Artists' materials - Visual Design Manufacturing Co. Inc.
DECO-SAURS - Pet products - Penn-Plax, Inc.
DECO SEAL - Sealing compounds - Tec Inc.
DECO SHELLS - Pet products - Penn-Plax, Inc.
DECO-SLEV - Flower bouquet holder - DBR Inc.
DECO-SORTER - Office supplies ☆ - Esselte Corp.
DECO-S.P.C. - Pharmaceutical preparations ☆ - Wesley Pharmacal Co. Inc.
DECO SPECTRUM - Bedding–linen - Dan River Inc.
DECO STAR - Frames–picture - North American Enclosures Inc.
DECO-TAGS - Labels–paper ☆ - Stephen Lawrence Co.
DECO-TEX - Artists' materials - Vogart Crafts Corp.
DECO-TEX - Paint rollers - Bestt-Liebco
DECO-TEX - Paints - Color Master
DECO-TEX - Paints - Evans Paint
DECO-TILE - Decals and transfers - Philadelphia Ceramics Inc.
DECO TILE - Tiles–enamel - Lucky America Inc.
DECO TIN - Housewares - Brockway Standard Inc.

☆ = Now out of production

DECO TRIM - Wood products ☆ - Maywood Inc.
DECO TRIMS - Paperboard - Paper Magic Group, Inc.
DECO-WEB - Paints ☆ - DecoArt, Inc.
DECO WEIGHTS - See **QUILT/PATTERN WATE**
DECO WRAP - Paper–gift wrap ☆ - Cleo Inc.
DECO-WRITE - Pedestals–wood - Vogart Crafts Corp.
DECOBEL - Pharmaceutical preparations - Lannett Co. Inc.
DECOC - Computers - Digital Equipment Corp.
DECODINE - Pharmaceutical preparations - Blair Pharmacal
DECODULT - Pharmaceutical preparations - Wesley Pharmacal Co. Inc.
DECOEDGE - Garbage disposal units–household - O.C. & Associates, Inc.
DECOEDGE PLUS - Building materials - O.C. & Associates, Inc.
DECOFED - Pharmaceutical preparations ☆ - Barre-National, Inc.
DECOFILE - Office supplies - Esselte Corp.
DECOFLAME - Candles - Biedermann & Sons Inc.
DECOFLEX - Office supplies - Esselte Corp.
DECOGEST - Pharmaceutical preparations ☆ - Wesley Pharmacal Co. Inc.
DECOGLASS - Artists' materials ☆ - Shiva Inc.
DECOGLAZE - Paints - Jones Blair Co.
DECOGLO - Paints - Dunn Edwards Corp.
DECOGLOSS - Paints ☆ - Dunn Edwards Corp.
DECOHIST - Pharmaceutical preparations - Barre-National, Inc.
DECOLAC - Lacquers - Dunn Edwards Corp.
DECOLAM, INC. - Wood products - Decolam, Inc.
DECOLAQ - Window treatments - A.J. Boyd Industries Inc.
DECOLATE - Pharmaceutical preparations - Wesley Pharmacal Co. Inc.
DECOLITE - Boat-building materials - Baltek Corp.
DECOLITE - Lighters - Scripto-Tokai Corp.
DECOLLETE - Skin care products ☆ - Borlind of Germany
DECOLONE - Health care products - Kay Pharmacal Co. Inc.
DECOMAGIC - Paints - DecoArt, Inc.
DECOMATIC - Blinds–vertical - Benthin Co.
DECOMETAL - Adhesives and sealants - Formica Corp.
DECOMINIC - Pharmaceutical preparations - Wesley Pharmacal Co. Inc.
DECOMIRROR - Mirrors - Headwest Inc.
DECOMIST - Pharmaceutical preparations ☆ - Wesley Pharmacal Co. Inc.
DECON-PLUS - Cold remedies ☆ - Pharmex Inc.
DECONADE - Pharmaceutical preparations ☆ - Moore Medical Corp.
DECONCHEST - Pharmaceutical preparations - Home Health Products, Inc.
DECONGEST - Pharmaceutical preparations - C.O. Truxton Inc.
DECONGEST - Vitamins and nutritional supplements ☆ - Thompson Medical Co., Inc.
DECONGEST HERBAL - Health care products - McZand Herbal, Inc.
DECONGESTADE - Pharmaceutical preparations - David A. Rosow Inc.
DECONGEX - Prescription drug - IDE-Interstate Inc.
DECONGISTAMIN - Pharmaceutical preparations - Consolidated Midland Corp.
DECONSAL - Pharmaceutical preparations - Adams Laboratories Inc.
DECONTABS - Pharmaceutical preparations ☆ - Zenith Laboratories, Inc.
DECONTAM-17 - Vitamins and nutritional supplements - Amrion, Inc.
DECONVOLUTION TOOLBOX - Computer software - VayTek, Inc.
DECOPAK - Packaging–paper ☆ - Z-Barten Productions
DECOPICS - Decorations - McGlynn Bakeries Inc.
DECOPLAS - Office supplies - Stempel Manufacturing Co.
DECOPLEAT - Fabrics - Guilford Mills, Inc.
DECOPOUR - Fins–aircraft ☆ - Flecto Co. Inc.
DECOR - Blinds–venetian - Hunter Douglas Intermountain Fabrication Co.
DECOR - Desks - Wood Design Inc.
DECOR - Dinnerware–glass ☆ - Lenox, Inc.
DECOR - Drapery hardware - Newell Window Furnishing Co.
DECOR - Floor coverings–carpet and rugs - Value Carpets Inc.
DECOR - Mats - Majestic Mat Co.
DECOR - Mirrors - National Products Inc.
DECOR - Paints - Valspar Corp.
DECOR - Paints ☆ - American Art Clay Co. Inc.
DECOR - Shelving units–metal - Dorfile Manufacturing Co.
DECOR - Steps ☆ - Dowcraft Corp.
DECOR - Tiles–ceramic ☆ - Wenczel Tile Co.
DECOR 2 - Tiles–ceramic - Wenczel Tile Co.
DECOR 7 - Floor coverings - Parquet de France Inc.
DECOR 8 - Limestone products - Georgia Marble Co.
DECOR BATHWARE - Bathroom accessories - Franklin Brass Manufacturing Co.
DECOR-BOND - Fabric binding - Freudenberg Nonwovens Apparel Division
DECOR BY SHIBA - Tablecloths ☆ - Town & Country Linen Corp.
DECOR DE SOLEIL - Wallpaper - Decor International Wallcovering Inc.
DECORS-DECALS - Decals and transfers ☆ - Carnival Arts, Inc.

DECOR DELIGHTS - Candy - McCormick & Co., Inc.
DECOR DIARY - Wallpaper - Decor International Wallcovering Inc.
DECOR DIMENSIONS - Wallpaper - Decor International Wallcovering Inc.
DECOR EFFECTS - Wallpaper - Decor International Wallcovering Inc.
DECOR EFFECTS 2 - Wallpaper - Decor International Wallcovering Inc.
DECOR ELEGANCE - Wallpaper ☆ - Decor International Wallcovering Inc.
DECOR-ETT - Cording - Novelty Cord and Tassel Co. Inc.
DECOR-GLAZE - Automotive parts and accessories ☆ - Trenwyth Industries Inc.
DECOR JOLIE - Paper–gift wrap ☆ - Cleo Inc.
DECOR-KEYED - Housewares ☆ - Arden Corp.
DECOR-KRAFT - Paints ☆ - Benjamin Moore & Co.
DECOR-LIGHT - Windows - Frantz Manufacturing Co.
DECOR LINE, THE - Bulletin boards–cork - Quartet Manufacturing Co.
DECOR-LITE - Lighting equipment - Hobby Hill Inc.
DECOR-LOK - Furniture ☆ - Spacemaster Home Products
DECOR-MATCH - Power switching equipment ☆ - Lomar Industries Inc.
DECOR-NAILS - Hardware - Tremont Nail
DECOR SELECTS - Cake decorations - Signature Brands, LLC
DECOR-SHAKE - Roofing materials–concrete ☆ - Alcan Aluminum Corp. Alcan Building Products Div.
DECOR-SPAR - Bricks - Pasvalco
DECOR-STONE - Paving materials–stone ☆ - Dur-A-Flex Inc.
DECOR-TEX - Paints - Chemex Paint & Coatings Inc.
DECOR TWEED - Synthetic turf - Instant Turf Industries Inc.
DECOR TWIST - Floor coverings–carpet and rugs ☆ - Porter Carpet Mills Inc.
DECOR TWISTS - Flowers, plants, and seeds - Exotic Wood Flowers Inc.
DECORA - Benches–metal - Artesian Industries
DECORA - Cabinets - Aristokraft, Inc.
DECORA - Dishes–china - Decora Imports Inc.
DECORA - Fabrics - Janlynn Corp.
DECORA - Glass products - Pittsburgh Corning Corp.
DECORA - Paints ☆ - Parks Corp.
DECORA - Skin care products - Takara Belmont USA, Inc.
DECORA - Switches–electric - Leviton Manufacturing Co., Inc.
DECORA 28 - Tubes–plastic - Voltarc Technologies, Inc.
DECORA CORD - Flowers, plants, and seeds - Lifesake Faster-Form Co.
DECORACK - Racks - Esselte Corp.
DECORACK JR. - Racks - Esselte Corp.
DECORAFAN - Fans–ceiling - Northwest Envirofan
DECORALITES - Candles ☆ - Will & Baumer, Inc.
DECOR'ALL - Paint rollers - Bestt-Liebco
DECORAMA - Draperies - Decorator Industries Inc.
DECORAMA - Giftware - Bentley Gifts Inc.
DECORAMA - Novelty items - Beistle Co.
DECORAMA - Paints ☆ - Royal Lustre Brands
DECORATE-IT! - Wallpaper - Minnesota Mining & Manufacturing Co.
DECORATE 'N DAZZLE - Dolls - Mattel, Inc.
DECORATE YOUR BASKET BUNNY - Toys–stuffed - Dan-Dee International Ltd.
DECORATE YOUR LIFE - Paints - Benjamin Moore & Co.
DECORATED VIOLETS - Glassware–household ☆ - Fenton Art Glass Co.
DECORATEUR - Floor coverings–carpet and rugs - J.L. Benson Co.
DECORATING DEN SYSTEMS INC. - Interior design services - Decorating Den Systems Inc.
DECORATING MAGIC - Spray glitter - Chase Products Co.
DECORATING PASTE - Paints - DecoArt, Inc.
DECORATING WITH BORDERS II - Wallpaper - Imperial Wallcoverings, Inc.
DECORATING WIZARD - Computer software - Power Solutions, Inc.
DECORATIONS OF INDEPENDENCE - Apparel and accessories - Teximpor Inc.
DECORATIONS SARA SINAIKO - Apparel and accessories - Sinaiko-Weber Inc.
DECORATIVE AIDES - Window coverings - Vertical Blind Factory
DECORATIVE DIFFERENCE, THE - Window coverings - Allpro Corp.
DECORATIVE DIMENSIONS - Wallpaper ☆ - Horizon Wallcoverings
DECORATIVE GROUP II - Hardware ☆ - Amerock Corp.
DECORATIVE GROUP I - Hardware ☆ - Amerock Corp.
DECORATIVE IMPRESSIONS - Wallpaper - Linon Home Decor Products, Inc.
DECORATIVE ORIGINALS - Floor coverings - Custom Decor Inc.
DECORATIVE SERIES - Faucets - Chicago Faucet Co.
DECORATIVE TEXTURES VOL. IV - Wallpaper - Stamford Wall Paper Co. Inc.
DECORATIVE TILE - Tiles–ceramic - Porcelanite, Inc.
DECORATIVE TOUCHES - Paints - L & F Products Inc.
DECORATONE - Unframed reproductions of oil paintings ☆ - Goes Lithographing Co.

DECORATOR - Artists' materials - Robert Simmons Inc.
DECORATOR - Bathroom fixtures ☆ - Artesian Industries
DECORATOR - Blinds–venetian - Kenney Manufacturing Co.
DECORATOR - Cabinets - National Lock Hardware
DECORATOR - Cork centerpieces, coaster sets, hot pads ☆ - Corcoran Manufacturing Co., Inc.
DECORATOR - Deodorizers - Dial Corp.
DECORATOR - Desk sets ☆ - Park Sherman
DECORATOR - Door mats ☆ - Royal Rubber & Manufacturing Co.
DECORATOR - Doors–garage - McKee Door, Inc.
DECORATOR - Drapery hardware ☆ - Spring Window Fashions Division, Inc.
DECORATOR - Fans–electric - Nutone Inc.
DECORATOR - Floor coverings - Tarkett, Inc.
DECORATOR - Hardware - Prisma Unlimited
DECORATOR - Hardware - Woodward-Wanger Co.
DECORATOR - Hooks - Vogel Peterson Furniture Co.
DECORATOR - Ladders–wood - John S. Tilley Ladders Co. Inc.
DECORATOR - Paints - Jones Blair Co.
DECORATOR - Paints - Plaid Enterprises, Inc.
DECORATOR - Thread - Threads USA Div.
DECORATOR BLOCKS - Stencils - Muskoka Cottage Products, Inc.
DECORATOR COLORS - Tiles–ceramic - Cambridge Tile Manufacturing Co.
DECORATOR HOUSE - Kitchenware–earthenware - Glazer Associates Inc.
DECORATOR LYKEWOOD - Hardware - Marley Mouldings Inc.
DECORATOR RAIL - Fencing–wood - Gerber Industries Inc.
DECORATOR SERIES - Door mats - Royal Floor Mats
DECORATOR, THE - Giftware ☆ - General Housewares Corp.
DECORATOR TURF - Synthetic turf - Instant Turf Industries Inc.
DECORATORS - China cabinets–wood - C.H. Stuart & Co. Inc.
DECORATORS - Paints - Carnival Arts, Inc.
DECORATORS - Paints - Somay Products Inc.
DECORATORS - Shingles–wood - Marshall Manufacturing Inc./Cedar Valley Shingle Systems
DECORATORS - Stainless steel - Nobility-Prestige Co.
DECORATOR'S CHOICE - Cabinets–wood - Harbor Sales Co.
DECORATORS CHOICE - Paints ☆ - Flo-Rite Coating & Chemical Co.
DECORATOR'S CHOICE - Wallpaper - Allpro Corp.
DECORATOR'S GALLERY - Fabrics - Everfast Inc.
DECORATORS GILT - Finishing agents - Carnival Arts, Inc.
DECORATORS' SUPREME - Paints - Kwal-Howells Inc.
DECORBOARD - Hardware - Scott Sign Systems, Inc.
DECOREBOX - Mail boxes ☆ - Flambeau Products Corp.
DECOREGGER - Dyes–food - Spearhead Industries Inc.
DECOREL FINE ART - Pictures and prints - Decorel Inc.
DECORETTE - Apparel–women's ☆ - Bali Co. Inc.
DECORETTE - Ribbons - Minnesota Mining & Manufacturing Co.
DECORETTES - Greeting cards ☆ - Evergreen Press
DECORETTES - Tiles–ceramic ☆ - Wenczel Tile Co.
DECOREX - Decorative plating - Enthone-OMI
DECORITE - Hardware - Advanced Affiliates Inc.
DECORITE - Pillows - Decorite, Inc.
DECORLETTERS - Hardware - Scott Sign Systems, Inc.
DECORLINE - Faucets - Gerber Plumbing Fixtures Corp.
DECORLUX - Lighting equipment - Diffusa-Lite Co.
DECORMIST - Skin care products - Delta Industries International, Inc.
DECOROL - Paper–rolls - Riverside Paper Corp.
DECORP - Apparel and accessories ☆ - Kellwood Co.
DECORPLATE - Housewares - Olfa Products Corp.
DECORPOXY - Epoxy - Garon Products Inc.
DECORPRINTS - Napkins–paper - Erving Paper Mills
DECORTEN - Adhesives and sealants - Vitricon
DECORTEX - Wallpaper ☆ - Pickhardt & Siebert USA Inc.
DECORUM - Ceiling fans - Davoil, Inc.
DECORUM - Floor coverings–carpet and rugs ☆ - Gulistan Carpet Inc.
DECORUM - Furniture - Steelcase Inc.
DECORUM - Furniture ☆ - Bassett Furniture Industries, Inc.
DECORWARE - Giftware - Ballonoff Home Products
DECOS - Floor coverings–tile ☆ - Kepcor, Inc./SSI Tiles
DECOSHEEN - Paints - Dunn Edwards Corp.
DECOSPAN - Pharmaceutical preparations ☆ - Wesley Pharmacal Co. Inc.
DECOSTA - Chocolate candy - Bell'amore Imports Inc.
DECOSTA - Meat products - Kayem Foods, Inc.
DECOSTAT - Pharmaceutical preparations ☆ - Wesley Pharmacal Co. Inc.
DECOSTYLE - Paints - Sherwin-Williams Automotive Finishes Corp.
DECOT - Thread - Synthetic Thread Co. Inc.
DECOTEL - Personal telephones - American Telecommunications Corp.

DECOTEX - Athol Corp.
DECOTHANE - Dunn Edwards Corp.
DECOTRAY - Trays - Esselte Corp.
DECOTUCK - Fabrics - Guilford Mills, Inc.
DECOTUSSIN - Pharmaceutical preparations ☆ - Wesley Pharmacal Co. Inc.
DECOTY'S MIRACLE DIP BREADING MIX - Bread crumbs - Decoty Coffee Co.
DECOTY'S SPICES/SEASONINGS - Spices and extracts - Decoty Coffee Co.
DECOTY'S WESTERN GOLD - Coffee - Decoty Coffee Co.
DECOUTIQUES - Decals and transfers ☆ - Walnut Hollow Farm, Inc.
DECOUVE - Apparel–women's ☆ - Leslie Fay Companies Inc.
DECOVEL - Paints - Dunn Edwards Corp.
DECOY - Furniture - Lee Industries Inc.
DECOY - Glassware–household - Owens-Illinois Inc. (Libbey Div.)
DECOY - Shoes - Craddock-Terry Inc.
DECOY - Wines - Duckhorn Vineyards
DECOYS - Floor coverings–carpet and rugs - Capel, Inc.
DECPRO - Lighting fixtures - Kenall Manufacturing Co.
DECRA - Lamps - Genlyte Group Inc.
DECRA-LOC - Blocks–paving - Decra-Loc U.S.A., Inc.
DECRA-MOLD - Molding compounds–plastics - Kay-Wood Industries Inc.
DECRA-TEX - Paints - Steelcote Manufacturing Corp.
DECRAFORM - Window coverings - Avista Industries, Inc.
DECRAGUARD - Plywood - Harbor Sales Co.
DECRAMASTIC - Roof tile - Automated Building Components
DECRATONE - Paints ☆ - Kyanize Paint Co.
DECRISTOFARO - Furniture - Lexington Furniture Industries, Inc.
DECRO-BRICK - Concrete products - Masonry Processes, Inc.
DECRO-FACE - Concrete products - Masonry Processes, Inc.
DECRO-GRAPHICS - Blocks–concrete - Masonry Processes, Inc.
DECRO-PAVERS - Concrete products - Masonry Processes, Inc.
DECROBEAD - Hardware - Bead Industries Inc. (Bead Chain Div.)
DECROCOLOR - Fabrics–tapestry ☆ - Coloroll Inc.
DECROLITE - Lighting equipment - Diffusa-Lite Co.
DECROLON - Paints - Dutch Boy Group
DECROTEX - Window coverings - Vertical Blind Factory
DECSPELL - Computer software - Digital Equipment Corp.
DECSTITCH - Thread ☆ - American & Efird, Inc.
DECTAPE - Magnetic tape–blank - Digital Equipment Corp.
DECTEXT - Computer software - Digital Equipment Corp.
DECTO-STICK - Wood products - H.F. Staples & Co. Inc.
DECTOMAX - Pet products - Pfizer Inc.
DECTONE - Nautical instruments - Fiamm Technologies
DECTONE - Paints - Sinclair Paint Co.
DECTUSS - Pharmaceutical preparations ☆ - Marlop Pharmaceuticals Inc.
DECTYPE - Computer software - Digital Equipment Corp.
DECUB-A-GUARD - Mattresses ☆ - Penox Technologies Inc.
DECUBICARE - Medical apparatus - Guardian Products Inc.
DECUBITEX - Pharmaceutical preparations - I.C.P. Pharmaceuticals
DECURA - Medical apparatus - Senior Technologies, Inc.
DECWORD - Computer software - Digital Equipment Corp.
DECWORD/DP - Computer software - Digital Equipment Corp.
DECWRITER - Computer software - Digital Equipment Corp.
DECYLENES - Pharmaceutical preparations - Rugby Laboratories Inc.
DECYPHER - Computer software - Time Logic, Inc.
DEDICATED - Recording label - BMG Entertainment North America
DEDICATED TO BEER - Beverages–malt - Boston Beer Co. LP
DEDICATED TO HEART HEALTH - Salad dressings–bottled - GFA Brands Inc.
DEDICATED TO SERVICE - Nuts and bolts - Capital Fasteners, Inc.
DEDICATED TO YOU SERIES - Compact discs–prerecorded - Original Sound Record Co. Inc.
DEDICATED TO YOUR COMMITMENTS - Courier services–land - Nationwide Express, Inc.
DEDICATED TRANSPORT, INC. - Railroad transportation–freight - Dedicated Transport, Inc.
DEDICATION - Clocks - General Time Corp. (Westclox/Seth Thomas Div.)
DEDICATION - Floor coverings–carpet and rugs - Monticello Carpet Mills
DEDICATOR - Diagnostic apparatus - Instrumentation Northwest, Inc.
DEDICATOR - Facsimile equipment - TT Systems Corp.
DEDO - Statuary - American Eagle Co., Inc.
DEDOES - Machinery - Dedoes Industries, Inc.
DEDURA - Paints ☆ - Demert & Dougherty, Inc.
DEE 2 N/R - Disinfectant ☆ - Intex Chemical Inc.
DEE 10 - Pharmaceutical preparations ☆ - Scrip-Physician Supply Co.
DEE BURGER - Food products - Dee's, Inc.

☆ = Now out of production

DEE CEE - Apparel and accessories - Washington Manufacturing Co.

DEE CEE FOR GALS - Apparel–women's - Washington Manufacturing Co.

DEE DEE - Dolls - Mattel, Inc.

DEE-DEE'S - Footwear ☆ - Glamour Footwear

DEE-DO - Hair care products ☆ - Stanley Fay Co.

DEE FOUNTAINS - Fountains - Dee Co.

DEE GEE - Slippers - Daniel Green Co.

DEE-LISH - Relish ☆ - Aunt Jane's Foods

DEE-LITE-FULS - Posters - C.M. Paula Co.

DEE LUX - Stationery - Diagraph Corp.

DEE-MURE - Underwear and nightwear - Spirite Industries Inc.

DEE PET - Pet products - Dee Pet Products

DEE PET GLAMOUR - Pet products - Dee Pet Products

DEE PRINCESS FASHIONS - Pet products - Dee Pet Products

DEE-RAX - Plastics - Deep Flex Plastic Molds Inc.

DEE ZEE - Motor vehicle parts and accessories - Dee Zee, Inc.

DEE-ZOL - Fuel additives - Bell Additives, Inc.

DEE-ZOL PLUS - Fuel additives - Bell Additives, Inc.

DEEDRUNNER - Computer software - Mapsync-Maplink Co.

DEEKISHA - Recording label - Toro'na International

DEEKO - Doilies ☆ - Freund-Mayer & Co. Inc.

DEELITE - Sandals - Playazul International Inc.

DEELITEFUL - Food products - BarB-Que Industries Inc.

DEELY BOBBERS - Novelty items - Ace Novelty Co. Inc.

DEEMER - Ophthalmic goods ☆ - Rozin Optical Export Corp.

DEENA - Apparel and accessories - Deena Inc.

DEEP - Apparel–athletic - Tracy Fong

DEEP - Food products - Deep Foods, Inc.

DEEP 6 - Insecticides - Speer Products, Inc.

DEEP ACTION - Cleaning preparations–carpet and rug - Hillyard Enterprises, Inc.

DEEP AMBER - Skin care products ☆ - T.N. Dickinson Co.

DEEP BABY N - Fishing lures - Howe Now Inc.

DEEP BLUE SECRET - Dolls - Mattel, Inc.

DEEP CLEAN - Hair care products - Gene-Metre Professional Salon Products

DEEP COUNTRY - Apparel and accessories - Spinnerstown Shuttle

DEEP COUNTRY - Lighting fixtures - Big Beam Emergency Systems Inc.

DEEP CREEK CELLARS - Wines - Worden's Washington Winery

DEEP CREEPERS - Toys - Toymax Inc.

DEEP CRYSTAL - Automotive parts and accessories - Meguiar's, Inc.

DEEP CYCLE - Pistons - Child & Albert Inc.

DEEP DARK SUNLESS - Suntan lotions - Procter & Gamble Co.

DEEP DEEP - Nail care products - Revlon Consumer Products Corp.

DEEP DEEP - Seafood products–fresh or frozen - Atlantic Coast Fisheries Corp.

DEEP DIGGERS - Garden equipment - Brewer Design Service, Inc.

DEEP DIMENSION - Molding compounds–plastics - Gossen Corp.

DEEP-DISH - Ashtrays–glass - Frank J. Curran-Esquire Chemical Co.

DEEP DISH - Recording label - Jazz Composer's Orchestra Association Inc.

DEEP DIVING RIVER RUNT - Sporting goods ☆ - James Heddon's Sons

DEEP DOWN - Analgesics - Smithkline Beecham Corp.

DEEP E - Bags - Deep E Co.

DEEP EARTH - Hair care products - Modern Research Laboratories

DEEP EARTH - Skin care products - Image Laboratories, Inc.

DEEP-EASE - Bath salts - Newton Laboratories Inc.

DEEP END - Shirts - Millennium Marketplace, Inc.

DEEP FACIAL - Skin care products - New England Natural Sponge, Inc.

DEEP FLATTERY - Apparel–women's - Exquisite Form Industries

DEEP FLEX - Hobby kits - Deep Flex Plastic Molds Inc.

DEEP FOREST - Air purification systems ☆ - Medo Industries, Inc.

DEEP FREEZ! - Hair care products - Image Laboratories, Inc.

DEEP FREEZE - Ice chests–plastic - Igloo Products Corp.

DEEP FREEZE - Veterinary pharmaceutical preparations - Zirin Laboratories International

DEEP FRIES - Vegetables–frozen - Ore-Ida Foods, Inc.

DEEP HEAT - Giftware - Pollenex Corp.

DEEP IMPRESSION - Floor coverings–carpet and rugs - Mohawk Industries Inc.

DEEP JR. THUNDERSTICK - Fishing lures - Storm Manufacturing Co.

DEEP LITTLE N - Fishing lures - Howe Now Inc.

DEEP LOCK - Gutters–plastic - National Aluminum Products Co.

DEEP-LUBE - Lubricants ☆ - Dykem Co.

DEEP LUSTRE - Polishing rouge - Park Metallurgical Corp.

DEEP MAGIC - Floor coverings–carpet and rugs ☆ - Lees Carpets

DEEP MAGIC - Skin care products - Gillette Co.

DEEP MUSCLE THERAPY SPORTS MASSAGE - Health care products - Lakon Herbals Inc.

DEEP 'N BOUNCY - Hair care products - Helene Curtis Industries Inc.

DEEP NIGHT - Cookies - Stella D'Oro Biscuit Co. Inc.

DEEP OAK - Aluminum products ☆ - National Aluminum Products Co.

DEEP ORCHID - Cosmetics ☆ - Honey & Spice Toiletries

DEEP PENETRATOR - Ammunition ☆ - Olin Corp. (Winchester Div.)

DEEP PENETRATOR - Hair care products - Gelle-International Ltd.

DEEP PLUNGE - Brassieres (Bras) - Lady Marlene

DEEP POCKETS - Plates–paper - Temple-Eastex Inc.

DEEP PREP - Massage products - Smith & Nephew Inc. (Rehabilitation Div.)

DEEP PURPLE - Beverages–carbonated - Hampton Associates and Son, Inc.

DEEP RELIEF - Health care products - Lakon Herbals Inc.

DEEP RELIEF - Orthopedic products - Gustave Rick Rinz

DEEP RICH - Instant coffee and tea - American Instants Inc.

DEEP RIVER - Recording label ☆ - Olivia Records Inc.

DEEP-ROCK - Cement - Dependable Chemical Co.

DEEP ROCK - Oils–lubricating ☆ - Kerr-McGee Chemical Corp.

DEEP ROCK - Water–bottled or canned - Deep Rock Water South

DEEP ROCK - Water–distilled ☆ - Wometco Enterprises Inc.

DEEP ROOT - Garden equipment - W. Atlee Burpee and Co.

DEEP ROOTS - Labels–paper - Koala Records Inc.

DEEP SEA - Salmon–smoked, salted, dried, or pickled - Wards Cove Packing Co.

DEEP SEA - Shrimp–fresh or frozen - Deep Sea Shrimp Importing Co. Inc.

DEEP SEA - Skin care products - GPS, Inc.

DEEP SEA - Watches - Bulova Corp.

DEEP SEA FISH OIL - Vitamins and nutritional supplements - Horizon Worldwide Export Corp.

DEEP SEA GOLD - Oils–essential - United Natural Resources, Inc.

DEEP SEAL - Adhesives and sealants - Midland Chicago Corp.

DEEP SECRET - Fishing lures - Luhr Jensen & Sons, Inc.

DEEP SECRET - Floor coverings–carpet and rugs - Queen Carpet Corp.

DEEP SHINE - Shoe polish ☆ - Ronson Consumer Products Corp.

DEEP-SIX - Archery equipment - Saunders Archery Co.

DEEP SIX - Ice chests–plastic ☆ - Glacier Ware Inc.

DEEP SKID - Tires - Bridgestone/Firestone, Inc.

DEEP SLEEP - Apparel–men's - Mission Control

DEEP SPACE NINE STATION - Toys–models - ERTL Co., Inc.

DEEP SPACE: OPERATION COPERNICUS - Computer software ☆ - Sir-Tech Software, Inc.

DEEP SPACE TRANSPORT - Toys–models ☆ - Estes Industries

DEEP STRENGTH - Analgesics ☆ - Schering-Plough Healthcare Products

DEEP STRIP - Wax removers - Calgon Vestal Laboratories

DEEP TALKIN' BASS - Musical instrument accessories - E. & O. Mari Inc.

DEEP THERAPY - Hair care products - Amital Spinning Corp.

DEEP THERAPY - Pharmaceutical preparations - United Research Laboratories, Inc.

DEEP THROAT - Saws–power - CS Unitec Inc.

DEEP THUNDERSTICK - Fishing lures - Storm Manufacturing Co.

DEEP THUNDERSTICK JR. - Fishing lures ☆ - Storm Manufacturing Co.

DEEP TINY N - Fishing lures - Howe Now Inc.

DEEP TONES - Hosiery - 21st Century Hosiery Inc.

DEEP TRAG - Tires - Bridgestone/Firestone, Inc.

DEEP-TREAT - Floor waxes ☆ - Klean-Strip

DEEP V - Boating equipment and accessories - Molded Parts Specialists, Inc.

DEEP-V - Shirts - Narcy Novack

DEEP VIOLET - Dinnerware–glass ☆ - Nikko Ceramics Inc.

DEEP VISION - Electronic equipment - Medi-Vision Technologies, Inc.

DEEP WATER - Bathroom accessories - Better Sleep, Inc.

DEEP WATER - Fishing tackle - U.S. Line Co.

DEEP WATER EXPRESS - Fishing tackle - Minnesota Mining & Manufacturing Co.

DEEP WINE - Lipsticks - Honey & Spice Toiletries

DEEP WOODS - Perfumes ☆ - Avon Products, Inc.

DEEP WOODS OFF - Insecticides - S.C. Johnson & Son, Inc.

DEEPEST ORCHID - Cosmetics - Lancome

DEEPFREEZE - Refrigerators - Amana Refrigeration Inc.

DEEPGROOVE - Machine tools - Lenore E. Perry

DEEPHAVEN - Cabinets ☆ - Medallion Kitchens of Minnesota Inc.

DEEPIES - Frames–picture - Cider Mill Art & Frame

DEEPROOT - Agricultural products - Deep Root Partners, L.P.

DEEPSET - Anchors ☆ - Rule Industries, Inc.

DEEPSLEEP - Mattresses - Simmons USA

DEEPSPRINGS - Floor coverings–carpet and rugs - West Point-Pepperell Mill Store

DEEPTAN - Suntan lotions - Solar Cosmetic Labs, Inc.
DEEPTAN SUPREME - Tanning agents - Solar Cosmetic Labs, Inc.
DEEPTAN-X - Sunblocks ☆ - Solar Cosmetic Labs, Inc.
DEEPTEX - Fabrics–tapestry ☆ - Coloroll Inc.
DEER - Food products - Taormina Co.
DEER ALERT - Automotive parts and accessories - Save-a-Life
DEER BRAND - Fruits–canned - Western Overseas Trade and Development Corp.
DEER CANE - Veterinary nutritional supplements - Matthew Newman
DEER-COY - Sporting goods - Orbex Inc.
DEER CREEK - Apparel–men's - M. Fine & Sons Manufacturing Co. Inc.
DEER CREEK - Fruits and vegetables - Grand View Heights Citrus Association
DEER CREEK - Rice - Creek Wild Rice Exchange
DEER CREEK COLLECTION - Furniture - Oakwood Interiors
DEER DIARY - Books–blank - David & Roy's Outdoor Classics
DEER GARDEN - Oils–edible - Deer Garden Foods-Rejuvenative Foods
DEER HAVEN - Wines - Delvista Vineyards
DEER HUNTER - Leatherware - Paristar Trading Co.
DEER ISLE - Building materials - New England Stone Industries, Inc.
DEER ISLE - Furniture - Moosehead Manufacturing Co.
DEER LURE - Traps–animal - G-96 Products Co. Inc.
DEER ME - Dolls - Mattel, Inc.
DEER MEER - Sporting goods - John Joseph Archer
DEER MUFFS - Apparel and accessories - Ernest J. Copper
DEER-OFF - Chemical preparations - Deer-Off, Inc.
DEER-ONE - Fruit ☆ - Florida Fresh
DEER ONES - Figurines - Flowertowr Inc.
DEER PARK - Water–bottled or canned ☆ - Clorox Co.
DEER PARK - Water–mineral - Deer Park Spring Water Inc.
DEER PARK INTERNATIONAL - Cosmetic applicators - Sentinel Consumer Products, Inc.
DEER PARK SPRING WATER - Water–mineral - Perrier Group of America Inc.
DEER PARK WINERY - Wines - Deer Park Winery
DEER RIVER OUTDOOR APPAREL - Apparel - Berco, Inc.
DEER RUN - Wines - Allied Management, Inc.
DEER SENSE - Hunting equipment - Deer Quest Ltd.
DEER STAGS - Footwear - Deer Stags, Inc.
DEER STAGS ORIGINAL - Footwear - Deer Stags, Inc.
DEER-THIN - Gloves - Dakota Corp.
DEER VALLEY - Beverages–alcohol - Canandaigua Wine Co. Inc.
DEER VALLEY - Food products - Martori Bros. Distributors
DEER VALLEY - Wines ☆ - Smith & Hook Winery
DEER VALLEY FARM - Health care products - Deer Valley Farm
DEER WARNING - Electronic equipment - Cobbs Manufacturing Co.
DEER WEAR - Apparel and accessories ☆ - Mid-Western Sport Togs
DEERBUSTERS - Veterinary pharmaceutical preparations - Trident Enterprises
DEERFIELD - Apparel–children's - Charles Greenberg & Sons Inc.
DEERFIELD - Bicycles - Columbia Manufacturing Inc.
DEERFIELD - Clocks - General Time Corp. (Westclox/Seth Thomas Div.)
DEERFIELD - Floor coverings - Tarkett, Inc.
DEERFIELD - Floor coverings–carpet and rugs - Colonial Mills Inc.
DEERFIELD - Food products - Gerawan Foods Inc.
DEERFIELD - Knives ☆ - Precise International/Wenger
DEERFIELD COURT - House furnishings - Lea Industries Inc.
DEERFIELD GROVES ORCHID ISLAND - Citrus fruits - Florida Fresh
DEERFIELD, THE - Construction equipment - Sentry Building
DEERFIELD VINEYARDS - Wines - Wine Cellars Inc.
DEERFOOT - Boats–skiffs - Deerfoot Yachts
DEERFOOT - Jackets - Omnisport Inc.
DEERHUNTERS - Pharmaceutical preparations - Wisconsin Pharmacal Co. Inc.
DEERING - Food products - Deering Ice Cream Corp.
DEERING - Musical instrument accessories - Deering Banjo Co.
DEERING CROSSFIRE - Banjos - Deering Banjo Co.
DEERLENE - Toys - Tonka Corp.
DEERSCOUTS - Footwear - Osceola Shoe Co. Inc.
DEERSKIN - Abrasive products - Advanced Affiliates Inc.
DEERSKIN - Apparel and accessories - Melton Shirt Co., Inc.
DEERSLAYER - Knives ☆ - Precise International/Wenger
DEERSLAYER - Shotguns - Ithaca Gun Co. Inc.
DEERSLAYER 500 - Archery equipment - Martin Archery Inc.
DEERSLAYERS - Footwear–men's ☆ - Jarman Shoe Co.
DEERSTAG - Shoes - Osceola Shoe Co. Inc.
DEERWOOD - Food products - Maple Leaf Foods Inc.
DEERWOOD - Screws - Deerwood Fasteners Int'l.
DEE'S - Bakery products - Dee's Cheesecake Factory

DEE'S - Bakery products–frozen - Dee's All Natural Baking
DEE'S DELICIOUS - Spaghetti sauces - Diamond Partnership
DEEYA - Skin care products - Deeya Cosmetics (Heads Inc.)
DEF - Computer software - Applied Software, Inc.
DEF - Defoliants - Bayer Corp. (Agriculture Div.)
DEF - Recording label - Pandisc Records
DEF CONTROL - Recording label - State of Fresh American Entertainment
DEF HYPE CLIPS - Recording label - MCA Universal Studios
DEF SOUL - Audio equipment - DJR Holdings, LLC
DEF WISH WAX - Recording label - Slamdek/Scramdown
DEFACER ERASER - Cleaning preparations - ProSoCo Inc.
DEFCO EYE EASE - Pharmaceutical preparations - Detroit First Aid Co.
DEFCON 5 - Computer software - Cosmi Corp.
DEFEN-L.A. TABLETS RX - Pharmaceutical preparations - Horizon Pharmaceutical Corp.
DEFENCE - Thread - Threads USA Div.
DEFEND - Chewing gum ☆ - Purdue Frederick Co.
DEFEND - Dog insecticide - Pitman-Moore Inc.
DEFEND - Skin care products - Barcolene Inc.
DEFEND-DOOR - Doors - Caradon America, Inc. (Caradon Thermal-Gard)
DEFEND-U - Pepper spray - International Business Development Corp.
DEFEND YOUR HEALTH NATURALLY - Vitamins and nutritional supplements - Naturally Vitamin Supplements Inc.
DEFENDAMINS - Vitamins and nutritional supplements - Nature's Way Products, Inc.
DEFENDEARS - Headphones - Westone Laboratories Inc.
DEFENDER - Adhesives and sealants - Dap Products Inc.
DEFENDER - Boats - Defender Industries
DEFENDER - Chemical preparations - Kristee Products Co.
DEFENDER - Filters–water - Jon-Don Products, Inc.
DEFENDER - Firearms, accessories, and parts - Welsh Sporting Goods Corp. (Boyt Div.)
DEFENDER - Floor coverings–carpet and rugs - Aladdin Mills, Inc.
DEFENDER - Floor coverings–carpet and rugs - Criterion Mills Inc.
DEFENDER - Floor coverings–carpet and rugs - Miles Carpets Inc.
DEFENDER - Floor coverings–carpet and rugs - Mohawk Carpet Corp.
DEFENDER - Flowers, plants, and seeds - Loft's Seed Inc.
DEFENDER - Furniture - Bassick Casters
DEFENDER - Lighting fixtures - Kenall Manufacturing Co.
DEFENDER - Mufflers–motor vehicle - Maremont Exhaust Products Inc.
DEFENDER - Ophthalmic goods - Foremost Optical Products
DEFENDER - Padlocks ☆ - American Lock Co.
DEFENDER - Pet products - Glo-Marr Products Inc.
DEFENDER - Thermometers - Popper & Sons Inc.
DEFENDER - Toys–models ☆ - Estes Industries
DEFENDER - Watches - Fossil Inc.
DEFENDER - Window-insulation system - Auburn Plastic Engineering
DEFENDER - Wire–barbed - Keystone Steel & Wire Co.
DEFENDER-1 - Glass–window - Defender Inc.
DEFENDER 90 - Motor vehicles–all-terrain - Land Rover North America Inc.
DEFENDER BVM - Pharmaceutical preparations - Amrion, Inc.
DEFENDER RED - Chemical preparations - Citizens Against Crime, Inc.
DEFENDER SRX+4 - Tires - Uniroyal Goodrich Licensing Services, Inc.
DEFENDER T3 - Toys - Hasbro, Inc.
DEFENDERS - Hair care products - Helene Curtis Industries Inc.
DEFENDERS - Notebooks and notepads - Earthshine Wildlife Notecards
DEFENDERS INFECTIOUS WASTE STEP CANS - Wastebaskets - United Receptacle Inc.
DEFENDING CHAMPION - Floor coverings–carpet and rugs - Barrett Carpet Mills Inc.
DEFENDOOR - Hardware - Blackfeet Writing Instruments Inc.
DEFENDOR - Toys - Tonka Corp.
DEFENDUM - Paper ☆ - Parsons Paper Co.
DEFENSE - Skin care products - Pharmagen, Inc.
DEFENSE BOOSTER - Health care products - Natural Laboratories Corp.
DEFENSE FORCE - Toys–guns - Daisy Manufacturing Co.
DEFENSE FORCE - Vitamins and nutritional supplements - Planetary Formulas
DEFENSE MAINTENANCE - Vitamins and nutritional supplements - Lifetrends International
DEFENSE RULES - Apparel and accessories - Borneo Group, Inc.
DEFENSE SERIES - Sporting goods - Figgie Licensing Corp.
DEFENSE-SHIELD - Vitamins and nutritional supplements - Nature's Sunshine Products, Inc.
DEFENSE, THE - Golf clubs - Founders Club Golf Co.
DEFENSOR - Veterinary pharmaceutical preparations - SmithKline Beecham Animal Health Products

☆ = Now out of production

DEFI-RUST - Paints - Harrison Paint Corp.
DEFIANCE - Bicycles ☆ - Huffy Corp.
DEFIANCE - Flags - Annin and Co.
DEFIANCE - Floor coverings—carpet and rugs ☆ - Patcraft Mills Inc.
DEFIANCE - Furniture - Bassick Casters
DEFIANCE - Knee braces - Smith & Nephew DonJoy Inc.
DEFIANCE - Office supplies - R.A. Stewart Superior
DEFIANCE - Stoves—wood-burning - Fabridyne Inc.
DEFIANT - Books—comic - Enlightened Entertainment Partners, L.P.
DEFIANT - Brushes—paint - Allpro Corp.
DEFIANT - Floor coverings—carpet and rugs ☆ - Criterion Mills Inc.
DEFIANT ENCORE - Stoves—wood-burning - Vermont Castings, Inc.
DEFIANT, THE - Shoes—athletic ☆ - Titleist & Foot-Joy Worldwide
DEFICIT - Apparel and accessories - Michael D. Thies
DEFILE - Posters - Aegis Entertainment, Inc.
DEFINE - Chemical preparations - Becker-Underwood, Inc.
DEFINE - Vitamins and nutritional supplements - Diane Wakat
DEFINE & DAZZLE - Cosmetics - Del Pharmaceuticals, Inc.
DEFINITELY DINOSAURS - Toys - Playskool, Inc.
DEFINITELY NOT NEUTRAL - Fabrics—tapestry ☆ - Combeau Industries
DEFINITION - Furniture - Thomasville Furniture Industries Inc.
DEFINITION - Window coverings - Levolor Inc.
DEFINITION SD - Floor coverings—carpet and rugs - Karastan-Bigelow Inc.
DEFINITIONS - Hair care products - Conair Corp.
DEFINITIVE CLOTHING CO. - Apparel—women's - Christina James Ltd.
DEFINITIVE TECHNOLOGY - Audio equipment - Definitive Technology Inc.
DEFLECT - Sunblocks - SBS Products, Inc.
DEFLECT-O - Heating equipment - Deflecto Corp.
DEFLECTA-SHIELD - Motor vehicle parts and accessories - Deflecta-Shield
DEFLECTOJET - Nozzles - Spraying Systems Co.
DEFLECTOR - Goggles—safety - Ektelon
DEFLECTOR - Windshield frames—motor vehicle ☆ - National Cycle Inc.
DEFOAMER - Cleaning preparations - Hillyard Enterprises, Inc.
DEFOAMER - Cleaning preparations—carpet and rug - Dependable Chemical Co.
DEFOCUS IMAGE CONTROL - Cameras - Nikon Inc.
DEFORD - Musical instruments ☆ - Emerson Musical Instruments Inc.
DEFORMULA 1 - Toys—automobiles - Mattel, Inc.
DEFRIZZ'N SHINE - Hair care products - Dowbrands L.P.
DEFROSTERS - Boots - Kaufman Footwear
DEFROSTMASTER 2000 - Heating equipment - Personalized Products, Inc.
DEFT - Finishing agents - Deft Inc.
DEFTHANE - Varnishes - Deft Inc.
DEFTOIL - Finishing agents - Deft Inc.
DEFUSER PLUS - Electronic equipment - Gabriel, Inc.
DEFY - Floor coverings—carpet and rugs ☆ - Patcraft Mills Inc.
DEFY - Pharmaceutical preparations ☆ - Akorn Inc.
DEFY - T-shirts—women's - Defy
DEG - Musical instruments - Deg Music Products Inc.
DEG POWERSTAR - Musical instrument accessories ☆ - Deg Music Products Inc.
DEGAS - Artists' materials - M. Grumbacher Inc.
DEGAS - Floor coverings ☆ - Congoleum Corp.
DEGAS - Lighters - Colibri Inc.
DEGAS - Paper ☆ - Hunt Manufacturing Co.
DEGAS - Wallcoverings - Stretchwall Fabrics Co.
DEGAS ROSE - Lipsticks - Lancome
DEGEST 2 - Ophthalmic goods - Barnes-Hind Inc.
DEGEST 2 - Pharmaceutical preparations ☆ - Akorn Inc.
DEGILDE - Furniture—public buildings - Worden Co.
DEGLON - French cutlery - Cook Things
DEGLOSSER - Paint and wallpaper cleaners - Savogran Co.
DEGRAFFENREID - Food products - J.L. Degraffenreid & Sons Inc.
DEGRAH - Paints ☆ - Valspar Corp.
DEGRAZIA - Figurines ☆ - Goebel of North America
DEGRAZIA - Novelty items - Artists of the World
DEGREAS-IT - Degreasing solvents - Surco Products Inc.
DEGREASER PLUS - Cleaning preparations - Stanley Home Products Inc.
DEGREASOL - Degreasing solvents - Kleer Flo Co. Inc.
DEGREE - Deodorants—personal - Helene Curtis Industries Inc.
DEGREES - Sunglasses - Revo, Inc.
DEGREEZER - Stain removers ☆ - ITW Fluid Products
DEGRIP - Motorcycles - Gold Belt Line Inc.
DEHART - Paints - Dehart Paint & Varnish Co.
DEHIST - Pharmaceutical preparations ☆ - Forest Pharmaceuticals Inc.
DEHLINGER WINERY - Wines - Dehlinger Winery

DEHNERS - Leather goods - Dehner Co. Inc.
DEHYBOR - Insecticides - U.S. Borax Inc.
DEHYDRATINE - Waterproofing compounds - A.C. Horn Co.
DEI - Alarm systems - Directed Electronics, Inc.
DEI - Identification tags - Rockwell Shops Ltd.
DEI FRATELLI PRIMA QUALITA BRAND FRESH & READY - Vegetables—canned - Hirzel Canning Co.
DEIDRE - Dolls - Mattel, Inc.
DEIGHTONS TRANSFERS - Handwork supplies - American Crewel & Canvas Studio
DEIMOS - Golfing equipment - Mars Golf Supply
DEINHARD - Wines ☆ - Kobrand Corp.
DEINHARD GREEN LABEL - Beverages—alcohol - Deinhard & Partners
DEITERWINKLER - Pet products - Active Pet Supplies
DEITRINTINO - Binoculars ☆ - Ercona Corp.
DEJA - Apparel and accessories - Deja Inc.
DEJA VIEWS - Stencils - C-Thru Ruler Co.
DEJA VU - Computer software - Mindscape Software Inc.
DEJA VU - Computer software - VNM Inc.
DEJA VU - Floor coverings—carpet and rugs - Customweave Carpets Inc.
DEJA VU - Floor coverings—carpet and rugs - Patcraft Mills Inc.
DEJA VU - Sunglasses - Nassau Lens Co. Inc.
DEJA VUE - Greeting cards ☆ - Thought Factory
DEJACQUES - Musical instrument accessories - Dejacques Musical Accessories Co.
DEJASHOE - Shoes - Northwest Quality Innovations Inc.
DEJEAN'S - Food products ☆ - Borden, Inc.
DEJORIA BOTANICAL WHITE OAK FACIAL CLEANSER - Cosmetics - John Paul Jones Dejoria
DEJORIA FACIAL FRESH - Cosmetics - John Paul Jones Dejoria
DEJUNO - Apparel and accessories - Dejuno Watch Corp.
DEK-MAT - Floor coverings - American Floor Products Co. Inc.
DEK-PRO-TECH - Sealing compounds - Monsey Products Co.
DEK-QUIN - Pharmaceutical preparations - C.O. Truxton Inc.
DEK RX - Varnishes - Pro Shop Co.
DEKA - Artists' materials - Dec-Art Co.
DEKA - Batteries - East Penn Manufacturing Co., Inc.
DEKA IRONON - Artists' materials - Dec-Art Co.
DEKA-MOSAIK - Puzzles - Kadon Enterprises Inc.
DEKA-STAR - Puzzles - Kadon Enterprises Inc.
DEKADOOR - Wood products - Georgia-Pacific Corp.
DEKAFFO - Coffee - Van Rooy Coffee Co.
DEKALB - Flowers, plants, and seeds - Dekalb Genetics Corp.
DEKALEATHER - Wood products - Georgia-Pacific Corp.
DEKALUX - Wood products - Georgia-Pacific Corp.
DEKAPLEX - Waterproofing compounds ☆ - Andek Corp.
DEKARA - Jewelry - Karadolian Jewelry
DEKAREM - Binoculars ☆ - Ercona Corp.
DEKARIS - Binoculars ☆ - Ercona Corp.
DEKARISMO - Binoculars ☆ - Ercona Corp.
DEKASOL - Pharmaceutical preparations - Seatrace Co.
DEKATILE - Wood products - Georgia-Pacific Corp.
DEKCHOICE - Building materials - Pro Shop Co.
DEKCLEAR - Sealant - Pro Shop Co.
DEKEN'S - Health care products - Deken's Products
DEKMOP - Mops - Ecot, Inc.
DEKO COVER - Flower pots—earthenware - Dek Marketing, Inc.
DEKODAR - Toys - Mattel, Inc.
DEKOR - Paints - Vanguard Paints & Finishes Inc.
DEKOTONES - Tiles—ceramic ☆ - American Olean Tile Co.
DEKRALITE - Floor coverings—tile - Mer-Kote Products, Inc.
DEKS OLJE - Finishing agents - Flood Co.
DEKS RENS - Cleaning preparations ☆ - Flood Co.
DEKSIDE - Metal finishing equipment - Pro Shop Co.
DEKSWOOD - Cleaning preparations - Flood Co.
DEKTOL - Photographic equipment - Eastman Kodak Co.
DEKTOMATIC - Photographic equipment - Eastman Kodak Co.
DEKTRA - Glass products ☆ - Globe-Amerada Glass Co.
DEL-AIR - Paints - M.A. Bruder & Sons Inc.
DEL ALPE - Food products - Fred Montesi Super Markets
DEL-AQUA - Pharmaceutical preparations ☆ - Del-Ray Labs, Inc.
DEL BETA - Pharmaceutical preparations - Del-Ray Labs, Inc.
DEL CABO - Fruits and vegetables - Jacobs Farm/Del Cabo Inc.
DEL CANTO - Guitars - WMI Corp.
DEL CARA - Fruits—dried - Central California Raisin Packing Co. Inc.
DEL CARIBE - Cheese - V & V Food Products, Inc.

DEL-CARMEN - Tortillas - Puebla Foods, Inc.

DEL CENTRO - Crackers - Vista Bakery, Inc.

DEL CERRO - Nuts–salted, roasted, cooked, or canned - Stahmann Farms Inc.

DEL-CLENS - Skin care products - Del-Ray Labs, Inc.

DEL CONCA - Tiles–ceramic - Maxsam Sales, Inc.

DEL CONCA - Tiles–mosaic - TJ Imports

DEL CONTE - Novelty items - N. Villar, Inc.

DEL CORONADO - Cooking utensils–cast iron ☆ - National Housewares

DEL DESTINO - Olive oil - Atalanta Corp.

DEL DIXIE - Pickles - Mrs. Dalton's Best Maid Products

DEL-E-TAPE - Ribbons–inked ☆ - Aetna Products Co. Inc.

DEL FALEGNAME - Wines - Vintwood International Ltd.

DEL FINO - Floor coverings ☆ - Congoleum Corp.

DEL FINO II - Floor coverings ☆ - Congoleum Corp.

DEL-FIX - Adhesives and sealants - Lilly Industrial Coatings Inc. (Delkote Div.)

DEL FRATELLI - Food products - Hirzel Canning Co.

DEL GAIZO - Tomato pastes and sauces - A. Sargenti Co. Inc.

DEL GRECO - Floor coverings - Mannington Resilient Floors

DEL GROSSO - Food products - Del Grosso Foods Inc.

DEL HAVEN - Food products - S.M. Flickinger Co. Inc.

DEL LAGO - Floor coverings - Tarkett, Inc.

DEL-LITE - Yarn - Delaine Worsted Mills

DEL MAR - Apparel and accessories - Del Mar Thoroughbred Club

DEL MAR - Cabinets - Del Mar Cabinets

DEL MAR - Candles - Knorr Beeswax Products Inc.

DEL MAR - Floor coverings - Congoleum Corp.

DEL MAR - Floor coverings–carpet and rugs - Cabin Crafts Carpets

DEL MAR - Floor coverings–carpet and rugs ☆ - Regal Rugs Inc.

DEL MAR - Food products - Ambassador Seafoods Inc.

DEL MAR - Food products ☆ - Del Mar Food Products Corp.

DEL MAR - Furniture - Hooker Furniture Corp.

DEL MAR - Furniture ☆ - Universal Flooring

DEL MAR - Medical apparatus - Del Mar Avionics

DEL MAR - Trailers–travel - Leader Enterprises

DEL MAR - Watches - La Costa Time L.C.

DEL MAR - Window coverings - Del Mar Window Coverings

DEL MAR - Window coverings - Vertical Blind Factory

DEL MAR BEDFORD - Cabinets - Del Mar Cabinets

DEL MAR NORDIC - Cabinets - Del Mar Cabinets

DEL MAR PLAID - Bedding–linen - Dan River Inc.

DEL MARIOS - Pizzas–frozen - Chicago Brothers, Inc.

DEL-MAX - Flowers, plants, and seeds - Delta and Pine Land Co.

DEL MAYAB - Spices and extracts - La Perla Spice Co., Inc.

DEL MONTE - Food products - Del Monte Corp.

DEL MONTE FRUIT BLENDS - Beverages - Del Monte Corp.

DEL MONTE LITE - Fruits–canned - Del Monte Corp.

DEL MONTE QUALITY TROPICAL FRUIT BLENDS - Fruit drinks–bottled or canned - Del Monte Corp.

DEL MONTE SPECIALTIES - Vegetables–canned - Del Monte Corp.

DEL MUNDO - Food products ☆ - Calavo Growers of California

DEL-NORTE - Food products - Eureka Fisheries

DEL PAIS - Shortening - Colita Beverage Corp.

DEL-PHOS - Insecticides for animals, crops - Pitman-Moore Inc.

DEL-PHOS - Veterinary pharmaceutical preparations - Schering-Plough Animal Health

DEL PINO'S - Pasta - Moran Foods, Inc.

DEL RAY - Boats–motor - Thompson Boat Co.

DEL RAY - Furniture–upholstered ☆ - Mersman Furniture Co.

DEL RAY - Guitars - WMI Corp.

DEL-RAY - Hair care products - Del-Ray Labs, Inc.

DEL RAY - Handbags - Tandem Imports Corp.

DEL RAY DOBBY - Fabrics - Rosebar Textile Co.

DEL REAL - Cabinets - Superior Woodwork Inc.

DEL REY - Food products - Del Rey Tortilleria Inc.

DEL REY - Furniture ☆ - Universal Flooring

DEL REY - Publisher's imprints - Random House, Inc.

DEL REY PLAID - Bedding–linen - Dan River Inc.

DEL-RICHES - Vegetables–frozen - J.G. Townsend Jr. & Co. Inc.

DEL RIO - Apparel stores–sports - Jem Sportswear Inc.

DEL RIO - Fabrics - Dan River Inc.

DEL RIO - Floor coverings ☆ - Congoleum Corp.

DEL RIO - Food products - Del Rio Orchards

DEL RIO - Furniture - Homecrest Industries Inc.

DEL RIO - Olives–pickled or brined - A. Camacho Inc.

DEL RIO - Recording label ☆ - Marsal Productions Inc.

DEL RIO - Wines ☆ - Bardenheier Wine Cellars

DEL RIO GOLD - Floor coverings–carpet and rugs - Coronet Carpets Inc.

DEL ROYALE - Fabrics - Dan River Inc.

DEL SOL - Fans–electric - Hunter Fan Co.

DEL SOL - Fruits and vegetables - West Indies Tropical Sales Co.

DEL SOL - Motor vehicles–automobiles - American Honda Motor Co. Inc. (Acura Div.)

DEL SOL - Recording label - Musimex Inc.

DEL SOL - Tomato pastes and sauces - Purcell International

DEL SOL SERIES - Skylights - Sun-Tek Industries Inc.

DEL-STAT - Skin care products - Del-Ray Labs, Inc.

DEL TERRA - Tomato pastes and sauces - Furman Foods, Inc.

DEL-TRAC - Pharmaceutical preparations - Del-Ray Labs, Inc.

DEL TUSSEX - Pharmaceutical preparations - Deleon Laboratories Inc.

DEL-VAL FILTER - Fabrics - Delaware Valley Corp.

DEL-VAL FLUFF - Fabrics - Delaware Valley Corp.

DEL VECCHIO - Apparel–men's - Pennshire Shirt Corp.

DEL-VI-A - Pharmaceutical preparations ☆ - Del-Ray Labs, Inc.

DEL WARE - Floor coverings ☆ - Congoleum Corp.

DELA CUISINE - Housewares - Ernest Sohn Creations

DELACORT - Pharmaceutical preparations ☆ - Mericon Industries Inc.

DELACORTE PRESS - Publisher's imprints - Bantam Doubleday Dell Publishing Group, Inc.

DELACOUR - Brandy - Blair Importers Ltd.

DELACOUR - Brandy - David Sherman Corp.

DELACRE - Cookies - Campbell Soup Co.

DELACRE - Cookies - Morris National Inc.

DELACRE - Cookies - Prince of Peace Enterprises Inc.

DELADUMONE - Pharmaceutical preparations - Bristol-Myers Squibb Co.

DELAFIELD - Sinks–metal - Kohler Co.

DELAFORCE - Wines - Palace Brands Co.

DELAFORCE - Wines ☆ - Shaw-Ross International Importers

DELAGAR - Skin care products - Delagar

DELALATE - Pharmaceutical preparations ☆ - Wesley Pharmacal Co. Inc.

DELAMAIN - Wines - European Beverage Co., Inc.

DELAMAIN & CO. - Wines - Kobrand Corp.

DELAMINE-500 - Pharmaceutical preparations - Vista Laboratories Inc.

DELAMONT - Watches - Hampden Corp.

DELANCY - Tiles–ceramic - American Olean Tile Co.

DELAND'S DECK - Novelty items - S.S. Adams Co.

DELANEY BOOK, THE - Publisher's imprints - Delaney Books Inc.

DELANO FARMS - Fruits and vegetables - Delano Farms Co.

DELANO GROWER'S - Beverages - Delano Grower's Grape Products

DELANO STUDIOS - Giftware - Low Country Guild

DELAPAV - Pharmaceutical preparations - Dunhall Pharmaceuticals Inc.

DELAR SMALL BURNET - Flowers, plants, and seeds - Jacklin Seed

DELAS FRERES - Wines ☆ - Dreyfus Ashby Inc.

DELASEPTIC - Soap - Delta Medical Products Corp.

DELAUNE'S - Spices and extracts - Louisiana Food & Packaging, Inc.

DELAVAN - Skin care products ☆ - Miles Inc.

DELAVAN - Transport trailers and equipment and parts - Ryder Automotive Operations, Inc.

DELAVERDE - Olive oil - Bertolli USA, Inc.

DELAVISION - Computer storage devices–optical - Delmar Co.

DELAWARE - Cabinets - Imperial Cabinet Co. Inc.

DELAWARE - Furniture - Dinaire Corp.

DELAWARE - Wines - Bully Hill Vineyards, Inc.

DELAWARE PUNCH - Beverages–carbonated - Barq's Inc.

DELAWARE PUNCH - Food products - Delaware Punch Co.

DELAWARE SAMPLER, THE - Chocolate candy - The Planning Factory, Inc.

DELAXIN - Health care products ☆ - Ferndale Laboratories, Inc.

DELAYED MAGNETIC UNCOUPLING - Toys–trains - Kadee Quality Products

DELAYED REACTION - Sporting goods - Advanced Polishing Products

DELAZINC - Pharmaceutical preparations - Mericon Industries Inc.

DELCARO - Floor coverings–carpet and rugs - Evans-Black Carpet Mills

DELCATH - Intercontinental Enterprises Ltd.

DELCIA - Barrettes - Accessories International

DELCID - Antacids - Marion Merrell Dow

DELCI'S - Jewelry - Ramodi's

DELCLEAR - Thread ☆ - American & Efird, Inc.

DELCO - Motor vehicle parts and accessories - General Motors Corp. (Delco Moraine Div.)

DELCO - Pencils - Empire Berol USA

DELCO - Thread ☆ - American & Efird, Inc.

DELCO - Washing machine parts - Alto U.S. Inc.

☆ = Now out of production

DELCO ELECTRONICS - Automotive-audio equipment - Delco Electronics Corp.

DELCO FREEDOM BATTERIES - Batteries - General Motors Corp. (AC Delco Div.)

DELCO-GM/BOSE - Automotive-audio equipment - Delco Electronics Corp.

DELCO LOC - Automotive-stereo security system - Delco Electronics Corp.

DELCO-REMY - Electrical equipment - General Motors Corp. (AC Delco Div.)

DELCO SUPREME - Brake fluids - General Motors Corp. (Delco Moraine Div.)

DELCOFILE - Office supplies - Delco Associates Inc.

DELCORE - Thread ☆ - American & Efird, Inc.

DELCORT - Pharmaceutical preparations - Roberts/Hauck Pharmaceuticals Inc.

DELCOTRON - Alternators–automotive - General Motors Corp. (AC Delco Div.)

DELDAN - Giftware ☆ - Towle Silversmiths

DELEAL - Skin care products - Cutter Laboratories

DELECTA - Colognes ☆ - Avon Products, Inc.

DELECTA - Furniture - Tomlinson of High Point Inc.

DELECTA-RAY - Food products - Tyson Foods Inc.

DELECTABLE - Cookies ☆ - Sunshine Biscuits, Inc.

DELECTABLE - Floor coverings–carpet and rugs - Lees Carpets

DELECTABLE COLLECTIBLES - Candy - Miss Saylor's Candies

DELECTABLE LIPCOLOR - Lipsticks - Ilona, Inc.

DELECTABLES - Underwear and nightwear - Maidenform Inc.

D'ELEGANCE - Cabinets - Flair Cabinetware

D'ELEGANCE - Plumbing fixtures–porcelain - Speakman Co. (Manufacturing Div.)

DELEGATE! - Computer software - Precision Dataquest

DELEGATE - Floor coverings–carpet and rugs - Criterion Mills Inc.

DELEGATE - Floor coverings–carpet and rugs - Cumberland Mills Inc.

DELEGATE - Luggage - Samsonite Corp.

DELEGATE - Mattresses and box springs - Ohio Mattress Co.

DELEGATE - Office supplies - Alvin and Co. Inc.

DELEGATE - Trailers–travel - Royals International

DELEGATE, THE - Binders ☆ - 20th Century Plastics

DELEGATI - Wines ☆ - Prestige Wine Imports Corp.

DELEMONT - Knives–pocket - Buck Knives, Inc.

DE'LEON - Posters - Winbar Designs

DELESTROGEN - Pharmaceutical preparations - Bristol-Myers Squibb Co.

DELET OLMER RECORDS - Recording label - Meda Records Inc.

DELETE - Beauty aids - American Cosmetic Manufacturing Laboratories Inc.

DELETE - Cleaning preparations–household - Hank Landau

DELETE - Cosmetics - Cameo Coutures

DELETE - Herbicides - Nomix, Inc.

DELETE - Skin care products - Les Femmes Inc.

DELETE! - T-shirts–men's - Whodunit Design, Inc.

DELETE SENTRY - Computer software - Central Point Software Inc.

DELEWARE - Wines - Heritage Wine Cellars

DELEX - Mouthwashes - Delex Products

DELF - Yarn - Brunswick Yarns

DELFEN - Pharmaceutical preparations - Ortho Pharmaceutical Corp.

DELFETA-SED - Pharmaceutical preparations - Eastern Research Laboratories

DELFETAMINE - Pharmaceutical preparations - Eastern Research Laboratories

DELFINO - Floor coverings–carpet and rugs - Lees Carpets

DELFINO - Whirlpools - Jacuzzi Inc.

DELFLEET - Paints - PPG Industries, Inc.

DELFT - Gingerbread–mixes - Holland-American Importing Co. Inc.

DELFT - Tiles–ceramic ☆ - Wenczel Tile Co.

DELFT BLUE - Glassware–household ☆ - Lenox Crystal, Inc.

DELFTREE - Mushrooms - Delftree Corp. Inc.

DELFUTS - Vinegar - Dean & Deluca Inc.

DELGADO - Food products - El Chico Foods

DELGADO OF LONDON - Greeting cards ☆ - Fran Mar Greeting cards Ltd.

DELGADOL - Pharmaceutical preparations - Vartex Pharmaceuticals Inc.

DELGARD - Fencing–iron - Delair Group Inc.

DELHI - Bicycles - Columbia Manufacturing Inc.

DELHI - Floor coverings–tile ☆ - Kentile Floors Inc.

DELHI - Rice - Southwest Rice Mill Co. Inc.

DELHI II - Floor coverings–tile ☆ - Kentile Floors Inc.

DELI - Meat products–poultry - Snowball Foods, Inc.

DELI BOARD - Bakery products - Original Oatmeal Baking Co.

DELI BUDDY - Food products machinery - M & E Manufacturing Co., Inc.

DELI-CATESSEN - Food products - Vobma Inc.

DELI CRACKERS - Crackers - Gilda Industries Inc.

DELI DILLS - Pickles - Vlasic Foods Inc.

DELI DINNERS - Meat products - Ringling Bros.-Barnum & Bailey Combined Shows, Inc.

DELI-DIXI - Pickles - Mrs. Dalton's Best Maid Products

DELI-DOUBLES - Meat products–beef - Armour Swift-Eckrich

DELI EXPRESS - Sandwiches–prepackaged - E.A. Sween Co.

DELI EXPRESS HOME STYLE - Sandwiches–prepackaged - E.A. Sween Co.

DELI-FARMS - Breads - International Baking Co.

DELI FRESH - Food products - Reser's Fine Foods Inc.

DELI-FRESH - Meat products–canned - Detroit City Dairy Inc.

DELI FRESH - Pizzas–frozen - Circle K Corp.

DELI HEARTH - Breads - Roush Products Co., Inc.

DELI INTERNATIONAL - Cheese ☆ - Olympia Cheese Co. LLC

DELI KING - Food products - Pocino Foods Co.

DELI KNIT - Crocheted and knitted items - Dickson Industries, Inc.

DELI LEAN - Meat products - Marsh Supermarkets, Inc.

DELI LINKS - Dog food - Heinz Pet Products Co.

DELI-LITE - Sausages - Vienna Sausage Manufacturing Co.

DELI MASTER - Food products ☆ - Design Foods

DELI MELT - Sandwiches–prepackaged - Denny's Inc.

DELI-N-DASH - Sandwiches–prepackaged - Golden Valley Farms Commodity Group, Inc.

DELI NOW - Meat products - Bessin Corp.

DELI NUTRITION EXPERTS, THE - Meat products–canned - Hansel 'n Gretel Brand, Inc.

DELI OLIVES - Olives–pickled or brined - Musco Olive Products Inc.

DELI ON THE RUN - Food products ☆ - Pillsbury Co.

DELI PICK-UPS - Meats - Perdue Farms Inc.

DELI POCKETS - Sandwiches–prepackaged - General American Foods Manufacturing Corp.

DELI-PRIDE - Sandwiches–prepackaged - Circle K Corp.

DELI-QUIK - Food products - Nash-Finch Co.

DELI READY - Food products - Tyson Foods Inc.

DELI RESERVE - Cheese - Golden Cheese Co. of California

DELI-RITE - Meats–luncheon - Emmber Foods, Inc.

DELI ROAST COLLECTION, THE - Turkeys - Cuddy Farms, Inc.

DELI SALAD - Food products ☆ - J.G. Van Holten & Son Inc.

DELI-SELECT - Meats–luncheon - Hillshire Farm Co.

DELI SHOPPE - Bakery products - Allied Bakers Co.

DELI SHOPPE - Meat products - Fresh Mark, Inc.

DELI SHOPPE - Sandwiches–prepackaged - Southland Corp.

DELI SINGLES - Cheese - Swissrose International Inc.

DELI SMART - Meat products–beef - Royal Quality Foods, Inc.

DELI SMOOTH - Cheese - Churny Co., Inc.

DELI SNAX - Dog food - Heinz Pet Products Co.

DELI SPEARS - Pickles - Curtice-Burns Foods, Inc.

DELI-SPREADS - Cheese - Heidi's Cheese Products

DELI SUPREME - Cheese - Sargento Cheese Co. Inc.

DELI SUPREME - Food products ☆ - Longmont Foods

DELI SUPREME - Meat products–poultry - Snowball Foods, Inc.

DELI, THE - Food products - Publix Super Markets, Inc.

DELI-THIN - Meats–luncheon - Oscar Mayer Foods Corp.

DELI TO GO - Salads–prepackaged - Mrs. Giles Country Kitchens Inc.

DELI TRAY - Meats–luncheon - Conagra, Inc.

DELI TRIM - Meat products - John Morrell & Co.

DELI USA - Cheese - Dan Carter Inc.

DELI WRAP - Food products - Minnesota Foodservice, Inc.

DELIA - Caviar ☆ - Smith Brothers Food Service Inc.

DELIA - Tableware–china - Villeroy and Boch Tableware Ltd.

DELIA'S - Apparel and accessories - Delia's, Ltd

DELICACIES - Candy - Creole Delicacies Kitchens Inc.

DELICACIES - Underwear and nightwear - Maidenform Inc.

DELICACIES DIRECT - Food products - Caviar & Caviar Corp.

DELICACY - Sinks–metal - American Standard Inc.

DELICACY - Underwear and nightwear - Maidenform Inc.

DELICADO - Ophthalmic goods - Foremost Optical Products

DELICADOS - Cigarettes - G.A. Georgopulo & Co. Inc.

DELICARE - Detergents - Smithkline Beecham Corp.

DELICASEAS - Seafood products–fresh or frozen ☆ - Kibun Products International Inc.

DELICATE CYCLE - Detergents - Andrew Jergens Co.

DELICATE LILY - Dinnerware ☆ - Corning Inc.

DELICATE POWDER - Deodorants–personal - Bristol-Myers Squibb Co.

DELICATE ROSE - Skin care products - Maybelline Co.

DELICATE SPLENDOR - Nail care products ☆ - Shiseido Cosmetics (America) Ltd.

DELICATE TRIO - Dinnerware ☆ - Corning Inc.

DELICATES - Underwear and nightwear - J.C. Penney Co., Inc.

DELICATESSEN - Breads - Schmidt Baking Co., Inc.

DELICATO - Tomato pastes and sauces - Delicato Foods, Inc.
DELICATO - Wines - Delicato Vineyards
DELICATO - Wines ☆ - Winequest
DELICATO FAMILY VINEYARDS - Wines - Winequest
DELICATO GRAPE STOMP - Wines ☆ - Delicato Vineyards
DELICE - Biscuits - Bahlsen Inc.
DELICE - Lipsticks - Lancome
DELICE AU CHOCOLAT - Cookies - Pepperidge Farm Inc.
DELICE DE DIJON - Food products - Casino North America
DELICE DE FRANCE - Cheese - Bongrain Cheese USA
DELICE DE FRANCE - Dairy products - Bc-USA, Inc.
DELICE DE STRASBOURG - Food products ☆ - Liberty Richter Inc.
DELICE MYSTERE - Cosmetics - Lancome
DELICIA - Accordions - Castiglione Accordion
DELICIAS - Food products - Delicias, Inc.
DELICIAS - Food products ☆ - Southern Frozen Foods Inc.
DELICIAS - Fruits and vegetables - Gourmet America
DELICIEUX - Cheese ☆ - Raskas Foods, Inc.
DELICIOUS - Cakes - Grandma's Bake Shoppe
DELICIOUS - Cookies - Delicious Brands, Inc.
DELICIOUS - Cookies - Delicious Cookies
DELICIOUS - Food products - Clements Food Co. Inc.
DELICIOUS - Food products - Eastrend International Inc.
DELICIOUS - Food products - John Labatt Foods
DELICIOUS - Food products - W.F. Straub & Co.
DELICIOUS - Food products - Veronica Foods Co.
DELICIOUS - Ice cream - Drigg's Dairy Farms Inc.
DELICIOUS - Vegetables–frozen - Delicious Foods Co.
DELICIOUS BEVELY HILLS - Perfumes - La Parfumerie Inc.
DELICIOUS DARLINGS - Brassieres (Bras) ☆ - Lovable Co.
DELICIOUS DUOS - Baby foods ☆ - Beech-Nut Nutrition Corp.
DELICIOUS FEELINGS - Perfumes - La Parfumerie Inc.
DELICIOUS FEELINGS BEVERLY HILLS - Perfumes - La Parfumerie Inc.
DELICIOUS FOODS - Meat products - Delicious Foods, Inc.
DELICIOUS FRUITS - Tiles–ceramic - Monarch Tile Inc.
DELICIOUS MEMORIES - Publisher's imprints - Delicious Memories, Inc.
DELICIOUS PERFECTION - Coffee - Brad Barry Co. Ltd.
DELICIOUS WISHES - Candy ☆ - Marsyl Inc. (Marsyl Enterprises, Inc.)
DELICIOUSLY LIGHT - Salad dressings–bottled - Kraft Foods, Inc.
DELICO - Cheese - Dairy Fresh Products Co.
DELICO - Cheese - Kolb-Lena Cheese Co.
DELIGHT - Beverages–malt - Hudepohl-Schoenling Brewing Co.
DELIGHT - Clocks ☆ - Sunbeam Precision Measurement
DELIGHT - Floor coverings–carpet and rugs - Quaker Inc.
DELIGHT - Pet products - Strongheart Products, Inc.
DELIGHT - Rings–jewelry - Artcarved Inc.
DELIGHT, THE - Golfing equipment - Izzo Systems, Inc.
DELIGHT TO WRITE - Stationery - Gibson Greetings, Inc.
DELIGHTFORM - Apparel stores–lingerie - Formflex Foundations Inc.
DELIGHTFUL - Floor coverings–carpet and rugs ☆ - Carpet Crafts Inc.
DELIGHTFUL - Floor coverings–carpet and rugs ☆ - S and S Mills Inc.
DELIGHTFUL MUSICALS - Figurines - Delfino Products Inc.
DELIGHTFULLY BARE - Apparel stores–lingerie - Formflex Foundations Inc.
DELIGHTFULLY DELICIOUS DESSERTS - Ice cream - Blue Ridge Farms, Inc.
DELIGHTFULLY DOTTY - Fabrics - Gretchen Bellinger Inc.
DELIGHTS - Cakes - Svenhard's Swedish Bakery Inc.
DELIGHTS - Candy - Crown Candy Corp.
DELIGHTS - Candy - Grand Specialties Co.
DELIGHTS - Television equipment - Zenith Electronics Corp.
DELIGHTS FRUITASTIC - Cookies - Keebler Co.
DELIGHTT - Floor coverings ☆ - Tarkett, Inc.
DELIHOST - Deli meats - Emet Provisions Inc.
DELIKUT - Sauerkraut - Rea-D-Pack Foods Inc.
DELILAH - Glassware–household ☆ - Oneida Ltd.
DELILAH - Medical apparatus ☆ - Camp, Inc.
DELILLE CELLARS - Wines - Delille Cellars, Inc.
DELIMA - Lubricating oils - Shell Oil Co.
DELIMER - Water heaters–household - Mor-Flo Industries Inc.
DELINDA - Shoes - Edison Brothers Stores, Inc.
DELINEASCOPE - Electronic equipment - Kalart Victor Corp.
DELINEATOR - Shirts - Butterick Co. Inc.
DELIO - Neckties - World Wide Ties Inc.
DELIPCIOUS - Lip balms - Desert Essence Cosmetics
DELI'S - Sandwiches–prepackaged ☆ - Pepperidge Farm Inc.
DELISA - Hats - Henschel Manufacturing Co.
DELISE - Food products ☆ - De Medici Imports Ltd.

DELISO - Footwear–women's - Samuels Shoe Co.
DELI'SSANT - Bakery goods - Chatel Corp.
DELISSIO - Pizzas–mixes - Kraft Foods, Inc.
DELITE - Beef - Excel Corp.
DELITE - Chocolate syrup ☆ - Deer Garden Foods-Rejuvenative Foods
DELITE - Ice cream ☆ - Drigg's Dairy Farms Inc.
DELITE - Meat products–pork - Hoffman Brothers Packing Co. Inc.
DELITEFUL - Floor coverings–carpet and rugs - Queen Carpet Corp.
DELITEFUL SCENTS - Candles ☆ - Corning Inc.
DELITES - Candy - Nabisco Foods Group
DELIVER - Animal feed supplements - Miles Inc. (Animal Health Div.)
DELIVER 2.0 - Nutritional supplement - Mead Johnson & Co.
DELIVER-EASE - Computer software - Vance Young
DELIVERING THE FUTURE TODAY - Video production - Synergistic Systems, Inc.
DELIWARE - Dinnerware–plastic - Continental/SiLite International Inc.
DELIWARE RECTANGULAR CROCKS - Cookware - Carlisle Foodservice Products, Inc.
DELIWRAPS - Food products - Del Monte Corp.
DELIZIA - Food products - Veronica Foods Co.
DELIZIO'S - Cheese - Medaris Hamilton Corp.
DELIZIOSO - Cookies - Delizioso Foods
DELKER - Foil–aluminum - Delker Corp.
DELKRON - Motor vehicle parts and accessories - Rivera Engineering, Inc.
DELL - Computers–personal - Dell Computer Corp.
DELL - Food products - Beatreme Foods, Inc.
DELL - Food products - Beatrice Cos. Inc.
DELL - Ophthalmic goods ☆ - Rozin Optical Export Corp.
DELL BOOKS - Publisher's imprints - Bantam Doubleday Dell Publishing Group, Inc.
DELL DIMENSION - Computer peripheral equipment - Dell Computer Corp.
DELL FLORALS - Novelty items - Pat Dellacroce Studio
DELL OLMO - Housewares - Arteriors
DELL PURSE BOOKS - Publisher's imprints - Bantam Doubleday Dell Publishing Group, Inc.
DELLA - Corn oil - Food Oils Corp.
DELLA CASA - Beverages–alcohol ☆ - Parrott & Co.
DELLA ROBBIA - Artists' materials - Sculpture House Inc.
DELLA ROBBIA - Glass products - Westmoreland Glass Co.
DELLA ROBBIA - Teas - Eastern Shore Tea Co.
DELLA ROSA - Floor coverings - Mannington Resilient Floors
DELLA SUPREMA - Doughs–frozen - Rich Products Corp.
DELLACO CLASSIC CONFECTIONS - Candy - Dellaco Industries, Inc.
DELLACROCE - Apparel–men's - Castle Neckwear Inc.
DELLALOS - Food products - Bernardi Italian Foods Co.
DELLAPE - Accordions - Castiglione Accordion
DELLFORD - Food products - United Grocers Inc.
DELL'ORTO - Carburetors - Rivera Engineering, Inc.
DELLORTO CARBURETORS - Carburetors - Cosmopolitan Motors Inc.
DELL'S SECRET GARDEN - Fertilizer - Dell's Secret Garden, Inc.
DELLWOOD - Dairy products - Dellwood Foods, Inc.
DELLWOOD - Floor coverings–carpet and rugs ☆ - Barrett Carpet Mills Inc.
DELLWOOD - Recording label - Dellwood Music Co. Inc.
DELLWOOD PLACE - Furniture–upholstered ☆ - Webb Furniture Enterprises Inc.
DELMAG - Electrical equipment - Pileco, Inc.
DELMAID - Margarine - Miami Margarine Co. Inc.
DELMAN - Footwear–women's - Nina Footwear Co., Inc.
DELMAR - Floor coverings–carpet and rugs ☆ - Porter Carpet Mills Inc.
DELMAR - Margarine - Miami Margarine Co. Inc.
DELMAR - Sandals - Playazul International Inc.
DELMAR PUBLISHERS INC. - Textbooks - Delmar Publishers Inc.
DELMARK - Recording label - Delmark Records
DELMARK - Vitamins and nutritional supplements - Novartis Nutrition Corp.
DELMARK QUICK - Desserts - Novartis Nutrition Corp.
DELMARVA - Food products - Williamsburg Canning Co.
DELMED - Pharmaceutical preparations - Delmed Inc.
DELMHORST INSTRUMENT CO. - Electrical equipment - Delmhorst Instrument Co.
DELMONICO - Luggage - United States Luggage Corp.
DELMONICO - Macaroni ☆ - Pastamania
DELMONICO - Pasta - Hershey Pasta Group
DELMONICO - Seafood products–canned or cured - Bumble Bee Seafoods, Inc.
DELMONICO - Spices and extracts - Roosa & Ratliff Drug Co.
DELMONT SQUARE - Floor coverings - Tarkett, Inc.

☆ = Now out of production

DELMONTE - Cases–musical instrument ☆ - St. Louis Music Supply Co.
DELO - Health care products - Unicare Health & Fitness Co.
DELOBA - Biscuits - Bahlsen Inc.
DELODUR - Glass–window - Crystal International Corp.
DELONG - Apparel and accessories - DeLong Sportswear Inc.
DELONG - Glass products - Bellco Glass Inc.
DELONG'S - Food products - Delong's Pine Tree Packing Co.
DELORE - Cosmetics - American International Industries
DELORE FOR NAILS - Manicure preparations - Delore International
DELORES - Apparel and accessories - Ross of Florida Inc.
DELORME - Computer software - Delorme Publishing Co., Inc.
DELORME GLOBAL EXPLORER - Computer software - Delorme Publishing Co., Inc.
DELORO - Cologne and aftershave ☆ - London International U.S. Holdings
DELORO - Floor coverings ☆ - Congoleum Corp.
DELOS - Apparel and accessories - Perry Manufacturing Co.
DELOS - Chairs–upholstered ☆ - Fixtures Furniture
DELOS - Pet products - Fishy Farmacy
DELOS - Recording label - Delos Records International
DELOS - Vases - Durand International
DELOS-FY - Recording label ☆ - Delos Records International
DELOUIS - Food products - Bel Canto Fancy Foods Ltd.
DELOUIS FILS - Food products - Gourmet America
DELOVELY - Floor coverings–carpet and rugs ☆ - S and S Mills Inc.
DELPHI - Cabinets - Del Mar Cabinets
DELPHI - Cigarettes - G.A. Georgopulo & Co. Inc.
DELPHI - Flatware - Reed and Barton Corp.
DELPHI - Floor coverings–carpet and rugs - Roxbury Carpet Co.
DELPHI - Footwear–men's - Baker-Benjes, Inc.
DELPHI - Frames–picture - Terragrafics Inc.
DELPHI - Glass products - Pittsburgh Corning Corp.
DELPHI - Rings–jewelry - Artcarved Inc.
DELPHI - Telephones - TIE Communications Inc.
DELPHI - Wallpaper - S.R. Wood Inc.
DELPHIC - Lighting fixtures - Holophane Corp.
DELPHINA'S - Bakery products - Neighborhood Baking Co.
DELPHINIUS - Whirlpools - Lasco Products Group
DELPHINUS - Furniture ☆ - Bassett Furniture Industries, Inc.
DELPHOS - Gutters–metal - New Delphos Manufacturing
DELPHUS - Computer software - Delphus Inc.
DELPROOF - Thread ☆ - American & Efird, Inc.
DELPUMP - Pumps - CHPT, Inc.
DELRAY - Floor coverings - American Floor Products Co. Inc.
DELRAY - Thread - Threads USA Div.
DELRAY FARMS FRESH MARKET - Apparel–athletic - Delray Farms, Inc.
DELREY - Floor coverings - Mannington Resilient Floors
DELREY - Lamps - International Product Concepts, Inc.
DELRICH - Margarine - Cudahy Co.
DELRIN - Hair care products - Fromm Industries
DELRIN - Musical instrument accessories - J. D'Addario & Co. Inc.
DELRIO - Bathroom fixtures - Crane Plumbing/Fiat Products
DELRON - Fabrics–polyester - Dale Lichy
DEL'S - Beverages - Del's Lemonade & Refreshments
DEL'S BELLS - Fishing lures - Den Manufacturing Co.
DEL'S LIGHT - Lemonade - Del's Lemonade & Refreshments
DEL'S SOFT FROZEN CLASSIC - Lemonade - Del's Lemonade & Refreshments
DELSAFE - Thread ☆ - American & Efird, Inc.
DELSAN - Windows - Delsan Industries, Inc.
DELSAY - Liquors - Crestfield Importers Ltd.
DELSEA - Food products - Suzuki of America Automotive Corp.
DELSEY - Paper–toilet - Kimberly-Clark Corp.
DELSEY'S - Food products - Wilson Products Co. Inc.
DELSEY'S BURRITO - Food products - Wilson Products Co. Inc.
DELSHEEN - Thread ☆ - American & Efird, Inc.
DELSIDE ACRES STUDIOS - Stationery - Upstate Teaching Materials
DELSO - Crocheted and knitted items - New Era Knitting Mills
DELSOFT - Yarn - Delaine Worsted Mills
DELSPUN - Thread ☆ - American & Efird, Inc.
DELSYM - Cough medicines - Fisons Corp.
DELT-A-ROLLA - Infant product - Delta Enterprise Corp.
DELTA - See **EDCOR MAGNETIC**
DELTA - Apparel and accessories - Duck Head Apparel Co., Inc.
DELTA - Automated money order machines - Travelers Express Co., Inc.
DELTA - Bicycles ☆ - Roadmaster Corp.
DELTA - Boats - Glen-L Marine Designs

DELTA - Boats–motor - Great River Marine Inc.
DELTA - Boats–motor ☆ - Thunderbird Products
DELTA - Boats–skiffs - Delta Class Association
DELTA - Brushes–paint - Corona Brushes Inc.
DELTA - Cabinets - Imperial Cabinet Co. Inc.
DELTA - Cabinets–wood ☆ - Kemper
DELTA - Chairs–upholstered - United Chair Co., Inc.
DELTA - Cigarettes - West Park Tobacco Inc.
DELTA - Dust mops, housewares - Bouras Mop Manufacturing Co.
DELTA - Electrical equipment ☆ - Delta International Marine Products Inc.
DELTA - Fabrics - Interface, Inc.
DELTA - Fabrics - Vertilux-Louverlux Inc.
DELTA - Fans–attic - Delta Fan Ventilation Products
DELTA - Faucets - Peerless Faucet Co. (Plumbing Products Div.)
DELTA - Files–tools - Clemson Brothers Inc.
DELTA - Fishing lures - Den Manufacturing Co.
DELTA - Floor coverings ☆ - Aladdin Mills, Inc.
DELTA - Floor coverings–carpet and rugs - Mohawk Industries Inc.
DELTA - Floor coverings–carpet and rugs ☆ - Regal Rugs Inc.
DELTA - Flowers, plants, and seeds - Hooven Allison
DELTA - Frames–eyeglass - Rozin Optical Export Corp.
DELTA - Furniture - Haworth, Inc.
DELTA - Gasoline - Mapco Petroleum Inc.
DELTA - Glass–window - Croft Metals Inc.
DELTA - Hair care products - Rusk Inc.
DELTA - Health care products - Rajowalt Corp.
DELTA - Health care products ☆ - Freeman Industries LLC
DELTA - Insulation board - Rock Wool Manufacturing Co.
DELTA - Lighting equipment - Durimex Inc.
DELTA - Motor vehicle parts and accessories - Delta Consolidated Industries, Inc.
DELTA - Ophthalmic goods - Vision Ease
DELTA - Paints - Shiva Inc.
DELTA - Paper - Fay Paper Products Inc.
DELTA - Paper–toilet - Georgia-Pacific Corp.
DELTA - Partitions–wood - Advanced Equipment Corp.
DELTA - Pens ☆ - Long's Dixie Pens
DELTA - Pet products - Hartz Mountain Corp.
DELTA - Playing cards - Brown and Bigelow Inc.
DELTA - Publisher's imprints - Bantam Doubleday Dell Publishing Group, Inc.
DELTA - Recording label - Delta Entertainment Corp.
DELTA - Respirators - Racal Health and Safety Inc.
DELTA - Rings–jewelry - Delta Manufacturing Co.
DELTA - Sporting goods - Oceanic
DELTA - Sprinklers–lawn ☆ - L.R. Nelson Corp.
DELTA - Syrup - Gem Inc.
DELTA - Tableware–china - Villeroy and Boch Tableware Ltd.
DELTA - Tape–adhesive - Time Med Labeling Systems Inc.
DELTA - Tiles–ceramic - Kowa Texas Inc.
DELTA - Tires - Delta Tire Corp.
DELTA - Watches - Swiss Army Brands, Ltd.
DELTA - Yarn ☆ - JCA, Inc.
DELTA 3 - Radio magnetic instrumentation - Moore-O-Matic Inc.
DELTA-4 - Insulating materials - Rock Wool Manufacturing Co.
DELTA 5 - Boats–motor ☆ - Monark Boat Co.
DELTA-6 - Insulating materials - Rock Wool Manufacturing Co.
DELTA-8 - Insulating materials - Rock Wool Manufacturing Co.
DELTA-10 - Insulating materials - Rock Wool Manufacturing Co.
DELTA-12 - Insulating materials - Rock Wool Manufacturing Co.
DELTA 88 - Motor vehicles–automobiles ☆ - General Motors Corp. (Oldsmobile Div.)
DELTA 88 ROYALE - Motor vehicles–automobiles ☆ - General Motors Corp. (Oldsmobile Div.)
DELTA 88 ROYALE BROUGHAM - Motor vehicles–automobiles ☆ - General Motors Corp. (Oldsmobile Div.)
DELTA 200 SERIES - Lighting fixtures - Juno Lighting Inc.
DELTA AFFINITY - Prosthetic apparatus ☆ - Coloplast Corp.
DELTA AIR - Fans - Delta Fan Ventilation Products
DELTA ALBAPLEX - Pharmaceutical preparations - Upjohn Co.
DELTA AMP - Hearing aids - Beltone Electronics Corp.
DELTA BLOWING WOOL - Insulating materials - Rock Wool Manufacturing Co.
DELTA BURKE - Apparel–women's - Lady Ester Lingerie Corp.
DELTA BURKE COLLECTION - Jewelry - Roman Co.
DELTA-CAL - Medical apparatus - Utah Medical Products, Inc.
DELTA CITY - Recording label - Airwax Records Productions

DELTA CLASSIC - Musical instrument accessories - GRH Inc.
DELTA CLIPPER - Space vehicles - McDonnell Douglas Corp.
DELTA CLIPPER - Toys—models ☆ - Estes Industries
DELTA COLOR ACCENTS - Paints—artists' - Delta Technical Coatings, Inc.
DELTA-CORTEF - Pharmaceutical preparations - Upjohn Co.
DELTA CREST - Floor coverings - Mannington Resilient Floors
DELTA CW - Insulating materials - Rock Wool Manufacturing Co.
DELTA D - Water—bottled or canned - Delta D Inc.
DELTA D3 - Vitamins and nutritional supplements - Freeda Vitamins Inc.
DELTA DART - Sporting goods - O'Brien International
DELTA DART - Toys—airplanes - Comet Montrose Ltd.
DELTA DAWN - Floor coverings—carpet and rugs - Mohawk Carpet Corp.
DELTA DIAMOND - Drill bits - Diamant Boart America
DELTA-DOME - Pharmaceutical preparations ☆ - Miles Inc.
DELTA DOUBLE DART - Sporting goods - O'Brien International
DELTA DRAWING - Computer software - Spinnaker Software Corp.
DELTA DRY - Calcium compounds - Delta-Therm Corp.
DELTA ELITE - Pistols - Colt's Manufacturing Co. Inc.
DELTA FAUCET - Faucets - Masco Corp.
DELTA FAUCET - Faucets - Masco Corp. (Plumbing Products Div.)
DELTA-FLOW - Medical apparatus - Utah Medical Products, Inc.
DELTA FOIL - Ships—hydrofoils - Ackley Marine Products
DELTA FORCE - Fireworks - China Pyrotechnics, Inc.
DELTA-FPF - Insulating materials - Rock Wool Manufacturing Co.
DELTA GOLD - Potato chips - Frito-Lay, Inc.
DELTA GOLD CUP - Pistols - Colt's Manufacturing Co. Inc.
DELTA HIGH TEMP - Insulating materials - Rock Wool Manufacturing Co.
DELTA IMPORTS - Footwear—men's ☆ - Delta Shoe Group
DELTA KING - Boats - Glen-L Marine Designs
DELTA KING - Flowers, plants, and seeds - Lawhon Farm Services, Inc.
DELTA LAMELLA - Insulating materials - Rock Wool Manufacturing Co.
DELTA-LUTIN - Pharmaceutical preparations - Bolan Pharmaceutical Inc.
DELTA MAGNETICS - Electronic equipment ☆ - Edcor Electronics
DELTA MAID - Insulating materials - Rock Wool Manufacturing Co.
DELTA MANOR - Trailers—travel - Fleetwood Enterprises, Inc.
DELTA MARINE - Insulation board - Rock Wool Manufacturing Co.
DELTA METAL-MESH - Insulating materials - Rock Wool Manufacturing Co.
DELTA NO-TANGLE - Safety products - D B Industries, Inc.
DELTA ONE SHOT - Insulating materials - Rock Wool Manufacturing Co.
DELTA PC - Insulating materials - Rock Wool Manufacturing Co.
DELTA PERSONALLY - Prosthetic apparatus - Coloplast Corp.
DELTA PF - Insulating materials - Rock Wool Manufacturing Co.
DELTA PRIDE - Fish—fresh or frozen - Delta Pride Catfish Inc.
DELTA QUEEN - Fruits and vegetables - Jack Klein Trust Partnership
DELTA QUEEN - Jewelry - Delta Queen Steamboat Co.
DELTA ROSE - Rice - Louis Dreyfus Holding Co. Inc.
DELTA SA-FIRE - Insulating materials ☆ - Rock Wool Manufacturing Co.
DELTA SA-FIRE BOARD - Insulating materials - Rock Wool Manufacturing Co.
DELTA SAFING - Insulation board - Rock Wool Manufacturing Co.
DELTA-SCAN - Laboratory apparatus - Opti-Vue, Inc.
DELTA SCOUT - Insecticides - Hercon Environmental Corp.
DELTA SPORTCRUISER - Boats—motor ☆ - Larson Boat Div.
DELTA STAR - Electronic equipment - Delta Star Inc.
DELTA STAR - Kites - Hi-Flier Manufacturing Co.
DELTA STAR - Rice - Riceland Foods, Inc.
DELTA STAR - Toys—models ☆ - Estes Industries
DELTA STREAK - Toys—airplanes - Paul K. Guillow Inc.
DELTA-SX - Radios - General Electric Co.
DELTA TEC - Drafting supplies - Martin Universal Design Inc.
DELTA TRIMMER - Machinery - Muller Martini Corp.
DELTA-V - Archery equipment ☆ - Bear Archery Inc.
DELTA-V - Computer software - Media Technology Ltd.
DELTA VEHICLE SECURITY - Automotive parts and accessories - Delta
  Vehicle Security
DELTA-WARM - Calcium compounds - Delta-Therm Corp.
DELTA WEDGE - Toys—models ☆ - Estes Industries
DELTA WING - Toys—airplanes ☆ - Life-Like Products Inc.
DELTA WING GLIDERS - Toys—airplanes ☆ - Paul K. Guillow Inc.
DELTABAC - Floor coverings - Mannington Carpets, Inc.
DELTABELLS - Exercising equipment - Excel Sports Science Inc.
DELTAGARD - Insecticides - Agrevo Environmental Health, Inc.
DELTAGEL - Food products - Quest International Flavors & Food Ingredients
  Co.
DELTAGRIP - Pens - Sheaffer Inc.
DELTAGUARD - Lighting fixtures - Ruud Lighting
DELTAH - Jewelry - Imperial-Deltah Inc.

DELTALIN - Pharmaceutical preparations - Eli Lilly and Co.
DELTALINE - Paving materials—concrete - Brite-Line Industries, Inc.
DELTALLOY - Wire—aluminum - Aluminum Co. of America
DELTAMAT - Mats - Rubbermaid Office Products Inc.
DELTAMATE - Medical apparatus - Data Instruments, Inc.
DELTAMAX - Amplifiers - Electro-Voice, Inc.
DELTAPINE - Flowers, plants, and seeds - Delta and Pine Land Co.
DELTAPOINT ANIMATED DESKTOP - Computer software - DeltaPoint Inc.
DELTAPOL - Abrasive products - Famtec International, Inc.
DELTAR - Automotive parts and accessories - Illinois Tool Works Inc.
DELTASCAN - Computer hardware - Teradyne, Inc.
DELTASCREEN - Projection screens - Quartet Manufacturing Co.
DELTASLEEP - Mattresses - Sealy Inc.
DELTASMYL - Barbituates ☆ - Roussel-Uclaf Corp.
DELTASONE - Pharmaceutical preparations - Upjohn Co.
DELTAVILLE DEADRISE - Boats—motor - Hulls Unlimited East Inc.
DELTAVILLE GARVEY - Boats—motor - Hulls Unlimited East Inc.
DELTEC - Electrical equipment - Deltec Electronics Corp.
DELTEX - Artists' materials ☆ - Binney & Smith Inc.
DELTEX - Musical instrument accessories - Ultimate Support Systems Inc.
DELTEX - Thread ☆ - American & Efird, Inc.
DELTINA - Thread ☆ - American & Efird, Inc.
DELTIQUE - Faucets ☆ - Masco Corp.
DELTOID AID - Health care products - Activeaid Inc.
DELTON - Apparel and accessories ☆ - Pincus Bros., Inc.
DELTORO - Thread ☆ - American & Efird, Inc.
DELTRAN - Medical apparatus - Utah Medical Products, Inc.
DELTRAN PLUS - Medical apparatus - Utah Medical Products, Inc.
DELUBE - Health care products - E-Gal Corp.
DELUGE - Sporting goods - Primex Marketing, Inc.
DELUSCIOUS - Mustard - Boston Knish
DELUX - Cabinets - Hanak Millwork
DELUX - Dinnerware—glass ☆ - Kenro Inc.
DELUX - Drums—musical instruments - Castiglione Accordion
DELUX - Recording label - Charta Records
DELUX MONOGRAM - Mats - Cactus Mat Manufacturing Co.
DELUX RUMMY Q SET - Games - Kingstone International Corp.
DELUXE - Automotive parts and accessories - Ford Motor Co.
DELUXE - Baked beans—canned - Bush Brothers and Co.
DELUXE - Bicycles - Columbia Manufacturing Inc.
DELUXE - Bowling balls - Master Industries Inc.
DELUXE - Breads - Wolferman's Inc.
DELUXE - Buckets—plastic ☆ - Arctic Products Inc.
DELUXE - Buckets—plastic ☆ - Kelley Manufacturing Co.
DELUXE - Chairs—folding ☆ - E-Z Sales & Manufacturing, Inc.
DELUXE - Cigar boxes—wood - Consolidated Cigar Corp.
DELUXE - Cosmetics ☆ - Spilo/Mehaz Worldwide
DELUXE - Fabrics - Gretchen Bellinger Inc.
DELUXE - Glassware—household - Federal Glass
DELUXE - Jewelry, watches ☆ - Disegno Collection
DELUXE - Ladders—plastic - John S. Tilley Ladders Co. Inc.
DELUXE - Lighting fixtures - General Electric Co.
DELUXE - Markers—felt-tip - Sanford Corp.
DELUXE - Mops - Royal Maid Association for the Blind Inc.
DELUXE - Mops - Zephyr Manufacturing Co.
DELUXE - Pet food - Reinders, Inc.
DELUXE - Recording label - Gusto Records Inc.
DELUXE - Shower stalls—plastic - Plaskolite Inc.
DELUXE - Siding—metal - Alcan Aluminum Corp. Alcan Building Products Div.
DELUXE - Sponges - Acme Sponge & Chamois Co., Inc.
DELUXE - Sporting goods ☆ - Wright & McGill Co.
DELUXE - Trays ☆ - Artex-Green Corp. of N.Y.
DELUXE - Vacuum cleaners and accessories ☆ - Bissell Inc.
DELUXE - Window coverings - Draco Corp.
DELUXE 5-PT. - Seats—automobile - Cosco, Inc.
DELUXE 10 - Pet products - Rolf C. Hagen (USA) Corp.
DELUXE 18 - Photographic equipment - Richard Manufacturing Co.
DELUXE 500 HONE - Abrasive products - American Hone Co.
DELUXE AGGRAVATION - Games - Lakeside Games
DELUXE ARRIVA - Seats—automobile - Cosco, Inc.
DELUXE BIG STEP - Stools—metal - Cosco, Inc.
DELUXE CANDIES - Candy - Keppel's Inc.
DELUXE CAPRICE - Organs—musical instrument ☆ - Kimball International,
  Inc.
DELUXE CHAMPION - Tires - Bridgestone/Firestone, Inc.
DELUXE CONTEMPORARY FLAIR CHAIR - High chairs ☆ - Cosco, Inc.

☆ = Now out of production

DELUXE COOTIE - Games - Tyco Toys
DELUXE CORDLESS CLIPPER CASE - Barber shop equipment - Kim Laube & Co. Inc.
DELUXE DESIGNER - Saunas - Trayco, Inc.
DELUXE DINNER MIX - Animal feeds - Pennington Seed, Inc.
DELUXE EAGLE - Sporting goods ☆ - Wright & McGill Co.
DELUXE ENGLISH MUFFINS - Breads - Saramar Corp.
DELUXE FARM - Toys–models ☆ - CBS Toys
DELUXE FLASH - Glassware–household ☆ - Delfino Products Inc.
DELUXE GRAHAMS - Cookies - Keebler Co.
DELUXE GRAND OAK - Swimming pools - Lomart Industries
DELUXE GREYSTONE - Swimming pools - Lomart Industries
DELUXE HEALTH BIKE - Exercising equipment - Battle Creek Equipment Co.
DELUXE ISLAND - Saunas ☆ - Trayco, Inc.
DELUXE KISMET - Games - Lakeside Games
DELUXE KLEENCUT - Scissors–hand-operated - Acme United Corp.
DELUXE MODEL B - Projection screens - Da-Lite Screen Co. Inc.
DELUXE MODULE - Hearing aids - Qualitone
DELUXE MOON PIE BRAND - Bakery products - Chattanooga Bakery Inc.
DELUXE MUSIC CONSTRUCTION SET - Computer software - Electronic Arts Inc.
DELUXE NADINOLA - Cosmetics - Chattem Inc.
DELUXE NAIL GENIE - Beauty shop equipment - Protec International
DELUXE OLYMPIAN - Seats–automobile - Cosco, Inc.
DELUXE PADDLE RESCUE BOARD - Swimming pools - Recreonics, Inc.
DELUXE PET-DOR - Pet products - Johnson Pet-Dor Inc.
DELUXE PILLOW - Pillows - Cascade Designs, Inc.
DELUXE PRESTO-SPARKLE PAINTS - Paint sets–hobby ☆ - Kenner Products
DELUXE PRO-SHOW - Binders - 20th Century Plastics
DELUXE QUIET TIME SWING - Infant product - Cosco, Inc.
DELUXE RANGER - Lanterns–kerosene ☆ - Dorco Manufacturing Inc.
DELUXE SATIN - Paints ☆ - Kwal-Howells Inc.
DELUXE SOCIALITE - Luggage - United States Luggage Corp.
DELUXE STURDY PLUS - Ironing boards - Design Trend, Inc.
DELUXE SUNDOWN - Window shades - Draco Corp.
DELUXE TREND - Shelving units–wood ☆ - Hirsh Co.
DELUXE TRIPPPLES - Games ☆ - Avalon Hill Game Co.
DELUXE TURF - Flowers, plants, and seeds - Seed Corp. of America
DELUXE TURNABOUT - Infant product - Cosco, Inc.
DELUXE VELVET - Seat covers - Saddleman, Inc.
DELUXE WORKCENTER - Work benches ☆ - Hirsh Co.
DELUXEHUGGER - Infant product ☆ - Cosco, Inc.
DELUXEPAINT II - Computer software - Electronic Arts Inc.
DELUXEPRINT - Computer software - Electronic Arts Inc.
DELUXEVIDEO - Computer software - Electronic Arts Inc.
DELUZE - Beverages–alcohol - David Sherman Corp.
DELVAL - Lighting fixtures - Delval Lighting
DELVERDE - Food products - Tosi Trading Co.
DELVISTA AURORE - Wines - Delvista Vineyards
DELVISTA ESTATE - Wines - Delvista Vineyards
DELVIT - Tiles–ceramic - Capitol Tile Import Co.
DELVO - Concrete–mixture - Master Builders Inc.
DELVOCID - Yeast - Gist-Brocades Food Ingredients Inc.
DELWA STAR - Medical apparatus - Zewa, Inc.
DELWEACO - Clocks - Andy H. Weaver Co.
DELWINE - Wines ☆ - Delano Grower's Grape Products
DEM - Jewelry–precious - De Merini Inc.
DEM BONES - Candy - Brach and Brock Confections Inc.
DEM-KOTE - Paints - Grainger Division
DEMA - Glassware–household - Denby USA Limited
DEMA - Pharmaceutical preparations ☆ - Rhone-Poulenc Rorer Pharmaceuticals Inc.
DEMADEX - Pharmaceutical preparations - Boehringer Mannheim Corp.
DEMAGLOW - Skin care products - Heritage Store Inc.
DEMAKUP - Skin care products - Temco USA Inc.
DEMALOGICA SOLAR DEFENSE SYSTEM - Skin care products - Dermalogica Inc.
DEMAND - Dog food - Best Feeds and Farm Supplies Inc.
DEMAND - Recording label - Cookin' Records
DEMAND FLOW - Manuals - J-I-T Institute of Technology, Inc.
DEMAND MANAGEMENT PROGRAMS - Computer software - Health Decisions, Inc.
DEMAND STREAM - Computer software - Oce Printing Systems USA, Inc.
DEMAND THE TRUTH - Paper–rolls - Fibre Glass-Evercoat Co. Inc.
DEMANDPRINT - Computer hardware ∑ Gammagraphx, Inc.

DEMAQUILLANT POUR CILS - Skin care products - Ella Bache Inc.
DEMAR - Bakery products - Demar Desserts
DEMARCATION - Dining room furniture ☆ - Daystrom Furniture Inc.
DEMARCATION I - Dining room furniture ☆ - Daystrom Furniture Inc.
DEMAREST - Luggage - American Flyer
DEMARK - Connectors–electrical - E & J Demark, Inc.
DEMARLY - Apparel and accessories - W. Seitchik & Sons Inc.
DEMASONE - Pharmaceutical preparations ☆ - Bock Pharmacal Co.
DEMASONE-LA - Pharmaceutical preparations ☆ - Bock Pharmacal Co.
DEMAX - Measuring instruments - Demax Corp.
DEMAZIN - Antihistamine preparations - Schering-Plough Healthcare Products
DEMCO - Belts–industrial ☆ - Grainger Division
DE'MEDICI - Giftware ☆ - Gorham Inc.
DEMENSIA - Floor coverings–carpet and rugs ☆ - World Carpets, Inc.
DEMEO - Cosmetics - De Meo Brothers
DEMERARA - Food products - Haze-Line International Inc.
DEMERICO - Food products - Demerico Corp.
DEMERITS - Candy - Brownie Points Natural Bakers
DEMEROL - Analgesics - Winthrop Pharmaceuticals
DEMERT - Manicure preparations - Demert & Dougherty, Inc.
DEMERT NAIL DRYER - Manicure preparations - Demert & Dougherty, Inc.
DEMERT TRAVEL SHAVE - Razors - Demert & Dougherty, Inc.
DEMETRE - Sweaters - Demetre Ski Sweaters
DEMETRIUS - Hair care products - Peter Moschera
DEMEYE - Ophthalmic goods - Foremost Optical Products
DEMI - Cosmetics - Revlon Consumer Products Corp.
DEMI - Hearing aids - Oto-Sonic Inc.
DEMI - Pencils–mechanical ☆ - Yasutomo
DEMI-5 - Pencils–mechanical ☆ - Yasutomo
DEMI-BAS - Figurines ☆ - Ideal Originals
DEMI-GIRDLE - Apparel–women's ☆ - Bali Co. Inc.
DEMI GLOSS - Paints ☆ - Pratt & Lambert United, Inc.
DEMI-JOUR - Perfumes - Houbigant, Inc.
DEMI-LOAF - Bakery products–frozen - Bridgford Foods Corp.
DEMI-MATTE - Cosmetics - Estee Lauder Inc.
DEMI-REGROTON - Pharmaceutical preparations - Rhone-Poulenc Rorer Pharmaceuticals Inc.
DEMI-SANTS - Snack foods - Premier Gourmet Products Inc.
DEMI-SHEER - Lipsticks - Revlon Consumer Products Corp.
DEMI-TASSE - Beverages–alcohol - Paddington Corp.
DEMI TASSE - Fabrics–tapestry ☆ - Columbus Coated Fabrics Co.
DEMI-TASSE - Frames–eyeglass - May Optical Co. Inc.
DEMI VELOUR - Pillows - Pacific Coast Feather Co.
DEMIDO - Pharmaceutical preparations ☆ - Wendt-Bristol Co.
DEMIHIST - Pharmaceutical preparations ☆ - Veratex Group
DEMILL - Cheese - Noon Hour Food Products
DEMILLE - Furniture ☆ - Lane Co. Inc.
DEMING - Watches - Hampden Corp.
DEMING'S - Salmon–smoked, salted, dried, or pickled - Peter Pan Seafoods, Inc.
DEMI'S - Apparel–women's - Milaca Mills, Inc.
DEMIS - Greeting cards ☆ - Yorkraft Inc.
DEMITASSE - Cookies - Sherwood Brands, Inc.
DEMITASSE AFTER DINNER - Teas - Grace Tea Co. Ltd.
DEMITASSE EXTRAS - Cookies - Sherwood Brands, Inc.
DEMITRIA - Ophthalmic goods ☆ - Luxottica
DEMITRI'S BLOODY MARY SEASONINGS - Beverages - Demitri Pallis
DEMITRI'S BLOODY MARY SEASONINGS - Seasonings - Gourmet Mixes
DEMLER'S - Food products - Lyndonville Vinegar Inc.
DEMO DONKEY - Toys–stuffed - Dakin Inc.
DEMO-GRAPHICS - Computer software ☆ - CONDUIT
DEMO MASTER - Video production - Corporate Visions Inc.
DEMOCRACY - Jeans–women's - Group B Clothing Co.
DEMOGRAPHS - Computer software - Benefit Design Consultants, Ltd.
DEMO'ING STAND - Office furniture–metal - D'ing Products
DEMOISELLE - Cosmetics - Chem Spray Aerosols Inc.
DEMOISELLE - Jewelry - Bruce Donald Co.
DEMOISELLE - Lenses–optical - Ditto Industries Inc.
DEMOLITION CLASSIC - Game machines ☆ - Brunswick Corp.
DEMOLITION DERBY - Games - Smethport Specialty Co.
DEMOLITION DIVISION - Computer software - SRA/McGraw-Hill (Div. of The McGraw-Hill Companies)
DEMOLITION EXPRESS - Power switching equipment - Robert J. Johnson
DEMOLITION GEAR - Apparel and accessories - Gary Alan Adams
DEMON - Bicycles - Ross Bicycles USA, Ltd.
DEMON - Bicycles ☆ - Muskin Leisure Products Inc.

☆ = Now out of production

DEMON - Kites ☆ - Gayla Industries Inc.
DEMON - Recording label - Titan Records
DEMON - Sporting goods - Ektelon
DEMON - Sporting goods - Wellington Leisure Products, Inc.
DEMON DESTROYER GUNN - Computer peripheral equipment - Tac Systems, Inc.
DEMON/ORC - Games - Gamescience
DEMORGAN CLASSICS - Wallpaper ☆ - Eisenhart Wallcoverings Co.
DEMOSAN - Fungicides - Kincaid Enterprises, Inc.
DEMOSHIELD - Computer software - Stirling Technologies, Inc.
DEMOZ - Food products machinery - M & E Manufacturing Co., Inc.
DEMPCO - Pumps - Dempster Industries Inc.
DEMPSEY DAIRY - Milk - Dempsey Bros. Dairies Inc.
DEMPSEYS - Beverages–malt - Joseph Huber Brewing Co., Inc.
DEMSER - Pharmaceutical preparations - Merck & Co., Inc. (Merck Research Laboratories)
DEMULEN - Pharmaceutical preparations - G. D. Searle & Co.
DEMURE - Pharmaceutical preparations - Richardson-Vicks USA
DEMURE BEIGE - Cosmetics ☆ - Sally Hansen
DEN - Food products - North Coast Processing
DEN - Sporting goods - Den Manufacturing Co.
DEN-BERE - Food products - Den-Bere International Ltd.
DEN CLENZ - Denture cleaners - L.T. Laboratories
DEN HAAN - Lamps - Weems & Plath, Inc.
DEN OUDSTEN & ZN - Giftware - Dutch Trading Co. Inc.
DEN-PAK - Handbags - Dental Concepts Inc.
DEN PERMANENTE - Candles - Den Permanente
DEN TITE - Weather stripping - W.J. Dennis & Co.
DENA - Hair care products - Dena Corp.
DENA VIE - Hair care products - Dena Corp.
DENAKA - Vodka - Sazerac Co. Inc.
DENALAN - Denture cleaners - Whitehall Laboratories
DENALI - Computer peripheral equipment - Kubota Pacific Computer, Inc.
DENALI ESPRESSO - Carts - Denali Espresso
DENALI LLAMA - Snowshoes - Mountain Safety Research, Inc.
DENALI MT. MCKINLEY - Ice cream and frozen yogurt - General Container Co. of Michigan, Inc.
DENBY - Dishes–earthenware - Denby USA Limited
DENBY GLASS - Glassware–household - Denby USA Limited
DENCIDE - Pharmaceutical preparations - Dentsply International Inc.
DENCITY - Apparel and accessories - Central Trading Enterprises, Inc.
DENCLENZ - Denture cleaners - Sandoz Pharmaceuticals Corp.
DENCO - Emery products - Belcam Inc.
DENCO - Lead products - Deniston Co.
DENCO - Recording label - Terock Records
DENCO - Scissors–hand-operated - Delagar
DENCO SUPER II - Sporting goods ☆ - Wright & McGill Co.
DENCORUB - Analgesics - Alvin Last Inc.
DENDHUR - Furniture - Haworth, Inc.
DENDRID - Ophthalmic goods ☆ - Alcon Laboratories, Inc.
DENEER - Furniture ☆ - Woodmark International, Inc.
DENEUL - Garden equipment - Seymour Manufacturing Co.,Inc.
DENEUVE - Colognes ☆ - Avon Products, Inc.
DENIC - Cigarettes - Philip Morris Companies Inc.
DENICLEAN - Tobacco products ☆ - Alfred Dunhill of London Inc.
DENICOTEA - Tobacco products - Alfred Dunhill of London Inc.
DENICOTIN - Toothpaste ☆ - The Montclair Co.
DENICOTIZER - Pharmaceutical preparations - Save-A-Life Today, Inc.
DENIM - Eyeglasses - Martin-Copeland Eyewear Corp.
DENIM - Pet collars - Leatherite-Nylorite Manufacturing Inc.
DENIM - Skin care products - Lever Brothers Co. Inc.
DENIM BLUES - Stationery - Crane & Co. Inc.
DENIM BUSTER - Sewing machines–household - Tacony Corp.
DENIM D/K - Fabrics–broadcloth ☆ - Desire Mills Co. Inc.
DENIM EXPRESS - Apparel and accessories - Kmart Properties, Inc.
DENIM FUN - Dolls - Mattel, Inc.
DENIM GENERATION - Apparel and accessories - Bugle Boy Industries, Inc.
DENIM MATES - Apparel and accessories - Levi Strauss & Co. (Accessory Div.)
DENIM 'N LACE - Dolls - Mattel, Inc.
DENIM 'N RUFFLES - Dolls - Mattel, Inc.
DENIM-PAPER - Stationery - Denim-Paper Products Corp.
DENIM PENCILS - Pencils - Watson Paper Co.
DENIM PRO - Sewing machines–household - Tacony Corp.
DENIM REPUBLIC - Apparel–women's - Kmart Properties, Inc.
DENIM TREE - Pencils - Watson Paper Co.

DENIM WEAR - Apparel and accessories - Dorothea A. Lorber
DENIM WORKS - Apparel and accessories - Dickinson Retailing Co.
DENIMITE - Fabric softeners - Ideal Chemical and Supply Co.
DENIMITE - Fabrics - Guilford Mills, Inc.
DENINTONE-BLACKOUTS - Fabrics - Rockland Industries Inc.
DENISE - Crocheted and knitted items - P.G. Roberts Manufacturing Co.
DENISE - Dolls ☆ - Effanbee Doll Corp.
DENISE - Pajamas–women's - I. Amsterdam Co. Inc.
DENISE AUSTIN - Sporting goods - Divajex
DENISE RICHARDS - Cosmetics - Cellouette Inc.
DENISON - Cosmetics - Denison Laboratories Inc.
DENISON HYDRAULICS - Machine parts - Denison Hydraulics Inc.
DENISON LIBRARY - Publisher's imprints - T.S. Denison and Co.
DENISON MUSIC CO. - Music–sheet ☆ - T.S. Denison and Co.
DENITECH - Facsimile equipment - Denitech Corp.
DENITIP - Cigarette filters - Denicotea, Inc.
DENITRATE - Pet products ☆ - Seachem Laboratories
DENIZATE - Repellent - Nortech Forest Products, Inc.
DENK & KUEHN - Ornamental products–metal - Rolf Wallach Inc.
DENLINGER BOOKS - Publisher's imprints - Denlinger's Publishers Ltd.
DENMAN - Brushes–hair - Denman Inc.
DENMARK - Dinnerware–glass - Franciscan by Johnson Brothers, USA, Inc.
DENMARK - Frames–eyeglass ☆ - Universal/Univis Inc.
DENMARK HOUSE - Giftware - Baekgaard Ltd.
DENNERY - Food products - Charles Dennery Co.
DENNESEN - Audio equipment - Dennesen Electrostatics Inc.
DENNEY SENSITIVE - Skin care products - Frances Denney
DENNIE - Hats ☆ - Henschel Manufacturing Co.
DENNIS AND HIS FRIENDS - Office supplies ☆ - Bemiss-Jason Corp.
DENNIS COMEAU - Handbags - Visione Footwear Inc.
DENNIS GOLDSMITH - Apparel and accessories - Dennis Goldsmith
DENNIS GOLDSMITH - Apparel and accessories ☆ - Kellwood Co.
DENNIS GOLDSMITH - Patterns–clothing ☆ - Simplicity Pattern Co., Inc.
DENNIS WICK - Musical instruments - Boosey & Hawkes Buffet Crampon USA
DENNISON - Cabinets–wood - UltraCraft Co.
DENNISON - Printing trades machinery - Avery Dennison Corp.
DENNISON'S - Chili con carne - American Home Food Products Inc.
DENNISON'S LITE - Chili - American Home Food Products Inc.
DENNISON'S SELECT - Lima beans, chili beans, etc. - American Home Food Products Inc.
DENNY - Building materials - Amerimark Building Products, Inc.
DENNY - Ophthalmic goods ☆ - Luxottica
DENNYBURGER - Sandwiches–prepackaged - Denny's Inc.
DENNY'S - Sporting goods - Den Manufacturing Co.
DENNY'S PIZZA OMELETTE - Food products - Denny's Inc.
DENOBILI - Cigars - Avanti Cigar Co.
DENOL - Analgesics - Church and Dwight Co. Inc.
DENON - Audio tapes–blank - Denon America Inc.
DENOREX - Shampoos - Whitehall Laboratories
DENQUEL - Hair care products - Thompson and Formby
DENRICH - Recording label - Denny Somach Productions
DENRIL - Film - Borden & Riley Paper Co.
DENS-CORE - Gypsum products - Georgia-Pacific Corp.
DENS-COTE - Gypsum products - Georgia-Pacific Corp.
DENS-DECK - Gypsum products - Georgia-Pacific Corp.
DENS-GLASS - Gypsum products - Georgia-Pacific Corp.
DENS-SHIELD - Gypsum products - Georgia-Pacific Corp.
DENSATITE - Paints - Diamond/Kuhn Paint Co.
DENSCAL - Gypsum products - Georgia-Pacific Corp.
DENSCAST - Plaster–wallboard - Georgia-Pacific Corp.
DENSCRETE - Cement - Georgia-Pacific Corp.
DENSEVEYOR - Conveyors - Michael F. Crawley
DENSFLOR - Floor coverings - Georgia-Pacific Corp.
DENSI-TIMER - Photographic equipment - Lektra Service Corp.
DENSITE - Plaster–wallboard - Georgia-Pacific Corp.
DENSITY - Hair care products ☆ - Lusan Inc.
DENSITY PATCH - Circuit boards - Sheldahl, Inc.
DENSIWOOD - Drums–musical instruments ☆ - Cappella Wood Enterprises
DENSKA - Computers - Tensor Corp.
DENSLITE - Frames–eyeglass ☆ - U.S. Optical Frame Co.
DENSO - Paints ☆ - Waterlox Coatings Corp.
DENSO-CHEM - Paints ☆ - Waterlox Coatings Corp.
DENSO-DEV - Artists' materials - Momentum Graphics
DENSO-GARD - Paints ☆ - Waterlox Coatings Corp.
DENSO-KOTE - Paints ☆ - Waterlox Coatings Corp.
DENSO STICK-TITE - Paints ☆ - Waterlox Coatings Corp.

☆ = Now out of production

DENSOCHLOR - Enamels ☆ - Waterlox Coatings Corp.
DENSOCHROME - Paints ☆ - Waterlox Coatings Corp.
DENSOLITE - Sporting goods ☆ - Shakespeare Fishing Tackle
DENSOLUME - Enamels ☆ - Waterlox Coatings Corp.
DENSOLUSTRE - Enamels ☆ - Waterlox Coatings Corp.
DENSOTONE - Paints ☆ - Waterlox Coatings Corp.
DENSTAR - Dental equipment - Denstar Corp.
DENSTONE - Floor finishing machines–commercial ☆ - Densol Co.
DENSWALL - Gypsum products - Georgia-Pacific Corp.
DENT/ALERT ONLINE - Advertising agencies - Health Care Marketing Services, Inc.
DENT CLINIC - Automotive repair shops - Dennis Brooks
DENT-O-PILLOW - Pillows - Linda H. Dixon
DENT-X - Chemical preparations - AFP Imaging Corp.
DENT X DRY PACK - Chemical preparations - AFP Imaging Corp.
DENT-ZEL-ITE - Dental compounds - Alvin Last Inc.
DENTA-CHEQ - Toothbrushes - Cococare Products Inc.
DENTA-FIT - Electric toothbrushes - Salton/Maxim Housewares, Inc.
DENTA-FL - Pharmaceutical preparations ☆ - Saron Pharmacal Corp.
DENTA PLUS - Denture cleaners ☆ - Connoisseurs Products Corp.
DENTACAINE - Toothpaste ☆ - Pharm-A-Lab
DENTACHE - Ointment - American Laboratories Inc.
DENTAFORCE - Health care products - Bioforce of America Ltd.
DENTAGARD - Toothbrushes - Colgate-Palmolive Co.
DENTAL - Snuff - Conwood Co. L.P.
DENTAL-ACE - Computer software - Data Systems Northwest, Inc.
DENTAL BATH - Dental equipment - Regent Labs, Inc.
DENTAL CARE - Gloves–rubber - Tillotson Healthcare Corp.
DENTAL CARE - Toothpaste - Church and Dwight Co. Inc.
DENTAL CARE TARTAR CONTROL - Toothpaste - Church and Dwight Co. Inc.
DENTAL FRESH - Toothpaste - Viva America Marketing, Inc.
DENTAL GRIP - Gloves - Innovative Healthcare Supply
DENTAL KONG - Pet products - Kong Co.
DENTAL LINK - Computer software - E-Scan Inc.
DENTAL MATE, THE - Racks - North American Corp.
DENTAL PIK - Dental equipment - Regent Labs, Inc.
DENTAL RESOURCE - Catalogs - Brasseler USA, Inc.
DENTAL THERAPY-PAK - Dental equipment - Colgate-Palmolive Co.
DENTAL UCR PAYMENT SYSTEM - Computer storage devices - Medicode, Inc.
DENTALDYNE - Pharmaceutical - American Hygienic Laboratories Inc.
DENTALED - Computer software - HCC Communications, Inc.
DENTALGESIC - Pharmaceutical - American Hygienic Laboratories Inc.
DENTALIFE - Vitamins and nutritional supplements - Solaray
DENTALL - Toothpaste - Regent Labs, Inc.
DENTALOOP - Dental compounds - Marion Donovan
DENTAL*PARTNER - Computer software - Integra Software, Inc.
DENTALTRAC - Computer software - Dental Services Corp. of North Dakota
DENTALUBE - Lubricants - James S. Mellos
DENTALWORKS - Pet products - Farnam Cos. Inc.
DENTAMINT - Mouthwashes - Cameo Inc.
DENTAPAINE - Pharmaceutical preparations - Reese Chemical Co.
DENTASTIC - Dental materials - Pulpdent Corp.
DENTAVIT - Denture materials - Dentorium Products, Co. Inc.
DENTAVITE - Pharmaceutical preparations ☆ - Solvay Pharmaceuticals Inc.
DENTAX - Dental floss - Carewell Industries, Inc.
DENTAX - Lubricants - Shell Oil Co.
DENTAX S - Oils–lubricating - Shell Oil Co.
DENTEC 4000 - Health care products - Dentec Corp.
DENTELLE - Apparel and accessories - Romance Du Jour, Inc.
DENTEMP - Dental compounds - Majestic Drug Co., Inc.
DENTENA - Dental equipment - Micro Dental Laboratories
DENTERGEMS - Beverages–alcohol ☆ - Phoenix Imports Ltd.
DENTEX - Shoes - Dentex Shoe Corp.
DENTEXX - Gloves–rubber ☆ - Latex Partners, Inc.
DENTEXX - Medical uniforms - First Medical Infection Control Associates, Inc.
DENTI-CARE SYSTEM - Health care products - Melaleuca, Inc.
DENTI-FIT - Denture materials - Mueller Sports Medicine Inc.
DENTIFLEX - Toothbrushes–electric - Philips Electronics North America Corp.
DENTIL MOLDINGS - Moldings and trim - Woodwaves Inc.
DENTINBLOC - Pharmaceutical preparations - Colgate-Palmolive Co.
DENTIST DIRECT - Advertising agencies - Michael Lomas
DENTIST'S FORMULA - Toothpaste - Dentists' Formula Inc.
DENTLOCK - Adhesives and sealants - Medtech Laboratories Inc.
DENTON - Frames–eyeglass ☆ - U.S. Optical Frame Co.

DENTONE - Mouthwashes - Denison Laboratories Inc.
DENTOTAPE - Dental equipment - Johnson & Johnson
DENTOX - Vitamins and nutritional supplements - Pronatura, Inc.
DENTRIX - Computer peripheral equipment - Dentrix Dental Systems, Inc.
DENTROL - Health care products - Block Drug Co., Inc.
DENT'S - Health care products - Grandpa Brands Co.
DENT'S LOTION-JEL - Dental compounds ☆ - Grandpa Brands Co.
DENTU-CREME - Toothpaste - Block Drug Co., Inc.
DENTU-FOAM - Toothpaste - Block Drug Co., Inc.
DENTU-GEL - Toothpaste - Block Drug Co., Inc.
DENTU GRIP - Health care products - Block Drug Co., Inc.
DENTUR-EZE - Denture cleaners ☆ - Blistex Inc.
DENTUR-KLEEN - Denture cleaners ☆ - Blistex Inc.
DENTURE SHIELD - Dental preparation - Essential Dental Systems, Inc.
DENTURE WHITE - Denture cleaners - Faria Ltd. (Sheffield Laboratories)
DENTUREX - Hair care products ☆ - Rexall Nutritional Products Inc.
DENTURFIT - Denture adhesive - Regent Labs, Inc.
DENTURITE - Denture materials - Brimms Inc.
DENTYNE - Candy - American Chicle Co.
DENTYNE SUGAR FREE - Chewing gum - American Chicle Co.
DENUSHA - Vodka ☆ - SPAR Inc.
DENVER - Brushes - Corona Brushes Inc.
DENVER - Fabrics ☆ - Dan River Inc.
DENVER - Frames–eyeglass - Pathway Optical Prods.
DENVER - Photographic equipment - Eastman Kodak Co.
DENVER - Publisher's imprints - Denver Metro Convention & Visitors Bureau, Inc.
DENVER - Solder - Allied Manufacturing Corp.
DENVER CHICAGO TRUCKING - Toys–automobiles - Toy Truck Lines, Inc.
DENVER DAN - Meat products–beef - Curtice-Burns Meat Snacks Inc.
DENVER GOLD - Games - United States Football League
DENVER INTERNATIONAL WESTERN/ENGLISH APPAREL & EQUIPMENT MARKET - Trade Associations - Western & English Sales Association
DENVER JEANS - Apparel and accessories - Kellwood Co.
DENVER JOE - Food products - Janson's Foods Inc.
DENVER MATTRESS CO. - Furniture - Big Sur Waterbeds, Inc.
DENVER NUGGETS - Apparel–athletic - Denver Nuggets
DENVER SWEETS - Cigars - Thompson & Co., Inc.
DENVER'S CLASSIC - Coffee - Brothers Gourmet Coffees, Inc.
DENYER-DANS - Food products - Beatrice Cos. Inc.
DENZER'S - Chowders–canned - Denzer's Food Products
DENZYME - Dental compounds - RMO, Inc.
DEO-GRAN - Deodorizers - Frank Miller and Sons Inc.
DEO-POGZ - Deodorizers - Surco Products Inc.
DEO-SECT - Insecticides ☆ - National Chemsearch Corp.
DEO WIX - Deodorizers ☆ - Atmosphere Products Co. Inc.
DEODOR-GRANS - Deodorizers - Vaportek, Inc.
DEODOR-LITE - Lamps–ultraviolet ☆ - Atlantic Ultraviolet Corp.
DEODORANTS - Deodorants–personal - Kiss My Face
DEODORIFIC - Pet products - Natra Pet Inc.
DEODORINE - Paints - Mautz Paint Co.
DEODRITE - Air purification systems - Barnebey and Sutcliffe Corp.
DEORO - Toothbrushes - Deoro Corp.
DEOTA - Luggage - Novatex Trading Co.
DEOX - Paints - Standard T Chemical Co. Inc.
DEOX - Pharmaceutical preparations - Ultradent Products, Inc.
DEOX - Pipes - Deox, Inc.
DEOXAL - Paints ☆ - Parker & Amchem
DEOXALUME - Cleaning preparations - Henkel Corp. (Functional Products Div.)
DEP - Filters–water - Sta-Rite Industries Inc.
DEP - Hair care products - Dep Corp.
DEP ANDROGYN - Pharmaceutical preparations ☆ - Forest Pharmaceuticals Inc.
DEP BLO-DRY - Hair care products ☆ - Dep Corp.
DEP FOR MEN - Hair care products - Dep Corp.
DEP FOR SHINE - Hair care products - Dep Corp.
DEP FOR STYLING - Hair care products - Dep Corp.
DEP FRIZZ - Hair care products - Dep Corp.
DEP GYNOGEN - Pharmaceutical preparations - Forest Pharmaceuticals Inc.
DEP LIQUA MOUSSE - Hair care products ☆ - Dep Corp.
DEP MEDALONE - Pharmaceutical preparations - Forest Pharmaceuticals Inc.
DEP NET - Hair care products ☆ - Dep Corp.
DEPAKENE - Pharmaceutical preparations - Abbott Laboratories
DEPAKOTE - Pharmaceutical preparations - Abbott Laboratories
DEPANDRO - Pharmaceutical preparations ☆ - Forest Pharmaceuticals Inc.

☆ = Now out of production

DEPART STRETGEAR - Apparel–athletic - Linda L. Rice
DEPARTMENT OF CORONER COUNTY OF LOS ANGELES - Glassware–household - Department of Coroner
DEPARTMENT OF CORONER LOS ANGELES COUNTY - Apparel and accessories - Department of Coroner
DEPARTMENT OF CORRECTIONS - T-shirts–men's - Francisco N. Dao
DEPARTURE - Luggage - Airway Industries, Inc.
DEPAZ - Rum - Paterno Imports, Ltd.
DEPEN TITRATABLE - Pharmaceutical preparations - Wallace Laboratories
DEPEND - Adhesives and sealants - Loctite Corp.
DEPEND - Diapers–disposable - Kimberly-Clark Corp.
DEPEND 330 - Adhesives and sealants - Loctite Corp.
DEPEND-A-FRY - Shortening - Ventura Foods LLC (Lou Ana Division)
DEPEND-A-LITE - Flashlights ☆ - Garrity Industries
DEPEND ACTIVATOR 738 - Adhesives and sealants - Loctite Corp.
DEPEND-AID - First aid kits - Sellstrom Manufacturing Co.
DEPEND-O - Cleaning preparations–household - Boyle-Midway
DEPEND ON IT! - Batteries - Johnson Controls Inc.
DEPENDA - Markers–felt-tip - Micropoint Inc.
DEPENDABLE - Eyeglasses - Martin-Copeland Eyewear Corp.
DEPENDABLE - Tools - O.P. Link Handle Co. Inc.
DEPENDABLE CARE - Washing machines–household - Maytag Corp.
DEPENDABLE-PERSONAL - Deodorizers - D-P Lotion Co.
DEPENDABLES - Luggage ☆ - American Tourister, Inc.
DEPENDABUILT - Automotive parts and accessories - W.W. Williams Co.
DEPENDALAX - Laxatives ☆ - Nature's Way Products, Inc.
DEPENDENT SOCIETY, A - Recording label - Peter Mahoney
DEPENDO - Furniture–wood - Dependable Manufacturing Co.
DEPENDO - Paper - Butler Paper Co.
DEPESTRO - Health care products - Kay Pharmacal Co. Inc.
DEPIL-A-TWEEZ - Depilatories - Mehaz International, Inc.
DEPIL-A-TWEEZ - Tweezers - Spilo/Mehaz Worldwide
DEPIL TWEEZ - Depilatories ☆ - P-Ryton Corp.
DEPILATOR G - Depilatories - Nemectron Skin Care Inc.
DEPILEVE - Depilatories - Divi International Co.
DEPLOY - Herbicides - Monsanto Co.
DEPO - Hormone preparations - Upjohn Co.
DEPO-CLAD - Paints ☆ - Wescon Products Co.
DEPO COBOLIN - Pharmaceutical preparations - Legere Pharmaceuticals Inc.
DEPO-ESTRADIOL - Pharmaceutical preparations - Upjohn Co.
DEPO-MEDROL - Pharmaceutical preparations - Upjohn Co.
DEPO-PRED - Pharmaceutical preparations ☆ - Vortech Pharmaceuticals
DEPO-PREDATE - Pharmaceutical preparations - Legere Pharmaceuticals Inc.
DEPO-PROVERA - Pharmaceutical preparations - Upjohn Co.
DEPO-TESTADIOL - Pharmaceutical preparations - Upjohn Co.
DEPO-TESTOSTERONE CYPIONATE - Pharmaceutical preparations ☆ - Upjohn Co.
DEPOCAST - Computer hardware - Indata Corp.
DEPOE BAY - Seafood products–fresh or frozen - Depoe Bay Fish Co.
DEPOGEN - Pharmaceutical preparations - Hyrex Pharmaceuticals
DEPOMED - Pharmaceutical preparations - Depomed, Inc.
DEPONIT - Pharmaceutical preparations - Schwarz Pharma
DEPOPRED - Pharmaceutical preparations - Hyrex Pharmaceuticals
DEPOSIT LINK - Computer software - WBA Financial Institution Products Corp.
DEPOSITIONDIRECTOR - Computer hardware - Indata Corp.
DEPOSITRON - Machinery - National Instrument Co. Inc.
DEPOT - Eyeglasses - Art-Craft Optical Co.
DEPOT PAC - Disinfectants - PortionPac Chemical Corp.
DEPOT SUDS - Detergents - Glissen Chemical Co., Inc.
DEPOT TECH TIPS - Educational materials - Apogee Enterprises, Inc.
DEPOTEST - Health care products - Kay Pharmacal Co. Inc.
DEPOTESTOGEN - Pharmaceutical preparations - Hyrex Pharmaceuticals
DEPPREDALONE - Pharmaceutical preparations ☆ - Forest Pharmaceuticals Inc.
DEPRESSOR, THE - Books–comic - Anthony Masino
DEPROIST - Health care products - Geneva Generics Inc.
DEPROL - Pharmaceutical preparations ☆ - Wallace Laboratories
DEPROLUTIN-250 - Pharmaceutical preparations ☆ - Seatrace Co.
DEPTH ALARM - Navigational instruments - Raytheon Co.
DEPTH CHARGER - Toys - Tonka Corp.
DEPTH-O-MATIC - Sporting goods ☆ - Outdoor Technologies Group
DEPTH-O-PLUG - Fish sounder - Bornemann Products Co.
DEPTHMASTER - Lasers - Laser Alignment, Inc.
DEPTHOMATIC - Watches - Croton Watch Co., Inc.
DEPUTY - Knives - Buck Knives, Inc.
DEPUTY - Paper–writing ☆ - School Stationers Corp.

DEPUTY - Shirts ☆ - Horace Small Apparel Co.
DEPUTY - Slacks–men's ☆ - Cowden Manufacturing Co.
DEPUTY DAN - Candy - R.M. Palmer Co.
DEPUTY MARSHALL - Gun holsters and belts - American Sales & Manufacturing Co.
DEPUY - Braces–orthopedic - Depuy Inc.
DEQ - Audio equipment - Oxmoor Corp.
DEQUEST - Chemical preparations - Monsanto Co.
DEQUEVEDO - Statuary - Richard D. Freemon
DEQUIBOLIN-100 - Pharmaceutical preparations ☆ - Vortech Pharmaceuticals
DER LACHS GOLDWASSER - Beverages–alcohol - Niche Marketing Corp.
DER SAURE FRITZ - Beverages–alcohol - Leonard Kreusch Inc.
DER-TEX - Wood products - Der-Tex Corp.
DER V-3 - Toys–models ☆ - Estes Industries
DERAN - Candy ☆ - Haviland Candy Inc.
DERAN - Chocolate candy - New England Confectionery Co.
DERBAC - Shampoos - J.T.L.K. Inc.
DERBI - Trailers–travel - Marina Mobili Inc.
DERBIBOARD - Insulating materials - Performance Roof Systems, Inc.
DERBY - Apparel and accessories - Dan River Inc.
DERBY - Bicycles - Ross Bicycles USA, Ltd.
DERBY - Binders - Steego Corp.
DERBY - Brass products - F. Kelly Co.
DERBY - Brushes–paint - Wooster Brush Co.
DERBY - Envelopes - Western States Envelope Co.
DERBY - Food products - Beatrice Cos. Inc.
DERBY - Garden furniture - Rubbermaid Inc.
DERBY - Gasoline - Derby Refining Co.
DERBY - Grass seed - International Seeds, Inc.
DERBY - Ladders–metal - Rich Ladder Co.
DERBY - Office furniture–metal - Haskell of Pittsburgh, Inc.
DERBY - Office supplies ☆ - Arrow Rubber Products Inc.
DERBY - Relishes - Green Bay Foods Co.
DERBY - Upholstery leather ☆ - American Leather Manufacturing Co.
DERBY - Whirlpools - Lasco Products Group
DERBY - Yarn ☆ - William Unger & Co. Inc.
DERBY DOGS - Frankfurters - Fischer Packing Co.
DERBY FARMS - Dairy products - Southwestern Dairies Inc.
DERBY PRETZEL HOME OF THE BIERHAUS BRETZEL - Pretzels - Derby Pretzel, Inc.
DERBY RED - Paints - Sherwin-Williams Automotive Finishes Corp.
DERBY ROPE - Cordage and twine - Wellington Leisure Products, Inc.
DERBY SUPREME - Grass seed - International Seeds, Inc.
DERBY TIME - Invitations - Steven H. Lyverse
DERBY'S - Slippers ☆ - Tru-Stitch Footwear (Div. of Wolverine World Wide)
DERBY'S ULTRA-LIFE - Oils–lubricating - Derby Refining Co.
DERBYSHIRE - Wood products - Georgia-Pacific Corp.
DERBYSHIRE - Yarn ☆ - Lion Brand Yarn Co.
DERBYSTAR - Sporting goods - Continental Sports Supply Inc.
DERCO - Fruits–dried - Derco Associates, Inc.
DEREK - Dolls - Mattel, Inc.
DEREK - Tobacco products - Quiktrip Corp.
DEREMI - Shirts - Prince Deremi Martins
DERFORT - Analgesics ☆ - Cole Pharmacal Co. Inc.
DERGONG - Pharmaceutical preparations ☆ - U.S. Ethicals Inc.
DERI-DEL - Soft drink - Bottlers International Ltd.
DERIFIL - Pharmaceutical preparations - Rystan Co. Inc.
DERIGUEUR - Apparel and accessories - J. Schoeneman Inc.
DERIVATION I - Furniture - Thayer Coggin Inc.
DERM ADVANTAGE - Skin care products - Cosmedical Technologies, Inc.
DERM AESTHETICS - Skin care products - Dermatologic Specialty Products, Inc.
DERM AFFAIR - Skin care products - Newbury Park Mountain Marketing
DERM-APPLY - Skin moisturizers - Snuva Inc.
DERM SYSTEM - Health care products - Geritrex Corp.
DERM SYSTEM, THE - Health care products - Geritrex Corp.
DERMA - Skin care products - FMG/Tsumara Medical
DERMA - Soap ☆ - Ferndale Laboratories, Inc.
DERMA - Towels - Helga Van Dyke Skin Care
DERMA 2000 - Skin-care products - Benchmark Enterprises
DERMA-ANALYZER - Skin care products - Helga Van Dyke Skin Care
DERMA BLANCH - Cosmetics ☆ - Chattem Inc.
DERMA-BUFF - Skin care products - Karlen Manufacturing, Inc.
DERMA-CAINE - Skin care products - Metropolitan Pharmacy, Inc.
DERMA-CAP - Pharmaceutical preparations - Progressive Laboratories, Inc.
DERMA CARE - Skin care products ☆ - Nature's Answer (Bio Botanica)

☆ = Now out of production

DERMA CARE - Snuff - Blue Cross Laboratories Inc.
DERMA CAS - Pharmaceutical preparations - Hill Dermaceuticals
DERMA CENTRE - Skin care products - ElectroDerma International Inc.
DERMA CIDOL - Pharmaceutical preparations - Jones Medical Industries, Inc. (Medical Div.)
DERMA-CORRECTIVE COSMETICS - Skin care products - M.G. Westmore Co.
DERMA-COVER - Product description unknown ☆ - Scrip-Physician Supply Co.
DERMA DAN - Shampoos - Mahdeen Laboratory
DERMA-DIP - Veterinary pharmaceutical preparations - Pitman-Moore, Inc.
DERMA-DRY - Skin care products ☆ - Skin Culture Co.
DERMA E - Skin care products - Stearn's Products Inc.
DERMA FIVE - Hair care products ☆ - Mahdeen Laboratory
DERMA-FLEUR - Skin care products - Zee Medical Inc.
DERMA FRESH - Skin care products - Alberto-Culver Co.
DERMA-FUSE - Skin care products - Alfa Services USA Inc.
DERMA-GLO - Skin care products - Nutri-Cell Inc.
DERMA-GRO-2 - Pet products - M & P Laboratories
DERMA GUARD - Pet products - Pro-Tec Pet Health
DERMA GUARD - Vitamins and nutritional supplements - Great Life Laboratories Inc.
DERMA-KLEAR - Skin care products - Enzymatic Therapy, Inc.
DERMA KWIK - Cleaning preparations ☆ - Lee Products Co.
DERMA LUV - Skin care products - Santa Barbara Medco, Inc.
DERMA LUX - Soap - Karlen Manufacturing, Inc.
DERMA MAGIC - Skin care products ☆ - Derma Magic
DERMA-MOIST - Skin care products - Monaco Import/Export Inc.
DERMA MOIST - Skin care products ☆ - Parthenon Co. Inc.
DERMA NAIL - Nail care products - Summers Laboratories Inc.
DERMA-PAX - Skin care products - Recsei Laboratories
DERMA POW'R - Bath salts - Alacer Co.
DERMA-PURE - Skin care products - Celmark International, Inc.
DERMA-RUB - Analgesics ☆ - Robinette Inc.
DERMA RX - Pharmaceutical preparations - Barry I. Bockow
DERMA-SAFE - Laundry detergent - American Home Products Corp.
DERMA-SAFE - Surgical supplies - Derma-Safe Co.
DERMA-SAN - Cleaning preparations ☆ - Lee Products Co.
DERMA-SAN ANTI-BAC HAND CLEANER - Cleaning preparations - Uncle Sam Chemical Co., Inc.
DERMA SCRUB - Pharmaceutical preparations - Jones Medical Industries, Inc. (Medical Div.)
DERMA SCRUB - Skin care products - FMG/Tsumara Medical
DERMA SCRUB - Skin care products ☆ - Moore Beauty Inc.
DERMA-SECT - Pet products ☆ - Boehringer Ingelheim Animal Health, Inc.
DERMA SHEEN - Pet products - Revere Manufacturing
DERMA SHEEN - Veterinary nutritional supplements - Petco Animal Supplies, Inc.
DERMA SHIELD - Skin-care products - Benchmark Enterprises
DERMA-SMOOTH - Skin care products - Metropolitan Pharmacy, Inc.
DERMA SMOOTHE - Pharmaceutical preparations - Hill Dermaceuticals
DERMA-SOFT - Pharmaceutical preparations - Sandoz Pharmaceuticals Corp.
DERMA-SONE - Pharmaceutical preparations - Hill Dermaceuticals
DERMA SOOTHE - Pharmaceutical preparations - Jones Medical Industries, Inc. (Medical Div.)
DERMA SPA - Hair care products - W.W. Grainger, Inc.
DERMA-SPEC - Skin care products ☆ - Avon Products, Inc.
DERMA STAT - Pharmaceutical preparations - Jones Medical Industries, Inc. (Medical Div.)
DERMA SURE - Skin care products - United-Guardian, Inc. (Guardian Laboratories Div.)
DERMA-SURE - Skin care products ☆ - General Scientific Equipment Co.
DERMA SWABS - Pharmaceutical preparations - Hydromer Inc.
DERMA SWISS 3000 - Skin care products - Derma Swiss 3000 Skincare Manufacturing, Inc.
DERMA-TECH - Soap - Go-Jo Industries Inc.
DERMA-TONE - Pet shops - Dermo Inc.
DERMA TOUCH - Medical gloves - Medline, Industries, Inc.
DERMA TREAT - Antiseptics - Mary Grossman Meeks
DERMA-TRODE - Health care products - American Imex
DERMA-VET - Veterinary pharmaceutical preparations - Med-Pharmex, Inc.
DERMA ZAPP - Skin care products - Odor Zapper Inc.
DERMABALM - Skin care products - Nexxus Products Co.
DERMABASE - Cosmetics - Lachine Inc.
DERMABATH - Antipruritic bath oil ☆ - Ion Laboratories Inc.
DERMABATH - Skin care products - Nexxus Products Co.
DERMABLEND - Skin care products - Flori Roberts Inc.

DERMABRASE/35 - Cosmetics - Tri Tech Laboratories, Inc.
DERMACARE - Pet products - Rolf C. Hagen (USA) Corp.
DERMACARE - Skin care products - Johnson & Johnson
DERMACARE - Vitamins and nutritional supplements - Ayurvedic Concepts Ltd.
DERMACEA - Bandages - Sherwood Medical Co.
DERMACEA - Skin care products ☆ - Pettibone Laboratories Inc.
DERMACIN - Pharmaceutical preparations ☆ - Pedinol Pharmacal Inc.
DERMACLEANSER - Skin care products - Nexxus Products Co.
DERMACOAT - Antiseptics - Century Pharmaceuticals Inc.
DERMACOLOR - Cosmetics - European Skin & Haircare
DERMACOOL - Pet products - Virbac, Inc.
DERMACOOL - Skin care products - Afassco
DERMACORT - Pharmaceutical preparations - Solvay Pharmaceuticals Inc.
DERMACULTURE - Astringents - Arc Group, LLC
DERMADEW - Skin care products - Nexxus Products Co.
DERMADROX - Skin care products - Geritrex Corp.
DERMAFILM - Health care products - Vygon Corp.
DERMAGARD - Pet products - Gerard-Pellham Co.
DERMAGEL - Plastics - Douglas & Sturgess
DERMAGEN - Hair care products - J. Cannon Inc.
DERMAGEN - Skin care products - Tishcon Corp.
DERMAGLIDE - Skin care products - General Physiotherapy, Inc.
DERMAGLOW - Skin care products - Nexxus Products Co.
DERMAGRAFT - Dental compounds - Advanced Tissue Sciences Inc.
DERMAGRAN - Bandages - Derma Sciences Inc.
DERMAGRAN II - Pharmaceutical preparations - Derma Sciences Inc.
DERMAGUARD-SKIN BARRIER - Skin care products - Pedinol Pharmacal Inc.
DERMAJETICS - Skin care products - Herbalife International, Inc.
DERMAJOY - Skin care products - Theon, Inc.
DERMAL - Gloves - George Glove Co. Inc.
DERMAL-RUB - Pharmaceutical preparations ☆ - Roberts/Hauck Pharmaceuticals Inc.
DERMALAB - Pharmaceutical preparations - Dermalab Ltd.
DERMALEVEL - Medical apparatus - USMS, Inc.
DERMALITE - Soap - Go-Jo Industries Inc.
DERMALIVE - Skin care products - Earth Solutions
DERMALOGICA SPA BODY - Skin care products - Dermalogica Inc.
DERMALOGICA TREATMENT FOUNDATIONS - Skin care products - Dermalogica Inc.
DERMAMAP - Medical apparatus - USMS, Inc.
DERMAMASQUE - Skin care products - Nexxus Products Co.
DERMAMEND - Skin care products - Derma Rx Corp.
DERMAMIST - Skin care products - Nexxus Products Co.
DERMAMYCIN - Skin care products - Pfeiffer Pharmaceuticals Inc.
DERMANEED - Pharmaceutical preparations - Hanlon Drug Products
DERMANET - Medical bandage - Deroyal Industries, Inc.
DERMAPLAST - Footwear ☆ - Apex Foot Health Industries, Inc.
DERMAPLEX - Pet products - Bioglan Animal Products Inc.
DERMAPLEX - Veterinary pharmaceutical preparations - Happy Jack, Inc.
DERMAPOINTS - Nerve stimulator ☆ - Intercontinental Enterprises Ltd.
DERMAPON - Skin care products ☆ - RBI Distributors
DERMAPOR - Gloves - W.L. Gore & Associates, Inc.
DERMAPRO - Soap - Go-Jo Industries Inc.
DERMAREST - Pharmaceutical preparations - Del Pharmaceuticals, Inc.
DERMAREST DRICORT - Skin care products - Del Pharmaceuticals, Inc.
DERMAREX - Pharmaceutical preparations ☆ - Hyrex Pharmaceuticals
DERMAROSE - Skin care products - ElectroDerma International Inc.
DERMASAFE - Gloves–rubber - American Health Products Corp.
DERMASAFE - Pharmaceutical preparations - Postamatic Co. Inc.
DERMASCAN - Skin care products - Proteus Inc.
DERMASCIENCE - Cosmetics - Clientele, Inc.
DERMASEPT - Skin care products ☆ - Organics Corp. of America (Ambix Laboratories Div.)
DERMASIL - Skin care products - Chesebrough-Pond's USA Co.
DERMASOL - Pet products - Bioglan Animal Products Inc.
DERMASORB - Surgical supplies - E.R. Squibb & Sons, Inc.
DERMASQUARE - Medical apparatus - USMS, Inc.
DERMASSAGE - Skin care products - Colgate-Palmolive Co.
DERMASSIST - Bandages - Wilshire Technologies, Inc.
DERMATEC - Health care products ☆ - Parke-Davis
DERMATELL - Bandages–surgical - Gentell, Inc.
DERMATELL SECURE - Bandages–surgical - Gentell, Inc.
DERMATIN - Skin care products - Valley Laboratories
DERMATOLOGISTS PRODUCTS LTD. - Skin care products - Dermatologists Products, Ltd.
DERMATONE - Ski suits–children's - Swix Sport USA, Inc.

DERMATONE CAMPHOR ICE - Skin care products - Dermatone Laboratories, Inc.

DERMATOX - Pharmaceutical preparations ☆ - Reese Chemical Co.

DERMATROPHIN PMG - Vitamins and nutritional supplements - Standard Process Inc.

DERMAVAL - Pharmaceutical preparations ☆ - Pal-Pak Inc.

DERMAVIEW - Skin analysis machine - Aramis Inc.

DERMAWARE - Skin care products - Gul Celebi Zone

DERMAWAY - Skin care products - Dermaway Corp.

DERMAXIN - Skin care products - Trimas Laboratories Inc.

DERMBASICS - Skin care products - Rhonda Rand M.D., Inc.

DERMED - Pet products - New England Serum Co.

DERMED - Skin care products ☆ - Abana Pharmaceuticals, Inc.

DERMELLE BOTANICAL - Skin care products - Essque Bodycare

DERMETHRIN - Pet flea/tick dip - American Home Products Corp.

DERMICEL - Tape–adhesive - Johnson & Johnson

DERMICORT - Pharmaceutical preparations - Republic Drug Co. Inc.

DERMIDON - Pharmaceutical preparations - Republic Drug Co. Inc.

DERMLINE - Computer software - Aries Systems Corp.

DERMO - Pet shops - Dermo Inc.

DERMO-PEDIC - Pharmaceutical preparations - Consolidated Midland Corp.

DERMO-VITE - Pet shops - Dermo Inc.

DERMOCAINE - Pharmaceutical preparations - Walker Pharmacal Co.

DERMOFLEX - First aid kits ☆ - Zila Pharmaceuticals Inc.

DERMOID - Pharmaceutical preparations ☆ - Ulmer Pharmacal Co.

DERMOL - Skin care products - Teaco International

DERMOLATE - Antipyretics - Schering-Plough Healthcare Products

DERMOLIN - Pharmaceutical preparations - Roberts/Hauck Pharmaceuticals Inc.

DERMOLOGICA - Pharmaceutical preparations - Dermalogica Inc.

DERMOPLAST - Pharmaceutical preparations - Whitehall Laboratories

DERMOVAN - Pharmaceutical preparations - Owen/Galderma Laboratories Inc.

DERMOZONE - Cosmetics - Donigan Natural Health, Inc.

DERMPAK - Gauze–surgical - Dermpak International

DERMSOL - Vitamins and nutritional supplements - Parnell Pharmaceuticals Inc.

DERMTEX - Pharmaceutical preparations - Pfeiffer Pharmaceuticals Inc.

DERMX - Veterinary pharmaceutical preparations - Animal Health Products

DERNIER CRI - Apparel stores–lingerie ☆ - Formfit Rogers

DERNIER CRI - Frames–eyeglass - Hudson Optical Corp.

DERO - Prosthetic apparatus - Klaus H. Lohmann

DERONIL - Pharmaceutical preparations ☆ - Schering-Plough Healthcare Products

DEROYAL - Orthopedic products - Deroyal Industries, Inc.

DERRICK COSTA - Apparel–children's - A.C. Reed

DERRIERES - Apparel and accessories ☆ - Edison Brothers Stores, Inc.

DERRINGER - See **RICK DERRINGER**

DERRY - Urinals–enameled - Kohler Co.

DERRY FARM - Cheese - Hawthorn Mellody Inc.

DERSU UZALA - Teas - Preston F. Zoller

DERUSTO - Enamels - Dap Products Inc.

DES - Jewelry–precious - Fantasia Jewelry, Inc.

DES ARTISTE - Musical instrument accessories - B. Portnoy Clarinet Accessories

DES LAURIERS - Musical instruments - Roberto Ciarfella Inc.

DES MOINES - Water–bottled or canned - Stonebridge Co.

DES-O-E - Pharmaceutical preparations ☆ - Wendt-Bristol Co.

D.E.S. PLUS - Computer software - Biodynamic Research Corp.

DESA - Heaters–space ☆ - Desa International, Inc.

DESA - Shoes - Desa Shoe Co. Inc.

DESA-HIST - Pharmaceutical preparations - Pharmics Inc.

DESAFIN - Pet products - Tetra Sales USA

DESAG - Glass products - D & L Stained Glass Supply, Inc.

DESAMYCIN - Antibiotics - Pharmics Inc.

DESATRATE - Pharmaceutical preparations - Pharmics Inc.

DESBUTAL - Pharmaceutical preparations ☆ - Abbott Laboratories

DESCALEJET - Nozzles - Spraying Systems Co.

DESCAMPS - Bedding–linen - Descamps

DESCARTES' DELIGHT - Computer software ☆ - Krell Software Corp.

DESCENDENTS - Posters - Descendents Partners

DESCENT - Toys–musical - Interplay Productions

DESCENTE - Sporting goods ☆ - Sports Imports Inc.

DESCHET - Apparel–children's - Coastline Designs

DESCHLER'S MONOGRAM - Cigars ☆ - House of Windsor Inc.

DESCHUTES BREWERY - Beverages–malt - Deschutes Brewery

DESCO - Belts, hair accessories, jewelry, etc - Honey Fashions Ltd.

DESCO - Handkerchiefs - David E. Schwab & Co. Inc.

DESCOLATE - Cough medicines - Vita-Fore Products Co.

DESCOTE - Health care products - Particle Dynamics Inc.

DESCOWARE - Cooking equipment–household ☆ - General Housewares Corp.

DESCRIPTIONS NOW - Computer software - KnowledgePoint

DESCRIPTO-CARDS - Textbooks - Communication Skill Builders, Inc.

DESDEMONA - Computer software ☆ - Zephyr Services

DESEAL - Paint removers - Advance Cleaning Products Inc.

DESELEX - Chemical preparations - United-Guardian, Inc. (Guardian Laboratories Div.)

DESEMPACHO - Health care products - D'Franssia Corp.

DESENEX - Health care products - Fisons Corp.

DESENEX - Pharmaceutical preparations - Ciba-Geigy Corp.

DESERET - Floor coverings–carpet and rugs ☆ - Customweave Carpets Inc.

DESERET MUSIC - Music–sheet - Jackman Music Corp.

DESERPA - Pharmaceutical preparations - Deleon Laboratories Inc.

DESERT - Lenses–optical - Kelley & Hueber

DESERT - Shoes - Clarks of England Inc.

DESERT - Toilet seats ☆ - Ginsey Industries, Inc.

DESERT BARS - Candy - Hershey Chocolate USA

DESERT BEAUTY - Skin care products - Desert Beauty Cosmetics, Inc.

DESERT BIKE - Scooters–children's - Peg Perego USA Inc.

DESERT BLEND - Stones–synthetic - Stone Products Corp.

DESERT BLITZ - Fireworks - American Promotional Events, Inc.

DESERT BLOSSOM - Dinnerware ☆ - Corning Inc.

DESERT BLOSSOM COLORS - Skin care products - Schering-Plough Healthcare Products

DESERT BOOT - Shoes - Clarks of England Inc.

DESERT BOWLING - Bowling balls - Center of the World, Inc.

DESERT BRAND TAG GARD - Coatings ☆ - Hill Brothers Chemical Co.

DESERT BRONZE - Suntan lotions - Roy M. Duleba, II

DESERT CASUALS - Shoes ☆ - Clarks of England Inc.

DESERT CAT - Bicycles - Murray, Inc.

DESERT CITRUS - Soft drink - Creative Beverage Co.

DESERT CLIMATE - Skin care products - Patricia Anne Eaton

DESERT DEMON - Toys–automobiles - Mattel, Inc.

DESERT DESIGNS - Sunglasses - Oroton USA Inc.

DESERT DEW - Skin care products - Scott/Franklin International

DESERT DOG - Books–comic - Modern Thought Combine

DESERT DREAMS - Floor coverings–carpet and rugs - Karastan-Bigelow Inc.

DESERT DRINX - Beverages - BCB USA Corp.

DESERT DRY - Fabrics–quilted - Confab, Inc.

DESERT DUNES - Bedding–linen - Dan River Inc.

DESERT ESSENCE - Tea-tree oil - Desert Essence Cosmetics

DESERT FLAME - Frames–picture - Framemica Co.

DESERT FLOWER - Bicycles - Murray, Inc.

DESERT FLOWER - Floor coverings - Mannington Resilient Floors

DESERT FLOWER - Greeting cards - Henry R. Mockel's

DESERT FLOWER - Rings–jewelry - Artcarved Inc.

DESERT FLOWERS - Floor coverings–carpet and rugs ☆ - Capel, Inc.

DESERT FOAM - Cleaning preparations–carpet and rug - Damon Industries, Inc.

DESERT FOAM - Hobby kits - Flora Craft Inc.

DESERT FOX - Motorcycles ☆ - Certified Parts Corp.

DESERT GARAGE - Toys–automobiles - Mattel, Inc.

DESERT GARDENS CHILE & SPICE CO. - Spices and extracts - Desert Gardens Chile & Spice Co.

DESERT GATHERINGS - Candy - Desert Gatherings, Inc.

DESERT GOLD - Honey - Nickabood's Inc.

DESERT GOURMET - Fruits and vegetables - Desert Gourmet Foods Inc.

DESERT GRASS - Fresh asparagus - Desert Harvest Packing, Inc.

DESERT GREEN - Food products - P.R. Hagadorns

DESERT HEALTH - Health care products - Desert Health Products, Inc.

DESERT HIGHLANDS - Floor coverings–carpet and rugs - Catalina Carpet Mills Inc.

DESERT HILLS - Floor coverings–carpet and rugs - Evans-Black Carpet Mills

DESERT IMPRESSIONS - Apparel and accessories - Desert Images

DESERT ISLAND - Beverages–alcohol - Consolidated Distilled Products Inc.

DESERT ISLAND DISCS - Recording label - Stanyan Record Co.

DESERT JADE - Fruits and vegetables - Dresick Farms Inc.

DESERT KING - Eyeglasses - Art-Craft Optical Co.

DESERT LENS - Ophthalmic goods - Breger Mueller Welt Corp.

DESERT LIGHTS - Floor coverings–carpet and rugs - Roxbury Carpet Co.

DESERT MIST - Fruits and vegetables - Ocean Mist Farms

DESERT MOON - Publisher's imprints ☆ - Roadshow Music Corp.

☆ = Now out of production

DESERT MORN - Dinnerware–glass ☆ - Lenox, Inc.
DESERT MORNING - Recording label - House of Knox Music Publishing
DESERT NECTAR - Beverages–alcohol - Jenkins Spirits Corp., Ltd.
DESERT NECTAR - Colognes - Aramis Inc.
DESERT NOTES - Harmonicas - Henry R. Mockel's
DESERT OASIS - Suntan lotions - Lars Desert Oasis Sun Care Inc.
DESERT PEPPER - Food products - Desert Pepper Trading
DESERT PRIDE - Herbal food supplement, hair- and skin-care products - Botanical Products
DESERT PURE - Calcium supplement - Cal-White Mineral Co.
DESERT RACER - Frames–eyeglass ☆ - Universal/Univis Inc.
DESERT RAIN - Candles ☆ - A.K.A. Saunders, Inc.
DESERT RAIN - Fountains - Aquatic Dynamics, Inc.
DESERT RAINMAKER - Toys - Arte Indigena Imports, Inc.
DESERT RAT - Toys–automobiles - Mattel, Inc.
DESERT ROSE - Binoculars - Nikon Inc.
DESERT ROSE - Building materials - Cavco Industries, Inc.
DESERT ROSE - Dinnerware–glass - Franciscan by Johnson Brothers, USA, Inc.
DESERT ROSE - Dishes–china - Waterford Wedgewood USA, Inc.
DESERT ROSE - Lipsticks - Merle Norman Cosmetics
DESERT ROSE - Skin care products - Magick Mud
DESERT ROSE - Vegetable sauces - Desert Rose Foods, Inc.
DESERT SAGE - Shampoos - Aramis Inc.
DESERT SAND - Copper compounds ☆ - Regal Ware, Inc.
DESERT SAND - Floor coverings - B.F. Goodrich Co.
DESERT SAND - Frames–eyeglass ☆ - Universal/Univis Inc.
DESERT SAND - Wallcoverings - Cork Products Co. Inc.
DESERT SAND - Wallpaper - Koroseal Wallcoverings
DESERT SAND TEDLAR - Wallpaper - Koroseal Wallcoverings
DESERT SANDS - Floor coverings–tile - Kentile Floors Inc.
DESERT SANDS - Glassware–household - Owens-Illinois Inc. (Libbey Div.)
DESERT SATIN - Blinds–venetian ☆ - Hunter Douglas, Inc.
DESERT SECRET - Soap - Cameo Inc.
DESERT SECRETS - Skin care products - J's Alternatives Inc.
DESERT SHIELD - Apparel and accessories - Brigade Quartermasters Ltd.
DESERT SHIELD - Prophylactics - Big Star Concepts Inc.
DESERT SHIELD - Watches ☆ - Hirsch Speidel Inc.
DESERT SKY COLLECTION - Bedding–linen - Dan River Inc.
DESERT SON - Shoes - Desert Son Inc.
DESERT SONG - Floor coverings - Mannington Resilient Floors
DESERT SONG - Floor coverings–carpet and rugs ☆ - Callaway Carpets
DESERT SPEEDTRAP - Video games - Sega of America, Inc.
DESERT SPORT - Automotive parts and accessories - Electrodyne, Inc.
DESERT SPRING - Soft drinks - Tri-States Double-Cola Bottling Co., Inc.
DESERT STAR - Frames–eyeglass ☆ - Universal/Univis Inc.
DESERT STAR - Lumber - Allied Forest Products, Inc.
DESERT STAR - Rings–jewelry - Artcarved Inc.
DESERT STAR - Swimming pools ☆ - Doughboy Recreational Inc.
DESERT STONE - Floor coverings–tile - American Biltrite Inc.
DESERT STORM - Fireworks - American Promotional Events, Inc.
DESERT STRIPE - Floor coverings–carpet and rugs ☆ - Regal Rugs Inc.
DESERT SUN - Spices and extracts - Marnie Smith
DESERT SUN - Wallpaper - Four Seasons
DESERT SUNSET - Floor coverings–carpet and rugs - Lotus Carpets
DESERT SUNSET - Giftware - Russ Berrie and Co., Inc.
DESERT SWEET - Fruit drinks–bottled or canned - Sunkist Growers, Inc.
DESERT SWEET - Juices - Sunkist Growers Inc.
DESERT TAN - Lamps - Sperti Sunlamp
DESERT THUNDER - Toys–automobiles - Saban Entertainment, Inc.
DESERT TONE - Tableware–earthenware ☆ - Anchor Hocking Glass, Inc.
DESERT TOUGH - Motor vehicle parts and accessories ☆ - KozaK Auto Drywash Inc.
DESERT WAR - Games - Avalon Hill Game Co.
DESERT WEAVES - Wallpaper - Preferred Prints
DESERT WIND - Deodorants–personal - Shaklee Corp.
DESERT WIND - Floor coverings–carpet and rugs - Dan River Inc.
DESERT WIND - Floor coverings–carpet and rugs - Downs Carpet Co. Inc.
DESERT WINDS - Craft supplies - Sharmark Las Vegas, Inc.
DESERT WINDS - Wallpaper ☆ - Pickhardt & Siebert USA Inc.
DESERT WONDER - Health-care products - Botanical Products
DESERTBOOST - Vitamins and nutritional supplements - Desert Health Products, Inc.
DESERTICA - Ceramic tile ☆ - Interceramic Inc.
DESERTKING - Air conditioning equipment ☆ - Nordyne Inc.
DESERTSPICE - Seasonings - Nile Spice Foods Inc.

DESERTSTONE II - Tiles–ceramic - American Marazzi Tile, Inc.
DESFERAL - Pharmaceutical preparations - Ciba-Geigy Corp.
DESI/AIR - Heating equipment - Engelhard/ICC
DESI-CATES - Vitamins and nutritional supplements - Alacer Co.
DESI-PLUS - Pet products - Nekton USA Inc.
DESI-ROPE - Insulating materials - Lauren Manufacturing Co.
DESIC - Briefcases - Caribou Mountaineering Inc.
DESICOL KAPSEALS - Pharmaceutical preparations ☆ - Parke-Davis
DESIDERIO - Leather goods - Attaches International
DESIGELITE - Glass products - Guardian Jamestown
DESIGN - Beauty aids - International Beauty Design, Inc.
DESIGN - Clocks ☆ - Sunbeam Precision Measurement
DESIGN - Fragrance - Paul Sebastian, Inc.
DESIGN - Hair care products ☆ - Kenra Laboratories, Inc.
DESIGN - Measuring instruments - Rolatape Corp.
DESIGN - Office supplies - Faber-Castell Corp.
DESIGN - Paints - Millmaster Onyx Group Inc.
DESIGN - Pesticides–household - Ciba-Geigy Corp.
DESIGN - Tableware–china ☆ - Villeroy and Boch Tableware Ltd.
DESIGN - Typewriters - Smith Corona Corp.
DESIGN 1 - Clocks - Continental/SiLite International Inc.
DESIGN 1 - Craft items - Design 1
DESIGN 2 - Markers–felt-tip - Faber-Castell Corp.
DESIGN 70 - Dinnerware–glass - Taylor, Smith & Taylor Co.
DESIGN-77 - Eyeglasses - Martin-Copeland Eyewear Corp.
DESIGN 80 - Furniture ☆ - White Furniture Co.
DESIGN 90 - Apparel and accessories - NCC Sportswear Corp.
DESIGN 2000 - Coolers–electric - Elkay Manufacturing Co.
DESIGN-A-COVER - Office supplies - Mead Corp.
DESIGN-A-DOOR - Door frames - R & R Woodworking
DESIGN A FACE - Cosmetics - Paper Magic Group Inc.
DESIGN-A-FACE - Toys - Spearhead Industries Inc.
DESIGN-A-LINER - Window shades - Designer Shades
DESIGN A MUG - Containers - Maryland China Co.
DESIGN-A-ROOM - Door frames - R & R Woodworking
DESIGN-A-SCREEN - Hobby kits - Crown Art Products
DESIGN-A-SPACE - Office supplies - Rubbermaid Inc.
DESIGN ACCENTS - House furnishings ☆ - Gear Holdings, Inc.
DESIGN ADVANTAGE - Computer software - Supercads Inc.
DESIGN AMERICA - Bedding–linen - Dan River Inc.
DESIGN-AN-EGG - Dyes–food - Spearhead Industries Inc.
DESIGN AN EGG - Novelty items - Paper Magic Group Inc.
DESIGN & COMBINE - Lighting fixtures - Angelo Brothers Co.
DESIGN ARCHITECT - Computer software - Mentor Graphics Corp.
DESIGN ARTS - Wallcoverings - Sherman & Associates International
DESIGN BOOK - Games - Leisure Learning Products
DESIGN BY ANN NOMTAK - Wallpaper ☆ - Wallquest, Inc.
DESIGN BY DATAMAX - Computer hardware - Datamax Bar Code Products Corp.
DESIGN BY MARV ALPERN - Giftware ☆ - Artique Inc.
DESIGN CARE - Furniture - Sauder Woodworking Co.
DESIGN CENTER - Floor coverings–carpet and rugs - Lees Carpets
DESIGN CENTER - Patches, insignia, and emblems - Happiness Inc.
DESIGN CENTER - Wallcovering - Interials Inc.
DESIGN CLASSIC - Nail care products - Gena Laboratories Inc.
DESIGN CLASSICS - Furniture - CTH/Sherrill Occasional
DESIGN CLASSICS - Paper products - C.R. Gibson Co.
DESIGN CLEAN - Shower stalls–plastic - Thomas A. Davis
DESIGN COATS - Pottery - Duncan Enterprises
DESIGN COLLECTION - Paper - Paper Co.
DESIGN COLLECTION, THE - Glassware–household ☆ - Country Originals Inc.
DESIGN COMPANION - Computer software - Woodbourne Inc.
DESIGN CONCEPTS - Plastics–laminated - Formica Corp.
DESIGN CONNECTION, THE - Jewelry–costume - Victoria Creations Inc.
DESIGN COTTAGE - Curtains–shower - Glenhil Inc.
DESIGN COTTAGE - Housewares - Barth-Dreyfuss of California
DESIGN CRAFT - Craft supplies ☆ - Winbar Designs
DESIGN CRAFT - Lighting fixtures - Hunter Fan Co.
DESIGN CREATIONS - Floor coverings–carpet and rugs - Hartford Carpet Mills
DESIGN DECOR - Flowers, plants, and seeds - Exotic Wood Flowers Inc.
DESIGN DIMENSIONS - Floor coverings - Beaulieu of America, Inc.
DESIGN DIMENSIONS - Lamination material - Reneer Films Corp.
DESIGN-EARS - Jewelry–costume - Design Ears International Inc.
DESIGN EDGE - Artists' materials - Plaid Enterprises, Inc.

☆ = Now out of production

DESIGN EFFECTS - Hair care products - Alberto-Culver Co.
DESIGN ELEMENTS BY FINLA - Wallpaper ☆ - Imperial Wallcoverings, Inc.
DESIGN ENVIRONMENT - Apparel and accessories - Capital Mercury Shirt Corp.
DESIGN ESSENTIALS - Hair care products - McBride Research Laboratories Inc.
DESIGN ETNIKA - Handbags - East O'Java Trading Co.
DESIGN EXPRESSIONS - Plates–paper - C.R. Gibson Co.
DESIGN FOODS - Food products - Design Foods
DESIGN FOODS EGGCEPTIONAL PREPARED EGG PRODUCTS - Egg products - Saramar Corp.
DESIGN FOR MEN - Perfumes - Paul Sebastian, Inc.
DESIGN FOUR - Dinnerware–glass - Sango Co. Ltd. (Sango USA Div.)
DESIGN FREEDOM - Hair care products - Zotos International Inc.
DESIGN FREEDOM COLOURS - Hair care products - Zotos International Inc.
DESIGN GALLERY - Leather goods - Buxton Inc.
DESIGN-GUARD - Skateboards - Moth Studios
DESIGN GUILD - Lamps - Crystal Clear Industries, Inc.
DESIGN HOUSE - Calendars - Cullman Ventures Inc.
DESIGN HOUSE - Cutlery - Robeson Industries
DESIGN HOUSE - Fans–electric - Design House, Inc.
DESIGN I - Furniture - Thomasville Furniture Industries Inc.
DESIGN I - Ophthalmic goods - Embassy Creations Inc.
DESIGN II - Ophthalmic goods - Embassy Creations Inc.
DESIGN III - Floor coverings–carpet and rugs ☆ - Lees Carpets
DESIGN IMAGES - Dinnerware - Corning Inc.
DESIGN IMAGES - Wallpaper ☆ - Fidelity Industries, Inc.
DESIGN IMPRESSIONS - Wallpaper - Palette Prints Inc.
DESIGN IMPRESSIONS - Wallpaper ☆ - Forbo Industries, Inc.
DESIGN-IN-PINE - Furniture ☆ - R & R Woodworking
DESIGN INK - Apparel - Design Ink Corp.
DESIGN INSIGHT - Computer software - Chrysalis Symbolic Design, Inc.
DESIGN INSPIRATION COLLECTION - Floor coverings–carpet and rugs - Mohawk Carpet Corp.
DESIGN INTRIGUE - Floor coverings–carpet and rugs ☆ - Karastan-Bigelow Inc.
DESIGN-IT - Craft supplies ☆ - Clayton Corp.
DESIGN-IT! - Dyes and pigments - CPC International Inc.
DESIGN-IT - Hair care preparations - Schering-Plough Healthcare Products
DESIGN IV - Floor coverings–carpet and rugs - Lees Carpets
DESIGN LINE - Chairs–folding - Krueger International, Inc.
DESIGN LINE - Golfing equipment - John Rouzee Green Co., Inc.
DESIGN LINE - Pet products - Penn-Plax, Inc.
DESIGN LINE - Telephones - At&T Corp.
DESIGN LINE THE PERSONAL TOUCH - Heating equipment - Mestek Inc.
DESIGN-LINES - Blinds–venetian - Bamboo Abbott Florida Corp.
DESIGN-LINES - Office supplies - Safco Products Co.
DESIGN-LOK - Floor coverings–carpet and rugs - Shaw Industries Inc.
DESIGN M - Lighting fixtures - Light Inc.
DESIGN MARKETTE - Pens ☆ - Faber-Castell Corp.
DESIGN MASTER - Moldings and trim - Mid-America Building Products Corp.
DESIGN MASTER - Paints - Design Master
DESIGN-MATE - Toilet seats - Sanderson Plumbing Products, Inc.
DESIGN MISTRESS - Paints ☆ - Design Master
DESIGN MIX - Building materials - Mutual Materials Co.
DESIGN 'N' DOODLE - Toys - Rose Art Industries, Inc.
DESIGN NETWORK - Towels - Cecil Saydah Co.
DESIGN OF DOG - Luggage - Wolverine World Wide, Inc.
DESIGN OF FEMALE SILHOUETTE - Apparel and accessories - Playtex Apparel, Inc.
DESIGN OF PIG - Leather goods - Wolverine World Wide, Inc.
DESIGN OPTIONS - Floor coverings–carpet and rugs - Olympic Carpets Inc.
DESIGN PERFECT - Skin care products - Plasto Tech Co. International
DESIGN PERSPECTIVES - Fans–electric - Montgomery Ward & Co. Inc.
DESIGN PLUS - Floor coverings–carpet and rugs ☆ - Playfield International Inc.
DESIGN POINT - Floor coverings–carpet and rugs ☆ - Dorsett Carpet Mills Inc.
DESIGN POINT - Floor coverings–carpet and rugs ☆ - Downs Carpet Co. Inc.
DESIGN POPS - Candy - Murray-Allen International Inc.
DESIGN PORTFOLIO - Paper–gift wrap - Paperplains, Inc.
DESIGN PRO - Curling irons–electric - Windmere Corp.
DESIGN RACK - Racks - Fabric Marketing Association
DESIGN REFERENCE COUSTIC - Audio equipment - Concept Enterprises, Inc.
DESIGN SERIES 1 - Wallpaper - Bayview Wallcoverings

DESIGN SHOJI - Draperies - Design Shoji
DESIGN SPAN - Roofing materials–slate - ASC Pacific Inc.
DESIGN SPECTRUM - Paints - Courtaulds Coatings Inc.
DESIGN STAR - Culinary vessels and utensils ☆ - Corning Inc.
DESIGN STRIPE - Pencils ☆ - Faber-Castell Corp.
DESIGN STUDIO - Flatware ☆ - Gorham Inc.
DESIGN STUDIO - Frames–eyeglass - May Optical Co. Inc.
DESIGN STUDIO - Greeting cards ☆ - American Greetings Corp.
DESIGN STUDIO - Lamps - Service Merchandise Co. Inc.
DESIGN STUDIO FOR KIDS - Computer software - Parsons Technology, Inc.
DESIGN SYSTEM - Funnels ☆ - KMS Research Inc.
DESIGN TEAM - Computer Software - Scopus Technology, Inc.
DESIGN-TEC - Lockers–metal - W & W Sales Ltd.
DESIGN TECH - Floor coverings–carpet and rugs ☆ - World Carpets, Inc.
DESIGN TEK - Floor coverings–carpet and rugs ☆ - Customweave Carpets Inc.
DESIGN-TEX - Fireplace equipment ☆ - Temtex Products Inc.
DESIGN TEX - Floor coverings–carpet and rugs ☆ - J.L. Benson Co.
DESIGN TEX - Window coverings - Covoc Corp.
DESIGN TEX 1 - Floor coverings–carpet and rugs - J.L. Benson Co.
DESIGN TEX III - Floor coverings–carpet and rugs ☆ - J.L. Benson Co.
DESIGN TEX IV - Floor coverings–carpet and rugs - J.L. Benson Co.
DESIGN TEXT - Computer software - Alpine Press, Inc.
DESIGN TIME - Watches - Design Time USA Inc.
DESIGN TODAYS INC. - Apparel–athletic - Design Todays Inc.
DESIGN TOSCANO - Catalogs - Design Toscano, Inc.
DESIGN TRENDS - Drapery hardware - Kirsch Co.
DESIGN TRENDS FASHION SOFT SEATS - Toilet seats - Ginsey Industries, Inc.
DESIGN TRIM - Hardware ☆ - Marley Mouldings Inc.
DESIGN TWO - Dinnerware–glass - Sango Co. Ltd. (Sango USA Div.)
DESIGN U.S.A. - Bedding–linen - Dan River Inc.
DESIGN VERIFYER - Computer software - Chrysalis Symbolic Design, Inc.
DESIGN VERONIQUE - Medical apparatus - My True Image Manufacturing, Inc.
DESIGN VI FUTURES - Floor coverings–carpet and rugs - Lees Carpets
DESIGN VIEW - Curtains ☆ - Kawneer Co., Inc.
DESIGN: VIGNELLI - Apparel and accessories - Vignelli Designs, Ltd.
DESIGN-VUE - Eyeglasses - McKesson Home Health Care
DESIGN WALL - Wood products - Homasote Co.
DESIGN WORKS - Wallpaper - Wallcoverings Unlimited Inc.
DESIGN YOUR OWN - Jewelry - QVC, Inc.
DESIGN YOUR OWN - Patterns–clothing ☆ - Simplicity Pattern Co., Inc.
DESIGN YOUR OWN HOME - Computer software - Abracadata Ltd.
DESIGN2-TITE - Machinery - Ready Tech Inc.
DESIGNACOLOR - Paints - PPG Industries, Inc.
DESIGNAIR - Motor vehicle parts and accessories - Preview Products
DESIGNAIRE - Ventilation equipment - Tomkins Industries Inc.
DESIGNASAURUS - Computer software - Compton's NewMedia
DESIGNASAURUS - Shirts - United American Video Corp.
DESIGNATED DRIVER - Glassware–household - Culver Glass Inc.
DESIGNATED DRIVER - Golfing equipment - Golfsmith International Inc.
DESIGNATED HITTER GAME, THE - Computer software - Martin Lowry
DESIGNBOOK - Computer software - Escalade
DESIGNCASE - Magazine-storage containers - Gaylord Bros. Inc.
DESIGNCHECK - Computer software - Systems of Merritt, Inc.
DESIGNCOMPOSER - Computer software - Software Productivity Consortium, Inc.
DESIGNE FULL VIEW - Fireplace equipment - Schaefer Co.
DESIGNED BY RAGO - Underwear and nightwear - Rago Foundations Inc. LLC
DESIGNED EDGE - Animal feed - Cenex/Land O'Lakes AG Services
DESIGNED FOR LIVING - Dinnerware - Corning Inc.
DESIGNED IDEAS - Bathroom accessories - H.M. Coby Associates Inc.
DESIGNEDGE - Landscaping timbers - Thompson Industries, Inc.
DESIGNER - Aquariums–household - All Glass Aquarium Co. Inc.
DESIGNER - Ashtrays–glass - Peter Pan Industries
DESIGNER - Bathtubs–enameled - Pearl Baths Inc.
DESIGNER - Benches–metal - Artesian Industries
DESIGNER - Blinds–venetian - Kenney Manufacturing Co.
DESIGNER - Cash registers - Auer Register Co.
DESIGNER - Floor coverings–carpet and rugs ☆ - Criterion Mills Inc.
DESIGNER - Garment racks - Vogel Peterson Furniture Co.
DESIGNER - Hair care products - Mastey De Paris
DESIGNER - Hobby kits ☆ - Accento Plastic Manufacturing Inc.
DESIGNER - Irons–electric - Sunbeam Corp.

☆ = Now out of production

DESIGNER - Jewelry - Jacoby-Bender Inc.
DESIGNER - Lighting fixtures - Visador Co.
DESIGNER - Office supplies - Alvin and Co. Inc.
DESIGNER - Office supplies - Bates Manufacturing Co.
DESIGNER - Paints - Dutch Boy Group
DESIGNER - Paper–gift wrap - Stephen Lawrence Co.
DESIGNER - Rings–jewelry ☆ - Artcarved Inc.
DESIGNER - Sponges - Acme Sponge & Chamois Co., Inc.
DESIGNER - Stencils - The Stencil Shoppe Inc.
DESIGNER - Tiles–ceramic ☆ - KPT Inc.
DESIGNER - Toys - Jak-Pak Inc.
DESIGNER 2 - Desk sets - Rubbermaid Commercial Products Inc.
DESIGNER ACCENT - Paints - Devoe & Raynolds Co.
DESIGNER ACCENTS - Tiles–ceramic ☆ - American Olean Tile Co.
DESIGNER BAY - Fireplace equipment - Jack-Post Corp.
DESIGNER CARE CO., LTD. - Gloves–rubber - Designer Care Co., Ltd.
DESIGNER CAREFREE - Floor coverings - Congoleum Corp.
DESIGNER CHOICE - Floor coverings–carpet and rugs ☆ - Blue Ridge Carpet Mills
DESIGNER CHOICES - Wallcoverings - Intex Plastics Sales Co. (Wallcovering Div.)
DESIGNER CLASSIC ALTERNATIVES - Perfumes - Tristar Corp.
DESIGNER CLASSICS - Furniture ☆ - Chromcraft Corp.
DESIGNER COLLECTION - Electrical equipment - General Electric Co.
DESIGNER COLLECTION - Eyeglasses - Art-Craft Optical Co.
DESIGNER COLLECTION - Floor coverings ☆ - Azrock Commercial Flooring
DESIGNER COLLECTION 10 - Wallpaper - Pantasote Inc. (Wallcovering Div.)
DESIGNER COLOR COLLECTION - Toys - Imperial Toy Corp.
DESIGNER COLORS - Wood fillers ☆ - Natural Products Corp.
DESIGNER CONTRACT - Frames–picture - Designer Moulding
DESIGNER COTTONS - Fabrics - Dan River Inc.
DESIGNER CURLS - Hair care products - Waverly Beauty Products
DESIGNER DIMENSIONS - Wallpaper ☆ - Horizon Wallcoverings
DESIGNER DIMENSIONS 2 - Wallpaper ☆ - Horizon Wallcoverings
DESIGNER DIRECT - Women's apparel - Home Shopping Club, Inc.
DESIGNER DIRT - Soil–potting - Gold Kist Inc.
DESIGNER DISPLAYWARE - Cookware - Carlisle Foodservice Products, Inc.
DESIGNER DRAWER - Furniture - Clairson International Corp.
DESIGNER EDITION - Wallcoverings - Beverly Stevens Ltd.
DESIGNER FABRIC - Bulletin boards–wood - Claridge Products and Equipment Inc.
DESIGNER FOODS - Meat products - Designer Foods, Inc.
DESIGNER FOODS - Vitamins and nutritional supplements - Durk Pearson & Sandy Shaw Partnership
DESIGNER GALLERY - Floor coverings–carpet and rugs ☆ - Alexander Smith Carpets
DESIGNER GALLERY - Frames–picture - Two's Co. Inc.
DESIGNER GOLF - Games - Scott J. Bassler
DESIGNER GUILD COLLECTION LIMITED EDITION ORIGINAL ARTIST DOLLS - Dolls - Blackall Associates, Inc.
DESIGNER HOME - Toys - Walmer Dollhouses
DESIGNER HOMESPUN - Yarn ☆ - Tahki Imports Ltd.
DESIGNER I - Drafting supplies - Pickett Industries
DESIGNER IMPOSTERS - Perfumes - Parfum de Coeur Ltd.
DESIGNER INLAY - Furniture - Dinaire Corp.
DESIGNER INTRASCAPES - Window treatments - Intrascapes
DESIGNER JEWELS - Jewelry - Designer Jewels Inc.
DESIGNER KIT - Hobby kits - Binney & Smith Inc.
DESIGNER LAMPKITS BY GARRY - Lamps - Max C's Ceramic & Craft
DESIGNER LINE - Containers - Hedges Manufacturing Co.
DESIGNER-LINER - Stationery - Pen Notes Inc.
DESIGNER LITE - Bathroom fixtures - Artesian Industries
DESIGNER LITES - Lamps - Pansy Ellen Products, Inc.
DESIGNER MATES - Frames–picture - Designer Moulding
DESIGNER METALLICS - Paints - Tulip Productions
DESIGNER MISTS - Colognes - Thomas E. McCann
DESIGNER MODEL B - Projection screens - Da-Lite Screen Co. Inc.
DESIGNER MOULDING BY CARDINAL - Frames–picture - Designer Moulding
DESIGNER NATURALS - Tiles–ceramic ☆ - American Olean Tile Co.
DESIGNER OPTIMA - Floor coverings - Tarkett, Inc.
DESIGNER PACESETTER II - Wallpaper ☆ - Pantasote Inc. (Wallcovering Div.)
DESIGNER PACESETTER III - Wallpaper - Pantasote Inc. (Wallcovering Div.)
DESIGNER PALETTE - Floor coverings ☆ - Kentile Floors Inc.
DESIGNER PENCILS - Pencils - Musgrave Pencil Co. Inc.

DESIGNER PLUS - Lamps - Osram Sylvania Inc.
DESIGNER PLUS - Shelving units–metal - Hirsh Co.
DESIGNER PLUS CRYSTALS - Lamps - Osram Sylvania Inc.
DESIGNER PODGE - Finishing agents ☆ - Tulip Productions
DESIGNER PROP - Propellers - Ameritech Industries, Inc.
DESIGNER REPRODUCTIONS - Sunglasses - Visual Effects Inc.
DESIGNER ROLLS - Paper–rolls - Paper Manufacturers Co.
DESIGNER SERIES - Cameras - CCTV Corp./GBC
DESIGNER SERIES - Fireplace equipment - Schaefer Co.
DESIGNER SERIES - Housewares - Wilton Co.
DESIGNER SERIES - Motor vehicles - Jayco Inc.
DESIGNER SILKS - Fabrics–silk - Joscar Industries Inc.
DESIGNER SLATE - Floor coverings - National Floor Products Co., Inc.
DESIGNER SOLIDS - Floor coverings - Azrock Commercial Flooring
DESIGNER STEPS - Footwear - Wang's International, Inc.
DESIGNER STONE - Masonry blocks - Designer Blocks, Inc.
DESIGNER-STRIPE - Floor coverings–carpet and rugs - Ludlow Composites Corp.
DESIGNER TEXTILES - Wallpaper - Thomas Ray Designs Inc.
DESIGNER, THE - Housewares stores - Butterick Co. Inc.
DESIGNER, THE - Jewelry - Helzbergs Diamond Shops Inc.
DESIGNER, THE - Paper ☆ - Hunt Manufacturing Co.
DESIGNER TOUCH - Floor coverings–carpet and rugs - Dan River Inc.
DESIGNER TOUCH, THE - Paper–gift wrap - Clark Imports Inc.
DESIGNER TREASURES - Apparel–women's - Warnaco Inc.
DESIGNER TRENDMARK - Wallpaper - Surface Industries Inc.
DESIGNER VASES - Flower pots–plastic - Syndicate Sales, Inc.
DESIGNER WEAVES - Fabrics - Decorative Aides Co. Inc.
DESIGNER WHEELS - Toys - Shure Products, Inc.
DESIGNER WOOD STAINS - Paints - Gray Seal Paint Manufacturing Co. Inc.
DESIGNER WOODS - Frames–picture - Rare Woods Inc.
DESIGNERLINE - Doors–glass ☆ - Material Corp. Inc.
DESIGNERLINE - Tiles–ceramic ☆ - Porcelanite, Inc.
DESIGNERLINE - Window shades - Conrad Imports, Inc.
DESIGNERPLUS - Artists' materials ☆ - Plan Hold Corp.
DESIGNERS - Artists' materials ☆ - M. Grumbacher Inc.
DESIGNERS - Cosmetics - Honey & Spice Toiletries
DESIGNER'S - Paints - Winsor & Newton
DESIGNERS & ILLUSTRATORS - Greeting cards - American Artists Group Inc.
DESIGNERS BARGAIN PAK - Jewelry - Stanislaus Imports, Inc.
DESIGNER'S CACHET - Floor coverings–carpet and rugs ☆ - Callaway Carpets
DESIGNERS' CERAMIC ARTS M I - Glassware–household - Marina Isetta
DESIGNER'S CHOICE - Beads - Greene Plastics Corp.
DESIGNER'S CHOICE - Fans–electric - Hunter Fan Co.
DESIGNER'S CHOICE - Furniture - Hickory Manufacturing Co.
DESIGNERS CHOICE - Glass–leaded - Albert E. Price, Inc.
DESIGNERS CHOICE - Health care products ☆ - Sunrise Medical
DESIGNER'S CHOICE - Laminate moldings - Milton W. Bosley & Co. Inc.
DESIGNER'S CHOICE - Paper–gift wrap - Gift Wrap Co.
DESIGNER'S CHOICE - Ships–sailing vessels - Howmar Boat Corp.
DESIGNER'S CHOICE - Tiles–ceramic - United States Ceramic Tile Co.
DESIGNER'S CHOICE - Wallpaper - Robert Crowder & Co.
DESIGNER'S CHOICE - Wallpaper - K.M.L. Industries
DESIGNER'S CHOICE - Wallpaper - Wallcoverings Unlimited Inc.
DESIGNERS CHOICE COLLECTION - Sofabeds - Aireloom Bedding Co.
DESIGNER'S CLUB - Computer software - Dynamic Graphics Inc.
DESIGNERS COLLECTION - Figurines ☆ - Ideal Originals
DESIGNERS COLLECTION - Giftware - Designers Collection
DESIGNERS' COLLECTION - Greeting cards - American Greetings Corp.
DESIGNERS COLLECTION - Greeting cards ☆ - Paper Magic Group Inc.
DESIGNER'S COLOSSAL CARDS - Greeting cards - Designer Greetings Inc.
DESIGNER'S CONCEPTS - Wallpaper - Galaxie Handprints
DESIGNER'S CONNECTION - Greeting cards - Designer's Connection
DESIGNER'S EDGE - Computer software - Allen Communication Inc.
DESIGNER'S EDITION - Greeting cards - Nu-Art Inc.
DESIGNER'S ENSEMBLE - Floor coverings–carpet and rugs ☆ - Callaway Carpets
DESIGNER'S FIRST EDITION - Wallpaper - Pickhardt & Siebert USA Inc.
DESIGNERS FOUNTAIN - Lighting fixtures - Designers Fountain
DESIGNER'S GALLERY - Floor coverings–carpet and rugs - Galaxy Carpet Mills Inc.
DESIGNER'S GALLERY - Furniture ☆ - Norwalk Furniture Corp.
DESIGNERS GOLD - Business cards - Stationery House Inc.
DESIGNERS GUILD - Dinnerware–plastic - Plastics Manufacturing Co.

DESIGNERS GUILD - Drapery hardware - Newell Operating Co.
DESIGNERS GUILD - Drapery hardware - Newell Window Furnishing Co.
DESIGNERS ORIGINAL - Glass products ☆ - Thomas Industries Inc.
DESIGNERS ORIGINALS - Crocheted and knitted items ☆ - Hampshire Hosiery, Inc.
DESIGNERS ORIGINALS - Sweaters - Hampshire Group, Ltd.
DESIGNERS ORIGINALS STUDIO - Sweaters - Hampshire Group, Ltd.
DESIGNER'S PALETTE - Floor coverings–tile ☆ - Kepcor, Inc./SSI Tiles
DESIGNER'S PENCIL, THE - Computer software - Activision, Inc.
DESIGNER'S PREFERENCE - Tiles–ceramic ☆ - United States Ceramic Tile Co.
DESIGNERS RESOURCE - Jewelry - Stanislaus Imports, Inc.
DESIGNERS ROW - Greeting cards - Amscan Inc.
DESIGNERS SHOWCASE - Greeting cards - Regency Thermographers Inc.
DESIGNER'S SPECIAL - Toys–models - Estes Industries
DESIGNERS' SPECTRUM - Wallpaper - Pantasote Inc. (Wallcovering Div.)
DESIGNER'S TOUCH - Floor coverings–carpet and rugs - Lees Carpets
DESIGNER'S TOUCH - Wallpaper - Benson Manufacturing Corp.
DESIGNER'S TOUCH II - Wallpaper - Norwall Wallcoverings
DESIGNERS WORKSHOP - Figurines ☆ - Hagen-Renaker Inc.
DESIGNERSTYLE - Refrigerators - Whirlpool Properties, Inc.
DESIGNERWALL - Shelving units–metal - Design Components Inc.
DESIGNERWARE - Plates–plastic - WNA Comet
DESIGNEXPRESS - Computer software - Microvision Development, Inc.
DESIGNFLEX - Floor coverings–carpet and rugs - Shaw Industries Inc.
DESIGNFOLD - Greeting cards - Designfold, Inc.
DESIGNGARD - Frames–eyeglass - Hudson Optical Corp.
DESIGNGUARD - Finishing agents - Designer Wood Products Inc.
DESIGNING BETTER CHEMICAL PRODUCTS - Computer software - Molecular Knowledge Systems, Inc.
DESIGNIT - Computer software - Standard Register Co.
DESIGNLAB - Computer software - Microsim Corp.
DESIGNLAB - Stationery - Designlab, Inc.
DESIGNLAB START TO FINISH - Computer software - Microsim Corp.
DESIGNLAND - Hobby kits - M. Ginsburg & Co.
DESIGNLAND CRAFTS - Toys - M. Ginsburg & Co.
DESIGNLIGHT - Lamps–desk - Art Specialty Co. Inc.
DESIGNLINE - Flowers–artificial - Caffco International
DESIGNMASTER - Computer software - SourceView Software International
DESIGNMASTER - Dining room furniture - Designmaster Furniture Inc.
DESIGNMATE - Toilet seats - Magnolia Products
DESIGNMODE - Tiles–ceramic ☆ - Dal-Tile Corp.
DESIGNO DINO'S - Dolls ☆ - Totsy Manufacturing Co., Inc.
DESIGNOSAURUS - Dinnerware–plastic - Design Imports Ltd.
DESIGNOTE - Computer software - First International Computer of America, Inc.
DESIGNPOST - Computer software - Computervision Corp.
DESIGNPRO - Blinds–vertical - Ambassador Industries
DESIGNREALITY - Computer software - Ashlar Inc.
DESIGNS BY AARON - Jewelry - Modern Art Jewelry
DESIGNS BY ANTHONY - Pottery - Freeman-McFarlin Potteries Inc.
DESIGNS BY BOBBY - Greeting cards - Designs by Bobby
DESIGNS BY BONNIE - Glassware–household - Bonnie Burns
DESIGNS BY EDA - Statuary - Seymour Mann Inc.
DESIGNS BY HETRICK - Pottery - Freeman-McFarlin Potteries Inc.
DESIGNS BY J. WRIGHT - Pottery - Freeman-McFarlin Potteries Inc.
DESIGNS BY KAY FINCH - Pottery - Freeman-McFarlin Potteries Inc.
DESIGNS BY KUMA - Aprons ☆ - Coe & Dru Inc.
DESIGNS BY LINDA - Hobby kits - H.P. & H.F. Hunt Co.
DESIGNS BY MALINDA - Hobby kits - Lake City Craft Co.
DESIGNS BY ME - Hobby kits - Western Publishing Co., Inc.
DESIGNS BY METZKE - Giftware - Faroy Sales
DESIGNS BY RUTLEDGE - Pottery - Freeman-McFarlin Potteries Inc.
DESIGNS BY VICTORIA - Wallpaper - Designs by Victoria, Inc.
DESIGNS FOR HEALTH - Cookies - Designs for Health
DESIGNS FOR LIVING - Floor coverings - L.D. Brinkman & Co. Inc.
DESIGNS FOR WORLD-CLASS QUALITY - Video production - Juran Institute, Inc.
DESIGNS FOR YOU - Wallcoverings - Intex Plastics Sales Co. (Wallcovering Div.)
DESIGNS IN COPPER - Copper products - Designs in Copper
DESIGNS IN STRINGS - Blinds–venetian ☆ - Decorative Aides Co. Inc.
DESIGNS IN TEXTURE - Wallpaper ☆ - Kingfisher Wallcoverings
DESIGNS IN VINES - Baskets–wood - McCann Bros., Inc.
DESIGNS OF TODAY - Wallpaper ☆ - Richard E. Thibaut, Inc.
DESIGNS TOO - Giftware - Faroy Sales

DESIGNS UNCOVERED - Apparel and accessories - Herman Pearl Button Co., Inc.
DESIGNS UNLIMITED - Wallpaper ☆ - Royal Products
DESIGNS WEST - Wallpaper - Bob Mitchell Designs
DESIGNS WEST 5 - Wallpaper - Bob Mitchell Designs
DESIGNS WITH LIGHT - Housewares - Dansk International Designs, Ltd.
DESIGNSCAPE - Floor coverings–carpet and rugs - Karastan-Bigelow Inc.
DESIGNSETTER - Curling irons–electric - Helen of Troy Corp.
DESIGNSOURCE - Computer peripheral equipment - Synopsys, Inc.
DESIGNSTEIN - Apparel and accessories - Designstein, Inc.
DESIGNSTUDIO - Computer software ☆ - Esselte Corp.
DESIGNTEAM - Computer software - Scopus Technology, Inc.
DESIGNTEC - Floor coverings–carpet and rugs - Karastan-Bigelow Inc.
DESIGNTECH - Electronic equipment - Designtech International, Inc.
DESIGNWARE - Computer software - Synopsys, Inc.
DESIGNWARE - Paper products - American Greetings Corp.
DESIGNWAY - Carpets, now out of production - Couristan Inc.
DESIGNWORKSHOP - Computer software - Artifice, Inc.
DESIGNWRAP - Paper–gift wrap - American Greetings Corp.
DESINCRUSTOR - Skin care products - Dynex International
DESIRABLE - Floor coverings–carpet and rugs - Trend Carpet
DESIRABLES - Bottles, jars - Italglass Group USA Corp.
DESIRE - Christmas tree ornaments - Cracker Box Inc.
DESIRE - Dinnerware–glass ☆ - Lenox, Inc.
DESIRE - Floor coverings–carpet and rugs ☆ - Galaxy Carpet Mills Inc.
DESIRE - Glassware–household ☆ - Lenox Crystal, Inc.
DESIRE - Ophthalmic goods - Embassy Creations Inc.
DESIRED EFFECTS - Wallpaper ☆ - Andover Wallcovering
DESIREE - Bedding–linen - Dan River Inc.
DESIREE - Fabrics - Guilford Mills, Inc.
DESIREE - Floor coverings–carpet and rugs ☆ - Regal Rugs Inc.
DESIREE - Glassware–household ☆ - Oneida Ltd.
DESIREE - Lipsticks - Lancome
DESIROUS - Floor coverings–carpet and rugs - World Carpets, Inc.
DESI'S FAMOUS PIZZA AND RESTAURANT - Pizzas–frozen - Desi's Pizza Inc.
DESIST - Health care products - Halsey Drug Co. Inc.
DESITIN - Skin care products - Pfizer Inc.
DESK BUDDY - Pen holders - Nina Enterprises, Inc.
DESK COMPANION - Computers ☆ - Fidelity Electronics International Inc.
DESK DISC - Table-top organizer - Ingenious Designs, Inc.
DESK DIVOT - Novelty items - Two Putts, Inc.
DESK ESSENTIALS - Office supplies - American Trading and Production Corp.
DESK GALLERY - Computer software - Zedcor Inc.
DESK JOCKEY - Calendars - Mach 1, Inc.
DESK-LITER - Lamps–desk ☆ - Cannon Products Inc.
DESK MASTER - Books–blank - Myron Manufacturing Corp.
DESK-MASTER - Desk sets - Master Woodcraft Inc.
DESK MASTER - Paper–gummed ☆ - Park Sherman
DESK MATE - Desk sets ☆ - Newell Office Products
DESK MATE - Markers–felt-tip - National Pen & Pencil Co.
DESK MATE - Staplers - Markwell Manufacturing Co. Inc.
DESK MATES - Office supplies ☆ - Park Sherman
DESK-N-DOOR - Nameplates–engraved - Spear Engineering Co.
DESK-O-MATIC - Drafting supplies - Mayline/Hamilton
DESK PAC - Desk sets ☆ - Sainberg and Co. Inc.
DESK PALS - Office supplies ☆ - Faber-Castell Corp.
DESK PARTITIONER - Desk sets - Marnay Sales & Manufacturing Co. Inc.
DESK PORTFOLIO EXPRESS - Office supplies - McBee Loose Leaf Binders
DESK SAVER - Computers - Duracom Computer Systems
DESK SETS - Desk sets - Quill Co. Inc.
DESK STONE - Novelty items - S.J. Miller Co.
DESK SUSAN - Office supplies - Park Sherman
DESK SYSTEMS - Office furniture–metal - Marvel Group Inc.
DESK TO DINNER - Shoes - QVC, Inc.
DESK TOP - Office supplies - Artistic Office Products
DESK TOP - Photographic equipment - Logan Electric Specialty Manufacturing Co.
DESK TOP LINOLEUM - Desks - Forbo Industries, Inc.
DESK TOPPERS - Paper products - Trend Enterprises, Inc.
DESK WORKS - Scissors–hand-operated - Fiskars Inc.
DESKCONNECT - Computer software - Traveling Software, Inc.
DESKDATE - Calendars - Ad-a-Day Co. Inc.
DESKDIRECT - Computer peripheral equipment - Hewlett-Packard Co.
DESKJET - Printers–computer - Hewlett-Packard Co.
DESKMAIL - Computer software - Western Union Commercial Services

DESKMANAGER - Computer software - Hewlett-Packard Co.
DESKMASTER - Lamps–desk ☆ - Eagle Electric Manufacturing Co., Inc.
DESKMASTER - Pens ☆ - Faber-Castell Corp.
DESKMATE - Computer software - Tandy Corp.
DESKNET SYSTEMS INC. - Electronic equipment - Desknet Systems, Inc.
DESKPOD - Furniture - Stanley James Kotkosky
DESKPRO - Computers–personal ☆ - Compaq Computer Corp.
DESKRETARY - Calendars - Ad-a-Day Co. Inc.
DESKS INCORPORATED - Furniture - Desks Inc.
DESKSET - Adhesives and sealants - Loctite Corp.
DESKTOP - Desk sets ☆ - Franmara Co. Inc.
DESKTOP ACCOUNTANT - Computer software - SourceView Software International
DESKTOP ADVENTURES - Video games - Lucasarts Entertainment Co.
DESKTOP ART - Computer software ☆ - Dynamic Graphics Inc.
DESKTOP CDPD - Computer software - Wireless Connect, Inc.
DESKTOP COLORFOIL - Foil paper - Paper Direct, Inc.
DESKTOP DESIGN - Paper - Paper Direct, Inc.
DESKTOP DUST PUPPY - Dusters–feather - H.W. Products, Inc.
DESKTOP LIBRARY - Computer storage devices–optical - Sony Electronics Inc.
DESKTOP MBA - Computer software - C-Sharp Software
DESKTOP MESSAGES - Paper - Paper Direct, Inc.
DESKTOP OBSERVATORY - Computer software - Pinnacle Technology, Inc.
DESKTOP PLAYGROUND - Computer software - 7th Level, Inc.
DESKTOP PRACTICE SYSTEMS - Computer software - West Publishing Co.
DESKTOP SEMINARS - Computer software - Icon Associates, Inc.
DESKTOP SUPPORT FACTORY - Computer software - Usability Sciences Corp.
DESKTOP TODAY - Computer software - Regency Thermographers of California, Inc.
DESKTOP TOYS - Computer software - Cortex Software, LLC
DESKTRACY - Computer software - Kansasbay Systems, Inc.
DESKUBE - Electronic equipment ☆ - Tandy Corp.
DESKWINDOWS - Plastic pockets - Barbara P. Lott
DESKWRITER C - Printers–computer - Hewlett-Packard Co.
DESNOES & GEDDES - Beverages–carbonated - Reggae Imports
DESOGEN - Pharmaceutical preparations - Organon Inc.
DESOLVE - Degreasing solvents - Surco Products Inc.
DESOLVE-IT - Degreasing solvents - Surco Products Inc.
DESOTO - Bicycles - Trailmate Inc.
DESOTO - Cleaning preparations - Desoto, Inc.
DESOTO - Detergents - Valspar Corp.
DESOTO - Flooring–hardwood - DeSoto Hardwood Flooring Co.
DESOTO - Recording label - Slamdek/Scramdown
DESOTO OUTDOORS - Hosiery - Desoto Hosiery Mills, Inc.
DESOWEN - Pharmaceutical preparations - Owen/Galderma Laboratories Inc.
DESOXEMMS - Pharmaceutical preparations ☆ - C.O. Truxton Inc.
DESOXY-CELL PLUS - Pharmaceutical preparations - Quaker City Pharmacal Co.
DESOXYN - Pharmaceutical preparations - Abbott Laboratories
DESPANA BRAND - Food products - 86-17 Northern Boulevard Corp.
DESPARD - Switches–electric - Pass & Seymour, Inc.
DESPERADO - Beverages–malt - Coast Range Brewing Co.
DESPERADO - Bicycle - Rand International, Inc.
DESPERADO - Fishing lures - Paul Warner Industries
DESPERADO - Furniture - Bean Station Furniture Factory Inc.
DESPERADO - Knives - Cold Steel Inc.
DESPERADO - Optical scanners–computer - Titmus Optical, Inc.
DESPERADO - Ships–sailing vessels - Tanton
DESPERADO SALSA - Spices and extracts - Marksell, Inc.
DESPERADO WESTERNWEAR - Apparel and accessories - Putnam Industries
DESPERATELY SEEKING C - Juices - Fresh Samantha Inc.
DESPLEX - Electronics equipment - Secur-Data Systems, Inc.
DESPOT - Posters - Aegis Entertainment, Inc.
DESQUAM-X - Pharmaceutical preparations - Westwood-Squibb Pharmaceuticals, Inc.
DESQVIEW - Computer software - Quarterdeck Corp.
DESSAUX FILS - Food products ☆ - Liberty Richter Inc.
DESSERT BOOTS - Footwear - Wolverine World Wide, Inc.
DESSERT CREATIONS - Cakes - Heidi's Pastry, Inc.
DESSERT CREATIONS CHOCOLATE MOUSSE PIES - Desserts - Dessert Creations
DESSERT DELIGHT - Desserts - Desert Rose Corp.
DESSERT FAVORITES - Cookies - PF Brands, Inc.
DESSERT-LOVER - Confections - Irwin L. Gold & Assoc.

DESSERT-MATE - Pies–fresh - Nestle USA
DESSERT MINT - Teas–herbal - Lipton Investments, Inc.
DESSERT MINTS - Candy - Brach and Brock Confections Inc.
DESSERT SECRETS - Food products - Signature Brands, LLC
DESSERT THINS - Candy - Superior Fruit & Confections
DESSERTS BY DAVID GLASS - Bakery products - Desserts by David Glass
DESSERTS ELITE - Confections - Sara Lee Corp.
DESSERTS ETCETERA - Bakery products - Desserts Etcetera
DESSERTS IN THE ROUND - Food products ☆ - Just Desserts Inc.
DESSERTS ON THE SQUARE - Food products ☆ - Just Desserts Inc.
DESSERTS ON US - Food products - Desserts On Us Baklava
DESSERTS, THE - Bakery products ☆ - Allied Bakers Co.
DESSERTS TO DIE FOR - Bakery products - TDF, Inc.
DEST - Pet products ☆ - Sera Aquaristik USA Inc.
DESTAB - Health care products - Particle Dynamics Inc.
DESTANE - Cleaning preparations - Advance Cleaning Products Inc.
D'ESTE - Pipes–tobacco - James B. Russell Inc.
DESTEFANO'S - Footwear - Somerset Footwear
DESTIM - Pharmaceutical preparations - 206 Macopin Corp.
DESTIN CLOTHING CO. - Apparel and accessories - Destin Clothing Co.
DESTINATION - Cosmetics - AnnTaylor, Inc.
DESTINATION SERVER - Computer hardware - Gammagraphx, Inc.
DESTINATION UNKNOWN - Infant product ☆ - Ming Ta Supply
DESTINATION: VACATION - Games - Brown and Bigelow Inc.
DESTINATIONS - Apparel and accessories - Swingster Co.
DESTINATIONS - Fabrics–cotton ☆ - Wallquest, Inc.
DESTINATIONS - Luggage - Service Merchandise Co. Inc.
DESTINATIONS AMERICA - Computer software - Parsons Technology, Inc.
DESTINATIONS IN SCIENCE - Recording label - Addison-Wesley Publishing Co.
DESTINY - Agricultural products - Durant Distributing, Inc.
DESTINY - Apparel stores–lingerie - Goddess Bra
DESTINY - Artists' materials ☆ - Artoptic International Corp.
DESTINY - Bicycles ☆ - Huffy Corp.
DESTINY - Clocks - General Time Corp. (Westclox/Seth Thomas Div.)
DESTINY - Computer software - At&T Corp.
DESTINY - Fabrics - Majilite Corp.
DESTINY - Flatware ☆ - Lifetime Hoan Corp.
DESTINY - Floor coverings–carpet and rugs - Conquest Carpet Mills Inc.
DESTINY - Floor coverings–carpet and rugs - Hartford Carpet Mills
DESTINY - Flowers, plants, and seeds - Jonathan Green, Inc.
DESTINY - Flowers, plants, and seeds - Jacklin Seed
DESTINY - Frames–eyeglass - Kenmark Optical Co.
DESTINY - Games - Gamescience
DESTINY - Guitars - Peavey Electronics Corp.
DESTINY - Health care products - National Wheel-O-Vator Co. Inc.
DESTINY - Hearing aids - Pittsburgh Hearing Aid Co.
DESTINY - Herbicides - Cenex/Land O'Lakes AG Services
DESTINY - Luggage ☆ - Maximillian Luggage Corp.
DESTINY - Motor vehicles–motor homes - Coachmen Industries, Inc.
DESTINY - Perfumes - Marilyn Miglin L.P.
DESTINY - Printers–computer - Destiny Technology Corp.
DESTINY - Recording label - Destiny Records
DESTINY - Skin care products - Veeco Manufacturing Co.
DESTINY - Trailers–travel - Fleetwood Enterprises, Inc.
DESTINY - Wallets - Accurate Leather & Novelty Co. Inc.
DESTINY I - Beds–wood - Watercloud Bed Co.
DESTINY II - Beds–wood - Watercloud Bed Co.
DESTINY III - Beds–wood - Watercloud Bed Co.
DESTINY PRESS - Publisher's imprints - Walsh-Haloska
DESTINY II - Wallpaper - J. Josephson, Inc.
DESTRO - Toys - Hasbro, Inc.
DESTROOPER - Cookies - Liberty Richter Inc.
DESTROY - Footwear–children's - Lvichiny Destroy Imports Inc.
DESTROYER - Bicycles ☆ - Huffy Corp.
DESTROYER - Sporting goods ☆ - Prince Sports Group, Inc.
DESTROYER - Steering mechanisms–boat - Edson Corp.
DESTROYER - Toys - Tonka Corp.
DESTROYER ESCORT - Computer software ☆ - Microprose Software, Inc.
DESTROYIT - Office supplies - Michael Business Machines
DESTROYS PET ODORS - Candles - Arizona Natural Resources
DESVIGNES AINE & FILS - Wines - European Beverage Co., Inc.
DESYREL - Pharmaceutical preparations - Bristol-Myers Squibb Co.
DET - Giftware - David E. Trabich Inc.
DET-MAR - Steering mechanisms–motor vehicle - Detroit Marine Engineering
DET-O-JET - Detergents - Alconox Inc.

DETACHABLE PLUS - Hair clippers–veterinary - Andis Co.
DETACHATIP - Medical equipment - Microsurge Inc.
DETACHE - Leather goods - St. Thomas Inc.
DETACHOL - Adhesives and sealants - Ferndale Laboratories, Inc.
DETAIL - Agricultural products - American Cyanamid Co.
DETAIL - Detergents - Procter & Gamble Co.
DETAIL - Frames–eyeglass - Hoya Corp. USA
DETAIL - Paints ☆ - DecoArt, Inc.
DETAIL FUSIBLE - Fabrics–canvas - Crown Textile Co.
DETAIL TOUCH - Brushes–paint - Al C. Salazar
DETAILER'S CHOICE - Cleaning preparations - First Brands Properties Inc.
DETAILER'S CHOICE, THE - Chamois cloths and brushes - Clean-Rite
Products Co.
DETAILS - Apparel and accessories - Fishman and Tobin Inc.
DETAILS - Apparel–women's - Details Sportswear Inc.
DETAILS - Coffee makers–electric - Mr. Coffee, Inc.
DETAILS - Decorations - Ogren Companies Inc.
DETAILS - Fabrics–tapestry - Comark Wallcoverings
DETAILS - Fixtures - Georgia-Pacific Corp.
DETAILS - Floor coverings–tile - Interface, Inc.
DETAILS - Shoes - MSF Corp.
DETAILS - Wallpaper - Benchmark Preferred Wallcoverings
DETAILS - Wallpaper ☆ - Imperial Wallcoverings, Inc.
DETAILS-2000 - Publisher's imprints - Edwin Shaver
DETAILS BY E.E.H. - Apparel and accessories - E & E Hosiery Inc.
DETAILS EYEWEAR - Eyeglasses - Windsor Optical Inc.
DETAILS II - Wallpaper - Imperial Wallcoverings, Inc.
DETALES - Apparel and accessories - Novatex Trading Co.
DETALIA - Tiles–ceiling ☆ - Florida Tile Industries, Inc.
DETAMINATR - Cleaning equipment - Contec, Inc.
DETANE - Skin care products - Del Pharmaceuticals, Inc.
DETANGLE - Hair care products - Fromm Industries
DETANGLE - Hair care products - Sebastian International, Inc.
DETECATEST - Health care products ☆ - C.B. Fleet Co. Inc.
DETECT-A-FIRE - Smoke detectors - Kidde-Fenwal, Inc.
DETECT-A-JEWEL - Jewelry - Michael Steinfeld
DETECT-A-LEAK - Pipes–tobacco - Flamort Chemical Co.
DETECT-O-GRAPH - Pencils ☆ - Faber-Castell Corp.
DETECTABLE WARNING - Concrete products - Hanover Architectural
Products Businesstrust
DETECTASSETTE - Measuring instruments - Baker Hughes Inc.
DETECTIVE - Ophthalmic goods - Embassy Creations Inc.
DETECTIVE - Tools - Monadnock Lifetime Products, Inc.
DETECTIVE BOOK CLUB - Publisher's imprints - Walter J. Black Inc.
DETECTIVE KIT GAME, THE - Games - University Games Corp.
DETECTIVE SPECIAL - Firearms, accessories, and parts - New Colt Holding
Corp.
DETECTIVE SPECIAL - Revolvers ☆ - Colt's Manufacturing Co. Inc.
DETECTIVE TOOL KIT - Computer software - Detective Tools Corp.
DETECTIVE TRIO MYSTERIES - Jigsaw puzzle - Lombard Marketing, Inc.
DETECTO - Scales–bathroom - Detecto Scale Co.
DETECTOR SYSTEMS - Electronic equipment - Intersection Development
Corp.
DETENSIONIZE - Orthopedic products - Clayton M. Reynolds, III
DETENTE - Eyeglasses - Art-Craft Optical Co.
DETENTE - Office furniture–metal - Invincible Metal Furniture Co.
DETER - Deodorants–personal - Amway Corp.
DETER-MITE - Alarm systems - Astro-Guard Industries Inc.
DETERGADYNE - Iodine sanitizer - Continental Labs Inc.
DETERGENT-8 - Detergents - Alconox Inc.
DETERGEZYME - Cleaning preparations - Metrex Research Corp.
DETERGICLENE - Cleaning preparations - General Medical Corp.
DETERGISAN - Disinfectant - Continental Chemical Corp.
DETERMINATOR - Electrical equipment - Environmental Instruments Co.
DETERMINED PRODUCTIONS - Infant product ☆ - European Toy Collection/
Crocodile Creek
DETERMINED PRODUCTIONS INC. - Toys–stuffed - Determined Productions,
Inc.
DETER'S BEST - Health care products ☆ - Particle Dynamics Inc.
DETHBLO - Toys - Tonka Corp.
DETONATOR - Guitars - Peavey Electronics Corp.
DETONATOR - Toys - Hasbro, Inc.
DETONATOR - Toys - Tonka Corp.
DETOUR - Frames–eyeglass - Zylo Ware Corp.
DETOUR - Repellent - Security Products Co.
DETOUR - Sunglasses ☆ - Mountain Shades

DETOUR, THE - Guardrails - SCS Healthcare Products, Inc.
DETOX - Health care products - East Earth Herb Inc.
DETOX - Vitamins and nutritional supplements - Reese Chemical Co.
DETOX-21 - Beauty shop equipment - Focus 21 International Inc.
DETOXACARE - Vitamins and nutritional supplements - Natrol, Inc.
DETOXCLEANSE - Vitamins and nutritional supplements - Amrion, Inc.
DETOXIFY - Vitamins and nutritional supplements - Royal Source, Inc.
DETOXIL - Pharmaceutical preparations ☆ - Fibertone Co.
DETOXINAL - Vitamins and nutritional supplements - Amrion, Inc.
DETOXO VITE - Vitamins and nutritional supplements - Natural Organics, Inc.
DETOXOL - Vitamins and nutritional supplements - Bio San Laboratories Inc.
DETOXYGEN - Vitamins and nutritional supplements - Natural Organics, Inc.
DETREX - Cleaning preparations - Detrex Corp.
DETROIT & MACKINAC - Beer - Detroit Brewery Inc.
DETROIT BAGEL FACTORY - Bagels - Detroit Bagel Factory
DETROIT CAR STYLING KIT - Toys - Milton Bradley Co.
DETROIT DIESEL - Electronic equipment - Detroit Diesel Corp.
DETROIT JEWEL - Cooking equipment–household - Welbilt Appliances Inc.
DETROIT NEON - Balls - Arena Associates, Inc.
DETROIT PISTONS - Apparel–athletic - Detroit Pistons Basketball Co.
DETROIT STEEL - Hardware - Blaine Window Hardware Inc.
DETROITER - Briefcases - NSM Industries Inc.
DETROITER - Pingpong tables - Martin-Kilpatrick Table Tennis Co.
DETROITER, THE - Pingpong tables ☆ - Michigan Ladder Co. Inc.
DETTLING SWISS KIRSCHWASSER - Cordials - Kobrand Corp.
DETTRA - Flags - Flags International Inc.
DETUSS - Pharmaceutical preparations ☆ - Zenith Laboratories, Inc.
DETUSSIN - Pharmaceutical preparations - Barre-National, Inc.
DETWA - T-shirts–men's - Regular Guys
DEUCE - Frames–eyeglass ☆ - Universal/Univis Inc.
DEUCE - Games ☆ - Milton Bradley Co.
DEUCE - Hosiery ☆ - Wigwam Mills Inc.
DEUCE - Medical apparatus - APT Technology, Inc.
DEUCE JUICE - Wines - Monarch Wine Co. of Georgia
DEUCES WILD - Candy ☆ - Leaf, Inc.
DEUCES WILD - Frames–eyeglass - Zylo Ware Corp.
DEUCES WILD - Game machines - Bally Gaming International, Inc.
DEUCES WILD - Toys - Tonka Corp.
DEUER - Pulleys–industrial - Deuer Manufacturing Inc.
DEUS BOOKS - Publisher's imprints - Paulist Press
DEUTSCH - Automotive parts and accessories - Autozone, Inc.
DEUTSCHE EINHEIT - Cigars - Gesty Trading & Manufacturing Corp.
DEUTSCHE GRAMMOPHON - Recording label - Polygram Records, Inc.
DEUTSCHLITE - Tubes–aluminum - Deutsch Metal Components
DEUTSCHLOK - Metals - Deutsch Metal Components
DEUTZ - Wines - C & B Vintage Cellars
DEUTZ-ALLIS - Toys - ERTL Co., Inc.
DEUX AMIS - Needles–sewing - Deux Amis
DEUX FLEUR BORDERS - Floor coverings–carpet and rugs - Langhorne
Carpet Co. Inc.
DEV - Apparel and accessories - Dev Imports Ltd.
DEV-TEC - Tile cleaner - Slipsafe Professional Products, Inc.
DEV-TUBE - Plastic solder ☆ - Devcon Consumer Products (ITW Devcon)
DEVA - Broadcasting equipment - Zaxcom, Inc.
DEVA FLOWER REMEDIES - Pharmaceutical preparations - Natural
Laboratories Corp.
DEVAC - Windows–storm - Devac Inc.
DEVALCOURT - Cases–plastic ☆ - Sazerac Co. Inc.
DEVALE D NEEDLES - Pharmaceutical preparations - Beutlich L.P.
Pharmaceuticals
DEVALUM - Paints - Grow Group, Inc.
DEVAN - Caulking compounds - Devan Sealants Inc.
DEVAN - Toys - Tonka Corp.
DEVAN DESIGNS - Furniture - Devan Designs Inc.
DEVANCY - Crocheted and knitted items - Hoffman Mills Inc.
DEVASTATOR - Alarm systems - Astro-Guard Industries Inc.
DEVASTATOR - Archery equipment - Bear Archery Inc.
DEVASTATOR - Golfing equipment - Tokuda International Corp.
DEVASTATORS - Toys–automobiles - Mattel, Inc.
DEVCO - Tools–hand-operated - Devco Enterprises Inc.
DEVCON - Repair material ☆ - Devcon Consumer Products (ITW Devcon)
DEVELOP 10 - Nail care products - Vital Nails Inc.
DEVELOPER - Computer software - Arnett Development Corp.
DEVELOPER - Floor coverings–carpet and rugs - Trend Carpet
DEVELOPER - Manufactured homes - Redman Industries, Inc.
DEVELOPER PLUS - Hair coloring preparations - Helene Curtis Industries Inc.

☆ = Now out of production

DEVELOPER STUDIO - Computer software - Microsoft Corp.

DEVELOPING BIORATIONAL SOLUTIONS FOR AGRICULTURE - Pesticides–agricultural - CCT Corp.

DEVELOPING HEARTS - Greeting cards - Pre-Emptive Products, Inc.

DEVELOPINGLIFELONG LEARNERS - Video production - Canter and Associates, Inc.

DEVER - Beds–metal ☆ - HARD Manufacturing Co. Inc.

DEVERE COLLECTION - Tools - A.D. Johnson Engraving Co.

DEVERE INTERNATIONAL - Cleaning preparations–carpet and rug - Harris Research, Inc.

DEVEREAUX - Floor coverings - Mannington Resilient Floors

DEVI - Apparel and accessories - Outback

DEVI - Lenses–optical - National Optical Co.

DEVICE - Apparel and accessories - Abe Maya

DEVICE LUBE PLUS - Lubricants ☆ - Von Duprin, Inc.

DEVIL - Frames–eyeglass - Zylo Ware Corp.

DEVIL AND MR. WEBSTER, THE - Computer software ☆ - Krell Software Corp.

DEVIL BARRACUDA - Toys - Tonka Corp.

DEVIL BUG - Fishing lures - Eppinger Manufacturing Co.

DEVIL DOGS - Cakes - Drake Bakeries, Inc.

DEVIL GUM - Chewing gum ☆ - Fleer Corp.

DEVIL MOUNTAIN BREWERY - Beverages–alcohol - Boston Beer Co. LP

DEVIL MOUNTAIN BREWERY RAILROAD ALE - Beverages–malt - Boston Beer Co. LP

DEVIL MOUNTAIN RAILROAD ALE BREWERY - Beverages–malt - Boston Beer Co. LP

DEVIL SHAKE - Beverages ☆ - Yoo-Hoo Chocolate Beverage Corp.

DEVIL SPINNER - Fishing lures ☆ - Hildebrandt Corp.

DEVIL WIND - Recording label - Music Craftshop Inc.

DEVIL WINGS - Meat products–poultry ☆ - McIlhenny Co.

DEVILBISS - Paint sprayers - Illinois Tool Works Inc.

DEVILBISS - Vaporizers ☆ - Sunrise Medical (Respiratory Products Division)

DEVILBISS/HANKSCRAFT - Vaporizers ☆ - Sunrise Medical (Respiratory Products Division)

DEVILIQUE - Underwear and nightwear ☆ - Alba-Waldensian, Inc.

DEVILISH - Lenses–optical - Ditto Industries Inc.

DEVILLE - Floor coverings–carpet and rugs ☆ - Galaxy Carpet Mills Inc.

DEVILLE - Motor vehicles–automobiles - General Motors Corp. (Cadillac Motor Car Div.)

DEVILLE - Motor vehicles–automobiles - General Motors Corp.

DEVILLE - Rings–jewelry ☆ - Artcarved Inc.

DEVILLE - Typewriters - Smith Corona Corp.

DEVILLE CONCOURS - Motor vehicles–automobiles - General Motors Corp. (Cadillac Motor Car Div.)

DEVILLE VSOP - Brandy - Guinness Import Co.

DEVILLIER - Musical instruments - European Crafts/USA

DEVIL'S BREW PORTER - Beverages–alcohol - Boston Beer Co. LP

DEVIL'S CAPE, THE - Toys–stuffed - Fun World Inc.

DEVIL'S DELIGHT - Fireworks - American Promotional Events, Inc.

DEVIL'S DELITE - Cakes - American Bakeries Co.

DEVIL'S HELPER - Safety products - Meeco Manufacturing Co.

DEVIL'S HORSE - Fishing tackle - Smithwick Lures, Inc.

DEVIL'S OWN RUBBER HOOD, THE - Toys–stuffed - Fun World Inc.

DEVIL'S POTION, THE - Colognes ☆ - Pfizer Inc.

DEVILS SPRING - Vodka - Black Prince Distillery, Inc.

DEVIL'S TINGLE - Food products - Sauces & Salsas, Ltd.

DEVILS TRIANGLE - Fireworks - B.J. Alan Co. Inc.

DEVILS TRIANGLE - Games ☆ - Pressman Toy Corp.

DEVIN - Cosmetics - Estee Lauder Inc.

DEVIN - Ophthalmic goods ☆ - Rozin Optical Export Corp.

DEVINA ESTATES - Wines - Geerlings & Wade, Inc.

DEVINE'S - Health care products ☆ - Blistex Inc.

DEVINGER PLACE - Floor coverings–carpet and rugs - Gulistan Carpet Inc.

DEVITO'S - Tomato pastes and sauces - Roberts Bros. Inc.

DEVKO - Deodorants–personal - Parthenon Co. Inc.

DEVLE BUGS - Fishing lures - Eppinger Manufacturing Co.

DEVLE DOG - Fishing lures - Eppinger Manufacturing Co.

DEVLIEG - Machine tools - Devlieg-Bullard Services Group

DEVLIN - Wines - Devlin Wine Cellars

DEVO - See **DEVILBISS**

DEVOE - Paints - Devoe & Raynolds Co.

DEVOE EAGLE - Tobacco products - United States Tobacco Co.

DEVOID - Herbicides - Puritan-Churchill Chemical Co.

DEVOLD - Apparel and accessories - Devold Inc.

DEVON - Apparel–women's - Devon Apparel

DEVON - Cabinets - Aristokraft, Inc.

DEVON - Cabinets - Contempri Kitchens

DEVON - Candy ☆ - Pet Inc. (Whitman's Chocolates Div.)

DEVON - Canvas–artists' ☆ - Winsor & Newton

DEVON - Dolls - Mattel, Inc.

DEVON - Floor coverings - Bruce Hardwood Floors

DEVON - Floor coverings - Mannington Resilient Floors

DEVON - Furniture - Hammary Furniture Co. Inc.

DEVON - Ophthalmic goods - Swank Optical

DEVON - Tires - Target Tire and Automotive Corp.

DEVON - Watches ☆ - Design Time USA Inc.

DEVON - Weather tracking equipment ☆ - Bausch & Lomb Inc.

DEVON - Window frames - Certainteed Corp. (Roofing Products Group)

DEVON AIRE - Apparel and accessories - Devon-Aire, Inc.

DEVON COUNTRY - Food products ☆ - Christopher Brookes Distinctive Foods

DEVON HILL - Floor coverings–carpet and rugs - Bloomsburg Carpet Industries

DEVON MANOR - Floor coverings–carpet and rugs - Bloomsburg Carpet Industries

DEVON MANOR - Floor coverings–carpet and rugs ☆ - Downs Carpet Co. Inc.

DEVON MANOR BORDER - Floor coverings–carpet and rugs - Bloomsburg Carpet Industries

DEVON SPRAYS BROWN - Dinnerware–glass ☆ - Johnson Brothers, USA, Inc.

DEVON SYSTEM, THE - Computer software - SunGard Software Inc.

DEVON TWEED - Ophthalmic goods - Fidelity Case Corp.

DEVON VIOLETS - Skin care products - Freund-Mayer & Co. Inc.

DEVONCOURT - Furniture - Drexel Heritage Furnishings, Inc.

DEVONDALE - Frozen yogurt and confections - Devondale, Inc.

DEVONIAN - Frames–eyeglass ☆ - Universal/Univis Inc.

DE'VONS - Eyeglasses - De'Vons, Inc.

DEVONSHEER - Breads - CPC International Inc.

DEVONSHIRE - Dinnerware–glass ☆ - Johnson Brothers, USA, Inc.

DEVONSHIRE - Floor coverings ☆ - Congoleum Corp.

DEVONSHIRE - Floor coverings–carpet and rugs - Eligere Carpets

DEVONSHIRE - Floor coverings–tile ☆ - Kentile Floors Inc.

DEVONSHIRE - Furniture ☆ - Bassett Furniture Industries, Inc.

DEVONSHIRE - Furniture ☆ - Hooker Furniture Corp.

DEVONSHIRE - Furniture ☆ - Mersman Furniture Co.

DEVONSHIRE - Lamps - Kaadan Ltd.

DEVONSHIRE - Saddles ☆ - Outdoor Sports Industries

DEVONSHIRE - Scotch ☆ - Charles Jacquin et Compagnie Inc.

DEVONSHIRE - Trailers–travel - Fleetwood Enterprises, Inc.

DEVONSHIRE GARDENS - Wallpaper - Bob Mitchell Designs

DEVONSHIRE LACE - Bedding–linen - Dan River Inc.

DEVONSHIRE ROYAL - Cream liqueur - Charles Jacquin et Compagnie Inc.

DEVOS LEMMENS - Food products - Universal Foods Corp.

DEVOSEAL - Stationery - American Tape Corp.

DEVOTEE - Brassieres (Bras) - Goddess Bra

DEVOTEE - Colognes ☆ - Avon Products, Inc.

DEVOTION - Floor coverings–carpet and rugs - Karastan-Bigelow Inc.

DEVOTION - Rings–jewelry - Artcarved Inc.

DEVOTION-LITES - Candles - Emkay Candles

DEVOTIONAL CREATIONS - Statuary - Seymour Mann Inc.

DEVOUR - Cleaning preparations - R.R. Street & Co. Inc.

DEVOUR CITRUS CLEANER & DEGREASER - Cleaning preparations–household - Enviro-Chem Inc.

DEVOURING SNIZARD LIPS - Toys - Saban Entertainment, Inc.

DEVPRO - Insecticides - Devpro Machine Inc. (Insectocutor Div.)

DEVRAN - Paints - Grow Group, Inc.

DEVROM - Pharmaceutical preparations - Parthenon Co. Inc.

DEVTEC - Surgical supplies - Sertec International, Inc.

DEW - Hair care products - Sequel Products Inc.

DEW BERRY - Lipsticks ☆ - Honey & Spice Toiletries

DEW DISTILLED ECOLOGICAL WATER - Water distillation units - Dew Enterprises, Inc.

DEW DROP - Dolls - Uneeda Doll Co., Inc.

DEW FLEX - Sporting goods ☆ - Outdoor Technologies Group

DEW IT - Hair care products - John Amico Expressive Hair Care Products

DEW IT! - Skin care products - Matrix Essentials, Inc.

DEW KISS LIP DEW - Lip balms - Avon Products, Inc.

DEW KIST - Food products - Jewel Food Stores Inc.

DEW ME - Apparel–athletic - Richard J. Gibbons

DEW MIST - Hair care products - Madame C.J. Walker Inc.

DEW MIST - Skin care products - Goubaud

☆ = Now out of production

DEW MIST - Skin care products - Helene Curtis Industries Inc.

DEW-UP KILKARREN - Beverages–alcohol ☆ - Kentucky Brands of California Inc.

DEWAAL - Statuary ☆ - Eastern Shore Trading Co.

DEWALT - Toys–automobiles - Black & Decker Corp.

DEWAR'S - Candy - Dewar's Candy Shop Inc.

DEWARS ANCESTOR - Whiskey - Schenley Industries Inc.

DEWARS WHITE LABEL - Whiskey - Schenley Industries Inc.

DEWDROP - Jewelry - Jacoby-Bender Inc.

DEWDROP - Watches - Bulova Corp.

DEWDROPS - Christmas tree ornaments - Cracker Box Inc.

DEWDROPS - Dinnerware–glass ☆ - Lenox, Inc.

DEWEATHERIZE - Computer software - Strategic Weather Services

DEWEESE - Bathing suits - Deweese Inc.

DEWEESE DESIGNS - Bathing suits - Deweese Inc.

DEWEY - Musical instrument accessories - Carpenter Co.

DEWEY - Water–bottled or canned - Talawanda Springs Inc.

DEWEY, CHEETHAM & HOWE - Apparel and accessories - Dewey Cheetham & Howe

DEWEY PERCUSSION - Drums–musical instruments ☆ - L.A. Sax Co.

DEWEY STEVENS - Wines ☆ - Anheuser-Busch Companies Inc.

DEWEY'S - Candy - Dewey's Candy Co.

DEWEY'S - Meat products - Group Four Marketing, Inc.

DEWIND - Shrimp–canned or cured - Eastern Fish Co.

DEWITT'S PILLS - Pharmaceutical preparations - Monticello Drug Co.

DEWITT'S TABLE READY MEALS - Precooked entrees - Bil Mar Foods

DEWKIST - Pickles - W.B. Roddenbery Co., Inc.

DEWMIST - Beverages - N & N International Ltd.

DEWORMEX - Pet products ☆ - Aquatronics-Filtronics

DEWPLEX - Hair care products - Redmond Products, Inc.

DEWRISTER GRIP - Golfing equipment ☆ - John Rouzee Green Co., Inc.

DEWSCO - Pharmaceutical preparations - Summa Pharmaceutical Laboratories Inc.

DEWY FRESH - Fruits and vegetables - Nash-Finch Co.

DEX-A-DIET - Pharmaceutical preparations ☆ - Columbia Laboratories Inc.

DEX-A-DRON - Pharmaceutical preparations ☆ - R.A. McNeil Co.

DEX-O-TEX - Floor coverings - Cincinnati Floor Co. Inc.

DEX-RAY - Laboratory apparatus - Landauer, Inc.

DEX4 - Glucose - Can-Am Care Corp.

DEXA-KLOR - Insecticides ☆ - Dexol Industries

DEXA-PED - Vitamins and nutritional supplements ☆ - Xttrium Laboratories Inc.

DEXACEN-4 - Pharmaceutical preparations ☆ - Central Pharmaceutical Inc.

DEXACEN LA-8 - Pharmaceutical preparations - Central Pharmaceutical Inc.

DEXACIDIN - Prescription ophthalmic - Iolab Pharmaceuticals

DEXACORT - Pharmaceutical preparations - Medeva, Inc.

DEXACORTEN - Pharmaceutical preparations - Bolan Pharmaceutical Inc.

DEXADAR - Health care products - Republic Drug Co. Inc.

DEXADROL - Pharmaceutical preparations - Wesley Pharmacal Co. Inc.

DEXAFED - Pharmaceutical preparations - Roberts/Hauck Pharmaceuticals Inc.

DEXALYTE - Veterinary pharmaceuticals - American Veterinary Products, Inc.

DEXALYTE PLUS - Veterinary pharmaceuticals - American Veterinary Products, Inc.

DEXAMETH - Vitamins and nutritional supplements ☆ - Rhone-Poulenc Rorer Pharmaceuticals Inc.

DEXAMINE - Pharmaceutical preparations - Alva-Amco Pharmacal Co.

DEXAMPEX - Pharmaceutical preparations ☆ - Lemmon Co.

DEXAMYL - Barbituates - Smithkline Beecham Corp.

DEXAPLEX 15 - Pharmaceutical preparations ☆ - Coast Laboratories Inc.

DEXASONE - Pharmaceutical preparations - Legere Pharmaceuticals Inc.

DEXASONE - Pharmaceutical preparations - Roberts/Hauck Pharmaceuticals Inc.

DEXASONE-LA - Pharmaceutical preparations - Roberts/Hauck Pharmaceuticals Inc.

DEXASPAN - Pharmaceutical preparations ☆ - Rhone-Poulenc Rorer Pharmaceuticals Inc.

DEXATIP - Pharmaceutical preparations - Cardiac Pacemakers Inc.

DEXATONE - Pharmaceutical preparations ☆ - Hyrex Pharmaceuticals

DEXATRIM - Health care products - Thompson Medical Co., Inc.

DEXATRON - Pharmaceutical preparations - Alva-Amco Pharmacal Co.

DEXDELAY - Pharmaceutical preparations ☆ - C.O. Truxton Inc.

DEXEDRINE - Pharmaceutical preparations - Smithkline Beecham Corp.

DEXFERRUM - Pharmaceutical preparations - American Regent Laboratories, Inc.

DEXI-TAC - Pharmaceutical preparations - Republic Drug Co. Inc.

DEXIGLAS - Fabrics - Dexter Corp.

DEXLO - Locks–door ☆ - Dexter Lock

DEXLOCK - Locks–door ☆ - Dexter Lock

DEXOIL - Pharmaceutical preparations - Dade Pharmaceuticals Inc.

DEXOL - Automotive parts and accessories - Marwan Y. Ghosn

DEXOL - Pesticides–household - Dexol Industries

DEXOL - Pharmaceutical preparations - Legere Pharmaceuticals Inc.

DEXOLEV - Pharmaceutical preparations ☆ - C.O. Truxton Inc.

DEXON - Health care products - Kay Pharmacal Co. Inc.

DEXON L.A. - Health care products - Kay Pharmacal Co. Inc.

DEXONE - Pharmaceutical preparations - Solvay Pharmaceuticals Inc.

DEXONE LA - Pharmaceutical preparations - Keene Pharmaceuticals Inc.

DEXPHEMMS - Pharmaceutical preparations ☆ - C.O. Truxton Inc.

DEXRON II - Transmission fluids ☆ - Castrol, Inc.

DEXRON III/MERCON - Oils–lubricating - Castrol, Inc.

DEXSAN - Fabrics - Dexter Corp.

DEXSONATE - Pharmaceutical preparations ☆ - JMI-Canton Pharmaceuticals

DEXSONE - Pharmaceutical preparations ☆ - Vortech Pharmaceuticals

DEXSONE-E - Pharmaceutical preparations ☆ - Vortech Pharmaceuticals

DEXSONE L.A. - Pharmaceutical preparations ☆ - Vortech Pharmaceuticals

DEXSTAR - Fabrics - Dexter Corp.

DEXTECH - Hardware - Dextech

DEXTER - Boots - Dexter Shoe Co.

DEXTER - Cutlery - Russell Harrington Cutlery, Inc.

DEXTER - Locks–door ☆ - Dexter Lock

DEXTER - Magnets - Dexter Corp.

DEXTER - Pencil sharpeners - Empire Berol USA

DEXTER - Postcards ☆ - Ketchian Photographers

DEXTER - Urinals–enameled - Kohler Co.

DEXTER FREEBISH - Recording label - Copper Moon Productions

DEXTER LONDRES - Cigars - Swisher International, Inc.

DEXTER PLUS - Shoes - Dexter Shoe Co.

DEXTER RUSSELL - Knives - Russell Harrington Cutlery, Inc.

DEXTER THE DINOSAUR - Fabrics - Cranston Print Works Co.

DEXTEX - Fabrics - Dexter Corp.

DEXTITE - Packaging–paper - Dexter Corp.

DEXTRA-LITES - Lighting fixtures - Swivelier Co. Inc.

DEXTRAM - Health care products - Halsey Drug Co. Inc.

DEXTRI-MALTOSE - Infant product ☆ - Bristol-Myers Squibb Co.

DEXTRIN - Pharmaceutical preparations - Pfanstiehl Laboratories Inc.

DEXTRO-FETAMINE - Pharmaceutical preparations ☆ - Vita-Fore Products Co.

DEXTRO-REX - Pharmaceutical preparations ☆ - Rex Research Laboratories

DEXTRO-TRIPLE - Pharmaceutical preparations ☆ - Harvey Laboratories Inc.

DEXTRO-TUSS GG - Pharmaceutical preparations ☆ - Ulmer Pharmacal Co.

DEXTROLYTE - Vitamins and nutritional supplements - Frye Co.

DEXTROPAN - Pharmaceutical preparations ☆ - Keene Pharmaceuticals Inc.

DEXTROSTAT - Pharmaceutical preparations - Richwood Pharmaceutical Co., Inc.

DEXTROSTIX - Chemical preparations - Miles Inc.

DEXTROTABS - Pharmaceutical preparations - Cramer Products Inc.

DEXUS - Chemical preparations - Dexus Laboratories, Inc.

DEXXA - Computer peripheral equipment - Dexxa International, Inc.

DEXXA D - Computer peripheral equipment - Logitech, Inc.

DEY-DOSE - Pharmaceutical preparations ☆ - Dey Laboratories Inc.

DEY-LUBE - Pharmaceutical preparations ☆ - Dey Laboratories Inc.

DEY-LUTE - Medical apparatus ☆ - Dey Laboratories Inc.

DEY-METRIC - Shoe accessories - T.O. Dey Service Corp.

DEY-MIST - Pharmaceutical preparations ☆ - Dey Laboratories Inc.

DEY-PAK - Pharmaceutical preparations ☆ - Dey Laboratories Inc.

DEY-SYSTEM - Pharmaceutical preparations ☆ - Dey Laboratories Inc.

DEY-VIAL - Pharmaceutical preparations ☆ - Dey Laboratories Inc.

DEY-WASH - Medical apparatus ☆ - Dey Laboratories Inc.

DEY'S - Adhesives and sealants - Magic Match Patch Co.

DEZEST - Pharmaceutical preparations - Armenpharm Ltd.

DEZIGNER TRIM - Trimmings–metal - Mascotech, Inc.

DEZINE - Apparel and accessories - Urban Legend, Inc.

DEZINE - Figurines - Dezine Ltd.

DF - Jewelers' findings - Dover Findings Inc.

DF - Meat products - Saramar Corp.

DF - Ships–sailing vessels - Dyna-Yacht, Inc.

D.F. METALWORKS DANIEL JOSEPH - Lighting fixtures - D.F. Meatlworks

DFA - Ammunition - Delta Defense, Inc.

DFA - Ammunition - Delta Defense, Inc.

DFA'S FAMILY BUSINESS ASSESSMENT TOOL - Publisher's imprints - Dean R. Fowler

D.F.C. - Apparel - Advanced Trading Co., Inc.

DFC - Kilns ☆ - Kennedy Van Saun Corp.

DFE - Apparel and accessories - Designs for Education, Inc.

☆ = Now out of production

DFG 100 - Sporting goods - Lisco, Inc.
DFG 3000 - Sporting goods - Lisco, Inc.
DFI - Automotive parts and accessories ☆ - Echlin Inc.
DFI - Silverware ☆ - Estus Export-Import
DFJ - Timeclocks–office - A.D. Joslin Manufacturing Co.
D'FLEA - Insecticides - Environmental Chemical Group Inc.
D'FLEA-III - Insecticides - Environmental Chemical Group Inc.
DFOS - Computer software - Crown International, Inc.
DFR - Electronic equipment - Identicator Technology
DFS - Fruits–canned - Dicarlo Distributors, Inc.
DFS - Hosiery - EBI Medical Systems, Inc.
DFSMS/MVS - Computer software - International Business Machines Corp.
DFW/HPI - Couplings ☆ - Hefco Plastics Inc.
DG - Degreasing solvents ☆ - Hertron International Inc.
D.G. - Fireplace equipment ☆ - Pine Mountain Corp.
DG - Jewelry - Designs By Glory Ltd.
DG - Recording label - Polygram Records, Inc.
DG - Software - Data General Corp.
DG - Video equipment - Digital Graphix, Inc.
D.G. DOMINANT GEANS - Apparel and accessories - Dominant Geans, Inc.
DG SIGNATURE - Skin care products - Dollar General Corp.
DG TEEZERS - Frozen foods - J.R. Simplot Co.
DG/UX - Computer software - Data General Corp.
DG/VIISION - Computers - Data General Corp.
DGB - Chemical preparations - Oil Chem Technologies, Inc.
DGC - Computer software - Dangerous Goods Council
DGC - Recording label - Geffen Records, Inc.
DGD - Tools–power-driven - Cooper Industries, Inc.
DGF-10 - Sports rackets and accessories - Victor Sports
DGI ART SHOP - Computer software ☆ - Decision Graphics Inc.
DGI CRYPTOGRAM - Computer software - Decision Graphics Inc.
DGI LOTTO MANAGER - Computer software - Decision Graphics Inc.
DGI MATCH IT - Computer software - Decision Graphics Inc.
DGI NUMBER SEARCH - Computer software - Decision Graphics Inc.
DGI ORGANIZATION - Computer software - Decision Graphics Inc.
DGI SIGN MAKER - Computer software - Decision Graphics Inc.
DGI TYPE SHOP - Computer software - Decision Graphics Inc.
DGI WORD PUZZLES #2 - Computer software - Decision Graphics Inc.
DGI WORD SCRAMBLE - Computer software - Decision Graphics Inc.
DGI WORD SEARCH PRO - Computer software - Decision Graphics Inc.
DGM - Meat products–pork - Calumet Diversified Meats Inc.
DGM MERCHANDISING STRUCTURES - Metal building materials - DGM Enterprises, Inc.
D'GREASE - Pet products - Purepet Co.
DGS - Jewelry - David G. Steven Inc.
DGS - Zippers - Azuma Trimming Inc.
D.G.T. - Degreaser - Vibe Records Inc.
DGW BACKS TO BASICS - Video production - Diane G. Wall
DH - Recording label - Statue Records
DH PROTEIN DRINK - Vitamins and nutritional supplements - Desert Health Products, Inc.
DHASCO - Pharmaceutical preparations - Martek Corp.
DHCPLUS - Analgesics ☆ - Purdue Pharma L.P.
DHE - Hearing aids - G.N. Danavox Inc.
D.H.E.-45 - Pharmaceutical preparations - Sandoz Pharmaceuticals Corp.
DHEA - Vitamins and nutritional supplements - Body Wise International, Inc.
DHEA - Vitamins and nutritional supplements - Reese Chemical Co.
DHEA - Vitamins and nutritional supplements - Scandinavian Natural Health & Beauty Products, Inc.
DHEA - Vitamins and nutritional supplements - Vitamin Research Products Inc.
DHEA FUEL - Vitamins and nutritional supplements - Twin Laboratories, Inc.
DHEA-POWER - Vitamins and nutritional supplements - Twin Laboratories Inc.
DHEA SUPER HORMONE - Vitamins and nutritional supplements - Natural Balance, Inc.
DHEA THERAPEUTIC - Pharmaceutical preparations - Reese Chemical Co.
DHEA ULTRA - Vitamins and nutritional supplements - Freelife International LP
DHEAX - Health care products - Healthwatchers System
DHG DUTCH HARBOR GEAR - Apparel and accessories - Pearl Northwest, Inc.
DHS - Hair care products - Person and Covey Inc.
DHT - Seafood products–fresh or frozen ☆ - Coast to Coast Seafood Inc.
DHURRIES - Floor coverings–carpet and rugs - Capel, Inc.
DI - Floor coverings–carpet and rugs - E.R. Carpenter Co.
DI - Machine parts - Carbide Products International, Inc.
DI-100 - Electrical equipment - General Electric Co.
DI AFRO - Pharmaceutical preparations ☆ - Legere Pharmaceuticals Inc.

DI-ALL - Paints - Diall Chemical Co. Inc.
DI-ATLANTIS - Computer software - Dimensional Insight, Inc.
DI-AZO - Health care products - Kay Pharmacal Co. Inc.
DI BORGHESE - Fragrance - Borghese Cosmetics Inc.
DI-CALS - Vitamins and nutritional supplements - Vita-Fore Products Co.
DI CICCO - Food products - Di Cicco Ravioli Co. Inc.
DI COSTA - Apparel–women's - Di Costa Knits Ltd.
DI-CYCLONEX - Pharmaceutical preparations ☆ - Pasadena Research Laboratories, Inc.
DI-D KLIPS - Diapers–cloth ☆ - Gala Industries Inc.
DI-DELAMINE - Skin care products - Del Pharmaceuticals, Inc.
DI DESTINATION IMAGES - Video production - Destination Images, LLC
DI DIENER INDUSTRIES - Pencils - WINCRAFT
DI-DIVER - Computer software - Dimensional Insight, Inc.
DI-EST - Pharmaceutical preparations ☆ - Central Pharmaceutical Inc.
DI-ET - Chewing gum ☆ - Clark Gum Co.
DI FERRI - Apparel–men's - Di Ferri Inc.
DI-FERRIN - Pharmaceutical preparations ☆ - Ulmer Pharmacal Co.
DI-GAS - Cleaning preparations - Vapor Products
DI-GEL - Antacids - Schering-Plough Healthcare Products
DI-GESIC - Analgesics ☆ - Central Pharmaceutical Inc.
DI GIORGIO - Guitars - Juan Orozco Corp.
DI GIORNO - Cheese - Kraft Food Ingredients Corp.
DI GIORNO - Pasta - Kraft Foods, Inc.
DI-HYDRA - Health care products - Halsey Drug Co. Inc.
DI-HYDROTIC - Pharmaceutical preparations ☆ - Legere Pharmaceuticals Inc.
DI-ISOPACIN - Pharmaceutical preparations ☆ - Consolidated Midland Corp.
DI LEO - Musical instruments - Newark Musical Merchandise Co.
DI LEWIS - Housewares - Di Lewis Studios, Ltd.
DI LI DO - Leather goods - A & L Seamon Inc.
DI LI DO ORIGINALS - Leather goods - A & L Seamon Inc.
DI-LOG - Electrical equipment - Universal Enterprises
DI-LOK - Pipes - Grinnell Corp.
DI LULLO - Food products - G. Di Lullo & Son
DI LUSSO - Meat products–pork - Hormel Foods Corp.
DI/MAC TECHNOLOGIES, INC. - Computer peripheral equipment - DI/Mac Technologies, Inc.
DI MEDICI - Fabrics–velvet - Dan River Inc.
DI-METRIC PLUS - Computer software - Optical Gaging Products, Inc.
DI MITRI - Hosiery–men's ☆ - Keepers International
DI NOBILI - Attache cases - Ventura Travelware Inc.
DI-OCTO SOFTEZE - Pharmaceutical preparations - Global Pharmaceutical Corp.
DI-PAC - Health care products - Domino Sugar Corp.
DI PANDINI - Breads - Mason/Sundahl Co., Inc.
DI-PHEN - Pharmaceutical preparations ☆ - Vortech Pharmaceuticals
DI-PRED - Pharmaceutical preparations ☆ - Central Pharmaceutical Inc.
DI PRINTER - Stationery - Diagraph Corp.
DI-SANITE - Cleaning preparations ☆ - Oakite Products, Inc.
DI-SIGN - Nameplates–engraved - Adjusta Bulletin Board System Inc.
DI-SPAZ - Pharmaceutical preparations ☆ - Vortech Pharmaceuticals
DI-STEROID - Pharmaceutical preparations ☆ - Schwarz Pharma
DI-URIFORM - Diuretics ☆ - P. & S. Laboratories Inc.
DI VILLAROSA - Neckties - Ram Tiemakers Inc.
DI VINA - Shoes - Interco Inc.
DI-WEBDIVER - Computer software - Dimensional Insight, Inc.
DIA - Jewelry - Diaco International Corp.
DIA BET TEA - Teas - Vincent Trading Co.
DIA-BUD - Jewelry - Jackmail Jewelry Inc.
DIA-CARB - Pet products ☆ - Lee-Mar Pet Supplies
DIA-CHECKS - Diabetes-management journal ☆ - Informative Amenities Inc.
DIA-CONE - Furniture ☆ - Altec Lansing Consumer Products
DIA DRIVE PAD - Cleaning preparations - Verona Marble Co.
DIA-EZE - Pharmaceutical preparations ☆ - Central Pharmaceutical Inc.
DIA-FORM - Aluminum products - Jim Payne Sales, Inc.
DIA-LOCK - Jewelry - Unigem International
DIA-PAK - Diabetic organizer - Atwater Carey Ltd.
DIA-PERFECTOR - Binoculars ☆ - Ercona Corp.
DIA-QUEL - Pharmaceutical preparations - Milance Laboratories Inc.
DIA SCOPE - Electronic equipment - Leica USA Inc.
DIA-SHEAR - Construction equipment - Hessian Co. Ltd.
DIA-SPAN - Pharmaceutical preparations - Alva-Amco Pharmacal Co.
DIA TRIM - Corsets - Sears, Roebuck and Co.
DIA-TROL - Apparel and accessories - Vanity Corset Co. Inc.
DIAB-A-SOLES - Footwear - Langer Biomechanics Group, Inc.
DIABE VITE - Vitamins and nutritional supplements - Vitamin Specialties Corp.

DIABET-X - Skin care products - FNC Medical Corp.

DIABETA - Pharmaceutical preparations - Hoechst-Roussel Pharmaceuticals Inc.

DIABETES INFORMATION CENTER - Publisher's imprints - On Target Media, Inc.

DIABETES PACK - Food products - Snyder Communications, L.P.

DIABETESDEK - Paper - Infodek Inc.

DIABETIC TUSSIN - Cough medicines - Hi-Tech Pharmacal Co., Inc.

DIABETIC'S CHOICE - Health care products - Nature's Design Ltd.

DIABETIC'S DELIGHT! - Food products - Diabetic's Delight Inc.

DIABETIC'S TRAVELER - Medical apparatus - Chillynex Corp.

DIABETIL - Vitamins and nutritional supplements - Nutrifit International Corp.

DIABETIVITE PLUS - Vitamins and nutritional supplements - Jordan Medical Enterprises, Inc.

DIABEX - Health care products - Healthwatchers System

DIABISMUL - Pharmaceutical preparations ☆ - Forest Pharmaceuticals Inc.

DIABLO - Cleaning preparations - Takeo Enterprises Corp.

DIABLO - Cooking equipment–commercial - Le-Jo Enterprises, Inc.

DIABLO - Floor coverings ☆ - Tarkett, Inc.

DIABLO - Printers–computer - Diablo Systems Xerox Corp. (Information Products Div.)

DIABLO 630 - Printers–computer ☆ - Diablo Systems Xerox Corp. (Information Products Div.)

DIABLO VALLEY - Wines - J.E. Digardi Winery

DIABLO VALLEY CABINETRY - Cabinets - Diablo Valley Cabinetry

DIABLO VISTA - Wines ☆ - Lake Sonoma Winery

DIABLOS - Musical instrument accessories - Guild Music Corp.

DIABOND - Clay products - Universal Agri Products, Inc.

DIACEL - Aquarium product - Imi Cornelius Inc.

DIACIN - Pharmaceutical preparations ☆ - Lemmon Co.

DIACRYST - Sugar–granulated, refined, or powdered ☆ - E. Fougera & Co. Inc.

DIACTION - Pharmaceutical preparations ☆ - Boots Pharmaceuticals Inc.

DIADAX - Pharmaceutical preparations ☆ - Columbia Laboratories Inc.

DIADEM - Floor coverings–carpet and rugs ☆ - Navan Carpets Inc.

DIADEM - Recording label - Diadem Music Group

DIADEM - Sewing machines–household - Beta/Unitex Inc.

DIADON - Floor coverings ☆ - Tarkett, Inc.

DIADOT - Pharmaceutical preparations - Virus Reference Laboratory, Inc.

DIAFINE - Photographic equipment - Acufine Inc.

DIAFOLD - Tools - Diamond Machining Technology Inc.

DIAFOODS THICK-IT - Food products - Precision Foods, Inc.

DIAGEL-C - Pharmaceutical preparations - Mayer Laboratories, Inc.

DIAGENEX, INC. - Water purification systems - Diagenex, Inc.

DIAGNOSIS ENGINE - Computer software - Clarify Inc.

DIAGNOSISPRO - Computer software - Medtech USA, Inc.

DIAGNOSTEC 2000 - Dental equipment - Video Dental Concepts, Inc.

DIAGNOSTIC ULTRASOUND - File folders - Gillooly, Inc. (Echo Files Division)

DIAGNOSTICALLY FOCUSED TREATMENT PROFILE - Computer software - National Assessment Corp.

DIAGO - Ceramic tile - Integrity Tile Co.

DIAGONAL - Floor coverings–carpet and rugs - Daltonian Carpet & Cushion Inc.

DIAGONAL DOUBLES - Video equipment - New Gaming Systems

DIAGONAL SLASH - Apparel–women's - Jezebel-Renee of Hollywood

DIAGONALE - Floor coverings–carpet and rugs - Karastan-Bigelow Inc.

DIAGONALS - Floor coverings–carpet and rugs - Alliance Industries Inc.

DIAGRAM IT - Computer software - Soft Craft Technologies

DIAGRAPH BRADLEY - Stationery - Diagraph Corp.

DIAGSOFT - Computer diagnostic program - Diagsoft, Inc.

DIAHANN CARROLL - Watches - Fada Industries Inc.

DIAKOOL - Diabetic organizer - Cherokee 4000

DIAL - Publisher's imprints - Penguin Books USA Inc.

DIAL - Soap - Dial Corp.

DIAL 5 - Sprinklers–lawn - L.R. Nelson Corp.

DIAL-A-BEAD - Hobby kits - Chenille Kraft Co.

DIAL-A-BIT - Driver bits - Wilmar Corp.

DIAL-A-BLEND - Machinery - Dema Engineering Co.

DIAL-A-BREW - Coffee makers–electric ☆ - Philips Electronics North America Corp.

DIAL-A-COLOR - Artists' materials - Art Enterprises

DIAL-A-DEADLINE - Paper products - Deadline Management, Inc.

DIAL-A-DEPARTMENT - Office machines - Interoffice Express, LLC

DIAL-A-DIET - Fish food ☆ - Wardley Corp.

DIAL-A-DROP - Agricultural machinery - Spray-Air USA, Inc.

DIAL-A-FIT - Novelty items - Kolcraft Enterprises, Inc.

DIAL-A-FLO - Pharmaceutical preparations - Abbott Laboratories

DIAL-A-HEAT JALAPENOS - Preserved foods–prepackaged - Basic Vegetable Products Inc.

DIAL A LASH - Cosmetics - Maybelline Co.

DIAL-A-LITE - Lamps ☆ - Eagle Electric Manufacturing Co., Inc.

DIAL-A-LITE - Mirrors - Monaco Import/Export Inc.

DIAL-A-MATCH - Antennas - Valor Enterprises, Inc.

DIAL-A-MATIC - Vacuum cleaners and accessories - The Hoover Co.

DIAL-A-MED PEN - Health care products - Apothecary Products, Inc.

DIAL-A-MIX - Tools–garden - Gilmour Manufacturing Co.

DIAL-A-NAP - Vacuum cleaners and accessories - The Eureka Co.

DIAL-A-POINT - Office supplies ☆ - Alvin and Co. Inc.

DIAL-A-POWER - Power switching equipment - Pulizzi Engineering Inc.

DIAL-A-RAIN - Sprinklers–lawn - L.R. Nelson Corp.

DIAL-A-SEAL - Tools–power-driven - Loctite Corp.

DIAL-A-SPRAY - Tools–garden - Gilmour Manufacturing Co.

DIAL-A-STREAM - Nozzles ☆ - H.B. Sherman Manufacturing Co.

DIAL A STYLE - Dolls - Mattel, Inc.

DIAL-A-STYLE - Hair curlers ☆ - Sunbeam-Oster Household Products

DIAL-A-SWAG - Machinery - S. Morantz Inc.

DIAL-A-SWITCH - Power switching equipment - Pulizzi Engineering Inc.

DIAL-A-TAN - Tanning agents - Quintessence Inc.

DIAL-A-TEACHER - Toys–electronic - Video Technology U.S. Inc.

DIAL-A-TORQUE - Artists' materials - Hamilton Industries

DIAL-A-VERSE - Calendars - Rainfall Inc.

DIAL-A-VISION - Sunglasses - USA Sport Eyewear

DIAL-A-WATT - Heating equipment - King Electrical Manufacturing Co.

DIAL BOOKS FOR YOUNG READERS - Publisher's imprints - E.P. Dutton Inc.

DIAL DEX - Telephone accessories - Rest-a-Phone Corp.

DIAL-ESE - Bathroom fixtures - Crane Plumbing/Fiat Products

DIAL FOR KIDS - Soap - Dial Corp.

DIAL IN STYLE - Telephones - Universal Security Instruments Inc.

DIAL KING - Nozzles ☆ - H.B. Sherman Manufacturing Co.

DIAL MASSAGE - Giftware - Pollenex Corp.

DIAL MASTER - Nozzles ☆ - H.B. Sherman Manufacturing Co.

DIAL ME - Toys - Gerber Products Co.

DIAL ME PRETTY - Mirrors - Mechanical Mirror Works Inc.

DIAL 'N SPELL - Games ☆ - Milton Bradley Co.

DIAL 'N SPRAY - Nozzles - Chevron Chemical Co.

DIAL N STYLE - Curling irons–electric ☆ - Helen of Troy Corp.

DIAL-O-MATIC - Luggage ☆ - Hartmann Luggage Co.

DIAL-O-RAMA - Watches - Hampden Corp.

DIAL-ON - Toilet seats ☆ - Bemis Manufacturing Co.

DIAL PLUS - Soap - Dial Corp.

DIAL PRESS - Publisher's imprints - Bantam Doubleday Dell Publishing Group, Inc.

DIAL TECH - Computer software - Dialing Technology, LLC

DIAL-TEMP - Heating equipment - Coleman Co., Inc.

DIAL-TOUCH - Gloves - Dial Medical of Florida, Inc.

DIAL ULTRA SKIN CARE - Soap - Dial Corp.

DIALA - Lubricating oils - Shell Oil Co.

DIALASSIST - Computer software - Apple Computer Inc.

DIALITE - Clocks - General Time Corp. (Westclox/Seth Thomas Div.)

DIALITE - Dental compounds - Brasseler USA, Inc.

DIALMATE - Telephone apparatus - Edilberto A. Punzalan

DIALMATIC - Locks–door ☆ - Dexter Lock

DIALOCK BOOT - Computer software - Com&Dia, LLC

DIALOG - Alarm systems ☆ - Kaye Instruments Inc.

DIALOG - Computer software - Dialog Information Services, Inc.

DIALOGIC - Computer hardware - Secure Data Systems, Inc.

DIALOGUE - Wallpaper - Secrest Handprints Inc.

DIALOGUE II - Wallpaper - Secrest Handprints Inc.

DIALOSE - Laxatives - McNeil Pharmaceuticals

DIALPOWER - Communications equipment–mobile - Action Systems Co.

DIAL'S EASY-TO-READ BOOKS - Publisher's imprints - E.P. Dutton Inc.

DIALTROL - Tubes–vacuum ☆ - E-Z Clor Systems

DIALUME - Pharmaceutical preparations ☆ - Armour Pharmaceutical Co.

DIALWORX - Pagers - Pagenet

DIALYT - Binoculars - Carl Zeiss Optical Inc.

DIAM-O-LAST - Jewelry - Lasting Impressions Inc.

DIAMALLOY - Chemical preparations - Sulzer Metco (US) Inc.

DIAMALT - Malt syrup - Premier Malt Products, Inc.

DIAMALT - Syrup - Nabisco Foods Group

DIAMANT - Floor coverings–tile ☆ - Monarch Tile Inc.

DIAMANT - Glassware–household - Durand International

DIAMANT - Tableware–china ☆ - Villeroy and Boch Tableware Ltd.

☆ = Now out of production

DIAMANT - Toys ☆ - DGI/Buki
DIAMANT BOART TARGET - Machinery - DBNA Trademarks Holding Inc.
DIAMANTE - Floor coverings–carpet and rugs - Dorsett Carpet Mills Inc.
DIAMANTE - Food products - Mexican-American Specialties Inc.
DIAMANTE - Furniture - Nucraft Furniture Co.
DIAMANTE - Motor vehicles–automobiles - Mitsubishi Motor Sales of America Inc.
DIAMANTES - Cigar boxes–wood - Consolidated Cigar Corp.
DIAMAR - Computer software - Diamar Interactive Corp.
DIAMAR - Marble products - S.V.I. Inc.
DIAMEDIX - Pharmaceutical preparations - Diamedix Corp.
DIAMETRESS - Shampoos - Nexxus Products Co.
DIAMETRIC - Floor coverings–carpet and rugs ☆ - Burtco Enterprises Inc.
DIAMETRICS MEDICAL - Medical apparatus - Diametrics Medical, Inc.
DIAMINOS - Playing cards - John Feeley
DIAMITE - Epoxy floor covering - Metalcrete Industries Inc.
DIAMITE CELL SALTS - Pharmaceutical preparations - Boericke & Tafel
DIAMO - Floor coverings–carpet and rugs ☆ - Evans-Black Carpet Mills
DIAMO - Footwear - Vans, Inc.
DIAMON DEB - Nail care products - London International U.S. Holdings
DIAMON GEL - Cosmetics ☆ - London International U.S. Holdings
DIAMON GLAZE - Cosmetics ☆ - London International U.S. Holdings
DIAMON KING - Cosmetics ☆ - London International U.S. Holdings
DIAMONAIR - Jewelry - Diamonair
DIAMONAL - Tools–power-driven - Joseph A. Thomas Ltd.
DIAMOND - See **ATLAS**
DIAMOND - Automotive parts and accessories - Diamond Industries Inc.
DIAMOND - Bathroom accessories - Wilardy Originals Inc.
DIAMOND - Bicycles - Columbia Manufacturing Inc.
DIAMOND - Cabinets - Diamond Cabinets
DIAMOND - Cabinets - White Consolidated Industries, Inc.
DIAMOND - Cases–camera - Lefkowitz and Santangelo Co.
DIAMOND - Cosmetics ☆ - Duart Industries Ltd.
DIAMOND - Crackers - Diamond Bakery Co. Ltd.
DIAMOND - Darts and dart games - Kulite Tungsten Corp.
DIAMOND - Dog food - W.A. Davis Milling Co. Inc.
DIAMOND - Enamels - Paris Paint & Varnish Co.
DIAMOND - Envelopes ☆ - Marvin Envelope & Paper Co.
DIAMOND - Finishing agents - Flecto Co. Inc.
DIAMOND - Floor coverings - American Floor Products Co. Inc.
DIAMOND - Floor coverings - Congoleum Corp.
DIAMOND - Floor coverings–carpet and rugs - Matworks
DIAMOND - Flowers, plants, and seeds - Florida Group
DIAMOND - Food products - Diamond Blueberry Inc.
DIAMOND - Food products - Diamond Fruit Growers
DIAMOND - Frames–picture - Terragrafics Inc.
DIAMOND - Furnaces–electric - York International Corp.
DIAMOND - Game machines - Bally Gaming International, Inc.
DIAMOND - Games ☆ - Warren Industries Inc.
DIAMOND - Gasoline - Rogers Oil Co.
DIAMOND - Gauging instruments - Diamond Power International, Inc.
DIAMOND - Giftware ☆ - Gorham Inc.
DIAMOND - Handbags - Magnum Fashions Inc.
DIAMOND - Handles–wood - Turner, Day and Woolworth Handle Corp.
DIAMOND - Hardware ☆ - Masback Hardware Co.
DIAMOND - Health care products - Divina Products Co.
DIAMOND - Hoses - Colorite Plastic Co.
DIAMOND - Housewares - Amaza Laboratories Inc.
DIAMOND - Licorice - Henry Heide, Inc.
DIAMOND - Luggage - Diamond Baseball Co., Inc.
DIAMOND - Mattresses - Easyrest Inc.
DIAMOND - Motor vehicle parts and accessories - Sun Co. Inc.
DIAMOND - Musical instruments - White Eagle Rawhide Manufacturing Co.
DIAMOND - Nozzles - H.B. Sherman Manufacturing Co.
DIAMOND - Nuts–salted, roasted, cooked, or canned - Diamond Walnut Growers Inc.
DIAMOND - Office accessories - Newell Office Products
DIAMOND - Paints - Somay Products Inc.
DIAMOND - Pet products - Diamond Feeds
DIAMOND - Pharmaceutical preparations - Lumex, Inc.
DIAMOND - Recreational vehicles - Diamond Coach Corp.
DIAMOND - Rope - Wellington Leisure Products, Inc.
DIAMOND - Shoelaces ☆ - Mitchellace Inc.
DIAMOND - Shoes - Interco Inc.
DIAMOND - Soy sauce - Honolulu Sake Brewery Co. Ltd.
DIAMOND - Syrup - H. Fox & Co., Inc.

DIAMOND - Tiles–ceramic - Wenczel Tile Co.
DIAMOND - Tires - Uniroyal Goodrich Tire Co.
DIAMOND - Tools - Diamond/Triangle Tool Group Inc.
DIAMOND - Tools–hand-operated - Diamond Tool & Horseshoe Co.
DIAMOND - Tools–hand-operated - Triangle Tool Group Inc.
DIAMOND - Vaccines - Diamond Animal Health, Inc.
DIAMOND - Wallcoverings - Stretchwall Fabrics Co.
DIAMOND - Water purification systems - Safe-T-Serv Corp.
DIAMOND - Water–bottled or canned - Diamond Water, Inc.
DIAMOND - Wines - Diamond Island Cellars Inc.
DIAMOND A - Vegetables–canned - Agripac, Inc.
DIAMOND A RANCHWEAR - Apparel and accessories - Ridgefield, Inc.
DIAMOND ACE - Apparel stores–sports ☆ - Bee Hat Co.
DIAMOND ADDABLES - Jewelry - Keen Jewelry Manufacturing Corp.
DIAMOND AIRE - Floor coverings - Congoleum Corp.
DIAMOND AND STRUCTURAL CARBON NEWS - Office supplies - Business Communications Co. Inc.
DIAMOND-ARROW - Furniture - Bassick Casters
DIAMOND ARROW - Wire products - Kaspar Wire Works, Inc.
DIAMOND B - Lumber - Woodex Lumber Corp.
DIAMOND BACK - Bicycle parts and accessories - Diamondback
DIAMOND-BACK - Machine parts - Environmental Procedures, Inc.
DIAMOND BEACH - Apparel and accessories - Diamond Beach Inc.
DIAMOND BITS - Manicure preparations - Dubl Duck/Jet Set Inc.
DIAMOND BRITE - Detergents - Melaleuca, Inc.
DIAMOND BRITE - Epoxy - Diamond Brite Industries Inc.
DIAMOND BRITE - Knives–pocket ☆ - Imperial Schrade Corp.
DIAMOND BRITE - Motor vehicle parts and accessories - Lancaster Colony Automotive Group
DIAMOND BRITE - Signs - American Electronic Sign Co.
DIAMOND BRITE - Windows - Nordam
DIAMOND CABLE - Blinds–venetian ☆ - Hunter Douglas, Inc.
DIAMOND CARESSE - Watches - Bulova Corp.
DIAMOND CARPETS - Floor coverings–carpet and rugs - Diamond Rug & Carpet Mills
DIAMOND CLASSIC - Watches - Bulova Corp.
DIAMOND CLEAR - Laboratory apparatus - Columbia Diagnostics, Inc.
DIAMOND CLUB - Floor coverings - Mannington Resilient Floors
DIAMOND COAT - Cosmetics - Worldwide Cosmetics
DIAMOND COLLECTION - Boxes - Delta Consolidated Industries, Inc.
DIAMOND COLLECTION - Luggage ☆ - Hartmann Luggage Co.
DIAMOND COLLECTION, THE - Bridal gowns and headpieces - Diamond Bridal Collection Ltd.
DIAMOND CONTROL - Computer software - Mitsubishi Electronics America Inc.
DIAMOND COOLER - Wines ☆ - Hudepohl-Schoenling Brewing Co.
DIAMOND CREEK - Wines - Diamond Creek Vineyards
DIAMOND CREEK VINEYARDS - Wines - Diamond Creek Vineyards
DIAMOND CROWN - Cigars - M & N Cigar Manufacturing Inc.
DIAMOND CROWN - Cigars - J.C. Newman Cigar Co.
DIAMOND CRUISER - Bicycles - Ross Bicycles USA, Ltd.
DIAMOND CRYSTAL - Glassware–household - Mayflower Glass Works
DIAMOND CUT - Cutlery - B and F System Inc.
DIAMOND CUT - Meat products–pork - Pork Packers, Inc.
DIAMOND CUT - Musical instrument accessories - United Musical Instruments USA Inc.
DIAMOND CUT - Roofing materials - Building Materials Corp. of America
DIAMOND D - Trailers - Diamond D Trailer Manufacturing, Inc.
DIAMOND DATE CALENDAR - Jewelry - Baby Gold Jewelry, Inc.
DIAMOND DEC ENTERTAINMENT CORPORATION - Video production - Diamond Entertainment Corp.
DIAMOND DEFENDER - Archery equipment - Saunders Archery Co.
DIAMOND DEKPLATE - Floor coverings - American Floor Products Co. Inc.
DIAMOND DELIGHT - Cosmetics - Revlon Consumer Products Corp.
DIAMOND DEMON - Machinery - Diamond Demon, Inc.
DIAMOND DIMPLE - Musical instrument accessories ☆ - Carpenter Co.
DIAMOND DIVIDEND - Jewelry - The Diamond Registry
DIAMOND DOLLARS - Jewelry - DuBarry Fifth Ave. Inc.
DIAMOND DREAM - Watches - Bulova Corp.
DIAMOND DUET II - Watches - Bulova Corp.
DIAMOND DUO - Linen - Medline, Industries, Inc.
DIAMOND DUST - Christmas tree ornaments - Cracker Box Inc.
DIAMOND DUST - Games - International Gamco, Inc.
DIAMOND DUST - Pottery - Duncan Enterprises
DIAMOND DUST BLADE - Fishing lures - Strike King Lure Co.
DIAMOND DUST BZ - Sporting goods - Earth & Ocean Sports, Inc.

☆ = Now out of production

DIAMOND DUST SKIRT - Fishing lures - Strike King Lure Co.
DIAMOND E - Food products - Diamond E Packers
DIAMOND EDGE - Cutlery - Imperial Schrade Corp.
DIAMOND ELECTRONICS - Electronic equipment - Diamond Electronics Inc.
DIAMOND ELEGANCE - Watches - Bulova Corp.
DIAMOND EMBOSSED DESIGN - Paper–toweling - Georgia-Pacific Corp.
DIAMOND EMPRESS - Watches - Bulova Corp.
DIAMOND ETCH - Tools - Armour Products
DIAMOND EXCELLENCE - Watches - Longines-Wittnauer Watch Co.
DIAMOND EYE - Manicure preparations - Burmax Co. Inc.
DIAMOND EYE - Pet products - Berolina Imports
DIAMOND EYES - Sunglasses ☆ - International Tropic-Cal Inc. (I SKI Div.)
DIAMOND EZE - Nail care products - Opi Products, Inc.
DIAMOND F - Lighting fixtures - Diamond F Corp.
DIAMOND F - Vegetables–canned - Feldman & Co. Inc.
DIAMOND FALCON - Fuel additives - Petrolon Management, Inc.
DIAMOND FIRE - Fireplaces ☆ - Malm Fireplaces Inc.
DIAMOND FLEX - Coatings - PPG Industries, Inc.
DIAMOND FLEX - Footwear ☆ - E.S. Originals, Inc.
DIAMOND FLOOR FINISH - Varnishes - Flecto Co. Inc.
DIAMOND FOREST - Cosmetics - Almay Inc.
DIAMOND FORMULA - Manicure preparations ☆ - Bonne Bell, Inc.
DIAMOND G - Food products - Southern Packaging & Storage Co. Inc.
DIAMOND G - Rice - Farmers' Rice Cooperative
DIAMOND G BRAND - Rice - Farmers' Rice Cooperative
DIAMOND GALLERY - Trading cards and stamps - Upper Deck Co.
DIAMOND GARD - Fencing–steel - Gilbert and Bennett Manufacturing Co.
DIAMOND GEM - Food products - SPADA enterprise, ltd.
DIAMOND GIRL - Footwear - BCNY International Inc.
DIAMOND GLIDERS - Jewelry - Maico Industries Inc.
DIAMOND GODDESS - Watches - Bulova Corp.
DIAMOND GOLD - Glassware–household - Gorham Inc.
DIAMOND-GRATE - Barbecues and grills - Stewart Steel Corp.
DIAMOND GRAVERS - Tools - Armour Products
DIAMOND GRIP - Cushions ☆ - Graham-Field Inc.
DIAMOND GUARD - Paints - Sureguard, Inc.
DIAMOND GUARD SUPREME - Paints - Sureguard, Inc.
DIAMOND HARD - Manicure preparations - Max Factor & Co.
DIAMOND HEAD - Floor coverings - Moulder-Oldham Co.
DIAMOND HEAD - Floor coverings–carpet and rugs - Hartford Carpet Mills
DIAMOND HEAD - Floor coverings–carpet and rugs - Patcraft Mills Inc.
DIAMOND HEAD - Video equipment - Samsung Electronics America, Inc.
DIAMOND HEAD 15 - Wallpaper - Pantasote Inc. (Wallcovering Div.)
DIAMOND HEAD SPORTSWEAR - Apparel–men's - Pacific Clothing Co., Inc.
DIAMOND HEAD TRI-BEAD - Beads - Greene Plastics Corp.
DIAMOND HILL VINEYARDS - Wines - Diamond Hill Vineyards
DIAMOND ICE - Scissors–hand-operated - Burmax Co. Inc.
DIAMOND IMAGES - Posters - Diamond Images, Inc.
DIAMOND IN THE ROUND - Jewelry - S. Bellara Diamonds, Inc.
DIAMOND INCENTIVES - Jewelry - DuBarry Fifth Ave. Inc.
DIAMOND INTRIGUE - Floor coverings–carpet and rugs - Karastan-Bigelow Inc.
DIAMOND ISLAND - Seafood products–fresh or frozen - Diamond Island Seafood Co.
DIAMOND JEWEL - Motorcycle parts and accessories - Richard H. Savitski
DIAMOND JEWEL - Pet collars ☆ - Leatherite-Nylorite Manufacturing Inc.
DIAMOND JIM - Jewelry - Jacoby-Bender Inc.
DIAMOND JIM - Pianos ☆ - Universal Player Piano Co.
DIAMOND JOY - Underwear and nightwear ☆ - Lovable Co.
DIAMOND JUBILEE - Christmas tree ornaments - Cracker Box Inc.
DIAMOND JUBILEE - Floor coverings–carpet and rugs - Lees Carpets
DIAMOND JUBILEE - Fruits–candied - L. Karp & Sons, Inc.
DIAMOND JUBILEE - Toys - Tonka Corp.
DIAMOND JUBILEE - Watches ☆ - Longines-Wittnauer Watch Co.
DIAMOND K - Health care products - J.J. Keller & Associates
DIAMOND L - Apparel - Jones of Dallas Manufacturing
DIAMOND LABEL - Men's shirts - Levi Strauss & Co.
DIAMOND LADY - Jewelry - Jacoby-Bender Inc.
DIAMOND LIFE - Jewelry - Vargas Manufacturing Co.
DIAMOND LIGHTS - Wallpaper - Seabrook Wallcoverings, Inc.
DIAMOND LITE - Eyeglasses ☆ - Cable Car Eyeware
DIAMOND LITES - Apparel and accessories - Warnaco Inc.
DIAMOND-LOK - Garden equipment - Valley View Specialties Co.
DIAMOND LOOK - Jewelry - Kramer Jewelry Creations Inc.
DIAMOND LUSTER - Christmas tree ornaments - Cracker Box Inc.
DIAMOND LUSTRE - Christmas tree ornaments - Cracker Box Inc.

DIAMOND M - Flour–blended - Morrison Milling Co.
DIAMOND MIND - Vitamins and nutritional supplements - Diamond Herpanacine Associates
DIAMOND MINI-SHARP - Tools - Diamond Machining Technology Inc.
DIAMOND MIST - Floor coverings–carpet and rugs - Barrett Carpet Mills Inc.
DIAMOND MOUNTAIN RANCH - Wines - Sterling Vineyards
DIAMOND NAIL - Nail care products - Pantresse Inc.
DIAMOND NET - Netting - Jetnet Corp.
DIAMOND O - See **B & R**
DIAMOND O - Meat products–poultry - Ottman & Co.
DIAMOND OAKS VINEYARD - Wines - Diamond Oaks Vineyard
DIAMOND OCCIDENTAL - Lumber - Woodex Lumber Corp.
DIAMOND PARTNERS - Rings–jewelry - Feature Enterprises
DIAMOND PLATE - Eyeglasses - Cable Car Eyeware
DIAMOND PLUS - Engines–internal combustion - Briggs & Stratton Corp.
DIAMOND POINT - Fishing tackle ☆ - Wright & McGill Co.
DIAMOND POINT - Pressed glassware - Indiana Glass Co.
DIAMOND POSTER - Frames–picture - North American Enclosures Inc.
DIAMOND POWER - Engines–internal combustion - Briggs & Stratton Corp.
DIAMOND-POWER - Incense - Shoyeido Corp.
DIAMOND PRINCE - Watches - Longines-Wittnauer Watch Co.
DIAMOND PRINCESS - Watches - Longines-Wittnauer Watch Co.
DIAMOND PRO - Monitors–electronic - Mitsubishi Electronics America Inc.
DIAMOND PUMPS - Pumps–water - Aermotor Pumps Inc.
DIAMOND PUMPS AND WATER SYSTEMS - Pumps - Aermotor Pumps Inc.
DIAMOND RAIL - Surfboards - Packaging Industries Group Inc.
DIAMOND RAINBOW - Puzzles - Kadon Enterprises Inc.
DIAMOND READERS - Eyeglasses - Cable Car Eyeware
DIAMOND REGISTRY, THE - Jewelry - The Diamond Registry
DIAMOND REO - Motor vehicles–trucks - Diamond Reo Trucks Inc.
DIAMOND RIB - Aluminum products ☆ - Kaiser Aluminum & Chemical Corp.
DIAMOND RING FACTORY - Rings–jewelry - John M. Marshall's Diamond Import Co.
DIAMOND RIO - Games - International Gamco, Inc.
DIAMOND ROCK - Seafood products–fresh or frozen - Multimar Products, Inc.
DIAMOND ROYALE - Wines - Cap*Rock Winery, Inc.
DIAMOND RUNNERS - Jewelry - Maico Industries Inc.
DIAMOND SAVOY - Jewelry - Richelieu Corp.
DIAMOND SCAN - Monitors–electronic - Mitsubishi Electronics America Inc.
DIAMOND SCREEN - Projection screens - Draper Shade and Screen Co. Inc.
DIAMOND SEEDS - Novelty items - Kenneth R. Smith
DIAMOND SERIES - Steering mechanisms–boat - Edson Corp.
DIAMOND SERIES, THE - Furnaces–electric - York International Corp.
DIAMOND-SHAD - Fishing lures - Strike King Lure Co.
DIAMOND SHAMROCK - Gasoline - Diamond Shamrock Inc.
DIAMOND SHIELD - Fabrics ☆ - Surface Industries Inc.
DIAMOND SHINE - Polishing rouge - Star Brite
DIAMOND SHINE - Shampoos - Kim Laube & Co. Inc.
DIAMOND SLIM - Eyeglasses ☆ - Cable Car Eyeware
DIAMOND SOLITAIRE - Tiles–ceramic - Dal-Tile Corp.
DIAMOND SOLUTIONS - Jewelry–precious - Diamond Solutions, Inc.
DIAMOND SPARKLE - Cleaning preparations - Rual Products Co.
DIAMOND STAR - Apparel–athletic - A & G Inc.
DIAMOND STATION - Coffee - Ephrata Diamond Spring Water Co., Inc.
DIAMOND STEEL - Cosmetics ☆ - Dubl Duck/Jet Set Inc.
DIAMOND-STIK - Jewelry - Kurt Wayne Inc.
DIAMOND STREET - Footwear–men's - Nozaki America Inc.
DIAMOND TEAM - Noodles - Diamond Team International, Inc.
DIAMOND TECH - Adhesives and sealants - Ardex Laboratories, Inc.
DIAMOND TILE - Paneling - ABT Co., Inc.
DIAMOND TIP - Cigar boxes–wood - Consolidated Cigar Corp.
DIAMOND TIP - Musical instruments - Joseph Porcaro
DIAMOND TIP - Sporting goods - Surfco Hawaii Inc.
DIAMOND TOE - Hosiery - Marlex Trading Corp.
DIAMOND TOP - Counter tops–laminated - Hartson-Kennedy Cabinet Top Co., Inc.
DIAMOND TOP - Mats - Superior Manufacturing Group/Notrax Floor Matting
DIAMOND TOUCH - Electronic equipment - Premier Technology
DIAMOND TOUR - Golfing equipment - Korex Corp.
DIAMOND TRIBUTE - Trading cards and stamps - Fleer Corp.
DIAMOND TURF - Synthetic turf - Instant Turf Industries Inc.
DIAMOND TWIST - Floor coverings–carpet and rugs - Porter Carpet Mills Inc.
DIAMOND-UTICA - Tools–hand-operated - Cooper Industries, Inc.
DIAMOND V - Veterinary nutritional supplements - Diamond V Mills Inc.
DIAMOND V AO - Veterinary nutritional supplements - Diamond V Mills Inc.
DIAMOND V LS - Veterinary nutritional supplements - Diamond V Mills Inc.

☆ = Now out of production

DIAMOND V XP - Veterinary nutritional supplements - Diamond V Mills Inc.

DIAMOND V YC - Veterinary nutritional supplements - Diamond V Mills Inc.

DIAMOND V YEAST CULTURE - Veterinary nutritional supplements - Diamond V Mills Inc.

DIAMOND VANE - Sporting goods - Easton Aluminum Inc.

DIAMOND VAULT - Safes - Empire Safe Co. Inc.

DIAMOND VELVET - Seat covers - Saddleman, Inc.

DIAMOND-VOGEL - Paints - Vogel Paint and Wax Co., Inc.

DIAMOND W - Ribbons–inked - Western Carbon Paper Manufacturing Co.

DIAMOND WALKER - Footwear–women's ☆ - E.S. Originals, Inc.

DIAMOND WATER - Perfumes - Mon Jardin Secret Inc.

DIAMOND WATER CONDITIONING - Water treating compounds - Diamond Water, Inc.

DIAMOND WELD - Fencing–gates and posts - Northwestern Steel and Wire Co.

DIAMOND WHETSTONE - Tool boxes - Diamond Machining Technology Inc.

DIAMOND WHITE - Beverages–malt - Miller Brewing Co.

DIAMOND WORLD - Jewelry ☆ - Rogers Enterprises, Inc.

DIAMOND WRIGHT - Electrical industrial apparatus - Cold Spring Granite Co.

DIAMONDBACK - Binders - U.S. Ring Binder Corp.

DIAMONDBACK - Landscape border - Valley View Specialties Co.

DIAMONDBACK - Motor vehicle parts and accessories - Tensar Corp.

DIAMONDBACK - Pistols ☆ - Colt's Manufacturing Co. Inc.

DIAMONDBACK SHAD - Fishing lures - Sports Design and Development, Inc.

DIAMONDBOARD - Marine rigging - General Boats Corp.

DIAMONDBUCK - Knife sharpener - Buck Knives, Inc,

DIAMONDCORE - Boats–motor - Skeeter Products Inc.

DIAMONDFLEUR - Colognes ☆ - Avon Products, Inc.

DIAMONDFLOR - Floor coverings - Congoleum Corp.

DIAMONDFORCE - Sunglasses - Spy Optic, Inc.

DIAMONDHARD - Sunglasses - Bausch & Lomb Inc.

DIAMONDHEAD - Furniture ☆ - Bassett Furniture Industries, Inc.

DIAMONDI LIMITED EDITION - Apparel–women's - Diamondi, Inc.

DIAMONDINE - Jewelry - Tiara Corp.

DIAMONDITE - Apparel and accessories - Richton International Corp.

DIAMONDLITE - Christmas tree lights - Direct Source International Inc.

DIAMONDPLY - Fabrics - Albany International Corp.

DIAMONDROPE - Jewelry - OroAmerica Inc.

DIAMONDS - Bicycles ☆ - Huffy Corp.

DIAMONDS - Blinds–vertical - U.S. Polymers, Inc.

DIAMONDS - Fans–electric ☆ - Nutone Inc.

DIAMONDS - Floor coverings–carpet and rugs ☆ - Quaker Inc.

DIAMONDS - Floor coverings–carpet and rugs ☆ - Regal Rugs Inc.

DIAMOND'S - Shrimp–fresh or frozen - Darik Enterprises Inc.

DIAMONDS & EMERALDS - Perfumes - Parfums International Ltd.

DIAMONDS AND EMERALDS - Toiletries - Conopco, Inc.

DIAMONDS & ROSES - Game machines - Bally Gaming International, Inc.

DIAMONDS AND RUBIES - Perfumes - Conopco, Inc.

DIAMONDS & RUBIES - Perfumes - Parfums International Ltd.

DIAMONDS AND SAPPHIRES - Perfumes - Conopco, Inc.

DIAMONDS & SAPPHIRES - Perfumes - Parfums International Ltd.

DIAMONDS & STUDS - Puzzles ☆ - Ben Cooper Inc.

DIAMONDS AND TRIANGLES DESIGN - Paper - Georgia-Pacific Corp.

DIAMONDS ARE A MAN'S BEST FRIEND, TOO. - Cigars - C.A.O. International, Inc.

DIAMONDS ARE FOR EVERYONE - Jewelry - American Concept Inc.

DIAMONDS ARE FOREVER - Christmas tree ornaments - Cracker Box Inc.

DIAMONDS CAN BE DEADLY - Puzzles - Hasbro, Inc.

DIAMONDS IN BLOOM - Jewelry–precious - Charles Bloom & Co.

DIAMONDS IN THE ROUGH - Fabrics - Gretchen Bellinger Inc.

DIAMONDS INTERNATIONALE - Jewelry - House of Commans Inc.

DIAMONDS OF THE SEA - Shrimp–fresh or frozen - United Seafood Imports, Inc.

DIAMONDSTEP - Bumpers–motor vehicle - Wedgestone Automotive Corp.

DIAMONDSUN - Sunblocks - European Tanning Systems Inc.

DIAMONDVEE - Tools - Diamond Machining Technology Inc.

DIAMONDWALL - Wallpaper - PCI Industries Inc.

DIAMONDWARE - Tableware–plastic - Diamond Brands Inc.

DIAMONEER - Floor coverings–carpet and rugs - Roxbury Carpet Co.

DIAMONESS - Jewelry - Peter Brams Designs, Ltd.

DIAMONEX - Lenses–optical - Monsanto Co.

DIAMONFIRE - Jewelry - Bates Creations Inc.

DIAMONIDE - Jewelry - Tiara Corp.

DIAMONIQUE PREMIERE - Perfumes - Diamonique Corp.

DIAMONIZE FOR NAILS - Nail care products - Finger Mates Inc.

DIAMONIZER - Lubricating oils - We Innovex, Inc.

DIAMONLITE - Lamps - Public Service Lamp Corp.

DIAMONT - Cosmetics - Colour Grow Cosmetics Intl.

DIAMONTE - Dishes–china - Pasmantier Co. Inc.

DIAMONTE - Harnesses - Weaver Leather Goods, Inc.

DIAMONTE - Rings–jewelry - Artcarved Inc.

DIAMONTINA - Jewelry - Tiara Corp.

DIAN MERI - Furniture - Marianna Imports, Inc.

DIANA - Apparel and accessories - Image Equity Management, Inc.

DIANA - Bathroom fixtures - Crane Plumbing/Fiat Products

DIANA - Brushes–paint - Corona Brushes Inc.

DIANA - Clocks - General Time Corp. (Westclox/Seth Thomas Div.)

DIANA - Coffee - Pearl Coffee Co.

DIANA - Floor coverings–carpet and rugs ☆ - Karastan-Bigelow Inc.

DIANA - Food products - Diana Fruit Preserving Co.

DIANA - Food products - Goya Foods, Inc.

DIANA - Glassware–household ☆ - Oneida Ltd.

DIANA - Needles–sewing ☆ - Boye Needle

DIANA - Olive oil - Moscahlades Bros. Inc.

DIANA - Recording label - Starman Records

DIANA - Sporting goods ☆ - S & R Sport/Maric

DIANA - Watches - Bulova Corp.

DIANA COLLECTION - Belts, handbags, jewelry, etc. - Italtrade

DIANA FASHIONS - Shoes - Shoe Masters Inc.

DIANA HOME FASHIONS - Placemats - Avon Glove Corp.

DIANA LEIGH DESIGNER FASHIONS - Hobby kits - A + A

DIANA MARCO - Apparel–women's - Miller-Wohl Co., Inc.

DIANA MARSH - Bags–cosmetic - A.J. Siris Products Corp.

DIANA ROSS - Hosiery–women's ☆ - Nantucket Industries Inc.

DIANA'S - Sausages - Piqua Pizza Supply Co.

DIANA'S CALIFORNIA COOKIES - Food products - Diana's California Cookies

DIANA'S CHAMOMILE SHAMPOO - Shampoos - Annabelle's Inc.

DIANE - Cheese - Mike Hudson Distributing Inc.

DIANE - Dolls ☆ - Effanbee Doll Corp.

DIANE - Floor coverings–carpet and rugs ☆ - Regal Rugs Inc.

DIANE - Frames–eyeglass ☆ - U.S. Optical Frame Co.

DIANE - Hair care products - Chicago Hair Good Inc.

DIANE - Hair care products - Diane Products Inc.

DIANE-CAPS - Cosmetics - Diane Products Inc.

DIANE COLLECTIBLE'S - Giftware - Peterson Pacific Co. Inc.

DIANE GILMAN - Footwear, belts, ties, etc. - DGD Inc.

DIANE K. - Apparel–women's - Ormond Shops Inc.

DIANE MIRAGE - Mirrors - Diane Products Inc.

DIANE NIPPERS - Cosmetics - Diane Products Inc.

DIANE TAYLOR DESIGNS - Eyeglasses - Mark R. Feldman

DIANE VON FURSTENBERG - Apparel–women's - Avon Products, Inc.

DIANE VON FURSTENBERG - Dresses–women's - Jody Apparel Group

DIANE VON FURSTENBERG - Handbags - Empress Handbags Inc.

DIANE VON FURSTENBERG - Luggage - York Luggage Co.

DIANE VON FURSTENBERG - Luggage ☆ - Verdi Travelware

DIANE VON FURSTENBERG - Ophthalmic goods - Optique du Monde Ltd.

DIANE VON FURSTENBERG - Paper–toweling ☆ - Orchids Paper Products, Inc.

DIANE VON FURSTENBERG - Perfumes - Quintessence Inc.

DIANE VON FURSTENBERG THE COLOR AUTHORITY - Eyeglasses - Diane Von Furstenberg Studio

DIANE VON FURSTENBURG - Hosiery ☆ - McCubbin Hosiery Inc.

DIANE WINTER - Jewelry - Costume Jewelry Co.

DIANE YOUNG - Dresses–women's - Anne Klein & Co.

DIANE'S - Corn chips - Mission Foods Corp.

DIANES' GARDEN - Wallpaper - Hunting Valley Prints

DIANE'S KIDS SIZE - Tortillas - Mission Foods Corp.

DIANGLE - Games - Enginuity

DIANIXX - Health care products - Pharma Botanixx

DIANNA, THE HUNTRESS - Shirts - Converse Pointe

DIANO - Spectrographs - Milton Roy Co.

DIANOGAH - Musical instrument stores - Dianogah Partnership

DIAPA-KARE - Skin care products - Perry Products

DIAPARENE - Dermatological preparations - L & F Consumer Products

DIAPARENE - Infant product - Sterling Winthrop Inc.

DIAPASON - Pianos - Kawai America Corp.

DIAPASON MODULE - Audio equipment - Shahinian Acoustics Ltd.

DIAPECTIN - Antacids - Fleetwood Co.

DIAPER AND MORE TO-GO - Infant product - Diaper To-Go, Inc.

DIAPER BASIC - Infant product - Kooshies Diapers International Inc.

DIAPER-DEPOT - Infant product - Safe-Strap Co., Inc.

DIAPER DOUBLERS - Diapers–disposable - Weyerhaeuser Co.

DIAPER GANG, THE - Cloth diapers, diaper liners, and pants - Diaper Gang
DIAPER GENIE - Diaper disposal container - Mondial Industries, Ltd.
DIAPER GUARD - Pharmaceutical preparations - Del Pharmaceuticals, Inc.
DIAPER KING - Diaper covers - Alam & Wills
DIAPER PLUS - See DIAPER BASIC
DIAPER RASH - Greeting cards ☆ - Amberley Greeting Card Co.
DIAPER ROLL SYSTEM - Infant product - RMED International Inc.
DIAPERAP LITES - Diaper covers - SynCro Internation Corp.
DIAPERAPS - Infant product - SynCro Internation Corp.
DIAPERBRIEFS - Incontinence products - George Disposables
DIAPERENE NURSERY FRESH - Deodorizers - Sterling Winthrop Inc.
DIAPERS AWAY - Bags–trash - Changing World Products, Inc.
DIAPERS ETC. - Bags–storage - Boston Bag Co. of New York, Inc.
DIAPHANIQUE - Apparel and accessories - Vanity Fair Mills Inc.
DIAPHOS RX - Insecticides - Y-Tex Corp.
DIAPID - Pharmaceutical preparations - Sandoz Pharmaceuticals Corp.
DIAPREX - Infant product - Diaprex Marketing Inc.
DIAPURE - Pharmaceutical preparations - Fresenius USA, Inc.
DIAQUA - Pharmaceutical preparations ☆ - Roberts/Hauck Pharmaceuticals Inc.
DIAR-ADE - Health care products - Halsey Drug Co. Inc.
DIAR-AID - Health care products - Thompson Medical Co., Inc.
DIAR-EASE - Health care products ☆ - Nature's Herbs
DIAR-RELIEF - Veterinary pharmaceutical preparations - Dr. Goodpet
DIARAL - Pharmaceutical preparations - Roberts/Hauck Pharmaceuticals Inc.
DIARCON - Pharmaceutical preparations - Consolidated Midland Corp.
DIARD SOCKS - Socks - Diard, Inc.
DIAREX - Veterinary pharmaceutical preparations - G.C. Hanford Manufacturing Co.
DIARID - Pharmaceutical preparations ☆ - Nature's Way Products, Inc.
DIARREST - Pharmaceutical preparations - Dover Pharmaceutical Inc.
DIARREX - Pharmaceutical preparations - Standard Homeopathic Co., Inc.
DIARRID - Pharmaceutical preparations - Stellar Health Products, Inc.
DIARY S.O.S. - Publisher's imprints - Daniel Weiss Associates, Inc.
DIARYCRAFT - Stationery - Advertising Corp. of America
DIARYLINK - Computer software - The Arbitron Co.
DIASAL - Salt ☆ - E. Fougera & Co. Inc.
DIASCAN - Home health care products - Home Diagnostics Inc.
DIASCRIPTOR - Electronic equipment - Leica USA Inc.
DIASONE SODIUM - Pharmaceutical preparations ☆ - Abbott Laboratories
DIASORB - Pharmaceutical preparations - Columbia Laboratories Inc.
DIASPORAL - Skin care products ☆ - Doak Dermatologics
DIASPRON - Office supplies - Olivetti North America Inc. (Consumer Products Div.)
DIASTAT - Pharmaceutical ☆ - Upsher-Smith Laboratories, Inc.
DIASTAY - Pharmaceutical preparations ☆ - ICN Pharmaceuticals Inc.
DIASTIX - Chemical preparations - Miles Inc.
DIASTONE - Tiles–ceramic - Impo Glaztile Inc.
DIASTOP - Pharmaceutical preparations ☆ - ICN Pharmaceuticals Inc.
DIATBUSTER - Pressure-washer system - Blue Lustre, LLC
DIATEK 600 - Electronic equipment - Diatek Inc.
DIATOM - Aquariums–household - Vortex Innerspace Products Inc.
DIATOMAGIC FILTER - Pet products - Tetra Sales USA
DIATROL - Pharmaceutical preparations - Buffington
DIATROL - Pharmaceutical preparations - Otis Clapp & Son Inc.
DIATRON - Novelty items–paper - Epoca Corp.
DIAX - Lenses–photographic ☆ - Heitz Service Corp.
DIAX BY TENSOR - Lamps - Tensor Corp.
DIAZINON - Pesticides–household - Bonide Products, Inc.
DIAZOURACIL - Pharmaceutical preparations ☆ - City Chemical Corp.
DIBAGGIO - Business cases - W.K. Leathers
DIBATROL - Pharmaceutical preparations ☆ - Lexis Laboratories Inc.
DIBBI DUCK - Toys–stuffed - Russ Berrie and Co., Inc.
DIBBLES DUCK - Toys–stuffed - Dakin Inc.
DIBENCOPLEX - Health care products - Anabol Naturals
DIBENEDETTO - Apparel–men's - Crown Clothing Corp.
DIBENIL - Pharmaceutical preparations - H.R. Cenci Laboratories Inc.
DIBENT - Pharmaceutical preparations ☆ - Roberts/Hauck Pharmaceuticals Inc.
DIBENT-PB - Pharmaceutical preparations ☆ - Roberts/Hauck Pharmaceuticals Inc.
DIBENZYLINE - Pharmaceutical preparations - Smithkline Beecham Corp.
DIBI - Apparel–women's - Christian Fletcher Surf, Inc.
DIBS - Disposable bibs - Procter & Gamble Co.
DIC - Games - Darwell Import Co. Inc.
DIC-HK - Novelty items - Darwell Import Co. Inc.
DIC-O-LON - Tools–power-driven ☆ - Dico Products Corp.

DIC-TION-AR-Y DER-BY - Games - Charles Rodriguez
DICAL - Vitamins and nutritional supplements ☆ - Legere Pharmaceuticals Inc.
DICAL-D - Pharmaceutical preparations - Abbott Laboratories
DICARBOSIL - Antacids - Smithkline Beecham Corp.
DICASOL - Pharmaceutical ☆ - IDE-Interstate Inc.
DICE - Fuel additives - Aviation Laboratories, Inc.
DICE BEADS - Novelty items - Koplow Games
DICE POINTS 10,000 - Games - True Image Audio
DICE-SIONS - Games - David L. Battaglia
DICE SPORTS - Games - Michael A. Vernon
DICHROGLASS - Glassware–household - Optical Coating Laboratory Inc.– Santa Rosa Div.
DICIN - Pharmaceutical preparations - C.S. Ruckstuhl Co. Inc.
DICK BARTLEY PRESENTS COLLECTOR'S ESSENTIALS - Recording label - D.B. Productions, Inc.
DICK BREWER SURFBOARDS - Apparel and accessories - Brewer Bros. Inc.
DICK CLARK'S AMERICAN BANDSTAND GRILL AB - Novelty items - Olive Enterprises, Inc.
DICK HELD - Sporting goods ☆ - Gill Sports Equipment, Inc.
DICK KNOX - Dinnerware–glass - Vohann of California Inc.
DICK TRACY - Candy - Topps Co., Inc.
DICK TRACY SPARKLE PAINTS - Paint sets–hobby ☆ - Kenner Products
DICK TWINNEY - Housewares ☆ - Chase Collection, Inc.
DICK WEBER - Bowling balls ☆ - Master Industries Inc.
DICKENS - Eggnog ☆ - Montebello Brands, Inc.
DICKENS DELIGHT - Fruits–dried - Rocky Peanut Co., Inc.
DICKENS ON THE STRAND - Spoons - Galveston Historical Foundation
DICKENS' VILLAGE SERIES - Figurines - D 56, Inc.
DICKENS' VILLAGE SERIES - Figurines - Department 56 Inc.
DICKENSCENT - Colognes - Glenn E. Arnett, Jr.
DICKENSON - Flatware - Reed and Barton Corp.
DICKERSON - Ships–sailing vessels - Dickerson Boatbuilders Inc.
DICKERSON - Shoes - Drew Shoe Corp.
DICKEY - Health care products - First Aids Inc.
DICKEY BETTS - Musical instrument accessories - Gibson Strings & Accessories
DICKIE - Thread ☆ - American & Efird, Inc.
DICKIES - Apparel and accessories - Williamson-Dickie Manufacturing Co.
DICKINSON - Chocolate candy - Maxfield Candy Co.
DICKINSON - Jams and jellies - Dickinson Family Inc.
DICKINSON - Sinks–metal - Kohler Co.
DICKINSON & LEE - Sportscoats, slacks and ties - Stone & Thomas
DICKINSON FAMILY, THE - Food products - Dickinson Family Inc.
DICKINSON'S - Pharmaceutical preparations - E.E. Dickinson Co.
DICKSON - Health care products - Thermo-Electric Co.
DICKSON - Measuring instruments - Dickson/Unigage, Inc.
DICKSON - Sporting goods and fishing tackle - American Import Co.
DICKSON ELBERTON - Fabrics - Dickson Elberton Mills, Inc.
DICKY - Archery equipment - Dicky Golf
DICO - Artists' materials - DICO Group Inc.
DICO - Cooking utensils–aluminum - Darwell Import Co. Inc.
DICO - Tires - Dico Tire Inc.
DICO - Tools–power-driven - Dico Products Corp.
DICO KWIK-KLEEN - Photographic equipment - DICO Group Inc.
DICODETHAL - Cold remedies - Lannett Co. Inc.
DICOHIST - Pharmaceutical preparations - Wesley Pharmacal Co. Inc.
DICOLE - Health care products - Halsey Drug Co. Inc.
DICOM - Computer software - Eastman Kodak Co.
DICON - Electronic equipment - Eastman Kodak Co.
DICONIX - Printers–computer - Eastman Kodak Co.
DICOPAQUE - Photographic equipment - DICO Group Inc.
DICTA SCRIBE - Electronic equipment ☆ - Hamilton Electronics Corp.
DICTABELT - Dictating machines ☆ - Dictaphone Corp.
DICTACADDY - Dictating machines ☆ - Dictaphone Corp.
DICTACALL - Remote control devices ☆ - Dictaphone Corp.
DICTACHRON - Telephone answering machines ☆ - Dictaphone Corp.
DICTACLEAN - Tape recorders ☆ - Dictaphone Corp.
DICTACOIL - Telephone answering machines ☆ - Dictaphone Corp.
DICTACOM - Telephone answering machines ☆ - Dictaphone Corp.
DICTACORD - Dictating machines ☆ - Dictaphone Corp.
DICTAGRAM - Stationery ☆ - Dictaphone Corp.
DICTALERT - Telephone answering machines - Dictaphone Corp.
DICTALOG - Telephone answering machines - Dictaphone Corp.
DICTAMAILER - Packaging–blisterwrap ☆ - Dictaphone Corp.
DICTAMASTER - Dictating machines ☆ - Dictaphone Corp.
DICTAMATE - Dictating machines - Dictaphone Corp.

☆ = Now out of production

DICTAMATIC - Office machines - Dictaphone Corp.

DICTAMATION - Dictating machines ☆ - Dictaphone Corp.

DICTAMAX - Dictating machines ☆ - Dictaphone Corp.

DICTAMETER - Office machines - Dictaphone Corp.

DICTAMITE - Dictating machines - Dictaphone Corp.

DICTAPAK - Packaging–blisterwrap ☆ - Dictaphone Corp.

DICTAPHONE - Telephone answering machines - Dictaphone Corp.

DICTARASER - Office machines ☆ - Dictaphone Corp.

DICTASCAN - Office machines - Dictaphone Corp.

DICTASCRIBE - Office machines - Dictaphone Corp.

DICTASETTE - Office machines - Dictaphone Corp.

DICTATAPE - Tape recorders–cassette - Dictaphone Corp.

DICTATIMER - Office machines ☆ - Dictaphone Corp.

DICTATION - Pencils ☆ - Staedtler, Inc.

DICTATOR, THE - Tires - Dealers Tire Supply Inc.

DICTEL - Dictating machines - Dictaphone Corp.

DICTET - Tape recorders–cassette ☆ - Dictaphone Corp.

DICTIONARY - Apparel and accessories - Bodywaves, Inc.

DICTIONARY FOR THE REST OF US!, A - Computer software - International Data Group, Inc.

DICTIONARY OF COLOR, THE - Wallpaper ☆ - Stroheim & Romann, Inc.

DICTIONARY OF COLOR VOL. II, THE - Wallpaper - Stroheim & Romann, Inc.

DICTRONIC - Microphones ☆ - Dictaphone Corp.

DICURIN PROCAINE - Pharmaceutical preparations ☆ - Eli Lilly and Co.

DICYCLON - Pharmaceutical preparations ☆ - Kenyon Drug Co. Inc.

DID-IT - Games - Advanced Innovations, Inc.

DIDDLE COW - Toys–stuffed - Russ Berrie and Co., Inc.

DIDDLE DADDLE - Pens ☆ - Sanford Corp.

DIDDLIES - Toys - Flambeau Products Corp.

DIDECA - Recording label - Sonotone Corp.

DIDGER - Computer software - Golden Software, Inc.

DIDI - Ophthalmic goods ☆ - Rozin Optical Export Corp.

DIDIER - Logging equipment - Didier Log Splitters

DIDREX - Pharmaceutical preparations - Upjohn Co.

DIDRONEL - Pharmaceutical preparations - Norwich-Eaton Pharmaceuticals

DIDWARE - Wood products - Independent Stave Co. Inc.

DIE PLANK - Plastics - Tool Chemical Co., Inc.

DIE RUNNER - Tools–hand-operated - Power House Tool, Inc.

DIE-SAVER - Glass products ☆ - Corning Inc.

DIE-TAN - Apparel–men's - Anthrocore Inc.

DIEBOLD - Filing cabinets–metal - Diebold Inc.

DIECRAT MQ - Metals - Precision Industries, Inc.

DIEFAST - Insecticides - Lynwood Laboratories, Inc.

DIEGO - Wines - Monterey Peninsula Winery

DIEHARD - Automotive parts and accessories - Sears, Roebuck and Co.

DIEHARD - Books–comic - Rob Liefeld, Inc.

DIEHL - Tobacco–chewing or smoking - Cornell & Diehl Inc.

DIEHL - Woodworking machinery - Diehl Machines, Inc.

DIEHL'S - Juices ☆ - Diehl's Orchard & Cider Mill

DIEHL'S ORCHARD - Cider - Diehl's Orchard & Cider Mill

DIELECTRIC COATING INDUSTRIES - Optical reflectors - Dielectric Coating Industries

DIELEKTROL - Capacitors - General Electric Co.

DIEMASTER 2 - Band-saw blades - American Saw & Manufacturing Co.

DIEMATE - Connectors–electronic - Texas Instruments Inc.

DIEMATE - Electronic equipment - Texas Instruments Inc.

DIEMITECH - Metals - Mi-Tech Metals, Inc.

DIENER - Erasers - Diener Industries Inc.

DIERDRA - Bedding–linen - Dan River Inc.

DIESEL - Toys - Titan Sports, Inc.

DIESEL 190 - Vodka - Sazerac Co. Inc.

DIESEL BLASTER - Toys–trains - Life-Like Products Inc.

DIESEL CHARGER - Toys–trains - Life-Like Products Inc.

DIESEL DEVIL, THE - Horns–motor vehicle - Anes Electronics Burglar Alarm Systems

DIESEL EMPIRE - Toys–trains - Life-Like Products Inc.

DIESEL FUEL GARD - Lubricants - Gard Corp.

DIESEL HEET - Fuel additives ☆ - Demert & Dougherty, Inc.

DIESEL MASTER - Toys–trains - Life-Like Products Inc.

DIESEL PEP - Fuel additives - Spray Products Corp.

DIESEL PLUS - Fuel additives - Conklin Co., Inc.

DIESEL PRO-FLO - Fuel additives - Berryman Products Inc.

DIESEL-SEAL - Gaskets - AE Clevite Inc.

DIESEL TREET - Fuel additives ☆ - Fibre Glass-Evercoat Co. Inc.

DIESELDRIVE - Engines–marine - Stewart and Stevenson Services Inc.

DIESELEZE - Motor vehicle parts and accessories - Sunland Refining Corp.

DIESELJET - Engines–marine - Stewart and Stevenson Services Inc.

DIESSE - Footwear–women's - Diesse Shoes Inc.

DIESSE SPORT - Footwear–women's - Diesse Shoes Inc.

DIESTORE - Racks - Jarke Corp.

DIET - Health care products - East Earth Herb Inc.

DIET - Jewelry - William Donovan

DIET 7 UP - Beverages–carbonated - Dr. Pepper/Seven Up, Inc.

DIET A & W - Beverages–carbonated - A and W Brands Inc.

DIET-AID - Pharmaceutical preparations ☆ - Parmed Pharmaceuticals, Inc.

DIET ANALYSIS - Computer software - SourceView Software International

DIET ASSISTANCE - Vitamins and nutritional supplements - Hall Laboratories, Inc.

DIET BARQ'S - Beverages–carbonated - Barq's Inc.

DIET BIG RED - Beverage ☆ - Big Red Inc.

DIET BIRCH BEER - Soft drink - Briar's USA Inc.

DIET BLUE BELL - Ice cream - Blue Bell Creameries, L.P.

DIET BUBBLE UP - Beverages–carbonated - Monarch Co., Inc.

DIET CAFFEINE-FREE DR. PEPPER - Beverages–carbonated - Dr. Pepper/ Seven Up, Inc.

DIET-CAL - Syrup - IFP Co.

DIET CALIFORNIA NATURAL - Beverages–carbonated ☆ - Vernors Inc.

DIET CENTER - Giftware ☆ - Papel Freelance, Inc.

DIET CHASER - Beverages–carbonated - Double Cola Co.-USA

DIET CHEERWINE - Beverages–carbonated - Carolina Beverage Inc.

DIET CHERRY 7-UP - Beverages–carbonated - Dr. Pepper/Seven Up, Inc.

DIET CHERRY COKE - Beverages–carbonated - Coca-Cola Co.

DIET CHROME-CARE - Vitamins and nutritional supplements - Bluebonnet Nutrition Corp.

DIET CITRA - Beverages–carbonated ☆ - Global Beverage Co.

DIET CITRUS 7 - Beverages–carbonated ☆ - Dr. Pepper/Seven Up, Inc.

DIET-COFFEE - Vitamins and nutritional supplements - Natural Organics, Inc.

DIET COKE - Beverages–carbonated - Coca-Cola Co.

DIET COOL FROM NESTEA - Iced tea–bottled or canned - Coca-Cola Co.

DIET CRUSH - Beverages–carbonated - Cadbury Beverages Inc.

DIET DAD'S - Beverages–carbonated - Monarch Co., Inc.

DIET DELIGHT - Food products - Tri Valley Growers, Inc.

DIET DOUBLE-COLA - Beverages–carbonated - Double Cola Co.-USA

DIET DOWN - Fruit drinks–bottled or canned - Science Foods, Inc.

DIET DR PEPPER - Beverages–carbonated - Dr. Pepper/Seven Up, Inc.

DIET EASY - Pharmaceutical preparations - Sportstar Health & Fitness

DIET EMPORIUM, A - Food products - Muffin Lady Inc.

DIET-EZE - Salad dressings–bottled ☆ - Nalley's Fine Foods

DIET FORCE - Beverages - Weider Nutrition Group, Inc.

DIET FORCE WITH CITRIMAX - Vitamins and nutritional supplements - American Body Building Products, Inc.

DIET FUEL - Iced tea–bottled or canned - Twinlab

DIET GARD - Vitamins and nutritional supplements ☆ - Whitehall Laboratories

DIET GREEN RIVER - Beverages–carbonated - Green River Corp.

DIET HERBAL UNCLE LEE'S - Teas - Uncle Lee's Tea

DIET HIRES - Root beer–bottled or canned - Schweppes USA Ltd.

DIET IBC - Beverages–carbonated - Dr. Pepper/Seven Up, Inc.

DIET IMPERIAL - Margarine - Lever Brothers Co. Inc.

DIET JOLT - Beverages–carbonated ☆ - Global Beverage Co.

DIET K - Health care products - Futurebiotics

DIET MATE - Apparel–women's - Cupid Foundations Inc.

DIET MATE - Teas - Prince of Peace Enterprises Inc.

DIET MELLO YELLO - Beverages–carbonated - Coca-Cola Co.

DIET MINDED - Underwear and nightwear - Rago Foundations Inc. LLC

DIET MINUTE MAID - Beverages–carbonated - Coca-Cola Co.

DIET MOUNTAIN DEW - Beverages–carbonated - Pepsi-Cola Co.

DIET MR. PIBB - Beverages–carbonated - Coca-Cola Co.

DIET MUG - Beverages–carbonated - Pepsi-Cola Co.

DIET NESTEA - Iced tea–bottled or canned - Coca-Cola Co.

DIET NOW - Vitamins and nutritional supplements - Shay Lee Corp.

DIET, NUTRITION & ENERGY NEWS - Catalogs - 206 Macopin Corp.

DIET ORIGINAL NEW YORK SELTZER - Beverages–carbonated - Original New York Seltzer

DIET PEP - Vitamins and nutritional supplements - Natural Balance, Inc.

DIET PEP MEAL REPLACEMENT AND ENERGY DRINK - Food products - Natural Balance, Inc.

DIET PEP MEAL REPLACEMENT AND ENERGY DRINK - Vitamins and nutritional supplements - Caroline Owens

DIET PEPSI - Beverages–carbonated - Pepsi-Cola Co.

DIET PEPSI - Beverages–carbonated - Pepsico, Inc.

DIET PEPSI FREE - Beverages–carbonated - Pepsi-Cola Co.

DIET POTENCY - Vitamins and nutritional supplements - Pharmavite Corp.

DIET-POWER - Vitamins and nutritional supplements - Country Life

DIET QUENCH - Beverages–carbonated - Monarch Co., Inc.

DIET RAMBLIN' ROOT BEER - Beverages–carbonated - Coca-Cola Co.

DIET RAZCAL - Beverages - Razcal Corp.

DIET RC - Beverages–carbonated - Royal Crown Cola Co.

DIET RIDE - Land vehicle - Richard A. Lombardi

DIET-RITE - Beverages–carbonated - Royal Crown Cola Co.

DIET RUBY RED SQUIRT - Beverages–carbonated - Squirtco

DIET SHASTA - Beverages–carbonated - Shasta Beverages, Inc.

DIET SKI - Beverages–carbonated - Double Cola Co.-USA

DIET SKINNY WAIST - Apparel and accessories - Strouse, Adler Co.

DIET SLICE - Beverages–carbonated - Pepsi-Cola Co.

DIET SPRITE - Beverages–carbonated - Coca-Cola Co.

DIET SQUIRT - Beverages–carbonated - Squirtco

DIET SQUIRT PLUS - Beverages–carbonated ☆ - Squirtco

DIET SUNDROP - Beverages–carbonated - Cadbury Beverages Inc.

DIET SUNKIST - Beverages–carbonated - Sunkist Growers Inc.

DIET SUNKIST PLUS - Beverages–carbonated - Sunkist Growers Inc.

DIET SYSTEM 6 - Vitamins and nutritional supplements - Irwin Naturals

DIET THERAPY - Vitamins and nutritional supplements - Polyionics Inc.

DIET TIME - Confections - Tuscan

DIET TRAIL MIX - Food products - Hickory Harvest Foods

DIET-TRIM - Health care products ☆ - Pharmex Inc.

DIET-TRIM 70 - Health care products - Bernard Food Industries Inc. (Consumer Products Div.)

DIET-UP - Vitamins and nutritional supplements - N.I.S.M. Inc.

DIET VERNORS - Beverages–carbonated - Vernors Inc.

DIET VESS - Beverages - Vess Beverages Inc.

DIET VITE - Vitamins and nutritional supplements - Natural Organics, Inc.

DIET WILD CHERRY PEPSI - Beverages–carbonated - Pepsi-Cola Co.

DIET WORKSHOP - Weight-control franchise - Diet Workshop Inc.

DIETABS - Pharmaceutical ☆ - Blaine Co. Inc.

DIETAC - Health care products ☆ - SmithKline Beecham Consumer Healthcare

DIETARY SPECIALTIES - Bakery products - Dietary Specialties

DIETARY SUPPLEMENT FOR CATS - Pet products - Natra Pet Inc.

DIETARY SUPPLEMENT FOR DOGS - Pet products - Natra Pet Inc.

DIETCAP - Reducing aid ☆ - Blaine Co. Inc.

DIETENE - Vitamins and nutritional supplements - Sandoz Pharmaceuticals Corp.

DIETERB - Vitamins and nutritional supplements - Pronatura, Inc.

DIETER'S BEST - Teas–herbal - Nature's Design Ltd.

DIETER'S EDGE - Vitamins and nutritional supplements - Body Breakthrough, Inc.

DIETER'S EMERGENCY SURVIVAL KIT - Novelty items ☆ - American National Glass

DIETERS' HERBAL DRINK - Teas - Prestige Chinese Teas Co.

DIETER'S NATURE - Teas - Connex Enterprises Inc.

DIETER'S SUPER TEA - Teas - Reese Chemical Co.

DIETER'S SWEETENER FRUIT SUGAR - Sugar - Motasim H. Agha

DIETETIC-NO/SALT-NO SUGAR COOKIES - Cookies - Bell'amore Imports Inc.

DIETMANNAN - Health care products - Bioenergy Inc.

DIETMASTER - Computer software - Dietmaster Systems

DIETMATE - Scales–bathroom - Health Innovations

DIETMAX - Nutritional supplement - Makers of Kal, Inc.

DIETRICH - Milk - Dietrich's Milk Products Inc.

DIETRISK - Computer peripheral equipment - Technology Sciences Group Inc.

DIETROL - Tofu - Unique Products Co.

DIETTIME - Health care products - Republic Drug Co. Inc.

DIETZ - Wicking - Hooper Industries Inc.

DIETZ & WATSON - Meat products - Dietz & Watson

DIEUTRIM - Pharmaceutical preparations - Legere Pharmaceuticals Inc.

DIEZ TALENTOS - Publisher's imprints - Ten Talents Distributors

DIF - Scrapers - William Zinsser & Co. Inc.

DIFFERENCE - Garment hangers–wire - American & Efird, Inc.

DIFFERENCE IS STRIKING!, THE - Bags–duffel - Sports Technologies, Inc.

DIFFERENCE IS YOU, THE - Video production - Morse Bros., Inc.

DIFFERENCE, THE - Vitamins and nutritional supplements - Merle Norman Cosmetics

DIFFERENT DRUMMER - Recording label - Ripete Music Group

DIFFERENT PERSPECTIVE, A - Furniture - Different Perspective, Inc.

DIFFERENT THINGS - Toys - Lauri Inc.

DIFFERENT VIEWPOINT, A - Fabrics–tapestry ☆ - Columbus Coated Fabrics Co.

DIFFICULT STAINS - Cleaning preparations ☆ - Albatross USA Inc.

DIFFOIL - Laboratory apparatus - Kurt J. Lesker Co.

DIFFRACTION HORN - Amplifiers ☆ - Electro-Voice, Inc.

DIFFRIENT - Tables–wood - Howe Furniture Corp.

DIFFSPIN SLIDE SPINNER - Medical apparatus - Statspin Technologies

DIFFUSAIRE - Deodorizers - Surco Products Inc.

DIFFUSION - Colognes ☆ - Avon Products, Inc.

DIFFUSION - Computer software ☆ - CONDUIT

DIFFUSOR - Perfumes - Karen Carson Creations

DIFIL-TEST - Veterinary medical equipment - Evsco Pharmaceuticals

DIF'RENT STROKES - Wallpaper - Fine Art Wallcoverings Ltd.

DIFRINSE - Cleaning preparations - Richardson-Vicks USA

DIFULERON - Laxatives - Lannett Co. Inc.

DIFUSO - Insecticides ☆ - Tanglefoot Co.

DIG - Computer software - Wff'n Proof Learning Games Associates

DIG - Recording label - Dig

DIG - Toys - Tonka Corp.

DIG A LITTLE DEEPER - Apparel and accessories - Tonney Sparks

DIG AMERICA - Trowels - Cobraco Manufacturing, Inc.

DIG-EZY - Shovels - Ames Lawn & Garden Tool Co.

DIG-IT - Sporting goods - Excel Sports Products

DIG-IT-ALL - Garden equipment - Seymour Manufacturing Co.,Inc.

DIG, SET, SPIKE - Balls ☆ - Mikasa Sports

DIG, THE - Computer software - Lucasarts Entertainment Co.

DIGACOM - Broadcasting equipment - EMCEE Broadcast Products

DIGARDI - Wines - J.E. Digardi Winery

DIGAS - Gasoline - Tesoro Petroleum Corp.

DIGENZYMES - Pharmaceutical preparations - Maurry Biological Co. Inc.

DIGESPLEN - Pharmaceutical preparations - Medical Products Panamericana Inc.

DIGEST A - Feed additive - Loveland Industries, Inc.

DIGEST AID - Pet products - Farnam Cos. Inc.

DIGEST AID - Vitamins and nutritional supplements - Momentum Marketing Inc.

DIGEST-AIDS - Antacids ☆ - Chex Co.

DIGEST-ALL - Vitamins and nutritional supplements ☆ - ICN Pharmaceuticals Inc.

DIGEST B - Animal feed supplements - Loveland Industries, Inc.

DIGEST-EASE - See **NATURE'S DIGEST-EASE**

DIGEST-EFX - Vitamins and nutritional supplements - Natural Efx, Inc.

DIGEST HELPER - Health care products - Above All Health Inc.

DIGEST HERBAL - Health care products - McZand Herbal, Inc.

DIGEST-IT - Vitamins and nutritional supplements - Sundown Vitamins, Inc.

DIGESTA-LAC - Health care products - Natren Inc.

DIGESTABILITEA - Teas–herbal - Unitea Herbs

DIGESTABS - Health care products - Futurebiotics

DIGESTAHERB - Vitamins and nutritional supplements ☆ - J.R. Carlson Laboratories Inc.

DIGESTALIN - Pharmaceutical preparations ☆ - Vortech Pharmaceuticals

DIGESTAMIC - Pharmaceutical preparations ☆ - Lexis Laboratories Inc.

DIGESTAMIC 2 - Pharmaceutical preparations ☆ - Lexis Laboratories Inc.

DIGESTAMIC H.P. - Pharmaceutical preparations ☆ - Lexis Laboratories Inc.

DIGESTANT-M - Health care products ☆ - Fibertone Co.

DIGESTAZYME - Vitamins and nutritional supplements - Nature's Sunshine Products, Inc.

DIGESTCHEWS - Vitamins and nutritional supplements - Earthnet

DIGESTEA - Health care products - Natureworks Inc.

DIGESTESE - Pharmaceutical - American Hygienic Laboratories Inc.

DIGESTEX - Pharmaceutical preparations - Pasadena Research Laboratories, Inc.

DIGESTIN - Pharmaceutical preparations - Rugby Laboratories Inc.

DIGESTIT - Degreasing solvents - Surco Products Inc.

DIGESTIVE GRAPE BITTERS - Vitamins and nutritional supplements - Planetary Formulas

DIGESTO-REX - Pharmaceutical preparations - Rex Research Laboratories

DIGESTONE - Health care products ☆ - Futurebiotics

DIGESTONE - Vitamins and nutritional supplements ☆ - Nature's Way Products, Inc.

DIGEZYME - Vitamins and nutritional supplements - Sabinsa Corp.

DIGEZYME - Vitamins and nutritional supplements - Vitamin Research Products Inc.

DIGGER - Bicycles - Sears, Roebuck and Co.

DIGGER - Games ☆ - Milton Bradley Co.

DIGGER DAN'S - Toys–automobiles ☆ - Revell-Monogram, Inc.

DIGGER T. ROCK - Video games - Rare Coin-It Inc.

DIGGERS - Crackers - Nabisco Foods Group

DIGGERS - Garden equipment - Cobraco Manufacturing, Inc.

DIGGITY - Toys–stuffed - Gund, Inc.

DIGI - Computer peripheral equipment - Digi International Inc.

DIGI - Headware - California Sportsound, Inc.

☆ = Now out of production

DIGI-BLOCK - Exercising equipment - Smith & Nephew Inc. (Rehabilitation Div.)

DIGI-COMP - Bicycles - Columbia Manufacturing Inc.

DIGI-CUE - Electronic equipment ☆ - Minnesota Mining & Manufacturing Co.

DIGI-CURE - Pharmaceutical preparations - RBR Productions, Inc.

DIGI-FAX - Facsimile equipment - Universal Design, Inc.

DIGI FLEX - Health care products - Innovative Medical Engineering Inc.

DIGI-GLO - Watches - Medana Watch Corp.

DIGI-GLO - Watches - Webster Watch Co. Associates

DIGI GRIP - Medical apparatus - Instrument Specialists, Inc.

DIGI-KEY - Screws - Digi-Key Corp.

DIGI-LINK - Laboratory apparatus - Kaye Instruments Inc.

DIGI-MED - Medical apparatus - Micro-Med, Inc.

DIGI-MOLD ID - Circuit boards–printed - Fast Heat, Inc.

DIGI-PRO - Computer software - Bo Fred Diversified, Inc.

DIGI-RE-DU - Artists' materials - Jacquet Arts, Inc.

DIGI-READY - Electronic equipment - California Amplifier

DIGI-STAR, INC. - Scales–bathroom - J-Star Industries, Inc.

DIGI-SYNCH - Automotive parts and accessories - Harrel Inc.

DIGI-TEK - Chemical preparations - Graphic Technologies, Inc.

DIGI THERMO - Thermometers - A.W. Sperry Instruments, Inc.

DIGI-TIME - Clocks - Sunbeam Precision Measurement

DIGI-TRACKER - Treadmills - Battle Creek Equipment Co.

DIGIAPPLY - Computer software - Cleveland Motion Controls, Inc.

DIGICAL - Electronic equipment - Leeds and Northrup Co.

DIGICALL - Electronic equipment - Fleetwood Furniture Co.

DIGICEIVER - Communications equipment - International Communications Products

DIGICLIPS - Computer software - R.K. Investments

DIGICON - Electronic equipment - Environmental Elements Corp.

DIGICONTROL - Computer software - Cleveland Motion Controls, Inc.

DIGICORDER - Medical apparatus - Del Mar Avionics

DIGIDATER - Thermometers ☆ - Airguide Instrument Co.

DIGIDIAL - Thermometers - Universal Enterprises, Inc.

DIGIDRIVE - Motor vehicles–automobiles - Division Driving Systems Inc.

DIGIDRUMS - Computer software - Digidesign Inc.

DIGIFAST - Inks–duplicating - Western Duplicating, Inc.

DIGIFORTIS - Digitalis ☆ - Parke-Davis

DIGIGAL - Computer software - Omicron Computer Technologies, Inc.

DIGIGLUSIN - Digitalis ☆ - Eli Lilly and Co.

DIGIGUIDE - Thermometers ☆ - Airguide Instrument Co.

DIGILITE - Lighting equipment - Sunergy Inc.

DIGILOCK - Electronic equipment - Security People, Inc.

DIGIMAC - Telephone answering machines ☆ - MacKenzie Laboratories Inc.

DIGIMATIC - Computer software - Huvard Research and Consulting Inc.

DIGIMATIC - Photographic equipment - Electronic Systems Engineering Co.

DIGIMAX - Computer software - Dictaphone Corp.

DIGIONIC - Digital sequencer ☆ - Ionic Industries Inc.

DIGIORNO - Spaghetti sauces - Kraft Foods, Inc.

DIGIPACE - Battery chargers - Ace R/C

DIGIPAD - Motor vehicles–automobiles - Division Driving Systems Inc.

DIGIPHONE - Computer software - Third Planet Publishing, Inc.

DIGIPULSE - Health care products - Elexis Corp.

DIGIQUARTZ - Watches - Bulova Corp.

DIGIREADER - Electronic equipment - Westinghouse Electric Corp.

DIGISAUR - Clocks - Phorm Concept and Design Inc.

DIGISAVER - Surveillance equipment - Alpha Systems Lab, Inc.

DIGISCALE - Scales - Counselor Co.

DIGISCAN - Engines - J.P. Instruments

DIGISCAN - File folders - Kardex Systems, Inc.

DIGISCAN - Radar systems and equipment - Fox Electronics & Technology, Inc.

DIGISCAN - Scales - Counselor Co.

DIGISCORE - Electronic equipment - Fleetwood Furniture Co.

DIGISEAL - Cables–coaxial - Antec Corp.

DIGISENSE - Laboratory apparatus - Cole-Parmer Instrument Co.

DIGISIGN - Computer software - Apple Computer Inc.

DIGISIM - Computer software - Bioanalytical Systems Inc.

DIGISNAP - Electrical equipment - A.W. Sperry Instruments, Inc.

DIGISTRIP - Laboratory apparatus - Kaye Instruments Inc.

DIGIT - Pencils–mechanical - Sanford Corp.

DIGIT - Toys - Maryland Toy Corp.

DIGIT 3 - Footwear - L.A. Gear, Inc.

DIGIT DESIGNS BY TRIM - Clippers–nail - W.E. Bassett Co.

DIGIT GRABBER - Telephone apparatus - Metro-Tel Corp.

DIGIT GRABBET - Telephone apparatus - Metro-Tel Corp.

DIGITAL - Audio equipment ☆ - Cerwin-Vega Inc.

DIGITAL - Computers–personal - Digital Equipment Corp.

DIGITAL - Floor coverings–carpet and rugs - Whitecrest Carpet Mills

DIGITAL - Playing cards - Old Bridge Playing Card Co., Inc.

DIGITAL 4-COLOR - Computer software - Trumatch, Inc.

DIGITAL 500 - Audio equipment ☆ - J.C. Penney Co., Inc.

DIGITAL ACOUSTICS - Electronic equipment - Digital Acoustics, Inc.

DIGITAL ANTENNA - Antennas - Digital Antenna, Inc.

DIGITAL BAUHAUS - Computer software - Byron Preiss Multimedia Co., Inc.

DIGITAL BLUEPRINT PAPER II - Computer software - Ideal Scanners & Systems, Inc.

DIGITAL BOX OFFICE - Computer software - Power Training, Inc.

DIGITAL BUSINESS CARD, THE - Computer software - Seth Resnick

DIGITAL BY QUALCOMM - Electronic equipment - Qualcomm Inc.

DIGITAL CADDY - Golfing equipment - Innovative Golf Corp.

DIGITAL CELEBRIS - Computer software - Digital Equipment Corp.

DIGITAL CHOICE - Phonographic turntables - Digital Recorders Inc.

DIGITAL D - Electronic equipment - Thomson Consumer Electronics, Inc.

DIGITAL DISCOUNTS - Advertising agencies - Joseph H. Voyles

DIGITAL DITTIES - Recording label - Zapset, Inc.

DIGITAL DJ - Computer hardware - Digital D.J. Inc.

DIGITAL DOMINATOR - Antennas - Allen Telecom Group, Inc.

DIGITAL DOOR LOCK - Mechanical locks - Door Systems Inc.

DIGITAL DOVE - Electronic equipment - AVL

DIGITAL DUNGEON - Recording label - Metropolitan Recording Corp.

DIGITAL DYNAMICS - Computers - Digital Dynamics, Inc.

DIGITAL EFFECTS - Audio equipment - Kraco Enterprises Inc.

DIGITAL EXPRESS - Electronic equipment - Dictaphone Corp.

DIGITAL FLEXOPROOF - Computer software - Professional Software Technologies, Inc.

DIGITAL FLIPCHART - Computer software - Tegrity, Inc.

DIGITAL FOUNDRY, THE - Computer software - Digital Foundry, Inc.

DIGITAL IMAGES FOR SCIENCE - Computer software - Ventura Educational Systems

DIGITAL IMAGING ASSOCIATES DATABASE OF IMAGES - Computer storage devices–optical - Digital Imaging Associates Inc.

DIGITAL IMPACT - Recording label - Digital Impact

DIGITAL ISLAND - Communications equipment - Digital Island, Inc.

DIGITAL LIGHT PROCESSING - Electric lighting equipment - Texas Instruments Inc.

DIGITAL LINK - Radios - Sony Corp. of America

DIGITAL MAGIC - Antennas - Winegard Co.

DIGITAL MAGIC - Computer peripheral equipment - Advanced Digital Imaging

DIGITAL MAMMOGRAPHICS INCORPORATED - Medical apparatus - Digital Mammographics, Inc.

DIGITAL MESSAGE SHUTTLE - Telephone answering machines - Sony Electronics Inc.

DIGITAL METEOR - Computer software - Digital Media International, Inc.

DIGITAL MUSIC MENTOR - Computer software - Electronic Courseware Systems Inc.

DIGITAL NETWORK - Telephones–cellular - McCaw Cellular Communications, Inc.

DIGITAL NOISE - Watches - Timex Corp.

DIGITAL PHOTOPRINTER FROM NUTEK - Photographic equipment - Nutek Inc.

DIGITAL PICTURES - Video games - Digital Pictures, Inc.

DIGITAL PICTURES DP - Video games - Digital Pictures, Inc.

DIGITAL POSTCARDS - Computer software - Pugdog Enterprises, Inc.

DIGITAL PRINT EXECUTIVE - Computer hardware - Gammagraphx, Inc.

DIGITAL PRIORIS - Computer software - Digital Equipment Corp.

DIGITAL PROFESSOR - Computer software - Spectrum Universal

DIGITAL PROFILE DETECTOR - Electronic equipment - Forney Corp.

DIGITAL REALTY - Computer software - At&T Corp.

DIGITAL RIVER - Computer software - Digital River, Inc.

DIGITAL SCIENCE - Photographic equipment - Eastman Kodak Co.

DIGITAL SEMICONDUCTOR - Computer hardware - Digital Equipment Corp.

DIGITAL SIGNAL PROCESSING - Computer software - Pentek Inc.

DIGITAL SOUND PRO - Computer peripheral equipment - Cardinal Technologies, Inc.

DIGITAL STOREFRONT - Computer software - Pleiades Research Corp.

DIGITAL STUDIOS - Computer software - Digital Studios

DIGITAL TALK - Telephones–cellular - NEC America, Inc.

DIGITAL TECHNOLOGY INC. - Computers - Digital Technology Inc.

DIGITAL THEATER - Computer software - Digital Theater, Inc.

DIGITAL TO DISC - Recording label - Pet Records

DIGITAL VENTURIS - Computer software - Digital Equipment Corp.

DIGITAL VIDEO PRODUCER - Computer software - Asymetrix Corp.
DIGITAL VIEWBOOK - Computer software - Rezun Interactive Concepts, Inc.
DIGITAL VISC ALERT - Measuring instruments - Diagnetics, Inc.
DIGITAL VISION - Compact discs–prerecorded - Digital Vision, Inc.
DIGITAL WATCH - Watches - By Design Corp.
DIGITAL WISDOM - Computer storage devices–optical ☆ - Digital Wisdom, Inc.
DIGITALES - Computer storage devices–optical - UBI Soft Inc.
DIGITALMICROGRAPH - Computer software - Gatan, Inc.
DIGITALPAPER - Computer software - No Hands Software, Inc.
DIGITALWHEEL - Computer software - Digitalwheel Corp.
DIGITECH - Audio equipment - Dod Electronics
DIGITECH - Telephones - Comdial Corp.
DIGITEMP - Thermometers - Elexis Corp.
DIGITEX - Fabrics - Industrial Coatings Group, Inc.
DIGITEX - File folders ☆ - Cel-U-Dex Corp.
DIGITEX - Gloves–rubber - Mayer Laboratories, Inc.
DIGITHERM - Thermal printer paper and film - Eastman Kodak Co.
DIGITHERM - Thermostats - Alnor Instrument Co.
DIGITICER - Computer peripheral equipment - Management Computer Controls, Inc.
DIGITILE - Tiles–ceramic - Michael J. McNamara
DIGITIME - Tape recorders - Stancil Corp.
DIGITIZER 4 - Audio equipment ☆ - ADA Signal Processors Inc.
DIGITLINE - Transmitting apparatus - General Signal Corp.
DIGITOE - Measuring instruments - Alan H. Zerobnick
DIGITONE - Telescopes - Northern Telecom, Inc.
DIGITONIN - Pharmaceutical preparations - City Chemical Corp.
DIGITOR - Electronic equipment - Educational Insights, Inc.
DIGITORA - Pharmaceutical preparations ☆ - Upjohn Co.
DIGITORQUE - Electrical testing instruments - Automation Technology Inc.
DIGITRAC - Electronic equipment - Rockford Acromatic Products Co.
DIGITRAK - Electrical industrial apparatus - Commercial Intertech Corp.
DIGITRAK - Electronic equipment - AVL
DIGITRAX - Compact discs–prerecorded - Hottrax Records
DIGITRAX INC - Toys–models - Digitrax, Inc.
DIGITRON - Electronic equipment ☆ - Gutmann Cutlery Inc.
DIGITRON - Watches - Bulova Corp.
DIGITRONIC - Blood pressure apparatus - Lumiscope Co. Inc.
DIGITS - Apparel–children's - Camptown Togs Inc.
DIGITS - Toys–electronic - Hasbro, Inc.
DIGITS - Watches - Hyo Sam Byun
DIGITS - Watches - Digits Co.
DIGITUS - Computer peripheral equipment - Assmann Data Products
DIGIVIEW - Computer terminals - Continental Technology, Inc.
DIGIX - Computer programming services - Qualex Financial Corp.
DIGMATE - Electronic equipment - General Electric Co.
DIGNITARY - Luggage - Samsonite Corp.
DIGNITARY - Radio communications equipment - Motorola, Inc. (Land Mobile Products Sector)
DIGNITY - Clocks - General Time Corp. (Westclox/Seth Thomas Div.)
DIGNITY - Health care products - Humanicare International, Inc.
DIGNITY - Incontinence product - Convatec
DIGNITY DINER - Apparel–children's - Suzanne Y. Horlacher
DIGNITY LITES STACKABLES - Home health care products - Humanicare International, Inc.
DIGOLASE - Pharmaceutical preparations ☆ - Boyle & Co.
D.I.G.S. - Hardware - Duchamp's Irreverant Guiding Spirit, Inc.
DIGWELL - Augers - Seymour Manufacturing Co.,Inc.
DIHISTINE - Pharmaceutical preparations - Barre-National, Inc.
DIHYCON - Pharmaceutical preparations ☆ - Consolidated Midland Corp.
DIHYDREX - Health care products - Kay Pharmacal Co. Inc.
DIIMO - Computer peripheral equipment - Diimo Technologies, Inc.
DIIMOCACHE - Computer peripheral equipment - Diimo Technologies, Inc.
DIJICOMP - Computer software - Eastman Kodak Co.
DIJIMAX - Recording label - Dejazmatch Tikim Coombs
DIJIRI-TUBE - Musical instruments - Toot & Hoot Primitive Instruments
DIJIT - Computers - Eastman Kodak Co.
DIJITEL - Electronic equipment - Arion Corp.
DIJON - Apparel–children's - Dijon Apparel Inc.
DIJON - Furniture - Broyhill Furniture Industries, Inc.
DIJON - Rings–jewelry - Artcarved Inc.
DIJON - Watches - I.D. Enterprises
DIJON MUSTARD - Food products - Europa Foods Ltd.
DIKE - Cement - Gibraltar National Corp.
DIKE - Radiators–motor vehicle - Conklin Co., Inc.

DIKES - Shoes ☆ - Tingley Rubber Corp.
DIKLEIN - Umbrellas - D. Klein & Son
DIKLN 32 - Fabrics - Dickson Elberton Mills, Inc.
DIKLON 32 - Fabrics - Astrup Co.
DILAC 80 - Pharmaceutical preparations ☆ - B.F. Ascher & Co. Inc.
DILACOR - Pharmaceutical preparations - Rhone-Poulenc Rorer Pharmaceuticals Inc.
DILANTIN - Pharmaceutical preparations - Parke-Davis
DILATRATE-SR - Health care products - Reed & Carnrick
DILATTO - Cheese - Suprema Specialties Inc.
DILAUDID - Cough medicines - Knoll Pharmaceutical Co.
DILBERT - Apparel and accessories - United Feature Syndicate, Inc.
DILCOL - Stationery ☆ - Mead Corp.
DILEMMAS - Games ☆ - Avalon Hill Game Co.
DILETTANTE - Chocolate candy - Dilettante Chocolates, Inc.
DILIJAN - Spices and extracts - Castle Food Products
DILIJAN - Spices and extracts - Dilijan Products Inc.
DILIN - Pharmaceutical preparations ☆ - Roberts/Hauck Pharmaceuticals Inc.
DILITHIUM PRESS - Embossing plates - Dilithium Press
DILITUSS - Cough medicines ☆ - Columbia Drug Co. Inc.
DILL & CINNABERRIES - Toys–stuffed ☆ - Gund, Inc.
DILL HAVARTI SAGA - Cheese - Tholstrup Cheese USA Inc.
DILL PICKLE RELISH - Relishes - Flamm Pickle and Packing Co. Inc.
DILLARD HOUSE - Fruits–pickled or brined - Dillard House Inc.
DILLARDS - Apparel and accessories - Dillard Department Stores Inc.
DILLARD'S - Barbecue sauce - Dillard's Bar-B-Q Sauce
DILLBY AND PEPPERBY - Cheese - Swiss American Import Co.
DILLETANTE - Floor coverings–carpet and rugs - Milliken & Co. Inc.
DILLICIOUS - Spices and extracts - To Market to Market
DILLMAN FARM - Food products - Dillman Farm, Inc.
DILLO - Games - Dillo, Inc.
DILLON - Floor coverings–carpet and rugs - Bloomsburg Carpet Industries
DILL'S - Tobacco products - United States Tobacco Co.
DILL'S BEST - Tobacco products ☆ - House of Windsor Inc.
DILLS-CHALLSTROM - Awnings - Dills-Challstrom Inc.
DILLY - Apparel and accessories - Banner Industries, Inc.
DILLY - Fishing lure - Mister Twister, Inc.
DILLY BAG - Bags - Kapella Originals
DILLY DALLY - Apparel–children's - Alpha Shirt Co., Inc.
DILLY DUCK - Toys–stuffed - Russ Berrie and Co., Inc.
DILLY OF A THYME - Salads–prepackaged - Buckeye Beans & Herbs, Inc.
DILLY'S TOY BOX - Game - Toy Box Inc.
DILOCAINE - Pharmaceutical preparations - Roberts/Hauck Pharmaceuticals Inc.
DILOMINE - Health care products - Kay Pharmacal Co. Inc.
DILOR - Pharmaceutical preparations - Savage Laboratories Inc.
DILOR G - Pharmaceutical preparations - Savage Laboratories Inc.
DILOREX - Pharmaceutical preparations - C.S. Ruckstuhl Co. Inc.
DILOVASIC - Vitamins and nutritional supplements - Great Life Laboratories Inc.
DILTON - Floor coverings–carpet and rugs ☆ - Lees Carpets
DILUMAT - Gravimetric dilutor ☆ - Intercontinental Enterprises Ltd.
DILUTE-A-JET - Medical apparatus - International Medication Systems, Limited
DILUTE 'N SHOOT - Irrigation equipment - Aquatrols Corp. of America, Inc.
DILYS - Bath products - Laura Ashley
DIM-A-LITE - Electric lighting equipment - Eagle Electric Manufacturing Co., Inc.
DIM-N-GLO - Electric lighting equipment - Lutron Electronics Co., Inc.
DIMACID - Pharmaceutical preparations - Otis Clapp & Son Inc.
DIMACOL - Cough medicines - A.H. Robins Co. Inc.
DIMAHIST - Pharmaceutical preparations - H.R. Cenci Laboratories Inc.
DIMANGO - Electrical equipment - Dimango Products Corp.
DIMARCO - Food products - Travel Trade Corp.
DIMAREX - Pharmaceutical preparations - C.S. Ruckstuhl Co. Inc.
DIMARZIO - Musical instruments ☆ - Dimarzio, Inc.
DIMARZIO 8'S - Musical instrument accessories - Dimarzio, Inc.
DIMARZIO 9'S - Musical instrument accessories - Dimarzio, Inc.
DIMARZIO 10'S - Musical instrument accessories - Dimarzio, Inc.
DIMARZIO 45'S - Musical instrument accessories - Dimarzio, Inc.
DIMARZIO MODEL J - Musical instrument accessories - Dimarzio, Inc.
DIMARZIO MODEL P - Musical instrument accessories - Dimarzio, Inc.
DIMARZIO MODEL P+J - Musical instrument accessories - Dimarzio, Inc.
DIMATROL - Electric lighting equipment - Eagle Electric Manufacturing Co., Inc.
DIMAX CONTROLS - Electronic equipment - Dimax Controls Inc.
DIME - Milking machines - Borden, Inc.

☆ = Now out of production

DIME 'N' PENDANT - Jewelry - Just A Little Stock Co., Inc.

DIME 'N' PIN - Jewelry - Just A Little Stock Co., Inc.

DIME'N - Jewelry - Just A Little Stock Co., Inc.

DIMENHYDRINATE - Pharmaceutical preparations ☆ - Legere Pharmaceuticals Inc.

DIME'NS ARE A GIRL'S BEST FRIEND - Jewelry - Just A Little Stock Co., Inc.

DIMENSIA - Electronic equipment ☆ - Thomson Consumer Electronics, Inc.

DIMENSION - Boats–canoes - Johnson Worldwide Associates, Inc.

DIMENSION - Buoyancy compensators - Sea Quest, Inc.

DIMENSION - Chemical preparations - Alliedsignal Inc.

DIMENSION - Computers–personal - Northstar

DIMENSION - Cooking equipment–household - General Housewares Corp.

DIMENSION - Floor coverings–carpet and rugs - Coronet Carpets Inc.

DIMENSION - Floor coverings–carpet and rugs ☆ - Lees Carpets

DIMENSION - Floor coverings–carpet and rugs ☆ - Regal Rugs Inc.

DIMENSION - Furniture ☆ - Fancher Furniture Co. Inc.

DIMENSION - Glassware–household - Mikasa Co.

DIMENSION - Glassware–household ☆ - Lenox Crystal, Inc.

DIMENSION - Heat pumps - Lennox Industries Inc.

DIMENSION - Lighting equipment - General Electric Co.

DIMENSION - Nail care products - Opi Products, Inc.

DIMENSION - Photo albums ☆ - D. Davis Kenny Co.

DIMENSION - Shampoos - Lever Brothers Co. Inc.

DIMENSION - Tableware–china - Lenox, Inc.

DIMENSION - Telephones - At&T Corp.

DIMENSION - Tiles–ceramic ☆ - Porcelanite, Inc.

DIMENSION - Vacuum cleaners and accessories - The Hoover Co.

DIMENSION - Watches - Bulova Corp.

DIMENSION - Windows–storm - Duo-Temp

DIMENSION 2 - Hardware - National Lock Hardware

DIMENSION 3 - Dinnerware–plastic - Plastics Manufacturing Co.

DIMENSION 3 - Electronic equipment - Techsonic Industries, Inc.

DIMENSION 3 - Lighting equipment - Sound Off Inc.

DIMENSION III - Trading cards and stamps - Topps Co., Inc.

DIMENSION BEAM - Musical instrument accessories - Interactive Light, Inc.

DIMENSION IV - Glass dinnerware ☆ - Corning Inc.

DIMENSION IV - Kitchenware–earthenware ☆ - Arita Sales Co. Inc.

DIMENSION MASTER - Ultrasonic testing equipment - Calculated Industries, Inc.

DIMENSION PLUS - Plastics - Gerber Scientific, Inc.

DIMENSION SIX - Recording label - Sonic Arts Corp.

DIMENSION STORAGE SYSTEMS - Furniture - Dimension Storage Systems, Inc.

DIMENSION WELD - Apparel–children's - Playskool Baby Inc.

DIMENSIONAL LIVING - Wallpaper - Norwall Wallcoverings

DIMENSIONAL METALLIC - Paints ☆ - Wellington Leisure Products, Inc.

DIMENSIONAL PEOPLE SKILLS - Recording label - Psychological Associates, Inc.

DIMENSIONAL SHAKE - Shingles–asphalt or tar - Celotex Corp.

DIMENSIONALS - Adhesives and sealants - Formica Corp.

DIMENSIONALS II - Wallpaper ☆ - Imperial Wallcoverings, Inc.

DIMENSIONALS III - Wallpaper ☆ - Imperial Wallcoverings, Inc.

DIMENSIONE - Wallpaper - Textile Wallcoverings International Ltd.

DIMENSIONE - Wallpaper ☆ - Wall Fashion Inc.

DIMENSIONS - Benches–metal - Artesian Industries

DIMENSIONS - Checkbooks - Clarke American Checks, Inc.

DIMENSIONS - Dinnerware–glass - Arita Sales Co. Inc.

DIMENSIONS - Floor coverings - Congoleum Corp.

DIMENSIONS - Floor coverings–carpet and rugs - Southern Carpet Mills

DIMENSIONS - Floor coverings–carpet and rugs ☆ - Burtco Enterprises Inc.

DIMENSIONS - Floor coverings–carpet and rugs ☆ - Porter Carpet Mills Inc.

DIMENSIONS - Frames–eyeglass - Creative Optiks

DIMENSIONS - Furniture–wood ☆ - Ficks Reed Co. Inc.

DIMENSIONS - Notebooks and notepads - GraphiGallery

DIMENSIONS - Tiles–ceramic ☆ - American Olean Tile Co.

DIMENSIONS - Wallpaper - Winfield Design Associates, Inc.

DIMENSIONS '80 - Furniture ☆ - Keller Manufacturing Co.

DIMENSIONS FOR LIVING - Publisher's imprints - United Methodist Publishing House

DIMENSIONS I - Wallpaper - Bart Klion & Associates Inc.

DIMENSIONS II - Furniture - Weiman Co.

DIMENSIONS PLUS - Wallpaper - Winfield Design Associates, Inc.

DIMENSIONS UNLIMITED - Floor coverings–carpet and rugs - Philadelphia Carpets

DIMENTABS - Pharmaceutical preparations ∑ - JMI-Canton Pharmaceuticals

DIMETANE - Antihistamine preparations - A.H. Robins Co. Inc.

DIMETAPP - Antihistamine preparations - A.H. Robins Co. Inc.

DIMETAPP PLUS - Analgesics - A.H. Robins Co. Inc.

DIMEZONE - Photographic equipment - Eastman Kodak Co.

DIMI-CLIP - Stationery - Dimitex Co.

DIMICA - Apparel–women's - Michael Carrie Inc.

DIMILIN - Insecticides - Uniroyal Chemical Co. Inc. (Crop Protection Div.)

DIMINUENDO - Brassieres (Bras) - Goddess Bra

DIMITRI - Apparel–men's ☆ - Cavaliero Cravats

DIMITRI - Beverages–alcohol - Consolidated Distilled Products Inc.

DIMITRI - Colognes - Dimitri of Italy Inc.

DIMITRIA DELIGHTS - Food products - Dimitria Delights Inc.

DIMITRINO - Cigarettes - G.A. Georgopulo & Co. Inc.

DIMITRINO BOTSCHAFTER - Cigarettes - G.A. Georgopulo & Co. Inc.

DIMITRIUS - Neckties - Norseman Neckwear, Inc.

DIMITY BLUE - Kitchenware–china - H. Wittur & Co.

DIMLITER - Electrical equipment - Lutron Electronics Co., Inc.

DIMMCHECK - Electronic equipment - Innoventions, Inc.

DIMMING MOUSE - Lighting equipment - Electronic Ballast Technology, Inc.

DIMO - Seafood products–fresh or frozen - Penguin Frozen Foods, Inc.

DIMOTAL - Pharmaceutical preparations ☆ - Roberts/Hauck Pharmaceuticals Inc.

DIMPLE - Cushions - Mark One Healthcare Products Inc.

DIMPLE - Office supplies - American Tombow Inc.

DIMPLE II - Sporting goods - SSK America Inc.

DIMPLE MINDED - Umbrellas - Robert W. Aamodt

DIMPLE MUGS - Giftware - Charles Zahn-Import Merchant

DIMPLE POWER - Sporting goods - SSK America Inc.

DIMPLE, THE - Orthodontic equipment - Ultimate Wireforms, Inc.

DIMPLER, THE - Drills–electric - Disston Co.

DIMPLES - Cosmetics - Todd Bijan

DIMPLES - Novelty items - LNG, Inc.

DIMPLES - Paper–toilet - Moran Foods, Inc.

DIMPLES - Toys–stuffed - Dakin Inc.

DIMPLES - Toys–stuffed ☆ - Fun World Inc.

DIMPLEX - Darts and dart games - Dart World Inc.

DIMYCOR - Pharmaceutical preparations - Standard Drug Products Inc.

DINA - Frames–picture - Iron-A-Way, Inc.

DINA - Recording label ☆ - Joey Records International Inc.

DINA - Toys–stuffed ☆ - CBS Toys

DINA BAR-EL - Apparel - Hi Tech Fashions, Inc.

DINA-MITE - Cereal - Cal-Leaf Health Products Inc.

DINAH - Frames–eyeglass - Rozin Optical Export Corp.

DINAH-MITE - Toys ☆ - Mego Financial Corp.

DINAH SHORE - Fabrics–linen ☆ - West Point-Pepperell Inc.

DINAIR - Cosmetics - Dinair Airbrush Make-Up System, Inc.

DINAIRE - Furniture - Dinaire Corp.

DINAPOLI - Food products - Sun Garden Packing Co., Inc.

DINARA - Floor coverings–carpet and rugs - Evans-Black Carpet Mills

DINASOUR EGGS - Candy - Willy Wonka Brands

DINASTIA NORTENA - Recording label - Fidencio Gomez

DINATURA - Syrup - Stearns and Lehman Inc.

DINE-A-HEAT - Cooking equipment–commercial - Le-Jo Enterprises, Inc.

DINE-EASE - Publisher's imprints - Evart Enterprises Inc.

DINE HEALTHY - Computer software - Dine Systems, Inc.

DINE IN DENIM - Containers–insulated ☆ - Aladdin Industries, Inc.

DINE MOOR - Coffee ☆ - Decoty Coffee Co.

DINE-MOR - Coffee - Dine-Mor Foods, Inc.

DINE 'N WITH - Sauces ☆ - Hudson Foods, Inc.

DINE RIGHT - Computer software - Public Interest Software

DINELLE - Tables–wood - Solid Surface Acrylics, Inc.

DINER - Catsup - Brooks Foods

DINER MITE - Food service equipment - Diner-Mite, Inc.

DINER MUG, THE - Glassware–household - Majestic Gifts

DINERO - Frozen foods - Deli International of Omaha, Inc.

DINERO PIZZA - Pizzas–frozen - Deli International of Omaha, Inc.

DINERSAURS - Cereal - Ralston Purina Co.

DINESTY - Glassware–household ☆ - Crystal Clear Importing Co. Inc.

DINETTE - Vegetables–canned - Lucca Packing Co. of California Inc.

DINEWELL - Hams - John Hofmeister & Son, Inc.

DINEX - Containers - Dinex International, Inc.

DINEX - Tableware–plastic ☆ - Thermos Co.

DING DANG - Toys - Mattel, Inc.

DING DEFENDER - Safety products - TLC Enterprises

DING DONG - Frozen confectioneries - International Ice Cream Corp.

DING DONG SCHOOL - Finger paints, poster paints ☆ - Coloron Industries

DING DONGS - Snack cakes - Interstate Brands Corp.
DING GOOP - Adhesives and sealants ☆ - Eclectic Products Inc.
DING GUA GUA - Seafood products–fresh or frozen - Carmine N. Romano
D'ING STAND - Office furniture–metal - D'ing Products
DINGAC - Wines - Stanley Stawski Distributing Co.
DINGBAT - Candy - Nabisco Foods Group
DINGBAT - Pet products - Pet Affairs, Inc.
DINGBATS - Clocks - Unitex Trading Corp.
DINGEZE - Cranes ☆ - Middy Marine Products Inc.
DINGHY - Brushes - Wright-Bernet
DINGHY DOGS - Marine rigging - Harvey Products
DINGHY DUCK - Toys–stuffed - Dakin Inc.
DINGLE BERRIES - Candy ☆ - Ce De Candy Inc.
DINGLE THE DINODEER - Novelty items - Papel Freelance, Inc.
DINGO - Boots - Acme Boot Co., Inc.
DINGO - Gocarts - Manco Products, Inc.
DINGO BARON - Footwear - Acme Boot Co., Inc.
DINGO FOR JEANS - Footwear - Acme Boot Co., Inc.
DINGO JIG - Fishing lures ☆ - Lindy Little Joe Inc.
DINGOS - Pet products - Renick Farms Inc.
DINGSEAL - Adhesives and sealants - Kevin M. Zunich
DINH-Z - Air conditioners and dehumidifiers - Heat Pipe Technology Inc.
DINH Z-COIL - Dehumidifiers - Heat Pipe Technology Inc.
DINING A LA CARTE - Furniture - Lane Upholstery (Venture Furniture Div.)
DINING BY PIANOLIGHT - Video production - Pianolight Music
DINING CAR - Coffee - Manhattan Coffee Co.
DINING IN - Dinners–frozen - Conagra, Inc.
DINING-IN - Food products - Topco Associates, Inc.
DINING IN - Publisher's imprints - Peanut Butter Publishing
DINING LITE - Food products - Conagra, Inc.
DINING TREAT - Food products - Conagra, Inc.
DINK-GARD - Rubber–molded - W.H. Salisbury & Co.
DINK, THE - Sailboat - American Sail
DINKELACKER - Beverages–malt - Dieter Steinmann Inc.
DINKELACKER DARK - Beverages–malt - Grolsch Importers Inc.
DINKELACKER PILS - Beverages–malt - Grolsch Importers Inc.
DINKELACKER WEISS - Beverages–malt - Grolsch Importers Inc.
DINKEL'S - Bakery products - Dinkel's Bakery
DINKIE DOG - Toys–stuffed - Russ Berrie and Co., Inc.
DINKUM - Apparel and accessories - David Scholem
DINKY - Boats - Glen-L Marine Designs
DINKY DIPPERS - Ice cream cones - Craigador
DINKY DONUTS - Cereal - Ralston Purina Co.
DINKY DOODLE - Stationery - Phoenix Stationery Products, Inc.
DINKY-ELEPHANT - Toys–stuffed ☆ - Gund, Inc.
DINKY LINKS - Meat products–pork - Carver's Classic Meat Products, Inc.
DINKY MC DIVER - Toys–stuffed - Dakin Inc.
DINKY TOYS - Die-cast models and die-cast model kits - Ava International Inc.
DINKY TWINKIES - Snack cakes ☆ - Interstate Brands Corp.
DINKYTOWN DAY CARE KIDS - Publisher's imprints - Cultural Exchange Corp.
DINKYTOWN DAYCARE KIDS - Dolls - Cultural Exchange Corp.
DINNER! - Computer software - Culinary Concepts, Inc.
DINNER AT EIGHT - Fabrics - F. Schumacher & Co.
DINNER BELL - Meats–luncheon - Dinner Bell Foods Inc.
DINNER BELL LEAN N' LO - Meats–luncheon - John Morrell & Co.
DINNER CLASSICS - Food products - Conagra, Inc.
DINNER DATE - Dolls - Mattel, Inc.
DINNER DELIGHTS - Candy ☆ - Van Melle Inc.
DINNER HOUR - Coffee - Davis-Le Grand Co.
DINNER HOUR - Napkins–paper ☆ - Plainwell Tissue
DINNER KING - Food products ☆ - Stokely USA, Inc.
DINNER MIX - Dog food - Ralston Purina Co.
DINNER PARTY - Candy ☆ - Food Producers International Inc.
DINNER ROUNDS - Dog food - Heinz Pet Products Co.
DINNER SLICES - Vegetables–frozen ☆ - Lamb-Weston, Inc.
DINNER SUPREME - Dinners–frozen ☆ - Stouffer Foods Corp.
DINNER SURPRISE - Dolls - Mattel, Inc.
DINNERMATE - Pet products ☆ - Doskocil Manufacturing Co., Inc.
DINNERTIME - Cat food - Heinz Pet Products Co.
DINO - Cereal - Hanna-Barbera Productions, Inc.
DINO - Cooking utensils–aluminum - Ensar Corp.
DINO - Gasoline - Sinclair Oil Corp.
DINO - Measuring instruments - A.M.D. North America Corp.
DINO - Spaghetti sauces - Ventre Packing Co. Inc.
DINO & DAVID - Pasta - Ital American Foods, Inc.

DINO AUTO-RESTRAINT TRANSPORT - Toys - Hasbro, Inc.
DINO BLASTERS - Toys - Trendmasters, Inc.
DINO BONALBERTI - Figurines - Omnisport Inc.
DINO BRITES - Dolls - Happiness Express Inc.
DINO-BUDDIES - Shirts - Rivercrest Industries, Inc.
DINO CHALK - Toys - Bandai America Inc.
DINO CHART - Infant product - Mary A. Zellem
DINO CHASE - Games - Smethport Specialty Co.
DINO CHECKERS - Pet products - Educational Insights, Inc.
DINO-DAMAGE - Toys - Hasbro, Inc.
DINO DINOLENE - Oils–lubricating - Sinclair Oil Corp.
DINO DISARDI - Apparel–men's - Sar-Dun Knitwear
DINO DUDES - Video games - Atari Games Corp.
DINO ECONOIL - Oils–lubricating - Sinclair Oil Corp.
DINO FLIP - Games - Smethport Specialty Co.
DINO FORCE - Footwear–children's - Payless Shoesource Worldwide, Inc.
DINO-GLOW - Novelty items–paper - Romar Enterprises Ltd.
DINO-LIFE - Vitamins and nutritional supplements - Life-Line Inc.
DINO-MANIACS - Toys - Weberworks
DINO MASTER - Bicycles ☆ - Huffy Corp.
DINO-MAT HABITAT - Sporting goods ☆ - Brimms Inc.
DINO MATS - Placemats - Russ Berrie and Co., Inc.
DINO-MITE - Office accessories - Acco World Corp.
DINO NITE LITES - Lighting fixtures - Eagle Electric Manufacturing Co., Inc.
DINO ORSINI - Neckties - Cornell of California Inc.
DINO O'SAUR - Cookies - Street Kids
DINO-PAK - Pet products - Classic Products
DINO PARK TYCOON - Computer software - Softkey International Inc.
DINO POPS - Candy - Adams & Brooks, Inc.
DINO RIDE 'EM - Toys - Steven Manufacturing Co.
DINO-ROARRRRRS - Toys–stuffed - Fisher-Price, Inc.
DINO ROCK & ROLL'EM - Toys - Steven Manufacturing Co.
DINO SOAP - Toys - Chase Holding Co. Inc.
DINO-SOAR JUMP - Toys–automobiles - Mattel, Inc.
DINO SPLASH - Swimming pools - Buddy L Inc.
DINO SPORTS - Candy - Homestead, Inc.
DINO SQUIRTS - Toys ☆ - Xonex International, Inc.
DINO-STARS - Apparel and accessories - Harry P. Capers, Jr.
DINO-STRIKE - Toys - Hasbro, Inc.
DINO STUFFS - Dolls - Meritus Industries, Inc.
DINO TALK - Electronic equipment - Creative Critters International
DINO TEAM SPORTS - Apparel–men's - Dino DiMilano Corp.
DINO-TRACKERS - Toys - Hasbro, Inc.
DINO TYKES - Toys & games - Linda Kay Florence
DINOBABY - Diapers–disposable - VMG Products Inc.
DINOBONE - Pet products - Classic Products
DINOBONES - Games - Warren Industries Inc.
DINOBONES - Toys - Diversified Plastics, Inc.
DINOCAPS - Games - Mark Ponte
DINOCHIPS - Snack foods - Variety Foods, Inc.
DINOFORMS - Apparel and accessories - Lifeforms International, Inc.
DINOLAND - Play map - Integra Toys, Inc.
DINOMANIA - Giftware - Russ Berrie and Co., Inc.
DINOPALS - Vitamins and nutritional supplements - Freelife International LP
DINOPARK TYCOON - Games - Softkey International Inc.
DINOPASTE - Toothpaste - Perio Products
DINOPRINT - Apparel and accessories - Peter C. Tomassetti
DINO'S PRIMO - Doughs–frozen - Health Jet, Inc.
DINOSAR EGGS - Cakes - Hazelwood Farms
DINOSAUCE - Chocolate syrup - Traffic Jam, Inc.
DINOSAUR - Fireworks - North Central Industries, Inc.
DINOSAUR - Gasoline - Polothink Petroleum Inc.
DINOSAUR - Mattresses - R.F. Simmons Co.
DINOSAUR - Soups–canned - Campbell Soup Co.
DINOSAUR - Vitamins and nutritional supplements - Dr. Willard's Water Products
DINOSAUR ACTION SET - Publisher's imprints - Price Stern Sloan Inc.
DINOSAUR BONES - Cheese - Frigo Cheese Corp.
DINOSAUR CHICK'N CHUNKS - Food products - Tyson Foods Inc.
DINOSAUR DAYS - Computer software - Teach Yourself By Computer Software Inc.
DINOSAUR DICE - Novelty items - Koplow Games
DINOSAUR DIG - Computer software - CBS Software
DINOSAUR DISCOVERY KIT - Computer software - First Byte Inc.
DINOSAUR DOMINOES - Games ☆ - World Traveler Ltd.
DINOSAUR DUST - Candy - Allen Mitchell Products

☆ = Now out of production

DINOSAUR EGG - Fruits and vegetables - Mike Jackson Farms

DINOSAUR EGG - Soap - Colossus Corp.

DINOSAUR EGGS - Candy ☆ - New England Confectionery Co.

DINOSAUR GRRRAHAMS - Cookies - Sunshine/Salerno Inc.

DINOSAUR HATCHLINGS - Toys–stuffed - Dakin Inc.

DINOSAUR IN MY POCKET - Toys - Morrison Entertainment Group

DINOSAUR ISLAND - Toys - Tonka Corp.

DINOSAUR JUICE - Juices - Givaudan Rare Flavors

DINOSAUR JUICE DRINKS - Fruit drinks–bottled or canned - Givaudan Rare Flavors

DINOSAUR MUD PIT - Toys - Mattel, Inc.

DINOSAUR MUSEUM - Computer software - Perspective Visuals, Inc.

DINOSAURABET - Clothing - Jeb Biemiller

DINOSAURS - Bandages - Kendall Co.

DINOSAURS - Computer software - Advanced Ideas

DINOSAURS - Cookies - A.V. Olsson Trading Co., Inc.

DINOSAURS - Erasers - Diener Industries Inc.

DINOSAURS - Games - Avalon Hill Game Co.

DINOSAURS - Games - Milton Bradley Co.

DINOSAURS - Kites ☆ - Hi-Flier Manufacturing Co.

DINOSAURS - Vitamins and nutritional supplements - Makers of Kal, Inc.

DINOSAURS CREAMY COOLERS - Fruit drinks - Cosmos International

DINOSAURUS - Computer peripheral equipment - Dinosaurus, Inc.

DINOSAVER - Computer software - Fiore Industries Inc.

DINOSIPPER - Containers - Eagle Affiliates, Inc.

DINOSLIDE - Exercising equipment - I.H.P. Inc.

DINOSNAPS - Cookies - Westbrae Natural Foods, Inc.

DINOSNORES - Toys–stuffed ☆ - Commonwealth Toy and Novelty Co. Inc.

DINOSOFT - Computer software - Maverick Software Inc.

DINOSORB - Toys - Mattel, Inc.

DINOSUAR DUEL - Games - Smethport Specialty Co.

DINOTABS - Vitamins and nutritional supplements - Nature's Sunshine Products, Inc.

DINOTOPIA - Recording label - Greenwich Workshop, Inc.

DINOTREATS - Bakery products - Alan W. Nayes

DINOZOO - Games - Dinozoo, Inc.

DINOZORD - Toys - Saban Entertainment, Inc.

DINSMORE - Electronic equipment - Dinsmore Instrument Co.

DINTESA - Health care products - Texas International Commodities Association Inc.

DINTY MOORE - Food products - Hormel Foods Corp.

DIO-MEDICONE - Laxatives ☆ - E.E. Dickinson Co.

DIO-SOL - Paints - Floquil-Polly S Color Corp.

DIO-SUL - Pharmaceutical preparations ☆ - Vortech Pharmaceuticals

DIOCHON - Fabrics - Leimtex Corp.

DIOCTALOSE - Pharmaceutical preparations ☆ - Schein Pharmaceutical Inc.

DIOCTO - Pharmaceutical preparations - Barre-National, Inc.

DIOCTO-C - Pharmaceutical preparations - Consolidated Midland Corp.

DIOCTO-K - Pharmaceutical preparations - Rugby Laboratories Inc.

DIOCTYN - Pharmaceutical preparations - Dixon-Shane Inc.

DIODOQUIN - Pharmaceutical preparations ☆ - G. D. Searle & Co.

DIOEZE - Pharmaceutical preparations - Century Pharmaceuticals Inc.

DIOGENES - FDA MEDICAL DEVICES - Computer storage devices–optical - Diogenes

DIOL - Pharmaceutical preparations ☆ - C.O. Truxton Inc.

DION - Recording label - Universal Record

DION UNCORKING MACHINE - Housewares - Franmara Co. Inc.

DIONAR - Cameras ☆ - Edixa Camera Co.

DIONE - Apparel–women's ☆ - Palm Beach Co., Inc.

DIONE - Footwear - Aztec Imports Inc.

DIONETTE - Rings–jewelry - Artcarved Inc.

DIONEX - Chemical preparations - Dionex Corp.

DIONEX - Pharmaceutical - IDE-Interstate Inc.

DIONIC - Batteries - Anton/Bauer, Inc.

DIONNE - Floor coverings–carpet and rugs ☆ - Regal Rugs Inc.

DIONYSOS - Vases - Durand International

DIOPTICS - Eyeglasses - Dioptics Medical Products, Inc.

DIOR - Apparel–women's - Lily of France Inc.

DIOR JUNIOR - Apparel and accessories - Carole Hochman Designs Inc.

DIORAMA - Skin care products ☆ - Christian Dior Perfumes Corp.

DIORELLA - Perfumes - Christian Dior Perfumes Corp.

DIORESSENCE - Perfumes - Christian Dior Perfumes Corp.

DIORISSIMO - Perfumes - Christian Dior Perfumes Corp.

DIORISSIMO - Perfumes - Parfums Christian Dior U.S. Corp.

DIORLING - Perfumes ☆ - Christian Dior Perfumes Corp.

DIOSOL - Pharmaceutical - Iodent Co.

DIOSTATE D - Pharmaceutical preparations ☆ - Upjohn Co.

DIOSUCCIN - Pharmaceutical preparations - Consolidated Midland Corp.

DIOSUL - Pharmaceutical preparations - C.S. Ruckstuhl Co. Inc.

DIOTHANE - Pharmaceutical preparations ☆ - Marion Merrell Dow

DIOTHRON - Pharmaceutical preparations ☆ - Vortech Pharmaceuticals

DIOVAL - Pharmaceutical preparations ☆ - Keene Pharmaceuticals Inc.

DIOWEED - Pesticides–household ☆ - Bonide Products, Inc.

DIOXYCHLOR - Pharmaceutical preparations - American Biologics

DIP - Cleaning preparations - Harvey Co. Inc.

DIP-A-FLOWER - Craft supplies - Milton Bradley Co.

DIP-A-WAY - Veterinary pharmaceutical preparations ☆ - Aquatronics-Filtronics

DIP-AN-EGG - Dyes–food - Spearhead Industries Inc.

DIP & CRISP - Seasonings - Old Bay

DIP-CHA-MACALLIT - Food serving dish - H.S., Inc.

DIP CLASSICS - Seasonings - McCormick & Co., Inc.

DIP DOTS - Paint sets–hobby ☆ - Kenner Products

DIP FIXINS - Spices and extracts - Mayacamas Fine Foods, Inc.

DIP-IDY-DILL - Spices and extracts - Jodie's Kitchen Inc.

DIP IN A CHIP - Crackers - Nabisco Foods Group

DIP-IT - Cleaning preparations–household ☆ - RCN Products Inc.

DIP IT WHIP IT - Rope - Star Brite

DIP-LESS - Office supplies ☆ - Faber-Castell Corp.

DIP-LOMAT - Food products - Chips Inc.

DIP MATES - Crackers ☆ - Keebler Co.

DIP-N-BREAD - Breads–frozen - Chef-Fresh Frozen, Inc.

DIP-N-CLEAN - Disinfectants - Gabel's Cosmetics Inc.

DIP N CLIP - Lubricants - Gabel's Cosmetics Inc.

DIP 'N DAB - Hobby kits - Hinkle Easter Products

DIP N' DONE - Pottery - Duncan Enterprises

DIP-N-DRI - Detergents ☆ - Alconox Inc.

DIP 'N EAT - Food products - Lipton Investments, Inc.

DIP 'N GRIP - Rubber–acrylic ☆ - Loctite Corp.

DIP N JOY - Sauces - Gold Pure Food Products Inc.

DIP N' LIK - Candy ☆ - S.L. Kaye Co., Inc.

DIP 'N SNACK - Dairy products - Circle K Corp.

DIP 'N SPREAD - Mustard - R.T. French Co.

DIP 'N STRIP - Furniture repair shops - Dip 'n Strip Inc.

DIP 'N STRIPS - Turkeys - Ralston Purina Co.

DIP-OFF - American International Industries

DIP QUIK - Food products - Dawn Food Products Inc.

DIP QUIK - Pet products ☆ - Farnam Cos. Inc.

DIP S TICKS - Medical products - Integrated Diagnostics, Inc.

DIP SEAL - Coatings - Dip Seal Plastics, Inc.

DIP SHIELD - Insect repellents - Landco

DIP STICK - Pet products - Classic Products

DIP STIX - Toys–electronic - Lewis Galoob Toys, Inc.

DIP TEN - Sporting goods - Ziffco

DIP 'UM - Salad dressings–bottled - R.T. French Co.

DIPANE ITALIANO - Bakery products - Lewis Brothers Bakeries Inc.

DIPASA - Health care products - Texas International Commodities Association Inc.

DIPASA - Oils–edible - Dipasa USA, Inc.

DIPCRAFT - Embossing plates - Dipcraft Manufacturing Co.

DIPEL - Pesticides–household - Bonide Products, Inc.

DIPENDRATE - Pharmaceutical preparations ☆ - Kenyon Drug Co. Inc.

DIPENTUM - Pharmaceutical preparations - Kabi Pharmacia Inc.

DIPEX - Veterinary pharmaceutical preparations ☆ - Aquatronics-Filtronics

DIPHEDRYL - Health care products - Esquire Pharmaceuticals Inc.

DIPHELIN - Health care products - Esquire Pharmaceuticals Inc.

DIPHEN - Pharmaceutical preparations - Morton Grove Pharmaceuticals

DIPHENACEN - Pharmaceutical preparations ☆ - Central Pharmaceutical Inc.

DIPHENACEN-50 - Pharmaceutical preparations ☆ - Central Pharmaceutical Inc.

DIPHENADRIL - Pharmaceutical preparations ☆ - Vitarine Pharmaceuticals Inc.

DIPHENATOL - Pharmaceutical preparations - Rugby Laboratories Inc.

DIPHENHIST - Pharmaceutical preparations - Rugby Laboratories Inc.

DIPHENYLAN - Pharmaceutical preparations - Lannett Co. Inc.

DIPIMAL - Health care products ☆ - Everett Laboratories Inc.

DIP'ITY STIX - Snack foods - Marco Food Products Inc.

DIPLANAR - Amplifiers ☆ - Magnepan Inc.

DIPLO-DINO - Hobby kits - Pamela Drake Imports, Inc.

DIPLO MATS - Mats - Service Products Inc.

DIPLOMA - Floor coverings–carpet and rugs - J and J Industries Inc.

DIPLOMA - Floor coverings–carpet and rugs - Karastan-Bigelow Inc.

DIPLOMA - Pencils ☆ - Faber-Castell Corp.

DIPLOMA - Spices and extracts - Herbert Marmorek & Son, Inc.

☆ = Now out of production

DIPLOMA FACTORY - Frames–picture - Diploma Factory, Inc.
DIPLOMA MILL, THE - Greeting cards - Diploma Mill
DIPLOMACY - Floor coverings–carpet and rugs ☆ - Criterion Mills Inc.
DIPLOMACY - Games - Avalon Hill Game Co.
DIPLOMACY - Leather–parchment ☆ - Saxon Paper Co.
DIPLOMAT - Aluminum foil paper - Highland Supply Corp.
DIPLOMAT - Apparel and accessories ☆ - Campus Sportswear Co.
DIPLOMAT - Bicycles - Kent International Inc.
DIPLOMAT - Binoculars - Nikon Inc.
DIPLOMAT - Boats–motor ☆ - Checkmate Boats Inc.
DIPLOMAT - Burial vaults–concrete - Cardinal/Embassy Group, Inc.
DIPLOMAT - Canned foods - East Coast Sales Co. Inc.
DIPLOMAT - Dinnerware–glass - Sango Co. Ltd. (Sango USA Div.)
DIPLOMAT - Dishes–china ☆ - Pickard Inc.
DIPLOMAT - Doors–wood ☆ - Peachtree Doors and Windows Inc.
DIPLOMAT - Drafting materials - Dietzgen Corp.
DIPLOMAT - Duplicating machines - Bell & Howell Co.
DIPLOMAT - Fabrics - Greenwood Mills Inc.
DIPLOMAT - Faucets - Kallista Inc.
DIPLOMAT - Flags - Annin and Co.
DIPLOMAT - Flashlights - Accutec Inc.
DIPLOMAT - Floor coverings–carpet and rugs - Johnson's Carpets Inc.
DIPLOMAT - Floor coverings–carpet and rugs - Lees Carpets
DIPLOMAT - Floor coverings–carpet and rugs - Regal Rugs Inc.
DIPLOMAT - Floor coverings–carpet and rugs ☆ - Patrick Carpet Mills
DIPLOMAT - Frames–picture - Framemica Co.
DIPLOMAT - Globes - Replogle Globes Inc.
DIPLOMAT - Greeting cards - Ambassador Cards
DIPLOMAT - Jewelry - Jacoby-Bender Inc.
DIPLOMAT - Knives–pocket ☆ - Swiss Army Brands, Ltd.
DIPLOMAT - Lighters - Colibri Inc.
DIPLOMAT - Luggage - Samsonite Corp.
DIPLOMAT - Mail boxes - Steel City Corp.
DIPLOMAT - Motor vehicles ☆ - Chrysler Corp. (Dodge Car Div.)
DIPLOMAT - Motor vehicles–motor homes ☆ - Coachmen Industries, Inc.
DIPLOMAT - Motor vehicles–motor homes ☆ - Honey Recreational Vehicles Inc.
DIPLOMAT - Office furniture–metal - Joyce International Inc.
DIPLOMAT - Ophthalmic goods ☆ - Rozin Optical Export Corp.
DIPLOMAT - Pens ☆ - Koh-I-Noor, Inc.
DIPLOMAT - Plastic silverware - Van Brode Milling Co. Inc.
DIPLOMAT - Plates–plastic - Genpak Corp.
DIPLOMAT - Plywood - Plywood & Panels Inc.
DIPLOMAT - Projection screens - Draper Shade and Screen Co. Inc.
DIPLOMAT - Switches–electric - Pass & Seymour, Inc.
DIPLOMAT - Tables–wood - Riverside Furniture Corp.
DIPLOMAT - Telescopes - Northern Telecom, Inc.
DIPLOMAT - Tires - Kelly-Springfield Tire Co.
DIPLOMAT - Toilet seats ☆ - Magnolia Products
DIPLOMAT - Trailers–travel - Royals International
DIPLOMAT - Trailers–travel ☆ - Carriage, Inc.
DIPLOMAT - Wallpaper ☆ - Marburg Wallcoverings Inc.
DIPLOMAT - Watchbands–base metal - Regal Industries, Inc.
DIPLOMAT MEDALLION - Motor vehicles ☆ - Chrysler Corp. (Dodge Car Div.)
DIPLOMAT SALON - Motor vehicles ☆ - Chrysler Corp. (Dodge Car Div.)
DIPLOMAT, THE - Ophthalmic goods - Chums Ltd.
DIPLOMATE MMP - Ophthalmic apparatus - Allergan Medical Optics
DIPLOMATS - Footwear - Mason Shoe Manufacturing Co.
DIPLOMATTE - Artists' materials - Custom Case Co.
DIPLOMAX - Surgical instruments - Allergan Elite, Inc.
DIP'N CHIK'N - Meat products–poultry - Pierce Foods Corp.
DIP'N-DRAPE - Fabrics - Zims Inc.
DIP'N STICK - Pretzels - Toad-Ally Snax Inc.
DIPNFLOW - Brushes–paint - Muralo Co. Inc.
DIPOL - Machinery - IMT Systems, Inc.
DIPOL-VINYLS - Paints ☆ - Briner Paint Manufacturing Co. Inc.
DIPPED TATERS - Snack foods ☆ - General Mills, Inc.
DIPPER - Dolls - Tonka Corp.
DIPPER - Toys–stuffed ☆ - Gund, Inc.
DIPPER MATE - Ice cream cones - Derby Cone Co. Inc.
DIPPERS - Potato chips - Nalley's Fine Foods
DIPPETTES - Snack foods - Karen Peterson
DIPPIN' FRESH - Meat sauces ☆ - Hormel Foods Corp.
DIPPIN STIK - Sporting goods ☆ - Outdoor Technologies Group
DIPPIT - Paint and wallpaper cleaners ☆ - H.F. Staples & Co. Inc.
DIPPITY DEW - Toys–banks - A.J. Renzi Plastic Corp.

DIPPITY-DO - Hair care products - Gillette Co.
DIPPITY-DYE - Paper–tissue - Crystal Tissue Co. Inc.
DIPPITY-FLIP - Dolls - Dakin Inc.
DIPPY DUCKY - Toys - Gerber Products Co.
DIPRIVAN - Pharmaceutical preparations - Zeneca Inc.
DIPROLENE - Pharmaceutical preparations - Schering-Plough Healthcare Products
DIPROLIN - Prescription drug ☆ - American Hygienic Laboratories Inc.
DIPROSONE - Pharmaceutical preparations - Schering-Plough Healthcare Products
DIPROZINE - Pharmaceutical preparations ☆ - Legere Pharmaceuticals Inc.
DIPS FOR CATS - Pet products - Natra Pet Inc.
DIPS FOR DOGS - Pet products - Natra Pet Inc.
DIPSEY DOODLE - Candy - Nestle USA
DIPSEY DUCK - Toys–stuffed ☆ - Gund, Inc.
DIPSEY SWIVEL - Fishing tackle - Water Gremlin Co.
DIPSSCOVERY - Dips–sour cream based ☆ - Dr. Pepper/Seven Up, Inc.
DIPSTERS - Sporting goods - Fabrication Enterprises
DIPSTICKS - Ice cream - Premium Leasing Limited Liability Co.
DIPSY DIVER - Fishing tackle - Luhr Jensen & Sons, Inc.
DIQUINOL - Pharmaceutical preparations - Consolidated Midland Corp.
DIRAC - Metals - W.P. Hickman Co.
DIRECSTAR - Antennas - Winegard Co.
DIRECT - Cleaning preparations - L & F Consumer Products
DIRECT - Cleaning preparations - Sterling Winthrop Inc.
DIRECT - Gasoline - Tenneco Oil Co.
DIRECT - Hair care products - Redken Laboratories, Inc.
DIRECT 1 WORLDWIDE - Computers - CLN Enterprises, Inc.
DIRECT 60-BAY - Photographic equipment ☆ - Tiffen Manufacturing Corp.
DIRECT-A-COM - Telephone apparatus - Nutone Inc.
DIRECT-A-LURE - Paper–photographic - Eastman Kodak Co.
DIRECT-A-PRINT - Paper–photographic - Eastman Kodak Co.
DIRECT ACTION - Soap - Andrew Jergens Co.
DIRECT-ADD - Fabric softeners - Malco Products, Inc.
DIRECT AID - Cosmetics - Andrew Jergens Co.
DIRECT AIR - Dryers–commercial - Clarke Industries, Inc.
DIRECT AXXESS - Pumps - ECR Technologies, Inc.
DIRECT CONNECT AXSYS - Communications equipment - Spectrum Cellular Corp.
DIRECT CONTROL - Brassieres (Bras) - LCA Intimates
DIRECT DISPATCH - Computer software - MCI Communications Corp.
DIRECT-DOCS - Real estate agencies - Document Processing Systems, Inc.
DIRECT DRIVE - Exercising equipment - Cybex
DIRECT EFFECT - Hair care products - Matrix Essentials, Inc.
DIRECT EXPRESS - Wallpaper - Surface Industries Inc.
DIRECT FARM FRESH - Flowers, plants, and seeds - Vans, Inc.
DIRECT FARM FRESH ADVANTAGE - Flowers, plants, and seeds - Vans, Inc.
DIRECT-GRIP - Gloves - W.L. Gore & Associates, Inc.
DIRECT-GRIP GORE-TEX - Gloves - W.L. Gore & Associates, Inc.
DIRECT IMPACT - Sporting goods - Lifetime Products, Inc.
DIRECT LINE - Colognes ☆ - Avon Products, Inc.
DIRECT LINE - Footwear ☆ - Conjac Inc.
DIRECT LINE PLUS ON LINE - Computer software - Countrywide Credit Industries Inc.
DIRECT MAIL II - Computer software - Mail Order Systems Inc.
DIRECT NAME - File folders - Yawman and Erbe of California Corp.
DIRECT NET - Computer software - E-Z Data, Inc.
DIRECT PRINT - Photographic equipment - Portage Newspaper Supply Co.
DIRECT PROTECT - Sporting goods - Markwort Sporting Goods Co.
DIRECT RESPONSE - Recording label - Ernie Cash Enterprises
DIRECT ROOT - Water dispensers - Andrew D. Rose
DIRECT-SEAL - Valves - Quality Assured Products, Inc.
DIRECT SELECT - Computer software - Direct Marketing Technology, Inc.
DIRECT TEES - Apparel and accessories - Direct Apparel Corp.
DIRECT VENT GS - Pipes - Simpson Dura Vent Co., Inc.
DIRECT-VISION - Antennas - Kaul-Tronics, Inc.
DIRECT VISION - File folders - Yawman and Erbe of California Corp.
DIRECTAIRE - Water heaters–household - Lochinvar Corp.
DIRECTAMOTION - Remote control devices - Eiki International Inc.
DIRECTED PERCEPTION - Computer peripheral equipment - Directed Perception, Inc.
DIRECTION - Glassware–household - Toscany Imports Ltd.
DIRECTION - Hair care products - Mastey De Paris
DIRECTION - Pesticides–household - Becker-Underwood, Inc.
DIRECTION-AIRE - Dryers–hair ☆ - Sunbeam-Oster Household Products
DIRECTIONAL SOUND - Audio equipment - Califone International Inc.

☆ = Now out of production

DIRECTIONALE - Cosmetics - Elizabeth Arden Inc.
DIRECTIONARY - Stationery - Betty Jo Abraham
DIRECTIONS - Apparel and accessories ☆ - Lovable Co.
DIRECTIONS - Dinnerware–glass - Arita Sales Co. Inc.
DIRECTIONS - Glass products ☆ - Baum Bros. Imports Inc.
DIRECTIONS - Handbags - Sarne Co. Inc.
DIRECTIONS - Ophthalmic goods - Foremost Optical Products
DIRECTIONS - Wallpaper - Dekortex Inc.
DIRECTIONS - Wallpaper - Secrest Handprints Inc.
DIRECTIONS 2 - Wallpaper ☆ - Walldesigns
DIRECTIONS FOR PETITES - Apparel–women's ☆ - Bobbie Brooks Inc.
DIRECTIONS II - Furniture ☆ - Lane Co. Inc.
DIRECTIONS III - Garden furniture - Directions III Displays, Inc.
DIRECTIVE SPORTS - Apparel–women's - Periscope Sportswear, LLC
DIRECTLINE PLUS - Computer programs - Countrywide Credit Industries Inc.
DIRECTLINK - Computer software - Direct Travel, Inc.
DIRECTLY FROM THE HEART - Labels–gummed - Valerie Bosselman
DIRECTMAIL - Computer hardware - Gammagraphx, Inc.
DIRECTO-MATIC - Electrical equipment - General Electric Co.
DIRECTO-PRESS - Starch - Mississippi Blending Co.
DIRECTOJET - Nozzles - Spraying Systems Co.
DIRECTOR - Barometers - Airguide Instrument Co.
DIRECTOR - Bicycles ☆ - Roadmaster Corp.
DIRECTOR - Computer software - Macromedia, Inc.
DIRECTOR - Floor coverings–carpet and rugs ☆ - Porter Carpet Mills Inc.
DIRECTOR - Furniture–upholstered ☆ - Mersman Furniture Co.
DIRECTOR - Golfing equipment - Ben Hogan Co.
DIRECTOR - Leather goods - AR Accessories Group Inc.
DIRECTOR - Musical instrument accessories - Whirlwind Music Distributors, Inc.
DIRECTOR - Musical instruments - United Musical Instruments USA Inc.
DIRECTOR - Office supplies - Bates Manufacturing Co.
DIRECTOR - Rackets–tennis - Head Sports USA
DIRECTOR - Surgical supplies - Microsurge Inc.
DIRECTOR - Tables–metal ☆ - Belmont Equipment Corp.
DIRECTOR - Telephones - At&T Corp.
DIRECTOR - Toiletries - Gera Dist. Inc.
DIRECTOR - Watches - Bulova Corp.
DIRECTOR CHAIR COLLECTION - Furniture - Telescope Casual Furniture Inc.
DIRECTOR II - Pagers - Motorola, Inc. (Land Mobile Products Sector)
DIRECTOR LINE - Office furniture–metal - Art Metal-U.S. Corp.
DIRECTOR LITE - Lighting fixtures–street - Bright Star Industries Inc.
DIRECTOR, THE - Electronic equipment - AudioControl
DIRECTOR, THE - Projectors–photographic ☆ - Buhl Industries, Inc.
DIRECTOR, THE - Signs - Desutter Enterprises Inc.
DIRECTOR, THE - Heaters–kerosene - Kero-Sun Inc.
DIRECTOR, THE - Lamp bulbs - Philips Lighting Co.
DIRECTOR TXD - Rackets–tennis - Head Sports USA
DIRECTORATE - Floor coverings–carpet and rugs ☆ - Mannington Carpets, Inc.
DIRECTORIESIVR - Computer software - Geoaccess, Inc.
DIRECTORIESONLINE - Computer software - Geoaccess, Inc.
DIRECTORS - Cigars ☆ - Swisher International, Inc.
DIRECTOR'S CHAIR - Computer software - Knowledge Adventure, Inc.
DIRECTORS CHOICE - Floor coverings–carpet and rugs - Conquest Carpet Mills Inc.
DIRECTOR'S CHOICE - Floor coverings–carpet and rugs ☆ - Lees Carpets
DIRECTOR'S CHOICE - Tobacco products - NCC
DIRECTORS CHOICE - Wines ☆ - Guild Wineries
DIRECTOR'S SHOWCASE - Apparel and accessories - G & S Products, Inc.
DIRECTORSHIP - Floor coverings–carpet and rugs ☆ - Karastan-Bigelow Inc.
DIRECTORY ASSISTANCE - Computer software - Individual Software Inc.
DIRECTORY OF EXECUTIVE RECRUITERS, THE - Directories - Kennedy Information
DIRECTORY OF EXECUTIVE TEMPORARY PLACEMENT FIRMS, THE - Dishwashers–household - Kennedy Information
DIRECTORY OF MANAGEMENT CONSULTANTS, THE - Dishwashers–household - Kennedy Information
DIRECTORY OF OUTPLACEMENT AND CAREER MANAGEMENT FIRMS, THE - Dishwashers–household - Kennedy Information
DIRECTORY USA - Computer software - Parsons Technology, Inc.
DIRECTORYEXPERT - Computer software - Geoaccess, Inc.
DIRECTOVALVE - Valves–industrial - Spraying Systems Co.
DIRECTPHONE - Computer software - Pro CD Inc.
DIRECTRAC - Computer software - Directory Distributing Associates, Inc.
DIRECTREE! - Computer software - Inside Technologies Inc.

DIRECTRESS - Hair care products - Vogue Laboratories
DIRECTRESS - Leather goods ☆ - AR Accessories Group Inc.
DIRECTROUTE - Computer software - Symplex Communications Corp.
DIRECTTALK - Computer peripheral equipment - International Business Machines Corp.
DIREKT - Electronic equipment - Direkt, Inc.
DIREKT TO DIGITAL - Recording label - Sonic Arts Corp.
DIREKT TO DISK - Recording label - Sonic Arts Corp.
DIREKTOR - Amplifiers ☆ - Electro-Voice, Inc.
DIREX - Pesticides–household - Griffin Corp.
DIREZIONE - Apparel and accessories - Union Apparel, Inc.
DIRGE - Insecticides - Puritan-Churchill Chemical Co.
DIRGES, THE - Recording label - The Dirges
DIRILYTE - Awards, plaques and medals - The Dirilyte Line
DIRK COURAGE - Toys - Tonka Corp.
DIRLABEL - Computer software - SourceView Software International
DIRLS - Thread - Dirls
DIRLS SIT-UPON - Furniture - Dirls
D.I.R.T. - Microscopes - Microview USA, Inc.
DIRT BARRIER - Mats - Superior Manufacturing Group/Notrax Floor Matting
DIRT BLAZER - Bicycles - Murray, Inc.
DIRT BOSS - Tires - Carlisle Tire & Rubber Co.
DIRT BUSTER - Bicycles ☆ - Roadmaster Corp.
DIRT CHEAP LAND - Soil–potting - Andyland Concepts Inc.
DIRT DART - Toys–automobiles - Mattel, Inc.
DIRT DEMON - Brooms ☆ - Laitner Brush Co.
DIRT DEMON - Filters–air - American Air Filter International (Replacement Filter Products)
DIRT DESTROYER - Cleaning preparations - Color Tile, Inc.
DIRT DEVIL - Vacuum cleaners and accessories - Marathon Projects
DIRT DEVIL - Vacuum cleaners and accessories - Royal Appliance Manufacturing Co.
DIRT DEVIL CLASSIC - Vacuum cleaners and accessories - Royal Appliance Manufacturing Co.
DIRT DEVIL RACING - Apparel–athletic - Royal Appliance Manufacturing Co.
DIRT DEVIL RACING TEAM - Vacuum cleaners and accessories ☆ - Royal Appliance Manufacturing Co.
DIRT DIGGER - Toys - CPG Products Corp.
DIRT DOG - Bicycles ☆ - Huffy Corp.
DIRT DUSTER - Bicycles - Western Auto Supply Co.
DIRT FIGHTER - Paints - Dutch Boy Group
DIRT FINDER - Vacuum cleaners and accessories - The Hoover Co.
DIRT GEAR - Shirts–polo - Hines Fine Soil, LLC
DIRT IS GOOD - Apparel–athletic - Enba Corp.
DIRT MAGNET - Filters–air - ICS Corp.
DIRT MAGNET AQUARIUM FILTER - Aquariums–household - Jungle Laboratories Corp.
DIRT MASTER - Shoes–athletic - Wilson Sporting Goods Co.
DIRT MONSTER - Bicycles ☆ - Huffy Corp.
DIRT MOVERS - Toy vehicles - Intex Recreation Corp.
DIRT RECORDS - Recording label - Dirt Records, Inc.
DIRT REMOVING EQUIPMENT - Soap ☆ - Colossus Corp.
DIRT RESEARCH - Bicycle accessories - Strictly BMX/Off Road
DIRT RIDER - Bicycles - Recreational Equipment, Inc.
DIRT ROVER - Toys–automobiles - Mattel, Inc.
DIRT SQUIRT - Motorcycles ☆ - Pabatco
DIRT SQUIRT - Skin care products - Memphis Contract Packaging, Inc. (Softee Products Division)
DIRT THROWER - Bicycles ☆ - Huffy Corp.
DIRT WATER - Bicycles ☆ - Huffy Corp.
DIRT WRANGLER - Detergents - Harris Research, Inc.
DIRT ZASTER - Bicycles - Dynacraft Industries Inc.
DIRTBAG - Filters–industrial - Atlantic Construction Fabrics, Inc.
DIRTBAG - Tools - Arcoa Industries
DIRTBLASTER - Pressure washers - Alfred Karcher Inc.
DIRTBLASTERS - Pumps - Minne Jet Inc.
DIRTBOARD - Skateboards - Mort Heilig
DIRTBUSTERS - Giftware ☆ - Tinkerbell
DIRTEX - Cleaning preparations–window - Savogran Co.
DIRTLIFTER - Vacuum cleaners and accessories - Bissell Inc.
DIRTMAGNET - Vacuum cleaners and accessories - Regina Co.
DIRTWIZARD - Vacuum cleaners and accessories - Tammie P. Wu
DIRTY BIRD - Apparel–athletic - Douglas G. Patterson
DIRTY CAT - Bicycles - Murray, Inc.
DIRTY DAWGS - Pet products - Mara Casey
DIRTY DIAPER - Novelty items - Cal Themes Inc.

DIRTY DICE - Games ☆ - Pacific Game Co.
DIRTY DISHES - Dishes–earthenware - Tal Creations
DIRTY DOG - Pet products - Nature's Choice
DIRTY DOG GRUNGE WEAR DIRTY DOG TAG - Apparel and accessories - Daniel K. Schmitt
DIRTY DUCK - Water purification systems - Great Lakes Biochemical Co., Inc.
DIRTY ERNIE - Balls–billiard - Dirty Ernie
DIRTY LAUNDRY - Candy ☆ - Topps Co., Inc.
DIRTY POTATO CHIPS - Food products - Chickasaw Foods
DIRTYBIRD - Fishing lures - Plastics Research and Development Co.
DIRX - Sporting goods - Schutt Manufacturing Co.
DIS - Computer software - Lucent Technologies Inc.
DI'S - Shoe insoles - Sentinel Consumer Products, Inc.
DIS-ARM - Sporting goods ☆ - Magic American Corp.
DIS-IS-IT - Apparel and accessories - Slippery Noodle Inn, Inc.
DISA - Filters–air - DISA
DISABLED FRIENDLY - Menus - Friendly Productions of Texas, Inc.
DISABLED LIST - Apparel–athletic - Injured Reserve, Inc.
DISABLER 10-13, THE - Personal defense products - Personal Safety Outlet Inc.
DISAG - Computer software - Association for Effective Schools, Inc.
DISALCID - Pharmaceutical preparations - Minnesota Mining & Manufacturing Co.
DISANTHROL - Laxatives - Lannett Co. Inc.
DISAPPEAR - Recording label - Disappear Records
DISAPPEARING EGGS - Novelty items ☆ - Easter Unltd. Inc.
DISAPPEARING TREASURE - Toys - Fisher-Price, Inc.
DISARITA - Beverages–alcohol - Paddington Corp.
DISASTER RECOVERY PLAN - Computer software - Caroline Pratt and Associates, Inc.
DISASTER RECOVERY SOFTWARE - Computer software - Caroline Pratt and Associates, Inc.
DISASTER X - Deodorizers - Surco Products Inc.
DISBURSEMATE - Computer hardware and software - Equitrac Corp.
DISBURSEMATE - Computer hardware and software - ERB Industries, Inc.
D.I.S.C. - Rifles - Modern Muzzle Loading, Inc.
DISC-AD - Writing product - Island Pen Manufacturing Corp.
DISC CHECKBOOK-PLUS - Computer software - Disc, Inc.
DISC DETECTIVE - Computer storage devices–optical - VSMT Productions, Inc.
DISC-EYES - Mascara-remover pads - American Hygienic Laboratories Inc.
DISC-FINDER - Cases–plastic - Brandt Weibezahn
DISC-IT - Games ☆ - Mantua/Cosom Sporting Goods
DISC JOCKEY - Audio equipment - Sony Corp. of America
DISC MATES - Cases–plastic ☆ - Recoton Corp.
DISC N' DAT - Recording label - Lindberg Records
DISC-O - Toys ☆ - Flambeau Products Corp.
DISC-O-COFFEE - Coffee makers–electric - Gourmet Center
DISC-O-FELT - Fabrics–felt - Roberts Colonial House Inc.
DISC-O-NAIL - Fingernail files and buffers - International Beauty Design, Inc.
DISC-O-PADS - Adhesives and sealants - Roberts Colonial House Inc.
DISC-O-TILE - Floor coverings–tile - R.C. Musson Rubber Co.
DISC-O-TRED - Staircases–wood - R.C. Musson Rubber Co.
DISC PAC - Photographic equipment - Tension Envelope Corp.
DISC RESCUE - Cleaning preparations - B.C. International, Inc.
DISC SHOT - Toys–guns - Edison Toys USA Inc.
DISC SUPPORT - Health care products - Healthwatchers System
DISC TAXI - Cardboard - Cadmus Communications Corp.
DISC-TEK - Cleaning preparations - Disc-Tek, Inc.
DISC TROPHY - Recording label - PPX Enterprises Inc.
DISC-TWIST - Floor coverings–carpet and rugs ☆ - Olympic Carpets Inc.
DISC VUE PAC - Photographic equipment - Tension Envelope Corp.
DISCABINET - Furniture - Wallach & Associates Inc.
DISCADDY - Bags–duffel - John David
DISCAPON - Recording label - Apon Record Co., Inc.
DISCASSETTE - Electronic equipment - Diamond Electronics Inc.
DISCCOVER - Motor vehicle parts and accessories - Keeter Manufacturing, Inc.
DISCDISK - Audio cabinets - Epic Design Studios
DISCERNE - Prosthetic apparatus - Coloplast Corp.
DISCHARGE SURVIVAL - Health care products - Maddak Inc.
DISCIDE - Disinfectants - Palmero Health Care
DISCIDE - Health care products - Cramer Products Inc.
DISCIPLE - Apparel–athletic - Cold Cuts Boardwear
DISCIPLINE - Skin care products - Compar Inc.
DISCIPLINE AEROSOL SPRAY - Hair care products - Peter Hantz Co.
DISCIPLINE II - Health care products - Promatek Medical Systems Inc.

DISCJET - Nozzles - Spraying Systems Co.
DISCKIT - Audio equipment - Recoton Corp.
DISCLEAN - Cleaning preparations - Recoton Corp.
DISCLINC - Computer storage devices–optical - Thomson Legal Publishing Inc.
DISCLOSE - Pharmaceutical preparations - Beutlich L.P. Pharmaceuticals
DISCLOSED ADDITIONAL DRIVER SYSTEM (DADS), THE - Computer software - Trans Union/Dateq
DISCLOSURE - Apparel–women's - Dixietex International, Inc.
DISCLOSURE - Computer software - Disclosure Inc.
DISCLOSURE PRESENTER - Computer software - Disclosure Inc.
DISCMAN - Compact disc players - Sony Corp. of America
DISCMIST - Cleaning preparations - Record-Rama Sound Archives
DISCMOBILE - Furniture - Wallach & Associates Inc.
DISCO - Dinnerware–glass - Block China Co.
DISCO - Hardware - Blaine Window Hardware Inc.
DISCO - Ophthalmic goods ☆ - Rozin Optical Export Corp.
DISCO - Steel-wool pads ☆ - American Steel Wool Manufacturing Co. Inc.
DISCO - Underwear and nightwear ☆ - Spencer Supports Ltd.
DISCO - Yarn ☆ - William Unger & Co. Inc.
DISCO-BRUSH - Brushes–hair - Magic Distributing Ltd.
DISCO-CHEF - Blenders - Sunbeam-Oster Household Products
DISCO DANCE - Floor waxes - Boyer Corp.
DISCO DARLINGS - Underwear and nightwear ☆ - Lovable Co.
DISCO DOLLY RECORDS - Recording label - Nervous, Inc.
DISCO-DUST - Paints - Glitterex Corp.
DISCO FUENTES - Recording label - Sonotone Corp.
DISCO GOLD - Toys - Tonka Corp.
DISCO SOLIDS - Floor coverings–carpet and rugs - Trend Carpet
DISCO STRIPES - Floor coverings–carpet and rugs - Trend Carpet
DISCO-VISION - Video tapes–blank - MCA Universal Studios
DISCO-VITAL - Pet products - Aquatronics-Filtronics
DISCO-WORM - Pet products - Aquatronics-Filtronics
DISCOLOR - Recording label - Kubaney Publishing Corp.
DISCOMANIA - Recording label - Lindberg Records
DISCOMED - Pet products ☆ - Aquatronics-Filtronics
DISCOMODA - Recording label - Sonotone Corp.
DISCONEX - Switches–electric - Hubbell Inc.
DISCORGANIZER - Recording label ☆ - Recoton Corp.
DISCOS MONICA - Recording label - Peer-Southern Organization
DISCOS VICTORIA - Recording label - Sonotone Corp.
DISCOTEST - Computer storage devices - Scientific American, Inc.
DISCOTHEQUE - Apparel stores–lingerie - Goddess Bra
DISCOTHEQUE - Watches - Hampden Corp.
DISCOV-R-SCOPE - Kaleidoscopes - Wild Planet Toys, Inc.
DISCOVER - Computer peripheral equipment - Don Johnston Inc.
DISCOVER - Computer software ☆ - Sunburst Communications, Inc.
DISCOVER - Detergents - ADCO Inc.
DISCOVER - Floor coverings - Congoleum Corp.
DISCOVER - Skin care products - Fingerpaints
DISCOVER - Underwear and nightwear - Youthcraft-Charmfit
DISCOVER:BOARD - Computer software - Don Johnston Inc.
DISCOVER GENEALOGY - Computer software - Parsons Technology, Inc.
DISCOVER HOW OUR CELLS WORK FOR YOUR CELLS - Cushions - Supracor Systems, Inc.
DISCOVER: KENX - Computer software - Don Johnston Inc.
DISCOVER NEW WORLDS OF FLAVOR WITH NEAREAST - Food products - Golden Grain Co.
DISCOVER RETIREMENT - Computer software - Principal Mutual Life Insurance Co.
DISCOVER:SCREEN - Computer software - Don Johnston Inc.
DISCOVER SPACE - Computer software ☆ - Broderbund Software, Inc.
DISCOVER:SWITCH - Computer software - Don Johnston Inc.
DISCOVER TAZO - Teas - Tazo, Inc.
DISCOVER THE ADIRONDACKS - Book series ☆ - Countryman Press Inc.
DISCOVER THE WORLD - Computer software - Hartley Courseware Inc.
DISCOVER YOUR EYE Q! - Educational materials - Foundation of the American Academy of Ophthalmology
DISCOVERED - Trailers–travel ☆ - Shasta Industries Inc.
DISCOVERER - Binoculars - Bushnell Corp.
DISCOVERER - Telescopes - Bausch & Lomb Inc.
DISCOVERER - Trailers–travel - Forest River, Inc.
DISCOVERIES - Jewelry and giftware - Discoveries
DISCOVERIES - Publisher's imprints - Harry N. Abrams Inc.
DISCOVERIES OF THE DEEP - Computer software - Capstone Software
DISCOVERING ALABAMA - Video production - Douglas J. Phillips
DISCOVERING AMERICA - Computer software ☆ - Knowledge Adventure

☆ = Now out of production

DISCOVERING AUTHORS - Computer software - The Gale Group
DISCOVERING THE WORLD WITH STAMPS - Toys - ZOE Arts
DISCOVERY - Audio visual supplies - Firstmedia Music
DISCOVERY - Boats–canoes - Old Town Canoe Co.
DISCOVERY - Boats–motor ☆ - Bayliner Marine Corp.
DISCOVERY - Chairs–upholstered - Fixtures Furniture
DISCOVERY - Christmas tree ornaments - Cracker Box Inc.
DISCOVERY - Electronic equipment - Tandy Corp.
DISCOVERY - Envelopes–paper - Cavert Wire Co. Inc.
DISCOVERY - Floor coverings–carpet and rugs - Lees Carpets
DISCOVERY - Floor coverings–carpet and rugs - Mattel Carpet & Rug Inc.
DISCOVERY - Floor coverings–carpet and rugs ☆ - Regal Rugs Inc.
DISCOVERY - Footwear and apparel ☆ - Rockport Co. Inc.
DISCOVERY - Furniture ☆ - Vaughan Furniture Co. Inc.
DISCOVERY - Garden equipment ☆ - Dayco Products, Inc.
DISCOVERY - Guitars - Heritage Industries
DISCOVERY - Hair care products - Helene Curtis Industries Inc.
DISCOVERY - Luggage - Airway Industries, Inc.
DISCOVERY - Mattresses - Sealy Inc.
DISCOVERY - Mattresses - Vinyl Products
DISCOVERY - Motor vehicles–automobiles - Land Rover North America Inc.
DISCOVERY - Pet products - Ginger, Inc.
DISCOVERY - Pottery - Duncan Enterprises
DISCOVERY - Prefabricated buildings–wood - Champion Enterprises Inc.
DISCOVERY - Skates–roller - Rollerblade, Inc.
DISCOVERY - Sporting goods ☆ - Fuji America, Inc.
DISCOVERY - Toys–models ☆ - Estes Industries
DISCOVERY - Underwear and nightwear - Bestform Foundations, Inc.
DISCOVERY - Wallpaper ☆ - ICI Americas Inc.
DISCOVERY - Watches - Hampden Corp.
DISCOVERY - Wines - Belvedere Winery
DISCOVERY 1000 ZOOM - Cameras - Fuji Photo Film USA Inc.
DISCOVERY 2000 - Cleaning preparations - Hillyard Enterprises, Inc.
DISCOVERY BLOCKS - Educational materials - Educational Teaching Aids
DISCOVERY BOOKS - Publisher's imprints - Fisher-Price, Inc.
DISCOVERY BUNNY - Toys - Fisher-Price, Inc.
DISCOVERY CANDLE - Candles - Steidle Enterprises, Inc.
DISCOVERY CHANNEL PICTURES - Film - Discovery Communications, Inc.
DISCOVERY CHANNEL PRESS, THE - Publisher's imprints - Discovery Channel
DISCOVERY COLLECTION - Cooking equipment–household ☆ - West Bend Co.
DISCOVERY COLLECTION - Furniture ☆ - Pulaski Furniture Corp.
DISCOVERY COLLECTION, THE - Wallpaper - Seabrook Wallcoverings, Inc.
DISCOVERY COTTAGE - Toys - Fisher-Price, Inc.
DISCOVERY EXPRESS - Motor vehicles–motor homes - Mallard Coach
DISCOVERY FOLDING TRAVEL - Trailers–travel ☆ - Sun-Lite Inc.
DISCOVERY FOREST - Toys - Mattel, Inc.
DISCOVERY GARDEN - Flowers, plants, and seeds - Advance Seed Co.
DISCOVERY GLOBE - Toys - Fisher-Price, Inc.
DISCOVERY HEART - Vitamins and nutritional supplements - Carter-Wallace, Inc.
DISCOVERY III - Windows–storm ☆ - Malta Co.
DISCOVERY IV - Floor coverings–carpet and rugs - Western Carpet Mills
DISCOVERY JOURNALS - Book stores - Abbey Press Inc.
DISCOVERY JR. - Toys - Tedco Inc.
DISCOVERY KIT - Health care products - Above All Health Inc.
DISCOVERY MAP - Toys - Fisher-Price, Inc.
DISCOVERY MS92 - Ships–sailing vessels - Snark Boats
DISCOVERY MUSIC - Recording label - Discovery Music
DISCOVERY PAK - Toys - Tedco Inc.
DISCOVERY PALS - Toys–stuffed - Kids II, Inc.
DISCOVERY READERS - Publisher's imprints - Ideals Publishing Co.
DISCOVERY SCHOOLHOUSE - Toys - Fisher-Price, Inc.
DISCOVERY STONE - Figurines - Denis Brand
DISCOVERY TABLE - Toys - Learning Products Inc.
DISCOVERY TOYS - Toys–musical - Discovery Toys, Inc.
DISCOVERY TWO BABY CARRIER - Infant product - Noel Joanna, Inc.
DISCOVERY ZX - Computer software - Discovery Products, Inc.
DISCOVERYLAND - Toys - Mattel, Inc.
DISCOVERYMATE - Computers - Cascade Technology Corp.
DISCPAGES - Computer software - Bell Atlantic Network Services, Inc.
DISCPHILE - Containers–plastic - Edward Bydalek
DISCPICKABLES - Index cards - Mactec Products
DISCPOOL - Games - Conrad R. Medina
DISCPORT - Computer hardware - Microtest, Inc.

DISCREET - Floor coverings–carpet and rugs ☆ - Columbus Mills, Inc.
DISCREET - Hearing aids - Finetone Hearing Instruments, Inc.
DISCREET - Pharmaceutical preparations - Pro Care Industries Ltd.
DISCRENE - Brassieres (Bras) - Coloplast Corp.
DISCRETION - Bags–plastic - Barna Ltd.
DISCRETION - Brassieres (Bras) ☆ - Playtex Apparel, Inc.
DISCRETION - Cosmetics - Madison Cosmetics, Inc.
DISCRETION - Flatware - Utica Cutlery Co.
DISCRETION - Floor coverings–carpet and rugs - Hollytex Carpet Mills Inc.
DISCRETION - Floor coverings–carpet and rugs - Monticello Carpet Mills
DISCRETION - Skin care products - Beaumont Products, Inc.
DISCRIMINATING ALARM SYSTEMS - Electronic equipment - Child Alert Rapid Eyedentification, Inc.
DISCRIMINATING MALE - Hosiery–men's - Clovermere Sales Corp.
DISCS-ON-A-RING - Toys - Gerber Products Co.
DISCSAFE 5 - Cleaning preparations - Geneva Group of Cos. Inc.
DISCSERV - Computer hardware - Microtest, Inc.
DISCSET - Cleaning preparations - Recoton Corp.
DISCTRAKER - Phonographic needles ☆ - Recoton Corp.
DISCUS - Apparel stores–sports - Tultex Corp.
DISCUS - Computer software - Eastman Kodak Co.
DISCUS - Floor coverings–carpet and rugs ☆ - Olympic Carpets Inc.
DISCUS - Furniture - Knoll, Inc.
DISCUS - Publisher's imprints ☆ - Hearst Corp.
DISCUS - Recording label - Stanyan Record Co.
DISCUS - Watches - Croton Watch Co., Inc.
DISCUS ATHLETIC - Apparel and accessories - Tultex Corp.
DISCUS BUFFER - Pet products - Seachem Laboratories
DISCUS DENTAL - Dental compounds - Discus Dental Impressions, Inc.
DISCUS NUTRIBITS - Pet products - Nippon Pet Food
DISCUSS - Computer software - Massachusetts Institute of Technology
DISCVIEW - Computer hardware - Microtest, Inc.
DISCWASHER - Computer peripheral equipment - Recoton Corp.
DISCWIPES - Cleaning preparations - Geneva Group of Cos. Inc.
DISEASE STOPPER - Fertilizers - Seacoast Laboratories Inc.
DISERONA - Pasta - International Multi-Products, Ltd.
DISETRONIC V100 - Insulin pump - Disetronic Medical Systems
DISFUNKTIONAL - Apparel and accessories - L'koral, Inc.
DISGUISE - Lipstick - American Hygienic Laboratories Inc.
DISGUISE FOR LINES - Cosmetics - Parlux Fragrances, Inc.
DISGUISE GUYS, THE - Antennas - Sti-Co Industries, Inc.
DISGUISE THE LIMIT - Costumes - Disguise Inc.
DISH AND THE SPOON - Bakery products - Trish Albers
DISH-EZE - Cleaning preparations - Flo-Pac Corp.
DISH IT UP! - Games - Gamewright, Inc.
DISH MAGIC - Detergents ☆ - Care-Tech Laboratories Inc.
DISH MASTER SATELLITE PROTECTION - Regulators–voltage - Electronic Specialists, Inc.
DISH-N-POT - Brooms - Lighthouse Industries
DISH O'GOLD - Vegetables–canned - Northland Canning Co.
DISH-PALS - Detergents ☆ - Hy-Ko Products Co.
DISH-POD - Broadcasting equipment - Trudell, Inc.
DISH QUIK - Housewares - Kirkhill Inc.
DISH, THE - Pet products - Fletcher Products Corp.
DISHGUARD - Pet products - Petcraft, Inc.
DISHIST - Pharmaceutical preparations ☆ - Veratex Group
DISHMAID - Dishwashers–household ☆ - SES Industries Inc.
DISHMASTER - Plumbing fixtures–metal - Manville Manufacturing Corp.
DISHSCRUB - Brushes - Suburbanite Industries
DISHTERGENT - Dishwashing compounds - Harley Chemicals
DISHWASHER ALERT - Signs - G.S. Design, Inc.
DISHWASHER GLISTEN - Dishwashing compounds - Brady Enterprises Inc.
DISHWASHER KLEEN - Cleaning preparations - G.G. Bean Inc.
DISILVER - Apparel–men's - Crown Clothing Corp.
DISINTEGRATION TESTED FORMULA - Health care products - Pharmavite Corp.
DISINTEGRATOR - Cleaning preparations - Phoenix Pharmaceutical, Inc.
DISIPAL - Pharmaceutical preparations - Minnesota Mining & Manufacturing Co.
DISK ACCESS - Computer software - Seven Hills Software
DISK ADVISOR - Computer software - W. Quinn Associates, Inc.
DISK ASSISTANT - Computer software ☆ - Spectrum Universal
DISK CADDY, THE - Computer diskettes–blank - Key Productions
DISK DEFENDER - Computer software - Alliance Systems & Programming, Inc.
DISK FINDER II - Electronic equipment ☆ - Bates Manufacturing Co.
DISK HELPER - Computer software ☆ - Spectrum Universal

☆ = Now out of production

DISK LISA - Brushes ☆ - SCI Scandicrafts Inc.
DISK MAT - Electronic equipment - Bell & Howell Co.
DISK OF DOOM - Toys - Mattel, Inc.
DISK PACK - Electronic equipment - Mass Memory Systems Inc.
DISK-PICK - Computer-disk storage units - GP Technologies Inc.
DISK SCRIPSIT - Computer software ☆ - Tandy Corp.
DISK SPINNER - Toys - Skitters
DISK, THE - Sponges - Delby System
DISK VALET - Audio cabinets–plastic ☆ - Ramstar Mills, Inc.
DISKALOIDS - Cough drops - Claflin Co.
DISKARD - Medical apparatus - Florida Manufacturing Corp.
DISKDOUBLER - Computer peripheral equipment - Datran Periphals
DISKDUP PRO - Computer software - Roger D. Bates
DISKETTE MANAGER - Computer software ☆ - IMSI
DISKETTE MANAGER III - Computer peripheral equipment - Lassen Software Inc.
DISKETTO - Markers–felt-tip ☆ - Staedtler, Inc.
DISKEXTENDER - Computer software ☆ - OTG Software
DISKFOLIO - Office supplies ☆ - Esselte Corp.
DISKIN - Health care products - Knobble Associates
DISKINS - Candy - Grace Cocoa Associates, L.P.
DISKIONARY - Computer software - International Data Group, Inc.
DISKMAKER - Computer software - Advanced Systems Concepts
DISKMIZER - Computer software - Intersecting Concepts, Inc.
DISKNET - Computer software - Reflex, Inc.
DISKOS - Lighting fixtures - Swivelier Co. Inc.
DISKPIC - Bar fixtures–plastic - Spir-it Inc.
DISKPMP - Computer software - Iloc, Inc.
DISKPROTEK - Computer disc covers - W. Parke Young
DISKPUMP - Computer software - P.G. Soft, Inc.
DISKRIBE - Pens - Sanford Corp.
DISKSTIR - Bar fixtures–plastic - Spir-it Inc.
DISKTOP - Computer software ☆ - CE Software, Inc.
DISKTOTE - Computer storage devices ☆ - Bates Manufacturing Co.
DISKUS - Hardware - Abus Lock Co.
DISKWARE - Computer software - Apple Computer Inc.
DISKXTENDER - Computer peripheral equipment - OTG Software
DISMISS - Pharmaceutical preparations - Schering-Plough Healthcare Products
DISMUTASE - Health care products ☆ - Marcor Development Corp.
DISNEY - Apparel–men's ☆ - Keepers International
DISNEY - Bathing suits - Catalina
DISNEY - Bop bags, tent sets, etc. - Intex Recreation Corp.
DISNEY - Eyeglasses - Marchon and Marcolin Eyewear Inc.
DISNEY - Furniture ☆ - Dolly, Inc.
DISNEY - Games - Ben Cooper Inc.
DISNEY - Games - Milton Bradley Co.
DISNEY - Games - Tyco Toys
DISNEY - Giftware - Applause, Inc.
DISNEY - Giftware ☆ - Enesco Corp.
DISNEY - Hats ☆ - Stetson Hat Co. Inc.
DISNEY - Motion picture distributors–prerecorded - Walt Disney Co.
DISNEY - Music boxes - Schmid Inc.
DISNEY - Pillows ☆ - A.D. Sutton & Sons Inc.
DISNEY - Publisher's imprints - Grosset & Dunlap Inc.
DISNEY - Toys - Knickerbocker Toy Co. Inc.
DISNEY - Toys - F.J. Strauss Co. Inc.
DISNEY - Toys–blocks - Playskool, Inc.
DISNEY - Umbrellas - Shaw Creations Inc.
DISNEY - Watches - Mayfair
DISNEY ALL ABOARD - Games ☆ - Milton Bradley Co.
DISNEY BABIES - Figurines ☆ - Goebel of North America
DISNEY BABIES - Lamps - Dolly, Inc.
DISNEY BABIES - Wallpaper - Priss Prints Inc.
DISNEY CHARACTERS - Pet products - Precious Paws
DISNEY CIRCUS - Lamps ☆ - Dolly, Inc.
DISNEY DANGLE DOLLS - Dolls ☆ - Diener Industries Inc.
DISNEY DUO'S - Cosmetics - Cosrich Inc.
DISNEY EASY READERS - Publisher's imprints ☆ - Western Publishing Co., Inc.
DISNEY FOLLOW THAT MOUSE - Games ☆ - Milton Bradley Co.
DISNEY FROZEN TREATS - Ice cream - Good Humor Corp.
DISNEY LIGHT & LEARN - Games - Milton Bradley Co.
DISNEY ON PARADE - Kitchen utensils–aluminum - Bonny Products Inc.
DISNEY PARKS SERIES - Figurines - Department 56 Inc.
DISNEY POPPIN' PALS - Toys–stuffed - CBS Toys
DISNEY PULL-MEES - Toys–stuffed ☆ - CBS Toys

DISNEY SQUEEZ-MEES - Toys–stuffed - CBS Toys
DISNEY WATERFULS - Games - Milton Bradley Co.
DISNEY WORLD - Games ☆ - Milton Bradley Co.
DISNEY WORLD STEAMBOAT - Toys - Marlin Toy Products Inc.
DISNEYLAND CASEY JR. - Furniture ☆ - Dolly, Inc.
DISNEYLAND PIN-UPS - Posters ☆ - Dolly, Inc.
DISNEY'S ANIMATED STORYBOOK - Computer storage devices–optical - Walt Disney Co.
DISNEY'S CLASSIC VALUE STORIES - Publisher's imprints ☆ - Western Publishing Co., Inc.
DISNEY'S ENCHANTED PLACES - Statuary - Walt Disney Co.
DISNEY'S MICKEY MOUSE - Furniture - American Toy & Furniture Co.
DISNEY'S MUSIC BOX ARTIST - Recording label - Walt Disney Records
DISNEY'S POCOHONTAS - Lunch boxes - Thermos Co.
DISNEY'S SNOW WHITE - Shoes ☆ - S. Goldberg and Co. Inc.
DISNEY'S SPOTLIGHT ARTIST - Recording label - Walt Disney Records
DISNEY'S THE LITTLE MERMAID - Lunch boxes - Thermos Co.
DISNEY'S WONDERFUL WORLD OF READING - Publisher's imprints - Random House, Inc.
DISNEY'S WORLD OF ADVENTURE - Publisher's imprints - Random House, Inc.
DISOBROM - Pharmaceutical preparations - Geneva Generics Inc.
DISOCAP - Pharmaceutical preparations ☆ - Coast Laboratories Inc.
DISOGRIN SEAL - Sealing devices - Freudenberg-Nok General Partnership
DISOLAN - Laxatives - Lannett Co. Inc.
DISOMER CHRONOTAB - Pharmaceutical preparations - Schering-Plough Healthcare Products
DISONATE - Laxatives - Lannett Co. Inc.
DISOPHROL - Antihistamine preparations - Schering-Plough Healthcare Products
DISOPHROL CHRONOTAB - Pharmaceutical preparations - Schering-Plough Healthcare Products
DISOPLEX - Laxatives - Lannett Co. Inc.
DISORDERLY CONDUCT - Games ☆ - Western Publishing Co., Inc.
DISORIENTED EXPRESS - Greeting cards - American Greetings Corp.
DISOTATE - Pharmaceutical preparations ☆ - Forest Pharmaceuticals Inc.
DISPATCH - Apparel and accessories - Russ Togs Inc.
DISPATCH - Disinfectants - Caltech Industries, Inc.
DISPATCH - Luggage - Samsonite Corp.
DISPATCH - Paper ☆ - Mead Corp.
DISPATCH WRITER - Printing presses - Motorola, Inc. (Land Mobile Products Sector)
DISPATCHER'S CHOICE - Toys–trains - Life-Like Products Inc.
DISPATCHIT - Computer hardware - PDA Dimensions, Inc.
DISPATCHWORKS - Computer peripheral equipment - Baker Audio, Inc.
DISPEN-SI-MATIC - Machinery - Si Handling Systems, Inc.
DISPENS-A-BAG - Medical apparatus - Duramark, Inc.
DISPENS-EZE - Beverages–carbonated - Universal Flavor USA
DISPENS-O-PACK - Wire - Anchor Wire Corp.
DISPENS-O-WIRE - Wire - Anchor Wire Corp.
DISPENSA PLATE - Plate holders - LA Fads Inc.
DISPENSA-WHEEL - Paints - Padco Companies, Inc.
DISPENSALL - Housewares ☆ - World Wide Manufacturing Inc.
DISPENSE-A-LINER - Bags–trash - Witt Co.
DISPENSE-A-WRAP - Skin care products - Rudolph International, Inc.
DISPENSE-RITE - Cups–paper - Diversified Metal Products Inc.
DISPENSER-MATE - Jars–plastic ☆ - Gent-L-Kleen Products Inc.
DISPESMAR - Shrimp–canned or cured ☆ - Darik Enterprises Inc.
DISPIRO - Medical apparatus - Utah Medical Products, Inc.
DISPLAWALL - Paneling - Marlite
DISPLAY - Floor waxes ☆ - Brulin & Co., Inc.
DISPLAY - Ophthalmic goods - Foremost Optical Products
DISPLAY-A-YEAR - Calendars - Skinner & Kennedy Co.
DISPLAY BOOK-N-EASEL - Easels - Lion Office Products, Inc.
DISPLAY COAT - Cakes - Coast Novelty Manufacturing Co.
DISPLAY + EXHIBIT SOURCE, THE - Display cases–metal - Architectural Source, Inc.
DISPLAY LABS - Computer peripheral equipment - Display Laboratories, Inc.
DISPLAY-MASTER - Easels - William A. Crook Co. Inc.
DISPLAYBRIGHT - Lighting fixtures - Brightman Design
DISPLAYBUILDER - Computer software - Brento Corp.
DISPLAYCO - Racks - Reborn Products Co., Inc.
DISPLAYMAKER - Computer peripheral equipment - Lasermaster Corp.
DISPLAYMAKER - Projectors–photographic - Eastman Kodak Co.
DISPLAYMATE - Computer software - Cactus Computers Inc.
DISPLAYMATE - Electronic equipment ☆ - Charles Beseler Co.

☆ = Now out of production

DISPLAYMATE - Video equipment - Matsushita Electric Corp. of America

DISPLAYPHONE - Telescopes - Northern Telecom, Inc.

DISPLAYPIE - Containers - Wilkinson Manufacturing Co.

DISPLAYRITE - Refrigerators - Ardco Inc.

DISPLAYVOICE - Computer peripheral equipment - Syntellect, Inc.

DISPLAYWRITE 1 - Computer software - International Business Machines Corp.

DISPO-BRIEF - Health care products - MB Products Ltd.

DISPO-ZYME - Garbage-disposal cleaner ☆ - Vibe Records Inc.

DISPOS-A-KLOZ - Work clothes - Cleveland Cotton Products Co.

DISPOS-ALL-FRESH - Cleaning preparations - AmeriPlus Inc.

DISPOSA-FILE - File folders - W.W. Holes Manufacturing

DISPOSA-FLEX - File folders ☆ - W.W. Holes Manufacturing

DISPOSA-HOOD - Medical apparatus - Utah Medical Products, Inc.

DISPOSA-PUFFS - Sponges - Sterling Winthrop Inc.

DISPOSABALLS - Golfing equipment - Decision Point, Inc.

DISPOSABLE DECORATING BAGS - Bakery products - Kopykake

DISPOSABLE DECUBITOUS MEASURING GUIDE - Medical apparatus - Trademark Corp.

DISPOSABLE PLOTTER PEN - Pens - Koh-I-Noor, Inc.

DISPOSABLE PLUS - Cameras - Sakar International Inc.

DISPOSADOR - Mailbox accessories - Babco

DISPOSALENE - Cleaning preparations ☆ - Malco Products, Inc.

DISPOSALL - Garbage disposal units–household - General Electric Co.

DISPOSAMED - Health care products - Aedline, Industries, Inc.

DISPOSAWARE - Plates–plastic - Continental/SiLite International Inc.

DISPOSEZE - Diapers–disposable - Whitestone Products Inc.

DISPOSO TREET - Mops - Golden Star Inc.

DISPOZ-A-BAG - Health care products - C.R. Bard, Inc.

DISPOZ-A-SCOOP - Pet products - Petpro Products Inc.

DISPOZ-ALL - Drain pipe cleaners - Alumin-Nu Corp.

DISPOZOIL - Automobile engine-oil-collection device - Altech Corp.

DISQ - Amplifiers–musical instrument - Bbe Sound, Inc.

DISQ - Audio equipment - At&T Corp.

DISQUES SWING - Recording label ☆ - DRG Records Inc.

DISRUPT - Insecticides - Hercon Environmental Corp.

DISS-CHROME - Saws–power ☆ - Disston Co.

DISSAPEER - Pharmaceutical preparations ☆ - Vita Plus Industries Inc.

DISSECT-AN-ALIEN - Toys - Mattel, Inc.

DISSECTABLE HUMAN, THE - Compact discs–prerecorded - Mosby-Year Book, Inc.

DISSECTIONS - Computer storage devices–optical - Digital Imaging Associates Inc.

DISSEN - Machete sheaths - Lengemann of Florida, Inc.

DISSING - Figurines - Swe-Den Inc.

DISSOLUTION TEST STATION - Laboratory instruments - Vankel Industries, Inc.

DISSOLUTION TESTED FORMULA - Health care products - Pharmavite Corp.

DISSOLUTION TESTED RELEASE ASSURED - Health care products - Leiner Health Products Inc.

DISSOLVE - Pesticides–agricultural - Riverdale Chemical Co., Inc.

DISSOLVE - Rust removers - Binford Products, Inc.

DISSOLVE - Wallcoverings-adhesive remover - Golden Harvest Adhesives

DISSOLVE - Water treating compounds - Great Lakes Biochemical Co., Inc.

DISSOLVE - Yarn - Staflex Harotex

DISSOLVE-A-BAG - Bags - American Packaging Corp.

DISSOLVE-A-PAK - Waste-system chemical ☆ - ITT Jabsco

DISSOLVE AWAY - Manicure preparations - Flying Emery Board Inc.

DISSOLVE II - Industrial chemicals - Binford Products, Inc.

DISSPLA - Computer software - Computer Associates International, Inc.

DISSTON - Tools - Disston Co.

DISSTON-CARLSON - Tools ☆ - Disston Co.

DISSTON SELECT - Saws–hand-operated - Disston Co.

DIST-O-MAP - Maps - Rand McNally & Co.

DISTA - Pharmaceutical preparations - Eli Lilly and Co.

DISTANCE-FINDER - Golfing equipment ☆ - Double Products Co.

DISTANCE MASTER - Golfing equipment - Ralph Maltby Enterprises Inc.

DISTANCE TEACHER - Communications equipment - Scientific-Atlanta, Inc.

DISTANCE WHIP, THE - Golfing equipment - Network Golf Ltd. Partnership

DISTANT ECHOES - Bells - B-J Enterprises Inc.

DISTANT RAINBOW - Christmas tree ornaments - Cracker Box Inc.

DISTAVIEW - Lenses ☆ - Daktronics Inc.

DISTEN - Pharmaceutical preparations - Blair Pharmacal

DISTILLATA - Water–distilled - Distillata Co.

DISTILLATE - Guitars - Alembic Inc.

DISTILLATE 38 - Fuel additives - Lincoln Laboratory

DISTILLER - Computer software - Adobe Systems Inc.

DISTILLERIES PERRAUX - Fruits–candied ☆ - Dean & Deluca Inc.

DISTILLER'S BOND - Whiskey - Old Boone Distillery Co.

DISTILLER'S PRIDE - Gin - Old Boone Distillery Co.

DISTINCT - Recording label - Westwood Entertainment Group

DISTINCTION - Clocks - General Time Corp. (Westclox/Seth Thomas Div.)

DISTINCTION - Floor coverings - Congoleum Corp.

DISTINCTION - Floor coverings–carpet and rugs - Calladium & Marglen

DISTINCTION - Floor coverings–carpet and rugs - S and S Mills Inc.

DISTINCTION - Floor coverings–carpet and rugs ☆ - Lees Carpets

DISTINCTION - Towels - Southern Terry, Inc.

DISTINCTION FRANKLIN SILK - Mattresses - Simmons USA

DISTINCTION MADISON LUXURY - Mattresses - Simmons USA

DISTINCTIONS - Tiles–ceramic ☆ - American Olean Tile Co.

DISTINCTIONS - Wallpaper - Essex Wallcoveringss

DISTINCTIVE - Crackers - Pepperidge Farm Inc.

DISTINCTIVE - Diaries - Distinctive Diaries Ltd.

DISTINCTIVE - Floor coverings–carpet and rugs - Carpeting Concepts

DISTINCTIVE BLUSH - Beverages ☆ - Labatt Importers Inc.

DISTINCTIVE DESIGNS - Furniture - Edward Hostmann, Inc.

DISTINCTIVE DESIGNS BY CROWN CRAFTS, INC. - Linen - Crown Crafts, Inc.

DISTINCTIVE DINNERS - Pet products - ALPO Petfoods Inc.

DISTINCTIVE FINIALS - Lamps - American-De Rosa Lamparts, Inc.

DISTINCTIVE MILANO - Cookies - Pepperidge Farm Inc.

DISTINCTLY DAMASK - Wallpaper - Stroheim & Romann, Inc.

DISTINCTLY DAMASK II - Wallpaper - Stroheim & Romann, Inc.

DISTINCTLY DIFFERENT - Apparel–women's - Kmart Corp.

DISTINCTLY MINT - Teas - Lipton Investments, Inc.

DISTINO - Shoes - Globe Footwear Corp.

DISTINQT - Beverages–alcohol - Munico International Corp.

DISTINQT DIAMANTE - Beverages–alcohol - Munico International Corp.

DISTINQT LEMONY - Beverages–alcohol - Munico International Corp.

DISTINQT ORANGY - Beverages–alcohol - Munico International Corp.

DISTO-GUARD-5-K - Pet products - Thomas Veterinary Drug

DISTOGUIDE - Maps - Rand McNally & Co.

DISTON - Shower stalls–metal - Craft-Diston Industries Inc.

DISTOPINE - Disinfectants - Sanitek Products Inc.

DISTRACTIONS - Hair accessories, jewelry, belts, etc. - Parrish Inc.

DISTRAN - Sporting goods ☆ - Ranging Inc.

DISTRESS FLASH - Lighting equipment - GTE Corp.

DISTRESSED LEATHER CONDITIONER - Sporting goods - Bee Natural Leathercare Inc.

DISTRIBOJET - Nozzles - Spraying Systems Co.

DISTRIBULINK - Computer software - Legent Corp.

DISTRIBUNE - Publisher's imprints - Aluminum Co. of America

DISTRIBUTED DATABASE CONNECTION SERVICES/2 - Computer software - International Business Machines Corp.

DISTRIBUTED SNIFFER SYSTEM - Computer software - Network General Holding Corp.

DISTRIBUTEDPRINT - Computer hardware - Gammagraphx, Inc.

DISTRIBUTION MANAGEMENT 2000 - Business software - Software 2000, Inc.

DISTRIBUTION STREAM - Computer software - Dun and Bradstreet Software Services, Inc.

DISTRIBUTOR - Pipes - Pomona Pipe Products Co.

DISTRICT - Apparel–women's - Siena Group

DISTRICT MATCH - Computer software - Data Systems & Mapping, Inc.

DISTRINET - Computer software - K2 Micro Systems Inc.

DISTRIVISION - Computer software - Vertical Technologies, Inc.

DISTRO BOX - Electrical equipment - Union Connector Co.

DISTROID - Toys ☆ - ERTL Co., Inc.

DISTURBULATOR - Vacuum cleaners and accessories - The Eureka Co.

DISULANS - Pharmaceutical preparations ☆ - P.J. Noyes Co., Inc.

DISYSTON - Pesticides–household - Bonide Products, Inc.

DITA - Dolls - Out of This World Projects Inc.

DITA - Hockey equipment - Dita USA

D'ITALIANO - Breads - American Bakeries Co.

D'ITALIANO FRESH BAKED - Breads - Stroehmann Bakeries Inc.

DITATE - Pharmaceutical preparations ☆ - Savage Laboratories Inc.

DITCH DIGGER - Tires - Denman Tire Corp.

DITCH THE BITCH - Novelty items - Unlimited Ltd. Inc.

DITCHERS - Machinery - Alamo Industrial

DITEK - Electrical surge protectors - Diversified Technology Group, Inc.

DITEL - Communications equipment - Ditel, Inc.

DITHANE - Fungicides - Rohm and Haas Co.

DITHANE F-45 - Fungicides - Rohm and Haas Co.

DITHER DUCK - Toys - Tonka Corp.

DITHIREX - Pharmaceutical preparations - C.S. Ruckstuhl Co. Inc.

D.I.T.I.-2 - Pharmaceutical preparations - Dunhall Pharmaceuticals Inc.

DITKIT - Pet products - Adri

DITO DITO - Apparel–women's - In-Port Ltd.

DITOMITE THE MIRACLE MINERAL - Soil testing kits - Agriscience and Technologies, Inc.

DITON-A - Cleaning preparations - Diversey Wyandotte Corp.

DITRACE - Electrical equipment - SEEQ Technology Inc.

DITRONIC - Batteries - Rayovac Corp.

DIT'S - Lamps - World of Clothing, Inc.

DIT'S - Nuts–salted, roasted, cooked, or canned - R.D. Williams

DITTAFONO - Dictating machines ☆ - Dictaphone Corp.

DITTING - Coffee makers–electric - First Colony Coffee and Tea Co. Inc.

DITTMARK - Paper ☆ - Lincoln Paper Co.

DITTO - Dinnerware–glass - Dansk International Designs, Ltd.

DITTO - Duplicating machines - Starkey Chemical Process Co.

DITTO - Floor coverings–carpet and rugs ☆ - Masland Corp.

DITTO BIRD - Dolls - Mattel, Inc.

DITTOS - Potato chips ☆ - Laura Scudder's

DITTY BUDDY - Bags - Marcor, Inc.

DIU-SCRIP - Pharmaceutical preparations ☆ - Scrip-Physician Supply Co.

DIUCARDIN - Pharmaceutical preparations - Wyeth-Ayerst Laboratories

DIUCEN - Pharmaceutical preparations ☆ - Central Pharmaceutical Inc.

DIULO - Pharmaceutical preparations - G. D. Searle & Co.

DIUPRES - Pharmaceutical preparations - Merck & Co., Inc. (Merck Research Laboratories)

DIURESE - Pharmaceutical preparations - American Urologicals Inc.

DIURESE-R - Pharmaceutical preparations ☆ - American Urologicals Inc.

DIURESS - Vitamins and nutritional supplements - Bioenergy Nutrient's Inc.

DIURETIC FACTORS - Vitamins and nutritional supplements - Consac Industries, Inc.

DIURETON - Health care products ☆ - D'Franssia Corp.

DIUREX - Pharmaceutical preparations - Alva-Amco Pharmacal Co.

DIUREX-2 - Pharmaceutical preparations - Alva-Amco Pharmacal Co.

DIUREX MPR - Pharmaceutical preparations - Alva-Amco Pharmacal Co.

DIURFLO - Health care products - Healthwatchers System

DIURIGEN - Pharmaceutical preparations - Goldline Laboratories, Inc.

DIURIL - Diuretics - Merck & Co., Inc. (Merck Research Laboratories)

DIURITE - Vitamins and nutritional supplements - Planetary Formulas

DIURTAB - Health care products ☆ - Nature's Herbs

DIUTABS - Pharmaceutical preparations - Vita-Fore Products Co.

DIUTENSEN-R - Pharmaceutical preparations - Wallace Laboratories

DIV-I-DEX - File folders ☆ - Cel-U-Dex Corp.

DIVA - Apparel and accessories ☆ - Palm Beach Co., Inc.

DIVA - Boats–motor - Forester Boats Inc.

DIVA - Cabinets - Aristokraft, Inc.

DIVA - Cheese - Ambriola Co. Inc.

DIVA - Computer peripheral equipment - Oxford Molecular Group

DIVA - Cosmetics - Parfums Ungaro Inc.

DIVA - Dinnerware–glass - Arita Sales Co. Inc.

DIVA - Dolls - Mattel, Inc.

DIVA - Draperies - Maya Romanoff Corp.

DIVA - Electric lighting equipment - Lutron Electronics Co., Inc.

DIVA - Fabrics - Gretchen Bellinger Inc.

DIVA - Helmets–athletic - Troxel-West

DIVA - Metals - Wenger Corp.

DIVA - Negligees ☆ - Marja Foundations

DIVA - Rings–jewelry - Artcarved Inc.

DIVA - Wood products - Grosfillex Inc.

DIVA BRAND - Cheese - Ambriola Co. Inc.

DIVA COMPANY - Jewelry - Diva Co.

DIVE-! - Apparel–athletic - Mission Control

DIVE-AIDE - Food products - Horizon Worldwide Export Corp.

DIVE-ALERT - Sporting goods - Ideations Design Inc.

DIVE-DIVE - Toys - Tonka Corp.

DIVE DOTS - Swimming pools - Recreonics, Inc.

DIVE FLASH CARDS - Swimming pools - Recreonics, Inc.

DIVE GEAR - Apparel and accessories - First Step

DIVE-IN THEATRE - Video production - Porpoise Pool & Patio, Inc.

DIVE MASTER - Computers - Cochran Consulting, Inc.

DIVE PROFILER - Computer software - Savant, Ltd.

DIVE-TRAK - Navigational instruments - RJE International, Inc.

DIVEMASTER - Watches - Rolex Watch USA, Inc.

DIVEN - Tomato pastes and sauces - Diven Packing Co.

DIVEN TOMATO JUICE - Tomato pastes and sauces - Diven Packing Co.

DIVEN WHOLE PEELED TOMATOES - Tomato pastes and sauces - Diven Packing Co.

DIVEOPTX - Lenses–optical - OPTX 20/20

DIVER - Fishing lines - Cortland Line Co., Inc.

DIVER BELOW - Swimming gear - Poolmaster Inc.

DIVER PELICAN - Toys–stuffed - Dakin Inc.

DIVERCILLIN - Pharmaceutical preparations ☆ - B.F. Ascher & Co. Inc.

DIVERS CHOICE, THE - Sporting goods - Underwater Diving Inc.

DIVERS DEPOT - Scuba diving equipment - EKS Enterprises, Inc.

DIVERSEY WYANDOTTE - Chemical preparations - Diversey Wyandotte Corp.

DIVERSI - Dishes–china - Global/Guzzini

DIVERSI-BOARD - Plastics - Diversi-Plast Div.

DIVERSIDE K - Insecticides - Diversey Wyandotte Corp.

DIVERSIPHASE - Electronic equipment - Shure Brothers, Inc.

DIVERSIPIPE - Hoses - Goodyear Tire & Rubber Co.

DIVERSITY - Apparel–women's - J.C. Penney Co., Inc.

DIVERSITY GAME, THE - Games - Quality Education Development, Inc.

DIVERSIWALL - Insulating materials - Gencorp Inc.

DIVERSOL CX - Health care products - Diversey Wyandotte Corp.

DIVERSTRIP - Paint removers - Diversey Wyandotte Corp.

DIVERTENTE - Footwear–women's - Marx & Newman Co. Inc.

DIVERTER EWA, THE - Electronic equipment - Electronic Warfare Associates, Inc.

DIVESKINS - Apparel and accessories - Oztex, Inc.

DIVETALKER - Computers - Steelex Inc.

DIVEX - Games ☆ - Avalon Hill Game Co.

DIVIDA KILN - Decals ☆ - Commercial Decal Inc.

DIVIDEND DOZEN - Handkerchiefs - J.C. Penney Co., Inc.

DIVIDEND EXPRE$$ - Banks–commercial - Northwest Natural Gas Co.

DIVIDENDS - Apparel–women's - J.C. Penney Co., Inc.

DIVIDENT - Health care products - Block Drug Co., Inc.

DIVINA - Food products - Food Match, Inc.

DIVINA - Hair care products - Divina Products Co.

DIVINA ALOESSENTIAL POLISH REMOVER - Cosmetics - Divina Products Co.

DIVINA COMPLETE CARE - Cosmetics - Divina Products Co.

DIVINA PINK PARFAIT - Cosmetics ☆ - Divina Products Co.

DIVINA PRO - Hair care products ☆ - Divina Products Co.

DIVINA SEA SPLASH ASTRINGENT - Cosmetics - Divina Products Co.

DIVINE - Floor coverings - Aladdin Mills, Inc.

DIVINE - Recording label - Jazz Composer's Orchestra Association Inc.

DIVINE DESIGN BY HARRIET MARCUS - Jewelry - Harriet Marcus

DIVINE FOODS - Health care products ☆ - CC Pollen Co.

DIVINE GUIDANCE SYSTEMS - Golfing equipment - Brian S. Baggott

DIVINE INSPIRATION - Greeting cards - Divine Inspiration

DIVINE INTENTIONS - Candy - J.B.R, Inc.

DIVINE MADNESS - Games - Elizabeth J. Merrick Vecchio

DIVINE NIGHTLIGHTS, THE - Lighting equipment - Divine Nightlight Co., Inc.

DIVINE NINE - Golfing equipment - Callaway Golf Co.

DIVINE NO. 10 - Perfumes - Perfumer's Workshop Ltd.

DIVINE RIPE - Fruits and vegetables ☆ - Sun World International

DIVINE TOUCH - Floor coverings–carpet and rugs - Ashley Commercial Carpets

DIVINE TOUCH - Hosiery–women's ☆ - J.C. Penney Co., Inc.

DIVINE WORD MISSIONARIES - Notebooks and notepads - Sormani Inc.

DIVING DEVILS - Toys–automobiles - Tyco Toys

DIVING DOLPHIN - Massage products - Robin Haynes

DIVING GIRL - Apparel and accessories ☆ - Jantzen Inc.

DIVING SYSTEMS INTERNATIONAL - Apparel–athletic - Lanco Corp.

DIVINITY BY DAVE - Candy - David Alan Tombaugh

DIVISION 23 - Sporting goods - Carmate, Inc.

DIVISION SHOOTING GALLERY - Computer software - Gamco Industries Inc.

DIVISION STREET - Sausages - Andy's Deli & Mikolajczyk Sausage Shop, Inc.

DIVISIONS - Cabinets - A-Bee Syndicate Inc.

DIVISUMMA 24 - Calculators ☆ - Olivetti North America Inc. (Consumer Products Div.)

DIVOLUXE - Cleaning preparations - Diversey Wyandotte Corp.

DIVON - Furniture - United Industries of New England

DIVORCE CALENDAR - Calendars - Ladybug Press

DIVORCECARE - Recording label - Steve Grissom

DIVOT MATE - Containers - Par Aide Products Co.

DIX-LOCK - Hardware - Dixon Valve and Coupling Co.

DIXACT - Pharmaceutical preparations ☆ - Dixon-Shane Inc.

DIXADE - Pharmaceutical preparations - Dixon-Shane Inc.

DIXAHIST - Pharmaceutical preparations ☆ - Dixon-Shane Inc.

☆ = Now out of production

DIXANA - Food products - Gerawan Foods Inc.
DIXATAL - Pharmaceutical preparations - Dixon-Shane Inc.
DIXATAP - Pharmaceutical preparations - Dixon-Shane Inc.
DIXCEL - Brushes - Mascot Precision Tools
DIXIANA - Food products - Draper-King Cole Inc.
DIXIE - Artists' materials ☆ - M. Grumbacher Inc.
DIXIE - Beverages–malt - Dixie Brewing Co.
DIXIE - Candy - Ferrara Pan Candy Co., Inc.
DIXIE - Containers–trash ☆ - Cyclops Industries (Empire-Detroit Steel Div.)
DIXIE - Dog food - Pet Center, Inc.
DIXIE - Dolls - Mattel, Inc.
DIXIE - Envelopes–paper - Specialty Envelopes Inc.
DIXIE - Floor coverings–carpet and rugs - Tack Levye
DIXIE - Floor coverings–carpet and rugs ☆ - Regal Rugs Inc.
DIXIE - Food products ☆ - Moody Dunbar Inc.
DIXIE - Fruits and vegetables - Paradise Fruit Co., Inc.
DIXIE - Furniture - Lexington Furniture Industries, Inc.
DIXIE - Furniture ☆ - Masco Corp.
DIXIE - Furniture–upholstered - Eagle Ottawa Leather Co.
DIXIE - Games - Columbia Games, Inc.
DIXIE - Gasoline - Dixie Oil Co. Inc.
DIXIE - Kitchen appliances - Magic Chef Inc.
DIXIE - Ladders–wood - John S. Tilley Ladders Co. Inc.
DIXIE - Musical instrument accessories - Trophy Music Co.
DIXIE - Paints ☆ - Blue Ridge Talc Co. Inc.
DIXIE - Paper dinnerware, cup dispensers - James River Corp.
DIXIE - Refuse cans ☆ - Bowman Metal Deck
DIXIE - Shoes–athletic - Coast Shoes Inc.
DIXIE - Tar - Bickmore Inc.
DIXIE - Twine - Blue Mountain Industries, Inc.
DIXIE - Window shades - A & E Blind & Awning Co.
DIXIE AMBER LIGHT - Beverages–malt - Dixie Brewing Co.
DIXIE ANA - Vegetable oil - Ventura Foods LLC (Lou Ana Division)
DIXIE BELL - Cookies - Ralston Purina Co.
DIXIE BELL - Jackets - Dixie, USA, Inc.
DIXIE BELLE - Ice boxes–household - Richmond Cedar Works Manufacturing Corp.
DIXIE BELLE - Snack foods ☆ - Bremner Inc.
DIXIE BEST - Mayonnaise ☆ - Piknik Products Co. Inc.
DIXIE BLACKENED VOODOO LAGER - Beverages–malt - Dixie Brewing Co.
DIXIE BRAND - Food products - Paradise Fruit Co., Inc.
DIXIE BWICK - Wicking - Hooper Industries Inc.
DIXIE CCA - Lumber - Hoover Treated Wood Products Inc.
DIXIE CHEF - Poultry feeds - Sweet Sue Kitchens
DIXIE CHOPPER - Lawn mowers - Magic Circle Corp.
DIXIE CLAY - Clay products - R.T. Vanderbilt Co., Inc.
DIXIE CREAM - Doughnuts - Dixie Cream Flour Co.
DIXIE CRIMSON VOODOO ALE - Beverages–malt - Dixie Brewing Co.
DIXIE CRYSTALS - Sugar–granulated, refined, or powdered - Savannah Foods and Industries Inc.
DIXIE DAIRY - Milk - Dixie Dairy Co.
DIXIE-DANDY - Food products - Pierce Foods Corp.
DIXIE DAN'S - Dips–sour cream based - Jardine's Texas Foods
DIXIE DARLING - Jewelry - Jacoby-Bender Inc.
DIXIE DAY - Detergents - Clo White Co.
DIXIE-DEALERS - Meat products–poultry - Hester Industries, Inc.
DIXIE DELITE - Milk - Pic a Pac Inc.
DIXIE DELITES - Candy ☆ - Visitation Home Made Candies
DIXIE DEW DROPS - Food products - Jardine's Texas Foods
DIXIE-DIPPERS - Food products - Pierce Foods Corp.
DIXIE DOG - Flour–blended - Rio Grande Amusements, Inc.
DIXIE DOG CHEW CIGARS - Dog food - Pet Center, Inc.
DIXIE DOUBLE - Computer peripheral equipment - Sigma Game Inc.
DIXIE DRUMMERS - Food products - Whistlin' Dixie Fried Chicken Inc.
DIXIE DUCK - Toys–stuffed - Russ Berrie and Co., Inc.
DIXIE FIFE - Toys–musical - Trophy Music Co.
DIXIE FLYER - Brooms - Fluffo Mop & Broom Co. Inc.
DIXIE FLYER - Ladders–metal - Davidson Ladders Inc.
DIXIE FRESH DELITE - Bakery products - Dixie Fresh Inc.
DIXIE GARDEN - Vegetables–frozen - Chiquita Brands, Inc.
DIXIE-HEARTS - Food products - Hester Industries, Inc.
DIXIE-HEARTS - Food products - Pierce Foods Corp.
DIXIE HOT CUPS - Paper cups - James River Corp.
DIXIE HOT SAUCE - Sauces - Commonwealth Brands, Inc.
DIXIE JAZZ - Beverages–malt - Dixie Brewing Co.
DIXIE-JOE - Food products - Pierce Foods Corp.

DIXIE KIDS - Plates–paper - James River Paper Co., Inc.
DIXIE LIGHT - Beverages–malt - Dixie Brewing Co.
DIXIE LILY - Food products - Beatrice Cos. Inc.
DIXIE LIVINGWARE - Paper plates, cups - James River Corp.
DIXIE LOAF - Meats–luncheon - Fischer Packing Co.
DIXIE MAID - Cigars - Swisher International, Inc.
DIXIE MILLS - Fabrics - Natex Inc.
DIXIE MINT - Candy - Nestle USA
DIXIE OVEN - Food products - Whistlin' Dixie Fried Chicken Inc.
DIXIE PEACH - Hair care products - Lander Co., Inc.
DIXIE PEACH - Juices - Snapple Beverage Corp.
DIXIE PEACH WHITE CORN - Tortillas - Native South Service
DIXIE PERFECTOUCH - Cups–paper - James River Paper Co.
DIXIE PRESS - Publisher's imprints - Pelican Publishing Co. Inc.
DIXIE PRIDE - Confections ☆ - Central Carolina Grocers Inc.
DIXIE PRIDE - Food products - Golden Pantry West Inc.
DIXIE PURE - Candy ☆ - Southwestern Candy Co. Inc.
DIXIE PWF - Lumber - Hoover Treated Wood Products Inc.
DIXIE QUEEN - Food containers - Farmhouse Foods
DIXIE QUEEN - Jewelry - Jacoby-Bender Inc.
DIXIE ROSE - Jewelry - Jacoby-Bender Inc.
DIXIE SONG BIRD - Harmonicas - William Kratt Co.
DIXIE SPECIAL - Tools - Railway Handle Corp.
DIXIE SPRINGS SPRING WATER - Water–mineral - New Orleans Water Co.
DIXIE SQUARE - Floor coverings–carpet and rugs ☆ - Hollytex Carpet Mills Inc.
DIXIE-STARS - Poultry - Hester Industries, Inc.
DIXIE-STIX - Meat products–poultry - Whistlin' Dixie Fried Chicken Inc.
DIXIE SUPERWARE - Paper plates, cups, and bowls - James River Corp.
DIXIE-SUPREME - Meat products–poultry - Whistlin' Dixie Fried Chicken Inc.
DIXIE-TENDERS - Meat products–poultry - Whistlin' Dixie Fried Chicken Inc.
DIXIE-TURK'Y STIX - Meat products–poultry - Whistlin' Dixie Fried Chicken Inc.
DIXIE WHITE - Turkeys - Continental Grain Co.
DIXIE WHITE MOOSE - Beverages–malt - Dixie Brewing Co.
DIXIE-WINGS - Meat products–poultry - Whistlin' Dixie Fried Chicken Inc.
DIXIE-WRITER - Pens ☆ - Long's Dixie Pens
DIXIEBELLE - Mops - Piedmont Mop Co.
DIXIELAND - Food products - Renfro Foods Inc.
DIXIELAND JUBILEE - Recording label - GNP Crescendo Record Co. Inc.
DIXIENAMEL - Enamels ☆ - Blue Ridge Talc Co. Inc.
DIXIES - Candy - Fanny Farmer Candy Shops Inc.
DIXIES - Crackers - Nabisco Foods Group
DIXIES DRUMSTICK - Crackers - Nabisco Foods Group
DIXIEVIM - Gasoline ☆ - Charter Marketing Co.
DIXIEWARE - Disposable ovenwear - James River Corp.
DIXILINK - Fence fabric ☆ - Atlantic Steel Co.
DIXIPAK - Tie wire coils ☆ - Atlantic Steel Co.
DIXISTEEL - Fence fabric, wire, etc ☆ - Atlantic Steel Co.
DIXON - Artists' materials - American Blueprint Co. Inc.
DIXON - Cleaning preparations - Khadija Dixon
DIXON - Lawn mowers - Dixon Industries Inc.
DIXON - Pencils - Dixon Ticonderoga Co.
DIXON - Shoes ☆ - Hyde Athletic Industries Inc.
DIXON - Thermometers - Airguide Instrument Co.
DIXON - Toys–musical - Davitt and Hanser Music Co.
DIXON - Window shades - John Dixon Inc.
DIXON - Wood products - Dixon Lumber Co. Inc.
DIXON BEST - Pencils - Dixon Ticonderoga Co.
DIXON DARLIN' CLAYMATES - Figurines - H.T. Fues & Associates Inc.
DIXON-SHANE - Pharmaceutical preparations ☆ - Dixon-Shane Inc.
DIXON TICONDEROGA - Pencils - Dixon Ticonderoga Co.
DIXONEX - Pharmaceutical preparations - Dixon-Shane Inc.
DIXON'S CRAFT - Erasers - Dixon Ticonderoga Co.
DIXOTUSS - Pharmaceutical preparations - Dixon-Shane Inc.
DIXSTEEL - Tools ☆ - Mascot Precision Tools
DIY - Mats - Colmar Industries, Inc.
DIY - Video production - Do It Yourself Inc.
D.I.Y. BRAND - Caulking compounds - Red Devil Inc.
DIZ-ZINE PAX - Patterns–clothing ☆ - Stangren Co.
DIZ-ZIT - Brushes ☆ - Stangren Co.
DIZMISS - Pharmaceutical preparations - JMI-Canton Pharmaceuticals
DIZYMES - Pharmaceutical preparations ☆ - Recsei Laboratories
DIZZLE-DIZZLE - Paints - Colortex Co.
DIZZY - Peanut butter ☆ - Ventura Foods
DIZZY DINOSAURS - Games ☆ - Pressman Toy Corp.

☆ = Now out of production

DIZZY DISC - Toys - Steven Manufacturing Co.
DIZZY DIZZY DINOSAURS - Games - Pressman Toy Corp.
DIZZY FRIZZY - Yarn - Dizzy Frizzy
DIZZY GRIZZLIES - Snack foods - Nabisco Foods Group
DIZZY LIZZY - Candy ☆ - Sunline Brands
DIZZY LIZZY - Dolls ☆ - Fun World Inc.
DIZZY LIZZY PRODUCTIONS - Greeting cards - Dizzy Lizzy Productions
D.J. - Flatware - Oneida Ltd.
DJ - Garden equipment ☆ - Rubens Originals
DJ - Remote controls - International Cablecasting Technologies Inc.
DJ DOTSON - Beverages - D J Dotson
DJ DOTSON RUM RUNNER MIX - Beverages - D J Dotson
D.J. DOTSON TRIPLE SEC - Beverages - D J Dotson
DJ FARMS - Food products - L & B Distributors Inc.
DJ WEST - Recording label - Def Jam Recordings, Inc.
DJ WEST - Recording label - DJR Holdings, LLC
DJAKARTA - Floor coverings–carpet and rugs ☆ - Regal Rugs Inc.
DJARUM - Cigarettes - G.A. Georgopulo & Co. Inc.
DJARUM INTERNATIONAL - Cigarettes - G.A. Georgopulo & Co. Inc.
DJARUM SAFARI - Cigarettes - G.A. Georgopulo & Co. Inc.
DJARUM SPECIAL - Cigarettes - G.A. Georgopulo & Co. Inc.
DJARUM SUPER - Cigarettes - G.A. Georgopulo & Co. Inc.
DJC - Bags–storage - DJC Design Studio, Inc.
DJC DESIGN STUDIO, INC. - Jewelry - DJC Design Studio, Inc.
DJD - Apparel–women's - Meijer, Inc.
DJD SPORT - Apparel–women's - Meijer, Inc.
DJEEP - Lighters - General Cigar Co., Inc.
DJER-KISS - Skin care products - All Clubman
DJI SAM SOE - Cigarettes - G.A. Georgopulo & Co. Inc.
DJINN - Floor coverings–carpet and rugs ☆ - Regal Rugs Inc.
DJO - Recording label - Daran Records
DJ'S - Apparel and accessories - DJ's Custom Designs Inc.
DJ'S BAKERY - Breads - DJ's Bakery, Inc.
D.J.'S CHOICE - Amplifiers - Marketing Insights, Inc.-Frank Luppino Jr., and
  Associates
+D'JULIA - Footwear ☆ - Glamour Footwear
DJW - Jewelry - Direct Jewelry Wholesale, Inc.
DK - Bicycles - DK Products Inc.
DK - Hair-replacement product and services - International Hairgoods Inc.
DK - Skin care products - Gabrielle Studio, Inc.
D.K. GOLD - Apparel–women's - Donnkenny Inc.
DK MEN - Colognes - Gabrielle Studio, Inc.
DKC MUSIC - Recording label - Dkc Music, Inc.
DKE - Decals and transfers - Duke University
DKNY - Hosiery - Donna Karan Co.
DKNY EYES - Sunglasses - Solargenics
DKP - Fertilizers - JH Biotech, Inc.
D.K.S. - Golfing equipment - Mitsushiba International, Inc.
DKSA - Exercising equipment - DKSA
DL - Cleaning preparations - DL/Banite
DL - Metals - Driv-Lok, Inc.
DL 2000 - Hair care products - Carson Products Co.
DL-BU - Locks–door - Powerbrace Corp.
DL GROUP - Office furniture–metal ☆ - Metier Furniture Corp.
DL LANGUAGE - Computer software - Open+Voice, Inc.
DL-NORLEUCINE - Pharmaceutical preparations - City Chemical Corp.
D'LAURA - Perfumes - Rugby Laboratories Inc.
DLC - Chalk ☆ - Claridge Products and Equipment Inc.
DLC - Tires - Bridgestone/Firestone, Inc.
DLC-100 - Tires - Bridgestone/Firestone, Inc.
DLD - Jewelry - Dennis Lee Folk
+D'LECO - Guitars - D'leco Acoustic Instruments, Inc.
D'LEON - Boots - Jamie Castro
DLI WATCHMAN - Microscopes - DLI Engineering Corp.
D'LISH - Yogurt–frozen - SC Acquisition Corp.
D'LITA - Shoes - Canter Shoe Co.
D'LITE - Beverages–carbonated - Sara Lee Corp.
+D'LITE! - Cheese ☆ - Rose International
+D'LITTER CRITTERS - Statuary ☆ - Faultless Starch/Bon Ami Co.
DLM - Flexible doors and partitions - DLM Plastics Corp.
DLO - Measuring instruments - Chemtrac Systems, Inc.
DLPA - Analgesics ☆ - Natrol, Inc.
D.L.R. BY DE LA RENTIS - Footwear–men's - Fred E. Goldstein
DLS - Electrical equipment - D.L.S. Enterprise, Inc.
DLS DRUM LABEL SOLUTIONS - Computer software - Labels One, Inc.
DLTSTOR - Computer peripheral equipment - Quantum Corp.

DLUBAK - Glass–stained - Dlubak Bending Studios
DLW - Furniture - Blue Inc.
DLX - Eyeglasses - Crews, Inc.
DLX - Jewelry - Violetta Jewelry Co.
DLX PLUS - Guitars - Dimarzio, Inc.
D'LYLE - Jewelry - Lyles-DeGrazier Co.
DM - Computer storage devices–magnetic - OCLC Online Computer Library
  Center
DM - Cough medicines - Morton Grove Pharmaceuticals
DM - Spices and extracts - David Michael & Co., Inc.
DM-3 - Cutlery - Lenore E. Perry
DM CHOICE - Juices - David Michael & Co.
DM DOOR MAIL - Electronic equipment - BMW Enterprises, Inc.
D.M. FERRY - Flowers, plants, and seeds - Ferry-Morse Seed Co.
DM PLUS - Computer software - Mchugh, Freeman & Associates, Inc.
DM RECORDS - Recording label - DM Records, Inc.
DM RECORDS - Recording label - DM Records, Inc.
DM4/DL DUAL MULTI - Gauging instruments - Krautkramer-Branson Inc.
DMA - Medical apparatus - Del Mar Avionics
DMAE 100 PLUS - Vitamins and nutritional supplements - Vitamin Research
  Products Inc.
DMAE-H3 - Vitamins and nutritional supplements - Twinlab
D'MAG - Tape players–cassette - Recoton Corp.
DMAN - Apparel–men's - Leland-Byron Investments, Inc.
D'MARIE - Furs–pelts - Fur Outlet Inc.
D!MATCH - Computer peripheral equipment - WizardWorks Group Inc.
DMB - Cosmetics - De Meo Brothers
DMB - Golfing equipment - Dunlop Maxfli Sports Corp.
DMB - Musical instruments - Design Direct Sound
DMC - Paints ☆ - Valspar Corp.
DMC - Thread - DMC Corp.
DMC CONSULTING, INC. - Computer software - DMC Consulting, Inc.
DMC NET - Computer hardware - Digital Microwave Corp.
DME - Health care products - Tubular Fabricators Industry, Inc.
DME/PEN - Computer peripheral equipment - COMPuAIMS Inc.
DME PRO - Health care products - Sandata Inc.
+D'MEDICI USA - Jewelry - Norman T. Kanel Corp.
DMF - Vegetables–canned - Oxford Chemicals
DMG - Vitamins and nutritional supplements ☆ - Ethical Nutrients
DMI - Surgical instruments - Dean Medical Instruments, Inc.
DMI-7000 - Automotive parts and accessories ☆ - Edelbrock Corp.
DMJ - Jewelry - DMJ Jewelers, Inc.
DMJ CLIPCATCH - Personal care products - M.J. Dana Corp., Inc.
DMK ELECTRONIC LIBRARY - Computer software - Direct Medical
  Knowledge
DML - Jewelry - M.J. Harrington & Co., Inc.
DML - Skin care products - Person and Covey Inc.
DMMS - Computer software - Applied Systems Technologies, Inc.
DMR - Lighting fixtures - Hubbell Lighting, Inc. (Lighting Div.)
DMS - Amplifiers–musical instrument - Dean Markley Strings, Inc.
DMS - Computer peripheral equipment - Inspex Inc.
DMS - Medical apparatus - Del Mar Avionics
DMS DESIGNS - Paper - Daniel Martinez
DMS/IB - Computer software - Software Laboratories Inc.
DMS TREASURES - Incense - Root Candle Co.
DMSCIENTIFIC - Medical apparatus - Del Mar Avionics
DMT - Lighting fixtures - Hubbell Lighting, Inc. (Lighting Div.)
DMT - Paper adhesive - Lany Fax of America Inc.
DMU - Database management software - Information Retrieval Companies Inc.
DMV - Contact lenses ☆ - Camelot Laboratories
DMV II - Contact lenses ☆ - Camelot Laboratories
DMW - Jewelry - Stone-Margulis
DMX DJ - Remote control devices - International Cablecasting Technologies
  Inc.
DMZ SAFE ZONE - Apparel and accessories - EWH Investment Co.
DN - Boats - Frank M. Weeks Yacht Yard
DN - Boats–fishing - Doyle/Boston Sailmakers
DN - Caps–baseball - Denver Nuggets
DN - Floor coverings ☆ - Venturi, Inc.
DN - Hardware - Dyson Corp.
DN-24 - Skin care products - Pharmagel Corp.
DNA - Perfumes - Fashion World, Inc.
DNA - Recording label - DNA Records
DNA - Sporting goods ☆ - Prince Sports Group, Inc.
DNA MULTIPREP - Laboratory apparatus - Biotecx Laboratories, Inc.
DNA TUTOR - Computer software - SourceView Software International

☆ = Now out of production

DNASE SHOTGUN - Chemical preparations - Novagen, Inc.
DNAZOL - Chemical preparations - Molecular Research Center, Inc.
DNE - Vitamins and nutritional supplements - D & E Pharmaceuticals, Inc.
D'NEALIAN ALPHABET PUZZLES - Puzzles - Lauri Inc.
DNI - Communications equipment - Telect, Inc.
D.N.I. BASICS - Apparel - Manhattan Trade International Inc.
DNIEPER RIVER LINE - Games ☆ - Avalon Hill Game Co.
DNJ - Jewelry - Star of New York Inc.
DNR - Electronic equipment - National Semiconductor Corp.
DO-A-BAK - Bathroom accessories - CCMA Products, Inc.
DO-A-DUCK - Hobby kits - Stoney Point Decoys Ltd.
DO A NUMBER ON ME - Apparel and accessories - Bentley Lingerie, Inc.
DO A NUMBER ON ME ESLEEP - Apparel and accessories - Bentley Lingerie, Inc.
DO A NUMBER ON SOMEBODY - Apparel and accessories - Bentley Lingerie, Inc.
DO-ALL - Brassieres (Bras) - Q-T Foundations Co. Inc.
DO-ALL - Floor coverings - American Floor Products Co. Inc.
DO-ALL - Paint rollers ☆ - Arsco International Inc.
DO-ALL - Wood products - Homasote Co.
DO-ALL +PLUS - Furnace and refractory cement - Vibe Records Inc.
DO & LEARN - Electronic equipment - Hudson Photographic Industries Inc.
DO AS I SAY - Toys ☆ - Placo Products Co.
DO AT THE ZOO - Apparel and accessories - Cheryl Gowdy International, Inc.
DO-BEST - Paints ☆ - Finnaren & Haley Inc.
DO DROP II - Golfing equipment - John H. Rees
DO DUDS PLAY CLOTHES - Apparel–children's - Doduds, Inc.
DO GAN JIN KYU - Vitamins and nutritional supplements - Chang Lee Bok
DO-GOODERS - Cleaning preparations - Swiss-Tex Inc.
DO HWI IT - Knives–pocket - Hardware Wholesalers, Inc.
DO I DARE - Apparel–women's ☆ - Bali Co. Inc.
DO I HAVE ENOUGH? - Computer software - Moneythink, Inc.
DO I LOOK OK? - Recording label - Patricia Farnack
D.O. INDUSTRIES - Lenses ☆ - Navitar, Inc.
DO-IT - Fertilizers - Hardware Wholesalers, Inc.
DO IT - Health care products - East Earth Herb Inc.
DO-IT - Office supplies - Do-It Corp.
DO IT - Tools ☆ - Argee Corp.
DO-IT-ALL - Lighting fixtures - Swivelier Co. Inc.
DO-IT-ALL - Multipurpose totes - Coordinated Products Corp.
DO IT ALL - Tools–hand-operated - Olympia Industrial Inc.
DO-IT-ART - Novelty items - Paper Magic Group Inc.
DO IT BEST HWI - Paint removers - Hardware Wholesalers, Inc.
DO-IT-RIGHT - Paints - United Coatings, Inc.
DO-IT-RIGHT - Paints - United Coatings Inc.
DO-IT-WELL - Brushes–paint ☆ - Linzer Products Corp.
DO IT WITH A PARTNER - Vitamins and nutritional supplements - Ultravit Enterprises, Inc.
DO-IT-YOURSELF - Artists' materials ☆ - M. Grumbacher Inc.
DO-IT-YOURSELF - Lighting fixtures ☆ - Thomas Industries Inc.
DO-IT-YOURSHELF - Shelving units–metal - Dalen Products Inc.
DO-JIGGER - Fishing lures - Bay De Noc Lure Co.
DO-LITTLE AQUARIUMS - Hobby kits - Biosand International, Inc.
DO-MOR - Paints - Schulte Paint & Lacquer Manufacturing Co., Inc.
DO-NOTHING WORM - Fishing lures - Jack Chancellor Lure Co.
DO-NUT - Toys ☆ - Cal-June Inc.
DO-QUICK - Dough conditioners - Archer Daniels Midland Co.
DO-RE-ME - Apparel–women's - USA in Sync, Inc.
DO-RE-MI - Musical instruments - Trophy Music Co.
DO SPEAK - Recording label - Jazz Composer's Orchestra Association Inc.
DO SPORTS - Tote bags - Lawrence J. Purgliese
DO WHAT YOU WANT - Braces–orthopedic - Sportstech, Inc.
DO WHAT'S RIGHT CLUB SKIPPY DRUGPHREY, THE - Shirts - Mobile Bay Area Partnership for Youth
DO WHAT'S RIGHT CLUB, THE - Educational materials - Mobile Bay Area Partnership for Youth
DO-WIKKI - Games - Omnicor
DO YOU REMEMBER? - Publisher's imprints - Gitter's Guides
DO YOUR BODY A FLAVOR - Beverages - Healthtek International, LLC
DO YOUR TASTE BUDS A FLAVOR AND THE ENVIRONMENT A FAVOR - Coffee makers–electric - Manufacturers Components, Inc.
D.O.A. - Fishing lures - D.O.A., Inc.
D.O.A. - Sauces - Victoria's Treasure Inc.
DO+ABLE PRODUCTS - Furniture - Do+Able Products, Inc.
DOAK DERMOTOLOGISTS - Skin care products - Doak Dermatologics
DOAL - Lighting equipment - Northeast Robotics, Inc.

DOAN'S - Analgesics - Ciba-Geigy Corp.
DOB - Skin care products ☆ - Person and Covey Inc.
DOBBEY - Blinds–venetian ☆ - Hunter Douglas, Inc.
DOBBHOFF - Medical apparatus ☆ - Biosearch Medical Products Inc.
DOBBINS - Garden equipment - Master Manufacturing Co.
DOBBS - Hats - Resistol Hats
DOBBS - Hats–felt - Stetson Hat Co. Inc.
DOBBYWEAVE - Wallpaper ☆ - Osborne & Little
DOBE-KOTE - Paints ☆ - Triangle Coatings Inc.
DOBERT - Milk - Dobert Dairy Inc.
DOBIE - Apparel–children's - Dobie Industries Inc.
DOBIE - Scouring pads - Dial Corp.
DOBIE ORIGINALS - Sporting goods - Dobie Industries Inc.
DOBLE XX - Paints ☆ - Everseal International Sales Co. Inc.
DOBLER - Beverages–malt - Piel Bros. Ltd.
DOBRA - Vodka - Sazerac Co. Inc.
DOBRA-NOL - Tranquilizers - Polam Wholesale Inc.
DOBRE - Recording label ☆ - Ray Lawrence Ltd.
DOBRE NON-THIO - Hair care products - Dobre Products Inc.
DOBRE PROTEAN - Hair care products - Dobre Products Inc.
DOBRO - Guitars - Original Musical Instruments Co. Inc.
DOBRO HOUND DOG - Guitars - Original Musical Instruments Co. Inc.
DOBUTREX - Pharmaceutical preparations - Eli Lilly and Co.
DOBY DOBERMAN - Toys–stuffed - Dakin Inc.
DOC - Animal feeds - Bush Brothers and Co.
D.O.C. - Denture cleanser - Harry J. Bosworth Co.
DOC - Sealing compounds - Wall Firma Inc.
DOC & EDDY'S - Billiard-lounge/restaurant franchise - Corner Pockets of America Inc.
DOC BONES - Pet products - EPP, Inc.
DOC CHAOS - Apparel and accessories - Mitchel D. Perlman
DOC/FLOW PLUS - Computer software - Micro Telesis Corp.
DOC HANCOCK - Leather goods - Smith-Worthington Saddlery Co. Inc.
DOC-IN-A-BOX - Computer software - Robert Epstein
DOC-IT - Cameras - UVP Inc.
DOC JOC - Sporting goods ☆ - Worth Inc.
DOC MARTENS - Shoes ☆ - Saga House Inc.
DOC RAIL - Sporting goods - Doc Rail USA, Inc.
D.O.C. SEXY SPECS - Eyeglasses - D.O.C. Optics Corp.
DOC SHASTA - Beverages–carbonated - Shasta Beverages, Inc.
DOC SMITH'S - Beverages–carbonated - Creative Beverage Co.
DOC-U-MAILER - Business forms - Goodwin Graphics, Inc.
DOC-U-NOTES - Pre-printed note pads - Harmony Printing Co., Inc.
DOC WELLFISH - Pet products - Aquarium Pharmaceuticals, Inc.
DOCA - Pharmaceutical preparations ☆ - Organon Inc.
DOCDIRECT - Computer software - Notis Systems, Inc.
DOCJET - Nozzles - Spraying Systems Co.
DOCK & DECK - Paints - C.A. Nash & Son Inc.
DOCK COP - Alarm systems - Sharon Traxler
DOCK-GARD - Rubber–molded - W.H. Salisbury & Co.
DOCK HAND - Tools - Pacific Metal Fabricators
DOCK MONSTER - Tools - Cepco Tool Co.
DOCK SHOCK - Boats - Paul J. Rapa
DOCK STREET - Beverages–malt - Dock Street Brewing Co.
DOCK TENDER - Sporting goods - Dock Tender, Inc.
DOCKAIDE - Machinery - Braj Enterprise Inc.
DOCKCOTE - Paints ☆ - Valspar Corp.
DOCKER - Boats - Docker Marine
DOCKERS - Apparel - Levi Strauss & Co.
DOCKERS - Belts–apparel - Humphrey's Inc.
DOCKERS - Neckties - Randa Corp.
DOCKER'S - Watches - Genender International, Inc.
DOCKERS AUTHENTIC - Apparel–men's - Levi Strauss & Co.
DOCKET - Office supplies - Wallace Computer Services, Inc.
DOCKLINE CATCHING CLEAT - Marine rigging - Robert T. Grange
DOCKMASTER - Tractors ☆ - HME Inc.
DOCKMASTERS - Shoes–athletic - Marty Shoes, Inc.
DOCKMATE - Electrical equipment - General Electric Co.
DOCKMATE, THE - Marine-cable adapter kits - Charles Industries Ltd.
DOCKMATES - Footwear - Morse Shoe, Inc.
DOCKRELL - Ships–sailing vessels - Dockrell Yachts Ltd.
DOCKSIDE - Food products ☆ - Sea Harvest Packing Co.
DOCKSIDE - Hoists - Dethmers Manufacturing Co.
DOCKSIDE - Sauces - Chelten House Products Inc.
DOCKSIDE - Whirlpools - Kohler Co.
DOCKSIDES - Footwear - Sebago Inc.

☆ = Now out of production

DOCKSON - Welding equipment - Dockson Corp.
DOCKTOR PET CENTERS - Pet shops - Docktor Pet Holdings Ltd.
DOCLINK/VB - Computer software - Napersoft, Inc.
DOCLOGIK - Computer software - Infologistik, Inc.
DOCRITE - Forms–preprinted - Docrite, Inc.
DOCROS - Forms–preprinted - Docrite, Inc.
DOC'S - Beverages–carbonated ☆ - Eastern Brewing Corp.
DOC'S - Food products - Dawkins Market Inc.
DOC'S - Footwear–men's - Lowell Shoe, Inc.
DOC'S FINEST KIND - Beverages - Finest Kind Products, Llc
DOC'S HANDY BANDAGES - Novelty items - Doc's Apothecary
DOCS INTERCHANGE - Computer software - Pc Docs Inc.
DOC'S KNUCKLE RUB - Soap - Coast Novelty Manufacturing Co.
DOC'S KNUCKLE RUB CITRUS - Soap - Coast Novelty Manufacturing Co.
DOC'S MAKE-BELIEVE PILLS - Novelty items - Doc's Apothecary
DOCS OPEN - Computer peripheral equipment - Pc Docs Inc.
DOC'S PERSONALIZED LABELS - Novelty items - Doc's Apothecary
DOC'S PREMIUM - Dairy products - Brackman Brothers, Inc.
DOC'S PROMOLD - Plugs–ear - Doc's Proplugs, Inc.
DOC'S PROPLUGS - Plugs–ear - Doc's Proplugs, Inc.
DOC'S PROTUNE - Plugs–ear - Doc's Proplugs, Inc.
DOC'S RABBIT ENHANCER - Animal feeds - Hubbard Milling Co.
DOC'S TALCUM FOR STINKIN PEOPLE - Novelty items - Doc's Apothecary
DOCSTEP - Boats–motor - International Marine
DOCTATE - Pharmaceutical preparations - Glaxo Wellcome Inc.
DOCTER - Binoculars ☆ - Bogen Photo Corp.
DOCTIENT HC - Health care products ☆ - Suppositoria Laboratories
DOCTOR - Fishing lures - Fred Arbogast Co. Inc.
DR. ALOE - Shampoos - Kim Laube & Co. Inc.
DR. ALOE - Skin care products - Sarah Aloe Essence Cosmetics & Accessories, Inc.
DR. ARRILLAGA - Vitamins and nutritional supplements - Abenamar Arrillaga
DR. B - Beverages–carbonated - H.E. Butt Grocery Co.
DR. B. WHOLESOME - Food products - Imperial Catering, Inc.
DR. BAKER'S CHILDREN'S ASPIRIN - Analgesics - Health Products Corp.
DR. BALJIT'S - Skin care products - Baljit Khalsa
DR. BALLARDS - Dog food - Nabisco Foods Group
DR. BARBIE - Dolls - Mattel, Inc.
DR. BARMAKIAN'S - Health care products - Alta Health Products
DR. BENJAMIN S. FRANK - Pharmaceutical preparations ☆ - Bio-Nutritional Products
DR. BEVERLY CRUSHER - Toys - Paramount Pictures Corp.
DR. BOB'S GOLF LESSONS - Shirts - Marathon Corp.
DR. BRAIN - Computer software - Knowledge Adventure
DR. BRONNER'S - Health care products - All-One-God-Faith Inc.
DR. BROOKS' - Arch supports - Jeffrey S. Brooks, Inc.
DR. BROWNS - Beverages–carbonated - Canada Dry Corp.
DR. B'S NATURAL PRODUCTS - Medical apparatus ☆ - Dr. B's Natural Products, Inc.
DR. BUSSAN'S - Herbal products - Health Tech Industries, Inc.
DR. CALDWELL'S - Laxatives - Sterling Winthrop Inc.
DOCTOR CERTIFIED - Socks - Performance Hosiery, Inc.
DR. CHANG'S - Health care products ☆ - Lotus Brands Inc.
DR. CHEDDAR - Cheese - Alpine Lace Brands, Inc.
DR. COUSTIC - Electronic audio equipment - Concept Enterprises, Inc.
DR. CRANKENSTEIN'S CREEPS - Toys–stuffed - Toy Works, Inc.
DR. CREAM ARTHRITIC'S DREAM - Health care products - DAPAT Inc.
DR. CUSH - Footwear - Right Stuff, Inc.
DR. D. SCHWAB - Skin care products - Ca Botana International, Inc.
DR. DANIELS - Veterinary pharmaceutical preparations - Dr. A.C. Daniels Inc.
DR. DEALS - Skin care products - Teaco International
DR. DEAN EDELL - Eyeglasses - Cable Car Eyeware
DR. DEDO'S - Health care products - Panex Corp.
DR. DEEBEE - Computer software - Syware, Inc.
DR. DENTON - Apparel and accessories - Manhattan International
DR. DENTON - Apparel and accessories - Salant/Manhattan Industries
DR. DENTON - Apparel–children's - Salant Corp.
DR. DENTON - Apparel–men's ☆ - Obion Denton
DR. DIESEL - Chemical preparations - Transcontinental Petroleum Industries, Inc.
DR. DIGGER P.H.D. POST HOLE DIGGER - Drills–electric - Roger James Burnett
DR. DINGLEHUM - Mushrooms - Paul Philips
DOCTOR DOCTOR - Toys–stuffed ☆ - CBS Toys
DR. DOGKATZ - Veterinary pharmaceutical preparations - Growth Plus Laboratories Inc.

DR. DOGKATZ'S CRITTER CHASER - Veterinary pharmaceutical preparations - Growth Plus Laboratories Inc.
DOCTOR DOOM - Books–comic - Marvel Entertainment Group, Inc.
DR. DOOM'S REVENGE - Computer software ☆ - Microprose Software, Inc.
DR. DOS LANPACK - Computer software - Novell, Inc.
DR. DRAIN - Cleaning preparations - ATM America Corp.
DR. DRAIN - Cleaning preparations–household - Mapco Inc.
DOCTOR DRAIN - Sewerage systems - Winston Co., Inc.
DR. DRAIN, PHD. - Drain pipe cleaners - Black Swan Manufacturing Co.
DOCTOR DREADFUL DRINK LAB - Toys - Tyco Industries, Inc.
DOCTOR DREADFUL FOOD LAB - Toys - Tyco Industries, Inc.
DOCTOR DREADFUL LUNCH LAB - Toys - Tyco Industries, Inc.
DOCTOR DRILL'N FILL - Toys–stuffed ☆ - Kenner Products
DR. D'S - Pet products - Avi-Sci Inc.
DR. EARL - Sandwiches–prepackaged - Git-N-Go Inc.
DR. EARLES HAIR & SCALP TREATMENT - Shampoos - Renee Earles
DR. EDWARDS OLIVE TABLETS - Laxatives - Oakhurst Co.
DR. EDWARDS OLIVE TABLETS LAXATIVE - Health care products - Woolfoam Corp.
DOCTOR ELAM'S LA VIE - Hair care products - La Vie Cosmetics Inc.
DR. FENNER'S - Pharmaceutical preparations - Brown Manufacturing Co.
DR. FFEINE'S BEANS - Coffee - Terry A. Day
DR. FISH - Pet products - Aquatrol, Inc.
DR. FLEE - Shampoos - Kim Laube & Co. Inc.
DR. FLOSSER - Dental equipment - Flossrite Corp.
DOCTOR FORMULATED - Foot-care products - M.T.S. Associated
DR. FRANKEN - Computer software - Kemco America Inc.
DR. FRANKENSTEIN - Toys - Hirsch Co.
DR. FRANK'S - Furniture - Directions East
DR. FRED PALMER - Skin care products ☆ - Carson Products Co.
DOCTOR FRIENDLY - Computer software - Doctor Friendly, Ltd.
DR. FULLER - Mattresses - U.S. Mattress Corp.
DR. GAUSS THE EMF DETECTIVE - Electronic equipment - Huntar Co., Inc.
DR. GEORGE HILL PET DRINKS - Pet food - Pet Drinks, Inc.
DR. GEORGE'S - Hair care products ☆ - Giovanni Cosmetics Inc.
DR. GEORGE'S - Toothpaste - Telebrands
DR. GEORGE'S DENTAL WHITE - Toothpaste - Telebrands Corp.
DR. GIBSON'S BABY OINTMENT - Pharmaceutical preparations - Rhodes & Rhodes Products, Co.
DR. GOMEZ - Shampoos - Jojoba Resources Inc.
DR. GOOD - Food products ☆ - VIP Sales Co. Inc.
DR. GOODBONES - Mattresses - Kingsdown, Inc.
DR. GOODPET - Veterinary pharmaceutical preparations - Dr. Goodpet
DR. GORDSHELL'S - Skin care products - Gordshell Salve Co.
DR. GRABOW - Pipes–tobacco - Dr. Grabow Pre-Smoked Pipes Inc.
DR. GRABOW - Tobacco products - United States Tobacco Co.
DR. GRAF'S AGENDA - Hair care products - Graf Skin Care, Inc.
DR. GRANDEL - Skin care products - Dr. Grandel Inc.
DR. GRIP - Pens - Pilot Pen Corp. of America
DR. G'S - Lotions - Woodward Laboratories, Inc.
DR. G'S CLEAR NAIL - Cosmetics - Woodward Laboratories, Inc.
DR. H. THANISCH MULLER-BURGGRAEF - Wines - Heublein, Inc.
DR. HACKETT - Surgical supplies - Brooks Appliance Co.
DR. HANDS - Infant product - Medtech Laboratories Inc.
DR. HANSON'S BULLSEYE - Pet products - Professional Specialties Inc.
DR. HAPPY TOOTH - Publisher's imprints - Arnold & Wilson, DDS
DR. HARVEY'S - Cleaning preparations–household - Harvey Universal Inc.
DR. HARVEY'S COPPER MOUNTAIN SNAIL & SLUG BARRIER - Garden equipment - Harvey Universal Inc.
DR. HARVEY'S FRESH AIR - Deodorizers - Harvey Universal Inc.
DR. HARVEY'S FRESH FISH - Aquarium water additive - Harvey Universal Inc.
DR. HAUSCHKA - Skin care products - Dr. Hauschka Cosmetics
DR. HILLCARE - Toys–stuffed - Tradewinds Enterprises, Inc.
DR. HILLS - Pharmaceutical preparations - Light Force Inc.
DR. HISS - Shoes - Drew Shoe Corp.
DR. HOOK PLUS - Automotive parts and accessories - American Auto Accessories, Inc.
DR. HOOK-UP - Cables - R.B. Sales Corp.
DR. HUBBARD'S - Disinfectants ☆ - J. Hubbard Co. Inc.
DR. HYPO - Shampoos - Kim Laube & Co. Inc.
DR. I.B. BIDERMAN'S BEND IT ANY WAY YOU WANT RESIN APPLICATOR BRUSH - Dental equipment - Foremost Dental Manufacturing Inc.
DR. I.Q. - Stationery - NCN Interstate Distributors, Inc.
DR. J - Canvas footwear - Converse Inc.
DOCTOR J - Fabrics - Dan River Inc.

☆ = Now out of production

DR. J AND LARRY BIRD GO ONE-ON-ONE - Computer software - Electronic Arts Inc.

DR. J SCORE - Games - Tyco Toys

DR. JACKS - Dog food ☆ - Best Feeds and Farm Supplies Inc.

DR. JACKSONS - Leather goods - Tandy Leather Co.

DR. JARDINIERS - Flower pots–earthenware - Jardiniers

DR. JAZZ - Tape players–cassette - Sony Music Entertainment Inc.

DR. J.H. MCLEAN MEDICINE CO. - Health care products - Woolfoam Corp.

DR. JIMENEZ'S MENTOL FORTE - Pharmaceuticals - Mentol Forte, Ltd.

DR. JOFFRE'S - Personal-care product - American Cosmetic Manufacturing Laboratories Inc.

DR. JOHN R. CHRISTOPHER - Health care products - Nature's Way Products, Inc.

DR. JOHN'S FISHERMANS SOAP - Soap - Dr. John's Laboratory, Inc.

DR. JUICE - Sporting goods - Normark Corp.

DR. KARBUNKLE - Toys - Brentwood Television Funnies, Inc.

DR. KARR'S - Skin care products - Atida H. Karr

DR. KARR'S SUN-STATIN - Suntan lotions - Eton Derma Laboratories, Inc.

DR. KELLEYS - Beverages–alcohol - White Rock Distilleries Inc.

DR. KEYS - Computer software ☆ - Dr. T's Music Software Inc.

DR. KILLEMOFF - Toys - Troma, Inc.

DR. KNOLL - Potato flakes - Haram-Christensen Corp.

DR. KNOW - Computer software - Ventura Educational Systems

DR. KONSTANTIN FRANK - Wines - Dr. Frank's Vinifera Wine Cellars Ltd.

DOCTOR K'S COMFORT PACK - Medical apparatus - William Harry Kurtz

DR. LANE - Health care products ☆ - Cumberland-Swan, Inc.

DR. LANGERS SELF HELP GUIDES - Publisher's imprints ☆ - Keats Publishing Co.

DR. LICKS - Publisher's imprints - Hal Leonard Corp.

DR. LYON'S - Toothpaste - Sterling Winthrop Inc.

DR. MARIO - Video games - Nintendo of America Inc.

DR. MCCOY - Skin care products - Dr. McCoy Health Products Inc.

DR. MCCOY - Toys - Paramount Pictures Corp.

DR. MCDOUGALL'S RIGHT FOODS - Food products - Dr. Mcdougall's Right Foods Inc.

DR. MCDOUGALL'S RIGHT FOODS - Soups–canned - Dr. Mcdougall's Right Foods Inc.

DR. MCGILLICUDDY'S - Beverages–alcohol - Joseph E. Seagram & Sons, Inc.

DR. MCGILLICUDDY'S - Beverages–alcohol - SPAR Inc.

DR. MCGILLICUDDY'S - Root beer–bottled or canned - Sazerac Co. Inc.

DR. MELODY - Pet products - Deep Run Packing Co. Inc.

DR. METAL - T-shirts–men's - Richard M. Kashmanian

DR. MINDELL MEDICAL REFERENCE - Publisher's imprints - Book Margins, Inc.

DOCTOR MIRAGE - Books–comic - Voyager Communications Inc.

DR. NAYLOR - Veterinary medical equipment - H.W. Naylor Co.

DR. NED - Apparel and accessories - Badger Co. Inc.

DR. NO ADVENTURE - Games - Avalon Hill Game Co.

DR. OETKER - Housewares stores - SCI Scandicrafts Inc.

DR. PATI'S - Tea - Auromere Inc.

DR. PAULY-BERGWEILER - Wines - Winesellers Ltd.

DR PEPPER - Beverages–carbonated - Dr. Pepper/Seven Up, Inc.

DR. PEPPER MINI-WHEELS - Toys–electronic - Bird Bromiticous Inc.

DR. PERTSCHUK'S HIP & THIGH FIRMER - Exercising equipment - Specialty Fitness Products Inc.

DR. PETER'S HOBOKO - Laxatives - Dr. Peter Fahrney & Sons Co.

DR. PETER'S KURIKO - Laxatives - Dr. Peter Fahrney & Sons Co.

DOCTOR PH - Cleaning preparations - W.W. Grainger, Inc.

DR. PH. MARTIN - Water colors - Salis International, Inc.

DR. PH. MARTIN 80 - Pens - Salis International, Inc.

DR. PIERCE'S GOLDEN MEDICAL DISCOVERY - Health care products - Woolfoam Corp.

DR. PIERRES - Mouthwashes - Consolidated Midland Corp.

DR. PIRANOID - Dolls - Mattel, Inc.

DR. POCKET - Office supplies - Nina Enterprises, Inc.

DR. PUMP - Pumps - Carter Bridgman, Inc.

DR. PUTTS' - Golfing equipment - Roger Wolk

DR. Q'S - Fertilizers - Star Nursery, Inc.

DR. QUENDT - Bakery products - Haram-Christensen Corp.

DR. QUINN MEDICINE WOMAN - Jewelry - CBS Inc.

DR. R. A. ECKSTEIN - Skin care products - Martha Damboise Biokosmetik

DR. RAWSTOCK - Film - Dr. Rawstock

DR. REDDY'S - Vitamins and nutritional supplements - Reddy Foods

DR. RING - Jewelry - QT, Inc.

DR. RINGSDORF'S - Vitamins and nutritional supplements - Ringsdorf Research, L.L.C.

DR. RODENTALL - Pet products - Animal Lovers

DR. ROSS - Pet products - Lewis Food Co.

DR. RUMNEY'S - Snuff - James B. Russell Inc.

DR. RUTH'S GAME OF GOOD SEX - Games - Avalon Hill Game Co.

DR. SACHS - Health care products - Dr. Sachs Laboratories

DR. SAM'S - Vitamins and nutritional supplements - Sammy J. Walters

DR. SCAT - Cleaning preparations - Starkey Chemical Process Co.

DR. SCHENCK'S - Pharmaceutical preparations ☆ - Hays Pharmaceutical Co.

DR. SCHNEE - Beverages - Vess Beverages Inc.

DR. SCHOLL'S - Pharmaceutical preparations - Schering-Plough Healthcare Products

DR. SCHOLL'S - Pharmaceutical preparations - Schering-Plough Healthcare Products, Inc.

DR. SCHOLL'S - Skin care products - Dazey Corp.

DR. SCHOLL'S CAREERS - Footwear - Schering-Plough Healthcare Products, Inc.

DR. SCHUELER'S SELF-HEALTH - Computer storage devices–optical - Pixel Perfect Inc.

DR. SCHULTZ - Shoes–orthopedic ☆ - Tru-Mold Shoes Inc.

DR. SELTZER'S HANGOVER HELPER - Pharmaceutical preparations - Rexall Sundown, Inc.

DR. SHOCK - Bicycles ☆ - Huffy Corp.

DR. SIMONSEN'S - Animal feeds - Dr. Simonsen's Pet Food

DR. SLICE - Beverages–carbonated - Pepsico, Inc.

DR. SLICK - Barber shop equipment - Kim Laube & Co. Inc.

DR. SMITH'S DIAPER OINTMENT - Pharmaceutical preparations - Esrubar, Inc.

DR. SONG - Recording label - Mark Taylor, Inc.

DR. SOYBEAN - Beverages - Big Beans, Inc.

DR. SPICE - Computer peripheral equipment - Deutsch Technology Research

DR. SPOT - Cleaning preparations–carpet and rug - Certified International

DR. STAIN - Cleaning preparations–carpet and rug - Certified International

DR. STUART'S - Teas - Gilway Co. Ltd.

DR. STUART'S - Teas–herbal ☆ - Chase Collection, Inc.

DR. TAR - Shampoos - Kim Laube & Co. Inc.

DR. TEDDY, M.D. - Toys–stuffed - Dakin Inc.

DR. TERROR - Toys - Tonka Corp.

DR. TEX - Beverages–carbonated - Texas Beverage Packers, Inc.

DR., THE - Garden equipment - Country Home Products Inc.

DOCTOR, THE - Medical apparatus - Milt Besen Industries, Inc.

DOCTOR, THE - Skateboards ☆ - Nash Manufacturing Inc.

DR. THE LANE - Sporting goods - Lifetime Products, Inc.

DR. THEISS - Pharmaceutical preparations - Merz Apothecary Inc.

DR. THIRST - Beverages - BCB USA Corp.

DR. THOMASTIK - Musical instrument accessories - John M. Connolly & Co. Inc.

DR. TICHENORS - Skin care products - Dr. G.H. Tichenor Antiseptic Co.

DR. TIMA - Beverages - Dr. Tima Natural Products

DR. TOUCH-UP - Painting kits - Indco Inc.

DR. T.RX - Thermometers - Steridyne Corp.

DR. T'S SING-A-LONG - Computer software - Dr. T's Music Software Inc.

DR. TSUNG'S - Teas–herbal - Tsung Corp.

DR. TURTLE - Pet products - Aquatrol, Inc.

DR. UP - Cleaning preparations - Specialty National, Inc.

DR. VINCENT'S - Health care products - Rex Research Laboratories

DR. VINCENTS #11 - Pharmaceutical preparations - Rex Research Laboratories

DR. WALKER - Footwear - Galleria International Inc.

DR. WALLACH'S VIRGIN EARTH - Soil testing kits - Joel D. Wallach

DR. WATSON - Computer software - Empirical Tools and Technologies, Inc.

DR. WELLBOOK - Publisher's imprints - Tim Peters and Co., Inc.

DR. WELLS - Beverages–carbonated - Monarch Co., Inc.

DR. WEST'S - Toothbrushes - Oral B Laboratories

DR. WHO - Candy - Sterling Candy Corp.

DR. WILD - Shoe polish ☆ - Edison Brothers Stores, Inc.

DR. WILLARD'S WATER - Medical apparatus - Caw Industries Inc.

DR. WISELY - Games - William J. Funk, Jr. and Paul E. Funk Partnership

DR. X - Footwear - J.P. Original Corp.

DR. YOUNG'S RED ROOSTER PILLS - Pharmaceutical preparations - Roberts/Hauck Pharmaceuticals Inc.

DR. ZIPP - Beverages–carbonated - United Packers, Inc.

DOCTOR'S - Cases–eyeglass - Cable Car Eyeware

DOCTOR'S - Health-care products - Dental Concepts Inc.

DOCTOR'S + - Vitamins and nutritional supplements - Moneytree Management

DOCTOR'S ALL NATURAL DEFENDER - Vitamins and nutritional supplements - Swanson Health Products, Inc.

DOCTORS BOOK OF HOME REMEDIES, THE - Publisher's imprints - Rodale Press, Inc.

DOCTORS BOOK, THE - Publisher's imprints - Rodale Press, Inc.

DOCTOR'S CHOICE - Filters–air - Vortek Industries, Inc.

DOCTOR'S CHOICE - Pharmaceutical preparations - Derma Skin Products Inc.

DOCTOR'S EXCLUSIVE COLLECTION, THE - Skin care products - Doctor's Private Collection, Inc.

DOCTOR'S ORDERS - Pies–frozen - Doctor's Orders Inc.

DOCTOR'S PREMIUM - Vitamins and nutritional supplements - Almark Products, Inc.

DOCTOR'S PRESCRIPTION FOR ENHANCED SPINE REHABILITATION, THE - Medical apparatus - Physicians Consulting, Inc.

DOCTORS' PRIDE - Vitamins - Nature's Bounty, Inc.

DOCTOR'S WEIGH - Food products - Health-Style USA, Inc.

DOCU-ART - Paints–artists' - Greenwich Workshop, Inc.

DOCU PLUS - Paper–writing - Willamette Industries, Inc.

DOCU-SOFT - Pharmaceutical preparations - Reese Chemical Co.

DOCU-SOFT PLUS - Pharmaceutical preparations - Reese Chemical Co.

DOCU-TAB - Stationery - Tab Products Co.

DOCUCAL PLUS - Laxatives - Chase Laboratories Inc.

DOCUCHECK - Paper - Appleton Papers Inc.

DOCUDEX - Plastics–laminated - E-Z Machine Corp.

DOCUFEED - Machinery - Standard Duplicating Machines Corp.

DOCUGRIP - Office supplies - Avery Dennison Corp.

DOCUGUARD - Paper - Paper Systems Inc.

DOCUJET - Facsimile equipment - Relisys

DOCUMARK - Computer software - Midmark Corp.

DOCUMATE - File folders - Wright Line Inc.

DOCUMATIC - Optical scanners–computer - Optowand, Inc.

DOCUMAX - Printers–computer - Datasouth Computer Corp.

DOCUMENT AGENT SEARCH - Computer software - Caere Corp.

DOCUMENT COMPANY, THE - Paper - Xerox Corp.

DOCUMENT MANAGER 9000 - Computer software - Powerway, Inc.

DOCUMENT NAVIGATOR - Computer software - Datalogics Inc.

DOCUMENT PORTAL - Computer hardware - Gammagraphx, Inc.

DOCUMENT VIEWING SERVICES - Computer software - Document Sciences Corp.

DOCUMENT WORKPLACE - Computer hardware - Gammagraphx, Inc.

DOCUMENTA - Wallpaper ☆ - Osborne & Little

DOCUMENTARY HAND PRINTS - Wallcoverings - Arthur Sanderson and Sons North America Ltd.

DOCUMENTATION - Paper - Scott Paper Co.

DOCUMENTATION PLUS - Computer software - Management Software Inc.

DOCUMENTATION STUDIO - Computer peripheral equipment - Wextech Systems, Inc.

DOCUMENTBASE - Computer software - Information Systems Corp.

DOCUMENTDIRECTOR - Computer hardware - Indata Corp.

DOCUMENTOR - Computer peripheral equipment - Notable Solutions Inc.

DOCUMENTORS WORKBENCH - Computer software - At&T Corp.

DOCUMENTS ON A DISK - Computer software - Insmark, Inc.

DOCUMETRIX WORKFLOW - Computer software - Universal Systems Inc.

DOCUMINT - Computer software - Honeywell Inc.

DOCUPAC - File folders - Xerox Corp.

DOCUPLEX - Computer peripheral equipment - Xerox Corp.

DOCUPOWER - Computer software - Computing!

DOCUPRINT - Printers–computer - Xerox Corp.

DOCURATOR - Computer software - Paige Document Automation Resources

DOCURIGHT - Computer software - Postalsoft, a Firstlogic Technology

DOCUROM - Computer storage devices - Ask Group, Inc.

DOCUSCAN PLUS - Electrical equipment - Terminal Data Corp.

DOCUSERV - Computer software - Standard Register Co.

DOCUSOFT - Computer software - Docusoft, Inc.

DOCUSOFT - Laxatives - G and W Laboratories Inc.

DOCUSOLVE - Computer software - Image Sciences Inc.

DOCUSP - Computer software - Xerox Corp.

DOCUTABS - Paper products - Dlm Associates

DOCUTAG - Paper industry machinery - James T. Higgins

DOCUTECH - Office machines - Xerox Corp.

DOCUTIME - Computer software - Chronology Corp.

DOCUTRAN - Computer peripheral equipment - Tangent Systems, Inc.

DOCUTRAX - Recording label - Cyclops Records, Inc.

DOCWORX - Computer software - Innovatech Corp.

DOD - Audio equipment - Dod Electronics

D.O.D. - Costumes - Lifeforms International, Inc.

DODD, MEAD & CO. INC. - Publisher's imprints - Dodd, Mead & Co. Inc.

DODDLE BUG - Fishing tackle - Schumann's Fly Fish Kit Co.

DODECCAMENTE - Games ☆ - Kadon Enterprises Inc.

DODEX - Pharmaceutical preparations ☆ - Organon Inc.

DODGE - Floor coverings - Dodge-Regupol Inc.

DODGE - Motor vehicles - Chrysler Corp. (Dodge Car Div.)

DODGE - Thread - Threads USA Div.

DODGE CITY - Footwear - Acme Boot Co., Inc.

DODGE-CITY - Meat products–beef - Meat-O-Mat Corp.

DODGE CORK - Floor coverings–tile - Dodge-Regupol Inc.

DODGE DAIRY - Milk - Mid-America Dairymen Inc. Southern Div.

DODGE 'EM - Video games - Atari Games Corp.

DODGEM - Amusement rides - Designs International, Inc.

DODGER - Apparel stores–sports - Dodger Industries Inc.

DODGER - Bicycles - Columbia Manufacturing Inc.

DODGER - Fishing tackle ☆ - Worth Co.

DODIE DUCK - Toys–stuffed - Russ Berrie and Co., Inc.

DODII DEFENDER OF DIGNITY IN ILLNESS - Dolls - Cynthia J. Plewinski

DODO ON THE GOGO - Publisher's imprints - Dodo Unlimited, Inc.

DODON'S - Cheese ☆ - Krinos Foods, Inc.

DODSON TRUCKER TOUGH - Gloves–work - Dodson Specialties Inc.

DODWELL - Duplicating machines - Dodwell & Co. Ltd.

DOE-IN-RUT - Sporting goods - Wellington Leisure Products, Inc.

DOE MILL - Wines ☆ - Calera Wine Co.

DOE RUN - Floor coverings–carpet and rugs - Sheridan Carpet Mills

DOE-SPUN - Apparel and accessories - Doe Spun Group, Inc.

DOE SPUN - Apparel–children's - Doe Spun Inc.

DOERFLER - Musical instrument accessories - International Violin Co. Ltd.

DOES-IT - Paint removers ☆ - H. Behlen & Bro. Inc.

DOES IT ALL - Detergents - Lustre-Glo Chemical

DOES IT ALL! - Waterproofing compounds - Gloucester Co., Inc.

DOFF - Epoxy coatings - Sterling-Clark-Lurton Corp.

DOFI - Computer peripheral equipment - Dofi Communications, Inc.

DOFINO - Cheese - MD Foods USA Inc.

DOFO - Cheese ☆ - MD Foods USA Inc.

DOG & PONY SHOW - Computer software - Scientific Development Corp.

DOG AWAY - Pet products - Farnam Cos. Inc.

DOG BEDS - Pet products - Black Sheep Inc.

DOG BLOOM - Veterinary nutritional supplements - J.E. Ronicker Labs Inc.

DOG BREATH - Pet products - Zema Corp.

DOG BYTES - Computer software - Tiedway Software

DOG-CAT-CHER - Pet products - Pet Deckers Ltd.

DOG CATCHER - Pet products - Novalek, Inc.

DOG-CHECK - Chemical preparations ☆ - Nott Manufacturing Co. Inc.

DOG CHOVIES - Pet products - Lone Toy Tree Inc.

DOG CHOW - Pet products - Ralston Purina Co.

DOG DAZE INACTIVEWEAR - Apparel and accessories - Pioneer Industries, Inc.

DOG DELIGHT - Dog food - Gimborn U.S., Inc.

DOG DELIGHT DELI - Pet products - Gimborn U.S., Inc.

DOG DELIGHT WEEKENDER - Pet products - Gimborn U.S., Inc.

DOG DELITES - Dog food - J. Narby Inc.

DOG DEN - Pet products - Handy Home Products

DOG DEN - Pet products - Insul-House

DOG DICE - Games - Gamewright, Inc.

DOG DOME - Pet products ☆ - Diverse Designs

DOG-E-O - Pet products - Richard Hanau Pet Foods Corp.

DOG EAR - Bags–laundry - Cafco, Inc.

DOG FIGHTERS - Toys–airplanes ☆ - Cox Products Inc.

DOG FOUNTAIN - Pet products - Molor Products Co.

DOG FUN - Pet products - Europet Inc.

DOG-GONE - Games ☆ - Parker Brothers

DOG-GONE - Pet products - J.M. Saddler, Inc.

DOG GONE - Pet products - San-Jo, Inc.

DOG GONE - Stain removers - Glenlo Products Co. Inc.

DOG GONES - Novelty items - Tom and Sally's Handmade Chocolates, Inc.

DOG HOUSE - Kitchen appliances ☆ - Sunbeam-Oster Household Products

DOG HOUSE - Puppets ☆ - Dakin Inc.

DOG JOGGER - Pet products - Charlee Bear Farms, Inc.

DOG-JOGS - Pet products - Debonair Pets of California

DOG KABIN - Pet products ☆ - Dogloo Inc.

DOG KABINS XT - Pet products - R.C. Steele Co.

DOG KNITS - Pet products - Tawn Chi & Associates Inc.

DOG LEG RIGHT - Sporting goods - Dogleg Right Corp.

DOG LIFE - Dog food - Pet Life Foods Inc.

DOG LOSHES - Dog boots - Items Inc.

☆ = Now out of production

DOG MAGIC PEMICAN - Dog food - American Superior Feeds, Inc.
DOG MANE - Hair care products - Jung Woo Lee
DOG MATE - Pet products - Ani Mate Co.
DOG 'N SUDS - Restaurants–fast food - Dog 'n Suds Restaurants
DOG NAPPERS - Pet products - R.C. Steele Co.
DOG-O-DONTICS - Pet products - Canine Dental Health
DOG-O-DONTICS - Pet products - St. Jon Pet Care Products Inc.
DOG-OFF - Deodorizers - Thornell Corp.
DOG ON A LOG - Electronic equipment - Texas Instruments Inc.
DOG PACK - Pet products ☆ - Diverse Designs
DOG PORTRAIT NOTE PAPER BY EARL SHERWAN - Stationery - Lakeshore Artisans
DOG POUND BREW - Beverages–alcohol ☆ - Evansville Brewing Co.
DOG POUND BREW - Beverages–malt - Great American Brew Co. Inc.
DOG POUND BREW DP - Beverages–malt - Great American Brew Co. Inc.
DOG-RADARTRON - Pet products - Mr. Mutt Pet Products Inc.
DOG REFLECTORIZED I.D. TAG - Pet products - Molor Products Co.
DOG-S-CAT - Pet products - J. & L. Adikes Inc.
DOG SHOWMANSHIP - Pet products - Florida Films
DOG SNAPS - Pet products - Prime Pet Products
DOG SPOONZ - Dog food - Alan F. Lilly
DOG TAGS - Toys–stuffed - Russ Berrie and Co., Inc.
DOG TAGS - Trading cards and stamps - Christopher Martin
DOG TEE PEE - Pet products ☆ - Dogloo Inc.
DOG-TEX - Stain removers - Consolidated Chemical Co.
DOG TOTES - Pet products - Dog-Togs
DOG TOWN - Apparel and accessories - Lance Lemond
DOG TOWN - Skateboards - Izumi Shirase
DOG TYE - Pet products - Village Products
DOG WATCH - Pet products - R.C. Steele Co.
DOG-WICK - Pet products ☆ - National Scent Co.
DOG WORKS - Pet products - Dog Works, Inc.
DOGBURGER - Dog food ☆ - Central Soya Co. Inc.
DOGCRAZY TEAM DESIGN MARKETING - Pet products - Designers Express
DOGEST-IONS - Health care products - Ion Laboratories Inc.
DOGETTE - Pet products - Lora Laboratories Inc.
DOGFEAT - Toys–stuffed - Gund, Inc.
DOGGIDUDS - Pet products - Doggiduds, Inc.
DOGGIDUDS - Pet products - R.C. Steele Co.
DOGGIE - Infant product ☆ - Binky-Griptight Co.
DOGGIE BAG - Dog food - MCS (USA) Marketing, Service & Commerce, Inc.
DOGGIE BAG - Pet products - Collar Craft/Petite Originals
DOGGIE BAG-GRR - Pet products - Dualle Products
DOGGIE BAG TREATS - Dog food - Nabisco Holdings Corp.
DOGGIE BAGEL BITES - Pet products - Doggie Bagel Bites
DOGGIE BANDANA, THE - Pet products - St. John's Herb Garden Inc.
DOGGIE BISCOTTI - Dog food - Christina Canas Stinchcomb
DOGGIE BOWS - Pet products - Leatherite-Nylorite Manufacturing Inc.
DOGGIE BROWN'S GOURMET BONES - Dog treats - JW Products Co.
DOGGIE CHIN - Pet products - Dee Pet Products
DOGGIE CUTS - Video production - Kevin Martin Corp.
DOGGIE DANGLES - Pet products - Pet Concepts
DOGGIE DISCUIT - Dog food - Michael Simone
DOGGIE DIVINES - Pet food - Brunzi's Best, Inc.
DOGGIE DOGTOR FIRST AID FOR DOGS - Publisher's imprints - Jill Lynne Turnbull
DOGGIE DONUTS - Dog food - Pet Life Foods Inc.
DOGGIE DOOLEY - Toilets–porcelain - Hueter Toledo, Inc.
DOGGIE DOORBELL HAPPY PAW - Electronic equipment - Delightful Living Ventures
DOGGIE FRIES - Toys - Russ Berrie and Co., Inc.
DOGGIE IN THE WINDOW - Toys–stuffed ☆ - Gund, Inc.
DOGGIE LINKS - Pet products - Gimborn U.S., Inc.
DOGGIE MAN - Chewing gum - Philadelphia Chewing Gum Corp.
DOGGIE MUNCHIE - Pet products - St. John's Herb Garden Inc.
DOGGIE-'N-A-BAG - Toys–stuffed ☆ - Bradley Import Co.
DOGGIE PANTIES - Pet products - Leatherite-Nylorite Manufacturing Inc.
DOGGIE-SOX - Pet products - Doggie-Sox Manufacturing Co.
DOGGIE UNIQUE - Pet products - Doggie Unique
DOGGONE GOOD COOKIES - Cookies - Doggone Good, Inc.
DOGGONIT - Apparel stores–sports ☆ - Tultex Corp.
DOGGY BAG - Dog food - Doggy Bag, Inc.
DOGGY DENT - Pet products - Doggy Dent International Inc.
DOGGY DISK - Pet products - Phydeaux Enterprises Inc.
DOGGY POPS - Dog food - The James Valley Co. Inc.
DOGGY RUN - Pet products - Prestige Products Co.

DOGGY RUN - Pet products - Roccorp, Inc.
DOGGY VIBE - Massage products - HWE Inc.
DOGHOUSE - Dog food - Gimborn U.S., Inc.
DOGHOUSE - Recording label - Godwin Music Group
DOGHOUSE GREETINGS - Greeting cards - Kersten Bros. Studios
DOGHOUSE GREETINGS - Greeting cards ☆ - Nova Greetings
DOGI-DECO - Pet products - Gerard-Pellham Co.
DOGIE - Apparel and accessories - Wrangler Co.
DOGLAS HOUNDSWORTH III - File folders - Lisa Frank, Inc.
DOGLOO - Pet products - R.C. Steele Co.
DOGLOO BAUX'R - Pet products - Dogloo Inc.
DOGLOO INDIGO - Pet products - Dogloo Inc.
DOGLOVERS FARM - Dog food - Heinz Pet Products Co.
DOGMATIC - Pet products - Mininome Inc.
DOGMEDIC - Veterinary pharmaceutical preparations - Loki Enterprises
DOGNAPPER - Pet products - Flexi-Mat Corp.
DOGONEX - Chemical preparations ☆ - Hydroponic Chemical Co. Inc.
DOGONIT - Chemical preparations - Millennium Lawns, Inc.
DOGPATCH - Pet shops - Olema Valley Pharmaceuticals Inc.
DOG'S BEST - Dog food - Pet Products, Inc.
DOGS KNOW - Dog food - Nabisco Foods Group
DOGS OWN - Pet products - V.K. Industries Inc.
DOGTOGS - Pet products - Dog-Togs
DOGTRAX - Computer software - TGM Software
DOGUI - Dog food - Stevens Industries Inc.
DOGUI - Pet food - Cargill, Inc.
DOGWALKER'S VALET - Pet products - Petpro Products Inc.
DOGWILD - Pet products - Dana Rice
DOGWOOD - Giftware - Doranne
DOGWOOD - Glassware–household ☆ - WMF/USA
DOGWOOD - Vases–stone - R.H. Nagel Distributing Co., Inc.
DOGZ - Video games - Pf. Magic, Inc.
DOGZIX - Repellent - Bonide Products, Inc.
DOILY - Clocks - General Time Corp. (Westclox/Seth Thomas Div.)
DOINKER - Sporting goods - William L. Leven
DOJO CONTROL - Computer software - James D. Philbin
DOK-STEP - Boats - Taylor & Gaskin Inc. (Marine Products Div.)
DOKAINE DU FIEFGUERIN - Wines - Bercut-Vandervoort & Co.
DOKSTAR - Lighting fixtures - Hubbell Lighting, Inc. (Lighting Div.)
DOKTORS - Cold remedies ☆ - Schering-Plough Healthcare Products
DOKUMENTAL - Inks - Hedra Inc.
DOK'UMENTATION - Binders - Boorum & Pease Co.
DOKUTS - Doughs–frozen - Mel-O-Cream Donuts International, Inc.
DOL-END - Pharmaceutical preparations - Dade Pharmaceuticals Inc.
DOL-FIN - Candy ☆ - Y & S Candies Inc.
DOL-FYN - Water purification systems - West Bend Co.
DOL-WEAR - Pet products - Dol-Wear Inc.
DOLACET - Pharmaceutical preparations - Roberts/Hauck Pharmaceuticals Inc.
DOLAFORT - Pharmaceutical preparations - Vista Laboratories Inc.
DOLAN BULLOCK - Jewelry - Park Lane Associates, Inc.
DOLAN DESIGNS - Electric lighting equipment - A-Boy Supply Co.
DOLAN<bul>BULLOCK - Jewelry - Park Lane Associates, Inc.
DOLANEX - Pharmaceutical preparations - Lannett Co. Inc.
DOLBI - Housewares - Vincent Lippe Co.
DOLBY - Audio equipment - Dolby Laboratories Licensing Corp.
DOLBY 3 STEREO - Audio equipment - Dolby Laboratories Licensing Corp.
DOLCE - Housewares ☆ - Berarducci Bros. Manufacturing Co. Inc.
DOLCE - Juices - Mira International Foods Inc.
DOLCE - Syrup - Stearns and Lehman Inc.
DOLCE - Wines - Dolce Winery Inc.
DOLCE & FABULOSO - Apparel–women's - Essendi, Inc.
DOLCE BLUE - Tobacco products ☆ - Avanti Cigar Co.
DOLCE BY PIERRE - Shoes - Pierre Shoes Inc.
DOLCE FAR NIENTE 1871 - Cigars - Caribe Imported Cigars, Inc.
DOLCE GOLD BY PIERRE - Shoes - Pierre Shoes Inc.
DOLCE VITA - Computer software - Ann DeWees Allen
DOLCE VITA - Computer software - Pierre Lutard
DOLCE VITA - Cosmetics - Parfums Christian Dior U.S. Corp.
DOLCE VITA - Handbags - Jackson Corp.
DOLCE VITA - Perfumes - Christian Dior Perfumes Corp.
DOLCEZZA - Shampoos - Modafini Inc.
DOLCEZZA - Sweaters - Montgomery Ward & Co. Inc.
DOLCH PAC - Computers - Dolch Computer System
DOLCHEM - Adhesives and sealants - Dolphin Paint & Chemical Co.
DOLCI CALZE - Socks ☆ - TGC INC.
DOLCI FRUTTA - Chocolate syrup - Saco Foods, Inc.

DOLCI ITALIANI - Cookies - Bertolli USA, Inc.
DOLCIN - Pharmaceutical preparations ☆ - Dolgin Acme Foods
DOLCINO - Rings–jewelry - Artcarved Inc.
DOLCITAL - Chocolate candy - Bell'amore Imports Inc.
DOLCITOL - Candlesticks - Bell'amore Imports Inc.
DOLCO-VAR - Paints ☆ - C.B. Dolge Co.
DOLCOBUFF - Floor waxes ☆ - C.B. Dolge Co.
DOLCOROCK - Paints ☆ - C.B. Dolge Co.
DOLD - Meat products–pork ☆ - Dold Foods Inc.
DOLD EXQUISIT - Clocks - Staufen Studio
D'OLE - Computer software - Next Software, Inc.
DOLE - Food products - Dole Food Co., Inc.
DOLE - Raisins - Dole Dried Fruit & Nut Co.
DOLE DARE - Fruits–dried - Dole Food Co., Inc.
DOLEJO - Recording label - Summit Enterprises
DOLEWHIP - Snack foods - Dole Food Co., Inc.
DOLFEN - Pharmaceutical preparations - Pharmics Inc.
DOLFIN - Bathing suits - Dolfin Corp.
DOLFINITE - Finishing agents - Woolsey Marine Industries
DOLFINO - Sporting goods - Aqua-Leisure Industries, Inc.
DOLFINO COLLECTION, THE - Apparel and accessories - Imperial Knitting Co. Inc.
DOLFINO DIVE GEAR - Sporting goods - Aqua-Leisure Industries, Inc.
DOLGESIC - Pharmaceutical preparations ☆ - Marlop Pharmaceuticals Inc.
DOLGRAY - Apparel and accessories - Dol-Gray Enterprises, Inc.
DOLISINUS - Pharmaceutical preparations - Dolisos America, Inc.
DOLIUM - Lubricants - Shell Oil Co.
DOLL ARTISTRY - Dolls - Hobby House Press Inc.
DOLL BABY - Dolls ☆ - Fibre-Craft Materials Corp.
DOLL CLASSICS - Dolls - Uneeda Doll Co., Inc.
DOLL COLLECTORS GUILD - Dolls - Seymour Mann Inc.
DOLL CRAFTIN' - Dolls - Mangelsen's (VDI)
DOLL-E-TOYS - Toys ☆ - South Bend Toy Manufacturing Co.
DOLL FACE - Dolls - D & B Leis
DOLL HOUSE MINIATURES - Wallpaper - Milbrook Wallcoverings
DOLL PINS - Dolls - Forster Inc.
DOLL PLAY - Dolls - Daval N.Y., Inc.
DOLL QUBE - Containers–plastic - Sportscubes, L.C.
DOLL RAGS - Apparel–women's ☆ - Gem-Dandy, Inc.
DOLL READER - Novelty items - Hobby House Press Inc.
DOLL-UP - RAGGEDY ANN doll with talc and cologne ☆ - Cosrich Inc.
DOLL-UP - Skin care products - Elliot Pharmacal Co.
DOLLAR - Tools–hand-operated - Dollar Trading, Inc.
DOLLAR BILL POKER - Games ☆ - Milton Bradley Co.
DOLLAR TRADING, INC. - Tools–hand-operated - Dollar Trading, Inc.
DOLLARS & SCENTS - Underwear and nightwear ☆ - Lovable Co.
DOLLARS DELUXE - Game machines - IGT - North America
DOLLARS FOR SCHOLARS - Computer software ☆ - Cambridge Educational
DOLLARS FOR SCHOLARS - Novelty items - Citizens' Scholarship Foundation of America, Inc.
DOLLHOUSE - Apparel and accessories - Joujou Designs Inc.
DOLLHOUSE CENTER, THE - Toys - Real Good Toys
DOLLHOUSE COORDINATES II - Wallpaper ☆ - Andover Wallcovering
DOLLHOUSE COORDINATES III - Wallpaper ☆ - Andover Wallcovering
DOLLHOUSE COORDINATES IV - Wallpaper ☆ - Andover Wallcovering
DOLLHOUSE COORDINATES V - Wallpaper ☆ - Andover Wallcovering
DOLLHOUSE INTIMATES - Apparel–women's - Jacques Moret, Inc.
DOLLHOUSE PRETTY SOUNDS PIANO - Toys - Playskool, Inc.
DOLLIKIN - Dolls ☆ - Uneeda Doll Co., Inc.
DOLLIPOP - Toys–stuffed - Gund, Inc.
DOLLMATES - Leotards - Jacques Moret, Inc.
DOLLS BY BERENGUER - Dolls - J.C. Toys Group, Inc.
DOLLS BY BRADLEY - Dolls - Bradley Import Co.
DOLLS BY PAULINE - Dolls ☆ - International Playthings Inc.
DOLLS OF ALL NATIONS - Dolls - Seymour Mann Inc.
DOLLS PLUS - Dolls - Goldberger Doll Manufacture Co.
DOLLS THAT TOUCH YOUR HEART - Dolls ☆ - Effanbee Doll Corp.
DOLLSANDDREAMS - Toys - Dollsandreams
DOLLSPART SUPPLY - Dolls - Dollspart Supply Co.
DOLLUP'S - Ice cream - Silverado Foods, Inc.
DOLLY - Automotive parts and accessories - Mirror Lite Co.
DOLLY - Dolls - Dolly Hosiery Mills Inc.
DOLLY - Floor coverings–carpet and rugs - Alexander Smith Carpets
DOLLY - Furniture - Bean Station Furniture Factory Inc.
DOLLY - Publisher's imprints ☆ - Dolly, Inc.
DOLLY - Wigs - Dolly Parton Inc.

DOLLY - Yarn ☆ - William Unger & Co. Inc.
DOLLY BEAR - Toys–stuffed ☆ - Dakin Inc.
DOLLY CARE - Toys - Meritus Industries, Inc.
DOLLY CARRIERS - Infant product - Cozy Carriers
DOLLY CRAFT - Toys - Marlon Creations
DOLLY DINGBE - Dolls - Alaska Momma
DOLLY DOLPHIN - Apparel and accessories - Sea World, Inc.
DOLLY DOWNS - Dolls - Camp Venture, Inc.
DOLLY DUZIT - Sponges ☆ - Springfield Wire Inc.
DOLLY II - Bakery products - Interstate Brands Corp.
DOLLY MADISON - Baked goods - Interstate Brands Corp.
DOLLY MADISON - Cigars - A.J. Golden Inc.
DOLLY MADISON - Fruits and vegetables - Comstock Michigan Fruit
DOLLY MADISON - Glass–leaded - Seneca Glass Co.
DOLLY MADISON - Ice cream - Calip Dairies, Inc.
DOLLY MADISON - Kitchen appliances ☆ - Sunbeam-Oster Household Products
DOLLY MADISON - Milk - Shoenberg Farms Inc.
DOLLY MADISON - Paper–tissue - Fort Howard Corp.
DOLLY MADISON - Watches - Bulova Corp.
DOLLY MADISON BAKERY FUN PACKS - Snack foods - Interstate Brands Corp.
DOLLY MADISON, THE - Jewelry ☆ - Napier Co.
DOLLY PARTON - Wigs - Dolly Parton Inc.
DOLLY PARTON - Wigs - Revlon General Wig Manufacturers, Inc.
DOLLY PARTON DOLLY'S SECRET - Wigs - Revlon General Wig Manufacturers, Inc.
DOLLY PARTON GOOF-PROOF - Wigs - Revlon General Wig Manufacturers, Inc.
DOLLY PARTON WIGS - Wigs - Revlon General Wig Manufacturers, Inc.
DOLLY PARTON'S BEAUTY CONFIDENCE - Video production - Dolly Parton Inc.
DOLLY POPS - Toys - Knickerbocker Toy Co. Inc.
DOLLY SURPRISE - Toys - Playskool, Inc.
DOLLY TOTE - Dolls - Uneeda Doll Co., Inc.
DOLLY TOY - Lamps - Dolly, Inc.
DOLLYPOD - Photographic equipment - Acme-Lite Manufacturing Co.
DOLLY'S KITCHEN CENTER - Toys - Tyco Toys
DOLLYS NEEDS - Dolls ☆ - Totsy Manufacturing Co., Inc.
DOLLY'S SECRET - Wigs - Dolly Parton Inc.
DOLMAR - Pharmaceutical preparations ☆ - Marlop Pharmaceuticals Inc.
DOLMETSCH - Musical instruments - Theodore Presser Co.
DOLOBID - Analgesics - Merck & Co., Inc. (Merck Research Laboratories)
DOLOCAP - Pharmaceutical preparations - Vista Laboratories Inc.
DOLOMETTE - Aquarium accessories - Kordon
DOLOMETTE - Aquarium accessories - Novalek, Inc.
DOLOMITE - Pet products ☆ - Aqua Stock/Petcetera Inc.
DOLOMITE - Sporting goods ☆ - Elan-Monark
DOLOMITI - Tiles–ceramic - American Marazzi Tile, Inc.
DOLONIL - Analgesics ☆ - Parke-Davis
DOLOPHINE HCl - Analgesics - Eli Lilly and Co.
DOLORES - Food products - Dolores Canning Co.
DOLORO - Floor coverings ☆ - Congoleum Corp.
DOLOTIC - Pharmaceutical preparations - Marlop Pharmaceuticals Inc.
DOLPHIN - Bicycles - Ross Bicycles USA, Ltd.
DOLPHIN - Binoculars ☆ - Swift Instruments, Inc.
DOLPHIN - Boating equipment and accessories - Dolphin Boat Lifts, Inc.
DOLPHIN - Boats - McKenzie Boat Manufacturing Co.
DOLPHIN - Boats - Nalad Corp.
DOLPHIN - Boats ☆ - John G. Alden Inc.
DOLPHIN - Boats–canoes - Carstens Industries Inc.
DOLPHIN - Boats–motor ☆ - Grady-White Boats, Inc.
DOLPHIN - Cleaning preparations–household - Puritan-Churchill Chemical Co.
DOLPHIN - Cosmetics - Spornette International, Inc.
DOLPHIN - Ear plugs - Pacific Coast Laboratories Inc.
DOLPHIN - Enamels - Somay Products Inc.
DOLPHIN - Fabrics - Uniroyal Engineered Products
DOLPHIN - Floor coverings - American Floor Products Co. Inc.
DOLPHIN - Floor coverings–carpet and rugs - Roxbury Carpet Co.
DOLPHIN - Food products - Dolphin Dispensers
DOLPHIN - Housewares - Lipper International Inc.
DOLPHIN - Lanterns–electric - Burgess Inc.
DOLPHIN - Motor vehicles–motor homes - National RV, Inc.
DOLPHIN - Nail care products - Tweezerman Corp.
DOLPHIN - Paints - Dolphin Paint & Chemical Co.
DOLPHIN - Plumbing fixtures - Sloan Valve Co.

☆ = Now out of production

DOLPHIN - Publisher's imprints - Bantam Doubleday Dell Publishing Group, Inc.

DOLPHIN - Razors - C.A. Daniels & Co.

DOLPHIN - Seafood products–fresh or frozen - Iceland Seafood Corp.

DOLPHIN - Sporting goods ☆ - Pompanette Inc.

DOLPHIN - Steering mechanisms–motor vehicle - Detroit Marine Engineering

DOLPHIN - Watches - Bulova Corp.

DOLPHIN - Watches - Croton Watch Co., Inc.

DOLPHIN BOATS - Boats - Michael Courtney

DOLPHIN COURT - Floor coverings - Mannington Resilient Floors

DOLPHIN FAMILY - Candy - Tropicana Hawaii Candy, Inc.

DOLPHIN MY FRIEND - Pendant - Explorer's Exchange Inc.

DOLPHIN-SAFE - Tuna–canned ☆ - Tri-Union International, LLC

DOLPHIN-STAR - Boats - Besicorp Group, Inc.

DOLPRN #3 - Pharmaceutical preparations - Bock Pharmacal Co.

DOLSEAL - Adhesives and sealants - V.J. Dolan & Co. Inc.

DOLSED - Pharmaceutical preparations - American Urologicals Inc.

DOLSOX - Pet products - Dol-Wear Inc.

DOLTHANE - Finishing agents ☆ - C.B. Dolge Co.

DOLVAR - Paints - V.J. Dolan & Co. Inc.

DOM BRAU - Beverages–malt ☆ - Safeway Stores Inc.

DOM DECHANT WERNER - Wines - Chrissa Imports Ltd.

DOM DES PERDRIX - Wines - Winesellers Ltd.

DOM PERIGNON - Beverages–alcohol - Schieffelin & Co.

DOM PERIGNON - Wines - Schieffelin and Somerset Co.

DOM PERIGNON - Wines ☆ - European Beverage Co., Inc.

DOM PIERRE - Wines ☆ - Weibel Vineyards

DOM RUINART - Wines - Schieffelin and Somerset Co.

DOMAIN - Audio equipment - MB Quart Electronics USA, Inc.

DOMAIN - Floor coverings–carpet and rugs - Bloomsburg Carpet Industries

DOMAIN - Floor coverings–carpet and rugs - Criterion Mills Inc.

DOMAIN - Floor coverings–carpet and rugs ☆ - Playfield International Inc.

DOMAIN - Furniture - LUI Corp.

DOMAIN - Furniture ☆ - Hammary Furniture Co. Inc.

DOMAIN - Publisher's imprints - Bantam Doubleday Dell Publishing Group, Inc.

DOMAIN - Toys - Tonka Corp.

DOMAIN/DACS - Computer software - Utimaco Mergent

DOMAIN HILL & MAYES - Wines - William H. Hill and John W. Mayes Partnership

DOMAIN SAN MARTIN - Wines ☆ - San Martin Winery Inc.

DOMAINE - Floor coverings–carpet and rugs ☆ - Patrick Carpet Mills

DOMAINE - Glassware–household - Oneida Ltd.

DOMAINE - Liqueurs ☆ - Charles Jacquin et Compagnie Inc.

DOMAINE ALFRED - Wines - Chamisal Vineyard

DOMAINE ALOUETTE - Beverages–alcohol - Margus Co.

DOMAINE ANTONIN GUYON - Wines - Seagram's Chateau & Estate Wines Co.

DOMAINE ARMAND ROUSSEAU - Wines - Frederick Wildman and Sons Ltd.

DOMAINE BACHELET DELAGRANGE - Wines - Seagram's Chateau & Estate Wines Co.

DOMAINE BARRE - Wines ☆ - Kobrand Corp.

DOMAINE BERNARD MUGNERET - Wines - Seagram's Chateau & Estate Wines Co.

DOMAINE BERTAGNA - Wines ☆ - Maison Jomere Ltd.

DOMAINE BONNEAU DE MARTRAY - Wines - Seagram's Chateau & Estate Wines Co.

DOMAINE BOUDON - Wines - Chartrand Imports

DOMAINE BOURMONT - Beverages–alcohol - Brimstone Hill Winery

DOMAINE BRETON - Wines ☆ - Guenoc & Langtry Estate Vineyards and Winery

DOMAINE BUENA VISTA - Wines ☆ - Buena Vista Winery, Inc.

DOMAINE CARNEROS - Wines - Kobrand Corp.

DOMAINE CECI LEYMARIE - Wines - Wine House Ltd.

DOMAINE CHANDON - Wines - Schieffelin and Somerset Co.

DOMAINE COMTE DE LAUZE - Wines - Seagram's Chateau & Estate Wines Co.

DOMAINE COOPERATIVE - Wines ☆ - Golden State Vintners

DOMAINE CORDIER-TEXAS - Wines - Seagram's Chateau & Estate Wines Co.

DOMAINE D. ARGENS - Candy - International Gourmet

DOMAINE DE BOUTEILLEY - Wines - European Beverage Co., Inc.

DOMAINE DE CABRIERES - Wines - Parliament Import Co.

DOMAINE DE COURCEL - Wines - Seagram's Chateau & Estate Wines Co.

DOMAINE DE COYEUX - Wines ☆ - Dreyfus Ashby Inc.

DOMAINE DE GARTIEUX - Wines ☆ - European Beverage Co., Inc.

DOMAINE DE LA BATADIERE - Wines - Seagram's Chateau & Estate Wines Co.

DOMAINE DE LA BOUBEE - Wines - Admiral Wine Merchants

DOMAINE DE LA MALADIERE - Wines - Seagram's Chateau & Estate Wines Co.

DOMAINE DE LA RENARDS - Wines ☆ - Admiral Wine Merchants

DOMAINE DE LA ROQUETTE - Wines - Seagram's Chateau & Estate Wines Co.

DOMAINE DE LA VENNE - Wines - Oasis Vineyard

DOMAINE DE LAUZE - Wines - Seagram's Chateau & Estate Wines Co.

DOMAINE DE L'HYVERNIERE - Wines - Dreyfus Ashby Inc.

DOMAINE DE L'OISELLNIERE - Wines - Seagram's Chateau & Estate Wines Co.

DOMAINE DE LONGVAL - Wines - Seagram's Chateau & Estate Wines Co.

DOMAINE DE MONT-REDON - Wines ☆ - Kobrand Corp.

DOMAINE DE POUSSE D'OR - Beverages–alcohol ☆ - Diamond Wine Merchants

DOMAINE DE PROVENCE - Olive oil - Friendly Fruit, Inc.

DOMAINE DE SAINT-LAURENT-L'ABBAYE - Wines - Seagram's Chateau & Estate Wines Co.

DOMAINE DE TRIENNES - Wines - Wilson Daniels Ltd.

DOMAINE DELAGRANGE BACHELET - Wines - Seagram's Chateau & Estate Wines Co.

DOMAINE DES CEDRES - Wines - Chartrand Imports

DOMAINE DOPFF - Beverages–alcohol ☆ - Kobrand Corp.

DOMAINE D'ORMESSON - Wines - Wine Imports Ltd.

DOMAINE DROUHIN OREGON - Wines - Dreyfus Ashby Inc.

DOMAINE DU CELLIER - Wines - Admiral Wine Merchants

DOMAINE DU CHATEAU - Wines - Finest Wines Inc.

DOMAINE DU SAC - Wines - Wollersheim Winery, Inc.

DOMAINE DU SOLEIL - Wines ☆ - McDowell Cellars Inc.

DOMAINE DU VIGNEAU - Beverages–alcohol - Margus Co.

DOMAINE DUJAC - Wines - Wilson Daniels Ltd.

DOMAINE DUPONT-TISSERANDOT - Wines - Seagram's Chateau & Estate Wines Co.

DOMAINE EDOUARD DELEGER - Wines - Seagram's Chateau & Estate Wines Co.

DOMAINE G. ROUMIER - Wines - Seagram's Chateau & Estate Wines Co.

DOMAINE GELIN-MOLIN - Wines - Seagram's Chateau & Estate Wines Co.

DOMAINE J. GUILLEMARD - Wines - Seagram's Chateau & Estate Wines Co.

DOMAINE JEAN CHAVY - Wines - Seagram's Chateau & Estate Wines Co.

DOMAINE JEAN GRIVOT - Wines - Seagram's Chateau & Estate Wines Co.

DOMAINE L. GEOFFROY - Wines - Seagram's Chateau & Estate Wines Co.

DOMAINE LEFLAIVE - Wines - Frederick Wildman and Sons Ltd.

DOMAINE MANIERE-NOIROT - Wines - Wine House Ltd.

DOMAINE MARQUIS D'ANGERVILLE - Wines - Seagram's Chateau & Estate Wines Co.

DOMAINE NAPA CELLARS - Wines - Bronco Wine Co.

DOMAINE NOEL - Wines - Bianchi Vineyards

DOMAINE P. DE MARCILLY - Wines ☆ - Seagram's Chateau & Estate Wines Co.

DOMAINE PICASSO - Wines - Pablo Picasso International Licensing Co.

DOMAINE PIERRE MATROT - Wines - Seagram's Chateau & Estate Wines Co.

DOMAINE PINSON - Beverages–alcohol ☆ - Diamond Wine Merchants

DOMAINE RABAT - Wines - Palm Bay Imports, Inc.

DOMAINE ROBERT DUBOIS - Wines - Seagram's Chateau & Estate Wines Co.

DOMAINE ROYAL - Beverages–alcohol - R. Torre & Co.

DOMAINE ST. CHARLES - Wines ☆ - Wilson Daniels Ltd.

DOMAINE SAINT GEORGE - Wines - Cannon Wines Ltd.

DOMAINE ST. GEORGE - Wines - Domaine St. George Winery & Vineyards

DOMAINE STE. MICHELLE - Wines - Stimson Lane Vineyards & Estates

DOMAINE SONOMA - Wines - Cannon Wines Ltd.

DOMAINE TOLLOT-BEAUT - Wines - Seagram's Chateau & Estate Wines Co.

DOMAINE VALOUIT - Wines - Admiral Wine Merchants

DOMAINE WILLIAM FEVRE - Wines - Seagram's Chateau & Estate Wines Co.

DOMAINES DES ASTRUC - Wines ☆ - Maison Jomere Ltd.

DOMAINES LOUBERE - Wines - Seagram's Chateau & Estate Wines Co.

DOMAINES OTT - Wines - House of Burgundy Inc.

DOMAINES PRATS - Wines ☆ - Kobrand Corp.

DOMAINES VITICOLES DU CREDIT FONCIER - Wines ☆ - Admiral Wine Merchants

DOMAINWEAR - Apparel and accessories - Broadbent & Williams, Inc.

DOMAN - Lumber - Woodex Lumber Corp.

DOMANI - Food products - DFC Food Corp.

☆ = Now out of production

DOMANI - Food products - Ore-Ida Foods, Inc.
DOMANI - Pasta - Food Service Products Co.
DOMANI - Plumbing fixtures–metal ☆ - Barclay Products Ltd.
DOMANI - Shoes ☆ - Genesco Inc.
DOMANI - Skin care products - Domani
DOMANI - Toys - Peg Perego USA Inc.
DOMANI - Wallpaper - Capital Carousel Inc.
DOMANI - Wallpaper - K.M.L. Industries
DOMANI - Wallpaper ☆ - Royaleigh Designs Ltd.
DOMANI BRILLIANT - Skin care products - Domani
DOMANI UOMO - Apparel–men's - D & L, Inc.
DOMASCO - Bakery products ☆ - California Milling Corp.
DOMCRETE - Cement - Georgia-Pacific Corp.
DOMCRETE & DESIGN - Cement - Georgia-Pacific Corp.
DOME - Jar tops–metal - Alltrista Corp.
DOME - Office supplies - Dome Publishing Co., Inc.
DOME - Recording label - Universal Record
DOME BY NUMBER - Ceiling dome kits - Joan N. Barszcz
DOME CLIMBER - Exercising equipment ☆ - Roadmaster Corp.
DOME-INATOR - Tents - Creative Energies Inc.
DOME KIT I - Hobby kits - Avionics Plastics Corp.
DOME-LITES - Lighting fixtures - Swivelier Co. Inc.
DOME-PASTE - Bandages - Miles Inc.
DOME SHADOWS - Cosmetics - Cici Cosmetic Co.
DOME-TOP - Electrical equipment - Panduit Corp.
DOME-TOP - Wastebaskets - F.H. Lawson Co.
DOMEBORO - Antiseptics - Miles Inc.
DOMEBORO - Pharmaceutical preparations - Bayer Corp. (Consumer Care Div.)
DOMED - Cosmetics - Maybelline Co.
DOMEFORM-HC - Antibiotics ☆ - Miles Inc.
DOMENICA LAMANDO - Shoes ☆ - Atsco Footwear Inc.
DOMENICO GALBANI - Cheese - Bel Canto Fancy Foods Ltd.
DOMEPLEX - Audio equipment ☆ - MTX
DOMER - Helmets–athletic - Domer Sportswear
DOMERINE - Shampoos - Miles Inc.
DOMES OF SILENCE - Hardware - Robert E. Miller & Co. Inc.
DOMESTIC - Bedding–linen - Dan River Inc.
DOMESTIC - Furniture - Roy McMakin
DOMESTIC - Sewing machines–household - VWS Inc.
DOMESTIC - Thread - Threads USA Div.
DOMESTIC ARTS - Floor coverings–carpet and rugs ☆ - Callaway Carpets
DOMESTICATIONS - Bedding–linen - Hanover Companies
DOMETIC - Refrigerators - Dometic Corp.
DOMETIC-AIRE - Air conditioning equipment ☆ - Dometic Corp.
DOMEX - Handbags - Domex Handbag Trading Co. Ltd.
DOMI-NOTES - Games ☆ - Cramer Products Co.
DOMINADE - Lemonade - Domino Sugar Corp.
DOMINANT - Drills–electric - Arthur Gomez
DOMINANTE - Floor coverings–carpet and rugs - Milliken & Co. Inc.
DOMINATE - Cleaning preparations - W.W. Grainger, Inc.
DOMINATOR - Amplifiers ☆ - Electro-Voice, Inc.
DOMINATOR - Archery equipment - Thomas J. Grimaldi
DOMINATOR - Batteries - East Penn Manufacturing Co., Inc.
DOMINATOR - Bicycles ☆ - Hedstrom Corp.
DOMINATOR - Boats–motor - Alumacraft Boat Co.
DOMINATOR - Floor coverings–carpet and rugs - Dorsett Carpet Mills Inc.
DOMINATOR - Floor coverings–carpet and rugs ☆ - Blue Ridge Carpet Mills
DOMINATOR - Flour - Inland Mills Co.
DOMINATOR - Rackets–tennis - Pro Kennex, Inc.
DOMINATOR - Searchlights - National Event Marketing Inc.
DOMINATOR - Sporting goods - Gear 2000, Ltd.
DOMINATOR - Sports rackets and accessories ☆ - Gexco Enterprises
DOMINATOR - Toys–guns - Hasbro, Inc.
DOMINATOR - Trailers - Classic Manufacturing Inc.
DOMINATOR - Veterinary pharmaceutical preparations - Schering-Plough Animal Health
DOMINATOR, THE - Pizza - Domino's Pizza Inc.
DOMINGO - Breads ☆ - American Naturavit Inc.
DOMINGO OLOR HANDMADE IMPORTED - Cigars - Famous Smoke Shop, Inc.
DOMINIC BROTHERS - Games - Mattel, Inc.
DOMINICAN CLUB - Beverages - Prime Foods Inc.
DOMINICAN NOIR - Coffee - First Colony Coffee and Tea Co. Inc.
DOMINICKS - Food products - Dominick's Finer Foods, Inc.
DOMINION - Cutlery - Washington Forge Inc.

DOMINION - Floor coverings–carpet and rugs ☆ - Ebsco Carpet Mills
DOMINION - Furniture ☆ - Bernhardt Industries
DOMINION - Hardware - Evanite Fiber Corp. (Evanite Hardboard Div.)
DOMINION - Housewares - Dominion Electric Supply Co.
DOMINION - Juice extracting devices ☆ - Hamilton Beach/Proctor-Silex Inc.
DOMINION - Labels–paper - K-Tel International, Inc.
DOMINION - Mattresses - Stearns & Foster Bedding Co.
DOMINION - Shoes - Genesco Inc.
DOMINION - Spices and extracts - Herbert Marmorek & Son, Inc.
DOMINION - Tools - Railway Handle Co.
DOMINION - Watches - North American Watch Corp.
DOMINION ALE - Beverages–malt - Old Dominion Brewing Co.
DOMINION COLLECTION - Furniture–wood - Flexsteel Industries Inc.
DOMINION LOCK - Locks–padlocks - ILCO Unican Corp.
DOMINION POST, THE - Toys–banks - West Virginia Newspaper Publishing Co.
DOMINION STOUT - Beverages–malt - Old Dominion Brewing Co.
DOMINIQUE - Boats ☆ - Correct Craft Inc.
DOMINIQUE - Footwear–women's - Wohl Shoe Co.
DOMINIQUE - Rings–jewelry - Artcarved Inc.
DOMINIQUE - Toys–stuffed ☆ - Gund, Inc.
DOMINIQUE - Underwear and nightwear - Heavenly Intimate Inc.
DOMINIQUE DESIGNS - Greeting cards - Schurman Fine Papers
DOMINO - Apparel and accessories - Salant/Manhattan Industries
DOMINO - Cigarettes - House of Edgeworth
DOMINO - Floor coverings - Harris-Tarkett, Inc.
DOMINO - Food products ☆ - General Mills, Inc.
DOMINO - Footwear - Chadwick Industries
DOMINO - Games - Carrom Co.
DOMINO - Sugar–granulated, refined, or powdered - Domino Sugar Corp.
DOMINO - Toys–stuffed ☆ - Gund, Inc.
DOMINO CIRCUS - Toys - Discovery Toys, Inc.
DOMINO COMPUTERS - Computers - Domino Computer Services, Inc.
DOMINO KITTY - Toys–stuffed - Dakin Inc.
DOMINO LTD. - Recording label ☆ - Domino Ltd.
DOMINO PANDA - Toys–stuffed - Dakin Inc.
DOMINO RALLY - Games - Pressman Toy Corp.
DOMINOES - Bathing suits - Ocean Pool Co.
DOMINOES - Floor coverings–carpet and rugs - Quaker Inc.
DOMINOES USA TRIP 50 - Games ☆ - Pal Productions Inc.
DOMINOES WORLD 7 - Games ☆ - Pal Productions Inc.
DOMINOOOS - Games ☆ - CBS Toys
DOMINO'S - Pizzas–mixes - Domino's Pizza Inc.
DOMINO'S PIZZA - Chewing gum ☆ - Amurol Confections Co.
DOMINO'S PIZZA - Restaurants–pizzerias - Domino's Pizza Inc.
DOMINOWIZARD - Computer software - Wandel & Goltermann Technologies, Inc.
DOMINUCCI - Handbags - Oroton USA Inc.
DOMINUS - Video games - Gregory A. Thomas
DOMKE - Cases–camera - The Tiffen Co.
DOMKE - Photographic equipment - Tiffen Manufacturing Corp.
DOMMANATE - Pharmaceutical preparations ☆ - Forest Pharmaceuticals Inc.
DOMODIDOVO - Furniture - Domodidovo Ltd.
DOMODOTS - Games - Learning Games Inc.
DOMOGYN - Chemical preparations ☆ - Miles Inc.
DOMOL - Bath salts - Miles Inc.
DOMOTEX - Wallpaper ☆ - Marburg Wallcoverings Inc.
DOMOTEX 8 - Wallpaper - Marburg Wallcoverings Inc.
DOMPE - Food products - Dompe Warehouse Co.
DOMS - Computer software - Alpha & Omega Integrated Control Systems Inc.
DOM'S - Seafood products–fresh or frozen - Mobile Freezers Inc.
DOMSEA - Seafood products–fresh or frozen - Domsea Farms Inc.
DOMSKI - Vodka - Italian and French Wine Co. of Buffalo Inc.
DOMUS - Flatware - W.M.F. of America Inc.
DOMUS - Floor coverings–carpet and rugs ☆ - World Carpets, Inc.
DOMUS - Giftware - Sasaki
DOMUS CIRCULATION MAPS - Maps - On Target Communications, Inc.
DON - Food products - Universal Foods Corp.
DON - Ophthalmic goods ☆ - Rozin Optical Export Corp.
DON - Recording label - Kubaney Publishing Corp.
DON-A-BELT - Girdles - Nuvogue Creations
DON-A-SPAS - Pharmaceutical preparations ☆ - Murray Drug Corp.
DON ALDO PASTA ITALIANA DI GRAGNANO NAPOLI - Pasta - Best Way Food Dist., Inc.
DON AND DAVE - Fruits and vegetables - Per-Clin Orchards Inc.
DON BARTOLO - Cigars - Cattle Crest Group

☆ = Now out of production

DON BRUNO - Spices and extracts - Bruno Scheidt, Inc.
DON BRUNO - Vinegar, olive oil - American Roland Food Corp.
DON BUDGE - Sporting goods - Gold Medal Recreational Products
DON CARLENO - Window coverings - Paramount Fabrics Inc.
DON CARLOS - Footwear ☆ - Brown Shoe Co.
DON CE SAR - Cigars - Havatampa Inc.
DON CHARLES ROSS - Wines - Napa Valley Wines
DON CHATEO - Recording label - Kubaney Publishing Corp.
DON COSSACK - Vodka - M.S. Walker Inc./Seacoast
DON COYOTE - Food products - Swiss American Import Co.
DON COYOTE - Hats - Coyote-Crow Productions, Inc.
DON DE PRIMOS - Pasta - Primo's Italian Foods
DON DIEGO - Cigar boxes–wood - Consolidated Cigar Corp.
DON DIEGO PRELUDES - Cigar boxes–wood - Consolidated Cigar Corp.
DON ELITO - Cigars - IP & L, Ltd. Cigars International
DON EMILIO - Beverages–alcohol - Bacardi Imports Inc.
DON ENRIQUE - Food products - World Variety Produce Inc.
DON-EZE - Girdles - Nuvogue Creations
DON FRANCISCO - Cigars - Goodarz Haydarzadeh
DON FRANCISCO - Coffee - F. Gavina and Sons Inc.
DON FRANCISCO - Dairy products - Don Francisco Foods, Inc.
DON G. - Food products - Don G. Orchards Inc.
DON GIOVANNI'S ESPRESSO BELLISSIMO - Coffee - John Eugene Martinez
DON HERMANN & SONS - Seasonings - Hermann Pickle Co.
DON-ITE - Lacquers - Don V. Davis Co.
DON JAMES PETAGREE COLLECTABLES - Toys–stuffed ☆ - Commonwealth Toy and Novelty Co. Inc.
DON JANUARY - Balls–golf - Plymouth Golf Ball Co.
DON JOE - Vegetables–canned - Mercantum Corp.
DON JOSE - Beverage - Paradise Valley Foods, Inc.
DON JOSE - Food products ☆ - Tommy's Foods Inc.
DON JUAN - Tobacco products - Tropical Tobacco, Inc.
DON JUAN - Wines ☆ - Laird and Co.
DON JUANE - Perfumes - Chanel Inc.
DON JULIO - Cigars - Swisher International, Inc.
DON JULIO AUTHENTIC - Food products - Craig Fisher
DON LAPIZZIN - Publisher's imprints - Izaskun Gaminde
DON LOPER - Apparel–men's - Superba, Inc.
DON LOPER - Leather goods - Tandy Brands Accessories Inc.
DON LOPER OF BEVERLY HILLS - Leather goods ☆ - Gary's Leather Creations
DON-LOU - Bottled water - Buffalo Don's Artesian Wells Ltd.
DON LUIS - Wines - Val Verde Winery
DON MANUEL - Coffee - Coffee Holding Co.
DON-MAR - Recording label - Casa Grande Records
DON MARCOS - Cigar boxes–wood - Consolidated Cigar Corp.
DON MARTINO - Pizzas–mixes - Crestar Food Products, Inc.
DON MATTINGLY - Sporting goods ☆ - Franklin Sports, Inc.
DON MAXIMO - Fruits and vegetables - Leo Martinez
DON MELO - Cigars ☆ - Tropical Tobacco, Inc.
DON MIGUEL - Cigar boxes–wood - Consolidated Cigar Corp.
DON MIGUEL - Food products - Alex Foods, Inc.
DON-O-TRED - Paints - Shaheen Paint Co.
DON PABLO LIGHT - Tobacco products - Lane Ltd.
DON PASQUALE - Food products - Paisano Food Products Inc.
DON PEDRO - Brandy - Domecq Importers Inc.
DON PEDRO - Food products - Camino Real Foods
DON PEPINO - Food products - Violet Packing Co.
DON PONCHO - Food products - Reser's Fine Foods Inc.
DON Q GRAND ANEJO - Rum - Destileria Serralles Inc.
DON QUIJOTE - Olive oil - Goya Foods, Inc.
DON QUIJOTE - Perfumes - Helene Curtis Industries Inc.
DON QUIXOTE'S WINDMILL - Weather vanes - Vitos Products
DON RAMON - Shrimp–fresh or frozen ☆ - Darik Enterprises Inc.
DON RENE - Cigars - Cigar Connection, Inc.
DON REY - Cigars - T.E. Brooks & Co.
DON RICARDO - Beverages–alcohol - Turret Imports Ltd.
DON RICO - Coffee - Hansen Good Coffee
DON SALVATORE - Humidifiers - Nina Enterprises, Inc.
DON SENOR - Tortillas - Mexi-Food Distributors Inc.
DON THE BEACHCOMBER - Beverages - Vita-Pakt Citrus Products Co.
DON TOMAS - Cigars - United States Tobacco Co.
DON TOMAS - Fruit drinks–bottled or canned - Empresas Don Tomas, Inc.
DON TOWT - Tools–garden - Lawn & Garden Supply Co.
DON TROIANI'S BATTLES THAT FORGED A NATION SERIES - Posters - Don Troiani

DON VICENTE - Cigars - V. Guerrieri Cigar Co. Inc.
DON VITO - Shoes - Futura Shoe Corp.
DONA - Pottery - Tortilla Press
DONA DOULAS OF NORTH AMERICA - Video production - Doulas of North America
DONA LAPINA - Flour–blended - General Mills, Inc.
DONA MARGARITA - Sauces - Avo-King International, Inc.
DONA-PAUL - Cosmetics - Dona-Paul Co.
DONABARB - Pharmaceutical preparations ☆ - ICN Pharmaceuticals Inc.
DONAHUE - Tables–wood ☆ - Howe Furniture Corp.
DONALD BROOKS - Apparel–men's - Greif Cos.
DONALD DUCK - Fruit drinks–bottled or canned - Citrus World Inc.
DONALD DUCK - Wallpaper ☆ - Priss Prints Inc.
DONALD DUCK STICKS - Candy ☆ - American Candy Co.
DONALD DUCK'S PLAYGROUND - Computer software - Sierra On-Line, Inc.
DONALD J. PLINER - Handbags - Donald J. Pliner Concepts, Inc.
DONALD JONS' - Hair care products - Donald Johns' Systems, Inc.
DONALD RICHARD'S - Jewelry - Don-Lin Jewelry Co. Inc.
DONATELLO - Toys - Playmates World Wide Inc.
DONATO D'ANGELO - Wines - Paterno Imports, Ltd.
DONATO MARRONE - Footwear - Donato Marrone Ltd.
DONATONI WINERY - Wines - Donatoni Winery
DONATUS - Meat products–poultry - Lactoprot USA, Inc.
DONATUS ROYAL VIKING - Cheese - Lactoprot USA, Inc.
DONATUSSIN - Pharmaceutical preparations - Laser Inc.
DONATUSSIN DC - Pharmaceutical preparations - Laser Inc.
DONAX - Lubricants - Shell Oil Co.
DONCASTER - Apparel–men's - J. Schoeneman Inc.
DONCASTER - Apparel–women's - Tanner Companies Inc.
DONCASTER - Coats–men's - Schoeneman Enterprises, Inc.
DONDE ESTA CARMEN SANDIEGO? - Computer software - Gessler Publishing Co., Inc.
DONDI - Fruits–candied ☆ - Liberty Richter Inc.
DONDI MOSTRARDA - Fruits–candied ☆ - Liberty Richter Inc.
DONDOLINO - Toys - Peg Perego USA Inc.
DONDRIL - Cough medicines - Whitehall Laboratories
DONE IT! - Meat products–poultry - Perdue Farms Inc.
DONEAGLE - Neckties - M. Aron Corp.
DONEGAL - Earthenware ☆ - Waterford Wedgewood USA, Inc.
DONEGAL - Floor coverings–carpet and rugs - Mohawk Industries Inc.
DONEGAL - Floor coverings–carpet and rugs - Patcraft Mills Inc.
DONEGAL - Men's apparel - Interco Inc.
DONEGAL - Yarn ☆ - Tahki Imports Ltd.
DONEGAL BAY - Floor coverings–carpet and rugs - Hartford Carpet Mills
DONELI - Cheese - Mid-America Dairymen Inc. Southern Div.
DON'EM IN DANIMS - Fabrics ☆ - Dan River Inc.
DONG HUNG VIEN - Bakery products - Loan Kim Hoang
DONG QUAIL/DAMIANA - Vitamins and nutritional supplements - Desert Health Products, Inc.
DONG SARONG - Underwear and nightwear - Wanda R. Michie
DONGHIA - Fabrics - Donghia Textiles Inc.
DONGHIA - Furniture - Donghia Furniture Co. Ltd.
DONI - Athletic shoes - Turning Point Sports
DONI - Dinnerware–glass ☆ - Thornton White Group
DONIE - Furniture - Donie Chair Co. Inc.
DONINGTON - Pillows - Pillowtex Corp.
DONITS - Crocheted and knitted items - Hercules-Carnation Knitwear Inc.
DONIZETTI - Glassware–household - Spiegelau Inc.
DONJOY - Braces–orthopedic - Smith & Nephew DonJoy Inc.
DONKERS - Candy - Westdale Foods Co.
DONKEY KONG - Candy ☆ - Topps Co., Inc.
DONKEY KONG - Cereal - Ralston Purina Co.
DONKEY KONG - Toys–electronic - Hasbro, Inc.
DONKEY KONG COUNTRY - Video games - Nintendo of America Inc.
DONKEY KONG JUNIOR - Cereal - Ralston Purina Co.
DONKEY KONG JR. - Toys–electronic - Hasbro, Inc.
DONKEY KONG MAZE - Candy ☆ - Fleer Corp.
DONLAR - Chemical preparations - Donlar Corp.
DONMAR - Automotive parts and accessories - Donmar Enterprises Inc.
DONMOOR - Apparel and accessories - Cluett, Peabody & Co.
DONNA - Cabinets - Formitex Inc.
DONNA - Dolls - Uneeda Doll Co., Inc.
DONNA - Food products - US Foodservice
DONNA - Frames–eyeglass ☆ - Rozin Optical Export Corp.
DONNA - Watches - Bulova Corp.
DONNA - Wigs ☆ - Jean Paree Weegs Inc.

☆ = Now out of production

DONNA ADAMS - Apparel and accessories - Donna F. Adams, Inc.
DONNA EXTENDTABS - Pharmaceutical preparations ☆ - A.H. Robins Co. Inc.
DONNA GRAY NEW YORK SELECTIONS - Apparel–women's - Allgrain International Export Corp.
DONNA KARAN - Apparel and accessories - Sara Lee Corp.
DONNA KARAN - Eyewear - Solargenics
DONNA KARAN NEW YORK - Patterns–clothing - Donna Karan Co.
DONNA KARAN NEW YORK - Skin care products - Gabrielle Studio, Inc.
DONNA KETTY MADE IN ITALY - Shoes - Fe. Ma. Inc.
DONNA LEE - Cosmetics - Donna Lee Cosmetics Inc.
DONNA MAIONE - Apparel and accessories - Donna Maione Inc.
DONNA MARIA VINEYARD - Wines ☆ - Chalk Hill Winery
DONNA MARIE - Apparel–women's - Jason Fok
DONNA NICOLE - Apparel and accessories - Pacific Teaze
DONNA-SED - Pharmaceutical preparations ☆ - Vortech Pharmaceuticals
DONNA THE KANGAROO - Furniture–children's - Maze Inc.
DONNA VALENTINA - Wines - Tyfield Importers
DONNA VINCI - Apparel–women's - Brasseur, Inc.
DONNACIN - Pharmaceutical preparations ☆ - Pharmex Inc.
DONNAGEL - Pharmaceutical preparations - A.H. Robins Co. Inc.
DONNALATE - Antacids ☆ - A.H. Robins Co. Inc.
DONNAPRIN - Analgesics - Dunhall Pharmaceuticals Inc.
DONNAS - Footwear - Chesapeake Shoe Co. of California
DONNASEP - Analgesics ☆ - A.H. Robins Co. Inc.
DONNEGAL - Aluminum foil wrap - Highland Supply Corp.
DONNER - Bathroom accessories - VSI Donner
DONNER MOUNTAIN - Shoes - Atsco Footwear Inc.
DONNIE D. PRODUCTIONS - Posters - Donnie D. Productions Inc.
DONNIE'S - Hair care products - Samlo
DONNIE'S ACTIVATOR - Hair care products - Samlo
DONNIE'S LITE - Hair care products - Samlo
DONNIE'S REJUVENATION - Hair care products - Samlo
DONNING - Publisher's imprints - Donning Co./Publishers
DONNKENNY - Apparel–women's - Donnkenny Inc.
DONNY - Handbags - Donny Handbags Inc.
DONNYBROOK - Beverages - The Sqwincher Corp.
DONNYSPUN - Crocheted and knitted items - Garland Knitting Mills
DONOHUE - Publisher's imprints ☆ - Rand McNally & Co.
DONORART - Tiles–ceramic - Recognition Resources
DONORSAURUS - Paper - Southwest Florida Blood Bank Inc.
DONOVAN-GALVANI - Apparel and accessories - TJ Designs Inc.
DONPHEN - Pharmaceutical preparations ☆ - Lemmon Co.
DONRUSS - Trading cards and stamps - Leaf, Inc.
DON'S CHUCK WAGON - Food products - Hodgson Mill
DON'S DELICIOUS GOURMET CREAM CHEESE SPREADS - Cheese - Aldon Food Corp.
DON'T - Pharmaceutical preparations ☆ - Del Pharmaceuticals, Inc.
DON'T ASK - Games ☆ - Mayfair Games, Inc.
DON'T ASK Y - Apparel–children's - D.A.Y. Kids Sportswear Inc.
DON'T BE A VICTIM - Recording label - Jan L. Warner
DON'T BE BLUE - Toys–stuffed - Bonnie Sugar
DON'T BITE IT - Nail care products - Gena Laboratories Inc.
DON'T BLAME US - Video production - Mitchell Video Productions
DON'T BLEND IN KATS - Apparel–children's - Don't Blend in Kats
DON'T BLOW YOUR TOP - Games - Tyco Toys
DON'T BREAK THE ICE - Games - Milton Bradley Co.
DON'T COMMIT DATACIDE! - Safes - Empire Safe Co. Inc.
DON'T COOK YOUR GOOSE - Games - Tyco Toys
DON'T DARE CALL IT JELLY! - Fruit butters - M. Polaner Inc.
DON'T EAT WITHOUT IT - Mouthwashes - Breath Asure, Inc.
DON'T GET RATTLED - Toys - Hasbro, Inc.
DON'T GIVE UP! - Legal services - Independent Paralegal Services, Inc.
DON'T GO OVERBOARD - Games - Tyco Toys
DON'T GO WITHOUT THEM! - Footwear - Caressa Inc.
DON'T HOLD BACK - Golfing equipment - Taylor Made Golf Co. Inc.
DON'T JUST SIT THERE! - Apparel and accessories - Interfilm Technologies, Inc.
DON'T JUST STAND THERE STEP ON IT - Exercising equipment - Sports Step Inc.
DON'T JUST WATCH.LISTEN! - Radios - Sportronics Radios, Inc.
DON'T LET UP - Apparel and accessories - Mark McPerry
DON'T LET YOUR FEARS STAND IN THE WAY OF YOUR DREAMS - Apparel and accessories - No Fear, Inc.
DON'T LOSE IT - Computer software - Dantz Development Corp.
DON'T LOSE YOUR TOOL! - Belts–apparel - Kane Products, Inc.

DON'T MEAN A THING WITHOUT THE RING - Apparel and accessories - Kick 10 Promotions, Inc.
DON'T MISS THE BOAT - Games - Tyco Toys
DON'T PANIC - Apparel and accessories - Don't Panic Designs, Inc.
DON'T PANIC - Games - Milton Bradley Co.
DON'T POSTPONE JOY - Toys - Last Wound-Up Inc.
DON'T SPILL THE BEANS - Games - Milton Bradley Co.
DON'T SPILL THE BEANS - Soups–mixes - Wildwood Creations
DON'T STICK ME - Pins–safety ☆ - Gerber Products Co.
DON'T STOP - Apparel and accessories - Levad Fashion Inc.
DON'T TREAD ON ME - Cutlery - Russell Harrington Cutlery, Inc.
DON'T USE - Computer software - Synopsys, Inc.
DON'T WAKE THE DRAGON - Games - Tonka Corp.
DON'T WORRY - Health care products - Herbs of China Ltd.
DON'T WORRY, BE HAPPY - Food products - Herbs of China Ltd.
DONTESO - Jams and jellies - Doneteso Co.
DONUT-ALL - Kitchen appliances ☆ - Nordic Ware
DONUT BANK - Bakery products - Donut Bank Inc.
DONUT BEAD - Fabrics - Lumured Corp.
DONUT BOX - Food containers - Skinner & Kennedy Co.
DONUT COUPE - Infant product ☆ - Century Products Co.
DONUT DELITES - Doughnuts - Drake Bakeries, Inc.
DONUT DISASTER - Parlor game equipment - Tonka Corp.
DONUT HEEL PADS - Health care products - Professional Foot Care Products Inc.
DONUT HEEL PADS - Heels–boot and shoe - Professional Product Research, Inc.
DONUT MAN, THE - Food products machinery - American Specialty Foods Inc.
DONUT MAN, THE - Cooking equipment–commercial - Quantum Group, Inc.
DONUT PALACE - Bakery products - Donut Palace and Equipment Co., Inc.
DONUT SHOP - Doughnuts–frozen - Conagra, Inc.
DONUTLAND - Restaurants–coffee shops - Donutland Inc.
DONUTS - Apparel and accessories - Jays Industries Inc.
DONUTZ - Cereal - General Mills, Inc.
DONZI - Boats–motor - Donzi Marine Corp.
DONZI - Boats–motor - Outboard Marine Corp.
DONZIS - Automotive repair shops - Byron A. Donzis
DOO-ALL SCRUBBER - Cleaning preparations - Swiss-Tex Inc.
DOO-DADS - Artists' materials ☆ - Hunt Manufacturing Co.
DOO DADS - Snack foods - Nabisco Foods Group
DOO-GLUE - Hair care products - Posner Laboratories Inc.
DOO GRO - Hair care products - Altman Enterprises, Inc.
DOO IT UP - Hair curlers - Earthly Essentials, Inc.
DOO-WAVE - Hair care products - Alaion Products Inc.
DOO-Z - Paint rollers - Wooster Brush Co.
DOOBIE - Toys–stuffed - Gund, Inc.
DOOBY - Toys–stuffed ☆ - Russ Berrie and Co., Inc.
DOOD-ITS - Frames–picture - Cider Mill Art & Frame
DOODADS - Candy ☆ - Leaf, Inc.
DOODANA - Apparel and accessories - Tamami, Inc.
DOODIE SCOOP - Pet products ☆ - Mapes Industries Inc.
DOODLE - Binders - Rundel Products Inc.
DOODLE - Fruits and vegetables ☆ - Stapleton-Spence Packing Co.
DOODLE - Telescopes - Northern Telecom, Inc.
DOODLE ART - Artists' materials - Price Stern Sloan Inc.
DOODLE BALLS - Toys - Smethport Specialty Co.
DOODLE BOPS - Hosiery - Clayson Knitting Co. Inc.
DOODLE BUZZ - Fishing lures - Plastics Research and Development Co.
DOODLE DINOSUAR - Toys - Smethport Specialty Co.
DOODLE DOGS - Greeting cards - James Thomas Burnett
DOODLE-DOO - Artists' materials - Artistic Office Products
DOODLE IN' - Office supplies - Avery Dennison Corp.
DOODLE MARKERS - Artists' materials - Price Stern Sloan Inc.
DOODLE-MATION - Computer storage devices - Screenmagic, Inc.
DOODLE O'S - Snack foods - Borden, Inc.
DOODLE POODLE - Toys - Smethport Specialty Co.
DOODLE ROLL - Paper products - Fay Paper Products Inc.
DOODLE SNIFFS - Artists' materials - Price Stern Sloan Inc.
DOODLE SOCON - Fishing tackle - Skyline Industries Inc.
DOODLE TOOLS - Artists' materials - Jonathan Bradley Pens Inc.
DOODLE TWISTERS - Corn chips - Borden, Inc.
DOODLEBUGGY - Trucks and all-terrain vehicles - Western Atlas International Inc.
DOODLEKEEPER - Publisher's imprints - Five Star Productions, LLC
DOODLEMANIA - Calendars - T.J. Bohme
DOODLER - Pipes - National Briar Pipe Co.

☆ = Now out of production

DOODLER'S DELIGHT - Office supplies - People Systems Inc.
DOODLES - Cosmetics - Maybelline Co.
DOODLES AND VERSES - Greeting cards - Doodles and Verses Inc.
DOODLEWONKERS - Trading cards and stamps - Treat Entertainment, Inc.
DOODLEYBOPPER - Massage products - Touch of Life
DOOFFLES - Bags - Wilshire Group Inc.
DOOLEY DINGHY - Ships–sailing vessels - Glander Boats Inc.
DOOLEY GRABBER, THE - Shovels - Hueter Toledo, Inc.
DOOLEY'S - Snack foods - Mars, Inc.
DOOLITTLE - Office supplies - House of Doolittle
DOOLITTLE - Toys–stuffed ☆ - Gund, Inc.
DOOM - Insecticides - Fairfax Biological Laboratory
DOOM II - Computer software - 3do Co.
DOOM LOOP, THE - Educational materials - Dory Hollander
DOOMCOPTER - Toys–airplanes - Mattel, Inc.
DOOM'S IV - Books–comic - Rob Liefeld, Inc.
DOOMSDAY 2000 - Computer software - Emil D. Scheifler
DOOMSDAY PROGRAM, THE - Games ☆ - Mayfair Games, Inc.
DOOMSLAYERS - Toy figures - Russ Berrie and Co., Inc.
DOOR - Games - Flying Buffalo Inc.
DOOR 1 - Lubricants - Denco Marketing Co.
DOOR-AID - Electrical equipment - Medical Surgical Specialties, Ltd.
DOOR BOSS, THE - Metals - Watson Co.
DOOR BUDDY - Locks–door - Independent Livings Products, Llc
DOOR CLUB - Alarm systems–burglar - Winner International Corp.
DOOR CLUB - Hinges - James E. Winner Jr.
DOOR COM - Telephone apparatus - Nutone Inc.
DOOR COUNTY - Seafood products–canned or cured - Aldo's Spices
DOOR COUNTY - Wines - Door Peninsula Winery
DOOR DELIGHT - Beverages - Door Peninsula Winery
DOOR-EASE - Lubricants - American Grease Stick Co.
DOOR FIXER, THE - Weather stripping - KEL-EEZ
DOOR-GUARD - Floor coverings–carpet and rugs - Ludlow Composites Corp.
DOOR KEEPER - Alarm systems - Delfino Products Inc.
DOOR KNOB - Bags–plastic - Saket Co.
DOOR KNOB - Labels–paper - Gene Kennedy Enterprises
DOOR-LITE - Electrical equipment ☆ - Cable Electric Products
DOOR MATES - Floor coverings ☆ - Congoleum Corp.
DOOR-MATIC - Hardware - Advanced Affiliates Inc.
DOOR-N-WALL - Shelving units–wood ☆ - Hirsh Co.
DOOR PALS - Safety products - Wayne Salvador
DOOR PENINSULA - Wines - Door Peninsula Winery
DOOR SECURITY - Electrical equipment - Rittenhouse
DOOR SNUGLER - Draft preventer ☆ - Intromark Inc.
DOOR STEP - Enamels - Lasting Paints Inc.
DOOR SWEEP - Weather stripping - KEL-EEZ
DOOR TATTOOS - Paper products - Fepco, Inc.
DOOR THING - Exercise apparatus - Diversified Products Corp.
DOOR TREE, THE - Hardware - Door Tree, Inc.
DOOR VALET - Door openers–electronic ☆ - Stanley Home Automation Inc.
DOORKEEPER - Door openers–electronic ☆ - Stanley Home Automation Inc.
DOORKNOBBER - Candy ☆ - Topps Co., Inc.
DOORMAN, THE - Electronic equipment - CSI/Speco
DOORMAN, THE - Alarm systems ☆ - Midwest Sunroofs
DOORMASTER - Cabinets–wood - Ampco Products Inc.
DOORMISER - Doors–storm ☆ - Norandex, Inc.
DOORNAMENTS - Pillows - Barth-Dreyfuss of California
DOORNOBS - Fishing lures - Area Rule Engineering Inc.
DOORS OF DUBLIN - Christmas tree ornaments - Cracker Box Inc.
DOORSAVER - Automotive parts and accessories - Popeil Industries Inc.
DOORSEAL - Caulking compounds ☆ - Myro, Inc.
DOORSHIELD - Hardware - Key Control Systems Inc.
DOORVISION - Television equipment - CCTV Corp./GBC
DOORWAYS TO ADVENTURE - Games - Pressman Toy Corp.
DOORWAYS TO HORROR - Games - Pressman Toy Corp.
DOOZER - Toys - Jim Henson Productions, Inc.
DOOZY - Brushes - Tico Industries Inc.
DOOZY - Polishes - Mr. Furniture Finisher LLC
DOOZY AUTOMOTIVE - Polishes - Mr. Furniture Finisher LLC
DOOZY DOES IT - Polishes - Mr. Furniture Finisher LLC
DOOZY HI-TECH - Polishes - Mr. Furniture Finisher LLC
DOPAL 8 - Cosmetics ☆ - Cosmair Inc.
DOPAR - Pharmaceutical preparations - Norwich-Eaton Pharmaceuticals
DOPASCAN - Pharmaceutical preparations - Guilford Pharmaceuticals Inc.
DOPE BUSTERS - Publisher's imprints - Dopebust*Rs International, Inc.
DOPE ON A ROPE - Soap - Compass Development Corp.

DOPE PRODUCTS! - Apparel - Benjamin Johnston Enterprises
DOPES, THE - Recording label - W.D.O.P., Inc.
DOPF & IRON - Wines ☆ - Bercut-Vandervoort & Co.
DOPFF AU-MOULIN - Wines - Kobrand Corp.
DOPIE DOPE - Dolls - Grin-A-Bit Co., Inc.
DOPP - Bags–cosmetic - Buxton Inc.
DOPPEL DARK - Beverages–malt ☆ - Hudepohl-Schoenling Brewing Co.
DOPPERT - Cameras ☆ - Edixa Camera Co.
DOPRAD - Radar systems and equipment - Advanced Designs Corp.
DOR - Lamps - Harris Lamps Co.
+D'OR - Wines - St. Julian Wine Co.
DOR-C - Cold remedies - Dorsey Laboratories
DOR-FLO - Deodorizers ☆ - Vaportek, Inc.
DOR-LITES - Floodlights - Chris Kaye Plastics Corp.
DOR MOR - Anchors - Dor-Mor, Inc.
DOR PAK - Cartons–paperboard - Carry Pack, Inc.
DOR-STOP - Hardware - Portaseal Inc.
DOR-SWEEP - Hardware - Portaseal Inc.
DOR WAL - Doors–glass - Acorn Window Systems Inc.
DORADO - Beverages–alcohol - Black Prince Distillery, Inc.
DORADO - Cigarettes ☆ - Liggett Group Inc.
DORADO - Crackers ☆ - FCW Imports
DORADO - Desks - Stylex Inc.
DORADO - Dog food - Valley Feed and Supply, Inc.
DORADO - Floor coverings ☆ - National Floor Products Co., Inc.
DORADO - Mobile homes - Wick Building Systems Inc. (Manufactured Home Div./North)
DORADO - Musical instruments ☆ - Fred Gretsch Enterprises
DORADO - Paper–carbon ☆ - Curtis-Young Corp.
DORADO BEACH - Floor coverings - Mannington Resilient Floors
DORADO BEACH CHAMPIONSHIP COURSE - Computer software - Access Software Inc.
DORADO CARTON - Paper products - Dorado Carton Co., Inc.
DORADO COLLECTION, THE - Wallpaper - Lawrence Wallcoverings
DORADO GOLD - Beverages–alcohol - U.S. Beverage, LLC
DORAL - Apparel and accessories - Champion Products Inc.
DORAL - Cigarettes - R.J. Reynolds Tobacco Co.
DORAL - Floor coverings–carpet and rugs - Cumberland Mills Inc.
DORAL - Floor coverings–carpet and rugs - Playfield International Inc.
DORAL - Furniture - Pilliod Co.
DORAL - Mobile homes - Wick Building Systems Inc. (Manufactured Home Div./North)
DORAL - Pharmaceutical preparations - Wallace Laboratories
DORAL GERMANY - Cigarettes - General Cigar Co., Inc.
DORAL SUAVE - Cigarettes - R.J. Reynolds Tobacco Co.
DORANA - Pharmaceutical preparations - Wyeth-Ayerst Laboratories
DORANN - Food products ☆ - Agway Country Foods Inc.
DORCHESTER - Bicycles - Ross Bicycles USA, Ltd.
DORCHESTER - Cigarettes - R.J. Reynolds Tobacco Co.
DORCHESTER - Dinnerware–glass - Nikko Ceramics Inc.
DORCHESTER - Floor coverings - Mannington Resilient Floors
DORCHESTER - Floor coverings–carpet and rugs - Queen Carpet Corp.
DORCHESTER - Floor coverings–carpet and rugs ☆ - Dorsett Carpet Mills Inc.
DORCHESTER - Floor coverings–carpet and rugs ☆ - Kelly Group Inc.
DORCHESTER - Lamps ☆ - Lamplight Farms, Inc.
DORCHESTER HOUSE - Furniture ☆ - Romweber Co.
DORCO - Windows–storm - Dorco Manufacturing Co. Inc.
DORCOL - Cough medicines - Dorsey Laboratories
DORCY - Bicycles - Cycle Products Co.
DORCY - Flashlights - Rothco Inc.
DORDEN - Squeegees - Dorden & Co.
DORE - Wines - Winequest
DOREEN - Glassware–household ☆ - Oneida Ltd.
DOREL - Suntan lotions - Lever Brothers Co. Inc.
DORELLE - Cheese - Swissrose International Inc.
DOREMI - Colognes ☆ - Avon Products, Inc.
DORET - Cheese - Lactoprot USA, Inc.
DORETTE - Ophthalmic goods ☆ - Luxottica
DORFMAN-PACIFIC - Apparel stores–sports - Dorfman-Pacific Co. Inc.
DORGALI - Apparel stores–sports - Dodger Industries Inc.
DORIA - Recording label - Jazz Composer's Orchestra Association Inc.
DORIA - Rings–jewelry - Artcarved Inc.
DORIAN - Bathroom fixtures ☆ - Crane Plumbing/Fiat Products
DORIAN - Chimes ☆ - J.W. Stannard Co.
DORIAN - Floor coverings - Congoleum Corp.
DORIAN - Rings–jewelry - Artcarved Inc.

DORIAN - Vases ☆ - Lenox Crystal, Inc.
DORIAN - Wallpaper - Brewster Wallcovering Co.
DORIAN FOR MEN - Wigs - Dorian for Men Ltd.
DORIAN RECORDINGS - Recording label - Dorian Group, Ltd.
DORIANI - Men's apparel - Ital Clothing, Inc.
DORIC - Floor coverings–carpet and rugs ☆ - Langhorne Carpet Co. Inc.
DORIC - Food products - Sundor Brands Inc.
DORIC - Mushrooms - Krinos Foods, Inc.
DORIC - Pens ☆ - Keuffel & Esser Co.
DORIC - Pens ☆ - Parker Pen USA
DORIC - Recording label - Organ Literature Foundation
DORIC - Wallpaper - Seabrook Wallcoverings, Inc.
DORIDEN - Pharmaceutical preparations - Rhone-Poulenc Rorer Pharmaceuticals Inc.
DORIO - Computers - Digital Equipment Corp.
DORIS - Dresses–girls' - Doris Brosk Inc.
DORISON HOUSE PUBLISHERS - Publisher's imprints - Dorison House Publishers
DORITOS - Snack foods - Frito-Lay, Inc.
DORITOS 3D - Snack foods - Frito-Lay, Inc.
DORITOS TACO SUPREME - Snack foods - Frito-Lay, Inc.
DORK - Candy - Classic Caramel Co.
DORK - Candy - Lukas & Co.
DORKO - Scissors–hand-operated - Norsk Engros USA Inc.
DORKS - Chewing gum ☆ - Amurol Confections Co.
DORKY MULLET - Fishing lures - Kalin Co.
DORLAND'S - Waxes–paraffin - Siphon Art Products
DORM BASKET - Giftware - Harper's Fabric Centers Inc.
DORMA - Door openers–electronic - Dorma Properties, Inc.
DORMA-REST - Pharmaceutical preparations - Pharmex Inc.
DORMALUX - Furniture - Dinaire Corp.
DORMAN - Vehicle parts - SDI Operating Partners
DORMAN'S - Cheese - Swissrose International Inc.
DORMAN'S FINE CHEESE SPECIALISTS SINCE 1896 - Cheese - Dorman-Roth Foods, Inc.
DORMAREX - Health care products - Republic Drug Co. Inc.
DORMAREX 2 - Health care products - Republic Drug Co. Inc.
DORMASTER - Furniture - Serta, Inc.
DORMATE - Staircases–wood ☆ - Goodhue Lumber Co. Inc.
DORMEASAN - Health care products - Bioforce of America Ltd.
DORMIE - Slippers - Daniel Green Co.
DORMIN - Pharmaceutical preparations - Randob Laboratories Ltd.
DORMIREX - Fabrics ☆ - Fateh International Inc.
DORN - Recording label - AKO Records
DORNIER LITHOTRIPTER COMPACT - Medical therapeutic apparatus - Dornier Medical Systems, Inc.
DORO - Cases–eyeglass ☆ - California Optical Leather Inc.
D'ORO - Dinnerware–glass - WMF/USA
D'ORO - Men's suits, blazers, slacks - International Clothing of Florida Inc.
D'ORO - Shoes - Canter Shoe Co.
D'ORO - Spaghetti sauces - Cantisano Foods, Inc.
D'ORO U.S.A. - Nail care products - Lal Rewachand
DOROFIN - Pet products - Tetra Sales USA
DOROGREEN - Pet products - Tetra Sales USA
DOROMENU - Pet products - Tetra Sales USA
DOROMIN - Pet products - Tetra Sales USA
DORORED - Pet products - Tetra Sales USA
DOROTHEE BIS - Yarn ☆ - Knitting Fever Inc.
DOROTHY - Dolls - Effanbee Doll Corp.
DOROTHY - Ophthalmic goods - Styl-Rite Optical Manufacturing Co., Inc.
DOROTHY BAUER - Belts - A Piece of the Rainbow
DOROTHY DAY JUNIORS - Crocheted and knitted items - Garland Knitting Mills
DOROTHY DEAR DESIGNS OLD-FASHIONED DESIGNS - Fabrics - Dorothy Dear Designs
DOROTHY DODD - Shoes - Interco Inc.
DOROTHY DUNCAN - Cakes ☆ - Safeway Stores Inc.
DOROTHY GRAY - Health care products - Dorothy Gray Cosmetics Ltd.
DOROTHY GRAY - Skin care products - L & F Products Inc.
DOROTHY HAFNER - Housewares - Dorothy Hafner
DOROTHY HAMMILL - Sporting goods - Bollinger Industries
DOROTHY LYNCH - Salad dressings–bottled - Tasty Toppings Inc.
DOROTHY THORPE - Glassware–household - Vincent Lippe Co.
DOROTHY'S RUFFLED ORIGINALS - Curtains - Dorothy's Ruffled Originals Inc.
DORRIE - Floor coverings–carpet and rugs - Masland Corp.

DORRIE'S CLAY CREATIONS CLAY BUSINESS CARD HOLDERS - Desk sets - Delores L. Storrs
DORSACAINE - Pharmaceutical preparations - Dorsey Laboratories
DORSAL - Chairs–wood - Krueger International, Inc.
DORSEAL - Hardware - Croft Metals Inc.
DORSEL'S - Corn–flour or meal - Wilson's Corn Products Inc.
DORSEL'S - Flour–blended - Dorsel Co.
DORSET - Bicycles - Columbia Manufacturing Inc.
DORSET - Brushes–hair ☆ - Harry D. Koenig & Co.
DORSET - Cabinets ☆ - Yorktowne Inc.
DORSET - Frames–eyeglass ☆ - Universal/Univis Inc.
DORSET - Furniture ☆ - Telescope Casual Furniture Inc.
DORSET - Housewares ☆ - Scio Pottery Co.
DORSET SQUARE - Furniture - Lane Co. Inc.
DORSET WOOD - Wood products ☆ - J.K. Adams Co. Inc.
DORSETTE - Glassware–household - Crystal Clear Importing Co. Inc.
DORSETTE HOUSE - Mobile homes - Western Homes Corp.
DORSEY INTERNATIONAL - Tools–garden - Lawn & Garden Supply Co.
D'ORSINI - Cosmetics - Transamerica Mailings, Inc.
DORSIWEDGE - Bandages–orthopedic - Walkwell International, Inc.
DORT - Motor vehicles–automobiles ☆ - Dort Motor Car Co.
D'ORTEGA - Sandals - Mosinger-Cohn Inc.
DORTMUNDER ACTION DRAUERIE (DAD) - Beverages–malt ☆ - HDT Importers Inc.
DORTMUNDER KRONEN - Beverages–alcohol ☆ - Chrissa Imports Ltd.
DORTMUNDER UNION - Beverages–malt - Dortmunder Union Import
DORVAL - Candy - Dorval Trading Co., Ltd.
DORVILLE - Wines ☆ - Frank Sutton & Co.
DORY - Boats - Glen-L Marine Designs
DORY - Novelty items - Dory Development Corp.
DORYX - Pharmaceutical preparations - Parke-Davis
D.O.S. - Pharmaceutical preparations - Goldline Laboratories, Inc.
DOS AMIGOS - Vegetables–canned - Basic American Foods
DOS BUILD - Computer software - Eason Technology, Inc.
DOS EQUIS - Beverages–malt - Labatt Importers Inc.
DOS EQUIS - Beverages–malt - Montezuma Imports Inc.
DOS GRINGOS - Spices and extracts - Adobe Milling
DOS GUSANOS - Beverages–alcohol - David Sherman Corp.
DOS MARIAS - Coffee - Dos Marias, SA
DOS PADRES - Food products - Dos Padres, Inc.
DOS PAGE - Computer software - EX Machina, Inc.
DOS PICOS - Salsa - Price Co.
DOS ROSAS PROD. - Film–motion picture - Eucharist Films Distribution
DOSAGE KORC - Health care products - Apothecary Products, Inc.
DOSCIM - Computer software - Compuserve Inc.
DOSE - Apparel–athletic - Snowboard Connection, Inc.
DOSE-MAP - Measuring instruments - ISP Investments Inc.
DOSE OF COLOR - Cosmetics - Beauticontrol Cosmetics Inc.
DOSE-RITE - Ophthalmic goods - InSite Vision Inc.
DOSEASSIST - Computer software - Simkin, Inc.
DOSECALC - Computer software - Glaxo Wellcome Inc.
DOSER - Medical apparatus - New-Med Corp.
DOSHA 793 - Apparel and accessories ☆ - Edison Brothers Stores, Inc.
DOSILIFT - Medical apparatus - Capintec, Inc.
DOSIO VIGNETI - Beverages–alcohol - Alseca Corp.
DOSKOCIL - Cases–camera - Doskocil Manufacturing Co., Inc.
DOSKOCIL - Meat products–beef - Foodbrands America, Inc.
DOSKOCIL - Pet products - R.C. Steele Co.
DOSKOCIL A STRONG CASE FOR QUALITY - Sporting goods - Doskocil Manufacturing Co., Inc.
DOSKOW - Silverware - Leonore Doskow Inc.
DOSS - Recording label - Stardust/Wizard/Doss Records
DOSS - Soccer equipment - Soccer Sport Supply Co. Inc.
DOSS CHAMPIONS - Soccer equipment - Soccer Sport Supply Co. Inc.
DOSS DIAMOND - Sporting goods - Soccer Sport Supply Co. Inc.
DOSS MAXI SKILL - Sporting goods ☆ - Soccer Sport Supply Co. Inc.
DOSS SUPER 9 - Soccer equipment - Soccer Sport Supply Co. Inc.
DOSS WORLD CUP - Soccer equipment - Soccer Sport Supply Co. Inc.
DOSSIER - Luggage - Lifestyle International, Inc.
DOSSIER - Recording label - Jazz Composer's Orchestra Association Inc.
DOSTOPS - Computer software - Sitka Corp.
DOSWEDGE - Computer software - Tal Technologies, Inc.
DOT - Balls–golf - Spalding Sports Worldwide
DOT - Cleaning preparations ☆ - White Cap Inc.
DOT - Computer storage devices–optical - Pinnacle Micro, Inc.
DOT - Flower pots–earthenware - Kevin X. Domurat

☆ = Now out of production

DOT - Recording label - MCA Universal Studios

DOT - Skin care products - Holder Images

DOT & PEG - Footwear ☆ - R.G. Barry Corp.

DOT ART - Product description unknown - Amav Sales Ltd.

DOT COAT - Packaging–paper - Oliver Products Co.

DOT DURABLES - Fasteners–snap - American Engineer Components

DOT JONES-COCONUT GROVE HOT & SPICEY - Barbecue sauce - Jones Barbeque Sauce, Inc.

DOT LINER - Automotive parts and accessories - James P. Wright

DOT-O - Games - Brown and Bigelow Inc.

DOT SNAPPERS - Fasteners–snap - American Engineer Components

DOTCO - Pneumatic tools - Cooper Industries, Inc.

DOTLESS - Artists' materials - Apple Arts Ltd.

DOTLURE - Fishing lures - Dot Lure Inc.

DOTMAN - Publisher's imprints - Progressive Training, Inc.

DOTPRINT - Printers–computer - Linotype-Hell Co. Inc.

DOTS - Candy - Tootsie Roll Industries, Inc.

D.O.T.S. - Fertilizers - Howard Johnson's Enterprises, Inc.

DOTS - Sugar–granulated, refined, or powdered - Domino Sugar Corp.

DOT'S DAISIES - Bedding–linen - Dan River Inc.

DOTS ON METAL - Wallcoverings - Worldwalls International Inc.

DOTSMANN - Cylinders - Thoma Imports

DOTTED LINE - Computer software - Scientific-Atlanta, Inc.

DOTTED SUN DESIGN - Paper - Georgia-Pacific Corp.

DOTTED SWISS - Glassware–household ☆ - Crisa Corp.

DOTTI - Apparel and accessories - Dotti Original Inc.

DOTTI - Apparel and accessories - Kellwood Co.

DOTTIE - Food products - Golden Pantry West Inc.

DOTTIE - Wigs - Jean Paree Weegs Inc.

DOTTIE II - Apparel and accessories - Carole Hochman Designs Inc.

DOTTIE'S ORIGINALS - Pet products - Leatherite-Nylorite Manufacturing Inc.

DOTTO - Games ☆ - T.J. Bohme

DOTTY, CHARLIE & SAM - Toys–stuffed - Tomy America, Inc.

DOTTY MANN - Apparel–women's - Euclid Sportswear Co.

DOTTY SMITH - Apparel and accessories - Dotty Smith

DOUBLE - Hair care products - Ry-Al Beauty Corp.

DOUBLE - Ophthalmic goods - Foremost Optical Products

DOUBLE - Sporting goods - Sports 'N' More Corp.

DOUBLE 2, THE - Fabrics - Ack-Ti-Linings Inc.

DOUBLE A - Ammunition - Olin Corp. (Winchester Div.)

DOUBLE A - Eggs - Double A Poultry Farm

DOUBLE-A - Pharmaceutical preparations ☆ - Edwards Pharmaceuticals, Inc.

DOUBLE A - Recording label - Sarg Recording Co.

DOUBLE-AA - Dog food - W.A. Davis Milling Co. Inc.

DOUBLE AA - Fruits and vegetables ☆ - Idaho Fruit Sales Inc.

DOUBLE ACTION - Cleaning preparations–carpet and rug ☆ - Bissell Inc.

DOUBLE ACTION - Pet products - Red Bell Inc.

DOUBLE AGENT - Drain pipe cleaners - Hercules Chemical Co. Inc.

DOUBLE AGENT - Publisher's imprints ☆ - Tsr, Inc.

DOUBLE B - Apparel–children's - Buster Brown Apparel Inc.

DOUBLE B - Meat products–beef - Double B Foods Inc.

DOUBLE B - Onions - Bosgraaf Sales Co.

DOUBLE BACK - Paper - Penn-Plax, Inc.

DOUBLE BALL - Pet products - Novalek, Inc.

DOUBLE BARB - Fishing tackle - Wright & McGill Co.

DOUBLE BARREL - Degreasing solvents - Calgon Vestal Laboratories

DOUBLE BARREL - Toys–automobiles - Mattel, Inc.

DOUBLE BARREL TARGET - Toys - Placo Products Co.

DOUBLE BATCH - Food products machinery - Dynamics Corp. of America

DOUBLE BEAUTY - Lenses–optical - Kelley & Hueber

DOUBLE BERBER - Floor coverings–carpet and rugs - Prestige Mills Inc.

DOUBLE BLACK STOUT - Beverages–alcohol - Starbucks Corp.

DOUBLE-BLADE - Sporting goods ☆ - Shaw & Tenney Inc.

DOUBLE BLOCK - Floor coverings–carpet and rugs ☆ - Regal Rugs Inc.

DOUBLE BLUEBERRY - Bakery products - Martha White Foods Inc.

DOUBLE-BRELLA - Umbrellas ☆ - Double Products Co.

DOUBLE/BUBBLE - Adhesives and sealants - Hardman

DOUBLE BUBBLE - Health care products - HNE Healthcare

DOUBLE BUBBLER - Faucets - Faucet-Queens Inc.

DOUBLE BUCKS - Games - International Gamco, Inc.

DOUBLE BUG - Fishing lures - Storm Manufacturing Co.

DOUBLE C HAWAIIAN PUNCH - Fruit drinks–bottled or canned - Procter & Gamble Co.

DOUBLE CENTURY - Wines ☆ - Domecq Importers Inc.

DOUBLE CHECK - Electronic equipment - Victoreen, Inc.

DOUBLE-CHECKER - Office supplies ☆ - Wescosa Inc.

DOUBLE-CHEK - Pregnancy test kits - Bio-Medical Products Corp.

DOUBLE CHERRIES - Game machines - Sigma Game Inc.

DOUBLE CHEX - Cereal - Ralston Purina Co.

DOUBLE CHIPS! - Cookies - Mother's Cake & Cookie Co.

DOUBLE-COLA - Beverages–carbonated - Double Cola Co.-USA

DOUBLE-COLA - Syrup - The Atlantic Beverage Group, USA, Inc.

DOUBLE COLOR - Cosmetics - Estee Lauder Inc.

DOUBLE COMFORT - Pillows - American Fiber Industries Corp.

DOUBLE COULEUR - Cosmetics - Chanel Inc.

DOUBLE CRISP - Candy - R.M. Palmer Co.

DOUBLE CROSS - Brassieres (Bras) ☆ - Lovable Co.

DOUBLE CROSS - Game machines - Amutronics, Inc.

DOUBLE CROSS - Games - International Gamco, Inc.

DOUBLE CROSS - Games - Lakeside Games

DOUBLE CROSSER - Frames–eyeglass - Zylo Ware Corp.

DOUBLE CROSSING - Games ☆ - Lionel Trains Inc.

DOUBLE-CUSHION - Weather stripping - W.J. Dennis & Co.

DOUBLE CUT - Games - Mogi Co.

DOUBLE-D - Ophthalmic goods - Vision Ease

DOUBLE D - Pharmaceutical preparations ☆ - C.O. Truxton Inc.

DOUBLE D. WESTERN - Publisher's imprints - Bantam Doubleday Dell Publishing Group, Inc.

DOUBLE DANDERINE - Shampoos ☆ - Medtech Laboratories Inc.

DOUBLE DARE - Games ☆ - Pressman Toy Corp.

DOUBLE DATE - Apparel–women's - Wacoal America Inc.

DOUBLE DECKER - Cases–camera - SP Systems/Saratons

DOUBLE DECKER - Cosmetics - Comare Corp.

DOUBLE DECKER - Electronic equipment - Logan Electric Specialty Manufacturing Co.

DOUBLE DECKER - Glassware–household - L & L Products, Inc.

DOUBLE-DECKER - Ice chests ☆ - Poloron Products Inc.

DOUBLE DECKER - Sandwiches–prepackaged - Taco Bell Corp.

DOUBLE DEER BRAND - Rice - Imex House International, Inc.

DOUBLE DELIGHT - Game machines - Sigma Game Inc.

DOUBLE DELIGHT - Meat products–beef - Sigman Meat Co. Inc.

DOUBLE DELIGHTS - Yogurt - Dannon Co., Inc.

DOUBLE DELUXE - Game machines - Bally Gaming International, Inc.

DOUBLE DEMON - Toys–automobiles - Mattel, Inc.

DOUBLE DEUCE - Beverages–malt - The Stroh Brewery Co.

DOUBLE DEVON - Cheese - Chesman Inc.

DOUBLE DIAMOND - Beverages–malt - Associated Importers Co.

DOUBLE DIAMOND - Beverages–malt - Canandaigua Wine Co. Inc.

DOUBLE DIAMOND - Food products - Northern Star Co.

DOUBLE DIAMOND DELUXE - Game machines - IGT - North America

DOUBLE DIAMOND LEAN - Meat products - Excel Corp.

DOUBLE DIAMONDS - Apparel and accessories - Playtex Apparel, Inc.

DOUBLE DIAMONDS - Jewelry–precious - Unigem International

DOUBLE DIGITS - Candy ☆ - Sunline Brands

DOUBLE DIMENSION - Apparel and accessories ☆ - Playtex Apparel, Inc.

DOUBLE DIMPLE - Apparel and accessories - Double Dimple Partners

DOUBLE DIP - Apparel–children's - Little Funky Knits, Inc.

DOUBLE DIP - Candy - R.L. Albert & Son, Inc.

DOUBLE DIP - Toys ☆ - Today's Kids Inc.

DOUBLE DIP CRUNCH - Cereal ☆ - Kellogg Co.

DOUBLE-DIPPED - Hardware - Maze Nails

DOUBLE DIPPERS - Candy - Brach and Brock Confections Inc.

DOUBLE DISC - Video games - Taito America Corp.

DOUBLE DISK CONVERTER - Computer peripheral equipment - Biological Engineering/High Tech Pet Products

DOUBLE DIVIDE - Bicycles - Dynacraft Industries Inc.

DOUBLE DOOZ - Toys - Mattel, Inc.

DOUBLE DOUBLES - Cookies - Topco Associates, Inc.

DOUBLE DOUGH - Clay–modeling - Botanical Science

DOUBLE DOWN STUD - Board game - D.D. Stud, Inc.

DOUBLE DRAGON - Video games - Nintendo of America Inc.

DOUBLE DRAGON - Video games ☆ - Taito America Corp.

DOUBLE DREAD - Toys ☆ - Those Characters from Cleveland, Inc.

DOUBLE DRIBBLE - Video games ☆ - Konami (America) Inc.

DOUBLE DRIBBLE-THE PLAYOFF EDITION - Computer software ☆ - Konami (America) Inc.

DOUBLE DRUM DINNER - Turkeys - Cooper's Turkey Place, Inc.

DOUBLE-DRY - Beverages–carbonated - Double Cola Co.-USA

DOUBLE DUAL - Alarm systems - Crow Electronic Engineering, Inc.

DOUBLE DUNK - Toys - SLM Inc.

DOUBLE DUSTER - Pet products - Pueblo Chemical & Supply Co.

DOUBLE DUTCH - Siding - Variform, Inc.

DOUBLE DUTY - Chemical preparations ☆ - Sanford Corp.

DOUBLE-DUTY - Cleaner - Intex Chemical Inc.

DOUBLE DUTY - Floor coverings–carpet and rugs ☆ - Blue Ridge Carpet Mills

DOUBLE DUTY - Floor coverings–tile - Tec Inc.

DOUBLE-DUTY - Gypsum products - Georgia-Pacific Corp.

DOUBLE DUTY - Marker pens ☆ - Itoya of America, Ltd.

DOUBLE DUTY - Ovens–microwave - General Electric Co.

DOUBLE-DUTY - Paint sprayers - Wagner Spray Tech Corp.

DOUBLE DUTY - Pencils ☆ - Faber-Castell Corp.

DOUBLE-DUTY - Signs - Fasteners for Retail, Inc.

DOUBLE DUTY - Tools - Century Drill & Tool Co.

DOUBLE DUTY - Tools - Vaughan & Bushnell Manufacturing Co.

DOUBLE DUTY - Toys–automobiles - Mattel, Inc.

DOUBLE E - Food products - Maple Leaf Foods Inc.

DOUBLE E - Health care products - Keystone Laboratories Inc.

DOUBLE EAGLE - Audio equipment - Shahinian Acoustics Ltd.

DOUBLE EAGLE - Batteries - Goodyear Tire & Rubber Co.

DOUBLE EAGLE - Beverages–carbonated - Decca Financial & Consulting, Inc.

DOUBLE EAGLE - Bicycles - Columbia Manufacturing Inc.

DOUBLE EAGLE - Boats - Glen-L Marine Designs

DOUBLE EAGLE - Boots - Double Eagle Custom Boots

DOUBLE-EAGLE - Coffee - Herold & Miller Inc.

DOUBLE EAGLE - Floor coverings–carpet and rugs - Gulistan Carpet Inc.

DOUBLE EAGLE - Knives–pocket - Imperial Schrade Corp.

DOUBLE EAGLE - Motors–outboard - Byrd Industries Inc.

DOUBLE EAGLE - Pistols - Colt's Manufacturing Co. Inc.

DOUBLE EAGLE - Saws–chain ☆ - McCulloch Corp.

DOUBLE EAGLE - Sporting goods ☆ - Wright & McGill Co.

DOUBLE EAGLE - Tobacco products - Sterling Tobacco Co.

DOUBLE EAGLE - Toys–airplanes ☆ - Cox Products Inc.

DOUBLE EFFECTS - Cosmetics - Revlon Consumer Products Corp.

DOUBLE ELEPHANT PRESS - Publisher's imprints - Ten Speed Press

DOUBLE ESTERLON - Rope - Yale Cordage, Inc.

DOUBLE EXPOSURE - Apparel–children's - M. Rubin & Sons Inc.

DOUBLE EXPOSURE - Apparel–women's - Jezebel-Renee of Hollywood

DOUBLE EXPOSURE - Frames–eyeglass - May Optical Co. Inc.

DOUBLE EXPOSURE - Games - Bob Stupak

DOUBLE FAULT - Apparel and accessories - Hi Joon Woo

DOUBLE FEATURE - Apparel–women's - Wacoal America Inc.

DOUBLE-FEATURE - Frames–eyeglass - Liberty Optical Manufacturing Co.

DOUBLE FEATURE - Lighters - Colibri Inc.

DOUBLE-FEATURE - Mirrors - Wimmer-Ferguson Inc.

DOUBLE FEATURE - Recording label - Musicor Records Inc.

DOUBLE FRESH - Pet products - Applied Industrial Materials

DOUBLE FRONT - Ladders–wood - John S. Tilley Ladders Co. Inc.

DOUBLE FRUIT COOLER - Fruit drinks–bottled or canned ☆ - Coca-Cola Co.

DOUBLE FUDGE - Candy ☆ - Holland American Wafer Co.

DOUBLE FUDGE PLUNGE - Ice cream - Dean Foods Co.

DOUBLE FUN - Toys - Mattel, Inc.

DOUBLE GARD - Windows–storm - National Aluminum Products Co.

DOUBLE GLO - Paints - C.M. Athey Paint Co.

DOUBLE GRIP - Balls–football - Charles O. Finley

DOUBLE GRIP - Clothespins - Penley Corp.

DOUBLE GUARD - Filters–oil - Alliedsignal Inc.

DOUBLE GUARD - Hardware - Tufco Technologies Inc.

DOUBLE GUARD - Pharmaceutical preparations - C.R. Bard, Inc.

DOUBLE H - Footwear - H.H. Brown Shoe Co., Inc.

DOUBLE H - Footwear - Double-H Boot Co.

DOUBLE-H - Meats–luncheon ☆ - Halperin Distributing Corp.

DOUBLE HATTER - Hats - Gary Adam Sherman

DOUBLE HEADER - Balls–baseball - J. De Beer & Son Inc.

DOUBLE HEADER - Bathing suits - Catalina

DOUBLE HEADER - Crocheted and knitted items - Schuessler Knitting Mills Inc.

DOUBLE HEADER - Crocheted and knitted items ☆ - Reliable of Milwaukee

DOUBLE HEADER - Nail care products - Spilo/Mehaz Worldwide

DOUBLE HEADERS - Trading cards and stamps - Topps Co., Inc.

DOUBLE HEELIX - Apparel and accessories - Douglas C. Siegel

DOUBLE HELIX - Computer software - Odesta Corp.

DOUBLE HELIX - Glass–plate - Sasaki

DOUBLE HI - Food products - U.S. Enterprise Corp.

DOUBLE HORSES BRAND - Rice - J & A Importers, Inc.

DOUBLE HYATAL - Pharmaceutical preparations ☆ - Mericon Industries Inc.

DOUBLE IMAGE - Bicycles - Roadmaster Corp.

DOUBLE IMAGE - Computer software - Host Interface International, Inc.

DOUBLE IMAGE - Cosmetics - Maybelline Co.

DOUBLE INTERWELT - Fabrics–cotton - J.P. Stevens & Co. Inc. (Knit & Narrow Fabric Div.)

DOUBLE ISOPACIN - Pharmaceutical preparations ☆ - Consolidated Midland Corp.

DOUBLE J - Apparel and accessories ☆ - Jantzen Inc.

DOUBLE J SADDLERY YOAKUM, TEXAS - Belts–apparel - Double J Saddlery, Inc.

DOUBLE JACKPOT - Games - Sigma Game Inc.

DOUBLE JACKPOT DOUBLE - Games - Sigma Game Inc.

DOUBLE K - Pharmaceutical preparations - Consolidated Midland Corp.

DOUBLE KAY - Nuts–salted, roasted, cooked, or canned ☆ - CPC International Inc.

DOUBLE KOTE - Machinery - D & K Custom Machine Design, Inc.

DOUBLE KOTE - Paints - C.M. Athey Paint Co.

DOUBLE KOTE JR. - Machinery - D & K Custom Machine Design, Inc.

DOUBLE L - Sporting goods - L.L. Bean Inc.

DOUBLE-LOC - Floor coverings - Congoleum Corp.

DOUBLE LOC - Tape–adhesive - Capitol Adhesives Inc.

DOUBLE LOIHES - Candy - Ce De Candy Inc.

DOUBLE-LOK - Bottle caps - Aluminum Co. of America

DOUBLE LOLLIE - Candy - Swizzels Matlow (USA) Ltd.

DOUBLE LOOPER - Games ☆ - Tyco Toys

DOUBLE LUCKY - Food products - Vitarroz

DOUBLE MAC - Kitchen appliances ☆ - Hamilton Beach/Proctor-Silex Inc.

DOUBLE MALT - Beverages–malt - G. Heileman Brewing Co., Inc.

DOUBLE MASTIC - Varnishes ☆ - Winsor & Newton

DOUBLE-MATES - Sofas - LZB Properties, Inc.

DOUBLE MATRIX - Safety products - U.S. Safety Corp.

DOUBLE MATTE - Cosmetics - Estee Lauder Inc.

DOUBLE MIX - Food processors - Dynamics Corp. of America

DOUBLE N TROUBLE - Computer software - Hartley Courseware Inc.

DOUBLE NINE - Firearms, accessories, and parts - High Standard Manufacturing Corp.

DOUBLE NOISET - Candy ☆ - Bahlsen Inc.

DOUBLE NOODLE - Soups–canned - Campbell Soup Co.

DOUBLE NURTZ - Playing cards - United States Playing Card Co.

DOUBLE NUTTY - Cookies ☆ - Keebler Co.

DOUBLE-O - Deodorizers - Surco Products Inc.

DOUBLE O - Enamels - Cerdec Corp.

DOUBLE O COMPLEX - Skin care products - Flori Roberts Inc.

DOUBLE O TUBE - Sporting goods ☆ - O'Brien International

DOUBLE-O-WIRE - Binders - Spiral Binding Co. Inc.

DOUBLE OO - Animal feeds - Okie Ostrich Ranch, Inc.

DOUBLE OPTION - Toys - Tonka Corp.

DOUBLE O'S - Chocolate candy - Meijer, Inc.

DOUBLE PEACHES - Lipstick and nail polish ☆ - Cosrich Inc.

DOUBLE PEANUT CLUSTER - Candy - Ben Myerson Candy Co.

DOUBLE PENCIL SHARPENERS - Cosmetics - Victoria Vogue, Inc.

DOUBLE-PHEN - Pharmaceutical preparations ☆ - C.O. Truxton Inc.

DOUBLE PLAY - Apparel and accessories ☆ - Warnaco Inc.

DOUBLE PLAY - Collectible baseball cards - ANCO Collector Supplies, Inc.

DOUBLE PLAY - Lenses–optical - Ditto Industries Inc.

DOUBLE PLAY - Pens - Sheaffer Inc.

DOUBLE PLAY - Pizzas–frozen ☆ - Mr. Z's Fund Raising Corp.

DOUBLE PLAY - Stereos ☆ - Quasar Co.

DOUBLE PLEASURE - Cookies - Interbake Foods Inc.

DOUBLE PLUS - Calculators - Zelco Industries, Inc.

DOUBLE POINT - Pens ☆ - Illustrator Pen Products Inc.

DOUBLE POPPERS - Candy - R.L. Albert & Son, Inc.

DOUBLE POPPERS - Toy motorcycles ☆ - Intex Recreation Corp.

DOUBLE POTENCY EVENING PRIMROSE - Vitamins and nutritional supplements - Schiff Products, Inc.

DOUBLE POWER - Detergents - Lever Brothers Co. Inc.

DOUBLE POWER ARM & HAMMER - Detergents - Church and Dwight Co. Inc.

DOUBLE PUMP - Athletic footwear - Reebok International Ltd.

DOUBLE Q - Salmon–smoked, salted, dried, or pickled - Peter Pan Seafoods, Inc.

DOUBLE Q - Tuna–canned - Mitsui & Co. Inc.

DOUBLE Q DELI - Sandwiches–prepackaged - Double Q Corp.

DOUBLE QUARTET - Candy - Murray-Allen International Inc.

DOUBLE QUICK - Yarn ☆ - Lily Craft Products

DOUBLE R - Food products - Cap's Italian Foods Inc.

DOUBLE RAY - Accordions - Hohner Inc.

☆ = Now out of production

DOUBLE REED - Sporting goods ☆ - Penn's Woods Products Inc.

DOUBLE REED FINGERINGS - Computer software - Electronic Courseware Systems Inc.

DOUBLE RINGER - Tools - Diamond/Triangle Tool Group Inc.

DOUBLE RL - Apparel–men's - Polo Ralph Lauren Corp.

DOUBLE S - Food products - Sadler's Bar-B-Que Sales Inc.

DOUBLE S - Pet products - Double S Dog Fashions

DOUBLE-SAL - Pharmaceutical preparations ☆ - Pal-Pak Inc.

DOUBLE SCRUB - Brushes - Clarke Industries, Inc.

DOUBLE SEAL - Health care products - Tecnol Medical Products, Inc.

DOUBLE SEAL - Plumbing fixtures–plastic - Sanitary-Dash Manufacturing Co. Inc.

DOUBLE SEMI-U - Construction equipment - Caron Compactor Co.

DOUBLE SERVICE - Lubricants - SF Services, Inc.

DOUBLE-SEWED - Erasers - Quartet Manufacturing Co.

DOUBLE SHADOW - Knives–pocket ☆ - United Cutlery Corp.

DOUBLE SHIELD - Insect repellent and sunscreen - Winning Solutions Inc./ Miracle of Aloe

DOUBLE SHINE PLUS - Lip balms - Del Pharmaceuticals, Inc.

DOUBLE SHOT - Basketball game - Lifetime Products, Inc.

DOUBLE SHOT - Games ☆ - CBS Toys

DOUBLE SHOT TOWER - Amusement rides - S & S Power, Inc.

DOUBLE SHUTTLE - Motor vehicles–trucks - Automated Waste Equipment Co., Inc.

DOUBLE SIDE SLEEPER - Infant product - Children on the Go, Inc.

DOUBLE SIX PACKER - Food containers ☆ - Thermos Co.

DOUBLE SQUARE - Tools - Lowell Corp.

DOUBLE SQUEAKIES - Games - Tyco Toys

DOUBLE STAR - Hardware, pipe, fence product - BP & N Inc.

DOUBLE STRENGTH - Detergents - First Preference Products Corp.

DOUBLE STRENGTH - Detergents - First Team Sports, Inc.

DOUBLE STRETCH PLEASURE - Underwear and nightwear ☆ - Lovable Co.

DOUBLE STUF - Cookies - Nabisco Brands Co.

DOUBLE STUF - Cookies - Nabisco Foods Group

DOUBLE SUPPORT - Apparel–women's - Bali Co. Inc.

DOUBLE SWITCH - Video games - Sega of America, Inc.

DOUBLE T - Apparel and accessories ☆ - Playtex Apparel, Inc.

DOUBLE T - Socks - Trenway Textiles Inc.

DOUBLE TAKE - Alarm systems - Mirror Lite Co.

DOUBLE TAKE - Bicycles ☆ - Huffy Corp.

DOUBLE-TAKE - Computer software - Network Specialists, Inc.

DOUBLE TAKE - Cosmetics - Del Pharmaceuticals, Inc.

DOUBLE TAKE - Costumes - Disguise Inc.

DOUBLE TAKE - Dental equipment - Ivoclar North America, Inc.

DOUBLE TAKE - Electronics equipment - Grass Valley Group Inc.

DOUBLE TAKE - Eyeglasses - Martin-Copeland Eyewear Corp.

DOUBLE TAKE - Floor coverings–carpet and rugs - Philadelphia Carpets

DOUBLE TAKE - Key rings - Park Lane Associates, Inc.

DOUBLE TAKES - Notebooks and notepads - Moore U.S.A. Inc.

DOUBLE TALK - Games - Boyle & Elggren, Inc.

DOUBLE TANGOES - Games - Rex Games, Inc.

DOUBLE THREAT - Fishing tackle and lures - Go Fish. Inc.

DOUBLE TIME - Hitches–trailer - Jerome J. Gerber

DOUBLE TIME - Ophthalmic goods - Embassy Creations Inc.

DOUBLE TIMER - Timers–appliance - West Bend Co.

DOUBLE TOP - Pizzas–frozen - Tombstone Pizza Corp.

DOUBLE TOUGH - Glass products ☆ - Corning Inc.

DOUBLE/TRAC - Mats–rattan - Samuel Furiness Mat Co.

DOUBLE TREASURE - Cookies - Interbake Foods Inc.

DOUBLE TREAT - Hair coloring preparations - Helene Curtis Industries Inc.

DOUBLE TROUBLE - Fishing lures ☆ - Joe's Flies

DOUBLE TROUBLE - Games - Brown and Bigelow Inc.

DOUBLE TROUBLE - Games - Meyers List Inc.

DOUBLE TROUBLE - Games - Milton Bradley Co.

DOUBLE TROUBLE - Sporting goods ☆ - Wellington Leisure Products, Inc.

DOUBLE TROUBLE - Toys - Mattel, Inc.

DOUBLE TUFF - Footwear - Cove Shoe Co.

DOUBLE TUSSIN BM - Cough medicines - Polam Wholesale Inc.

DOUBLE-TUSSIN DM - Cough medicines - Reese Chemical Co.

DOUBLE TWIST - Cosmetics - Revlon-Realistic Professional Products Inc.

DOUBLE TWIST - Nail care products - Revlon Consumer Products Corp.

DOUBLE U - Meat products–beef - Weiss Packing Co. Inc.

DOUBLE UP - Candy ☆ - Leaf, Inc.

DOUBLE UP - Closet organizers - Lynk, Inc.

DOUBLE UP - Frames–eyeglass - May Optical Co. Inc.

DOUBLE-UP - Juice extracting devices - High Performance Appliances, Inc.

DOUBLE-UP SKILLET - Breakfast entree - Country Hospitality Corp.

DOUBLE-UP, THE - Infant product - Natural Choice Co.

DOUBLE UPS - Jewelry ☆ - Hirsch Speidel Inc.

DOUBLE V - Apparel and accessories ☆ - Playtex Apparel, Inc.

DOUBLE-VIEW - Calendars ☆ - House of Doolittle

DOUBLE VISION - Novelty items - Hasbro, Inc.

DOUBLE VISION - Trading cards and stamps - Double Vision Enterprises

DOUBLE-VU - Office supplies - 20th Century Plastics

DOUBLE-VUE - Toys ☆ - Tyco Toys

DOUBLE W - Fruits and vegetables - Warren Wagner Inc.

DOUBLE-WALL MOUNTAIN - Cups–plastic - Coleman Co., Inc.

DOUBLE WAVE SCREW - Machine tools - HPM Corp.

DOUBLE-WEAR - Gloves - Midwest Glove Co.

DOUBLE WHACK PACK - Candy ☆ - Ferrero U.S.A Inc.

DOUBLE WHAMMY - Guitars - Dimarzio, Inc.

DOUBLE-WHITE - Pigments - Samuel Cabot Inc.

DOUBLE WHITE LIE - Apparel stores–lingerie - Formflex Foundations Inc.

DOUBLE-WING FLIER - Toys - Beyond Design Corp.

DOUBLE WISH - Greeting cards - Norcross Inc.

DOUBLE X - Ammunition - Olin Corp. (Winchester Div.)

DOUBLE-X - Photographic equipment - Eastman Kodak Co.

DOUBLE X - Vitamins and nutritional supplements - Nutrilite, Div. of Amway Corp.

DOUBLE ZERO - Apparel–men's - Sportailor Inc.

DOUBLEBARREL - Veterinary pharmaceutical preparations - Schering-Plough Animal Health

DOUBLECAP - Laxatives - Breckenridge Pharmaceutical, Inc.

DOUBLEDAY GALILEE - Publisher's imprints - Bantam Doubleday Dell Publishing Group, Inc.

DOUBLEGUARD - Motor vehicle parts and accessories - Directed Electronics, Inc.

DOUBLEHEADER - Highlighter - Itoya of America, Ltd.

DOUBLEHEADER - Razors - Philips Electronics North America Corp.

DOUBLEHEADER - Squeegees ☆ - Clean-Rite Products Co.

DOUBLELIFE - Stamps–hand - Dayton Stencil Works Co.

DOUBLEMINT - Chewing gum - Wm. Wrigley Jr. Co.

DOUBLEPLAY - Cosmetics - Revlon Consumer Products Corp.

DOUBLERES - Computer hardware - Personal Computer Products, Inc.

DOUBLERIB - Siding–metal - Alcan Aluminum Corp. Alcan Building Products Div.

DOUBLERS - Diapers–disposable - Paragon Trade Brands, Inc.

DOUBLERS - Diapers–disposable - Weyerhaeuser Co.

DOUBLERS - Furniture - Mitchell Manufacturing Co.

DOUBLES - Cookies ☆ - Sunshine Biscuits, Inc.

DOUBLES - Glassware–household - Anchor Hocking Glass, Inc.

DOUBLES WILD - Games - Enginuity

DOUBLESCAN - Computer software - PC Video Conversion

DOUBLESHOT - Markers–felt-tip - Pentech International Inc.

DOUBLESPACE - Computer software - Microsoft Corp.

DOUBLESUEDE - Fabrics - Fab. Industries Inc.

DOUBLET - Flags ☆ - Flags International Inc.

DOUBLET - Floor coverings–carpet and rugs - Masland Corp.

DOUBLETAKE - Wallpaper - Bolta Wallcoverings

DOUBLETONE - Artists' materials - Vogart Crafts Corp.

DOUBLETREE - Hotels and motels - Doubletree Hotels Inc.

DOUBLEUP WAKEBOARDS - Sporting goods - Denny Kidder Enterprises, Inc.

DOUBLEVISION - Computer software - Maximum Computer Technologies Inc.

DOUBLEWALE - Fabrics - Greenwood Mills Inc.

DOUBLEWEAR MICARTA - Plastics - Westinghouse Electric Corp. (Decorative Micarta Div.)

DOUBLEWIDE - Frames–picture ☆ - Fellowes Manufacturing Co.

DOUBLOGRAM - Enlargers–photographic ☆ - SP Systems/Saratons

DOUBLPURE - Water–distilled - Distilled Water Co. of Tulsa

DOUCEDIN - Pharmaceutical preparations ☆ - U.S. Ethicals Inc.

DOUCEVITE - Pharmaceutical preparations ☆ - U.S. Ethicals Inc.

DOUCHETTES - Personal-hygiene product - American Hygienic Laboratories Inc.

DOUCIEL - Cheese ☆ - Swissrose International Inc.

DOUG - Recording label - Viacom International Inc.

DOUG FLUTIE - Sporting goods ☆ - Franklin Sports, Inc.

DOUG MURDICK'S - Fudge - Doug Murdick's Fudge Inc.

DOUG WILSON - Hockey equipment ☆ - Right Gard Corp.

DOUGEL - Bakery products - Stanley J. Pelczar

DOUGH - Erasers ☆ - Bright Boy Abrasives

DOUGH BAIT STIK - Sporting goods ☆ - Brown Bear Bait Co.

DOUGH-IT-YOURSELF - Pizzas–mixes - Pasta Via

☆ = Now out of production

DOUGH RELAXER - Breads—mixes - Lora Brody Products, Inc.
DOUGH-TO-GO - Doughs—frozen - Dough-To-Go
DOUGHBOY - Swimming pools - Doughboy Recreational Inc.
DOUGHDISH - Ships—sailing vessels - Doughdish Inc.
DOUGHKNOTS - Breads - Ruba Ltd.
DOUGHMAKER - Chemical preparations - Elf Atochem North America, Inc.
DOUGHNUGGETS - Doughnuts - Flowers Family Bakeries, Inc.
DOUGHTY BIRDS - Figurines ☆ - Royal China & Porcelain Companies Inc.
DOUGLAR - Toys - Tonka Corp.
DOUGLAS - Corn starch - Penford Products Co.
DOUGLAS - Frames—eyeglass ☆ - Universal/Univis Inc.
DOUGLAS - Garden equipment - Ames Lawn & Garden Tool Co.
DOUGLAS - Inks ☆ - Bic Corp.
DOUGLAS - Seafood products—fresh or frozen ☆ - Pocasset Seafoods Inc.
DOUGLAS - Sporting goods - Douglas Industries Inc.
DOUGLAS - Sweaters - Binghamton Knitting Co.
DOUGLAS - Tools - Radiator Specialty Co.
DOUGLAS - Vacuum cleaners and accessories - Douglas/Quikut
DOUGLAS - Watches - Hampden Corp.
DOUGLAS CASUAL LIFESTYLE - Furniture - Douglas Furniture of California, Inc. (Bedrord Park)
DOUGLAS CLASSIC CASUAL - Furniture - Douglas Furniture of California, Inc. (Bedrord Park)
DOUGLAS FACETS - Furniture - Douglas Furniture of California, Inc. (Bedrord Park)
DOUGLAS FEATHOR - Oars ☆ - Alden Ocean Shells Inc.
DOUGLAS IONIC PEDESTAL - Furniture - Douglas Furniture of California, Inc. (Bedrord Park)
DOUGLAS LEGACY POWER SYSTEM - Chemical preparations - Douglas Battery Manufacturing Co.
DOUGLAS NO-HOLDS - Furniture - Douglas Furniture of California, Inc. (Bedrord Park)
DOUGLAS OAKTON - Furniture - Douglas Furniture of California, Inc. (Bedrord Park)
DOULTON - Glassware—household - Royal Doulton-Somerset UK Ltd.
DOURO - Cooking equipment—household - Benjamin & Medwin Inc.
DOUVILLE - Bakery products ☆ - Oven Fresh Bakery
DOUWANNA? - Novelty items - Criton Products
DOUWE EGBERTS - Coffee - Acme Food Specialties Inc.
DOUX DE MONTAGNE - Cheese ☆ - Bongrain Cheese USA
DOUZIE'S - Tiles—ceramic - Amsterdam Corp.
DOV ENTERPRISES - Notebooks and notepads - Dov Enterprises
DOVA - Handbags - Dover Handbag Corp.
DOVACET - Pharmaceutical preparations ☆ - Pal-Pak Inc.
DOVAN - Dishes—china - Taylor, Smith & Taylor Co.
DOVE - Allpro Corp.
DOVE - American International Industries
DOVE - Apparel and accessories - L & L Manufacturing Co.
DOVE - Candy - Dove International
DOVE - Chimes ☆ - J.W. Stannard Co.
DOVE - Confections - Mars, Inc.
DOVE - Detergents - Lever Brothers Co. Inc.
DOVE - Frames—eyeglass - Zylo Ware Corp.
DOVE - Mushrooms - Dove Foods
DOVE - Musical instruments - Gibson Guitar Corp.
DOVE BOOKS ON TAPE - Publisher's imprints - Dove Books on Tape Inc.
DOVE DESIGN - Cookware - West Bend Co.
DOVE FEATHER - Frames—eyeglass - Zylo Ware Corp.
DOVE GRAY - Dinnerware—glass - Nikko Ceramics Inc.
DOVE MATE - Frames—eyeglass - Zylo Ware Corp.
DOVE OF PEACE - Kites ☆ - Airplane Kite Co.
DOVE PROMISES - Chocolate candy - Mars, Inc.
DOVE QUILL - Frames—eyeglass - Zylo Ware Corp.
DOVE SUEDE - Ophthalmic goods ☆ - Fidelity Case Corp.
DOVE TAIL - Frames—eyeglass - Zylo Ware Corp.
DOVE WING - Frames—eyeglass - Zylo Ware Corp.
DOVE X - Electronic equipment ☆ - AVL
DOVE X2 - Electronic equipment - AVL
DOVEDELIGHT - Ice cream - Dove International
DOVEKIE - Ships—sailing vessels - Edey & Duff, Ltd.
DOVEPRINT - Paper—tissue - Potlatch Corp.
DOVER - Apparel and accessories - Host Apparel Inc.
DOVER - Artists' materials ☆ - Andrews/Nelson/Whitehead
DOVER - Blankets - Pillowtex Corp.
DOVER - Cabinets - Marsh Furniture Co.
DOVER - Cabinets - H.J. Scheirich Co.

DOVER - Chimes - Nutone Inc.
DOVER - Cigarettes - Brown & Williamson Tobacco Corp.
DOVER - Cribs—wood ☆ - Welsh Co.
DOVER - Floor coverings—carpet and rugs - Glen Eden Wool Carpets
DOVER - Floor coverings—carpet and rugs ☆ - Royalweve Carpet Mills
DOVER - Frames—eyeglass - May Optical Co. Inc.
DOVER - Glassware—household ☆ - Crystal Clear Importing Co. Inc.
DOVER - Handbags - Dover Handbag Corp.
DOVER - Lighting fixtures ☆ - Liteway
DOVER - Pipes—galvanized - Dover Parkersburg Co.
DOVER - Scrapers - Zephyr Manufacturing Co.
DOVER - Sponges - Quality Rubber Co.
DOVER - Wines - Dover Vineyards Inc.
DOVER BRAND - Fruits and vegetables - Walden-Sparkman, Inc.
DOVER CASTLE - Artists' materials ☆ - Andrews/Nelson/Whitehead
DOVER CLASSIC - Fruits and vegetables - Walden-Sparkman, Inc.
DOVER KIDZ - Handbags - Dover Handbag Corp.
DOVER PARK - Apparel—men's - Nulook Fashions Menswear Inc.
DOVER SLATE - Finishing agents ☆ - Flintkote Co.
DOVER SLATE - Floor coverings ☆ - Azrock Commercial Flooring
DOVER SLATE - Paints ☆ - GS Roofing Products Co.
DOVER UROLOGICALS - Medical apparatus - Sherwood Medical Co.
DOVER VELLUM - Stationery ☆ - Berkshire Stationery Inc.
DOVERCLOTH - Knitting machines - Fox-Wells & Co. Inc.
DOVERIN - Pharmaceutical preparations - Lannett Co. Inc.
DOVERSTONE - Bathroom fixtures - Artesian Industries
DOVERTWIST - Knitting machines - Fox-Wells & Co. Inc.
DOVERWOOD BLINDS - Window coverings - Bamboo-Abbott Inc.
DOVETAIL INN - Wallpaper - Belmont Wallcoverings
DOVETAIL RIDGE - Wines - Chateau Diana
DOVETAILS - Diapers—cloth - Family Clubhouse
DOVETOWN - Crocheted and knitted items - Garland Knitting Mills
DOVETS - Pharmaceutical preparations ☆ - Wesley Pharmacal Co. Inc.
DOVIS DESIGNS - Giftware - Eastern Shore Trading Co.
DOVO - Skin care products - Hess Hair Milk Laboratories Inc.
DOVOSAL - Pharmaceutical preparations ☆ - JMI-Canton Pharmaceuticals
DOVRE - Sporting goods - Shelburne Corp.
DOW - Cleaning preparations - Dowbrands L.P.
DOW - Wines ☆ - European Beverage Co., Inc.
DOW CORNING - Adhesives and sealants - Dow Corning Corp.
DOW CORNING STI - Silicon products - Dow Corning Corp.
DOW-ISONIAZID - Pharmaceutical preparations - Marion Merrell Dow
DOW JONES/ECONOMICS - Glassware—household - Ceraglass Inc.
DOWDY - Candy - Wellons Candy Co. Inc.
DOWEL - Doors—wood - Weyerhaeuser Co.
DOWEL-FAST - Adhesive - Rawlplug Co., Inc.
DOWELL-PACE HIGH PERFORMANCE LEADERSHIPINDICATOR - Forms—preprinted - Ronald Dowell and Associates
DOWEX OPTIPORE - Chemical preparations - Dow Chemical Co.
DOWKER - Meat products—beef - Dowker Packing Co.
DOWLING MAGNETS - Magnets - Dowling Miner Magnetics Corp.
DOWMYCIN-E - Antibiotics - Marion Merrell Dow
DOWN A DUSTY ROAD - Recording label - Hummingbird Recording Co. Inc.
DOWN & DIRTY - Clothing - Great Threads, Inc.
DOWN & DIRTY - Pet products - Lynco Pet Products Inc.
DOWN & OUT - Water treating compounds - Robarb Inc.
DOWN & OUTERS - Sporting goods - North Face
DOWN AROUND - Pillows - Pacific Coast Feather Co.
DOWN BABY LANE - Publisher's imprints - McMillin Foley Publishing Co.
DOWN CHRISTMAS LANE - Greeting cards - American Greetings Corp.
DOWN DOWN UP UP LEFT RIGHT ON LINE - Golfing equipment - On Line Golf Products, Inc.
DOWN-DRAIN - Chemical preparations - Harley Chemicals
DOWN EAST - Confections ☆ - Lou-Rod Candy Inc.
DOWN-EAST - Fishing tackle - L.L. Bean Inc.
DOWN EAST - Seafood - F.J. O'Hara & Sons Inc.
DOWN-EAST CRAFTS - Giftware - Cape Shore Inc.
DOWN EAST SQUALL SURVIVORS - Slippers ☆ - Acorn
DOWN EASTER - Food products ☆ - One Pie Canning Co.
DOWN EASTER - Footwear—men's - L.B. Evans' Son Co.
DOWN EMBRACE - Pillows - Pacific Coast Feather Co.
DOWN HOME - Glassware—household - Owens-Illinois Inc. (Libbey Div.)
DOWN IT! - Computer software - Compusci, Inc.
DOWN LIGHTS - Lighting fixtures - Lucifer Lighting Co.
DOWN ON THE FARM - Glassware—household ☆ - Fenton Art Glass Co.
DOWN ON TOP - Pillows - Pacific Coast Feather Co.

☆ = Now out of production

DOWN SANTA CLAUS LANE - Paper–gift wrap - Papercraft Corp.
DOWN SELECT PLUS - Fibers–synthetic - United Feather & Down Inc.
DOWN SIDE UP - Pillows - Pacific Coast Feather Co.
DOWN SOUTH - Comforters and pillows - Belk Stores Services, Inc.
DOWN SOUTH - Labels–paper - King Walk Inc.
DOWN-SPOUT-O-MATIC - Downspouts ☆ - H.D. Campbell Co.
DOWN STUFF - Apparel and accessories - Outerstuff, Ltd.
DOWN SURROUND - Pillows - Pacific Coast Feather Co.
DOWN-THE-DRAIN - Drain pipe cleaners - L & F Consumer Products
DOWN THE DRAIN - Games ☆ - Lakeside Games
DOWN THE MIDDLE - Golfing equipment - Down the Middle, Inc.
DOWN THE OCEAN - Apparel and accessories - James G. Barrett
DOWN-TO-EARTH - Computer software ☆ - Spectrum Universal
DOWN TO EARTH - Computer software ☆ - Synergex
DOWN TO EARTH - Cosmetics - Arizona Natural Resources
DOWN TO EARTH - Luggage - Buenos Aires Imports
DOWN TO EARTH KIDS - Bags–duffel - Down to Earth Products, Inc.
DOWN TO EARTH PRODUCTS - Bags–duffel - Down to Earth Products, Inc.
DOWN TO THE WIRE - Jewelry - JPR Jewelry Co.
DOWN TOWN LIGHTS - Apparel and accessories - Comint Leather Goods Inc.
DOWN UNDER - Computer software - Voyager Software Corp.
DOWN-UNDER - Fishing tackle - Mason Tackle Co.
DOWN UNDER - Paper–gift wrap - World's Finest Chocolate, Inc.
DOWN UNDER - Pet products ☆ - Wald Designs Acrylic Idea Factory
DOWN UNDER AUSTRALIAN OUTFITTERS - Apparel and accessories - Gammon Co. & Associates, Inc.
DOWN UNDER DIPPER - Golfing equipment - Down Under Dipper Co.
DOWN UNDER SADDLE SUPPLY - Sporting goods - Down Under Saddle Supply, Inc.
DOWN VEHICLE FLAG - Novelty items - Madeleine Conway
DOWN WITH THE KING - Games ☆ - Avalon Hill Game Co.
DOWN WITH X - Apparel and accessories - MVP Products, Inc.
DOWNBEAT - Musical instrument accessories - David Wexler & Co.
DOWNDEEP - Fishing lures - Normark Corp.
DOWNDUS - Uncle Sam Chemical Co., Inc.
DOWNEAST - Beverages–carbonated - Coca-Cola Bottling Co. of Northern New England, Inc.
DOWNEAST - Breads - F.R. Le Page Bakery
DOWNEAST - Coffee - Excellent Coffee Co. Inc.
DOWNEAST - Lobsters - Claw Island Foods Inc.
DOWNEAST - Meat products–beef ☆ - Lollipop Tree
DOWNEAST DECADENT DESSERTS - Desserts - Schlotterbeck and Foss Co.
DOWNEAST OUTFITTERS - Apparel and accessories - Downeast Outfitters, Inc.
DOWNEAST PASTA - Pasta - Downeast Pasta, Inc.
DOWNEAST TRADING CO. - Jewelry - Downeast Trading Co.
DOWNEASTER - Boats–motor - Thurston Co.
DOWNERWEAR - Sports apparel ☆ - Jansport Inc.
DOWNEY - Toys–stuffed ☆ - Gund, Inc.
DOWNEY COLLECTION, THE - Glass–flat ☆ - Downey Glass
DOWNEY-SPUN - Crocheted and knitted items - Garland Knitting Mills
DOWNEY'S - Cakes - Downey's Products
DOWNEY'S - Food products - Dairy Fresh Products Co.
DOWNEY'S - Honey - Honey Butter Products Co.
DOWNEY'S GOURMET - Soups - Downey Foods, Inc.
DOWNEY'S IRISH SOUPS - Soups–canned - Europa Foods Ltd.
DOWNEY'S SAUCES - Sauces - Europa Foods Ltd.
DOWNFALL - Games ☆ - Western Publishing Co., Inc.
DOWNHILL - Frames–eyeglass ☆ - Universal/Univis Inc.
DOWNHILL DAN - Candy ☆ - R.M. Palmer Co.
DOWNHILL MANIA - Sports clubs - Team Big Bear Mountain Bikes, Inc.
DOWNHILL RACER - Ski suits–women's - Robern Skiwear, Inc.
DOWNHILL SHOWER CURTAIN - Curtains–shower - James D. Benson
DOWNHOME COUNTRY FINS - Fish–fresh or frozen - Fish King Processors Inc.
DOWNHOME PUNCH - Beverages–alcohol - Jack Daniel's Distillery
DOWNING - Toilets–enameled - Kohler Co.
DOWNING SQUARE - Dolls ☆ - Effanbee Doll Corp.
DOWNING STREET - Floor coverings–carpet and rugs - Wunda Weve Carpet Co.
DOWNING STREET - Ophthalmic goods - Embassy Creations Inc.
DOWNING STREET GROUP - Furniture - Bean Station Furniture Factory Inc.
DOWNJIGGER - Fishing lures - Strike Line, Inc.
DOWNLITE - Lighting fixtures - Hubbell Lighting, Inc. (Lighting Div.)
DOWNLOCK - Comforters - Pacific Coast Feather Co.
DOWNPOUR - Plumbing fixtures - Resources Park

DOWNRIGHT LTD. - Bedding–linen - Downright Ltd.
DOWNRIVER COMPETITOR - Boats–kayaks ☆ - Old Town Canoe Co.
DOWNS - Ophthalmic goods - Foremost Optical Products
DOWNS FARE - Food produots - Tony Downs Foods Co.
DOWNSTAIRS - Frames–eyeglass - Liberty Optical Manufacturing Co.
DOWNTOWN - Balls–basketball - Wilson Sporting Goods Co.
DOWNTOWN - Frames–eyeglass - Liberty Optical Manufacturing Co.
DOWNTOWN - Wallpaper ☆ - Sandpiper Studios
DOWNTOWN BROWN - Beverages–malt - Table Bluff Brewing, Inc.
DOWNTOWN BROWN ALE - Beer - Lost Coast Brewery & Cafe
DOWNTOWN GIRL - Perfumes - Revlon Consumer Products Corp.
DOWNTOWN SHOOT OUT - Toy action figures - Tonka Corp.
DOWNTOWNER MOTOR INN - Hotels and motels - Downtowner-Passport International Hotel Corp.
DOWNWIND - Eyeglasses - Martin-Copeland Eyewear Corp.
DOWNY - Fabric softeners - Procter & Gamble Co.
DOWNY - Paper–toilet - Stevens & Thompson Paper Co.
DOWNY LIQUID ULTRA - Detergents - Procter & Gamble Co.
DOWNY-SOFT - Apparel–women's ☆ - Bali Co. Inc.
DOWNY TC - Fabric softeners - Procter & Gamble Co.
DOWNYFLAKE - Pancakes–frozen - Pet Inc.
DOWNYFLAKE BREAKFAST CLASSIC - Pancakes–frozen - Pet Inc.
DOWPEN VK - Antibiotics - Marion Merrell Dow
DOWPON - Garden equipment ☆ - Dowelanco
DOWRIES - Floor coverings–tile - Kohler Co.
DOW'S & GRAHAM'S - Beverages–alcohol - Ginday Imports Ltd.
DOX - Chemical preparations - Diamond Technologies Co.
DOX - Paint thinners - Reliable Finishing Products, Inc.
DOX-100 - Pharmaceutical preparations ☆ - Lunsco Inc.
DOX HEAD BANZ - Adhesives and sealants - Markwort Sporting Goods Co.
DOX-SL - Pharmaceutical preparations - Liposome Technology, Inc.
DOXATE-D - Pharmaceutical preparations - Dunhall Pharmaceuticals Inc.
DOXEGEST - Pharmaceutical preparations ☆ - Sterling Winthrop Inc.
DOXIDAN - Laxatives - Upjohn Co.
DOXIE - Fencing–gates and posts - Semmerling Fence and Supply Inc.
DOXIL - Health care products - Liposome Technology, Inc.
DOXSEE - Dyes–food - Doxsee Food Corp.
DOXY-CAPS - Pharmaceutical preparations - Edwards Pharmaceuticals, Inc.
DOXY-II - Antibiotics ☆ - Rhone-Poulenc Rorer Pharmaceuticals Inc.
DOXY-LEMMON - Pharmaceutical preparations ☆ - Lemmon Co.
DOXYMINE - Pharmaceutical preparations ☆ - Kenyon Drug Co. Inc.
DOY - Food products - Gama Trading Co. Inc.
DOZ GUYS - Adhesives and sealants - Genteel Corp.
DOZER LOADER - Toys - Fisher-Price, Inc.
DOZORB - Yeast - Dutch Boy Co.
DOZ'RS - Skateboards ☆ - Nash Manufacturing Inc.
DOZY OAT - Cakes - Drake Bakeries, Inc.
DP - Ammunition ☆ - Olin Corp. (Winchester Div.)
DP - Apparel and accessories - Daniel James Pena
DP - Chemical preparations - Dwight Products Inc.
DP - Jewelry - Doris Panos Designs, Ltd.
DP - Jewelry–precious - DoPaso Corp.
D.P. - Paint rollers - Elder & Jenks, Inc.
DP - Plumbing fixtures - Duracraft Plastics, Inc.
DP - Recording label - Harcourt Brace & Co.
DP - Sporting goods - Diversified Products Corp.
DP - Sports apparel - Detroit Pistons Basketball Co.
DP - Vials - National Scientific Co.
DP-25 - Lubricants - Rectorseal Corp.
DP II - Film - SKC America Inc.
DP LIGHT - Lighting equipment - Lowel-Light Manufacturing Inc.
DP LOW PROTEIN - Bakery products - Dietary Specialties
DPASSETS - Computer software - UVS Associates, Inc.
DPC - Amplifiers–radio - Peavey Electronics Corp.
DPF - Animal feeds - Purina Mills, Inc.
DPF - Golfing equipment - Daiwa Corp.
DPF YACHT WHITE - Hardware ☆ - Boatlife Inc.
DPI - Recording label - Counter Culture
DPL - Cosmetics - Dermatologists Products, Ltd.
DPL - Jewelry - Diplomat Jewelry Manufacturing Corp.
DPL - Lubricants - Chemtronics Inc.
DPL - Machinery - Genie Industries, Inc.
DPL-2 - Lubricants - Chemtronics Inc.
DPL QUIK START - Dairy products - Rhone-Poulenc Specialty Chemicals Co.
D.P.M. - Food products ☆ - Cargill Corp.
DPM - Skin-care products - Marion M. Vujevich

☆ = Now out of production

643

DPM - Sporting goods - Dental Concepts Inc.
DPOS - Printers–computer - Destiny Technology Corp.
DPR-11 - Hair care products - Kenra, Inc.
DPS/EXPERT PUBLISHER - Computer software - Database Publishing Software, Inc.
DPS PERSONAL ANIMATION RECORDER - Electronic equipment - Digital Processing Systems, Inc.
DPT - Waterproofing compounds - United States Borax & Chemical Corp.
DPWL - Pillows - Pawleys Island Rope Hammock
DQ - Jewelry - Diamonique Corp.
DQ BASKET DEAL - Combination meal - International Dairy Queen Inc.
DQ CLASSIC CAKES - Ice cream products - International Dairy Queen Inc.
DQ TREATZZA PIZZA - Ice milk - American Dairy Queen Corp.
DQBROKER - Computer peripheral equipment - Decision Support, Inc.
DQE - Computer software - PRC Inc.
DQI - Perfumes - Designer Quality Impressionists International, Ltd.
DQR III - Computer software - W. Quinn Associates, Inc.
DQR II - Computer software ☆ - W. Quinn Associates, Inc.
DR. - See **DOCTOR**
DR - Fabrics - Dan River Inc.
DR - Hair care products - Daniel Rizzardi
DR - Hair care products - Waverly Beauty Products
DR - Hearing aids - Magnatone Hearing Aid Corp.
DR DURABLE RALPH - Pet products - Durable Ralph, Inc.
DR PEPPER - Chewing gum ☆ - Amurol Confections Co.
DRA - Computer software - Data Research Associates, Inc.
DRA FIND - Computer software - Data Research Associates, Inc.
DRAB OUT - Shampoos - Nu-Tress Laboratories Inc.
DRABBERS - Hair coloring preparations - Cosmair Inc.
DRAC - Games - Tonka Corp.
DRACHEN FIRE - Apparel and accessories - Busch Entertainment Corp.
DRACO - Sunglasses - Spy Optic, Inc.
DRACOBRA - Kites ☆ - Gayla Industries Inc.
DRACOR - Thread ☆ - Synthetic Thread Co. Inc.
DRACOULL - Shirts - Cameron Pearce
DRAC'S BATS - Candy - Fleer Corp.
DRACSTER, THE - Toys - Bandai America Inc.
DRACUBEAR - Toys–stuffed - Russ Berrie and Co., Inc.
DRACULA - Mounting equipment - Holtsch Corp.
DRACULA - Toys–electronic - Hasbro, Inc.
DRACULA BLOOD - Toys - Topstone Industries Inc.
DRACULA UNLEASHED - Computers - Viacom International Inc.
DRACULAS - Beverages–alcohol - Leonard Kreusch Inc.
DRAEGER INTERLOCK - Safety products - National Draeger, Inc.
DRAFT - Health care products - GB Marketing USA Inc.
DRAFT - Helmets–athletic - Giant Bicycle, Inc.
DRAFT-ART - Office supplies - Alvin and Co. Inc.
DRAFT BUSTERS - Home weather stripping - Manco, Inc.
DRAFT-CLEAN - Artists' materials - Keuffel & Esser Co.
DRAFT DODGER - Housewares - Blue Ridge International Products Co., Inc.
DRAFT DODGER - Novelty items - Item Co., Inc.
DRAFT DODGER - Window frames ☆ - Hartwig-Hartoglass Inc.
DRAFT DODGERS - Electrical equipment ☆ - Z-Flex U.S. Inc.
DRAFT EVADER - Dolls - Tradewinds Enterprises, Inc.
DRAFT-KING - Fireplace equipment - Hy-C Co. Inc.
DRAFT-LINE - Pencils–mechanical - Alvin and Co. Inc.
DRAFT/MATIC - Office supplies - Alvin and Co. Inc.
DRAFT-O-STAT - Dampers - Dornback Furnace Division
DRAFT SEAL - Tape–adhesive ☆ - Custom Tapes, Inc.
DRAFT-SEAL - Weather stripping - W.J. Dennis & Co.
DRAFT SEALERS - Insulators–electrical ☆ - Oatey Co.
DRAFTEC/GRAPHIC - Office supplies - Alvin and Co. Inc.
DRAFTETTE - Artists' materials - PMC Industries Inc. (Draftette Div.)
DRAFTETTE - Office supplies - Alvin and Co. Inc.
DRAFTEX - Inks–drawing ☆ - Andrew Jeri Co. Inc.
DRAFTING DOTS - Drafting supplies - Koh-I-Noor, Inc.
DRAFTITE - Caulking compounds ☆ - Gibson-Homans Co.
DRAFTITE - Weather stripping ☆ - The Standard Products Co.
DRAFTMASTER - Bicycle racks - Anew Development, Inc.
DRAFTMASTER - Roofing materials–concrete - O.D. Funk Co.
DRAFTMASTER - Tables–wood - Stacor Corp.
DRAFTMASTER CHIMNEY CAP - Building materials - O.D. Funk Co.
DRAFTMASTER II - Tables–wood - Stacor Corp.
DRAFTON - Electronic equipment - GAF Corp.
DRAFTSMAN - Pencil sharpeners - Empire Berol USA
DRAG-A-MOUSE - Pet products - Drag-A-Mouse Co.

DRAG & FILE - Computer software - Canyon Software
DRAG & VIEW - Computer software - Canyon Software
DRAG & VIEW GOLD - Computer software - Canyon Software
DRAG & ZIP - Computer software - Canyon Software
DRAG, DROP, DONE - Computer peripheral equipment - Visio Corp.
DRAG FLIP - Toys–automobiles - Mattel, Inc.
DRAG NET - Netting - Nicolas P. Lessick
DRAG-ON - Mufflers–motor vehicle ☆ - Merit Automotive Exhaust Systems
DRAG ON FLOATS - Building materials - Great Northern Docks, Inc.
DRAG SLICK - Bicycles - Sears, Roebuck and Co.
DRAG STRIP DUEL - Toys–automobiles - Mattel, Inc.
DRAGGED PAPERS - Wallpaper - Christopher Hyland
DRAGGER - Bicycles - Columbia Manufacturing Inc.
DRAGGIN' DRAGON - Toys - Thomas Lowe Ventures, Inc.
DRAGINSTALL - Computer software - Ray Sauers Associates Inc.
DRAGMASTER - Scooters–children's ☆ - Peg Perego USA Inc.
DRAGMULES - Recording label - Dragmules
DRAG'N FLY - Toys - Dumas Products Inc.
DRAGO - Food products - Bison Canning Co. Inc.
DRAGON - Beverages–malt ☆ - Labatt Importers Inc.
DRAGON - Bicycles - Columbia Manufacturing Inc.
DRAGON - Blow torches - Microflame Inc.
DRAGON - Dishes–china ☆ - Royal China & Porcelain Companies Inc.
DRAGON - Eyeglasses - Dragon Optical, Inc.
DRAGON - Fruit and vegetable markets - Riverside Fruit Sales, Inc.
DRAGON - Games - Mayfair Games, Inc.
DRAGON - Games - Milton Bradley Co.
DRAGON - Insecticides - Dragon Chemical Corp.
DRAGON - Musical instrument accessories - Dimarzio, Inc.
DRAGON - Recording label - Dragon Records (Div. of Agon Productions)
DRAGON - Rice - Comet American Marketing
DRAGON BALL - Shoes ☆ - S. Goldberg and Co. Inc.
DRAGON BALM - Analgesics - Superior Trading Co.
DRAGON BAT - Kites - Gayla Industries Inc.
DRAGON BLADE - Toys - TMP International, Inc.
DRAGON BLASTER - Toys - Mattel, Inc.
DRAGON BREATH - Chewing gum ☆ - Zeebs Enterprises, Inc.
DRAGON CHASE - Games - Smethport Specialty Co.
DRAGON CLAW - Tools–garden - Lawn & Garden Supply Co.
DRAGON CRYSTAL - Games - Sega of America, Inc.
DRAGON DAGGER - Toys ☆ - Henry Gordy International Inc.
DRAGON DANCE - Toilets–enameled - Kohler Co.
DRAGON DICE - Games - Tsr, Inc.
DRAGON DOUBLE NINE - Games - Milton Bradley Co.
DRAGON DOUBLE SIX - Games - Milton Bradley Co.
DRAGON DROP - Computer software - NovaStor Corp.
DRAGON EGGS - Vitamins and nutritional supplements - Lotus Brands Inc.
DRAGON FLIES - Flower pots–earthenware ☆ - Blue Ribbon Flower Holder Co.
DRAGON FLY - Toys - North Pacific Products Inc.
DRAGON FLY - Toys–models ☆ - Estes Industries
DRAGON FLY LINE - Fishing lures - Shannon Lure Co.
DRAGON GREEN - Eyeglasses - Art-Craft Optical Co.
DRAGON I - Sauces - W.M. Associates LLC
DRAGON KEEP - Figurines - Marty Sculpture
DRAGON KICK - Toys - Hasbro, Inc.
DRAGON LADY - Artificial fingernails - International Beauty Design, Inc.
DRAGON LADY - Self-defense video series - E-Ztech Books, Videos & Seminars
DRAGON LORDS - Toys–models - Grenadier Models
DRAGON MASTER - Games - Tsr, Inc.
DRAGON MELT - Deicing fluid - Hersch's, Inc.
DRAGON MIX - Computer software - SRA/McGraw-Hill (Div. of The McGraw-Hill Companies)
DRAGON MOUNTAIN - Games - Tsr, Inc.
DRAGON OPTICAL - Sunglasses - Dragon Optical, Inc.
DRAGON PAL - Infant product - Leachco Inc.
DRAGON PASS - Games ☆ - Avalon Hill Game Co.
DRAGON PUTTY - Toys - Jak-Pak Inc.
DRAGON QUEST - Games - Tsr, Inc.
DRAGON RIDERS OF PERN - Computer software - Epyx Inc.
DRAGON SEED - Apparel–women's - Sultra Corp.
DRAGON SLAYER - Kites - Gayla Industries Inc.
DRAGON STAR - Rice - U.S. Trading Enterprise, Inc.
DRAGON STONE - Toys - Tonka Corp.
DRAGON STRIKE - Games - Tsr, Inc.

☆ = Now out of production

DRAGON TEARS - Food products - Minh Food Corp.
DRAGON, THE - Skin care products - Marcott Industries Inc.
DRAGON TREE - Shampoos - Holistic Laboratories
DRAGON WAGON - Toys–automobiles - Mattel, Inc.
DRAGON WALKER - Toys–automobiles - Mattel, Inc.
DRAGON WEAR - Apparel–athletic - Cameron Pearce
DRAGON WING - Flowers, plants, and seeds - Panamerican Seed
DRAGON-WINGS - Meat products–poultry - Pierce Foods Corp.
DRAGONDICTATE - Computers - Dragon Systems, Inc.
DRAGONFLY - Apparel and accessories - Drummer Boy Sportswear, Inc.
DRAGONFLY - Boats - Deep Ocean Engineering Inc.
DRAGONFLY - Computer hardware - ITT Industries, Inc.
DRAGONFLY - Food products - U.S. Trading Enterprise, Inc.
DRAGONFLY - Posters - Gale Bartlett Nemec
DRAGONFLY - Ships–sailing vessels - Scandinavian Yachts
DRAGONFLY - Toys–airplanes - Cox Products Inc.
DRAGONFLY BOOKS - Publisher's imprints - Alfred A. Knopf Inc.
DRAGONFLY MEGABUG - Toys - Tonka Corp.
DRAGONHUNT - Games ☆ - Avalon Hill Game Co.
DRAGONLADY - Computer software - Epyx Inc.
DRAGONLANCE - Games - Tsr, Inc.
DRAGONLORD - Computer software - John Myers
DRAGONRIDERS OF PERN - Games ☆ - Mayfair Games, Inc.
DRAGONRIDERS OF THE STYX - Toys - Multi Toys Corp.
DRAGON'S - Calculators - Cathay International
DRAGONS - Games ☆ - Mayfair Games, Inc.
DRAGONS - Sunglasses - Dragon Optical, Inc.
DRAGON'S CROWN - Games - Tsr, Inc.
DRAGON'S DREAM - Publisher's imprints - A & W Publishers Inc.
DRAGON'S FURY - Computer software - Tengen Inc.
DRAGON'S LAIR - Chewing gum ☆ - Fleer Corp.
DRAGON'S MILK - Beverages ☆ - Good Word Co.
DRAGONS OF WENG T'SEN - Games ☆ - Mayfair Games, Inc.
DRAGONSHIP 7 - Toys–models ☆ - Estes Industries
DRAGONSKIN - Paper–sand - Red Devil Inc.
DRAGONSLAYER - Apparel and accessories - Jim J. Barrett
DRAGONSTRIKE - Games - Tsr, Inc.
DRAGONSWITCH - Computer peripheral equipment - Ungermann-Bass, Inc.
DRAGONWELL - Teas - Eastern Shore Tea Co.
DRAGONZORD - Toys - Saban Entertainment, Inc.
DRAGOON - Frames–eyeglass - Hudson Optical Corp.
DRAGOON - Sporting goods - EMF Co. Inc.
DRAGOON & HUSSAR - Toys - War House
DRAGSTER - Boats - Glen-L Marine Designs
DRAGWAY DEMON - Toys–automobiles - Mattel, Inc.
DRAIN A MATIC - Drain pipe cleaners - Vibe Records Inc.
DRAIN-A-WAY - Quaker Plastic Corp.
DRAIN B CLEAN - Cleaning preparations - William R. Lamb
DRAIN CARE - Cleaning preparations - Enforcer Products Inc.
DRAIN CLEAN - Drain pipe cleaners - Cobra Products Inc.
DRAIN COVER - Mats - Jomac Products Inc.
DRAIN DEMON - Drains - State Chemical Manufacturing Co.
DRAIN DIAPER - Filters–water - Metrochem, Inc.
DRAIN DROPS - Drain pipe cleaners ☆ - Holloway House, Inc.
DRAIN-E-ZE - Drain opener - Jancyn Manufacturing Corp.
DRAIN EZ - Mats - JCH International Inc.
DRAIN EZ - Rubber–molded - Lancaster Colony Automotive Group
DRAIN FLOW - Cleaning preparations–household - Win-Chekd Inc.
DRAIN INVADERS - Candy ☆ - Bohemian Biscuit Co.
DRAIN-IT - Drainage systems - Atlantic Construction Fabrics, Inc.
DRAIN KING - Drain pipe cleaners - G.T. Water Products Inc.
DRAIN KING - Mats - Matworks
DRAIN KLEAN - Drain pipe cleaners - Malco Products, Inc.
DRAIN MAGIC - Cleaning preparations - Analab Inc.
DRAIN MAGIC - Drain pipe cleaners - Flow-Eze Co.
DRAIN MASTER - Machinery - Dema Engineering Co.
DRAIN OPENERS - Cleaning preparations - Black Swan Manufacturing Co.
DRAIN OUT - Cleaning preparations - Iron Out, Inc.
DRAIN OUT CRYSTAL - Cleaning preparations - Iron Out, Inc.
DRAIN OUT ENZYME - Cleaning preparations - Iron Out, Inc.
DRAIN OUT EXTRA - Cleaning preparations - Iron Out, Inc.
DRAIN POWER - Cleaning preparations - Airwick Industries
DRAIN SHIELD DRAIN BARRIER - Mats - New Pendulum Corp.
DRAIN-SOLVE - Cleaning preparations - Nyco Products Co.
DRAIN SYRUP - Chemical cleaning preparations ☆ - Jancyn Manufacturing Corp.

DRAIN TABS - Drain pipe cleaners - Coughlan Products Corp.
DRAIN TAINER - Containers - Rubbermaid Inc.
DRAIN THRU - Mats - JCH International Inc.
DRAIN VALVE LUBRICANT - Lubricants - Thetford Corp.
DRAIN WELL - Floor coverings - Pawling Corp. (Standard Products Div.)
DRAIN WORKS - Chemical preparations - Covington Enterprises, Inc.
DRAINMASTER - Drain pipe cleaners - Binford Products, Inc.
DRAINMASTER SUPREME - Drain pipe cleaners - Binford Products, Inc.
DRAINO - Golfing equipment - U.S. Precision Inc.
DRAINOSAUR - Pumps - Little Giant Pump Co.
DRAINTRAK - Plaster–wallboard - Basement Systems, Inc.
DRAINTRINE - Cleaning preparations–household ☆ - Applied Biochemists, Inc.
DRAINZ - Cesspool and tank cleaner - Jancyn Manufacturing Corp.
DRAINZYME - Bacteria booster - Jancyn Manufacturing Corp.
DRAKE - Cakes - Drake Bakeries, Inc.
DRAKE - Frames–eyeglass - Zylo Ware Corp.
DRAKE - Gloves - Netz Glove & Mitten Co.
DRAKE - Marine rigging ☆ - Woolsey Marine Industries
DRAKE - Trailers–travel ☆ - Mallard Coach
DRAKE - Watches - Bulova Corp.
DRAKE - Wheelchairs - AM Scooters
DRAKE BEAM MORIN, INC. - Publisher's imprints - Drake Beam Morin, Inc.
DRAKE SMITH & CO. - Furniture - Colonial Furniture Co. Inc.
DRAKE'S - Bakery products - Drake Bakeries, Inc.
DRAKES - Beverages–alcohol - Black Prince Distillery, Inc.
DRAKE'S - Beverages–malt - Lind Brewing Co.
DRAKE'S - Gasoline - Drake's Refining Station
DRAKE'S CRISPY FRYMIX - Cakes–mixes - Drake Batter Mix Co. Inc.
DRAKE'S DUCKS - Sauces - Drake's Ducks
DRAKE'S X-1 LEATHER DRESSING - Leather tanning and finishing - Leather Factory Inc.
DRAKKAR - Cosmetics - Lancome
DRAKKAR NOIR - Cosmetics - Lancome
DRAKKHEN - Video games - Nintendo of America Inc.
DRALON - Window coverings - Arquati Inc.
DRALSERP - Pharmaceutical preparations ☆ - Lemmon Co.
DRALZINE - Pharmaceutical preparations ☆ - Lemmon Co.
DRAM TREE - Sport steins - CUI Inc./Dram Tree
DRAMA - Clocks - General Time Corp. (Westclox/Seth Thomas Div.)
DRAMA - Frames–eyeglass - Pathway Optical Prods.
DRAMA - Paints - Valspar Corp.
DRAMA-FOLD - Folding doors ☆ - American Fold Doors Inc.
DRAMA SOUNDBOOKS - Recording label - Harper Audio
DRAMABOOKS - Magazines - Farrar, Straus and Giroux Inc.
DRAMAMINE - Pharmaceutical preparations - Upjohn Co.
DRAMAMINE II - Pharmaceutical preparations - Upjohn Co.
DRAMAMINE JR. - Pharmaceutical preparations ☆ - Upjohn Co.
DRAMANATE - Pharmaceutical preparations - Pasadena Research Laboratories, Inc.
DRAMAREX - Pharmaceutical preparations - C.S. Ruckstuhl Co. Inc.
DRAMATEYES - Cosmetics - Lord & Berry, Ltd.
DRAMATIC - Floor coverings–carpet and rugs - Downs Carpet Co. Inc.
DRAMATIC - Health care products - Saxony Products Inc.
DRAMATIC FIRMING CREAM - Skin care products - Avon Products, Inc.
DRAMATIC FX - Skin care products - L'anza Research International
DRAMATIC RESULTS - Skin care products - Conopco, Inc.
DRAMATIC RESULTS - Skin care products ☆ - Prince Matchabelli
DRAMATICA - Computer software - Screenplay Systems, Inc.
DRAMATICALLY LONG - Cosmetics - Olay Co., Inc.
DRAMATICAT - Toys–blocks - Guidecraft Inc.
DRAMATICS NYC - Hair care products - Dramatics for Hair, Inc.
DRAMATIQUE - Cosmetics - Lancome
DRAMATIST - Eyeglasses - Martin-Copeland Eyewear Corp.
DRAMATIX - Publisher's imprints - Dramatix, Inc.
DRAMATTEICS - Cosmetics - Nu Skin International, Inc.
DRAMBUIE - Beverages–alcohol - Hiram Walker & Sons, Inc.
DRAMEX - Paints ☆ - Bondex International Inc.
DRAMILIN - Health care products - Kay Pharmacal Co. Inc.
DRAMM - Garden equipment - Dramm Corp.
DRAMOCEN - Pharmaceutical preparations ☆ - Central Pharmaceutical Inc.
DRAMOJECT - Pharmaceutical preparations ☆ - Merz Inc.
DRANO - Cleaning preparations - Drackett Co.
DRANO BUILD-UP REMOVER - Drain pipe cleaners - S.C. Johnson & Son, Inc.
DRANO PLUS - Cleaning preparations–household - S.C. Johnson & Son, Inc.

DRANOCHOL - Pharmaceutical preparations - Marin Pharmaceuticals
DRAPE-A-SWAG - Machinery - S. Morantz Inc.
DRAPE-A-WINDOW - Machinery - S. Morantz Inc.
DRAPE FAB - Hobby kits - Mangelsen's (VDI)
DRAPE STAR - Draperies - Protech Shading Inc.
DRAPEBOSS - Electrical equipment - Daniel V. Boss
DRAPELINE - Draperies - MFM Drapeline
DRAPER - Projection screens - Nelson Beck of Washington
DRAPER - Window coverings - Covoc Corp.
DRAPER-CRAFT - Steel springs–railroad - Needlecraft Industries
DRAPER VALLEY FARMS - Meat products–poultry - Draper Valley Farms, Inc.
DRAPERS OF ENGLAND - Footwear - R.J. Draper & Co. Ltd.
DRAPEWELL - Drapery hardware - Kenney Manufacturing Co.
DRAPO - Thread - Cincinnati Thread Co.
DRAPRED - Pharmaceutical preparations - Ascent Pharmaceuticals, Inc.
DRASTIC - Bicycles - Huffy Corp.
DRAUGHTING - Pencils - Empire Berol USA
DRAW & SAW - Tracing film ☆ - Grafix Plastics
DRAW-KLEEN - Cleaning preparations - Vogart Crafts Corp.
DRAW 'N' DO - Toys - Binney & Smith Inc.
DRAW 'N SPELL - Toys - Playskool, Inc.
DRAW OUT SALVE - Pharmaceutical preparations - Reese Chemical Co.
DRAW PLAY - Computer software - Cramer Products Inc.
DRAW PLUS - Computer software ☆ - Novell, Inc.
DRAW RINGS - Toys - Tonka Corp.
DRAW-TITE - Tents ☆ - Johnson Camping Inc.
DRAW TODAY - Video production - Walter Foster Publishing, Inc.
DRAWER STACKERS - Shelving units–wood ☆ - Hirsh Co.
DRAWERS FOR ALL - Cabinets - A-Bee Syndicate Inc.
DRAWERSTOP - Cabinets - Keller Products Inc.
DRAWING BOARD - Greeting cards ☆ - Drawing Board Greeting Cards Inc.
DRAWINGMASTER - Computer printers - Calcomp Inc.
DRAWITOL - Pharmaceutical preparations - Republic Drug Co. Inc.
DRAWLS - Clothing - Drawls
DRAW!MATE - Computer software - Stahls' Inc.
DRAWMATIC - Hardware ☆ - Endisco Supply Co.
DRAWMEE - Dolls - JLW & Co.
DRAWN FROM NATURE - Skin care products - Crabtree & Evelyn, Ltd.
DRAWPERFECT - Computer software - Wordperfect Corp.
DRAWS-A-LOT - Crayons - Avery Dennison Corp.
DRAWVISION - Computer software - Hellmuth, Obata Kassabaum, Inc.
DRAYCO - Paints - Vogart Crafts Corp.
DRAYDECK - Plywood ☆ - Harbor Sales Co.
DRAYPE - Racks ☆ - A.J. Ganz Co. Inc.
DRB III - Measuring instruments - DaimlerChrysler
DRC - Motor vehicle parts and accessories - Morse Controls
D.R.C. - Pharmaceutical preparations ☆ - Xttrium Laboratories Inc.
DRD - Electronic equipment - Matsushita Electric Corp. of America
DRDA - Computers - International Business Machines Corp.
DREAD HEAD - Hair care products - BodyFX Co.
DREAD HEADS - Toys - Hasbro, Inc.
DREAD LAUNCHERS - Toys - Tonka Corp.
DREAD L'OPS - Dolls - Susan Sona
DREAD MOUNTAIN CO. - Apparel and accessories - Jamaican Style, Inc.
DREADED HEADS - Chewing gum ☆ - Amurol Confections Co.
DREADED SHREDS - Chewing gum ☆ - Amurol Confections Co.
DREADFORCE, THE - Toys - Tonka Corp.
DREADNAUGHT - Fishing tackle ☆ - Gladding Braided Products Inc.
DREADNAUGHT - Paints - Orleans Paint Co. Inc.
DREADNOUGHT - Sporting goods - Gold Medal Recreational Products
DREADNOUGHTS - Games ☆ - Avalon Hill Game Co.
DREADY TEDDY - Dolls - Susan Sona
DREAM - Mat boards - Callen Photo Mount Corp.
DREAM - Recording label - Jazz Composer's Orchestra Association Inc.
DREAM - Rings–jewelry - Artcarved Inc.
DREAM - Scissors–hand-operated - F.W. Engels Inc.
DREAM - Shampoos - Edward & Sons Trading Co., Inc.
DREAM - Underwear and nightwear - Maidenform Inc.
DREAM - Wallpaper - Just for You Wallcoverings
DREAM - Wallpaper ☆ - J.C. Prints
DREAM-AIRE - Underwear and nightwear - Maidenform Inc.
DREAM & KEEP - Toys ☆ - Sun Products Corp. (Wellington)
DREAM AWHILE - Floor coverings–carpet and rugs ☆ - Walter Carpet Mills
DREAM BABY - Dolls - Doll Factory, Inc.
DREAM BEAM - Medical apparatus - Futrex, Inc.

DREAM BEAMS - Toys - Leisure Concepts, Inc.
DREAM BEAR - Bedding–linen - Dan River Inc.
DREAM BEARS - Candy ☆ - Gourmet Confections Inc.
DREAM BOAT - Toys - Mattel, Inc.
DREAM BOATS - Cookies - Parco Foods, Inc.
DREAM BRIDE - Dolls - Mattel, Inc.
DREAM BUILDERS - Toys - Tyco Toys
DREAM BY MAIDENFORM - Underwear and nightwear - Maidenform Inc.
DREAM CAFE - Apparel–women's - Charles Komar and Sons Inc.
DREAM CARE - Mattresses - Bemco Associates, Inc.
DREAM CASTLE - Christmas tree ornaments - Cracker Box Inc.
DREAM CASTLE COLLECTION - Giftware ☆ - Reco International Corp.
DREAM CATCHER - Archery equipment - Martin Archery Inc.
DREAM CATCHER - Cosmetics - Judith Ann Diss
DREAM CATCHER - Game machines - New Gaming Systems
DREAM CHASERS - Greeting cards - Genie's Quickprint
DREAM CLOUD - Floor coverings–carpet and rugs ☆ - Zenith Carpets
DREAM CORD - Fabrics–velvet - Dan River Inc.
DREAM COTTAGE - Dolls - Mattel, Inc.
DREAM-CREAM - Skin care products - Frank Robinson
DREAM CREAMS - Snack foods - R.W. Frookies Inc.
DREAM CREME - Candy ☆ - Standard Candy Co. Inc.
DREAM DANCERS - Calendars ☆ - American Greetings Corp.
DREAM DATE - Dolls - Mattel, Inc.
DREAM DELIGHT - Floor coverings–carpet and rugs - Alexander Smith Carpets
DREAM DESIGN - Mattresses - King Koil Licensing Co., Inc.
DREAM DOLL HOUSE - Computer software ☆ - Knowledge Adventure
DREAM DOLL HOUSE - Toys ☆ - Arrow Industries, Inc.
DREAM DOLLS - Dolls - Dakin Inc.
DREAM DRESSER - Clothing - Dream Dresser, Inc.
DREAM FANTASY - Dolls - Mattel, Inc.
DREAM FASHION - Lenses–optical - Ditto Industries Inc.
DREAM FIT - Bedding–linen - Homtex, Inc.
DREAM FLEX - Footwear - United States Shoe Corp.
DREAM FLIGHT - Beds–wood - Watercloud Bed Co.
DREAM FORM - Brassieres (Bras) ☆ - Gelmart Industries Inc.
DREAM FORTUNE - Game machines - Universal Distributing of Nevada, Inc.
DREAM FURNITURE - Dolls - Mattel, Inc.
DREAM GIRL - Apparel–children's ☆ - Gerber Products Co.
DREAM GIRL - Cosmetics - Nu-Art Beauty Products
DREAM GLIDER - Exercising equipment - Richard Simmons
DREAM GLO - Cosmetics - Andrew Jergens Co.
DREAM GLOW - Dolls - Mattel, Inc.
DREAM HOME - Paints - Kwal-Howells Inc.
DREAM HORSE - Toys - Mattel, Inc.
DREAM HOUSE - Computer software - CBS Software
DREAM HOUSE - Dolls - Mattel, Inc.
DREAM HOUSE - Paints ☆ - Morton International Traffic Markings
DREAM ISLE - Floor coverings–carpet and rugs ☆ - World Carpets, Inc.
DREAM KIDS - Furniture - Shuchter, Inc.
DREAM KITCHEN - Toys - Mattel, Inc.
DREAM LICKS - Ice cream ☆ - Thin's Inn Inc.
DREAM-LITE - Food products - Dream-Meals, Inc.
DREAM MACHINE - Bicycles - Columbia Manufacturing Inc.
DREAM MACHINE - Games ☆ - Mayfair Games, Inc.
DREAM MACHINE - Radios - Sony Corp. of America
DREAM MACHINE - Vacuum cleaners and accessories - White Consolidated Industries, Inc.
DREAM MACHINE - Wallpaper - Pickhardt & Siebert USA Inc.
DREAM MACHINE II - Wallpaper - Advance Wallcoverings
DREAM MACHINE, THE - Computer software - Electromedia Productions, Inc.
DREAM MACHINE, THE - Wallpaper - Southport
DREAM MACHINE, THE - Wallpaper - Cheri L. Strole
DREAM MAGIC - Floor coverings–carpet and rugs ☆ - Mohawk Carpet Corp.
DREAM MAID - Mattresses - Bemco Associates, Inc.
DREAM MAKER - Brassieres (Bras) - Lovable Co.
DREAM MAKERS - Recording label - Survivor Records/Dream Makers Inc.
DREAM MANOR - Mobile homes - Fleetwood Enterprises, Inc.
DREAM NET - Nail care products ☆ - W.R. Rayson Co., Inc.
DREAM NUGGETS - Candy - Ann Beth Goldblum
DREAM ON - Apparel and accessories - MCA Television Entertainment, Inc.
DREAM O'PEDIC - Mattresses - Sleepwell Mattress Co. Inc.
DREAM PARK - Trailers–travel - Fleetwood Enterprises, Inc.
DREAM-PEAT - Apparel and accessories - Gordon A. Kuehl.
DREAM PEDLAR - Greeting cards - Green Tiger Press

☆ = Now out of production

DREAM PHONE - Games - Milton Bradley Co.
DREAM PIE - Snack foods - Natural Nectar Corp.
DREAM POOL - Dolls - Mattel, Inc.
DREAM PRINCESS - Bicycles - Huffy Corp.
DREAM PRINCESS - Dolls - Mattel, Inc.
DREAM PUDDINGS - Puddings–canned ✰ - Imagine Foods Inc.
DREAM PUFF - Bedding–linen - Whiting Manufacturing Co. Inc.
DREAM PUFF - Dolls and accessories, now out of production - American Greetings Corp.
DREAM PUFFS - Cookies - Nabisco Holdings Corp.
DREAM PUFFS - Toys–stuffed - Russ Berrie and Co., Inc.
DREAM REST - Mattresses - Bio Clinic Corp.
DREAM RIDE - Seats–automobile - Cosco, Inc.
DREAM ROSES - Flower pots–plastic - Anthony Tesselaar USA Inc.
DREAM SCAPE - Toiletries - Beauty International Fragrances, Ltd.
DREAM SCENTS - Deodorizers - Natural Image Botanicals Inc.
DREAM SEAMER - Quilts - Extra Special Products Corp.
DREAM SENSATIONS - Pillows - Pacific Coast Feather Co.
DREAM SEQUENCE - Recording label - Dream Sequence Music Ltd.
DREAM SHEET - Infant product - Judi's Orijinals
DREAM STAR - Lenses–optical - Ditto Industries Inc.
DREAM STATE - Apparel–women's - Wal-Mart Stores Inc.
DREAM STONE - Novelty items - S.J. Miller Co.
DREAM SUPREME - Lenses–optical - Ditto Industries Inc.
DREAM SUPREME II - Floor coverings–carpet and rugs - Sears, Roebuck and Co.
DREAM SWING - Golfing equipment - Dream Swing
DREAM TAN - Skin care products - Mohamed N. Mohsen
DREAM TEAM - Paper products - Dream Team Collectibles, Inc.
DREAM-TEE'S - Underwear and nightwear - A.H. Schreiber Co.
DREAM TIME - Floor coverings–carpet and rugs ✰ - S and S Mills Inc.
DREAM TIME - Vitamins and nutritional supplements - Amrion, Inc.
DREAM TRACER - Floor coverings–carpet and rugs - Columbus Mills, Inc.
DREAM TREE - Trees–artificial - Dream Tree
DREAM TYME - Mattress pads ✰ - Child Craft Industries Inc.
DREAM VACATION - Dolls - Mattel, Inc.
DREAM VAN XGW - Toys–automobiles - Mattel, Inc.
DREAM 'VETTE - Toys–automobiles - Mattel, Inc.
DREAM WARDROBE - Dolls - Mattel, Inc.
DREAM WEAVE - Floor coverings–carpet and rugs - LaVelle Textile Marketing Inc.
DREAM WEAVE - Washboards - Kimberly-Clark Corp.
DREAM WEAVER - Mattresses - Vinyl Products
DREAM WEAVER - Wallpaper ✰ - Somerville Designs
DREAM WEAVER SUPREME CENTER - Bars–steel - Vinyl Products
DREAM WEAVERS - Dinnerware–glass ✰ - Denby USA Limited
DREAM WEAVING - Jewelry - Norine A. Newton
DREAM WEDDING - Dolls - Mattel, Inc.
DREAM WEDDING - Toys - Tonka Corp.
DREAM X POWER - Hair care products - Apex Products Co.
DREAMBEDS - Furniture–wood - Dreambeds
DREAMBOAT - Ophthalmic goods - Embassy Creations Inc.
DREAMCALE - Bedding–linen - Eckerd Corp.
DREAMCALE - Bedding–linen ✰ - Dreamtex Corp.
DREAMCANDY - Chocolate bars - Sorbee International, Ltd.
DREAMCOATS - Robes - Kingley Manufacturing Corp.
DREAMEDIA TECHNOLOGIES - Computer software - Thomas A. Gotuzzo
DREAMER - Frames–eyeglass - May Optical Co. Inc.
DREAMER - Motor vehicles–motor homes - Western Recreational Vehicles Inc.
DREAMETTES - Underwear and nightwear - Maidenform Inc.
DREAMFACTORY - Computer software - Cyberflix, Inc.
DREAMFIRE - Heating equipment - Lennox Industries Inc.
DREAMFLOWER - Talcum powders ✰ - Prince Matchabelli
DREAMFORGE - Computer software - Event Horizon Software, Inc.
DREAMGLOW - Fireplace logs–treated - Temco Fireplace Products, Inc.
DREAMHOUSE - Bedding–linen ✰ - Dan River Inc.
DREAMIN' COLORS - Cosmetics - Cosmo Cosmetics, Inc.
DREAMJET - Bathroom accessories - Watkins Manufacturing Corp.
DREAMKEEPER - Figurines - Kirk's Folly, Inc.
DREAMKNIT - Fabrics ✰ - Vanity Fair Mills Inc.
DREAMLAB - Computer software - Crown Software International, Inc.
DREAMLAN 5 - Cables - General Cable Industries, Inc.
DREAMLAND - Apparel–children's - Gerber Products Co.
DREAMLAND - Bedspreads - Dan River Inc.
DREAMLAND - Christmas tree ornaments - Cracker Box Inc.

DREAMLEARNING - Recording label - Innerquest, Inc.
DREAMLINE - Mattresses - Dreamline Manufacturing, Inc.
DREAMLITE - Watches - Elgin Watch Co.
DREAMPUFF - Crocheted and knitted items ✰ - Alpha Mills Corp.
DREAMRIDER - Frames–eyeglass ✰ - Universal/Univis Inc.
DREAMS - Flowers, plants, and seeds - Panamerican Seed
DREAMS + ACTION = REALITY - Apparel and accessories - Richard J. Racosky
DREAMS & SEAMS - Apparel and accessories - Winchel Associates, Inc.
DREAMS BY EMUNIVERSAL - Skin care products - Jo Jones
DREAMS BY TABU - Perfumes - Dana Perfumes Corp.
DREAMS COME TRUE - Frames–picture - Terragrafics Inc.
DREAMS EVERLASTING - Invitations - Classic Thermographers Ltd.
DREAMS OF THE DANCE - Calendars - American Greetings Corp.
DREAMSCOPE - Telescopes - Beachcombers International Inc.
DREAMSHAKE - Ice cream - Quiktrip Corp.
DREAMSHEET - Bedding–linen - Originals Bi Judi Inc.
DREAMSICLE - Apparel–children's - Popsicle Playwear Ltd.
DREAMSICLE - Ice cream ✰ - Good Humor Corp.
DREAMSICLES - Figurines - Cast Art Industries, Inc.
DREAMSICLES HEAVENLY CLASSICS - Figurines ✰ - Cast Art Industries, Inc.
DREAMSICLES, THE - Giftware - Cast Art Industries, Inc.
DREAMSOFT - Bedding–linen - Dreamtex Corp.
DREAMSPACE - Cribs–wood - Newborne Co.
DREAMSPACE - Garden furniture - Thermal Industries Inc.
DREAMSPORT - Women's apparel - Ideas Apparel Group Inc.
DREAMSPUN - Crocheted and knitted items - Garland Knitting Mills
DREAMSPUN - Floor coverings–carpet and rugs - Evans-Black Carpet Mills
DREAMSTEAMER - Steamers–apparel - A/C Enterprises, Inc.
DREAMSTYLES - Linen - Bibb Co.
DREAMTEX - Bedding–linen - Dreamtex Corp.
DREAMTIME - Dolls - Mattel, Inc.
DREAMTIME - Footwear ✰ - Terra Australis Inc.
DREAMTIME - Pillows - DreamTime Inc.
DREAMTIME - Underwear and nightwear - Maidenform Inc.
DREAMTIME CAROUSEL - Toys–musical - Mattel, Inc.
DREAMWALK - Floor coverings–carpet and rugs ✰ - Carpet Crafts Inc.
DREAMWARE - Electronic equipment - Arthur Meyer
DREAMWEAR - Apparel–women's - Sanmark-Stardust Inc.
DREAMWEAR - Underwear and nightwear - Maidenform Inc.
DREAMWEAVER - Eyeglasses - Art-Craft Optical Co.
DREAMWEAVER - Floor coverings–carpet and rugs - Carpet Crafts Inc.
DREAMWORKS - Toys - Toy Soldiers Inc.
DREAMWRAP - Paper–gift wrap - Glitterwrap Inc.
DREAMY - Floor coverings–carpet and rugs ✰ - Gulistan Carpet Inc.
DREAMY ANGEL - Toys–stuffed - Jolly U.S.A., Inc.
DREAMY-EYE - Frames–eyeglass - Liberty Optical Manufacturing Co.
DREAMY NIGHTS - Blankets–electric ✰ - Sunbeam-Oster Household Products
DREAMY WHITE - Candy - Ethel M. Chocolates, Inc.
DREEMS INTL. - Cosmetic applicators - Sentinel Consumer Products, Inc.
DREFT - Soap - Procter & Gamble Co.
DREHER - Pickles - Green Bay Foods Co.
DREHMANN - Epoxy coatings - Drehmann Paving and Flooring Co.
DREI GLOCKEN - Pasta - C. & J. Willenborg Inc.
DREI PAULY - Bakery products ✰ - Dietary Specialties
DREIDL - Novelty items ✰ - S.J. Miller Co.
DREISBACH'S STEAKS - Meat products–beef - Rocking Beef, Inc.
DREIZACK-SOLINGEN - Cutlery ✰ - S.I. Moss Co. Inc.
DREK - Apparel–athletic - SDO Sports, Ltd.
DREME CREME - Skin care products - Fanie International
DREMEL - Tools–power-driven - Dremel
DRENATROPHIN PMG - Vitamins and nutritional supplements - Standard Process Inc.
DRENCH - Hair care products - Brocato International
DRENCHER - Fruit drinks–bottled or canned - Pepsi-Cola Co.
DRENCHING SOLUTION - Cosmetics - Origins Natural Resources Inc.
DRESCO - Candy - Raymond Foods Inc.
DRESDEN - Christmas tree ornaments - Cracker Box Inc.
DRESDEN - Dinnerware–glass - WMF/USA
DRESDEN - Figurines ✰ - Reco International Corp.
DRESDEN - Glassware–household - Crystal Clear Importing Co. Inc.
DRESDEN - Tableware–china ✰ - Susquehanna Glass Co.
DRESDEN - Wallpaper - Gloria Merrill Enterprises
DRESDEN - Wallpaper ✰ - Capital Carousel Inc.

✰ = Now out of production

DRESDEN ROSE - Dishes–earthenware ☆ - Gorham Inc.
DRESDEN ROSE - Flatware - Reed and Barton Corp.
DRESDEN ROSE - Giftware - Arnart Imports Inc.
DRESDEN ROSE - Lipsticks - Lancome
DRESDEN TOUR BASKET - Bassinets - Longaberger Co.
DRESHER - Beds–metal - Dresher Inc.
DRESS - Paints - Somay Products Inc.
DRESS BLUES - Jeans–women's ☆ - Lee Apparel Co. Inc.
DRESS CIRCLE - Apparel stores–lingerie - Formflex Foundations Inc.
DRESS CIRCLE - Leather goods ☆ - Buxton Inc.
DRESS CODE - Floor waxes - Mission Kleensweep Products, Inc.
DRESS DOWN FRIDAY - Footwear - Freeman International, Inc.
DRESS-IT - Wax removers - Auto Wax Co., Inc.
DRESS IT UP - Novelty items - Jesse James
DRESS LITES - Footwear - Wolverine World Wide, Inc.
DRESS ME BEAR - Toys–stuffed ☆ - Dakin Inc.
DRESS ME UP - Dolls - J.C. Toys Group, Inc.
DRESS-ME-UP ERNIE - Toys - Playskool, Inc.
DRESS-ME-UPS - Toys–stuffed - Fun World Inc.
DRESS N' DAZZLE - Costumes - Rubie's Costume Co., Inc.
DRESS 'N DAZZLE - Toys - Tonka Corp.
DRESS 'N FUN - Dolls - Mattel, Inc.
DRESS RIGHT - Garment hangers–wire ☆ - Latama Inc.
DRESS SHAPERS - Apparel stores–lingerie ☆ - Formfit Rogers
DRESS SIZED - Apparel stores–lingerie - Formfit Rogers
DRESS TO WIN - Signals–traffic - American Soccer Co. Inc.
DRESS UP - Brassieres (Bras) ☆ - Lovable Co.
DRESS UP BAGS - Bags - Allsorts Premium Packaging
DRESS-UP VANITY - Toys - Fisher-Price, Inc.
DRESS UP YOUR HOME - Hardware ☆ - Amerock Corp.
DRESS UPS - Apparel–women's - Russ Togs Inc.
DRESS UPS - Socks - Lea-Wayne Knitting Mills Inc.
DRESS-WALKERS - Shoes–athletic - Titleist & Foot-Joy Worldwide
DRESS WHITES - Jewelry ☆ - Hirsch Speidel Inc.
DRESS-YOUR-OWN - Dolls - Standard Doll Co.
DRESSABOUT - Footwear - Mason Shoe Manufacturing Co.
DRESSED BY DAD - Childrens apparel - Richard P. Proctor, Jr.
DRESSED IN DIAMONDS - Apparel - Saramar Corp.
DRESSED-IN-STYLE - Food products - Amato-Chase Inc.
DRESSED LESTERS - Toys–stuffed - Russ Berrie and Co., Inc.
DRESSED MICE PROFESSIONALS - Toys–stuffed - Russ Berrie and Co., Inc.
DRESSED TO KILL - Puzzles - Hasbro, Inc.
DRESSEL'S - Cakes - Dressels Bakeries Inc.
DRESSEL'S - Food products - American Bakeries Co.
DRESSEL'S CRUNCH CAKE - Baked goods - Dressels Bakeries Inc.
DRESSER - Sandwiches–prepackaged - H-D Michigan, Inc.
DRESSEROBE - Furniture ☆ - Hedstrom Corp.
DRESSEZ - Shoe accessories ☆ - Arcoa Industries
DRESSING FOR PLEASURE - Apparel and accessories - Constance Enterprises Ltd.
DRESSING FOR SUCCESS - Salad dressings–bottled ☆ - Johnny's Enterprises Inc.
DRESSING ROOMS - Fabrics–tapestry - Comark Wallcoverings
DRESSING-TO-GO - Salad dressings–bottled ☆ - Henri's Food Products Co. Inc.
DRESSLINERS - Apparel stores–lingerie ☆ - Formfit Rogers
DRESSMAKER - Sewing machines–household ☆ - Nelco Sewing Machine Sales Corp.
DRESSMAKERS HAM - Hams - June Tailor Inc.
DRESSMASTER - Sewing machines–household - VWS Inc.
DRESSPORTS - Footwear–men's - Rockport Co. Inc.
DRESSWORKS BY ALBEROY - Crocheted and knitted items - Beldoch Industries Corp.
DRESSY BESSY - Dolls - Playskool, Inc.
DRESSY DREAMS - Dolls - Mattel, Inc.
DREST - Hair care products ☆ - Dermik Laboratories Inc.
DREW - Insulating materials–foam - Drew Foam Co. Inc.
DREW - Shoes - Drew Shoe Corp.
DREW OCCASIONAL - Furniture - LADD Furniture Inc.
DREW PICTURES - Computer software - Drew Pictures
DREW SMITH - Statuary - Drew Smith Glasshouse
DREWBROM - Chemical preparations - Drew Chemical Corp.
DREWCOR - Corrosion inhibitor - Ashland Oil, Inc.
DREWERY - Food products ☆ - C-Corp.
DREWRYS - Beverages–alcohol - Evansville Brewing Co.

DREXAR 530 - Chemical preparations - Drexel Chemical Co.
DREXEL - Cleaning preparations - Drexel House of Draperies
DREXEL - Furniture - Drexel Heritage Furnishings, Inc.
DREXEL - Hosiery - Dan River Inc.
DREXEL HERITAGE - Furniture - Drexel Heritage Furnishings, Inc.
DREXEL HILL - Floor coverings - Mannington Resilient Floors
DREXLER'S - Spices and extracts - Stache Foods
DREXLITE - Shoes - Shoe Show, Inc.
DREYER/SONOMA - Wines - House of Burgundy Inc.
DREYERS' - Ice cream - Dreyer's Grand Ice Cream, Inc.
DREYER'S GRAND LIGHT - Ice cream - Dreyer's Grand Ice Cream, Inc.
DRG - Recording label - DRG Records Inc.
DRG ARCHIV - Recording label ☆ - DRG Records Inc.
DRI - Chemical preparations - State Chemical Manufacturing Co.
DRI-AID - Health care products - Hal-Hen Co. Inc.
DRI-BABIES - Bedding–linen - Gotham Industries II
DRI-BACK - Cosmetics - Andre Fantasies Inc.
DRI-BALL - Steel springs–railroad - Dri-Sports Co.
DRI BED - Pet products - Southdown Pet Products Ltd.
DRI-BORE - Cleaning preparations ☆ - Selmer Co. Inc.
DRI-BOTTOMS - Diapers–disposable - Arquest, Inc.
DRI-BOTTOMS DIAPERS FOR BOYS - Diapers–disposable - Arquest, Inc.
DRI-BOTTOMS DIAPERS FOR GIRLS - Diapers–disposable - Arquest, Inc.
DRI-BOTTOMS SUPREME - Diapers - Arquest, Inc.
DRI-CALC - Computer software - Dri-Steem Humidifier Co.
DRI-CATCH - Fishing lures - Fred Arbogast Co. Inc.
DRI-COOL - Cosmetics - Carter Co.
DRI-CORE - Apparel–athletic - Dri-Core Inc.
DRI-COTTON - Apparel and accessories ☆ - Terramar Sports Worldwide, Ltd.
DRI-DEK - Mats - Drehmann Paving and Flooring Co.
DRI-DEK - Pet products - Kendall Products
DRI-DEK - Tiles–ceramic - Dri-Dek Corp.
DRI DISC - Saw blades - DBNA Trademarks Holding Inc.
DRI-DOC - Hearing aids - Harc Mercantile Ltd.
DRI-DOCK - Boats - Ve-Ve Inc.
DRI-DON - Fabrics–cotton - Dan River Inc.
DRI-DOWN - Pillows - Pacific Coast Feather Co.
DRI-EAR - Pharmaceutical preparations - Pfeiffer Pharmaceuticals Inc.
DRI-EST - Cleaning preparations–carpet and rug ☆ - C.B. Dolge Co.
DRI-F.I.T. - Apparel and accessories - Nike, Inc.
DRI-F.I.T. REMOVES SWEAT - Apparel–athletic - Nike, Inc.
DRI-FLO - Sanitary napkins - Kinetic Concepts, Inc.
DRI FLOR - Bathroom accessories - Akay Corp.
DRI-FOOT - Health care products - Chaska Inc./Medihome-Doctors Podiatry
DRI G GARD - Gloves - Grandoe Corp.
DRI-GARD - Gloves - Grandoe Corp.
DRI HOLD - Sporting goods - Unique Sports Products Inc.
DRI-INK - Inks ☆ - Floquil-Polly S Color Corp.
DRI-KEM - Health care products - Thetford Corp.
DRI-KLEEN - Pet products - Farnam Cos. Inc.
DRI-KLEEN - Sanitary napkins - Kleinert's Inc.
DRI-LABELS - Office supplies - Esselte Corp.
DRI-LINE - Pencils ☆ - Faber-Castell Corp.
DRI-LOC - Adhesives and sealants - Loctite Corp.
DRI MARK - Markers–felt-tip - Dri Mark Products, Inc.
DRI MARK JUMBO - Markers–felt-tip - Dri Mark Products, Inc.
DRI-NEX - Paper–toweling - Misc Elaineous Marquetter Enterprises
DRI OUT - Dehumidifiers - Coughlan Products Corp.
DRI-PAINT - Paints–artists' - Markwell Manufacturing Co. Inc.
DRI PANTS - Health care products ☆ - Nelkin/Piper Health Products
DRI-PIPE - Adhesives and sealants ☆ - Mystik Corp.
DRI-POINT - Paper - Stuart Hall Co., Inc.
DRI-PREP - Chemical preparations - Garon Products Inc.
DRI-RAC - Dryers–household - Deccofelt Corp.
DRI-REX - Pharmaceutical preparations - C.S. Ruckstuhl Co. Inc.
DRI-RIND - Fishing lures - Fred Arbogast Co. Inc.
DRI-RITE - Ribbons–inked - Standard Manifold Co.
DRI-RITE - Skin care products ☆ - Aquamint Laboratories Inc.
DRI SET - Hair care products - Vienna Beauty Products Co.
DRI-SLIDE - Lubricants - Guardsman Products, Inc.
DRI-SPOT - Clay products ☆ - Golden Cat Corp.
DRI-STEEM - Humidifiers - Dri-Steem Humidifier Co.
DRI-TACK - Printing presses - Lawrence S. Vaughan
DRI-TEX - Tents ☆ - Coleman Co., Inc.
DRI-TITE - Archery equipment - Bohning Co. Ltd.
DRI-TOUCH - Rustproofing compounds - Birchwood Casey

☆ = Now out of production

DRI-TOXEN - Antipyretics ☆ - Walker Corp. & Co. Inc.

DRI-TUBE - Hearing aids - Earmold Design Inc.

DRI UP - Detergents ☆ - Coughlan Products Corp.

DRI WASH 'N GUARD - Cleaning preparations–household - Enviro-Tech International

DRI-WICK - Desoldering braid - American Electrical Heater Co. (American Beauty Div.)

DRI-WIPE MARKERS - Markers–felt-tip - Dri Mark Products, Inc.

DRI-WOOL - Apparel and accessories ☆ - Terramar Sports Worldwide, Ltd.

DRI-ZIT - Cleaning preparations–household - Waverly Mineral Products Co.

DRI-ZORB - Chemical preparations - Andersons Management Corp.

DRIAD - Paints ☆ - Binney & Smith Inc.

DRIBBLE WAY - Paints - Fitzgerald Enterprises Inc.

DRIBBLES - Toys–stuffed - Gund, Inc.

DRIBECK'S - See **BECK'S LIGHT**

DRICHEM - Exercising equipment - Pathway Bellows, Inc.

DRICLAD - Fiberboard - Stan Chem Inc. (Albi Div.)

DRICORT - Pharmaceutical preparations - Del Pharmaceuticals, Inc.

DRIEHOEK BANKET - Pastries - Holland-American Importing Co. Inc.

DRIFLEX - Apparel and accessories - Stearns Manufacturing Co.

DRIFT - Apparel and accessories - Robern Skiwear, Inc.

DRIFT BUSTER - Tires - Montgomery Ward & Co. Inc.

DRIFT TIDE - Floor coverings–carpet and rugs ☆ - Catalina Carpet Mills Inc.

DRIFTED SNOW - Flour–blended - General Mills, Inc.

DRIFTER - See **WINDSOR**

DRIFTER - Boats - Glen-L Marine Designs

DRIFTER - Boats–houseboats - Boating Corp. of America

DRIFTER - Boats–houseboats ☆ - Cron Houseboats

DRIFTER - Toys - North Pacific Products Inc.

DRIFTERS - Shoes - Craddock-Terry Inc.

DRIFTING CLOUDS - Floor coverings–carpet and rugs - Evans-Black Carpet Mills

DRIFTMASTER - Sporting goods - Black River Tools, Inc.

DRIFTWOOD - Fabrics–cotton - Milliken & Co.

DRIFTWOOD - Furniture ☆ - A. Brandt Co. Inc.

DRIFTWOOD - Garden equipment - Far West Forests

DRIFTWOOD - Motor vehicles–motor homes - Baron Motor Homes Inc.

DRIFTWOOD - Recording label - Driftwood Records

DRIFTWOOD - Siding–metal - Alcan Aluminum Corp. Alcan Building Products Div.

DRIFTWOOD - Yarn - William Unger & Co. Inc.

DRIFTWOOD CASUAL - Glass–leaded - Seneca Glass Co.

DRIGEL - Electrodes - Physiometrix, Inc.

DRIGEN - Pharmaceutical preparations - Goldline Laboratories, Inc.

DRIGG'S FARMS - Ice cream - Drigg's Dairy Farms Inc.

DRIHAND - Gloves - Heyman Corp.

DRIKETTE - Desiccant paper - Multiform Desiccants Inc.

DRIL-KWICK - Screws - Parker-Kalon Inc.

DRILCO INDUSTRIAL - Tools–power-driven - Carbide Products International, Inc.

DRILDEX - Hardware - Huot Manufacturing Co.

DRILL - Apparel and accessories - Drill Clothing Co.

DRILL BUDDY - Drill bits - Disston Co.

DRILL-OUT BOLT EXTRACTOR KIT - Tools - Auto Vehicle Parts Co.

DRILL QUEST - Computer software - Technology Source, Inc.

DRILL-RITE - Hardware - Barrett Manufacturing Co.

DRILL SERGEANT - Toys - Mattel, Inc.

DRILL TEAM - Drill bits - Credo Co.

DRILL-THIN - Drills–electric - Drilling Specialties Co.

DRILL-TITE - Hardware - Barrett Manufacturing Co.

DRILLDOWN - Computer storage devices–magnetic - Medline, Industries, Inc.

DRILLIA - Giftware - REO Co.

DRILLMAKER - Computer software - John M. Eubanks

DRILLMAKER - Computer software ☆ - CONDUIT

DRILLMASTER - Electronic equipment - Vermax Inc.

DRILLPRO - Computer software - Resources Engineering Systems, Inc.

DRILLSHELL - Computer software ☆ - CONDUIT

DRILLSTATION - Computers–personal - Baker Hughes Inc.

DRILOCK - Gloves - Olympia Sports Co. Inc.

DRILTEC - Drill bits - Driltec, Drilling and Fastening Technics, Inc.

DRIMA - Thread - Coats and Clark Inc.

DRIMARQUETTE - Marking inks - Irwin-Hodson Co.

DRIMESTAN - Flowers, plants, and seeds - Stanford Seed Co.

DRIMISOL - Dairy products - Valley Lea Dairies Inc.

DRINA - Cigarettes - G.A. Georgopulo & Co. Inc.

DRINASE - Cold remedies ☆ - Chase Laboratories Inc.

DRINK - Apparel - Late Night, Inc.

DRINK-BUOY - Glassware–household - Orbex Inc.

DRINK CHILL - Housewares - SGI Inc.

DRINK CONNECTION, THE - Portable beverage container and cups ☆ - Ingrid

DRINK GENIE - Plastics - Drink Genie, Inc.

DRINK-IN-BUDDY - Containers - Diversified Specialty Printing, Inc.

DRINK-KING - Vending machines - Omega Products Corp.

DRINK-LITE - Novelty items ☆ - Crossbow Inc.

DRINK MACHINE - Blenders - Vita-Mix Corp.

DRINK 'N SAVE - Water–bottled or canned - Pure Water Inc.

DRINK STIX - Cups–plastic - Joy Plastics Enterprises Ltd.

DRINK-UP - Drink holder ☆ - Attwood Corp.

DRINK WITH A PEEL, THE - Beverages–carbonated - Dansig Inc.

DRINK YOUR VEGETABLES - Beverages - Campbell Soup Co.

DRINKEE BABY - Dolls - Horsman

DRINKEE WALKER - Dolls - Horsman

DRINKER'S WILD - Games ☆ - Avalon Hill Game Co.

DRINKEYS - Paper–gummed ☆ - Wry Idea Co.

DRINKING DEBBIE - Dolls ☆ - Fun World Inc.

DRINKLESS - Pipes–tobacco - S.M. Frank & Co. Inc. (Kaywoodie-Yello-Bole-Medico)

DRINKMASTER - Blenders - Hamilton Beach/Proctor-Silex Inc.

DRINKMORE WATER STORE, THE - Water–bottled or canned - The Drinkmore Water Store, Inc.

DRINKWATER - Flour–blended - Stevens Industries Inc.

DRINKWATER - Mops - Piedmont Mop Co.

DRINOPHEN - Pharmaceutical preparations - Lannett Co. Inc.

DRION - Apparel and accessories - Montbell America Inc.

DRION - Pipes - Triple G Coatings Inc.

DRIONE - Pet products - Roussel-Uclaf Corp.

DRIONIC - Health care products - General Medical Co.

DRIP CLIP - Clamps–hose - Paine Co.

DRIP DRY - Garment storage bags - Laidlaw Corp.

DRIP-FIXER - Tools–plumbing - Moen Inc.

DRIP-GRIP - Cookware - Dazey Corp.

DRIP-LESS - Housewares - Tupperware Co.

DRIP LIP - Jewelry - Hartwell Corp.

DRIP MASTER - Garden equipment ☆ - Pro-Mark Corp.

DRIP MIST - Sprinklers–lawn ☆ - Hardie-Toro Irrigation

DRIP NOT - Kitchen cabinets–metal - Foge Jensen Imports

DRIP-O-MATIC - Deodorizers - Surco Products Inc.

DRIP STOP - Thread - Belding Heminway Co. Inc.

DRIP-STOP ULTIMA - Irons–electric - Philips Electronics North America Corp.

DRIP STOPPERS - Tools - Edward O'Malley Valve Co.

DRIP THINKER - Hardware - DIG Corp.

DRIPCUT - Tableware–china - Dripcut Corp.

DRIPLESS - Caulking guns - Dripless, Inc.

DRIPLESS - Furniture - Tables International Corp.

DRIPLESS - Paints - Lee Paint & Varnish Co.

DRIPLESS OIL - Lubricating oils - American Grease Stick Co.

DRIPLESS THE ORIGINAL DRIPLESS CAULKING GUN - Caulking guns - Dripless, Inc.

DRIPMASTER - Sprinklers–lawn - Orbit Irrigation Products, Inc.

DRIPPITY DO DRY - Padding–foam - Franic Creations

DRIPRIDE - Incontinence products ☆ - Scott Health Care

DRIPRINT - Dry diazo media - Dietzgen Corp.

DRIPS AND DRIZZLES - Waterproof outerwear - Pyramid Handbags Inc.

DRIQUIK - Lamps - DriQuik, Inc.

DRISCOLL - Fruits and vegetables ☆ - J.R. Simplot Co.

DRISDOL - Vitamins and nutritional supplements - Winthrop Pharmaceuticals

DRISTAN - Cold remedies - Whitehall Laboratories

DRISTAN MIX-IN - Cold remedies - Whitehall Laboratories

DRISTAN ULTRA - Cold remedies ☆ - Whitehall Laboratories

DRISTAR - Health care products - Davstar California, Inc.

DRISTEX - Pharmaceutical preparations ☆ - Veratex Group

DRISTIK - Chemical preparations - Elite Ink & Coatings, Ltd.

DRITAIL - Veterinary pharmaceutical preparations - Mardel Laboratories, Inc.

DRITEST - Computer software - LCS/Telegraphics Inc.

DRITHERM - Calcium compounds - Dritherm, Inc.

DRITZ - Craft supplies - Prym Dritz Corp.

DRIVE - Animal feed supplements - DDI Pharmaceuticals Inc.

DRIVE - Detergents - Lever Brothers Co. Inc.

DRIVE - Pet products ☆ - Farnam Cos. Inc.

DRIVE - Skin care products - International Wholesale Products

DRIVE ALERT - Electrical equipment - Sanford M. Stein

DRIVE & EAT - Toys - Mattel, Inc.

DRIVE CLEANER - Computer software - Seven Hills Software
DRIVE FOR SHOW, PUTT FOR DOUGH - Balls–golf - Pro Glow Sports Inc.
DRIVE-GUIDE - Motor vehicle parts and accessories ☆ - SAFCO Corp.
DRIVE HIDE - Cement - M.A. Bruder & Sons Inc.
DRIVE IN - Vegetables–frozen - Norpac Services, Inc.
DRIVE-IN, THE - Video equipment - Desktop Video Systems
DRIVE-IT - Hooks - Paine Co.
DRIVE-IT - Staples - Porcelain Products Co.
DRIVE-IT-CLEAN - Toys - Mattel, Inc.
DRIVE MASTER - Golfing equipment - Drive Master Inc.
DRIVE-N-ANCHOR - Anchors ☆ - Steel City Corp.
DRIVE 'N BANK - Toys - Mattel, Inc.
DRIVE-N-MOUNT - Mail boxes - Steel City Corp.
DRIVE 'N PLAY - Toys–electronic - CBS Toys
DRIVE 'N POP - Toys - Mattel, Inc.
DRIVE-R-DRILL - Tools - S-B Power Tool Co.
DRIVE-RITE - Aluminum nails - Independent Nail Inc.
DRIVE STAND - Clamps–metal - Sign-Up Corp.
DRIVE TENDORE - Driveway signals - Signal-U Manufacturing
DRIVE TIME - Antennas - Antenna Co.
DRIVE WITH PRIDE - Video production - California Detailing
DRIVE YA NUTS - Puzzles ☆ - Milton Bradley Co.
DRIVEALIGN - Pulleys–industrial - Gates Rubber Co. (Automotive
   Aftermarket/Hardware Sales Div.)
DRIVEAWAY - Cleaning preparations - TRJN, Inc.
DRIVEBACK - Sporting goods - Marty Gilman Inc.
DRIVEBOSS - Adhesives and sealants - BossWorks Inc.
DRIVECOATE - Asphalt felts and coatings - Building Protective Industries
DRIVEGAUGE - Measuring instruments - GK Inc.
DRIVEGUARD - Hardware - Aluminum Coating Manufacturers Inc.
DRIVEKLEEN - Machinery - Drivekleen, Inc.
DRIVELINE 50 - Paving materials–stone - Paver Systems, Inc.
DRIVELINK - Radio communications equipment - Futaba Corp. of America
DRIVEMASTER - Tools - Great Neck Saw Manufacturers, Inc.
DRIVEMATIC - Clutches–industrial - Access Unlimited
DRIVEN' - Computer software - Hartley Courseware Inc.
DRIVEN BY A PASSION FOR PERFECTION - Motor vehicles - Carlin
   Manufacturing Inc.
DRIVEN TO PERFORM - Furniture–factory - Utility Composites, Inc.
DRIVEPRO - Computer peripheral equipment - Micro House International, Inc.
DRIVER - Toys - Disc Golf Association, Inc.
DRIVER-21 - Tools - Disstim Corp.
DRIVERIGHT - Speedometers - Davis Instruments Corp.
DRIVERS - Boots ☆ - Durango Boot Co. Inc.
DRIVERS - Eyeglasses - Solar-Mates Sunglasses
DRIVERS - Sunglasses - Corning Inc.
DRIVERS AID - First aid kits - E.H. Kneen Co.
DRIVER'S CHOICE - Eyeglasses - Foster Grant Co. Inc.
DRIVER'S FRIEND - Gloves - Plenge Trading Co.
DRIVER'S FRIEND - Vitamins and nutritional supplements - Tishcon Corp.
DRIVERS PLUS - Gloves–work - Adams Global Industries, Inc.
DRIVERX - Computer peripheral equipment - Winstar Technologies
DRIVESALL - Wrenches - Great Bay Tool Corp.
DRIVESHAFT - Golfing equipment - Nicklaus Golf Equipment Co.
DRIVESHARE - Computer software - Casa Blanca Works Inc.
DRIVETIME - Computer programs - Drivetime Inc.
DRIVEWAY CARE - Paving materials–concrete - Neyra Industries, Inc.
DRIVEWAY DEALS - Games - Celia Weiner
DRIVEWAY DETAILER - Cleaning preparations - Blue Coral, Inc.
DRIVEWAY HEAT - Deicing fluid - Prestone Products Corp.
DRIVEWAY SNOWMASTER - Snowblowers - Ferance Construction Co.
DRIVEWAY TENNIS - Sporting goods - Tennis Farm
DRIVEWORKS - Adhesives and sealants - Master's Choice Inc.
DRIVEX - Electronic equipment - General Electric Co.
DRIVIN - Hardware - Barrett Manufacturing Co.
DRIVIN' DAN - Toys - Mattel, Inc.
DRIV'IN EASE - Cushions - Homedics Inc.
DRIVING FORCE - Batteries - Johnson Controls Inc.
DRIVING ME CRAZY - Recording label - Folger Entertainment Co.
DRIVING STYLES - Apparel and accessories - Waldron Enterprises
DRIV'NPLOW - Motor vehicles–snowplows - Solotec Corp.
DRIWATER - Chemical preparations - Driwater, Inc.
DRIXORAL - Antihistamine preparations - Schering-Plough Healthcare Products
DRIXORAL - Cough medicines - Schering Corp.
DRIZE - Motor vehicles–buses ☆ - B.F. Ascher & Co. Inc.

DRIZE - Pharmaceutical preparations - Jones Medical Industries, Inc. (Medical
   Div.)
DRIZZLE - Hair care products - John Amico Expressive Hair Care Products
DRIZZLE ETC. - Apparel–women's - Drizzle, Inc.
DRIZZLER - Apparel and accessories - Mcgregor Corp.
DRO - Electrical equipment - Acu-Rite Inc.
D'RO TOO - Handbags - D-Rossana Associates, LLC
+D'RO-TOO BY SCOTT RANKINS - Footwear–women's - D'Rossana
   Associates LLC
DROID FACTORY - Toys–models ☆ - Kenner Products
DROL - Giftware - Lorac Co.
DROLBAN - Pharmaceutical preparations ☆ - Eli Lilly and Co.
DROLLS - Greeting cards ☆ - Hallmark Cards Inc.
DROMEDARY - Bakery products - Specialty Brands Inc.
DROMEDARY BAKERY - Bakery products - Dole Dried Fruit & Nut Co.
DROOL - Toys - Mattel, Inc.
DROOLERS - Animal feeds - Marcy, Inc.
DROOLERS - Candy - P.T.C. Brands, Inc.
DROOLIE - Infant product - Tailored Baby Inc.
DROOLIES - Infant product - Kidsco
DROOPERS BRADY BEAR - Toys–stuffed - Dakin Inc.
DROOPERS DOG - Toys–stuffed - Dakin Inc.
DROOPERS LEROY LION - Toys–stuffed - Dakin Inc.
DROOPERS MORTON MONKEY - Toys–stuffed - Dakin Inc.
DROOPY DRAGON, THE - Electronic equipment ☆ - Texas Instruments Inc.
DROP - Clothing - Tom Vincent Gelinas
DROP - Footwear–children's ☆ - Bidegain Inc.
DROP-A-DOODLE - Books–blank - Jack Taylor
DROP-A-LINE - Paper - Whitehall Inc.
DROP AT A TIME - Cleaning preparations ☆ - Scentex Inc.
DROP-BOX - Toilets–portable - Semi-Vacuum Systems, Inc.
DROP D - Music stands - Kyser Musical Products, Inc.
DROP DOSE - Pharmaceutical preparations - Burroughs Wellcome Co.
DROP-GRIP - Nuts and bolts - Star Anchors & Fasteners
DROP IN THE BUCKET - Games - Lakeside Games
DROP-INS - Cleaning preparations - Drackett Co.
DROP-INS - Infant product - Playtex Beauty Care, Inc.
DROP-LOCK - Artists' materials - Artcadi Products
DROP-LOK - Bottle caps - Aluminum Co. of America
DROP-MATE - Medical apparatus - Ocular Designs, Inc.
DROP 'N BAKE - Cookies - Leon's Bakery Inc.
DROP 'N BOP - Games - Play-Tech, Inc.
DROP N' VAC - Chemical preparations - Great Lakes Biochemical Co., Inc.
DROP-O-MATIC - Buttons ☆ - Nilodor Inc.
DROP OCTAGON - Clocks ☆ - General Time Corp. (Westclox/Seth Thomas
   Div.)
DROP ON GEL KIT - Cosmetics - American International Industries
DROP SHOTS - Greeting cards ☆ - Duck Press
DROP SPRED II - Garden equipment - Greenview Lawn & Garden Products
DROP-STOP - Adhesives and sealants - Dynamic Fastener Service, Inc.
DROP TOP MUSIC - Recording label - Rooster Blues Records
DROP ZONE - Vending machines - Parkway Machine Corp.
DROPLET - Medical apparatus - International Technidyne Corp.
DROPPERETTES - Pharmaceutical applicator - Iolab Pharmaceuticals
DROPS OF YOUTH - Skin care products ☆ - Palm Beach Beauty Products
DROPS O'GOLD - Food products - Everfresh Foods Corp.
DROPSIDE - Wagons–children's ☆ - Little Tikes Co.
DROP$TEAM - Machinery - Ace USA, Inc.
+D'ROSSANA - Footwear–women's ☆ - D'Rossana Associates LLC
+D'ROSSANA BY CHARNA - Footwear–women's - D'Rossana Associates
   LLC
DROTIC - Pharmaceutical preparations ☆ - B.F. Ascher & Co. Inc.
DROUGH PARIS - Skin care products - European Cosmetics Inc.
DROUGHT BUSTER - Fertilizers - Bandini Fertilizer Co.
DROUGHT TOUGH - Flowers, plants, and seeds - Jonathan Green, Inc.
DROUGHTMASTER - Electronic equipment - Max Ray Systems
DROVER STATION NO. 4 - Apparel–athletic - Australian Outback Collection
DROWSE - Clocks - General Time Corp. (Westclox/Seth Thomas Div.)
DROWSER BOWSER - Pillows - Joan Lorraine Stone
DROWSY - Dolls - Mattel, Inc.
DROXEMMS - Pharmaceutical preparations ☆ - C.O. Truxton Inc.
DROXINE - Pharmaceutical preparations - Shear Kershman Laboratories Inc.
DROXYLLINE - Pharmaceutical preparations ☆ - Wesley Pharmacal Co. Inc.
DROZINE - Health care products ☆ - Solvay Pharmaceuticals Inc.
DRUCON - Pharmaceutical preparations ☆ - Scrip-Physician Supply Co.
DRUEKE - Games - Carrom Co.

☆ = Now out of production

DRUEKE CO., THE - Bags - Eclipse Inc.

DRUEKE COMPANY, THE - Games - H.C. Meyers Co.

DRUG ABUSE PREVENTION LIBRARY - Publisher's imprints - Rosen Publishing Group & Pelion Press

DRUG ABUSE PREVENTION LIBRARY, THE - Publisher's imprints - Rosen Publishing Group & Pelion Press

DRUG BUST - Games - Federal Ideas, Inc.

DRUG-CHEK - Pregnancy test kits - Bio-Medical Products Corp.

DRUGFIRE - Computer software - Mnemonic Systems Inc.

DRUGPAD - Computer software - Hearst Corp.

DRUGPHREY - Paper - Mobile Bay Area Partnership for Youth

DRUGS AND HEARTBEAT - Computer software - Cross Educational Software Inc.

DRUGS: IT'S ALL RIGHT TO SAY NO - Computer software - Orange Cherry Software

DRUID-DAEMONS OF THE MIND - Computer software - Sir-Tech Software, Inc.

DRUKCHEN - Apparel–women's - Sonia Trussardi

DRUM - Tables–wood - Krueger International, Inc.

DRUM - Tools - Tri Lite

DRUM-BOY - Recording label - Jay Jay Record & Tape Co.

DRUM BUDDY - Drums–musical instruments - Tamarkin Co.

DRUM BUG - Musical instrument accessories - J.T. Enterprises

DRUM CLINIC - Musical instruments - Trophy Music Co.

DRUM CORP - Musical instruments - Trophy Music Co.

DRUM DEFENDER - Rubber–molded ☆ - Tri-Solutions Inc.

DRUM DROP - Toys ☆ - Playskool, Inc.

DRUM FIXX - Musical instrument accessories - Slobeat Industries

DRUM-FX - Musical instrument accessories ☆ - JTG of Nashville

DRUM MAJOR - Food products - Umatilla Citrus Growers Association

DRUM-PLEX - Electric lighting equipment - Legion Lighting Co., Inc.

DRUM ROLLS - Candy ☆ - Spangler Candy Co.

DRUM RUNNER - Motor vehicles–trucks - Thurman Manufacturing Co.

DRUM RUNNERS - Cases–musical instrument - SKB Corp.

DRUM SHOE - Musical instrument accessories - RKG Enterprises

DRUM-STICK - Mixer - Pulsair Systems, Inc.

DRUM STICKY - Musical instrument accessories - Ethos International Corp.

DRUM TALK - Apparel - Dean Sanderson and Peter Cowley Partnership

DRUM TRIBE - T-shirts–men's - Mark Vollenweider

DRUM-X - Drums–musical instruments ☆ - Pearl Corp.

DRUMATIC - Air conditioning equipment - Skuttle Manufacturing Co.

DRUMBEAT RED - Nail care products - Cosmair Inc.

DRUMBEATERS OF AMERICA - Compactors - Drumbeaters of America Inc.

DRUMCRAFT - Drums–musical instruments - Newark Musical Merchandise Co.

DRUMDIAL - Drums–musical instruments - Big Bang Distribution/A.P.I.

DRUMETTES - Meat products–poultry - Conagra, Inc.

DRUMMARA - Apparel–men's - Drummond Knitwear Ltd.

DRUMMER - Musical instruments - Gibson Guitar Corp.

DRUMMERMAN - Musical instrument accessories ☆ - Carpenter Co.

DRUMMER'S CHOICE, THE - Drums–musical instruments - Drum Workshop, Inc.

DRUMMOND - Apparel–men's - Drummond Knitwear Ltd.

DRUMMOND BROS. - Beverages–alcohol - Evansville Brewing Co.

DRUMPHONES - Headphones - Gordon Knudtson

DRUMROLL - Computer peripheral equipment - Mediaware Technology, Inc.

DRUMSETTER - Printing trades machinery - Ecrm Inc.

DRUMSLINGER - Cases–musical instrument - Tough Traveler Inc.

DRUMSTICK SUNDAE CONE - Ice cream - Nestle USA

DRUMSTICKS - Candy - Swizzels Matlow (USA) Ltd.

DRUMSTIX - Meat products–poultry - Pierce Foods Corp.

DRUMTECH - Drums–musical instruments - Mechanical Music Corp.

DRUMULATOR - Musical instruments ☆ - E-Mu Systems, Inc.

DRUMZ - Covers–seat - Tom Drum, Inc.

DRUNKEN HOT BULLETS - Olives - Miss Scarlett

DRUSILATE - Pharmaceutical preparations ☆ - U.S. Pharmaceutical Corp.

DRUTHER'S - Restaurants–fast food ☆ - Druther's System Inc.

DRUVAN - Vinegar - Haram-Christensen Corp.

DRUWHIT - Hardware - Blaine Window Hardware Inc.

DRX - Skin care products - Paula Payne Products Co. Inc.

DRX - Wheelchairs - Dura-Med Equipment Corp.

DRX NUTRITIONAL RESEARCH - Vitamins and nutritional supplements - DRX Nutritional Research Inc.

DRY - Deodorants–personal - Mennen Co.

DRY - Waterproofing compounds - Merix Chemical Co.

DRY-A-WAY - Plumbing fixtures–metal ☆ - Matarah Industries Inc.

DRY & CLEAR - Pharmaceutical preparations - Whitehall Laboratories

DRY & NATURAL - Hair care products - Alberto-Culver Co.

DRY AND SWEATER - Sweaters - Pletz Imports

DRY & WET FLYS - Fishing lures - Joe's Flies

DRY ART - Paints–artists' - Palmer Paint Products, Inc.

DRY-B-LO DESIGNER DECK DRAIN SYSTEM - Drains - Grant M. Moore

DRY BAK - Apparel–athletic - Red Head Brand Corp.

DRY BAN - Deodorants–personal - Bristol-Myers Squibb Co.

DRY BLACKTHORN CIDER - Cider - Martlet Importing Co.

DRY BLACKTHORNE - Cider - Miller Brewing Co.

DRY-BLOCK - Waterproofing compounds - Grace Construction Products

DRY BLOSSOMS - Glassware–household - Lenox, Inc.

DRY BOND - Adhesives and sealants - Chartpak

DRY BOND - Adhesives and sealants ☆ - Laticrete International Inc.

DRY BREEZE - Deodorizers - Dymon, Inc.

DRY BREEZES - Air and fabric freshener - American Home Products Corp.

DRY BRUSH - Brushes–hair - The Montclair Co.

DRY CHUM - Fishing lures - Mickey Jacobs, Inc.

DRY CLEAN - Cleaning preparations–household - J. Goddard & Sons

DRY CLEAN - Computer software - Xerox Corp.

DRY CLEAN YOUR STREET MACHINE - Cleaning preparations - Miracle Mist

DRY CLIMATE - Skin care products ☆ - Hy-Grade Laboratories

DRY CREEK - Apparel and accessories - Bugle Boy Industries, Inc.

DRY CREEK VINEYARD - Wines - Dry Creek Vineyard Inc.

DRY-CRISP - Chemical preparations - Merix Chemical Co.

DRY CURE - Mortars–clay - Mapei East Corp.

DRY CURL - Hair care products - Pro-Capa Products Inc.

DRY DOCKER - Boat lifts - Spec Mar Manufacturing Co., Inc.

DRY DOUBLE SEAL - Pens - Koh-I-Noor, Inc.

DRY DOWN - Pillows - Pacific Coast Feather Co.

DRY ENDS - Hair care products - Roberts Research Laboratories, Inc.

DRY ERASE PLUS - Office supplies - Ghent Manufacturing Inc.

DRY EYE SOLUTION - Pharmaceutical preparations - Vision Pharmaceuticals, Inc.

DRY FALLOUT - Paints - Finnaren & Haley Inc.

DRY FAST - Cosmetics ☆ - Monique Quality Products Co. Inc.

DRY FLY - Beverages–alcohol ☆ - SPAR Inc.

DRY FLY - Traps–animal - G-96 Products Co. Inc.

DRY FOG - Insecticides - Dymon, Inc.

DRY FOGGER - Machinery - Interesting Products, Inc.

DRY FOOT - Hosiery - Wigwam Mills Inc.

DRY FORMULA FOODS - Pet products - Tetra Sales USA

DRY GATOR - Apparel–athletic - Colorado Dry Gator Limited Liability Co.

DRY GRIP - Antiperspirant lotion - Innova International Inc.

DRY GRIP - Health care products - DBA Products Co.

DRY GUARD - Silica - Engelhard Corp.

DRY GUY - Dryers–hair - Remington Products Co.

DRY HANDS - Skin care products - Nelson Sports Products, Inc.

DRY HARD - Pet products ☆ - Aaronco Grooming Products

DRY HARD II - Pet products ☆ - Aaronco Grooming Products

DRY ICE - Apparel and accessories - Go! Graphics

DRY ICE - Skates–roller - Motiv Sports, Inc.

DRY ICE SELTZER - Water–bottled or canned - Artlom USA, Inc.

DRY IDEA - Deodorants–personal - Gillette Co.

DRY IT - Rope ☆ - Crow Rope Industries LLC

DRY JERK RUB - Spices and extracts - Cinnabar Specialty Foods, Inc./Neera's Products

DRY-KUT - Pumps - Ansimag Inc.

DRY-KUT STARTER - Pumps - Ansimag Inc.

DRY KWIK - Manicure preparations - Del Pharmaceuticals, Inc.

DRY-LAM - Lany Fax of America Inc.

DRY LAYER PLUS SERENITY - Health care products - Johnson & Johnson

DRY LOOK, THE - Hair care products - Gillette Co.

DRY-LUBE - Lubricants - Reardon Products

DRY-MAST - Veterinary pharmaceutical preparations ☆ - Boehringer Ingelheim Animal Health, Inc.

DRY MY HAIR - Infant product - Rock-A-Bye Baby Inc.

DRY 'N HAPPY - Diapers–disposable - Weyerhaeuser Co.

DRY NOBLE - Wines - Old South Winery

DRY OIL - Hair care products ☆ - Madame C.J. Walker Inc.

DRY ON CLEAR - Sealing compounds - Wall Firma Inc.

DRY ONE, THE - Deodorants–personal ☆ - Carter-Wallace, Inc.

DRY ONE, THE - Apparel and accessories - Performance Contracting, Inc.

DRY PAINT - Plastic films - Avery Dennison Corp.

DRY-PLUS - Apparel and accessories - Cabela's Inc.

DRY PLUS - Cosmetics - Stephan Co.

DRY-PRO - Vacuum cleaners and accessories - Nash Engineering Co.
DRY RING - Golfing equipment - J. Marches Sheet Metal Inc.
DRY ROOTS - Fertilizers - Lisa Products Corp.
DRY-RUN - Clamp - James Maynard Magee
DRY SACK - Beverages–alcohol - Hiram Walker & Sons, Inc.
DRY SET - Grouting material - Super-Tek Products Inc.
DRY SHU - Shoes ☆ - Clarks of England Inc.
DRY SIZE - Cleaning preparations - R.R. Street & Co. Inc.
DRY SLITZ - Cigars - M. Marsh & Son
DRY SOX - Footwear - Washington Shoe Co.
DRY SPOTS - Pharmaceutical - American Hygienic Laboratories Inc.
DRY STOP - Pet products - Pet Biotics Inc.
DRY STRIP - See **POWDER/PLUS**
DRY SWEATS - Sweat pants - Arthur Kahn Co. Inc.
DRY-TAB - Office supplies - Dry-Tab Package Sealer Co.
DRY-TAB - Pet products - Aquarium Pharmaceuticals, Inc.
DRY TECH - Film - Polaroid Corp.
DRY TECH - Footwear - Marco Distributing Inc.
DRY-TEMP - Paints–artists' - Palmer Paint Products, Inc.
DRY UMBRELLA, THE - Umbrellas - Saramar Corp.
DRY-UR-FLY - Fly-fishing accessories - Cortland Line Co., Inc.
DRY VENTURE - Luggage ☆ - Cascade Designs, Inc.
DRY WEAR - Apparel and accessories - Stearns Manufacturing Co.
DRY WORKOUT, THE - Towels - Mark E. Kuwahara
DRY WORLD - Deodorants–personal - Alberto-Culver Co.
DRY ZONE - Paints - Valspar Corp.
DRY-ZYME - Veterinary pharmaceutical preparations - Dyna Pet Inc.
DRYACIDE - Insecticides - David M. Stang
DRYAD - Deodorants–personal - Andrew Jergens Co.
DRYAD - Hobby kits - Brittoys
DRYBONES - Labels–gummed - Keith Cooper Marshall
DRYBOY - Bathroom accessories - R-Z Co. of America Inc.
DRYCOMFORT - Health care products - Cascades
DRYCON - Brush-on waterproof coating - IPA Systems Inc.
DRYCON - Cleaning preparations–carpet and rug - Miracle Carpet Cleaning, Inc.
DRYCRETE - Cement ☆ - W.R. Bonsal Co.
DRYDEN - Furniture - Triangle Pacific Corp. (Cabinet Division)
DRYDEN - Recording label - Harcourt Brace & Co.
DRYDEN & COMPANY - Food products - New York Extract Co. Inc.
DRYDEN & PALMER - Candy - Dryden & Palmer Inc.
DRYDEN PRESS, THE - Recording label - Harcourt Brace & Co.
DRYDENE - Oils–lubricating - Castrol Heavy Duty Lubricants Inc.
DRYDOT - Inks - Matthews International Corp.
DRYDUNK - Hardware - FasTest Inc.
DRYEASE - Laboratory apparatus - Novel Experimental Technology
DRYEDGE - Photographic equipment ☆ - Buckingham
DRYER MATE - Dryers–household - Nemco Inc.
DRYER NET - Sporting goods - Unique Sports Products Inc.
DRYER VALET - Hair care products - KEF Enterprises
DRYFAST STYLING PRODUCTS - Hair care products - Roberts Research Laboratories, Inc.
DRYFIL - Fabrics - Veratec
DRYFIT - Health care products - Sonnenschein Batteries
DRYFLOW - Air conditioning equipment - Johnson Controls Inc.
DRYGARD - Veterinary pharmaceutical preparations - Upjohn Co.
DRYHALER - Inhalers - Dura Pharmaceuticals, Inc.
DRYIT - Chemical preparations - American Patent Group, Inc.
DRYJOYS - Shoes - Titleist & Foot-Joy Worldwide
DRYJOYS - Shoes–athletic - Titleist & Foot-Joy Worldwide
DRYJOYS GX - Shoes–athletic - Titleist & Foot-Joy Worldwide
DRYLAYER - Apparel and accessories - InSport International Inc.
DRYLETE - Fabrics - Hind, Inc.
DRYLINER - Insulating materials - Furon Co.
DRYLITE - Waterproof outerwear ☆ - Plastimayd Corp.
DRYLO - Dog food - Dry Fork Milling Co. Inc.
DRYLOC - Floor coverings - Mannington Resilient Floors
DRYLOCKER - Furniture - Gregory Dhaemers
DRYLOFT - Sleeping bags - W.L. Gore & Associates, Inc.
DRYLOK - Adhesives and sealants - United Gilsonite Laboratories
DRYLOK - Metals - Dover Corp.
DRYLOK FAST PLUG - Cement - United Gilsonite Laboratories
DRYNAL - Prescription drug ☆ - Blaine Co. Inc.
DRYNAMIC - Machinery - Castex Industries Inc.
DRYNAMITE - Pumps - Goulds Pumps, Inc.
DRYONEX - Chemical preparations ☆ - Hydroponic Chemical Co. Inc.

DRYOX 10 - Pharmaceutical preparations - C&M Pharmacal, Inc.
DRYPERS - Diapers–disposable - Drypers Corp. (Veragon Div.)
DRYPERS BIG GIRL - Disposable training pants - Classic Premiums
DRYPHITE - Lubricants - Kano Laboratories Inc.
DRYRUN - Footwear - Wolfpax, Inc.
DRYSAC - Knapsacks - Coleman Co., Inc.
DRYSDALE OF EDINBURGH - Teas ☆ - Dean & Deluca Inc.
DRYSEAL - Copper products - York Manufacturing Inc.
DRYSIDES - Footwear - Sebago Inc.
DRYSMOKE - Pipes - National Briar Pipe Co.
DRYSOL - Pharmaceutical preparations - Person and Covey Inc.
DRYSPORT - Sunblocks - Solar Gear Inc.
DRYSTIX - Paper–gummed - Labelblank Corp.
DRYSUM - Shampoos ☆ - Summers Laboratories Inc.
DRYTAC - Office supplies - Drytac USA
DRYTERGENT - Skin care products - C&M Pharmacal, Inc.
DRYTEX - Skin care products - C&M Pharmacal, Inc.
DRYTHERM - Sporting goods - Kellwood Co.
DRYTIME - Diagnostic apparatus - Health Sense International, Inc.
DRYTON - Floor coverings–tile - Federal Tile Imports Inc.
DRYTRAIL - Shoes - Amtrail, Inc.
DRYTRAK - Plaster–wallboard - Basement Systems, Inc.
DRYTYPE - Stencils - Kores Nordic USA Corp.
DRYVAX - Pharmaceutical preparations ☆ - Wyeth-Ayerst Laboratories
DRYVE - Snowboards - Bruce G. Witkin
DRYVIN - Nuts and bolts - Star Anchors & Fasteners
DRYWALL 1ST COAT - Coatings - Coronado Paint Co.
DRYWASH - Motor vehicle parts and accessories - KozaK Auto Drywash Inc.
DRYWEAR - Leather - Horween Leather Co.
DRYXCEL - Fabrics - Hind, Inc.
DRYZON - Insecticides - Y-Tex Corp.
DS - Ammonia - Rual Products Co.
DS - Apparel and accessories - Dukes Baseball Corp.
D.S. - Hair care products - Madame C.J. Walker Inc.
DS 2000 - Golfing equipment - Dorson Sports Inc.
DS DIVISION SCALE - Transducers - Division Scale Co. Inc.
DS STANDARD - Computer software - Preferred Systems, Inc.
D'S UNIQUES - Hairpins - D's Uniques
DS6 - Computer hardware - Pentax Technologies Corp.
DS10 - Computer hardware - Pentax Technologies Corp.
D'SAN JULIAN - Health care products - D'San Julian, Inc.
DSASIGN - Construction equipment rental services - Information Security Corp.
D.S.C. - Skin care products - Cococare Products Inc.
DSC - Waterproof outerwear - Distributors Service Corp.
DSC SLICKER - Footwear - Distributors Service Corp.
DSC SUPER NEO - Footwear ☆ - Distributors Service Corp.
DSD - Antennas - Alliance Telecommunications Corp.
DSE - Musical instruments - Design Direct Sound
DSERTWHIP - Whipped topping–frozen - Presto Food Products, Inc.
DSET DISTRIBUTED SOFTWARE SOLUTIONS - Computer software - DSET Corp.
DSF - Catalogs - Diabetic Supply Foundation, Inc.
DSI SYSTEM 2000 - Garbage disposal units–commercial ☆ - MediVators Inc.
DSKT STUMPER - Archery equipment - Dskt Kick Target, Inc.
DSL - Computer software - Deseret Book Co.
DSL - Data loggers - National Metal Industries (Utility Metal Products Div.)
DSL - Jewelry - Di-Star, Ltd.
DSL - Oils–vulcanized - Davis-Howland Oil Corp.
D.S.M.C. - Pharmaceutical preparations - Geneva Generics Inc.
DSO - Sunglasses - Patrick Dale Boisvert
DSP - Audio equipment - Valley Audio Products, Inc.
DSP - Skin care products - Dermatologic Specialty Products, Inc.
DSP - Thread ☆ - SCT Yarns Inc.
DSP 100 - Wheel alignment sensors - Hunter Engineering Co.
DSP 9000 - Machinery - Hunter Engineering Co.
DSP WORKBENCH - Audio equipment - G Prime Limited
DSPACK - Computer hardware - Domain Technologies, Inc.
DSPC - Metals - Soligen, Inc. (Soligen Technologies Inc.)
DSPDAQ - Computer hardware ☆ - R.C. Electronics Inc.
DSPOWER - Computer software - Signalogic, Inc.
DSS - Apparel–athletic - De Soto Clothing Co., Inc.
DSS - Computer peripheral equipment - Ontrak Systems, Inc.
DSS - Computer software - Document Storage Systems, Inc.
DSS - Computer storage devices - Hughes Communications, Inc.
DSS ALC HOME COLLECTION KIT - Medical apparatus - Diabetes Support Systems, Inc.

☆ = Now out of production

DSS PRODIESEL - Engines–diesel - DSS/Prodiesel, Inc.
DSS PRODIESEL - Sealing devices - DSS/Prodiesel, Inc.
DSSMANAGER - Computer storage devices - Document Storage Systems, Inc.
D.S.T. - Cosmetics - Alleghany Pharmacal Corp.
DST - Diagnostic substances - Access Medical Systems, Inc.
D'STAT - Phonographs - Recoton Corp.
DSTFOIL - Electronic equipment - Polyclad Laminates, Inc.
DSW DO SOMETHING WILD - Computer peripheral equipment - Do Something Wild, LLC
DSX - Chemical preparations - Henkel Corp. (Functional Products Div.)
DT - Cleaning preparations - Roebic Laboratories Inc.
DT - Screws - G.B. Dupont Co., Inc.
DT 2000 - Pens - Design Technology Corp.
DT-CONNECT - Computers - Data Translation, Inc.
DT FAX - Facsimile modems - DataTrek Corp.
DT-IRIS - Computer software - Data Translation, Inc.
DT-LIB - Computer software ☆ - Data Translation, Inc.
DT-OPEN LAYERS - Computer software - Data Translation, Inc.
DT1R - Computer software - Destiny Technology Corp.
DT710 - Tires - Goodyear Tire & Rubber Co.
DT730 - Tires - Goodyear Tire & Rubber Co.
DT810 - Tires - Goodyear Tire & Rubber Co.
DT820 - Tires - Goodyear Tire & Rubber Co.
DTAK - Dust cloths - Photographic Solutions, Inc.
DTC - Alarm systems - Dynatech Tactical Communications Inc.
DTC - Chemical preparations - B. D. Chemicals, Inc.
DTC DIRECT TORQUE CONTROL - Electrical equipment - ABB Industrial Systems, Inc.
DTD - Recording label - Sonic Arts Corp.
DTECH - Computer software - Document Technologies, Inc.
DTED - Computer peripheral equipment - Defense Mapping Agency
DTH - Amplifiers - Peavey Electronics Corp.
DTI - Plastics film - MSC Specialty Films Inc.
D.T.I. - Recording label - Holy Bible Gospel Ministry of The Body of Christ, Yeshua, of the Holy Land,
DTI DIMENSION TECHNOLOGIES, INC. - Liquid crystal displays - Dimension Technologies Inc.
DTK - Jewelry - Douglas Koorey
DTM - Lathes - Dovetail Tool Manufacturing Co.
DTR - Pencils - Dixon Ticonderoga Co.
DTS DIGITAL SOUND - Film–motion picture - Digital Theater Systems, L.P.
DTS STEREO - Recording label - Digital Theater Systems, L.P.
DTSEARCH - Computer software - DT Software, Inc.
DTX DIGITAL TECHNOLOGY EXCHANGE - Computer - Digital Technology Exchange, Inc.
DTXPLUS - Medical apparatus - Ohmeda Medical Devices Division Inc.
DU-AL-CLIP - Frames–eyeglass - Teco/Lumberlok
DU-ALL - Mops - Du-All Manufacturing Co.
DU-ALL - Pencil sharpeners - Wescosa Inc.
DU BERRY OIL - Oils–edible - Europa Foods Ltd.
DU BOA - Brushes–hair - Jatai International
DU BOIS - Enamels - Pep Boys Manny, Moe & Jack
DU BRO - Food products - Alpine Distributors
DU CAIR - Bathroom accessories ☆ - Tsumura International Inc.
DU-CARE - Air mattresses - Lotus Health Care Products/Connecticut Art Craft
DU FOAM - Skin care products - Waverly Beauty Products
DU-IT - Wheelchairs - APT Technology, Inc.
DU-LITE - Paints - E.I. Dupont de Nemours and Co.
DU LONG FRERES - Wines - Prestige Wine Corp.
DU MAURIER - Cigarettes - Brown & Williamson Tobacco Corp.
DU-MIN - Product description unknown ☆ - Scrip-Physician Supply Co.
DU-O-MATIC - Vestments–academic and clerical - Ponsness-Warren
DU-OL - Automotive parts and accessories - Unival Corp.
DU-ONS - Apparel and accessories ☆ - Duofold Inc.
DU PONT - Chemical preparations - E.I. Dupont de Nemours and Co.
DU PONT REFINISH RACING - Apparel and accessories - E.I. Dupont de Nemours and Co.
DU SHARME - Hair care products - J. Strickland & Co.
DU-TER - Fungicides ☆ - Uniroyal Chemical Co. Inc. (Crop Protection Div.)
DU-ZEE - Pet products - Du-Zee Products
DUA-DROME - Bicycle parts and accessories - Richard Anthony Kozlowski
DUA-LUX - Paper–toilet - Georgia-Pacific Corp.
DUADACIN - Cold remedies - Kenwood Laboratories Inc.
DUAL - Audio equipment - Dual
DUAL - Tools–hand-operated - Robilco, Inc.
DUAL-ACTION - Hardware ☆ - Amerock Corp.

DUAL ACTION - Insecticides - Hillyard Enterprises, Inc.
DUAL ACTION - Oils–lubricating - Witco Corp.
DUAL ACTION - Skin care products - Lancome
DUAL ACTION - Skin care products ☆ - Scruples Professional Salon Products, Inc.
DUAL AXIS TECHNOLOGY - Exercising equipment - Lumex, Inc.
DUAL BEAD - Clamps - Murray Corp.
DUAL C 600 - Vitamins and nutritional supplements - Nutra-Source Corp.
DUAL CEMENT - Dental compounds - Ivoclar North America, Inc.
DUAL CHANNEL - Pet products - Sandpoint Aquarium Products
DUAL COIL COMFORT - Furniture - Klaussner Corporate Services, Inc.
DUAL CONTROL - Apparel and accessories - Marshall Gobuty International USA, Inc.
DUAL CONTROL - Hair care products - Helene Curtis Industries Inc.
DUAL CONVERTER - Machinery - Neward Enterprises Inc.
DUAL CORE - Ammunition ☆ - Federal Cartridge Co.
DUAL CPU-COOL - Computer hardware - PC Power and Cooling, Inc.
DUAL CYCLE - Cosmetics - Revlon Consumer Products Corp.
DUAL-D - Cables - General Cable Corp.
DUAL-D SCREENED - Cables - General Cable Corp.
DUAL DAY - Watches - Bulova Corp.
DUAL DIFFERENTIAL DISCRETE TOPOLOGY - Amplifiers - Electro-Voice, Inc.
DUAL DOLPHIN - Recording label - Dual Dolphin Publishing Inc.
DUAL-DRI - Photographic equipment ☆ - Omega/Arkay
DUAL DUTY - Thread - Coats and Clark Inc.
DUAL DUTY II - Thread - Coats and Clark Inc.
DUAL DUTY PLUS - Thread - Coats and Clark Inc.
DUAL DUTY XTRA - Thread - Coats and Clark Inc.
DUAL DYNAMO - Toys - Tonka Corp.
DUAL FINISH - Cosmetics - Lancome
DUAL-FLAME - Cigarette lighters - Park Lane Associates, Inc.
DUAL FLAME - Lighters - Colibri Inc.
DUAL-FLEX - Bandages–orthopedic - Allegro Industries
DUAL-FLEX - Footwear - Quabaug Corp.
DUAL FOIL WET/DRY - Razors–electric - Remington Products Co.
DUAL FORCE - Golfing equipment - Odyssey Sports, Inc.
DUAL/FUEL - Fireplaces - Majestic Co.
DUAL FUEL - Lanterns–kerosene - Coleman Co., Inc.
DUAL GARD - Filters–oil - Amsoil, Inc.
DUAL/GATE - Automotive parts and accessories - Hurst Performance Inc.
DUAL GRIP - Cutlery - JMP-Newcor International, Inc.
DUAL GROUP - Computers - Dual Group, Inc.
DUAL GUARD - Hardware - Centryco Inc.
DUAL HOODLIFTERS - Motor vehicle parts and accessories - Target Motorsports
DUAL J-T-E-K - Thermometers - Cole-Parmer Instrument Co.
DUAL KICK SYSTEM - Golfing equipment - Mitsushiba International, Inc.
DUAL KLEEN - Vacuum cleaners and accessories–commercial - White Consolidated Industries, Inc.
DUAL-LOC - Binders - Steego Corp.
DUAL-LUCIFERASE - Research–business - Promega Corp.
DUAL MEET - Scoreboards - Daktronics Inc.
DUAL-MELT - Furnaces–industrial - Inductotherm Corp.
DUAL-MESH - Pet products - Penn-Plax, Inc.
DUAL MIX - Mortars–clay - Super-Tek Products Inc.
DUAL PAC - Luggage - Airway Industries, Inc.
DUAL PACK - Popcorn - Great Western Products Inc.
DUAL PD - Belts–rubber - Goodyear Tire & Rubber Co.
DUAL PERFORMANCE - Cosmetics - Janet Sartin, Inc.
DUAL PHASE - Pet products - Marine Environment/Aqua Craft
DUAL PILLOW - Pillows - Body Care Inc.
DUAL-POWER - Magnifying glasses - Uncle Milton Industries Inc.
DUAL PURPOSE - Easels ☆ - Winsor & Newton
DUAL PURPOSE - Stepladders - W.W. Babcock Co. Inc.
DUAL RANGE - Automotive repair shops–transmission - Subaru of America, Inc.
DUAL-RITER - Pens ☆ - Empire Berol USA
DUAL-RULE - Rulers–metal - Quality Circle Products
DUAL SAFETY - Lanterns–kerosene ☆ - Dorco Manufacturing Inc.
DUAL-SEALOR - Gaskets - Newcourt, Inc.
DUAL SHADE - Window shades - Mecho Shade Corp.
DUAL SHARP - Pens - Avery Dennison Corp.
DUAL SHIELD WEATHER BARRIER - Weather stripping ☆ - The Standard Products Co.

DUAL SHOWMAN - Amplifiers–musical instrument - Fender Musical Instruments

DUAL SHREET - Floor coverings–linoleum - Forbo Industries, Inc.

DUAL SIX - Guitars - Fender Musical Instruments

DUAL SOUND - Guitars - Dimarzio, Inc.

DUAL SURFACE - Cleaning preparations - Flo-Pac Corp.

DUAL-TAB - Bags - Bob De Matteis Co.

DUAL-TAB - Pharmaceutical preparations - Vista Laboratories Inc.

DUAL TABLE - Furniture - Ymt International, Inc.

DUAL-TAC - Building materials - Minnesota Mining & Manufacturing Co.

DUAL TEC - Electronic equipment - C & K Systems, Inc.

DUAL TILE - Floor coverings–linoleum - Forbo Industries, Inc.

DUAL TONES - Hair care products - Conair Corp.

DUAL TOUGH - Batteries - Globe-Union Inc.

DUAL TWISTER - Manicure preparations - Nail Gems by Cara

DUAL USE E.C. - Insecticides - Agrevo Environmental Health, Inc.

DUAL-VIEW - Office supplies ☆ - Barkley Filing Supplies

DUAL-WEB - Paper - Data Documents, Inc.

DUAL-WET - Ophthalmic goods ☆ - Alcon Laboratories, Inc.

DUALASTIC - Health care products - Bell-Horn

DUALDOT - Firearms, accessories, and parts - Emerging Technologies Inc.

DUALDRAW - Fans–exhaust - Sportsman Manufacturing Co.

DUALENS - Ophthalmic goods ☆ - Bausch & Lomb Inc.

DUALEVEL - Audio equipment - Dana Innovations

DUALFIT - Exercising equipment - Giant Bicycle, Inc.

DUALIFE - Hair care products ☆ - Scruples Professional Salon Products, Inc.

DUALIFT - Brassieres (Bras) ☆ - Lovable Co.

DUALINE - Hardware ☆ - Stanley Hardware Div.

DUALITE - Sign - Dualite Inc.

DUALL - Luggage - Airway Industries, Inc.

DUALLOCK - Car-security systems - Audiovox Corp.

DUALLY - Musical instrument accessories - Actodyne General, Inc.

DUALOAD - Tires ☆ - Bridgestone/Firestone, Inc.

DUALOBE - Connectors–electrical - Nanonics Corp.

DUALOGR - Thermometers - Cole-Parmer Instrument Co.

DUALOUVRE - Hardware - Leslie-Locke, Inc.

DUALPACK - Toys–electronic - MRC

DUALPATH - Computer hardware - Eigen Video

DUALPDA - Measuring instruments - Dantec Measurement Technology Inc.

DUALPLEX - Tires - Bridgestone/Firestone, Inc.

DUALSPUN - Apparel and accessories - Patagonia, Inc.

DUALSTAR RECORDS - Recording label - Dualstar Entertainment Group, Inc.

DUALSTAR VIDEO - Video production - Dualstar Entertainment Group, Inc.

DUALTABS - Vitamins and nutritional supplements - Twinlab

DUALTEC - Sporting goods - Rossignol Ski Co., Inc.

DUALTHANE - Adhesives and sealants - W.R. Meadows Inc.

DUALTHRUST - Air conditioning equipment ☆ - General Electric Co.

DUALTONE - Paper products - Wallace Computer Services, Inc.

DUANE EDDY - Guitars ☆ - Guild Music Corp.

DUART - Cosmetics ☆ - Duart Industries Ltd.

DUB-L-COP - Paints - Mobile Paint Manufacturing Co.

DUBA - Sporting goods - Bishop Freeman Co.

DUBAI - Floor coverings–carpet and rugs ☆ - Eurotex Inc.

DUBARRY - Skin care products ☆ - Carme Inc.

DUBARRY - Watches - Bulova Corp.

DUBARRY II - House furnishings ☆ - Lexington Furniture Industries, Inc.

DUBBL-DARK - Window shades ☆ - C-Mor Co.

DUBBLE BUBBLE - Chewing gum - Fleer Corp.

DUBBLE BUBBLE - Toys - Imperial Toy Corp.

DUBBLES - Apparel and accessories - Dubbles, Inc.

DUBBLEWEAR - Apparel and accessories - Hoffman Apparel International Corp.

DUBE - Toys - Brian Dube, Inc.

DUBEARY - Toys–stuffed ☆ - Gund, Inc.

DUBELU - Apparel and accessories - Circus Distribution, Inc.

DUBILETS - Troches - Concord Chemists

DUBL AIR - Cosmetics ☆ - Dubl Duck/Jet Set Inc.

DUBL-COVERAGE - Asphalt - GAF Corp.

DUBL DUCK - Cosmetics - Dubl Duck/Jet Set Inc.

DUBL-DUTY - Vacuum cleaners and accessories - The Hoover Co.

DUBL-FRESH - Packaging–paper - Bagcraft Corp. of America

DUBL-FRONT - File folders ☆ - ACCO USA, Inc.

DUBL-GARD - Enamels - Perry & Derrick Co.

DUBL-GRIP - Envelopes - Westvaco Corp.

DUBL HANDI - Washboards - Columbus Washboard Co.

DUBL-HANDLE - Bags–paper - Bagcraft Corp. of America

DUBL-LIFE - Enamels - Perry & Derrick Co.

DUBL-NATURE - Towels - Mosinee Paper Corp.

DUBL-STIK - Tape–adhesive - Compac Corp. (Pressure Sensitives Div.)

DUB'L-TUF - Plastics film ☆ - Monsanto Co.

DUBL-VUE - Envelopes - Westvaco Corp.

DUBL-WAX - Bags–paper - Bagcraft Corp. of America

DUBLBOND - Padding–foam - Foamex LP

DUBLIN - Fans–electric - Nutone Inc.

DUBLIN - Floor coverings–carpet and rugs ☆ - Atlas Carpet Mills Inc.

DUBLIN - Furniture - Singer Furniture Co.

DUBLIN - Thread - Cincinnati Thread Co.

DUBLIN TILE - Floor coverings - Congoleum Corp.

DUBLLOCK - Binders - ACCO USA, Inc.

DUBLOCK - Office supplies - ACCO USA, Inc.

DUBOIS - Floor coverings–carpet and rugs - Bloomsburg Carpet Industries

DUBOIS - Tables–wood - Mersman Furniture Co.

DUBON - Food products - Bush Brothers and Co.

DUBONNET - Furniture ☆ - Stanley Furniture Co. Inc.

DUBONNET - Wines - Schenley Industries Inc.

DUBOSC - Wines ☆ - IDV Wines (Beaulieu Vineyard)

DUBREQ - Electronic organs ☆ - Audio Arts Records

DUBUQUE - Meat products–beef - Dubuque Foods, Inc.

DUBUQUE SUPREME - Food containers - Dubuque Foods, Inc.

DUC DE BOURGOGONE - Tiles–ceramic - La France

DUC DE VERVINS - Colognes - Houbigant, Inc.

DUC D'O - Confections - Morris National Inc.

DUCADOS - Cigarettes - G.A. Georgopulo & Co. Inc.

DUCADOS INTERNATIONAL - Cigarettes - G.A. Georgopulo & Co. Inc.

DUCARE - Photographic equipment - E.I. Dupont de Nemours and Co.

DUCATI - Motorcycles - Cagiva of North America

DUCATTI - Coats–men's - Gallron

DUCCO - Plumbing fixtures–plastic - Ductilic Inc.

DUCHENE - Wines - Fred Bofird Co.

DUCHESS - Aircraft–airplanes ☆ - Beech Aircraft Corp.

DUCHESS - Bakery products - Alfred Nickles Bakery Inc.

DUCHESS - Bathroom fixtures ☆ - Crane Plumbing/Fiat Products

DUCHESS - Boats–motor ☆ - Regal Marine Industries Inc.

DUCHESS - Brushes–hair - Phillips Brush Corp.

DUCHESS - Carpet matting ☆ - American Floor Products Co. Inc.

DUCHESS - Cotton batting - National Patent Medical

DUCHESS - Doors–metal ☆ - Remington Building Products

DUCHESS - Fireplaces ☆ - Malm Fireplaces Inc.

DUCHESS - Floor coverings–carpet and rugs - Mohawk Industries Inc.

DUCHESS - Flour–blended ☆ - Stevens Industries Inc.

DUCHESS - Food products - Super Valu Inc.

DUCHESS - Furniture–upholstered - Imperial of Morristown Inc.

DUCHESS - Giftware - Ebeling and Reuss Co.

DUCHESS - Giftware - Norcrest China Co.

DUCHESS - Hair care products - Helene Curtis Industries Inc.

DUCHESS - Hair care products ☆ - Dubl Duck/Jet Set Inc.

DUCHESS - Hobby kits ☆ - Gibbs Manufacturing Co.

DUCHESS - Mops - Piedmont Mop Co.

DUCHESS - Nail care products - Nailtex Inc.

DUCHESS - Opera glasses - Swift Instruments, Inc.

DUCHESS - Watches - Bulova Corp.

DUCHESS III - Yarn ☆ - Henry's Attic

DUCHESS CUT - Jewelry - Suberi Brothers, Inc.

DUCHESS DIRE - Toys - Tonka Corp.

DUCHESS GEAR - Strollers–baby ☆ - Welsh Co.

DUCHESS OF MARLBORO COLLECTION - Furniture ☆ - Hooker Furniture Corp.

DUCHESS OF WINDSOR FASHIONS, THE - Apparel and accessories - Duchess of Windsor Inc.

DUCHESS OF WINDSOR JEWELRY, THE - Jewelry–costume - Duchess of Windsor Inc.

DUCHESS RETREAT - Pet furniture - Lydia Evans

DUCHESS, THE - Fans–electric - Davoil, Inc.

DUCHESSE - Rings–jewelry - Artcarved Inc.

DUCHY - Biscuits - De Medici Imports Ltd.

DUCK - Boats–motor - Carstens Industries Inc.

DUCK - Dinnerware - Corning Inc.

DUCK - Stationery ☆ - Mead Corp.

DUCK - Tape–adhesive - Manco, Inc.

DUCK BALL - Balls–rubber - Llumar Star Kites Inc.

DUCK BLUES - Dinnerware–glass ☆ - Metlox Pottery Shoppe

DUCK BOAT - Boats - Glen-L Marine Designs

☆ = Now out of production

DUCK CROSSING - Apparel and accessories - Avenues Inc.
DUCK D, THE - Recreational vehicle dealers - Thor Tech, Inc.
DUCK DUCK GOOSE - Dolls ☆ - Effanbee Doll Corp.
DUCK FEET - Sporting goods - Voit Corp.
DUCK GLOVES - Gloves ☆ - William Bay Trading Co.
DUCK HARBOR - Apparel stores–sports - Names Sportswear Inc.
DUCK HARBOR - Apparel–children's - Kids R Us Co.
DUCK HEAD - Apparel–children's - Liberty Childrenswear Co., LLC
DUCK HEAD - Food products - Umatilla Citrus Growers Association
DUCK HEAD - Shoes - Duck Head Apparel Co., Inc.
DUCK HEAD EXPEDITION 1865 - Footwear - Alchem Capital Corp.
DUCK HUNTER - Fabrics - Graniteville Co.
DUCK L'ORANGE - Kites ☆ - Hi-Flier Manufacturing Co.
DUCK-O-METER - Thermometers - Aquacide
DUCK OIL - Suntan lotions ☆ - Jason Natural Products, Inc.
DUCK PIN - Decals and transfers - Decorator and Craft Corp.
DUCK POND - Apparel–men's ☆ - J.C. Penney Co., Inc.
DUCK POND - Wallpaper - Taylor Wallcoverings Inc.
DUCK POND - Wine - Stone Cellars
DUCK POND CELLARS - Wines - D. & J.F. Cellars, Inc.
DUCK POND CELLARS - Wines - HDT Importers Inc.
DUCK PUDDLE FARM - Mustard - Wagner Gourmet Foods, Inc.
DUCK SASS/FOWL ATTITUDE CLUB - Glassware–household - Joe A. Taylor
DUCK SHOOT - Toys - Brumberger Co. Inc.
DUCK T - Trailers–travel ☆ - Jayco Inc.
DUCK TAIL - T-shirts–men's - Duck Head Apparel Co., Inc.
DUCK TALES - Games - Milton Bradley Co.
DUCK THE WEATHER - Umbrellas - Tony Marterie & Associates
DUCK TUCKS - Apparel and accessories - Alchem Capital Corp.
DUCK WEAR - Tool belts - Portable Products, Inc.
DUCKBACK - Labels - Epsen Hillmer Graphics Co.
DUCKBILL - Anchors - Foresight Products Inc.
DUCKBILL - Visors - Tom Hemmer
DUCKBUCKERS - Musical instrument accessories - Seymour Duncan Pickups
DUCKHEAD - Apparel and accessories - Duck Head Apparel Co., Inc.
DUCKHEAD - Apparel–athletic - Cooper Sportswear Manufacturing Co., Inc.
DUCKHEAD FOR HER - Apparel–women's - Wilkins Industries Inc.
DUCKHORN VINEYARDS - Wines - Duckhorn Vineyards
DUCKIES - Apparel and accessories - Brazabra Corp.
DUCKLING - Surgical instruments - Acufex Microsurgical, Inc.
DUCKLING - Trailers–travel ☆ - Mallard Coach
DUCKMAN - Apparel and accessories - Paramount Pictures Corp.
DUCKOTA - Bags - Hair by Stewarts, Inc.
DUCKS AHOY! - Computer software - CBS Software
DUCKS & BUNNIES - Giftware - Diener Industries Inc.
DUCK'S BACK - Waterproofing compounds - Masterchem Industries, Inc.
DUCKS-BAK - Waterproofing compounds - Briner Paint Manufacturing Co. Inc.
DUCKS/DRAKES - Glassware–household ☆ - Lotus Glass Co.
DUCKS ON THE POND - Apparel and accessories ☆ - Dee-Yah, Inc.
DUCKS, THE - Apparel and accessories - Walt Disney Co.
DUCKS UNLIMITED - Apparel and accessories - Ducks Unlimited, Inc.
DUCKS UNLIMITED - Furniture - Hammary Furniture Co. Inc.
DUCKS UNLIMITED - Knives–pocket - W.R. Case & Sons Cutlery Co.
DUCKSTER - Office supplies - Plastic Fabricators Inc.
DUCKSTER - Waterproof outerwear ☆ - Arnold Palmer Golf Co.
DUCKWALL - Food products - Duckwall-Pooley Fruit Co.
DUCKWALL-POOLEY - Food products - Duckwall-Pooley Fruit Co.
DUCKWEAR BY MISTY HARBOR - Coats–women's - United Merchants and Manufacturers Inc.
DUCKY - Chairs–metal ☆ - Century Products Co.
DUCKY - Infant product ☆ - Sanitoy Inc.
DUCKY BRAND - Rice - V. W. Trading Corp.
DUCKY DELIGHT - Dinnerware–plastic - Design Imports Ltd.
DUCKY DRYS - Diapers–disposable - Weyerhaeuser Co.
DUCKY FLOAT - Sporting goods - Ziffco
DUCKY TREATER - Sporting goods - Ziffco
DUCKYS - Diapers–disposable - Weyerhaeuser Co.
DUCO - Adhesive cement - Devcon Consumer Products (ITW Devcon)
DUCO STIK-TAK - Adhesive - Devcon Consumer Products (ITW Devcon)
DUCOA - Mold inhibitors for food production - Ducoa
DUCON - Antacids - Smithkline Beecham Corp.
DUCROS - Mustard ☆ - Lifetone International Inc.
DUCT-BLOWER - Fans–electric - A.J. Carlow Inc.
DUCT BOOSTER - Air conditioning equipment - Tjernlund Products Inc.
DUCT GRIP - Ventilation equipment ☆ - Snappy A.D.P.
DUCT TAPE - Tape–adhesive - Black Swan Manufacturing Co.

DUCT-VISION - Optical machinery - Shamrock Heating and Air Conditioning
DUCT-WHIP - Cleaning equipment - Power Vacuum Trailers, Inc.
DUCT WHIP - Cleaning equipment - PVT Systems Inc.
DUCTSOX - Ventilation equipment - Rite-Hite Corp.
DUCTWORKS - Ducts–metal - Ductworks, Inc.
DUD SPORTSWEAR - Apparel and accessories - Michael N. Utterback
DUDA - Food products ☆ - A. Duda & Sons, Inc.
DUDA MAN - Apparel and accessories - George K. Setka
DUDE - Dolls - Mattel, Inc.
DUDE SHAPERS - Apparel stores–lingerie ☆ - Formfit Rogers
DUDEK - Food products - Dudek Deli Foods Inc.
DUDEK - Soups–mixes - Dudek Foods, Inc.
DUDENHOEFER - Wines - Lost Hills Winery
DUDETTE - Sportswear - Dude Sportswear Inc.
DUDLEY - Apparel and accessories ☆ - Palm Beach Co., Inc.
DUDLEY - Sporting goods - Dudley Sports Co.
DUDLEY - Toys–stuffed - Spearhead Industries Inc.
DUDLEY ACTION RIDER - Wagons–children's ☆ - Little Tikes Co.
DUDLEY DOG - Toys–stuffed - Russ Berrie and Co., Inc.
DUDLEY FARMS - Vegetables–canned - Nature's Pride Inc.
DUDLEY PRODUCTS - Hair care products - Dudley Products Inc.
DUDLEY THE DINOSAUR - Book series - Warner Press, Inc.
DUDLEY THE DRAGON - Lunch boxes - Thermos Co.
DUDLEY THE DRAGON - Shoes ☆ - S. Goldberg and Co. Inc.
DUDLEY'S - Dyes–food - Spearhead Industries Inc.
DUDS - Blouses–women's ☆ - Kaufman Knitting Co. Inc.
DUDSBERRY - Games - Janelle Publications Inc.
DUE CARE/DISCOVERY SYSTEM, THE - Computer software - Hemisphere Group Inc.
DUE FRATI - Vinegar - Dean & Deluca Inc.
DUE PER DUE - Apparel and accessories - Equals 4 Inc.
DUECO - Construction equipment - Utility Equipment Co., Inc.
DUEIT - Printers–computer - Brodart Co.
DUEL - Amplifiers - Peavey Electronics Corp.
DUEL SYSTEMS - Electrical equipment - Methode Electronics, Inc.
DUEL, THE - Games ☆ - Avalon Hill Game Co.
DUELER - Tires - Bridgestone/Firestone, Inc.
DUELIN' DRAGSTERS - Toys–automobiles - Matchbox Toys USA
DUELIN' DUDES - Toys - Azrak-Hamway International, Inc.
DUELL - Games ☆ - Lakeside Games
DUELTRACK - Games - Steve Jackson Games Inc.
DUENDE - Apparel and accessories - Anthony G. McIntosh
DUERR'S ENGLISH TRADITIONAL - Food products - British Wholesale Imports
DUESANG - Apparel and accessories - Kwang Soo Kang
DUESENBERG - Floor coverings - American Floor Products Co. Inc.
DUET - Apparel–women's - Duet Creations Inc.
DUET - Bicycles - Ross Bicycles USA, Ltd.
DUET - Candy - Ethel M. Chocolates, Inc.
DUET - Electrical equipment - Nady Systems Inc.
DUET - Faucets - U.S. Brass Corp.
DUET - Floor coverings - Mannington Resilient Floors
DUET - Floor coverings ☆ - Tarkett, Inc.
DUET - Flowers, plants, and seeds - Jonathan Green, Inc.
DUET - Food products ☆ - Liberty Richter Inc.
DUET - Glassware–household - Oneida Ltd.
DUET - Office supplies - Master Caster Co.
DUET - Pet products - Lambert-Kay
DUET - Respirators - Respironics, Inc.
DUET - Rings–jewelry - Artcarved Inc.
DUET - Yarn ☆ - William Unger & Co. Inc.
DUET PRINTS - Posters ☆ - Blue Mountain Arts Inc.
DUET SET - Hair curlers ☆ - Sunbeam-Oster Household Products
DUET V - Bathtubs–enameled - Pearl Baths Inc.
DUET VI - Bathtubs–enameled - Pearl Baths Inc.
DUETS - Candy - American Licorice Co.
DUETS - Paper–gift wrap ☆ - Stephen Lawrence Co.
DUETT - Floor coverings–carpet and rugs ☆ - Mannington Carpets, Inc.
DUETT - Giftware ☆ - Sangray Corp.
DUETT - Pet products - Vitakraft Pet Products Co., Inc.
DUETTE - Cosmetics - Pfizer Inc.
DUETTE - Photographic flash unit ☆ - Saul Bower Inc.
DUETTE - Toys - Peg Perego USA Inc.
DUETTE - Wallpaper ☆ - Pantasote Inc. (Wallcovering Div.)
DUETTE - Window coverings - Hunter Douglas, Inc.
DUETTE - Window coverings - Hunter Douglas Intermountain Fabrication Co.

☆ = Now out of production

DUETTE CLASSIC - Blinds–venetian - Hunter Douglas, Inc.
DUETTE DESIGNS III - Wallpaper - Pantasote Inc. (Wallcovering Div.)
DUETTE DOUBLE HONEYCOMB - Window coverings - Hunter Douglas, Inc.
DUETTE ECLIPSE - Window coverings - Hunter Douglas, Inc.
DUETTE ELITE - Window coverings - Hunter Douglas, Inc.
DUETTE EXPRESSIONS - Window coverings - Hunter Douglas, Inc.
DUETTE PHENOMENA - Window coverings - Hunter Douglas, Inc.
DUETTE SHEER - Window coverings - Hunter Douglas, Inc.
DUETTE SMART SHADE - Window shades - Comfortex Corp.
DUETTE SPLENDOR - Window coverings - Hunter Douglas, Inc.
DUETTO - Bicycles - Ross Bicycles USA, Ltd.
DUETTO - Filters–water - Aquarium Systems, Inc.
DUEX - Photographic equipment - Eastman Kodak Co.
DUF-COTE - Paint removers - Duffy Products Co.
DUF-OYL - Paint removers - Duffy Products Co.
DUFCO - Wheelchairs - Quickie Designs Inc.
DUFF STUFF - Greeting cards - Recycled Paper Products, Inc.
DUFFEL DOGGIE - Toys–stuffed - Russ Berrie and Co., Inc.
DUFFER - Apparel and accessories - Walden Rhodes, Inc.
DUFFER - Apparel–women's - David Smith
DUFFERS - Toys–stuffed - DCN Industries Inc.
DUFFER'S DEMISE - Games - Golf Gifts, Inc.
DUFFLE COOL - Infant product - J.L. Childress Co.
DUFFS - Apparel and accessories - Chase Co., Inc.
DUFF'S - Food products - Gilster-Mary Lee Corp.
DUFFTOWN - Beverages–malt - European Beverage Co., Inc.
DUFFTOWN-GLENLIVET - Beverages–malt - European Beverage Co., Inc.
DUFFY DOG - Health care products - Apothecary Products, Inc.
DUFFY-MOTT - Food products - Mott's Inc.
DUFFY NOTES - Greeting cards ☆ - Kersten Bros. Studios
DUFFY'S - Beverages–carbonated - Duffy's Draft Beverage
DUFFY'S - Cleaning preparations ☆ - Klean-Strip
DUFFY'S - Food products - Milnot Co.
DUFFY'S DRAUGHT - Beverages–malt ☆ - Labatt Importers Inc.
DUFLEX - Identification tags - Fearing Manufacturing Co. Inc.
DUFONTE - Watches - Lucien Piccard/Arnex
DUFOUR: BRISTOL HALL - Wallpaper - Sterling Prints
DUFRAIS - Vinegar - Nestle USA
DUGGAL - Shoes - D & D Enterprises
DUGGAN'S - Burial caskets - Duggan's Funeral Service
DUGOUT SMOKING SYSTEM - Pharmaceutical preparations - Music City Marketing, Inc.
DUICE - Recording label - Isbell Records, Inc.
DUIT - Paints - Key Products Inc.
DUJARDIN VSOP - Beverages–alcohol - Carradale Import Co.
DUK-IT - Cigarettes - McDonald Products
DUKANE - Audio equipment - Dukane Corp.
DUKE - Aircraft–airplanes ☆ - Beech Aircraft Corp.
DUKE - Animal feeds - Bush Brothers and Co.
DUKE - Balls–football - Wilson Sporting Goods Co.
DUKE - Boats - MCP Co.
DUKE - Brushes - Corona Brushes Inc.
DUKE - Cigars ☆ - Phillies Cigar Co.
DUKE - Drums–musical instruments - Lo Duca Bros. Musical Instruments Inc.
DUKE - Floor coverings–carpet and rugs - Mohawk Industries Inc.
DUKE - Flowers, plants, and seeds - Jonathan Green, Inc.
DUKE - Footwear - Distributors Service Corp.
DUKE - Gasoline - Englefield Oil Co.
DUKE - Handles–wood - Fleischmann Handle Co.
DUKE - Health care products - Supreme Beauty Products Co.
DUKE - Hosiery - Kayser-Roth Corp.
DUKE - Pipes–tobacco - Dr. Grabow Pre-Smoked Pipes Inc.
DUKE - Plastic pocket stamps - Consolidated Stamp Manufacturing Co. Inc.
DUKE - Plastics ☆ - Rubens Originals
DUKE - Record books, slip cases, etc. - American Superior
DUKE - Recording label - MCA Universal Studios
DUKE - Sports rackets and accessories ☆ - Victor Sports
DUKE - T-shirts–men's - Royal Textile Mills Inc.
DUKE - Thread - Threads USA Div.
DUKE - Toys - Hasbro, Inc.
DUKE - Toys–stuffed ☆ - Kenner Products
DUKE BOYD - Apparel and accessories - Francis L. Boyd III
DUKE DELUXE - Wigs ☆ - Jean Paree Weegs Inc.
DUKE FOR MEN - Connectors–electrical - Kiehl's Since 1851, Inc.
DUKE GERMAN SHEPHERD - Toys–stuffed - Dakin Inc.
DUKE KAHANAMOUKU - Bathing suits - Catalina

DUKE L'ORANGE - Toys - Mattel, Inc.
DUKE NUKEM - Toys - TBS Productions, Inc.
DUKE OF DEVON - Cigars - General Cigar Co., Inc.
DUKE OF GLOUCESTER - Floor coverings–carpet and rugs ☆ - Bloomsburg Carpet Industries
DUKE OF MODENA - Vinegar ☆ - Europa Foods Ltd.
DUKE OF WELLINGTON - Cigars - General Cigar Co., Inc.
DUKE-OF-WHIRL - Toys - Duke-of-Whirl
DUKE OF YORK - Cigars - Casa Blanca Cigar Co. Inc.
DUKE WILLABY - Toys–stuffed - Dakin Inc.
DUKE'EM - Recording label ☆ - Westwood Entertainment Group
DUKES - Cigars - Faber, Coe & Gregg Inc.
DUKE'S - Ice cream - Danken's Gourmet Ice Creams
DUKES - Valves - Danfoss, Inc. (Danfoss Fluid Power)
DUKE'S - Vegetable sauces - C.F. Sauer Co.
DUKE'S 2-TONED DOG SHOES - Pet products - Duke's Dog Fashions
DUKE'S BACK TO BASICS - Pet products ☆ - Duke's Dog Fashions
DUKE'S DESCENT, THE - Games - Decipher Inc.
DUKES OF DIXIELAND - Apparel and accessories - GCI Inc. (Great Chefs Television/Publishing Div.)
DUKES OF HAZZARD - Toys–automobiles ☆ - ERTL Co., Inc.
DUKES OF HAZZARD, THE - Apparel and accessories - Time Warner Entertainment Co., L.P.
DUKE'S TOTALLY AWESOME CAT FASHIONS - Pet products - Duke's Dog Fashions
DUKE'S TROPICALS - Pet products - Duke's Dog Fashions
DUKE'S ULTIMATE DOG WARMER - Pet products - Duke's Dog Fashions
DUKI KAHANAMOUKU - Bathing suits - Authentic Fitness Corp.
DUKKI - Health care products ☆ - Pin Dot Products
DUKOFF - Musical instrument accessories - Bobby Dukoff Mouthpieces
DUL-GLO - Paints ☆ - C.A. Nash & Son Inc.
DULAC - Shrimp–canned or cured - Buquet Canning Co.
DULAMEL - Enamels - Benjamin Moore & Co.
DULANY - Food products - Dulany Foods Inc.
DULCAGEN - Laxatives - Goldline Laboratories, Inc.
DULCET - Hearing aids - Beltone Electronics Corp.
DULCET - Paper–writing - Monadnock Paper Mills Inc.
DULCET LINES - Floor coverings–carpet and rugs - Capel, Inc.
DULCIA - Hair care products - Cosmair Inc.
DULCIE - Watches - Bulova Corp.
DULCIMER SHOPPE - Musical instrument accessories - McSpadden Musical Instruments
DULCITAR - Musical instruments - Ledfords Musical Instruments
DULCITO - Vegetables–canned - Trappey's Fine Foods Inc.
DULCITOL - Pharmaceutical preparations ☆ - City Chemical Corp.
DULCOLAX - Pharmaceutical preparations - Boehringer Ingelheim Pharmaceuticals Inc.
DULCONITE - Paints - Remien & Kuhnert Co.
DULCRAFT - Varnishes - Perry & Derrick Co.
DULGLOS - Paints ☆ - Dean and Barry Co.
DULL C POWDER - Vitamins and nutritional supplements - Freeda Vitamins Inc.
DULL GLO - Varnish removers - M.A. Bruder & Sons Inc.
DULL-KOTE - Paints - Conco Paint Co.
DULL LUSTRE - Paints - M.A.B. Paints
DULL 'N BOND - Hardware - Allpro Corp.
DULL SPRAY - Photographic equipment - Century Labs Inc.
DULLCOTE - Enamels - The White Co.
DULSE - Noodles - San Francisco Herb & Natural Food Co.
DULSEAL - Adhesives and sealants - Keuffel & Esser Co.
DULTINE - Paints ☆ - Blatz Paint Co. Inc.
DULTONE - Paints - Perry & Derrick Co.
DULTONE - Paints ☆ - Foy-Johnston Inc.
DULUTH - Enamels - American Paints
DULUTH ESKIMOS - Apparel and accessories - National Football League Properties, Inc.
DULUX - Paints - Glidden Co.
DULUX NATURAL WHITES - Paints - E.I. Dupont de Nemours and Co.
DULVAR - Varnishes ☆ - Valspar Corp.
DULZIT - Paint removers - Masury Paint Co.
DUM DUM - Candy - Spangler Candy Co.
DUMAIN - Musical instruments ☆ - Grossman Music Corp.
DUMAR - Clocks ☆ - General Time Corp. (Westclox/Seth Thomas Div.)
DUMAS - Toys - Dumas Products Inc.
DUMAURIER - Optical machinery - Dumaurier Co.
DUMB - Recording label - Jazz Composer's Orchestra Association Inc.

☆ = Now out of production

DUMB AND DUMBER - Trading cards and stamps - New Line Productions, Inc.

DUMB CLOTHING CO., THE - Apparel and accessories - Dumb Clothing and Design Co., Inc.

DUMB DABS - Chewing gum ☆ - Fleer Corp.

DUMBARTON - Beverages–malt - European Beverage Co., Inc.

DUMBBELLS HEALTH AND FITNESS A BODIES BEST FRIEND - Apparel–athletic - Dumbbells Health and Fitness Club, Inc.

DUMBO PIN-UPS - Posters ☆ - Dolly, Inc.

DUMBO POPS - Candy ☆ - American Candy Co.

DUMBO PRINTS - Paper–gift wrap ☆ - Stephen Lawrence Co.

DUMO LABS - Vitamins and nutritional supplements ☆ - Phoenix Laboratories, Inc.

DUMONT - Apparel–men's ☆ - After Six Inc.

DUMONT - Health care products - Lean & Jones Inc.

DUMONT - Watches - Phoenix Co. Inc.

DUMONT - Wines ☆ - Renault Winery

DUMOWY OGOREK - Pickles - Heifetz Pickling Co.

DUMP RATS - Apparel and accessories - David G. Roach

DUMP, THE - Computer software ☆ - Dr. T's Music Software Inc.

DUMP THE CHUMP - Novelty items - Unlimited Ltd. Inc.

DUMP TRUCK - Toys - Steven Manufacturing Co.

DUMPA - Audio equipment ☆ - Kevek Speaker Technology

DUMPIN' DIGGER - Toys–automobiles - SLM Inc.

DUMPLING - Toys–stuffed - Eden LLC

DUMPLING - Toys–stuffed - Gund, Inc.

DUMPLING & CO. - T-shirts, intimate apparel, sweaters, etc. - Advanced Trading Co., Inc.

DUMPLING DUCK - Toys–stuffed - Dakin Inc.

DUMPLING THE DINOSAUR & CO. - Apparel - Advanced Trading Co., Inc.

DUMPLINGS - Toys–stuffed - DCN Industries Inc.

DUMPLINGS - Toys–stuffed ☆ - Mighty Star Inc. (Special Effects Div.)

DUMPSTAT - Computer software - Robert D. Gibbons, Ltd.

DUMPSTER DOCTOR - Cleaning preparations - Puritan-Churchill Chemical Co.

DUN A JAY - Apparel–men's - Sar-Dun Knitwear

DUN-AGED - Musical instrument accessories - Seymour Duncan Pickups

DUN-BRITE - Enamels ☆ - Kelly-Moore Paint Co. Inc.

DUN DEAL - Apparel and accessories - R. Cousins Ltd.

DUN-EZY - Enamels ☆ - Kelly-Moore Paint Co. Inc.

DUN-FAST - Paints ☆ - Kelly-Moore Paint Co. Inc.

DUN-LAC - Floor finish ☆ - Cook and Dunn Paint Corp.

DUN-PRIDE - Paints ☆ - Kelly-Moore Paint Co. Inc.

DUN-PRIME - Paints ☆ - Kelly-Moore Paint Co. Inc.

DUN-PRO - Paints ☆ - Kelly-Moore Paint Co. Inc.

DUN SON - Apparel–men's - Sar-Dun Knitwear

DUN-SYN - Paints ☆ - Kelly-Moore Paint Co. Inc.

DUN-TEC - Enamels ☆ - Kelly-Moore Paint Co. Inc.

DUN-TONE - Paints ☆ - Kelly-Moore Paint Co. Inc.

DUN-VAR - Varnishes ☆ - Kelly-Moore Paint Co. Inc.

DUNA - Wines - Monsieur Henri Wines Ltd.

DUNAMEL - Enamels ☆ - Kelly-Moore Paint Co. Inc.

DUNAMIS - Computer software - Dunamis Inc.

DUNAVAR - Wines - Victoire Imports Co.

DUNBAR - Furniture - Dunbar Furniture

DUNBAR - Seafood products–canned or cured - Southern Shell Fish Co.

DUNBAR BOOT - Boots - Dunbar Boot Co.

DUNBAR LTD. - Footwear - H. Gordon Shoe Corp.

DUNBARS - Food products - Moody Dunbar Inc.

DUNBARS - Food products - Garlic Festival Foods

DUNBARTON MANOR - Floor coverings ☆ - Tarkett, Inc.

DUNBERRY'S FINES - Biscuits, scones, and english muffins - Interstate Brands Corp.

DUNBERRY'S FINEST - Baked foods - Interstate Brands Corp.

DUNBROOKE DISTINCTIVE IMAGES - Apparel and accessories - American Marketing Industries Inc.

DUNCAN - Automotive parts and accessories - Automatic Equipment Manufacturing Co.

DUNCAN - Musical instrument accessories - Seymour Duncan Pickups

DUNCAN - Pottery products - Duncan Enterprises

DUNCAN - Toys - Duncan Toys Co.

DUNCAN - Toys - Flambeau Products Corp.

DUNCAN - Watches - Bulova Corp.

DUNCAN & DUGAN - Apparel–men's - Pier Connection, Inc.

DUNCAN COMPLIMENTS - Paints–artists' - Duncan Enterprises

DUNCAN CUSTOM - Musical instrument accessories - Seymour Duncan Pickups

DUNCAN DECORATOR ACRYLICS - Pottery products - Duncan Enterprises

DUNCAN DESIGNED - Musical instrument accessories - Seymour Duncan Pickups

DUNCAN DISTORTION - Musical instrument accessories - Seymour Duncan Pickups

DUNCAN DRAGON - Toys–stuffed - Dakin Inc.

DUNCAN FORBES - Leather goods - Enger-Kress Co.

DUNCAN GLITTER WRITERS - Craft supplies - Duncan Enterprises

DUNCAN GRANITE STONE - Paints - Duncan Enterprises

DUNCAN HINES - Bakery products - Procter & Gamble Co.

DUNCAN HINES - Steel - Regal Ware, Inc.

DUNCAN HINES ANGEL CUPS - Food products - Procter & Gamble Co.

DUNCAN HINES BAKERY STYLE - Bakery products - Procter & Gamble Co.

DUNCAN HINES CHOCOLATE LOVERS' EXXTRA - Bakery products - Hines-Park Foods Inc.

DUNCAN HINES DELIGHTS - Bakery products - Procter & Gamble Co.

DUNCAN HINES KIDS CUPS - Bakery products - Procter & Gamble Co.

DUNCAN MCINTOSH - Greeting cards - Brick Mill Studios

DUNCAN PEAK VINEYARDS - Wines - Duncan Peak Vineyards

DUNCAN PHYFE - Varnishes - Valspar Corp.

DUNCAN ROYALE - Figurines - Duncan Royale Avenue

DUNCANS - Beverages–alcohol - Star Liquor Imports Inc.

DUNCANS CUPS - Baking cups - Procter & Gamble Co.

DUNCEY - Recording label - Sun-Ray & Sky-Vue Records

DUNCRAFT BIRD FEEDERS - Pet products - Duncraft, Inc.

DUNDEE - Beverages–malt - Genesee Brewing Co., Inc.

DUNDEE - Cigars - General Cigar Co., Inc.

DUNDEE - Floor coverings–carpet and rugs ☆ - Royalweve Carpet Mills

DUNDEE - Towels - Dundee Mills, Inc.

DUNDEE - Wallpaper - Koroseal Wallcoverings

DUNDEE - Watches - Dundee Watch Co.

DUNDEE BARIGARD - Health care products - Dundee Mills, Inc.

DUNDEER - Footwear–men's - L.B. Evans' Son Co.

DUNE - Chewing gum ☆ - Fleer Corp.

DUNE - Deodorants–personal - Gillette Co.

DUNE - Games ☆ - Avalon Hill Game Co.

DUNE - Games ☆ - Parker Brothers

DUNE - Perfumes - Christian Dior Perfumes Corp.

DUNE - Perfumes - Parfums Christian Dior U.S. Corp.

DUNE BUSTER - Toys - Fisher-Price, Inc.

DUNE DIGGER M/T - Tires - Jetzon/Telstar Tire

DUNE RAT - Toys–automobiles - Mattel, Inc.

DUNE RIDER - Bicycles - Ross Bicycles USA, Ltd.

DUNE ROAD - Apparel–children's - Montgomery Ward & Co. Inc.

DUNE SCOOT - Toys ☆ - Steven Manufacturing Co.

DUNE SLIDER - Tires–airplane - Greenball Corp.

DUNE SPOONS - Toys - Emsco Inc.

DUNE TRACKER - Tires–airplane - Greenball Corp.

DUNE TRIKESTER - Toys - Empire of Carolina Inc.

DUNEBUGGY - Recording label - Jon-Michael Procopio

DUNES - Fabrics - Greenwood Mills Inc.

DUNES - Fabrics - Vertilux-Louverlux Inc.

DUNES - Floor coverings–carpet and rugs ☆ - Interloom Ltd.

DUNES - Shoes ☆ - Endicott Johnson Corp.

DUNES PHOTOS - Framing supplies - Anthony J. Yadouga

DUNES WEST - Real estate agencies - Georgia-Pacific Corp.

DUNES WEST & DESIGN - Real estate agencies - Georgia-Pacific Corp.

DUNESMERE - Floor coverings–carpet and rugs - Kelly Group Inc.

DUNGENESS - Wines - Olympic Cellars

DUNGEON! - Games - Tsr, Inc.

DUNGEON BLAST - Fireworks - American Promotional Events, Inc.

DUNGEON DOOM TYPING GAME - Computer software - Gamco Industries Inc.

DUNGEON MASTER - Board game - Tsr, Inc.

DUNGEON MASTER - Computer software - FTL Games

DUNGEON MASTER - Toys–guns - Imperial Toy Corp.

DUNGEON MASTER DECKS - Games - Tsr, Inc.

DUNGEON OF PERIL - Computer software - Orange Cherry Software

DUNGEONBUILDER - Computer software - BMS, Inc.

DUNGEONS & DRAGONS - Candy ☆ - Amurol Confections Co.

DUNGEONS & DRAGONS - Games - Tsr, Inc.

DUNGEONS & DRAGONS - Puzzles - Tyco Toys

DUNGLO - Enamels ☆ - Kelly-Moore Paint Co. Inc.

DUNHAM BROTHERS COLLECTION, THE - Footwear - Dunham Boot Makers

DUNHAM-BUSH - Air conditioning equipment - Dunham Bush, Inc.

DUNHAM CASTLE - Beverages–malt - Old European Brewery Co.

☆ = Now out of production

DUNHAM DOUBLE COVERAGE TOES - Footwear - Falcon Shoe Manufacturing Co.
DUNHAM DURAFLEX - Footwear - Dunham Boot Makers
DUNHAM RAINBOWS - Footwear - Dunham Boot Makers
DUNHAM TYROLEANS - Footwear - Dunham Boot Makers
DUNHARROW - Floor coverings–carpet and rugs - Masland Corp.
DUNHEATH - Beverages–alcohol - Kasser Laird Distilling Co.
DUNHILL - Beverages–alcohol ☆ - Laird and Co.
DUNHILL - Jewelry - Jacoby-Bender Inc.
DUNHILL - Recording label - MCA Universal Studios
DUNHILL - Steel springs–railroad - Needlecraft Industries
DUNHILL - Sunglasses ☆ - Carrera Eyewear Corp.
DUNHILL - Tobacco–chewing or smoking - Alfred Dunhill of London Inc.
DUNHILL DOG - Toys–stuffed - Russ Berrie and Co., Inc.
DUNHILL INTERNATIONAL 100'S - Cigarettes - G.A. Georgopulo & Co. Inc.
DUNHILLS - Candy ☆ - R.L. Albert & Son, Inc.
DUNIA - Jewelry - Dunia Ltd.
DUNITE - Enamels ☆ - Kelly-Moore Paint Co. Inc.
DUNK - Cleaning preparations ☆ - Nowstar
DUNK-IS - Bathing suits - Rexx of London
DUNK-IT - Toys - Tyco Toys
DUNKAROOS - Crackers - General Mills, Inc.
DUNKEL WEIZEN - Beverages–malt - Sprecher Brewing Co. Inc.
DUNKELD RECORDS - Recording label - Alcazar Productions
DUNKER - Hardware - AM-Source International
DUNKER POPPLE - Toys–stuffed ☆ - Mattel, Inc.
DUNKERMUG - Glassware–household - J.S. English Co.
DUNKIN - Chewing gum - Richardson Brands
DUNKIN' DECAF - Coffee - Dunkin' Donuts of America Inc.
DUNKIN' DONUTS - Restaurants–coffee shops - Dunkin' Donuts of America Inc.
DUNKIN' DONUTS UNIVERSITY - Novelty items - Dunkin' Donuts of America Inc.
DUNKIN' THE TIMBERPUP - Toys–stuffed - Dayton Hudson Corp.
DUNKIRK - Heating equipment - Dunkirk Radiator Corp.
DUNKIT DUNK - Bags–duffel - E-Z Sales & Manufacturing, Inc.
DUNLAP - Health care products - Bruder Healthcare Co.
DUNLEIGH - Neckties - Dunleigh Tuxton Inc.
DUNLOGGIN - Blouses–women's - Shelburne Shirt Co. Inc.
DUNLOGGIN - Shirts - Sunrise Apparel, Inc.
DUNLOP - Cosmopolitan Motors Inc.
DUNLOP - Apparel and accessories - Sigallo Ltd.
DUNLOP - Bags - Sirco International Corp.
DUNLOP - Belts–industrial - Hal E. Verble & Son Inc. (Veri Products Div.)
DUNLOP - Handbags - Sirco International Corp.
DUNLOP - Musical instrument accessories - Dunlop Manufacturing, Inc.
DUNLOP - Sporting goods - Dunlop Maxfli Sports Corp.
DUNLOP - Tires - Dunlop Tire Corp.
DUNLOP - Travelware - Action Travelware
DUNLOP SP - Tires - Dunlop Tire Corp.
DUNMAR - Clocks - General Time Corp. (Westclox/Seth Thomas Div.)
DUNMARK - Flowers–artificial - Dunmark Inc.
DUNMORE - Earthenware ☆ - Waterford Wedgewood USA, Inc.
DUNN BROS COFFEE - Coffee - Roasters Edge, Inc.
DUNNE COLOR SUITED - Paints ☆ - Kelly-Moore Paint Co. Inc.
DUNNEWOOD - Beverages–alcohol - Canandaigua Wine Co. Inc.
DUNNEWOOD - Wines - Guild Wineries
DUNNEWOOD VINEYARDS - Wines - Guild Wineries
DUNOON - Dinnerware–glass - Franciscan by Johnson Brothers, USA, Inc.
DUNOONS - Shoes - Red Wing Shoe Co. Inc.
DUNORD - Ashtrays–glass ☆ - Nordic Ware
DUNQUICK - Enamels ☆ - Kelly-Moore Paint Co. Inc.
DUNRITE - Timers–appliance - Minnesota Mining & Manufacturing Co.
DUN'S PRIDE WHITE - Paint ☆ - Cook and Dunn Paint Corp.
DUN'S SUNLITE - Paint ☆ - Cook and Dunn Paint Corp.
DUNSANY - Floor coverings–carpet and rugs - Navan Carpets Inc.
DUNSBORO - Pipes–tobacco ☆ - Mastercraft Pipes Inc.
DUNSEAL - Varnishes ☆ - Kelly-Moore Paint Co. Inc.
DUNSEN - Sporting goods - Sports Imports Inc.
DUNSEN SPORTS GROUP, THE - Sporting goods - Sports Imports Inc.
DUNSPAR - Varnishes ☆ - Kelly-Moore Paint Co. Inc.
DUNSWORTH P. DRAGON - Publisher's imprints - Frank C. McQuilliams
DUNTINE - Thinner, varnish, enamel, etc. - Cook and Dunn Paint Corp.
DUNVALOX - Paints ☆ - Kelly-Moore Paint Co. Inc.
DUNVARLITE - Varnishes ☆ - Kelly-Moore Paint Co. Inc.
DUNVEGAN - Floor coverings–carpet and rugs - Milliken & Co. Inc.

DUNWOODY DRAGON - Toys–stuffed ☆ - Dakin Inc.
DUO - Adhesives and sealants - Smithkline Beecham Corp.
DUO - Boats–motor - Tennessee Acquisition Corp.
DUO - Brushes–hair - Nino Originals
DUO - Cheese ☆ - Swissrose International Inc.
DUO - Chimes ☆ - Nutone Inc.
DUO - Dinnerware ☆ - Corning Inc.
DUO - Erasers - Dixon Ticonderoga Co.
DUO - Furniture–upholstered - Sealy Furniture of Maryland/IHFC
DUO - Leather goods - St. Thomas Inc.
DUO - Locks–door - Illinois Lock Co.
DUO - Medical apparatus - Cobe Laboratories, Inc.
DUO - Motor vehicle parts and accessories - Kar-Rite LP
DUO - Tricycles ☆ - GT Bicycles Inc.
DUO - Tripods–photographic ☆ - Raven Screen Corp.
DUO - Wallpaper - S.R. Wood Inc.
DUO-AQUA-DRIN - Health care products - McKesson Home Health Care
DUO-ART - Pianos - Aeolian Pianos Inc.
DUO-BACK - Erasers - Claridge Products and Equipment Inc.
DUO-BELLOWSCOPE - Photographic equipment - SP Systems/Saratons
DUO-BIND - Binders - Duo Tang, Inc.
DUO-BIT - Tools - New England Carbide
DUO-BLEND - Bird feeds - Reinders, Inc.
DUO-BLEND - Cigarettes - G.A. Georgopulo & Co. Inc.
DUO-BLUE - Pharmaceutical preparations ☆ - Murray Drug Corp.
DUO-BORDER - Floor coverings–carpet and rugs ☆ - Capel, Inc.
DUO-BRIGHT - Binders ☆ - Duo Tang, Inc.
DUO-BRITE - Scouring pads - Minnesota Mining & Manufacturing Co.
DUO-CAL PAB - Vitamins and nutritional supplements ☆ - Freeda Vitamins Inc.
DUO-CEN - Pharmaceutical preparations ☆ - Solvay Pharmaceuticals Inc.
DUO-CHEK - Hardware - Yale Security Inc.
DUO CIDE - Pesticides–household - Allerderm Inc.
DUO-CITROCORB - Health care products ☆ - Halsey Drug Co. Inc.
DUO-CITRUS BIOFLAV - Pharmaceutical preparations ☆ - Schein Pharmaceutical Inc.
DUO CLEAN - Hair care products - Zotos International Inc.
DUO-CLICK - Binders - Duo Tang, Inc.
DUO-CLINE - Health care products - Bodyline Comfort Systems
DUO-COIL - Furniture–upholstered - Lancer Inc.
DUO CONTROL - Switches–power - Power Controls Corp.
DUO-C.V.P. - Pharmaceutical preparations - Rhone-Poulenc Rorer Pharmaceuticals Inc.
DUO-CYP - Pharmaceutical preparations ☆ - Keene Pharmaceuticals Inc.
DUO DE-HUMMER - Fans–electric - Power Controls Corp.
DUO DECKEM - Insecticides - Fearing Manufacturing Co. Inc.
DUO DECOR - Weather stripping - W.J. Dennis & Co.
DUO DELIGHTS - Chocolate candy - Duo Delights, Inc.
DUO-DENT - Dental equipment - James V. D'Alise
DUO-DERM - Hair care products - Allerderm Inc.
DUO DISH - Nail care products - E.O.H. Industries, Inc.
DUO-DRIVE - Tools - Cleveland Twist Drill Co.
DUO DUTY - Paints - Proctor Paint & Varnish Co. Inc.
DUO-FAST - Staplers - Duo-Fast Corp.
DUO FILE - Office supplies ☆ - Safco Products Co.
DUO-FLEX - Paper - Rotary Printing Co. Inc.
DUO-FLOW - Cleaner for contact lenses - CooperVision Inc.
DUO-FORM - Medical apparatus ☆ - Lumex, Inc.
DUO-FRESH - Sewage treatment equipment - Satellite Industries, Inc.
DUO-GLASS - Automotive parts and accessories - Minnesota Mining & Manufacturing Co.
DUO GLIDE - Hardware - Seal Rite Windows
DUO GLO - Paper - Whitehall Products Ltd.
DUO GRIP - Containers–plastic - Laclede Chain Manufacturing Co.
DUO-HIST - Pharmaceutical preparations ☆ - Schein Pharmaceutical Inc.
DUO/JET - Apparel and accessories ☆ - Duofold Inc.
DUO-JOBMASTER - Fastening tool ☆ - ITW Ramset/Red Head
DUO-K - Pharmaceutical preparations - Barre-National, Inc.
DUO-LEG - Medical apparatus - Columbus Mckinnon Corp.
DUO LIFT - Trailers - Duo Lift Manufacturing Co., Inc.
DUO-LINED - Pipes–tobacco ☆ - S.M. Frank & Co. Inc. (Kaywoodie-Yello-Bole-Medico)
DUO LITE - Flashlights - Vincent Yee
DUO-LITE - Lighting fixtures - Swivelier Co. Inc.
DUO-LITE - Paints ☆ - Waterlox Coatings Corp.
DUO LITE - Window coverings - Hunter Douglas, Inc.

☆ = Now out of production

DUO-LOC - Sporting goods - Omni Scientific Inc.

DUO MAT - Mats–grass, reed, and jute ☆ - Hunt Manufacturing Co.

DUO-MATIC - Pens - Erwin Pearl Inc.

DUO-MEDIHALER - Pharmaceutical preparations - Minnesota Mining & Manufacturing Co.

DUO MINDER - Calendars ☆ - Keith Clark Inc.

DUO-MOUNT - Fans–electric - Crest Industries Inc.

DUO-PAD - Adhesives and sealants - W.R. Meadows Inc.

DUO-PANE - Insulating materials - Western Insulated Glass Co.

DUO PILLOW - Pillows - Pillowtex Corp.

DUO-PLAIN - Floor coverings–carpet and rugs ☆ - Capel, Inc.

DUO-PLEAT II - Window shades - Verosol

DUO-PLEAT I - Window shades - Verosol

DUO PLY - False eyelashes ☆ - Cosrich Inc.

DUO-POINT - Audio equipment - Shure Brothers, Inc.

DUO-POST - Envelopes - Tension Envelope Corp.

DUO-PRED - Pharmaceutical preparations ☆ - Keene Pharmaceuticals Inc.

DUO-PRIMER - Paints - Kwal-Howells Inc.

DUO-PURPOSE - Labels–paper - The Eureka Co.

DUO-RAIL - Hardware ☆ - Hettich America L.P.

DUO RIB - Tires - Bridgestone/Firestone, Inc.

DUO-ROW - File folders - Stacor Corp.

DUO-SAFETY - Ladders–metal - Duo-Safety Ladder Corp.

DUO-SCRIBE - Pens ☆ - Mastercraft Pen Co.

DUO SCRUB - Skin care products - Excelcis

DUO SET - Hair care products - Helene Curtis Industries Inc.

DUO-SHADE - Artists' materials - Grafix Plastics

DUO-SIL - Adhesives and sealants - Siroflex, Inc.

DUO-SITE - Ophthalmic goods ☆ - Bausch & Lomb Inc.

DUO-SONIC - Guitars - Fender Musical Instruments

DUO SPA - Whirlpool baths and spas - Marquis Corp.

DUO SPAN - Pharmaceutical preparations ☆ - Primedics Laboratories

DUO-SPAN II - Pharmaceutical preparations ☆ - Primedics Laboratories

DUO SPAR - Varnish - American Paints

DUO-STICK - Hair care products - New Image

DUO-STICK - Tape–adhesive - Daubert Coated Products, Inc.

DUO-STICK - Tape–adhesive ☆ - Kasen Industries (Circle K Tape Div.)

DUO-SUPPORT 2 - Health care products - Shamrock Medical Inc.

DUO-SWEEP - Brooms - Flo-Pac Corp.

DUO-SYNCRO - Furniture - Knoll Group

DUO-SYNCRO - Swimming pools - Precision Multiple Controls, Inc.

DUO SYSTEM - Microwave ovens - Whirlpool Properties, Inc.

DUO TANG - Binders - Duo Tang, Inc.

DUO-TAPTITE - Screws - Research Engineering & Manufacturing Inc.

DUO TECH - Golfing equipment - Knight Golf, Inc.

DUO TEMP - Health care products - Cramer Products Inc.

DUO-TEMP - Thermometers - Republic Drug Co. Inc.

DUO-TEMP - Windows–storm - Duo-Temp

DUO TEST - Chemical preparations - Sta-Rite Industries Inc.

DUO TEX - File folders - Duo Tang, Inc.

DUO TEX - Hair care products - Johnson Products Co., Inc.

DUO-THERM - Air conditioning equipment - Dometic Corp.

DUO-THERM - Doors–storm - Duo-Temp

DUO-THERM - Hair care products - Zotos International Inc.

DUO-TOOL - Cleaning equipment - Flo-Pac Corp.

DUO-TREAT - Apparel–women's - Cupid Foundations Inc.

DUO-TROL - Brassieres (Bras) - Cupid Foundations Inc.

DUO TROVEL - Monuments–stone - Eagle Affiliates, Inc.

DUO TUBE - Lamps - Wiko Ltd.

DUO-TUSSIN - Cold remedies ☆ - Pharmex Inc.

DUO-VAC - Vacuum cleaners and accessories ☆ - Regina Co.

DUO-WAY - Paint rollers - Wooster Brush Co.

DUO WIND - Watches - Bulova Corp.

DUO-WR - Pharmaceutical preparations - Whorton Pharmaceuticals Inc.

DUO WRAP - Hairpins - Claire's Boutiques, Inc.

DUOBARB - Pharmaceutical preparations ☆ - C.O. Truxton Inc.

DUOBELT 202 - Tires ☆ - Bridgestone/Firestone, Inc.

DUOBRIDGE - Games - Just Games

DUOCOMFORT - Mattresses ☆ - Cosco, Inc.

DUOCRAFT - Apparel and accessories ☆ - Duofold Inc.

DUODENAL-80 - Pharmaceutical preparations ☆ - Fibertone Inc.

DUODERM - Bandages - E.R. Squibb & Sons, Inc.

DUODEX - Pharmaceutical preparations - Misemer Pharmaceuticals Inc.

DUODISK - Computer peripheral equipment - Apple Computer Inc.

DUOFACE - Labels–paper - Moore Business Forms, Inc.

DUOFADE - Electronics equipment - Kimchuk Inc.

DUOFILE - Computer peripheral equipment - Apple Computer Inc.

DUOFILM - Pharmaceutical preparations - Schering-Plough Healthcare Products

DUOFILM - Pharmaceutical preparations ☆ - Stiefel Laboratories, Inc.

DUOFLANGE - Pipes–steel - Improved Piping Products, Inc.

DUOFLEX - Compressors–air - Marshalltown Trowel Co.

DUOFOLD - Apparel and accessories - Duofold Inc.

DUOFOLD - Leather goods - St. Thomas Inc.

DUOFOLD - Paper - Klearfold Inc.

DUOFOLD - Pens - Parker Pen USA

DUOFOLD CENTENNIAL - Pens - Parker Pen USA

DUOFONE - Electronic equipment - Tandy Corp.

DUOGARD - Concrete–mixture - W.R. Meadows Inc.

DUOGEN L.A. - Pharmaceutical preparations ☆ - Vortech Pharmaceuticals

DUOLATE-Q - Pharmaceutical preparations ☆ - Wesley Pharmacal Co. Inc.

DUOLENE - Rope - Tubbs Cordage Co.

DUOLITE - Projectors–photographic ☆ - Kalart Victor Corp.

DUOLITES - Cosmetics - Redken Laboratories, Inc.

DUOLOCK - Medical apparatus - E.R. Squibb & Sons, Inc.

DUOLOK - Fittings–cast iron - SSP Fittings Corp.

DUOLONE - Pharmaceutical preparations ☆ - C.O. Truxton Inc.

DUOLUBE - Pharmaceutical preparations - Bausch & Lomb Inc.

DUOLYTE - Veterinary pharmaceutical preparations ☆ - Vineland Laboratories Inc.

DUOMAT - Photographic equipment - Eastman Kodak Co.

DUOMATE - Computers - Rasterops Corp.

DUOMATIC - Cameras - Avant Inc.

DUOMINE - Prescription drug - IDE-Interstate Inc.

DUOMO - Tables–wood - Nucraft Furniture Co.

DUONET - Computer hardware - Leunig Communications, Inc.

DUOPAK - Window shades - Draper Shade and Screen Co. Inc.

DUOPAQUE - Paper ☆ - Silver Leaf Paper Co.

DUOPHRAM - Brassieres (Bras) ☆ - Milady Brassiere & Corset Co., Inc.

DUOPLANT - Pharmaceutical preparations - Schering-Plough Healthcare Products

DUOPLANT - Pharmaceutical preparations ☆ - Stiefel Laboratories, Inc.

DUOPOCKET - Office supplies - Ames Safety Envelope Co.

DUOPRIN - Analgesics - Dunhall Pharmaceuticals Inc.

DUOPRINT - Artists' materials ☆ - Duostat Corp.

DUORUN - Paper ☆ - Lincoln Paper Co.

DUOS - Yogurt - Marigold Foods Inc.

DUOSCORB - Renal-dialysis product ☆ - Upsher-Smith Laboratories, Inc.

DUOSEAL - Kitchenware - Reynolds Metals Co.

DUOSETTE - Apparel–women's - Lily of France Inc.

DUOSHIELD 100 - Cables–coaxial - Cable Design Technologies, Inc.

DUOSLEEP - Pillows - Perfect Fit Industries, Inc.

DUOSOL - Paint removers - Pratt & Lambert, Inc.

DUOSTAT - Photographic equipment - Duostat Corp.

DUOSTAT - Photographic equipment - Graphline, Inc.

DUOSTONE - Aquariums–household - Willinger Bros., Inc.

DUOSTRAINER - Drains - Kohler Co.

DUOSWAB - Pharmaceutical preparations - Nice-Pak Products, Inc.

DUOTECTOR - Electronic equipment - NJR Corp.

DUOTONE - Blinds–venetian - Hunter Douglas, Inc.

DUOTONE - Furniture - Winsome Trading, Inc.

DUOTONE - Recording label - Jazz Composer's Orchestra Association Inc.

DUOTONE - Snowboards ☆ - Earth & Ocean Sports, Inc.

DUOTONE - Watches - Gruen Marketing Corp.

DUOTRACK - Bicycle parts and accessories - SR Suntour USA, Inc.

DUOTROL - Hair care products - Helene Curtis Industries Inc.

DUOTRON - Floor coverings–carpet and rugs - Mohawk Carpet Corp.

DUOTRUSS - Shelving units–metal ☆ - Clairson International Corp.

DUOVAL P.A. - Pharmaceutical preparations ☆ - Solvay Pharmaceuticals Inc.

DUOVIN-S - Pharmaceutical preparations - G.O. Spanner Inc.

DUOVISC - Pharmaceutical preparations - Alcon Laboratories, Inc.

DUOVOX - Musical instrument accessories - Trophy Music Co.

DUP-A-TAPE - Electronic equipment - Brandons Inc.

DUPAGE - Film - Du Page Metal Products Inc.

DUPE-PRO - Photographic equipment - Radmar Inc.

DUPER - Photographic equipment - Wess Plastic

DUPHALAC - Pharmaceutical preparations - Solvay Pharmaceuticals Inc.

DUPHRENE - Antihistamine preparations ☆ - Pal-Pak Inc.

DUPLA - Pet products - J.P. Burleson Inc.

DUPLA FOOD POINT - Pet products ☆ - Aquarium Products Inc.

DUPLA-VAN - Bakeries - Bush, Boake, Allan Inc.

DUPLARIN - Pet products ☆ - Aquarium Products Inc.

DUPLARIN COMPRETTEN - Pet products ☆ - Aquarium Products Inc.
DUPLARIN MICRO - Pet products ☆ - Aquarium Products Inc.
DUPLAST - Bandages ☆ - Beiersdorf Inc.
DUPLESSIS - Wines - Dreyfus Ashby Inc.
DUPLEX - Artists' materials ☆ - M. Grumbacher Inc.
DUPLEX - Cookies ☆ - D.F. Stauffer Biscuit Co., Inc.
DUPLEX - Crepe paper ☆ - Creative Expressions Group
DUPLEX - Dishes–china - Mikasa Co.
DUPLEX - Erasers ☆ - Bright Boy Abrasives
DUPLEX - Fabrics–linen - West Point-Pepperell Inc.
DUPLEX - Floor coverings - Congoleum Corp.
DUPLEX - Floor-finish applicator - American Textile Products Co.
DUPLEX - Lubricants - Coastal Unilube Inc.
DUPLEX - Lubricants - Quaker State Oil Refining Corp.
DUPLEX - Musical instrument accessories - Trophy Music Co.
DUPLEX - Pet products - American Cat Emporium
DUPLEX - Rulers–wood ☆ - Keuffel & Esser Co.
DUPLEX - Shampoos - C&M Pharmacal, Inc.
DUPLEX - Sights–gun - Leupold and Stevens Inc.
DUPLEX - Snack foods ☆ - Holland American Wafer Co.
DUPLEX - Sweaters - T.J. Manalo, Inc.
DUPLEX - Tires - Bridgestone/Firestone, Inc.
DUPLEX - Tripods–photographic ☆ - QuickSet International Inc.
DUPLEX 2000 - Tires - Bridgestone/Firestone, Inc.
DUPLEX MANAGEMENT SYSTEMS - Computers - Duplex Products Inc.
DUPLEX T - Shampoos - C&M Pharmacal, Inc.
DUPLEXO - Musical instrument accessories - Micro Musical Products Corp.
DUPLI-COLOR - Enamels - Krylon/Dupli-Color
DUPLI-KEY - Cabinets–metal - Major Metalfab Co.
DUPLI-LITE - Photographic equipment - SP Systems/Saratons
DUPLI-RAIL - Photographic equipment - SP Systems/Saratons
DUPLI-RITER - Office supplies - Reynolds and Reynolds Co.
DUPLICATES - Hair care products - R & W Marketing, Inc.
DUPLICUT - Surgical instruments - Alcon Laboratories, Inc.
DUPLIGRAVE - Automotive repair shops–glass ☆ - Lamps Ltd.
DUPLIKIN - Electronics equipment - Century Precision Optics
DUPLIMAT - Photocopy machines - SP Systems/Saratons
DUPLIMATIC - Duplicators and supplies ☆ - Copy Plus Inc.
DUPLIN - Wines - Duplin Wine Cellars
DUPLISAFE - Office supplies - Repeat-O-Type Manufacturing Corp.
DUPLISCOPE - Photographic equipment - SP Systems/Saratons
DUPLISTRIP - Photographic equipment - SP Systems/Saratons
DUPLITEK - Video equipment - Audio Visual Systems, Inc.
DUPLIVAR - Photographic equipment - SP Systems/Saratons
DUPLO - Toys–blocks - Lego Systems Inc.
DUPLO BABY - Toys–erector sets - Lego Systems Inc.
DUPLOFOL - Tape–adhesive - Weco Trading of Maryland
DUPLOTEX - Tape–adhesive - Weco Trading of Maryland
DUPLUX - Lighting fixtures - Edison Price Lighting
DUPONOL - Shampoos ☆ - C&M Pharmacal, Inc.
DUPRE - Musical instrument accessories - Hershman Musical Instrument
DUPROS - Adhesives and sealants ☆ - James B. Day and Co.
DUQUESNE D DUKES UNIVERSITY - Shirts - Duquesne University of the Holy Ghost
DUQUESNE UNIVERSITY SPIRITUS EST QUI VIVIFICAT 1878 - Apparel and accessories - Duquesne University of the Holy Ghost
DUR-A-CRETE - Epoxy - Dur-A-Flex Inc.
DUR-A-EDGE - Furniture - Plymold Seating
DUR-A-FILLER - Putties - Dur-A-Flex Inc.
DUR-A-FLEX - Sealing compounds - Dur-A-Flex Inc.
DUR-A-GARD - Epoxy coatings - Dur-A-Flex Inc.
DUR-A-GLAZE - Finishing agents - Dur-A-Flex Inc.
DUR-A-HOSE - Automotive parts and accessories ☆ - Pirelli Power Transmission Corp.
DUR-A-LIFE - Automotive parts and accessories ☆ - Pirelli Power Transmission Corp.
DUR-A-LITE - Lighting equipment - General Manufacturing Inc.
DUR-A-POXY - Epoxy - Dur-A-Flex Inc.
DUR-A-PRENE - Rubber–urethane ☆ - Dur-A-Flex Inc.
DUR-A-QUARTZ - Floor coverings - Dur-A-Flex Inc.
DUR-A-SHIELD - Concrete products - Dur-A-Flex Inc.
DUR-A-TEX - Cement - Dur-A-Flex Inc.
DUR-A-TEX - Gloves–rubber - Duracraft Corp.
DUR-A-TUFF - Batteries - Exide Corp.
DUR-A-WEAR - Floor waxes - Uncle Sam Chemical Co., Inc.
DUR-A-ZZO - Xerrazzo epoxy ☆ - Dur-A-Flex Inc.

DUR-ABEL - Office supplies ☆ - Abel Products
DUR-ABLE - Pegboard hooks - Dur-O-Peg
DUR-ANG-O - Boomerang - American Eagle Co./Teacher's Discovery
DUR APLEX - Building materials - Aliquot, Ltd.
DUR-COR - Glass products ☆ - Corning Inc.
DUR-EL MOP-ON RESTORER - Cleaning preparations - Uncle Sam Chemical Co., Inc.
DUR-FLEX - Violins - Fender Musical Instruments
DUR-O-JAC - Jackets–leather - Schott Brothers Inc.
DUR-O-LITE - Pens - Dur-O-Lite Inc.
DUR-O-MATIC - Pencils ☆ - Dur-O-Lite Inc.
DUR-O-PANE - Plastics ☆ - Warp Bros.
DUR-O-TUNE - Paper - French Paper Co.
DUR-X-ACCUSLOT - Doors–screen - Durex Products Inc.
DUR-X-LITE - Doors–screen - Durex Products Inc.
DURA - Adhesives and sealants - Monsey Products Co.
DURA - Cleaning preparations - Durawool Inc.
DURA - Footwear ☆ - Conjac Inc.
DURA - Golfing equipment - Exim Manufacturers, Inc.
DURA - Lighting equipment - Dura Electric Lamp Co. Inc.
DURA - Mops - Lighthouse Industries
DURA - Paints - Norton & Sons
DURA - Pet products - Flexi-Mat Corp.
DURA - Sporting goods - Sport Fun, Inc.
DURA - Tiles–ceramic ☆ - Dal-Tile Corp.
DURA-20 - Roofing materials - NCI Building Systems, Inc.
DURA-ACE - Sporting goods - Shimano American Corp.
DURA AMP 2 - Motors–outboard - Zebco Corp.
DURA-BILT - Bathroom accessories - Selfix, Inc.
DURA-BLACK - Ducts–metal - Simpson Dura Vent Co., Inc.
DURA BLOCK - Deodorizers ☆ - Olfactory Corp.
DURA-BLU - Cleaning preparations - Durawool Inc.
DURA-BODY - Audio equipment - Shure Brothers, Inc.
DURA-BOND - Doors–metal - Pioneer Industries
DURA-BOND - Fabric binding - Freudenberg Nonwovens Apparel Division
DURA-BOND - Padding–foam - Bondafoam Inc.
DURA BONDED - Abrasive products ☆ - Norton Co.
DURA BONE - Pet products - Dura Pro Products
DURA BRAID - Pet products - Mustang Products, Inc.
DURA-BRASS - Bathroom accessories - Selfix, Inc.
DURA-BRASS - Brass products - Curtis Industries Inc.
DURA-BRAZE - Cables - W.L. Gore & Associates, Inc.
DURA BROOM - Housewares - Alwin Products
DURA BRUSH - Housewares - Alwin Products
DURA-BUILD - Varnishes - Valspar Corp.
DURA-BUILT - Aluminum products - National Aluminum Products Co.
DURA-CAP - Gypsum products - Maxxon Corp.
DURA-CARB - Vitamins and nutritional supplements - Source Naturals
DURA-CASE - Containers–plastic - Alpha Enterprises, Inc.
DURA-CAST - Barbecues and grills - Arkla Products Co.
DURA CAST - Hardware - Holo-Krome Co.
DURA-CHANNEL - Drains - Zurn Industries, Inc.
DURA CHECK - Floor coverings–carpet and rugs - Milliken & Co. Inc.
DURA CHIMNEY - Building materials–concrete - Simpson Dura Vent Co., Inc.
DURA-CHOCK - Tires - Durable Corp.
DURA-CHROME - Bathroom accessories - Selfix, Inc.
DURA-CLAD - Containers–insulated ☆ - Aladdin Industries, Inc.
DURA-CLAD - Ophthalmic goods - Pan Optics, Inc.
DURA-CLAD - Paints - Duron, Inc.
DURA-CLAD - Publisher's imprints - Booksource, Inc.
DURA CLAY - Clay products - Uniflame, Inc.
DURA CLEAR - Garment storage bags - Manco, Inc.
DURA-COATED - Wire products - Selfix, Inc.
DURA-COLOR - Cables–coaxial - General Cable Corp.
DURA COLOR - Office supplies - American Trading and Production Corp.
DURA-COLOR - Pet products - Novalek, Inc.
DURA-COLOR - Siding–asphalt ☆ - GAF Corp.
DURA/CONNECT - Pipes - Simpson Dura Vent Co., Inc.
DURA-CORD - Hats - American Hat Co. Inc.
DURA COTE - Glass products - Dura-Cote Corp.
DURA-COVE - Rubber–molded - Johnsonite Flooring Products
DURA-COVER - Cases–musical instrument - M & M Distributing Co.
DURA-COVER - Office supplies - Esselte Corp.
DURA-CRAFT - Paints - Sherwin-Williams Automotive Finishes Corp.
DURA-CREST - Paints ☆ - Duron, Inc.
DURA-CRETE - Concrete–ready-mix - Cemstone Products Co.

☆ = Now out of production

DURA-CRETE - Paints - Duron, Inc.
DURA-CRYSTAL - Watches - Bulova Corp.
DURA-DECOR - Fabrics–coated - Duracote Corp.
DURA-DIE - Pharmaceutical preparations - E & D Dental Products, Inc.
DURA-DINER - Containers–insulated - Aladdin Industries, Inc.
DURA-DIP - Pet products - Davis Manufacturing
DURA DISC - Brakes–motor vehicle - Rockwell International Corp.
DURA-DOCK - Bumpers–motor vehicle - Durable Corp.
DURA-DUMONE - Pharmaceutical preparations ☆ - Roberts/Hauck
    Pharmaceuticals Inc.
DURA-EDGE - Fabrics - Technical Textiles, Inc.
DURA-ESTRIN - Pharmaceutical preparations - Roberts/Hauck
    Pharmaceuticals Inc.
DURA FAME - Varnishes - McCloskey Corp.
DURA FELT - Hats - GWB, Inc.
DURA-FILE - Envelopes - Acorn Industries, Inc.
DURA FILE - File folders - W.W. Holes Manufacturing
DURA FINISH - Finishing agents - Dura Seal
DURA-FIT - Medical apparatus - Safeskin Corp.
DURA FIX - Abrasive products - Conros Corp.
DURA-FLAT - Containers - Molded Container Corp.
DURA-FLEECE - Fabrics - Delta Mills Inc.
DURA-FLEX - Antennas - Allen Telecom Group, Inc.
DURA-FLEX - Lighters - Colibri Inc.
DURA-FLEX - Shelving - Impact Products, Inc.
DURA FLEX - Ventilation equipment - Simpson Dura Vent Co.
DURA-FLEX - Wheels - Faultless Caster Co.
DURA-FLO - Concrete products ☆ - Fosroc Inc.
DURA-FLO - Pipes–steel - Berger Industries Inc.
DURA FLOW - Flues - Stan Sievers Research & Development Corp.
DURA-FOAM - Foam rubber - Foam Rubber Fabricators Inc.
DURA-FOLD - Doors–metal - Elkhart Door Inc.
DURA-FOLD - Socks - Saramar Corp.
DURA-FRESH - Paints ☆ - Duron, Inc.
DURA-GARD - Gloves–safety - Saf-T-Gard International, Inc.
DURA-GLAS - Pumps - Sta-Rite Industries Inc.
DURA GLASS DG - Bathtubs–enameled - Dura Glass Products Inc.
DURA-GLAZE - Finishing agents - Porter Paint Co.
DURA-GLAZE - Plates–paper - Premier Industries Inc.
DURA-GLIDE - Pencils ☆ - Faber-Castell Corp.
DURA GLOSS - Enamels - Columbia Paint Co.
DURA GLOSS - Floor coverings - Azrock Commercial Flooring
DURA-GLOSS - Floor waxes ☆ - Care-Tech Laboratories Inc.
DURA-GRIP - Paints - Atlas Chemical Co.
DURA-GRO - Pesticides–household - Platte Chemical Co.
DURA-GUARD - Goggles–safety - Aearo Co.
DURA-GUARD - Medical apparatus - Bio-Vascular, Inc.
DURA-GUARD - Paints ☆ - United Coatings Inc.
DURA HINGE - Stationery - Dennison National Co.
DURA-HOG - Drill bits - Fitzpatrick Manufacturing Co.
DURA-INK - Markers–felt-tip - Markal Co.
DURA-JET - Spray nozzle - Delavan Inc.
DURA-KAP - Uniforms–tailored - Red Kap
DURA KEELIN - Pharmaceutical preparations ☆ - Pharmex Inc.
DURA KING - Paints - Graham Paint and Varnish Co.
DURA-KOLD - Medical apparatus - Dura*Kold Corp.
DURA-KOOL - Cooking equipment–commercial - Dura-Ware of America Inc.
DURA-KOTE - Paints - Duron, Inc.
DURA-KOTER - Cleaning preparations - Mega Manufacturing Co. Inc.
DURA-LAGG - Building materials - Don Morin, Inc.
DURA-LAM - Mattresses - Evenflo Juvenile Furniture Co.
DURA-LAP - Aluminum products - Edco Products Inc.
DURA-LAR - Plastics film - Grafix Plastics
DURA-LAST - Drafting supplies - Koh-I-Noor, Inc.
DURA-LATTICE - Roofing materials - Texas Aluminum Industries Inc.
DURA LIFE - Medical apparatus - Diemolding Corp.
DURA-LIFE - Windows–storm - Duo-Temp
DURA LIFT - Doors–garage ☆ - Clopay Millwork
DURA-LIGN - Window coverings - Gilmore Enterprises Window Coverings, Inc.
DURA/LINER - Building materials–concrete - Simpson Dura Vent Co., Inc.
DURA LITE - Flags - Dettra Flag Co. Inc.
DURA-LITE - Shoe accessories - Meramec Group, Inc.
DURA-LITE - Step ladders and stools - Dura-Lite Ladder Co.
DURA-LITE - Windshield frames–motor vehicle - Dura Mechanical
    Components Inc.
DURA-LITH - Lubricants - Chevron Corp.

DURA-LOCK - Racks - Frazier Industrial Co.
DURA-LUBE - Oils–lubricating - Dura-Lube Corp.
DURA-LUSTER CLEANER - Cleaning preparations - Bruce Hardwood Floors
DURA MAG - Automotive parts and accessories - Echlin Inc.
DURA-MAID - Gloves–rubber - Duracraft Corp.
DURA-MARINE - Fabrics–coated ☆ - Duracote Corp.
DURA MASK - Floor coverings - Poly-Tak Protection Systems
DURA-MASTER - Brakes–motor vehicle - Rockwell International Corp.
DURA-MATE - Marine pumps ☆ - ITT Jabsco
DURA-MATIC - Pistols - High Standard Manufacturing Corp.
DURA-MAX - Boilers - A.O. Smith Corp.
DURA-MAX - Machine parts - Lenore E. Perry
DURA MED - Pharmaceutical preparations - Duramed Pharmaceuticals, Inc.
DURA-MESH - Respirators - Moldex-Metric Inc.
DURA-MOLY - Pistons - Child & Albert Inc.
DURA-NAP - Blankets - Medline, Industries, Inc.
DURA-NEB - Medical apparatus - Pari Respiratory Equipment Inc.
DURA NEB-2000 - Health care products - Dura Pharmaceuticals, Inc.
DURA-PAC - Drill bits - Drillmaster, Inc.
DURA-PACK - Concrete products ☆ - Fosroc Inc.
DURA-PACK - Glue–household or industrial - Polymer Engineering Corp.
DURA PARK - Floor coverings ☆ - Harris-Tarkett, Inc.
DURA-PATCH - Sealing compounds - Maxxon Corp.
DURA-PAVERS - Tiles–ceramic ☆ - Laufen Ceramic Tile
DURA-PEL - Finishing agents ☆ - Kelly-Moore Paint Co. Inc.
DURA-PEN - Pens - Rolamech Inc.
DURA PERF - Roofing materials–clay - Hollinee Corp.
DURA-PLASTIC - Racks - Dura-Ware of America Inc.
DURA-PLATE - Epoxy coatings - Pratt & Lambert United, Inc.
DURA-PLAY - Sporting goods - Sport Fun, Inc.
DURA-PLUS - Building materials–concrete - Simpson Dura Vent Co., Inc.
DURA-PLUS - Buttons - Emsig Manufacturing Corp.
DURA-POX - Paints - Pratt & Lambert United, Inc.
DURA PREME - Paints–artists' - MCI Quality Coatings
DURA-PRO - Fabrics–coated - Duracote Corp.
DURA PRO - Pet products - Dura Pro Products
DURA-QUILT - Cribs–wood - Evenflo Juvenile Furniture Co.
DURA-RAMIC - Antennas - Ward Products Corp.
DURA-RIB - See SPECTRA-RIB
DURA-RIB - Plastics - Robertson-Ceco Corp.
DURA RICH - Ladders–metal ☆ - Rich Ladder Co.
DURA-RUG 400 - Floor coverings - Durable Corp.
DURA-SEAL - Adhesives and sealants ☆ - Custom Building Products
DURA SEAL - Cleaning preparations - Thompson-Minwax Co.
DURA-SEAL - Finishing agents - Dura Seal
DURA-SEAL - Finishing agents - Duron, Inc.
DURA-SEAL - Paper–kraft ☆ - Canson-Talens Inc.
DURA SERIES - Skylights - Sun-Tek Industries Inc.
DURA-SET - Yarn - Bentley Mills, Inc.
DURA-SHADE - Fabrics–coated - Duracote Corp.
DURA-SHAKE - Siding–asphalt ☆ - GAF Corp.
DURA-SHARP - Drill bits ☆ - Credo Co.
DURA SHARP - Scissors–hand-operated - Fiskars Inc.
DURA-SHIELD - Paint - Interstate Paint Corp.
DURA-SHIELD - Tarpaulins - Test-Rite Products Corp.
DURA-SHINE - Floor waxes - Knight Marketing Corp.
DURA-SKID - Finishing agents - Pratt & Lambert United, Inc.
DURA-SLUG - Bowling balls - DBA Products Inc.
DURA-SOFT - Bumpers–motor vehicle - Durable Corp.
DURA-SOFT - Fabrics–linen - Hydro Dynamics Inc.
DURA-SOFT - Medical apparatus - Dura*Kold Corp.
DURA-SONIC - Fabrics–coated - Duracote Corp.
DURA-SORB - Wet mops ☆ - American Textile Products Co.
DURA-SPRAY - Insecticides - PBI/Gordon Corp.
DURA-STAG - Knives–pocket - Camillus Cutlery Co.
DURA-STAIN - Finishing agents - Duron, Inc.
DURA-STAKES - Flowers, plants, and seeds ☆ - Security Products Co.
DURA-STAR - Roofing materials - Texas Aluminum Industries Inc.
DURA STARS - Stones–synthetic - Max Duraffourg Gem Co. Inc.
DURA-STAT - Fabrics–coated - Duracote Corp.
DURA-STAT - Radiator steam trap - ITT Corp.
DURA-STEEL - Siding–metal ☆ - Aluminum Co. of America
DURA-STIK - Office supplies - Barkley Filing Supplies
DURA STONE - Dry powder fillers - Arizona Cultured Stone Products, Inc.
DURA-STONE - Sculptures - Austin Sculpture Inc.
DURA STOP - Brakes–motor vehicle - General Motors Corp.

☆ = Now out of production

DURA-STRAN - Fibers–fluorocarbons - Multi-Tex Products INC.

DURA-TAC - Oils–lubricating - Quaker State Corp.

DURA-TECH - Tires - Bridgestone/Firestone, Inc.

DURA TEK - Drafting supplies - Saga Cad & Drafting Supplies

DURA-TERRY - Towels - Fieldcrest Cannon, Inc.

DURA TESTOSTERONE - Pharmaceutical preparations - C.S. Ruckstuhl Co. Inc.

DURA-TESTRONE - Pharmaceutical preparations ☆ - Pharmex Inc.

DURA TEX - Ceiling panels - Armstrong World Industries, Inc.

DURA-TEX II LASER MATTE - Paper - Duratech Paper Specialties, Inc.

DURA-THERM - Fabrics–coated - Duracote Corp.

DURA-TILE - Floor coverings–tile - Pawling Corp. (Standard Products Div.)

DURA-TILE-II - Floor coverings - Durable Corp.

DURA-TIP - Bathroom accessories - Empire Brushes, Inc.

DURA-TIP - Markers–felt-tip ☆ - Faber-Castell Corp.

DURA TOOL - Knives–hunting - Camillus Cutlery Co.

DURA TOOL - Tools–power-driven - Foremost International Trading Inc.

DURA TOP - Counter tops–laminated - Hartson-Kennedy Cabinet Top Co., Inc.

DURA TOP - Finishing agents - Dura Seal

DURA TORQ - Fasteners–hook and eye - Curtis Industries Inc.

DURA-TOUCH - Gloves–safety - Edmont

DURA-TRAC - Measuring instruments - Chemtrac Systems, Inc.

DURA-TRACK - Floor coverings–carpet and rugs - No-Muv Corp., Inc.

DURA TRAK - Shelving system - Newell Operating Co.

DURA TRAK 90 - Audio equipment - Broadcast Electronics, Inc.

DURA-TREND - Paints ☆ - Fuller-O'Brien Paints Inc.

DURA-TRIM - Fabrics–coated - Duracote Corp.

DURA TRIM - Lace - Narrow Fabric Industries Inc.

DURA-TUFF - Concrete products - Dura-Tuff Engineered Products, Inc.

DURA-TUFF - Elevators - Maxi-Lift, Inc.

DURA-TUFF - Fabrics–coated ☆ - Duracote Corp.

DURA-TUFF - Paints - Titan Corp.

DURA-TURF - Floor coverings–carpet and rugs - Mica Inc.

DURA-TURF - Flowers, plants, and seeds - Jonathan Green, Inc.

DURA TURF - Synthetic turf - Instant Turf Industries Inc.

DURA-TWIST - Mops - Zephyr Manufacturing Co.

DURA-VENT - Fabrics–coated ☆ - Duracote Corp.

DURA VUE - Drapery hardware ☆ - Spring Window Fashions Division, Inc.

DURA-VUE - Fabrics–coated ☆ - Duracote Corp.

DURA-WARE - Kitchen utensils–aluminum - Dura-Ware of America Inc.

DURA-WASH - Cleaning preparations - Media Group, Inc.

DURA WEAR - Floor coverings–carpet and rugs - Coronet Industries, Inc.

DURA-WEVE - Floor coverings–carpet and rugs - Sweetwater Carpet Corp.

DURA-WHELP - Pet products - Fawn Run Corp.

DURA-WHITE - Glassware–household - Federal Glass

DURA-WHITE - Tiles–facing ☆ - Chicago Adhesive Products Co.

DURA WHITE - Wainscotting - Georgia-Pacific Corp.

DURA-WICKER - Furniture - Runnells Manufacturing Inc.

DURA-WIRE - Kitchen utensils–aluminum - Dura-Ware of America Inc.

DURABAKE - Furniture - Tomlinson of High Point Inc.

DURABAKE - Mirrors - Willard Mirrors Inc.

DURABAND - Saw blades - Clemson Brothers Inc.

DURABASE - Gypsum products - National Gypsum Co.

DURABASE - Shower stalls–plastic - E.L. Mustee & Sons Inc.

DURABEAM - Flashlights - Duracell Co. USA

DURABEAUTY - Laminates - Consolidated Papers, Inc.

DURABIB - Apparel–children's - Bibco

DURABIDE - Silicon carbide coatings - Dura-Tech Processes, Inc.

DURABILITY - Office supplies - Barkley Filing Supplies

DURABILITY PLUS - Paints - Montgomery Ward & Co. Inc.

DURABILT - Hardware - Blaine Window Hardware Inc.

DURABILT - Paint rollers - Bestt-Liebco

DURABILT - Watches - Bulova Corp.

DURABIND - Office supplies - Cardinal Products

DURABLADE - Automotive accessories - Lifetime Automotive Products Inc.

DURABLE - Containers - Durable Fibre Sample Case Co.

DURABLE - Hardware - United Manufacturers Supplies Inc.

DURABLE - Ribbons–inked - Phillips Ribbon & Carbon Co.

DURABLE ARTS - Glass–stained ☆ - Siphon Art Products

DURABLE COLORS - Paints - Plaid Enterprises, Inc.

DURABLE FLORCOTE - Cleaning preparations ☆ - Chalmers Chemical Co.

DURABLE RALPH - Pet shops - Durable Ralph, Inc.

DURABLE STORABLES - Containers–plastic - Safety 1st, Inc.

DURABLEND - Automotive parts and accessories - Ashland Inc.

DURABLEND - Oils–lubricating - Ashland Oil, Inc.

DURABLEND - Underwear and nightwear ☆ - Henson-Kickernick Inc.

DURABLES - Furniture–upholstered - Gilford Corp.

DURABOARD - Artists' materials - Gilman Brothers Co.

DURABOARD - Melamine-surfaced board - Consolidated Papers, Inc.

DURABOLIC - Pharmaceutical preparations ☆ - Roberts/Hauck Pharmaceuticals Inc.

DURABOLIN - Pharmaceutical preparations - Organon Inc.

DURABOND - Adhesives and sealants - Dap Products Inc.

DURABOND - Cooking equipment–household - Jacksonville Manufacturing

DURABOND - Hair care products - Helene Curtis Industries Inc.

DURABOOT - Replacement boots - Aircraft Gear Corp.

DURABRIDGE - Scales–industrial - Weigh-Tronix, Inc.

DURABRITE - Essential Industries, Inc.

DURABRITE - Food products - Kalsec, Inc.

DURABUCK - Boots - United States Shoe Corp.

DURABUILT - Clamps - Alltrade Inc.

DURABUILT - Leather goods ☆ - McGuire-Nicholas Co., Inc.

DURACAL - Cement - United States Gypsum Co.

DURACALK - Caulking compounds - United Gilsonite Laboratories

DURACARE - Ophthalmic goods ☆ - Blairex Laboratories, Inc.

DURACARE II - Ophthalmic goods - Blairex Laboratories, Inc.

DURACARTRIDGE - Toners - Duracartridge, Inc.

DURACAST - Cooking equipment–household - Jacksonville Manufacturing

DURACELL - Batteries - Duracell Co. USA

DURACHEM - Barber shop equipment - Kim Laube & Co. Inc.

DURACHLOR - Chemical preparations - Haviland Consumer Products, Inc.

DURACHROME - Engines - WCI Outdoor Products, Inc.

DURACHROME - Office supplies ☆ - Faber-Castell Corp.

DURACID - Pharmaceutical preparations ☆ - Fielding Pharmaceutical Co.

DURACIDE - Cement - Durako Paint & Color Corp.

DURACILLIN A.S. - Antibiotics - Eli Lilly and Co.

DURACITE - Blackboards–slate - Claridge Products and Equipment Inc.

DURACLEAN - Gloves - Wilshire Technologies, Inc.

DURACLEAR - School supplies - Manco, Inc.

DURACLIP - Office supplies - Cardinal Products

DURACLOTH - Dropcloths ☆ - Rexam Flexible Packaging

DURACLOTH - Manicure and pedicure products - International Beauty Design, Inc.

DURACOAT - Adhesives and sealants ☆ - Induron Coatings Inc.

DURACOAT - Cooking equipment–household - Southeastern Coatings Inc.

DURACOAT - Paints ☆ - Devoe & Raynolds Co.

DURACOLOR - Floor coverings - Burlington Industries, Inc.

DURACOLOR - Wallpaper - The Creative Edge, Inc.

DURACOM - Computers - Duracom Computer Systems

DURACOM-4 - Office supplies ☆ - Alliance America

DURACON - Floor coverings - Mannington Resilient Floors

DURACON II - Floor coverings - Mannington Resilient Floors

DURACONOMY - Paints ☆ - Everseal International Sales Co. Inc.

DURACORD - Floor coverings–carpet and rugs - Porter Carpet Mills Inc.

DURACOTE - Cooking equipment–household - Regal Ware, Inc.

DURACOTE - Hardware - Duke City Lumber Co.

DURACOVER - Binders - Boorum & Pease Co.

DURACRAFT - Air conditioning equipment - Duracraft Corp.

DURACRAFT - Bird cages - Nature House Inc.

DURACRAFT - Boats–motor - Duracraft Boats Inc.

DURACRAFT - Photographic equipment - Arel Inc.

DURACRAFT - Photographic equipment - Argraph Corp. (Samigon Div.)

DURACRIB - Cribs–wood - Paris Co. Inc.

DURACURE - Adhesives and sealants - Nowstar

DURACUSHION - Mattresses - Ohio Mattress Co.

DURACUT - Lubricating oils - Enterprise Oil Co.

DURACUT - Machine parts - Teknor Apex Co.

DURADATER - Stamps–hand - Schwaab, Inc.

DURADERM - Health care products ☆ - Sentry Medical Products

DURADISC - Plastics - Anchor Swan

DURADIX - Adhesives and sealants ☆ - Mascot Precision Tools

DURADOOR - Shower stalls–metal - E.L. Mustee & Sons Inc.

DURADOR - Doors–metal - Taylor Building Products Co.

DURADRY - Dryers–commercial - Kent Co.

DURADUCK - Duck decoys ☆ - Boss Manufacturing Co.

DURADUDS - Work clothes - Duraduds Workware, Inc.

DURADYNE - Cold remedies ☆ - Forest Pharmaceuticals Inc.

DURADYNE D.H.C. - Analgesics ☆ - Forest Pharmaceuticals Inc.

DURAEDGE - Mattresses - Lisco, Inc.

DURAFAB - Apparel and accessories - Durafab Inc.

DURAFAST - Paints - California Products Corp.

☆ = Now out of production

DURAFELT - Fabrics–felt - Allied Felt Group
DURAFIBER - Machinery - J and M Laboratories Inc.
DURAFIBER - Paper–toweling - Georgia-Pacific Corp.
DURAFILL - Pillows - Pacific Coast Feather Co.
DURAFILM - Lubricants - Enterprise Oil Co.
DURAFIN - Photographic equipment - Eastman Kodak Co.
DURAFIRE - Spark plugs - SL Auburn Industries, Inc.
DURAFLAME - Fireplace equipment - Duraflame, Inc.
DURAFLECT - Game machines - Micro Manufacturing, Inc.
DURAFLEX - Blinds–venetian - Spring Window Fashions Division, Inc.
DURAFLEX - File folders - Dur-A-Flex Inc.
DURAFLEX - File folders ☆ - K & M Co.
DURAFLEX - Footwear - Iron Age Corp.
DURAFLEX - Hardware - Caribbean Lumber Co. Inc.
DURAFLEX - Heating equipment - Senseatherm, Inc.
DURAFLEX - Mattress pads - L & P Property Management Co.
DURAFLEX - Office supplies - Ames Safety Envelope Co.
DURAFLEX - Paints - Triangle Coatings Inc.
DURAFLEX - Paints ☆ - Fuller-O'Brien Paints Inc.
DURAFLEX - Photographic equipment - Eastman Kodak Co.
DURAFLEX - Pipes–plastic - Shell Oil Co.
DURAFLEX - Rackets–tennis ☆ - Prince Sports Group, Inc.
DURAFLEX - Watchbands–base metal - Regal Industries, Inc.
DURAFLEX PREMIER COLLECTION, THE - Footwear - Dunham Boot Makers
DURAFLINT - Coatings - Reichhold Chemicals, Inc.
DURAFLITE - Boats–motor ☆ - Duracraft Boats Inc.
DURAFLO - Paints - Dunn Edwards Corp.
DURAFLO - Photographic equipment - Eastman Kodak Co.
DURAFLO - Plumbing fixtures–metal - Mansfield Plumbing Products, Inc.
DURAFLOR - Tiles–ceramic - Dal-Tile Corp.
DURAFLOR - Varnishes - Dunn Edwards Corp.
DURAFLOW - Nipples–rubber - Kiddie Products, Inc.
DURAFOAM - Cables - General Cable Corp.
DURAFOAM - Garden equipment - Teknor Apex Co.
DURAFOAM - Health care products - Scott Specialties, Inc.
DURAFOAM - Health care products ☆ - Sammons Preston
DURAFOLD - Boxes - Mason Box Co. Inc.
DURAFOLD - Tires - Armtec Industries Inc.
DURAFORGED - Key rings - Nelson B. Boone Co., Inc.
DURAFORM - Cases–musical instrument ☆ - Selmer Co. Inc.
DURAFRAME - Furniture - Kwalu Inc.
DURAFRAME - Window frames - Duraframe Window Shutter Systems, Inc.
DURAFREE - Chemical preparations - Duracraft Corp.
DURAFUSION - Inks - Printronix, Inc.
DURAGARD - Plugs–electric - Amerace Corp.
DURAGARD - Toys - Sport Fun, Inc.
DURAGAS - Pipes - Shapco, Inc.
DURAGEN - Pharmaceutical preparations - Roberts/Hauck Pharmaceuticals Inc.
DURAGESIC - Pain medication - Janssen Pharmaceutica Inc.
DURAGESTIC - Pharmaceutical preparations - Glaxo Wellcome Inc.
DURAGLAS - Glassware–household - Owens-Illinois Inc. (Libbey Div.)
DURAGLAZE - Adhesives and sealants - Induron Coatings Inc.
DURAGLIDE - Marine rigging - Windline Marine
DURAGLO - Paints - Triangle Coatings Inc.
DURAGLOSS - Automotive parts and accessories - Brothers Research Corp.
DURAGLOSS - Floor cleaning equipment - White Consolidated Industries, Inc.
DURAGLOSS - Floor finishing machines–commercial - Kent Co.
DURAGLOVE - Gloves–rubber - Advanced Mittworks, Inc.
DURAGLOVE - Gloves–rubber - Arbitrage Imports Inc.
DURAGLOW - Lighting equipment - General Electric Co.
DURAGOLD - Pens - Quill Co. Inc.
DURAGOLD - Tableware–earthenware - Great China Industrial, Inc.
DURAGRAIN - Siding - Variform, Inc.
DURAGRIP - Adhesives and sealants - Bil-Dry Corp.
DURAGRIP - Gloves–rubber - Johnson & Johnson
DURAGUARD - Cleaning preparations ☆ - Duraclean International Inc.
DURAGUARD - Dishwashers–household - Maytag Corp.
DURAGUARD - Floor coverings - Congoleum Corp.
DURAGUIDE - Machine parts - Fort Wayne Wire Die, Inc.
DURAHEAD - Office supplies - Esselte Corp.
DURAHOLD - Floor coverings–carpet and rugs - No-Muv Corp., Inc.
DURAHOPPER - Containers - Cew Products, Inc.
DURAJOINT PVC WATERSTOP - Waterproofing compounds - A.C. Horn Co.
DURAKOL - Paints - Briner Paint Manufacturing Co. Inc.

DURAKON INDUSTRIES - Liners and covers–Swimming pool - Durakon Industries Inc.
DURAKOOL - Health care products - Foam Products Inc.
DURAKOOL - Toys - Wonderline
DURAKORE - Boat-building materials - Baltek Corp.
DURAKOTA - Seminola–flour or meal - North Dakota Mill and Elevator Association
DURAKOTE - Epoxy - Tamms Industries Co.
DURAKOTE - Paints - Triangle Coatings Inc.
DURAKYL - Veterinary pharmaceutical preparations - DVM Pharmaceuticals, Inc.
DURAL - Epoxy - Tamms Industries Co.
DURALAC - Pens - Quill Co. Inc.
DURALACE - Fabrics–broadcloth - Chicopee
DURALAMB - Fabrics ☆ - Alconox Inc.
DURALAMP - Lamp bulbs - Action Media Technologies, Inc.
DURALAR - Brake parts - Carlisle Corp.
DURALASH - Cosmetics - Ardell International Inc.
DURALASH LASH FREE - Cosmetics - American International Industries
DURALASH LASHTITE - Cosmetics - American International Industries
DURALASH STUDENT KIT - Cosmetics - American International Industries
DURALAST - Floor coverings–carpet and rugs - Aladdin Mills, Inc.
DURALAST - Wheels - Hamilton Caster & Manufacturing Co.
DURALASTIC - Crocheted and knitted items - M and M Woolen Co. Inc.
DURALAY - Padding–foam - Hobbs Bonded Fibers
DURALENS - Knives–pocket - Imperial Schrade Corp.
DURALEX - Glassware–household - St. Gobain International Glassware
DURALEX - Pharmaceutical preparations - American Urologicals Inc.
DURALIFE - Hosiery - Kayser-Roth Corp.
DURALIGHT - Core shafts - Double E Co., Inc.
DURALIGHT II - Window coverings - Duratex Inc.
DURALIN - Floor coverings - Congoleum Corp.
DURALINE - Drums–musical instruments ☆ - Duraline Industries Inc.
DURALINE - Filing cabinets ☆ - Corry Hiebert
DURALINE - Photographic equipment - Harrison & Harrison
DURALINE - Rope - Crow Rope Industries LLC
DURALIP - Automotive parts and accessories - Chicago Rawhide
DURALITE - Carousels - Millrock Inc.
DURALITE - Glass products - Lasco Products Group
DURALITE - Insecticides ☆ - H.D. Hudson Manufacturing Co.
DURALITE - Luggage - Airway Industries, Inc.
DURALITE - Mops - W.E. Kautenberg Co.
DURALITE - Paints ☆ - Fuller-O'Brien Paints Inc.
DURALITE - Sanitary napkins ☆ - Kleinert's Inc.
DURALITE - Trailers - Aero Industries, Inc.
DURALITE - Wire - Raychem Corp.
DURALITH - Concrete–mixture - L.D. Sterns Corp.
DURALL - Paints - Triangle Coatings Inc.
DURALL EAGLE - Tools–hand-operated - Durall-Eagle Tools
DURALOC - Coatings - Grillers' World, Inc.
DURALOC - Metals - Buffers USA Inc.
DURALOCK - Floor coverings–tile - Roope Corp.
DURALOCK - Locks–door ☆ - Dexter Lock
DURALOFT - Pillows - E.I. Dupont de Nemours and Co.
DURALOK - Furnaces–electric - Lennox Industries Inc.
DURALOK PLUS - Furnaces–electric - Lennox Industries Inc.
DURALON - Bathroom accessories - Consolidated Industries Corp.
DURALON - Concrete products - Metalcrete Industries Inc.
DURALON - Knitting machines - Peter Freund Knitting Mills
DURALON - Ribbons–inked - Eaton Allen Ko-Rec-Type Corp.
DURALONE - Pharmaceutical preparations - Roberts/Hauck Pharmaceuticals Inc.
DURALOOP - Door mats - Royal Rubber & Manufacturing Co.
DURALOX - Spices and extracts - Kalsec, Inc.
DURALOY - Drills–mining - Curtis Industries Inc.
DURALTEX - Floor finishing machines–commercial - Tamms Industries Co.
DURALUBE - Oils–lubricating - Dura-Lube Corp.
DURALUCENT - Window coverings - Duratex Inc.
DURALUME - Paints ☆ - Fuller-O'Brien Paints Inc.
DURALUMES - Chemical preparations - Lindgren-Pitman, Inc.
DURALUTIN - Pharmaceutical preparations - Roberts/Hauck Pharmaceuticals Inc.
DURALUX - Enamels ☆ - Sigma Coatings USA BV.
DURALUX - Paints - Gray Seal Paint Manufacturing Co. Inc.
DURALUX - Paints - Triangle Coatings Inc.
DURALUX - Tableware–plastic - Design Specialties Inc.

☆ = Now out of production

DURAMAG - Magnets - Dura Magnetics, Inc.
DURAMAIL - Mail boxes ☆ - Flambeau Products Corp.
DURAMARK - Crayons - Faber-Castell Corp.
DURAMASTER - Paints - Glidden Co.
DURAMASTIC - Epoxy - Briner Paint Manufacturing Co. Inc.
DURAMAT - Insulating materials - Manville/Schuller
DURAMATE - Insulating materials - Dow Chemical Co.
DURAMATIC - Lighting equipment - Dura Electric Lamp Co. Inc.
DURAMAX - Easels - Quartet Manufacturing Co.
DURAMAX - Health care products - Softcare Corp.
DURAMAX - Hosiery - Kayser-Roth Corp.
DURAMAX - Paints - Valspar Corp.
DURAMENT - Hardware - C.E. Kaiser Co.
DURAMESH - Insulating materials ☆ - Manville/Schuller
DURAMIC - Bricks - Glen-Gery Corp.
DURAMILL - Treadmills - Pacer Fitness Systems
DURAMINE - Epoxy - Briner Paint Manufacturing Co. Inc.
DURAMIST - Pharmaceutical preparations - Pfeiffer Pharmaceuticals Inc.
DURAMITE - Cylinders - Greenco Manufacturing Corp.
DURAMITE - Photographic equipment ☆ - Dura Electric Lamp Co. Inc.
DURAMITT - Apparel and accessories - Advanced Mittworks, Inc.
DURAMITT - Gloves–rubber - Arbitrage Imports Inc.
DURAMUNE - Veterinary product - American Home Products Corp.
DURAMYL - Floor coverings - Congoleum Corp.
DURAN - Fabrics - Uniroyal Engineered Products
DURAN DURAN - Apparel and accessories - DD Productions, Ltd.
DURAN DURAN - Games ☆ - Milton Bradley Co.
DURANAIL - Cosmetics - Cumberland-Swan, Inc.
DURANAMEL - Paints - Briner Paint Manufacturing Co. Inc.
DURANAUTIC - Boats–fishing - Reichman Inc.
DURANAUTIC - Boats–motor - Marathon Boat Group, Inc.
DURAND - Computer software - Durand Communications Network, Inc.
DURAND - Kitchen utensils–aluminum ☆ - Reston Lloyd Ltd.
DURAND - Music–sheet - Theodore Presser Co.
DURAND - Pet products - Durand Distributors
DURAND - Tool carts - Durand Products, Inc.
DURAND - Vases - Durand International
DURANDRO - Pharmaceutical preparations ☆ - B.F. Ascher & Co. Inc.
DURANDROL - Pharmaceutical preparations ☆ - Pharmex Inc.
DURANGA - Garden equipment - Mount Washington Enterprises, Inc.
DURANGA SWEEPER - Brooms - Mount Washington Enterprises, Inc.
DURANGO - Beverages–carbonated - Dairy Fresh Products Co.
DURANGO - Bicycles - Huffy Corp.
DURANGO - Boots - Durango Boot Co. Inc.
DURANGO - Cigar boxes–wood ☆ - Consolidated Cigar Corp.
DURANGO - Colognes - Melaleuca, Inc.
DURANGO - Firearms, accessories, and parts - High Standard Manufacturing Corp.
DURANGO - Firearms, accessories, and parts - Welsh Sporting Goods Corp. (Boyt Div.)
DURANGO - Floor coverings ☆ - Congoleum Corp.
DURANGO - Flowers, plants, and seeds - Panamerican Seed
DURANGO - Liquors - United States Distilled Products Co.
DURANGO - Luggage - Atchison Products, Inc.
DURANGO - Thread - Threads USA Div.
DURANGO - Tiles–ceramic - Porcelanite, Inc.
DURANGO COFFEE COMPANY - Coffee - Durango Coffee Co.
DURANGO DICK'S CAROLINA FIRE - Seasonings - Richard C. Bradley
DURANGO DINER GREEN CHILI - Seasonings - Durango Diner, Inc.
DURANGO PLANK - Floor coverings - Bruce Hardwood Floors
DURANITE - Pens - Staedtler, Inc.
DURANT - Fabrics - Gretchen Bellinger Inc.
DURANT - Motor vehicles–automobiles ☆ - Durant Motors Inc.
DURANYL - Siding–insulating - Aluminum Co. of America
DURAPAC - Video tapes–blank - Microplas Inc.
DURAPACK - Plastics - Eaglebrook Plastics, Inc.
DURAPAINT - Paints - Major Paint Co.
DURAPATCH - Concrete products - Sosroc Inc.
DURAPHOS - Lubricant - Albright & Wilson Americas, Inc.
DURAPHYL - Pharmaceutical preparations ☆ - Forest Pharmaceuticals Inc.
DURAPINK - Construction equipment - UC Industries, Inc.
DURAPINK - Roofing materials - Owens Corning
DURAPLANX - Flooring–hardwood - Harris-Tarkett, Inc.
DURAPLAS - Paints - Red Spot Paint & Varnish Co., Inc.
DURAPLASTIC - Gasoline ☆ - Lehigh Portland Cement Co.
DURAPLUGS - Footwear–athletic - K-Swiss Inc.

DURAPLUSH - Floor coverings–carpet and rugs - BASF Corp.
DURAPLY - Thread ☆ - SCT Yarns Inc.
DURAPLY - Waterproofing compounds - Briner Paint Manufacturing Co. Inc.
DURAPLY - Wood products - Champion International Corp.
DURAPOL - Floor waxes - Harley Chemicals
DURAPON - Epoxy - Briner Paint Manufacturing Co. Inc.
DURAPOT - Electrical equipment - North Atlantic Instruments, Inc.
DURAPOWER - Watches - Helbros International
DURAPOXY - Epoxy coatings - Garon Products Inc.
DURAPOXY - Hardware - C.E. Kaiser Co.
DURAPRIME - Paints - Frazee Paint
DURAPRO - Anti-inflammatory - American Home Products Corp.
DURAPRO - Brushes–paint - Wooster Brush Co.
DURAPRO - Fabrics - Lowell Shoe, Inc.
DURAPROOF - Naphthalene chips - Duraclean International Inc.
DURAQUIN - Pharmaceutical preparations ☆ - Parke-Davis
DURARINSE - Chemical preparations - Duracraft Corp.
DURAROME - Seasonings - Firmenich Inc.
DURAROPE - Jewelry–precious - Dalow Industries, Inc.
DURAS DINNERWARE - Dinnerware - Carlisle Foodservice Products, Inc.
DURASAFE - Glass–tempered - Guardian Jamestown
DURASAFE - Medical apparatus - Becton, Dickinson and Co.
DURASAFE - Safes ☆ - Meilink Safe Co.
DURASAL - Pharmaceutical preparations ☆ - Seatrace Co.
DURASAN - Gypsum products - National Gypsum Co.
DURASAND - Abrasive sponges - Dallas Stephens
DURASCAPE - Limestone products - Medusa Minerals Co.
DURASCAPE - Tiles–ceramic - Dal-Tile Corp.
DURASCREEN - Sunscreen ☆ - Penederm Inc.
DURASCRIM - Sporting goods - Sage Manufacturing Corp.
DURASCRUB - Floor cleaning equipment - Kent Co.
DURASCRUB - Floor finishing machines–commercial - White Consolidated Industries, Inc.
DURASEAL - Adhesives and sealants - Geocel Corp.
DURASET - Hair care products - Lusan Inc.
DURASEW - Thread - Threads USA Div.
DURASHAPE - Fabrics - Rubie's Costume Co., Inc.
DURASHEEN - Paints - Triangle Coatings Inc.
DURASHEET - Plastics ☆ - Rexam Flexible Packaging
DURASHIELD - Doors–metal - Amweld Building Products
DURASHIELD - Paints - Briner Paint Manufacturing Co. Inc.
DURASHIELD - Scientific apparatus - Desalination Systems, Inc.
DURASHIELD - Tires - Uniroyal Goodrich Tire Co.
DURASHIELD PLUS - Stain removers - Duraclean International Inc.
DURASHINE - Floor waxes - Amway Corp.
DURASHINE - Paints - Master Lock Co.
DURASIGN - Paper - Insignia Systems, Inc.
DURASIL - Pharmaceutical preparations - Seatrace Co.
DURASIL DURABLE SILICONE SHEET - Medical apparatus - S.F. Group, Inc.
DURASIL DURABLE SILICONE SHEET - Medical apparatus - Paule Stiefler
DURASILK - Fabrics - Hind, Inc.
DURASILK - Wallpaper ☆ - Wall-Pride Inc.
DURASITE - Laser systems–medical - Kentek Corp.
DURASMOCK - Apparel–children's - Bibco
DURASOFT - Contact lenses - Wesley-Jessen Co.
DURASOFT - Footwear - Morse Shoe, Inc.
DURASOFT - Handles–rubber - Marshalltown Trowel Co.
DURASOFT - Insulating materials - Water Adventures, Inc.
DURASOFT COLORS - Contact lenses - Wesley-Jessen Co.
DURASOFT OPTFIT - Contact lenses - Wesley-Jessen Co.
DURASOFT SUPERSOFT - Contact lenses ☆ - Wesley-Jessen Co.
DURASOLE - Shoe soles - Durasole, Inc.
DURASOLE - Shoes ☆ - Endicott Johnson Corp.
DURASONE - Pharmaceutical preparations ☆ - Roberts/Hauck Pharmaceuticals Inc.
DURASORB - Diapers–disposable - Professional Medical Products, Inc.
DURASPAN - Glass–tempered - Guardian Jamestown
DURASPER - Paints - Multicolor Specialties Inc.
DURASPORT - Bicycles - Huffy Corp.
DURASPORT - Floor coverings–tile - American Biltrite Inc.
DURASPORT - Toys - Playskool, Inc.
DURASPOUT - Downspouts - Genova Products Inc.
DURASPRAY - Lubricants - Kent Oil Co., Inc.
DURASPRAY - Nozzles - L.R. Nelson Corp.
DURASPUN - Thread ☆ - SCT Yarns Inc.
DURASTALL - Shower stalls–metal - E.L. Mustee & Sons Inc.

☆ = Now out of production

DURASTAND - Cabinets–metal - Ampco/Rosedale Fabricators
DURASTAR - Food processors - Longwood Elastomers, Inc.
DURASTART - Chemical preparations - Duracraft Corp.
DURASTAT - Medical apparatus - Mentor O & O Inc.
DURASTAT - Wheelchairs - Theradyne Healthcare Product Div.
DURASTEEL - Blackboards–slate ☆ - Claridge Products and Equipment Inc.
DURASTEEL - Watches - E. Gluck Corp.
DURASTILL - Housewares - Durastill Inc.
DURASWEEP - Brooms - Perfex Corp.
DURASWEEP - Carpet sweepers - Kent Co.
DURASYSTEM - Machinery - J and M Laboratories Inc.
DURASYSTEM - Skin care products - American Salon Products
DURATAB - Office supplies - Esselte Corp.
DURATACK - Adhesives - Consolidated Papers, Inc.
DURATACK - Mats - Hartco Inc.
DURATAPE - Insulating tape ☆ - Manville/Schuller
DURATAPE - Tape players–cassette ☆ - Duracell Co. USA
DURATEARS NATURALE - Ophthalmic goods - Alcon Laboratories, Inc.
DURATEC - Motor vehicles - Ford Motor Co.
DURATEC - Paints - Frazee Paint
DURATEC - Paints - Hawkeye Industries, Inc.
DURATECH - Shoes–athletic - Diadora America
DURATEK - Paints - Triangle Coatings Inc.
DURATEMP - Paints - Triangle Coatings Inc.
DURATEST - Pharmaceutical preparations - Roberts/Hauck Pharmaceuticals Inc.
DURATEST - Tools–hand-operated - Custom Accessories, Inc.
DURATEST - Watches - Elgin Watch Co.
DURATESTRIN - Pharmaceutical preparations - Roberts/Hauck Pharmaceuticals Inc.
DURATEX - Bags–trash - Rexam Flexible Packaging
DURATEX - Draperies - Maharam Vertical Surfaces
DURATEX - Floor coverings–carpet and rugs - Porter Carpet Mills Inc.
DURATEX - Luggage - Airway Industries, Inc.
DURATEX - Novelty items - Pacific Balloon Co., Inc.
DURATEX - Siding–insulating - Champion International Corp.
DURATEX - Sports rackets and accessories - Victor Sports
DURATEX - Sports rackets and accessories - Winn, Inc.
DURATEX - Window coverings - Duratex Inc.
DURATEXTILES - Wallpaper - Walldesigns
DURATHANE - Varnishes - Pettit Paint Co. Inc.
DURATHATE - Pharmaceutical preparations ☆ - Roberts/Hauck Pharmaceuticals Inc.
DURATHERM - Filters–water - Desalination Systems, Inc.
DURATHESIA - Pharmaceutical preparations ☆ - Vortech Pharmaceuticals
DURATHIN - Sporting goods ☆ - Prince Sports Group, Inc.
DURATHON III - Aluminum products - Hubbell Lighting, Inc. (Lighting Div.)
DURATILE - Mats - U.S. Mat & Rubber Co. Inc.
DURATILE - Shower stalls–plastic - Aqua Glass Corp.
DURATION - Cement - Para-Chem Southern, Inc. (Parabond Adhesives Division)
DURATION - Cold remedies - Schering-Plough Healthcare Products
DURATION - Fabrics–linen - West Point-Pepperell Inc.
DURATION - Floor coverings ☆ - Masco Corp.
DURATION - Floor coverings–carpet and rugs - Olympic Carpets Inc.
DURATION - Floor coverings–carpet and rugs - Sheridan Carpet Mills
DURATION - Siding - Amerimark Building Products, Inc.
DURATION MILD - Cold remedies - Schering-Plough Healthcare Products
DURATION SYSTEM - Paints ☆ - Proko Industries Inc.
DURATITE - Wood products - Dap Products Inc.
DURATONE - Paints ☆ - Devoe & Raynolds Co.
DURATONE - Pens - Quill Co. Inc.
DURATONE - Playing cards - United States Playing Card Co.
DURATONE 95 - Pens - Quill Co. Inc.
DURATOOL - Photographic tool - Graphic Technology Inc.
DURATOUCH - Computers–personal - Gagetalker Corp.
DURATOUGH - Adhesives and sealants - Enecon Corp.
DURATRAC - Floor cleaning equipment - Kent Co.
DURATRAC - Garden equipment - Bolens Corp.
DURATRAC - Nails–horseshoe - Mustad, Inc.
DURATRACE - Electronic equipment - GAF Corp.
DURATRAD - Pharmaceutical preparations ☆ - B.F. Ascher & Co. Inc.
DURATRANS - Photographic equipment - Eastman Kodak Co.
DURATRAX - Conveyors - Scandura, Inc.
DURATRAX - Golfing equipment - Cadillac Rubber & Plastics, Inc.
DURATRAX - Motors - Hobbico Inc.

DURATRAY - Trays - Lancaster Colony Automotive Group
DURATRED - Footwear - Soletech, Inc.
DURATRODE - Solder - NCH Corp.
DURATRONIC - Electrical equipment - Curtis Industries Inc.
DURATUB - Laundry tubs–plastic - E.L. Mustee & Sons Inc.
DURATUFF - Adhesives and sealants - Titan Corp.
DURATUFF - Glassware–household - Owens-Illinois Inc. (Libbey Div.)
DURATUFF - Plastics film ☆ - Dick Blick Co.
DURATUSS - Pharmaceutical preparations - Whitby Pharmaceuticals, Inc.
DURATWEED - Floor coverings–carpet and rugs - Roxbury Carpet Co.
DURATWIST - Floor coverings–carpet and rugs - Barrett Carpet Mills Inc.
DURATYPE - Office accessories - Kroy, Inc.
DURAVAC - Vacuum cleaners and accessories–commercial - Kent Co.
DURAVAL II - Floor coverings–carpet and rugs ☆ - Playfield International Inc.
DURAVAULT - Safes ☆ - Meilink Safe Co.
DURAVIDER - Truck beds - Martec Products International
DURAVINYL - Floor coverings - Congoleum Corp.
DURAVIS - Chemicals - Albright & Wilson Americas, Inc.
DURAVISION - File folders - Forward Industries, Inc.
DURAVITES - Vitamins and nutritional supplements ☆ - Chase Laboratories Inc.
DURAWALL - Bathroom fixtures - E.L. Mustee & Sons Inc.
DURAWALL - Floor coverings–carpet and rugs ☆ - LaVelle Textile Marketing Inc.
DURAWALL - Paints - Dunn Edwards Corp.
DURAWALL 7 - Wallpaper - Durawall Inc.
DURAWAND - Computer peripheral equipment - Videx, Inc.
DURAWARE - Computer peripheral equipment - Quality Value Service, Inc.
DURAWEAR - Paper–carbon - Codo Manufacturing Corp.
DURAWEAVE - Wallpaper - Durawall Inc.
DURAWEVE - Floor coverings–carpet and rugs ☆ - Karastan-Bigelow Inc.
DURAWOOD - Building materials - Eaglebrook Products, Inc.
DURAY - Bags - Duray Co.
DURAY TAKE ALONGS - Bottles–glass - Duray Co.
DURAZINC - Paints - Briner Paint Manufacturing Co. Inc.
DURB EASE - Apparel–children's - Franklin-Durbin, Inc.
DURBAN - Floor coverings–carpet and rugs ☆ - Eurotex Inc.
DURBAN - Recording label - Sweet 'N Smooth Productions
DURBAN'S - Toothpaste - Chesebrough-Pond's USA Co.
DURDILLY - Wines - Wine Imports Ltd.
DUREIN - Stationery - American/Durein Co.
DURELCO - Lighting equipment - Dura Electric Lamp Co. Inc.
DURELENE - Flexible plastic tubing - Auburn Plastic Engineering
DURELLE - Bathtubs–enameled - Burnett & Associates, Inc.
DURENE - Yarn - Dixie Yarns, Inc.
DURER - Artists' materials - Riebe's Artist Materials Inc.
DURESSENCE - Perfumes - Parfums Christian Dior U.S. Corp.
DURETHENE - Plastics - ADPI Enterprises Inc.
DUREX - Badminton equipment - General Sportcraft Co. Ltd.
DUREX - Lighting equipment - Duro-Test Corp.
DUREX - Paints - Procos Group
DUREX - Towels ☆ - Durafab Inc.
DUREX AVANTI - Prophylactics - Durex Consumer Products
DUREX RAMSES - Prophylactics - Durex Consumer Products
DUREX SHEIK - Prophylactics - Durex Consumer Products
DURFAST CHAIR - Beds–metal - M. Craig Cabinetmaker
DURHAM - Dishes–china ☆ - Royal China & Porcelain Companies Inc.
DURHAM - Floor coverings ☆ - Anderson Hardwood Floors Inc.
DURHAM - Furniture - Boling Co.
DURHAM - Furniture - General Housewares Corp.
DURHAM - Wallets - Enger-Kress Co.
DURHAM HERITAGE - Furniture ☆ - Moosehead Manufacturing Co.
DURHAM'S - Ice cream - Durham's Products Co.
DURHAM'S ROCK HARD - Boats ☆ - Donald Durham Co.
DURHAM'S ROCK HARD WATER PUTTY - Putties - Donald Durham Co.
DURIA - Glassware–household - Crystal Glass Tube & Cylinder Co.
DURIBILKNIT - Sporting goods - John B. Flaherty Co. Inc.
DURIBRAKE - Brake pads - Durilon Brake Co.
DURICEF - Antibiotics - Bristol-Myers Squibb Co.
DURICOL - Veterinary pharmaceutical preparations - Pharmeral Inc.
DURID - Deodorants–personal ☆ - Carter-Wallace, Inc.
DURILITE - Paints - Conco Paint Co.
DURIPAL - Permanent masonry sealer - IPA Systems Inc.
DURIPLAST - Furniture - Tradeways Inc.
DURITE - Abrasive products - Norton Co.
DURITE - Cases–musical instrument - Elkhart Cases Inc.

☆ = Now out of production

DURITE 108 - Floor coverings - Durable Corp.
DURKEE - Spices - Burns Philp Food Inc.
DURKEE BEEF EASY - Spices and extracts - Specialty Brands Inc.
DURKEE BUFFALO WINGS - Seasonings - Burns Philp Food Inc.
DURKEE CALIFORNIA STYLE BLENDS - Spices and seasonings - Burns Philp Food Inc.
DURKEE FAMOUS SAUCE - Gravy - Durkee French Foods
DURKEE GRILL CREATIONS - Marinade bag and seasonings - Burns Philp Food Inc.
DURKEE JUMBO! - Snack foods - Reckitt & Colman, Inc.
DURKEE JUMBO POTATO STICKS - Snack foods - Specialty Brands Inc.
DURKEE QUALITY SINCE 1850 - Seasonings - Burns Philp Food Inc.
DURKEE SALAD SENSATIONS - Seasonings - Burns Philp Food Inc.
DURKEE'S - Food products - Durkee French Foods
DURKEE'S EASY MEALS - Spices and extracts - Specialty Brands Inc.
DURKIN PARK BRICK - Floor coverings ☆ - Tarkett, Inc.
DURLAST - Stains - Tool World, Inc.
DURLING FARMS - Meat products - C. Correll Durling
DURLING FARMS - Milk - Readington Farms
DURLING FARMS APPLE CIDER - Cider - Readington Farms
DURLING FARMS SPRING WATER - Water–bottled or canned - Readington Farms
DURLON - Combs - Ajax Comb Co. (Div. of Antonio's Manufacturing, Inc.)
DURLYNE - Apparel and accessories ☆ - Durlacher & Co., Inc.
DURNEY VINEYARD - Beverages–alcohol - Durney Vineyard
DURNEY VINEYARDS - Wines - Durney Winery Corp.
DURO - Automotive parts and accessories - Loctite Corp.
DURO - Blinds–venetian - Wellington Leisure Products, Inc.
DURO - Decals and transfers - Duro Art Industries Inc.
DURO - Floor coverings–carpet and rugs - Whitecrest Carpet Mills
DURO - Motor vehicle parts and accessories - Budge Industries, Inc.
DURO - Oils–lubricating - Lyondell Petrochemical Co.
DURO - Thread - Cincinnati Thread Co.
DURO - Water filters and softeners - Duro Co.
DURO-7 - Valves–engine - Tomco, Inc.
DURO 1400 - Dryers–hair - Helene Curtis Industries Inc.
DURO-CEL - Sponges - Acme Sponge & Chamois Co., Inc.
DURO-CHROME - Tools–hand-operated ☆ - Duro Metal Products Inc.
DURO DARN - Adhesives and sealants ☆ - Loctite Corp.
DURO DOT - Floor coverings–carpet and rugs ☆ - Quaker Inc.
DURO FLEX - Adhesives and sealants - R.P.C., Inc.
DURO FLEX - Hoses - Gates Rubber Co. (Automotive Aftermarket/Hardware Sales Div.)
DURO-GARD - Lamp bulbs–fluorescent - Duro-Test Corp.
DURO-GEL - Pharmaceutical preparations - Duro Med Industries Inc.
DURO GOLD - Artists' materials - Duro Art Industries Inc.
DURO/INDESTRO - Tools–hand-operated - Duro Metal Products Inc.
DURO-KRETE - Floor coverings - Colonial Refining and Chemical Co.
DURO-LITE - Lighting equipment - Duro-Test Corp.
DURO-LITH - Printing trades machinery - A-Korn Roller, Inc.
DURO-MATIC - Pharmaceutical preparations - Duro Med Industries Inc.
DURO-MED - Pharmaceutical preparations - Duro Med Industries Inc.
DURO PATCH - Hardware - Maxus Energy Corp.
DURO PERM - Sporting goods ☆ - Duro Finishing Corp.
DURO RIB - Floor coverings - Apache Mills Inc.
DURO-RIM - Binders ☆ - Master-Craft Corp.
DURO-SAN - Cans–metal - Stainless Metals Inc.
DURO-SHEEN - Floor waxes - Uncle Sam Chemical Co., Inc.
DURO-SHIELD - Fireplace equipment - Hy-C Co. Inc.
DURO SPECS - Adhesives and sealants - Loctite Corp.
DURO/STRAND - Brooms - Zephyr Manufacturing Co.
DURO-TABLE - Furniture - Camelot West Corp.
DURO-TONE - Dinnerware–glass ☆ - Homer Laughlin China Co.
DURO TONE - Finishing agents - Porter Paint Co.
DURO/TYPE - Decals and transfers - Duro Art Industries Inc.
DURO WOODCARE - Adhesives and sealants ☆ - Loctite Corp.
DURO-WOODHILL - Automotive parts and accessories ☆ - Loctite Corp.
DUROBACK - Electronic equipment - Fuji Photo Film USA Inc.
DUROCAST - Musical instruments ☆ - United Musical Instruments USA Inc.
DUROCEL - Vinyl ☆ - Aluminum Co. of America
DUROCK - Cement - United States Gypsum Co.
DUROCK - Tiles–ceramic - Dap Products Inc.
DUROL - Cleaning preparations - Reliance Pen & Pencil Corp.
DUROLAST - Gaskets - Plastic Specialties and Technologies, Inc.
DUROLATUM - Health care products - King Laboratories
DUROLEAD - Pencils - Reliance Pen & Pencil Corp.

DUROLITE - Aprons–leather - Custom Leathercraft Manufacturing
DUROMAT - Mats - C/S Group/DecoGard Products
DURON - Artists' materials ☆ - Sculpture House Inc.
DURON - Paints - Duron, Inc.
DURON - Pharmaceutical preparations ☆ - Wesley Pharmacal Co. Inc.
DURON DELUXE - Paints - Duron, Inc.
DURON PLUS - Paints - Duron, Inc.
DURON-TEX - Wallpaper - Duron, Inc.
DURONG NAIL - Cosmetics ☆ - Nature's Answer (Bio Botanica)
DUROPEL - Sporting goods ☆ - Duro Finishing Corp.
DUROPLEX - Paints - Triangle Coatings Inc.
DUROS - Pumps–water - Eldex Laboratories, Inc.
DUROSHEEN - Thread ☆ - American & Efird, Inc.
DUROSLATE - Office supplies - Ghent Manufacturing Inc.
DUROTHERM - Soldering equipment - Hexacon Electric Co.
DUROTHERM - Weather tracking equipment ☆ - Watrous & Co. Inc.
DUROTREAD - Floor coverings–carpet and rugs ☆ - Karastan-Bigelow Inc.
DUROTRED - Mats - C/S Group/DecoGard Products
DUROTYPE - Inks–duplicating ☆ - A.B. Dick Co.
DUROX - Bleach ☆ - Mid-America Chemical Inc.
DURRAN - Blinds–vertical - Tontine/VyTech Industries Inc.
DURRAX - Pharmaceutical preparations ☆ - Dermik Laboratories Inc.
DURRSCHMIDT - Musical instrument accessories ☆ - St. Louis Music Supply Co.
DURSBAN - Insecticides - Dowelanco
DURTEX - Finishing agents - Tool World, Inc.
DURUG - Floor coverings - Duracote Corp.
DURULITE - Doors - Chase Industries, Inc.
DURUS - Cases–camera - Bee Electronics Inc.
DURUS - Dinnerware–plastic - Plastics Manufacturing Co.
DURUSLIDE - Doors - Chase Industries, Inc.
DURVAC - Pharmaceutical preparations - Durvet, Inc.
DURVET DEALER SELECT HORSECARE - Animal feed supplements - Durvet, Inc.
DURVIL - Fabrics - Avtex Fibers Inc.
DURWARD - Sporting goods - McNett Corp.
DURWELD - Adhesives and sealants - American Durweld Sales Inc.
DURWELD 2000 - Resins–synthetic - American Durweld Sales Inc.
DURYEA'S - Corn starch - CPC International Inc.
DUS-TROL - Mops - Golden Star Inc.
DUSARDIN VSOP BRANDY - Beverages–alcohol - Niche Marketing Corp.
DUSCURE - Concrete–mixture ☆ - Reardon Industries Inc.
DUSK - Dinnerware ☆ - Corning Inc.
DUSK & DAWN - Binoculars - Ranging Inc.
DUSK SHADOW - Glassware–household ☆ - Lenox Crystal, Inc.
DUSK TO DAWN - Lighting fixtures - Test-Rite Products Corp.
DUSKY - Boats–motor - Dusky Marine Inc.
DUSKY DRIVE - Boats–motor - Dusky Marine Inc.
DUSO'S FINEST - Food products - Duso Food Distributors
DUSOTAL - Pharmaceutical preparations ☆ - Harvey Laboratories Inc.
DUST - Computer software - Cyberflix, Inc.
DUST-A-MATIC - Dusters ☆ - Latham Studios
DUST ABATER - Filters–air - Air Kontrol Inc.
DUST-AIDE - Cleaning preparations ☆ - Herbert Stanley Co.
DUST ALL - Dust cloths - Louis M. Gerson Co. Inc.
DUST-AWAY - Pottery products ☆ - Duncan Enterprises
DUST BOWL DENIM - Jeans–women's ☆ - Labelon Corp.
DUST BRAIN - Toys ☆ - Those Characters from Cleveland, Inc.
DUST BUFF, THE - Flower pots–plastic - Liberty Ridge
DUST-DEMON - Respirators - Aearo Co.
DUST DEVIL - Cleaning preparations - FOMO PRODUCTS Inc.
DUST DEVIL - Vacuum cleaners and accessories - Royal Appliance Manufacturing Co.
DUST DEVIL DUNKEL - Beverages–malt - Super Hops!, Inc.
DUST EATER - Health care products - Permatron Corp.
DUST-EEZ - Furniture polish and wax - Nordic Industries Inc.
DUST FIGHTER - Health care products - Dust Free Inc.
DUST FREE - Air purifying and filtering units - Dust Free Inc.
DUST-GARD - Concrete products - W.R. Meadows, Inc.
DUST-GO - Mops ☆ - Golden Star Inc.
DUST GRABBER - Dust cloths - National Allergy Supply, Inc.
DUST GRABBER - Motor vehicle parts and accessories - Purolator Products Co.
DUST-GUARD - Adhesives and sealants - W.R. Meadows Inc.
DUST GUARD - Cleaning preparations - Alberto-Culver Co.
DUST GUARD - Health care products - Medical Industries America, Inc.

☆ = Now out of production

DUST HANDLERS - Mops - Suburbanite Industries

DUST HOPPER - Vacuum cleaners and accessories - Conant Custom Brass, Inc.

DUST KLEEN'R - Mops - Empire Brushes, Inc.

DUST-KLING - Cleaning preparations - Zephyr Manufacturing Co.

DUST KONTROLLER - Filters–air - Air Kontrol Inc.

DUST-LESS - Blinds–venetian - 3 Day Blinds, Inc.

DUST LOC - Dust-mop treatment - American Textile Products Co.

DUST-MAGNET - Electronic equipment - Benjamin Electroproducts Inc. (Robins Div.)

DUST MINDER - Trays - Afco Sales Co.

DUST MITT - Cleaning preparations ☆ - Liberty Ridge

DUST 'N SHINE - Cleaning preparations - K & W Products

DUST 'N SHINE - Cleaning preparations–upholstery - Missouri Hickory Corp.

DUST 'N SHINE - Furniture polish and wax - Amrep Inc.

DUST-NO-MORE - Cleaning preparations - Kleen Chemical Manufacturing Co.

DUST-OFF - Cleaning preparations - Aiken Chemical Co., Inc.

DUST-OFF - Dusting and spraying equipment–aircraft - Falcon Safety Products, Inc.

DUST-OFF PLUS - Dusting and spraying equipment–aircraft - Falcon Safety Products, Inc.

DUST-PAK - Filters–air - Airflow Systems, Inc.

DUST PATROLLER - Filters–air - Air Kontrol Inc.

DUST PLUS - Health care products - Permatron Corp.

DUST-PRO - Dust cloths - Veratec

DUST PUFF - Dust cloths - Sunshine Industries Inc.

DUST PUPPY - Dusters–feather - H.W. Products, Inc.

DUST QUEEN - Vacuum cleaners and accessories ☆ - Home Care Industries, Inc.

DUST RUNNER - Dusters–feather - Sunshine Industries Inc.

DUST SHEEN - Cleaning preparations - W.W. Grainger, Inc.

DUST TERMINATOR - Chemical preparations - Amcol International Corp.

DUST UP - Dusters - Claire Manufacturing Co.

DUST WRANGLER - Housewares - Wool Shop

DUST-X - Cleaning preparations ☆ - W.J. Hagerty & Sons Ltd. Inc.

DUSTABOUT - Vacuum cleaners and accessories ☆ - Eazypower Corp.

DUSTAC - Chemical preparations - Georgia-Pacific Corp.

DUSTAMATIC - Brushes - Pickering and Co. Inc.

DUSTAR - Air purification systems - Hein-Werner Corp.

DUSTBAN - Filters–air ☆ - Skuttle Manufacturing Co.

DUSTBUSTER - Cleaning preparations - Patrick Mastronardo

DUSTBUSTER - Respirators - Glendale Protective Technologies Inc.

DUSTBUSTER - Vacuum cleaners and accessories - Black & Decker Corp.

DUSTBUSTER PLUS - Vacuum cleaners and accessories - Black & Decker Corp.

DUSTBUSTER POWERPRO - Vacuum cleaners and accessories - Black & Decker Corp.

DUSTEATER - Skin care products - Rudolph International, Inc.

DUSTEEZ - Slippers ☆ - R.G. Barry Corp.

DUSTER - Boats–canoes - Black River Canoes

DUSTER - Motor vehicle parts and accessories - Cricket Camper Manufacturing Co.

DUSTER - Motor vehicles–automobiles ☆ - Chrysler Corp. (Chrysler-Plymouth Div.)

DUSTER - Motorcycles ☆ - Suzuki of America Automotive Corp.

DUSTER PLUS - Cleaning preparations - S.C. Johnson & Son, Inc.

DUSTERAL-MOP - Cleaning preparations - Analab Inc.

DUSTERS - Dust cloths - S.C. Johnson & Son, Inc.

DUSTERSHAL - Vitamins and nutritional supplements - Pasadena Research Laboratories, Inc.

DUSTERZ - Paper products - IFC Disposables, Inc.

DUSTFREE - Dental equipment - Dux Sales, Inc.

DUSTFYGHTER - Chemical preparations - Midwest Industrial Supply, Inc.

DUSTGRABBER - Mops - O-Cedar/Vining Household Products Co.

DUSTGUARD - Blinds–venetian - Newell Operating Co.

DUSTIKIN - Paper–tissue ☆ - Whitestone Products Inc.

DUSTIN - Apparel–women's - Eber International

DUSTIN - Cleaning implements - Sunshine Industries Inc.

DUSTIN - Ophthalmic goods ☆ - Rozin Optical Export Corp.

DUSTIN BRITTANY - Apparel–women's - Eber International

DUSTIN SAMUEL - Apparel–women's - Eber International

DUSTLOK - Fabrics–broadcloth - Fiberbond Corp.

DUSTMASTER - Dust mops - American Textile Products Co.

DUSTMASTER - Dusters - Reeves Photo Sales Inc.

DUSTMOPS - Slippers ☆ - Tru-Stitch Footwear (Div. of Wolverine World Wide)

DUSTPAN CAN, THE - Housewares ☆ - Fesco Plastics Corp.

DUSTR - Static eliminator - A-Loop Offroads

DUSTRACT - Chemical preparations - Midwest Industrial Supply, Inc.

DUSTROYER - Dust mops - American Textile Products Co.

DUSTUP - Cleaning preparations - Sprayway Inc.

DUSTY - Skin care products - Dusty Fleming

DUSTY - Toys ☆ - Mego Financial Corp.

DUSTY - Toys–stuffed ☆ - Kenner Products

DUSTY DEATH - Insecticides - Mylen Co.

DUSTY FLEMING - Hair care products - Dusty Fleming

DUSTY HAYES - Toys - Tonka Corp.

DUSTY MAUVE - Cosmetics - Lancome

DUSTY MILLER - Wines - Breitenbach Wine Cellars

DUSTY RD. - Apparel and accessories - Alexxus, Inc.

DUSTY ROSE - Colognes - Eurostar Corp.

DUSTY ROSE - Glassware–household - Fenton Art Glass Co.

DUSTY SOREBACK - Agricultural products - M-K Distributors, Inc.

DUSTY STRINGS - Musical instruments - Dusty Strings Co.

DUTCH - Cleaning preparations - Dial Corp.

DUTCH - Floor coverings ☆ - Congoleum Corp.

DUTCH ANN - Bakery products–frozen - Herold & Miller Inc.

DUTCH APPLE - Skin care products - American Image

DUTCH APPLE TREAT - Pizzas–mixes - Mr. Gatti's, Inc.

DUTCH BLEND - Tobacco products - Shepherd Tobacco Co.

DUTCH BOY - Paints - Dutch Boy Group

DUTCH BOY - Tobacco–chewing or smoking ☆ - Republic Tobacco L.P.

DUTCH BOY - Yeast - Dutch Boy Co.

DUTCH BRAND - Paints - Perry & Derrick Co.

DUTCH BRAND PLUS - Paints - Perry & Derrick Co.

DUTCH BURLEY - Tobacco products - Shepherd Tobacco Co.

DUTCH COLONY - Food products - Brokers Choice Inc.

DUTCH COUNTRY - Mushrooms - Georgio Foods Plant II

DUTCH CUPBOARD - Cookies - H.C. Brill Co., Inc.

DUTCH DELIGHT - Fruits and vegetables - John Cope's Food Products, Inc.

DUTCH ENTREES - Food products ☆ - Tyson Foods Inc.

DUTCH FAMILY - Turkeys ☆ - Wampler Foods Inc.

DUTCH FARMS - Food products - Dutch Farms, Inc.

DUTCH FARMS - Vegetables–frozen - Hanover Foods Corp.

DUTCH FAVORITE - Mushrooms - Giorgio Foods Inc.

DUTCH FRYE - Food products - Tyson Foods Inc.

DUTCH-GARD - Paints ☆ - Harrison Paint Corp.

DUTCH GARDEN - Clocks - General Time Corp. (Westclox/Seth Thomas Div.)

DUTCH GARDEN - Food products - Swiss American Import Co.

DUTCH GARDEN FARMS - Fruits and vegetables - Medina Imports, Inc.

DUTCH GIRL - Fruit butters - J.M. Smucker Co.

DUTCH GIRL - Milk - Valley of the Rogue Dairy

DUTCH GIRL - Skin care products - American Image

DUTCH GUILD - Paints ☆ - Reliable Finishing Products, Inc.

DUTCH GUILDER POTATOES - Precooked baby potatoes - Windmill Farms, Inc.

DUTCH HARBOR - Crab meat–canned or cured - Dutch Harbor Seafoods Ltd.

DUTCH HEARTH - Bread - Interstate Brands Corp.

DUTCH HENRY WINERY - Wines - Oat Hill Corp.

DUTCH KETTLE - Jams and jellies ☆ - Owen & Mowrey Inc.

DUTCH LACE - Sunblocks - Euro Rustic Inc.

DUTCH LAND - Candy - Hospitality Products & Services Inc.

DUTCH LAP - Roofing materials - GAF Corp.

DUTCH LATTICE - Dinnerware ☆ - Corning Inc.

DUTCH MAID - Brooms - Hamburg Broom Works Inc.

DUTCH MAID - Food products - Timmer Brothers

DUTCH MAID - Whipped topping–powdered ☆ - Presto Food Products, Inc.

DUTCH MASTERS - Cigar boxes–wood - Consolidated Cigar Corp.

DUTCH MASTERS - Meat products–pork - Dutch Masters Meats Inc.

DUTCH MASTERS - Paints - General Coating Technologies, Inc.

DUTCH MILK - Candy - Miss Saylor's Candies

DUTCH MILL - Breads - Dutch Mill Baking Co.

DUTCH MILL - Flowers, plants, and seeds - M.L. de Lange

DUTCH MILL BRAND - Milk–canned or powdered - Intertrade Import-Export, Inc.

DUTCH QUALITY HOUSE - Chickens - Dutch Quality House

DUTCH STANDARD - Paints - Harrison Paint Corp.

DUTCH STAR - Trailers–travel - Newmar Corp.

DUTCH SUPREME BALER TWINE - Twine - Twine Producers' Sales, Inc.

DUTCH TREAT - Bedding–linen - Dan River Inc.

DUTCH TREAT - Candy ☆ - Holland American Wafer Co.

DUTCH TREAT - Dolls ☆ - Effanbee Doll Corp.

DUTCH TREAT - Jams and jellies - Dawn Food Products Inc.

☆ = Now out of production

DUTCH TREAT - Sauerkraut ☆ - Rea-D-Pack Foods Inc.
DUTCH TREATS - Cigar boxes–wood - Consolidated Cigar Corp.
DUTCH TULIP - Glassware–household - Durand International
DUTCH TWINS - Snack foods - Holland American Wafer Co.
DUTCH VALLEY - Brisket - Brown Packing Co. Inc.
DUTCH VALLEY - Food products - Weis Markets Inc.
DUTCH VELVET - Cocoa–powders or mixes - Sara Lee Corp.
DUTCH VILLAGE - Candy - Lovelace Candy Manufacturing Co. Inc.
DUTCH WEAVE - Dinnerware–glass ☆ - Franciscan by Johnson Brothers, USA, Inc.
DUTCH WHIFFS - Cigars - Gesty Trading & Manufacturing Corp.
DUTCH WONDERLAND - Amusement parks - Earl Realty, Inc.
DUTCHBOY - Solder - Metalico Granite, Inc.
DUTCHESS - Apparel and accessories - Dutchess Lingerie
DUTCHESS - Cabinets - Crisa Corp.
DUTCHESS - Doughnuts–mixes - Dawn Food Products Inc.
DUTCHESS - Motor vehicles–motor homes ☆ - Honey Recreational Vehicles Inc.
DUTCHESS - Plastics ☆ - Rubens Originals
DUTCHESS - Postage meters - Pelouze Scale Co.
DUTCHESS - Thread ☆ - Kreinik Manufacturing Co. Inc.
DUTCHESS - Wines - Ziem Vineyards
DUTCHESS FOR WOMEN - Perfumes - Kiehl's Since 1851, Inc.
DUTCHESS JRS. - Apparel and accessories ☆ - Dutchess Lingerie
DUTCHESS MANOR - Floor coverings ☆ - Tarkett, Inc.
DUTCHIE - Pretzels - Wege Pretzel Co.
DUTCHIE - Snack food - J & J Snack Foods Corp.
DUTCHLAND FARMS - Food products - Howard Johnson Co.
DUTCHMAN MOTORSPORTS INC. - Motor vehicle parts and accessories - Dutchman Motorsports, Inc.
DUTCHNSUCH - Cookies - Sunshine/Salerno Inc.
DUTCH'S CHOICE - Cheese - Lactoprot USA, Inc.
DUTCHTECH - Apparel and accessories - Pearl Northwest, Inc.
DUTCHWOOD - Siding–insulating - Bird Inc.
DUTTON RANCH CHARDONNAY - Wines - Sebastiani Vineyards, Inc.
DUTY - Mops ☆ - Helen Keller Services for the Blind
DUTY - Safety products - Armament Systems and Procedures, Inc.
DUTY GRADE LASER - Sights–gun - Laser Devices, Inc.
DUTY MAN - Belts–apparel - Duty Man Inc.
DUVA - Apparel–athletic - Monarch Knit and Sportswear Inc.
DUVALL - Floor coverings–carpet and rugs - Duvall Adhesives
DUVALL COMPETITION SKIS - Apparel and accessories - Sammy Duvall
DUVEL - Beverages–malt - Mannekin-Brussel Imports
DUVEL - Liquors ☆ - European Beverage Co., Inc.
DUVET - Comforters - Sufolla Industries Inc.
DUVET - Crocheted and knitted items ☆ - Hampshire Hosiery, Inc.
DUVINAGE - Staircases–metal - Duvinage Corp.
DUVOID - Pharmaceutical preparations - Norwich-Eaton Pharmaceuticals
DUX - Computers - Dux Software Corp.
DUX - Crackers - Goya Foods, Inc.
DUX - Furniture - Dux Interiors Inc.
DUX-BAK - Tents - San Antonio Tent & Awning Co.
DUX BAK - Waterproofing compounds - Whittemore Polish Co.
DUX-TOX - Wood preservative ☆ - Valspar Corp.
DUX WATER WEIGHTS - Exercising equipment - Judy Ann Day
DUXBAK - Adhesives and sealants ☆ - Evans Adhesive Corp.
DUXBAK - Apparel and accessories - Duxbak Inc.
DUXBAK - Apparel and accessories - Walls Industries, Inc.
DUXBAK - Shoes - Liberty Finance Co., Inc.
DUXBURY - Publisher's imprints - PWS Publishing
DUXBURY - Water–bottled or canned - Duxbury Vermont Springs
DUXBURY LTD. - Neckties - Cornell of California Inc.
DUXIANA - Beds–wood - Dux Interiors Inc.
DUZ - Detergents - Procter & Gamble Co.
DUZ-KLEEN - Detergents - Uncle Sam Chemical Co., Inc.
DUZ-SEAL - Adhesives and sealants ☆ - Watson-Standard Co.
DUZIA DUPLA - Cartons–paperboard - Mead Corp.
DUZITAL - Paints - Lasting Paints Inc.
DUZITALL - Cleaning preparations ☆ - Uncle Sam Chemical Co., Inc.
DV - Vitamins and nutritional supplements - Healthy 'N Fit Nutritionals
DV 8 RECORDS - Recording label - Conundrum Productions Inc.
DV/DTGUARD - Electrical equipment - Trans-Coil Inc.
DV2 - Fuel additives - Getty Petroleum Marketing, Inc.
DV8 - Nail care products - Finger Mates Inc.
DV90 - Hardware - Inter-City Products Corp. (USA)
DVC - Vacuum cleaners and accessories - Home Care Industries, Inc.

DVD BROWSER PAKS - Fixtures - Chicago One Stop/Browser Display
DVD EXPRESS - Computer software - DVD Express, Inc.
DVEATOR - Video equipment - Pinnacle Systems, Inc.
D'VERSIBIT - Greenlee Textron Inc.
DVI - Catheters - Devices for Vascular Intervention, Inc.
DVIDEO - Electronic equipment ☆ - AVL
DVITS - Video communications equipment - Harris Corp.
DVL - Ducts–metal - Simpson Dura Vent Co., Inc.
DVM - Pet products ☆ - Doggy Dent International Inc.
DVM/VPI - Pet products - Veterinary Pet Insurance Co.
D.V.O. - Deodorizers - W.J. Deevy & Sons
DVP - Artists' materials - Da Vinci Paint Co. Inc.
DVR - Audio equipment - Colorado Computer Associates, Inc.
DVRT - Electronic equipment - Microstrain Co.
DVS - Computer software - Document Sciences Corp.
DVTR - Computer hardware - Indata Corp.
DVX - Wines - Domaine Mumm, Inc.
DW - Apparel and accessories - DW Partners, Inc.
DW - Drums–musical instruments - Drum Workshop, Inc.
DW - Fencing–chain link - Davis-Wire
DW - Photographic equipment - Argraph Corp. (Samigon Div.)
D.W. - Toys–stuffed - Marc & Laurie Brown, Inc.
D.W. - Toys–stuffed - Eden LLC
DW FW - Contact lenses - O.S.I. Corp.
DW LASER WALL - Wallcovering - D.W. Wallcovering, Inc.
DW3 - Apparel–women's - David Warren Enterprises, Inc.
DWALYNE - Apparel stores–lingerie - Character Foundations Inc.
DWANGO - Computer software - Interactive Visual Systems Corp.
DWARF - Projection screens - Draper Shade and Screen Co. Inc.
DWARVES - Games ☆ - Mayfair Games, Inc.
DWAYN PETERS - Skateboards ☆ - Santa Cruz Skateboards
DWAYNE HEIKES FARMS - Food products - Heikes Produce, Inc.
DWC - Watches - Daltron, Inc.
DWEEBS - Candy - Willy Wonka Brands
DWF - Pet equipment - Dog Wear Fashions Inc.
D.W.F. - Vitamin - Diet Workshop Inc.
DWICK - Wicking - Hooper Industries Inc.
DWINKLES - Food products - Moran Holding Co., Inc.
DWM - Firearms - New Helvetia Trade Group
DWORK - Toys - Mattel, Inc.
DWR DECK & WOOD PRODUCTS - Cleaning preparations - Chemique Inc.
DWSF - Apparel–children's - Shane Hunter Inc.
DWYER - Housewares - Dwyer Products Corp.
DWYER - Meters–electric - Dwyer Instruments, Inc.
DWYER MARK II - Meters–electric - Dwyer Instruments, Inc.
DX - Apparel and accessories - M. Rubin & Sons Inc.
DX - Audio equipment - Cerwin-Vega Inc.
DX - Electronic equipment - Intel Corp.
DX - Golfing equipment - MacGregor Golf Co.
DX - Herbal products - Zeneca Inc.
DX - Photographic equipment - Eastman Kodak Co.
DX - Wellcasings - Dril-Quip, Inc.
DX 25 - Sporting goods - Donnay USA
DX 111 - Pet products ☆ - Nala Barry Laboratories
DX-114 - Pharmaceutical - American Laboratories Inc.
DX-CONNECT - Computer software - Mimetics Corp.
DX DANEXX - Footwear - Medallion Shoe Corp.
DX, MDX - Generators–gas - Surface Combustion, Inc.
DX MULTI SCAN - Antennas - Wintenna Inc.
DX PATCH - Computer software ☆ - Dr. T's Music Software Inc.
DX SOLUTION SERIES - Computer software - Knowledge Industries, Inc.
DXB - Musical instruments - Design Direct Sound
DXI-RATEMASTER - Computer software - DXI Inc.
DXIX - Photographic equipment - Eastman Kodak Co.
DXL2000 - Binders - Samsill Corp.
DXPLAIN - Computer software - General Hospital Corp.
DXPRESS - Computer software - Knowledge Industries, Inc.
DY - Jewelry - Yurman Designs, Inc.
DY DEE - Dolls ☆ - Effanbee Doll Corp.
DY DEE BABY - Dolls - Effanbee Doll Corp.
DY-DEE DARLIN' - Dolls ☆ - Effanbee Doll Corp.
DY-O-DERM - Pharmaceutical preparations - Owen/Galderma Laboratories Inc.
D.Y. SPECIAL - Boats–canoes ☆ - Sawyer Composite Products
DY-TAP - Tools ☆ - Dykem Co.
DY-ZOFF - Stain removers - King Research, Inc.
DYACIDE - Aquatic pharmacuetical preparations ☆ - Aquatronics-Filtronics

☆ = Now out of production

DYACIDEX - Aquatic pharmacuetical preparations ☆ - Aquatronics-Filtronics

DYAD - Computer software - Dyad Software Corp.

DYAD - Electronic equipment - Cp Clare Corp.

DYAD - Insulating materials - Soundcoat Co., Inc.

DYANAP - Herbicides ☆ - Uniroyal Chemical Co. Inc. (Crop Protection Div.)

DYANITE LIGHTNING - Tools–hand-operated - Vermont American Corp.

DYANSHINE - Shoe polish - C.A. Zoes Manufacturing Co. Inc.

DYAX - Candles - Lumi-Lite Candle Co. Inc.

DYAZIDE - Diuretics - Smithkline Beecham Corp.

DYBELON - Veterinary pharmaceutical preparations - Boehringer Ingelheim Animal Health, Inc.

DYCE - David & Young Co., Inc.

DYCEM - Mats - Sammons Preston

DYCILL - Pharmaceutical preparations - Smithkline Beecham Corp.

DYCOR - Prosthetic apparatus - Michael T. Wilson

DYCREST - Automotive parts and accessories - NI Industries Inc.

DYCREST AUTOMOTIVE - Motor vehicle parts and accessories - Mascotech, Inc.

DYCURA - Uniforms–tailored - Angelica Uniform Group

DYDES - Infant product - Tailored Baby Inc.

DYE-A-PHOTO - Markers–felt-tip ☆ - Giorgi Process Inc.

DYE HARDS - Candy ☆ - Foreign Candy Co. Inc.

DYE HOUSE - Enamels ☆ - PPG Industries, Inc.

DYE IT - Dyes–household - G & K Craft Industries, Ltd.

DYE IT RIGHT - Dyes–household ☆ - Carnival Arts, Inc.

DYE-LITE - Dyes and pigments - Spectronics Corp.

DYE MAGNET - Detergents - Project Strategies Corp.

DYE MANAGEMENT - Medical apparatus - Abbott Laboratories

DYE-NAMICS - Stationery ☆ - Scentex Inc.

DYE NAMITE RADIANCE - Paints - Carnival Arts, Inc.

DYEABLES - Footwear - Dyeables Inc.

DYED - Floor coverings - Apache Mills Inc.

DYEING TO PLEASE YOU ! - Dyes and pigments - Hexaco, Inc.

DYENAMITE - Dyes–household ☆ - Carnival Arts, Inc.

DYENE - Photographic equipment - Retouch Methods Co. Inc.

DYER - Boats–motor - Anchorage Inc.

DYER BENNET - Recording label - Dyer-Bennet Records

DYER DELTA - Ships–sailing vessels ☆ - Anchorage Inc.

DYER DHOW - Ships–sailing vessels - Anchorage Inc.

DYER DHOW MIDGET - Ships–sailing vessels - Anchorage Inc.

DYER DINK - Ships–sailing vessels - Anchorage Inc.

DYER FLYER - Ships–sailing vessels - Anchorage Inc.

DYERCRAFT - Boats–motor - Anchorage Inc.

DYERSPORT - Fabrics - Dyersburg Fabrics Inc.

DYFLEX - Pharmaceutical preparations - Econo Med Pharmaceuticals Inc.

DYFLEX-G - Pharmaceutical preparations - Econo Med Pharmaceuticals Inc.

DYFONATE - Insecticides - Chesebrough-Pond's USA Co.

DYFORMS - Wire products - Bridon American Corp.

DYING FLUTTER - Sporting goods - James Heddon's Sons

DYKEM - Inks - Dykem Co.

DYKHOUSE - Pickles - Dykhouse Pickle Co.

DYLATE - Pharmaceutical preparations ☆ - ICN Pharmaceuticals Inc.

DYLIX - Pharmaceutical preparations - Lunsco Inc.

DYLON - Paints - E-Z Paintr Corp.

DYLOX - Insecticides - Bayer Corp. (Agriculture Div.)

DYMACEL - Footwear - Jack Schwartz Shoes, Inc.

DYMACRYL - Finishing agents - Dampney Co., Inc.

DYMAX - Adhesives and sealants - Dymax Corp.

DYMELOR - Pharmaceutical preparations - Eli Lilly and Co.

DYMENATE - Pharmaceutical preparations ☆ - Keene Pharmaceuticals Inc.

DYMETEC - Electronic equipment - Dymetrol Co., Inc.

DYMO - Office supplies - Esselte Corp.

DYMO 1000 - Labeling machinery - Esselte Corp.

DYMO 2000 - Labeling machinery - Esselte Corp.

DYMO EXECUTIVE - Embossing machines - Esselte Corp.

DYMON - Cleaning preparations–household - Dymon, Inc.

DYMORIG - Tools–power-driven - Milwaukee Electric Tool Corp.

DYMOS - Amplifiers–musical instrument ☆ - Fender Musical Instruments

DYMOSIGN - Office supplies ☆ - Esselte Corp.

DYN-A-PAK - Chemical preparations - Abbott Laboratories

DYN-O-FLO - Solar energy collectors - Heliodyne Inc.

DYN-O-LITES - Lighting fixtures ☆ - Prestigeline Inc.

DYN-O-LOG - Computer software - Patient Medical Records, Inc.

DYN-O-MAT - Floor coverings - Dyn-O-Mat, Inc.

DYN-O MELT - Deicing fluid - Cargill Salt

DYN-O MELT - Deicing fluid - Stevens Industries Inc.

DYN-O-MITE - Computer software - Patient Medical Records, Inc.

DYN-O-MOUSE D - Fireworks - Morton Kapp

DYNA - Construction equipment - Dynacrafters Inc.

DYNA - Generators–electric - Renewable Energy Ventures

DYNA - Guitars - Peavey Electronics Corp.

DYNA - Kilns - L & L Manufacturing Co.

DYNA - Mops - Lighthouse Industries

DYNA - Sandwiches–prepackaged - H-D Michigan, Inc.

DYNA - Wigs - Jean Paree Weegs Inc.

DYNA ART - Televisions ☆ - Quasar Co.

DYNA-BASS - Guitars - Peavey Electronics Corp.

DYNA-BLACK - Paints ☆ - Kyanize Paint Co.

DYNA-BOR PLUS - Health care products - Dynamic Power Laboratories

DYNA-BRIDGE - Computer software - Bell Atlantic Network Services, Inc.

DYNA-CARE - Medical apparatus - Grant Airmass Corp.

DYNA-CHARGE - Health care products - Dynamic Power Laboratories

DYNA-CHEK - Valves - Dynamic Air, Inc.

DYNA CHROME - Chromium products - Caroline Owens

DYNA COIL - Tape–masking - Superior Tape Corp.

DYNA-COIN - Nozzles - William Steinen Manufacturing Co.

DYNA CORE - Balls–baseball - J. De Beer & Son Inc.

DYNA CORR - Tape–masking - Superior Tape Corp.

DYNA-CUT - Agricultural machinery - Kondex Corp.

DYNA DISC - Wheels - Hamilton Caster & Manufacturing Co.

DYNA-DRIVE - Farm machinery - Alamo Group Inc.

DYNA DROPS - Cleaning preparations ☆ - Alleghany Pharmacal Corp.

DYNA FILTER - Filters–air - Kaz Business Systems Inc.

DYNA-FIT - Golfing equipment - Wilson Sporting Goods Co.

DYNA-FLAME - Fireplaces - Dyna Corp.

DYNA-FLAME - Kilns - Swindell-Dressler International Co.

DYNA-FLASH - Adhesives and sealants - Dynamic Fastener Service, Inc.

DYNA-FLEX - Bandages - Johnson & Johnson

DYNA FLEX - Box springs - Steadley Co.

DYNA-FLEX - Tape–masking - Superior Tape Corp.

DYNA-FLITES - Toy airplanes - Intex Recreation Corp.

DYNA-FLOW - Pens–fountain - Universal Fountain Pen & Pencil Co.

DYNA-FLOW - Sprinklers–lawn - American Tube Co. Inc.

DYNA-FORCE - Tools–plumbing ☆ - Moen Inc.

DYNA-FORM-IT - Health care products - Maddak Inc.

DYNA-FUEL - Health care products - Dynamic Power Laboratories

DYNA-GARD - Audio equipment ☆ - Renkus-Heinz Inc.

DYNA-GLIDE - Door openers–electronic ☆ - Stanley Home Automation Inc.

DYNA GLIDE - Windshields–plastic - Harley-Davidson, Inc.

DYNA-GLO - Fireplace logs–electric - RMC International, Ltd.

DYNA GRIP - Sporting goods - Ace Mitchells Bowlers Mart

DYNA GRIP - Tires - Goodyear Tire & Rubber Co.

DYNA-HOIST - Hoists ☆ - Douglas Dynamics Inc.

DYNA JET - Toys–airplanes ☆ - Victor Stanzel and Co.

DYNA-LIFT - Cranes - Machine Products Corp.

DYNA-LIGHT - Sprinklers–lawn - American Tube Co. Inc.

DYNA-LITE - Medical apparatus - Dyna Corp.

DYNA-LITE - Window shades ☆ - Bristolite Skylights

DYNA-LOK - Screws - Danek Medical, Inc.

DYNA-MATCHED - Sporting goods - Lisco, Inc.

DYNA-MATE - Fabrics - Guilford Mills, Inc.

DYNA-MATE II - Electrical equipment - General Electric Co.

DYNA-MATIC - Appliance parts - Dyna Corp.

DYNA-MATIC - Mops - Drackett Co.

DYNA-MAX - Health care products - Dynamic Power Laboratories

DYNA MECHTRONICS - Machinery - Dyna Mechtronics

DYNA MICA - Frames–picture - North American Enclosures Inc.

DYNA MIST - Air purification systems - Kaz Business Systems Inc.

DYNA-MITE - Golfing equipment - Golfsmith International Inc.

DYNA MITE - Shoes ☆ - Atsco Footwear Inc.

DYNA-MITES - Fishing lures - Brown Bear Bait Co.

DYNA-MO - Hardware - Aqua-Dyne, Inc.

DYNA MYTE - Machine tools - Dyna Mechtronics

DYNA-OPTIMO - Health care products - Dynamic Power Laboratories

DYNA-PANEL - Construction equipment - Dyna Corp.

DYNA POWER - Batteries - Conagra, Inc.

DYNA PPS - Tape–masking - Superior Tape Corp.

DYNA-PURGE - Cleaning compounds - Shuman Plastics Inc.

DYNA-QUARTZ - Insulating materials ☆ - Manville/Schuller

DYNA-RACE - Hardware ☆ - Hettich America L.P.

DYNA-ROLL - Machine parts - Dynagear Inc.

DYNA-ROPE - Pet products - For the Birds

☆ = Now out of production

DYNA S - Motor vehicle parts and accessories - Rivera Engineering, Inc.
DYNA SAND - Filters–water - Muskin Leisure Products Inc.
DYNA-SAW - Hardware - Aqua-Dyne, Inc.
DYNA-SCRUB - Cleaning preparations - Flo-Pac Corp.
DYNA-SEAL - Bags - Dynasel Corp.
DYNA-SHIELD - Fabrics - Top-Line USA Inc.
DYNA SIXTY - Tape–masking - Superior Tape Corp.
DYNA SPLICE - Tape–masking - Superior Tape Corp.
DYNA STAR - Darts and dart games - PenUltimate, Inc.
DYNA-START HERO - Batteries - Conagra, Inc.
DYNA-STAT - Measuring and dispensing pumps - Ashby-Cross Inc.
DYNA SWEET - Flowers, plants, and seeds - Tri-State Chemicals, Inc.
DYNA-SYNC - Audio equipment ☆ - Barcus-Berry Inc.
DYNA-TECH - Bicycles ☆ - Raleigh USA Bicycle Co.
DYNA-TECH - Televisions ☆ - Quasar Co.
DYNA-TEMP - Air conditioning equipment - Suburban Manufacturing Co.
DYNA-THANE - Adhesives and sealants - Siroflex, Inc.
DYNA-TONE - Health care products ☆ - Sunbeam-Oster Household Products
DYNA-TOT - Video production - Dyna-Tot Karate, Inc.
DYNA TRAK - Boats–motor - Ebbtide Corp.
DYNA-TRED - Wheels - Faultless Caster Co.
DYNA-TWIN - Electronic equipment - Telex Communications, Inc.
DYNA TWIST - Machine parts - Anderson Products, Inc.
DYNA-VALVE - Hardware - Aqua-Dyne, Inc.
DYNA VAP - Skin care products - Dynex International
DYNA VENT - Appliance parts - Dyna Corp.
DYNA-VITE - Veterinary pharmaceutical preparations - Dyna Pet Inc.
DYNA VITES - Pet products - Trophy Animal Health Care
DYNA VOX - Intercom - J & M Corp.
DYNA WRAP - Plastics film - Superior Tape Corp.
DYNAACCESS - Computer software - Cornerstone Software, Inc.
DYNABAC - Pharmaceutical preparations - Eli Lilly and Co.
DYNABACK - Braces–orthopedic - Fla. Orthopedics, Inc.
DYNABAND - Ophthalmic goods - Amcon Laboratories, Inc.
DYNABASE - Computer software - Dyna Software & Consulting, Inc.
DYNABEE - Exercising equipment - Dynabee/Variety Plastic Products
DYNABIT - Drill bits ☆ - ITW Ramset/Red Head
DYNABOLT - Golfing equipment - Plawood Mormac Corp.
DYNABOLT - Masonry sleeve anchors - ITW Ramset/Red Head
DYNABRADE - Abrasive products - Dynabrade, Inc.
DYNABRITE - Television tubes ☆ - Quasar Co.
DYNABURGERS - Dog food - Hubbard Milling Co. (Landon Div.)
DYNACE - Computer software - Algorithms Corp.
DYNACEIL - Heaters–gas - Suburban Manufacturing Co.
DYNACHEM - Chemical preparations - Morton International Inc. (Morton Salt Div.)
DYNACHROME - Vitamins and nutritional supplements - Natural Balance, Inc.
DYNACHRON - Giftware - Wyler Sales Corp.
DYNACIRC CR - Pharmaceutical preparations - Sandoz Pharmaceuticals Corp.
DYNACO - Electronic equipment - Dynaco Inc.
DYNACOIL - Footwear–athletic - KangaROOS USA Inc.
DYNACOL - Paints ☆ - Kop-Coat, Inc.
DYNACOLOR - Pearlescent pigments - Mearl Corp.
DYNACOLOR - Televisions ☆ - Quasar Co.
DYNACOLOR PLUS - Televisions ☆ - Quasar Co.
DYNACOMM/OPENCONNECT - Computer software - Openconnect Systems, Inc.
DYNACOMP - Computer software - Image Sciences Inc.
DYNACORD - Audio equipment - EVI Pro Audio Group
DYNACORD - Drums–musical instruments - Drum Workshop, Inc.
DYNACRAFT - Automotive parts and accessories - Paccar Inc.
DYNACUBE - Electronic equipment - A-Tech Corp.
DYNACURL - Hair care products ☆ - Willat Co.
DYNACYCLE - Air purification systems - Monsanto Co.
DYNACYCLE - Bicycles - Ross Bicycles USA, Ltd.
DYNACYCLE - Exercising equipment - Dicor Fitness, LLC
DYNADEPTH - Reagent filter - Vitek Systems, Inc.
DYNADERM - Bandages - Ferris Corp.
DYNADISQ - Disk drives–computer - Fujitsu Computer Products of America, Inc.
DYNADRILL - Electric tools ☆ - ITW Ramset/Red Head
DYNAFED - Pharmaceutical preparations - Body Dynamics Inc.
DYNAFILE - Tools - Dynabrade, Inc.
DYNAFILTER - Filters–air - Kaz, Inc.
DYNAFIX - Medical apparatus - EBI Medical Systems, Inc.
DYNAFLEX - Adhesives and sealants - Neyra Industries, Inc.

DYNAFLEX - Floor coverings - Congoleum Corp.
DYNAFLEX - Lasers - Laser Power Corp.
DYNAFLEX - Microwave components - Dynawave Inc.
DYNAFLEX - Razors–electric - Wahl Clipper Corp.
DYNAFLEX - Roofing materials - Schuller International, Inc.
DYNAFLO - Pet products - Rolf C. Hagen (USA) Corp.
DYNAFLOR - Adhesives and sealants - Polymer Plastic Corp.
DYNAFLOW - Engines - Gale Banks Engineering
DYNAFLOW - Heaters–space ☆ - Desa International, Inc.
DYNAFLOW 1 - Pumps–water - Lomart Industries
DYNAFLOW 2 - Pumps–water - Lomart Industries
DYNAFOLD - Office supplies ☆ - Michael Business Machines
DYNAFORM - Construction equipment - Fibergrate Corp.
DYNAFORM - Microwave components - Dynawave Inc.
DYNAGLAS PLUS - Panels - Specialty Products & Services Corp.
DYNAGLASS - Tires - Sears, Roebuck and Co.
DYNAGLAZE - Automotive parts and accessories - Nord-Viscount Corp.
DYNAGLIDE - Strollers–baby - Century Products Co.
DYNAGLOW - Heaters–space ☆ - Desa International, Inc.
DYNAGRIP - Balls–basketball - Voit Corp.
DYNAGRIP - Gloves–rubber - Granet Inc.
DYNAGRIP - Pens - Gillette Co.
DYNAGRIP - Screw drivers - Stanley Works
DYNAHAULER - Motor vehicle parts and accessories - Somerset Welding & Steel, Inc.
DYNAHEX - Skin care products ☆ - Xttrium Laboratories Inc.
DYNAHIDE - Wallpaper - Polymer Plastic Corp.
DYNAJET - Fireplaces - S and S Industries Inc. (Thermo Saver Div.)
DYNAK - Cleaning preparations - Restortek, Inc.
DYNAKUT - Abrasive products - SIA America
DYNALEVEL - Musical instruments ☆ - United Musical Instruments USA Inc.
DYNALIFE - Antifreeze ☆ - Conoco Inc.
DYNALIFT - Braces–orthopedic - Fla. Orthopedics, Inc.
DYNALINE - Air conditioning equipment - Suburban Manufacturing Co.
DYNALINK - Automotive parts and accessories - MacLean-Fogg Co.
DYNALITE - Shovels - True Temper Hardware Co.
DYNALITE GOLD - Golf club shafts - Emhart Inc.
DYNALL - Coatings - Kano Laboratories Inc.
DYNALOC - Communications equipment–microwave - Dynawave Inc.
DYNALOCK - Pipes - Explosive Fabricators, Inc.
DYNALUBE - Motor vehicle parts and accessories - Sun Co. Inc.
DYNALZER - Meters–electric - Radcal Corp.
DYNAM-EQ - Hearing aids - Qualitone
DYNAMASTER - Heaters–gas ☆ - Desa International, Inc.
DYNAMASTER - Pumps - Eugene G. Danner Manufacturing Inc.
DYNAMATCH - Paints - Niles Chemical Paint Co., Inc.
DYNAMATE - Electrical equipment - General Electric Co.
DYNAMATE - Mops - Geerpres Wringer Co.
DYNAMATIC - Television equipment - Blonder-Tongue Laboratories Inc.
DYNAMAX - Mufflers–motor vehicle - Centek Industries, Inc.
DYNAMETRIC - Bathtubs–enameled - Kohler Co.
DYNAMIC - Amplifiers–public address - Peavey Electronics Corp.
DYNAMIC - Audio equipment - TDK Electronics Corp.
DYNAMIC - Automotive parts and accessories ☆ - Lancaster Colony Automotive Group
DYNAMIC - Batteries - East Penn Manufacturing Co., Inc.
DYNAMIC - Electrical equipment - Dynamic Sales Co. Inc.
DYNAMIC - Electronic equipment - Neumade Products Corp.
DYNAMIC - Floor coverings–carpet and rugs - Eagle Carpets Inc.
DYNAMIC - Floor coverings–carpet and rugs ☆ - Len Dal Carpets
DYNAMIC - Health care products - JUZO
DYNAMIC - Machinery - Antec, Inc.
DYNAMIC - Mobile homes - Dynamic Homes Inc.
DYNAMIC - Musical instrument accessories ☆ - G. Leblanc Corp.
DYNAMIC - Thread - United Thread Mills Corp.
DYNAMIC - Vitamins and nutritional supplements - Unipro Inc.
DYNAMIC II - Clarinets ☆ - G. Leblanc Corp.
DYNAMIC ACCENT - Lipsticks ☆ - Shiseido Cosmetics (America) Ltd.
DYNAMIC BALANCE - Loudspeakers - Polk Investment Corp.
DYNAMIC COLA - Beverages–carbonated - Golden Eagle Beverages Corp.
DYNAMIC CUSHIONING - Footwear - Reebok International Ltd.
DYNAMIC DIMENSIONS! - Vitamins and nutritional supplements - Frank J. Lageman
DYNAMIC DISTRIBUTION OF FORCE - Fittings–cast iron - Ward Manufacturing Inc.
DYNAMIC DRIVE - Health care products - East Earth Herb Inc.

☆ = Now out of production

DYNAMIC DUO - Massage products - Homedics Inc.

DYNAMIC EDUCATION - Electronics equipment - American Animation Inc.

DYNAMIC FINISHES - Wallcovering - Gencorp Inc.

DYNAMIC FIT CONCEPT - Footwear–athletic - Dolomite America, Inc.

DYNAMIC FORCE - Braces–orthopedic - Generation II USA, Inc.

DYNAMIC FORCE STRAP - Braces–orthopedic - Generation II USA, Inc.

DYNAMIC FUR COLLECTION - Pet products ✰ - Flexi-Mat Corp.

DYNAMIC GEOMETRY - Computer software - Key Curriculum Press, Inc.

DYNAMIC GOLD - Golfing equipment - True Temper Sports Inc.

DYNAMIC GRAPHICS ARTWORKS - Computer storage devices–optical - Dynamic Graphics Inc.

DYNAMIC LENS - Lenses–optical - State Optical Co.

DYNAMIC LIST DISPLAY - Electronic equipment - Accom, Inc.

DYNAMIC LITE - Golf clubs - Emhart Inc.

DYNAMIC MUSCLE BUILDER - Vitamins and nutritional supplements - Weider Health and Fitness

DYNAMIC PEAKING - Radio communications equipment - JPS Communications, Inc.

DYNAMIC PLANNING WORKBENCH - Computer software - Integrated Solutions Group, Inc.

DYNAMIC POSTURE CHAIR - Wheelchairs - Ortho-Kinetics, Inc.

DYNAMIC POWER STONES - Jewelry - Jan Martin

DYNAMIC PRECISION FEEDING - Animal feeds - Purina Mills, Inc.

DYNAMIC REFERENCE FRAME, THE - Computer hardware - Imge Guided Technologies, Inc.

DYNAMIC SCHEDULING - Computer software - Gensym Corp.

DYNAMIC SEATING - Wheelchairs - American Ergonomics Corp.

DYNAMIC SIGNAL PROCESSING - Circuit boards - Electro-Voice, Inc.

DYNAMIC SOLUTIONS INTERNATIONAL - Computer peripheral equipment - Dynamic Solutions International Corp.

DYNAMIC TRIO - Vitamins and nutritional supplements - CC Pollen Co.

DYNAMIC VINYLS - Wallpaper - I. Gottlieb & Associates

DYNAMIC WARRIOR - Health care products - East Earth Herb Inc.

DYNAMICACHE - Video equipment - Ocean Information Systems, Inc.

DYNAMICELECTROCARDIOGRAPHY - Medical apparatus - Del Mar Avionics

DYNAMICRON - Electronic equipment - Sony Corp. of America

DYNAMICS - Food products - Energen Products Inc.

DYNAMICS - Wallpaper - Thybony Wallcoverings Co.

DYNAMICS 2000 PHAROH MAKING POWERFUL CONNECTIONS - Computer software - C4 Network Inc.

DYNAMICS C/S+ - Computer software - Great Plains Software Inc.

DYNAMICS OF CREATIVE SELLING - Recording label - Success Motivation, Inc.

DYNAMICS OF PERSONAL GOAL SETTING - Recording label - Success Motivation, Inc.

DYNAMICS OF PERSONAL TIME CONTROL - Recording label - Success Motivation, Inc.

DYNAMICVECTORCARDIOGRAPHY - Medical apparatus - Del Mar Avionics

DYNAMICWEB - Computer software - Dynamicweb Transaction Systems, Inc.

DYNAMIGHT - Generators–electric - Renewable Energy Ventures

DYNAMIGHTS - Toys ✰ - Intex Recreation Corp.

DYNAMINTS - Candy ✰ - American Chicle Co.

DYNAMIQUE - Clocks - General Time Corp. (Westclox/Seth Thomas Div.)

DYNAMIST - Housewares - Kaz, Inc.

DYNAMITE - Adhesives and sealants - Gibson-Homans Co. (Sealant Technology)

DYNAMITE - Apparel–men's ✰ - Munsingwear, Inc.

DYNAMITE - Dialing devices–telephone - Baltimore Luggage Co.

DYNAMITE - Games - Tonka Corp.

DYNAMITE - Headphones ✰ - Koss Corp.

DYNAMITE - Microwave components - Dynawave Inc.

DYNAMITE - Musical instrument accessories - Valley Audio Products, Inc.

DYNAMITE - Paint sprayers ✰ - Wooster Brush Co.

DYNAMITE - Popcorn ✰ - Popcorn World Inc.

DYNAMITE - Snack foods - Haydenergy Inc.

DYNAMITE - Vitamins and nutritional supplements - Dynamite Marketing Inc.

DYNAMITE 8 - Tape recorders–cassette - Matsushita Consumer Electronics Co.

DYNAMITE CROSSING - Toys–automobiles - Mattel, Inc.

DYNAMITE HOT - Chili–canned - Stagg Foods, Inc.

DYNAMITE IN DENIM - Dolls ✰ - Totsy Manufacturing Co., Inc.

DYNAMITE PLANT FOOD - Fertilizers - Lovell Farms, Inc.

DYNAMITE VITES - Vitamins and nutritional supplements - Haydenergy Inc.

DYNAMIXX - Footwear–athletic - Etonic Inc.

DYNAMO - Computer storage devices - Fujitsu Computer Products of America, Inc.

DYNAMO - Detergents - Colgate-Palmolive Co.

DYNAMO - Fishing tackle - Truline Glass Rod Manufacturing Co.

DYNAMO - Floor coverings–carpet and rugs ✰ - Southern Carpet Mills

DYNAMO - Recording label - Musicor Records Inc.

DYNAMO - Scooters–motorized - Pride Health Care, Inc.

DYNAMO - Toys - Tonka Corp.

DYNAMO - Vitamins and nutritional supplements - Tishcon Corp.

DYNAMO 2 - Detergents - Colgate-Palmolive Co.

DYNAMO ACTION PLUS - Detergents - Colgate-Palmolive Co.

DYNAMO HEAVY DUTY GENERATOR SETS - Generators–electric - Reagan Equipment Co., Inc.

DYNAMO TRIAL - Model of BENELLI minibike ✰ - Cosmopolitan Motors Inc.

DYNAMO ULTRA - Detergents - Colgate-Palmolive Co.

DYNAMO WOODSBIKE - Model of BENELLI minibike ✰ - Cosmopolitan Motors Inc.

DYNAMOMETERS - Computer hardware - Yudan, Ltd.

DYNAMOTE - Generators - Dynamote Corp.

DYNAMOTE SUPERCHARGER - Battery chargers - Dynamote Corp.

DYNAMOUNT - Tools - Dynabrade, Inc.

DYNAMOW - Lawn mowers - Dynamow, Inc.

DYNAPAC - Microwave components - Dynawave Inc.

DYNAPAD - Personal computers - Toshiba America Information Systems, Inc.

DYNAPERT - Machinery - Emhart Inc.

DYNAPHASE - Headphones ✰ - Stanton Magnetics Inc.

DYNAPHENE - Cleaning preparations ✰ - Dynasurf Corp.

DYNAPLAN - Watches - Movado Time Corp.

DYNAPLUG - Sealing compounds - Hector Engineering Co. Inc.

DYNAPOINT - Ammunition ✰ - Olin Corp. (Winchester Div.)

DYNAPOINT - Computer peripheral equipment - DynaPoint Inc.

DYNAPON - Paints - Valspar Corp.

DYNAPORE - Metals–liquid - Martin Kurz & Co., Inc.

DYNAPOWER - Cables - General Cable Corp.

DYNAPRIME - Primers - Valspar Corp.

DYNAPROBE - pH sensors - Broadley-James Corp.

DYNAPULSE - Medical apparatus - Pulse Metric, Inc.

DYNARAID - Computer storage devices - Fujitsu Computer Products of America, Inc.

DYNARAY - Heaters–space - Suburban Manufacturing Co.

DYNAREP - Computer software - Aristacom International, Inc.

DYNARISK - Computer software - Systems Development Corp.

DYNAROTOR - Combines–agricultural - Korvan Industries, Inc.

DYNASCAN - Electrical equipment - Lasertechnics, Inc.

DYNASCOPE - Toys - Criterion Co.

DYNASCRIBE - Computer software - Cornerstone Software, Inc.

DYNASET - Anchor bolts ✰ - ITW Ramset/Red Head

DYNASHEAR - Industrial machinery - Dapra Corp.

DYNASIEVE - Construction machinery - Andritz Sprout-Bauer, Inc.

DYNASOAR - Kites ✰ - Gayla Industries Inc.

DYNASOL 4 - Health care products ✰ - Sherman Pharmaceuticals, Inc.

DYNASONIC - Musical instruments - Fender Musical Instruments

DYNASONICS, INC. - Measuring instruments - Racine Federated, Inc.

DYNASORB - Adhesives and sealants ✰ - Stockhausen, Inc.

DYNASOUND - Audio and video accessories ✰ - CoStar Corp.

DYNASQL - Computer software - Cornerstone Software, Inc.

DYNASTAR - Computer software - Decision Dynamics, Inc.

DYNASTAR - Sporting goods - Skis Dynastar, Inc.

DYNASTARS - Toys ✰ - Jak-Pak Inc.

DYNASTAT - Industrial machinery - Fluid Dynamics, Inc.

DYNASTEAM - Vaporizers - Kaz Business Systems Inc.

DYNASTEP - Golfing equipment - Wilson Sporting Goods Co.

DYNASTONE - Lighting fixtures - Dynasty Classics Corp.

DYNASTORE - Computer software - Electric Power Research Institute Inc.

DYNASTRETCH - Apparel–women's - Exquisite Form Industries

DYNASTY - Air conditioning equipment - R & R Marketing Inc.

DYNASTY - Bathroom accessories - J.C. Penney Co., Inc.

DYNASTY - Batteries - Johnson Controls Inc.

DYNASTY - Bedding–linen - Sufolla Industries Inc.

DYNASTY - Bicycles - Sears, Roebuck and Co.

DYNASTY - Blinds–vertical - Steelwood Extruding Corp.

DYNASTY - Boats - Webbcraft

DYNASTY - Boats–motor - Godfrey Marine Co.

DYNASTY - Boats–motor ✰ - Bluewater

DYNASTY - Bugles - Deg Music Products Inc.

DYNASTY - Carpets, now out of production - Couristan Inc.

DYNASTY - Christmas tree ornaments - Cracker Box Inc.

DYNASTY - Cosmetics - Monaco Import/Export Inc.

✰ = Now out of production

DYNASTY - Cutlery ☆ - Regent Sheffield, Ltd.
DYNASTY - Draperies - Maharam Vertical Surfaces
DYNASTY - Fabrics - Handler Textile Corp.
DYNASTY - Fans–electric - Classic Concepts Inc.
DYNASTY - Fireplace equipment - Thomas Industries Inc. (Portland Willamette Div.)
DYNASTY - Floor coverings - Congoleum Corp.
DYNASTY - Floor coverings ☆ - Sponge-Cushion Inc.
DYNASTY - Floor coverings–carpet and rugs - Dan River Inc.
DYNASTY - Floor coverings–carpet and rugs - Gulistan Carpet Inc.
DYNASTY - Footwear - Dynasty Footwear, Ltd.
DYNASTY - Furniture - Hammary Furniture Co. Inc.
DYNASTY - Furniture ☆ - Bassett Furniture Industries, Inc.
DYNASTY - Furniture ☆ - Lane Co. Inc.
DYNASTY - Giftware - Mike Mendelson & Associates Inc.
DYNASTY - Giftware ☆ - Gorham Inc.
DYNASTY - Glassware–household - Owens-Illinois Inc. (Libbey Div.)
DYNASTY - Golfing equipment ☆ - Hillerich & Bradsby Co.
DYNASTY - Hardware - Harloc, Inc.
DYNASTY - Jewelry - Dynasty Import Co.
DYNASTY - Manicure preparations - Nailtex Inc.
DYNASTY - Motor homes - Monaco Coach Corp.
DYNASTY - Motor vehicles ☆ - Chrysler Corp. (Dodge Car Div.)
DYNASTY - Recording label - West Records
DYNASTY - Soy sauce - JFC International, Inc.
DYNASTY - Strollers–baby - Combi International Corp.
DYNASTY - Sunglasses ☆ - International Tropic-Cal Inc. (I SKI Div.)
DYNASTY - Tea kettles–nonelectric ☆ - National Housewares
DYNASTY - Telephones - Motorola, Inc. (Land Mobile Products Sector)
DYNASTY - Toys–electronic ☆ - Philips Consumer Electronics Co.
DYNASTY - Vases ☆ - Lenox Crystal, Inc.
DYNASTY - Wallpaper - Capital Carousel Inc.
DYNASTY - Watches - Pedre Co. Inc.
DYNASTY - Wheelchairs - Jaken Co., Inc.
DYNASTY - Wigs ☆ - Paula Young
DYNASTY - Wood products - Anchor Sales Corp.
DYNASTY BY NOLAN MILLER - Suits–women's - Leslie Fay Companies Inc.
DYNASTY CLASSICS - Lamps - Holiday Classics
DYNASTY CLASSICS EXPRESSIONS - Lamps - Dynasty Classics Corp.
DYNASTY COLLECTION - Bowls - Knobler International Ltd.
DYNASTY COLLECTION, THE - Tuxedos ☆ - After Six Inc.
DYNASTY DOLL COLLECTION - Dolls - Cardinal Inc.
DYNASTY PEARLS - Wallpaper - Sellers & Josephson
DYNASTY PLUS - Golfing equipment - Hillerich & Bradsby Co.
DYNASTY SACS - Luggage - Dynasty Sacs Corp.
DYNASTY SKATEBOARDS - Skateboards - Watson Laminates, Inc.
DYNASTY THE T.V. SERIES COLLECTION - Jewelry - Les Bernard Inc.
DYNASTY THREE - Wallpaper ☆ - Bob Mitchell Designs
DYNASTY TREASURES - Wallpaper - Payne Fabrics
DYNASTY TV SERIES COLLECTION - Hosiery–women's ☆ - Easton International
DYNASURF - Cleaning preparations - Dynasurf Corp.
DYNASWIVEL - Connectors–electrical - Dynabrade, Inc.
DYNASYMS - Computer software - Sentient Systems Technology Inc.
DYNATE - Pharmaceutical preparations ☆ - Hyrex Pharmaceuticals
DYNATEC - Valves–industrial - KF Enterprises, Inc.
DYNATECH - Windows–vinyl - Modern Builders Supply Inc.
DYNATEK - Motor vehicle parts and accessories - Rivera Engineering, Inc.
DYNATEL - Cables - Minnesota Mining & Manufacturing Co.
DYNATEX - Protective fabrics - Milliken & Co.
DYNATEXT - Computer software - Electronic Book Technologies, Inc.
DYNATONE - Musical instruments - Fender Musical Instruments
DYNATOUCH - Computer hardware - Dynatouch Corp.
DYNATOUCH - Computer stores ☆ - Golden Star Inc.
DYNATOUR - Golfing equipment - Northwestern Golf Co.
DYNATOUR - Golfing equipment - Pro Select Sports USA
DYNATRAIL - Heating equipment - Suburban Manufacturing Co.
DYNATREAT - Chemical preparations - Environmental Dynamics, Inc.
DYNATRIM - Pharmaceutical preparations - Lederle Laboratories
DYNATRON - Computer software - Dynatronics Research Corp.
DYNATRON - Hardware - Bondo Corp.
DYNATWIN - Air conditioning equipment - Suburban Manufacturing Co.
DYNAVALVE - Machine parts - Dynamo Enterprises
DYNAVECTOR - Phonographic needles - GNP Audio Video Inc.
DYNAVENT - Heaters–gas - Desa International, Inc.
DYNAVENT - Machinery - Albany International Corp.

DYNAVITE - Pharmaceutical preparations ☆ - Majestic Drug Co., Inc.
DYNAVOX - Computer software - Sentient Systems Technology Inc.
DYNAWALL - Heaters–space ☆ - Desa International, Inc.
DYNAWARE - Cooking equipment–household - Creative Specialty Manufacturing, Inc.
DYNAWELD - Trailers–industrial - Dynaweld, Inc.
DYNAWHEELS - Toy race cars - Intex Recreation Corp.
DYNAWHITE - Paper–bond - Weyerhaeuser Co.
DYNAWRITE - Computer software - Sentient Systems Technology Inc.
DYNAX - Rackets–racquetball - Ektelon
DYNAZONE - Fertilizers–nitrogenous - Chemical Dynamics, Inc.
DYNE TECH - Audio equipment - Shure Brothers, Inc.
DYNECO - Machinery - Dyneco International Inc.
DYNED INTERNATIONAL - Computer software - Dyned International, Inc.
DYNELASTIC - Rackets–tennis - Wilson Sporting Goods Co.
DYNEMMS - Pharmaceutical preparations ☆ - C.O. Truxton Inc.
DYNETIC - Audio equipment - Shure Brothers, Inc.
DYNEX - Skin care products - Dynex International
DYNEX - Vitamins and nutritional supplements - McKesson Home Health Care
DYNEX III - Health care products - Medtronic Nortech
DYNIQUE - Floor coverings–carpet and rugs ☆ - Columbus Mills, Inc.
DYNO - Adhesives and sealants - Superior Sewing Machine and Supply Corp.
DYNO - Batteries - Dyno Battery Inc.
DYNO - Bicycles - GT Bicycles Inc.
DYNO - Crocheted and knitted items - Schuessler Knitting Mills Inc.
DYNO - Darts and dart games ☆ - Dart World Inc.
DYNO - Explosives - Dyno Nobel Inc.
DYNO - Resins–synthetic - Dyno Overlays Inc.
DYNO CAMS - Camshafts - Bordeaux Dyno Cams
DYNO-DOTS - Goggles–safety - Sellstrom Manufacturing Co.
DYNO DUMPER - Toys - Tonka Corp.
DYNO HOLDS - Exercising equipment - Long Island Rocks, Inc.
DYNO-O-SEAL - Sealing devices - Heliodyne Inc.
DYNO-POWER - Motor vehicle parts and accessories - Custom Chrome, Inc.
DYNO-QUEST - Computer software - Mind Play
DYNO SLAMMER - Paper products - Hof, Inc.
DYNO SWEETIE - Candy - Confections by Sandra
DYNO-TOT - Apparel–children's - Baby Togs, Inc.
DYNO WAVE - Children's apparel - Advanced Trading Co., Inc.
DYNOJET - Automotive parts and accessories - Dynojet Research, Inc.
DYNOLITE - Explosives - Dyno Nobel Inc.
DYNOMAX - Exhaust systems–motor vehicle - Walker Manufacturing Co.
DYNOMITE - Infant product - Evenflo Co.
DYNOMITE - Notebooks and notepads ☆ - Agent Andy Inc.
DYNORBITAL - Sanders and grinders - Dynabrade, Inc.
DYNOSEIS - Explosives - Dyno Nobel Inc.
DYNOTAR - Electronic equipment ☆ - Navitar, Inc.
DYNOTECH PERFORMANCE - Computer peripheral equipment - Dynotech Performance, Inc.
DYNOTHANE - Cables - Peterson Systems International, Inc.
DYOT - Hats - Dyot Ventures, Inc.
DYPESRT CUSHION - Infant product - Tailored Baby Inc.
DYPHENADRYL - Pharmaceutical preparations - Schein Pharmaceutical Inc.
DYPHIL - Pharmaceutical preparations ☆ - Hyrex Pharmaceuticals
DYPROTEX - Infant product - Blistex Inc.
DYQEX - Chemical preparations - Georgia-Pacific Corp.
DYRACT - Dental compounds - Dentsply International Inc.
DYRENE - Fungicides ☆ - Bayer Corp. (Agriculture Div.)
DYRENIUM - Diuretics - Smithkline Beecham Corp.
DYRETIC - Pharmaceutical preparations ☆ - Keene Pharmaceuticals Inc.
DYREX - Veterinary product - American Home Products Corp.
DYS - Recording label - Jazz Composer's Orchestra Association Inc.
DYSART GLAZE - Vases–glass ☆ - Waterford Wedgewood USA, Inc.
DYSEAL - Dyes–household - Cello Chemical Co.
DYSONIL - Analgesics ☆ - Circle Pharmaceuticals Inc.
DYSPAS - Pharmaceutical preparations ☆ - Vortech Pharmaceuticals
DYSPEL - Pharmaceutical preparations - Dover Pharmaceutical Inc.
DYSYSTON - Insecticides - Bayer Corp. (Agriculture Div.)
DYTROL - Paint removers ☆ - Monsanto Co.
DYTUSS - Pharmaceutical preparations - Lunsco Inc.
DZ - Apparel and accessories - Discovery Zone L.P.
DZL - Fuel additives - Bell Additives, Inc.
DZL LENE - Fuel systems–motor vehicle - Texas Refinery Corp. (Lubricants Div.)
D!ZONE - Video games - WizardWorks Group Inc.
DZZACKK!! - Apparel - Paoling Hsia

☆ = Now out of production

DZZACKK!! - Footwear - Verden Imports Co. Ltd.

E

Addresses and phone numbers for the companies cited in the brands below
are available in the Company Listings section immediately following the brands listings.

E - Apparel - A.G.E.
E - Apparel and accessories - Spiegel, Inc.
E - Bowling balls - Ebonite International, Inc.
E - Outerwear - Tomen-Ein Inc.
E - Recording label - West Records
E - Vitamins and nutritional supplements - Global World Media Corp.
E-3 - Vitamins and nutritional supplements - Econo Med Pharmaceuticals Inc.
E 8 - Computer software - E-8 Publications, Inc.
E 14K - Jewelry - Eastern Jewelry Manufacturing Co. Inc.
E-200 - Health care products - Above All Health Inc.
E-400 - Health care products - Above All Health Inc.
E-1000 - Health care products - Above All Health Inc.
E-2020 - Automotive fuel - EnviroFuels Corp.
E-6000 - Adhesives and sealants - Eclectic Products Inc.
E-A - Furniture - Eck-Adams Corp.
E-A-R - Plugs–ear - Aearo Co.
E-A-R - Recording label - Edel America Records, Inc.
E & B - Dyes and pigments - E & B Manufacturing Co.
E & B - Outdoor product - Bissell Inc.
E & J - Beverages–alcohol - Ernest and Julio Gallo Winery
E & J - Cider ☆ - Diehl's Orchard & Cider Mill
E & J - Paint rollers - Elder & Jenks, Inc.
E & J - Paints - Muralo Co. Inc.
E & J PEAKE - Apparel–men's - Hubert W. White, Inc.
E & J'S DESIGNER SHOE OUTLET - Shoe stores - Famous Brand Shoes, Inc.
E AND K - Wines - E & K Wine Co.
E & M LTD. - Apparel and accessories - H.L. Miller and Son, Inc.
E & S - Mattresses - E & S Vinyl Manufacturing Inc.
E. ANTONIO'S - Bakery products - Edward A. Thompson
E ARIUS -EICKERT - Scissors–hand-operated - A. Eickert Co., Inc.
E AWARDS - Novelty items - Doc's Apothecary
E. B. FOOTE WINERY - Wines - E.B. Foote Winery
E. B. FRYE & SON - Wood products - E.B. Frye & Son Inc.
E. B. MARKS - Music–sheet - Hal Leonard Corp.
E. B. RICHFIELD - Beverages - Vero Beach Groves Inc.
E-BIOTIC - Antibiotics ☆ - Saron Pharmacal Corp.
E-BLEND - Pharmaceutical preparations - Republic Drug Co. Inc.
E-BOND 100 - Adhesives and sealants - Induron Coatings Inc.
E-BOOK - Computer storage devices–optical - Dator Corp.
E. BURNHAM - Skin care products - E. Burnham, Inc.
E. C. CARTER - Wallpaper - Greeff Fabrics Inc.
E/C LEVEL - Pharmaceutical preparations ☆ - DDI Pharmaceuticals Inc.
E CARD - Health care products - EmergencyCARD
E-CARPINE - Ophthalmic goods ☆ - Alcon Laboratories, Inc.
E CHEM - Cleaning preparations - Environmental Biotech, Inc.
E-CLASS - Motor vehicles–automobiles - Mercedes-Benz of North America Inc.
E-CLASS - Motor vehicles–automobiles ☆ - DaimlerChrysler
E CLIPS - Housewares - Candice Carter-Mann
E-CLIPSE - Animal feeds - Kentucky Equine Research, Inc.
E COAT - Paints - Kelly-Moore Paint Co. Inc.
E-COAT - Sheet metal products - Aluminum Co. of America
E COAT RECYCLED PAINT PRODUCTS - Pigments - Kelly-Moore Paint Co. Inc.
E-COL-O-GARD - Paints - John L. Armitage & Co.

E-COL-O-HIDE - Paints - John L. Armitage & Co.
E-COL-O-PLATE - Adhesives and sealants - John L. Armitage & Co.
E-COL-O-TEX - Paints - John L. Armitage & Co.
E-COLO-BEEF - Beef - Monfort, Inc.
E-CON - Electric lighting equipment - E-Mon Corp.
E-CON-O-VAC - Vacuum cleaners and accessories ☆ - General Floorcraft Inc.
E CONFERENCE - Electronic equipment - PMB Corp.
E-CREAM - Cosmetics - Elysee Scientific Cosmetic Co.
E-CUTTER - Dental equipment - Brasseler USA, Inc.
E-CYPIONATE - Pharmaceutical preparations - Legere Pharmaceuticals Inc.
E/D - Lenses–optical - Sola Optical USA, Inc.
E D B - Jewelry–precious - Equity Diamond Brokers Inc.
E. #DILLON & CO. - Blocks–concrete - E. Dillon and Co.
E-DISK - Electronics equipment - Grass Valley Group Inc.
E-DRUM - Musical instruments ☆ - E-Mu Systems, Inc.
E EASTPORT - Apparel and accessories - Starter Corp.
E EDGE - Photographic equipment - Edge Reps, Ltd.
E EFCO - Windows - Efco Corp.
E ELITE MICROELECTRONICS INC. - Computers–mainframe - Elite Microelectronics Inc.
E ENSEC - Computers - Ensec, Inc.
E ENTERPRISE - Automotive repair shops - Enterprise Rent-A-Car Co.
E ENVIROSENSE - Paints - Interface, Inc.
E EPITAPH - Compact discs–prerecorded - Epitaph
E ERGO PLUS - Computer software - Ford Motor Co.
E ESTAR FASHIONS - Apparel–women's - Fashion Fun, Inc.
E. F. DEAN - Musical instruments - Custom Music Co.
E-F TONE - Skin care products - Lois Yee Cosmetics Inc.
E F X ELLIPTICAL FITNESS CROSSTRAINING - Exercising equipment - Precor Inc.
E-FAB - Electronic equipment - Xerox Corp.
E-FILE - Computer software - Edwin J.Stolarz
E FILES - Office supplies - Rubbermaid Office Products Inc.
E-FLEX - Alarm systems–burglar - Stellar Security Products, Inc.
E-FLOW - Cooking equipment–commercial - Wolfe Electric Co.
E FONTS - Computer peripheral equipment ☆ - Harvey-Hunt Inc.
E-FORM - Computer software - Computer Language Research Inc.
E-FOUNT - Farm machinery - Ahrens Agricultural Industries, Inc.
E. G. SMITH - Socks - World Love Productions Inc.
E. G. SMITH SOCKS - Hosiery - E.G. Smith Socks
E. GADD! - Apparel–women's - Decorp Inc.
E-GARD HARDWARE - Hardware - Truth Hardware Corp.
E-GARD PROTECTED - Hardware - Truth Hardware Corp.
E-GEM - Skin care products - J.R. Carlson Laboratories Inc.
E-GEMS - Skin care products - J.R. Carlson Laboratories Inc.
E-GEMS PLUS - Vitamins and nutritional supplements - J.R. Carlson Laboratories Inc.
E-GLOSS - Lip makeup - Cabot Laboratories Inc.
E GRANDE EPICURE - Cutting boards - Foley-Martens Co.
E-GROUP - Computer software - Lebhar-Friedman, Inc.
E. GUIGAL - Wines - Classic Wine Imports Inc.
E-I-E-I-O - Toys - EIEIO Inc.
E-IONATE P.A. - Pharmaceutical preparations ☆ - Solvay Pharmaceuticals Inc.
E. J. GITANO - Socks - Renfro Corp.
E-JAY - Shoes ☆ - Endicott Johnson Corp.
E. JOVEN - Apparel–men's - Farah Inc.

☆ = Now out of production

675

E/L - Exercising equipment - Precor Inc.

E-LAB - Furniture–laboratory - Case Systems, Inc.

E-LEGAL BOOKS - Books–blank - E-Z Legal Forms, Inc.

E-LEMONATOR, THE - Cleaning preparations - Nutrition for Life International, Inc.

E-LINE - Calendars - Skinner & Kennedy Co.

E-LINE - Computer furniture ☆ - Invincible Metal Furniture Co.

E-LINE - Ophthalmic goods - Sola Optical USA, Inc.

E-LINE - Trailers - U.S. Cargo, Inc.

E-LINE - Wire products - Jesco Industries, Inc.

E-LINK - Computer software - Electronic Form Systems Inc.

E-LITE - Vitamins and nutritional supplements - Solaray

E-LOC - Electronic equipment - Etco Specialty Products Inc.

E-LOC - Electronic equipment - General Motors Corp.

E-LOY - Valves–engine - S.B. International, Inc.

E-MAG - Computer storage devices–optical - Gametek, Inc.

E. MAGRATH - Apparel–men's ☆ - Haggar Corp.

E-MAIL CONNECTION - Computer software - Adonis Corp.

E-MAILMCI - Computer software - MCI Communications Corp.

E MALAMA I KA MOANA - Apparel - Leprevost Corp.

E-MANUAL - Computer peripheral equipment - Scott I. Turner

E. MARTIN SACHSEN - Musical instruments - C. Bruno & Son Inc.

E MASTER - Welding and cutting kits - Esab Welding & Cutting Products

E-MAX - Golfing equipment - Slotline Golf

E-MEM - Electronics equipment - Grass Valley Group Inc.

E-MERGE - Computer software - Vanier

E-MF - Insulating materials - High Voltage Engineering Corp.

E-MID CARD - Paper–coated - Phyllis Abbott

E-MSG! - Electronic equipment - Masterminds Premier Business Consultants, Inc.

E-MU - Musical instruments - E-Mu Systems, Inc.

E MYCIN - Pharmaceutical preparations - Boots Pharmaceuticals Inc.

E-MYCIN - Pharmaceutical preparations - Upjohn Co.

E N - Computer hardware - En Technology Corp.

E-NA MOLLYE - Craft supplies - Philadelphia Ceramics Inc.

E-NEWS - Computer software - Ion Systems, Inc.

E NOS LIVES - Computer software - Sony Interactive Entertainment Inc.

E/NU - T-shirts–men's - Mobius VI

E/NU - T-shirts–men's - Mobius VI

E-OK - Envelopes–paper - E-OK Inc.

E ON - Remote control devices - TV Answer, Inc.

E. ORSINI FINE ART - Toys ☆ - Arthur Court Designs Inc.

E/P - Dental compounds - Implant Innovations, Inc.

E P - Hair care products - Edwin Paul, Inc.

E-P - Radio communications equipment - Motorola, Inc. (Land Mobile Products Sector)

E. P. DUTTON - Publisher's imprints - E.P. Dutton Inc.

E-PATROL - Bags–paper - Planet Productions, Inc.

E-PHICIENT - Cleaning preparations - Polychem Corp.

E-PHORESIS - Skin care products - Fanie International

E-PILO - Prescription ophthalmic - Iolab Pharmaceuticals

E-PLEX - Lawn mowers - Ransomes-Cushman-Ryan

E-PLUS - Motors–hydraulic - Magnetek Inc.

E-POLY-KOTE - Epoxy - American Chem-Tech Inc.

E-POX-E - Glue–household or industrial ☆ - Loctite Corp.

E-QUALIDYNE - Microphones ☆ - Shure Brothers, Inc.

E-QUIP - Computer software - Alacrity Systems Inc.

E-R-O - Cold remedies - Schering-Plough Healthcare Products

E. REMINGTON - Ammunition ☆ - Remington Arms Co., Inc.

E-ROV - Water transportation - Benthos Inc.

E-RUNNER - Computer software - I.R.S.C., Inc.

E. S. LOWE - Games - Milton Bradley Co.

E-SEA SAIL - Computer software - Innovative Logistics Inc.

E-SEEL - Rubber–silicone - A.P.M. Hexseal Corp.

E-SEL - Vitamins and nutritional supplements - J.R. Carlson Laboratories Inc.

E SERIES - Filing cabinets–metal - Krueger International, Inc.

E SERIES - Musical instrument accessories - J. D'Addario & Co. Inc.

E-SERIES 5000 - Escalators - Montgomery Kone Inc.

E SERIES MINI FRAME - Fireplace equipment - Schaefer Co.

E SERIES MINI FRAME CLASSIC - Fireplace equipment - Schaefer Co.

E-SERIES TR - Escalators - Montgomery Kone Inc.

E-SMART - Electrical equipment - Eagle Electric Manufacturing Co., Inc.

E. SOLUTIONS - Computer software - GTE Service Corp.

E-SOLVE - Pharmaceutical preparations - Syosset Laboratories Inc.

E SOURCE - Vitamins and nutritional supplements - Nutra-Source Corp.

E-SPACE - Hotels and motels - Holiday Inns, Inc.

E-SQUARED - Recording label - E-Squared, LLC

E STEP WATCH - Measuring instruments - Theodore J. Batlas

E STREET - Apparel and accessories - Pyke Manufacturing Co.

E STYLE - Apparel and accessories - Spiegel, Inc.

E-STYLE - Lenses–optical - X-Cel Optical Co.

E STYLE E - Apparel and accessories - Spiegel, Inc.

E-SWITCH - Electronic equipment - Electronic Components Groupe, Inc.

E-TAPP - Pharmaceutical preparations ☆ - Edwards Pharmaceuticals, Inc.

E-TEA - Vitamins and nutritional supplements - Lifetrends International

E-THERM - Doors–glass - Acorn Window Systems Inc.

E THREADS - Apparel and accessories - Educational Wear Inc.

E TICKET - Computer software - Rick Gibson

E-TOP - Counter tops–laminated - Hartson-Kennedy Cabinet Top Co., Inc.

E-TUBE - Air purification systems - Geoenergy International Corp.

E TUI - Crocheted and knitted items - Walbead Inc.

E-V - Amplifiers - Electro-Voice, Inc.

E-VAP - Electronic equipment - MDC Vacuum Products Corp.

E-VISTA - Pharmaceutical preparations - Seatrace Co.

E-VITAL - Skin care products - Pasadena Research Laboratories, Inc.

E. W. DANIELS - Hardware - Sea Spike Marine Supply Co. Inc.

E. W. KNEIP - Corned beef - Pioneer Food Sales Inc.

E. WALDO WARD - Marmalade - E. Waldo Ward & Son

E WEAR - Apparel and accessories - Nordstrom, Inc.

E-WIPE - Cleaning preparations - Photographic Solutions, Inc.

E WIRES - Eyeglasses - Oakley, Inc.

E-XL - Computer hardware - Exlibris

E-Z - Adhesives and sealants - Elroy Turpentine Co.

E-Z - Brushes - Wright-Bernet

E-Z - Easels ☆ - Martin F. Weber Co.

E-Z - Electronic equipment - Screen Works

E-Z - Fencing–wood - Master Halco Inc.

E-Z - Fencing–wood ☆ - Pan Am Agri Fabric

E-Z - Food products ☆ - Enzo-Pac Inc.

E-Z - Garden equipment - Kinsman Co. Inc.

E-Z - Locks–door - Lewis Hyman, Inc.

E Z - Medical apparatus - Home Hospital Equipment Co.

E-Z - Motor vehicle parts and accessories - KP Industries

E-Z - Musical instrument accessories - Humes & Berg Manufacturing Co. Inc.

E-Z - Novelty items - Creative Balloons Manufacturing Inc.

E-Z - Paint sets–hobby ☆ - Canson-Talens Inc.

E-Z - Rakes - Evergreen International, Inc.

E-Z - Stencils - E-Z Industries Inc.

E Z - Sunglasses ☆ - Bolle' America, Inc.

E-Z - Tools–garden ☆ - Compac Industries Inc.

E-Z - Tripods–photographic ☆ - Edixa Camera Co.

E-Z - Varnishes - E.E. Zimmerman Co.

E-Z - Washers–metal - Viking Engineering Inc.

E-Z-2 VUE - Optical machinery - Coburn Optical Industries Inc.

E-Z 15 - Paints ☆ - Montgomery Ward & Co. Inc.

E-Z ACCESS - Trays - Houck Industries Inc.

E-Z ACCOUNTING, INC. - Stationery - E-Z Accounting, Inc.

E-Z ACTION - Footwear–women's - E.S. Originals, Inc.

E-Z AJUST - Cabinets–metal - B-O-F Corp.

E-Z ANCHORS - Nuts and bolts - Auto Vehicle Parts Co.

E-Z ANCOR - Self-drilling anchors - ITW Ramset/Red Head

E-Z ANGEL BOWZ - Tools–hand-operated - E-Z Bowz, LLC

E-Z ANGLE - Tables–metal - Tapco International Corp.

E-Z-AP - Veterinary medical equipment - Y-Tex Corp.

E-Z-BAKE - Flour–blended - Acme-Evans/A.D.M. Milling Co.

E-Z BAKER - Bakery products - G & S Metal Products Co., Inc.

E-Z BAKER INSULATED - Bakery products - G & S Metal Products Co., Inc.

E-Z BALLOON DISC - Toys - Creative Balloons Manufacturing Inc.

E-Z BEE - Toys–airplanes ☆ - Cox Products Inc.

E-Z BEE II - Toys–airplanes ☆ - Cox Products Inc.

E-Z BEE SPORT - Toys–airplanes - Cox Products Inc.

E-Z BEST - Petroleum - E.E. Zimmerman Co.

E-Z BLEED - Brake parts - EIS Brake Parts

E-Z BLO - Chewing gum ☆ - Spangler Candy Co.

E-Z BLO - Tools–garden ☆ - Evergreen International, Inc.

E-Z BLOCK - Hardware - Vagedes Industries Inc.

E-Z BOND - Window coverings - Solar-Screen Corp.

E-Z BORE - Drill bits - Greenlee Textron Inc.

E-Z BOW MAKER - Tools–hand-operated - E-Z Bowz, LLC

E-Z BREAK - Lubricants - La-Co Industries, Inc.

E-Z BREATHERS - Health care products - EZ Kare Good Health Systems, Inc.

E-Z BREEZE - Fans–electric - Lomanco Inc.

☆ = Now out of production

E Z BREEZE - Veterinary nutritional supplements - Oralx Corp.
E-Z BUSINESS SOFTWARE - Computer software - E-Z Legal Forms, Inc.
E-Z-C - Stationery - Dennison National Co.
E-Z CALL - Sporting goods ☆ - Penn's Woods Products Inc.
E-Z CAM - Cameras - Proex Photo Systems, Inc.
E-Z CANNING - Condiments ☆ - Dean Pickle & Specialty Products Co.
E-Z CARE - Cribs–metal ☆ - HARD Manufacturing Co. Inc.
E-Z CARE - Swimming pools ☆ - E-Z Clor Systems
E-Z CARE-E - Sporting goods - Rec Aids Co.
E-Z CARVE - Food products - Bar S Food Co. Inc.
E-Z CATCH - Traps–animal - Estelle Jonason
E-Z CHANGE - Mops ☆ - American Textile Products Co.
E-Z CHECK'R - Fishing tackle - GHS, Inc.
E-Z CLEAN - Bulletin boards–cork ☆ - Congoleum Corp.
E-Z CLEANER - Vacuum cleaners and accessories - Penn-Plax, Inc.
E-Z CLOR - Swimming pools - E-Z Clor Systems
E-Z COAT - Shortening - Bunge Foods Corp.
E-Z COLOR - Paints - RG Enterprises
E-Z-COMB - Pet products - E-Z Grip Ltd.
E-Z CONNECT - Amplifiers - Proctor and Associates Inc.
E-Z CONSTRUCTION ESTIMATOR - Computer software - E-Z Legal Forms, Inc.
E-Z CONTRACTORS FORMS - Forms–preprinted - E-Z Legal Forms, Inc.
E-Z COOK-IN' - Cooking equipment–household ☆ - E-Z-Por Corp.
E-Z CUT - Hams - Chiquita Brands, Inc.
E-Z CUT - Plates–steel - Dick Blick Co.
E-Z CUTTER - Hardware - Rothenberger USA, Inc.
E-Z D - Cleaning preparations - Armor All Products Corp.
E-Z-DIP - Stain removers - Unit Chemical Corp.
E-Z DO - Electrical equipment - Triangle Wire & Cable, Inc.
E-Z DOES IT - Tableware–plastic - E-Z-Por Corp.
E-Z-DOOR-LOKS - Locks–door ☆ - M.A.G. Engineering & Manufacturing Co. Inc.
E-Z DOZIT - Fuel additives - Berryman Products Inc.
E-Z DRIVES - Computer storage devices - Syquest Technology, Inc.
E-Z DU SCENIC MURALS - Wallpaper ☆ - Imperial Wallcoverings, Inc.
E-Z EDGE - Construction machinery - Idrs, Inc.
E-Z EDGE - Hair care products - Fromm Industries
E-Z ELECTRICS - Toys–models - Cox Products Inc.
E-Z ELEGANCE - Trays - E-Z-Por Corp.
E Z EMPTY - Vacuum cleaners and accessories - The Hoover Co.
E-Z-EST - Cleaning preparations - Aervoe-Pacific Co. Inc.
E-Z FEED - Fertilizers - Aqua-Trol Corp.
E-Z FILL - Funnels - Dazey Corp.
E Z FILL - Pet products - Van Ness Plastics Molding Co., Inc.
E-Z FILTER CLEANER - Cleaning preparations - Robarb Inc.
E-Z FIT - Barbecue-grill parts and accessories - American Wick Co. Inc.
E-Z FIX - Hardware - Wal-Rich Corp.
E-Z-FLEX - Abrasive products - Norton Co.
E-Z FLEX - Automotive parts and accessories - Pirelli Power Transmission Corp.
E-Z FLO - Breathing equipment - Figgie Licensing Corp.
E-Z-FLO - Shortening - Kraft Food Ingredients Corp.
E-Z FLOW - Bottles–plastic - First Brands Properties Inc.
E-Z FLOW - Pottery products - Duncan Enterprises
E-Z FLOW - Solvents ☆ - Fry Technology
E-Z FOIL - Foil–aluminum - E-Z-Por Corp.
E-Z FOLD - Containers–paper - Georgia-Pacific Corp.
E-Z FOLD - Eyewear - Criterion/Cool-Ray Corp.
E-Z-FOLD - Musical instrument accessories - Humes & Berg Manufacturing Co. Inc.
E-Z FOLD - Projection screens - Screen Works
E-Z FOLD GIANT ROLL CARTS - Carts - Screen Works
E-Z FOLD ROLL CARTS - Carts - Screen Works
E-Z FORM - Formable vinyl ☆ - Athol Corp.
E-Z FRAME - Frames–picture - Lightpost Publishing, Inc.
E-Z FREE - Lubricants - X-I-M Products Inc.
E-Z GARD - Mouth guards - E-Z Gard Industries, Inc.
E-Z GARD - Seats–automobile - Kolcraft Enterprises, Inc.
E-Z-GLIDE - Automotive parts and accessories ☆ - Midwest Sunroofs
E-Z GLIDE - Hardware - Engineered Products Co.
E-Z GLIDE - Lamps–desk - Art Specialty Co. Inc.
E-Z GLIDER - Pet products - Carter-Wallace, Inc.
E Z GO - Barbecues and grills - E Z Q Products, Inc.
E Z GO - Barbecues and grills - EZQ Products, Inc.
E-Z-GO - Housewares - Amaza Laboratories Inc.

E-Z GO - Strollers–baby - Century Products Co.
E-Z-GO - Toys ☆ - Imperial Toy Corp.
E-Z-GO BLUE - Housewares ☆ - Amaza Laboratories Inc.
E-Z-GO GRITS - Housewares - Amaza Laboratories Inc.
E-Z-GRAPH - Medical apparatus - E-Z Graph of Victoria, Inc.
E-Z GRIP - Drafting supplies - Mayline/Hamilton
E-Z GRIP - Film - Scherer Manufacturing Co.
E/Z GRIP - Hooks - Vulcan-Volner Manufacturing Corp.
E-Z GRIP - Pet products - E-Z Grip Ltd.
E-Z GROUND - Electrical equipment - Eagle Electric Manufacturing Co., Inc.
E-Z HANDY HELPER - Cooking utensils–enameled - G & S Metal Products Co., Inc.
E-Z HANDY HELPER SMART GRIPS - Cooking utensils–enameled - G & S Metal Products Co., Inc.
E-Z HEAT - Starch - American Maize-Products Co.
E-Z HINGE - Hinges - Cardinal Aluminum Co.
E-Z HOLD - Glue–household or industrial - Handcraft Designs Inc.
E-Z HOLD - Tools - Adjustable Clamp Co. Inc.
E Z I PADSTER - Binders - Angler's Roslyn Group Ltd.
E-Z ICE MAKER - Ice buckets - E-Z-Por Corp.
E/Z ICER - Health care products - Icer International Inc.
E-Z-JAX - Sailboat control system - E-Z-Jax Systems, Inc.
E-Z JECT - Health care products - Can-Am Care Corp.
E-Z JELLY - Lubricating oils - Chester Labs, Inc.
E-Z JIVE - Bicycles - Neal Enterprises
E-Z KARE - Health care products - EZ Kare Good Health Systems, Inc.
E-Z KARE - Paint - Cotter & Co.
E-Z KARE - Pigments–paint - Tru-Test Manufacturing
E-Z KEEP - Cheese - American Cheeseman Inc.
E-Z KITCHEN - Furniture - Vartta, Inc.
E-Z KLAMP - Electrical equipment - Eagle Electric Manufacturing Co., Inc.
E-Z KLEEN - Palettes - Anco Wood Specialties Inc.
E-Z KLEEN - Palettes - Winsor & Newton
E-Z KLENZ - Napkins–paper ☆ - Robert Burton Associates Ltd.
E-Z KNIT - Yarn ☆ - Coats and Clark Inc.
E-Z KOTE - Paints ☆ - Plasti-Kote Co. Inc.
E-Z-KURL - Exercising equipment - York Barbell Co., Inc.
E-Z LATCH - Fencing–gates and posts - Master Halco Inc.
E Z LEDGER - Computer software - Right on Programs
E-Z LEGAL - Business forms - American Legal Forms Inc.
E-Z LEGAL FORMS - Forms–preprinted - E-Z Legal Forms, Inc.
E-Z LEGAL SOFTWARE - Computer software - E-Z Legal Forms, Inc.
E-Z LETTER - Stencils - E-Z Industries Inc.
E Z LIFT - Medical apparatus - Home Hospital Equipment Co.
E-Z LIFT - Motor vehicles–trucks - Atlas Lift Truck Rentals & Sales, Inc.
E-Z LIFTER - Moldings and trim - PCS Co.
E-Z LIK POPS - Candy - Gladstone Candies
E-Z LINERS - Machinery - EZ-Liner Industries
E-Z-LINK - Electronics equipment - Grass Valley Group Inc.
E-Z LITE - Golf carts - Global Edge, Inc.
E-Z LOADER CARRYING BAGS - Saddles - Thornhill Enterprises, Inc.
E-Z LOCK - Knives–pocket - Sea Quest, Inc.
E-Z-LOK - Tobacco pouches - Allied Products Corp.
E-Z-M JIVE - Bicycles - Neal Enterprises
E-Z MAGIC - Toys - D. Robbins & Co. Inc.
E-Z MARK - Tools - Adjustable Clamp Co. Inc.
E Z MASK - Hardware - Ambroid Co.
E-Z MATE - Golf carts - Global Edge, Inc.
E-Z-MATIC - Tools–hand-operated ☆ - Durall-Eagle Tools
E-Z MERC - Lamps - General Electric Co.
E-Z MERGE - Paper products - CBR Information Group, Inc.
E-Z MINI ANCOR - Anchors - Illinois Tool Works Inc.
E-Z MIX - Veterinary products - Ecolab Inc.
E-Z MIXER - Mixers–concrete - Garon Products Inc.
E-Z MOUNT - Frames–picture - Adolph Burkland & Sons Inc.
E-Z MOUNT - Plow blade mountings - Louis Berkman Co.
E-Z-ON - Apparel stores–lingerie - Goddess Bra
E-Z-ON - Dampers - Gerett Products Div.
E-Z-ON - Paints - Farwest Paint Manufacturing Co. Inc.
E-Z ON - Pet products - Nor-Con Knits
E-Z ON - Toilet seats - Magnolia Products
E-Z ON/E-Z OFF - Toilet seats - Magnolia Products
E-Z OPEN - Briefcases - Standard Brief Case Co. Inc.
E-Z OUT - Carbon and graphite products - Uarco Inc.
E-Z-PACK - Automotive parts and accessories - General Motors Corp.
E-Z PAK - Containers–plastic - E-Z Pak Amenities Inc.

☆ = Now out of production

E-Z PAVE - Asphalt - Tough Patch, Inc.
E-Z PEEL - Paints ☆ - Vanguard Paints & Finishes Inc.
E-Z-PERMA-SEAL - Sealing compounds - CGM Inc.
E-Z PICKENS - Skin care products - Crown Health Equipment Co.
E Z PICKER - Golfing equipment - Easy Picker Golf Products Inc.
E-Z PILOT - Computer software - Hartley Courseware Inc.
E-Z PLAQUE - Computer software - E-Z Legal Forms, Inc.
E-Z PLAY TODAY - Musical instrument accessories - Hal Leonard Corp.
E-Z POND - Pet products - Golden Pond Inc.
E-Z-POP - Oils–edible - Detroit Popcorn Co.
E-Z-POP POPCORN - Popcorn - Micro-Pop Distributors, Inc.
E-Z POR - Housewares - E-Z-Por Corp.
E-Z POST - Mail boxes ☆ - American Vinyl Products
E-Z POUR - Containers - Bunn-O-Matic Corp.
E-Z POUR - Insulating materials–foam - Casco Mineral Wool
E-Z-PREP - Paints - Allpro Corp.
E-Z PRIME - Paints - Dunn Edwards Corp.
E-Z PRO - Binders - Columbus Mckinnon Corp.
E-Z PULL - Rivets–metal - Arrow Fastener Co. Inc.
E-Z REACH - Bathroom accessories - Better Sleep, Inc.
E-Z REACHER - Tools - Arcoa Industries
E-Z READ - Braille slates - Howe Press
E-Z-READ - Glassware–household - Crossbow Inc.
E-Z READ - Pet products - D & D Enterprises
E-Z-READ - Tools ☆ - Durall-Eagle Tools
E-Z READER - Thermometers ☆ - Hawaiian Marine Imports Inc.
E-Z READERS - Eyeglasses - AAI/ACCESSORIES Associates Inc.
E-Z RECORD - Telephone directories - E-Z Industries Inc.
E-Z REDI - Food products - Chiquita Brands, Inc.
E-Z RESIN - Food products - Givaudan Roure
E-Z RIDER - Automotive parts and accessories - Thor Tech, Inc.
E-Z RIM - Wood products - Willamette Industries, Inc.
E-Z RITE - Electronic equipment - Advance Products Co. Inc.
E-Z-ROL - Hats - Henschel Manufacturing Co.
E-Z-ROL - Kitchen utensils–aluminum - Omessi Group
E-Z ROLL - Golf carts - Climax Clothing Industries, Inc.
E-Z ROLLER - Infant product ☆ - Graco Children's Products
E-Z ROSE MAKER - Tools–hand-operated - E-Z Bowz, LLC
E-Z SAMPLER - Laboratory apparatus - Wheaton Holding, Inc.
E-Z SANTA BOWZ - Tools–hand-operated - E-Z Bowz, LLC
E-Z SCAN - Photographic equipment - Eastman Kodak Co.
E-Z SCARF - Window coverings - CHF Industries, Inc.
E-Z SCOOP - Pet products - Nel-Rich Products Inc.
E-Z SEAL - Sealing compounds - Gibson-Homans Co.
E-Z SEAM - Tape–adhesive - Capitol Adhesives Inc.
E-Z SET - Fireplaces ☆ - Superior Fireplace Co.
E Z SHARP - Knife blades - Creative Products International Inc.
E-Z SHOE-ON - Health care products ☆ - Arcoa Industries
E-Z SOAK-OFF - Paints ☆ - Vanguard Paints & Finishes Inc.
E-Z SPACER - Medical apparatus - We Pharmaceuticals, Inc.
E-Z SPIN - Tiles–asphalt - Garden Way Inc.
E-Z SPREAD - Frosting - J.W. Allen & Co.
E-Z STAC - Trays - Stainless Metal Products Co. Inc.
E-Z STAMP - Stamps–hand - Diener Industries Inc.
E-Z STAMP - Stamps–hand - WINCRAFT
E Z STAND - Medical apparatus - Home Hospital Equipment Co.
E-Z-STOR - Office supplies - Safco Products Co.
E-Z STRIP - Paints ☆ - Steelcote Manufacturing Corp.
E-Z STUFF - Fibers–polyester - Fairfield Processing Corp.
E-Z SWEEP - Cables - Ralph C. Kendrick, Jr.
E-Z SWING - Tools - Vaughan & Bushnell Manufacturing Co.
E-Z SYTE - Chalk - Binney & Smith Inc.
E-Z TAIL - Tools–hand-operated - Nils P. Fornell
E-Z TILE GROUT - Sealing compounds - CGM Inc.
E-Z TILT - Office machines - Stenograph Corp.
E-Z TILT - Windows–storm - Marvin Windows and Doors
E-Z TILT PAC - Windows–storm - Marvin Windows and Doors
E-Z TITE - Rope - Hooven Allison
E-Z TONE - Musical instrument accessories - United Musical Instruments USA Inc.
E-Z-TOP - Pet products - Novalek, Inc.
E-Z-TOTE - Dumbwaiters - Sedgwick Lifts Inc.
E-Z TRACE - Wire - Falcon Fine Wire and Wire Products, Inc.
E-Z TRACK - Computer storage devices - E-Z Data, Inc.
E-Z TRACT - Tools - Granberg International
E-Z TRAIL - Trailers–truck - E-Z Trail Inc.

E-Z TRAVELER - Luggage ☆ - Lark Luggage Co. Inc.
E-Z TREATS - Vitamins and nutritional supplements - Landco
E-Z TRIMMER - Razors - Wahl Clipper Corp.
E-Z TUCK TOP - Containers - Technology Container Corp.
E-Z TWIRL - Fasteners - B-Line Systems, Inc.
E-Z UP - Awnings - International EZ Up, Inc.
E-Z UP - Cardboard - Gibson Greetings, Inc.
E-Z-UP - Clamps - Lectro-Stik Corp.
E-Z USE - Food products - J.W. Allen & Co.
E-Z-V - Cooking equipment–household - Trepte Wire and Metal Works
E-Z VAC - Cleaning equipment - Kreepy Krauly USA, Inc.
E-Z VAC - Tools–garden - Evergreen International, Inc.
E-Z VIEWER - Electronic equipment - Telex Communications, Inc.
E-Z VINYL - Wallpaper ☆ - Imperial Wallcoverings, Inc.
E-Z VISION - Cleaning preparations ☆ - National Aerosol Products Co.
E-Z WALL TILE - Tools–garden ☆ - Compac Industries Inc.
E-Z-WATERPROOFER - Sealing compounds - CGM Inc.
E-Z-WAY - Tools–garden - Gilmour Manufacturing Co.
E-Z WELD - Solvents - Fry Technology
E-Z WELD - Welding alloys - SDI Operating Partners
E-Z WET-PLUG - Sealing compounds - CGM Inc.
E-Z WHEELER - Luggage - Lark Luggage Co. Inc.
E-Z WIDER - Paper–cigarette - Robert Burton Associates Ltd.
E-Z-WIN - Housewares ☆ - Amaza Laboratories Inc.
E-Z WIND - Skis - Ve-Ve Inc.
E-Z WIRE - Electrical equipment - Eagle Electric Manufacturing Co., Inc.
E-Z WRAPS - Health care products - Salter Labs
E-ZDUIT - Conduits–electrical - Carlon
E-ZEE - Brushes–paint ☆ - Laitner Brush Co.
E-ZEE RIDERS - Toys ☆ - Intex Recreation Corp.
E-ZEE SPREAD - Brushes–paint ☆ - Laitner Brush Co.
E-ZRASER - Bulletin boards–wood - Bycin Industries, Inc.
E1-WATCHER - Communications equipment - Electrodata, Inc.
E2 - Toys - Centuri Corp.
E2 - Toys–models - Estes Industries
E2-60 - Motor vehicle parts and accessories - Crow River Industries Inc.
E2 SQUARED - Recording label - E-Squared, LLC
E2B2 - Computer software ☆ - JT&A, Inc. (EnviroScope Models)
E2COTS - Computer peripheral equipment - Raytheon Co.
E2E - Snow skis - Sitca East Inc.
E2X - Toys - Centuri Corp.
E2X - Toys–models - Estes Industries
E300 - Motor vehicles–automobiles - Mercedes-Benz of North America Inc.
E320 - Motor vehicles–automobiles - Mercedes-Benz of North America Inc.
E420 - Motor vehicles–automobiles - Mercedes-Benz of North America Inc.
EA - Eyeglasses - Eli Lilly and Co.
EA - Office supplies - Eaton Allen Ko-Rec-Type Corp.
EA - Skin care products - Unopco Sub, Inc.
EA DELUXE - Paper–carbon - Eaton Allen Ko-Rec-Type Corp.
EA ELITE AGLAONEMA HYBRID-SERIES - Flowers, plants, and seeds - Sunshine Foliage World
EA KIDS - Games - Electronic Arts Inc.
EA LIFT-OFF - Ribbons - Eaton Allen Ko-Rec-Type Corp.
EA SPORTS - Computer software - Electronic Arts Inc.
EA SPORTS ELECTRONIC ARTS - Video games - Electronic Arts Inc.
EA70 - Sporting goods - Easton Aluminum Inc.
EAASE - Vitamins and nutritional supplements - Matrix Technologies Inc.
EAC - Cases–musical instrument ☆ - D'Andrea Manufacturing Co. Inc.
E.A.C. - Skin care products ☆ - Stearn's Products Inc.
EACAREY - Tobacco products - E.A. Carey of Ohio, Inc.
EACH BITE IS RITE - Agricultural products - Am Agra Inc.
EAD-ALL - Health care products ☆ - CTS Laboratories Inc.
EAGALINE - Electrical equipment - Eagle Electric Manufacturing Co., Inc.
EAGER BEAVER - Brooms - Perfex Corp.
EAGER BEAVER - Frames–eyeglass - Pathway Optical Prods.
EAGER BEAVER - Saws–chain - McCulloch Corp.
EAGER BEAVER - Toys–stuffed ☆ - Gund, Inc.
EAGLE - Air conditioning equipment - Eagle Engineering & Manufacturing, Inc.
EAGLE - Apparel and accessories - Donnkenny Inc.
EAGLE - Apparel and accessories - Eagle Button Inc.
EAGLE - Bats–baseball - Pacers Sports
EAGLE - Batteries ☆ - Best Laboratories
EAGLE - Binders - Dennison National Co.
EAGLE - Boats - Glen-L Marine Designs
EAGLE - Boats–canoes ☆ - Marathon Boat Group, Inc.
EAGLE - Boats–motor ☆ - Old Town Canoe Co.

☆ = Now out of production

EAGLE - Boats–motor ☆ - Skeeter Products Inc.
EAGLE - Boats–motor ☆ - Yar-Craft, Inc.
EAGLE - Brooms - American Water Broom Co.
EAGLE - Brooms - Braun Bruch Co.
EAGLE - Burden carriers, now out of production - Ransomes-Cushman-Ryan
EAGLE - Calendars - Skinner & Kennedy Co.
EAGLE - Candy ☆ - Haviland Candy Inc.
EAGLE - Carbon paper - American Coated Products Inc.
EAGLE - Chocolate candy - Maillard Corp.
EAGLE - Chocolate candy ☆ - Ghirardelli Chocolate Co.
EAGLE - Coffee - Eagle Coffee Co.
EAGLE - Computer peripheral equipment - Digicom Systems, Inc.
EAGLE - Computer peripheral equipment - Tekelec Inc.
EAGLE - Containers - Eagle Affiliates, Inc.
EAGLE - Cosmetics - Spilo/Mehaz Worldwide
EAGLE - Desks - Hamilton Industries
EAGLE - Doors–garage - Eagle Window & Door Inc.
EAGLE - Dusters - R.E. Chapin Manufacturing Works Inc.
EAGLE - Electrical equipment - Bindicator Co.
EAGLE - Electronic equipment - AVL
EAGLE - Enamels - Bridges Smith & Co.
EAGLE - Eyeglasses - Art-Craft Optical Co.
EAGLE - File folders ☆ - Yawman and Erbe of California Corp.
EAGLE - Floor coverings - American Floor Products Co. Inc.
EAGLE - Food products - Eagle Agricultural Products Inc.
EAGLE - Food products ☆ - Hunt-Wesson, Inc.
EAGLE - Frames–eyeglass ☆ - U.S. Optical Frame Co.
EAGLE - Fruits and vegetables - Rice Fruit Co. Inc.
EAGLE - Fruits and vegetables - Stemilt Growers, Inc.
EAGLE - Game tables - American International Shuffleboard Corp.
EAGLE - Garden equipment - Ames Lawn & Garden Tool Co.
EAGLE - Gasoline - Colonial Oil Industries Inc.
EAGLE - Glassware–household ☆ - Lotus Glass Co.
EAGLE - Gliders–metal - Turner and Seymour Manufacturing Co.
EAGLE - Gocarts ☆ - Manco Products, Inc.
EAGLE - Golfing equipment - Brandell Products, Inc.
EAGLE - Greeting cards ☆ - Recycled Paper Products, Inc.
EAGLE - Hair care products ☆ - S.R. Droescher Inc.
EAGLE - Handles–wood - Turner, Day and Woolworth Handle Corp.
EAGLE - Health care products - National Wheel-O-Vator Co. Inc.
EAGLE - Health care products ☆ - Binky-Griptight Co.
EAGLE - Health care products ☆ - Smith and Davis Manufacturing Co.
EAGLE - Heels–boot and shoe - Star Heel Plate Co.
EAGLE - Ice cream - Riser Foods Inc.
EAGLE - Kites - Hi-Flier Manufacturing Co.
EAGLE - Lamps - Thermwell Products Co. Inc.
EAGLE - Lighting fixtures - Eagle Electric Manufacturing Co., Inc.
EAGLE - Machinery - Eagle Compressors, Inc.
EAGLE - Men's shirts - Crystal Brands Inc.
EAGLE - Milking machines - Borden, Inc.
EAGLE - Mobile homes - Oakwood Homes Corp.
EAGLE - Mops - Eagleware Manufacturing Co. Inc.
EAGLE - Motor vehicles - DaimlerChrysler
EAGLE - Motor vehicles–motor homes ☆ - Fleetwood Enterprises, Inc.
EAGLE - Motor vehicles–trucks - Navistar International Transportation Corp.
EAGLE - Motors–outboard - Byrd Industries Inc.
EAGLE - Musical instrument accessories - Performance Products Inc.
EAGLE - Musical instrument accessories - Stewart-MacDonald Manufacturing
EAGLE - Musical instruments ☆ - Fred Gretsch Enterprises
EAGLE - Navigational instruments - Lowrance Electronics, Inc.
EAGLE - Paints - General Coating Technologies, Inc.
EAGLE - Pencils - Empire Berol USA
EAGLE - Pencils - Sanford Corp.
EAGLE - Printing presses - Crestliner Boats Inc.
EAGLE - Recording label - Pet Records
EAGLE - Sardines–canned - North Lubec Manufacturing & Canning Co.
EAGLE - Sealing compounds - Monsey Products Co.
EAGLE - Ships - Marine Trading International Inc.
EAGLE - Signs - Fasteners for Retail, Inc.
EAGLE - Ski boat - American Skier Boat Co.
EAGLE - Skis ☆ - Wellington Leisure Products, Inc.
EAGLE - Snack foods ☆ - Anheuser-Busch Companies Inc.
EAGLE - Sporting goods - American Wholesale Hardware Co.
EAGLE - Stamps–hand - U.S. Stamp
EAGLE - Telephones–cellular - Omni Telecommunications Inc.
EAGLE - Tires - Goodyear Tire & Rubber Co.

EAGLE - Tools - Sunbeam-Oster Household Products
EAGLE - Tools ☆ - Regent Sheffield, Ltd.
EAGLE - Toys–airplanes - Paul K. Guillow Inc.
EAGLE - Toys–airplanes - North Pacific Products Inc.
EAGLE - Toys–guns ☆ - Ray Plastic Inc.
EAGLE - Traffic speed measuring apparatus - Kustom Signals, Inc.
EAGLE - Trailers–travel - Sun-Lite Inc.
EAGLE - Twine - Blue Mountain Industries, Inc.
EAGLE - Video equipment - Pro Mark Technologies, Inc.
EAGLE - Vinegar - Martin Gillet and Co. Inc.
EAGLE - Watches - Accusplit Inc.
EAGLE - Water heaters–household - Mor-Flo Industries Inc.
EAGLE - Wheelchairs - AM Scooters
EAGLE - Yeast - Gist-Brocades Food Ingredients Inc.
EAGLE 20'S - Cigarettes - Eve Holdings Inc.
EAGLE 28 - Floor coverings–carpet and rugs - Eagle Carpets Inc.
EAGLE 2001 - Footwear - Bottoms USA, Inc.
EAGLE AQUATRED - Tires - Goodyear Tire & Rubber Co.
EAGLE BASKETS - Baskets–wood - John Hess and Chris Holmes Partnership
EAGLE BRAND - Candy ☆ - New England Confectionery Co.
EAGLE CANYON - Food products - Goodmark Foods, Inc.
EAGLE CLASSIC - Golfing equipment - PC International, Inc.
EAGLE CLAW - Fishing tackle - Wright & McGill Co.
EAGLE CLAW - Hardware - Austin International Manufacturing Inc.
EAGLE CLAW - Hoists - Miller Industries Towing Equipment, Inc.
EAGLE CLUB - Socks - Kilgore Hosiery Inc.
EAGLE COMPRESSORS - Machinery - Eagle Compressors, Inc.
EAGLE COMPUTERS - Computer peripheral equipment - Inland Business Systems Inc.
EAGLE COUNTRY BUTCHER - Grocery stores - Eagle Food Centers, Inc.
EAGLE CREEK - Luggage - Eagle Creek, Inc.
EAGLE CREEK - Luggage - Eagle Creek Travel Gear
EAGLE CREST - Bags - Daniel C. Libera
EAGLE CREST - Wines - Eagle Crest Vineyard Inc.
EAGLE DANGER - Jams and jellies - Mountain Maid Gourmet Jelly
EAGLE EDGE - Cutlery - Ginkgo International Ltd.
EAGLE EQUIPMENT - Machinery - Minuteman Distributors, Inc.
EAGLE-EYE - Frames–eyeglass - Liberty Optical Manufacturing Co.
EAGLE EYE - Golfing equipment - Raymon W. Cook
EAGLE EYE - Paper–carbon - Phillips Ribbon & Carbon Co.
EAGLE EYE - Sporting goods - Ranging Inc.
EAGLE EYE - Toys–guns - Tonka Corp.
EAGLE EYE MYSTERIES - Computer software - Electronic Arts Inc.
EAGLE EYE PUBLISHERS INC. - Compact discs–prerecorded - Eagle Eye Publishers Inc.
EAGLE FLIGHT STAINLESS STEEL LINERS - Wheel covers - JAE Enterprises, Inc.
EAGLE FORCE - Toys ☆ - Mego Financial Corp.
EAGLE FOUNDRY - Buckles ☆ - Wm. K. Walthers Inc.
EAGLE GLC - Fishing tackle - Fenwick
EAGLE GLC - Fishing tackle - Outdoor Technologies Group
EAGLE HARBOR - Underwear and nightwear - Rapid Transit Ltd., Inc.
EAGLE II - Powerboat - American Skier Boat Co.
EAGLE II - Toys–airplanes ☆ - Cox Products Inc.
EAGLE-IRON - Fertilizers ☆ - Eagle-Picher Industries Inc.
EAGLE KINGDOMS - Games - Gamewright, Inc.
EAGLE KNIT - Apparel–children's ☆ - Eagle Knitting Mills Inc.
EAGLE MALT LIQUOR - Beverages–alcohol - Evansville Brewing Co.
EAGLE MILLS - Flour–blended - Conagra, Inc.
EAGLE NEST - Computer terminals - Exabyte Corp.
EAGLE OK - Electrical equipment - Eagle Electric Manufacturing Co., Inc.
EAGLE ONE - Cleaning preparations - Egl 1, Inc.
EAGLE OTTAWA - Leather cleaner - Albert Trostel & Sons Co.
EAGLE PACK - Pet products - Eagle Products, Inc.
EAGLE PASS - Bicycles ☆ - Huffy Corp.
EAGLE POINT - Shirts - Sea World, Inc.
EAGLE PREMIER PREMIUM ABRASIVE SYSTEMS - Grinders - Eagle Industries of America, Inc.
EAGLE PREMIERE - Trailers–truck ☆ - Sun-Lite Inc.
EAGLE PREMIUM - Beverages–malt ☆ - Stevens Point Beverage Co.
EAGLE PREMIUM, THE - Beverages–alcohol - Evansville Brewing Co.
EAGLE PRESS - Publisher's imprints - Eagle Press
EAGLE PROFESSIONAL PACK - Pet products - Eagle Products, Inc.
EAGLE R-40 AMP - Amplifiers - PRO Manufacturing
EAGLE RANCH THINS - Tortillas - Campbell Taggart Inc.

EAGLE RARE 101 - Beverages–alcohol - Sazerac Co. Inc.
EAGLE RIDGE - Bicycles ☆ - Huffy Corp.
EAGLE RIDGE - Siding - Georgia-Pacific Corp.
EAGLE RIDGE - Watches - Genender International, Inc.
EAGLE RIVER - Juices - Cranberry Products Inc.
EAGLE RIVER CLASSICS - Fruit butters - Cranberry Products Inc.
EAGLE RIVER TRADERS - Women's apparel - Sunny South Fashions, Inc.
EAGLE ROCK - Apparel and accessories - Kinney Shoe Corp.
EAGLE RS-A - Tires - Goodyear Tire & Rubber Co.
EAGLE RUBBER - Balls ☆ - Hedstrom Corp.
EAGLE SAUNDERS - Computer hardware - Richard Young Journal, Inc.
EAGLE SERIES - Antennas and parts - Radio Frequency Systems, Inc.
EAGLE SHADOW - Fishing tackle - Wright & McGill Co.
EAGLE STOKERS - Furnaces–electric - Fabridyne Inc.
EAGLE THINS - Snack foods ☆ - Anheuser-Busch Companies Inc.
EAGLE-TOUCH - Computer hardware - Wentek Technology, Inc.
EAGLE TOUR - Golfing equipment - Akshun & Akshun, Inc.
EAGLE TRACE - Floor coverings–carpet and rugs ☆ - World Carpets, Inc.
EAGLE TRACE - Trailers–travel - Fleetwood Enterprises, Inc.
EAGLE TWIN SWEEP - Brushes - Wright-Bernet
EAGLE V - Electronics equipment - Grass Valley Group Inc.
EAGLE VALLEY - Vegetables–frozen - Chase Farms Inc.
EAGLE VIEW - Publisher's imprints - Eagle View
EAGLE VISION! - Apparel and accessories ☆ - Bolle' America, Inc.
EAGLE XP - Motors–outboard - Byrd Industries Inc.
EAGLE XR - Fishing tackle - Wright & McGill Co.
EAGLE XR REELS - Sporting goods - Wright & McGill Co.
EAGLECONF.COM - Computer peripheral equipment - Eagle Teleconferencing, Services
EAGLECREST - Floor coverings–carpet and rugs - Mid America Carpet Distributor, Inc.
EAGLEEYE - Computer software - Greenhouse Products, Inc.
EAGLEFEATHER - Computer software - Frank Lloyd Wright Foundation
EAGLELINE - Paper ☆ - Northwest Blueprint and Supply
EAGLEMOBILE - Computer peripheral equipment - Raptor Systems, Inc.
EAGLES - Computer software - Trycon Associates
EAGLES - Recording label - Eagles, Ltd.
EAGLES - Trading cards and stamps - Columbia Games, Inc.
EAGLES 7 - Bait - Bacon Products Corp.
EAGLES-7 FLY RIBBONS - Insecticides - Bacon Products Corp.
EAGLE'S CLAW - Glue–household or industrial ☆ - Evans Adhesive Corp.
EAGLES CRISS CROSS - Games - International Gamco, Inc.
EAGLES LANDING - Floor coverings–carpet and rugs - Gulistan Carpet Inc.
EAGLE'S NEST - Ice chests - Mathews Witte International Inc.
EAGLESIGHT - Computer software - Stratagene
EAGLESOFT WET LENS - Contact lenses - Eagle Vision, Inc.
EAGLET - Eyeglasses - Art-Craft Optical Co.
EAGLETON - Flowers, plants, and seeds - Jacklin Seed
EAGLETRAK - Computer software - Eagle Insurance Group
EAGLEVISION - Apparel and accessories ☆ - Bolle' America, Inc.
EAGLEVISION - Video equipment - Automatic/Eagle Holding, LLC
EAGLEWARE - Cooking utensils–aluminum - Harold Leonard & Co. Inc.
EAGLEWRITE - Computer software - Eagle Insurance Group
EAGLEYE - Cameras–video - Eagleye Technologies, Inc.
EAGLEZEPHYR - Inks, markers - Consolidated Stamp Manufacturing Co. Inc.
EAGLO - Paints - Eaglo Paint & Varnish Corp.
EAGLO 5TH AVE. - Paints - Eaglo Paint & Varnish Corp.
EAGLO C.P. - Paints - Eaglo Paint & Varnish Corp.
EAGLO EPVAR - Finishing agents - Eaglo Paint & Varnish Corp.
EAGLO M.P. - Paints - Eaglo Paint & Varnish Corp.
EAGLO POXY - Paints - Eaglo Paint & Varnish Corp.
EAGLYTE - Filters–water ☆ - Eagle Spring Filtration, Inc.
EAJ - Jewelry - Jewels by Sergio Inc.
EAMES - Chairs–metal - Herman Miller, Inc.
EAMES FINECRAFT - Drums–musical instruments - Eames Drum Co.
EAMON GLASS - Glassware–household - Fragrances of Ireland Accent on Irish Wares Ltd.
EANDEAVOR - Golfing equipment - Besco USA
EAP - Asphalt - Engineered Asphalt Products Co.
EAP - Brakes–motorcycle - Eurasian Automotive Products Inc.
EAR - Goggles–safety - Aearo Co.
E.A.R. - Musical instrument accessories - David Wexler & Co.
EAR-ALL - Pet products - Glo-Marr Products Inc.
EAR BAND-IT - Headbands - Jaco Enterprises, Inc.
EAR BOOK - Book series on tape - Audio Books on Cassette Distributors, Inc.
EAR BUFF - Telephone accessory - Ronald L. Brito

EAR CARE - Jewelry - R.N. Koch Inc.
EAR CHALLENGER - Computer software - Electronic Courseware Systems Inc.
EAR CHANGES - Jewelry - Pepi Kelman Inc.
EAR-CLEAR - Pet products - Ear-Clear Corp.
EAR-CLEEN - Pet earwash - B-Elegant Products
EAR CLENS - Veterinary pharmaceutical preparations - Doctors Foster & Smith, Inc.
EAR CORP - Plugs–ear - Rockford Medical & Safety Co.
EAR COUPLERS - Infant product - Natus Medical Inc.
EAR DEFENDERS - Plugs–ear - MSA
EAR DROPS - Pharmaceutical preparations - D'Franssia Corp.
EAR DRY - Pharmaceutical preparations - Schering-Plough Healthcare Products
EAR-EASE - Eyeglasses - Chaska Inc./Medihome-Doctors Podiatry
EAR-EZE - Pharmaceutical preparations - Hyrex Pharmaceuticals
EAR FORCE RANGER - Veterinary pharmaceutical preparations ☆ - Boehringer Ingelheim Animal Health, Inc.
EAR FORCE TAGS - Veterinary pharmaceutical preparations ☆ - Boehringer Ingelheim Animal Health, Inc.
EAR FREE - Medical apparatus - Ear Technology Corp.
EAR GEAR - Headphones - Recoton Corp.
EAR GROOM - Pet products - Lambert-Kay
EAR IT IS! - Cases–vanity - Karen Ellingsworth
EAR KLEAR - Pet products - Natra Pet Inc.
EAR LABS - Hearing aids - Natural Ear Inc.
EAR LENZES - Electronic equipment - National Market Makers Inc.
EAR-LOKS - Eyeglasses - Chaska Inc./Medihome-Doctors Podiatry
EAR MAGIC - Health care products - Concept Marketing Inc.
EAR MAGIK - Pharmaceutical preparations ☆ - Reese Chemical Co.
EAR-MIKE - Audio equipment - Telex Communications, Inc.
EAR-OL - Pharmaceutical preparations ☆ - Lexis Laboratories Inc.
EAR PLUGS - Plugs–ear - Glenwood LLC
EAR POPS - Apparel and accessories - WorkAbles for Women
EAR RELIEF - Veterinary pharmaceutical preparations - Dr. Goodpet
EAR-REPLACEABLES - Jewelry - Roman Research, Inc.
EAR-RESISTABLES - Toys ☆ - Imperial Toy Corp.
EAR-RESISTIBLE - Jewelry - Mercury Ring Corp.
EAR RESISTIBLES - Pet food - Smokey's Smokehouse, Inc.
EAR-REST - Health care products ☆ - J.I. Morris Co.
EAR REVERENCE - Jewelry - Ear Reverence
EAR RITE - Pet products - Lambert-Kay
EAR SWEATERS - Crocheted and knitted items - Reliable of Milwaukee
EAR TABS - Ophthalmic goods - Apex Medical Corp.
EAR, THE - Computer software - Steinberg/Jones Corp.
EAR VINES - Jewelry - Alex Simkin
EAR WASH - Pet shops - Dermo Inc.
EAR WAXX - Apparel and accessories - Outcast Surf & Sport, Inc.
EAR-X - Pet products - St. Lawrence Sales Inc.
EARACHE - Recording label - Relativity/Combat/In-Effect
EARAMID - Display cases–plastic - Joseph Difranco
EARCRAFT - Hearing aids - Earcraft Technologies, Inc.
EARDOWN - Plugs–ear - Bilsom International Inc.
EARGARD - Pet products ☆ - Gerard-Pellham Co.
EARGENE - Pharmaceutical preparations - Priscilla Laboratories Inc.
EARHUGGER - Electronic equipment - M-Squared, Inc.
EARIGATOR - Medical apparatus - Irwin A. Ginsberg
EARL - Brushes–paint - Corona Brushes Inc.
EARL - Frames–eyeglass - Hudson Optical Corp.
EARL - Recording label ☆ - Ray Lawrence Ltd.
EARL & ED'S - Bags–storage - Richard D. Labrie
EARL BEECHER - Publisher's imprints - Outstanding Records
EARL CAMPBELL'S - Sauces - Earl Campbell Foods, Inc.
EARL CAULFIELD - Tobacco–chewing or smoking - Swisher International, Inc.
EARL-GLO - Fabrics–cotton - N. Erlanger, Blumgart & Co. Inc.
EARL GREY - Beverages–alcohol ☆ - Brown-Forman Corp.
EARL GREY - Teas - R.C. Bigelow, Inc.
EARL GREY - Teas - Eastern Shore Tea Co.
EARL GREY SUPERIOR MIXTURE - Teas - Grace Tea Co. Ltd.
EARL GREY VINAIGRE DE T - Vinegar - Golden Whisk Pasta Partners
EARL JEAN - Apparel and accessories - Earl Jean
EARL MAY EM EDIBLES - Corn–malt - Earl May Seed and Nursery L.P.
EARL 'N PATS - Fertilizers ☆ - Plantabbs Products
EARL OF LONSDALE - Cigars - General Cigar Co., Inc.
EARL SCHEIB - Automotive repair shops - Earl Scheib Inc.

☆ = Now out of production

EARL SCRUGGS - Musical instrument accessories - Gibson Strings & Accessories

EARL THE DEAD CAT - Toys–stuffed - Mad Dog Productions Inc.

EARL WEAVER BASEBALL - Computer software - Electronic Arts Inc.

EARLE EYVIND - Greeting cards - American Artists Group Inc.

EARLI-GARD - Smoke detectors ☆ - Square D Co.

EARL'S COURT - Furniture - Lane Co. Inc.

EARLY AGE - Frames–eyeglass - Liberty Optical Manufacturing Co.

EARLY AMERICA IV - Wallpaper ☆ - Imperial Wallcoverings, Inc.

EARLY AMERICA STENCIL III: CAROUSEL EDITION - Wallpaper ☆ - Imperial Wallcoverings, Inc.

EARLY AMERICAN - Floor coverings–carpet and rugs ☆ - American Carpet Mills

EARLY AMERICAN - Furniture - Twilight Oil Refining Co.

EARLY AMERICAN - Knives–pocket ☆ - W.R. Case & Sons Cutlery Co.

EARLY AMERICAN - Paints - Passonno Paints

EARLY AMERICAN - Paper ☆ - Fox River Paper Co.

EARLY AMERICAN - Ribbons–inked - Eaton Allen Ko-Rec-Type Corp.

EARLY AMERICAN - Stationery - Burgoyne Inc./Curtis Swann

EARLY AMERICAN - Wood products - Champion International Corp.

EARLY AMERICAN ANTIQUE - Glassware–household ☆ - Lenox Crystal, Inc.

EARLY AMERICAN CANDLE CRAFTSMEN - Candles - Early American Candle Shop

EARLY AMERICAN HARVEST - Cabinets ☆ - Haas Cabinet Co. Inc.

EARLY AMERICAN HEARTH - Bakery products - Campbell Taggart Inc.

EARLY AMERICAN HEARTH - Bread and bread mixes - Roush Products Co., Inc.

EARLY AMERICAN RECIPES - Bakery products - Roush Products Co., Inc.

EARLY AMERICAN SHARP - Cheese - Cabot Creamery Cooperative, Inc.

EARLY AMERICANA - Giftware - Doranne

EARLY ANN - Gloves - Wells Lamont Corp.

EARLY AUTUMN - Rings–jewelry - Artcarved Inc.

EARLY BIRD - Food products - Gold Kist Inc.

EARLY BIRD - Frames–eyeglass - Liberty Optical Manufacturing Co.

EARLY BIRDS - Games - Tonka Corp.

EARLY CALIFORNIA - Food products - Vlasic Foods Inc.

EARLY CHILDHOOD - Computer software - Interactive Digital Software Association

EARLY COLONIAL - Flatware - Lunt Silversmiths

EARLY DAWN - Dinnerware–glass ☆ - Nikko Ceramics Inc.

EARLY DAWN - Mushrooms ☆ - Manfredini Enterprises

EARLY DAWN - Rings–jewelry - Artcarved Inc.

EARLY DETECTOR - Medical apparatus ☆ - Warner-Lambert Co.

EARLY DEVELOPMENT - Musical instrument stores - Shar Products, Inc.

EARLY DISCOVERIES: COLORS AND SHAPES - Computer software - Hartley Courseware Inc.

EARLY DISCOVERIES: CONSERVATION AND COUNTING - Computer software - Hartley Courseware Inc.

EARLY DISCOVERIES: OBSERVATION AND CLASSIFICATION - Computer software - Hartley Courseware Inc.

EARLY DISCOVERIES: PARQUETRY AND PICTURES - Computer software - Hartley Courseware Inc.

EARLY DISCOVERIES: PATTERNS AND SEQUENCES - Computer software - Hartley Courseware Inc.

EARLY DISCOVERIES: SIZE AND LOGIC - Computer software - Hartley Courseware Inc.

EARLY EDGE - Animal feeds - Land O'Lakes, Inc.

EARLY EDGE - Fertilizers - Agway Country Foods Inc.

EARLY EMERGING RULES - Computer software - Laureate Learning Systems Inc.

EARLY HARVEST - Food products - California & Washington Co.

EARLY I CAN READ BOOKS - Publisher's imprints - Harper Junior Books Group

EARLY LEARNING - Publisher's imprints - MacMillan Publishing Co. Inc.

EARLY LEARNING CONCEPTS - Toys ☆ - The Coleman Co.

EARLY LITERACY INTERVENTION - Printed teacher training materials - Rena M. Walker & Assoc., Inc.

EARLY MORN - Food products - Thornton's Flav-O-Rich Bakery Inc.

EARLY MORN FRESH - Dairy products - Guth Dairy Inc.

EARLY MORNING PIPE - Tobacco–chewing or smoking - Alfred Dunhill of London Inc.

EARLY MUSIC SKILLS - Computer software - Electronic Courseware Systems Inc.

EARLY REMEDY II - House furnishings ☆ - Apothecary Products, Inc.

EARLY REMEDY I - House furnishings ☆ - Apothecary Products, Inc.

EARLY RISER - Teas ☆ - R.C. Bigelow, Inc.

EARLY SKILLS - Computer software - Hartley Courseware Inc.

EARLY SKILLS PROGRAMS - Educational materials - EDCON Publishing

EARLY SPRING - Lumber - Georgia-Pacific Corp.

EARLY SPRING - Silverware ☆ - Imperial Schrade Corp.

EARLY START CHILD DEVELOPMENT TOYS - Toys - International Playthings Inc.

EARLY SUMMER BERRY - Beverages ☆ - Golden Brands Marketing

EARLY TIMES - Whiskey - Brown-Forman Corp.

EARLY TIMES - Whiskey - Early Times Distillery Co.

EARLY TIMES MINT JULEP - Beverages–alcohol - Brown-Forman Corp.

EARLY TIMES TRIPLE TURF - Jewelry - Early Times Distillery Co.

EARLY WARNING - Radar systems and equipment - Sunkyong America, Inc.

EARLY WARNING EFFECT - Alarm systems–fire - RJF International Corp.

EARLY WEAN - Vitamins and nutritional supplements - Vicortone AG Products Inc.

EARLY WRITER - Computer software - Hartley Courseware Inc.

EARLY YEARS SERIES FERRELL'S OLD WEST, THE - Leather - Lanny Keith Ferrell

EARLY YEARS, THE - Wallpaper ☆ - Motif Designs, Inc.

EARLY YEARS....AND LATER ON, THE - Wallpaper ☆ - Motif Designs, Inc.

EARLYLAC - Animal feeds - Stevens Industries Inc.

EARLY'S - Paper - Whitehall Inc.

EARLYWORKS - Playground equipment - Kompan, Inc.

EARMARK - Communications equipment–mobile - Earmark Inc.

EARN-IT/PLAY-IT - Computer software - Dynacomp Inc.

EARN MILES FOR YOUR MEALS - Advertising agencies - Signature Financial/ Marketing, Inc.

EARNEST - Paints - Earnest Machine Products

EARNEST LEE! - Dolls - Blue Squirrel Concepts

EAROBICS - Educational materials - Cognitive Concepts Inc.

EAROCOL - Pharmaceutical preparations ☆ - Roberts/Hauck Pharmaceuticals Inc.

EAROPA - Apparel and accessories - Windy Tree, Inc.

EAROXIDE - Pet products - Tomlyn Products

EARRING - Frames–picture - Nancy Tucker

EARRING CENTRAL - Earring tree - Jeffrey A. Nornberg

EARRING ELEGANCE - Jewelry - Earring Elegance Inc.

EARRING ESSENTIAL'S - Jewelry - Earring Essential's

EARRING MAGIC - Dolls - Mattel, Inc.

EARRINGRIPS - Jewelry–costume - Chaska Inc./Medihome-Doctors Podiatry

EARS - Agricultural machinery - Osborne Industries Inc.

EARS - Audio equipment - Renkus-Heinz Inc.

EARS A POPPIN - Popcorn on the cob - In-Cahoots Creative Services, Inc.

EARS LOOKING AT YOU - Giftware - Russ Berrie and Co., Inc.

EARSCOPE - Medical apparatus - Notoco

EARSKOPE - Medical apparatus - Techno-Optic, Inc.

EARSPLITTER - Alarm systems - Kolin Industries Inc.

EARSPRINGS - Jewelry - Exclusive Creations, Inc.

EARTEC - Communications equipment - Porta Phone Co. Inc.

EARTH - Cosmetics - Ida Grae Cosmetics

EARTH - Cosmetics - Hard Candy, Inc.

EARTH - Greeting cards ☆ - Recycled Paper Products, Inc.

EARTH - Hardware - Niagara Conservation Corp.

EARTH - Shoes - Kalso Systemet Inc.

EARTH - Skin care products - Aveda Corp.

EARTH ACADEMY - Video production - Laidlaw Environmental Services, Inc.

EARTH ACCENT - Hosiery - Shogren Industries, Inc.

EARTH AGE - Apparel–women's - Rielly Co. Inc.

EARTH & BODY CARE - Skin care products ☆ - ABRA Inc.

EARTH & GLOW - Skin care products - Janelle Mignon Cosmetics

EARTH & ITS COMPOSITION, THE - Computer software - Right on Programs

EARTH & LIFE ALL ORGANIC PASTA - Pasta - Pasta USA Inc.

EARTH & LIFE ALL ORGANIC PASTA BOUNTIFUL BELLS - Ovens– smelting - Pasta USA Inc.

EARTH & LIFE ALL ORGANIC PASTA BUTTERFLY BOWS - Pasta - Pasta USA Inc.

EARTH & LIFE ALL ORGANIC PASTA HEAVENLYHEARTS - Ovens– smelting - Pasta USA Inc.

EARTH & LIFE ALL ORGANIC PASTA TASTY TREES - Pasta - Pasta USA Inc.

EARTH ANGEL - Jewelry - Treasures & Trinkets, Inc.

EARTH ANGELS - Underwear and nightwear - Charles Komar and Sons Inc.

EARTH ANIMAL - Animal feed supplements - Northern Skies Animal Co.

EARTH ANIMALS - Jewelry–costume - Phillips International Jewelry & Souvenirs Inc.

EARTH BALLS - Confections - Sunspire Foods

EARTH BASKET - Baskets–wood - Earth Basket Inc.

EARTH BEAT! - Recording label - Music for Little People

EARTH BOOKS - Publisher's imprints ☆ - Morgan & Morgan

EARTH BORN - Dinnerware–glass ☆ - Franciscan by Johnson Brothers, USA, Inc.

EARTH BORN - Pharmaceutical preparations - Barth's Nutra Products

EARTH BORN - Skin care products - Gillette Co.

EARTH BOUND BROWN - Cosmetics ☆ - Noxell Corp.

EARTH BOUQUETS - Flowers, plants, and seeds - Sunshine Bouquet Co.

EARTH BOX - Containers - Blake Whisenant

EARTH BREAD - Breads - Campbell Taggart Inc.

EARTH CAMP - Apparel and accessories - Yippee International

EARTH CARDS - Greeting cards - Earthcard Inc.

EARTH CARE - Automotive parts and accessories - United Industries Corp.

EARTH CARE - Bleach - Earth Wise, Inc.

EARTH CLOTH - Fabrics - Guilford Mills, Inc.

EARTH COLORS - Publisher's imprints - Color Communications, Inc.

EARTH CONCERNS - Shirts - Capital Mercury Shirt Corp.

EARTH CUT - Tobacco products - Earth Cut, Inc.

EARTH DAWN - Hair care products - Bluebonnet Pharmaceuticals Inc.

EARTH DAY EARTH TRUSTEE - Posters - Earth Society Foundation, Inc.

EARTH DAY EVERY DAY - Sweaters, t-shirts, tote bags, etc ☆ - National Wildlife Federation

EARTH DIVISION - Apparel and accessories - Fernando Sakuray

EARTH ELEMENTS - Oils–essential - Carol Laino

EARTH ESSENCE - Cosmetics - Essential Holdings Inc.

EARTH EXCELLENCE - Skin care products - Cosmyl, Inc.

EARTH EYES - Cosmetics - Ida Grae Cosmetics

EARTH FIBERS - Wallpaper - Maya Romanoff Corp.

EARTH FLAG PEACE FIVE RACES-ONE PEOPLE - Shirts - Gert Ragnar Sjoberg

EARTH FRAGRANCE - Perfumes - Ida Grae Cosmetics

EARTH FREINDLY - Pesticides–household - Bonide Products, Inc.

EARTH FRIENDLY - Chemical preparations - Harvey Universal Inc.

EARTH GALLERY - Office supplies - Climax Paper Converters Inc.

EARTH GARDEN - Spices and extracts - Scentex Inc.

EARTH GEL - Soil–potting - Steven Craig Lumbley

EARTH GIRL - Frames–eyeglass - Zylo Ware Corp.

EARTH GLOW - Cosmetics - Earth Glow Inc.

EARTH GRAIN PIZZA ROUNDS - Breads - Campbell Taggart Inc.

EARTH GRAINS - Bakery products - Campbell Taggart Inc.

EARTH GRAINS LITE 35 - Breads - Campbell Taggart Inc.

EARTH GREEN - Melamine product - Boonton Molding Co. Inc.

EARTH-GUARD - Chemical preparations - Polymer Chemistry Innovations, Inc.

EARTH GUARD - Cleaning preparations - Descale-It Products Co.

EARTH GUARD - Cleaning preparations ☆ - Omega Products Corp.

EARTH HARVEST - Food products - Health Best Distributors Inc.

EARTH HARVEST - Spices and extracts - Scentex Inc.

EARTH HERBAL - Health care products ☆ - Earthnet

EARTH HERBAL GREENS - Health care products ☆ - Earthnet

EARTH HERO - Bathroom fixtures - Susan M. Linnell

EARTH HOME - Figurines ☆ - United Design Corp.

EARTH JUICE - Juices - Chiquita Brands, Inc.

EARTH JUICE CATALYST - Fertilizers - Thomas M. Shelsky

EARTH KIDS EARTH-FRIENDLY FUNWEAR - Apparel–children's - Karen L. Wiand and Mary E. Bush

EARTH KING - Post-hole diggers ☆ - E.F. Brewer Co.

EARTH LAND - Footwear - Dynasty Footwear, Ltd.

EARTH LIKABLE - Stationery - BOK Industries Inc.

EARTH-LINK - Television equipment–cable - Channel One Communications Corp.

EARTH MAGIC - Skin-care products - Gloria J. Olmstead

EARTH MARK - Stationery - Griffin Envelope Inc.

EARTH MATTERS - Checkbooks - Check Gallery, Inc.

EARTH MATTERS - Mats–rattan - Golden Star Inc.

EARTH MATTERS - Neckties - TBAC-Prince Gardner Inc.

EARTH METAL - Agricultural machinery - Case Corp.

EARTH MOP - Mops - Wilen Companies, Inc.

EARTH MORSELS - Fertilizers - National By-Products, Inc.

EARTH MOVER - Toys–automobiles - Mattel, Inc.

EARTH MUSIC - Recording label - Earth Music Productions

EARTH ORIGINS - Candles ☆ - Our Secret, Ltd.

EARTH PAK - Packaging–paper - Protective Packaging Inc.

EARTH PATROL - Apparel and accessories - Earth Patrol, Inc.

EARTH PENCIL - Pencils - Blackfeet Writing Instruments Inc.

EARTH PERFECT - Compost - Earth Perfect, Inc.

EARTH PLAN - Greeting cards - Earth Plan Inc.

EARTH PLEDGE - Posters - John F. Ince

EARTH PLUGS - Plugs–ear - Karlen Manufacturing, Inc.

EARTH POSTERS - Posters ☆ - Kersten Bros. Studios

EARTH PRESERV - Skin care products - Earth Preserv, Ltd.

EARTH PRIDE - Vitamins and nutritional supplements - Nature's Products Inc.

EARTH PRO - Soil–potting - Kurtz Bros., Inc.

EARTH PRODUCTS - Food products ☆ - Green Grown Products Inc.

EARTH PROFILE - Globes ☆ - Geo. F. Cram Co.

EARTH PROTECTION SYSTEMS - Air purification systems - Earth Protection Systems, Inc.

EARTH QUAKE - Pet products - Saket Co.

EARTH REVERENCE - Hair care products - Earth Reverence Inc.

EARTH ROUGE - Cosmetics - Ida Grae Cosmetics

EARTH SAFE - Gloves - Norman Librett, Inc.

EARTH SAVER - Netting - R.H. Dyck, Inc.

EARTH SCENTS - Spices and extracts - Scentex Inc.

EARTH SCENTS DESIGNER - Cleaning preparations - Scentex Inc.

EARTH SCENTS NATURALS - Deodorizers - Scentex Inc.

EARTH SCIENCE - Computer software - Orange Cherry Software

EARTH SENSE - Apparel and accessories - Aramark Corp.

EARTH SENSE - Cleaning preparations - Earth Sense, Inc.

EARTH SHAKER - Chewing gum - Philadelphia Chewing Gum Corp.

EARTH SHAKER - Construction set - Intex Recreation Corp.

EARTH SHAKES - Dairy products - Merritt Technical Assoc., Inc.

EARTH SHINE GLOBAL CLEANER - Cleaning preparations - Earth Shine, Inc.

EARTH SITUATION ROOM - Computers - Tom Van Sant, Inc.

EARTH SITUATION ROOM - Electronic equipment - CH Products Div.

EARTH SMART - Cleaning preparations - James Fobair

EARTH SONG - Food products - Earth Song Whole Foods

EARTH SONG - Greeting cards - Sunrise Publications, Inc.

EARTH SOURCE - Collar buttons - H. Alpert and Co.

EARTH SOURCE - Vitamins and nutritional supplements - Solgar Vitamin and Herb Co., Inc.

EARTH SOURCE GREENS & MORE - Vitamins and nutritional supplements - Solgar Vitamin and Herb Co., Inc.

EARTH-SPUN - Yarn - Patrick Yarn Mill, Inc.

EARTH STALKERS - Colognes ☆ - Avon Products, Inc.

EARTH STOVE, THE - Stoves–wood-burning - Earth Stove Inc.

EARTH STRUCK - T-shirts–men's - Earth Struck Corp.

EARTH STUFF - Apparel and accessories - National Shirt Sales Inc.

EARTH THERAPEUTICS - Cleaning preparations - Earth Therapeutics Group

EARTH TONE - Recording label - Artifex Records Inc.

EARTH TONES - Apparel and accessories - Impulse Wear

EARTH TONES - Candles - Nordstrom, Inc.

EARTH TOUCH ORGANIC PEST CONTROL - Pesticides–household - Earth Touch Franchise Corp.

EARTH TOWEL - Towels - Kay Dee Designs Inc.

EARTH TREASURES - Artists' materials ☆ - Dick Blick Co.

EARTH TREKS - Computer software - Earthquest Inc.

EARTH TRIBE - Apparel and accessories - Earth Goods USA, Inc.

EARTH TRIBE AROMATICS - Oils–essential - Earth Tribe Aromatics

EARTH TV - Apparel and accessories - Kevan Khanamirian

EARTH VENUS - Skin care products - Ida Grae Cosmetics

EARTH WAGON - Children's wagons - Radio Flyer Inc.

EARTH WASH - Apparel and accessories - Blue Bell, Inc.

EARTH WASH - Apparel and accessories - Wrangler Apparel Co.

EARTH WATCH - Apparel and accessories - Capital Mercury Shirt Corp.

EARTH WATCH - Cleaning preparations - Kleenco Products, Inc.

EARTH WATCH - Toys - Trend Enterprises, Inc.

EARTH WATCH - Watches - Priority Earth Co.

EARTH WEAR - Apparel stores - Jeffrey E. Young

EARTH, WIND & STONE - Wallpaper - Archetonic

EARTH-WISE GIFT BAGS - Bags–printed - Earth-Wise Enterprise, Inc.

EARTH WOOD CARE - Paints - Pettibone Corp.

EARTH WORDS - Greeting cards ☆ - Stevenson Industries Inc.

EARTH WORKS - Cleaning preparations - T Square, Inc.

EARTH WOVE - Envelopes - New York Envelope Corp.

EARTH WRAP - Hardware - Niagara Conservation Corp.

EARTHBATH - Pet products - Earthwhile Endeavors, Inc.

EARTHBOND - Adhesives and sealants - Roberts

EARTHBORN - Hosiery - Shogren Industries, Inc.

EARTHBOUND ENVIRONMENTAL CREATIONS - Jewelry - Earthbound Environmental Creations

EARTHCELL - Batteries - Astron Cosmetics, Inc.

EARTHCHILD - Baby powder, oil ☆ - Autumn-Harp, Inc.

☆ = Now out of production

EARTHCHILD - Dolls - Environments, Inc.
EARTHDAWN - Computer software - Fasa Corp.
EARTHDAY LEATHER - Leather goods - Feuer Leather Corp.
EARTHDAY SOLUTIONS - Degreasing solvents - Geo International, Inc.
EARTHDESIGN, LTD. - Crocheted and knitted items - Earthdesign Ltd.
EARTHEN POT - Spices and extracts - Singapore Trade Development Board
EARTHEN WEAR - Socks - Renfro Corp.
EARTHGRO - Fertilizers - Earthgro Inc.
EARTHGRO'S BEST - Fertilizer - Earthgro Inc.
EARTHGUARD - Bags–paper - Portco Corp.
EARTHGUARD - Electronic equipment - Earth Protection Systems, Inc.
EARTHGUARDS - Bicycle parts and accessories - Ken Hassen
EARTHLAB - Toys ☆ - Revell-Monogram, Inc.
EARTHLINE - Binders - McBee Loose Leaf Binders
EARTHLINGS - Cosmetics - Cosmania, Inc.
EARTHLINGS - Jewelry ☆ - Anson Inc.
EARTHLY ENERGY - Vitamins and nutritional supplements - Barth-Spencer Corp.
EARTHLY ESSENTIALS - Cosmetics - Earthly Essentials, Inc.
EARTHLY ESSENTIALS - Toiletries - T.D. Sales & Marketing, Inc.
EARTHLY MATTERS - Bags–trash - Earthly Matters Inc.
EARTHMADE - Vitamins and nutritional supplements - Natural Organics, Inc.
EARTHMATE - Compost - PRS Materials, Inc.
EARTHMATE ORGANICS - Fertilizers - Southern Indiana Rehabilitation Services, Inc.
EARTHNEEDS - Figurines - Vincent Lippe Co.
EARTHOOD - Apparel and accessories - Earthood Environmental A-Wear-Ness
EARTHPAC - Backpacks and tote bags - Earth Sense Inc.
EARTHPAPERS - Stationery - Paper Co.
EARTHQUACK - Recording label - Jazz Composer's Orchestra Association Inc.
EARTHQUAKE - Augers - Ardisam, Inc.
EARTHQUAKE - Clothing - Earthquake Sound Corp.
EARTHQUAKE - Sporting goods - Tonka Corp.
EARTHRIGHT - Lubricants - Earthright Technologies, Inc.
EARTHRISE - Health care products - Earthnet
EARTHRISE - Notebooks and notepads - Earthrise
EARTHRITE - Cleaning preparations - RCN Products Inc.
EARTHRITE - Cleaning products - EarthRite Cleaning Products
EARTH'S 911 - Video production - Clean Up, Inc.
EARTH'S BEST - Food products - Earth's Best Inc.
EARTH'S BOUNTY - Vitamins and nutritional supplements - Matrix Health Products, Inc.
EARTH'S CHOICE - Vitamins and nutritional supplements - Earth Industries Inc.
EARTH'S FUTURE - Educational materials - Thomas Doyle
EARTH'S MOST COMFORTABLE SHOES, THE - Footwear - Wolverine World Wide, Inc.
EARTH'S MOST PERFECT WATER, THE - Water–bottled or canned - Chippewa Springs, Ltd.
EARTH'S PHARMACY - Vitamins and nutritional supplements - Tanza Ltd.
EARTH'S RESOURCES - Vitamins and nutritional supplements - Earth's Resources, Inc.
EARTH'S TURF - Flowers, plants, and seeds - Loft's Seed Inc.
EARTHSAFE - Measuring instruments - Earth Protection Systems, Inc.
EARTHSAVER - Industrial machinery - Clinton, L.P.
EARTHSAVER - Paper - Fay Paper Products Inc.
EARTHSCAPE - Fabrics - Synthetic Industries, Inc.
EARTHSCOPE - Environmental trivia cards - Good Medicine Inc.
EARTHSEARCH - Educational materials - Klutz Press
EARTHSHELL - Containers–plastic - Earthshell Container Corp.
EARTHSHELL FOR EARTH'S SAKE - Building materials–concrete - Earthshell Container Corp.
EARTHSMART - Fireplace equipment - West End Gardens
EARTHSMART - Skin care products - HT Marketing, Inc.
EARTHSMART PRODUCTS - Computer diskettes–blank - Prism Group, Inc.
EARTHSONG - Jewelry - Kenneth S. Kantro
EARTHSPELL - Colognes ☆ - Avon Products, Inc.
EARTHSPRING - Water–bottled or canned - Morningstar Group Inc.
EARTHSPUN - Yarn - Cascade Fibers Co.
EARTHSTAR - Jewelry–precious - Earthstar Enterprises
EARTHSTONE - Cleaning preparations ☆ - Scentex Inc.
EARTHSTONE - Concrete products - Andre M. Lugo
EARTHSTONE - Cosmetics - Cosmair Inc.
EARTHSTONE - Dinnerware–glass - Trend Pacific Inc.
EARTHSTONE - Tiles–ceramic - Florida Tile Industries, Inc.
EARTHSTONES - Jewelry–precious - H.S. Strygler & Co. Inc.

EARTHTONE - Tiles–ceramic - Capitol Tile Import Co.
EARTHTONE - Varnishes ☆ - Klean-Strip
EARTHUES - Yarn - Caracol
EARTHWALKER - Bicycle parts and accessories - Phoenix Risen International
EARTHWARE - Paper plates - Heartland Manufacturing Corp.
EARTHWEAR - Ceramic tile ☆ - Integrity Tile Co.
EARTHWEB - Computer software - Jack D. Hidary
EARTHWISE - Apparel and accessories - Dixie Yarns, Inc.
EARTHWISE - Office supplies - Esselte Corp.
EARTHWISE ENNOVATIONS - Floor coverings–carpet and rugs - Milliken & Co.
EARTHWISE WINDOW SYSTEMS - Windows–vinyl - RJT Industries, Inc.
EARTHWOOD - Guitar strings - Ernie Ball Inc.
EARTHWORKS - Filters–air - Jacuzzi Brothers
EARTHWORKS - Skin care products - Jolie Guy
EARTHWORM - Aerator, now out of production - Ransomes-Cushman-Ryan
EARTHWORM - Machinery - Earthworm, Inc.
EARTHWORM JIM - Footwear ☆ - S. Goldberg and Co. Inc.
EARTHWORM JIM - Toys - Playmates World Wide Inc.
EARTHWORM, THE - Computer software - Ventura Educational Systems
EARTHWORMS - Stuffed animal - Big Fun Toy Co.
EARTHWRAP - Plastics - J.C. Parry & Sons Co. Inc.
EARTHWRITE - Nibs–pen - Tuttle Law Print Inc.
EARVISION - Hearing aids - Creative Hearing Solutions, Inc.
EARWIG - Recording label - Earwig Music Co. Inc.
EARWISE - Jewelry - Roman Research, Inc.
EARZ - Apparel and accessories - Direct Success, Inc.
EAS - Computer hardware - DataWare Development, Inc.
EAS - Vitamins and nutritional supplements - Experimental & Applied Sciences, Inc.
EAS-ALL - Binders - Key Sales Co.
EASA-GRIP - Electronic equipment - Chief Manufacturing Co.
EASA-MATE - Electronic equipment - Chief Manufacturing Co.
EASA-SET - Easels - Chief Manufacturing Co.
EASACOLD - Cold treatment - True Quality Pharmacies Inc.
EASARAIL - Health care products - Temco Health Care
EASE - Computer software - Center for Healthcare Industry Performance Studies
EASE - Computer software - Lifease, Inc.
EASE - Computer software - Renkus-Heinz Inc.
EASE - Deodorizers - Gentell, Inc.
EASE - Frames–eyeglass - Zylo Ware Corp.
EASE - Medical apparatus - Omnitrition International, Inc.
EASE - Paints - Smith Paint Products
EASE - Waxes–mineral ☆ - Fox Run Craftsmen
EASE/ADMISSION - Computer software - Exeter Educational Management Systems, Inc.
EASE-AWAY - Cleaning preparations - CMC Inc.
EASE AWAY - Horseshoes ☆ - Farnam Cos. Inc.
EASE BACK ROOM SAVERS - Recliners - Flexsteel Industries Inc.
EASE EDGE - Garden equipment - Cobraco Manufacturing, Inc.
EASE-IT - Silicon products ☆ - Dap Products Inc.
EASE OFF 990 - Adhesives and sealants - Texacone Co.
EASE PETITE CHEMISE - Apparel and accessories ☆ - Kellwood Co.
EASE PETITE FEMME - Apparel and accessories ☆ - Kellwood Co.
EASE PETITE FEMME - Apparel–women's - En Chante
EASE SPORT - Apparel and accessories - Kellwood Co.
EASE SPORT - Apparel–women's - En Chante
EASE-U - Brassieres (Bras) ☆ - Lovable Co.
EASE YOUR MIND - Pillows - Beso De Luna, Inc.
EASEL - Apparel and accessories - KSK International Inc.
EASEL - Computer software ☆ - Time Arts Inc.
EASEL - Frames–picture - Andy Designs, Ltd.
EASEL-ART - Paint sets–hobby ☆ - Canson-Talens Inc.
EASEL WORKBENCH - Computer software - Easel Corp.
EASEL-Y - Binders - Dennison National Co.
EASEMASTER - Furniture - Tomlinson of High Point Inc.
EASEOUT - Machine parts - GTI, Inc.
EASESTOP - Dental equipment - Js Dental Manufacturing, Inc.
EASEY - Computer software - Expert Systems, Inc.
EASEY FRAMEWORKS - Computer software - Expert Systems, Inc.
EASI - Computer software - Faxon Co. Inc.
EASI - Furniture - Eck-Adams Corp.
EASI-BILD - Publisher's imprints - Easi-Bild Directions Simplified Inc.
EASI-BOOK - Computer software - U.S. Recognition, Inc.
EASI FILL - Camping appliance fuel filler - Coleman Co., Inc.

EASI-HOLD BOOKMASTER - Book ends ☆ - Latham Studios

EASI-MECHE - Hair care products - Cosmair Inc.

EASI/PACE - Computer software - PCI Remote Sensing Corp.

EASI-READER - Furniture - Hoyle Products Inc.

EASICLIP - Office supplies - Ames Safety Envelope Co.

EASICON - Televisions - Matsushita Electric Corp. of America

EASICORDER - Tape recorders–cassette - APT Technology, Inc.

EASIEST WAY TO PROOFREAD YOUR WRITING, THE - Computer software - Reference Software International

EASIFLAGS - Office supplies - Ames Safety Envelope Co.

EASILOK - Office supplies - Ames Safety Envelope Co.

EASIMAP - Computer software - 21st Century Innovations, Inc.

EASISHARP - Housewares - Serr-Edge Machine Co.

EASIZIP FLAP - Office supplies - Ames Safety Envelope Co.

EASLBACK - Binders - S.I. Jacobson Manufacturing Co.

EASLEY'S & CAPE - Wines - Easley Enterprises

EASON TECHNOLOGY - Computer hardware - Eason Technology, Inc.

EASPORT - Powerboat ☆ - Boston Whaler, Inc.

EASPRIN - Analgesics - Warner-Lambert Co.

EAST AND WEST LIBRARY - Publisher's imprints - Hebrew Publishing Co.

EAST ASIA - Food products - Holland-American Importing Co. Inc.

EAST BALT. - Bakery products–frozen - East Balt. Inc.

EAST BEST - Chickens - East Poultry Co.

EAST COAST - Gasoline - East Coast Oil Corp.

EAST COAST ATHLETIC CLUB - Footwear - Pic 'n Pay Stores, Inc.

EAST COAST BAGEL DOG - Frankfurters - Wilton Foods Inc.

EAST COAST BEGGEL - Eggs - East Coast Bagel Co., Inc.

EAST COAST ORIGINAL FROZEN CUSTARD - Yogurt–frozen - Ivan Platt

EAST COAST WEST - Dairy products - Barbara L. Ochsner

EAST FALLS - Floor coverings–carpet and rugs ☆ - Evans-Black Carpet Mills

EAST FIFTH - Footwear - J.C. Penney Co., Inc.

EAST GATE - Wallpaper - K.M.L. Industries

EAST GATE - Wallpaper - Textile Wallcoverings International Ltd.

EAST HAMPTON - Tools - East Hampton Industries Inc.

EAST HAMPTON PERFUMERY - Perfumes - East Hampton Perfumery, Inc.

EAST HILLS - Wallpaper ☆ - Lawrence Wallcoverings

EAST INDIA - Coffee - Coffee & Tea Ltd.

EAST INDIA - Teas - East India Coffee & Tea

EAST INDIAN TIKKA - Spices and extracts - Finest Kind Spices

EAST OF SIAM - Shrimp - Continental Seafoods Inc.

EAST OF SUEZ - Colognes - Dynamic Classics Ltd.

EAST OF THE SUN - Wallpaper - Artisan Handprints Inc.

EAST OF THE SUN - Wallpaper - Kirk-Brummel

EAST POINT - Seafood products–fresh or frozen - East Point Seafood Co.

EAST PORT - Seafood products–fresh or frozen - East Coast Sea Port Corp.

EAST SIDE - Bicycles - Ross Bicycles USA, Ltd.

EAST SIDE - Floor coverings–carpet and rugs - Masland Corp.

EAST SIDE - Furniture - Bean Station Furniture Factory Inc.

EAST STREET - Shoes - Charm Step Shoes

EAST-TENN - Sporting goods - East-Tenn Mills Inc.

EAST TEXAS FAIR - Food products - Allen Canning Co.

EAST TOTEM WEST - Greeting cards ☆ - Pomegranate Publications

EAST VALLEY - Chickens ☆ - East Poultry Co.

EAST WEST - Coats - Orbit International Corp.

EAST WEST AMERICA - Recording label - Atlantic Records

EAST/WEST COLLECTION - Wallpaper - Wall Fabrics Inc.

EAST WIND - Apparel–men's - Alps Sportswear Manufacturing Co.

EAST WIND - Dishes–china ☆ - Gorham Inc.

EAST WIND - Eyeglasses - Martin-Copeland Eyewear Corp.

EAST WIND - Food products - East Wind Nut Butters

EAST WINDS - Wallpaper - Maharam Vertical Surfaces

EASTBAY - Apparel–athletic - Eastbay, Inc.

EASTCLOX - Clocks ☆ - General Time Corp. (Westclox/Seth Thomas Div.)

EASTCOM - Computer software - Eastman Kodak Co.

EASTEK - Coatings - Eastman Chemical Co.

EASTER ACTION - Toys–stuffed - Fun World Inc.

EASTER AVENUE - Figurines - Frederick Atkins, Inc.

EASTER BABIES - Puppets - Dakin Inc.

EASTER BASKET CAKES - Snack foods - McKee Foods Corp.

EASTER BASKET EXPRESS - Chewing gum - Philadelphia Chewing Gum Corp.

EASTER BUDDY - Paper products - Lisa Frank, Inc.

EASTER BUNNY FAMILY, THE - Figurines - United Design Corp.

EASTER BUTTERCREME CRITTERS - Candy - Brock Candy Co. Inc.

EASTER CHICK - Paper–gift wrap ☆ - American Greetings Corp.

EASTER EGG - Snack foods - Flowers Family Bakeries, Inc.

EASTER EGG HUNT - Candy ☆ - R.M. Palmer Co.

EASTER EGG SNACK CAKE - Bakery products - Flowers Family Bakeries, Inc.

EASTER EGGS - Candy - Naron Candy Co. Inc.

EASTER FANTASY - Candy - Rosemary Candy Co.

EASTER FUN - Dolls - Mattel, Inc.

EASTER GALLERY - Candy ☆ - R.M. Palmer Co.

EASTER HEADLINER - Toys–stuffed ☆ - Fun World Inc.

EASTER HUNT EGGS - Candy - Brock Candy Co. Inc.

EASTER JORDAN - Nuts–candied - Brach and Brock Confections Inc.

EASTER PALS - Pins–jewelry - Russ Berrie and Co., Inc.

EASTER PARADE - Candy - Brock Candy Co. Inc.

EASTER PARADE - Chocolate candy - Superior Fruit & Confections

EASTER PARADE - Toys–stuffed ☆ - Fun World Inc.

EASTER PARADE BUNNY - Greeting cards - Morehead, Inc.

EASTER PARTY - Dolls - Mattel, Inc.

EASTER PET SHOW - Candy ☆ - R.M. Palmer Co.

EASTER SPRING BACKS - Toys–stuffed - Dakin Inc.

EASTER SWEET GREETS - Candy - R.M. Palmer Co.

EASTER TAILS - Chocolate candy - Superior Fruit & Confections

EASTER VALE - Statuary - Collins International Co., Ltd.

EASTER WORLD - Novelty items–paper - Kurt S. Adler Inc.

EASTERLING FARMS - Onions - Easterling Farms

EASTERN - Batteries - Exide Corp.

EASTERN - Extension ladders - W.W. Babcock Co. Inc.

EASTERN - Musical instruments - Eastern Music Co.

EASTERN - Prefabricated buildings–metal ☆ - Roper Corp.

EASTERN - Safes - Boston Lock & Safe Co.

EASTERN - Safety products - Aearo Co.

EASTERN - Window coverings - Rex Venetian Blind Co.

EASTERN ELEGANCE - Wallpaper ☆ - Greeff Fabrics Inc.

EASTERN FLAVOR - Food products ☆ - Lehmann Farms, Inc.

EASTERN FOODS - Dairy products and condiments - Eastern Foods, Inc.

EASTERN HARMONY - Wallpaper - Dekortex Inc.

EASTERN HARMONY - Wallpaper ☆ - Singer Wallcoverings, Inc.

EASTERN HOME PRODUCTS INC. - Bedding–linen - Eastern Home Products Inc.

EASTERN MARKET - Beef - Cattleman's Inc.

EASTERN MIND: THE LOST SOULS OF TONG NOU - Computer software - Sony Interactive Entertainment Inc.

EASTERN PLAIN - Water–bottled or canned - Eastern Plains

EASTERN SHORE - Apparel and accessories - Commander Garment Co.

EASTERN SHORE - Seafood products–fresh or frozen - Eastern Shore Seafood

EASTERN SHOREMAN EXPRESS, THE - Sporting goods - Sean Mann

EASTERN SHOREMAN, THE - Decoys - Sean Mann

EASTERN STANDARD - Window coverings - Eastern Standard Corp.

EASTERN TECHNOLOGIES - Motor vehicles - Eastern Technologies Ltd.

EASTERN TRADITIONS - Food products - Uncle Ben's, Inc.

EASTERN WIND - Apparel–children's - House of Bargains, Inc.

EASTERN WINDS - Furniture ☆ - Bassett Furniture Industries, Inc.

EASTERNER - Doors–wood ☆ - Ropert General Electric

EASTERNER - Wood products - Rex Venetian Blind Co.

EASTERVALE - House furnishings - Collins International Co., Ltd.

EASTERVILLE FARMS - Candy ☆ - R.M. Palmer Co.

EASTFIELD - Firearms, accessories, and parts - Smith & Wesson Corp.

EASTGATE - Floor coverings–carpet and rugs - Hollytex Carpet Mills Inc.

EASTGATE - Furniture ☆ - Broyhill Furniture Industries, Inc.

EASTHAMPTON - Wallpaper - Magic Appliques Inc.

EASTHAMPTON II - Wallpaper - Magic Appliques Inc.

EASTLAKE - Wallpaper - Belmont Wallcoverings

EASTLAND - Shoes - Eastland Shoe Manufacturing Corp.

EASTMAN - Hardware - U.S. Brass Corp.

EASTMAN - Photographic equipment - Eastman Kodak Co.

EASTMAN - Watches - Eastman Watch Co. Inc.

EASTMAN - Yarn - Eastman Chemical Co.

EASTMAN HOUSE - Bedding–linen ☆ - Chittenden & Eastman Co. Inc.

EASTMAN, INC. - Pens - Eastman, Inc.

EASTMAN OUTDOORS - Mattresses - Game Tracker, Inc.

EASTOBOND - Adhesives and sealants - Eastman Kodak Co.

EASTON - Frames–eyeglass - Zylo Ware Corp.

EASTON - Sporting goods - Easton Sports Inc.

EASTON E - Sport bags - Easton Aluminum Inc.

EASTON INSTINCT - Hockey equipment - Easton Aluminum Inc.

EASTONE - Dyes and pigments - Eastman Kodak Co.

EASTOZONE - Vitamins and nutritional supplements - Eastman Kodak Co.

☆ = Now out of production

EASTPAK - Apparel and accessories - Eastpak
EASTPAK - Bags–duffel - Eastpak Corp.
EASTPAK - Stationery - Eastpak Corp.
EASTPARK INTERNATIONAL AQUARIUM BRAND - Seafood products–fresh or frozen - Cheun Hing Trading Co., Inc.
EASTPOINT - Frames–eyeglass - May Optical Co. Inc.
EASTPORT - Frames–eyeglass ☆ - Universal/Univis Inc.
EASTPRINT - Publisher's imprints - Eastprint Inc.
EASTSIDE - Wallpaper ☆ - Linden Street Gallery
EASTWAY - Wallpaper - Secrest Handprints Inc.
EASTWAY 3 - Wallpaper - Secrest Handprints Inc.
EASTWIND - Adhesives and sealants - Eastwind Lapidary, Inc.
EASTWIND, THE - Recliners - Lane Co. Inc.
EASTWINDS - Furniture ☆ - Stanley Furniture Co. Inc.
EASTWINDS - Rice - Connell Co.
EASTWOOD - Wallpaper ☆ - Manuscreens
EASTWOOD COLLECTION - Furniture ☆ - Southern Furniture Co. of Conover
EASY - Computer software ☆ - WordStar International Inc.
EASY - Cosmetics - SBS Beauty Systems
EASY - Dairy products - Dean Foods Co.
EASY - Food products - Van Den Bergh Foods Co.
EASY - Mops - Royal Maid Association for the Blind Inc.
EASY - Washing machines–household - White Consolidated Industries, Inc.
EASY - Window frames - Lakeshore Products Ltd.
EASY 3 - Remote control devices - Gemini Industries, Inc.
EASY 7'S - Game machines - Sigma Game Inc.
EASY 8 - Filters–air - Air Kontrol Inc.
EASY ACCENTS - Hobby kits - JCA, Inc.
EASY ACCESS - Alarm systems–burglar - Interactive Technologies, Inc.
EASY ACES - Candy - Ph. Wunderle Inc.
EASY-ACID - Chemical preparations - Fritz Industries, Inc.
EASY ADDRESS - Computer software - Simplesoft Corp.
EASY AIM - Golfing equipment - Ernst F. Sturm
EASY ALKALINITY - Water treating compounds - United Chemical Corp.
EASY & NATURAL - Beverages ☆ - The Atlantic Beverage Group, USA, Inc.
EASY ANGLE - Knives–pocket ☆ - G-96 Products Co. Inc.
EASY ART - Paint-by-number sets ☆ - Coloron Industries
EASY AUGER - Tools–hand-operated - Tioga, Inc.
EASY AUTOMOTIVE - Automotive-oil-changing kit - Easy Automotive Products Inc.
EASY BACK - Faucets - Gerber Plumbing Fixtures Corp.
EASY-BAKE - Toys - Tonka Corp.
EASY BAKE - Toys–electronic - Kenner Products
EASY BASICS - Patterns–clothing ☆ - Simplicity Pattern Co., Inc.
EASY BLEND - Medical apparatus - W.W. Grainger, Inc.
EASY BLEND STENCIL PAINT - Paints - DecoArt, Inc.
EASY BLOCK - Horse feed - Purina Mills, Inc.
EASY BLUE - Apparel - Bugle Boy Industries, Inc.
EASY BREADS - Breads–mixes - General Mills, Inc.
EASY-BRIEF - Health care products - MB Products Ltd.
EASY BUFF - Cosmetics - SBS Beauty Systems
EASY BUTTON - Audio equipment - Telequest Inc.
EASY CAESAR - Salad dressings–mixes - Saco Foods, Inc.
EASY CALC 64 - Computer software ☆ - Commodore Business Machines Inc.
EASY-CARE - Finishing agents ☆ - Flintkote Co.
EASY CARE - Floor coverings–carpet and rugs ☆ - Johnsonite Flooring Products
EASY CARE - Mats - Roope Corp.
EASY-CARE - Medical apparatus - Guardian Products Inc.
EASY-CARE - Paints ☆ - GS Roofing Products Co.
EASY CARE - Siding–insulating - Ashland-Davis Co.
EASY CARE - Toys - Tonka Corp.
EASY CARE - Yarn ☆ - Caron International Inc.
EASY CARE 2000 - Health care products - Sunrise Medical
EASY CARE JUST WEAR - Apparel and accessories - Bugle Boy Industries, Inc.
EASY CARE KNITS - Apparel–men's - Haspel Brothers Inc.
EASY-CATCH - Medical apparatus - Superior Healthcare Group, Inc.
EASY CHANGE - Hair coloring preparations ☆ - Roux Laboratories, Inc.
EASY CHARGE - Cigarette lighters - Fidelitone Inc.
EASY CHECK - Gauging instruments - Hammerhead Tower, Inc.
EASY CHEESE - Cheese - Nabisco Foods Group
EASY CLEAN - Faucets - Moen Inc.
EASY-CLEAN - Glass–window - Great Lakes Window, Inc.
EASY CLEAN - Paints - Kyanize Paint Co.
EASY CLEAR - Water purification systems - Bunn-O-Matic Corp.

EASY CLICK - Computer peripheral equipment ☆ - Pelikan, Inc.
EASY CLIP - Photographic equipment - Stainless Steel Products
EASY COLOR - Pigments–paint - Tru-Test Manufacturing
EASY COLOR ATTITUDE, THE - Hair care products - Almay Inc.
EASY COMBING - Hair care products - Johnson & Johnson
EASY COMPUTER SYSTEMS INC. - Computers - Easy Computer Systems
EASY CONTROL - Vitamins and nutritional supplements - Advanced Physicians Products, Inc.
EASY CORNER - Building materials - Triad Group Inc.
EASY COUNTRY - Basket-weaving craft kit - Rainbow Trading Co. Inc.
EASY-COVER - Office supplies ☆ - Newell Office Products
EASY COVER - Paper - Kent Adhesive Products Co.
EASY CRISP - Housewares - Tupperware Co.
EASY CURL - Curling irons–electric ☆ - Marianna Imports, Inc.
EASY CURL - Toys - Tonka Corp.
EASY CURTAIN - Motor vehicle parts and accessories - Frank Nenstiel
EASY CUT - Clippers–barber - Andis Co.
EASY CUT - Garden equipment ☆ - Nelson Roanoke Corp.
EASY DAY - Deodorants–personal ☆ - Carter-Wallace, Inc.
EASY DAY - Mops - Easy Day Manufacturing Co.
EASY DAYS CALMNESS - Health care products - Futurebiotics
EASY DIAMOND - Garden equipment - Valley View Specialties Co.
EASY-DO - Can openers–hand-operated - Lewart Co. Inc.
EASY DOES IT - Adhesives and sealants ☆ - Loctite Corp.
EASY DOES IT - Floor coverings - Congoleum Corp.
EASY-DOES-IT - Food products - Murry's Inc.
EASY DOES IT - Frames–eyeglass - May Optical Co. Inc.
EASY DOG DOOR - Pet products - Gun Dog House Door Co.
EASY DOSE - Chemical preparations - Fritz Industries, Inc.
EASY DRIVER - Health care products - Remington Products Co.
EASY DRY - Infant product - Rock-A-Bye Baby Inc.
EASY EASEL - Furniture - Swartz Framing Studio
EASY EASEL - Photographic equipment ☆ - Omega/Arkay
EASY-EASTER - Hobby kits ☆ - Hinkle Easter Products
EASY EATIN' - Apparel–children's - Playskool Baby Inc.
EASY-EDGE - Plastics - Warp Bros.
EASY EDGE - Seat covers - Rubbermaid Inc.
EASY-EDIT - Trays ☆ - GAF Corp.
EASY EGGS - Eggs - Milton G. Waldbaum Co.
EASY ELEGANCE - Floor coverings–carpet and rugs - Tuftex Carpet Mills, Inc.
EASY ELEGANCE - Mushrooms ☆ - Mushroom Cooperative Co.
EASY ELEGANCE - Paints - Valspar Corp.
EASY EMBERS - Circuit breakers–air - Alma Products Inc.
EASY ENTRY - Apparel and accessories - Orvis Co., Inc.
EASY ESSENTIALS - Patterns–clothing ☆ - Simplicity Pattern Co., Inc.
EASY ETCH - Cleaning preparations - Klein & Co.
EASY ETCH - Decals and transfers - Color-Clings, Inc.
EASY EXTRA - Computer software - WordStar International Inc.
EASY FACES - Novelty items - Imagineering Inc.
EASY FARM - Computer software - Vertical Solutions, Inc.
EASY FEAST - Meat products–poultry - Jerome Foods Inc.
EASY FILLER - Faucets - Gerber Plumbing Fixtures Corp.
EASY FILTER - Aquarium accessories - Kordon
EASY FILTER - Filters–water - Novalek, Inc.
EASY FINISH - Adhesives and sealants - National Gypsum Co.
EASY-FIT - Floor coverings - Tarkett, Inc.
EASY FIT - Hair care products - SBS Beauty Systems
EASY-FIT - Toys - Aqua-Leisure Industries, Inc.
EASY FIT - Window shades - Kenney Manufacturing Co.
EASY-FIT - Windows - A-J Manufacturing
EASY FIT COLLECTIBLES - Patterns–clothing ☆ - Mccall Pattern Co.
EASY FIT-EASY SEW - Patterns–clothing ☆ - Mccall Pattern Co.
EASY FIVE - Floor coverings–carpet and rugs - Conquest Carpet Mills Inc.
EASY FIX - Pipes - Lasco Products Group
EASY FLAME - Fireplace equipment - Majestic Co.
EASY FLO - Automotive parts and accessories ☆ - Fibre Glass-Evercoat Co. Inc.
EASY FLOAT - Paints - DecoArt, Inc.
EASY-FLOW - Health care products - Schuco Inc.
EASY FOIL - Adhesives and sealants - Duncan Enterprises
EASY-FOLD-CASCADE - Machinery - S. Morantz Inc.
EASY FOLD DECOY - Decoys - Carry-Lite, Inc.
EASY FOOT - Mats - JCH International Inc.
EASY FOR YOU TO SAY - Games - John Huff
EASY FORMS - Nail care products - Superb Solutions

☆ = Now out of production

EASY FRAME - Frames–picture - North American Enclosures Inc.
EASY FRAME - Hardware - National Manufacturing Co.
EASY FROST - Vegetables–frozen ☆ - Hanover Foods Corp.
EASY FROST NEEDLES - Hair care products - SBS Beauty Systems
EASY GHCC ON - Diapers–cloth - General Health Care Corp.
EASY GLAMUR - Cleaning preparations–carpet and rug ☆ - Wagner Products
EASY GLAZE - Adhesives and sealants ☆ - Macklanburg-Duncan Co.
EASY GLIDE - Bowling balls - Master Industries Inc.
EASY GLIDE - Chairs–upholstered - Franklin Corp.
EASY GLIDE - Paper–coated - J.L. Hammett Co.
EASY GO! PLAY YARD - Infant product - Ming Ta Supply
EASY GOING - Antifreeze - Camco Manufacturing, Inc.
EASY GOING - Footwear–athletic - E.S. Originals, Inc.
EASY GOING - Luggage - Samsonite Corp.
EASY GOING FOR K & B - Fabrics–tapestry ☆ - Columbus Coated Fabrics Co.
EASY GOURMET, EVERYDAY! - Food products - Anna Lena's Cranberry Products, Inc.
EASY GRABBER - Pet products - Marineland Aquarium Products
EASY-GRADE - Lasers - Spectra-Physics Laserplane, Inc.
EASY GRAND - Game machines - Sigma Game Inc.
EASY GRASS - Fertilizers - Advanced Marketing Concepts Inc.
EASY GREASE - Pneumatic grease guns - Steven Nelson Joyner
EASY GREENS - Vitamins and nutritional supplements - Professional & Technical Services, Inc.
EASY GRILL - Barbecues and grills - Easy Grill, Inc.
EASY GRIP - Gauging instruments - Moeller Products Co. Inc.
EASY GRIP - Health care products - Crump Products Inc.
EASY-GRIP - Health care products - Maddak Inc.
EASY GRIP - Infant product - Playskool Baby Inc.
EASY GRIPPERS - Rubber–vulcanized - Manco, Inc.
EASY-GRO - Garden equipment ☆ - Novelcrafts Manufacturing Co.
EASY GRO SYSTEMS - Hoses - Gregory Deppe
EASY GROW - Garden equipment - Carefree Garden Products
EASY-GROW - Garden equipment - Warp Bros.
EASY GUN - Caulking compounds - Allpro Corp.
EASY GUN - Paint removers - Easy Time Wood Refinishing Products Corp.
EASY HANGER - Binders - Dennison National Co.
EASY HERBS - Herbal products - Fontina Foods
EASY HINGES - Craft supplies - Sig Manufacturing Inc.
EASY HIT - Bats–baseball - Little Tikes Co.
EASY HITCH - Motor vehicle parts and accessories - Teledyne Industries Inc.
EASY HITCH - Pet products - Aspen Pet Products
EASY HOLD - Manicure preparations - W.E. Bassett Co.
EASY HOOKER - Pipes - Anderson-Barrows Metals Corp.
EASY HOURS - Slippers - International Seaway Trading Corp.
EASY-IN - Bathroom fixtures ☆ - Artesian Industries
EASY-IRON - Fabrics–cotton - Dan River Inc.
EASY-IVY - Pharmaceutical preparations - Bethurum Research & Development Inc.
EASY JOINT - Tape–adhesive - Wall Tool & Tape Corp
EASY KEY - Remote control devices - Jasco Products Co. Inc.
EASY KIT - Rackets–tennis - Gexco Enterprises
EASY KNOT - Housewares - Charles O. Larson Co. Inc.
EASY KRETE - Cement - Colonial Refining and Chemical Co.
EASY KUTTER - Knives–pocket - Allway Tools Inc.
EASY LAYER BARS - Food products - General Mills, Inc.
EASY LEAF SCOOPER, THE - Tools–hand-operated - Scooper Corp.
EASY LIFE - Apparel and accessories - County Seat Stores Inc.
EASY LIFE - Floor coverings ☆ - Congoleum Corp.
EASY LIFE WRINKLE-LESS - Apparel and accessories - County Seat Stores Inc.
EASY-LIFT - Chair ☆ - Access Industries, Inc.
EASY-LIFT - Hairpins - Lessl, Inc.
EASY LIGHT - Wood products ☆ - Di Giorgio Corp.
EASY LINK - Hoses - Suncast Corp.
EASY LISTENER - Telephone apparatus - Phonic Ear, Inc.
EASY-LITE - Eyeglasses - Art-Craft Optical Co.
EASY-LITE - Lanterns–kerosene - Coleman Co., Inc.
EASY LIVING - Brushes–paint - E-Z Paintr Corp.
EASY LIVING - Floor coverings–carpet and rugs ☆ - Carpet Crafts Inc.
EASY LIVING - Floor coverings–carpet and rugs ☆ - Playfield International Inc.
EASY LIVING - Footwear ☆ - E.S. Originals, Inc.
EASY LIVING - Frames–eyeglass ☆ - Universal/Univis Inc.
EASY LIVING - Furniture–wood - Lloyd/Flanders Industries

EASY LIVING - Paints - Sears, Roebuck and Co.
EASY LIVING - Umbrellas - Service Merchandise Co. Inc.
EASY LOAD - Electronic equipment - Kalart Victor Corp.
EASY LOAD'R - Motor vehicle parts and accessories - Delta Consolidated Industries, Inc.
EASY-LOCATOR - Medical apparatus - Schautex Corp.
EASY-LOCK - Braces–orthopedic - Swede-O, Inc.
EASY-LOCK - Fencing–gates and posts - Mapes Industries Inc.
EASY LOCK - Pipes - GSW Jackes-Evans Manufacturing Co.
EASY-LOCK - Sealing devices - Gallo Manufacturing Co.
EASY-LOK - Office supplies - Globe-Weis
EASY MARKER - Paints - Fox Valley Systems Inc.
EASY-MASK - Tape–masking - Daubert Coated Products, Inc.
EASY MATIC - Ovens–microwave ☆ - Quasar Co.
EASY MEAL - Food products ☆ - Oregon Freeze Dry Inc.
EASY MEASURE - Kitchen utensils–enameled - Robbins Industries, Inc.
EASY MIX - Faucets - Gerber Plumbing Fixtures Corp.
EASY MIX & SET - Concrete products ☆ - Set Consumer Products Inc.
EASY MONEY - Eyeglasses - Martin-Copeland Eyewear Corp.
EASY MONEY - Game machines - WMS Gaming Inc.
EASY MONEY - Games ☆ - Milton Bradley Co.
EASY MOUNT - Air conditioning equipment - General Electric Co.
EASY MOUNT - Bathroom accessories - Miller Studio
EASY MOUNT - Hardware - National Manufacturing Co.
EASY-MOUNT - Hooks ☆ - Newell Office Products
EASY MOVER - Toys ☆ - Steven Manufacturing Co.
EASY MULCH - Lawn mowers - Toro Co.
EASY NAV - Navigational instruments - Pioneer Marketing & Research, Inc.
EASY NOTEBOOK OFFICE - Computer software - Apsley-Bolton Computers, Inc.
EASY NOW - Teas–herbal - Traditional Medicinals, Inc.
EASY OATS - Health care products - Futurebiotics
EASY-OFF - Cleaning preparations - Reckitt & Colman Subsidary Corp.
EASY-OFF - Cleaning preparations–household - Boyle-Midway
EASY-OFF - Crayons - Binney & Smith Inc.
EASY OFF - Sporting goods - Bear Archery Inc.
EASY-OFF TARP STOP - Tarpaulins - Shur-Co Inc.
EASY OMELETS - Eggs - Nabisco Brands Inc.
EASY ON - Concrete products ☆ - Set Consumer Products Inc.
EASY ON - Eyeglasses - Martin-Copeland Eyewear Corp.
EASY-ON - Golfing equipment - Golfsmith International Inc.
EASY-ON - Plastics film ☆ - Warp Bros.
EASY-ON - Skates–roller ☆ - Chicago Roller Skate Co.
EASY ON - Sporting goods - Mill Run Products Co.
EASY-ON - Starch–laundry - Boyle-Midway
EASY ON-EASY OFF - Wallpaper - Statter Wallpaper Mills
EASY-ON FASHIONS - Toys - M.&S. Shillman Inc.
EASY ON THE EYES - Cosmetics - Alexandra De Markoff, Ltd.
EASY OPEN - Ladders–metal - Carolina Ladder Co. Inc.
EASY-OUT - Infant product - Leachco Inc.
EASY PAGER - Computer software - Crockett & Associates
EASY PAKS - Cleaning preparations - S.C. Johnson & Son, Inc.
EASY PAKS - Luggage ☆ - Samsonite Corp.
EASY PATCH - Flowers, plants, and seeds - Pennington Enterprises, Inc.
EASY PATCH - Hardware - C.E. Kaiser Co.
EASY PICKENS - Flowers, plants, and seeds - D. Landreth Seed Co.
EASY PIECES - Apparel–athletic - Isaac Hazan & Co.
EASY PIECES - Shelving units–wood - Dawson Home Fashions, Inc.
EASY PITCH TENT - Toys - Fisher-Price, Inc.
EASY PLAID - Bedding–linen - Dan River Inc.
EASY PLANTER - Garden equipment - Union Wadding Co.
EASY-PLY - Roofing materials–slate - Homasote Co.
EASY PREP - Paints - Sinclair Paint Co.
EASY PREP - Paints - Standard Brands Paint Co.
EASY-PRINT - Office supplies - Alvin and Co. Inc.
EASY-PRINTS - Adhesives and sealants - Decora Manufacturing
EASY PRINTS - Decals and transfers - Stahls' Inc.
EASY-PRO - Bicycle parts and accessories - Finish Line Technologies, Inc.
EASY PRO WOOD PRODUCTS - Fencing–gates and posts - Capital Lumber Co.
EASY-PULL - Motors–outboard - Outboard Marine Corp.
EASY PUTTY - Plumber's putty - Comstar International Inc. (IPC Div.)
EASY QUICK STYLER - Skin care products ☆ - JRC Products Inc.
EASY RACER SUPER ZZIPPER - Apparel and accessories - Zzip Designs
EASY REACH - Clutches–industrial - Access Unlimited
EASY REACH - Mops - Drackett Co.

☆ = Now out of production

EASY REACH - Paint rollers - Panda Brush Co.
EASY REACH - Poles–wood - E-Z Paintr Corp.
EASY-REACH - Toys - Tonka Corp.
EASY REACHER - Housewares ☆ - Selfix, Inc.
EASY READ - Maps - CIR Products Inc.
EASY READ - Office supplies ☆ - Replogle Globes Inc.
EASY-READ - Scales–bathroom - Healthometer
EASY READER - Hobby kits - Extra Special Products Corp.
EASY READER - Watches - Timex Corp.
EASY READER, THE - Electronic equipment ☆ - Navitar, Inc.
EASY RECIPE - Vegetables–frozen - Dean Foods Co.
EASY REQ - Construction equipment rental services - Moore Business Forms, Inc.
EASY REST - Pillows - Town & Country Pillow
EASY RIDE - Health care products - Total Support
EASY RIDE - Tricycles ☆ - Little Tikes Co.
EASY RIDER - Bicycles - Raleigh USA Bicycle Co.
EASY RIDER - Bodyboards - Foam Design Consumer Products Inc.
EASY RIDER - Exercising equipment - Marcy Fitness Products
EASY RIDER - Infant product ☆ - Pearson Archery
EASY RIDER - Lenses–optical - Ditto Industries Inc.
EASY RIDER - Pet products - R.C. Steele Co.
EASY RIDER - Sporting goods ☆ - Hedstrom Corp.
EASY RIDERS - Jeans–women's - H.D. Lee Co., Inc.
EASY RIDERS - Safety equipment - Mine Safety Appliances Co.
EASY RIDE'UMS - Toys–stuffed - Mary Meyer Corp.
EASY RIDGE - Apparel and accessories - Wrangler Apparel Co.
EASY RISE - Window coverings - Hunter Douglas, Inc.
EASY-RISER - Health care products - Rajowalt Corp.
EASY RISER - High chairs - Gerry Baby Products Co.
EASY-RITE - Bulletin boards–wood - Marsh Chalkboard Co.
EASY ROCK - Sporting goods - Van Dyke's
EASY ROLLER - Eyeglasses - Martin-Copeland Eyewear Corp.
EASY ROLLER - Housewares - Home Equipment Manufacturing Co.
EASY ROLLER - Pens - Scripto-Tokai Corp.
EASY ROLLER - Skates–roller ☆ - Steven Manufacturing Co.
EASY ROLLERS - Roller skates - Brookfield Athletic Co. Inc.
EASY SAFE - Computer software - Eliashim Microcomputers, Inc.
EASY SAND - Paint removers - Fibre Glass-Evercoat Co. Inc.
EASY SCIENCE - Toys - Natural Science Industries, Ltd.
EASY SCOOP - Cat box litter - Excel-Mineral Co. Inc.
EASY SCRIPT - Computer software ☆ - Commodore Business Machines Inc.
EASY SCRUB - Cleaning preparations - Star Brite
EASY SEAT - Boats–canoes - Coleman Co., Inc.
EASY SEAT - Furniture - Creative Imaging
EASY SEE RED - Rope - Columbian Rope Co.
EASY SERVE - Food products - Bush Brothers and Co.
EASY-SET - Fishing tackle - Easy-Set Hook Co.
EASY SET - Tiles–ceramic ☆ - American Olean Tile Co.
EASY SHAPE 'N STIR - Toys - Playskool, Inc.
EASY SHAPES - Apparel–women's - Sanmark-Stardust Inc.
EASY SHINE - Cleaning preparations - Blue Lustre, LLC
EASY SHOT - Cameras - Keystone Camera Corp.
EASY SHOT - Staplers - Black & Decker Corp.
EASY SHREDS - Seafood products–fresh or frozen - Tyson Holding Co.
EASY SLEEP - Vitamins and nutritional supplements - Planetary Formulas
EASY SLIDE - Dental floss - Johnson & Johnson
EASY SLIDE - Weather stripping - KEL-EEZ
EASY SLIDER - Binders - Dennison National Co.
EASY SLIDER - Pipes - MRN Enterprises
EASY-SLIP - Hoses - Camco Manufacturing, Inc.
EASY-SNEAKS - Footwear - Keds Corp.
EASY SOLUTION, THE - Exercising equipment - Body Bat, Inc.
EASY SONGMAKER - Toys–musical - Mattel, Inc.
EASY SOW-STRAIGHT ROW - Garden equipment - W. Atlee Burpee and Co.
EASY-SPARE - Tires - Dutton-Lainson Co.
EASY SPELL - Computer software ☆ - Commodore Business Machines Inc.
EASY SPINNER - Pipes–tobacco - MRN Enterprises
EASY SPIRIT - Shoes - United States Shoe Corp.
EASY SPIRIT OUTDOORS - Footwear - United States Shoe Corp.
EASY SPRAY - DC - Paint sprayers - Evergreen International, Inc.
EASY SPREAD - Limestone products - Medusa Minerals Co.
EASY SPREAD - Paints - Dean and Barry Co.
EASY SQUEEZY DYE - See VOILA
EASY STACK - Shelving units–wood - Windquest Companies, Inc.
EASY STAIN - Paints - Wattyl Paint Corp.

EASY STAND - Health care products - ALTimate Medical Inc.
EASY START - Metals - Game Tracker, Inc.
EASY STEAM - Irons–electric - Philips Electronics North America Corp.
EASY STEEL - Cutlery - General Housewares Corp.
EASY STEER - Brakes–motor vehicle - Rockwell International Corp.
EASY STEP 1100 AND EASY STEP 1210 - Office supplies - Varitronic Systems, Inc.
EASY STEP 2500 - Labeling machinery - Varitronic Systems, Inc.
EASY STEP 4000 - Labeling machinery - Varitronic Systems, Inc.
EASY-STICK - Pens - Union Pen Co.
EASY STOR - Closet organizers - Windquest Companies, Inc.
EASY STREET - Computer software - Mind Play
EASY STREET - Floor coverings–carpet and rugs - Burlington House Carpets
EASY STREET - Floor finishing machines–commercial - Basic Coatings, Inc.
EASY STREET - Frames–eyeglass - Zylo Ware Corp.
EASY STREET - Shoes - Easy Street Shoe Co.
EASY STREET - Trailers–travel - New Adventures, Inc.
EASY STREET - Wallpaper - Sanitas Wallcoverings
EASY STREETS - Maps - Map Works, Inc.
EASY STREUSEL - Food products ☆ - General Mills, Inc.
EASY STRIDE - Exercising equipment - Icon Health & Fitness, Inc.
EASY STRIDE - Lawn mowers - Toro Co.
EASY STRIDER - Bicycles - Tri Industries, Inc.
EASY STRIDER - Ophthalmic goods - Foremost Optical Products
EASY STRINGER - Sporting goods - Guterman International Inc.
EASY STRIP - See DAD'S EASY SPRAY
EASY STRIP - Epoxy coatings ☆ - Star Bronze Co. Inc.
EASY STUFF - Breads–mixes - Roskam Baking Co.
EASY STYLER - Dryers–hair - Windmere Corp.
EASY SURFACE PREP - Cleaning preparations - Flood Co.
EASY SWAP - Batteries - Liebert Corp.
EASY SWITCH RAILROAD - Toys - Mattel, Inc.
EASY TAPE PLAYER - Toys–musical - Mattel, Inc.
EASY TAX - Computer tax program - Timeworks International Inc.
EASY-TEA - Tea kettles–electric - Bunn-O-Matic Corp.
EASY TEACH - Publisher's imprints - United Methodist Publishing House
EASY TEETHER - Infant product - Leachco Inc.
EASY TEMP - Thermostats - Lux Products Corp.
EASY TENS - Health care products - American Imex
EASY TEST - Air conditioning equipment - Harvey-Westbury Corp.
EASY TEST - Pet products - Aquarium Products Inc.
EASY TEXTURE - Paints–artists' - Duncan Enterprises
EASY TILT - Hardware - Newell Manufacturing Co.
EASY TIME - Finishing agents - Easy Time Wood Refinishing Products Corp.
EASY TIMES - Shoes - Mason Shoe Manufacturing Co.
EASY TO BE ME - Underwear and nightwear - Kayser-Roth Corp.
EASY-TO-DO-KITS - Paints - Leather Factory Inc.
EASY-TO-DRESS - Dolls - Mattel, Inc.
EASY TO GROW - Flowers, plants, and seeds - Davids & Royston Bulb Co. Inc.
EASY-TO-HOLD - Infant product - Ansa Co. Inc.
EASY TO LOVE - Frames–eyeglass - Zylo Ware Corp.
EASY TO PLAY - Music–sheet ☆ - Warner Bros. Publications
EASY-TO-READ FOLKTALES - Publisher's imprints - Scholastic Inc.
EASY-TO-READ TRAVEL ATLAS - Atlases - Rand McNally & Co.
EASY TO SEW - Patterns–clothing ☆ - Simplicity Pattern Co., Inc.
EASY TO WEAR - Cosmetics - Revlon Consumer Products Corp.
EASY TONE - Paints - Hartco Wood Flooring
EASY TONE - Skin care products - Fredric's
EASY TOSS - Sporting goods - Sports Tutor, Inc.
EASY TOTE - Paper–toweling - Scott Paper Co.
EASY TOUCH - Electric can opener - Rival Co.
EASY TOUCH - Massage products - Homedics Inc.
EASY TOUCH - Paints - Homax, Inc.
EASY TOUCH - Toys–musical - Mattel, Inc.
EASY TOUCH CLASP - Jewelers' findings - QVC, Inc.
EASY TOUCH TALKING PICTURES - Toys - Mattel, Inc.
EASY TRACK - Closet organizers - Windquest Companies, Inc.
EASY TRAIN R'S BY JACO'S - Apparel and accessories - Alice Janice Slaughter
EASY TRAINER - Pet products - R.C. Steele Co.
EASY TRAVELER - Luggage - Moffat Wire Products Co.
EASY TRAVELER - Men's pants - Hubbard Co.
EASY TRAVELLER - Artists' materials - Loew-Cornell Inc.
EASY TREAT - Vegetables–canned - FCX Inc.
EASY-TRIM - Christmas tree lights - General Enterprises Inc.

EASY TRIM - Floor coverings - National Floor Products Co., Inc.
EASY TRIM - Sprinklers–lawn ☆ - All-State Plastics
EASY TRIM - Vitamins and nutritional supplements - Barth-Spencer Corp.
EASY-TURN - Wood products ☆ - Gerber Industries Inc.
EASY TWIST - Corkscrews ☆ - Franmara Co. Inc.
EASY-TWIST REFILL SYSTEM - Mops - O-Cedar/Vining Household Products Co.
EASY-TYPE - Office supplies ☆ - Office Products Inc.
EASY-UP - Blinds–venetian - Spring Window Fashions Division, Inc.
EASY UP - Housewares - Xcel Industrial Group, Inc.
EASY UP - Wood products - Furman Lumber Inc.
EASY UP-EASY DOWN - Motors–outboard - Outboard Marine Corp.
EASY UP RAMP SYSTEMS - Ramps - Easy-Up Industries, Inc.
EASY VICTORIAN - Moldings–plaster of paris - Reliance Industries Inc.
EASY VIEW - Cameras - Concord Camera Corp.
EASY-VIEW - Office supplies - Office Products Inc.
EASY-VIEW - Photo albums - Pioneer Photo Albums, Inc.
EASY VOICE - Audio equipment - Adriana M. Vick
EASY-VOLT - Electrical equipment - A.W. Sperry Instruments, Inc.
EASY WALK TREADMILL - Exercising equipment - Bodyshaping, Inc.
EASY WALKER - Pet products - Premier Pet Products Inc.
EASY WALL - Shower stalls–plastic - Plaskolite Inc.
EASY-WASH - Detergents - Airwick Industries
EASY WASHING - Infant product - Rock-A-Bye Baby Inc.
EASY-WAVE - Furniture - Easyrest Inc.
EASY WAVE - Hair care products - Gold Medal Hair Products Inc.
EASY WAVE - Hair care products - Posner Laboratories Inc.
EASY WAY - Cleaning preparations–household - Trebol Co., Inc.
EASY-WAY - Mats ☆ - Royal Rubber & Manufacturing Co.
EASY-WAY - Paint sets–hobby - Stateside Products Inc.
EASY WAY - Paints - Plasti-Kote Co. Inc.
EASY WAY - Sporting goods - D & H Products Co.
EASY-WAY-V - Hair care products - Fleetwood Co.
EASY-WEAR - Health care products ☆ - Nelkin/Piper Health Products
EASY WEAVE - Hobby kits - National Spinning Co., Inc.
EASY WEEDER - Garden equipment - Ultimate Tool Group
EASY-WHEELER - Carts - Agri-Engineering, Inc.
EASY-WIPE - Inks - Graphic Chemical & Ink Co.
EASY WIPES - Washcloths - Magla Products Inc.
EASY WRITER - Computer software - Lynn Norton
EASY8 - Containers–paper - Georgia-Pacific Corp.
EASYACCT - Computer software - Tax and Accounting Software Corp.
EASYBALL - Computer peripheral equipment - Microsoft Corp.
EASYBOARD - Easels - Easy Graphics Corp.
EASYBOOK DELUXE - Computer software - Sunburst Communications, Inc.
EASYBREW - Coffee makers–electric - Douwe Egberts Coffee Service Inc.
EASYCARE - Shoes ☆ - Titleist & Foot-Joy Worldwide
EASYCELL - Electronic equipment - Ohio Electronic Engravers, Inc.
EASYCHEW - Shirts - Easychew Co.
EASYCHORD AUTOHARP - Zithers ☆ - Oscar Schmidt International Inc.
EASYCLEAN - Tools - Axia Inc.
EASYCLEAN/GP - Ophthalmic goods ☆ - Allergan, Inc.
EASYCOMPACT - Photographic equipment - E.I. Dupont de Nemours and Co.
EASYCOOLER - Water dispensers - Ebac Systems, Inc.
EASYCRAFT - Computer software ☆ - Commodore Business Machines Inc.
EASYDIJ - Computer software - Geocomp, Ltd.
EASYDRIVER - Tools ☆ - Creative Products Inc.
EASYDYE - Machinery - Applied Color Systems, Inc.
EASYEDIT - Computer software - Geotrace Technologies, Inc.
EASYEST AG - Computer software - Keithley Instruments, Inc.
EASYFILE - Filing cabinets–metal - Steelworks, Inc.
EASYFILT - Computer software - Geotrace Technologies, Inc.
EASYFINDER MAPS - Maps - Rand McNally & Co.
EASYFINDER PLUS - Maps - Rand McNally & Co.
EASYFLEX - Golf-club shafts - United Sports Technologies Inc.
EASYFLO - Brushes–paint - Wooster Brush Co.
EASYFLOPPY - Computer storage devices–magnetic - Sysgen Inc.
EASYFLOW - Paper ☆ - ACCO USA, Inc.
EASYGLIDE - Drapery hardware - Kirsch Co.
EASYGLIDE - Ironing board pads - Lear Siegler Seymour Corp.
EASYGRAFIX - Computer peripheral equipment - GCH Systems, Inc.
EASYGRIP - Paper–sand - Nicsand, Inc.
EASYHELP - Computer software - Interthink Consulting Group Inc.
EASYHOLD - Medical apparatus - Physicians Appliance Co.
EASYHORSE - Sawhorses - J & S Manufacturing Co.
EASYID - Computer software - Intellivoice Communications, Inc.

EASYINPUT - Telephone apparatus - SNI Innovation Inc.
EASYISDN - Computer software - Meret Communications, Inc.
EASYKEY - Computer software - CBS Software
EASYLEE - Recording label - Ichiban Records, Inc.
EASYLIFT - Forklifts - Nor-Tech B.S.M., Inc.
EASYLIGHT - Fireplace equipment - Pine Mountain Corp.
EASYLIGHT - Ladders–metal - White Metal Rolling & Stamping Corp.
EASYLOAD - Office supplies - 20th Century Plastics
EASYMARC - Computer software - Data Trek Inc.
EASYMATCH - Computer software - HunterLab
EASYMATH - Computer software - TCI Software Research, Inc.
EASYMENU - Computer software - Adtran
EASYMIX E-B - Paints - Flood Co.
EASYMOD - Computer software - Geotrace Technologies, Inc.
EASYON-EYES - Pet products - Sunbeam-Oster Household Products
EASYONE - Kitchen appliances - Easyone, Inc.
EASYORDER - Computer software - Micro*D, Inc.
EASYPATH - Software - TSI International
EASYPHOTO - Computer hardware - Storm Software, Inc.
EASYPICK - Hardware - Unarco Industries Inc. Materials Handling Div.
EASYPLEAT - Drapery hardware - Kirsch Co.
EASYPLOT - Pens - Koh-I-Noor, Inc.
EASYPLOT PLUS - Pens - Koh-I-Noor, Inc.
EASYPLY - Health care products - Biomedical Life Systems, Inc.
EASYPOINT - Decals and transfers - Flagship Group II, Inc.
EASYPOST - Building materials - Abco, Inc.
EASYPOXY - Paints - Pettit Paint Co. Inc.
EASYPRO - Carpet cleaning machine - Regina Co.
EASYRAKE - Tools–power-driven - Evergreen International, Inc.
EASYRAY - Computer software - Geotrace Technologies, Inc.
EASYREACH - Machinery - Suhar Corp.
EASYREAD - Telephones - Code-a-Phone Corp.
EASYRIDER - Audio equipment - Aphex Systems, Ltd.
EASYRIDERS - Cleaning preparations - Paisano Publications, Inc.
EASYRIDERS CAFE - Apparel and accessories - Paisano Publications, Inc.
EASYRISER - Pharmaceutical preparations ☆ - Jess Clarke & Sons Inc.
EASYROLL - Tools - Ames Taping Tool Systems Co.
EASYSAA - Computer software - Multi Soft Inc.
EASYSALES - Computer software - Adata Corp.
EASYSAMPLER - Medical apparatus - E.F. Brewer Co.
EASYSEAL - Office supplies - Oliner Fibre Co. Inc.
EASYSECT - Computer software - Geotrace Technologies, Inc.
EASYSET - Traps–animal - Woodstream Corp.
EASYSHRINK - Heating equipment - Research, Inc.
EASYSIGN - Signs ☆ - Webway, Inc.
EASYSOY - Vitamins and nutritional supplements - J.R. Carlson Laboratories Inc.
EASYSPOOLER - Computer software - Seay Systems, Inc.
EASYSPROUT - Soil–potting - Sproutamo Corp.
EASYSTART - Building materials - Abco, Inc.
EASYSTEP - Computer software - ChipSoft Inc.
EASYSTRAT - Computer software - Geotrace Technologies, Inc.
EASYSTREET - Fibers–synthetic - Veratec
EASYSTREET - Office furniture–metal ☆ - Hon Co.
EASYSUN - Skin care products - Almay Inc.
EASYSWITCH - Electrical equipment - Woods Industries, Inc.
EASYSYN - Computer software - Geotrace Technologies, Inc.
EASYTAC - Paper products - Decora Manufacturing
EASYTALK - Electrical equipment - Nady Systems Inc.
EASYTANK - Recycling tanks - York International Corp.
EASYTAPER - Office supplies ☆ - Sainberg and Co. Inc.
EASYTEL - Computer software - Tax and Accounting Software Corp.
EASYTIME - Computer software - Shawneesoft Systems, Inc.
EASYTOUCH - Pens - Pilot Corp. of America
EASYTOUCH - Welding equipment - Broco, Inc.
EASYTRACK - Computer software - Matthew J. Tomascik Associates, Inc.
EASYTRAINER - Pet products - Austin Innovations, Inc.
EASYTURN - Luggage - American Tourister, Inc.
EASYVAC - Garden equipment - Evergreen International, Inc.
EASYVIEW - Office supplies ☆ - McBee Loose Leaf Binders
EASYVUE - Easels - Rubbermaid Inc.
EASYWARE - Hardware - National Manufacturing Co.
EASYWASH WASHCLOTHS - Infant product - Rock-A-Bye Baby Inc.
EASYWEAVERS - Hair care products - Easy Weavers
EAT-A-BITE - Fruits and vegetables ☆ - Idaho Fruit Sales Inc.
EAT-A-SNAX - Food products - Tom's Foods Inc.

☆ = Now out of production

EAT-ALL - Seafood products–fresh or frozen - Eat-All Frozen Food Co.

EAT CHICKEN - Novelty items - Papel Freelance, Inc.

EAT-EM-ALIVE - Cleaning preparations–household - Imperial Manufacturing Co. Inc.

EAT 'EM UP - Chewing gum - Philadelphia Chewing Gum Corp.

EAT FIT NOT FAT - Rice - Pacific Grain Products, Inc.

EAT FOOTBALL, SLEEP FOOTBALL, DRINK COCA-COLA - Beverages - Coca-Cola Co.

EAT IN YOUR CAR - Tableware–earthenware ☆ - Anacapa Corp.

EAT-LESS - Vitamins and nutritional supplements ☆ - Mayor Pharmaceutical Laboratories

EAT-M INTERNATIONAL - Trade Associations - Euro American Trading-Merchants Inc.

EAT ME - Fishing lures - Agua Images

EAT-MOR - Catsup - Brooks Foods

EAT MY DUST - Toys - Mattel, Inc.

EAT-N-JOY - Food products ☆ - Gol-Pak Corp.

EAT 'N LOSE - Health care products - CCA Industries, Inc.

EAT-N-TIME - Crackers - Vista Bakery, Inc.

EAT-ON - Food products ☆ - Eaton Foods Inc.

EAT-OS - Nuts–candied - Aster Nut Products Co. Inc.

EAT ROCKS! - Candy - Squire Boone Caverns, Inc.

EAT SLEEP - Apparel–athletic - Jeffrey Evans Nelson

EAT SLEEP GOLF - Apparel–athletic - Jeffrey Evans Nelson

EAT THE DRAGON - Health care products - East Earth Herb Inc.

EAT THE PEACH GARDEN COLLECTION - Spices and extracts ☆ - Chase Collection, Inc.

EAT WELL, SNACK WELL - Cookies - Nabisco Foods Group

EAT WORMS - Candy - Squire Boone Caverns, Inc.

EAT YER FACE - Publisher's imprints - Michael E. Samonek

EAT YOUR SPINACH - Apparel–athletic - Garret T. Murphy

EAT YOUR VEGETABLES! - Spices and extracts - To Market to Market

EAT ZE BEST - Vegetables–frozen ☆ - Lake Erie Frozen Foods Inc.

EATABLE GREETABLES - Candy ☆ - Marsyl Inc. (Marsyl Enterprises, Inc.)

EAT'EM-UP - Dog food - Farmland Industries Inc.

EATER'S DIGEST - Teas–herbal - Traditional Medicinals, Inc.

EATICUS ANYTHINGUS - T-shirts–men's - Lifeforms International, Inc.

EATIN' TIME - Fruit and vegetable markets - Frigid Food Products Inc.

EATING MACHINE - Computer software - Queue Inc.

EATING RIGHT - Dinners–frozen - Kraft Foods, Inc.

EATMOR - Flour–blended - Allen Bros. Milling Co./ADLUH Flour Mills

EATMOR - Food products - Eatmor Cranberries Inc.

EATMOR - Seafood products–fresh or frozen - New England Fish Co.

EAT'N RUN - Vitamins and nutritional supplements - Pharmavite Corp.

EATON - Floor coverings–carpet and rugs ☆ - Capel, Inc.

EATON - Frames–eyeglass - Zylo Ware Corp.

EATON - Ribbons–inked - Eaton Allen Ko-Rec-Type Corp.

EATON ALLEN - Office supplies - Eaton Allen Ko-Rec-Type Corp.

EATON KNOLL - Tableware–china ☆ - Lenox, Inc.

EATON OAK - Cabinets - Del Mar Cabinets

EATON PARK - Manufactured homes - Redman Industries, Inc.

EATON PLACE - Floor coverings–carpet and rugs ☆ - Customweave Carpets Inc.

EATON VINEYARDS - Wines - Eaton Vineyards

EATON-YALE - Hardware - Blaine Window Hardware Inc.

EATON'S - Stationery ☆ - Berkshire Stationery Inc.

E.A.T.S. EASY ACCESS T-SHIRTS - Apparel–women's - E.A.T.S.

EATWELL - Food products ☆ - Ventura Foods

EATWELL - Sardines–canned - Star-Kist Foods, Inc.

EAU CLAIRE - Cheese - Besnier USA, Inc.

EAU CLAIRE - Juices ☆ - Eau Claire Packing Co.

EAU DE 1000 - Perfumes - Jean Patou, Inc.

EAU DE BLONDE - Perfumes - Advertising to Women, Inc.

EAU DE COLOGNE IMPERIALE - Perfumes - Guerlain Inc.

EAU DE DOLCE - Perfumes - Parfums Christian Dior U.S. Corp.

EAU DE FRAICHE - Colognes - Revlon Consumer Products Corp.

EAU DE GUCCI - Colognes - Frances Denney

EAU DE KANANGA - Colognes - FMG/Tsumara Medical

EAU DE MELISSE DES CARMES - Antacids ☆ - Caswell-Massey Co. Ltd.

EAU DE PORTUGAL - American International Industries

EAU DE QUININE - Hair care products - All Clubman

EAU DENNA - Hair care products - Hair Specialty Co.

EAU DENNA - Hair care products - Larkspur Group Inc.

EAU DU MATIN - Perfumes - Mon Jardinet, Ltd.

EAU FRESH - Colognes - Quintessence Inc.

EAU SAUVAGE - Cosmetics - Christian Dior Perfumes Corp.

EAU SAUVAGE - Perfumes - Parfums Christian Dior U.S. Corp.

EAU SAVAGE EXTREME - Colognes - Christian Dior Perfumes Corp.

EAU SVELTE - Perfumes - Parfums Christian Dior U.S. Corp.

EAU-TO-GO - Bags–duffel - Co. of Women Inc.

EAV - Audio equipment - Clearvue/EAV, Inc.

EAVERWEAVE - Wallpaper - Capital Carousel Inc.

EAW - Electronic equipment - EAW

EAWD - Automotive parts and accessories - Dana Corp.

EAZOL - See NAUS-A-WAY

EAZY-STRIP - Paint removers - Mantrose-Haeuser Co. Inc.

EB - Bakery products - East Balt. Inc.

EB - Computer diskettes–blank - Electronics Boutique, Inc.

EB - Footwear - Hy Line Inc.

EB - Jewelry - Edwin B. Cutshall

EB - Jewelry - Elizabeth Blair Ltd., Inc.

EB - Jewelry - Paul F. Rothstein Inc.

EB - Wood products - Standard Supply & Equipment Co., Inc.

EB ELECTRONICS BOUTIQUE - Computer peripheral equipment - Electronics Boutique, Inc.

E.B. KOWAL MY PRINT SERIES - Greeting cards - E.B. Kowal

EB1200 - Musical instrument accessories - Music Accessories Manufacturing Co. Inc.

EBANO - Ceramic wall tile - Interceramic Inc.

EBARA - Barbecue sauce - U.S. Ebara Foods Inc.

EBARA CRYO-MAG-TURBO - Pumps - Ebara Technologies Inc.

EBARA CRYO-TURBO - Pumps - Ebara Technologies Inc.

EBARA TARI - Soy sauce - JFC International, Inc.

EBB & FLO - Fabrics - Gretchen Bellinger Inc.

EBB TIDE - Apparel and accessories - Warnaco Inc.

EBB TIDE - Floor coverings–carpet and rugs ☆ - Catalina Carpet Mills Inc.

EBB-TIDE - Floor coverings–carpet and rugs ☆ - Masland Corp.

EBB TIDE - Frames–eyeglass - Zylo Ware Corp.

EBB TIDE - Furniture ☆ - Stanley Furniture Co. Inc.

EBB TIDE - Rings–jewelry - Artcarved Inc.

EBBETS FIELD - Mustard - Carl Jensen and Virginia Jensen Partnership

EBBTIDE - Boats–motor - Ebbtide Corp.

EBBTIDE - Christmas tree ornaments - Cracker Box Inc.

EBBTIDE - Floor coverings–carpet and rugs - Mohawk Industries Inc.

EBBTIDE - Swimming pools ☆ - Lomart Industries

EBBTIDE - Tiles–ceramic - Wenczel Tile Co.

EBBTIDE - Venetian blinds - Atlantic Venetian Blind & Drapery Co.

EBBTIDE - Wood products - Weyerhaeuser Co.

EBBTIDE BRITE - Tiles–ceramic - Wenczel Tile Co.

E'BEEZ - Diapers–disposable - Enchanted Beginnings Inc.

EBELING & REUSS - Giftware - Ebeling and Reuss Co.

EBELSKIVER - Cooking equipment–household ☆ - Nordic Ware

EBERHARD - Pens - Faber-Castell Corp.

EBERHARD FABER - Office supplies - Faber-Castell Corp.

EBERHARD FABER-BOARD - Office accessories ☆ - Faber-Castell Corp.

EBERLE - Wines - Eberle Winery

EBERTHAL - Dishes–china - Imperial Crystal and China Inc.

EBERWINE - Food products - McCall Farms Inc.

EBEX C500 - Pharmaceutical preparations ☆ - Edom Laboratories Inc.

EBFLEECE - Apparel and accessories - Eddie Bauer Inc.

EBG - Diamond powder - General Electric Co.

EBI X FIX - Orthopedic products - EBI Medical Systems, Inc.

EBIONEX - Hair care products - Helene Curtis Industries Inc.

EBL - Electronic circuit components - Staveley, Inc.

EBO-TONE - Clarinets - Ideal Musical Merchandise Co.

E'BOARD WEAR - Apparel and accessories - Teru Teraoka

EBOLIN - Musical instrument accessories ☆ - Selmer Co. Inc.

EBOLINE - Lubricants - Ashland Oil, Inc.

EBON-NAIL - Cosmetics - Alleghany Pharmacal Corp.

EBONE - Toiletries - Johnson Publishing Co., Inc.

EBONETTE - Hair care products - A.W. Curtis Laboratories, Inc.

EBONETTES - Gloves–work ☆ - Pioneer Industrial Products Co.

EBONEX - Jewelry - Jacoby-Bender Inc.

EBONIQUE - Stationery ☆ - Joli Greeting Card Co.

EBONITE - Bowling balls - Ebonite International, Inc.

EBONITE - Wheels - Hamilton Caster & Manufacturing Co.

EBONWARE - Cooking equipment–household ☆ - Mirro Corp.

EBONY - Brooms - Hamburg Broom Works Inc.

EBONY - Brushes–hair - Capitol Novelty Co.

EBONY - Chimes - Nutone Inc.

EBONY - Clocks - General Time Corp. (Westclox/Seth Thomas Div.)

EBONY - Dinnerware–glass - Nikko Ceramics Inc.

EBONY - Occasional furniture ☆ - JDI Group, Inc.

EBONY - Pencils - Faber-Castell Corp.

EBONY - Pipes–tobacco - S.M. Frank & Co. Inc. (Kaywoodie-Yello-Bole-Medico)

EBONY - Toys–stuffed ☆ - Gund, Inc.

EBONY & IVORY - Wallpaper - Roger Nicholson Designs Ltd.

EBONY E STYLE SPIEGEL - Apparel and accessories - Johnson Publishing Co., Inc.

EBONY: MANHATTAN COLLECTION - Locks–padlocks ☆ - Weiser Lock Corp.

EBONY MICA - Blackboards–slate ☆ - Anco Wood Specialties Inc.

EBONY ROSE - Tableware–china ☆ - Lenox, Inc.

EBONY SUPREME - Hosiery - Mayer/Berkshire Corp.

EBONY VISIONS - Figurines - Willitts Design International, Inc.

EBONY WAVE - Toilets–enameled - Kohler Co.

EBOW - Guitars - Heet Sound Products

EBS - Motor vehicle parts and accessories - Navistar International Transportation Corp.

EBS - Shoes - Edison Brothers Stores, Inc.

EBS XCHANGE - Construction equipment rental services - Engineered Business Systems Inc.

EBSON - Jewelry - Page Jewelers

EBT - Lighting equipment - Electronic Ballast Technology, Inc.

EBTECH - Soft drinks - EbTech Corp.

EBTECH THIRSTY - Drinking water dispensers - EbTech Corp.

EBTECH THIRSTY THE CAMEL - Beverage dispenser - EbTech Corp.

EBULANCE - Skin care products - Rajoc International

EBURNATED - Musical instrument accessories - Otto Link Inc.

EBY'S - Veterinary pharmaceutical preparations - Eby Remedy Co.

EC - Jewelry - Empire Continental

EC - Meat products–beef - Eaglecrest, Inc.

EC - Publisher's imprints - Jacqueline I. White

EC - Toys - ERTL Co., Inc.

E.C. CLUB - Waterproof outerwear - Gordon & Ferguson of Delaware, Inc.

EC-DESIGN - Computer peripheral equipment - Synthetic Industries, Inc.

EC II - Belts, hair accessories, jewelry, etc. - Elaine Coyne Galleries

EC-IMAGE - Computer software - Electro Communication Systems, Inc.

EC-NAPROSYN - Pharmaceutical preparations - Syntex Puerto Rico, Inc.

EC REGULAR - Gasoline - Atlantic Richfield Co.

EC4KDZ - Apparel and accessories - Kellwood Co.

EC4U - Apparel–women's - Kellwood Co.

ECAL - Lace - Los Angeles Creative Embroidery, Inc.

ECARTE - Skin care products ☆ - B & B Distributors

ECAT - Electronic equipment - Keytek Instrument Corp.

ECATALOG - Computer software - Provantage Corp.

ECC - Machinery - Enviro-Care Co.

ECCENTRICKS - Stamps–hand - Zsp Manufacturing, Inc.

ECCLESIA - Publisher's imprints ☆ - William Carey Library

ECCO - See MINITHERM

ECCO - Cleaning preparations - Electro-Chemical Products Corp.

ECCO - Computer software - Netmanage, Inc.

ECCO - Electromedical apparatus - Electronic Controls Co.

ECCO - Fragrance - Borghese Cosmetics Inc.

ECCO 1 - Wallpaper - Winfield Design Associates, Inc.

ECCO BELLA - Cosmetics - E.B. Botanicals Inc.

ECCO BELLA - Pasta - Ecco Bella Inc.

ECCO BELLA BOTANICALS - Skin care products - E.B. Botanicals Inc.

ECCO-BLEND - Milk - Erie Foods International Inc.

ECCO DOMANI - Wines - Ernest and Julio Gallo Winery

ECCO PRESS - Publisher's imprints - Ecco Press

ECCO VERONA - Footwear - Conjac Inc.

ECCOLO - Hair-care products and skin-care products - Christine Products Inc.

ECCOMATE - Chemical preparations - Neozyme International, Inc.

ECCOVISION - Diagnostic apparatus - E. Benson Hood Laboratories Inc.

ECCS - Paints - PDI Inc.

ECD - Watches - Elgin Watch Co.

ECDS - Electronics equipment ☆ - ITC, Inc.

ECEE - Pharmaceutical preparations ☆ - Edwards Pharmaceuticals, Inc.

ECEE PLUS - Pharmaceutical preparations - Edwards Pharmaceuticals, Inc.

ECFORMS - Computer software - International Business Machines Corp.

ECG LONG - Medical apparatus - Nellcor Puritan Bennett

ECG SIMULATOR - Medical apparatus - Nellcor Puritan Bennett

ECHATIN PLUS - Vitamins and nutritional supplements - NF Formulas, Inc.

ECHELON - Bicycles ☆ - Huffy Corp.

ECHELON - Computer software ☆ - Access Software Inc.

ECHELON - Golfing equipment - Echelon, Golf Inc.

ECHELON - Luggage - F & L Industries, Inc.

ECHELON - Ophthalmic goods ☆ - Allergan, Inc.

ECHELON - Tires - Hoffman Tire Co. Inc.

ECHELON - Tires–automobile - Jetzon/Telstar Tire

ECHELON - Zippers - YKK USA Inc.

ECHIHAFRESH - Vitamins and nutritional supplements - Enzymatic Therapy, Inc.

ECHINA GOLD - Dietary supplement - Basic Organics, Inc.

ECHINACARE - Herbal products - Bio-Therapeutics, Inc.

ECHINACEA & GOLDSEAL COMPLEX - Pharmaceutical preparations - Boericke & Tafel

ECHINACEA EXTRACTS, 150 MG. - Vitamins and nutritional supplements - Vitamin Research Products Inc.

ECHINACEA PLUS - Teas–herbal - Traditional Medicinals, Inc.

ECHINACEA PLUS - Vitamins and nutritional supplements ☆ - Ethical Nutrients

ECHINACEA-POWER - Health care products ☆ - Nature's Herbs

ECHINACEA TINTURE - Homeopathic remedies - Washington Homeopathic Products

ECHINACEAC - Vitamins and nutritional supplements - McZand Herbal, Inc.

ECHINAFORCE - Health care products - Bioforce of America Ltd.

ECHINAGUARD - Vitamins and nutritional supplements - Nature's Way Products, Inc.

ECHINASHIELD - Vitamins and nutritional supplements - NF Formulas, Inc.

ECHINCACEA-GOLDENSEAL - Vitamins and nutritional supplements - Reese Chemical Co.

ECHIP - Computer software - Echip, Inc.

ECHITE KROAZBERGE BLACKBERRY - Beverages–alcohol - Niche Marketing Corp.

ECHL EAST COAST HOCKEY LEAGUE - Broadcasting stations–television - East Coast Hockey League, Inc.

ECHLIN AUTOMOTIVE - Automotive parts and accessories - Echlin Inc.

ECHO - Apparel and accessories - Echo Speech Corp.

ECHO - Apparel and accessories ☆ - Leo's Dancewear, Inc.

ECHO - Boats–motor ☆ - Thunderbird Products

ECHO - Clocks - General Time Corp. (Westclox/Seth Thomas Div.)

ECHO - Coupons - Credit Verification Corp.

ECHO - Dishes–earthenware ☆ - Denby USA Limited

ECHO - Eyeglasses - Silhouette Optical Ltd.

ECHO - Faucets - Kallista Inc.

ECHO - Floor coverings - Congoleum Corp.

ECHO - Floor coverings–carpet and rugs - Len Dal Carpets

ECHO - Frames–eyeglass ☆ - Universal/Univis Inc.

ECHO - Garden equipment - Echo, Inc.

ECHO - Harmonicas - Hohner Inc.

ECHO - Health care products ☆ - Graham-Field Inc.

ECHO - Office furniture–wood ☆ - Haskell of Pittsburgh, Inc.

ECHO - Paper–tissue ☆ - Plainwell Tissue

ECHO - Pickles - W.B. Roddenbery Co., Inc.

ECHO - Protective headgear - Echo Products

ECHO - Recording label - Dana Publishing Co.

ECHO - Ribbons–inked ☆ - Eaton Allen Ko-Rec-Type Corp.

ECHO - Rings–jewelry - Artcarved Inc.

ECHO - Scarves - Echo Design Group

ECHO - Stamps–hand - Carolina Marking Devices, Inc.

ECHO - Stationery ☆ - Superior Marking Equipment Co.

ECHO+ - Stethoscopes - Richard J. Deslauriers

ECHO - Tableware–china - Susquehanna Glass Co.

ECHO - Tiles–ceramic - Latco Products

ECHO - Tiles–ceramic - Los Angeles Tile Co., Inc.

ECHO - Toys–electronic ☆ - Philips Consumer Electronics Co.

ECHO - Toys–models ☆ - Estes Industries

ECHO-ALARM - Sporting goods ☆ - Ray Jefferson

ECHO CANYON - Bicycles ☆ - Huffy Corp.

ECHO-FILE - File folders - Gillooly, Inc. (Echo Files Division)

ECHO GOLF REPORTER - Computer software - Eric C. Hansen

ECHO LAKE - Furniture - American Moulding & Millwork Co.

ECHO LAKE - Socks - Echo Lake Industries, Ltd.

ECHO LOGIC - Computer software - Echo Logic Inc.

ECHO MOUNTAIN - Recording label - Galaxy Mountain Music & Publishing

ECHO OF DECO - Floor coverings–carpet and rugs - Burtco Enterprises Inc.

ECHO PEAK PRODUCTIONS - Recording label - Joy Wake

ECHO PLUS - Computer software ☆ - Dr. T's Music Software Inc.

ECHO RIDGE - Bicycles - Dynacraft Industries Inc.

ECHO RIDGE - Wines - Fetzer Vineyards

ECHO ROUND - Faucets - Kallista Inc.

ECHO USA - Recording label - Echo Records Inc.

☆ = Now out of production

ECHO VALLEY - Water–bottled or canned - Misty Mountain Spring Water Co.

ECHO VALLEY FARMS - Fruit and vegetable markets - Swedesboro Produce Co.

ECHOCAL - Calibrating device - Dynatek Laboratories, Inc.

ECHOCHIME - Chimes - Yancy Co., Inc.

ECHODIDE - Ophthalmic goods ☆ - Alcon Laboratories, Inc.

ECHOES - Greeting cards - American Greetings Corp.

ECHOES - Wallpaper ☆ - Bob Mitchell Designs

ECHOES-MIDI - Computer software - Electronic Courseware Systems Inc.

ECHOES OF CHRISTMAS - Christmas tree ornaments - Cracker Box Inc.

ECHOES OF THE PAST - Toys–stuffed - Fagan International

ECHOGEN - Pharmaceutical preparations - Sonus Pharmaceuticals, Inc.

ECHOKING - Transmitting apparatus - Kobold Instruments, Inc.

ECHOLE - Ophthalmic goods - Styl-Rite Optical Manufacturing Co., Inc.

ECHOLS - Pesticides–household - Athena Products Corp.

ECHOMASTER - Radar systems and equipment - Davis Instruments Corp.

ECHORAY - Medical apparatus - Del Mar Avionics

ECHOS II - Computer software - Electronic Courseware Systems Inc.

ECHOTECH - Recording label - Progressive Awareness Research, Inc.

ECHOVISION - Scuba diving equipment - Armatron International Inc.

ECHT STONSDORFER - Beverages–alcohol - Dieter Steinmann Inc.

ECI - Electronic equipment - Electronic Controls, Inc.

ECI - Skin care products - European Cosmetics Inc.

ECI TACOMA WA - Engines–locomotive - Energy Conversions, Inc.

ECJ - Jewelry - Eclipse Collection Jewelry Corp.

ECK-ADAMS - Furniture - Eck-Adams Corp.

ECKADAMS - Furniture - EAC Integrated Furniture Solutions

ECKERD - Skin care products - Eckerd Corp.

ECKER'S - Sausages - Aries Prepared Beef Co.

ECKERT'S - Juices - Eckert Orchards Inc.

ECKERWORKS - Recording label ☆ - Rounder Records Corp.

ECKESPOINT - Flowers, plants, and seeds - Paul Ecke Ranch, Inc.

ECKHART - Hitches–trailer - Eckharts Trailer Hitch & Welding, Inc.

ECKO - Meats–luncheon - Dinner Bell Foods Inc.

ECKRICH - Meat products–beef - Armour Swift-Eckrich

ECL - Aquariums–household ☆ - GM Aquatics

ECL - Office supplies - Faber-Castell Corp.

ECLAIR - Frames–eyeglass - Pathway Optical Prods.

ECLAMIDE - Pharmaceutical preparations ☆ - U.S. Ethicals Inc.

ECLASUFED - Pharmaceutical preparations ☆ - U.S. Ethicals Inc.

ECLAT - Flatware - Couzon USA

ECLAT - Ophthalmic goods ☆ - Rozin Optical Export Corp.

ECLECTIC - Floor coverings–carpet and rugs - Dorsett Carpet Mills Inc.

ECLECTIC - Floor coverings–carpet and rugs ☆ - Customweave Carpets Inc.

ECLECTIC - Wallpaper - Textile Wallcoverings International Ltd.

ECLECTIQUE - Floor coverings–carpet and rugs - J.L. Benson Co.

ECLIPS - Sunglasses - Focal Point Opticians

ECLIPSE - Aircraft - American Polarizers Inc.

ECLIPSE - Audio equipment ☆ - Telequest Inc.

ECLIPSE - Automotive parts and accessories - Eclipse Inc.

ECLIPSE - Bats–baseball - Lisco, Inc.

ECLIPSE - Blinds–venetian - Hunter Douglas, Inc.

ECLIPSE - Boats - Wellcraft Marine Corp.

ECLIPSE - Cameras–video - CLI

ECLIPSE - Chemical preparations - Calgon Carbon Corp.

ECLIPSE - Chemical preparations - Metalline Chemical Corp.

ECLIPSE - Christmas tree ornaments - Cracker Box Inc.

ECLIPSE - Cigarettes - R.J. Reynolds Tobacco Co.

ECLIPSE - Cleaning preparations - Pioneer/Eclipse Corp.

ECLIPSE - Containers–paper - Georgia-Pacific Corp.

ECLIPSE - Cosmetics - Creative Nail Design, Inc.

ECLIPSE - Dinnerware–glass - Lenox, Inc.

ECLIPSE - Electronic equipment - Texecom, Inc.

ECLIPSE - Fishing tackle - South Bend Sporting Goods Inc.

ECLIPSE - Floor coverings–carpet and rugs - Regal Rugs Inc.

ECLIPSE - Floor coverings–carpet and rugs ☆ - Walter Carpet Mills

ECLIPSE - Flowers, plants, and seeds - Jacklin Seed

ECLIPSE - Food products - Original Trenton Cracker Co.

ECLIPSE - Food products ☆ - Globe Extracts Inc.

ECLIPSE - Frames–eyeglass - Zylo Ware Corp.

ECLIPSE - Fruits and vegetables ☆ - Sun World International

ECLIPSE - Furniture - Expo Displays

ECLIPSE - Furniture - Stanley Furniture Co. Inc.

ECLIPSE - Furniture ☆ - Bernhardt Industries

ECLIPSE - Furniture ☆ - Lane Co. Inc.

ECLIPSE - Games - Tedco Inc.

ECLIPSE - Gift pen/pencil set - Itoya of America, Ltd.

ECLIPSE - Glass–plate - Sasaki

ECLIPSE - Glassware–household ☆ - Lenox Crystal, Inc.

ECLIPSE - Gowns–hospital - Medline, Industries, Inc.

ECLIPSE - Hardware - Norita Precision, Inc.

ECLIPSE - Hearing aids - Argosy Electronics, Inc.

ECLIPSE - Insecticides - Ciba-Geigy Corp.

ECLIPSE - Liquors - Schramsberg Vineyards Co.

ECLIPSE - Locks–padlocks - Kwikset Powdered Metal Products

ECLIPSE - Manufactured homes - Redman Industries, Inc.

ECLIPSE - Medical apparatus - Ricon Corp.

ECLIPSE - Motor vehicles–automobiles - Mitsubishi Motor Sales of America Inc.

ECLIPSE - Non-stick coating cookware - General Housewares Corp.

ECLIPSE - Office supplies - McDonald Products

ECLIPSE - Office supplies ☆ - Globe-Weis

ECLIPSE - Oils–lubricating - Phillips Petroleum Co.

ECLIPSE - Ophthalmic goods ☆ - Rozin Optical Export Corp.

ECLIPSE - Paints - Sophir Morris Paint

ECLIPSE - Paper–writing ☆ - Kurtz Bros. Inc.

ECLIPSE - Plumbing fixtures - St. Thomas Creations

ECLIPSE - Projection screens - Claridge Products and Equipment Inc.

ECLIPSE - Recording label - Galaxie III Studios

ECLIPSE - Rope - Wellington Leisure Products, Inc.

ECLIPSE - Scales–bathroom - Fairbanks Inc.

ECLIPSE - Scissors–hand-operated - Acme United Corp.

ECLIPSE - Scooters–motorized - Leisure Lift, Inc.

ECLIPSE - Sewing machines–household - Tacony Corp.

ECLIPSE - Skin care products - Veeco Manufacturing Co.

ECLIPSE - Soccer equipment ☆ - Brine Inc.

ECLIPSE - Sporting goods - Camp-Cap Products

ECLIPSE - Sporting goods - Easton Aluminum Inc.

ECLIPSE - Suntan lotions - Dorsey Laboratories

ECLIPSE - Swimming pool sand filters - KDI American Products, Inc.

ECLIPSE - Syrup - Autocrat, Inc.

ECLIPSE - Tiles–ceiling - USG Interiors, Inc.

ECLIPSE - Tiles–ceramic ☆ - H & R Johnson Inc.

ECLIPSE - Toys - Tonka Corp.

ECLIPSE - Toys–models ☆ - Estes Industries

ECLIPSE - Video equipment - Draper Shade and Screen Co. Inc.

ECLIPSE - Wallpaper - Dekortex Inc.

ECLIPSE - Window coverings - Vertical Blind Factory

ECLIPSE - Window shades - C-Mor Co.

ECLIPSE - Window shades - Kenney Manufacturing Co.

ECLIPSE 3 - Veterinary pharmaceutical preparations - Schering-Plough Animal Health

ECLIPSE 2000 - Vitamins and nutritional supplements - Bob O'leary Health Food Distribution Co., Inc.

ECLIPSE BY TEMPO - Fabrics - Tempo Shain Corp.

ECLIPSE EXTRA STOUT - Beverages–malt - Brew Moon Enterprises Inc.

ECLIPSE FOLDING TRAVEL - Trailers–travel ☆ - Sun-Lite Inc.

ECLIPSE MASTER - Computer software - Zephyr Services

ECLIPSE SUN SHADE - Automotive parts and accessories - Jack Hays Inc.

ECLIPSE+ - Health care products - Medtronic Nortech

ECLIPSER - Electronic equipment - Optical Radiation Corp.

ECLISSE - Footwear - G.H. Bass and Co.

ECM - Computer peripheral equipment - Micro Chemical, Inc.

ECM - Motors–hydraulic - General Electric Co.

ECM - Recording label - Polygram Records, Inc.

ECM - Screws - East Coast Metals, Inc.

ECMLINK - Computer software - Learned-Mahn, Inc.

ECNER - Mechanical seals - Oem Components, Inc.

ECO - Chemical preparations - Nordost Corp.

ECO - Food products - C and E Canners Inc.

ECO - Rubber bands - Alliance Rubber Co.

ECO - Valves - Pulsafeeder, Inc.

ECO 10 - Hair care products - Ecoco, Inc.

ECO 100 - Containers - Green Bay Packaging, Inc.

ECO 2000 - Degreasing solvents - KC Products, Inc. (Sharon D. Spence)

ECO ACTIVE - Clothing - Sun Sportswear, Inc.

ECO AIR - Packaging–paper - Eco Air Co.

ECO-AMBER - Glass products - Owens-Illinois Inc. (Libbey Div.)

ECO-BEDDING - Pet products - Ranpak Corp.

ECO BLADE - Machine parts - J.B. Kidd, Inc.

ECO-BLOCK - Paints - Surface Protection Industries, Inc.

ECO BLUES - Apparel and accessories - Aalfs Manufacturing, Inc.

☆ = Now out of production

ECO BURGER - Meat substitute - Believe, Inc.
ECO-CAL - Calcium compounds - Minerals Technologies Inc.
ECO CAL - Fertilizers - Eco Soil Systems, Inc.
ECO-CAPSULE - Science kits - Dynamic Development
ECO-CHEF - Towels - Park B. Smith, Inc.
ECO-CHOICE - Bags–trash - Carlisle Plastics, Inc.
ECO-CLEAN - Cleaning preparations - Ecolab Inc.
ECO CLEAR - Boxes ☆ - Ultra Pac, Inc.
ECO-CLEAR - Cleaning preparations–household - Neozyme International, Inc.
ECO CUP - Inks - Imtran Industries, Inc.
ECO-DENT - Dentifrices - Marc Warsowe
ECO-DENT - Tooth powder - American Merfluan Inc.
ECO DISC - Computer storage devices - Eco Products, Inc.
ECO ELITE - Water purification systems - Ecowater Systems, Inc.
ECO-FARM - Food products - Eco-Farm Co.
ECO-FELT - Hats - Bollman Hat Co.
ECO-FOAM - Packaging–foam - American Excelsior Co.
ECO GAME - Games - Global Godmother
ECO-GLASS - Glass products - Owens-Illinois Inc. (Libbey Div.)
ECO-GREEN - Glass products - Owens-Illinois Inc. (Libbey Div.)
ECO-GUARD - Electronic equipment - Rust Evader Corp.
ECO HANGER - Garment hangers - Beaver Packaging
ECO-KIDS - Cosmetics - Red Rose Collection
ECO-KOR - Rustproofing compounds - National Chemical & Oil Corp.
ECO-KOTE - Paints - Brookwood Companies Inc.
ECO-LAC - Chemicals - Ecological Chemical Products Co.
ECO-LIG - Chemical preparations - Georgia-Pacific Corp.
ECO LITE - Faucets - Kohler Co.
ECO-LITTER - Pet products - Ranpak Corp.
ECO-LIZER - Machinery - Alan Ashby
ECO LOG - Aquarium accessories - Novalek, Inc.
ECO-LOGIC - Water purification systems - Atlantic Ultraviolet Corp.
ECO-LOGICA - Stationery - Lotus Marketing Group, Inc.
ECO-MATIC - Electrical equipment - Eco-Matic Salt Water Pool Systems, Inc.
ECO MELT - Deicing fluid - Ossian, Inc.
ECO-NATURALS - Underwear and nightwear - St. Eve International, Inc.
ECO-PAK - Herbicides - American Cyanamid Co.
ECO-PAK - Refills - American Merfluan Inc.
ECO PAKS - Vitamins and nutritional supplements - Michael's Naturopatic Products
ECO-PEN - Pens - Gillette Co.
ECO PLA - Resins–polymer - Stevens Industries Inc.
ECO-PLUS - Lubricants - Kent Oil Co., Inc.
ECO-PLY - Tissue stencils - Mason Marking Systems Corp.
ECO-POLY - Plastics film - Flex-O-Glass, Inc.
ECO-PRIME - Primers - Kelly-Moore Paint Co., Inc.
ECO PRODUCTS - Compost and fertilizer - New Solutions, Inc.
ECO-RAGS - Cleaning equipment - Josco Products (John Cole Chemical Corp.)
ECO SAFE - Pet products ☆ - Natural Animal Health Products, Inc.
ECO-SAVE - Chemical preparations - Jean L. Harrison
ECO-SCOOP - Paper products - CGS Pet Products Ltd.
ECO SCOOT - Scooters–motorized - Doran Motor Co.
ECO SENSORS - Gauging instruments - ECO Sensors Inc.
ECO-SHAKE - Shingles–shakes - Re-New Wood, Inc.
ECO-SNEAKS - Footwear - Deja Inc.
ECO SOLUTIONS - Fertilizers - Eco Solutions, Inc.
ECO SOURCE - Cleaning preparations - Eco Source, Inc.
ECO-SPOT - Paints - Nelson Paint Co., Inc.
ECO-STAR - Detergents - Ecolab Inc.
ECO STATION - Apparel and accessories - Glant Pacific Co.
ECO STUMP - Aquarium accessories - Novalek, Inc.
ECO-SUDS - Cleaning preparations - Earth-Safe, Inc.
ECO/TAG - Signs - Electromark Co.
ECO TECH - Degreasing solvents - Finish Line Technologies, Inc.
ECO-TECH - Machinery - Ecoair Corp.
ECO-THANE - Adhesives and sealants - Kelly-Moore Paint Co., Inc.
ECO THREADS - Apparel and accessories - Christine Owens
ECO TOYS PLAYABLE ART - Toys - Sha D' Lei, Inc.
ECO-TRED - Shoe soles - Hi-Tec Sports USA Inc.
ECO TRIM - Capacitors - Johanson Manufacturing Corp.
ECO VAC - Cleaning preparations - DCI International, Inc.
ECO-VALVES - Valves–industrial - Dresser Industries, Inc.
ECO-WARRIORS - Toys - Hasbro, Inc.
ECO-WHEY - Fertilizer - Ecological Chemical Products Co.
ECO WHITE - Paper products - Green Bay Packaging, Inc.

ECO-WRAP - Paper–gift wrap - Natural Products Corp.
ECO ZONE - Pet products - Natural Animal Health Products, Inc.
ECOAX - Electrical connectors - Phoenix Co. of Chicago, Inc.
ECOBLEND - Fabrics–cotton - Natural Cotton Colours, Inc.
ECOBOWLS - Containers–plastic - Winkler Forming, Inc.
ECOBRANCH - Aquarium accessories - Kordon
ECOBRANCH - Aquarium accessories - Novalek, Inc.
ECOBUBBLE - Plastics film - Tape Inc.
ECOBULB - Lamp bulbs–fluorescent - Feit Electric Co.
ECOCARE - Skin care products - Paul Mazzotta Inc.
ECOCARTON - Cartons–paperboard - Dole Food Co., Inc.
ECOCENTRIC - Catalogs - Terresa Lynn Gerger
ECOCHARGEBACK - Computer software - Compuware Corp.
ECOCHECK - Medical apparatus - AirSep Corp.
ECOCHEM - Chemical preparations - Ecological Chemical Products Co.
ECOCLEAN - Rustproofing compounds - Cortec Corp.
ECOCLEAR - Petroleum - Sunmarks, Inc.
ECOCOAT - Rustproofing compounds - Cortec Corp.
ECOCONNECTION - Apparel and accessories - Eco Depot, Inc.
ECOCRETE - Building materials - Eco Building Systems, Inc.
ECOCYCLE - Sinks–metal - Kohler Co.
ECODEK - Paper products - G. L. Packaging Products Inc.
ECODESIGNER - Computer software - Intelligen, Inc.
ECODISC - Electrical equipment - Quartet Manufacturing Co.
ECODUSTER - Compressors–air - Perfectdata Corp.
ECOENERGY - Hardware - Outokumpu Ecoenergy, Inc.
ECOEXPLORER - Computer software - Ecogroup, Inc.
ECOFILM - Adhesives and sealants - Coating Sciences Inc.
ECOFIT - Apparel and accessories - Fierres, Inc.
ECOFORM - Furniture panels - Baltek Corp.
ECOFRESH - Pet products - Absorption Corp.
ECOGARD - Lubricants - Ashland Oil, Inc.
ECOGAS - Ships–tankers - Ecogas Corp.
ECOGEN 851 - Vitamins and nutritional supplements - Econugenics, Inc.
ECOGRAIN - Flour–blended ☆ - InterNatural Foods
ECOGREEN - Oils–lubricating - Lilyblad Petroleum, Inc.
ECOGUARD - Air filters - International Manufacturing Center, Inc.
ECOL-O-VANE - Hardware - Levolor Inc.
ECOLAN - Circuit boards - Kyocera Electronics, Inc.
L'ECOLE NO. 41 - Wines - Lowden Schoolhouse Corp.
ECOLINE - Skin care products - Ya-Man Ltd.
ECOLINE - Water colors ☆ - Canson-Talens Inc.
ECOLINK - Cleaning preparations - Ecolink, Inc.
ECOLINK - Mats - Ashland Rubber Mat Co. Inc.
ECOLITE - Computer hardware - Progen Technology Inc.
ECOLITE - Lanterns–kerosene ☆ - Dorco Manufacturing Inc.
ECOLIZER - Automotive parts and accessories - Emissions Technology Inc.
ECOLIZER - Tools–garden ☆ - Lawn & Garden Supply Co.
ECOLLECTION - Jewelry - Esprit De Corp.
ECOLLOGEN - Hair-care products - Tri-Institute of Trichology
ECOLO-CHAMP - Agricultural machinery - DMI, Inc.
ECOLO KRYSTAL KLEER - Hair care products - Organifyl Laboratories
ECOLO-TIGER - Agricultural machinery - DMI, Inc.
ECOLOAM - Soil mixture - Horsehead Resource Development Co. Inc.
ECOLOCOTE - Paper–writing - P.H. Glatfelter Co.
ECOLOG - Aquarium accessories ☆ - Kordon
ECOLOG - Fireplace logs–treated - US Fiber, Inc.
ECOLOGIC - Computer software - Berkeley Systems, Inc.
ECOLOGIC, INC. - Furniture - Ecologic, Inc.
ECOLOGIC SOLUTIONS - Vitamins and nutritional supplements - Ecologic Solutions, Inc.
ECOLOGICA - Skin care products - Malibu Skin Care Systems, llc
ECOLOGICAL CHOICE, THE - Office supplies - Repeat-O-Type Manufacturing Corp.
ECOLOGICAL TRUST FOUNDATION - Vases–stone - Ecological Trust Foundation
ECOLOGY - Aquariums–household - Willinger Bros., Inc.
ECOLOGY - Paper - Riverside Paper Corp.
ECOLOGY BAG - Grocery totes - Coordinated Products Corp.
ECOLOGY CLUB - Apparel–women's - Rich & Me, Inc.
ECOLOGY KIDS - Bedding–linen - Diplomat Corp.
ECOLOGY SEAL - Sealing compounds - Surebond, Inc.
ECOLOGY SYSTEMS & DESIGN - Trash compactors–household - Ecology Systems & Design, Inc.
ECOLOGY TECH - Air purification systems ☆ - Northwest Envirofan
ECOLOQUIP - Sewage treatment equipment - Noyes & Associates, Inc.

☆ = Now out of production

ECOLOR - Dyes–synthetic - Allegro Natural Dyes, Inc.
ECOLUTION - Paper products - Ecolution, Inc.
ECOLY - Cosmetics - Carlton Hair International, Inc.
ECO*MASTERS - Computer video games - New Media Magic
ECOMER NATRA-BIO - Health care products - Peterson's Health Products
ECOMID - Electrical equipment - Quartet Manufacturing Co.
ECOMOTION - Motor vehicles - Allegheny Power Service Corp.
ECOMOVE - Moving box - Ecomove Corp.
ECON - Fabrics–silk - H.T. Herbert Co. Inc.
ECON - Gasoline - Southern Union Co.
ECON AIR - Cooking equipment–commercial - Econ Air, Inc.
ECON-O-CYCLE - Medical apparatus ✰ - American Walker Inc.
ECON-O-GARD - Mats ✰ - Ludlow Composites Corp.
ECON-O-GROOVE - Lathes - Valenite Inc.
ECON-O-LITE - Fishing tackle - Frabill Inc.
ECON-O-LOC - Hardware - Sash Controls Inc.
ECON-O-MERSE - Pumps ✰ - ITT Marlow
ECON-O-METS - Dog food - Dad's Products Co. Inc.
ECON-O-PAR - Lamps - Philips Lighting Co.
ECON-O-POST - Hardware - Tel-O-Post Co.
ECON-O-SIGN V - Letterpress plates - Leteron
ECON-O-STAK - Office supplies ✰ - Plasticoid Manufacturing Inc.
ECON-O-TILE - Wainscotting - Georgia-Pacific Corp.
ECON-O-VINYL - Floor coverings - Mannington Resilient Floors
ECON-O-WATT - Lamps - Philips Lighting Co.
ECON-O-WIPE GOLDEN DUSTERS - Fabrics - Erikson Nonwoven Textiles Inc.
ECON-O-ZIP - Attache cases - Angler's Roslyn Group Ltd.
ECON-TIPS - Sporting goods - Hocks Laboratories
ECONATURAL - Oils–essential - Mario Cader
ECONEX - See VIKING
ECONMOBILE MFG. CO. - Engines - Econmobile Manufacturing, Inc.
ECONO - Bicycles - Hunt-Wilde Corp.
ECONO - Binders - Boorum & Pease Co.
ECONO - Building materials–concrete - F.E. Schumacher Co.
ECONO - Cabinets - Saco Industries Inc.
ECONO - Carpet-cleaning supplies - American Textile Products Co.
ECONO - Display units - Paul Flum Ideas, Inc.
ECONO - Floor coverings - Dexter Corp. (Mercer Plastics Div.)
ECONO - Food processors - Wapsie Produce Inc.
ECONO - Gasoline ✰ - Conoco Inc.
ECONO - Hardware ✰ - Hettich America L.P.
ECONO - Health care products - Stand Aid of Iowa Inc.
ECONO - Kilns - L & L Manufacturing Co.
ECONO - Meat products–poultry - Snowball Foods, Inc.
ECONO - Oak moldings - Larson-Juhl Manufacturing
ECONO - Podiatric product - Aetna Felt Corp.
ECONO - Rubber cement - Econo Products Inc.
ECONO II - Ophthalmic goods ✰ - Rozin Optical Export Corp.
ECONO 2 - Oxygen ✰ - Caire
ECONO III - Ophthalmic goods ✰ - Rozin Optical Export Corp.
ECONO-AIRE - Mats ✰ - Ludlow Composites Corp.
ECONO BAKE - Dairy products - Foremost Farms USA
ECONO BRAID - Cordage and twine - Wonder Craft
ECONO-CAVITY-LOK - Building materials–concrete - AA Wire Products Co.
ECONO-CELL - Lighting fixtures ✰ - Kenall Manufacturing Co.
ECONO-CERV - Traction apparatus–medical - Shamrock Medical Inc.
ECONO-CLASSIFILE - Office supplies ✰ - Barkley Filing Supplies
ECONO-CLING - Signs - Joseph Struhl Co., Inc.
ECONO CLUB - Motorcycle parts and accessories - James E. Winner Jr.
ECONO-COIR - Fabrics - Belton Industries Inc.
ECONO COMMANDER - Vehicle mounted spreaders - Louis Berkman Co.
ECONO-CORD - Bedspreads - Tuf-Tex, Inc.
ECONO CORD - Cordage and twine - Wonder Craft
ECONO-CUSH - Orthopedic products - Kinetic Diversified Industries, Inc.
ECONO-EZE - Health care products - L & M Medical Inc.
ECONO-FENCE - Fencing–gates and posts - Northwestern Steel and Wire Co.
ECONO-FLO - Flour–blended - Econo-Flo Flour Service Inc.
ECONO-FLOAT - Health care products - Jefferson Industries Inc.
ECONO FLOOR - Wood products - Mitek Industries Inc.
ECONO-FRY - Seafood products–canned or cured - Rose Frozen Shrimp Inc.
ECONO-GUARD - Pet products - Ginger, Inc.
ECONO-HORSE - Garden equipment - Garden Way Inc.
ECONO-JET - Shoes–athletic - Econo-Jet
ECONO KAP - Blocks–chimney ✰ - Field Controls Co.
ECONO-KIT - Door frames - Crest Metal Doors, Inc.

ECONO-KRINKLE - Gloves–rubber - Duracraft Corp.
ECONO LIFE SHIELD - Vitamins and nutritional supplements - Vitamin Research Products Inc.
ECONO-LIFT - Swimming pools - Spectrum Pool Products
ECONO-LINER - Brake linings - Rockwell International Corp.
ECONO-LODGE - Hotels and motels - Choice Hotels International Inc.
ECONO-LOK - Building materials–concrete - AA Wire Products Co.
ECONO-MATE - Ophthalmic goods - Apex Medical Corp.
ECONO MATE - Ophthalmic goods - Karlen Manufacturing, Inc.
ECONO-MATIC - Cleaning preparations - Uncle Sam Chemical Co., Inc.
ECONO-MATTE - Writing product - Island Pen Manufacturing Corp.
ECONO-MISER - Air conditioning equipment - Manumark Inc.
ECONO-MISER - Lamps - Philips Lighting Co.
ECONO-MIST - Oxygen ✰ - Caire
ECONO-MIST 2000 - Water purification systems - Web Products, Inc.
ECONO-MULCH - Garden equipment - Dalen Products Inc.
ECONO PAC - Office supplies ✰ - Barkley Filing Supplies
ECONO PAV - Asphalt - Reclaim, Inc.
ECONO PINE - Deodorizers - Sun-Pine Corp.
ECONO-PLEX - Mirrors ✰ - Fred Silver and Co. Inc.
ECONO-POST - Mail boxes - Steel City Corp.
ECONO-PRO - Dog food - Merrick Petfoods Inc.
ECONO-PRO - Pet food - Hereford Bi-Products, Inc.
ECONO-QUAT - Disinfectants - Unit Chemical Corp.
ECONO-RAIL - Railings–wood - Newman Brothers Inc.
ECONO-SCENT - Deodorizers - Surco Products Inc.
ECONO-SHARP - Pencils–mechanical - Pentel of America, Ltd.
ECONO-SLIDE - Hardware ✰ - Hettich America L.P.
ECONO SPOT - Paints - Nelson Paint Co., Inc.
ECONO-SPRAY - Lubricants - Slide Products, Inc.
ECONO-SPROUTER TOPPERS - Garden equipment - Sprout-Ease Co.
ECONO START - Batteries - Montgomery Ward & Co. Inc.
ECONO/STOR - Filing cabinets–metal - Fellowes Manufacturing Co.
ECONO SUN - Suntan lotions - Cumberland-Swan, Inc.
ECONO-SWEEP - Sweeping compounds - Paxon Manufacturing Co.
ECONO TAC - Adhesives and sealants - Sta'-Put Inc.
ECONO-TAC - Plastics film - Protac, Inc.
ECONO TERRY - Apparel and accessories - Dan River Inc.
ECONO TOPFLOR - Floor coverings ✰ - Halstead International
ECONO TRADING - Hardware - Econo Trading Co.
ECONO TRANSPORTERS - Motor vehicles - Turtle Top Specialty Products
ECONO TREAD - Floor coverings - Dexter Corp. (Mercer Plastics Div.)
ECONO TUBE - Mail boxes ✰ - Steel City Corp.
ECONO TURF - Synthetic turf - Instant Turf Industries Inc.
ECONO TURF STRIPE - Floor coverings - R.W. Beattie Carpet Industries Inc.
ECONO-WAY - Milk - Borden, Inc.
ECONO X - Frames–eyeglass - Rozin Optical Export Corp.
ECONO XI - Frames–eyeglass - Rozin Optical Export Corp.
ECONOBAY - Lighting fixtures ✰ - Hubbell Lighting, Inc. (Lighting Div.)
ECONOCHLOR - Ophthalmic goods ✰ - Alcon Laboratories, Inc.
ECONOCLEAT - Mats - Rubbermaid Office Products Inc.
ECONOCLEAT - Seat covers - Rubbermaid Inc.
ECONOCO - Metals - Econoco Corp.
ECONODECK - Building materials - Mapes Industries Inc.
ECONOEASE - Chairs–metal - Stacor Corp.
ECONOETCH - Printing trades machinery - Dick Blick Co.
ECONOFLO - Filters–air - Air Kontrol Inc.
ECONOFLOOD - Lighting fixtures ✰ - Hubbell Lighting, Inc. (Lighting Div.)
ECONOFOLD - Paper–toweling - Georgia-Pacific Corp.
ECONOFOODS - Breads - Nash-Finch Co.
ECONOFRAME - Frames–eyeglass - Denver International Eyewear Inc.
ECONOFRY - Cooking equipment–commercial - Hobart Corp.
ECONOGLASS - Antennas - Antenna Co.
ECONOGUARD - Filters–air - International Manufacturing Center, Inc.
ECONOKOTE - Toys–models - Top Flite Models
ECONOL-LIFT - Elevators - Econol Lift Corp.
ECONOLEVEL - Levels - Johnson Level & Tool Manufacturing Co. Inc.
ECONOLIFT - Orthopedic products - Ortho-Kinetics, Inc.
ECONOLINE - Floor coverings - Congoleum Corp.
ECONOLINE - Inks–duplicating - Heyer Inc.
ECONOLINE - Mattresses ✰ - E & S Vinyl Manufacturing Inc.
ECONOLINE - Motor vehicles–automobiles - Ford Motor Co.
ECONOLINE - Musical instrument accessories - Humes & Berg Manufacturing Co. Inc.
ECONOLINE - Paint rollers - Wooster Brush Co.
ECONOLINE - Shelving units–metal - Tap Fabrication

✰ = Now out of production

ECONOLINE - Shutters–wood - Maywood Inc.
ECONOLITE - Flashlights - Accutec Inc.
ECONOLITE I - Safety eyewear - H.L. Bouton Co. Inc.
ECONOLITE II - Safety eyewear - H.L. Bouton Co. Inc.
ECONOLUX - Lighting fixtures ✩ - Hubbell Lighting, Inc. (Lighting Div.)
ECONOM-EASEL - Office supplies ✩ - JM Co.
ECONOMALT - Flour–blended - Ross Industries Inc.
ECONOMASTER - Brushes–paint ✩ - Laitner Brush Co.
ECONOMASTER - Tools–garden - Gilmour Manufacturing Co.
ECONOMATE - Medical apparatus - Respironics, Inc.
ECONOMATIC - Paper–toilet - Georgia-Pacific Corp.
ECONOME - Shampoos - Mastey De Paris
ECONOMEASURE - Marine rigging - Outboard Marine Corp.
ECONOMIC ERGONOMICS - Office furniture–metal ✩ - Marvel Group Inc.
ECONOMICS: WHAT, HOW AND FOR WHOM? - Computer software - Focus Media Inc.
ECONOMIES - Books–comic - AccuServe Corp.
ECONOMIR - Mirrors - Bunker Industries, Inc.
ECONOMISER - Bathroom fixtures - Crane Plumbing/Fiat Products
ECONOMIST - Eyeglasses - Martin-Copeland Eyewear Corp.
ECONOMITE - Heating equipment - Midco International Inc.
ECONOMIX - Gelatin - Vyse Gelatin Co.
ECONOMIXER - Marine rigging ✩ - Outboard Marine Corp.
ECONOMIZER - Air conditioning equipment - Carrier Corp.
ECONOMIZER - Audio equipment - Pro-Co. Sound Co. Inc.
ECONOMIZER - Bathroom fixtures - Artesian Industries
ECONOMIZER - Office supplies - McBee Loose Leaf Binders
ECONOMIZER - Ophthalmic goods - Styl-Rite Optical Manufacturing Co., Inc.
ECONOMIZER - Wood products - Georgia-Pacific Corp.
ECONOMIZER PLUS - Mufflers–motor vehicle - Midas International Corp.
ECONOMOUNT - Television cabinets - Luxor
ECONOMY - Artists' materials - Hamilton Industries
ECONOMY - Binders ✩ - Stationers Loose Leaf Co.
ECONOMY - Blinds–venetian - Wellington Leisure Products, Inc.
ECONOMY - Boats–motor ✩ - Harris-Kayot Inc.
ECONOMY - Containers–insulated ✩ - Aladdin Industries, Inc.
ECONOMY - Cooking equipment–commercial - Comstock Castle Stove Co.
ECONOMY - Fertilizers ✩ - Grovco Sales Co. Inc.
ECONOMY - Files–tools - O.P. Link Handle Co. Inc.
ECONOMY - Gloves - Jasper Glove Co.
ECONOMY - Guitars ✩ - Guild Music Corp.
ECONOMY - Kitchen appliances - Vaughan Manufacturing Co. Inc.
ECONOMY - Macaroni ✩ - Pastamania
ECONOMY - Medical apparatus ✩ - Monterey, Inc.
ECONOMY - Metals - Hubbell Inc.
ECONOMY - Mops ✩ - Royal Maid Association for the Blind Inc.
ECONOMY - Musical instruments - White Eagle Rawhide Manufacturing Co.
ECONOMY - Office furniture–metal - Joyce International Inc.
ECONOMY - Pasta - American Beauty Macaroni
ECONOMY - Pens - Empire Berol USA
ECONOMY - Photographic equipment - Leedal Inc.
ECONOMY - Sporting goods - Cramer Products Inc.
ECONOMY - Steel - St. Paul Corrugating Co.
ECONOMY - Stencils ✩ - Heyer Inc.
ECONOMY - Tractors ✩ - Engineering Products Co.
ECONOMY - Wet mops - American Textile Products Co.
ECONOMY 595 - Hair care products - Fromm Industries
ECONOMY BALL BUCKET - Sporting goods - Lob-Ster Inc.
ECONOMY BASICS - Apparel–women's ✩ - Maidenform Inc. (True Form Foundations Div.)
ECONOMY KOI FOOD - Pet products - Hikari Sales USA Inc.
ECONOMY LITE - Chimes - Nutone Inc.
ECONOMY PACK - Stationery ✩ - Pratt & Austin Co.
ECONOMY PAK - Noodles - Homestead, Inc.
ECONOMY PET-DOR - Pet products - Johnson Pet-Dor Inc.
ECONOMY ROLL - Abrasive products - Carborundum Abrasives North America
ECONOMY ROLL - Wallpaper - Pantasote Inc. (Wallcovering Div.)
ECONOPAK - Fasteners–hook and eye - VSI Fasteners, Inc.
ECONOPAK - Vacuum cleaners and accessories ✩ - Home Care Industries, Inc.
ECONOPLEX - Hardware - Lexco Cable Manufacturing & Distributing
ECONOPRED - Ophthalmic goods - Alcon Laboratories, Inc.
ECONOPRED PLUS - Ophthalmic goods ✩ - Alcon Laboratories, Inc.
ECONOPROP - Housewares - Carbo Ceramics Inc.
ECONORISE - Health care products - Temco Health Care
ECONOROOF - Machinery - M.I.C. Industries, Inc.

ECONOSAN - Disinfectants - Unit Chemical Corp.
ECONOSENS - Electronic equipment - Kistler Instrument Corp.
ECONOSERV - Napkins–paper - Georgia-Pacific Corp.
ECONOSET - Building materials - P-G Industries, Inc.
ECONOSIL - Rubber–molded - F.E. Knight, Inc.
ECONOSOURCE - Paper - Saxon Paper Co.
ECONOSTAT - Mats - Rubbermaid Office Products Inc.
ECONOSTAT - Seat covers - Rubbermaid Inc.
ECONOTAB - Office supplies - Yawman and Erbe of California Corp.
ECONOTECH - Automotive parts and accessories - Auto Accessories of America
ECONOTEMP - Dryers–hair - Helene Curtis Industries Inc.
ECONOTIG - Welding equipment - Miller Electric Manufacturing Co.
ECONOTROL - Thermostats - Robertshaw Controls Co.
ECONOWALL - Movable partitions ✩ - Yates Furniture Systems Corp.
ECONOZORB - Chemical preparations - Matarah Industries Inc.
ECOPAC - Catheters - Cordis Corp.
ECOPAC - Paper–toweling - Marcal Paper Mills, Inc.
ECOPAD - Paper–writing - Riverside Paper Corp.
ECOPAINT - Paints - Atlantic County Utilities Authority
ECOPAK - Packaging–blisterwrap - Ranpak Corp.
ECOPALLET - Paper products - Ecological Pallets, Ltd.
ECOPANELS ARCHITECTURAL FOREST ENTERPRISES - Building materials - Architectural Forest Enterprises
ECOPAQUE - Paper - Simpson Paper Co.
ECOPASTE - Solder - Ecosol Technologies, Inc.
ECOPET - Pet products - Cardinal Laboratories, Inc.
ECOPHRST - Limestone products - National Lime & Stone Co.
ECOPILE - Fabrics–polyester - Draper Knitting Co. Inc.
ECOPLY - Plywood - Springfield Forest Products, L.P.
ECOPOP - Hosiery - Renfro Corp.
ECOPOWER - Cleaning preparations - Ecolab Inc.
ECOPOWER - Household cleaners - Earthway Ltd.
ECOQUEST - Computer software - Sierra On-Line, Inc.
ECORE - Antennas–satellite - KVH Industries, Inc.
ECORE - Cables–fiber optic - Andrew Corp.
ECOREL - Paper - REXAM DSI
ECOS - Detergents - Venus Laboratories, Inc.
ECOSANE - Plant growth regulators - Ekma, Inc.
ECOSCAN - Forms–preprinted - National Computer Systems, Inc.
ECOSCIENCE - Insecticides - Ecoscience Corp.
ECOSCRUBS - Medical uniforms - Angelica Corp.
ECOSHIELD - Plastics film - Cortec Corp.
ECOSHINE - Cleaning preparations - Ecolab Inc.
ECOSHIRT - Apparel and accessories - Terrasystems/Ecoshirt Inc.
ECOSIS - Apparel–women's - Viva Sportswear Inc.
ECOSLAT - Wood products - Hudson ICS
ECOSNAX - Nuts - Ames International Inc.
ECOSORB - Acoustical insulation for vehicles - Cascade Engineering
ECOSOY - Inks - Sun Chemical Corp.
ECOSPACE - Electrical equipment - Quartet Manufacturing Co.
ECOSPHERE - Computer software - Compuware Corp.
ECOSPLICE - Splicing tape - Coating Sciences Inc.
ECOSPORT - Apparel - Ecosport, Inc.
ECOSPRAY - Rustproofing compounds - Cortec Corp.
ECOSPRING - Water purification systems - Fountainhead Technologies, Inc.
ECOSSIA - Thread - DMC Corp.
ECOSTAKE - Building materials - North American Green, Inc.
ECOSTAR - Dishwashing compounds - Ecolab Inc.
ECOSTAR - Hair care products - Ecostyle, Inc.
ECOSTAR - Motor vehicles–automobiles - Ford Motor Co.
ECOSTAR - Paints - Ecostar Technologies, Inc.
ECOSTAR II-E - Flowers, plants, and seeds - Jacklin Seed
ECOSTUMP - Aquarium accessories - Kordon
ECOSUN - Solar energy collectors - Aquatherm Industries, Inc.
ECOSYSTEM - Quartet Manufacturing Co.
ECOSYSTEM - Cleaning preparations–household - Neozyme International, Inc.
ECOSYSTEM - Hair care products - Joico Laboratories, Inc.
ECOSYSTEMS - Water filtration units - Ecological Systems, Inc.
ECOTAPE - Video tapes–blank - Studio Film & Tape, Inc.
ECOTERRA - Hair care products - Image Laboratories, Inc.
ECOTIMBER - Lumber - Ecotimber International, Inc.
ECOTIP - Fuel systems–motor vehicle - Interstate Diesel Service, Inc.
ECOTONE - Bedding–linen - Watkins Manufacturing Corp.
ECOTONE - Pet products - Keisler Corp.

✩ = Now out of production

ECOTOOLS - Computer software - Compuware Corp.

ECOTOTE - Bags ☆ - Ramstar Mills, Inc.

ECOTOX - Abrasive products - Whitemetal, Inc.

ECOTRACK - Blocks–paving - Bike Track, Inc.

ECOTRAP - Drains - Waterless Co.

ECOTRIM - Fiberboard - Pueblo Millwork, Inc.

ECOTRIN - Analgesics - SmithKline Beecham Consumer Healthcare

ECOTTON - Apparel–children's - Sara's Prints, Inc.

ECOUSTIC - Guitars - Peavey Electronics Corp.

ECOVAC - Tubes–vacuum - Abar Ipsen Industries, Inc.

ECOVER - Cleaning preparations - Ecover Inc.

ECOVIEW - Computer software - Environmental Protection Agency

ECOVILLAGE - Food products - Global Village Institute

ECOWATER - Water purification systems - Ecowater Systems, Inc.

ECOWATER SYSTEMS INC. - Water treating compounds - Ecowater Systems, Inc.

ECOWEAVE - Plastics film - Cortec Corp.

ECOWOOD - Blinds–venetian - Source Northwest, Inc.

ECOWOOD - Landscaping products - Monroe Partners Inc.

ECOWOOL - Yarn - Joseph Galler Inc.

ECOWRITER - Pencils - Faber-Castell Corp.

ECOZ - Deodorizers - Vaportek, Inc.

ECOZONE - Water purification systems - Gatsby Spas Inc.

ECP - Computer software - Stockholder Systems, Inc.

ECP - Veterinary pharmaceutical preparations - Upjohn Co.

ECREVISSE ACADIENNE U S A - Seafood products–fresh or frozen - Ecrevisse Acadienne USA

ECREVISSE ACADIENNE U.S.A. - Crab meat–fresh - Ecrevisse Acadienne USA

ECRIDOR - Pens - Caran D'Ache of Switzerland Inc.

ECRINAL - Hair care products - Nailtex Inc.

ECRIS - Computer software - Rand Corp.

ECRM - Printing trades machinery - Graphline, Inc.

ECRU - Apparel and accessories - Timely Trends, Inc.

ECRU - Colognes ☆ - Avon Products, Inc.

ECRU - Photographic cameras ☆ - Olympus America Inc.

ECS - Computer software - ITT Commercial Finance Corp.

ECS - Publisher's imprints - Exchange Computing Systems, Inc.

ECS - Saws–power - DBNA Trademarks Holding Inc.

ECS TECHNOLOGICAL LEADERSHIP - Computer hardware - Eden Computer Systems, Inc.

ECSTASIES IN SPACE - Fabrics–tapestry - Jeppson Galleries Inc.

ECSTASY - Christmas tree ornaments - Cracker Box Inc.

ECSTASY - Eyeglasses - Art-Craft Optical Co.

ECSTASY - Jams and jellies - Mountain Maid Gourmet Jelly

ECSTASY - Mattresses ☆ - Kingsdown, Inc.

ECSTASY - Motorcycles - Ecstasy Cycles Corp.

ECSTASY - Towels - Fieldcrest Cannon, Inc.

ECSTASY - Underwear and nightwear - Bestform Foundations, Inc.

ECSTRA - Animal feeds - SF Services, Inc.

ECT - Air purification systems - QVC, Inc.

ECT - Fabrics - Liberty Fabrics, Inc.

ECTO ACCELERATOR - Toys - Saban Entertainment, Inc.

ECTO SKEL QUALITY BUG WEAR - Computer software - Ecto Skel, Inc.

ECTO WRIST COMMUNICATOR - Toys - Saban Entertainment, Inc.

ECTOFLEX - Waterproofing compounds - Synthetic Industries, Inc.

ECTOKYL - Veterinary pharmaceutical preparations - DVM Pharmaceuticals, Inc.

ECTOPLAZM - Chewing gum ☆ - Amurol Confections Co.

ECX - Audio equipment - Scosche Industries, Inc.

ECX - Electrical equipment - Toro Co.

ED - Amplifiers–musical instrument ☆ - Peavey Electronics Corp.

ED - Filters–industrial - Ahlstrom Filtration Inc. Industrial Products Group

ED - Ophthalmic goods ☆ - Luxottica

ED - Snack foods - Everson Distributing Co.

ED - Wines - E. & J. Gallo Winery

ED-2 - Glass products - Owens-Illinois Inc. (Libbey Div.)

ED-4 - Glass products - Owens-Illinois Inc. (Libbey Div.)

ED & DON'S - Candy - Ed & Dons Hawaii

ED AND JOAN DELUCA - Pasta - Deluca Inc.

ED BURYN - Publisher's imprints - Ed Buryn

ED-CHARTPAD - Computer software - Compass Systems Corp.

ED-CORE - Tools - Edington Sales Co.

ED DONOVAN'S - Ice cream - Protein Group Inc.

ED DORTCH - Paintbrushes - Corona Brushes Inc.

ED DWIGANS PRIVATE STOCK - Paints - United Coatings Inc.

ED/IT - Video production - Sima Products Corp.

ED MYERS - Musical instrument accessories - Ed Myers Co.

ED NORTON - Dolls ☆ - Effanbee Doll Corp.

ED. PINAUD - American International Industries

E.D. PUBLICATIONS - Music–sheet - Ernest Deffner Inc.

ED-TECH - Electronics equipment - Educational Technology Inc.

ED THOMAS THIN GRIP - Sporting goods - Ace Mitchells Bowlers Mart

EDA MANN ORIGINALS - Statuary - Seymour Mann Inc.

EDA PUBLISHER - Computer software - Concurrent CAE Solutions, Inc.

EDA/SQL - Computer software - Information Builders, Inc.

EDAC - Connectors–electronic - ARS Electronics

EDA'S - Candy - Lehman SUGARFREE Confections

EDATA - Computers - Hein-Werner Corp.

EDAVALIDATOR - Computer software - Harris Electronic Design Automation, Inc.

E.D.B. EVERY DAY BASIC - Shorts–men's - Pacific Teaze

EDC CRACK - Computer software - Kinetics Technology International Corp.

EDCO - Jewelry - Elite Distributing Co.

EDCO - Siding–insulating - Edco Products Inc.

EDCOR - Electronic equipment - Edcor Electronics

EDCOR MAGNETIC - Electronic equipment ☆ - Edcor Electronics

EDCOR SOUND PRODUCTS - Audio equipment - Edcor Electronics

EDCOR TRANSFORMERS - Audio equipment - Edcor Electronics

EDD-BOND - Thread - Eddington Thread Manufacturing Co.

EDD-CLEAR - Thread - Eddington Thread Manufacturing Co.

EDD-CORE - Thread - Eddington Thread Manufacturing Co.

EDD-COTT - Thread ☆ - Eddington Thread Manufacturing Co.

EDD-SPUN - Thread - Eddington Thread Manufacturing Co.

EDD-TEX - Thread - Eddington Thread Manufacturing Co.

EDDIA - Floor coverings–carpet and rugs - Jaunty Co., Inc.

EDDIE BAUER - Luggage ☆ - Eclipse Inc.

EDDIE BAUER - Sporting goods - Eddie Bauer Inc.

EDDIE BAUER ADVENTURER - Colognes - Quintessence Inc.

EDDIE BAUER BEACH CLUB - Umbrellas - Eddie Bauer Inc.

EDDIE BAUER GOURMET - Knives–pocket - Eddie Bauer Inc.

EDDIE BAUER HERO - Knives–pocket - Eddie Bauer Inc.

EDDIE BAUER HOME COLLECTION - Soap - Eddie Bauer Inc.

EDDIE BAUER JOURNEYMAN - Knives–pocket - Eddie Bauer Inc.

EDDIE BAUER LEGENDS - Catalogs - Eddie Bauer Inc.

EDDIE BAUER LODGE - Pancake mix - Eddie Bauer Inc.

EDDIE BELL - Chord diagram stamps - Jan-Mar Industries

EDDIE MCTUNE'S NOTE TUTOR - Music–sheet - Jean R. Newberg

EDDIE PEPPERS - Food products - Schwan's Sales Enterprises, Inc.

EDDIE WALKER - Figurines - Midwest of Cannon Falls Inc.

EDDIE'S - Meat products–canned - E.Z.A. Inc.

EDDIE'S WORLD - Pet products - HTZ Investment Corp.

EDDING - Markers–felt-tip ☆ - Koh-I-Noor, Inc.

EDDORABLES - Shoes - Eddy Shoe Co.

EDDY - Gasoline - Eddy Refining Co.

EDDY - Testing apparatus - SE Systems, Inc.

EDDY BROS. - Hats - Eddy Bros. Co. Inc.

EDDY CURRENT - Tools - Krautkramer-Branson Inc.

EDDY J - Recording label - Eddy J Enterprises

EDDY SHIRE - Shoes - Eddy Shoe Co.

EDDYLEON - Candy - Eddyleon Chocolate Co. Inc.

EDDYVISION - Computer software - Vortex Applications, Ltd.

EDECRIN - Diuretics - Merck & Co., Inc. (Merck Research Laboratories)

EDEL - Food products - George C. Brown's Biscuits & Confections

EDEL DE CLERON - Cheese - Crystal Food Import Corp.

EDEL LACE - Cheese - Brewster Dairy Inc.

EDEL SCREEN - Recording label - Edel America Records, Inc.

EDEL WEISS - Beverages–malt - The Stroh Brewery Co.

EDELBROCK - Automotive parts and accessories - Edelbrock Corp.

EDELMAN - Automotive parts and accessories - Stant Corp.

EDELMANN - Motor vehicle parts and accessories - Epicor Industries, Inc.

EDELRID - Helmets–athletic - Climb High Inc.

EDELTALER - Cheese - Lactoprot USA, Inc.

EDELTON - Compact discs–prerecorded - Edel America Records, Inc.

EDELWEISS - Comforters - Pillowtex Corp.

EDELWEISS - Cooking equipment–household - Charles Zahn-Import Merchant

EDELWEISS - Floor coverings–carpet and rugs - Cabin Crafts Carpets

EDELWEISS - Floor coverings–carpet and rugs - Walter Carpet Mills

EDELWEISS - Jewelry - German Products Distributing Inc.

EDELWEISS - Jewelry–costume ☆ - Safari Ltd.

EDELWEISS - Rings–jewelry - Artcarved Inc.

EDELWEISS - Ski suits–men's - Authentic Fitness Corp.

☆ = Now out of production

EDELWEISS - Sporting goods - Omni International Distributors Inc.

EDELWEISS DUNKEL - Beverages–malt - Phoenix Imports Ltd.

EDELWEISS HEFETRUB - Beverages–malt - Phoenix Imports Ltd.

EDELWEISS KRISTALL - Beverages–malt - Phoenix Imports Ltd.

EDELZEIT - Clocks - La Crosse-McCormick

EDEMCO - Pet products - Edemco Dryers Inc.

EDEN - Cheese - Walker Foods

EDEN - Cigars - Villazon and Co.

EDEN - Dinnerware–glass - Dansk International Designs, Ltd.

EDEN - Dishes–china - Waterford Wedgewood USA, Inc.

EDEN - Floor coverings–carpet and rugs ☆ - Robertex Associates Inc.

EDEN - Food products - Eden Foods, Inc.

EDEN - Melamine product - Boonton Molding Co. Inc.

EDEN - Ophthalmic goods - Styl-Rite Optical Manufacturing Co., Inc.

EDEN - Recording label - Starbound Publishing

EDEN - Rings–jewelry - Artcarved Inc.

EDEN - Toys–stuffed - Eden LLC

EDEN - Wallpaper - Surface Industries Inc.

EDEN - Wallpaper ☆ - Capital Carousel Inc.

EDEN - Whirlpools - Lasco Products Group

EDEN BALLS - Health care products - Eden Foods, Inc.

EDEN BLEND - Beverages - Eden Foods, Inc.

EDEN BRIDALS - Wedding gowns - Eden Bridals, Inc.

EDEN COLLECTION - Floor coverings–carpet and rugs - Callaway Carpets

EDEN COLLECTION - Floor coverings–carpet and rugs ☆ - Feizy Rugs

EDEN ELECTRONICS - Amplifiers - Eden Electronics Inc.

EDEN EXCEL - Filters - Jeffrey I. Edens

EDEN FORMU;AS SKIN CARE - Vitamins and nutritional supplements - Bay to Bay Distribution, Inc.

EDEN GRASS SEED - Flowers, plants, and seeds - Agrono-Tec Seed Co.

EDEN HOUSE - Furniture - Bassett Furniture Industries, Inc.

EDEN HOUSE II - Furniture ☆ - Bassett Furniture Industries, Inc.

EDEN-OA - Computer utility program - Wyndgate Technologies

EDEN ORGANIC - Food products - Eden Foods, Inc.

EDEN PARK - Glassware–household ☆ - Anchor Hocking Glass, Inc.

EDEN PRAIRIE - Lighting fixtures - Holophane Corp.

EDEN RICE - Beverages–carbonated - Eden Foods, Inc.

EDEN ROC - Wines - Ernest and Julio Gallo Winery

EDEN SOY - Beverages - Eden Foods, Inc.

EDEN TRACE - Health care products - Nellcor Puritan Bennett

EDEN TREND - Health care products - Nellcor Puritan Bennett

EDEN VALLEY - Furniture - Dinaire Corp.

EDENBURGH - Lamps ☆ - Lamplight Farms, Inc.

EDENFRUIT - Food products - Edenfruit Products Co.

EDEN'S FRUIT - Vitamins and nutritional supplements - Century Systems Inc.

EDENSIDE - Food products ☆ - Norpac Services, Inc.

EDENTON - Cabinets - Marsh Furniture Co.

EDENTRACE - Medical apparatus - Nellcor Puritan Bennett

EDER - Flags ☆ - Flags International Inc.

E.D.G. - Degreasing solvents ☆ - Sanitek Products Inc.

EDGAR - Cigars - SJI Wholesale, Inc.

EDGAR - Computer software - U.S. Securities and Exchange Commission

EDGAR ALLAN PRINT - Paper - Riverside Paper Corp.

EDGAR DEGAS - Artists' materials ☆ - M. Grumbacher Inc.

EDGAR MORRIS - Astringents - Edgar Morris Inc.

EDGAR POMEROY - Apparel and accessories - Edgar Pomeroy, Ltd.

EDGAR WATKINS - Serving carts ☆ - National Housewares

EDGARLINK - Software - U.S. Securities and Exchange Commission

EDGARTOWN - Floor coverings–carpet and rugs - Trans-Ocean Import Co. Inc:

EDGARTOWN - Frames–eyeglass ☆ - Universal/Univis Inc.

EDGE - Brushes - Corona Brushes Inc.

EDGE - Chemical preparations - Akzo America Inc.

EDGE - Cymbals - Avedis Zildjian Co.

EDGE - Floor coverings - National Floor Products Co., Inc.

EDGE - Footwear–athletic - Puma Inc.

EDGE - Golfing equipment - Ben Hogan Co.

EDGE - Heart monitors - Polar Electro Inc.

EDGE - Microscopes - Edge Scientific Instrument Corp.

EDGE - Oil machinery - Howe-Baker Engineers, Inc.

EDGE - Pet products - F.L. Emmert Co., Inc.

EDGE - Rackets–tennis - Head Sports USA

EDGE - Shaving preparations - S.C. Johnson & Son, Inc.

EDGE - Sponges - Magla Products Inc.

EDGE - Sporting goods - Brine Inc.

EDGE - Sporting goods - Comfort Cushion Mills, Inc.

EDGE - Veterinary pharmaceutical preparations - Boehringer Ingelheim Animal Health, Inc.

EDGE - Wheelchairs - Fortress Inc.

EDGE - Window frames - Quaker Window Products Co.

EDGE 2001, THE - Knives–carving - S.C. Chang & Co.

EDGE-A-LINE - Weed killer ☆ - National Scent Co.

EDGE CITY - Computer software - Joel R. Garreau

EDGE COMPANY, THE - Telephones - Edge Co.

EDGE CONTROL - Shoes–orthopedic - Northwest Podiatric Laboratory, Inc.

EDGE EATER - Tools–hand-operated - Genesis Materials International

EDGE FOR CATS - Pet products - Edge Products

EDGE FOR DOGS - Pet products - Edge Products

EDGE FREE - Steel strappings - Acme Packaging Corp.

EDGE-GUARD - Hardware - Trim-Lok Inc.

EDGE II - Footwear–athletic - Head Sports USA

EDGE II - Wheelchairs - Fortress Inc.

EDGE IT - Garden equipment ☆ - Pro Inc.

EDGE-IT - Machinery - Our Tool & Cutter, Inc.

EDGE KLEENER - Vacuum cleaners and accessories - The Eureka Co.

EDGE NATURAL SUPPLEMENT - Vitamins and nutritional supplements - Emmert Grain Co.

EDGE OF ELEGANCE - Vinyl - National Floor Products Co., Inc.

EDGE ROCK - Blocks–concrete - Keystone Retaining Wall Systems, Inc.

EDGE SAVER - Razor blades - Anshal II , Inc.

EDGE SCIENTIFIC INSTRUMENTS - Microscopes - Edge Scientific Instrument Corp.

EDGE SYSTEM, THE - Vitamins and nutritional supplements - Nutri Science Inc.

EDGE TECH - Apparel and accessories - Authentic Fitness Corp.

EDGE, THE - Wood products - Artistry In Veneers, Inc.

EDGE, THE - Bicycles - Columbia Manufacturing Inc.

EDGE, THE - Glassware–household ☆ - Crisa Corp.

EDGE, THE - Kites - Go Fly A Kite Inc.

EDGE, THE - Trailers - Haulmark Industries, Inc.

EDGE, THE - Elevators - Montgomery Kone Inc.

EDGE, THE - Elevators - Quartet Manufacturing Co.

EDGE-TO-EDGE - Fabrics - Rockland Industries Inc.

EDGE TV - Video production - Edge Communications, Inc.

EDGE TXE - Rackets–tennis - Head Sports USA

EDGE USA - Skates–ice - Edge Specialties, Inc.

EDGE20 - Water–mineral - Beverage Alternatives, Inc.

EDGEBROOK - Furniture ☆ - Cosco, Inc.

EDGEBROOK MANOR - Hardware ☆ - Amerock Corp.

EDGECO - Cutlery - Edge Co.

EDGECRAFT - Knives - Edgecraft Corp.

EDGECRAFT DIAMOND FILE SET - Tools–hand-operated - Edgecraft Corp.

EDGECRAFTED - Blinds–vertical ☆ - Louverdrape Inc.

EDGECRAFTER - Hardware - Edgecraft Corp.

EDGECRAFTER DIAMOND HONE SET - Files and sharpeners - Edgecraft Corp.

EDGEGARD - Vitamins and nutritional supplements - Baker Co. Inc.

EDGEGUARD - Mattresses - Ohio Mattress Co.

EDGELESS - Pencils ☆ - Faber-Castell Corp.

EDGELIGHT - Metals - Fort Wayne Plastics, Inc.

EDGELITE - Cutlery - Gutmann Cutlery Inc.

EDGELITE - Signs - Clearr Corp.

EDGEMAIL - Computer software - Advantage Communications, Inc.

EDGEMARK - Cutlery - Gutmann Cutlery Inc.

EDGEMASTER - Garden equipment - Master Mark Plastic Products

EDGEMASTER - Scissors–hand-operated - Gutmann Cutlery Inc.

EDGEMATE - Wood products - Westvaco Corp.

EDGEMONT - Flatware - Gorham Inc.

EDGEMONT - Paper–bond ☆ - Parsons Paper Co.

EDGEMONT GOLD - Dishes–china - Gorham Inc.

EDGEPRO - Lawn edging - Dimex Corp.

EDGER - Mops - O-Cedar/Vining Household Products Co.

EDGEROY - Balls–tennis - Edgeroy Co. Inc.

EDGERPLUS - Garden equipment - Ryobi America Corp.

EDGESITE - Optical machinery ☆ - Gutmann Cutlery Inc.

EDGESTIK - Tools–hand-operated - Colorstik Ltd.

EDGEWATER - Bathroom accessories - Baldwin Hardware Corp.

EDGEWATER - Paper–gift wrap ☆ - Papercraft Inc.

EDGEWATER - Wallpaper ☆ - Pickhardt & Siebert USA Inc.

EDGEWOOD - Beverages–alcohol - Golden State Vintners

EDGEWOOD - Cabinets–wood - Edgewater Cabinets

EDGEWOOD - Clocks - General Time Corp. (Westclox/Seth Thomas Div.)

☆ = Now out of production

EDGEWOOD - Flatware ☆ - Utica Cutlery Co.
EDGEWOOD - Floor coverings–carpet and rugs - Colonial Mills Inc.
EDGEWOOD - Floor coverings–carpet and rugs ☆ - Alexander Smith Carpets
EDGEWOOD - Furniture–upholstered ☆ - Webb Furniture Enterprises Inc.
EDGEWOOD - Jewelry - Jacoby-Bender Inc.
EDGEWOOD - Manufactured homes - Redman Industries, Inc.
EDGEWOOD - Tools–woodworking - Shopsmith Inc.
EDGEWOOD - Trailers–travel - Fleetwood Enterprises, Inc.
EDGEWOOD ESTATE - Wines - Golden State Vintners
EDGEWORTH - Floor coverings - Oregon Lumber Products Inc.
EDGEWORTH - Tobacco products - Lane Ltd.
EDGEWORTH EXPORT - Cigarettes ☆ - House of Edgeworth
EDGEWORX - Computer software - Antares Alliance Group
EDGIE WEDGIE - Ski teaching aid - Vernon W. Miller
EDGY LEMON - Beverages - The Stroh Brewery Co.
EDI - Computer hardware - Daniel F. Lin
EDI ABLE - Computer software - Edi Able, Inc.
EDI/E - Computer software - Premenos Corp.
EDI MANAGER - Computer software - Edi Able, Inc.
EDI OFFICE - Computer software - Genesis Data Systems, Inc.
EDI YELLOW PAGES - Publisher's imprints - Phillips Publishing International, Inc.
EDIBELTS - Belts - Frances Goldmark
EDIBLE ART - Desserts - Kenneth Prehart
EDIBLE EMPIRE - Pasta - Salem Food Co. of New York, Inc.
EDIBLE FLORAL CREATIONS - Fruits and vegetables - Incredibly Edible Delites Inc.
EDIBLE FLOWERS - Flowers, plants, and seeds ☆ - Applewood Seed & Garden Group
EDIBLE IMAGE - Food products - Lucks Co.
EDIBLE ORNAMENT, THE - Candy - Geoffrey Boehm Chocolates Inc.
EDIE ADAMS CUT AND CURL - Beauty shops - Cutco Industries Inc.
EDIE BEE - Robes - Waterbury Garment Corp.
EDIEASY - Computer software - EDI Solutions Inc.
EDIFICE - Computer software - SourceView Software International
EDILCOUGHI - Ceramic tile - Integrity Tile Co.
EDILGRES - Ceramic tile ☆ - Integrity Tile Co.
EDILGRES - Tiles–ceramic - Federal Tile Imports Inc.
EDILINX - Computer software - EDI Solutions Inc.
EDINA - Cameras ☆ - Edixa Camera Co.
EDINBOROUGH - Manufactured homes - Redman Industries, Inc.
EDINBOROUGH - Mobile homes - Western Homes Corp.
EDINBURGH - Artists' materials ☆ - Andrews/Nelson/Whitehead
EDINBURGH - Cabinets ☆ - Medallion Kitchens of Minnesota Inc.
EDINBURGH - Cigarettes - Faber, Coe & Gregg Inc.
EDINBURGH - Mattresses - Stearns & Foster Bedding Co.
EDINBURGH COURT - Furniture - Sherrill Furniture Co.
EDIQIT - Editing equipment–photographic - Strassner Video Enterprises
EDIQUIP - Film/tape equipment - J and R Film Co. Inc.
EDISON - Apparel and accessories - New Era Knitting Mills
EDISON - Computer peripheral equipment - Shahram Bidsal
EDISON - Computer software - Designware, Inc.
EDISON - Dehumidifiers ☆ - Martin Industries, Inc.
EDISON - Fans–electric ☆ - Toastmaster Inc.
EDISON - Infant product - Edison Industries Inc.
EDISON - Lighting fixtures and outdoor lanterns - Cooper Industries, Inc.
EDISON CRAFT - Hand tools - Midwest Air Technologies, Inc.
EDISON DESIGN GROUP - Computer software - Edison Design Group, Inc.
EDISON PRICE LIGHTING - Lighting fixtures - Edison Price Lighting
EDISTO - Fabrics - Greenwood Mills Inc.
EDISTO SHRIMP CO. - Seafood - Edisto Shrimp Co. Inc.
EDISYS - Computer software - Edisys Corp.
EDIT CUTTER - Electronic equipment - Comprehensive Video Supply Corp.
EDIT LISTER - Computer software - Comprehensive Video Supply Corp.
EDIT MASTER - Electronic equipment - Comprehensive Video Supply Corp.
EDIT POINT - Video editing system - Edit Point, Inc.
EDITALL - Audio equipment - Xedit
EDITCAM - Video equipment - Ikegami Electronics (USA) Inc.
EDITECH - Televisions - Electronics Distributors, Inc.
EDITH - Glassware–household - H. Wittur & Co.
EDITH IMRE - Beauty aids - Edith Imre Hair Fashions Inc.
EDITH LANCES - Brassieres (Bras) - Edith Lances Corp.
EDITH LEIGHTON - Skin care products - Ritornelle Inc.
EDITH'S GOURMET COOKIE CO. - Bakery goods - Edith's Gourmet Cookie Co., Inc.
EDITION DELUXE - Glassware–household - Oneida Ltd.

EDITION FAZER - Music–sheet - MMB Music Inc.
EDITION MEDIZIN - Publisher's imprints - VCH Publishers Inc.
EDITION STEMMLE - Publisher's imprints - Abbeville Press, Inc.
EDITION WILHELM HANSEN - Music–sheet - Music Sales Corp.
EDITIONS - Apparel and accessories - Phillips-Van Heusen Corp.
EDITIONS CHANSON - Music–sheet - Stanyan Record Co.
EDITIONS DU BUOT - Posters - Graphic Arts Unltd. Inc.
EDITIONS EG - Recording label - EG Records
EDITIONS F. HAZAN - Posters - Graphic Arts Unltd. Inc.
EDITIONS IN FASHION - Dresses–women's - Anne Klein & Co.
EDITIONS LTD. - Greeting cards - Editions Ltd.
EDITIONS MUGERON - Posters ☆ - Classico San Francisco Inc.
EDITIONS NOVOS - Calendars - Sormani Inc.
EDITOR 2 - Typewriters ☆ - Olivetti North America Inc. (Consumer Products Div.)
EDITOR IN CHIEF - Publisher's imprints - Critical Thinking Press & Software
EDITOR, THE - Audio equipment - Recoton Corp.
EDITORIAL PORTAVOZ - Publisher's imprints - Kregel Publications & Bookstores
EDITORIALS ON FILE - Publisher's imprints - Facts on File Inc.
EDITORS - Paper–writing - P.H. Glatfelter Co.
EDITOR'S CHOICE - Eyeglasses - Lantis Corp.
EDITRON - Electronic equipment - Hudson Photographic Industries Inc.
EDITWINDOWS - Computer software - Microsoft Corp.
EDIX - Computer software - Emerging Technology Consultants Inc.
EDIXA - Cameras ☆ - Edixa Camera Co.
EDIZIONI D'ARTE M. DORDONI - Posters - Graphic Arts Unltd. Inc.
EDJER - Health care products - Andis Co.
EDKO - Door openers–electronic - McKee Door, Inc.
EDL PRO - Computer software - Alba Editorial, Inc.
EDLOS - Recording label ☆ - Prince/SF Productions
EDMAC - Beef - Edmac Foods Inc.
EDMARK - Computer software - Edmark Corp.
EDME - Dishes–china - Waterford Wedgewood USA, Inc.
EDMEADES - Wines - Kendall Jackson Winery, Ltd.
EDMEADES VINEYARDS - Wines - Edmeades Inc.
EDMOND BOIVERT - Watches - Belair Watch Corp.
EDMONT - Gloves ☆ - Edmont
EDMONTON - Floor coverings–carpet and rugs - Bellbridge Carpets
EDMONTON - Floor coverings–carpet and rugs ☆ - Atlas Carpet Mills Inc.
EDMONTON - Occasional tables - JDI Group, Inc.
EDMONTON BOOT CO. - Food products - Shonac Corp.
EDMUND - Optical machinery - Edmund Scientific Co.
EDMUND MELVIN WHITE - Wines - St. Croix Winery
EDNA - Skin care products - Edna 4czns, Inc.
EDNA B. - Apparel–women's - Julie Lawson
EDNA KAUFMANN - Women's clothing - Suzanne Schaeffer
EDNA LOONEY - Hobby kits - Edna Looney Products
EDNA VALLEY VINEYARD - Wines - Edna Valley Vineyard
EDNA VALLEY VINEYARD - Wines - Paragon Vineyard Co. Inc.
EDNALITE - Projection screens - D'San Corp.
EDNOVATION - Computer software - Ednovation, Inc.
E.DOC - Gas machinery - Innovative Engineering Solutions, Inc.
EDOM - Vitamins and nutritional supplements - Edom Laboratories Inc.
EDON - Paper–tissue ☆ - Fort Howard Corp.
EDOPAK - Pet products - Ranpak Corp.
EDOX - Watches - Holzerwatch Co. Inc.
EDR - Computer hardware and software ☆ - Donovan Data Systems, Inc.
E'DRADOUR - See AUSTIN NICHOLS
EDROBAY - Luggage - Jinwoong Inc.
EDROY'S - Lenses–magnifying - Edroy Products Co.
EDS - Battery chargers - Electronic Design & Sales Inc.
E.D.S. - Compressors–air ☆ - Sofragraf Unifix Inc.
ED'S - Glue–household or industrial ☆ - DecoArt, Inc.
EDS - Jewelry - Europa Diamond Syndicate Inc.
ED'S - Rice - Falcon Rice Mill Inc.
EDS: ENZYME DELIVERY SYSTEM - Chemical preparations - National Enzyme Co. Inc.
ED'S FAVORITE POPCORN - Popcorn - Twin Valley Development Services Inc.
ED'S ORIGINAL CAVE CREEK - Beer - Shamrock Imports
ED'S OWN - Salad dressings–bottled - Ed's Own
EDSEL - Motor vehicles–automobiles ☆ - Ford Motor Co.
EDSON - Steering mechanisms–boat - Edson Corp.
EDTA - Pharmaceutical preparations - Legere Pharmaceuticals Inc.
EDU-BLOX - Toy building tiles - PI Consumer Products Corp.

☆ = Now out of production

EDU-CASSETTE - Audio equipment ☆ - BASF Corp.

EDU-CRAFT - Rope ☆ - Wellington Leisure Products, Inc.

EDU FUN - Computer software ☆ - Milliken Publishing Co. (Computer Software Div.)

EDU-KEE - Publisher's imprints - Kee Inc.

EDU-LASE - Laser systems–medical - Kentek Corp.

EDU-RING - Toys - Learning Products Inc.

EDU-TAPE - Audio equipment ☆ - BASF Corp.

EDUBENCH - Desks - Learning Products Inc.

EDUBLOC - Toys - Learning Products Inc.

EDUCALUX - Toys ☆ - Reeves International, Inc.

EDUCASE - Publisher's imprints - Education Design, Inc.

EDUCATED NUT - Automotive parts and accessories ☆ - Pacific Lubricants

EDUCATION INDUSTRY DIRECTORY - Publisher's imprints - Education Investing, Inc.

EDUCATION IS GOLD - Jewelry - Education is Gold, Inc.

EDUCATION PLACE - Educational materials - Houghton Mifflin Co.

EDUCATIONAL - Puzzles - Derek H. Chan

EDUCATIONAL ACTIVITIES - Recording label - Folkraft/Dance Record

EDUCATIONAL ALTERNATIVES - Textbooks ☆ - Communication Skill Builders, Inc.

EDUCATIONAL EXCHANGE - Educational materials - Educational Exchange

EDUCATIONAL FAMILY - Dolls - R. William Gilbert Associates Inc.

EDUCATIONAL IN NATURE - Educational materials - Georgia-Pacific Corp.

EDUCATIONAL STRUCTURES - Educational materials - American Cybercasting Corp.

EDUCATOR - Clocks - General Time Corp. (Westclox/Seth Thomas Div.)

EDUCATOR - Electronic equipment - Sharp Electronics Corp.

EDUCATOR - Harmonicas - Hohner Inc.

EDUCATOR - Musical instrument accessories - G. Leblanc Corp.

EDUCATOR - Office supplies ☆ - Newell Office Products

EDUCATOR - Projection screens - Da-Lite Screen Co. Inc.

EDUCATOR OVERHEAD - Calculators - Stokes Publishing Co., Inc.

EDUCATOR, THE - Games - Classic Games Co. Inc.

EDUCATORSONLINE - Computer software - Executive Resource Associates, Inc.

EDUCLIP IMAGES 1 - Computer software - Teach Yourself By Computer Software Inc.

EDUCLIP IMAGES 2 - Computer software - Teach Yourself By Computer Software Inc.

EDUCLIP IMAGES 3 - Computer software - Teach Yourself By Computer Software Inc.

EDUCLIP IMAGES 4 - Computer software - Teach Yourself By Computer Software Inc.

EDUCLIP IMAGES 5 - Computer software - Teach Yourself By Computer Software Inc.

EDUCTOR - Medical apparatus - Eductor Partnership

EDUCUBE - Toys - Learning Products Inc.

EDULATOR - Adding machines ☆ - Monroe Systems for Business Inc.

EDUMAT - Paper products - Edumat, Inc.

EDUQUEST - Computer hardware - International Business Machines Corp.

EDURA - Mats - Matworks

EDUSCHO - Coffee - C. & J. Willenborg Inc.

EDUSERV OASIS - Computer software - Eduserv Technologies, Inc.

EDUSOFT - Educational materials - Scott Steketee

EDUTEL - Telephones - Teleconferencing Systems International Inc.

EDUTRAX - Construction equipment rental services - Randy Engle Microsystems

EDUVIEW - Computer software - Network Connection, Inc.

EDVANTAGE - Food products - Edlong Corp.

EDWAL - Photographic equipment - Edwal Scientific Products Corp.

EDWAL G - Photographic equipment ☆ - Edwal Scientific Products Corp.

EDWARD & SONS - Food products - Edward & Sons Trading Co., Inc.

EDWARD ARNOLD - Publisher's imprints - Routledge

EDWARD ARNOLD/HODDER & STOUGHTON - Publisher's imprints - Routledge

EDWARD ARTZNER - Meat products–canned - Haddon House Food Products Inc.

EDWARD G. ROBINSON - Tobacco pouches - Consolidated Cigar Corp.

EDWARD G. ROBINSON - Tobacco pouches - Sutliff Tobacco Co.

+EDWARD #KING ESTATE - Wines - King Estate Vineyards, Inc.

EDWARD WARREN - Crocheted and knitted items - Garland Knitting Mills

EDWARD WESTON - Posters - Edward Weston Fine Arts

EDWARDIAN - Frames–picture - Terragrafics Inc.

EDWARDIAN COLLECTION - Luggage - Textile Brokers Ltd.

EDWARDIAN GARDEN - Wallpaper ☆ - Sandpiper Studios

EDWARDIAN GARDEN II - Wallpaper - Sandpiper Studios

EDWARDS - Coffee - Safeway Stores Inc.

EDWARDS - Footwear - Stride Rite Corp.

EDWARDS - Musical instruments - Getzen Co.

EDWARDS - Pies–fresh - Edwards Baking Co.

EDWARDS - Pumps - Edwards Manufacturing, Inc.

EDWARDS - Sporting goods - Edwards Sports Products

EDWIN - Meat products–beef - Edwin Beef Co.

EDWIN K. WILLIAMS & CO. - Business-aids and services franchise - Edwin K. Williams & Co.

EDWIN PAUL - Hair care products - Edwin Paul, Inc.

EDX - Coils–ignition - Rite Autotronics Corp.

EDY'S - Ice cream, frozen yogurt - Edy's Grand Ice Cream Inc.

EDY'S LIGHT - Ice cream, frozen yogurt - Edy's Grand Ice Cream Inc.

EE - Furniture - Wright Line Inc.

EE STYLE - Catalogs - Spiegel, Inc.

EE-Z CAJUN - Food products ☆ - Bodin Foods Inc.

EE Z EE - Brackets - Crawford Products Inc.

EEE LTD - Recording label - Ripete Music Group

EEE-ZZZ-LAY DRAIN CO. - Drains - Eee-Zzz Lay Drain Co., Inc.

EEEKS - Toys - Toymax Inc.

EEGEE - Dolls - Goldberger Doll Manufacture Co.

EEGOR - Electrical equipment - GB Electrical Inc.

EEI - Automotive parts and accessories - Ernie Elliott Enterprises, Inc.

EEK - Pet products - Fuhrman Diversified

EEK! THE CAT - Dolls - Twentieth Century Fox Film Corp.

EEK THE CAT - Games - Fox Children's Network, Inc.

EEKO - Luggage - Holiday Fair, Inc.

EEL BY ERNIE - Apparel and accessories - Pletz Imports

EELY-OSS - Surgical instruments - Mason Laboratories, Inc.

EEMS - Computer peripheral equipment - Eems, Inc.

EEN - Pharmaceutical preparations ☆ - Lexis Laboratories Inc.

EENSY & FRIENDS - Computer software - Don Johnston Inc.

EERDMANS BOOKS FOR YOUNG READERS - Publisher's imprints - Wm. B. Eerdmans Publishing Co.

EERIE - Apparel and accessories - Eerie Entertainment, Inc.

EERIE - Books–comic - Harris Publications, Inc.

EERIE SERIES, THE - Publisher's imprints ☆ - Harper Junior Books Group

EERIE TISSUE SILHOUETTES - Novelty items - Paper Magic Group Inc.

E.E.S. - Pharmaceutical preparations - Abbott Laboratories

EEV - Electron tubes - ARS Electronics

EEZ - Health care products - McKesson Home Health Care

EEZ-IN - Marine rigging - Garelick Manufacturing Co.

EEZ-ON - Plumbing fixtures - Jameco Industries, Inc.

EEZ-THRU - Dental equipment - John O.Butler Co.

EEZBEE - Gyroscopes - Kenneth L. Pravitz

EEZEE-GO RINSE FREE FINISH & WAX STRIPPER - Cleaning preparations - Uncle Sam Chemical Co., Inc.

EEZEL - Paints - Schulte Paint & Lacquer Manufacturing Co., Inc.

EEZY STAK - Wire products - Jesco Industries, Inc.

E.F. #JOHNSON - Radio communications equipment - E.F. Johnson Co.

E.F.A. - Hair care products - Playtex Beauty Care, Inc.

EFA - Vitamins and nutritional supplements ☆ - Great Life Laboratories Inc.

EFA PRIMROSE - Hair care products - Jason Natural Products, Inc.

EFA Z PLUS - Pet products - Allerderm Inc.

EFACOM - Vitamins and nutritional supplements ☆ - Nature's Way Products, Inc.

EFADINA - Cough medicines - Luyties Pharmacal Co.

EFALOCK - Hair care products - Efalock International

EFAMAX - Vitamins and nutritional supplements ☆ - Nature's Way Products, Inc.

EFAMOL - Shampoos ☆ - Jason Natural Products, Inc.

EFC - Pet products - Eastern Findings Corp.

EFCO - Building materials - Efco Corp.

EFD - Nuts and bolts - Express Fasteners And Distribution Ltd.

EFED II - Pharmaceutical preparations - Alto Pharmaceuticals Inc.

EFEDRON - Pharmaceutical preparations - Hyrex Pharmaceuticals

EFF-STOP - Paints - Dunn Edwards Corp.

EFFACER: HANGMAN FROM THE 25TH CENTURY - Computer software - Capitol Multimedia, Inc.

EFFACIL - Skin care products - Lancome

EFFANJAY - Office supplies - Effanjay Pens Inc.

EFFASOL - Hair care products - Cosmair Inc.

EFFECI - Clothing - B. Boston & Associates

EFFECT - Hair care products - Advantage Cosmetics, Inc.

EFFECT - Recording label - Luke Records Inc.

☆ = Now out of production

EFFECTIVE MOTIVATIONAL MANAGEMENT - Publisher's imprints - Success Motivation, Inc.

EFFECTIVE PERSONAL LEADERSHIP - Publisher's imprints - Success Motivation, Inc.

EFFECTIVE SELLING STRATEGIES - Publisher's imprints - Success Motivation, Inc.

EFFECTIVE SUPERVISORY MANAGEMENT - Publisher's imprints - Success Motivation, Inc.

EFFECTIVE TIME MANAGEMENT - Publisher's imprints - Success Motivation, Inc.

EFFECTIVE VEHICLE SECURITY - Alarm systems - Directed Electronics, Inc.

EFFECTO - Paints - Pratt & Lambert, Inc.

EFFECTONE - Paints - Jones Blair Co.

EFFECTS - Electrical equipment - Lamson & Sessions Co.

EFFECTS - Fabrics–tapestry - Christopher Prints

EFFECTS - Hair care products - Scruples Professional Salon Products, Inc.

EFFECTS - Wallpaper ✩ - Old Deerfield Fabrics Inc.

EFFERDENT - Denture cleaners - Warner-Wellcome

EFFERDENT PLUS - Denture cleaners - Warner-Lambert Co.

EFFERDENT PLUS - Denture cleaners - Warner-Wellcome

EFFERFIT - Vitamins and nutritional supplements - American BioGir Corp.

EFFERGRIP - Denture materials - Warner-Wellcome

EFFERSAN - Disinfectants - Micrel Limited, Inc.

EFFERSYLLIUM - Laxatives - McNeil Pharmaceuticals

EFFERZYME - Cleaning preparations - Cross Country Paper Products, Inc.

EFFET DU SOLEIL - Skin care products - Cosmair Inc.

EFFEX - Lighting equipment - Genlyte Group Inc.

EFFEX - Wallpaper ✩ - National Products Inc.

EFFICIENC - Soups–mixes - Campbell Soup Co.

EFFICIENCY - Duplicating machines ✩ - Heyer Inc.

EFFICIENCY - Floor coverings–carpet and rugs ✩ - Lees Carpets

EFFICIENCY - Paper–writing - Ampad Corp.

EFFICIENCY - Sinks–metal - Kohler Co.

EFFICIENCY PLUS - Dehumidifiers - Lennox Industries Inc.

EFFICIENT STORE FIXTURING - Fixtures - Milton Merl & Associates, Inc.

EFFIGY - Cosmetics - Nexxus Products Co.

EFFIKAL - Flues - Meyer Furnace Co.

EFFORTLESS - Floor coverings–carpet and rugs - Lees Carpets

EFFRETTO COMPLEX - Skin care products - Ya-Man Ltd.

EFI - Food products - Eastern Foods, Inc.

EFI - Fuel systems–motor vehicle - EFI Technology, Inc.

E.F.I. - Furniture ✩ - Custom Sound Corp.

EFI - Gas turbine cartridge filters - TDC Filter Manufacturing, Inc.

EFI - Power control devices - EFI Electronics Corp.

EFI LIFT-A-LIMB - Orthopedic products - Equip for Independence, Inc.

EFICA CC - Medical apparatus - SSI Medical Services, Inc.

EFICALE - Pharmaceutical preparations ✩ - U.S. Ethicals Inc.

EFICOLOR - Computer software - Electronics for Imaging, Inc.

EFIDAC/24 - Pharmaceutical preparations - Ciba-Geigy Corp.

EFIDIL - Pharmaceutical preparations ✩ - U.S. Ethicals Inc.

EFLON - Thread - Belding Heminway Co. Inc.

EFLONE - Pharmaceutical preparations - Ciba-Geigy Corp.

E.F.M. - Heating equipment - Electric Furnace-Man

EFO-CAN - Health care products ✩ - E. Fougera & Co. Inc.

EFO-TUSSIN - Cough medicines ✩ - E. Fougera & Co. Inc.

EFODINE - Pharmaceutical preparations - E. Fougera & Co. Inc.

.E FONTS - Computer software - Berthold Direct Corp.

E.FORCE - Aerotic rides exercise equipment ✩ - CSA, Inc.

EFRATOM - Electronic equipment - Efratom Time and Frequency Products, Inc.

EFRICON - Cough medicines - Lannett Co. Inc.

EFS - Computer software - Excalibur Technologies Corp.

EFS - Jewelry - EFS International Corp.

EFS - Seasonings - Flavor & Fragrance Specialties Inc.

EFS LAMBDA - Electronic equipment ✩ - Phoenix Systems LLC

EFT - Electronic equipment - Seaboard-Arval Corp.

EFT WIZARD - Computer software - Systemax Corp.

EFTEE - Floor coverings - Compass Concepts

EFTG - Jewelry - Anita Rene' Goudeau

EFUDEX - Pharmaceutical preparations - Roche Laboratories

EFURD - Machinery - Pierce Construction and Maintenance Co., Inc.

EFX - Pharmaceutical preparations - Natural Efx, Inc.

EFX - Recording label - MGM Grand Hotel, Inc.

EFX PLUS2 - Projectors–photographic - City Theatrical Inc.

EG - Amplifiers ✩ - Music Industries Inc.

EG - Lighting fixtures - Hubbell Lighting, Inc. (Lighting Div.)

EG - Recording label - Caroline Records, Inc.

EG+ - Video tapes–blank ✩ - Minnesota Mining & Manufacturing Co.

E.G. CREATIONS - Jewelry–costume - Blue Delft Co. Inc.

E.G. SMITH E.MAGINATION - Apparel and accessories - World Love Productions Inc.

EG&G FLOW TECHNOLOGY - Measuring instruments - EG&G Flow Technology, Inc.

EG&G ROTRON - Pet products - Area Inc.

EGBERT - Brushes–hair - Robert Simmons Inc.

EGBOK - Novelty items - ABC Inc.

EGC - Recording label ✩ - Combo Records

EGC - Sound-reinforcement equipment - Valley Audio Products, Inc.

EGE - Floor coverings–carpet and rugs - EGE Area Rugs Inc.

EGEKVIST - Breads - Metz Baking Co.

L'EGENT - Handbags - Legent International, Ltd.

EGERMANN - Ruby glass - Continental Art-Craft

EGERMEIER'S - Publisher's imprints - Warner Press, Inc.

EGF - Food products machinery - E.G. Forrest Co.

EGG - Apparel–children's - Designs By Egg Inc.

EGG AND YOU, THE - Hair care products - Helene Curtis Industries Inc.

EGG BASKETS - Doughs–frozen ✩ - Pillsbury Co.

EGG BEATERS - Eggnog - Nabisco Brands Inc.

EGG BEATERS - Eggs - Nabisco Foods Group

EGG BEATERS WITH CHEEZ - Eggs - Nabisco Foods Group

EGG BOOSTER 16 CRUMBLES - Animal feeds - Bluebonnet Milling Co.

EGG BOOSTER 16 NIBBLETS - Animal feeds - Bluebonnet Milling Co.

EGG-CETERA - Kitchen appliances ✩ - Sunbeam-Oster Household Products

EGG COLORS - Novelty items - Paper Magic Group Inc.

EGG CRATES - Toys ✩ - Henry Gordy International Inc.

EGG DAZZLERS - Dyes–food - Spearhead Industries Inc.

EGG FOAM YELLOW - Cosmetics - Nutrine Ltd.

EGG GEMS - Novelty items - Easter Unltd. Inc.

EGG GOURMET - Dishes–plastic - Maywood Industries Inc.

EGG HAMLETTE - Sandwiches–prepackaged - Southland Corp.

EGG HARBOR - Boats–motor - Egg Harbor Boat Co.

EGG HARBOR - Boats–motor - Egg Harbor Yacht Co., Inc.

EGG HARBOR - Rope - Sea Spike Marine Supply Co. Inc.

EGG HARBOR ORCHARDS - Food products - Egg Harbor Orchards Inc.

EGG-HEAD - Musical instrument accessories ✩ - Music Accessories Manufacturing Co. Inc.

EGG HEAD - Sporting goods - Yakima Bait Co.

EGG HEADS - Hobby kits ✩ - Hinkle Easter Products

EGG LADY, THE - Figurines - Egg Lady

EGG LAND'S BEST - Dairy products - Eggland's Best Inc.

EGG-LITES - Candles - Lancaster Colony Corp.

EGG MAGIC - Egg substitutes - Sandoz Pharmaceuticals Corp.

EGG MANNA - Pet products ✩ - Aquatronics-Filtronics

EGG MCMUFFIN - Sandwiches–prepackaged - Mcdonald's Corp.

EGG N OMELET - Ovens–microwave - Nordic Ware

EGG NOG - Toys - Russ Berrie and Co., Inc.

EGG NOGGIN - Hats - Raymond D. Kiefer

EGG-O-GRAM - Novelty items - Jeffrey Allan Umstead

EGG-O-RAMA - Toys–stuffed ✩ - Fun World Inc.

EGG-O-RUM - Hair care products ✩ - Gena Laboratories Inc.

EGG PARADE - Novelty items - Paper Magic Group Inc.

EGG PASTAS IN A BASKET - Food products - Colavita USA, Inc.

EGG PICTURES - Recording label - Egg Pictures, Inc.

EGG PRO PLUS - Vitamins and nutritional supplements - AST Research, Inc.

EGG ROLL SELECT - Food products - Jimmies Food Packing

EGG ROLLS - Food products - Health is Wealth

EGG SCAPE - Games - Toyvision, Inc.

EGG-SORTMENT - Candy - Planters LifeSavers Co.

EGG-SPRESSION - Toys–stuffed ✩ - Fun World Inc.

EGG-STRA - Frames–picture - Russ Berrie and Co., Inc.

EGG-STRAVAGANZA - Novelty items - Russ Berrie and Co., Inc.

EGG, THE - Artists' materials - Visual Design Manufacturing Co. Inc.

EGG TOTE - Sporting goods - Brown Bear Bait Co.

EGG WATCHERS - Food products - Tofutti Brands Inc.

EGG WELL'S - Egg substitutes - Nabisco, Inc.

EGG-YOKE - Musical instrument accessories ✩ - Music Accessories Manufacturing Co. Inc.

EGGANENE - Food products ✩ - Sleepy Eye Foods

EGGBERT - Giftware ✩ - Enesco Corp.

EGGCESSORIES - Hobby kits - Imagineering Inc.

EGGCETERA - Novelty items - Geoffrey Inc.

EGGCITING - Games - Creatnetics

EGGER - Candy - Haram-Christensen Corp.

EGGERCIZER - Computer peripheral equipment - ACCO USA, Inc.
EGGHEADS - Candy - Frankford Candy & Chocolate Co. Inc.
EGGIT - Food products ☆ - Eggit Inc.
EGGLETS - Chocolate candy - Superior Fruit & Confections
EGGLITE - Food products ☆ - Sanovo-Seymour USA, Inc.
EGGO - Waffles–frozen - Kellogg Co.
EGGPLANT PEOPLE, THE - Frozen foods - Dominex, L.C.
EGGS/DEADHATCH - Insecticides ☆ - Valent USA Corp.
EGGS DECO - Hobby kits - Hinkle Easter Products
EGGS D'LITE - Egg substitutes - M.G. Waldbaum Co.
EGGS IN THE ATTIC - Candy ☆ - R.M. Palmer Co.
EGGS 'N MUFFIN - Cooking equipment–household ☆ - Nordic Ware
EGGS ON WHEELS - Novelty items - Paper Magic Group Inc.
EGGS ON WHEELS - Toys - Spearhead Industries Inc.
EGGS SMOKEHOUSE - Food products ☆ - Morrison Restaurants Inc.
EGGSACT - Animal feed supplements - International Ingredient Corp.
EGGSACT - Eggtimers - Hammerhead Products
EGGSCAVATORS - Toys ☆ - Henry Gordy International Inc.
EGGSCHANGE - Egg substitutes - Echo Lake Farm Produce Co., Inc.
EGGSEVERYWAY - Kitchen appliances ☆ - National Presto Industries, Inc.
EGGSPESSIONS - Toys–stuffed - Fun World Inc.
EGGSPRESS - Toys–models ☆ - Estes Industries
EGGSQUISITES - Novelty items - Eggspressions, Inc.
EGGSS PLUS - Food products - Pilgrim's Pride Corp.
EGGSTASY - Eggs - Century Acres Eggs
EGGSTENDABLE - Eggs - Papetti's Hygrade Egg Products, Inc.
EGGSTENDER - Veterinary pharmaceutical preparations - Feed Products & Service Co.
EGGSTRA - Food products - Pet Inc.
EGGSTSTARTS - Egg product - Pureggs Brands, Inc.
EGGSVILLE USA - Toys - Bleyer Industries (Peoria Plastics Div.)
EGGUMS - Candy - Leaf, Inc.
EGGVANTAGE - Eggs - Papetti's Hygrade Egg Products, Inc.
EGGZ - Glass–illuminating - EGGZ
EGGZILLA - Games ☆ - Milton Bradley Co.
EGI - Jewelry - Eurogold, Inc.
EGII AWARENESS - Computer software - Envision Graphics Inc.
EGMOND - Guitars - Multivox/Sorkin Music Co. Inc.
EGNELL - Health care products - Ameda/Egnell Corp.
EGO - Apparel–men's - Ego Underwear Co.
EGO - Apparel–women's - E. Greenwald & Sons Inc.
EGO - Compact discs–prerecorded - Eric John Focht
EGO - Shaving preparations - Triumph Associates
EGO ENVIRO GEAR OUTFITTERS - Apparel and accessories - Sherwood Group, Inc.
EGOISTE - Perfumes - Chanel Inc.
EGOISTE PLATINUM - Toiletries - Chanel Inc.
EGON MULLER - Wines - Seagram's Chateau & Estate Wines Co.
EGON SCHIELE - Oils–essential - Lena Sklenar
EGON VON FURSTENBERG - Apparel and accessories - Neema Clothing, Ltd.
EGON VON FURSTENBERG - Neckties ☆ - Randa Corp.
EGON VON FURSTENBERG - Shirts - Shelburne Shirt Co. Inc.
EGON VON FURSTENBERG - Shoes ☆ - Atsco Footwear Inc.
EGONE - Sporting goods - Egon Egone
E.G.P. - Glass products - Shatterproof Glass Corp.
EGRET - Binoculars - Nikon Inc.
EGRET - Binoculars ☆ - Swift Instruments, Inc.
EGRET - Boats–kayaks - Old Town Canoe Co.
EGRET - Boats–motor - Egret Boat Co., Inc.
EGRET - Brushes - Wright-Bernet
EGRI BIKAVER - Wines - Monsieur Henri Wines Ltd.
EGS - Bicycle parts and accessories - Giant Bicycle, Inc.
EGS - Health care products - Electro-Med Health Industries
EGS - Surgical devices - Endovascular Technologies Inc.
EGW EVOLUTION GUN WORKS - Firearms, accessories, and parts - Evolution Gun Works
EGXTRA - Health care products - Electro-Med Health Industries
EGYPTIAN CAMOMILE - Teas - Grace Tea Co. Ltd.
EGYPTIAN EARTH - Skin care products - Colora Henna
EGYPTIAN EYES - Cosmetics - Bare Essentials
EGYPTIAN HENNA - Hair care products - American International Industries
EGYPTIAN HENNA - Hair coloring preparations - All Clubman
EGYPTIAN OIL - Massage products - Heritage Store Inc.
EGYPTIAN PAPYRUS SERIES - Pottery products - Henriksen Imports Inc.
EGYPTIAN QUEEN - Dolls - Mattel, Inc.
EGYPTIAN TREASURE - Game machines - Ramparts Inc.

EGYPTISCHE I - Cigarettes - G.A. Georgopulo & Co. Inc.
EGYPTO NUBIAN AMERICAN - Apparel and accessories - Kirkland Properties, Inc.
EGYPTSTONES - Tiles–ceramic - American Olean Tile Co.
E.H. ROTH - Musical instruments - International Violin Co. Ltd.
EHB - Lighting equipment - General Electric Co.
EHC - Skin care products ☆ - Stearn's Products Inc.
EHL - Apparel and accessories - Eddie Haggar Ltd., Inc.
EHL NO-WRINKLE - Apparel–women's - Eddie Haggar Limited, Inc.
EHL NO-WRINKLE COTTON - Apparel–women's - Eddie Haggar Ltd., Inc.
EHL SOFT STRETCH - Apparel–women's - Eddie Haggar Ltd., Inc.
EHMANN - Olives–canned - Ehmann Olive Co. Inc.
EHRLE BROS. - Wines - Ehrle Bros. Inc.
EHRLICH MULTIMEDIA - Computer software - Times Mirror Multimedia Corp.
EHRLICH OF GRAND RAPIDS - Furniture–upholstered ☆ - Grand Rapids Leather Furniture Co.
EHRMAN - Yarn - Ehrman Kits, Ltd.
EI-90 - Golfing equipment - Emhart Industries Inc.
EI OXIDIZER - Agricultural machinery - Environmental Instruments Co.
EICHHORN - Frames–picture - Staufen Studio
EICHHORN - Toys - Merry Thoughts Inc.
EICHHORN - Toys - Small World Toys
EICHNER - Electrical equipment - Fellowes Manufacturing Co.
EICKERT - Scissors–hand-operated - Arius-Eickert Co. Inc.
EICO - Musical instruments ☆ - EICO Electronic Instrument Co. Inc.
EICODERM - Cosmetics - Surfactant Technologies, Inc.
EICOTEC - Dietary supplements - Surfactant Technologies, Inc.
EIDEMAX - Computer hardware - Promise Technology
EIDEPRO - Computer hardware - Promise Technology
EIDETIC - Computer software - Blank, Berlyn & Co., Inc.
EIDETICS - Aircraft - Eidetics Corp.
E.I.E.I.O. - Animal feeds - Alan Ritchey Inc.
EIFA - Seafood products–fresh or frozen - Ocean Duke Corp.
EIFERT - Musical instrument accessories - Allegro Woodwind Supply
EIFFEL - Leather–chamois - Schroeder & Tremayne, Inc.
EIFFEL NEW YORK - Apparel and accessories - Eiffel Apparel Manufacturing Co., Inc.
EIFFEL TOWER - Cheese - Chesman Inc.
EIGENTECH - Communications equipment - Neutron Systems, Inc.
EIGHT - Motor vehicles–automobiles ☆ - Bentley Motors Inc.
EIGHT BALL - Air purification systems - Medo Industries, Inc.
EIGHT BALL - Automotive parts and accessories - Ward Products Corp.
EIGHT BALL - Boats - Glen-L Marine Designs
EIGHT BALL DELUXE - Video games - Midway Manufacturing Co.
EIGHT-BALL STOUT - Beverages–malt - Table Bluff Brewing, Inc.
EIGHT-MATE - Electronic equipment ☆ - Buhl Optical Co.
EIGHT O'CLOCK - Beverages - Compass Foods Inc.
EIGHT O'CLOCK - Coffee - Great Atlantic & Pacific Tea Co., Inc.
EIGHT O'CLOCK FRESH CUP - Coffee ☆ - Compass Foods Inc.
EIGHT O'CLOCK ROYALE - Coffee - Compass Foods Inc.
EIGHTBALL RECORDS - Recording label - Shakedown Records, Ltd.
EIGHTEEN GOOD DESIGNS - Wallpaper ☆ - Blumenthal
EIGHTEEN HOUR COMFORT STRETCH - Brassieres (Bras) - Playtex Apparel, Inc.
EIGHTEENTH CENTURY COLLECTION - Furniture reproductions ☆ - Victorian Classics
EIGHTEENTH CENTURY TRADITIONS - Furniture ☆ - Bernhardt Industries
EIGHTEENTH CENTURY TREASURES - Furniture ☆ - Lexington Furniture Industries, Inc.
EIGHTY-TWO - Guns ☆ - Weatherby Inc.
EII - Electronic sockets and connectors - Augat Inc.
EIKI - Projectors–photographic - Eiki International Inc.
EIKIMATIC - Projectors–photographic - Eiki International Inc.
EIKIVISION - Electronic equipment - Eiki International Inc.
EIKO - Lamps - Wiko Ltd.
EIKON - Computer software - Eikon Systems Inc.
EIKON - Watches - Eikon Inc.
EILEEN - Earthenware ☆ - Waterford Wedgewood USA, Inc.
EILEEN - Furniture - Tropitone Furniture Co. Inc.
EILEEN AMSTER - Leather goods - Accessories to the Fact
EILEEN WEST - Bedding–linen - San Francisco Mercantile Co.
EILEEN WEST - Footwear ☆ - S. Goldberg and Co. Inc.
EILEEN #WEST - Novelty items–paper - San Francisco Mercantile Co.
EILEEN WEST - Wallpaper - Old Stone Mill
EILER'S - Cheese ☆ - Dan Carter Inc.
EILISH - Glassware–household - Gorham Inc.

☆ = Now out of production

EILON - Mosaic ware - Israeli Accents

EIMAC - Electron tubes ☆ - ARS Electronics

EINBECKER - Beverages—malt ☆ - Acme Food Specialties Inc.

EINSTEIN - Floor coverings—carpet and rugs - Patcraft Mills Inc.

EINSTEIN'S FAVORITE - Multi-vitamin - Super Nutrition Life Extension Research

EINTECS - Fabrics - Tomen-Ein Inc.

EIP - Construction equipment - European Industrial Products, Inc.

EIS - Automotive parts and accessories - Standard Motor Products, Inc.

EIS - Computer software and hardware - Electronic Information Systems, Inc.

EISBERG - Beverages - Private Cellars Ltd.

EISBOCK - Beverages—malt - Adolph Coors Co.

EISELE - Thermometers - Popper & Sons Inc.

EISEMAN BOYS - Apparel—children's - Florence Eiseman Inc.

EISENBERG - Food products - Eisenberg Co.

EISENBERG ICE - Jewelry—costume - Import Ltd.

EISENHART - Wallpaper ☆ - Eisenhart Wallcoverings Co.

EISENHART BORDER BOOK I - Wallpaper ☆ - Eisenhart Wallcoverings Co.

EISENHART BORDER BOOK II - Wallpaper ☆ - Eisenhart Wallcoverings Co.

EISENHART FOLIO COLLECTION - Wallpaper ☆ - Eisenhart Wallcoverings Co.

EISENHART KIDS - Wallpaper ☆ - Eisenhart Wallcoverings Co.

EISENHART KITCHEN AND BATH - Wallpaper - Eisenhart Wallcoverings Co.

EISENZUCKER - Pharmaceutical preparations ☆ - Wesley Pharmacal Co. Inc.

EISYS - Furniture - Ergonomically Integrated Systems, Inc.

EITECH - Toys ☆ - Reeves International, Inc.

EITHER OR - Skin care products - Waverly Beauty Products

EITRA - Recording label - Jazz Composer's Orchestra Association Inc.

EJ - Shoes - Endicott Johnson Corp.

EJ CHECK - Computer software - DSD Associates, Inc.

E.J. #HARPER - Apparel—women's - Jessica Hale Inc.

EJ PRO - Shoes - Endicott Johnson Corp.

EJA - Fish—fresh or frozen - M.L. de Lange

EJAZ - Recording label - Jazz Composer's Orchestra Association Inc.

EJECTOMATIC - Lead products ☆ - Koh-I-Noor, Inc.

EJECTOR - Cigarette holders ☆ - S.M. Frank & Co. Inc. (Kaywoodie-Yello-Bole-Medico)

(E)JES - Computer software - Phoenix Computer Corp.

(E)JES/2 - Computer software - Phoenix Computer Corp.

EJETHA RECORDING - Recording label - Black Diamond Records, Inc.

EJM - Apparel—women's - H.L. Miller and Son, Inc.

EK - Cameras - Eastman Kodak Co.

EK - Jewelry—precious - Eichhorn & Kocian Jewelers

EK - Lenses—optical - Eye-Kraft Optical, Inc.

EK - Office supplies - Ekonomik Systems

E.K. - Wallets - Enger-Kress Co.

EKAPTURE - Chemical preparations - Novagen, Inc.

EKC - Photographic equipment ☆ - Eastman Kodak Co.

EKCO - Housewares - Ekco Housewares, Inc.

EKDISTEN - Vitamins and nutritional supplements - Atletika Inc.

EKEY - Computer peripheral equipment - Integrated Technologies of America, Inc.

EKI - Building materials - E. Khashoggi Industries

EKI - Electronic equipment - Electronic Kits International, Inc.

EKLP - Thread - Elmore-Pisgah, Inc.

EKM - Publisher's imprints - Hal Leonard Corp.

EKO - Beverages—carbonated - V. & E. Kohnstamm Inc.

EKO - Musical instruments - Lo Duca Bros. Musical Instruments Inc.

EKO - Photographic equipment ☆ - Eastman Kodak Co.

E.K.O. - Recording label - Stark Records & Tape Co.

EKO - Soldering equipment - Pace, Inc.

EKO - Watches - E.K.O. International

EKONO SET - Paint rollers - Corona Brushes Inc.

EKONOMIK - Office supplies - Ekonomik Systems

EK'SELANT - Hair care products - Ausome Inc.

EKSTRA - Floor coverings ☆ - Tarkett, Inc.

EKTA-CLEAR - Waxes—sealing - Ektelon

EKTABOND - Adhesives and sealants - Eastman Kodak Co.

EKTABROME - Paper—photographic - Eastman Kodak Co.

EKTACHROME - Photographic equipment - Eastman Kodak Co.

EKTACHROME 400 HC - Film - Eastman Kodak Co.

EKTACHROME-X - Film - Eastman Kodak Co.

EKTACOLOR - Film - Eastman Kodak Co.

EKTACOLOR GOLD - Film - Eastman Kodak Co.

EKTACOLOR ROYAL - Paper—photographic - Eastman Kodak Co.

EKTAFAX - Photographic equipment - Eastman Kodak Co.

EKTAFLEX - Photographic equipment - Eastman Kodak Co.

EKTAFLO - Photographic equipment - Eastman Kodak Co.

EKTAGRAPHIC - Projectors—photographic - Eastman Kodak Co.

EKTAJET - Photographic equipment - Eastman Kodak Co.

EKTALINE - Photographic equipment - Eastman Kodak Co.

EKTALITE - Photographic equipment - Eastman Kodak Co.

EKTALITH - Duplicating machines - Eastman Kodak Co.

EKTALOG - Computers - Eastman Kodak Co.

EKTALON - Leather goods - Enger-Kress Co.

EKTALURE - Paper—photographic - Eastman Kodak Co.

EKTALUX - Photographic equipment - Eastman Kodak Co.

EKTAMARK - Photographic equipment - Eastman Kodak Co.

EKTAMATE - Photographic equipment - Eastman Kodak Co.

EKTAMATIC - Photographic equipment - Eastman Kodak Co.

EKTAMAX - Film - Eastman Kodak Co.

EKTAMITE - Flashlights - Eastman Kodak Co.

EKTANAR - Photographic equipment - Eastman Kodak Co.

EKTANON - Photographic equipment - Eastman Kodak Co.

EKTAPAN - Film - Eastman Kodak Co.

EKTAPRESS GOLD - Film - Eastman Kodak Co.

EKTAPRINT - Duplicating machines - Eastman Kodak Co.

EKTAR - Photographic equipment - Eastman Kodak Co.

EKTASCAN - Photographic equipment - Eastman Kodak Co.

EKTASOUND - Photographic equipment - Eastman Kodak Co.

EKTATHERM - Photographic equipment - Eastman Kodak Co.

EKTATRANS - Photographic equipment - Eastman Kodak Co.

EKTAVISION - Television equipment - Eastman Kodak Co.

EKTAVOLT - Photographic equipment - Eastman Kodak Co.

EKTAWRITE - Film - Eastman Kodak Co.

EKTELON - Balls—tennis - Prince Sports Group, Inc.

EKTELON - Sporting goods - Ektelon

EKTON - Photographic equipment - Eastman Kodak Co.

EKTONOL - Photographic equipment - Eastman Kodak Co.

EKTRA - Cameras - Eastman Kodak Co.

EKTRA - Pharmaceutical preparations - Colgate Healthcare Laboratories

EKTRA FAMILY MEDICINE - Pharmaceutical preparations - Colgate Healthcare Laboratories

EKTRALITE - Cameras - Eastman Kodak Co.

EKTRAMAX - Cameras - Eastman Kodak Co.

EKTRON - Automotive parts and accessories - Standard Motor Products, Inc.

EKTRON - Photographic equipment - Eastman Kodak Co.

EKU - Beverages—malt - Joseph Gies Import

EKW* MANAGER - Computer software - Edwin K. Williams & Co.

E.L. - Beverages—alcohol - Mccormick Distilling Co., Inc.

EL - Brake parts ☆ - Raybestos/Brake Parts Inc.

EL - Cash boxes - Indiana Cash Drawer Co.

EL - Cosmetics - Estee Lauder Inc.

EL - Golfing equipment - Hurricane Sports, Inc.

EL - Jewelry - Elizabeth Locke

EL - Lighting fixtures - American Auto Accessories, Inc.

EL - Publisher's imprints - Alfred A. Knopf Inc.

EL-60 - Valves—industrial - Knorr Brake Holding Corp.

EL ACAPULCO - Food products - El Acapulco Tamales

EL AGUILA - Tortillas - El Aguila Food Products, Inc.

EL AL - Panty hose - Lincolnwood Merchandising Co. Inc.

EL ARISTO - Drapery hardware ☆ - Spring Window Fashions Division, Inc.

EL ASTURIANO - Meat products - Meats of Spain, Inc.

EL AUTOBUS MAGICO - Publisher's imprints - Scholastic Inc.

EL BARA - Clothing - El Bara Designs, Inc.

EL BATURRO - Sausages - Corte & Co.

EL BRONCO - Chewing gum - Philadelphia Chewing Gum Corp.

EL BUBBLE - Chewing gum - Philadelphia Chewing Gum Corp.

EL BURRITO - Food products - Dairy Fresh Products Co.

EL BURRITO - Food products - El Burrito Mexican Food Products

EL CALDERO - Seasonings - Pet Inc.

EL CAMINO - Fireplaces - Dyna Corp.

EL CAMINO - Floor coverings - Congoleum Corp.

EL CAMINO - Floor coverings—carpet and rugs ☆ - Royalweve Carpet Mills

EL CAMINO - Housewares - Elon Inc.

EL CAMINO - Motor vehicles ☆ - General Motors Corp. (Chevrolet Motor Div.)

EL CAMINO - Office supplies - Faber-Castell Corp.

EL CAMINO - Sporting goods - K-2 Corp.

EL CAMINO - Trailers—travel - Compact Equipment Co.

EL CAMPEON - Sausages - Sparrer Sausage Co., Inc.

EL CANARIO - Food products ☆ - American Naturavit Inc.

EL CAPITAN - Guitars - Gibson Guitar Corp.

EL CARIBE - Rum - Paramount Distillers Inc.

EL CAUTO - Cigars - Mike's Cigars Distributors Inc.

EL CENTENARIO - Harmonicas - Hohner Inc.

EL CERDITO - Sausages - Arnold's Meat Food Products Inc.

EL CESAR - Beverages–alcohol - Leonard Kreusch Inc.

EL CHARRITO - Food products - Alex Foods, Inc.

EL CHARRITO - Food products - Eagle Crest Foods Inc.

EL CHARRO - Beverages–carbonated - Vernor Food Products Inc.

EL CHARRO - Tortillas - Mission Foods Corp.

EL CHARRO SILVER - Liquors - House of Seagram

EL CHE - Shirts - United World Jeans Co., Inc.

EL CHEAPO - Garbage bags - North American Plastics & Chemical Co.

EL CHEAPO - Giftware ☆ - Bernard W. Bernthal Inc.

EL-CHEM - Water purification systems - Juhani Ilves

EL CHUPACABRAS - Fruits and vegetables - Khavogh, Inc.

EL COCINERO - Oils–edible - Goya Foods, Inc.

EL CONDOR - Beverages–alcohol - Montebello Brands, Inc.

EL COQUI - Food products - Mexi-Frost Specialties Co.

EL CORTEZ - Shrimp–fresh or frozen - Deep Sea Shrimp Importing Co. Inc.

EL-DA-MINT - Pharmaceutical preparations ☆ - ICN Pharmaceuticals Inc.

EL DIABLO - Cigars - Heaven Group, LLC

EL DORADO - Boots - Texas Boot Co.

EL DORADO - Boots - United States Shoe Corp.

EL DORADO - Cabinets - Superior Woodwork Inc.

EL DORADO - Coffee - El Dorado Coffee

EL DORADO - Food products - Borden Brands Foodservice Co.

EL DORADO - Motor vehicles–motor homes - Honorbuilt Industries Inc.

EL DORADO - Scissors–hand-operated - Windmere Corp.

EL DORADO - Shrimp–fresh or frozen - New England Shrimp Co. Inc.

EL DORADO - Strollers–baby ☆ - Welsh Co.

EL DORADO GOLD - Beverages–malt - El Dorado Brewing Co.

EL DORADO VALLEY BREW - Beverages–malt - Creighton Younnel

EL-DUR SPRAY-ON MAINTAINER - Cleaning preparations - Uncle Sam Chemical Co., Inc.

EL EBRO - Food products - Ebro Foods Inc.

EL FIORE - Wines - Southwest Distributing Inc.

EL FLACO - Recording label - El Flaco Enterprises

EL FLEESO - Fabrics - Dan River Inc.

E.L. FUDGE - Cookies - Keebler Co.

EL GALL O - Knives–carving - Knife Importers Inc.

EL GARTERO SIDRA - Beverages–malt - V & P Import

EL GATO - Bicycles ☆ - Muskin Leisure Products Inc.

EL GATO BANDOLERO - Toys–stuffed - Rane Toy Co. Inc.

EL GLORIOSO DOMINICANO - Cigars - Rex Pipe Shop Inc.

EL GOLINDO MEXICAN - Food processors - SWB Co. Inc.

EL GORDO BURRITO - Food products - M.C.I. Foods Inc.

EL GRANADA - Motor vehicle parts and accessories - Van Conversion Inc.

EL GRANDE - Flour–blended ☆ - Safeway Stores Inc.

EL GRANDE - Food products - Gold Medal Products Co.

EL GRANDE - Glassware–household - Benner Glassware Inc.

EL GRANDE - Hardware - National Lock Hardware

EL GRANDE - Musical instruments ☆ - Grossman Music Corp.

EL GRANGERO - Cigars - Wein-Bauer, Inc.

EL GRECO - Artists' materials ☆ - Binney & Smith Inc.

EL GRECO - Floor coverings ☆ - Congoleum Corp.

EL GUAPO - Spices and extracts - Richard Adlai Corp.

EL HORNO - Tortillas - Santa Fe Tortilla Co.

EL JEFE - Seeds–salted, roasted, cooked, or canned ☆ - Moscow Idaho Seed Co.

EL KANATER - Food products ☆ - Mira International Foods Inc.

EL-KAY - Paints ☆ - Valspar Corp.

EL KHAYAL - Food products ☆ - Mira International Foods Inc.

EL KIDDO - Candy ☆ - Leaf, Inc.

EL MACCO - Cigars - National Cigar Corp.

EL MAGNIFICO - Floor coverings–carpet and rugs ☆ - Royalweve Carpet Mills

EL MAMBO - Coffee ☆ - Casino North America

EL MANZANAR - Juices - Hudson Valley Apple Products Co. Inc.

EL MAR - Fish–canned or cured - Purcell International

EL MARINO - Coffee - Daymar Corp.

EL MARKO - Markers–felt-tip - Gillette Co.

EL MASRI - Food products - Tut's International Export and Import Co.

EL MASURO - Paints ☆ - Masury Paint Co.

EL MATADOR - Pharmaceutical preparations - Yago Enterprises Ltd.

EL MERCADO - Tortillas - C & C Bakery, Inc.

EL MINO - Sausages - S. Abuin Packing Inc.

EL MOLINO - Food products - El Molino Foods Inc.

EL MOLINO - Food products - El Molino Mills

EL MONTE - Food products - El Monte Rabbit Co.

EL MONTEREY - Frozen foods - Ruiz Food Products Inc.

EL MONTEREY - Meat products–beef - Bob Ostrow Co.

EL-NIKKOR - Photographic enlarging lenses - Nikon Inc.

EL NINO - Wines - St. Julian Wine Co.

EL NINO CLASSIC WEAR - Apparel and accessories - El Nino Classic Wear

EL NOPAL - Food products - La Manzanillera Food Processing, Inc.

EL NOPAL BAKERY EL PAN DE SU HOGAR - Bakery products - El Nopal Bakery, Inc.

EL NORUEGO - Fish–canned or cured - Dolphin Fisheries, Inc.

EL PALOMAR - Dishes–earthenware - N.S. Gustin Co.

EL PANADERO - Crackers - Sunshine Biscuits, Inc.

EL PARAISO - Cigars - Northstar Imports Inc.

EL PASO - Beverages - El Paso Chili Co.

EL PASO - Boots ☆ - Georgia Boot Inc.

EL PASO - Building materials–concrete - Jobe Concrete Products Inc.

EL PASO - Candy ☆ - Crystal Pure Candy Co.

EL PASO - Floor coverings ☆ - Tarkett, Inc.

EL PASO - Seat covers - Saddleman, Inc.

EL PASO - Wines - El Paso Winery

EL PASO CHILE CO., THE - Seasonings - El Paso Chili Co.

EL PASO ONYX - Games - Music City Marketing, Inc.

EL PATIO - Serving carts ☆ - National Housewares

EL PATO - Food products - Walker Foods Inc.

EL PEQUENO PANADERO - Bakery products ☆ - Campagna-Turano Bakery Inc.

EL PICE - Paint removers - Klean-Strip

EL PICO - Cleaning preparations - Klean-Strip

EL PIONERO - Beverages–carbonated - Florida Brewing Co.

EL PODER MENTAL - Recording label - Almanauta, Inc.

EL POLLO LOCO - Restaurants–fast food - El Pollo Loco

EL PORTAL - Fruits and vegetables - Suma Fruit International (USA) Inc.

EL PRESIDENTE - Food products ☆ - Darik Enterprises Inc.

EL PRO - Cigar boxes–wood - Consolidated Cigar Corp.

EL PRODUCTO - Cigar boxes–wood - Consolidated Cigar Corp.

EL RANCHO - Fencing–wood - Machalk Enterprises Inc.

EL RANCHO - Floor coverings–carpet and rugs - Newport Carpet Mills Inc.

EL RANCHO - Fruits–dried - Garry Packing Inc.

EL RANCHO - Paints - Devoe Paint Co.

EL REAL - Tortillas - Morrison Milling Co.

EL-REES-SO - Cigars - T.E. Brooks & Co.

EL REGAL - Hardware - National Lock Hardware

EL REY - Food products - Tony Ingoglia Salami and Cheese Co. Inc.

EL-REY - Paints - Impervious Paint Industries Ltd.

EL REY DE FLOREZ - Cigars - Flor De Florez Distribution, Inc.

EL REYECITO - Dairy products - Swissrose International Inc.

EL RICO - Floor coverings - Mannington Resilient Floors

EL RIO - Food products - World Finer Foods, Inc.

EL RIO GRANDE - Food products - World Finer Foods, Inc.

EL ROSA Y EL AZUL - Broadcasting stations–television - Gems International Television

EL SABINAR CIGARS - Cigars - Compania De Tobacos De Las Antillas, SA

EL SABROSO - Bacon - Snak King Corp.

EL SABROSO - Snack foods - El Sabroso

EL SANTIAGUERO - Cheese - JS Cheeses, Inc.

EL SEGUNDO - Floor coverings ☆ - Tarkett, Inc.

EL SUBLIMADO - Tobacco–chewing or smoking - Jean Claude Marty

EL TACO - Chili sauce ☆ - Golden Specialty Foods Inc.

EL TACO - Trays ☆ - Ullman Co. Inc.

EL TANNIN - Floor coverings ☆ - Congoleum Corp.

EL TESORO - Food products - El Tesoro Foods Inc.

EL TESORO DE DON FELIPE - Beverages–alcohol - Jim Beam Brands Co.

EL TESORO DE DON FELIPE - Tequila - Tequila Tepatio, SA

EL TIGRE - Pins–jewelry - Arctco, Inc.

EL TIGRE - Sporting goods - Cut 'n Jump Ski Corp.

EL TOLNA - Cigars - A.J. Golden Inc.

EL TOLUQUENO - Cheese - Francisco Vega

EL TOPE - Food products - Tommy's Foods Inc.

EL TORENO - Apparel–men's - Alps Sportswear Manufacturing Co.

EL TORO - Boats–dinghies - Moore Boats

EL TORO - Dried beans - KBL Trading and Processing Co.

EL TORO - Food products - Amigos Canning Co. Inc.

EL TORO - Food products - Reser's Fine Foods Inc.

EL TORO - Liquors - Canandaigua Wine Co. Inc.

EL TORO - Rice - Southwest Rice Mill Co. Inc.
EL TORO - Seasonings - McCormick & Co., Inc.
EL TORO - Seasonings - Mojave Foods Corp.
EL TORO - Ships–sailing vessels - El Toro International Yacht Racing Association
EL TORO - Teas - Service Foods Inc.
EL TORO BRAVO - Apparel and accessories - M. Rubin & Sons Inc.
EL TRIUNFO - Cigars - Te-Amo
EL-TRON - Lamps - Philips Lighting Co.
EL VAZCO - Meat products–beef - High Top Products Corp.
EL VEGETAMAL - Snack foods - Eden Guerra
EL VERSO - Cigars - National Cigar Corp.
EL VIDEO DEL AMOR - Recording label - Arturo Rodriguez
EL VIEJITO - Beverages–alcohol - Robert E. Lloyd
EL VISTA - Food products - El Vista Orchards Inc.
EL Z - Water-bed risers - Bil-Built Manufacturing Co.
ELA - Canes - ELA Systems, Inc.
ELA - Medical apparatus - Xmr, Inc.
ELA VITES - Vitamins and nutritional supplements - Natural Organics, Inc.
ELAAN - Neckties - Mallory and Church Corp.
ELAH TOFFAIRS - Candy ☆ - R.L. Albert & Son, Inc.
ELAINE GOLD - Scarves - Collection XIIX Ltd.
ELAINE POWERS - Exercising equipment - Living Well Lady
ELAM - Apparel–men's - Genexus Marketing Inc.
ELAMINATOR - Metals - Energy Blanket of Texas Inc.
ELAM'S - Bakery products - Elam's
ELAN - Boxes–corrugated paperboard ☆ - Mason Box Co. Inc.
ELAN - Cabinets - Grandview Products Co.
ELAN - Cabinets - Quality Cabinets
ELAN - Computer software - Elan Associates (GreenLight Software Division)
ELAN - Dinnerware–plastic - Plastics Manufacturing Co.
ELAN - Floor coverings–carpet and rugs - Collins & Aikman Corp.
ELAN - Floor coverings–carpet and rugs - Customweave Carpets Inc.
E'LAN - Floor coverings–carpet and rugs ☆ - Regal Rugs Inc.
ELAN - Food products - Elan Foods Inc.
ELAN - Furniture - Henredon Furniture Industries Inc.
ELAN - Guitars - Alembic Inc.
ELAN - Hair care products - Wella Corp. (Consumer Products Div.)
ELAN - Handbags - Pantera International Corp.
ELAN - Hardware ☆ - Amerock Corp.
ELAN - Mat boards - Onyx Mat Board
ELAN - Pens - Gillette Co.
ELAN - Perfume, dusting powder, etc ☆ - Coty Inc.
ELAN - Printers–computer - Domino Amjet Inc.
ELAN - Publisher's imprints - Cynthia D. Elam
ELAN - Salad dressings–bottled - Korbro Oil Corp.
ELAN - Shoes - Elano Shoe Co.
ELAN - Skis - Elan-Monark
E'LAN - Stoves–wood-burning ☆ - Travis Industries
ELAN - Sunglasses - Nassau Lens Co. Inc.
ELAN - Telephones - Square D Co.
ELAN - Telescopes - Northern Telecom, Inc.
ELAN - Water treating compounds - Watercare Corp.
ELAN BY BARCO - Medical uniforms - Barco of California
E'LAN CLASSICS - Guitars ☆ - Shane Music Products
ELAN II - Fabrics–tapestry ☆ - Coloroll Inc.
ELAN PITCHER - Kitchen appliances - Carlisle Foodservice Products, Inc.
ELAN VITAL - Vitamins and nutritional supplements - Source Naturals
ELANA CHOCOLATES - Chocolate candy - Sherwood Brands, Inc.
ELANCE - Pens - Staedtler, Inc.
ELANCE - Underwear and nightwear - Jockey International, Inc.
ELANCYL - Skin care products ☆ - Spilo/Mehaz Worldwide
ELANDAN - Motor vehicles–motor homes - Winnebago Industries, Inc.
ELANIX - Computer software - Elanix Inc.
ELANO - Shoes - Elano Shoe Co.
ELANTE - Boats–motor - Holiday Mansion
ELANTE' - Motor vehicles–motor homes - Winnebago Industries, Inc.
ELANTRA - Motor vehicles–automobiles - Hyundai Motor America
ELAQUA - Skin care products ☆ - ICN Pharmaceuticals Inc.
ELARA - Fabrics - Superior Shade & Blind Co. Inc.
ELARA - Perfumes - Elara Inc.
ELARCO - Dinnerware–glass - Reusche & Co.
ELARCO - Tableware–earthenware - Maurice Ceramics of California
ELAST O LACE - Laces–boot and shoe - Ilsan Associates
ELAST-O-MERIC - Waterproofing compounds - Coronado Paint Co.
ELAST-O-PATCH - Adhesives and sealants - Sinclair Paint Co.

ELASTA CARE - Hair care products - Kenra Laboratories, Inc.
ELASTA-CORD - Apparel trimmings - Minnetonka Mills Inc.
ELASTA FIL - Coatings - American Paints
ELASTAGRAPH - Gaskets - Acadia Elastomers Corp.
ELASTEC DRUM SKIMMER - Oil machinery - Elastec Inc.
ELASTECH - Paints - Columbia Paint and Coatings, Inc.
ELASTEEL - Golfing equipment - Golfsmith International Inc.
ELASTESSE - Hair care products - Richardson-Vicks USA
ELASTEX - Cement - F.H. Leinweber Co. Inc.
ELASTI-GARD - Roof cements and coatings - Pioneer Manufacturing Co.
ELASTI NEW - Paint - Connor Aga Sports Flooring Corp.
ELASTI PLUS - Flooring - Connor Aga Sports Flooring Corp.
ELASTI-POXI - Epoxy coatings - Rock-Tred Corp.
ELASTIC STOP NUT - Nuts and bolts - MacLean-Fogg Co.
ELASTIC STOP NUTS - Nuts and bolts ☆ - MacLean-ESNA
ELASTIC SUPER - Drill bits ☆ - Hawera Inc.
ELASTICAP - Adhesives and sealants - Missouri Paint & Varnish Co.
ELASTICITY-A-DERM - Skin care products - University Medical Products/USA, Inc.
ELASTICLAD - Adhesives and sealants - Missouri Paint & Varnish Co.
ELASTICORD - Ironing board pads - Seymour Housewares Corp.
ELASTIKON - Tape–adhesive - Johnson & Johnson
ELASTIKRAFT - Paper–crepe - Cindus Corp.
ELASTIMENT - Adhesives and sealants - Boiardi Products Corp.
ELASTIN MASSAGE LOTION - Skin care products - Fanie International
ELASTIQUE - Skin-care products - Cabot Laboratories Inc.
ELASTISIZER - Drafting supplies ☆ - Lutz Superdyne Inc.
ELASTO - Mops - Zephyr Manufacturing Co.
ELASTO CREME - Skin care products - Ella Bache Inc.
ELASTO CROSS - Sporting goods - Babolat
ELASTO-FLEX - Paints - Jones Blair Co.
ELASTO-GEL - Health care products - Southwest Technologies Inc.
ELASTO-GEL - Splints - Smith & Nephew Inc. (Rehabilitation Div.)
ELASTO-PREENE - Orthopedic products - Tru-Fit Marketing Corp.
ELASTO SACRO - Medical apparatus - Nelkin/Piper Health Products
ELASTO-SEAL - Caulking compounds ☆ - Farwest Paint Manufacturing Co. Inc.
ELASTO-SHIELD - Waxes–sealing - Tnemec Co. Inc.
ELASTOCOL - Adhesives and sealants - Gerbert Ltd.
ELASTODECK 350 - Paints - Edison Coatings, Inc.
ELASTOFORM - Roofing materials–clay - Carlisle Corp.
ELASTOGEL - Skin care products ☆ - Ella Bache Inc.
ELASTOID - Rubber–synthetic - Dampney Co., Inc.
ELASTOLACE - Lace - Liberty Fabrics, Inc.
ELASTOLOGY - Skin care products - Clientele, Inc.
ELASTOMASTIC - Adhesives and sealants - Henry Co.
ELASTOMASTIC 352 - Paints - Edison Coatings, Inc.
ELASTOMER PRODUCTS EP - Rubber goods - Elastomer Products, Inc.
ELASTOMERIC - Paints - Mobile Paint Manufacturing Co.
ELASTOMERIC ONE - Adhesives and sealants - Gibson-Homans Co. (Sealant Technology)
ELASTOMUFFLE - Mufflers–motor vehicle - Apex Equipment Inc.
ELASTOMULL - Bandages - Beiersdorf Inc.
ELASTONET - Fabrics - Liberty Fabrics, Inc.
ELASTOPLAST - Bandages - Beiersdorf Inc.
ELASTOPLAST T.P.N. - Bandages - Beiersdorf Inc.
ELASTOTAPE - Tape–adhesive - W.W. Henry Co.
ELASTOWALL 357 - Paints - Edison Coatings, Inc.
ELASTOX - Filters–industrial - Baker Hughes Inc.
ELATION - Colognes - Lever Brothers Co. Inc.
ELATION - Floor coverings–carpet and rugs ☆ - Karastan-Bigelow Inc.
ELATION - Lighting equipment - Elation Lighting, Inc.
ELAVIL - Pharmaceutical preparations - Zeneca Inc.
ELAYNA JONS - Jewelry ☆ - Latham Studios
ELBA - Carpets - Couristan Inc.
ELBA - Dishes–china - Pasmantier Co. Inc.
ELBE ACCRA - Cocoa–powders or mixes ☆ - K.H. McClure & Co. Inc.
ELBECO - Apparel–men's - Elbeco Inc.
ELBERT MALLORY SAUSAGE CO., THE - Sausages - Elbert Mallory
ELBO - Straws–drinking - Clear Shield National Inc.
ELBO-ARM GUARD - Sporting goods - Trace Athletic Corp.
ELBO-GUARD - Sporting goods - Trace Athletic Corp.
ELBO-RONI - Pasta - American Beauty Macaroni
ELBON - Watches - Nicolet International Inc.
ELBOW CAP - Sporting goods - Unique Sports Products Inc.
ELBOW EASE - Sporting goods - Fem Gard Inc.

☆ = Now out of production

ELBOW GREASE - Lubricants ☆ - Klean-Strip
ELBOW GREASE - Polishes - Master Products Inc.
ELBOW-TECTOR - Exercising equipment - DBA Products Co.
ELBOW VELVET - Skin care products - Cameo Inc.
ELBOWRANGER - Braces–orthopedic - Professional Care Products Inc.
ELBOWSPORT - Health care products - Camp, Inc.
ELC - Switches–electric - Easter-Owens Electric Co.
ELCAR - Motor vehicles–automobiles ☆ - Elkhart Carriage & Motor Car Co.
ELCATTO - Pet products - R.A.F. Trading Inc.
ELCHIM 2001 - Skin care products - Elchim USA Inc.
ELCI FASHIONS INC. - Apparel–women's - Elci Fashions Inc.
ELCID - Computer software - Multi-Link, Inc.
ELCO - Cleaning preparations - Elco Laboratories Inc.
ELCO - Office supplies - Elco Manufacturing Co. Inc.
ELCO - Office supplies - Elgin School Supply Co. Inc.
ELCO LIGHTING - Lighting fixtures - AMP Plus, Inc.
ELCOM - Computer software - Elcom International
ELCONA - Food products ☆ - Plumrose Inc.
ELCOR - Paper ☆ - Plainwell Tissue
ELCROSS - Orthopedic corset - Camp, Inc.
ELCYS - Computers - Brother International Corp.
ELD - Flutes - Emerson Musical Instruments Inc.
ELDADRYL - Pharmaceutical preparations ☆ - ICN Pharmaceuticals Inc.
ELDAJON - Palettes ☆ - Winsor & Newton
ELDATAPP - Pharmaceutical preparations ☆ - ICN Pharmaceuticals Inc.
ELDEC - Pharmaceutical preparations ☆ - Parke-Davis
ELDECORT - Pharmaceutical preparations - ICN Pharmaceuticals Inc.
ELDEFED - Pharmaceutical preparations ☆ - ICN Pharmaceuticals Inc.
ELDEMOL - Pharmaceutical preparations ☆ - ICN Pharmaceuticals Inc.
ELDER & JENKS - Paint rollers - Muralo Co. Inc.
ELDER BLOSSOM - Wines ☆ - Yamhill Valley Vineyards
ELDER COMPOUND 65 - Pharmaceutical preparations ☆ - ICN Pharmaceuticals Inc.
ELDER SCROLLS, THE - Computer software - Media Technology Ltd.
ELDER SECRETS - Games - Avalon Hill Game Co.
ELDERADO - Apparel and accessories - Elder Manufacturing Co., Inc.
ELDERBERRIES - Greeting cards - Hourglass Editions
ELDERBERRY-POWER - Vitamins and nutritional supplements - Natur-Pharma, Inc.
ELDERBERRYC - Vitamins and nutritional supplements - McZand Herbal, Inc.
ELDERBLOSSOM - Skin care products - Blackmores
ELDERBRIEF - Apparel and accessories - Warren Fisher
ELDERCAPS - Pharmaceutical preparations - Merz Inc.
ELDERTONIC - Pharmaceutical preparations - Merz Inc.
ELDEZOL - Pharmaceutical preparations ☆ - ICN Pharmaceuticals Inc.
ELDIABLO - Boats–motor ☆ - Eldocraft
ELDITAS - Women's shoes - Italian Leather Co. Inc.
ELDO - Mats - Eldo Inc.
ELDOCRAFT - Boats–motor - Eldocraft
ELDODRAM - Pharmaceutical preparations ☆ - ICN Pharmaceuticals Inc.
ELDON - Bedding–linen - Dan River Inc.
ELDON - Desk sets - Newell Office Products
ELDON - Jewelry–costume - Howard Eldon Ltd.
ELDON - Office supplies - Rubbermaid Office Products Inc.
ELDONWAL SYSTEM - Office supplies - Rubbermaid Office Products Inc.
ELDOPAQUE - Skin care products - ICN Pharmaceuticals Inc.
ELDOPAQUE-FORTE - Pharmaceutical preparations - ICN Pharmaceuticals Inc.
ELDOQUIN - Skin care products - ICN Pharmaceuticals Inc.
ELDOQUIN-FORTE - Pharmaceutical preparations - ICN Pharmaceuticals Inc.
ELDOR - Toys - Mattel, Inc.
ELDORADO - Area rugs - Couristan Inc.
ELDORADO - Bathroom accessories ☆ - Franklin Brass Manufacturing Co.
ELDORADO - Beverages - Eldorado Artesian Springs Inc.
ELDORADO - Boats–motor ☆ - Eldocraft
ELDORADO - Cigars - Gesty Trading & Manufacturing Corp.
ELDORADO - Fabrics - Superior Shade & Blind Co. Inc.
ELDORADO - Floor coverings ☆ - Congoleum Corp.
ELDORADO - Floor coverings–carpet and rugs ☆ - Blue Ridge Carpet Mills
ELDORADO - Glassware–household - Federal Glass
ELDORADO - Motor vehicle parts and accessories - Seats Inc.
ELDORADO - Motor vehicles–automobiles - General Motors Corp. (Cadillac Motor Car Div.)
ELDORADO - Motor vehicles–motor homes - Eldorado Motor Corp.
ELDORADO - Musical instruments ☆ - Grossman Music Corp.
ELDORADO - Pencils ☆ - Dixon Ticonderoga Co.

ELDORADO - Pipes–tobacco - Dr. Grabow Pre-Smoked Pipes Inc.
ELDORADO - Shrimp–canned or cured ☆ - Arista Industries Inc.
ELDORADO - Tools–power-driven - PCC Specialty Products, Inc.
ELDORADO BIARRITZ - Motor vehicles–automobiles - General Motors Corp. (Cadillac Motor Car Div.)
ELDORADO CONTINENTAL - Pipes–tobacco ☆ - Dr. Grabow Pre-Smoked Pipes Inc.
ELDORADO FUTURA - Pipes–tobacco ☆ - Dr. Grabow Pre-Smoked Pipes Inc.
ELDORADO VIP - Motor vehicle parts and accessories - Seats Inc.
ELDOSPORT - Boats–motor ☆ - Eldocraft
ELDRIDGE GRADE - Bicycles - Marin Mountain Bikes, Inc.
ELE HANG - Hardware - Martin Paint Stores
ELE-VERT - Hoists - Ace Boat Hoist
ELEANOR - Glassware–household - ACC
ELEANOR ROOSEVELT - Dolls ☆ - Effanbee Doll Corp.
ELEC-TRA-MATE - Sporting goods - Electric Fishing Reel Systems Inc.
ELEC TRAK - Tractors–lawn - Wheel Horse Toro Inc.
ELECAL - Pharmaceutical preparations - Western Research Laboratories
ELECOMPACK - Shelving units–plastic - Automated Storage & Retrieval Systems of America, Inc.
ELECON - Metals - Mi-Tech Metals, Inc.
ELECT AIRE - Air conditioning equipment - Nordyne Inc.
ELECTA - Office furniture–metal ☆ - Stow/Davis Furniture Co.
ELECTA-POINT - Pens - Gillette Co.
ELECTA RIDE - Electronic equipment - Palmer Industries
ELECTHAL - Dishes–china - Imperial Crystal and China Inc.
ELECTION - Pencils ☆ - Dixon Ticonderoga Co.
ELECTION CENTRAL - Computer software - James Brodsky
ELECTIVE ELEMENTS-1 - Office furniture–metal - Stow/Davis Furniture Co.
ELECTONE - Hearing aids - Electone Inc.
ELECTOR - Floor coverings–carpet and rugs ☆ - Blue Ridge Carpet Mills
ELECTORAL COLLEGE - Computer software ☆ - Krell Software Corp.
ELECTR-A-SCENT - Deodorizers - Neptune Plastics & Manufacturing Corp.
ELECTRA - Bicycles - Ross Bicycles USA, Ltd.
ELECTRA - Blinds–vertical - C-Mor Co.
ELECTRA - Darts and dart games - Dart Mart Inc.
ELECTRA - Floor coverings - American Floor Products Co. Inc.
ELECTRA - Floor coverings–carpet and rugs ☆ - Hollytex Carpet Mills Inc.
ELECTRA - Furniture–upholstered ☆ - Patrician Furniture Co.
ELECTRA - Guitars - European Crafts/USA
ELECTRA - Harnesses - Weaver Leather Goods, Inc.
ELECTRA - Ice - Strike Master Inc.
ELECTRA - Lighters - Scripto-Tokai Corp.
ELECTRA - Medical apparatus - Avionix Medical Devices
ELECTRA - Musical instrument accessories ☆ - St. Louis Music Supply Co.
ELECTRA - Musical instrument accessories ☆ - SLM Marketplace
ELECTRA - Paint rollers - Corona Brushes Inc.
ELECTRA - Paper–carbon - Phillips Ribbon & Carbon Co.
ELECTRA - Pens ☆ - Faber-Castell Corp.
ELECTRA - Rings–jewelry - Artcarved Inc.
ELECTRA - Skis - Wellington Leisure Products, Inc.
ELECTRA - Toys–airplanes - Comet Montrose Ltd.
ELECTRA - Trailers–travel ☆ - Hop-Cap Inc.
ELECTRA - Underwear and nightwear ☆ - Elegante Foundations Inc.
ELECTRA - Wines - Quady Winery
ELECTRA - Yarn - William Unger & Co. Inc.
ELECTRA 225 - Motor vehicles–automobiles ☆ - General Motors Corp. (Buick Motor Div.)
ELECTRA BICYCLE CO. - Bicycles - Benno Baenziger
ELECTRA CARE - Electronic equipment ☆ - Madison Equipment Co.
ELECTRA CURL - Curling irons–electric ☆ - Standard Products Corp.
ELECTRA ESTATE WAGON - Motor vehicles–automobiles - General Motors Corp. (Buick Motor Div.)
ELECTRA GLIDE ROAD KING - Motorcycles - Harley-Davidson, Inc.
ELECTRA GLOW - Watches - Ruby International, Inc.
ELECTRA-LIFT - Antennas - Winegard Co.
ELECTRA LIMITED - Motor vehicles–automobiles - General Motors Corp. (Buick Motor Div.)
ELECTRA MAGIC - Health care products - Thetford Corp.
ELECTRA PARK AVENUE - Motor vehicles–automobiles - General Motors Corp. (Buick Motor Div.)
ELECTRA-PERK - Coffee - Maxwell House
ELECTRA-PLOT - Drafting materials - Dietzgen Corp.
ELECTRA-POWER SENTRY - Electrical equipment - Cable Electric Products
ELECTRAC - Drapery hardware - Kirsch Co.

☆ = Now out of production

ELECTRACAT - Pest-control device - Electracat Inc.

ELECTRACRAFT - Electric lighting equipment - Waxman Industries Inc.

ELECTRALURE - Fishing lures - Maxx Technologies Inc.

ELECTRAMAC - Saws–chain - McCulloch Corp.

ELECTRAMAIL - Telephone answering machines ☆ - NEC America, Inc.

ELECTRAMATES - Cleaning preparations - Aervoe-Pacific Co. Inc.

ELECTRAMATIC - Pianos ☆ - Kimball International, Inc.

ELECTRAMOUNT - Video equipment - Draper Shade and Screen Co. Inc.

ELECTRAY - Hardware - Mphusky Corp.

ELECTRETTE - Hearing aids - Qualitone

ELECTRI-CARS - Golfing equipment - Tommy Armour Golf Co.

ELECTRI CD - Computer software - Millennium Media Group, Inc.

ELECTRI-FONE - Headsets - L & M Auto Supply

ELECTRI-THERM CONTROL - Hair-care products - Tri-Institute of Trichology

ELECTRIC - Ladders–metal - Carolina Ladder Co. Inc.

ELECTRIC - Recording label - Peak Records, Inc.

ELECTRIC ART - Electrical equipment ☆ - Majestic Gifts

ELECTRIC BEACH - Apparel and accessories - Jantzen Inc.

ELECTRIC BLUE - Cosmetics - Flori Roberts Inc.

ELECTRIC BLUE - Nail care products - Pavion Ltd.

ELECTRIC BRAIN SUPPLEMENT - Vitamins and nutritional supplements ☆ - Oakmont Investments Co.

ELECTRIC BREAD - Innovative Cooking Enterprises

ELECTRIC BREAD - Spices and extracts - Innovative Cooking Enterprises * I.C.E., Inc.

ELECTRIC CAFE - Barbecues and grills - Sunbeam Outdoor Products Inc.

ELECTRIC COMPANY, THE - Computer software - Children's Television Workshop

ELECTRIC CONNECTION - Games - Addison-Wesley Publishing Co.

ELECTRIC DYNAMO - Apparel and accessories - Synchronal Corp.

ELECTRIC FACTORY - Greeting cards - Gibson Greetings, Inc.

ELECTRIC FIZZ - Bedding–linen - Dan River Inc.

ELECTRIC IGLOO, THE - Ice chests–plastic - Igloo Products Corp.

ELECTRIC KNIT CO. - Knitting machines - Fortune Knits Inc.

ELECTRIC KRAYON - Cosmetics - Burmax Co. Inc.

ELECTRIC LIGHT - Skin care products - Schering-Plough Healthcare Products

ELECTRIC LUMINARIAS - Lighting equipment - RC Co.

ELECTRIC MAGIC COMPANY, THE - Computer software - Andrew S. Green

ELECTRIC MALIBU - Toys–airplanes ☆ - Cox Products Inc.

ELECTRIC MOBILITY - Scooters–motorized - Electric Mobility Corp.

ELECTRIC MUSK IMPULSE - Deodorants–personal - Lever Brothers Co. Inc.

ELECTRIC NECKWEAR - Neckties - Impact Apparell, Inc.

ELECTRIC PILLOW - Electronic equipment - Peavey Electronics Corp.

ELECTRIC PINK - Nail care products - Maybelline Co.

ELECTRIC PUMPKIN - Pet products - Hill Top Enterprises

ELECTRIC SOK! - Socks - Ditto Legwear

ELECTRIC SUN - Lamps - McGuire Sun & Fitness Inc.

ELECTRIC SUNDANCE - Toys–airplanes - Cox Products Inc.

ELECTRIC-WARE - Computer software - Crasur, Inc.

ELECTRIC WORKS, THE - Cooking equipment–household ☆ - Mirro Corp.

ELECTRIC XPRESS - Motor vehicles - Electric Mobility Corp.

ELECTRIC YO YO - Video games - Taito America Corp.

ELECTRIC YOUTH - Perfumes - Revlon Consumer Products Corp.

ELECTRICALC - Calculators - Calculated Industries, Inc.

ELECTRICAR - Motor vehicles–trucks - Commonwealth Edison Co.

ELECTRICIAN - Ladders–wood - John S. Tilley Ladders Co. Inc.

ELECTRICITEA - Teas–herbal - Unitea Herbs

ELECTRICOOKER - Nuts–salted, roasted, cooked, or canned ☆ - Fairmont Snacks Group Inc.

ELECTRICORD - Extension cords - Pacific Electricord Co.

ELECTRICORR - Rustproofing compounds - Cortec Corp.

ELECTRICS - Musical instrument accessories - E. & O. Mari Inc.

ELECTRICS - Musical instrument accessories - E. & O. Mari Inc.

ELECTRIFIED - Water–distilled - Deep Rock Fontenelle

ELECTRIFIER - Computer software - Electrifier, Inc.

ELECTRIGARD - Infant product - BB Marketing Inc.

ELECTRIKBROOM - Vacuum cleaners and accessories - Regina Co.

ELECTRIM - Lawn mowers - Trim-a-Lawn Sales Co.

ELECTRIMAID - See MICRO AIR

ELECTRIPAK - Electric lighting equipment - Electripak

ELECTRIX - Lamps - Electrix Inc.

ELECTRIX - Pet products ☆ - Aquatronics-Filtronics

ELECTRO - Aluminum products - Hanover Wire Cloth

ELECTRO - Banjos ☆ - International Music Corp.

ELECTRO - Darts and dart games - Dart World Inc.

ELECTRO - Electronic equipment - Electro Brand Inc.

ELECTRO - Epoxy - Niles Chemical Paint Co., Inc.

ELECTRO - Guitars - Rickenbacker International Corp.

ELECTRO - Tape recorder - L & M Auto Supply

ELECTRO - Tape–adhesive - Textile Concepts

ELECTRO - Thread - Perfect Thread Co. Inc.

ELECTRO - Tools - Electro Engineering Products Co. Inc.

ELECTRO ALOE - Vitamins and nutritional supplements - Body Wise International, Inc.

ELECTRO-AMP - Musical instruments - Fender Musical Instruments

ELECTRO-ARC - Hair care products ☆ - Fromm Industries

ELECTRO BLADES HEATED WINDSHIELD WIPER BLADES - Windshield wiper blades - KEAPM, Inc.

ELECTRO BLENDER - Blenders ☆ - Sunbeam-Oster Household Products

ELECTRO-BLUE - Health care products - Labeltape Meditect Inc.

ELECTRO BRAIN CORP. - Computer software - Electro Brain Corp.

ELECTRO BRAND - Radios - Electrobrand, Inc.

ELECTRO-C - Vitamins and nutritional supplements - NutriBiotic

ELECTRO CARB - Vitamins and nutritional supplements - Nutra-Source Corp.

ELECTRO-CELLULITE - Skin care products - ElectroDerma International Inc.

ELECTRO/CONNECT - Wiring devices - Thomas Industries Inc.

ELECTRO DRIVE - Staplers ☆ - Duo-Fast Corp.

ELECTRO-FIRM - Skin care products - ElectroDerma International Inc.

ELECTRO FLAME - Cigarette lighters - Colibri Inc.

ELECTRO-FLAME - Cigarette lighters - Park Lane Associates, Inc.

ELECTRO-FOAM - Cleaning preparations–carpet and rug - Bissell Inc.

ELECTRO-GEL - Beauty shop equipment - Focus 21 International Inc.

ELECTRO GROOM - Pet products - Electric Cleaner Co.

ELECTRO-GROUND - Electronic equipment ☆ - RMS Electronics, Inc.

ELECTRO-GUN - Exterminating products - Etex Ltd.

ELECTRO-JET - Toys–airplanes ☆ - Victor Stanzel and Co.

ELECTRO-KLENE - Cleaning preparations - Stoner Inc.

ELECTRO-LIFT - Electrical equipment ☆ - Chamberlain Group Inc.

ELECTRO LIFT - Skin care products - ElectroDerma International Inc.

ELECTRO-LITE - Health care products - Damaco Inc.

ELECTRO-MASTER - Ladders–metal - Werner Co.

ELECTRO-MATIC - Sporting goods - Court & Slope Inc.

ELECTRO-MATIC - Staplers - Arrow Fastener Co. Inc.

ELECTRO-MATIC - Staplers - Electro-Matic Staplers, Inc.

ELECTRO MAXX - Transmission equipment–motor vehicle - Morse Controls

ELECTRO-MEG - Amplifiers–public address ☆ - Sonar Radio Corp.

ELECTRO-OPTIX - Mirrors ☆ - Electro-Optix Inc.

ELECTRO-PAD - Health care products ☆ - Medical Science Products Inc.

ELECTRO-PAK - Veterinary pharmaceutical preparations - Farnam Cos. Inc.

ELECTRO-PATCHES - Valves–industrial ☆ - J.W. Speaker Corp.

ELECTRO-PLEX - Veterinary nutritional supplements - Oralx Corp.

ELECTRO POINTER - Pencil holders ☆ - ACCO USA, Inc.

ELECTRO PROBE - Voltmeters - A.W. Sperry Instruments, Inc.

ELECTRO-PULSE - Audio equipment ☆ - Electro-Voice, Inc.

ELECTRO-QUAD - Cameras - Avant Inc.

ELECTRO-QUARTZ - Lighters - Colibri Inc.

ELECTRO QUARTZ - Lighters - Park Lane Associates, Inc.

ELECTRO-RAIL - Electrical equipment - Universal Sewing Supply, Inc.

ELECTRO-REG - Lighting fixtures - Hubbell Lighting, Inc. (Lighting Div.)

ELECTRO SHIELD - Mats - Aldan Rubber Co.

ELECTRO SKYJACK - Electronic equipment - Fahmee Hakeem

ELECTRO SNARE - Drums–musical instruments - Multivox/Sorkin Music Co. Inc.

ELECTRO-SOUND - Cleaning preparations - Chem-Pak Inc.

ELECTRO STYLUS - Markers–felt-tip - Electro Stylus

ELECTRO-SYNC - Tape recorder - L & M Auto Supply

ELECTRO-TACH - Electronic equipment ☆ - Lafayette Instrument Co. Inc.

ELECTRO-TECH - Toys - Natural Science Industries, Ltd.

ELECTRO-THERM - Digital thermometers - Cooper Instrument Corp.

ELECTRO THERM - Heating pads–electric - Chromalox

ELECTRO-TIME - Beads - Electro-Time

ELECTRO-VOICE - Audio equipment - Electro-Voice, Inc.

ELECTRO WASH - Cleaning preparations - Chemtronics Inc.

ELECTRO-WRITE - Paper–carbon ☆ - Codo Manufacturing Corp.

ELECTRO-ZIP - Electrolyte diagnostic agents - Farnam Cos. Inc.

ELECTROBLAST - Computer software - Maxwell Technologies, Inc.

ELECTROBLOC - Electromedical apparatus - TH Charters, Inc.

ELECTROBLOC - Electronic equipment - Daido Corp.

ELECTROCARDIOCHART - Medical apparatus - Del Mar Avionics

ELECTROCHEMICAL FUEL CELLS - Electrical equipment - Public Service Technologies, Inc.

ELECTROCOLOR - Television equipment - Blonder-Tongue Laboratories Inc.

☆ = Now out of production

ELECTRODE TESTER - Medical apparatus - Nellcor Puritan Bennett

ELECTRODERMA - Skin care products - ElectroDerma International Inc.

ELECTRODYNE - Watches - Elgin Watch Co.

ELECTROFILE - Index cards ☆ - ACME Design Technology

ELECTROFORM/400 - Computer software - Digital Designs, Inc.

ELECTROFUEL - Petroleum ☆ - Crown Central Petroleum Corp.

ELECTROHOME - Electronic equipment - Mitsubishi Electric America, Inc.

ELECTROHOME - Health care products - Fasco Industries Inc.

ELECTROKLEAN - Filters–air - American Air Filter International (Replacement Filter Products)

ELECTROKOTE - Paints and coatings - Insl-X Products Corp.

ELECTROL - Electronic equipment ☆ - Da-Lite Screen Co. Inc.

ELECTROL - Pharmaceutical preparations - Buffington

ELECTROL - Pharmaceutical preparations - Otis Clapp & Son Inc.

ELECTROLATES - Hair care products - Genesis Research International

ELECTROLET - Electronic equipment ☆ - Da-Lite Screen Co. Inc.

ELECTROLIGHT - Bicycles - Huffy Corp.

ELECTROLINE - Hardware - Esmet, Inc.

ELECTROLITE II - Lighting equipment - Bristolite Skylights

ELECTROLUBE PLUS - Computer software - Software Dynamics Corp.

ELECTROLUX - Vacuum cleaners and accessories - Electrolux Corp.

ELECTROLYTE & APPETITE STIMULANT - Veterinary pharmaceutical preparations - Mardel Laboratories, Inc.

ELECTROLYTE ENERGY - Pharmaceutical preparations - Marine Biotherapies

ELECTROMATIC - Clippers–barber - Sunbeam-Oster Household Products

ELECTROMATIC - Electrical industrial apparatus - BWI Kartridgpak Co.

ELECTROMATIC - Guitars ☆ - Fred Gretsch Enterprises

ELECTROMATICS - Electric cookware ☆ - Corning Inc.

ELECTROMIC - Toys–airplanes ☆ - Victor Stanzel and Co.

ELECTROMIST - Health care products - Pharmaceutical Innovations

ELECTRON BEAM - Toys - Estes Industries

ELECTRON CASCADE PURIFIER - Air purification systems - Netco International, Inc.

ELECTRON EAR - Hearing aids - Telex Communications, Inc.

ELECTRON ESD - Floor coverings–carpet and rugs ☆ - Heuga USA

ELECTRON II - Floor coverings–carpet and rugs - Heuga USA

ELECTRONI-CORD - Tires - Bridgestone/Firestone, Inc.

ELECTRONIC - Adhesives and sealants - Textile Concepts

ELECTRONIC - Office furniture–wood - Engineered Data Products Inc.

ELECTRONIC ARTS - Computer software - Electronic Arts Inc.

ELECTRONIC BATTLESHIP - Games - Milton Bradley Co.

ELECTRONIC BODYGUARD PORTABLE ALARM SYSTEM - Alarm systems - Edge Co.

ELECTRONIC BROCHURES - Computer software - Mariners' Museum

ELECTRONIC BUSINESS QUEUE - Computer software - Omr Systems Corp.

ELECTRONIC BUTLER - Electronic equipment - Electronic Butler

ELECTRONIC CLASSICAL LIBRARY - Computer software - World Library, Inc.

ELECTRONIC CLIPPER - Artists' materials - Dynamic Graphics Inc.

ELECTRONIC COMMAND - Electronic equipment - Moore-O-Matic Inc.

ELECTRONIC COMPONENTS GROUPE - Electronic equipment - Stein Industries, Inc.

ELECTRONIC DATA AND RATES - Computer software ☆ - Donovan Data Systems, Inc.

ELECTRONIC DAUBER, THE - Games - Bingo Card Minder Corp.

ELECTRONIC EAR - Alarm systems - Anes Electronics Burglar Alarm Systems

ELECTRONIC FIELD BOOK - Computer software - Sokkia Technology, Inc.

ELECTRONIC INNOVATORS - Electronic equipment - Electronic Innovators Inc.

ELECTRONIC LIBRARY OF SCIENCE, THE - Recording label - Springer-Verlag New York, Inc.

ELECTRONIC MUSICAL SOFT TUNES - Toys–electronic - CBS Toys

ELECTRONIC NIGHTSTICK - Motor vehicle parts and accessories - Kraco Enterprises Inc.

ELECTRONIC NOTEBOOK - Dictating machines - Craig Consumer Electronics

ELECTRONIC PAPER - Computer software ☆ - Mindgate Technologies Inc.

ELECTRONIC PARAMEDIC - Toys ☆ - Playskool, Inc.

ELECTRONIC PUTTING CHALLENGE - Golfing equipment - G.L. Technology Inc.

ELECTRONIC ROOM - Recreational vehicle dealers - Space Craft Manufacturing Inc.

ELECTRONIC TALK 'N PLAY - Toys–electronic - CBS Toys

ELECTRONIC TEACHER - Electronic equipment ☆ - Sight & Sound Inc.

ELECTRONIC TEAK - Chimes - Nutone Inc.

ELECTRONIC TINI ARCADE - Toys–electronic - Video Technology U.S. Inc.

ELECTRONIC WORKFORCE - Computer software - Edify Corp.

ELECTRONICO - Dryers–hair - Nino Originals

ELECTRONICS BOUTIQUE - Computer hardware - Electronics Boutique, Inc.

ELECTRONICS EB BOUTIQUE - Computers - Electronics Boutique, Inc.

ELECTROPILE - Weather stripping ☆ - The Standard Products Co.

ELECTROPLEAT - Filters–air - American Air Filter International (Replacement Filter Products)

ELECTROPOR - Laboratory apparatus - Cuno Inc.

ELECTROSHADES - Window shades - Mecho Shade Corp.

ELECTROSILVER - Photographic equipment - Eastman Kodak Co.

ELECTROSOL - Dishwashing compounds - Benckiser Consumer Products Inc.

ELECTROSTAR - Circuit boards–printed - Electrostar, Inc.

ELECTROSTIM - Health care products - Promatek Medical Systems Inc.

ELECTROTIME - Watches - Bulova Corp.

ELECTROTRONICS - Televisions - Morfi International, Inc.

ELECTROTUNE - Audio equipment - Paso Sound Products Inc.

ELECTROVOICE - Audio equipment - Speakerkits Inc.

ELECTRUCK - Utility truck - Taylor-Dunn Manufacturing Co.

ELECTRUM - Guitars - Alembic Inc.

ELEFUN - Games - Tonka Corp.

ELEGANA - Floor coverings–carpet and rugs ☆ - Colonial Mills Inc.

ELEGANCE - Bathroom accessories - Franklin Brass Manufacturing Co.

ELEGANCE - Blankets–electric - Sunbeam-Oster Household Products

ELEGANCE - Blown glassware - Indiana Glass Co.

ELEGANCE - Cabinets - Nutone Inc.

ELEGANCE - Ceramic floor tile - Interceramic Inc.

ELEGANCE - Deodorizers - S.C. Johnson & Son, Inc.

ELEGANCE - Dishes–china - Viletta China Co.

ELEGANCE - Dishes–china ☆ - Gorham Inc.

ELEGANCE - Drapery hardware ☆ - Spring Window Fashions Division, Inc.

ELEGANCE - Flatware - Salem China Co.

ELEGANCE - Floor coverings - Azrock Commercial Flooring

ELEGANCE - Floor coverings - National Floor Products Co., Inc.

ELEGANCE - Floor coverings–carpet and rugs - Barrett Carpet Mills Inc.

ELEGANCE - Floor coverings–carpet and rugs ☆ - Robertex Associates Inc.

ELEGANCE - Frames–eyeglass - U.S. Optical Frame Co.

ELEGANCE - Furniture - Pilliod Co.

ELEGANCE - Furniture - Yates Furniture Systems Corp.

ELEGANCE - Glass–leaded - Seneca Glass Co.

ELEGANCE - Glassware–household - Lenox Crystal, Inc.

ELEGANCE - Golfing equipment - Golfsmith International Inc.

ELEGANCE - Health care products - MB Products Ltd.

ELEGANCE - Health care products ☆ - Sunrise Medical

ELEGANCE - Hearing aids - Qualitone

ELEGANCE - House furnishings - L.E. Smith Glass Co.

ELEGANCE - Housewares - Leeber Ltd. USA

ELEGANCE - Leather goods - Accessories to the Fact

ELEGANCE - Napkins–paper - Erving Paper Products Inc.

ELEGANCE - Plastics–laminated - Plaskolite Inc.

ELEGANCE - Skin care products ☆ - Salon Essentials

ELEGANCE - Steel ☆ - Regal Ware, Inc.

ELEGANCE - Tablecloths - Hoyne Industries Inc.

ELEGANCE - Tiles–ceramic ☆ - American Olean Tile Co.

ELEGANCE - Toilet seats - Ginsey Industries, Inc.

ELEGANCE - Watches - Hampden Corp.

ELEGANCE - Watches ☆ - SMH (US) Inc.

ELEGANCE - Wigs - Paula Young

ELEGANCE - Yarn - Rainbow Gallery, Inc.

ELEGANCE & ZESTY - Recording label - Elegance & Zesty Records Co.

ELEGANCE BY CROSS YOUR HEART - Brassieres (Bras) - Playtex Apparel, Inc.

ELEGANCE IN MARBLE - Wallpaper - Prestige Screen Prints Ltd.

ELEGANCE IN TEXTILES - Wallpaper - H & S Sales Inc.

ELEGANCE IN TEXTURES - Wallpaper ☆ - H & S Sales Inc.

ELEGANCE NOUVELLE - Golfing equipment - Lynx Golf, Inc.

ELEGANCE RIBBON - Ribbons - Quilters' Resource Inc.

ELEGANCE TREND - Window coverings - All Strong Industry (USA) Inc.

ELEGANCE WITH EASE - Curtains - Beacon Looms Inc.

ELEGANCY - Greeting cards ☆ - American Artists Group Inc.

ELEGANT - Awnings - Acme Awning Co.

ELEGANT - Candy - McDonald Candy Co. Inc.

ELEGANT - Detergents - Sage Laboratories Inc.

ELEGANT - Dolls - Bradley Import Co.

ELEGANT - Floor coverings–carpet and rugs ☆ - Customweave Carpets Inc.

ELEGANT - Floor waxes - Uncle Sam Chemical Co., Inc.

ELEGANT - Glassware–household ☆ - Dansk International Designs, Ltd.

ELEGANT - Gloves–work ☆ - Pioneer Industrial Products Co.

☆ = Now out of production

ELEGANT - Invitations - Nu-Art Inc.

ELEGANT - Signs - Sachs-Lawlor Co.

ELEGANT - Wallpaper ☆ - Wallpaper Imports Inc.

ELEGANT AGE - Floor coverings–carpet and rugs - Monticello Carpet Mills

ELEGANT BABY - Infant product - Baby Needs Inc.

ELEGANT CHOICE - Floor coverings–carpet and rugs - Alexander Smith Carpets

ELEGANT CHRISTMAS - Greeting cards ☆ - Nu-Art Inc.

ELEGANT CLASSICS - Furniture ☆ - White Furniture Co.

ELEGANT CLASSICS - Wallpaper - Queens Decorative Wallcoverings Inc.

ELEGANT CLASSICS II - Wallpaper - Queens Decorative Wallcoverings Inc.

ELEGANT CONTOURS - Brassieres (Bras) ☆ - Coloplast Corp.

ELEGANT DELIGHTS - Meat products–poultry ☆ - Nichirei Foods America

ELEGANT DESIGNS - Jewelry - Kirchner Corp.

ELEGANT DIRECTION - Floor coverings–carpet and rugs - Olympic Carpets Inc.

ELEGANT DIRECTIONS - Floor coverings–carpet and rugs - Philadelphia Carpets

ELEGANT DIRECTIONS - Wallpaper - Advent Industries Inc.

ELEGANT EGGS - Dyes–food - Spearhead Industries Inc.

ELEGANT EIGHTEEN - Jewelry - K & M Associates

ELEGANT ENDINGS - Cakes - Sara Lee Corp.

ELEGANT ENTREES - Food products - Gold Kist Inc.

ELEGANT EXPRESSIONS - Floor coverings–carpet and rugs - Evans-Black Carpet Mills

ELEGANT EXPRESSIONS - Greeting cards - John Henry Co.

ELEGANT EXPRESSIONS - Wallpaper - Warner Co.

ELEGANT FLAIR - Floor coverings–carpet and rugs - Cabin Crafts Carpets

ELEGANT FLOOR FINISH - Cleaning preparations - Uncle Sam Chemical Co., Inc.

ELEGANT GRAINS - Rice - Fantastic Foods Inc.

ELEGANT GROUNDS - Wallpaper ☆ - Robert Crowder & Co.

ELEGANT HEIR - Apparel and accessories - Esskay Manufacturing Co.

ELEGANT HERB GOURMET, THE - Food products - Mix-In's Ltd.

ELEGANT HIGH PERFORMANCE SHOWER, THE - Bathroom fixtures - Interbath, Inc.

ELEGANT HOME - Stencils - Plaid Enterprises, Inc.

ELEGANT ICE - Jewelry - Southern Belle Dairy Co.

ELEGANT IMAGES - Mirrors ☆ - Advanced Technology Inc.

ELEGANT INTERIORS - Fabrics–tapestry ☆ - Columbus Coated Fabrics Co.

ELEGANT INTERIORS - Wallpaper - Imperial Wallcoverings, Inc.

ELEGANT INVITATIONS, THE - Invitations ☆ - Evergreen Press

ELEGANT JOURNEY - Floor coverings–carpet and rugs ☆ - Lees Carpets

ELEGANT LEGACY - Wallpaper - Ambiance

ELEGANT LIVING - Fabrics–tapestry ☆ - Columbus Coated Fabrics Co.

ELEGANT LIVING - Wallcovering - BDH Two, Inc.

ELEGANT MOMENTS - Glassware–household - Consolidated Stores Corp.

ELEGANT PERVERSITIES - Apparel and accessories - Romantasy, Inc.

ELEGANT RICE PUDDING - Prepared foods - Lundberg Family Farms

ELEGANT SATINS - Wallpaper - Queens Decorative Wallcoverings Inc.

ELEGANT SILK - Flowers–artificial - Sin Kuang Enterprises Inc.

ELEGANT SILKIES - Wallpaper - Blumenthal

ELEGANT SUEDE - Wallpaper - Queens Decorative Wallcoverings Inc.

ELEGANT THRONE, THE - Toilet seats - H.M. Coby Associates Inc.

ELEGANT TOUCH - Floor coverings–carpet and rugs - Calladium & Marglen

ELEGANT TOWER - Floor coverings–carpet and rugs - World Carpets, Inc.

ELEGANT TRADITION - Floor coverings–carpet and rugs ☆ - Cabin Crafts Carpets

ELEGANT WALLS - Wallpaper ☆ - Wall Fashion Inc.

ELEGANT WALLS 2 - Wallpaper ☆ - Wall Fashion Inc.

ELEGANT WALLS 3 - Wallpaper - Wall Fashion Inc.

ELEGANT WALLS 4 - Wallpaper - Wall Fashion Inc.

ELEGANT WRITER - Markers–felt-tip - Hunt Manufacturing Co.

ELEGANTE - Boats–motor ☆ - Cruisers

ELEGANTE - Cabinets - Kabom Kitchen & Bath Manufacturing

ELEGANTE - Fabrics ☆ - Rosebar Textile Co.

ELEGANTE - Floor coverings–carpet and rugs - E.R. Carpenter Co.

ELEGANTE - Floor coverings–carpet and rugs - Dorsett Carpet Mills Inc.

ELEGANTE - Floor coverings–carpet and rugs - Omalon

ELEGANTE - Frames–eyeglass - Pan Optics, Inc.

ELEGANTE - Girdles ☆ - Elegante Foundations Inc.

ELEGANTE - Glassware–household - ACC

ELEGANTE - Glassware–household ☆ - Culver Glass Inc.

ELEGANTE - Hair care products - Conair Corp.

ELEGANTE - Luggage - United States Luggage Corp.

ELEGANTE - Paints ☆ - PPG Industries, Inc.

ELEGANTE - Pens - Accutec Inc.

ELEGANTE - Sinks–metal - Moen Inc.

ELEGANTE - Toys - Peg Perego USA Inc.

ELEGANTE BABY BEAR - Toys–stuffed - Dakin Inc.

ELEGANTE BENTLEY BEAR - Toys–stuffed ☆ - Dakin Inc.

ELEGANTE BLACKIE - Toys–stuffed - Dakin Inc.

ELEGANTE BY DAKIN - Toys–stuffed - Dakin Inc.

ELEGANTE CHANG CHOW - Toys–stuffed - Dakin Inc.

ELEGANTE DOLLS BY DAKIN - Dolls - Dakin Inc.

ELEGANTE HANA SIAMESE - Toys–stuffed - Dakin Inc.

ELEGANTE KOKO - Toys–stuffed - Dakin Inc.

ELEGANTE LADY - Toys–stuffed - Dakin Inc.

ELEGANTE LIMA LLAMA - Toys–stuffed - Dakin Inc.

ELEGANTE LOLLY LHASA - Toys–stuffed - Dakin Inc.

ELEGANTE MAMA BEAR - Toys–stuffed - Dakin Inc.

ELEGANTE OLLIE ORANGUTAN - Toys–stuffed - Dakin Inc.

ELEGANTE PAPA BEAR - Toys–stuffed - Dakin Inc.

ELEGANTE PEKOE - Toys–stuffed - Dakin Inc.

ELEGANTE PENGUIN AND BABY - Toys–stuffed - Dakin Inc.

ELEGANTE SANDY GOLDEN RETRIEVER - Toys–stuffed - Dakin Inc.

ELEGANTE SHEFFIELD SHEEPDOG - Toys–stuffed - Dakin Inc.

ELEGANTE SHONG SHONG PANDA - Toys–stuffed - Dakin Inc.

ELEGANTE SUSHI SIAMESE - Toys–stuffed - Dakin Inc.

ELEGANTE WICKI TUT - Toys–stuffed - Dakin Inc.

ELEGANTE WOEBEGONE BASSET - Toys–stuffed - Dakin Inc.

ELEGANTLY GRAY - Hair coloring preparations ☆ - Avon Products, Inc.

ELEGANTS - Fruits–canned - Cascadian Fruit Shippers

ELEGANZA - Floor coverings - Mannington Resilient Floors

ELEGANZA - Motor vehicles–motor homes ☆ - Fleetwood Enterprises, Inc.

ELEGANZA - Wallpaper ☆ - Wallpaper Imports Inc.

ELEGANZA - Yarn ☆ - Brunswick Yarns

ELEGENT - Colognes ☆ - Rosal Laboratories

ELEGENTE - Darts and dart games ☆ - Dart World Inc.

ELEGON - Floor coverings–tile ☆ - Vida Mosaic Co. Inc.

ELEK-PRO-TEK - Drill bits - Pate Manufacturing, Inc.

ELEKAP - Pharmaceutical preparations - Western Research Laboratories

ELEKTRA - Batteries - E.E. Electronic Components Inc.

ELEKTRA - Dishes–china - Pickard Inc.

ELEKTRA - Rackets–racquetball - Head Sports USA

ELEKTRA - Recording label - Warner Music International

ELEKTRA/EVEREST LEGACY SERIES - Recording label - Everest Record Group

ELEKTRA-II - Heaters–swimming pool - Teledyne Laars

ELEKTRA II - Water heaters–household - Teledyne Industries Inc.

ELEKTRA NAILS - American International Industries

ELEKTRA STAR - Heaters–swimming pool - Teledyne Industries Inc.

ELEKTRAPURE - Vacuum cleaners and accessories–commercial - HMI Industries Inc.

ELEKTRIM - Motors - American Contex Corp.

ELEMA-SCHONANDER - Teas - Siemens Medical Systems, Inc.

ELEMENT - Computers - SoftBase/Eventum

ELEMENT HUNT - Computer software - Queue Inc.

ELEMENTAL MUSIC - Recording label - T.E.C. Tones/Ralph Records

ELEMENTARY MATH GRAPHICS CD LIBRARY - Computer software - Ventura Educational Systems

ELEMENTRA - Vitamins and nutritional supplements - Clintec Nutrition Co.

ELEMENTS - Dinnerware–glass - Arita Sales Co. Inc.

ELEMENTS - Eyewear - NuVision Inc.

ELEMENTS - Floor coverings–carpet and rugs ☆ - J and J Industries Inc.

ELEMENTS - Furniture - Hammary Furniture Co. Inc.

ELEMENTS - Furniture - Weiman Co.

ELEMENTS - Furniture ☆ - Bernhardt Industries

ELEMENTS - Furniture ☆ - Lane Co. Inc.

ELEMENTS - Housewares - P.T. Kedaung Industrial Glass Ltd.

ELEMENTS - Lighting equipment - Sterner Lighting Systems Inc.

ELEMENTS - Slacks–men's - Glen Oaks Industries Inc.

ELEMENTS BY EVAN-PICONE - Apparel and accessories - Plaid Holdings Corp.

ELEMENTS BY J.G. HOOK - Apparel–men's - J.G. Hook, Inc.

ELEMENTS OF MATHEMATICS - Computer software - Electronic Courseware Systems Inc.

ELEMENTS OF MUSIC - Computer software - Electronic Courseware Systems Inc.

ELEMENTS OF STYLE - Computer software - Microlytics Inc.

ELEMENTS, THE - Baskets–wood ☆ - Royal Cathay Trading Co.

☆ = Now out of production

ELEMIGUM - Pharmaceutical preparations - Spectrum Chemical Manufacturing Corp.

ELENA - Food products - Elena's Food Specialties Inc.

ELENA MARIA - Spices and extracts - Scentique Ltd.

ELENA'S - Pasta - Houlihan's Culinary Traditions, Ltd.

ELENENTS - Shoes - MSF Corp.

ELENI'S GOURMET - Spaghetti sauces - Eleni's Gourmet Foods Inc.

ELENTE - Girdles - Lord & Taylor

ELEPHANT - Steel-wool pads, etc ☆ - International Steel Wool Corp.

ELEPHANT BAR - Chocolate bars - Famous Pacific Dessert Co.

ELEPHANT GLUE - Glue—household or industrial ☆ - Sanford Corp.

ELEPHANT HIDE PAPER - Paper - Permalin Products Co.

ELEPHANT-HYDE - Industrial machinery - Republic Roller Corp.

ELEPHANT JOHN - File folders - Lisa Frank, Inc.

ELEPHANT MALT LIQUOR - Beverages—malt - Anheuser-Busch Companies Inc.

ELEPHANT RED - Beverages—malt - Anheuser-Busch Companies Inc.

ELEPHANT RED LAGER - Beverages—malt - Anheuser-Busch Companies Inc.

ELEPHANT ROCK & ROLL'EM - Toys - Steven Manufacturing Co.

ELEPHANT-VAC - Vacuum-type trash collector - Hollowell Products Corp.

ELEPHANT WALK - Apparel and accessories - Immanuel Enterprises, Ltd.

ELEPHANT WALK - Floor coverings—carpet and rugs ☆ - Concord/Aldon Industries Inc.

ELEPHANTS 2 IN LOVE - Toys—stuffed ☆ - Dakin Inc.

ELERT - Electronic equipment - Digequip Security Industries Inc.

ELESIA - Rings—jewelry - Artcarved Inc.

ELETRO-LIGHT - Bicycles - Huffy Corp.

ELETTROSUMMA - Calculators ☆ - Olivetti North America Inc. (Consumer Products Div.)

ELEUTHERO GINSENG EXTRACT ORAL LIQUID - Beverages - Chung, Inc.

ELEVA TRUCK - Carts - Hamilton Caster & Manufacturing Co.

ELEVABED - Beds—metal ☆ - Hickory Springs Manufacturing Co.

ELEVAGE - Wines - Chimney Rock Winery

ELEVATION - Floor coverings—carpet and rugs ☆ - Regal Rugs Inc.

ELEVATIONS - Fabrics - Interface, Inc.

ELEVATIONS - Floor coverings—carpet and rugs ☆ - Concepts International

ELEVATIONS - Wallpaper - Capital Carousel Inc.

ELEVATIONS - Wallpaper - Ozite Corp.

ELEVATOR ACTION - Video games ☆ - Taito America Corp.

ELEVATORS - Footwear—men's - Richlee Shoe Co.

ELEVEN - Floor coverings—carpet and rugs ☆ - Alexander Smith Carpets

ELEVEN - Recording label - Geffen Records, Inc.

ELEVEN EAST - Floor coverings—carpet and rugs - Burlington Industries, Inc.

ELEVEN STAR - Wines ☆ - Canandaigua Wine Co. Inc.

ELEVETTE - Elevators - Inclinator Co. of America

ELEVETTE HYDRARIDE - Elevators - Inclinator Co. of America

ELEVETTE HYDRARIDE 2100 - Elevators - Inclinator Co. of America

ELEVONIC 311MV - Elevators - Otis Elevator Co.

ELEVONIC 411MV - Elevators - Otis Elevator Co.

ELF - Audio equipment - Adcom Technologies Corp.

ELF - Bicycles - Kenneth E. Pendergraft

ELF - Candy ☆ - Super Valu Inc.

ELF - Circuit boards - Atlanta Signal Processors, Inc.

ELF - Electrical equipment - Emerson Electric Co.

ELF - Herring—smoked, salted, dried, or pickled - Lyon Food Products Inc.

ELF - Lubricants - Cosmopolitan Motors Inc.

ELF - Office supplies - Rubbermaid Office Products Inc.

ELF BOOKS - Publisher's imprints ☆ - Rand McNally & Co.

ELF BURGERS - Sandwiches—prepackaged - Summit Meat Processors Inc.

ELF KIN - Dolls - Lynnda Hagen

ELF MOTO - Lubricants - Elf Lubricants North America, Inc.

ELFA-BET - Games - Maurice O. Reiber

ELFAST - Office supplies - Rubbermaid Office Products Inc.

ELFCO - Diaries - E.L. Freeman Co.

ELFIN - Dinnerware—glass - Nikko Ceramics Inc.

ELFIN - Greeting cards - Vivian Greene Inc.

ELFIN - Insulators—electrical - Dare Products Inc.

ELFIN - Jewelry - George Walter Boucher

ELFIN - Paper—tissue - Fort Howard Corp.

ELFIN DELIGHTS - Cookies - Keebler Co.

ELFIN LOAVES - Breads ☆ - Keebler Co.

ELFIN' MAGIC - Metal wire figures - Cobraco Manufacturing, Inc.

ELFKINS - Cookies ☆ - Keebler Co.

ELFQUEST - Games - Chaosium Inc.

ELFQUEST - Games ☆ - Mayfair Games, Inc.

ELF'S ARM, THE - Tools—hand-operated - Michael E. Hedtke

ELGIN - Clocks - Burwood Products Co.

ELGIN - Food products - Elgin-Honey Hill Corp.

ELGIN - Office supplies - Elgin School Supply Co. Inc.

ELGIN - Sewing machines—household - VWS Inc.

ELGIN - Stationery - Ginn Card & Paper Co. Inc.

ELGIN - Vegetables—canned - Elgin Canning Co.

ELGIN - Watches - Elgin Watch Co.

ELGIN COURT DESIGNS - Greeting cards - Evergreen Press

ELGIN ELECTRIC - Tools - Test-Rite Products Corp.

ELGIN-MACOR - Hardware - Blaine Window Hardware Inc.

ELGIN SPORTSMAN - Watches - Elgin Watch Co.

ELGINART - Stationery - Ginn Card & Paper Co. Inc.

ELGINITE - Watches - Elgin Watch Co.

ELGINIUM - Watches - Elgin Watch Co.

ELI CUTTER - Cigarettes - Brown & Williamson Tobacco Corp.

ELI LILLY - Pharmaceutical preparations - Eli Lilly and Co.

ELI ORIGINAL - Footwear - Blue Jasper Inc.

ELI STONER - Tents - Academy Broadway Corp.

ELI WEATHERBY EXTERIOR STAINS - Varnishes - Davis Paint Co.

ELIA - Skin care products - Elia Cosmetics, Inc.

ELIAM - Jewelry - EliaM Enterprise

ELIB - Computer software - Entropic Research Laboratory, Inc.

ELICO - Athletic footwear - Elico Shoe Corp.

ELIDANSE - Hair care products - Lever Brothers Co. Inc.

ELIGERE - Floor coverings—carpet and rugs - Collins & Aikman Corp.

ELIJAH CRAIG - Liquors - Heaven Hill Distilleries, Inc.

ELIJOHN - Outerwear - Janeman International, Inc.

ELIKI - Tiles—ceramic ☆ - Maxsam Sales, Inc.

ELIMA-MATIC - Pumps - Versa-Matic Tool, Inc.

ELIMI-STAT - Cleaning preparations—household ☆ - Guardsman Products, Inc.

ELIMIN ODOR - Deodorizers - Pfizer Inc.

ELIMINA - Skin care products - Revlon Consumer Products Corp.

ELIMINALL - Health care products - Natural Laboratories Corp.

ELIMINATE - Cleaning preparations—household - HERC, Inc.

ELIMINATOR - Alarm systems - Boatsafe Products Inc.

ELIMINATOR - Audio equipment - MTX

ELIMINATOR - Audio equipment ☆ - Electro-Voice, Inc.

ELIMINATOR - Bicycles - Murray, Inc.

ELIMINATOR - Chemical preparations - Challenger Manufacturing, Inc.

ELIMINATOR - Containers—plastic - James C. Lloyd

ELIMINATOR - Filters—industrial - T/M Industrial Supply, Inc.

ELIMINATOR - Firearms, accessories, and parts - Matz Rubber Co., Inc.

ELIMINATOR - Floor coverings—carpet and rugs ☆ - Calladium & Marglen

ELIMINATOR - Garden equipment - Bolens Corp.

ELIMINATOR - Guitars - St. Blues Guitars

ELIMINATOR - Hardware - Emerson Electric Co.

ELIMINATOR - Inner tubes—bicycles - Eliminator Airless Division

ELIMINATOR - Machine parts - Esco Corp.

ELIMINATOR - Machinery - Clipper Belt Lacer Co.

ELIMINATOR - Machinery - Enviroquip Systems, Inc.

ELIMINATOR - Orthopedic products - JSB Orthotics Inc.

ELIMINATOR - Pesticides—household - Pennington Enterprises, Inc.

ELIMINATOR - Pharmaceutical preparations - New Vision Concepts, Inc.

ELIMINATOR - Plants - Greiling Farms, Inc.

ELIMINATOR - Power transformers - States Engineering Corp.

ELIMINATOR - Pumps - Little Giant Pump Co.

ELIMINATOR - Sporting goods - Dunlop Maxfli Sports Corp.

ELIMINATOR - Sporting goods - Wellington Leisure Products, Inc.

ELIMINATOR - Tools—masonry - Cleform Tool Co.

ELIMINATOR - Toys - Tyco Industries, Inc.

ELIMINATOR - Toys—models - Estes Industries

ELIMINATOR - Windows - Jeld-Wen, Inc.

ELIMINATOR II - Automotive parts and accessories - Loctite Corp.

ELIMINATOR PLUS - Lawn mowers - Bolens Corp.

ELIMINATOR, THE - Water purification systems - John A. Hansen

ELIMINATOR, THE - Lawn mowers ☆ - K-W Manufacturing Co. Inc.

ELIMINATOR, THE - Deodorizers ☆ - Ole Time Woodsman

ELIMINATOR, THE - Deodorizers ☆ - Olfactory Corp.

ELIMINATOR, THE - Fans—electric - Pettibone Corp.

ELIMINATOR, THE - Cleaning equipment - Wheel-Chair Care, Inc.

ELIMINATORS - Engines—motor vehicle - Springfield Remanufacturing Corp.

ELIMINATORS - Toys—automobiles - Playskool, Inc.

ELIMINATORS, THE - Toys - Tonka Corp.

ELIMINATR - Cleaning equipment - Contec, Inc.

ELIMINATR - Water purification systems - Flint & Walling Industries, Inc.

☆ = Now out of production

ELIMITE - Skin care products - Allergan, Inc.
ELIMSTAPH - Pharmaceutical preparations - Walter G. Legge Co., Inc.
ELIMSTAT LX - Electrical testing instruments - Walter G. Legge Co., Inc.
ELIMSTAT SD - Electrical testing instruments - Walter G. Legge Co., Inc.
ELINCHROM - Photographic equipment - Bogen Photo Corp.
ELION - Apparel–athletic - Elion International Inc.
ELIOS - Ceramic tile ☆ - Integrity Tile Co.
ELIPSE - Bread crumbs ☆ - Prepco
ELIPSE - Rings–jewelry - Artcarved Inc.
ELIPSUS - Whirlpools - Lasco Products Group
ELI'S - Bakery products–frozen - Eli's Chicago Finest Inc.
ELI'S CHEESECAKE WORLD - Pastries - Elimarc Associates, Inc.
ELI'S DREAM TEAM - Pastries - Elimarc Associates, Inc.
ELI'S UNCHEESECAKE - Bakery products - Elimarc Associates, Inc.
ELISA CELLI - Frozen foods ☆ - Wilton Foods Inc.
ELISABETH - Apparel–women's - Liz Claiborne Inc.
ELISABETH STEWART - Bathing suits - Apparel Ventures, Inc.
ELISABETH STEWART - Bathing suits - Elisabeth Stewart Swimwear
ELISABETTA ROGIANI - Clothing - Elisabetta Rogiani
ELISE - Clocks - General Time Corp. (Westclox/Seth Thomas Div.)
ELISE - Dolls - Alexander Doll Co. Inc.
ELISE - Floor coverings–carpet and rugs ☆ - Regal Rugs Inc.
ELISIA - Rings–jewelry - Artcarved Inc.
ELITCH GARDENS - Office supplies - New Elitch Gardens, Ltd.
ELITE - See **IMPACT**
ELITE - Antifreeze and chemicals - Ionics, Inc.
ELITE - Apparel and accessories - Atco Truelife International
ELITE - Apparel–women's - Oxford Industries, Inc.
ELITE - Audio equipment ☆ - Yorkville Sound
ELITE - Automotive parts and accessories - Edelbrock Corp.
ELITE - Automotive parts and accessories - Hop-Cap Inc.
ELITE - Automotive parts and accessories - Lancaster Colony Automotive Group
ELITE - Barbecues and grills - M.E. Heuck Co. Inc.
ELITE - Bicycles - Roadmaster Corp.
ELITE - Bicycles ☆ - Huffy Corp.
ELITE - Binoculars - Bausch & Lomb Inc.
ELITE - Bird feeds - Kellogg Inc.
ELITE - Blankets–electric - Sunbeam-Oster Household Products
ELITE - Blinds–venetian - Hunter Douglas, Inc.
ELITE - Blinds–vertical - Louverdrape Inc.
ELITE - Boats ☆ - Wellcraft Marine Corp.
ELITE - Boats–pontoons ☆ - Forester Boats Inc.
ELITE - Bottle caps - APM Inc.
ELITE - Brushes–hair ☆ - Phillips Brush Corp.
ELITE - Brushes–paint - Wooster Brush Co.
ELITE - Cabinets - American Woodmark Corp.
ELITE - Cabinets - Quality Cabinets
ELITE - Computers–mainframe - Elite Microelectronics Inc.
ELITE - Containers–metal - Wisconsin Tissue Mills Inc.
ELITE - Converters–electric - Advanced Digital Systems
ELITE - Cosmetics ☆ - Elysee Scientific Cosmetic Co.
ELITE - Desk sets - Samuel Ward Manufacturing Inc.
ELITE - Desks - Vanguard Corp.
ELITE - Dinnerware - Genpak Corp.
ELITE - Electrical equipment - Tork Inc.
ELITE - Electronic equipment - Micro Motion Inc.
ELITE - Embossing machines - A.D. Joslin Manufacturing Co.
ELITE - Exercising equipment - ESB Enterprises, Inc.
ELITE - Fasteners–hook and eye - Universal Fasteners Inc.
ELITE - Film - Eastman Kodak Co.
ELITE - Fireplace equipment - Design Specialties Inc.
ELITE - Fishing tackle - South Bend Sporting Goods Inc.
ELITE - Fishing tackle ☆ - Gladding Braided Products Inc.
ELITE - Flatware - Reed and Barton Corp.
ELITE - Floor coverings - Tarkett, Inc.
ELITE - Floor coverings–carpet and rugs - E.R. Carpenter Co.
ELITE - Floor coverings–carpet and rugs ☆ - Blue Ridge Carpet Mills
ELITE - Floor coverings–carpet and rugs - Columbus Mills, Inc.
ELITE - Floor coverings–carpet and rugs ☆ - World Carpets, Inc.
ELITE - Food products - Elite Mushroom Co., Inc.
ELITE - Food products ☆ - Sea Greene Co.
ELITE - Footwear–athletic ☆ - Nike, Inc.
ELITE - Frames–picture - North American Enclosures Inc.
ELITE - Fungicides - Bayer Corp. (Agriculture Div.)
ELITE - Furniture - King Koil Licensing Co., Inc.

ELITE - Furniture - Samsonite Furniture Co. (Consumer Products Div.)
ELITE - Furniture - Singer Furniture Co.
ELITE - Giftware ☆ - W.M.F. of America Inc.
ELITE - Glassware–household - Federal Glass
ELITE - Glassware–household - Owens-Illinois Inc. (Libbey Div.)
ELITE - Gloves - Fownes Brothers & Co., Inc.
ELITE - Goggles–underwater - Skyline Northwest Corp.
ELITE - Guitars - Ovation Instruments
ELITE - Hair care products - Fromm Industries
ELITE - Hair care products - Roux Laboratories, Inc.
ELITE - Hardware - Liberty Hardware Manufacturing Corp.
ELITE - Health care products - Geri-Care Products, LLC
ELITE - Hearing aids - Hearing Services Inc.
ELITE - Hearing aids - Widex Hearing Aid Co., Inc.
ELITE - Hosiery - Kayser-Roth Corp.
ELITE - Housewares - Horizon Ventures, Inc.
ELITE - Jewelry - Elite Imports Inc.
ELITE - Kitchen appliances ☆ - R & R Mill Co. Inc.
ELITE - Lamps - Metro Mark, Inc.
ELITE - Laser systems–medical - McMahan Corp.
ELITE - Lighting fixtures - Meyda Tiffany Inc.
ELITE - Luggage - Airway Industries, Inc.
ELITE - Makeup brushes and manicure tools ☆ - London International U.S. Holdings
ELITE - Meat products–poultry ☆ - Snowball Foods, Inc.
ELITE - Mobile homes - Oakwood Homes Corp.
ELITE - Motor vehicles–automobiles - General Motors Corp. (Oldsmobile Div.)
ELITE - Motor vehicles–motor homes - Travco
ELITE - Musical instrument accessories - E. & O. Mari Inc.
ELITE - Napkins–fabric ☆ - Carolina Manufacturing Inc.
ELITE - Occasional furniture - JDI Group, Inc.
ELITE - Oils–lubricating - Witco Corp.
ELITE - Ophthalmic goods - Europa Co.
ELITE - Paints - Graham Paint and Varnish Co.
ELITE - Paints ☆ - Glidden Co.
ELITE - Paper–bond ☆ - Southworth Co.
ELITE - Pens - Staedtler, Inc.
ELITE - Personal-care shower - Interbath, Inc.
ELITE - Pet products - Farnam Cos. Inc.
ELITE - Pet products - Rolf C. Hagen (USA) Corp.
ELITE - Pet products - Vortex Innerspace Products Inc.
ELITE - Pharmaceutical preparations - Vector Laboratories, Inc.
ELITE - Plastics–laminated - Plaskolite Inc.
ELITE - Playing cards - Old Bridge Playing Card Co., Inc.
ELITE - Publisher's imprints - Lusan Inc.
ELITE - Pumps - Titan Tool Inc.
ELITE - Puzzles ☆ - Warren Industries Inc.
ELITE - Rackets–racquetball - Head Sports USA
ELITE - Recording label - No-Bull Records
ELITE - Regulators–automotive - Carotron, Inc.
ELITE - Ribbons - Princess Ribbon Corp.
ELITE - Rulers–metal - Alvin and Co. Inc.
ELITE - Soccer equipment ☆ - Brine Inc.
ELITE - Sporting goods - Nordictrack, Inc.
ELITE - Sporting goods ☆ - O'Brien International
ELITE - Strollers–baby - Century Products Co.
ELITE - Telephone directories ☆ - Park Sherman
ELITE - Telephones - At&T Corp.
ELITE - Thread - Witten Sales Corp.
ELITE - Tiles–ceramic - Dal-Tile Corp.
ELITE - Tiles–ceramic ☆ - Laufen Ceramic Tile
ELITE - Toothbrushes - Ranir Corp.
ELITE - Toys–automobiles - Kyohei Murakami
ELITE - Trailers–horse - Merhow Industries
ELITE - Trailers–travel - Travel Line Enterprises Inc.
ELITE - Trailers–travel ☆ - Excel Trailer Co. Inc.
ELITE - Vacuum cleaners and accessories - The Hoover Co.
ELITE - Vans–conversion - Coachmen Industries, Inc.
ELITE - Veterinary pharmaceutical preparations - Elite Pet Products, Inc.
ELITE - Wallets ☆ - Enger-Kress Co.
ELITE - Wallpaper - Capital Carousel Inc.
ELITE - Washing machines–household - White Consolidated Industries, Inc.
ELITE - Watches - Precise International/Wenger
ELITE - Water heaters - Reco Industries, Inc.
ELITE - Water treating compounds - Aquacare Systems, Inc.
ELITE - Wheelchairs - Jaken Co., Inc.

☆ = Now out of production

ELITE - Wheels–motor vehicle - Progressive Custom Wheels

ELITE - Wiring devices - Erico International Corp.

ELITE 4 - Veterinary pharmaceutical preparations - Boehringer Ingelheim Animal Health, Inc.

ELITE 4-HS - Veterinary pharmaceutical preparations - Boehringer Ingelheim Animal Health, Inc.

ELITE 9 - Veterinary pharmaceutical preparations - Boehringer Ingelheim Animal Health, Inc.

ELITE 9-HS - Veterinary pharmaceutical preparations - Boehringer Ingelheim Animal Health, Inc.

ELITE 16 - Computer hardware - Profit Systems Inc.

ELITE ACCESS SYSTEMS, INC. - Electronic equipment - Elite Access Systems, Inc.

ELITE BRAND - Food products - Saval Foods Corp.

ELITE BREED - Pet product - American Leather Specialties

ELITE BY REGENCY - Greeting cards - Regency Thermographers Inc.

ELITE COLLECTION - Dinnerware–glass - Sango Co. Ltd. (Sango USA Div.)

ELITE DIAMOND - Finishing agents - Flecto Co. Inc.

ELITE EDITION - Apparel and accessories - Blue Bell, Inc.

ELITE EMERALD - Bedding - Ohio Mattress Co.

ELITE GLASS-SEAL - Shingles - Tamko Roofing Products, Inc.

ELITE GLASS-SEAL AR - Shingles - Tamko Roofing Products, Inc.

ELITE HOME THEATRE - Electronic equipment - Pioneer Electronics USA Inc.

ELITE JUNIOR - Greeting cards - Regency Thermographers Inc.

ELITE KNITS - Crocheted and knitted items - Le Roy Knitted Sportswear Inc.

ELITE LOGOS BY IRELAND - Computer storage devices–optical - Ireland Enterprises, Inc.

ELITE MASSAGE - Personal-care shower - Interbath, Inc.

ELITE OPAL - Bedding - Ohio Mattress Co.

ELITE PERFORMANCE U.S.A - Vitamins and nutritional supplements - Lawrence Kaye

ELITE RIDER - Footwear–athletic - Puma Inc.

ELITE RUBY - Bedding - Ohio Mattress Co.

ELITE SAPPHIRE - Bedding - Ohio Mattress Co.

ELITE SERIES, THE - Baseball trading cards - Leaf, Inc.

ELITE SOIR - Fabrics ☆ - Charter Fabrics Inc.

ELITE SPORT - Apparel–women's - Colberts.

ELITE SPORT COATING SYSTEM - Paints - A.D. Rossi Corp.

ELITE STAINLESS STEEL COUNTRY CLUB - Cooking equipment–household - LazyMan, Inc.

ELITE TACTICAL EQUIPMENT - Guns - Gustavo Rodriguez

ELITE TE - Boats–motor - Glasstream Boats Inc.

ELITE, THE - Binders ☆ - 20th Century Plastics

ELITECLONE - Fruits and vegetables - Epitope Inc.

ELITES - Doors–glass - Jeld-Wen, Inc.

ELITES - Musical instrument accessories - Meisel Music Inc.

ELITES - Paints - Surface Protection Industries, Inc.

ELITES - Seafood products–fresh or frozen - Fishery Products International USA

ELITSES - Olives–canned - Peloponnese

ELIX - Fishing lures - Sheldons', Inc.

ELIX - Vitamins and nutritional supplements - Wellness Beverage Co.

ELIXIR - Computer software - Majiq, Inc.

ELIXIR - Pollen extracts - CC Pollen Co.

ELIXIR DE HOJAS DE NOGAL NEGRO - Pharmaceutical preparations - Vartex Pharmaceuticals Inc.

ELIXIR DE LIQUEUR - Beverages–alcohol ☆ - Westin Inc.

ELIXIR OF LIFE - Health care products - Natural Laboratories Corp.

ELIXIR OF LIFE - Vitamins and nutritional supplements - Planetary Formulas

ELIXIR OF LOVE - Skin care products - Caswell-Massey Co. Ltd.

ELIXIR OF LOVE NO. 1 - Colognes - Caswell-Massey Co. Ltd.

ELIXIRAL - Pharmaceutical preparations - Vita Elixir Co. Inc.

ELIXOMIN - Pharmaceutical preparations - H.R. Cenci Laboratories Inc.

ELIXOPHYLLIN - Pharmaceutical preparations - Forest Pharmaceuticals Inc.

ELIXOPHYLLIN ELIXIR - Pharmaceutical preparations - Forest Pharmaceuticals Inc.

ELIYA - Posters - Aegis Entertainment, Inc.

+ELIZA #CHOI - Apparel–women's - Joneli Fabrics Inc.

ELIZA DUCK - Housewares ☆ - Shafford Co. Inc.

ELIZABETH - Bedding–linen ☆ - Dan River Inc.

ELIZABETH - Clocks - General Time Corp. (Westclox/Seth Thomas Div.)

ELIZABETH - Dolls ☆ - Effanbee Doll Corp.

ELIZABETH - Glassware–household - Anchor Hocking Glass, Inc.

ELIZABETH - Hosiery–women's - Vida Enterprise Corp.

ELIZABETH ARDEN - Cosmetic bags - Unopco Sub, Inc.

ELIZABETH ARDEN - Cosmetics - Elizabeth Arden Inc.

ELIZABETH ARDEN ONE GREAT SOAP - Soap - Unopco Sub, Inc.

ELIZABETH CAROLE COLLECTION, THE - Dolls - Moore Enterprises, Inc.

ELIZABETH CLAIRE - Apparel–women's ☆ - Malouf Co.

ELIZABETH COLLECTION - Glassware–household ☆ - Fenton Art Glass Co.

ELIZABETH DREW - Tablecloths - Standard Terry Mills Inc.

ELIZABETH GRADY - Skin care products - Elizabeth Grady Face First, Inc.

ELIZABETH GRADY FACE FIRST - Beauty shops - Elizabeth Grady Face First Inc.

ELIZABETH +KAYE COLLECTION - Apparel–women's - Elizabeth Kaye Collection

ELIZABETH KODA-CALLAN'S MAGIC CHARM BOOKS - Publisher's imprints - Elizabeth Koda-Callan

ELIZABETH LOCKE - Jewelry - Elizabeth Locke

ELIZABETH MEY - Skin care products - Mentos Products Co.

ELIZABETH POST - Hair care products - Lander Co., Inc.

ELIZABETH RAE - Cosmetics - Donovan Industries, Inc.

ELIZABETH TAYLOR - Perfume and cologne - Elizabeth Taylor Cosmetics Co.

ELIZABETH TAYLOR'S PASSION - Perfumes - Prince Matchabelli

ELIZABETH TAYLOR'S PASSION FOR MEN - Perfumes - Prince Matchabelli

ELIZABETH VAN BUREN - Oils–essential - Elizabeth Van Buren Aromatherapy

ELIZABETH WOOD - Apparel and accessories - Elizabeth Wood Inc.

ELIZABETH YORK - Food products - Wakefern Food Corp.

ELIZABETHAN - Floor coverings–carpet and rugs ☆ - World Carpets, Inc.

ELIZABETHAN - Giftware - Norcrest China Co.

ELIZABETHAN - Jams and jellies - Christopher Brookes Distinctive Foods

ELIZABETHAN - Tobacco–chewing or smoking - Alfred Dunhill of London Inc.

ELIZABETHAN ENGLAND - Jams and jellies ☆ - Christopher Brookes Distinctive Foods

ELJAY - Meat products–poultry - El Jay Poultry Corp.

ELJER - Plumbing fixtures–metal - Eljer Plumbingware

ELK - Bicycles - Columbia Manufacturing Co.

ELK - Paints - Olympic Paint & Varnish Co.

ELK - Work clothes - Elk Brand Manufacturing

ELK BUGLING SCENT - Hunting equipment - Wildlife Research Center, Inc.

ELK CAPSTONE - Shingles - Elk Corp. of Dallas

ELK COVE VINEYARDS - Wines - Elk Cove Vineyards

ELK CREEK - Furniture ☆ - Vaughan Furniture Co. Inc.

ELK-FIRE - Hunting equipment - Wildlife Research Center, Inc.

ELK HILL VINEYARDS - Wines - La Abra Farm & Winery Inc.

ELK HUNTER - Sleeping bags - Coleman Co., Inc.

ELK MOON MURDER, THE - Games - Activision, Inc.

ELK MOUNTAIN AMBER - Beverages–malt - Anheuser-Busch Companies Inc.

ELK MOUNTAIN HERBS - Vitamins and nutritional supplements - Elk Mountain Herbs, Inc.

ELK MOUNTAIN RED - Beverages–malt - Anheuser-Busch Companies Inc.

ELK PARK - Furniture ☆ - Kincaid Furniture Co. Inc.

ELK PRESTIQUE I HIGH DEFINITION - Shingles - Elk Corp. of Dallas

ELK PRESTIQUE II RAISED PROFILE - Shingles - Elk Corp. of Dallas

ELK PRESTIQUE PLUS HIGH DEFINITION - Shingles - Elk Corp. of Dallas

ELK RIDGE VINEYARDS - Wines - Gibson Wine Co.

ELK SEAL-A-RIDGE PLUS - Shingles - Elk Corp. of Dallas

ELK Z - Shingles - Elk Corp. of Dallas

ELKA - Amplifiers–musical instrument - Colombo & Sons Accordion Co.

ELKA - Audio equipment ☆ - Music Industries Inc.

ELKA - Food products - Elka Gilmore

ELKA - Jewelry - Elka Jewel Industries Inc.

ELKAN-VOGEL - Music–sheet - Theodore Presser Co.

ELKAVOX - Accordions - Castiglione Accordion

ELKAY - Fountains–drinking - Elkay Manufacturing Co.

ELKAY - Padding–foam - Elkay Products Co. Inc.

ELKAY WATER SENTRY - Water coolers - Elkay Manufacturing Co.

ELKCOTE - Paints ☆ - Steelcote Manufacturing Corp.

ELKE'S - Biscuits - Murray-Allen International Inc.

ELKES BISCUITS - Cookies - Cornwall Group Inc.

ELKHAN - Apparel–men's - Elkhan Inc.

ELKHART - Firefighting apparatus - Elkhart Brass Manufacturing Co. Inc.

ELKHART - Musical instrument accessories ☆ - Selmer Co. Inc.

ELKHORN - Musical instruments ☆ - Getzen Co.

ELKHORN - Trailers–travel - Fleetwood Enterprises, Inc.

ELKIE - Dolls - Mattel, Inc.

ELKIN - Coffee - Elkin Coffee, Inc.

ELKLAND - Footwear - Kobacker Co.

ELL - Packaging machines ☆ - International Paper Co.

ELLA BACHE - Skin care products - Ella Bache Inc.

☆ = Now out of production

ELLANAR - Cleaning preparations - L & R Manufacturing Co.
ELLE - Handbags - Magnum Fashions Inc.
ELLE - Mirrors - Nailtex Inc.
ELLEGANCE COLOURS - Cosmetics - NaturElle Cosmetics
ELLEN ASHLEY - Apparel and accessories - Hit or Miss Inc.
+ELLEN #ASHLEY - Apparel–women's - Hit or Miss Inc.
ELLEN B - Apparel–women's - Lane Bryant, Inc.
ELLEN JAY - Apparel and accessories - T.J. & E. Sales and Services Corp.
ELLEN LANGE - Skin care products - Ellen Lange
ELLEN MCCARN - Patterns–clothing - McCarn Enterprises Inc.
ELLEN ORIGINALS - Craft supplies - Ross Manufacturing Co. Inc.
ELLEN TRACY - Belts - Cipriani
ELLEN TRACY - Housewares - Ellen Tracy, Inc.
ELLEN TRACY - Scarves - Collection XIIX Ltd.
ELLEN TRACY - Shoes - Intershoe Inc.
ELLEN TRACY - Sunglasses - Private Eyes Sunglass Corp.
ELLEN TRACY - Wallpaper - United Wallcoverings
ELLENDALE - Catsup - Brooks Foods
ELLENDALE VINEYARDS - Wines - Ellendale Vineyards Inc.
ELLEN'S RAINBOW SALT - Food products - Headway Market
ELLERIE FASHIONS - Coats–children's - MZL Fashions Corp.
ELLERY - Whirlpools - Kohler Co.
ELLERY AND GORDON - Apparel and accessories - Specialty Department Stores, Inc.
ELLERY QUEEN'S MYSTERY CLUB - Publisher's imprints - Walter J. Black Inc.
ELLESDALE MANOR - Furniture - Davis Cabinet Co.
ELLESSE - Shoes - Ellesse USA Inc.
ELLESSE SUNMIRRORS - Sunglasses ☆ - Marchon and Marcolin Eyewear Inc.
ELLESSEE - Giftware - Sasaki
ELLICOTT - Paints - Ellicott Paint Co. Inc.
ELLIE ELEPHANT - Toys–stuffed - Dakin Inc.
ELLIE LANCE - Skin care products - Ellie Lance Creations
ELLIE MAY CHOPPE - Dolls - Meritus Industries, Inc.
ELLIE'S CAKE RACK - Housewares - Ella Lockett
ELLIJAY APPLE BREAD - Bakery products - Life's Little Pleasures Bakery, Inc.
ELLIMAN'S - Pharmaceutical preparations - Consolidated Midland Corp.
ELLINGTON - Clocks ☆ - General Time Corp. (Westclox/Seth Thomas Div.)
ELLINGTON - Dishes–china - Pickard Inc.
ELLINGTON - Electronic equipment - Monotype Corp.
ELLINGTON - Toilets–enameled - Kohler Co.
ELLIO'S - Pizzas–frozen - McCain Ellio's Foods, Inc.
ELLIOT - Amplifiers - Bob White Associates
ELLIOT - Boats–motor ☆ - C.J. Hendry
ELLIOT STEVENS - Apparel–men's - Smart Style Industries Inc.
ELLIOTT - Apparel–men's - La Strada Fashions, Inc.
ELLIOTT - Dog food - Chapin Livestock Supplements
ELLIOTT - Frames–eyeglass ☆ - U.S. Optical Frame Co.
ELLIOTT - Paints ☆ - Valspar Corp.
ELLIOTT - Toys–stuffed - RPM Inc.
ELLIOTT - Trees - Burchell Nursery, Inc.
ELLIOTT FISHER - Office supplies ☆ - Olivetti North America Inc. (Consumer Products Div.)
ELLIOTT OF LONDON - Clocks - Kashlan Co.
ELLIOTT'S - Fruit drinks–bottled or canned - Amazing Beverages, Inc.
ELLIOTT'S - Wines ☆ - David Sherman Corp.
ELLIOTT'S AMAZING - Fruit drinks–bottled or canned - Amazing Beverages, Inc.
ELLIOTT'S BEST - Paints ☆ - Valspar Corp.
ELLIP-SEE-CON - Contact lenses - Conforma Contact Lenses
ELLIPS-ANGLE - Drafting supplies - Timely Products Co.
ELLIPSE - Computer database software - Cooperative Solutions, Inc.
ELLIPSE - Floor coverings–carpet and rugs ☆ - Regal Rugs Inc.
ELLIPSE - Office furniture–metal - Steelcase Inc.
ELLIPSE - Pens - Scripto-Tokai Corp.
ELLIPSE - Tiles–ceiling - United States Gypsum Co.
ELLIPSE - Toilets–enameled - Kohler Co.
ELLIPSE - Wheelchairs - Everest and Jennings International Ltd.
ELLIPSIS - Apparel and accessories - Ellipsis, Inc.
ELLIPSOID OF POWER - Golfing equipment - Hillerich & Bradsby Co.
ELLIPSYS - Computer software - Ellipsys Technologies, Inc.
ELLIPSYS TECHNOLOGIES - Computer software - Ellipsys Technologies, Inc.
ELLIPTIC - Erasers ☆ - Bright Boy Abrasives
ELLIS - Coffee - Ellis Coffee Co.

ELLIS - Food products - Stokes/Ellis Foods
ELLIS - Lighting fixtures - Hubbell Lighting, Inc. (Lighting Div.)
ELLIS-BARKER - Silverware - Ellis Barker Silver Co.
ELLIS CARROLL COLLECTION, THE - Apparel and accessories - Sweaters 'N' Things Ltd.
ELLIS-MASTER PRONUNCIATION - Computer software - Cali, Inc.
ELLIS SENIOR MASTERY - Computer software - Cali, Inc.
ELLISANTO REGE - Wines - Diamond Oaks Vineyard
ELLISON - Bicycles - Ellison Bicycles
ELLISON - Machinery - Ellison Educational Equipment, Inc.
ELLISSE - Bathroom fixtures and fittings - American Standard Inc.
ELLONGE - Nail care products - Monteil Paris
ELLSEY MALT VINEGAR - Vinegar - Europa Foods Ltd.
ELLSWORTH - Shoes - Allen-Edmonds Shoe Corp.
ELLSWORTH - Tableware–china ☆ - Lenox, Inc.
ELLSWORTH - Watches - Bulova Corp.
ELLUSION - Skin care products ☆ - Fanie International
ELLYP-TECH, THE - Rackets–tennis - Spalding Sports Worldwide
ELLYPSE - Furniture–children's - Child Craft Industries Inc.
ELLYPSE - Glassware–household - Durand International
ELM - Food products - Allen Canning Co.
ELM - Recording label - Jazz Composer's Orchestra Association Inc.
ELM DALE - Food products - Associated Wholesalers Inc.
ELM GROUNDS - Wallcoverings - Elm Grounds
ELM GROUNDS - Wallpaper - Hawthorne Prints Inc.
ELM GROVE DAIRY - Dips–sour cream based - Elm Grove Dairy
ELM RIDGE - Toilets–porcelain - Mansfield Plumbing Products, Inc.
ELM STREET - Furniture ☆ - Broyhill Furniture Industries, Inc.
ELM VALLEY - Beverages–alcohol - L. Mawby Vineyards-Winery
ELMAR - Photographic equipment - Leica USA Inc.
ELMAR - Toys - Elmar Products Co.
ELMARIT - Photographic equipment - Leica USA Inc.
ELMARON - Photographic equipment - Leica USA Inc.
ELMAS - Food products - House of Yemen Inc.
ELMENTRY - Computer input keyboard - Elmentry Enterprises
ELMER - Trophies–metal - Tropar Manufacturing Co., Inc.
ELMER CLOWN - Dolls ☆ - Effanbee Doll Corp.
ELMER EGGPLANT AND HIS WORLD - Toys–stuffed - Beth J. Geiges
ELMER FUDD - Apparel and accessories - Time Warner Entertainment Co., L.P.
ELMER LITTLE - Gloves - Swany America Corp.
ELMER T. LEE - Beverages–alcohol - R.H. Farms Inc.
ELMER T. LEE SINGLE BARREL - Beverages–alcohol - Sazerac Co. Inc.
ELMER'S - Adhesives and sealants - Elmer's Products, Inc.
ELMER'S - Candy - Elmer Candy Corp.
ELMER'S NEW ORLEANS CHOCOLATE SELECTIONS - Candy - Elmer Candy Corp.
ELMER'S WEATHER - TITE - Glue–household or industrial - T.M.I. Associates, LP
ELMHURST - Apparel–men's - Nulook Fashions Menswear Inc.
ELMHURST - Floor coverings - Mannington Resilient Floors
ELMHURST DAIRY - Milk - Honeywell Farms
ELMO - Cheese ☆ - Stella Foods, Inc.
ELMO - Office machines ☆ - Elmo Manufacturing Corp.
ELMO PIO - Wines - Ernest and Julio Gallo Winery
ELMODA - Thread - United Thread Mills Corp.
ELMORE - Thread - Elmore-Pisgah, Inc.
ELMOTIL - Pharmaceutical preparations ☆ - ICN Pharmaceuticals Inc.
ELMS AGAIN - Flowers, plants, and seeds - Raymond H. Smith
ELMS, THE - Wallpaper - Exeter Wallcoverings
ELMWOOD - Furniture ☆ - Mersman Furniture Co.
ELNA - Food products - Frank's Food Mart
ELNA - Sewing machines–household - Tacony Corp.
ELNOR - Food products - W & W Meats Inc.
ELO TOUCHSYSTEMS - Computer hardware - ELO Touchsystems, Inc.
ELO TOUCHSYSTEMS - Computer hardware - ELO Touchsystems, Inc.
ELOCON - Skin care products - Schering-Plough Healthcare Products
ELODER - Boats–motor ☆ - Checkmate Boats Inc.
ELOISE - Dinnerware–glass ☆ - Royal China & Porcelain Companies Inc.
ELOISE ELEPHANT - Toys–stuffed - Russ Berrie and Co., Inc.
ELON - Photographic equipment - Eastman Kodak Co.
ELONGATE - Pet products - Kidco, Inc.
ELOQUENCE - Bedding–linen ☆ - Fieldcrest Cannon, Inc.
ELOQUENCE - Christmas tree ornaments - Cracker Box Inc.
ELOQUENCE - Clocks - General Time Corp. (Westclox/Seth Thomas Div.)
ELOQUENCE - Computer software - Hewlett-Packard Co.

☆ = Now out of production

ELOQUENCE - Floor coverings–carpet and rugs - Karastan-Bigelow Inc.
ELOQUENCE - Furniture ☆ - Stanley Furniture Co. Inc.
ELOQUENCE - Hearing aids - Rexton Inc.
ELOQUENCE - Pillows - E.I. Dupont de Nemours and Co.
ELOQUENCE - Rings–jewelry - Artcarved Inc.
ELOQUENCE - Silverware - Lunt Silversmiths
ELOQUENCE - Tableware–china ☆ - Lenox, Inc.
ELOQUENCE - Vases ☆ - Lenox Crystal, Inc.
ELOQUENCE - Wallpaper - Bill Villetto Designs Inc.
ELOQUENCE - Wallpaper ☆ - Bob Mitchell Designs
ELOQUENCE II ACCENTS - Floor coverings–carpet and rugs ☆ - Karastan-Bigelow Inc.
ELOQUENT - Electronic equipment repair shops - Eloquent, Inc.
ELOQUENT - Floor coverings–carpet and rugs ☆ - Downs Carpet Co. Inc.
ELOQUENT - Floor coverings–carpet and rugs ☆ - Regal Rugs Inc.
ELOQUENT EXPRESSIONS - Tables–metal ☆ - Samsonite Corp.
ELOQUENT TOUCH - Floor coverings–carpet and rugs - Queen Carpet Corp.
ELOXAL - Cigarette holders - Gesty Trading & Manufacturing Corp.
ELOXYL - Pharmaceutical preparations ☆ - ICN Pharmaceuticals Inc.
ELPAR - Motor vehicles–trucks - Elwell-Parker Electric Co.
ELPECO SYRUP - Cough medicines - Luyties Pharmacal Co.
ELPETN - Pharmaceutical preparations ☆ - ICN Pharmaceuticals Inc.
ELPIS - Golfing equipment - Imax Corp.
ELPO - Novelty items–glass - Elpo Products Inc.
ELR - Electrical equipment - High Voltage Supply, Inc.
ELRIC - Games - Chaosium Inc.
ELRIC - Games ☆ - Avalon Hill Game Co.
ELROY - Computer software - Headbone Interactive, Inc.
ELROY HITS THE PAVEMENT - Video tapes–blank - Headbone Interactive, Inc.
ELS - Hardware - Electronic Locking Specialties Inc.
EL'S - Prepared foods - Elmer J. Lambert
ELS ELS LANGUAGE CENTERS - Publisher's imprints - Els Educational Services, Inc.
ELSA WILLIAMS - Yarn - JCA, Inc.
ELSANE - Desk sets - Sainberg and Co. Inc.
ELSENHAM - Jams and jellies - C. & J. Willenborg Inc.
ELSENHAM 1890 - Meat products–pork - JMS Specialty Foods Inc.
ELSET - Bandages - Tecnol Medical Products, Inc.
ELSEVE - Hair care products - Cosmair Inc.
ELSEWORLDS - Books–comic - DC Comics
ELSIE STIX - Confections - Borden, Inc.
ELSINORE - Flatware - Dansk International Designs, Ltd.
ELSINORE - Floor coverings–carpet and rugs ☆ - Eurotex Inc.
ELSOL - Apparel and accessories - Georges Marciano
ELSON'S - Candy - W.H. Smith Inc.
ELSPAR - Pharmaceutical preparations - Merck & Co., Inc. (Merck Research Laboratories)
ELSV - Hardware ☆ - Wasco Products, Inc.
ELT - Electronics equipment - Physical Health Devices Inc.
ELT - Vitamins and nutritional supplements - Essential Life Tech, Inc.
ELTA - Cosmetics - Swiss-American Products, Inc.
ELTEK - Electronic equipment - Eltek, Inc.
ELTEK LC - Watches - Commodore Business Machines Inc.
ELTONE - Paints ☆ - Valspar Corp.
ELTRA - Watches - Elgin Watch Co.
ELTREX - Telephone accessories - Comex Systems Co.
ELTRON - Heating pads–electric - Chromalox
ELTRON - Razors–electric ☆ - Hampton-Haddon Marketing
ELTTAB - Apparel and accessories - Elttab Inc.
ELUPATCH - Pharmaceutical preparations - Transdermal Products, Inc.
ELURA - Wigs ☆ - Monsanto Co.
ELUSIVE IMAGE NATURE PHOTOGRAPHY - Greeting cards - Carol Davis
ELUSIVE LEGEND - Giftware ☆ - Enesco Corp.
ELUSTRA - Apparel and accessories ☆ - Munsingwear, Inc.
ELVEN BANNER - Games ☆ - Mayfair Games, Inc.
ELVES - Games ☆ - Mayfair Games, Inc.
ELVES CHRISTMAS FOREST, THE - Christmas trees - Ampro, Inc.
ELVIN ELEPHANT - Puppets - Dakin Inc.
ELVIRA - Cosmetics - London International U.S. Holdings
ELVIRA - Novelty items - Imagineering Inc.
ELVIRA MISTRESS OF THE DARK - Novelty items - Imagineering Inc.
ELVIS - Colognes - Brandy Harvest
ELVIS - Toys–stuffed - Elvis Presley Enterprises Inc.
ELVIS GUNDY - Toys–stuffed - Gund, Inc.
ELVIS PRESLEY - Dolls ☆ - Toy Works, Inc.

ELVIS PRESLEY - Novelty items - Elvis Presley Enterprises Inc.
ELVIS: THE LEGEND LIVES ON - Games - S. Alden Inc.
ELVIS WEEK - Postcards - Elvis Presley Enterprises Inc.
ELVOX - Audio equipment - Paso Sound Products Inc.
ELWELL - Chickens - Elwell Farms
ELWOOD - Trailers–travel ☆ - Shasta Industries Inc.
ELX - Audio equipment - Electro-Voice, Inc.
ELY - Shirts - Ely and Walker Co.
ELY DIAMOND - Apparel–men's - Ely and Walker Co.
ELY WOULD - Golfing equipment - Callaway Golf Co.
ELYESSE - Furniture ☆ - Bassett Furniture Industries, Inc.
ELYON - Marshmallows - Shimon Eider
ELYSEE - Cigars ☆ - Tropical Tobacco, Inc.
ELYSEE - Dinnerware–glass ☆ - Royal China & Porcelain Companies Inc.
ELYSEE - Pens - Erwin Pearl Inc.
ELYSEE - Rings–jewelry - Artcarved Inc.
ELYSEE - Skin care products - Elysee Scientific Cosmetic Co.
ELYSEE - Wallpaper - Bayview Wallcoverings
ELYSEE - Watches ☆ - Crawford Watch Co. Inc.
ELYSEE ROYALE - Wines ☆ - Parliament Import Co.
ELYSEES - Frames–picture - Louis Michel Cie.
ELYSIAN FIELDS - Toiletries - Elysian Fields, Inc.
ELYSIAN GOLD - Vitamins and nutritional supplements ☆ - Great Life Laboratories Inc.
ELYSIUM - Floor coverings–carpet and rugs ☆ - Evans-Black Carpet Mills
ELYSIUM - Food products - Stache Foods
ELYSIUM - Perfumes - Clarins USA Inc.
ELYSIUM - Wines - Quady Winery
ELYSIUM BLOOM - Dinnerware–glass ☆ - Arita Sales Co. Inc.
ELZYME 303 - Pharmaceutical preparations ☆ - ICN Pharmaceuticals Inc.
ELZZUP - Puzzles ☆ - Carrom Co.
EM - Electrical equipment - Electro-Matic Products, Inc.
EM - Electronics equipment - Educational Media Inc.
EM - Floor coverings - Congoleum Corp.
EM - Industrial machinery - Greenfield Tap & Die
EM - Jewelry - Easom Manufacturing Corp.
EM - Metal fasteners - Eastwood Manufacturing
EM - Paint sprayers - Graco Inc.
EM - Pet products - Aquarium Pharmaceuticals, Inc.
EM - Tools–machine - Greenfield Industries Inc.
EM 1 - Exercising equipment - Marcy Fitness Products
EM-55 - Artists' materials ☆ - LogEtronics Corp.
EM-97 - Mirrors–optical - Viratec Thin Films, Inc.
EM/DATA - Computer software - Blade Software, Inc.
EM ES - Paint removers ☆ - Lilly Perfection Paint
EM-K - Vitamins and nutritional supplements ☆ - Econo Med Pharmaceuticals Inc.
E.M. MERCK COLLECTION - Nutcrackers - Old World Christmas
EM-NI - Tools - Greenfield Industries Inc.
EM-SS - Tools - Greenfield Industries Inc.
EM-TI - Tools - Greenfield Industries Inc.
EM TUFF - Industrial machinery - Greenfield Tap & Die
EM-TUFF - Tools–machine - Greenfield Industries Inc.
EM-VAR-CO - Lacquers - Waterlox Coatings Corp.
EM-VAR-CO-LAC - Lacquers - Waterlox Coatings Corp.
EMA - Jewelry - EMA Jewelry Inc.
EMACK AND BOLIO'S - Restaurants–fast food - Emack & Bolio's
EMACK & BOLIO'S ICE CREAM AND YOGURT FOR THE CONNOISSEUR - Ice cream - Gone Troppo Inc.
EMACO - Adhesives and sealants - Master Builders Inc.
EMAGRIN - Analgesics - Otis Clapp & Son Inc.
EMAGRIN FORTE - Analgesics - Otis Clapp & Son Inc.
EMAIL DIAMANT - Toothpaste - Caswell-Massey Co. Ltd.
EMALINE - Hardware - Sigma Coatings USA BV.
EMALJ - Paints - Masury Paint Co.
EMAM - Hair care products - Emam Inc.
EMANELO - Cigars - National Cigar Corp.
EMANUEL UNGARO - Cosmetics - Parfums Ungaro Inc.
EMANUEL UNGARO - Ophthalmic goods - Luxottica
EMANUEL UNGARO - Suits–men's - Wm. B. Kessler Inc.
EMANUEL WILFER - Violins - Ideal Musical Merchandise Co.
EMANUELE CRAVATTE - Apparel and accessories - Pure Luck Enterprises, Inc.
EMARKURE - Pet products - Emark Tropical Imports
EMAX - Building materials - Exhibitgroup Inc.
EMAX - Musical instruments ☆ - E-Mu Systems, Inc.

EMBA - Floor coverings–carpet and rugs ☆ - Columbus Mills, Inc.

EMBA VECTOR - Heating equipment ☆ - Embassy Industries Inc.

EMBALMING - Recording label - New Renaissance Records

EMBARC - Boxes - Star Case Manufacturing Co. Inc.

EMBARCADERO COLLECTION - Apparel–men's - Big & Tall Associates

EMBARK - Moldings and trim - Contact Lumber Co.

EMBASA - Sauces - Ingro

EMBASSADOR - Doors–garage - McKee Door, Inc.

EMBASSY - Burial vaults–concrete - Cardinal/Embassy Group, Inc.

EMBASSY - Cabinets ☆ - Aristokraft, Inc.

EMBASSY - Cases–musical instrument - St. Louis Music Supply Co.

EMBASSY - Cutlery ☆ - Carvel Hall Inc.

EMBASSY - Dishes–china - Pickard Inc.

EMBASSY - Dishes–china ☆ - Royal China & Porcelain Companies Inc.

EMBASSY - Doors–wood ☆ - Peachtree Doors and Windows Inc.

EMBASSY - Fabrics - Uniroyal Engineered Products

EMBASSY - Flatware - Reed and Barton Corp.

EMBASSY - Floor coverings - Mannington Resilient Floors

EMBASSY - Floor coverings–carpet and rugs - American Carpet Mills

EMBASSY - Floor coverings–carpet and rugs - Ebsco Carpet Mills

EMBASSY - Floor coverings–carpet and rugs - Quaker Inc.

EMBASSY - Furniture ☆ - Broyhill Furniture Industries, Inc.

EMBASSY - Glass–leaded - Seneca Glass Co.

EMBASSY - Glassware–household - Owens-Illinois Inc. (Libbey Div.)

EMBASSY - Hardware - National Lock Hardware

EMBASSY - Heating equipment - Embassy Industries Inc.

EMBASSY - Intimate apparel - E.S. Industries Inc.

EMBASSY - Milk - Embassy Dairy

EMBASSY - Musical instruments - C. Bruno & Son Inc.

EMBASSY - Occasional tables ☆ - JDI Group, Inc.

EMBASSY - Radio communications equipment - Motorola, Inc. (Land Mobile Products Sector)

EMBASSY - Trimmings–fabric - Wm. E. Wright Ltd.

EMBASSY - Watches - Gruen Marketing Corp.

EMBASSY COLLECTION - Fans–electric - Hunter Fan Co.

EMBASSY COLLECTION - Floor coverings–carpet and rugs - Roxbury Carpet Co.

EMBASSY COLLECTION - Luggage ☆ - Hartmann Luggage Co.

EMBASSY COURT - Floor coverings–carpet and rugs - Bloomsburg Carpet Industries

EMBASSY HOUSE - Furniture - Union National Inc.

EMBASSY OAK - Floor coverings - National Floor Products Co., Inc.

EMBASSY ROW - Apparel–men's ☆ - Nulook Fashions Menswear Inc.

EMBASSY ROW - Floor coverings–carpet and rugs - Barrett Carpet Mills Inc.

EMBASSY ROW - Floor coverings–carpet and rugs - Tuftex Carpet Mills, Inc.

EMBASSY ROW - Furniture ☆ - Lane Co. Inc.

EMBASSY STONE - Concrete products ∑ - SES Ltd.

EMBASSY SUITE - Floor coverings–carpet and rugs - Bloomsburg Carpet Industries

EMBASSY SUITE - Floor coverings–carpet and rugs - Lees Carpets

EMBASSY SYSTEMS - Heating equipment - Embassy Industries Inc.

EMBASSY'S LUCKY BOY - Cookies - Emco Foodservice Systems, Inc.

EMBECO - Adhesives and sealants - Master Builders Inc.

EMBEDSPARC - Computers - Sparc International, Inc.

EMBEDTEC - Computer hardware - Embedtec Corp.

EMBEE - Hardware - Embee Corp.

EMBELLIR - Cosmetics - Designed Management, Inc.

EMBELLISH - Floor coverings–carpet and rugs - Patcraft Mills Inc.

EMBELLISHMENTS - Apparel and accessories - Associated Merchandising Corp.

EMBELLISHMENTS - Patches, insignia, and emblems - Blumenthal/Lansing Co.

EMBELLISHMENTS - Wallpaper - Sunnyside Prints

EMBER - Food products - Peck Foods Corp.

EMBER-GLO - Food warming equipment - Midco International Inc.

EMBER HEARTH - Fireplaces - Rinnai America Corp.

EMBER MUSK - Shampoos - S.C. Johnson & Son, Inc.

EMBER-STAT - Fireplace equipment - Desa International, Inc.

EMBERDALE - Food products - Sugardale Foods Inc.

EMBERDALE - Meat products–pork - Fresh Mark, Inc.

EMBERMATIC - Barbecues and grills - Preway Industries Inc.

EMBERMATIC - Barbecues and grills - Sunbeam Outdoor Products Inc.

EMBERS - Clocks ☆ - General Time Corp. (Westclox/Seth Thomas Div.)

EMBERS - Food products - Bob's Processing

EMBLAZON - Perfumes ☆ - Hair Specialty Co.

EMBLEM - Computer software - Emblem Interactive Inc.

EMBLEM - Fungicides ☆ - ISK Biosciences Corp.

EMBLEM - Oils–lubricating - United Refining Co.

EMBLEM - Ophthalmic goods - Foremost Optical Products

EMBLEM - Thread ☆ - SCT Yarns Inc.

EMBLEM - Vegetables–canned ☆ - Johnston Farms

EMBLEM OF ELEGANCE - Greeting cards - Norcross Inc.

EMBO-GUARD - Pharmaceutical preparations - Tetra Medical Supply Corp.

EMBOLEX - Pharmaceutical preparations - Sandoz Pharmaceuticals Corp.

EMBOSS - Stamps–hand - Tsukineko, Inc.

EMBOSS-O - Artists' materials - Scratch-Art Co., Inc.

EMBOSSART - Manicure preparations - EmbossArt for Nails

EMBOSSED DIMENSIONALS - Wallpaper - Carlton-Metro Wallcoverings

EMBOSSED TULIP DESIGN - Napkins–paper - Georgia-Pacific Corp.

EMBOSSING POWDERS - Craft supplies - Ranger Industries

EMBOSSING POWDERZ - Craft supplies - Z-Barten Productions

EMBRACE - Apparel–women's - Cupid Foundations Inc.

EMBRACE - Cosmetics - Pro Finish USA, Ltd.

EMBRACE - Floor coverings–carpet and rugs ☆ - Gulistan Carpet Inc.

EMBRACE - Lipsticks - Lancome

EMBRACE - Pillows - Pacific Coast Feather Co.

EMBRACE - Rings–jewelry - Artcarved Inc.

EMBRACE LETTES - Jewelry - Jacoby-Bender Inc.

EMBRACE ME - Apparel and accessories - Thomas P. Foley

EMBRACEABLE - Floor coverings–carpet and rugs - Galaxy Carpet Mills Inc.

EMBRACEABLE - Floor coverings–carpet and rugs ☆ - Gulistan Carpet Inc.

EMBRACEABLE - Watches - Hampden Corp.

EMBRACEABLE LACE - Apparel and accessories ☆ - Vanity Fair Mills Inc.

EMBRACEABLE YOU - Floor coverings–carpet and rugs ☆ - Mohawk Carpet Corp.

EMBRACEABLES - Greeting cards - C.M. Paula Co.

EMBRACEABLES - Jewelry - Sandberg & Sikorski Diamond Corp.

EMBRACELETTE - Watches - Hampden Corp.

EMBRACING - Colognes ☆ - Mem Co., Inc.

EMBRACING TECHNOLOGY - Labels–paper - Standard Register Co.

EMBRAPESCA - Seafood products–canned or cured ☆ - Arista Industries Inc.

EMBRASERS - Erasers - Diener Industries Inc.

EMBRO - Olive oil - Moscahlades Bros. Inc.

EMBRO - Thread - United Thread Mills Corp.

EMBROID-A-KIT - Needles–sewing ☆ - Best Emblem & Insignia Co. Inc.

EMBROID-A-MATS - Place mats - Convergence Corp.

EMBROID-O-CARDS - Greeting cards - Reeve Sales Co.

EMBROID-O-PRINTS - Pharmaceutical preparations - Reeve Sales Co.

EMBROID-ON - Fabrics - Stahls' Inc.

EMBROIDERED DAWN - Apparel–women's - Wacoal America Inc.

EMBROIDERY - Dinnerware ☆ - Corning Inc.

EMBROIDERY THEME - Note cards ☆ - American Crewel & Canvas Studio

EMBROS - Wines - Monarch Wine Co. of Georgia

EMBRYO - Recording label - Atlantic Records

EMBRYOVAL - Skin care products ☆ - Christine Valmy, Inc.

EMBSO - Thread ☆ - Perfect Thread Co. Inc.

EMC - Electrical equipment - Underwriters Laboratories Inc.

EMC - Envelope stuffing and sealing machines - Electro-Mechanics Corp.

EMC - Hearing aids ☆ - Magnatone Hearing Aid Corp.

EMC - Jewelry - Bijou Bebe

EMC - Motors–automotive ☆ - Howard Industries Inc.

EMC ELECTRONIC MEDICAL CHART - Computer software - EMC, Inc.

EMC FILMS - Broadcasting stations–television - Educational Marketing Concepts, Inc.

EMC MODULE - Computer software - Automation & Management Services, Inc.

EMC PLU$ - Computer storage devices - Automated Health Systems, Inc.

EMC SQUARED - Pharmaceutical preparations - Soil Stabilization Products Co., Inc.

EMC STATION MANAGER - Computer software - Environmental Monitoring Co., Inc.

EMC SYSTEM MANAGER - Computer software - Environmental Monitoring Co., Inc.

EMC VAC - Veterinary pharmaceutical preparations - Oxford Veterinary Laboratories, Inc.

EMC2 - Computer software - EMC Corp.

EMCELLE - Vitamins and nutritional supplements - Stuart Products, Inc.

EMCI - Guitars ☆ - Fred Gretsch Enterprises

EMCO - Epworth Morehouse-Cowles

EMCO - Badges–uniform - Eagle Metalart Co.

EMCO - Doors–storm - Emco Enterprises, Inc.

EMCO - Electronic equipment - CSI/Speco

EMCO - Lighting fixtures - Thomas Industries Inc.
EMCO - Paints ☆ - Everseal International Sales Co. Inc.
EMCO - Paper–bond ☆ - Esleeck Manufacturing Co., Inc.
EMCO COLA - Food products - Essential Products Co. Inc.
EMCO-REX - Woodworking machinery ☆ - Emco-Maier Corp.
EMCO-STAR - Woodworking machinery ☆ - Emco-Maier Corp.
EMCO USA - Epworth Morehouse-Cowles
EMCOR - Furniture - Crenlo, Inc.
EMCRITIS - Musical instruments ☆ - Armstrong Woodwinds
EMCYT - Pharmaceutical preparations - Kabi Pharmacia Inc.
EMD - Chemical preparations - Chemetals Inc.
EMDEC - Engines–diesel - General Motors Corp.
EMDEE - Pharmaceutical preparations - Marion Merrell Dow
EMED - Computer hardware - E-Systems, Inc.
EMEER - Rings–jewelry - Artcarved Inc.
EMEL-TONE - Paints - Seagraves Coatings
EMELITE - Paints - Seagraves Coatings
EMERAL COVE SEA - Great Eastern Sun Trading Co. Inc.
EMERALAIR - Jewelry ☆ - Litton Systems, Inc. (Airtron Division)
EMERALD - Amplifiers - Essence
EMERALD - Area rugs ☆ - Couristan Inc.
EMERALD - Bicycles - Columbia Manufacturing Inc.
EMERALD - Cakes–mixes - L. Karp & Sons, Inc.
EMERALD - Desk sets - Crystal Clear Importing Co. Inc.
EMERALD - Electronics equipment - Irish Magnetic Industries
EMERALD - Erasers ☆ - Faber-Castell Corp.
EMERALD - Faucets - Flair Cabinetware
EMERALD - Fireplaces ☆ - Malm Fireplaces Inc.
EMERALD - Flatware - Reed and Barton Corp.
EMERALD - Floor coverings–carpet and rugs ☆ - Rugby Rugs Inc.
EMERALD - Frames–picture - Terragrafics Inc.
EMERALD - Generators - Onan Corp.
EMERALD - Glassware–household - ACC
EMERALD - Glassware–household ☆ - Lenox Crystal, Inc.
EMERALD - Grass seed - International Seeds, Inc.
EMERALD - Nuts–salted, roasted, cooked, or canned - Diamond Walnut
Growers, Inc.
EMERALD - Paper–tissue - James River Paper Co., Inc.
EMERALD - Pet products ☆ - Zoo Med Laboratories, Inc.
EMERALD - Recording label - Fiesta Record Co. Inc.
EMERALD - Shampoos - Johnson T&C, Inc.
EMERALD - Toys–stuffed - Dakin Inc.
EMERALD - Trailers–travel ☆ - Carriage, Inc.
EMERALD 2000 - Lubricants - Emerald 2000, Inc.
EMERALD-AWARENESS - Incense - Shoyeido Corp.
EMERALD BAY - Fabrics - Thompson of California Inc.
EMERALD BAY - Floor coverings–carpet and rugs ☆ - Catalina Carpet Mills
Inc.
EMERALD BAY - Furniture ☆ - Hooker Furniture Corp.
EMERALD BAY - Seafood products–fresh or frozen - Emerald Bay Inc.
EMERALD BAY - Tents ☆ - Jinwoong Inc.
EMERALD BAY - Wines - Chateau Julien
EMERALD BAY II - Floor coverings–carpet and rugs ☆ - Walter Carpet Mills
EMERALD BRAID - Dinnerware - Dansk International Designs, Ltd.
EMERALD BRAND - Cleaning preparations - Hocking International Chemical
Corp.
EMERALD BRAND - Fish–fresh or frozen - Pacific Sea Foods Co.
EMERALD CITY - Christmas tree ornaments - Cracker Box Inc.
EMERALD CITY ALE - Beverages–malt - The Stroh Brewery Co.
EMERALD CLASSIC - Garden equipment - Garden Pals, Inc.
EMERALD COLLECTION - Candy - Kraft Foods, Inc.
EMERALD COLLECTION - Fabrics - Vertilux-Louverlux Inc.
EMERALD COLLECTION - Vacuum cleaners and accessories ☆ - Royal
Appliance Manufacturing Co.
EMERALD COVE - Floor coverings–carpet and rugs ☆ - Catalina Carpet Mills
Inc.
EMERALD COVE - Food products - Great Eastern Sun Trading Co. Inc.
EMERALD CREAM - Coffee - Sara Lee Corp.
EMERALD CROWN - Meat products–poultry ☆ - Snowball Foods, Inc.
EMERALD-CUT ROPE - Jewelry - Grando, Inc.
EMERALD EDGE - Rubber–molded - Emerald Products, Inc.
EMERALD ELEGANCE - Dolls - Mattel, Inc.
EMERALD EMBERS - Dolls - Mattel, Inc.
EMERALD EMPRESS - Toys ☆ - Imperial Toy Corp.
EMERALD ENERGY - Vitamins and nutritional supplements - Emerald
Products

EMERALD EYES - Kites ☆ - Hi-Flier Manufacturing Co.
EMERALD FARMS - Milk–canned or powdered - Coastlog Industries Ltd.
EMERALD FOREST - Skin care products - Andrew Ungerleider
EMERALD FOREST - Trees - Emerald Forest, Inc.
EMERALD FOUNTAIN - Flowers, plants, and seeds - Monrovia Nursery Co.
EMERALD GARDENS - Agricultural products - Kevlaur Industries, Inc.
EMERALD GARDENS - Teas - Celestial Seasonings, Inc.
EMERALD GLEN - Floor coverings ☆ - Congoleum Corp.
EMERALD GREEN - Food products - C.M. Holtzinger Fruit Co. Inc.
EMERALD GREEN TEA - Vitamins and nutritional supplements - Amrion, Inc.
EMERALD ISLE - Beverages–alcohol - Beverage America, Inc.
EMERALD ISLE - Dolls ☆ - Effanbee Doll Corp.
EMERALD ISLE - Wallpaper - Scalamandre Silks Inc.
EMERALD ISLE COLLECTION - Furniture–factory ☆ - Clayton Marcus Co.
Inc.
EMERALD MIST - Christmas tree ornaments - Cracker Box Inc.
EMERALD NEWTOWN - Food products ☆ - Diamond Fruit Growers
EMERALD POINT - Furniture ☆ - Vaughan Furniture Co. Inc.
EMERALD POOL - Whirlpools - Geritrex Corp.
EMERALD RADIANCE - Tableware–china - Pfaltzgraff Investment Co.
EMERALD RESIN PAPER - Paper–sand - Swimc, Inc.
EMERALD SARI, THE - Christmas tree ornaments - Cracker Box Inc.
EMERALD SCROLL - Glassware–household ☆ - Culver Glass Inc.
EMERALD SKY - Dolls - Tonka Corp.
EMERALD SNOW - Christmas tree ornaments - Cracker Box Inc.
EMERALD STAR - Rings–jewelry - Artcarved Inc.
EMERALDS TO COCONUTS - Apparel and accessories - Emeralds to
Coconuts, Inc.
EMERAUDE - Glassware–household - Durand International
EMERAUDE - Perfume, dusting powder, bath oil, etc. - Coty Inc.
EMERAUDE SOFTWEAR - Skin-care products - Coty Inc.
EMERCAL - Bird feeds ☆ - Lafeber Co.
EMERFAX - Facsimile equipment - Emerson Radio Corp.
EMERG-ALERT - Identification tags - Apothecary Products, Inc.
EMERGE - Skin care products - Helene Curtis Industries Inc.
EMERGE! PRO - Computer software ☆ - Caroline Pratt and Associates, Inc.
EMERGEN-C - Vitamins and nutritional supplements - Alacer Co.
EMERGEN-C-CARD - Health care products - C.M. Morelli Enterprises, Inc.
EMERGENCE - Footwear–athletic - L.A. Gear, Inc.
EMERGENCEE - Hair care products - Nexxus Products Co.
EMERGENCY - Apparel and accessories - William Hudson & Associates
EMERGENCY - Blankets - Dynamic Development
EMERGENCY - Cleaning preparations - Geritrex Corp.
EMERGENCY - Hosiery ☆ - Mayer/Berkshire Corp.
EMERGENCY 911 FEELERS - Telephone accessories - John Tobish
EMERGENCY BALM - First aid kits - Origins Natural Resources Inc.
EMERGENCY BEAR - Dolls - Mattel, Inc.
EMERGENCY EXIT - Apparel and accessories - Meijer, Inc.
EMERGENCY MANAGER 2000 - Computer peripheral equipment - Specialized
Disaster Systems, Inc.
EMERGENCY MEDICAL SERVICES - Machinery - Summer Communications,
Inc.
EMERGENCY MEDICAL UPDATE - Recording label - Lockert-Jackson &
Associates
EMERGENCY PREPAREDNESS PLAN - Computer software - Caroline Pratt
and Associates, Inc.
EMERGENCY PREPAREDNESS SOFTWARE - Computer software - Caroline
Pratt and Associates, Inc.
EMERGENCY STATION - Toys - Mattel, Inc.
EMERGENCY STIK'R - Skin care products - Backscratchers, Inc.
EMERGENCYCARD - Health care products - EmergencyCARD
EMERGERE - Handbags - Herb Yussim
EMERGI-SCRIPT - Antihistamine preparations - UDL Laboratories, Inc.
EMERGIN C - Skin care products - Renature Skin Care, Inc.
EMERGING GLOBAL MARKETS - Publisher's imprints - McGraw-Hill
Companies, Inc.
EMERGO - Recording label ☆ - Roadrunner Records, Inc.
EMERITE - Varnishes - Seagraves Coatings
EMERITUS - Musical instruments ☆ - Armstrong Woodwinds
EMERITUS ENTERPRISES - Publisher's imprint - Borgo Press
EMERLITE - Shampoo - Costec 20 Inc.
EMERSAL - Pharmaceutical preparations - Medco Lab Inc.
EMERSON - Audio equipment - Emerson Radio Corp.
EMERSON - Cigars - National Cigar Corp.
EMERSON - Floor coverings–carpet and rugs ☆ - Quaker Inc.
EMERSON - Frames–picture ☆ - D & L Stained Glass Supply, Inc.

☆ = Now out of production

EMERSON - Hardware stores - Emerson Electric Co.

EMERSON - Musical instruments - Emerson Musical Instruments Inc.

EMERSON - Watches ☆ - SMH (US) Inc.

EMERSON-IMPERIAL - Lighting fixtures - Emerson Electric Co.

EMERSON-QUIET KOOL - Hardware - Emerson-Quiet Kool Co.

EMERSON UPS - Hardware - Emerson Electric Co.

EMERY - Candles ☆ - Candle-Lite Co.

EMERY PUFF - Balls–rubber - Barristo Ltd.

EMERY WAND - Manicure preparations - Barristo Ltd.

EMERYL - Nail care products - Revlon Consumer Products Corp.

EMES - Food products - Emes Provisions, Inc.

EMETE-CON - Pharmaceutical preparations - J.B. Roerig & Co.

EMEX - Iron products - Endisco Supply Co.

EMFABID - Pharmaceutical preparations ☆ - Saron Pharmacal Corp.

EMFASEEM - Pharmaceutical preparations - Saron Pharmacal Corp.

EMFOTEC - Computer hardware - Emfotec Information Systems Corp.

EMG - Medical apparatus ☆ - Biosig Instruments Inc.

EMG - Musical instruments - EMG Inc.

EMGE - Meat products - Excel Corp.

EMGE - Meat products–canned - Emge Packing Co. Inc.

EMGEE - Thread - Threads USA Div.

EMGEL - Explosives - Mining Services International Corp.

EMGLO - Compressors–air - Emglo Products L.P. (Emglo Air Compressors)

EMGLO - Compressors–air - Illinois Fastening Systems

EMGO - Motorcycles - Emgo International Ltd.

EMH - Drills–electric - S-B Power Tool Co.

EMI - Recording label - Capitol-EMI Music Inc.

EMI-TOOLKIT - Computer software - Kimmel Gerke Associates, Ltd.

EMIGRE - Backpacks - Dan-Dee International Ltd.

EMIGRE - Recording label - Emigre Music

EMIL KAHN - Jewelry - Emil Kahn, Ltd.

EMILE BARAN - Violins - Dekalb Musicians Supply Co. Inc.

EMILE CHAMPET - Beverages–alcohol - Wine House Ltd.

EMILE GALLE COLLECTION - Lamps - Meyda Tiffany Inc.

EMILE'S - Wines - Emilio Guglielmo Winery

EMILIE ROBIN - Skin care products - Belcam Inc.

EMILIO FRANCO - Footwear - Emilio Franco Imports Inc.

EMILIO LUSTAV - Beverages–alcohol ☆ - Diamond Wine Merchants

EMILIO OF CAPRI - Shirts - Crystal Brands Inc.

EMILIO PUCCI - Apparel stores–lingerie ☆ - Formfit Rogers

EMILIO PUCCI - Eyeglasses ☆ - Windsor Optical Inc.

EMILIO PUCCI - Handbags - Nova Imports Inc.

EMILIO TEZZA - Frames–picture - Lionvale

EMILIO'S - Breads - D'Forte/La Cantina Brands

EMILIO'S - Food products - Lindsay Olive Growers

EMILITA - Food products - Olympia Cheese Co. LLC

EMIL'S ORIGINAL HOME STYLE OVEN ROAST TURKEY BREAST - Meat products–poultry - E.G. Emil & Son, Inc.

EMILY - Occasional tables ☆ - JDI Group, Inc.

EMILY - Tableware–china - Lenox, Inc.

EMILY - Watches - Bulova Corp.

EMILY - Whirlpools - Jason International, Inc.

EMILY - Yarn - Brunswick Yarns

EMILY ASHFORD - Apparel–women's - Gateway Apparel, Inc.

EMILY DANIELL - Handbags - Federated Department Stores, Inc.

EMILY JANE - Stationery ☆ - Chase Collection, Inc.

EMILY POST - Greeting cards - Regency Thermographers Inc.

EMILY REGER - Apparel–women's - Malcolm & Co., LLC

EMILY'S ART GARDEN - Greeting cards - Emily's Art Garden Inc.

EMINENCE - Amplifiers–musical instrument - David Wexler & Co.

EMINENCE - Audio equipment - Speakerkits Inc.

EMINENCE - Brushes–hair - I. Sekine Co. Inc.

EMINENCE - Floor coverings–carpet and rugs - Calladium & Marglen

EMINENCE - Floor coverings–carpet and rugs ☆ - Blue Ridge Carpet Mills

EMINENCE - Loudspeakers - Eminence Speaker Corp.

EMINENCE - Mattresses - R.F. Simmons Co.

EMINENCE - Rings–jewelry - Artcarved Inc.

EMINENT - Sheet vinyl flooring - Tarkett, Inc.

EMINENT ACOUSTIFLOR - Sheet vinyl flooring - Tarkett, Inc.

EMINENT TECHNOLOGY - Phonographs - GNP Audio Video Inc.

EMIR - Colognes ☆ - Dana Perfumes Corp.

EMIR - Floor coverings–carpet and rugs - Bloomsburg Carpet Industries

EMIR - Recording label ☆ - Connoisseur Society Inc.

EMISSARY - Briefcases - Samsonite Corp.

EMISSARY - Computer software - Information Technology Solutions

EMISSARY - Floor coverings–carpet and rugs - Mohawk Carpet Corp.

EMISSARY - Trailers–travel - Royals International

EMISSION CONTROL - Chemical preparations - Wynn Oil Co.

EMISSION CONTROL PLUS - Chemical preparations - Wynn Oil Co.

EMISSION-PAK - Machine parts - Neles-Jamesbury, Inc.

EMISSION SENTRY - Automotive parts and accessories - Kohler Co.

EMISSION TECHNICIAN, THE - Industrial machinery - Emi-Tech, Inc.

EMIT MANAGER - Computer software - Intelligen, Inc.

EMITASOL - Pharmaceutical preparations - Rugby Laboratories Inc.

EMIVAN - Vitamins and nutritional supplements ☆ - Rhone-Poulenc Rorer Pharmaceuticals Inc.

EMIX - Pet products ☆ - Clifford W. Estes Co. Inc.

EMJOI - Health care products - Conair Corp.

EMKAY - Candles - Emkay Candles

EMKAY - Recording label - Country International Records

EMKO - Pharmaceutical preparations - Schering-Plough Healthcare Products

EMLA - Anesthetics - Astra Pharmaceutical Products, Inc.

EMLIN - Skin care products - Neiman Marcus Co.

EMMA BELLA - Food products - Escalon Frozen Foods

EMMA MAE - Cookies - Service America Corp.

EMMA ROSE - Toys–stuffed - Dakin Inc.

EMMALJUNGA - Infant product - Bandaks Emmaljunga Inc.

EMMANUEL WILFER - Musical instruments - St. Louis Music Supply Co.

EMMANUELLE KAHN - Eyeglasses ☆ - B. Robinson Sunglasses

EMMANUELLE KHANH PARIS - Sunglasses - Private Eyes Sunglass Corp.

EMMBER - Meat products–beef - Emmber Foods, Inc.

EMME - Carts - Datel, Inc.

EMMENTAL - Cheese ☆ - H.J. Gasser Specialty Foods

EMMETS IRISH CREAM - Beverages–alcohol - Sunbelt Beverage Corp.

EMMETT KELLY - Dolls - Goldberger Doll Manufacture Co.

EMMEVI - Tiles–ceramic - Federal Tile Imports Inc.

EMMEVI - Tiles–terrazzo - Imperial Tile and Marble Corp.

EMMIE MACH ONE - Strollers–baby ☆ - Evenflo Co.

EMMIE MACH TWO - Strollers–baby ☆ - Evenflo Co.

EMMITT, INC. - Apparel and accessories - Emmitt, Inc.

EMMITT ZONE - Posters - Emmitt, Inc.

EMMITT ZONE, THE - Signs - Emmitt, Inc.

EMMIVI - Tiles–mosaic - TJ Imports

EMMO - Sporting goods - Set Tennis Co.

EMMONS - Guitars - Emmons Guitar Co. Inc.

EMMY - Lenses–optical - Ditto Industries Inc.

EMNLSO - Degreasing solvents - National Purity Inc.

EMOLLIA - Skin care products - Gordon Laboratories

EMON RAVIVETT - Hair care products - Framesi USA/Roffler Industries Inc.

EMORI - Fabrics–silk - Jelliff Corp.

EMORY & DOUGLAS - Barometers - Sign of the Crab Ltd.

EMORY MOJAVE - Bicycles - Emory Manufacturing Co.

EMOTION - Computer software - Emotion, Inc.

EMOTION - Office supplies - Action Cartoons

EMOTIONAL BALANCE - Vitamins and nutritional supplements - Planetary Formulas

EMOTIONAL BLOCKS - Games - Tom Blackwell

EMOTIONAL FLOWERS - Chemical preparations - International Flavors & Fragrances Inc.

EMOTIONAL RESEARCH, INC. - Research–business - Emotional Research, Inc.

EMOTIONALS - Greeting cards - C.M. Paula Co.

EMOTIONS - Dolls - Mattel, Inc.

EMOTIONS - Wallpaper - Pickhardt & Siebert USA Inc.

EMOTIONS FOREVER - Greeting cards - Mason and Eyres, Inc.

EMP EMERGENCY MED PAK - First aid kits - Solid G Investments, Ltd.

EMPACADORA ANAHUAC - Food products - Empacadora Anahuac SA

EMPACADORA INTER-MEX - Food products - Betters International Food Corp.

EMPACT - Computer software - Triad Software, Inc.

EMPANADAS UNLIMITED - Kosher food products ☆ - Aristocrat International Corp.

EMPATH - Computer software - LDS Inc.

EMPCO-LITE - Safety products - Elgin Molded Plastics, Inc.

EMPECO - Thread - Threads USA Div.

EMPERADOR - Food products - Atlas Horn Food Service

EMPERADOR - Musical instrument accessories - Westheimer Corp.

EMPEREAU - Floor coverings–carpet and rugs ☆ - Karastan-Bigelow Inc.

EMPERIA - Accordions - Fred Gretsch Enterprises

EMPEROR - Accordions - Titano Accordion Co. International

EMPEROR - Bathroom fixtures - Crane Plumbing/Fiat Products

EMPEROR - Building materials - Pacific Coast Building Products, Inc.

EMPEROR - Candles - Merrill-West Publishing

EMPEROR - Dinnerware–glass ☆ - Royal China & Porcelain Companies Inc.
EMPEROR - Flowers, plants, and seeds - Randall Lane Brackin
EMPEROR - Flutes - Boosey & Hawkes Buffet Crampon USA
EMPEROR - Food products - Wei-Chuan U.S.A., Inc.
EMPEROR - Frames–eyeglass - Zylo Ware Corp.
EMPEROR - Furniture–upholstered ☆ - Mersman Furniture Co.
EMPEROR - Garment hangers - Mission Industries Inc.
EMPEROR - Guns ☆ - Armsport Inc.
EMPEROR - Mats - Majestic Mat Co.
EMPEROR - Musical instruments - Westheimer Corp.
EMPEROR - Sauces - Rhee Bros., Inc.
EMPEROR - Silverware - Reed and Barton Corp.
EMPEROR - Watches - Bulova Corp.
EMPEROR ARTS - Candles - Vincent Lippe Co.
EMPEROR O2 - Health care products - Roman Labs Inc.
EMPEROR'S CH'I - Herbal products - Equinox International Corp.
EMPEROR'S CHOICE - Floor coverings–carpet and rugs - Galaxy Carpet Mills Inc.
EMPEROR'S CHOICE - Teas–herbal - Celestial Seasonings, Inc.
EMPEROR'S GARDEN - Vitamins and nutritional supplements - Tea Garden Products, Inc.
EMPEROR'S KITCHEN - Seasonings - Great Eastern Sun Trading Co. Inc.
EMPHASIS - Floor coverings–carpet and rugs ☆ - Walter Carpet Mills
EMPHASIS - Furniture ☆ - Lane Co. Inc.
EMPHASIS - Hair care products - Scruples Professional Salon Products, Inc.
EMPHASIS - Pens - Empire Berol USA
EMPHASIS - Plastics–laminated - Plaskolite Inc.
EMPHASIS - Stationery - Moore Business Forms, Inc.
EMPHASIS - Underwear and nightwear - Maidenform Inc.
EMPHASIS II - Furniture ☆ - Broyhill Furniture Industries, Inc.
EMPHASIZER - Pens - Empire Berol USA
EMPHASYS - Electronics equipment - Grass Valley Group Inc.
EMPI - Motor vehicle parts and accessories - Empi Inc.
EMPIRAL - Analgesics ☆ - Burroughs Wellcome Co.
EMPIRE - Ashtrays–glass - Ashtray Specialty Co./Marion Products Co.
EMPIRE - Audio equipment - Empire Scientific Corp.
EMPIRE - Bicycles - Columbia Manufacturing Inc.
EMPIRE - Binoculars - Bausch & Lomb Inc.
EMPIRE - Blinds–vertical - U.S. Polymers, Inc.
EMPIRE - Books–blank - Boorum & Pease Co.
EMPIRE - Brushes - Cook Things
EMPIRE - Candles ☆ - Will & Baumer, Inc.
EMPIRE - Cleaning preparations ☆ - Empire Brushes, Inc.
EMPIRE - Clocks - Empire Clock Inc.
EMPIRE - Clocks - General Time Corp. (Westclox/Seth Thomas Div.)
EMPIRE - Dental equipment - Schein Dental Equipment Co.
EMPIRE - Dinnerware–glass - Nikko Ceramics Inc.
EMPIRE - Electric lighting equipment - Empire Industries
EMPIRE - Exercising equipment - Titan Exercise Equipment Inc.
EMPIRE - Filing cabinets–metal ☆ - Yawman and Erbe of California Corp.
EMPIRE - Flags - Annin and Co.
EMPIRE - Floor coverings–carpet and rugs ☆ - Capel, Inc.
EMPIRE - Food products - Empire Kosher Poultry Inc.
EMPIRE - Food products - Fairtry Fisheries Group
EMPIRE - Food products - Midtown Provision Co. Inc.
EMPIRE - Footwear - Empire Shoe Co.
EMPIRE - Furniture - Stanley Furniture Co. Inc.
EMPIRE - Furniture ☆ - Hammary Furniture Co. Inc.
EMPIRE - Hardware ☆ - Amerock Corp.
EMPIRE - Housewares ☆ - Metal Ware Corp.
EMPIRE - Ladders–metal - John S. Tilley Ladders Co. Inc.
EMPIRE - Lamp glasses and globes ☆ - Corning Inc.
EMPIRE - Machinery - S. Morantz Inc.
EMPIRE - Manufactured homes ☆ - Redman Industries, Inc.
EMPIRE - Office furniture - Inwood Office Furniture
EMPIRE - Office supplies - Empire Berol USA
EMPIRE - Oils–lubricating - Warren Oil Co., Inc.
EMPIRE - Recording label - Jazz Composer's Orchestra Association Inc.
EMPIRE - Rope ☆ - American Manufacturing Co. Inc.
EMPIRE - Safes - Empire Safe Co. Inc.
EMPIRE - Silver products - Empire Silver Co. Inc.
EMPIRE - Tiles–ceramic - American Marazzi Tile, Inc.
EMPIRE - Tools–hand-operated - Empire Level Manufacturing Corp.
EMPIRE - Toys - Empire of Carolina Inc.
EMPIRE - Trailers–travel - Empire RV
EMPIRE - Trees - Schichtel's Nursery Oregon Inc.

EMPIRE - Varnishes ☆ - Sampson Coatings Inc.
EMPIRE - Video tapes–blank - New Products Group
EMPIRE - Wallpaper - Studio IV Graphics Inc.
EMPIRE - Wet mops ☆ - American Textile Products Co.
EMPIRE BLENDED - Adhesives and sealants - Empire Blended Products Co.
EMPIRE BREWING COMPANY - Beverages–malt - Empire Brewery of Syracuse, Inc.
EMPIRE BUILDER - Fruits–canned - Cashmore Pioneer Growers
EMPIRE BUILDER - Games - Mayfair Games, Inc.
EMPIRE BUILDER - Toys–trains - Digitrax, Inc.
EMPIRE CITY 1931 - Video games - Taito America Corp.
EMPIRE EMBERS - Heaters–aircraft - Empire Comfort Systems Inc.
EMPIRE ENTERTAINMENT - Recording label - State of Fresh American Entertainment
EMPIRE FITNESS CLUBS - Physical fitness centers - Empire Fitness Clubs, Inc.
EMPIRE GAS - Liquefied gas - Empire Gas Corp.
EMPIRE HEARTH - Heaters–aircraft - Empire Comfort Systems Inc.
EMPIRE I: WORLD BUILDERS - Computer software - Encyclopaedia Britannica Inc.
EMPIRE II: INTERSTELLAR SHARKS - Computer software - Encyclopaedia Britannica Inc.
EMPIRE III: ARMAGEDDON - Computer software - Encyclopaedia Britannica Inc.
EMPIRE IN ARMS - Games - Avalon Hill Game Co.
EMPIRE INDIGLO - Heating equipment - Empire Comfort Systems Inc.
EMPIRE LOGS - Heaters–aircraft - Empire Comfort Systems Inc.
EMPIRE-MATIC - Housewares ☆ - Metal Ware Corp.
EMPIRE NATIONAL - Meat products–beef - A to Z Kosher Meat Products Co., Inc.
EMPIRE OF THE OVERMIND - Games ☆ - Avalon Hill Game Co.
EMPIRE PREMIUM - Food products ☆ - Empire Kosher Poultry Inc.
EMPIRE STATE - Food products ☆ - Curtice-Burns Foods, Inc.
EMPIRE STATE - Paints ☆ - A. Flohr Co. Inc.
EMPIRE STRIKES BACK, THE - Candles - Lucasfilm Ltd.
EMPIRE SUPREME - Housewares ☆ - Metal Ware Corp.
EMPIRE TERRACE - Manufactured homes - Redman Industries, Inc.
EMPIRE VINEYARDS - Beverages–carbonated - Felton-Empire Vineyards Inc.
EMPIRE WHITE - Adhesives and sealants - Empire Blended Products Co.
EMPIRE WREATH - Floor coverings–carpet and rugs - Callaway Carpets
EMPIRES - Cigars - Faber, Coe & Gregg Inc.
EMPIRE'S FINEST - Soups–mixes - Empire Dehydrated Products Inc.
EMPIRIA - Cheese - Imperia Foods Inc.
EMPIRICAL TOOLS AND TECHNOLOGIES - Computer software - Empirical Tools and Technologies, Inc.
EMPIRIN - Cold remedies ☆ - Warner-Wellcome
EMPIRITE - Paints - Muralo Co. Inc.
EMPLAST - Shelving units–plastic - Emplast, Inc.
EMPLOY ABILITY - Publisher's imprints - Woolworth Corp.
EMPLOYEE APPRAISER - Computer software - Austin-Hayne Corp.
EMPLOYEE GUIDE TO HEALTH AND SAFETY - Publisher's imprints - Employment Risk Systems, Inc.
EMPLOYEE RECOGNITION BACKGROUNDS - Posters - Clement Communications Inc.
EMPORE - Filters–industrial - Minnesota Mining & Manufacturing Co.
EMPORER - Faucets - Kallista Inc.
EMPORIA - Coffee - Emporia Wholesale Coffee Co.
EMPORIA - Wallpaper ☆ - David Merritt Handprints Inc.
EMPORIO - Ophthalmic goods - Luxottica
EMPORIO CHEMISE - Apparel and accessories - Spearhead Development of New Jersey, Inc.
EMPORIO HOMME - Apparel–men's - United Clothing, Inc.
EMPORIUM - Floor coverings–carpet and rugs - Philadelphia Carpets
EMPORIUM - Wallpaper - Vymura
EMPOWER - Skin care products - Kenra Laboratories, Inc.
EMPOWER - Vitamins and nutritional supplements - Intracell Nutrition Inc.
EMPOWER E NET - Telephones - Empower Net, LLC
EMPOWERED LEARNING - Recording label - Empowered Learning, Inc.
EMPOWERING WHEAT - Bagels - Spot Bagel Bakery, Inc.
EMPOWERMENTS - Jewelry - Planetary Plaything
EMPRACET - Pharmaceutical preparations ☆ - Burroughs Wellcome Co.
EMPRAZIL - Pharmaceutical preparations ☆ - Burroughs Wellcome Co.
EMPRECETTE - Apparel and accessories ☆ - Strouse, Adler Co.
EMPREINTE DE BEAUTE - Skin care products - Lancome
EMPRESS - Artists' materials - Robert Simmons Inc.
EMPRESS - Bathing suits - Ocean Pool Co.

☆ = Now out of production

EMPRESS - Bathroom accessories - Kinkead/Tub/Shower Doors
EMPRESS - Bathroom fixtures - Crane Plumbing/Fiat Products
EMPRESS - Bedding–linen - Fieldcrest Cannon, Inc.
EMPRESS - Blinds–venetian ☆ - Hunter Douglas, Inc.
EMPRESS - Boats–motor - Lyn-Craft Boat Co.
EMPRESS - Boats–motor - Regal Marine Industries Inc.
EMPRESS - Candles - Merrill-West Publishing
EMPRESS - Candlesticks ☆ - Lenox Crystal, Inc.
EMPRESS - Carpets, now out of production - Couristan Inc.
EMPRESS - Clocks ☆ - Ridgeway Clock Co.
EMPRESS - Dishes–china ☆ - Gorham Inc.
EMPRESS - Dishes–china ☆ - Pickard Inc.
EMPRESS - Doughnuts–mixes ☆ - Dawn Food Products Inc.
EMPRESS - Drapery hardware ☆ - Spring Window Fashions Division, Inc.
EMPRESS - Fabrics–velvet - Minnetonka Mills Inc.
EMPRESS - Flatware - The Dirilyte Line
EMPRESS - Floor coverings - American Floor Products Co. Inc.
EMPRESS - Floor coverings - Mannington Resilient Floors
EMPRESS - Floor coverings–carpet and rugs - Providence Rug Co.
EMPRESS - Floor coverings–carpet and rugs - Rugby Rugs Inc.
EMPRESS - Floor coverings–carpet and rugs - Trans-Ocean Import Co. Inc.
EMPRESS - Food products - Empress International Ltd.
EMPRESS - Food products - Mitsui & Co. Inc.
EMPRESS - Food products - Mitsui Foods, Inc.
EMPRESS - Frames–picture ☆ - Acme Frame Products, Inc.
EMPRESS - Furniture ☆ - Stanley Furniture Co. Inc.
EMPRESS - Giftware ☆ - W.M.F. of America Inc.
EMPRESS - Glassware–household - Svend Jensen of Denmark Inc.
EMPRESS - Glassware–household - Rezler & Howell Co.
EMPRESS - Glassware–household - Culver Glass Inc.
EMPRESS - Golf clubs - Mitsushiba International, Inc.
EMPRESS - Hair care products - Helene Curtis Industries Inc.
EMPRESS - Handbags - Empress Handbags Inc.
EMPRESS - Handbags - Jaclyn, Inc.
EMPRESS - Manicure preparations - Nailtex Inc.
EMPRESS - Mops - Piedmont Mop Co.
EMPRESS - Padding–foam - Crain Industries Inc.
EMPRESS - Personal telephones - American Telecommunications Corp.
EMPRESS - Rings–jewelry - Artcarved Inc.
EMPRESS - Rope - Samson Cordage Works
EMPRESS - Tables–wood - Riverside Furniture Corp.
EMPRESS - Tableware–china ☆ - Villeroy and Boch Tableware Ltd.
EMPRESS - Toys - M. Pressner and Co. Inc.
EMPRESS - Underwear and nightwear ☆ - Youthform Co.
EMPRESS - Vegetable sauces ☆ - Safeway Stores Inc.
EMPRESS - Watches - Bulova Corp.
EMPRESS - Window coverings - Conso Products Co.
EMPRESS - Wines - James Moroney, Inc.
EMPRESS BRIDALS BY EUGENIE - Wedding gowns - Empress Bridals Inc.
EMPRESS BRIDE - Dolls - Mattel, Inc.
EMPRESS CARLOTTA - Watches - Bulova Corp.
EMPRESS CATHERINE - Watches - Bulova Corp.
EMPRESS CROWN - Jewelry - Imperial-Deltah Inc.
EMPRESS ELIZABETH - Watches - Bulova Corp.
EMPRESS EUGENIE - Watches - Bulova Corp.
EMPRESS II - Doors–glass - Sterling Plumbing Group Inc.
EMPRESS II - Floor coverings–carpet and rugs - Shaheen Carpet Mills
EMPRESS JOANNA - Watches - Bulova Corp.
EMPRESS MARGARET - Watches - Bulova Corp.
EMPRESS' SECRET - Cosmetics - Irwin Baker
EMPRESS SECRET BATH - Bath salts - Pacific Spirit Corp.
EMPRESS SILKS - Wallpaper - Capital Carousel Inc.
EMPRESS SILKS - Wallpaper - Coverwalls Inc.
EMPRESS SILKS - Wallpaper ☆ - Wall Fashion Inc.
EMPRESS STRIPE - Wallpaper - Koroseal Wallcoverings
EMPRESS VALERIE - Watches - Bulova Corp.
EMPRIDE - Computer software - Huntington Laboratories Inc.
EMPRISE - Pens - Emprise Financial Corp.
EMPRISE - Perfumes ☆ - Avon Products, Inc.
EMPRIZONE - Skin care products - Emprise International, Inc.
EMPRO - Computer software - Electronic Information Systems, Inc.
EMPRO - Pharmaceutical preparations - Econo Med Pharmaceuticals Inc.
EMPRO - Signs - Kemlite Co., Inc.
EMPROVIAN - Dairy products ☆ - DMV USA Inc.
EMPTY POCKETS - Giftware - Bamboo Inc.
EMPULSE - Heating equipment ☆ - Empire Comfort Systems Inc.

EMPURE PLATE - Floor coverings–carpet and rugs - Milliken & Co. Inc.
EMREX - Pharmaceutical preparations - Econo Med Pharmaceuticals Inc.
EMS - Electronic equipment - Moor Electronics Inc.
EMS - Sporting goods - Eastern Mountain Sports, Inc.
EMS 5000 - Health care products - Wholesale Medical Import
EMS POWERPAK - Computer software - Intergraph Corp.
EMS-PRO - Computer software - James Lindsay Davison
EMS-PRO - Computer software - James Lindsay Davison
EMS SOLUTIONS - Computer software - Dynastat, Inc.
EMS+2 - Health care products - Staodyn, Inc.
EMSER 555 - Dairy products ☆ - DMV USA Inc.
EMSER 736 - Dairy products ☆ - DMV USA Inc.
EMSER 747 - Dairy products ☆ - DMV USA Inc.
EMSON - Housewares - E. Mishan & Sons, Inc.
EMS+ - Health care products - Essex Medical Products
EMSPRITT - Jewelry - Combine International, Inc.
EMSTATION - Computer software - Clinical Information Advantages, Inc.
EMT - Audio equipment - G Prime Limited
EMT - Medical device - Mallinckrodt Medical, Inc.
EMTAP - Computer software - EDSA Micro Corp.
EMTEK - Locks–door - Emtek Products, Inc.
EMTET - Pharmaceutical preparations - Econo Med Pharmaceuticals Inc.
EMTRAK - Sporting goods - Empak, Inc.
EMTRYL - Veterinary pharmaceutical preparations - Solvay Animal Health, Inc.
EMU - Apparel–athletic - Eastern Michigan University
EMU - Electrical equipment - Benchmarq Microelectronics, Inc.
EMU-GESIC - Pharmaceutical preparations - Kylemu, Inc.
EMU/ROBIN - Yarn ☆ - Plymouth Yarn Co.
EMUL-O-BALM - Analgesics ☆ - Fisons Corp.
EMULATOR IV - Musical instruments - E-Mu Systems, Inc.
EMULSA BOND - See **EASYMIX E-B**
EMULSICLEAN - Degreasing solvents - Texwipe Co. LLC
EMULSION ELASTIC COLLAGENE - Skin care products - Ella Bache Inc.
EMULSION EQUILIBRANTE - Skin care products - Ella Bache Inc.
EMULSIONE - Skin care products - Mastey De Paris
EMULSOIL - Pharmaceutical preparations - Paddock Laboratories Inc.
EMULSONATOR - Electronic equipment - Electronic Controls Design, Inc.
EMULUS - Computer software ☆ - Sas Institute Inc.
EMUNIQUE - Skin care products - Superior Products
EMUNITION - Skin care products - Esta Kronberg
EMUREX - Pharmaceutical preparations - EMU Ranchers Inc.
EMURI - Cosmetics - EMU Ranchers Inc.
EMURIA - Perfumes - EMU Ranchers Inc.
EMURIEL - Toiletries - Box L Emu Ranch, Inc.
EMURL - Computer software - Seattle Lab, Inc.
EMUVERA - Skin care products - American Outback, Inc.
EMX - Computer software - Information Retrieval Companies Inc.
EMX - Jewelry - Matrix Creations, Inc.
EMX TECHNOLOGY - Computer hardware - EMX Corp.
EMY - Ophthalmic goods ☆ - Luxottica
EMYL SERE - Copper products - Galleria Petromilli Imports
EN-CEBRIN - Pharmaceutical preparations - Eli Lilly and Co.
EN CHANTE - Apparel and accessories - Kellwood Co.
EN CHANTE CHEMISE - Apparel and accessories - Kellwood Co.
EN CHANTE KIDS - Apparel and accessories - Kellwood Co.
EN-CHLOR - Pharmaceutical preparations ☆ - Ulmer Pharmacal Co.
EN CLEAN - Motor vehicle parts and accessories - Triangle Corp.
EN-DURE - Floor waxes - Uncle Sam Chemical Co., Inc.
EN-DURO - Pharmaceutical preparations - Bricker Laboratories
EN GARDE - Fabrics - Guilford Mills, Inc.
EN GARDE - Leather goods - Service Manufacturing Corp.
EN GARDE - Pens ☆ - Sanford Corp.
EN GARDE - Sunblocks - Caribia, Cosmetic Research Laboratories Inc.
EN GARDE OXY-MOXY - Vitamins and nutritional supplements - En Garde Health Products, Inc.
EN MASSE! - Computer software - Avatar Technologies, Inc.
EN-PAIN - Pharmaceutical preparations ☆ - Roberts/Hauck Pharmaceuticals Inc.
EN PROVENCE - Wallpaper ☆ - Bob Mitchell Designs
EN-R-TECH - Furnaces–electric - Meyer Furnace Co.
EN ROUTE - Computer software ☆ - CE Software, Inc.
EN-STRESS - Health care products ☆ - Enzymatic Therapy, Inc.
EN-TOUT-CAS (LAVIS FIDELIS) - Paper ☆ - Canson-Talens Inc.
EN VIRON MENT - Apparel and accessories - Robert G. Walder
EN VOGUE - Apparel stores–sports - 2 Tuff-E-Nuff Productions, Inc.
EN VOGUE - Dinnerware–glass - WMF/USA

☆ = Now out of production

EN VOGUE - Furniture - National/Mt. Airy Furniture

EN-ZY-MEX - Pharmaceutical preparations - Nutrition Enterprises

E.N.A. - Apparel and accessories - E.N.A. Clothing, Inc.

ENA - Frames–eyeglass ☆ - U.S. Optical Frame Co.

E.N.A. - Paints ☆ - ARK Laboratory, Inc.

ENA-C-T - Diagnostic apparatus - Actimed Laboratories, Inc.

ENABLE - Computer software - Enable Software, Inc.

ENABLER - Computer software - USA Administration Services, Inc.

ENABLER - Health care products - Damaco Inc.

ENACA GOLD - Frozen food - Pan American Seafood, Inc.

ENACARD - Veterinary pharmaceutical - Merck & Co., Inc. (Merck Research Laboratories)

ENACT - Blood derivatives - Actimed Laboratories, Inc.

ENAJ - Colognes - Fragranhaus

ENAMATEX - Enamels - Warren Paint & Color

ENAMEL-GLOW - Enamel - Iowa Paint Manufacturing Co. Inc.

ENAMEL PEN - Paints - Testor Corp.

ENAMEL PEN - Paints ☆ - Plasti-Kote Co. Inc.

ENAMEL SAVER - Toothpaste - Squigle, Inc.

ENAMELAC - Enamels - Mantrose-Haeuser Co. Inc.

ENAMELEASE - Enamel - Continental Products Co.

ENAMELED PUPS - Jewelry - Terr-If-Ick Flair, Inc.

ENAMELETTES - Nail care products - Arthur Matney Co., Inc.

ENAMELFLO - Paints ☆ - Mac-O-Lac Paints Inc.

ENAMELHIDE - Paints ☆ - PPG Industries, Inc.

ENAMELOID - Enamels ☆ - Sherwin-Williams Automotive Finishes Corp.

ENAMELUX - Paint-roller sleeves ☆ - Corona Brushes Inc.

ENAMOR - Eyeglasses - Martin-Copeland Eyewear Corp.

ENARAX - Tranquilizers ☆ - Smithkline Beecham Corp.

ENARDOE - Novelty items–paper - Morris House of Drane

ENASCENT - Skin care products - Enascent Inc.

ENAZ - Apparel and accessories - Enaz, Ltd.

ENBIROMED - Skin care products - Enbiromed, Inc.

ENC 150 - Electrical equipment - Acu-Rite Inc.

ENCAP - Chemical preparations - Loctite Corp.

ENCAP - Footwear–athletic - New Balance Athletic Shoe, Inc.

ENCAPRIN - Analgesics - Procter & Gamble Co.

ENCAPSALL - Waterproofing compounds - Andek Corp.

ENCAPSULATED NUTRITION - Vitamins and nutritional supplements - Solaray

ENCAPSULATIONS - Pharmaceutical preparations - Chase Laboratories Inc.

ENCAPSULON - Gaskets - Frederickseal, Inc.

ENCARE - Health care products - Thompson Medical Co., Inc.

ENCARTA - Computer software - Microsoft Corp.

ENCAUSTO - Wallcovering - Innovations in Wallcoverings, Inc.

ENCEPHAL - Pharmaceutical preparations ☆ - U.S. Ethicals Inc.

ENCEPHALON - Computer software - Andent DCN

ENCERA - Pottery - Brastoff Designs Inc.

ENCHANCERS, THE - Frames–eyeglass ☆ - Universal/Univis Inc.

ENCHANCETTES - Apparel–women's - Lily of France Inc.

ENCHANT - Spices and extracts - CF Technologies, Inc.

ENCHANT-MINTS - Candy ☆ - Leaf, Inc.

ENCHANTA - Toys - Mattel, Inc.

ENCHANTE - Apparel–women's - En Chante

ENCHANTE - Brassieres (Bras) - Lady Marlene

ENCHANTE - Floor coverings–carpet and rugs - J.L. Benson Co.

ENCHANTE - Floor coverings–carpet and rugs - Mandate-Dawn Carpet Mills

ENCHANTE - Glass products ☆ - Thomas Industries Inc.

ENCHANTE - Luggage - Luggage America Inc.

ENCHANTE - Prosthetic apparatus ☆ - Jobst Institute Inc.

ENCHANTE - Window treatments - Home Fashions Inc.

ENCHANTE COLLECTION - Apparel and accessories - Kellwood Co.

ENCHANTE POUR LA DAME - Apparel and accessories - Kellwood Co.

ENCHANTE SPORT - Apparel–women's - En Chante

ENCHANTE SPORT - Apparel–women's - Kellwood Co.

ENCHANTED - Floor coverings - Beaulieu of America, Inc.

ENCHANTED - Floor coverings–carpet and rugs - Ashley Commercial Carpets

ENCHANTED - Floor coverings–carpet and rugs ☆ - Interloom Ltd.

ENCHANTED - Floor coverings–carpet and rugs ☆ - World Carpets, Inc.

ENCHANTED - Lenses–optical - Ditto Industries Inc.

ENCHANTED - Pillows - Pacific Coast Feather Co.

ENCHANTED BEARS - Greeting cards - American Greetings Corp.

ENCHANTED BEAUTY - Jewelry - Paul F. Rothstein Inc.

ENCHANTED CIGARDEN, THE - Flowers–artificial - Sheila Wolfson

ENCHANTED CORAL - Nail care products - Cosmair Inc.

ENCHANTED CREATIONS - Pet products - Blue Ribbon Pet Products, Inc.

ENCHANTED DANCER, THE - Apparel and accessories - Enchanted Dancer

ENCHANTED EVENING - Dolls - Mattel, Inc.

ENCHANTED FOREST - Christmas tree ornaments - Cracker Box Inc.

ENCHANTED FOREST PRODUCTS - Giftware ☆ - Blair Cedar and Novelty Works

ENCHANTED GARDEN - Dolls ☆ - Effanbee Doll Corp.

ENCHANTED GARDEN - Skin care products ☆ - Delagar

ENCHANTED GARDEN - Toiletries - Belcam Inc.

ENCHANTED GEMS - Jewelry - Siddha International Import/Export

ENCHANTED GINSENG GARDEN - Teas - Seelect, Inc.

ENCHANTED HOUR - Tableware–china ☆ - Lenox, Inc.

ENCHANTED ISLAND SANDI - Dolls ☆ - Totsy Manufacturing Co., Inc.

ENCHANTED ISLE - Fruits–canned ☆ - Safeway Stores Inc.

ENCHANTED LEGENDS - Wallpaper ☆ - Legend Wallcoverings

ENCHANTED MEMORIES - Tin products - Giordano Art, Ltd.

ENCHANTED ORCHARD INC., THE - Novelty items - Enchanted Orchard Inc.

ENCHANTED PRINCESS - Dolls - Mattel, Inc.

ENCHANTED ROSE - Silver products ☆ - International Silver Co.

ENCHANTED SEASONS COLLECTION - Dolls - Mattel, Inc.

ENCHANTED TALES - Video production - Sony Music Entertainment Inc.

ENCHANTED TAROT, THE - Computer software - Zerner/Farber Editions, Ltd.

ENCHANTED TREASURES - Wallpaper - Archetonic

ENCHANTED TREE - Giftware - Cadillac Co., Inc.

ENCHANTEEN - Apparel–women's - Wacoal America Inc.

ENCHANTER - Computer software - Activision, Inc.

ENCHANTER - Musical instruments - Zachary Organ

ENCHANTER TRILOGY - Computer software - Activision, Inc.

ENCHANTICA - Figurines - Munro Enterprises Inc.

ENCHANTING - Apparel and accessories - Kellwood Co.

ENCHANTING - Floor coverings–carpet and rugs ☆ - Patcraft Mills Inc.

ENCHANTING MOMENTS - Teas - Farmer Bros. Co.

ENCHANTING TOUCH - Floor coverings–carpet and rugs ☆ - Karastan-Bigelow Inc.

ENCHANTMENT - Blankets–electric - Sunbeam-Oster Household Products

ENCHANTMENT - Dinnerware–glass ☆ - Nikko Ceramics Inc.

ENCHANTMENT - Floor coverings–carpet and rugs - Cabin Crafts Carpets

ENCHANTMENT - Floor coverings–carpet and rugs - Dorsett Carpet Mills Inc.

ENCHANTMENT - Floor coverings–carpet and rugs - Regal Rugs Inc.

ENCHANTMENT - Floor coverings–carpet and rugs - Walter Carpet Mills

ENCHANTMENT - Frames–eyeglass - May Optical Co. Inc.

ENCHANTMENT - Furniture - Henredon Furniture Industries Inc.

ENCHANTMENT - Glassware–household ☆ - Lotus Glass Co.

ENCHANTMENT - Hearing aids - Rexton Inc.

ENCHANTMENT - Rings–jewelry - Artcarved Inc.

ENCHANTMENT - Swimming pools ☆ - Lomart Industries

ENCHANTMENT - Wallpaper - Advent Industries Inc.

ENCHANTMENT - Wallpaper - Capital Carousel Inc.

ENCHANTMENTS - Dolls - Victoria Impex Corp.

ENCHANTMINTS - Candy - Dragonfly and Co., Inc.

ENCHANTOR - Boats–motor ☆ - Checkmate Boats Inc.

ENCHANTRESS - Christmas tree ornaments - Cracker Box Inc.

ENCHANTRESS - Flatware - Wallace International Silversmiths, Inc.

ENCHANTRESS - Floor coverings–carpet and rugs - Lees Carpets

ENCHANTRESS - Frames–eyeglass - May Optical Co. Inc.

ENCHANTRESS - Jewelry - Jacoby-Bender Inc.

ENCHANTRESS - Jewelry - Town & Country Corp.

ENCHANTRESS - Lighting fixtures - Lava-Simplex Internationale

ENCHANTRESS - Watches - Borel Watch Co.

ENCHILADA FIESTA - Food products - Night Hawk Foods Inc. (Frozen Foods Div.)

ENCINA BUILDER - Computer software - Transarc Corp.

ENCINA/WINDSOR - Office furniture–wood - Anderson Desk Inc.

ENCINO - Floor coverings–carpet and rugs - Evans-Black Carpet Mills

ENCIRCLE - Publisher's imprints - Quinco Consulting Center, Inc.

ENCLAVE DE PAPES - Wines ☆ - European Beverage Co., Inc.

ENCLOZER, THE - Fabric covers - Lisa Payne

ENCLUME - Racks - Enclume Design Products, Inc.

ENCO - Petroleum - Exxon Corp.

ENCOMPAS - Furniture ☆ - U.S. Furniture Industries Inc.

ENCOMPASS - Brassieres (Bras) - Montgomery Ward & Co. Inc.

ENCOMPASS - Computer software - Blue Marble Development Group, Inc.

ENCOMPASS - Computer software - Tempus Software, Inc.

ENCON - Hardware - Encon Industries Inc.

ENCOPRIN - Pharmaceutical preparations - Republic Drug Co. Inc.

ENCORE - Aircraft - Mooney Aircraft Corp.

ENCORE - Automotive parts and accessories ☆ - Lancaster Colony Automotive Group

☆ = Now out of production

ENCORE - Batteries - Tocad America, Inc. (Tocad Co. Ltd.)
ENCORE - Bicycles ☆ - Roadmaster Corp.
ENCORE - Brassieres (Bras) - Goddess Bra
ENCORE - Cabinets - Del Mar Cabinets
ENCORE - Cabinets - Nutone Inc.
ENCORE - Cabinets–wood - Fleetwood Furniture Co.
ENCORE - Candy ☆ - American Chicle Co.
ENCORE - Clarinets ☆ - G. Leblanc Corp.
ENCORE - Colognes - Richelieu Corp.
ENCORE - Computer language apparatus - Proficiency
ENCORE - Computer software - Passport Designs Inc.
ENCORE - Consulting services - Encore Marketing International Inc.
ENCORE - Dinnerware–glass ☆ - Johnson Brothers, USA, Inc.
ENCORE - Dishes–china - Pickard Inc.
ENCORE - Display cases–metal - Channel-Kor Systems, Inc.
ENCORE - Doors–garage - Taylor Building Products Co.
ENCORE - Electrodes - Uni-Patch
ENCORE - Electronics equipment - Colortran Inc.
ENCORE - Electronics stores - Encore Electronics Inc.
ENCORE - Floor coverings - Azrock Commercial Flooring
ENCORE - Floor coverings - Mannington Resilient Floors
ENCORE - Floor coverings–carpet and rugs - Porter Carpet Mills Inc.
ENCORE - Floor coverings–carpet and rugs - Quaker Inc.
ENCORE - Floor coverings–carpet and rugs - S and S Mills Inc.
ENCORE - Floor coverings–carpet and rugs ☆ - American Carpet Mills
ENCORE - Floor coverings–carpet and rugs ☆ - Mannington Carpets, Inc.
ENCORE - Furniture - Inwood Office Furniture
ENCORE - Furniture - Lane Co. Inc.
ENCORE - Furniture ☆ - Bassett Furniture Industries, Inc.
ENCORE - Furniture ☆ - Halcyon Inc.
ENCORE - Furniture–children's - Child Craft Industries Inc.
ENCORE - Furniture–wood - Charleston Forge Inc.
ENCORE - Games - Tonka Corp.
ENCORE - Garden furniture–metal - Lloyd/Flanders Industries
ENCORE - Giftware ☆ - Clinton Packaging Co.
ENCORE - Glassware–household - Owens-Illinois Inc. (Libbey Div.)
ENCORE - Health care products ☆ - Wheel Ring Inc.
ENCORE - Jewelry - Victoria International.
ENCORE - Lamps ☆ - Cannon Products Inc.
ENCORE - Luggage - Airway Industries, Inc.
ENCORE - Motor vehicles - Renault Inc.
ENCORE - Motor vehicles–motor homes - Eldorado Motor Corp.
ENCORE - Occasional tables - JDI Group, Inc.
ENCORE - Office furniture–wood - Anderson Desk Inc.
ENCORE - Office furniture–wood ☆ - Haskell of Pittsburgh, Inc.
ENCORE - Paints - Suntec Paint Inc.
ENCORE - Pens - Accutec Inc.
ENCORE - Pet products - Francodex Labs
ENCORE - Pet products - Ralston Purina Co.
ENCORE - Printers–computer - Comtec Information Systems, Inc.
ENCORE - Puzzles - Warren Industries Inc.
ENCORE - Rifles - Thompson/Center Arms
ENCORE - Rings–jewelry - Artcarved Inc.
ENCORE! - Soil–potting - Reuse Technology, Inc.
ENCORE - Sporting goods - Lisco, Inc.
ENCORE - Sports rackets and accessories - Winn, Inc.
ENCORE! - Stamps–hand - Tsukineko, Inc.
ENCORE - Thread - Sew-Art International
ENCORE - Tiles–ceramic ☆ - American Olean Tile Co.
ENCORE - Vacuum cleaners and accessories - The Hoover Co.
ENCORE - Vitamins and nutritional supplements - Diane Wakat
ENCORE - Wheelchairs ☆ - Ortho-Kinetics, Inc.
ENCORE - Wigs ☆ - Paula Young
ENCORE - Window coverings - ESI
ENCORE - Window shades - Fashion Tech, Inc.
ENCORE - Yarn - Plymouth Yarn Co.
ENCORE GOLD - Glassware–household - Lenox, Inc.
ENCORE II - Electrodes ☆ - Uni-Patch
ENCORE PERFORMANCE RECORDINGS - Recording label - Ron Meyer Recordings
ENCORE PLATINUM - Glassware–household - Lenox, Inc.
ENCORE PLUS - Electrodes - Uni-Patch
ENCORE PLUS - Floor coverings–carpet and rugs ☆ - Regal Rugs Inc.
ENCORE QUICKIE SOLUTION - Skin care products - Fanie International
ENCORE! SALES AND SERVICE - Computer software - CFI Pro Services, Inc.

ENCORE SCRAPE AND DRY - Floor coverings–carpet and rugs - Superior Manufacturing Group/Notrax Floor Matting
ENCORE SERIES - Tape players–cassette ☆ - Sony Music Entertainment Inc.
ENCORE SHOWMOBILE - Trailers - Wenger Corp.
ENCORE SOFTWARE - Computer software - Encore Software, Inc.
ENCORE STUDIOS - Stationery - Encore Studios, Inc.
ENCORE TANTONE - Electrodes - Uni-Patch
ENCORE ULTIMATE METALLIC - Stamps–hand - Tsukineko, Inc.
ENCORE ZODIAC - Shoes - Encore Shoe Corp.
ENCORES - Candy - Boehm's Candies, Inc.
ENCOUNTER - Boats–motor ☆ - Bayliner Marine Corp.
ENCOUNTER - Computer peripheral equipment - American Management Systems, Inc.
ENCOUNTER - Floor coverings–carpet and rugs - Hollytex Carpet Mills Inc.
ENCOUNTER - Floor coverings–carpet and rugs ☆ - Masland Corp.
ENCOUNTER - Floor coverings–carpet and rugs ☆ - Regal Rugs Inc.
ENCOUNTER - Frames–eyeglass - Liberty Optical Manufacturing Co.
ENCOUNTER - Motor vehicles–motor homes - Georgie Boy Manufacturing, Inc.
ENCOUNTER - Skin care products - Veeco Manufacturing Co.
ENCOUNTER - Toiletries - Victoria's Secret Stores, Inc.
ENCOUNTER - Wet suits–rubber ☆ - Parkway Systems
ENCOUNTERBAT - Toys - Uniquity
ENCOUNTERS - Electronic equipment - Carl E. Hewitt
ENCOUNTERS - Glassware–household - Culver Glass Inc.
ENCURVE - Building materials - Pittsburgh Corning Corp.
ENCYCLOFLORA - Educational materials - National Florist Directory, Inc.
ENCYCLOPEDIA AMERICANA - Compact discs–prerecorded - Grolier Inc.
ENCYCLOPEDIA OF BORDERS VOL. 1 - Wallpaper - I. Gottlieb & Associates
ENCYCLOPEDIA OF DRUGS - Computer software - Parsons Technology, Inc.
ENCYCLOPEDIA OF LIFE - Computer software - EDUCORP
END-A-FLAT - Adhesives and sealants - Endrust Industries
END-A-STAIN - Adhesives and sealants - Endrust Industries
END-ALL - Deodorizers - Cosmic Cat Corp.
END CIRCLE - Pens - Sheaffer Inc.
END FOG - Automotive parts and accessories ☆ - Turtle Wax, Inc.
END-ICATOR - Staples ☆ - Bates Manufacturing Co.
END ICE - Deicing fluid - E.C. Grow Inc.
END-IF - Computer software - End-If Software Inc.
END IRON - Slacks - American Trouser Inc.
END LICE - Health care products - Thompson Medical Co., Inc.
END-O-MATIC - Jewelry - Jacoby-Bender Inc.
END OF ENDINGS, THE - Computer software ☆ - Right on Programs
END OF THE COUCH, THE - Pet products - James M. Healey and Karen E. Bruno Partnership
END OF THE LINE - Games - Brown and Bigelow Inc.
END OF THE RAINBOW - Christmas tree ornaments - Cracker Box Inc.
END SMOKE - Deodorizers - Surco Products Inc.
END, THE - Broadcasting stations–television - Harmoney Holdings Inc.
END, THE - Frames–eyeglass - Liberty Optical Manufacturing Co.
END!, THE - Apparel and accessories - Warnaco Inc.
END-X - Filters–industrial - Associates of Cape Cod, Inc.
ENDAC - Skin care products - Helene Curtis Industries Inc.
ENDAGE - Trading cards and stamps - Vincent Pepi
ENDAGEN-HD - Cough medicines - Abana Pharmaceuticals, Inc.
ENDAGEN-HD - Pharmaceutical preparations - Jones Medical Industries, Inc. (Medical Div.)
ENDAL - Pharmaceutical preparations - Forest Pharmaceuticals Inc.
ENDAL-HD PLUS - Pharmaceutical preparations - Forest Pharmaceuticals Inc.
ENDAMINE - Vitamins and nutritional supplements - Armenpharm Ltd.
ENDANGERED ANIMALS - Footwear - R & S Affiliates Inc.
ENDANGERED SPECIES - Apparel and accessories - Wemco, Inc.
ENDANGERED SPECIES - Games - Teaching Concepts Inc.
ENDANGERED SPECIES - Neckties - Randa Corp.
ENDANGERED SPECIES - Puzzles ☆ - Decipher Inc.
ENDANGERED YOUNG'UNS - Hobby kits - Morehead, Inc.
ENDCOAT GREEN - Finishing agents - Osmose Wood Preserving Inc.
ENDCOR - Epoxy coatings - Dampney Co., Inc.
ENDEARMENT - Floor coverings–carpet and rugs - Mohawk Carpet Corp.
ENDEARMENT - Jewelry - Morris Rosenbloom & Co. Inc.
ENDEARMENT - Rings–jewelry - Artcarved Inc.
ENDEAVOR - Cameras - Fuji Photo Film USA Inc.
ENDEAVOR - Floor coverings–carpet and rugs ☆ - Cabin Crafts Carpets
ENDEAVOR - Furniture - Stanley Furniture Co. Inc.
ENDEAVOR - Motor vehicles - Holiday Rambler Corp.
ENDEAVOR - Orthopedic products - Fla. Orthopedics, Inc.

☆ = Now out of production

ENDEAVOR - Pagers - Uniden America Corp.
ENDEAVOR STARSONG - Recording label - Endeavor Starsong Records
ENDEAVOR YACHT - Boats–houseboats - Boatel Marine, Inc.
ENDEAVORS - Bags–duffel - H. Bernbaum Import-Export Co.
ENDEAVORS - Lamps - Harris Lamps Co.
ENDEAVORS - Lighting fixtures - Harris Industries
ENDEAVOUR - Boats–skiffs - Endeavour Yacht
ENDEAVOUR - Finishing agents - Hillyard Enterprises, Inc.
ENDECO - Cheese - Swissrose International Inc.
ENDECON - Health care products ☆ - Du Pont Pharmaceuticals
ENDEMIC - Recording label - Jazz Composer's Orchestra Association Inc.
ENDEN - Hair care products - Helene Curtis Industries Inc.
ENDEP - Pharmaceutical preparations - Roche Laboratories
ENDERES - Tools - Enderes Tool Co. Inc.
ENDGATE - Antennas - Endgate Technology Corp.
ENDICO - Food products - Endico Potatoes Inc.
ENDICO POTATOEY - Food products - Endico Potatoes Inc.
ENDICOTT - Floor coverings ☆ - Tarkett, Inc.
ENDICOTT JOHNSON - Shoes - Endicott Johnson Corp.
ENDIMAL - Deodorizers - Pettibone Laboratories Inc.
ENDIT - Pharmaceutical preparations - ENDIT Laboratories
ENDLESS - Audio equipment - TDK Electronics Corp.
ENDLESS - Floor coverings–carpet and rugs - Patcraft Mills Inc.
ENDLESS BEAUTY - Floor coverings–carpet and rugs - Evans-Black Carpet Mills
ENDLESS BEAUTY - Floor coverings–carpet and rugs ☆ - World Carpets, Inc.
ENDLESS-LIGHTS - Christmas tree ornaments - Wolfe Nursery Inc.
ENDLESS LOVE - Floor coverings–carpet and rugs ☆ - World Carpets, Inc.
ENDLESS QUEST - Publisher's imprints - Tsr, Inc.
ENDLESS SAIL - Apparel and accessories - Bugle Boy Industries, Inc.
ENDLESS SEARCH FOR ADVENTURE - Bags - Sundog Inc.
ENDLESS SHADOWS - Floor coverings–carpet and rugs ☆ - World Carpets, Inc.
ENDLESS SUMMER - Wallpaper - Judscott Handprints Ltd.
ENDLESS SUMMER - Wallpaper - K.M.L. Industries
ENDLESS TUBES - Pasta - Eden Foods, Inc.
ENDLESS TWIST - Mops - Golden Star Inc.
ENDLESS VARIATIONS - Floor coverings - Aladdin Mills, Inc.
ENDLESS WAVE - Watersports equipment - David Strickland
ENDLOSS FORMULA - Shampoos - Klee M. Irwin
ENDNOTE - Computer software - Niles & Associates, Inc.
ENDO - Pharmaceutical preparations - Dupont Merck Pharmaceutical Co.
ENDO - Publisher's imprints - Endocrine Society
ENDO-AVITENE - Pharmaceutical - MedChem Products Inc.
ENDO BOARD - Medical apparatus - Specialty Medical Systems, Inc.
ENDO-BUTTON - Surgical fasteners - Acufex Microsurgical, Inc.
ENDO CLOSE - Medical apparatus - United States Surgical Corp.
ENDO-EZE - Dental equipment - Ultradent Products, Inc.
ENDO IMAGE - Medical apparatus - Optik, Inc.
ENDO-MILK - Lubricants - Snowden Pencer, Inc.
ENDO MINI-RETRACT - Medical apparatus - United States Surgical Corp.
ENDO POOL - Medical apparatus - American Hydro-Surgical Instruments, Inc.
ENDO-QA - Computer software ☆ - Gastroenterology Associates of Cleveland, Inc.
ENDO RETRACT MAXI - Medical apparatus - United States Surgical Corp.
ENDO-SCRUB - Medical apparatus - Xomed-Treace, Inc.
ENDO SHEARS - Medical apparatus - United States Surgical Corp.
ENDO-SHOPPER - Dental equipment - Becker-Parkin Dental Equipment and Supply Co., Inc.
ENDO-SIM - Video games - Ixion, Inc.
ENDO-SNARE - Medical apparatus - Cook Urological Inc.
ENDO-STAPH - Medical apparatus - Meridian Diagnostics, Inc.
ENDO-STAT - Fabrics - Burlington Industries, Inc.
ENDO TA - Medical apparatus - United States Surgical Corp.
ENDO-TUBE - Medical apparatus ☆ - Biosearch Medical Products Inc.
ENDO-VALUE - Surgical instruments - Snowden Pencer, Inc.
ENDOBAG - Surgical supplies - Dexide, Inc.
ENDOCLEAR - Cleaning preparations - Smith & Nephew Richards, Inc.
ENDOCOIL - Medical apparatus - Instent Inc.
ENDOFLEX - Health care products ☆ - Pin Dot Products
ENDOFLEX - Surgical biopsy forceps - Endo-Therapeutics, Inc.
ENDOGLOBIN FORTE - Pharmaceutical preparations ☆ - Du Pont Pharmaceuticals
ENDOGRAFT - Medical apparatus - Endovascular Technologies Inc.
ENDOGRINS - Lenses–optical - Gradient Lens Corp.
ENDOLOR - Pharmaceutical preparations - Keene Pharmaceuticals Inc.

ENDOMAX - Medical apparatus - T. Koros Surgical Instruments, Corp.
ENDOMOVE - Health care products ☆ - Intercontinental Enterprises Ltd.
ENDONET - Computers ☆ - Pentax Corp.
ENDOPACK - Scientific apparatus - Clonetics Corp.
ENDOPUMP - Medical apparatus - Frantz Medical Development Ltd.
ENDOQUENCH - Heating equipment - Surface Combustion, Inc.
ENDOR FOREST RANGER - Toys–automobiles - Lucasfilm Ltd.
ENDORA - Crackers - Vista Bakery, Inc.
ENDORFUN - Games - Onesong Partners, Inc.
ENDORPHIN WARRIOR - Apparel and accessories - Endorphin Warriors
ENDORSEMENT - Floor coverings–carpet and rugs - Lees Carpets
ENDOSHEATH - Medical apparatus - Vision-Sciences, Inc.
ENDOTAK DSP - Medical apparatus - Cardiac Pacemakers Inc.
ENDOTEX - Vitamins and nutritional supplements - Apex Energetics Inc.
ENDOTRAX - Computer software - Leadmark Services LLC
ENDOTUSSIN-NN - Cough medicines - Du Pont Pharmaceuticals
ENDOVISE - Surgical apparatus - Nusurg Medical, Inc.
ENDOWED - Fabrics - Graniteville Co.
ENDOWMENT - Clocks ☆ - General Time Corp. (Westclox/Seth Thomas Div.)
ENDPOINT - Medical apparatus - International Technidyne Corp.
ENDRE'S WALKAMALS - Toys - Barbara Christensen
ENDRUST - Rust removers - Endrust Industries
ENDS - Frames–eyeglass - Zylo Ware Corp.
ENDS - Novelty items ☆ - Chase Collection, Inc.
ENDSLIP - Adhesives and sealants - Endslip Products Co.
ENDSLIP SPRAY - Adhesives and sealants - Endslip Products Co.
ENDU-THANE - Epoxy coatings - Pratt & Lambert, Inc.
ENDUCRYL - Enamels - Pratt & Lambert, Inc.
ENDUE - Skin care products - HDS Cosmetic Lab, Inc.
ENDUR-RING - Key rings - Nelson B. Boone Co., Inc.
ENDURA - See RIDGELINE
ENDURA - Automotive parts and accessories - A.M.E. International Inc.
ENDURA - Cabinets–wood - Southeast Millwork & Casework Manufacturers
ENDURA - Chemical preparations - Baker Hughes Inc.
ENDURA - Computers–personal - Gagetalker Corp.
ENDURA - Containers ☆ - Roadrunner Cases Inc.
ENDURA - Floor coverings–carpet and rugs - Hartford Carpet Mills
ENDURA - Floor coverings–carpet and rugs ☆ - Robertex Associates Inc.
ENDURA - Hardware - Alside Div.
ENDURA - Hardware - Endura Rubber Flooring
ENDURA - Labels–paper - B & H Manufacturing Co., Inc.
ENDURA - Metals - Darman Manufacturing Co. Inc.
ENDURA - Projection screens - Claridge Products and Equipment Inc.
ENDURA - Skin care products - Johnson & Johnson
ENDURA - Television cabinets - Luxor
ENDURA - Tiles–ceramic - Ferro Corp.
ENDURA - Toilet seats ☆ - Bemis Manufacturing Co.
ENDURA - Vitamins and nutritional supplements - Metagenics, Inc.
ENDURA - Vitamins and nutritional supplements ☆ - Tomlyn Products
ENDURA - Weather stripping - Endura Products Inc.
ENDURA ALL SPORT - Vitamins and nutritional supplements - Unipro Inc.
ENDURA-CLEAR - Waxes–sealing - Tnemec Co. Inc.
ENDURA-FLEX - Surface coatings - Vass Industries, Inc.
ENDURA-JEL - Pet products - Tomlyn Products
ENDURA-LITE - Electric lighting equipment ☆ - Bass Products
ENDURA LITE - Paper–rolls - W.R. Grace & Co.
ENDURA OAK - Cutlery ☆ - National Housewares
ENDURA OPTIMIZER - Vitamins and nutritional supplements - Metagenics, Inc.
ENDURA PRO - Ladders–metal - White Metal Rolling & Stamping Corp.
+ENDURA SUPREME - Hardware - Alside Div.
ENDURA-TEC - Laboratory apparatus - Endura-Tec Systems Corp.
ENDURABLE - Floor coverings–carpet and rugs ☆ - Olympic Carpets Inc.
ENDURABLE II - Floor coverings–carpet and rugs ☆ - Olympic Carpets Inc.
ENDURABLES - Hoses - Sears, Roebuck and Co.
ENDURABOND - Hardware - Endura Rubber Flooring
ENDURACIDE - Particle accelerators - Happy Jack, Inc.
ENDURACOAT - Insulating materials - Owens Corning
ENDURACOLOR - Wood products - Enduracolor Hardwood Flooring Inc.
ENDURACRYL - Paints - Dunn Edwards Corp.
ENDURAFIRM - Pillows - E.I. Dupont de Nemours and Co.
ENDURAGLOSS - Paints - Dunn Edwards Corp.
ENDURALIGHT - Ladders–metal - White Metal Rolling & Stamping Corp.
ENDURALITE - Flashlights - Accutec Inc.
ENDURALL - Apparel and accessories - Champion Products Inc.
ENDURALL - Veterinary pharmaceutical preparations - SmithKline Beecham Animal Health Products

☆ = Now out of production

ENDURALUME - Lighting fixtures - Holophane Corp.

ENDURAMID - Brake parts - Carlisle Corp.

ENDURANCE - Bicycles - Ross Bicycles USA, Ltd.

ENDURANCE - Boats–skiffs - European Custom Yachts Ltd.

ENDURANCE - File folders - U-File-M Binder Manufacturing Co. Inc.

ENDURANCE - Floor coverings - Congoleum Corp.

ENDURANCE - Gloves - Netz Glove & Mitten Co.

ENDURANCE - Housewares - Barth-Dreyfuss of California

ENDURANCE - Paints - Glidden Co.

ENDURANCE - Sports rackets and accessories - Victor Sports

ENDURANCE - Sportswear - Comstock Load Inc.

ENDURANCE - Thread - Threads USA Div.

ENDURANCE - Tiles–ceramic - KPT Inc.

ENDURANCE - Vitamins and nutritional supplements - Twinlab

ENDURANCE - Wheelchairs - Essential Medical Supply Inc.

ENDURANCE - Wire products - Bridon American Corp.

ENDURANCE 101 - Animal feeds - Buckeye Feed Mills, Inc.

ENDURANCE COMSTOCK - Coats - Comstock Load Inc.

ENDURANCE CONDITIONER - Hair care products - Peter Hantz Co.

ENDURANCE OPTIMIZER - Vitamins and nutritional supplements - Vitamin Research Products Inc.

ENDURANCE PACKS - Health care products - Health Maintenance Programs Inc.

ENDURANCE WALLS - Wallpaper ☆ - Wall Fashion Inc.

ENDURANCE WALLS II - Wallpaper ☆ - Wall Fashion Inc.

ENDURANCE XL - Floor coverings–carpet and rugs ☆ - Fieldturf & Carpet Inc.

ENDURAPRENE - Hardware - Endura Rubber Flooring

ENDURASEAL - Adhesives and sealants - Dunn Edwards Corp.

ENDURASOFT - Bedding items - E.I. Dupont de Nemours and Co.

ENDURATEC - Paints - Dunn Edwards Corp.

ENDURATOP - Counter tops–laminated - Resin Partners, Inc.

ENDURAWALL - Finishing agents - Dunn Edwards Corp.

ENDURAWEAR - Apparel and accessories - Muncie Endurathon, Inc.

ENDURE - Chemical preparations - Angus Chemical Co.

ENDURE - Cordage and twine ☆ - Winchester-Auburn Mills Inc.

ENDURE - Veterinary pharmaceutical preparations - Babson Bros. Co.

ENDURE 50 - Concrete products - Conspec Marketing & Manufacturing Co. Inc.

ENDURE-A-BILT - Garages - Endure Products Inc.

ENDURE-A-DOR - Doors–metal - Endure Products Inc.

ENDURE-O-CELL - Foam rubber - Eastern Foam Products Inc.

ENDURECON - Brake parts - Carlisle Corp.

ENDURING - Lenses–optical - Ditto Industries Inc.

ENDURING - Lipsticks - Cosmair Inc.

ENDURING - Rings–jewelry - Artcarved Inc.

ENDURING ELEGANCE - Floor coverings–carpet and rugs - World Carpets, Inc.

ENDURING ELEGANCE - Paints - Pratt & Lambert, Inc.

ENDURING LOVE - Glassware–household ☆ - Fenton Art Glass Co.

ENDURING LOVE - Rings–jewelry - Artcarved Inc.

ENDURING QUALITY - Jewelry - Stainless Steelcraft Co.

ENDURO - Apparel–athletic - Jobst Institute Inc.

ENDURO - Awnings - Enduro Fabric Awnings

ENDURO - Balls - Voit Corp.

ENDURO - Beverages–carbonated - Enduro Inc.

ENDURO - Bicycles - Schwinn Cycling & Fitness Inc.

ENDURO - Binoculars - Celestron International

ENDURO - Computer software - Activision, Inc.

ENDURO - Engines - Tecumseh Products Co.

ENDURO - Fibers–synthetic - Hendee Enterprises, Inc.

ENDURO - Frames–eyeglass ☆ - Universal/Univis Inc.

ENDURO - Fuel additives - Conklin Co., Inc.

ENDURO - Health care products - Wheel Ring Inc.

ENDURO - Helmets–athletic - Troxel-West

ENDURO - Measuring instruments - Rolatape Corp.

ENDURO - Musical instrument accessories - Humes & Berg Manufacturing Co. Inc.

ENDURO - Pencil sharpeners ☆ - Dixon Ticonderoga Co.

ENDURO - Sandals - ALP Sport Sandals

ENDURO - Saws–hand-operated - Credo Inc.

ENDURO-FLEX - Springs–furniture - Hickory Springs Manufacturing Co.

ENDURO WAT-R-BASE - Sealant - Compliant Spray Systems

ENDUROBLOCK - Furniture - Blockhouse Co., Inc.

ENDUROCAST - Scales - Fairbanks Inc.

ENDUROFOAM - Foam rubber - Hickory Springs Manufacturing Co.

ENDUROL - Plastics - Watkins Manufacturing Corp.

ENDUROLOFT - Fibers–synthetic - Hickory Springs Manufacturing Co.

ENDURON - Diuretics - Abbott Laboratories

ENDURON - Molding compounds–plastics - Fiberite, Inc.

ENDURONAMEL PANELS - Signs - Wagner Zip-Change Inc.

ENDURONYL - Diuretics - Abbott Laboratories

ENDUROTHANE - Wheelchairs - American Airless

ENDUROX - Vitamins and nutritional supplements - Pacifichealth Laboratories, Inc.

ENDUROX EXCEL - Vitamins and nutritional supplements - Pacifichealth Laboratories, Inc.

ENDUROXR4 - Vitamins and nutritional supplements - Pacifichealth Laboratories, Inc.

ENDUST - Cleaning preparations - Drackett Co.

ENDUST FOR ELECTRONICS - Cleaning preparations - Kiwi Brands, Inc.

ENDUSTRA - Filters–air - Endustra Filter Manufacturing

ENECRETE - Adhesives and sealants - Enecon Corp.

ENEMY - Books–comic - Steven D. Grant

ENENCHI - Vitamins and nutritional supplements ☆ - Nature's Way Products, Inc.

ENER-B - Vitamins and nutritional supplements - Nature's Bounty, Inc.

ENER-G - Apparel and accessories - Garan Services Corp.

ENER-G - Food products - Ener-G Foods Inc.

ENER-G-POLARI-T PRODUCTS - Electronic equipment - Energ-T-Polari-T Products, Inc.

ENER-G-TITE - Glass–window - Defender Inc.

ENER-GRID - Building materials - Rastra Building Systems, Inc.

ENER-RADIANT - Heaters–gas - Enerco Technical Products

ENER SAVER - Thermostats - Ener Saver (USA), Inc.

ENER-VESCENT - Vitamins and nutritional supplements - Nature's Bounty, Inc.

ENERBOND - Adhesives and sealants - Flexible Products Co.

ENERCELL - Batteries - Tandy Corp.

ENERCHRON - Paints - Helios Energy Products Inc.

ENERCO - Heaters–gas - Enerco Technical Products

ENEREX - Lighting fixtures - Enerex Technology, Inc.

ENERG H4 - Health care products - Futurebiotics

ENERGAIN NEW EARTH - Agricultural products - Energy Saver International

ENERGAIRE - Athletic shoes - Reebok International Ltd.

ENERGEE - Pet products - Espree Animal Products, Inc.

ENERGEN - Confections ☆ - C. & J. Willenborg Inc.

ENERGEN - Vitamins and nutritional supplements - Energen Products Inc.

ENERGENIUS - Thermostats - Jameson Home Products Inc.

ENERGETIC - Flour–blended - Acme-Evans/A.D.M. Milling Co.

ENERGEX - Finishing agents - Polymer Plastic Corp.

ENERGIA - Vitamins and nutritional supplements - Richardson Labs, Inc.

ENERGIA VITALE CAPELLI - Hair care products - Korff USA

ENERGIE FIRMANTE - Skin care products - Revlon Consumer Products Corp.

ENERGISAVER - Swimming-pool and spa pumps - ITT Marlow

ENERGISTIC - Hair coloring preparations - Stylors Inc.

ENERGITE - Pharmaceutical - IDE-Interstate Inc.

ENERGIZE - Uncle Sam Chemical Co., Inc.

ENERGIZE! - Computer software - Kona Software, Inc.

ENERGIZE - Computer software - Lucid Inc.

ENERGIZE - Vitamins and nutritional supplements - Healthy 'N Fit Nutritionals

ENERGIZE - Vitamins and nutritional supplements - Vitamin Research Products Inc.

ENERGIZE YOUR DAY! - Teas - Sportea

ENERGIZED - Balls–baseball ☆ - J. De Beer & Son Inc.

ENERGIZED - Snack foods ☆ - Health is Wealth

ENERGIZED FITNESS - Pharmaceutical preparations - Energized Fitness, Inc.

ENERGIZED WITH CHITOSAN - Hair care products - Wella Corp.

ENERGIZED WITH CHITOSAN FOR HUMIDITY RESISTANT HOLD & SHINE - Hair care products - Wella Corp.

ENERGIZER - Aquariums–household - Willinger Bros., Inc.

ENERGIZER - Batteries - Eveready Battery Co., Inc.

ENERGIZER - Beverages - Original Smoothie Co., Inc.

ENERGIZER - Furniture ☆ - Bassett Furniture Industries, Inc.

ENERGIZER - Golfing equipment - Terrill R. McCabe

ENERGIZER - Hair care products - Hobe Labs Inc.

ENERGIZER - Vitamins and nutritional supplements - Nature's Way Products, Inc.

ENERGIZER - Windows ☆ - Continental Aluminum Products Co. Inc.

ENERGIZER II - Fireplaces ☆ - Superior Fireplace Co.

ENERGIZER BUNNY - Flashlights - Eveready Battery Co., Inc.

ENERGIZER RECHARGEABLE POWER SYSTEMS - Batteries - Eveready Battery Co., Inc.

☆ = Now out of production

ENERGY - Floor coverings–carpet and rugs - Milliken & Co.
ENERGY - Health care products - East Earth Herb Inc.
ENERGY - Juices - Gregory Packaging Inc.
ENERGY - Pet products ☆ - Super Valu Inc.
ENERGY - Pollen extracts - CC Pollen Co.
ENERGY - Vitamins and nutritional supplements - Jessica Lee Inc.
ENERGY AID - Veterinary nutritional supplements - Oralx Corp.
ENERGY ALFA - Pharmaceutical preparations - Dolisos America, Inc.
ENERGY AT WORK - Computer software - Right on Programs
ENERGY BAGELBAR - Snack foods - Broadmoor Baker, Inc.
ENERGY BALANCER - Toiletries - California Fragrance Co.
ENERGY BAR - Breads - New York Bagel Factory
ENERGY BAR - Food products - York Barbell Co., Inc.
ENERGY BAR - Vitamins and nutritional supplements - Shaklee Corp.
ENERGY BLAST - Vitamins and nutritional supplements - Brent Laboratories, Inc.
ENERGY BLOCKS - Exercising equipment - Gerstung/Gym-Thing Inc.
ENERGY-BOND - Doors–wood - E.A. Nord Co. Inc.
ENERGY BOOSTER - Beverages - Mistic Brands, Inc.
ENERGY BOOSTER, THE - Pharmaceutical preparations - Alva-Amco Pharmacal Co.
ENERGY-BRACE - Construction equipment - Fiber-Lam Inc.
ENERGY BUILDER - Vitamins and nutritional supplements - Celebrities Plus, Inc.
ENERGY CENTER - Electrical equipment - General Cable Corp.
ENERGY CHECK - Plastics film - MSC Specialty Films Inc.
ENERGY CHECKERS - Hobby kits ☆ - Carousel Crafts Co.
ENERGY CHOICE - Lamp bulbs–incandescent - General Electric Co.
ENERGY CLUB - Confections - Energy Club, Inc.
ENERGY CLUB - Leotards - Krystal K. International Inc.
ENERGY COMMAND - Housewares - Amana Refrigeration Inc.
ENERGY COOKIES - Bakery products - Lifelong Inc.
ENERGY CUP - Soups–mixes - Dr. Mcdougall's Right Foods, Inc.
ENERGY DENSE - Flowers, plants, and seeds - Land O'Lakes Inc.
ENERGY DIET - Dietary supplement - Crystal Springs
ENERGY DIET - Dog food ☆ - Burris Pet Food
ENERGY DIET - Health care products - Herbs of China Ltd.
ENERGY DYNAMICS POWER SYSTEMS - Generators–electric - Energy Dynamics, Inc.
ENERGY EDGE - Window frames - Hygrade Metal Moulding Manufacturing Corp.
ENERGY FACTORS - Vitamins and nutritional supplements - Innner Health Group, Inc.
ENERGY FIT - Footwear - Elan-Polo, Inc.
ENERGY GAGE - Monitors–electronic - Frezzolini Electronics, Inc.
ENERGY GUARD - Doors–storm - Green Hammer Metal Products Co.
ENERGY-GUARD - Glass–window - Reynolds Metals Co.
ENERGY HERBS - Food products - Herbs of China Ltd.
ENERGY HERBS - Vitamins and nutritional supplements - Wendell E. El
ENERGY KNIGHT - Heat pumps - Heat Controller Inc.
ENERGY KNIGHT, THE - Air conditioning equipment - Heat Controller Inc.
ENERGY LIFT - Vitamins and nutritional supplements - Basic Organics, Inc.
ENERGY LOCK - Skin care products - Graham Webb International
ENERGY MANAGER - Thermostats - Robertshaw Controls Co.
ENERGY MASTER - Fireplaces - Heat-N-Glo Fireplace Products, Inc.
ENERGY MAT - Floor coverings–carpet and rugs - Milliken & Co.
ENERGY MC2 - Vitamins and nutritional supplements - Kershenstine's Diamond Beer
ENERGY MC2 - Vitamins and nutritional supplements - Kershenstine's Diamond Beer
ENERGY MEDICINE - Pharmaceutical preparations - Dolisos America, Inc.
ENERGY MISER - Lighting fixtures ☆ - Liteway
ENERGY NOW - Health care products - Foodscience Laboratories Inc.
ENERGY NOW - Vitamins and nutritional supplements - Midland Funds, Ltd.
ENERGY ORAL - Vitamins and nutritional supplements ☆ - Mayor Pharmaceutical Laboratories
ENERGY OVERLOAD - Lighting fixtures - Big Beam Emergency Systems Inc.
ENERGY PATROL - Weather stripping - W.J. Dennis & Co.
ENERGY PAYBACK BUILDING - Building materials - Modular Energy Systems, Inc.
ENERGY PERFORMER - Prefabricated buildings–metal - Morton Buildings, Inc.
ENERGY PLUS - Animal feeds - Bluebonnet Milling Co.
ENERGY PLUS - Golfing equipment - Pinseeker Golf Corp.
ENERGY PLUS - Health care products - Futurebiotics
ENERGY PLUS - Pet food - Purina Mills, Inc.

ENERGY PLUS - Skin care products - Graham Webb International
ENERGY PLUS - Veterinary nutritional supplements - American Superior Feeds, Inc.
ENERGY-PLUS - Veterinary nutritional supplements - Oralx Corp.
ENERGY QUICK - Teas–herbal - Key Products Co.
ENERGY RECORDS - Recording label - Charles A. Caronia
ENERGY SAFE - Doors - Jeld-Wen, Inc.
ENERGY SAVER - Caulking compounds - Dap Products Inc.
ENERGY SAVER - Lighting fixtures - Lights of America Inc.
ENERGY $AVER - Motors–hydraulic - General Electric Co.
ENERGY SAVER - Paints - Atlas Chemical Co.
ENERGY SAVER - Pottery products - Duncan Enterprises
ENERGY SAVER - Rope - Wellington Leisure Products, Inc.
ENERGY SAVERS, THE - Weather stripping ☆ - Compac Industries Inc.
ENERGY SAVINGS - Refrigerators - Amana Refrigeration Inc.
ENERGY SCREEN - Electronic equipment - Copytele, Inc.
ENERGY SENTRY - Monitors–electronic - Brayden Automation Corp.
ENERGY SHAKE, THE - Health care products ☆ - Oakmont Investments Co.
ENERGY STAR - Lighting equipment - Bristolite Skylights
ENERGY STAR - Skylights - Bristol Fiberlite Industries
ENERGY SUPPLEMENTS - Health care products - Natural Organics, Inc.
ENERGY SURGE - Energy drink mix - Hansen & Frank, Inc.
ENERGY TO GO FURTHER, THE - Lubricants - Texaco Lubricants Co.
ENERGY TRANSFER - Golfing equipment - Square Two Golf
ENERGY TUBES - Heat-storage tubes - Boardman Energy Systems Inc.
ENERGY UNLIMITED - Vitamins and nutritional supplements - Y. K. Kim Productions, Inc.
ENERGY WALL - Windows–storm - Vega Industries, Inc.
ENERGY WATCH - Indoor thermometer - American Thermometer Co.
ENERGY WISER - Lamp bulbs–fluorescent - Bulbrite Industries, Inc.
ENERGY WRAP - Bakery products - Raybern Quality Foods
ENERGY2 BURN - Recording label - American Council on Exercise
ENERGYMATE - Power switching equipment ☆ - National Presto Industries, Inc.
ENERGYMAX - Ventilation systems - Research Products Corp.
ENERGYMISER - Windows–storm ☆ - Norandex, Inc.
ENERGYRISE - Health care products - Earthnet
ENERGYRISE ALIVE - Vitamins and nutritional supplements - Earthnet
ENERGYRITE - Pool heaters - Lochinvar Corp.
ENERGYSAVER - Space heaters - Rinnai America Corp.
ENERGYSLIM - Vitamins and nutritional supplements - Female Success Products
ENERJET - Food processors - APV Baker Inc.
ENERJETS - Pharmaceutical preparations ☆ - Vapon, Inc.
ENERJOY - Heaters–space - Solid State Heating
ENERJUICE - Beverages - Lang Naturals
ENERLINK - Computer software - Southern Co.
ENERLUX - Lighting fixtures - Enersys3 Inc.
ENERPRIME - Vitamins and nutritional supplements - Impax International
ENERQUENCE BAR - Food products - Weider Health and Fitness
ENERQUENCH - Beverages ☆ - Weider Health and Fitness
ENERVESCENT - Vitamins and nutritional supplements - Nature's Bounty, Inc.
ENERVITE - Pet products - 8 in 1 Pet Products Inc.
ENERVITE - Pet products - St. Aubrey
ENERVITE - Vitamins and nutritional supplements - United Vitamin Manufacturing Corp.
ENERYDA - Figurines - Charles Norman Inc.
ENERZEST - Vitamins and nutritional supplements - Tishcon Corp.
ENESCO - Musical instruments - Ideal Musical Merchandise Co.
ENESCO DESIGNED - Giftware - Enesco Corp.
ENESCO GIFT GALLERY - Giftware - Enesco Corp.
ENESCO SMALL WORLD OF MUSIC - Giftware - Enesco Corp.
ENESEAL - Adhesives and sealants - Enecon Corp.
ENESWEAR - Mops ☆ - Piedmont Mop Co.
ENF - Bicycles - Schwinn Cycling & Fitness Inc.
ENFAMIL - Infant product - Bristol-Myers Squibb Co.
ENFAMIL NURSETTE - Infant product - Bristol-Myers Squibb Co.
ENFANT - Medical apparatus - Neurotech Corp.
ENFIELD - Frames–eyeglass - Hudson Optical Corp.
ENFIELD - Jewelry ☆ - Hirsch Speidel Inc.
ENFIELD - Shoes ☆ - Allen-Edmonds Shoe Corp.
ENFIELD - Stationery - Harold-Lawrence Associates Inc.
ENFLEX - Communications equipment - Conservation Through Innovation, Ltd.
ENFOLD - Apparel stores–lingerie - Goddess Bra
ENFORCE - Hair care products - Scruples Professional Salon Products, Inc.

☆ = Now out of production

ENFORCE PLUS - Hair care products - Scruples Professional Salon Products, Inc.

ENFORCER - Amplifiers–musical instrument - Fender Musical Instruments

ENFORCER - Automotive parts and accessories - AP Parts

ENFORCER - Bicycles - Murray, Inc.

ENFORCER - Boats–motor ☆ - Checkmate Boats Inc.

ENFORCER - Bulletproof vests - Tim Tyler Zufle

ENFORCER - Field-sport shoes ☆ - Jaclar

ENFORCER - Firearms, accessories, and parts - Welsh Sporting Goods Corp. (Boyt Div.)

ENFORCER - Frames–eyeglass - Hudson Optical Corp.

ENFORCER - Gloves - Ektelon

ENFORCER - Herbicides - Enforcer Products Inc.

ENFORCER - Lighting fixtures ☆ - Hubbell Lighting, Inc. (Lighting Div.)

ENFORCER - Meters–parking - Positran, Inc.

ENFORCER - Mufflers–motor vehicle - Goerlich's

ENFORCER - Rackets–racquetball - Lisco, Inc.

ENFORCER - Skates–roller ☆ - Rollerblade, Inc.

ENFORCER - Toys - Tonka Corp.

ENFORCER - Toys–automobiles - Mattel, Inc.

ENFOUR - Paints - Endeavour IV, Inc.

ENFUELS - Compressed natural gas - Enfuels Corp.

ENFUSE - Health care products - Entech Inc./Enteral Technology

ENGADIN PRESS - Postcards ☆ - Transworld Visions

ENGAGE - Insecticides - Whitmire Research Laboratories, Inc.

ENGAGE - Pesticide - Platte Chemical Co.

ENGAGE RECORDS - Recording label - Engage Records

ENGAGEMENT - Frames–eyeglass ☆ - Universal/Univis Inc.

ENGAGEMENT - Glass–plate - Sasaki

ENGAGING - Floor coverings–carpet and rugs - Lees Carpets

ENGARDE - Disinfectants - T.K. X-Ray, Ltd.

ENGARDE - Mirrors - Gardner Mirror Corp.

ENGEL - Electronic equipment - Micro Mo Electronics, Inc.

ENGELBERT SCHMID - Musical instruments ☆ - Orpheus Music Inc.

ENGELHARDT - Musical instruments - Engelhardt-Link Inc.

ENGELS - Scissors–hand-operated - F.W. Engels Inc.

ENGER KRESS - Leather - Enger-Kress Co.

ENGEVITA - Yeast - Gist-Brocades Food Ingredients Inc.

ENGINAIR - Automotive parts and accessories - G.H. Meiser & Co.

ENGINE - Games ☆ - Warren Industries Inc.

ENGINE 1 - Barbecue sauce ☆ - Chelten House Products Inc.

ENGINE 2 - Barbecue sauce ☆ - Chelten House Products Inc.

ENGINE-AIR - Toys–airplanes - Mattel, Inc.

ENGINE BLOX - Cardboard - Performance Packaging

ENGINE BRITE - Cleaning preparations - Radiator Specialty Co.

ENGINE CLENE - Cleaning preparations ☆ - Klean-Strip

ENGINE CO. NO. 28 - Apparel and accessories - Griego Enterprises, Inc.

ENGINE CONNECTION INC., THE - Engines–internal combustion - Engine Connection, Inc.

ENGINE DOCTOR - Power steering fluid - Packaging Group Corp.

ENGINE DYNAMICS - Metals - AE Clevite Inc.

ENGINE EXPERT - Automotive parts and accessories - E Group

ENGINE FOG - Cleaning preparations - Engine Fog, Inc.

ENGINE LOCK - Electronic equipment ☆ - Digequip Security Industries Inc.

ENGINE MASTER - Lubricants - JTS Corp.

ENGINE MIST - Cleaning preparations - Engine Fog, Inc.

ENGINE MUSCLE - Fuel additives - Engine Muscle

ENGINE PROTECTOR, THE - Oils–lubricating - Sunmarks, Inc.

ENGINE STETHOSCOPE - Scientific apparatus - William M. Kayser

ENGINE STOR - Lubricants - CRC Chemicals USA/Siloo

ENGINEBOOSTER - Oils–lubricating - Saveco, Inc.

ENGINEER - Watches - Bulova Corp.

ENGINEERED CONVERSION - Refrigerators - American Standard Inc.

ENGINEERED EXCELLENCE - Building materials - Simpson Dura Vent Co., Inc.

ENGINEERED FIBER SELECTION - Computer software - Cotton Inc.

ENGINEERED LUMBER & DESIGN - Lumber - Georgia-Pacific Corp.

ENGINEERED WORK GARMENTS - Uniforms–tailored ☆ - Garment Corp. of America

ENGINEQUEST - Automotive parts and accessories - Hams Inc.

ENGINKOOL - Engine coolant - CRC Chemicals USA/Siloo

ENGINSEAL - Adhesives and sealants - CRC Chemicals USA/Siloo

ENGINUITY - Games - Enginuity

ENGITECH - Pharmaceutical preparations - Engitech Inc.

ENGLANDER - Mattresses - Englander Co. Inc.

ENGLAZE - Adhesives and sealants - Endrust Industries

ENGLEFIELDS - Metals ☆ - Kirk Stieff Co.

ENGLERT SERIES 1000 - Construction equipment - Englert Inc.

ENGLERT SERIES 2000 - Construction equipment - Englert Inc.

ENGLEWOOD - Bedding–linen - Dan River Inc.

ENGLHOFER - Confections ☆ - R.L. Albert & Son, Inc.

ENGLISH - Fruit drinks–bottled or canned - English

ENGLISH - Paper–bond ☆ - Fox River Paper Co.

ENGLISH ACCENTS - Furniture - Councill Craftsmen Inc.

ENGLISH BOAR - Apparel and accessories - Wal-Mart Stores Inc.

ENGLISH BOUQUETS - Skin care products - Natural Attitudes Inc.

ENGLISH BREAKFAST - Dinnerware - Corning Inc.

ENGLISH BRICK - Floor coverings - Congoleum Corp.

ENGLISH CHEF - Cutlery ☆ - Lifetime Hoan Corp.

ENGLISH CHIPPENDALE - Silverware - Reed and Barton Corp.

ENGLISH CLASSIC - Hardware ☆ - Amerock Corp.

ENGLISH CLUB - Recliners - Sears, Roebuck and Co.

ENGLISH COUNTRY - Chimes - Nutone Inc.

ENGLISH COUNTRY - Furniture ☆ - Cosco, Inc.

ENGLISH COUNTRY - Wallpaper ☆ - Raintree Designs Inc.

ENGLISH COUNTRY CLASSIC - Furniture ☆ - Cosco, Inc.

ENGLISH COUNTRY COTTAGE - Wallpaper - Old Stone Mill

ENGLISH COUNTRY GARDEN II - Wallpaper - Imperial Wallcoverings, Inc.

ENGLISH COUNTRY GARDENS - Flowers, plants, and seeds - English Country Gardens Inc.

ENGLISH COUNTRY HOME - Wallpaper - Imperial Wallcoverings, Inc.

ENGLISH COUNTRYSIDE - Dishes–earthenware - Mikasa Licensing, Inc.

ENGLISH COUNTRYSIDE - Furniture ☆ - Southern Furniture Co. of Conover

ENGLISH COUNTRYSIDE - Potpourri - Countryside Fragrances Inc.

ENGLISH CROWN - Silverware - Reed and Barton Corp.

ENGLISH ELEGANCE - Fabrics–tapestry - Coloroll Inc.

ENGLISH EXPRESS - Computer software ☆ - Knowledge Adventure

ENGLISH FAIR - Housewares - Kirk & Matz Ltd.

ENGLISH FLOWERS - Wallpaper ☆ - Greeff Fabrics Inc.

ENGLISH GARDEN - Baskets–wood ☆ - Royal Cathay Trading Co.

ENGLISH GARDEN - Clocks - General Time Corp. (Westclox/Seth Thomas Div.)

ENGLISH GARDEN - Dinnerware–glass - Royal China & Porcelain Companies Inc.

ENGLISH GARDEN - Dishes–china ☆ - Denby USA Limited

ENGLISH GARDEN - Flowers–artificial - Creative Home Collections Inc.

ENGLISH GARDEN - Glassware–household - Mikasa Licensing, Inc.

ENGLISH GARDEN - Herbal tea - Donovan Coffee Co., Inc.

ENGLISH GARDEN - Tableware–china ☆ - Robinson Knife & Fiddlers Plastics

ENGLISH GARDEN - Umbrellas - Totes, Inc.

ENGLISH GARDEN - Wood products ☆ - Spaulding & Frost Co. Inc.

ENGLISH GARDENS - Wallpaper ☆ - Sanitas Wallcoverings

ENGLISH GENTRY - Silverware - Reed and Barton Corp.

ENGLISH GUARD - Liquors - United States Distilled Products Co.

ENGLISH HOBNAIL - Glass products - Westmoreland Glass Co.

ENGLISH IVY - Dinnerware ☆ - Corning Inc.

ENGLISH LAVENDER - Cosmetics - Yardley of London Inc.

ENGLISH LEATHER - Bags - Archer Worldwide

ENGLISH LEATHER - Colognes - Mem Co., Inc.

ENGLISH LEATHER - Luggage - Pierre Cardin Electronique

ENGLISH LEATHER - Tobacco–chewing or smoking - Amar Blends Co.

ENGLISH LINKS - Apparel–women's - Gillman Knitwear Co.

ENGLISH MANOR HOUSE - Fabrics–tapestry - Coloroll Inc.

ENGLISH MASTERY - Computer software - American Language Academy Inc.

ENGLISH MEADOW - Dinnerware - Corning Inc.

ENGLISH MEADOW - Wallpaper - Exeter Wallcoverings

ENGLISH MORN - Dinnerware ☆ - Corning Inc.

ENGLISH MOUNTAIN - Food products - Bush Brothers and Co.

ENGLISH MUFFIN - Breads - Natural Ovens of Manitowoc Inc.

ENGLISH NOW! - Computer software - Transparent Language, Inc.

ENGLISH OAK - Furniture - Pennsylvania House

ENGLISH OAK REPRODUCTIONS - Furniture - Link-Taylor Corp.

ENGLISH OVALS - Cigarettes - Philip Morris Companies Inc.

ENGLISH OVALS - Pet products - Rawhide Brand Inc.

ENGLISH PRINTS - Fabrics - Capital Carousel Inc.

ENGLISH PROVINCIAL - Silverware - Reed and Barton Corp.

ENGLISH PUB - Fabrics - Uniroyal Engineered Products

ENGLISH PUB - Mustard - Lea and Perrins Inc.

ENGLISH RAIN - Cosmetics - Madeleine Mono Ltd.

ENGLISH RIB - Socks - Kayser-Roth Corp.

ENGLISH ROSE - Dishes–china - Waterford Wedgwood USA, Inc.

ENGLISH ROSE - Luggage - Leisure Merchandising Corp.

ENGLISH ROSE - Skin-care products - Intellectual Property Holding Co.
ENGLISH ROSE - Tableware—china ☆ - Lenox, Inc.
ENGLISH ROSE - Wallpaper - Milbrook Wallcoverings
ENGLISH ROYALE - Furniture - Keller Manufacturing Co.
ENGLISH SCRAMBLE - Food products - Denny's Inc.
ENGLISH SERIES - Computer software - Electronic Courseware Systems Inc.
ENGLISH SPRING FLOWERS - Cosmetics - Yardley of London Inc.
ENGLISH SQUIRE - Apparel—men's - Masterpiece Apparel, Inc.
ENGLISH SQUIRE - Men's apparel - Dick Lynott Inc.
ENGLISH TAPESTRY - Floor coverings ☆ - Congoleum Corp.
ENGLISH TEATIME - Teas - R.C. Bigelow, Inc.
ENGLISH TOFFEE - Apparel—children's - Kid Duds
ENGLISH TOFFEE - Cookies - Nikki's Cookies, Inc.
ENGLISH TRADITION - Teas - Farmer Bros. Co.
ENGLISH TRELLIS - Toilets—enameled - Kohler Co.
ENGLISH TUDOR - Furniture ☆ - Virginia House Furniture Corp.
ENGLISH TWEED - Luggage ☆ - Mercury Luggage Manufacturing Co.
ENGLISH ULTRA - Shotguns - Ithaca Gun Co. Inc.
ENGLISH VELLUM - Paper - A.I. Friedman Inc.
ENGLISH VILLAGE - Dinnerware—glass - Salem China Co.
ENGLISH WALKER - Footwear—women's - B. Levy & Son
ENGLISH WALKER - Hosiery - Hole-in-None Hosiery
ENGLISHWOOD - Clocks - Ridgeway Clock Co.
ENGOL DOLLS - Dolls ☆ - DGI/Buki
ENGRALITE - Lighting fixtures ☆ - Hubbell Lighting, Inc. (Lighting Div.)
ENGRAN HP - Pharmaceutical preparations - Bristol-Myers Squibb Co.
ENGRAVABLES - Frames—picture - Contemporary Inc.
ENGRAVABLES - Giftware - Cawley Co.
ENGRAVED ELEGANCE - Mirrors - Contractors Wardrobe, Inc.
ENGRAVEMATE - Computer software - Scanvec Inc.
ENGSPAN - Computer software - Pan American Health Organization
ENGSTROM - Sporting goods ☆ - Texwood Furniture
ENGUARD - Computer software - Grapevine Systems, Inc.
ENHAN-SIT - Furniture - American Dream International
ENHANCE - Cleaning preparations - Blue Lustre, LLC
ENHANCE - Fertilizers - Lange-Stegmann Co.
ENHANCE - Floor coverings - American Floor Products Co. Inc.
ENHANCE - Floor waxes - Harley Chemicals
ENHANCE - Frames—eyeglass - Hudson Optical Corp.
ENHANCE - Girdles - Lily of France Inc.
ENHANCE - Hair care products ☆ - S.C. Johnson & Son, Inc.
ENHANCE - Medical apparatus ☆ - Spenco Medical Corp.
ENHANCE - Paints - Benjamin Moore & Co.
ENHANCE! - Paper - International Paper Co.
ENHANCE - Plastics—laminated - Plaskolite Inc.
ENHANCE FLAKE PLUS - Fish food ☆ - Aquatronics-Filtronics
ENHANCE-HER - Brassieres (Bras) - Jodee Bra Co.
ENHANCE KINS - Jewelry - Aurafin Corp.
ENHANCE PERSONAL LUBRICANT - Health care products - Xandria Collection
ENHANCEABLE Y NECKLACE - Jewelry - David Emsellem
ENHANCED - Computer hardware - Enhanced Memory Systems, Inc.
ENHANCED AUDIO PRODUCT AP - Computer software ☆ - Selectware Technologies, Inc.
ENHANCED FINGER CALS - Cosmetics - Coburn Corp.
ENHANCED PERFORMANCE II - Vitamins and nutritional supplements - Desert Health Products, Inc.
ENHANCED STATEMENT PRESENTATION - Computer software - CSG Systems, Inc.
ENHANCEDACCESS - Handles—plastic - Meridian, Inc.
ENHANCEMENT - Floor coverings—carpet and rugs ☆ - Galaxy Carpet Mills Inc.
ENHANCEMENT - Ophthalmic goods - Foremost Optical Products
ENHANCEMENT COURSES - Video production - Murray and Jacobs Associates, Inc.
ENHANCEMENTS - Dinnerware - Corning Inc.
ENHANCEMENTS - Plastics - Gencorp Polymer Products
ENHANCER - Food products machinery - Par-Way Group
ENHANCER - Hair care products - Trionics Systems Corp.
ENHANCER - Health care products - Roho, Inc.
ENHANCER - Heating equipment - York International Corp.
ENID - Ophthalmic goods - Styl-Rite Optical Manufacturing Co., Inc.
ENIGMA - Perfumes - Alexandra De Markoff, Ltd.
ENIGMA - Puzzles - Enigma
ENIGMA - Recording label - Capitol-EMI Music Inc.

ENIGMA COMMUNICATIONS - Computer integrated systems design services - Enigma Communications
ENISYL - Pharmaceutical preparations ☆ - Person and Covey Inc.
ENJA - Recording label - Creav Inc. USA
ENJAIE INTERNATIONAL - Boxes - Buyers International Inc.
ENJAY - Food products - Ralston Purina Co.
ENJOLI - Perfumes - Revlon Consumer Products Corp.
ENJOLI MIDNIGHT - Perfumes - Revlon Consumer Products Corp.
ENJOUR - Floor coverings—carpet and rugs ☆ - Evans-Black Carpet Mills
ENJOY - Grass seed - International Seeds, Inc.
ENJOY - Snack foods - Enjoy Foods International, Inc.
ENJOY BEEF JERKY - Food products - Enjoy Foods International, Inc.
ENJOY LIFE - Bakery products - Food For Life Baking Co.
ENKA - Frames—eyeglass ☆ - U.S. Optical Frame Co.
ENKAID - Pharmaceutical preparations - Bristol-Myers Squibb Co.
ENKASONIC - Mats - Akzo America Inc.
ENLARGER-LITE - Lamps - American Crewel & Canvas Studio
ENLIGHTEN - Bakery products - Safeway Inc.
ENLIGHTEN - Cosmetics - Estee Lauder Inc.
ENLIGHTEN - Eyeglasses - Martin-Copeland Eyewear Corp.
ENLIGHTEN - Fabrics - Astrup Co.
ENLIGHTEN - Vitamins and nutritional supplements - Ellon USA, Inc.
ENLIGHTENED AUDIO DESIGNS - Electronic equipment - Enlightened Audio Designs Corp.
ENLIGHTENMENT - Apparel and accessories - Jeffrey Peter Gabica
ENLIGHTENMENTS - Paper - Scafa-Tornabene Art Publishing Co., Inc.
ENLITENED CONCERNS - Bakery products - L. Karp & Sons, Inc.
ENLON - Tools—machine - Enlon Import Corp.
ENM - Electrical equipment - ENM Co.
ENNDS - Pharmaceutical preparations - Oakhurst Co.
ENNDS CHLOROPHYLL TABLETS - Health care products - Woolfoam Corp.
ENNESI - Shoes - Ennesi Shoe Co. Inc.
ENNESI GOLD - Shoes - Ennesi Shoe Co. Inc.
ENNIS - Business forms - National Sales Co.
ENNIS - Tools - Ennis Manufacturing Co.
ENNIS HOWARD'S - Barbecue sauce - Earsie Howard's Old Time Foods Inc.
ENNSBROOK - Floor coverings—carpet and rugs ☆ - Columbus Mills, Inc.
ENO - Antacids - Smithkline Beecham Corp.
ENO - Apparel and accessories - Implus Corp.
ENOCH WEDGWOOD - Dinnerware—glass ☆ - S.P. Skinner Co. Inc.
ENOLOGICA VALTELLINESE - Wines ☆ - Pellegrini Bros. Wines Inc.
ENON SPRINGS - Beverage dispensing equipment - Emro Marketing
ENOSIS - Office supplies - Metro Form Systems, Ltd.
ENOSPUN - Fibers - Ridgewood Textiles, Inc.
ENOTEX - Fibers - Ridgewood Textiles, Inc.
ENOTRIA - Beverages—alcohol - Valley Cheese, Wine & Food Co.
ENOVE - Shampoos - Mastey De Paris
ENOVID - Pharmaceutical preparations - G. D. Searle & Co.
ENOVIL - Pharmaceutical preparations ☆ - Roberts/Hauck Pharmaceuticals Inc.
ENOX - Machine parts - Enox Technologies, Inc.
ENOZ - Deodorizers - Willert Home Products, Inc.
ENPAC - Motors—outboard - Marine Power Inc.
ENPAC CORPORATION - Containers—plastic - Enpac Corp.
ENPAYNE - Pharmaceutical preparations ☆ - Morton Pharmaceuticals Inc.
ENPHYMIN - Vitamins and nutritional supplements - Horizons Marketing Group, Inc.
ENPLACE - Hair care products - Mastey De Paris
ENPOWER - Computers - PC Club
ENQUIRER - Frames—eyeglass - Pathway Optical Prods.
ENQYR - Computer peripheral equipment - O'Pin Systems, Inc.
ENRICH - Hair care products - Ardell International Inc.
ENRICH - Hair care products - Naturelle, Inc.
ENRICH - Luggage - Henry A. Enrich & Co. Inc.
ENRICH - Pharmaceutical preparations - Enrich International, Inc.
ENRICH - Pigments—paint - Tru-Test Manufacturing
ENRICH - Varnish - Cotter & Co.
ENRICH - Vitamins and nutritional supplements - Ross Laboratories
ENRICH BITS - Animal feeds - Purina Mills, Inc.
ENRICHLIFE PLUS - Vitamins and nutritional supplements ☆ - Carlsbad Technology
ENRICHMENT - Ophthalmic goods - Foremost Optical Products
ENRICHMENT DE PANTENE - Hair care products ☆ - Procter & Gamble Co.
ENRICO - Lenses—optical - Ditto Industries Inc.
ENRICO FRATELLI - Apparel—women's - KGR, Inc.
ENRICO GELINI - Apparel—men's - Kingsport, Int'l, Inc.
ENRICO GUCCINI - Neckties - Cornell of California Inc.

☆ = Now out of production

ENRICO ROMANO - Sweaters - DLR Trading
ENRICO SERGIO - Footwear - J. Baker Inc.
ENRICO'S - Spaghetti sauces - Ventre Packing Co. Inc.
ENRIDOLE 3-C - Vitamins and nutritional supplements - Enrich Corp.
ENRLAC - Milk substitute ☆ - Corning Inc.
ENRO - Apparel–men's - Enro Shirt Co. Inc.
ENRO - Shirts - Apparel Group, Ltd.
ENRO - Water heaters–household - Meyer Furnace Co.
ENROUTE - Computer software - Scanvec Inc.
ENROUTE - Frames–eyeglass - Liberty Optical Manufacturing Co.
ENS - Computer programs - Banyan Systems Inc.
ENSEMBLE - Apparel–athletic ☆ - Tighe Industries Inc.
ENSEMBLE - Computer software - GeoWorks
ENSEMBLE - Computer software - Teletrol Systems Inc.
ENSEMBLE - Dishes–china - Pickard Inc.
ENSEMBLE - Erasers ☆ - Bright Boy Abrasives
ENSEMBLE - Mallets - Mike Balter Mallets
ENSEMBLE - Musical instrument accessories ☆ - Selmer Co. Inc.
ENSEMBLE - Musical instruments ☆ - Oscar Schmidt International Inc.
ENSEMBLE - Office furniture–wood - Marvel Group Inc.
ENSEMBLE - Violins - St. Louis Music Supply Co.
ENSEMBLE - Window shades - Verosol
ENSEMBLE - Window shades - Vertical Blind Factory
ENSEMBLE 77 - Furniture - Universal Flooring
ENSEMBLE BLUSH - Glassware–household ☆ - Lenox Crystal, Inc.
ENSEMBLE CLUTCH - Handbags - DHP Limited Parnership
ENSEMBLE COBALT - Glassware–household ☆ - Lenox Crystal, Inc.
ENSENADA - Dresses–women's - Anne Klein & Co.
ENSENADA - Floor coverings ☆ - Kentile Floors Inc.
ENSENDA - Frames–eyeglass - May Optical Co. Inc.
ENSHRINE - Rings–jewelry - Artcarved Inc.
ENSIDUR - Rubber goods - Ensinger, Inc.
ENSIGHT - Computer software - Computational Engineering International, Inc.
ENSIGN - Binoculars - Bausch & Lomb Inc.
ENSIGN - Boats–motor - Trophy Marine Co.
ENSIGN - Flag stands - Annin and Co.
ENSIGN - Floor coverings–carpet and rugs - Coronet Carpets Inc.
ENSIGN - Frames–eyeglass ☆ - Universal/Univis Inc.
ENSIGN - Freezers - Frigibar Industries Inc.
ENSIGN - Fungicides ☆ - ISK Biosciences Corp.
ENSIGN - Navigational instruments - Rule Industries, Inc.
ENSIGN - Office supplies - Alvin and Co. Inc.
ENSIGN - Pencils - Empire Berol USA
ENSIGN - Recording label - Chrysalis Records
ENSIGN - Ships–sailing vessels - Sunfish Laser Inc.
ENSIGN - Telephone apparatus ☆ - RF Communications Div.
ENSIGN - Watches - Bulova Corp.
ENSIGN HARRY KIM - Toys - Paramount Pictures Corp.
ENSIPRO - Polypropylene film sheets - Ensinger Industries, Inc.
ENSIS COMPOUND - Oils–lubricating ☆ - Shell Oil Co.
ENSOLITE - Wet suits–rubber - Wellington Leisure Products, Inc.
ENSONIQ - Musical instruments - Ensoniq
ENSOTROL - Chemical preparations - Pharmavene, Inc.
ENSTAR - Computer software - Electronic Data Systems Corp.
ENSUPPLE - Hair care products - Gillette Co.
ENSURANCE - Deodorants–personal - Nu Skin International, Inc.
ENSURE - Detergents - Stearns Technical Textiles Co.
ENSURE - Hair care products - Nexxus Products Co.
ENSURE - Vitamins and nutritional supplements - Ross Laboratories
ENSYLVA - Grass seed - International Seeds, Inc.
ENTABLATURE, THE - Lighting fixtures - Kim Lighting Inc.
ENTAC - Emulsifiers - Entac Northeast, Inc.
ENTAGON - Pharmaceutical preparations - Smithkline Beecham Corp.
ENTAPRIN - Analgesics - Caraco Pharmaceutical Laboratories Ltd.
ENTASIS - Televisions - Entasis, LLC.
ENTEC - Computer software - Entec Consulting, Inc.
ENTEC - Metals - Kadee Industries, Inc.
ENTEC - Stereos - GNP Audio Video Inc.
ENTEGRA - Roofing materials - Eterna Roof Tile Corp.
ENTELA CERTIFIED - Furniture - Entela, Inc.
ENTELE - Rice - Natraj International, Inc.
ENTENMANN'S - Bakery products - Entenmann's Inc.
ENTENTE - Frames–eyeglass - Zylo Ware Corp.
ENTER HERE - Video production - Enter Here, LLC
ENTER MEMORY - Vitamins and nutritional supplements - Reyman Drug Co., Inc.

ENTERA - Health care products - Fresenius Pharma
ENTERA FLO - Health care products - Fresenius Pharma
ENTERALITE - Medical apparatus - Zevex, Inc.
ENTERGY - Doors–metal - Robertson-Ceco Corp.
ENTERIC DISEASE - Pharmaceutical preparations - Wampole Laboratories Div.
ENTERIGAR - Vitamins and nutritional supplements - Global Marketing Associates, Inc.
ENTERLINK - Loudspeakers - Unitec, Inc.
ENTERO C - Medical apparatus - Smith & Nephew Richards, Inc.
ENTERPLEX'S - Telephones - Cathay International
ENTERPREX - Calculators - Enterprex International Corp.
ENTERPRISE - Antennas - Valor Enterprises, Inc.
ENTERPRISE - Artists' materials ☆ - Hamilton Industries
ENTERPRISE - Bicycles - Murray, Inc.
ENTERPRISE - Clocks - General Time Corp. (Westclox/Seth Thomas Div.)
ENTERPRISE - Computer software - Enterprise Computer Systems Inc.
ENTERPRISE - Floor coverings–carpet and rugs - Dan River Inc.
ENTERPRISE - Furniture ☆ - Bombay Co. Inc.
ENTERPRIZE - Gasoline - Enterprise Products Co.
ENTERPRISE - Mats–grass, reed, and jute - Everett Associates Inc.
ENTERPRISE - Paint - Insilco Corp.
ENTERPRISE - Paints - Valspar Corp.
ENTERPRISE - Photographic equipment ☆ - Omega/Arkay
ENTERPRISE - Recording label ☆ - London Records Inc.
ENTERPRISE - Stoves - Enterprise Appliance Corp.
ENTERPRISE 2000 - Beds–hospital - Sci-O-Tech Inc.
ENTERPRISE ASSET MANAGER - Computer software - Chrysler Systems Inc.
ENTERPRISE AUTHORING SYSTEM - Computer software - DataWare Development, Inc.
ENTERPRISE CERT - Computer software - Transcender Corp.
ENTERPRISE DOCUMENT SOLUTIONS - Forms–preprinted - Enterprise Computer Systems Inc.
ENTERPRISE ELEMENTS - Computer storage devices - Enterprise Engines, Inc.
ENTERPRISE HUB - Computer hardware - Hughes Aircraft Co.
ENTERPRISE ONLINE - Advertising agencies - Gordon A. Haines
ENTERPRISE PRINT SERVICES - Computer software - Interlink Computer Sciences Inc.
ENTERPRISE SELF-SERVICE - Computer software - ESSENSE Systems Inc.
ENTERPRISE SERVER - Computer software - Bristol Babcock Inc.
ENTERPRISE SOLUTIONS MAIL - Computer software - Enterprise Solutions Limited
ENTERPRISE SYSTEM/9000 - Computer peripheral equipment - International Business Machines Corp.
ENTERPRISE, THE - Golf clubs - Solo Enterprise Corp.
ENTERPRISE WIDE - Computer software - Techsmith Corp.
ENTERPRISE WINDOWS - Computer software - Bristol Babcock Inc.
ENTERPRISES - Food products - Green Turtle Cannery
ENTERPRIZE - Computer software - Cincinnati Bell Information Systems Inc.
ENTERSAFE - Home-security system - Invention Prototypes & Marketing Corp.
ENTERTAINER - Boats–motor ☆ - Checkmate Boats Inc.
THE +ENTERTAINER - Electrical equipment - West Bend Co.
ENTERTAINER - Furniture - American Furniture Co. Inc.
ENTERTAINER - Glassware–household ☆ - Lancaster Colony Corp.
ENTERTAINER - Ophthalmic goods - Embassy Creations Inc.
ENTERTAINER - Organs–musical instrument ☆ - Kimball International, Inc.
ENTERTAINER - Projectors–photographic - Tyco Toys
ENTERTAINER - Sinks–metal - Kohler Co.
ENTERTAINER, THE - Horns–motor vehicle - Anes Electronics Burglar Alarm Systems
ENTERTAINER, THE - Audio equipment - Electro-Voice, Inc.
ENTERTAINER, THE - Vending machines - JR Vending, Inc.
ENTERTAINER, THE - Refrigerators ☆ - Magic Chef Inc.
ENTERTAINERS - Furniture ☆ - Bassett Furniture Industries, Inc.
ENTERTAINERS - Glassware–household - Anchor Hocking Corp.
ENTERTAINERS - Serving carts ☆ - Artex-Green Corp. of N.Y.
ENTERTAINER'S SECRET THROAT RELIEF - Pharmaceutical preparations - KLI Corp.
ENTERTAINERS, THE - Occasional furniture - American Furniture Co. Inc.
ENTERTAINERS, THE - Glassware–household - Anchor Hocking Glass, Inc.
ENTERTAINERS, THE - Cookware, servingware ☆ - Corning Inc.
ENTERTAINMENT BUYERS CLUB - Advertising agencies - Budget Marketing, Inc.
ENTERTAINMENT CENTER, THE - Dinnerware–plastic - Grainware Co.
ENTERTAINMENT TONIGHT: THE TRIVIA GAME - Games - Lakeside Games

☆ = Now out of production

ENTEX - Pharmaceutical preparations - Norwich-Eaton Pharmaceuticals

ENTEX - Toys–electronic ☆ - Placo Products Co.

ENTHAICE - Coffee - Classic Beverage Corp.

ENTHOVEN - Sinks–porcelain - American Standard Inc.

ENTHUSIAST - Eyeglasses - Art-Craft Optical Co.

ENTHUSIASTIC ENTERPRISES - Greeting cards - Enthusiastic Enterprises

ENTICE - Apparel–women's ☆ - Maidenform Inc. (True Form Foundations Div.)

ENTICE - Hair care products - Jingles International

ENTICE - Ophthalmic goods - Foremost Optical Products

ENTICEMENT - Floor coverings–carpet and rugs ☆ - Blue Ridge Carpet Mills

ENTICEMENTS - Apparel–women's - Kellwood Co.

ENTICER - Boats–motor ☆ - Checkmate Boats Inc.

ENTICING - Floor coverings–carpet and rugs - Milliken & Co. Inc.

ENTICING DELIGHTS - Candy ☆ - Falcon Trading Co.

ENTIQUE - Doors–glass - Robertson-Ceco Corp.

ENTIRE NET-WORK - Computer software - Software AG of North America, Inc.

ENTITLED - Apparel and accessories - M.B.E International Resources, Inc.

ENTOURAGE - Cosmetics - SRA Industries Inc.

ENTRA VISION - Computer storage devices–magnetic - Northern Computers, Inc.

ENTRAC - Catheters - American Medical Systems, Inc.

ENTRACO - Abrasive products - Engineered Transitions Co. Inc.

ENTR'ACTE - Recording label - Fifth Continent Music Corp.

ENTRADA - Signs - Entrada Inc.

ENTRALITER - Lighting fixtures - Hubbell Lighting, Inc. (Lighting Div.)

ENTRALUX - Lighting fixtures - Hubbell Lighting, Inc. (Lighting Div.)

ENTRANCE GUARD - Mats - U.S. Mat & Rubber Co. Inc.

ENTRANCE MAKER - Ophthalmic goods - Foremost Optical Products

ENTRANCE SENTRY - Mats ☆ - Superior Manufacturing Group/Notrax Floor Matting

ENTRAPMENT - Puzzles - Tyco Toys

ENTRAPTA - Toys - Mattel, Inc.

ENTRATA - Computer software - National Computer Systems, Inc.

ENTRE - Audiovisual and computer products - Entre Electronics Corp.

ENTRE - Ballet slippers - Art Stone Theatrical Corp.

ENTRE - Cigars ☆ - Avanti Cigar Co.

ENTRE NOUS - Apparel and accessories ☆ - Swirl II Ltd.

ENTRE NOUS - Apparel stores–lingerie - Goddess Bra

ENTRE NOUS - Candy - S.L. Kaye Co., Inc.

ENTRE NOUS - Furniture - Roche-Bobois USA

ENTREE - Cabinets - Riviera Cabinets Inc.

ENTREE - Fabrics - Greenwood Mills Inc.

ENTREE - Floor coverings–carpet and rugs - E.R. Carpenter Co.

ENTREE - Floor coverings–carpet and rugs - Omalon

ENTREE - Furniture - Lane Co. Inc.

ENTREE - Sinks–metal - Kohler Co.

ENTREE - Sporting goods - Moody & Co. Inc.

ENTREE EXPRESS - Dinners–frozen - Conagra, Inc.

ENTREE SALADS-TO-GO - Salads–prepackaged - Carl Karcher Enterprises Inc.

ENTREE SEA - Seafood products–fresh or frozen - Nova Fisheries, Inc.

ENTREE XPRESS - Food products - Park 100 Foods Inc.

ENTREES - Cooking utensils–earthenware ☆ - Anchor Hocking Glass, Inc.

ENTREMED - Pharmaceutical preparations - Entremed, Inc.

ENTREPRENEUR - Deodorants–personal ☆ - Jan Stuart Co.

ENTREPRENEUR - Frames–eyeglass - May Optical Co. Inc.

ENTREPRENEUR EDITION - Calendars - Day Runner, Inc.

ENTRIA - Computer hardware - Hewlett-Packard Co.

ENTRIFLEX - Medical apparatus ☆ - Biosearch Medical Products Inc.

ENTRIMIT - Medical apparatus ☆ - Biosearch Medical Products Inc.

ENTRITION - Medical apparatus - Clintec Nutrition Co.

ENTROBAN - Pharmaceutical preparations - Norwich-Eaton Pharmaceuticals

ENTRON - Medical apparatus ☆ - Biosearch Medical Products Inc.

ENTROPY - Furniture - Haworth, Inc.

ENTROSET - Enteral-feeding system ☆ - Intercontinental Enterprises Ltd.

ENTRUST - Health care products - McKesson Home Health Care

ENTRY GARD - Hardware - Truth Hardware Corp.

ENTRY LITE - Lighting fixtures - Regent Lighting Corp. (Consumer Products Div.)

ENTRYVISION - Television equipment - CCTV Corp./GBC

ENTUBE - Health care products - Entech Inc./Enteral Technology

ENTUBE-MEER BRIDLE - Health care products - Entech Inc./Enteral Technology

ENTUSS - Pharmaceutical preparations - Roberts/Hauck Pharmaceuticals Inc.

ENTUSS-D - Pharmaceutical preparations - Roberts/Hauck Pharmaceuticals Inc.

ENTWINE - Dinnerware–glass ☆ - Nikko Ceramics Inc.

ENTWINE - Rings–jewelry - Artcarved Inc.

ENUCLENE - Ophthalmic goods - Alcon Laboratories, Inc.

E.N.U.F. - Apparel–men's - E.N.U.F. Internationale, Inc.

E.N.U.F. INTERNATIONALE - Apparel and accessories - E.N.U.F. Internationale, Inc.

E.N.U.F. S.T.U.F. - Bags - E.N.U.F. Internationale, Inc.

ENUF STUF - Bolts, screws, nails, etc. - Independent Fastener Co.

E.N.U.F. TIME - Watches - E.N.U.F. Internationale, Inc.

ENURAID - Pharmaceutical preparations - P. & S. Laboratories Inc.

ENURAID - Pharmaceutical preparations - Standard Homeopathic Co., Inc.

ENUREMINDER - Medical apparatus ☆ - Mid-Island Medical Supply Co.

ENURETROL - Pharmaceutical preparations ☆ - Berlex Laboratories, Inc.

ENV-2000 - Paperboard - Bradford Co.

EN'VE - Apparel and accessories - En've, Inc.

ENVELOCK - Office supplies - Ames Safety Envelope Co.

ENVELOK - Office supplies - Mead Corp.

ENVELOPE 2000 - Wood products - Weyerhaeuser Co.

ENVELOPE TOASTER - Printers–computer - Addressease, Inc.

ENVELOPENER - Office supplies - Omation Corp.

ENVELOPER MTR - Machinery - Buhrs Americas, Inc.

ENVENOTE - Stationery - West America Graphics Corp.

ENVERGURE - Colognes - Bourjois Ltd.

ENVI - Computer software - Better Solutions Consulting, LLC

ENVI-RO-FUGE 2000 - Filters–oil - Green Isle Environmental Services, Inc.

ENVI-RO-TECH - Cleaning preparations - Tech Spray, Inc.

ENVIGRO ENVIRONMENTALLY SOUND GROWER PRODUCTS - Trays - Karthauser & Sons, Inc.

ENVION - Vitamins and nutritional supplements - Pure Distributors, Inc.

ENVION LINE - Filters–industrial - Pure Distributors, Inc.

ENVIR-ASEPTIC - Uniforms–tailored - Angelica Uniform Group

ENVIRA-LAC - Paints - Kelly-Moore Paint Co., Inc.

ENVIRA-LAC - Paints - Kelly-Moore/Preservative Paints

ENVIRA-NAMEL - Paints - Kelly-Moore/Preservative Paints

ENVIRA-SHIELD - Paints - Kelly-Moore Paint Co. Inc.

ENVIRA-THANE - Paints - Kelly-Moore/Preservative Paints

ENVIRACAIRE - Health care products - Enviracaire

ENVIRACOR - Veterinary pharmaceutical preparations - Upjohn Co.

ENVIREX - Health care products - Surco Products Inc.

ENVIRO - Bicycles - Huffy Corp.

ENVIRO - Tiles–ceramic - KPT Inc.

ENVIRO-AIR - Ventilation equipment - Environmental Air Technologies

ENVIRO BLEND - Chemical preparations - American Minerals, Inc.

ENVIRO BLEND - Oils–lubricating - Primrose Oil Co., Inc.

ENVIRO-BLEND - Paper - Data Documents, Inc.

ENVIRO CARE - Fertilizers - Vigoro Industries, Inc.

ENVIRO CARE - Floor waxes - Rochester Midland Corp.

ENVIRO-CHOICE - Cleaning preparations - Ecolab Inc.

ENVIRO-CLEAN - Housewares - Southwest Manufacturers & Distributors, Inc.

ENVIRO-COAT - Paints - Harrison Paint Corp.

ENVIRO COP - Board games - Enviro Times, Inc.

ENVIRO-CORE - Soil testing kits - Precision Sampling Inc.

ENVIRO-CURE - Paints - Gilbert Spruance Co.

ENVIRO-CURE - Polyurethane foam - Crain Industries Inc.

ENVIRO ECONOMICS - Machinery - Green Oasis Environmental, Inc.

ENVIRO FIBER - Paperboard - Gulf States Paper Corp.

ENVIRO-FLEX - Conduits–electrical - Cantex Inc.

ENVIRO FLOC - Water purification systems ☆ - Coughlan Products Corp.

ENVIRO FORMS - Business forms, labels, envelopes, etc. - Office Electronics Inc.

ENVIRO-GARD - Insect repellents ☆ - Landco

ENVIRO/GEOPHYSICAL - Electronic equipment - Gisco-Geophysical/ Geological Instrument & Supply Co.

ENVIRO GRAN - Water purification systems ☆ - Coughlan Products Corp.

ENVIRO GUARD - Antifreeze - Marcus International Inc.

ENVIRO-GUARD - Paints - Pratt & Lambert United, Inc.

ENVIRO GUARD - Protective covers - Continental Disc Corp.

ENVIRO-HEALTH - Surgical supplies - Tidi Products, Inc.

ENVIRO-KOTE - Coatings - Brookwood Companies Inc.

ENVIRO-LAWN - Flowers, plants, and seeds - Willamette Seed Co.

ENVIRO-LINER - Motor vehicle parts and accessories - Insta-Bulk, Inc.

ENVIRO-LOG - Fireplace logs - James P. Dunham

ENVIRO-LOOB - Lubricants - Alu-Tech, Inc.

ENVIRO-MAG - Waste treatment additives - American Minerals, Inc.

☆ = Now out of production

ENVIRO-MAGIC - Cleaning preparations - Amazon Lumber & Trading Corp.

ENVIRO-MARINE - Degreasing solvents - Lehrco Inc.

ENVIRO MAX PLUS - Fuel additives - James Kenneth Sanders

ENVIRO MELT - Ice and snow melters - Coughlan Products Corp.

ENVIRO MIST - Air purification systems - Environmental Engineering Concepts Inc.

ENVIRO-MOTIVE - Cleaning preparations ☆ - Green Island Research, Inc.

ENVIRO-NOVOC - Paints - Spectra-Tone Paint Corp.

ENVIRO-PEAT - Agricultural products - Applied Environmental Technologies, Inc.

ENVIRO-PHOS - Waste treatment additives - American Minerals, Inc.

ENVIRO-PLEX - Paints - Con-Lux Coatings Inc.

ENVIRO-RAGS - Cloths - Row Clothing Enterprises, Inc.

ENVIRO-REZ - Chemical preparations - Corrugated Chemicals, Inc.

ENVIRO-SAFE - Cleaning preparations - Loctite Corp.

ENVIRO-SAFE - Dinnerware–plastic - Essex Marketing Inc.

ENVIRO-SAFE - Disinfectants - OBF Industries, Inc.

ENVIRO-SAFE - Inks - Pinnacle Technologies, Inc.

ENVIRO-SAFE - Thermometers - H-B Instrument Co.

ENVIRO SAN - Vaporizers ☆ - Coughlan Products Corp.

ENVIRO-SEAL - Containers - E.S. Robbins Corp.

ENVIRO SEAL - Protective film - Lustra Line, Inc.

ENVIRO-SLIDE - Chemical preparations - Rhomar Industries, Inc.

ENVIRO-SPA - Shower rods - USI Environmental Reclamation, Ltd.

ENVIRO SPAT - Welding equipment - Dynaflux, Inc.

ENVIRO-SPHERE - Globes - Geo. F. Cram Co.

ENVIRO SPOT - Paints - Nelson Paint Co., Inc.

ENVIRO SPRAY - Adhesives and sealants ☆ - Environmental Technology, Inc.

ENVIRO-SPUN - Yarn - Patrick Yarn Mill, Inc.

ENVIRO TAB - Vaporizers - Coughlan Products Corp.

ENVIRO-TAR - Epoxy - Pratt & Lambert, Inc.

ENVIRO-TECH INTERNATIONAL - Cleaning preparations - Enviro-Tech International

ENVIRO-TEK - Boxes–corrugated paperboard - Bell Packaging Corp.

ENVIRO-TEK - Hair care products - Focus 21 International Inc.

ENVIRO-TREAD - Waxes–sealing - Tnemec Co. Inc.

ENVIRO-WALL - Curtain wall - American Home Improvement

ENVIRO-WATE - Chemical preparations - J.E. Beall

ENVIRO-WATER - Containers - E.S. Robbins Corp.

ENVIRO-WIPE - Cleaning preparations - Bycin Industries, Inc.

ENVIROAMP - Chemical preparations - Roche Molecular Systems, Inc.

ENVIROBASE - Fertilizers - Harmony Products, Inc.

ENVIROBLIND - Shutters–wood - Environmental Seal & Security

ENVIROBOX - Prefabricated corrugated boxes - Beaverton Packaging

ENVIROCIDE - Disinfectants ☆ - Viro Research International Inc.

ENVIROCLAM - Containers - Robert J. Petcavich

ENVIROCLOTH - Fabrics - Apollo Environmental Corp.

ENVIROCOTE - Paperboard - Federal Paper Board Co., Inc.

ENVIROCRON - Paints - PPG Industries, Inc.

ENVIRODIAPER - Diapers–cloth - Envirodiaper Inc.

ENVIRODRI - Veterinary medical equipment ☆ - Ranpak Corp.

ENVIROFAN - Fans–ceiling - Northwest Envirofan

ENVIROFIBER - Wood fillers - Gulf States Paper Corp.

ENVIROFILLER - Machinery - Environmental Packing LP

ENVIROFLEX - Water-filtering units - Healthguard, Inc.

ENVIROFORM - Prefabricated buildings–wood - Simpson Timber Co.

ENVIROGANICS - Apparel and accessories - David Lindsay

ENVIROGARD - Bags–trash ☆ - North American Plastics Corp.

ENVIROGARD - Monitors–electronic - Clarke Industries, Inc.

ENVIROGEL - Fire extinguishing compositions - Powsus, Inc.

ENVIROGLAZE - Cleaning preparations - USI Environmental Reclamation, Ltd.

ENVIROGLOSS - Floor waxes - Brulin & Co., Inc.

ENVIROGRAPHIC - Paper–bond - Badger Paper Mills, Inc.

ENVIROGUARD - Lighting fixtures - Guth Lighting

ENVIROGUARD TUBE - Lighting fixtures - Guth Lighting

ENVIROHOME - Prefabricated buildings–wood - Home Builders International Inc.

ENVIROKARTON - Packaging–blisterwrap - Textile Printing Co.

ENVIROKEM - Display cases–plastic - Envirokem, Inc.

ENVIROKIND - Cleaning preparations - Delta Industries International, Inc.

ENVIROKLEEN - Packaging–paper - Kliegman Brothers, Inc.

ENVIROLINE - Adhesives and sealants - Industrial Environmental Coatings Corp.

ENVIROLINK - Computer software - Georgia-Pacific Corp.

ENVIROLITE - Fiberboard - Gridcore Systems International, Inc.

ENVIROLOCK - Plastic cable connector seal - Raychem Corp.

ENVIROLUBE - Lubricants - Envir-O-Lube, Inc.

ENVIROMAC - Paperboard - MacMillan Bloedel Packaging Inc.

ENVIROMAN - Insect repellents - EnviroMan, Inc.

ENVIROMARK - Markers–felt-tip - Sanford Corp.

ENVIROMAX - Analyzers–industrial - Liston Scientific Corp.

ENVIROMAX - Furnaces–electric - Inter-City Products Corp. (USA)

ENVIROMINS - Vitamins and nutritional supplements - Twinlab

ENVIROMULCH - Mulchers - Sonoco Products Co.

ENVIRON - Building materials - Phenix Biocomposites Inc.

ENVIRON-RICHMENT - Cages–wire - Britz-Heidbrink, Inc.

ENVIRON-V - Shirts - Alexxus, Inc.

ENVIRONAMEL - Paints - Ponderosa Paint Manufacturing Co. Inc.

ENVIRONAMICS - Machine parts - Environamics Corp.

ENVIRONET - Filters–water - Filtration Manufacturing, Inc.

ENVIRONICS - Generators–gas - Environetics Inc.

ENVIRONMAT - Floor coverings ☆ - Congoleum Corp.

ENVIRONMENT - Controls–heating systems - Kohler Co.

ENVIRONMENT 25 - Paper–writing - Neenah Paper Co.

ENVIRONMENT & ENERGY EFFICIENT - Motion-detector - Larry C.Y. Lee

ENVIRONMENT FRIENDLY - Insulating materials–foam - FOMO PRODUCTS Inc.

ENVIRONMENT MASTERBATH - Curtains–shower - Kohler Co.

ENVIRONMENT ON FILE - Publisher's imprints - Facts on File Inc.

ENVIRONMENT/ONE - Electrical equipment - Environment One Corp.

ENVIRONMENTAL - Cups–plastic - Wes Design & Supply Co. Ltd.

ENVIRONMENTAL ARTWEAR - Apparel and accessories - Environmental Artwear, Inc.

ENVIRONMENTAL CHOICE - Recycled computer and fax paper - West Shore Group (USA) Ltd.

ENVIRONMENTAL CLEANSE - Vitamins and nutritional supplements - Kroeger Herb Products Co. Inc.

ENVIRONMENTAL CLOTHING CO. - Apparel–men's - Almax Sportswear Corp.

ENVIRONMENTAL CLOTHING CO. - Sweaters - Phil Kriegel Associates Inc.

ENVIRONMENTAL CONCEPTS - Pool-, spa-, and plant-care products - Environmental Concepts, Inc.

ENVIRONMENTAL ECHOES - Chimes - Richmond Goodwill Industries, Inc.

ENVIRONMENTAL ELEMENTS CORPORATION - Electronic equipment - Environmental Elements Corp.

ENVIRONMENTAL GRAPHICS - Wallpaper - Environmental Graphics Inc.

ENVIRONMENTAL HEMP - Apparel and accessories - Hemposphere

ENVIRONMENTAL LIGHTING - Fluorescent fixtures - IMS Corp.

ENVIRONMENTAL MANAGEMENT 2000 - Business software - Software 2000, Inc.

ENVIRONMENTAL MATE - Educational materials - Little, Brown and Co., Inc.

ENVIRONMENTAL NOTEBOOK, THE - Computer storage devices–optical - Digital Imaging Associates Inc.

ENVIRONMENTAL RUB ON SYMBOLS - Decals and transfers - Real Estate Graphics, Inc.

ENVIRONMENTAL SAFETY SEAL - Adhesives and sealants - Para-Chem Southern, Inc. (Parabond Adhesives Division)

ENVIRONMENTAL SELF ASSESSMENT PROGRAM - Computer software - International Business Machines Corp.

ENVIRONMENTAL SOLUTIONS - Magazines - Advantage Communications, Inc.

ENVIRONMENTAL SOLUTIONS, INC. - Polypropylene film sheets - Environmental Solutions, Inc.

ENVIRONMENTAL TESTING KIT - Toys - Natural Science Industries, Ltd.

ENVIRONMENTALIST 2000 - Water treatment apparel - Superior Manufacturing Division

ENVIRONMENTALIST/ZERO-BLEED - Superior Manufacturing Division

ENVIRONMENTALLY AWARE - Chemical preparations - Kurtz Bros. Inc.

ENVIRONMENTALLY AWARE - Fertilizers - Kurtz Bros., Inc.

ENVIRONMENTALLY FRIENDLY - Charcoal starter - GSW Jackes-Evans Manufacturing Co.

ENVIRONMENTALLY SAFE-VOC COMPLIANT - Adhesives and sealants ☆ - Macklanburg-Duncan Co.

ENVIRONMENTALLY SPEAKING - T-shirts–women's - Prelude Designs

ENVIRONMENTS - Recording label - Syntonic Research Inc.

ENVIRONMENTS 20/20 - Furniture - Corry Hiebert

ENVIRONMENTS OLEFIN II - Wallpaper - Wallquest, Inc.

ENVIRONMENTS OLEFIN KINSALE - Wallpaper - Wallquest, Inc.

ENVIRONMODES - Tiles–ceramic - Dal-Tile Corp.

ENVIRONNEMENTAL AIR SPONGE - Deodorizers - Regina Trainor

ENVIRONWARE - Paper plates - Heartland Manufacturing Corp.

ENVIROPAK - Cables - Belden Wire & Cable Co.

☆ = Now out of production

ENVIROPAK - Garden equipment - Womack Nursery Co.
ENVIROPAN - Automotive parts and accessories - Amersave Products Corp.
ENVIROPATCH - Asphalt felts and coatings - Vulcan Materials Co.
ENVIROPAVE - Asphalt felts and coatings - Vulcan Materials Co.
ENVIROPAVE/ENVIROPATCH - Asphalt - Vulcan Materials Co.
ENVIROPLUS 90 - Furnaces–electric - Inter-City Products Corp. (USA)
ENVIROPREME - Antifreeze - Dynachem Technologies, Inc.
ENVIROPRO - Computer software - Heartland Technologies, Inc.
ENVIROPRO - Machinery - Autoclave Engineers Inc.
ENVIROQUEST - Facial tissues - Ashdun Inc.
ENVIROQUEST - Fishing tackle - Danielson Co.
ENVIRORESEARCH - Hair care products - Windmere Corp.
ENVIROSAFE - Machinery - John W. Wade
ENVIROSAFE - Pesticides–household - Envirosafe Bug Control Corp.
ENVIROSAFE - Pet products - Consep Inc.
ENVIROSAVE - Agricultural products - Rivard's Quality Seeds Inc.
ENVIROSCOPE - Computer software - JT&A, Inc. (EnviroScope Models)
ENVIROSEAL - Paints - Ponderosa Paint Manufacturing Co. Inc.
ENVIROSEAL - Plastic film - Milprint Inc.
ENVIROSENSE - Coatings - Interface, Inc.
ENVIROSET - Foundry binders - Delta Resins & Refractories
ENVIROSHADE - Pet products - Enviroworks
ENVIROSHAPE - Hair care products - Tigi Linea, Inc.
ENVIROSHEEN - Cartons–paperboard - Carton Service, Inc.
ENVIROSHIELD - Air conditioning equipment - Lindgren RF Enclosures, Inc.
ENVIROSHIELD - Filters–air - Kleen Air Research
ENVIROSHIELD - Windows–vinyl - Enlight Industries LLC
ENVIROSILV - Chemical preparations - Fuji Hunt Photographic Chemicals, Inc.
ENVIROSOL - Cleaning preparations - Twin Rivers Technologies, L.P.
ENVIROSOL - Fertilizers - Envirosol Organic Products Inc.
ENVIROSPORTS - Apparel and accessories - Envirosports, Inc.
ENVIROSPRAY - Housewares - Delta Industries International, Inc.
ENVIROSPRAY - Paints ☆ - Environmental Technology, Inc.
ENVIROSPRAY - Sprayers - Wynn Oil Co.
ENVIROSTAT - Static eliminator - Simco
ENVIROSTONE - Blocks–concrete - Future Stone, Inc.
ENVIROSTORM - Vacuum cleaners and accessories - Schoettler Research and Engineering Co.
ENVIROSTRIPE - Paints - Adhesive Coatings Co.
ENVIROSURE - Oil recovering chemicals - Betz Energy Chemicals Inc.
ENVIROTEC HEALTHGUARD - Adhesives and sealants - W.F. Taylor Co.
ENVIROTECH - Camping equipment - CW Group
ENVIROTECH - Paints - Triangle Coatings Inc.
ENVIROTEX - Adhesives and sealants - Environmental Technology, Inc.
ENVIROTEX LITE - Adhesives and sealants - Environmental Technology, Inc.
ENVIROTOWEL - Cleaning preparations - Sentinel Products Inc.
ENVIROTRADE - Computer software - U.S. Department of Energy
ENVIROTRON - Cleaning preparations - Gaines Industries, Inc.
ENVIROVIEW - Computer software - Applied Graphic Solutions Corp.
ENVIROVU - Egg cartons - Envirosys L.P.
ENVIROWARE - Scientific equipment - Fisher Scientific Co.
ENVIROWHITE - Packaging–paper - Innovative Machinery Co.
ENVIROWOOD - Plastics - Chicagoland Processing Corp.
ENVIROZONE - Water purification systems - Pure Flow Water Co., Inc.
ENVISION - Computer software - Deneb Robotics, Inc.
ENVISION - Computer software - Health Care Data Systems, Inc.
ENVISION - Computer software - Softchec, Inc.
ENVISION - Contact lenses - Polymer Technology Corp.
ENVISION - Diagnostic apparatus - C. R. Bard, Inc.
ENVISION - Skin care products ☆ - Parker Taylor, Inc.
ENVIZEX - Computer peripheral equipment - Hewlett-Packard Co.
ENVOGUE - Hair care products - Lady Di Enterprises, Inc.
ENVOL - Flatware ☆ - Couzon USA
ENVOPAK - Office supplies - Envopak Reusable Envelopes
ENVOY - Briefcases - Samsonite Corp.
ENVOY - Briefcases ☆ - Master Products Manufacturing Inc.
ENVOY - Cabinets - Oxford Furniture Corp.
ENVOY - Catheters - Cordis Endovascular Systems, Inc.
ENVOY - Chairs–metal - Hon Co.
ENVOY - Chimes - Friedland, Inc.
ENVOY - Dinnerware–glass ☆ - Royal China & Porcelain Companies Inc.
ENVOY - Electronic equipment - American Locker Security Systems
ENVOY - Electronic equipment - Motorola, Inc. (Land Mobile Products Sector)
ENVOY - Fabrics - Greenwood Mills Inc.
ENVOY - Faucets - Kallista Inc.
ENVOY - Flags - Annin and Co.

ENVOY - Furniture ☆ - Stanley Furniture Co. Inc.
ENVOY - Jewelry - Anson Inc.
ENVOY - Luggage - United States Luggage Corp.
ENVOY - Mats - Matworks
ENVOY - Musical amplifiers - Peavey Electronics Corp.
ENVOY - Paper - Strathmore Paper Co.
ENVOY - Pens - Accutec Inc.
ENVOY - Pipes–tobacco - Bradberry Briar Pipe Corp.
ENVOY - Projection screens - Draper Shade and Screen Co. Inc.
ENVOY - Shirts ☆ - Horace Small Apparel Co.
ENVOY - Trailers–travel - Royals International
ENVOY - Vaults - Cardinal/Embassy Group, Inc.
ENVOY - Watches - Bulova Corp.
ENVOY - Wheelchairs - Theradyne Healthcare Product Div.
ENVOY DINNERWARE - Dinnerware - Carlisle Foodservice Products, Inc.
ENVOY II - Furniture ☆ - Stanley Furniture Co. Inc.
ENVOYS - Boots - KangaROOS USA Inc.
ENVUE - Computer software - Video Technics, Inc.
ENVY - Colognes - Elijah Hogan
ENVY - Dishes–paper - Bunzl Plastics, Inc.
ENVY - Eyeglasses - Art-Craft Optical Co.
ENVY - Fertilizers - National Liquid Fertilizer Corp.
ENWOOD - Floor coverings–carpet and rugs - Whitecrest Carpet Mills
ENWRAPTURE - Tables–wood - Dab Design, Inc.
ENZ - Vitamins and nutritional supplements - Kroeger Herb Products Co. Inc.
ENZ PAIN - Vitamins and nutritional supplements ☆ - Ethical Nutrients
ENZ VINEYARDS - Wines - ENZ Vineyards
ENZA B. - Educational materials - Forlang Foreign Language Services
ENZACTIN - Pharmaceutical preparations - Whitehall Laboratories
ENZAMINE - Vitamins and nutritional supplements - Bioscript International Inc.
ENZEC - Veterinary pharmaceutical preparations - Merck & Co., Inc. (Merck Agvet Division)
ENZEL - Shoes - Kinney Shoe Corp.
ENZIO - Bridal gowns - Phillie Bridals, Inc.
ENZIVATOR - Sewage treatment equipment - Boyer Corp.
ENZKIN - Computer software ☆ - CONDUIT
ENZO - Footwear - Roman Sandal, Inc.
ENZO - Lenses–optical - Ditto Industries Inc.
ENZO & MARCO - Footwear - G.H. Bass and Co.
ENZO ANGIOLINI - Footwear - Fisher Camuto Corp.
ENZO ANGIOLINI - Handbags - Nine West Group Inc.
ENZO-B - Pharmaceutical ☆ - Ion Laboratories Inc.
ENZO-SNAKE - Drain pipe cleaners - Share Corp.
ENZO-SWEET - Food products ☆ - Enzo-Pac Inc.
ENZOBILE - Pharmaceutical preparations - Roberts/Hauck Pharmaceuticals Inc.
ENZONE - Hemorrhoidal treatment - Biozone Laboratories
ENZONE - Insecticides - Union Oil Co. of California
ENZONE - Safety products - Enzone Inc.
ENZONE CREAM - Pharmaceutical preparations - Forest Pharmaceuticals Inc.
ENZO'S MAGIC GRILL - Housewares - Creative Process, Inc.
ENZY-CLEAN - Chemical preparations - Aqua Clear Industries Inc.
ENZYMATIC - Health care products - Deer Valley Farm
ENZYMATIC THERAPY - Health care products - Enzymatic Therapy, Inc.
ENZYME COCKTAIL - Hair care products - Trionics Systems Corp.
ENZYME EX-CELL - Skin care products - Gary E. Loest
ENZYME ICE - Analgesics - Nutri-West
ENZYME SOLAR ICE - Analgesics - Nutri-West
ENZYMEACTIVE - Vitamins and nutritional supplements - Nature's Way Products, Inc.
ENZYMESFORLIFE - Juices - Lifenzyme Americas, Inc.
ENZYMINT - Candy - Randal Nutritional Products Inc.
ENZYNK - Chemical preparations - Enzymatic Deinking Technologies, LLC
ENZYPAN - Pharmaceutical preparations ☆ - Norgine Laboratories Inc.
ENZYTEC - Pesticide-detection kit - Enzytec Inc.
EO - Computers - EO, Inc.
EO2 - Hair care products - KMS Research Inc.
EOC - Seasonings - Flavor & Fragrance Specialties Inc.
EOCF/2 - Computer software - International Business Machines Corp.
EODRADOUR - Scotch whiskey - Austin, Nichols & Co., Inc.
E'OLA AMP II PRO DROPS - Vitamins and nutritional supplements ☆ - E'ola Products, Inc. (Biogenics)
E'OLA ARTHRITIS PLUS - Vitamins and nutritional supplements - E'ola Products, Inc. (Biogenics)
E'OLA CALCIMIN - Vitamins and nutritional supplements ☆ - E'ola Products, Inc. (Biogenics)

☆ = Now out of production

E'OLA LIFE JUICE - Vitamins and nutritional supplements ☆ - E'ola Products, Inc. (Biogenics)

E'OLA NO SUN TAN - Skin care products ☆ - E'ola Products, Inc. (Biogenics)

E'OLA PYNOGEMIN - Vitamins and nutritional supplements ☆ - E'ola Products, Inc. (Biogenics)

E'OLA VITAMIN - Vitamins and nutritional supplements ☆ - E'ola Products, Inc. (Biogenics)

EON - Audio equipment - JBL Inc.

EON - Clocks - Ann A. Fleming

EON - Electrical equipment - Eon Corp.

EON - Glass–plate - Sasaki

E'ON 5 - Skin care products - ATM America Corp.

EON LABS - Pharmaceutical preparations - Eon Labs, Inc.

EONITE - Glass–optical - Schott Glass Technologies Inc.

EOP - Bags–duffel - Dower

EOS - Computer software - Viewsoft, Inc.

EOS - Mattresses - Simmons USA

EOS - Ophthalmic apparatus - Alcon Laboratories, Inc.

EOS - Sporting goods - Earth & Ocean Sports, Inc.

EOS-1 - Cameras - Canon USA, Inc.

EOS A-2 - Cameras - Canon USA, Inc.

EOS AE-1 - Cameras - Canon USA, Inc.

EOS REBEL - Cameras - Canon USA, Inc.

EOSTATION - Office supplies - Eos Technologies Inc.

EOSTONE - Stone products - Nancy Cheryl Albrecht

EOTEC - Modems - Weed Fiber-Optics, Inc.

EOTIQUE - Wallpaper - Pantasote Inc. (Wallcovering Div.)

EP - Life preservers - Wellington Leisure Products, Inc.

EP - Luggage - Palm Beach Co., Inc.

EP - Sporting goods ☆ - Hedstrom Corp.

EP-2 - Primers - House of Kolor, Inc.

EP-680 - Cleaning preparations - Diana Industries International

EP-2000 - Beauty shop equipment - Proteus Inc.

EP ECONODRAFT - Furnaces–steam - E/S Corp.

EP ELANEX - Pharmaceutical - Elanex Pharmaceuticals, Inc.

E.P. MYCIN - Pharmaceutical preparations ☆ - Edwards Pharmaceuticals, Inc.

EP-PO - Paints - Miller Paint Co., Inc.

EP SPORTS - Skis ☆ - Hedstrom Corp.

EP-XT - Medical apparatus - C.R. Bard, Inc.

EPA - Hair care products - John Amico Expressive Hair Care Products

EPA-PURE 700 - Food products - Nature's Pride Inc.

EPA SELECT - Vitamins and nutritional supplements - Jenek, Inc.

EPACHOL 300 - Health care products - Esquire Pharmaceuticals Inc.

EPALINE - Oils–edible ☆ - Grifair Co.

EPAMARINE - Vitamins and nutritional supplements - Arista Industries Inc.

EPARON - Paints ☆ - Surface Protection Industries, Inc.

EPAULET - Colognes ☆ - Avon Products, Inc.

EPAULET - Frames–eyeglass - Hudson Optical Corp.

EPC LOUDON - Containers–plastic - Engineered Polymers Corp.

EPC PAK - Pharmaceutical preparations ☆ - Lexis Laboratories Inc.

EPCO - Cleaning preparations ☆ - Erbrich Products Co. Inc.

EPCO - Hardware - Engineered Products Co.

EPCON - Epoxy-anchoring system - ITW Ramset/Red Head

EPCON - Pencils - Empire Berol USA

E.P.D.M. - Weather stripping - Mortite Inc.

EPEC - Paints - Vogel Paint and Wax Co., Inc.

EPERNAY - Furniture ☆ - Bassett Furniture Industries, Inc.

EPHED-ORGANIDIN - Pharmaceutical preparations ☆ - Wallace Laboratories

EPHEDRILINE - Pharmaceutical preparations - Sherwood Laboratories Inc.

EPHEDRINE PLUS - Pharmaceutical bronchodilators - DMD Sales, Inc.

EPHEDRIX - Nasal decongestant - True Quality Pharmacies Inc.

EPHEDROL - Cold remedies ☆ - Eli Lilly and Co.

EPHEDSOL - Cold remedies - Lannett Co. Inc.

EPHEMERA - Office supplies ☆ - Evergreen Press

EPHENYLLIN - Pharmaceutical preparations - Consolidated Midland Corp.

EPHEX SR - Pharmaceutical preparations - Teral Laboratories

EPHRATA DIAMOND - Water–bottled or canned - Ephrata Diamond Spring Water Co., Inc.

EPHROGEST - Pharmaceutical preparations - Michigan Pharmaceutical

EPI - Boats - Englehart Products Inc.

EPI - Giftware - Engineered Plastics Inc.

EPI - Jewelry - Ear Piercing Industries, Inc.

EPI - Stereos - Harman Consumer Group

EPI CENTER - Displays - Epi Products USA, Inc.

EPI-CLASP - Oil machinery - Tri Hawk Corp.

EPI-KLENZ - Toiletries - Ecolab Inc.

EPI LOCK - Apparel stores–sports - CMO Inc.

EPI-LOCK - Bandages - Merck & Co., Inc.

EPI-MER - Adhesives and sealants - Environmental Purification Industries

EPI-OTIC - Skin care products - Allerderm Inc.

EPI-PURE - Resins–acrylic - EPI Technologies, Inc.

EPI-SCAN - Medical apparatus - EPI Scan Corp.

EPI SPORTS - Toys–stuffed - Environmental Preservation, Inc.

EPIBOND - Epoxy - Furane Aerospace Products Div.

EPIC - Apparel–women's - Evan-Picone Inc.

EPIC - Cabinets - Actua

EPIC - Cigarettes - Southland Corp.

EPIC - Coffee - Folger Coffee Co.

E.P.I.C. - Computer software - Equitrac Corp.

EPIC - Computer software - Futurevision of America Corp.

EPIC - Computer software - Gallaher Business Development Corp.

EPIC - Corks - Epic Products Inc.

EPIC - Dental compounds - Parkell Products Inc.

EPIC - Electrical equipment - General Electric Co.

EPIC - Electrical equipment - National Tank Co.

EPIC - Faucets ☆ - Masco Corp.

EPIC - Floor coverings–carpet and rugs - Regal Rugs Inc.

EPIC - Floor waxes ☆ - Chemway Corp.

EPIC - Frames–eyeglass - Hudson Optical Corp.

EPIC - Guitars - Alembic Inc.

EPIC - Hardware - Baldwin Hardware Corp.

EPIC - Health care products - Medical Data Institute

EPIC - Heating equipment - Lennox Industries Inc.

EPIC - Pens - Gillette Co.

EPIC - Saw blades - Simonds Industries Inc.

EPIC - Tape players–cassette - Sony Music Entertainment Inc.

EPIC - Thread - Coats and Clark Inc.

EPIC - Tools - Titan Tool Inc.

EPIC - Vacuum cleaners and accessories - Sle, Inc.

EPIC - Vacuum cleaners and accessories ☆ - Home Care Industries, Inc.

EPIC - Water purification systems - EPI Corp.

EPIC - Wheelchairs - Everest and Jennings International Ltd.

EPIC 2000 - Engines–internal combustion - Altronic, Inc.

EPIC PRINTING SYSTEM - Printers–computer - Uarco Inc.

EPIC SOUNDTRAX - Tape players–cassette - Sony Music Entertainment Inc.

EPIC SOUNDTRAX E - Tape players–cassette - Sony Music Entertainment Inc.

EPIC SPECIAL EVENTS - Apparel and accessories - Epic Special Events, Inc.

EPIC STREET - Recording label - Sony Music Entertainment Inc.

EPIC WAVES - Hair care products - Gillette Co.

EPIC XTRA - Thread - Coats and Clark Inc.

EPIC4 - Computers–personal - Dataware Electronics Inc.

EPICA - Tiles–ceramic - American Marazzi Tile, Inc.

EPICAR - Ophthalmic goods ☆ - Barnes-Hind Inc.

EPICARE - Skin care products - Ecolab Inc.

EPICDANCE - Recording label - Sony Music Entertainment Inc.

EPICENTER - Bicycle parts and accessories - Schwinn Cycling & Fitness Inc.

EPICENTER, THE - Electronic equipment - AudioControl

EPICENTRE - Computer software - Petrotechnical Open Software Corp.

EPICORT - Pharmaceutical preparations - Glaxo Wellcome Inc.

EPICS - Computer peripherals - Varityper Inc.

EPICURE - Audio equipment ☆ - Harman Consumer Group

EPICURE - Cooking utensils–aluminum - Commercial Aluminum Cookware Co.

EPICURE - Crab meat–fresh - The J.M. Clayton Co.

EPICURE - Dinnerware–plastic ☆ - Plastics Manufacturing Co.

EPICURE - Faucets - Kohler Co.

EPICURE - Glass–leaded - Seneca Glass Co.

EPICURE - Napkins–paper - Georgia-Pacific Corp.

EPICURE - Publisher's imprints - Peanut Butter Publishing

EPICURE DELI - Meat products–beef - Tav Brands Inc.

EPICURE DINNERWARE - Dinnerware - Carlisle Foodservice Products, Inc.

EPICUREAN - Coffee - First Colony Coffee and Tea Co. Inc.

EPICUREAN - Containers - Epicurean International Corp.

EPICUREAN - Food products - Rice Food Markets, Inc.

EPICUREAN - Housewares - Doranne

EPICUREAN - Sinks–metal - Kohler Co.

EPICUREAN BREAKFAST BLEND - Coffee - Rice Food Markets, Inc.

EPICUREAN COFFEE COMPANY - Coffee - Rice Food Markets, Inc.

EPICUREAN HOUSE BLEND - Coffee - Rice Food Markets, Inc.

EPICUREAN ROTISSERIE CHICKEN RICE - Meat products–poultry - Rice Food Markets, Inc.

EPICUREAN SPECIALTIES - Food products - Westworks Inc.

EPICUREAN'S DELIGHT GARLIC - Food products - Hosgoods

EPICURES, THE - Kitchen utensils–aluminum - Bonny Products Inc.

EPIDAURE - Vases - Durand International

EPIDENT - Dental compounds - Epi Products USA, Inc.

EPIDERM - Health care products - Pedinol Pharmacal Inc.

EPIDIASCOPE - Electronic equipment - Leica USA Inc.

EPIDOL - Pharmaceutical preparations ☆ - Spirt & Co.

EPIDRAL - Veterinary pharmaceutical preparations - Daliff Corp.

EPIFLEX - Protective device - Hollister Inc.

EPIFOAM - Health care products - Reed & Carnrick

EPIFRIN - Ophthalmic goods - Allergan, Inc.

EPIGEN - Health care products - Epigen International, Inc.

EPIGRAFS - Wood products - Makepeace Colony Press Inc.

EPIHEAT - Hair care products - Epi Products USA, Inc.

EPIKURE - Chemical preparations - Shell Oil Co.

EPILADY - Hair care products - Epi Products USA, Inc.

EPILADY ULTRA - Hair care products - Epi Products USA, Inc.

EPILASER - Lasers - Spectrum Medical Technologies, Inc.

EPILATOR - Beauty shop equipment - Lois Yee Cosmetics Inc.

EPILATOR - Cosmetics - R.A. Fischer Co. Inc.

EPILEX - Skin care products - Epilex Associates, Inc.

EPILIN - Pharmaceutical preparations ☆ - Fibertone Co.

EPILOGUE - Frames–eyeglass ☆ - Universal/Univis Inc.

EPILOR - Medical apparatus - Becton, Dickinson and Co.

EPILOTION - Skin care products - Epi Products USA, Inc.

EPILYT - Skin care products - Stiefel Laboratories, Inc.

EPIMAX - Pharmaceutical preparations - Parker Taylor, Inc.

EPINAL - Ophthalmic goods - Alcon Laboratories, Inc.

EPINEPHRENE - Veterinary pharmaceutical preparations ☆ - Boehringer Ingelheim Animal Health, Inc.

EPINEPHRICAINE - Pharmaceutical preparations ☆ - Upjohn Co.

EPINEPHRINE - Ophthalmic prescription drug ☆ - Iolab Pharmaceuticals

EPINGLE - Hair care products - Capitol Novelty Co.

EPIPED - Skin care products - Epi Products USA, Inc.

EPIPHANY - Computer software ☆ - Quad-S Consultants, Inc.

EPIPHANY RECORDINGS - Recording label - Epiphany Recordings, Ltd.

EPIPHONE - Musical instrument accessories - Gibson Strings & Accessories

EPIPHONE G.A.S. - Electrical equipment ☆ - Gibson Strings & Accessories

EPIPRAM - Pharmaceutical preparations - Block Drug Co., Inc.

EPIQURE - Dishes–china - Mikasa Co.

EPIRUS - Footwear ☆ - Asics Tiger Corp.

EPI*SAFE - Skin care products - Burnishine Products

EPISAUNA - Skin care products - Epi Products USA, Inc.

EPISEAL - Medical bandage - Deroyal Industries, Inc.

EPISMILE - Dentifrices - Epi Products USA, Inc.

EPISODE - Apparel stores - Episode USA, Inc.

EPISODE - Floor coverings–carpet and rugs ☆ - Richmond Carpet Mills

EPISODE - Frames–eyeglass - May Optical Co. Inc.

EPISODE - Recording label - T.E.C. Tones/Ralph Records

EPISODE PROFILER - Computer software - HPR Inc.

EPI*SOFT - Skin care products - Burnishine Products

EPISSAGE - Toothbrushes - Epi Products USA, Inc.

EPISSENTIA - Skin care products - Epi Products USA, Inc.

EPISTIK - Health care products - Medi Inc.

EPITAPH - Shirts - Epitaph

EPITECH - Bandages–surgical - Rynel Ltd., Inc.

EPITOL - Pharmaceutical preparations - Lemmon Co.

EPITOME - Audio equipment - GC Thorsen, Inc.

EPITOME - Connectors–electrical - Thomas & Betts Holdings, Inc.

EPITOME - Fabrics - Dan River Inc.

EPITOME - Frames–eyeglass - Pathway Optical Prods.

EPITOME - Furniture ☆ - Lane Co. Inc.

EPITOME - Medical apparatus - Utah Medical Products, Inc.

EPITOME - Pet products - Bennett Mineral

EPITONE - Hair care products - Nexxus Products Co.

EPITOPE - Medical apparatus - Epitope Inc.

EPITRATE - Pharmaceutical preparations - Wyeth-Ayerst Laboratories

EPIVENT - Medical apparatus - Smith & Nephew Richards, Inc.

EPIVERA E - Soaps - Ecolab Inc.

EPIX - Apparel and accessories - Epix Collection

EPIX - Medical apparatus - Empi Inc.

EPIX XL - Medical apparatus - Empi Inc.

EPL - Leather goods - Borsack Group, Inc.

EPL - Leather goods - El Portal of Nevada, Inc.

EPL - Lighting fixtures - Edison Price Lighting

EPLANS - Computer software - At&T Corp.

EPLUCHE - Skin care products - Gailshay Worldwide Inc.

E+PLUS - Solder - Engrowtronic, Inc.

EPLUS - Woven webbing material - Elizabeth Webbing Mills Co.

E+C - Tools–hand-operated - Eutectic Corp.

EPO - Floor waxes - Consolidated Coatings Corp.

EPO-FLOOR TOP - Paints - Steelcote Manufacturing Corp.

EPO-GEL - Concrete repair products - Chemrex Inc.

EPO-GLAZE - Floor waxes - Consolidated Coatings Corp.

EPO-GRIP - Concrete repair products - Chemrex Inc.

EPO-LINE - Paints - Steelcote Manufacturing Corp.

EPO-LUX - Epoxy coatings - Steelcote Manufacturing Corp.

EPO-PLEX - Paints - Con-Lux Coatings Inc.

EPO PRIME - Paints - Sinclair Paint Co.

EPO-X - Paints - Steelcote Manufacturing Corp.

EPOC - Floor waxes - Epoca Corp.

EPOC 5 - Floor waxes - Epoca Corp.

EPOC-A-POOL - Paints - Diasyde Corp.

EPOCA - Pens - Bic Corp.

EPOCAP - Epoxy - Hardman

EPOCAST - Resins–acetal - Furane Aerospace Products Div.

EPOCH - Audio equipment - Spiritus, Inc.

EPOCH - Computer software - Stockholder Systems, Inc.

EPOCH - Dinnerware - Euromarket Design Inc.

EPOCH - Doors–storm - Canyon Creek Cabinet Co.

EPOCH - Floor coverings–carpet and rugs ☆ - American Carpet Mills

EPOCH - Orthopedic products - Zimmer, Inc.

EPOCH 2000 - Artists' materials - Artoptic International Corp.

EPOCH 2000 - Computer software - Farpoint Research

EPOCH IMAGES - Postcards - Kustom Quality

EPOCHSAT - Medical apparatus - Invivo Research, Inc.

EPOCLEAR 25 - Adhesives and sealants ☆ - Spartan Chemical Co., Inc.

EPOCRYL - Epoxy - STO Corp.

EPODUR - Epoxy coatings - Dampney Co., Inc.

EPOGEN - Prescription drug - Amgen Inc.

EPOGLOSS - Epoxy - Sinclair Paint Co.

EPOKOTE - Paints - Frazee Paint

EPOKOTE II - Floor waxes - Epoca Corp.

EPOL - Polishing rouge - Williams-Hayward Protective Coatings Inc.

EPOLITE - Adhesives and sealants - Hexcel Corp.

EPON - Asphalt - Shell Oil Co.

EPONA - Skin care products - Epona, Ltd.

EPONOX - Epoxy coatings - L.D. Sterns Corp.

EPOQUE - Photographic equipment - R.T.S. Inc.

EPOQUE ELEGANTE - Wallpaper - Robert Crowder & Co.

EPOQUE UNDERWATER - Cameras - Charles Beseler Co.

EPORSTER - Laces–boot and shoe - St. Louis Braid Co.

EPOSET - Adhesives and sealants - Hardman

EPOSOLVE - Cleaning preparations - Hardman

EPOTILT - Paints - Frazee Paint

EPOWELD - Epoxy - Hardman

EPOWER - Tools–power-driven - Epower

EPOX-E-SET - Cement - W.R. Bonsal Co.

EPOX-E-SET - Epoxy - Cambridge Tile Manufacturing Co.

EPOX-EASE - Putties - Vibe Records Inc.

EPOX TECHNOLOGY - Insulating materials - Hotsplicer Corp.

EPOXATHANE - Paints - Flo-Rite Coating & Chemical Co.

EPOXI-FIL - Epoxy - Porter Paint Co.

EPOXO - Epoxy coatings - American Safety Technology

EPOXO - Finishing agents ☆ - Falcon Safety Products, Inc.

EPOXOLITE - Finishing agents ☆ - Allied Compositions

EPOXOLITE - Putties - Sig Manufacturing Inc.

EPOXOLV - Epoxy coatings - Dap Products Inc.

EPOXOMIDE - Epoxy coatings - Standard Paint Co.

EPOXON - Finishing agents - Uncle Sam Chemical Co., Inc.

EPOXON TERRA-SEAL - Finishing agents - Uncle Sam Chemical Co., Inc.

EPOXY 45 - Glue–household or industrial - Loctite Corp.

EPOXY 350 - Sealing compounds - Hillyard Enterprises, Inc.

EPOXY GREAT HAZE REMOVER - Cleaning preparations - Custom Building Products

EPOXY GUARD - Lithographic plates - C.M. Athey Paint Co.

EPOXY IC-48 INSERT KIT - Golfing equipment - Club Kit Inc.

EPOXY KOTE - Adhesives and sealants ☆ - Atlas Chemical Co.

EPOXY RED LIFE - Paints ☆ - Zynolyte Products Co.

EPOXY STONE II - Binder of decorative stones for floors, patios, etc. - Construction Adhesives Co.

☆ = Now out of production

EPOXY-TABS - Epoxy - La-Co Industries, Inc.

EPOXY-TIE - Adhesives and sealants - Simpson Strong-Tie Co., Inc.

EPOXY-TYTE - Putties - J.C. Whitlam Manufacturing Co.

EPOXY WOOD REBUILDER - Wood fillers - H.F. Staples & Co. Inc.

EPOXYBOND - Waterproof adhesives, moldable putty, etc. - Atlas Minerals & Chemicals, Inc.

EPOXYCAST - Transformers - AFP Transformers, Inc.

EPOXYKOTE - Paints - Triangle Coatings Inc.

EPP CORP. - Machine parts - Engineered Plastic Products Corp.

EPPENS SMITH IMPORTERS COFFEE AND TEA SINCE 1855 - Coffee - Chock Full O'Nuts Corp.

EPPINGER - Fishing lures ☆ - Eppinger Manufacturing Co.

EPPLEY'S - Popcorn ☆ - Weaver Popcorn Co. Inc.

EPPY/N - Ophthalmic goods - Barnes-Hind Inc.

EPR - Computer software - C & P Press

EPRINEX - Veterinary pharmaceutical preparations - Merck & Co., Inc.

EPRIS - Colognes - Max Factor & Co.

EPRO - Tiles–ceramic - Epro Inc.

EPROLIN - Pharmaceutical preparations - Eli Lilly and Co.

E.P.S. - Apparel–women's - Evan-Picone Inc.

E.P.S. - Foam rubber - Modern Milltex Corp.

EPS - Resins–synthetic - Valspar Corp.

EPS EXCHANGE - Computer software - Altsys Corp.

EPS TECHNOLOGIES - Computer peripheral equipment - EPS Technologies Inc.

EPSAL - Artists' materials - Press Chemical & Pharmaceutical Laboratories

EPSILON - Couplings - Aeroquip Corp.

EPSILON - Luggage - Samsonite Corp.

EPSO-PINE - Bath salts - Majestic Drug Co., Inc.

EPSON - Printers–computer - Epson America, Inc.

EPSON EPL - Printers–computer ☆ - Epson America, Inc.

EPSON STYLUS - Printers–computer - Epson America, Inc.

EPSWORD - Computer software - SourceView Software International

EPT - Catheters - EP Technologies, Inc.

EPT - Machine parts - Emerson Electric Co.

E.P.T. - Pregnancy test kits ☆ - Warner-Lambert Co.

EPT-1000 - Medical apparatus - EP Technologies, Inc.

E.P.T. PLUS - Pregnancy test kits ☆ - Warner-Lambert Co.

EPTI - Battery chargers - Electronic Power Technology, Inc.

EPURE - Hardware ☆ - Vance Industries Inc.

EPX - Audio equipment - Rockford Corp.

EP(X) - Computer software - Vestra Resources, Inc.

EQ - Electronic equipment ☆ - Peavey Electronics Corp.

EQ - Hair care products - Jean Alexander Cosmetics, Inc.

EQ - Wigs - Eva Gabor International, Ltd.

EQ 20/20 SPORTS VISION OF THE FUTURE - Apparel and accessories - Andrew Gause

E.Q. 335 - Veterinary pharmaceutical preparations - C.J. Martin Co.

EQ2 - Computer software - EQ2, Inc.

EQCEL - Computer software - HCIA, Inc.

EQL - Electronic equipment - AudioControl

EQQ - Electronic equipment - AudioControl

EQT - Electronic equipment - AudioControl

EQUA - Chairs–metal - Herman Miller, Inc.

EQUA - Musical instrument accessories ☆ - Gibson Strings & Accessories

EQUA - Recording label - Equa Records

EQUA 2 - Office furniture–metal - Herman Miller, Inc.

EQUA FLOW - Oils–lubricating - Maxus Energy Corp.

EQUA-LINER - Machinery - Servants Inc.

EQUA-LYTE - Pharmaceutical preparations - Abbott Laboratories

EQUAFLEX - Box springs - Spring Air Bedding Inc.

EQUAFUGE - Centrifuges–laboratory - Curtin Matheson Scientific, Inc.

EQUAGESIC - Pharmaceutical preparations - Wyeth-Ayerst Laboratories

EQUAGESIC-M - Pharmaceutical preparations ☆ - Wyeth-Ayerst Laboratories

EQUAL - Dishes–plastic - NutraSweet Co.

EQUAL - Herbicides - BASF Corp.

EQUAL - Wood furniture finish - Hydrocote Co., Inc.

EQUAL DARTS - Games - Merit Industries

EQUAL EXCHANGE - Coffee - Equal Exchange Inc.

EQUAL-FX - Hair care products - Matrix Essentials, Inc.

EQUAL MEASURE - Sweeteners–artificial - NutraSweet Co.

EQUAL PACKETS - Sweeteners–artificial - NutraSweet Co.

EQUAL TABLETS - Sweeteners–artificial - NutraSweet Co.

EQUAL TIME ATHLETES - Apparel–athletic - Equal Time Athletics LLC

EQUAL TIME II - Floor coverings–carpet and rugs - Evans-Black Carpet Mills

EQUALACSIN - Pharmaceutical preparations - Pfizer Inc.

EQUALAMP - Electric lighting equipment - Sun Systems International, LLC

EQUALATIN - Laxatives - Numark Laboratories Inc.

EQUIPMENTATP - Pharmaceutical preparations - Bricker Laboratories

E=QUALITY - Apparel - Jaya Melwani

EQUALITY - Hair care products - Helene Curtis Industries Inc.

EQUALITY-AIR - Fans–electric - Recovery Systems, Inc.

EQUALIZER - Alarm systems - Directed Electronics, Inc.

EQUALIZER - Cleaning preparations–carpet and rug - Evsco Pharmaceuticals

EQUALIZER - Door openers–electronic - LCN Closers

EQUALIZER - Drainboards - Infiltrator Systems, Inc.

EQUALIZER - Electrical equipment - Innovative Technology, Inc.

EQUALIZER - Hand trucks - Magline Inc.

EQUALIZER - Machinery - Wilden Pump & Engineering Co.

EQUALIZER - Medical apparatus - Royce Medical Co.

EQUALIZER - Scuba diving equipment - Beuchat-USA Inc.

EQUALIZER 3 - Hair care products - Helene Curtis Industries Inc.

EQUALIZER AIR WALKER - Orthopaedic devices - Centec Orthopaedics

EQUALIZER II - Skates–roller - Seneca Sports, Inc.

EQUALIZER, THE - Bats–baseball - Baum Research and Development Co.

EQUALIZER, THE - Sporting goods - Stearns Manufacturing Co.

EQUALIZER, THE - Remote-controlled-vehicle motors - Trinity Products Inc.

EQUALS - Apparel and accessories - Anthony J. Nappi and Emily Vass Partnership

EQUAL'S COMEBACK - Sauces - Equal Lee Smith

EQUANIL - Pharmaceutical preparations - Wyeth-Ayerst Laboratories

EQUANITRATE - Pharmaceutical preparations ☆ - Wyeth-Ayerst Laboratories

EQUANOX 2000 - Exercising equipment - Gerstung/Gym-Thing Inc.

EQUASION - Skin-care products ☆ - Coty Inc.

EQUATE - Cosmetics - Wal-Mart Stores Inc.

EQUATION - Golfing equipment - Dunlop Maxfli Sports Corp.

EQUATIONS - Computer software - Wff'n Proof Learning Games Associates

EQUATOR - Cocoa butter - Van Den Bergh Foods Co.

EQUATOR - Heaters–space - Rinnai America Corp.

EQUATOR - Iced tea–bottled or canned - Hansen Beverage Co.

EQUATOR - Thread - Threads USA Div.

EQUATOR - Watches - Croton Watch Co., Inc.

EQUATOR ED'S - Food products - Milnot Co.

EQUATOR PLUS - Lenses–optical - Volk Optical, Inc.

EQUAZINE-M - Pharmaceutical preparations - Rugby Laboratories Inc.

EQUENNE - Shampoos - Pamb Corp.

EQUESTRIAN - Trailers–horse ☆ - Merhow Industries

EQUI-BOOT - Medical apparatus - Equi-Pro

EQUI-CIDE - Veterinary pharmaceutical preparations ☆ - Agri Laboratories, Ltd.

EQUI-DERM - Pet products - Glo-Marr Products Inc.

EQUI-EASE WITH IBUPROFEN - Analgesics - No Pain, Inc.

EQUI-ETTES - Doilies ☆ - Jo-An Imports

EQUI-FIT - Saddles - Steele Saddle Tree Co., Inc.

EQUI-GLO - Pet products - Farnam Cos. Inc.

EQUI-LIZER - Vitamins and nutritional supplements - Equinox International Corp.

EQUI-PREP - Animal feeds - Manna Pro Corp.

EQUI-SHEEN - Pet products - Natra Pet Inc.

EQUI-TRITION - Vitamins and nutritional supplements - Equinox International Corp.

EQUI-TROL - Veterinary pharmaceutical preparations - Farnam Cos. Inc.

EQUIBALM - Veterinary pharmaceutical preparations - Macsil Inc. (Balmex Div.)

EQUIBAL'S YOU CAN SHAVE TOO! - Skin care products - Equibal, Inc.

EQUIBLOC - Pet products - Farnam Cos. Inc.

EQUIBOLIN-50 - Pharmaceutical preparations ☆ - Vortech Pharmaceuticals

EQUIBOT-TC - Veterinary pharmaceutical preparations - Farnam Cos. Inc.

EQUICINE - Veterinary pharmaceutical preparations - Miles Inc.

EQUIDESK - Computer software - Commscan, Inc.

EQUIDYNE - Metals - Starr E. Paton

EQUIFAB - Fabrics - Astrup Co.

EQUIFLEX - Footwear ☆ - E.S. Originals, Inc.

EQUIFLO - Fuel systems–motor vehicle - Freightliner Corp.

EQUIFOAL - Veterinary pharmaceutical preparations - Farnam Cos. Inc.

EQUIL - Computer peripheral equipment - Abbott Laboratories

EQUILABS - Veterinary pharmaceutical preparations - Agri Laboratories, Ltd.

EQUILAR - Sporting goods - Equilar Inc.

EQUILENE - Animal feeds - Bluebonnet Milling Co.

EQUILENE NATURAL 12 - Animal feeds - Bluebonnet Milling Co.

EQUILENE THERAPY - Animal feeds - American Superior Feeds, Inc.

EQUILENE THERAPY - Animal feeds - Bluebonnet Milling Co.

EQUILET - Antacids ☆ - Mission Pharmacal Co.

EQUILIBRANT - Skin care products - Lendan USA Co.

EQUILIBRIUM - Hair care products - Helene Curtis Industries Inc.

EQUILIBRIUM - Hair care products ☆ - Shape-Up

EQUILIBRIUM - Publisher's imprints - Equilibrium, Inc.

EQUILIBRIUM - Vitamins and nutritional supplements - NF Formulas, Inc.

EQUILITE - Trailers–horse - Merhow Industries

EQUIMECTRIN - Veterinary pharmaceutical preparations - Merck & Co., Inc.

EQUIMIN - Horse vitamins - Southern States Cooperative Inc.

EQUIMIX - Horse feed supplement - Trade One Inc. (Equine Specialty Feed Co.)

EQUINE - Jewelry–precious - Equine Designs

EQUINE BLOOM - Veterinary nutritional supplements - J.E. Ronicker Labs Inc.

EQUINE ELEGANCE - Cosmetics - C. K. Products Inc.

EQUINE ENERGY - Animal feed supplements - Buckeye Feed Mills, Inc.

EQUINE JUNIOR - Animal feeds - Purina Mills, Inc.

EQUINE LMT - Animal feed supplements - Hubbard Milling Co.

EQUINE RACING FORMULA - Animal feeds - Kentucky Equine Research, Inc.

EQUINE SHIELD - Veterinary pharmaceutical preparations - Skin Biology, Inc.

EQUINE TECHNOLOGIES - Veterinary medical equipment - Equine Technologies, Inc.

EQUINE'S CHOICE - Pet products - Marianna Imports, Inc.

EQUINEX - Pharmaceutical preparations ☆ - Wyeth-Ayerst Laboratories

EQUINOTE - Musical instrument accessories ☆ - Scherl & Roth Inc.

EQUINOX - Air purification systems - Equinox International Corp.

EQUINOX - Audio cables and accessories - Wireworld by David Salz, Inc.

EQUINOX - Fabrics - Greenwood Mills Inc.

EQUINOX - Finishing agents - Pioneer/Eclipse Corp.

EQUINOX - Floor coverings–carpet and rugs - Patcraft Mills Inc.

EQUINOX - Floor coverings–carpet and rugs ☆ - Mannington Carpets, Inc.

EQUINOX - Luggage - H. Bernbaum Import-Export Co.

EQUINOX - Publisher's imprints ☆ - Hearst Corp.

EQUINOX - Skin care products - Veeco Manufacturing Co.

EQUINOX - Sleeping bags - Coleman Co., Inc.

EQUINOX - Wallpaper ☆ - Koroseal Wallcoverings

EQUINOX - Wines - Bully Hill Vineyards, Inc.

EQUINOX COLLECTION - Furniture - BDO Seidman

EQUINOX COLLECTION - Wallpaper - Dekortex Inc.

EQUINOX TOURLITE - Trailers–travel - Equinox Industries Inc.

EQUINOXE - Pens - Caran D'Ache of Switzerland Inc.

EQUINU - Novelty items - Chrishawn Associates Inc.

EQUIOPATHICS - Herbal products - Homeopet LLC

EQUIOPATHICS - Homeopathic remedies - Washington Homeopathic Products

EQUIPE - Skates–roller - Rollerblade, Inc.

EQUIPE - Socks - Kayser-Roth Corp.

EQUIPLEX - Veterinary nutritional supplements - International Nutrition, Inc.

EQUIPMENT - Shoes–athletic - Adidas USA Inc.

EQUIPMENT HANGERS - Sporting goods - Dacon Manufacturing

EQUIPMENT SCHEDULER - Computer software - Right on Programs

EQUIPMENT SOLUTIONS - Tools - Snap-On Technologies, Inc.

EQUIPMENTITY - Computer software - Financial Engineering Associates, Inc.

EQUIPOISE - Golfing equipment - Spangler Classic, Inc.

EQUIPOISE - Toiletries - A-Veda Corp.

EQUIPPED FOR THE FUTURE - Golfing equipment - Dunlop Maxfli Sports Corp.

EQUIPTO - Shelving units–metal - Equipto

EQUIPTO-ROBE - Lockers–metal - Equipto

EQUIS - Computer software - Equis Software Systems, Inc.

EQUIS - Golfing equipment - Triumph Golf Co.

EQUISOFT - Computer software - Equisoft, Inc.

EQUISOUS - Riding clothes - Libertyville Saddle Shop, Inc.

EQUISTAR - Trailers–horse - Merhow Industries

EQUISTEEL - Rope - American Saddlery, Inc.

EQUISUEDE - Saddles - Miller Harness Co., Inc.

EQUITARD - Horse covering - Newtech Enterprises Inc.

EQUITAX - Computer software - John G. Cleminshaw Inc.

EQUITE - Cosmetics - Parfums Christian Dior U.S. Corp.

EQUITE CHRISTIAN DIOR PARIS - Cosmetics - LVMH Moet Hennesy Louis Vuitton Inc.

EQUITEC - Veterinary pharmaceutical preparations - Zema Corp.

EQUITECH - Animal feeds - Southern States Cooperative Inc.

EQUITECH - Pet products - Robert J. Ferrand

EQUITEK II - Microphones ☆ - C.T.I. Audio Inc.

EQUITONE - Musical instrument accessories ☆ - Scherl & Roth Inc.

EQUITRAC WIRELESS-COMLINK - Computer peripheral equipment - Equitrac Corp.

EQUITRADE - Computer software - Robert F. Deming

EQUITRI - Veterinary pharmaceutical preparations - Nutra-Vet Research Corp.

EQUITY - Clocks - Equity Industries Corp.

EQUITY - Floor coverings–carpet and rugs - Eagle Carpets Inc.

EQUITY - Floor coverings–carpet and rugs ☆ - Hollytex Carpet Mills Inc.

EQUITY - Insecticides - Dowelanco

EQUITY - Plaster–wallboard - Westinghouse Electric Corp.

EQUITY - Printers–computer ☆ - Epson America, Inc.

EQUITY - Thread - Threads USA Div.

EQUITY LT - Computers–personal ☆ - Epson America, Inc.

EQUITYWISE - Computer software - Residential Funding Corp.

EQUIVALENT - Floor coverings–carpet and rugs ☆ - Calladium & Marglen

EQUIVALENTS - Hair care products - RC International

EQUIVET - Veterinary pharmaceutical preparations - Farnam Cos. Inc.

EQUIX - Computers - Equix Computer Corp.

EQUIZOLE - Veterinary pharmaceutical preparations - Merck & Co., Inc. (Merck Agvet Division)

EQULINE - Window frames - Kawneer Co., Inc.

EQUUS - Apparel and accessories - America's Cup Inc.

EQUUS - Fireplace equipment ☆ - Majestic Co.

EQUUS - Veterinary pharmaceutical preparations - NNQ Inc.

EQUUS IV MAN - Apparel–men's ☆ - Equus Group, Inc.

EQUUS COLLECTION - Apparel–men's - Equus Group, Inc.

EQUUS GOLF - Apparel–men's - Equus Group, Inc.

EQUUS POLYMER LTD. - Pet products - St. Lawrence Sales Inc.

EQVALAN - Veterinary pharmaceutical preparations - Merck & Co., Inc. (Merck Agvet Division)

EQWIESE - Veterinary nutritional supplements - Wiese Vet Supply, Inc.

EQX - Electronic equipment - AudioControl

ER - Apparel and accessories - Time Warner Entertainment Co., L.P.

ER - Bandages - Crackle Creations, Inc.

ER - Hair care products - Scruples Professional Salon Products, Inc.

ER - Hearing aids - Etymotic Research Inc.

ER-GO COMFORT - Office supplies - Safco Products Co.

ER MAPPER - Computer software - Unisys Corp.

ER90 - Data loggers - E-Systems, Inc.

ERA - Detergents - Procter & Gamble Co.

ERA - Footwear–athletic - Vans, Inc.

ERA - Furniture - Homecrest Industries Inc.

ERA - Grass seed - International Seeds, Inc.

ERA - Labels–paper - K-Tel International, Inc.

ERA - Real estate agencies - Era Franchise Systems, Inc.

ERA-1 - Furniture - Haworth, Inc.

ERA II - Fabrics - Guilford Mills, Inc.

ERACE - Cosmetics - Max Factor & Co.

ERACE COLOUR PRECISE - Cosmetic - Noxell Corp.

ERADICANE - Herbicides - Chesebrough-Pond's USA Co.

ERADICATOR 60 - Chemical preparations - Challenger Manufacturing, Inc.

ERADICATOR, THE - Tools - IQ Distribution, Inc.

ERAMOSA - Marble products ☆ - Carl Schilling Stoneworks

ERAMYCIN - Pharmaceutical preparations - Wesley Pharmacal Co. Inc.

ERAS-CIL - Erasers - National Pen & Pencil Co.

ERASABLES TRANSFORMERS - Pens - Pentech International Inc.

ERASALL - Erasers ☆ - Empire Berol USA

ERASCO - Soups–canned - Haram-Christensen Corp.

ERASE - Deodorizers - Geritrex Corp.

ERASE - Deodorizers ☆ - Benckiser Consumer Products Inc.

ERASE - Health care products - Block Drug Co., Inc.

ERASE - Paints - Lilly Perfection Paint

ERASE - Pet products - Vo-Toys Inc.

ERASE - Shampoos - Tressa, Inc.

ERASE - Soap - Camp-Cap Products

ERASE A SLATE - Toys ☆ - Henry Gordy International Inc.

ERASE-A-WORD - Typewriters - Smith Corona Corp.

ERASE-AWAY - Chalk ☆ - Listo Pencil Corp.

ERASE-EASE - Paper–bond - Dennison National Co.

ERASE-EAZE - Computer equipment - Keyboard Advances, Inc.

ERASE-ITT - Deodorizers - Surco Products Inc.

ERASE RAS-POURI - Deodorizers - Geritrex Corp.

ERASER MATE - Pens - Paper Mate Co.

ERASER PEN - Pens - Micropoint Inc.

ERASER PET - Erasers ☆ - Newell Office Products

ERASER POPS - Artists' materials - Lisa Frank, Inc.

ERASERR - Erasers - Yasutomo

ERASERSTIK - Erasers - Faber-Castell Corp.

ERASIT - Erasers ☆ - Dixon Ticonderoga Co.

ERASIT - Hair care products ☆ - Majestic Drug Co., Inc.

☆ = Now out of production

ERASMUS EDITIONS - Publisher's imprints ☆ - Bandanna Books
ERASOL - Cleaning preparations - American Polymer Corp.
ERATH VINEYARDS - Wines - Erath Vineyards Winery
ERB - Helmets–athletic - ERB Industries, Inc.
ERBACTIV - Hair care products - Helene Curtis Industries Inc.
ERBE - Hair care products - L'erboristeria, Ltd.
ERBO-LAX - Pharmaceutical preparations - Herb Products Co.
ERC - Bats–baseball - Worth Inc.
ERC - Cameras - L.F. Deardorff & Sons Inc.
ERC - Welding equipment - Electron Beam Technologies, Inc.
ERC INDUSTRIES - Valves - ERC Industries, Inc.
ERC POWERCELL - Bats–baseball - Worth Inc.
ERCAF - Pharmaceutical preparations - Geneva Generics Inc.
ERCATAB - Pharmaceutical preparations ☆ - Parmed Pharmaceuticals, Inc.
ERCO - Badges–uniform - Eagle Metalart Co.
ERCO - Candy ☆ - E. Rosen Co.
ERCOLANO - Dishes–china - Pasmantier Co. Inc.
ERCONA - Cameras ☆ - Ercona Corp.
ERCPEEL AWAY - Catheters - Cook Imaging Corp.
ERDENKLANG - Recording label - American Gramaphone Records
ERDI - Woodworking products - American Clamping Corp.
ERDMAN-TEDESCHI - Wines - Tedeschi Vineyards Ltd.
ERDOS - Apparel and accessories - All America International Group Inc.
EREBE - Artists' materials - Riebe's Artist Materials Inc.
EREBUNI - Liquors - Saharex, Inc.
ERECAID - Health care products - Osbon Medical Systems, Ltd.
ERECTA SHELF - Shelving - InterMetro Industries Corp.
ERECTA SWITCH - Switches–electric - Compac Engineering, Inc.
ERECTO CUP - Decorations - A.J. Ganz Co. Inc.
ERECTO-PAT - Brackets - Oakwood Manufacturing Co.
ERECTOR SET - Toys–erector sets - CBS Toys
ERENA - Wigs - Hair Access
ERETZ - Mineral water - Hafco Video Boutique, Inc.
EREV - Jewelry - Harold Freeman Jewelry Co.
EREWHON - Cereal - U.S. Mills, Inc.
EREZ - Apparel - Erez Fashions Inc.
EREZ EXTERIOR - Apparel–women's - Erez Fashions Inc.
ERG-15 - Lubricants - Envir-O-Lube, Inc.
ERG ENTERTAINMENT RESOURCES GROUP - Recording label - Entertainment Resources USA, Inc.
ERG-O-NOMIC - Mats - Ludlow Composites Corp.
ERGAMISOL - Colon cancer treatment - Janssen Pharmaceutica Inc.
ERGEE - Hosiery - Ergee International Inc.
ERGEE TREND - Hosiery - Ergee International Inc.
ERGI - Office furniture–metal - Grahl Industries, Inc.
ERGO - Computers–personal - The Brick Computer Co.
ERGO - Footwear - Interco Inc.
ERGO-AIR - Carts - Air Systems, Inc.
ERGO-BENCH - Furniture - Lye Metal, Inc.
ERGO BY FLORSHEIM - Footwear ☆ - Wolverine World Wide, Inc.
ERGO-CAFF - Pharmaceutical preparations - Rugby Laboratories Inc.
ERGO-CHAISE - Medical apparatus - JB Research, Inc.
ERGO-COMP - Furniture–metal - Par Metal Products Inc.
ERGO CONCEPT - Tools - Ames Lawn & Garden Tool Co.
ERGO-CRATE - Crates - International Container Systems
ERGO-EDGE - Computer storage devices - Innovative Ergonomics, Inc.
ERGO EXPERT - Construction equipment rental services - Steelcase Inc.
ERGO-EZE - Food products - Brechteen Co.
ERGO-MATE - Furniture ☆ - Mead-Hatcher, Inc.
ERGO-ONE - Carts - Lakeside Manufacturing, Inc.
ERGO-PULL - Micro-chip puller - Advanced Tool Technologies
ERGO QUEST - Software - Gary Nederveld & Associates
ERGO-RITE - Carts - Richard McCluhan & Associates, Inc.
ERGO SAFE - Stamps–hand - GB Products International Corp.
ERGO SHARP - Knives–butcher - Southampton Cutting Industry, Inc.
ERGO SPACE - Computer storage devices - Engineered Data Products Inc.
ERGO/STAK - Chairs–upholstered - United Chair Co., Inc.
ERGO-STEP - Exercising equipment - Battle Creek Equipment Co.
ERGO-TRED - Ladders–wood - D.R. Bulkley Co., Inc.
ERGO-ZIN - Pharmaceutical preparations ☆ - Ulmer Pharmacal Co.
ERGOARM - Forearm rest - Sit-Rite Group Inc.
ERGOBUDDY - Chairs–metal - Johnson Technologies Corp.
ERGOCISERS - Exercising equipment ☆ - Maximus Fitness Products
ERGOCYCLE - Health care products - Unicare Health & Fitness Co.
ERGODESIGN - Computers - NEC Technologies, Inc.
ERGODYNAMIC - Cushions - Ergo Air, Inc.

ERGODYNE - Video production - Ergodyne Corp.
ERGOEASE - Computer software - Ease Inc.
ERGOFEED - Paper industry machinery - BDI Products Inc.
ERGOFORM - Computer peripheral equipment - Gemini Industries, Inc.
ERGOFORM - Therapeutic cold packs - Ergomed, Inc.
ERGOGENIC - Furniture - John Larson
ERGOKINETICS: SAFETY IN MOTION - Video production - Prentice-Hall, Inc.
ERGOLINK - Computer hardware - R & R Industries, Inc.
ERGOMAR - Health care products ☆ - Fisons Corp.
ERGOMAT - Mats - Superior Manufacturing Group/Notrax Floor Matting
ERGOMAT - Mats - Tinby LLC
ERGOMAT - Sporting goods - Stearns Manufacturing Co.
ERGOMATIC - Mops - Empire Brushes, Inc.
ERGOMATIC - Tools–machine - Reelcraft Industries, Inc.
ERGOMATION - Measuring instruments - Woodhead Industries, Inc.
ERGOMAX - Wheelchairs - American Ergonomics Corp.
ERGOMET - Exercising equipment - Ergometrx Corp.
ERGOMETER - Exercising equipment - Tunturi, Inc.
ERGOMETER PRO-FIT - Exercising equipment ☆ - Exercycle Corp.
ERGOMETRIC - Bicycles - Schwinn Cycling & Fitness Inc.
ERGOMETRX - Computer software - Ergometrx Corp.
ERGON - Chairs–metal - Herman Miller, Inc.
ERGON 3 - Furniture - Herman Miller, Inc.
ERGONAL - Pharmaceutical preparations - Vita Elixir Co. Inc.
ERGONOMIC SOLUTIONS - Wrist and foot rests - Ergonomic Technology Corp.
ERGONOMIX - Scissors–hand-operated - Wolff Industries Inc.
ERGOPEDIC - Air mattresses - Basic Designs, Inc.
ERGOPEDIC - Sporting goods - Stearns Manufacturing Co.
ERGOPHENE - Pharmaceutical preparations ☆ - Upjohn Co.
ERGOPLEX - Vitamins and nutritional supplements - Unipro Inc.
ERGOPLUS - Computer software - Ford Motor Co.
ERGOSCOOP - Scoops - United Associates Group Inc.
ERGOSMART - Computer software - Envirovisions
ERGOSOFT-GRIP - Tools–hand-operated - Lockwell Corp.
ERGOSOFTGRIP - Tools–hand-operated - Lockwell Corp.
ERGOSTAND - Office furniture–wood - ErgoWorks Inc.
ERGOSTAT - Pharmaceutical preparations ☆ - Parke-Davis
ERGOTAL - Pharmaceutical preparations ☆ - Whitby Pharmaceuticals, Inc.
ERGOTAR - Musical instruments - Willis Whiteside
ERGOTASK - Chairs - Globe Business Furniture, Inc.
ERGOTECH - Health care products - Rudolph International, Inc.
ERGOTECH - Splints - Smith & Nephew Inc. (Rehabilitation Div.)
ERGOTEK - Chairs–metal - GF Office Furniture Ltd.
ERGOTOUCH - Recliners ☆ - Flexsteel Industries Inc.
ERGOTRATE MALEATE - Pharmaceutical preparations - Eli Lilly and Co.
ERGOTRON - Office furniture - Ergotron, Inc.
ERGOVIEW - Electronic equipment - Sigma Designs Inc.
ERGOWARE - Computer peripheral equipment - LB Innovators, Inc.
ERGOWEAR - Orthopedic products - Steven Florman
ERGOWOOD - Office furniture–plastic - Jeffery Saull
ERI - Puppets - Dollsandreams
ERI - Surgical instruments - ERI Inc.
E.R.I.C. - Computer software - Westech Corp.
ERIC - Construction equipment rental services - David C. Cook Publishing Co.
ERIC - Frames–eyeglass ☆ - Rozin Optical Export Corp.
ERIC - Frames–eyeglass ☆ - U.S. Optical Frame Co.
ERIC - Sweaters - Heritage Sportswear
ERIC - Thread ☆ - SCT Yarns Inc.
ERIC BOYSWEAR - Shoes ☆ - Combine Group Division Inc.
ERIC BRISTOW - Darts and dart games ☆ - Dart World Inc.
ERIC CARLE - Toys - Eric Carle
ERIC FOR MEN - Footwear–men's ☆ - Combine Group Division Inc.
ERIC GURNEY - Greeting cards ☆ - Woodbridge Graphics
ERIC MORGAN - Audio cabinets–wood ☆ - Bush Industries, Inc.
ERIC MORGAN BY BUSH - Furniture–wood - Bush Industries, Inc.
ERIC STAUFFER - Figurines - Arnart Imports Inc.
ERIC STEVEN - Apparel–women's - Toula Manufacturing Ltd., Inc.
ERIC TURBOTREADS - Footwear–men's ☆ - Combine Group Division Inc.
ERICA - Bathroom fixtures - Crane Plumbing/Fiat Products
ERICA - Dinnerware–glass - Franciscan by Johnson Brothers, USA, Inc.
ERICA - Glassware–household ☆ - Dansk International Designs, Ltd.
ERICA - Harmonicas - Hohner Inc.
ERICA - Looms ☆ - Northfield Loom
ERICA - Rings–jewelry - Artcarved Inc.
ERICA - Tableware–china - Lenox, Inc.

ERICA HANSON - Hair accessories, jewelry - Loom Co.
ERICH HAUSNER - Cellos - Deltex Music Corp.
ERICH S. HERRMANN - Posters - Graphic Arts Unltd. Inc.
ERICH WERNER - Musical instruments - St. Louis Music Supply Co.
ERICKSON-SWEDEN - Glassware–household ☆ - Kuhn Concepts
ERICOMP - Scientific apparatus - Ericomp, Inc.
ERICSON - Boats - Pacific Seacraft Corp.
ERIDIUM - Antiseptics - Roberts/Hauck Pharmaceuticals Inc.
ERIE - Brushes - Wright-Bernet
ERIE - Brushes–paint - Corona Brushes Inc.
ERIE - Ladders–plastic - John S. Tilley Ladders Co. Inc.
ERIE - Seafood products–fresh or frozen - C.E. Lixie Fisheries Inc.
ERIE SHINER-FISH LURES - Fishing lures - Hildebrandt Corp.
ERIETTE - Medical apparatus ☆ - Erie Medical (Div. of Ocenco Incorporated)
ERIEZ - Magnets - Eriez Manufacturing Co.
ERIK - Cigars - Havatampa Inc.
ERIK - Furniture–wood ☆ - Gold Medal Inc.
ERIK ELITE M - Stoves - American Road Equipment Co.
ERIKA - Apparel–women's - Miss Erika, Inc.
ERIKA - Cooking equipment–household - Jacksonville Manufacturing
ERIKA - Dining room furniture - Daystrom Furniture Inc.
ERIKA - Glassware–household - ACC
ERIKA - Mattresses - Namaco Industries, Inc.
ERIKA - Ophthalmic goods ☆ - Rozin Optical Export Corp.
ERIKA - Shampoo - Iodent Co.
ERIKA COLLECTION - Jewelry - House of Bangles Inc.
ERIKNIT - Apparel–men's ☆ - Michaels/Stern & Co. Inc.
ERIK'S - Food products - Erik's DeliCafe Inc.
ERIMA - Sporting goods - Continental Sports Supply Inc.
ERIN - Computer software - Lucent Technologies Inc.
ERIN - Floor coverings–carpet and rugs - Regal Rugs Inc.
ERIN - Giftware - Franciscan by Johnson Brothers, USA, Inc.
ERIN - Glassware–household - Crate and Barrel
ERIN - Tableware–china - Lenox, Inc.
ERIN - Toys - Tonka Corp.
ERIN - Yarn - Brunswick Yarns
ERIN BEAR - Toys–stuffed - Dakin Inc.
ERIN GOLD - Cheese - Swissrose International Inc.
ERIN LOUIS - Floor coverings–carpet and rugs - Regal Rugs Inc.
ERINGOLD - Tobacco products - Lane Ltd.
ERINMORE - Tobacco products - House of Edgeworth
ERINORE - Tablecloths - William Ewart & Son New York Ltd.
ERIN'S LITTLE BITS OF SHORTBREAD - Cookies - M.A. O'Halloran
ERINSTONE - Dishes–china - Mikasa Co.
ERIPS - Computer software - Environmental Research Institute of Michigan
ERIS - Electronic equipment - General Electric Co.
ERKY & FRIENDS - Dolls - Kenneth Lockwood
ERLAND - Food products ☆ - Dole Food Co., Inc.
ERLANGER - Beverages–malt - The Stroh Brewery Co.
ERLIWORM - Pet products - St. Aubrey
ERLON - Apparel–women's - Devon Apparel
ERMA MEYER - Dolls ☆ - Foley & Robinson Inc.
ERMENEGILDO ZEGNA - Skin care products - Ermenegildo Zegna Corp.
ERMENEGILDO ZEGNA - Toiletries - Ermenegildo Zegna Corp.
ERMET - Tables–metal - Ermet Products
ERMETO - Watches - Movado Time Corp.
ERMETOPHON - Watches - Movado Time Corp.
ERMEX - Watches - Nationwide Time Inc.
ERMI - Dental products - U.S. Biomaterials Corp.
ERMINE - Paper ☆ - Hunt Manufacturing Co.
ERMINETTE - Artists' materials - M. Grumbacher Inc.
ERMINEX - Artists' materials - Stangren Corp.
ERN - Computer software - Electronic Realty Associates, L.P.
ERNEST & JULIO GALLO - Wines - Ernest and Julio Gallo Winery
ERNEST & JULIO GALLO SONOMA - Wines - Ernest and Julio Gallo Winery
ERNEST BOREL - Watches - Borel Watch Co.
ERNEST GALLO - Wines - Ernest and Julio Gallo Winery
ERNEST SOHN CREATIONS - Housewares - Ernest Sohn Creations
ERNESTO PALLA - Guitar strings - Ernie Ball Inc.
ERNESTO W. - Apparel–women's - Howard B. Wolf Inc.
ERNIE - Toys - Jim Henson Productions, Inc.
ERNIE BALL - Guitar strings and accessories - Ernie Ball Inc.
ERNIE BEAR - Measuring instruments - Ernest John Panek
ERNIE GARDENER'S AMERICA'S CHOICE - Gardening products - Channel Home Centers Inc.

ERNIE'S APPEARANCE CENTER - Home health care products - Baylor Health Care System
ERNIE'S BIG SPLASH - Computer software - CBS Software
ERNIES CASH MUSIC - Recording label - Ernie Cash Enterprises
ERNIE'S MAGIC SHAPES - Computer software - CBS Software
ERNIE'S RUBBER DUCKIE - Toys - Playskool, Inc.
ERNO LASZLO - Skin care products - Chesebrough-Pond's USA Co.
ERNST HEINRICH ROTH - Musical instruments - Ideal Musical Merchandise Co.
ERNST OF SAN FRANCISCO - Neckwear ☆ - Cornell of California Inc.
ERNTEDANK - Food containers - Purity Foods Inc.
ERNUCOI - Pet products ☆ - Bioglan Animal Products Inc.
ERO - Electrical equipment - Ero, Inc.
ERO - Health care products - Scherer Laboratories Inc.
ERO - Sporting goods - Alpina Sports Corp.
ERO - Sporting goods - Hedstrom Corp.
EROGEL - Cosmetics - Taylor-Wright Pharmacals, Inc.
EROGRAPH - Pens–fountain ☆ - Canson-Talens Inc.
EROS - Floor coverings–carpet and rugs ☆ - Hollytex Carpet Mills Inc.
EROS - Jewelry - Frederick Goldman, Inc.
ERO'S MARKETPLACE - Meat products - Ero Meat Co.
EROSION PATCH - Fertilizers - Amturf
EROTIC ESCAPADES - Video production - Erotic Escapades
EROTICA - Prophylactics - Ansell Inc. (Personal Products Div.)
EROTICA - Underwear and nightwear - Bentley Lingerie, Inc.
EROTISENSE - Skin care products - John Langhorne Jr.
EROX - Cosmetics - Erox Corp.
ERPACE - Pharmaceutical preparations - Dolisos America, Inc.
ERPX - Computer software - J.D. Edwards & Co.
ERRE UNO - Apparel–men's - Superba, Inc.
ERROR-EATER - Office supplies - Repeat-O-Type Manufacturing Corp.
ERROT'S - Meat products–beef - Blue Ridge Beefalo, Inc.
ERS - Electronic equipment - Electronic Retailing Systems International, Inc.
ERSKINE - Motor vehicles–automobiles ☆ - Studebaker-Packard Corp.
ERT - Heating equipment - Surface Combustion, Inc.
ERTE - Posters - One-of-a-Kind Workshop
ERTE - Puzzles ☆ - Milton Bradley Co.
ERTH FOOD - Compost - Erth Group, Inc.
ERTL - Toys–models - ERTL Co., Inc.
ERTL'S 50TH ANNIVERSARY COMMEMORATIVE FARM TOYS - Toys– automobiles - ERTL Co., Inc.
ERUDITE SOFTWARE - Computer software - Erudite Software and Consulting, Inc.
ERUPTING VOLCANOES - Aquarium accessories - Blue Ribbon Pet Products, Inc.
ERUPTION - Bicycles - Roadmaster Corp.
ERVING - Paper–toweling - Erving Paper Mills
ERWIN - Computer database programs - Logic Works, Inc.
ERWIN BURGER - Italian art in glass - Intercontinental Industries Inc.
ERWIN-LAMBETH - Furniture - Erwin-Lambeth Inc.
ERWIN PEARL - Pens - Erwin Pearl Inc.
ERY-MUNE-C - Veterinary pharmaceutical preparations ☆ - Boehringer Ingelheim Animal Health, Inc.
ERY-TAB - Antibiotics - Abbott Laboratories
ERYC - Pharmaceutical preparations - Parke-Davis
ERYCETTE - Pharmaceutical preparations - Ortho Pharmaceutical Corp.
ERYDERM - Antibiotics - Abbott Laboratories
ERYGEL - Skin care products - Allergan, Inc.
ERYMAX - Pharmaceutical preparations - Allergan, Inc.
ERYMAX SOLUTION - Skin care products - Allergan, Inc.
ERYN'S ABC'S - Computer software - SourceView Software International
ERYPAR - Antibiotics ☆ - Parke-Davis
ERYPED - Antibiotics - Abbott Laboratories
ERYTHRA-DERM - Pharmaceutical preparations - Paddock Laboratories Inc.
ERYTHRO-PAK - Skin care products - Dermik Laboratories Inc.
ERYTHROCIN - Antibiotics - Abbott Laboratories
ERYTHROCOT - Pharmaceutical preparations - C.O. Truxton Inc.
ERYTHROMYCIN - Pharmaceutical preparations - Akorn Inc.
ERZ TRASH BAG HOLDER - Housewares ☆ - Edwards Creative Products, Inc.
ERZGEBIRGE - Figurines - Staufen Studio
ERZGEBIRGE FOLKART - Ornamental products–glass - Old World Christmas
ERZQEBINGE - Novelty items - Whitehurst Imports
ES - Apparel and accessories - Pierre Andre Senizergues
ES - Audio equipment - Sony Corp. of America
ES - Brake parts - Raybestos/Brake Parts Inc.

☆ = Now out of production

ES - Computer software - Enersoft Corp.
ES - Floor coverings - Congoleum Corp.
ES - Hair care products - Fromm Industries
ES - Medical apparatus - Ventana Medical Systems, Inc.
ES/9000 - Computers - International Business Machines Corp.
ES-A-CORT-E - Skin care products ☆ - Miles Inc.
ES CLASSIC - Shoes - Ephrata Shoe Co. Inc.
E.S. DURALIM - Sporting goods - Avant Garde
ES-GEN - Skin care products - Professional & Technical Services, Inc.
E.S. ORIGINALS - Footwear–women's - E.S. Originals, Inc.
ES PARANZA - Recording label - Atlantic Records
ES-SE - Skirts–women's - ES-SE Clothing LLC
ES UNA SALSA.MUY SALSA! - Seasonings - Empacadora Tapatio
ES2 - Hearing aids - Widex Hearing Aid Co., Inc.
ESA - Computer software - Softmed Systems, Inc.
ESA - Measuring instruments - Surface Combustion, Inc.
ESAB RACING - Apparel and accessories - Esab Welding & Cutting Products
ESANTE - Sewing machines–household - Tacony Corp.
ESAR - Recording label ☆ - Bill Rase Productions Inc.
ESAS - Radio equipment - Uniden America Corp.
ESAT - Automotive parts and accessories - Automotive Products (USA) Inc.
ESATTA GRAPPA BAROLO - Wines - Tempo Imports Ltd.
ESAW - Connectors–electrical - Esaw Industries, Inc.
ESB - Beverages–malt - Redhook Ale Brewery, Inc.
ESB - Recording label - ESB Records
ES*BEAR*DRILLES - Footwear - Bear Feet
ESBILAC - Dog food - Pet-Ag, Inc.
ESCA - Pharmaceutical preparations - Michigan Pharmaceutical
ESCA - Recording label ☆ - Rounder Records Corp.
ESCADA - Apparel stores–sports - Escada Beaute Ltd.
ESCADA - Footwear–women's - Pancaldi
ESCADRILLE - Apparel–women's - Hart Schaffner & Marx
ESCADRILLE - Furniture ☆ - Tropitone Furniture Co. Inc.
ESCADRILLE - Slacks–men's - Jaymar-Ruby Inc.
ESCALADE - Computer software - Escalade
ESCALATION P.S.E. - Health care products - Enzymatic Therapy, Inc.
ESCALATOR - Escalators - Otis Elevator Co.
ESCALATOR - Wallpaper - Koroseal Wallcoverings
ESCALERT - Health care products - Enzymatic Therapy, Inc.
ESCALITE - Health care products ☆ - Enzymatic Therapy, Inc.
ESCALLOPE - Floor coverings–carpet and rugs - Regal Rugs Inc.
ESCALON - Food products - Escalon Frozen Foods
ESCAP - Stepper motors - Portescap U.S. Inc.
ESCAPADE - Boats - Glen-L Marine Designs
ESCAPADE - Flatware - Yamazaki Tableware Inc.
ESCAPADE - Floor coverings - Parquet de France Inc.
ESCAPADE - Floor coverings–carpet and rugs - Coronet Carpets Inc.
ESCAPADE - Luggage - Airway Industries, Inc.
ESCAPADE - Motor vehicles–motor homes - Skylark Industries Inc.
ESCAPADE - Publisher's imprints ☆ - Maxwell/McMellan Inc.
ESCAPADE - Tires - Dico Tire Inc.
ESCAPADE - Toilets–enameled - Kohler Co.
ESCAPADE - Yarn - William Unger & Co. Inc.
ESCAPADE COLLECTION - Draperies - Maharam Fabric Corp.
ESCAPADES - Apparel and accessories - Lady Ester Lingerie Corp.
ESCAPADES - Furniture - Stanley Furniture Co. Inc.
ESCAPE - Bicycles ☆ - Raleigh USA Bicycle Co.
ESCAPE - Boats–motor - Forester Boats Inc.
ESCAPE - Boats–motor - Grady-White Boats, Inc.
ESCAPE - Colognes - Calvin Klein Ltd.
ESCAPE - Exercising equipment - Bench Press Escape, Inc.
ESCAPE - Household cleaner - Ecolab Inc.
ESCAPE - Luggage ☆ - Hartmann Luggage Co.
ESCAPE-AID - Ladders–metal - St. Pierre Manufacturing Corp.
ESCAPE ARTIST - Recording label - Alek Vila
ESCAPE FOR MEN - Colognes - Calvin Klein Ltd.
ESCAPE FROM TERROR CAVE - Games ☆ - Cadaco Div.
ESCAPE GEAR - Sleeping bags - Erickson Outdoors
ESCAPE GOAT - Bicycles ☆ - Mountain Goat Cycles
ESCAPE LIGHT - Smoke detectors - BRK Electronics Inc.
ESCAPE TO PARADISE - Wallpaper - Jack Denst Designs
ESCAPE TO THE FRESH SIDE - Cigarettes - R.J. Reynolds Tobacco Co.
ESCAPE VELOCITY - Sunglasses - Escape Velocity
ESCAPE WEAR - Apparel and accessories - Edison Brothers Stores, Inc.
ESCAPEZE - Apparel and accessories - Martin Enterprises
ESCAPING JAIL - Puzzles - University Games Corp.

ESCENTIAL ESSENCES - Incense - Matchless Gifts Inc.
ESCENTIALS - Beauty aids, hair-care products - Escentials Inc.
ESCENTUAL - Skin care products - Starwest Botanicals Inc.
ESCEPCIONALES - Cigar boxes–wood - Consolidated Cigar Corp.
ESCHATIN - Pharmaceutical preparations ☆ - Parke-Davis
ESCHER - Posters ☆ - Icart Vendor Graphics Inc.
ESCHER - Puzzles - Importoys
ESCH'S - Syrup - Esch's Maple Products
ESCO - See **J. HOFERT**
ESCO - Food products - Esco Foods Inc.
ESCO - Giftware - Esco Products Inc.
ESCO - Paper–rolls - Autron Inc.
ESCODARA - Floor coverings–carpet and rugs - Tuftex Carpet Mills, Inc.
ESCOFFIER - Food products - Nabisco Foods Group
ESCOLITE - Paints ☆ - Valspar Corp.
ESCOLUX - Paints - Valspar Corp.
ESCONDIDO MILLS - Food products - Health Best Distributors Inc.
ESCOPLAN - Paper–carbon - Kores Nordic USA Corp.
ESCOPY - Paper–rolls - Autron Inc.
ESCOR - Computer software - Tegra, Inc.
ESCORT - Attache cases - Buhl Industries, Inc.
ESCORT - Automotive parts and accessories - Lancaster Colony Automotive Group
ESCORT - Bags - Interstate Packaging Corp.
ESCORT - Bicycles - Murray, Inc.
ESCORT - Boats - Glen-L Marine Designs
ESCORT - Calculators ☆ - Citizen America Corp.
ESCORT - Cameras–motion picture - Eastman Kodak Co.
ESCORT - Cases–musical instrument - Calzone Case Co.
ESCORT - Computer software - Passport Designs Inc.
ESCORT - Computer software - Sonex Corp.
ESCORT - Cosmetics - Spornette International, Inc.
ESCORT - Crackers - Nabisco Foods Group
ESCORT - Cutlery - Gerber Legendary Blades
ESCORT - Dryers–hair ☆ - Dubl Duck/Jet Set Inc.
ESCORT - Dryers–hair ☆ - Ronson Consumer Products Corp.
ESCORT - Floor coverings–carpet and rugs - Calladium & Marglen
ESCORT - Floor coverings–carpet and rugs - Catalina Carpet Mills Inc.
ESCORT - Footwear–athletic - KangaROOS USA Inc.
ESCORT - Garden equipment - Geerpres Wringer Co.
ESCORT - Glassware–household - Owens-Illinois Inc. (Libbey Div.)
ESCORT - Glassware–household ☆ - Anchor Hocking Glass, Inc.
ESCORT - Globes - Replogle Globes Inc.
ESCORT - Herbicides - E.I. Dupont de Nemours and Co.
ESCORT - Infant product - Gerry Baby Products Co.
ESCORT - Locks–door - Handy Andy Home Improvement Centers, Inc.
ESCORT - Luggage ☆ - American Tourister, Inc.
ESCORT - Measuring and dispensing pumps - Landauer, Inc.
ESCORT - Medical apparatus - Wilson-Cook Medical Inc.
ESCORT - Motor vehicles–automobiles - Ford Motor Co.
ESCORT - Oxygen ☆ - Caire
ESCORT - Paper - L.L. Brown Paper Co.
ESCORT - Shirts ☆ - Horace Small Apparel Co.
ESCORT - Skin care products - William Stevens Perfumers
ESCORT - Sweaters - Binghamton Knitting Co.
ESCORT - Veterinary pharmaceutical preparations - Schering-Plough Animal Health
ESCORT - Veterinary pharmaceutical preparations ☆ - Schering-Plough Animal Health
ESCORT - Watches - Precise International/Wenger
ESCORT - Wigs - Jean Paree Weegs Inc.
ESCORT - Window shades ☆ - Superior Shade & Blind Co. Inc.
ESCORT 720 - Staplers - ACCO USA, Inc.
ESCORT GT - Motor vehicles–automobiles - Ford Motor Co.
ESCORT PLUSH - Automotive parts and accessories - Lancaster Colony Automotive Group
ESCORT RX - Cart - Geerpres Wringer Co.
ESCORT, THE - Projectors–photographic - Buhl Industries, Inc.
ESCORT TO HELL - Games ☆ - Mayfair Games, Inc.
ESCOT - Pharmaceutical preparations ☆ - Solvay Pharmaceuticals Inc.
ESCOTE - Paints ☆ - Valspar Corp.
ESCOTS - Computer software - E.S. Consultants, Inc.
ESCRIBIEN - Computer software - Bilingual Software Co.
ESCUDO - Beverages–malt - Logret Import & Export Co.
ESCUDO - Tobacco–chewing or smoking - James B. Russell Inc.
ESCURIAL - Wallpaper ☆ - Wallquest, Inc.

ESD - Cleaning preparations ☆ - Marshall Industries
ESDEE - Paper–sand - Canson-Talens Inc.
ESE - Vitamins and nutritional supplements - Sunrider International
ESEMCO - Giftware - Shiman Industries Inc.
ESENZIA - Fabrics - Burlington Industries, Inc.
ESERINE SULFATE - Ophthalmic prescription drug - Iolab Pharmaceuticals
ESFRESH PRODUCE - Fruits and vegetables - Esfresh Produce, Inc.
E.S.G. - Food products - Giulianos' Specialty Foods
E.S.G. - Musical instruments - Valerie J. Scroggins
ESGIC - Analgesics - Forest Pharmaceuticals Inc.
ESGIC PLUS - Analgesics - Forest Pharmaceuticals Inc.
ESHCOL CABERNET SAUVIGNON - Wines - Trefethen Vineyards Winery Inc.
ESHCOL CHARDONNAY - Wines - Trefethen Vineyards Winery Inc.
ESHELMAN - Animal feeds - Manna Pro Corp.
ESHOP - Computer software - Ink Development Corp.
ESI - Switches–electric - Electric Switches, Inc.
ESI-CRYL - Chemical preparations - Cook Composites and Polymers Co.
ESI TRACKER - Publisher's imprints - Deltatrends, Inc.
ESICO - Tools–soldering - Esico Triton
ESICONTROL - Electronic equipment - Esico Triton
ESIDRIX - Diuretics - Ciba-Geigy Corp.
ESIMIL - Pharmaceutical preparations - Ciba-Geigy Corp.
ESKA - Motors–outboard ☆ - Certified Parts Corp.
ESKABARB SPANSULE - Barbituates - Smithkline Beecham Corp.
ESKALITH - Tranquilizers - Smithkline Beecham Corp.
ESKAPHEN B - Barbituates - Smithkline Beecham Corp.
ESKATROL - Pharmaceutical preparations - Smithkline Beecham Corp.
ESKAY - Food products - Spice King Corp.
ESKI - Apparel and accessories ☆ - Alpine Crafts Co. Inc.
ESKI - Sleeping bags - Coleman Co., Inc.
ESKI CAP - Crocheted and knitted items - Schuessler Knitting Mills Inc.
ESKIMO - Apparel and accessories ☆ - Eagle Knitting Mills Inc.
ESKIMO - Augers - Ardisam, Inc.
ESKIMO - Fans–electric ☆ - Toastmaster Inc.
ESKIMO - Floor coverings - American Floor Products Co. Inc.
ESKIMO - Gloves ☆ - Alpine Crafts Co. Inc.
ESKIMO - Sleeping bags - Coleman Co., Inc.
ESKIMO PENGUIN - Toys–stuffed - Dakin Inc.
ESKIMO PIE - Ice cream - Eskimo Pie Corp.
ESKIMO PIE BUTTERSCOTCH CRUNCH - Frozen foods - Eskimo Pie Corp.
ESKIMO PIE NORTHERN LITES - Ice cream ☆ - Eskimo Pie Corp.
ESKIMO PIE PUDDING BARS - Ice cream - Eskimo Pie Corp.
ESKIMO ROCKET POPS - Ice cream - Eskimo Pie Corp.
ESKIMO SEAL - Toys–stuffed - Dakin Inc.
ESKIMOX - Footwear ☆ - Tru-Stitch Footwear (Div. of Wolverine World Wide)
ESKIMUFFS - Apparel and accessories - Arlington Hat Co. Inc.
ESKIPADES - Footwear ☆ - Dunham Boot Makers
ESKOFOT - Cameras - Graphline, Inc.
ESL - Eggs - Stevens Industries Inc.
E.S.L. - Jewelry - E.S.L. Jewelers, Inc.
ESL - Machinery ☆ - International Paper Co.
ESL EXTENDED SHELF LIFE - Machinery ☆ - International Paper Co.
ESL PICTURE GRAMMAR - Computer software - Gessler Publishing Co., Inc.
ESL TUTOR - Computer software - DPI Services, Inc.
ESLABON - Publisher's imprints - Eslabon International, Inc.
ESLEEP - Apparel and accessories - Esleep, Inc.
ESLEEP & CO. - Apparel–women's - Bentley Lingerie, Inc.
ESLEEP EQUIPMENT - Apparel and accessories - Esleep, Inc.
ESLEEP POETS SHIRT - Apparel and accessories - Esleep, Inc.
ESLEEP SIGNATURE - Apparel–athletic - Esleep, Inc.
ESLEEP SOFTWEAR - Nightgowns - Esleep, Inc.
ESLEEP TEAM - Apparel and accessories - Esleep, Inc.
ESLOK - Nuts and bolts - MacLean-ESNA
ESLON - Electrical equipment - Sekisui Products Inc.
ESM - Electrical equipment - Auburn International, Inc.
ESM ELECTRONIC SERVICE MANUAL - Computer software - L-Cube Innovative Solutions, Inc.
ESMARK - Shortening - Beatrice Cos. Inc.
ESMOND - Blankets - Chatham Manufacturing Co.
ESNA - Nuts and bolts - MacLean-Fogg Co.
ESNA - Nuts and bolts - New York Fasteners Co.
ESO NEW YORK - Footwear–women's - E.S. Originals, Inc.
ESOS ELECTRONIC SUPPLY ORDERING SYSTEM - Computer software - Standard Register Co.
ESOTERIC - Drums–musical instruments ☆ - LP Music Group
ESOTERIC - Recording label - Everest Record Group

ESOTERIC - Wallpaper - Academy Handprints Ltd.
ESOTERICA - Skin care products - Smithkline Beecham Corp.
ESP - Agricultural machinery - Clark Equipment Co.
ESP - Air conditioning equipment - Inter-City Products Corp. (USA)
ESP - Cleaning preparations - ESP, Inc.
ESP - Cleaning preparations - Louis C. Landman
E.S.P. - Deodorants–personal - Smithkline Beecham Corp.
E.S.P. - Electric lighting equipment - Intelectron Products Co.
ESP - Fishing tackle ☆ - Cortland Line Co., Inc.
ESP - Games ☆ - Milton Bradley Co.
ESP - Guitars - E.S.P. Guitar Co. Inc.
ESP - Hair care products - John Amico Expressive Hair Care Products
E.S.P. - Hair care products ☆ - Syosset Laboratories Inc.
ESP - Machinery - ESAB Automation Inc.
ESP - Patterns–clothing ☆ - Simplicity Pattern Co., Inc.
ESP - Pharmaceutical preparations - Elements Inc.
ESP - Recording label - ESP-Disk Ltd.
ESP - Vacuum cleaners and accessories - The Eureka Co.
ESP-2 - Electronic equipment - AudioControl
ESP-3 - Electronic equipment - AudioControl
ESP CARE - Motor vehicle parts and accessories - Ford Motor Co.
ESP EDUCATIONAL SOFTWARE PRODUCTS, INC. - Computer software - Educational Software Products, Inc.
ESP G - Bicycle parts and accessories - Sram Corp.
ESP G OPERATING SYSTEM - Gears–bicycle - Sram Corp.
ESP PERFORMANCE - Bathing suits - Ocean Pool Co.
ESP PLUS - Motor vehicle parts and accessories - Ford Motor Co.
ESP THE EXPERT SUPPORT PROGRAM - Computer software - Teubner & Associates, Inc.
ESPACE - Footwear - Eliot Co. Inc.
ESPALIER - Apparel–women's - Charles Sakmann Golf, Inc.
ESPALMA - Towels - Cobra Trading Corp.
ESPANA - Dinnerware–glass - Block China Co.
ESPANA - Fireplaces - Dyna Corp.
ESPANA - Floor coverings - Congoleum Corp.
ESPANA - Novelty items ☆ - Decorative Crafts
ESPANA - Shelving units–wood - Woodland Products Inc.
ESPANA - Tiles–ceramic - Dal-Tile Corp.
ESPANOL - Shelving units–wood - Naomi Gale Wall Systems
ESPARTO - Floor coverings–carpet and rugs - Milliken & Co. Inc.
ESPE - Hair clippers–veterinary - Friends Imports Inc.
ESPECIAL - Beverages–alcohol ☆ - Domecq Importers Inc.
ESPECIAL, INC. - Laboratory apparatus - Especial, Inc.
ESPECIALLY FOR YOU - Candy - Russell Stover Candies, Inc.
ESPECIALLY FOR YOU - Flower pots–earthenware - Russ Berrie and Co., Inc.
ESPECIALLY FOR YOU - Giftware - N.S. Gustin Co.
ESPECIALLY FOR YOU - Wallcoverings - Beverly Stevens Ltd.
ESPECIALLY YOU - Apparel–women's - Sanmark-Stardust Inc.
ESPECIALLY YOURS - Dolls - Geoffrey Inc.
ESPECIALLY YOURS - Floor coverings–carpet and rugs ☆ - Callaway Carpets
ESPECOL - Pharmaceutical preparations - Pfeiffer Pharmaceuticals Inc.
ESPER DELUXE - Food products - Esper Products Deluxe
ESPERANCE - Faucets - Sterling Plumbing Group Inc.
ESPERANT - Computer software - Software AG of North America, Inc.
ESPERANTO - Apparel–athletic ☆ - Cooper Sportswear Manufacturing Co., Inc.
ESPERANTO - Artists' materials ☆ - M. Grumbacher Inc.
ESPERANTO - Computer software - Jay-Martin Systems, Inc.
ESPERANTO - Shoes - Canter Shoe Co.
ESPERE - Wallpaper - Koroseal Wallcoverings
ESPERFOAM - Fire extinguishing compositions - Witco Corp.
ESPIAL - Skin care products - Espial, Inc.
ESPILLON - Apparel and accessories - Casero's & Associates
ESPIRIT DE CORP EDC GROUP - Apparel and accessories - Esprit De Corp.
ESPIRIT SAN FRANCISCO - Handbags - Esprit De Corp.
ESPLANADE - Floor coverings - Mannington Resilient Floors
ESPLANADE - Floor coverings–carpet and rugs ☆ - Atlas Carpet Mills Inc.
ESPLANADE - Lighting fixtures - Holophane Corp.
ESPLENDIDO - Cheese - Kraft Food Ingredients Corp.
ESPLENDIDO - Tortillas - Kraft Foodservice Holding Corp.
ESPLENDIDO GARVEY - Brandy - European Beverage Co., Inc.
ESPN - Computer software - ESPN, Inc.
ESPN BASEBALL TONIGHT - Video game - ESPN, Inc.
ESPO - Jewelry - Esposito Jewelry, Inc.

☆ = Now out of production

ESPO-FLEX - Jewelry - Esposito Jewelry, Inc.
ESPOMA ORGANIC - Flowers, plants, and seeds - Espoma Co.
ESPORT - Uniforms–athletic - Pennine Computer Consulting, Inc.
ESPORTAZIONE - Paper - Fabriano America Inc.
ESPO'S COOKIES - Bakery products - Tony R. Esposito
ESPOSITO HOCKEY - Games ✩ - Parker Brothers
ESPRE - Furniture - Lane Co. Inc.
ESPREE - Cleaning preparations - Blue Coral, Inc.
ESPREE - Dryers–hair - Belson Products
ESPREE - Hobby kits ✩ - Unicraft Products
ESPREE - Scooters–motorized - Leisure Lift, Inc.
ESPREE - Sewing machines–household - Tacony Corp.
ESPREE - Whirlpool spa ✩ - Jacuzzi Inc.
ESPREE WHEEL RESTORER - Automotive parts and accessories - Blue Coral, Inc.
ESPRESS THIS - Coffee - Tetley Inc.
ESPRESSO - Cigars ✩ - General Cigar Co., Inc.
ESPRESSO - Containers–insulated - Robert E. Karns
ESPRESSO - Cosmetics - Lancome
ESPRESSO - Crocheted and knitted items - Martin D. Zucker
ESPRESSO - Furniture - Homecrest Industries Inc.
ESPRESSO - Modems - Beond Communications
ESPRESSO - Sporting goods - Montgomery Ward & Co. Inc.
ESPRESSO AMERICANO - Coffee makers–electric - Espresso Americano USA Inc.
ESPRESSO ARMANDO - Coffee makers–electric - Basis Audio, Inc.
ESPRESSO BEAN CHOCOLATE - Candy - Champlain Chocolate
ESPRESSO BROWN - Glassware–household ✩ - Lenox Crystal, Inc.
ESPRESSO DECADENCE - Confections - Famous Pacific Dessert Co.
ESPRESSO DOLCE - Coffee - P.J.'s USA, Inc.
ESPRESSO ENTERTAINMENT CENTER - Carts - Boyd Coffee Co.
ESPRESSO EXPRESS - Coffee - Hasco International, Inc.
ESPRESSO LUNA - Coffee - Starbucks Corp.
ESPRESSO MINI - Coffee makers–electric - Robert Krups North America
ESPRESSO NOVO - Coffee makers–electric - Robert Krups North America
ESPRESSO ROYALE CAFFE - Coffee - Espresso Caffe Corp.
ESPRESSO SOLO - Coffee - Boyd Coffee Co.
ESPRESSO STOUT - Beverages–malt - Hart Brewing, Inc.
ESPRESSO, THE - Coffee - Thomas A. Campbell Co.
ESPRESSO USA - Electrical equipment - Espresso USA, Inc.
ESPRESSOLES - Candy - Nordstrom, Inc.
ESPRION - Dairy products ✩ - DMV USA Inc.
ESPRIT - Apparel and accessories - Esprit De Corp.
ESPRIT - Beverages–alcohol - Canandaigua Wine Co. Inc.
ESPRIT - Bicycles ✩ - Roadmaster Corp.
ESPRIT - Boats–motor - Cruisers
ESPRIT - Clarinets - G. Leblanc Corp.
ESPRIT - Cookies - Pepperidge Farm Inc.
ESPRIT - Doors–storm - Canyon Creek Cabinet Co.
ESPRIT - Floor coverings - Azrock Commercial Flooring
ESPRIT - Floor coverings–carpet and rugs - Cumberland Mills Inc.
ESPRIT - Floor coverings–carpet and rugs ✩ - Columbus Mills, Inc.
ESPRIT - Fruit drinks–bottled or canned - Hamilton Foods Co. Inc.
ESPRIT - Furniture - Universal Flooring
ESPRIT - Furniture ✩ - Bassett Furniture Industries, Inc.
ESPRIT - Giftware ✩ - Gorham Inc.
ESPRIT - Glassware–household ✩ - Anchor Hocking Glass, Inc.
ESPRIT - Jewelry ✩ - Hirsch Speidel Inc.
ESPRIT - Men's apparel - Interco Inc.
ESPRIT - Motor vehicles–automobiles ✩ - General Motors Corp. (Pontiac/GMC Div.)
ESPRIT - Occasional tables ✩ - JDI Group, Inc.
ESPRIT - Rings–jewelry - Artcarved Inc.
ESPRIT - Skin care products - Veeco Manufacturing Co.
ESPRIT - Sports rackets and accessories - Victor Sports
ESPRIT - Strollers–baby - Evenflo Co.
ESPRIT - Sunglasses ✩ - Carrera Eyewear Corp.
ESPRIT - Telescopes - Northern Telecom, Inc.
ESPRIT - Video equipment - AmPro Corp.
ESPRIT - Wallpaper - Capital Carousel Inc.
ESPRIT - Wallpaper - Style-Tex Wallcoverings
ESPRIT - Wheelchairs - Ortho-Kinetics, Inc.
ESPRIT - Whirlpool ✩ - Jacuzzi Inc.
ESPRIT - Yogurt - Pace Foods, Ltd.
ESPRIT DE CUISINE - Cooking equipment–household ✩ - Mirro Corp.
ESPRIT DE FRANCE - Furniture ✩ - Kaylyn Inc.

ESPRIT DE VIE - Water–bottled or canned ✩ - Canandaigua Wine Co. Inc.
ESPRIT DU SEL - Salt - De Medici Imports Ltd.
ESPRIT KIDS - Apparel and accessories - Esprit De Corp.
ESPRIT SPORT - Apparel and accessories - Esprit De Corp.
ESPRIT TIMEWEAR - Watches - Esprit De Corp.
ESPRIT TODDLER - Apparel and accessories - Esprit De Corp.
ESPS - Neckties - Randa Corp.
ESPY - Computer program - Apple Computer Inc.
ESPY - Electrical equipment - Fluoroware, Inc.
ESQ - Chemical preparations - Lexicon Genetics Inc.
ESQA - Computer storage devices - Prospective Computer Analysts Inc.
ESQUIRE - Belts–apparel - Dan Dee Belt and Bag Co. Inc.
ESQUIRE - Beverages–malt - Jones Brewing Co.
ESQUIRE - Cabinets–wood ✩ - Kemper
ESQUIRE - Floor coverings–carpet and rugs ✩ - American Carpet Mills
ESQUIRE - Giftware ✩ - Bar & Barbeque Products Inc.
ESQUIRE - Glassware–household - Owens-Illinois Inc. (Libbey Div.)
ESQUIRE - Golfing equipment ✩ - Northwestern Golf Co.
ESQUIRE - Guitars - Fender Musical Instruments
ESQUIRE - Hosiery - Kayser-Roth Corp.
ESQUIRE - Knives - Precise International/Wenger
ESQUIRE - Mobile homes - Wick Building Systems Inc. (Manufactured Home Div./North)
ESQUIRE - Paper–bond - Saxon Paper Co.
ESQUIRE - Pool tables - American International Shuffleboard Corp.
ESQUIRE - Publisher's imprints - Hearst Corp.
ESQUIRE - Recording label - Little Major Record Distributors Inc.
ESQUIRE - Shoe accessories - Kiwi Brands, Inc.
ESQUIRE - Shoe polish - Hickory Industries, Inc.
ESQUIRE - Thread - Threads USA Div.
ESQUIRE - Tiles - TileCera Inc.
ESQUIRE - Toys - Esquire Novelty Corp.
ESQUIRE - Watches - Movado Time Corp.
ESQUIRE COLLECTION - Housewares - Karen Carson Creations
ESQUIRE EXTRA - Beverages–malt ✩ - Jones Brewing Co.
ESQUIRE EXTRA DRY LIGHT - Beverages–malt ✩ - Jones Brewing Co.
ESQUIRE GOLF - Shoe accessories - Hickory Industries, Inc.
ESQUIRE/NICHOLS - Toys–guns - Esquire Novelty Corp.
ESQUIRE NOVELTY - Toys–guns - Esquire Novelty Corp.
ESQUIRE PAPERS - Stationery ✩ - Royal Imprints Corp.
ESR - Brakes–motor vehicle - Eaton Corp.
ESR - Jewelry - Sansom Refining Co.
ESS - Sporting goods ✩ - O'Brien International
ESS/400 - Computer software - Dataflex Systems Inc.
ESS G.H. - Pharmaceutical - American Hygienic Laboratories Inc.
ESS INDUSTRIES - Office equipment - Ess Industries
ESS-PAK - Hardware - Free-Flow Packaging Corp.
ESS-PHERIC - Contact lenses - Chariotstar Inc.
ESSA - Air purification systems - Aqua-Air Technologies, Inc.
ESSAI - Clothing - Pretty Talk, Inc.
ESSATIONS - Hair care products - Easy Pro, Inc.
ESSAY - Apparel - Geneco Inc.
ESSAY - Recording label - Koch International
ESSAY EASE - Computer software - Mind Play
ESSCAPE - Wallcovering - Gencorp Inc.
ESSCENT - Hair coloring preparations - Stylors Inc.
ESSCOR - Giftware - Esslinger & Co.
ESSE - Paper - Mead Corp.
ESSE - Paper–writing - Gilbert Paper Co.
ESSE - Skin care products - Catalog Ventures, Inc.
ESSE SALON & SPA - Skin and hair care products - Catalog Ventures, Inc.
ESSELTE - Office supplies - Esselte Corp.
ESSELTE DT 2500 - Office accessories - Esselte Corp.
ESSEN - Salads–prepackaged - Essen Nutrition Corp.
ESSENCE - Amplifiers - Essence
ESSENCE - Bicycles - Schwinn Cycling & Fitness Inc.
ESSENCE - Cabinets–wood - Decora
ESSENCE - Chairs–folding ✩ - Cramer Inc.
ESSENCE - Clocks - General Time Corp. (Westclox/Seth Thomas Div.)
ESSENCE - Floor coverings–carpet and rugs - Regal Rugs Inc.
ESSENCE - Floor coverings–carpet and rugs - Alexander Smith Carpets
ESSENCE - Floor coverings–carpet and rugs ✩ - Hollytex Carpet Mills Inc.
ESSENCE - Flowers, plants, and seeds - International Seeds, Inc.
ESSENCE - Frames–eyeglass - Diaco
ESSENCE - Furniture ✩ - Broyhill Furniture Industries, Inc.
ESSENCE - Furniture ✩ - Hammary Furniture Co. Inc.

ESSENCE - Guitars - Alembic Inc.

ESSENCE - Jewelry–costume - Diamond Essence Co.

ESSENCE - Lighting fixtures - Progress Lighting Inc.

ESSENCE - Luggage - American Tourister, Inc.

ESSENCE - Napkins–paper - Fort Howard Corp.

ESSENCE - Panty hose - Essence Communications, Inc.

ESSENCE - Photo albums - International Silver Co.

ESSENCE - Rings–jewelry - Artcarved Inc.

ESSENCE - Soap - Baudelaire Inc.

ESSENCE - Tiles–ceiling ☆ - Florida Tile Industries, Inc.

ESSENCE - Tiles–ceramic - Monarch Tile Inc.

ESSENCE - Wallpaper - Fidelity Industries, Inc.

ESSENCE - Whirlpools ☆ - Jacuzzi Inc.

ESSENCE 2000 NATURALLY - Skin care products - Natural Essence Inc.

ESSENCE BY MAIL - Apparel and accessories - Essence Communications, Inc.

ESSENCE GOLD ACCENT - Flatware ☆ - Yamazaki Tableware Inc.

ESSENCE II - Wallpaper - Fidelity Industries, Inc.

ESSENCE IN HARMONY - Perfumes - Avon Products, Inc.

ESSENCE OF INDIA - Health care products - Lakon Herbals Inc.

ESSENCE OF MAN - Colognes - Faberge Co.

ESSENCE OF OREGON - Jams and jellies - Essence of Oregon

ESSENCE OF SPRING - Soap - Intellectual Property Holding Co.

ESSENCE OF TASTE - Food products ☆ - Ajinomoto USA, Inc.

ESSENCE OF THE GAME - Posters - Successories, Inc.

ESSENCE OF THE SEASON - Perfumes - Garden Botanika, Inc.

ESSENCE OF TIME - Exercising equipment - Home Shopping Club, Inc.

ESSENCE OF XMAS - Candles - San Francisco Candle Co.

ESSENCE RARE - Perfumes ☆ - Houbigant, Inc.

ESSENCE RELE - Oils–essential - Essence Rele Inc.

ESSENDI - Apparel and accessories - Origin Industries, Inc.

ESSENSA - Skin care products - Regent Bond Inc.

ESSENSIA - Wines - Quady Winery

ESSENTIA - Cabinets - Actua

ESSENTIAL - Floor coverings–carpet and rugs ☆ - J and J Industries Inc.

ESSENTIAL - Foam products - Essential Medical Supply Inc.

ESSENTIAL - Freezers - General Signal Corp.

ESSENTIAL - Furniture - Avant Industries

ESSENTIAL - Pharmaceutical preparations - Leiner Health Products Inc.

ESSENTIAL - Pharmaceutical preparations ☆ - Dermalogica Inc.

ESSENTIAL - Shampoos - La Coupe

ESSENTIAL 1 - Milk - Richfood, Inc.

ESSENTIAL ACCENTS - Framing supplies - Potomac Corp.

ESSENTIAL ACTIVITY SERUM - Skin care products ☆ - Sothys USA Inc.

ESSENTIAL BALANCE - Vitamins and nutritional supplements - Omega Nutrition USA Inc.

ESSENTIAL CALCIUM - Vitamins and nutritional supplements - Body Wise International, Inc.

ESSENTIAL CARE - Health care products - Lakon Herbals Inc.

ESSENTIAL COLLECTION, THE - Hair care products - Demert & Dougherty, Inc.

ESSENTIAL COLOR THERAPY - Hair care products - Matrix Essentials, Inc.

ESSENTIAL CRIBBAGE BOARD, THE - Games - Gene David Cohen

ESSENTIAL E - Vitamins and nutritional supplements - Bioenergy Nutrient's Inc.

ESSENTIAL ELEMENT - Skin care products - Ross Cosmetics Inc.

ESSENTIAL ELEMENTS - Apparel–women's - Nordstrom, Inc.

ESSENTIAL ELEMENTS - Recording label - Hal Leonard Corp.

ESSENTIAL ENERGY - Cosmetics - Shiseido Cosmetics (America) Ltd.

ESSENTIAL ENZYMES - Vitamins and nutritional supplements - Source Naturals

ESSENTIAL EQUIPMENT - Balls - Mikasa Sports

ESSENTIAL EYES - Eyeglasses - Pennsylvania Optical

ESSENTIAL FACE - Skin care products - Elysee Scientific Cosmetic Co.

ESSENTIAL FLUID - Cosmetics - Olay Co., Inc.

ESSENTIAL FOODS - Food products - Essential Foods, Inc.

ESSENTIAL GRAMMAR - Computer software - Gamco Industries Inc.

ESSENTIAL GREENS - Vitamins and nutritional supplements - Vitaquest International, Inc.

ESSENTIAL LEARNING - Publisher's imprints - Highlights for Children, Inc.

ESSENTIAL LIFE - Vitamins and nutritional supplements - Country Life

ESSENTIAL LUXURIES - Skin care products - Chasalco Inc.

ESSENTIAL MINERALS - Vitamins and nutritional supplements - Vitamin Research Products Inc.

ESSENTIAL NAIL - Health care products - Select Brands

ESSENTIAL NOURISHER - Skin care products - Stephan Co.

ESSENTIAL OIL - Hair care products - Raymac Corp. Hair & Skin Technology

ESSENTIAL OIL BLENDS - Oils–essential - Elizabeth Van Buren Aromatherapy

ESSENTIAL ORGANICS - Vitamins and nutritional supplements - Bio San Laboratories

ESSENTIAL PUNCTUATION - Computer software - Gamco Industries Inc.

ESSENTIAL REMEDIES - Health care products - Smith & Vandiver, Inc.

ESSENTIAL STEPS - Computer software - Mastery Rehabilitation Systems

ESSENTIAL, THE - Sauces - Essential Foods, Inc.

ESSENTIAL THERAPY - Hair care products - Matrix Essentials, Inc.

ESSENTIAL TONERS - Hosiery - Sara Lee Corp.

ESSENTIAL TREATMENTS - Hair care products - California Essential Products Co.

ESSENTIALLY ALL - Vitamins and nutritional supplements - Alacer Co.

ESSENTIALLY YOURS - Hair care products ☆ - W.R. Rayson Co., Inc.

ESSENTIALS - Apparel and accessories ☆ - Hartwell Garment Co.

ESSENTIALS - Apparel–men's - D. Stone Industries, Inc.

ESSENTIALS - Clocks - Timex Corp.

ESSENTIALS - Floor coverings - Mannington Resilient Floors

ESSENTIALS - Footwear–women's - Thom McAn Shoe Co.

ESSENTIALS - Frames–eyeglass ☆ - Universal/Univis Inc.

ESSENTIALS - Furniture ☆ - Bassett Furniture Industries, Inc.

ESSENTIALS - Glassware–household - Toscany Imports Ltd.

ESSENTIALS - Glue–household or industrial - Stanley Works

ESSENTIALS - Patterns–clothing ☆ - Simplicity Pattern Co., Inc.

ESSENTIALS - Prophylactics - Sime Health Ltd. (Sime Darby Group)

ESSENTIALS - Publisher's imprints - Research and Education Assn.

ESSENTIALS - Wallpaper - Essex Wallcoveringss

ESSENTIALS BY AMCO - Shelving units–metal - Amco Corp.

ESSENTIALS TOO - Apparel–children's - D. Stone Industries, Inc.

ESSENTIALSEA - Vitamins and nutritional supplements - Seaborne, Inc.

ESSEX - Artists' materials - Andrews/Nelson/Whitehead

ESSEX - Bicycles - Columbia Manufacturing Inc.

ESSEX - Binders - Dennison National Co.

ESSEX - Brushes–hair - I. Sekine Co. Inc.

ESSEX - Cabinets - Canyon Creek Cabinet Co.

ESSEX - Cabinets - Major Line Products Co. Inc.

ESSEX - Cabinets - Wellborn Cabinet, Inc.

ESSEX - Computer software ☆ - Broderbund Software, Inc.

ESSEX - Cutlery - Washington Forge Inc.

ESSEX - Dinnerware–glass - Crystal Clear Importing Co. Inc.

ESSEX - Dishes–china - Viletta China Co.

ESSEX - Faucets - Kohler Co.

ESSEX - Floor coverings–carpet and rugs - Galaxy Carpet Mills Inc.

ESSEX - Floor coverings–carpet and rugs ☆ - Cumberland Mills Inc.

ESSEX - Food products ☆ - Empire Kosher Poultry Inc.

ESSEX - Furniture - Haworth, Inc.

ESSEX - Glass products - Pittsburgh Corning Corp.

ESSEX - Glassware–household - Anchor Hocking Glass, Inc.

ESSEX - Hardware - National Lock Hardware

ESSEX - House furnishings - Dan River Inc.

ESSEX - Jars–glass - Apothecary Products, Inc.

ESSEX - Lamps - Lamplight Farms, Inc.

ESSEX - Lighting fixtures - Liteway

ESSEX - Luggage - Airway Industries, Inc.

ESSEX - Motor vehicle parts and accessories - Lancaster Colony Automotive Group

ESSEX - Musical instrument accessories ☆ - Willis Music Co.

ESSEX - Nuts–salted, roasted, cooked, or canned - Aster Nut Products Co. Inc.

ESSEX - Occasional furniture - American Furniture Co. Inc.

ESSEX - Occasional furniture ☆ - JDI Group, Inc.

ESSEX - Organs–musical instrument ☆ - Rodgers Instrument Corp.

ESSEX - Paper - Willmann Paper Co., Inc.

ESSEX - Saddles - State Line Tack, Inc.

ESSEX - Ships–sailing vessels - E/Boats

ESSEX - Trailers–travel ☆ - Starcraft Corp.

ESSEX - Wallpaper - Gencorp Polymer Products

ESSEX - Watches - Hampden Corp.

ESSEX, BY DESIGN - Wallcovering - Gencorp Inc.

ESSEX COLLECTION - Housewares - Himark Enterprises Inc.

ESSEX HOUSE - Floor coverings - Mannington Resilient Floors

ESSEX HOUSE - Floor coverings–carpet and rugs - Atlas Carpet Mills Inc.

ESSEX KIDS - Wallpaper - Essex Wallcoveringss

ESSEX MASTERPIECE - Brushes–hair - I. Sekine Co. Inc.

ESSEX NIGHT - Housewares - Himark Enterprises Inc.

☆ = Now out of production

ESSEX SQUARE - Floor coverings - Congoleum Corp.

ESSEX SQUARE - Floor coverings–carpet and rugs - Downs Carpet Co. Inc.

ESSIAC - Food products - Mankind Research Unltd. Inc.

ESSIAX - Health care products - Healthwatchers System

ESSICK - Plaster–wallboard - Mayco Essick

ESSIE COSMETICS - Lipsticks - Essie Cosmetics Ltd.

ESSIX - Dental equipment - Raintree Essix, Inc.

ESSIX & ARS MATERIALS - Dental equipment - Raintree Essix, Inc.

ESSJEE - Shirts - Marble Sportswear, Inc.

ESSKAY - Candy - Koppers Chocolate Specialty Co. Inc.

ESSKAY - Food products - Esskay Inc.

ESSKAY - Office supplies ☆ - S-K Forms Co.

ESSLINGER - Beverages–malt ☆ - Lion Brewery, Inc.

ESSO - Petroleum - Exxon Corp.

ESSTECH - Contact lenses - Chariotstar Inc.

ESSTURE - Shampoos - Redken Laboratories, Inc.

E.S.T. - Beverages–alcohol - Consolidated Distilled Products Inc.

EST - Sporting goods - Estusa Corp.

E.S.T. - Steel springs–railroad - Needlecraft Industries

EST-AID - Vitamins and nutritional supplements - Crystal Star Herbal Nutrition, Inc.

EST-CA - Sporting goods - Estusa Corp.

ESTABLISHMENT - Motor vehicles–motor homes - Thor Industries West

ESTAL - Skin care products - Esta Kronberg

ESTAMPA - Greeting cards - Gibson Greetings, Inc.

ESTANCIA ESTATE - Wines - Franciscan Vineyards, Inc.

ESTANCIA VINEYARDS - Wines ☆ - Franciscan Vineyards, Inc.

ESTAPOL - Paints - Wattyl Paint Corp.

ESTAQUA - Health care products - Kay Pharmacal Co. Inc.

ESTAR - Film - Eastman Kodak Co.

ESTAR - Pharmaceutical preparations - Westwood-Squibb Pharmaceuticals, Inc.

ESTAR-AH - Film - Eastman Kodak Co.

ESTATE - See **LIBRARY**

ESTATE - Bathroom accessories - American Standard Inc.

ESTATE - Bathroom fixtures - Artesian Industries

ESTATE - Bathtubs–enameled ☆ - Lasco Products Group

ESTATE - Bicycles - Columbia Manufacturing Inc.

ESTATE - Cabinets - Superior Woodwork Inc.

ESTATE - Cabinets–wood - Decora

ESTATE - Cabinets–wood ☆ - Kemper

ESTATE - Coffee products - J. Martinez and Co.

ESTATE - Cooking equipment–household ☆ - Mirro Corp.

ESTATE - Cupolas - CW Ohio Inc.

ESTATE - Dining room furniture ☆ - Daystrom Furniture Inc.

ESTATE - Dishes–china - Viletta China Co.

ESTATE - Dishwashers–household - Whirlpool Properties, Inc.

ESTATE - Doors–glass ☆ - Remington Building Products

ESTATE - Drapery hardware - Kirsch Co.

ESTATE - Floor coverings - Ply-Gem Manufacturing Corp.

ESTATE - Floor coverings ☆ - Bruce Hardwood Floors

ESTATE - Floor coverings–carpet and rugs - E.R. Carpenter Co.

ESTATE - Floor coverings–carpet and rugs ☆ - Daltonian Carpet & Cushion Inc.

ESTATE - Furniture ☆ - Cosco, Inc.

ESTATE - Furniture–wood - Design Line Cabinets

ESTATE - Glassware–household - Owens-Illinois Inc. (Libbey Div.)

ESTATE - Heaters–kerosene - Sunbeam-Oster Household Products

ESTATE - Kitchenware–china - H. Wittur & Co.

ESTATE - Mail boxes - Leigh

ESTATE - Motor vehicles - Estate Manufacturing Inc.

ESTATE - Padding–foam ☆ - Foamex LP

ESTATE - Pharmaceutical preparations ☆ - Savage Laboratories Inc.

ESTATE - Recording label - Heath & Associates

ESTATE - Shingles–asphalt or tar ☆ - GS Roofing Products Co.

ESTATE - Storm doors - Cole Sewell Corp.

ESTATE - Wainscotting - Georgia-Pacific Corp.

ESTATE - Wines - Bully Hill Vineyards, Inc.

ESTATE - Wines - Sky Vineyards

ESTATE CABERNET SAUVIGNON - Wines - Trefethen Vineyards Winery Inc.

ESTATE CELLARS BY INGLENOOK - Beverages–alcohol - Canandaigua Wine Co. Inc.

ESTATE CHARDONNAY - Wines - Trefethen Vineyards Winery Inc.

ESTATE CLASSIC - Furniture ☆ - Cosco, Inc.

ESTATE COLLECTION - Furniture ☆ - Mersman Furniture Co.

ESTATE COLLECTION - Giftware - Service Merchandise Co. Inc.

ESTATE COLLECTION - Watches - Bulova Corp.

ESTATE GOLD - Coffee - Coffee Beanery Ltd.

ESTATE GOURMET COFFEE - Coffee - Dine-Mor Foods, Inc.

ESTATE MASTER - File folders - Curt Ramsey

ESTATE MASTER - Garden equipment - Parker Sweeper Co.

ESTATE MERLOT - Wines - Trefethen Vineyards Winery Inc.

ESTATE PFARRKIRCHE - Wines ☆ - H. Schmitt Soehne, Inc.

ESTATE PLANNING ADVISOR - Computer software - Thomson Information Services Inc.

ESTATE PRACTICE SYSTEMS - Computer software - Shepard's/McGraw-Hill Inc.

ESTATE RECIPE - Meat products - Cargill, Inc.

ESTATE RIESLING & GEWURTZRAMINER - Wines ☆ - Kobrand Corp.

ESTATE SELECTIONS - Coffee - Millstone Coffee, Inc.

ESTATE VINEYARD SELECTION - Wines - Chalk Hill Winery

ESTATE WM. BACCALA - Wines ☆ - Estate William Baccala

ESTATEKEEPER - Housewares - Sow Easy Inc.

ESTATES - Furniture - Bean Station Furniture Factory Inc.

ESTATES - Furniture - Drexel Heritage Furnishings, Inc.

ESTATES - Furniture ☆ - Bassett Furniture Industries, Inc.

ESTATES - Furniture ☆ - Hammary Furniture Co. Inc.

ESTATES COLLECTION - Housewares - Dayton Hudson Corp.

ESTATES GROUP - Wines ☆ - Sebastiani Vineyards, Inc.

ESTATURIA - Figurines ☆ - Penco Industries Inc.

ESTE - Modems - Joel Gomez

ESTE - Tableware–china ☆ - Villeroy and Boch Tableware Ltd.

ESTEAM - Steamers–apparel - Jiffy Steamer Co.

ESTEE - Food products - Estee Corp.

ESTEE - Perfumes - Estee Lauder Inc.

ESTEE - Shoes - Shoe Masters Inc.

ESTEE LAUDER - Cosmetics - Estee Lauder Inc.

ESTEE LAUDER PLEASURES - Colognes - Estee Lauder Inc.

ESTEE LAUDER SIGNATURE - Cosmetics - Estee Lauder Inc.

ESTEE LITE - Ice cream ☆ - Estee Corp.

ESTEE TASTE, NUTRITION AND HEALTH - Food products - Estee Corp.

ESTEEM - Automotive parts and accessories - American Suzuki Motor Corp.

ESTEEM - Beverages - Estee Corp.

ESTEEM - Clocks - General Time Corp. (Westclox/Seth Thomas Div.)

ESTEEM - Clothing - Mr. Sid Inc.

ESTEEM - Floor coverings - Congoleum Corp.

ESTEEM - Floor coverings–carpet and rugs - E.R. Carpenter Co.

ESTEEM - Floor coverings–carpet and rugs - Mica Inc.

ESTEEM - Floor coverings–carpet and rugs ☆ - World Carpets, Inc.

ESTEEM - Luggage - Samsonite Corp.

ESTEEM - Motor vehicles–automobiles - Suzuki of America Automotive Corp.

ESTEEM PLUS - Health care products - Esteem Products Ltd.

ESTEK - Semiconductors - Eastman Kodak Co.

ESTELAR - Agricultural products - Morning Star Paso Fino Farm, LLC

ESTELLE - Watches - Bulova Corp.

ESTELLO - Cooking utensils–earthenware - French & Pacific Trading Corp.

ESTER-C - Vitamins and nutritional supplements - Inter-Cal Corp.

ESTER-C MAXITABS - Vitamins and nutritional supplements - Ethical Nutrients

ESTER-CMZ - Vitamins and nutritional supplements - Inter-Cal Corp.

ESTER DROPLETS - Skin care products - Shaklee Corp.

ESTERBROOK - Office supplies - Faber-Castell Corp.

ESTEREL - Glassware–household - Durand International

ESTEREOFONO - Recording label - Musimex Inc.

ESTEREX - Fabrics–polyester - Jelliff Corp.

ESTERLENE - Rope - Tubbs Cordage Co.

ESTERLINE - Clamps–metal - Esterline Technologies Corp.

ESTERLON - Rope - Wall Industries Inc.

ESTEROL - Vitamins and nutritional supplements - Oxycal Laboratories, Inc.

ESTEROLA-C - Vitamins and nutritional supplements - Oxycal Laboratories, Inc.

ESTEROM - Pharmaceutical preparations - Entropin, Inc.

ESTERON - Garden equipment ☆ - Dowelanco

ESTES - Luggage - Samsonite Corp.

ESTES - Toys–models - Estes Industries

ESTETA - Perfumes ☆ - Frances Denney

ESTETICA - Beauty shops - Amekor Industries

ESTETICA - Dryers–hair - Dona-Paul Co.

ESTETICA OF ITALY - Cosmetics - Dona-Paul Co.

ESTEY - Shelving units–metal - Tennsco Corp.

ESTHEDERM - Skin care products - Aesthetic Skin Care Importers Ltd.

ESTHER BONNEY - Skin care products ☆ - Comfort Manufacturing Co.

ESTHER DESIGN - Jewelry - Esther Design Inc.

☆ = Now out of production

ESTHER PRICE - Ice cream - Esther Price Candies Corp.

ESTHER'S - Wines - Shallon Winery

ESTHETIC RESEARCH - Skin care products - Mana Products, Inc.

ESTIK - Hair care products - Cassidy Inc.

ESTILO - Apparel and accessories - Rich & Me, Inc.

ESTIMA - Vitamins and nutritional supplements - Healthline Institute, Inc.

ESTIMATE PLUS - Computer software - PPG Industries, Inc.

ESTIMATOR, THE - Computer software - SourceView Software International

ESTIMEASURE - Games - Dale Seymour Publications, Inc.

ESTINYL - Pharmaceutical preparations - Schering-Plough Healthcare Products

ESTIVIN - Pharmaceutical preparations - Alcon Laboratories, Inc.

ESTO-REX - Pharmaceutical preparations - Rex Research Laboratories

ESTOMASAN - Pharmaceutical preparations - Vartex Pharmaceuticals Inc.

ESTOMPE - Cosmetics - Chanel Inc.

ESTORAL - Pharmaceutical preparations - Andropharm Inc.

ESTORIL - Copper products - Cutlers Owens

ESTORIL - Dinnerware–glass - WMF/USA

ESTORIL - Floor coverings - Mannington Resilient Floors

ESTRA - Floor coverings–carpet and rugs ☆ - Evans-Black Carpet Mills

ESTRA-L - Pharmaceutical preparations - Pasadena Research Laboratories, Inc.

ESTRA-PRO - Veterinary pharmaceutical preparations ☆ - New England Serum Co.

ESTRA-TESTRIN - Pharmaceutical preparations - Pasadena Research Laboratories, Inc.

ESTRACE - Hormone preparations - Bristol-Myers Squibb Co.

ESTRACELL - Sponges - Armaly Sponge Co.

ESTRADERM - Hormone preparations - Ciba-Geigy Corp.

ESTRADURIN - Pharmaceutical preparations - Wyeth-Ayerst Laboratories

ESTRAGUARD - Pharmaceutical preparations ☆ - Solvay Pharmaceuticals Inc.

ESTRALATE - Pharmaceutical preparations ☆ - Wesley Pharmacal Co. Inc.

ESTRALLITA - Floor coverings - Mannington Resilient Floors

ESTRANATE - Pharmaceutical preparations - Physician Sales & Service

ESTRATAB - Pharmaceutical preparations - Solvay Pharmaceuticals Inc.

ESTRATEST - Pharmaceutical preparations - Solvay Pharmaceuticals Inc.

ESTRAVAL - Health care products - Kay Pharmacal Co. Inc.

ESTRELLA - Floor coverings–carpet and rugs ☆ - Alexander Smith Carpets

ESTRELLA - Floor coverings–carpet and rugs ☆ - Stanton Carpet Corp.

ESTRELLA - Food products - Estrella Tortilla Factory & Deli Store

ESTRELLA - Glassware–household ☆ - National Housewares

ESTRELLA - Guitars - European Crafts/USA

ESTRELLA - Wallcoverings - Cork Products Co. Inc.

ESTRELLA DEL MAR - Floor coverings–carpet and rugs - Catalina Carpet Mills Inc.

ESTRELLA RIVER - Wines ☆ - House of Burgundy Inc.

ESTRELLA RIVER WINERY - Wines - Bronco Wine Co.

ESTRELLAS DE LA LITERATURA - Recording label - Harcourt Brace & Co.

ESTRELLITA - Rings–jewelry - Artcarved Inc.

ESTRIE - Floor coverings - Congoleum Corp.

ESTRIN Q.S. - Pharmaceutical preparations ☆ - Pasadena Research Laboratories, Inc.

ESTRO-CYP - Pharmaceutical preparations - Keene Pharmaceuticals Inc.

ESTRO-DEL - Pharmaceutical preparations ☆ - R.A. McNeil Co.

ESTRO FEM - Vitamins and nutritional supplements - Highland Laboratories

ESTRO-MED - Pharmaceutical preparations ☆ - U.S. Pharmaceutical Corp.

ESTRO SPAN - Pharmaceutical preparations - Primedics Laboratories

ESTROATE - Health care products - Kay Pharmacal Co. Inc.

ESTROCARE - Vitamins and nutritional supplements - Pharmanex, Inc.

ESTROFEM - Pharmaceutical preparations - Pasadena Research Laboratories, Inc.

ESTROFOL - Pharmaceutical preparations ☆ - Solvay Pharmaceuticals Inc.

ESTROGATE - Pharmaceutical preparations ☆ - Legere Pharmaceuticals Inc.

ESTROJECT - Pharmaceutical preparations ☆ - Merz Inc.

ESTROL - Health care products - Kay Pharmacal Co. Inc.

ESTROLAN - Pharmaceutical preparations - Lannett Co. Inc.

ESTRON - Yarn - Eastman Kodak Co. (Eastman Chemicals Div.)

ESTRONE-A - Health care products - Kay Pharmacal Co. Inc.

ESTRONEX - Pharmaceutical preparations - Lyphomed Inc.

ESTRONOL - Pharmaceutical preparations ☆ - Central Pharmaceutical Inc.

ESTRONOL-LA - Pharmaceutical preparations ☆ - Central Pharmaceutical Inc.

ESTROSOL - Pharmaceutical preparations ☆ - Wesley Pharmacal Co. Inc.

ESTROVAL-10 - Pharmaceutical preparations - Solvay Pharmaceuticals Inc.

ESTROVIS - Pharmaceutical preparations ☆ - Parke-Davis

ESTRUGEN - Pharmaceutical preparations - Wesley Pharmacal Co. Inc.

ESTRUSCAN SUITE - Lighting fixtures - Angelo Brothers Co.

ESTRUST - Sporting goods - Camp-Cap Products

ESTUS - Plastics ☆ - Estus Export-Import

ESTUS GOURMET - Rice - Estus Gourmet

ESTUSA - Athletic bags, sportswear, etc. - Sportstech Industries Inc.

ESTUSA - Rackets–badminton - Rackets International (Racket Sports Div.)

ESTUSA - Sporting goods - Estusa Corp.

ESTWING - Tools - Estwing Manufacturing Co.

ESTY - Skin care products - Nemectron-Belmont Inc.

ESTY JOY - Chairs–metal - Nemectron-Belmont Inc.

ESW - Computer software - VIASOET

ESW/PC - Computer software - VIASOET

E.T. - Candy ☆ - Topps Co., Inc.

ET - Computer peripheral equipment - Emulation Technology, Inc.

ET - Electronic equipment ☆ - Texas Instruments Inc.

ET - Furniture ☆ - H. Wilson Co.

ET - Pharmaceutical preparations - Alra Laboratories, Inc.

E.T. - Toys–stuffed - Kamar International Inc.

E.T. - Video games - Atari Games Corp.

E.T. - Vitamins and nutritional supplements - Bristol-Myers Squibb Co.

ET-C - Automotive parts and accessories - Dana Corp.

ET CALC - Computer software - Irrigation Management Group

ET CETERA - Floor coverings–carpet and rugs - Trend Carpet

ET CETERA - Furniture - Drexel Heritage Furnishings, Inc.

ET CETERA - Tableware–china - Susquehanna Glass Co.

E.T. COMPLETE FIBERGLASS SYSTEM - Cosmetics - European Touch Co.

ET DRAG - Tires - Max-Trac Tire Co.

E.T. EXCEPTIONAL TEXTILES - Wallpaper - I. Gottlieb & Associates

ET STRANDED - Electronic equipment ☆ - Texas Instruments Inc.

ET TRACKER - Measuring instruments - Rain Master Irrigation Systems, Inc.

ETA - Fabrics - Interface, Inc.

ETA - Furniture - Brooks Furniture Manufacturing Inc.

ETA - Maternity clothing - ETA

ETA - Paints–artists' ☆ - Canson-Talens Inc.

ETACOL - Fabrics - Harodite Finishing Co. Inc.

ETAGE XV - Apparel and accessories - Sherne Lingerie Inc.

ET&F - Washers–metal - Erico Tool & Fasteners, Inc.

ETAP - Ships–sailing vessels - North East Wind Yacht Group

ETBAR - Skin care products ☆ - Cosmetic Firsts Ltd.

ETC - Circuit breakers - Satin American Corp.

ETC. - Cleaning preparations - Tech Spray, Inc.

ETC. - Furniture–children's - Child Craft Industries Inc.

ETC. - Golfing equipment ☆ - John Rouzee Green Co., Inc.

ETC - Metals - Econo Trading Co.

ETC - Modems - At&T Corp.

ETC - Paper–carbon - Kores Nordic USA Corp.

ETC. BY CATO - Jewelry - Cato Corp.

ETC., ETC., ETC. - Advertising agencies - Mail Boxes Etc. USA, Inc.

ETC. PLUS BY CATO - Handbags - Cato Corp.

ETCC - Educational materials - Dynamics Research Corp.

ETCETERA BY J. G. HOOK - Apparel and accessories ☆ - J.G. Hook, Inc.

ETCH-A-SKETCH - Toys - Ohio Art Co.

ETCH-ART - Glassware–household - Gainsborough Product Ltd.

ETCH BATH - Silver compounds - Armour Products

ETCH-IT! - Computer software - Directed Electronics, Inc.

ETCH MARK - Paper - Zoecon Corp.

ETCH-MASK - Stencils - Richards Distributing, Inc.

ETCH-MASTER - Craft supplies - Meistergram Inc.

ETCH-N-BOND - Paints ☆ - Surface Protection Industries, Inc.

ETCHALL - Artists' materials - Etchall Co.

ETCHALL - Chemical preparations - B & B Products, Inc.

ETCHARREST - Dental compounds - Ultradent Products, Inc.

ETCHCRAFT - Greeting cards ☆ - Nu-Art Inc.

ETCHCRAFT - Hobby kits ☆ - Creative Concepts

ETCHED IN STONE - Desk sets - Successories, Inc.

ETCHED IN STONE - Novelty items - Celebrating Excellence, Inc.

ETCHED IN TIME - Watches - Etched in Time Inc.

ETCHEDWOOD - Floor coverings ☆ - Robbins Inc.

ETCHINGS - Floor coverings–carpet and rugs - Burtco Enterprises Inc.

ETCHINGS - Floor coverings–carpet and rugs - Criterion Mills Inc.

ETCHINGS - Floor coverings–carpet and rugs - Mohawk Carpet Corp.

ETCHINGS - Floor coverings–carpet and rugs - Trend Carpet

ETCHINGS - Floor coverings–carpet and rugs ☆ - J and J Industries Inc.

ETCHINGS - Mirrors - Hoyne Industries Inc.

ETCHINGS - Shirts - Tica Industries Inc.

ETCHINGS - Wallcoverings - Pinnacle Wallcoverings

ETCHIPRINTS - Posters - Henry R. Mockel's

ETCHLIGHT - Doors–glass ☆ - Pease Industries, Inc.

☆ = Now out of production

ETCHMASTER - Giftware - Herbert J. Ballon Co.

ETCHO - Stationery ☆ - Superior Marking Equipment Co.

ETCO - Connectors–electrical - Etco Inc.

ETCO2 - Health care products - Criticare Systems Inc.

ETD FOOD MART - Candy - Shell Oil Co.

ETE MOD - Hair care products - Waverly Beauty Products

ETEMP - Air conditioning equipment - Eventemp Corp.

ETEQ - Integrated circuits - ETEQ Microsystems Inc.

ETERNA - Bathroom fixtures - General Marble Co.

ETERNA - Brushes–hair - William Marvy Co., Inc.

ETERNA - Hair care products - Marianna Imports, Inc.

ETERNA - Musical instruments - Getzen Co.

ETERNA - Musical instruments - Yamaha Corp. of America

ETERNA - Recording label ☆ - Lyrichord Discs Inc.

ETERNA - Skin care products - Revlon Consumer Products Corp.

ETERNA 27 - Skin care products - Revlon Consumer Products Corp.

ETERNA II - Musical instruments - Getzen Co.

ETERNA ROSE - Flowers, plants, and seeds - Donald McQueen Moore

ETERNAFLEX - Caulking compounds ☆ - Gibson-Homans Co.

ETERNAGOLD - Bronze products - Obron Atlantic Corp.

ETERNAL - Floor coverings–carpet and rugs ☆ - American Carpet Mills

ETERNAL - Glassware–household ☆ - Lenox Crystal, Inc.

ETERNAL - Rings–jewelry - Artcarved Inc.

ETERNAL - Tableware–china - Lenox, Inc.

ETERNAL - Teas - Satori Fine Herbals

ETERNAL BEAUTY - Skin care products ☆ - Ella Bache Inc.

ETERNAL BLACK - Inks - Faber-Castell Corp.

ETERNAL BLISS - Rings–jewelry - Cana-Nuptial

ETERNAL BLOOM - Chemical preparations - Unifinium Ltd.

ETERNAL BLOSSOMS - Lipsticks - Maybelline Co.

ETERNAL FASHION - Cosmetics - W.E.A.R. Laboratories Inc.

ETERNAL GOLD - Glassware–household - Lenox, Inc.

ETERNAL HEALTH - Vitamins and nutritional supplements - Tishcon Corp.

ETERNAL RHYTHMS - Posters - Group Durrance Photography, Inc.

ETERNAL SOLE - Shoe soles - Runner's Products Inc.

ETERNAL SPRING - Pottery ☆ - Rubens Originals

ETERNAL STAR - Jewelry - Tiara Corp.

ETERNAL TOE - Shoe soles - Runner's Products Inc.

ETERNAL TREASURES - Statuary - Eternal Treasures, Inc.

ETERNAL VOW - Rings–jewelry - Artcarved Inc.

ETERNAL WOMAN, THE - Puzzles - Hasbro, Inc.

ETERNAL YOUTH - Underwear and nightwear - Bestform Foundations, Inc.

ETERNALAMP - Lamp bulbs - Standard Enterprises, Inc.

ETERNALLY - Rings–jewelry - Artcarved Inc.

ETERNALLY YOURS - Jewelry - Sterling Inc.

ETERNALUX - Candles - Candle Corp. of America

ETERNAM - Computer software - Capstone Software

ETERNAWALL - Gypsum products - Georgia-Pacific Corp.

ETERNEAU - Floor coverings–carpet and rugs ☆ - Karastan-Bigelow Inc.

ETERNIA - Toys - Mattel, Inc.

ETERNITE - Water–bottled or canned - P.C. Eternite, Inc.

ETERNITY - Archery equipment - Archer Sports Inc.

ETERNITY - Christmas tree ornaments - Cracker Box Inc.

ETERNITY - Colognes - Calvin Klein Ltd.

ETERNITY - Flatware - Yamazaki Tableware Inc.

ETERNITY - Floor coverings - Aladdin Mills, Inc.

ETERNITY - Floor coverings–carpet and rugs - Alliance Industries Inc.

ETERNITY - Gold products - OroAmerica Inc.

ETERNITY - Housewares - Barth-Dreyfuss of California

ETERNITY - Whirlpools - Kohler Co.

ETERNITY - Windows–storm - Sugarcreek Window & Door Corp.

ETERNITY ACCENTS - Floor coverings–carpet and rugs ☆ - Karastan-Bigelow Inc.

ETERNITY BANGLE - Jewelry - OroAmerica Inc.

ETERNITY GOLD ACCENT - Flatware - Yamazaki Tableware Inc.

ETERNITY INC. - Games ☆ - Mayfair Games, Inc.

ETERNITY, THE - Furnaces - Bard Manufacturing Co.

ETERNO - Pencils ☆ - Dixon Ticonderoga Co.

ETEX - Exterminating products - Etex Ltd.

ETHAFOAM - Insulating materials–foam - Dow Plastics

ETHAMIDE - Pharmaceutical preparations ☆ - Allergan, Inc.

ETHAMOLIN - Pharmaceutical preparations - Reed & Carnrick

ETHAN ALLEN - Furniture - Ethan Allen, Inc.

ETHAN ALLEN - Guns ☆ - Hoppe's

ETHAN ALLEN - Malt beverages - Catamount Brewing Co.

ETHAN ALLEN - Umbrellas - Ethan Allen Finance Corp.

ETHAN ANDREWS - Slacks–men's - Target Licensing Corp.

ETHAN ELEPHANT - Dolls - Mattel, Inc.

ETHAQUIN - Pharmaceutical preparations ☆ - B.F. Ascher & Co. Inc.

ETHATAB - Pharmaceutical preparations - Glaxo Wellcome Inc.

ETHAVEROL-75 - Pharmaceutical preparations ☆ - Pharmex Inc.

ETHAVEX-100 - Pharmaceutical preparations - Econo Med Pharmaceuticals Inc.

ETHEL IDA'S ORIGINAL PECAN TAFFY - Candy - Bedre Nut Co., Inc.

ETHEL M. - Candy - Ethel M. Chocolates, Inc.

ETHERCELL - Computer peripheral equipment - Synoptics Communications, Inc.

ETHERCOM - Computers - Quanta Electro

ETHERCORE - Electronic equipment - NCR Corp.

ETHEREA - Skin care products - Revlon Consumer Products Corp.

ETHERIA - Toys–erector sets - Mattel, Inc.

ETHERLITE - Computer peripheral equipment - Central Data Corp.

ETHERPAC - Circuit boards - Asante Technologies Inc.

ETHERPAGE - Computer software - Personal Productivity Tools Inc.

ETHERPOINT - Computer hardware - Photonics Corp.

ETHERSTACK - Electronic equipment - Whitaker Corp.

ETHERSTREAMER - Computer hardware - International Business Machines Corp.

ETHERSWITCH - Computer peripheral equipment - Kalpana Inc.

ETHERTALK - Computer peripheral equipment - Apple Computer Inc.

ETHERTEST - Computer software - Frontline Test Equipment, Inc.

ETHERTHIN - Computers - Farallon Computing, Inc.

ETHERX - Computer hardware - Kingston Technology Corp.

ETHI GAR - Vitamins and nutritional supplements ☆ - Ethical Nutrients

ETHI-HIST - Prescription drug ☆ - Ion Laboratories Inc.

ETHIBORO - Pharmaceutical preparations ☆ - U.S. Ethicals Inc.

ETHICAL - See BONE BUILDER

ETHICAL - Pet products - Ethical Products Inc.

ETHICAL PHARMACEUTICALS - Pharmaceutical preparations - Ferndale Laboratories, Inc.

ETHICARBON - Pharmaceutical preparations ☆ - U.S. Ethicals Inc.

ETHICOL - Pharmaceutical preparations ☆ - U.S. Ethicals Inc.

ETHICON ENDO-SURGERY - Medical apparatus - Johnson & Johnson

ETHICORT - Pharmaceutical preparations ☆ - U.S. Ethicals Inc.

ETHICS IN ACTION - Video production - Sony Electronics Inc.

ETHIDELTA - Pharmaceutical preparations ☆ - U.S. Ethicals Inc.

ETHILIVER - Pharmaceutical preparations ☆ - U.S. Ethicals Inc.

ETHIMENS - Pharmaceutical preparations - Lanpar Co.

ETHINIQUE SHADES - Sunglasses - Sungold Enterprises Ltd.

ETHIODOL - Pharmaceutical preparations - Savage Laboratories Inc.

ETHIONAMIDE - Pharmaceutical preparations - Wyeth-Ayerst Laboratories

ETHITABS - Vitamins and nutritional supplements ☆ - U.S. Ethicals Inc.

ETHITEK - Pharmaceutical preparations - Ethitek Pharmaceuticals Co.

ETHIVITE - Vitamins and nutritional supplements ☆ - U.S. Ethicals Inc.

ETHNIC - Hair care products - Cornrows & Co.

ETHNIC GOLD - Lotions - Ethnic Gold Corp.

ETHNIC MILWAUKEE SEASONINGS - Seasonings - William T. Penzey

ETHNICWARE - Housewares - Geoffrey G. Macon

ETHNO - Clocks - Wai Kin Ng

ETHNO TECHNO - Recording label - Tee Vee Toons, Inc.

ETHNOGRAPHICS - Greeting cards - Carol A. Weinstock

ETHNOS - Cigarettes - G.A. Georgopulo & Co. Inc.

ETHOBRAL - Pharmaceutical preparations ☆ - Wyeth-Ayerst Laboratories

ETHOCYN - Cosmetics - Chantal Pharmaceutical Corp.

ETHOS - Tableware–china - Pfaltzgraff Investment Co.

ETHOSPACE - Furniture - Herman Miller, Inc.

ETHOX - Medical apparatus - Ethox Corp.

ETHQUINOL - Pharmaceutical preparations ☆ - Ulmer Pharmacal Co.

ETHRIL - Pharmaceutical preparations - Bristol-Myers Squibb Co.

ETHYLENE GLYCOL - Chemical preparations - Consolidated Recycling Co, Inc.

ETHYLEPA 1,000 MG. - Vitamins and nutritional supplements - Vitamin Research Products Inc.

ETI - Computer software - Evolutionary Technologies, Inc.

ETI - Electrical equipment - Electro-Test, Inc.

ETI - Electrical supplies - Fredericks Co.

ETI - Electronics equipment - Educational Technology Inc.

ETI-EXTRACT - Computer software - Evolutionary Technologies, Inc.

ETI SYSTEMS - Valves - ETI Systems, Inc.

ETIDERM - Veterinary pharmaceutical preparations - Virbac, Inc.

ETIENNE - Watches - Webster Watch Co. Associates

ETIENNE AIGNER - Apparel and accessories - Jonathan Logan Inc.

☆ = Now out of production

ETIENNE AIGNER - Apparel and accessories - Phillips-Van Heusen Corp.
ETIENNE AIGNER - Apparel—men's - Swank Inc.
ETIENNE AIGNER - Shoes - Etienne Aigner, Inc.
ETIENNE ALGNIR - Jewelry ☆ - Danecraft, Inc.
ETIENNE BRANA EAUX-DE-VIE - Cordials ☆ - Kobrand Corp.
ETIENNE GILBERT - Wines ☆ - Beauvignot International Inc.
ETINCELLE - Pillows - Etincelle Inc.
ETINNE - Bedding—linen - Dan River Inc.
ETIQUETTE - Furniture ☆ - Bernhardt Industries
ETITAR - Skin care products - Etitar
ETL LISTED - Windows—storm - ETL Testing Laboratories, Inc.
ETM - Thread - Threads USA Div.
ETMS - Computer software - Bear, Stearns & Co. Inc.
ETNA - Automotive parts and accessories - Echlin Inc.
ETNA - Gasoline - Etna Oil Co. Inc.
ETNA - Gasoline - Mobil Oil Corp.
ETNABEX C - Pharmaceutical preparations ☆ - U.S. Ethicals Inc.
ETNABOLATE - Pharmaceutical preparations ☆ - U.S. Ethicals Inc.
ETNACYCLIN - Pharmaceutical preparations ☆ - U.S. Ethicals Inc.
ETNAPA - Pharmaceutical preparations ☆ - U.S. Ethicals Inc.
ETNATOL - Pharmaceutical preparations ☆ - U.S. Ethicals Inc.
ETNAVITE - Pharmaceutical preparations ☆ - U.S. Ethicals Inc.
ETNERGAN V.C. - Pharmaceutical preparations ☆ - U.S. Ethicals Inc.
ETNIKO - Apparel and accessories - Acorn Partners
ETNOFRIL - Pharmaceutical preparations ☆ - U.S. Ethicals Inc.
ETNOLAX - Pharmaceutical preparations ☆ - U.S. Ethicals Inc.
ETOILE - Apparel—women's - R. & A. Collections Inc.
ETOILE - Furniture ☆ - Harden Furniture Co. Inc.
ETOILE - Music—sheet - MMB Music Inc.
ETOILE BACATELLE - Floor coverings - Parquet de France Inc.
L'ETOILE COLLECTION, THE - Lighting fixtures - Marvin Alexander, Inc.
ETOILE MUSIC PRESS - Music—sheet - MMB Music Inc.
ETON - Dishes—china - Sterling China Co. Inc.
ETON - Flatware - Wallace International Silversmiths, Inc.
ETON - Flatware ☆ - Svend Jensen of Denmark Inc.
ETON - Food products - V. & E. Kohnstamm Inc.
ETON - Furniture - Haworth, Inc.
ETON - Glassware—household ☆ - ACC
ETON - Jewelry - Eton Jewelry Manufacturing Corp.
ETON - Pencils - J.L. Hammett Co.
ETON - Watches - Dundee Watch Co.
ETON HARROW - Gin - John Gross & Co.
ETONA - Staplers ☆ - Al Nyman and Son
ETONIC - Shoes - Etonic Inc.
ETONIC ACTIVEWEAR - Apparel—women's - Jacques Moret, Inc.
ETONNE BY SARAH RICHARDS - Apparel—women's - Cato Corp.
ETOPOFOS - Pharmaceutical preparations - Bristol-Myers Squibb Co.
ETOUFFEE - Food products - Tone Brothers, Inc.
ETOX - Monitors—electronic - Mine Safety Appliances Co.
ETOX-DX - Veterinary medical equipment ☆ - Hess & Clark, Inc.
ETR - Recording label - Euro Tec Records
ETRA - Handbags - Etra Handbags Inc.
ETRAC - Chemical preparations - Etrac Inc.
ETRAFON - Pharmaceutical preparations - Schering-Plough Healthcare Products
ETRO - Neckties - Salant/Manhattan Industries
ETRUNK - Two-way radios - Etrunk Systems, Inc.
ETRUSCA - Tiles—ceramic - American Marazzi Tile, Inc.
ETRUSCAN - Dishes—china - Taylor, Smith & Taylor Co.
ETRUSCAN - Rings—jewelry - Artcarved Inc.
ETRUSCAN FRIEZE - Glassware—household ☆ - Ceraglass Inc.
ETRUSCAN WALL - Wallpaper - Blumenthal
ETRUSCAN WALL METALLICA - Wallpaper - Blumenthal
ETS - Pharmaceutical preparations ☆ - Paddock Laboratories Inc.
ETS. D. HEBRARD - Wines - Winesellers Ltd.
ETS PIERRE BONNET - Wines - Maison Jomere Ltd.
ETSC - Diagnostic apparatus - Diagsoft, Inc.
ETTER FRAMBOISE - Beverages—alcohol - Jim Beam Brands Co.
ETTER GRAPPA - Beverages—alcohol - Jim Beam Brands Co.
ETTER KIRSCH - Beverages—alcohol - Jim Beam Brands Co.
ETTER POIRE WILLIAMS - Beverages—alcohol - Jim Beam Brands Co.
ETTER POMME ROYALE - Beverages—alcohol - Jim Beam Brands Co.
ETTORE LABBATE - Olive oil - Made in France
ETTORE SOTTSASS - Flatware - Reed and Barton Corp.
ETU - Computer software - Hearst Corp. (Capital Newspapers)
ETU/400 - Computer software - Andrew Corp.

ETUDE - Clarinets - Ideal Musical Merchandise Co.
ETUDE - Computer software - Gpu Nuclear Corp.
ETUDE - Dishes—china ☆ - WMF/USA
ETUDE - Furniture ☆ - Bassett Furniture Industries, Inc.
ETUNA - Musical instrument accessories ☆ - Scherl & Roth Inc.
ETX-2002 - Motors - Engelhard Corp.
EU-MINT HONEES - Candy - Andre Prost Inc.
EUBANK - Frames—picture - Eubank Frame Inc.
EUCA-RUB - Health care products - Energy Factors
EUCALYPTUS - Cooking utensils—stoneware - Custom Crafts
EUCAPINE - Cold remedies - Lannett Co. Inc.
EUCERIN - Skin care products - Beiersdorf Inc.
EUCERIN PLUS - Skin care products - Beiersdorf Inc.
EUCLID - Ribbons—inked ☆ - Buckeye Business Products Inc.
EUCNTONE STAINS & FINISHES - Varnishes - Davis Paint Co.
EUDAL SR - Pharmaceutical preparations - Forest Pharmaceuticals Inc.
EUDICANE - Pharmaceutical preparations ☆ - Rexall Nutritional Products Inc.
EUDORA - Computer software - Qualcomm Inc.
EUDORA LIGHT - Computer software - Qualcomm Inc.
EUDORA PRO - Computer software - Qualcomm Inc.
EUELL LOVETT - Chocolate syrup ☆ - Novartis Nutrition Corp.
EUFECTIN - Chemical preparations - Novagen, Inc.
EUFORA - Hair care products - Eden Beauty Concepts
EUGA-LEIN - Pharmaceutical preparations ☆ - Bio-Nutritional Products
EUGALAN FORTE - Pharmaceutical preparations - Bio-Nutritional Products
EUGALAN FORTE BIFIDUS - Health care products - Bio-Nutritional Products
EUGALAN TOPER - Health care products - Peterson's Health Products
EUGEL - Pharmaceutical preparations ☆ - Solvay Pharmaceuticals Inc.
EUGENE - Computer software - Daniben Systems, Inc.
EUGENIA DUKAS COLLECTION - Dolls - Effanbee Doll Corp.
EUGENIE - Lamps - Kaadan Ltd.
EUKANUBA - Dog food - Iams Co.
EUKANUBA JUNIOR - Pet food - Iams Co.
EUKANUBA NATURAL - Animal feeds - Iams Co.
EUKANUBA VETERINARY DIETS - Animal feeds - Iams Co.
EULEXIN - Pharmaceutical preparations - Schering-Plough Healthcare Products
EUNECE - Colognes - Fashion Fair Cosmetics
EUNINA - Apparel—women's - Eunina, Inc.
EUNUCH CORPORATION, THE - Paper products - Michael Russell
EUPHONIC SERIES - Amplifiers - Southern Audio Services Inc.
EUPHORIA - Floor coverings—carpet and rugs ☆ - World Carpets, Inc.
EUPHORIA - Greeting cards ☆ - Moderne Card Co. Inc.
EUPHRASIASAN - Health care products ☆ - Bioforce of America Ltd.
EUPHRATES - Crackers - Sunshine/Salerno Inc.
EURA - Whirlpools - Jacuzzi Inc.
EURA-FIL - Mattresses - Somma Mattress Co.
EURA-WOOL - Mattresses - Somma Mattress Co.
EURADA - Automotive parts and accessories ☆ - Peterson Manufacturing Co.
EUREKA - Beverages—malt - Los Angeles Brewing
EUREKA - Boats - Glen-L Marine Designs
EUREKA - Books—blank - Eureka Blank Book Co.
EUREKA - Computer software - Gamco Industries Inc.
EUREKA - Electronic equipment - Frank W. Morse Co.
EUREKA - Floor coverings—carpet and rugs - Cabin Crafts Carpets
EUREKA - Floor coverings—carpet and rugs ☆ - Len Dal Carpets
EUREKA - Food products - Eureka Fisheries
EUREKA! - Machinery - Dry-Tab Package Sealer Co.
EUREKA - Musical instruments - Fred Gretsch Enterprises
EUREKA - Novelty items—paper - Paper Magic Group Inc.
EUREKA - Paper products - Paper Magic Group, Inc.
EUREKA - Post hole diggers—hand-operated - Seymour Manufacturing Co.,Inc.
EUREKA - Tents - Johnson Camping Inc.
EUREKA! - Tents - Johnson Worldwide Associates, Inc.
EUREKA - Vacuum cleaners and accessories - The Eureka Co.
EUREKA - Vegetables—canned ☆ - Lakeside Packing Co.
EUREKA - Wallpaper - Cavalier Handprints Ltd.
EUREKA - Water—bottled or canned - Eureka Water Co.
EUREKA - Wood products - Eureka Manufacturing Co.
EUREKA 1881 - Beverages—malt - Jones Brewing Co.
EUREKA BLACK & TAN - Benches—plastic - Jones Brewing Co.
EUREKA EXPRESS - Vacuum cleaners and accessories - The Eureka Co.
EUREKA GALVANITE - Paints - Graham Paint and Varnish Co.
EUREKA GOLD LAGER - Beverages—malt - Jones Brewing Co.
EUREKA GOLD LIGHT LAGER - Beverages—malt - Jones Brewing Co.

☆ = Now out of production

EUREKA IMPERIAL - Vacuum cleaners and accessories - White Consolidated Industries, Inc.

EUREKA KARAT - Rope - Columbian Rope Co.

EUREKA MIL-WHITE - Paints - Graham Paint and Varnish Co.

EUREKA MUSIC - Recording label - Eureka Music, Inc.

EUREKA RED IRISH AMBER - Beverages—malt - Jones Brewing Co.

EUREKA SHOP BOSS - Vacuum cleaners and accessories—commercial - White Consolidated Industries, Inc.

EUREKA: THE SOLVER - Computer software - Borland International, Inc.

EUREKA TREASURE CHEST - Children's book series - McDougal, Littell & Co.

EUREKA UNICORN - Toys—stuffed ☆ - Dakin Inc.

EURFORMA - Mattresses - Somma Mattress Co.

EURION - Hearing aids - United Hearing Systems Inc.

EURITA - Kitchen utensils—aluminum - Reston Lloyd Ltd.

EURO - Automotive parts and accessories - Lancaster Colony Automotive Group

EURO - Brushes—paint - Imperial Paint Applicators Ltd.

EURO - Cabinets - Del Mar Cabinets

EURO - Coffee - Euro

EURO - Combs - Spornette International, Inc.

EURO - Health care products - Tubular Fabricators Industry, Inc.

EURO - Office supplies - Da-Lite Screen Co. Inc.

EURO - Socks ☆ - Moretz Hosiery Mills Inc.

EURO - Watches - Helbros International

EURO 6 - Cabinets - KraftMaid Cabinetry Inc.

EURO AIRE - Dryers—hair - Windmere Corp.

EURO AMERICAN - Pastries - L. Karp & Sons, Inc.

EURO-BAGS - Bags - Stephen Lawrence Co.

EURO BATH - Bathroom accessories - Selfix, Inc.

EURO BLOCK - Floor coverings - American Floor Products Co. Inc.

EURO/BREW - Coffee makers—electric ☆ - Robert Krups North America

EURO-BRICK - Tools—masonry - Anita Scherping

EURO BRIEF - Bathing suits - Authentic Fitness Corp.

EURO-CARD - Games ☆ - Wff'n Proof Learning Games Associates

EURO-CHEKS - Games - Asgard Enterprises

EURO-CLIP - Frames—picture - Structural Industries

EURO COLLECTIONS - Cosmetics - Eurostar Corp.

EURO CRIB - Cribs—metal - Cosco, Inc.

EURO-CUT - Tools—machine - National Steel Rule Co.

EURO DESIGN COLLECTIONS - Colognes - Tristar Corp.

EURO DIAL - Giftware - Pollenex Corp.

EURO-ESPRESSO BLEND - Coffee - Coffee Masters, Inc.

EURO FIBER - Vitamins and nutritional supplements - Desert Health Products, Inc.

EURO-FLEX - Shoes - Beacon Shoe Co.

EURO FOAM - Polishing cloths - Lake Country Manufacturing, Inc.

EURO-FOLD I - Tables—wood - Stacor Corp.

EURO GARDEN COLLECTIONS - Colognes - Tristar Corp.

EURO GLAZE - Chemical preparations - European Coatings, Inc.

EURO-GLAZE - Putties - Fibre Glass-Evercoat Co. Inc.

EURO HAIR - Hairpieces, etc. - International Hairgoods Inc.

EURO HEALTH - Cookies - Grandma Kahn's

EURO I - Furniture - Triangle Pacific Corp. (Cabinet Division)

EURO JUICE - Fruit juices - Business Consulting Group Inc.

EURO LINEA - Apparel and accessories - CMT Enterprises, Inc.

EURO-PACK - Plastics - James Desiderio, Inc.

EURO PALM - Furniture - European Touch, Ltd. II

EURO-PENN - Pet products - Penn-Plax, Inc.

EURO POINTS - Hairpiece tape - International Hairgoods Inc.

EURO POWER - Dryers—hair - Conair Corp.

EURO PREP - Shoes and handbags - Ramerica International Inc.

EURO-RING - Jewelry - American Foreign Trade Inc.

EURO SHARP - Cutlery - Washington Forge Inc.

EURO-SNAP - Frames—picture - Structural Industries

EURO-SOFT - Putties - Fibre Glass-Evercoat Co. Inc.

EURO SPAN - Mattresses - Paramount Industrial Companies Inc.

EURO SPORT - Dryers—hair - Windmere Corp.

EURO SPORT - Ophthalmic goods - Foremost Optical Products

EURO SPORTS - Health care products - Euro-Care Products & Services Co.

EURO STARS - Trading cards and stamps - Upper Deck Co.

EURO-TANK - Pet products - Penn-Plax, Inc.

EURO-TANK - Tanks—gas - Euro Tank and Ecosafe Systems, Inc.

EURO-TECH - Automotive parts and accessories - Dick Cepek, Inc.

EURO-TECH - Furniture ☆ - Halstead International

EURO-TECH - Housewares - Royal Cathay Trading Co.

EURO TECH - Soccer equipment - Franklin Sports, Inc.

EURO TEEZER - Combs - Judit Ford

EURO-VENETIAN - Candles - Candle Corp. of America

EURO-VENT - Ventilation equipment - Transpec Inc.

EURO-WAX - Automobile wax - Encino Center Car Wash Inc.

EURO-WIRE - Jewelry - Peter Brams Designs, Ltd.

EURO-X - Apparel—women's - X.E.S./NY Ltd.

EUROBAHN - Automotive parts and accessories - Optronics Inc.

EUROBAKE - Ovens—convection - Lucks Co.

EUROBATH - Soap - Sani-Fresh International Inc.

EUROBED - Furniture - Sico Inc.

EUROBENCH - Furniture - Tennessee Hardwood Co.

EUROBROWN - Lenses—optical - Transitions Optical, Inc.

EUROBUTT - Hinges - Eurobutt Systems, Inc.

EUROC - Knives ☆ - Selfix, Inc.

EUROCALM - Vitamins and nutritional supplements - Solaray

EUROCASE - Attache cases - Samsonite Corp.

EUROCASE - Cabinets - Fleetwood Furniture Co.

EUROCELL - Antennas - Scala Electronic Corp.

EUROCERAM - Dishes—china - Mikasa Co.

EUROCHASSE - Apparel—athletic - Hafez & Hafez Co., Inc.

EUROCHEF - Cooking equipment—household ☆ - Mirro Corp.

EUROCLASS - Automotive parts and accessories - Stant Corp.

EUROCLOSET - Furniture - Eurodesign Ltd.

EUROCOACH - Motor vehicles—motor homes - Champion Enterprises Inc.

EUROCOAT - Paints - Bega/US, Inc.

EUROCOLORS - Toilet seats ☆ - Bemis Manufacturing Co.

EUROCRAFT - Cutlery - J.A. Henckels Zwillingswerk Inc.

EURODATA - Computer software - Personal Programs

EURODOWN - Pillows - Pacific Coast Feather Co.

EUROFEATHER - Pillows - Pacific Coast Feather Co.

EUROFILL - Pillows - Pacific Coast Feather Co.

EUROFLAIR - Floor coverings - Aladdin Mills, Inc.

EUROFLAIR - Washing machines—household - White Consolidated Industries, Inc.

EUROFLEX - Floor coverings—carpet and rugs - Harbinger Co.

EUROFLEX - Office furniture—plastic - Nina Enterprises, Inc.

EUROFLEX - Razors—electric - Wahl Clipper Corp.

EUROFLEX - Watchbands—base metal - Hirsch Speidel Inc.

EUROFOME - Hair care products - Bonat Inc.

EUROFORM - Footwear - Morse Shoe, Inc.

EUROFRAME - Bulletin boards—cork - Davson Inc.

EUROFRESH - Fruits and vegetables - Eurofresh Ltd.

EUROFROST - Furniture - Triangle Pacific Corp. (Cabinet Division)

EUROGELLE - Hair care products - Bonat Inc.

EUROGLO - Watches - Jean Carel Co.

EUROKLAR - Skin care products - Bonat Inc.

EUROKRAFT - Hand, platform, shop, and shelf trucks and stock carts - C and H Distributors Inc.

EUROKURL - Hair care products - Bonat Inc.

EUROLINE - Furniture ☆ - Lexington Furniture Industries, Inc.

EUROLINE - Health care products - Melard Manufacturing Corp.

EUROLINE - Wood products ☆ - Penn Wood Products, Inc.

EUROLINE/CONTEMPO - Wood products ☆ - Penn Wood Products, Inc.

EUROLINE EXCLUSIVE - Ophthalmic goods - Rozin Optical Export Corp.

EUROLUCE - Lamps - Grandrich Corp.

EUROLUXE - Lighting fixtures - Hubbell Lighting, Inc. (Lighting Div.)

EUROMA 10 - American International Industries

EUROMARK - Guns - Weatherby Inc.

EUROMATE - Furniture - V.T. Industries

EUROMATES - Cases—vanity - Paris Presents Ltd.

EUROMAX - Tires - Trillium Group

EUROMIST - Cosmetics ☆ - Delta Industries International, Inc.

EUROMODA - Footwear - Aztec Imports Inc.

EUROMOULD - Moldings and trim - Barber & Ross Co.

EUROMOUND - Cabinets - Worth Products Inc.

EUROPA - Barrettes - Fantasia Accessories Ltd.

EUROPA - Baskets—wood ☆ - Royal Cathay Trading Co.

EUROPA - Bicycles - Ross Bicycles USA, Ltd.

EUROPA - Blinds—venetian ☆ - Hunter Douglas, Inc.

EUROPA - Brushes - Corona Brushes Inc.

EUROPA - Cabinets - Trendlines Inc.

EUROPA - Coffee - Excellent Coffee Co. Inc.

EUROPA - Computer peripheral equipment - Fraser's Hill Ltd.

EUROPA - Doors—vinyl ☆ - Panelfold Inc.

EUROPA - Fabrics—tapestry - Europa Co.

EUROPA - Faucets - Kohler Co.
EUROPA - Floor coverings - Mannington Resilient Floors
EUROPA - Floor coverings–carpet and rugs ☆ - Lees Carpets
EUROPA - Floor coverings–tile ☆ - Halstead International
EUROPA - Footwear–women's ☆ - World Import Co. Inc.
EUROPA - Furniture - Dinaire Corp.
EUROPA - Furniture - Haworth, Inc.
EUROPA - Furniture - Thomasville Furniture Industries Inc.
EUROPA - Furniture ☆ - Bassett Furniture Industries, Inc.
EUROPA - Games - Game Designers' Workshop, Inc.
EUROPA - Glass products ☆ - Baum Bros. Imports Inc.
EUROPA - Glassware–household ☆ - Oneida Ltd.
EUROPA - Guitars - Alembic Inc.
EUROPA - Lighting fixtures ☆ - Roxter Lighting
EUROPA - Luggage - Airway Industries, Inc.
EUROPA - Recording label - Fiesta Record Co. Inc.
EUROPA - Sunglasses - Europa Eyewear Corp.
EUROPA - Tiles–ceramic - Latco Products
EUROPA - Tiles–ceramic - Los Angeles Tile Co., Inc.
EUROPA - Wallpaper - Durawall Inc.
EUROPA - Wallpaper - Koroseal Wallcoverings
EUROPA 2000 - Coffee tables - Bruce Loder Designs
EUROPA CANDY DROPS - Tiles–ceramic - Latco Products
EUROPA CANDY STICKS - Tiles–ceramic - Latco Products
EUROPA COIN - Tiles–ceramic ☆ - Latco Products
EUROPA HARLEQUINS - Tiles–ceramic - Latco Products
EUROPA SPECIAL - Motor vehicles–automobiles - Lotus/Cars USA Inc.
EUROPA-TOTE - Plastic shopping/tote bag ☆ - Continental Extrusion Corp.
EUROPAD - Office supplies - Artistic Office Products
EUROPANEL - Hardware - Runtal North America Inc.
EUROPE ABLAZE - Computer software ☆ - Electronic Arts Inc.
EUROPE-AMERICA & THE WORLD - Infant product - European Toy Collection/Crocodile Creek
EUROPEAN - Cosmetics - European Cosmetics Inc.
EUROPEAN AMERICAN - Apparel and accessories - European American, Inc.
EUROPEAN BEACH TOLEDOHH! - Apparel - Ethy A. Toledo, Inc.
EUROPEAN BLEND - Coffee - Equal Exchange Inc.
EUROPEAN BODY - Depilatories - Lois Yee Cosmetics Inc.
EUROPEAN CHOICE - Chocolate candy - Grace Cocoa Associates, L.P.
EUROPEAN CLASSIC - Furniture ☆ - Broyhill Furniture Industries, Inc.
EUROPEAN CLASSICS - Cookies - Allied Marketing, Inc.
EUROPEAN COATINGS - Coatings - European Coatings, Inc.
EUROPEAN COFFEEHOUSE COLLECTION - Coffee makers–electric - Kraft General Foods, Inc.
EUROPEAN COFFEEHOUSE COLLECTION - Containers - Kraft Foods, Inc.
EUROPEAN COLLAGEN COMPLEX - Skin care products - Revlon Consumer Products Corp.
EUROPEAN COLLECTION - Fabrics - Interials Inc.
EUROPEAN COLLECTION - Hair curlers - Helen of Troy Corp.
EUROPEAN CONNECTION - Furniture - Hickory Chair Co.
EUROPEAN CONNECTION - Wallpaper ☆ - Wolf-Gordon Inc.
EUROPEAN CONNECTION VII - Wallpaper ☆ - Wolf-Gordon Inc.
EUROPEAN COUNTRY CLASSICS - Bakery products - Rich Products Corp.
EUROPEAN DELUXE - Coffee - Harvel Corp.
EUROPEAN DESIGNER - Perfumes - Cosmair Inc.
EUROPEAN EDITIONS - Adhesives and sealants - Formica Corp.
EUROPEAN ELEGANCE - Wallpaper - Maharam Vertical Surfaces
EUROPEAN FASHION - Underwear and nightwear - LCA Intimates
EUROPEAN GOLD XL ULTRA RICH - Skin care products - Creative Laboratories Inc.
EUROPEAN HEARTH - Bakery products - Gai's Seattle French Baking Co., Inc.
EUROPEAN HERITAGE COLLECTION - Kitchen utensils–enameled ☆ - Revere Ware Corp.
EUROPEAN INTERPRETATIONS - Furniture - Harden Furniture Co. Inc.
EUROPEAN LADY - Cooking equipment–household ☆ - West Bend Co.
EUROPEAN LEAD - LEATHER - Pet products - Hamilton Products Inc.
EUROPEAN LUXURY - Floor coverings–carpet and rugs ☆ - Calladium & Marglen
EUROPEAN MASTERPIECE - Furniture - White Furniture Co.
EUROPEAN MYSTIQUE - Hair care products - Dena Corp.
EUROPEAN NATURALS - Hair care products - Alberto-Culver Co.
EUROPEAN PROFILE - Floor coverings ☆ - Congoleum Corp.
EUROPEAN RACERS - Toys - Revell-Monogram, Inc.
EUROPEAN ROAST - Coffee - Nestle Beverage Co.
EUROPEAN ROASTERIE INC - Coffee - European Roasterie, Inc.

EUROPEAN ROYALTY - Jams and jellies - Gourmet Award Foods
EUROPEAN SECRET - Nail care products - Windmere Corp.
EUROPEAN SECRETS - Nail care products - American International Industries
EUROPEAN SPA - Skin care products - Barth's Nutra Products
EUROPEAN SPORTS CAR - Toys–automobiles - Kingsbury Mini Motors of America Inc.
EUROPEAN SPORTS ROADSTER - Toys–electronic - Bird Bromiticous Inc.
EUROPEAN STYLE - Chocolate milk - Nestle Beverage Co.
EUROPEAN TRADITION - Salad dressings–bottled - Gourmet Classic Inc.
EUROPEAN TRADITIONS - Dining room furniture ☆ - Lexington Furniture Industries, Inc.
EUROPEAN WALL DECOR - Posters - Fabulous Forgeries Ltd.
EUROPEAN WAY - Cosmetics ☆ - Duart Industries Ltd.
EUROPEENNE DE CONDIMENT - Mustard - Gilway Co. Ltd.
EUROPEN - Pens - Marketex Corp.
EUROPET USA - Pet products - Aqua Stock/Petcetera Inc.
EUROPHONE, THE - Skin care products - American Communication Technology
EUROPI'S - Shoes - Willits Footwear Worldwide, Inc.
EUROPONIC - Plant growth kits - Superior Growers Supply, Inc.
EUROPREP - Footwear–athletic ☆ - E.S. Originals, Inc.
EUROPRO - Skin care products - Salon Designs Products
EUROPURE - Skin care products - Puretek Corp.
EUROPVIN - Wines - Prestige Wine Corp.
EURORAILS - Games - Mayfair Games, Inc.
EUROROMAN - Computer software - Philip B. Payne and Nancy C. Payne
EUROS COLLECTION - Bathroom fixtures - Showerlux USA
EUROSCRIPT - Computer software - Payne Loving Trust
EUROSHELF - Shelving units - Clairson International Corp.
EUROSILK - Flowers–artificial - European Imports of California Inc.
EUROSLAVIC - Computer software - Philip B. Payne and Nancy C. Payne
EURO*SPEL - Flowers, plants, and seeds - Equiflor Corp.
EUROSPORT - Automotive parts and accessories ☆ - Lancaster Colony Automotive Group
EUROSPORT - Bicycles - Ross Bicycles USA, Ltd.
EUROSPORT - Motor homes and travel trailers - Gulf Stream Coach Inc.
EUROSPRITZ - Hair care products - Bonat Inc.
EURO'SSAGE - Massage products - Baja Products, Ltd.
EUROSTAR USA - Machinery - Elmer N. Strauss
EUROSTEAK - Meat products–beef - M & M Provisions Inc.
EUROSTONE - Paving materials–stone - Fergus Concrete Products Co., Inc.
EUROSTYLE - Frames–eyeglass - Hudson Optical Corp.
EUROSTYLE - Wallpaper ☆ - Marburg Wallcoverings Inc.
EUROSTYLE - Wallpaper ☆ - Winfield Design Associates, Inc.
EUROSTYLE COLLECTION - Cutting boards ☆ - Vermillion Inc.
EUROSTYLERS - Brushes - American Greetings Corp.
EUROSUEDE - Fabrics - Burlington Industries, Inc.
EUROSUEDE - Fabrics–tapestry - Guilford Mills, Inc.
EUROSUPREME - Yarn - Amital Spinning Corp.
EUROSYSTEM - Pens ☆ - Newell Office Products
EUROSYSTEME - Bathtubs–enameled - Regina Co.
EUROTAN - Building materials - Southwest Recreational Industries, Inc.
EUROTAN - Sunblocks - Eurotan International
EUROTEC - Furniture - Thomasville Furniture Industries Inc.
EUROTEC NUTRITION - Animal feed supplements - Eurotec of America, Inc.
EUROTECH - Floor coverings–carpet and rugs ☆ - Kelly Group Inc.
EUROTECH - Tools–hand-operated - First National Bank of Boston
EUROTECH - Watches - Uti Time Corp.
EUROTEK FINISHES - Paints - Eurotek Finishes, Inc.
EUROTEST - Electronic equipment - Eurotest Environmental Technology, Ltd.
EUROTINTER - Dispensers - Fluid Management
EUROTOUCH - Women's intimate apparel - Ithaca Industries Inc.
EUROTOUR - Bicycles - Ross Bicycles USA, Ltd.
EUROTRANS - Motor vehicles - Metrotrans Corp.
EUROTREND - Bicycles - Ross Bicycles USA, Ltd.
EUROTRENDS - Fabrics - Dan River Inc.
EUROVAR - Varnishes - Earl Campbell Manufacturing Co., Inc.
EUROVEIL - Window shades - Mecho Shade Corp.
EUROVELOUR - Floor coverings–carpet and rugs ☆ - Mohawk Industries Inc.
EUROVIEW - Glass products - Heights Glass & Mirror Co.
EUROVITAL - Vitamins and nutritional supplements - Royal Medical Group Ltd.
EUROWALL - Wallpaper ☆ - Blumenthal
EUROWAV - Hair care products - Bonat Inc.
EUROWAY - Trailers–travel - Fleetwood Enterprises, Inc.
EUROWOOD - Floor coverings - Congoleum Corp.
EUROWOOD - Kitchen utensils–aluminum - Global/Guzzini

☆ = Now out of production

EUROWOODS - Furniture - Michigan Tube Swagers and Fabricators, Inc.
EURY - Toys - Eury International Inc.
EUSCOCLENZ - Soap ☆ - Evsco Pharmaceuticals
EUSCOCLENZ 4 - Veterinary pharmaceutical preparations ☆ - Evsco Pharmaceuticals
EUSYNTH - Computer software - Euphonics
EUTECDUR - Coating - Eutectic Corp.
EUTHROID - Pharmaceutical preparations ☆ - Parke-Davis
EUTHYROID - Thyroid preparations - Warner-Lambert Co.
EUTONYL - Pharmaceutical preparations - Abbott Laboratories
EUTRON - Pharmaceutical preparations - Abbott Laboratories
EV-4 - Violins - T.F. Barrett Co.
EV-5 - Violins - T.F. Barrett Co.
EV DISC LOCK - Cables–steel - Kryptonite Corp.
EV FORK LOCK - Cables–steel - Kryptonite Corp.
EV GAME - Audio equipment - Russell Industries Inc.
EV-I - Electrical equipment - General Electric Co.
EV-I-DENT - Labels–paper - Ten-Eight Products, Inc.
EV III - Shoes - Ennesi Shoe Co. Inc.
EV-JETSETTER - Lasers - Konica Imaging U.S.A., Inc.
EV-N-SPRED - Fertilizers - Earthway Products Inc.
EV PARTS - Machine parts - Kimball Physics, Inc.
EV PRODUCTS - Scientific apparatus - II-VI Inc.
EV/TAPCO - Amplifiers ☆ - Electro-Voice, Inc.
EV WARRIOR - Bicycles - Electric Bicycle Co.
EV4 - Gastroscopes - Pathway Bellows, Inc.
EVA - Film - Favorite Plastics Corp.
EVA - Skin care products - Eva T. Friederichs
EVA - Wigs ☆ - Jean Paree Weegs Inc.
EVA-BLITZ - Tripods, photographic flash units ☆ - Saul Bower Inc.
EVA GABOR - Wigs - Eva Gabor International, Ltd.
EVA GABOR INTERNATIONAL - Wigs - Eva Gabor International, Ltd.
EVA JOIA GITANO - Apparel stores–sports - E.J. Gitano Inc.
EVA MARINE - Photographic equipment - R.T.S. Inc.
EVA-PRESS - Electronic equipment - Evatype
EVABRITE - Mirrors - Precision Bache Glass
EVAC - Pharmaceutical preparations - Physician Sales & Service
EVAC-Q-SERTS - Medical apparatus - NMC Laboratories Inc.
EVAC-U-GEN - Pharmaceutical preparations - Walker Corp. & Co. Inc.
EVAC-U-LAX - Pharmaceutical preparations - Roberts/Hauck Pharmaceuticals Inc.
EVAC-U-TRAP - Dental equipment - Pinnacle Products Inc.
EVACU-TRAC - Medical apparatus - Garaventa Ltd.
EVACUATOR - Alarm systems ☆ - Warn Industries, Inc.
EVACUCIL - Vitamins and nutritional supplements - Tishcon Corp.
EVACULAX - Laxatives - Tishcon Corp.
EVACUPAC - Refrigeration equipment - American Standard Inc.
EVADE - Deodorants–personal - Camp-Cap Products
EVADE - Pesticides–household - Platte Chemical Co.
EVADIN - Electronic equipment - Aiko Corp.
EVAGEN - Pharmaceutical preparations ☆ - Hyrex Pharmaceuticals
EVALAST - Mirrors - Precision Bache Glass
EVALOSE - Laxatives - Copley Pharmaceutical, Inc.
EVALUATOR - Electronics equipment - RTI Research Technology International
EVALUATOR - Medical apparatus - Del Mar Avionics
EVALUSITE - Chemicals - Eastman Kodak Co.
EVAN CHAIN COLLECTION - Jewelry - Mercury Products Corp.
EVAN DAVIES - Apparel and accessories - May Department Stores Co.
EVAN-PICONE - Apparel and accessories - Crystal Brands Inc.
EVAN-PICONE - Apparel–women's - Evan-Picone Inc.
EVAN-PICONE - Frames–eyeglass - Creative Optiks
EVAN PICONE - Neckties - Randa Corp.
EVAN PICONE - Shoes - Marx & Newman Co. Inc.
EVAN PICONE PETITES - Apparel–women's - Evan-Picone Inc.
EVAN-PICONE SPORT - Apparel and accessories - Plaid Holdings Corp.
EVAN WILLIAMS - Liquors - Heaven Hill Distilleries, Inc.
EV&EL - Handbags - Evandel Corp.
EVANESCE - Vitamins and nutritional supplements - Bioenergy Nutrient's Inc.
EVANGELINE - Colognes - Leon Hirsh & Son
EVANGELINE - Food products - Vlasic Foods Inc.
EVANGERS - Dog food - Evanger's Dog & Cat Food Co.
EVANS - Bakery products - Evans Bakery Inc.
EVANS - Food products - E.B. Evans
EVANS - Food products - Evans Packing Co.
EVANS - Food products - Trinidad/Benham Holding Co.
EVANS - Footwear–men's - L.B. Evans' Son Co.

EVANS - Furs–pelts - Evans Inc.
EVANS - Lighters–cigarette - Evans Case Co.
EVANS - Musical instruments - Evans CAD-CAM Drumheads
EVANS - Popcorn - Hopewell Enterprises
EVANS - Tape measures ☆ - L.S. Starrett Co. Inc. (Consumer Products Div.)
EVANS - Watches ☆ - Sun Coast Merchandise Corp.
EVANS-BLACK - Floor coverings–carpet and rugs - Evans-Black Carpet Mills
EVANS DESIGNS - Figurines - Evans Designs/California
EVANS EYELITERS - Ophthalmic goods - Evans Case Co.
EVANS FITS-ALL - Ophthalmic goods - Evans Case Co.
EVANS STUDIO - Giftware - N.S. Gustin Co.
EVANS SUNLITERS - Ophthalmic goods - Evans Case Co.
EVANSTON - Occasional tables - JDI Group, Inc.
EVANSTON - Paper–bond ☆ - Lincoln Paper Co.
EVANSTON, THE - Beds–wood - Evans Manufacturing
EVAPOMIST - Humidifiers - Field Controls Co.
EVASHIN WOOD - Window coverings - Evashin Wood U.S. Co.
EVASION - Fragrance - Bourjois Ltd.
EVASIVE ACTION - Computer software - Software Toolworks, Inc.
EVAY HAIR CARE PRODUCTS - Hair care products - Evay Cosmetics Lab, Inc.
EVC - Vitamins and nutritional supplements - Enervite Corp.
EVCO - Motor vehicles–ambulances - Emergency Vehicle Corp. of Ohio
EVCO - Office supplies - Evans & Convery Inc.
EVE - Cigarettes - Liggett Group Inc.
EVE - Footwear–women's - Samuels Shoe Co.
EVE - Glassware–household - Lenox, Inc.
EVE - Jewelry - Eve J. Alfille, Ltd.
EVE - Skin care products - Bonat Inc.
EVE - Wigs - Paula Young
EVE-A-NEEN - Pharmaceutical preparations - G.O. Spanner Inc.
EVE ALFILLE - Jewelry - Eve J. Alfille, Ltd.
EVE CARRIE - Apparel–women's - Jean Gancarcik
EVE LIGHTS - Cigarettes - Eve Holdings Inc.
EVE LIGHTS - Cigarettes - Liggett Group Inc.
EVE-N-FIX - Fingernail reconstruction products - International Beauty Design, Inc.
EVE-N-TIPS - Fingernail reconstruction products - International Beauty Design, Inc.
EVE OF MILADY - Gowns - Eve of Milady Inc.
EVE SLIM LIGHTS - See EVE ULTRA LIGHTS
EVE ULTRA LIGHTS - Cigarettes - Liggett Group Inc.
EVEL KNIEVEL - Games ☆ - CBS Toys
E.V.E.L.T. - Wines - Tempo Imports Ltd.
EVELYN - Boats–canoes - Formula Yachts
EVELYN - Skin care products - Crabtree & Evelyn, Ltd.
EVELYN WOOD DYNAMIC READER - Computer software - Timeworks International Inc.
EVEN-BAKE - Pans - Wilton Industries, Inc.
EVEN FLOW - Hoses - Colorite Plastic Co.
EVEN HEAT - Hair care products - Helene Curtis Industries Inc.
EVEN SO. BAKING CO. - Breads–mixes - Even So Baking Co.
EVEN SONG - Mushrooms - Emil Lerch Inc.
EVEN TIDE - Mushrooms - Emil Lerch Inc.
EVEN TONES - Cosmetics - IL-Makiage
EVEN TOUGH GUYS DO DISHES - Sponges - Innovative Homeware Concepts, Inc.
EVEN-UP - Searchlights ☆ - Cowman-Campbell Paint Co.
EVENAIR - Ventilation equipment - Field Controls Co.
EVENALL - Hair care products - Waverly Beauty Products
EVENFLO - Backpacks - Lisco, Inc.
EVENFLO - Infant product - Evenflo Co.
EVENFLO 7 - Infant product - Evenflo Co.
EVENFLO BABY CARE - Strollers–baby - Evenflo Co.
EVENFLO INFINITE INNERSPRING - Mattresses - Evenflo Juvenile Furniture Co.
EVENFLOW - Pet products - Rolf C. Hagen (USA) Corp.
EVENIN' STAR - Apparel and accessories - Dancin' Cowboy Inc.
EVENING BREEZE - Rings–jewelry - Artcarved Inc.
EVENING ELEGANCE - Dolls - Mattel, Inc.
EVENING ENCHANTMENT - Dolls - Mattel, Inc.
EVENING EXTRAVAGANZA - Dolls - Mattel, Inc.
EVENING FANTASY - Bedding–linen - Dan River Inc.
EVENING FLAME - Dolls - Mattel, Inc.
EVENING GARDEN - Perfumes - Container Store, Inc.
EVENING GLORY - Apparel and accessories - Bonwit Teller & Co.

EVENING GROSBEAK - Christmas tree ornaments - Cracker Box Inc.
EVENING IN PARIS - Women's toiletries - Bourjois Ltd.
EVENING IN YBOR - Colognes ☆ - Old 97 Co.
EVENING MIST - Flatware ☆ - Wallace International Silversmiths, Inc.
EVENING MIST - Floor coverings—carpet and rugs ☆ - World Carpets, Inc.
EVENING MIST - Floor coverings—carpet and rugs ☆ - Zenith Carpets
EVENING MUSK - Perfumes - Avon Products, Inc.
EVENING PRIMROSE - Shampoos - Jason Natural Products, Inc.
EVENING PRIMROSE - Skin care products - Bio-Nutritional Products
EVENING REFLECTION - Floor coverings—carpet and rugs ☆ - Callaway Carpets
EVENING ROSE - Flatware ☆ - Utica Cutlery Co.
EVENING SENSATION - Dolls - Mattel, Inc.
EVENING SHADES - Bathing suits ☆ - Jantzen Inc.
EVENING SHADOW - Glassware—household ☆ - Lenox Crystal, Inc.
EVENING SONG - Floor coverings—carpet and rugs - Milliken & Co. Inc.
EVENING SPARKLE - Dolls - Mattel, Inc.
EVENING SPLENDOR - Toys - Tonka Corp.
EVENING STAR - Christmas tree ornaments - Cracker Box Inc.
EVENING STAR - Colognes - Del Pharmaceuticals, Inc.
EVENING STAR - Floor coverings—carpet and rugs - Mohawk Carpet Corp.
EVENING STAR - Glassware—household ☆ - Lenox Crystal, Inc.
EVENING STAR - Rings—jewelry - Artcarved Inc.
EVENING STAR - Sleeping bags - Coleman Co., Inc.
EVENING SUNSET - Colognes ☆ - Old 97 Co.
EVENING TREASURES - Handbags - Creative Imports
EVENING WHISPER - Floor coverings—carpet and rugs - Monticello Carpet Mills
EVENING WHISPER - Mattresses - Simmons USA
EVENIT - Underwear and nightwear - NCC Industries, Inc.
EVENLITE - Projectors—photographic - Sima Products Corp.
EVENMIST - Humidifiers - The Field Controls Co.
EVENMIST - Humidifiers - Field Controls Co.
EVENMOR GAB - Fabrics - Dan River Inc.
EVENPLEAT - Window shades - Spring Window Fashions Division, Inc.
EVENROLL - Projection screens - Draper Shade and Screen Co. Inc.
EVENRUM - Abrasive products - Minnesota Mining & Manufacturing Co.
EVENSONG - Toilets—enameled - Kohler Co.
EVENSPUN - Thread - Quality Thread Co.
E'VENT - Computer software - Merasoft Corp.
EVENT/CAD - Computer software - Blade Software, Inc.
EVENT-LINK - Health care products - Corometrics Medical Systems Inc.
E'VENT MANAGER - Computer software - Merasoft Corp.
EVENT MEDIA - Packaging—paper - Sterling Advance Packaging, Inc.
EVENT MINDER - Computer software - Hallmark Cards Inc.
EVENT STAFF - Intimate apparel - Bentley Lingerie, Inc.
EVENT TAPE - Banners - Moose Lake Products Co., Inc.
EVENTCAPTURE - Video equipment - Roush Electronics, Inc.
EVENTIDE - Christmas tree ornaments - Cracker Box Inc.
EVENTIDE NIGHT - Sunblocks - European Tanning Systems Inc.
EVENTLOGGER - Tape recorders - Hecon Corp.
EVENTPAC - Luggage - Promac, Inc.
EVENTPRO - Computer programs - Vector Teknologies, Inc.
EVENTUM - Computer software - SoftBase/Eventum
EVENWAVE - Ovens—microwave - Sears, Roebuck and Co.
EVER AFTER - Colognes - Avon Products, Inc.
EVER-BEST - Water—bottled or canned - Purity Bottling Co.
EVER-BRIGHT - Paints - Davis Paint Co.
EVER BRITE - Oils—illuminating - Candle Station, Ltd.
EVER-BRITE - Plumbing fixtures - National Fiber Glass Products
EVER CLEAN - Agricultural products - A & M Products Inc.
EVER CLEAN - Cat-box litter - A & M Pet Products Inc.
EVER COLOR - Lipsticks - Cosmo Cosmetics, Inc.
EVER CRETE - Mortars—clay - Ohio State Waterproofing, Inc.
EVER-DRI - Housewares - Tyz-All Plastics Inc.
EVER-DRI - Pipes—tobacco ☆ - S.M. Frank & Co. Inc. (Kaywoodie-Yello-Bole-Medico)
EVER-DRI - Tools ☆ - Zorbite Corp.
EVER-DRI - Waterproofing compounds - M.A.B. Paints
EVER-DRY - Deodorants—personal ☆ - Scherer Laboratories Inc.
EVER-FIRM - Fabric stores - Conso Products Co.
EVER FLEX - Footwear - Wolverine World Wide, Inc.
EVER-FLEX - Gloves - Edmont
EVER-FLO - Aquarium accessories - Consolidated Models, Inc.
EVER-FLO - Ventilation equipment - R & V Products Inc.
EVER-FLUFFY - Comforters - Pacific Coast Feather Co.

EVER-FOLD - Doors—metal - Elkhart Door Inc.
EVER FOR EXCELLENCE - Computer peripheral equipment - Everex Systems, Inc.
EVER FRESH - Doughnuts - Rich Products Corp.
EVER-FRESH - Food products ☆ - Dairy Fresh Products Co.
EVER GENTLE - Pet products - Lambert-Kay
EVER-GLO - Paints - Spencer-Adams Paint Co. Inc.
EVER-GO-ROUND - Playground equipment ☆ - Kenner Products
EVER-GO-ROUND - Toys - Tonka Corp.
EVER-GRIP - Floor coverings - Dodge-Regupol Inc.
EVER-GUARD - Laser systems—medical - Kentek Corp.
EVER-HOT - Heating equipment ☆ - Bradford-White Corp.
EVER LAND - Recording label - Word, Inc.
EVER LAND ENTERTAINMENT - Tape players—cassette - Word, Inc.
EVER-LOCK - Jewelry—precious - Chicago Diamond Brokers
EVER LOCK - Tape—adhesive - Conso Products Co.
EVER LOVELY - Floor coverings—carpet and rugs - Lees Carpets
EVER-MOIST CAKE - Ice cream - Baskin-Robbins USA Co.
EVER-PERM - Hair care products - Helene Curtis Industries Inc.
EVER-PLAY - Radios - Gulton Industries Inc.
EVER-PRIME - Paints - Ponderosa Paint Manufacturing Co. Inc.
EVER-READY - Brushes, shaving soaps ☆ - American Safety Razor Co.
EVER READY - Calendars - Keith Clark Inc.
EVER-READY - Cleaning preparations—household - Ever-Ready Appliance Manufacturing Co.
EVER-READY - Enamels ☆ - James B. Day and Co.
EVER-READY - Glue—household or industrial - Evans Adhesive Corp.
EVER READY - Health care products - Ever Ready First Aid Medical Supply Corp.
EVER-READY - Labels—paper - Ever-Ready Label Corp.
EVER-READY - Office supplies - Ever-Ready Co.
EVER READY - Pickles - Paramount Foods Inc.
EVER READY - Toys - Eveready Battery Co., Inc.
EVER-READY SHAVING BRUSHES - Shaving preparations - American Safety Razor Co.
EVER-ROLL - Floor coverings—tile - Dodge-Regupol Delaware, Inc.
EVER-ROLL - Floor coverings—tile - Dodge-Regupol Inc.
EVER-SCRUB - Paint ☆ - Cook and Dunn Paint Corp.
EVER-SERV - Paper—toilet - Georgia-Pacific Corp.
EVER SET - Thread ☆ - Perfect Thread Co. Inc.
EVER-SHIELD - Screws - Independent Fastener Co.
EVER SLENDER - Vitamins and nutritional supplements ☆ - Nature's Herbs
EVER-SMOOTH - Hair care products - Form-U-La-Hair Co.
EVER-SO-FITTING - Brassieres (Bras) ☆ - Lovable Co.
EVER SO GOOD - Food products - Giulianos' Specialty Foods
EVER SO KIND - Cosmetics - Kathleen White
EVER SOFT - Linen - American Textile Co.
EVER SPRING - Water—bottled or canned - North East Mississippi Coca-Cola Bottling Co.
EVER-STRAIT - Doors - Pease Industries, Inc.
EVER THINE - Rings—jewelry - Artcarved Inc.
EVER-WEAR - Cooking equipment—household ☆ - John L. Chaney Instrument Co.
EVER-WEAR - Lubricants - Quantum Marketing, Inc.
EVER-WELD - Hardware - Silver Line Building Products Corp.
EVER YOURS - Dishes—earthenware - Taylor, Smith & Taylor Co.
EVERBAKE - Vegetable oil - Creative Products Inc. of Rossville
EVERBEARING - Flowers, plants, and seeds - D. Landreth Seed Co.
EVERBEST - Food products - Thistledown Farms
EVERBEST - Paper—carbon ☆ - Curtis-Young Corp.
EVERBEST - Pickles - Green Bay Foods Co.
EVERBLUM - Cleaning preparations - Albatross USA Inc.
EVERBOUND WB - Adhesives and sealants - Triangle Pacific Corp. (Cabinet Division)
EVERBRIGHT - Artists' materials - Riebe's Artist Materials Inc.
EVERBRITE - Cooking equipment—household - Jacksonville Manufacturing
EVERBRITE - Mirrors - Tele Vue Optics Inc.
EVERBRITE - Sheet metal products - Aluminum Co. of America
EVERCANE - Sugar—granulated, refined, or powdered - Savannah Foods and Industries Inc.
EVERCAST - Cooking equipment—household - Jacksonville Manufacturing
EVERCEL - Tape—adhesive ☆ - Sekisui Products Inc.
EVERCLEAN - Paints - Sherwin-Williams Automotive Finishes Corp.
EVERCLEAN - Shampoos - Home Health Products, Inc.
EVERCLEAR - Automotive parts and accessories - World Wide Equipment Inc.
EVERCLEAR - Beverages—alcohol - David Sherman Corp.

☆ = Now out of production

EVERCLEAR - Blinds–vertical - Louverdrape Inc.
EVERCLEAR - Filters–industrial ☆ - Everpure Inc.
EVERCLEAR - T-shirts–men's - Everclear
EVERCLEAR PURPLE PASSION - Beverages–alcohol - David Sherman Corp.
EVERCLOR - Filters–industrial ☆ - Everpure Inc.
EVERCOAT - Finishing agents - Fibre Glass-Evercoat Co. Inc.
EVERCOLD - Ice - Cold Ice Corp.
EVERCOLOR - Color prints - Evercolor Corp.
EVERCREASE - Apparel–men's - J.C. Penney Co., Inc.
EVERCUT - Scissors–hand-operated - Acme United Corp.
EVERE - Colognes - Chesebrough-Pond's USA Co.
EVEREADY - Flashlights - Eveready Battery Co., Inc.
EVEREADY - Juices - Hollywood Health Foods
EVEREADY - Juices ☆ - Dole Food Co., Inc.
EVEREADY SUPER HEAVY DUTY - Batteries - Eveready Battery Co., Inc.
EVEREADY SUPERIOR PRODUCTS - Hobby kits - Stanislaus Imports, Inc.
EVEREADY TRAVEL GEAR - Flashlights - Eveready Battery Co., Inc.
EVEREDGE - Cutlery - J.A. Henckels Zwillingswerk Inc.
EVEREDY - Cooking equipment–household ☆ - Jacksonville Manufacturing
EVERENE - XLPE - Insulating materials - Triangle Wire & Cable, Inc.
EVEREST - Bicycles - Columbia Manufacturing Inc.
EVEREST - Floor coverings–carpet and rugs - Karastan-Bigelow Inc.
EVEREST - Footwear - Hershberg Shoe Co. Inc.
EVEREST - Knives - Precise International/Wenger
EVEREST - Luggage - American Flyer
EVEREST - Luggage - Everest Trading Corp.
EVEREST - Paper products - International Paper Co.
EVEREST - Publisher's imprints - Panamerican Associates, Inc.
EVEREST - Recording label - Everest Record Group
EVEREST - Tiles–ceramic - Porcelanite, Inc.
EVEREST - Tires - Solcoor Inc.
EVEREST - Water–bottled or canned - Everest Drinking Water Co.
EVEREST & JENNINGS - Wheelchairs - Everest and Jennings International Ltd.
EVEREST ELITE - Sporting goods - Kellwood Co.
EVEREST GROUP - Furniture - Bean Station Furniture Factory Inc.
EVEREST IMAGING - Video equipment - Welch Allyn, Inc.
EVEREST SOFTWARE - Computer software - Everest Software Corp.
EVEREST SPRING - Paperboard ☆ - International Paper Co.
EVERETT - Pianos ☆ - Everett Piano Co.
EVERETT - Watches - Bulova Corp.
EVERETT AQUASOX - Apparel and accessories - Everett Giants, Inc.
EVEREVE - Perfumes - FMG/Tsumara Medical
EVEREX - Computers - Everex Systems, Inc.
EVERFAST - Fabrics - Everfast Inc.
EVERFAST - Hardware - Ambroid Co.
EVERFAST - Thread - Cincinnati Thread Co.
EVERFIX - Epoxy - Fibre Glass-Evercoat Co. Inc.
EVERFLASH - Cameras - Keystone Camera Corp.
EVERFLAT - Desk sets - Sainberg and Co. Inc.
EVERFLEX - Cables - Esterline Technologies Corp.
EVERFLEX - Office supplies - Everflex Aluminum Products
EVERFLEX BONDAPRENE - Adhesives and sealants - Surebond, Inc.
EVERFLEX MONKEY GRIP - Gloves–work - Ansell Edmont Industrial Inc.
EVERFLOW - Antifreeze - Irving Oil Corp.
EVERFRESH - Dishes–china - Mikasa Co.
EVERFRESH - Food products - Beatrice Cheese Co.
EVERFRESH - Food products - Everfresh Foods Corp.
EVERFRESH - Food products - Opta Food Ingredients, Inc.
EVERFRESH - Fruit drinks–bottled or canned - Everfresh Beverages, Inc.
EVERFRESH - Fruits and vegetables - Pitsweet Inc.
EVERFRESH - Nuts–salted, roasted, cooked, or canned - Jimbo's Jumbos Inc.
EVERFRESH JUICE CO. PREMIUM - Beverages - Everfresh Beverages, Inc.
EVERFRESH PREMIUM - Fruit drinks–bottled or canned - Everfresh Beverages, Inc.
EVERFRESH PREMIUM LIGHT - Beverages–carbonated - Everfresh Beverages, Inc.
EVERFRESH WAX - Flowers, plants, and seeds - Bill Suyeyasu Wholesale Florist, Inc.
EVERFULL - Dresses–women's - Malco Modes Inc.
EVERGLADES - Synthetic turf - Instant Turf Industries Inc.
EVERGLADES COMBINATION - Food products - Salad Werks
EVERGLADES WINGS - Seafood products–fresh or frozen - Salad Werks
EVERGLASS - Automotive parts and accessories - Fibre Glass-Evercoat Co. Inc.

EVERGLAZE - Epoxy coatings - Perry & Derrick Co.
EVERGLIDE - Blinds–vertical ☆ - Spring Window Fashions Division, Inc.
EVERGLIDE - Machine parts - Unitron, Inc.
EVERGLIDE - Pens - Scripto-Tokai Corp.
EVERGLIDE - Shaving preparations - Nu Skin International, Inc.
EVERGLO - Fireplace logs–treated - Vaquero Leasing Co. Inc.
EVERGLO - Fireplaces ☆ - Heat-N-Glo Fireplace Products, Inc.
EVERGLO - Novelty items - Lite-Up Corp.
EVERGLOW - Christmas tree lights - J. Hofert Co.
EVERGLOW - Musical instrument accessories - Humes & Berg Manufacturing Co. Inc.
EVERGLOW - Watches - Abraham Laniado
EVERGOLD - Bronze products - Obron Atlantic Corp.
EVERGOOD - Mayonnaise ☆ - Wilsey Foods, Inc.
EVERGOOD - Rice - Wehah Farm, Inc.
EVERGOOD - Toys - Evergood
EVERGREEN - Agricultural products - Evergreen/Ridge, Inc.
EVERGREEN - Christmas tree stands - Industrial Molding Corp.
EVERGREEN - Dinnerware–glass - Nikko Ceramics Inc.
EVERGREEN - Dog food - Evergreen Mills Inc.
EVERGREEN - Doors–metal - Castlegate Inc.
EVERGREEN - Electrical equipment - Oneac Corp.
EVERGREEN - Floor coverings–carpet and rugs ☆ - American Excelsior Co.
EVERGREEN - Flowers, plants, and seeds - D. Landreth Seed Co.
EVERGREEN - Food products ☆ - Harry and David Inc.
EVERGREEN - Lighting fixtures - Fluorescent Supply Co. Inc.
EVERGREEN - Packaging machines - International Paper Co.
EVERGREEN - Paper - Simpson Paper Co.
EVERGREEN - Paper–bond - Fox River Paper Co.
EVERGREEN - Publisher's imprints - Grove/Atlantic, Inc.
EVERGREEN - Stoneware dinnerware - Iron Mountain Stoneware Inc.
EVERGREEN - Toys - Little Tikes Co.
EVERGREEN - Veterinary pharmaceutical preparations - Evergreen Mills, Inc.
EVERGREEN - Vitamins and nutritional supplements - Sunrider Corp.
EVERGREEN - Yarn ☆ - Seventh Generation Wholesale Inc.
EVERGREEN COLLECTION - Jams and jellies - J.M. Smucker Co.
EVERGREEN COLLECTION, THE - Greeting cards - Evergreen Press
EVERGREEN FLAGS - Flags - Evergreen Flags
EVERGREEN FOREST - Potpourri - Countryside Fragrances Inc.
EVERGREEN MUSIC RECORDINGS - Compact discs–prerecorded - Evergreen Music Recordings
EVERGREEN PRINCESS BARBIE - Dolls - Mattel, Inc.
EVERHANDY - Pencils ☆ - Hunt Manufacturing Co.
EVERHARD LIFT - Elevators - Aging Technologies, Inc.
EVERHEALTH - Toiletries - Everhealth Natural Vitamin Co.
EVERHOT - Barbecues and grills ☆ - Toastmaster Inc.
EVERITE - Artists' materials - Gilman Brothers Co.
EVERITE - Frosting - Mallet and Co.
EVERKLEEN - Ophthalmic goods - Everkleen Products
EVERKLEEN - Water heaters–household - Rheem Manufacturing Co.
EVERKROME - Paints ☆ - Everseal International Sales Co. Inc.
EVERLAND - Recording label - Word, Inc.
EVERLAST - Bags - Everlast World's Boxing Headquarters Corp.
EVERLAST - Floor coverings–tile - Dodge-Regupol Inc.
EVERLAST - Floor waxes - Twi-Laq Industries Inc.
EVERLAST - Luggage - Rose Trunk Manufacturing Co. Inc.
EVERLAST - Watches - Webster Watch Co. Associates
EVERLAST TILE - Floor coverings - Dodge-Regupol Inc.
EVERLASTING - Calendars - Boone International, Inc.
EVERLASTING - Floor coverings–carpet and rugs - Cabin Crafts Carpets
EVERLASTING - Floor coverings–carpet and rugs - Walter Carpet Mills
EVERLASTING - Floor coverings–carpet and rugs ☆ - American Carpet Mills
EVERLASTING - Hair care products - Alaion Products Inc.
EVERLASTING - Paints - United States Refining Co.
EVERLASTING ARRANGEMENTS - Flowers, plants, and seeds - Aroma Design Group Inc.
EVERLASTING EDITIONS - Greeting cards - American Greetings Corp.
EVERLASTING ELEGANCE - Epoxy - Greenstreet Co., Inc.
EVERLASTING PLATINUM - Jewelry - OE Design Inc.
EVERLAWN - Floor coverings–carpet and rugs - Conquest Carpet Mills Inc.
EVERLIP - Cosmetics - Everlip, Inc.
EVERLOCK - Hardware - Everlock Systems
EVERLOFT - Fibers–synthetic - Veratec
EVERLON - Draperies - Fabrican Inc.
EVERLOVE - Jewelry–precious - David Dattner, Inc.
EVERLY - Skin care products - Frances Denney

EVERMASK - Paper - Fibre Glass-Evercoat Co. Inc.

EVERMORE - Cigars - National Cigar Corp.

EVERMORE - Floor coverings–carpet and rugs - Columbus Mills, Inc.

EVERMORE - Health care products - Eurostar Corp.

EVERMORE - Skin care products - Bonat Inc.

EVERON - Lip balms - Weleda Inc.

EVERONE - Pharmaceutical preparations - Hyrex Pharmaceuticals

EVERPRESS - Apparel–men's - Oxford Industries, Inc.

EVERPRIME - Paints - Ponderosa Paint Manufacturing Co. Inc.

EVERPURE - Water purification systems - Everpure Inc.

EVERQUEST - Computer peripheral equipment - Sony Interactive Entertainment Inc.

EVERREADY - Lighter fluid ☆ - Cumberland-Swan, Inc.

EVERREADY - Photographic equipment ☆ - SP Systems/Saratons

EVERSAFE - Cabinets–metal - Eversafe Corp.

EVERSCENT - Deodorizers - Creative Products Inc. of Rossville

EVERSEAL - Adhesives and sealants - Pennzoil Products Co.

EVERSEAL - Paints - Everseal International Sales Co. Inc.

EVERSHARP - Cutlery - J.A. Henckels Zwillingswerk Inc.

EVERSHARP - Knives–carving ☆ - Lifetime Hoan Corp.

EVERSHARP - Knives–electric - National Presto Industries, Inc.

EVERSHARP - Pens - Astro Pen Co.

EVERSHARP - Pens - Eversharp Pen Co.

EVERSHARP - Pens - Ray Rosato

EVERSHARP - Scissors–hand-operated - Acme United Corp.

EVERSHARP-PRO - Cutlery - J.A. Henckels Zwillingswerk Inc.

EVERSHARP SHEFFIELD - Knives–carving ☆ - Lifetime Hoan Corp.

EVERSHEARS - Medical equipment - Everest Medical Corp.

EVERSHIELD - Paints - Dunn Edwards Corp.

EVERSLICK P.B.T. SKIN - Skateboards - NHS, Inc.

EVERSOFT - Cosmetics - Andrew Jergens Co.

EVERSOFT - Denture materials - Austenal, Inc.

EVERSOFT - Dust cloths - Louis M. Gerson Co. Inc.

EVERSOFT - Fabric - Crown Textile Co.

EVERSOFT - Footwear ☆ - E.S. Originals, Inc.

EVERSOFT - Golf gloves - Austad Co.

EVERSOFT - Handkerchiefs ☆ - Carolina Manufacturing Inc.

EVERSOFT - Water purification systems - Eversoft, Inc.

EVERSPUN - Fabrics - Veratec

EVERSTAR - Epoxy - Fibre Glass-Evercoat Co. Inc.

EVERSTONE - Wood products - Safas Corp.

EVERSYS CORPORATION - Computer software - Eversys Corp.

EVERT-FRESH - Atomizers - Evert-Fresh Corp.

EVERTEMP - Boxes–corrugated paperboard - Cold Ice Corp.

EVERTHANE - Paints - Ponderosa Paint Manufacturing Co. Inc.

EVERTITE - Adhesives and sealants ☆ - Franklin International, Inc.

EVERTOL - Paints ☆ - Everseal International Sales Co. Inc.

EVERTONE - Paints ☆ - Everseal International Sales Co. Inc.

EVERTUF - Paper - ATAPCO Office Products Group

EVERTUFF - Floor waxes - Uncle Sam Chemical Co., Inc.

EVERTWIST - Floor coverings–carpet and rugs - Quaker Inc.

EVERVESS - Beverages ☆ - Vess Beverages Inc.

EVERVIEW - Computer hardware - Everview, Inc.

EVERWARM - Linen - Danaher Sheets & Co.

EVERWAY - Trading cards and stamps - Wizards of the Coast, Inc.

EVERWEAR - Aluminum products - N.H. Rudeen Co.

EVERWEAR - Floor coverings–carpet and rugs ☆ - Playfield International Inc.

EVERWEAR - Jewelry - Pearl Trend Ltd.

EVERWEAR - Sporting goods - Lisco, Inc.

EVERWET - Brushes ☆ - Brushtech Inc.

EVERWHITE - Grouting material - C-Cure Corp.

EVERWHITE - Paints - Binney & Smith Inc.

EVERWOOD - Wood products - Watkins Manufacturing Corp.

EVERY COLOR GOES WITH EVERY COLOR - Apparel–children's - Mamiye Brothers, Inc.

EVERY-DAY - Pharmaceutical preparations - G.O. Spanner Inc.

EVERY DAY CHAIR - Furniture - Hon Co.

EVERY DAY SUNDAE CONTAINER - Product for hiding valuables ☆ - Iwasaki Images of America

EVERY HUNTER DESERVES A TROPHY - Binoculars - Bausch & Lomb Inc.

EVERY MAN - Food supplements - New Moon Extracts, Inc.

EVERY MOVE - Apparel–women's - Perry Manufacturing Co.

EVERY OCCASION - Napkins–paper - Converting, Inc.

EVERY STEP OF THE WAY - Footwear - SRL, Inc.

EVERY SWITCH WAY - Underwear and nightwear ☆ - Lovable Co.

EVERY WHICH WAY - Mops - Drackett Co.

EVERY-WHICH-WAY - Photographic equipment - SP Systems/Saratons

EVERYBODI IZ SOMEBODI - Apparel and accessories - Kulcha, Inc.

EVERYBODY LOVES A NUT - Nuts–candied - Nabisco Foods Group

EVERYBODY NEEDS ONE - Dinnerware - Treasures & Trinkets, Inc.

EVERYBODY'S - Skin care products - Hytrous/Flash Sales Inc.

EVERYDAY - Books–blank - Sun Graphix

EVERYDAY - Foil–aluminum - Reynolds Metals Co.

EVERYDAY - Fruits and vegetables - Regal Fruit Cooperative

EVERYDAY - Hosiery ☆ - Sara Lee Corp.

EVERYDAY - Office supplies - Globe-Weis

EVERYDAY - Pet products - Hartz Mountain Corp.

EVERYDAY - Skin care products - Texas Pharmacal Co.

EVERYDAY COOKBOOKS, THE - Publisher's imprints - Time Life Inc.

EVERYDAY CREATIVITY - Publisher's imprints - McGoff Enterprises, Inc.

EVERYDAY DISCIPLESHIP - Publisher's imprints - Sunday School Board of the Southern Baptist Convention

EVERYDAY ESSENTIALS - Apparel–women's - Sara Lee Corp.

EVERYDAY ESSENTIALS! - Luggage - Pacific Connections of California, Inc.

EVERYDAY EXPRESSIONS - Stationery - Elite Greetings Inc.

EVERYDAY GOURMET - Glass products ☆ - Corning Inc.

EVERYDAY GOURMET - Meat and poultry - G and R Felpausch Co.

EVERYDAY GOURMET, THE - Video production - Kathleen Perry

EVERYDAY MATHEMATICS - Video production - Everyday Learning Corp.

EVERYDAY TEACHING - Publisher's imprints - Everyday Learning Corp.

EVERYDAYPAVE' - Jewelry - Roman Co.

EVERYMAN LIBRARY - Publisher's imprints - Littlefield, Adams & Co.

EVERYMAN VITALITY FACTORS - Vitamins and nutritional supplements - New Moon Extracts, Inc.

EVERYNIGHT - Hair care products - Helene Curtis Industries Inc.

EVERYONE'S CATCHING IT - Balls - Signature Marketing Group, Ltd.

EVERYOUTH - Conditioning cremes - Wilson Marketing Enterprises, Inc.

EVERYOUTH - Hair coloring preparations - Everyouth Products Inc.

EVERYTHING - Glassware–household ☆ - Lancaster Colony Corp.

EVERYTHING - Recording label ☆ - Parr-X Corp.

EVERYTHING BABY NEEDS - Wallpaper - Imperial Wallcoverings, Inc.

EVERYTHING BUT THE KITCHEN SINK - Kitchen utensils–aluminum - Robinson Knife & Fiddlers Plastics

EVERYTHING BUT THE KITCHEN SINK COOKIE - Bakery products - Creative Confections

EVERYTHING BUTT - T-shirts–men's - James K. Benton

EVERYTHING ELSE IS JUST A GAME - Apparel and accessories - Pro Rodeo Sports, Inc.

EVERYTHING ELSE WAS JUST PRACTICE - Apparel and accessories - Streetball Partners, Inc.

EVERYTHING FOR EYES - Cosmetics - Del Pharmaceuticals, Inc.

EVERYTHING FRAME - Frames–picture - North American Enclosures Inc.

EVERYTHING FROM NOTHING - Bakery products - Two Two Chefs on a Roll, Inc.

EVERYTHING IN WRITING - Pencils ☆ - Faber-Castell Corp.

EVERYTHING NICE - Apparel–women's - Wacoal America Inc.

EVERYTHING PLUS - Vitamins and nutritional supplements ☆ - Thompson Medical Co., Inc.

EVERYTHING RACK - Drums–musical instruments - LP Music Group

EVERYTHING SAUCE - Sauces ☆ - Festive Foods, Inc.

EVERYTHING YOU CONNECT WITH - Pagers - Comcast Corp.

EVERYTHING YOU HEAR IS TRUE - Recording label - Telarc International Corp.

EVERYTHING YOU NEED. MORE THAN YOU EXPECT. - Calendars - Music City Marketing, Inc.

EVERYTIME - Hair care products - Helene Curtis Industries Inc.

EVERYWARE - Housewares - Glass Products, Inc.

EVERYWARE - Plates–plastic ☆ - Genpak Corp.

EVERYWEAR - Clothing - Blair Corp.

EVERYWHERE - Floor coverings–carpet and rugs - Quaker Inc.

EVERYWHERE DESK - Toys ☆ - Natural Science Industries, Ltd.

EVERYWHERE, EVERYWEAR - Apparel and accessories - Breton Industries

EVERYWOMAN VITALITY FACTORS - Vitamins and nutritional supplements - New Moon Extracts, Inc.

EVERYWOMAN'S WORKOUT - Video production - Mary Tyler Moore Levine

EVE'S GARDEN - Juices ☆ - Apple and Eve Inc.

EVE'S GARDEN - Perfumes - Windlestraw

EVE'S REVENGE - Fruits–candied - Paron Chocolatier

EVESHAM - Dinnerware–glass - Royal China & Porcelain Companies Inc.

EVESHAM MICRO-WAVE - Dinnerware–glass - Royal China & Porcelain Companies Inc.

☆ = Now out of production

EVESHAM VALE - Dinnerware–glass - Royal China & Porcelain Companies Inc.

EVETTE - Clarinets - Boosey & Hawkes Buffet Crampon USA

EVG - Apparel–men's - Nordstrom, Inc.

EVIAN - Wallpaper - Koroseal Wallcoverings

EVIAN - Water–mineral - Evian Waters of France

EVIAN BRUMISATEUR - Water–mineral - The Wilkes Group

EVICT - Pet products - Carter-Wallace, Inc.

EVICT - Pet products - Lambert-Kay

EVIDENCE - Paper - Ampad Corp.

EVIDENCE - Recording label - Jazz Composer's Orchestra Association Inc.

EVIDENCE - Skin care products ☆ - Whitehall Laboratories

EVIDENCE FILM - Film - Chief Supply Corp.

EVIDENCE MATE - Educational materials - Little, Brown and Co., Inc.

EVIDENT CRIME SCENE PRODUCTS - Fingerprinting equipment - Evident, Inc.

EVIDEX - Pharmaceutical preparations - J & W Scientific

EVIE MADISON - Breads - Evie Madison

EVIL - Colognes - Design Air

EVIL BY ELVIRA - Perfumes - Design Air

EVIL EEL - Fishing lures - Kalin Co.

EVIL EYE - Fishing lures - Eppinger Manufacturing Co.

EVIL EYE - Novelty items - Imagineering Inc.

EVIL EYE ALE - Beverages–malt - Pittsburgh Brewing Co.

EVIL HORDE - Toys - Mattel, Inc.

EVIL-LYN - Toys - Mattel, Inc.

EVIL RAT PACK - Toys–automobiles - Mattel, Inc.

EVIL SPACE ALIENS - Toys - Saban Entertainment, Inc.

EVIL TEETH - Novelty items - Imagineering Inc.

EVIL WARRIORS - Toys - Mattel, Inc.

EVIL WEEVIL - Toys–automobiles - Mattel, Inc.

EVINRUDE - Motors–outboard - Outboard Marine Corp.

EVINRUDE SPITFIRE - Motors–outboard - Outboard Marine Corp.

EVINRUDE XP - Motors–outboard - Outboard Marine Corp.

EVINS - Shoes - Marx & Newman Co. Inc.

EVISION - Computer software - St. Paul Software

EVITA PERONI - Socks, hair accessories, jewelry, etc. - Desmark Inc.

EVM - Audio equipment - Electro-Voice, Inc.

EVO - Furniture - American Seating Co.

E.V.O. - Olive oil - Thomas A. Keller

EVO - Skates–roller - Rollerblade, Inc.

EVO MAX - Skates–roller - Rollerblade, Inc.

EVO-PEN - Pen cartridge - Evolutionary Pen & Instrument Co., Inc.

EVOC AL MUTRJEM - Computers–micro - Adam Michael Sacks

EVOKE - Apparel and accessories - Crystal Brands Inc.

EVOLITE - Cables–steel - Kryptonite Corp.

EVOLO - Sports apparel - Converse Inc.

EVOLUT - Computer software ☆ - CONDUIT

EVOLUTION - Board game - Intromark Inc.

EVOLUTION - Boating equipment and accessories - Evolution Co., Inc.

EVOLUTION - Flatware ☆ - Yamazaki Tableware Inc.

EVOLUTION - Floor coverings - American Biltrite Inc.

EVOLUTION - Floor coverings - Congoleum Corp.

EVOLUTION - Floor coverings–carpet and rugs - Robertex Associates Inc.

EVOLUTION - Food products - H-D Michigan, Inc.

EVOLUTION - Health care products - Medical Industries America, Inc.

EVOLUTION - Infant product - Newborne Co.

EVOLUTION - Irrigation equipment - Rain Master Irrigation Systems, Inc.

EVOLUTION - Musical instrument accessories - Dimarzio, Inc.

EVOLUTION - Paper - Datacom Inc.

EVOLUTION - Paper - Kimberly-Clark Corp.

EVOLUTION - Paper–carbon ☆ - Eaton Allen Ko-Rec-Type Corp.

EVOLUTION - Pencils - Bic Corp.

EVOLUTION - Tires - Pirelli Armstrong Tire Corp.

EVOLUTION - Vitamins and nutritional supplements - Organic Diversions, Inc.

EVOLUTION 2000 - Cables–steel - Kryptonite Corp.

EVOLUTION 2000 - Locks–padlocks - Kryptonite Corp.

EVOLUTION 2000 - Paints - Surface Protection Industries, Inc.

EVOLUTION GOLD ACCENT - Flatware - Yamazaki Tableware Inc.

EVOLUTION MOUSSE - Hair care products - Peter Hantz Co.

EVOLUTION SERIES - Computer hardware - Colorgrahic Communications Corp.

EVOLUTIONARY TECHNOLOGIES, INC. - Computer software - Evolutionary Technologies, Inc.

EVOLVE - Vitamins and nutritional supplements - Nutragenics

EVON'S - Nuts–salted, roasted, cooked, or canned - John B. Sanfilippo & Son, Inc.

EVOSEAL 80 - Waterproofing compounds ☆ - Andek Corp.

EVR - Computers - Microlog Corp.

EVR 3 - Lighting fixtures - Elsco Lighting

EV'R CLEAR - Water–bottled or canned ☆ - Hinckley & Schmitt (Bottled Water Group)

EVR-GLO - Floor coverings–tile - Harbor Sales Co.

EVR-TITE - Cement - L.D. Sterns Corp.

EVRON GEL - Health care products - Pharmaceutical Innovations

EVRY THINS - Apparel–women's ☆ - Bali Co. Inc.

EVRYWEAR - Apparel and accessories - Determined Productions, Inc.

EVS - Braces–orthopedic - Fairway Import Export, Inc.

EV'S - Cakes–mixes - Bon Melange Inc.

EVS - Electrical equipment - Elevator Video Systems

EVSCOZYME - Veterinary pharmaceutical preparations ☆ - Evsco Pharmaceuticals

EVT - Audio equipment ☆ - Electro-Voice, Inc.

EVT - Medical products - Endovascular Technologies Inc.

EVTECH - Coatings - Eastman Chemical Co.

EVTEK - Computer peripheral equipment - Evtek Corp.

EVYAN - Perfumes - Evyan Perfumes Inc.

EW - Food products - Wallace Foods Inc.

EWA - Cases–camera - Pioneer Marketing & Research, Inc.

EWA MARINE - Photographic equipment - R.T.S. Inc.

EWAHH BAGS! - Novelty items ☆ - Reed Productions

EWART'S - Bakery products ☆ - Ewarts Frozen Foods

EWEEY - Toys–stuffed - Gund, Inc.

EWESON - Composting machines - Bedminster Bioconversion Corp.

EWF - Paints - Evans Paint

EWICK - Wicking - Hooper Industries Inc.

EWING - Footwear - Dream Inc.

EWOK - Calendars - Lucasfilm Ltd.

EWOKS - Laces–boot and shoe - Lucasfilm Ltd.

EWOKS - Toys–stuffed - Kenner Products

EWP - Lumber - Western Wood Products Association

EWS - Alarm systems - Anes Electronics Burglar Alarm Systems

EWSM - Communications equipment - Siemens Stromberg-Carlson

EWTF - Veterinary pharmaceutical preparations - Schering Corp.

EX - Beverages–malt - The Stroh Brewery Co.

EX - Deodorizers - American Auto Accessories, Inc.

EX - Lighting fixtures - Big Beam Emergency Systems Inc.

EX-BAND - Brassieres (Bras) ☆ - Lovable Co.

EX BLACK ALE - Beverages–malt - The Stroh Brewery Co.

EX CALIBER - Bicycles - Ross Bicycles USA, Ltd.

EX-CALORIC - Health care products - Eastern Research Laboratories

EX-CEL - Clay products - Ex-Cel Inc.

EX CEL - Pottery - House of Ceramics Inc.

EX-CEL-CIS - Cosmetics - Sorenson Development, Inc.

EX-CELL - Laboratory apparatus - Corning Inc.

EX-CELL - Skin care products - Pharmagel Corp.

EX CON - Jewelry - Frank G. D'Amato

EX-COR - Tape–adhesive ☆ - Nashua Corp.

EX EXPORT LIGHT - Beverages–malt - G. Heileman Brewing Co., Inc.

EX FACTOR 4 - Guitars - Philip Kubicki Technology

EX-HUSBANDS CLUB - Apparel and accessories - Thomas Joseph Kellgren

EX ICE - Beverages–malt - The Stroh Brewery Co.

EX-IN-CO SYSTEMS BUSINESS PARTNER - Computer software - Ex.In.Co Systems, Inc.

EX-IT - Hair care products - Tressa, Inc.

EX-LAX - Laxatives - Sandoz Pharmaceuticals Corp.

EX LIBRIS - Forms–preprinted - BlumbergExcelsior, Inc.

EX LIBRIS - Publisher's imprints - Oryx Press, Inc.

EX LIGHT - Beverages–malt - The Stroh Brewery Co.

EX-O-FIT - Sports apparel - Reebok International Ltd.

EX-O-MATIC - Fishing tackle ☆ - Martin Reel Co.

EX-OBESE - Pharmaceutical preparations ☆ - Kay Pharmacal Co. Inc.

EX OFFICIO - Apparel and accessories - EX Officio

EX-PLAC - Dental equipment - Preventive Dentistry Products, Inc.

EX PONTO - Computer peripheral equipment - Adobe Systems Inc.

EX-RELATED GREETINGS - Greeting cards - Anne Vincent

EX RUBY RED ALE - Beverages–malt - The Stroh Brewery Co.

EX-SPAN - Pharmaceutical preparations - Rotex Pharmaceuticals Inc.

EX SPECIAL EXPORT - Beverages–malt - G. Heileman Brewing Co., Inc.

EX-STAT - Soap - Imperial Manufacturing Co. Inc.

EX-STATIC - Posters - Service Litho-Print Inc.

☆ = Now out of production

EX-STRESS - Vitamins and nutritional supplements - Nature's Way Products, Inc.

EX-XIT 5 - Apparel and accessories - Plutus Creations Inc.

EXA - Apparel and accessories - Exa Designs, Inc.

EXA - Computers - Exa Corp.

EXA-SOFT - Computer software - Exabyte Corp.

EXAC-PAC - Seasonings - Flavorite Laboratories Inc.

EXACCT - Computer peripheral equipment - Realty Executives

EXACOM - Electronic equipment - Exacom

EXACOMPTA - Notebooks and notepads - Exaclair Inc.

EXACT - Computer software - Intuit Inc.

EXACT - Dental compounds - Jeneric/Pentron Inc.

EXACT - Hardware - Exact Level & Tool Inc.

EXACT - Insecticides ☆ - D-Con Co. Inc.

EXACT - Office supplies - Alvin and Co. Inc.

EXACT - Paper–writing - Wausau Paper Mills Co.

EXACT - Pharmaceutical preparations - Advanced Polymer Systems

EXACT - Recording label ☆ - Alshire International Inc.

EXACT - Shampoos ☆ - Spilo/Mehaz Worldwide

EXACT 20 - Hair care products - Mahdeen Laboratory

EXACT BRIGHTS - Paper–writing ☆ - Wausau Paper Mills Co.

EXACT CHANGE - Coin purses - E.L. Donson Manufacturing Co. Inc.

EXACT COULEUR - Hair care products - Thompson and Formby

EXACT DIMENSION - Window shades - Kirsch Co.

EXACT DIMENSIONS - Cleaning preparations–window - Clopay Building Products Co., Inc.

EXACT-I-RIP - Saws–power - Emerson Electric Co.

EXACT MIX - Oils–lubricating - Homelite, Inc.

EXACT-PAC - Food products - Prepared Foods Inc.

EXACT WORD, THE - Educational materials - Exact Word Inc.

EXACTA - Floor coverings–carpet and rugs ☆ - Criterion Mills Inc.

EXACTA - Games - Twinson Co.

EXACTA - Hair care products - Matrix Essentials, Inc.

EXACTA - Pens - Accutec Inc.

EXACTA - Sporting goods - AFC

EXACTA-CHUTE - Fabrics - Performance Textiles, Inc.

EXACTA LITE - Lamp bulbs–fluorescent - Marvel Lighting Corp.

EXACTACAST - Dental equipment - Essential Dental Systems, Inc.

EXACTECH - Health care products - Medisense, Inc.

EXACTING - Hair care products - ABBA Products Inc.

EXACTLY - Classic Time Watch Co.

EXACTLY FOR WOMEN - Vitamins and nutritional supplements - Diane Wakat

EXACTLY RED - Lipsticks - Estee Lauder Inc.

EXACTO - Metronomes - Stringer Industries Inc.

EXACTRON - Watches - Bulova Corp.

EXACTUS - Health care products - Omron Healthcare, Inc.

EXADERM - Cream - National Chemsearch Corp.

EXAKT - Pencils–mechanical - Alvin and Co. Inc.

EXAKT-PAK - Containers - Exakt Technologies, Inc.

EXAKTA - Cameras - Exakta Camera Co. Inc.

EXAKTA LUMINAX - Photographic equipment - Exakta Camera Co. Inc.

EXAKTOR - Cutlery ☆ - Mundial Inc.

EXALTED - Floor coverings - Aladdin Mills, Inc.

EXALTONE - Chemical preparations - Firmenich Inc.

EXALTOR - Batteries - Suncoast Security Distributors, Inc.

EXAM MASTER - Computer software - Cramer Products Inc.

EXAM NOTES - Publisher's imprints - Research and Education Assn.

EXAM-TEX - Gloves–rubber - Ansell Inc. (Personal Products Div.)

EXAMCO EDGE - Publisher's imprints - Examco Inc.

EXAMGLO - Gloves–rubber - Kossan Gloves, Inc.

EXAMINATOR - Computer software ☆ - Transcender Corp.

EXAMINER - Electronic equipment - Telex Communications, Inc.

EXAMODULE - Computer storage devices - ECCS, Inc.

EXANDRA - Apparel and accessories - Nygard

EXANTE - Motorcycles - Suzuki of America Automotive Corp.

EXAPAK - Audio equipment - Exabyte Corp.

EXAQUARTZ - Watches - North American Watch Corp.

EXBOR - Giftware - Superlux Ltd.

EXCALIBEAR - Toys–stuffed - New Castle Corp.

EXCALIBER - Bicycles - Montgomery Ward & Co. Inc.

EXCALIBER - Footwear - Distributors Service Corp.

EXCALIBER - Musical instruments ☆ - Deg Music Products Inc.

EXCALIBER GROUP - Furniture - Bean Station Furniture Factory Inc.

EXCALIBOR - Motor vehicles–motor homes ☆ - Georgie Boy Manufacturing, Inc.

EXCALIBUR - Management Prescriptives, Inc.

EXCALIBUR - Apparel and accessories - Horace Small Apparel Co.

EXCALIBUR - Apparel and accessories - I. Spiewak and Sons Inc.

EXCALIBUR - Audio equipment - Pro-Co. Sound Co. Inc.

EXCALIBUR - Automotive parts and accessories - Turtle Wax, Inc.

EXCALIBUR - Beds–hospital - Sci-O-Tech Inc.

EXCALIBUR - Billiards and darts equipment, bowling bags - J-S Sales Co. Inc.

EXCALIBUR - Boats - Genmar Industries Inc.

EXCALIBUR - Boats - Wellcraft Marine Corp.

EXCALIBUR - Boats–kayaks - Noah Corp.

EXCALIBUR - Boats–motor ☆ - Excalibur Marine

EXCALIBUR - Brushes - Corona Brushes Inc.

EXCALIBUR - Colognes ☆ - Avon Products, Inc.

EXCALIBUR - Computers - American Megatrends, Inc.

EXCALIBUR - Cutlery - Gerber Legendary Blades

EXCALIBUR - Dehydrating equipment - Excalibur Products Inc.

EXCALIBUR - Doors–storm - Quik-Fab Aluminum Manufacturing Co. Inc.

EXCALIBUR - Eaves - English Greenhouse Products Corp.

EXCALIBUR - Flatware ☆ - Kirk Stieff Co.

EXCALIBUR - Floor coverings–carpet and rugs ☆ - Interloom Ltd.

EXCALIBUR - Floor coverings–carpet and rugs ☆ - Royalweve Carpet Mills

EXCALIBUR - Foam rubber - Rosen's Inc.

EXCALIBUR - Food dehydrator - Killer Baits Inc.

EXCALIBUR - Frames–picture - Terragrafics Inc.

EXCALIBUR - Furniture - Homecrest Industries Inc.

EXCALIBUR - Garden equipment ☆ - Nupla Corp.

EXCALIBUR - Guitars - St. Blues Guitars

EXCALIBUR - Hardware - Alside Div.

EXCALIBUR - Kitchen appliances ☆ - R & R Mill Co. Inc.

EXCALIBUR - Locks–padlocks - Illinois Lock Co.

EXCALIBUR - Mattresses and box springs - Ohio Mattress Co.

EXCALIBUR - Musical instruments - McCormick's

EXCALIBUR - Paper - Strathmore Paper Co.

EXCALIBUR - Pens - Pentel of America, Ltd.

EXCALIBUR - Plastics film - AEP Industries, Inc.

EXCALIBUR - Safety products - Crews, Inc.

EXCALIBUR - Sinks–metal - Moen Inc.

EXCALIBUR - Vacuum cleaners and accessories - The Eureka Co.

EXCALIBUR - Veterinary pharmaceutical preparations - Farnam Cos. Inc.

EXCALIBUR - Vitamins and nutritional supplements ☆ - Natural Balance, Inc.

EXCALIBUR - Wallpaper - Royaleigh Designs Ltd.

EXCALIBUR - Watches - Criterion Watch Co. Inc.

EXCALIBUR - Whiskey - John Gross & Co.

EXCALIBUR - Window coverings - Blinds & Designs Inc.

EXCALIBUR BY HOYO DE MONTERREY - Cigars - Danby-Palicio

EXCALIBUR CONCOURS - Automotive parts and accessories - Turtle Wax, Inc.

EXCALIBUR GOURMET CUTS - Kippered beef and sausages - Inorex Inc.

EXCALIBUR TECHNOLOGIES - Computer software - Excalibur Technologies Corp.

EXCAPE2 - Apparel - Cucci International Inc.

EXCEDO - Cleaning preparations - Twi-Laq Industries Inc.

EXCEDRIN - Analgesics - Bristol-Myers Squibb Co.

EXCEDRIN EXTRA STRENGTH - Analgesics - Bristol-Myers Squibb Co.

EXCEDRIN P.M. - Analgesics - Bristol-Myers Squibb Co.

EXCEED - Beverages - Ross Laboratories

EXCEED! - Computer software - Technology Resource Assistance Center

EXCEED - Herbicides - Ciba-Geigy Corp.

EXCEED - Paper–toweling - Wisconsin Tissue Mills Inc.

EXCEED - Pens - Faber-Castell Corp.

EXCEED - Tiles–ceramic - Innovative Ceramics, Inc.

EXCEED 1 - Food products - Kraft Food Ingredients Corp.

EXCEL - Anchors - Barrett Manufacturing Co.

EXCEL - Beef - Excel Corp.

EXCEL - Bicycles - Excel International Group Inc.

EXCEL - Building materials - Texas Aluminum Industries Inc.

EXCEL - Computer software - Microsoft Corp.

EXCEL - Cookware - Revere Ware Corp.

EXCEL - Dog food - Pet Products Plus

EXCEL - Ear plugs - Safety Supply America Corp.

EXCEL - Escalators - Access Industries, Inc.

EXCEL - Exercising equipment - Excel, The Exercise Co.

EXCEL - Exercising equipment - Rocket Industries

EXCEL - Fibers–synthetic - American Excelsior Co.

EXCEL - File folders - Warrensville File & Knife, Inc.

EXCEL - Filters–industrial - Jason Inc.

EXCEL - Fishing rods - Bass Pro Shops Inc.

☆ = Now out of production

EXCEL - Floor coverings–carpet and rugs - Cabin Crafts Carpets
EXCEL - Flowers, plants, and seeds - NK Lawn & Garden Co.
EXCEL - Golfing equipment - Lisco, Inc.
EXCEL - Guitars - Davitt and Hanser Music Co.
EXCEL - Hair care products - Amole Inc.
EXCEL - Health care products - Key Products Co.
EXCEL - Health care products ☆ - Leisure Lift, Inc.
EXCEL - Kilns - American Art Clay Co. Inc.
EXCEL - Luggage - Samsonite Corp.
EXCEL - Manicure preparations - Fromm Industries
EXCEL - Medical apparatus - McKesson Home Health Care
EXCEL - Motor vehicles - Excel Trailer Co. Inc.
EXCEL - Motor vehicles–automobiles ☆ - Hyundai Motor America
EXCEL - Occasional tables - JDI Group, Inc.
EXCEL - Pacemakers - Cardiac Pacemakers Inc.
EXCEL - Paper - Fay Paper Products Inc.
EXCEL - Pens - Faber-Castell Corp.
EXCEL - Pet products - 8 in 1 Pet Products Inc.
EXCEL - Photographic equipment - LogEtronics Corp.
EXCEL - Rackets–racquetball - Ektelon
EXCEL - Razors - Gillette Co.
EXCEL - Rope ☆ - Wellington Leisure Products, Inc.
EXCEL - Shoes - MSF Corp.
EXCEL - Trailers–travel - Peterson Industries Inc.
EXCEL - Vitamins and nutritional supplements - Ross Laboratories
EXCEL - Water purification systems - American Cyanamid Co.
EXCEL II - Rope ☆ - Wellington Leisure Products, Inc.
EXCEL II - Rope ☆ - Wellington Leisure Products, Inc.
EXCEL 4 - Veterinary pharmaceutical preparations ☆ - Boehringer Ingelheim Animal Health, Inc.
EXCEL 5000 - Computer monitoring system - Honeywell Inc.
EXCEL-A-TAN - Suntan lotions - Super Sun
EXCEL BRITE - Billboards - Sunnywell Display System, Inc.
EXCEL DEGREASER CONCENTRATE - Cleaning preparations - Uncle Sam Chemical Co., Inc.
EXCEL-FINISH - Thread ☆ - Coats and Clark Inc.
EXCEL-GLACE - Thread ☆ - Coats and Clark Inc.
EXCEL KOI FOOD - Pet products - Hikari Sales USA Inc.
EXCEL-LERATED LEARNING - Recording label - I.M.P.A.C.T. Publishing, Inc.
EXCEL-LITE - Brackets - Exclusive Specialty Products, LLC
EXCEL-LYTE - Lighting fixtures - Genlyte Group Inc.
EXCEL PLUS - Veterinary nutritional supplements - 8 in 1 Pet Products Inc.
EXCEL-R - Brushes–paint - Wooster Brush Co.
EXCEL STRINGS - Wallpaper - Advance Wallcoverings
EXCEL SUPREME - Food products - Excel Corp.
EXCELAIR - Deodorizers - Vaportek, Inc.
EXCELAMINS - Vitamins and nutritional supplements - Tishcon Corp.
EXCELAVITES - Vitamins and nutritional supplements - Tishcon Corp.
EXCELCIDE - Insecticides - Huge Co. Inc.
EXCELE - Watches - Elgin Watch Co.
EXCELER - Golfing equipment - Daiwa Corp.
EXCELERASE - Paper–bond ☆ - Fox River Paper Co.
EXCELERATE - Photographic equipment ☆ - Minnesota Mining & Manufacturing Co.
EXCELERATION - Vitamins and nutritional supplements - Excel Sports Science Inc.
EXCELERATOR - Rope ☆ - Wellington Leisure Products, Inc.
EXCELERATOR - Toys–automobiles - Mattel, Inc.
EXCELERATOR II - Sporting goods ☆ - Wellington Leisure Products, Inc.
EXCELGAR - Vitamins and nutritional supplements ☆ - Solaray
EXCELGARD - Diapers–disposable ☆ - Whitestone Products Inc.
EXCELIDE - Electronic equipment - Ox Products Inc.
EXCELIGHT - Ladders–metal - White Metal Rolling & Stamping Corp.
EXCELITE - Hearing aids - Earmold Design Inc.
EXCELL - Batteries - Argraph Corp. (Samigon Div.)
EXCELL - Binders - Steego Corp.
EXCELL - Drill bits - Credo Co.
EXCELL - Fabrics - BBA Nonwovens Simpsonville, Inc.
EXCELL - Hair care products - Kenra Laboratories, Inc.
EXCELL - Health care products - Rockline Industries Inc.
EXCELL - Hosiery - Emby Hosiery Corp.
EXCELL - Jewelry - Excell Manufacturing Co.
EXCELL - Pet products ☆ - Lightning Products
EXCELL - Skates–roller - Variflex, Inc.
EXCELL-40 - Lighting equipment - Excell Technology Inc.
EXCELL-A3 - Skin care products - Cosmair Inc.

EXCELLA - Audio equipment - Hiraoka New York Corp.
EXCELLA - Lighting equipment - Marvel Lighting Corp.
EXCELLA - Motor vehicles - Airstream Inc.
EXCELLE - Antiseptics - Cottrell, Ltd.
EXCELLE - Hair care products - Carson Products Co.
EXCELLENCE - Floor coverings ☆ - Congoleum Corp.
EXCELLENCE - Food products - Fairco, Inc.
EXCELLENCE - Glassware–household ☆ - Oneida Ltd.
EXCELLENCE - Hair coloring preparations - Cosmair Inc.
EXCELLENCE - Lacquers and varnishes - Gemini Coatings, Inc.
EXCELLENCE - Shoes - Life Shoes
EXCELLENCE - Yarn - Nomis Yarn Co.
EXCELLENCE BY DESIGN - Luggage - Tumi Luggage, Inc.
EXCELLENCE TRANSLATES EVERYWHERE - Automotive repair shops - ITT Automotive, Inc.
EXCELLENCE UNDER PRESSURE - Machine parts - Starr Hydraulics Electro Controls, Co.
EXCELLENCY - Cabinets - Prestige Inc.
EXCELLENCY - Floor coverings–carpet and rugs ☆ - Karastan-Bigelow Inc.
EXCELLENCY - Glassware–household - Anchor Hocking Glass, Inc.
EXCELLENT - Coffee - Excellent Coffee Co. Inc.
EXCELLENT - Scissors–hand-operated - J.A. Henckels Zwillingswerk Inc.
EXCELLENT - Thread - Belding Heminway Co. Inc.
EXCELLENT APPAREL COMPANY - Apparel and accessories - Graj & Gustavsen
EXCELLENT MARINARA - Food products - Uncle Dave's Kitchen
EXCELLENT MARINARA W/MUSHROOMS - Tomato pastes and sauces - Uncle Dave's Kitchen
EXCELLENT PERFORMANCE 1995 - Leotards - Krystal K. International Inc.
EXCELLERATOR - Audio/video cables - Audio Authority Corp.
EXCELLINE - Food products - Dairy Fresh Products Co.
EXCELLINE - Frozen foods - Excelline Foods Inc.
EXCELLINES - Audio equipment - Pro-Co. Sound Co. Inc.
EXCELLITE - Reflectors–vehicular - Reflectory
EXCELLO - Artists' materials - Advance Process Supply Co.
EXCELLO - Batteries - Ebco Battery Co.
EXCELLO - Binders ☆ - Stationers Loose Leaf Co.
EXCELLO - Chalk - Dixon Ticonderoga Co.
EXCELLO - Floor coverings ☆ - Congoleum Corp.
EXCELLO - Flour–blended - North Dakota Mill and Elevator Association
EXCELLO - Hotplates - Fashioncraft-Excello
EXCELLO - Shirts - Pandora Sportswear Industries
EXCELLO - Shirts - Tica Industries Inc.
EXCELLO - Towels - Excello Ltd.
EXCELLO SQUARES - Chalk - Dixon Ticonderoga Co.
EXCELLOLITE - Paints ☆ - Dunn Edwards Corp.
EXCELLOVAN - Spices and extracts - Crompton & Knowles Corp.
EXCELON - Bathroom accessories - Consolidated Industries Corp.
EXCELS - Boats - Wellcraft Marine Corp.
EXCEL'S SPECIAL LEAN - Food products - Excel Corp.
EXCELSALL - Tools - O.P. Link Handle Co. Inc.
EXCELSAN - Detergents - Huge Co. Inc.
EXCELSIOLA - Musical instruments - Excelsior Accordions Inc.
EXCELSIOR - Accordions - Castiglione Accordion
EXCELSIOR - Bicycles - Schwinn Cycling & Fitness Inc.
EXCELSIOR - Clocks - Excelsior Collection Inc.
EXCELSIOR - Diaries - Dennison National Co.
EXCELSIOR - Eyeglasses - Uvex Safety LLC
EXCELSIOR - Glassware–household - Dalzell-Viking
EXCELSIOR - Golfing equipment - Raven Golf Services, Inc.
EXCELSIOR - Hams - Atalanta Corp.
EXCELSIOR - Milk - Excelsior Dairy Ltd.
EXCELSIOR - Musical instruments - Excelsior Accordions Inc.
EXCELSIOR - Needles–sewing ☆ - Torrington Co.
EXCELSIOR - Nuts and bolts - Berry Brothers
EXCELSIOR - Office accessories - Fasteners for Retail, Inc.
EXCELSIOR - Pasta - Borinquen Macaroni Corp.
EXCELSIOR - Pencils - Reliance Pen & Pencil Corp.
EXCELSIOR - Pins–jewelry - Excelsior-Hendersn Motorcycle Manufacturing Co.
EXCELSIOR - Tape measures ☆ - Keuffel & Esser Co.
EXCELSIOR - Water–bottled or canned - Excelsior Spring Water
EXCELSIOR BOND - Office supplies - BlumbergExcelsior, Inc.
EXCELSIOR BOTANICAL HAIR SYSTEMS - Hair care products - For Women Only Inc.
EXCELSIOR/EDITION DELUXE - Glassware–household - Oneida Ltd.

☆ = Now out of production

EXCELSIOR KNIFE CO. - Pocket knives - Tennessee River Valley Knife Association Inc.

EXCELSIOR MIDIVOX III SYSTEMS - Sound equipment - Castiglione Accordion

EXCELSIOR MUSIC - Music–sheet - Theodore Presser Co.

EXCELSIOR SUPERIOR - Incense - Excelsior Incense Works

EXCELSIOR WOOD-PAK - Packaging–paper - Cedar-Al Products

EXCELSIS-PL - Jams and jellies - Edwin R. Sage Co.

EXCELTAG - Paper products - Beekley Corp.

EXCELUBE - Thread - Advance Thread Corp.

EXCELYTE - Electrolyte diagnostic agents - Excel Technology

EXCENTIA - Tires–automobile - Uniroyal Goodrich Licensing Services, Inc.

EXCENTRIQUE - Apparel–women's - Excentrique, Inc.

EXCEPTION - Computer software - Infraspection Institute, Inc.

EXCEPTIONAL - Floor coverings–carpet and rugs - World Carpets, Inc.

EXCEPTIONAL - Wallpaper - I. Gottlieb & Associates

EXCEPTIONAL ATHLETE MATTERS, THE - Apparel and accessories - World T.E.A.M. Sports

EXCEPTIONAL CHOCOLATES - Candy ☆ - Maillard Corp.

EXCEPTIONAL EYES - Cosmetics - Prince Matchabelli

EXCEPTIONAL TEXTILE II - Wallpaper - I. Gottlieb & Associates

EXCEPTIONAL TEXTILES - Wallcoverings - Cork Products Co. Inc.

EXCEPTIONAL TEXTILES - Wallpaper - K.M.L. Industries

EXCEPTIONAL TEXTILES II - Wallcoverings - Cork Products Co. Inc.

EXCEPTIONAL VALUE - Food products - Scrivner, Inc.

EXCEPTIONELLE - Floor coverings–carpet and rugs ☆ - J.L. Benson Co.

EXCEPTIONELLE - Floor coverings–carpet and rugs ☆ - Olympic Carpets Inc.

EXCERLITES - Health care products - Ginny Inc.

EXCERTIGHTS - Leotards - Learsi Collection

EXCESS - Pens - Pen Werks, LLC.

EXCESS - Skis - Rossignol Ski Co., Inc.

EXCESS WORDS - Computer software ☆ - Right on Programs

EXCESSALITE - Electronic equipment - Bell & Howell Co.

EXCHANGE - Beverages - Sunkist Growers Inc.

EXCHANGE BLADE - Cutlery - Gerber Legendary Blades

EXCHANGE SPORT - Apparel - Bradlees Stores, Inc.

EXCHANGE UNLIMITED - Women's and children's apparel - Bradlees Stores, Inc.

EXCHANGECERT - Computer software - Transcender Corp.

EXCHANGEFONE - Telephones - Ipc Information Systems, Inc.

EXCHANGEMAX - Telecommunications products - At&T Corp.

EXCITA - Prophylactics - Schmid Laboratories

EXCITABLES, THE - Automotive parts and accessories ☆ - Hedstrom Corp.

EXCITE BIKE MINI-BIKES - Bicycle parts and accessories - Lakeland Manufacturing Co. Inc.

EXCITEMENT - Floor coverings–carpet and rugs - Burlington House Carpets

EXCITEMENT - Floor coverings–carpet and rugs ☆ - Downs Carpet Co. Inc.

EXCITEMENT - Frames–eyeglass - Zylo Ware Corp.

EXCITER - Boats–motor ☆ - Checkmate Boats Inc.

EXCITERS - Frames–eyeglass - May Optical Co. Inc.

EXCITIMO - Frames–eyeglass - Zylo Ware Corp.

EXCITING - Floor coverings–carpet and rugs ☆ - Karastan-Bigelow Inc.

EXCITING - Frames–eyeglass - Pathway Optical Prods.

EXCITING GAME OF WINE, THE - Games - Carajean Entertainment, Inc.

EXCITING HOUR - Video games - Taito America Corp.

EXCITING OVATION - Floor coverings–carpet and rugs ☆ - Karastan-Bigelow Inc.

EXCITING WORLD OF FASTENERS, THE - Computer storage devices - National Fastener Distributors Association

EXCITOR - Air purification systems - CRS Industries, Inc. (Cosatron)

EXCLAIM - Occasional tables - JDI Group, Inc.

EX'CLA'MA'TION - Fragrance - Coty Inc.

EXCLAMATION - Frames–eyeglass - Liberty Optical Manufacturing Co.

EXCLAMATION - Furniture ☆ - White Furniture Co.

EXCLIMATIC - Drums–musical instruments - Tucson Wholesale Music

EXCLOID - Audio equipment - Audiological Engineering Corp.

EXCLOSURES - Leather goods ☆ - Design Circle Ltd.

EXCLUSIV - Watches - Medana Watch Corp.

EXCLUSIVE - Bathroom fixtures - Showerlux USA

EXCLUSIVE - Bicycles ☆ - Roadmaster Corp.

EXCLUSIVE - Dishes–china - Ellis Barker Silver Co.

EXCLUSIVE - Hair coloring preparations - Cosmair Inc.

EXCLUSIVE - Hotels and motels - Trusthouse Forte Hotels International Inc.

EXCLUSIVE - Jewelry - N. Gogolick & Son Inc.

EXCLUSIVE - Nail care products - Opi Products, Inc.

EXCLUSIVE AREA RUGS - Floor coverings–carpet and rugs - Salzburg Creations Inc.

EXCLUSIVE ARTISTS - Greeting cards - Exclusive Co.

EXCLUSIVE BOGOLAN - Fabrics - Setma/Afritex Inc.

EXCLUSIVE CARE - Hair care products - Montana-Steinberg Corp.

EXCLUSIVE CREATIONS - Catalogs - Straight Status, Inc.

EXCLUSIVE CREATIONS - Greeting cards - Exclusive Co.

EXCLUSIVE DIAMOND - Jewelry - Veejai Creations

EXCLUSIVE FOIL - Paper–gift wrap - Exclusive Co.

EXCLUSIVE LINES - Artists' materials - National Art Supply, Inc.

EXCLUSIVE MIXTURES - Beverages–malt - Brazos Country Foods

EXCLUSIVELY BORDERS - Floor coverings–carpet and rugs - J and J Industries Inc.

EXCLUSIVELY DOG - Dog food - General Pet Supply, Inc.

EXCLUSIVELY FOR YOU - Apparel–women's - May Department Stores Co.

EXCLUSIVELY FRUIT - Jams and jellies - Allied Old English, Inc.

EXCLUSIVELY JESS ROBBIN - Footwear - New York City Shoes Inc.

EXCLUSIVELY OURS - Wallpaper ☆ - Wallpaper Imports Inc.

EXCLUSIVELY SANTA'S - Lamps–plastic - North American Marketing Corp.

EXCLUSIVELY YOURS - Candy - World's Finest Chocolate, Inc.

EXCLUSIVELY YOURS - Ribbons–inked ☆ - Distinguished Brands Inc.

EXCLUSIVELY YOURS FROM SLM AND MOTHER NATURE - Swimming pools - SLM Inc.

EXCLUSIVES BY GEORGETTE MOSBACHER - Cosmetics - Georgette Mosbacher Enterprises Inc.

EXCON - Apparel and accessories - Frank G. D'Amato

EXCOR - Electrical equipment - Rogers Corp.

EXCUISITE - Cooking utensils–aluminum - Bahrain Industrial Investment Co.

EXCULPATOR - Golfing equipment - Tommy Armour Golf Co.

EXCURSION - Women's apparel - Florida Adams, Ltd.

EXCURSIONS - Furniture ☆ - Lane Co. Inc.

EXCUSES - Apparel–women's - No Excuses Sportswear Ltd.

EXE - Apparel and accessories - Intersport, Inc.

EXEC - Air conditioning equipment ☆ - Dometic Corp.

EXEC - Apparel–men's - Munsingwear, Inc.

EXEC - Carpet - Global Contract Carpets Inc.

EXEC - Dictating machines - Dictaphone Corp.

EXEC - Luggage - United States Luggage Corp.

EXEC-SEC PEN - Pens ☆ - K-9 Pen Co.

EXEC, THE - Lighting fixtures - Big Beam Emergency Systems Inc.

EXEC U PUTT - Golfing equipment - Executive Golf Co.

EXECARDS - Stationery - PSI Research

EXECMASTER - Office machines - Dictaphone Corp.

EXECONTROL - Computer software - George M. Hartley

EXECSET - Computers ☆ - Compaq Computer Corp.

EXECTALK - Dictating machines - Dictaphone Corp.

EXECU-CARD - Greeting cards - Regency Thermographers Inc.

EXECU-DOODLES - Calendars - Jack Taylor

EXECU-LINE - Office supplies ☆ - JM Co.

EXECU-RIGHT - Paper products - One-Right Systems, Inc.

EXECU-RIGHT THE EXECUTIVE CHECKBOOK - Paper products - One-Right Systems, Inc.

EXECU-TURF - Grass seed - Cisco Companies

EXECUCOACH - Motor vehicles - Noventa Fm 90, Inc.

EXECUFAX - Calendars - Bugatti Inc.

EXECUFILE - File folders ☆ - Anthes Universal

EXECULINE - Furniture - Virco Manufacturing Corp.

EXECUMARK - Pens - Accutec Inc.

EXECUPET TOYS - Pet products - Diverse Designs

EXECUSOX - Socks - Thomas C. Cullop

EXECUSYS - Computer software - Execusys, Inc.

EXECUTAIRE - Office supplies ☆ - Bentson Industries Inc.

EXECUTARY - Office machines - International Business Machines Corp.

EXECUTEUR - Eyeglasses - Martin-Copeland Eyewear Corp.

EXECUTILE - Floor coverings–tile - Matworks

EXECUTIONER, THE - Skateboards ☆ - Nash Manufacturing Inc.

EXECUTIVE - Audio cabinets–wood - Luxor

EXECUTIVE - Bathroom fixtures - Melard Manufacturing Corp.

EXECUTIVE - Boats–houseboats ☆ - Holiday Mansion

EXECUTIVE - Boats–motor - Thompson Boat Co.

EXECUTIVE - Boats–motor ☆ - Ebko Industries Inc.

EXECUTIVE - Boats–pontoons - Forester Boats Inc.

EXECUTIVE - Briefcases ☆ - Master Products Manufacturing Inc.

EXECUTIVE - Cigars ☆ - Phillies Cigar Co.

EXECUTIVE - Diaries - Distinctive Diaries Ltd.

EXECUTIVE - Drums–musical instruments - J.W. Enterprises

                                  ☆ = Now out of production

EXECUTIVE - Electric vehicle - Ransomes-Cushman-Ryan
EXECUTIVE - Envelopes - Westvaco Corp.
EXECUTIVE - Exercising equipment ☆ - Jugglebug
EXECUTIVE - Floor coverings–carpet and rugs - J.L. Benson Co.
EXECUTIVE - Floor coverings–carpet and rugs ☆ - Cumberland Mills Inc.
EXECUTIVE - Furniture - Bretford Manufacturing, Inc.
EXECUTIVE - Furniture ☆ - Domore/DO3
EXECUTIVE - Glassware–household - Federal Glass
EXECUTIVE - Glassware–household - Svend Jensen of Denmark Inc.
EXECUTIVE - Golfing equipment - Spalding Sports Worldwide
EXECUTIVE - Greeting cards - Masterpiece Studios Inc.
EXECUTIVE - Jewelry - Jacoby-Bender Inc.
EXECUTIVE - Motor vehicles–automobiles ☆ - DaimlerChrysler
EXECUTIVE - Motor vehicles–automobiles ☆ - General Motors Corp. (Pontiac/GMC Div.)
EXECUTIVE - Motor vehicles–motor homes ☆ - Honey Recreational Vehicles Inc.
EXECUTIVE - Motor vehicles–motor homes ☆ - Mitchell & Sons Inc.
EXECUTIVE - Office furniture–metal ☆ - Joyce International Inc.
EXECUTIVE - Office supplies - Stuart Hall Co., Inc.
EXECUTIVE - Office supplies - McDonald Products
EXECUTIVE - Ophthalmic goods - American Optical Corp.
EXECUTIVE - Ophthalmic goods ☆ - Rozin Optical Export Corp.
EXECUTIVE - Pencils - Dixon Ticonderoga Co.
EXECUTIVE - Pens ☆ - K-9 Pen Co.
EXECUTIVE - Pipes - National Briar Pipe Co.
EXECUTIVE - Playing cards ☆ - United States Playing Card Co.
EXECUTIVE - Plywood - Plywood & Panels Inc.
EXECUTIVE - Portable partition ☆ - Brewster Corp.
EXECUTIVE - Powerboat - Invader Marine Inc.
EXECUTIVE - Staplers - Markwell Manufacturing Co. Inc.
EXECUTIVE - Stationery ☆ - Pratt & Austin Co.
EXECUTIVE - Thread - Witten Sales Corp.
EXECUTIVE - Toys–stuffed ☆ - Commonwealth Toy and Novelty Co. Inc.
EXECUTIVE - Trailers–travel - Franklin Coach Co.
EXECUTIVE - Vans–conversion - Coachmen Industries, Inc.
EXECUTIVE - Watches - Gruen Marketing Corp.
EXECUTIVE - Windows–storm ☆ - Miller Industries Inc.
EXECUTIVE 707 - Trailers–travel ☆ - Seven O Seven Industries Inc.
EXECUTIVE 727 - Trailers–travel ☆ - Seven O Seven Industries Inc.
EXECUTIVE 2000 - Dryers–commercial ☆ - American Dryer Inc.
EXECUTIVE ACTION - Fishing rods - Michael J. Grossman
EXECUTIVE ADVISOR - Computer software - Career Interactive, Inc.
EXECUTIVE ANTROPOLIS - Toys ☆ - Uncle Milton Industries Inc.
EXECUTIVE APPOINTMENTS - Desk sets - Crystal Clear Importing Co. Inc.
EXECUTIVE BEANBAG, THE - Furniture ☆ - Jeanine M. Rogers
EXECUTIVE BELLS - Sporting goods - Diversified Products Corp.
EXECUTIVE BENEFITS SYSTEMS - Computer software - Insmark, Inc.
EXECUTIVE BERBER II - Floor coverings–carpet and rugs - Milliken & Co. Inc.
EXECUTIVE BOARD - Trading cards and stamps - Upper Deck Co.
EXECUTIVE BRASS - Darts and dart games - Dart World Inc.
EXECUTIVE BUCK PASSER - Novelty items ☆ - Wry Idea Co.
EXECUTIVE BUFF - Manicure preparations - American Manicure Corp.
EXECUTIVE CARPETS - Floor coverings–carpet and rugs - Queen Carpet Corp.
EXECUTIVE CHEF - Meat products–poultry - Snowball Foods, Inc.
EXECUTIVE CHEF - Seasonings - Milwaukee Seasonings, Inc.
EXECUTIVE CHEF - Seasonings - Pet Inc.
EXECUTIVE CHEF - Sinks–metal - Kohler Co.
EXECUTIVE CHESS - Computer software - SourceView Software International
EXECUTIVE CHOICE - Greeting cards - Nu-Art Inc.
EXECUTIVE CLASS - Stationery - Geographics Inc.
EXECUTIVE CLUB - Eyeglasses - Art-Craft Optical Co.
EXECUTIVE CLUB - Luggage - Travelers Club Luggage Inc.
EXECUTIVE COLLECTION - Furniture ☆ - Hooker Furniture Corp.
EXECUTIVE COLLECTION - Giftware - Lenox, Inc.
EXECUTIVE COMIC CARDS - Novelty items - BRC Corp.
EXECUTIVE COMMAND - Floor coverings–carpet and rugs ☆ - Karastan-Bigelow Inc.
EXECUTIVE CONTROL - Electronic equipment - Ecolab Inc.
EXECUTIVE COUNCIL - Floor coverings–carpet and rugs - Trend Carpet
EXECUTIVE COURIER - Cases–plastic - Custom Case Co.
EXECUTIVE CUP, THE - Educational materials - JM Perry Corp.
EXECUTIVE CUTTERS - Tools - LRH Enterprises Inc.
EXECUTIVE DECISION - Games ☆ - Avalon Hill Game Co.

EXECUTIVE DESK FILE - Office supplies ☆ - Quality Park Products Co.
EXECUTIVE DREAM BY ATS - Motor vehicles–all-terrain - American Travel Systems, Inc.
EXECUTIVE DRESSING - Apparel–athletic - Alexander's Inc.
EXECUTIVE EDGE - Floor coverings–carpet and rugs ☆ - American Carpet Mills
EXECUTIVE ELECTROL - Electronic equipment ☆ - Da-Lite Screen Co. Inc.
EXECUTIVE EXPRESS - Furniture - Sligh Furniture Co.
EXECUTIVE EYES - Ophthalmic goods - Foremost Optical Products
EXECUTIVE FIRST AID KIT - Housewares ☆ - Sperry Owens Inc.
EXECUTIVE FLAIR - Pens ☆ - Paper Mate Co.
EXECUTIVE FORUM - Computer software - IMRS Operations Inc.
EXECUTIVE GERIATRIC - Health care products - Fleetwood Co.
EXECUTIVE GIFT - Games - Tedco Inc.
EXECUTIVE GOLF LTD. 19 - Visors - Executive Golf Ltd.
EXECUTIVE IBM - Typewriters - International Business Machines Corp.
EXECUTIVE IMAGE - Floor coverings–carpet and rugs - Lotus Carpets
EXECUTIVE JAZZ - Panty hose - TGC INC.
EXECUTIVE KEYLESS ENTRY & SECURITY - Alarm systems - Kenneth E. Flick
EXECUTIVE KNIT - Crocheted and knitted items - Heritage Sportswear
EXECUTIVE KNOCKING BLOCK - Novelty items - Wry Idea Co.
EXECUTIVE KO-REC-TYPE - Ribbons - Eaton Allen Ko-Rec-Type Corp.
EXECUTIVE LEATHERWARE - Luggage - New England Leather Accessories
EXECUTIVE LIBRARIAN, THE - Computer software - Imagine Products, Inc.
EXECUTIVE LOUNGE - Motor vehicles–motor homes ☆ - Georgie Boy Manufacturing, Inc.
EXECUTIVE MANOR - Floor coverings–carpet and rugs ☆ - S and S Mills Inc.
EXECUTIVE MARBLES - Giftware - Russ Berrie and Co., Inc.
EXECUTIVE MEMBERS - Luggage - Universal Trav-ler Inc.
EXECUTIVE MEMO MASTER - Paper–gummed ☆ - Park Sherman
EXECUTIVE MIXTURE - Tobacco products - Lane Ltd.
EXECUTIVE OFFICE - Computer software ☆ - DataPak Software Inc.
EXECUTIVE ORDER - Floor coverings–carpet and rugs ☆ - Karastan-Bigelow Inc.
EXECUTIVE ORGANIZER, THE - Binders - Samsill Corp.
EXECUTIVE PENTIUS SYSTEMS - Computers - Mitsuba Corp.
EXECUTIVE PICTURE SHOW - Computer software - PCSoftware
EXECUTIVE PLUS - Floor coverings–carpet and rugs - Heuga USA
EXECUTIVE PONY - Toys ☆ - Hartco Inc.
EXECUTIVE POWERS - Computer software - Advanced Business Language Group Inc.
EXECUTIVE PRO - Motors–outboard - G. & R. Industries Inc.
EXECUTIVE PROGRAM, THE - Publisher's imprints - MacMillan Publishing Co. Inc.
EXECUTIVE QUARTERS - Office supplies - J.C. Penney Co., Inc.
EXECUTIVE ROLLING ORGANIZER - Carts - E.D. Dunn, Jr.
EXECUTIVE ROW - Frames–eyeglass ☆ - Universal/Univis Inc.
EXECUTIVE ROWE II - Floor coverings–carpet and rugs - Milliken & Co. Inc.
EXECUTIVE SELF-SERVICE - Computer storage devices - ESSENSE Systems Inc.
EXECUTIVE SERIES - Electronics equipment - Crestron Electronics Inc.
EXECUTIVE SERIES, THE - Jewelry - Novell Enterprises, Inc.
EXECUTIVE SESSION - Floor coverings–carpet and rugs - Barrett Carpet Mills Inc.
EXECUTIVE SLIM - Pens - Paper Mate Co.
EXECUTIVE SOFTWARE - Computer software - Executive Software International, Inc.
EXECUTIVE STRESS FORMULA - Vitamins and nutritional supplements - Better Health Products
EXECUTIVE SUITE - Fabrics - Valley Forge Fabrics Inc.
EXECUTIVE SUITE - Floor coverings–carpet and rugs ☆ - Criterion Mills Inc.
EXECUTIVE SUITE - Wallcoverings - Wallcovering Industries Inc.
EXECUTIVE SUITE - Wallpaper - Benchmark Preferred Wallcoverings
EXECUTIVE SUITE, THE - Apparel–men's - Jones Investment Co., Inc.
EXECUTIVE SUMMARY PROGRAM, THE - Publisher's imprints - MacMillan Publishing Co. Inc.
EXECUTIVE SWEET, THE - Pollen extracts - CC Pollen Co.
EXECUTIVE SWEET, THE - Chocolate candy - K & L Associates, Inc.
EXECUTIVE, THE - Office supplies - Mayflower Glass Works
EXECUTIVE, THE - Computer software - SourceView Software International
EXECUTIVE TOTE - Bags–duffel - Ektelon
EXECUTIVE TOURNAMENT - Computer software ☆ - Access Software Inc.
EXECUTIVE TOWER - Floor coverings–carpet and rugs ☆ - Blue Ridge Carpet Mills
EXECUTIVE TRANSPORTER - Motor vehicles - Turtle Top Specialty Products

---

☆ = Now out of production

EXECUTIVE VIP - Boats–houseboats ☆ - Boatel Marine, Inc.
EXECUTIVE WOOD - Wallpaper - S.R. Wood Inc.
EXECUTIVE WOOLS FOR THE WALL - Wallpaper - Maharam Vertical
  Surfaces
EXECUTOR - Doughnuts - McKee Door, Inc.
EXECUTOR, THE - Binders ☆ - 20th Century Plastics
EXECUTOUR - Golfing equipment - Korex Corp.
EXECUTRA - Pens - Accutec Inc.
EXECUTRON - Watches - Movado Time Corp.
EXECUVOICE - Computer software - Media Vision Technology Inc.
EXECUWALL II - Wallpaper - Capital Carousel Inc.
EXEL - See SUNNY SQUARE
EXEL - Sporting goods - Exel Marketing Inc.
EXELENTO - Hair care products - Murray's Worldwide Inc.
EXELLENCE BY L'OREAL - Hair coloring preparations - Cosmair Inc.
EXELPET - Pet products - Kal Kan Foods, Inc.
EXELTAX - Computer software - IMP Group Ltd.
EXELTHERM XTRA - Insulating materials ☆ - Kop-Coat, Inc.
EXEMPLAR - Apparel–men's - Haspel Brothers Inc.
EXEMPLAR - Computer hardware - Convex Computer Corp.
EXER-BALL - Exercising equipment - Exer-Ball Inc.
EXER-GENIE - Exercising equipment - Physical Fitness Inc.
EXER-PEDIC - Health care products - Thermo-Electric Co.
EXER-SIT - Stools–metal - Sherrill Corey
EXER-STIK - Health care products - Omni Group Inc.
EXER-STIM - Electromedical apparatus - TH Charters, Inc.
EXER-STIM 2 - Electromedical apparatus - TH Charters, Inc.
EXER-STIM CONTROLLER - Electromedical apparatus ☆ - TH Charters, Inc.
EXER-STRESS - Recording label ☆ - Fit Net
EXER-TONER - Exercising equipment ☆ - Camp Forest Springs
EXER-TWIST - Health care products - Maddak Inc.
EXERAIRE - Floor coverings - Trotmar, Inc.
EXERBIKE - Exercising equipment ☆ - World Famous Trading Co., Ltd.
EXERCARDS - Paper products - Bithian Empire Mercantile Corp.
EXERCARE - Exercising equipment - Exercare, Inc.
EXERCISE - Pencils - General Pencil Co.
EXERCISE IV - Floor coverings–carpet and rugs ☆ - Regal Rugs Inc.
EXERCISE MATE - Apparel–women's - Cupid Foundations Inc.
EXERCISE SINGLE - Exercising equipment - Coffey Racing Shells
EXERCISEBREAK - Computer software - Hopkins Technology LLC
EXERCLIP - Hardware - Trotmar, Inc.
EXERCYCLE - Exercising equipment - Exercycle Corp.
EXERFLEX - Exercising equipment - Trotmar, Inc.
EXERFLEX - Shoes - Melville Corp.
EXERFLEXER - Men's aerobic shoes ☆ - Jaclar
EXERGRIP - Exercising equipment - DBA Products Co.
EXERION - Video games - Taito America Corp.
EXERKIT - Exercising equipment - Patricia Schwarzmann
EXERLOPERS - Medical apparatus ☆ - Biosig Instruments Inc.
EXEROW - Exercising equipment - Battle Creek Equipment Co.
EXERREVIEW - Computer software - Ergometrx Corp.
EXERSANDER - Health care products - Sammons Preston
EXERSAUCER - Rocking chairs - Lisco, Inc.
EXERSAUCER BABY - Toys - Lisco, Inc.
EXERSAUCER DELUXE PLUS - Toys - Lisco, Inc.
EXERSAUCER TOY - Toys - Lisco, Inc.
EXERSCIENCE - Sporting goods - Nordictrack, Inc.
EXERSCRIBE - Computer software - Ergometrx Corp.
EXERSOLE - Shoes - Thom McAn Shoe Co.
EXERSTIK - Exercising equipment - Personally Fit Inc.
EXERSTRESS - Medical apparatus - Del Mar Avionics
EXERSTRIDER - Exercising equipment - Exerstrider Products Inc.
EXERT - Pharmaceutical preparations - Bretney Corp.
EXERTAINMENT - Electronic equipment ☆ - Life Fitness
EXERTRON - Exercising equipment - Exertron Inc.
EXERTUBING - Health care products ☆ - Sammons Preston
EXESCAN - Computer software - Exescan, Inc.
EXESTICKS - Cosmetics ☆ - Redken Laboratories, Inc.
EXETER - Artists' materials - Light Impressions Corp.
EXETER - Canvas–artists' ☆ - Winsor & Newton
EXETER - Floor coverings - Congoleum Corp.
EXETER - Floor coverings–carpet and rugs - Atlas Carpet Mills Inc.
EXETER - Lenses–optical - Kelley & Hueber
EXETER - Rings–jewelry - Artcarved Inc.
EXETER - Telephones - At&T Corp.
EXETER PLACE - Floor coverings–carpet and rugs - Atlas Carpet Mills Inc.

EXFODERM - Skin care products - Worldwide Products, Inc.
EXFOLE - Skin care products - Cosmetic Solutions, Inc.
EXGEST LA - Pharmaceutical preparations - Carnick Laboratories Inc.
EXHAUST-A-LITE - Lighting fixtures - O.C. White Co.
EXHAUST AID - Engines–diesel - Exhaust Aid Co. Inc.
EXHAUST AUTHENTIC ORIGINAL - Apparel–men's - Traffic Sportswear Ltd.
EXHAUST-GARD - Boating equipment and accessories - W.H. Salisbury & Co.
EXHIBIT - Insecticides - Ciba-Geigy Corp.
EXHIBIT - Projectors–photographic ☆ - MPO Videotronics Inc.
EXHIBIT - Wallpaper coverings - Exhibit Corp.
EXHIBIT J - Recording label - Bomp Records Inc.
EXHIBITMAKER - Computer software - Coopers & Lybrand
EXHIBITOR TIMES - Magazines - Virgo Publishing, Inc.
EXHIBITOUR - Furniture–public buildings - Randall Bailey
EXHILARAMA THE ULTIMATE INDOOR PLAYGROUND - Amusement
  parks ☆ - Edison Brothers Stores, Inc.
EXHILARATING SKINSCENT - Skin care products - Cosmair Inc.
EXHILARATION - Eyeglasses - Martin-Copeland Eyewear Corp.
EXHILARATION - Furniture ☆ - Bassett Furniture Industries, Inc.
EXI - Audio equipment - Entronix International, Inc.
EXI-PEL - Coatings - Aegis Coating Technologies Corp.
EXI-POST - Office machines - Park Sherman
EXIDE - Batteries - Exide Corp.
EXIDE BATTERIES RACING TEAM - Hats - Exide Corp.
EXIDE ELECTRONICS STRATEGIC POWER MANAGEMENT - Electrical
  equipment - Exide Electronics Corp.
EXIDY - Toys - Exidy Inc.
EXIDY'S MOUSE TRAP - Toys–electronic - Hasbro, Inc.
EXILE - Cleaning preparations–carpet and rug - W.W. Grainger, Inc.
EXILES - Books–comic - Malibu Comics Entertainment, Inc.
EXILUME - Lighting fixtures ☆ - Kenall Manufacturing Co.
EXIMER - Golfing equipment - Ram Golf Corp.
EXISS - Trailers - Exiss Aluminum Trailers, Inc.
EXISTENCE - Frames–eyeglass ☆ - Universal/Univis Inc.
EXIT - Adhesives and sealants - Nu-Brite Chemical Co. Inc.
EXIT - Insecticide ☆ - Atlas Chemical Corp.
EXIT - Motor vehicles–armored - Clarklift Services, Inc.
EXIT - Sporting goods - Denali International Inc.
EXIT - Sporting goods ☆ - Action Clothing Technology
EXIT-1 - Apparel–rubberized - USA Fashions Inc.
EXIT SIGNS - Lighting equipment - ProLight
EXIT, STAGE RIGHT - Office machines - Jeanne K. Smith
EXIT STOPPER - Alarm systems–fire - Safety Technology International, Inc.
EXIT STRATEGY - Skin care products - Philosophy, Inc.
EXIT-ZERO - Apparel and accessories - Excellmodes Exclusives, Inc.
EXITO - Computer software - Analysas Corp.
EXITRONIX - Signs - Barron Manufacturing Corp.
EXLEY - Diaries - Chase Collection, Inc.
EXLITE - Electric lighting equipment - Flexlite Inc.
EXLOX - Chemical preparations - Novagen, Inc.
EXM - Computer software - Enterprise Solutions Business Corp.
EXMORE - Vegetables–frozen - Exmore Foods Inc.
EXO - Paper–gift wrap - Tommy R. Savage
EXO-BED - Medical apparatus - Florida Manufacturing Corp.
EXO-DOOR - Medical apparatus - Florida Manufacturing Corp.
EXO-FOAM - Medical apparatus - Florida Manufacturing Corp.
EXO-KOL - Cough medicines - Barrows Pharmacal Inc.
EXO-KON - Pharmaceutical preparations - Barrows Pharmacal Inc.
EXO SQUAD - Toys - Playmates World Wide Inc.
EXO-STATIC - Medical apparatus - Florida Manufacturing Corp.
EXO WORLD CLASS HEAT EXCHANGERS - Heating equipment -
  Exothermics, Inc.
EXOCAINE - Analgesics - Del Pharmaceuticals, Inc.
EXOCELITE - Fibers–acrylic - Faulkner Plastics Inc.
EXOCET - Toys–models ☆ - Estes Industries
EXOCLEAR - Medical apparatus - Econoline Products, Inc.
EXOCORT - Skin care products ☆ - TDC Dermatologicals
EXODE - Paint removers ☆ - Pratt & Lambert, Inc.
EXODENT - Dental compounds ☆ - E. Fougera & Co. Inc.
EXODUS - Boots - Red Wing Shoe Co.
EXODUS - Floor coverings–carpet and rugs ☆ - Criterion Mills Inc.
EXODUS - Video games - Origin Systems, Inc.
EXOLIT - Fire retardant - American Vamag Co. Inc.
EXOLITE - Molding compounds–plastics - Cyro Industries
EXOLIVA - Olives–pickled or brined - Joseph Caragol Inc.
EXOR - Exercising equipment - Henry V. Hall

☆ = Now out of production

EXOS - Lenses - Capo, Inc.

EXOSCOPE - Computer software - Radionics Software Applications, Inc.

EXOSKIN - Apparel and accessories - Enterprise Coatings Co., Ltd.

EXOSQUAD - Toys - Universal Cartoon Studios, Inc.

EXOTEC - Braces–orthopedic - Professional Products, Inc.

EXOTECH - Apparel and accessories - K-2 Corp.

EXOTHERM TERMIL - Fungicides - Maxus Energy Corp.

EXOTHERMIC - Hair care products - Cosmair Inc.

EXOTIC - Floor coverings–carpet and rugs ☆ - World Carpets, Inc.

EXOTIC - Flowers, plants, and seeds - Exotic Wood Flowers Inc.

EXOTIC - Frames–eyeglass ☆ - Universal/Univis Inc.

EXOTIC - Pet products - The Crab Connection

EXOTIC-AIR - Deodorizers - Louis T. Anderson

EXOTIC ANGEL - Flowers, plants, and seeds - Hermann Engelmann Greenhouses, Inc.

EXOTIC BLEND - Suntan lotions - ETS, Inc.

EXOTIC CAR SHOWROOM - Computer software - Capstone Software

EXOTIC ENVIRONMENTS - Aquarium accessories - Blue Ribbon Pet Products, Inc.

EXOTIC GARDENS, THE - Flowers, plants, and seeds - Exotic Gardens Inc.

EXOTIC GEMS - Marble products - Vitro Agate Corp.

EXOTIC-HC - Pharmaceutical preparations - Doral Pharmamedics Inc.

EXOTIC LADY - Frames–eyeglass ☆ - U.S. Optical Frame Co.

EXOTIC MILK SHAKES - Beverages - Hamburger Museum, Inc.

EXOTIC SIENNA - Lipsticks ☆ - Honey & Spice Toiletries

EXOTICA - Cosmetics - I. Sekine Co. Inc.

EXOTICA - Floor coverings–carpet and rugs ☆ - Regal Rugs Inc.

EXOTICA - Prophylactics - Ansell Inc. (Personal Products Div.)

EXOTICALS - Incense - Vineyard Group, Inc.

EXOTICS - Toys–models - ERTL Co., Inc.

EXOTICS BY ENNESI - Shoes - Ennesi Shoe Co. Inc.

EXOTICS FROM THE TROPICS - Flowers, plants, and seeds - International Floral Corp.

EXOTICS, THE - Bedding–linen - Pillowtex Corp.

EXOTIQUE - Wallpaper - Pantasote Inc. (Wallcovering Div.)

EXOTIQUES - Brushes–hair - Windmere Corp.

EXOTIX - Fruit drinks–bottled or canned - Planter's Pride, Inc.

EXP - Motor vehicles–automobiles ☆ - Ford Motor Co.

EXP - Ribbons–inked - Corporate Express Inc.

EXP 400 - Bicycles - Huffy Corp.

EXP-NT - Computers - ACMA Computers Inc.

EXP: SYS - Computer software - Brooks/Cole Publishing Co.

EXPAN - Computer software - College Entrance Examination Board

EXPAN - Hearing aids ☆ - Oticon Corp.

EXPAN-DESK - Furniture - Knoll Group

EXPAND - Shampoos - Gabel's Cosmetics Inc.

EXPAND-A-BAR - Computer software - Quick Scan, Inc.

EXPAND-A-CLOSET - Closet organizers ☆ - Hirsh Co.

EXPAND-A-GRIP - Padding–foam - Louisville Bedding Co.

EXPAND-A-LIGHT - Aquariums–household - California Aquarium Supply Corp.

EXPAND-A-LOPE - Attache cases - Angler's Roslyn Group Ltd.

EXPAND-A-NOTE - Computer programs - Quick Scan, Inc.

EXPAND-A-PAK - Envelopes - Wallace Computer Services, Inc.

EXPAND-A-PLAN - Electronic equipment ☆ - Methods Research Corp.

EXPAND-A-POCKET - Office goods - American Trading and Production Corp.

EXPAND-A-PRONG - Office supplies - Charles Leonard Inc.

EXPAND A SHELF - Shelving units–plastic - Softalk Inc.

EXPAND-A-SIZER - Apparel and accessories ☆ - Tiger Button Co., Inc.

EXPAND-A-TUBE - Tubes–plastic - Alvin and Co. Inc.

EXPAND-IT - Tools - Homelite, Inc.

EXPAND-IT - Tools–power-driven - Mark Macline Inc.

EXPAND-O-BOTTLE - Health care products ☆ - C.R. Bard, Inc.

EXPAND-O-FILE - File folders - Angler's Roslyn Group Ltd.

EXPAND-O-MATIC - Slacks–men's - Haggar Corp.

EXPAND YOUR HORIZONS - Audio tapes–blank - International Cultural Enterprises Inc.

EXPANDA-DECK - Wood products - Penco Products Div.

EXPANDA-FILE - File folders ☆ - Quality Park Products Co.

EXPANDA-SHELF - Pet products - Penn-Plax, Inc.

EXPANDABAK - Office supplies - McBee Loose Leaf Binders

EXPANDABLE-PLUS - Doors–storm ☆ - Therma-Tru Corp.

EXPANDABLES - Paper–gift wrap - Beistle Co.

EXPANDABLES, THE - Furniture - Sico Inc.

EXPANDAR - Lenses–photographic ☆ - SP Systems/Saratons

EXPANDED CHOICE - Hardware - Stanley Hardware Div.

EXPANDED EXPRESSIONS - Wallpaper - Marburg Wallcoverings Inc.

EXPANDED HORIZONS - Wallpaper - Marburg Wallcoverings Inc.

EXPANDED NOTATION - Computer software - Hartley Courseware Inc.

EXPANDED VINYL - Wallpaper - Lin-Gor Wallcoverings

EXPANDER - Toys - Strombecker Corp.

EXPANDET - Screws - Danish Import Inc.

EXPANDEX - Expansion mailing envelopes - American Fiber-Velope Manufacturing Co.

EXPANDEX - Office supplies - Ameriforms Inc.

EXPANDI-MATIC - Office machines - Mead-Hatcher, Inc.

EXPANDING POINT - Bullets - Olin Corp. (Winchester Div.)

EXPANDING YOUR UNIVERSE THROUGH LEARNING - Software - Education Achievement Corp.

EXPANDO - Luggage - Shalam Imports Inc.

EXPANDO - Office supplies ☆ - Datacom Inc.

EXPANDO SEAL - Sealing devices - W. Braun Co. Inc.

EXPANDOVER - Health care products - Sherwood Medical Co.

EXPANDRA - Fabrics - Burlington Industries, Inc.

EXPANKO - Floor coverings - Expanko Cork Co.

EXPANSIONS - Furniture - Bean Station Furniture Factory Inc.

EXPANSIONS - Luggage - Jinwoong Inc.

EXPANSO - Caulking compounds - L.D. Sterns Corp.

EXPANSO - Pajamas–men's - Knothe Corp.

EXPANTABLE - Furniture - A.A. Laun Furniture Co.

EXPANZ - Computer storage devices–magnetic - InfoChip Systems Inc.

EXPAR - Insecticides - Mallinckrodt Veterinary, Inc.

EXPAR - Veterinary pharmaceutical preparations - Schering-Plough Animal Health

EXPEC - Pharmaceutical preparations - C.O. Truxton Inc.

EXPEC II - Cough medicines - Naturade Inc.

EXPECT THE UNEXPECTED - Toys - Mattel, Inc.

EXPECTATIONS - Educational materials - James A. Bagaloff

EXPECTATIONS - Furniture - Arbek Furniture Manufacturing Inc.

EXPECTATIONS - Wallpaper - Chapters Wallcoverings

EXPECTORINE - Pet products - Farnam Cos. Inc.

EXPEDIO - Bathroom fixtures - Crane Plumbing/Fiat Products

EXPEDITE - Computer software - IEX Corp.

EXPEDITE - Herbicides - Monsanto Co.

EXPEDITE - Paint removers - Pratt & Lambert, Inc.

EXPEDITER - Cleaning preparations - Hillyard Enterprises, Inc.

EXPEDITER - Computer software - Sungard Investment Ventures, Inc.

EXPEDITER - Eyeglasses - Art-Craft Optical Co.

EXPEDITION - Bicycles ☆ - Huffy Corp.

EXPEDITION - Computer software - Primavera Systems, Inc.

EXPEDITION - Luggage - Airway Industries, Inc.

EXPEDITION - Motor vehicles - Ford Motor Co.

EXPEDITION - Pens - Expedition Pens, Inc.

EXPEDITION - Women's apparel - India Garments Inc.

EXPEDITION AFRICA SERIES - Pens - Expedition Pens, Inc.

EXPEDITION GEAR - Coats - Londontown Corp.

EXPEDITION HARDGEAR - Sporting goods - Kellwood Co.

EXPEDITION SERIES - Sporting goods - Outdoor Technologies Group

EXPEDITION TRAILS - Sleeping bags - M.Z.H. Inc.

EXPEDITIONS - Eyeglasses - Art-Craft Optical Co.

EXPEDITIONS - Watches - Timex Corp.

EXPEDITIONS INTERNATIONAL - Sporting goods ☆ - Action Clothing Technology

EXPEDITOR - Bags–duffel - Ektelon

EXPEDITOR - Luggage - Airway Industries, Inc.

EXPEDITOR - Veterinary pharmaceutical preparations - Moorman Manufacturing Co.

EXPEND-A-CAPES - Capes - A & J of Oshkosh Inc.

EXPENDABLE - Artists' materials ☆ - Winsor & Newton

EXPENSABLE - Computer software - Intuit Inc.

EXPENSELINK - Computer software - Gelco Information Network

EXPENSEPLUS - Computer software - State of the Art, Inc.

EXPERFAX - Computer software - Expervision, Inc.

EXPERIENCE - Computer software - Stores Automated Systems, Inc.

EXPERIENCE - Paper–writing - Kurtz Bros. Inc.

EXPERIENCE ANONYMES - Recording label ☆ - Lyrichord Discs Inc.

EXPERIENCE THE CHANGING OF THE GUARD - Sporting goods - Tru-Fit Marketing Corp.

EXPERIENCE THE WILD - Video production - Grunko Films, Inc.

EXPERIENCED - Balls–golf - Southwest Regional Sports Inc.

EXPERIENCING GOD - Publisher's imprints - Sunday School Board of the Southern Baptist Convention

---

☆ = Now out of production

EXPERIMENTAL AND APPLIED SCIENCES - Vitamins and nutritional supplements - Experimental & Applied Sciences, Inc.
EXPERT - Bicycles - Murray, Inc.
EXPERT - Exercising equipment - Proform Fitness Products, Inc.
EXPERT - Health care products - JUZO
EXPERT - Notebooks and notepads - Pen-Tab Industries
EXPERT - Pencils ☆ - Faber-Castell Corp.
EXPERT - Pet products ☆ - Kal Kan Foods, Inc.
EXPERT - Sewing machines–household - Tacony Corp.
EXPERT - Tools–garden ☆ - Gamble-Skogmo Inc.
EXPERT - Traps–animal - Remington Arms Co., Inc.
EXPERT ASTRONOMER - Computer software - Softsync Inc.
EXPERT AUTOSTATS - Computer software - 4n6xprt Systems
EXPERT BRAND SOFTWARE - Computer software - Expert Software Inc.
EXPERT COLOR PAINT - Computer software - Softsync Inc.
EXPERT CREDIT SYSTEM - Computer programs - ITT Commercial Finance Corp.
EXPERT EASE - Computer software - Expert Software Inc.
EXPERT EDGE - Medical supplies - Chiron Corp.
EXPERT EVOLUTION - Computer software - Software Artistry, Inc.
EXPERT EXPRESS - Office supplies - Pen-Tab Industries
EXPERT EXTRA - Paper–writing - Pen-Tab Industries
EXPERT EYES - Cosmetics - Maybelline Co.
EXPERT EYES - Cosmetics ☆ - Noxell Corp.
EXPERT EYES - Skin care products - Maybe Holding Co.
EXPERT FOUNDATION MANAGER - Computer software - Software Artistry, Inc.
EXPERT LEASE - Computer software - Charles R. Hart
EXPERT LINE - Medical apparatus - Julius Zorn, Inc.
EXPERT MOUSE - Computer peripheral equipment - Kensington
EXPERT QWIC CALCS - Computer software - 4n6xprt Systems
EXPERT RATING - Computer software - AIQ Systems Inc.
EXPERT SENSOR - Electronic equipment - Advanced Optical Controls, Inc.
EXPERT SOFTWARE - Computer software - Expert Software Inc.
EXPERT SOLICITATION - Computer software - Integrated Decision Support Corp.
EXPERT SYSTEM, THE - Pet products - Texmark Enterprises Inc.
EXPERT, THE - Coffee makers–electric - Mr. Coffee, Inc.
EXPERT TIRE STUF - Computer software - 4n6xprt Systems
EXPERT TOUCH - Cosmetics - Maybelline Co.
EXPERT VIN DECODER - Computer software - 4n6xprt Systems
EXPERT WRITER - Computer software - Softsync Inc.
EXPERTALERT - Microscopes - DLI Engineering Corp.
EXPERTALIGN - Electronic equipment - Hunter Engineering Co.
EXPERTISE - Apparel–athletic - Warnaco Inc.
EXPERTISE - Computer peripheral equipment - Software Artistry, Inc.
EXPERTISSE - Shampoos ☆ - Wella Corp. (Consumer Products Div.)
EXPERTS SPEAKING TO NONEXPERTS - Electrical equipment - Carlson Quinn Enterprises, Inc.
EXPIRED - Snowboards - Expired Snowboards USA
EXPLICIT - Eyeglasses - Martin-Copeland Eyewear Corp.
EXPLODE - Zylo Ware Corp.
EXPLODED-TIP - Brushes–paint - Wooster Brush Co.
EXPLODER - Exercising equipment - MLH Marketing, Inc.
EXPLORACENTER - Educational kits - Exploratorium
EXPLORAPEDIA - Computer software - Microsoft Corp.
EXPLORASCOPE - Microscopes - Educational Insights, Inc.
EXPLORATION - Publisher's imprints - Paulist Press
EXPLORATIONS - Apparel and accessories - Body Shops of America Inc.
EXPLORATOY - Toys - Educational Insights, Inc.
EXPLORAWEAR - Shirts - Exploratorium
EXPLORE AMERICA - Games - Curwood, Inc.
EXPLORE PROTEIN SKIMMERS - Aquariums–household - California Aquarium Supply Corp.
EXPLORE SAN DIEGO - Publisher's imprints - Coda Publications
EXPLORE SAN DIEGO(R) - Publisher's imprints - Auto Book Press
EXPLORER - Bags–duffel ☆ - Eclipse Inc.
EXPLORER - Bicycles - Murray, Inc.
EXPLORER - Boat - Hydro-Bikes Inc.
EXPLORER - Boats ☆ - Alumitech Inc.
EXPLORER - Boats ☆ - Valco Aluminum Boats
EXPLORER - Boats–canoes - Black River Canoes
EXPLORER - Boats–motor - Broadwater Boat Co.
EXPLORER - Boats–motor - Lund Boat Co.
EXPLORER - Boats–motor - Penn Yan Boats Inc.
EXPLORER - Boats–motor ☆ - Bayliner Marine Corp.

EXPLORER - Boats–motor ☆ - Grady-White Boats, Inc.
EXPLORER - Cameras - Eastman Kodak Co.
EXPLORER - Cleaning preparations–carpet and rug - Castex Industries Inc.
EXPLORER - Compasses–gyroscopic - E.S. Ritchie & Sons Inc.
EXPLORER - Compasses–magnetic - Tedco Inc.
EXPLORER - Cots–metal - E-Z Sales & Manufacturing, Inc.
EXPLORER - Dictating machines ☆ - Lanier Voice Products
EXPLORER - Firearms, accessories, and parts - Welsh Sporting Goods Corp. (Boyt Div.)
EXPLORER - Floor coverings–carpet and rugs ☆ - Regal Rugs Inc.
EXPLORER - Globes - Trippensee Corp.
EXPLORER - Golfing equipment - Mars Golf Supply
EXPLORER - Hoses - Goodyear Tire & Rubber Co.
EXPLORER - Ice chests–plastic ☆ - Igloo Products Corp.
EXPLORER - Knives–hunting - Gutmann Cutlery Inc.
EXPLORER - Motor vehicles–trucks - Ford Motor Co.
EXPLORER - Motorized scooters - Burke Mobility Products, Inc.
EXPLORER - Motors–outboard ☆ - Eska Corp.
EXPLORER - Pens - Pilot Pen Corp. of America
EXPLORER - Photographic equipment - Bausch & Lomb Inc.
EXPLORER - Radios - Pollenex Corp.
EXPLORER - Seats–automobile - Cosco, Inc.
EXPLORER - Synthesizers–musical instrument - Fender Musical Instruments
EXPLORER - Toys–models - Estes Industries
EXPLORER - Watches - Rolex Watch USA, Inc.
EXPLORER II - Watches - Rolex Watch USA, Inc.
EXPLORER AQUARIUS - Toys–models ☆ - Estes Industries
EXPLORER BREWER - Knives–hunting - Gutmann Cutlery Inc.
EXPLORER CERT 4.0 - Computer software - Transcender Corp.
EXPLORER II - Guns ☆ - Charter Arms
EXPLORER METROS: A METRIC ADVENTURE - Computer software ☆ - Sunburst Communications, Inc.
EXPLORER RC5 - Drills–mining - Sandvik Rock Tools, Inc.
EXPLORER SOLINGEN - Knives–hunting - Gutmann Cutlery Inc.
EXPLORER SPORT - Motor vehicles–trucks - Ford Motor Co.
EXPLORER XL - Orthopedic products - Ortho-Kinetics, Inc.
EXPLORERS - Publisher's imprints ☆ - MacMillan Publishing Co. Inc.
EXPLORERS - Toys ☆ - Intex Recreation Corp.
EXPLORER'S GUIDE - Publisher's imprints - Countryman Press Inc.
EXPLORERS' WORLD - Publisher's imprints - Little People's Workshop, Inc.
EXPLORERSCOPE - Microscopes - Learning Things Inc.
EXPLORING CAREERS - Publisher's imprints - Rosen Publishing Group & Pelion Press
EXPLORING ECOLOGY - Science kits - Educational Insights, Inc.
EXPLORING FIRST VERBS - Computer software - Laureate Learning Systems Inc.
EXPLORING FIRST WORDS - Computer software - Laureate Learning Systems Inc.
EXPLORING FIRST WORDS II - Computer software - Laureate Learning Systems Inc.
EXPLORING MATHEMATICS - Computer software - ScottForsman & Co.
EXPLORING OUR UNIVERSE - Publisher's imprints ☆ - Harper Junior Books Group
EXPLORING PLACES - Publisher's imprints - Price Stern Sloan Inc.
EXPLORING SERIES - Publisher's imprints - Bantam Doubleday Dell Publishing Group, Inc.
EXPLORING TABLES & GRAPHS 1 - Computer software ☆ - Optimum Resource, Inc.
EXPLORING TABLES AND GRAPHS 2 - Computer software ☆ - Optimum Resource, Inc.
EXPLORING THE LOST MAYA - Compact discs–prerecorded - Sumeria, Inc.
EXPLORZ - Computer software ☆ - B & N Companies, Inc.
EXPLOSION - Frames–eyeglass - Zylo Ware Corp.
EXPLOSION OF COLOR - Wallpaper - Capital Carousel Inc.
EXPLOSION OF ENERGY - Vitamins and nutritional supplements - Tribro, Inc.
EXPLOSIONS - Wallpaper - Dekortex Inc.
EXPLOSIVE - Apparel and accessories - Explosive Clothing, Inc.
EXPLOSIVE - Frames–eyeglass - Zylo Ware Corp.
EXPLOSIVE CLOTHING - Apparel and accessories - Explosive Clothing, Inc.
EXPLOSIVE POP-UPS - Greeting cards - Second Nature
EXPLOUR - Fishing tackle - South Bend Sporting Goods Inc.
EXPO - Erasers - Sanford Corp.
EXPO - Eyeglasses - Trecom Safety Corp.
EXPO - Floor coverings–carpet and rugs - Prestige Mills Inc.
EXPO - Motor vehicles–automobiles - Mitsubishi Motor Sales of America Inc.
EXPO - Motor vehicles–motor homes - Winnebago Industries, Inc.

☆ = Now out of production

EXPO - Occasional tables ☆ - JDI Group, Inc.

EXPO - Radio communications equipment ☆ - Motorola, Inc. (Land Mobile Products Sector)

EXPO 43 - Cement - Edison Coatings, Inc.

EXPO CLEANER - Erasers - Sanford Corp.

EXPO-ERA - Apparel and accessories - Polomate Corp.

EXPO-GLOSS - Concrete–mixture - W.R. Meadows Inc.

EXPO II - Markers–felt-tip - Sanford Corp.

EXPO POWWOW - Paperboard ☆ - Sanford Corp.

EXPO-RITE - Photographic equipment - SP Systems/Saratons

EXPO SOLAR SAILER - Ships–sailing vessels - Newport R & D Inc.

EXPO STAR - Boxes - Star Case Manufacturing Co. Inc.

EXPO TECH - Computers - Vtech Industries, Inc.

EXPO TICKLER - Paperboard - Sanford Corp.

EXPO TOUCH-CODE - Radio communications equipment ☆ - Motorola, Inc. (Land Mobile Products Sector)

EXPO XP II - Paperboard - Sanford Corp.

EXPOAIRE - Furniture - Expo Displays

EXPOFRAME - Furniture - Expo Displays

EXPOMANAGER, THE - Computer software - Harry Eisenberg

EXPOMAR - Seafood products–fresh or frozen - Bayside Foods Inc.

EXPOMAT - Photographic equipment - SP Systems/Saratons

EXPONENT GRAPHICS - Computer software - IMSL Inc.

EXPOPLUS - Display cases–metal - Chroma Copy Franchising of America, Inc.

EXPORT - Cigars - Gesty Trading & Manufacturing Corp.

EXPORT - Drums–musical instruments - Pearl Corp.

EXPORT - Pens - Schneider Pens USA

EXPORT A - Cigarettes - R.J. Reynolds Tobacco Co.

EXPORT ALE - Beverages–malt - Martlet Importing Co.

EXPORT PRO - Drums–musical instruments - Pearl Corp.

EXPOSE - Frames–eyeglass - May Optical Co. Inc.

EXPOSER - Tool boxes - Richard J. Blitz

EXPOSET - Computer peripheral equipment - Infimed, Inc.

EXPOSITION - Bedding–linen - Dan River Inc.

EXPOSTAR DISPLAYS - Display cases–plastic - Expostar Displays, Inc.

EXPOSURE - Computer software - Technical Assessment Systems, Inc.

EXPOSURE - Ophthalmic goods - Foremost Optical Products

EXPOSURE - Skin care products - California SunCare, Inc.

EXPOSURE BASE - Computer programs - Travelers Corp.

EXPOSURE LOTION - Health care products - Tec Laboratories, Inc.

EXPOSURSELF - Apparel and accessories - Shelley L. Watson

EXPOTEL - Photographic equipment - SP Systems/Saratons

EXPOTROL - Photographic equipment - SP Systems/Saratons

EXPOZAY - Ophthalmic goods - Foremost Optical Products

EXPRESEP - Laboratory apparatus - Biotecx Laboratories, Inc.

EXPRESS - Ammunition - Remington Arms Co., Inc.

EXPRESS - Apparel and accessories - Limited Inc.

EXPRESS - Automotive parts and accessories - C & D Charter Power Systems, Inc.

EXPRESS - Boats–motor - Broadwater Boat Co.

EXPRESS - Boats–motor ☆ - Century Boat Co.

EXPRESS - Boats–motor ☆ - Cruisers

EXPRESS - Boats–motor ☆ - Tollycraft Corp.

EXPRESS - Boats–motor ☆ - Trojan Yacht

EXPRESS - Catheters - Scimed Life Systems, Inc.

EXPRESS - Compasses–gyroscopic ☆ - Rule Industries, Inc.

EXPRESS - Computer peripheral equipment - Videomedia, Inc.

EXPRESS - Computer software - Seven Hills Software

EXPRESS - Computer software - Stores Automated Systems, Inc.

EXPRESS - Dialing devices–telephone - Baltimore Luggage Co.

EXPRESS - Floor coverings–carpet and rugs - World Carpets, Inc.

EXPRESS - Frames–eyeglass ☆ - Vanity Optical Manufacturing Co. Inc.

EXPRESS - Guitars ☆ - Philip Kubicki Technology

EXPRESS - Health care products - East Earth Herb Inc.

EXPRESS - Medical apparatus - Western Atlas International Inc.

EXPRESS - Model kits - Express Design Inc.

EXPRESS - Motor vehicles–motor homes - Eldorado Motor Corp.

EXPRESS - Motorcycles - American Honda Motor Co. Inc. (Acura Div.)

EXPRESS - Office supplies - Better Packages

EXPRESS - Paint rollers - Wooster Brush Co.

EXPRESS - Pens - Schneider Pens USA

EXPRESS - Playing cards - Mayfair Games, Inc.

EXPRESS - Plugs–ear - Aearo Co.

EXPRESS - Radiofrequency measuring equipment - Lockheed Information Management Services Co., Inc.

EXPRESS - Refractory castables - A.P. Green Industries Inc.

EXPRESS - Sporting goods - Wellington Leisure Products, Inc.

EXPRESS - Thread - Threads USA Div.

EXPRESS - Wheelchairs - Ortho-Kinetics, Inc.

EXPRESS 96 - Computer peripheral equipment - Hayes Microcomputer Products Inc.

EXPRESS-A-LITE - Lighters - Scripto-Tokai Corp.

EXPRESS ACCESS - Computer software - Advanced Computer Communications

EXPRESS ADS - Computer software - Val-Pak Direct Marketing Systems, Inc.

EXPRESS & CHILL - Bags–duffel - Lisco, Inc.

EXPRESS APPETITE - Food products - Party Foods, Inc.

EXPRESS BAR - Cosmetics - Charles of the Ritz Group Ltd.

EXPRESS BRIDGE - Boats–motor ☆ - Cruisers

EXPRESS COMBINATION PACKAGE - Recording label - Disc Makers

EXPRESS CRUISER - Boats–motor - Chris Craft Boats

EXPRESS DELIGHTS - Sandwiches–prepackaged - Classic Delight Inc.

EXPRESS DESIGNS - Heat transfers - Express Designs, Inc.

EXPRESS EGGS - Food products - Papetti's Hygrade Egg Products, Inc.

EXPRESS EVENT - Computer software - Pro Enterprises, Inc.

EXPRESS FIT - Coats–men's - Cliftex Corp.

EXPRESS FOODS FLOUR TORTILLAS - Tortillas - Express Foods Flour Tortillas

EXPRESS ICE CREAM - Ice cream - Carrie Concessions, Inc.

EXPRESS LINE - Cosmetics - Sassaby, Inc.

EXPRESS MAIL NEXT DAY SERVICE - Office supplies - United States Postal Service

EXPRESS MEALS - Stoves - Sunbeam-Oster Household Products

EXPRESS METER - Computer software - HDC Computer Corp.

EXPRESS METER AUDIT KIT - Computer software - Express Systems, Inc.

EXPRESS-NEWS FLYBALL - Broadcasting stations–cable television - Hearst Corp.

EXPRESS PICS - Transmitting apparatus - Presearch Inc.

EXPRESS POINT - Computer hardware - Express Point Technology Services, Inc.

EXPRESS QUEUING - Computer software - Advanced Computer Communications

EXPRESS RIDER - Boots - Wal-Mart Stores Inc.

EXPRESS SWITCHING - Computer software - Ascom Timeplex, Inc.

EXPRESS-TRACK - Computer software - Data General Corp.

EXPRESS TRICOT - Apparel and accessories - Expressco, Inc.

EXPRESS WAGON - Trailers–travel - Wells Cargo Inc.

EXPRESS XL - Communications equipment - Adtran

EXPRESS XLT - Communications equipment - Adtran

EXPRESS XR - Communications equipment - Adtran

EXPRESS XRT - Communications equipment - Adtran

EXPRESS YOURSELF - Hair care products - John Amico Expressive Hair Care Products

EXPRESSBUNDLE - Computer software - Legent Corp.

EXPRESSDOCS - Computer software - Wordperfect Corp.

EXPRESSDRIVE - Disk drives–computer - La Cie. Ltd.

EXPRESSION - Dinnerware–glass - Noritake Co. Inc.

EXPRESSION - Floor coverings ☆ - Durable Corp.

EXPRESSION - Floor coverings–carpet and rugs ☆ - Regal Rugs Inc.

EXPRESSION - Photographic equipment - Epson America, Inc.

EXPRESSION - Rings–jewelry - Artcarved Inc.

EXPRESSION - Skin care products - Frances Denney

EXPRESSION - Trailers–travel - Fleetwood Enterprises, Inc.

EXPRESSION '94 - Cameras - Rollei of America Inc.

EXPRESSION PLUS - Audio components ☆ - J.L. Cooper Electronics

EXPRESSIONIST - Mats–rattan ☆ - Golden Star Inc.

EXPRESSIONS - Apparel–men's - Kmart Properties, Inc.

EXPRESSIONS - Clocks - General Time Corp. (Westclox/Seth Thomas Div.)

EXPRESSIONS - Costume jewelry - Almar Sales Co., Inc.

EXPRESSIONS - Craft supplies - Textile Enterprises Inc.

EXPRESSIONS - Craft supplies ☆ - Prym Dritz Corp.

EXPRESSIONS - Exercising equipment - Giant Bicycle, Inc.

EXPRESSIONS - Fabrics - Uniroyal Engineered Products

EXPRESSIONS - Floor coverings - Tarkett, Inc.

EXPRESSIONS - Floor coverings–carpet and rugs - Dorsett Carpet Mills Inc.

EXPRESSIONS - Floor coverings–carpet and rugs - Edgecrest Carpet Mills

EXPRESSIONS - Floor coverings–carpet and rugs - Lotus Carpets

EXPRESSIONS - Floor coverings–carpet and rugs ☆ - Downs Carpet Co. Inc.

EXPRESSIONS - Floor coverings–carpet and rugs ☆ - J and J Industries Inc.

EXPRESSIONS - Floor coverings–carpet and rugs ☆ - Mannington Carpets, Inc.

EXPRESSIONS - Furniture - Expressions in Fabrics Ltd.

EXPRESSIONS - Furniture ☆ - Bassett Furniture Industries, Inc.

EXPRESSIONS - Furniture ☆ - Tell City Chair Co.

EXPRESSIONS - Glass dinnerware - Corning Inc.

EXPRESSIONS - Greeting cards ☆ - Amberley Greeting Card Co.

EXPRESSIONS - Hair permanent - Jheri Redding Products Inc.

EXPRESSIONS - Hardware - Amerock Corp.

EXPRESSIONS - Hearing aids - Rexton Inc.

EXPRESSIONS - Luggage ☆ - Samsonite Corp.

EXPRESSIONS - Lumber - Georgia-Pacific Corp.

EXPRESSIONS - Manicure preparations - M. Kamenstein, Inc.

EXPRESSIONS - Plastics–laminated - Plaskolite Inc.

EXPRESSIONS - Skin care products - Beneficial International

EXPRESSIONS - Stationery - Texan House Inc.

EXPRESSIONS - Wallpaper - Regency Mills Inc.

EXPRESSIONS - Wallpaper - Royson's Corp.

EXPRESSIONS - Wallpaper - Secrest Handprints Inc.

EXPRESSIONS BY BENEKE - Toilet seats ☆ - Sanderson Plumbing Products, Inc.

EXPRESSIONS BY FOREVER YOURS - Gowns - Forever Yours International Corp.

EXPRESSIONS FROM HALLMARK - Greeting cards - Hallmark Licensing, Inc.

EXPRESSIONS IN WOOL - Furniture–upholstered - Maharam Vertical Surfaces

EXPRESSIONS OF FAITH - Greeting cards - Current, Inc.

EXPRESSIONS OF GRAND TRAVERSE - Wines - Chateau Grand Traverse Ltd.

EXPRESSIT - Furniture - TWC Enterprises Ltd.

EXPRESSIVE - Floor coverings–carpet and rugs - Downs Carpet Co. Inc.

EXPRESSIVE ELEVATIONS - Wallpaper ☆ - Capital Carousel Inc.

EXPRESSIVE IMAGES - Calendars - Cullman Ventures Inc.

EXPRESSLANE - Computer software - XDB Systems, Inc.

EXPRESSLINE - Educational materials - Ziff-Davis Publishing Co.

EXPRESSLINE - Outerwear and accessories - Outfitters Express, Inc.

EXPRESSLITE - Lighting fixtures - Holophane Corp.

EXPRESSLY ORIENTAL - Food products - Golden Whisk Pasta Partners

EXPRESSNACKS - Snack foods - Hershey Import Co. Inc.

EXPRESSO - Computer software - Berkeley Systems, Inc.

EXPRESSO - Cordials - David Sherman Corp.

EXPRESSO - Frames–eyeglass - May Optical Co. Inc.

EXPRESSO - Greeting cards ☆ - Handprints

EXPRESSO - Liquors - Foreign Vintages Inc.

EXPRESSO - Pens - Sanford Corp.

EXPRESSO SILK - Wallpaper - Queens Decorative Wallcoverings Inc.

EXPRESSO TERMINI - Coffee - Expresso Termini Franchise Group, Inc.

EXPRESSPAD - Computer hardware - National Laboratory Center, Inc.

EXPRESSSIONS - Blinds–venetian ☆ - Hunter Douglas, Inc.

EXPRESSTOP - Vending machines - Vending Intelligence Co.

EXPRESSTRAC - Medical apparatus - Del Mar Avionics

EXPRESSTRAK - Billing machines - Bell Atlantic Network Services, Inc.

EXPRESSWATCH - Computer software - Microcom Systems, Inc.

EXPRESSWAY - Computers - Eventide Inc.

EXPRESSWAY - Floor coverings–carpet and rugs - Trend Carpet

EXPRESSWAYS TO MATH - Software and prerecorded audio cassettes - Expressways to Learning, Inc.

EXPRESSWAYS TO READING - Multi-media educational system - Expressways to Learning, Inc.

EXPRESSWORKS - Computer software - Roadway Express, Inc.

EXPRESSWRITER - Printers–computer - Toshiba America Information Systems, Inc.

EXPRESSWRITER - Recording label - Dictaphone Corp.

EXPREST - Archery equipment - Saunders Archery Co.

EXQUIS - Lenses–optical - Ditto Industries Inc.

EXQUISA - Cheese ☆ - Swissrose International Inc.

EXQUISIT - Wallpaper - Seabrook Wallcoverings, Inc.

EXQUISITE - Coffee - Amway Corp.

EXQUISITE - Eyeglasses - Art-Craft Optical Co.

EXQUISITE - Floor coverings–carpet and rugs - Calladium & Marglen

EXQUISITE - Floor coverings–carpet and rugs - Carpeting Concepts

EXQUISITE - Floor coverings–carpet and rugs ☆ - Gulistan Carpet Inc.

EXQUISITE - Footwear - Southern Shoe Importers Inc.

EXQUISITE - Hair care products - Master Chemical Co.

EXQUISITE - Prophylactics - Pharmex Inc.

EXQUISITE - Silver compounds - Blue Delft Co. Inc.

EXQUISITE COLLECTION - Candy - Ethel M. Chocolates, Inc.

EXQUISITE FORM - Underwear and nightwear - Exquisite Form Industries

EXQUISITE RAIN - Perfumes - Kiehl's Since 1851, Inc.

EXQUISITELY YOURS - Candy - Ethel M. Chocolates, Inc.

EXR - Film - Eastman Kodak Co.

EXRUST - Rust removers - Kano Laboratories Inc.

EX'S - Skis - Rossignol Ski Co., Inc.

EXSATIVA - Health care products - Scandinavian Natural Health & Beauty Products, Inc.

EXSEL - Hair care products - Allergan, Inc.

EXSIL - Lubricants ☆ - General Electric Co.

EXSILON - Coatings - Engelhard Corp.

EXSO - Yarn - Dixie Yarns, Inc.

EXSOTROL - Blinds–venetian - Baumann Inc.

EXSRP - Prosthetic apparatus - Wright Medical Technology, Inc.

EXSTREAM - Boots - Simms Fishing Products Corp.

EXSULATION - Insulating materials ☆ - Dryvit Systems, Inc.

EXSUPE - Spices and extracts - Herbert Marmorek & Son, Inc.

EXT - Animal feeds - Purina Mills, Inc.

EXT - Golfing equipment - Pro Kennex, Inc.

EXT - Helmets–athletic - Giant Bicycle, Inc.

EXT INTERNATIONALE - Golfing equipment - Pro Kennex, Inc.

EXTANG - Boats - Extang Corp.

EXTANT - Computer hardware - Documented Medical Monitoring, Inc.

EXTARDER - Motor vehicle parts and accessories - Diesel Engine Retarders, Inc.

EXTASE - Perfumes - Frances Denney

EXTASKI - Apparel and accessories - Patrick Brian O'Shea

EXTEK - Photographic equipment - Houston Fearless 76 Inc.

EXTEMPORE - Computer software - Delno S. Zane, Jr.

EXTEN-A-KUT - Machine parts ☆ - Alamo Industrial

EXTENAR - Photographic equipment ☆ - Edixa Camera Co.

EXTEND - Animal feed supplements - Purina Mills, Inc.

EXTEND - Finishing agents - Pioneer/Eclipse Corp.

EXTEND - Pencils–mechanical - Sanford Corp.

EXTEND - Rust removers - Loctite Corp.

EXTEND - Shortening - Wilsey Foods, Inc.

EXTEND 12 - Cough medicines ☆ - A.H. Robins Co. Inc.

EXTEND-A-BOOTH - Awnings - John W. Ross, III

EXTEND-A-BRUSH - Poles–wood - Star Brite

EXTEND A BUTTON - Buttons - J.H.T. Imports, Inc.

EXTEND-A-DUCT - Heating equipment ☆ - Deflecto Corp.

EXTEND-A-FILE - File folders - Newell Office Products

EXTEND-A-LEAD - Pet products - Rolf C. Hagen (USA) Corp.

EXTEND-A-MATCH - Matches ☆ - Dinsmore Instrument Co.

EXTEND-A-PHONE - Telephones ☆ - Uniden America Corp.

EXTEND A RAMP - Medical apparatus - Med World

EXTEND A SPONJ - Cleaning preparations ☆ - Duchess Royale Inc.

EXTEND-A-TONE - Games - Knight & Hale Game Calls, Inc.

EXTEND-A-WAIST - Apparel and accessories ☆ - Tiger Button Co., Inc.

EXTEND-AIR - Springs–mechanical - Goodyear Tire & Rubber Co.

EXTEND-O-DRAIN - Plumbing fixtures–plastic - Extend-O-Drain Inc.

EXTEND ONE - Vitamins and nutritional supplements - Vitamin Research Products Inc.

EXTENDA-LITE - Floodlights - GFE Manufacturing, Inc.

EXTENDAC - Cold remedies ☆ - Vitarine Pharmaceuticals Inc.

EXTENDAN-ARM - Tool boxes ☆ - Red Devil Inc.

EXTENDAR - Toys - Mattel, Inc.

EXTENDED CARE - Containers–glass - AAA Supplies Inc.

EXTENDED CARE - Soap - AAA Supplies Inc.

EXTENDED DEBUGGING CONTROLLER - Computer software - Cole Software L.L.C.

EXTENDED DYNAMIC RANGE - Electronic equipment - Galileo Corp.

EXTENDED FIT SYSTEM - Skates–roller - Rollerblade, Inc.

EXTENDED LONG LIFE - Food products machinery ☆ - International Paper Co.

EXTENDED PLAY - Apparel and accessories - Environs

EXTENDED RANGE - Audio equipment - Electro-Voice, Inc.

EXTENDED SERVICES - Computer software - International Business Machines Corp.

EXTENDED SERVICES FOR OS/2 - Computer software - International Business Machines Corp.

EXTENDED SHELF LIFE - Cartons–paperboard ☆ - International Paper Co.

EXTENDED SOFTWARE SOLUTIONS - Computer software - Dataflex Systems Co.

EXTENDED STYLES - Computer software ☆ - DataPak Software Inc.

EXTENDER - Footwear ☆ - Asics Tiger Corp.

EXTENDHUB - Computer hardware - Extended Systems, Inc.

☆ = Now out of production

EXTENDO - Hardware - Imperial Paint Applicators Ltd.

EXTENDO - Scrapers - Karmichael Industries Inc.

EXTENDRYL - Antihistamine preparations - Fleming & Co.

EXTENSION - Cosmetics - Noxell Corp.

EXTENSION - Pharmaceutical preparations - Republic Drug Co. Inc.

EXTENSION - Vitamins and nutritional supplements - Vitamin Research Products Inc.

EXTENSION ANTIOXIDANT - Vitamins and nutritional supplements - Vitamin Research Products Inc.

EXTENSION B-PLEX - Vitamins and nutritional supplements - Vitamin Research Products Inc.

EXTENSION-BAY - Windows–storm - Habitek Inc.

EXTENSION CALCIUM - Vitamins and nutritional supplements - Vitamin Research Products Inc.

EXTENSION HAIR & NAILS - Vitamins and nutritional supplements - Vitamin Research Products Inc.

EXTENSION I.Q. - Vitamins and nutritional supplements - Vitamin Research Products Inc.

EXTENSION I.Q. DRINK MIX - Vitamins and nutritional supplements - Vitamin Research Products Inc.

EXTENSION OLYMPIAN - Vitamins and nutritional supplements - Vitamin Research Products Inc.

EXTENSION PHYTONUTRIENT - Vitamins and nutritional supplements - Vitamin Research Products Inc.

EXTENSION PRESS - Publisher's imprints - Lowell House

EXTENSION VISION - Vitamins and nutritional supplements - Vitamin Research Products Inc.

EXTENSIONS IN CARE - Video production - Extensions in Care, Inc.

EXTENSIVE THERAPY - Hair care products - Jheri Redding Products Inc.

EXTENT - Medical apparatus - Allan J. Walling

EXTENZYME - Ophthalmic goods ☆ - Allergan, Inc.

EXTERIOR - Greeting cards - Sunrise Publications, Inc.

EXTERIOR-FIRE X - Lumber - Hoover Treated Wood Products Inc.

EXTERIOR PATCH-N-PAINT - Putties ☆ - Custom Building Products

EXTERIOR SOLAR CONTROL - Blinds–venetian - Baumann Inc.

EXTERIORS - Apparel and accessories - William Bay Trading Co.

EXTERMINATOR - Musical instruments ☆ - Fred Gretsch Enterprises

EXTERNAL CONTROL INTERNAL CONTROL - Veterinary pharmaceutical preparations - Merck & Co., Inc.

EXTESEAL - Adhesives and sealants - Rock-Tred Corp.

EXTING - Paints - Touraine Paints Inc.

EXTINGUISHSURE - Fire extinguishers - R. & G. Sloane Manufacturing Co. Inc.

EXTNDNFLEX - Exercising equipment - Proctor Development, Inc.

EXTOL - Frames–eyeglass - Hudson Optical Corp.

EXTOL CORPORATION - Tools - Extol Corp.

EXTON SQUARE - Floor coverings - Mannington Resilient Floors

EXTRA - Chewing gum - Wm. Wrigley Jr. Co.

EXTRA - Digitalis - Dualle Products

EXTRA - Frames–eyeglass - Hudson Optical Corp.

EXTRA - Hair care products - Conair Corp.

EXTRA - Handbags - Edison Brothers Stores, Inc.

EXTRA - Pens - Sunmex Imports Corp.

EXTRA - Rackets–racquetball - Wilson Sporting Goods Co.

EXTRA - Vitamins and nutritional supplements - Topper Bird Ranch West

EXTRA-AIRE - Pet products - Kennel-Aire Inc.

EXTRA BASES - Toys–electronic - Bandai America Inc.

EXTRA BASES - Trading cards and stamps - Fleer Corp.

EXTRA BERRIES - Jams and jellies - Knott's Berry Farm

EXTRA BIG BLAST, THE - Horns–motor vehicle - Anes Electronics Burglar Alarm Systems

EXTRA BOOST - Cosmetics - Ray Hayes Inc.

EXTRA BRIGHT - Paper ☆ - Hunt Manufacturing Co.

EXTRA CALM - Mattresses - E & S Vinyl Manufacturing Inc.

EXTRA CARE - Hair care products - Treslure Hair Cosmetics

EXTRA CONTROL - Skin care products - Elizabeth Arden Inc.

EXTRA COVER - Cosmetics - Almay Inc.

EXTRA-CRUNCHY - Pickles - Nalley's Fine Foods

EXTRA-CURRICULAR - Brassieres (Bras) ☆ - Lovable Co.

EXTRA CURRICULAR LEARNING - Recording label - Extra Curricular Learning

EXTRA DEPTH - Footwear - P.W. Minor & Son Inc.

EXTRA DIMENSION - Cosmetics - Jheri Redding Products Inc.

EXTRA DRY - Nail care products ☆ - Cosmair Inc.

EXTRA DYNAMIC - Audio equipment ☆ - TDK Electronics Corp.

EXTRA EDGE - Mattresses - Spring Air Co.

EXTRA EDGE - Vitamins and nutritional supplements ☆ - Quantum, Inc.

EXTRA EFFORT PEOPLE, THE - Real estate agencies - Colonial Realty LP

EXTRA ELEMENTS - Apparel and accessories - Wal-Mart Stores Inc.

EXTRA EXCEPTIONAL - Hair care products - Jheri Redding Products Inc.

EXTRA EXTRA - Cereal - Topco Associates, Inc.

EXTRA! EXTRA! - Floor coverings–carpet and rugs - Mohawk Industries Inc.

EXTRA! EXTRA! - Games - Lombard Marketing, Inc.

EXTRA EXTRA - Ice cream - Pierre's French Ice Cream Distributing Co. of Akron

EXTRA EXTRA - Potato chips ☆ - State Line Potato Chip Co.

EXTRA EXTRA CRYSTALLINE - Nail care products - Revlon Consumer Products Corp.

EXTRA FORCE - Automotive parts and accessories - G.M.B. Battery Inc.

EXTRA FRUIT - Jams and jellies - J.M. Smucker Co.

EXTRA-GO - Vitamins and nutritional supplements ☆ - Nature's Concept Inc.

EXTRA-GRIP - Adhesives and sealants - Mantrose-Haeuser Co. Inc.

EXTRA HAND - Playing cards ☆ - Carrom Co.

EXTRA HAND, THE - Braiding - Style-A-Braid, Inc.

EXTRA-HANDS - Gloves - Magla Products Inc.

EXTRA HANDS - Tableware–plastic - P.J. Maxwell Co., Inc.

EXTRA-HEAT - Heating equipment - Deflecto Corp.

EXTRA-HELP - Lip balms - Alexandra De Markoff, Ltd.

EXTRA HELPINGS - Dinners–frozen - Conagra, Inc.

EXTRA HOLD STYLING SPRITZ - Hair care products - Viviane Woodard Industries, Ltd.

EXTRA INNINGS - Games - Sony Electronic Publishing Co.

EXTRA LARGE - Cigarette holders - S.M. Frank & Co. Inc. (Kaywoodie-Yello-Bole-Medico)

EXTRA LEAN - Food products - Bar S Food Co. Inc.

EXTRA LIFE - Batteries - Bridgestone/Firestone, Inc.

EXTRA LIFE - Chemical preparations - Dennis Green Design Group Ltd.

EXTRA LIFE - Cosmetics - Revlon-Realistic Professional Products Inc.

EXTRA LIGHT - Beverages–malt - Peter Hand Brewing Co.

EXTRA-LIGHTS - Shoes–athletic - Titleist & Foot-Joy Worldwide

EXTRA-LITE - Ammunition - Federal-Hoffman, Inc.

EXTRA LITE - Luggage ☆ - Universal Trav-ler Inc.

EXTRA LIVELY - Guitars - Emmons Guitar Co. Inc.

EXTRA-LOFT - Fabrics - Fairfield Processing Corp.

EXTRA LONG-LASHES - Cosmetics - Almay Inc.

EXTRA-M - Gasoline - Marathon Oil Co.

EXTRA MELT - Cheese - Land O'Lakes Inc.

EXTRA MILE - Tires ☆ - Cooper Tire & Rubber Co.

EXTRA MILER - Tires - Uniroyal Goodrich Tire Co.

EXTRA MOISTURIZING AFRIN - Pharmaceutical preparations - Schering-Plough Healthcare Products

EXTRA OLDSTOCK - Beverages–alcohol - Century Importers Inc.

EXTRA POINT - Frames–eyeglass ☆ - Universal/Univis Inc.

EXTRA POINT - Game machines ☆ - WMS Gaming Inc.

EXTRA POINTS - Cosmetics ☆ - Chattem Inc.

EXTRA RANGE GREASE - Lubricants - Citgo Petroleum Corp.

EXTRA REPS - Health care products - Nature Health

EXTRA-REST - Air mattresses - Intex Recreation Corp.

EXTRA RICH - Cosmetics - Dr. Babor Natural Cosmetics

EXTRA RICH - Incense - Genie Co. Inc.

EXTRA ROOM - Furniture - Taylor-Ramsey Corp.

EXTRA SAVE - Food products - Associated Wholesale Grocers, Inc.

EXTRA SCENSTORY - Incense - Olfactory Corp.

EXTRA SEAL - Adhesives and sealants - Mepac Enterprises, Corp.

EXTRA SHAPING POWER - Apparel and accessories - Playtex Apparel, Inc.

EXTRA SHINY SILVER - Cosmetics - Jheri Redding Products Inc.

EXTRA SPECIAL - Beverages–malt - The Stroh Brewery Co.

EXTRA SPECIAL PUP - Dog food - Farmland Industries Inc.

EXTRA STRENGTH - Adhesives and sealants - Roman Adhesives, Inc.

EXTRA STRENGTH BAYER - Analgesics - Bayer Corp. (Consumer Care Div.)

EXTRA STRENGTH CSP - Cleaning preparations - Hillyard Enterprises, Inc.

EXTRA STRENGTH GAS-X - Antacids - Sandoz Pharmaceuticals Corp.

EXTRA STRENGTH GELTABS - Analgesics - McNeil Consumer Products Co.

EXTRA STRENGTH GOLD BOND MEDICATED POWDER - Skin care products - Martin Himmel Inc.

EXTRA STRENGTH GUARANA - Vitamins and nutritional supplements - Natural Balance, Inc.

EXTRA STRENGTH TYLENOL PM GELCAPS - Analgesics - McNeil Pharmaceuticals

EXTRA-STRONG - Solder - L.B. Allen Co. Inc.

EXTRA-TERRESTRIAL, THE - Electronic equipment ☆ - Texas Instruments Inc.

EXTRA TEXTURE - Fabrics - Valley Forge Fabrics Inc.

EXTRA TIME - Apparel–men's - Made in the Shade by Prime Time

EXTRA TOUCH - Hair care products - Hair Research X Inc.

EXTRA TREAT - Fruits and vegetables - George F. Joseph Orchard Siding Inc.

EXTRA VALUE - Cigarettes - R.J. Reynolds Tobacco Co.

EXTRA VALUE - Meat products–beef - Holten Meat, Inc.

EXTRA WHITE - Brushes–paint ☆ - PPG Industries, Inc.

EXTRA WINNER - Brushes–paint ☆ - PPG Industries, Inc.

EXTRA YIELD - Coffee - Continental Coffee Products Co.

EXTRAAS - Ice cream - Haagen-Dazs Co. Inc.

EXTRACOPY - Computer software - Intex Solutions Inc.

EXTRACTA - Beverages–alcohol - Distributors & Condal Imports

EXTRACTA - Paper–carbon - Robert F. De Castro, Inc.

EXTRACTA - Pumps ☆ - Marley Pump Co.

EXTRACTA-MAT - Floor coverings - Apache Mills Inc.

EXTRACTACAPS - Health care products - Nature's Answer (Bio Botanica)

EXTRACTO - Cleaning preparations–carpet and rug - Uncle Sam Chemical Co., Inc.

EXTRACTOR - Filters–air - Air Kontrol Inc.

EXTRACTOR VAC - Cleaning preparations–carpet and rug - Host/Racine Industries Inc.

EXTRACTORSPONGES - Cleaning preparations–carpet and rug - Host/Racine Industries Inc.

EXTRACTORVAC - Carpet cleaning equipment - Racine Industries, Inc.

EXTRACTS - Trade Associations - George Little Management, Inc.

EXTRAFLEX - Gloves - Granet Inc.

EXTRAFLEX - Hoses - Hose Master, Inc.

EXTRAGESIC - Pharmaceutical preparations - Rex Research Laboratories

EXTRAKLASSE - Cutlery ☆ - W.M.F. of America Inc.

EXTRALIGHT - Bicycles - Columbia Manufacturing Inc.

EXTRALIN - Pharmaceutical preparations ☆ - Eli Lilly and Co.

EXTRALITE - Paints ☆ - Dunn Edwards Corp.

EXTRALOW - Cooking equipment–commercial - Thermador

EXTRAMALT - Vitamins and nutritional supplements - Novartis Nutrition Corp.

EXTRAORDINAIRE - Cookware - Kaiser Bakeware, Inc.

EXTRAORDINAIRE - Floor coverings–carpet and rugs - J.L. Benson Co.

EXTRAORDINAIRE - Floor coverings–carpet and rugs - E.R. Carpenter Co.

EXTRAORDINAIRE - Floor coverings–carpet and rugs - Omalon

EXTRAORDINAIRE - Frames–eyeglass - Liberty Optical Manufacturing Co.

EXTRAORDINAIRE - Wallpaper - K.M.L. Industries

EXTRAORDINAIRE - Wallpaper - Textile Wallcoverings International Ltd.

EXTRAORDINARY - Wallcoverings - Cork Products Co. Inc.

EXTRAORDINARY CLIMBING GEAR - Sporting goods - Trango USA, Ltd.

EXTRAORDINARY EARL GREY - Teas–herbal - Celestial Seasonings, Inc.

EXTRAORDINARY TEXTILES II - Wallcoverings - Cork Products Co. Inc.

EXTRAORDIWEAR - Apparel and accessories - Extraordiwear

EXTRAPONES - Spices and extracts - Dragoco Inc.

EXTRAVAC - Cleaning preparations–carpet and rug - Castex Industries Inc.

EXTRAVAC - Floor cleaning equipment - Tennant Trend Inc.

EXTRAVAGANCE - Luggage - Totes, Inc.

EXTRAVAGANCE - Wallpaper - Fine Art Wallcoverings Ltd.

EXTRAVAGANT - Cookies - American Stores Co.

EXTRAVAGANZA - Chocolate candy - Pangburn Candy Co.

EXTRAVAGANZA - Frames–eyeglass - Hudson Optical Corp.

EXTRAVAGANZZA, THE - Pizzas–mixes - Domino's Pizza Inc.

EXTREME - Bicycles ☆ - Raleigh USA Bicycle Co.

EXTREME - Cleaning preparations - Betco Corp.

EXTREME - Detergents - Babson Bros. Co.

EXTREME - Hair care products - Redken Laboratories, Inc.

EXTREME - Lighting fixtures - National Service Industries, Inc.

EXTREME - Sporting goods - Easton Aluminum Inc.

EXTREME - Sporting goods - HO Sports Inc.

EXTREME - Sporting goods - Wellington Leisure Products, Inc.

EXTREME AROMATHERAPY - Deodorizers - Vent Scents, Inc.

EXTREME CARDIO - Physical fitness centers - Better Bodies Inc.

EXTREME CHAMPIONSHIP WRESTLING - Broadcasting stations–television - H H G Corp.

EXTREME CORDLESS - Tools–power-driven - Black & Decker Corp.

EXTREME CREATINE - Vitamins and nutritional supplements - TSN Labs, Inc.

EXTREME DINOSAURES - Footwear–children's - S. Goldberg and Co. Inc.

EXTREME FX - Costumes - Rob Liefeld Inc.

EXTREME GHOSTBUSTERS - Footwear - S. Goldberg and Co. Inc.

EXTREME IMPACT - Golfing equipment - Golfsmith International Inc.

EXTREME MEASURES - Vitamins and nutritional supplements - Blackwell, Thompson & Harris Holdings

EXTREME PRECISION - Measuring instruments - Zircon Corp.

EXTREME SLED - Sleds ☆ - Mad River Rocket Co. Inc.

EXTREME SMIRNOFF - Beverages - Heublein, Inc.

EXTREME SOFTWARE - Computer software - Patrick Husting

EXTREME STACK - Vitamins and nutritional supplements - TSN Labs, Inc.

EXTREME TEA - THE ULTIMATE CAFFEINE RUSH - Teas - Scott J. Weiner

EXTREME TIMES CALL FOR EXTREME HEROES - Toys - Hasbro, Inc.

EXTREMELY COLORADO - Stationery - Winter Park Recreational Association

EXTREMELY GENTLE - Cosmetics - Noxell Corp.

EXTREMISTS, THE - Video production - Bennett Productions, Inc.

EXTREMITIES - Apparel–athletic - Climb High Inc.

EXTREMITY PUMP - Compressors–gas - Jobst Institute Inc.

EXTRIVAN - Butter vanilla - American Flavor & Fragrance Corp.

EXTROM - Telephones - Panor Corp.

EXTRON - Computer peripheral equipment - RGB Systems, Inc.

EXTRORDINAIR - Cash registers - Continental Industries Inc.

EXTRORDINAIRE - Recording label - Essex Entertainment, Inc.

EXTROVERT - Colognes ☆ - Avon Products, Inc.

EXTROVERT - Frames–eyeglass - Hudson Optical Corp.

EXTRUDA-FORM - Siding–insulating ☆ - Aluminum Co. of America

EXTRUDA-LOK - Siding–insulating ☆ - Aluminum Co. of America

EXTRUDICOTE - Phosphates - Detrex Corp.

EXTRUSIONLOCK - Medical apparatus - Smith & Nephew Richards, Inc.

EXTUSSIVE - Cough medicines - Ion Laboratories Inc.

EXUBERANCE - Hair care products - Nicole Research Inc.

EXUBERANT - Floor coverings–carpet and rugs - Patcraft Mills Inc.

EXUBERANT - Floor coverings–carpet and rugs - Philadelphia Carpets

EXUBERANTE - Frames–eyeglass ☆ - Universal/Univis Inc.

EXUBERANTLY SINGLE - Recording label - Shelton International

EXUDE - Apparel and accessories - Exude Inc.

EXUVIANCE - Pharmaceutical preparations - Neostrata Co., Inc.

EXVELOPER - Photographic equipment - Douthitt Corp.

EXWATER - Plugs–ear ☆ - Woltra Corp.

EXX/OIL - Shampoos - Nexxus Products Co.

EXXAIRE - Plastics film - Exxon Corp.

EXXCOOL - Lubricants - Exxon Corp.

EXXCUT - Lubricants - Exxon Corp.

EXXENTIALE FORTE - Vitamins and nutritional supplements - Biotech (N.A.) Corp.

EXXFIX - Plant growth enhancers - Exxon Corp.

EXXMAR - Oils–lubricating - Exxon Corp.

EXXON - Gasoline - Exxon Corp.

EXXON CHEMICAL - Drycleaning preparations - Exxon Corp.

EXYLIN - Bags–duffel - Exylin Co.

EXYMOL - Health care products - Exymol Laboratories

EXZIT - Skin care products ☆ - Miles Inc.

EXZOOMA - Computer software - B & N Companies, Inc.

EYAK - Salmon–smoked, salted, dried, or pickled - Eyak Packing Co.

EYE - Knives–carving - Knife Importers Inc.

EYE - Recording label - Jazz Composer's Orchestra Association Inc.

EYE ACCENTO - Cosmetics - Revlon Consumer Products Corp.

EYE ACCENTS - Cosmetics - American International Industries

EYE ALLURE - Frames–eyeglass ☆ - Universal/Univis Inc.

EYE APPEAL - Eyeglasses - Martin-Copeland Eyewear Corp.

EYE AREA - Skin care products - Barbara Salomone and Associates, Inc.

EYE ARMOR - Exercising equipment - Pro-Tec Inc.

EYE-BALLS - Candy - Leaf, Inc.

EYE-BATH - Pet products - Aquatronics-Filtronics

EYE BEAUTE - Skin care products - Pharmagel Corp.

EYE BEAUTIQUE - Frames–eyeglass ☆ - Universal/Univis Inc.

EYE BELIEVE - Cosmetics - Cosmedic Concepts, Inc.

EYE BIZ - Eyeglasses - Art-Craft Optical Co.

EYE BLACK - Sporting goods - Unique Sports Products Inc.

EYE BOUTIQUE - Frames–eyeglass ☆ - Universal/Univis Inc.

EYE-BRITE - Pet products - Lambert-Kay

EYE BRYTE - Cleaning preparations - Dean Rubber Co.

EYE-C - Veterinary pharmaceutical preparations - Dr. Goodpet

EYE CAN - Note holders - Robert G. Phipps

EYE CARE AND CURE - Pharmaceutical preparations - Eye Care and Cure, Inc.

EYE CARE DRESSING - Bandages - Karlen Manufacturing, Inc.

EYE CARE EYE WEAR - Ophthalmic goods - Vision Ease

EYE-CATCHERS - Costumes - Russ Berrie and Co., Inc.

EYE CATCHING DESIGN - Apparel - Norbac Inc.

EYE-CEE SYSTEM FOR VDT USERS, THE - Computer software - Jeffrey Anshel

EYE-CITEMENT - Ophthalmic goods - Foremost Optical Products

EYE CLEAR - Veterinary pharmaceutical preparations - Gimborn U.S., Inc.

EYE CONS - Games - Hersch and Co.

EYE CONTACT - Computer software - Stephen Arthur Hellerstein, Jr.

EYE-CORT - Pharmaceutical preparations ☆ - Roberts/Hauck Pharmaceuticals Inc.

EYE CRAYONS - Cosmetics - Revlon Consumer Products Corp.

EYE-CROSSER - Sporting goods ☆ - Shakespeare Fishing Tackle

EYE CUE - Games - Dale Seymour Publications, Inc.

EYE DEFENSE - Cosmetics - Cosmair Inc.

EYE DESIGNER - Cosmetics - Noxell Corp.

EYE DESIGNS - Cosmetics - Max Factor & Co.

EYE DETECTOR - Alarm systems–burglar ☆ - General Binding Corp.

EYE-DIL-EYES - Mascara-remover pads - American Hygienic Laboratories Inc.

EYE DOCTOR - Cosmetics - Origins Natural Resources Inc.

EYE DROPS - Pharmaceutical preparations - Reese Chemical Co.

EYE EASE - Health care products - Maddak Inc.

EYE-EASE - Paper - Dennison National Co.

EYE-EASE - Pet products - Thomas Veterinary Drug

EYE EXPRESS - Cosmetics - Del Pharmaceuticals, Inc.

EYE EXPRESSIONS - Cosmetics - Del Pharmaceuticals, Inc.

EYE-EYE-EYE! - Eyeglasses - Eye-Eye-Eye, Inc.

EYE FERME - Skin care products - Pharmagel Corp.

EYE FISH - Sunglasses - Sungold Enterprises Ltd.

EYE-FIX - Cosmetics - Elizabeth Arden Inc.

EYE FOCAL - Ophthalmic goods - Breger Mueller Welt Corp.

EYE-FUNGEX - Aquatic pharmacuetical preparations ☆ - Aquatronics-Filtronics

EYE GENE EYE DROPS - Health care products - Woolfoam Corp.

EYE GLEAMERS - Cosmetics - Revlon Consumer Products Corp.

EYE-GORE - Toys - Mattel, Inc.

EYE-GUARD - Plastics - Spray Sok Co. Inc.

EYE JACKET - Goggles–safety - Oakley, Inc.

EYE JACKETS - Eyeglasses - Oakley, Inc.

EYE JEWEL - Eyeglass-frame Jewelry - Designs by Elgo Inc.

EYE KIT - Cosmetics - Cici Cosmetic Co.

EYE LAV - Pharmaceutical preparations ☆ - Schein Pharmaceutical Inc.

EYE-LIFT - Cosmetics ☆ - Beauty Aids Inc.

EYE-LIGHTS - Cosmetics - Honey & Spice Toiletries

EYE-LITE - Ophthalmic goods - Eye-Kraft Optical, Inc.

EYE LITES - Cosmetics - Mimi's Discount Beauty Supply

EYE LOVE YOU - Dolls - Blue Squirrel Concepts

EYE MAGNIFY - Sunglasses - Sungold Enterprises Ltd.

EYE MATES BY NURSE MATES - Eyeglasses - Lowell Shoe, Inc.

EYE OF HORUS - Computer software - Compton's NewMedia

EYE OF THE HAWK - Beverages–malt - Mendocino Brewing Co., Inc.

EYE OF +THE HAWK SELECT ALE - Beverages–malt - Mendocino Brewing Co., Inc.

EYE OF THE PHARAOH, THE - Novelty items - Hasbro, Inc.

EYE OF THE SWAN - Wines - Sebastiani Vineyards, Inc.

EYE OF THE SWAN CELLARS - Wines - Sebastiani Vineyards, Inc.

EYE OF THE TIGER - Sportswear - Eye of the Tiger Inc.

EYE OF THE ZEBRA - Golfing equipment - Ram Golf Corp.

EYE-OPENER - Bleacher seating–portable - W.L. Gore & Associates, Inc.

EYE OPENERS - Greeting cards - American Greetings Corp.

EYE OPENERS - Pharmaceutical preparations - Paul Oesterman

EYE PARADE - Eye-makeup kits ☆ - Cosrich Inc.

EYE PATCH - Health care products - Karlen Manufacturing, Inc.

EYE PERFECTOR - Cosmetics ☆ - Avon Products, Inc.

EYE PLEX - Skin care products - Garcoa Labs/Vitamin Classics

EYE POPPER - Markers–felt-tip - Yasutomo

EYE POPPERS - Chewing gum - Leaf, Inc.

EYE POWER - Eye-makeup kits ☆ - Cosrich Inc.

EYE POWER - Eyeglasses - International Tropic-Cal Inc. (I SKI Div.)

EYE-POWER - Vitamins and nutritional supplements - Natur-Pharma, Inc.

EYE PRO - Pet products - Classic Products

EYE PROTECH - Sunglasses - Capo, Inc.

EYE Q'S - Cotton–sterilized - American International Industries

EYE QUEST - Microscopes - Educational Insights, Inc.

EYE-RASORS - Mascara-remover pads - American Hygienic Laboratories Inc.

EYE RESCUE - Skin care products - Monteil Paris

EYE-SED - Pharmaceutical preparations - Schering-Plough Healthcare Products

EYE SENTRY - Goggles–safety - Ektelon

EYE SHADOW - Cosmetics - Viviane Woodard Industries, Ltd.

EYE SHADOW THEATER - Now out of production ☆ - Cosrich Inc.

EYE SHADOWS THAT CHANGE - Sunglasses ☆ - Corning Inc.

EYE SHAFT - Golfing equipment - Putt Masters, Inc.

EYE-SINE - Pharmaceutical preparations - Akorn Inc.

EYE SITE - Skin care products - Charles Revson Inc.

EYE SPECIALIST - Cosmetics - Estee Lauder Inc.

EYE-SPY - Computer software - Ultimis Corp.

EYE SPY - Eyeglasses - E-M International

EYE STEALS - Eyeglasses - Eye Deals Eyewear

EYE-STREAM - Ophthalmic goods - Alcon Laboratories, Inc.

EYE STROKES - Cosmetics ☆ - Bonne Bell, Inc.

EYE SURPRISE - Puzzles ☆ - Ceaco, Inc.

EYE TEASERS - Eye-makeup kits ☆ - Cosrich Inc.

EYE TECH - Cosmetics - Chesebrough-Pond's USA Co.

EYE TECH - Operating tables - Olympus America Inc.

EYE, THROAT AND COMPLEXION OIL - Skin care products - Viviane Woodard Industries, Ltd.

EYE TIME - Cosmetics - Aramis Inc.

EYE TO EYE - Cosmetics - Estee Lauder Inc.

EYE TO EYE - Hats - Benkel Manufacturing Co.

EYE TONE - Paper - Reynolds and Reynolds Co.

EYE TREATS - American International Industries

EYE VISOR - Eye moisturizer - Cabot Laboratories Inc.

EYE VITE - Vitamins and nutritional supplements - Makers of Kal, Inc.

EYE WASH - Ophthalmic goods - Flents Products Co. Inc.

EYE WASH CUP - Health care products - Karlen Manufacturing, Inc.

EYE WITNESS - Toys - Tonka Corp.

EYE WONDER - Lenses–magnifying - C. Bennett Scopes Inc.

EYE WONDER - Skin care products - California Cosmetics, Inc.

EYE WONDER - Toys - Mattel, Inc.

EYE WRITERS - Cosmetics - Maybelline Co.

EYE-X-CEL - Cosmetics - Beauticontrol Cosmetics Inc.

EYE-X-L - Knives–carving ☆ - Knife Importers Inc.

EYEASE - Lighting equipment - Philips Lighting Co.

EYEBALL - Golfing equipment - Paul E. Schwab, Jr.

EYEBALL MAKER - Toys - Mattel, Inc.

EYEBLASSES - Frames–eyeglass ☆ - Universal/Univis Inc.

EYECAM - Cameras - Silicon Vision, Inc.

EYECATCHERS - Cosmetics - Honey & Spice Toiletries

EYECATCHERS - Hosiery - Mayer/Berkshire Corp.

EYECESSORIES - Ophthalmic goods - Eyecessories

EYECOLOR APPLICATORS - Cosmetics - Karlen Manufacturing, Inc.

EYECOOL - Ophthalmic goods - Whitby Pharmaceuticals, Inc.

EYECORP - Eyeglasses - Eyecorp International Corp.

EYECREM - Skin care products - Mastey De Paris

EYEFIX - Ophthalmic apparatus - Eye Fix, Inc.

EYEFUL - Boxes - Lerner Manufacturing Inc.

EYEGARD - Pet products ☆ - Gerard-Pellham Co.

EYEGENE - Pharmaceutical preparations - Oakhurst Co.

EYEGENIC - Pharmaceutical preparations - Schmid Laboratories

EYEGLASS-AIDS - Eyeglasses - Penny Pendleton Manufacturing Inc.

EYEGLASS HUGGY - Sporting goods - Unique Sports Products Inc.

EYEGLOVE - Eyeglass bands - Dive N' Surf, Inc.

EYEKING CO. - Sunglasses - Sungold Enterprises Ltd.

EYELASH - Yarn - Melrose Yarn Co. Inc.

EYELINE - Cosmetics - Cici Cosmetic Co.

EYELINE - Sporting goods ☆ - Bomark Group Inc.

EYELINER PENCIL - Cosmetics - Viviane Woodard Industries, Ltd.

EYELO - Pharmaceutical preparations ☆ - Rexall Nutritional Products Inc.

EYEMART EXPRESS - Eyeglasses - Eye-Mart Express, Inc.

EYEMO - Electronic equipment - Bell & Howell Co.

EYEMOIST - Skin care products - Key West Aloe Inc.

EYEPAC - Cosmetics - L.T. Laboratories

EYEPLY - Contact lenses - Earl Holtzclaw

EYERENUE COMPLEX - Skin care products - Viviane Woodard Industries, Ltd.

EYES HAVE IT - Greeting cards ☆ - American Greetings Corp.

EYES OF AMERICA - Cosmetics ☆ - Noxell Corp.

EYES OF THE HUNTER, THE - Binoculars - Bausch & Lomb Inc.

EYES PLUS - Skin care products - Donna Lee Cosmetics Inc.

EYES R DRY - Bathroom accessories - Prince Lionheart, Inc.

EYES SO NATURAL - Cosmetics - Hazel Bishop International

EYESCRUB - Hypoallergenic eye-cleansing solution - Cooper Companies Inc.

EYESCRUB - Pharmaceutical preparations - Ciba-Geigy Corp.

EYESEXXXY - Cosmetics - Charles Revson Inc.

EYESHADES - Sunglasses - Oakley, Inc.

EYESILKS - Cosmetics - Matrix Essentials, Inc.

EYESTATION - Computer software - Clinical Information Advantages, Inc.

EYESYS LABORATORIES - Optical machinery - EyeSys Technologies Inc.

EYETAMINS - Vitamins and nutritional supplements - Sundown Vitamins, Inc.

☆ = Now out of production

EYETEES - Cosmetic applicators - Wilson Marketing Enterprises, Inc.

EYETHLETICS - Goggles - Associates in Vision Rehabilitation

EYETIQUE - Shirts - Kim Jon Ltd.

EYEVIEW - Construction equipment rental services - Vision Sciences Research Corp.

EYEWEAR - Cosmetics - Estee Lauder Inc.

EYEWEAR CONCEPTS - Eyeglasses - Eyewear Concepts

EYEWEAR HANGERS - Jewelry - Cyd Roche, Inc.

EYEWISE - Goggles ☆ - Advanced Consumer Products, Inc.

EYGEL - Cosmetics - L.T. Laboratories

EYKISILK - Wallpaper - Capital Carousel Inc.

EYREVILLE - Food products ☆ - Nature's Pride Inc.

EYRIE VINEYARDS, THE - Wines - Eyrie Vineyards

EYZE BAG - Pharmaceutical preparations - Tetra Medical Supply Corp.

EYZONE - Cosmetics - Estee Lauder Inc.

EYZZON - Frames—eyeglass - Richard Schatzberg

EZ - Cameras - Vivitar Corp.

E.Z. - Cleaning preparations - National Sponge Corp.

EZ - Converters—electric - Anes Electronics Burglar Alarm Systems

EZ - Exercising equipment - Paramount Electronic Corp.

EZ - Floor coverings—carpet and rugs - Mattel Carpet & Rug Inc.

EZ - Health care products - Temco Health Care

EZ - Hearing aids - Hearing Services Inc.

EZ - Oils—lubricating - Derby Refining Co.

EZ - Sewing machines—household - E Z International, Inc.

EZ - Window coverings - EZ Distributors Ltd.

EZ-1 - Bicycles - Easy Racers Inc.

EZ-1 - Plastics - Zin-Plas Corp.

EZ-1 - Whirlpool tubs and spas - Conway Products Corp.

EZ 2 DO - Toys - Tonka Corp.

EZ 2 VUE - Lenses—optical - Sola Optical USA, Inc.

EZ-3 - Sporting goods ☆ - Penn's Woods Products Inc.

EZ-7 - Adhesives and sealants - EZ-Seal, LLC

EZ-8 - Sanders and grinders - Clarke Industries, Inc.

EZ-12 - Whirlpools - Emerald Spa Corp.

EZ 250 - Electronic equipment - Ametek, Inc. (Mansfield & Green Division)

EZ-A-BELT - Apparel—women's - Nuvogue Creations

EZ-ACCESS - Medical apparatus - Home Care Products Inc.

EZ-ADD - Fuel additives - Lubrizol Corp.

EZ-ADDER - Fishing-line release device - Walker Downriggers Inc.

EZ-ADJUST - Tools - Cepco Tool Co.

EZ AIR - Cleaning preparations - DCI Industries Ltd.

EZ AIR - Medical apparatus ☆ - Dome Publishing Co., Inc.

EZ ALERT - Signs - Mobilemedia Communications, Inc.

EZ ARCHIVE - Computer software - EZ Image Inc.

EZ-ATTACH - Health care products - Premier Solutions Ltd.

EZ BALLOON KIT - Novelty items - Creative Balloons Manufacturing Inc.

EZ-BAR - Steel products - Southington Tool & Manufacturing Corp.

EZ-BATHE - Medical apparatus - Home Care Products Inc.

EZ-BELT - Belts—apparel - Richie & John, Inc.

E.Z. BIGBBY - Snack foods - Crawford Group, Inc.

EZ BINS - Containers - Empak, Inc.

EZ-BLUE - Deodorizers - J+J Chemical Co., Inc.

EZ BOOT - Motor vehicle parts and accessories - Alloy Industries, Inc.

EZ BREAKER - Tools—hand-operated - Kenneth Smith

E.Z.-C - Chewing gum - Finnfoods Div.

EZ CAN RECYCLER - Trash compactors—household - Empak, Inc.

EZ CAP - Computer software - Fred Rothenberg & Associates, Inc.

EZ-CATCH! - Games - Bravo International Corp.

EZ-CD - Audio cabinets - Mactec Products

EZ-CHEK - Furs—artificial - Stuart Entertainment, Inc.

E.Z. CHRISTMAS - Christmas tree stands - HMS Manufacturing Co.

EZ-CMM - Computer software - Bridgeport Machines, Inc.

EZ COIL - Plastics - Southwest Plastic Binding Co.

EZ COMBI - Ovens—convection - MJR Industries, Inc.

EZ-COMM - Telephones - Comdial Corp.

EZ-CONNECT - Plumbing fixtures - B & K Industries, Inc.

EZ COVER - Containers—plastic - Ropak Corp.

EZ CURL - Hair care products - Alberto-Culver Co.

EZ CURVE - Baseball-pitching machine - Granada Pitching Machines

EZ-CUT - Window shades ☆ - C-Mor Co.

EZ DOC REQUEST - Computer software - Randall C. Sorensen

EZ DRI - Pet products - Dura Pro Products

EZ DRIVE - Computer peripheral equipment - Micro House International, Inc.

EZ DRIVER - Golf clubs - Austad Co.

EZ DROPPER - Semiconductor manufacturing machinery - Semtech Corp.

EZ DU - Wallpaper ☆ - Imperial Wallcoverings, Inc.

EZ-DUIT - Computer software - Digi-Fonts Inc.

EZ DUST IT - Texas Feathers Inc.

EZ DUZ IT - Enamels ☆ - North Jersey Paint Co. Inc.

EZ-DUZ-IT - Packaging machines - Infra Pak, Inc.

E.Z. DUZZIT - Toys - Mattel, Inc.

EZ EAS - Theft prevention apparatus - Security Tag Systems, Inc.

EZ EATER - Animal feed supplements - Zema Corp.

EZ EATER - Pet products - Zema Corp.

EZ ELECTRONIC ENCLOSURES - Electrical equipment - B-Line Systems, Inc.

EZ EXPRESS - Computer hardware - Micro Design International, Inc.

EZ-EYES - Optical goods stores - ETS, Inc.

EZ-FINISH - Steel products - Armco Inc.

E.Z. FIT - Barbecue and grill accessories - GSW Jackes-Evans Manufacturing Co.

EZ FIT - Health care products - Mor-Loc Corp.

EZ FLEX - Conduits—electrical - Cantex Inc.

EZ-FLEX - Hardware - Amerock Corp.

EZ-FLEX - Tools—hand-operated - Union Fork and Hoe Co.

EZ-FLIP - Containers - Keith T. White

EZ FLOOD - Floodlights - RAB Electric

EZ-FLOW - Computer software - Encor-America, Inc.

EZ FOLD - Sporting goods - Draper Shade and Screen Co. Inc.

EZ-FORM - Roofing materials—slate - ASC Pacific Inc.

EZ FORM 400 - Plates—steel - High Strength Holding Co.

EZ FRAME BRACE - Hardware - Newco, Inc.

EZ FRY - Shortening - Interstate Foods Corp.

EZ GAGE - Gauging instruments ☆ - Roper Whitney of Rockford, Inc.

EZ GARD - Sporting goods - E-Z Gard Industries, Inc.

E.Z. GEAR - Apparel and accessories - Ames Department Stores, Inc.

EZ GLOSS - Cleaning preparations - Robarb Inc.

EZ GRADE - Computer software ☆ - Cambridge Educational

EZ GRIP - Bags—plastic - Mason Box Co. Inc.

EZ GROMMET - Motor vehicle parts and accessories - S & J Products, Ltd.

EZ HANG - Wallpaper ☆ - Brewster Wallcovering Co.

EZ HANG II - Wallpaper ☆ - Brewster Wallcovering Co.

EZ HANG TEXTURES III - Wallpaper - Brewster Wallcovering Co.

EZ HAULER - Carts - E.B.S. Equipment Brokers Service, Inc.

EZ HEAT - Heating pads—electric - Prism Enterprises, Inc.

EZ-HOE - Tillers—rotary - Hoffco Inc.

EZ HOLD GRIPS - Office accessories - Ten-Eight Products, Inc.

EZ-HUB - Computer hardware - Millennet

EZ HUTCH - Building materials—concrete - Holtkamp Implement, Inc.

EZ-INSTALL - Computer software - Software Factory, Inc.

EZ JACK - Tools—hand-operated - Blaylock Industries, Inc.

EZ JAPANESE READER - Computer software - Ej Bilingual, Inc.

E.Z. JUST - Hardware - Moore Push-Pin Co.

EZ-KEY - Machinery - EZ Key Corp.

EZ KLEEN - Filters—air - Research Products Corp.

EZ KLEEN - Vacuum cleaners and accessories - The Eureka Co.

EZ KNIFE - Knives—pocket - Sog Specialty Knives, Inc.

EZ KNOT - Fabrics ☆ - Hickory Industries, Inc.

EZ LANGUAGE - Computer software - International Microcomputer Software, Inc.

EZ LEAN - Vitamins and nutritional supplements - Windsor International Co., Inc.

EZ LEAN - Vitamins and nutritional supplements - Windsor International Co., Inc.

EZ-LEARN - Computer storage devices—optical - Seiko Instruments U.S.A., Inc.

EZ-LEDGER - Computer software - Spectrum Universal

EZ-LETS - Medical apparatus - Palco Laboratories

EZ-LIFT - Shovels - Hardware & Industrial Tool Co., Inc.

EZ-LINK - Computer software - Fred Rothenberg & Associates, Inc.

EZ-LITE - Lighting fixtures - Thomas & Betts Holdings, Inc.

EZ LITE - Petroleum - The Di-Bar Co.

EZ LITE - Wheelchairs ☆ - Everest and Jennings International Ltd.

EZ-LOAD - Computer software - Universal Enterprises

EZ-LOAD - Mixers - Fluid Management

EZ LOAD - Notebooks and notepads - General Binding Corp.

EZ LOC - Locks—padlocks - Brammall Inc.

EZ LOCK - Connectors—electrical - Raychem Corp.

EZ MAKE EZ - Cabinets - Angela J. Durrah

E.Z. MAX - Dental equipment - Eurotek Dental Studios, Inc.

EZ-MIX - Artists' materials - Smooth-On Inc.

EZ MOUNT - Automotive parts and accessories ☆ - Optronics Inc.

        ☆ = Now out of production

EZ MOUNT - Mail boxes ✩ - Flambeau Products Corp.

EZ NUTRITION - Vitamins and nutritional supplements - Oxygen for Life, Inc.

EZ OFFICE SYSTEMS - Furniture - O'Sullivan Industries, Inc.

EZ-ON-EZ-OFF - Musical instrument accessories - Sottile Manufacturing Co.

EZ-ON PAK - Tubes–plastic - VisiPak

EZ-ONE - Housewares - Nation/Ruskin, Inc.

EZ ONE! - Skin care products - Alberto-Culver Co.

EZ ORANGE - Degreasing solvents - Martin A. Kahn

EZ-ORGANIZER - Housewares - Grayline Housewares

EZ-OUT - Inverted tongs - Alloway Industries, Inc.

EZ-PAC - Headphones - Avid Corp.

EZ PAIL - Containers - Ring Can Corp.

EZ PAINTR - Paint rollers - E-Z Paintr Corp.

EZ-PAK - Business cards - Moore Business Forms, Inc.

EZ-PAK - Cables–coaxial - Comm/Scope Inc.

EZ PAK - Containers–plastic - Ropak Corp.

EZ-PALLET - Cardboard - Paper Systems, Inc.

EZ PANEL - Paneling ✩ - Louisiana-Pacific Corp.

EZ-PARTNER - Computer software - Fred Rothenberg & Associates, Inc.

EZ PITCH - Baseball-pitching machine - Granada Pitching Machines

EZ PLAN - Publisher's imprints - EZ Plan Corp.

EZ-PLOW - Shovels - Kent & Spiegel Direct, Inc.

EZ PLUMB - Hardware - U.S. Brass Corp.

EZ POINT - Computer peripheral equipment - Gateway 2000, Inc.

EZ-PORT - Computer peripheral equipment - Hayes Microcomputer Products Inc.

EZ PORT - Docks - Ez Dock, Inc.

E.Z. PORT - Pharmaceutical preparations - Izi Corp.

EZ-PROBE - Electrical equipment - Cascade Microtech, Inc.

EZ PUMP - Pumps - Hilo Industries

EZ-QUANT - Chemical preparations - Editek, Inc.

EZ-QUILTING PRODS. - Fabrics–quilted - E Z International, Inc.

EZ READ - Clocks - General Time Corp. (Westclox/Seth Thomas Div.)

EZ - READER - Magnifier - Continental Quest Research Corp.

EZ RECALL - Computer software - EZ Image Inc.

EZ REEL - Tape recorders–reels - Plastic Reel Corp. of America

EZ RETURN - Envelopes - EZ Return Remailable Envelopes and Forms

EZ RIDE - Bicycles - Trailmate Inc.

EZ-RIZER - Step stool - Curd Enterprizes, Inc.

EZ ROLL - Doughnuts ✩ - Johnson Kart Manufacturing

E.Z. ROLL - Hardware - Aluma Trim EZ Roll Manufacturing Co.

EZ ROLLER - Garden equipment - Ames Lawn & Garden Tool Co.

EZ ROLLER - Paint rollers - E-Z Paintr Corp.

EZ RTA - Furniture - O'Sullivan Industries, Inc.

EZ RUNNER - Vacuum cleaners and accessories - CFR Corp.

EZ SCRAPE - Machinery ✩ - Agway, Inc.

EZ-SCSI - Computer software - Adaptec, Inc.

EZ SERV - Trays - Home-Aid Distributors

EZ-SERVE - Plates–paper - Gulf States Paper Corp.

EZ-SHAMPOO - Medical apparatus - Home Care Products Inc.

EZ SHOPPER - Orthopedic products - Ortho-Kinetics, Inc.

EZ-SHOWER - Medical apparatus - Home Care Products Inc.

EZ SIDER - Motor vehicle parts and accessories - Superior Industries International, Inc.

EZ-SLIDE - Paints - Van Sickle Paint Manufacturing Co.

EZ-SLIDER - Motor vehicles–trucks - Superior Industries International, Inc.

EZ SNAP - Cosmetics - Pavion Ltd.

EZ SORT - Cabinets - Empak, Inc.

EZ SPANISH - Games - Candelario G. Camos

EZ-SPC - Computer software - Production Tool & Gage, Inc.

EZ START - Tape–adhesive - Manco, Inc.

EZ STAT - Mats - JCH International Inc.

EZ STEPS - Staircases–metal - Quaker Plastic Corp.

EZ STOCK - Shelving units–metal - Universal Display & Fixtures Co.

EZ STOP - Safety products - D B Industries, Inc.

EZ STOR - Containers–plastic - Ropak Corp.

EZ STREET - Apparel and accessories - Kellwood Co.

EZ-STROKE - Pottery products - Duncan Enterprises

EZ-SWALLOW - Pill-crushers and pill-splitters - American Medical Industries

EZ TABLE - Furniture - Ford B. Cauffiel

E.Z. TAG - Medical apparatus - Izi Corp.

EZ TAPER - Tools–hand-operated - Krystan Manufacturing, Inc.

EZ TEAR - Tape–adhesive - Manco, Inc.

EZ-TESTER - Electronic equipment - Electrodata, Inc.

EZ THAW - Deicing fluid - Swiss Valley Farms Co.

EZ TILT - Glassware–household - Valerie J. Kolle

EZ TILT - Golfing equipment - Ronald P. Jaworski

EZ-TO-STORE EZ-TO-START - Fuel additives - Star Brite

EZ TOTE - Tool boxes - Empak, Inc.

EZ TOUCH - Nozzles - Krylon/Dupli-Color

EZ TRACK - Labels - EZ Track Systems, Inc.

EZ TRACTOR SPREADER - Fertilizers - Republic Tool and Manufacturing Co.

EZ-TRAK - Machinery - Bridgeport Machines, Inc.

EZ-TRAP - Filters–fuel - Lubrizol Corp.

EZ-TRIM - Floor coverings - National Floor Products Co., Inc.

EZ TRODE - Health care products - Mettler Electronics Corp.

EZ-TURN - Garden equipment - Dalen Products Inc.

EZ UP - Exercising equipment - STL International, Inc.

EZ UP FASTTRAX - Electric lighting equipment - Byers Corp.

EZ UZE - Housewares - S J International Corp.

EZ VAC - Cleaning equipment - Kreepy Krauly USA, Inc.

EZ VIEW - Photographic equipment - Logan Electric Specialty Manufacturing Co.

EZ WAXER - Mops - Stanley Home Products Inc.

EZ-WAY - Hardware - EZ Way Sales Inc.

EZ WEEDER - Tools - Stahls' Inc.

EZ-WEEDER - Weed-puller - Advanced Tool Technologies

EZ WHEELER - Luggage - Samsonite Corp.

EZ WIRE - Wire products - Husky Systems, Inc.

EZ-WRAP - Electrical equipment - Preformed Line Products Co.

EZ-WRAP - Rubber–molded ✩ - Johnsonite Flooring Products

EZ-XPERT - Computer software - Richard C. Hicks

EZ ZOOM - Cameras - Yashica Inc.

EZ2B - Dolls - Legacy Products, Inc.

EZ2B RESPONSIBLE FOR ME - Publisher's imprints - Legacy Products, Inc.

EZ2C - Photo albums - 20th Century Plastics

EZ2C - Sporting goods - Professional Printing

EZ135 DRIVE - Disk drives–computer - Syquest Technology, Inc.

EZA-BRIEF - Apparel–women's - Nuvogue Creations

EZA-PANTY - Apparel–women's - Nuvogue Creations

EZAPP - Computer software - Plyware Systems Development, Inc.

EZBACK - Wheelchairs ✩ - APT Technology, Inc.

EZBACK 2 - Medical apparatus - APT Technology, Inc.

EZBOOK - Computers–personal - CTX International, Inc.

EZC - Stencils ✩ - Repeat-O-Type Manufacturing Corp.

EZC EXTRA - Electrical equipment - Triangle Wire & Cable, Inc.

EZC KEYLIGHT - Key rings - Prince Song International

EZCORP-EZDAWN - Ezcorp, Inc.

E.Z.D.GLAZER - Tools–hand-operated - RSKB, LLC

EZE - Herbicides - Security Products Co.

EZE - Mops - Royal Maid Association for the Blind Inc.

EZE - Pencils–mechanical - Sanford Corp.

EZE-A-WAY - Recliners - Bean Station Furniture Factory Inc.

EZE-BENCH - Work benches ✩ - Marshall Industries

EZE-CLEAN - Cleaning preparations–window ✩ - Flo-Pac Corp.

EZE-FIT - Medical apparatus - Storz Instrument Co.

EZE-FLEX - Brassieres (Bras) - Bi-Flex International

EZE-FLO - Paints ✩ - Progress Paint Manufacturing Co.

EZE-GROUTER - Tools–hand-operated - Tile EZ USA, Inc.

EZE-IMAGE - Labels–paper - Fitchburg Coated Products Inc.

EZE-LAX - Pharmaceutical preparations ✩ - JMI-Canton Pharmaceuticals

EZE-LITE - Welding equipment - Goss, Inc.

EZE-MOUNT - Tape–adhesive - Scott Sign Systems, Inc.

EZE-READ - Thermometers - Popper & Sons Inc.

EZE REEL - Cables - M & P Cable Trailer Manufacturing Co.

EZE-SAVE - Tools–machine - Eze Products, Inc.

EZE SHEAR - Hair care products - Tweezerman Corp.

EZE SOCK I.D. - Identification tags - Ross Brothers, Inc.

EZE-STIK - Labels–paper - Fitchburg Coated Products Inc.

EZE-TEX - Paints - Synkoloid Co.

EZE-TRANSFER - Labels–paper - Fitchburg Coated Products Inc.

EZE-VIEW - Cloth–asbestos - June Tailor Inc.

EZE VUE - Photo albums ✩ - McMillin Foley Publishing Co.

EZE WAX - Depilatories ✩ - Bobby Co.

EZE-WAY - Finishing agents - Pioneer Manufacturing Co.

EZEE - Paints - Liberty Distributors Group

EZEE-SWEEP - Garden equipment ✩ - Parker Sweeper Co.

EZEFORM - Orthopedic products - Smith & Nephew Inc. (Rehabilitation Div.)

EZEFORM LIGHT - Splints - Smith & Nephew Inc. (Rehabilitation Div.)

EZEKIEL - Apparel and accessories - Vincent De La Pena

EZELOK - Cosmetics ✩ - Duart Industries Ltd.

EZEMIX - Health care products - Smith & Nephew Inc. (Rehabilitation Div.)

✩ = Now out of production

EZERA - Apparel and accessories - Ezera
EZGC - Computer software - Analytical Innovations, Inc.
EZI GRIP - Pens ☆ - Sanford Corp.
EZIDE - Pharmaceutical preparations - Econo Med Pharmaceuticals Inc.
EZINA - Watches - J.R. Azizollahoff
EZJACK - Telephone apparatus - Hayes Microcomputer Products Inc.
EZJECT - Herbicides - Monsanto Co.
EZLIFE - Vitamins and nutritional supplements - Ezlife Co., Ltd.
EZLINKS TEE TIME NETWORK - Athletic associations - Linksource, Inc.
EZLITE - Computer software - At Systems, Inc.
EZLOGIC - Electronic equipment - Hytrol Conveyor Co., Inc.
EZNOTE - Computer hardware - CTX International, Inc.
EZO - Denture materials - Medtech Laboratories Inc.
EZPORT - Computer peripheral equipment - Archive Corp.
EZPOWER - Computer software - Ezpower Systems, Inc.
EZPULL - Housewares - Prodyne Enterprises Inc.
EZRA BROOKS - Whiskey - David Sherman Corp.
EZREC - Computer software - J.P. Instruments
EZREPORT - Computer software - Raosoft, Inc.
EZRITE - Wallpaper - Walltalkers, Inc.
EZS - Slacks–men's - Haggar Corp.
EZSIGHT - Sights–gun - Tasco Sales, Inc.
EZSPEED - Power switching equipment - Saftronics, Inc.
EZSURVEY - Computer software - Raosoft, Inc.
EZTV - Television equipment - Elcom Technologies Corp.
EZUP - Lighting fixtures - Byers Corp.
EZVU - Lighting equipment - Alvin and Co. Inc.
EZVU - Lighting equipment - Plasticoid Manufacturing Inc.
EZWRITER - Computer software - Lynn Norton

EZXS - Ammunition ☆ - Olin Corp. (Winchester Div.)
EZY CARE - Braces–orthopedic - Apothecary Products, Inc.
EZY-CROWN - Machine parts - RGT
EZY DOSE - Medical apparatus - Apothecary Products, Inc.
EZY DROP - Medical apparatus - Apothecary Products, Inc.
EZY-DUST - Mops - Zephyr Manufacturing Co.
EZY-FILE - File folders ☆ - Jacob North Printing Co. Inc.
EZY FIX - Handles–wood - Fleischmann Handle Co.
EZY FLOSS - Medical apparatus - Apothecary Products, Inc.
EZY FLOSS 'N' PIX - Medical apparatus ☆ - Apothecary Products, Inc.
EZY GRIP - Containers–shipping - Drug Plastic and Glass Co.
EZY-INFANT CARE - Medical apparatus ☆ - Apothecary Products, Inc.
EZY LIFT - Medical apparatus - Professional Products, Inc.
EZY LOCK - Office supplies - American Trading and Production Corp.
EZY-OUT - Tools - Cleveland Twist Drill Co.
EZY PUPPEEZ - Orthopedic products - Professional Products, Inc.
EZY PUPPEEZ ORTHOPAEDIC HEEL CUSHIONS - Orthopedic products - Professional Products, Inc.
EZY PUPPEEZ ORTHOPAEDIC INSOLES - Orthopedic products - Professional Products, Inc.
EZY-RASE - Chalk - Arcana Products Co.
EZY-RUG - Rubber–molded ☆ - Lancaster Colony Automotive Group
EZY-SLEEP - Pharmaceutical preparations - Apothecary Products, Inc.
EZY-SPRAYS - Pesticides–household - Dexol Industries
EZY-TILT - Tools - Kraft Tool Co.
EZY TOUCH - Drains - Jameco Industries, Inc.
EZY-TURN - Lubricants - Jet-Lube, Inc.
EZYINDEX - Office supplies - Globe-Weis
EZZY - Masts–wood - Ezzy Sails Maui, Inc.
EZZY CLEAN - Cleaning preparations - Ezzy Clean-Up, Inc.

☆ = Now out of production

Addresses and phone numbers for the companies cited in the brands below
are available in the Company Listings section immediately following the brands listings.

F - Computer program - Financialware, Inc.

F - Computer storage devices - Franklin Electronic Publishers, Inc.

F - Furnaces–electric - Fuchs Systems, Inc.

F - Guitars - Fender Musical Instruments

F - Hardware - Ring Screw Works

F - Projection screens - Fairtron Corp.

F - Snack foods - BDH Two, Inc.

F-1 - Bicycle parts and accessories - Foes Fabrications Inc.

F-1 - Computer peripheral equipment - Husco Engineering Co. Inc.

F 1 - Motor vehicle parts and accessories - Atlas Imports-Exports, Inc.

F-1 SUPER BATTLE - Video games - Jaleco USA, Inc.

F-1X - Audio equipment - Alembic Inc.

F-2B - Audio equipment - Alembic Inc.

F-4 PHANTOM - Toys–models - Estes Industries

F-4G WILD WEASEL - Fireworks - American Promotional Events, Inc.

F-8 - Sprockets–industrial - Steiner Co., Inc.

F-14 - Boats - Ray Industries, Inc.

F-14 TOMCAT - Toys–models - Estes Industries

F-15 EAGLE - Fireworks - American Promotional Events, Inc.

F-15 EAGLE - Toys - Fisher-Price, Inc.

F-15 EAGLE - Toys–airplanes - Cox Products Inc.

F-15 JET - Kites ☆ - Hi-Flier Manufacturing Co.

F-15 STRIKE EAGLE - Computer software ☆ - Microprose Software, Inc.

F-16 FALCON - Toys–models - Estes Industries

F-16 FLCS - Computer software - Thrustmaster, Inc.

F-16 STICK - Computer peripheral equipment - Joystick Technologies (CH Products Division)

F-16 TQS - Computer software - Thrustmaster, Inc.

F 18 - Tools–hand-operated - Salco, Inc.

F-18 HORNET - Toys–models - Estes Industries

F-19 STEALTH FIGHTER - Computer software ☆ - Microprose Software, Inc.

F-22 AIR SUPERIORITY FIGHTER - Toys–models - Estes Industries

F-26 - Adhesives and sealants - Leech Products Inc.

F-26 - Boats–motor - Grady-White Boats, Inc.

F-61 STARFIGHTER - Toys–models ☆ - Estes Industries

F-68 - Agricultural products - Fenic Co.

F-85 - Motor vehicles–automobiles ☆ - General Motors Corp. (Oldsmobile Div.)

F-117 STEALTH NIGHTHAWK - Toys–models - Estes Industries

F-402 - Pens - Zebra Pen Corp.

F-570 - Tires - Bridgestone/Firestone, Inc.

F & C - Putties - BASF Corp.

F & C INTERNATIONAL, INC. - Chemicals ☆ - Wild Flavors, Inc.

F & D - Paints - Valspar Corp.

F & F - Dinnerware–glass - Fitz & Floyd, Inc.

F & F - Health care products ☆ - F & F Laboratories, Inc.

F & H - Potato flakes ☆ - Fowler & Huntting Co.

F AND J - Fruit drinks–bottled or canned - Foote & Jenks Corp.

F & L - Recording label - F & L Records

F & P - Food products - Tri Valley Growers, Inc.

F & S - Beverages–malt - Fuhrmann & Schmidt Brewing Co.

F & T - Pet products - Professional Pet Products

F & W - Water purification systems - Flint & Walling Industries, Inc.

F. B. ROGERS - Giftware ☆ - Towle Silversmiths

F. B. ROGERS - Silver products ☆ - National Housewares

F. BESSON - Musical instruments - Boosey & Hawkes Buffet Crampon USA

F C C ROM. 10:17 EDUCATING THE BELIEVERS - Publisher's imprints - Faith Christian Church Inc.

F. CHAUVENET - Wines - Paterno Imports, Ltd.

F. E. BARBER - Crackers - FCW Imports

F. E. OLDS & SON - Musical instruments ☆ - L.A. Sax Co.

F-E-P - Pharmaceutical preparations - Boots Pharmaceuticals Inc.

F. E. TRIMBACH - Wines - Seagram's Chateau & Estate Wines Co.

F F FRANKLIN SERVICE SYSTEMS - Computer software - Simpson Kalisher

F F INC. - Machinery - Fortville Feeders, Inc.

F FLAVORLAND - Beef - Conagra, Inc.

F FLEX PRODUCTS INC. - Pigments ☆ - Flex Products, Inc.

F FREEDA VITAMINS - Vitamins and nutritional supplements - Freeda Vitamins Inc.

F FREEMAN - Skin care products - Freeman Cosmetics Corp.

F/G - Furniture - Jofco, Inc.

F-K - Electronic equipment ☆ - Ercona Corp.

F. L. & J. A. RADDINS - Snuff ☆ - Byfield Snuff Co.

F-L-T - Veterinary pharmaceutical preparations ☆ - Boehringer Ingelheim Animal Health, Inc.

F-LINE - Sandals - Playazul International Inc.

F-M - Mirrors - Faries-McMeekan Inc.

F-METER - Electrical equipment - Allen Face & Co., L.C.

F. MONTANT - Wines ☆ - Alimar & Cie. Inc.

F-O-C - Archery equipment - Saunders Archery Co.

F-P HIDEAWAY CHANGER - Infant product - Fisher-Price, Inc.

F-P HOP SKIP JUMPER - Toys - Fisher-Price, Inc.

F-P TRIPLE TOTE - Toys - Fisher-Price, Inc.

F-PROT PROFESSIONAL - Computer software ☆ - Command Software Systems, Inc.

F Q - Seasonings - Flavorite Laboratories Inc.

F R, A - Ashtrays–metal - One Eleven Corp.

F. R. WUNDERLICH - Musical instrument accessories - Fred Gretsch Enterprises

F/S - Cleaner/degreaser - Intex Chemical Inc.

F S - Nuts and bolts - National Welders Supply Co. Inc.

F SERIES - Lighting equipment - Fox Lite Inc.

F-SERIES - Motor vehicles–trucks - Ford Motor Co.

F/STOP - Apparel and accessories - Focus Apparel Group Inc.

F. W. FISCHER - Coats–children's - MZL Fashions Corp.

F/X FUNDAMENTALS - Wallcoverings - Sinclair Wallcovering

F-X INTERCEPTOR - Toys–airplanes - Cox Products Inc.

F/X TAP - Electronic equipment - Commercial Video Services

F-ZERO - Video games - Nintendo of America Inc.

F2 - Snowboards ☆ - Earth & Ocean Sports, Inc.

F3 - Computer software - BLOC Development Corp.

F3 - Machinery - Quamco, Inc.

F4 - Cameras - Nikon Inc.

F4 - Electrical equipment - Omega Holdings, LLC

F8 - Apparel and accessories - Faith

F8F BEARCAT - Toys–models - Cox Products Inc.

F32 ALL WINTER - Tires - Goodyear Tire & Rubber Co.

F100 - Tires ☆ - Bridgestone/Firestone, Inc.

F100 PRECISION SWIM RING - Toys - Aqua-Leisure Industries, Inc.

F301 - Pens - Zebra Pen Corp.

F605 - Pens - Zebra Pen Corp.

F911 - Tanks–steel - Steel Tank Institute

☆ = Now out of production

F921 - Tanks–steel - Steel Tank Institute
F1500 - Projection screens - Draper Shade and Screen Co. Inc.
FA-12 - Agricultural products - Gustafson Inc.
FA-18 HORNET - Toys–airplanes - Cox Products Inc.
FA 200 - Oils–lubricating - Triple T Marketing
FA 700S/FA 900S/FA 2000 - Chemical preparations - Westwood Chemical Corp.
FA SPORTS - Shirts - Fabricart, Inc.
FA2ST - Computer software - Sys-Tech Solutions, Inc.
FA1010 - Adhesives and sealants - Franklin International, Inc.
FAAM - Licorice - Holland-American Importing Co. Inc.
FAAR - Computer storage devices - NMT Corp.
FAB - Artists' materials - Fabco Products Inc.
FAB - Detergents - Colgate-Palmolive Co.
FAB - Shelving units–metal - Tennsco Corp.
FAB 1 SHOT - Detergents - Colgate-Palmolive Co.
FAB-A-FRAME - Doors–metal - Amweld Building Products
FAB-A-FRAME - Metals - Pro-De-Co Inc.
FAB CAB - Toys–automobiles - Mattel, Inc.
FAB FOAM - Pet products ☆ - Texas Recreation Corp.
FAB-LINED - Girdles ☆ - Playtex Apparel, Inc.
FAB PHONICS - Publisher's imprints - Learning Quest
FAB RINGS - Shower rods - SRCO Inc.
FAB SILK - Flowers–artificial ☆ - First American Artificial Flowers Inc.
FAB-SOFT - Fabric softeners ☆ - Elcal Enterprises Ltd.
FAB-TEX - Paints - Stencil-Ease
FAB-TEX - Wallcoverings - Sherman & Associates International
FAB TONE - Musical instruments - Evets Corp.
FAB-U-DRAPE - Hobby kits - Craft World International Inc.
FAB-U-FIBER - Nail care products - W.R. Rayson Co., Inc.
FAB WORKS - Computer software - Texas Instruments Inc.
FAB9 - Automotive parts and accessories - Chris Alston's Chassisworks, Inc.
FABBRI - Desserts - Bell'amore Imports Inc.
FABBRI - Syrup - De Choix Specialty Foods Co.
FABCO - Mats–rattan - Fabco Rubber Inc.
FABCO - Meat products–poultry - O.K. Foods Inc.
FABCO - Office supplies ☆ - IDL Manufacturing & Sales Corp.
FABCO - Sporting goods - F.A. Baker Co. Inc.
FABCOR - Wallpaper ☆ - Expanko Cork Co.
FABCRAFT - Metals - Fabcraft Inc.
FABCRO - Inks ☆ - Crown Art Products
FABER - Photographic equipment - Adams Retouching Machine Co.
FABER - Window shades - Plastic Sun Shade Co. Inc.
FABER CASTELL - Office supplies - Faber-Castell Corp.
FABERGE - Air purification systems ☆ - Medo Industries, Inc.
FABERGE - Apparel–men's - James Edmond Inc.
FABERGE - Colognes - Faberge Co.
FABERGE - Deodorants–personal - CPI Fab, Inc.
FABERGE - Leather goods ☆ - I.J.K. Sales Corp.
FABERGE - Luggage - Monarch Luggage Co., Inc.
FABERGE - Underwear and nightwear - Nantucket Industries Inc.
FABERGE - Watches - M.Z. Berger & Co. Inc.
FABERGE LADY POWER - Deodorants–personal - CPI Fab, Inc.
FABERGE ORGANICS - Skin care products - Faberge Co.
FABERPEL - Shampoos - Faberge Co.
FABIANA - Fabrics - Fab. Industries Inc.
FABIANO - Footwear–athletic - Fabiano Shoe Co. Inc.
FABIANO - Sporting goods ☆ - Regina Imports
FABIELLA - Fabrics - Fab. Industries Inc.
FABIO - Luggage - Orgama Ltd.
FABIO - Ophthalmic goods ☆ - Luxottica
FABIOLA - Glass products - Primex International Corp.
FABKIT - Window treatments - A.J. Boyd Industries Inc.
FABLE - Floor coverings–carpet and rugs - Regal Rugs Inc.
FABLE - Jewelry and watches - Shube's Manufacturing, Inc.
FABLE - Whipped topping–frozen - Presto Food Products, Inc.
FABLES - Floor coverings–carpet and rugs ☆ - Alliance Industries Inc.
FABLES & FLOWERS - Toilets–enameled - Kohler Co.
FABLES FLYING BEAR - Toys–stuffed - Frivals n Friends
FABLIQUE - House furnishings - Carousel Crafts Co.
FABMET - Machine tools - Mitsubishi Materials USA Corp.
FABRA-DECOR - Frames–picture - Repcon International, Inc.
FABRA-FRAME - Frames–picture - Repcon International, Inc.
FABRA-TEX - Wallpaper - Ozite Corp.
FABRAID - Floor coverings–carpet and rugs - Colonial Mills Inc.
FABRATIQUE - Fabric - Patricia J. Cockrell

FABRAY - Fabrics - Stearns Technical Textiles Co.
FABRETE - Blinds–venetian - Hunter Douglas, Inc.
FABREX - Cleaning preparations - Associated Chemists, Inc.
FABREZON - Window treatments - A.J. Boyd Industries Inc.
FABRI - Wallpaper ☆ - Decorative Coverings Inc.
FABRI-CLEAN - Cleaning preparations–upholstery - Minnetonka Mills Inc.
FABRI-COATE - Cleaning preparations - Guardsman Products, Inc.
FABRI-COMB - Brushes–hair - Helmac Products Corp.
FABRI-COMP - Hydraulic presses - Pacific Press and Shear Inc.
FABRI CRYLIC - Paints–artists' - Palmer Paint Products, Inc.
FABRI-KLEEN - Cleaning preparations - Guardsman Products, Inc.
FABRI-SAFE - Cleaning preparations - H. Behlen & Bro. Inc.
FABRI-SHIELD - Cleaning preparations - Guardsman Products, Inc.
FABRI-TECH - Packaging–paper ☆ - NPS
FABRI WRAP - Paper–gift wrap ☆ - Gift Wrap Co.
FABRIANO - Coffee - 1 Uno Espresso, Inc.
FABRIANO - Eyeglasses - Martin-Copeland Eyewear Corp.
FABRIANO - Paper - Fabriano America Inc.
FABRIANO - Stationery - Oldcastle Associates Inc.
FABRIB - Siding–metal - Alcan Aluminum Corp. Alcan Building Products Div.
FABRIC ANCHORS - Garden equipment - Teknor Apex Co.
FABRIC ELEGANCE - Fabrics–linen - Maytex Mills
FABRIC-FORM - Paper–thermoplastics coated - Unnatural Resources Inc.
FABRIC FRESH - Cleaning preparations - S.C. Johnson & Son, Inc.
FABRIC FUN - Markers–felt-tip - Pentel of America, Ltd.
FABRIC IN PRINT - Paper–gift wrap - Gibson Greetings, Inc.
FABRIC-LOCK - Paint rollers - Wooster Brush Co.
FABRIC MASTER - Artists' materials - Robert Simmons Inc.
FABRIC-MATIC - Washing machines–household - Maytag Corp.
FABRIC OF AMERICA - Dolls - Lawton Doll Co.
FABRIC ONE - Fabrics - Frankel Associates, Inc.
FABRIC PAINTERS - Markers–felt-tip ☆ - Hunt Manufacturing Co.
FABRIC RUG CUSTOMIZER - Floor coverings–carpet and rugs - Colonial Mills Inc.
FABRIC SILHOUETTES - Decals and transfers - Christy Crafts, Inc.
FABRIC SNOW-TEX - Paints ☆ - DecoArt, Inc.
FABRIC SOURCE - Fabrics–broadcloth - Norman Lacoff & Associates Inc.
FABRIC TRAYS - Trays - Knobler International Ltd.
FABRIC X - Paint rollers ☆ - Wooster Brush Co.
FABRICA - Floor coverings–carpet and rugs - Fabrica International
FABRICA - Paper–bond ☆ - Fox River Paper Co.
FABRICA DE TORTILLA - Tortillas - Mega Marts, Inc.
FABRICA INTERNATIONAL - Floor coverings–carpet and rugs - Fabrica International
FABRICADABRA - Apparel–women's - Exquisite Form Industries
FABRICAID+ - Stain remover - Heartland Corp.
FABRICARTS - Paints - Ivy Imports Inc.
FABRICARTS ANTIFUSANT - Paints - Ivy Imports Inc.
FABRICARTS GUTTAS - Paints - Ivy Imports Inc.
FABRICARTS LIQUID ALL FABRIC PAINTS - Paints - Ivy Imports Inc.
FABRICARTS RESIST - Paints - Ivy Imports Inc.
FABRICAT - Cages–wire - Hoff Fabrication
FABRICATS - Appliques - JCA, Inc.
FABRICLIFE - Waterproofing compounds - Dap Products Inc.
FABRICMATE - Markers–felt-tip - Yasutomo
FABRICO - Stamps–hand - Tsukineko, Inc.
FABRICON - Girdles ☆ - Playtex Apparel, Inc.
FABRICORD - Floor coverings–carpet and rugs - Colonial Mills Inc.
FABRICORK - Bulletin boards–cork - Claridge Products and Equipment Inc.
FABRICRAFT - Fabrics - Rubbermaid Inc.
FABRICRAFTER - Cleaning preparations–upholstery - Duraclean International Inc.
FABRICS NOW - Fabric stores - Streamline Industries, Inc.
FABRICS OF FAITH - Giftware ☆ - Cronar Ltd.
FABRICS PLUS - Fabrics–broadcloth - Fabrics Plus
FABRICTEX - Wallcovering - Panelfold Inc.
FABRICUT - Fabrics - Fabricut Inc.
FABRICWAL - Doors - Panelfold Inc.
FABRIELLA'S - Skin care products ☆ - Victoria Vogue, Inc.
FABRIFOIL - Fabrics–coated - Duracote Corp.
FABRIFORGE - Machinery - Esco Corp.
FABRIFRAME - Hardware ☆ - Astrup Co.
FABRIHANCE - Fabrics - Veratec
FABRIK-LOK - Projection screens ☆ - Draper Shade and Screen Co. Inc.
FABRILUX - Luggage - Marcor, Inc.
FABRIMATIC - Rug cleaning machines–commercial - Castex Industries Inc.

☆ = Now out of production

FABRINI - Scarves - Handcraft Manufacturing Corp.
FABRIOLLA - Ophthalmic goods - Styl-Rite Optical Manufacturing Co., Inc.
FABRIQUE - Dishes–china - Taylor, Smith & Taylor Co.
FABRIQUE - Wallpaper - Carlton-Metro Wallcoverings
FABRIQUE DELICES - Meat products–poultry - Made in France
FABRIQUE DELICES - Pate - Fabrique Delices
FABRIQUES MOVADO - Watches - Movado Time Corp.
FABRISCAPES - Quilts ✩ - Martingale & Co.
FABRITECH - Blinds–vertical - Gilmore Enterprises
FABRITONE - Soap - Imperial Manufacturing Co. Inc.
FABRIWALL - Wallpaper - Payne Fabrics
FABRIZON - Cleaning preparations–window ✩ - John Dixon Inc.
FAB'S SUPERSUEDE II - Apparel - Fab. Industries Inc.
FABSHOP - Welding equipment - Hobart Corp.
FABSPRAY - Paints - Glidden Co.
FABSPRAY - Paints - Zynolyte Products Co.
FABSTIC - Adhesives and sealants - Dap Products Inc.
FABSTRAN - Wallpaper ✩ - Thomas Strahan Wallcoverings
FABTAC - Covers–seat - Kittrich Corp.
FABTEX - Fabrics - Fabrite Laminating Corp.
FABU-SILK - Hair care products - Revlon Consumer Products Corp.
FABUCORD - Fabrics - Majestic Mills Inc.
FABUFIT - Hosiery - Volt USA Inc.
FABULACE - Apparel and accessories - Lane Bryant, Inc.
FABULAND - Toys–blocks - Lego Systems Inc.
FABULASH - Cosmetics - Revlon Consumer Products Corp.
FABULAXER - Hair care products - Revlon Consumer Products Corp.
FABULIFT - Bathing suits - A & H Sportswear Co., Inc.
FABULINER - Cosmetics - Revlon Consumer Products Corp.
FABULITE - Frames–eyeglass ✩ - Vanity Optical Manufacturing Co. Inc.
FABULITE - Giftware - Wm. V. Schmidt Co. Inc.
FABULON - Decals and transfers ✩ - Sangray Corp.
FABULON - Paints - Pratt & Lambert, Inc.
FABULON - Varnishes - Pratt & Lambert, Inc. (Specialty Products Div.)
FABULOSO - Cleaning preparations - Colgate-Palmolive Co.
FABULOUS - Candy - Pangburn Candy Co.
FABULOUS - Flags - Outside Design Inc.
FABULOUS - Frames–eyeglass - Zylo Ware Corp.
FABULOUS - Paints - Lee Paint & Varnish Co.
FABULOUS - Perfumes ✩ - Spilo/Mehaz Worldwide
FABULOUS EYES - Skin care products ✩ - Freeman Cosmetics Corp.
FABULOUS FACES - Cosmetics - Del Pharmaceuticals, Inc.
FABULOUS FACES - Cosmetics - Robert Rosso
FABULOUS FAKES - Canvas–artists' - Fabulous Forgeries Ltd.
FABULOUS FAKES - Wigs - Revlon General Wig Manufacturers, Inc.
FABULOUS FANGS - Toy imitation teeth - Peter Alan Inc.
FABULOUS FANNY'S - Desserts - Margaret Van Der Blom Sapp
FABULOUS FANNY'S NEW YORK STYLE CHEESECAKE - Desserts - Margaret Van Der Blom Sapp
FABULOUS FAUX FINISHES - Wallpaper - Capital Carousel Inc.
FABULOUS FAVORS - Novelty items–paper - Impact International Inc.
FABULOUS FEATHERS - Veterinary pharmaceutical preparations - Nickers International Ltd.
FABULOUS FEET - Skin care products - Freeman Cosmetics Corp.
FABULOUS FELINES - Calendars ✩ - American Greetings Corp.
FABULOUS FIBER - Health care products - Lewis Laboratories International Ltd.
FABULOUS FIDDLESTIX - Toys–guns - T-N-T International, Inc.
FABULOUS FIFTEEN - Jewelry - K & M Associates
FABULOUS FINISH - Nail care products - Posner Laboratories Inc.
FABULOUS FIT - Mannequins - Jill Ralston Goray
FABULOUS FLORENCE - Christmas tree ornaments - Cracker Box Inc.
FABULOUS FOLDERS - Furniture ✩ - Regional Respotary
FABULOUS FONTS - Computer software - Parsons Technology, Inc.
FABULOUS FOODS - Computer software ✩ - Broderbund Software, Inc.
FABULOUS FRAGRANCES - Deodorizers - Candles Et Cetera Inc.
FABULOUS FUR - Veterinary pharmaceutical preparations - Nickers International Ltd.
FABULOUS HAIR - Hair care products - Nickers International Ltd.
FABULOUS HAIR FRIENDS - Dolls - Tyco Industries, Inc.
FABULOUSFILLABLES - Tote bags - Fact Games, Ltd.
FABULOUSLY CLEAN - Shampoos - Playtex Beauty Care, Inc.
FABULOY - Varnishes - Pratt & Lambert, Inc. (Specialty Products Div.)
FABULUSE - Perfumes - Classic Fragrances Ltd.
FABUNAIL - Cosmetics - Revlon Consumer Products Corp.
FABWEL - Gutters–metal - Fabwel, Inc.

FABWIPE - Multi-purpose wiper - Texwipe Co. LLC
FABWORLD - Motoman, Inc.
FAC - Locks–door - Amerisafe Industries, Inc.
FAC-ETTE - Machinery - Fac-Ette Manufacturing, Inc.
FAC-PAC - Paper products ✩ - Dev-Tec, Inc.
FACADE - Furniture - American Furniture Co. Inc.
FACADES - Wallpaper - Essex Wallcoveringss
FACADES - Wallpaper - Gencorp Polymer Products
FACCENT - Markers–felt-tip - Sanford Corp.
FACCIA BRUTTA - Fruits and vegetables - Bruno Dispoto
FACE-A-GLOW - Lipsticks ✩ - Avon Products, Inc.
FACE & BODY SPA - Vitamins and nutritional supplements - Fong Chiropractic Medical Center, Inc.
FACE CHEMISTRY - Skin care products - Alton L. Hayes Jr.
FACE COLOURS - Cosmetics - Zauder Bros. Inc.
FACE DESIGNS - Cosmetics ✩ - Honey & Spice Toiletries
FACE-ETTES - Skin care products - Reina Claire
FACE FAX - Cosmetics - Lana Toni Gersman
FACE FIRST - Eyeglasses - Martin-Copeland Eyewear Corp.
FACE FIRST - Skin care products - Elizabeth Grady Face First Inc.
FACE-FIT - Goggles - Trademark Corp.
FACE FITNESS - Skin care products - PRL USA Holdings, Inc.
FACE FLOWERS - Beauty product - Aubrey Organics, Inc.
FACE FRAMER, THE - Cutting boards - Gianfarro, Inc.
FACE GLEAMER - Cosmetics - Revlon Consumer Products Corp.
FACE GUARD - Lotions ✩ - P.J. Maxwell Co., Inc.
FACE GUARD - Razor blades Now out of production ✩ - American Safety Razor Co.
FACE GUARD, THE - Sporting goods - Advanced Sports Concepts Inc.
FACE IN THE SHADE - Pillows - Harold Harrison
FACE IT - Picture frames - Sansom, Inc.
FACE KOTE - Skin care products - Aloe Gator Suncare Co.
FACE LIFE - Video production - Face Life, Inc.
FACE LIFE FOR FACIAL EXERCISE - Video equipment - Face Life, Inc.
FACE LIFT - Cleaning preparations - Thompson and Formby
FACE LIFT - Skin care products - Beauty Aids Inc.
FACE LIFT - Skin care products ✩ - Elysee Scientific Cosmetic Co.
FACE MAGIC - Cosmetics - Covermark Cosmetics
FACE MAKER - Computer software - SourceView Software International
FACE OFF - Fabrics - Greenwood Mills Inc.
FACE OFF! - Games - Global Giggles
FACE OFF - Skin care products - Patricia Anne Eaton
FACE OFF HOCKEY - Games - Carrom Co.
FACE PILLOW - Skin care products - Yellowbird Inc.
FACE-SAVER - Apparel–athletic ✩ - Sport Obermeyer Ltd.
FACE SAVER - Computer software - Lighten Up Software Inc.
FACE SAVER - Hats - Preston Leather Products
FACE SAVER - Shaving preparations - Gillette Co.
FACE SAVERS - Frames–eyeglass - May Optical Co. Inc.
FACE SHAPERS - Cosmetics - Del Pharmaceuticals, Inc.
FACE STOCKHOLM - Health care products - Face Stockholm, Ltd.
FACE SYSTEM FIVE - Skin care products - Face System Five
FACE, THE - Novelty items - Imagineering Inc.
FACE THE BUZZ - Apparel and accessories - Face the Buzz Inc.
FACE-THERAPY - Skin care products ✩ - Para Laboratories Inc.
FACE TO FACE - Computer software - Groupware Authors
FACE TO FACE - Skin-care products - American Hygienic Laboratories Inc.
FACE TO FACE - Skin care products - Mary Kay Cosmetics Inc.
FACE 2 FACE - Sunglasses - Face 2 Face Corp.
FACE TOOLS - Accessories - Norine L. Fuller
FACE VALUE - Cosmetic applicators - Earthly Essentials, Inc.
FACE VALUES - Eyeglasses - Shopko Stores, Inc.
FACEBALLS - Toys ✩ - South Bend Toy Manufacturing Co.
FACEGLOW - Cosmetics - Noxell Corp.
FACEKIT - Computer software - Infotec Development, Inc.
FACELESS - Clocks ✩ - By Design Corp.
FACELETS - Glass–optical ✩ - Willson/Dalloz Safety
FACELIFTERS - Cabinets - Facelifters Home Systems Inc.
FACELLI - Wines - Facelli Winery
FACEMAKER - Computer software ✩ - Queue Inc.
FACEMAKER - Skin care products ✩ - Sunbeam-Oster Household Products
FACEMAKER - Tools–woodworking - Blount International, Inc. (Sporting Equipment Group)
FACEMATE - Frames–eyeglass ✩ - Universal/Univis Inc.
FACE'N REALITY - Apparel–women's - Trina L. Forte
FACEOLOGY - Publisher's imprints - Facemaker Enterprises

✩ = Now out of production

FACERSIZER - Medical apparatus - Edward A. Carosi

FACES - Computer software - Spectrum Holobyte, Inc.

FACES OF. - Novelty items–paper - Z'atelier, Inc.

FACES PLUS - Suntan lotions - Sun Pharmaceuticals Corp.

FACESAVER - Wood products ☆ - Pluswood Inc.

FACESEPTIC - Cosmetics - Aristocrat Hairseptic Co.

FACESPACE - Computer software - Digital Technology International

FACESPAN - Computer software - Software Designs Unlimited Inc.

F.A.C.E.T. - Computer software - Lab-Volt Systems, Inc.

FACET - Floor coverings ☆ - Congoleum Corp.

FACET - Furniture ☆ - Hammary Furniture Co. Inc.

FACET - Motor vehicle parts and accessories - Purolator Products Co. (Motor Components Div.)

FACET - Recording label - Delos Records International

FACET BRITE - Jewelry - Elgin Watch Co.

FACETED ELEGANCE - Beads - Greene Plastics Corp.

FACETS - Apparel–women's - Antigua Knits, Inc.

FACETS - Colognes ☆ - Avon Products, Inc.

FACETS - Computer software - Erisco Inc.

FACETS - Floor coverings–carpet and rugs - Collins & Aikman Corp.

FACETS - Furniture - Lane Co. Inc.

FACETS - Furniture ☆ - Broyhill Furniture Industries, Inc.

FACETS - Glassware–household - Owens-Illinois Inc. (Libbey Div.)

FACETS - Wallpaper - Essex Wallcoveringss

FACETTE - Cosmetics - Kris Evans

FACETTE - Eyeglasses - Martin-Copeland Eyewear Corp.

FACETTE - Glassware–household - Dansk International Designs, Ltd.

FACETTE - Rings–jewelry - Artcarved Inc.

FACETTE - Tableware–china ☆ - Villeroy and Boch Tableware Ltd.

FACFILE - Computer software - Thomson Financial Publishing Inc.

FACHO - Apparel and accessories - Facho Wear

FACIA - Wallpaper ☆ - Combo Industries

FACIAL ACTIVATOR - Skin care products - Viviane Woodard Industries, Ltd.

FACIAL AESTHETICS MD - Skin care products - Medical Aesthetic Foundation, Inc.

FACIAL CLEANSING SYSTEMS - Cosmetics ☆ - E.E. Dickinson Co.

FACIAL FIRM - Skin care products - Facial Firm Inc.

FACIAL-FLEX - Medical device - Facial Concepts, Inc.

FACIAL FLOWER - Cosmetics - Sponge Factory, Inc.

FACIAL-GLACIAL - Skin care products - Reliable Plastics

FACIAL MAGIC - Recording label - Rejenuve

FACIAL OPTICS - Cosmetics ☆ - Redken Laboratories, Inc.

FACIAL SCRUBS - Skin care products - Para Laboratories Inc.

FACIAL SENSATION - Massage products - Facial Sensation Products

FACIALIN - Napkins–paper - Fort Howard Corp.

FACILE - Bedding–linen - Springs Industries, Inc.

FACILE - Corsets - Marshall Field's

FACILE - Yarn - Brunswick Yarns

FACILITAPE - Computer software - Legent Corp.

FACILITATOR - Computer software - Johnson Service Co.

FACILITIES 10 - Floor coverings–carpet and rugs - Lees Carpets

FACILITIES GROUP - Furniture - Jofco, Inc.

FACILITRAY - Medical apparatus - Lumex, Inc.

FACILITY - Floor coverings–carpet and rugs - Mohawk Industries Inc.

FACILITY ASSOCIATE - Computer software - Environmental Support Solutions, Inc.

FACILITY ENGINEERING SUITE - Computer software - Procomp Software, Inc.

FACIT - Computer peripheral equipment - Ahearn & Soper Co., Inc. (Facit Div.)

FACKELMANN - Cooking equipment–commercial - Kreiner Imports

FACS - Computer software - Joseph Madison Associates Inc.

FACSIMILE - Games - Sterten & Co.

FACSIMLE - Surgical supplies - Flexbar Machine Corp.

F-A-C-T - Apparel and accessories - Eagle Button Inc.

FACT - Cigarettes - Brown & Williamson Tobacco Corp.

FACT - Frames–eyeglass - Pathway Optical Prods.

FACT - Pregnancy test kits - Ortho Pharmaceutical Corp.

FACT-1 - Paint removers - Great Lakes Chemical Corp.

FACT FINDER - Pens - National Pen & Pencil Co.

FACT OR OPINION - Computer software - Hartley Courseware Inc.

FACT-PACK - Containers–shipping ☆ - Dev-Tec, Inc.

FACT PACK - Hobby kits - Peabody's-Toys that Teach Inc.

FACT PLUS - Pregnancy test kits - Ortho Pharmaceutical Corp.

FACT SHEETS - Computer software - Hartley Courseware Inc.

FACTIVITY - Computer software - Manufacturing Decision Support Systems,Inc.

FACTOR - Exercising equipment - Parabody, Inc.

FACTOR - Golfing equipment - Knight Golf, Inc.

FACTOR - Guitars - Philip Kubicki Technology

FACTOR - Water bottles–rubber - Connelly Skis, Inc.

FACTOR II - Floor coverings–carpet and rugs ☆ - Mannington Carpets, Inc.

FACTOR BLAST - Computer software ☆ - Spinnaker Software Corp.

FACTOR EXPRESS - Computer software - Federal National Mortgage Association

FACTORATE - Pharmaceutical preparations ☆ - Armour Pharmaceutical Co.

FACTORY - Brushes–paint ☆ - PPG Industries, Inc.

FACTORY ART - Candlesticks - Factory Art Inc.

FACTORY BEAT - Recording label - Factory Beat Records Inc.

FACTORY EXPLORER - Computer software - Chance Industrial Solutions

FACTORY FAVORITES - Cigars - G.W. Van Slyke & Horton

FACTORY PERFORMANCE - Automotive parts and accessories - Polyproducts Corp.

FACTORY RACING - Motorcycle parts and accessories - Boyesen Engineering

FACTORY, THE - Apparel–children's ☆ - Jonbil Inc.

FACTORYMATE PLUS - Computers–mainframe - Eaton IDT Inc.

FACTORYMOUSE - Computer peripheral equipment - Eaton IDT Inc.

FACTOTUM - Computer software - Micra, Inc.

FACTREL - Pharmaceutical preparations - Wyeth-Ayerst Laboratories

FACTROL - Computer software - Fluid Air, Inc.

FACTS - Computer software - Telic Corp.

FACTS AND FALLACIES - Computer software - Hartley Courseware Inc.

FACTS FINDER - Markers–felt-tip - Micropoint Inc.

FACTS IN FIVE - Games - Avalon Hill Game Co.

FACTS MATCH - Computer programming services - Berta-Max Inc.

FACTS 'N FUN - Toys ☆ - Small World Toys

FACTS ON FILE - Publisher's imprints - Facts on File Inc.

FACTS REPLAY - Pagers ☆ - NEC America, Inc.

FACTS SPORT - Communications equipment–mobile ☆ - NEC America, Inc.

FACTUARY - Computer software - ViewPlan Inc.

FACULTY - Floor coverings–carpet and rugs - Lees Carpets

FACULTY CLUB - Apparel–men's - Palm Beach Co., Inc.

FACULTY CLUB, THE - Eyeglasses - Art-Craft Optical Co.

FACULTY II - Floor coverings–carpet and rugs - Lees Carpets

FACULTY II FUTURES - Floor coverings–carpet and rugs - Lees Carpets

FAD - Panty hose ☆ - Stevens Hosiery

FAD - Veterinary pharmaceutical preparations ☆ - Zirin Laboratories International

FAD & FASHION - Eyeglasses ☆ - Cable Car Eyeware

FAD FASHION AND DESIGN TELEVISION - Broadcasting stations–television - Saxon Cable, Inc.

FAD-T.F. - Veterinary pharmaceutical preparations ☆ - Zirin Laboratories International

FADCO - Pet products - Perky-Pet Products Co.

FADE! - Apparel and accessories - Fade! Golf Apparel

FADE - Concrete–ready-mix ☆ - Sakrete Inc.

FADE-AWAY - Artists' materials - Bee Paper Co. Inc.

FADE AWAY - Fabrics - Graniteville Co.

FADE AWAY - Skin care products - Frances Denney

FADE FAST - Skin care products - Pharmagel Corp.

FADE FAST - Skin care products ☆ - Alleghany Pharmacal Corp.

FADE OUT - Fabrics - Graniteville Co.

FADE SAFE - Glass products - Globe-Amerada Glass Co.

FADE SURF - Apparel and accessories - Glenn Matsumoto

FADEBLOK - Cleaning preparations - Blue Coral, Inc.

FADED DENIM - Ophthalmic goods ☆ - Fidelity Case Corp.

FADED GLORY - Leather - Faded Glory, Ltd.

FADELESS - Paper - Bemiss-Jason Corp.

FADELESS DUET - Paper - Bemiss-Jason Corp.

FADERMASTER - Electronic equipment - J.L. Cooper Electronics

FADERMASTER PROFESSIONAL - Electronic equipment - J.L. Cooper Electronics

FADING CREAM PIGMENT EQUALIZER - Skin care products - T.R. International

FADO - Apparel and accessories - Irish Pub Co. Ltd.

FADS - Apparel–women's - Chadwick's of Boston, Ltd.

FAE - Jewelry - Peter Brams Designs, Ltd.

FAEMINO - Espresso - Euromark Inc.

FAF - Antifreeze - Malco Products, Inc.

FAFARD - Soil–potting - Conrad Fafard, Inc.

FAFFCO - Snack foods - Fayette Frozen Foods Inc.

FAFIX - Electronic equipment - Rofu International Corp.

FAFNIR TDC - Automotive parts and accessories - Torrington Co.

☆ = Now out of production

FAG - Automotive parts and accessories - Echlin Inc.
FAHREN-LITE - Fabrics - Guilford Mills, Inc.
FAHRENHEAT - Heaters–space - Fahrenheat
FAHRENHEIT - Apparel–women's - Lee Yin Inc.
FAHRENHEIT - Circuit boards - Orchid Technology
FAHRENHEIT - Colognes - Christian Dior Perfumes Corp.
FAHRENHEIT - Perfumes - Parfums Christian Dior U.S. Corp.
FAHRENHEIT 451 - Computer software - Trillium Research Inc.
FAHRENHEIT FABRICS - Fabrics - Guilford Mills, Inc.
FAI - Housewares ☆ - Chase Collection, Inc.
FAICHNEY - Thermometers - Chesebrough-Pond's USA Co.
FAIENCE - Floor coverings ☆ - Tarkett, Inc.
FAIENCE - Housewares - Wilton Co.
FAIENCERIE DE LA SORGUE - Cooking utensils–earthenware - French & Pacific Trading Corp.
FAIENCERIES DE QUIMPER - Dinnerware–glass - Quimper Faience Inc.
FAIL SAFE - Ammunition - Olin Corp.
FAIL SAFE - Bullets - Olin Corp. (Winchester Div.)
FAIL SAFE - Underwear and nightwear ☆ - Elegante Foundations Inc.
FAILLETRIQUE - Fabrics ☆ - Dan River Inc.
FAILLI - Vinegar ☆ - Liberty Richter Inc.
FAILSAFE - Alarm systems ☆ - EICO Electronic Instrument Co. Inc.
FAILSAFE - Ammunition - Olin Corp.
FAILSAFE - Detergents - Hydrite Chemical Co.
FAILSAFE - Plumbing fixtures–metal - Marshall Brass
FAILSAFE - Toys–airplanes - Cox Products Inc.
FAIR 30 - Chemical preparations - Fair Products, Inc.
FAIR 80 SP - Chemical preparations - Fair Products, Inc.
FAIR ACRES - Vegetables–frozen - Patterson Frozen Foods, Inc.
FAIR BABY - Dolls ☆ - Effanbee Doll Corp.
FAIR BLONDE - Floor coverings–carpet and rugs - Glen Eden Wool Carpets
FAIR CATCH - Sporting goods - Marty Gilman Inc.
FAIR CHILD MEADOWS - Baby-care products - Aurora Henna Co.
FAIR-COURT - Electronic equipment - Porter Athletic Equipment Co.
FAIR GAME - Jewelry - International Bullion & Metal Brokers (USA) Inc.
FAIR HAVEN - Crocheted and knitted items - Valor
FAIR HAVEN - Flatware - Washington Forge Inc.
FAIR HAVEN - Food products ☆ - Seneca Foods Corp.
FAIR HAVEN - Seafood products–fresh or frozen - Connors Brothers Inc.
FAIR ISAAC - Computer software - Fair, Isaac and Co., Inc.
FAIR ISLE - Crocheted and knitted items ☆ - Jacques De Loux Inc.
FAIR ISLE - Slippers ☆ - Acorn
FAIR ISLE - Tableware–china ☆ - Lenox, Inc.
FAIR LADY - Bicycles - Schwinn Cycling & Fitness Inc.
FAIR LADY - Floor coverings–carpet and rugs ☆ - Cabin Crafts Carpets
FAIR LADY - Glassware–household ☆ - Lenox Crystal, Inc.
FAIR LADY - Golfing equipment - Golfsmith International Inc.
FAIR LADY - Rings–jewelry - Artcarved Inc.
FAIR LADY - Tableware–china ☆ - Lenox, Inc.
FAIR LADY - Watches - Hampden Corp.
FAIR-LAWN - Sprinklers–lawn - La Fayette Brass Co. Inc.
FAIR-LITE - Eyeglasses - Art-Craft Optical Co.
FAIR MARKET VALUE - Apparel and accessories ☆ - Gordon & Ferguson of Delaware, Inc.
FAIR 'N COOLER - Apparel and accessories ☆ - Warnaco Inc.
FAIR OAKS - Floor coverings–carpet and rugs ☆ - Hollytex Carpet Mills Inc.
FAIR PLAY - Floor coverings–carpet and rugs - Walter Carpet Mills
FAIR SEAS - Stationery - Fairchild Art
FAIR, THE - Colognes - Brandy Harvest
FAIR WATER - Canned vegetables - American Stores Co.
FAIR WEATHER MARINER - Boats–houseboats - Fair Weather Marine
FAIR WINDS - Floor coverings - Congoleum Corp.
FAIRBANKS - Cabinets - American Woodmark Corp.
FAIRBANKS - Frames–eyeglass ☆ - U.S. Optical Frame Co.
FAIRBANKS - Wines - Ernest and Julio Gallo Winery
FAIRBANKS INSULATED VINYL WINDOWS - Windows - Idrs, Inc.
FAIRBANKS PENGUIN - Toys–stuffed - Russ Berrie and Co., Inc.
FAIRBROOK ARCH - Cabinets–wood - Kemper
FAIRBURY - Bacon - Westin Inc.
FAIRCHESTER - Watches - Croton Watch Co., Inc.
FAIRCHILD - Brushes–paint ☆ - PPG Industries, Inc.
FAIRCHILD - Machinery - Fairchild Technologies USA, Inc.
FAIRCHILD - Perfumes - Parfum de Coeur Ltd.
FAIRCHILD - Photographic equipment - Sentry Test Systems
FAIRCHILD - Posters - Aegis Entertainment, Inc.
FAIRCHILD 24 - Toys–airplanes - Cox Products Inc.

FAIRCHILD DATA - Electronic equipment - Fairchild Data Corp.
FAIRCHILD DATA DART - Audio equipment - Fairchild Data Corp.
FAIRCHILD INDUSTRIAL PRODUCTS COMPANY - Transmission equipment–industrial - Fairchild Industrial Products Co.
FAIRCHILD PHOENIX - Giftware - Fairchild Art
FAIRCO - Food products - Fairco, Inc.
FAIRCRAFT - Padding–foam - Montgomery Ward & Co. Inc.
FAIRDALE FARMS - Milk - Fairdale Farms Inc.
FAIREST ONE - Floor coverings–carpet and rugs - Galaxy Carpet Mills Inc.
FAIRFAX - Brushes–paint ☆ - PPG Industries, Inc.
FAIRFAX - Cabinets - HomeCrest Corp.
FAIRFAX - Cigarettes ☆ - G.A. Georgopulo & Co. Inc.
FAIRFAX - Cribs–wood ☆ - Welsh Co.
FAIRFAX - Eyeglasses - Art-Craft Optical Co.
FAIRFAX - Flatware - Gorham Inc.
FAIRFAX - Floor coverings - Mannington Resilient Floors
FAIRFAX - Floor coverings–carpet and rugs ☆ - Dorsett Carpet Mills Inc.
FAIRFAX - Furniture ☆ - Lane Co. Inc.
FAIRFAX - Jewelry - Sterling Inc.
FAIRFAX - Metals - Weiser Lock Corp.
FAIRFAX - Siding–insulating - Georgia-Pacific Corp.
FAIRFAX COUNTY - Liquors ☆ - A. Smith Bowman Distillery Inc.
FAIRFAX HALL - Food products ☆ - J.D. Dawson Co.
FAIRFAX PRINTS - Posters - Fairfax Prints Ltd.
FAIRFAX WOODSMITHS - Cigars ☆ - Te-Amo
FAIRFIELD - Brushes–paint ☆ - Winsor & Newton
FAIRFIELD - Cabinets - American Woodmark Corp.
FAIRFIELD - Cabinets - Yorktowne Inc.
FAIRFIELD - Cabinets ☆ - Medallion Kitchens of Minnesota Inc.
FAIRFIELD - Cabinets–wood - UltraCraft Co.
FAIRFIELD - Clocks ☆ - General Time Corp. (Westclox/Seth Thomas Div.)
FAIRFIELD - Cotton–sterilized ☆ - Parke-Davis
FAIRFIELD - Dishes–china - Tienshan, Inc.
FAIRFIELD - Dishes–china - Waterford Wedgwood USA, Inc.
FAIRFIELD - Floor coverings - Congoleum Corp.
FAIRFIELD - Floor coverings–carpet and rugs - Dan River Inc.
FAIRFIELD - Floor coverings–carpet and rugs - Philadelphia Carpets
FAIRFIELD - Giftware - N.S. Gustin Co.
FAIRFIELD - Glassware–household ☆ - Anchor Hocking Glass, Inc.
FAIRFIELD - Paper - Strathmore Paper Co.
FAIRFIELD - Rings–jewelry - Artcarved Inc.
FAIRFIELD - Sporting goods ☆ - Maurice Sporting Goods, Inc.
FAIRFIELD - Tableware–china ☆ - Lenox, Inc.
FAIRFIELD - Thread - Threads USA Div.
FAIRFIELD COLLECTION - Fabrics - Dan River Inc.
FAIRFIELD COLLECTION - Furniture ☆ - Bassett Furniture Industries, Inc.
FAIRFIELD FARM KITCHEN - Food products - Fairfield Farm Kitchens
FAIRFIELD-HANOVER - Gloves - Fairfield Line, Inc.
FAIRFIELD INN - Furniture ☆ - Bassett Furniture Industries, Inc.
FAIRFIELD MANOR - Furniture ☆ - Athens Furniture Industries Inc.
FAIRFORM - Apparel stores–lingerie - Gold Seal Garter Corp.
FAIRFORM FLYER - Boats–motor - Huckins Yacht Corp.
FAIRGATE - Measuring instruments - Fairgate Rule Co. Inc.
FAIRGROUNDS - Meat products–beef - Moran Foods, Inc.
FAIRGROUNDS COLLECTION - Figurines - Delfino Products Inc.
FAIRGROVE - Housewares - Aluminum Housewares Co. Inc.
FAIRHAVEN - Awnings - Alcan Aluminum Corp. Alcan Building Products Div.
FAIRHAVEN - Frames–eyeglass - May Optical Co. Inc.
FAIRHAVEN - Shoes - Allen-Edmonds Shoe Corp.
FAIRHAVEN - Yarn - Brunswick Yarns
FAIRHAVEN PEACH - Candles - Fragrance Innovations
FAIRHILL - Candy - Pet Inc. (Whitman's Chocolates Div.)
FAIRINGTON - Furniture–upholstered ☆ - Southwood Furniture Corp.
FAIRISLE - Flatware - Pfaltzgraff Investment Co.
FAIRLADY - Footwear–women's - P.H. Volk Co.
FAIRLANE - Hosiery ☆ - Liberty Hosiery Mills Inc.
FAIRLANE - Motor vehicles–automobiles ☆ - Ford Motor Co.
FAIRLAWN - Clocks - Ridgeway Clock Co.
FAIRLAWN - Lawn mowers ☆ - Bridgestone/Firestone, Inc.
FAIRLAWN - Vinyl floor covering - Congoleum Corp.
FAIRLEE - Brushes–paint ☆ - PPG Industries, Inc.
FAIRLIGHT - Computer software - Mindscape Software Inc.
FAIRLINE - Frames–eyeglass ☆ - Universal/Univis Inc.
FAIRLITE - Awnings - Alcan Aluminum Corp. Alcan Building Products Div.
FAIRMONT - Cabinets ☆ - Decora
FAIRMONT - Cheese - Hotel Bar Foods Inc.

FAIRMONT - Cigarettes - Philip Morris Companies Inc.
FAIRMONT - Floor coverings ☆ - Congoleum Corp.
FAIRMONT - Furniture ☆ - Barclay Furniture Co.
FAIRMONT - Furniture ☆ - Harter
FAIRMONT - Glassware–household ☆ - Oneida Ltd.
FAIRMONT - Jewelry–precious - Belenke Co.
FAIRMONT - Milk - Fairmont-Zarda Dairy
FAIRMONT - Motor vehicles–automobiles ☆ - Ford Motor Co.
FAIRMONT - Popcorn - Circle K Corp.
FAIRMONT PLAZA - Floor coverings–carpet and rugs - Western Carpet Mills
FAIRMONT TAMPER - Transportation vehicles and equipment - Harsco Corp.
FAIRMONT-ZARDA - Dairy products - Fairmont-Zarda Dairy
FAIRMOUNT - Frames–eyeglass ☆ - U.S. Optical Frame Co.
FAIRMOUNT - Shoes ☆ - Allen-Edmonds Shoe Corp.
FAIRMOUNT - Thread - Threads USA Div.
FAIRMOUNT - Wood products - Georgia-Pacific Corp.
FAIRPLAY - Fishing lines - Cortland Line Co., Inc.
FAIRPLAY ORCHARDS - Food products ☆ - A. D'Amico & Sons Inc.
FAIRPORT - Floor coverings–carpet and rugs - Milliken & Co. Inc.
FAIRS - Software - University of Florida
FAIRSEX - Frames–eyeglass - Zylo Ware Corp.
FAIRSKIN - Skin care products ☆ - Hair Specialty Co.
FAIRSPRAY - Apparel–men's ☆ - Michaels/Stern & Co. Inc.
FAIRTAX - Tripods–photographic ☆ - QuickSet International Inc.
FAIRTEX - Yarn - Metlon Corp.
FAIRTIME - Candy - Adams & Brooks, Inc.
FAIRTY - Food products - Bay Trading Co.
FAIRVEL - Fabrics - A. Wimpfheimer & Brother Inc.
FAIRVIEW - Frames–eyeglass - Zylo Ware Corp.
FAIRVIEW - Furniture - Thomasville Furniture Industries Inc.
FAIRVIEW - Furniture ☆ - Bassett Furniture Industries, Inc.
FAIRVIEW - Liquors - White Rock Distilleries Inc.
FAIRVIEW - Mobile homes ☆ - Kit Manufacturing Co.
FAIRVIEW FARMS - Meat products–cured - Stevens Industries Inc.
FAIRWAY - Brushes - Chesal Golf
FAIRWAY - Brushes–paint - PPG Industries, Inc.
FAIRWAY - Computer software - Telematics International, Inc.
FAIRWAY - Floor coverings–carpet and rugs - Kelly Group Inc.
FAIRWAY - Handkerchiefs ☆ - Carolina Manufacturing Inc.
FAIRWAY - Ice cream - David Michael & Co.
FAIRWAY - Mats - Matworks
FAIRWAY - Sporting goods - Rocky Mountain Sports
FAIRWAY - Sprinklers–lawn - Champion Irrigation Products
FAIRWAY - Urinals–porcelain - Mansfield Plumbing Products, Inc.
FAIRWAY & GREENE - Apparel and accessories - Fairway & Greene, Ltd.
FAIRWAY DARTS - Darts and dart games - PGI Industries
FAIRWAY GREEN - Oils–essential - Herb Gilbertie's & Garden Center
FAIRWAY VINEYARDS - Wines - Mark West Vineyards
FAIRWAYS - Candy - Harbor Sweets Inc.
FAIRWEATHER - Heat pumps - O.E.M. Products Inc.
FAIRWEATHER GARDENS - Live plants - Fairweather Gardens
FAIRWINDS - Coffee - Fairwinds Gourmet Coffee Co. Inc.
FAIRWINDS - Wallpaper - S.M. Hexter Co.
FAIRWINDS III - Wallpaper ☆ - Fairwinds Studio
FAIRWOOD - Cabinets–wood - Richmond Lumber Co. Inc.
FAIRY - Candles ☆ - Candle-Lite Co.
FAIRY BELLE - Dolls - Tonka Corp.
FAIRY BOX BOOK, A - Publisher's imprints - Wendy Wallin Malinow
FAIRY DELL - Dishes–earthenware ☆ - Royal China & Porcelain Companies Inc.
FAIRY FANTASY - Toys - Mattel, Inc.
FAIRY FIND-ME'S - Dolls and accessories - Tonka Corp.
FAIRY FINERY - Toys - Toddler Teepee, Inc.
FAIRY FUN COLLECTION - Toys - Mattel, Inc.
FAIRY GEM - Polished stones - Explorer's Exchange Inc.
FAIRY LIGHT WONDERLAND - Sporting goods - Mattel, Inc.
FAIRY LIGHTS - Giftware - Fenton Art Glass Co.
FAIRY MESSAGES - Greeting cards - Baker & Peterson
FAIRY OF THE MONTH - Figurines - Papel Freelance, Inc.
FAIRY PRETTIES - Dolls - Tonka Corp.
FAIRY RING - Mushrooms - Mushroom Growers Association Sales Co.
FAIRY SWEETS - Dolls - Tonka Corp.
FAIRY TALE - Dolls ☆ - Totsy Manufacturing Co., Inc.
FAIRY TALE - Footwear - Polly of California
FAIRY TALE - Games ☆ - Decipher Inc.
FAIRY TALE - Greeting cards - Green Tiger Press

FAIRY TALE - Ophthalmic goods - Foremost Optical Products
FAIRY TALE CLASSICS - Dolls - Sky Kids Inc.
FAIRY TALE CLASSICS - Games - Cardinal Industries, Inc.
FAIRY TALE WEDDING CUVEE - Wine - Iron Horse Vineyards
FAIRY TALES - Computer software - Orange Cherry Software
FAIRY TALES - Footwear–children's - Roy Mantelman Shoe Co.
FAIRY TALES COME TRUE - Dolls - Seymour Mann Inc.
FAIRY WISHING WORLD - Toys - Mattel, Inc.
FAIRYLAND - Furniture - Fairyland Corp.
FAIRYLAND - Jewelry–costume - B.B. Greenberg Co.
FAIRYLAND - Ophthalmic goods - Foremost Optical Products
FAIRYLAND COLLECTION - Dolls ☆ - Uneeda Doll Co., Inc.
FAIRYTALE - Flowers, plants, and seeds ☆ - R.J. Reynolds Tobacco Co.
FAIRYTALE - Foil–aluminum ☆ - RJR Archer Inc.
FAIRYTALE FRAGRANCES - Colognes - Fairytale Fragrances, Inc.
FAIRYTALE TREASURES - Dolls - Brass Key, Inc.
FAIRYTUNES - Recording label - Robert Farnsworth
FAIRYWINKLES - Dolls - Tonka Corp.
FAIT BEAU - Lenses–optical - Ditto Industries Inc.
FAITH - Dresses–women's - Surya, Inc.
FAITH - Greeting cards - Masterpiece Studios Inc.
FAITH - Ophthalmic goods ☆ - Luxottica
FAITH - Toys–stuffed - Jolly U.S.A., Inc.
FAITH DAIRY - Milk - Faith Dairy Inc.
FAITH MOUNTAIN - Bags–canvas - Faith Mountain, Inc.
FAITH NO MORE - Recording label - Faith No More
FAITH STORIES - Games - FNDI L.P.
FAITHFUL - Food products ☆ - Pillsbury Co.
FAITHFUL - Pet products ☆ - Avon Products, Inc.
FAITHFUL WITNESS - Giftware ☆ - Warner Press, Inc.
FAITHFULLY YOURS - Greeting cards - Galleria Publishing Corp.
FAITHQUEST - Publisher's imprints - Church of the Brethren General Board
FAITHWARE - Computer software - Liguori Publications
FAJITA DUST - Spices and extracts - Cajun Dust, LLC
FAJITA-EAZY - Meat products - Dewey's Foods Inc.
FAJITA GOURMET - Spices and extracts - Finest Kind Spices
FAJITA LEMON LIME - Spices and extracts - Finest Kind Spices
FAJITA RED - Wines ☆ - McDowell Cellars Inc.
FAJITA SUPERBA - Sauces - Curtice-Burns Foods, Inc.
FAJITA TAMER - Kitchen appliances - Le-Jo Enterprises, Inc.
FAJITAS - Barbecue sauce - Lawry's Foods Inc.
FAJITAS CHIQUITAS - Food products - El Torito Restaurants Inc.
FAKE BRAINS - Computer software - Fake Brains
FAKE JEANS THE ORIGINAL - Jeans–women's - Fake the Original, Inc.
FAKE SKIN - Toys - Collegeville/Imagineering
FAKE SPACE - Computer hardware - Mark Bolas
FAKER - Toys - Mattel, Inc.
FAKESPACE - Computer software - Fakespace, Inc.
FAKIN' BACON - Food products - Lightlife Foods, Inc.
FALAISE - Floor coverings–carpet and rugs ☆ - Mohawk Industries Inc.
FALBO - Cheese - Avonmore-Kent Inc.
FALCINELLI - Tiles–ceramic - Mediterranean Exports
FALCO - Computers–mainframe - Falco Data Products Inc.
FALCOAT II - Mirrors ☆ - Guardian Jamestown
FALCON - Apparel and accessories ☆ - Talon Inc.
FALCON - Archery equipment ☆ - Bear Archery Inc.
FALCON - Barbecues and grills - Preway Industries Inc.
FALCON - Barbecues and grills - Sunbeam Outdoor Products Inc.
FALCON - Beverages–carbonated - Hampton Associates and Son, Inc.
FALCON - Bicycles - Commonwealth Inc.
FALCON - Bicycles - Roadmaster Corp.
FALCON - Binoculars ☆ - Swift Instruments, Inc.
FALCON - Boats–motor - Thunderbird Products
FALCON - Boats–motor ☆ - Seaswirl Boats Inc.
FALCON - Candy - Falcon Candy Co.
FALCON - Communications equipment - Gulf Coast Avionics Corp.
FALCON - Computer software - Spectrum Holobyte, Inc.
FALCON - Computers–personal - Falcon Systems, Inc.
FALCON - Conveyors - Falcon Belting, Inc.
FALCON - Darts and dart games ☆ - Dart Mart Inc.
FALCON - Electronic equipment - Ag-Chem Equipment Co. Inc.
FALCON - Fans–electric - International Development Corp.
FALCON - Filters–water ☆ - Sta-Rite Industries Inc.
FALCON - Fishing tackle - Mason Tackle Co.
FALCON - Furniture - Falcon Products Inc.
FALCON - Guitars - Peavey Electronics Corp.

☆ = Now out of production

FALCON - Health care products - Falcon Rehabilitation Products Inc.
FALCON - Health care products - National Wheel-O-Vator Co. Inc.
FALCON - Knives–hunting - Normark Corp.
FALCON - Mirrors - Guardian Jamestown
FALCON - Motor vehicles–automobiles ☆ - Ford Motor Co.
FALCON - Musical instrument accessories - Ernest Deffner Inc.
FALCON - Pens - Micropoint Inc.
FALCON - Photographic equipment - Falcon Safety Products, Inc.
FALCON - Publisher's imprints - Bantam Doubleday Dell Publishing Group, Inc.
FALCON - Puzzles ☆ - Warren Industries Inc.
FALCON - Recreational vehicles - International Vehicle Corp.
FALCON - Rice - Falcon Rice Mill Inc.
FALCON - Rug cleaning machines–commercial - Castex Industries Inc.
FALCON - Rulers–wood - Falcon Rule
FALCON - Skin care products - Falcon Health & Fitness Systems Inc.
FALCON - Snack foods - Millner Trading Co. Inc.
FALCON - Tape–adhesive - Adhesive Tapes International, Inc.
FALCON - Tires - Bridgestone/Firestone, Inc.
FALCON - Tools–garden - O. Ames Co.
FALCON - Tools–machine - Cincinnati Machine
FALCON - Trailers–truck ☆ - Sun-Lite Inc.
FALCON - Uniforms–tailored - Amplaco Group Inc.
FALCON - Wallpaper ☆ - Wolf-Gordon Inc.
FALCON - Watches - Wai Kin Ng
FALCON - Wheelchairs - AM Scooters
FALCON-2 - Archery equipment - Saunders Archery Co.
FALCON 2000 - Aircraft parts - Dassault Falcon Jet Corp.
FALCON CLASSIC - Guitars - Peavey Electronics Corp.
FALCON COMMANDER - Toys–models ☆ - Estes Industries
FALCON CORPORATION - Ladders–plastic - Falcon Corp.
FALCON/DMS - Computer software - Tom Synnott Associates Inc.
FALCON ELECTRONICS - Electronic equipment - Bob Bartlett & Associates Inc.
FALCON EYE - Lighting equipment - Falcon Eye Inc.
FALCON-FLEX - Rulers–metal - Falcon Rule
FALCON FRAMEWORK - Computer software - Mentor Graphics Corp.
FALCON HALON - Fire extinguishers ☆ - Falcon Safety Products, Inc.
FALCON HOG - Machine tools - Clarke's Sheet Metal, Inc.
FALCON LIGHTS - Cigarettes - Brown & Williamson Tobacco Corp.
FALCON LOWRIDER - Fishing rods - Beckwith Sales, Inc.
FALCON NEW YORKER - Tires ☆ - Bridgestone/Firestone, Inc.
FALCON PRINT - Photographic equipment ☆ - Falcon Safety Products, Inc.
FALCON R-60 AMP - Amplifiers - PRO Manufacturing
FALCON SEABOARD - Electrical industrial apparatus - Falcon Seaboard Holdings, LP
FALCON SEAL - Glass products - Guardian Jamestown
FALCON TRADING - Food products - Falcon Trading Co.
FALCONE - Pianos - Sohmer Corp.
FALCONE - Tobacco products - Consolidated Cigar Corp.
FALCONE'S COOKIELAND - Cookies - Falcone's Cookieland Ltd.
FALCONET - Apparel and accessories - Talon Inc.
FALCONHURST DAIRY - See IDAHO COUNTRY
FALCONS - Cigar boxes–wood - Consolidated Cigar Corp.
FALCRAFT - Housewares - Fox Specialty Co. Inc.
FALERNO - Glass–leaded - Seneca Glass Co.
FALERNUM - Syrup - Sazerac Co. Inc.
FALF-N-OATS BITS - Pet products - Novalek, Inc.
FALFA - Pet products - Novalek, Inc.
FALFA BALES - Pet products - Novalek, Inc.
FALFA BITS - Pet products - Novalek, Inc.
FALFA CUBES - Pet products - Novalek, Inc.
FALFA-N-OAT CUBES - Animal feeds - Novalek, Inc.
FALFA NUGGETS - Pet products - Novalek, Inc.
FALFLAX - Tablecloths - Fallani & Cohn Inc.
FALKEN - Tires - Chatani Enterprises Inc.
FALL-A-WAY - Archery equipment ☆ - Martin Archery Inc.
FALL BLOSSOMS - Dinnerware–glass ☆ - Lenox, Inc.
FALL BOUNTY - Dinnerware–glass ☆ - Lenox, Inc.
FALL BRAWL - Broadcasting stations–television - World Championship Wrestling, Inc.
FALL CALL - Alarm systems - Eagle Electronics Inc.
FALL CAT - Heating equipment - Coleman Co., Inc.
FALL CITY - Beverages–malt - The Stroh Brewery Co.
FALL CITY - Buckets–plastic - Our Own Hardware Co.
FALL COLORS - Soap - Hewitt Soap Co., Inc.
FALL CREEK VINEYARDS - Wines - Fall Creek Vineyards

FALL-EZ - Fabrics–acetate - Distinct Medical Supplies, Ltd.
FALL FEST ALE - Beverages–malt ☆ - Rockies Brewing Co.
FALL GUY - Toys ☆ - ERTL Co., Inc.
FALL MAGIC - Flowers, plants, and seeds - Jonathan Green, Inc.
FALL PREMIERES COLLECTION - Cosmetics - Pfizer Inc.
FALL RIVER - Fasteners - Fall River Manufacturing Co., Inc.
FALL RIVER - Rice - California Wild Rice Growers Association Inc.
FALL RIVER COTTON COLLECTION - Apparel–women's - Nap, Inc.
FALL VISAGE - Cosmetics - Chanel Inc.
FALLGUARD - Safety products - Plasteco, Inc.
FALLING LEAVES - Christmas tree ornaments - Cracker Box Inc.
FALLING LEAVES - Musical instrument accessories - Sottile Manufacturing Co.
FALLING SQUARES - Glassware–household ☆ - Crisa Corp.
FALLING STAR - Christmas tree ornaments - Cracker Box Inc.
FALLING STAR - Rings–jewelry - Artcarved Inc.
FALLING WATER - Faucets - Kohler Co.
FALLLINE - Apparel and accessories - Fallline Corp.
FALLON - Brushes–paint - PPG Industries, Inc.
FALLON - Toys - Tonka Corp.
FALLS - Fruits–canned - Butler Trading Co. Inc.
FALLS - Meat products–poultry ☆ - Hebrew Foods Inc.
FALLS CITY - Beverages–alcohol - Evansville Brewing Co.
FALLS CREEK - Apparel and accessories - Meijer, Inc.
FALLSCANYON - Wood products - Dawson Co. Manufacturing
FALMOUTH - Frames–eyeglass ☆ - Universal/Univis Inc.
FALMOUTH - Stoves–wood-burning - Portland Franklin Stove Foundry Inc.
FALSE ALARM - Sportswear - LJJ Inc.
FALSE ALARM - Thread ☆ - Perfect Thread Co. Inc.
FALSE BOTTOMS - Infant product - American Baby Concepts
FALSIES - Cosmetics - Charles Revson Inc.
FALSPUN - Tablecloths - Fallani & Cohn Inc.
FALSTAFF - Beverages–malt - Falstaff Brewing Corp.
FALSTAFF - Beverages–malt - Pearl Brewing Co.
FALSTAFF LITE BEER - Beverages–malt - Falstaff Brewing Corp.
FALSTAFF NA - Beverages–malt - Falstaff Brewing Corp.
FAM - Laxatives - Schering-Plough Healthcare Products
FAM - Negligees - Gibor Sabrina Ltd.
FAM-COLSOF - Pharmaceutical preparations - F.A. Mitchell Co. Inc.
FAM-IRON - Pharmaceutical preparations - F.A. Mitchell Co. Inc.
FAM-OB 6 - Vitamins and nutritional supplements ☆ - F.A. Mitchell Co. Inc.
FAM-PERICOLSOF - Laxatives - F.A. Mitchell Co. Inc.
FAM-PLEX C - Vitamins and nutritional supplements ☆ - F.A. Mitchell Co. Inc.
FAM-PREN FORTE - Vitamins and nutritional supplements - F.A. Mitchell Co. Inc.
FAM-THERA - Vitamins and nutritional supplements ☆ - F.A. Mitchell Co. Inc.
FAM-VITA - Vitamins and nutritional supplements ☆ - F.A. Mitchell Co. Inc.
FAME - Amplifiers, guitars - International Music Corp.
FAME - Aprons - ERB Industries, Inc.
FAME - Flatware ☆ - Lifetime Hoan Corp.
FAME - Floor coverings - Aladdin Mills, Inc.
FAME - Floor coverings - Congoleum Corp.
FAME - Floor coverings–carpet and rugs - Galaxy Carpet Mills Inc.
FAME - Floor coverings–carpet and rugs ☆ - Calladium & Marglen
FAME - Food products - Nash Finch Super Food Services, Inc.
FAME - Fruit drinks–bottled or canned - Golden Gem Growers Inc.
FAME - Thread - Cincinnati Thread Co.
FAME - Vinyl-floor dressing ☆ - Pratt & Lambert, Inc. (Specialty Products Div.)
FAME & FORTUNE - Recording label - Jazz Composer's Orchestra Association Inc.
FAMEL - Cough medicines ☆ - Consolidated Midland Corp.
FAMEX - Hair care products ☆ - Fromm Industries
FAMI-LEAVES - Jewelry - Clyde Duneier Inc.
FAMILIA - Cereal - Novartis Nutrition Corp.
FAMILIAR THINGS - Toys - Lauri Inc.
FAMILIE - Cooking equipment–household - West Bend Co.
FAMILY - Bathroom accessories - Watkins Manufacturing Corp.
FAMILY - Camp furniture–metal ☆ - Huffy Plastics
FAMILY - Flowers, plants, and seeds - Scotts Co. (Organics Business Group)
FAMILY - Fruits and vegetables - Family Food Co., Inc.
FAMILY - Greeting cards ☆ - American Greetings Corp.
FAMILY - Meat products–beef - Ohio Packing Co.
FAMILY 17 - Boats–canoes - Sawyer Composite Products
FAMILY ADVENTURE THEATER - Video production - Metacom Inc.
FAMILY AFFAIR - Frames–eyeglass ☆ - Universal/Univis Inc.
FAMILY ALBUM - Dolls - Seymour Mann Inc.

☆ = Now out of production

FAMILY ALBUM - Jewelry ☆ - Anson Inc.

FAMILY ALBUM - Photo albums - Holson Co.

FAMILY & FRIENDS FOLIO - Giftware - Avon Products, Inc.

FAMILY ATLAS - Computer software - Parsons Technology, Inc.

FAMILY BEGINNINGS - Jewelry - SE Designs

FAMILY BIBLE TRIVIA - Games - Rapid Mounting and Finishing Co.

FAMILY BUDGET ANALYSIS - Computer software - SourceView Software International

FAMILY BUSINESS - Playing cards - Mayfair Games, Inc.

FAMILY CARE - Health-care product - Iodent Co.

FAMILY CENTER - Playground equipment - Hedstrom Corp.

FAMILY CHANNEL, THE - Broadcasting stations–television - International Family Entertainment, Inc.

FAMILY CHEF - Knives–electric - Windmere Corp.

FAMILY CHOICE! - Food products - Little Caesar Enterprises, Inc.

FAMILY CHOICE - Hair and skin care products - American Household Products, Inc.

FAMILY CHOICE - Toothpaste - Iodent Co.

FAMILY CHOICES - Burial caskets - Batesville Casket Co., Inc.

FAMILY CHRISTMAS - Dinnerware–glass - Cuthbertson Imports Inc.

FAMILY CHRISTMAS - Housewares ☆ - Vermillion Inc.

FAMILY CLASSIC - Hams - Hatfield, Inc.

FAMILY CLASSIC - Hams - Hqm, Ltd.

FAMILY CLASSIC - Meat products–pork - HGM, Ltd.

FAMILY COLLECTIBLES - Dolls - Golden Ribbon Playthings Inc.

FAMILY COLLECTION - Figurines - Lenox, Inc.

FAMILY CONNECTIONS - Computer software - Quinsept Inc.

FAMILY CORNERS - Dolls - Mattel, Inc.

FAMILY CRAFT - Hobby kits - Edna Looney Products

FAMILY CREST - Linen - Notra Trading, Inc.

FAMILY CREST - Rings–jewelry - Heraldica Imports

FAMILY CROWN - Jewelry - B. David Co.

FAMILY CYCLE - Exercising equipment ☆ - Tunturi, Inc.

FAMILY D'ADANT - Candles - D'Adant and Sons Inc.

FAMILY DATA - Scales–bathroom ☆ - Robert Krups North America

FAMILY DESIGN STUDIO - Computer software - Parsons Technology, Inc.

FAMILY DINER - Apparel–men's - Joe Boxer Corp.

FAMILY ENTREE - Food products - Conagra, Inc.

FAMILY FACES - Cosmetics - Paper Magic Group Inc.

FAMILY FARE - Food products - Hill Bros. Inc.

FAMILY FARMS - Meat - Family Farms, Inc.

FAMILY FAST FRY - Kitchen appliances ☆ - Philips Electronics North America Corp.

FAMILY FAVORITE - Food products - Tradewell Stores Inc.

FAMILY FAVORITES - Dinners–frozen - Conagra, Inc.

FAMILY FAVORITES - Food products - Lipton Investments, Inc.

FAMILY FAVORITES - Meat products–beef - Lykes Bros. Inc. (Meat Packing Div.)

FAMILY FAVORITES - Syrup - Green Bay Foods Co.

FAMILY FEUD - Games ☆ - Milton Bradley Co.

FAMILY FISHERMAN - Boats–motor ☆ - Sport-Craft Inc.

FAMILY FLOORING - Floor coverings - Carpax Associates, Inc.

FAMILY FOREST - Computer software - Millisecond Publishing Co., Inc.

FAMILY FORTUNE - Juices - Mon Chong Loong Trading Corp.

FAMILY FRAME - Frames–picture - Rare Woods Inc.

FAMILY FRAMES - Frames–picture ☆ - M.W. Carr & Co. Inc.

FAMILY FRESH - Fruits and vegetables - Mann Packing Co., Inc.

FAMILY FRIEND - Recording label - Jazz Composer's Orchestra Association Inc.

FAMILY FUN - Boats–pontoons ☆ - Duracraft Boats Inc.

FAMILY FUN - Candy - Charms Co.

FAMILY FUN - Telescopes - Bausch & Lomb Inc.

FAMILY GARD - Smoke detectors - BRK Electronics Inc.

FAMILY GATHERING - Computer software - Palladium Interactive, Inc.

FAMILY GLOSSINE - Hair care products - Madame C.J. Walker Inc.

FAMILY GROUPS - Toys–blocks - Guidecraft Inc.

FAMILY GUIDEX - Research–educational - Centaur Records

FAMILY HARVEST - Breads - Elam's

FAMILY HEALTH NEWS - Catalogs - Family News Inc.

FAMILY HERITAGE - Baskets–wood - Berlin Fruit Box Co.

FAMILY HOLIDAY BEARS - Toys–stuffed - Dan-Dee International Ltd.

FAMILY HOME - Fabrics–linen - Notra Trading, Inc.

FAMILY HUG - Apparel - Jack L. Lentz Jr.

FAMILY IDENTIFICATION - Computer software ☆ - CONDUIT

FAMILY INNS OF AMERICA - Hotels and motels - Family Inns of America

FAMILY JEWELRY COLLECTION - Jewelry - Family Jewelry Collection, Inc.

FAMILY KEEPSAKES - Frames–picture - Bradson Press, Inc.

FAMILY KITCHEN - Food products - Nabisco Foods Group

FAMILY KITS - Pharmaceutical preparations - Dolisos America, Inc.

FAMILY LAWYER - Computer programming services - Parsons Technology, Inc.

FAMILY LEARNING CENTER - Computer software - Mick Tarel

FAMILY LINE - Paper–gift wrap - Allison Greetings

FAMILY LINKS - Computer software ☆ - Quinsept Inc.

FAMILY LIVING - Wallpaper ☆ - Brewster Wallcovering Co.

FAMILY LOCATOR - Research–engineering - Parallel Communications Inc.

FAMILY MAN DT - Recording label - Family Man Dt, Inc.

FAMILY MATTERS - Computer software - Matterware

FAMILY MEDIC - Health care products - Tender Corp.

FAMILY MEDIC AFTERBURNS - Health care products - Tender Corp.

FAMILY MOMENTS - Jewelry - BC Creations Ltd.

FAMILY MOVE - Computer software ☆ - Quinsept Inc.

FAMILY OF ALES - Glassware–household - Crisa Corp.

FAMILY OPTICS - Sunglasses - Lantis Corp.

FAMILY ORIGINS - Computer software - Parsons Technology, Inc.

FAMILY ORIGINS - Novelty items - Papel Freelance, Inc.

FAMILY PACK - Meat products–beef - Colonial Beef Co.

FAMILY PACK - Pigments–paint - Leshner Corp.

FAMILY PAGER, THE - Radio pagers - RAM/BSE Communications, L.P.

FAMILY PAK - Fruits and vegetables - R.C. McEntrire & Co., Inc.

FAMILY PORTRAIT - Dolls - Seymour Mann Inc.

FAMILY PRIDE - Food products - Shelton Farms

FAMILY PRIDE - Meat products–poultry - Norbest Inc.

FAMILY PRIDE - Toys–stuffed - Dakin Inc.

FAMILY PUZZLE - Puzzles - GMG Publishing Inc.

FAMILY READING NIGHT - Posters - Demco Inc.

FAMILY RECIPE - Breads - Campbell Taggart Inc.

FAMILY RECIPE - Food products - Tyson Foods Inc.

FAMILY RECIPE - Meat products–cured - Bryan Foods, Inc.

FAMILY RECIPE - Processed meats - Saramar Corp.

FAMILY RECIPE - Rice - Comet American Marketing

FAMILY RECORD ORGANIZER - Forms–preprinted - E-Z Legal Forms, Inc.

FAMILY REUNION - Preserved foods–prepackaged - Prepco

FAMILY ROOTS - Computer software - Quinsept Inc.

FAMILY SAVER - Talcum powders - Niemand Industries Inc.

FAMILY SAVINGS CARD - Coupons - Fundraising Solutions, Inc.

FAMILY SCOTT - Paper–toilet - Scott Paper Co.

FAMILY SCRAPBOOK - Computer software - Visionary Endeavors

FAMILY SECRET - Pies–frozen - Rich Products Corp.

FAMILY SELECT - Cleaning preparations - Grow Group, Inc.

FAMILY SIGNATURE SERIES - Giftware - Fenton Art Glass Co.

FAMILY SPREAD - Food products - Van Den Bergh Foods Co.

FAMILY STYLE - Ice cream - Anderson Erickson Dairy Co.

FAMILY SUN - Fruits and vegetables - Debenedetto Farms, Inc.

FAMILY TIES - Jewelry–costume - the Name Game

FAMILY TIES - Pager - Ram Communications of Michigan Inc.

FAMILY TIES - Paper–gift wrap - Paperwork Ltd.

FAMILY TOUCH - Recording label - Sunday School Board of the Southern Baptist Convention

FAMILY TRADITION - Meat products–poultry - Norbest Inc.

FAMILY TRADITION - Scrapbooks - Makepeace Colony Press Inc.

FAMILY TREASURES - Jewelry - Donald Bruce & Co.

FAMILY TREAT - Ice cream - House of Flavors, Inc.

FAMILY TREE - Cleaning preparations–household - Calusa Chemical Co. Inc.

FAMILY TREE - Games - Legacy Games Ltd.

FAMILY TREE - Jewelry - Aaron Perry

FAMILY TREE - Knives–pocket - Tennessee River Valley Knife Association Inc.

FAMILY TREE HOUSE - Toys - Tonka Corp.

FAMILY TREE MAKER DELUXE - Computer software - Broderbund Software, Inc.

FAMILY VALUE - Breads - Storck Baking Co., Inc.

FAMILY VALUE - Dairy products - H.P. Hood & Sons Inc.

FAMILY VINEYARD - Wines - Bella Napoli Winery

FAMILY VISIONS - Bags–cosmetic - Family Visions, Inc.

FAMILY WAGON - Vans–conversion - Compact Equipment Co.

FAMILY WISDOM - Recording label - Apostolate for Family Consecration, Inc.

FAMILYTAINMENT FOR ALL AGES - Computer software - Terraglyph Interactive, LP

FAMINE CHILDREN OF THE WORLD - Dolls - Nellie Ruth Ingram

FAMIS - Paper products - Famis, Inc.

FAMISE - Girdles ☆ - Kellogg Industries Inc.

☆ = Now out of production

FAMOGLAZE - Wood fillers - Beverly Manufacturing Co.

FAMOLARE - Shoes - Famolare Inc.

FAMOLARE ELEGET - Footwear–men's - Famolare Inc.

FAMOR - Jewelry - Famor Inc.

FAMOUS - Brushes–paint ☆ - PPG Industries, Inc.

FAMOUS - Ophthalmic goods - Foremost Optical Products

FAMOUS - Seafood products–fresh or frozen - Pocasset Seafoods Inc.

FAMOUS 4TH ST. COOKIE CO., THE - Bakery products - Bainbridge Group, Inc.

FAMOUS AMOS - Beverages - White Rock Products Corp.

FAMOUS AMOS - Cookies - Famous Amos Chocolate Chip Cookie Co.

FAMOUS AMOS DIET - Beverages - White Rock Products Corp.

FAMOUS ARTISTS - Greeting cards - American Artists Group Inc.

FAMOUS ARTISTS - Greeting cards - Famous Artists Studios

FAMOUS CHICK - Sandwiches–prepackaged - Olga's Kitchen Licensing, Inc.

FAMOUS CHICKEN - Chewing gum ☆ - Amurol Confections Co.

FAMOUS CLASSICS - Greeting cards - American Greetings Corp.

FAMOUS COURSES - Computer software - Accolade Inc.

FAMOUS DEAD DUDES - Trading cards and stamps - The Learning Experience Inc.

FAMOUS DESIGNS - Bathroom accessories - Ransburg Accessories Inc.

FAMOUS FACES - Cosmetics - Ben Cooper Inc.

FAMOUS FACES - Stamps–hand - Clearsnap, Inc.

FAMOUS FARE - Floor coverings–carpet and rugs ☆ - Evans-Black Carpet Mills

FAMOUS FARE II - Floor coverings–carpet and rugs - Evans-Black Carpet Mills

FAMOUS FARE NATURALS - Floor coverings–carpet and rugs ☆ - Evans-Black Carpet Mills

FAMOUS FARE SUPREME - Floor coverings–carpet and rugs - Evans-Black Carpet Mills

FAMOUS FIDO'S - Pet products - Gimborn U.S., Inc.

FAMOUS FIGHTERS - Toy airplanes - Intex Recreation Corp.

FAMOUS FOLLIES - Apparel–women's ☆ - Treasures of Paris-Monogram Manufacturing Co.

FAMOUS FONSZWORTH - Pet products ☆ - Gimborn U.S., Inc.

FAMOUS FROZEN FRUITS - Fruits–frozen - Heikes Produce, Inc.

FAMOUS GATE, THE - Wines - Domaine Carneros, Ltd.

FAMOUS GROUSE, THE - Whiskey - Heublein, Inc.

FAMOUS HERO - Toys - Ben Cooper Inc.

FAMOUS HOME RUN - Frozen pizza - Famous Home Run Inn

FAMOUS ITALIAN STYLE NORTH BEACH - Cheese - Pacific Cheese Co., Inc.

FAMOUS JAMES SANDWICHES - Sandwiches–prepackaged - Famous James Sandwich Co., Inc.

FAMOUS LAST WORDS - Recording label - John Morgan Reilly

FAMOUS LOCOMOTIVES - Erasers - Diener Industries Inc.

FAMOUS LONGHORN GRILL - Spices and extracts - Bernard Food Industries Inc. (Consumer Products Div.)

FAMOUS MARIETTA - Paints - Vanguard Paints & Finishes Inc.

FAMOUS PACIFIC DESSERT COMPANY, THE - Confections - Famous Pacific Dessert Co.

FAMOUS PLACES - Computer software - Orange Cherry Software

FAMOUS READING - Oils–lubricating - Reading Anthracite Co.

FAMOUS RESTAURANTS - Salad dressings–bottled - Arcobasso Foods, Inc.

FAMOUS SCIENTISTS - Computer software - Hartley Courseware Inc.

FAMOUS SPORTSWEAR - Apparel and accessories - Famous-Fraternity Sportswear Sales Co.

FAMOUS STOLLEN - Cakes - Dinkel's Bakery

FAMOUS TRAILS - Apparel–athletic - Famous Trails

FAMOWOOD - Wood fillers - Beverly Manufacturing Co.

FAMOWOOD - Wood fillers - Eclectic Products Inc.

FAMOWOOD - Wood fillers - Harbor Sales Co.

FAMOWOOD PROPATCH - Building materials ☆ - Eclectic Products Inc.

FAMOX - Labels–paper - Litton Industrial Automation Systems

FAMS - Electronics stores - Farmstead Asset Management Services, LLC

FAN - Trailers–travel ☆ - Coachmen Industries, Inc.

FAN - Trailers–travel ☆ - Shasta Industries Inc.

FAN A CLAIM - Computer software - Racing Concepts Inc.

FAN-A-SIGN - Signs - Sportniks, Inc.

FAN-AIR - Air conditioning equipment - United Metal Products, Inc.

FAN CALL - Communications equipment–satellite - Keith Conrad

FAN-CEE NOTIONS - Hobby kits - Debbie Legg Lloyd

FAN CHIC - Glass products - Glass Inc.

FAN CLASS - Motor vehicles–motor homes ☆ - Shasta Industries Inc.

FAN FAIR - Toys–stuffed - Bantam Collections Inc.

FAN-FAN - Cosmetics ☆ - Cassidy Inc.

FAN FAN - Ophthalmic goods ☆ - Luxottica

FAN FARE - Brushes - Quickie Manufacturing Corp.

FAN FARE - Floor coverings - Compass Concepts

FAN-FILE - Computer diskettes–blank - Fellowes Manufacturing Co.

FAN FLARE - Lighting fixtures ☆ - Hubbell Lighting, Inc. (Lighting Div.)

FAN FUELER - Containers - Frederick Miller, III

FAN GEAR - Pet products - Hunter Manufacturing Group, Inc.

FAN HAND - Novelty items–stitched - Douglas A. Williams

FAN HORSE OWNERS CLUB - Computer software - Racing Concepts Inc.

FAN IN A CAN - Furnaces–electric - Pettibone Corp.

FAN JET - Dryers–hair ☆ - Sunbeam-Oster Household Products

FAN-LOGI - Ceiling fans and accessories - Beverly Hills Trading Co. Inc.

FAN LOYALTY - Sporting goods - Eddie J. Buford Jr.

FAN MAIL - Novelty items–paper - Fan Mail Greeting Card Co.

FAN MINI - Motor vehicles–motor homes ☆ - Shasta Industries Inc.

FAN OUT - Tools - D & L Stained Glass Supply, Inc.

FAN RADIO - Electronic equipment - Sportronics Radios, Inc.

FAN-RAKE - Rakes - Rugg Manufacturing Co. Inc.

FAN SCENTS - Ceiling-fan air fresheners - Lines Unlimited

FAN SHELL - Dinnerware–glass - Franciscan by Johnson Brothers, USA, Inc.

FAN-TA-SEAS - Hobby kits - Burke

FAN-TAG - Novelty items - Beistle Co.

FAN-TAS-STICK - Housewares ☆ - Deflecto Corp.

FAN-TAS-TIC - Fans–electric - Sanyo Fisher (USA) Corp.

FAN, THE - Broadcasting stations–radio - Infinity Broadcasting Corp.

FAN TOP - Girdles - Youthcraft-Charmfit

FAN WING - Fishing lures - Sunset Line and Twine Co.

FANA OF ENGLAND - Greeting cards - H. George Caspari Inc.

FANAGLE THE BAGEL - Bagels - Queen Bee Enterprises Corp.

FANALYZE - Paper - Reynolds and Reynolds Co.

FAN*A*RAMA - Computer software - Sterling Technologies, Inc.

FANATICS ONLY FO - Apparel and accessories - Fanatics Only, LLC

FANCARDS - Novelty items - Gretchen G. Walberg

FANCEE FREE - Apparel stores–lingerie - Fancee Free Manufacturing Co.

FANCHER - Furniture ☆ - Fancher Furniture Co. Inc.

FANCI - Pet products ☆ - Gone to the Dogs

FANCI CRAFTS - Hobby kits ☆ - JCA, Inc.

FANCI-CURL - Hair care products - Roux Laboratories, Inc.

FANCI-FULL - Hair care products - Revlon Consumer Products Corp.

FANCI-FULL - Hair care products - Roux Laboratories, Inc.

FANCI PAC - Food products - Bush Brothers and Co.

FANCI-TONE - Hair coloring preparations - Roux Laboratories, Inc.

FANCIFOIL - Foil–aluminum - E-Z-Por Corp.

FANCIFOOD WESTERN GOURMET - Snack foods - Tree of Life, Inc.

FANCIFORM - Frames–eyeglass - Zylo Ware Corp.

FANCIFUL - Clocks - General Time Corp. (Westclox/Seth Thomas Div.)

FANCIFUL - Floor coverings–carpet and rugs - Milliken & Co. Inc.

FANCIFUL - Floor coverings–carpet and rugs ☆ - Columbus Mills, Inc.

FANCIFUL - Frames–eyeglass - Zylo Ware Corp.

FANCIFUL - Rings–jewelry - Artcarved Inc.

FANCIFUL - Tableware–china ☆ - Lenox, Inc.

FANCIFUL - Underwear and nightwear ☆ - Lovable Co.

FANCIFUL COLLECTION - Wallpaper - Judscott Handprints Ltd.

FANCIFUL PLUM - Lipsticks - Honey & Spice Toiletries

FANCO - Easels - Anco Wood Specialties Inc.

FANCORSIL - Vitamins and nutritional supplements - Fanning Corp.

FANCRAFT - Electric lighting equipment ☆ - Waxman Industries Inc.

FANCY - Condiments - Cains Foods, Inc.

FANCY - Cookies - Fancy Fortune Cookies

FANCY - Frames–eyeglass - Pathway Optical Prods.

FANCY - Glassware–household - Federal Glass

FANCY - Gliders–metal - Turner and Seymour Manufacturing Co.

FANCY - Placemats - Jersey Blanke Designs Inc.

FANCY - Toys - Tonka Corp.

FANCY ACETATES - Publisher's imprints - Pen-Tab Industries

FANCY ADDRESS - Dresses–girls' - Sugar Plum, Inc.

FANCY BEST - Dolls - Mattel, Inc.

FANCY CAKES - Snack cakes - McKee Foods Corp.

FANCY CAT - Pet products - JT Industries

FANCY CHANGES - Dolls - Mattel, Inc.

FANCY CURLS FRIENDS - Toys - Tonka Corp.

FANCY CUTS - Hardware - Shakertown Inc.

FANCY DANCER - Toys - Tonka Corp.

FANCY DANCIN' - Dolls - Mattel, Inc.

FANCY DELANCY - Crocheted and knitted items - Valor

FANCY DRY - Infant product - Rock-A-Bye Baby Inc.

FANCY EUREKA - Seafood products–fresh or frozen - Eureka Fisheries

FANCY FAN - Fans–electric ☆ - Sunbeam-Oster Household Products

FANCY FASHIONS - Dolls - Mattel, Inc.

FANCY FEAST - Cat food - Nestle USA

FANCY FELINE - See FELINE SUPREME

FANCY FIESTA - Toys - Tonka Corp.

FANCY FINGERS - Manicure preparations - Lee Pharmaceuticals

FANCY FLAGS - Flags - Windsport, Inc.

FANCY FLOWERS - Flowers–artificial ☆ - Natcol Crafts & Hobbies

FANCY FOLDS - Greeting cards - Stephen Lawrence Co.

FANCY FOODS - Food containers - Fancy Foods of Virginia Inc.

FANCY FOOTWORK - Floor coverings–carpet and rugs - E.R. Carpenter Co.

FANCY FOOTWORK - Infant product ☆ - Ming Ta Supply

FANCY FORTY - Glassware–household - Federal Glass

FANCY FRAGRANCE - Deodorizers - Norpak Companies Ltd.

FANCY FREE - Apparel–women's - MB Products Ltd.

FANCY FREE - Boats - Glen-L Marine Designs

FANCY FREE - Dinnerware–glass ☆ - Lenox, Inc.

FANCY FREE - Floor coverings–carpet and rugs - Coronet Carpets Inc.

FANCY-FREE - Frames–eyeglass - Pathway Optical Prods.

FANCY FREE - Furniture - Lyon-Shaw Inc.

FANCY FREE - Luggage - Airway Industries, Inc.

FANCY FREE - Wallpaper - Pageant Wallpaper Corp.

FANCY FRIENDS - Toys–stuffed ☆ - Fun World Inc.

FANCY FRILLS - Dolls - Mattel, Inc.

FANCY FRUIT - Pet products - L/M Animal Farms, Inc.

FANCY FRUITS - Candy - Planters LifeSavers Co.

FANCY FRUITS - Game machines - IGT - North America

FANCY FRUITY - Dolls - Mattel, Inc.

FANCY FULLY - Apparel–women's - Exquisite Form Industries

FANCY FURRY - Cushions - R & R Sales

FANCY GIRL - Eyeglasses - Art-Craft Optical Co.

FANCY HAIR - Dolls - Mattel, Inc.

FANCY KITTY - Toys–stuffed - Dakin Inc.

FANCY KORDE - Craft supplies - Textile Enterprises Inc.

FANCY LACES - Laces–boot and shoe ☆ - Mitchellace Inc.

FANCY LADIES' BOUTIQUE - Cigarette holders - Gesty Trading & Manufacturing Corp.

FANCY ME - Apparel stores–lingerie - Fancee Free Manufacturing Co.

FANCY NANCY - Seasonings - Eric Martin and Katie Martin Partnership

FANCY NOTES - Paper–writing - Carol Wilson Fine Arts, Inc.

FANCY NUT CHEW - Food products - Honeypot Treats

FANCY PAC - Seafood - Bayside Imports Inc.

FANCY PANTRY - Food products ☆ - Dean Pickle & Specialty Products Co.

FANCY PANTS - Dolls - Meritus Industries, Inc.

FANCY PANTS - Dolls - Uneeda Doll Co., Inc.

FANCY PASTELS - Candy - Fanny Farmer Candy Shops Inc.

FANCY PETS - Pet products - JT Industries

FANCY PRANCERS - Toys–stuffed - Mary Meyer Corp.

FANCY PROPS - Apparel–women's ☆ - Wilkins Industries Inc.

FANCY SHRED - Cheese - Sargento Cheese Co. Inc.

FANCY SKAMP - Underwear and nightwear ☆ - Henson-Kickernick Inc.

FANCY SNAPS - Fasteners–snap - Prym Dritz Corp.

FANCY STEPS - Frames–eyeglass ☆ - Universal/Univis Inc.

FANCY THAT - Apparel–children's - Montgomery Ward & Co. Inc.

FANCY THAT - Floor coverings–carpet and rugs - Sweetwater Carpet Corp.

FANCY THAT - Floor coverings–carpet and rugs ☆ - Regal Rugs Inc.

FANCY THAT - Frames–eyeglass - May Optical Co. Inc.

FANCY THAT - Jewelry - Dayton Hudson Corp.

FANCY WORKS - Apparel and accessories - Warnaco Inc.

FANCYFULL YOU - Brassieres (Bras) - Vanity Fair Mills Inc.

FANCYMATS - Paper products - Kaibab Artistic, Inc.

FANCYNAIL GEMS - Nail care products - SRA Industries Inc.

FANCYPANTS - Diapers–disposable ☆ - West Point-Pepperell Inc.

FANCYPLANTS - Aquarium accessories - Aquarium Systems, Inc.

FANCYS EXTRA - Cigars ☆ - Havatampa Inc.

FANCY'S FINEST - Pickles - Fancy Foods of Virginia Inc.

FANCYTIME - Dolls - Mattel, Inc.

FANCYWORK - Christmas tree lights - Overly-Raker

FANCYWORK CHARLEY - Infant product ☆ - Overly-Raker

FANCYWORK CHECKERS - Infant product ☆ - Overly-Raker

FANCYWORK FRIENDS - Toys - Overly-Raker

FANCYWORKS - Apparel–women's - Warnaco Inc.

FANDANGLES - Skin care products ☆ - Premiere Salon Products

FANDANGO - Christmas tree ornaments - Cracker Box Inc.

FANDANGO - Colognes ☆ - Key West Aloe Inc.

FANDANGO - Eyeglasses - Art-Craft Optical Co.

FANDANGO - Musical instruments ☆ - Carpenter Co.

FANDEMONIUM - Apparel–athletic - Bismarck Enterprises of Illinois, Inc.

FANDI FAWN - Toys–stuffed - Russ Berrie and Co., Inc.

FANDIAL - Electrical equipment - Lutron Electronics Co., Inc.

FANFAIR - Paints ☆ - United Coatings Inc.

FANFANNER - Novelty items–paper - KLF Designs, Inc.

FANFARE - Aluminum foil wrap - Highland Supply Corp.

FANFARE - Bedding–linen - Dan River Inc.

FANFARE - Chairs–folding - Cosco, Inc.

FANFARE - Cheese - Walker Foods

FANFARE - Christmas tree ornaments - Cracker Box Inc.

FANFARE - Flatware - Utica Cutlery Co.

FANFARE - Floor coverings–carpet and rugs - Tuftex Carpet Mills, Inc.

FANFARE - Floor coverings–carpet and rugs ☆ - Regal Rugs Inc.

FANFARE - Food products - Land O'Lakes Inc.

FANFARE - Food products - Seneca Foods Corp.

FANFARE - Furniture ☆ - Hooker Furniture Corp.

FANFARE - Giftware ☆ - Gorham Inc.

FANFARE - Glassware–household - Owens-Illinois Inc. (Libbey Div.)

FANFARE - Glassware–household ☆ - Towle Silversmiths

FANFARE - Hair care products - Helene Curtis Industries Inc.

FANFARE - Invitations ☆ - John Henry Co.

FANFARE - Publisher's imprints - Bantam Doubleday Dell Publishing Group, Inc.

FANFARE - Rings–jewelry - Artcarved Inc.

FANFARE - Wallpaper ☆ - Gloria Merrill Enterprises

FANFARE - Yarn ☆ - William Unger & Co. Inc.

FANFARES - Footwear–women's - Wohl Shoe Co.

FANFARON - Wines ☆ - Wine Group Inc.

FANFX - Paints - OEM Paints, Inc.

FANG THE SNEEFY SNAKE - Toys - Imperial Toy Corp.

FANG TIRE, THE - Tires–bicycles - Answer Products Inc.

FANG WHITE - Pet products - Faria Ltd. (Sheffield Laboratories)

FANGLEY'S - Dentifrices - Amway Corp.

FANGMATO - Toys - Mattel, Inc.

FANGS - Candy - Glenn Confections Inc.

FANGS - Eyeglasses - Oakley, Inc.

FANGS - Toys - Tonka Corp.

FANGSTER - Toys–automobiles - Mattel, Inc.

FANIE - Skin care products - Fanie International

FANIE INTERNATIONAL - Skin care products - Fanie International

FANIMATION - Trading cards and stamps - Upper Deck Co.

FANLIGHT - Giftware ☆ - Lenox Crystal, Inc.

FANMIX - Gas burners - Tuthill Corp. (Coppus Murray Group)

FANNER-50 - Toys - Mattel, Inc.

FANNER, THE - Motorcycle parts and accessories - O.P. Racing

FANNFITTER ANYWHERE CHAIR - Furniture - Sound Business Concepts Inc.

FANNIE MAY - Candy - Archibald Candy Corp.

FANNY - Artists' materials - Stangren Co.

FANNY FARMER - Candy - Fanny Farmer Candy Shops Inc.

FANNY FLAG - Novelty items - AG-Tronic Inc.

FANNY FRIDGE - Bags - Seattle Sports Manufacturing Co., Inc.

FANNY-MATE - Chairs - Robert A. Nordmeyer

FANNY PIG - Toys–stuffed - Russ Berrie and Co., Inc.

FANNY SKIS - Sleds ☆ - Laid Back Enterprises, Inc.

FANNY WARMER - Apparel–women's - Tammy Lynn Comstock

FANNYKINS - Figurines - Samalo

FANNY'S NO FAT - Cakes - Fat Free Food Corp.

FANO - Glassware–household - Dansk International Designs, Ltd.

FANO SATELLITE - Guitars - Dennis Fano

FANON/COURIER - Communications equipment–mobile - Fanon Courier Inc.

FANS - Coffee - Luban International, Inc.

FANS - Communications equipment - Fans Telecom, Inc.

FANSEA - Seafood products–canned or cured - Long Beach Seafoods Co.

FANSIDAR - Pharmaceutical preparations - Roche Laboratories

FANSINK - Electronic component cooling system - Nidec America Corp.

FANSPRAY - Lawn mowers ☆ - Thompson Manufacturing Co.

FANT-A-GEM - Adhesives and sealants - Marli Industries Inc.

FANTA - Beverages–carbonated - Coca-Cola Corp.

FANTA-SEEDS - Bird feeds - Andrea Brown

FANTABULOUS CATS - Posters - Aaronco Grooming Products

FANTAGRAPH - Draperies - Standard Textile Co., Inc.

FANTAIL - Bicycles - Columbia Manufacturing Inc.

FANTAIL - Fishing lure - Mister Twister, Inc.

☆ = Now out of production

FANTAISIE - Wines - Folie A Deux Winery
FANTAN - Thread - Threads USA Div.
FANTANA - Floor coverings–carpet and rugs - Queen Carpet Corp.
FANTASCENES - Photographic equipment - Eastman Kodak Co.
FANTASEA - Apparel and accessories ☆ - Kellwood Co.
FANTASEA CASTLE - Paper products - Lisa Frank, Inc.
FANTASIA - Artists' materials - Sakura Color Products of America, Inc.
FANTASIA - Belts–apparel - Great American Leatherworks Inc.
FANTASIA - Bicycles - Huffy Corp.
FANTASIA - Cakes - Fancy Foods of Virginia Inc.
FANTASIA - Candy - Beacon Sweets, Inc.
FANTASIA - Cigarettes - Nat Sherman, Inc.
FANTASIA - Clocks - General Time Corp. (Westclox/Seth Thomas Div.)
FANTASIA - Dinnerware–glass - Princess House, Inc.
FANTASIA - Electronic equipment - Vicon Fiber Optics Corp.
FANTASIA - Fabrics - Thompson of California Inc.
FANTASIA - Floor coverings ☆ - Congoleum Corp.
FANTASIA - Floor coverings–carpet and rugs - Philadelphia Carpets
FANTASIA - Frames–picture - Framemica Co.
FANTASIA - Furniture ☆ - Bassett Furniture Industries, Inc.
FANTASIA - Greeting cards - American Artists Group Inc.
FANTASIA - Hair care products - Fantasia Accessories Ltd.
FANTASIA - Hair care products - Fantasia Industries Corp.
FANTASIA - Kitchenware–earthenware - Arnart Imports Inc.
FANTASIA - Lighting fixtures ☆ - Cable Electric Products
FANTASIA - Musical instruments - Miracle Music
FANTASIA - Novelty items - J.W. Stannard Co.
FANTASIA - Rings–jewelry ☆ - Artcarved Inc.
FANTASIA - Skin care products - Goubaud
FANTASIA - Underwear and nightwear - NCC Industries, Inc.
FANTASIA - Wallpaper - Thomas Ray Designs Inc.
FANTASIA - Yarn ☆ - Joseph Galler Inc.
FANTASIA COLLECTION - Greeting cards ☆ - Cleo Inc.
FANTASIA IC - Hair care products - Fantasia Industries Corp.
FANTASIA LIGHTS - Cigarettes - Nat Sherman, Inc.
FANTASIA LION - Puppets - Russ Berrie and Co., Inc.
FANTASIA WATERCOLORS - Artists' materials - Sakura of America
FANTASIC - Footwear–men's ☆ - Nozaki America Inc.
FANTASIE OF ENGLAND - Apparel–women's - Stirling Brands, Inc.
FANTASIES - Floor coverings–carpet and rugs - Coronet Carpets Inc.
FANTASIES IN LACE - Apparel–women's - Jezebel-Renee of Hollywood
FANTASIO - Perfume - Bourjois Ltd.
FANTASMA - Apparel and accessories - Fantasma Productions, Inc. of Florida
FANTASPORTS - Trading cards and stamps - Topps Co., Inc.
FANTASQUE - Colognes ☆ - Avon Products, Inc.
FANTASTAKES OF AMERICA - Golfing equipment - Palm Beach Plastics Inc.
FANTASTEC - Lighting equipment - Kidselebration Inc.
FANTASTEX - Ribbons–inked - Leedall Products Manufacturing Co.
FANTASTEX - Wallpaper ☆ - Wolf-Gordon Inc.
FANTASTIC - Apparel stores–lingerie - Formflex Foundations Inc.
FANTASTIC - Candles ☆ - L.J. Rench & Co.
FANTASTIC - Floor coverings - Aladdin Mills, Inc.
FANTASTIC - Floor coverings–carpet and rugs - Galaxy Carpet Mills Inc.
FANTASTIC - Floor coverings–carpet and rugs - LaVelle Textile Marketing Inc.
FANTASTIC - Floor coverings–carpet and rugs - Mohawk Carpet Corp.
FANTASTIC - Snack foods - Golden Stream Quality Foods
FANTASTIC - Wallcoverings - Cork Products Co. Inc.
FANTASTIC - Window coverings ☆ - Hunter Douglas, Inc.
FANTASTIC COLOR - Hair care products - Fantastic Sam's International, Inc.
FANTASTIC CRYSTAL CREATIONS - Hobby kits - Hasbro, Inc.
FANTASTIC FACES - Toys–stuffed - Fun World Inc.
FANTASTIC FAKES - Canvas–artists' - Fabulous Forgeries Ltd.
FANTASTIC FALAFIL - Food products - Fantastic Foods Inc.
FANTASTIC FASHIONS - Dolls - Mattel, Inc.
FANTASTIC FIFTEEN - Jewelry - K & M Associates
FANTASTIC FINGER FOODS - Vegetable sauces - Fred's Frozen Foods Inc.
FANTASTIC FINGERNAILS - Toys - Hasbro, Inc.
FANTASTIC FOAM - Cleaner - Comstar International Inc. (IPC Div.)
FANTASTIC FORCE - Books–comic ☆ - Marvel Entertainment Group, Inc.
FANTASTIC FOUR - Chewing gum ☆ - Amurol Confections Co.
FANTASTIC FOUR - Toys - Marvel Entertainment Group, Inc.
FANTASTIC FRUITY! - Frozen foods - Good Humor Corp.
FANTASTIC FUCHSIA - Stationery - Lisa Frank, Inc.
FANTASTIC KIDS - Dolls - F.W. Woolworth Co.
FANTASTIC NOODLES - Soups–mixes - Fantastic Foods Inc.
FANTASTIC ORANGE - Teas - Harris Tea Co.

FANTASTIC PLASTIC - Artists' materials - Aleene's
FANTASTIC PLASTIC - Toys ☆ - Henry Gordy International Inc.
FANTASTIC RECALL - Computer software - Binar Graphics, Inc.
FANTASTIC SAND SURPRISES - Hobby kits - Hasbro, Inc.
FANTASTIC STICKER MAKER - Toys - Hasbro, Inc.
FANTASTIC STRINGS - Wallpaper - K.M.L. Industries
FANTASTIC TREASURES - Games - Mayfair Games, Inc.
FANTASTICA - Dolls - Mattel, Inc.
FANTASTICA - Yarn - William Unger & Co. Inc.
FANTASTICARDS - Trading cards and stamps - Educational Insights, Inc.
FANTASTICKS - Decals and transfers ☆ - Compac Industries Inc.
FANTASTICO - Cleaning preparations–household - Blue Cross Laboratories Inc.
FANTASTICO - Lighting fixtures - Angelo Brothers Co.
FANTASTICS - Candy ☆ - Price Candy Co. Inc.
FANTASTIK - Cleaning preparations - Dowbrands L.P.
FANTASTIK - Erasers - Wescosa Inc.
FANTASTIK - Glue–household or industrial - Natcol Crafts & Hobbies
FANTASTIK - Hair care products ☆ - P.S. Pibbs Inc.
FANTASTIK S'WIPES - Skin care products ☆ - Dowbrands L.P.
FANTASTIKARTS - Mining cars - Commonwealth Inc.
FANTASTIQUE - Floor coverings–carpet and rugs - Aldon Industries Inc.
FANTASTIX KA-BOBS - Food products - Fantastix Inc.
FANTASY - Artists' materials - Andrews/Nelson/Whitehead
FANTASY - Bicycles - Roadmaster Corp.
FANTASY - Computer software - U.S. Integrated Technologies
FANTASY - Dinnerware–glass - Block China Co.
FANTASY - Dolls ☆ - Gorham Inc.
FANTASY - Fabrics - Guilford Mills, Inc.
FANTASY - Fabrics ☆ - Thompson of California Inc.
FANTASY - Fans–electric - Holmes Products, Corp.
FANTASY - Floor coverings–carpet and rugs ☆ - American Carpet Mills
FANTASY - Floor coverings–carpet and rugs ☆ - World Carpets, Inc.
FANTASY - Furniture - Halcyon Inc.
FANTASY - Furniture - Weiman Co.
FANTASY - Jewelry - Fantasy Diamond Corp.
FANTASY - Lamps ☆ - Lamplight Farms, Inc.
FANTASY - Nail care products - Rudolph International, Inc.
FANTASY - Novelty items - Destini Productions Inc.
FANTASY - Paper–tissue - Crystal Tissue Co. Inc.
FANTASY - Phonographs - Fantasy Inc.
FANTASY - Plates–paper ☆ - Potlatch Corp.
FANTASY - Posters - Fairfax Prints Ltd.
FANTASY - Rings–jewelry ☆ - Artcarved Inc.
FANTASY - Shoes - Genesco Inc.
FANTASY - Skin care products - Niche Research Inc.
FANTASY - Skin care products - Takara Belmont USA, Inc.
FANTASY - Toys - Cardinal Teen Toy Inc.
FANTASY - Toys–stuffed - Fun World Inc.
FANTASY - Wallpaper - Morton Jonap Co. Inc.
FANTASY AIRBRUSH - Recording label - Fantasy Airbrush
FANTASY ART FURNITURE - Furniture - Sutton House, Inc.
FANTASY BALL DINOSAURS - Candy - Uniconfis Corp.
FANTASY BLANKE BAER - Food products - Fantasy Blankebaer
FANTASY BY FOREVER YOURS - Wedding gowns - Forever Yours International Corp.
FANTASY CHESS - Games - John Paul Bakshoian
FANTASY COLLECTION - Footwear–women's - Hawaii Shoe Co.
FANTASY CREATURES - Toys - Processed Plastic Co.
FANTASY FACES - Beauty shops - R.S. Noggins, Inc.
FANTASY FACES - Toys - Anagram International, Inc.
FANTASY FACTORY - Compact discs–prerecorded - Peter Pan Industries
FANTASY FASHION - Pet products - Fantasy Farm Products Co.
FANTASY FEAST - Paper - Lisa Frank, Inc.
FANTASY FILES - Skin care products - Rudolph International, Inc.
FANTASY FINISH - Mat boards - Dahle USA
FANTASY FLIGHT - Floor coverings–carpet and rugs - Ashley Commercial Carpets
FANTASY FLYER SERIES - Fans–electric - Hunter Fan Co.
FANTASY FOREST - Games - Tsr, Inc.
FANTASY FOREST - Toys ☆ - Today's Kids Inc.
FANTASY FORTRESS - Toys - Tyco Toys
FANTASY FORTUNE - Playing cards - United States Playing Card Co.
FANTASY FRIENDS - Dolls ☆ - Totsy Manufacturing Co., Inc.
FANTASY FROST - Hobby kits - Tri-Chem Inc.
FANTASY FUN - Dolls ☆ - Totsy Manufacturing Co., Inc.

FANTASY FUR - Hobby kits - Mangelsen's (VDI)

FANTASY GAMERS COMPENDIUM - Games - Gamescience

FANTASY GENERAL - Computer software - Strategic Simulations, Inc.

FANTASY HOCKEY - Computer software - Fantasy Sports Properties, Inc.

FANTASY IN LIGHTS - Jewelry - Ida Cason Callaway Foundation

FANTASY IN WOOD - Giftware ☆ - Crisa Corp.

FANTASY ISLAND - Wallpaper - Advance Wallcoverings

FANTASY LADIES - Dolls ☆ - Totsy Manufacturing Co., Inc.

FANTASY LIQUID - Toys ☆ - Steven Manufacturing Co.

FANTASY LORDS - Toys–models - Grenadier Models

FANTASY MAKERS - Jewelry–costume - Pavion Ltd.

FANTASY SAND - Agricultural products - Coastal Supply Co., Inc.

FANTASY SANDI - Dolls ☆ - Totsy Manufacturing Co., Inc.

FANTASY SEEDS - Novelty items - Chase Collection, Inc.

FANTASY SPARKLE - Bicycles ☆ - Huffy Corp.

FANTASY UNICORN - Puppets - Dakin Inc.

FANTASY/WMOT - Phonographs ☆ - Fantasy Inc.

FANTASYLAND - Dolls ☆ - Effanbee Doll Corp.

FANTAVISION - Computer software ☆ - Broderbund Software, Inc.

FANTAZAMADAZZLE MAGICAL CHOCOLATE FACTORY, THE - Chocolate candy - Leah Gold Confectioners, Ltd.

FANTAZE - Furniture - JZS, Inc.

FANTAZIE - Apparel–children's - Kessner and Rabinowitz, Inc.

FANTAZMA - Kites - Gayla Industries Inc.

FANTAZMA GORDO - Kites - Gayla Industries Inc.

FANTAZOO - Candy - Usher Products International, Inc.

FANTESSA - Fabrics ☆ - West Point-Pepperell Inc.

FANTI - Hair care products - Roux Laboratories, Inc.

FANTOM - Fans–electric - Delwyn

FANTOM FLEX - Electrical equipment ☆ - Wiremold Co.

FANTOM FORM - Girdles - Bi-Flex International

FANTOMFINGERS - Pianos ☆ - Baldwin Piano & Organ Co.

FANTURA - Footwear–women's - Benjamin Walk Corp.

FANTUSY - Giftware - Fantus Paper Products

FANWATCH - Electronic equipment - Lexar Computers

FANZY TYE - Apparel and accessories - Ernest F. Romero

FAPPS - Computer software - Bechtel Group, Inc.

FAR & SURE - Golfing equipment - Gamecock Collection Ltd.

FAR AWAY - Colognes - Avon Products, Inc.

FAR CORNERS - Furniture ☆ - Harden Furniture Co. Inc.

FAR EAST - Furniture ☆ - Lane Co. Inc.

FAR EAST - Seasonings - House of Herbs Inc.

FAR EAST - Wallpaper ☆ - Wolf-Gordon Inc.

FAR EAST COLLECTION - Furniture - Jackson of Danville Inc.

FAR EAST STIR FRY - Fruits and vegetables - Patterson Frozen Foods, Inc.

FAR EASTERN - Coconut–shredded - Far Eastern Coconut Co.

FAR EASTERN - Wallpaper - Durawall Inc.

FAR EASTERN SILKY SMOOTH - Hair care products - Revlon Consumer Products Corp.

FAR FAMED - Hosiery ☆ - Chipman-Union Inc.

FAR-GO - Product description unknown - American Stone-Mix Inc.

FAR-GO FLOW STONE - Product description unknown - American Stone-Mix Inc.

FAR-GO SMOOTH'R FILL - Product description unknown - American Stone-Mix Inc.

FAR HILLS - Syrup - Far Hills Maple Syrup

FAR HILLS RACE MEETING - Posters - Far Hills Race Meeting Association, Inc.

FAR HORIZONS II - Wallpaper ☆ - Capital Carousel Inc.

FAR LIBRARY, THE - Computer software - Legislative Information Systems Corp.

FAR-MAR-CO - Health care products - Farmland Industries Inc.

FAR-MOR-LITE - Paints - Harrison Paint Corp.

FAR NIENTE - Wines - Far Niente Winery

FAR-OUT - Brushes–hair - Nino Originals

FAR OUT - Insecticides - Dymon, Inc.

FAR PRO SERIES - Legal services - Florida Association of Realtors

FAR STAR - Computer software - Random House, Inc.

FAR VILLAGE - Apparel and accessories - Hanah Jane Exley

FAR WEST - Electronic equipment - America's Favorite Chicken Co.

FAR WEST PUBLISHING COMPANY - Publisher's imprints - Sun Publishing Co.

FARA SAN MARTINO - Pasta - Ferrara Food Co., Inc.

FARADAY - Alarm systems–fire - Faraday Inc.

FARADAY - Magnetic coded cards - DeLaRue Inc.

FARAH - Frames–eyeglass - U.S. Optical Frame Co.

FARAH - Slacks–men's - Farah Inc.

FARAH FITS - Apparel–children's - Farah Inc.

FARAH NO WRINKLES - Apparel - Farah Inc.

FARALLON - Computer hardware - Farallon Computing, Inc.

FARALLON - Food containers - Farallon Foods Inc.

FARALLON - Scuba diving equipment - Peter Vickers

FARALLOY - Thermoplastic pellet - Polymer Materials, Inc.

FARANDOLE - Floor coverings - Parquet de France Inc.

FARANDOLE - Glassware–household - Durand International

FARAWAY FRIENDS - Dolls - Georgetown Collection, Inc.

FARBEE - Pharmaceutical preparations - Michigan Pharmaceutical

FARBER - Cookware - Farberware Inc.

FARBER PEEL - Electrical equipment - Farberware Inc.

FARBERPEEL - Kitchen appliances - Farberware Inc.

FARBERWARE - Cooking equipment–household - Farberware Inc.

FARBERWARE - Cutlery - Lifetime Hoan Corp.

FARBERWARE - Food containers - Frye International Corp.

FARBERWARE - Glassware–household - Excel Cutlery Inc.

FARBIGEM - Glass–flat ☆ - Willet Stained Glass Studios Inc.

FARCAL - Plastics film - Farco Plastics Supply Inc.

FARD PAUPIERES - Cosmetics - Sothys USA Inc.

FARFANA - Fruits–canned - Marglo Products Corp.

FARFELU VINEYARD - Wines - Farfelu Vineyard

FARFISA - Accordions - Castiglione Accordion

FARGO - Flour–blended ☆ - Ross Industries Inc.

FARGO - Printers–computer - Fargo Electronics Inc.

FARIBO - Blankets - Faribault Woolen Mill Co.

FARIES-MCMEEKAN - Mirrors - Faries-McMeekan Inc.

FARINA - Cereal ☆ - Pillsbury Co.

FARINA - Fabrics - Dan River Inc.

FARINA CREAMY HOT WHEAT CEREAL - Cereal - Holden Foods, Inc.

FARINA GEGENUEBER - Colognes ☆ - Noymer Leather and Gifts Ltd.

FARINA MILLS - Cereal - Holden Foods, Inc.

FARING ROAD - Floor coverings–carpet and rugs - Atlas Carpet Mills Inc.

FARKAS - Musical instrument accessories - G. Leblanc Corp.

FARLEY - Brushes–paint - PPG Industries, Inc.

FARLEY - Fruits–candied - Farley Candy Co.

FARLEY - Stuffed animals ☆ - Russ Berrie and Co., Inc.

FARLEY SELECT - Candy - Farley Candy Co.

FARLEY'S - Beverages–alcohol - Gibson Wine Co.

FARLEY'S - Fruits–candied - Farley Candy Co.

FARLEY'S ZESTY CHIPS 'N STIX - Snack foods - Farley Candy Co.

FARM - Tableware–earthenware - Anacapa Corp.

FARM & FAMILY - Paints - Central Tractor Farm & Family Center, Inc.

FARM & RANCH - Battery chargers - Schumacher Electric Corp.

FARM AND RANCH - Boots - Durango Boot Co. Inc.

FARM & RANCH - Boots - Georgia Boot Inc.

FARM & TRACK - Dog food - Merrick Petfoods Inc.

FARM BARN - Paints - Graham Paint and Varnish Co.

FARM BEST - Beverages–carbonated - Dairymen Inc. (Farm Best Div.)

FARM BEST - Dairy products - Challenge Dairy Co.

FARM BEST - Dairy products - Flav-O-Rich, Inc.

FARM BOSS - Saws–chain - Stihl Inc.

FARM BOY - Raisins - Dole Dried Fruit & Nut Co.

FARM BRAND - Fruits and vegetables - Desert Wealth Resources Inc.

FARM BRAND - Skin care products - Richard Charles Regan, Jr.

FARM CHARM - Dairy products - Big Star Food Stores

FARM CLUB - Animal feeds - Purina Mills, Inc.

FARM COUNTRY - Glassware–household - Anchor Hocking Glass, Inc.

FARM COUNTRY - Toys - ERTL Co., Inc.

FARM DELIGHT - Seafood products–fresh or frozen - Empress International Ltd.

FARM FAMILIES - Games - Hasbro, Inc.

FARM FAMILY - Toys–stuffed - Fun World Inc.

FARM FARE - Food products ☆ - Agway Country Foods Inc.

FARM FEAST - Turkeys - Foster Poultry Farms

FARM FLAVOR - Food products - Wakefern Food Corp.

FARM FOODS - Food products - Barricini Foods Inc.

FARM FRESH - Candy ☆ - Eddyleon Chocolate Co. Inc.

FARM FRESH - Fish–fresh or frozen - Farm Fresh Catfish Co.

FARM FRESH - Food products - Borden, Inc.

FARM FRESH - Food products - Victoria Packing Corp.

FARM FRESH - Meat products–beef - Super Valu Inc.

FARM FRESH - Milk - Shoenberg Farms Inc.

FARM FRESH DAIRY - Milk - Farm Fresh Dairy Inc.

FARM FRIEND - Toys–stuffed - Dakin Inc.

☆ = Now out of production

FARM FRIENDS - Toys–stuffed - Russ Berrie and Co., Inc.
FARM GUARD - Paints - Martin-Senour Co.
FARM HARVEST - Turkeys - Foster Poultry Farms
FARM HOUSE - Furniture - Bassett Furniture Industries, Inc.
FARM HOUSE BISCUITS - Cookies - Cornwall Group Inc.
FARM KETTLE - Food products ☆ - Sanofi Bio-Industries Inc.
FARM KING - Food products - Red Wing Co., Inc.
FARM KING - Garden equipment ☆ - Union Fork and Hoe Co.
FARM KITCHEN - Vegetables–canned - Beatrice Cos. Inc.
FARM LAX - Health care products - Old Amish Herbs
FARM MADE - Dairy products - Imperial Frozen Novelties Inc.
FARM MASTER - Shoes ☆ - Endicott Johnson Corp.
FARM N BARN - Vacuum cleaners and accessories - Sunbeam-Oster Household Products
FARM O' THE SEA - Shrimp–fresh or frozen ☆ - Neptune Sea Food Co.
FARM-PAC - Meat products–canned - Yoakum Packing Co.
FARM PACK - Nuts and bolts - Rockford Products Corp. (International Group)
FARM PACKT - Pickling salt - Farm Packt Pickle Co.
FARM PRIDE - Food products - Red Food Stores Inc.
FARM PRIDE - Shrimp–fresh or frozen ☆ - Southeast Foods Inc.
FARM PROTECTIVE - Paints - Morris Paint & Varnish Co.
FARM RAISED - Food products - Maple Leaf Farms Inc.
FARM RAISED FOODS - Meat products - Farm Raised Foods, Inc.
FARM-RANCH-HOME - Paints - Schulte Paint & Lacquer Manufacturing Co., Inc.
FARM-RATED - Motors–hydraulic - Magnetek Inc.
FARM RICH - Breads - Rich-Seapak Corp.
FARM RICH - Eggnog - Rich Products Corp.
FARM ROSE - Food products - P.J. Rhodes Corp.
FARM SKILLET - Breakfast entree - Country Hospitality Corp.
FARM STAND - Food products - Jewel Food Stores Inc.
FARM STAR - Farm machinery - Worksaver, Inc.
FARM STEAD - Animal feeds - Purina Mills, Inc.
FARM STORES - Beverages–carbonated - Farm Stores
FARM TABLE - Vegetables–pickled or brined ☆ - Paisley Farm
FARM, THE - Glassware–household ☆ - Fenton Art Glass Co.
FARM TOUGH - Batteries - Ford Motor Co.
FARM VIEW - Food products - Pick-n-Pay Super Markets Inc.
FARMACY - Dog food ☆ - Central Soya Co. Inc.
FARMANS - Relishes - Curtice-Burns Foods, Inc.
FARMAN'S - Sauerkraut - Farman Bros. Pickle Co.
FARMASTER - Fencing–gates and posts - Behlen Manufacturing Co.
FARMAVITA - Skin care products - Sukesha
FARMBELT - Food products - Beatrice Cos. Inc.
FARMBROOK - Furniture ☆ - Lane Co. Inc.
FARMCO - Musical instrument accessories - French American Reeds Manufacturing
FARMCOTE - Paints - Valspar Corp.
FARMCREST - Garden equipment ☆ - Gamble-Skogmo Inc.
FARMDALE - Processed foods - American Stores Co.
FARMED CAVIAR - Caviar - Tsar Nicoulai Caviar
FARMELLE - Food products - Jersey Farms Corp.
FARMER BOBS - Food products - All Fresh Products Inc.
FARMER BROTHERS - Coffee - Farmer Bros. Co.
FARMER GIRL - Food products - Hanover Foods Corp.
FARMER-IN-THE-DELL - Vegetables–canned - Draper-King Cole Inc.
FARMER JACKS - Cookies - Simmers Products
FARMER JOHN - Chickens - Markel-Johnson Poultry Co.
FARMER JOHN - Meat products–beef - Clougherty Packing Co.
FARMER KING - Oils–edible - Wei-Chuan U.S.A., Inc.
FARMER PEETS - Bacon - Peet Packing Co.
FARMER SAYS, THE - Toys - Mattel, Inc.
FARMER SY LOWE - Toys - Mattel, Inc.
FARMER TILLIE LOWE - Toys - Mattel, Inc.
FARMERS' - Dairy products - Farmers Cooperative Dairy of West Hazleton, Inc.
FARMERS - Horseradish - Brede Inc.
FARMERS BEST - Veterinary nutritional supplements - A.L. Gilbert & Co.
FARMERS BRANCH - Floor coverings–carpet and rugs ☆ - Evans-Black Carpet Mills
FARMER'S BUTTER - Butter - V.S. Distributors
FARMER'S CHOICE - Fruits and vegetables - J.R. Simplot Co.
FARMER'S CHOICE - Popcorn poppers - Felknor International Inc.
FARMERS CO-OP DAIRY - Milk - Farmers Cooperative Dairy of West Hazleton, Inc.
FARMERS CRATE - Fruits–dried - California Hi-Lites, Inc.

FARMERS DAIRIES - Milk - Farmers Dairies
FARMER'S DAUGHTER - Apparel and accessories - Anne Elizabeth Alper
FARMER'S DAUGHTER, THE - Meat products - Michael L. Whalen
FARMER'S FRIEND - Soap - Burt's Bees Inc.
FARMER'S HARVEST - Vegetables–frozen - California & Washington Co.
FARMER'S MARKET - Fruit drinks–bottled or canned - Knudsen & Sons Inc.
FARMER'S MARKET - Tableware–china - Pfaltzgraff Investment Co.
FARMER'S MARKET - Wallpaper ☆ - Imperial Wallcoverings, Inc.
FARMER'S PLATTER - Turkeys - Cooper's Turkey Place, Inc.
FARMER'S PRIDE - Pet products ☆ - 8 in 1 Pet Products Inc.
FARMERS SEAFOOD - Seafood products–fresh or frozen - Farmers Seafood Co., Inc.
FARMERS SELECT - Food products - Northern Star Co.
FARMERS STORE - Dairy products - Farmers Store Co.
FARMER'S STRIPES - Bedding–linen - Dan River Inc.
FARMER'S WIFE, THE - Hair care products - Farmer's Wife Co.
FARMFIELD - Juices ☆ - Pokka, Inc.
FARMFRESH - Fruits and vegetables - Pacific Marketing Group
FARMGARD - Animal health-care products - Purina Mills, Inc.
FARMHAND - Hair care products - Thompson and Formby
FARMHANDS - Aprons - Barth-Dreyfuss of California
FARMHOUSE - Clocks - General Time Corp. (Westclox/Seth Thomas Div.)
FARMHOUSE - Rice - Farmhouse Foods Co.
FARMHOUSE COLLECTION - Furniture - Vaughan Furniture Co. Inc.
FARMHOUSE COLLECTION, INC. - Furniture - Farmhouse Collection, Inc.
FARMHOUSE FOODS - Food containers - Farmhouse Foods
FARMHOUSE IN PROVENCE, A - Wallpaper ☆ - Raintree Designs Inc.
FARMING FLAGS - Flags - Flag Co., Inc.
FARMINGDALE - Floor coverings–carpet and rugs - Gulistan Carpet Inc.
FARMINGTON - Baskets–wood ☆ - Royal Cathay Trading Co.
FARMINGTON - Cabinets - Haas Cabinet Co. Inc.
FARMINGTON - Fabrics - Dan River Inc.
FARMINGTON - Footwear–men's - Livermore-Farmington Shoe Co.
FARMINGTON - Furniture - Lane Co. Inc.
FARMINGTON - Furniture ☆ - Singer Furniture Co.
FARMINGTON - Lumber - Georgia-Pacific Corp.
FARMINGTON - Occasional tables - JDI Group, Inc.
FARMINGTON - Toilets–enameled - Kohler Co.
FARMINGTON FRESH - Fruits and vegetables - Farmington Packing Co., Inc.
FARMINGTON HILL - Trailers–travel - Fleetwood Enterprises, Inc.
FARMKIST - Food products - Mayfair Packing Co.
FARMLAND - Chickens - Markel-Johnson Poultry Co.
FARMLAND - Food containers - Farmland Foods, Inc.
FARMLAND - Petroleum - Farmland Industries Inc.
FARMLAND - Toys - Bullyland Inc.
FARMLAND DAIRIES - Milk - Farmland Dairies Inc.
FARMS CREAMERY - Dairy products - J. & J. Farms Creamery Co., Inc.
FARMSHIRE - Cheese ☆ - Swissrose International Inc.
FARMSTAND FEEDERS - Pet products - Pets International, Ltd.
FARMSTEAD - Cabinets - Haas Cabinet Co. Inc.
FARMVIEW - Maps - Institute for Technology Development
FARMYARD - Infant product ☆ - Reliance Products Corp.
FARMYARD FRIENDS - Housewares - Pampered Chef, Ltd.
FARNAM - Pet products - Farnam Cos. Inc.
FARNAM DRIVE - Cigars - National Cigar Corp.
FARNHAM - Dinnerware–glass ☆ - Wallace International Silversmiths, Inc.
FARNSWORTH ARMORED, INC. - Motor vehicles–armored - Farnsworth Armored, Inc.
FARO - Beverages–malt - Merchant du Vin Corp.
FAROE ISLAND - Seafood products–fresh or frozen ☆ - Pocasset Seafoods Inc.
FAROS - Cigarettes - G.A. Georgopulo & Co. Inc.
FAROY - Giftware - Faroy Sales
FARR - Boats–pontoons - Farr International
FARRAGO COLLECTIONS - Apparel and accessories - Landmark Tailors
FARRAGUT - Watches - Bulova Corp.
FARRAH FAWCETT - Hair care products - Faberge Co.
FARRANGER - Antennas - Communications & Energy Corp., Inc.
FARRAR, STRAUS & GIROUX - Publisher's imprints - Farrar, Straus and Giroux Inc.
FARRIER'S CHOICE - Animal feed supplements - Advanced Biological Concepts
FARRIER'S CHOICE - Horseshoes - Journeys End International, Inc.
FARRINGTON - Music boxes - Mele Manufacturing Co. Farrington Packaging Co.
FARRO-HEAT - Air conditioning equipment ☆ - Easy Heat Inc.

FARRON RIDGE - Wines - Stimson Lane Vineyards & Estates
FARROW & HUMPHREYS - Soap - Global Marketing (US) Inc.
FARSIGHT - Computer software - Interface Technologies Inc.
FARSIGHT - Computer software - D.E. Shaw & Co., L.P.
FARSNI - Hair care products - Farsn, Inc.
FART CORK - Novelty items - JOCO
FARUCHOC - Food products - George C. Brown's Biscuits & Confections
FARVIEW FARMS - Food products - Joanne B. Losurdo
FARWELL O.K. - Paints - United Hardware
FARWEST - Apparel and accessories - Farwest Garments Inc.
FARWEST - Paints - Farwest Paint Manufacturing Co. Inc.
FARX-PVC - Plastics film - Farco Plastics Supply Inc.
FAS - Audio equipment - FAS Industries
FAS - Hardware - Scovill Inc.
FAS - Jewelry - FMC Manufacturing Corp.
FAS-DRIVE - Screws - Fas-Drive
FAS-GEL - Glue—household or industrial - Richard L. Stephens
FAS GLO - Paints - Vanguard Paints & Finishes Inc.
FAS-LOK - Adhesives and sealants - Richard L. Stephens
FAS-LOK - Couplers - Fulton Manufacturing Corp.
FAS-LOK - Hardware - Teco/Lumberlok
FAS-N-FREE - Cement - Tremco Inc.
FAS-N-IT - Nuts and bolts - Elco Industries, Inc.
FAS-SET - Fireplace equipment ☆ - Malm Fireplaces Inc.
FAS-TAK - Tools—hand-operated - Woodstock International, Inc.
FAS TECH - Boats—motor - Thunderbird Products
FAS-TIQUE - Antique stores - Impervious Paint Industries Ltd.
FAS TRED - Paints - Vanguard Paints & Finishes Inc.
FAS-WELD - Expoxy repair putty - Richard L. Stephens
FAS1000 - Computer software - Best Programs, Inc.
FAS2000 - Computer software - Best Programs, Inc.
FASA - Food products ☆ - Transmudo Co. Inc.
FASAD - Artists' materials - Gilman Brothers Co.
FASAD FR - Artists' materials - Gilman Brothers Co.
FASAR - Hearing aids - Hearing Health Group Inc.
FASBIN - Racks - Fastec Industrial Corp.
FASBO - Ribbons - Vaban Ribbons International
FASCIA - Frames—picture - Letraset USA Inc.
FASCIA-THERM - Insulating materials - Chicago Bridge and Iron Co. (Technical Services Div.)
FASCINATING SHEERS - Hosiery - Jack Constant Inc.
FASCINATION - Christmas tree ornaments - Cracker Box Inc.
FASCINATION - Fabrics - Robert Kaufman Co., Inc.
FASCINATION - Floor coverings—carpet and rugs - Regal Rugs Inc.
FASCINATION - Floor coverings—carpet and rugs ☆ - Gulistan Carpet Inc.
FASCINATION - Glassware—household - Durand International
FASCINATION - Hosiery—women's - Kayser-Roth Corp.
FASCINATION - Occasional tables - JDI Group, Inc.
FASCINATION - Rings—jewelry - Artcarved Inc.
FASCINATION - Underwear and nightwear - Bestform Foundations, Inc.
FASCINATION - Watches ☆ - SMH (US) Inc.
FASCINATION ST. GALLERY - House furnishings - Fascination St. Gallery
FASCINATIONS - Lighting fixtures - General Electric Co.
FASCINATIONS - Toys - Fascinations Toys and Gifts Inc.
FASCO - Enamels—dental - Fasco Industries Inc. (Consumer Products Div.)
FASCO CEIL-N-WALL - Building materials—concrete ☆ - Fasco Industries Inc. (Consumer Products Div.)
FASCOM - Amplifiers—public address - Fasco Industries Inc. (Consumer Products Div.)
FASCUT - Tools - Osborn Manufacturing Corp.
FASDRIV - Screws - Southern Screw Products, Inc.
FASERVER - Computer software - Network Appliance Corp.
FASET - Skin care products - Waverly Beauty Products
FASFACTS - Pencils—mechanical - Avery Dennison Corp.
FASFIX - Hair-care products - Costec 20 Inc.
FASGAS - Gasoline ☆ - Conoco Inc.
FASGRIP - Fasteners—hook and eye - Fasnap Corp.
FASH-N-TACK - Bulletin boards—cork - Masonite Corp.
FASHAN - Floor coverings—carpet and rugs - Trans-Ocean Import Co. Inc.
FASHION - Cooking equipment—household ☆ - Mirro Corp.
FASHION - Cosmetics - Nu-Art Beauty Products
FASHION - Curtain rods - Kenney Manufacturing Co.
FASHION - Floor coverings - Congoleum Corp.
FASHION - Floor coverings—carpet and rugs - Alexander Smith Carpets
FASHION - Hairstyling mousse - Tri-Institute of Trichology
FASHION - Locks—door - Weiser Lock Corp.

FASHION - Paints - Proctor Paint & Varnish Co. Inc.
FASHION - Paints—artists' - Plaid Enterprises, Inc.
FASHION - Pens - Sheaffer Inc.
FASHION - Perfumes - Classic Fragrances Ltd.
FASHION - Strollers—baby - Fashion Associated International Inc.
FASHION - Watchbands—leather - Regal Industries, Inc.
FASHION 2-GO - Clothing - Sun Sportswear, Inc.
FASHION 10 - Shoes ☆ - Endicott Johnson Corp.
FASHION 20 - Medical apparatus - Freeman Manufacturing Co.
FASHION 1920 - Giftware - Gold Crown Inc.
FASHION-A-BOWL - Housewares - Kyjen Co., Inc.
FASHION ACCENTS - Hosiery - Kayser-Roth Corp.
FASHION ACCESSORY CLUB - Luggage - Travelers Club Luggage Inc.
FASHION ACTION - Hosiery—women's - Magnolia Hosiery Mill Inc.
FASHION ADD VANTAGE - Underwear and nightwear - Lovable Co.
FASHION AIRE - Dryers—hair - Sunbeam-Oster Household Products
FASHION-AIRE - Lighters - Colibri Inc.
FASHION ALERT - Apparel and accessories - Stitches Inc.
FASHION & FUN - Toys - Mattel, Inc.
FASHION APPLIQUES - Patches, insignia, and emblems ☆ - Best Emblem & Insignia Co. Inc.
FASHION AVENUE - Artists' materials - Artoptic International Corp.
FASHION BAR - Soap ☆ - Carolina Designs Ltd.
FASHION BED GROUP - Furniture - Berkshire Furniture Co. Inc.
FASHION BOATS - Inflatable boats - Intex Recreation Corp.
FASHION BOUTIQUE - Children's coloring set - Coloron Industries
FASHION BOW - Barrettes - American Greetings Corp.
FASHION BRIGHTS - Dolls - Mattel, Inc.
FASHION BY JODI - Footwear - Fashion Slippers Import USA
FASHION CAFE - T-shirts—women's - Tommaso Buti
FASHION CHAIN - Ophthalmic goods - Karlen Manufacturing, Inc.
FASHION CHOICE - Floor coverings—carpet and rugs - Evans-Black Carpet Mills
FASHION CLASSICS - Dolls - Mattel, Inc.
FASHION CLASSICS - Underwear and nightwear - Maidenform Inc.
FASHION COLLECTION - Dinnerware—glass - Mt. Clemens Pottery Co.
FASHION COLOR - Paints - Proctor Paint & Varnish Co. Inc.
FASHION COLOR - Panty hose - No Nonsense Fashions Inc.
FASHION COLOR - Paper—gift wrap - Penn Corp.
FASHION COLORS - Paper - Contempo Colours, Inc.
FASHION CONSPIRACY - Apparel and accessories ☆ - Edison Brothers Stores, Inc.
FASHION COORDINATED - Giftware - Kraftware Corp. (Morgan Div.)
FASHION-COTE - Housewares - Magla Products Inc.
FASHION CRAFT - Furniture - Edward Hostmann, Inc.
FASHION CRAFT - Jewelry - Fashion Craft Corp.
FASHION CRAFT - Markers—felt-tip ☆ - Sakura of America
FASHION CRAZE - Bicycles ☆ - Huffy Corp.
FASHION CROSSROADS - Apparel and accessories - Breton Industries
FASHION-CURL - Hair curlers ☆ - Sunbeam-Oster Household Products
FASHION DECORATOR - Hobby kits - Mattel, Inc.
FASHION DESIGN - Brushes—paint ☆ - Winsor & Newton
FASHION DESIGN CENTER - Coloring activity sets - Coloron Industries
FASHION DESIGNER - Computer software - Mattel, Inc.
FASHION DESIGNER CLUB - Luggage - Travelers Club Luggage Inc.
FASHION EDGE - Glassware—household ☆ - Anchor Hocking Glass, Inc.
FASHION ESSENTIAL - Hairpins - Wal-Mart Stores Inc.
FASHION ESSENTIALS - Jewelry—costume - Burgess Manufacturing Corp.
FASHION ESSENTIALS - Socks - High Point Knitting Inc.
FASHION EXPRESS - Handbags - Fashion Express
FASHION EXPRESS - Watches - Timex Corp.
FASHION FABRIC - Fabric stores ☆ - John Boyle & Co., Inc.
FASHION FACE - Toys - Mattel, Inc.
FASHION FAIR - Cosmetics - Fashion Fair Cosmetics
FASHION FANTASY - Dolls - Mattel, Inc.
FASHION FAUX - Wallpaper - Andover Wallcovering
FASHION FAVORITES - Toys - Mattel, Inc.
FASHION FAVORITES - Underwear and nightwear - Bestform Foundations, Inc.
FASHION FEELINGS - Toys - Tonka Corp.
FASHION FIFTY - Floor coverings—carpet and rugs - Barrett Carpet Mills Inc.
FASHION FINDS - Dolls - Mattel, Inc.
FASHION FINISH - Paints ☆ - General Coating Technologies, Inc.
FASHION FIRM-UPS - Underwear and nightwear - Bestform Foundations, Inc.
FASHION FIRST - Paints ☆ - Valspar Corp.
FASHION FIRST - Watches - Gruen Marketing Corp.

☆ = Now out of production

FASHION FIT - Gloves - Magla Products Inc.
FASHION FIVER - Apparel–men's - Palm Beach Co., Inc.
FASHION FLAIR - Barrettes - Florean Mader Corp.
FASHION FLAIR - Bathroom accessories - General Marble Co.
FASHION FLAIR - Bathroom fixtures - Leucadia, Inc.
FASHION FLAIR - Floor coverings–carpet and rugs - Barrett Carpet Mills Inc.
FASHION FLAIR - Floor coverings–carpet and rugs - Alexander Smith Carpets
FASHION-FLAIR - Hair care products - Russ Berrie and Co., Inc.
FASHION FLAIR - Leather goods ✫ - Designers Collection
FASHION FLAIR - Paints - Bruning Paint Co.
FASHION FLEX - Shoes ✫ - Endicott Johnson Corp.
FASHION-FLEX - Watchbands–base metal - Regal Industries, Inc.
FASHION FLING - Floor coverings–carpet and rugs - Mohawk Carpet Corp.
FASHION FLORALS - Brushes–hair - American Greetings Corp.
FASHION FLOWER - Housewares ✫ - Venturi, Inc.
FASHION FLUSH - Floor coverings–carpet and rugs - Alexander Smith Carpets
FASHION FOAM - Dolls - Mattel, Inc.
FASHION FOIL - Paper–gift wrap - Norcross Inc.
FASHION FOLD - Furniture–metal ✫ - All-Luminum Products Inc.
FASHION-FOLD - Musical instrument accessories - Humes & Berg Manufacturing Co. Inc.
FASHION FORMER - Fabrics–canvas - Crown Textile Co.
FASHION FORMULAS - Apparel–women's - QVC, Inc.
FASHION FORWARD - Handbags - Bagland
FASHION FORWARD - Ophthalmic goods - Foremost Optical Products
FASHION FRAMES - Frames–picture ✫ - Accento Plastic Manufacturing Inc.
FASHION FRIENDS - Dolls - Mattel, Inc.
FASHION FRONTIER - Apparel and accessories - Wrangler Co.
FASHION FROST - Hair care products - Wella Corp. (Consumer Products Div.)
FASHION FUN - Dolls - Mattel, Inc.
FASHION FUN - Hobby kits ✫ - Craft House Corp.
FASHION GEAR - Apparel and accessories - Worldwood Industries, Inc.
FASHION GEMS - Nail care products - SRA Industries Inc.
FASHION GENIE - Dolls - Mattel, Inc.
FASHION GIRL - Toys - Processed Plastic Co.
FASHION GLITZ - Bicycles ✫ - Huffy Corp.
FASHION HARVEST - Floor coverings–carpet and rugs ✫ - Calladium & Marglen
FASHION HOUND - Apparel and accessories - Fashion Hound, Inc.
FASHION HUES - Enamel ✫ - Cook and Dunn Paint Corp.
FASHION I BY ALTA - Footwear ✫ - Alta Products Corp.
FASHION IMPORTS - Handbags - Fashion Imports
FASHION IN COLOR - Paints ✫ - Nowstar
FASHION JEANS - Apparel and accessories ✫ - Levi Strauss & Co.
FASHION KOTE - Paints ✫ - Lilly Perfection Paint
FASHION LASHES - Cosmetics - American International Industries
FASHION LEADER, THE - Apparel and accessories - Y.M.L.A., Inc.
FASHION LEG WEAR - Panty hose - Jockey International, Inc.
FASHION LINE - Pillowcases - Crawford Home Fashions Inc.
FASHION LINE - Weather stripping - W.J. Dennis & Co.
FASHION LINE - Window shades - Allied Extrusions
FASHION LINE-SPORT - Sunglasses ✫ - Vangurd Sunglasses Inc.
FASHION LUNCHEON - Dolls - Mattel, Inc.
FASHION MAGIC - Apparel and accessories - Playtex Apparel, Inc.
FASHION MAGIC - Dolls - Mattel, Inc.
FASHION MAGIC - Jewelry - Emmons Jewelers Inc.
FASHION MAGIC - Party goods ✫ - American Greetings Corp.
FASHION MAKER - Hobby kits - Rose Art Industries, Inc.
FASHION MALL - Dolls - Mattel, Inc.
FASHION MARK COLLECTION - Floor coverings–carpet and rugs ✫ - Columbus Mills, Inc.
FASHION MASTER - Furniture - Master Design Furniture
FASHION MATE - Toilet seats - Magnolia Products
FASHION-MATE AIROGRATE - Pipes–tobacco ✫ - S.M. Frank & Co. Inc. (Kaywoodie-Yello-Bole-Medico)
FASHION MATES - Fabrics - Liberty Fabrics, Inc.
FASHION MATES - Fabrics ✫ - J.C. Penney Co., Inc.
FASHION MICHELLE - Toys - Eugene Doll & Novelty Co. Inc.
FASHION MINI - Audio tapes–blank ✫ - Quasar Co.
FASHION MISS - Bicycles - Roadmaster Corp.
FASHION MODE - Fabrics - Dyno Merchandise
FASHION NAIL - Cosmetics - American International Industries
FASHION NOTE - Floor coverings–carpet and rugs - Mohawk Carpet Corp.
FASHION NOTES - Apparel–women's - Wacoal America Inc.
FASHION NOUVEAU - Greeting cards ✫ - Cleo Inc.

FASHION PAL - Dolls - Mattel, Inc.
FASHION PASSPORT - Apparel–women's - Fashion Passport
FASHION PEACH - Makeup ✫ - Cosrich Inc.
FASHION PERFORMANCE - Floor coverings–carpet and rugs - Mohawk Carpet Corp.
FASHION PERSUADER - Intimate apparel - H.F. Robbins
FASHION PET - Pet products - Ethical Products Inc.
FASHION PICTURE - Hosiery - Kayser-Roth Corp.
FASHION PLACE - Floor coverings–carpet and rugs - World Carpets, Inc.
FASHION PLACE - Floor coverings–carpet and rugs ✫ - Customweave Carpets Inc.
FASHION PLATE - Communications equipment–mobile - AG Communication Systems Inc.
FASHION PLATE - Switches–electric ✫ - Bryant Electric Co.
FASHION PLATES - Hair care products - Conair Corp.
FASHION PLATES - Jewelry ✫ - Hirsch Speidel Inc.
FASHION PLAY - Dolls - Mattel, Inc.
FASHION PLUS - Apparel and accessories - Hutter Sales Co.
FASHION PLUS - Medical apparatus - Freeman Manufacturing Co.
FASHION + COMFORT = CROSSTOWN - Shoes - AmAsia International Ltd.
FASHION QUEEN - Floor coverings–carpet and rugs - Barrett Carpet Mills Inc.
FASHION RITE - Yarn ✫ - Caron International Inc.
FASHION ROCKER - Audio tapes–blank ✫ - Quasar Co.
FASHION ROSE - Bathroom accessories ✫ - Syroco
FASHION ROYALE - Floor coverings–carpet and rugs ✫ - World Carpets, Inc.
FASHION SCENTS - Fragrances, toiletries ✫ - Delagar
FASHION SCOOP - Apparel–women's - Olga Co.
FASHION SEAL - Uniforms–academic - Superior Surgical Manufacturing Co. Inc.
FASHION SEAL - Uniforms–tailored - Fashion Seal Uniforms
FASHION SECRETS - Underwear and nightwear - Maidenform Inc.
FASHION SELECT - Carpeting - Shaw Industries Inc.
FASHION SELECTIVES - Underwear and nightwear - Maidenform Inc.
FASHION SHADE - Visors - Gexco Enterprises
FASHION SHAPERS - Apparel and accessories - Playtex Apparel, Inc.
FASHION SHOW - Paints - DKM Ltd.
FASHION SHOWCASE - Window coverings - Elmar Supply Co.
FASHION SOFT - Toilet seats - Magnolia Products
FASHION-SPORT - Sunglasses - Vangurd Sunglasses Inc.
FASHION SPREE - Dolls - Mattel, Inc.
FASHION SQUARE - Paper–writing ✫ - The Rytex Co.
FASHION STEP - Orthopedic products - JSB Orthotics Inc.
FASHION STEPS BY MESSINA - Shoes - Messer Import Corp.
FASHION STORIES - Stationery - Gitano Licensing, Ltd.
FASHION STRETCH - Apparel and accessories ✫ - Manhattan International
FASHION STRINGS - Wallpaper - K.M.L. Industries
FASHION SUEDE - Leather goods ✫ - Tandy Leather Co.
FASHION SUEDE - Paints - Tulip Productions
FASHION SUPPORT - Apparel–women's - NCC Industries, Inc.
FASHION TAN - Tanning agents - Aloe Creme Laboratories
FASHION TARGETS BREAST CANCER COUNCIL OF FASHION DESIGNERS OF AMERICA - T-shirts–women's - CFDA Foundation, Inc.
FASHION TILE - Metals - Metalco Industries Inc.
FASHION TIME - Jewelry - Yonoss Inc.
FASHION TIME - Underwear and nightwear - Maidenform Inc.
FASHION TIP - Floor coverings–carpet and rugs ✫ - Masland Corp.
FASHION TONE - Food products - Jewel Food Stores Inc.
FASHION TONE - Needles–sewing ✫ - Coats and Clark Inc.
FASHION TONE - Needlework supplies ✫ - Susan Bates Inc.
FASHION TONES - Hearing aids - Ed Staton
FASHION TOUCH - Floor coverings–carpet and rugs ✫ - Callaway Carpets
FASHION TREAD - Tiles–ceramic ✫ - Huntington/Pacific Ceramics Inc.
FASHION TRENDS - Drapery hardware - Cooper Industries, Inc.
FASHION TRENDS - Drapery hardware - Kirsch Co.
FASHION TRENDS - Paints - Olympic Paint & Varnish Co.
FASHION TRESS - Brushes–hair - Helen of Troy Corp.
FASHION TRIM - Sewing accessories - Kahaner Co.
FASHION TRIM COLLECTIOM - See DECORATOR LYKEWOOD
FASHION TRIMS - Craft supplies - Walbead Inc.
FASHION TWIST - Floor coverings–carpet and rugs ✫ - Columbus Mills, Inc.
FASHION TWO TWENTY - Cosmetics - Fashion Two Twenty Inc.
FASHION UPDATE - Publisher's imprints - Fashion News, Inc.
FASHION VALUE - Underwear and nightwear - Maidenform Inc.
FASHION-VUE - Fabric stores - Streamline Industries, Inc.
FASHION WEAR - Hosiery - Virginia Maid Hosiery Mills Inc.
FASHION WOOD - Floor coverings ✫ - Congoleum Corp.

✫ = Now out of production

FASHION WRAPS - Dolls - Mattel, Inc.

FASHION WRAPS - Paper–gift wrap - Stephen Lawrence Co.

FASHION WRITE - Office supplies ☆ - Mead Corp.

FASHIONABLE - Floor coverings–carpet and rugs - Mohawk Industries Inc.

FASHIONABLE - Floor coverings–carpet and rugs ☆ - Calladium & Marglen

FASHIONABLES - Glass–leaded - Seneca Glass Co.

FASHIONAIRE - Air conditioning equipment ☆ - General Electric Co.

FASHIONAIRE - Apparel–men's - Hartmarx Corp.

FASHIONAIRE - Fabrics - Greenwood Mills Inc.

FASHIONAIRE - Floor coverings - Congoleum Corp.

FASHIONAIRE CAREER CLOTHING - Uniforms–tailored - Hartmarx Corp.

FASHIONAIRE II - Fabrics - Greenwood Mills Inc.

FASHIONART - Patches, insignia, and emblems - Dimensions, Inc.

FASHIONATION - Computer software - Modamagic, Inc.

FASHIONATOR - Window shades - Acme Window Coverings Ltd.

FASHIONBERRY - Neckties - Countess Mara Inc.

FASHIONCOVE - Floor coverings - Tarkett, Inc.

FASHIONCRAFT - Floor coverings ☆ - Tarkett, Inc.

FASHIONCRAFT - House furnishings ☆ - Miller Studio

FASHIONCRAFT - Mattress pads - Fashioncraft-Excello

FASHIONELLA - Yarn - Melrose Yarn Co. Inc.

FASHIONETTE - Tiles–ceramic ☆ - Wenczel Tile Co.

FASHIONFILES - Cosmetics - Sunfiles, LLC

FASHIONFLOR - Floor coverings - Congoleum Corp.

FASHIONGLO - Paper - Astronics Corp.

FASHIONISTICS - Jewelry - Feature Enterprises

FASHIONLINE - Window coverings - Fashionline Window Shades

FASHIONLITES - Ophthalmic goods - Foremost Optical Products

FASHIONMASTER - Fasteners–hook and eye ☆ - Boye Needle

FASHIONPLEAT - Blinds–venetian - Spring Window Fashions Division, Inc.

FASHIONS - Toys - Mattel, Inc.

FASHIONS BY JULI LTD. - Pajamas–women's - Carole Hochman Designs Inc.

FASHIONS BY TERRY - Apparel and accessories - Terry Manufacturing Co. Inc.

FASHIONS FOR COMFORT - Apparel and accessories - Glamorise Foundations Inc.

FASHIONS IN DINING - Dining room furniture ☆ - Imperial Manufacturing Co.

FASHIONS ON PARADE - Figurines ☆ - Goebel of North America

FASHIONSTAR FILLIES - Toys - Tonka Corp.

FASHIONTONE - Stereos ☆ - Jasco Products Co. Inc.

FASHIONWARE - Flatware ☆ - Towle Silversmiths

FASHIONWISE - Underwear and nightwear - Maidenform Inc.

FASH'N FUN - Jewelry - Acme Premium Supply Corp.

FASHON - Wallpaper - Gencorp Polymer Products

FASHON BORDER - Wallcovering - Fashon Wallcoverings

FASHON CLASSICS - Wallcovering ☆ - Fashon Wallcoverings

FASIA - Ceramic wall tile - Interceramic Inc.

FASINATING - Apparel and accessories - Chester County Sportswear Co. Inc.

FASLINE - Tools–hand-operated - Prince Castle Inc.

FASLOCK - Adhesives and sealants - Federal Process Co.

FASMATE - Hardware - FasTest Inc.

FAS'N-ALL - Hardware - Ambroid Co.

FAS'N-IT - Hardware - Ambroid Co.

FASOLV - Cleaning preparations - Sterling Winthrop Inc.

FASON - Novelty items - Fason Souvenirs and Novelties, Inc.

FASPAK - Office supplies - P.A. Plymouth, Inc.

FASPIN - Marine rigging - Aerofast Inc.

FASS-DRI - Asphalt felts and coatings - Maintenance Inc.

FASS MASS - Pharmaceutical preparations - Bricker Laboratories

FASSATI - Wines - Palm Bay Imports, Inc.

FASSBIND - Brandy - Dieter Steinmann Inc.

FASSBIND EAUX-DE-VIE - Beverages–alcohol - Paterno Imports, Ltd.

FASSEAL-ATS - Adhesives and sealants - Federal Process Co.

FASSETTS - Breads - Fassetts Bakery Inc.

FASSON - Decals and transfers - Avery Dennison Corp.

FAST - Apparel and accessories - Fast Sportswear, Inc.

FAST - Computer software - West Publishing Co.

F.A.S.T. - Drill bits - Dresser Industries, Inc.

FAST - Microwave components - Superconducting Core Technologies, Inc.

FAST - Nail care products - Nu-Tress Laboratories Inc.

FAST - Paint removers - Savogran Co.

FAST - Pipes - R.W. Lyall & Co., Inc.

F.A.S.T. - Roofing materials–concrete - Tremco Inc.

FAST - Solder - La-Co Industries, Inc.

F.A.S.T. - Towels - Aspect Inc.

FAST - Transducers - Sikorski & Pfannenstiel Innovative Non-Destructive Examinations, LLC.

FAST 50 - Adhesives and sealants - Capitol Adhesives Inc.

FAST 111'S - Coloring books - CPG Products Corp.

FAST 111'S - Toys - Tonka Corp.

FAST ACTION - Apparel and accessories - Dillard Department Stores Inc.

FAST ACTIVES - Vitamins and nutritional supplements - Nature's Way Products, Inc.

FAST ALERT - Pharmaceutical preparations - Apothecary Products, Inc.

FAST AND EASY - Trees–artificial - General Foam Plastics Corp.

FAST & FABULOUS - Patterns–clothing ☆ - Simplicity Pattern Co., Inc.

FAST & FINE - Flowers, plants, and seeds - NK Lawn & Garden Co.

FAST AND GENTLE - Manicure preparations - Max Factor & Co.

FAST & HOT - Vitamins and nutritional supplements - Chemopharm Laboratory, Inc.

FAST ASLEEP - Pharmaceutical preparations - Frontier Cooperative Herbs

FAST ATTACK - Computer software - Writing Wizardry, Inc.

FAST BATH - Glassware–scientific - Corning Inc.

FAST BLAST - Vitamins and nutritional supplements ☆ - Vitamin Research Products Inc.

FAST BREAK - Cleaning preparations - Loctite Corp.

FAST BREAK - Computer software - Cramer Products Inc.

FAST BREAK - Frozen foods - Schwan's Sales Enterprises, Inc.

FAST BREAK - Fruit drinks–bottled or canned - Ocean Spray Cranberries Inc.

FAST BREAK - Housewares - Pepsico, Inc.

FAST-BREAK - Pharmaceutical preparations - Pdk Labs, Inc.

FAST BREAK - Trading cards and stamps - Treat Entertainment, Inc.

FAST BREAK BASKETBALL - Games - Lakeside Games

FAST BROWNS - Vegetables–frozen ☆ - Lamb-Weston, Inc.

FAST BUS - Electrical equipment - Siemens Energy & Automation, Inc.

FAST CAST - Artists' materials ☆ - Sculpture House Inc.

FAST CAST - Paints - OEM Paints, Inc.

FAST CAST RESIN - Paints and paint sundries - Industriline Co.

FAST-CAT - Cleaning preparations - Prowers S. Hudnall

FAST CAT THE SHARPEST CLAWS IN CLEANING - Cleaning preparations - Elhoco Manufacturing, Inc.

FAST CHOICE - Food products - Pierre Frozen Foods Inc.

FAST CLASP - Jewelry - Jacoby-Bender Inc.

FAST COLOR - Paints ☆ - Nowstar

FAST COPPER TECHNOLOGY - Computer hardware - Tut Systems, Inc.

FAST-COUNT - Computer software - Megaplex Software, Inc.

FAST CURE EPOXY 45 - Adhesives and sealants - Loctite Corp.

FAST CURVES - Hair care products - Roux Laboratories, Inc.

FAST-CUT - Abrasive products - Park Metallurgical Corp.

FAST-CUT - Tools–hand-operated - Great Neck Saw Manufacturers, Inc.

FAST-DAQ - Computer software - Fast-Daq

FAST DOG - Apparel and accessories - Fast Dog Clothing Co.

FAST DRAW - Elastic - Southern Webbing Mills, Inc.

FAST DRAW - Toys ☆ - Ray Plastic Inc.

FAST DRY - Finishing agents - Dura Seal

FAST ENERGY - Vitamins and nutritional supplements - New Success International, Inc.

FAST FABRICATORS, INC. - Pipes–iron - Fast Fabricators, Inc.

FAST FACTS - Computer software ☆ - Edusoft

FAST FARE - Petroleum - Crown Central Petroleum Corp.

FAST-FEED - Clippers–barber - Sunbeam Corp.

FAST FEED - Clippers–barber - Sunbeam-Oster Household Products

FAST FEET - Footwear–athletic ☆ - Gulbenkian Swim Inc.

FAST-FIL - Faucets - Sterling Plumbing Group Inc.

FAST FINANCIAL ANALYTICS STRUCTURED TRANSACTIONS - Computer software - Bear, Stearns & Co. Inc.

FAST FINISH - Antiseptics - Ladyfingers

FAST FINISH - Automotive parts and accessories - Blue Coral, Inc.

FAST FINISHER - Finishing agents - Pioneer/Eclipse Corp.

FAST-FIT - Compressors–gas - Jobst Institute Inc.

FAST FIT STRETCHER STRIPS - Artists' materials - Wolsey Co.

FAST FIXIN'S - Food products - Glenmark Industries, Ltd.

FAST FLIGHT - Sporting goods - Edwards Sports Products

FAST FLO - Lactose - Foremost Farms USA

FAST FLUSH - Vitamins and nutritional supplements - Royal Source, Inc.

FAST FLUSH CAPS - Vitamins and nutritional supplements - Royal Source, Inc.

FAST FOAM - Insulating materials - FOMO PRODUCTS Inc.

FAST FOG - Lenses ☆ - Courtaulds Performance Plus

FAST FOLD - Electronic equipment - Da-Lite Screen Co. Inc.

FAST-FOLD - Office supplies ☆ - Safco Products Co.

☆ = Now out of production

FAST FOLD - Toys ☆ - Evenflo Co.

FAST FOOD ISLANDS - Food products machinery - M & E Manufacturing Co., Inc.

FAST FRAME - Frames–picture - Martin F. Weber Co.

FAST FRANK - Kitchen appliances ☆ - Hamilton Beach/Proctor-Silex Inc.

FAST FREDDIE'S HONG KONG DICE - Games - Jax Ltd.

FAST FREEZE - Hair care products - LaDove Inc.

FAST FREEZE - Pharmaceutical preparations - American Pharmacal Inc.

FAST-FRET - Musical instrument accessories - Kenyon International Inc.

FAST FRET - Musical instruments - GHS Strings

FAST FRIEND - Apparel–children's - May Apparel Group, Inc.

FAST GAP - Machine parts - Extrusion Dies, Inc.

FAST GAS ! - Vitamins and nutritional supplements - National Health Products, Inc.

FAST GEAR - Skis - Fast Gear Racing Sports, Inc.

FAST-GLASS - Automotive parts and accessories ☆ - Marson Creative Fastener Group

FAST GLUES - Adhesives - Atlas Minerals & Chemicals, Inc.

FAST GRIP - Sporting goods - Wright & McGill Co.

FAST GROW - Flowers, plants, and seeds - Jonathan Green, Inc.

FAST-GUN - Gun holsters and belts - American Sales & Manufacturing Co.

FAST HINGES - Toys–models - Charles S. Fist

FAST ICE - Ice making machinery - Ice Production Products, Inc.

FAST KILL - Insecticides - Claire Manufacturing Co.

FAST LANE - Apparel–children's - Hortex Inc.

FAST LANE - Boots - Bates Leathers

FAST LANE - Teas - Celestial Seasonings, Inc.

FAST LATCH - Machine parts - FMC Corp.

FAST LATCH - Tools–hand-operated - D. Michael Reese

FAST LOCK - Adhesives and sealants - Orcon Corp.

FAST LOK - Clamps–hose - Deco Products Co. (Fast-Lok Div.)

FAST-LOK - Fencing–gates and posts - Mapes Industries Inc.

FAST-LOK - Hardware - Dixon Valve and Coupling Co.

FAST MAILER - Business forms ☆ - Hano Business Forms Inc.

FAST-MASK - Hardware - Tufco Technologies Inc.

FAST-MASK - Soldering equipment - Eldon Industries Inc. (Ungar Div.)

FAST MENU - Food products - Health Valley Food

FAST MOVES - Apparel–children's - Kids R Us Co.

FAST-N EASY - Cleaning preparations - Manhattan Products Inc.

FAST 'N EASY - Food products - Hormel Foods Corp.

FAST 'N FINAL - Adhesives and sealants - Dap Products Inc.

FAST 'N FRESH - Coffee makers–electric ☆ - West Bend Co.

FAST 'N LIGHT - Hair care products - Helene Curtis Industries Inc.

FAST 'N TASTY - Sausages - Johnsonville Foods Co.

FAST-N-TITE - Hardware - Universal Strap Co.

FAST NEVER TASTED THIS GOOD - Food products - Tanimura & Antle, Inc.

FAST-N'TUFF - Grass seed - Kellogg Inc.

FAST-ON - Paints ☆ - Nowstar

FAST ONES - Games ☆ - Testor Corp.

FAST ORANGE - Soap - Loctite Corp.

FAST PACK - Beverages - The Sqwincher Corp.

FAST-PAK - Medical products - Mallinckrodt Medical, Inc.

FAST PAK - Travel accessories - American Guard-It Manufacturing Co. Inc.

FAST PASSAGE - Ships–sailing vessels ☆ - Tollycraft Corp.

FAST PATCH - Floor coverings ☆ - Tarkett, Inc.

FAST PATCH - Hardware - C.E. Kaiser Co.

FAST PATCH - Patching compound - Construction Adhesives Co.

FAST POOLS START AT THE SURFACE - Swimming pools - Grate Technologies, Inc.

FAST-PREP - Food products - Oscar Mayer Foods Corp.

FAST-RESPONSE - Generators - Kohler Co.

FAST-RESPONSE II - Generators - Kohler Co.

FAST RIDER - Footwear–athletic - Puma Inc.

FAST-RITER - Pens - K-9 Pen Co.

FAST SET - Flowers, plants, and seeds - Lifesake Faster-Form Co.

FAST SET - Tiles–ceramic ☆ - American Olean Tile Co.

FAST SHAKE - Pancakes–mixes - Little Crow Foods

FAST SHINE - Cleaning preparations - Valco Cincinnati Inc.

FAST SHIP - Wallpaper - I. Gottlieb & Associates

FAST SLIDE - Archery equipment - Saunders Archery Co.

FAST START - Fabrics - Easy Gardener Inc.

FAST START - Medical apparatus - J.D. Medical Inc.

FAST STEEL - Epoxy - Polymeric Systems, Inc.

FAST STEMS - Flowers, plants, and seeds - Lifesake Faster-Form Co.

FAST STIK - Photo albums - Pioneer Photo Albums, Inc.

FAST SWING - Sporting goods - Easton Aluminum Inc.

FAST-TAB - Apparel and accessories - GWB, Inc.

FAST TAB - Office supplies - Transkrit

FAST TACK - Bostik Inc.

FAST TAN & KEEP IT! - Tanning agents ☆ - Jason Natural Products, Inc.

FAST TOUCH - Grinders - Robert Krups North America

FAST TRAC - Beverages–carbonated - Guida's Seibert Dairy

FAST TRAC - Juices - Fast Trac Inc.

FAST TRAC - Snowmobiles - Weiland Fast-Trac Industries

FAST TRACK - Caulking compounds - Gibson-Homans Co. (Sealant Technology)

FAST TRACK - Health care products - Procter & Gamble Co.

FAST TRACK - Key rings - Russ Berrie and Co., Inc.

FAST TRACK - Medical apparatus - Wright Medical Technology, Inc.

FAST TRACK - Ophthalmic goods - Foremost Optical Products

FAST TRACK - Research–opinion - Conway/Milliken & Associates, Inc.

FAST TRACK - Skin care products - VMS Corp.

FAST TRACK - Trading cards and stamps - ANCO Collector Supplies, Inc.

FAST TRACK 1 - Guitars - Dimarzio, Inc.

FAST TRACK 2 - Musical instrument accessories - Dimarzio, Inc.

FAST TRACK COMMUNICATIONS - Electronics equipment - Fast Track Communications Inc.

FAST TRACK T - Musical instrument accessories - Dimarzio, Inc.

FAST TRACK, THE - Publisher's imprints - MacMillan Publishing Co. Inc.

FAST TRACKERS - Toys–automobiles - Life-Like Products Inc.

FAST TRACKS - Bicycles ☆ - Huffy Corp.

FAST TRACKS - Kites ☆ - Hi-Flier Manufacturing Co.

FAST TRACT - Medical apparatus - Transtracheal Systems, Inc.

FAST TRAK - Footwear - Illinois Footwear Co.

FAST TRAK - Maps - Ralph Muniz

FAST TRAK - Pregnancy test kits ☆ - Wampole Laboratories Div.

FAST TRAKS - Toys - Tonka Corp.

FAST TRAX - Calendars - Brown and Bigelow Inc.

FAST TRAXX - Toys–automobiles - Tyco Toys

FAST TRUSS - Prefabricated buildings–wood - Fast Truss Inc.

FAST-TWITCH SPORTS TRAINING CENTERS - Exercising equipment - Fast Twitch, Inc.

FAST UNLOAD - Computer peripheral equipment - Platinum Technology, Inc.

FAST WHEELS - Toy cars - Intex Recreation Corp.

FAST WIPES - Cosmetics - Gojo Industries, Inc.

FAST WIRING - Catalogs - Calterm, Inc.

FAST WRAP - Electrical equipment - Thomas Industries Inc. (Tool & Fastener Div.)

FAST WRAP - Medical apparatus - Camp, Inc.

FAST WRAP - Pet products - Mustang Products, Inc.

FASTAC - Window coverings - Conso Products Co.

FASTACCESS - Filing cabinets–metal - Counterpoint

FASTACK - Glue–household or industrial - Craft World International Inc.

FASTAMP - Stamps–hand ☆ - Artistic Greetings, Inc.

FASTANSWER - Computer software - Village Software, Inc.

FASTAPP - Computer software - General Electric Capital Corp.

FASTBACK - Bicycles ☆ - Huffy Corp.

FASTBACK - Building materials–concrete - Southern Imperial Inc.

FASTBACK - Clippers–barber ☆ - Sunbeam-Oster Household Products

FASTBACK - Darts and dart games - Kulite Tungsten Corp.

FASTBACK - Floor coverings - Dexter Corp. (Mercer Plastics Div.)

FASTBACK - Hardware - Shepherd Products U.S. Inc.

FASTBACK - Jewelry ☆ - Hirsch Speidel Inc.

FASTBACK TAPE - Computers - Fifth Generation Systems Inc.

FASTBALL - Cleaning preparations - Pioneer Manufacturing Co.

FASTBALL - Pens - Pentech International Inc.

FASTBANK - Communications equipment - Dynatech Communications, Inc.

FASTBELT - Electrometallurgical products - FKI Industries Inc.

FASTBLAZER - Modems - Telebit Corp.

FASTBREAK POCKETS - Food products - Tony's Pizza Service

FASTBURN - Vitamins and nutritional supplements - PR Nutrition, Inc.

FASTCAP - Computer software - Roy Vincent Giorgio

FASTCAP - Housewares - Johnson & Johnson

FASTCAST - Metals - Rokop Corp.

FASTCHECK - Electrical testing instruments - Kohler Co.

FASTCLIP - Hardware - Milliken Industries

FASTCO - Food products - Fastco Food Stores

FASTCUT - Abrasive products ☆ - Carborundum Abrasives North America

FASTCUT - Tools - Norton Co.

FASTDNA - Diagnostic substances - Bio 101, Inc.

FASTDRAIN - Machine parts - Baker Hughes Inc.

FASTECH - Boats–motor - Porter, Inc.

FASTECH - Games - Tyco Toys
FASTECH - Towels - Fastech Corp.
FASTECH INTEGRATION - Construction equipment rental services - Fastech Integration, Inc.
FASTEETH - Denture materials - Richardson-Vicks USA
FASTEK - Photographic equipment - Eastman Kodak Co.
FASTEN-AIDING - Belts–apparel - Mary Anne Bourke
FASTEN-ATOR, THE - Staplers ☆ - Al Nyman and Son
FASTENER, THE - Adhesives and sealants - Chemray Coatings Corp.
FASTENMASTER - Adhesives and sealants - Olympic Manufacturing Group, Inc.
FASTENT - Sporting goods - Upland Enterprises Inc.
FASTER PLASTER - Plaster–patching - Plaid Enterprises, Inc.
FASTER PLASTER - Wallpaper - Flexi-Wall Systems
FASTEST - Water treating compounds - Aquarium Systems, Inc.
FASTEST WAY TO RESTORE THE PAST, THE - Paint removers - Creative Technologies Group Inc.
FASTEX - Hardware - Illinois Tool Works Inc.
FASTFILER - File folders ☆ - Anthes Universal
FASTFINDER - Computer software - Fastfinder Systems, L.C.
FASTFIT - Windows–storm ☆ - Aluminum Co. of America
FASTFOLDERS - File folders - Filmkote Corp.
FASTFORM - Hair care products - Matrix Essentials, Inc.
FASTFORMS - Computer software - Data Systems Consulting, Inc.
FASTFORWARD - Computer hardware - Cisco Systems, Inc.
FASTGLOVE - Containers - Becky Johnson-Rabbett
FASTGRAPH - Computer software - Ted Gruber Software, Inc.
FASTHREAD - Packaging machines - Infra Pak, Inc.
FASTHUB - Computers - Grand Junction Networks, Inc.
FASTIK - Adhesives and sealants - Chicago Adhesive Products Co.
FASTIME - Electronics equipment - Allen Avionics, Inc.
FASTIME - Enamels - M.A.B. Paints
FASTIN - Pharmaceutical preparations - Smithkline Beecham Corp.
FASTINGE - Hinges - Edward Leeds Co.
FASTITCH - Industrial machinery - High Tech Engineering
FASTJACKET - Jackets - Ken Jenks
FASTLANE - Computer software ☆ - Datatec Industries Inc.
FASTLANE - Shoes–athletic - Fastlane Footwear Inc.
FASTLINE - Holding bins - H & K Dallas
FASTLINE - Roofing materials ☆ - Trimline Building Products
FASTLINK - Computer hardware - Grand Junction Networks, Inc.
FASTLIST - Computer software - Chicago Interface Group, Inc.
FASTLOAN - Computer software - Recreational Mathemagical Software
FASTLOCK II - Cables - Intermatic Inc.
FASTMASTER - Computers - Electronic Technology Services, Inc.
FASTMATCH - Paints - Propaint & Decorating, Inc.
FASTMORE - Varnishes ☆ - Nowstar
FAST'N FUN - Shoes ☆ - Edison Brothers Stores, Inc.
FAST'N HOT - Sandwiches–prepackaged - E.A. Sween Co.
FASTNIC - Computer hardware and software - Grand Junction Networks, Inc.
FASTNURS - Brassieres (Bras) - Leading Lady Companies Inc.
FASTOAST - Toasters - Black & Decker Corp.
FASTOMATIC - Water heaters–household ☆ - Bel-Aire Sales Corp.
FASTON - Electrical equipment - AMP Inc.
FASTONE - Fabrics - Manart-Hirsch Co. Inc.
FASTOP - Motor vehicle parts and accessories - Brake-Guard Products, Inc.
FASTOPT - Computer software - Georgia-Pacific Corp.
FASTPAC - Humphrey Systems
FASTPACE - Computer software - James Martin & Co., Inc.
FASTPAGE - Pagers - Indyme Electronics, Inc.
FASTPAK - Insulating materials - Manville/Schuller
FASTPAK - Nautical instruments ☆ - Signet Marine
FASTPASS - Computer software - Micromash
FASTPLAN - Computer software - Georgia-Pacific Corp.
FASTPREP - Laboratory apparatus - Bio 101, Inc.
FASTPRO - First aid kits - First Aids Inc.
FASTPRO - Modems - General Datacomm, Inc.
FASTPROJECT - Software - James Martin & Co., Inc.
FASTQUOTER - Paper products - Orix Credit Alliance, Inc.
FASTRAC - Electronic equipment - General Electric Co.
FASTRAC - Floor waxes - S.C. Johnson & Son, Inc.
FASTRACC - Computer hardware - Meret Communications, Inc.
FASTRACK - Building materials–concrete - Southern Imperial Inc.
FASTRACK - Hardware - Stanley Hardware Div.
FASTRACK - Trailers–industrial - Vulcan International, Inc.
FASTRACKER - Catheters - Target Therapeutics, Inc.

FASTRACS - Computer software - Applied Microsystems Inc.
FASTRAK - Computer software - Layout Concepts Inc.
FASTRAK - Hammers–electric - Desa International, Inc.
FASTRAK - Pens - Pilot Pen Corp. of America
FASTRAK - Sporting goods - Bell Sports Corp.
FASTRAK - Sporting goods - Marker International Co.
FASTRAK - Tires - Uniroyal Goodrich Tire Co.
FASTR&D - Computer software - Quality Sciences, Inc.
FASTRANS - Video equipment - Odetics, Inc.
FASTRAP - Leather goods - Bruce Heggeland, Inc.
FASTRAX - Industrial machinery - I.S.I. Robotics, Inc.
FASTRAX - Paint rollers - E-Z Paintr Corp.
FASTREFRESH - Computer monitors - North American Philips Corp.
FASTRENGTH - Nail-care products - American Cosmetic Manufacturing Laboratories Inc.
FASTRIP - Cleaning preparations - United Gilsonite Laboratories
FASTROKE - Brushes–paint - Andrew Mack & Son Brush Co.
FASTROLLER - Boats - Zodiac of North America
FASTROPE - Rope - Columbian Rope Co.
FAST'S - Machinery parts - Kop-Flex, Inc.
FASTSHAPE - Food products ☆ - Little Crow Foods
FASTSYSTEM - Medical apparatus - Minnesota Scientific, Inc.
FASTTAKE - Medical apparatus - LifeScan Inc.
FASTTEST - Audio equipment and computer software - Audio Precision, Inc.
FASTTRACK - Adhesives and sealants - Sealmaster, Inc.
FASTTRACK - Computer hardware - Fastech, Inc.
FASTTRACK FRACTIONS - Computer software - SRA/McGraw-Hill (Div. of The McGraw-Hill Companies)
FASTVIEW - Binoculars - Bausch & Lomb Inc.
FASTVIEW - Computer storage devices - NMT Corp.
FASTVSAM - Computer software - Software Engineering of America, Inc.
FASTWALKER - Footwear - Propet USA, Inc.
FASTWALL - Bathroom accessories - Consolidated Industries Corp.
FASTWARE - Hardware - Frame Tek, Inc.
FASTWAY - Gasoline - Flying J Inc.
FASTWAY HAM-R-TOOL - Tools - Thomas Industries Inc. (Tool & Fastener Div.)
FASTWAYS - Computer software - Software Support Products, LLC
FASTWIN - Motors–outboard ☆ - Outboard Marine Corp.
FASTWIST - Building materials–concrete - Southern Imperial Inc.
FASTYLES - Wigs - Linda Sendowski
FASWEET - Sugar–granulated, refined, or powdered - Fasweet Co.
FAT A - Fishing lures - Bomber Bait Co.
FAT ABSORBER - Vitamins and nutritional supplements - Nature's Products Inc.
FAT ALBERT - Games ☆ - Milton Bradley Co.
FAT ALBERT SHAKE - Candy ☆ - Phoenix Confections Inc.
FAT BAT - Kites ☆ - Gayla Industries Inc.
FAT-BE-GONE - Food products - Food Innovations International, Inc.
FAT BOB - Motorcycles ☆ - Harley-Davidson, Inc.
FAT BOY - Beverages–malt - McKenzie River Partners
FAT BOY - Confections - Caspers Ice Cream Inc.
FAT BOY - Confections - H-D Michigan, Inc.
FAT BURNERS - Vitamins and nutritional supplements - Weider Health and Fitness
FAT CAT - Bicycles - Ross Bicycles USA, Ltd.
FAT CAT - Pet products - Cat Craft Co.
FAT CAT - Seasonings - M & M Specialties
FAT CAT SNARES - Drums–musical instruments - Big Bang Distribution/A.P.I.
FAT CATS - Giftware ☆ - Gessner Products Co. Inc.
FAT CATS - Pins–jewelry - Patray's
FAT CHANCE - Bicycles - Fat City Cycles
FAT CHANCE - Games ☆ - Milton Bradley Co.
FAT CHANCE - Greeting cards - Chesapeake Press Inc.
FAT CITY - Computer software - Optimum Resource, Inc.
FAT DARTS - Fishing lures - Boone Bait Co. Inc.
FAT EDNA - Dolls - Melodie Kleiman
FAT FAIRY - Statuary - Marilyn Palsha
FAT FENDERED '40 - Toys–automobiles - Mattel, Inc.
FAT FIGHTER - Health care products ☆ - Above All Health Inc.
FAT FOOT II SKID STEER - Tires–automobile - Galaxy Tire & Wheel, Inc.
FAT FREDDIE - Meat products–cured - Carl Buddig & Co.
FAT FREDDIE - Snack foods - Old Wisconsin Sausage
FAT FREE - Skates–roller - Rollerblade, Inc.
FAT-FREE CAROTENE - Soups–canned - Health Valley Food
FAT FREE CORNY SALSA - Food products - Uncle Dave's Kitchen

☆ = Now out of production

FAT FREE CRACKERS - Crackers - Tree of Life, Inc.
FAT FREE CRACKERS - Crackers - Venus Wafers, Inc.
FAT FREE FIG BARS - Cookies - Barbara's Bakery, Inc.
FAT FREE GOURMET - Snack foods - Harry's Premium Snacks
FAT FREE GOURMET, THE - Snack foods - Original Hampton Potato Chip Co.
FAT FREE HOMESTYLE COOKIES - Cookies - Barbara's Bakery, Inc.
FAT FREE KEEBLER MINIS - Pretzels ☆ - Keebler Co.
FAT FREE LIVING - Publisher's imprints - Fat Free Living, Inc.
FAT FREE MINI COOKIES - Cookies - Barbara's Bakery, Inc.
FAT FREE NEWTONS - Cookies - Nabisco Foods Group
FAT FREE RAMEN - Soups–mixes - Sanwa Foods Inc.
FAT FREE SOURDOUGH PRETZELS - Pretzels ☆ - Barbara's Bakery, Inc.
FAT FREE SPAGHETTI SAUCE - Spaghetti sauces - Uncle Dave's Kitchen
FAT FREEDOM - Ice cream ☆ - Eskimo Pie Corp.
FAT FRENCHY - Toys - Mattel, Inc.
FAT FROG - Ice cream - Good Humor Corp.
FAT HANDLE - Handles–wood - Riviera Brokerage, Inc.
FAT HAT - Helmets–athletic - Giro Sport Design
FAT HEAD - Guitars - Groove Tubes
FAT-HEAD - Hardware - Maze Nails
FAT JACK - Fabrics - Robert D. Hummmel
FAT JOB - Fishing lures - Hildebrandt Corp.
FAT KATS - Toys - Strombecker Corp.
FAT LACES - Laces–boot and shoe - Mitchellace Inc.
FAT LADY SWINGS, THE - Golfing equipment - Bobby Grace Classic Clubs
FAT MAN, THE - Golfing equipment - Bobby Grace Golf Design, Inc.
FAT MAX - Travel accessories - American Guard-It Manufacturing Co. Inc.
FAT 'N FIBER - Animal feeds - Consolidated Nutrition, L.C.
FAT NOT! - Food products - Dixie, USA, Inc.
FAT ON THE FARM - Veterinary pharmaceutical preparations - Griffin Industries Inc.
FAT OTTO - Dolls - Melodie Kleiman
FAT RABBIT - Sachets - Fat Rabbit
FAT RAP - Fishing lures - Normark Corp.
FAT-SO - Fishing lures - Storm Manufacturing Co.
FAT-SOLVE - Health care products - Nature's Concept Inc.
FAT TERMINATOR SYSTEM, THE - Vitamins and nutritional supplements - First Fitness International, Inc.
FAT TERMINATOR, THE - Slide-rule calculator - Herbert Davis
FAT TIRE - Beverages–malt - New Belgium Brewing Co.
FAT TO FIRM - Health care products - Fiske Industries Inc.
FAT TRACK - Toys–automobiles - Mattel, Inc.
FAT TUESDAY - Apparel–athletic - David Briggs Enterprises, Inc.
FAT VAT - Cooking equipment–commercial - Pitco Frialator, Inc.
FAT WRECK CHORDS - Recording label - Fat Wreck Chords, Inc.
FATA - Food containers - VanEerden Distribution Co.
FATAL ATTRACTION - Fishing lures - South Bend Sporting Goods Inc.
FATAL ATTRACTION - Perfumes - Juvenesse by Elaine Gayle
FATAL FROG - Fishing lures - Humphrey's H & H Lure Co., Inc.
FATAL RUN - Video games - Atari Games Corp.
FATALELUR - Colognes - Fragranhaus
FATAR - Musical instruments - Music Industries Inc.
FATA'S BEST - Food products - VanEerden Distribution Co.
FATBOY - Saxophones - Dave Guardala Inc.
FATBOY - Tires–bicycles - Specialized Bicycle Components, Inc.
FATBOY AMPS - Amplifiers–musical instrument - Norbert H.K. Funk
FATE - T-shirts–men's - NCI Manufacturing
FATHER AND CHILD - Jewelry - Kirchner Corp.
FATHER & SON - Pizzas–frozen - Nation Pizza Products L.P.
FATHER & SON - Shoes ☆ - Endicott Johnson Corp.
FATHER JOHN'S HEAT PLASTER - Health care products - Woolfoam Corp.
FATHER JOHN'S MEDICINE - Cough medicines - Oakhurst Co.
FATHER JOHN'S MEDICINE - Health care products - Woolfoam Corp.
FATHER JOHN'S MEDICINE PLUS - Health care products - Woolfoam Corp.
FATHER JOHN'S PLUS - Vitamins and nutritional supplements - Oakhurst Co.
FATHER NATURE - Bird feeders - Calvin Baynard
FATHER SAM'S - Pita bread - Father Sam's Syrian Bread Inc.
FATHER TIME - Cheese - Heluva Good Cheese Inc.
FATHOM - Colognes - Mem Co., Inc.
FATHOM - Computer software and hardware - Quarterdeck Systems
FATHOM - Recording label - Hearts of Space Inc.
FATHOM - Wet suits–rubber - Water Adventures, Inc.
FATHOM-40 - Sporting goods - Dreier Co.
FATHOM-MASTER - Fishing tackle - Penn Fishing Tackle Manufacturing Co.
FATHOM-TROL - Fishing tackle - Penn Fishing Tackle Manufacturing Co.
FATHOMETER - Navigational instruments - Raytheon Co.

FATIGUE BUSTERS - Video production - Total Life Creations
FATIGUE FIGHTER - Floor coverings–carpet and rugs - Heuga USA
FATIGUE FIGHTER - Health care products - Fiske Industries Inc.
FATIGUE FIGHTER - Hosiery - Ridgeview Inc.
FATIMA - Cigarettes ☆ - Liggett Group Inc.
FATMASTER - Measuring instruments - Rainbow Charts
FATMOX - Apparel and accessories - L.A. Gear, Inc.
FATORIA LA RIPA - Wines - European Beverage Co., Inc.
FATRACS - Tricycles ☆ - Hedstrom Corp.
FATRIDE - Apparel and accessories - Fatride
FATS GRAMM - Greeting cards - Baggs Brothers Enterprises, Inc.
FATSCO - Poison–ant - Fatsco
FATSCO ANCHOR MASTER - Anchors - Fatsco
FATSO - Food products ☆ - Goodmark Foods, Inc.
FATTED CALF, THE - Restaurants ☆ - American Snacks Inc.
FATTIBASE - Pharmaceutical preparations - Paddock Laboratories Inc.
FATTIES - Toys–stuffed - Kamar International Inc.
FATTORIA DEI BARBI - Wines - Blair Importers Ltd.
FATTORIA DEL BARBI - Wines - Palm Bay Imports, Inc.
FATTORIA DI PETROGNANO - Wines - Pellegrini Bros. Wines Inc.
FATTORIE & PANDEA - Breads - Liberty Richter Inc.
FATTRAX - Tires - Fisher Mountain Bikes
FATTY KNEES - Boats–dinghies - Edey & Duff, Ltd.
FAUB, THE - Jewelry - Orogem Corp.
FAUCET BRITE - Cleaning preparations - TR Industries
FAUCET FOUNTAIN - Novelty items - Jokari/US, Inc.
FAUCET FRIENDS - Novelty items - Waco Products Corp.
FAUCET KING - Plumbing fixtures–plastic ☆ - Waxman Industries Inc.
FAUCET MATE - Water purification systems - Cuno Inc.
FAUCET-QUEEN - Hair care products - Faucet-Queens Inc.
FAUCET, THE - Housewares - Metrokane
FAUCHON - Wines - Hilton Commercial Group Inc.
FAUCHON-USA - Food products - Richard Adlai Corp.
FAUGIER - Candy ☆ - Liberty Richter Inc.
FAUGIER - Nuts–salted, roasted, cooked, or canned - De Choix Specialty Foods Co.
FAULBAKER - Electronic equipment - Micro Mo Electronics, Inc.
FAULT-XPERT - Computer software - Compuware Corp.
FAULTFINDER - Electronic equipment - Schlumberger Technologies, Inc.
FAULTLESS - Binders - Stationers Loose Leaf Co.
FAULTLESS - Health care products - Abbott Laboratories
FAULTLESS - Hooks - Klauer Manufacturing Co.
FAULTLESS - Metals - FKI Industries Inc.
FAULTLESS - Pharmaceutical preparations - Abbott Laboratories
FAULTLESS - Starch–laundry - Faultless Starch/Bon Ami Co.
FAULTLESS - Wheels - Faultless Caster Co.
FAULTLESS FABRICRAFT - Fabric softeners ☆ - Faultless Starch/Bon Ami Co.
FAULTLESS FRONT - Apparel and accessories ☆ - Strouse, Adler Co.
FAULTLESS FUSCHIA - Lipsticks - Estee Lauder Inc.
FAUNA - Flatware - Wilton Co.
FAUST - Beverages–malt - Anheuser-Busch Companies Inc.
FAUST - Pencils ☆ - Koh-I-Noor, Inc.
FAUST - Salmon–smoked, salted, dried, or pickled - Trident Seafoods Corp.
FAUSTINO WINES FROM SPAIN - Wines - Palm Bay Imports, Inc.
FAUTA - Furniture - All-Luminum Products Inc.
FAUTEX II - Wallpaper - Advance Wallcoverings
FAUVE - Veterinary pharmaceutical preparations - Nutra-Vet Research Corp.
FAUVE ULTRA - Pet products - Nutra-Vet Research Corp.
FAUX - Wines - Preston Vineyards
FAUX ART - Wallpaper - Aresda Design Associates
FAUX BRICK - Concrete repair products - Artcrete, Inc.
FAUX CREATIONS - Paint sprayers - Bloch/New England, Inc.
FAUX FINISH - Paints - Plaid Enterprises, Inc.
FAUX FINISH - Wallpaper ☆ - Sandpiper Studios
FAUX FINISH ENCORE - Wallpaper - Sandpiper Studios
FAUX FINISHES - Wallpaper - Marburg Wallcoverings Inc.
FAUX FITNESS - Apparel and accessories - Authentic Fitness Corp.
FAUX FUN - Wallpaper - Scalamandre Silks Inc.
FAUX FUR - Yarn - Rainbow Gallery Inc.
FAUX GLAZING MEDIUM - Paints - DecoArt, Inc.
FAUX MARBLE - Floor coverings - Tarkett, Inc.
FAUX NATUREL - Fabrics - Interials Inc.
FAUX PAS - Jewelry - Nailtex Inc.
FAUX PAW - Toys–stuffed ☆ - Gund, Inc.
FAUX REAL - Shirts - Sandra Maroney

☆ = Now out of production

FAUX TEX - Finishing agents - JSA Inc.
FAUXCIO - Wallpaper - Stroheim & Romann, Inc.
FAUXSOLE - Floor coverings–carpet and rugs - Trans-Ocean Import Co. Inc.
F.A.V. MILITARY HOPPER - Toys–automobiles - Tyco Toys
FAVARGER - Chocolate bars ☆ - C. & J. Willenborg Inc.
FAVOLS - Candy - International Gourmet
FAVOR - Brushes–paint - PPG Industries, Inc.
FAVOR - Cigarettes - Advanced Tobacco Products Inc.
FAVOR - Furniture polish and wax - S.C. Johnson & Son, Inc.
FAVOR - Heart monitors - Polar Electro Inc.
FAVOR - Occasional furniture - CTH/Sherrill Occasional
FAVOR - Thread - Cincinnati Thread Co.
FAVOR - Toys - Key Novelty Manufacturing Co.
FAVOR-IT - Novelty items - House of Favors
FAVOR MAKER - Novelty items - Rose Manufacturing
FAVORABLE IMPRESSIONS - Publisher's imprints - Omnigraphics Inc.
FAVORETTA - Rings–jewelry - Artcarved Inc.
FAVORIN - Skin care products - Fima Biotechnology
FAVORITA - Cigar boxes–wood - Consolidated Cigar Corp.
FAVORITA - Grinders - Favorita Usa Corp.
FAVORITE - Bakery products - Flowers Bakeries (West Virginia Div.)
FAVORITE - Bicycles - Columbia Manufacturing Inc.
FAVORITE - Cooking utensils–aluminum ☆ - W.E. Kautenberg Co.
FAVORITE - Floor coverings–carpet and rugs ☆ - Calladium & Marglen
FAVORITE - Food containers - Farmhouse Foods
FAVORITE - Garden equipment ☆ - H.D. Hudson Manufacturing Co.
FAVORITE - Hair care products - Helene Curtis Industries Inc.
FAVORITE - Housewares - John Chatillon & Sons
FAVORITE - Office supplies - ACCO USA, Inc.
FAVORITE - Paints - Wilson Paint Co.
FAVORITE - Paper–writing - Kurtz Bros. Inc.
FAVORITE - Pens ☆ - Empire Berol USA
FAVORITE - Pipes - National Briar Pipe Co.
FAVORITE - Sporting goods ☆ - Wright & McGill Co.
FAVORITE - Stationery ☆ - Mead Corp.
FAVORITE - Tape measures ☆ - Keuffel & Esser Co.
FAVORITE - Tobacco–chewing or smoking - Taylor Bros. Inc.
FAVORITE 3-LETTER WORDS - Publisher's imprints - Fast Learners Co.
FAVORITE 4'S - Cheese - Alpine Lace Brands, Inc.
FAVORITE ALTERNATIVE TO WALKERS, THE - Exercising equipment - Lisco, Inc.
FAVORITE BEAR - Toys–stuffed ☆ - Dakin Inc.
FAVORITE BOND - Paper - Reynolds and Reynolds Co.
FAVORITE CHEF - Food products - Continental Food Products Inc.
FAVORITE FIRSTS - Infant product - Mattel, Inc.
FAVORITE FLAVORS - Toys ☆ - Henry Gordy International Inc.
FAVORITE PLACES - Fabrics–tapestry - Comark Wallcoverings
FAVORITE PLACES II - Wallpaper - Style-Tex Wallcoverings
FAVORITE SPICE - Seasonings - Continnuus
FAVORITES - Candy - Nabisco Foods Group
FAVORITES - Posters ☆ - Thought Factory
FAVORITES - Wallpaper - Quality House Wallcoverings
FAVORITES CLUB - Food products - Harry and David Inc.
FAVORITT - Floor coverings - Tarkett, Inc.
FAVORS - Doilies - S.A. Leart Co.
FAVRENE - Glassware–household ☆ - Fenton Art Glass Co.
FAWCETT - Publisher's imprints - Random House, Inc.
FAWCETT COLUMBINE - Publisher's imprints - Random House, Inc.
FAWCETT JUNIPER - Publisher's imprints - Ballantine Books Inc.
FAWN - Clocks - General Time Corp. (Westclox/Seth Thomas Div.)
FAWN - Cosmetics ☆ - Elysee Scientific Cosmetic Co.
FAX - Computer software - STF Technologies, Inc.
FAX - Recording label ☆ - Instinct Records Corp.
FAX - Stoves - Rohn
FAX ANIMATION - Artists' materials - Alan Gordon Enterprises Inc.
FAX CONDUCTOR - Computer storage devices - Octus, Inc.
FAX DESCRIPTION LANGUAGE (FDL) - Computer software - Ibex Technologies Inc.
FAX EMILY - Facsimile equipment - Fax Emily Inc.
FAX-LINE - Telephone apparatus - Perma Power Electronics Inc.
FAX MANAGER - Printers–computer - Communication Control Systems International
FAX MATE - Computer peripheral equipment - Interactive Products Corp.
FAX MAX - Paper - Labelon Corp.
FAX NIKKOR - Photographic enlarging lenses ☆ - Nikon Inc.
FAX-OUT - Correction fluid - Bic Corp.

FAX REPORTER, THE - Computer software - Contour Software Inc.
FAX RESOURCE - Computer software - IMECOM Group, Inc.
FAX SUPPORT - Computer software - CTL, Inc.
FAXAIDE - Computer hardware - Zenith Electronics Corp.
FAXALYZER - Computer peripheral equipment - At&T Corp.
FAXBACK - Computer software - Intel Corp.
FAXBRIDGE - Computer software - Wygant Scientific, Inc.
FAXCARDS - Greeting cards - First & Second, Inc.
FAXCENTRAL - Computer software - Ring Zero Systems, Inc.
FAXCILITATE - Computer software - PSI Integration, Inc.
FAXFX - Computer software - Devcom Mid-America, Inc.
FAXIMIZER - Computers - Western Telematic Inc.
FAXIPHONE - Computer software - Martin Green
FAXLAB - Computer peripheral equipment - Genoa Technology Inc.
FAXLINE - Weather tracking equipment - AccuWeather, Inc.
FAXLINK - Telephone answering machines - Spear Voice Systems, Inc.
FAXLINKPLUS - Computer software - AudioFax Inc.
FAXON SOURCE - Computer software - Faxon Co. Inc.
FAXPAD - Computer peripheral equipment - Anchor Pad International Inc.
FAXPOINT - Computer hardware - Syntellect, Inc.
FAXPROBE - Computer hardware - Genoa Technology Inc.
FAXSTATUS - Computer software ☆ - STF Technologies, Inc.
FAXTALK - Computer software - Thought Communications
FAXWEB - Computer peripheral equipment - NetOffice, Inc.
FAY - Frames–eyeglass - Rozin Optical Export Corp.
FAY - Tools - L.S. Starrett Co. Inc. (Consumer Products Div.)
FAY-FAX - Paper - Fay Paper Products Inc.
FAY VINEYARD - Wines - Stag's Leap Wine Cellars
FAY-VO-RITE - Paper - Fay Paper Products Inc.
FAYD - Health care products - Fleetwood Co.
FAYE - Apparel and accessories - Duck Head Apparel Co., Inc.
FAYE BY O'BRYAN BROTHERS - Apparel–women's - O'Bryan Brothers, Inc.
FAYE ROSE - Notebooks and notepads - Pentech International Inc.
FAYE'S - Bakery products - Bubbles Baking Co.
FAYE'S 1 - Cosmetics - Faye Mendelsohn Cosmetics, Inc.
FAYETTE - Glassware–household ☆ - L.E. Smith Glass Co.
FAYETTE - Pianos ☆ - Everett Piano Co.
FAYETTE - Recording label - Parr-X Corp.
FAYETTE - Tables–wood - Riverside Furniture Corp.
FAYGO - Beverages–carbonated - Faygo Beverages, Inc.
FAY'S CLOSET - Apparel–women's ☆ - Leslie Fay Companies Inc.
FAYVA - Footwear - Morse Shoe, Inc.
FAZER - Sleds - SLM Inc.
FAZI BATTAGLIA - Wines - Palm Bay Imports, Inc.
FAZIT TEA TREE - Skin care products - Thursday Plantation Ltd.
F.B. EYE - Sunglasses - Sun Creations, Inc.
FBA NAVIGATOR - Computer software - Unisys Corp.
FBC II - Pharmaceutical preparations ☆ - ICN Pharmaceuticals Inc.
FBG - Furniture - L & P Property Management Co.
FBI FOR BODY AND IMAGE - Sportswear - C & S Sales & Merchandising Associates
FBS - Apparel and accessories - Fat Bastard Sportswear
FBT - Amplifiers–musical instrument - Colombo & Sons Accordion Co.
F.B.V. - Paints - Dunn Edwards Corp.
FBX - Amplifiers–public address - Sabine Musical Manufacturing Co. Inc.
FC - Apparel and accessories - Free Clothes, Inc.
FC - Jewelry - Fashion Craft Corp.
FC - Jewelry–precious - Fred Crabtree and Associates
FC - Rods–steel - Fabsco Corp.
FC 101 - Floor coverings–carpet and rugs ☆ - Cumberland Mills Inc.
FC-900 - Communications equipment - Danka Corp.
FC FLIGHT CONTROL - Sporting goods - Lisco, Inc.
FC JUNIOR - Apparel–women's - Fashions Crossroads Inc.
FC LTD. - Apparel and accessories - Edison Brothers Stores, Inc.
FC PLANK - Building materials–concrete - F.C.P., Inc.
FC SEARCH - Computer software - Foundation Center
FC TROTTER - Apparel and accessories ☆ - Edison Brothers Stores, Inc.
F.C.A.H. - Pharmaceutical preparations ☆ - Schering-Plough Healthcare Products
FC&S BULLETINS - Computer software - National Underwriter Co.
FCBLOCK - Diagnostic preparations - Pharmingen
FCC - Distributors–automotive - FCC Export Inc.
FCE - Giftware - Fine Casting Enterprises & FCE
FCF - Jewelry - FCF Jewelry Manufacturing Co.
FCI - Brake parts - James L. Parker
FCI - Flagpole accessories - Concord Industries Inc.

☆ = Now out of production

FCI FIRE CONTROL INSTRUMENTS - Fire alarms - Fire Control Instruments, Inc.

FCM - Golfing equipment - Brunswick Bowling & Billiards Corp.

FCP - Cement - F.C.P., Inc.

FCS - Computer peripheral equipment - Ancor Communications, Inc.

FCS - Video equipment - Thrustmaster, Inc.

FCS-FLIGHT CONTROL SYSTEM - Computer software - Thrustmaster, Inc.

FD-29 - Skin care products - Frances Denney

F.D. BLUES - Apparel and accessories - Family Dollar Services, Inc.

FD FAIRMONT DESIGNS - Boxes–corrugated paperboard - Cambium Business Group Inc.

F.D. GRAVE - Cigars - F.D. Grave & Son, Inc.

F.D. PIERCE - Paints - General Coating Technologies, Inc.

F.D. SHOE FUMIGANT - Fungicides ☆ - Noble Pine Products Co.

FDC - Containers - FDC Packaging Inc.

FDC - Jewelry - Schachter-Fein Designs, Ltd.

FDC - Nuts–salted, roasted, cooked, or canned - F.D.C. Wholesale Corp.

FDF - Jewelry - Sam Herman

FDH-PAC - Hair-care products - Cheveux Inc.

FDL MARKETING/DUBUQUE - Food products - Pioneer Food Sales Inc.

FDMERU - Pet products - Tetra Sales USA

F.D.R. - Optical scanners–computer - Tart Optical

FDS - Computer software - Nestor, Inc.

FDS - Health care products - Alberto-Culver Co.

FDS FIRM DELIVERY SCHEDULE - Machine tools - Dayton Progress Corp.

FDSI FINANCIAL DECISION SYSTEMS, INC. - Computer software - Financial Decision Systems, Inc.

F.DULAC - Wines ☆ - Alimar & Cie. Inc.

FDV-TC - Veterinary pharmaceutical preparations ☆ - Schering-Plough Animal Health

FDX - Index cards - File-A-Dex Inc.

FDX-400 - Printers–computer - Integrated Payment Systems Inc.

FE - Jewelry - Frank Ellman Co. Inc.

F.E. - Sporting goods ☆ - L & M Distribution Inc.

FE-8 - Fertilizers - Rootsinc

FE 50 - Vitamins and nutritional supplements - Northampton Medical, Inc.

FE-TRACIN & DESIGN - Chemical preparations - Georgia-Pacific Corp.

FEAGENT - Computer software - Great American Insurance Co.

FEAR GOD - Novelty items - Don Tardiff

FEAR THIS - Decals and transfers ☆ - Vortech Engineering, Inc.

FEARC - Furniture - Samuel Clayton

FEARLESS - Brushes - Wright-Bernet

FEARLESS - Floor coverings–carpet and rugs - Patcraft Mills Inc.

FEARLESS - Footwear - No Fear, Inc.

FEARN - Health care products - Fearn Natural Foods, Division of Modernproducts, Inc.

FEARN - Soups–canned - CPC Food Service

FEARSOME FACE-OFF - Toys - Mattel, Inc.

FEAST - Pet products ☆ - Aquatronics-Filtronics

FEAST & TALBERT - Food products machinery - Food Services of America, Inc.

FEAST OF EDEN - Fruits–dried - California Hi-Lites, Inc.

FEAST, THE - Recording label - Guerilla Records

FEASTER - Food products - Westin Inc.

FEASTING IN THE FAST LANE - Publisher's imprints - Holly Anne Rudin-Braschi

FEASTING ON THE LIGHT SIDE - Recording label - Mary Ann Pickard

FEASTMASTER - Barbecues and grills ☆ - Superior Fireplace Co.

FEATHAIRE - Apparel–women's - Barbizon Lingerie

FEATHAIRE - Fabric stores - Jaunty Textile Div.

FEATHER - Boats - Glen-L Marine Designs

FEATHER - Candles - Candles International

FEATHER - Lawn mower - American Lawn Mower Co.

FEATHER - Markers–felt-tip - Blackfeet Writing Instruments Inc.

FEATHER - Pet products - Vee Enterprises

FEATHER - Razor blades - Jatai International

FEATHER - Recording label - Wizard & Feather Brown Productions

FEATHER - Stoves - Coleman Co., Inc.

FEATHER - Wigs - Jean Paree Weegs Inc.

FEATHER BIRD - Pet products - Mason Distributing

FEATHER BRANCHED - Flowers, plants, and seeds - John Holmlund Nursery

FEATHER BRIGHT - Pet products - Gerard-Pellham Co.

FEATHER BRITE - Pet products - Four Paws Products Ltd.

FEATHER CONSTRUCTION - Footwear–women's - United States Shoe Corp.

FEATHER EASE - Furniture - Schottenstein Stores Corp.

FEATHER EDGE - Mattresses - Vinyl Products

FEATHER EDGE AIR SUPPORT - Mattresses - Vinyl Products

FEATHER EDGER - Paint removers ☆ - Klean-Strip

FEATHER-EZE - Underwear and nightwear ☆ - Lovable Co.

FEATHER FANCY - Pet products - Professional Pet Products

FEATHER FENCE - Netting - Dawn W. O'Neil

FEATHER-FILL - Automotive parts and accessories - Fibre Glass-Evercoat Co. Inc.

FEATHER FINERY - Apparel–children's - Feather Your Nest

FEATHER FLEX - Decoys - Sport-Flex, Inc.

FEATHER-FLO - Brushes–paint - Sherwin-Williams Automotive Finishes Corp.

FEATHER FLUFF - Desserts - J.W. Allen & Co.

FEATHER FRINGE - Craft supplies - Meadowbrook Inventions Inc.

FEATHER GLO - Pet products - Rich Health

FEATHER II - Razors - Stature Field

FEATHER-LIFE - Health care products - Electric Wheel Chair Manufacturing Corp.

FEATHER-LITE - Adhesives and sealants - Icare Industries Inc.

FEATHER LITE - Bicycles - Hunt-Wilde Corp.

FEATHER-LITE - Tools - Ames Taping Tool Systems Co.

FEATHER LITE - Toys–trains - Douglas Goodsell

FEATHER-LUX - Furniture - Bench Craft Inc.

FEATHER RIVER - Compost ☆ - National Bark Sales

FEATHER SELECT - Fibers–synthetic - United Feather & Down Inc.

FEATHER-SOF - Furniture - Universal Furniture Industries, Inc.

FEATHER SOFT - Paper–toweling - Von Drehle Corp.

FEATHER SUEDE - Apparel and accessories - Neema Clothing, Ltd.

FEATHER SWEEP - Brooms - Perfex Corp.

FEATHER TIP - Brooms - O-Cedar/Vining Household Products Co.

FEATHER-TIP - Brushes–paint - Baker Brush Co. Inc.

FEATHER TIPS - Backscratcher - Backscratchers, Inc.

FEATHER TOUCH - Chairs–upholstered - Franklin Corp.

FEATHER TOUCH - Musical instruments ☆ - Barclay Music

FEATHER-TOUCH - Printing trades machinery - Republic Roller Corp.

FEATHER TOUCH CLEANSER - Skin care products - Charles of the Ritz Group Ltd.

FEATHER WEIGHT - Fishing lures - Thomas and Thomas Rodmakers Inc.

FEATHER WIND - Bicycles - Columbia Manufacturing Inc.

FEATHER YOUR NEST - Pillows - Feather Your Nest

FEATHERAIRE - Shotguns ☆ - Marble Arms Corp.

FEATHERBLEND - Pillows - Pacific Coast Feather Co.

FEATHERBLEND KOHLINER - Cosmetics - Max Factor & Co.

FEATHERED FANCYS - Pet products - M.I.L.D. Kingdom

FEATHERED FRIEND - Bird feeds - Agway Country Foods Inc.

FEATHERED FRIENDS - Novelty items - Papel Freelance, Inc.

FEATHERED FRIENDS - Toys–stuffed - Russ Berrie and Co., Inc.

FEATHERETTE - Underwear and nightwear - Rago Foundations Inc. LLC

FEATHERFLEX - Fishing tackle ☆ - Perfection Tip Co.

FEATHERFLITE - Containers ☆ - Poloron Products Inc.

FEATHERFLO - Pet products - Rich Health

FEATHERFONE - Headphones ☆ - Pickering and Co. Inc.

FEATHERGAB - Suits and sportcoats - M. Wile & Co., Inc.

FEATHERIDE - Audio equipment - Electro-Voice, Inc.

FEATHERIES - Cosmetics - Revlon Consumer Products Corp.

FEATHERKNIT - Apparel and accessories ☆ - Geltman Industries

FEATHERLIGHT - Bicycles - Columbia Manufacturing Inc.

FEATHERLIGHT - Firearms and parts - Ithaca Gun Co. Inc.

FEATHERLIGHT - Fishing tackle - Wright & McGill Co.

FEATHERLITE - Building materials - Arizona Cultured Stone Products, Inc.

FEATHERLITE - Cushions - La-Z-Boy Chair Co.

FEATHERLITE - Gloves - Fairfield Line, Inc.

FEATHERLITE - Golfing equipment - Ram Golf Corp.

FEATHERLITE - Knives–pocket - Featherlite Manufactuing, Inc.

FEATHERLITE - Pet products - National Display Materials

FEATHERLITE - Photographic equipment - American Photographic Instrument Co.

FEATHERLITE - Scissors–hand-operated - Clauss Cutlery Co.

FEATHERLITE - Tent campers ☆ - Damon Corp.

FEATHERLITE - Trailers - Featherlite Manufacturing, Inc.

FEATHERLITE FISHHOOKS - Fishing tackle - Wright & McGill Co.

FEATHERLITE FORMULA - Display cases–wood - Media/Graphics, Inc.

FEATHERLOCK - Pillows - Pacific Coast Feather Co.

FEATHERLY THE OWL - Furniture–children's - Maze Inc.

FEATHERNAP - Girdles ☆ - Kleinert's Inc.

FEATHERPROOF - Lipsticks - Estee Lauder Inc.

FEATHERS - Footwear–women's - Diesse Shoes Inc.

FEATHERS - Pet products ☆ - Kal Kan Foods, Inc.

☆ = Now out of production

FEATHERS - Toys–stuffed - American Greetings Corp.
FEATHERS FEATHER - Jewelry - Angelique Inc.
FEATHERSOFT - Fabrics - Lackawanna Leather Co. Inc.
FEATHERSOFT - Medical apparatus ☆ - Monterey, Inc.
FEATHERSOFT - Sponges ☆ - Schroeder & Tremayne, Inc.
FEATHERSPUN - Apparel and accessories ☆ - Playtex Apparel, Inc.
FEATHERSTONE - Flower pots–plastic - Potpourri Press, Inc.
FEATHERSTONE - Toilets–portable - Oldcastle Architectural West, Inc.
FEATHERSUEDE - Apparel and accessories - Genesco Inc.
FEATHERTOP OUTDOOR CLOTHING - Apparel and accessories - Feathertop
   Outdoor Clothing
FEATHERTOUCH - Knives - RonCo Inc.
FEATHERTOUCH - Pillows - Pacific Coast Feather Co.
FEATHERVEIN - Floor coverings ☆ - Congoleum Corp.
FEATHERWEIGHT - Bicycles - Bridgestone/Firestone, Inc.
FEATHERWEIGHT - Boats–canoes ☆ - Old Town Canoe Co.
FEATHERWEIGHT - Books–blank - Uarco Inc.
FEATHERWEIGHT - Chemical preparations - Georgia-Pacific Corp.
FEATHERWEIGHT - Cutlery - Utica Cutlery Co.
FEATHERWEIGHT - Furniture - International Colorcast Corp.
FEATHERWEIGHT - Health care products - Novartis Nutrition Corp.
FEATHERWEIGHT - Lenses–magnifying ☆ - Edroy Products Co.
FEATHERWEIGHT - Medical apparatus - Medsource, Inc.
FEATHERWEIGHT - Pens ☆ - K-9 Pen Co.
FEATHERWEIGHT - Strollers–baby ☆ - Welsh Co.
FEATHERWEIGHT - Vitamins and nutritional supplements - Sandoz
   Pharmaceuticals Corp.
FEATHERWEIGHTS - Luggage - Multiple Choice
FEATHERWIND PRODUCTIONS - Video production - Featherwind
   Productions, Inc.
FEATHERWRITER - Markers–felt-tip - Blackfeet Writing Instruments Inc.
FEATHERZ - Craft supplies - Z-Barten Productions
FEATURE - Apparel–women's - Bi-Flex International
FEATURE - Fertilizers - Platte Chemical Co.
FEATURE - Hardware ☆ - Masonite Corp.
FEATURE - Rings–jewelry - Feature Enterprises
FEATURE-FLASH - Rings–jewelry - Feature Enterprises
FEATURE FLAVOR - Cakes - Tasty Baking Co.
FEATURE-FLEX - Rings–jewelry - Feature Enterprises
FEATURE-GLO - Rings–jewelry - Feature Enterprises
FEATURE-LOCK - Rings–jewelry - Feature Enterprises
FEATURECHIPS - Circuit boards - Cirrus Logic, Inc.
FEBREZE - Deodorizers - Procter & Gamble Co.
FEBRIGESIC - Pharmaceutical preparations ☆ - Seatrace Co.
FEBRINOL - Analgesics ☆ - Vitarine Pharmaceuticals Inc.
FEBRO-BAR - Pharmaceutical preparations ☆ - JMI-Canton Pharmaceuticals
FEBROL - Analgesics - Scot-Tussin Pharmacal Co.
FEC - Machinery - Food Engineering Corp.
FECALYZER - Veterinary medical equipment - Evsco Pharmaceuticals
FECHHEIMER - Coats - Fechheimer Brothers Co.
FECO - Drapery hardware - Ralph Friedland and Brothers Inc.
FECO-T - Pharmaceutical ☆ - Blaine Co. Inc.
FECOPLEX - Prescription drug ☆ - Blaine Co. Inc.
FED-CO - Adhesives and sealants ☆ - Nowstar
FED DEP INS CALC - Computer software - Great Pond Technologies, Inc.
FED/NIT - Tiles–ceramic ☆ - Federal Tile Imports Inc.
FED-RED & WHITE - Meat products–canned - Zartic, Inc.
FED STONE - Tiles–ceramic - Federal Tile Imports Inc.
FED UP - Antihistamine preparations - DMD Sales, Inc.
FEDAHIST - Cold remedies - Schwarz Pharma
FEDCO - Automotive parts and accessories - FEDCO Automotive Components
   Co. Inc.
FEDCO - Batteries - Fedco Electronics Inc.
FEDCO - Boxes - Federal Fibre Corp.
FEDCO/INDIAN - Fire extinguishers - The Fountainhead Group, Inc.
FEDDERS - Air conditioning equipment - Fedders North America Inc.
FEDELLA - Playing cards ☆ - United States Playing Card Co.
FEDER & FLEISCHER - Wigs - Joseph Fleischer Natural Coiffures, Inc.
FEDERAL - Ammunition - Federal Cartridge Co.
FEDERAL - Bathroom fixtures ☆ - Crane Plumbing/Fiat Products
FEDERAL - Batteries - East Penn Manufacturing Co., Inc.
FEDERAL - Binders - Champion International Corp.
FEDERAL - Brushes–paint - Rubberset Co.
FEDERAL - Floor coverings–carpet and rugs ☆ - Eurotex Inc.
FEDERAL - Floor coverings–tile ☆ - Kentile Floors Inc.
FEDERAL - Hardware - Blaine Window Hardware Inc.

FEDERAL - Jewelry, watches ☆ - Disegno Collection
FEDERAL - Paper–sand - Biwenco Industries Inc.
FEDERAL - Personal defense products - Armament Systems and Procedures,
   Inc.
FEDERAL - Recording label - Gusto Records Inc.
FEDERAL - Sinks–metal ☆ - Federal Home Products
FEDERAL - Stepladders - W.W. Babcock Co. Inc.
FEDERAL - Tableware–china - Lenox, Inc.
FEDERAL/AMERICAN - Sinks–metal - Federal Home Products
FEDERAL ARTGLO - Flags - Annin and Co.
FEDERAL BLUE - Glassware–household ☆ - Fenton Art Glass Co.
FEDERAL COBALT - Tableware–china - Lenox, Inc.
FEDERAL ELECTRIC - Small household appliances - Samhill Enterprises, Inc.
FEDERAL EXPRESS - Courier services–air - Federal Express Corp.
FEDERAL FLEX - Propellers - Federal Marine Motors Co.
FEDERAL FORMULA - Chemical preparations - Valspar Corp.
FEDERAL GOLD - Tableware–china - Lenox, Inc.
FEDERAL GRANDEUR - Tableware–china - Lenox, Inc.
FEDERAL HILL - Furniture - National/Mt. Airy Furniture
FEDERAL LOCK COMPANY - Metals - Federal Lock Co.
FEDERAL-MOGUL - Engines - Federal-Mogul Corp.
FEDERAL OAK - Cabinets–wood ☆ - Haas Cabinet Co. Inc.
FEDERAL PLATINUM - Dinnerware–glass - Lenox, Inc.
FEDERAL PREMIUM SAFARI - Ammunition - Federal Cartridge Co.
FEDERAL SQUARE - Furniture ☆ - Singer Furniture Co.
FEDERAL STORE FIXTURES - Capital Hardware Inc.
FEDERAL WING & CLAY - Educational materials - Federal-Hoffman, Inc.
FEDERALIST, THE - Lamps - Federalist, Inc.
FEDERALLOY - Metals - Federal Metal Co.
FEDERATED - Refrigerators - Federated Department Stores, Inc.
FEDERICO - Food products - Suzuki of America Automotive Corp.
FEDEX - Courier services–air - Federal Express Corp.
FEDEX DOCUMENT PREP - Computer software - Federal Express Corp.
FEDEX EXPRESS DISTRIBUTION CENTER - Aircraft - Federal Express Corp.
FEDEX INTERNETSHIP - Computer software - Federal Express Corp.
FEDEX ORANGE BOWL - Paper products - Orange Bowl Committee, Inc.
FEDEX TRACKING - Computer software - Federal Express Corp.
FEDEX USA AIRBILL - Forms–preprinted - Federal Express Corp.
FEDOSKINO - Papier-mache articles - Siamese Imports Co.
FEDOSKINO PEGOCKUHO - Novelty items - Marina's Russian Collection, Inc.
FEDRACS - Computer software - Mellon Bank N.A.
FEDRALUBE - Oils–lubricating - Federal Mining & Manufacturing Co.
FEDRATHANE - Cleaning preparations ☆ - Federal Mining & Manufacturing
   Co.
FEDRATONE - Cleaning preparations - Federal Mining & Manufacturing Co.
FEDRAVAN - Cleaning preparations - Federal Mining & Manufacturing Co.
FEDRAZIL - Antihistamine preparations ☆ - Burroughs Wellcome Co.
FEDRELEN - Pharmaceutical preparations ☆ - Scrip-Physician Supply Co.
FEDRENE - Cleaning preparations - Federal Mining & Manufacturing Co.
FEDRIN - Pharmaceutical preparations - Afassco
FEDRINAL - Pharmaceutical preparations - Barre-National, Inc.
FEDRIPAL - Cleaning preparations - Federal Mining & Manufacturing Co.
FEDROID II - Cleaning preparations - Federal Mining & Manufacturing Co.
FEDRON - Cleaning preparations - Federal Mining & Manufacturing Co.
FEDS-TRACKER - Computer software - Intek Corp.
FEDTRAX - Compact discs–prerecorded - International Data Group, Inc.
FEDUP - Vegetables–canned - Simpson Imports, Ltd.
FEE BEE - Recording label - Fee Bee Record Co.
FEE BROTHERS - Syrup - Fee Brothers Inc.
FEE(CALC) - Computer software - National Business Systems, Inc.
FEED BAGS - Pet products - Sacramento Bag Manufacturing Co.
FEED IN A DRUM, THE - Animal feed supplements - Animal Feed Supplement,
   Inc.
FEED-MATE 68 - Veterinary pharmaceutical preparations - Boehringer
   Ingelheim Animal Health, Inc.
FEED-MATE 68 FEED MIX - Veterinary pharmaceutical preparations -
   Boehringer Ingelheim Animal Health, Inc.
FEED-MATE CALF/VEAL - Veterinary pharmaceutical preparations -
   Boehringer Ingelheim Animal Health, Inc.
FEED-MATE EQUINE - Veterinary pharmaceutical preparations - Boehringer
   Ingelheim Animal Health, Inc.
FEED-MATE RELOAD GEL - Veterinary pharmaceutical preparations -
   Boehringer Ingelheim Animal Health, Inc.
FEED-MATE RUMINANT - Veterinary pharmaceutical preparations - Boehringer
   Ingelheim Animal Health, Inc.
FEED ME - Games ☆ - Milton Bradley Co.

☆ = Now out of production

FEED ME FRANKIE - Decorations - Industrial Molding Corp.

FEED MILL EXPRESS - Animal feeds - Farmers Mill & Elevator, Inc.

FEED 'N NUZZLE - Toys - Empire Industries

FEED-N-WAX - Furniture polish and wax - Howard Products

FEED POWER - Dog food ☆ - Central Soya Co. Inc.

FEED-SAVER - Pet products - Stromberg's Chicks & Pets Ltd.

FEED THE CHILDREN BLEND - Coffee - Frontier Cooperative Herbs

FEED THE FROG - Games - Mattel, Inc.

FEEDBACK - Retractable mechanical pencils ☆ - Autopoint Inc.

FEEDBACK ACTION PLANNING TRAINING & DEVELOPMENT FOLLOW UP - Computer software - CCI Assessment Group, Inc.

FEEDBACK CONTROLLER - Electronic equipment - Polyfusion Electronics Inc.

FEEDBACK MANAGER - Computer software - Service Measurement Group, Inc.

FEEDBACK WHEEL, THE - Paper–book - Career Systems, Inc.

FEEDER CUBE - Electronic equipment - Rodix, Inc.

FEEDER GOLDFISH CONDITIONER - Aquariums–household - Jungle Laboratories Corp.

FEEDER GOLDFISH KEEPER - Aquariums–household - Jungle Laboratories Corp.

FEEDER METER - Hunting equipment - Product Innovations, Inc.

FEEDERMASTER - Computer software - Livestock Marketing Services Corp.

FEEDER'S CHOICE - Pet products - Seaboard Seed Co.

FEEDING FRENZY - Games - Aristoplay, Ltd.

FEEDING SYSTEMS - Food products - Camino Real Foods

FEEDING YOUR BUSINESS - Apparel and accessories - Union Oil Co. of California

FEEDSTORE - Agricultural chemicals - Conklin Co., Inc.

FEEDTECH - Animal feed supplements - Alfa Laval Agri Inc.

FEEL - Golfing equipment - West Point Industries Inc.

FEEL & MATCH - Toys ☆ - Lauri Inc.

FEEL BETTER BABY - Dolls - Toy Biz, Inc.

FEEL BRIGHT LIGHT - Health care products - Physician Engineered Products

FEEL FIT - Health care products - Garcoa Labs/Vitamin Classics

FEEL FREE - Deodorants–personal - Gillette Co.

FEEL GREAT PRODUCTS - Vitamins and nutritional supplements - Feel Great Products

FEEL HEALTHY, FEEL GREAT, OR YOUR MONEYBACK! - Vitamins and nutritional supplements - Enzymatic Therapy, Inc.

FEEL LOVELY - Hair care products ☆ - Demert & Dougherty, Inc.

FEEL PRETTY - Girls' lingerie and sleepwear - Inner World Inc.

FEEL PRODUCTIONS - Recording label - Afterschool Publishing Co.

FEEL SAFE - Self defense spray - Feel Safe Corp.

FEEL THE POWER - Golfing equipment ☆ - Penley Sports, LLC

FEEL THE POWER - Shirts - Get On-Line Sportswear Inc.

FEEL THE SHIELD - Toothpaste - Bioglobe Tech. Inc.

FEEL THE SOLE OF AFRICA - Sandals - Ilizwe Trading Co.

FEEL-WET LINER - Diapers–disposable - Procter & Gamble Co.

FEELBETTER FIT, THE - Apparel and accessories - Munsingwear, Inc.

FEELEY-MEELEY - Games ☆ - Milton Bradley Co.

FEELIN' FANCY - Toys - Tonka Corp.

FEELIN' FINE - Pet products - Feline Enterprises Inc.

FEELIN' FIT - Vitamins and nutritional supplements - Twinlab

FEELIN' GOOD - Chewing gum - Philadelphia Chewing Gum Corp.

FEELIN' GOOD - Health care products ☆ - Philips Electronics North America Corp.

FEELIN' GREAT - Hosiery - Van Raalte Gloves

FEELIN' GROOVY - Dolls - Mattel, Inc.

FEELIN' JAZZY - Health care products - Stanley Home Products Inc.

FEELIN' SILKY - Footwear - Americal Corp.

FEELIN' SPECIAL - Dolls - Mattel, Inc.

FEELIN' TRIM - Hosiery - Kayser-Roth Corp.

FEELING - Flatware ☆ - Regent Sheffield, Ltd.

FEELING ALIVE - Recording label - Feeling Alive Records Inc.

FEELING BETTER - Computer software - Dynacomp Inc.

FEELING FREE - Teas–herbal ☆ - R.C. Bigelow, Inc.

FEELING FRIENDS - Balls–rubber - Karen Cuthrell

FEELING FUN - Dolls - Mattel, Inc.

FEELING GOOD - Vitamins and nutritional supplements - Unipro Inc.

FEELING INTIMATE - Greeting cards - Georgia L.M. Roulo

FEELING IS BELIEVING - Electronic equipment - SWR Sound Corp.

FEELING MIGHTY GOOD - Shoes - Bernie Mev Shoes Inc.

FEELING PRETTY - Dolls - Mattel, Inc.

FEELING SAUCY - Food products - Monterey Mushrooms Inc.

FEELING SPECIAL - Brassieres (Bras) ☆ - Playtex Apparel, Inc.

FEELING YOUNG - Vitamins and nutritional supplements - Freelife International LP

FEELINGS - Floor coverings–carpet and rugs - Lees Carpets

FEELINGS - Floor coverings–carpet and rugs ☆ - Lowe's Carpet Corp.

FEELINGS - Shirts - Monticello Manufacturing Co.

FEELINGS - Wallpaper ☆ - ICI Americas Inc.

FEELINGS - Wallpaper ☆ - Vymura

FEELINGS II - Wallpaper - ICI Americas Inc.

FEELINGS III - Wallpaper - ICI Americas Inc.

FEELINGS 'N FLOWERS - Flowers–artificial - Feelings N' Flowers Inc.

FEELINGS OF THE HEART - Greeting cards - American Greetings Corp.

FEELS LIKE REAL - Yarn - Glen Raven Mills Inc.

FEELS OF COTTON - Underwear and nightwear ☆ - Lovable Co.

FEELS-SO-GOOD - Underwear and nightwear ☆ - Lovable Co.

FEELS SO LIVELY - Hair care products - Zotos International Inc.

FEEMSTERS - Slicing machines - M.E. Heuck Co. Inc.

FEEN-A-MINT - Laxatives - Schering-Plough Healthcare Products

FEENEY'S IRISH CREME - Beverages–alcohol - Sazerac Co. Inc.

FEESEARCH - Computer software - Practice Perfect Inc.

FEET FIRST - Hosiery ☆ - Sara Lee Corp.

FEET HEAT - Pet products - Pet Heating Products Inc.

FEET READ ALONG - Computer programming services - Berta-Max Inc.

FEET RELIEF - Giftware - Pollenex Corp.

FEETS - Apparel–athletic ☆ - Jobst Institute Inc.

FEETS OF FANCY - Slippers - Feets of Fancy

FEG - Computer software - Procomp Software, Inc.

FEG - Firearms, accessories, and parts - K.B.I.

FEHR - Sporting goods - D.L.C. Fabricating Co. Inc.

FEHRS - Wines ☆ - Anheuser-Busch Companies Inc.

FEI AMERICA - Computers - FEI America, Inc.

FEINSCHMECKER - Meat products–beef ☆ - Armour Swift-Eckrich

FEINT - Computer software - Thiokol Corp.

FEINWERKBAU - Firearms, accessories, and parts - Beeman Precision Airguns

FEISTY - Floor coverings–carpet and rugs - Wunda Weve Carpet Co.

FEIT ELECTRIC - Lamps - Feit Electric Co.

FEITSEW - Sewing machines–household - Feit Co. Inc.

FEIZY RUGS - Floor coverings–carpet and rugs - Feizy Rugs

FEL-COBOND - Adhesives and sealants - Fel-Pro Inc.

FEL-COPRENE - Gaskets - Fel-Pro Inc.

FEL-O-GUARD-3-K - Pet products - Thomas Veterinary Drug

FEL-O-TABS - Pet products - Thomas Veterinary Drug

FEL-O-VAX - Veterinary product - American Home Products Corp.

FEL-POXY - Epoxy - Fel-Pro Inc.

FEL-PRO IMPORT - Gaskets - Fel-Pro Inc.

FEL-PROTECTOR - Rust removers - Fel-Pro Inc.

FELA - Food products - Gonzalez & Tapanes Inc.

FELAXIN - Pet products ☆ - Schering-Plough Animal Health

FELBATOL - Pharmaceutical preparations - Carter-Wallace, Inc.

FELBATOL - Pharmaceutical preparations - Wallace Laboratories

FELCO - Apparel–athletic - Felco Athletic Wear Co.

FELCO - Oils–lubricating ☆ - Cenex/Land O'Lakes AG Services

FELCOID/PLUS - Gaskets - Fel-Pro Inc.

FELDEN - Brushes–paint ☆ - PPG Industries, Inc.

FELDHEIM PUBLISHERS LTD. - Publisher's imprints - Philipp Feldheim, Inc.

FELDINI - Apparel–men's - Supreme International Corp.

FELDMANN - Garden equipment - Feldmann Engineering & Manufacturing Co., Inc.

FELDMARX - Markers–felt-tip - Action Technology Co.

FELESCA - Pet products - Nutra-Vet Research Corp.

FELICE - Slippers - Daniel Green Co.

FELICE MOOR - Housewares - Alladin Plastics Inc.

FELICI - Jewelry - Felici

FELICIANA - Toys–stuffed ☆ - Russ Berrie and Co., Inc.

FELICIANA - Flatware ☆ - Wallace International Silversmiths, Inc.

FELICITA - Shoes - Canter Shoe Co.

FELICITY - Dinnerware–glass ☆ - Royal China & Porcelain Companies Inc.

FELICITY - Vases ☆ - Lenox Crystal, Inc.

FELICS - Computer peripheral equipment - Amdyne Corp.

FELIDE' - Apparel and accessories - Pornkumpoo Phaksuwan

FELIN-L - Pharmaceutical preparations - Boehringer Ingelheim Animal Health, Inc.

FELINA - Underwear and nightwear - Spencer Supports Ltd.

FELINA LINGERIE - Apparel and accessories - Piege Co., Inc.

FELINE - American International Industries

FELINE BALANCE - Pet products - Biogenetics Food Corp.

FELINE CASTLE - Pet products - Pet Castle Co.

FELINE CHALANGER - Pet products - R.A.F. Trading Inc.

FELINE CHECKS - Pet products - Kansas Bank Note Co.

FELINE DIGESTIVE ENZYMES - Veterinary pharmaceutical preparations - Dr. Goodpet

FELINE EXPRESSIONS - Figurines ☆ - United China and Glass Co.

FELINE-FARE - Pet products ☆ - Reliable Protein Products

FELINE FEEDER - Pet food - Doggiduds, Inc.

FELINE FISHING - Pet products - Lazy Pet Products

FELINE FOILER - Pet products - Pilot Enterprises Inc.

FELINE FOLLY - Pet products - Pet Concepts

FELINE FRIEND FONZWORTH - Cat food ☆ - Gimborn U.S., Inc.

FELINE FRITTERS - Pet products - Gimborn U.S., Inc.

FELINE FUN BALL - Pet products - Protect-A-Pet Inc.

FELINE RESORT - Pet products - Aboolhassan Zoroufy

FELINE SUPREME - Cat food - Buckeye Feed Mills, Inc.

FELINERS - Pet products - Colgate-Palmolive Co.

FELINFOEL - Beverages–malt - Wolfgang Morandell Import

FELINFOEL - Beverages–malt ☆ - Thames America Trading Co. Ltd.

FELINS - Boating equipment and accessories - Felins, Inc.

FELIPE II - Brandy - Domecq Importers Inc.

FELIPE II - Liquors - Foreign Vintages Inc.

FELIPE SUAVE - Cigars ☆ - Danby-Palicio

FELIX - Brushes–paint ☆ - PPG Industries, Inc.

FELIX - Food products - Haram-Christensen Corp.

FELIX - Fruits and vegetables - Gourmet America

FELIX - Fruits and vegetables - Jaret Specialties Inc.

FELIX - Hand splint - O.C.S.

FELIX - Pet products - Strongheart Products, Inc.

FELIX - Toys–stuffed - Toy Works, Inc.

FELIX - Veterinary pharmaceutical preparations - NNQ Inc.

FELIX COMICS, INC. - Books–comic - Felix the Cat Productions, Inc.

FELIX THE CAT - Books–comic - Felix the Cat Productions, Inc.

FELIX THE CAT - Toys–stuffed - Determined Productions, Inc.

FELIX +THE CAT - Toys–stuffed - Toy Works, Inc.

FELIZ NAVIDAD - Coffee - Santa Cruz Coffee Roasting Co.

FELLER - Apparel and accessories ☆ - George D. Donovan & Sons Inc.

FELLER OF AUSTRIA - Apparel–athletic ☆ - George D. Donovan & Sons Inc.

FELLER OF AUSTRIA - Slacks - George D. Donovan & Sons Inc.

FELLING - Trailers–semi - Sauk Centre Welding & Machine Works, Inc.

FELLOWES - Magazines - Fellowes Manufacturing Co.

FELLOWSHIP - Office supplies - Effanjay Pens Inc.

FELLOWSHIP OF CHRISTIAN COWBOYS - Jewelry–costume - Fellowship of Christian Cowboys

FELLOWSHIP PUBLISHERS - Publisher's imprints - John Sullivan

FELLSGATE - Apparel stores–children's - Goodman Knitting Co. Inc.

FELO-PET - Pet products ☆ - BenePet Pet Care Products

FELOBITS - Veterinary pharmaceutical preparations - SmithKline Beecham Animal Health Products

FELOCELL - Veterinary pharmaceutical preparations ☆ - SmithKline Beecham Animal Health Products

FELOCINE - Veterinary pharmaceutical preparations ☆ - SmithKline Beecham Animal Health Products

FELOMUNE CVR - Veterinary pharmaceutical preparations - SmithKline Beecham Animal Health Products

FELON - Rackets–racquetball - Lisco, Inc.

FELONY - Cosmetics - Hard Candy, Inc.

FELONY - Musical instrument accessories - Adder Plus Corp.

FELOVITE - Veterinary pharmaceutical preparations - Evsco Pharmaceuticals

FELOVITE II - Veterinary pharmaceutical preparations - Evsco Pharmaceuticals

FELRAMIC 200 - Gaskets - Fel-Pro Inc.

FELS - Apparel–athletic - Sportco Corp.

FELS - Cleaning preparations - Dial Corp.

FELS NAPTHA - Soap - Dial Corp.

FELSTE - Machine parts - Felste Co., Inc.

FELT-LOK - Hardware - Integrity Weatherproofing Systems Inc.

FELT ORIGINALS - Hobby kits ☆ - Blumenthal/Lansing Co.

FELT RITER - Office supplies ☆ - Faber-Castell Corp.

FELT-TACT - Decals and transfers - Rubbermaid Inc.

FELTA SPRINGS - Wines - Mill Creek Vineyards

FELTER FAST - Ventilation equipment - Triangle Metal and Manufacturing Inc.

FELTGUARD - Chemical preparations - Quaker Chemical Corp.

FELTKIDS - Toys - Shetland Toys, Inc.

FELTON - Brushes - Felton Brush Inc.

FELTON - Fabrics - Dan River Inc.

FELTON-EMPIRE - Wines - Felton-Empire Vineyards Inc.

FELTSHAPES - Fabrics–felt - National Nonwovens

FELTSTIK - Markers–felt-tip ☆ - Faber-Castell Corp.

FELTWEAVE - Paper - Georgia-Pacific Corp.

FELTWORKS - Hobby kits - Dimensions, Inc.

FEM-ACTIN - Vitamins and nutritional supplements - Natural Organics, Inc.

FEM CAL - Vitamins and nutritional supplements - Freeda Vitamins Inc.

FEM-CAL - Vitamins and nutritional supplements - Nature's Way Products, Inc.

FEM-CAP - Vitamins and nutritional supplements - Banner-Pharmacaps Inc. (Advanced Nutritional Technology Division)

FEM-COOL PETITE - Medical apparatus - Anago Inc.

FEM-EEZ - Pharmaceutical preparations - Lunsco Inc.

FEM-ETTS - Pharmaceutical preparations - Roberts/Hauck Pharmaceuticals Inc.

FEM FLORA - Health care products - Nature's Own Inc.

FEM FLORA - Health care products - VMC Corp.

FEM-GARD - Apparel stores–lingerie - Fem Gard Inc.

FEM-H - Pharmaceutical preparations ☆ - Saron Pharmacal Corp.

FEM-H - Vitamins and herbal diet aids - Nutrition Professionals Inc.

FEM-LIFE-CHANGE - Vitamins and nutritional supplements ☆ - Ethical Nutrients

FEM MEND - Vitamins and nutritional supplements - Nature's Way Products, Inc.

FEM-PLUS - Vitamins and nutritional supplements - Advanced Nutritional Technology

FEM-TABS - Vitamins and nutritional supplements - Bio San Laboratories Inc.

FEM-TIME - Vitamins and nutritional supplements - Nutrition Headquarters, Inc.

FEM-TIME 36 - Vitamins and nutritional supplements ☆ - Schiff Products, Inc.

FEM-TOTE - Bags - William Blankenship

FEMADULIN - Vitamins and nutritional supplements - Winning Laboratories Corp.

FEMAHERB - Vitamins and nutritional supplements ☆ - J.R. Carlson Laboratories Inc.

FEMAID - Vitamins and nutritional supplements - Armenpharm Ltd.

FEMALE ADVANTAGE - Vitamins and nutritional supplements - Body Wise International, Inc.

FEMALE ADVANTAGE, THE - Publisher's imprints - Sally Helgesen

FEMALE BOOSTER - Health care products - Natural Laboratories Corp.

FEMALE CONTRACEPTIVE YOU CAN'T FEEL!, THE - Pharmaceutical preparations - Apothecus, Inc.

FEMALE DRI - Health care products ☆ - Nelkin/Piper Health Products

FEMALE ESSENTIAL - Pharmaceutical preparations - Longevity Pure Medicine

FEMALE FUEL - Vitamins and nutritional supplements - Twin Laboratories, Inc.

FEMALE SAGE - Vitamins and nutritional supplements - Traditional Medicinals, Inc.

FEMALE TONE - Skin care products - Equinox Botanicals, Inc.

FEMALE TONER - Teas–herbal - Traditional Medicinals, Inc.

FEMALT - Pet products - Lambert-Kay

FEMAPRIN - Vitamins and nutritional supplements - Nature's Way Products, Inc.

FEMARONE - Skin care products - Wise Essentials Inc.

FEMAYLE INSTINCT - Apparel and accessories - Monte Gillespie

FEMBILD - Lenses–photographic ☆ - Ercona Corp.

FEMCAPS - Pharmaceutical preparations - Buffington

FEMCAPS - Pharmaceutical preparations - Otis Clapp & Son Inc.

FEMCARE - Pharmaceutical preparations - Schering-Plough Healthcare Products

FEMCET - Analgesics - Northampton Medical, Inc.

FEMCO - Bicycles - Pikula Associates

FEMCO - Coconut–shredded - Far Eastern Coconut Co.

FEMENAL - Oral contraceptives - American Home Products Corp.

FEMENIL - Vitamins and nutritional supplements - Million Minks, Corp.

FEMENO - Vitamins and nutritional supplements - Bio San Laboratories Inc.

FEMEST - Pharmaceutical preparations ☆ - Laser Inc.

FEMGUARD - Pharmaceutical preparations ☆ - Solvay Pharmaceuticals Inc.

FEMI FORMS - Deodorants–personal ☆ - G and W Laboratories Inc.

FEMICINE - Pharmaceutical preparations - Lake Consumer Products

FEMILAX - Laxatives - G and W Laboratories Inc.

FEMINA - Health care products - East Earth Herb Inc.

FEMINA - Perfume, cosmetics - Bourjois Ltd.

FEMINAID - Vitamins and nutritional supplements - Beso Biological Research Center, Inc.

FEMINEASE - Health care products - Parnell Pharmaceuticals Inc.

FEMININ - Colognes - Faberge Co.

FEMININE BALANCE - Vitamins and nutritional supplements ☆ - Ethical Nutrients

FEMININE FACETS - Greeting cards - Jeri Galloway

☆ = Now out of production

FEMININE GOLD - Lotion - Au Pharmaceuticals Inc.

FEMININE MYSTIQUE - Fabrics - Guilford Mills, Inc.

FEMININE-PLUS - Housewares - Barnhart Industries Inc.

FEMININE SCENTSATIONS - Cleaning preparations - Cambridge Laboratories, Inc.

FEMININE STYLE - Underwear and nightwear - Fruit of the Loom Inc.

FEMININE SUPPORT - Vitamins and nutritional supplements - Nature's Bounty, Inc.

FEMININE WASH - Health care products - C.B. Fleet Co. Inc.

FEMININITEA - Teas–herbal - Unitea Herbs

FEMINIQUE - Health care products - Bristol-Myers Squibb Co.

FEMINIQUE - Health care products - London International U.S. Holdings

FEMINIQUE - Prosthetic apparatus ☆ - Jobst Institute Inc.

FEMINIST PRESS, THE - Publisher's imprints - Feminist Press

FEMINOL - Vitamins and nutritional supplements - Synergy Plus

FEMINONE - Pharmaceutical preparations ☆ - Upjohn Co.

FEMIRON - Vitamins and nutritional supplements - Smithkline Beecham Corp.

FEMITONE - Beverages ☆ - Standard Homeopathic Co., Inc.

FEMIZOL - Pharmaceutical preparations - Lake Consumer Products

FEMIZOL-7 - Pharmaceutical preparations - Lake Consumer Products

FEMLIN - Apparel–women's ☆ - Gem-Dandy, Inc.

FEMME - Frames–eyeglass - Rozin Optical Export Corp.

FEMME - Skin care products - Femme Manufacturing Corp.

FEMME BALANCE - Health care products - Healthwatchers System

FEMME FAIRE - Cream bleach ☆ - Iodent Co.

FEMME FASHIONS - Apparel stores–lingerie - Best Manufacturing Inc.

FEMME FATALE - Apparel–women's - No Excuses Sportswear Ltd.

FEMME FATALE - Cosmetics - Maybelline Co.

FEMME FATALE - Dolls ☆ - Effanbee Doll Corp.

FEMME FORM - Brassieres (Bras) - Finebrand Inc.

FEMME HALF EYE C.V. - Optical scanners–computer - Tart Optical

FEMME INTERNATIONAL ACCESSORIES - Hair ornaments - Atlantic Industries Inc.

FEMME-PAC - Cases–vanity - M.B.G. Enterprises, Inc.

FEMME T-72 - Goggles–underwater - TYR Sport, Inc.

FEMME TABS - Pet products - Vo-Toys Inc.

FEMODE - Apparel–women's - Jezebel-Renee of Hollywood

FEMOPAUSE - Vitamins and nutritional supplements - Herbal Magic, Inc.

FEMOTRONE - Pharmaceutical preparations ☆ - Bluco Inc.

FEMPATCH - Pharmaceutical preparations - Warner-Lambert Co.

FEMPOTANE - Vitamins and nutritional supplements - Health Products Corp.

FEMPOUCH - Diapers–disposable - Vision Medical, Inc.

FEMPREN - Pharmaceutical preparations - Alva-Amco Pharmacal Co.

FEMRX - Surgical instruments - Femrx, Inc.

FEMS - Tampons - Kimberly-Clark Corp.

F.E.M.S.(FUGITIVE EMISSION MANAGEMENT SYSTEM) - Computer software - EnviroMetrics Software Inc.

FEMSTAT - Pharmaceutical preparations - Syntex USA, Inc.

FEMSTRUATION - Vitamins and nutritional supplements - Herbal Magic, Inc.

FEMTEX - Personal products - First Quality Hygienic, Inc.

FEMTOGUARD - Electrical equipment - Cascade Microtech, Inc.

FEMULA - Health care products - Goldline Laboratories, Inc.

FEN-THIN - Vitamins and nutritional supplements - Golden Pride-Rawleigh, Inc.

FENCE ALL - Sporting goods - J.A. Cissel Manufacturing Co.

FENCE CONNECTION, THE - Fencing–plastic - Fence Connection

FENCE FUNDAMENTALS - Fencing–wood - Universal Forest Products, Inc.

FENCE-IT - Fencing–wood - Dalen Products Inc.

FENCE PACK - Fencing–gates and posts - Gilbert and Bennett Manufacturing Co.

FENCE WEAVE - Vinyl - Patrician Products Inc.

FENCEMENT - Building materials - Dale E. Vesper

FENCES - Glassware–household - Ceraglass Inc.

FENCET - Hardware - Sealwall Products Inc.

FENCO - Apparel and accessories - Fenncco Cashmere, Inc.

FENCO - Cameras ☆ - Edixa Camera Co.

FENCOLOR - Sporting goods ☆ - Woodstream Corp.

FEND-AIRE - Bumpers–motor vehicle ☆ - Ashland Plastics Inc.

FEND-AIRE H-T-M - Sporting goods ☆ - Wellington Leisure Products, Inc.

FEND-R-CLIP - Fenders–automotive - C. Sherman Johnson Co. Inc.

FENDALL OPTIX - Eyeglasses - Fendall Co.

FENDER - Musical instruments - Fender Musical Instruments

FENDER BENDER - Giftware - Russ Berrie and Co., Inc.

FENDER BENDER - Ships - C. Sherman Johnson Co. Inc.

FENDER BENDER - Toys - Tyco Toys

FENDER FLARE - Automotive parts and accessories ☆ - Peterson Manufacturing Co.

FENDER-MATE - Boating equipment and accessories - Attwood Corp.

FENDERLOCK - Fasteners–snap - Westwood Inventive Technology Corp.

FENDERS & MORE, INC. - Automotive parts and accessories - Fenders and More, Inc.

FENDI - Eyeglasses - Marchon and Marcolin Eyewear Inc.

FENDI - Footwear–women's ☆ - United States Shoe Corp.

FENDI - Gloves - Portolano Products Inc.

FENDI - Handbags and leather goods - Manetti Farrow

FENDI - Neckties - Mallory and Church Corp.

FENDI - Perfumes - Parfums International Ltd.

FENDI - Watches - Ultima Brands USA Inc.

FENDI CLASSIC - Perfumes - La Parfumerie Inc.

FENDI FANTASIA - Perfumes - La Parfumerie Inc.

FENDOL - Pharmaceutical preparations - Buffington

FENDON - Analgesic - American Pharmaceutical Co.

FENELLA - Lubricating oils ☆ - Shell Oil Co.

FENESHIELD - Yarn - PPG Industries, Inc.

FENESTRA - Doors–metal - Fenestra Corp.

FENESTRA - Hardware - Blaine Window Hardware Inc.

FENESTRA - Wines - Fenestra Winery

FENG YUN - Water purification systems - Morton Industrial (USA) Inc.

FENIX - Fruits and vegetables - Marglo Products Corp.

FENJAL - Soap ☆ - Caswell-Massey Co. Ltd.

FENN - Candy ☆ - Fenn Brothers Inc.

FENN - Garden equipment - Seymour Manufacturing Co.,Inc.

FENN VALLEY - Wines - Fenn Valley Vineyards

FENNELL - Ships–sailing vessels - Liberty Yachts Inc.

FENNER - Automotive parts and accessories - Fenner Drives

FENNER - Electrical equipment - Fenner U.S., Inc.

FENOBELL - Pharmaceutical preparations ☆ - Harvey Laboratories Inc.

FENOFON - Pharmaceutical preparations - Pharmics Inc.

FENSLING - Brackets - Dec-Kor, Inc.

FENTON - Brushes–paint - PPG Industries, Inc.

FENTON - Musical instrument accessories - Fenton Music

FENTON ACRES - Wines ☆ - J. Rochioli Vineyards

FENTON CARNIVAL - Glassware–household ☆ - Fenton Art Glass Co.

FENTON COLORS - Giftware - Fenton Art Glass Co.

FENTON FLY - Fishing lures - Yakima Bait Co.

FENTRON - Hardware - Blaine Window Hardware Inc.

FENWAL - Fire extinguishers - Kidde-Fenwal, Inc.

FENWAY - Meats–luncheon - Colonial Provision Co.

FENWICK - Brushes–paint ☆ - PPG Industries, Inc.

FENWICK FLOAT-ORS - Nautical instruments - Fenwick Float-Ors

FEOCYTE - Pharmaceutical preparations - Dunhall Pharmaceuticals Inc.

FEODORA - Chocolates - Carl Brandt

FEODORA WUNDERBAR - Candy bar - Carl Brandt

FEOSOL - Vitamins and nutritional supplements - SmithKline Beecham Consumer Healthcare

FEOSOL - Vitamins and nutritional supplements - Smithkline Beecham Corp.

FEOSOL PLUS - Health care products ☆ - SmithKline Beecham Consumer Healthcare

FEOSTAT - Pharmaceutical preparations - Forest Pharmaceuticals Inc.

FER - Colognes ☆ - Avon Products, Inc.

FER-B-TONE - Veterinary tonic ☆ - American Equine Products Inc.

FER-IN-SOL - Pharmaceutical preparations - Bristol-Myers Squibb Co.

FER-SUL - Pharmaceutical preparations - Pharmex Inc.

FER-X-CON - Vitamins and nutritional supplements ☆ - Great Life Laboratories Inc.

FERACID - Diet supplement - Major Pharmaceuticals

FERALITE - Fishing tackle - Fenwick

FERANCEE - Pharmaceutical preparations - McNeil Pharmaceuticals

FERARRI - Ceramic tile ☆ - Integrity Tile Co.

FERASCORB - Pharmaceutical preparations ☆ - Shannon Chemical Co. Inc.

FERATE-C - Pharmaceutical preparations ☆ - Pal-Pak Inc.

FERBERDENT - Dentifrices - Ferberdent International Inc.

FERBETRIN - Vitamins and nutritional supplements ☆ - U.S. Ethicals Inc.

FERBUS - Toys - Saban Entertainment, Inc.

FERDO DESIGNS - Bathrobes - Kemo Enterprises, Inc.

FEREN - Fruits–pickled or brined - Riser Foods Inc.

FERENGI - Toys - Paramount Pictures Corp.

FERENTINA - Skin care products - Caesars World Inc.

FEREX - Lubricants ☆ - Shell Oil Co.

FERGLUCON - Pharmaceutical preparations - Liquipharm Inc.

FERGON - Pharmaceutical preparations - Bayer Corp. (Consumer Care Div.)

FERGUS - Brushes–paint ☆ - PPG Industries, Inc.

FERGUSON HEALTH AND NUTRITION - Recording label - Ferguson Health and Nutrition, Inc.

FERGUSON SYSTEM ONE - Vitamins and nutritional supplements - Ferguson Health and Nutrition, Inc.

FERGUSON ATLANTIC - Apparel and accessories - Cluett, Peabody & Co.

FERIA - Wallcovering - The Creative Edge, Inc.

FERKY - Toys–stuffed ✫ - Russ Berrie and Co., Inc.

FERLIVIT - Pharmaceutical preparations ✫ - Medical Products Panamericana Inc.

FERM LAC - Skin care products - Waverly Beauty Products

FERM SET - Skin care products - Waverly Beauty Products

FERMALOX - Pharmaceutical preparations - Rhone-Poulenc Rorer Pharmaceuticals Inc.

FERMENTA - Pet products ✫ - Fermenta Animal Health

FERMENTASE - Beverages–alcohol ✫ - Premier Malt Products, Inc.

FERMENTATO - Tobacco products ✫ - Avanti Cigar Co.

FERMENZYME - Chemical preparations - Solvay Enzymes, Inc.

FERMI-FET - Computer peripheral equipment - Thunderbird Technologies, Inc.

FERMIBLANC - Yeast - Gist-Brocades Food Ingredients Inc.

FERMICHAMP - Yeast - Gist-Brocades Food Ingredients Inc.

FERMIPAN - Yeast - Gist-Brocades Food Ingredients Inc.

FERMIROUGE - Yeast - Gist-Brocades Food Ingredients Inc.

FERMIVIN - Yeast - Gist-Brocades Food Ingredients Inc.

FERMO BRITE - Hair care products - Revlon Consumer Products Corp.

FERMO CARESSE - Shampoos - Revlon Consumer Products Corp.

FERMODYL - Hair care products - Revlon Consumer Products Corp.

FERMOMETER - Thermometers - Tkach Enterprises

FERMONT - Bathroom fixtures ✫ - Crane Plumbing/Fiat Products

FERMUS - Paper–carbon - Kores Nordic USA Corp.

FERN - Floor coverings–carpet and rugs ✫ - American Excelsior Co.

FERN BRATTEN - Apparel–women's - Kellwood Co.

FERN COURT - Floor coverings–carpet and rugs ✫ - Hollytex Carpet Mills Inc.

FERN RIDGE FARMS POTATOES - Fruits and vegetables - Circle C Marketing, Inc.

FERN ROSE - Dishes–china - Taylor, Smith & Taylor Co.

FERN-WARE - Giftware - Terrace Ceramics Inc.

FERNANDES - Guitars ✫ - Chandler Industries

FERNANDEZ USA PUBLISHING CO. - Publisher's imprints - Fernandez USA Publishing Co., Inc.

FERNANDO - Cigars - Gesty Trading & Manufacturing Corp.

FERNANDO ROMERO BEVERLY HILLS - Hair care products - Fernando Romero Management Co., Inc.

FERNANDO SANCHEZ - Slippers - Fernando Sanchez Ltd.

FERNANDO STRAPPA COLLECTION - Footwear–men's - Stracam of Italy, Inc.

FERNBROOK - Dishes–china ✫ - WMF/USA

FERNBROOK - Floor coverings - Mannington Resilient Floors

FERNCROFT - Furniture - Bassett Furniture Industries, Inc.

FERNDALE - Floor coverings - Mannington Resilient Floors

FERNDALE - Floor coverings–carpet and rugs ✫ - Walter Carpet Mills

FERNDALE - Food products - Davis-Cleaver Foods Inc.

FERNDALE FARMS - Breads - Fluhrer Bakeries, Inc.

FERNDELL - Fruits and vegetables - Comstock Michigan Fruit

FERNDEX - Health care products ✫ - Ferndale Laboratories, Inc.

FERNET BRANCA - Beverages–alcohol - Carillon Importers Ltd.

FERNET-BRANCA - Health care products - Fratelli Branca & Co. Inc.

FERNGULLY - Computer software - Capstone Software

FERNGULLY - Kites - Hi-Flier Manufacturing Co.

FERNHIST - Health care products ✫ - Ferndale Laboratories, Inc.

FERNISOLONE - Health care products ✫ - Ferndale Laboratories, Inc.

FERNISONE - Health care products ✫ - Ferndale Laboratories, Inc.

FERNLEAF - Foil–aluminum - Highland Supply Corp.

FERNO WASHINGTON - Medical apparatus - Rockford Medical & Safety Co.

FERNSTON - Stone products - Endless Mountain Stone Co.

FERNWOOD - Drapery hardware - Kenney Manufacturing Co.

FERNWOOD - Garden equipment ✫ - Carefree Garden Products

FERNWOOD - Musical instrument accessories - Distex Corp.

FERO-FOLIC 500 - Pharmaceutical preparations - Abbott Laboratories

FERO-GRAD-500 - Pharmaceutical preparations - Abbott Laboratories

FERO-GRADUMET - Pharmaceutical preparations - Abbott Laboratories

FERON T-D - Pharmaceutical preparations ✫ - Perry Laboratories

FERONCLEAN - Chemical preparations - Gordon Feron & Co., Inc.

FERONFINISH - Chemical preparations - Gordon Feron & Co., Inc.

FERONGARD - Chemical preparations - Gordon Feron & Co., Inc.

FERONIM - Pharmaceutical preparations - Pasadena Research Laboratories, Inc.

FERON'S SPORTS - Sporting goods - Feron's Events, Inc.

FERON'S WOOD PRESERVATIVE/MILDEW PREVANTATIVE - Chemical preparations - Gordon Feron & Co., Inc.

FEROSORB-C - Pharmaceutical preparations ✫ - Roberts/Hauck Pharmaceuticals Inc.

FEROTRINSIC - Pharmaceutical preparations - Rugby Laboratories Inc.

FEROX - Cleaning preparations - Joan Maroney

FERPECT - Vitamins and nutritional supplements - Damino AS

FERPLAST - Pet products ✫ - Finny World Class Pet Products Inc.

FERR-L-TITE - Archery equipment - Bohning Co. Ltd.

FERRA - Pharmaceutical preparations - Goldline Laboratories, Inc.

FERRACOMP - Pharmaceutical preparations - Roberts/Hauck Pharmaceuticals Inc.

FERRALET - Vitamins and nutritional supplements ✫ - Mission Pharmacal Co.

FERRALET PLUS - Vitamins and nutritional supplements ✫ - Mission Pharmacal Co.

FERRALET S.R. - Vitamins and nutritional supplements ✫ - Mission Pharmacal Co.

FERRALYN - Pharmaceutical preparations - Lannett Co. Inc.

FERRANDIZ - Music boxes ✫ - Schmid Inc.

FERRANTE - Wines - Ferrante Winery & Vineyard

FERRARA - Food products - Ferrara Food Co., Inc.

FERRARA - Wines - Ferrara Winery

FERRARA PAN - Snack foods - Ferrara Pan Candy Co., Inc.

FERRARELLE - Water–mineral - Evian Waters of France

FERRARI - Floor coverings–carpet and rugs - Patcraft Mills Inc.

FERRARI - Motor vehicles–automobiles - Ferrari North America Inc.

FERRARI - Tires ✫ - Bridgestone/Firestone, Inc.

FERRARO'S - Juices - Ferraro's Fine Juices

FERRASTONE - Statuary - Rolf Stone, Inc.

FERRATE - Pharmaceutical preparations - Parmed Pharmaceuticals, Inc.

FERRATIN - Pharmaceutical preparations - Pasadena Research Laboratories, Inc.

FERREE'S - Musical instrument accessories - Ferree's Tools Inc.

FERREE'S B.I.T.S. - Musical instrument accessories ✫ - Ferree's Tools Inc.

FERREIRA - Brandy - Sogrape USA Inc.

FERRELL-ROSS - Sifting machines - Bluffton Agri/Industrial Corp.

FERRELLGAS - Oils–mineral - Ferrellgas, Inc.

FERRELLMETER - Electronic equipment - Ferrellgas, Inc.

FERRELL'S V NECK - Uniforms–athletic - Ferrells V Neck

FERRERO - Bakery products ✫ - Ferrero U.S.A Inc.

FERRERO - Chocolate candy - Holland-American Importing Co. Inc.

FERRERO ROCHER - Candy - Ferrero U.S.A Inc.

FERRERO ROCHER - Candy - Prince of Peace Enterprises Inc.

FERRERRO - Food products - Made in France

FERRE'S TOOLS - Musical instrument accessories - Ferree's Tools Inc.

FERRET - Automobiles - Ferret Corp.

FERRET - Personal defense products - Mace Security International, Inc.

FERRET BOTTLE - Pet products - Novalek, Inc.

FERRET CASTLE - Pet products - Pet Castle Co.

FERRET FRIEND - Pet products - Ryter Corp.

FERRET FUN FACTORY - Pet products - Duke's Dog Fashions

FERRET GLOW - Pet products - Four Paws Products Ltd.

FERRET-GO-ROUND - Pet products - Ferret World Inc.

FERRET HAMMOCK - Pet products - Ferret Stuff

FERRET KLEEN - Deodorizers - G.G. Bean Inc.

FERRET MARK I - Binoculars ✫ - Swift Instruments, Inc.

FERRET-OFF - Deodorizers - Thornell Corp.

FERRET SPHERE - Pet products - Pet Castle Co.

FERRET TEE - Pet products - Ferret Stuff

FERRET TUBE - Pet products - R.A.F. Trading Inc.

FERRETEER - Apparel and accessories - Four Ferreteers

FERRETONE - Pet products - 8 in 1 Pet Products Inc.

FERRETPAK - Pet products - Ferret World Inc.

FERRETRAIL - Pet products - Pets International, Ltd.

FERRETTS - Pharmaceutical preparations - Pharmics Inc.

FERRIGNO VINEYARDS - Wines - Ferrigno Vineyards & Winery

FERRINAL - Vitamins and nutritional supplements - H.R. Cenci Laboratories Inc.

FERRINI - Apparel–men's - Profile Menswear International Ltd.

FERRINI - Leather goods - Ferrini USA, Inc.

FERRINOVA - Vitamins and nutritional supplements - Winning Laboratories Corp.

FERRIS - Brushes–paint ✫ - PPG Industries, Inc.

FERRIS - Food products - Ferris Coffee & Nut Co.

FERRIS & ROBERTS - Teas–herbal - Gourm-E-Co Imports

✫ = Now out of production

FERRIS & ROBERTS FINEST QUALITY - Teas - Gourm-E-Co Imports

FERRIS WHEEL - Index cards ☆ - ACME Design Technology

FERRIS WHEEL - Infant product - Marlin Toy Products Inc.

FERRIS WHEEL - Pet products - American Cat Emporium

FERRISPERSE - Pigments–iron - Harcros Pigments, Inc.

FERRITABS - Chemical preparations - Aqua Clear Industries Inc.

FERRITRINSIC - Pharmaceutical preparations ☆ - Upjohn Co.

FERRO - Barbecues and grills - Ferro Corp.

FERRO - Hardware - Sequentia Inc. (Reinforced Plastics Div.)

FERRO-3 - Hardware - Travaco Laboratories Inc.

FERRO-12 - Pharmaceutical preparations - Biosante Distributors Inc.

FERRO B VITA - Pharmaceutical preparations ☆ - Rugby Laboratories Inc.

FERRO-BOB - Pharmaceutical preparations - Scot-Tussin Pharmacal Co.

FERRO-BOND - Paints ☆ - Valspar Corp.

FERRO CAPS - Pharmaceutical preparations - Michigan Pharmaceutical

FERRO COBALPLEX - Pharmaceutical preparations ☆ - C.O. Truxton Inc.

FERRO-CYTE - Pharmaceutical preparations - G.O. Spanner Inc.

FERRO-DSS - Pharmaceutical preparations - Geneva Generics Inc.

FERRO EXTRA I - Recording label - BASF Corp.

FERRO-FAX - Sealing compounds ☆ - A.C. Horn Co.

FERRO-FUMATRIN - Pharmaceutical preparations ☆ - U.S. Ethicals Inc.

FERRO MAXIMA I - Recording label - BASF Corp.

FERRO-SEQUELS - Vitamins and nutritional supplements - Lederle Laboratories

FERRO-SHEEN - Electronics equipment - Ampex Corp.

FERRO SUPER I - Recording label - BASF Corp.

FERRO-TECH-DISC-PELLETIZER - Machinery - Ferro-Tech, Inc.

FERRO-TECH-TURBULATOR - Machinery - Ferro-Tech, Inc.

FERROBID - Pharmaceutical preparations - Glaxo Wellcome Inc.

FERROBOND - Epoxy - Abatron, Inc.

FERROCHEL FE - Vitamins and nutritional supplements - Albion Laboratories, Inc.

FERROGRIT - Floor coverings - Wooster Products Inc.

FERROGUANATE - Pharmaceutical preparations ☆ - U.S. Ethicals Inc.

FERROLAC - Pharmaceutical preparations ☆ - U.S. Ethicals Inc.

FERROLIP - Pharmaceutical preparations ☆ - Boots Pharmaceuticals Inc.

FERROMAX - Loudspeakers - Weber Vintage Sound Technology

FERRONEED - Pharmaceutical preparations - Hanlon Drug Products

FERRONEX - Pharmaceutical preparations ☆ - Pasadena Research Laboratories, Inc.

FERRONORD - Pharmaceutical preparations ☆ - Berlex Laboratories, Inc.

FERROREX - Vitamins and nutritional supplements - Rex Research Laboratories

FERROSEL B KOTES - Pharmaceutical preparations ☆ - Harvey Laboratories Inc.

FERROSYN - Health care products - Halsom Home Care

FERROTHANE - Finishing agents ☆ - Flecto Co. Inc.

FERROTHANE 32 - Finishing agents ☆ - Flecto Co. Inc.

FERROTHANE SURFA-BOND - Finishing agents ☆ - Flecto Co. Inc.

FERROWATT - Lamp bulbs - Aamsco Lighting, Inc.

FERROX - Epoxy coatings - American Safety Technology

FERRY - Electrical equipment - General Cable Corp.

FERRY TALES - Greeting cards - Advance Seed Co.

FERRY'S FLOWER GARDEN - Flowers, plants, and seeds - Advance Seed Co.

FERT-A-PLY - Fertilizers - Earthway Products Inc.

FERTIBOR - Fertilizers - U.S. Borax Inc.

FERTIL-ADE-FERTILIZER - Fertilizers - Plant Marvel Laboratories

FERTIL-TONE - Soil–potting - Espoma Co.

FERTILIFE - Garden equipment - Scotts Co. (Organics Business Group)

FERTILITY MONITOR - Computer software - NFP Software

FERTILMIX - Soil–potting - A.H. Hoffman Inc.

FERTILO-PAKS - Tampons - Milex Products Inc.

FERUCCI - Wallpaper - Koroseal Wallcoverings

FERULIC ACID/GAMMA ORYZANOL CAPS - Vitamins and nutritional supplements - Vitamin Research Products Inc.

FERVID - Ophthalmic goods - Foremost Optical Products

FERVOR - Floor coverings–carpet and rugs - Gulistan Carpet Inc.

FERVOR TONES - Floor coverings–carpet and rugs ☆ - Gulistan Carpet Inc.

FERYL - Pharmaceutical preparations ☆ - Central Pharmaceutical Inc.

FES - Health care products - Flower Essence Services

FESCO - Toys ☆ - Fesco Plastics Corp.

FESCUEBLEND - Flowers, plants, and seeds - Ampac Seed Co.

FESOTYME - Pharmaceutical preparations ☆ - ICN Pharmaceuticals Inc.

FESTA - Food products - Alberico & Son Co.

FESTA BELLISSIMA - Sandwiches–prepackaged ☆ - Swissrose International Inc.

FESTAL - Food products - Owatonna Canning Co.

FESTAL - Vegetables–canned - Chiquita Processed Food, LLC

FESTEX - Health care products - Halsey Drug Co. Inc.

FESTIDA - Food products - Festia Foods Ltd.

FESTITOS - Food products - McLane Foods

FESTIVA - Area rugs, now out of production - Couristan Inc.

FESTIVA - Motor vehicles–automobiles - Ford Motor Co.

FESTIVA - Napkins–paper - Erving Paper Products Inc.

FESTIVA - Spas–home ☆ - Jacuzzi Inc.

FESTIVAAL - Dishes–wood ☆ - Dansk International Designs, Ltd.

FESTIVAL - Audio equipment - Harman Kardon Inc.

FESTIVAL - Candles - W and F Products Inc.

FESTIVAL - Dinnerware–glass - Nikko Ceramics Inc.

FESTIVAL - Dishes–china ☆ - Pickard Inc.

FESTIVAL - Electric organs - Lowrey Organ Co.

FESTIVAL - Eyeglasses - Art-Craft Optical Co.

FESTIVAL - Floor coverings - Mannington Resilient Floors

FESTIVAL - Floor coverings–carpet and rugs - Barrett Carpet Mills Inc.

FESTIVAL - Floor coverings–carpet and rugs - J and J Industries Inc.

FESTIVAL - Floor coverings–carpet and rugs - Southern Carpet Mills

FESTIVAL - Floor coverings–carpet and rugs ☆ - Patrick Carpet Mills

FESTIVAL - Food products - Acme Food Sales Inc.

FESTIVAL - Food products - National Preserve Co.

FESTIVAL - Food products ☆ - Globe Extracts Inc.

FESTIVAL - Furniture ☆ - Bemis Manufacturing Co.

FESTIVAL - Furniture ☆ - Hooker Furniture Corp.

FESTIVAL - Glass products - Tiffin Glass Co. Inc.

FESTIVAL - Housewares - Fesco Plastics Corp.

FESTIVAL - Kitchenware–earthenware - Arnart Imports Inc.

FESTIVAL - Tableware–china ☆ - Villeroy and Boch Tableware Ltd.

FESTIVAL - Trailers–travel - Fleetwood Enterprises, Inc.

FESTIVAL - Wallpaper - Capital Carousel Inc.

FESTIVAL - Wines - Breitenbach Wine Cellars

FESTIVAL II - Floor coverings–carpet and rugs - J and J Industries Inc.

FESTIVAL BOOKS - Publisher's imprints - Abingdon Press

FESTIVAL ICE CREAM - Ice cream - Smith's Dairy Products Co.

FESTIVAL MUSICAL BUDWEISER - Beverages–malt - Anheuser-Busch Companies Inc.

FESTIVAL OF FLOWER FAIRIES, A - Giftware ☆ - Enesco Corp.

FESTIVAL POT - Flowers, plants, and seeds - Hines Nurseries, Inc.

FESTIVAL TRAYS - Cookware - Carlisle Foodservice Products, Inc.

FESTIVAL USA - Luggage - Harris Trading Co.

FESTIVE - Calendars ☆ - C. & J. Willenborg Inc.

FESTIVE - Dinnerware–glass ☆ - WMF/USA

FESTIVE - Food products - Associated Food Stores Inc.

FESTIVE - Greeting cards ☆ - Cleo Inc.

FESTIVE - Ophthalmic goods - Foremost Optical Products

FESTIVE ALE - Beverages–malt - Thames America Trading Co. Ltd.

FESTIVE DINNER - Dinners–frozen - Pet Inc.

FESTIVE FIXINGS - Stationery - McCormick & Co., Inc.

FESTIVE HARVEST - Servingware - Corning Inc.

FESTIVE HARVEST - Spices and extracts ☆ - Chipurnoi Inc.

FESTIVE NIGHTS - Frames–eyeglass - Liberty Optical Manufacturing Co.

FESTIVE PINE - Deodorizers - Dial Corp.

FESTIVE RED - Lipsticks - Estee Lauder Inc.

FESTIVE SEASONINGS - Christmas tree ornaments - Mangelsen's

FESTIVE SEASONINGS - Craft supplies - Mangelsen's (VDI)

FESTIVE SPIRIT - Floor coverings–carpet and rugs - Evans-Black Carpet Mills

FESTIVE TREATS - Cookies - Sunshine/Salerno Inc.

FESTIVITEA - Teas–herbal - Unitea Herbs

FESTIVITY - Dinnerware–glass ☆ - Kenro Inc.

FESTIVITY - Dishes–china - Waterford Wedgwood USA, Inc.

FESTIVITY - Floor coverings–carpet and rugs ☆ - Karastan-Bigelow Inc.

FESTIVO - Baskets–wood ☆ - Royal Cathay Trading Co.

FESTIVO - Recording label - Organ Literature Foundation

FESTIVO LATINO - Iced tea–bottled or canned ☆ - Eastern Brewing Corp.

FESTOON - Frames–eyeglass - Hudson Optical Corp.

FET - Amplifiers–musical instrument ☆ - Seymour Duncan Pickups

FET 5000 - Medical apparatus ☆ - Hoggan Health Industries Inc.

FETAL PIG - Computer software - Ventura Educational Systems

FETAMIN - Pharmaceutical preparations ☆ - Mission Pharmacal Co.

FETCH - Computer software - Aldus Corp.

FETCH ARMSTRONG - Toys - Cap Toys, Inc.

FETCH STICKS - Pet products - Inn the Doghouse

FETCH TREDS - Pet products - Weiss Twice Toys, Inc.
FETCHING - Frames—eyeglass - Hudson Optical Corp.
FETCH'M - Tools—hand-operated - Breezy Inc.
FETCH'N CHEW - Pet products - HTZ Investment Corp.
FETCH'N SIT - Furniture ☆ - Gem Manufacturing Corp.
FETCH'N STEP - Stools—metal ☆ - Gem Manufacturing Corp.
FETCO INTERNATIONAL - Photo albums - Fetco International Corp.
FETE DE NUIT - Lipsticks - Lancome
FETEC - Veterinary pharmaceutical preparations - Upjohn Co.
FETHERLITE - Prophylactics - Schmid Laboratories
FETHERNIT - Apparel and accessories ☆ - Duofold Inc.
FETHERWATE - Lighting equipment - Acme-Lite Manufacturing Co.
FETINIC - Pharmaceutical preparations ☆ - Roberts/Hauck Pharmaceuticals Inc.
FETINIC-MW - Pharmaceutical preparations ☆ - Roberts/Hauck Pharmaceuticals Inc.
FETRIN - Pharmaceutical preparations - Lunsco Inc.
FETTUCCINE BROS. - Pasta - Great West Foods
FETTUCINNI LAMBORGHINI - Food products - My Favorite Year Inc.
FETZEN - Apparel and accessories - Patricia E. Byers
FETZER VINEYARDS - Wines - Fetzer Vineyards Inc.
FEU FROID - Perfumes - Helene Curtis Industries Inc.
FEUDAL - Furniture - Jamestown Lounge Co.
FEUDAL - Games - Avalon Hill Game Co.
FEUILLE - Glassware—household - Durand International
FEVA-GARD - Thermometers - Popper & Sons Inc.
FEVAXYN - Veterinary pharmaceutical preparations - Schering-Plough Animal Health
FEVER - Shoes - Stephen K. Fleming
FEVER-ALERT - Infant product - Prosonics Inc.
FEVER-DROP - Health care products - Natural Laboratories Corp.
FEVER INDICATOR PACIFIER - Infant product ☆ - American Baby Concepts
FEVER METER - Health care products - Steridyne Corp.
FEVER SCAN - Forehead thermometer - American Thermometer Co.
FEVER-SCAN-10 - Forehead thermometer - American Thermometer Co.
FEVER TESTER - Thermometer ☆ - American Thermometer Co.
FEVERFEW-POWER - Vitamins and nutritional supplements ☆ - Nature's Herbs
FEVERLINE - Thermometers - Liquid Crystal Sciences Inc.
FEVERNOL - Pharmaceutical preparations ☆ - Upsher-Smith Laboratories, Inc.
FEVITOL - Vitamins and nutritional supplements - Petland, Inc.
FEY - Bumpers—motor vehicle - Wedgestone Automotive Corp.
FEY & COMPANY - Jewelry - Edgar H. Fey Jewelers, Inc.
FEZZIWIG - Toys—stuffed ☆ - Dakin Inc.
FF - Computer software - Fastfinder Systems, L.C.
FF - Dinnerware—glass - Fitz & Floyd, Inc.
FF - Housewares stores - Fleet Wholesale Supply Co., Inc.
FF - Jewelry - F & F Creations Inc.
FF - Jewelry - Fragments, Inc.
FF - Jewelry - Frederica, Ltd.
FFF - Fruit drinks—bottled or canned - Flavors From Florida Inc.
FFF FORDE'S FUNCTIONAL FASHIONS, INC. - Apparel and accessories - Forde's Functional Fashions, Inc.
FFM - Automotive parts and accessories - Hayes Wheels International, Inc.
FFM - Food containers - Fast Food Merchandisers Inc.
FFMS - Computer software - Radian Corp.
FFP - Abrasive products - Practical Systems, Inc.
FFV - Cookies - Interbake Foods Inc.
FFV - Vegetables—frozen ☆ - Hanover Foods Corp.
FG - Apparel and accessories - Fashion Group International, Inc.
FG - Eyeglasses - BEC Distribution, Inc.
FG - Eyeglasses - Foster Grant Co. Inc.
FG - Shelving units—metal ☆ - Frick-Gallagher Manufacturing Co.
FG DEWAXER - Wax removers - Pettit Paint Co. Inc.
FG FRICK GALLAGHER - Motor vehicles—trucks ☆ - Frick-Gallagher Manufacturing Co.
FGSPORT - Sunglasses - BEC Distribution, Inc.
F.H. - Cabinets - Jim Walters Custom Cabinets
FH - Cooking utensils—stoneware - Pampered Chef, Ltd.
FH - Jewelry - F & H Repair Service Inc.
F.H. GILLINGHAM & CO. - Food products - F.H. Gillingham & Sons Inc.
FHI - Garment hangers - Batts, Inc.
FHI - Giftware - Fred Hill Inc.
FHMA - Radio communications equipment - Powerspectrum, Inc.
FHRED - Musical instrument accessories - Quodlibet, Inc.
FI - Giftware - Findings Inc.

FI - Nuts and bolts - Flexalloy Inc.
FI-1 SOY FIBRE - Grain products—flour - Fibred, Inc.
FI-BAR - Yogurt - Natural Nectar Corp.
FI-BAR BERRY BEST - Snack foods - Natural Nectar Corp.
FI-BAR FAT FREE - Snack foods - Natural Nectar Corp.
FI-BAR NECTAR - Food products - Natural Nectar Corp.
FI-CORD - Dictating machines ☆ - Heitz Service Corp.
FI FO FUM - Pens ☆ - Paper Mate Co.
FI-ROK - Gypsum products - Celotex Corp.
FI-ROK PLUS - Gypsum products - Celotex Corp.
FI RST NOTES - Notebooks and notepads - First Notes Co.
FI-SHOCK - Electrical equipment - Fi-Shock Inc.
FI-TECH - Tobacco products - Fi-Tech, Inc.
FI:X - Wood fillers - OSI Sealants, Inc.
FI:X TOUCH UP STIK - Caulking compounds - OSI Sealants, Inc.
FIALDINI - Apparel stores—men's - Apparel Imports, Inc.
FIA'LE COLLECTION - Apparel and accessories - Roy Smith Shoes, Inc.
FIAMMA - Fragrance - Borghese Cosmetics Inc.
FIAMMA - Frames—eyeglass - Pathway Optical Prods.
FIANCEE'S - Shoes - Interco Inc.
FIANDRE - Ceramic tile - Integrity Tile Co.
FIASCO - Apparel—women's - Resource Productions
FIASCO - Eyeglasses - Art-Craft Optical Co.
FIASCOWARE - Kitchen utensils—enameled - Mindy Schneider
FIAT - Hardware - Blaine Window Hardware Inc.
FIAT - Motor vehicles—automobiles - Fiat USA, Inc.
FIAT PRODUCTS - Plumbing fixtures—metal - CR-PL L.P.
FIBAMINS - Health care products - Astra Associates
FIBER 7 - Cereal - Health Valley Food
FIBER-7 - Vitamins and nutritional supplements - Naturally Vitamin Supplements Inc.
FIBER 7 FLAKES - Cereal - Health Valley Food
FIBER 28 - Vitamins and nutritional supplements - Vita Source, Inc.
FIBER 88 - Health care products ☆ - Natrol, Inc.
FIBER AQUABOX - Mattresses - Del Astra Industries Inc.
FIBER BLEND - Vitamins and nutritional supplements - Shaklee Corp.
FIBER BONDED CARPETS - Floor coverings—carpet and rugs - Daltonian Carpet & Cushion Inc.
FIBER BRACE - Building materials - Temple-Inland Forest Products Corp.
FIBER/CASE - Chemicals - Fiberglass Encasements, Inc.
FIBER-CLASSIC - Glass products - Therma-Tru Corp.
FIBER-CRAFT - Doors ☆ - Therma-Tru Corp.
FIBER CRISP - Crackers ☆ - Fantastic Foods Inc.
FIBER DELIGHT - Vitamin and mineral supplements - Diet Fitness Weight Loss Centers, Inc.
FIBER EDGE - Paper - Woodtape Co.
FIBER-ETCH - Chemical preparations - Michele Hester
FIBER FACE - Wood products - Georgia-Pacific Corp.
FIBER FEAST - Snack foods ☆ - El Molino Mills
FIBER-FLASH - Photographic equipment - SP Systems/Saratons
FIBER FLEX - Clamps—metal - Sign-Up Corp.
FIBER-FLEX CROSS BRACES - Clamps—metal - Sign-Up Corp.
FIBER FLOATS - Beverages - Energy Factors
FIBER FLUFF - Apparel—women's ☆ - Bali Co. Inc.
FIBER FORCE-6 - Vitamins and nutritional supplements - Nutrition Warehouse, Inc.
FIBER FULL - Vitamins and nutritional supplements ☆ - Thompson Medical Co., Inc.
FIBER GLASS SHEEN - Fiberglass cleaner - Comstar International Inc. (IPC Div.)
FIBER GOLD - Vitamins and nutritional supplements - Health Maintenance Programs Inc.
FIBER GOODNESS - Breads - Campbell Taggart Inc.
FIBER GUARD - Vitamins and nutritional supplements - Wyeth-Ayerst Laboratories
FIBER JUMBOS - Cookies - Health Valley Food
FIBER KING - Fibers—polyester - Fairfield Processing Corp.
FIBER-KING - Mats—grass, reed, and jute - Koffler Sales Co.
FIBER-LAX - Pharmaceutical preparations - Rugby Laboratories Inc.
FIBER LEAN - Health care products ☆ - Reese Chemical Co.
FIBER LINK - Rope - Fiberlink Webbing Products LLC
FIBER-LITE - Doors—garage - Calder Manufacturing Co.
FIBER-LITE - Firearms, accessories, and parts - Modern Muzzle Loading, Inc.
FIBER-LOK - Floor coverings—carpet and rugs - Environmental Technology, Inc.
FIBER MASTER - Cleaning preparations—carpet and rug - Promaster

☆ = Now out of production

FIBER N' FLAX - Vitamins and nutritional supplements - Tishcon Corp.
FIBER 'N TOFU - Snack foods ☆ - Above All Health Inc.
FIBER NAIL - Nail care products - Fiber Nail Inc.
FIBER NATURALS - Floor cleaning equipment - Glit, Inc.
FIBER ONE - Cereal - General Mills, Inc.
FIBER OPTIC CABLES - Medical apparatus - Luxtec Corp.
FIBER OPTIC DEEP SPACE NINE - Toys–models - ERTL Co., Inc.
FIBER OPTIC STAR DESTROYER - Toys–models - ERTL Co., Inc.
FIBER OPTIC U.S.S. ENTERPRISE - Toys–models - ERTL Co., Inc.
FIBER OPTICS - Lighting fixtures - Lucifer Lighting Co.
FIBER PLEX - Vitamins and nutritional supplements - Natural Organics, Inc.
FIBER PLUS - Nail care products - Worldwide Cosmetics
FIBER PLUS - Vitamins and nutritional supplements - Yerba Prima, Inc.
FIBER PLUSH SYSTEM B-II - Mattresses ☆ - Vinyl Products
FIBER-PLY - Plywood - Georgia-Pacific Corp.
FIBER PROTECT - Cosmetics ☆ - Nina International, Inc.
FIBER-PURSE - Tubes–plastic - National Fiberstok Corp.
FIBER RICH - Crackers - A.V. Olsson Trading Co., Inc.
FIBER RICH - Juices - Well Creek Farms
FIBER RICH - Pharmaceutical preparations ☆ - Columbia Laboratories Inc.
FIBER-RITE, 800 MG. - Vitamins and nutritional supplements - Vitamin Research Products Inc.
FIBER-SOL - Vitamins and nutritional supplements - Twinlab
FIBER SONIC - Golfing equipment - TourEdge Golf Manufacturing Inc.
FIBER STAR - Golfing equipment - Golfsmith International Inc.
FIBER STUDIO PRESS - Publisher's imprints - Martingale & Co.
FIBER SUPREME - Vitamins and nutritional supplements - ND Labs Inc.
FIBER-TECH - Sporting goods - Total Sports Source
FIBER TO THE DESK - Computer peripheral equipment - Dual-Tek Corp.
FIBER TRENDS - Publisher's imprints - Beverly J. Galeskas
FIBER-VELOPE - Filing supplies and wallets - American Fiber-Velope Manufacturing Co.
FIBER YEAST - Vitamins and nutritional supplements - Lewis Laboratories International Ltd.
FIBER YOU CAN COUNT ON - Cables–fiber optic - Corning Inc.
FIBERALL - Laxatives - Ciba-Geigy Corp.
FIBERBASE - Computer software - ADC Telecommunications, Inc.
FIBERBILT - Cases–compacts - Fiberbilt Cases Inc.
FIBERBOND - Adhesives and sealants ☆ - Bil-Dry Corp.
FIBERBOND - Chemical preparations - CPC International Inc.
FIBERBOND - Fabrics–broadcloth - Fiberbond Corp.
FIBERBOND - Paper industry machinery - Albany International Corp.
FIBERBRITE - Panels - Harbor Sales Co.
FIBERCLEANSE - Laxatives - Nature's Way Products, Inc.
FIBERCO - Musical instruments - Fibre Case & Novelty Co.
FIBERCOAT - Adhesives and sealants - Garon Products Inc.
FIBERCON - Laxatives - Lederle Laboratories
FIBERCOR - Particle board - Georgia-Pacific Corp.
FIBERCOR - Sports rackets and accessories - Gexco Enterprises
FIBERCOR - Water filtering units - Minntech Corp.
FIBERCRAFT - Garden furniture–rattan ☆ - Lloyd/Flanders Industries
FIBERDOPHILUS - Health care products - Longevity Network, Ltd.
FIBEREYE - Diagnostic apparatus - Microtest, Inc.
FIBERFLAKE - Particle board - Roseburg Forest Products Co.
FIBERFLEX - Luggage - Samsonite Corp.
FIBERFLEX - Medical apparatus - Spenco Medical Corp.
FIBERFLEX - Suits–men's - Pincus Bros., Inc.
FIBERFLIGHT - Bicycles - Edo Sports
FIBERFLUF - Insulation ☆ - Conwed Plastics
FIBERFORM - Laxatives - G and W Laboratories Inc.
FIBERGARD - Stain removers - Fibergard Chemical Corp.
FIBERGEN - Vitamins and nutritional supplements - Bioenergy Nutrient's Inc.
FIBERGIZER BAR - Snack foods - Twinlab
FIBERGLASS ETC. - Cleaning preparations - Dial Corp.
FIBERGLASS MAGIC - Furniture polish and wax - Magic American Corp.
FIBERGLO - Lighting equipment - Fiberstars, Inc.
FIBERGLO - Translucent place mats - Convergence Corp.
FIBERGRAFIX - Computer software - At&T Corp.
FIBERGRATE - Building materials - Fibergrate Composite Structures
FIBERGRATE - Gratings–floor - Fibergrate Corp.
FIBERGUARD - Guns ☆ - Weatherby Inc.
FIBERGY - Vitamins and nutritional supplements - Usana, Inc.
FIBERHEALTH - Vitamins and nutritional supplements - Health Products Corp.
FIBERHYDE - Binders - National Fiberstok Corp.
FIBERHYDRANT - Computer software - Visual F/X, Inc.
FIBERIFIC - Granola bars - Nature's Plus

FIBERKOTE - Binders - National Fiberstok Corp.
FIBERLENE - Filters–oil - Fiberlene Filters, Inc.
FIBERLIFE - Breads - DCB, Inc.
FIBERLITE - Health care products ☆ - Nature's Way Products, Inc.
FIBERLITE - Lighting equipment - Bristolite Skylights
FIBERLITE - Wastebaskets ☆ - Globe-Weis
FIBERLOC - Fabrics–broadcloth - Felters Co.
FIBERLOFT - Fibers–synthetic - Stearns Technical Textiles Co.
FIBERLON - Fibers–synthetic - Georgia-Bonded Fibers, Inc.
FIBERLUX - Cases–musical instrument - Scanlan Music Sales Inc.
FIBERLUX - Doors–glass - Ethyl Corp.
FIBERLUX - Fibers–polyester - Ohio Mattress Co.
FIBERMARK - Guns - Weatherby Inc.
FIBERMATE - Plant growth regulators - PRS Materials, Inc.
FIBERMAX - Fencing–gates and posts - Common Sense Fence
FIBERMED - Pharmaceutical preparations - Purdue Frederick Co.
FIBERMESH - Nail care products - E.O.H. Industries, Inc.
FIBERMINI - Ophthalmic goods - Tektronix, Inc.
FIBERMUX - Computer software - ADC Fibermux
FIBER'N MOR - Nutritional supplements - Omnitrition International, Inc.
FIBEROCK - Containers–shipping - Weyerhaeuser Co.
FIBEROK - Containers–trash - Federal Fibre Corp.
FIBEROLLS - Tape–adhesive - Thermopatch Corp.
FIBERPAK - Electrical equipment - Antec Corp.
FIBERPDA - Measuring instruments - Dantec Measurement Technology Inc.
FIBERPLETE - Vitamins and nutritional supplements - Great Life Laboratories Inc.
FIBERPRESS - Binders - National Fiberstok Corp.
FIBERPRO - Handles–plastic - Woodings-Verona Tool Works Inc.
FIBERRY - Sporting goods - Nu Skin International, Inc.
FIBER'S A-WEIGH - Health care products - Fiske Industries Inc.
FIBERSCAPE - Electric lighting equipment - Fiberstars, Inc.
FIBERSEAL - Cable splice enclosures - Reliance Comm/Tec Corp.
FIBERSEAL - Communications equipment - ADC Telecommunications, Inc.
FIBERSENTRY - Computer hardware - Tacan Corp.
FIBERSKIN - Paneling - Georgia-Pacific Corp.
FIBERSKYN - Drums–musical instruments - Remo, Inc.
FIBERSOFT - Fibers–polyester - Ohio Mattress Co.
FIBERSPOOL - Packaging–blisterwrap - Myriadlase, Inc.
FIBERSPORT - Sporting goods - Sport Supply Group, Inc.
FIBERSTOK - Binders - National Fiberstok Corp.
FIBERSTRATE - Lumber - Georgia-Pacific Corp.
FIBERSTRONG - Lumber - Georgia-Pacific Corp.
FIBERSWITCH - Electrical equipment - Fiber Switch Technologies
FIBERTECH - Animal feeds - Ralston Purina Co.
FIBERTECH - Wallpaper - Gencorp Polymer Products
FIBERTHERM - Solid fuel products - Cemtech L.P.
FIBERTHERM PLUS - Solid fuel products - Cemtech L.P.
FIBERTHIN - Health care products - Esquire Pharmaceuticals Inc.
FIBERTONE - Vitamins and nutritional supplements - Sunrider Corp.
FIBERTOUCH - Fishing rods - Scott Powr-Ply Co.
FIBERTUBE - Measuring instruments - Pruett Industries, Inc.
FIBERTUBE - Tubes–plastic - National Fiberstok Corp.
FIBERTUFF - Paperboard - Scott Paper Co.
FIBERTWIST - Electric lighting equipment - Fiberstars, Inc.
FIBERVAULT - Tanks–storage - Hoover Group, Inc.
FIBERWALL - Concrete products - Wall Firma Inc.
FIBERWEAR - Glass products - Sloss Industries Corp.
FIBERWEVE - Housewares ☆ - American Textile Products Co.
FIBERWISE - Cereal ☆ - Kellogg Co.
FIBERWOOD - Building materials–concrete - Weyerhaeuser Co.
FIBERWOVEN - Blankets - Chatham Manufacturing Co.
FIBLAST - Pharmaceutical preparations - Scios Nova Inc.
+FIBONACCI +BOX - Boxes - Gerald L. Koenig
FIBRACOL - Bandages - Johnson & Johnson
FIBRAMENT - Kitchenware–earthenware - AWMCO Inc.
FIBRASOL - Fibers–synthetic - Axim Concrete Technologies Inc.
FIBRATEX SCUFF PADS - Paper–sand - Carborundum Abrasives North America
FIBRE - Cases–musical instrument - Anvil Cases
FIBRE 500 - Pharmaceutical preparations ☆ - Vita Plus Industries Inc.
FIBRE BOX - Tool boxes - Fibre Body Industries Inc.
FIBRE COAT - Cement - Tamms Industries Co.
FIBRE-CRAFT - Bells - Fibre-Craft Materials Corp.
FIBRE FAST - Insulating materials–foam - C.G.I.-Silvercoat Inc.
FIBRE-GLASS - Boats - Frank M. Weeks Yacht Yard

FIBRE-LAM - Wood products ☆ - Fibreboard Corp.
FIBRE LASTIC - Finishing agents - Plastics & Resins Ltd.
FIBRE LOCK - Sporting goods ☆ - Duro Finishing Corp.
FIBRE PURE - Cleaning preparations–household - Aquacide
FIBRE SNACK - Food products - Hydromer Inc.
FIBRE-TITE - Wood fillers ☆ - Gibson-Homans of Iowa Inc.
FIBRE TRIM - Vitamins and nutritional supplements - Schering-Plough Healthcare Products
FIBRE WAY - Vitamins and nutritional supplements - 206 Macopin Corp.
FIBREAD - Breads - Broadmoor Baker, Inc.
FIBRE(B)LOCK - Floor coverings - Norman Kaswell
FIBRE(B)LOCK - Padding–foam - Kaswell & Co., Inc.
FIBREC - Dyes and pigments ☆ - Norma Dharma Trading Co.
FIBRECAST - Computer peripheral equipment - Videomedia, Inc.
FIBRECLAD INFRANGIBLE - Giftware - Universal Statuary Corp.
FIBRECRAFT - Hobby kits - Fibre-Craft Materials Corp.
FIBREDEX - File folders - Hollinger Corp.
FIBREDYNE - Fabrics - National Nonwovens
FIBREGARDE - Cleaning preparations–carpet and rug ☆ - Castex Industries Inc.
FIBREKOR - Dental compounds - Jeneric/Pentron Inc.
FIBRELITE - Electronic equipment - Fairtron Corp.
FIBRELOK - Mops ☆ - Golden Star Inc.
FIBREMATRIX - Golfing equipment - Brunswick Bowling & Billiards Corp.
FIBRES MEET FABRIC - Fabrics–tapestry ☆ - Combeau Industries
FIBRESEAL - Fireplace equipment ☆ - Heatsafe
FIBRESLIDE - Fiberboard - Harpo Investment, Inc.
FIBRESTORE - Vitamins and nutritional supplements - Reliv' International, Inc.
FIBREWORKS - Floor coverings - Fibreworks Corp.
FIBREX - Health care products - Delta Fibre Foods
FIBREX - Office supplies - Oliner Fibre Co. Inc.
FIBRIJET - Medical apparatus - Micromedics, Inc.
FIBRIM - Food products - Protein Technologies
FIBRINOGEN - Pharmaceutical preparations - City Chemical Corp.
FIBRISTAT - Medical products - Fibratek, Inc.
FIBRO - Brooms ☆ - Lighthouse Industries
FIBRO - Fabrics–rayon - Courtaulds Fibres Inc.
FIBRO-CLAY - Clay–modeling ☆ - Milton Bradley Co.
FIBRON - Windows - Owens Corning
FIBRWRAP - Epoxy - Hexcel-Fyfe LLC
FIBULA - Jewelry - Fibula
FIC - Shoes - Genesco Inc.
FICGO - Coffee substitutes - Cal-Leaf Health Products Inc.
FICHE-SAFE - Electronic equipment - Luxor
FICHE V-FILE - Office supplies ☆ - Rolodex Corp.
FICHEFINDER - Computer software - Lightspeed Dealer Management Systems Inc.
FICKLE FILM - Toys - James Industries, Inc.
FICKLE FINGER - Hair care products - Waverly Beauty Products
FICKLE FOAM - Plaything - James Industries, Inc.
FICKLE PICKLE - Toys - Gym Rat, Inc.
FICKLE PICKLES - Toys ☆ - Steven Manufacturing Co.
FICKLIN - Wines - Parrott & Co.
FICKLIN PORTS - Wines - Shaw-Ross International Importers
FICKLIN VINEYARDS - Wines - Ficklin Vineyards
FICKS FEATURES - Furniture–wood - Ficks Reed Co. Inc.
FICKS REED - Furniture–wood - Ficks Reed Co. Inc.
F.I.C.S.I.T. - Racks - Warner Press, Inc.
FICTIONARY - Games ☆ - Mayfair Games, Inc.
FICTIONMASTER - Computer software - WritePro Corp.
FID ALLER - Rope splicing and threading tools - James H. Marthaller
FID-O - Knife blades - Fid-O/McGrew Splicing Tool Co.
FIDA - Snack foods - Bell'amore Imports Inc.
FIDASS - Confections ☆ - R.L. Albert & Son, Inc.
FIDCO - Jewelry - Feature Enterprises
FIDDLE FACTORY - Novelty items - Sell-O Manufacturing Inc.
FIDDLE FADDLE - Popcorn - Novartis Nutrition Corp.
FIDDLE-RIB - Silver products - Kirk & Matz Ltd.
FIDDLE STICK - Tiles–ceramic - Latco Products
FIDDLE STICKS - Jewelry - K & M Associates
FIDDLE STICKS - Pens - Sanford Corp.
FIDDLE-STIX - Frames–eyeglass - Pathway Optical Prods.
FIDDLE, THREAD & SHELL - Flatware ☆ - Towle Silversmiths
FIDDLEPAK - Cases–musical instrument - M & M Distributing Co.
FIDDLER - Recording label ☆ - Rounder Records Corp.
FIDDLER SOLIDS - Fabrics - Charter Fabrics Inc.

FIDDLERS - Candy - Elmer Candy Corp.
FIDDLER'S GREEN - Apparel and accessories - Sally Gee Inc.
FIDDLERS PEOPLE BY DAVID KAPLAN - Statuary–wood - David Kaplan Studio
FIDDLESTICKS - Hobby kits - Current, Inc.
FIDDLESTIX - Floor coverings–carpet and rugs - Galaxy Carpet Mills Inc.
FIDDLESTX - Lacrosse sticks and balls - STX, Inc.
FIDDLETOWN - Wines - Renwood Winery, Inc.
FIDEK - Loudspeakers - Fidek Audio Corp.
FIDELIA - Rings–jewelry - Artcarved Inc.
FIDELIO - Cigars - James B. Russell Inc.
FIDELIO - Fabrics - J.B. Martin Co. Inc.
FIDELIO - Watches - Seville Watch Corp.
FIDELIS - Artists' materials ☆ - Hunt Manufacturing Co.
FIDELIS - Brandy - Safeway Stores Inc.
FIDELIS - Thread - Threads USA Div.
FIDELITONE - Audio equipment - Fidelitone Inc.
FIDELITY - Apparel and accessories - Fidelity Sportswear Co.
FIDELITY - Brushes–paint ☆ - PPG Industries, Inc.
FIDELITY - Cases–eyeglass - Fidelity Case Corp.
FIDELITY - Computer software - Omniview, Inc.
FIDELITY - Games - Fidelity Electronics International Inc.
FIDELITY - Health care products ☆ - Medicine Shoppe International Inc.
FIDELITY - Hearing aids - Starkey Labs Inc.
FIDELITY - Paper - Esleeck Manufacturing Co., Inc.
FIDELITY - Spices and extracts - Herbert Marmorek & Son, Inc.
FIDELITY - Thread - Threads USA Div.
FIDELITY ACCESSLINE - Banks–commercial - FMR Corp.
FIDELITY LEATHER - Apparel and accessories ☆ - Fidelity Sportswear Co.
FIDELITY ON-LINEXPRESS - Computer software - FMR Corp.
FIDEO OLE' - Spices and extracts - Bolner's Fiesta Products, Inc.
FIDGET - Fishing lures - Fred Arbogast Co. Inc.
FIDGET FRIENDS - Dolls - Erin Louise Voorhies
FIDJI - Frames–eyeglass - Zylo Ware Corp.
FIDJI - Perfumes - Lancome
FIDO - Animal feeds - Bush Brothers and Co.
FIDO - Clocks - James D. Cofer Inc.
FIDO - Golfing equipment - Tech Sports Inc.
FIDO - Housewares - Metro/Thebe, Inc.
FIDO - Pet collars - Fido, Inc.
FIDO BONES - Dog food ☆ - Gimborn U.S., Inc.
FIDO CASTRO - Dog food - Mark Holden and John P. Kempf Jr. Partnership
FIDO DIDO - Dolls - Fido Dido Inc.
FIDO DIDO - Frames–picture - Terragrafics Inc.
FIDO DIDO - Watches ☆ - E. Gluck Corp.
FIDO FLEECE - Pet products - Mann Designs Ltd.
FIDO-SHOCK - Electrical equipment - Fi-Shock Inc.
FIDO'S COOKIES - Dog food - Topographic Chocolate Co.
FIE-Z-GARD - Gloves–safety - Food Industry Equipment International, Inc.
FIEBING - Chemical preparations - St. Lawrence Sales Inc.
FIEKL PEN - Pens ☆ - Eversharp Pen Co.
FIELD - Floor coverings–carpet and rugs ☆ - Regal Rugs Inc.
FIELD - Meat products–beef - Field Packing Co.
FIELD - Wallets - Brigade Quartermasters Ltd.
FIELD ADVENTURE KIT - Binoculars - Sakar International Inc.
FIELD & SHOW - Compasses - Shopko Stores, Inc.
FIELD & SHOW - Pet food - Doane Products Co.
FIELD & STREAM - Apparel and accessories - Gordon & Ferguson of Delaware, Inc.
FIELD & STREAM - Boxes - Field & Stream Licenses Co.
FIELD & STREAM - Cigarettes - Philip Morris Companies Inc.
FIELD & STREAM - Eyeglasses - Art-Craft Optical Co.
FIELD & STREAM - Fabrics–tapestry ☆ - Coloroll Inc.
FIELD & STREAM - Motor vehicles–automobiles - Field & Stream Licenses Co.
FIELD & STREAM - Shoe polish - Mason Shoe Manufacturing Co.
FIELD & STREAM - Tobacco products - House of Windsor Inc.
FIELD BLOCKS - Bathing suits - E.D. Murphy Corp.
FIELD BOXES - Cartons–paperboard - H. Field & Sons, Inc.
FIELD COMMAND - Games - Vist Marketing, Inc.
FIELD COMMANDER - Sporting goods - Glovesmith, Inc.
FIELD CONTROL - Electronic equipment - General Electric Co.
FIELD DAY - Frames–eyeglass - Liberty Optical Manufacturing Co.
FIELD DRESSER - Knives - Precise International/Wenger
FIELD EXCHANGE - Apparel and accessories - Galt Sand Co.
FIELD EXPLORER - Toys - Fisher-Price, Inc.

☆ = Now out of production

FIELD FLOWERS - Colognes ☆ - Avon Products, Inc.

FIELD FLOWERS - Tableware–china ☆ - Villeroy and Boch Tableware Ltd.

FIELD FLOWERS - Wallpaper ☆ - Thomas Strahan Wallcoverings

FIELD FLOWERS II - Fabrics–tapestry - Comark Wallcoverings

FIELD FRESH - Cat litter - Andersons Management Corp.

FIELD FRESH - Flowers, plants, and seeds ☆ - J.C. Penney Co., Inc.

FIELD GATES - Cheese - First District Association

FIELD GLASS - Wallpaper - Blumenthal

FIELD GOAL - Collectible trading cards - ANCO Collector Supplies, Inc.

FIELD GUIDE - Games - Chaosium Inc.

FIELD GUN - Shotguns - Armsport Inc.

FIELD ISSUE - Watches - Precise International/Wenger

FIELD KING - Bicycles - Columbia Manufacturing Inc.

FIELD KING - Garden equipment - The Fountainhead Group, Inc.

FIELD MARSHALL - Frames–eyeglass ☆ - Universal/Univis Inc.

FIELD MASTER - Dog food - Ralston Purina Co.

FIELD MOUSEPAD - Computer peripheral equipment - Fieldworks, Inc.

FIELD 'N FARM - Dog food - Ralston Purina Co.

FIELD 'N FARM CLASSIC - Dog food - Ralston Purina Co.

FIELD OF CLOVER - House furnishings - Kellwood Co.

FIELD OF DREAMS - Floor coverings–carpet and rugs - Gulistan Carpet Inc.

FIELD PAL - Footwear - Southern Leather & Shoe Co.

FIELD PEN - Pens - Eversharp Pen Co.

FIELD POPPIES - Bedding–linen - Dan River Inc.

FIELD-PRO - Computer storage devices ☆ - Amherst International Enterprises Co.

FIELD RATION - Dog food - Farmland Industries Inc.

FIELD RULES - Computer software - Alpha Software Corp.

FIELD SCOUT - Agricultural machinery - Quimby Brothers

FIELD STONE - Fabrics–tapestry - Comark Wallcoverings

FIELD STONE - Wines - Field Stone Winery

FIELD STONE CELLARS - Wines - Field Stone Winery

FIELD STONE VINEYARD - Wines - Field Stone Winery

FIELD STONE WINERY - Wines - Field Stone Winery

FIELD TO FIELD - Computer software - AGA Computer Services Inc.

FIELD TRIAL - Dog food - American Pet Food Co.

FIELD TRIP TO THE RAINFOREST, A - Computer software - Sunburst Communications, Inc.

FIELD WORKSTATION - Computer peripheral equipment - Fieldworks, Inc.

FIELDALE - Floor coverings–carpet and rugs - Karastan-Bigelow Inc.

FIELDALE FARMS - Meat products–poultry - Fieldale Farms Corp.

FIELDBATH - Medical apparatus - Incline Technologies, Inc.

FIELDBROOK SOFTWARE - Computer software - MLM-Fieldbrook Inc.

FIELDBROOK VALLEY WINERY - Wines - Fieldbrook Valley Winery

FIELDCAM TLV - Cameras–video - Fuhrman Diversified

FIELDCAM WCRYS - Cameras–video - Fuhrman Diversified

FIELDCRAFT - Knives - Marble Arms Corp.

FIELDCREST - Dairy products - Dean Foods Co.

FIELDCREST - Frames–eyeglass ☆ - Universal/Univis Inc.

FIELDCREST - Towels - Fieldcrest Cannon, Inc.

FIELDCREST CANNON - Towels - Fieldcrest Cannon, Inc.

FIELDER'S CHOICE - Candy - Russ Berrie and Co., Inc.

FIELDER'S CHOICE - Pizzas–frozen ☆ - Mr. Z's Fund Raising Corp.

FIELDERS' CHOICE - Sporting goods - General Sportcraft Co. Ltd.

FIELDFORMS - Computer software - Penmetrics, Inc.

FIELDHOUSE - Floor coverings - AstroTurf Industries Inc.

FIELDING - Glassware–household ☆ - Crownford Giftware Co. Inc.

FIELDING TRAVEL BOOKS - Publisher's imprints - William Morrow and Co. Inc.

FIELDING WORLDWIDE - Publisher's imprints - Fielding Worldwide, Inc.

FIELDJET - Nozzles - Spraying Systems Co.

FIELDLAB - Scientific apparatus - Unifet Inc.

FIELDLINE - Sporting goods - Outdoor Recreation Group

FIELDLINK - Optical machinery - Dicon

FIELDMARK - Towels ☆ - Needlecraft Industries

FIELDMASTER - Apparel and accessories - Sears, Roebuck and Co.

FIELDMASTER - Electrical equipment - Trippensee Corp.

FIELDMASTER - Guns - Remington Arms Co., Inc.

FIELDMASTER - Knives–pocket - Swiss Army Brands, Ltd.

FIELDMASTER - Measuring instruments - Rolatape Corp.

FIELDPAK - Computer storage devices - Avid Technology, Inc.

FIELDPRO - Computer software - Heartland Technologies, Inc.

FIELDPRO - Computer software - Resources Engineering Systems, Inc.

FIELD'S - Bakery products–frozen - Field's Inc.

FIELDS - Blinds–vertical - Tontine/VyTech Industries Inc.

FIELDS - Floor coverings - Mannington Resilient Floors

FIELDS & MADISON - Eyeglasses - D.O.C. Optics Corp.

FIELDS OF GREENS - Vitamins and nutritional supplements - Aloe Vera of America, Inc.

FIELDS OF PROVENCE - Wallpaper ☆ - Eisenhart Wallcoverings Co.

FIELDS OF WAR - Toys - Mattel, Inc.

FIELD'S WORLDS BEST - Bakery products–frozen - Field's Inc.

FIELDSCHOICE - Soil testing kits - Premier Environmental Products, Inc.

FIELDSPEC - Spectrometers - Analytical Spectral Devices Inc.

FIELDSTON - Coats–children's - S. Rothschild & Co., Inc.

FIELDSTONE - Cabinets - Fieldstone Cabinetry

FIELDSTONE - Cabinets - Masco Corp.

FIELDSTONE - Fireplaces - Dyna Corp.

FIELDSTONE - Floor coverings - Congoleum Corp.

FIELDSTONE - Floor coverings–carpet and rugs - Colonial Mills Inc.

FIELDSTONE - Gloves ☆ - Gates Gloves

FIELDSTONE - Posters - Flashco

FIELDTURF - Floor coverings–carpet and rugs - Fieldturf & Carpet Inc.

FIELDTURF 35OZ UF - Floor coverings - Fieldturf & Carpet Inc.

FIELDTURF 48 UF - Floor coverings - Fieldturf & Carpet Inc.

FIELDVIEW - Computer software - Dicon

FIEND - Apparel and accessories - Adrian Donald Gross

FIEND FOLIO - Games ☆ - Tsr, Inc.

FIERA - Ophthalmic goods - Foremost Optical Products

FIERCE GRIP - Darts and dart games - Dart Mart Inc.

FIERO - Bicycles ☆ - Kung Hsue She, Inc.

FIERO - Boats–motor ☆ - Century Boat Co.

FIERO - Floor coverings–carpet and rugs ☆ - Galaxy Carpet Mills Inc.

FIERO - Footwear–athletic - KangaROOS USA Inc.

FIERO - Gloves - Gordini USA Inc.

FIERO - Motor vehicles–automobiles ☆ - General Motors Corp. (Pontiac/GMC Div.)

FIERO - Watches - Bulova Corp.

FIERO PLUS - Audio equipment ☆ - Telequest Inc.

FIERRO MOIRE - Window shades ☆ - Superior Shade & Blind Co. Inc.

FIERY - Computer peripheral equipment - Electronics for Imaging, Inc.

FIERY BRONZE - Pet products - Tomlyn Products

FIERY COLORLASER - Printers–computer - Electronics for Imaging, Inc.

FIERY FINS - Seafood products–fresh or frozen - Fish King Processors Inc.

FIERY FLAPPERS - Food products - Brakebush Brothers Inc.

FIERY FURNACE - Stoves–wood-burning - Hunt County Lumber

FIERY SUNSET - Hair care products - Redmond Products, Inc.

FIERY SWEET PEACH - Tortillas - Native South Service

FIESOLE - Dishes–china - Pasmantier Co. Inc.

FIESTA - Accordions - Pancordion Inc.

FIESTA - Apparel–men's - J. Schoeneman Inc.

FIESTA - Area rugs ☆ - Couristan Inc.

FIESTA - Awnings - Anchor Industries Inc.

FIESTA - Bean sprouts - Kinfolk Sprout Farm

FIESTA - Bicycles - Schwinn Cycling & Fitness Inc.

FIESTA - Boats–motor - Rinker Boat Co. Inc.

FIESTA - Cabinets - Mid-America Cabinets Inc.

FIESTA - Cakes - Ferrero U.S.A Inc.

FIESTA - Cameras - Eastman Kodak Co.

FIESTA - Candy ☆ - Food Producers International Inc.

FIESTA - Cigar boxes–wood ☆ - Consolidated Cigar Corp.

FIESTA - Confections ☆ - R.L. Albert & Son, Inc.

FIESTA - Corn chips ☆ - Sunshine Biscuits, Inc.

FIESTA - Crocheted and knitted items - Lana Inc.

FIESTA - Dinnerware–glass - Nikko Ceramics Inc.

FIESTA - Dishes–china - Homer Laughlin China Co.

FIESTA - Door mats ☆ - Royal Rubber & Manufacturing Co.

FIESTA - Enameled ware ☆ - Knobler International Ltd.

FIESTA - Fireworks - F & S Co., Inc.

FIESTA - Floor coverings–carpet and rugs - Coronet Carpets Inc.

FIESTA - Floor coverings–carpet and rugs ☆ - Karastan-Bigelow Inc.

FIESTA - Floor coverings–carpet and rugs ☆ - Regal Rugs Inc.

FIESTA - Food products - Dole Food Co., Inc.

FIESTA - Food products - Mitsui & Co. Inc.

FIESTA - Food products - Sauces & Salsas, Ltd.

FIESTA - Food products - Taco Bell Corp.

FIESTA - Frames–eyeglass ☆ - Universal/Univis Inc.

FIESTA - Furniture - Homecrest Industries Inc.

FIESTA - Giftware - Fiesta Wedding Car Kits

FIESTA - Glassware–household ☆ - Crisa Corp.

FIESTA - Ice chests–foam ☆ - Fiesta Products Co.

FIESTA - Jewelry ☆ - Hirsch Speidel Inc.

FIESTA - Kitchen utensils–aluminum - Bonny Products Inc.
FIESTA - Liquors - Gaetano Specialties Ltd.
FIESTA - Mayonnaise - Kennedy Mayonnaise Products
FIESTA - Meat products–pork - Hygrade Food Products Corp.
FIESTA - Motor vehicles–automobiles ☆ - Ford Motor Co.
FIESTA - Office furniture–wood ☆ - Haskell of Pittsburgh, Inc.
FIESTA - Office supplies ☆ - Empire Berol USA
FIESTA - Oils–lubricating - Witco Corp.
FIESTA - Paper - Strathmore Paper Co.
FIESTA - Paper–construction ☆ - Canson-Talens Inc.
FIESTA - Paper–toweling ☆ - Scott Paper Co.
FIESTA - Pet food - Kaytee Products Inc.
FIESTA - Pies–frozen - Rich Products Corp.
FIESTA - Prophylactics - Schmid Laboratories
FIESTA - Recording label - Fiesta Record Co. Inc.
FIESTA - Rice - AC Humko Rice Specialties
FIESTA - Rings–jewelry - Artcarved Inc.
FIESTA - Seasonings ☆ - McCormick & Co., Inc.
FIESTA - Seat covers - Saddleman, Inc.
FIESTA - Snack foods - Curtice-Burns Foods, Inc.
FIESTA - Snack foods - Granny Goose Foods Inc.
FIESTA - Soap - Andrew Jergens Co.
FIESTA - Soups–mixes - Columbia Bean & Produce Co., Inc.
FIESTA - Spices and extracts - Bolner's Fiesta Products, Inc.
FIESTA - Syrup - L. Karp & Sons, Inc.
FIESTA - Tea kettles–nonelectric ☆ - Revere Ware Corp.
FIESTA - Teas ☆ - R.C. Bigelow, Inc.
FIESTA - Thread - Threads USA Div.
FIESTA - Tiles–ceramic ☆ - American Olean Tile Co.
FIESTA - Tires ☆ - Bridgestone/Firestone, Inc.
FIESTA - Vegetable oil - Imperial Foods
FIESTA - Water–bottled or canned - RV Industries, Inc.
FIESTA - Window shades ☆ - Draper Shade and Screen Co. Inc.
FIESTA BOWL - Apparel and accessories - Arizona Sports Foundation
FIESTA CHARM - Outdoor furniture - Jack-Post Corp.
FIESTA CROCK-ETTE - Housewares - Rival Co.
FIESTA DEL MAR - Seafood products–fresh or frozen - State Fish Co., Inc.
FIESTA DEL SOL - Chili–canned - Fiesta Canning Co. Inc.
FIESTA DIPPY - Hobby kits ☆ - Yaley Enterprises
FIESTA EXPRESS - Kitchen appliances - High Performance Appliances, Inc.
FIESTA FAIR - Detergents - Federated Foods Inc.
FIESTA FANTASY - Jams and jellies - Mountain Maid Gourmet Jelly
FIESTA FLOWERS - Paper–tissue - Bemiss-Jason Corp.
FIESTA GLO - Posters ☆ - Datacom Inc.
FIESTA GRANDE - Dinners–frozen ☆ - Pillsbury Co.
FIESTA HIP-CHIK - Meat products–poultry - Pierce Foods Corp.
FIESTA KITCHENS U.S.A. - Giftware - Party Foods, Inc.
FIESTA LEADER - Electronic equipment - Neumade Products Corp.
FIESTA LIGHT - Lamps ☆ - Lamplight Farms, Inc.
FIESTA LUNCHBREAK - Ice chests–foam ☆ - Fiesta Products Co.
FIESTA MESH - Fabrics - Lumured Corp.
FIESTA PACK - Food products - Ruiz Food Products Inc.
FIESTA PARTY PAN - Pans ☆ - Nordic Ware
FIESTA PIZZA FEAST - Pizza - Domino's Pizza Inc.
FIESTA POPS - Candy - Tootsie Roll Industries, Inc.
FIESTA RANCH - Salad dressings–bottled - HVR Co.
FIESTA ROSE - Silverware ☆ - Imperial Schrade Corp.
FIESTA ROYALE - Outdoor furniture - Jack-Post Corp.
FIESTA SANTA FE - Soups–canned - Pet Inc.
FIESTA STICKS - Snack foods - Rich-Seapak Corp.
FIESTA STIX - Food products - Design Foods
FIESTA STORE - Apparel and accessories - Fiesta San Antonio Commission, Inc.
FIESTA SWEEP - Brushes - O-Cedar/Vining Household Products Co.
FIESTA TEXAS - Statuary - Hospitality & Leisure Management Co. Inc.
FIESTA TIME - Cheese ☆ - T. Marzetti Co.
FIESTA TROPICAL - Ice cream ☆ - Welsh Farms Inc.
FIESTA VEE - Boats–motor - Rinker Boat Co. Inc.
FIESTADA - Food products - Schwan's Sales Enterprises, Inc.
FIESTAS - Cigars ☆ - General Cigar Co., Inc.
FIF-TEENS - Pharmaceutical preparations ☆ - Chex Co.
FIFE & DRUM - Eyeglasses - Art-Craft Optical Co.
FIFI - Eyeglasses - Art-Craft Optical Co.
FIFI - Yarn - Bernat Yarn & Craft Corp.
FIFTH AVE. - Apparel–men's - I. Wolfmark Inc.
FIFTH AVE. - Pencils - Empire Berol USA

FIFTH AVE. CLASSICS - Footwear - United States Shoe Corp.
FIFTH AVENUE - Coffee - Coffee Holding Co.
FIFTH AVENUE - Computer software - Silicon Logics
FIFTH AVENUE - Dolls ☆ - Effanbee Doll Corp.
FIFTH AVENUE - Fans–electric - Dan's Fan City
FIFTH AVENUE - Floor coverings - Bellbridge Carpets
FIFTH AVENUE - Floor coverings ☆ - Robbins Inc.
FIFTH AVENUE - Floor coverings–carpet and rugs - Galaxy Carpet Mills Inc.
FIFTH AVENUE - Frames–eyeglass - Liberty Optical Manufacturing Co.
FIFTH AVENUE - Furniture ☆ - Bassett Furniture Industries, Inc.
FIFTH AVENUE - Glassware–household - Crystal Clear Importing Co. Inc.
FIFTH AVENUE - Motor vehicles–automobiles ☆ - DaimlerChrysler
FIFTH AVENUE - Pens ☆ - Parker Pen USA
FIFTH AVENUE - Perfumes ☆ - Avon Products, Inc.
FIFTH AVENUE - Sextants–surveying ☆ - Allen-Edmonds Shoe Corp.
FIFTH AVENUE - Skin care products - Hygiene Industries
FIFTH AVENUE - Wallpaper - Pantasote Inc. (Wallcovering Div.)
FIFTH AVENUE - Yarn ☆ - JCA, Inc.
FIFTH AVENUE CRYSTAL LTD. - Lighting fixtures - Crystal Clear Industries, Inc.
FIFTH AVENUE GIRL - Toys - Libby Lee Toys Inc.
FIFTH AVENUE STYLE - Dolls - Mattel, Inc.
FIFTH AVENUE SUITE - Floor coverings–carpet and rugs ☆ - Durkan Patterned Carpets
FIFTH BURNER - Hotplates - Hamilton Beach/Proctor-Silex Inc.
FIFTH COLUMN - Recording label - The Bank Nightclub
FIFTH GEAR - Footwear - J.C. Penney Co., Inc.
FIFTH STREET - Frames–eyeglass ☆ - Universal/Univis Inc.
FIFTH SUIT, THE - Computer software ☆ - B & N Companies, Inc.
FIFTH SYMPHONY - Floor coverings–carpet and rugs - Barrett Carpet Mills Inc.
FIFTH WHEEL - Food products ☆ - Pierre Frozen Foods Inc.
FIFTHSBURGH - Apparel and accessories - Eleuterio Simon Cruz, Jr.
FIFTY 50 - Candy - Fifty 50 Foods Inc.
FIFTY-BELOW - Antifreeze ☆ - Mid-America Chemical Inc.
FIFTY-MINUTE - Instructional videos - Crisp Publications, Inc.
FIFTY SIDED - Games - Gamescience
FIG CHEWIES - Cookies ☆ - Sunshine Biscuits, Inc.
FIG NEWTONS - Cakes - Nabisco Foods Group
FIGALI - Jewelry - Perfect Timing of New York, Inc.
FIGARO - Brushes–hair - Nino Originals
FIGARO - Cat food - Bumble Bee Seafoods, Inc.
FIGARO - Clippers–barber - William Marvy Co., Inc.
FIGARO - Frames–eyeglass - May Optical Co. Inc.
FIGARO 1993 CREATION MOULIN DE GASSAC VIN DU VENT DE LA MEDITERRANEE VIN DE PAYS - Wines - Kysela Pere Et Fils, Ltd.
FIGARRO-CIGARRO - Cookies - William E. Baker
FIGGY - Fruit butters ☆ - Sarabeth's Kitchen
FIGHT - Deodorant soap - Hubert Inc.
FIGHT - Recording label - Rob Halford Music Ltd.
FIGHT BACK - Chemical preparations ☆ - Garrity Industries
FIGHT CHAMP - Punching bags - Logan Electric Specialty Manufacturing Co.
FIGHT NIGHT - Broadcasting stations–television - Fight Night, Inc.
FIGHTBACK - Sporting goods - Marty Gilman Inc.
FIGHTER - Floor waxes ☆ - C.B. Dolge Co.
FIGHTER BRAND - Forms–preprinted - Scott Printing Corp.
FIGHTER BRAND EXPORT FORMS - Forms–preprinted - Scott Printing Corp.
FIGHTER COMBAT SYSTEM - Games - Gamescience
FIGHTER PILOT - Games ☆ - Gamescience
FIGHTER TOWN - Wallpaper ☆ - Image Crafter
FIGHTIN' CRAWDAD - Fishing lures - Mister Twister, Inc.
FIGHTING FALCON. - See F-16 FLCS
FIGHTING FALCON - Toys–models - Comet Montrose Ltd.
FIGHTING FOR THE PAST - Publisher's imprint, calendars, etc. - Cool Spring Associates Inc.
FIGHTING YANK - Toys ☆ - Mego Financial Corp.
FIGHTMAN - Drums–musical instruments ☆ - Pearl Corp.
FIGHTSTERS! - Audio equipment - Harrison Nutkins
FIGMENTS - Greeting cards - Figments Greeting Cards
FIGMENTS OF FOLKLORE - Figurines - International Silver Co.
FIGURAMA - Apparel–women's ☆ - Maidenform Inc. (True Form Foundations Div.)
FIGURANTE - Toilets–enameled - Kohler Co.
FIGURE 5 - Computer software - Columbia Ultimate Business Systems, Inc.
FIGURE 8 - Flour–blended - Western Star Mill Co.
FIGURE 8 CRASH COURSE - Toys–automobiles ☆ - CBS Toys

☆ = Now out of production

FIGURE ANALYZER - Apparel and accessories ☆ - Glamorise Foundations Inc.

FIGURE BUILDER - Brassieres (Bras) - Bi-Flex International

FIGURE DESIGNS FASHION CAD - Computer software - Figure Designs

FIGURE FACTORY - Toys - Natural Science Industries, Ltd.

FIGURE FIRMER - Panty hose - National Wholesale Co., Inc.

FIGURE FORMER - Apparel–women's - Nuvogue Creations

FIGURE FRIEND - Apparel–women's - Wacoal America Inc.

FIGURE INTIMATE - Apparel and accessories - Figureplane

FIGURE PERFECT - Apparel and accessories - Alba-Waldensian, Inc.

FIGURE PHONE - Communications equipment–mobile - Circuit Service Inc.

FIGURE TRIM - Health care products - Futurebiotics

FIGUREFLEX - Sporting goods - Nordictrack, Inc.

FIGUREHEAD ALE - Beverages–malt - HDT Importers Inc.

FIGURETTE - Mannequins ☆ - Canson-Talens Inc.

FIGURETTES - Vitamins and nutritional supplements - Cameo Coutures

FIGUREWRITE - Stationery - Filer Inc.

FIGURFIT - Slips, sleepwear - Indera Mills Co.

FIGURINE AMERICANA - Figurines - Arnart Imports Inc.

FIGURINES - Vitamins and nutritional supplements - Pillsbury Co.

FIJI - Housewares - Royal Cathay Trading Co.

FIJI - Ophthalmic goods - Foremost Optical Products

FIJI FLARE - Candles - Empire Manufacturing Co.

FIKES WORLDWIDE - Deodorizers - Pestco, Inc.

FIL-A-FIL - Wallpaper - Limonta USA Inc.

FIL-MAR - Food products - Sundor Brands Inc.

FIL-N-GLU - Concrete products - Diasyde Corp.

FIL-O - Candles - Filardo Products Co.

FIL-R-KOTE - Paints ☆ - Devoe & Raynolds Co.

FIL TEC INCORPORATED - Filters–air - Fil Tec Inc.

FIL-TENNA - Antennas - Pacific Monolithics

FILA - Bags–duffel - Sirco International Corp.

FILA - Footwear–athletic - Fila USA, Inc.

FILA FOR KIDS - Footwear - Fila USA, Inc.

FILABOND - Fabric binding ☆ - Kwik-Affix Products

FILAMENT - Apparel stores–women's - Sinolink Apparel Inc.

FILANTO - Footwear - Pamjon Corp.

FILAR - Flatware ☆ - Yamazaki Tableware Inc.

FILAR GOLD ACCENT - Flatware ☆ - Yamazaki Tableware Inc.

FILARE - Paper–bond - Fox River Paper Co.

FILARE - Paper–writing - Simpson Paper Co.

FILARIBITS - Veterinary pharmaceutical preparations - SmithKline Beecham Animal Health Products

FILARMONICA - Hair care products - Perfector Products

FILARMONICA - Hair care products ☆ - Peter J. Michels Inc.

FILASPUN - Thread ☆ - Belding Heminway Co. Inc.

FILAXIS - Pharmaceutical - American Laboratories Inc.

FILBERT ACTION ROCKERS - Rocking chairs ☆ - Little Tikes Co.

FILBERT FANCIES - Candy ☆ - Brock Candy Co. Inc.

FILE - Computer software - Microsoft Corp.

FILE-A-DEX - File folders - File-A-Dex Inc.

FILE-A-FOTO - Computer software - Tropich Software, Inc.

FILE-A-WAY - Giftware - Ballonoff Home Products

FILE ALERT - Computer software - Executive Software International, Inc.

FILE-ALL - Files–tools - Simonds Industries Inc.

FILE AWAY - Storage products - Spectrum International, Inc.

FILE BEST - Office supplies - Pen-Tab Industries

FILE CADDY - Office supplies - Esselte Corp.

FILE COMPRESSPRO - Computer software - Software Builders, Inc.

FILE DIRECTOR - Computer software - Fifth Generation Systems Inc.

FILE-EEZ - Shelf filing jackets - Quality Park Products Co.

FILE-ETTE - Cabinets - Wells Industries

FILE GUARD - Locks–padlocks - Abloy Security Inc.

FILE HAVEN - Computer software - Intessera, LP

FILE-IN-A-BOX - Office supplies ☆ - Globe-Weis

FILE IT - Boxes–corrugated paperboard ☆ - Esselte Corp.

FILE MAGIC - Computer software - Westbrook Technologies Inc.

FILE MAGIC EXPERT - Computer software - Westbrook Technologies Inc.

FILE MAGIC EXPERT FOR LANS - Computer software - Westbrook Technologies Inc.

FILE MAGIC PLUS - Computer software - Westbrook Technologies Inc.

FILE-MASTER - Cabinets ☆ - Knoll Group

FILE MASTER - Computer software - J.A. Business Services Inc.

FILE MATES - Desk sets - Artwire Creations Inc.

FILE MAX - Filing cabinets–metal - Steelworks, Inc.

FILE-N-GUIDE - Tools - Granberg International

FILE-N-JOINT - Tools - Granberg International

FILE-N-SEND - Binders - Lion Office Products, Inc.

FILE OF LIFE - Bags–plastic - File of Life, Inc.

FILE PAL - File folders - Newell Office Products

FILE PLUS PERSONAL - Computer software - Timeworks International Inc.

FILE PLUS PROFESSIONAL - Computer software - Timeworks International Inc.

FILE PRO - Computers - Duracom Computer Systems

FILE PRO - Nail-care products - Cosmar Corp.

FILE PRO - Office supplies ☆ - Esselte Corp.

FILE PRODUCT - Office supplies ☆ - Esselte Corp.

FILE SHUTTLE - Office supplies ☆ - Leelo Industries, Inc.

A FILE, THE - Beauty aids - International Beauty Design, Inc.

FILE TRACKER - Stationery - Tab Products Co.

FILE VELOPE - Envelopes - Marvin Envelope & Paper Co.

FILE WIZARD - Computer software - Knozall Systems Inc.

FILEMAN 48 - Computer software - Ramss, Inc.

FILEMAN LAUNCHER - Computer software ☆ - Canyon Software

FILEMANAGER - Boxes–paperboard - Anthes Universal

FILEMASTER - Computer software - Synex

FILEMASTER - Office supplies - McBee Loose Leaf Binders

FILE!MATE - Computer software - Stahls' Inc.

FILEMATION - Computer software - Bibbero Systems, Inc.

FILEO - Wines - Barboursville Winery Inc.

FILEPAD - Computer storage devices - Healthcare Communications, Inc.

FILEPOWER - Computer software - Optika Imaging Systems, Inc.

FILEPRO - Computer software - Small Computer Co. Inc.

FILERUNNER - Personal-computer software - MBS Technologies Inc.

FILESECURE - Computer software - Tallgrass Technologies Corp.

FILESTAR/2 - Computer software - Softouch Systems, Inc.

FILESWEEP - Computer storage devices–magnetic - Core Technology Corp.

FILET-O-FISH - Sandwiches–prepackaged - Mcdonald's Corp.

FILET O'BREST - Meat products–poultry - Hester Industries, Inc.

FILET O'BREST - Meat products–poultry - Pierce Foods Corp.

FILET O'CHICKEN - Meat products–poultry - Pierce Foods Corp.

FILET OF HAM - Meat products–beef - Armour Swift-Eckrich

FILETRAX - Computer software - Docutech Data Systems, Inc.

FILETTE - Cosmetics ☆ - London International U.S. Holdings

FILETTO - Tableware–china ☆ - Villeroy and Boch Tableware Ltd.

FILEVUE - Humphrey Systems

FILEWARE - Computer software - Apple Computer Inc.

FILEWEDGE - Computer software - Tal Technologies, Inc.

FILEX - Office furniture–metal ☆ - Martin Industries, Inc.

FILEX INTERNATIONAL - Binders - Suplee Envelope Co., Inc.

FILGREE - Floor coverings - Bellbridge Carpets

FILIBON - Vitamins and nutritional supplements - Lederle Laboratories

FILIBUSTER - Brassieres (Bras) ☆ - Vanity Fair Mills Inc.

FILIGRAN - Perfumes ☆ - Frances Denney

FILIGREE - Enamels ☆ - Star Bronze Co. Inc.

FILIGREE - Floor coverings–carpet and rugs - Alexander Smith Carpets

FILIGREE - Rings–jewelry ☆ - Artcarved Inc.

FILIGREE - Skin care products - Thymes Limited

FILIGREE - Tableware–china ☆ - Lenox, Inc.

FILIGREE - Tableware–earthenware - Pfaltzgraff Investment Co.

FILIGREE - Wood products ☆ - Masonite Corp.

FILING GIRL - Office supplies ☆ - Esselte Corp.

FILING WIZARD - Computer storage devices - Corbel

FILIPINA - Apparel–men's - Sportailor Inc.

FILIPINO - Hair care products - Dubl Duck/Jet Set Inc.

FILIPINO 88 - Hair care products - Dubl Duck/Jet Set Inc.

FILIPPONI - Belts–apparel ☆ - Leon Fleischer, International Marketing

FILKO TRIPLE SILICONE - Spark plugs - F & B Manufacturing Co.

FILL-A-BAR - Computer software - Quick Scan, Inc.

FILL-A-FAVOR - Novelty items - Unique Industries, Inc.

FILL-A-GAP - Foam rubber - Fill-A-Gap

FILL-AIR - Packaging–paper - Sealed Air Corp.

FILL AND FINISH - Paints ☆ - Proko Industries Inc.

FILL AND SEAL - Caulking compounds - Insta-Foam Products, Inc.

FILL 'EM FAST - Gasoline ☆ - Diamond Shamrock Inc.

FILL-IT - Craft supplies ☆ - Clayton Corp.

FILL 'N FINISH - Wood fillers - Elmer's Products, Inc.

FILL 'N SAVE - Water–distilled - Pure Water Inc.

FILL 'N THRILL - Toys - Bleyer Industries (Peoria Plastics Div.)

FILL 'N WASH STATION - Toys - Playskool, Inc.

FILL R UP - Toys - Gerber Products Co.

FILL THE BILL - Pet products - Klenatron Co. Inc.

FILLAUER, INC. - Prosthetic apparatus - Fillauer, Inc.
FILLED TILE - Fabrics - Lumured Corp.
FILLER - Flowers, plants, and seeds - BDH Two, Inc.
FILLER - Snack foods - Nabisco Foods Group
FILLER SNACKS - Potato chips - BDH Two, Inc.
FILLER UP - Nail care products - Worldwide Cosmetics
FILLET-A-FISH - Fish nets ☆ - G-96 Products Co. Inc.
FILLET GALLEY - Fishing tackle - Aquasea Inc.
FILLET-O-PIZZA - Pizzas–frozen - Eat-All Frozen Food Co.
FILLETER'S FRIEND - Cutting boards - Maurice Sporting Goods, Inc.
FILLETMASTER - Knives–hunting - Rival Manufacturing Co.
FILLETS FRISCO - Fruits and vegetables - Merrill Farms
FILLETTA - Fish–fresh or frozen ☆ - Slade Gorton and Co. Inc.
FILLIOUX FILS - Wines ☆ - Admiral Wine Merchants
FILLIT - Cement - Sealwall Products Inc.
FILLIT + - Putties ☆ - Fibre Glass-Evercoat Co. Inc.
FILLITE - Porcelain electrical supplies ☆ - Hastings Plastics Co.
FILLMASTER - Electronic equipment - R.M. Schultz & Associates, Inc.
FILLMORE - Glassware–household ☆ - Lenox Crystal, Inc.
FILLMORE REFILL INK - Inks - Fillmore Group
FILLO CLASSIC - Doughs–frozen - Athens Pastries & Frozen Foods Inc.
FILLPRO - Toilets–enameled - Fillpro Products Inc.
FILLY - Apparel and accessories - Warnaco Inc.
FILLY - Apparel–women's - Lucia, Inc.
FILLY - Brushes–paint ☆ - PPG Industries, Inc.
FILLY - Exercising equipment - Physical Fitness Inc.
FILLY=TAC - Jewelry - Bart Thompson Enterprises
FILM-A-RECORD - Electronic equipment - Kardex Systems, Inc.
FILM COMPOSER - Computer software - Avid Technology, Inc.
FILM-GARD - Plastics film - Carlysle Plastics
FILM-IN - Cameras - Konica USA Inc.
FILM-KING - Pencils - Dur-O-Lite Inc.
FILM MASTER - Electronic equipment - Telex Communications, Inc.
FILM MIRACLE - Electronics equipment - Marty Bahn & Co.
FILM SAVER - Switches–power - Eiki International Inc.
FILM STRIP - Adhesive removers - Klein & Co.
FILM-TAK - Photographic equipment - DICO Group Inc.
FILMAKER - Photographic equipment - Radmar Inc.
FILMAR - Pencils ☆ - Faber-Castell Corp.
FILMASKS - Photographic equipment - Rollei of America Inc.
FILMATIC - Projectors–photographic - Rollei of America Inc.
FILMBILL - Pre-printed theater programs - Steven Duchovnay
FILMCO - Plastic film - Viskase Corp.
FILMCORE - Office supplies - Avery Label Systems
FILMCURE - Film - Thompson Technology, Inc.
FILMGUARD - Photo albums - Pacific Foto/Supply Co.
FILMO - Electronic equipment - Bell & Howell Co.
FILMOGRAPH - Pencils - Empire Berol USA
FILMOLUX - Film - Interlam Inc.
FILMOPAQUER - Pens - Mark-Tex Corp.
FILMORAMA - Lenses–photographic ☆ - Eiki International Inc.
FILMORE - Watches - Bulova Corp.
FILMOSONIC - Electronic equipment - Bell & Howell Co.
FILMOSOUND - Projectors–photographic - Eiki International Inc.
FILMOSS - Cleaning preparations - National Development Corp.
FILMOSTO - Photographic equipment ☆ - Heitz Service Corp.
FILMOVARA - Electronic equipment - Bell & Howell Co.
FILMPAK - Tubes–plastic ☆ - Sima Products Corp.
FILMPOCKETS - Protective cases - Schwabe Consulting, Ltd.
FILMRITE - Photographic equipment - Rosco Laboratories Inc.
FILMSHIELD - Lead products - Sima Products Corp.
FILMSTAR 2 - Computer peripheral equipment - Xante Corp.
FILMSTIK - Electronic equipment ☆ - Steck-Vaughn/EDL
FILMTAX - Paperboard - Savage Universal Corp.
FILO - Surgical instruments - Intramedica, Inc.
FILO - Tablecloths and bedspreads - Interdec Corp.
FILON - Motor vehicle parts and accessories - Kemlite Co., Inc.
FILON - Plastics - BP Chemicals Inc. (Filon Products Div.)
FILON-STRIPES - Glass products - BP Chemicals Inc. (Filon Products Div.)
FILOPLATED - Motor vehicle parts and accessories - Kemlite Co., Inc.
FILOR KNITS - Crocheted and knitted items - Hercules-Carnation Knitwear Inc.
FILPAX - Coffee makers–electric - Lancer Corp.
FILSILK - Fabrics - Cameo Coutures
FILSINGER - Wines - Filsinger Vineyards & Winery
FILSON - Apparel and accessories - C.C. Filson Co.
FILSTIKS - Wood fillers - Star Finishing Products Inc.

FILT-A-CARB - Water purification systems - Penn-Plax, Inc.
FILT AIR - Medical apparatus ☆ - Apex Medical Corp.
FILTAIR - Medical apparatus - Karlen Manufacturing, Inc.
FILTAIRETTE - Hardware - General Scientific Equipment Co.
FILTER - Recording label - Richard Patrick
FILTER 1ST AS-U-SPRAY - Filters–industrial - MCKenzie Product Co.
FILTER-AID - Pet products - Aquarium Products Inc.
FILTER ALERT - Alarm systems ☆ - Oatey Co.
FILTER BOSS - Plates–plastic - Spray Sok Co. Inc.
FILTER CLEAN - Cleaning preparations - LifeTime Filter Inc.
FILTER CLEANSE - Cleaning preparations - Great Lakes Biochemical Co., Inc.
FILTER EZZ - Kitchen utensils–enameled - Ransburg Accessories Inc.
FILTER-FLO - Water purification systems - General Electric Co.
FILTER FRESH - Cleaning preparations - Great Lakes Biochemical Co., Inc.
FILTER FRESH - Vacuum cleaners and accessories - Figgie International Inc.
FILTER-FRY - Pans ☆ - Research Products Corp.
FILTER KLEAN - Aquariums–household - Zip Pet Products
FILTER LINK - Water purification systems - Link Automation, Inc.
FILTER PLUS - Filters–air - Air Kontrol Inc.
FILTER PLUS - Filters–oil ☆ - Monroe Auto Equipment Co.
FILTER PLUS - Filters–water - N.R.G. Enterprises, Inc./Mistra Inc.
FILTER PLUS - Motor vehicle parts and accessories - James Cheng, Darryl Wright, Norman P. Butler and Li Kam Pui
FILTER POWER - Vacuum cleaners and accessories ☆ - Home Care Industries, Inc.
FILTER PURE - Filters–water - A.K.S. of Clearwater, Inc.
FILTER QUEEN - Vacuum cleaners and accessories - Health-Mor Inc.
FILTER RINSE - Cleaning preparations - Great Lakes Biochemical Co., Inc.
FILTERAIRE - Bags–paper - The Eureka Co.
FILTERBANK - Photographic equipment - SP Systems/Saratons
FILTERCOLD - Water purification systems - Delta International Marine Products Inc.
FILTERCUP - Coffee makers–electric ☆ - Salton/Maxim Housewares, Inc.
FILTERED FENCE - Electronic equipment - Richard H. Colburn and Donald Hosmer Partnership
FILTEREDFLO - Blankets - Cincinnati Sub-Zero Products, Inc.
FILTERELA - Cigars ☆ - Phillies Cigar Co.
FILTERFLEX - Photographic equipment ☆ - Tiffen Manufacturing Corp.
FILTERFLOW - Medical apparatus - B. Braun Medical Inc.
FILTERGLOW - Lighting equipment - General Electric Co.
FILTERGRABBER - Wrenches ☆ - Normark Corp.
FILTERNET - Building materials - SLT North America, Inc.
FILTERSPUN - Filters–oil - Service Filtration Corp.
FILTERTRINE - Cleaning preparations–household ☆ - Applied Biochemists, Inc.
FILTERVEYOR - Conveyors - Jorgensen Conveyors, Inc.
FILTERWELD - Welders' hoods - Aearo Co.
FILTEX - Vacuum cleaners and accessories - M and S Systems Inc.
FILTEX - Varnishes ☆ - Pratt & Lambert, Inc.
FILTH - Apparel and accessories - Scott Steven Ganser
FILTHY ANIMAL - Shampoos - Kim Laube & Co. Inc.
FILTHY RICH - Video games - WMS Gaming Inc.
FILTR-GARD - Lighting equipment - General Electric Co.
FILTRACHECK-UTI - Pharmaceutical preparations - Meridian Diagnostics, Inc.
FILTRATOR - Coffee makers–electric ☆ - Mr. Coffee, Inc.
FILTRCOTE - Ophthalmic goods - Benson Optical Co., Inc.
FILTRESSE - Medical apparatus - Utah Medical Products, Inc.
FILTRETTE - Air purification systems - Barnebey and Sutcliffe Corp.
FILTREX - Sunblocks - Borghese Trademarks Inc.
FILTREX - Vacuum cleaners and accessories - Filtrex Inc.
FILTREZ - Pet products - Penn-Plax, Inc.
FILTRIDGE - Water purification systems ☆ - Aquatrol, Inc.
FILTRIX - Pet products - Rolf C. Hagen (USA) Corp.
FILTRON - Cookware - Same Day Distributing, Inc.
FILTRONICS - Pet products ☆ - Aquatronics-Filtronics
FILTRONICS - Pumps–water - Dimension Engineering
FILTROPA - Food products - Acme Food Specialties Inc.
FILTY - Aquariums–household - Rena Corp.
FILUMA - Doors–garage - Frantz Manufacturing Co.
FIM DE SECULO - Wines - Admiral Wine Merchants
FIM SAVR - Packaging machines - Infra Pak, Inc.
FIM STUFF - Fibers–polyester - Fairfield Processing Corp.
FIMBAND - Publisher's imprints - Jon Weingarten
FIMCO - Garden equipment - Fimco Inc.
FIN++ - Computer software - Infinity Financial Technology, Inc.
FIN-ACKY - Fishing lures - Slim Pelican

FIN & FEATHER - Boat and trailers - Fin & Feather Boats Inc.
FIN AND FEATHER - Footwear - Mason Shoe Manufacturing Co.
FIN-BORE - Sporting goods ☆ - Normark Corp.
FIN CARE - Pet products - Rolf C. Hagen (USA) Corp.
FIN DE NERT - Wines - Guild Wineries
FIN-ITE - Fishing tackle - Fin-Nor Corp.
FIN-L-FILTER - Water purification systems - Poly-Bio-Marine Inc.
FIN-N-SEAL - Waxes–sealing ☆ - Uncle Sam Chemical Co., Inc.
FIN-NOR - Fishing lures - United Sports Specialists Corp.
FIN-NOR - Fishing tackle - United Sports Scecialists Corp.
FIN-NOR LIGHT - Fishing tackle ☆ - United Sports Scecialists Corp.
FIN-ONYX - Sporting goods ☆ - Parkway Systems
FIN-OPAL - Sporting goods ☆ - Parkway Systems
FIN PALS - Fishing tackle - Strike King Lure Co.
FIN PALS - Pet products - Rolf C. Hagen (USA) Corp.
FIN-S - Fishing tackle - Lunker City Fishing Specialties
FIN-S - Lighting equipment - Lowel-Light Manufacturing Inc.
L'FINA - Cosmetics - Infina, Inc.
FINA - Fibers–acrylic - Monsanto Polymer Products
FINA - Sandals - Playazul International Inc.
FINA - Wallets - Fina Oil and Chemical Co.
FINA S.A. - Oils–lubricating - Fina Oil and Chemical Co.
FINA SPECIAL - Oils–lubricating ☆ - Fina Oil and Chemical Co.
FINA UNIVERSAL - Oils–lubricating - Fina Oil and Chemical Co.
FINAC - Pharmaceutical preparations - C&M Pharmacal, Inc.
FINAFTA - Pharamauceuticals - Efficient Laboratories, Inc.
FINAGLE A BAGEL - Bagels - Julian's Cheesecakes, Inc.
FINAL - Cleaning preparations ☆ - CMC Inc.
FINAL - Siding–insulating ☆ - Aluminum Co. of America
FINAL-AIR - Filters–air - AIFCO Co.
FINAL ANALYSIS - Computer software - Final Analysis, Inc.
FINAL ANSWER - Cleaning equipment - Tech Enterprises Inc.
FINAL BITE - Bait - Bacon Products Corp.
FINAL CALL - Health care products - U.S. Alcohol Testing of America Inc.
FINAL CHALLENGE, THE - Games ☆ - Mayfair Games, Inc.
FINAL CHARGE - Antifreeze - Old World Industries, Inc.
FINAL CHECK - Artists' materials - Graphic Products Corp.
FINAL CHOICE - Clothespins - Michael Daswani
FINAL CUT - Vitamins and nutritional supplements ☆ - Nature's Way Products, Inc.
FINAL DRAFT - Computer software - Computer Place Inc.
FINAL DRAFT - Computer software - Final Draft, Inc.
FINAL EXAM - Computer software - Earthware Computer Services
FINAL EXAM - Computer software - Platinum Technology, Inc.
FINAL FEAST - Rodenticide - Purina Mills, Inc.
FINAL FINISH - Coatings - Coronado Paint Co.
FINAL FINISH - Cosmetics - Madeleine Mono Ltd.
FINAL FINISH - Drycleaning preparations ☆ - Edison Brothers Stores, Inc.
FINAL FINISH - Varnishes - McCloskey Corp.
FINAL IMPRESSION - Cosmetics - Chem Spray Aerosols Inc.
FINAL NET - Hair care products - Clairol Inc.
FINAL NET ULTIMATE HOLD - Hair care products - Clairol Inc.
FINAL ONE - Hair care products - Revlon-Realistic Professional Products Inc.
FINAL PREP, THE - Steel wool - International Steel Wool Corp.
FINAL ROUND GOLFWEAR - Apparel–athletic - Freeman Golf Marketing
FINAL SCORE - Apparel and accessories - Chester County Sportswear Co. Inc.
FINAL SECONDS - Sporting goods - Lifetime Products, Inc.
FINAL STAND, THE - Furniture - Final Stand, Inc.
FINAL STRIP H.D. - Wax removers - Pioneer/Eclipse Corp.
FINAL TOUCH - Cleaning preparations - Ultra Finish Products
FINAL TOUCH - Fabric softeners - Lever Brothers Co. Inc.
FINAL TOUCH - Interior finishes - Interstate Paint Corp.
FINAL TOUCH - Nail care products ☆ - Spilo/Mehaz Worldwide
FINAL TOUCH - Paints - United Coatings Inc.
FINAL TOUCH - Pet products ☆ - Gerard-Pellham Co.
FINAL TOUCH - Sporting goods - Marshall Manufacturing Inc.
FINAL VINYL - Siding–insulating ☆ - Aluminum Co. of America
FINAL WORD - Novelty items - Barami Corp.
FINALE - Audio tapes–blank - Finale Inc.
FINALE - Computer software - Coda Music Technology, Inc.
FINALE - Fabric softeners - Faultless Starch/Bon Ami Co.
FINALE - Floor coverings–carpet and rugs - S and S Mills Inc.
FINALE - Floor coverings–carpet and rugs ☆ - Mannington Carpets, Inc.
FINALE - Frames–eyeglass - Pathway Optical Prods.
FINALE - Hair curlers ☆ - Nino Originals

FINALE - Herbicides - Agrevo Environmental Health, Inc.
FINALE - Herbicides - Hoechst-Roussel Agri-Vet Co.
FINALE - Musical instrument accessories - J.M. Sahlein Music Co. Inc.
FINALE - Ophthalmic goods - Pilkington Visioncare, Inc.
FINALE - Pet products - Best n' Show Pet Products Inc.
FINALE - Printers–computer - Samsung Information Systems
FINALE - Window shades ☆ - Verosol
FINALE - Wines - WHC Inc.
FINALE ALLEGRO - Computer software - Coda Music Technology, Inc.
FINALE BARS - Candy - Grand Finale Confections
FINALE COLLECTION - Cleaning preparations - Meguiar's, Inc.
FINALFORM - Computer software - IMRS Operations Inc.
FINALIST - Fishing tackle - South Bend Sporting Goods Inc.
FINALIST - Luggage - SGI Inc.
FINALIST - Mattresses - Simmons USA
FINALIST - Sporting goods ☆ - Excel Sports Products
FINALIST, THE - Apparel–men's - Richman Brothers Co.
FINALLY FIXED! - Swimming pools - L.W. Products
FINALLY FRESH - Cleaning preparations - Knight Marketing Corp.
FINALLY GONE - Deodorizers - C & M Group, Inc.
FINALLY NATURAL CARE - Medical apparatus ☆ - FNC Medical Corp.
FINALLY!...OVEN QUALITY FOOD - Ovens–convection - Alternative Pioneering Systems Inc.
FINANCE - Games ☆ - Parker Brothers
FINANCE ANALYSIS MODEL FOR EDUCATION - Computer peripheral equipment - Coopers & Lybrand
FINANCE LITE - Computer software - Shaws-Lawson Associates
FINANCE PLUS - Computer programming services - Ford New Holland Credit Co.
FINANCER - Computer software - Zephyr Services
FINANCER II - Floor coverings–carpet and rugs - Milliken & Co. Inc.
FINANCIAL AID FINDER - Computer software - Wintergreen/Orchard House, Inc.
FINANCIAL ASSET BUILDER - Computer software - DST Systems, Inc.
FINANCIAL CALCULATOR, THE - Computer software - Meca Software, Inc.
FINANCIAL COMPETENCE - Computer software - Competence Software
FINANCIAL COOKBOOK - Computer software ☆ - Electronic Arts Inc.
FINANCIAL EXPLORER - Computer software - Footprint Software Corp.
FINANCIAL INDEPENDENCE - Computer software ☆ - Broderbund Software, Inc.
FINANCIAL RATIOS - Computer software - Lassen Software Inc.
FINANCIAL STREAM - Computer software - Dun and Bradstreet Software Services, Inc.
FINANCIAL TUNE-UP - Computer software ☆ - Furistics Corp.
FINANCIAL VISION TOOLS - Computer software - 1st Partners & Co., Inc.
FINANCIAL WHIZ KIDS - Publisher's imprints - Charles J. Givens Organization, Inc.
FINANCIALLY IN TUNE - Computer software - Business Resource Services, Inc.
FINANCIER - Computer peripheral equipment - Wolffpack, Inc.
FINANCIER II - Computer software - Financier Inc.
FINARTE - Floor coverings–carpet and rugs ☆ - Foreign Accents
FINAS - Cigar boxes–wood - Consolidated Cigar Corp.
FINAVIA - Floor coverings–carpet and rugs ☆ - Colonial Mills Inc.
FINAZZIO'S - Breads ☆ - Super Valu Inc.
FINBAR & BROWN - Hams - Wis-Pak Foods, Inc.
FINCH - Brushes–paint ☆ - PPG Industries, Inc.
FINCH - Chimes ☆ - J.W. Stannard Co.
FINCH - Paper - Finch, Pruyn and Co.
FINCH INDUSTRIES - Mirrors - Finch Industries, Inc.
FINCO - Electrical equipment - Finney Co.
FIND-A-FILE - Office supplies - Wallace Computer Services, Inc.
FIND-A-KEY - Labels–paper - Dennis J. Gager
FIND AND SEEK - Toys - Mattel, Inc.
FIND (FAMILY INFORMATION NETWORK DATABASE) - Publisher's imprints - Guideposts Associates, Inc.
FIND IR - Apparel–athletic - Mountain Light Technology, LLC
FIND IT - Furniture ☆ - Esselte Corp.
FIND OUT WHY - Confections - Anthony Bonviso
FIND R PET - Pet products - Steve Cohen
FIND-R-SCOPE - Telescopes - FJW Optical Systems Inc.
FIND YOUR STRENGTH - Apparel and accessories - John K Kurtz
FIND YOURSELF IN BALI - Apparel and accessories - Saramar Corp.
FINDER - Computer software - Apple Computer Inc.
FINDER - Computer software - Arrays Inc./Continental Software
FINDER - Computer software - Finder Information Tools, Inc.

☆ = Now out of production

FINDER/DRIVER - Tools–power-driven - Makita USA, Inc.

FINDERS - Toys - Tonka Corp.

FINDER'S PATH - Furniture - Kincaid Furniture Co. Inc.

FINDERS-SEEKERS - Paper - Audio Listing Service, Inc.

FINDEX - Leather goods - AR Accessories Group Inc.

FINDEX - Office supplies - Gemaco Playing Card Co.

FINDING-OUT BOOKS - Publisher's imprints - Enslow Publishers, Inc.

FINDIT SYSTEM - Office supplies - Barkley Filing Supplies

FINDLATER'S SCOTCH - Beverages–alcohol - Marie Brizard Wines & Spirits, USA

FINDLEX - Brakes–motor vehicle - Findlex Corp.

FINDPLUS - Computer software - DT Software, Inc.

FINDS, THE - Kitchen display racks, books - Finds

FINDUSA - Telephone directories - American Business Information, Inc.

FINE - Cigarettes - G.A. Georgopulo & Co. Inc.

FINE - Flour–blended - King of Potatoes Inc.

FINE - Paints ☆ - Rich Art Color Co., Inc.

FINE-A SET - Skin care products - Waverly Beauty Products

FINE ART - Artists' materials ☆ - American Art Clay Co. Inc.

FINE ART - Floor coverings–carpet and rugs ☆ - Burtco Enterprises Inc.

FINE ART - Lamps - Fine Art Lamps

FINE ART CANVAS - Educational materials - Dynacolor Graphics, Inc.

FINE ART CAPPUCCINO & VINO OF LINGERING, THE - Food products - Cappuccino & Vino, Inc.

FINE ART FASHIONS - Apparel–men's - Fine Art Fashions, Ltd.

FINE ART OF BARBECUE, THE - Barbecue sauce - Southern Ray's Foods, Inc.

FINE ART OF GARNISHING, THE - Kitchen utensils–aluminum ☆ - Latham Studios

FINE ART TRUST - Picture frames - Azteca Frame Co.

FINE ARTIST QUALITY - Paints–artists' - Martin F. Weber Co.

FINE ARTS - Fabrics–linen - West Point-Pepperell Inc.

FINE ARTS - Floor coverings–carpet and rugs - Mohawk Carpet Corp.

FINE ARTS - Pottery - Freeman-McFarlin Potteries Inc.

FINE ARTS - Wallpaper - Bayview Wallcoverings

FINE ARTS - Whiskey - Canada Dry Corp.

FINE ARTS OF CHINA - Computer software - Hopkins Technology LLC

FINE ARTS SERIES - Hobby kits - Serendipity Designs Inc.

FINE BITES - Food products - Giumarra Vineyards

FINE CARE - Soap - USA Detergents Inc.

FINE CHOICE - Soap - Transmacro, Inc.

FINE CRAFT - Cooking equipment–household - New Era Co.

FINE CUT - Hair care products - Fromm Industries

FINE DINERS ULTRA PAC - Containers–plastic - Ultra Pac, Inc.

FINE DINING COLLECTION, THE - Meat products - Johnsonville Sausage, Inc.

FINE EDGE - Cutlery - Regent Sheffield, Ltd.

FINE-EDGE - Frames–eyeglass - Pathway Optical Prods.

FINE FARE - Food products - Hale-Halsell Co.

FINE FARE - Laundry and dish detergents - Federated Foods Inc.

FINE FEATHERS - Bird feeds - O.H. Kruse Grain and Milling Corp.

FINE FIELDS - Floor coverings - Mannington Resilient Floors

FINE FINISH - Waxes–paraffin - Hi-Temp Products Co.

FINE FINISHES - Wallcovering ☆ - Fashon Wallcoverings

FINE FIT - Frames–eyeglass - Pathway Optical Prods.

FINE FLOOR - Floor waxes - S.C. Johnson & Son, Inc.

FINE FOOD - Caviar - Caviar & Fine Foods Inc.

FINE FORM - Underwear and nightwear ☆ - Lovable Co.

FINE FORME - Cheese - Fromark

FINE FRUIT - Jams and jellies - Berry Best Farm

FINE FURNITURE - Cleaning preparations–household - Butcher Co.

FINE HIGH TOAST - Snuff - Faber, Coe & Gregg Inc.

FINE IDEA - Pet products - Carter-Wallace, Inc.

FINE ITALIAN FOODS CARMELA'S - Bakery products - Carmela's, Inc.

FINE-L-KOTE - Coatings - Tech Spray, Inc.

FINE LINE - Archery equipment - Archer Sports Inc.

FINE LINE - Electrical industrial apparatus - Ross Laboratories Inc.

FINE LINE - Food products - Trappe Packing Corp.

FINE LINE - Mats - Roope Corp.

FINE LINE EYE CREAM - Skin care products - Fanie International

FINE LINE, THE - Greeting cards - Avanti Press, Inc.

FINE LINES - Musical instrument accessories ☆ - Carl Dudash Harpsichords

FINE METALIX - Wallpaper - Blumenthal

FINE MISTER - Deodorizers - Quality of Life Associates

FINE 'N' SHINE - Cleaning preparations - Damon Industries, Inc.

FINE NOTE - Floor coverings–carpet and rugs - Mohawk Carpet Corp.

FINE NUGGETS - Candy - Fine Products Co. Inc.

FINE PLAY - Racket strings - Babolat

FINE PRINT - Posters ☆ - Signprint, Inc.

FINE QUALITY - Posters - Fine Art Lamps

FINE-RITER - Pens - Union Pen Co.

FINE SHINE JEWELERS POLISHING BATON - Polishing equipment–jewelry - L. Lawrence Products Inc.

FINE SOLUTIONS - Hair care products - Helene Curtis Industries Inc.

FINE STIK - Markers–felt-tip - Micropoint Inc.

FINE TUNE - Apparel and accessories - Brazabra Corp.

FINE TUNED - Floor coverings–carpet and rugs ☆ - Columbus Mills, Inc.

FINE TUNER - Skin care products - Origins Natural Resources Inc.

FINE VINYL - Window shades - Allied Extrusions

FINE-X FEEDER - Pet products - Bass Equipment Co.

FINECOAT - Paint sprayers - Wagner Spray Tech Corp.

FINECRAFT - Drums–musical instruments - Eames Drum Co.

FINEDGE - Glassware–household - Owens-Illinois Inc. (Libbey Div.)

FINEFLEX - Machine parts - Wangner Systems Corp.

FINELINE - Brushes–paint - Wooster Brush Co.

FINELINE - Cosmetics - Almay Inc.

FINELINE - Cosmetics - Revlon Consumer Products Corp.

FINELINE - Doors–wood ☆ - Stanley Hardware Div.

FINELINE - Hair care products - Mebco Industries, Inc.

FINELINE - Hardware - Diversified Dynamics Corp.

FINELINE - Medical apparatus - Staar Surgical Co., Inc.

FINELINE - Pencils–mechanical - Sheaffer Inc.

FINELINE - Tools–hand-operated - Transworld Products, Inc.

FINELINER - Pens - Pilot Pen Corp. of America

FINELINES - Blinds–venetian - Spring Window Fashions Division, Inc.

FINELON - Yarn ☆ - Lion Brand Yarn Co.

FINEMARK - Luggage - Airway Industries, Inc.

FINEMIX - Gelatin - Vyse Gelatin Co.

FINEPOINT - Technical pens - Itoya of America, Ltd.

FINEPOWER - Cameras–video - Yashica Inc.

FINER 1 - Hardware - Securtech Co.

FINER ARTS - Recording label - Bernstein Corp.

FINER DESIGNER - Hobby kits - A + A

FINER FILE - Skin care products - Tweezerman Corp.

FINER FOODS - Food products - Commercial Aluminum Cookware Co.

FINER FRIES - Frozen foods - J.R. Simplot Co.

FINER TOUCH - Tools–hand-operated - Tweezerman Corp.

FINERAIES - Wallpaper ☆ - Wallquest, Inc.

FINES FACE - Particle board - Georgia-Pacific Corp.

FINES HERBES - Seasonings - McCormick & Co., Inc.

FINESEAM - Thread - Threads USA Div.

FINESPUN - Thread - Lewis Threads Inc.

FINESS - Health care products - Halsey Drug Co. Inc.

FINESSA - Apparel–women's - I. Appel Corp.

FINESSE - Bathroom accessories - Kinkead/Tub/Shower Doors

FINESSE - Bedspreads - Glendale Hosiery Co.

FINESSE - Chimes - Nutone Inc.

FINESSE - Dishes–china - Viletta China Co.

FINESSE - Faucets - Kohler Co.

FINESSE - Fishing lures - Maurice Sporting Goods, Inc.

FINESSE - Flatware ☆ - W.M.F. of America Inc.

FINESSE - Floor coverings–carpet and rugs - Couristan Inc.

FINESSE - Floor coverings–carpet and rugs - Philadelphia Carpets

FINESSE - Floor coverings–carpet and rugs ☆ - Robertex Associates Inc.

FINESSE - Footwear - Polo International Inc.

FINESSE - Furniture ☆ - Broyhill Furniture Industries, Inc.

FINESSE - Glassware–household - Oneida Ltd.

FINESSE - Hair care products - Helene Curtis, Inc.

FINESSE - Hair care products - Helene Curtis Industries Inc.

FINESSE - Handbags - Finesse Imports Inc.

FINESSE - Herbicides - E.I. Dupont de Nemours and Co.

FINESSE - Hosiery ☆ - Stevens Hosiery

FINESSE - Jewelry - Alabaster Originals, Ltd.

FINESSE - Leather goods ☆ - AR Accessories Group Inc.

FINESSE - Luggage - Verdi Travelware

FINESSE - Medical apparatus - Utah Medical Products, Inc.

FINESSE - Paint rollers - Rol-Brush Manufacturing, Div. (Michigan Brush Mfg. Co., Inc.)

FINESSE - Pens - Accutec Inc.

FINESSE - Playing cards - United States Playing Card Co.

FINESSE - Thread ☆ - Coats and Clark Inc.

FINESSE - Tiles–ceramic - Latco Products

FINESSE - Underwear and nightwear - Kellwood Co.

☆ = Now out of production

FINESSE - Watchbands–precious metal - Admiral Watchband Co. Inc.

FINESSE FARMS - Flowers, plants, and seeds - Finesse Farms East Inc.

FINESSE PLUS - Shampoos - Helene Curtis Industries Inc.

FINESSE TEXTURED - Tiles–ceramic - Latco Products

FINEST - Artists' materials - M. Grumbacher Inc.

FINEST - Computer software - Scanvec Inc.

FINEST - Food products ☆ - Rubenstein Foods Inc.

FINEST - Paints–artists' - Koh-I-Noor, Inc.

FINEST - Vegetables–canned - Faribault Foods Inc.

FINEST BERRIES IN THE WORLD, THE - Fruits and vegetables - Driscoll Strawberry Associates, Inc.

FINEST CALL - Food products - American Beverage Marketers, Inc.

FINEST COFFEE & TEAS ESTABLISHED 1907 - Coffee - Longo Coffee & Tea Inc.

FINEST FINISH - Paints - Finnaren & Haley Inc.

FINEST HOMES DEMAND CROFT QUALITY, THE - Glass–window - Croft Metals Inc.

FINEST HOUR - Floor coverings–carpet and rugs - Coronet Carpets Inc.

FINEST QUALITY - Flowers, plants, and seeds - Rivard's Quality Seeds Inc.

FINEST QUALITY PEARLS - Trimmings–millinery - Novtex Corp.

FINEST QUALITY RICE KASHU-KOSHIHIKARI - Rice - California Akita Growers Assoc.

FINEST QUALITY TEA - Vitamins and nutritional supplements - Tea Garden Products, Inc.

FINEST, THE - Floor waxes ☆ - Penn Champ Inc.

FINEST TRADITIONS - Meat products - Coborn's Inc.

FINESTIK - Markers–felt-tip ☆ - Faber-Castell Corp.

FINESTONE - Adhesives and sealants - Simplex Products Div.

FINESTRA - Floor coverings - Mannington Resilient Floors

FINETEX - Toys–stuffed - Finetex International, Inc.

FINETONE - Drums–musical instruments - Eames Drum Co.

FINETONE - Hearing aids - Finetone Hearing Instruments, Inc.

FINFURNACE - Heaters–space - Pelonis USA Ltd.

FING-O-TIP - Racks ☆ - A.J. Ganz Co. Inc.

FING-R-FLEX - Exercising equipment - Nortech Laboratories

FINGER ART - Decals and transfers - Metra Inc.

FINGER BOWL - Games - Tiger Electronics, Inc.

FINGER-BRUSH - Dental equipment - Convenience Packaging Co.

FINGER COTS - First aid kits - Flents Products Co. Inc.

FINGER-EASE - Lubricants - Chem-Pak Inc.

FINGER-FILETS - Meat products–poultry - Pierce Foods Corp.

FINGER-FLICK - Games - Finger-Sports, Inc.

FINGER-FLICK SPORTS - Games - Finger-Sports, Inc.

FINGER FOOD - Skin care products - Forbess Corp.

FINGER FRIENDS - Hobby kits - Lisa Frank, Inc.

FINGER FUN - Cartoon prints - Kevin Gene Larson

FINGER GEMS - Nail care products - Nail Emporium & Nail Fashion

FINGER-GRIP - Medical apparatus - Genesis Industries Inc.

FINGER LAKES - Cans–metal - Curtice-Burns Foods, Inc.

FINGER LAKES - Meat products–poultry - Dudley Poultry Co.

FINGER LAKES - Socks - Seneca Knitting Mills Corp.

FINGER LAKES WINE CELLARS - Wines - Glenora Wine Cellars, Inc.

FINGER MAID - Gloves - Aparco Inc.

FINGER N TOE - Skin care products - Claire Topper Enterprises

FINGER OAK - Floor coverings ☆ - Bruce Hardwood Floors

FINGER PAINTS - Gloves - Swany America Corp.

FINGER PINKIES - Paper–toweling - Liquid Paper Corp.

FINGER POPS - Toys - Tonka Corp.

FINGER PUMPS - Weightlifting equipment - Peter C. Reilly

FINGER PUPPETS - Toys - Imperial Toy Corp.

FINGER ROLLERS - Massagers - Kinsei Shiatsu, Inc.

FINGER SAVER - Housewares - James Comaianni

FINGER-SPORTS - Games - Finger-Sports, Inc.

FINGER, THE - Key rings - Innovid

FINGER THINGS - Rings–jewelry ☆ - Other Mother Co.

FINGERBALL - Games ☆ - CBS Toys

FINGERKEY - Computer software - Optomation, Inc.

FINGERMAJIG - Pet products - Hearthsong Inc.

FINGERNAIL FITNESS - Nail care products ☆ - Spilo/Mehaz Worldwide

FINGEROOS - Toys - Tonka Corp.

FINGERPAINTS - Manicure preparations - Fingerpaints

FINGERPASS - Alarms–personal - Micro Identification Systems, Inc.

FINGERPRINT - Paper - Byron Weston Div.

FINGERPRINTS - Manicure preparations - Nailtex Inc.

FINGERSLIP - Cooking equipment–household - Dorcas' Door, Inc.

FINGERTIP - Cribs–wood - HARD Manufacturing Co. Inc.

FINGERTIP - Mats - Ludlow Composites Corp.

FINGERTIP FANTASY - Manicure preparations - Nails Naturally, Inc.

FINGERTIP STORAGE - Furniture - Datel, Inc.

FINGERTIPS - Cosmetics - Scherrer Laboratories Inc.

FINGERTITE - Couplings - Plastic Specialties and Technologies Investments, Inc.

FINGLES - Clay–modeling - Tonka Corp.

FINGLINE - Plastics - Plastruct Inc.

FINGOS - Cereal - General Mills, Inc.

FINI - Cereal ☆ - C. & J. Willenborg Inc.

FINIAL - Faucets - Kohler Co.

FINICKY BITS - Cat food - Heinz Pet Products Co.

FINIS. - Apparel and accessories - Corde a Linge, Inc.

FINIS - Cleaning preparations ☆ - Scott's Liquid Gold Inc.

FINIS - Skin care products - Paula Payne Products Co. Inc.

FINIS - Sporting goods - Finis Inc.

FINISH - Dishwashing compounds - Benckiser Consumer Products Inc.

FINISH - Lime products - Western Lime Corp.

FINISH - Mouthwashes - Lever Brothers Co. Inc.

FINISH 52, A - Animal feeds - Carl S. Akey Inc.

FINISH 58, A - Animal feeds - Carl S. Akey Inc.

FINISH 500 - Paints - Duron, Inc.

FINISH 2001 - Waxes–sealing - Turtle Wax, Inc.

FINISH-CURE - Glue–household or industrial - Bob Smith Industries

FINISH LINE - Floor coverings–carpet and rugs - Barrett Carpet Mills Inc.

FINISH LINE - Footwear–athletic - Finish Line, Inc.

FINISH LINE - Health care products ☆ - Avon Products, Inc.

FINISH-LINE - Tools - David White Inc.

FINISH LINE - Trading cards and stamps - West Sports Marketing, Inc.

FINISH LINE, THE - Building materials - ABT Co., Inc.

FINISH LINE, THE - Paint rollers - Bestt-Liebco

FINISH LINE, THE - Apparel and accessories - Finish Line, Inc.

FINISH MASTER - Mops - Piedmont Mop Co.

FINISH OF THE FUTURE - Paper–toilet - Jado Bathroom and Hardware Manufacturing Corp.

FINISH OFF - Paint removers - Savogran Co.

FINISH ON DEMAND - Office machines - C.P. Bourg Inc.

FINISH-RUB - Abrasive products - Park Metallurgical Corp.

FINISH RUB - Chemical preparations - H. Behlen & Bro. Inc.

FINISH STRIPPER - Cleaning preparations ☆ - Custom Building Products

FINISH TEC - Paints - Tremco Inc.

FINISH UP - Hair care products - Nutrine Ltd.

FINISHEEN - Hair care products - Revlon Consumer Products Corp.

FINISHER - Clippers–barber - Sunbeam-Oster Household Products

FINISHER - Cosmetics - Jatai International

FINISHER'S FRIEND - Concrete finisher - Century Floors

FINISHES - Wallpaper ☆ - Motif Designs, Inc.

FINISHES FOR LIFE TARNISH-FREE GUARANTEED - Brass products - Colonial Bronze Co.

FINISHING LINE - Steel wool - International Steel Wool Corp.

FINISHING MACHINE, THE - Tools–power-driven - Black & Decker Corp.

FINISHING TOUCH - Cleaning preparations - American Piano Service and Supply Corp.

FINISHING TOUCH - Cleaning preparations - Blue Coral, Inc.

FINISHING TOUCH - Electronic equipment - General Electric Co.

FINISHING TOUCH - Floor coverings–carpet and rugs - Mohawk Industries Inc.

FINISHING TOUCH - Floor coverings–carpet and rugs - National Floor Products Co., Inc.

FINISHING TOUCH - Floor waxes - L & F Consumer Products

FINISHING TOUCH - Furniture ☆ - Ridgeway Clock Co.

FINISHING TOUCH - Hair care products - Edward A. Sport Laboratory

FINISHING TOUCH - Hosiery–women's ☆ - Easton International

FINISHING TOUCH - Lotions - Photographic Solutions, Inc.

FINISHING TOUCH - Paint sprayers - Wagner Spray Tech Corp.

FINISHING TOUCH - Shelving units–metal - Robert Swanson Inc.

FINISHING TOUCH - Shutters–plastic - Kentech Plastics, Inc.

FINISHING TOUCH - Wallpaper - Rainbow Creations Inc.

FINISHING TOUCH, THE - Garden equipment - Cobraco Manufacturing, Inc.

FINISHING TOUCH, THE - Paper–gift wrap - CPS Corp.

FINISHING TOUCH, THE - Binders - Ibico Inc.

FINISHING TOUCH, THE - Switches–electric - Leviton Manufacturing Co., Inc.

FINISHING TOUCH, THE - Housewares - Merrick Industries Inc.

FINISHING TOUCH, THE - Lotions - Photographic Solutions, Inc.

FINISHING TOUCH, THE - Floor coverings–carpet and rugs - Tuftex Carpet Mills, Inc.

☆ = Now out of production

FINISHING TOUCHES - Deodorizers - Scentex Inc.
FINISHING TOUCHES - Dolls - Mattel, Inc.
FINISHING TOUCHES - Fireplace equipment - The Adams Co.
FINISHING TOUCHES - Jewelry - Duncan Enterprises
FINISHING TOUCHES - Socks - DML Marketing Group, Inc.
FINISHING TOUCHES - Wallpaper - Royaleigh Designs Ltd.
FINISHLINE - Shelving units—wood ☆ - Lundia
FINITA'S FANCIES BLAZING BULL BBQ SAUCE - Sauces - Finita's Fancies, Inc.
FINITA'S FANCIES SPOTTED BULL BBQ SAUCEBBQ SAUCE A GENTLE GIANT - Sauces - Finita's Fancies, Inc.
FINITE - Hair care products - Helene Curtis Industries Inc.
FINITY - Paints—artists' - Winsor & Newton
FINITY - Women's apparel - Delta Holdings, Inc.
FINITY NATURALS - Apparel—women's - Delta Holdings, Inc.
FINK - Apparel—men's - U.O.D., Inc.
FINK - Recording label ☆ - Fink-Pinewood Records & Productions (Pinewood Productions)
FINK - Wedding gowns - Fink Brothers Inc.
FINK - Wines - Fink Winery
FINK'S SUPERIOR CUT - Jewelry—precious - Fink's Jewelers Inc.
FINK'S SUPERIOR QUALITY - Jewelry—precious - Fink's Jewelers Inc.
FINLANDER - Boats—motor ☆ - Nord Yachts
FINLANDIA - Bedding—linen - Dan River Inc.
FINLANDIA - Cheese - Atalanta Corp.
FINLANDIA - Dinnerware—glass ☆ - Johnson Brothers, USA, Inc.
FINLANDIA - Floor coverings—carpet and rugs ☆ - Mandate-Dawn Carpet Mills
FINLANDIA - Glassware—household ☆ - Anchor Hocking Glass, Inc.
FINLANDIA - Jewelry - Marius Hansen Ltd.
FINLANDIA - Vodka - Heublein, Inc.
FINLANDIA LITE - Cheese - Atalanta Corp.
FINLAYSON OF SCANDANAVIA - Wallpaper - Sterling Prints
FINLESS - Jams and jellies - Berry Best Farm
FINLEY - Coffee - Sara Lee Corp.
FINLEY - Vegetables—frozen - Seabrook Brothers & Sons Inc.
FINN - Boats - Vanguard Racing Sailboats
FINN - Fishing lures - The Finn Co., Inc.
FINNAREN & HALEY - Paints - Finnaren & Haley Inc.
FINNCLIPPER - Ships—sailing vessels - North East Wind Yacht Group
FINNDIA - Bedding—linen - Dan River Inc.
FINNEGAN SEAL - Toys—stuffed - Dakin Inc.
FINNEGAN'S IRISH STYLE CHEESE - Cheese - Pacific Cheese Co., Inc.
FINNFLAIR - Bedding—linen - Dan River Inc.
FINNFOODS - Confections - Finnfoods Div.
FINNGLAS - Glass products - Seaply International
FINNGRIP - Sporting goods ☆ - Exel Marketing Inc.
FINNIANS - Figurines - Roman, Inc.
FINNISH ACCENT - Tablecloths ☆ - Dansk International Designs, Ltd.
FINNISH COLLECTION - Food products - Entre-Nous Fragrances Ltd.
FINNISH LINE - Bedding—linen - Dan River Inc.
FINNISH STAR - Cheese - Noon Hour Food Products
FINNLANDIA - Saunas - Cedarbrook Sauna Inc.
FINNLEO - Saunas - Cedarbrook Sauna Inc.
FINNSAILER - Ships—sailing vessels ☆ - Nord Yachts
FINNTASTIC - Bedding—linen - Dan River Inc.
FINNY - Pet products - Finny World Class Pet Products Inc.
FINO - Boats - Stephen Yadvish
FINO - Frames—picture - Fino, Inc.
FINO II - Fabrics—canvas - Crown Textile Co.
FINOLIC - Model-rocket accessories - Microbrick Technologies Inc.
FINS-UP - Pet products - Lake Products Co. Inc.
FINSEL - Fishing lures ☆ - Lindy Little Joe Inc.
FINSEW - Thread - New Bedford Thread Co. Inc.
FINSIM - Computer software - Fintronic USA Inc.
FINSKA - Saunas - Cedarbrook Sauna Inc.
FINSTER - Toys - Saban Entertainment, Inc.
FINSTRIP - Heating pads—electric - Chromalox
FINSURE - Pet products - Lake Products Co. Inc.
FINSWEEP - Cleaning equipment - Let's Clear the Air, Inc.
FINTASTIC - Fish food - Golden State Aquatics Inc. (Fintastic Div.)
FINWEAR - Apparel and accessories - J. Steven Slade
FINYL - Windows—plastic ☆ - Aluminum Co. of America
FINYL BOND - Floor coverings ☆ - Tec Inc.
FINYL-SEAL - Epoxy coatings - Sterling-Clark-Lurton Corp.
FINZ - Trading cards and stamps - Aqua-Signz, Inc.
FIOGESIC - Pharmaceutical preparations - Sandoz Pharmaceuticals Corp.

FIOR DI LATTE - Cheese - Pollio Dairy Products Corp.
FIOR D'ITALIA - Apparel - Fior D'Italia Inc.
FIORD - Sporting goods - Acme Tackle Co.
FIORD SPOON - Fishing lures - Acme Tackle Co.
FIORE - Food products - Bel Canto Fancy Foods Ltd.
FIORE - Scarves, neckwear - Continental Scarf Corp.
FIORE - Whirlpools - Jacuzzi Inc.
FIORE DI MIMOSA - Underwear and nightwear - Intapp Group, Inc.
FIORE D'ORO - Pasta - The Pasta Fresca Co. Inc.
FIORELLA - Plumbing fixtures—metal ☆ - Barclay Products Ltd.
FIORELLA - Shoes ☆ - Atsco Footwear Inc.
FIORELLA - Soybean oil - Venice Importing Co.
FIORELLO - Vegetables—canned - Lico Brands, Inc.
FIORENZA - Paper - Ohlendorf Imports
FIOREX - Pharmaceutical preparations - C.S. Ruckstuhl Co. Inc.
FIORGEN - Pharmaceutical preparations - Goldline Laboratories, Inc.
FIORI - Tableware—china ☆ - Villeroy and Boch Tableware Ltd.
FIORI - Wallpaper - Doshi Wallcoveringss Inc.
FIORICET - Pharmaceutical preparations - Sandoz Pharmaceuticals Corp.
FIORINAL - Pharmaceutical preparations - Sandoz Pharmaceuticals Corp.
FIORINO - Olive oil - Messinia USA, Inc.
FIORITO - Yarn - William Unger & Co. Inc.
FIORLINI SPORT - Women's apparel - Cato Corp.
FIORMOR - Pharmaceutical preparations - Moore Medical Corp.
FIORUCCI - Food products ☆ - Fred Montesi Super Markets
FIPA - Jewelry - Hobe Cie. Ltd.
F.I.Q.D. - Electrical equipment - Molex-Etc Inc.
FIRCRAFT - Wood products - Willamette Industries, Inc.
FIRCREST - Frankfurters - Fircrest Farms
FIRDA - Seafood products—canned or cured - B. Westergaard & Co. Inc.
FIRE - Apparel and accessories - Breton Industries
FIRE - Lipsticks - Cosmair Inc.
FIRE - Tools - Railway Handle Corp.
FIRE 66 - Sporting goods ☆ - Gold Eagle/Arnold Palmer
FIRE-A-LATOR - Fireplaces ☆ - Superior Fireplace Co.
FIRE ALARM - Thread ☆ - Perfect Thread Co. Inc.
FIRE ALERT - Smoke detectors ☆ - Kidde-Fenwal, Inc.
FIRE & ICE - Candy ☆ - Leaf, Inc.
FIRE & ICE - Christmas tree ornaments - Cracker Box Inc.
FIRE & ICE - Colognes - Revlon Consumer Products Corp.
FIRE & ICE - Dishes—china - Mikasa Co.
FIRE & ICE - Fabrics—tapestry - Comark Wallcoverings
FIRE AND ICE - Game machines - Bally Gaming International, Inc.
FIRE & ICE - Games ☆ - Mayfair Games, Inc.
FIRE AND ICE - Lamps - Lamplight Farms, Inc.
FIRE & ICE - Oils—lubricating - Shell Oil Co.
FIRE & SPICE - Colognes - Old 97 Co.
FIRE & SPICE - Perfumes - Stephan Co.
FIRE ART - Fireplace equipment - Rosewood
FIRE ATTACKER - Motor vehicles—trucks - Abbe Schmidt, Inc.
FIRE AWAY - Fire extinguishers - Kidde Safety
FIRE BALL - Ammunition - Remington Arms Co., Inc.
FIRE BALLS - Lighters ☆ - Lamplight Farms, Inc.
FIRE BARRIER II - Chemical preparations - Fire Doctor, Inc.
FIRE BLAST - Chewing gum - Richardson Brands
FIRE BLASTER - Fire extinguishing compositions - Midwest Environmental Safety Supply
FIRE-BLOCK - Bags - Block and Co., Inc.
FIRE BLOCK - Mattresses - Serta, Inc.
FIRE BLOX - Charcoal - Seymour Manufacturing Co.,Inc.
FIRE BOX - Thread ☆ - Perfect Thread Co. Inc.
FIRE-BRICK - Fireplace equipment ☆ - Sportsline
FIRE BRITE - Cleaning preparations - Sonju Corp.
FIRE BURNS, THE - Jewelry - Lazare Kaplan International Inc.
FIRE BY NITE - Recording label - Willie George Ministries, Inc.
FIRE CHEF - Sauces - Fire Chief Sauces
FIRE CHIEF - Bicycles - Kent International Inc.
FIRE CHIEF - Fabrics - Graniteville Co.
FIRE CHIEF - Filters—industrial - Standard-Keil Hardware Manufacturing Co.
FIRE CHIEF - Recording label - Argus Asset Management, Inc.
FIRE CHIPS - Snack foods - Salem Food Co. of New York, Inc.
FIRE/CLAD - Electrical cable - Coleman Cable Systems, Inc.
FIRE COMPANY 16 - Apparel and accessories - Tri-Equity Trading Ltd.
FIRE CONTROL - Fire extinguishers - Kidde Safety
FIRE DANCE - Fireplace equipment ☆ - Earth Stove Inc.
FIRE DANCE - Floor coverings—carpet and rugs - World Carpets, Inc.

☆ = Now out of production

FIRE DOT - Fabrics - Graniteville Co.

FIRE DRUM - Fireplaces - Malm Fireplaces Inc.

FIRE DRUM 2 - Fireplaces - Malm Fireplaces Inc.

FIRE DRUM 3 - Fireplaces - Malm Fireplaces Inc.

FIRE-EATER - Toys—automobiles - Mattel, Inc.

FIRE ELEMENT - Vitamins and nutritional supplements - Aveda Corp.

FIRE ERASER - Firefighting apparatus - Integrity International, Inc.

FIRE-ESCAPE - Golfing equipment - Network Golf Ltd. Partnership

FIRE EXTERMINATOR - Fire extinguishers - Stout Corp.

FIRE FIGHT - Fireworks - China Pyrotechnics, Inc.

FIRE FIGHTER - Filters—industrial - Standard-Keil Hardware Manufacturing Co.

FIRE FIGHTER - Paints ☆ - Colony Paints Div.

FIRE-FIGHTER - Thread - Threads USA Div.

FIRE FIGHTER - Toys - Tonka Corp.

FIRE FIGHTER - Toys—automobiles - Mattel, Inc.

FIRE FIGHTERS - Wastebaskets - United Receptacle Inc.

FIRE FIGHTER'S SODA - Beverages—carbonated - Creative Beverage Co.

FIRE-FILE - Cabinets—metal - Knoll Group

FIRE FLAKES - Fireplace equipment - Pine Mountain Corp.

FIRE-FLEX - Cables—coaxial - Firestik Antenna Co.

FIRE FLIES - Footwear - Sylvania Shoe Manufacturing Corp.

FIRE FLIGHT - Hardware - Fire Flight, Inc.

FIRE FLOWER - Bicycles ☆ - Roadmaster Corp.

FIRE FLOWER - Dinnerware—glass ☆ - Lenox, Inc.

FIRE FLOWERS - Clocks - General Time Corp. (Westclox/Seth Thomas Div.)

FIRE FLY - Fishing lures - Gemmy Industries Corp.

FIRE FLY - Fishing lures ☆ - Hildebrandt Corp.

FIRE-FLY - Paint removers - H. Behlen & Bro. Inc.

FIRE FLY - Soccer equipment ☆ - Brine Inc.

FIRE FOR SURE - Fireplace equipment - West End Gardens

FIRE FOX - Tricycles ☆ - Hedstrom Corp.

FIRE-FYTER - Safes - Center Manufacturing Co.

FIRE-GLASS III - Shingles - Manville/Schuller

FIRE GLAZED HAM - Hams - The Swiss Colony, Inc.

FIRE GUARD - Insulating materials - Edmar Technical Systems Inc.

FIRE GUARD - Paints - Parker Paint Manufacturing Co.

FIRE GUARD - Roofing materials—clay ☆ - GAF Corp.

FIRE-GUARD - Tape—adhesive - Manco, Inc.

FIRE GUARDIAN - Gloves - Knoxville Glove Co.

FIRE HALT - Gypsum products - Georgia-Pacific Corp.

FIRE-HALT - Shingles—asphalt or tar ☆ - GS Roofing Products Co.

FIRE HAWK - Golfing equipment - Leroy P. Rosasco

FIRE/IRONS - Toys ☆ - Henry Gordy International Inc.

FIRE JESTER - Fireplaces ☆ - Malm Fireplaces Inc.

FIRE-K-TROL - Paints - C.M. Athey Paint Co.

FIRE KING - Cooking utensils—earthenware - Anchor Hocking Glass, Inc.

FIRE KING - Safes - Fire King International, Inc.

FIRE-KING - Shingles - Manville/Schuller

FIRE KING 25 - Filing cabinets—metal - Fire King International, Inc.

FIRE KNOX - Gloves - Knoxville Glove Co.

FIRE KOTE - Pigments - Tremco Inc.

FIRE LOAD - Cleaning preparations - Thomas R. Lucenta

FIRE LOGS YOUR WAY - Machinery - Richard Green

FIRE MAGIC - Barbecues and grills - Robert H. Peterson Co.

FIRE MARSHALL - Filters—industrial - Standard-Keil Hardware Manufacturing Co.

FIRE MARSHALL - Metals - Nystrom, Inc.

FIRE MONKEY - Recording label - Fire Monkey

FIRE MOUNTAIN - Bicycles ☆ - Huffy Corp.

FIRE MOUNTAIN - Food products - Fire Mountain Enterprises

FIRE 'N ICE - Chewing gum ☆ - Fleer Corp.

FIRE ON ICE - Trading cards and stamps - Donruss Trading Cards, Inc.

FIRE OUT - Fire extinguishers - Real Ideas Inc.

FIRE PLUG #5 - Pet products - Richard Hanau Pet Foods Corp.

FIRE PLUGS - Dog food ☆ - Gimborn U.S., Inc.

FIRE-POINT - Telescopic sight - Fontaine Industries Inc.

FIRE POWER - Batteries - Exide Corp.

FIRE POWER - Bicycles - Kent International Inc.

FIRE POWER - Cleaning preparations - 1st Ayd Corp.

FIRE POWER - Fireworks - American Promotional Events, Inc.

FIRE POWER - Sporting goods ☆ - Gold Eagle/Arnold Palmer

FIRE POW'R - Sporting goods - Crosman Corp.

FIRE PUMPER - Toys - Fisher-Price, Inc.

FIRE QUEEN - Cooking utensils—earthenware ☆ - Anchor Hocking Glass, Inc.

FIRE QUEEN - Fireplaces ☆ - Malm Fireplaces Inc.

FIRE RESEARCH - Paints - Budeke's Paint

FIRE ROCK PALE ALE - Beverages—malt - Kona Brewing Co.

FIRE-SAFE - Safes - Sentry Group

FIRE SAUSAGE - Meat products - Woodroast Systems, Inc.

FIRE-SCAPE - Fabrics - Dan River Inc.

FIRE SENTRY - Fire extinguishers - Fyrnetics Inc.

FIRE SHIELD - Containers - Century Container Corp.

FIRE-SHIELD - Gypsum products - National Gypsum Co.

FIRE SHUT - Doors—metal - Alpine Overhead Doors Inc.

FIRE SMART - Measuring instruments - Gaztech International Corp.

FIRE SMASHER - Toys—automobiles - Mattel, Inc.

FIRE SMOLDER - Thread ☆ - Perfect Thread Co. Inc.

FIRE STAR - Bicycles ☆ - Roadmaster Corp.

FIRE STAR - Golfing equipment - Golfsmith International Inc.

FIRE STARTER - Flashlights ☆ - Garrity Industries

FIRE STARTER - Sporting goods ☆ - Gerber Legendary Blades

FIRE STARTERS - Giftware - Hanna's Potpourri Specialties, Inc.

FIRE STIX - Candy - Leaf, Inc.

FIRE STRIKE - Chemical preparations - Biocenter, Inc.

FIRE TAPE - Tape—adhesive - E-Z Taping System, Inc.

FIRE TEST - Paneling - Marlite

FIRE TITE - Doors—metal - Alpine Overhead Doors Inc.

FIRE TO GO - Fireplace logs—treated - Green Fields Inc.

FIRE-TOOTH - Saw blades - Vermont American Corp.

FIRE TRAK - Building materials - Duane Wm. Becker

FIRE TRUCK - Toys - Steven Manufacturing Co.

FIRE-UP - Pharmaceutical preparations - Light Force Inc.

FIRE WARDEN - Home fire extinguishers ☆ - American General Products Inc.

FIRE WATER - Beverages—alcohol - White Rock Distilleries Inc.

FIRE WATER EARTH - Luggage - VT International Ltd.

FIRE WICK - Solid-fuel starter for wood stoves ☆ - Coughlan Products Corp.

FIRE WORKS - Tableware—plastic - Design Works International Inc.

FIRE X CRACKER - Firefighting apparatus - Marco, Inc.

FIRE-X GLASBORD - Fiberboard - Kemlite Co., Inc.

FIREAERO - Toys—models ☆ - Estes Industries

FIREARM - Books—comic - Malibu Comics Entertainment, Inc.

FIREARROW - Bicycles - Columbia Manufacturing Inc.

FIREBALL - Bicycles - Columbia Manufacturing Inc.

FIREBALL - Christmas tree ornaments - Cracker Box Inc.

FIREBALL - Cordials - Marie Brizard Wines & Spirits, USA

FIREBALL - Footwear ☆ - E.S. Originals, Inc.

FIREBALL - Games - Sipa Sipa Games

FIREBALL - Golfing equipment - Pinseeker Golf Corp.

FIREBALL - Recording label - Fireball Records

FIREBALL - Sporting goods ☆ - K Lin Specialties

FIREBALL - Sunglasses, ophthalmic lenses ☆ - Corning Inc.

FIREBALL - Toys - North Pacific Products Inc.

FIREBALL - Trailers—travel - Fireball Industry Inc.

FIREBALL 78 - Clocks - Fisher's Products

FIREBALL ISLAND - Games ☆ - Milton Bradley Co.

FIREBAN - Insecticides - Zeneca Inc.

FIREBASE - Computer software - Mapping Solutions, Inc.

FIREBEAM - Automotive parts and accessories - Federal Signal Corp.

FIREBIRD - Bicycles ☆ - Roadmaster Corp.

FIREBIRD - Binoculars - Pioneer Marketing & Research, Inc.

FIREBIRD - Fabrics - Graniteville Co.

FIREBIRD - Fireplace equipment - Cardinal Home Products

FIREBIRD - Glassware—household ☆ - Crisa Corp.

FIREBIRD - Hair care products - Fromm Industries

FIREBIRD - Kites - Gayla Industries Inc.

FIREBIRD - Lighters - Park Lane Associates, Inc.

FIREBIRD - Luggage ☆ - Samsonite Corp.

FIREBIRD - Motor vehicles—automobiles - General Motors Corp. (Pontiac/GMC Div.)

FIREBIRD - Sporting goods - Shakespeare Fishing Tackle

FIREBIRD - Toys—models - Cox Products Inc.

FIREBIRD - Trailers—truck ☆ - Sun-Lite Inc.

FIREBIRD ARTS & MUSIC, INC. - Recording label - Firebird Arts & Music of Oregon, Inc.

FIREBIRD MUSIC - Recording label - Firebird Arts & Music of Oregon, Inc.

FIREBIRD THUNDERZORD - Toys - Saban Entertainment, Inc.

FIREBIRDS - Fireworks - L. W. Loyd Co., Inc.

FIREBLEND - Tiles—ceramic - Buchtal USA

FIREBLOCK - Building materials—concrete - Lasco Products Group

FIREBLOCKS - Fireplace equipment ☆ - Duraflame, Inc.

FIREBOLT - Bicycles - Columbia Manufacturing Inc.

FIREBOLT - Bowling balls ☆ - Ebonite International, Inc.
FIREBOX - Enamels - Fulton Co.
FIREBRAKE ZB - Insecticides - U.S. Borax Inc.
FIREBRAND - Candles - American Candle Co. Inc.
FIREBRAND - Lighters - Park Lane Associates, Inc.
FIREBRAND - Meat products–beef - Armour Swift-Eckrich
FIREBREAK - Door frames - Contact Lumber Co.
FIREBRIGHT - Rings–jewelry - Artcarved Inc.
FIRECAT - Archery equipment - Martin Archery Inc.
FIRECAT - Toys–models ☆ - Estes Industries
FIRECHEK - Floor coverings - Congoleum Corp.
FIRECHEK - Valves - Memry Corp.
FIRECHIEF - Playground equipment - Child Life Inc.
FIRECOOLER - Safes - Safe Supplies
FIRECRACKER - Bathing suits - Ocean Pool Co.
FIRECRACKER - Flowers, plants, and seeds - G.S. Grimes Seeds
FIRECRACKER - Game machines - Bally Gaming International, Inc.
FIRECRACKER - Toys - Tonka Corp.
FIRECRACKER, THE - Crab meat–canned or cured - Jerry's Seafood
FIRECRAFT HANDMADE CANDLES - Candles - Steidle Enterprises, Inc.
FIREFALLS - Fireplaces - Hearth & Home Distributors, Inc.
FIREFET - Electronic equipment - Wilcoxon Research, Inc.
FIREFIGHTER - Paints - Valspar Corp.
FIREFLEX - Glass products - Lasco Products Group
FIREFLIES - Fireworks - China Pyrotechnics, Inc.
FIREFLIES - Floor coverings–carpet and rugs - Eurotex Inc.
FIREFLY - Antennas - Firestik Antenna Co.
FIREFLY - Bicycles - Ross Bicycles USA, Ltd.
FIREFLY - Christmas tree ornaments - Cracker Box Inc.
FIREFLY - Computer equipment - Applied Intelligent Systems Inc.
FIREFLY - Computer software - Firefly Software Corp.
FIREFLY - Fishing floats - Blue Fox Tackle Co.
FIREFLY - Furniture ☆ - Bassett Furniture Industries, Inc.
FIREFLY - Furniture–metal - E-Z Sales & Manufacturing, Inc.
FIREFLY - Kites ☆ - Hi-Flier Manufacturing Co.
FIREFLY - Lamps ☆ - Tensor Corp.
FIREFLY - Lenses–magnifying - Swift Instruments, Inc.
FIREFLY - Lighting equipment - ACR, Electronics, Inc.
FIREFLY - Toys - Tonka Corp.
FIREFLY - Underwater transportation apparatus - Deep Ocean Engineering Inc.
FIREFLY FLASHCARDS - Pet products - Firefly Flashcards Inc.
FIREFLY GREETINGS - Greeting cards - Intouch Technologies, Inc.
FIREFLY PLUS - Flashlights - ACR, Electronics, Inc.
FIREFLY SAFETY VEST - Safety equipment - Firefly Safety Vest, Inc.
FIREFOAM - Fire-extinguishing chemicals - Chemonics Industries, Inc.
FIREFORCE - Toys - Tonka Corp.
FIREFORM - Fireplaces ☆ - Superior Fireplace Co.
FIREGARD - Fabrics - M. Lowenstein Corp.
FIREGLOW - Christmas tree ornaments - Cracker Box Inc.
FIREGUARD - Paints - Parker Paint Manufacturing Co.
FIREGUARD - Shelving units–metal - Schwab Corp.
FIREGUARD - Tanks–storage - Steel Tank Institute
FIREGUARD & DESIGN - Gypsum products - Georgia-Pacific Corp.
FIREHAWK - Firearms, accessories, and parts - Thompson/Center Arms
FIREHAWK - Tires - Bridgestone/Firestone, Inc.
FIREHAWK - Toys–models ☆ - Estes Industries
FIREHAWK GT - Tires - Bridgestone/Firestone, Inc.
FIREHAWK RMT - Tires - Bridgestone/Firestone, Inc.
FIREHAWK SV - Tires - Bridgestone/Firestone, Inc.
FIREHEAD - Apparel and accessories - Colin O'Hara
FIREHOOD - Fireplace equipment ☆ - Majestic Co.
FIREHORSE FILMS - Film - Firehorse Films
FIREHOUSE - Barbecue sauce ☆ - Liberty Richter Inc.
FIREHOUSE - Food products - Gourmet Specialties
FIREHOUSE - Fruit drinks–bottled or canned - Ocean Spray Cranberries Inc.
FIREHOUSE FRITZ - Puppets - Dakin Inc.
FIREHOUSE JALAPENO - Bagels - Spot Bagel Bakery, Inc.
FIREHOUSE NO. 1 - Barbecue sauce - Mad Will's Food Co. (Products Div.)
FIREKING - Safes - Meilink Safe Co.
FIRELANDS - Furniture - Norwalk Furniture Corp.
FIRELANDS - Wines - Firelands Winery
FIRELIGHT - Glassware–household - Lenox Crystal, Inc.
FIRELIGHT - Hardware - Turner Industries Ltd.
FIRELIGHT - Seafood products–fresh or frozen - Connors Brothers Inc.
FIRELIGHT - Seat covers - Saddleman, Inc.
FIRELIGHT - Tableware–china - Lenox, Inc.

FIRELIGHT - Wainscotting - Georgia-Pacific Corp.
FIRELIGHT COLLECTION - Glassware–household ☆ - National Housewares
FIRELIGHT GLASS - Oils–illuminating - Vitrico Corp.
FIRELIGHT GOLD - Glassware–household - Lenox, Inc.
FIRELIGHT PLATINUM - Glassware–household - Lenox, Inc.
FIRELIGHT SPICE - Teas - Celestial Seasonings, Inc.
FIRELIGHTS - Footwear ☆ - E.S. Originals, Inc.
FIRELINE - Shingles–asphalt or tar - Bird Inc.
FIRELURE NITWIT - Sporting goods - Weber Industries Inc.
FIREMAN BEAR - Toys–stuffed - Dakin Inc.
FIREMAN HOSER - Toys - Mattel, Inc.
FIREMAN IN A CAN - Fire extinguishers - Green Leaf Products, Inc.
FIREMAN'S GYM - Playground equipment - Child Life Inc.
FIREMARK - Smoke detectors - Rixson Firemark Inc.
FIREMASTER - Office supplies ☆ - Victor Systems & Equipment Co.
FIREMASTER - Paints - Kelly-Moore/Preservative Paints
FIREMASTER - Safety products - Thermal Ceramics Inc.
FIREMASTER - Shoes ☆ - Endicott Johnson Corp.
FIREMEN'S - Mustard - Universal Foods Corp.
FIREMEN'S BOOT - Footwear ☆ - West Coast Shoe Co.
FIRENZA - Apparel and accessories - Crystal Brands Inc.
FIRENZA - Golf equipment - King Par Corp.
FIRENZA - Jewelry - Firenza
FIRENZA - Motor vehicles–automobiles ☆ - General Motors Corp. (Oldsmobile Div.)
FIRENZA - Motor vehicles–motor homes ☆ - Eldorado Motor Corp.
FIRENZA CRUISER - Motor vehicles–automobiles ☆ - General Motors Corp. (Oldsmobile Div.)
FIRENZA GT - Motor vehicles–automobiles ☆ - General Motors Corp. (Oldsmobile Div.)
FIRENZA LC - Motor vehicles–automobiles ☆ - General Motors Corp. (Oldsmobile Div.)
FIRENZA LX - Motor vehicles–automobiles ☆ - General Motors Corp. (Oldsmobile Div.)
FIRENZE - Artists' materials - Andrews/Nelson/Whitehead
FIRENZE - Coffee - 1 Uno Espresso, Inc.
FIRENZE - Dishes–china - Pasmantier Co. Inc.
FIRENZE - Doors–wood - Peachtree Doors and Windows Inc.
FIRENZE - Flatware ☆ - Wallace International Silversmiths, Inc.
FIRENZE - Hardware - Caliber Computer Corp.
FIRENZE - Tiles–ceramic - H & R Johnson Inc.
FIRENZE - Wallcoverings - Scancelli Prints, Inc.
FIRENZE - Wallpaper - Wallprints
FIRENZE - Wallpaper ☆ - Jolie Papier
FIREPAN - Portable fireplaces - Firepan, Inc.
FIREPIT - Fireplace equipment - Whalen Manufacturing Co.
FIREPLACES BY MARTIN - Fireplaces - Martin Industries, Inc.
FIREPLEX - Smoke detectors - Rauland-Borg Corp.
FIREPLUG - Candy - Fleer Corp.
FIREPLUG - Paint ☆ - Iowa Paint Manufacturing Co. Inc.
FIREPLUGS, INC. - Paper–book - Fireplugs, Inc.
FIREPLUS - Fireplaces - Superior Fireplace Co.
FIREPORT - Computer hardware - Diamond Multimedia Systems, Inc.
FIREPOWER - Adhesives and sealants - Gibson-Homans Co. (Sealant Technology)
FIREPOWER - Automotive parts and accessories - Outboard Marine Corp.
FIREPOWER - Games - Avalon Hill Game Co.
FIREPOWER - Golfing equipment - Raven Golf Services, Inc.
FIREPOWER - Video production - Video Ordnance Inc.
FIREPUCK - Hockey equipment - Firepuck Co., Inc.
FIREQUEST - Ammunition - Firequest International, Inc.
FIRE'S OUT - Cleaning preparations–household - Promaster
FIRESAFE - Glass products ☆ - Glass Inc.
FIRESAFE - Tanks–storage - San Luis Tank Piping Construction Co., Inc.
FIRESCAPE - Kitchen appliances ☆ - Rival Manufacturing Co.
FIRESCREEN - Shingles–asphalt or tar - Bird Inc.
FIRESCREEN - Shingles–asphalt or tar ☆ - GS Roofing Products Co.
FIRESCREEN PLUS - Shingles–asphalt or tar ☆ - GS Roofing Products Co.
FIRESHIELD - Office furniture–metal - Hon Co.
FIRESHIELD - Prefabricated buildings–metal - Safety Storage, Inc.
FIRESIDE - Bedding–linen - Thomaston Mills Inc.
FIRESIDE - Cabinets ☆ - Mouser Kitchens Inc.
FIRESIDE - Clocks ☆ - General Time Corp. (Westclox/Seth Thomas Div.)
FIRESIDE - Cookies - Consolidated Biscuit Co.
FIRESIDE - Fireplace equipment ☆ - GSW Jackes-Evans Manufacturing Co.
FIRESIDE - Fireplace logs–treated - Conros Corp.

☆ = Now out of production

FIRESIDE - Floor coverings - Bruce Hardwood Floors

FIRESIDE - Furniture - Henredon Furniture Industries Inc.

FIRESIDE - Ovenware - Corning Inc.

FIRESIDE - Publisher's imprints - Fireside Bible Publishers

FIRESIDE - Publisher's imprints - Simon & Schuster, Inc.

FIRESIDE - Tobacco products - Consolidated Cigar Corp.

FIRESIDE BRANDY - Coffee - Saramar Corp.

FIRESIDE MIXTURE - Tobacco products - Shepherd Tobacco Co.

FIRESIDE NATURALS - Cookware and basket holder - Corning Inc.

FIRESIDE SCENTS - Spices and extracts - Scentex Inc.

FIRESIDE SCONES - Fireplace logs–treated - Lumi-Lite Candle Co. Inc.

FIRESIDE SKEWERS - Cooking utensils ☆ - Invention Marketing Inc.

FIRESIDE TARTAN - Floor coverings–carpet and rugs ☆ - Trans-Ocean Import Co. Inc.

FIRESIDER - Chairs–folding - E-Z Sales & Manufacturing, Inc.

FIRESIDER - Sleeping bags - Coleman Co., Inc.

FIRESIDERS - Slippers - Thorp Direct Sales, Inc.

FIRESIDERS - Slippers - Wolverine World Wide, Inc.

FIRESIDERS PLUS DESIGN - Slippers - Wolverine World Wide, Inc.

FIRESIDES - Footwear - Wolowick Shoe Co.

FIRESIST - Fabrics - Glen Raven Mills Inc.

FIRESNO - Fire extinguishers - Baker Boy, Inc.

FIRESONG - Floor coverings–carpet and rugs ☆ - Hollytex Carpet Mills Inc.

FIRESOUT - Ashtrays–glass - Jeannette Corp.

FIRESOX - Cement - Specrete-Ip Inc.

FIREST FROST - Christmas tree ornaments - Cracker Box Inc.

FIRESTALL - Roofing materials–slate - Homasote Co.

FIRESTALL TUPS - Roofing materials–slate - Homasote Co.

FIRESTAR - Bicycles - Columbia Manufacturing Inc.

FIRESTAR I - Toys - Fisher-Price, Inc.

FIRESTAR SIGHT - Archery equipment - Martin Archery Inc.

FIRESTART - Fireplace equipment - Duraflame, Inc.

FIRESTEED - Apparel and accessories - Firesteed Corp.

FIRESTICK - Golfing equipment - Wilson Sporting Goods Co.

FIRESTICK - Rods–steel - Vermeer Manufacturing Co.

FIRESTIK - Antennas - Firestik Antenna Co.

FIRESTIX - Wood products - F.M. Industries, Inc.

FIRESTONE - Tires - Bridgestone/Firestone, Inc.

FIRESTONE CHAMPIONSHIP COURSE - Computer software - Access Software Inc.

FIRESTONE VINEYARD, THE - Wines - Firestone Vineyard

FIRESTOP - Plaster–wallboard - Georgia-Pacific Corp.

FIRESTOPPER - Fire extinguishers - Bombay Productions, Inc.

FIRESTOPPER - Fire extinguishing compositions - Ranji Bedi

FIRESTREAK - Toys–models - Estes Industries

FIRETENDER-STOKERMATIC - Fireplace equipment - Chippewa Traders Ltd.

FIRETHERM - Paneling - Geobond International, Inc.

FIRETHORN - Apparel–athletic - Charles Sakmann Golf, Inc.

FIRETRAC - Computer hardware - Del Mar Avionics

FIRETRAK - Tires - Carlisle Tire & Rubber Co.

FIREVIEW - Cleaning preparations–household - Knight Marketing Corp.

FIREWALKER - Shoes ☆ - Endicott Johnson Corp.

FIREWALL - Automotive parts and accessories - Gates Rubber Co. (Automotive Aftermarket/Hardware Sales Div.)

FIREWALL FRB - Flame retardant sheet plastic - Coroplast Inc.

FIREWALL/PLUS - Computer software - Network-1 Software and Technology, Inc.

FIREWALLS - Publisher's imprints - Jack Ewing

FIREWATER - Drain pipe cleaners - Boyer Corp.

FIREWEAR - Fabrics - Springs Industries, Inc.

FIREWIRE - Computer peripheral equipment - Apple Computer Inc.

FIREWORK ALTERNATIVES - Fireworks - Frank G. Davidson

FIREWORKS - Beverages - Silver Palate Kitchen

FIREWORKS - Computer software - Emergency Management Solutions, Inc.

FIREWORKS - Floor coverings–carpet and rugs - Karastan-Bigelow Inc.

FIREWORKS - Glassware–household - Durand International

FIREWORKS - Jewelry - Tiffany and Co.

FIREWORKS - Pet collars ☆ - Leatherite-Nylorite Manufacturing Inc.

FIREWORKS - Recording label - Sugo Records Inc.

FIREWORKS - Rings–jewelry - Artcarved

FIREWORKS - Wallpaper - Jack Foley Associates Inc.

FIREWORKS - Wallpaper ☆ - W.H.S. Lloyd

FIREWORKS OVER AMERICA - Fireworks - Ingram Enterprises, Inc.

FIREWORKS THRU THE CROSS - Posters - Foto Mechanic

FIREX - Smoke detectors - Maple Chase Co.

FIREY - Toys–stuffed ☆ - Dakin Inc.

FIREY - Vegetable sauces - Baumer Foods, Inc.

FIRFFELS - Toys - Azrak-Hamway International, Inc.

FIRGROVE - Plywood - MacMillan Bloedel Building Materials

FIRING LINE - Toys–models ☆ - Estes Industries

FIRLOK - Wood products - Willamette Industries, Inc.

FIRM - Apparel and accessories - Firm Inc.

FIRM - Computer software ☆ - CONDUIT

FIRM - Toothbrushes - Johnson & Johnson

FIRM-A-CURVE - Underwear and nightwear ☆ - Lovable Co.

FIRM & DRY - Hair care products - Bonat Inc.

FIRM & FAST - Hair care products ☆ - Palm Beach Beauty Products

FIRM & FILL - Hair care products ☆ - Palm Beach Beauty Products

FIRM & FIT - Vitamins and nutritional supplements - Vita-Vista

FIRM & NORMAL - Cosmetics ☆ - Stephan Co.

FIRM BELIEVERS - Apparel and accessories - Firm Inc.

FIRM CONTROL - Cosmetics - Revlon-Realistic Professional Products Inc.

FIRM DEFENSE - Skin care products - Matrix Essentials, Inc.

FIRM-FILL - Floor slabs–concrete - Hacker Industries Inc.

FIRM FOOT - Paints - Restore-X

FIRM FOOT - Sporting goods - Beacon Ballfields

FIRM GRIP - Eyelash applicator ☆ - Cosrich Inc.

FIRM GRIP - Sporting goods - Cramer Products Inc.

FIRM HOLD - Hair care products - Nexxus Products Co.

FIRM-HOLDER - Hair care products - Gelle-International Ltd.

FIRM N FIT - Health care products - Garcoa Labs/Vitamin Classics

FIRM 'N FLATTER - Apparel and accessories - Playtex Apparel, Inc.

FIRM 'N' FRUITY - Yogurt - H.P. Hood & Sons Inc.

FIRM NAME - Floor coverings–carpet and rugs - Zapotec McLarty Indian Rugs

FIRM-O-PEDIC - Mattresses ☆ - Kingsdown, Inc.

FIRM REWARDS - Skin-care products - Frances Denney

FIRM-STEP - Floor coverings–tile - Kentile Floors Inc.

FIRM THIGHS LOTION - Skin care products - Health Products Corp.

FIRM-TOUCH - Mattresses - Sealy Inc.

FIRM UP - Hair care products ☆ - Select Brands

FIRM VESSEL - Health care products - East Earth Herb Inc.

FIRMA NAIL - Nail care products - Revlon Consumer Products Corp.

FIRMABOND - Sealing compounds - Wall Firma Inc.

FIRMACLEAR - Sealing compounds - Wall Firma Inc.

FIRMACOTE - Coatings - Wall Firma Inc.

FIRMACRYL - Sealing compounds - Wall Firma Inc.

FIRMAGLE - Skin care products - Revlon Consumer Products Corp.

FIRMAGRIP - Concrete repair products - Wall Firma Inc.

FIRMALASTIC - Coatings - Wall Firma Inc.

FIRMALON - Thread - Perfect Thread Co. Inc.

FIRMALOSS - Vitamins and nutritional supplements ☆ - Weider Health and Fitness

FIRMAMENT - Apparel and accessories - Firmament, Inc.

FIRMANI - Footwear - Emilio Franco Imports Inc.

FIRMAPLEX - Skin care products - Nexxus Products Co.

FIRMAPLUG - Concrete repair products - Wall Firma Inc.

FIRMASHEEN - Coatings - Wall Firma Inc.

FIRMASOME - Skin care products - Almay Inc.

FIRMATA - Hair care products - Aveda Corp.

FIRMAWELD - Adhesives and sealants - Wall Firma Inc.

FIRMDENT - Denture materials - Moyco Industries, Inc.

FIRMDOR - Paper–toilet - Clark Paper Converting Corp.

FIRMESH - Furniture ☆ - Ever-Ready Appliance Manufacturing Co.

FIRMESSCENCE 770 - Skin care products - Charles of the Ritz Group Ltd.

FIRMFLEX - Exercising equipment - Diversified Products Corp.

FIRMLY IN CONTROL - Hair care products - Shape-Up

FIRMNALE - Iodine - Halsey Drug Co. Inc.

FIRMTEX - Erasers ☆ - Empire Berol USA

FIRMWARE - Plates–paper - Fonda Group, Inc.

FIRP - Paneling - Elk River Enterprises, Inc.

FIRST - Computer software - Amr Training & Consulting Group, Inc.

FIRST - Floor coverings–carpet and rugs - Calladium & Marglen

FIRST - Sporting goods - Beneteau USA Inc.

FIRST ACRYLIC - Caulking compounds - Gibson-Homans Co. (Sealant Technology)

FIRST ACTIVITY - Medical apparatus - Caremark International Inc.

FIRST AID - Pharmaceutical preparations ☆ - Chex Co.

FIRST AID FOR SORE THROATS - Pharmaceutical preparations - Tec Laboratories, Inc.

FIRST ALERT - Electronic equipment - First Alert Trust

FIRST ALERT - Smoke detectors - BRK Electronics Inc.

FIRST ALERT PROFESSIONAL - Alarm systems - First Alert Trust

FIRST AMENDMENT - Recording label - Universal Record
FIRST AND GRAND - Shampoos - White Cross Supply Corp.
FIRST ANIMAL READER - Computer software - Orange Cherry Software
FIRST ARMY - Apparel and accessories - David J. Polk
FIRST ARTISTS - Recording label - Polygram Records, Inc.
FIRST AVENUE EDITIONS - Publisher's imprints - Lerner Publishing Group
FIRST BASE - Nail care products - Worldwide Cosmetics
FIRST BATH - Portable bathtubs - Infant Specialties, Inc.
FIRST BED - House furnishings ☆ - Kellwood Co.
FIRST BILINGUAL II - Computer software - Laureate Learning Systems Inc.
FIRST BORN - Dolls - Uneeda Doll Co., Ltd.
FIRST BOUQUET - Wallcovering - Gencorp Inc.
FIRST BRAND - Cheese ☆ - Cemac Foods Corp.
FIRST CABIN - Apparel–women's ☆ - Mount Vernon Mills Inc.
FIRST CABIN - Luggage - Lifestyle International, Inc.
FIRST CABIN - Shoes - Florida Shoe Inc.
FIRST CALL - Computer software - First Call Licensing Corp.
FIRST CATEGORIES - Computer software - Laureate Learning Systems Inc.
FIRST CELEBRATIONS - Dolls - Gata Box Ltd.
FIRST CHECK - Pharmaceutical preparations - Worldwide Medical Corp.
FIRST CHOICE - Balls–golf - Lisco, Inc.
FIRST CHOICE - Brushes–paint - Anderson Products, Inc.
FIRST CHOICE - Caulking compounds - Gibson-Homans Co. (Sealant Technology)
FIRST CHOICE - Cleaning preparations - Allen & Co., Inc.
FIRST CHOICE - Diapers–disposable - Weyerhaeuser Co.
FIRST CHOICE - Dinnerware–plastic - Nyman Manufacturing Co.
FIRST CHOICE - Fertilizers - Western Farm Service Inc.
FIRST CHOICE - Flour–blended - Groce-Wearden Co.
FIRST CHOICE - Flowers, plants, and seeds - Stanford Seed Co.
FIRST CHOICE - Food products - Golden Stream Quality Foods
FIRST CHOICE - Food products - Merkt Cheese Co., Inc.
FIRST CHOICE - Food products ☆ - Giant Markets Inc.
FIRST CHOICE - Glucose-meter test strips - Polymer Technology International
FIRST CHOICE - Insecticides ☆ - G-96 Products Co. Inc.
FIRST CHOICE - Nuts–salted, roasted, cooked, or canned ☆ - Leavitt Corp.
FIRST CHOICE - Plumbing fixtures–metal - Sterling Plumbing Group Inc.
FIRST CHOICE BRITES - Dinnerware–plastic - Nyman Manufacturing Co.
FIRST CHOICE EYEWEAR - Eyeglasses - United Optical Corp.
FIRST CHOICE V - Wallpaper ☆ - Imperial Wallcoverings, Inc.
FIRST CHOICE VI - Wallpaper ☆ - Imperial Wallcoverings, Inc.
FIRST CHRISTMAS - Greeting cards ☆ - Regency-Sonnell Greetings Inc.
FIRST CLASS - Floor coverings–carpet and rugs - Cabin Crafts Carpets
FIRST CLASS - Furniture - Newborne Co.
FIRST CLASS - Games - Fred David Charney
FIRST CLASS - Hair care products - Windmere Corp.
FIRST CLASS - Luggage ☆ - Gateway Travelware
FIRST CLASS - Motor vehicle parts and accessories ☆ - Lux Co. Inc.
FIRST CLASS - Skin care products - Crown Health Equipment Co.
FIRST CLASS - Strollers–baby - Aprica Kassai USA Inc.
FIRST CLASS - Telephone apparatus - Executone Information Systems Inc.
FIRST CLASS - Underwear and nightwear - Lovable Co.
FIRST CLASS - Wallpaper - Capital Carousel Inc.
FIRST CLASS - Wallpaper - Morton Jonap Co. Inc.
FIRST CLASS ASST. - Biscuits - Bahlsen Inc.
FIRST CLASS BASKETS - Cordage and twine - Eaton Imports Inc.
FIRST CLASS CREATIONS - Publisher's imprints - First Class Creations, Inc.
FIRST CLASS GOURMET - Can openers–electric - Windmere Corp.
FIRST CLASS KIDS - Waterproof outerwear - Swell-Wear Inc.
FIRST CLASS LEASE, THE - Motor vehicle dealers - Mercedes-Benz Credit Corp.
FIRST CLASS MALE U.S.A. - Apparel and accessories - Thomas Creative Apparel Inc.
FIRST CLASS ONLY - Seat covers ☆ - Saddleman, Inc.
FIRST CLASS SEATS - Furniture - Pima Leather, Inc.
FIRST CLASS TEACHER - Giftware - Papel Freelance, Inc.
FIRST CLASS VALET - Irons–electric - Windmere Corp.
FIRST COAST FAMILY - Recording label - Hallways to Fame Productions Inc.
FIRST COLONIAL CARD - Credit institutions - First Colonial Group, Inc.
FIRST COLONY - Coffee - First Colony Coffee and Tea Co. Inc.
FIRST COLONY - Floor coverings–carpet and rugs - Capel, Inc.
FIRST COLONY - Furniture ☆ - Bassett Furniture Industries, Inc.
FIRST COLONY COFFEE HOUSE - Coffee - First Colony Coffee and Tea Co. Inc.
FIRST COLONY DARK - Coffee - First Colony Coffee and Tea Co. Inc.

FIRST COLOR - Hair coloring preparations - Wella Corp. (Consumer Products Div.)
FIRST COLORS - Caulking compounds - Gibson-Homans Co. (Sealant Technology)
FIRST COURSE - Animal feeds - Hubbard Milling Co.
FIRST COUSINS - Frames–picture - Danielson Designs
FIRST CRUSH - Wines - Breitenbach Wine Cellars
FIRST CUT - Clippers–barber - Wahl Clipper Corp.
FIRST DATA CORP. - Computer software - American Express Information Services Corp.
FIRST DATE - Apparel–women's - Wacoal America Inc.
FIRST DE VAN CLEEF & ARPELS - Perfumes - Van Cleef & Arpels, Inc.
FIRST DEFENSE - Disinfectants - Seahawk Research Group, Inc.
FIRST DEFENSE - Guns - Defense Technology Corp. of America
FIRST DEFENSE - Pharmaceutical preparations - Miles Inc.
FIRST DINOSAUR READER - Computer software - Orange Cherry Software
FIRST DOLL - Toys ☆ - Those Characters from Cleveland, Inc.
FIRST DOWN - Apparel and accessories - Turbo Sportswear, Inc.
FIRST DOWN - Insecticides - Green Light Co.
FIRST DRAFT - Computer software - Scholastic Software Inc.
FIRST DRAFT CHOICE - Novelty items - Item Co., Inc.
FIRST DRAFT CHOICE - Novelty items ☆ - Blue Ridge International Products Co., Inc.
FIRST EDITION - Floor coverings–carpet and rugs - Whitecrest Carpet Mills
FIRST EDITION - Floor coverings–carpet and rugs ☆ - Dorsett Carpet Mills Inc.
FIRST EDITION - Floor coverings–carpet and rugs ☆ - Kelly Group Inc.
FIRST EDITION - Furniture ☆ - Bassett Furniture Industries, Inc.
FIRST EDITION - Hair care products - Helene Curtis Industries Inc.
FIRST EDITION - Manufactured homes - Redman Industries, Inc.
FIRST EDITION - Recording label - Louisville Orchestra First Edition Records
FIRST EDITION PLUS - Publisher's imprints - Herald House
FIRST FARM - Toys - Mattel, Inc.
FIRST FLASH - Banners - Moose Lake Products Co., Inc.
FIRST FLIGHT - Bird cages ☆ - Marineland Aquarium Products
FIRST FLIGHT - Floor coverings–carpet and rugs ☆ - Hollytex Carpet Mills Inc.
FIRST FLIGHT - Golfing equipment - Arnold Palmer Golf Co.
FIRST FLUSH - Teas - Republic of Tea, Inc.
FIRST FOCUS - Apparel–women's - Focus Apparel Group Inc.
FIRST FOLIO - Wallpaper - Bob Mitchell Designs
FIRST FOODS - Baby foods - Gerber Products Co.
FIRST FRIENDS - Toys - Playskool, Inc.
FIRST FROST - Christmas tree ornaments - Cracker Box Inc.
FIRST FRUITS - Infant product - Welcome to the World Inc.
FIRST FUN - Publisher's imprints ☆ - Western Publishing Co., Inc.
FIRST FUNDS - Consulting services - First Tennessee Bank National Association
FIRST GAMES - Games - Colorforms
FIRST GEAR - Bicycles - First Gear, Inc.
FIRST GEAR - Date planners - Mead Corp.
FIRST GEAR - Toys–automobiles - Limited Liability Co.
FIRST GENERATION - Recording label - 1st Generation Records
FIRST GIFT OF CHRISTMAS, THE - Jewelry - Crislu Corp.
FIRST GLANCE - Photo albums - Holson Co.
FIRST HARVEST - Food products - Heartland Foods, Inc.
FIRST HOME - Wallpaper - Capital Carousel Inc.
FIRST IMPRESSION - Cleaning preparations - Ecolab Inc.
FIRST IMPRESSION - Computer software - Visualtools, Inc.
FIRST IMPRESSION - Identification tags - Mark Master Inc.
FIRST IMPRESSION - Skin care products - Mennen Co.
FIRST IMPRESSION - Underwear and nightwear - Maidenform Inc.
FIRST IMPRESSIONS - Cabinets - Nutone Inc.
FIRST IMPRESSIONS - Fabrics–tapestry - Coloroll Inc.
FIRST IMPRESSIONS ☆ - Greeting cards - Barbara Linhard
FIRST IMPRESSIONS - Infant product ☆ - Noel Joanna, Inc.
FIRST IMPRESSIONS - Recording label - James Stanfield and Co., Inc.
FIRST IMPRESSIONS LAST - Advertising agencies - Omni 2000 Inc.
FIRST IMPRESSIONS NEWCOMER'S GUIDE - Publisher's imprints - Impressions Marketing Group, Inc.
FIRST IN - Health care products ☆ - Vector Products Inc.
FIRST IN FIRST OUT - Apparel–children's - Evy of California, Inc.
FIRST IN LINE - Apparel and accessories - Venture Stores, Inc.
FIRST IN THE FIELD - Ammunition - Remington Arms Co., Inc.
FIRST IN VALUE - Beverages - Sarvis Inc.
FIRST IN VALUE - Cleaning preparations - Sarvis Inc.

☆ = Now out of production

FIRST INTERVIEW - Apparel—women's - Nisha Sportswear Inc.

FIRST ISSUE FI - Apparel and accessories - L.C. Licensing, Inc.

FIRST KISS - Apparel—women's - Wacoal America Inc.

FIRST KISS - Rings—jewelry - Artcarved Inc.

FIRST KISS - Skin care products - Mana Products, Inc.

FIRST LADY - Cosmetics - Marianna Imports, Inc.

FIRST LADY - Floor coverings—carpet and rugs - Eagle Carpets Inc.

FIRST LADY - Foundation garments—women's - I. Amsterdam Co. Inc.

FIRST LADY - Glass—leaded - Seneca Glass Co.

FIRST LADY - Watches - Bulova Corp.

FIRST LADY'S LUNCH, THE - Vitamins and nutritional supplements - CC Pollen Co.

FIRST LADY'S SNACK BAR - Vitamins and nutritional supplements ☆ - CC Pollen Co.

FIRST LETTERS & WORDS - Computer software - First Byte Inc.

FIRST LIGHT - Apparel and accessories - Total Quality Apparel Resource

FIRST LIGHT - Breads - F.R. Le Page Bakery

FIRST LIGHT - Electric lighting equipment - Valley View Enterprises, Inc.

FIRST LITE - Recording label - Ripete Music Group

FIRST LOOK - Legal services - Merchant, Gould, Smith, Edell, Welter and Smith P.A.

FIRST LOOK - Ophthalmic goods - Foremost Optical Products

FIRST LOVE - Floor coverings—carpet and rugs - Monticello Carpet Mills

FIRST LOVE - Flowers, plants, and seeds - Monrovia

FIRST LOVE - Publisher's imprints - Silhouette Books

FIRST LUBE - Engines—motor vehicle - Blum Corp.

FIRST-MAN-UP - Safety products - D B Industries, Inc.

FIRST MATE - Cleaning preparations - Stanley Home Products Inc.

FIRST MATE - Cutlery ☆ - Precise International/Wenger

FIRST MATE - Food products, nonfood items - American Seaway Foods Inc.

FIRST MATE - Life preservers - Stearns Manufacturing Co.

FIRST MATE - Lubricants - Sta-Lube Inc.

FIRST-MATE - Marine rigging - Electro-Mechanical Products Inc.

FIRST MEADOW FESCUA - Flowers, plants, and seeds - Jacklin Seed

FIRST MEDIC - Computer software - Physio-Control Corp.

FIRST MOMENTS - Furniture—children's - Kohl's Department Stores, Inc.

FIRST MOVE - Colognes ☆ - Avon Products, Inc.

FIRST NAME IN CEILINGS, THE - Ceiling panels - Celotex Corp.

FIRST NATIONAL - Floor coverings—carpet and rugs - Miles Carpets Inc.

FIRST NIGHT - Coffee - Santa Cruz Coffee Roasting Co.

FIRST NIGHTER - Apparel and accessories - Knothe Corp.

FIRST NIGHTER - Apparel and accessories ☆ - Harwood Companies Inc.

FIRST NIGHTER - Musical instrument accessories - Ernest Deffner Inc.

FIRST NOTE - Toys—musical - Trophy Music Co.

FIRST OF SPRING - Dinnerware - Corning Inc.

FIRST OFFICER CHAKOTAY - Toys - Paramount Pictures Corp.

FIRST ON ANY MENU - Meat products—poultry - Peco Foods, Inc.

FIRST ORBICAL CHURCH OF ROCK-N-ROLL, THE - Shirts - Gregory N. Glauner

FIRST PAGE, THE - Apparel—women's - Jostens Inc.

FIRST PEARL - Jewelry - I.P.S. Jewelry, Inc.

FIRST PEEK - Toys—stuffed - Prestige Toy Corp.

FIRST PICK - Fruits and vegetables - Washington Rhubarb Growers Association

FIRST PICK - Pickles - Fleming Companies, Inc.

FIRST PLACE - Hair care products - First Place Inc.

FIRST PLACE AWARD WINNER COLLECTION - Food products ☆ - Shurfine International, Inc.

FIRST POINT - Dresses - High Point Fashion Inc.

FIRST POUR - Candles - Arizona Natural Resources

FIRST PRESS - Pamphlets - Barry D. Utsinger

FIRST PRIORITY - Furniture - Vaughan Furniture Co. Inc.

FIRST PRIORITY - Recording label - Atlantic Records

FIRST PRIZE - Apparel—women's - Wacoal America Inc.

FIRST PRIZE - Floor coverings—carpet and rugs - Lees Carpets

FIRST PRIZE - Flour—blended - Birkett Mills

FIRST PRIZE - Margarine - Ventura Foods

FIRST PRIZE - Meat products—beef - Tobin's First Prize Meat

FIRST PRIZE - Pet products - First Prize Pet Products Inc.

FIRST PRIZE - Pet products - Rotanis Pet Products Inc.

FIRST QUALITY - Sanitary napkins - First Quality Products, Inc.

FIRST QUALITY - Underwear and nightwear - First Quality Hygienic, Inc.

FIRST QUALITY - Water bottles—rubber - Farnam Cos. Inc.

FIRST QUEST - Games - Tsr, Inc.

FIRST R, THE - Computer software - Milliken Publishing Co. (Computer Software Div.)

FIRST RATE PERFORMANCE - Computer software - First Rate, Inc.

FIRST READER BUGTOWN - Computer software - Orange Cherry Software

FIRST READER COMPUTER SET - Computer software - Orange Cherry Software

FIRST RECOVERY - Gasoline antifreeze - Ashland Oil, Inc.

FIRST RESERVE LAGER - Beverages—malt - The Stroh Brewery Co.

FIRST RESERVE SOUTHERN BREW - Beverages—malt - The Stroh Brewery Co.

FIRST RESERVE TUPELO HONEY ALE - Beverages—malt - The Stroh Brewery Co.

FIRST RESPONDER SERIES - Tools - American Rescue Technology Inc.

FIRST RESPONSE - Fireplaces - S and S Industries Inc. (Thermo Saver Div.)

FIRST RESPONSE - Pregnancy test kits - Carter-Wallace, Inc.

FIRST RIDE - Seats—automobile ☆ - Cosco, Inc.

FIRST RIDE TRIKE - Toys - Hasbro, Inc.

FIRST RING - Apparel—women's - Wacoal America Inc.

FIRST ROW VIDEO - Video tapes—blank - First Row Video Inc.

FIRST SEED - Tennis footwear ☆ - Autry Industries Inc.

FIRST SETTLERS - Paints - C.A. Nash & Son Inc.

FIRST SHAPES - Computer software - First Byte Inc.

FIRST SHAPES - Puzzles - Lauri Inc.

FIRST SNOW - Christmas tree ornaments - Cracker Box Inc.

FIRST SNOW - Ornamental products—glass - United Design Corp.

FIRST STAR - Rings—jewelry - Artcarved Inc.

FIRST-START - Publisher's imprints - Troll Associates, Inc.

FIRST STEP - Adhesives and sealants - Pioneer/Eclipse Corp.

FIRST STEP - Computer software - Snelling & Snelling Personnel Services

FIRST STEP - First aid kits - First Step

FIRST STEP - Floor coverings—carpet and rugs - World Carpets, Inc.

FIRST STEP - Floor coverings—carpet and rugs ☆ - Zenith Carpets

FIRST STEP - Health care products - Sherman Pharmaceuticals, Inc.

FIRST STEP - Pencils ☆ - Faber-Castell Corp.

FIRST STEP - Primers - Valspar Corp.

FIRST STEP FOR ROSES - Flowers—artificial - Amlings Flowerland

FIRST STEP TO REALITY - Computer software - Fadal Engineering Co., Inc.

FIRST STRIKE - Archery equipment - Bear Archery Inc.

FIRST STRIKE - Insecticides - Green Light Co.

FIRST STRING - Apparel stores—sports - Jefferies Socks

FIRST STRING - Bandages - Cara, Inc.

FIRST STRING - Ophthalmic goods - Foremost Optical Products

FIRST SUPER - Hardware - Rhoton Corp.

FIRST SURPRISE - Dolls - Mattel, Inc.

FIRST TEETH - Toothpaste - Laclede Professional Products, Inc.

FIRST TEETH - Toothpaste - Nu-Tec Health Products

FIRST TELECOM - Computer software - First Tennessee Bank N.A.

FIRST THINGS FIRST - Publisher's imprints - Covey Leadership Center, Inc.

FIRST TIME - Hair care products - Helene Curtis Industries Inc.

FIRST TIME - Water treating compounds - Charity Games, Inc.

FIRST TO FIVE - Games - Tedco Inc.

FIRST TOUCH - Communications equipment - Touch 1 Communications, Inc.

FIRST TRY - Chemical preparations - Precision Brand Products, Inc.

FIRST VERBS - Computer software - Laureate Learning Systems Inc.

FIRST VERBS BILINGUAL - Computer software - Laureate Learning Systems Inc.

FIRST VIRTUAL FVC CORPORATION - Computer peripheral equipment - First Virtual Corp.

FIRST WATCH - Computer software - Tidalwave Technologies

FIRST WELLINGTON PRODUCTS - Antique stores - Wellington Galleries Ltd.

FIRST WHEELS - Toys—automobiles - Mattel, Inc.

FIRST WORDS - Computer software - Laureate Learning Systems Inc.

FIRST WORDS II - Computer software - Laureate Learning Systems Inc.

FIRST WORDS BILINGUAL - Computer software - Laureate Learning Systems Inc.

FIRST WORDS/PALABRAS II - Computer software - Laureate Learning Systems Inc.

FIRST YEAR - Pencils ☆ - Empire Berol USA

FIRST YEARS, THE - Infant product - The First Years Inc.

FIRSTAID FOR WRITERS - Computer software - WritePro Corp.

FIRSTAR EVE - Clothing - Firstar Corp.

FIRSTCHOICE - Orthopedic products - Langer Biomechanics Group, Inc.

FIRSTDERIVATIVE - Computer software - Global Advanced Technology

FIRSTFAX - Paper ☆ - Rite-Made Paper Converters Inc.

FIRSTFILE - Office equipment - Steelcase Inc.

FIRSTFILE - Office supplies - Globe-Weis

FIRSTGEAR - Apparel and accessories - Intersport Fashions West

FIRSTIE - Footwear - Stride Rite Corp.

FIRSTLIGHT VIDEOCLIPS - Computer software - Firstlight Productions Inc.
FIRSTLIGHT VIDEOPLAYER - Computer software - Firstlight Productions Inc.
FIRSTLINE - Helmets–athletic - R.C. First Enterprises
FIRSTLINE - Inks - Heyer Inc.
FIRSTLOOK - Video equipment - Fonet Inc.
FIRSTMATE - Batteries - Douglas Battery Manufacturing Co.
FIRSTMATE - Paint rollers - Bestt-Liebco
FIRST'N'GOAL - Confections - Good Humor Corp.
FIRSTNOVEL HANK SEARLS AUTHORS WORKSHOP - Computer software - Henry H. Searls
FIRSTPLAY - Playground equipment - Playworld Systems, Inc.
FIRSTRECOVERY - Research–chemical - Ashland Inc.
FIRSTRONICS - Toys–electronic - The First Years Inc.
FIRSTSERVE - Computer software - Cheyenne Software, Inc.
FIRSTSOUNDS - Medical apparatus - Spectrum Products, Inc.
FIRSTSOUNDS - Medical apparatus - Unisar, Inc.
FIRSTSQL - Computer software - Edward Lee Fesperman, III
FIRSTSTEP SINGLE SIGN-ON - Computer software - METAMOR SOFTWARE SOLUTIONS
FIRSTWEAR - Apparel–children's ☆ - Hasco International, Inc.
FIRZITE - Finishing agents ☆ - Champion International Corp.
FIS - Marble products - Mine Safety Appliances Co.
FISCA - Gasoline - Fisca Oil Co. Inc.
FISCAL DIMENSION - Computer software - Axsys, Inc.
FISCHEL - Apparel–children's - Johnston Inc.
FISCHER - Braids - Daystone International Corp.
FISCHER - Electrical equipment - Arizona Institute of Electrolysis
FISCHER PIGGIES - Sausages ☆ - Fischer Packing Co.
FISCHER WESTERN STYLE - Frankfurters ☆ - Fischer Packing Co.
FISCHERFORM - Infant product ☆ - Small World Toys
FISCHER'S - Meat products–cured - Fischer Packing Co.
FISCHER'S - Seasonings ☆ - House of Herbs Inc.
FISCHERS - Skin care products ☆ - WES Publishing
FISCHER'S LARD - Lard - Fischer Packing Co.
FISH - Boats - Wellcraft Marine Corp.
FISH-A-PIZZA - Pizzas–frozen - Eat-All Frozen Food Co.
FISH-A-VISION - Pet products - Fish-A-Vision Inc.
FISH AHOY - Cat food - Nestle USA
FISH ALIVE - Sporting goods - Mill Run Products Co.
FISH & SKI - Boats - O.M.C. Aluminum Boat Group
FISH & SKI - Boats–motor - Glasstream Boats Inc.
FISH & SKI - Boats–motor - Lund Boat Co.
FISH & SKI TE - Boats–fishing - Glasstream Boats Inc.
FISH BITE AND WON'T LET GO - Fishing lures - Outdoor Technologies Group
FISH BOAT BRAND, THE - Seafood products–fresh or frozen - Aslanis Seafoods Inc.
FISH BONE FRED ENTERPRISES INC. - Recording label - Fishbone Fred Enterprises, Inc.
FISH BRAND - Frozen foods - S.F. New Asia Trading Corp.
FISH BY GEORGE - Fish–fresh or frozen - Hormel Foods Corp.
FISH CAMP BRAND - Seafood products–fresh or frozen - Tampa Maid Seafoods, Inc.
FISH CARE MADE EASY - Aquariums–household - Jungle Laboratories Corp.
FISH-COMB - Cosmetics - Nino Originals
FISH DUDE - Video games - Nintendo of America Inc.
FISH EAGLE - Fishing lures - Cabela's Inc.
FISH EASY - Seasonings - Specialty Brands Inc.
FISH EGG GUARD - Pet products ☆ - Jungle Laboratories Corp.
FISH-EYE - Pet products - Aquarium Pharmaceuticals, Inc.
FISH EYE - Sporting goods ☆ - Ray Jefferson
FISH EYE DROPS - Automotive parts and accessories ☆ - Park Metallurgical Corp.
FISH FANCY - Dinnerware–glass ☆ - Cyclamen Studio
FISH FARM - Farm machinery - Sweetwater
FISH FARMERS CHOICE - Pet products - Mid-State Plastics
FISH FILET - Pet products - Reliable Protein Products
FISH FLASH - Fishing lures - Al E. Hazelquist
FISH FLASHER - Navigational instruments ☆ - Ray Jefferson
FISH FROLICS - Hair care products - Andre Fantasies Inc.
FISH GEAR - Fish food - Petland, Inc.
FISH GRABBER - Fishing tackle - Hypark Specialty Co., Inc.
FISH HAB - Sporting goods - Outdoor Technologies Group
FISH HAWK - Boats–motor - Crestliner Boats Inc.
FISH HAWK - Sporting goods - Edwards Sports Products
FISH HAWK - Sporting goods ☆ - Maurice Sporting Goods, Inc.
FISH HEAD - Watches - Cooper & Co., Inc.

FISH HOOK - Agricultural machinery - Decker Manufacturing Co.
FISH INVADER - Fishing lures - Sterling Lure Co.
FISH KING - Fish food - Fish King Inc.
FISH LINES - Greeting cards - Modern Thought Combine
FISH LO-K-TOR - Fishing tackle ☆ - Lowrance Electronics, Inc.
FISH MARKET - Seafood products–fresh or frozen - Perishable Distributors of Iowa, Ltd.
FISH MARKET - Wines - Bully Hill Vineyards, Inc.
FISH MATE - Pet products - Ani Mate Co.
FISH MEASURING TAPE - Fishing tackle - Akalak Products
FISH 'N - Knives–hunting - Normark Corp.
FISH N' CHIPS OCEAN SNAX - Cat food - Mardel Laboratories, Inc.
FISH-N-CRUISE - Boats–pontoons - Forester Boats Inc.
FISH-N-FLOAT - Fishing tackle - Lowrance Electronics, Inc.
FISH N FUN - Boats–motor ☆ - Marathon Boat Group, Inc.
FISH 'N FUN - Games - Smethport Specialty Co.
FISH N HUNT - Boats - Zodiac of North America
FISH-N-SKI - Boats - McDaniel Boats Inc.
FISH-N-SKI - Boats–motor - Forester Boats Inc.
FISH N' SKI - Boats–motor - Midwestern Industries Corp.
FISH-N-TEMP - Fishing tackle - Lowrance Electronics, Inc.
FISH NAUTIQUE - Boats ☆ - Correct Craft Inc.
FISH-O-METER - Water treating compounds - Fo-Mac Inc.
FISH-O-SAURS - Watches - Pet Inc.
FISH ODOR KLEEN - Deodorizers - G.G. Bean Inc.
FISH-ON - Apparel and accessories - Tempress, Inc.
FISH ONN - Jewelry - Specialty Cuisine, Inc.
FISH OR CUT BAIT - Games - Peace Harbor Inc.
FISH-PHONE - Communications equipment–marine - Echo Services
FISH PILL 1 - Pet products - Etani International Inc.
FISH PROBE - Thermometers ☆ - Ray Jefferson
FISH QUEEN - Fish food - Fish King Inc.
FISH RID - Deodorizers - Ryter Corp.
FISH RUNNER - Boats–motor - Hewes Marine Co.
FISH SAVER - Aquariums–household - Marine Metal Products
FISH SCALES - Computer software - SRA/McGraw-Hill (Div. of The McGraw-Hill Companies)
FISH SKATES - Skateboards - Greenroom Sales Inc.
FISH SPOTTER - Electronic equipment ☆ - Heath Co.
FISH STIX - Apparel and accessories - Fish Stix
FISH TALE - Beverages–malt - Fish Brewing Co.
FISH TALE ALES YOU SHOULD'VE TASTED THE ONE THAT GOT AWAY! - Beverages–malt - Fish Brewing Co.
FISH TALE INDIA PALE ALE - Beverages–malt - Fish Brewing Co.
FISH TALES - Games - Williams Electronics Games, Inc.
FISH-TAPE PULLER - Tools - Seatek Co. Inc.
FISH TENDER - Fish food ☆ - Aquatronics-Filtronics
FISH TENDER I - Fish food ☆ - Aquatronics-Filtronics
FISH TENDER II - Fish food ☆ - Aquatronics-Filtronics
FISH TONIC - Pet products - Weco Products Inc.
FISH TRAP - Prefabricated buildings–wood - USL Products Inc.
FISH TWISTER - Fishing rods - Tuzee Associates, Inc.
FISH-VET - Computer software - Aqua-Vet, Inc.
FISH WHISTLE - Fishing lures - Big Jon, Inc.
FISH WIDE OPEN - Electronic equipment - Techsonic Industries, Inc.
FISH WISH - Fishing lures ☆ - Ole Time Woodsman
FISHAH METER - Thermometers - Aquacide
FISHAMAJIG - Seafood products–fresh or frozen - Hershey Foods Corp.
FISHASAURUS REX - Fishing lures - Zebco Corp.
FISHBITES - Fish–fresh or frozen - Frionor USA Inc.
FISHER - Beverages–malt - General Brewing Co.
FISHER - Boats - Lanness K. McKee & Co.
FISHER - Boats–motor ☆ - Old Town Canoe Co.
FISHER - Cheese - R.W. Zant Co.
FISHER - Flour–blended - Fisher Mills Inc.
FISHER - Golfing equipment - J. Kennedy Fisher Inc.
FISHER - Lighting equipment - Fisher Skylights Inc.
FISHER - Motor vehicles–snowplows - Douglas Dynamics Inc.
FISHER - Nuts–salted, roasted, cooked, or canned - Fisher Nut Co.
FISHER - Televisions - Sanyo Fisher (USA) Corp.
FISHER - Valves–industrial - Fisher Controls International, Inc.
FISHER ALPINE SKIS - Skis - Raichle Molitor USA, Inc.
FISHER BOY - Seafood products–canned or cured - National Sea Products U.S. Corp.
FISHER CROSS COUNTRY SKIS - Skis - Raichle Molitor USA, Inc.
FISHER F-PAC - Golfing equipment - J. Kennedy Fisher Inc.

☆ = Now out of production

FISHER FAVORITES - Nuts–salted, roasted, cooked, or canned - Procter & Gamble Co.

FISHER FAVORITES - Snack foods - Fisher Food Products

FISHER HAMILTON - Furniture - Fisher Hamilton Scientific Inc.

FISHER PARK - Furniture - Thomasville Furniture Industries Inc.

FISHER-PRICE - Apparel–children's - H.H. Cutler Co.

FISHER-PRICE - Footwear - Chadwick Industries

FISHER PRICE - Lamps - Dolly, Inc.

FISHER-PRICE - Tricycles - Fisher-Price, Inc.

FISHER-PRICE 1-2-3'S - Computer software - Knowledge Adventure

FISHER-PRICE A-B-C'S - Computer software ☆ - Knowledge Adventure

FISHER-PRICE FOOTWEAR - Footwear–children's - Fisher-Price, Inc.

FISHER PRICE READ & PLAY LIBRARY - Computer software ☆ - Knowledge Adventure

FISHER-PRICE SCOOT AROUND - Toys - Fisher-Price, Inc.

FISHER-PRICE TRIPLE ARCADE - Toys - Fisher-Price, Inc.

FISHER RIDGE - Wines - Fisher Ridge Wine Co.

FISHER TOUCH - Golfing equipment - Fisher Bolf

FISHER VINEYARDS - Wines - Fisher Vineyards

FISHER VINEYARDS - Wines - Wilson Daniels Ltd.

FISHERMAN - See **FISH**

FISHERMAN - Boats - Glen-L Marine Designs

FISHERMAN - Boats–fishing - Glasstream Boats Inc.

FISHERMAN - Boats–motor - Dolphin Boats Ltd.

FISHERMAN - Boats–motor - Duracraft Boats Inc.

FISHERMAN - Boats–motor - Lund Boat Co.

FISHERMAN - Boats–motor - Sport-Craft Inc.

FISHERMAN - Boats–motor - Stamas Yacht Inc.

FISHERMAN - Boats–motor ☆ - Grady-White Boats, Inc.

FISHERMAN - Boats–motor - Hewes Marine Co.

FISHERMAN - Boats–motor ☆ - Marathon Boat Group, Inc.

FISHERMAN - Boats–pontoons - Harris-Kayot Inc.

FISHERMAN - Dishes–earthenware - Hadley Pottery Co. Inc.

FISHERMAN - Electrical industrial apparatus - Ross Laboratories Inc.

FISHERMAN - Motors–outboard - Outboard Marine Corp.

FISHERMAN - Publisher's imprints - Harold Shaw Publishers

FISHERMAN - Seafood products–fresh or frozen - Empress International Ltd.

FISHERMAN - Weather tracking equipment ☆ - Bausch & Lomb Inc.

FISHERMAN DELUXE - Boats–fishing - Glasstream Boats Inc.

FISHERMAN DELUXE - Boats–motor ☆ - Alumacraft Boat Co.

FISHERMAN EYEWEAR - Eyeglasses - Cable Car Eyeware

FISHERMAN, THE - Video production - Long Island Fisherman Publishing Corp.

FISHERMAN'S - Wines ☆ - Bully Hill Vineyards, Inc.

FISHERMAN'S CHOWDER - Chowders–canned ☆ - Campbell Soup Co.

FISHERMAN'S CLOSET - Fishing tackle - James E. Monson

FISHERMAN'S CLUB - Shrimp - Continental Seafoods Inc.

FISHERMAN'S FRIEND - Cough drops - Bristol-Myers Squibb Co.

FISHERMAN'S FRIEND - Detergents ☆ - Elcal Enterprises Ltd.

FISHERMAN'S FRIEND - Fishing tackle - Algoma Net Co.

FISHERMANS NET - Seafood products–canned or cured - L. Ray Packing Co.

FISHERMAN'S OUTLET - Shrimp–fresh or frozen - Ore-Cal Corp.

FISHERMAN'S PRIDE - Seafood products–fresh or frozen - BG Lobster & Shrimp Corp.

FISHERMAN'S, THE - Preserved foods–prepackaged - Aldo's Spices

FISHERMAN'S WHARF - Salad dressings–bottled - Nickabood's Inc.

FISHERS - Food products - Fisher Food Products

FISHER'S PEAK - Furniture - Vaughan Furniture Co. Inc.

FISHETS - Cat food - Heinz Pet Products Co.

FISHEYE - Electronic equipment - Kaman Aerospace Corp.

FISHFLAGE - Apparel and accessories - Fishflage

FISHGRIP - Sporting goods - Bear Paw Tackle Co.

FISHGUARD - Pet products - Penn-Plax, Inc.

FISHI - T-shirts–men's - De Armas Designs, Inc.

FISHIN' BUDDY - Fishing tackle - Hurricane Manufacturing Co.

FISHIN' BUDDY - Sonar systems and equipment - Computrol, Inc.

FISHIN' CHIPS - Fish food - P.J. Noyes Co., Inc.

FISHIN' HOLE - Sporting goods ☆ - Wright & McGill Co.

FISHIN' PARTNER - Sporting goods ☆ - Outdoor Technologies Group

FISHIN' PLACE, THE - Food products - Nicolov, Assen

FISHIN' PLACE, THE - Refrigerators - Assen Nicolov

FISHIN SKI - Boats–canoes - Fishin' Ski Barge

FISHIN' SKI BARGE - Boats–canoes - Fishin' Ski Barge

FISHIN' STUFF - Fishing tackle - Summer Stuff

FISHING HOT SPOTS - Publisher's imprints - Fishing Hot Spots, Inc.

FISHING HUT - Trailers–travel ☆ - Mitchell & Sons Inc.

FISHING LURE ORGANIZER - Display cases–plastic - Design Northwest

FISHING PRO - Fishing tackle - Fishing Pro Products, Inc.

FISHIN'MAGICIAN - Fishing tackle ☆ - K-Tel International, Inc.

FISHLADY - Publisher's imprints - Fishlady

FISHLETS - Seafood products–fresh or frozen - B. Manischewitz Co.

FISHLOCK - Fishing tackle - Paul R. Hutchins

FISHLOCKER - Fillet knives - Buck Knives, Inc.

FISHMARKET FRESH - Seafood products–fresh or frozen - Gorton Group

FISHMASTER - Boats–dinghies ☆ - C-G Industries Inc.

FISHMASTER - Boats–fishing - Klamath Boat Co. Inc.

FISHMASTER - Boats–motor - RSB Fiberglass Forms Inc.

FISHMASTER - Boats–motor ☆ - Sport-Craft Inc.

FISHMASTER - Fishing tackle - Mason Tackle Co.

FISHMASTER - Sporting goods ☆ - Bear Archery Inc.

FISHMASTER CUDDY - Boats–motor ☆ - Sport-Craft Inc.

FISHMASTER WALK AROUND CUDDY - Boats–motor ☆ - Sport-Craft Inc.

FISHMATE - Sporting goods ☆ - United States Stove Co. Inc.

FISH'N SKI - Boats–motor ☆ - Sport-Craft Inc.

FISHNET - Girdles - Beverly Vogue Co.

FISHNIKS 'N CHIPS - Seafood products–fresh or frozen - General Mills, Inc.

FISHSOL - Fertilizers - Dexol Industries

FISHSTARTLE - Nautical instruments - Sonalysts, Inc.

FISHSTICKS - Toys - International Leisure Products, Inc.

FISHTALE - Utility knives - Buck Knives, Inc.

FISHTAMIN - Pet products ☆ - Sera Aquaristik USA Inc.

FISHWELLS - Sporting goods - Pompanette Inc.

FISHWRAP - Computer software - Massachusetts Institute of Technology

FISHY AQUACIDE - Pet products - Fishy Farmacy

FISHY'S - Cat food - Ralston Purina Co.

FISK - Tires - Uniroyal Goodrich Tire Co.

FISKARS - Knives - Rothco Inc.

FISKARS - Scissors–hand-operated - Smith & Nephew Inc. (Rehabilitation Div.)

FISKARS - Tools–hand-operated - Fiskars Inc.

FISKARS SOFTOUCH - Sutures - Smith & Nephew Inc. (Rehabilitation Div.)

FISKELL'S - Health care products - Fiske Industries Inc.

FISONEB - Health care products ☆ - Fisons Corp.

FISON'S-SUNSHINE - Soil–potting - Lawn & Garden Supply Co.

FISSURETONE - Ceiling panels ☆ - Celotex Corp.

FIST FACE - Toys ☆ - Those Characters from Cleveland, Inc.

FIST: THE LEGEND CONTINUES - Computer software - Mindscape Software Inc.

FISTGLOVE - Sporting goods - UFG Enterprises

FISTO - Toys - Mattel, Inc.

FIT - Cleaning preparations - Procter & Gamble Co.

FIT - Computer software - Field Integration Technology, Inc.

FIT - Hardware - Alpha Wire Co.

FIT - Machine parts - Fit Bearings, Inc.

FIT - Medical apparatus - Pulse Medical Instruments, Inc.

F.I.T. - Vitamins and nutritional supplements - Montgomery Ward & Co. Inc.

FIT-A-FACE - Puzzles - Lauri Inc.

FIT-A-FRACTION - Toys - Lauri Inc.

FIT-A-GROUP - Toys ☆ - Lauri Inc.

FIT-A-SHAPE - Toys - Lauri Inc.

FIT-A-SIZE - Toys - Lauri Inc.

FIT-A-SPACE - Toys - Lauri Inc.

FIT-A-STATE - Toys - Lauri Inc.

FIT-A-WORLD - Toys ☆ - Lauri Inc.

FIT-AL - Tools - Rule Industries, Inc.

FIT-ALL - Faucets - Moen Inc.

FIT ALL - Faucets ☆ - Waxman Industries Inc.

FIT AMERICA - Vitamins and nutritional supplements - Fit America, Inc.

FIT & TRIM - Dog food - Ralston Purina Co.

FIT & TRIM - Ophthalmic goods - Foremost Optical Products

FIT BURNERS - Vitamins and nutritional supplements - Action Labs, Inc.

FIT CLASS - Biscuits ☆ - Bahlsen Inc.

FIT CONTROL - Scales–industrial ☆ - Robert Krups North America

FIT FATS - Vitamins and nutritional supplements - Fit America, Inc.

FIT FEET - Pharmaceutical products - Matrix Essentials, Inc.

FIT FIDELITY - Portable disk drives - Fidelity International Technologies

FIT-FIT - Pencils–mechanical - Sakura of America

FIT FOR FUN - Playground equipment - Olympic Recreation Inc.

FIT FOR LIFE - Pet products - Alliance Foods, Inc.

FIT FOR LIFE - Recording label - Life Science Institute, Inc.

FIT FOR LIFE BODY CYCLE - Mattresses - Paramount Industrial Companies Inc.

FIT FOR ME - Hosiery - Renfro Corp.

FIT FOR PETITE - Patterns–clothing ☆ - Simplicity Pattern Co., Inc.

FIT FOR SURVIVAL - Apparel and accessories - Lifeforms International, Inc.

FIT FOR WOMEN - Apparel–women's - Moving Comfort, Inc.

FIT-N-DEX - Computer software - Cramer Products Inc.

FIT 'N FASHION - Apparel–women's - Custom Maid Brassiere Co.

FIT PRODUCE RINSE - Cleaning preparations - Procter & Gamble Co.

FIT-RITE - Bicycles ☆ - Hedstrom Corp.

FIT-RITE - Cosmetics - Diane Products Inc.

FIT-RITE - Pet collars - Leatherite-Nylorite Manufacturing Inc.

FIT-RITE DELUXE - Publisher's imprints - Chesapeake Fiber Packaging Corp.

FIT/S/ACE - Paper products - Human Synergistics International

FIT SOFTWARE - Computer software - Field Integration Technology, Inc.

FIT SPORTS DRINK - Beverages - Tan USA International, Inc.

F.I.T. STRESSBLOCKER - Vitamins and nutritional supplements - Signature Financial/Marketing, Inc.

FIT STRIP - Sporting goods - Sharper Image Look, Inc.

FIT, THE - Sporting goods - Fit Kit Systems

FIT TO BE SHEER - Panty hose - Kayser-Roth Corp.

FIT TO BE TIED - Dolls - Mattel, Inc.

FIT TO BE TRIED! - Apparel and accessories ☆ - Warnaco Inc.

FIT/TODAY! - Paper products - Contemporary Fitness

FIT-WELL - Nail care products - H & H Products

FITALL - Electrical equipment - Kearney

FITALL - Leather goods - AR Accessories Group Inc.

FITALL - Shoe trees - C.S. Pierce Co.

FITALY - Stencils ☆ - MacPherson Sales Co.

FITCAPS - Pharmaceutical preparations - Winning Combination

FITCH - Brushes–paint - Corona Brushes Inc.

FITCH - Saddles ☆ - North and Judd Inc.

FITCHBURG - Clocks ☆ - General Time Corp. (Westclox/Seth Thomas Div.)

FITCO - Televisions - Pick Five Imports, Inc.

FITE BITE KIT - Insect repellant - Travel Medicine, Inc.

FITE-KITES - Kites - English Co.

FITEX - Wallpaper - Fidelity Industries, Inc.

FITFOODS - Potato chips - Fit Foods, Inc.

FITFORM - Exercising equipment - Michael F. Austin

FITH AVENUE PLANK - Floor coverings - Robbins Inc.

FITINA - Vitamins and nutritional supplements - Atlantic Licensing Corp.

FITIVA - Apparel–women's - J.A.C. Manufacturing, Inc.

FITMASTA - Monitors–electronic - Osung Electronic Co.

FITMAX - Vitamins and nutritional supplements - GT Merchandising & Licensing Corp.

FITNESOFT - Computer software - Fitnesoft, Inc.

FITNESS - Weightlifting equipment - Fitness Products Inc.

FITNESS AS SPORT - Sporting goods - Nordictrack, Inc.

FITNESS AWARD - Vitamins and nutritional supplements - Fitness Award Inc.

FITNESS BLEND - Breads - National Bakers Service Inc.

FITNESS BUILDER - Pharmaceutical preparations - Pro Cap

FITNESS BUILDER - Vitamins and nutritional supplements - Green Farm Herb Products

FITNESS CENTERS - Pet products - American Cat Emporium

FITNESS ESSENTIALS - Apparel–athletic - Nike, Inc.

FITNESS FAN - Apparel and accessories - Fitness Funatik Sportswear & Apparel

FITNESS FANATIC - Apparel–athletic - Otomix Inc.

FITNESS FIRST - Preserved foods–prepackaged - HFI Foods, Inc.

FITNESS FOR LIFE SERIES - Recording label - Score Productions, Inc.

FITNESS FORMAT - Exercising equipment - Life Fitness

FITNESS FUNATIK - Apparel and accessories - Fitness Funatik Sportswear & Apparel

FITNESS HEADQUARTERS, THE - Department stores - Fitness Depot, Inc.

FITNESS IS RELIGION - Apparel–athletic - Ray Kybartas

FITNESS MASTER - Weightlifting equipment - Fitness Master Inc.

FITNESS-MILL - Treadmills - Landice Products Corp.

FITNESS PAK - Health care products - Brite Years Vitamins

FITNESS PLUS - Fitness footwear ☆ - Autry Industries Inc.

FITNESS RIDER - Exercising equipment - Nordictrack, Inc.

FITNESS SOLUTIONS - Exercising equipment - Fitness Solutions, Inc.

FITNESS TRACK PLUS - Exercising equipment - World Famous Trading Co., Ltd.

FITNESS USA - Apparel–athletic - Detroit Health Corp.

FITNESSMAX - Exercising equipment - Energize International, Inc.

FITNESTEP - Exercising equipment - D.D. Chase Inc.

FITNET - Sporting goods - Universal Gym Equipment, Inc.

FITNITS - Apparel–women's - Sultra Corp.

FITOR - Toys - Tonka Corp.

FITPRINTS - Shoe insoles - Perfect Impression Footwear Co.

FITS - Computer software - Fits Imaging

FITS ALL - Apparel and accessories - RefrigiWear Inc.

FITS ALL - Bathroom accessories - Kirkhill Inc.

FITS-ALL - Doors–screen ☆ - Macklanburg-Duncan Co.

FITS-ALL - Frames–eyeglass - J.I. Morris Co.

FITS-ALL - Health care products - Hospitak Inc.

FITS-ALL - Pens - Micropoint Inc.

FITS-ALL - Sponges - Daily Dryer Co. Inc.

FITS-ANY - Mops - Royal Maid Association for the Blind Inc.

FITS LIKE A MILLION - Brassieres (Bras) ☆ - Playtex Apparel, Inc.

FITS MITS - Gloves - Up in the Air, Inc.

FITS-RITE - Gloves - National Glove Inc.

FITS TO YOU - Apparel–women's - Exquisite Form Industries

FITSALL - Hats ☆ - Imperial Headwear Inc.

FITSALL - Ribbons - Eaton Allen Ko-Rec-Type Corp.

FITSCAN - Computer software - ARA Human Factors

FITSRITE - Plugs–ear ☆ - Binky-Griptight Co.

FITSTEP - Exercising equipment - Universal Gym Equipment, Inc.

FITT MITT - Sporting goods - Divajex

FITTED HEAT - Heating pads–electric - Sunbeam-Oster Household Products

FITTED PLUS - Bedding–linen - Perfect Fit Industries, Inc.

FITTER'S CHOICE - Animal feeds - Bluebonnet Milling Co.

FITTI - Diapers–disposable ☆ - Associated Hygienic Products

FITTING BRUSHES - Brushes–paint - Black Swan Manufacturing Co.

FITTING CHOICE - Floor coverings–carpet and rugs ☆ - Alexander Smith Carpets

FITTING EASY - Apparel and accessories - Warnaco Inc.

FITTING FRIENDS - Toys - Play-Tech, Inc.

FITTING IMAGE - Jewelry - Woman's World Shops, Inc.

FITTING IN - Publisher's imprints ☆ - New Readers Press

FITTING PRETTY - Underwear and nightwear - Sara Lee Corp.

FITTING SOLUTIONS - Computer software - Fitting Solutions

FITWELL - Gloves - Jasper Glove Co.

FITZ - Shirts - Monticello Manufacturing Co.

FITZ-ALL - Appliance parts - Tops Manufacturing Co. Inc.

FITZ & FLOYD - Cooking utensils–china - Fitz & Floyd, Inc.

FITZ & FLOYD - Perfumes - Tsumura International Inc.

FITZ-E - Paints - Fitzgerald Enterprises Inc.

FITZ-HUGH LUDLOW LIBRARY - Publisher's imprints ☆ - And/Or Press

FITZ-IT - Faucets - Moen Inc.

FITZ-M-ALL - Switches–power - Precision Multiple Controls, Inc.

FITZBILLIES BAGEL BAKERY - Bagels - Fitzbillies Bagels, Inc.

FITZGERALD - Apparel–men's ☆ - Palm Beach Co., Inc.

FITZGERALD - Beverages–malt - Piel Bros. Ltd.

FITZGERALD FAIRFIELD - Spices and extracts - Fitzgerald Fairfield, Inc.

FITZGERALD SCOTTIE - Toys–stuffed ☆ - Dakin Inc.

FITZHUGH - Dinnerware–glass - Royal China & Porcelain Companies Inc.

FITZPATRICK - Wines - Fitzpatrick Winery

FITZU - Brassieres (Bras) - L. Bamberger & Co.

FIVE 5 HOLE - Apparel–athletic - Leonard G. Davis, Kelly Hrudey, and Lloyd Friedland

FIVE-65 - Zinc compounds - Briner Paint Manufacturing Co. Inc.

FIVE-A-SIDE - Balls - Mikasa Sports

FIVE-A-SIDE AMERICA - Balls - Mikasa Sports

FIVE ALIVE - Fruit drinks–bottled or canned - Coca-Cola Co.

FIVE ALIVE - Puzzles - University Games Corp.

FIVE BROS. - Tobacco - American Tobacco Co.

FIVE BROTHERS - Sauces - Conopco, Inc.

FIVE BROTHERS - Spaghetti sauces - Van Den Bergh Foods Co.

FIVE BROTHERS - Tobacco products - Swedish Match North America Inc.

FIVE CROWN - Apparel and accessories - Spot International, Inc.

FIVE CROWNS - Floor coverings–carpet and rugs ☆ - Customweave Carpets Inc.

FIVE-CROWNS - Games - Set Enterprises, Inc.

5 EASY PIECES - Video production - Conselle L.C.

FIVE ELEPHANT - Shrimp–fresh or frozen - Darik Enterprises Inc.

FIVE FLAVOR - Candy - Planters LifeSavers Co.

FIVE FLOWER FORMULA - Health care products - Flower Essence Services

FIVE GRAND - Soap - Malco Products, Inc.

FIVE KNUCKLE BULLET - Sporting goods - Five Knuckle Bullet

FIVE MINUTE POXY - Hardware - Ambroid Co.

FIVE MINUTE WEAR - Apparel–women's - Little Greene Apples, Inc.

FIVE O'CLOCK - Vodka - Laird and Co.

FIVE PLUS - Pet products - Penn-Plax, Inc.

☆ = Now out of production

FIVE PORTS - Furniture - Kmart Corp.
FIVE SERIES - Boats - Ray Industries, Inc.
FIVE SIDED - Games - Gamescience
FIVE SPICE - Food products ☆ - Shaffer, Clark & Co. Inc.
FIVE STAR - See **GROWCO**
FIVE STAR - Breads - Pepperidge Farm Inc.
FIVE STAR - Brushes–paint - Wooster Brush Co.
FIVE STAR - Candy bars - Five Star
FIVE STAR - Cigarettes - G.A. Georgopulo & Co. Inc.
FIVE STAR - Clarinets - Ideal Musical Merchandise Co.
FIVE STAR - Cleaning preparations–upholstery ☆ - Elcal Enterprises Ltd.
FIVE STAR - Coffee - Five Star Coffee, Inc.
FIVE STAR - Floor coverings–carpet and rugs - Criterion Mills Inc.
FIVE STAR - Floor coverings–carpet and rugs - Quaker Inc.
FIVE STAR - Fruits and vegetables ☆ - Idaho Fruit Sales Inc.
FIVE STAR - Hardware - Arnold Precision Manufacturers
FIVE STAR - Novelty items - Imagineering Inc.
FIVE STAR - Office supplies - Mead Corp.
FIVE STAR - Oils–lubricating ☆ - Diamond Shamrock Inc.
FIVE STAR - Pet food - Pet's Choice International, Inc.
FIVE STAR - Photographic equipment ☆ - Yashica Inc.
FIVE-STAR - Publisher's imprints - Oxmoor House Inc.
FIVE STAR - Recording label ☆ - Fidelity Sound Recordings
FIVE STAR - Scissors–hand-operated - Mehaz International, Inc.
FIVE STAR - Shoes - Norwich Shoe Co.
FIVE STAR - Shrimp–fresh or frozen ☆ - Southeast Foods Inc.
FIVE STAR - Tires - Armtec Industries Inc.
FIVE STAR - Toys - Newco Inc.
FIVE STAR - Whiskey - Laird and Co.
FIVE STAR DATE - Photographic equipment ☆ - Yashica Inc.
FIVE STAR DIAMONDS - Jewelry - Crescent Jewelers, Inc.
FIVE STAR FORMULA - Pet products - Tetra Sales USA
FIVE STAR RESTAURANT - Seafood products–fresh or frozen - Singleton Seafood Co.
FIVE STAR SEAL - Sealing devices - Flowserve Corp. (Fluid Sealing Division)
FIVE STAR SYSTEMS - Computer software - Five Star Systems, Inc.
FIVE STAR XL - Backpacks - Mead Corp.
FIVE STARS - Floor coverings–carpet and rugs - Lock Weave Carpet Mills Inc.
FIVE TO NINE - Nightgowns - Vanity Fair, Inc.
FIVE WINDERS - Toys - Tyco Toys
FIVE YEAR - Hardware - Melard Manufacturing Corp.
FIVER, THE - Apparel stores–lingerie - Formfit Rogers
FIVESTAR WEDDING - Toys - Tonka Corp.
FIVETOP V - Footwear - Boris Tang
FIX - Cleaning preparations - State Chemical Manufacturing Co.
FIX - Hair care products - Lusan Inc.
FIX 3 - Staplers ☆ - Sofragraf Unifix Inc.
FIX-A-CRETE - Mortars–clay ☆ - Custom Building Products
FIX-A-DRINK - Beverages - Doxsee Food Corp.
FIX-A-LEAK - Adhesives and sealants - Monsey Products Co.
FIX A LENS - Ophthalmic goods - Green Island Research, Inc.
FIX-A-MIRROR - Mirrors - Green Island Research, Inc.
FIX-A-THRED - Hardware - Hal E. Verble & Son Inc. (Veri Products Div.)
FIX-ALL - Waxes–sealing ☆ - Magic American Corp.
FIX DESIGN - Hair care products - Lusan Inc.
FIX GEL - Hair care products - Lendan USA Co.
FIX-IT - Adhesives and sealants - Plaid Enterprises, Inc.
FIX IT - Computer software - Random House, Inc.
FIX-IT - Pet products ☆ - Aquatronics-Filtronics
FIX-IT-KIT - Lawn product ☆ - Devcon Consumer Products (ITW Devcon)
FIX-IT KIT - Ophthalmic goods - Karlen Manufacturing, Inc.
FIX MI QUIK - Brushes - Better House Corp.
FIX-N-MIX - Housewares - Tupperware Co.
FIX 'N SHINE - Lip moisturizer - Cabot Laboratories Inc.
FIX 'N TOW - Toys - Mattel, Inc.
FIX RITE - Machinery - American Biltrite Inc.
FIX RUST - Paints - KCI Coatings, Inc.
FIX-UP - Varnishes ☆ - Lilly Perfection Paint
FIX VELOUR - Thread ☆ - Staple Sewing Aids Corp.
FIXALL - Gypsum products - Custom Building Products
FIXALL - Hardware - Dowman Products
FIXALL - Paints - KCI Coatings, Inc.
FIXATEUR VEGETAL - Hair care products - Rene Furterer
FIXATIF - Artists' materials ☆ - Empire Berol USA
FIXATIF - Charcoal - Martin F. Weber Co.

FIXATIF - Skin care products - La Coupe
FIXATIF PLUS - Skin care products - La Coupe
FIXATION - Candy - Fran's Chocolates
FIXATIVE - Hair care products - Image Laboratories, Inc.
FIXATIVE - Hair care products ☆ - Modern Research Laboratories
FIXCREAM - Hair care products - Paul Mazzotta Inc.
FIXE - Hair care products - Mastey De Paris
FIXED ASSETS 2000 - Business software - Software 2000, Inc.
FIXED N FANCY - Food products - Green Giant Co.
FIXED SLEEPER - Wood-floor covering systems - Superior Floor Co.
FIXIFYING - Hair care products - Revlon Consumer Products Corp.
FIXIN'S - Meat sauces ☆ - Hunt-Wesson, Inc.
FIXIN'S - Vegetables–frozen ☆ - Stokely USA, Inc.
FIXIT - Clay - Aves Inc.
FIXIT - Erasers ☆ - Faber-Castell Corp.
FIXIT - Recording label - Fixit Records Inc.
FIXIT-MIXES - Cement ☆ - W.R. Bonsal Co.
FIXIT PLUS - Computer software - Musick International, Inc.
FIXIT QUIK - Putties - Auto Vehicle Parts Co.
FIXLOOPERS - Footwear - Wolverine World Wide, Inc.
FIXMASTER - Paints ☆ - Rexnord Corp.
FIXMI - Housewares - Fixmi Corp.
FIX'N'STIX - Adhesives and sealants ☆ - Roman Adhesives, Inc.
FIXO - Pharmaceutical preparations ☆ - Schering-Plough Healthcare Products
FIXODENT - Denture materials - Richardson-Vicks USA
FIXODENT PLUS - Denture materials - Richardson-Vicks USA
FIXOMAT - Photographic equipment ☆ - Eastman Kodak Co.
FIXPENCIL - Pencil holders - Caran D'Ache of Switzerland Inc.
FIXSTRESS - Hair care products - St. Ives Laboratories, Inc.
FIXTONE - Paints ☆ - KCI Coatings, Inc.
FIXTURE PLANK - Plastics - Tool Chemical Co., Inc.
FIXX STUFF - Hair care products ☆ - Modern Research Laboratories
FIXXE - Hair care products - Grayson O. Group
FIXXIT - Knives–pocket - W.R. Case & Sons Cutlery Co.
FIZ COCO FINO SODA - Beverages–carbonated - Fiz Bottling Co. Inc.
FIZRIN - Antacids - Sterling Winthrop Inc.
FIZZ BARS - Candy - S.L. Kaye Co., Inc.
FIZZ-IN COLOUR - Hair coloring preparations - Sebastian International, Inc.
FIZZ-KEEPER - Bottle caps - Jokari/US, Inc.
FIZZ-O-WATER - Water–bottled or canned - Distilled Water Co. of Tulsa
FIZZ POPS - Candy - S.L. Kaye Co., Inc.
FIZZ TABS - Water purification systems ☆ - Coughlan Products Corp.
FIZZ WITH A QUIZZ - Candy bars ☆ - S.L. Kaye Co., Inc.
FIZZ WIZ - Candy - Confex Inc.
FIZZABLES - Novelty items - Paper Magic Group Inc.
FIZZARO - Shirts - Excelhigh, Inc.
FIZZERS - Candy - Swizzels Matlow (USA) Ltd.
FIZZIES - Beverages–carbonated - Premiere Innovations, Inc.
FIZZIES - Candy ☆ - American Chicle Co.
FIZZIT - Containers - Gas Cap Productions Inc.
FIZZMOS - Health care products - Smith & Vandiver, Inc.
FIZZY - Skin care products - Fanie International
FJ - Boats - Dynamic Plastics Inc.
FJG - Jewelry - Zale Corp.
FJORD - Breads - S-M Inc.
FJORD - Fabrics ☆ - Gretchen Bellinger Inc.
FJORD - Flatware ☆ - Dansk International Designs, Ltd.
FJORD - Furniture ☆ - Broyhill Furniture Industries, Inc.
FJORD - Glassware–household - Svend Jensen of Denmark Inc.
FJORD FARMS - Seafood products–fresh or frozen - Nordic Group Inc.
FJORD FRESH - Seafood products–fresh or frozen - Nordic Group Inc.
FJORDLAND - Cheese - Norseland Foods Inc.
FJ'S - Shoes ☆ - Titleist & Foot-Joy Worldwide
FJTB - Nuts and bolts - Eastern Unlimited
FK - Circuit breakers - General Electric Co.
FK - Paints - Patrick Media Group Inc.
F.K.T. - Recording label - Jazz Composer's Orchestra Association Inc.
FL - Jewelry - Fashion Line Ltd.
FL-7 PLUS - Chemical preparations - Texas United Chemical Co., LLC.
FL-8 - Electronic equipment - Vexilar, Inc.
FL-8 - Fishing tackle - Vexilar, Inc.
FL-B - Photographic equipment - Tiffen Manufacturing Corp.
FL-D - Photographic equipment - Tiffen Manufacturing Corp.
F.L. MALIK - Apparel and accessories - F.L. Malik Inc.
F.L. SPORT - Apparel and accessories - F.L. Malik Inc.
FL TOOL HOLDERS - Tool boxes - Air Gage Co.

FL2000 - Film - Rexam Release
FLA-O-GRAM - Vitamins and nutritional supplements - Alacer Co.
FLA-VOR-AID - Beverages–carbonated - Jel Sert Co.
FLA-VOR-ICE - Fruit pops–frozen - Jel Sert Co.
FLA-VOR-SOURS - Candy ☆ - Jel Sert Co.
FLAAVABEST - Salad dressings and oils - Supreme Oil Co.
FLACHSMANN - Spices and extracts ☆ - Particle Dynamics Inc.
FLAG - Cleaning preparations - Northern Automotive Corp.
FLAG - Floor coverings–carpet and rugs ☆ - Regal Rugs Inc.
FLAG - Playing cards - Brown and Bigelow Inc.
FLAG - Thread - Cincinnati Thread Co.
FLAG & SAIL - Apparel–men's - Vi-Jon Laboratories, Inc.
FLAG CAPTURE - Video games - Atari Games Corp.
FLAG DESIGN - Jewelry ☆ - Hirsch Speidel Inc.
FLAG FACTORY - Flags - Dunn Manufacturing Corp.
FLAG FIRE FLAG - Fire extinguishers - Flag Fire Inc.
FLAG GREETINGS - Flags - Securitag Corp.
FLAG GUARD - Chemical preparations - New Creative Enterprises, Inc.
FLAG IT - Office supplies - Omnimed Inc.
FLAG PRESS - Embossing plates - Devin-Adair Co. Inc.
FLAG RED/BLUE - Melamine product - Boonton Molding Co. Inc.
FLAG TIES - Ribbons - Bedford Industries, Inc.
FLAG-UP - Clamps–metal - Sign-Up Corp.
FLAG WINDCRAFTERS - Flags - Flag Windcrafters
FLAGCRAFTERS - Cloth banners - Robert Crowe
FLAGG - Dolls - R. William Gilbert Associates Inc.
FLAGG BROS. - Shoes - Genesco Inc.
FLAGG STAFF - Sporting goods - Bomark Group Inc.
FLAGNET - Magnets - Richard J. White
FLAGPIN - Playing cards ☆ - H.C. Meyers Co.
FLAGRAPHICS - Flags - Flagraphics Inc.
FLAGSHIP - Boats - Catalina Yachts Inc.
FLAGSHIP - Clocks - Ridgeway Clock Co.
FLAGSHIP - Construction equipment - Western Forms, Inc.
FLAGSHIP - Floor coverings–carpet and rugs - Catalina Carpet Mills Inc.
FLAGSHIP - Kites - Gayla Industries Inc.
FLAGSHIP - Paper–carbon - Eaton Allen Ko-Rec-Type Corp.
FLAGSHIP - Pens–fountain ☆ - Newell Office Products
FLAGSHIP - Plastics - Wood Kote Products, Inc.
FLAGSHIP - Sleeping bags - China Trade & Research, Inc.
FLAGSHIPS - Games - Lane & Lane Enterprise
FLAGSOURCE - Flags - J.C. Schultz Enterprises Inc.
FLAGSTAFF - Shoes - Allen-Edmonds Shoe Corp.
FLAGSTAFF - Trailers–travel - Forest River, Inc.
FLAGSTAFF - Wallpaper ☆ - Gilford Corp.
FLAGSTONE - Catalogs - Hanover Companies
FLAGSTONE - Floor coverings - Aladdin Mills, Inc.
FLAGYL - Pharmaceutical preparations - G. D. Searle & Co.
FLAGYL MR - Pharmaceutical preparations - G. D. Searle & Co.
FLAHERTY'S - Bakery products - HI-Q Bakery, Inc.
FLAIL AXE - Machinery - Alamo Industrial
FLAIL-MO - Fertilizers - Haban Manufacturing, Inc.
FLAIL MOWERS - Lawn mowers - Alamo Industrial
FLAIR - Cabinets - Schrock
FLAIR - Cigarettes - Brown & Williamson Tobacco Corp.
FLAIR - Deodorizers - Willert Home Products, Inc.
FLAIR - Dinnerware–plastic ☆ - Plastics Manufacturing Co.
FLAIR - Dryers–hair ☆ - Sunbeam-Oster Household Products
FLAIR - Electrical equipment - General Electric Co.
FLAIR - Faucets - Kohler Co.
FLAIR - Filters–air - Flair Corp.
FLAIR - Floor coverings–carpet and rugs - Mohawk Industries Inc.
FLAIR - Floor coverings–carpet and rugs - Quaker Inc.
FLAIR - Floor coverings–carpet and rugs ☆ - Hollytex Carpet Mills Inc.
FLAIR - Frames–picture - Ammak Manufacturing Corp.
FLAIR - Furniture - Bernhardt Industries
FLAIR - Furniture - Pilliod Co.
FLAIR - Furniture ☆ - Keller Manufacturing Co.
FLAIR - Furniture polish and wax - L & F Consumer Products
FLAIR - Giftware - Russ Berrie and Co., Inc.
FLAIR - Glassware–household ☆ - Anchor Hocking Glass, Inc.
FLAIR - Glassware–household ☆ - Lotus Glass Co.
FLAIR - Glassware–household ☆ - Oneida Ltd.
FLAIR - Globes - Trippensee Corp.
FLAIR - Golfing equipment - Precision Composites, Inc.
FLAIR - Hardware ☆ - Steel City Corp.

FLAIR - Jewelry - Flair Jewelry
FLAIR - Jewelry - Jacoby-Bender Inc.
FLAIR - Lamps ☆ - Luxo Corp.
FLAIR - Lighting fixtures - Swivelier Co. Inc.
FLAIR - Luggage - United States Luggage Corp.
FLAIR - Margarine - Kraft Food Ingredients Corp.
FLAIR - Mirrors ☆ - Lacolite Industries
FLAIR - Modular furniture - Indiana Desk Co. Inc.
FLAIR - Motor vehicles–motor homes - Fleetwood Enterprises, Inc.
FLAIR - Napkins–paper - Georgia-Pacific Corp.
FLAIR - Occasional furniture ☆ - JDI Group, Inc.
FLAIR - Paints - Muralo Co.
FLAIR - Pens - Gillette Co.
FLAIR - Perfumes - Ruckel Manufacturing Co. Inc.
FLAIR - Sunglasses - Capo, Inc.
FLAIR - Tableware–earthenware ☆ - National Housewares
FLAIR! - Tiles–ceramic - United States Ceramic Tile Co.
FLAIR - Trading cards and stamps - Fleer Corp.
FLAIR - Wallpaper - Secrest Handprints Inc.
FLAIR - Wallpaper ☆ - Wall Fashion Inc.
FLAIR - Yarn - Rainbow Gallery, Inc.
FLAIR ACCESSORIES - Dolls - Totsy Manufacturing Co., Inc.
FLAIR CABINETWARE - Cabinets - Flair Cabinetware
FLAIR CHAIR - High chairs ☆ - Cosco, Inc.
FLAIR FASHIONS - Dolls - Totsy Manufacturing Co., Inc.
FLAIR FI FO FUM - Pens - Gillette Co.
FLAIR FINISH - Varnishes - Walnut Hollow Farm, Inc.
FLAIR/FINN - Bedding–linen - Dan River Inc.
FLAIR FORM ORIGINALS - Lighting equipment - Creative Concepts
FLAIR GIFT SETS - Dolls - Totsy Manufacturing Co., Inc.
FLAIR, THE - Flowers, plants, and seeds - K-5 Coatings Inc.
FLAIRE - Musical instruments - Music Imports Ltd.
FLAIRE - Shelving units–metal ☆ - Stanley Hardware Div.
FLAIRHARBOR - Bedding–linen - Dan River Inc.
FLAIRLINE - Boats - Clark Craft Boat Co.
FLAIRMONT - Bathroom fixtures - Crane Plumbing/Fiat Products
FLAK - Computer software - Funsoft Inc.
FLAK - Sporting goods - Canstar Sports USA
FLAK TECH - Footwear–athletic - L.A. Gear, Inc.
FLAKE - Pet products - Richard Hanau Pet Foods Corp.
FLAKE AMERICAN THREADS - Apparel and accessories - William Scot Provost and Cameron Provost General Partnership
FLAKE FACE - Gypsum products - Georgia-Pacific Corp.
FLAKE FACE NOVOPLY - Plywood - Georgia-Pacific Corp.
FLAKE-OFF - Paints - Mar-Hyde Corp.
FLAKE-OFF - Skin care products - Unit Chemical Corp.
FLAKE ROYAL - Tobacco–chewing or smoking - G.A. Georgopulo & Co. Inc.
FLAKELINE - Adhesives and sealants - Master Builders Inc.
FLAKEPRIME - Adhesives and sealants ☆ - Master Builders Inc.
FLAKES O' BRAN - Cereal - Health Valley Food
FLAKES O FIRE - Fireplace equipment - West End Gardens
FLAKETAR - Tar - Master Builders Inc.
FLA.KIDS - Apparel–children's - Pixie Playmates, Inc.
FLAKO - Breads–mixes - Quaker Oats Co.
FLAKY JAKE, THE - Scrapers - Prodigy Products, Inc.
FLAMA - Handles–wood - Hartwell Brothers Handle Co.
FLAMAIR - Stoves–gas - Flamair Equipment Inc.
FLAMATIC - Giftware ☆ - Eastern Seaboard Products Inc.
FLAMBE - Lipsticks - Cosmair Inc.
FLAMBE FANFARE - Seasonings - Flambe Fanfare Inc.
FLAMBEAU - Apparel and accessories - Faberge Co.
FLAMBEAU - Coolers–electric - Flambeau Products Corp.
FLAMBEAU - Lighting fixtures ☆ - Hubbell Lighting, Inc. (Lighting Div.)
FLAMBEAU COLLECTION, THE - Artists' materials ☆ - Artisan House Inc.
FLAMBEAU RED - Paints - J.I. Case Co.
FLAMBO - Labels–paper - King Walk Inc.
FLAMBOYANT - Floor coverings–carpet and rugs - Coronet Carpets Inc.
FLAMBOYANT - Floor coverings–carpet and rugs - Mohawk Industries Inc.
FLAMBOYANT - Paints ☆ - Sherwin-Williams Automotive Finishes Corp.
FLAMBRO - Grocery stores - Flambro Imports, Inc.
FLAMCO - Building materials - Florida Metal Products, Inc.
FLAME - Fruit and vegetable markets - Deniz Packing Inc.
FLAME - Glassware–household ☆ - Crystal Clear Importing Co. Inc.
FLAME - Herbicides - Loveland Industries, Inc.
FLAME - Lipsticks - Lancome
FLAME 95 - Darts and dart games ☆ - Dart Mart Inc.

☆ = Now out of production

FLAME BARRIER - Fire extinguishing compositions - WHS Sales Inc.

FLAME BROILS - Food products - Stewart Foods

FLAME CENTER PRODUCTS - Charcoal - Zippo Manufacturing Co.

FLAME-CHECK - Thread - Elmore-Pisgah, Inc.

FLAME CHEF - Housewares ☆ - Lipper International Inc.

FLAME-CHEK - Mattresses - Bob Barker Co., Inc.

FLAME D'AMOUR - Frames–picture - Mikasa Licensing, Inc.

FLAME EDGE - Cutlery - Robeson Industries

FLAME FIGHTER - Chemical preparations - Anscott Chemical Industries, Inc.

FLAME FIGHTER - Fire extinguishers ☆ - Philips Electronics North America Corp.

FLAME-GLO - Cosmetics - Del Pharmaceuticals, Inc.

FLAME-GLO - Fireplace equipment ☆ - Sportsline

FLAME GRAIN - Pipes–tobacco - S.M. Frank & Co. Inc. (Kaywoodie-Yello-Bole-Medico)

FLAME GUARD - Paints - Enviro-Chem Inc.

FLAME-GUARD - Wood products - Weyerhaeuser Co.

FLAME HALT - Paints - Sinclair Paint Co.

FLAME-KING - Tools - Pro Hardware Inc.

FLAME MASTER - Gloves - Brookville Glove Manufacturing Co.

FLAME MASTER - Thermostats ☆ - Robertshaw Controls Co.

FLAME-MAX - Heating equipment - Desa International, Inc.

FLAME-OUT - Thread - Threads USA Div.

FLAME-OUT - Uniforms–academic ☆ - Superior Surgical Manufacturing Co. Inc.

FLAME RITE - Fuel additives - Index Industries Inc.

FLAME RUNNER - Toys–automobiles - Mattel, Inc.

FLAME-SAFE - Thread ☆ - Coats and Clark Inc.

FLAME SCREEN - Chemical preparations - Gam Industries, Inc.

FLAME SEAL - Tools - Railway Handle Corp.

FLAME SEASONED - Handles–wood - Fleischmann Handle Co.

FLAME SET - Thermostats ☆ - Robertshaw Controls Co.

FLAME SHIELD - Paints - M.A. Bruder & Sons Inc.

FLAME SMOLDER - Thread ☆ - Perfect Thread Co. Inc.

FLAME STIK - Antennas - Wintenna Inc.

FLAME STITCH - Floor coverings–carpet and rugs - Quaker Inc.

FLAME STOPPER - Toys–automobiles - Mattel, Inc.

FLAME-TAMER - Containers–trash ☆ - CAH Industries Inc.

FLAME TAMER - Toys - Tonka Corp.

FLAME-TEC - Paints - Kansas Paint & Color Co.

FLAME-TECH - Recreational vehicle dealers - Rainfair, Inc.

FLAME TEMPER - Fertilizers - Hartwell Brothers Handle Co.

FLAME-THROWER - Coils–ignition - Pertronix Inc.

FLAME THROWERS - Candy - Nabisco Foods Group

FLAME-VIEW - Photographic equipment - Superior Stove Co. Inc.

FLAME-VUE - Windows–storm - Sunbeam Outdoor Products Inc.

FLAME-WARE - Giftware - Terrace Ceramics Inc.

FLAME WEIGHT - Glassware–household - Nourot Glass Studio

FLAME ZERO PRODUCTS - Paints - National Certified Fire Retardants Inc.

FLAMEAWAY PLASTICS - Pipes–plastic - Flameaway Plastics Inc.

FLAMEBREAK - Plywood - Georgia-Pacific Corp.

FLAMEBUSTER - Fire extinguishers - Black & Decker Corp.

FLAMECLEAR - Thread - Signal Thread Co. Inc.

FLAMECRETE - Finishing agents ☆ - Fire Research Laboratories, Inc.

FLAMEFREE - Thread - Belding Heminway Co. Inc.

FLAMEGARD - Adhesives and sealants ☆ - Plastics & Resins Ltd.

FLAMEGARD - Fire detectors - Mine Safety Appliances Co.

FLAMEGUARD - Fabrics - Parvin Manufacturing Co.

FLAMEGUARD - Floor coverings–carpet and rugs ☆ - Ebsco Carpet Mills

FLAMEGUARD - Footwear - Lehigh Safety Shoe Co.

FLAMEGUARD - Lighters - Scripto-Tokai Corp.

FLAMELIGHT - Bicycles - Columbia Manufacturing Inc.

FLAMEN OIL - Pet products - Nutritional Research Associates Inc.

FLAMEN RED - Pet products - Nutritional Research Associates Inc.

FLAMENCO - Cigar boxes–wood - Consolidated Cigar Corp.

FLAMENCO - Cigars - Faber, Coe & Gregg Inc.

FLAMENCO - Floor coverings - Congoleum Corp.

FLAMENCO - Floor coverings–carpet and rugs - Couristan Inc.

FLAMENCO - Glassware–household ☆ - Oneida Ltd.

FLAMENCO - Mexican decorative accessories and furniture ☆ - Jacaman Gift Co. Inc.

FLAMENCO - Toilets–enameled - Kohler Co.

FLAMENCO FILTRO - Cigarettes - Faber, Coe & Gregg Inc.

FLAMENCO RED - Dinnerware–glass ☆ - Metlox Pottery Shoppe

FLAMENGO - Wigs - Jean Paree Weegs Inc.

FLAMENGO - Women's footwear - Ipanema Shoe Corp.

FLAMER - Boats–motor ☆ - Hobie Cat Co.

FLAMES - Blinds–vertical - U.S. Polymers, Inc.

FLAMES OF FREEDOM - Computer software - Microprose Software, Inc.

FLAMESCENT - Lamp bulbs - Duro-Test Corp.

FLAMESTITCH - Floor coverings–carpet and rugs - Regal Rugs Inc.

FLAMESTONE - Dishes–earthenware ☆ - Dansk International Designs, Ltd.

FLAMESTONE - Rings–jewelry ☆ - Artcarved Inc.

FLAMESTONE - Toys - Tonka Corp.

FLAMETEST - Awnings ☆ - John Boyle & Co., Inc.

FLAMEX - Chemical preparations - United American, Inc.

FLAMEX - Fire extinguishing compositions - Rosco Laboratories Inc.

FLAMEX - Lighters - Butane Products Corp.

FLAMIGNA AMARETTI FROM ITALY - Cookies - Daprano & Co.

FLAMIN' HOT - Snack foods - Frito-Lay, Inc.

FLAMIN' WINGS - Chickens - Conagra, Inc.

FLAMING ASS! - Spices and extracts - Richard W. Eastman and Sarah E. Webster-Eastman Partnership

FLAMING FUCHSIA - Nail care products - Pavion Ltd.

FLAMING PIT - Food products - Freda Corp.

FLAMINGO - Brassieres (Bras) - Bi-Flex International

FLAMINGO - Brooms - Wright-Bernet

FLAMINGO - Cement - Riverton Corp.

FLAMINGO - Coffee - Melkaz International Inc.

FLAMINGO - Containers ☆ - Poloron Products Inc.

FLAMINGO - Cosmetics - Lancome

FLAMINGO - Cosmetics - Morris-Flamingo Inc.

FLAMINGO - Furniture ☆ - Halcyon Inc.

FLAMINGO - Golfing equipment - Slotline Golf

FLAMINGO - Juices - Winter Garden Citrus Products Cooperative

FLAMINGO - Lamps - Lamplight Farms, Inc.

FLAMINGO - Manufactured homes - Redman Industries, Inc.

FLAMINGO - Office supplies - Lanir Trading Co., Inc.

FLAMINGO - Paper–tissue - Canover Industries Inc.

FLAMINGO - Serving carts ☆ - National Housewares

FLAMINGO - Toys–stuffed - Dakin Inc.

FLAMINGO CHANDELLE - Lamps - Lamplight Farms, Inc.

FLAMINGO COVE - Furniture ☆ - Bassett Furniture Industries, Inc.

FLAMINGO EGGS - Candy ☆ - Leaf, Inc.

FLAMINGO-FARE - Pet products - Reliable Protein Products

FLAMINGO RECORDS - Recording label - Joseph Pellecchia

FLAMINGO ROAD - Wallpaper - Seabrook Wallcoverings, Inc.

FLAMINGO SPRINGER - Toys–stuffed ☆ - Dakin Inc.

FLAMMARION - Postcards - Fotofolio Inc.

FLAMMARION - Publisher's imprints - Abbeville Press, Inc.

FLAMME - Perfume - Bourjois Ltd.

FLAMME - Yarn ☆ - Joseph Galler Inc.

FLAMM'S - Pickling salt ☆ - Flamm Pickle and Packing Co. Inc.

FLAMORT - Firefighting apparatus - Flamort Chemical Co.

FLAMY - Snack foods - Jim Fruity Products

FLAN - Fabrics–flannel - Sentinel Consumer Products, Inc.

FLAN-TEX - Garden furniture - Maytex Mills

FLANAGAN - Sauerkraut - Flanagan Bros. Inc.

FLANDERS - Blinds–vertical - Tontine/VyTech Industries Inc.

FLANDERS - Furniture–wood - Flanders Industries Inc.

FLANDERS - Meat products–beef - Flanders Provision Co.

FLANDERS - Motor vehicle parts and accessories - Flanders Co.

FLANDERS - Wallcoverings - James F. White & Co. Inc.

FLANDERS - Wallpaper - Surface Industries Inc.

FLANDERS II - Wallpaper - Surface Industries Inc.

FLANDERS CUT - Jewelry - QVC, Inc.

FLANDERS STRIPE - Wallpaper - Koroseal Wallcoverings

FLANDRIA - Mopeds - North American Cycles

FLANGE LOCKS - Transmitting apparatus–radio - Foxfire Microwave, Inc.

FLANGE SAVER - Brake shoes–railroad - Amsted Industries Inc.

FLANGE TYPE VINYL - Windows–storm - Yale Ogron Manufacturing Co. Inc.

FLANGER - Audio equipment - ADA Signal Processors Inc.

FLANKET - Infant product - Susan Polmanski

FLANNEL CARESS - Pillows - Pacific Coast Feather Co.

FLANNEL FLANNEL II - Fabrics - Guilford Mills, Inc.

FLANNELS - Paperboard - Miller Cardboard Corp.

FLANNIES - Apparel–women's - Elston Enterprises

FLANOL - Paint rollers ☆ - Jomac Products Inc.

FLAP JACK - Toilets–enameled - Fillpro Products Inc.

FLAP PAK - Medical supplies - Look, Inc.

FLAP-STIK - Envelopes - International Envelope Co.

FLAP WHEEL SANDER - Paint removers - Ali Industries, Inc.

FLAP WRAP - Food productss - International Multifoods Corp.
FLAPJACK - Toys–stuffed ☆ - Gund, Inc.
FLAP'N CHICKEN - Games ☆ - Cadaco Div.
FLAPPER - Dolls ☆ - Effanbee Doll Corp.
FLAPPER - Golfing equipment - Triumph Golf Co.
FLAPPER - Office supplies - Mead Corp.
FLAPPER FLAMINGO - Toys–stuffed - Dakin Inc.
FLAPPY - Hardware - Var E. Lordahl
FLAPPY JACKS - Pancakes–mixes - Dearborn
FLAPROTECT - File folders - Angler's Roslyn Group Ltd.
FLAPS UP - Apparel–children's - Knitwaves Inc.
FLAPSTICKS - Food products - Jimmy Dean Foods Div.
FLARE - Coatings - Sherwin-Williams Automotive Finishes Corp.
FLARE - Colognes - BC International Cosmetics & Image Services, Inc.
FLARE - Glassware–household - Denby USA Limited
FLARE - Publisher's imprints - Hearst Corp.
FLARE DURALASH - Cosmetics - Ardell International Inc.
FLARE GUARD - Barbecues and grills - Sunbeam Outdoor Products Inc.
FLARE JET - Machine parts - Nitrous Oxide Systems, Inc.
FLARE-TOP - Ice cream cones - Sweetheart Cup Co. Inc.
FLARE UP - Underwear and nightwear ☆ - Elegante Foundations Inc.
FLARE-UP TAMERS - Barbecues and grills - Vance Industries Inc.
FLARECRAFT - Jet boats - Flarecraft Corp.
FLAREX - Health care products - Alcon Laboratories, Inc.
FLARICO - Sporting goods - John B. Flaherty Co. Inc.
FLARING ROSE - Hoses ☆ - L.R. Nelson Corp.
FLASH - Rozin Optical Export Corp.
FLASH - Archery equipment ☆ - High Country American
FLASH - Automotive parts and accessories - Hop-Cap Inc.
FLASH - Darts and dart games - Dart Mart Inc.
FLASH - Decals and transfers - Midwest Plastics Inc.
FLASH - Girdles - H.F. Robbins
FLASH - Hardware - Seal-O-Matic Corp.
FLASH - Ice and snow melters - Coughlan Products Corp.
FLASH - Pens - Schwan-STABILO USA Inc.
FLASH - Skin care products - Hytrous/Flash Sales Inc.
FLASH - Skin care products - Mane Street Products USA
FLASH - Sporting goods ☆ - Outdoor Technologies Group
FLASH - Thread - Belding Heminway Co. Inc.
FLASH - Thread - Sew-Art International
FLASH - Toys - Animal Fair Inc.
FLASH - Watches - Vogue Watch Strap Creations
FLASH 20 - Cameras - Eastman Kodak Co.
FLASH 500 - Toys–airplanes ☆ - Victor Stanzel and Co.
FLASH ALERT - Lighting equipment–bicycles ☆ - Cycle Products Co.
FLASH ALERT - Pet products - Perimeter Technologies, Inc.
FLASH-BACK - Motor vehicle parts and accessories - Ronald S. Kauffman
FLASH BAGS - Apparel and accessories ☆ - Two's Co. Inc.
FLASH CARD - Lighting equipment - Lumatec Industries, Inc.
FLASH-CATH - Health care products - Baxter International Inc.
FLASH COAT - Cleaning preparations - Amway Corp.
FLASH CODE - Computer software - DBL Enterprises
FLASH DANCER - Fishing lures - Fred Arbogast Co. Inc.
FLASH DATA - Computer software - Flash Data, Inc.
FLASH DOT - Decals and transfers - CelloFoam North America Inc.
FLASH DRY - See **FAST**
FLASH DRY - Hair care products - Recreations
FLASH-DRY - Nail care products - Quintessence Inc.
FLASH DRY - Stationery - Superior Marking Equipment Co.
FLASH-FAR - Lighting fixtures - Swivelier Co. Inc.
FLASH FAX - Office supplies - Wallace Computer Services, Inc.
FLASH FILL - Building materials - American Electric Power Service Corp.
FLASH FINISH - Nail-polish dryer - Jonel Inc.
FLASH FINISH - Toys - Tonka Corp.
FLASH-FIRE - Balls–golf - Network Golf Ltd. Partnership
FLASH FLARE - Lighting equipment - Bright Star Industries Inc.
FLASH FOAM - Apparel stores–fur - Ballard Medical Products
FLASH FORWARD - Computer software - Electronic Ink Corp.
FLASH FREEZE - Beverages - Flash Freeze Inc.
FLASH GLANCES - Cosmetics - Del Pharmaceuticals, Inc.
FLASH GLO - Fishing lures - Yakima Bait Co.
FLASH JR. - Toys–stuffed ☆ - Fun World Inc.
FLASH LEGS - Hosiery–women's - Hampshire Hosiery, Inc.
FLASH LIGHT - Fabrics - Guilford Mills, Inc.
FLASH MASK - Tape–adhesive ☆ - Permacel
FLASH MATCH - Games - Mattel, Inc.

FLASH MATCH JUNIOR - Games - Mattel, Inc.
FLASH-N-DASH - Degreasing solvents ☆ - KC Products, Inc. (Sharon D. Spence)
FLASH-NOT - Cleaning preparations ☆ - Uncle Sam Chemical Co., Inc.
FLASH-O-LENS - Office supplies - E.W. Pike & Co.
FLASH-PAK - Sporting goods - Meadowbrook Products
FLASH POINT - Apparel–women's - Tri-North Department Stores, Inc.
FLASH POINT - Kites - Spectra Star Kites
FLASH RITE - Paints - Olympic Paint & Varnish Co.
FLASH SPELL HELICOPTER - Computer software - CBS Software
FLASH TAIL - Fishing lures - Storm Manufacturing Co.
FLASH-TECH 4 - Automobile burglar-alarm accessory ☆ - Auto Alarm Supply Corp.
FLASH TRACKS - Toys - Fisher-Price, Inc.
FLASH TYPING - Educational materials - Peter O. Dixon
FLASH WUZZY - Toys–stuffed ☆ - Gund, Inc.
FLASH20 - Computer software - Ramss, Inc.
FLASH55 - Computer software - Ramss, Inc.
FLASHBACK - Computer software - Berkeley Systems, Inc.
FLASHBACK - Electronic equipment - Comp General Corp.
FLASHBACK - Game machines - Bally Gaming International, Inc.
FLASHBACK - Medical apparatus - Medtronic, Inc.
FLASHBACK - Sandwiches–prepackaged - Give Pizza Chance, Inc.
FLASHBAKE - Ovens–microwave - Quadlux, Inc.
FLASHBALL - Games - Lewis Galoob Toys, Inc.
FLASHBAND - Aluminum products - Andek Corp.
FLASHBANK - Photographic equipment - SP Systems/Saratons
FLASHBOARD BINGO - Games - Bonanza Press, Inc.
FLASHBOND - Primers - X-I-M Products Inc.
FLASHCAP - Health care products - Global Products Inc.
FLASHCAP - Weather stripping - Zegers Inc.
FLASHCARD - Medical apparatus - Del Mar Avionics
FLASHCARDS - Notebooks and notepads - Flashcards Inc.
FLASHCHANGER - Lighting equipment–boat and ship - Automatic Power, Inc.
FLASHCOMM - Computer software - Flashtax Inc.
FLASHCOTE - Enamels - Akron Paint and Varnish, Inc.
FLASHDANCE - Christmas tree ornaments - Cracker Box Inc.
FLASHDANCE - Floor coverings–carpet and rugs ☆ - Hollytex Carpet Mills Inc.
FLASHDANCER - Fishing lures - Dennis G. Braid
FLASHDRY - Markers–felt-tip ☆ - Seal-O-Matic Corp.
FLASHEPOXY 580 - Epoxy - Edison Coatings, Inc.
FLASHER - Pet products - Togs for Dogs & Cats
FLASHERS - Costumes - Spearhead Industries Inc.
FLASHERS - Hardware - West Coast Washers, Inc.
FLASHES - Cosmetics - Sassaby Inc.
FLASHFIRE - Toys–automobiles - Mattel, Inc.
FLASHFUN - Cameras - Eastman Kodak Co.
FLASHGRILL - Cooking equipment–household - Quadlux, Inc.
FLASHGUARD - Tools–hand-operated - Calterm, Inc.
FLASHION STREAKS - Hair care products - Ardell International Inc.
FLASHIQUE - Clothing - Gerda Osward
FLASHJET - Machinery - Cold Jet, Inc.
FLASHLIGHTS - Footwear - BBC International Ltd.
FLASHLINE - Pet products - Hill Top Enterprises
FLASHLINK - Electronic equipment - Deltatrak, Inc.
FLASHLITER PLUS - Flashlights - Black & Decker Corp.
FLASHMASTER - Games - Leisure Learning Products
FLASHMITE - Cameras - Eastman Kodak Co.
FLASHPOINT - Adhesives and sealants - Gibson-Homans Co. (Sealant Technology)
FLASHPOINT - Computer hardware - Imge Guided Technologies, Inc.
FLASHPOINT - Computer software - McCaw Cellular Communications, Inc.
FLASHPOINT - Golfing equipment - EBT Corp.
FLASHPOINT - Posters - Wildstorm Productions
FLASHPOINT - Recording label - Black Diamond Records, Inc.
FLASHPOINT - Toys–models - Estes Industries
FLASHPOINT - Video equipment - Integral Technologies, Inc.
FLASHPOINT: GOLAN - Games - Avalon Hill Game Co.
FLASHPOINTS - Educational materials - National Academic & Licensing Study Aids, Inc.
FLASHRENDER - Computer software - Gnomon, Inc.
FLASHRITE - Lamps ☆ - Testrite Instrument Co. Inc.
FLASHSERVER - Computer peripheral equipment - Winchester Systems, Inc.
FLASHSPORT - Sporting goods - USA Sport Eyewear
FLASHSTANDS - Musical instrument accessories ☆ - Meisel Music Inc.

☆ = Now out of production

FLASHTAD - Circuit boards–printed - Lucent Technologies Inc.
FLASHTESTER - Battery testers ☆ - Bright Star Industries Inc.
FLASHTITE - Cement - GAF Corp.
FLASHTITE - Medical apparatus - Case Medical, Inc.
FLASHTRACKS - Toys - Fisher-Price, Inc.
FLASHVISION - Recording label - Unlimited Changes, Inc.
FLASHWARE - Cooking utensils–glass - Quadlux, Inc.
FLASHWIZARD - Radio communications equipment - Lab Partners Associates Inc.
FLASHY - Motor vehicle parts and accessories ☆ - SAFCO Corp.
FLASHY FEET - Kitchen appliances ☆ - Hamilton Beach/Proctor-Silex Inc.
FLASHY PANTS - Pet products ☆ - Four Paws Products Ltd.
FLASHYLIGHTS - Flashlights ☆ - Rayovac Corp.
FLAT AID - Tire inflators - Jetgo Auto Products, Inc.
FLAT-BAC - Pet products - Pets International, Ltd.
FLAT BALL - Balls ☆ - Voit Corp.
FLAT BLASTARD - Golfing equipment - Bob Mann
FLAT COLLIMATOR - Computer hardware - Briteview Technologies, Inc.
FLAT FIGHTER - Adhesives and sealants - Bridgestone/Firestone, Inc.
FLAT FLOOR - Motor vehicles - Navistar International Transportation Corp.
FLAT FOOT - Medical apparatus - Michael L. Pryce
FLAT FOOT FORKLIFT - Tires - Galaxy Tire & Wheel, Inc.
FLAT FOOT JIG - Fishing lures - Lindy Little Joe Inc.
FLAT FREE - Adhesives and sealants - Flat-Free Inc.
FLAT GRAIN - Knobs–wood - Baker Mcmillen Co., Inc.
FLAT HEADS - Toys - Skyline Toys Inc.
FLAT MAGIC - Paint - Continental Products Co.
FLAT-N-ZIT - Paints - C.M. Athey Paint Co.
FLAT-O - Binders - General Loose Leaf Bindery Co.
FLAT OUT - Toys–automobiles - Mattel, Inc.
FLAT PACK - Antennas - Electronics Research, Inc.
FLAT-PACK - Meat products–pork - Wright Brand Foods, Inc.
FLAT PACK - Tape–adhesive - Manco, Inc.
FLAT PACKS - Leather goods - AR Accessories Group Inc.
FLAT-PAKS - Batteries ☆ - Duracell Co. USA
FLAT-RITE - Paints ☆ - Sherwin-Williams Automotive Finishes Corp.
FLAT-ROUND - Heating equipment - Young Radiator Co.
FLAT SAVER - Sealing compounds - CRA International, Co.
FLAT SEAM - Printing trades machinery - Screen Printing Systems, Inc.
FLAT SHIELD - Automotive parts and accessories - PJH Brands
FLAT SHIELD - Paint rollers - Mr. Paintshield Inc.
FLAT STANLEY - Candy - S.L. Kaye Co., Inc.
FLAT/STOR - Containers - Fellowes Manufacturing Co.
FLAT-TEK - Paints - Passonno Paints
FLAT-TETE - Paints - Seagraves Coatings
FLAT TOP - Combs - Capitol Novelty Co.
FLAT TOP - Games - Avalon Hill Game Co.
FLAT-TOP - Motor vehicle parts and accessories - Bushwacker, Inc.
FLAT TOP 45 - Lenses–optical - Younger Optics
FLAT TOP POP - Candy - Colombina Candy Co., Inc.
FLAT TOPS - Musical instrument accessories - J. D'Addario & Co. Inc.
FLAT WART - Fishing lures - Storm Manufacturing Co.
FLATAMEL - Paints - Payson Corp.
FLATBALL - Toys ☆ - Tedco Inc.
FLATFISH - Fishing lures - Yakima Bait Co.
FLATFLO - Paints ☆ - Mac-O-Lac Paints Inc.
FLATFOOT - Signs - Flexstake, Inc.
FLATGLOBE - Maps - Streetwise Maps Inc.
FLATHEADS - Chewing gum - Leaf, Inc.
FLATHEADS - Games - Centsable Toys Inc.
FLATINE - Paints - Standard T Chemical Co. Inc.
FLATIRON - Mandolins - Gibson Guitar Corp.
FLATIRON BLEND - Coffee - Coffee Consultants, Inc.
FLATIRON BLEND - Coffee - Peaberry Coffee Ltd.
FLATIRON STRUCTURES - Work clothes - Flatiron Structures Co. LLC
FLATJACKS - Games - Diane L. Sadowski
FLATJET - Nozzles - Spraying Systems Co.
FLATLAND - Computer software - Ashcraft Architectural Computer Graphics
FLATLAQ - Paints - Savannah Paint Manufacturing Co.
FLATLINE - Fertilizers - Anchor Swan
FLAT'N SATIN - Paints - Proctor Paint & Varnish Co. Inc.
FLATON CLUTCH - Machine parts - Bushman Equipment, Inc.
FLATOUT - Labels–gummed - Brown-Bridge Industries
FLATOUT - Toys - Wilson Wheel & Tire Co.
FLATPAK - Aquarium accessories - Kordon
FLATPAK - Aquarium accessories - Novalek, Inc.

FLATPAK - Computer terminals - Spectrum Controls, Inc.
FLATPAK - Racks - Jarke Corp.
FLATPLATE - Exchangers–heat - Flatplate, Inc.
FLATPLUG - Thin-plug extension cords - STB Inc.
FLATS - Pens - Bic Corp.
FLATS FISHER - Boats–canoes - Fishin' Ski Barge
FLATSIDERS - Crayons - Sargent Art, Inc.
FLATSY - Doilies - Marvin Hellerman
FLATT - Brushes - Young's
FLATT STOPPER - Adhesives and sealants - Arlington Marketing Industries Corp.
FLATTER BOOTS - Fabrics - Dan River Inc.
FLATTER FIT - Slacks–women's - Koret North America
FLATTER LASH - Cosmetics ☆ - Jason Natural Products, Inc.
FLATTER STRETCH - Apparel–women's - Koret North America
FLATTERBAND - Brassieres (Bras) ☆ - Lovable Co.
FLATTERING - Floor coverings–carpet and rugs - Calladium & Marglen
FLATTERY - Brassieres (Bras) - Goddess Bra
FLATTOPPER - Skin care products - Phase One Distributing
FLATULENCE - Pharmaceutical preparations ☆ - Boiron Inc.
FLATWIRES - Musical instrument accessories - Gibson Strings & Accessories
FLAUBERT FLAMINGO - Toys–stuffed - Russ Berrie and Co., Inc.
FLAUM APPETIZING - Seafood products–fresh or frozen - Lee Avenue Food Products, Inc.
FLAURENT - Watches ☆ - SMH (US) Inc.
FLAV-A-BREW - Coffee makers–electric - Tops Manufacturing Co. Inc.
FLAV-A-BREW - Syrup - Tops Manufacturing Co. Inc.
FLAV-A-CHEWS - Candy ☆ - Y & S Candies Inc.
FLAV-A-DROPS - Candy ☆ - F.B. Washburn Candy Corp.
FLAV-A-POPS - Candy ☆ - F.B. Washburn Candy Corp.
FLAV-A-REDI - Food products - W & W Meats Inc.
FLAV-O-NATOR - Containers–metal - Pioneering Concepts Inc.
FLAV-O-RICH - Food products - Thornton's Flav-O-Rich Bakery Inc.
FLAV-O-RICH - Milk - Flav-O-Rich, Inc.
FLAV-O-ROAST - Spices and extracts - Crompton and Knowles Corp.
FLAV-O-SOY - Food products - Flavorite Laboratories Inc.
FLAV-R-CHURN - Food products - US Foodservice
FLAV-R-CLEAR - Seasonings - McCormick & Co., Inc.
FLAV-R-GRAIN - Food products - Quali Tech, Inc.
FLAV-R-PAC - Vegetables–frozen - Norpac Services, Inc.
FLAV-R-PAC QC FRIES - Frozen foods - Norpac Services, Inc.
FLAV-R-PAC VEGETABLE COLLECTION - Vegetables–frozen - Norpac Services, Inc.
FLAV-R-TATERS - Vegetables–frozen - Norpac Services, Inc.
FLAV-R-TOP - Vegetable oil - Ventura Foods LLC (Lou Ana Division)
FLAVA - Seasonings - Flava Manufacturing Co.
FLAVACOL - Seasonings - Gold Medal Products Co.
FLAVAROMA - Barbecue sauce - Flavorite Laboratories Inc.
FLAVETTE - Beverages–carbonated - Monarch Co., Inc.
FLAVEX - Spices and extracts - Crompton & Knowles Corp.
FLAVIA - Greeting cards - Gibson Greetings, Inc.
FLAVIGNY - Candy - Roth & Liebmann Inc.
FLAVIHIST - Cough syrup, nasal mist, lozenges - American Laboratories Inc.
FLAVIO - Colognes - Renee Distributors
FLAVITAB - Health care products ☆ - Ferndale Laboratories, Inc.
FLAVO-DRIP - Coffee makers–electric ☆ - West Bend Co.
FLAVO-FUL - Seasonings - Sigma Quality Foods Corp.
FLAVO-MATIC - Coffee makers–electric ☆ - West Bend Co.
FLAVO-PERK - Coffee makers–electric ☆ - West Bend Co.
FLAVO-RIPE - Fruits and vegetables - Kimura Farms, Inc.
FLAVO-SEAL - Cooking utensils–aluminum ☆ - West Bend Co.
FLAVOLIN - Seasonings - First Spice Mixing Co.
FLAVONALL - Vitamins and nutritional supplements - Advanced Medical Nutrition, Inc.
FLAVONOIDS - Pharmaceutical preparations - Barrows Pharmacal Inc.
FLAVONS - Vitamins and nutritional supplements - Freeda Vitamins Inc.
FLAVONS 500 - Vitamins and nutritional supplements - Freeda Vitamins Inc.
FLAVOPHOS - Seasonings - Flavorite Laboratories Inc.
FLAVOR-AGED - Seasonings - Meat Seasonings Inc.
FLAVOR ALL - Seasonings - Starport
FLAVOR BEARS - Novelty items–paper ☆ - Antioch Publishing Co.
FLAVOR BEST - Turkeys ☆ - Continental Grain Co.
FLAVOR-BITE - Tortillas - Arevalo Tortilleria, Inc.
FLAVOR BLEND - Pet products - Western Family Foods, Inc.
FLAVOR BURST - Food products machinery - Fantasy Blankebaer
FLAVOR CAPS - Games - Ben and Jerry's Homemade, Inc.

☆ = Now out of production

FLAVOR CHEF - Food products - Excel Corp.
FLAVOR CLASSICS - Spices and extracts - San Francisco Spice Co. Inc.
FLAVOR CORE - Seasonings - Colefield Foods Inc.
FLAVOR COUNTRY - Wines - Huber Orchard Winery
FLAVOR CREATIONS - Coffee - NSI Sweeteners, Inc.
FLAVOR CRISPS - Crackers - Nabisco Holdings Corp.
FLAVOR CRISPS - Crackers - Pepperidge Farm Inc.
FLAVOR CRUNCH - Nuts - Peanut Factory
FLAVOR-ETS - Candy ☆ - Miss Saylor's Candies
FLAVOR-ETTES - Food products - Quali Tech, Inc.
FLAVOR EXPRESS - Cooking equipment–household - ISPG, Inc.
FLAVOR FAST - Vitamins and nutritional supplements - American Harvest, Inc.
FLAVOR FEST - Jams and jellies - Flavor Fest Foods Inc.
FLAVOR FILTER - Coffee - Folger Coffee Co.
FLAVOR FOCUS - Coffee - Saramar Corp.
FLAVOR FRESH - Agricultural products - Hess Brothers Fruit Co.
FLAVOR FRESH - Snack foods - Fruit Salad
FLAVOR GEM - Food products - Douglas Food
FLAVOR GEMS - Candy - M-B Candies Inc.
FLAVOR-GLOW - Seasonings - Dean Distributors, Inc.
FLAVOR GUARD - Food products ☆ - Cargill Corp.
FLAVOR-GUARD - Glass products - Gallo Glass Co.
FLAVOR ISLANDS - Food products - Quali Tech, Inc.
FLAVOR KING - Food products - Supreme Meat Co. Inc.
FLAVOR KIST - Food products ☆ - Universal Frozen Foods Co.
FLAVOR KIST - Pastries ☆ - Schulze and Burch Biscuit Co.
FLAVOR KIST SNACKIN' FRUITS - Pastries - Schulze and Burch Biscuit Co.
FLAVOR KLEEN - Coffee-maker cleaner, now out of production - TKI Foods, Inc.
FLAVOR KRAZE - Frozen foods - Flavors Unlimited, USA
FLAVOR LIFT - Food products ☆ - Universal Foods Corp.
FLAVOR-LITE - Cream–canned or powdered - Vsa, Inc.
FLAVOR-LITES - Food products - Quali Tech, Inc.
FLAVOR-LOCK - Coffee makers–electric ☆ - Sunbeam-Oster Household Products
FLAVOR-LOK - Bottle caps - Aluminum Co. of America
FLAVOR LOVER'S - Popcorn - Golden Valley Microwave Foods, Inc.
FLAVOR MAGIC - Syrup - Magic Ice Products
FLAVOR MAID - Doughnuts - Leon AF Super
FLAVOR-MAKER - Coffee makers–electric - Thomas A. Campbell Co.
FLAVOR-MASTER - Food products - V. & E. Kohnstamm Inc.
FLAVOR MEISTER - Meat products–beef - Schweigert Foods
FLAVOR MILL - Seasonings - Chefmaster Products
FLAVOR MORE - Flowers, plants, and seeds - Ferry-Morse Seed Co.
FLAVOR OF SCRATCH, THE - Food products - J.R. Simplot Co.
FLAVOR OF THE SEA - Crab meat–canned or cured - Lewis Crab Factory Inc.
FLAVOR-ON - Pet products ☆ - Gimborn U.S., Inc.
FLAVOR-ONE INC. - Confections - Flavor-ONE Inc.
FLAVOR-PODS - Coffee - Thomas A. Campbell Co.
FLAVOR RICH - Coffee - Private Brands Coffee & Tea Inc.
FLAVOR RIGHT FR - Cream ☆ - Instantwhip Foods Inc.
FLAVOR-RITE - Fruits–frozen - Valley Packers Inc.
FLAVOR ROAST - Coffee - Nestle Beverage Co.
FLAVOR ROLLS - Candy - Tootsie Roll Industries, Inc.
FLAVOR ROUX - Sauces - Country Flavor, Inc.
FLAVOR SAVER - Pans - E-Z-Por Corp.
FLAVOR SAVER - Pie plates - Corning Inc.
FLAVOR SECRET - Food products - Beatrice Cos. Inc.
FLAVOR-SHIELD - Snuff - Brown & Williamson Tobacco Corp.
FLAVOR SNACK - Dog food - Nabisco Foods Group
FLAVOR SNACKS - Pet food - Nabisco Holdings Corp.
FLAVOR STRAWS - Candy - Philadelphia Chewing Gum Corp.
FLAVOR-SWEET - Bakery products ☆ - Super Valu Inc.
FLAVOR TABS - Veterinary pharmaceutical preparations - Ciba-Geigy Corp.
FLAVOR TIME - Beverages - Park Corp.
FLAVOR TOP - Vegetable oil - Bunge Foods Corp.
FLAVOR TOUCH - Food products - F.I.S. Inc.
FLAVOR TREAT - Margarine - Miami Margarine Co. Inc.
FLAVOR TREE - Candy - Herman Goelitz Candy Co., Inc.
FLAVOR TREE - Snack foods - Dolefam Corp.
FLAVOR TREE FRUIT NIBBLES - Snack foods - Lipton Investments, Inc.
FLAVOR UP - Meat products–beef - Armour Swift-Eckrich
FLAVOR YOUR COFFEE - Food products - Wagner Gourmet Foods, Inc.
FLAVORBANK - Seasonings - Castle Food Products
FLAVORBEST - Fruits and vegetables - Michigan Apple Committee

FLAVORBREW - Coffee makers–electric - Cuisinart Inc.
FLAVORBRITE - Food products - TKI Foods, Inc.
FLAVORBURST - Candy - Leaf, Inc.
FLAVORBURST - Food products - Givaudan Roure
FLAVORCELL - Food products - McCormick & Co., Inc.
FLAVORCUP - Coffee - Schapira Coffee Co.
FLAVORED BY NATURE - Rice - Ricetec, Inc.
FLAVORED COLESTID - Pharmaceutical preparations - Upjohn Co.
FLAVOREE - Food products ☆ - Super Valu Inc.
FLAVOREEDS - Musical instrument accessories - Mr. Music, Inc.
FLAVORFUL - Meat sauces - Schwartz Meat Co.
FLAVORIN - Seasonings - First Spice Mixing Co.
FLAVORITE - Food products - Maple Leaf Farms Inc.
FLAVORITE - Food products - Super Valu Inc.
FLAVORITE - Seasonings - Flavorite Laboratories Inc.
FLAVORITE - Steel ☆ - Regal Ware, Inc.
FLAVORITE FOR PETS - Pet food - Super Valu Inc.
FLAVORITE LABORATORIES, INC. - Seasonings - Flavorite Laboratories Inc.
FLAVORIZER - Barbecues and grills - Weber-Stephen Products Co.
FLAVORLAND - Food products - Flavorland Foods Inc.
FLAVORLAND - Fruits–frozen - J.R. Wood Inc.
FLAVORLAND U.S.A. - Fruits–frozen - Flavorland Foods Inc.
FLAVORLIFE - Food-flavoring product - American Flavor & Fragrance Corp.
FLAVORPAK - Chewing gum - Philadelphia Chewing Gum Corp.
FLAVORS - Chairs–folding ☆ - Cramer Inc.
FLAVORS - Tiles–ceramic ☆ - American Olean Tile Co.
FLAVORS OF FLORENCE - Salad dressings–bottled - Firenze Gourmet Foods Inc.
FLAVORS OF THE PACIFIC RIM - Cookies - East & West Gourmet, Inc.
FLAVORS UNLIMITED - Ice cream - Flavors Unlimited, USA
FLAVORSPICE - Syrup - McCormick & Co., Inc.
FLAVORTEX - Food products - Wynn Starr Foods Inc.
FLAVORTRAP - Food products - M-Cap Technologies International
FLAVORWOOD - Wood products - Bar-B-Q-Woods
FLAVORZ - Dentifrices - John D. Blue
FLAVORZEST - Vitamins and nutritional supplements - Vita-Fore Products Co.
FLAVOS - Food products - Matlaw's Food Products Inc.
FLAVOS - Pharmaceutical - American Laboratories Inc.
FLAVOTECH - Spices and extracts - Saramar Corp.
FLAVOUR CREATIONS - Coffee - NSI Sweeteners, Inc.
FLAVOUR'D - Rice ☆ - Mars, Inc.
FLAVOURS OF TASTE - Coffee - Jadee, Inc.
FLAV'R-BLEND - Cream–canned or powdered - Elgin-Honey Hill Corp.
FLAV'R-CREME - Whipped topping–powdered - Elgin-Honey Hill Corp.
FLAV'R FLO - Oils–edible - Kraft Food Ingredients Corp.
FLAV'R FLOW - Oils–edible - Kraft Food Ingredients Corp.
FLAV'R-PEAK - Whipped topping–powdered ☆ - Elgin-Honey Hill Corp.
FLAV'R TOP - Whipped topping–powdered - Elgin-Honey Hill Corp.
FLAV'R-WHIP - Whipped topping–powdered ☆ - Elgin-Honey Hill Corp.
F.L.A.W. - Veterinary pharmaceutical preparations - Dyna Pet Inc.
FLAWED FABLES - Greeting cards - Originals by Maris (O.B.M. Publishing)
FLAWLESS - Floor coverings - Aladdin Mills, Inc.
FLAWLESS - Food products ☆ - Diamond Fruit Growers
FLAWLESS 10 - Nail care products - Revlon Consumer Products Corp.
FLAWLESS FINISH - Cosmetics - Elizabeth Arden Inc.
FLAWLESS LOVE - Rings–jewelry - Artcarved Inc.
FLAWLESS SONG - Rings–jewelry - Artcarved Inc.
FLAWLESS STAR - Rings–jewelry - Artcarved Inc.
FLAX - Fixtures - Sanlu Art Industries Inc.
FLAX - Glass products - AFG Industries Inc. (Glass Group Div.)
FLAX N' FIBER - Vitamins and nutritional supplements - Tishcon Corp.
FLAX N HONEY - Breads - Natural Ovens of Manitowoc Inc.
FLAX N' PRUNE - Vitamins and nutritional supplements - Tishcon Corp.
FLAX-O-MEGA - Vitamins and nutritional supplements - Flora, Inc.
FLAX SPROUT BAG, THE - Garden equipment - Sprout House
FLAXEN BLONDE - Floor coverings–carpet and rugs - Glen Eden Wool Carpets
FLAXEN DECKLE - Stationery - Samuel Ward Manufacturing Inc.
FLAXO - Thread - Threads USA Div.
FLAXOAP - Cleaning preparations ☆ - JTM Products Inc.
FLAXSEEDS - Apparel–children's - Angelheart Designs
FLAYMBAR - Finishing agents ☆ - Fire Research Laboratories, Inc.
FLBUILDER - Computer software - Wright Strategies, Inc.
FLEA & TICK WIPES - Repellent - Kimberly-Clark Corp.
FLEA-B-GON - Insecticides - Chevron Chemical Co.
FLEA BEACON - Traps - Happy Jack, Inc.

☆ = Now out of production

FLEA BEATER - Pesticides–household - Bonide Products, Inc.
FLEA-BRITES - Pet products - Sergeant's Pet Products, Inc.
FLEA BUSTERS - Veterinary pharmaceutical preparations - Normera Resources Corp.
FLEA CATCHER - Pet products - Four Paws Products Ltd.
FLEA-CIDE - Pesticides–agricultural - Revere Manufacturing
FLEA-EX - Pet products ☆ - Nala Barry Laboratories
FLEA FIGHTER - Pet products ☆ - Vital Nutrition Products
FLEA FREE 5 - Shampoos - Edward V. Rippingille, III
FLEA-FREE-30 - Pet products - Zema Corp.
FLEA GARD - Veterinary pharmaceutical preparations - Happy Jack, Inc.
FLEA GRABBER - Pet products - Global Pet Time Products, Inc.
FLEA-HALT - Pet products - Farnam Cos. Inc.
FLEA-KILL - Pet products ☆ - Security Products Co.
FLEA OFF - Veterinary pharmaceutical preparations - Adams Veterinary Research Laboratories Inc.
FLEA PATROL - Pet products - Danklied Laboratories Ltd.
FLEA POW - Pet products - Farnam Cos. Inc.
FLEA PUFFER - Pet products - Lightning Products
FLEA RELIEF - Pet collars - Elexis Corp.
FLEA RELIEF - Veterinary pharmaceutical preparations - Dr. Goodpet
FLEA RID - Pet products - Glo-Marr Products Inc.
FLEA-SCAT - Insecticides ☆ - Security Products Co.
FLEA STOP - Pet products - Farnam Cos. Inc.
FLEA STOPPERS - Pesticides–household - Flea Stoppers Home Products, Inc.
FLEA TRAP - Pet products - Zema Corp.
FLEA TREATS - Pet products ☆ - FTI Pet Products
FLEA VAC - Pet products ☆ - Century Systems Inc.
FLEA ZINGER PLUS - Pesticides–household - Happy Jack, Inc.
FLEAFELLER'S FABULOUS FLEA CIRCUS - Statuary - Fleafeller's Fabulous Flea Circus
FLEAGARD - Pet products - Gerard-Pellham Co.
FLEAGO - Flea powder - Fleago Industries Inc.
FLEAGO - THE MAGIC CRYSTAL - Pet products - Fleago Industries Inc.
FLEAGO - THE MAGIC SHAMPOO - Pet products - Fleago Industries Inc.
FLEALAR - Insecticides - Enforcer Products Inc.
FLEAMASTER - Pet products - Breeders Equipment Co.
FLEAPOO - Pet products - K.C. Pharmacal Inc.
F.L.E.A.S. FAST, LASTING, EFFECTIVE, ARRESTING SYSTEM - Pesticides–household - Nature's Process Laboratories
FLEAS NO MORE - Pet products - Leisure Times of Destin, Inc.
FLEAS ON FRED - Games - Tyco Industries, Inc.
FLEAS-X - Veterinary pharmaceutical preparations - W.F. Young, Inc.
FLEAVOL - Veterinary pharmaceutical preparations - SmithKline Beecham Animal Health Products
FLEBOMEDIC - Pharmaceutical preparations ☆ - Medical Products Panamericana Inc.
FLEC IT GRANITE FINISH - Stains - Zynolyte Products Co.
FLECK/CHICK-CHICK - Eggs - J.J. Fleck Co.
FLECK STONE - Paints - Plasti-Kote Co. Inc.
FLECKS - Paper - Georgia-Pacific Corp.
FLECKS-N-SPECKS - Paints ☆ - Sequa Corp.
FLECT-AIRE - Controls–air conditioning systems ☆ - Deflecto Corp.
FLECTAN I - Photographic equipment - Nye Optical Co.
FLECTO - Finishing agents - Flecto Co. Inc.
FLECTORS - Footwear - Right Stuff, Inc.
FLEECE - Paints - Long Island Paint & Chemical Co.
FLEECE - Paper cutters ☆ - The Kroger Co.
FLEECE-A-NEW POLAR - Waterproofing compounds - Kenyon Consumer Products Inc.
FLEECE GOLD - Yarn ☆ - Oregon Worsted Co.
FLEECE ON EARTH - Apparel - Fleece on Earth
FLEECE SKINS - Cushions - Allman Products
FLEECENAP - Curtains–shower ☆ - Kleinert's Inc.
FLEECIE - Toys - Mattel, Inc.
FLEECY - Bleach - Dial Corp.
FLEECY - Footwear - Brown Wooten Mills Inc.
FLEECY FRIENDS - Pet products - Petstuff, Inc.
FLEECY LAMB - Toys–stuffed ☆ - Dakin Inc.
FLEEGLE FROG - Toys–stuffed - Russ Berrie and Co., Inc.
FLEER - Trading cards and stamps - Fleer Corp.
FLEER ULTRA - Trading cards and stamps - Fleer Corp.
FLEER ULTRA TEAM - Trading cards and stamps - Fleer Corp.
FLEER'S - Chewing gum ☆ - Fleer Corp.
FLEET - Bicycles - Schwinn Cycling & Fitness Inc.

FLEET - Oils–lubricating - Quaker State Oil Refining Corp.
FLEET - Pharmaceutical preparations - C.B. Fleet Co. Inc.
FLEET ACADEMIC EDITIONS INC. - Publisher's imprints - Fleet Press Inc.
FLEET ADVISOR - Computer hardware - Eaton Corp.
FLEET AIR - Truck cabs - Fleet Air Worldwide, Inc.
FLEET BAGENEMA - Health care products - C.B. Fleet Co. Inc.
FLEET CAD - Computer software - Quatron Inc.
FLEET CARRIER - Tires - Uniroyal Goodrich Tire Co.
FLEET DEFENDER - Computer software - Microprose Software, Inc.
FLEET DIRECTOR - Computer software - Airtouch Teletrac
FLEET-DRY - Paints - Vogel Paint and Wax Co., Inc.
FLEET-ERASE - Paper–bond - Esleeck Manufacturing Co., Inc.
FLEET-LUX - Enamel gloss - Automotive Finishes Inc.
FLEET-MAIL - Computer programming services - Transcommunications Inc.
FLEET-O-WING - Ships–sailing vessels - Pert Lowell Co. Inc.
FLEET PRESS - Publisher's imprints - Fleet Press Inc.
FLEET RELIEF - Health care products - C.B. Fleet Co. Inc.
FLEET SERVICE PACK - Filters–oil - Alliedsignal Inc.
FLEET SPEC - Radios - Custom Radio Corp.
FLEET STREET - Computer software - Newshound Corp.
FLEET UNIMASTER - Tires - Uniroyal Goodrich Tire Co.
FLEET VISION - Computer software - Trimble Navigation Ltd.
FLEETCLEAN SYSTEMS INC. - Cleaning preparations–carpet and rug - Fleetclean Systems, Inc.
FLEETCOM II - Radios ☆ - E.F. Johnson Co.
FLEETCON - Transportation vehicles and equipment - Arrowsmith Technologies, Inc.
FLEETDRY - Lithographic plates - Sherwin-Williams Automotive Finishes Corp.
FLEETFOOT - Shoes–athletic - Rawlings Sporting Goods Co., Inc.
FLEETFOOT - Vegetables–canned - Durand Canning Co.
FLEETLAR - Brake parts - Carlisle Corp.
FLEETLINE - Apparel and accessories - Wilson Brothers
FLEETLINE - Bicycles - Murray, Inc.
FLEETLINE - Hardware - Blaine Window Hardware Inc.
FLEETLINE - Office supplies ☆ - Faber-Castell Corp.
FLEETMAN - Computer software - Managed by Design
FLEETMASTER - Tires - Uniroyal Goodrich Tire Co.
FLEETMASTER DEEPLUG - Tires - Uniroyal Goodrich Tire Co.
FLEETMASTER TRIPLE TREAD - Tires - Uniroyal Goodrich Tire Co.
FLEET*MATE - Computer software - Multisystems, Inc.
FLEETRITE - Motor vehicle parts and accessories - Navistar International Transportation Corp.
FLEETSTAR - Computer software - Clay B. Winkler
FLEETWARE - Cutting boards - Fleet Manufacturing Co., Inc.
FLEETWASH - Cleaning preparations - Flo-Pac Corp.
FLEETWATCH - Computer peripheral equipment - S & A Systems, Inc.
FLEETWAY - Paper - Esleeck Manufacturing Co., Inc.
FLEETWIN - Motors–outboard - Outboard Marine Corp.
FLEETWOOD - Bicycles - Murray, Inc.
FLEETWOOD - Floor coverings - Mannington Resilient Floors
FLEETWOOD - Guitars ☆ - Fred Gretsch Enterprises
FLEETWOOD - Motor vehicles–automobiles - General Motors Corp. (Cadillac Motor Car Div.)
FLEETWOOD - Projectors–photographic - Brumberger Co. Inc.
FLEETWOOD - Shampoos - Fleetwood Co.
FLEETWOOD - Watches - Bulova Corp.
FLEETWOOD COINS - Giftware - Unicover Corp.
FLEETWOOD COLLECTION, THE - Giftware - Unicover Corp.
FLEETWOOD DESIGNER - Cutlery ☆ - Washington Forge Inc.
FLEETWOOD FIRST DAY COVERS - Paper products - Unicover Corp.
FLEETWOOD SIXTY SPECIAL - Motor vehicles–automobiles - General Motors Corp. (Cadillac Motor Car Div.)
FLEETWOOD SPORTSCARD ALBUM - Photo albums and binders ☆ - Unicover Corp.
FLEISCH - Oxygen - OEM Medical
FLEISCHER - Food products - John Sommer Inc.
FLEISCHER - Frames–picture - Fabulous Forgeries Ltd.
FLEISCHERS'S - Thread - Cincinnati Thread Co.
FLEISCHMANN'S - Almond pastes - Nabisco Foods Group
FLEISCHMANN'S - Liquors - Canandaigua Wine Co. Inc.
FLEISCHMANN'S CANOLA CHOICE - Food products - Nabisco Foods Group
FLEISCHMANN'S EXTRA LIGHT - See **FLEISCHMANN'S LOWER FAT**
FLEISCHMANN'S LIGHT - See **FLEISCHMANN'S LIGHT TASTE**
FLEISCHMANN'S LIGHT TASTE - Margarine - Nabisco Foods Group
FLEISCHMANN'S LOWER FAT - Margarine - Nabisco Foods Group
FLEISCHMAN'S FAT FREE SQUEEZE - Margarine - Nabisco Foods Group

☆ = Now out of production

FLEISHMAN - Pickles - Vlasic Foods Inc.
FLEMINGS OF BUCKHEAD - Leather goods - Fleming Roberts Childs, Jr.
FLEMINGTON - Furs–pelts - Flemington Fur Co. (Coat World Div.)
FLEMINGTON - Vases–glass - Flemington Cut Glass Co.
FLEMISH MANOR - Furniture–upholstered - Clyde Pearson Inc.
FLEMISH WONDER - Towels - John Ritzenthaler Co.
FLEMISH WONDER - Towels - Shen Manufacturing Co. Inc.
FLEN - Paints ☆ - Frazee Paint
FLENDER - Motors - American Contex Corp.
FLENSBORG - Cheese ☆ - Webeco Foods Inc.
FLENSTED - Novelty items - Swe-Den Inc.
FLENTS - Plugs–ear - Flents Products Co. Inc.
FLERE TRODER - Yarn - Delaine Worsted Mills
FLESH - Recording label - Jazz Composer's Orchestra Association Inc.
FLET - Video production - Logoi, Inc.
FLETCH-LAC - Archery equipment - Bohning Co. Ltd.
FLETCH MAGIC - Fishing tackle - Fly Fishing, Inc.
FLETCH-TITE - Archery equipment - Bohning Co. Ltd.
FLETCHER - Glass products - Fletcher-Terry Co.
FLETCHER - Seafood products–fresh or frozen - Missouri Fish Co.
FLETCHER AND OAKS - Beverages–alcohol - Jim Beam Brands Co.
FLETCHER'S - Chili sauce - Fletcher's Barbecue Inc.
FLETCHER'S - Meat products–beef - Fletcher's Fine Foods Inc.
FLETCHER'S CASTORIA - Laxatives - Mentholatum Co.
FLETCHER'S CORNY DOGS - Food products - State Fair Foods, Inc.
FLETCHUNTER - Archery equipment - Archer Sports Inc.
FLETKIDS PLAY SYSTEM - Toys - Learning Curve Toys, LLC
FLETT DAIRY - Milk - Flett Dairy Inc.
FLEUR - Bathroom accessories - Kohler Co.
FLEUR - Clocks - General Time Corp. (Westclox/Seth Thomas Div.)
FLEUR - Dinnerware–glass - Durand International
FLEUR - Paper ☆ - Super Valu Inc.
FLEUR 5 - Skin care products - Pharmagel Corp.
FLEUR BLANCHE - Cheese ☆ - Swissrose International Inc.
FLEUR D' ESPRIT - Apparel and accessories ☆ - Vanity Fair Mills Inc.
FLEUR DE CARNEROS - Wines ☆ - Cannon Wines Ltd.
FLEUR DE COLOUR - Hair care products - Matrix Essentials, Inc.
FLEUR DE FLEURS - Perfumes - Parfums Nina Ricci
FLEUR DE FRANCE - American International Industries
FLEUR DE LACE - Apparel and accessories - Strouse, Adler Co.
FLEUR-DE-LACE - Apparel–women's - Olga Co.
FLEUR DE LAIT - Cheese - Bongrain Cheese USA
FLEUR-DE-LIS - Breads - Fleur-De-Lis Products Inc.
FLEUR DE LIS - Colognes ☆ - T.N. Dickinson Co.
FLEUR-DE-LIS - Dinnerware–glass - WMF/USA
FLEUR-DE-LIS - Dinnerware–glass ☆ - Metlox Pottery Shoppe
FLEUR DE LIS - Fabrics - Gretchen Bellinger Inc.
FLEUR DE LIS - Food products - Henry Bresky & Sons Inc.
FLEUR-DE-LIS - Furniture - Hooker Furniture Corp.
FLEUR DE LIS - Girdles - Abraham & Straus/Jordan Marsh Co.
FLEUR DE LIS - Liquors - Hughes Markets Inc.
FLEUR DE LIS - Meat products–beef - Dubuque Foods, Inc.
FLEUR-DE-LIS - Pens ☆ - Park Sherman
FLEUR DE LIS - Shrimp–canned or cured - Reuther's Seafood Co. Inc.
FLEUR DE LOTTO - Containers - Pamela A. Barry
FLEUR DE LYS - Dinnerware–glass - Royal China & Porcelain Companies Inc.
FLEUR DE MONTAGNE - Wines - Diamond Wine Merchants
FLEUR DE NUIT - Wines - Admiral Wine Merchants
FLEUR DE ROSE - Colognes - Max Factor & Co.
FLEUR DECO - Housewares ☆ - Himark Enterprises Inc.
FLEUR DES CHAMPS - Bedding–linen - Dan River Inc.
FLEUR DES MERS - Dinnerware–glass ☆ - WMF/USA
FLEUR D'LACE - Apparel–women's - Jezebel-Renee of Hollywood
FLEUR D'OR - Cutlery ☆ - Lifetime Hoan Corp.
FLEURELLE - Floor coverings ☆ - Kentile Floors Inc.
FLEUREMEDY - Hair care products - Richard Stein Hair Care Products Inc.
FLEURETTE - Apparel–women's - Fleurette
FLEURETTE - Candy - McDonald Candy Co. Inc.
FLEURETTE - Dishes–china - Waterford Wedgwood USA, Inc.
FLEURETTE - Dishes–china ☆ - Pickard Inc.
FLEURETTE - Dolls ☆ - Effanbee Doll Corp.
FLEURETTE - Floor coverings–carpet and rugs - Milliken & Co. Inc.
FLEURETTE - Floor coverings–carpet and rugs ☆ - Stanton Carpet Corp.
FLEURETTE - Silverware - Imperial Schrade Corp.
FLEURI - Dinnerware–glass - Royal China & Porcelain Companies Inc.

FLEURIE - Floor coverings–carpet and rugs ☆ - Kelly Group Inc.
FLEURMONT - Wallpaper - Capital Carousel Inc.
FLEURON - Beverages–alcohol - Wine House Ltd.
FLEURON BLANCHE - Dinnerware–glass - WMF/USA
FLEURON PRINTEMPS - Dinnerware–glass - WMF/USA
FLEURON ROTONDE - Dinnerware–glass - WMF/USA
FLEURS CLASSIQUE - Perfumes and colognes - Jafra Cosmetics Inc.
FLEURS DE JONTUE - Perfumes - Revlon Consumer Products Corp.
FLEURS DE LA CHINE - Wallpaper - Greeff Fabrics Inc.
FLEURS D'ELLE - Perfumes - Nettie Rosenstein Inc.
FLEURS DU MONDE - Colognes - Faberge Co.
FLEURY - Glassware–household - Durand International
FLEX - Artists' materials - Flexcraft Industries
FLEX - Frames–eyeglass - Rozin Optical Export Corp.
FLEX - Frames–eyeglass ☆ - Universal/Univis Inc.
FLEX - Hair care products - Revlon Consumer Products Corp.
FLEX - Medical apparatus - PDT Systems
FLEX - Pagers - Motorola, Inc. (Land Mobile Products Sector)
FLEX - Paints - Energy Products Inc.
FLEX - Paints - Long Island Paint & Chemical Co.
FLEX - Sporting goods - Ektelon
FLEX - Toothbrushes - Desert Essence Cosmetics
FLEX - Vitamins and nutritional supplements - Unipro Inc.
FLEX 3 - Office supplies - Mead Corp.
FLEX 10 - Jewelry–precious - Metal Marketplace International
FLEX 14 - Jewelry–precious - Metal Marketplace International
FLEX-26 - Footwear - Illinois Footwear Co.
FLEX 90 - Footwear - Mercury International Trading Corp.
FLEX 250 - Water bottles–rubber ☆ - Connelly Skis, Inc.
FLEX-900 - Metal goods - Ebaa Iron Inc.
FLEX A BEAM - Lamps - Tacony Corp.
FLEX A BIT - Hardware - Eazypower Corp.
FLEX A BIT PLUS - Hardware - Eazypower Corp.
FLEX-A-BULL - Games - Custom Manufacturing, Inc.
FLEX-A-CHEST - Exercising equipment - Excel, The Exercise Co.
FLEX-A-COLOR - Floor coverings - American Floor Products Co. Inc.
FLEX-A-FITTING - Plumbing fixtures–metal - Genova Products Inc.
FLEX-A-FOAM - Apparel and accessories ☆ - Flexo Products Inc.
FLEX-A-GRIP - Exercising equipment - Excel, The Exercise Co.
FLEX-A-KRAFT - Envelopes ☆ - Quality Park Products Co.
FLEX-A-LASTIC - Bostik Inc.
FLEX-A-LITE - Apparel and accessories ☆ - Flexo Products Inc.
FLEX-A-MATIC - Pens ☆ - Union Pen Co.
FLEX-A-MIN - Vitamins and nutritional supplements - Barth's Nutra Products
FLEX-A-PEN - Artists' materials - Jonathan Bradley Pens Inc.
FLEX-A-PLUG - Plugs–electric - General Electric Co.
FLEX-A-POWER - Conduits - General Electric Co.
FLEX-A-PRENE - Apparel and accessories ☆ - Flexo Products Inc.
FLEX-A-PUMP - Pumps - Beckson Marine Inc.
FLEX A SOCKET - Hardware - Eazypower Corp.
FLEX-A-SPAN - Adhesives and sealants - Matrix Service Co.
FLEX-A-TONE - Drums–musical instruments - LP Music Group
FLEX A WRENCH - Hardware - Eazypower Corp.
FLEX ABILITY - Circuit boards - Altera Corp.
FLEX-ABILITY - Vitamins and nutritional supplements - Planetary Formulas
FLEX ABLE - Office supplies - Esselte Corp.
FLEX-ACTION - Frames–eyeglass - Liberty Optical Manufacturing Co.
FLEX ACTION - Massage products - Wahl Clipper Corp.
FLEX-AIM - Laser systems–medical - Kentek Corp.
FLEX-ALL - Analgesics - Signal Investment & Management Co.
FLEX ALL - Caulking compounds - Allpro Corp.
FLEX-ALL 454 - Cosmetics - Chattem Inc.
FLEX & GO - Shampoos - Revlon Consumer Products Corp.
FLEX & SET - Hardware - Melard Manufacturing Corp.
FLEX APPEAL - Cosmetics - Revlon Consumer Products Corp.
FLEX APPEAL - Footwear - Genesco Inc.
FLEX-BACK - Intimate apparel - Cortland Corset Co. Inc.
FLEX BACK - Underwear and nightwear - Cortland Corset Co. Inc.
FLEX BAG - Bins - Custom Metalcraft, Inc.
FLEX-BAND - Footwear - Penn Footwear Co.
FLEX-BAR - Tents ☆ - Coleman Co., Inc.
FLEX BASE - Plastics–laminated - Sheldahl, Inc.
FLEX-BEAM - Garden equipment - Union Fork and Hoe Co.
FLEX-BOND - Adhesives and sealants ☆ - Sandstrom Products Co.
FLEX BOND - Mortars–clay - Custom Building Products
FLEX-C-PAP - Medical apparatus - Kendall Co.

☆ = Now out of production

FLEX-CARE - Ophthalmic goods - Alcon Laboratories, Inc.
FLEX-CARE - Work benches - Metal Components Inc. (Flexible Furniture Div.)
FLEX CART - Portable storage shelving - Winsford Corp.
FLEX-CAULK - Putties ✩ - Sherwin-Williams Automotive Finishes Corp.
FLEX-COAT - Adhesives and sealants ✩ - Atlas Chemical Co.
FLEX-COAT - Sheet metal products - Aluminum Co. of America
FLEX COLD - Health care products - Medi Inc.
FLEX COLD JR. - Health care products - Medi Inc.
FLEX-CONNECT - Faucets ✩ - Jameco Industries, Inc.
FLEX-CONNECT - Plumbing fixtures–plastic - Eagle Industries Inc.
FLEX CONTROL - Skin care products - Braun Inc.
FLEX CORNER - Tape–adhesive - Goldblatt Tool Co.
FLEX-CORRECT - Drains ✩ - Jameco Industries, Inc.
FLEX-CRAFT - Eyeglasses - Art-Craft Optical Co.
FLEX-D-VIDER - Machine tools - Marathon Equipment Co.
FLEX-DRI - Sealing compounds - Champion Products Inc.
FLEX-DUIT - Conduits–electrical - Carlon
FLEX-E-FORM - Containers–paper - Sweetheart Cup Co. Inc.
FLEX E MAILER - Bags–plastic - Equitable Bag Co., Inc.
FLEX-E-WRAP - Packaging–paper - Prompac Industries, Inc.
FLEX-EVER - Pet products - Farnam Cos. Inc.
FLEX-EZE - Clamps - Ac-cetera Inc.
FLEX-EZE - Desks - Wood Design Inc.
FLEX FACTORY - Toys - Mattel, Inc.
FLEX FASHION - Wet suits–rubber - McNett Corp.
FLEX-FEED - Electrical equipment - Tecnetics Industries, Inc.
FLEX-FENCE - Fencing–chain link - Flex-Fence Manufacturing Co.
FLEX FENCE - Fencing–wood - Fence Parts, Inc.
FLEX FIRE - Vitamins and nutritional supplements - Weider Health and Fitness
FLEX FIT - Apparel and accessories - Zap-It, Inc.
FLEX-FIT - Bed sheets, mattress pads - Kimlor Mills Inc.
FLEX-FIT - Floor coverings - Tarkett, Inc.
FLEX-FIT - Gloves–rubber - Mapa Pioneer Corp.
FLEX-FIT - Helmets–metal - Muehleisen Manufacturing Co.
FLEX-FIT - Plumbing fixtures–plastic ✩ - Waxman Industries Inc.
FLEX FLO - Plastics - Lamp Products
FLEX FOAM BODY BRACE, THE - Medical apparatus - Spinal Technology, Inc.
FLEX FOLD - Steel-wool pads - American Steel Wool Manufacturing Co. Inc.
FLEX-FORM - Windshields–plastic ✩ - C.T.I. Audio Inc.
FLEX FORMULA - Toys - Mattel, Inc.
FLEX FRAME - Furniture - Suncast Corp.
FLEX-FRAME - Marine rigging - Garelick Manufacturing Co.
FLEX FREE - Animal feed supplements - Vita Flex Nutrition Co., Inc.
FLEX GARD - Automotive parts and accessories - Packard Electric Div.
FLEX-GAUGE - Electrical meters - Emico Inc.
FLEX GLIDE - Orthodontic equipment - Michael J. Pappas
FLEX GLOW - Paints - Parker Paint Manufacturing Co.
FLEX-GRIP - Microphones - Shure Brothers, Inc.
FLEX-GUARD - Apparel–athletic - S-Tek, Inc.
FLEX-GUARD - Sealing devices - Felton Brush Inc.
FLEX-GUARDS - Brushes - Felton Brush Inc.
FLEX GUN - Paint sprayers - Graco Inc.
FLEX-GUT - Medical apparatus - C.P. Medical
FLEX-I-PAK - Paper–sand - Moyco Industries, Inc.
FLEX-I-PAK - Wire products - Republic Fastener Products Corp.
FLEX-I-TIP - Toys–guns ✩ - Ray Plastic Inc.
FLEX-I-VISION - File folders - Smead Manufacturing Co.
FLEX II - Plastic piping - Environ Products, Inc.
FLEX IT AND PROTECT IT! - Boating equipment and accessories - Mark Alan Espinosa
FLEX-KING - Window coverings - Levolor Inc.
FLEX KLEEN - Air conditioning equipment - Plastic Techniques of Pennsylvania
FLEX-KOTE - Rope - Wire Rope Corp. of America Inc.
FLEX-LAG - Tiles–ceramic - Flexible Steel Lacing Co.
FLEX-LIFT - Brassieres (Bras) - Carmen Foundations Inc.
FLEX LIGHT & FREE - Hair care products - Revlon Consumer Products Corp.
FLEX-LINE - Frames–eyeglass ✩ - Universal/Univis Inc.
FLEX-LINE - Sporting goods - Rector Skatewear
FLEX-LITE - Eyeglasses - Art-Craft Optical Co.
FLEX-LITE - Flashlights - Bigsby Accessories Inc.
FLEX LITE - Hoses - Anchor Swan
FLEX-LOCK - Clamps–metal - Sign-Up Corp.
FLEX LOCK - File folders - K & M Co.
FLEX-LOK - Adhesives and sealants - Atlas Chemical Co.

FLEX-LOK - Motor vehicle parts and accessories - Flex Technologies, Inc.
FLEX MASTER - Bags - Pfeil & Holing, Inc.
FLEX-MATE - Medical apparatus - Breg, Inc.
FLEX-MIKE - Electronic equipment - Sonotone Corp.
FLEX-N-FIT - Automotive parts and accessories - Gates Rubber Co. (Automotive Aftermarket/Hardware Sales Div.)
FLEX 'N SAND - Abrasive products - Norton Co.
FLEX 'N SET - Dryers–hair ✩ - Belson Products
FLEX-NET - Hair care products - Revlon Consumer Products Corp.
FLEX-O-BAGS - Bags - Warp Bros.
FLEX-O-BAND - Apparel–women's ✩ - Bali Co. Inc.
FLEX-O-BOND - Thread - Needlecraft Industries
FLEX-O-BRUSH - Cosmetics - Comare Corp.
FLEX-O-CHANNEL - Hardware - Warp Bros.
FLEX-O-CRYLIC - Plastics film - Warp Bros.
FLEX-O-FILM - Plastics film - Warp Bros.
FLEX-O-FLASH - Plastics film ✩ - Warp Bros.
FLEX-O-FRY - Cooking equipment–commercial - Pitco Frialator, Inc.
FLEX-O-GLASS - Plastics film - Warp Bros.
FLEX-O-GLASS 2 - Plastics film - Warp Bros.
FLEX-O-GLAZE - Plastics - Warp Bros.
FLEX-O-GRAF - Scales–industrial ✩ - Pennsylvania Scale Co.
FLEX-O-GRIP - Sporting goods - Cut 'n Jump Ski Corp.
FLEX-O-HASPS - Locks - American Lock Co.
FLEX-O-JERCS - Ophthalmic goods - Chums Ltd.
FLEX-O-LATOR - Medical apparatus - Lumex, Inc.
FLEX-O-LOK - Building materials–concrete - AA Wire Products Co.
FLEX-O-MATE - Hoses - Beckson Marine Inc.
FLEX-O-MATIC - Door frames ✩ - Macklanburg-Duncan Co.
FLEX-O-MATIC - Eyeglasses - Fossil Inc.
FLEX-O-MATIC - Jewelry - Jacoby-Bender Inc.
FLEX-O-MIRRO - Hobby kits - Extra Special Products Corp.
FLEX-O-PANE - Plastics film - Warp Bros.
FLEX-O-PLASTIC - Plastics film - Warp Bros.
FLEX-O-SEAL - Waxes–sealing - J.C. Whitlam Manufacturing Co.
FLEX-O-STRIP - Magnets - Timewise
FLEX-O-TEX - Finishing agents - Plastics & Resins Ltd.
FLEX-O-TEX - Wallpaper - Andek Corp.
FLEX-O-WEIT - Shorts–children's - Willits Footwear Worldwide, Inc.
FLEX-O-WRAP - Plastics film ✩ - Warp Bros.
FLEX-ON - Health care products - Maddak Inc.
FLEX-ON - Watchbands–base metal - Regal Industries, Inc.
FLEX-OPAQUE - Paints–artists' - Salis International, Inc.
FLEX PAK - Chemical preparations - Turtle Wax, Inc.
FLEX-PAK - Pharmaceutical preparations - Merocel Corp.
FLEX PERFORMANCE SYSTEMS - Exercising equipment - Flex Equipment Inc.
FLEX-PLEET - Filters–air - Pneumafil Corp.
FLEX PLUS - Exercising equipment - Proform Fitness Products, Inc.
FLEX POINTE - Floor coverings–tile - Collins & Aikman Corp.
FLEX PRENE - Hoses - Colorite Plastic Co.
FLEX-QUEST - Bicycles - Columbia Manufacturing Inc.
FLEX REST - Computer peripheral equipment - Frederic C. Ambrose
FLEX RIB - Underwear and nightwear ✩ - Nantucket Industries Inc.
FLEX-RITE - Reaming machines - Union Butterfield Corp.
FLEX-ROLL - Kitchen appliances - Vaughan Manufacturing Co. Inc.
FLEX- S WASHER - Machine tools - Black Clawson Co.
FLEX SCRUB - Cleaning preparations - Empire Brushes, Inc.
FLEX-SEAL - Prosthetic apparatus - Flex-Foot Inc.
FLEX SHAFTS - Tools - Disston Co.
FLEX-SHEET - Mirrors - National Products Inc.
FLEX-SHIELD-STRIP - Curtains - Johnston Environmental
FLEX SHOP - Exercise equipment - Dynamic Classics Ltd.
FLEX-SLATE - Finishing agents ✩ - Flintkote Co.
FLEX-SLATE - Floor coverings - Azrock Commercial Flooring
FLEX-SLATE - Paints ✩ - GS Roofing Products Co.
FLEX-SPEC - Frames–eyeglass - Hudson Optical Corp.
FLEX SPLITTER - Conduit cutter - Greenlee Textron Inc.
FLEX SPRAY - Adhesives and sealants - Renew Roof Technologies Inc.
FLEX SQUEEGY - Squeegees - Milwaukee Dustless Brush Co.
FLEX-STICK - Fishing lures - American Cyanamid Co.
FLEX STRIP - Tires - Oliver Rubber Co.
FLEX-STRIPE - Adhesives and sealants ✩ - Sandstrom Products Co.
FLEX-SULATION - Air conditioning equipment - Grant Wilson Inc.
FLEX SWITCH - Switches–electric - Sheldahl, Inc.
FLEX SYSTEM - Exercising equipment - Interlectric Corp.

✩ = Now out of production

FLEX TAILORED - Apparel–men's - J. Schoeneman Inc.
FLEX TAPE - Bandages - Pedinol Pharmacal Inc.
FLEX-TEE - Apparel and accessories ☆ - Imperial Knitting Co. Inc.
FLEX-TEX - Finishing agents - Dunn Edwards Corp.
FLEX TILLER - Tractors ☆ - LMC Corp.
FLEX TILLERS - Tillers–rotary - LMC Corp.
FLEX TIMBER - Wood products - Environmental Design Concepts Inc.
FLEX-TIP - Brushes–paint - Baker Brush Co. Inc.
FLEX-TIP - Drums–musical instruments ☆ - Cappella Wood Enterprises
FLEX-TITE - Frames–eyeglass - J.I. Morris Co.
FLEX-TITE - Windows–plastic - Plaskolite Inc.
FLEX TOUCH - Printing trades machinery - Republic Roller Corp.
FLEX-TRAC - Adhesives and sealants ☆ - Sandstrom Products Co.
FLEX TRAINER - Footwear - Mercury International Trading Corp.
FLEX-TRED - Tape–adhesive - Wooster Products Inc.
FLEX-TRIM - Caulking compounds - Myro, Inc.
FLEX-TUFT - Floor coverings–tile - Flexco Co.
FLEX TWIST - Golfing equipment - Taylor Made Golf Co. Inc.
FLEX-U-SIL - Thermostats ☆ - Flexible Technologies Inc.
FLEX-VU - Film - Flexcon Co. Inc.
FLEX-VUE - Eyeglasses - McKesson Home Health Care
FLEX-WAX - Waxes–paraffin ☆ - Aleene's
FLEX-WEIGH - Mixing and weighing apparatus - Hough International, Inc.
FLEX WELT - Shoes - Clinic Shoe Co.
FLEX WING - Toys - Tonka Corp.
FLEX-WRAP - Bandages–orthopedic - Pelton Shepherd Industries
FLEX-X - Rope - Wire Rope Corp. of America Inc.
FLEX ZAP - Adhesives and sealants - Pacer Technology
FLEX-ZIP - Zippers ☆ - Coats and Clark Inc.
FLEX ZIPZ - Zippers - Flexsystems USA Inc.
FLEXA-ROAM - Pet products - Weller Co.
FLEXABALL - Exercising equipment - Fitness Quest Inc.
FLEXACHROME - Floor coverings–tile ☆ - GS Roofing Products Co.
FLEXACHROME - Tiles–terrazzo ☆ - Flintkote Co.
FLEXACRON CLAD - Doors–garage - Clopay Millwork
FLEXADDRESS - Binders - FlexAddress Systems
FLEXADE - Tools–hand-operated - Foredom Electric Co.
FLEXAFLOAT - Hoses - Coastal Industries Inc.
FLEXAFORM - Office supplies - FlexAddress Systems
FLEXAGON - Games - Gilbert M. Thompson
FLEXAHERB - Vitamins and nutritional supplements ☆ - J.R. Carlson Laboratories Inc.
FLEXALL - Mortars–clay - Custom Building Products
FLEXALLOY - Garden equipment - Teknor Apex Co.
FLEXALUM - Window shades - Aamglo Distributors Inc.
FLEXALUM DECOR - Blinds–venetian ☆ - Hunter Douglas, Inc.
FLEXAM - Health care products - Baxter International Inc.
FLEXANE - Moldings–plaster of paris - Crown Delta Corp.
FLEXAPEEL - Notebooks and notepads - FlexAddress Systems
FLEXARM - Lamps–desk - Art Specialty Co.
FLEXARM - Pet products - Rapid Electric/R & R Manufacturing
FLEXARRAY - Electronic equipment - Raidtec Corp.
FLEXATARD - Apparel–women's - Gilda Marx Inc.
FLEXATRON - Insulating materials - Kingsdown, Inc.
FLEXAVET - Bandages - Glenwood LLC
FLEXBAC - Abrasive products ☆ - Carborundum Abrasives North America
FLEXBAR - Frames–eyeglass ☆ - Universal/Univis Inc.
FLEXBAR - Surgical instruments - Flexbar Machine Corp.
FLEXBATCH - Computer software - Coherent Technologies Inc.
FLEXBOARD - Docks - R.L. Torbeck Industries Inc.
FLEXBOB - Thread - Threads USA Div.
FLEXBRIDGE - Eyeglass frames - Aptaker Co. Inc.
FLEXCAN - Plastic bins ☆ - Design Ideas Ltd.
FLEXCEIVER - Computer accessories - Advanced Concept Electronics
FLEXCEL - Machine parts - Flexovit USA Inc.
FLEXCEL - Printing trades machinery - Napp Systems, Inc.
FLEXCELL - Computer software - Vanguard Cellular Systems, Inc.
FLEXCELL - Concrete repair products - Celotex Corp.
FLEXCIM - Computer software - Vector Consulting Inc.
FLEXCO - Floor coverings–tile - Flexco Co.
FLEXCOIL - Hoses - Coilhose Pneumatics Inc.
FLEXCON & SYSTEMS, INC. - Bags–canvas - Flexcon & Systems, Inc.
FLEXCOR - Cables–fiber optic - Corning Inc.
FLEXCOR - Electrical equipment - Pass & Seymour, Inc.
FLEXCOR - Frames–eyeglass ☆ - Universal/Univis Inc.
FLEXCOR - Printing trades machinery - Polyfibron Technologies, Inc.

FLEXCORE - Computer hardware - Lsi Logic Corp.
FLEXCUT - Dyes and pigments - Flexcut, Inc.
FLEXCUTTER - Scissors–hand-operated - Flexcutter Inc.
FLEXDRIVE - Machine parts - Nutec Components Inc.
FLEXDROP - Hoses - Goodyear Tire & Rubber Co.
FLEXEE - Controls–heating systems - Cobra Products Inc.
FLEXEEL - Hoses - Coilhose Pneumatics Inc.
FLEXEES - Apparel–women's - Maidenform Inc. (True Form Foundations Div.)
FLEXEON - Electric lighting equipment - Flexlite Inc.
FLEXER - Frames–eyeglass - Hudson Optical Corp.
FLEXERIL - Pharmaceutical preparations - Merck & Co., Inc. (Merck Research Laboratories)
FLEXETTE - Frames–eyeglass ☆ - Universal/Univis Inc.
FLEXFILE - Computer software - Data Net Corp.
FLEXFILL - Wire - General Cable Corp.
FLEXFIN STABILIZER - Display units - Paul Flum Ideas, Inc.
FLEXFINISH - Cleaning preparations - Weiler Corp.
FLEXFIT - Ophthalmic goods - Capo, Inc.
FLEXFLOW - Hoses - Coilhose Pneumatics Inc.
FLEXFLYTE - Thermostats - Flexible Technologies Inc.
FLEXFOIL - Cables - General Cable Corp.
FLEXFORM - Health care products ☆ - Body Care Inc.
FLEXGEAR - Apparel and accessories - William L. Crawford
FLEXGLASS - Glass products - Georgia-Pacific Corp.
FLEXGOLD - Floor coverings–tile ☆ - GS Roofing Products Co.
FLEXGOLD - Tiles–terrazzo ☆ - Flintkote Co.
FLEXGRIP - Handles–metal - Gillette Co.
FLEXGRIP - Pens - Paper Mate Co.
FLEXGRIP ULTRA - Pens - Gillette Co.
FLEXGUARD - Containers–paper - Sweetheart Cup Co. Inc.
FLEXGUARD - Electronic equipment - C & K Systems, Inc.
FLEXGUARD - Medical apparatus - Kendall Co.
FLEXGUARD - Motor vehicle parts and accessories - Bentley-Harris Manufacturing Co.
FLEXGUARD - Wire - General Cable Corp.
FLEXHARD - Enamels - Pratt & Lambert United, Inc.
FLEXHEAD - Sprockets–industrial - MacDonald Mechanical, Inc.
FLEXHUB - Computer software - Celan Technology, Inc.
FLEXI - Cabinets ☆ - Borroughs Corp.
FLEXI - Caulking guns - Sven O. Olsson Engineering Co.
FLEXI - Infant product ☆ - Binky-Griptight Co.
FLEXI - Nail care products - Nailmate Inc.
FLEXI - Pet products - FLEXI USA, Inc.
FLEXI - Tools ☆ - Eller Manufacturing Co. Inc.
FLEXI-2 - Toys–automobiles - Parma International, Inc.
FLEXI-BLOCK - Electrical equipment - AMP Inc.
FLEXI-BOGGAN - Bobsleds and toboggans - Flexible Flyer Co.
FLEXI-BOND 540 - Adhesives and sealants - Edison Coatings, Inc.
FLEXI-BRUSH - Pet products - Marineland Aquarium Products
FLEXI - BRUSH TIPS - Dentifrices - E & D Dental Products, Inc.
FLEXI-CAL - Radios ☆ - Chase Collection, Inc.
FLEXI-CALK - Caulking compounds - Synkoloid Co.
FLEXI CHARGE - Tools–power-driven - S-B Power Tool Co.
FLEXI-CLIP-ON - Lighting equipment ☆ - Jobar International Inc./Bibi Products
FLEXI-CUT - Plates–steel - Dick Blick Co.
FLEXI-DECK 500 - Epoxy coatings - Edison Coatings, Inc.
FLEXI-DEXI - Games ☆ - Little Kenny Publications Inc.
FLEXI-DRAIN - Plumbing fixtures–plastic - Moen Inc.
FLEXI-DRIVER - Computer software - Adaptec, Inc.
FLEXI-DUCT - Air conditioning equipment ☆ - Grant Wilson Inc.
FLEXI-EZL - Easels ☆ - Stationers Loose Leaf Co.
FLEXI-FACT - Vitamins - Country Life
FLEXI-FIBER - Pet products ☆ - Flexi-Mat Corp.
FLEXI-FIN - Hardware - LSP Specialty Products Co.
FLEXI-FIRE - Hardware - Turner Industries Ltd.
FLEXI-FIT - Safety products - Columbus Mckinnon Corp.
FLEXI-FLANGE - Health care products - Natural Technologies Inc./White River
FLEXI FLANGE - Root canal posts - Essential Dental Systems, Inc.
FLEXI-FLASH - Polyvinyl sheets ☆ - Afco Products Inc.
FLEXI-FLO - Vitamins and nutritional supplements - Ross Laboratories
FLEXI-FLOR - Floor coverings - R.C.A. Rubber Co.
FLEXI-FLOW - Dental compounds - Essential Dental Systems, Inc.
FLEXI-FLYER - Pet products - Flexi-Mat Corp.
FLEXI-FOLDER - Binders ☆ - ACCO USA, Inc.
FLEXI-FONE - Toys–electronic - J.P. Fraser Inc.
FLEXI-FUR - Pet products - Flexi-Mat Corp.

☆ = Now out of production

FLEXI-GARD 500 - Epoxy coatings - Edison Coatings, Inc.
FLEXI-GLASS - Nail care products - Snails Italian Jewelry Inc.
FLEXI-GRIP - Shelving units–metal - Dorfile Manufacturing Co.
FLEXI-I-COLD - Health care products - Cramer Products Inc.
FLEXI-ICE - Health care products - AnaMed Healthcare
FLEXI-LIFT - Elevators - Access Industries, Inc.
FLEXI-LOFT - Furniture - Fleetwood Furniture Co.
FLEXI-MAGNET - Key rings - Norstar Enterprises
FLEXI-MATIC - Computer storage devices ☆ - Mead-Hatcher, Inc.
FLEXI-MATRIX 545 - Epoxy coatings - Edison Coatings, Inc.
FLEXI-MIST - Aquarium accessories - Blue Ribbon Pet Products, Inc.
FLEXI-MIX - Animal feeds - Blue Seal Feeds Inc.
FLEXI-MOUNT - Motors–automotive - Fasco Industries Inc.
FLEXI-MUTE - Musical instrument accessories ☆ - Selmer Co. Inc.
FLEXI-NETS - Traps–animal - Fuhrman Diversified
FLEXI-OVERDENTURE - Dental equipment - Essential Dental Systems, Inc.
FLEXI-PAPER - Plastics film - Repro-Tronics, Inc.
FLEXI-PATCH - Bandages–orthopedic - DBA Products Co.
FLEXI-PATCH - Paints - Synkoloid Co.
FLEXI-POST - Binders ☆ - Stationers Loose Leaf Co.
FLEXI-POST - Dental equipment - Essential Dental Systems, Inc.
FLEXI-QUARTZ - Epoxy coatings - Edison Coatings, Inc.
FLEXI RING - Infant product - Binky-Griptight Co.
FLEXI-SCAN - Medical apparatus - Shui Lai
FLEXI-SEAL 510 - Adhesives and sealants - Edison Coatings, Inc.
FLEXI SOFT - Footwear - Goodyear Tire & Rubber Co.
FLEXI SPRITZ - Hair care products ☆ - Colorful Products Corp.
FLEXI-STALL - Hardware - Western Products of Indiana
FLEXI-STAR - Respirators - Aearo Co.
FLEXI-STICK - Fuel gauges - Kaiser Aerospace Electronics Corp.
FLEXI-TEE - Golfing equipment - Floyd L. Gustine Co.
FLEXI-TEMP - Medical apparatus - Anago Inc.
FLEXI-TOP 550 - Epoxy - Edison Coatings, Inc.
FLEXI-TRACK - Moldings and trim - Roope Corp.
FLEXI-TRAK - Adhesives and sealants - E.R. Squibb & Sons, Inc.
FLEXI-VELVET - Dental impression material - Dyna Group, Inc.
FLEXI-VIEW - Mirrors ☆ - Ram Products Co.
FLEXI-WALL - Wallpaper - Flexi-Wall Systems
FLEXI-WELD 520 - Adhesives and sealants - Edison Coatings, Inc.
FLEXI-WRAP - Health care products - Cramer Products Inc.
FLEXIBAK - Office supplies - McBee Loose Leaf Binders
FLEXIBLE - Cabinets–metal - Meridian, Inc.
FLEXIBLE - Floor waxes ☆ - Foy-Johnston Inc.
FLEXIBLE - Frames–eyeglass - May Optical Co. Inc.
FLEXIBLE - Office furniture–metal - Joyce International Inc.
FLEXIBLE - Varnishes - Perry & Derrick Co.
FLEXIBLE ADVANCED MATERIALS - Insulated Fabric - Chemical Fabrics Corp.
FLEXIBLE BENEFITS 2000 - Business software - Software 2000, Inc.
FLEXIBLE ENGINEERED MATERIALS - Insulating materials - Chemfab Corp.
FLEXIBLE FILM - Housewares - Sealright Co., Inc.
FLEXIBLE FLYER - Bobsleds and toboggans - Flexible Flyer Co.
FLEXIBLE MIRROR - Wallpaper - National Products Inc.
FLEXIBLE PANCAKE - Electrical equipment - Wiremold Co.
FLEXIBLES - Furniture - Thayer Coggin Inc.
FLEXIBLOCKS - Toys - Flexitoys
FLEXIBOLTS - Bolts–door - Heartwood Furniture
FLEXIBOND - Coatings, etc. - Continental Products Co.
FLEXIBOND - Thread - Advance Thread Corp.
FLEXIBONE - Pet products - T.F.H. Publications, Inc.
FLEXIBONE EDIBLES - Pet food - T.F.H. Publications, Inc.
FLEXICO - Paints - Fuller-O'Brien Paints Inc.
FLEXICOLOR - Pencils ☆ - Koh-I-Noor, Inc.
FLEXICOLOR - Photographic equipment - Eastman Kodak Co.
FLEXICON - Computer software - Emerging Technology Consultants Inc.
FLEXICON - Paper–photographic - Luminos Photo Corp.
FLEXICOTE - Paints - Burgess Fobes Paint Co.
FLEXICOTE - Roofing materials–clay - L.D. Sterns Corp.
FLEXICURVE - Drafting supplies ☆ - Canson-Talens Inc.
FLEXIDOSE - Pharmaceutical preparations - Sidmak Laboratories Inc.
FLEXIDRILLES - Shoes ☆ - Beacon Shoe Co.
FLEXIDUCT - Electrical equipment - Geist Manufacturing Inc.
FLEXIES - Footwear–children's - Jumping-Jacks Shoes Inc.
FLEXIFILE - Office supplies ☆ - Victor Systems & Equipment Co.
FLEXIFILTER - Laboratory apparatus - Packard Instrument Co., Inc.
FLEXIFINANCIALS - Computer software ∑ - Flexiinternational Software, Inc.

FLEXIFLECTOR - Photographic equipment - SP Systems/Saratons
FLEXIFLO TPV - Medical apparatus - Abbott Laboratories
FLEXIFLOW - Hardware - Wal-Rich Corp.
FLEXIFOCAL - Ophthalmic goods - Breger Mueller Welt Corp.
FLEXIFURNACE - Fans–electric - Pelonis USA Ltd.
FLEXIGLAZE - Adhesives and sealants - Dap Products Inc.
FLEXIGLOW - Heating equipment - Commercial Aluminum Cookware Co.
FLEXIGRID - Mats - Tepromark International Inc.
FLEXIGRIP - Hardware - Amerock Corp.
FLEXIGRIP - Moldings and trim - Creative Extruded Products, Inc.
FLEXIKOOL - Motor vehicle parts and accessories - Wysco, Inc.
FLEXILAB - Computer software - Sunquest Information Systems, Inc.
FLEXILEDGER - Computer programs - Flexiware Corp.
FLEXILENS - Ophthalmic goods - Breger Mueller Welt Corp.
FLEXILINK - Computer software - Sunquest Information Systems, Inc.
FLEXILITY - Frames–eyeglass - Zylo Ware Corp.
FLEXILON - Fabrics - Veratec
FLEXIMAILER - Office supplies - Bell & Howell Phillipsburg Co.
FLEXIMATIC - Medical apparatus - General Physiotherapy, Inc.
FLEXIMAX - Metals - Koch Engineering Co., Inc.
FLEXIMESH - Curtains - Porter Athletic Equipment Co.
FLEXIN - Pharmaceutical preparations ☆ - Hyrex Pharmaceuticals
FLEXINYL - Ophthalmic goods - Breger Mueller Welt Corp.
FLEXION - Inks - A.I. Technology Inc.
FLEXIOPE - Ophthalmic goods - Breger Mueller Welt Corp.
FLEXIPLUG - Fertilizers - Grow-Tech Techniculture, Inc.
FLEXIPRENE - Adhesives and sealants - Polymeric Systems, Inc.
FLEXIPROBE - Photographic equipment ☆ - Photo Research, Inc.
FLEXIQUE - Fabrics - Burlington Industries, Inc.
FLEXIRECEIVABLES - Computer software - Flexiinternational Software, Inc.
FLEXIROD - Hair curlers - Burmax Co. Inc.
FLEXIROLLERS - Hair curlers - Caruso International, Inc.
FLEXIROLLS - Hair curlers - Caruso International, Inc.
FLEXIS - Chairs–upholstered - United Chair Co., Inc.
FLEXISCAN - Computer software - Amiable Technologies, Inc.
FLEXISCREEN - Fireplace equipment - Lentz Novelty Co.
FLEXISEAL - Caulking compounds ☆ - Dap Products Inc.
FLEXISEARCH - Computer software - Sunquest Information Systems, Inc.
FLEXISHOE - Footwear - Etta-Kit Enterprises
FLEXISIGN - Computer software - Amiable Technologies, Inc.
FLEXISOLE - Footwear - C.S.F. Corp.
FLEXISTAND - Photographic equipment - SP Systems/Saratons
FLEXISTORAGE - Furniture - Datel, Inc.
FLEXISWIVELS - Toys - Flexitoys
FLEXIT - Finger pads - Triangle Rubber Co. Inc.
FLEXIT - Frames–eyeglass ☆ - Universal/Univis Inc.
FLEXITE - Umbrellas - Haas-Jordan Co.
FLEXITEMP - Paints–artists' - QTL Corp.
FLEXITHERM - Medical apparatus - Diagnostic Thermographics, Inc.
FLEXITOYS - Toys - Flexitoys
FLEXIVENT - Awnings ☆ - Andersen Corp.
FLEXIVIDE - Curtains - Porter Athletic Equipment Co.
FLEXIVIEW - Window frames ☆ - Andersen Corp.
FLEXIWEAR - Contact lenses - Wesley-Jessen Co.
FLEXJET - Bathtubs–enameled - Kohler Co.
FLEXJET - Motor vehicles - Perry Tritech, Inc.
FLEXKLEAR - Filters–water - Baker Hughes Inc.
FLEXLAB - Motors - Flexlab Inc.
FLEXLAN - Fabrics - Borlan Industries Inc.
FLEXLINE - Burial caskets - Batesville Casket Co., Inc.
FLEXLINE - Computer peripheral equipment - Simian Arts, Inc.
FLEXLINE - Office supplies - Flexible Tape & Label Co. Inc. (Royce-Edwards Div.)
FLEXLINK - Circuit boards - M-Wave Inc.
FLEXLINK - Computer peripheral equipment - Celan Technology, Inc.
FLEXLINK - Hoses - Coilhose Pneumatics Inc.
FLEXLITE - Lenses–optical - Ditto Industries Inc.
FLEXLON - Thread - Threads USA Div.
FLEXMASTER - Doors - Modernfold, Inc.
FLEXMASTER - Tables–wood - Stacor Corp.
FLEXMATIC - Lenses–optical - Ditto Industries Inc.
FLEXMETL - Wainscotting - Georgia-Pacific Corp.
FLEXMOBILES - Toys ☆ - Unique Industries, Inc.
FLEXMOTION - Computer peripheral equipment - Nulogic Inc.
FLEX'N SOOTHE - Health care products ☆ - Sunbeam-Oster Household Products

---

☆ = Now out of production

FLEXNET - Apparel and accessories ☆ - Stearns Manufacturing Co.
FLEXNIT - Apparel–women's ☆ - Bali Co. Inc.
FLEXNIT - Gloves - Granet Inc.
FLEXO - Film - Eastman Kodak Co.
FLEXO - Lamps–desk - Art Specialty Co. Inc.
FLEXO - Shoe accessories ☆ - Schering-Plough Healthcare Products
FLEXO CRAFT - Giftware - Flexo Craft Prints Inc.
FLEXO-FEEDER - Pet products - Napro, Inc.
FLEXO FLYER - Printing trades machinery - Roller Technology, Inc.
FLEXO-PINK - Erasers ☆ - Empire Berol USA
FLEXOCAST - Pharmaceutical preparations ☆ - Ulmer Pharmacal Co.
FLEXOJECT - Pharmaceutical preparations ☆ - Merz Inc.
FLEXOLINE - Wood products - ACME Design Technology
FLEXOLON - Lacquers - Key Laboratories Inc.
FLEXOLON TRI-GLAZE - Paints - Key Laboratories Inc.
FLEXON - Adhesives and sealants - Garon Products Inc.
FLEXON - Bicycles - Hunt-Wilde Corp.
FLEXON - Fishing lures - Sunset Line and Twine Co.
FLEXON - Frames–eyeglass - Marchon and Marcolin Eyewear Inc.
FLEXON - Machine parts - Flexovit USA Inc.
FLEXON - Mops ☆ - Helen Keller Services for the Blind
FLEXON - Pharmaceutical preparations ☆ - Keene Pharmaceuticals Inc.
FLEXONITE - Wheels - Hamilton Caster & Manufacturing Co.
FLEXOPLAST - Bandages - Glenwood LLC
FLEXOPLATE - Radiators–furnace - Tranter Manufacturing Inc. (Edgefield Div.)
FLEXOPRINT - Paper–writing - Champion International Corp.
FLEXOR - Glass–optical - Welling International
FLEXOR - Gloves–work - Midwest Quality Gloves Inc.
FLEXOR - Medical apparatus - Cook Imaging Corp.
FLEXOR - Ski suits–children's - Swix Sport USA, Inc.
FLEXOS - Computer software ☆ - Novell, Inc.
FLEXOVERSAL - Bandages - Biomark Inc.
FLEXPAK - Vending machines - Dixie-Narco, Inc.
FLEXPERT - Computer software - Electronic Data Systems Corp.
FLEXPEX - Pipes–plastic - Elkhart Supply Corp.
FLEXPICK - Machinery - Electrocom Automation Inc.
FLEXPLATE - Communications equipment - Communications Systems, Inc.
FLEXPOINT - Office supplies - Bacon Felt Co. Inc.
FLEXPORT - Computer software - MarketWare Corp.
FLEXPRO - Headsets–telephone - Unex Corp.
FLEXQUEST - Computer software - Interaction Dynamics Systems, Inc.
FLEXRAKE - Tools–garden - California Flexrake Corp.
FLEXREADER - Eyeglasses - VSI International Inc.
FLEXRIDGED - Combs - Kim Laube & Co. Inc.
FLEXRITE - Artists' materials - Flexcraft Industries
FLEXRITE - Frames–eyeglass ☆ - Universal/Univis Inc.
FLEXRITE - Hoses - Plastic Specialties and Technologies Investments, Inc.
FLEXROLLER - Pumps ☆ - Hypro Corp.
FLEXROTOR - Pumps ☆ - Hypro Corp.
FLEXSEAL - Asphalt felts and coatings ☆ - DMF Industries Inc. (Al-Chroma Div.)
FLEXSEAL XT - Adhesives and sealants - Loctite Corp.
FLEXSHADE - Window shades - Draper Shade and Screen Co. Inc.
FLEXSHELL - Hot tubs–plastic ☆ - Coleman Spas
FLEXSHIELD - Filters–air - Baker Hughes Inc.
FLEXSHIELD - Tape–adhesive - Adhesives Research, Inc.
FLEXSIDE - Luggage - J.C. Penney Co., Inc.
FLEXSOCKET - Industrial machinery - Aetna Manufacturing Co.
FLEXSOFT - Adhesives and sealants - Adheso Graphics, Inc.
FLEXSOL - Ophthalmic goods ☆ - Alcon Laboratories, Inc.
FLEXSORT - Books–blank - Pinway International Inc.
FLEXSPAN - Prosthetic apparatus - Wright Medical Technology, Inc.
FLEXSPORTS INTERNATIONAL - Fitness equipment - Flexsports International, Inc.
FLEXSTAKE - Signs - Flexstake, Inc.
FLEXSTAR - Fabrics - Mcallister Mills Inc.
FLEXSTAR - Toys - Ryan R. Neading
FLEXSTATION - Furniture - Krueger International, Inc.
FLEXSTEEL - Hoses - Goodyear Tire & Rubber Co.
FLEXSTEEL SNEAK PREVIEW - Computer hardware - Flexsteel Industries Inc.
FLEXSTEM - Handlebars–bicycle - OSI Sports
FLEXSTIM - Medical apparatus - Perdell International, Inc.
FLEXSTONE - Mortars–clay - W.W. Henry Co.
FLEXSTRON - Tape–adhesive - Mystik Corp.

FLEXSWEEP - Brooms - California Flexrake Corp.
FLEXTAINER - Containers - Owens-Illinois Plastic Products Inc.
FLEXTARP - Tarpaulins - California Flexrake Corp.
FLEXTECH - Concrete products ☆ - Bomanite Corp.
FLEXTEEN - Brassieres (Bras) - Wacoal America Inc.
FLEXTEN - Hoses - Goodyear Tire & Rubber Co.
FLEXTERNAL - Sporting goods - Kellwood Co.
FLEXTHANE - Adhesives and sealants - Fosroc Inc.
FLEXTHANE - Chemical preparations - Air Products and Chemicals, Inc.
FLEXTIP - Brooms - Fluffo Mop & Broom Co. Inc.
FLEXTIQUE - Contact lenses - O.S.I. Corp.
FLEXTITE - Frames–eyeglass ☆ - Universal/Univis Inc.
FLEXTORQUE - Toys - Pegae Model Products Inc.
FLEXTOUR - Computer software - Computers for Business, Inc.
FLEXTRA - Packaging–paper - Astro-Valcour, Inc.
FLEXTRAC - Legal services - Flextrac Systems Corp.
FLEXTRAK - Housewares - B & K Industries, Inc.
FLEXTRAY - Wire products - GS Metals Corp.
FLEXTRON - Paints - Parker Paint Manufacturing Co.
FLEXTWIST - Thread - Threads USA Div.
FLEXURE - Frames–eyeglass - Zylo Ware Corp.
FLEXUS - Bandages - Kimberly-Clark Corp.
FLEXVENT - Thermostats - Flexible Technologies Inc.
FLEXVIEW - Motoman, Inc.
FLEXVISION - Video equipment - Asa Electronics Corp.
FLEXWALL - Mattress pads - Perfect Fit Industries, Inc.
FLEXWALL - Shelving units–metal ☆ - Knape and Vogt Manufacturing Co.
FLEXWARE - Containers–plastic - Dowbrands L.P.
FLEXWAX - Artists' materials - American Art Clay Co. Inc.
FLEXWELD - Adhesives and sealants - Imperial Adhesives Inc.
FLEXWELLIA - Pharmaceutical preparations - Barth-Spencer Corp.
FLEXWOOD - Wallpaper - Capital Carousel Inc.
FLEXWOOD - Wallpaper ☆ - Flexible Materials Inc.
FLEXWOOD - Wood products ☆ - Champion International Corp.
FLEXWOOD PLUS - Wallpaper ☆ - Flexible Materials Inc.
FLEXWORD - Computer software - At&T Corp.
FLEXX - Asphalt felts and coatings - Kimberton Enterprises, Inc.
FLEXX - Shelving units - A-Bee Syndicate Inc.
FLEXX-RAP - Tape–adhesive - D.F. Henry
FLEXXER - Pencils–mechanical - Empire Berol USA
FLEXXO - Toys ☆ - Henry Gordy International Inc.
FLEXXX - Audio equipment ☆ - Telequest Inc.
FLEXY - Markers–felt-tip - Micropoint Inc.
FLEXY FIRE TRUCK - Toys–automobiles ☆ - CBS Toys
FLEXYL - Artists' materials ☆ - Artoptic International Corp.
FLEXYL FORMULA 12 - Artists' materials ☆ - Artoptic International Corp.
FLEXYLON - Musical instrument accessories ☆ - Herco Products
FLEXZAN - Bandages–surgical ☆ - Dow Hickam Pharmaceuticals, Inc.
FLEYLITE - Ophthalmic goods - Rozin Optical Export Corp.
FLG - Jewelry - Flagstaff Inc.
FLI HI - Gloves - Jasper Glove Co.
FLI-MAP - Electronic equipment - John E. Chance & Associates, Inc.
FLIC-A-WRENCH - Wrenches ☆ - Invention Prototypes & Marketing Corp.
FLIC KICKERS - Games - Gladd Ladd
FLICK - Fabrics - Dan River Inc.
FLICK YOUR BIC - Cigarette lighters - Bic Corp.
FLICKA - Boats - Pacific Seacraft Corp.
FLICKA - Frames–eyeglass - May Optical Co. Inc.
FLICKBALL - Games - Mgwhiz, Inc.
FLICKBAR - Wallets - Buxton Inc.
FLICKEARING - Jewelry - Richelieu Corp.
FLICKER - Ladies' safety razors - American Safety Razor Co.
FLICKER - Pens - Hunt Manufacturing Co.
FLICKER - Toys ☆ - Henry Gordy International Inc.
FLICKER CHECKER - Toys - Motorola, Inc. (Land Mobile Products Sector)
FLICKER CLASSIC - Razors–electric ☆ - American Safety Razor Co.
FLICKER FLAME - Lamp bulbs–incandescent - Angelo Brothers Co.
FLICKER FLAME - Lighting equipment ☆ - Duro-Lite Lamps Inc.
FLICKER FREE - Lighting equipment - ProLight
FLICKER FROG - Puppets ☆ - Dakin Inc.
FLICKER RAINBOWS - Razors - American Safety Razor Co.
FLICKER-SPINNER - Fishing lures - Hildebrandt Corp.
FLICKER TAIL - Fishing lures ☆ - Storm Manufacturing Co.
FLICKERS - Decals and transfers ☆ - Creative Teaching Press
FLICKERS - Ophthalmic goods - Foremost Optical Products
FLICKEY - Apparel and accessories - Marguerite Charkalis

☆ = Now out of production

FLICKS - Chocolate candy ☆ - Ghirardelli Chocolate Co.
FLICKS - Frames–eyeglass ☆ - Universal/Univis Inc.
FLICKZONE - Games - Mgwhiz, Inc.
FLIGHT - Computer software - Estes Industries
FLIGHT - Dinnerware–glass - Block China Co.
FLIGHT - Glassware–household - Owens-Illinois Inc. (Libbey Div.)
FLIGHT - Helmets–athletic - Schwinn Cycling & Fitness Inc.
FLIGHT - Tools ☆ - Great Neck Saw Manufacturers, Inc.
FLIGHT 711 - Ophthalmic goods - Embassy Creations Inc.
FLIGHT COLLECTION - Computer software - SourceView Software International
FLIGHT COMMANDER - Computer peripheral equipment - Big Time Software, Inc.
FLIGHT DECK - Toys–airplanes - Mattel, Inc.
FLIGHT DECK U.S.A. - Apparel and accessories - I. Spiewak and Sons Inc.
FLIGHT DESK - Office supplies - Everflex Aluminum Products
FLIGHT EAGLE - Tires - Goodyear Tire & Rubber Co.
FLIGHT GEAR - Sunglasses - AO Sunwear USA, Inc.
FLIGHT LEADER - Games - Avalon Hill Game Co.
FLIGHT LEADER - Trailers–travel - Mallard Coach
FLIGHT LINE - Filing cabinets–metal - Top Flight Inc.
FLIGHT LINE - Frames–eyeglass ☆ - Universal/Univis Inc.
FLIGHT LINK - Computer software - Charles L. Henkenius
FLIGHT LUXE - Soap - Celeste Industries Corp.
FLIGHT MASTER - Targets - Blount, Inc.
FLIGHT MASTER - Toys–models - Estes Industries
FLIGHT NURSE - Watches - Bulova Corp.
FLIGHT OF FANCY - Dolls - Mattel, Inc.
FLIGHT OF FANCY - Jewelry - Avon Products, Inc.
FLIGHT OF THE INTRUDER - Computer software - Spectrum Holobyte, Inc.
FLIGHT PATTERNS - Statuary - William F. Monroe
FLIGHT PAX - Backpacks - A.D. Sutton & Sons Inc.
FLIGHT PROVEN - Paints - Randolph Products Co.
FLIGHT SIMULATOR - Computer software - Bruce Artwick Organization, Ltd.
FLIGHT SIMULATOR - Computer software - Microsoft Corp.
FLIGHT SIMULATOR II - Computer software - SubLogic Corp.
FLIGHT SONG - Bird feeds ☆ - Duncraft, Inc.
FLIGHT STUDIO GUILDWORKS - Games - Guildworks Flight Studio
FLIGHT SYSTEMS - Electronic equipment - Flight Systems, Inc.
FLIGHT THROUGH LIFE - Lithographic plates - Joseph F. Ruvolo
FLIGHT TIME - Dolls - Mattel, Inc.
FLIGHT TIME - Ophthalmic goods - Embassy Creations Inc.
FLIGHT UNLIMITED - Computer software - Looking Glass Technologies, Inc.
FLIGHT VECTOR - Computer software ☆ - Edusoft
FLIGHTCOM - Communications equipment - Flightcom Corp.
FLIGHTER - Pens ☆ - Parker Pen USA
FLIGHTGUIDE - Cables–fiber optic - Spectran Specialty Optics Co.
FLIGHTLIGHT - Bicycles - Columbia Manufacturing Inc.
FLIGHTLINER - Bicycles - Sears, Roebuck and Co.
FLIGHTLINES INTERNATIONAL - Toys–models - Flightlines International
FLIGHTMASTER - Toys–models - Centuri Corp.
FLIGHTMASTERS - Strollers–baby ☆ - Welsh Co.
FLIGHTS OF FANCY - Fabrics - Gretchen Bellinger Inc.
FLIGHTS OF FANCY - Garden equipment - W. Atlee Burpee and Co.
FLIGHTS OF FANCY - Infant product ☆ - European Toy Collection/Crocodile Creek
FLIGHTS OF FANCY - Needles–sewing - Carole J. Cree
FLIGHTS OF FANTASY - Games ☆ - Destini Productions Inc.
FLIGHTSOUNDS - Hearing aids - Hitec Group International, Inc.
FLIGHTSTAR - Aircraft - Thomas A. Peghiny
FLIGHTSTICK - Computer peripheral equipment - Joystick Technologies (CH Products Division)
FLIGHTSTICK PRO - Computer peripheral equipment - Joystick Technologies (CH Products Division)
FLIGHTUBE - Kites ☆ - Kite Factory
FLIK FLAK - Watches - SMH Corp.
FLIMM FIGHTER - Medical apparatus - General Physiotherapy, Inc.
FLINCH - Games ☆ - Parker Brothers
FLING - Boats - Outboard Marine Corp.
FLING - Cameras ☆ - Eastman Kodak Co.
FLING - Cleaning preparations–household - Chemed Corp.
FLING - Frames–eyeglass - May Optical Co. Inc.
FLING - Handbags - Accessories International
FLING - Wrapping paper - Highland Supply Corp.
FLING-A-THING - Games - Spaceworld, Inc.
FLING IT - Games - Let's Play...

FLING SOCK - Toys - Saturnian 1, Inc.
FLING TOSS - Games - Drybranch Inc./Sport Design
FLING WINGS - Toys ☆ - Hi-Flier Manufacturing Co.
FLINGER FOR FRIENDLY FLIPPING! - Dolls - Sonoma Trading Co., Inc.
FLINGS - Food products - Tyson Foods Inc.
FLINGS - Luggage ☆ - Samsonite Corp.
FLINGS - Shoes - Kinney Shoe Corp.
FLINGS - Snack foods - Nabisco Foods Group
FLINGSHOT - Toys - Oddzon Products, Inc.
FLINN - Shampoos - Hess Hair Milk Laboratories Inc.
FLINT - Cigarettes - Brown & Williamson Tobacco Corp.
FLINT - Tools - Railway Handle Corp.
FLINT & WALLING - Pumps - Masco Corp.
FLINT ARROW HEAD - Sporting goods - Ed Cumings Inc.
FLINT EDGE - Tools ☆ - True Temper Hardware Co.
FLINT-GLAZE - Paints - Suntec Paint Inc.
FLINT HIDE - Gloves - Brookville Glove Manufacturing Co.
FLINT INK - Inks - Flint Ink Corp.
FLINT 'N BRUSH - Tobacco products ☆ - S.M. Frank & Co. Inc. (Kaywoodie-Yello-Bole-Medico)
FLINT RIDGE - Furniture ☆ - Bassett Furniture Industries, Inc.
FLINT RIVER - Bedding–linen - Mouchet Corp.
FLINT ROCK - Gypsum products - Georgia-Pacific Corp.
FLINT SSD - See SSD
FLINTITE - Roofing materials–concrete - GS Roofing Products Co.
FLINTKOTE - Floor coverings ☆ - Flintkote Co.
FLINTKOTE - Floor coverings ☆ - GS Roofing Products Co.
FLINTLOK - Fabrics ☆ - Sero Sales
FLINTPATCH - Finishing agents ☆ - Flintkote Co.
FLINTPATCH - Paints ☆ - GS Roofing Products Co.
FLINTRIDGE 22 - Floor coverings–carpet and rugs - Western Carpet Mills
FLINTRIDGE 28 - Floor coverings–carpet and rugs - Western Carpet Mills
FLINTROCK - Floor coverings–carpet and rugs ☆ - Cumberland Mills Inc.
FLINTROCK - Ophthalmic goods - Styl-Rite Optical Manufacturing Co., Inc.
FLINTSTONE - Floor coverings–carpet and rugs - Barrett Carpet Mills Inc.
FLINTSTONE - Toothbrushes–electric ☆ - Kenner Products
FLINTSTONE & FRIENDS - Air purification systems ☆ - Medo Industries, Inc.
FLINTSTONE BEDROCK - Candy ☆ - Warner-Lambert Co.
FLINTSTONES - Candy - Glico Harmony Foods Corp.
FLINTSTONES - Children's melamine tableware - Boonton Molding Co. Inc.
FLINTSTONES - Children's toiletries - Cosrich Inc.
FLINTSTONES - Erasers ☆ - Diener Industries Inc.
FLINTSTONES - Footwear–athletic ☆ - E.S. Originals, Inc.
FLINTSTONES - Games ☆ - Milton Bradley Co.
FLINTSTONES - Key rings - Gift Creations, Inc.
FLINTSTONES - Kites - Hi-Flier Manufacturing Co.
FLINTSTONES - Pet products - Precious Paws
FLINTSTONES - Slippers ☆ - S. Goldberg and Co. Inc.
FLINTSTONES - Toys ☆ - Knickerbocker Toy Co. Inc.
FLINTSTONES - Video production - Hanna-Barbera Productions, Inc.
FLINTSTONES - Vitamins and nutritional supplements - Bayer Corp. (Consumer Care Div.)
FLINTSTONES FAMILY PLAYHOUSE - Toys - Intex Recreation Corp.
FLINTSTONES FRUIT PUSH-UPS - Desserts - Nestle USA
FLINTSTONES, THE - Lunch boxes - Thermos Co.
FLINTSTONES TWIST N' SHOOT - Games - Ben Cooper Inc.
FLINTWOOD - Wines - Clos du Bois Wines
FLINTWOOD PRODUCTS - Building materials - Flint Johnson, Inc.
FLIP - Maps ☆ - CIR Products Inc.
FLIP - Recording label - Flip Records Inc.
FLIP - Soap - Purex Industries Inc. (Kurly Kate Div.)
FLIP - Toys–stuffed - Russ Berrie and Co., Inc.
FLIP-A-CHIP - Action skills game - Kenneth Masaji Kudo
FLIP A FISH - Games - Smethport Specialty Co.
FLIP-A-LING PLAY N' SWING - Toys - Those Characters from Cleveland, Inc.
FLIP A NUT - Games - Smethport Specialty Co.
FLIP-A-PAGE - Electronic equipment ☆ - Logan Electric Specialty Manufacturing Co.
FLIP A ROO - Games - Smethport Specialty Co.
FLIP-A-WEEK - Calendars ☆ - Southworth Co.
FLIP & GRIP - Bags–plastic - Great Pacific Enterprises II Inc.
FLIP BUNNY - Toys–stuffed - Russ Berrie and Co., Inc.
FLIP CHART - Markers–felt-tip - Sanford Corp.
FLIP CHART - Paper ☆ - Da-Lite Screen Co. Inc.
FLIP CLIP - Apparel and accessories - Counterparts Sportswear, Inc.
FLIP CLIP - Artists' materials - Wolsey Co.

☆ = Now out of production

FLIP-CLIP - Frames–eyeglass - May Optical Co. Inc.
FLIP CLIP - Telephone apparatus - Haltof Product Design
FLIP CLIP - Toilet seats - Barrick Enterprises
FLIP CRASHERS - Toys - Tonka Corp.
FLIP CYCLES - Toy cycles - Intex Recreation Corp.
FLIP' EMS - Signs - Rockwell Dynamacs Inc.
FLIP-FILE - Photo albums - JM Co.
FLIP FINGERS - Toys - Gerber Products Co.
FLIP FLAP - Apparel and accessories - Brazabra Corp.
FLIP FLEET - Toys–automobiles - ERTL Co., Inc.
FLIP FLIP - Office supplies ☆ - McBee Loose Leaf Binders
FLIP FLOP - Blankets–electric ☆ - Sunbeam-Oster Household Products
FLIP-FLOP - Jewelry–costume - CNK International, Inc.
FLIP-FLOP - Nail-care product - International Beauty Design, Inc.
FLIP-FLOP - Squeegees - Milwaukee Dustless Brush Co.
FLIP FLOP - Toys - Little Tikes Co.
FLIP FLOP - Toys–electronic - Serenity Productions, Inc.
FLIP FLOP PUZZLE MATS - Floor coverings–carpet and rugs - Alessco, Inc.
FLIP FLOP ZOTS - Toys ☆ - Handsontoys, Inc.
FLIP FLOPS - Candy - Willy Wonka Brands
FLIP-GRIP - Vises - Wilton Corp.
FLIP-IT - Floor coverings–tile - Pawling Corp. (Standard Products Div.)
FLIP-IT - Hats ☆ - Resistol Hats
FLIP-IT - Novelty items - Concept/Research, Concept/Development
FLIP KLEAN KATJON - Pet products - Cielo Industries Inc.
FLIP LID - Electrical equipment - Pass & Seymour, Inc.
FLIP LIGHT - Lighting fixtures - Alltrade Inc.
FLIP 'N' FILE - Cases–plastic - Innovative Concepts Inc.
FLIP N FILE - Office accessories - Nina Enterprises, Inc.
FLIP 'N FILLET - Fishing tackle - Advanced Innovations, Inc.
FLIP 'N FIRE - Hockey equipment - Rapid Mounting and Finishing Co.
FLIP 'N FIRE - Toys–trains - Lionel Trains Inc.
FLIP 'N' FLY - Toys - Concept Products Inc.
FLIP 'N FUN - Games ☆ - Century Products Co.
FLIP N' GRIP - Frames–eyeglass - Hudson Optical Corp.
FLIP N' HARNESS - Fishing lures - Lindy Little Joe Inc.
FLIP 'N' PLAY - Compact-disc files, video-cassette-recorder covers ☆ - Innovative Concepts Inc.
FLIP 'N' POUR - Food containers - Thermos Co.
FLIP-N-SCRUB - Sponges ☆ - Duchess Royale Inc.
FLIP 'N SEAL - Bags–plastic - Arrowhead Plastic Engineering, Inc.
FLIP-N-SHOP - Strollers–baby - Central Specialties
FLIP 'N' SIP - Food containers - Thermos Co.
FLIP 'N SKIP - Games - Little Kenny Publications Inc.
FLIP-N-SLIP - Fishing lures ☆ - Fred Arbogast Co. Inc.
FLIP N' STIC - Paper products - Niagara Envelope Co., Inc.
FLIP - N - STICK - Plastic bags - Flip Cards, Inc.
FLIP-N-TELL - Desk sets - Lion Office Products, Inc.
FLIP 'N TELL - Toys ☆ - Reliance Products Corp.
FLIP 'N' TWIRL - Apparel–children's - Nita Novy
FLIP 'N TWIRL - Toys - Mattel, Inc.
FLIP 'N VIEW - Electronic equipment - SP Systems/Saratons
FLIP-O-POTAMUS - Games ☆ - Milton Bradley Co.
FLIP-O-RING - Binders ☆ - Spiral Binding Co. Inc.
FLIP-ONS - Hats - Sheldon Sontag
FLIP OUT! - Computer software - Gorilla Systems Corp.
FLIP OUT - Games - Mattel, Inc.
FLIP OUT - Toys - Kransco Manufacturing Inc.
FLIP OUTS - Toys–automobiles - Mattel, Inc.
FLIP OVER - Hardware - Brainerd Manufacturing Co.
FLIP PAD - Leather goods - Jack Georges Inc.
FLIP-PETS - Toys–stuffed - Fun World Inc.
FLIP-PHONE - Telephones - AG Communication Systems Inc.
FLIP SEAL - Weather stripping - W.J. Dennis & Co.
FLIP/SEAT - Furniture–wood ☆ - Fixtures Furniture
FLIP SIGN - Signs - Securitag Corp.
FLIP SLIDE - Playground equipment - Game Time, Inc.
FLIP SMACKERS - Cosmetics ☆ - Bonne Bell, Inc.
FLIP-STICK - Cleaning preparations - Hercules Chemical Co. Inc.
FLIP STIX - Hardware - Duro Dyne Corp.
FLIP SYSTEM - Electronic equipment - Avid Corp.
FLIP TARGET - Archery equipment - Packaging Industries Group Inc.
FLIP TITE - Boats - Detroit Marine Engineering
FLIP TOP - Boxes - Light Impressions Corp.
FLIP TOP - Cases–cigarette ☆ - Mautner Co. Inc.
FLIP TOP - Containers - Aqua-Tainer Co.

FLIP TOP - Leather goods - St. Thomas Inc.
FLIP-TOP - Pencils ☆ - Impact International
FLIP/TOP - Photographic equipment - Nu Arc Co. Inc.
FLIP-TOP - Photographic equipment - Royal-Pioneer Industries Inc.
FLIP-TOP - Projectors–photographic ☆ - Dukane Corp.
FLIP-TOP - Snow-cleaning brush/ice scraper ☆ - Clean-Rite Products Co.
FLIP TOP - Toys - Tonka Corp.
FLIP-TOP BAIT HUT - Sporting goods - Magic Products, Inc.
FLIP TOP BASKET - Dolls - Goldberger Doll Manufacture Co.
FLIP-UP - Ladders–metal ☆ - Werner Co.
FLIP UP SUNGLASSES - Eyeglasses - Karlen Manufacturing, Inc.
FLIP-UPS - Greeting cards - American Greetings Corp.
FLIP YOUR LID - Toys - Tedco Inc.
FLIP400 - Bicycles - Dynacraft Industries Inc.
FLIPBUSTER - Toys–automobiles - Mattel, Inc.
FLIPFLASH - Photographic equipment - General Electric Co.
FLIPFORMS - Musical instrument accessories - Wenger Corp.
FLIPIT - Automotive parts and accessories - Swiss-Tex Inc.
FLIPITS - Footwear - Sid Sharpstein
FLIPLOCK - Watches - Rolex Watch USA, Inc.
FLIP'N HARNESS - Fishing lures - Jim Fofrich, Sr.
FLIP'N TELL - Dolls - Gerber Products Co.
FLIPPER - Candy ☆ - Storck USA L.P.
FLIPPER - Cutlery ☆ - Clauss Cutlery Co.
FLIPPER - Footwear ☆ - S. Goldberg and Co. Inc.
FLIPPER - Hair curlers ☆ - Dubl Duck/Jet Set Inc.
FLIPPER - Machinery ☆ - Kreepy Krauly USA, Inc.
FLIPPER - Photographic equipment ☆ - Omega/Arkay
FLIPPER-SCRUBBER - Mops - New Knight Inc.
FLIPPER SHIPPER - Cardboard - Reynolds Consumer Products, Inc.
FLIPPERS - Games - Tedco Inc.
FLIPPERTOONS - Notebooks and notepads - William S. Reed
FLIPPIES - Hobby kits - Herbert R. Klischies, Sr.
FLIPPIN FLAPJACK - Games ☆ - Parker Brothers
FLIPPIN' FRENZY - Toys–automobiles - Mattel, Inc.
FLIPPIN' STIK - Fishing tackle - Fenwick
FLIPPO - Toys - Russ Berrie and Co., Inc.
FLIPPO - Toys ☆ - South Bend Toy Manufacturing Co.
FLIPPY - Computer diskettes–blank - Eastman Kodak Co.
FLIPROARIN' - Toys–automobiles - Mattel, Inc.
FLIPS - Crackers ☆ - Sunshine Biscuits, Inc.
F'LIPS - Lip balms - Randall Products International
FLIPSHOT - Toys - Mattel, Inc.
FLIPSIDE - Apparel and accessories - Starter Corp.
FLIPSIDE - Candy ☆ - Topps Co., Inc.
FLIPSIDE FICTION - Publisher's imprints ☆ - Rosen Publishing Group & Pelion Press
FLIPSTICKS - Lipsticks ☆ - Quintessence Inc.
FLIPTAIL CREATURE - Fishing lures - Plastics Research and Development Co.
FLIPTAIL FANDANGO - Flags - Plastics Research and Development Co.
FLIPTAIL FIESTY - Flags - Plastics Research and Development Co.
FLIPTAIL FLIRT - Flags - Plastics Research and Development Co.
FLIPTAIL FLOATING LIZARD - Flags - Plastics Research and Development Co.
FLIPTAIL HERTY GERTY SKIRT - Flags ☆ - Plastics Research and Development Co.
FLIPTAIL LIZARD - Flags - Plastics Research and Development Co.
FLIPTAIL SOFTFIN SHAD - Flags ☆ - Plastics Research and Development Co.
FLIPTAIL WORM - Flags - Plastics Research and Development Co.
FLIPTALK - Computer software - Microflip Inc.
FLIRT - Apparel–women's - Stanwood Corp.
FLIRT - Frames–eyeglass - Pathway Optical Prods.
FLIRT - Pens - Schneider Pens USA
FLIRT SHIRTS - Apparel and accessories - Harwood Companies Inc.
FLIRT SQUIRTS - Toys–guns - Hasbro, Inc.
FLIRTATION - Dinnerware ☆ - Corning Inc.
FLIRTATION - Tableware–china ☆ - Lenox, Inc.
FLIRTATION BRA - Underwear and nightwear - Bestform Foundations, Inc.
FLIRTATION WALK - Underwear and nightwear - Bestform Foundations, Inc.
FLIRTATIONS - Footwear–women's - St. Louis Shoe Co. Inc.
FLIRTATIONS - Wedding gowns - Alfred Angelo Inc.
FLIRTATIOUS - Frames–eyeglass ☆ - Universal/Univis Inc.
FLIRTATIOUS - Hosiery–men's - Clovermere Sales Corp.
FLIRT'S - Apparel and accessories - Lewis Frimel Co. Inc.
FLIRTS - Apparel–women's - Donnkenny Inc.

☆ = Now out of production

FLIRTS - Eyeglasses - Martin-Copeland Eyewear Corp.
FLIRTY - Dolls ☆ - Uneeda Doll Co., Inc.
FLIRTY - Frames—eyeglass - Zylo Ware Corp.
FLIT - Pesticides—household - Exxon Corp.
FLITE - Bicycles - D.J. Scott's Manufacturing Inc.
FLITE - Shoes ☆ - Hyde Athletic Industries Inc.
FLITE - Wines - Fenn Valley Vineyards
FLITE CONTROLS - Bicycle accessories - Flite Control Corp.
FLITE-KING - Bicycles - Ross Bicycles USA, Ltd.
FLITE-KING - Firearms, accessories, and parts - High Standard Manufacturing Corp.
FLITES - Sporting goods - NuSkate Inc.
FLITES - Toys—airplanes - Comet Montrose Ltd.
FLITESTAR - Garage door openers - Raynor Manufacturing Co.
FLITETRAK - Insect repellents - Trece, Inc.
FLITEWAGON - Trailers—travel ☆ - Wells Cargo Inc.
FLITEWAY - Luggage - United States Luggage Corp.
FLITZ - Polishing rouge - Flitz International Ltd.
FLITZ AEROSOL STAINLESS STEEL & CHROME CLEANER - Cleaning preparations—household - Flitz International Ltd.
FLIX - Footwear - San Shoe Trading Corp.
FLIX - Pet products - Gerard-Pellham Co.
FLIX FIRRE - Drums—musical instruments - Big Bang Distribution/A.P.I.
FLIXMIX - Computer software - Celeris Inc.
FLO - Computer software - Valis Group
FLO - Hardware - Flo Control Inc.
FLO AIRE - Heating equipment - Patton Electric Co. Inc.
FLO AND GLO - Paints - Tresco Paint Co. Inc.
FLO-AXIAL - Water filters - Healthguard, Inc.
FLO-CALK - Hardware ☆ - Boatlife Inc.
FLO CEL - Sponges - Florida Sponge & Chamois Co.
FLO-CILLIN - Veterinary pharmaceutical preparations - Bristol-Myers Squibb Co.
FLO-CONTROL - Paint rollers - E-Z Paintr Corp.
FLO DEVELOPER - Computer software - Image Innovation Solutions, Inc.
FLO-DOWN - Bathroom fixtures - Price Pfister Co.
FLO E ZEE - Paints - Bridges Smith & Co.
FLO-FILTER - Hardware - H.B. Sherman Manufacturing Co.
FLO-FLO - Infant product - Maria Schiess
FLO-FREE - Cleaning preparations—household - Frank Miller and Sons Inc.
FLO-GARD - Health care products - Baxter International Inc.
FLO-GEL - Hair care products ☆ - Lusan Inc.
FLO-GILT - Inks - Floquil-Polly S Color Corp.
FLO-GLO - Inks - Floquil-Polly S Color Corp.
FLO-GUARD - Heaters—swimming pool ☆ - Teledyne Laars
FLO-KING - Plumbing fixtures—plastic ☆ - Pro Hardware Inc.
FLO-LINE - Pipes - Semco, Inc.
FLO-LINE - Tables—metal - Flotron
FLO-LITE - Artists' materials - Plaid Enterprises, Inc.
FLO-LOK - Fasteners - Abbott-Interfast Corp.
FLO-LOK - Hardware - Predator Industries, Inc.
FLO-MATIC - Paint rollers - Rubberset Co.
FLO-MATIC - Signs ☆ - Webway, Inc.
FLO-MET - Herbicides - Micro-Flo Co.
FLO MOUSENGALE - Jewelry - Ruth Fanovich
FLO NASE - Antihistamine preparations - Glaxo Wellcome Inc.
FLO-ON - Paint rollers - PPG Industries, Inc.
FLO-PAC - Brushes - Flo-Pac Corp.
FLO-PAK - Packaging—blisterwrap - Free-Flow Packaging Corp.
FLO-PAQUE - Paints—artists' - Floquil-Polly S Color Corp.
FLO-PASTE - Housewares ☆ - Butcher Co.
FLO-PEARL - Inks - Floquil-Polly S Color Corp.
FLO-PLUG 50 - Cement - Edison Coatings, Inc.
FLO POINT - Pens - Gillette Co.
FLO-QUEEN - Faucets ☆ - Milwaukee Faucets Inc.
FLO-RESTER - Medical apparatus - Bio-Vascular, Inc.
FLO-RITE - Paints - Flo-Rite Coating & Chemical Co.
FLO-RITE - Pens ☆ - Faber-Castell Corp.
FLO-SMOOTH - Paints - V.J. Dolan & Co. Inc.
FLO-SPRAY - Paints ☆ - Premix-Marbletite Manufacturing Co.
FLO-STAIN - Paints - Floquil-Polly S Color Corp.
FLO-STAT - Surgical supplies - Femrx, Inc.
FLO-STRYP - Paint remover - International Chemical Co.
FLO TABS - Prescription drug - Misemer Pharmaceuticals Inc.
FLO-TAN - Sponges - Florida Sponge & Chamois Co.
FLO-TEC - Adhesives and sealants - Mobile Paint Manufacturing Co.

FLO-TEX - Finishing agents - Wright-Bernet
FLO-THRU - Brushes—paint - Rol-Brush Manufacturing, Div. (Michigan Brush Mfg. Co., Inc.)
FLO/TRAY - Machinery - Delta/Ducon Components Group Co.
FLO-TROL - Chemical preparations - M-I Drilling Fluids LLC
FLO-VAC 8 - Packaging machines - Free-Flow Packaging Corp.
FLO-WAY - Measuring instruments - Sauk Valley Systems, Inc.
FLO WHITE - Paints—artists' - Salis International, Inc.
FLO2 - Medical apparatus - Telecon, Inc.
FLOAM IN FLIGHT - Toys - Mattel, Inc.
FLOAM JEWELRY MAKER - Toys - Mattel, Inc.
FLOAM SHAPE SHOP - Hobby kits - Mattel, Inc.
FLOAM SHAPER - Toys - Mattel, Inc.
FLOAM SPORTS - Toys - Mattel, Inc.
FLOAMATIC - Clay—modeling - Mattel, Inc.
FLOAT A SLEEP - Pillows ☆ - Alger Creations Inc.
FLOAT BOAT - Boats—dinghies ☆ - Life-Like Products Inc.
FLOAT ME - Computer software - Floater Corp.
FLOAT 'N TAN - Mattresses - Seaway Importing Co.
FLOAT-ON - Trailers—boat - Float-On Corp.
FLOAT PLANE - Agricultural machinery - Reynolds International, Inc.
FLOATABLES - Life preservers - Outboard Marine Corp.
FLOATALINE - Sporting goods - Weber Industries Inc.
FLOATATION BY ATLANTIC - Footwear insoles - Atlantic Thermoplastics Co. Inc.
FLOATAWAYS - Footwear—men's - Wolverine World Wide, Inc.
FLOATER - Computer software - Floater Corp.
FLOATER - Fishing lures - Boone Bait Co. Inc.
FLOATER - Frames—picture - A.P.F. Master Framemaker
FLOATER - Pet products - Farnam Cos. Inc.
FLOATERS - Footwear - Wolverine World Wide, Inc.
FLOATERS - Gliders—metal ☆ - Expanded Technologies Corp.
FLOATERS - Toys - Lancer Industries Inc.
FLOATIE - Sporting goods - Hedstrom Corp.
FLOATIN' COOL - Dolls - Mattel, Inc.
FLOATING - Pens ☆ - Parker Pen USA
FLOATING ACTION - Apparel—women's - Exquisite Form Industries
FLOATING AIR - Air conditioning equipment - Friedrich Air Conditioning Co.
FLOATING BLOSSOM - Candles - Aloha Candle Manufacturing Co. Inc.
FLOATING CARBIDE - Auto parts - Mitch Atkinson
FLOATING COMFORT - Brassieres (Bras) ☆ - Montgomery Ward & Co. Inc.
FLOATING FAMILY - Toys - Fisher-Price, Inc.
FLOATING FREE - Dryers—hair ☆ - Sunbeam-Oster Household Products
FLOATING FUN - Toys - Fisher-Price, Inc.
FLOATING FUZZ-E-GRUB - Fishing lures - Lindy Little Joe Inc.
FLOATING MALLOWS - Fishing lures - Brown Bear Bait Co.
FLOATING MUSHROOM - Land vehicle parts - Mitch Atkinson
FLOATIVE - Candles - Hanna's Potpourri Specialties, Inc.
FLOATMASTER - Machinery - Lockmasters, Inc.
FLOATRON - Water purification systems - Medical SelfCare
FLOATS - Candy ☆ - Leaf, Inc.
FLOBOND - Housewares - Hopkins Manufacturing Corp.
FLOC RITE - Chemical preparations - Coastal Industries Inc.
FLOCATOR - Medical apparatus - Abbott Laboratories
FLOCK-A-LITE - Plastics - Disposable Linens L.P.
FLOCK AND FEAST - Bird feeds - Lawn & Garden Supply Co.
FLOCK-LOK - Adhesives and sealants - Lord Corp. (Chemical Products Div.)
FLOCK-SHOCK - Electrical equipment - Fi-Shock Inc.
FLOCOMB - Combs - Jack Forcelledo
FLODOSE - Computer software - FMC Corp.
FLODYNE - Pharmaceutical preparations - American Home Products Corp.
FLOETROL - Paints - Flood Co.
FLOGARD - Lubricants - Gard Corp.
FLOGG - Toys - Mattel, Inc.
FLOJOS - Sandals - Playazul International Inc.
FLOMAG - Chemical preparations - Martin Marietta Magnesia Specialties, Inc.
FLOMASTER - Sprayers - RL Flo-Master
FLOMATIC - Photographic equipment - Eastman Kodak Co.
FLOMAX - Health care products - Gainor Medical U.S.A. Inc.
FLOMAX - Machine parts - Spraying Systems Co.
FLOMAX - Water purification systems - MP Pumps Inc.
FLONE - Hair care products - Cosmair Inc.
FLOOD ALARM - Water-detecting device - Aquanot Ltd.
FLOOD-GUARD - Valves—industrial - General Wire Spring Co.
FLOOD-LITE - Lanterns—kerosene - Coleman Co., Inc.

FLOOD PUMPER - Rug cleaning machines–commercial - Castex Industries Inc.

FLOOD STOPPER - Plumbing fixtures - Morgan Wolf

FLOOD STOPPERS - Decals and transfers - Wry Idea Co.

FLOOD YOUR THIRST! NOAH'S GORILLA GRAPEGRAPE SODA - Beverages - Varni Brothers Corp.

FLOOD-ZONE - Life preservers - Thomas Craig Tiller

FLOODINFO - Computer software - Harvard Design and Mapping Co., Inc.

FLOODJET - Nozzles - Spraying Systems Co.

FLOODMASTER - Outdoor lights - American Electric

FLOODSAVER - Washing machines–household - AMI inc.

FLOOG-BALL - Toys - Aqua-Leisure Industries, Inc.

FLOOGAL - Greeting cards - Gibson Greetings, Inc.

FLOOR 24 - Computer software - Dancik-On-Disk International, Ltd.

FLOOR-A-MATIC - Vacuum cleaners and accessories ☆ - The Hoover Co.

FLOOR AID #1 - Finishing agents - Windsor Wax Co. Inc.

FLOOR ART - Floor coverings–carpet and rugs - Milliken & Co. Inc.

FLOOR ART - Posters - Service Litho-Print Inc.

FLOOR-BOND - Adhesives and sealants - Tarkett, Inc.

FLOOR BOSS - Cleaning preparations–carpet and rug - Flo-Pac Corp.

FLOOR CARE - Mop heads - Bouras Mop Manufacturing Co.

FLOOR-DAY - Paints ☆ - Klee Chemical Coatings

FLOOR DECOR - Floor coverings–carpet and rugs - Milliken & Co. Inc.

FLOOR DESIGNS - Floor coverings–carpet and rugs - Queen Carpet Corp.

FLOOR-EVER - Paints - Paris Paint & Varnish Co.

FLOOR FOAM - Cleaning preparations–household - Chemed Corp.

FLOOR GLIDE - Nozzles - TRC Acquisition Corp.

FLOOR GUARD - Cleaning preparations ☆ - Knight Marketing Corp.

FLOOR GUARD - Floor coverings–carpet and rugs - Jefferson Industries Inc.

FLOOR GUARD - Paints - Vanguard Paints & Finishes Inc.

FLOOR GUARD - Plastics–laminated - Seal Products Inc.

FLOOR-GUARDS - Furniture - Gerber Industries Inc.

FLOOR IMPRESSIONS, THE - Tiles–ceramic ☆ - Wenczel Tile Co.

FLOOR IN A BOX - Floor coverings–carpet and rugs - Carpet Crafts Inc.

FLOOR-INSUL - Insulating materials - Manville/Schuller

FLOOR KING - Hardware - Waxman Industries Inc.

FLOOR-KING - Mops - Geerpres Wringer Co.

FLOOR-KNIGHT - Mops - Geerpres Wringer Co.

FLOOR LASTIC - Cleaning preparations - M.A. Bruder & Sons Inc.

FLOOR LEVELER - Construction equipment - Custom Building Products

FLOOR MAGIC - Floor finishing machines–commercial - United Floor Machine Co.

FLOOR MASTER - Mop heads - Bouras Mop Manufacturing Co.

FLOOR-NU - Epoxy coatings ☆ - Steelcote Manufacturing Corp.

FLOOR OIL POLISH - Floor waxes - Analab Inc.

FLOOR POWER - Floor products - Blue Coral, Inc.

FLOOR-PRINCE - Mops - Geerpres Wringer Co.

FLOOR PROTECTOR - Mats - Akro Corp.

FLOOR SCIENCE - Cleaning preparations–carpet and rug - S.C. Johnson & Son, Inc.

FLOOR SENTRY - Mats - Akro Corp.

FLOOR SHOW - Floor waxes - R.M. Hollingshead Corp.

FLOOR SHOW - Vacuum cleaners and accessories - The Eureka Co.

FLOOR SPAN - Floor coverings - Timberco, Inc.

FLOOR STAT MAT - Mats - E.S. Robbins Corp.

FLOOR STOP - Floor coverings - Timothy Eugene Chavey

FLOOR STYLE - Sanders and grinders - Floor Style Products, Inc.

FLOOR TECH - Floor coverings–carpet and rugs - Porter Carpet Mills Inc.

FLOOR TREET - Concrete products ☆ - Grace Construction Products

FLOOR TRIM - Varnishes ☆ - Mac-O-Lac Paints Inc.

FLOOR WIZARD - Chemical preparations - State Chemical Manufacturing Co.

FLOOREVER - Finishing agents - Wood Kote Products, Inc.

FLOORFIN - Finishing agents - Daly's Inc.

FLOORGRES - Tiles–ceramic - Old World Tiles Inc.

FLOORGRIP - Hardware - ITW Paslode

FLOORIFIC - Finishing agents - Calgon Vestal Laboratories

FLOORITE - Floor finishing machines–commercial - United Floor Machine Co.

FLOORLEVEL - Water heaters–household - Hydrotherm

FLOORLINE - Mats - Tepromark International Inc.

FLOORMASTER - Mops ☆ - Helen Keller Services for the Blind

FLOORMASTER - Vacuum cleaners and accessories - Shop Vac Corp.

FLOORMAX - Floor waxes - The Hoover Co.

FLOORMOST - Finishing agents - PLC

FLOORPRO - Measuring instruments - Ytterberg Scientific Inc.

FLOORS & MORE - Cleaning preparations–household ☆ - Clorox Co.

FLOORS U.S.A. - Floor coverings–carpet and rugs - GCW Carpet Wholesalers, Inc.

FLOORSAVER - Mats - JCH International Inc.

FLOORSCAPE - Floor coverings–carpet and rugs ☆ - Kelly Group Inc.

FLOORSHIELD - Floor coverings–carpet and rugs - Shaw Industries Inc.

FLOORSHIELD - Floor waxes - L.D. Sterns Corp.

FLOORSONIC - Floor coverings - F.H. Leinweber Co. Inc.

FLOORSTONE - Cement - Tamms Industries Co.

FLOORTEX - Floor coverings - Congoleum Corp.

FLOORWORKS - Coatings - Master's Choice Inc.

FLOP-ABOUT BUNNY - Toys–stuffed - Fun World Inc.

FLOP-HERS - Footwear–women's - Flop-Hers Inc.

FLOP LOC - Electronic equipment - TBIG, Inc.

FLOPAC - Measuring instruments - Depac Corp.

FLOPPERS - Toys–stuffed ☆ - Gund, Inc.

FLOPPIE LIBRARIAN V - Computer software - Stuart-Matlock Corp. Inc.

FLOPPIES - Toys–stuffed - Kamar International Inc.

FLOPPY - Dolls ☆ - Effanbee Doll Corp.

FLOPPY - Toys - Lisco, Inc.

FLOPPY CUP - Fluid or material containers - InoTec Corp.

FLOPPY FACTORY - Computer software ☆ - B & N Companies, Inc.

FLOPPY-FLEX - Hoses - Tru-Flex Metal Hose Corp.

FLOPPY FLOWER BUNNIES - Toys–stuffed - Fun World Inc.

FLOPPY FLYER - Pet products - Biological Engineering/High Tech Pet Products

FLOPPY FLYERS - Toys–stuffed ☆ - Mighty Star Inc. (Special Effects Div.)

FLOPPY FOLKS - Figurines - FFSC, Inc.

FLOPPY GREETING - Computer software - Pickled Pixels, LLC

FLOPPY PENELOPE - Dolls - Uneeda Doll Co., Inc.

FLOPPY PUPPY - Toys–stuffed ☆ - Gund, Inc.

FLOPPY TOODLES - Dolls - Uneeda Doll Co., Inc.

FLOPSY - Candy - R.M. Palmer Co.

FLOPSY BUNNY - Toys–stuffed - Russ Berrie and Co., Inc.

FLOQUIL - Paints–artists' - Floquil-Polly S Color Corp.

FLOR - Floor coverings–tile - Interface, Inc.

FLOR - Vegetables–canned - J.M. Rodriguez & Co. Inc.

FLOR-A-DORN - Flower pots–earthenware ☆ - Cindus Corp.

FLOR-BRITE - Cleaning preparations ☆ - Elcal Enterprises Ltd.

FLOR DE APANAS - Coffee - Diedrich Coffee

FLOR DE CANA - Rum - Shaw-Ross International Importers

FLOR DE FLOREZ - Cigars - What's the Score, Inc.

FLOR DE MOSS - Cigars - A.J. Golden Inc.

FLOR DE ORLANDO - Cigars - Tampa Sweetheart Cigar Co.

FLOR DE VILLAR - Cigars - G.W. Van Slyke & Horton

FLOR DE YATERAS - Coffee - Jarrett Coffee Co.

FLOR DEL CARIBE - Cigars - Danby-Palicio

FLOR DEL MIRABELLE - Cigars - Villco Imports Inc.

FLOR DEL MUNDO - Cigars - Villazon and Co.

FLOR DO MINHO - Olive oil ☆ - Corte & Co.

FLOR - ESSENCE - Teas–herbal - Flora, Inc.

FLOR-EVER - Floor coverings - Congoleum Corp.

FLOR-FIX - Floor coverings - Tarkett, Inc.

FLOR-GARD - Paints - Coronado Paint Co.

FLOR-I-DUH - Shirts - Arnie Nathan

FLOR KARE - Cleaning preparations - Anderson Hardwood Floors Inc.

FLOR KLEEN - Cleaning preparations - Anderson Hardwood Floors Inc.

FLOR-LAK - Finishing agents - Lenmar Inc.

FLOR-MEND - Floor coverings ☆ - Congoleum Corp.

FLOR NEW - Cleaning preparations - Anderson Hardwood Floors Inc.

FLOR-S - Floor coverings–carpet and rugs - Heuga USA

FLOR S DECO - Floor coverings–carpet and rugs - Heuga USA

FLOR-SEAL - Adhesives and sealants ☆ - Elcal Enterprises Ltd.

FLOR SHINE - Cleaning preparations - Anderson Hardwood Floors Inc.

FLOR STAIN - Lacquers - Anderson Hardwood Floors Inc.

FLOR-TAC - Adhesives and sealants ☆ - Key Laboratories Inc.

FLOR-TEC - Paints - Frazee Paint

FLOR-TILE - Floor coverings - Hartco Wood Flooring

FLOR-TOP - Concrete products - CGM Inc.

FLOR-TRED - Enamels - Penn Crete Products Co. Inc.

FLOR-WELD - Enamels - Penn Crete Products Co. Inc.

FLOR X TEND - Chemical preparations - Siegmeister Saw Service, Inc.

FLORA - Artists' materials - Stangren Co.

FLORA - Baskets–wood ☆ - Royal Cathay Trading Co.

FLORA - Candles ☆ - Will & Baumer, Inc.

FLORA - Dolls ☆ - Fun World Inc.

FLORA - Floor coverings–carpet and rugs - Regal Rugs Inc.

☆ = Now out of production

FLORA - Foil–aluminum - Highland Supply Corp.
FLORA - Glassware–household - Crystal Clear Importing Co. Inc.
FLORA - Hobby kits - Modern Milltex Corp.
FLORA - Housewares ☆ - Dansk International Designs, Ltd.
FLORA - Jewelry - Richelieu Corp.
FLORA - Ophthalmic goods ☆ - Luxottica
FLORA - Pet products ☆ - Sera Aquaristik USA Inc.
FLORA - Tomato pastes and sauces - James Ferrera and Sons Inc.
FLORA AMERINDICA - Health care products - Top of the Line
FLORA AZZURRA - Tableware–china ☆ - Villeroy and Boch Tableware Ltd.
FLORA-BAMA - Clothing - Flora-Bama Lounge & Package Store, Inc.
FLORA BASICS - Hair care products - Revco D.S., Inc.
FLORA-BOOST - Pet products - Aquarium Products Inc.
FLORA-CARDS - Signs - John Henry Co.
FLORA DORA - Leather goods - Oppenheim Products Co.
FLORA EXPRESSION - Furniture - Maxim, Inc.
FLORA-FRESH - Filters–air - Research Products Corp.
FLORA FRESH - Oils–edible - Flora, Inc.
FLORA HEART - Hobby kits - Craft World International Inc.
FLORA-LAC - Health care products - Pierson Co.
FLORA LIBRARY - Publisher's imprints - Stemmer House Publishers Inc.
FLORA LITE - Chimes ☆ - Nutone Inc.
FLORA-LITES - Lighting equipment - J. Hermes
FLORA MASQUE - Wood products - Weyerhaeuser Co.
FLORA NIKROOZ - Apparel–women's - Flora Nikrooz Inc.
FLORA PREE - Soap - SBS Products, Inc.
FLORA ROYALE - Tableware–china - Pfaltzgraff Investment Co.
FLORA SATIN - Ribbons - Berwick Industries, Inc.
FLORA SEA WEES - Toys - Tonka Corp.
FLORA-SEAL - Floor waxes ☆ - Uncle Sam Chemical Co., Inc.
FLORA-SENTIAL - Vitamins and nutritional supplements - Bio-Energy Systems, Inc.
FLORA SPRAY - Chemical preparations - Rudd Co. Inc.
FLORA SPRINGS - Wines - Flora Springs Wine Co.
FLORA SUMA - Health care products - Top of the Line
FLORA TEC - Flowers, plants, and seeds - Equiflor Corp.
FLORA TEC FT-2000 - Flowers, plants, and seeds - Equiflor Corp.
FLORA-TEX - Tiles–ceramic - H & R Johnson Inc.
FLORA TROPIGAL - Toys - Tonka Corp.
FLORABELLE - Pianos ☆ - Universal Player Piano Co.
FLORABUNDA - Dinnerware - Cuthbertson Imports Inc.
FLORACEAN - Skin care products - Floraspa
FLORACRAFT - Glue–household or industrial - Flora Craft Inc.
FLORADA - Fertilizers ☆ - English Greenhouse Products Corp.
FLORADALE - Flowers, plants, and seeds - W. Atlee Burpee and Co.
FLORADALE - Honey - E.F. Lane & Son
FLORADERM - Vitamins and nutritional supplements - Perfectly Beautiful, Inc.
FLORADIX - Vitamins and nutritional supplements - Miracle Exclusives Inc.
FLORAFIN - Pet products - Tetra Sales USA
FLORAGLAS - Glass products - E.O. Brody Co.
FLORAGRANDE - Bedding–linen - Dan River Inc.
FLORAGRAPHICS BY PHYLLIS JUNE SIDNEY - Hats ☆ - Floragraphics
FLORAISON A ROSE - Tiles–ceramic ☆ - Monarch Tile Inc.
FLORAISON PLAIN - Tiles–ceramic ☆ - Monarch Tile Inc.
FLORAJEN - Calcium compounds - American Lifeline Inc.
FLORAL - Tiles–ceramic - Dal-Tile Corp.
FLORAL AFFAIR - Toothbrushes - Dental Concepts Inc.
FLORAL BALLET - Bedding–linen - Dan River Inc.
FLORAL BAROQUE - Floor coverings–carpet and rugs - Milliken & Co. Inc.
FLORAL BAROQUE - Silverware - Imperial Schrade Corp.
FLORAL BASKET - Skin care products - Longaberger Co.
FLORAL BIRTHDAY WISHES - Toys–stuffed - Dakin Inc.
FLORAL BOUQUET - Floor coverings–carpet and rugs - Glen Eden Wool Carpets
FLORAL BOUTIQUE - Furniture ☆ - Athens Furniture Industries Inc.
FLORAL CELEBRATIONS - Wallpaper - Warner Co.
FLORAL CONCEPTS - Display cases–metal - Structural Concepts Corp.
FLORAL CONCERTO - Wallpaper ☆ - Mirage Wallcovering Co.
FLORAL CONCERTO II - Wallpaper - Mirage Wallcovering Co.
FLORAL COROLLA - Floor coverings–carpet and rugs - Capel, Inc.
FLORAL CREST - Floor coverings - Mannington Resilient Floors
FLORAL DANCE - Dinnerware–glass ☆ - Franciscan by Johnson Brothers, USA, Inc.
FLORAL DELIGHT - Glassware–household - Owens-Illinois Inc. (Libbey Div.)
FLORAL DELIGHT - Wallpaper - Walls Alive
FLORAL DESIGN - Cookware - Corning Inc.

FLORAL DREAM - Frames–eyeglass ☆ - Universal/Univis Inc.
FLORAL ELEGANCE - Floor coverings–carpet and rugs ☆ - Bloomsburg Carpet Industries
FLORAL ELEGANCE - Wallpaper ☆ - Warner Co.
FLORAL FANCY PERSONALIZED PEN - Pens - Avon Products, Inc.
FLORAL FANCY STATIONERY PORTFOLIO - Stationery - Avon Products, Inc.
FLORAL FANTASIES - Flowers, plants, and seeds - Black Tie International
FLORAL FANTASY - Dinnerware–glass ☆ - Lenox, Inc.
FLORAL FANTASY - Flower pots–plastic - Ardel of America Inc.
FLORAL FANTASY - Giftware - Russ Berrie and Co., Inc.
FLORAL FANTASY - Stationery - Brushcreek Creative Co.
FLORAL FANTASY - Wallcoverings - Authentic Reproductions
FLORAL FRENZY - Perfumes - Colgate-Palmolive Co.
FLORAL FRESH - Bleach - Clorox Co.
FLORAL GARDENS - Fabrics–tapestry - Coloroll Inc.
FLORAL GLEN - Wines - Giumarra Vineyards
FLORAL HEART CLOCK - Clocks - Avon Products, Inc.
FLORAL HOLD - Craft supplies ☆ - Clayton Corp.
FLORAL ILLUSIONS - Craft supplies - Plaid Enterprises, Inc.
FLORAL IMPRESSIONS - Fabrics–tapestry ☆ - Coloroll Inc.
FLORAL IMPRESSIONS - Floor coverings ☆ - Bellbridge Carpets
FLORAL JOURNEY - Wallpaper - Scalamandre Silks Inc.
FLORAL KEY - Floor coverings - Tarkett, Inc.
FLORAL LACE - Incense - Circle of Beauty, Inc.
FLORAL LINE - Cosmetics - Caswell-Massey Co. Ltd.
FLORAL MAGIC - Frames–eyeglass - Hudson Optical Corp.
FLORAL MIST - Frames–eyeglass - Hudson Optical Corp.
FLORAL MIST - Housewares ☆ - Himark Enterprises Inc.
FLORAL NOTES - Skin care products ☆ - Thymes Limited
FLORAL PARK - Floor coverings - Congoleum Corp.
FLORAL PORTRAITS BY HENRY EVANS - Dinnerware–glass - Block China Co.
FLORAL SCENTS - Deodorizers - Aphrodisia Products
FLORAL SCROLL - Floor coverings–carpet and rugs - Regal Rugs Inc.
FLORAL SHOWER - Dinnerware–glass - Nikko Ceramics Inc.
FLORAL SPLENDOUR - Floor coverings–carpet and rugs - Customweave Carpets Inc.
FLORAL SPRAY - Dinnerware ☆ - Corning Inc.
FLORAL STRIPE - Floor coverings–carpet and rugs ☆ - Regal Rugs Inc.
FLORAL SUITE - Dinnerware–glass ☆ - Franciscan by Johnson Brothers, USA, Inc.
FLORAL SYMPHONY - Colognes - Saute Consultants Inc.
FLORAL TAPESTRY - Dinnerware–glass ☆ - Royal China & Porcelain Companies Inc.
FLORAL TERRACE - Floor coverings - Mannington Resilient Floors
FLORAL TOUCH - Stationery - Sangamon Co.
FLORAL TWISTER - Florists - David J. Bicknell
FLORAL WISE - Dinnerware ☆ - Corning Inc.
FLORAL WISP - Dinnerware - Corning Inc.
FLORALEA - Floor coverings - Mannington Resilient Floors
FLORALIA - Thread - DMC Corp.
FLORALIA - Wallcovering - Wall Trends, Inc.
FLORALIFE CRYSTAL CLEAR - Chemical preparations - Floralife, Inc.
FLORALITE - Candles ☆ - Gessner Products Co. Inc.
FLORALITE - Lighting fixtures ☆ - Hubbell Lighting, Inc. (Lighting Div.)
FLORALS & LACE - Tea kettles–nonelectric ☆ - Robinson Knife & Fiddlers Plastics
FLORALS COLLECTION - Perfumes - Quintessence Inc.
FLORAMA - Flowers–artificial - C & C Florists Supplies Inc.
FLORAMATIC - Garden equipment - Sodico Inc.
FLORAMIST - Skin care products - Delta Industries International, Inc.
FLORAMMUNE - Cold remedies - Flora Laboratories Inc.
FLORAMMUNE ENCHINACEA - Cold remedies - Flora Laboratories Inc.
FLORAN - Floor coverings - Congoleum Corp.
FLORANACEA - Herbicides - Flora Laboratories Inc.
FLORAPOT - Planters - Gale Group Inc.
FLORAPRIDE - Pet products - Tetra Sales USA
FLORAQUIN - Pharmaceutical preparations ☆ - G. D. Searle & Co.
FLORASAURUS - Bicycles - Raleigh USA Bicycle Co.
FLORASENSE - Flowers, plants, and seeds - Endar Corp.
FLORASILK - Flowers, plants, and seeds - Hub Floral Corp.
FLORASONE CARDIOSPERMUM CREAM - Pharmaceutical preparations - Boericke & Tafel
FLORASPA - Skin care products - Floraspa

☆ = Now out of production

FLORATEX - Flowers, plants, and seeds - Florida Foundation Seed Producers, Inc.

FLORATRICIAN - Flowers–artificial - C & C Florists Supplies Inc.

FLORAWALL - Building materials–concrete - Paver Systems, Inc.

FLORAY SPRAY - Bedding–linen - Dan River Inc.

FLORBATH - Bath salts - Nailtex Inc.

FLORCLAD - Floor coverings - Polymer Plastic Corp.

FLORE - Yarn - Joseph Galler Inc.

FLORE CAROLINA HERRERA - Cosmetics - Carolina Herrera, Ltd.

FLOREA - Bedding–linen - Dan River Inc.

FLOREAL - Wines ☆ - Flora Springs Wine Co.

FLOREAT - Craft supplies - Ziabicki Import Co.

FLOREL - Vitamins and nutritional supplements - Lotus Brands Inc.

FLORELATED - Furniture - Ethan Allen, Inc.

FLORENA - Pet products ☆ - Sera Aquaristik USA Inc.

FLORENCE - Dolls ☆ - Effanbee Doll Corp.

FLORENCE - Floor coverings ☆ - Tarkett, Inc.

FLORENCE - Floor coverings–carpet and rugs ☆ - LaVelle Textile Marketing Inc.

FLORENCE - Floor coverings–tile - Kowa Texas Inc.

FLORENCE - Furniture ☆ - Hammary Furniture Co. Inc.

FLORENCE - Hot tubs–fiberglass ☆ - Jacuzzi Brothers

FLORENCE - Ophthalmic goods - Rozin Optical Export Corp.

FLORENCE - Pasta - Florence Pasta and Cheese

FLORENCE - Toys ☆ - Peg Perego USA Inc.

FLORENCE - Wallpaper ☆ - Wallquest, Inc.

FLORENCE CLASSIC - Toys ☆ - Peg Perego USA Inc.

FLORENCE EISEMAN - Apparel–children's - Florence Eiseman Inc.

FLORENCE I - Wallcoverings - James F. White & Co. Inc.

FLORENCE JAMES - Handbags - Leather Accessories Inc.

FLORENCE NIGHTINGALE - Dolls ☆ - Effanbee Doll Corp.

FLORENCE STUDIO - Footwear–women's - Larry Stuart, Ltd.

FLORENCE/TC - Toys ☆ - Peg Perego USA Inc.

FLORENCE WILSON - Cosmetics ☆ - RH Cosmetics Corp.

FLORENCIAN - Floor coverings ☆ - Tarkett, Inc.

FLORENETTE - Pet products ☆ - Sera Aquaristik USA Inc.

FLORENTIA - See **GREENWICH COLLECTION**

FLORENTINA - Flatware - The Dirilyte Line

FLORENTINA - Glassware–household - Crystal Clear Importing Co. Inc.

FLORENTINA - Pens - Schneider Pens USA

FLORENTINE - See **AMBASSADOR**

FLORENTINE - Artists' materials - M. Grumbacher Inc.

FLORENTINE - Bedding–linen - Dan River Inc.

FLORENTINE - Candles - Will & Baumer, Inc.

FLORENTINE - Clocks - General Time Corp. (Westclox/Seth Thomas Div.)

FLORENTINE - Draperies - Maharam Vertical Surfaces

FLORENTINE - Flatware ☆ - Kirk Stieff Co.

FLORENTINE - Floor coverings - Mannington Resilient Floors

FLORENTINE - Floor coverings ☆ - Azrock Commercial Flooring

FLORENTINE - Floor coverings–carpet and rugs - Couristan Inc.

FLORENTINE - Floor coverings–carpet and rugs - Eligere Carpets

FLORENTINE - Floor coverings–carpet and rugs ☆ - Kelly Group Inc.

FLORENTINE - Frames–picture - Terragrafics Inc.

FLORENTINE - Giftware ☆ - Gorham Inc.

FLORENTINE - Glassware–household - Durand International

FLORENTINE - Lamps - Lamplight Farms, Inc.

FLORENTINE - Sinks–metal - Just Manufacturing Co.

FLORENTINE - Tiles–ceramic - American Marazzi Tile, Inc.

FLORENTINE - Toothpaste - Confi-Dental Products Co.

FLORENTINE BEAD - Silverware ☆ - Imperial Schrade Corp.

FLORENTINE BLACK - Dishes–china - Waterford Wedgwood USA, Inc.

FLORENTINE LASAGNA - Food products - My Own Meals Inc.

FLORENTINE SHOWER - Candles ☆ - Will & Baumer, Inc.

FLORENTINE TURQUOISE - Dishes–china - Waterford Wedgewood USA, Inc.

FLORENTINE VELVET - Floor coverings–carpet and rugs ☆ - Gulistan Carpet Inc.

FLORENTINI RUSTIC - Limestone products - Georgia Marble Co.

FLORENTINO - Beverages–alcohol - Western International Imports Inc.

FLORENZA - Beverages–alcohol - Remy Amerique Inc.

FLORENZI - Men's clothing - MGRR, Inc.

FLORENZO - Dinnerware–plastic - CCC Marketing Concepts

FLORES - Floor coverings–carpet and rugs ☆ - Regal Rugs Inc.

FLORES - Yarn ☆ - Joseph Galler Inc.

FLORES SONEU. - Apparel and accessories - Yaga, Inc.

FLORESCENCE - Hair care products - Helene Curtis Industries Inc.

FLORESCENCE - Skin care products - Naturelle, Inc.

FLORESS PROTEIN OIL - Shampoos - Fleetwood Co.

FLORET - Dinnerware–glass ☆ - Nikko Ceramics Inc.

FLORET - Perfumes - Antonia's Flowers, Inc.

FLORETT - Cigars - Gesty Trading & Manufacturing Corp.

FLORETTA - Yarn ☆ - William Unger & Co. Inc.

FLORETTE - Floor coverings ☆ - Congoleum Corp.

FLORETTE - Floor coverings–carpet and rugs ☆ - Couristan Inc.

FLORETTE - Floor coverings–carpet and rugs ☆ - Regal Rugs Inc.

FLOREVER - Garden equipment ☆ - L.J. Rench & Co.

FLOREX - Glass products - AFG Industries Inc. (Glass Group Div.)

FLOREX II - Hardware - English Greenhouse Products Corp.

FLOREX ITB - Hardware - English Greenhouse Products Corp.

FLORGARD - Paints - Sampson Coatings Inc.

FLORHIDE - Enamels ☆ - PPG Industries, Inc.

FLORI ROBERTS - Cosmetics - Color Me Beautiful, Inc.

FLORI ROBERTS - Cosmetics - Posner Laboratories Inc.

FLORI ROBERTS - Cosmetics - Flori Roberts Inc.

FLORIAN - Building materials - Florian Greenhouses, Inc.

FLORIAN - Cosmetics - Katco

FLORIAN - Flatware ☆ - Yamazaki Tableware Inc.

FLORIAN - Food products ☆ - Liberty Richter Inc.

FLORIAN - Hair- and skin-care products - Cabot Laboratories Inc.

FLORIAN - Pruning tools - American Standard Co.

FLORIAN GEYER - Cigars - Gesty Trading & Manufacturing Corp.

FLORIANA - Wines - Fruit Wines of Florida Inc.

FLORIBBEAN - Food products - Miami Interculinary Center

FLORIBUNDA - Dinnerware–glass ☆ - Cyclamen Studio

FLORIBUNDA - Wallpaper ☆ - Brewster Wallcovering Co.

FLORIBURDA - Wallpaper ☆ - Osborne & Little

FLORICAL - Pharmaceutical preparations - Mericon Industries Inc.

FLORIDA - Apparel and accessories - Florida Panthers Hockey, Ltd.

FLORIDA - Automotive parts and accessories ☆ - Toppertown Inc.

FLORIDA - Beverages–alcohol - Florida Distillers Co.

FLORIDA - Furniture - Homecrest Industries Inc.

FLORIDA - Imitation fur ☆ - Ivy International Ltd.

FLORIDA - Sponges - Florida Sponge & Chamois Co.

FLORIDA - Tiles–ceramic - Impo Glaztile Inc.

FLORIDA - Water–distilled - Aqua Plata Corp.

FLORIDA BAY - Fish food - Dynasty Marine Associates Inc.

FLORIDA BIRCH - Plywood - Georgia-Pacific Corp.

FLORIDA BIRD HOMES - Cages–wire ☆ - Pets International, Ltd.

FLORIDA CHIPS - Snack foods ☆ - Pelican Bay Ltd. Inc.

FLORIDA CITRUS - Juices–frozen - Johanna Foods, Inc.

FLORIDA CITRUS PUNCH - Beverages - Sundor Brands Inc.

FLORIDA CLUB - Citrus product - Bordo Products Co.

FLORIDA COBBLER - Shoes - Florida Shoe Inc.

FLORIDA COLUMNS - Building materials - Spaulding Craft, Inc.

FLORIDA CRYSTALS - Confections - Okeelanta Corp.

FLORIDA DAZE - Recording label - Rustron Music Productions

FLORIDA DESK - Furniture - Florida Desk Inc.

FLORIDA FIVE - Beverages ☆ - Veryfine Products, Inc.

FLORIDA FOAM - Pharmaceutical preparations - Hill Dermaceuticals

FLORIDA FRESH - Fruits and vegetables - Florida Fresh Citrus Sales, Inc.

FLORIDA GLOVE INC. - Gloves - Florida Glove Inc.

FLORIDA GOLD - Fruit drinks–bottled or canned - Lykes Services Co.

FLORIDA GOSPEL TRAIN - Recording label - Florida Swamper Records

FLORIDA GULF CITRUS - Food products - Gulf Citrus Growers Association, Inc.

FLORIDA JUICE INCORPORATED - Skin care products - Florida Juice, Inc.

FLORIDA KIST - Fruit drinks–bottled or canned ☆ - Lykes Services Co.

FLORIDA MAID - Honey - Sioux Honey Association

FLORIDA MELODY TRAIN - Recording label - Florida Swamper Records

FLORIDA ORANGE MIST MIMOSA - Wine coolers ☆ - H. Schmitt Soehne, Inc.

FLORIDA ORTHOPEDICS - Knives–surgical - Fla. Orthopedics, Inc.

FLORIDA PIK'T - Juices - Fresh Juice Co. Inc.

FLORIDA POOL PRODUCTS - Games - Florida Pool Products, Inc.

FLORIDA PRIDE - Fruits and vegetables - DNE World Fruit Sales

FLORIDA PRIDE - Seafood products–fresh or frozen ☆ - McRoberts Sales Co.

FLORIDA PROBE - Dental equipment - Florida Probe Corp.

FLORIDA QUALITY BRAND - Seafood products–fresh or frozen - Robert W. Hayman Inc.

FLORIDA QUEEN - Cigars - National Cigar Corp.

FLORIDA RF LABS - Microtomes - Florida RF Labs, Inc.

☆ = Now out of production

FLORIDA RUM RUNNER - Beverages–carbonated - Franco's Cocktail Products Inc.
FLORIDA RUSCUS - Flowers, plants, and seeds - Lake Ferns, Inc.
FLORIDA SEA - Food products - Florida Sea Inc.
FLORIDA SLIM - Yogurt - Energy Factors
FLORIDA SPECIAL - Insecticides - Web-Away Inc.
FLORIDA STATE JET - Air transportation–passengers - Comair, Inc.
FLORIDA SUN - Apparel and accessories - Cosmyl, Inc.
FLORIDA SUN - Lamps - Lighting Supplies
FLORIDA SUN - Vegetables–canned - Roberts Bros. Inc.
FLORIDA SUNSHINE - Chocolate bars - That's My Favorite Inc.
FLORIDA TILE - Tiles–ceramic - Florida Tile Industries, Inc.
FLORIDA UNTAMED - Paper products - George Rhodes Photography
FLORIDA WATER - Colognes - Lanman & Kemp-Barclay & Co. Inc.
FLORIDANA - Fruit drinks–bottled or canned - Floridana Citrus Products of Florida, Inc.
FLORIDANA - Orange and grapefruit juice - Inter-Floridana Import & Export
FLORIDA'S CHOICE - Window shades - Florida Shades Inc.
FLORIDA'S NATURAL - Fruit drinks–bottled or canned - Citrus World Inc.
FLORIDA'S OWN - Food products - United Citrus Products Corp.
FLORIDA'S PRIDE - Beverages–carbonated - Franco's Cocktail Products Inc.
FLORIDA'S SUNSHINE NECTAR DRINK - Juices - Salus Corp.
FLORIDIAN - Lamps - Lighting Supplies
FLORIDIAN - Novelty items - Floridian Card Products
FLORIDIAN - Swimming pools - Cascade Pools
FLORIDIAN - Windows–storm - Yale Ogron Manufacturing Co. Inc.
FLORIDIANS - Apparel and accessories - NBA Properties, Inc.
FLORIDOR - Awning window door ✩ - Continental Aluminum Products Co. Inc.
FLORIDOR - Crackers ✩ - Lifetone International Inc.
FLORIENT - Deodorizers - Colgate-Palmolive Co.
FLORIGOLD - Fruits and vegetables - Seald-Sweet Growers Inc.
FLORIKAN AC-CELL-ERATE - Chemical preparations - Florikan-E.S.A. Corp.
FLORIKAN TARGET FOR ORNAMENTALS INSECTICIDAL OIL - Insecticides - Florikan-E.S.A. Corp.
FLORIMEL - Rings–jewelry - Artcarved Inc.
FLORINA - Tableware–china - Villeroy and Boch Tableware Ltd.
FLORINDO - Food products - Mohawk Beverage Inc.
FLORINE WACHTER - Apparel and accessories - London Plain Corp.
FLORINE WACHTER BICCI - Apparel stores–women's - London Plain Corp.
FLORINSA - Flowers, plants, and seeds - Florinsa Farms Corp.
FLORISSA - Floor coverings–carpet and rugs ✩ - Evans-Black Carpet Mills
FLORIST PLANTER - Tableware–earthenware - Maurice Ceramics of California
FLORISTREE - Hobby kits ✩ - Latham Studios
FLORISTS' CHOICE - Flower holders - Syndicate Sales, Inc.
FLORITE - Lighting equipment - Acme-Lite Manufacturing Co.
FLORMATE - Floor coverings–carpet and rugs - Marchem Manufacturing
FLORMONT - Bathroom fixtures - Crane Plumbing/Fiat Products
FLORO FRY - Shortening - Florida Shortening Corp.
FLOROC - Paints ✩ - Valspar Corp.
FLOROCK - Epoxy coatings - Crawford Laboratories
FLOROLIN - Varnishes - Remien & Kuhnert Co.
FLORON - Epoxy coatings - Standard Paint Co.
FLORONE - Pharmaceutical preparations ✩ - Dermik Laboratories Inc.
FLOROPRYL - Pharmaceutical preparations - Merck & Co., Inc. (Merck Research Laboratories)
FLOROVA - Paints - Cloverleaf Paint & Varnish
FLORPINE - Wood products ✩ - Willamette Industries, Inc.
FLORPLY - Paints - Valspar Corp.
FLORSHEIM - Footwear - Interco Inc.
FLORSHEIM - Shoes - Wolverine World Wide, Inc.
FLORSHEIM COMFORTECH MAINTENANCE FREE - Shoes - Florsheim Shoe Co.
FLORSHEIM LIGHTWEIGHTS - Shoes - Interco Inc.
FLORSWEEP - Sweeping compounds - Frank Miller and Sons Inc.
FLORVAL - Cheese - Anco Foods Corp.
FLORVITE - Vitamins and nutritional supplements - Everett Laboratories Inc.
FLORVITE + IRON - Health care products - Everett Laboratories Inc.
FLORZEEL - Paints ✩ - Valspar Corp.
FLOSPUN - Thread - Quality Thread Co.
FLOSS-A-WAY'S - Embroidery-thread holders and totes - American Crewel & Canvas Studio
FLOSS FILE - Craft supplies - Metro Manufacturing & Supply
FLOSS FLY, THE - Dental equipment - Ramco Arts
FLOSSAID - Dental compounds - Floss Aid Corp.
FLOSSAWL - Dental floss - Brandir International, Inc.

FLOSSED HORIZONS - Floss and yarn organizer - Flossed Horizons
FLOSSMASTER - Thread - Creative Home Collections Inc.
FLOSSMATE - Dental equipment - John O.Butler Co.
FLOSSUPS - Dental equipment - Ranir Corp.
FLOSTAR - Containers - Davstar California, Inc.
FLOSTOP - Irrigation equipment - Hunter Industries Inc.
FLOTATION - Tires - Bridgestone/Firestone, Inc.
FLOTATION CONCEPTS - Mattresses ✩ - Sealy Inc.
FLOTATION FAMILY - Beds–wood - Waterworth
FLOTE-BIKE - Boats ✩ - Harris-Kayot Inc.
FLOTEBOTE - Boats–pontoons - Harris-Kayot Inc.
FLOTEDEK - Boats - Harris-Kayot Inc.
FLOTEK-90 - Sporting goods - Florek Co.
FLOTEROPE - Marine rope - American Manufacturing Co. Inc.
FLOTEX - Antifreeze - MMJ Corp.
FLOTEX - Floor coverings–carpet and rugs - Bonar & Flotex Inc.
FLOTILL - Food products - Pet Inc.
FLOTILLA - Boats–motor - Rinker Boat Co. Inc.
FLOTILLA - Fabrics–velvet - Dan River Inc.
FLOTO - Sporting goods - Weber Industries Inc.
FLOTONE - Photographic equipment - Argraph Corp. (Samigon Div.)
FLOTOX - Herbicides - Chevron Chemical Co.
FLOTRON - Industrial chemicals - Champion Technologies Inc.
FLOTTA - Food products - Pet Inc.
FLOTURA - Steel springs–railroad - Needlecraft Industries
FLOUR FINE - Gelatin - Vyse Gelatin Co.
FLOUR POT COOKIES - Cookies - Flour Pot Cookie Co., Inc.
FLOUR POWER - Baskets–wood ✩ - Rubens Originals
FLOURETTE - Dinnerware–glass ✩ - Nikko Ceramics Inc.
FLOURICON - Electronic equipment - General Electric Co.
FLOURISH - Dinnerware–glass ✩ - Lenox, Inc.
FLOURISH - Hair care products - Summit Laboratories
FLOURISH - Pet products - Seachem Laboratories
FLOURISH TABS - Pet products - Seachem Laboratories
FLOW CHECK - Labels–paper - Polysciences, Inc.
FLOW-EZE - Drain pipe cleaners - Flow-Eze Co.
FLOW FLEX - Surgical instruments - James R. Kendrick Co. Inc.
FLOW-GLO - Enamels ✩ - Kelly-Moore Paint Co. Inc.
FLOW-LATOR - Water purification systems ✩ - Bruner Corp.
FLOW-LOCK - Hardware - Lifeguard Medical Products Inc.
FLOW MASTER - Computer software - SourceView Software International
FLOW MATE - Pumps - Zoeller Co.
FLOW-MED - Measuring equipment - International Electronic Technology Corp.
FLOW PASTE - Bakery products - Kopykake
FLOW-PATH - Mufflers–motor vehicle - M.A.C. Products, Inc.
FLOW-RATOR - Plumbing fixtures–metal - Moen Inc.
FLOW RIDER - Apparel and accessories - Light Wave, Ltd.
FLOW-ROCK - Cement - Lyons Distributing, Inc.
FLOW SAFE - Safety products - Flow-Safe, Inc.
FLOW SOLUTION IV, THE - Analyzers–industrial - O.I. Corp.
FLOW SOLUTION, THE - Measuring instruments - Alpkem Corp.
FLOW-TOP - Cement ✩ - Consolidated Coatings Corp.
FLOW TOTALIZER - Fuel systems–motor vehicle - Floscan Instrument Co.
FLOW-TROLL - Fishing lures - Frabill Inc.
FLOW TRUE - Cement ✩ - Ardex, Inc.
FLOWARE - Computer software - Dantec Measurement Technology Inc.
FLOWAWAY - Diuretics - Church and Dwight Co. Inc.
FLOWAY - Degreasing solvents - Kano Laboratories Inc.
FLOWCHART - Games ✩ - Ampersand Press
FLOWCHECKER - Air purification systems - Lab Safety Supply, Inc.
FLOWCRETE - Concrete repair products - Lyons Distributing, Inc.
FLOWDATA - Measuring instruments - Flowdata, Inc.
FLOWEL - Brushes–paint - American Brush Co. Inc.
FLOWER - Hair care products - Nino Originals
FLOWER - Lighting fixtures - Planet Earth Inc.
FLOWER - Novelty items - Darwell Import Co. Inc.
FLOWER - Novelty items–paper - Bloomin' Roses
FLOWER - Vegetables–canned - Sun Hing Foods, Inc.
FLOWER - Wigs - Jean Paree Weegs Inc.
FLOWER ARRANGEMENTS MADE EASY - Recording label - Kim Alexander
FLOWER ART - Chemical preparations - Activa Products Inc.
FLOWER BABIES - Magnets - Kling Magnetics Inc.
FLOWER BALI - Apparel–women's - Bali Co. Inc.
FLOWER BELLS - Dinnerware–glass ✩ - Nikko Ceramics Inc.
FLOWER BLOSSOM - Glassware–household ✩ - National Housewares
FLOWER CANE BY SHEILA - Flowers–artificial - Dispo by Sheila

FLOWER CARPET - Flower pots–plastic - Anthony Tesselaar USA Inc.

FLOWER CHARMS - Brassieres (Bras) ☆ - Warnaco Inc.

FLOWER CRACKER - Fertilizers - Security Products Co.

FLOWER DESIGN I - Paper–toilet - Georgia-Pacific Corp.

FLOWER DESIGN II - Paper–toilet - Georgia-Pacific Corp.

FLOWER-DRI - Craft supplies - Plantabbs Products

FLOWER FABRIC - Flower and grass seeds - Proseed (USA), Inc.

FLOWER FACES - Novelty items - John Henry Co.

FLOWER FACTORY - Solar energy collectors - Vegetable Factory, Inc. (Sunbeam Structures Div.)

FLOWER FAIRIES - Greeting cards - Renaissance Greeting Cards Inc.

FLOWER FAIRY - Greeting cards - Green Tiger Press

FLOWER FANCY - Toys - Toymax Inc.

FLOWER FIX - Flowers, plants, and seeds - Fox Run Craftsmen

FLOWER FLAMES - Candles - Columbia Wax Products Inc.

FLOWER FRAGRANCE - Candles - Columbia Wax Products Inc.

FLOWER FRAMERS BY JAY - Housewares - Flower Framers L.P.

FLOWER FUN - Dolls - Mattel, Inc.

FLOWER GARD - Garden equipment - Gilbert and Bennett Manufacturing Co.

FLOWER GARDEN - Bedding–linen - Dan River Inc.

FLOWER GARDEN - Deodorizers - Sterling Co.

FLOWER GARDEN - Floor coverings–carpet and rugs - Daltonian Carpet & Cushion Inc.

FLOWER GARDEN - Housewares ☆ - Shafford Co. Inc.

FLOWER GARDEN - Teas ☆ - Alvita Products Co.

FLOWER GARDEN - Wallpaper - Imperial Wallcoverings, Inc.

FLOWER GIRL - Bicycles - Sears, Roebuck and Co.

FLOWER GIRL - Flowers–artificial - Horace Katz Sales Inc.

FLOWER GIRL LINE, THE - Flowers–artificial - D. Clarkson Ltd.

FLOWER GIRL OF BRITTANY - Dolls ☆ - Effanbee Doll Corp.

FLOWER GLASS - Jewelry ☆ - Snowflake Manufacturing Ltd.

FLOWER HILL - Wallpaper - Queens Decorative Wallcoverings Inc.

FLOWER KING - Housewares - Thermwell Products Co. Inc.

FLOWER MAGIC MARY - Dolls - Tyco Industries, Inc.

FLOWER MAKIN' BASKET - Toys - Tyco Toys

FLOWER MANIA - Flowers, plants, and seeds - W. Atlee Burpee and Co.

FLOWER OF HAWAII - Perfumes - House of Excellence

FLOWER OF THE DESERT - Fruits and vegetables - Pasquinelli Produce Co.

FLOWER OF THE MONTH - Novelty items - Papel Freelance, Inc.

FLOWER OF THE MONTH - Skin care products - Joyart Jewelry Co.

FLOWER PARADE - Floor coverings–carpet and rugs - Capel, Inc.

FLOWER PATH - Wallpaper - Essex Wallcoveringss

FLOWER PATTERNS - Video production - Sewing Arts, Inc.

FLOWER PETAL - Skin care products - K'Arsan Corp.

FLOWER PETALS - Deodorizers - Dial Corp.

FLOWER POPS - Craft supplies - Milton Bradley Co.

FLOWER POT BREAD BAKING KITS - Breads–mixes - Applewood Seed & Garden Group

FLOWER POT MUFFINS FOR KIDS - Breads–mixes - Applewood Seed & Garden Group

FLOWER POWER - Candy ☆ - Donruss Co.

FLOWER POWER - Colognes - Parfum de Coeur Ltd.

FLOWER POWER II - Dolls - Mattel, Inc.

FLOWER POWER - Fertilizers - Valley Fertilizer & Chemical Inc.

FLOWER-POWER - House furnishings - Aparco Inc.

FLOWER POWER - Pet products - Teddy Pets

FLOWER-PRO - Fertilizers - Dyna-Gro Nutrition Solutions

FLOWER RATTLE - Toys - Fisher-Price, Inc.

FLOWER SEED CRAYONS - Crayons - Applewood Seed & Garden Group

FLOWER SHOPPE - Sachets - Seasons Inc.

FLOWER SHOW - Girdles - Vanity Corset Co. Inc.

FLOWER SHOW, THE - Hobby kits ☆ - Latham Studios

FLOWER SOLUTIONS - Oils–essential - Flower Solutions, Inc.

FLOWER SONG - Colognes ☆ - Michael Duval Inc.

FLOWER SONG - Tableware–china ☆ - Lenox, Inc.

FLOWER SPOUTER - Toys - Bear Creek Toys, Inc.

FLOWER SURPRISE - Dolls - Mattel, Inc.

FLOWER TEA - Apparel and accessories - Kellwood Co.

FLOWER TURBAN - Wigs - Jean Paree Weegs Inc.

FLOWER VALLEY - Bowling pins - Bee Creek Botanicals

FLOWER WAREHOUSE - Flowers, plants, and seeds - Flower Warehouse, Inc.

FLOWER WEDDING LINE, THE - Greeting cards - Regency Thermographers Inc.

FLOWER WEIGHT - Glassware–household - Nourot Glass Studio

FLOWER WORLD - Flowers, plants, and seeds - Flower World of America Inc.

FLOWERAMA - Flowers, plants, and seeds - Flowerama of America Inc.

FLOWERANGER - Containers ☆ - Van Guard Studios of North Carolina

FLOWERCRAFTS - Bookmarks - Chase Collection, Inc.

FLOWERDRIFT - Colognes ☆ - Avon Products, Inc.

FLOWERGARDEN - Carpet sweepers ☆ - Bissell Inc.

FLOWERING - Dinnerware–glass - Nikko Ceramics Inc.

FLOWERING LACE - Underwear and nightwear - Warnaco Inc.

FLOWERIZED PRESENTATIONS - Christmas tree ornaments ☆ - Mr. Christmas, Inc.

FLOWERKINS - Dolls - Goldberger Doll Manufacture Co.

FLOWERPOWER - Scissors–hand-operated - Aaronco Pet Products, Inc.

FLOWERS - Apparel and accessories - At Last Sportswear Inc.

FLOWERS - Dinnerware–glass ☆ - Cyclamen Studio

FLOWERS - Snack foods - Flowers Industries Inc.

FLOWERS BY TETERS - Fabrics - Teters Floral Products Inc.

FLOWERS EXPRESS - Flowers, plants, and seeds - Sunburst Farms, Inc.

FLOWERS FERNS AND RAINFORESTS - Jewelry - Dian Malouf

FLOWERS IN A BOTTLE - Perfumes - Antonia's Flowers, Inc.

FLOWERS IN PERSON - Posters ☆ - One-of-a-Kind Workshop

FLOWERS IN THE AIR - Giftware ☆ - Avon Products, Inc.

FLOWERS 'N' BOWS - Giftware - Avon Products, Inc.

FLOWERS 'N FLOWERS - Flowers, plants, and seeds - Pickseed West, Inc.

FLOWERS OF CHRISTMAS - Glassware–household ☆ - Fenton Art Glass Co.

FLOWERS OF THE WORLD - Office supplies ☆ - Amcal Inc.

FLOWERS OF VAN GOGH - Flowers, plants, and seeds - White Swan, Ltd.

FLOWERS OF VENICE - Wallcoverings - Worldwalls International Inc.

FLOWERS WITH A FRAGRANCE - Cosmetics ☆ - May Cove Inc.

FLOWERSCAPES - Wallpaper - Benchmark Preferred Wallcoverings

FLOWERWORKS - Flowers, plants, and seeds - White Swan, Ltd.

FLOWERY - Manicure preparations - Flowery Beauty Products, Inc.

FLOWERY - Nail care products - Spilo/Mehaz Worldwide

FLOWERY - Skin care products - Major/Advance International

FLOWGRABBER - Laboratory apparatus ☆ - Dantec Measurement Technology Inc.

FLOWGRO - Garden equipment ☆ - Altra Corp.

FLOWGUARD GOLD - Adhesives and sealants - B.F. Goodrich Co.

FLOWGUARD GOLD - Pipes–plastic - B.F. Goodrich Co.

FLOWIN - Shirts - Daniel Bruckner

FLOWING SPRINGS - Water–bottled or canned - Daniel Kent Daniels

FLOWING SPRINGS - Water–bottled or canned - Hickory Springs Water Co. Inc.

FLOWING VELVET - Skin care products - Flowing Velvet

FLOWING WELLS - Water–bottled or canned - Southern Beverage Packers, Inc.

FLOWING WRITER - Pens - Pentel of America, Ltd.

FLOWLIN - Hair care products ☆ - Shiseido Cosmetics (America) Ltd.

FLOWLINE - Measuring instruments - Flowline Inc.

FLOWLITE - Measuring instruments - Dantec Measurement Technology Inc.

FLOWLOGIC - Computer software - Workflow Systems Inc.

FLOWMAKER - Computer software - Workflow, Inc.

FLOWMAN - Computer storage devices–magnetic - Logical Software Solutions Corp.

FLOWMANAGER - Computer software - Dantec Measurement Technology Inc.

FLOWMAP - Computer software - Dantec Measurement Technology Inc.

FLOWMARK - Computer software - International Business Machines Corp.

FLOWMATIC - Water heaters–household - Bel-Aire Sales Corp.

FLOWMAX - Containers - Georgia-Pacific Corp.

FLOWPAC - Health care products ☆ - HNE Healthcare

FLOWPLUS - Health care products - HNE Healthcare

FLOWPOWER - Computer software - J-I-T Institute of Technology, Inc.

FLOWPRESS - Health care products - HNE Healthcare

FLOWPULSE - Health care products ☆ - HNE Healthcare

FLOWRAP - Packaging machines - Shanklin Corp.

FLOWRIDER - Hats - Light Wave, Ltd.

FLOWSOFT - Computer software - Tesco Controls, Inc.

FLOWTECH - Exhaust systems–motor vehicle - Biggs Manufacturing, Inc.

FLOWTEX - Paints - Long Island Paint & Chemical Co.

FLOWTILE - Enamels ☆ - Everseal International Sales Co. Inc.

FLOWTOOL - Computer software - Ramss, Inc.

FLOWTOOLS - Computer software - Timothy J. Erskine

FLOWTRON - Health care products - HNE Healthcare

FLOWTRON - Insect repellents - Flowtron Outdoor Products

FLOWTRON ELECTRIC LEAF EATER - Machine parts - Armatron International Inc.

FLOWZ - Septic cleaner ☆ - Jancyn Manufacturing Corp.

☆ = Now out of production

FLOWZAN - Chemical preparations - Phillips Petroleum Co.

FLOXAID AWP - Veterinary pharmaceutical preparations ☆ - Merck & Co., Inc. (Merck Agvet Division)

FLOXAID BF - Veterinary pharmaceutical preparations ☆ - Merck & Co., Inc. (Merck Agvet Division)

FLOYD MALLOY - Toys - Tonka Corp.

FLOYD ROSE - Musical instruments - Floyd Rose Marketing, Inc.

FLOYD ROSE - Musical instruments ☆ - Kramer

FLOZE-OIL TREATMENT - Lubricating systems–motor vehicle - Analab Inc.

FLOZOL - Chemical preparations ☆ - Lubrizol Corp.

FLP - Containers–paper - Ivy Hill Corp.

FLS - Controls–heating systems - V.T.M. Industries, Inc.

F.L.S. - Veterinary astringent ☆ - American Equine Products Inc.

FLT - Electrical testing instruments - Fluid Components Intl, LLC.

FLU & COLD TIMES - Cold remedies - Natureworks Inc.

FLU-FLU - Sporting goods ☆ - Bear Archery Inc.

FLU SHIELD - Pharmaceutical - American Home Products Corp.

FLU SOLUTION - Pharmaceutical preparations - Dolisos America, Inc.

FLU SOLUTION PLUS - Pharmaceutical preparations - Dolisos America, Inc.

FLUAX - Vaccines ☆ - Merck & Co., Inc. (Merck Research Laboratories)

FLUBBER - Molding compounds–plastics - Cap Toys, Inc.

FLUE GLUE - Mortars–clay - CMS Industries, Inc.

FLUE-KAP - Blocks–chimney - Jomoco Products Co.

FLUE/LINE - Heating equipment - Slant/Fin Corp.

FLUE-MASTER - Hardware - Walter Emmich & Co. Inc.

FLUEFIN - Water heaters–household - Hudson Manufacturing Co.

FLUEGARD - Thermometers - Condar Co.

FLUENCY MASTER - Electronic equipment - Ronald L. Webster

FLUER - Flatware - Washington Forge Inc.

FLUER-DE-LIS - Bathroom accessories - Better Sleep, Inc.

FLUER LIGHTS - Lighting fixtures - General Electric Co.

FLUF-E-KOTE - Fabrics–flock - Bersted's Hobby-Craft

FLUF-PUFT - Marshmallows ☆ - Safeway Stores Inc.

FLUF-TEX - Thread and yarn - Coats American, Inc.

FLUF-TEX - Thread ☆ - SCT Yarns Inc.

FLUFA - Breads - Crystal Food Import Corp.

FLUFF - Crocheted and knitted items - Royal Knitting Mills Inc.

FLUFF - Fabric softener - James Austin Co.

FLUFF - Fabric softener - Graham Products

FLUFF - Pet products - K.C. Pharmacal Inc.

FLUFF-A-BED - Pet products - Gimborn U.S., Inc.

FLUFF-IN - Facial tissues - Marcal Paper Mills, Inc.

FLUFF 'N' BOB - Chains - Kmart Properties, Inc.

FLUFF-OUT - Animal grooming supplies - Davis Manufacturing

FLUFF OUT - Facial tissues - Marcal Paper Mills, Inc.

FLUFF PUFFS - Toys–stuffed - Fun World Inc.

FLUFF TIP - Housewares - Suburbanite Industries

FLUFFICUFF - Health care products - Vital Signs, Inc.

FLUFFIES - Dolls - Cal Themes Inc.

FLUFFIES 'N PUPPIES - Greeting cards - Paramount Cards Inc.

FLUFFLE - Toys–stuffed - Cozy's Inc.

FLUFFO - Brooms - Fluffo Mop & Broom Co. Inc.

FLUFFO - Food products - Procter & Gamble Co.

FLUFFY - Brassieres (Bras) - Wacoal America Inc.

FLUFFY - Dolls ☆ - Effanbee Doll Corp.

FLUFFY - Fabric softeners - Blue Cross Laboratories Inc.

FLUFFY - Greeting cards - Paramount Cards Inc.

FLUFFY - Medical apparatus ☆ - Monterey, Inc.

FLUFFY - Toys–stuffed ☆ - Russ Berrie and Co., Inc.

FLUFFY - Yarn - Carilorz Corp.

FLUFFY - Yarn ☆ - JCA, Inc.

FLUFFY BUNNY - Toys–stuffed ☆ - Fun World Inc.

FLUFFY DOWN - Food products ☆ - Semple Co.

FLUFFY DUFFY - Greeting cards ☆ - Fran Mar Greeting cards Ltd.

FLUFFY KITTY - Puppets - Dakin Inc.

FLUFFY LUVS - Toys–stuffed ☆ - Fun World Inc.

FLUFFY OMBRE - Yarn ☆ - William Unger & Co. Inc.

FLUFFY POPS - Candy - Creative Specialties Inc.

FLUFFY STUFF - Candy - OTec, Inc.

FLUFFY SUNSHINE - Toys–stuffed - Gund, Inc.

FLUFFY, THE - Skin care products - Opi Products, Inc.

FLUFFY'S - Pet products - Petco Pet Food & Supplies

FLUFFY'S LITTER - Pet products - Petco Pet Food & Supplies

FLUFTEX - Pie and cream fillings - American Maize-Products Co.

FLUGABONE - Trombones - King Musical Instruments

FLUGELS - Toys - Martin Carbone Inc.

FLUID, A - Antiseptics - Elysee Scientific Cosmetic Co.

FLUID ALARM SYSTEM - Medical apparatus - Medical Device Technologies, Inc.

FLUID BALL - Ammunition ☆ - Olin Corp. (Winchester Div.)

FLUID BLOC - Motor vehicle parts - Pullman Co.

FLUID CONTAINMENT - Electronic equipment - Fluid Containment, Inc.

FLUID FANTASY - Toys ☆ - Wham-O Manufacturing Co.

FLUID FILM - Cleaning preparations - Eureka Chemical Co.

FLUID-FLO - Plastics - Kvp Systems, Inc.

FLUID-LOK - Adhesives and sealants - Imperial Adhesives Inc.

FLUID MANAGER - Mixers - Fluid Management

FLUID MISER - Pipes - Charles Machine Works, Inc.

FLUID-TITE - Pipes - Certainteed Corp. (Roofing Products Group)

FLUIDCONTROLS - Valves - Danfoss, Inc. (Danfoss Fluid Power)

FLUIDE AUTO-BRONZANT - Cosmetics - Cosmair Inc.

FLUIDE SATINE - Cosmetics - Lancome

FLUIDEX - Diuretics ☆ - Columbia Laboratories Inc.

FLUIDLINE - Machine parts - LM76 Inc.

FLUIDMASTER - Plumbing fixtures - Fluidmaster, Inc.

FLUIDOT - Medical apparatus - Medrad, Inc.

FLUIDOTHERAPY - Pharmaceutical preparations - Maxxim Medical Inc.

FLUIDOTHERAPY T - Health care products - Neuromedics

FLUIDSHOOTER - Measuring and dispensing pumps - Asymptotic Technologies, Inc.

FLUIDTAME - Mattresses - Land and Sky Manufacturing Inc.

FLUIDTEC - Sealing devices - Garlock Inc.

FLUKE - Fishing lures - Zoom Bait Co.

FLUKE-TABS - Water treating compounds - Aquarium Products Inc.

FLUKES CONTROL - Pet products ☆ - Aquatronics-Filtronics

FLUKEVIEW - Computer software ☆ - Electrotek Concepts, Inc.

FLUMADINE - Pharmaceutical preparations - Forest Pharmaceuticals Inc.

FLUME - Faucets - Kohler Co.

FLUMEGLUMINE - Veterinary pharmaceutical preparations - Phoenix Pharmaceutical, Inc.

FLUMP - Toys - Sergeant's Pet Products, Inc.

FLUMPET - Musical instruments - David G. Monette Corp.

FLUNIXAMINE - Veterinary pharmaceutical preparations - American Home Products Corp.

FLUO-FLUX - Fluxes–welding and soldering - Aluminum Co. of America

FLUO-RECORD - Cameras - Sentry Test Systems

FLUO/VEYOR - Machinery - Delta/Ducon Components Group Co.

FLUOCINOLONE ACETONIDE - Health care products - G and W Laboratories Inc.

FLUOGEN - Vaccines - Parke-Davis

FLUOMERIC - Lamp bulbs–vapor - Duro-Test Corp.

FLUON - Wallpaper ☆ - ICI Americas Inc.

FLUONID - Skin care products - Allergan, Inc.

FLUOR-A-DIM - Power switching equipment - Jefferson Electric Co.

FLUOR-O-PAC - Lighting equipment - Magnetek Universal Manufacturing

FLUOR-OP - Ophthalmic prescription drug - Iolab Pharmaceuticals

FLUORACAINE - Pharmaceutical preparations - Akorn Inc.

FLUORAD - Chemical preparations - Minnesota Mining & Manufacturing Co.

FLUORART - Paints ☆ - Winsor & Newton

FLUORESCEIN - Ophthalmic prescription drug - Iolab Pharmaceuticals

FLUORESCEIN SODIUM - Ophthalmic goods - Alcon Laboratories, Inc.

FLUORESCENCE - Markers–felt-tip ☆ - Zebra Pen Corp.

FLUORESCENT GREEN - Nail care products - Pavion Ltd.

FLUORESCENT WEAVE - Vinyl - Sign-Up Corp.

FLUORESCITE - Ophthalmic goods - Alcon Laboratories, Inc.

FLUORESOFT - Pharmaceutical preparations - Akorn Inc.

FLUORESUNS - Lighting fixtures - Fleco Industries Inc.

FLUORETS - Ophthalmic goods - Akorn Inc.

FLUORI-METHANE - Anesthetics - Gebauer Co.

FLUORIDE FOAM - Dentifrices - Laclede Professional Products, Inc.

FLUORIGARD - Mouthwashes - Colgate-Palmolive Co.

FLUORINEED - Pharmaceutical preparations - Hanlon Drug Products

FLUORITAB - Health care products - Fluoritab Corp.

FLUORO-BRUSH - Toothbrushes - E & D Dental Products, Inc.

FLUORO-FREE - Health care products - Sims Deltec, Inc.

FLUORO/GLY - Pharmaceutical preparations - Pharmagen, Inc.

FLUORO-LITE - Dyes and pigments - Spectronics Corp.

FLUORO TECH - Refrigerators - Fluoro Tech, Inc.

FLUORO-TIP - Medical apparatus - B. Braun Medical Inc.

FLUORO TRI COLOR - Artists' materials ☆ - Printing Arts Research Laboratories

FLUOROAMP - Communications equipment - Galileo Corp.

FLUOROCLAD - Hardware ☆ - Sherwin-Williams Automotive Finishes Corp.
FLUOROCLEEN - Cleaning preparations - Stewart-Hall Chemical Corp.
FLUOROCOUNT - Measuring instruments - Packard Instrument Co., Inc.
FLUORODEX - Audio equipment ☆ - Hamilton Electronics Corp.
FLUORODEX - Prescription drug - IDE-Interstate Inc.
FLUOROFIL - Sutures - Pitman-Moore, Inc.
FLUOROFLEX - Contact lenses - Cooper Companies Inc.
FLUOROFLEX UV - Contact lenses - Cooper Companies Inc.
FLUOROLASE - Electronic equipment - Galileo Corp.
FLUOROLITE - Lighting fixtures - RGM Industries Inc.
FLUOROMOUNT-G - Adhesives and sealants - Southern Biotechnology Associates, Inc.
FLUORONYLINER - Bearings–industrial - Thomson Industries, Inc.
FLUOROPERM - Contact lenses - Pilkington Barnes Hind, Inc.
FLUOROPLEX - Skin care products - Allergan, Inc.
FLUOROSEAL - Pharmaceutical preparations - Scientific Pharmaceuticals, Inc.
FLUOROSENSOR - Chemical preparations - Atto Instruments, Inc.
FLUOROSENTRY - Boxes - Fluoroware, Inc.
FLUOROTECH - Packaging–foam - RM Engineered Products, Inc.
FLUOSOL - Pharmaceutical preparations - Alpha Therapeutic Corp.
FLUOTHANE - Anesthetics - Wyeth-Ayerst Laboratories
FLUOVIEW - Microscopes - Olympus America Inc.
FLUPPY DOG - Cosmetics for children ☆ - Cosrich Inc.
FLUPPY DOG - Shoes ☆ - Sidney Rich Associates Inc.
FLUPPY DOGS - Toys–stuffed - Kenner Products
FLUR-DRY - Paints - Klee Chemical Coatings
FLURAL SCROLL - Floor coverings–carpet and rugs - Langhorne Carpet Co. Inc.
FLURATE - Ophthalmic goods - Bausch & Lomb Pharmaceuticals, Inc.
FLURESEAL - Paints - Klee Chemical Coatings
FLURESS - Ophthalmic goods - Barnes-Hind Inc.
FLURESS - Pharmaceutical preparations - Akorn Inc.
FLURO - Photographic equipment - Eastman Kodak Co.
FLURO ETHYL - Anesthetics ☆ - Gebauer Co.
FLURO-SPRAY - Lamp bulbs - Duro-Test Corp.
FLUROETCH SAFETY SOLVENT - Cleaning preparations - Acton Technologies Inc.
FLUROPON - Paints - Valspar Corp.
FLUROSYN - Pharmaceutical preparations - Rugby Laboratories Inc.
FLURRYPAK - Machinery - Flurry International, Inc.
FLURSERV - Machinery - Flurry International, Inc.
FLUSH - Water treating compounds - General Environmental Science Corp.
FLUSH-A-BRUSH - Brushes - Plastics Manufacturing Co.
FLUSH ALL - Washers–metal ☆ - Goodall Manufacturing Co.
FLUSH ATTACK - Game machines - Sigma Game Inc.
FLUSH AWAY - Cleaning preparations - Roebic Laboratories Inc.
FLUSH-BRITE - Cleaning preparations ☆ - Willert Home Products, Inc.
FLUSH FREE - Health care products - Futurebiotics
FLUSH GUARD - Valves - Coast Foundry and Manufacturing Co., Inc.
FLUSH-IT - Cleaning preparations ☆ - Unival Corp.
FLUSH KLEEN - Pumps - Sterling Fluid Systems, Inc.
FLUSH METAL - Hardware - Blaine Window Hardware Inc.
FLUSH-MOUNT - Electrical meters - Emico Inc.
FLUSH 'N CLEAN - Cleaning preparations - Coughlan Products Corp.
FLUSH-RITE - Flush valves - Moeller Products Co. Inc.
FLUSH-SEAL - Hardware - Holo-Krome Co.
FLUSHAWAY - Pet products ☆ - Alfa-Pet Inc.
FLUSHCUTTER - Cutlery - Flushcutter International Corp.
FLUSHER FIXER - Plumbing fixtures - Fluidmaster, Inc.
FLUSHER FIXER KIT - Plumbing fixtures - Fluidmaster, Inc.
FLUSHING - Paints - Chilton Paint Co.
FLUSHMASTER - Machinery - Boattechs Corp.
FLUSHMATE - Flush valves - Water Control International Inc.
FLUSHMATE - Plumbing fixtures - Sloan Valve Co.
FLUSHOIL - Degreasing solvents - Hartline Products Co. Inc.
FLUSTER - Games ☆ - Parker Brothers
FLUTE SACK - Cases–musical instrument - JT Designs
FLUTE SLIP - Cases–musical instrument - JT Designs
FLUTE SPOON - Fishing lures - Bay De Noc Lure Co.
FLUTE SUIT - Musical instrument accessories - Anne Pollack
FLUTED RED SATIN - Glassware–household - Nourot Glass Studio
FLUTED SCROLL - Flatware - Reed and Barton Corp.
FLUTEX - Glass products - AFG Industries Inc. (Glass Group Div.)
FLUTEX - Pharmaceutical preparations - Syosset Laboratories Inc.
FLUTOPHONE - Musical instruments - Trophy Music Co.
FLUTTER BALL - Balls - Playskool, Inc.

FLUTTER BLOSSOM FAMILY, THE - Greeting cards - Linda Grayson Foster
FLUTTER BUG - Toys ☆ - Steven Manufacturing Co.
FLUTTER BY - Bath salts - GPS, Inc.
FLUTTER CHUCK - Fishing lures - Eppinger Manufacturing Co.
FLUTTER FETTI - Confetti - Flutter Fetti Inc.
FLUTTER FIN - Fishing tackle ☆ - Worth Co.
FLUTTER FLAGS - Flags - Flutter Flags of Wilson
FLUTTER FLYS - Exercising equipment ☆ - Jugglebug
FLUTTER LAKER TAKERS - Fishing lures - Bay De Noc Lure Co.
FLUTTER PACK - Bacon - Patcud Investments, Inc.
FLUTTERBURT BUTTERWINK - Kites ☆ - Gayla Industries Inc.
FLUTTERBY - Air purification systems ☆ - Medo Industries, Inc.
FLUTTERBYE - Dresses–women's ☆ - Huntington Industries Inc.
FLUTTERFLY - Games - Centsable Toys Inc.
FLUTTERINA - Toys - Mattel, Inc.
FLUTTERS - Crackers - Pepperidge Farm Inc.
FLUTTERS - Shoe accessories - Direct Source, Llc
FLUVAC - Veterinary product - American Home Products Corp.
FLUVAC PLUS - Vaccines - American Home Products Corp.
FLUVAL - Pet products - Rolf C. Hagen (USA) Corp.
FLUX-OFF - Electronic equipment - Chemtronics Inc.
FLUX-PEN - Solder - Kester Solder Co.
FLUX-STIK - Tools - La-Co Industries, Inc.
FLUX-TYTE - Fluxes–welding and soldering - J.C. Whitlam Manufacturing Co.
FLUX WEAR - Apparel and accessories - Boaz Sade, Inc.
FLUXES - Tools - L.B. Allen Co. Inc.
FLUXMARKER - Electrical equipment - EMF Co., Inc.
FLUXO - Tools - Binford Products, Inc.
FLUXO 50/50 - Solder - Binford Products, Inc.
FLUXOMATIC - Solder - Stewart-Hall Chemical Corp.
FLUXTAC - Iron ore pellets - USX Corp.
FLUZOL - Veterinary pharmaceutical preparations ☆ - Merck & Co., Inc. (Merck Agvet Division)
FLUZONE - Pharmaceutical preparations - Elkins-Sinn Inc.
FLX-O-LOC - Key rings - Lucky Line Products Inc.
FLX SERIES - Amplifiers - Performance Controls, Inc.
FLXIBLE - Buses and structural parts - Flxible Corp.
FLXO - Chore gloves - Boss Manufacturing Co.
FLXTITE - Plastics film - AEP Industries, Inc.
FLXX DEK - Fabrics–broadcloth - Fiberbond Corp.
FLY! - Computer software - PCI Remote Sensing Corp.
FLY - Footwear - Raffaella D'Arezzo
FLY-A-LATER - Fly swatters ☆ - Bravo International Corp.
FLY AND BUG GRABBER - Fly swatters - Plastics Development Corp.
FLY-AWAY - Uniforms–athletic - National Spirit Group, Ltd.
FLY BABIES - Toys - Catco, Inc.
FLY BOY - Video games - Taito America Corp.
FLY BY KNIGHTS - Games - Gamescience
FLY BY NIGHT - Apparel and accessories - Action Screen Printing
FLY DOPE - Insecticides ☆ - Ole Time Woodsman
FLY 'EM - Games ☆ - Testor Corp.
FLY FISHERMAN - Knives - Precise International/Wenger
FLY-FREE - Fly sprays - Farnam Cos. Inc.
FLY GIRLS - Apparel and accessories - Fly Industries, LLC
FLY GONE 7000 - Insecticides - Horseman's Dreams
FLY GUARD - Pet products - Farnam Cos. Inc.
FLY GUITAR - Guitars - Korg/Fishpark Associates
FLY INN - Flypaper - Security Products Co.
FLY IT - Rope ☆ - Crow Rope Industries LLC
FLY JINX - Insecticides - Claire Manufacturing Co.
FLY KIDS - Apparel–children's - Carter Herrera, Inc.
FLY MAGIC - Chemical preparations - Fly Fishing, Inc.
FLY MASK - Veterinary pharmaceutical preparations - Farnam Cos. Inc.
FLY-MATE - Containers - Janco, Inc.
FLY ME - Kites - Kite Factory
FLY ME - Skateboards ☆ - Nash Manufacturing Inc.
FLY N MOSQUITO - Insecticides - Vitarroz
FLY RELIEF - Fly swatters - Farnam Cos. Inc.
FLY RELIEF - Flypaper - Security Products Co.
FLY REPEL - Pet products - Farnam Cos. Inc.
FLY RETREEV - Tools - Fly-Tyer's Carry-All
FLY-SAFE - Fishing tackle ☆ - Martin Reel Co.
FLY SHOOTER - Fly swatters - Sell-O Manufacturing Inc.
FLY SKATERS - Apparel and accessories - Schwartz Communications Inc.
FLY SNIPER - Flypaper - Security Products Co.
FLY STIK - Fly swatters - Farnam Cos. Inc.

☆ = Now out of production

FLY STOP - Flypaper - Security Products Co.
FLY STOP - Pet products - Farnam Cos. Inc.
FLY TECH - Apparel–athletic - International Marketing Specialists, Inc.
FLY TERMINATOR - Fly swatters - Farnam Cos. Inc.
FLY TERMINATOR - Flypaper - Security Products Co.
FLY TRAP - Toys - Tonka Corp.
FLY WARS - Computer software - Sirius Software Development Inc.
FLY-WATE - Fishing tackle ☆ - Martin Reel Co.
FLY-WATE - Leather goods - St. Thomas Inc.
FLY WITH ME - Colognes - Parfum de Coeur Ltd.
FLY WRAPS - Pet products - Fly Wraps
FLYABILITY - Electronic equipment - Thot Technologies
FLYBACK - Sporting goods - Arena USA Inc.
FLYBALL - Computer software - Don Johnston Inc.
FLYBOT - Toys - Mattel, Inc.
FLYBOX - Computer hardware - BG Systems, Inc.
FLYBOY - Toys–airplanes - Cox Products Inc.
FLYBUSTER - Pesticides–household - Advanced Consumer Products, Inc.
FLYCYCLE - Fly swatters - Farnam Cos. Inc.
FLYDINE - Pet products ☆ - 8 in 1 Pet Products Inc.
FLYER - Golfing equipment - Triumph Golf Co.
FLYER - Motor vehicles–motor homes - Cruise America, Inc.
FLYER - Projection screens - Da-Lite Screen Co. Inc.
FLYER - Rackets–tennis - Dayton Racquet Co. Inc.
FLYER - Tires - Bridgestone/Firestone, Inc.
FLYER - Trailers–travel ☆ - Shasta Industries Inc.
FLYERS - Apparel–men's - Tropical Garment Manufacturing Co.
FLYERS - Food products - Tyson Foods Inc.
FLYER'S CHOICE - Bird feeds - Agway Country Foods Inc.
FLYERWARE - Computer software - Cybersight Software
FLYIN' ACES - Toys–airplanes - Mattel, Inc.
FLYIN' FREDDIE - Toys - Tonka Corp.
FLYIN' LION - Kites ☆ - Hi-Flier Manufacturing Co.
FLYIN' WEDGE - Toys - Tonka Corp.
FLYIN' ZOO CRU - Kites ☆ - Hi-Flier Manufacturing Co.
FLYING - Manicure preparations - Flying Emery Board Inc.
FLYING A - Apparel and accessories - Tropical Sportswear International Corp.
FLYING ACE - Clocks - General Time Corp. (Westclox/Seth Thomas Div.)
FLYING ACE - Fruits and vegetables - Ace Tomato Co. Inc.
FLYING ACE - Games ☆ - Avalon Hill Game Co.
FLYING ACE - Skates–roller ☆ - Lancaster Toy Co.
FLYING ARROW - Bicycles - Rideable Bicycle Replicas Inc.
FLYING ASTRONAUTS - Toys - Aims Education Foundation
FLYING BONES - Pet collars - Leatherite-Nylorite Manufacturing Inc.
FLYING BURRITO BROTHERS, THE - Video production - John Beland
FLYING C - Fishing lures - Sheldons', Inc.
FLYING CASINO - Toys - Concept Products Inc.
FLYING CIRCUS - Toys–airplanes - Paul K. Guillow Inc.
FLYING CLIPPER - Skin care products ☆ - Tinkerbell
FLYING CLIPPER - Watches - Bulova Corp.
FLYING CLOUD - Mushrooms - Hogan Associates
FLYING COLORS - Artists' materials ☆ - Sanford Corp.
FLYING COLORS - Bathroom fixtures - Price Pfister Co.
FLYING COLORS - Computer software - Edward Dejong
FLYING COLORS - Computer software ☆ - Knowledge Adventure
FLYING COLORS - Cosmetics ☆ - Noxell Corp.
FLYING COLORS - Flags ☆ - Flags International Inc.
FLYING COLORS - Floor coverings–carpet and rugs - Trend Carpet
FLYING COLORS - Floor coverings–carpet and rugs ☆ - Calladium & Marglen
FLYING COLORS - Wallpaper - Bob Mitchell Designs
FLYING DECOYS - Kites - Sports Innovations Inc.
FLYING DISC - Sleds - Paris Co. Inc.
FLYING DRAGONS - Toys–airplanes - Comet Montrose Ltd.
FLYING DUCKBACK - Labels–paper - Epsen Hillmer Graphics Co.
FLYING DUCKS - Luggage - United States Luggage Corp.
FLYING DUTCHMAN - Balls–golf ☆ - Gencorp Inc.
FLYING DUTCHMAN - Boats ☆ - Dynamic Plastics Inc.
FLYING DUTCHMAN - Boats–skiffs - Flying Dutchman Association
FLYING DUTCHMAN - Cigar boxes–wood - Consolidated Cigar Corp.
FLYING EAGLE - Fruits and vegetables - Rice Fruit Co. Inc.
FLYING EAGLE - Toys–airplanes - Comet Montrose Ltd.
FLYING FANTASIES - Toys–stuffed ☆ - Dakin Inc.
FLYING FINNEGAN - Toys–stuffed ☆ - Kenner Products
FLYING FISH - Bathing suits - Catalina
FLYING FISH - Recording label - Flying Fish Records Inc.
FLYING FISH - Ships–sailing vessels ☆ - Sunfish Laser Inc.

FLYING FISTS - Toys - Mattel, Inc.
FLYING FORTRESS - Wines - Bully Hill Vineyards, Inc.
FLYING FRENCH FRIES - Games ☆ - Western Publishing Co., Inc.
FLYING FRIENDS GARDEN - Flowers, plants, and seeds - W. Atlee Burpee and Co.
FLYING FROG PUBLISHING - Publisher's imprints - Flying Frog Publishing, Inc.
FLYING GOURMET - Bird feeds - Audubon Park Co.
FLYING HIGH - Recording label - Ridge Runner
FLYING HIGH - Wallpaper - Fine Art Wallcoverings Ltd.
FLYING HORSE - Beverages–alcohol - American United Breweries
FLYING JIB - Seafood products–fresh or frozen - King & Prince Seafood Corp.
FLYING JUNIOR - Boats ☆ - Vanguard Racing Sailboats
FLYING L - Fireplace equipment - Lincoln Steel Co.
FLYING LADY - Balls–golf - Spalding Sports Worldwide
FLYING MACHINE - Toys–airplanes - Paul K. Guillow Inc.
FLYING O - Bicycles - Otasco
FLYING OCTANES - Gasoline ☆ - Ashland Oil, Inc.
FLYING OFF SHELVES SINCE 1930 - Bakery products - Interstate Brands Co. - Licensing Co.
FLYING PANDA - Recording label - Jazz Composer's Orchestra Association Inc.
FLYING PIG FOOTBALL - Balls–football - Direct Connect International Inc.
FLYING PIG GALLERY - Office supplies - Stephen Black Design Inc.
FLYING PIRATES - Games ☆ - Parker Brothers
FLYING POINT - Apparel–women's ☆ - Russ Togs Inc.
FLYING QUACKER, THE - Toys - Welcome World Creations
FLYING SAUCER - Boats - Glen-L Marine Designs
FLYING SAUCER - Playground equipment - Learning Products Inc.
FLYING SAUCER - Toys–airplanes - Cox Products Inc.
FLYING SAUCER - Toys–models ☆ - Estes Industries
FLYING SAUCERS - Candy - American Chewing Gum Inc.
FLYING SAUCERS - Ice cream novelty - Carvel Corp.
FLYING SCOT - Ships–sailing vessels - Flying Scot Inc.
FLYING SCOTSMAN - Footwear - Washington Footwear Inc.
FLYING SCOTSMAN - Hosiery–men's ☆ - McCubbin Hosiery Inc.
FLYING SCOUT - Skates–roller ☆ - Chicago Roller Skate Co.
FLYING-SQUIRREL - Toys - Applied Elastomerics, Inc.
FLYING THINGS - Toys - Thomas Lowe Ventures, Inc.
FLYING TIGER - Boats - Nautical Boats Ltd.
FLYING TIGER - Toys–airplanes ☆ - Cox Products Inc.
FLYING TIGERS - Games - Gamescience
FLYING W - Fruits and vegetables - Warren Wagner Inc.
FLYKIL - Garden equipment - Vandermolen Corp.
FLYMASTERS - Fishing tackle - FlyMaster of Indianapolis Inc.
FLYNN - Hardware - Blaine Window Hardware Inc.
FLYNTFABRICS - Rolled fabric - Flynt Fabrics, Inc.
FLYPEL - Insect repellents - Virbac, Inc.
FLYS-AWAY - Insecticides - Farnam Cos. Inc.
FLY'S INN - Fly swatters - Farnam Cos. Inc.
FLYS-OFF - Pet products - Farnam Cos. Inc.
FLYS-X - Veterinary pharmaceutical preparations - W.F. Young, Inc.
FLYSCREEN - Windshield frames–motor vehicle ☆ - National Cycle Inc.
FLYSHACKER CLOTHING CO. - Apparel and accessories - T.C. Lyle, Inc.
FLYSTOP - Air curtain doors - Berner International Corp. (Miniveil Air Curtain Div.)
FLYT - Wet suits–rubber - Dacor Corp.
FLYTE - Tires–bicycles ☆ - Carlisle Tire & Rubber Co.
FLYTHRU - Computer software - Boeing Co.
FLYWARE - Computer software - Gray Matter Technologies, Inc.
FLYWATE - Lighting fixtures - Acme-Lite Manufacturing Co.
FLYWHEELS - Toys - Nylint Toy Corp.
FM - Boats–motor - Starcraft Corp.
FM - Chemical preparations - Oil Chem Technologies, Inc.
F.M. - Food containers - Fed Mart Corp.
FM - Golf club shafts - Brunswick Bowling & Billiards Corp.
FM - Recording label - TH Records & Tapes Inc.
FM-200 - Fire extinguishing compositions - Great Lakes Chemical Corp.
FM-III - Frames–eyeglass - Hoya Corp. USA
FM MUTUAL FUND MANAGEMENT - Computer software - LGBR, Inc.
FM TUBECRAFT - Foam rubber - FM Tubecraft Support Systems Inc.
FMALI - Herbal products - Fmali Herb Co.
FMC - Plastics–laminated - FMC Corp.
FMC - Recording label - Vandor Motion Pictures, Phonorecords & Music Publishing Group

☆ = Now out of production

FMD - Distributors–automotive - Coltec Industries Inc.
FMD - Radios - General Electric Co.
FMF FIELDS & MADISON - Eyeglasses - D.O.C. Optics Corp.
FMI FAMILY MOTIVATION INTERNATIONAL - Recording label - Family Motivation International, Inc.
FML FORTE - Ophthalmic goods - Allergan, Inc.
FML SOP - Ophthalmic goods - Allergan, Inc.
FMP - Cleaning preparations - Franklin Machine Products, Inc.
FMR - Fabrics - Boussac of France Inc.
FMS - Computer software - Servantis Systems, Inc.
FMS1000 - Facsimile enhancer - RICOH Corp.
FMV VALUE - Dog food - Fred Meyer, Inc.
FMX - Computer software - Information Retrieval Companies Inc.
FN - Jewelry - Foremost Novelty Co. Inc.
FN - Needles–sewing - Foster Needle Co. Inc.
FN - Shotguns - Browning Manufacturing Co.
FN-ESSE - Computer software - Toshiba America Information Systems, Inc.
FNA - Apparel and accessories - Future Nation, LLC
FNB - Computer software - Cabletron Systems, Inc.
FNDB - Hosiery - Atlantic Hosiery Inc.
FNL - Nuts and bolts - Fastenal Co.
FNM TABS - Pharmaceutical preparations - Enzyme Process Co. Inc.
FNT - Sporting goods - Victory Sports Nets
FO-TI TIENG - Health care products - Life-Renewal Inc.
FOAL FEEDER - Pet products - Farnam Cos. Inc.
FOAL-MATE - Animal feeds - Manna Pro Corp.
FOAL TO FURLONG - Animal feeds - Evergreen Mills, Inc.
FOAM 140 - Cleaning preparations - E.R. Squibb & Sons, Inc.
FOAM 240 - Disinfectants - E.R. Squibb & Sons, Inc.
FOAM-A-COIL - Cleaning preparations - Stewart-Hall Chemical Corp.
FOAM AIR MAT - Sporting goods - Stearns Manufacturing Co.
FOAM AND FRESH - Deodorizers - Cello Chemical Co.
FOAM AWAY - Paint removers - Kolor Koter Corp.
FOAM BLEND - Cushions - Hickory-Fry Furniture Co. Inc.
FOAM BRILLIANCE - Hair care preparations ☆ - Advanced Research Laboratories
FOAM BRUSH - Brushes–paint - Corona Brushes Inc.
FOAM BUSTER - Chemical preparations - Aqua Clear Industries Inc.
FOAM CARE - Cleaning preparations - Ballard Medical Products
FOAM-CLEEN - Cleaning preparations–household - Stewart-Hall Chemical Corp.
FOAM COAT - Resins–polypropylene ☆ - Flora Craft Inc.
FOAM COIL - Cushions–foam - Hickory Springs Manufacturing Co.
FOAM E - Hair care products - Naturelle, Inc.
FOAM EASE - Floor coverings - Congoleum Corp.
FOAM EASE - Pharmaceutical preparations ☆ - Schering-Plough Healthcare Products
FOAM-EZE - Medical apparatus - Guardian Products Inc.
FOAM FACTORY - Toy - Toymax Inc.
FOAM FARM - Toys - Poof Toy Products, Inc.
FOAM FILES - Nail care products - Rudolph International, Inc.
FOAM FINISH - Cleaning preparations - Auto Wax Co., Inc.
FOAM FLUSH - Engine degreaser ☆ - American Grease Stick Co.
FOAM FRILLS - Foam rubber - Beagle Manufacturing Co. Inc.
FOAM-GRID - Tiles–ceiling - CelloFoam North America Inc.
FOAM IN - Hair care products - Vogue Laboratories
FOAM IN LACE - Hair care products - Andre Fantasies Inc.
FOAM-IT - Sprayers - Innovative Cleaning Equipment Inc.
FOAM-IT-YOURSELF - Plastics - Fibre Glass-Evercoat Co. Inc.
FOAM KIDS - Toys - Berk Corp.
FOAM KILL - Aquariums–household ☆ - Jungle Laboratories Corp.
FOAM KING - Brushes–paint - Wooster Brush Co.
FOAM-LESS - Cleaning preparations–carpet and rug - Uncle Sam Chemical Co., Inc.
FOAM LINE COVER - Paint rollers - Corona Brushes Inc.
FOAM-LOOM - Floor coverings–carpet and rugs - Roxbury Carpet Co.
FOAM LUCK - Adhesives and sealants - Miracle Adhesives
FOAM-MATE - Aquarium accessories - Seafoood Aquavet
FOAM-MATE - Water treating compounds - Novalek, Inc.
FOAM-N-ETTE - Hair care products - Andre Fantasies Inc.
FOAM 'N SHINE - Cleaning preparations - Turtle Wax, Inc.
FOAM-OUT - Hair care products - Helene Curtis Industries Inc.
FOAM OUT - Whirlpools - Geritrex Corp.
FOAM PAC - Cleaning preparations–carpet and rug - PortionPac Chemical Corp.
FOAM PLUS - Foam sealant - Insta-Foam Products, Inc.

FOAM SET - Hair care products - N. Seligman Co.
FOAM-TEX - Chairs–upholstered - Foam Rubber Fabricators Inc.
FOAM-TILE - Floor coverings - Hartco Wood Flooring
FOAM TIME - Hobby kits - Chartpak
FOAM-UP - Hair care products - Helene Curtis Industries Inc.
FOAM WORKS - Hair care products - Revlon-Realistic Professional Products Inc.
FOAMADE - Tape–adhesive - Foamade Industries
FOAMART - Plastics ☆ - Adhesive Products, Inc.
FOAMASTER - Mattresses - Serta, Inc.
FOAMASTIK - Adhesives and sealants ☆ - Dacar Chemical Co.
FOAMATIC - Portable dry-foam shampooer - Advance Machine Co.
FOAMATION - Hair care products - Image Laboratories, Inc.
FOAMBOND - Adhesives and sealants - Sig Manufacturing Inc.
FOAMCLEN - Cleaning preparations–carpet and rug - J.N.T. Manufacturing Co. Inc.
FOAMCOR - Pillows - E.R. Carpenter Co.
FOAMCORE - Doors–garage - Wayne-Dalton Corp.
FOAMCRAFT - Floor coverings ☆ - Tarkett, Inc.
FOAMCUTTER - Saws–power - Kornylak Corp.
FOAMEDGE - Foam rubber - Foamedge Products
FOAMEE - Boats - Glen-L Marine Designs
FOAMFAST - Hardware - Moore Push-Pin Co.
FOAMFIT - Plugs–ear - Bilsom International Inc.
FOAMFLEX - Weather stripping - Mortite Inc.
FOAMGLAS - Insulating materials - Pittsburgh Corning Corp.
FOAMGUARD - Eyeglasses - Dioptics Medical Products, Inc.
FOAMGUARD - Roofing materials–clay ☆ - Flood Co.
FOAMIES - Garment hangers - Cleaners's Supply, Inc.
FOAMING VISTA GLISSEN - Cleaner - Intex Chemical Inc.
FOAMJET - Nozzles - Spraying Systems Co.
FOAMPRO - Foam rubber - Hypro Corp.
FOAMSIL - Glass products - Pittsburgh Corning Corp.
FOAMSULATE - Foam sealant - Insta-Foam Products, Inc.
FOAMTEC - Cleaning equipment - Contec, Inc.
FOAMTHANE - Glass products ☆ - Pittsburgh Corning Corp.
FOAMTON - Mattresses - Westcoast Fiber Inc.
FOAMTONE - Soap ☆ - Tempo Chemical Co. Inc.
FOAMTREADS - Slippers - Kaufman Footwear
FOAMULAR - Insulating materials - Owens Corning
FOAMULAR - Insulating materials - UC Industries, Inc.
FOAMY - Shaving preparations - Gillette Co.
FOAMZORB - Cleaning equipment - Contec, Inc.
FOATING TUBE - Machinery - Oil Skimmers, Inc.
FOBA MINI-SUPERBALL - Cameras - Sinar-Bron Inc.
FOCAL - Hardware - Triangle Brass Manufacturing Co.
FOCAL CREST - Tiles–ceiling - Artcrest Products Co. Inc.
FOCAL POINT - Apparel and accessories - N.A. Fashion, Ltd.
FOCAL POINT - Cosmetics - Alexandra De Markoff, Ltd.
FOCAL POINT - Floor coverings–carpet and rugs ☆ - Blue Ridge Carpet Mills
FOCAL POINT - House furnishings ☆ - Florida Furniture Industries Inc.
FOCAL POINT - Lighting fixtures - Focal Point Lighting
FOCAL POINT - Wallpaper ☆ - Imperial Wallcoverings, Inc.
FOCAL POWERED - Golfing equipment - Lisco, Inc.
FOCAL PRESS - Publisher's imprints - Butterworth Publishers Inc.
FOCALPIN - Binoculars ☆ - Heitz Service Corp.
FOCH - Wines - Bully Hill Vineyards, Inc.
FOCITRON - Frames–eyeglass - Hoya Corp. USA
FOCOMAT - Photographic equipment - Leica USA Inc.
FOCOMETER 2 - Photographic equipment - Leica USA Inc.
FOCOTAR - Photographic equipment - Leica USA Inc.
FOCOVARIO - Cameras ☆ - Heitz Service Corp.
FOCPAC - Computer software - Arisoft Inc.
FOCS - Electrical equipment - Fiberchem, Inc.
FOCUS - Apparel–athletic - JWA Scubapro Undersea Industries, Inc.
FOCUS - Apparel–women's - Newton Manufacturing Corp.
FOCUS - Contact lenses - Ciba Vision Corp.
FOCUS - Electrical equipment - Porta Systems Corp.
FOCUS - Envelopes - Paper Corp. of America
FOCUS - Floor coverings - Azrock Commercial Flooring
FOCUS - Floor finish and reconditioner ☆ - Intex Chemical Inc.
FOCUS - Furniture - Hammary Furniture Co. Inc.
FOCUS - Furniture ☆ - Harter
FOCUS - Furniture–public buildings - Myrtle Desk Co.
FOCUS - Golfing equipment - Slotline Golf
FOCUS - Hair care products - Focus 21 International Inc.

☆ = Now out of production

FOCUS - Hearing aids ☆ - Beltone Electronics Corp.
FOCUS - Medical apparatus - Empi Inc.
FOCUS - Mouthwashes - Lever Brothers Co. Inc.
FOCUS - Navigational instruments - Brookes & Gatehouse Inc.
FOCUS - Pens - Pentech International Inc.
FOCUS - Pet products - Seachem Laboratories
FOCUS - Vitamins and nutritional supplements - Sandy Shaw
FOCUS - Watches - Precision International Co. Inc.
FOCUS/ANF - Hearing aids - Beltone Electronics Corp.
FOCUS DIRECT - Advertising agencies - Focus Direct, Inc.
FOCUS FIVE - Heating equipment - Coleman Co., Inc.
FOCUS FUSION - Computer software - Information Builders, Inc.
FOCUS POINTE - Furniture ☆ - Bassett Furniture Industries, Inc.
FOCUS TEN - Heating equipment - Coleman Co., Inc.
FOCUS, THE - Stoves–wood-burning ☆ - Dovre Inc.
FOCUS, TOO - Apparel–women's - Focus Apparel Group Inc.
FOCUS TRUST - Banks–commercial - Lloyd, Leith & Sawin, Inc.
FOCUSED ON PERFORMANCE - Tools–power-driven - Stanley Works
FOCUSFREE - Electronic equipment - Elmo Manufacturing Corp.
FOCUSMASTER - Sporting goods - Focusmaster, Inc.
FOCUSWEAR - Apparel–women's - Broadway Stores, Inc.
FOCUSXTENDER - Photographic equipment - SP Systems/Saratons
FOCUZ - Frames–picture ☆ - Ammak Manufacturing Corp.
FODOR'S - Publisher's imprints - Fodor's Travel Publications Inc.
FODOR'S EXPLORING - Publisher's imprints - Fodor's Travel Publications Inc.
FODOR'S VIDEO - Video equipment - Fodor's Travel Publications Inc.
FOECKING - Beverages–malt - Loscalzo Inc.
FOG - Apparel and accessories - Londontown Corp.
FOG - Insecticides - H.D. Hudson Manufacturing Co.
FOG-A-YARD - Insecticides ☆ - Demert & Dougherty, Inc.
FOG BUSTER, THE - Mirrors - Showertek, Inc.
FOG BY DESIGN - Hair care products - Image Laboratories, Inc.
FOG CUTTER - Coats - Marshalls, Inc.
FOG FIGHTER - Cleaning preparations - J.I. Morris Co.
FOG-GARD - Food containers - Packaging Corp. of America
FOG-GONE - Cleaning preparations - Camp-Cap Products
FOG LITES - Luggage - Londontown Corp.
FOG MOUNTAIN - Wines - Jean-Claude Boisset Wines, USA, Inc.
FOG TOP MOTORCYCLE ACCESSORIES 13 - Motorcycle parts and accessories - James L. Nickolopoulos and Thomas L. Nickolopoulos Partnership
FOG-X - Antifreeze - Unelko Corp.
FOGACCI - Housewares - Miracle Exclusives Inc.
FOGAL - Hosiery - Fogal Legwear of Switzerland
FOGARTY'S COVE - Recording label - Alcazar Productions
FOGCITY - Plastics film - Modern World Ventures
FOGDOG - Office accessories - Dean C. Williams
FOGG - Industrial machinery - Fogg Filler Co.
FOGG-IT - Insecticides - Black Leaf Products Co.
FOGGER - Fuel systems–motor vehicle - Nitrous Oxide Systems, Inc.
FOGGY BOTTOM ALE - Beverages–malt - Olde Heurich Brewing Co.
FOGGY BOTTOM LAGER - Beverages–malt - Olde Heurich Brewing Co.
FOGHORN - Chocolate candy - Ghirardelli Chocolate Co.
FOGHORN LEGHORN - Video production - Time Warner Entertainment Co.
FOGJET - Nozzles - Spraying Systems Co.
FOGLIA - Tableware–china - Villeroy and Boch Tableware Ltd.
FOGMASTER - Electronic equipment - The Fogmaster Corp.
FOGNOT - Mirrors - John Daniels Inc.
FOGSPRAY - Adhesives and sealants - Imperial Adhesives Inc.
FOGSTAT - Electronic equipment - Mee Industries Inc.
FOHO - Hair care products - Gillette Co.
FOIL-AN-EGG - Novelty items - Easter Unltd. Inc.
FOIL ART - Hobby kits ☆ - Cindus Corp.
FOIL CREATIONS - Artists' materials - Quincrafts Corp.
FOIL FANTASIES - Greeting cards ☆ - Stephen Lawrence Co.
FOIL-FAST - Anchors - Rawlplug Co., Inc.
FOIL-FLEX - Insulating materials - Foil-Ray Inc.
FOIL-GARD - Paints - Perry & Derrick Co.
FOIL IT - Pigments–metallic ☆ - Carnival Arts, Inc.
FOIL-IT 5000 - Foil-stamping machines - Bind-It Corp.
FOIL-LOCK PROTECTS FLAVOR - Fruits and vegetables - Dean Foods Vegetable Co.
FOIL-RAY - Insulating materials - Foil-Ray Inc.
FOIL-RAY DS - Insulating materials - Foil-Ray Inc.
FOIL-RAY PLUS - Insulating materials - Foil-Ray Inc.
FOIL SIMPLICITY - Skin care products - A.J. Oster Foils Inc.

FOILED AGAIN - Greeting cards - P.S. Greetings
FOILED SPORTS - Notebooks and notepads - Norcom Inc.
FOILED SPORTS - Paper punches - Norcom Inc.
FOILER - Bird feeds ☆ - Duncraft, Inc.
FOILEX - Greeting cards ☆ - Royal Stationery Inc.
FOILFLAKE - Leafing powder - U.S. Bronze Powders Inc.
FOILLE - Health care products - Blistex Inc.
FOILLE PLUS - Health care products - Blistex Inc.
FOILMARK - Rolled foils and heat transfers - Foilmark Inc.
FOKKER - Toys–airplanes ☆ - Cox Products Inc.
FOKUS - Recording label ☆ - Northcott Productions Ltd.
FOLABEE - Pharmaceutical preparations ☆ - Vortech Pharmaceuticals
FOLACOLOR - Electronics equipment - Folex Film System
FOLAREX - Electronics equipment - Folex Film System
FOLATHERM - Electronics equipment - Folex Film System
FOLATRAN - Electronics equipment - Folex Film System
FOLAVIEW - Electronics equipment - Folex Film System
FOLD-A-CRIB - Cribs–wood - Evenflo Juvenile Furniture Co.
FOLD-A-DESK - Desks - Steelworks, Inc.
FOLD-A-FARM - Writing product ☆ - Binney & Smith Inc.
FOLD-A-GALAXY - Writing product ☆ - Binney & Smith Inc.
FOLD-A-JUG - Containers ☆ - Igloo Products Corp.
FOLD-A-JUNGLE - Writing product ☆ - Binney & Smith Inc.
FOLD-A-LEAF - Furniture - Michigan Tube Swagers and Fabricators, Inc.
FOLD A LEG - Carpet- and tile-removal equipment ☆ - Inventive Manufacturing
FOLD-A-MAT - Cardboard - Ralph Aranda
FOLD-A-MAT - Mats - E.S. Robbins Corp.
FOLD-A-MATIC - Office supplies - Alvin and Co. Inc.
FOLD-A-PLEAT - Machinery - S. Morantz Inc.
FOLD-A-SCISSOR - Scissors–hand-operated - Jobar International Inc./Bibi Products
FOLD-A-TOWN - Writing product ☆ - Binney & Smith Inc.
FOLD-ASIDE - Hardware ☆ - Stanley Hardware Div.
FOLD-AWAY - Baskets–wood - Fold-Away Basket Co. Inc.
FOLD-AWAY - Kitchen appliances - Rival Manufacturing Co.
FOLD-AWAY - Scales–industrial - Micro General
FOLD AWAY - Travel accessories - American Guard-It Manufacturing Co. Inc.
FOLD-AWAY II - Tables–wood - Stacor Corp.
FOLD BACK SIP LID - Disposable drinking lid - Disposable Products Corp.
FOLD FORM - Building materials - Lite-Form, Inc.
FOLD IT - Cardboard - Stephen E. Berglund
FOLD-LINE - Housewares - Tub-Master Corp.
FOLD LOCK - Photographic equipment - Light Impressions Corp.
FOLD N CLOSE - Plastics - Bedford Industries, Inc.
FOLD N' GO - Boxes - Industrial Molding Corp.
FOLD 'N GO - Carts - Carlisle Foodservice Products, Inc.
FOLD 'N GO - Strollers–baby - Century Products Co.
FOLD 'N GO ACTIVITY QUILT - Infant product - Playskool, Inc.
FOLD 'N GO DIRECTOR'S CHAIR - Chairs–metal - Century Products Co.
FOLD 'N' HOLD - Jewelry ☆ - Napier Co.
FOLD-N-HOLD - Signs - Fasteners for Retail, Inc.
FOLD-N LOK - Barbecues and grills - Thermos Co.
FOLD 'N' MAIL - Office supplies - Abbey Press Inc.
FOLD 'N' PRESS - Photographic equipment ☆ - Heindl Masks 'n' Mounts
FOLD 'N' RINSE - Mops - Empire Brushes, Inc.
FOLD-N-ROLL - Tables–wood - Mitchell Manufacturing Co.
FOLD N SEAL - Tape–adhesive - Mactac Inc. (Packaging Closures Systems Div.)
FOLD-N'-SET - Construction equipment - Sico Inc.
FOLD 'N STORE - Bicycles - Cycle Products Co.
FOLD-N-TOTE - Games - Mattel, Inc.
FOLD 'N TRAVEL - Infant product - Playskool Baby Inc.
FOLD-O-LEG - Tables–wood - Mitchell Manufacturing Co.
FOLD-O-WAY - Office furniture–metal - Art Metal-U.S. Corp.
FOLD-R-TABS - Office supplies - W.H. Brady Co.
FOLD-RITE - Fabrics - Freudenberg Nonwovens Apparel Division
FOLD UNI DRIVE - Screw drivers - Eklind Tool Co.
FOLD UNI KEY - Keys - Eklind Tool Co.
FOLDA SCOOT! - Scooters–motorized - Skoot!, Ltd.
FOLDALITE-B - Health care products - National Biological Corp.
FOLDARACK - Bicycles - Hollywood Engineering Inc.
FOLDAWAY - Furniture–metal ☆ - All-Luminum Products Inc.
FOLDAWAY - Lamps ☆ - Tensor Corp.
FOLDAWAY, THE - Tables–metal - Apollo Audiovisual Div.
FOLDAWAY WORKSHOP - Tools ☆ - Hirsh Co.
FOLDED SANDWICH - Sandwiches–prepackaged - Camino Real Foods

☆ = Now out of production

FOLDEM-UP - Publisher's imprints - Deflecto Corp.

FOLDER - Housewares - Fesco Plastics Corp.

FOLDER - Office supplies - Rubbermaid Office Products Inc.

FOLDER - Wheelchairs ☆ - X-L Manufacturing Co. Inc.

FOLDER-MATE - File folders - Fellowes Manufacturing Co.

FOLDER, THE - Office supplies - Rubbermaid Office Products Inc.

FOLDER-WAY - Hardware ☆ - Richards-Wilcox Manufacturing Co.

FOLDEX - Paper - Imperial Impressions

FOLDIN' PRO - Dryers–hair ☆ - Sunbeam-Oster Household Products

FOLDING FALCON - Archery equipment - Saunders Archery Co.

FOLDING-MITE - Photographic equipment - Rollei of America Inc.

FOLDING PRETTY - Dolls - Mattel, Inc.

FOLDING SAW - Saws–power - Allway Tools Inc.

FOLDING WING - Toys–airplanes - Paul K. Guillow Inc.

FOLDIR - Computer software - Quality Information Systems, Inc.

FOLDMASTER - Doors - Modernfold, Inc.

FOLDOOR - Partitions–wood - Foldoor/Holcomb & Hoke Manufacturing Co. Inc.

FOLDOOR - Partitions–wood - Holcomb & Hoke Manufacturing Co., Inc.

FOLDOVERS - Sandwiches–prepackaged - Maple Leaf Farms Inc.

FOLDSTIR - Tools - Goldblatt Tool Co.

FOLDTITE - Mail boxes - The C.J. Fox Co.

FOLDWING - Awnings ☆ - Alcan Aluminum Corp. Alcan Building Products Div.

FOLETTE - Apparel and accessories - Folette Design, Inc.

FOLEX - Cleaning preparations - RDH Chemical Co.

FOLEY - Catheters - Rochester Medical Corp.

FOLEY - Tools - Foley-Belsaw Co.

FOLEY-BELSAW - Woodworking machinery - Foley-Belsaw Co.

FOLEY DELUXE - Cooking equipment–household ☆ - Mirro Corp.

FOLEY ESTATES VINEYARD & WINERY - Wines - Foley Estates Vineyard and Winery

FOLEY ISLAND - Bedroom furniture - Impact Furniture

FOLEY MARTENS - House furnishings - Foley-Martens Co.

FOLGARD - Vitamins and nutritional supplements - Upsher-Smith Laboratories, Inc.

FOLGER'S - Coffee - Folger Coffee Co.

FOLGERS DARK & RICH SUPREME BEVERAGE - Coffee - Folger Coffee Co.

FOLGERS IRISH CREAM - Coffee - Folger Coffee Co.

FOLGERS T-BIRD - Toys–electronic - Bird Bromiticous Inc.

FOLI-GRO - Fertilizers - Wilbur-Ellis Co.

FOLIAGE - Colognes - Valley Spirit, Inc.

FOLIAGE - Floor coverings–carpet and rugs - Trans-Ocean Import Co. Inc.

FOLIAGE - Pottery ☆ - Doranne

FOLIAGE FRESH - Hobby kits - Flora Craft Inc.

FOLIAGE-PRO - Plant growth regulators - Dyna-Gro Nutrition Solutions

FOLICURE - Hair care products - Pantresse Inc.

FOLIE A DEUX - Wines - Folie A Deux Winery

FOLINI - Wines - Leonard Kreusch Inc.

FOLIO - Cabinets - Norren Manufacturing Inc.

FOLIO - Floor coverings–carpet and rugs ☆ - World Carpets, Inc.

FOLIO - Paper–kraft - Parsons Paper Co.

FOLIO - Wallpaper - Jolie Papier

FOLIO - Wallpaper ☆ - David Merritt Handprints Inc.

FOLIO - Wallpaper ☆ - Winfield Design Associates, Inc.

FOLIO 16 - Furniture ☆ - Henredon Furniture Industries Inc.

FOLIO BASIC - Bathroom fixtures - Kohler Co.

FOLIO D'ITALIA - Diaries - Cachet Products Inc.

FOLIO FOLDER - File folders - Brogdon Studios Inc.

FOLIO RAG - Paper–lithograph ☆ - ANW-Crestwood Paper Co.

FOLIO TEN - Furniture ☆ - Henredon Furniture Industries Inc.

FOLIOCRAFTS - Briefcases - Elizabeth Leather Bags

FOLIZER - Fertilizers - Plant Marvel Laboratories

FOLK/ART - Floor coverings–carpet and rugs ☆ - Concepts International

FOLK ART - Giftware - Enesco Corp.

FOLK ART - Stuffed-animal patterns - D.A. Brinkmann Designs

FOLK ART - Tableware–china ☆ - Pfaltzgraff Investment Co.

FOLK ARTIST - Artists' materials - Robert Simmons Inc.

FOLK COLLECTION, THE - Wallpaper - Eisenhart Wallcoverings Co.

FOLK CRAFT - Dinnerware–glass - Tienshan, Inc.

FOLK CRAFT FRUITS BY TIENSHAN - Tableware–china - Tienshan, Inc.

FOLK CRAFT HEARTS BY TIENSHAN - Tableware–earthenware - Tienshan, Inc.

FOLK ERA - Recording label - Aztec Corp.

FOLK-LORE - Fruit juices - Folk-Lore Natural Foods Inc.

FOLK NYLON - Musical instrument accessories - J. D'Addario & Co. Inc.

FOLK ROOTS - Musical instruments - Folkcraft Instruments

FOLK-STAR - Recording label - Goldband Recording Corp.

FOLK TALES AND FAIRY STORIES - Dolls - Lawton Doll Co.

FOLKART - Artists' materials - Plaid Enterprises, Inc.

FOLKBOATS - Ships–sailing vessels - Scandinavian Yachts

FOLKCRAFT - Housewares ☆ - Shafford Co. Inc.

FOLKCRAFT - Musical instruments - Folkcraft Instruments

FOLKLORE - Floor coverings–carpet and rugs - Coronet Carpets Inc.

FOLKLORE - Floor coverings–carpet and rugs - Trans-Ocean Import Co. Inc.

FOLKLORE - Furniture ☆ - Bassett Furniture Industries, Inc.

FOLKLORE - Lumber - Georgia-Pacific Corp.

FOLKLORE ASSOCIATES - Publisher's imprints - Omnigraphics Inc.

FOLKLORE COLLECTION - Barrettes ☆ - American Greetings Corp.

FOLKLORE HERBS - Health care products - Global Products Inc.

FOLKLYRIC - Recording label - Arhoolie Productions Inc.

FOLKRAFT - Recording label - Folkraft/Dance Record

FOLKS IN LITTLE - Figurines ☆ - Lance Corp.

FOLKSINGER - Musical instrument accessories - E. & O. Mari Inc.

FOLKSTONE - Dinnerware–glass - Noritake Co. Inc.

FOLKSTONE COLLECTION, THE - Figurines - Boyds Collection Ltd.

FOLKTAILS - Puppets - Folkmanis Inc.

FOLKWAYS - Compact discs–prerecorded - TRF Production Music Libraries

FOLKWAYS - Hobby kits - Canvas Creations Inc.

FOLKWAYS - Recording label ☆ - Rounder Records Corp.

FOLKWEAVE - Floor coverings–carpet and rugs - Mohawk Industries Inc.

FOLLANSBEE - Roofing materials - Follansbee Steel Corp.

FOLLETT - Publisher's imprints - Paramount Publishers

FOLLETT CAMPUS RESOURCES - Computer software - Follett Campus Resources

FOLLIFREE - Depilatories - Guaranty Hair Removal

FOLLIGEN - Hair care products - Skin Biology, Inc.

FOLLOW NO ONE - Apparel and accessories - InSport International Inc.

FOLLOW THE LEADER - Bedding–linen - Dan River Inc.

FOLLOW THE STAR - Craft supplies ☆ - VIP/VIP Crafts

FOLLOW YOUR DREAMS - Apparel and accessories - Darrell Conway Stone

FOLLOW YOUR DREAMS - Posters - Successores, Inc.

FOLLOW YOUR INSTINCTS - Glassware–household - Anheuser-Busch Companies Inc.

FOLLOWER, THE - Electronic equipment ☆ - Polyfusion Electronics Inc.

FOLLOWING DIRECTIONS: 1 & 2 - Computer software - Laureate Learning Systems Inc.

FOLLOWING DIRECTIONS LEFT & RIGHT - Computer software - Laureate Learning Systems Inc.

FOLLUTEIN - Pharmaceutical preparations - Bristol-Myers Squibb Co.

FOLLY - Brushes–paint - Wooster Brush Co.

FOLONARI - Wines - Frederick Wildman and Sons Ltd.

FOLTENE - Hair care products - FMG/Tsumara Medical

FOLTZ BROTHERS - Coffee - Foltz Tea & Coffee Co.

FOM - Footwear - Avia Group International Inc.

FOMAC - Pharmaceutical preparations ☆ - Dermik Laboratories Inc.

FOMASOL - Containers - Dri-Kleen, Inc.

FOMATE - Pharmaceutical preparations ☆ - Scrip-Physician Supply Co.

FOME-COR - Artists' materials - International Paper (Decorative Products Division)

FOME-COR - Artists' materials - Monsanto Co.

FOME-COR BOARD - Artists' materials - John Henry Co.

FOMECOTE - Paperboard - Federal Paper Board Co., Inc.

FOMOCO - Integrated circuits - Ford Motor Co.

FONCO - Jewelry - FCF Jewelry Manufacturing Co.

FONCOZY - Electronic equipment - Patricia C. Matheson and Lynda Burke Partnership

FOND DE ROBE - Slips - Henson-Kickernick Inc.

FOND DE TEINT - Cosmetics - Sothys USA Inc.

FOND DU CAVE - Beverages–alcohol - Vinos Argentinos Imports USA

FOND REMEMBRANCE - Floor coverings–carpet and rugs - Downs Carpet Co. Inc.

FONDA BLANCA - Liquors - David Sherman Corp.

FONDE YOUTH - Girdles - Fonde Youth

FONDERIE INCOLAY - Giftware - Incolay Studios Inc.

FONDEST MEMORIES - Dolls ☆ - Gorham Inc.

FONDETTES - Food products - Custom Industries Inc.

FONDI - Chairs–upholstered ☆ - Cramer Inc.

FONDL IT - Office supplies - C. Bennett Scopes Inc.

FONDLY - Toys - Playskool, Inc.

FONDO-ICE - Sugar–granulated, refined, or powdered - Sweetener Products Co.

FONDUE - Furniture ☆ - Bassett Furniture Industries, Inc.
FONE-A-LERT - Communications equipment–mobile - Floyd Bell Inc.
FONE LOCK - Communications equipment - Abdorreza Movassaghi
FONEAIDS - Electronic equipment ☆ - EICO Electronic Instrument Co. Inc.
FONEALIVE! - Telephones - Lynn Wayne Graves
FONEFAX - Directories - U.S. Equities, Inc.
FONET - Communications equipment - Fonet Inc.
FONEY BALONEY - Food products - Lightlife Foods, Inc.
FONG - Brushes–paint - Wooster Brush Co.
FONO-REX - Recording label - Sony Disco Inc.
FONOMUFF - Cushions–foam - Wescosa Inc.
FONOVISA TROPICAL - Recording label - Fonovisa, Inc.
FONSECA - Wines ☆ - European Beverage Co., Inc.
FONSECA GUIMARAENS - Wines - Kobrand Corp.
FONT CONNECTION - Computer software - Adonis Corp.
FONT DE MICHELLE - Beverages–alcohol ☆ - Diamond Wine Merchants
FONT FACTORY GS - Computer software - Seven Hills Software
FONT FREEDOM - Computer software - QMS, Inc.
FONT WIZARD - Computer software - Paper Direct, Inc.
FONTAIN - Watches - Helbros International
FONTAINBLEAU - Underwear and nightwear - Bestform Foundations, Inc.
FONTAINE - Floor coverings–carpet and rugs - Trans-Ocean Import Co. Inc.
FONTAINE - Furniture ☆ - Bernhardt Industries
FONTAINE - Glassware–household ☆ - Crystal Clear Importing Co. Inc.
FONTAINE - Glassware–household ☆ - Lenox Crystal, Inc.
FONTAINE - Pens - Empire Berol USA
FONTAINE - Tableware–china ☆ - Lenox, Inc.
FONTAINEBLEAU - Watches - Elgin Watch Co.
FONTANA - Clarinets ☆ - Deg Music Products Inc.
FONTANA - Floor coverings ☆ - Congoleum Corp.
FONTANA - Footwear - Cherokee Group
FONTANA - Glassware–household ☆ - ACC
FONTANA - Jewelry–costume - B.B. Greenberg Co.
FONTANA - Pens–fountain - Accutec Inc.
FONTANA - Perfumes ☆ - FMG/Tsumara Medical
FONTANA - Whirlpools - Jacuzzi Inc.
FONTANA ARTE - Glassware–household - Venini Ltd.
FONTANA ARTE - Lighting fixtures - Light Inc.
FONTANA CANDIDA - Wines - Brown-Forman Corp.
FONTANA DI TREVI - Beverages–alcohol - Arthur G. Lombardi & Son
FONTANAFREDDA - Wines - Brown-Forman Corp.
FONTANELLA - Pet products ☆ - Finny World Class Pet Products Inc.
FONTANELLE - Wines - Banfi Vintners
FONTANINI BRISTOL FALLS CAROLERS SOCIETY - Giftware - Roman, Inc.
FONTANINI FARMS - Meats - Capitol Wholesale Meats
FONTANINI HEIRLOOM - Giftware - Roman, Inc.
FONTCHAMELEON - Computer software - Ares Software Corp.
FONTENAX - Floor coverings ☆ - Congoleum Corp.
FONTENAY - Floor coverings - Congoleum Corp.
FONTENAY - Watches - Holzerwatch Co. Inc.
FONTENELLE - Jewelry - Elgin Watch Co.
FONTENELLE - Water–mineral - Deep Rock Fontenelle
FONTERUTOLI - Wines ☆ - Pellegrini Bros. Wines Inc.
FONTEVINO - Wines - Tempo Imports Ltd.
FONTHOPPER - Computer software - Ares Software Corp.
FONTINA - Food products - Fontina Foods
FONTINA FOODS - Sauces - Fontina Foods
FONTINELLA - Food products - Universal Foods Corp.
FONTMAKER - Computer peripheral equipment - Vivid Solutions Corp.
FONTMATIC - Computer software - CBF Systems, Inc.
FONTMINDER - Computer software - Ares Software Corp.
FONT'NETTES - Fountains - Henri Studio, Inc.
FONTOGRAPHER - Computer software - Altsys Corp.
FONTVAL - Water–mineral - Felipe A. Valls
FONTVILLAC - Wines - Bercut-Vandervoort & Co.
FONTVISION - Computer software - Lexmark International, Inc.
FONZ POPS - Candy ☆ - Beacon Sweets, Inc.
F.O.O. - Games - First One, Inc.
FOO FIGHTERS - Posters - McDonald & Quackenbush, P.S.
FOO FOO LITTLE SIGNS OF INTELLIGENCE - Novelty items - Michael W. Pfau
FOOBLITZKY - Computer software - Activision, Inc.
FOOD-A-RAMA - Food products - Basics Food Centers
FOOD/ANALYST - Computer software - Hopkins Technology LLC
FOOD/ANALYST PLUS - Computer software - Hopkins Technology LLC
FOOD AND WINE WINNERS - Computer software - E-8 Publications, Inc.

FOOD ANGEL - Jewelry - Anne Rooney
FOOD CENTER - Kitchen appliances - Nutone Inc.
FOOD CHAIN - Recording label - Platinum Music, Inc.
FOOD CLUB - Food products - Frank's Food Mart
FOOD CLUB MALTA - Beverages–carbonated - Florida Brewing Co.
FOOD COMBINING MADE EASY - Publisher's imprints - Ten Talents Distributors
FOOD COMPANION - Publisher's imprints - Weight Watchers International, Inc.
FOOD CYCLER - Bags - Woods End Research Laboratory, Inc.
FOOD FACTORY - Food processors - Sanyo Fisher (USA) Corp.
FOOD FIGHT - Video games - Atari Games Corp.
FOOD FIGHT & DESIGN - Toys - Mattel, Inc.
FOOD FIGHTERS - Toys - Mattel, Inc.
FOOD-FIGHTING - Toys - Mattel, Inc.
FOOD FILE - Office supplies - Rolodex Corp.
FOOD FLYER - Spoons - Harber Inc.
FOOD FOR THOUGHT - Food products - Swiss American Import Co.
FOOD FOR THOUGHT - Publisher's imprints - Iams Co.
FOOD FOR THOUGHT - Toys–stuffed - Mary Meyer Corp.
FOOD FRESH - Chemical preparations - G. P. Marketing, Inc.
FOOD FRESH - Gases and gas mixtures - BOC Group Inc.
FOOD GARDEN - Snack foods - Aspac Trading Corp.
FOOD GIANT - Grocery stores ☆ - Food Giant Inc.
FOOD GIFT GREETINGS - Greeting cards - Continnuus
FOOD GRADE INTERSTATE ICE - Ice - Interstate Ice Inc.
FOOD GROUPIE - Publisher's imprints - Food Groupie Inc.
FOOD INGREDIENTS TECHNOLOGY - Chickens - American Dehydrated Foods Inc.
FOOD KING - Food products ☆ - Shurfine International, Inc.
FOOD-LINE - Milk - Dairy Fresh Corp.
FOOD LION - Cleaning preparations - Food Lion, Inc.
FOOD MILL INC., THE - Food products - Food Mill, Inc.
FOOD 'N' FOUNTAIN - Pet products - Molor Products Co.
FOOD-N-WATA - Pet products - Blitz USA Inc.
FOOD-N-WATA II - Pet products - Blitz USA Inc.
FOOD OF NATURE - Pet products - Jones Manufacturing Co.
FOOD PAC - Machinery - Sweetheart Cup Co. Inc.
FOOD PRIDE - Fruits and vegetables - Nash-Finch Co.
FOOD PRODUCT - Food products - Andre Prost Inc.
FOOD PYRAMID LOTTO E D P V F G - Games - Yummy Designs
FOOD SERVICES OF AMERICA - Frankfurters ☆ - Olympic Foods Inc.
FOOD SHAPETTE - Kitchen appliances - Projectapix-II
FOOD SHOOTER - Food processors ☆ - National Presto Industries, Inc.
FOOD STAMPS - Stamps–hand - Nature Impressions
FOOD STATE - Vitamins and nutritional supplements - Bio San Laboratories Inc.
FOOD STATE - Vitamins and nutritional supplements - Biosan Laboratories, Inc.
FOOD TOTE - Copper compounds ☆ - Regal Ware, Inc.
FOOD TOWN - Seafood products–fresh or frozen ☆ - Singleton Seafood Co.
FOOD TRAIN - Cookware - Standex International Corp.
FOOD TREND - Food products - VIP Sales Co. Inc.
FOOD YOU FEEL GOOD ABOUT - Food products - Wegmans Food Markets, Inc.
FOODARAMA - Refrigerators - White Consolidated Industries, Inc.
FOODCO - Food products machinery - Kitchen-Quip Inc.
FOODCRAFT - Fruits–canned - Groce-Wearden Co.
FOODCRAFTER - Kitchen appliances - Sunbeam-Oster Household Products
FOODFORM - Vitamins, minerals - Intracell Nutrition Inc.
FOODFORM MANNA - Vitamins - Intracell Nutrition Inc.
FOODGUARD - Controls–refrigeration systems - Humidity Control Technologies, Inc.
FOODKEEPERS - Containers ☆ - Anchor Hocking Glass, Inc.
FOODKEEPERS - Housewares ☆ - Plastics, Inc. (Anchor Hocking Plastics)
FOODLAND - Food products - Super Valu Inc.
FOODLAND - Food products - Wetterau Inc.
FOODLES - Paper–newsprint - Newark Morning Ledger Co.
FOODMASTER - Kitchen appliances - Kitchen-Quip Inc.
FOODMASTER - Refrigerators - White Consolidated Industries, Inc.
FOODQUIP - Knives - Camilo Pereira
FOODS FROM THE SEA - Seafood products–fresh or frozen - Stavis Seafoods Inc.
FOODS OF NEW MEXICO - Food products - New Mexico Food Distributors, Inc.
FOODS PLUS - Dairy products - John C. Groub Co., Inc.
FOODSAVER - Packaging machines - Tilia, Inc.

FOODSERVICE PACK - Tuna–canned - Van Camp Seafood Co. Inc.

FOODSTAR INFORMATION SYSTEMS - Computer software - Pocahontas Foods USA Inc.

FOODSTUFFS - Fruits–dried - Foodstuffs Inc.

FOODTOWN - Pizza - Continental Food Products Inc.

FOODTOWN QUALITY & VALUE - Foil–aluminum - Foodtown

FOOFUR - Toys–stuffed - Dakin Inc.

FOOL-A-BUG - Insecticides - Alternative Control Systems Corp.

FOOLER, THE - Paint rollers - Redtree Industries, Inc.

FOOLPROOF - Computer software - Smartstuff Development Corp.

FOOL'S GOLD - Hair care products - Cosmair Inc.

FOON GOOS - Vitamins and nutritional supplements - Kroeger Herb Products Co. Inc.

FOON GOOS #2 - Vitamins and nutritional supplements - Kroeger Herb Products Co. Inc.

FOOT AND ALF OF ALE - Glassware–household - Crisa Corp.

FOOT & ANKLE - Shoe accessories - PediFix Footcare Co.

FOOT & CALLUS RUB - Skin care products - Set-N-Me-Free Aloe Vera Co.

FOOT BEAUTY - Skin care products - Schering-Plough Healthcare Products

FOOT BOWL - Bowls - B. Aronson Inc.

FOOT CHARGERS - Health care products - Remington Products Co.

FOOT COMFORT - Slippers ☆ - Schering-Plough Healthcare Products

FOOT COOLER - Footcare products - PediFix Footcare Co.

FOOT CUSHION - Door mats - Royal Rubber & Manufacturing Co.

FOOT EASE - Computer peripheral equipment - MicroComputer Accessories Inc.

FOOT EASE - Skin care products ☆ - Hess Hair Milk Laboratories Inc.

FOOT-EEZ - Floor coverings - American Floor Products Co. Inc.

FOOT FANCY - Cosmetics - Worldwide Cosmetics

FOOT FETISH - Novelty items - Nancy J. Wolff

FOOT FIXER, THE - Health care products ☆ - Remington Products Co.

FOOT FLEX FLOW THRU - Shoes - Warson Group Inc.

FOOT FREE SAFETY STIRRUP, THE - Sporting goods - Equestrian International Products

FOOT FRESH'NER - Deodorizers - L & A, Inc.

FOOT FRIENDS - Skin care products - Liberty Natural Products

FOOT FRILLS - Jewelry - Foot Flings, Inc.

FOOT GLOVES - Socks - Boss Manufacturing Co.

FOOT GUARD - Deodorants–personal - Gillette Co.

FOOT GYM - Footwear - PediFix Footcare Co.

FOOT-HUGGERS - Socks - Wigwam Mills Inc.

FOOT JINGLES - Infant product - Playskool Baby Inc.

FOOT-JOY - Shoes - Titleist & Foot-Joy Worldwide

FOOT-JOY 500 - Shoes–athletic ☆ - Titleist & Foot-Joy Worldwide

FOOT LIGHTNING - Drums–musical instruments ☆ - LP Music Group

FOOT LOOSE - Floor coverings–carpet and rugs ☆ - Columbus Mills, Inc.

FOOT LOVER - Mats - Ludlow Composites Corp.

FOOT MAGIC - Shoes - Colby Footwear, Inc.

FOOT MAGIC - Skin care products - Hair Specialty Co.

FOOT MAGIC - Skin care products - Nu-Tek Laboratories, Inc.

FOOT MASSAGING CREAM - Skin care products - Schering-Plough Healthcare Products

FOOT MATE - Massage tool - Jackson Enterprises Inc.

FOOT MATE - Nail care products - Nailmate Inc.

FOOT MATES - Footwear–children's - Badorf Shoe Co. Inc.

FOOT MIRACLE - Laxatives - Biopractic Group II Inc.

FOOT MOUSE - Computers ☆ - Versatron Corp.

FOOT NOTES - Musical instruments - Florida Entech Corp.

FOOT ODOR RESCUE - Skin care products - Benchmark Brands

FOOT OF BUBBLEGUM, A - Chewing gum - Sahagian & Associates, Inc.

FOOT-PALS - Shoes - Wall-Streeter Shoe Co.

FOOT PLOWS - Footwear - Summit Footwear Inc.

FOOT POINT - Shoes - Royal Footwear Co., Inc.

FOOT PRESERVER JRS. - Footwear–children's ☆ - Goodwear Shoe Co. Inc.

FOOT REJUVENATING CREAM - Skin care products - Sara Lee Corp.

FOOT REPAIR - Pharmaceutical preparations - Jess Clarke & Sons Inc.

FOOT REST - Foot support stand - Tiffin Systems

FOOT SACK - Health care products ☆ - Sunbeam-Oster Household Products

FOOT SAVER - Floor coverings - American Floor Products Co. Inc.

FOOT SAVER - Shoes - Drew Shoe Corp.

FOOT SAVER - Shoes - Tingley Rubber Corp.

FOOT SCENE - Shoes - Genesco Inc.

FOOT-SO-PORT - Shoes - Foot-So-Port

FOOT SPA - Bath salts - Clairol Inc.

FOOT STAT - Mats - Matworks

FOOT TENT - Bedding supports - Relaxacizor Products Inc.

FOOT THRILLS - Footwear–women's - Clinic Shoe Co.

FOOT TRAFFIC - Socks - Foot Traffic, Inc.

FOOT TRAIL - Sleeping bags - Ken Jenks

FOOT TRAITS - Shoes - W.L. Kreider's Sons Manufacturing Co. Inc.

FOOT TRAVELER - Massage tool - Jackson Enterprises Inc.

FOOT TREAT - Manicure preparations - Delore International

FOOT-TROL - Medical apparatus - CONMED Corp.

FOOT-TULE - Exercising equipment - Kenneth Lay

FOOT WARMER - Health care products ☆ - Sunbeam-Oster Household Products

FOOT WARMERS - Shoe soles ☆ - Combe Inc.

FOOT-Z - Shoes - Encore Shoe Corp.

FOOTAGE - Hosiery ☆ - Keepers International

FOOTBALL - Candy - Topps Co., Inc.

FOOTBALL - Floor coverings–carpet and rugs - Regal Rugs Inc.

FOOTBALL BASH IN A CAN - Novelty items - Great American Idea Co., Inc.

FOOTBALL BEAR - Toys–stuffed - Dakin Inc.

FOOTBALL BOOK, THE - Computer software - SourceView Software International

FOOTBALL FEVER - Napkins–paper ☆ - The Chinet Co.

FOOTBALL FIELD - Food products - Aiello's Golden Crust

FOOTBALL FLICKERS - Toys - Russ Berrie and Co., Inc.

FOOTBALL FLING - Health care products - Sammons Preston

FOOTBALL FOR BREAKFAST - Tape–adhesive - Breakfast Enterprizes Inc.

FOOTBALL FRENZY - Video machines, programs, and cartridges - Snk Corp. of America

FOOTBALL GOT ME HOOKED NOT DRUGS - Apparel and accessories - Dick Leon

FOOTBALL GOT ME HOOKED NOT DRUGS - Apparel and accessories - Palace Sports Center

FOOTBALL LOTTO FREE - Games - Rogert's Enterprises, Inc.

FOOTBALL MASTER - Computer software - SourceView Software International

FOOTBALL PARLAY FREE - Games - Rogert's Enterprises, Inc.

FOOTBALL SNACKS - Bakery products - Flowers Family Bakeries, Inc.

FOOTBALL SQUARES - Games - Miller Brewing Co.

FOOTBALL STRATEGY - Games - Avalon Hill Game Co.

FOOTBALL TEDDY - Toys–stuffed - Russ Berrie and Co., Inc.

FOOTBALL TODAY - Trading cards and stamps - Treat Entertainment, Inc.

FOOTCO - Shoe insoles - Benchmark Brands

FOOTEASE - Mats - Interstate Mat & Rubber

FOOTFIT - Shoe insoles - Donald C. Hodge

FOOTFITNESS - Footwear - Swenson Imports

FOOTFUR - Puzzles ☆ - Milton Bradley Co.

FOOTGARD - Shoes - Hershberg Shoe Co. Inc.

FOOTGARDS - Footwear - Handgards Inc.

FOOTHERAPY - Bath salts - General Therapeutics Inc.

FOOTHERAPY FOOT SALTS - Skin care products - Para Laboratories Inc.

FOOTHILL FARMS - Salad dressings–mixes - Benno Food Products Corp.

FOOTHILLS - Floor coverings–carpet and rugs ☆ - Kelly Group Inc.

FOOTHILLS LEATHER - Tools - Jural Manufacturing Co.

FOOTHOLD - Abrasive products ☆ - Norton Co.

FOOTHOLD - Exercising equipment - Randy Miller

FOOTHOLD - Footwear - Wolverine World Wide, Inc.

FOOTLETS - Socks - Leininger Mills Inc.

FOOTLIGHTS - Floor coverings–carpet and rugs - Mohawk Industries Inc.

FOOTLIGHTS - Toys - Mattel, Inc.

FOOTLITES - Brackets - Feetsie, Inc.

FOOTLITES - Footwear - Wolverine World Wide, Inc.

FOOTLOOSE - Floor coverings–carpet and rugs - Coronet Carpets Inc.

FOOTLOOSE - Hosiery - Belmont Hosiery Mills Inc.

FOOTLOOSE - Toys - Tonka Corp.

FOOTLOVER - Mats - Matworks

FOOTMATE, THE - Brushes - Footwork Corp.

FOOTMAXX - Orthopedic insoles - Physical Support Systems Inc.

FOOTMOBILE - Footwear - Stepperz, Inc.

FOOTNEWS - Footwear - Avanti Shoe

FOOTNOTES - Footwear–women's - Wohl Shoe Co.

FOOTNOTES - Hosiery - Mayer/Berkshire Corp.

FOOTNOTES - Musical instrument accessories - Wenger Corp.

FOOTNOTES - Pre-printed labels - Robert E. Korth

FOOTNOTES - Skin care products - Cosmedic Concepts, Inc.

FOOTNOTES IN TIME - Frames–picture - Footnotes in Time, Inc.

FOOTONIC II - Shoe accessories - Mason Shoe Manufacturing Co.

FOOTONIC ULTRA - Shoe accessories - Mason Shoe Manufacturing Co.

FOOTPATH - Floor coverings–carpet and rugs - Regal Rugs Inc.

FOOTPRINT - Furniture - Kimball International, Inc.

☆ = Now out of production

FOOTPRINT - Railroad equipment - ABC Rail Products Corp.
FOOTPRINT WORKS - Computer software - Footprint Software Corp.
FOOTPRINTS - Computer software - Hardy Software Systems, Inc.
FOOTPRINTS - Footwear - Birkenstock Footprint Sandals, Inc.
FOOTPRINTS - Mats - Mr. Tux, Inc.
FOOTQUARTERS - Socks - Kinney Shoe Corp.
FOOTREST - Footwear - Etta-Kit Enterprises
FOOTRESTS - Shoes - Wolverine World Wide, Inc.
FOOTSAVER - Health care products - Dazey Corp.
FOOTSAVERS - Footwear - Bostonian Shoe Co.
FOOTSHIELD - Footwear - Lehigh Safety Shoe Co.
FOOTSIE - Housewares - Deka Plastics Inc.
FOOTSIE - Skin care products - Gold Medal Hair Products Inc.
FOOTSIE WOOTSIES - Footwear–children's - Luna International USA Inc.
FOOTSKI - Steel springs–railroad - Morning Sun Inc.
FOOTSMART - Skin care products - Benchmark Brands
FOOTSOAKER - Medical apparatus - John P. Rothacker
FOOTSTEPS - Nail care products - Mary Kay Cosmetics Inc.
FOOTSTEPS - Shoes - Dentex Shoe Co.
FOOTSTONE - Natural lava stones - United States Pumice Co.
FOOTWARMERS - Apparel and accessories - R. Josephs Sportswear, Inc.
FOOTWORKS - Footwear ☆ - Brown Shoe Co.
FOOZZEE - Pet products - RHB Enterprises
FOP - Computer software - Four Horsemen Software
FOPPIANO VINEYARDS - Wines - L. Foppiano Wine Co.
FOPPIANO VINEYARDS - Wines - House of Burgundy Inc.
FOPP'S - Apparel–women's - Fopp's Design Ltd.
FOR A HEALTHY MOUTH - Toothpaste - Conopco, Inc.
FOR A HEALTHY PLANET - T-shirts–men's - Bugle Boy Industries, Inc.
FOR A KINDER, CLEANER AMERICA - Gloves - Intelligent Products Inc.
FOR ALL THE RIGHT REASONS - Beverages - Blue World, Inc.
FOR ALL THE WORLD TO SEE - Lenses–magnifying - MFD Enterprises, Inc.
FOR-ANY-JOB - Varnishes - United Hardware
FOR ANY JOB THAT'S TUFF-N-RUFF - Containers–paper - Tuff-E-Nuff Products, Inc.
FOR ARMS - Health care products - Service Associates
FOR ATHLETES ONLY - Vitamins and nutritional supplements ☆ - ICN Pharmaceuticals, Inc.
FOR-AZ-MA - Cough medicines ☆ - Vitarine Pharmaceuticals Inc.
FOR BATHROOMS ONLY - Wallpaper - United Wallcoverings
FOR BEAUTIFUL HAIR ONLY - Hair care products - Ecostyle, Inc.
FOR BEGINNERS - Publisher's imprints - Writers and Readers Publishing, Inc.
FOR BRAIDED HAIR ONLY - Hair care products - Ecostyle, Inc.
FOR BRIDES VIDEO WEDDING PLANNER - Video production - NWN Communications Group
FOR BRUNETTES ONLY - Hair care products - Alberto-Culver Co.
FOR CHARMSAKE - Hobby kits ☆ - Mangelsen's (VDI)
FOR CHOCOLATE LOVERS ONLY - Air purification systems ☆ - Medo Industries, Inc.
FOR-COAT - Adhesives and sealants ☆ - Grace Construction Products
FOR COMMENT - Computer software - Broderbund Software, Inc.
FOR DESSERT - Coffee - F. Gavina and Sons Inc.
FOR DIRTY KIDS - Skin care products ☆ - FMG/Tsumara Medical
.FOR DUMMIES - Publisher's imprints - International Data Group, Inc.
FOR EMERGENCY PERSONNEL TCISC - Decals and transfers - Critical Information Storage Center Corp.
FOR EVER - Floor waxes - Grow Group, Inc.
FOR EVERY SEASON - Greeting cards - Leanin' Tree Inc.
FOR EVERYTHING SWEET 'N SOUR - Food products - Skansen Food Packers
FOR EXAMPLE - Bedding–linen - For Example Inc.
FOR FACES ONLY - Suntan lotions - Schering-Plough Healthcare Products
FOR FEET THAT COMPETE - Hosiery - Wigwam Mills Inc.
FOR FRUIT N'STUFF - Food products - Regency Creative Foods
FOR FUN ON THE RUN - Games - Hasbro, Inc.
FOR-GIVING STONE - Giftware - For-Giving Stone
FOR GOODNESS FLAKES - Cereal - Sovex Foods, Inc.
FOR HEAT'S SAKE - Air conditioning equipment - Hercules Chemical Co. Inc.
FOR KEEPS - Cases–plastic ☆ - Newell Office Products
FOR KEEPS - Diapers–disposable - Koalakins Inc.
FOR KIDS ONLY - Cereal - Ralston Foods, Inc.
FOR KIDS ONLY - Vitamins and nutritional supplements - Only Natural, Inc.
FOR KIDS ONLY - Wallpaper - United Wallcoverings
FOR KIDS ONLY II - Wallpaper - United Wallcoverings
FOR KITCHENS ONLY - Wallpaper - United Wallcoverings
FOR LADIES ONLY - Briefcases ☆ - Belle Cadeaux Inc.

FOR LEADING PROPERTIES OF THE WORLD - Skin care products - Forest Essentials
FOR LIFE IN THE OPEN - Apparel and accessories - Walls Industries, Inc.
FOR MEN ON THE GO - Apparel and accessories - Gentry Inc.
FOR MEN ONLY - Footwear - Volpe Shoe Co.
FOR MEN ONLY - Vitamins and nutritional supplements - Only Natural, Inc.
FOR MEN ONLY - Wallpaper - United Wallcoverings
FOR MEN ONLY & WOMEN TOO! - Hair care products - Andre Fantasies Inc.
FOR MILITARY WE'RE IT - Apparel and accessories - Kaufman Surplus Inc.
FOR ONE OR MORE - Cooking equipment–household ☆ - Chicago Metallic Products Inc.
FOR OPENERS - Greeting cards - Sunrise Publications, Inc.
FOR OPENERS - Hair care products - Helene Curtis Industries Inc.
FOR PEOPLE WHO BUILD THINGS - Nuts and bolts - Bontel Fastener Corp.
FOR PERMS ONLY - Hair care products - For Perms Only Inc.
FOR PETS SAKE - Pet food - Super Valu Inc.
FOR PLAY - Biological products - Pharmaceutical Innovations
FOR REAL KIDS - Apparel stores–women's - Lady Ester Lingerie Corp.
FOR SALE - Automotive parts and accessories - John M. Sanders
FOR SEASONS - Pet products - City Dog Designed Co., Inc.
FOR SERIOUS INFORMATION - Consulting services - Nerac, Inc.
FOR TELEPHONES AND TELEPHONE ANSWERING MACHINES - Telephones - Conair Corp.
FOR THE ATHLETE IN ALL OF US - Beverages - California Sportseltzer Inc.
FOR THE BIRDS - Pet products - For the Birds
FOR THE BIRDS INC. - Housewares ☆ - For the Birds
FOR THE CULTURALLY REFINED - Apparel and accessories - Loyd Anthony Inc.
FOR THE ECOLOGY CONCERNED - Greeting cards ☆ - Recycled Paper Products, Inc.
FOR THE ELITE - Floor coverings–carpet and rugs ☆ - Prestige Mills Inc.
FOR THE LIFE OF YOUR BOAT - Paints - Life Industries Corp.
FOR THE LONG RUN - Exercising equipment - Woodway USA, Inc.
FOR THE LOVE OF ART - Greeting cards - Leanin' Tree Inc.
FOR THE LOVE OF DAIRY - Pharmaceutical preparations - Johnson & Johnson
FOR THE LOVE OF WOOD - Varnishes - Master Products Inc.
... FOR THE LOVE OF YOUR PET - Pet shops - Sergeant's Pet Products, Inc.
FOR THE MORE EXCITING WOMAN - Apparel and accessories ☆ - Edison Brothers Stores, Inc.
FOR THE ONES YOU LOVE - Water–bottled or canned - Absopure Water Co.
FOR THE OUTDOORS IN YOU - Footwear–athletic - KPR Sports International, Inc.
FOR THE RECORD - Computer software ☆ - Nolo Press/Folklaw Inc.
FOR THE WALL - Wallpaper ☆ - Wallpaper Imports Inc.
FOR THOSE OF YOU WHO THINK YOU KNOW - Games - Poole Enterprises, Inc.
FOR THOSE WHO KNOW BETTER - Apparel and accessories - Galt Sand Co.
FOR THOSE WHO LIVE BY A CODE - Apparel and accessories - Area Code Where? Ltd.
FOR TODAY'S CHILDREN AND TOMORROW'S - Furniture - Tyke Corp.
FOR TODAY'S SMARTER CARS - Lubricants - Ashland Oil, Inc.
FOR-TRESS - Hair care products - Nutrine Ltd.
FOR TWO. FOREVER. - Jewelry - CJC Holdings, Inc.
FOR UPSCALE FISH - Aquarium ornaments - Doug Stewart Photo
FOR VEGGIES N'STUFF - Puddings–mixes - Regency Creative Foods
FOR WOMEN, BY WOMEN. - Apparel stores–women's - Orvis Co., Inc.
FOR WOMEN ONLY - Apparel–women's - J. Schoeneman Inc.
FOR WOMEN ONLY - Vitamins and nutritional supplements - Only Natural, Inc.
FOR WOMEN ONLY - Vitamins and nutritional supplements - Vitaquest International, Inc.
FOR WOMEN ONLY - Wallpaper - United Wallcoverings
4 YOU - Apparel and accessories - Mondo, Inc.
FOR YOU ALONE - Greeting cards ☆ - American Greetings Corp.
FOR YOUR COMFORT - Pillows - Pacific Coast Feather Co.
FOR YOUR COMFORT...NATURALLY - Comforters - Pacific Coast Feather Co.
FOR YOUR EARS ONLY - Hearing aids - Hear Tronics
FOR YOUR EARS ONLY - Jewelry - Lori Greiner
FOR YOUR EYES ONLY - Cosmetics - Max Factor & Co.
FOR YOUR EYES ONLY - Games - Avalon Hill Game Co.
FOR YOUR EYES ONLY - Wallpaper - Sherburne Ewing Wallcovering Co.
FOR YOUR FACE ONLY - Skin care products - Home Health Products, Inc.
FOR YOUR FLIES ONLY - Fishing lures - Frank W. Sparkman
FOR YOUR HOMESTYLE - Wallpaper - Sherburne Ewing Wallcovering Co.
FOR YOUR INFORMATION GAMEMASTER - Games - Avalon Hill Game Co.

☆ = Now out of production

FOR YOUR LIFE STYLES - Wallpaper - Sherburne Ewing Wallcovering Co.
FOR YOUR LIPS - Sunblocks - Solar Sense Corp.
FOR YOUR NEXT ADVENTURE - Computer software ☆ - Sunburst Communications, Inc.
FORAGE - Computer software - Advanced Information Mgmt., Inc.
FORALL - Siding–insulating ☆ - Forestex Co.
FORAMBA - Insecticides ☆ - Uncle Sam Chemical Co., Inc.
FORANATE - Pharmaceutical preparations ☆ - Legere Pharmaceuticals Inc.
FORAY - Computer software - Techsmith Corp.
FORAY - Fire extinguishers - Ansul, Inc.
FORBES FOR BEST - Greeting cards - Paul P. Forbes
FORBIDDEN - Colognes ☆ - Dana Perfumes Corp.
FORBIDDEN FRAGRANCE, THE - Colognes - Les Parfums De Dana, Inc.
FORBIDDEN KNOWLEDGE - Computer software - David P. Solomon
FORBIDDEN RICE - Rice - Lotus Management Group
FORC-AIRE - Heating equipment - Surface Combustion, Inc.
FORCE - Adhesives and sealants - Dymax Corp.
FORCE - Amplifiers - Electro-Voice, Inc.
FORCE - Bicycles ☆ - Roadmaster Corp.
FORCE - Drycleaning machines - Kelleher Equipment Co., Inc.
FORCE - Footwear - BRS, Inc.
FORCE - Rackets–tennis ☆ - Wilson Sporting Goods Co.
FORCE - Skis - Stockli/Prestige USA
FORCE - Tool boxes - Flambeau Products Corp.
FORCE - Vitamins and nutritional supplements ☆ - Lustol Co.
FORCE - Weightlifting equipment ☆ - Maximus Fitness Products
FORCE 2 - Safety products - D B Industries, Inc.
FORCE 4 - Tires - Bridgestone/Firestone, Inc.
FORCE-5 - Fuel systems–motor vehicle - Tomco, Inc.
FORCE 5 - Ships–sailing vessels - Sunfish Laser Inc.
FORCE-5 - Shoes - Converse Inc.
FORCE-9 - Fire extinguishers ☆ - Kidde Safety
FORCE 15 POLYMER - Sporting goods - Moody & Co. Inc.
FORCE 109 - Lubricants - Loctite Corp.
FORCE 842 - Lubricants - LPS Laboratories, Inc.
FORCE CASE MARKER - Office machines - A.D. Joslin Manufacturing Co.
FORCE CONTINUUM - Educational materials - Armament Systems and Procedures, Inc.
FORCE ENERGIQUE - Health care products - Natural Approach
FORCE FIELD - Apparel–athletic - 3V Development Inc.
FORCE FIELD - Chemical preparations - Shield Industries, Inc.
FORCE FIELD - Games - Mattel, Inc.
FORCE FIVE - Boats - Frank M. Weeks Yacht Yard
FORCE FIVE - Windows–storm - Texas Aluminum Industries Inc.
FORCE FLOW - Helmets–athletic ☆ - Bell Sports Corp.
FORCE GUARD - Electrical equipment - Gmi Holdings, Inc.
FORCE I - Golfing equipment ☆ - Bost Enterprises, Inc.
FORCE II - Archery equipment - Pro Line Co.
FORCE MAJEURE - Health care products - Natural Approach
FORCE OF FREEDOM - Toys - Hasbro, Inc.
FORCE ONE - Toys–automobiles - ERTL Co., Inc.
FORCE OUTBOARDS - Apparel - Brunswick Corp.
FORCE SERIES - Skates–roller - Seneca Sports, Inc.
FORCE, THE - Chemical preparations - American Technologies Group, Inc.
FORCE WORKS - Books–comic ☆ - Marvel Entertainment Group, Inc.
FORCED AIR - Automotive parts and accessories - Franklin Yunes
FORCEFUL - Floor coverings–carpet and rugs ☆ - Kelly Group Inc.
FORCELITE - Lighting equipment - Bridgeport Metal Goods Manufacturing Co.
FORCEPOWER - Automotive parts and accessories - Vortech Engineering, Inc.
FORCHESS - Toys - SmalBook Associates
FORD - Chewing gum - Ford Gum and Machine Co.
FORD - Glass–flat - Ford Motor Co. (Glass Div.)
FORD - Motor vehicles - Ford Motor Co.
FORD - Recording label - Country International Records
FORD - Staircases–metal - SpaceGuard Products
FORD - Teas - Ford Tea Co.
FORD - Thread - Threads USA Div.
FORD - Underwear and nightwear ☆ - Nantucket Industries Inc.
FORD BOSS - Toys–automobiles - Ford Motor Co.
FORD EXP HOT STUFF - Toys - Fisher-Price, Inc.
FORD EXTREME - Chewing gum - Ford Gum and Machine Co.
FORD MUSTANG - Motor vehicles - Ford Motor Co.
FORDAN - Calendars - Advertising Unlimited Inc.
FORDHAM BREWING COMPANY - Beverages–malt - WM Enterprises, Inc.
FORDHAM UNIVERSITY PRESS - Publisher's imprints - Fordham University Press

FORDHOOK - Flowers, plants, and seeds - W. Atlee Burpee and Co.
FORDSON - Signs - Ford Motor Co.
FORDUSTIN - Skin care products - Sween Corp.
FORE - Golfing equipment - Fore Enterprises
FORE ATM - Computer peripheral equipment - Fore Systems, Inc.
FORE-GASM - Hats - Lloyd Petre
FORE 'N' AFT - Playtex Apparel, Inc.
FORE 'N AFT - Yarn - Brunswick Yarns
FORE-PAR - Golfing equipment - Western Golf Inc.
FORE PLAY - Colognes - Brothers Research Corp.
FORE-PLAYERS - Balls–golf - Russ Berrie and Co., Inc.
FORE RUNNER - Defibrillators - Heartstream, Inc.
FORE SYSTEMS - ATM equipment - Fore Systems, Inc.
FORE X FORE - Golfing equipment - Illah California, Inc.
FORECAST - Computer software - CBS Software
FORECAST - Dinnerware–glass ☆ - Johnson Brothers, USA, Inc.
FORECAST - Fabrics–tapestry ☆ - Coloroll Inc.
FORECAST - Floor coverings - Congoleum Corp.
FORECAST - Furniture ☆ - Broyhill Furniture Industries, Inc.
FORECAST - Hair care products - Zotos International Inc.
FORECAST - Luggage - Sears, Roebuck and Co.
FORECAST - Skin care products ☆ - House of Lowell Inc.
FORECAST COLORS - Paints - Pratt & Lambert, Inc.
FORECASTER - Barometers ☆ - Maximum Inc.
FORECASTER - Boats–motor - H & H Molded Products
FORECASTER - Pipes - National Briar Pipe Co.
FORECASTER OF BOSTON - Apparel–women's - Forecaster of Boston Inc.
FORECASTS - Shoes - Beacon Shoe Co.
FOREDOM - Tools–power-driven - Foredom Electric Co.
FOREDOM POWER GRAVER - Tools–machine - Blackstone Industries, Inc.
FOREE - Jewelry - Foree Hunsicker, Inc.
FOREFRONT - Computer software - Dexter & Chaney, Inc.
FOREFRONT - Recording label - Benson Music Group
FOREGGER - Respirators - Nova Tech
FOREGROUNDERS - Pet products - Penn-Plax, Inc.
FOREGROUNDS - Decals and transfers - 100% Products
FOREHELP - Computer software - Forefront, Inc.
FOREIGN CORRESPONDENT - Computer software - Toltran Ltd.
FOREIGN EXCHANGE - Games ☆ - Avalon Hill Game Co.
FOREIGN INTRIGUE - Apparel–men's - Almax Sportswear Corp.
FOREIGN INTRIGUE - Sunglasses - Opti-Ray, Inc.
FOREIGN LEGION - Apparel stores–sports - Brawn of California, Inc.
FOREIGNER - Music–sheet - Mick Jones
FORELLI - Candy - Allied International Corp.
FOREM - Watches - Jewelry Fashions Inc.
FOREM ASSOCIATES - Computer software - Forem Associates
FOREMAN - Office supplies - Alvin and Co. Inc.
FOREMOST - Apparel and accessories - Michael Angelo Enterprises Inc.
FOREMOST - Bicycles ☆ - J.C. Penney Co., Inc.
FOREMOST - Candy ☆ - Powers Pharmaceutical Corp.
FOREMOST - Cleaning preparations - Delta Foremost Chemical Corp.
FOREMOST - Dairy products - Kraft Foods, Inc.
FOREMOST - Dinnerware–glass ☆ - Nikko Ceramics Inc.
FOREMOST - Dog food - Lock Bros. Milling Co. Inc.
FOREMOST - Floor coverings–carpet and rugs - Calladium & Marglen
FOREMOST - Floor coverings–carpet and rugs ☆ - Regal Rugs Inc.
FOREMOST - Golfing equipment ☆ - Focus Golf Systems, Inc. (Dunlop Golf)
FOREMOST - Office furniture–wood ☆ - Sauder Woodworking Co.
FOREMOST - Pencils - Reliance Pen & Pencil Corp.
FOREMOST - Varnishes - Premier Coatings, Inc.
FOREMOST - Vitamins and nutritional supplements - Reliance Vitamin Co. Inc.
FOREMOST BODYGEAR - Apparel and accessories - Michael Angelo Enterprises Inc.
FOREMOST SELECT - Faucets - Foremost International Trading Inc.
FOREMOST SWINGER - Bicycles ☆ - J.C. Penney Co., Inc.
FORENZA - Apparel and accessories - Limited Inc.
FORENZA - Tiles–ceramic - Porcelanite, Inc.
FORENZA - Wallpaper - Koroseal Wallcoverings
FORERS, THE - Greeting cards ☆ - Brett-Forer Greetings Inc.
FORERUNNER - Computers ☆ - Data Translation, Inc.
FORERUNNER - Floor coverings–carpet and rugs ☆ - Blue Ridge Carpet Mills
FORERUNNER - Tires - Dico Tire Inc.
FORESEER - Computer software - Exide Electronics Group, Inc.
FORESIGHT - Computer software - Stratacom, Inc.
FORESIGHT - Slacks ☆ - Horace Small Apparel Co.
FORESIGHT - Wallpaper - Wall-Pride Inc.

☆ = Now out of production

FORESITE - Ophthalmic goods - Foremost Optical Products

FORESITE - Veterinary pharmaceutical preparations - SmithKline Beecham Animal Health Products

FORESQUARE - Sails - Davis Instruments Corp.

FOREST - Cabinets ☆ - American Woodmark Corp.

FOREST - Flowers, plants, and seeds - Crosman Corp.

FOREST - Glassware–household - Arrow International, Inc.

FOREST - Paper–writing - Hinkson Paper Co.

FOREST - Toys–stuffed - Eden LLC

FOREST & STREAM ORIGINALS - Apparel and accessories - T-Shirts of Florida Inc.

FOREST AREA SCHOOLS - Syrup - Forest Area Schools

FOREST BLEND - Siding–insulating - Bird Inc.

FOREST BROOK - Meat products–pork - Hygrade Food Products Corp.

FOREST CITY - Woodworking machinery - Forest City Tool

FOREST CRITTERS - Giftware - Roman, Inc.

FOREST ECHOES - Decals and transfers - Happiness Inc.

FOREST ESSENTIALS - Hair care products - Forest Essentials

FOREST ESTATE - Cabinets–wood ☆ - Kemper

FOREST FANCIES - Mixing bowls ☆ - Corning Inc.

FOREST FAWN - Toys–stuffed ☆ - Dakin Inc.

FOREST FLANNELS - Fabrics - Dan River Inc.

FOREST FLOOR - Agricultural products - Aguinaga Fertilizer Co., Inc.

FOREST FLOOR - Floor coverings–carpet and rugs - Milliken & Co.

FOREST FRESH - Chemical preparations - Unifinium Ltd.

FOREST FRESH - Wood products - Georgia-Pacific Corp.

FOREST FRIENDLY - Containers - Igloo Products Corp.

FOREST FRIENDS - Candy ☆ - R.M. Palmer Co.

FOREST FRIENDS - Jigsaw puzzles ☆ - American Publishing Corp.

FOREST FRIENDS - Puzzles - Milton Bradley Co.

FOREST FRIENDS - Toys–stuffed - Russ Berrie and Co., Inc.

FOREST FRIENDS - Wallpaper - Quality House Wallcoverings

FOREST FRUIT - Jams and jellies - Mille Lacs Maple Products Corp.

FOREST GLEN - Floor coverings - Congoleum Corp.

FOREST GLEN WINERY - Wines - Bronco Wine Co.

FOREST GOLD - Fertilizers - Gold Kist Inc.

FOREST HILL - Furniture - LUI Corp.

FOREST HILL - Wood products ☆ - Masonite Corp.

FOREST HILLS - Fabrics–tapestry - Comark Wallcoverings

FOREST HILLS - Floor coverings - Mannington Resilient Floors

FOREST HOME - Tents - Coleman Co., Inc.

FOREST INTERNATIONAL TRADING, INC. - Slacks–men's - Forest International Trading, Inc.

FOREST KING - Handles–wood - Turner, Day and Woolworth Handle Corp.

FOREST KING - Tools - O.P. Link Handle Co. Inc.

FOREST LAKE - Furniture - Khoury, Inc.

FOREST LAKE - Hosiery–men's - Clovermere Sales Corp.

FOREST LAKE - Water–bottled or canned - Cobb Mountain Spring Water Co.

FOREST LAKE NATURAL SPRING - Water–bottled or canned - Forest Lake Products Inc.

FOREST LANE - Floor coverings–carpet and rugs ☆ - Hollytex Carpet Mills Inc.

FOREST OAKS - Floor coverings–carpet and rugs - Gulistan Carpet Inc.

FOREST PARK - Apparel and accessories ☆ - Pannill Knitting Co. Inc.

FOREST PARK - Furniture - Vaughan Furniture Co. Inc.

FOREST PARK - Trailers–travel ☆ - Fleetwood Enterprises, Inc.

FOREST-PHANTOM - Fabrics - Shannon Outdoors, Inc.

FOREST PINE - Furniture ☆ - Broyhill Furniture Industries, Inc.

FOREST PINE TREE - Naphthalene chips - Coughlan Products Corp.

FOREST POINTE - Furniture - Vaughan Furniture Co. Inc.

FOREST PRESERVE - Fabrics ☆ - Gretchen Bellinger Inc.

FOREST PRODUCTS - Furniture - Wellington Home Products (Plastic Woven Products Div.)

FOREST PURE - Hair care products - Levlab, Inc.

FOREST RIDGE - Siding–insulating - Georgia-Pacific Corp.

FOREST RIDGE DESIGNS - Sweaters - Forest Ridge Designs, Inc.

FOREST RIDGE STUDIOS - Christmas tree ornaments - Dean William Griff

FOREST RIVERS - Trailers–travel - Forest River, Inc.

FOREST SHADOWS - Christmas tree ornaments - Cracker Box Inc.

FOREST STUMP THE TALKING TREE - Novelty items - Barbara Ashback

FOREST TEE-N-GEE - Siding–insulating ☆ - Forestex Co.

FOREST VILLE VINEYARD - Wines - Bronco Wine Co.

FOREST-WALL - Wood products ☆ - Bradley Plywood Corp.

FOREST WOODS - Toilet seats ☆ - Magnolia Products

FORESTCOTE - Fertilizers - OMS Investments, Inc.

FORESTCRAFT - Toy stores - Forestcraft Inc.

FORESTDALE - Furniture - Vermont Tubbs Inc.

FORESTER - Boats - American Marine Ltd.

FORESTER - Boats–canoes - Forester Boats Inc.

FORESTER - Drafting supplies - Mayline/Hamilton

FORESTER - Fireplace equipment - United States Stove Co. Inc.

FORESTER - Playground equipment - Hedstrom Corp.

FORESTER - Tools–garden - Porter-Ferguson, Inc.

FORESTER - Toys–stuffed ☆ - Gund, Inc.

FORESTER - Wood products ☆ - Masonite Corp.

FORESTER 1870 - Whiskey - Early Times Distillery Co.

FORESTEX - Siding–insulating - Forestex Co.

FORESTEX MAXI 500 - Siding–insulating - Forestex Co.

FORESTGLO - Wood products - Weyerhaeuser Co.

FORESTLAND - Water–distilled - Hudson Valley Apple Products Co. Inc.

FORESTRY - Computer storage devices–optical - Digital Imaging Associates Inc.

FORESTS OF THE WORLD - Flowers, plants, and seeds - Forests of the World, LLC

FORESTVIEW - Window coverings - Skagfield Corp.

FORESTWOOD - Siding–insulating ☆ - Forestex Co.

FORET DE FRAMBOISE - Apparel and accessories - Ben Elias Industries Corp.

FORET DE LA MERE - Bath and body products - Foret De La Mere

FORET DU MER - Wines ☆ - Haviland Vintners

FORETELL - Ophthalmic goods - Foremost Optical Products

FORETELL SOFT - Dishwashing compounds - Puritan-Churchill Chemical Co.

FORETHOUGHT CONNECTION, THE - Computer software - Forethought Life Insurance Co.

FORETIFIED - Ophthalmic goods - Foremost Optical Products

FORETITUDE - Ophthalmic goods - Foremost Optical Products

FORETRAVEL - Recreational vehicle dealers - Foretravel Inc.

FORETUNATE - Ophthalmic goods - Foremost Optical Products

FOREVA - Lighting equipment ☆ - Marvel Lighting Corp.

FOREVER - Batteries - Bridgestone/Firestone, Inc.

FOREVER - Colognes - Old 97 Co.

FOREVER - Deodorizers - PRH Products Co.

FOREVER - Floor coverings–carpet and rugs - Calladium & Marglen

FOREVER - Floor coverings–carpet and rugs ☆ - Royalweve Carpet Mills

FOREVER - Glassware–household - Crystal Clear Importing Co. Inc.

FOREVER - Jewelry–precious - Leo Pevsner & Co.

FOREVER - Novelty items–glass ☆ - Emco Enterprises, Inc.

FOREVER - Paints - Valspar Corp.

FOREVER - Rings–jewelry - Artcarved Inc.

FOREVER - Skin care products - Bonat Inc.

FOREVER - Synthetic turf - Instant Turf Industries Inc.

FOREVER - Tableware–china ☆ - Lenox, Inc.

FOREVER 29 - Skin care products - Palm Beach Beauty Products

FOREVER BEAUTIFUL - Floor coverings–carpet and rugs - Mohawk Carpet Corp.

FOREVER BEAUTIFUL - Flowers, plants, and seeds ☆ - Wilson Marketing Concepts

FOREVER BEAUTIFUL - Novelty items - Forever Beautiful

FOREVER BEE HONEY - Honey - Aloe Vera of America, Inc.

FOREVER BEE POLLEN - Vitamins and nutritional supplements - Aloe Vera of America, Inc.

FOREVER BEE PROPOLIS - Vitamins and nutritional supplements - Aloe Vera of America, Inc.

FOREVER BLESSINGS - Greeting cards - Warner Press, Inc.

FOREVER BLUE - Toilet-bowl cleaner - James Austin Co.

FOREVER BY SPEIDEL - Jewelry ☆ - Hirsch Speidel Inc.

FOREVER CARD, THE - Greeting cards ☆ - Papel Freelance, Inc.

FOREVER CLASSIC - Wallpaper - Gencorp Inc.

FOREVER DECK, THE - Plastics–laminated - Phoenix Recycled Plastics Corp

FOREVER ELEGANT - Ornamental products–glass - Coast Novelty Manufacturing Co.

FOREVER FAN - Fans–electric - Builders Square Inc.

FOREVER FLEXIBLE - Jewelry - Brendle's Stores Inc.

FOREVER FLORALS - Apparel–children's - Roanna Togs, Inc.

FOREVER FLORALS - Skin care products - Trade West, Inc.

FOREVER FLOWERS - Flowers–artificial - D.A. Glassco Inc.

FOREVER FOXY - Cosmetics - Arthur Matney Co., Inc.

FOREVER FRAGRANT - Deodorizers - PRH Products Co.

FOREVER FREE - Greeting cards ☆ - American Greetings Corp.

FOREVER FREE - Tools–hand-operated - Casey Cho

FOREVER FRESH - Flowers–artificial - Forever Fresh, Inc.

FOREVER FRESH - Pet products - Chip's Pet Products

FOREVER GARCINIA PLUS - Vitamins and nutritional supplements - Aloe Vera of America, Inc.

FOREVER GARLIC-THYME - Vitamins and nutritional supplements - Aloe Vera of America, Inc.

FOREVER-GOLD - Jewelry - Erwin Pearl Inc.

FOREVER GOLD - Recording label - Allegiance Records Ltd.

FOREVER GREEN - Fertilizers - Feeder Enterprises, Inc.

FOREVER GREEN - Paper - Statler Industries, Inc.

FOREVER GREETINGS - Giftware - Russ Berrie and Co., Inc.

FOREVER GUARD - Doors–storm ☆ - Emco Enterprises, Inc.

FOREVER KIDS - Apparel–children's - Forever Kids of Brightwaters, Inc.

FOREVER KRYSTLE - Perfumes - Yves St. Laurent Parfum Corp.

FOREVER LANCELOT - Jewelry - Forever Lancelot

FOREVER LASHLIGHT - Flashlights - C.J.M. Leasing Corp.

FOREVER LASTING - Floor coverings–carpet and rugs - Mohawk Carpet Corp.

FOREVER LINE - Motor vehicle dealers - Automotive Industries, Inc.

FOREVER LOFT - Pillows - Soft-Tex Manufacturing Co.

FOREVER LOVE - Greeting cards - American Greetings Corp.

FOREVER MASTERPIECE - Jewelry - Ramzor, Inc.

FOREVER MATTE - Cosmetics - Johnson Publishing Co., Inc.

FOREVER MINE - Dishes–china - Pickard Inc.

FOREVER NAILS - Nail care products - Flori Roberts Inc.

FOREVER NEVER WORRY - Window coverings - Levolor Inc.

FOREVER NEW - Cleaning preparations - Diamond Shield, Inc.

FOREVER NEW - Cleaning preparations - Forever New International, Inc.

FOREVER NYLONS - Liquid chemical - FX Environmental Products, Corp.

FOREVER PAGE - Pagers - Source One Wireless, Inc.

FOREVER PLAID - Bathing suits ☆ - Jantzen Inc.

FOREVER RADIANT - Skin care products - Hollywood Beauty Imports Inc.

FOREVER REGAL - Floor coverings–carpet and rugs - Mohawk Carpet Corp.

FOREVER SILVER - Jewelry - Erwin Pearl Inc.

FOREVER SPRING - Wallpaper - Pickhardt & Siebert USA Inc.

FOREVER SPRING - Wallpaper - Seabrook Wallcoverings, Inc.

FOREVER SPRING - Wallpaper - Southport

FOREVER STORM DOORS - Doors–storm - Emco Enterprises, Inc.

FOREVER SUMMER - Giftware ☆ - Avon Products, Inc.

FOREVER TAN PERFECT - Sunblocks - Forever Tan Inc.

FOREVER THIN - Health care products - Staple and Spice Market

FOREVER TOGETHER - Rings–jewelry - Feature Enterprises

FOREVER TREASURES - Keepsake boxes - Cheryl C. Walls

FOREVER VIEW - Computer software - INSCI Corp.

FOREVER WICKER - Furniture - Ransburg Accessories Inc.

FOREVER WILD CARDS - Greeting cards - Forever Wild Cards

FOREVER YOUNG - Doors–wood - Jeld-Wen, Inc.

FOREVER YOUNG - Dresses–women's - Anne Klein & Co.

FOREVER YOUNG - Health care products - Nutritional Gold

FOREVER YOUNG BY SOPHIA KAPLIN - Wigs - Troika International Inc.

FOREVER YOURS - Calendars - Wisconsin Woodcrafts

FOREVER YOURS - Candy bars - Mars, Inc.

FOREVER YOURS - Dinnerware - Corning Inc.

FOREVER YOURS - Dolls ☆ - Fun World Inc.

FOREVER YOURS - Ice cream - Dove International

FOREVER YOURS - Jewelry - Ullenberg Corp.

FOREVER YOURS - Stationery ☆ - Nu-Art Inc.

FOREVER YOURS BRIDALS - Wedding gowns - Forever Yours International Corp.

FOREVERFLEX - Cushions - Krause's Sofa Factory Inc.

FOREVERLAND - Jewelry - Kirk's Folly, Inc.

FOREVERS - Christmas tree ornaments - Prosperity Tree International

FOREVIEW - Computer software - Fore Systems, Inc.

FOREZ - Chocolate bars - Casino North America

FOREZA - Health care products ☆ - CTS Laboratories Inc.

FORFEX - Hair care products - Fromm Industries

FORFORA - Hair care products - Waverly Beauty Products

FORGE - Cases–musical instrument ☆ - Anvil Cases

FORGE CROSSING - Floor coverings–carpet and rugs ☆ - Lees Carpets

FORGE II - Cases–musical instrument - Anvil Cases

FORGE LTD. - Apparel–men's ☆ - Munsingwear, Inc.

FORGE LOOP - Hoses - Action Technology Co.

FORGE-MASTER - Wheels - Hamilton Caster & Manufacturing Co.

FORGECRAFT - Flatware ☆ - Washington Forge Inc.

FORGED - Handles–wood - Fleischmann Handle Co.

FORGED FEEL - Golfing equipment - Nassau Precision Casting Co., Inc.

FORGERON VINEYARDS - Wines - Forgeron Vineyards

FORGES - Hardware - Valli & Colombo USA Inc.

FORGET-IT - Batteries - Universal Cooperative Inc.

FORGET-ME-KNOTS INC. - Skin care products - Forget-Me-Knots, Inc.

FORGET-ME-NOT - Apparel stores–lingerie - Fancee Free Manufacturing Co.

FORGET-ME-NOT - Dinnerware ☆ - Corning Inc.

FORGET-ME-NOT - Dinnerware–glass - Franciscan by Johnson Brothers, USA, Inc.

FORGET-ME-NOT - Dinnerware–glass - Nikko Ceramics Inc.

FORGET ME NOT - Dinnerware–glass - Royal China & Porcelain Companies Inc.

FORGET ME NOT - Greeting cards - American Greetings Corp.

FORGET-ME-NOT - Housewares ☆ - Vermillion Inc.

FORGET-ME-NOT - Mattresses ☆ - DLM Plastics Corp.

FORGET ME NOT - Sunglasses - Esther Fuhrman Designs, Ltd.

FORGET ME NOT - Toys–stuffed ☆ - Gund, Inc.

FORGET-ME-NOT - Wigs ☆ - Paula Young

FORGET-ME-NOT CONDOMS - Prophylactics - Big Star Concepts Inc.

FORGIVENESS - Paper–writing - Bruce E. Regnier

FORGOTONIA - Shirts - Terry W. Finley

FORGOTTEN DREAMS - Floor coverings–carpet and rugs - Columbus Mills, Inc.

FORGOTTEN REALMS - Games - Tsr, Inc.

FORINDI - Apparel–women's - Melville Corp.

FORITE - Enamels ☆ - PPG Industries, Inc.

FORK CLEAN - Cleaning preparations - W.J. Hagerty & Sons Ltd. Inc.

FORKED HORN - Archery equipment - Saunders Archery Co.

FORKED LIGHTNING - Archery equipment ☆ - Bear Archery Inc.

FORKOLA JELL - Health care products - Bacorn Co. Inc.

FORLAC - Veterinary pharmaceutical preparations - Nutra-Vet Research Corp.

FORLIFE - Respirators - AirSep Corp.

FORM 2 - Flatware ☆ - W.M.F. of America Inc.

FORM 2 - Hair care products - Helene Curtis Industries Inc.

FORM 3 - Hair care products - Helene Curtis Industries Inc.

FORM 1000 - Desk sets - Rubbermaid Commercial Products Inc.

FORM A BROW - Stencils - Senna Cosmetics, Inc.

FORM-A-FAN - Boxes - Richard M. Patterson

FORM-A-GASKET - Adhesives and sealants - Loctite Corp.

FORM-A-LEAN - Animal feed supplements - Form-A-Feed, Inc.

FORM-A-LENS - Automotive parts and accessories - Loctite Corp.

FORM-A-SEAL - Adhesives and sealants - Loctite Corp.

FORM-A-THREAD - Adhesives and sealants - Loctite Corp.

FORM-A-TIONS - Construction toys - James Industries, Inc.

FORM-A-WEAN - Animal feed supplements - Form-A-Feed, Inc.

FORM-ALIGN - Trailers - American Ada Compliance Corp.

FORM & FASHION - Furniture - Erwin-Lambeth Inc.

FORM AND FINISH - Hair care products - Vidal Sassoon Inc.

FORM COIL - Cushions–foam - Hickory Springs Manufacturing Co.

FORM DEVINE - Corsets - Bonwit Teller & Co.

FORM-EZE - Concrete–mixture - Illinois Oil Products Inc.

FORM FACTOR - Computer software - Metapacific Systems, Inc.

FORM-FAST - Screw drivers - Fastron Co.

FORM-FIT - Chairs–plastic - Alladin Plastics Inc.

FORM-FIT - Gloves - Magla Products Inc.

FORM-FIT - Lighters - Colibri Inc.

FORM FIT - Orthopedic products - Royce Medical Co.

FORM-FIT - Sporting goods ☆ - Texas Recreation Corp.

FORM FITTER - Toys - Playskool, Inc.

FORM FIX - Computer software - Sequoia Data Corp.

FORM-FLEX - Fabrics - Handler Textile Corp.

FORM-FLEX - Girdles - Formflex Foundations Inc.

FORM FLEX - Pipes–plastic ☆ - Markel Corp.

FORM FLEX - Stencils - Highway Traffic Supply Corp.

FORM-FLOW - Business forms - Standard Register Co.

FORM-IT - Cardboard - Chesapeake Fiber Packaging Corp.

FORM-IT - Craft supplies ☆ - Clayton Corp.

FORM OF THE FUTURE IS TAKING SHAPE TODAY, THE - Business forms - Moore Business Forms, Inc.

FORM-ON-A-ROLL - Manicure preparations ☆ - Lee Pharmaceuticals

FORM-U-LIFE - Vitamins and nutritional supplements - Spectramin Inc.

FORM VIII - Furniture - Weiman Co.

FORM-X-FILM - Plastics film - Graphic Products Corp.

FORM14 - Furniture - Optima Enclosures

FORMA - Building materials–concrete - Forma Block, Inc.

FORMA - Chairs–upholstered - United Chair Co., Inc.

FORMA - Dinnerware–glass - Cyclamen Studio

FORMA - Glassware–household ☆ - National Housewares

FORMA - Plastics–laminated ☆ - Plaskolite Inc.

☆ = Now out of production

FORMA-RAY - Skin care products - Gordon Laboratories
FORMA-SPAR - Paints ☆ - Valspar Corp.
FORMA SPLIT UNIT - Health care products - Thermo-Electric Co.
FORMA VITRUM - Figurines - Forma Vitrum, Inc.
FORMACOTE - Paints ☆ - Valspar Corp.
FORMADON - Pharmaceutical preparations - Gordon Laboratories
FORMAFILM - Film - Joli Plastics & Chemical Corp.
FORMAFLEX - Hoses - Hose Master, Inc.
FORMAL - Candy - Pangburn Candy Co.
FORMAL - Floor coverings–carpet and rugs ☆ - Walter Carpet Mills
FORMAL CLASSICS - Tableware–china - Dalzell-Viking
FORMAL ELEGANCE - Floor coverings–carpet and rugs - Milliken & Co. Inc.
FORMAL ELEGANCE - Wallpaper - Preferred Prints
FORMALDEGEN - Veterinary pharmaceutical preparations - Vineland Laboratories Inc.
FORMALE - Kitchenware–china - H. Wittur & Co.
FORMALESQUE - Tiles–ceramic - Summitville Tiles, Inc.
FORMALIN 3 - Aquarium accessories - Kordon
FORMALIN 3 - Water treating compounds - Novalek, Inc.
FORMALINE - Artists' materials - Graphic Products Corp.
FORMALITE - Aquatic pharmacuetical preparations ☆ - Aquatronics-Filtronics
FORMALITE II - Pet products ☆ - Aquatronics-Filtronics
FORMALITIES - Giftware - Baum Bros. Imports Inc.
FORMALITIES - Wallpaper ☆ - Brewster Wallcovering Co.
FORMALITIES II - Wallpaper - Brewster Wallcovering Co.
FORMALITY - Furniture ☆ - Kaylyn Inc.
FORMALON - Ophthalmic goods - Foremost Optical Products
FORMALTABS - Cleaning preparations - King Research, Inc.
FORMALTEAS - Tea kettles–nonelectric - M. Kamenstein, Inc.
FORMALYDE-10 - Pharmaceutical preparations - Pedinol Pharmacal Inc.
FORMAN - Apparel and accessories - Forman's Apparel
FORMAN FORD - Varnishes ☆ - Valspar Corp.
FORMANITE - Paints ☆ - Valspar Corp.
FORMAN'S - Food products - Vlasic Foods Inc.
FORMANT - Water–bottled or canned - Teras Limited
FORMANT HYDRANT - Water–bottled or canned - Teras Limited
FORMASEAL - Hearing aids - Earmold Design Inc.
FORMASEAL - Varnishes ☆ - Valspar Corp.
FORMASOL - Hair care products - Helene Curtis Industries Inc.
FORMAT - Apparel–men's - Format, Inc.
FORMAT - Floor coverings–carpet and rugs ☆ - Mannington Carpets, Inc.
FORMAT - Motor vehicle parts and accessories - Lancaster Colony Automotive Group
FORMATIC - Computer peripheral equipment - CBF Systems, Inc.
FORMATIC - Tea kettles–electric - Forman Family Inc.
FORMATION - Furniture ☆ - Bassett Furniture Industries, Inc.
FORMATION - Manicure preparations - Creative Nail Design, Inc.
FORMATION - Ophthalmic goods - Foremost Optical Products
FORMATIONS - Furniture ☆ - Hammary Furniture Co. Inc.
FORMATIONS - Plastics–laminated - Formica Corp.
FORMATIONS - Shelving units–wood - Weyerhaeuser Co.
FORMATONE - Pharmaceutical preparations - Wyeth-Ayerst Laboratories
FORMATRIX - Pharmaceutical preparations ☆ - Wyeth-Ayerst Laboratories
FORMATT - Artists' materials - Graphic Products Corp.
FORMATTE - Fabrics - Dan River Inc.
FORMATTER - Cameras - General Electric Co.
FORMAX - Cushions - Mastex Industries, Inc.
FORMAX - Office machines - Tab Products Co.
FORMBRIDGE - Computer software - Texcel Systems, Inc.
FORMBUSTER - Computer software - Virtual Reality Laboratories, Inc.
FORMBY'S - Wood products - Thompson and Formby
FORMCAST - Metals - Amcast Industrial Corp.
FORMDOMAIN - Computer software - Reynolds and Reynolds Co.
FORME - Vitamins and nutritional supplements - Metagenics, Inc.
FORMELA - Cosmetics - Formela Inc.
FORMENT - Cement - Conproco Corp.
FORMFILE - Containers–paper - Rubbermaid Inc.
FORMFIT - Apparel stores–lingerie - Formfit Rogers
FORMFIT - Underwear and nightwear - Jockey International, Inc.
FORMFIT DESIGNERS COLLECTION - Apparel stores–lingerie - Formfit Rogers
FORMFIT INTIMATES - Underwear and nightwear - I. Appel Corp.
FORMFIT NEW YORK - Intimate apparel - I. Appel Corp.
FORMFIT ROGERS - Apparel stores–lingerie - Formfit Rogers
FORMFORAL - Health care products - Plex Products
FORMICA - Plastics–laminated - Formica Corp.

FORMICA COLOR & COLOR - Plastics–laminated - Formica Corp.
FORMICA FLOOR SHINE - Floor finishing machines–commercial ☆ - Formica Corp.
FORMICA LIGNA - Adhesives and sealants - Formica Corp.
FORMICA MCP - Floor finishing machines–commercial ☆ - Formica Corp.
FORMIDABLE - Sporting goods - Spalding Sports Worldwide
FORMIDABLE-TOTAL - Combs - Nino Originals
FORMING I.C.E. - Hair care products - Joico Laboratories, Inc.
FORMING TECHNOLOGIES - Paper industry machinery - Forming Technologies Inc.
FORMIT - Fabrics - Uniroyal Engineered Products
FORMITALIA - Furniture - Formitalia USA, Inc.
FORMITT - Hats - Staco Enterprises Inc.
FORMMANAGER - Computer peripheral equipment - MicroComputer Accessories Inc.
FORM'N'FIT - Plumbing fixtures–plastic - Moen Inc.
FORMOLD - Girdles - Associated Merchandising Corp.
FORMOPAQUE - Artists' materials - Graphic Products Corp.
FORMOSA OOLONG - Teas - Grace Tea Co. Ltd.
FORMPAC - Trays - W.R. Grace & Co.
FORMRUN - Paper - Georgia-Pacific Corp.
FORMS & FONTS - Computer software - LBM Systems Corp.
FORMS CADDY - Containers–shipping - Mead-Hatcher, Inc.
FORMS CARBON 500 - Spirit master units - Codo Manufacturing Corp.
FORMS ON DEMAND - Computer software - Hart Information Services, Inc.
FORMS UNLIMITED - Computer software - Parsons Technology, Inc.
FORMSET - Diamond powder - General Electric Co.
FORMSOURCE - Computer software - Computer Language Research Inc.
FORMSPRO - Computer software - Teknekron Customer Information Solutions, Inc.
FORMSTOR SYSTEMS - Computer software - Oblique Filing Systems
FORMTEK - Computer software - Formtek, Inc.
FORMTOOL - Computer software - BLOC Development Corp.
FORMTOOL GOLD - Computer software - IMSI
FORMUCARE - Cold medicine - Amway Corp.
FORMUFLEX - Adhesives and sealants - State Chemical Manufacturing Co.
FORMULA - Bicycles - Columbia Manufacturing Inc.
FORMULA - Boats–motor - Thunderbird Products
FORMULA - Coffee - Rione International Corp.
FORMULA - Deodorizers - Dualle Products
FORMULA - Motor vehicle parts and accessories - Delaware Capital Formation Inc.
FORMULA - Motor vehicles–automobiles - General Motors Corp. (Pontiac/GMC Div.)
FORMULA - Musical instrument accessories ☆ - GHS Strings
FORMULA - Scooters ☆ - Italjet USA
FORMULA - Skin care products - Soya System Inc.
FORMULA - Tires - Armtec Industries Inc.
FORMULA - Wheels–motor vehicle - Nankang Rubber Tire Corp. Ltd.
FORMULA 1 - Adhesives and sealants - VIP/Lighthouse Products
FORMULA 1 - Antennas - Allen Telecom Group, Inc.
FORMULA 1 - Automotive parts and accessories - Northern Labs, Inc.
FORMULA 1 - Fabrics–wool - Forstmann and Co. Inc.
FORMULA 1 - Nail care products - Nailtiques Cosmetic Corp.
FORMULA 1 TURBO HUNTER - Archery equipment - Golden Eagle Archery
FORMULA-2 - Chemical preparations - Mil-Du-Gas Co.
FORMULA 2 - Cosmetics - Revlon Consumer Products Corp.
FORMULA 2 - Fertilizers ☆ - Montgomery Ward & Co. Inc.
FORMULA II - Housewares ☆ - Shepherd Products U.S. Inc.
FORMULA 2 - Nail care products - Nailtiques Cosmetic Corp.
FORMULA 2 PLUS - Nail care products - Nailtiques Cosmetic Corp.
FORMULA 3 - Musical instrument accessories - United Musical Instruments USA Inc.
FORMULA 3/6/9 - Vitamins and nutritional supplements - Banner-Pharmacaps Inc. (Advanced Nutritional Technology Division)
FORMULA 3-D - Archery equipment - Golden Eagle Archery
FORMULA 4 - Gasoline - Kerr-McGee Chemical Corp.
FORMULA 4 - Pet products ☆ - Farnam Cos. Inc.
FORMULA 4 - Skin care products - Fanie International
FORMULA 6 - Pet products - Breeder's Choice Pet Foods, Inc.
FORMULA 7 - Hair care products - Winning Solutions Inc./Miracle of Aloe
FORMULA 8 - Adhesives and sealants - Fluoramics Inc.
FORMULA #9 - Hair care products - Gold Medal Hair Products Inc.
FORMULA 9 - Pharmaceutical preparations - Winning Solutions Inc./Miracle of Aloe
FORMULA 10 - Manicure preparations - Formula 10

FORMULA 10 - Nail care products - Finger Mates Inc.
FORMULA-10 - Scooters–motorized - Zenital Inc.
FORMULA 15 - Skin care products - Fanie International
FORMULA 17 - Skin care products - Rudolph International, Inc.
FORMULA 18 - Skin care products - Revlon Consumer Products Corp.
FORMULA 20 - Cleaning preparations - Sprayway Inc.
FORMULA 21 - Hair care products ☆ - Jerant Co. Inc.
FORMULA 21 - Vitamins and nutritional supplements - Dixon-Shane Inc.
FORMULA 22 - Cleaning preparations - L.D. Sterns Corp.
FORMULA 24 - Cosmetics ☆ - Lachine Inc.
FORMULA 27 - Plastics - Fibre Glass-Evercoat Co. Inc.
FORMULA 38 - Adhesives and sealants - Ohio Sealants Inc.
FORMULA 40 - Cleaning preparations - Sprayway Inc.
FORMULA 44 - Cough medicines - Richardson-Vicks USA
FORMULA 44/40 - Blueing - Brownells, Inc.
FORMULA 44/40 - Guns ☆ - Gun Parts Corp.
FORMULA 44-D - Cough medicines - Richardson-Vicks USA
FORMULA 44-M - Cough medicines - Richardson-Vicks USA
FORMULA 46 - Vitamins and nutritional supplements - Halsey Drug Co. Inc.
FORMULA 50 - Vitamins and nutritional supplements - Marlyn Co. Inc.
FORMULA 50 MEGA FORTE - Vitamins and nutritional supplements ☆ - Marlyn Co. Inc.
FORMULA 70 - Jewelry ☆ - Hobe Cie. Ltd.
FORMULA 77 - Adhesives and sealants - Kyanize Paint Co.
FORMULA 77 - Paints - Gulf States Paint Co.
FORMULA 79 - Nail care products ☆ - Claire Topper Enterprises
FORMULA 82/R - Musical instrument accessories - Dean Markley Strings, Inc.
FORMULA 99 - Paints - Mac-O-Lac Paints Inc.
FORMULA 105 - Deodorizers - Definitive Deodorant Co.
FORMULA 109 - Correction fluid - Bic Corp.
FORMULA '208' - Pharmaceutical preparations - Heritage Store Inc.
FORMULA '230' - Adhesives and sealants - Dap Products Inc.
FORMULA 300 - Pharmaceutical preparations ☆ - Pacific Mineral Industries
FORMULA 405 - Skin care products - Doak Dermatologics
FORMULA 409 - Cleaning preparations–household - Clorox Co.
FORMULA 523 - Pharmaceutical preparations - Enzyme Process Co. Inc.
FORMULA 545 - Pharmaceutical preparations - Heritage Store Inc.
FORMULA 582-H.D. - Degreasing solvents - Analab Inc.
FORMULA 602 - Cymbals - Paiste America, Inc.
FORMULA 636 - Pharmaceutical preparations - Heritage Store Inc.
FORMULA 707 - Pet products - John Ewing Co.
FORMULA 721 - Cleaning preparations ☆ - Flo-Pac Corp.
FORMULA 1447 - Pharmaceutical preparations - Rel-Eeze/JDM Enterprises
FORMULA 2000 - Veterinary nutritional supplements - Hubbard Milling Co.
FORMULA 2001 RAPID SHINE - Waxes–sealing - Turtle Wax, Inc.
FORMULA A - Paint removers ☆ - Klean-Strip
FORMULA B-2 - Laxatives - Herb Products Co.
FORMULA BMX - Bicycles - Western Auto Supply Co.
FORMULA BRONZE - Archery equipment ☆ - Bear Archery Inc.
FORMULA C/P - Animal feeds ☆ - Mardel Laboratories, Inc.
FORMULA CAMAY - Soap - Procter & Gamble Co.
FORMULA C.E. A-ONE - Cleaning preparations ☆ - Albatross USA Inc.
FORMULA D - Pharmaceutical preparations - Degree/Silverman M.D. Inc.
FORMULA D - Shampoos ☆ - Image Laboratories, Inc.
FORMULA DESERT DOG - Tires - Armtec Industries Inc.
FORMULA ELEVEN - Cleaner ☆ - Construction Adhesives Co.
FORMULA F-20 ENVIRO-CLEAR - Chemical preparations - Diversified Waterscapes, Inc.
FORMULA F21C - Soap - Fresh Inc.
FORMULA FACTORY - Computer software - True Basic, Inc.
FORMULA FEVER - Toys–automobiles - Mattel, Inc.
FORMULA FIX - Cosmetics - Nailtiques Cosmetic Corp.
FORMULA FOODS - Pet products - Ocean Nutrition Corp.
FORMULA FOR LIFE - Vitamins and nutritional supplements - Sundown Vitamins, Inc.
FORMULA G-510 - Cleaning preparations - Gaylord Industries, Inc.
FORMULA GLUE - Glue–household or industrial - Osment Models, Inc.
FORMULA GOLD - Archery equipment ☆ - Bear Archery Inc.
FORMULA-HAIR - Hair care products - Form-U-La-Hair Co.
FORMULA I - Bicycles - Murray, Inc.
FORMULA I - Chairs–upholstered ☆ - Haskell of Pittsburgh, Inc.
FORMULA I - Vitamins and nutritional supplements - Shaklee Corp.
FORMULA I RACERS - Toys - Imperial Toy Corp.
FORMULA II - Headphones - Westone Laboratories Inc.
FORMULA II CLEAR - Headphones - Westone Laboratories Inc.
FORMULA M - Adhesives and sealants - Stone Products Corp.

FORMULA MAGIC - Skin care products - Care-Tech Laboratories Inc.
FORMULA MAKER - Mixers - Fluid Management
FORMULA MICRO - Motor vehicles - Surfjet International Ltd.
FORMULA MPB - Paint removers - National Brands, Inc.
FORMULA MX OVERDRAW - Archery equipment - Martin Archery Inc.
FORMULA NO. 9 - Hair care products - Gold Medal Hair Products Inc.
FORMULA NUMBER 9 - Hair care products - Ronco Hairproducts, Inc.
FORMULA #10 - Cleaning preparations - Eplo Products Corp.
FORMULA ONE - Deodorizers - Ryter Corp.
FORMULA ONE - Dog food - Pet Products Plus
FORMULA ONE - Gloves–rubber - Tillotson Healthcare Corp.
FORMULA ONE - Lubricants - Outboard Marine Corp.
FORMULA ONE - Pet products - Ocean Nutrition Corp.
FORMULA ONE - Vitamins and nutritional supplements - Back to Health
FORMULA O.N.E. 1 - Shampoos - Sullivan Supply, Inc.
FORMULA Q - Sealing compounds - Ziebart International Corp.
FORMULA S-800 - Cleaning preparations - State Chemical Manufacturing Co.
FORMULA SHELL - Gasoline - Shell Oil Co.
FORMULA SILVER - Archery equipment ☆ - Bear Archery Inc.
FORMULA SOUR - Candy - Squire Boone Caverns, Inc.
FORMULA SR-X - Deodorizers - Fast Industries, Inc.
FORMULA T1 - Video games - Thrustmaster, Inc.
FORMULA TWO - Pet products - Ocean Nutrition Corp.
FORMULA U - Paints - Testor Corp.
FORMULA V - Veterinary pharmaceutical preparations - Pet-Ag, Inc.
FORMULA V/M/A - Animal feed supplements ☆ - Mardel Laboratories, Inc.
FORMULA VM75 - Vitamins and nutritional supplements - Solgar Vitamin and Herb Co., Inc.
FORMULA WB-20 - Laxatives ☆ - Bluco Inc.
FORMULA X - Wax removers - Pioneer/Eclipse Corp.
FORMULA X-10 - Drums–musical instruments ☆ - Aquarian Accessories Corp.
FORMULA X-11 - Toys - Empire of Carolina Inc.
FORMULA Z - Sealing compounds - Ziebart International Corp.
FORMULA Z-II - Skin care products ☆ - Alleghany Pharmacal Corp.
FORMULABS - Inks - Formulabs, Inc.
FORMULAE USP - Vitamins and nutritional supplements - Leiner Health Products Inc.
FORMULAS FOR HEALTH - Vitamins and nutritional supplements - Golden Pride-Rawleigh, Inc.
FORMULATE - Computer software - Seven Hills Software
FORMULATED FOR COMMERCIAL/RESIDENTIAL HOUSING MH 6600 MH QUALITY - Adhesives and sealants - TACC International Corp.
FORMULATED FOR THE ENVIRONMENT - Coatings - Kaupert Chemical and Consulting, Inc.
FORMULATION R - Health care products - G and W Laboratories Inc.
FORMULE EQUILIBRANTE - Skin care products ☆ - Sothys USA Inc.
FORMULE HUMECTANTE - Skin care products ☆ - Sothys USA Inc.
FORMULE HYDRATANTE - Skin care products ☆ - Sothys USA Inc.
FORMULE OXYGENANTE - Skin care products - Sothys USA Inc.
FORMULE RAFFERMISSANTE - Skin care products ☆ - Sothys USA Inc.
FORMULE SUPER VISAGE - Skin care products ☆ - Sothys USA Inc.
FORMULIFE - Pharmaceutical preparations ☆ - Highland Laboratories
FORMULITE - Hair coloring preparations - Helene Curtis Industries Inc.
FORMULITE - Liqueurs - Chembar, Inc.
FORMULOX - Cosmetics - Total Research Inc.
FORMVELOPE - Envelopes - Tension Envelope Corp.
FORMWOOD - Coatings - Formwood Industries, Inc.
FORMZ - Skin care products - Sequel Products Inc.
FORNACI DI TASSAROLO, GAVI - Wines - Kobrand Corp.
FORNAP - Napkins–paper - Fort Howard Corp.
FORNO - Breads - Gourmet America
FORNO BONOMI - Cookies - De Choix Specialty Foods Co.
FORPLAY - Toiletries - Trimensa Corp.
FORQE - Apparel and accessories - Munsingwear, Inc.
FORRELLI - Food products - R.J. Hirt Co.
FORRENCE ORCHARDS - Food products machinery - Forrence Orchards Inc.
FORREST GREEN - Recording label - Forrest Green Enterprises Inc.
FORREST HILL - Furniture ☆ - Bassett Furniture Industries, Inc.
FORREST PARK - Food products - Allen Canning Co.
FORRESTER - Handles–wood - Fleischmann Handle Co.
FORSA - Tableware–china ☆ - Villeroy and Boch Tableware Ltd.
FORSCHNER - See **R.H. FORSCHNER**
FORSELL - Yarn ☆ - Plymouth Yarn Co.
FORSGATE - Floor coverings–tile - Collins & Aikman Corp.
FORSHNER'S - Veterinary pharmaceutical preparations - Farnam Cos. Inc.
FORSTER - Wood products - Forster Inc.

☆ = Now out of production

FORSTMANN - Fabrics–wool ☆ - West Point-Pepperell Inc.

FORSTNER - Tools–woodworking - Connecticut Valley Manufacturing Co. of NB Inc.

FORSYTE - Chalk - Dixon Ticonderoga Co.

FORSYTE - Floor coverings–carpet and rugs - Burlington House Carpets

FORSYTH - Cabinets - Marsh Furniture Co.

FORSYTH - Furniture - Boling Co.

FORSYTHE - Cosmetics - Forsythe Cosmetic Group

FORSYTHIA - Integrated circuits - Infomedia Microelectronics, Inc.

FORT - Giftware - Fort USA

FORT AMERICA - Giftware ☆ - Africana Gifts & Shells Inc.

FORT APACHE - Toys - American Plastic Equipment Inc.

FORT ASTORIA - Wines - Shallon Winery

FORT BOISE - Onions - Fort Boise Produce Co.

FORT BRYAN - Musical instrument accessories - Bryan Enterprises, Inc.

FORT COLLEGE - Giftware - Fort USA

FORT COMMANCHE - Toys–automobiles - CBS Toys

FT. DODGE - Sporting goods - L.A. Steelcraft Products Inc.

FORT FRIDGE - Toys - Mattel, Inc.

FORT HOWARD - Food products ☆ - Stokely USA, Inc.

FORT HOWARD - Housewares - Fort Howard Corp.

FORT KNOX - Candy - Gerrit J. Verburg Co.

FORT KNOX - Computer software - Xiox Corp.

FORT LAREDO - Games ☆ - Warren Industries Inc.

FORT LOCK - Locks–padlocks - Fort Lock Corp.

FORT PITT - Beverages–malt - Jones Brewing Co.

FORT PITT FLAGPOLE - Flag poles - Ward Building & Highway Specialties, Inc.

FORT PITT LIGHT - Comforters - Jones Brewing Co.

FORT ROYAL - Floor coverings–carpet and rugs - Conquest Carpet Mills Inc.

FORT SCHUYLER - Beverages–malt ☆ - F.X. Matt Brewing Co.

FORT WALKER - Boots - Fort Walker, Inc.

FORT WAYNE ZOLLNER PISTONS - Apparel and accessories - Detroit Pistons Basketball Co.

FORT WHEAT - Crackers - Imperial Foods

FORT WORTH - Hats ☆ - Resistol Hats

FORTA - Vitamins and nutritional supplements - Ross Laboratories

FORTANT - Wines - Kobrand Corp.

FORTATIVE PERFORMANCE - Shampoos - Cosmair Inc.

FORTE - Amplifiers - Klipsch and Associates Inc.

FORTE - Cabinets - Aristokraft, Inc.

FORTE - Chemical preparations - Fuji Hunt Photographic Chemicals, Inc.

FORTE - Computer hardware - Forte Technologies, Inc.

FORTE - Computer peripheral equipment - Motorola, Inc. (Land Mobile Products Sector)

FORTE - Computer software - Forte' Advanced Management Software, Inc.

FORTE - Floor coverings–carpet and rugs ☆ - Lowe's Carpet Corp.

FORTE - Hair care products - Lendan USA Co.

FORTE - Hotels and motels - Trusthouse Forte Hotels International Inc.

FORTE - Mallets - Slobeat Industries

FORTE - Medical apparatus - Zimmer, Inc.

FORTE - Pencils–mechanical - Amblin' Entertainment, Inc.

FORTE - Pencils–mechanical - Pentel of America, Ltd.

FORTE - Photographic equipment - GMI Photographic Inc.

FORTE - Rings–jewelry - Artcarved Inc.

FORTE AUDIO - Audio equipment - Threshold Corp.

FORTE II - Fabrics–tapestry - Comark Wallcoverings

FORTE II - Wallpaper - Style-Tex Wallcoverings

FORTE INSTITUTE, THE - Computer software - Forte Interpersonal Communications, Inc.

FORTE-PLUS 24 - Vitamins and nutritional supplements ☆ - Parthenon Co. Inc.

FORTE-TOPICAL - Pharmaceutical preparations - Upjohn Co.

FORTEFITE - Paper–bond - Georgia-Pacific Corp.

FORTESAL - Pharmaceutical preparations ☆ - C.O. Truxton Inc.

FORTEX - Amplifiers - Hang-Kay Enterprise Inc.

FORTEX - Containers - Texamar Enterprises Inc.

FORTEZZA - Computer hardware - National Security Agency

FORTEZZE - Tiles–ceramic - American Marazzi Tile, Inc.

FORTGOLF - Giftware - Fort USA

FORTHANE - Cold remedies ☆ - Eli Lilly and Co.

FORTI-DIET - Pet products - Kaytee Products Inc.

FORTI-FLEX - Animal feed supplements - Agri-King Inc.

FORTICILS - Cosmetics - Lancome

FORTIFIBER - Floor coverings–carpet and rugs - Fortifiber Corp.

FORTIFIED - Golfing equipment - S.E.G., Inc.

FORTIFIED - Oils–lubricating - Getty Petroleum Marketing, Inc.

FORTIFIED FLAX - Food products - Omega-Life Inc.

FORTIFIED OSCAL - Vitamins and nutritional supplements - Hoechst Marion Roussel Inc.

FORTIFLEX - Containers - Texamar Enterprises Inc.

FORTIFY - Manicure preparations - Max Factor & Co.

FORTILAC - Milk - Hidden Valley Ranch

FORTINO WINERY - Wines - Fortino Winery

FORTIS - Dog food - Eugene Ingmand Co.

FORTIS - Floor coverings–carpet and rugs ☆ - Customweave Carpets Inc.

FORTISSIMO - Bedroom furniture - American Furniture Co. Inc.

FORTISSIMO - Hearing aids - Beltone Electronics Corp.

FORTITEC - Animal feeds - Farmland Foods, Inc.

FORTITUDE - Floor coverings–carpet and rugs - Karastan-Bigelow Inc.

FORTNUM & MASON - Food products - British American Imports

FORTO - Thread - Cincinnati Thread Co.

FORTRA - Computer peripheral equipment - JMR Electronics, Inc.

FORTREND - Handbags - Mister Ernest Handbags Inc.

FORTRESS - Product description unknown - American Window Fabricators Inc.

FORTRESS - Alarm systems–burglar - VSI Donner

FORTRESS - Apparel - Abanda Inc.

FORTRESS - Building materials - Brewer Co.

FORTRESS - Computer software - Science Applications International Corp.

FORTRESS - Computer software - Woodside Technologies Inc.

FORTRESS - Dental compounds - Chameleon Dental Products, Inc.

FORTRESS - Floor coverings - Congoleum Corp.

FORTRESS - Floor coverings–carpet and rugs - Matworks

FORTRESS - Floor coverings–carpet and rugs - Quaker Inc.

FORTRESS - Recording label - Refuge Music Group

FORTRESS - Skin care products - Conklin Co., Inc.

FORTRESS - Tires - Dunlop Tire Corp.

FORTRESS - Tubes–boiler - Smithkline Beecham Corp.

FORTRESS - Veterinary pharmaceutical preparations - SmithKline Beecham Animal Health Products

FORTRESS AMERICA - Games ☆ - Milton Bradley Co.

FORTRESS EUROPA - Games - Avalon Hill Game Co.

FORTRESS GOLD - Dental compounds - Chameleon Dental Products, Inc.

FORTRESS LITE - Wheelchairs ☆ - Fortress Inc.

FORTRESS OF DR. RADIAKI, THE - Video games - Future Visionary, Inc.

FORTRESS OF FANGS - Games ☆ - Tsr, Inc.

FORTRESS OF STEEL - Toys–automobiles - CBS Toys

FORTRESS OF THE WITCH KING - Games ☆ - Avalon Hill Game Co.

FORTRESS PRESS BOOKS - Publisher's imprints - Augsburg Fortress Publishers

FORTRESS, THE - Swing sets - Island Wood Products Inc.

FORTRON - Fibers–soybean - Fortron Industries

FORTRONICS - Electrical equipment - Fortronics Corp.

FORTRONICS - Locks–padlocks - Fort Lock Corp.

FORTSMITH - Furniture - Beatrice Cos. Inc.

FORTSTRESS - Hair care products - Recreations

FORTUIN - Candy - Holland-American Importing Co. Inc.

FORTUIN - Candy - Westdale Foods Co.

FORTUNA - Floor coverings ☆ - Congoleum Corp.

FORTUNA - Lighting fixtures - Angelo Brothers Co.

FORTUNA - Recording label - Celestial Harmonies

FORTUNA - Rings–jewelry - Artcarved Inc.

FORTUNADE HONDURAS - Cigars - Finck Cigar Co.

FORTUNAIRE - Floor coverings–carpet and rugs - World Carpets, Inc.

FORTUNATA - Floor coverings–carpet and rugs - Roxbury Carpet Co.

FORTUNATE OCCURRENCE - Greeting cards - Judith D. Drinks

FORTUNE - Candles - Merrill-West Publishing

FORTUNE - Candy ☆ - Melster Candies Inc.

FORTUNE - Clocks - General Time Corp. (Westclox/Seth Thomas Div.)

FORTUNE - Floor coverings–carpet and rugs - Calladium & Marglen

FORTUNE - Floor coverings–carpet and rugs - Columbus Mills, Inc.

FORTUNE - Food products - L. Karp & Sons, Inc.

FORTUNE - Glassware–household ☆ - Oneida Ltd.

FORTUNE - Golf clubs - King Par Corp.

FORTUNE - Meat products–canned - Sun Hing Foods, Inc.

FORTUNE - Pasta - JSL Foods, Inc.

FORTUNE - Recording label - Fortune & Hi-Q Records

FORTUNE - Shoes ☆ - Genesco Inc.

FORTUNE - Thread - Cincinnati Thread Co.

FORTUNE - Tires - National Tire Corp.

FORTUNE - Toys - Tonka Corp.

FORTUNE 32:16 - Computers–personal ☆ - SCI Systems, Inc.

FORTUNE 5000 - Computers–personal - SCI Systems, Inc.

☆ = Now out of production

FORTUNE AVENUE - Seafood products–fresh or frozen - Golden Crown Foods, Inc.

FORTUNE BALL - Games - Bet Technology, Inc.

FORTUNE BUBBLE - Chewing gum - R.L. Albert & Son, Inc.

FORTUNE CANDLE - Candles - Tops Malibu

FORTUNE CARD ROYAL MATCH 21 - Games - Bet Technology, Inc.

FORTUNE COOKIES - Dolls ☆ - Effanbee Doll Corp.

FORTUNE DELIGHT - Meat and vegetable extracts - Sunrider Corp.

FORTUNE FORMULA - Computers–personal ☆ - SCI Systems, Inc.

FORTUNE HEARTS - Candy - R.M. Palmer Co.

FORTUNE KCOOKIES - Stationery - Elaine I. Hindin

FORTUNE KNITS - Knitting machines - Fortune Knits Inc.

FORTUNE PASTA - Pasta - Fortune Macaroni Co.

FORTUNE QUIRKIES - Cookies - Eric Stromquist

FORTUNE SILKS - Artificial flowers - Fortune Silks, Inc.

FORTUNE UDON - Pasta - JSL Foods, Inc.

FORTUNE WRITER - Pens - Tiger Electronics, Inc.

FORTUNES - Coffee - Richard G. Cefola

FORTUNE'S - Coffee - Queen's Empire

FORTUNO - Games - Creatnetics

FORTUNY DIVA - Draperies - Maya Romanoff Corp.

FORTUNY GOLD ACCENT - Flatware ☆ - Yamazaki Tableware Inc.

FORTUS - Floor coverings–carpet and rugs - Daltonian Carpet & Cushion Inc.

FORTUS - Floor coverings–carpet and rugs - V & B Carpet

FORTWAYNE FURY - Apparel and accessories - Northern Indiana Basketball Corp.

FORTY BELOW - Jackets ☆ - Kellwood Co.

FORTY DRUMMERS - Wines - Wine Imports Ltd.

FORTY FATHOMS - Aquariums–household - Marine Enterprises International, Inc.

FORTY-MIGHT - Lighting fixtures - Kenall Manufacturing Co.

FORTY NINER - Bakery products - San Francisco French Bread Co.

FORTY-NINER - Eyeglasses - Art-Craft Optical Co.

FORTY-NINER - Jewelry ☆ - Hirsch Speidel Inc.

FORTY NINER - Kitchen utensils–aluminum - Bonny Products Inc.

FORTY-NINER - Ribbons - Eaton Allen Ko-Rec-Type Corp.

FORTY-SECOND STREET - Floor coverings ☆ - Tarkett, Inc.

FORTY-SECOND STREET - Furniture ☆ - Bassett Furniture Industries, Inc.

FORTY WINKS - Apparel and accessories - Bentley Lingerie, Inc.

FORTY WINKS - Fabrics - Guilford Mills, Inc.

FORUM - Bathroom accessories - Kohler Co.

FORUM - Bicycles - Columbia Manufacturing Inc.

FORUM - Drums–musical instruments - Pearl Corp.

FORUM - Floor coverings - Congoleum Corp.

FORUM - Floor coverings–carpet and rugs - Mannington Carpets, Inc.

FORUM - Floor coverings–carpet and rugs ☆ - Porter Carpet Mills Inc.

FORUM - Furniture ☆ - Boling Co.

FORUM - Pencils ☆ - Faber-Castell Corp.

FORUM - Pens ☆ - Bic Corp.

FORUM - Tables–wood - Fixtures Furniture

FORUM - Wallpaper - Koroseal Wallcoverings

FORUM DISPLAY FRAME SYSTEM, THE - Portable exhibit displays - Howard Glenn Godfrey

FORUM ENTERPRISES - Computer software - Forum Enterprises, Inc.

FORUM II - Office furniture–wood - Anderson Desk Inc.

FORUM LEADER - Office furniture–wood - Anderson Desk Inc.

FORUM SERIES - Desks and modular groups ☆ - American Desk Manufacturing Co.

FORUM VI - Furniture ☆ - Bassett Furniture Industries, Inc.

FORUMLA I - Luggage ☆ - Gateway Travelware

FORVISTA - Ophthalmic goods - Styl-Rite Optical Manufacturing Co., Inc.

FORWARD - Ophthalmic goods - Foremost Optical Products

FORWARD - Paper–bond - L.L. Brown Paper Co.

FORWARD - Pencils ☆ - Koh-I-Noor, Inc.

FORWARD FAN-OUT AGENT - Computer software - Technology Investments, Inc.

FORWARD FILE - Office furniture–metal - Haskell of Pittsburgh, Inc.

FORWEAR - Apparel–women's - Top Rank Apparel Corp.

FORZA - Boots - Track 'n Trail

FORZA - Hair care products - Modafini Inc.

FOS CAPS, 725 MG. - Vitamins and nutritional supplements - Vitamin Research Products Inc.

FOSC 200 - Cables–fiber optic - Raychem Corp.

FOSC 400 - Cables - Raychem Corp.

FOSFREE - Vitamins and nutritional supplements - Mission Pharmacal Co.

FOSILGLAS - Glass products - Coral Bay Inc.

FOSS - Spices and extracts - Schlotterbeck and Foss Co.

FOSS - Video production - Encyclopaedia Britannica Inc.

FOSS FLEX - Fabrics–broadcloth - Foss Manufacturing Co., Inc.

FOSS-SET - Brushes–paint - Wooster Brush Co.

FOSSETTE - Building materials–concrete - Burns & Russell Co.

FOSSFORM - Fabrics–broadcloth - Foss Manufacturing Co., Inc.

FOSSI - Wines ☆ - AHD Vinter's Ltd.

FOSSIL - Metals - Plastic Dress-Up Co.

FOSSIL - Recording label - Fossil Records

FOSSIL - Underwear and nightwear - Tugaloo River Boxer Co.

FOSSIL - Watches - Fossil Inc.

FOSSIL HUNT - Toys - Uncle Milton Industries Inc.

FOSSIL LORDS - Toys - Tonka Corp.

FOSSILI - Tiles–ceramic - American Marazzi Tile, Inc.

FOSSILMANIA - Art objects - Fossilmania, Inc.

FOSSPLIT - Fabrics–broadcloth - Foss Manufacturing Co., Inc.

FOSSTRETCH - Fabrics–broadcloth - Foss Manufacturing Co., Inc.

FOSTA - Optical services ☆ - Foster Grant Co. Inc.

FOSTA-GRANTLY - Optical services ☆ - Foster Grant Co. Inc.

FOSTER - Beds–metal ☆ - HARD Manufacturing Co. Inc.

FOSTER - Health care products - Abbey Home Health Care

FOSTER - Pet products - Colony Pet Goods

FOSTER - Tarpaulins - Foster Corp.

FOSTER - Valves–industrial - Foster Valve Corp.

FOSTER - Vegetables–canned - Foster Canning Inc.

FOSTER FARMS - Meat products–beef - Foster Poultry Farms

FOSTER FARMS SIGNATURE SERIES - Meat products–poultry - Foster Poultry Farms

FOSTER GRANT - Eyeglasses - Foster Grant Co. Inc.

FOSTER HOUSE - Tablecloths ☆ - Foster Corp.

FOSTER LIGHT - Beverages–alcohol ☆ - Century Importers Inc.

FOSTER MARSHALL - Water–bottled or canned - Foster Water Co.

FOSTER RAINEY - Boots - Larry's Standard Brand Shoes, Inc.

FOSTERS CLASSIC - Sandwiches–prepackaged - Fosters Freeze International, Inc.

FOSTERS FREEZE TWISTER - Ice cream - Fosters Freeze International, Inc.

FOSTER'S LAGER - Beverages–malt - Century Importers Inc.

FOSTER'S SPECINBITTER ALE - Beverages–malt - Century Importers Inc.

FOSTEX - Pharmaceutical preparations - Westwood-Squibb Pharmaceuticals, Inc.

FOSTEX - Recording label - Fostex Corp. of America

FOSTORIA - Barbecues and grills ☆ - Toastmaster Inc.

FOSTORIA INTERNATIONAL - Glassware–household - Colony Glass

FOSTORIA USA - Glassware–household - Colony Glass

FOSTRIL - Pharmaceutical preparations - Westwood-Squibb Pharmaceuticals, Inc.

FOT - Bathroom accessories - Flowery Beauty Products, Inc.

FOTA-LITE - Glass products - Corning Inc.

FOTI - Shoes - Frank Foti

FOTI - Shorts–men's - Foti Imports

FOTI TIENG - Health care products - Bio-Research Laboratories

FOTO-CART - Photographic equipment - Berkey Marketing Cos.

FOTO FEELINGS - Greeting cards - Foto Feelings, Inc.

FOTO FINNESSE - Photographic equipment - Reeves Photo Sales Inc.

FOTO-FLO - Photocopy machines ☆ - Xerox Corp.

FOTO FORMS - Statuary - Clearr Corp.

FOTO FRAME FRIENDS - Toys–stuffed - Fun World Inc.

FOTO FRISKET - Artists' materials - Badger Air-Brush Co.

FOTO FUN! - Printers–computer - Fargo Electronics Inc.

FOTO-MITE - Photographic equipment - Rollei of America Inc.

FOTO MORPHOSIS - Photographic equipment - American Alpha, Inc.

FOTO-O - Photographic equipment - Cincinnati Screen Printing Equipment Co.

FOTO PONG - Electronic equipment - Fotomark, Inc.

FOTO-R - Photographic equipment - Cincinnati Screen Printing Equipment Co.

FOTO/SPECTRUM - Scientific apparatus - Fotodyne Inc.

FOTO STIK - Adhesives and sealants - NCSI

FOTO-WEAR! - Paper–transfer - Foto-Wear Inc.

FOTOBRICK - Frames–picture - A/R Video, Inc.

FOTOCERAM - Glass products - Corning Inc.

FOTOFILE - Photo albums - Ensemble, Inc.

FOTOFINE - Photographic equipment - Acufine Inc.

FOTOFLAT - Electronic equipment - Seal Products Inc.

FOTOFOLIO - Postcards - Fotofolio Inc.

FOTOFORMS - Novelty items - Fabulous Fotoforms, Inc.

FOTOFUN! - Printers–computer - Fargo Electronics Inc.

FOTOFX - Computer software - Lasermaster Corp.

☆ = Now out of production

FOTOLARGER - Photographic equipment ✩ - Testrite Instrument Co. Inc.
FOTOLITE - Photographic equipment - Testrite Instrument Co. Inc.
FOTOMAN - Computer peripheral equipment - Logitech, Inc.
FOTOMAT - Film - Fotomat Corp.
FOTOMAX - Photographic equipment - Byers Corp.
FOTOMUG! - Glassware–household - Fargo Electronics Inc.
FOTONOTE - Stationery - Kimball Concepts Ltd.
FOTOPRINT - Posters - Kimball Concepts Ltd.
FOTORITE - Photographic equipment ✩ - Testrite Instrument Co. Inc.
FOTOSETS - Compact discs–prerecorded - Robco
FOTOSIGN - Posters - Metro Computer Signs Inc.
FOTOTAR - Pharmaceutical preparations - ICN Pharmaceuticals Inc.
FOTOTEX - Photographic equipment ✩ - Testrite Instrument Co. Inc.
FOTOTIRE - Novelty items–glass - Fotoball USA Inc.
FOTOVIEW - Photographic equipment - Fotoshow
FOTOVIX - Film - Tamron Industries Inc.
FOTOWITE - Paperboard ✩ - Sanlu Art Industries Inc.
FOUCHET - Brandy ✩ - Paramount Distillers Inc.
FOUGERA - Analgesics - E. Fougera & Co. Inc.
FOUGERE ROYALE - Skin care products - Houbigant, Inc.
FOUGERS - Glassware–household - Durand International
FOUL-BAN - Chemical preparations ✩ - Woolsey Marine Industries
FOUL PLAY - Socks - TGF Socks & Hosiery, Inc.
FOUL PLAY PRESS - Publisher's imprints - Countryman Press Inc.
FOUL SHOT - Sporting goods - Heart of America Sports Camps and Clinics, Ltd.
FOUL SHOT - Toys ✩ - Those Characters from Cleveland, Inc.
FOULARD - Blinds–venetian ✩ - Hunter Douglas, Inc.
FOULDS - Macaroni - Foulds Inc.
FOULEX - Veterinary pharmaceutical preparations - Y-Tex Corp.
FOULGARD - Paints - Valspar Corp.
FOULMOUTH - Generators–electric - S.R.M. Co., Inc.
FOUND A PEANUT - Desserts - Silver Palate Kitchen
FOUNDATION - Floor coverings–carpet and rugs - Coronet Carpets Inc.
FOUNDATION - Guitars - Peavey Electronics Corp.
FOUNDATION - Hair care products - Faberge Co.
FOUNDATION - Sinks–metal - Kohler Co.
FOUNDATION LH - Guitars - Peavey Electronics Corp.
FOUNDATION S - Guitars - Peavey Electronics Corp.
FOUNDATIONS - Communications equipment–satellite - Business Telecom, Inc.
FOUNDATIONS - Floor coverings - Congoleum Corp.
FOUNDATIONS - Stencils - Plaid Enterprises, Inc.
FOUNDATIONS - Wallpaper - Gencorp Inc.
FOUNDATIONS FOR HEALTH - Apparel and accessories - Glamorise Foundations Inc.
FOUNDATIONS IN READING - Computer software - Breakthrough, Inc.
FOUNDER'S - Adhesives and sealants - Plaid Enterprises, Inc.
FOUNDERS - Clocks - Ridgeway Clock Co.
FOUNDERS CLUB - Golf clubs - Founders Club Golf Co.
FOUNDERS OAK - Furniture ✩ - Virginia House Furniture Corp.
FOUNDERS WHITE - Wines - Bully Hill Vineyards, Inc.
FOUNDLINGS - Toys - Hugg-A-Planet
FOUNDRY ART - Decorations - Lowitz & Co.
FOUNT - Dinnerware–glass - Block China Co.
FOUNT - Publisher's imprints - World Publishing Co.
FOUNTABLES - Fountains - Henri Studio, Inc.
FOUNTAIN - Computer hardware - Fountain Technologies, Inc.
FOUNTAIN BLOCK - Water treating compounds - Jungle Laboratories Corp.
FOUNTAIN CLASSICS - Beverages–carbonated - Cable Car Beverage Corp.
FOUNTAIN FACTORY, THE - Figurines - Anna-Perenna Inc.
FOUNTAIN FRESH - Toothbrushes ✩ - Fountain Fresh
FOUNTAIN GROVE - Wines - Martini and Prati Wines Inc.
FOUNTAIN MERMAID - Dolls - Mattel, Inc.
FOUNTAIN MOISTENER - Office supplies - Bert M. Morris Co.
FOUNTAIN NATURAL SPRING WATER - Water–bottled or canned - Beverage Marketing International, Inc.
FOUNTAIN OF YOUTH - Health care products - Natural Laboratories Corp.
FOUNTAIN OF YOUTH - Juice extracting devices - Angel Life Corp.
FOUNTAIN PARK - Chocolate syrup - J. Hungerford Smith Co.
FOUNTAIN PENS - Pens–fountain - Quill Co. Inc.
FOUNTAIN PENTEL - Pens - Pentel of America, Ltd.
FOUNTAIN PLAZA - Floor coverings ✩ - Tarkett, Inc.
FOUNTAIN PRESS - Publisher's imprints - Price Stern Sloan Inc.
FOUNTAIN PRODUCTIONS - Recording label - Carmel Records
FOUNTAIN ROCK - Nurseries and garden stores - Dyna Corp.

FOUNTAIN SPRAY - Sporting goods - Alvimar Manufacturing Co. Inc.
FOUNTAIN STONE - Furniture - Wilderness Naturals Marketing Co.
FOUNTAIN WEIGHT - Glassware–household - Nourot Glass Studio
FOUNTAINBLEAU - Eyeglasses - Martin-Copeland Eyewear Corp.
FOUNTAINBLEAU - Furniture ✩ - Bernhardt Industries
FOUNTAINBLEAU - Glassware–household - Durand International
FOUNTAINBLEAU - Wallpaper - Rigo Wallcoverings Inc.
FOUNTAINEBLEAU - Dishes–china ✩ - WMF/USA
FOUNTAINEBLEAU - Tableware–china ✩ - Villeroy and Boch Tableware Ltd.
FOUNTAINHEAD - Floor coverings–carpet and rugs ✩ - Lees Carpets
FOUNTAINHEAD - Recording label - Fountainhead Records
FOUNTAINHEAD BY NEVAMAR - Counter tops–laminated - International Paper (Decorative Products Division)
FOUNTAINHEAD II - Floor coverings–carpet and rugs - Lees Carpets
FOUNTAINPURE - Fruit flavored drinks - Network Group
FOUNTAINS - Figurines - Anna-Perenna Inc.
FOUNTAINSIDE - Fountains - Bonsai World
FOUR 9'S - Solder - Metallic Resources, Inc.
FOUR ACES - Tobacco–chewing or smoking - Republic Tobacco L.P.
FOUR ACES WESTERN WEAR - Apparel and accessories - Joseph E. Cucuiat
FOUR A.M. - Apparel–athletic - Four A.M., Inc.
FOUR BOYS - Seafood products–fresh or frozen - Impex Shrimp & Fish Co.
FOUR CHIMNEYS - Wines - Four Chimneys Farm Winery
FOUR COLOR - Pencils ✩ - National Pen & Pencil Co.
FOUR CROWN - Dinnerware–glass - Sango Co. Ltd. (Sango USA Div.)
FOUR DAUGHTERS - Food products - Union Sea Foods Inc.
FOUR DOTS - Recording label - Jazz Composer's Orchestra Association Inc.
FOUR EDGE - Scrapers - Allway Tools Inc.
FOUR EYES - Frames–eyeglass - Zylo Ware Corp.
FOUR FINGER STOUT - Beverages–malt - KC Brewing Co.
FOUR FISHERMEN - Seafood products–fresh or frozen ✩ - Gorton Group
FOUR FLAGS - Recording label - Spotlite Records
FOUR/FOUR - Frames–eyeglass ✩ - Universal/Univis Inc.
FOUR-GARD - Medical apparatus - Karlen Manufacturing, Inc.
FOUR-GASM - Hats - Lloyd Petre
FOUR GENERATIONS - Apparel and accessories - Ray Strauss Unlimited Inc.
FOUR GINSENGS - Health care products - East Earth Herb Inc.
FOUR GREAT DIRECTIONS - Luggage - Jansport Apparel Corp.
FOUR HORSEMEN OF APOKOLIPS - Games ✩ - Mayfair Games, Inc.
FOUR HOUR FOGGER - Insecticides - Enforcer Products Inc.
FOUR-IN-LINE - Glassware–household - Owens-Illinois Inc. (Libbey Div.)
FOUR-IN-ONE - Cleaning preparations ✩ - Abbott Laboratories
FOUR-IN-ONE - Cooking equipment–household ✩ - Nordic Ware
FOUR-IN-ONE - Food products - Nasco Gourmet Foods
FOUR-IN-ONE - Hair curlers ✩ - Sunbeam-Oster Household Products
FOUR-IN-ONE'S - Hobby kits - A + A
FOUR J - Playground equipment ✩ - A.H. Schwab Co.
FOUR LEAF - Wines - American Vineyards Co. Inc.
FOUR LEAF CLOVER - Coffee - Coffee Beanery Ltd.
FOUR LEAF CLOVER - Recording label ✩ - Ozark Opry Records
FOUR-LETTER WORDS - Computer software ✩ - CONDUIT
FOUR-LIVES - Frames–eyeglass - Hudson Optical Corp.
FOUR MONKS - Tobacco products - Lane Ltd.
FOUR MONKS - Wine vinegar - American Foods Corp.
FOUR NAILS - Manicure preparations - Four Nails of Minnesota Inc.
FOUR-O-COFFEE - Coffee - Four-O-Coffee Co.
FOUR OF A KIND - Apparel and accessories - Motiva, Inc.
FOUR PALMS - Computer storage devices - Four Palms, Inc.
FOUR PAWS - Pet products - Four Paws Products Ltd.
FOUR PENNY - Shampoos - Four Penny Products Inc.
FOUR PLAY - Apparel and accessories - Bugle Boy Industries, Inc.
FOUR PLAY - Video production - Merit Industries
FOUR + FOUR - Headphones ✩ - Hamilton Electronics Corp.
FOUR-POINT - Hooks - Vulcan-Volner Manufacturing Corp.
FOUR POINT - Stationery - American Thermoplastic Co.
FOUR PURPOSE - Skin care products - Orjene Natural Cosmetics
FOUR QUEEN'S BLEND - Beverages–alcohol - Kasser Laird Distilling Co.
FOUR RIVERS - Computer software - Four Rivers Software Systems Inc.
FOUR ROSES - Flour–blended - Southeastern Mills Inc.
FOUR ROSES - Whiskey - Four Roses Distillers Co.
FOUR ROSES PREMIUM - Whiskey - Four Roses Distillers Co.
FOUR-S - Bread - Interstate Brands Corp.
FOUR SCORE - Boxes - Martin Carbone Inc.
FOUR SCORE - Video games - Nintendo of America Inc.
FOUR SEAS - Publisher's imprints - Branden Publishing Co., Inc.
FOUR-SEASON - Fencing ✩ - Conwed Plastics

FOUR SEASON - Fishing lures - Frabill Inc.
FOUR SEASON - Hair care products ☆ - P.S. Pibbs Inc.
FOUR-SEASON - Tiles–ceramic ☆ - Wenczel Tile Co.
FOUR SEASONS - Apparel and accessories ☆ - Halper Brothers Inc.
FOUR SEASONS - Automotive parts and accessories - Standard Motor Products, Inc.
FOUR SEASONS - Beverages–alcohol - Alpha Industries, Inc.
FOUR SEASONS - Boating equipment and accessories - Chemifax
FOUR SEASONS - Building materials - Brewer Co.
FOUR-SEASONS - Calendars - House of Doolittle
FOUR SEASONS - Candles ☆ - Emkay Candles
FOUR SEASONS - Cleaning preparations–household - Grow Group, Inc.
FOUR SEASONS - Dolls ☆ - Effanbee Doll Corp.
FOUR SEASONS - Doors–wood - Maywood Inc.
FOUR SEASONS - Eyeglasses - Martin-Copeland Eyewear Corp.
FOUR SEASONS - Fabrics - Greenwood Mills Inc.
FOUR SEASONS - Floor coverings ☆ - Aladdin Mills, Inc.
FOUR SEASONS - Floor coverings–carpet and rugs - Value Carpets Inc.
FOUR SEASONS - Furniture ☆ - Tropitone Furniture Co. Inc.
FOUR SEASONS - Health care products - Japlar Acquisition Co. (Japlar/Schauer)
FOUR SEASONS - House furnishings ☆ - Lexington Furniture Industries, Inc.
FOUR SEASONS - Indoor-outdoor carpet - Instant Turf Industries Inc.
FOUR SEASONS - Lighting fixtures ☆ - Hubbell Lighting, Inc. (Lighting Div.)
FOUR SEASONS - Mattresses - Spring Air Bedding Inc.
FOUR SEASONS - Paints - M.A. Bruder & Sons Inc.
FOUR SEASONS - Snack foods - Dolefam Corp.
FOUR SEASONS - Stationery ☆ - Doehla Greeting Cards Inc.
FOUR SEASONS - Tires - Bridgestone/Firestone, Inc.
FOUR SEASONS - Tobacco products - Lane Ltd.
FOUR SEASONS - Wallpaper - Bassett & Vollum Wallpapers
FOUR SEASONS - Wallpaper - Marburg Wallcoverings Inc.
FOUR SEASONS - Wallpaper ☆ - Fidelity Industries, Inc.
FOUR SEASONS AGRICULTURAL PRODUCTS - Film - Atlantis Group Inc.
FOUR SEASONS COLLECTION - Floor coverings–carpet and rugs - Karastan-Bigelow Inc.
FOUR SEASONS DESIGN AND REMODELING CENTERS - Building materials–asbestos - Four Seasons Solar Products
FOUR SEASONS MATCHMATE - Doors–wood - Maywood Inc.
FOUR SEASONS SHUTTER COLLECTION - Shutters–plastic - Blind Design Inc.
FOUR SEASONS SUNROOMS - Structural metal - Four Seasons Solar Products
FOUR SEASONS, THE - China - Classic Restaurants Corp.
FOUR SEASONS, THE - Floor coverings–carpet and rugs ☆ - Walter Carpet Mills
FOUR SEASONS VILLAGE, THE - Figurines - Kurt S. Adler Inc.
FOUR SHOT - Cleaner - Intex Chemical Inc.
FOUR SPEED - Sauces ☆ - Chris Cross Products Inc.
FOUR SQUARE - Apparel and accessories - J.C. Penney Co., Inc.
FOUR SQUARE - Floor coverings–tile ☆ - National Floor Products Co., Inc.
FOUR SQUARE - Frames–eyeglass - May Optical Co. Inc.
FOUR SQUARE - Tobacco products - Faber, Coe & Gregg Inc.
FOUR STAR - Candy ☆ - Beacon Sweets, Inc.
FOUR STAR - Cutlery - J.A. Henckels Zwillingswerk Inc.
FOUR STAR - Food products ☆ - Leavenworth Fruit Co.
FOUR STAR - Musical instrument accessories - Otto Link Inc.
FOUR STAR - Paper–bond - Southworth Co.
FOUR STAR - Pharmaceutical preparations ☆ - Hodgson Mill
FOUR STAR - Radios - Fortune Star Products Corp.
FOUR STAR - Sunglasses - Command Marketing Corp.
FOUR STAR - Tobacco–chewing or smoking - Amar Blends Co.
FOUR STAR - Wallpaper ☆ - Winfield Design Associates, Inc.
FOUR STAR DIAMONDS - Jewelry - Crescent Jewelers, Inc.
FOUR STAR MOBILE HOMES - Real estate agencies - Karen Reardon
FOUR STAR RESTAURANT BLEND - Coffee - Ephrata Diamond Spring Water Co., Inc.
FOUR STARS - Floor coverings–carpet and rugs - Lock Weave Carpet Mills Inc.
FOUR STRIPER - Apparel–athletic ☆ - Mighty-Mac
FOUR SWEET SISTERS, THE - Dairy products - Sweet Sisters, Inc.
FOUR WAY - Flowers, plants, and seeds - Seed Corp. of America
FOUR-WAY - Paints - Ponderosa Paint Manufacturing Co. Inc.
FOUR WAY CURLS - Curling irons–electric - Windmere Corp.
FOUR WHEEL DRIVE - Automotive parts and accessories - Quigley Motor Co. Inc.

FOUR WINDS - Dairy products - Schnuck Markets, Inc.
FOUR WINDS - Frames–eyeglass - May Optical Co. Inc.
FOUR WINDS - Wallpaper - Textile Wallcoverings International Ltd.
FOUR WINDS FARM - Food products - Staff Supermarket Associates, Inc.
FOUR WINDS FARM - Turkeys - Schnuck Markets, Inc.
FOUR WINDS PRESS - Publisher's imprints - MacMillan Publishing Co. Inc.
FOUR WINDS, THE - Music boxes - Giftec Ltd.
FOUR WINNS - Boats–motor - Outboard Marine Corp.
FOUR.1 - Electronic equipment - AudioControl
FOURBULOUS - Apparel–athletic - Dee-Yah, Inc.
FOUREX - Prophylactics - Durex Consumer Products
FOUREX - Prophylactics - Schmid Laboratories
FOURGEN - Computer software - Fourgen Software Technologies, Inc.
FOURGUARD - Chemical preparations - Professional Chemicals Corp.
FOURMOST - Recording label ☆ - Slep-Tone Entertainment Corp.
FOURNIER - House furnishings - Fournier Furniture, Inc.
FOURPLAY - Paper products - Samuel Chmell
FOURSED - Pharmaceutical preparations - Kraft Pharmaceutical Co.
FOURSOME - Kitchen appliances ☆ - Nordic Ware
FOURSOME - Luggage ☆ - Hartmann Luggage Co.
FOURSOME - Recliners - Sears, Roebuck and Co.
FOURSOMES - Candy ☆ - Leaf, Inc.
FOURTH ADDITION - Apparel–women's - Periphery Loungewear Inc.
FOURTH-COURT TENNIS - Tennis equipment - Sportime
FOURTH EDITION - Floor coverings–carpet and rugs - Queen Carpet Corp.
FOURTH FLOOR - Recording label - Northcott Productions Ltd.
FOURTH STREAM - Recording label - Jazz Composer's Orchestra Association Inc.
FOURWAYS - Salad dressings–bottled - Haddon House Food Products Inc.
FOURWORD/WORDLIFT - Computer software ☆ - Milliken Publishing Co. (Computer Software Div.)
FOUTENAY WATERCOLOR - Artists' materials - Canson-Talens Inc.
FOWITCO - Giftware - Four Winds Trading Co.
FOWL FOOLERS - Decoys - Fowl Foolers Decoy Co.
FOWL WEATHER GEAR - Apparel and accessories - Michael L. Arnold
FOWLER - Heating equipment ☆ - Bradford-White Corp.
FOWLER - Measuring instruments - Arthur H. Gaebel Inc.
FOWLER - Publisher's imprints - Fowler Music Enterprises
FOWLER'S - Peanut butter - Fowler & Huntting Co.
FOWLER'S FAMOUS - Food products - Fowler's Ltd.
FOWNES - Gloves - Fownes Brothers & Co., Inc.
FOX - Apparel and accessories - J.C. Penney Co., Inc.
FOX - Bassoons - Fox Products Corp.
FOX - Cables - Peterson Systems International, Inc.
FOX - Chemicals - Dow Corning Corp.
FOX - Electronic equipment ☆ - AVL
FOX - Firearms, accessories, and parts ☆ - Savage Arms Inc.
FOX - Gocarts - Manco Products, Inc.
FOX - Goggles - Glendale Protective Technologies Inc.
FOX - Hair-cutting shears ☆ - B.W. Boyd Shears Inc.
FOX - Motor vehicle parts and accessories - Certified Parts Corp.
FOX - Motor vehicles–automobiles - Volkswagen of America Inc.
FOX - Shovels - True Temper Hardware Co.
FOX - Syrup - H. Fox & Co., Inc.
FOX - Tripods–photographic - Phoenix Corp. of America
FOX 40 - Whistles - Tide-Rider Inc.
FOX-A-MATIC - Chlorine cartridges - Fox Pool Corp.
FOX BAT - Kites - Gayla Industries Inc.
FOX CREEK - Cooking utensils–stoneware - Fox Creek Pottery
FOX CREST - Floor coverings–carpet and rugs - Evans-Black Carpet Mills
FOX DELUXE - Beverages–malt - Cold Spring Brewing Co.
FOX DELUXE - Food products ☆ - Pillsbury Co.
FOX DEN - Wine - European Beverage Co., Inc.
FOX FIRE - Barbecue and grill accessories - Charlotte's Group, Inc.
FOX FIRE - Eyeglasses - Martin-Copeland Eyewear Corp.
FOX FIRE - Furniture - Singer Furniture Co.
FOX FIRE - Toys–models - Comet Montrose Ltd.
FOX FIRE - Toys–models ☆ - Estes Industries
FOX FRESH MESH - Bags–plastic - Kenneth Fox Supply Co.
FOX GL - Motor vehicles–automobiles - Volkswagen of America Inc.
FOX GLEN - Floor coverings–carpet and rugs ☆ - Evans-Black Carpet Mills
FOX HEAD 400 - Beverages–malt ☆ - Eastern Brewing Corp.
FOX HILL - Apparel–men's - M. Aron Corp.
FOX HILL - Floor coverings–carpet and rugs ☆ - Evans-Black Carpet Mills
FOX HILLS - Floor coverings–carpet and rugs ☆ - Royalweve Carpet Mills
FOX HOLLOW - Floor coverings–carpet and rugs - Evans-Black Carpet Mills

☆ = Now out of production

FOX HUNT - Floor coverings ☆ - Congoleum Corp.

FOX INTERACTIVE - Computer peripheral equipment - Twentieth Century Fox Film Corp.

FOX KIDS MUSIC - Recording label - Twentieth Century Fox Film Corp.

FOX KNAPP - Apparel–men's - David Peyser Sportswear Inc.

FOX KNAPP - Waterproof outerwear - Fox-Knapp Inc.

FOX LITE - Lighting equipment - Fox Lite Inc.

FOX MEADOW - Floor coverings ☆ - Tarkett, Inc.

FOX MOUNTAIN - Wines - L. Foppiano Wine Co.

FOX MOUNTAIN - Wines - House of Burgundy Inc.

FOX NUTRITION, INC. - Vitamins and nutritional supplements - Fox Nutrition, Inc.

FOX PLATFORM LADDER - Ladders–metal - Fox Products, Inc.

FOX POINT - Apparel stores–sports - Fox Point Sportswear Inc.

FOX RECORDS - Recording label - Twentieth Century Fox Film Corp.

FOX RIDGE WINERY - Wines - Geyser Peak Winery

FOX RIVER - Manufactured homes - Redman Industries, Inc.

FOX RIVER - Paper–bond - Fox River Paper Co.

FOX RIVER BRAKE - Firearms, accessories, and parts - Gander Mountain, Inc.

FOX RUN - Furniture - Singer Furniture Co.

FOX RUN - Furniture ☆ - Bassett Furniture Industries, Inc.

FOX RUN - Wines - Banfi Vintners

FOX RUN - Wines - Fox Run Vineyards

FOX RUN CRAFTSMEN - Kitchen cabinets–metal - Fox Run Craftsmen

FOX RUN VINEYARDS - Wines - Fox Run Vineyards

FOX SEARCHLIGHT PICTURES - Recording label - Twentieth Century Fox Film Corp.

FOX SPORTS DIRECT - Broadcasting stations–television - Twentieth Century Fox Film Corp.

FOX SPORTS WEST - Broadcasting stations–television - Twentieth Century Fox Film Corp.

FOX STUDIOS - Broadcasting stations–television - Twentieth Century Fox Film Corp.

FOX SYSTEM, THE - Furniture–children's - Fox System, Inc.

FOX TRAC - Motorcycles ☆ - Certified Parts Corp.

FOXALIN - Health care products - Halsom Home Care

FOXAPPER - Electronic equipment - Fox Electronics & Technology, Inc.

FOXBASE - Computer software - Microsoft Corp.

FOXBAT - Transmitting apparatus - Harris Corp.

FOXBAT PRECISION - Golfing equipment - Foxbat Precision Sports Inc.

FOXBORO - Computers - Foxboro Co.

FOXBORO - Frames–eyeglass ☆ - Universal/Univis Inc.

FOXBOROUGH - Furniture ☆ - A.A. Laun Furniture Co.

FOXCODER - Computer peripheral equipment - Foxfire, Inc.

FOXCROFT - Apparel and accessories - Enro Shirt Co. Inc.

FOXCROFT - Furniture - Moosehead Manufacturing Co.

FOXCROFT - Lenses–optical - National Optical Co.

FOXCROFT - Tableware–china ☆ - Lenox, Inc.

FOXES - Food products - F & F Laboratories, Inc.

FOXES PIN-UP GIRLS - Deodorizers ☆ - Car-Freshner Corp.

FOXFARM - Fertilizers - Foxfarm Soil & Fertilizer Co.

FOXFIBRE - Fabrics ☆ - Seventh Generation Wholesale Inc.

FOXFIRE - Colognes - Avon Products, Inc.

FOXFIRE! - Computer software - Micromega Systems, Inc.

FOXFIRE - Floor coverings–carpet and rugs - Coronet Carpets Inc.

FOXFIRE - Furniture - Athens Furniture Industries Inc.

FOXFIRE - Office supplies - Ghent Manufacturing Inc.

FOXFIRE - Type faces - John S. Hicks

FOXFIRE - Yarn ☆ - Caron International Inc.

FOXGLOVE - Wines - Park Wine Co., Inc.

FOXHEAD - Apparel–men's ☆ - Goodstein Bros. & Co. Inc.

FOXHILL - Mugs - Possible Dreams, Ltd.

FOXHOLLOW VINEYARD - Wines - Grand Cru Vineyards

FOXHOLM - Floor coverings–carpet and rugs ☆ - Mandate-Dawn Carpet Mills

FOXHUNT FARMS - Food products - Fox Hunt Farms LLC

FOXLINE - Paper–bond ☆ - Fox River Paper Co.

FOXLITE - Paper–bond ☆ - Fox River Paper Co.

FOXLOFT - Apparel and accessories - Fox River Mills, Inc.

FOXMOOR - Floor coverings–carpet and rugs - Patcraft Mills Inc.

FOXMOOR - Shoes - Melville Corp.

FOXPRO - Computer software - Microsoft Corp.

FOXRIDGE - Cabinets - Yorktowne Inc.

FOX'S - Biscuits ☆ - FCW Imports

FOX'S - Syrup - H. Fox & Co., Inc.

FOX'S PIZZA DEN - Apparel and accessories - Fox's Pizza Den, Inc.

FOX'S U-BET - Syrup - H. Fox & Co., Inc.

FOXTAIL FOODS - Bakery products - Perkins Restaurants Operating Co., L.P.

FOXTAILS - Apparel and accessories - Foxtails

FOXTROT - Apparel–men's ☆ - J.G. Hook, Inc.

FOXTROT - Fabrics - Gretchen Bellinger Inc.

FOXWOOD - Wines - Foxwood Wine Cellars

FOXWOOD TALES - Toys–stuffed ☆ - Toy Works, Inc.

FOXWORTH - Fabrics - Dan River Inc.

FOXWORTH HALL - Furniture - American Drew

FOXX - Exercising equipment - Weslo Inc.

FOXXE - Guitars ☆ - L.A. Sax Co.

FOXY - Animal figurine with cologne ☆ - Cosrich Inc.

FOXY - Floor coverings–carpet and rugs - World Carpets, Inc.

FOXY - Fruits and vegetables - Nunes Co., Inc.

FOXY - Hair care products - Stephan Co.

FOXY - Vegetables–dried - Nunes Co.

FOXY - Wallcoverings - Penthouse Wallcoverings Ltd.

FOXY - Wallpaper - Riverside Silkscreen

FOXY - Wigs - Jean Paree Weegs Inc.

FOXY FASHIONS FROM JOHNSON - Pet products ☆ - Johnson Pet-Dor Inc.

FOXY LADY - Apparel–women's - Shady Grove Inc.

FOXY LADY - Frames–eyeglass ☆ - Universal/Univis Inc.

FOXY LADY - Wines - Hunt Country Vineyards

FOXY LOX - Fresh vegetables - Nunes Co.

FOXY MATE - Traps–animal - Cuba Specialty Manufacturing Co.

FOXY MISS - Artists' materials ☆ - Artoptic International Corp.

FOXY MOCS - Footwear–women's ☆ - U.S. Water

FOXY POPS - Snack foods ☆ - H. Fox & Co., Inc.

FOXY SIPS - Beverages–carbonated ☆ - H. Fox & Co., Inc.

FOXY SOX FOR BEN BERGER - Socks ☆ - Ben Berger LLC.

FOYER - Floor coverings - Interface, Inc.

FOYLON - Fabrics–coated - Duracote Corp.

FOY'S - Barbecue sauce - D & D Foods Inc.

FOYS UBET - Syrup - Freskeeto Frozen Foods Inc.

FOYT - Trailers–travel ☆ - Giles Industries

FOZZIE BEAR - Toys - Jim Henson Productions, Inc.

FP - Machinery - Finn-Power International, Inc.

F.P. - Wines - Pesenti Winery

FP 2000 - Electronic equipment - Surface Systems, Inc.

FP2 - Sporting goods - Brine Inc.

FP4 PLUS - Film - ILFORD Photo Corp.

FPCB - Electronic equipment - Aptix Corp.

FPEDIT - Computer storage devices - Western Printing Machinery Co.

FPG - Trading cards and stamps - Friedlander Publishing Group, Inc.

FPGA ARCHITECT - Computer software - Neocad, Inc.

FPGA DESIGNER - Computer software - Cadence Design Systems, Inc.

FPGA STATION - Computer software - Mentor Graphics Corp.

FPGEC - Educational materials - National Association of Boards of Pharmacy

FPI - Food products - Beatrice Cos. Inc.

FPI - Seafood products–fresh or frozen - Fishery Products International USA

FPL LIGHTNING SHIELD - Power switching equipment - Florida Power and Light Co.

FPR - Analgesics - Rollerball International Inc.

FPR - Hearing aids - Maico Hearing Instruments Inc.

FPSELECT - Computer software - Western Printing Machinery Co.

FPSTATION - Computer software - Clinical Information Advantages, Inc.

FR - Apparel stores–lingerie ☆ - Formfit Rogers

FR - Business forms - Form-Right, Inc.

FR - Fabrics - Dan River Inc.

FR - Generators - Kohler Co.

FR - Nuts and bolts - Fast-Rite, Inc. Fasteners and Industrial Components

FR - Nuts and bolts - Rockford Products Corp. (International Group)

FR - Thread - Signal Thread Co. Inc.

FR-12 - Refrigerants - Intercool Energy Corp.

FR-40XD - Oils–vulcanized - Citgo Petroleum Corp.

FR II - Generators - Kohler Co.

FR-TEX - Thread - Signal Thread Co. Inc.

F.R. TUF-SKIN - Fibers–polyvinyl - Sto-Cote Products Inc.

FR360 - Automotive parts and accessories - Bridgestone/Firestone, Inc.

FR480 - Tires - Bridgestone/Firestone, Inc.

FRA DIAVOLO - Oils–edible - California Olive Oil Corp.

FRABILL - Fishing tackle - Frabill Inc.

FRAC-KIT - Health care products - Temco Health Care

FRACABOLIC 75 - Vitamins and nutritional supplements - Dener Management Inc.

FRACAS BY ROBERT PIGUET - Perfumes - Alfin Fragrances Inc.

FRACE' - Whey - Health Smart Products Inc.
FRACTAL - Electronic equipment - Oak Furniture Warehouse, Inc.
FRACTAL FIBEROPTICS - Electronic equipment - Galileo Corp.
FRACTALWEAR - Apparel - Berkeley Designs
FRACTILES - Games - Marc Pelletier
FRACTION ACTION - Computer software - Unicorn Software
FRACTION ACTION-ADDITION & SUBTRACTIONS - Playing cards - Game Geste, Inc.
FRACTION ACTION-SIMPLE TRACTIONS - Playing cards - Game Geste, Inc.
FRACTION ATTRACTION - Computer software - Sunburst Communications, Inc.
FRACTION BROS. CIRCUS - Games ☆ - Teaching Concepts Inc.
FRACTION BUILDER - Task cards - Ideal School Supply Corp.
FRACTION FACTORY - Toys - Ideal School Supply Corp.
FRACTION FLIP - Computer software - Southwest Edpsych Services Inc.
FRACTION FUEL-UP - Computer software - SRA/McGraw-Hill (Div. of The McGraw-Hill Companies)
FRACTION GAMES - Games - Lauri Inc.
FRACTION MACHINE, THE - Computer software - Southwest Edpsych Services Inc.
FRACTION-OIDS - Computer software - Mind Play
FRACTIONAL TILES - Games - Leon Tomash
FRACTOOLS - Computer software - Bourbaki Inc.
FRACTRIC - Calculators - Graphic Systems
FRACTRON - Calculators - Graphic Systems
FRACTURE FINISH - Finishing agents ☆ - Carnival Arts, Inc.
FRACTURE GROUT - Medical preparation - Norian Corp.
FRACTURED FORMALS - Stationery - Paramount Cards Inc.
FRACTURED GREETINGS - Greeting cards - X-Ray Duplications, Inc.
FRADELIS - Food products ☆ - Nalley's Fine Foods
FRAFLO - Enamels - Frazee Paint
FRAG BAG - Toys - Mamko Products Inc.
FRAGATA - Olives—canned - A. Camacho Inc.
FRAGGLE ROCK - Games ☆ - Milton Bradley Co.
FRAGGLE ROCK - Toys - Jim Henson Productions, Inc.
FRAGILE - Apparel—men's - Lola, Inc.
FRAGILE - Apparel—women's - J.C. Penney Co., Inc.
FRAGLOS - Enamels - Frazee Paint
FRAGMENTFIGHTER - Computer software - Raxco Software Inc.
FRAGOIS - Footwear - Southern Shoe Importers Inc.
FRAGOLA - Grocery stores - Joseph Fragola Inc.
FRAGRANCE CONTROLLED RELEASE SYSTEM - Chemical preparations - International Flavors & Fragrances Inc.
FRAGRANCE DE-LITE - Candles - Lancaster Colony Corp.
FRAGRANCE DESIGN - Perfumes - Shaw Mudge & Co.
FRAGRANCE DIPSTICKS - House furnishings - Gilbertie's Herb Gardens, Inc.
FRAGRANCE ENGINEERED - Chemical preparations - International Flavors & Fragrances Inc.
FRAGRANCE ENGINEERING - Chemical preparations - International Flavors & Fragrances Inc.
FRAGRANCE FOURSOME - Candles ☆ - American Candle Co. Inc.
FRAGRANCE FRIENDS - Dolls with cologne ☆ - Cosrich Inc.
FRAGRANCE IN THE AMERICAN SPIRIT - Colognes ☆ - Avon Products, Inc.
FRAGRANCE OF THE ISLANDS - Deodorizers - Waterbury Companies, Inc.
FRAGRANCE OILS - Natural Image Botanicals Inc.
FRAGRANCES OF IRELAND - Perfumes - Fragrances of Ireland Accent on Irish Wares Ltd.
FRAGRANT - Hair care products - Bonat Inc.
FRAGRANT DETAILS - Sachets - J.C. Penney Co., Inc.
FRAGRANT FACIALS - Skin care products - Liberty Natural Products
FRAGRANT FRANCES - Doll with cologne ☆ - Cosrich Inc.
FRAGRANT INTERLUDES - Bath salts - Twinscents
FRAGRANT JEWEL COLLECTION - Perfumes - Parfums International Ltd.
FRAGRANT KETTLE - Incense ☆ - Olfactory Corp.
FRAGRANT WISHES - Greeting cards - Neutron Industries, Inc.
FRAICHE - Colognes - Christian Dior Perfumes Corp.
FRAIDY CAT - Toys—stuffed ☆ - Gund, Inc.
FRAIDY CATS - Candy ☆ - R.M. Palmer Co.
FRAIDY CATS - Games - Hasbro, Inc.
FRAIS D'OR - Lipsticks - Lancome
FRAISE - Lipsticks - Cosmair Inc.
FRAISE DE BOIS - Liquors ☆ - House of Seagram
FRAKONIG - Chocolate candy - John Sommer Inc.
FRALINGER'S - Candy - Fralinger's Inc.
FRAM - Filters—oil - Alliedsignal Inc.
FRAM F - Filters—oil - Alliedsignal Inc.

FRAMABLES - Posters - Heartprint Inc.
FRAMALI PLANTER - Flower pots—plastic - Framali Planters, Inc.
FRAMAWAY - Fabric stores - Framaway Corp.
FRAMBOISE - Lipsticks - Cosmair Inc.
FRAMBOISE - Wines ☆ - Merchant du Vin Corp.
FRAMBOISE LAMBIC - Beverages—malt - Merchant du Vin Corp.
FRAMBROSIA - Wines - Oak Knoll Winery Inc.
FRAMCOLOR - Hair care products - Framesi USA/Roffler Industries Inc.
FRAME - Computer software - Frame Technology Corp.
FRAME - Tables—wood - Nancy Tucker
FRAME-A-CARD - Greeting cards - Aaron Brothers Art Marts Inc.
FRAME A MEMORY - Frames—picture ☆ - Roman, Inc.
FRAME-A-NOTES - Artists' materials ☆ - Conni Gordon Art Method Inc.
FRAME-A-SHADE - Window shades - Carefree/Scott Fetzer Co.
FRAME-ALL - Frames—picture ☆ - Structural Industries
FRAME ART - Easels - KB Design
FRAME FRIENDS - Frames—picture - Dakin Inc.
FRAME GAME - Frames—eyeglass ☆ - Universal/Univis Inc.
FRAME HOUSE - Recording label - Top's Records
FRAME-IT - Frames—picture ☆ - Structural Industries
FRAME-IT - Signs - Joseph Struhl Co., Inc.
FRAME-LITE - Eyeglasses - Art-Craft Optical Co.
FRAME MASTER - Calculators - Calculated Industries, Inc.
FRAME-N - Stencils - Mason Marking Systems Corp.
FRAME N FANCY - Frames—picture - Frames Inc.
FRAME N HANGS - Postcards ☆ - Gallant Greetings Corp.
FRAME-N-LITES - Eyeglasses - Frame-n-Lens Optical Inc.
FRAME OF THE YEAR - Frames—picture - Noteworthy
FRAME PAK - Frames—picture ☆ - Structural Industries
FRAME PHOTO KEEPER - Photo albums - Pioneer Photo Albums, Inc.
FRAME STRONG - Framing supplies - Herbert Suesholtz
FRAME-TECH - Hardware - Amerock Corp.
FRAME, THE - Sporting goods - Fit Kit Systems
FRAME-TO-FRAME - Tape—adhesive - Pro Tapes & Specialties, Inc.
FRAME-TRAY - Games - Golden Books Publishing Co., Inc.
FRAME-UP - Frames—picture ☆ - Structural Industries
FRAME-UP - Racks - Jarke Corp.
FRAME-UP - Underwear and nightwear - Maidenform Inc.
FRAME-UPS - Wood products - Makepeace Colony Press Inc.
FRAME VIEW - Bath packaging - Sterling Plumbing Group Inc.
FRAME WAY - Computer peripheral equipment ☆ - Jupiter Technology, Inc.
FRAMEBUILDER - Toys - Learning Materials Workshop
FRAMECAP - Framing supplies - Tom Kedzie Projects
FRAMECO - Frames—eyeglass - Liberty Optical Manufacturing Co.
FRAMED! - Games ☆ - Lombard Marketing, Inc.
FRAMED FOR MURDER - Puzzles - Hasbro, Inc.
FRAMEDECOR MANUFACTURING CORP. - Frames—picture - Frame Decor Manufacturing Corp.
FRAMEGUARD - Locks—door - Doors of Pontiac
FRAMEHANG - Craft supplies - Ziabicki Import Co.
FRAMEHOOK - Pumps - Goulds Pumps, Inc.
FRAMEIOLOGY - Frames—picture - United Design Corp.
FRAMEKIT - Frames—picture - Letraset USA Inc.
FRAMEKIT - Frames—picture - Nielsen & Bainbridge
FRAMEMASTER - Tools - Fletcher-Terry Co.
FRAMEMATE - Tools—woodworking - Fletcher-Terry Co.
FRAMEMICA - Frames—picture - Framemica Co.
FRAMEPEGS - Screws - Framepegs Ltd.
FRAMES UNLIMITED - Frames—picture - CBK Ltd. Inc.
FRAMESAKE - Stationery - Photostamp Co., Inc.
FRAMESCOPE - Computer peripheral equipment - Scope Communications Inc.
FRAMESHOP - Computer storage devices - Martin E. Ricks
FRAMESI - Hair care products - Framesi USA/Roffler Industries Inc.
FRAMESPACE - Frames—picture - Frame Tek, Inc.
FRAMESTATION - Computer hardware - ADC Telecommunications, Inc.
FRAMETASTIC! - Craft supplies - Rose Art Industries, Inc.
FRAMETTE - Frames—eyeglass - Zylo Ware Corp.
FRAMETTES - Frames—picture ☆ - A.J. Ganz Co. Inc.
FRAMEVILLE - Frames—eyeglass - Zylo Ware Corp.
FRAMEWAY - Computer software - Analogy, Inc.
FRAMEWORK - Floor coverings—carpet and rugs - Mannington Carpets, Inc.
FRAMEWORK FOR EFFECTIVE TEACHING - Publisher's imprints - Open Court Publishing Co.
FRAMEWORK II - Computer software - Borland International, Inc.
FRAMEWORKS - Furniture - Gaylord Bros. Inc.
FRAMEWORKS - Wallpaper - Wall Fashion Inc.

☆ = Now out of production

FRAMEWORKS - Wood products - Trus Joist MacMillan L.P.
FRAMEWORX - Computer software - Integrated Design Engineering Inc.
FRAMINGHAM - Clocks ☆ - General Time Corp. (Westclox/Seth Thomas Div.)
FRAMMIS - Recording label - Jazz Composer's Orchestra Association Inc.
FRAMO - Machine parts - Franz Morat, Inc.
FRAMOLINE - Furniture - Barbed Wire Publishers
FRAMONOIX - Cheese - Swissrose International Inc.
FRAMONT - Watches - Framont U.S. Inc.
FRAMOUS - Posters - Rogers F. Brackmann
FRAMOUS PRINTS - Posters - LBC Sports, Inc.
FRAMS FAST - Adhesives and sealants - Uncommon Conglomerates
FRAN - Optical scanners–computer - Tart Optical
FRAN KEENE - Apparel–women's - Perry Manufacturing Co.
FRAN LAWRENCE NAIL SYSTEMS - Nail care products - Fran Lawrence
FRAN MAR - Stationery - Fran Mar Greeting cards Ltd.
FRAN WILSON - Cosmetics - Fran Wilson Creative Cosmetics
FRANA - Blankets - Molly Roberts & Co. Inc.
FRANCAIS - Furniture - Stanley Furniture Co. Inc.
FRANCAISE - Lenses–optical - Ditto Industries Inc.
FRANCE 1940 - Games ☆ - Avalon Hill Game Co.
FRANCE 1944 - Games - Avalon Hill Game Co.
FRANCE EYEWEAR CHAINS - Eyeglasses - Private Eyes Sunglass Corp.
FRANCE LAURE - Skin care products - Dynex International
FRANCEES - Apparel stores–lingerie - H.F. Robbins
FRANCELLE - Sandwiches–prepackaged - Vie De France Corp.
FRANCES CLARK PIANO LIBRARY - Pianos - Summy-Birchard Inc.
FRANCES DENNEY - Cosmetics - Frances Denney
FRANCES DENNEY ULTIMATE EYE CARE - Cosmetics - Stephan Co.
FRANCES FOX - Health care products - Consolidated Midland Corp.
FRANCES HARRIET - Hair- and skin-care products, fragrance, etc. - Benjamin Ansehl Co.
FRANCES HOOK - Giftware - Roman, Inc.
FRANCES LYNN - Underwear and nightwear - Griffin Industries Inc.
FRANCES WEINSTOCK ORIGINALS - Poem plaques ☆ - Classic Plaques Inc.
FRANCES WOOD - Underwear and nightwear ☆ - Lovable Co.
FRANCESCA - Figurines ☆ - S.P. Skinner Co. Inc.
FRANCESCA - Frames–eyeglass - Hoya Corp. USA
FRANCESCA - Rings–jewelry - Artcarved Inc.
FRANCESCA BOTTA - Neckties - Francesca Botta Designs, Ltd.
FRANCESCA FOR DAMON SPORT - Apparel and accessories - Damon Creations Inc.
FRANCESCO RINALDI - Spaghetti sauces - Cantisano Foods, Inc.
FRANCESCO RINALDI ULTRA DOLCE - Sauces - Cantisano Foods, Inc.
FRANCESCO'S FINE FOODS - Spices and extracts - DeNiro Cheese Co.
FRANCESCO'S FRIENDLY WORLD - Video production - Edumundo Productions, Inc.
FRANCETTE - Apparel stores–lingerie - H.F. Robbins
FRANCHI - Cosmetics - Kast International, Inc.
FRANCHI - Shotguns - Fie Corp.
FRANCHISE FOOTBALL LEAGUE - Publisher's imprints - Fantasy Sports Properties, Inc.
FRANCHISE MANAGER - Computer software - Fantasy Sports Properties, Inc.
FRANCHISE, THE - Trading cards and stamps - Score Group, Inc.
FRANCHISOR - Window coverings - Visions 2000 Window Fashions, Inc.
FRANCIE - Dolls - Mattel, Inc.
FRANCINE - Toys–stuffed - Eden LLC
FRANCINE FANTIN - Cosmetics - Laboratoire Biosthetique Ltd.
FRANCINE OF FRANCE - Apparel–women's ☆ - Carmen Foundations Inc.
FRANCIS - Flatware - Reed and Barton Corp.
FRANCIS ASBURY PRESS - Publisher's imprints ☆ - Zondervan Publishing House
FRANCIS BACON - Pianos - Kohler & Campbell Inc.
FRANCIS DRAKE - Boats - Glen-L Marine Designs
FRANCISCAN - Ceramic tile, dinnerware - Franciscan by Johnson Brothers, USA, Inc.
FRANCISCAN - Eyeglasses - Art-Craft Optical Co.
FRANCISCAN - Guitars ☆ - Kaman Music Corp.
FRANCISCAN - Paints - Fredericks/Hansen Paint Manufacturing Co.
FRANCISCAN - Stoves ☆ - Malm Fireplaces Inc.
FRANCISCAN HERALD PRESS - Publisher's imprints - Franciscan Press
FRANCISCAN OAKVILLE ESTATE - Wines - Franciscan Vineyards, Inc.
FRANCISCAN PORTFOLIO COLLECTION - Tiles–ceramic - Franciscan by Johnson Brothers, USA, Inc.
FRANCISCAN SPECTRA - Tiles–ceramic - Franciscan by Johnson Brothers, USA, Inc.

FRANCISCAN TERRA - Tiles–ceramic - Franciscan by Johnson Brothers, USA, Inc.
FRANCISCAN TERRA CRAFT - Tiles–ceramic - Franciscan by Johnson Brothers, USA, Inc.
FRANCISCAN TERRA CROWN - Tiles–ceramic - Franciscan by Johnson Brothers, USA, Inc.
FRANCISCAN TERRA FLOOR - Tiles–ceramic - Franciscan by Johnson Brothers, USA, Inc.
FRANCISCAN TERRA GRANDE - Tiles–ceramic - Franciscan by Johnson Brothers, USA, Inc.
FRANCISCAN TERRA TAPESTRY - Tiles–ceramic ☆ - Franciscan by Johnson Brothers, USA, Inc.
FRANCISCAN TERRA VILLA - Tiles–ceramic - Franciscan by Johnson Brothers, USA, Inc.
FRANCISCAN TRACERY - Tiles–ceramic - Franciscan by Johnson Brothers, USA, Inc.
FRANCISCAN VINEYARDS - Wines ☆ - Franciscan Vineyards, Inc.
FRANCISCO - Apparel–women's ☆ - Jerell, Inc.
FRANCISCO - Breads - Best Foods Baking Group
FRANCISCO - Breads - CPC International Inc.
FRANCISCO - Shoes - Kotoni Trading Inc.
FRANCISCO'S EDISON ORANGES - Fruits and vegetables - Fillmore-Piru Citrus Association
FRANCITAL - Apparel stores–sports ☆ - French Dressing Inc.
FRANCO - Girdles - H.F. Robbins
FRANCO - Ophthalmic goods ☆ - Luxottica
FRANCO-AMERICAN - Pasta - Campbell Soup Co.
FRANCO BETTONI CLASSICS - Apparel and accessories - Echo Lake Industries, Ltd.
FRANCO BONBABA - Hosiery, socks - Kartex International Cos. Inc.
FRANCO BRINTINI - Fans–electric - Envirotech Electric, Inc.
FRANCO FIRENZE - Apparel–men's - Intrep Imports, Inc.
FRANCO FORTINI - Shoes - Rack Room Shoes, Inc.
FRANCO FOSSI - Apparel and accessories - Carter & Holmes
FRANCO STALLIONE - Apparel and accessories - Jolem Imports, Inc.
FRANCO VERDI - Apparel–women's - Russ Togs Inc.
FRANCOIS - Beverages–alcohol - Nor-Glo Import Co.
FRANCOIS LABET - Wines - HBB International
FRANCOIS LAURAY - Housewares - Arteriors
FRANCOISE - Dolls ☆ - Effanbee Doll Corp.
FRANCOISE - House furnishings - Dan River Inc.
FRANCONIA - Cases–camera ☆ - Edixa Camera Co.
FRANCONIA - Floor coverings ☆ - Tarkett, Inc.
FRANCONIA FARMS - Food products - Wampler Foods Inc.
FRANCO'S - Beverages–carbonated - Franco's Cocktail Products Inc.
FRANCO'S DELI - Sandwiches–prepackaged - Double B Foods Inc.
FRANES - Nuts–salted, roasted, cooked, or canned - Ciracor Ltd.
FRANE'S CRUNCH-WRAPPED PEANUTS - Snack foods - Ciracor Ltd.
FRANGELICO - Liquors - William Grant & Sons, Inc.
FRANGIPANI - Colognes - Key West Aloe Inc.
FRANGI'S - Pasta - Frangi's Italian Food Inc.
FRANGI'S TIMELESS ITALIAN CLASSICS - Pasta - Frangi's Italian Food Inc.
FRANGO - Chocolate candy - Marshall Field's
FRANGRANCE DELITES - Candles - Candle-Lite Co.
FRANGRANCE PUFFS - Headsets–telephone - Botanicus Inc.
FRANJO - Hair care products - International Beauty Connection Inc.
FRANK - Frames–eyeglass - Rozin Optical Export Corp.
FRANK A. HOPPE - Firearms, accessories, and parts - Hoppe's
FRANK & BRYAN'S - Food products - Frank & Bryan Foods, Inc.
FRANK & TERESSA'S ANCHOR BAR - Meat products–poultry - Snowball Foods, Inc.
FRANK BROTHERS - Shoes - Genesco Inc.
FRANK CANTON - Toys–guns - Daisy Manufacturing Co.
FRANK CERNE - Shelving units–metal - Flashco
FRANK COOPER - Jams and jellies - CPC International Inc.
FRANK FRITTER - Frankfurters ☆ - Olympic Foods Inc.
FRANK HARDY - Toys–stuffed ☆ - Kenner Products
FRANK K. WOOD'S PAIN RELIEF RUB - Pharmaceutical preparations - Frank W. Cawood & Associates, Inc.
FRANK LEITCH REVISITED - Wallpaper ☆ - Capital Carousel Inc.
FRANK LEWIS - Fruits and vegetables - Standex International Corp.
+FRANK LLOYD +WRIGHT - Publisher's imprints - Frank Lloyd Wright Foundation
FRANK MEISLER LTD. - Wood figures now out of production - Israeli Accents
+FRANK +MORA - Shoes - Saint Louis Trading Co. Inc.
FRANK-N-BURGER - Barbecues and grills ☆ - General Electric Co.

FRANK 'N STUFF - Frankfurters - Hormel Foods Corp.
FRANK OLIVER, THE - Apparel–men's - Hartz & Co., Inc.
FRANK OLIVIER - Apparel–men's - H.L. Hartz & Sons Inc.
FRANK ROMBAUER LARKMEAD CELLARS - Wines - Larkmead Vineyards
FRANK S. OLIVER & SON - Food products - Frank S. Oliver & Son
FRANK SALIBA - Attache cases - Elizabeth Leather Bags
FRANK SAVAGE/THERESE CHANG - Apparel–women's - Frank L. Savage
  Imports Inc.
FRANK SCHOONMAKER - Glass–leaded - Seneca Glass Co.
FRANK SCHOONMAKER - Wines ☆ - Seagram's Chateau & Estate Wines Co.
FRANK SINATRA LEGENDARY NECKWEAR - Neckties - Stonehenge Ltd.
FRANK SINATRA'S - Sauces - Sheffield Enterprises, Inc.
FRANK SMITH - Flatware ☆ - Towle Silversmiths
FRANK TROEH - Sweaters - Centralia Knitting Mills Inc.
FRANK WEBB - Palettes ☆ - Winsor & Newton
FRANK ZAPPA - Apparel and accessories - Zappa Family Trust
FRANKEL - Window coverings - Covoc Corp.
FRANKEN BERRY - Cereal - General Mills, Inc.
FRANKEN FRANK - Toys–stuffed - Toy Works, Inc.
FRANKENDATA - Computer software - Frankendata USA, Inc.
FRANKENHANGER - Seasonings - Frankfurt Products Co., Inc.
FRANKENMUTH BAVARIAN - Beverages–malt - Geyer Bros. Brewing Co.
FRANKENMUTH EXTRA LIGHT - Beverages–malt - Frankenmuth Brewery,
  Inc.
FRANKENMUTH SPARKLING WINE CELLARS - Wines ☆ - St. Julian Wine
  Co.
FRANKENSTEIN: THROUGH THE EYES OF THE MONSTER - Games -
  Interplay Productions
FRANKENSTUDE - Advertising agencies - Motorsport Koncepts, Inc.
FRANKENSTUDE - Automobiles - Frankenstude, Inc.
FRANKFOLD - Umbrellas - AAA Umbrella Co.
FRANKFORD - Candy - Frankford Candy & Chocolate Co. Inc.
FRANKFURT - Artists' materials - Andrews/Nelson/Whitehead
FRANKIE - Sausages - Fresh Mark, Inc.
FRANKIE AVALON'S TWILIGHT TAN - Suntan lotions - Frankie Avalon
  Products, Inc.
FRANKIES - Mushrooms - United Canning Corp.
FRANKIE'S CHICKEN SHACK - Barbecue sauce - Frankie's Chicken Shack,
  Inc.
FRANKIE'S FAVORITE - Snacks - Franklin Foods
FRANKIE'S GLOWING U.F.O. - Toys - Frank G. Davidson
FRANKIE'S SKY CLIMBER - Novelty items - Frank G. Davidson
FRANKINCENSE & MYRRH - Perfumes ☆ - Quintessence Inc.
FRANKLIN - Adhesives and sealants - Franklin International, Inc.
FRANKLIN - Apparel and accessories - Franklin Sports, Inc.
FRANKLIN - Bricks - Stanson Inc. (Dacor Brick Div.)
FRANKLIN - Brushes–paint - Corona Brushes Inc.
FRANKLIN - Clocks - Franklin Instrument Co. Inc.
FRANKLIN - Envelopes–paper - Western States Envelope Co.
FRANKLIN - Food products - American Home Food Products Inc.
FRANKLIN - Footwear–athletic - Mercury International Trading Corp.
FRANKLIN - Frames–picture - Franklin Picture Co.
FRANKLIN - Furniture - Boling Co.
FRANKLIN - Furniture - Dinaire Corp.
FRANKLIN - Glass products ☆ - Bradley Corp.
FRANKLIN - Glassware–household - Federal Glass
FRANKLIN - Hardware - Embassy Industries Inc.
FRANKLIN - Musical instrument accessories - David Wexler & Co.
FRANKLIN - Ophthalmic goods - Rozin Optical Export Corp.
FRANKLIN - Shelving units–metal - Storex Division
FRANKLIN - Tape–adhesive - Technical Paper Corp.
FRANKLIN - Tractors–industrial - Franklin Equipment Co.
FRANKLIN - Trailers–travel - Franklin Coach Co.
FRANKLIN - Traps–animal - Cuba Specialty Manufacturing Co.
FRANKLIN - Vegetables–canned - Rossville Packing Co.
FRANKLIN COLONY - Food containers - CPC Food Service
FRANKLIN DAY PLANNER, THE - Calendars - Franklin Quest Co.
FRANKLIN ELECTRIC - Machinery - Franklin Electric Co., Inc.
FRANKLIN FARMS - Fruits and vegetables - Franklin Farms, Inc.
FRANKLIN FARMS - Lighting equipment–aircraft ☆ - Dove Foods
FRANKLIN FARMS - Milk - Garelick Farms, Inc.
FRANKLIN FUTURE CHAMPS - Sporting goods - Franklin Sports, Inc.
FRANKLIN HEIRLOOM - Dolls - Franklin Mint
FRANKLIN HILL VINEYARD - Wines - Franklin Hill Vineyards
FRANKLIN LANGUAGE MASTER 5000 - Electronic dictionary/thesaurus -
  Technologies For Learning

FRANKLIN READING GLASSES - Eyeglasses - Shady Deal Corp.
FRANKLIN SPORTS - Sporting goods - Franklin Sports, Inc.
FRANKLIN SQUARE - Floor coverings ☆ - Congoleum Corp.
FRANKLIN T. BEAR - Toys–stuffed - Effanbee Doll Corp.
FRANKLIN VILLAGE - Pasta ☆ - Greenfield Noodle & Specialty
FRANKLY MUSIC - Publisher's imprints - Roadshow Music Corp.
FRANKLY SPEAKING - Novelty items - Russ Berrie and Co., Inc.
FRANKOMA POTTERY - Giftware - Frankoma Pottery
FRANK'S - Beverages–carbonated - Frank's of Philadelphia
FRANKS - Food products machinery - Frank Foods Co.
FRANK'S - Health care products ☆ - Speaco Foods Inc.
FRANK'S - Tomato pastes and sauces - Fremont Co.
FRANK'S SUPERCRAFTS - Hobby kits - Frank's Nursery & Crafts, Inc.
FRANK'S UNIVERSAL - Pet products - Fromm Industries
FRANMARA - Corkscrews - Franmara Co. Inc.
FRAN'S - Candy bars - Fran's Chocolates
FRAN'S PARK - Candy bars - Fran's Chocolates
FRAN'S PECANS - Food products - Tracy-Luckey Co. Inc.
FRANSK - Dinnerware–glass - Dansk International Designs, Ltd.
FRANTIC - Bicycles - Giant Bicycle, Inc.
FRANTOIO - Olive oil - Frantoio LP
FRANTZ - Doors–garage - Frantz Manufacturing Co.
FRANZ - Bakery products - United States Bakery
FRANZ - Musical instrument accessories - Franz Manufacturing Co. Inc.
FRANZ CLASSIC - Breads - Franz Bakery
FRANZ HALS - Artists' materials ☆ - M. Grumbacher Inc.
FRANZ HOFFMAN - Musical instruments - M & M Distributing Co.
FRANZ MORAT - Machine parts - Franz Morat, Inc.
FRANZ WEBER - Wines - Monsieur Henri Wines Ltd.
FRANZIA - Wines - Franzia Winery
FRANZIA - Wines - Wine Group Inc.
FRANZUS - Appliance parts - Franzus Co. Inc.
FRAP - Tape players–reels - Frap
FRAPPE - Cases–eyeglass - California Optical Leather Inc.
FRAPPE - Floor coverings–carpet and rugs ☆ - LaVelle Textile Marketing Inc.
FRAPPE CREMES - Candy - Pangburn Candy Co.
FRAPPELS - Candy - Woodward & Lothrop Inc.
FRAPPIER ACCELERATION - Apparel and accessories - Acceleration
  Products, Inc.
FRAPPUCCINO - Coffee - Coffee Connection, Inc.
FRAS - Computer peripheral equipment - Sense Technology Inc.
FRASCATI - Wallpaper - Carlton-Metro Wallcoverings
FRASER - Bedspreads - Fraser Collection
FRASER & CHURCH - Men's and women's apparel - Stone & Thomas
FRASER THOMSON - Apparel and accessories - Remington Apparel Co., Inc.
FRASER'S - Giftware ☆ - W.M.F. of America Inc.
FRASIER - Apparel and accessories - Paramount Pictures Corp.
FRASINETTI WINERY - Wines - James Frasinetti & Sons
FRASINETTI'S 97 - Wines - James Frasinetti & Sons
FRASSETTO FINE FRAGRANCE JARS - Pottery - Frassetto Inc.
FRATELLI - Cabinets - Les-Care Kitchens Inc.
FRATELLI BALZZANO - Apparel–men's - H.L. Hartz & Sons Inc.
FRATELLI BARALE - Wines - European Beverage Co., Inc.
FRATELLI BOTTO - Apparel–men's - H.L. Hartz & Sons Inc.
FRATELLI DESIGNS - Frames–picture - Rare Woods Inc.
FRATELLI ODDERO - Wines - William Grant & Sons, Inc.
FRATELLI ROSSETTI - Footwear - Fratelli Rossetti Boutique
FRATERNAL - Jewelry - Jacoby-Bender Inc.
FRATERNITY - Eyeglasses - Art-Craft Optical Co.
FRAUDBUSTER - Computer software - Coral Systems Inc.
FRAVESSI - Greeting cards - Fravessi Greetings, Inc.
FRAW - Ophthalmic goods - Styl-Rite Optical Manufacturing Co., Inc.
FRAY CHECK - Craft supplies - Prym Dritz Corp.
FRAY FREE RAYON CHENILLE 750 - Yarn - Henry's Attic
FRAY FREE RAYON CHENILLE 1000 - Yarn - Henry's Attic
FRAY STOP - Housewares - Sewing Organizer
FRAYED KNOT!!! - Apparel and accessories - Knotcorp
FRAZAR - Seafood products–canned or cured - Frazar Trading Corp.
FRAZEE - Paints - Frazee Industries, Inc.
FRAZETTA - Posters - Fairfax Prints Ltd.
FRAZIER - Worcestershire sauce - Frazier Extract Co.
FRAZIER RIVER - Apparel and accessories - Frazier River Band, Inc.
FRAZZLES - Apparel–children's - Doe Spun Inc.
FRC - Rice - Farmers' Rice Cooperative
FRC CARHARTT - Work apparel - Carhartt, Inc.
FRE - Electronic equipment - Wellfleet Communications, Inc.

☆ = Now out of production

F.R.E. - Skin care products - Chanel Inc.
FRE-ECO - Recording label - Freddie Records
FRE-FLO - Paint sprayers - Rubberset Co.
FRE-LINE - Sporting goods - Wright & McGill Co.
FREAK - Fishing lures - Triple Teazer Co.
FREAK - Fishing lures - Yakima Bait Co.
FREAK OF NATURE - Apparel - Mike Tramp
FREAKIES - Cereal - Ralston Purina Co.
FREAKIN' FUNKY FUZZBALLS - Computer software ☆ - Sir-Tech Software, Inc.
FREAKIN WEAR - Apparel and accessories - Arthur G. Meakin, Jr.
FREAKS - Writing instruments - Pentech International Inc.
FREAKY BEASTS - Greeting cards - Renaissance Greeting Cards Inc.
FREAKY FEATURES - Toys - Tara Toy Corp.
FREAKY FULLBACK - Toys ☆ - Those Characters from Cleveland, Inc.
FREART - Chalk - Dixon Ticonderoga Co.
FRECCIADORO - Wines - Transamerica Wine Corp.
FRECKLE FACTORY - Apparel and accessories - Freckle Factory, Inc.
FRECKLED FRIENDS - Dolls ☆ - Bradley Import Co.
FRECKLES - Bicycles - Murray, Inc.
FRECKLES - Confections ☆ - Good Humor Corp.
FRECKLES - Dog food - Archer Daniels Midland Co.
FRECKLES - Dolls - Effanbee Doll Corp.
FRECKLES - Dolls - Uneeda Doll Co., Inc.
FRECKLES - Greeting cards - Recycled Paper Products, Inc.
FRECKLES AND FROGS - Eyeglasses - Martin-Copeland Eyewear Corp.
FRECKLES CHOCOLATE COVERED CRISP RICE! - Chocolate candy - Chariot Corp.
FRECKLES 'N FRILLS - Health care products ☆ - Avon Products, Inc.
FRECKLES THE BUNNY - Chocolate candy - Superior Fruit & Confections
F.R.E.D. - Amplifiers - Recoton Corp.
FRED - Guitars - Dimarzio, Inc.
FRED - Surgical supplies - Dexide, Inc.
FRED AMAN LIMITED EDITIONS - Giftware ☆ - Enesco Corp.
FRED BEAR - Apparel–children's - Fred Meyer, Inc.
FRED BEAR - Sporting goods ☆ - Bear Archery Inc.
FRED FLINTSTONE - Bags–duffel ☆ - A.D. Sutton & Sons Inc.
FRED +HAYMAN BEVERLY HILLS - Wallets - Fred Hayman Beverly Hills Inc.
FRED HAYMAN PERSONAL SELECTION - Apparel and accessories - Fred Hayman Beverly Hills Inc.
FRED HAYMAN'S TOUCH - Skin care products - Fred Hayman Beverly Hills Inc.
FRED M LAWRENCE - Frames–picture - Fred M. Lawrence Co. Inc.
FRED MONTESI - Food products - Fred Montesi Super Markets
FRED MYERS - Statuary - Fred Myers Studio, Inc.
FRED PERRY - Apparel and accessories - Figgie International Inc.
FRED PERRY - Sporting goods - Sportsotron Inc.
FRED' RICO - Bakery products - Frederick's Fine Chocolates, Inc.
FRED SAMMONS - Health care products - Bissell Inc.
FRED STOLLE - Sporting goods - Set Tennis Co.
FREDA RAKER - Dolls - Overly-Raker
FREDDA - Ophthalmic goods ☆ - Luxottica
FREDDI - Food products - Confectionary World
FREDDI FISH - Computer software - Humongous Entertainment, Inc.
FREDDIE - Recording label - Freddie Records
FREDDIE FROGHAMMER'S - Apparel and accessories - Freddie Froghammer's, Inc.
FREDDIE THE FIREPLUG - Toys - Tyco Toys
FREDDIE THE FROG - Fishing lures - Paul Warner Industries
FREDDIE T'S TEXAS WINE-A-RITA - Wines - Hill Country Cellars, Inc.
FREDDO - Footwear - De La Rentis Imports Inc.
FREDDY BEAR - Dolls - Fisher-Price, Inc.
FREDDY FIELDMOUSE - Toys–stuffed - Dakin Inc.
FREDDY FOWLER - Toys–stuffed ☆ - Dakin Inc.
FREDDY FOX - Toys–stuffed ☆ - Gund, Inc.
FREDDY FROG - Toys–stuffed - Dakin Inc.
FREDDY PENGUIN - Toys–stuffed ☆ - Dakin Inc.
FREDDY'S BUBBLE GUM SHAKES - Candy - Topps Co., Inc.
FREDDY'S PUZZLING ADVENTURES - Computer software - SRA/McGraw-Hill (Div. of The McGraw-Hill Companies)
FREDERIC JEAN DUCLOS - Jewelry - AG Artwear
FREDERICIA - Glassware–household - Dansk International Designs, Ltd.
FREDERICK - Ophthalmic goods - Styl-Rite Optical Manufacturing Co., Inc.
FREDERICK BECK ORIGINALS - Greeting cards - Gene Bliley Stationery
FREDERICK EDWARD - Furniture ☆ - Masco Corp.
FREDERICK HEMKE - Musical instrument accessories - Rico International

FREDERICK THE GREAT - Games - Avalon Hill Game Co.
FREDERICK-THE-GREAT - Publisher's imprints - Hard Hat Records
FREDERICK THE GREAT'S - Cookies - Lady Walton's Cookies, Inc.
FREDERICK WARNE - Publisher's imprints - Penguin USA
FREDERICK WONG - Greeting cards - American Artists Group Inc.
FREDERICKSBURG - Games ☆ - Avalon Hill Game Co.
FREDERICKSBURG SELECT - Turkeys - Sunday House Foods Inc.
FREDERIKSEN - Ships–sailing vessels ☆ - Lewmar Marine Inc.
FREDERIQUE - Apparel–women's - Jacques Moret, Inc.
FREDERIQUE - Colognes - H2O Plus, L.P.
FREDONIA - Floor coverings - Mannington Resilient Floors
FREDONIA - Food products - Cliffstar Corp.
FREDONIA - Wines - Rheinfrank Cellars
FREDRIC REMINGTON - Eyeglasses - Gregory Dean Shideler
FREDRICK OF HOLLYWOOD - Footwear ☆ - Hawaii Shoe Co.
FREDRICKS - Musical instruments - Custom Music Co.
FREDRIK - Glassware–household - Denby USA Limited
FREDRIX - Canvas–artists' - Fredrix Artist Canvas Inc.
FRED'S - Beef - Dallas Dress Beef
FRED'S - Vegetables–frozen - Fred's Frozen Foods Inc.
FRED'S BERMUDA TRIANGLES - Onions - Fred's Frozen Foods Inc.
FRED'S BERMUDA TRIANGLES - Vegetables–frozen - International Multifoods Corp.
FRED'S CIDER - Wines - Mount Vernon Cidery, Inc.
FRED'S FRILLS & FREEBIES - Food products - International Multifoods Corp.
FRED'S POCO POSADA - Snack foods - Fred's Frozen Foods Inc.
FREE - Cheese ☆ - Rose International
FREE - Cigarettes - Philip Morris Companies Inc.
FREE - Cooking equipment–household ☆ - Kraftware Corp. (Morgan Div.)
FREE - Pet products - A & M Products Inc.
FREE AGENT - Apparel–athletic - Josten's Sportswear
FREE AGENT - Bicycle parts and accessories - Kung Hsue She, Inc.
FREE AGENT - Bicycles - KHS Inc.
FREE AGENT - Frames–eyeglass - Liberty Optical Manufacturing Co.
FREE ALL - Oils–lubricating - Federal Process Co.
FREE & ACTIVE - Health care products - Humanicare International, Inc.
FREE & CLEAR - Computer software - Harry L. Jensen
FREE & CLEAR - Hair care products - Pharmaceutical Specialties, Inc.
FREE AND EASY - Apparel stores–lingerie - Goddess Bra
FREE AND EASY - Frames–eyeglass - Zylo Ware Corp.
FREE & EASY - Tampons - Kimberly-Clark Corp.
FREE & FRESH - Sanitary napkins - Bently Manufacturing
FREE & LIGHT - Confections - Sara Lee Corp.
FREE BRA - Brassieres (Bras) - A Touch of Fashion
FREE CALC - Computer software - Stillwell Software Products
FREE CLIMBER - Exercising equipment - Tri-Tech Inc.
FREE-COASTING - Office supplies - Knoll Group
FREE COUNTRY - Jackets - Free Country, Ltd.
FREE CUT - Hair care products - Fromm Industries
FREE DIMENSIONAL - Office furniture–metal ☆ - Stow/Davis Furniture Co.
FREE ENTERPRISE - Games - Ken Monteiro
FREE EXPRESSION - Footwear–women's - J. Steiner Imports Inc.
FREE FILE - Computer software - Stillwell Software Products
FREE FLAME - Fireplace equipment - Majestic Co.
FREE-FLEX - Fabrics - Guilford Mills, Inc.
FREE-FLEX - Wet suits–rubber ☆ - Wellington Leisure Products, Inc.
FREE FLIGHT - Bicycles - Murray, Inc.
FREE-FLO - Pet products - Freeland Industries Inc.
FREE-FLO - Ventilation equipment - Triangle Metal and Manufacturing Inc.
FREE-FLO - Window coverings ☆ - Leslie-Locke, Inc.
FREE FLOW - Jackets - Coleman Co., Inc.
FREE FLOW - Novelty items - Concept/Research, Concept/Development
FREE FLOW - Surgical supplies - Marlen Manufacturing & Developing Co.
FREE-FLOW - Water purification systems - Penn-Plax, Inc.
FREE FORM - Electrodes - Uni-Patch
FREE-FORM BG MAG - Bicycles - Schwinn Cycling & Fitness Inc.
FREE-FORM EX - Bicycles - Schwinn Cycling & Fitness Inc.
FREE-FORM GS - Bicycles - Schwinn Cycling & Fitness Inc.
FREE-FORM PRO - Bicycles - Schwinn Cycling & Fitness Inc.
FREE-FORM TARTLETS - Pastries - Dufour Pastry Kitchens Inc.
FREE-FORM TC - Bicycles - Schwinn Cycling & Fitness Inc.
FREE HAND - Telephone apparatus - Superior Fabricators Inc.
FREE-HANDS - Lenses–magnifying - Ramco Arts
FREE HOLD - Hair care products - Cosmair Inc.
FREE HOOK - Fishing lures - Michael J. Brackus
FREE KICK - Game machines - IGT - North America

FREE KICK! SCORE - Confections - Good Humor Corp.
FREE-LIFT - Apparel and accessories ☆ - Warnaco Inc.
FREE-LOK - Lubricants - Travaco Laboratories Inc.
FREE N' EASY - Floor coverings–carpet and rugs - Queen Carpet Corp.
FREE 'N EASY - Oxygen tents ☆ - Western Enterprises
FREE 'N EASY - Shampoos - Gillette Co.
FREE 'N EASY - Stationery - Standard Manifold Co.
FREE 'N EASY - Underwear and nightwear - Bestform Foundations, Inc.
FREE N' LEAN - Cheese - Alpine Lace Brands, Inc.
FREE N' SOFT - Fabric softeners ☆ - RCN Products Inc.
FREE-O-FROST - Refrigerators - Amana Refrigeration Inc.
FREE PARKING - Games - Tonka Corp.
FREE PEOPLE - Clothing - U.O.D., Inc.
FREE PRESS - Publisher's imprints - MacMillan Publishing Co. Inc.
FREE RIDER - Frames–eyeglass ☆ - Universal/Univis Inc.
FREE SALT - Vitamins and nutritional supplements - Freeda Vitamins Inc.
FREE SHEAR - Drills–electric - Metal Cutting Systems, Inc.
FREE SHOCK - Swimming-pool chemicals - Harcros Chemicals Inc.
FREE SLIDE - Shelving units–metal - Lee-Rowan Co.
FREE SPIRIT - Beverages–alcohol - Heaven Hill Distilleries, Inc.
FREE SPIRIT - Bicycles - Sears, Roebuck and Co.
FREE SPIRIT - Boats - McDaniel Boats Inc.
FREE SPIRIT - Floor coverings–carpet and rugs - Coronet Carpets Inc.
FREE SPIRIT - Floor coverings–carpet and rugs - Galaxy Carpet Mills Inc.
FREE SPIRIT - Furniture ☆ - Bassett Furniture Industries, Inc.
FREE SPIRIT - Health care products - Demstar Corp.
FREE SPIRIT - Leather goods - Dame Belt Co. Inc.
FREE SPIRIT - Motor vehicles–motor homes ☆ - Holiday Rambler Corp.
FREE SPIRIT - Paints ☆ - Martin-Senour Co.
FREE SPIRIT - Skin care products - Better Living Products Inc.
FREE SPIRIT - Skin care products - Paula Payne Products Co. Inc.
FREE SPIRIT COLLECTION - Watches - Heidi Kummli
FREE SPORT - Apparel and accessories - Flynn Enterprises Inc.
FREE STICK - Posters - Service Litho-Print Inc.
FREE STYLE - Apparel - Dionysian Inc. (Jacobs Div.)
FREE STYLE - Beds–hospital - Sunrise Medical
FREE STYLE - Dryers–hair ☆ - Sunbeam-Oster Household Products
FREE STYLE - Eyeglasses - Martin-Copeland Eyewear Corp.
FREE SUPREME - Ice cream - Superior Dairy, Inc.
FREE SWING - Apparel and accessories ☆ - Glamorise Foundations Inc.
FREE THE GREEN - Apparel and accessories - Nick L. Paris
FREE THROW - Sporting goods - Porter Athletic Equipment Co.
FREE THROW - Sporting goods - Powersoft Corp.
FREE THROW - Trading cards and stamps - Treat Entertainment, Inc.
FREE-THUM - Beauty shop equipment - Diane Products Inc.
FREE-THUM 2000 - Beauty shop equipment - Diane Products Inc.
FREE TIME - Apparel–men's - Made in the Shade by Prime Time
FREE TO GO - Food products - Kraft Food Ingredients Corp.
FREE TO PEE BY CHERIE - Apparel–women's - Cherie Carter-Scott-Pomije
FREE TO READ. FREE TO WRITE. FREE TO EVERYONE. - Computer software - D.E. Shaw & Co.
FREE-TONE - Musical instrument accessories - Micro Musical Products Corp.
FREE-TOP - Sporting goods - Under Sea Industries, Inc.
FREE-TOX - Vitamins and nutritional supplements - Freeda Vitamins Inc.
FREE TRADE ZONE - Computer software - Accutrade, Inc.
FREE TRADER - Games ☆ - Avalon Hill Game Co.
FREE UP - Automotive parts and accessories - Barcolene Inc.
FREE WHEELER - Bicycles - Murray, Inc.
FREE WHEELER - Toys–stuffed - Fun World Inc.
FREE WHEELERS - Luggage ☆ - American Tourister, Inc.
FREE WHEELING - Toys–stuffed - Fun World Inc.
FREE WILL - Frames–eyeglass ☆ - Universal/Univis Inc.
FREE WORLD - Apparel and accessories - Zumiez Inc.
FREE YOUR MIND - Apparel and accessories - Raymond Robinson
FREEAHMAY - Bedding–linen - Dan River Inc.
FREEAIRE - Refrigerators - R.H. Travers Co.
FREECHEESE MINI - Toys–stuffed - Dakin Inc.
FREECLIMBER - Exercising equipment - Stairmaster Sports/Medical Products, Inc.
FREECOM - Air conditioning equipment - Northstar Industries, Inc.
FREED - Apparel and accessories - Freed Co.
FREED LTD. - Shoes–athletic - Victoria's Dance-Theatrical Supply
FREEDA - Vitamins and nutritional supplements - Freeda Vitamins Inc.
FREEDA FEM - Vitamins and nutritional supplements - Freeda Vitamins Inc.
FREEDALGIN - Vitamins and nutritional supplements - Freeda Vitamins Inc.
FREEDAVITE - Vitamins and nutritional supplements - Freeda Vitamins Inc.

FREEDCAPS-T - Vitamins and nutritional supplements ☆ - Freeda Vitamins Inc.
FREEDEEDS - Publisher's imprints - Garber Communications Inc.
FREEDENT - Chewing gum - Wm. Wrigley Jr. Co.
FREEDOM - Apparel–women's - Cupid Foundations Inc.
FREEDOM - Aquariums–household - Ginger, Inc.
FREEDOM - Awnings - Carefree of Colorado
FREEDOM - Boats–canoes - Freedom Yachts
FREEDOM - Boats–motor - Four Winns Inc.
FREEDOM - Boats–pontoons - Harris-Kayot Inc.
FREEDOM - Braces–orthopedic - Alimed, Inc.
FREEDOM - Braces–orthopedic - Smith & Nephew Inc. (Rehabilitation Div.)
FREEDOM - Broadcasting equipment - EMCEE Broadcast Products
FREEDOM - Cleaning preparations - Cleaning Systems, Inc.
FREEDOM - Colognes - Brandy Harvest
FREEDOM - Compasses–gyroscopic - Rule Industries, Inc.
FREEDOM - Denture cleaners - V.R. Myers Pump & Supply, Inc.
FREEDOM - Doors–garage - General American Door Co.
FREEDOM - Faucets - Nibco Hardware Marketing
FREEDOM - Floor coverings–carpet and rugs ☆ - Columbus Mills, Inc.
FREEDOM - Flowers, plants, and seeds - Jacklin Seed
FREEDOM - Furniture - Hooker Furniture Corp.
FREEDOM - Furniture - Virco Manufacturing Corp.
FREEDOM - Furniture ☆ - Athens Furniture Industries Inc.
FREEDOM - Furniture ☆ - Kincaid Furniture Co. Inc.
FREEDOM - Hair care products - Fromm Industries
FREEDOM - Health care products - American Medical Systems
FREEDOM - Health care products - Sunbeam-Oster Household Products
FREEDOM - Helmets–athletic ☆ - Bell Sports Corp.
FREEDOM - Herbicides - Monsanto Co.
FREEDOM - High chairs ☆ - Century Products Co.
FREEDOM - Lighting fixtures - Hubbell Lighting, Inc. (Lighting Div.)
FREEDOM - Motor vehicles–motor homes ☆ - Shasta Industries Inc.
FREEDOM - Pet collars - PlasTech Corp.
FREEDOM - Recording label - Malaco Records Inc.
FREEDOM - Trailers–travel - Snowy Mountain Recreational Products
FREEDOM - Vacuum cleaners and accessories ☆ - The Eureka Co.
FREEDOM - Vitamins and nutritional supplements ☆ - Solaray
FREEDOM II - Flowers, plants, and seeds - Jacklin Seed
FREEDOM II - Footwear - Iron Age Corp.
FREEDOM 5 PROGRESSIVE - Lenses–optical - X-Cel Optical Co.
FREEDOM 60 - Medical apparatus - Repro-Med Systems, Inc.
FREEDOM 2100 - Elevators - MP Elevator Products Corp.
FREEDOM-ART - Greeting cards - Freedom Greeting Card Co. Inc.
FREEDOM BLUE - Stoneware dinnerware - Iron Mountain Stoneware Inc.
FREEDOM BOWL - Pet products - P.M. Pet Products
FREEDOM CITY COFFEE - Coffee - Slape Brothers Enterprises, Inc.
FREEDOM CLEAR - Catheters - Mentor Corp.
FREEDOM CONTROL - Hair care products - Marianna Imports, Inc.
FREEDOM CUDDY CABIN - Boats–motor ☆ - Yar-Craft, Inc.
FREEDOM DESIGN - Motor vehicle parts and accessories - Electrodyne, Inc.
FREEDOM DUAL - Cameras ☆ - Minolta Corp.
FREEDOM ESCORT - Cameras - Minolta Corp.
FREEDOM FIGHTERS - Toys–electronic ☆ - Philips Consumer Electronics Co.
FREEDOM FIREWORKS - Fireworks - Freedom Fireworks, Inc.
FREEDOM FIT - Health care products - Geri-Care Products, LLC
FREEDOM FLYERS - Publisher's imprints ☆ - Western Publishing Co., Inc.
FREEDOM FORCE - Toys–automobiles - Nylint Toy Corp.
FREEDOM FOUNTAIN - Farm machinery - Behlen Manufacturing Co.
FREEDOM FRONT - Brassieres (Bras) - Olga Co.
FREEDOM-GREETINGS - Greeting cards - Freedom Greeting Card Co. Inc.
FREEDOM HAND - Medical apparatus - Alimed, Inc.
FREEDOM I - Cameras ☆ - Minolta Corp.
FREEDOM II - Cameras ☆ - Minolta Corp.
FREEDOM IMAGING SYSTEMS - Computer hardware - Freedom Business Machines, Inc.
FREEDOM IN THE GALAXY - Games ☆ - Avalon Hill Game Co.
FREEDOM LIFT - Elevators ☆ - Penox Technologies Inc.
FREEDOM-LIFT - Spas–home - Spectrum Pool Products
FREEDOM LIGHT - Lighting equipment - Sterling House
FREEDOM LINK - Telephones–cellular - Southwestern Bell Telecommunications, Inc.
FREEDOM LOGISTICS - Mobile classrooms - Tranzact Systems, Ltd.
FREEDOM MACHINE - Novelty items - AA World Class Corp.
FREEDOM MASTER - Furniture - Donna Difloe

☆ = Now out of production

FREEDOM MEDICAL SYSTEMS - Computer software - Custom Computing Corp.

FREEDOM-NEB - Health care products - Roman Labs Inc.

FREEDOM O2 - Health care products - Roman Labs Inc.

FREEDOM OF THE PRESS - Fabrics - Graniteville Co.

FREEDOM ONE - Wheelchairs - AmeriPower Inc.

FREEDOM PAGER - Pagers - Southwestern Bell Telecommunications, Inc.

FREEDOM PAK - Medical apparatus - Mentor Corp.

FREEDOM PLUS - Pillows - Pacific Spirit Corp.

FREEDOM PROGRESSIVE - Lenses–optical ☆ - X-Cel Optical Co.

FREEDOM REPORT WRITER - Computer software - Phase One Systems

FREEDOM RINGS - Flag poles - Brewer Design Service, Inc.

FREEDOM SEDAN DE VAN - Vans–conversion - Kentron Motor Coach Inc.

FREEDOM SERIES - Compressors–air - Champion Pneumatic Machinery Co., Inc.

FREEDOM SERIES - Computer software - Evans & Sutherland Computer Corp.

FREEDOM SERIES - Flowers, plants, and seeds - Hines Nurseries, Inc.

FREEDOM SPA - Bathtubs–enameled - W.W. Adcock Inc.

FREEDOM SPORTSFIT - Medical apparatus - Alimed, Inc.

FREEDOM STICK - Video games - Acemore International Ltd.

FREEDOM STREET - Footwear - 138 International, Inc.

FREEDOM, THE - Doors–storm - A-J Manufacturing

FREEDOM THUMB SPICA - Medical apparatus - Alimed, Inc.

FREEDOM THUMBKEEPER - Medical apparatus - Alimed, Inc.

FREEDOM TO CHANGE - Apparel–women's - Group B Clothing Co.

FREEDOM TO CREATE - Computer software - Cinovation, Inc.

FREEDOM TRAIL - Cheese - Crystal Food Import Corp.

FREEDOM WALKER - Treadmills - Roadmaster Corp.

FREEDOM WEB GLOSS - Paper - Scott Paper Co.

FREEDOM WORKFIT - Medical apparatus - Alimed, Inc.

FREEDOMAIRE - Air purification systems - Stackhouse, Inc.

FREEDOME - Lighting fixtures - Geometrica, Inc.

FREEDOMIKE - Microphones - Lectrosonics Inc.

FREEDOMLINE - Bathroom accessories - Lasco Products Group

FREEDOMLINE - Computer hardware - Compex, Inc.

FREEDOMLINK - Telecommunications equipment - Southwestern Bell Telecommunications, Inc.

FREEDOMSWITCH - Computer hardware - Compex, Inc.

FREEDOMVIEW - Computer software - Compex, Inc.

FREEDPLEX - Vitamins and nutritional supplements ☆ - Freeda Vitamins Inc.

FREED'S - Coffee - Freed Teller & Freed

FREEFALL - Books–comic - Aegis Entertainment, Inc.

FREEFALL - Cleaning preparations - Ramsey Co.

FREEFALL - Colognes - Shiara Holdings, Inc.

FREEFIX - Hair care products - Brocato International

FREEFLO - Machine parts - Magniflo Corp.

FREEFLOW - Apparel and accessories - Freeflowing International, Inc.

FREEFLOW - Hair curlers - Olivia Garden International, Inc.

FREEFORM - Exercising equipment ☆ - Maximus Fitness Products

FREEFORM - Fabricated metal products - Milliken & Co.

FREEFORM - Furniture ☆ - Bassett Furniture Industries, Inc.

FREEFORM - Underwear and nightwear - Henson-Kickernick Inc.

FREEFORM - Vitamins and nutritional supplements - Integrated Health, Inc.

FREEFORMING-ZIG-ZAG - Hair care products - Nino Originals

FREEHAND - Catheters - Schneider (USA) Inc.

FREEHAND - Pipes–tobacco - Dr. Grabow Pre-Smoked Pipes Inc.

FREEHAND - Wallpaper ☆ - Bolta Wallcoverings

FREEHOLD - Hair care products - European Tanning Systems Inc.

FREEJOE - Apparel and accessories - Freejoe Publications

FREELANCE - Footwear–women's ☆ - Cels Enterprises Inc.

FREELANCER - Tables–wood ☆ - Stacor Corp.

FREELAND - Firearms, accessories, and parts - Champion Shooters Supply

FREELAND KEG KOOLER - Beverages–malt ☆ - Freeland Industries Inc.

FREELAND-POLY-TUF - Pet products ☆ - Freeland Industries Inc.

FREELICIOUS - Salad dressings–bottled - Hudson Industries, Inc.

FREELINER - Printers–computer - Datasouth Computer Corp.

FREELINK - Computer hardware - Cabletron Systems, Inc.

FREELOADER, THE - Cameras - Auto Peeper Ltd.

FREELOOK - Computer software - Better Solutions Consulting, Inc.

FREEMAIL CHILD - Computer software - Freemail, Inc.

FREEMAN - Clocks - Freeman Products, Inc.

FREEMAN - Dust cloths - Las-Stik Manufacturing Co.

FREEMAN - Musical instruments - Ardsley Musical Instrument Co.

FREEMAN - Shoes - Freeman Shoe Co.

FREEMAN - Skin care products - Freeman Cosmetics Corp.

FREEMAN - Trophies–metal ☆ - Avnet, Inc.

FREEMAN AIR - Air transportation–passengers - Freeman Capital Co.

FREEMAN BEAUTIFUL SKIN - Dermatological preparations - Freeman Cosmetics Corp.

FREEMAN-MCFARLIN - Pottery - Freeman-McFarlin Potteries Inc.

FREEMAN MILITARY ULTRA LITES - Shoes - Freeman Shoe Co.

FREEMAN PROFESSIONAL - Skin care products - Freeman Cosmetics Corp.

FREEMARK ABBEY - Wines - Freemark Abbey Winery

FREEMEE - Pet collars - Steven Philip Kirsch

FREEPORT - Boats ☆ - Correct Craft Inc.

FREEPORT - Cigarettes - Philip Morris Companies Inc.

FREEPORT - Floor coverings–carpet and rugs - Queen Carpet Corp.

FREEPORT - Food products ☆ - Liberty Fish & Oyster Co.

FREEPORT - Motor vehicles–motor homes - Coachmen Industries, Inc.

FREEPORT - Trailers–travel - Shasta Industries Inc.

FREEPORT - Wireless digital networks - Windata Inc.

FREEPORT USA - Beverages–malt ☆ - F.X. Matt Brewing Co.

FREERIDER - Surfboards - Voit Corp.

FREERUNNER - Exercising equipment - Stairmaster Sports/Medical Products, Inc.

FREESCAN - Medical apparatus - K 3 Systems, Inc.

FREESIA - Bedding–linen - Dan River Inc.

FREESIA - Dinnerware–glass ☆ - Dansk International Designs, Ltd.

FREESIA - Glassware–household - Spiegelau Inc.

FREESIA - Lipsticks - Lancome

FREESIA - Shoes - JBI, Inc.

FREESIA - Vases - Crisa Corp.

FREESIA FIELDS - Deodorizers - Linden Corp.

FREESOLE - Shoe lasts - McNett Corp.

FREESOLE - Sporting goods - Gexco Enterprises

FREESOUND - Stereos - Sennheiser Electronic Corp.

FREESPACE - Loudspeaker systems - Bose Corp.

FREESPIRIT - Boats–motor - Glasstream Boats Inc.

FREESPIRIT - Radios - Motorola, Inc. (Land Mobile Products Sector)

FREESTONE - Footwear - Simms Fishing Products Corp.

FREESTONE - Pickles - Freestone Pickle Co. Inc.

FREESTYLE - Athletic shoes - Reebok International Ltd.

FREESTYLE - Bicycles - Columbia Manufacturing Inc.

FREESTYLE - Carpet cleaning equipment - Racine Industries, Inc.

FREESTYLE - Chairs–upholstered - United Chair Co., Inc.

FREESTYLE - Cleaning preparations–carpet and rug - Host/Racine Industries Inc.

FREESTYLE - Computer software - Wang Laboratories Inc.

FREESTYLE - Doors–glass - Sterling Plumbing Group Inc.

FREESTYLE - Electronic equipment ☆ - Arion Corp.

FREESTYLE - Finishing agents - Dryvit Systems, Inc.

FREESTYLE - Flowers, plants, and seeds - Goldsmith Seeds, Inc.

FREESTYLE - Greeting cards - AGC, Inc.

FREESTYLE - Greeting cards - American Greetings Corp.

FREESTYLE - Hair care products - Sunbeam Products, Inc.

FREESTYLE - Health care products - Sunrise Medical

FREESTYLE - Leotards - Danskin, Inc.

FREESTYLE - Prosthetic devices - Spenco Medical Corp.

FREESTYLE - Sporting goods - O'Brien International

FREESTYLE - Wallpaper - Fine Art Wallcoverings Ltd.

FREESTYLE - Wallpaper ☆ - Mayfair Wallcoverings

FREESTYLE - Watches - Sunburst Products Inc.

FREESTYLE - Wheelchairs - Fortress Inc.

FREESTYLE JAZZ - Apparel and accessories - Danskin, Inc.

FREESTYLES - Toys–erector sets - Lego Systems Inc.

FREETEXT - Computer software - John Hinsdale

FREETHROW II - Basketball footwear ☆ - Autry Industries Inc.

FREETIME - Footwear - Wolverine World Wide, Inc.

FREETRESS - Fibers–synthetic - Shake-N-Go Fashions, Inc.

FREEVALV - Chemical preparations - Edward V. Peterson

FREEWAX - Floor waxes ☆ - Dowbrands L.P.

FREEWAY - Computer software - Simpact Associates, Inc.

FREEWAY - Fabrics - Dan River Inc.

FREEWAY - Floor coverings–carpet and rugs ☆ - Cumberland Mills Inc.

FREEWAY - Food products - Ohio Steak and Barbecue Co.

FREEWAY - Health care products - Respironics, Inc.

FREEWAY - Herbicides - Loveland Industries, Inc.

FREEWAY - Inner tubes–automobile - Greenball Corp.

FREEWAY BEAR - Toys–stuffed - Gund, Inc.

FREEWAY DOG - Toys–stuffed - Gund, Inc.

FREEWAY FRENZY - Toys–automobiles - Mattel, Inc.

FREEWAY OFFSET - Paper - Turnquist, Inc.

☆ = Now out of production

FREEWAY PBD - Tires - Oliver Rubber Co.
FREEWHEEL FLYERS - Toys ☆ - Imperial Toy Corp.
FREEWILL - Shower stalls—metal - Kohler Co.
FREEWORD - Computer software - Stillwell Software Products
FREEZ! - Games - Freez! Games
FREEZ! - Hair care products - Image Laboratories, Inc.
FREEZ-CUT - Knives—carving ☆ - W.R. Case & Sons Cutlery Co.
FREEZ DRY - Hair care products - Image Laboratories, Inc.
FREEZ-FUN - Toys - Aluminum Hardgoods Inc.
FREEZ-MARK - Pens ☆ - Empire Berol USA
FREEZ-N-SAVE - Housewares - Tupperware Co.
FREEZ-PAK - Ice - Life-Like Products Inc.
FREEZE - Apparel—women's - Central Mills, Inc.
FREEZE - Chemical preparations - WorkAbles for Women
FREEZE - Dinnerware—plastic - Plastics Manufacturing Co.
FREEZE - Hair care products - Matrix Essentials, Inc.
FREEZE 2000 - Hair care products - Image Laboratories, Inc.
FREEZE & SERVE - Beverages ☆ - Mott's Inc.
FREEZE BAN - Antifreeze - Camco Manufacturing, Inc.
FREEZE-CLIK - Sprinklers—lawn - Glen-Hilton Products, Inc.
FREEZE DRIED BRINE SHRIMP - Fish food - Jungle Laboratories Corp.
FREEZE DRIED PEOPLE, THE - Flowers, plants, and seeds - Simpson & Turner Ltd.
FREEZE FINISH - Toys - Tonka Corp.
FREEZE-FIX - Plumbing fixtures—plastic - Eagle Industries Inc.
FREEZE FLASK - Containers - Igloo Products Corp.
FREEZE-FLO - Desserts - Rich Products Corp.
FREEZE FRAME - Computer software - DeltaPoint Inc.
FREEZE FRAME - Shoes - Sears, Roebuck and Co.
FREEZE FRAMES - Toys - Tonka Corp.
FREEZE FREE - Anti freeze - Comstar International Inc. (IPC Div.)
FREEZE-FREE - Chemical preparations - Midwest Industrial Supply, Inc.
FREEZE-FREE - Heating equipment ☆ - Easy Heat Inc.
FREEZE FREE-50 - Recreational vehicle dealers - Douglas Products and Packaging Co.
FREEZE FREE PLUS - Heating equipment - Easy Heat, Inc.
FREEZE-FREE PLUS - Heating equipment ☆ - Easy Heat Inc.
FREEZE GUARD - Batteries - Exide Corp.
FREEZE-GUIDE - Thermometers - Taylor Environmental Instruments
FREEZE, HEAT & SERVE - Cooking utensils—earthenware ☆ - Anchor Hocking Glass, Inc.
FREEZE HEAT N SERVE - Housewares ☆ - Plastics, Inc. (Anchor Hocking Plastics)
FREEZE-IT - Hair care products - Hayashi for Hair Inc.
FREEZE KIDS, LLC - Apparel—children's - Freeze
FREEZE N SQUEEZE - Confections - Jel Sert Co.
FREEZE-THAW - Whipped topping—frozen - Elgin-Honey Hill Corp.
FREEZE THEEZE - Water bottles—rubber - Songdog Packs
FREEZE-TITE - Plastics film - Polyvinyl Films Inc.
FREEZE WATCH - Health care products ☆ - Trimline Medical Products Corp.
FREEZEN - Veterinary product ☆ - American Equine Products Inc.
FREEZEPROOF - Antifreeze - Monson Companies, Inc.
FREEZER MATES - Housewares - Tupperware Co.
FREEZER/MILL - Laboratory apparatus - Spex CertiPrep, Inc.
FREEZER PLEASER - Ice cream - The Kroger Co.
FREEZER QUEEN - Meat extracts - Freezer Queen
FREEZER SAFETY - Thermometers - Tyz-All Plastics Inc.
FREEZERMATE - Insulation - Dow Chemical Co.
FREEZERTA - Ice cream - Kosto Food Products Co.
FREEZERVES - Jams and jellies - Sunfresh Foods, Inc.
FREEZETONE - Antifreeze - Freeztone Products, Inc.
FREEZETTE - Containers—plastic - Lawnware Products, Inc.
FREEZFLEX - Film - Plastic Suppliers, Inc.
FREEZITA - Beverages—carbonated - Soupmasters International, Inc.
FREEZITE - Epoxy - Garon Products Inc.
FREEZLOC - Plastics film ☆ - Dowbrands L.P.
FREEZONE - Pharmaceutical preparations - Whitehall Laboratories
FREEZRFLEX - Electrical tape - Imperial Industrial Supply Co.
FREEZY FREAKIES - Gloves - Swany America Corp.
FREEZYGEL - Novelty items - New Century Marketing & Distributors Inc.
FREEZZ FRAME - Greeting cards - Lawson Marden Post Card
FREHAIR - Hair care products - Mastey De Paris
FREI OL - Skin care products - Bouhon Cosmetics
FREI RANCH VINEYARD - Wines - Ernest and Julio Gallo Winery
FREIA - Chocolate candy - Haram-Christensen Corp.
FREIDEL'S FINEST - Food products - Inn Foods, Inc.

FREIGHT - Toys - Hasbro, Inc.
FREIGHT CONDUCTOR - Office supplies - R.A. Stewart Superior
FREIGHT MASTER - Toys—trains - Mattel, Inc.
FREIGHT MASTER - Toys—trains ☆ - Life-Like Products Inc.
FREIGHTLOGIC - Computer software - Pinnacle Distribution Concepts, LLC
FREIGHTMASTER - Scales—industrial - Sunbeam Precision Measurement
FREIGHTWORKS - Computer software - Computrex, Inc.
FREIHOF - Brandy - Dieter Steinmann Inc.
FREIHOFER'S - Bakery products - Charles Freihofer Baking Co.
FREIRICH - Sausages - Julian Freirich Food
FREIXENET - Wines - Freixenet USA
FREJO - Recording label - Fred Weinberg Productions Inc.
FRELEN ZIP LOCK - Pipes—tobacco - Frelen Corp.
FRELONIC - Footwear - Frelonic/Division of Dertek Corp.
FREM BETTER BY DESIGN - Plastics - Frem Corp.
FREMADA - Jewelry - Fremada Gold Inc.
FREMANTLE - Apparel—men's - Specialty Department Stores, Inc.
FREMONT - Cigarettes - Brown & Williamson Tobacco Corp.
FREMONT - Food products machinery ☆ - Fremont Co.
FREMONT COLLECTION - Furniture - Sumter Cabinet Co., Inc.
FREMWARE CLEARTAINERS - Frames—picture ☆ - Frem Corp.
FREN-L 650 - Lighting equipment - Lowel-Light Manufacturing Inc.
FRENCH - Handbags - S & H Pocketbook
FRENCH - Paper - French Paper Co.
FRENCH - Yarn - Henry's Attic
FRENCH ACCENT - Croissants - French Accent
FRENCH ACCENTS - Cosmetics - Chanel Inc.
FRENCH AFTERNOON - Fruits—dried - Agricultural Innovation & Trade Inc.
FRENCH & FANCY - Hair care products ☆ - Jason Natural Products, Inc.
FRENCH ARCHIVE - Wallpaper - Christopher Hyland
FRENCH AROMATICS - Oils—essential - Euro International
FRENCH BAKERY - Breads - Best Foods Baking Group
FRENCH BISQUE - Glass cookware, bakeware, etc ☆ - Corning Inc.
FRENCH BLEU - Glass cookware, bakeware, etc ☆ - Corning Inc.
FRENCH BLONDE - Floor coverings—carpet and rugs - Glen Eden Wool Carpets
FRENCH BLUE - Cosmetics - Lancome
FRENCH BOUQUET - Giftware - Seymour Mann Inc.
FRENCH BOUQUET - Perfumes ☆ - Carolina Designs Ltd.
FRENCH BOW - Floor coverings—carpet and rugs ☆ - Regal Rugs Inc.
FRENCH BOY - Popcorn - Purity Bottling Co.
FRENCH BRED - Wallpaper - Charles Barone Inc.
FRENCH BRED II - Wallpaper - Charles Barone Inc.
FRENCH BURNT PEANUTS - Candy - Brach and Brock Confections Inc.
FRENCH CAFE - Housewares - Aangela Ackerman
FRENCH CATHEDRAL - Dolls ☆ - Gorham Inc.
FRENCH CHEF - Pans - Marsh Industries Inc.
FRENCH CHERRY - Beverages—carbonated - Snapple Beverage Corp.
FRENCH CHEW - Candy bars - Doscher's Candies Inc.
FRENCH CHIPPENDALE - Silverware - Reed and Barton Corp.
FRENCH CHOCOLATE - Glassware—household - Seeley's Ceramics Inc.
FRENCH CLASSIC - Flatware - Gorham Inc.
FRENCH COLLECTION - Apparel—women's - Jezebel-Renee of Hollywood
FRENCH COLLECTION - Bottles, atomizers ☆ - Italia Collections
FRENCH COLLECTION, THE - Flatware - French Collection
FRENCH COLLECTION, THE - Furniture - Hickory Chair Co.
FRENCH COLLECTION, THE - Mirrors - Magic Distributing Ltd.
FRENCH COLONY - Hardware ☆ - Amerock Corp.
FRENCH CONNECTION - Hair care products - Capitol Novelty Co.
FRENCH CONNEX - Health care products - Healthwatchers System
FRENCH COOKERY - Dishes—wood - Royal Cathay Trading Co.
FRENCH CORDIAL CREME - Coffee ☆ - Boyd Coffee Co.
FRENCH CORNER - Coffee - Sodexho USA, Inc.
FRENCH COUNTRY - Floor coverings - Congoleum Corp.
FRENCH COUNTRY ALE ST. AMAND - Beverages—malt - Vanberg & Dewulf
FRENCH COUNTRY COLLECTION - Dolls - Effanbee Doll Corp.
FRENCH COUNTRY PRINTS - Wallpaper - Milbrook Wallcoverings
FRENCH COUNTRY PRINTS II - Wallpaper - Milbrook Wallcoverings
FRENCH COUNTRYSIDE - Potpourri - Countryside Fragrances Inc.
FRENCH COUNTRYSIDE - Wallpaper - Shelbourne Wallcoverings
FRENCH COURT - Furniture - Thomasville Furniture Industries Inc.
FRENCH CREAM - Cosmetics - Lancome
FRENCH CREAM - Glassware—household ☆ - Fenton Art Glass Co.
FRENCH CREAMS - Candy - Miss Saylor's Candies
FRENCH CREEK CELLARS - Wines - French Creek Cellars Inc.
FRENCH CUISINE - Food products ☆ - Westdale Foods Co.

☆ = Now out of production

FRENCH CURVE - Apparel–women's - Candice Inc.
FRENCH CURVE - Toilet seats - Kohler Co.
FRENCH DELICACIES - Pet products - Mon Cher Chouchou, Inc.
FRENCH DIMENSIONS - Pottery products - Duncan Enterprises
FRENCH DRESSING - Wallcoverings - Sherman & Associates International
FRENCH DRESSING - Wallpaper - Aresda Design Associates
FRENCH FANCY - Underwear and nightwear - Maidenform Inc.
FRENCH FARMHOUSE - Wallpaper ☆ - Imperial Wallcoverings, Inc.
FRENCH FIBRE GLACE - Nail care products - Nailtex Inc.
FRENCH FLIRTS - Apparel and accessories ☆ - Vanity Fair Mills Inc.
FRENCH FOLD - Window shades - Allied Extrusions
FRENCH FORMULA RICHE - Cosmetics - Cosmair Inc.
FRENCH FRAUDS - Food products ☆ - Pillsbury Co.
FRENCH FRIAR - Kitchen utensils–aluminum - Robinson Knife & Fiddlers Plastics
FRENCH FRIES - Pet products - Gimborn U.S., Inc.
FRENCH FROM THE PROVINCES - Furniture - Tomlinson of High Point Inc.
FRENCH FRY - Chewing gum ☆ - Leaf, Inc.
FRENCH FRY - Fishing lures - Worm World Inc.
FRENCH FRY DELIGHT - Food products - Wiener Works Group, Inc.
FRENCH FRYES - Dolls - Horsman
FRENCH FRYES - Hair accessories, jewelry - I.J. Grace Corp.
FRENCH FUSE - Fabrics - Staple Sewing Aids Corp.
FRENCH GARDEN - Clocks - General Time Corp. (Westclox/Seth Thomas Div.)
FRENCH GARDEN - Dinnerware ☆ - Corning Inc.
FRENCH GARDEN - Food products ☆ - Swiss American Import Co.
FRENCH GLOW - Cosmetics ☆ - M.L. Campbell Co.
FRENCH GOURMET FROZEN DOUGH - Bakery products - French Gourmet Inc.
FRENCH HANGMAN - Computer software - Dynacomp Inc.
FRENCH HILLS - Water–bottled or canned - Springwaters, Inc.
FRENCH ILLUSION - Hairpins - Jontee
FRENCH IMPRESSIONIST - Wallpaper ☆ - Sandpiper Studios
FRENCH IMPRESSIONIST II - Wallpaper - Sandpiper Studios
FRENCH JENNY - Apparel–women's - Richard Leeds International, Inc.
FRENCH KISS MADE IN FRANCE - Apparel and accessories - Chartered Merchants Inc.
FRENCH KISSES - Candy ☆ - Estus Export-Import
FRENCH KNOT - Floor coverings–carpet and rugs - Trend Carpet
FRENCH LACE - Doilies - Mafcote Industries, Inc.
FRENCH LACE - Plastic wrapping film - Highland Supply Corp.
FRENCH LACE - Ribbons - Heritage Designs Inc.
FRENCH LEAVES - Underwear and nightwear ☆ - Lovable Co.
FRENCH LILAC - Cosmetics - Lancome
FRENCH LINE - Stationery ☆ - Mead Corp.
FRENCH LINEN - Cases–eyeglass ☆ - California Optical Leather Inc.
FRENCH LINEN - Stationery - French Paper Co.
FRENCH LOUNGE - Chairs–upholstered - Cemanco
FRENCH MANICURE KIT - Nail care products - RTS Laboratories, Inc.
FRENCH MANICURE, THE - Nail care products - Orly International Inc.
FRENCH MANICURE WHITE TIP STYLE GUIDES - Nail care products - RTS Laboratories, Inc.
FRENCH MANOR - Doors–wood ☆ - Aluminum Co. of America
FRENCH MANOR - House furnishings ☆ - Lexington Furniture Industries, Inc.
FRENCH MANOR - Wood products - Caradco
FRENCH MARBLES - Artists' materials - Andrews/Nelson/Whitehead
FRENCH MARKET - Coffee - American Coffee Co. Inc.
FRENCH MARKET - Soups–mixes - Bon Melange Inc.
FRENCH MARKET SPECIALTY MEATS - Meat products - Meaux's Meat Market, Inc.
FRENCH MASTER, THE - Artists' materials - Solo-Horton Brush Co.
FRENCH MAXIMUM VOLUME - Hair care products - Revlon Consumer Products Corp.
FRENCH MERGUEZ SAUSAGE - Sausages - Merguez, Inc.
FRENCH MERGUEZ SAUSAGE LEAN BEEF SPICY - Sausages - Merguez, Inc.
FRENCH MESH - Crocheted and knitted items - Marcrest Knitting Mills
FRENCH MOIRE - Wallpaper ☆ - Wallpaper Imports Inc.
FRENCH MORNING - Fruits–dried - Agricultural Innovation & Trade Inc.
FRENCH NATURAL - Skin care products - American Manicure Corp.
FRENCH NECTAR CREME - Coffee ☆ - Boyd Coffee Co.
FRENCH NOW! - Computer software - Transparent Language, Inc.
FRENCH ONION SOUPERS - Snack foods ☆ - General Mills, Inc.
FRENCH OPERA - Coffee ☆ - American Coffee Co. Inc.
FRENCH ORGANZA - Manicure preparations - GG's Nail Systems

FRENCH PALACE - Floor coverings - Bangkok International Inc.
FRENCH PASTELS - Stationery - Stuart Hall Co., Inc.
FRENCH PASTRY II - Floor coverings–carpet and rugs ☆ - Mohawk Carpet Corp.
FRENCH PERM - Hair care products - Roux Laboratories, Inc.
FRENCH PRAIRIE - Food products - Dundee Brandied Fruit Co.
FRENCH QUARTER - Dinnerware–glass ☆ - United China and Glass Co.
FRENCH QUARTER - Floor coverings - Mannington Resilient Floors
FRENCH QUARTER - Furniture ☆ - Romweber Co.
FRENCH QUARTER - Lumber - Georgia-Pacific Corp.
FRENCH QUARTER - Tableware–china - Pfaltzgraff Investment Co.
FRENCH QUARTER - Tiles–ceramic - Dal-Tile
FRENCH QUARTERS - Game machines - Bally Gaming International, Inc.
FRENCH RAYON - Stationery - French Paper Co.
FRENCH REGENCY - Flatware - Wallace International Silversmiths, Inc.
FRENCH RIVIERA - Vitamins and nutritional supplements - Les Ruchers de la Cote d'Azur Inc.
FRENCH RIVIERA DIET - Vitamins and nutritional supplements - Abundant Life Custom-Made Food Supplements
FRENCH ROAST TANNING EXCELERATOR - Hair care products - Peter Hantz Co.
FRENCH ROOM - Shoes ☆ - Edison Brothers Stores, Inc.
FRENCH ROYALTY - Mustard - Tree of Life, Inc.
FRENCH SATINE - Hosiery - Danskin, Inc.
FRENCH SECRET - Apparel–women's - Olga Co.
FRENCH SHELL - Flatware ☆ - Wallace International Silversmiths, Inc.
FRENCH SHRINER - Shoes - French Shriner Shoe Co.
FRENCH SILK - Ice cream - Dreyer's Grand Ice Cream, Inc.
FRENCH STYLE - Wallpaper - Sanitas Wallcoverings
FRENCH SUEDE LUXE SHEER - Hosiery - Danskin, Inc.
FRENCH SUEDE OPAQUE - Hosiery - Danskin, Inc.
FRENCH TECHS - Shoes - French Shriner Shoe Co.
FRENCH TERGAL - Window coverings - Stead Textile Co. Inc.
FRENCH TIP - Manicure preparations - Creative Nail Design, Inc.
FRENCH TOAST - Artists' materials - Artoptic International Corp.
FRENCH TOAST - Gloves ☆ - Avon Glove Corp.
FRENCH TOAST - Hair ornaments - Lolly Togs, Ltd.
FRENCH TOAST - Socks - Sockyard Co. Inc.
FRENCH TOAST BOAT - Food products - Pierre Frozen Foods Inc.
FRENCH TOAST CRUNCH - Cereal - General Mills, Inc.
FRENCH TOAZT - Food products - Zartic, Inc.
FRENCH TWEED - Yarn ☆ - William Unger & Co. Inc.
FRENCH TWIRL - Pastries - Specialty Bakers Inc.
FRENCH TWIST - Candles ☆ - Candle-Lite Co.
FRENCH TWIST - Floor coverings–carpet and rugs ☆ - Regal Rugs Inc.
FRENCH TWIST - Pastries - Barry Yellen
FRENCH ULTRA SHEER - Panty hose - Danskin, Inc.
FRENCH VANILLA - Flowers, plants, and seeds - W. Atlee Burpee and Co.
FRENCH VANILLA - Furniture - Universal Flooring
FRENCH VANILLA - Teas–herbal - Traditional Medicinals, Inc.
FRENCH VILLAGE - Wallpaper ☆ - Imperial Wallcoverings, Inc.
FRENCH WASH - Paints - Plaid Enterprises, Inc.
FRENCH WAY BY LASALLE, THE - Skin care products - Allercare Inc.
FRENCH WEAVE - Wallpaper - Flexi-Wall Systems
FRENCH WEST INDIES - Luggage - Group III International Ltd.
FRENCH WHITE - Glass cookware, bakeware, etc. - Corning Inc.
FRENCHETTE - Salad dressings–bottled ☆ - T. Marzetti Co.
FRENCHIE TEDDY - Toys–stuffed - Dakin Inc.
FRENCH'S - Mustard - R.T. French Co.
FRENCH'S - Salad dressings–bottled - Marathon Projects
FRENCH'S SPECIAL BLEND - Tobacco products - Shepherd Tobacco Co.
FRENCHY - Pet products - Leather Brothers Inc.
FRENCO'S - Hair care products - Frenco Inc.
FRENESIE - Housewares ☆ - Doranne
FRENRY - See FLORIDA POOL PRODUCTS
FRENTA - Health care products - Fresenius Pharma
FRENZ CUDDLY & LOVABLE - Toys–stuffed - Gro-Well Enterprises Inc.
FRENZEE - Curling irons–electric ☆ - Wahl Clipper Corp.
FRENZEL - Sauerkraut and red cabbage - Carl Brandt
FRENZEL - Vegetables–canned - Kreiner Imports
FRENZY - Boats–kayaks - Ocean Kayak, Inc.
FRENZY - Colognes - Mem Co., Inc.
FRENZY - Games - Hasbro, Inc.
FRENZY - Tea - China Mist Tea Co.
FRENZY-FORENZI - Footwear–women's - Verden Imports Co. Ltd.
FREON - Refrigerators - E.I. Dupont de Nemours and Co.

☆ = Now out of production

FREOSTAT - Uniforms–tailored - Angelica Uniform Group
FREQUENCY FIT - Golfing equipment - Vulcan Golf Technology
FREQUENT FLIERS LIMITED - Novelty items - Carylle's
FREQUENT FLYER - Apparel and accessories - Norm Thompson Outfitters, Inc.
FREQUENT FLYER - Luggage ☆ - American Tourister, Inc.
FREQUENT FRYER PROGRAM - Meat products - Oscar Mayer Foods Corp.
FREQUENT TRAVELLER - Luggage - Pierre Cardin Electronique
FRERS - Sails - Carroll Marine Ltd.
FRES - Beverages–malt - Miller Brewing Co.
FRES' CIDER - Cider - Martlet Importing Co.
FRESCA - Beverages–carbonated - Coca-Cola Co.
FRESCA MEXICAN FOODS - Tortillas - Fresca Mexican Foods, Inc.
FRESCANTE - Coffee - Boyd Coffee Co.
FRESCHETTA - Pizzas–frozen - Schwan's Sales Enterprises, Inc.
FRESCO - Computer software - Infoscape, Inc.
FRESCO - Floor coverings - Congoleum Corp.
FRESCO - Floor coverings–carpet and rugs - French-Brown Wood Floors
FRESCO - Floor coverings–carpet and rugs ☆ - Gulistan Carpet Inc.
FRESCO - Pigments - H. Behlen & Bro. Inc.
FRESCO - Tiles–ceramic ☆ - American Olean Tile Co.
FRESCO - Wallpaper - Carlton-Metro Wallcoverings
FRESCO - Water colors - Rich Art Color Co., Inc.
FRESCO - Whirlpools - Jacuzzi Inc.
FRESCO BY PIERRE - Shoes - Pierre Shoes Inc.
FRESCO COLORS - Pigments - H. Behlen & Bro. Inc.
FRESCO II - Floor coverings–carpet and rugs - Mannington Carpets, Inc.
FRESCOES - Wallpaper - Robert Crowder & Co.
FRESCOMAR BRAND - Seafood products–fresh or frozen - Robert W. Hayman Inc.
FRESH - Health care products - ETAC USA Inc.
FRESH - Oils–edible ☆ - Arrowhead Mills, Inc.
FRESH - Pet products - Vitakraft Pet Products Co., Inc.
FRESH - Recording label - Charles Lowndes Conquest and Wesley E. Talbot Partnership
FRESH 7 - Bread - Interstate Brands Corp.
FRESH 1000 - Pet products - Oscar Enterprises Inc.
FRESH AGAIN - Deodorants–personal - Uncommon Conglomerates
FRESH AIR - Candles - Carolina Designs Ltd.
FRESH AIR - Greeting cards - Hallmark Licensing, Inc.
FRESH AIR - Paints - KCI Coatings, Inc.
FRESH AIR - Recording label - Moseka Records & Tapes
FRESH AIR - Shoes - Richman Gordman Stores Inc.
FRESH-AIR - Vending machines - Fresh Air International Express
FRESH AIR - Wallpaper - Frankford Wallcoverings Inc.
FRESH AIR - Wallpaper ☆ - Imperial Wallcoverings, Inc.
FRESH AIR CLIP - Deodorizers - Gold Eagle Co.
FRESH AIR FORMULA - Paints - KCI Coatings, Inc.
FRESH-AIRE MANUFACTURING CO. INC. - Air purification systems - Fletcher Manufacturing Co. Inc.
FRESH-ALL - Deodorizers - Vapor Products
FRESH ALL DAY - Cosmetics - Revlon Consumer Products Corp.
FRESH ALWAYS TASTES BEST - Dinners–frozen - Keystone Food Products
FRESH AMBROSIA - Juices ☆ - Odwalla, Inc.
FRESH AMERICAN ROYAL BANQUET LAMB - Lamb - Kash N'Karry Food Stores, Inc.
FRESH & CLEAN - Mouthwashes - Cosmetic Concepts, Inc.
FRESH & DRY - Deodorants–personal - Bristol-Myers Squibb Co.
FRESH & FRIENDLY - Soap - Water Resources International, Inc.
FRESH AND FUNKY - Patterns–clothing - One Heart...One Mind, LLC
FRESH & NATURAL - Bread - Interstate Brands Corp.
FRESH & NEW - Skin care products - Vitamin Shoppe Industries Inc.
FRESH & NEW THE VITAMIN SHOPPE - Skin care products - Vitamin Shoppe Industries Inc.
FRESH & SIMPLE - Wallcovering - Wall Trends, Inc.
FRESH APPEAL - Food products ☆ - Uncle Ben's, Inc.
FRESH APPEAL - Vitamins and nutritional supplements - MXM Essential Formulas Inc.
FRESH APPLE SPLASH - Shampoos - Softsoap Enterprises, Inc.
FRESH APPROACH - Shampoo, conditioner - Benjamin Ansehl Co.
FRESH APPROACH - Wallpaper ☆ - Imperial Wallcoverings, Inc.
FRESH-AS-A-BABY - Deodorizers - Surco Products Inc.
FRESH AS A DAISY - Cleaning preparations - New Ideas International, Inc.
FRESH BAKE SHOPPE - Containers–paper - Glenmark Industries, Inc.
FRESH BERRIES - Deodorizers - S.C. Johnson & Son, Inc.
FRESH BLOOM - Fruits and vegetables - River City Fruit Co.

FRESH-BREW - Cleaning preparations ☆ - Elcal Enterprises Ltd.
FRESH BURST LISTERINE - Mouthwashes - Warner-Wellcome
FRESH CARGO - Seafood products–fresh or frozen ☆ - J.F. Clarke Corp.
FRESH CARGO - Shrimp–fresh or frozen - Stevens Industries Inc.
FRESH CATCH - Cat food - Nestle USA
FRESH CHARGER - Pet products - Animal Medic Inc.
FRESH CHEF - Salads–prepackaged ☆ - Campbell Soup Co.
FRESH CHOICE - Juices - Freshco, Ltd.
FRESH CHOICE - Meat products–poultry - North Star Foods Inc.
FRESH CHOICE - Soap - Mistral Trade Corp.
FRESH CHOICE - Varnishes - Perry & Derrick Co.
FRESH CLASSIC'S - Sandwiches–prepackaged - Classic Delight Inc.
FRESH CLIP - Housewares - Lighthouse for the Blind Inc.
FRESH CLUB - Deodorants–personal - Philip B. Davis
FRESH COAT - Shampoos - Petland, Inc.
FRESH COLOR - Cosmetics - Almay Inc.
FRESH COMFORT - Mattresses - Kingsdown, Inc.
FRESH COUNTRY - Giftware - Enesco Corp.
FRESH CRANBERRY - Lipstick ☆ - Cosrich Inc.
FRESH CREATIONS - Candy - Kraft Foods, Inc.
FRESH CROP - Popcorn - National Oats Co. Inc.
FRESH CUP - Paper - Rockline Industries Inc.
FRESH CUT - Apparel–women's - Mcintosh & Seymour, Inc.
FRESH CUT - Fruits–canned ☆ - Coca-Cola Co.
FRESH CUT FLOWERS-FRAGRANCE COLLECTION - Perfumes ☆ - Dana Perfumes Corp.
FRESH CUTS - Meat products - Continental Deli Foods, Inc.
FRESH DAYS - Health care products - Confab Corp.
FRESH DELI GRANDISSIMO - Food products - A.M. Gilardi and Sons, Inc.
FRESH DIMENSION - Floor coverings–carpet and rugs ☆ - Playfield International Inc.
FRESH EDITION - Wallpaper - Newmarket Designs Ltd.
FRESH ENCOUNTER - Recording label - Sunday School Board of the Southern Baptist Convention
FRESH ESSENCE - Pet products - Four Paws Products Ltd.
FRESH EXPERIENCE - Floor coverings–carpet and rugs - Lees Carpets
FRESH EXPRESS - Fresh vegetables - Freshco Inc.
FRESH EXPRESS - Fruits and vegetables - Fresh Express Inc.
FRESH EXPRESS - Salads–prepackaged - Bruce Church Inc.
FRESH EXPRESS FARMS - Fruits and vegetables - Fresh Express Inc.
FRESH EXPRESSIONS - Apparel–women's - Exquisite Form Industries
FRESH EXPRESSIONS - Vegetables–canned - Celentano Brothers Inc.
FRESH FACE - Massage products - Wahl Clipper Corp.
FRESH FACE - Pet products - Gerard-Pellham Co.
FRESH FACE REHYD - Skin care products - Jason Natural Products, Inc.
FRESH FARE - Food products - Reser's Fine Foods Inc.
FRESH FARM - Furniture ☆ - Hammary Furniture Co. Inc.
FRESH FEELING - Floor coverings–carpet and rugs - Monticello Carpet Mills
FRESH FIELDS - Giftware ☆ - Avon Products, Inc.
FRESH FIESTA - Beverages - Azteca Restaurant Enterprises, Inc.
FRESH FINISH - Cosmetics - Almay Inc.
FRESH FLO VENTS - Deodorizers - Church & Dwight Co.
FRESH FLO VENTS - Deodorizers - Church and Dwight Co. Inc.
FRESH FLORALS - Wallpaper - Imperial Wallcoverings, Inc.
FRESH FLOWERS - Dinnerware–glass ☆ - Cyclamen Studio
FRESH FOCACCIA - Breads - Piemonte Foods Inc.
FRESH FOR YOU - Pies–frozen - Edwards Baking Co.
FRESH FREEDOM - Underwear and nightwear - Rago Foundations Inc. LLC
FRESH FRIDGE - Deodorizers - Cyril J.C. Brizard
FRESH FROM TEXAS - Spinach - Fresh From Texas
FRESH FROM THE BAY - Food products - Bay Trading Co.
FRESH FROM THE DELI - Meat products–beef - Armour Swift-Eckrich
FRESH FRUIT - Dinnerware–glass - Franciscan by Johnson Brothers, USA, Inc.
FRESH FRUIT - Dishes–china - Waterford Wedgewood USA, Inc.
FRESH FRY - Cooking equipment–commercial - Choo Choos
FRESH FUR - Pet products - Gerard-Pellham Co.
FRESH GAR - Vitamins and nutritional supplements - Nature's Way Products, Inc.
FRESH GLOSS - Lipsticks ☆ - Shiseido Cosmetics (America) Ltd.
FRESH GLOW - Cosmetics - Almay Inc.
FRESH GOES BETTER - Candy - Van Melle Inc.
FRESH GRIP - Cleaning preparations - Sico Golf Products
FRESH GROCER - Vegetables–canned - Flea Market, Inc.
FRESH GROUND - Horseradish - Silver Spring Gardens Inc.
FRESH GUY - Towels - Chicopee

☆ = Now out of production

FRESH HARVEST - Fruits and vegetables - Fagundes Agribusiness Co.
FRESH HARVEST - Juices - Farmland Dairies Inc.
FRESH HERB COMPANY, THE - Oils–edible - Fresh Herb Co.
FRESH HERBAL FOOT SOAK - Skin care products - Freeman Cosmetics Corp.
FRESH HOLD - Hair care products - Clairol Inc.
FRESH HORIZONS - Deodorizers ☆ - Sunbeam-Oster Household Products
FRESH HORIZONS - Reduced-calorie bread ☆ - Interstate Brands Corp.
FRESH IDEAS - Apparel–women's - Wacoal America Inc.
FRESH IDEAS - Seasonings - Lawry's Investments, Inc.
FRESH IMPRESSION - Cleaning preparations - National Interchem Corp.
FRESH IMPRESSIONS - Apparel - Gourmet Gear
FRESH-IT - Deodorizers ☆ - BG Products Inc.
FRESH JUICE - Apparel - Tomato, Inc.
FRESH KIDS - Infant's and children's apparel - H.J. Rashti & Co. Inc.
FRESH KING - Fruits and vegetables - Timothy Murphy
FRESH KOTE - Paints - M.A. Bruder & Sons Inc.
FRESH LASH - Cosmetics - Maybelline Co.
FRESH LEAVES - Cosmetics ☆ - Shiseido Cosmetics (America) Ltd.
FRESH LEE CUT - Fruits and vegetables - Sang Lee Farms, Inc.
FRESH LIDS - Hats - Fresh Lids
FRESH LITES - Snack foods ☆ - Dole Food Co., Inc.
FRESH-LOCK - Bags–plastic - Reynolds Consumer Products, Inc.
FRESH LOOK - Cleaning preparations–household - Dowbrands L.P.
FRESH LOOK - Contact lenses - Wesley-Jessen Co.
FRESH LOOK - Cosmetics - Almay Inc.
FRESH LOOKS - Wallpaper - Imperial Wallcoverings, Inc.
FRESH MADE - Juices - Ferraro's Fine Juices
FRESH MAID - Mayonnaise - Wilsey Foods, Inc.
FRESH MARK - Pork - Fresh Mark, Inc.
FRESH MAX - Fruits and vegetables - Chiquita Brands, Inc.
FRESH MEADOW - Tableware–china ☆ - Lenox, Inc.
FRESH MINT BOX - Candy - Fanny Farmer Candy Shops Inc.
FRESH MOISTURE - Lipstick ☆ - Cosrich Inc.
FRESH MOUTH - Candy - American Chewing Gum Inc.
FRESH MUSK - Perfumes - Revlon Consumer Products Corp.
FRESH 'N BRITE - Denture cleaners - Warner-Wellcome
FRESH 'N CLEAN - Cosmetics - American International Industries
FRESH 'N' CLEAN - Fans–electric - Duracraft Corp.
FRESH 'N CLEAN - Pet products - Lambert-Kay
FRESH 'N DRY - Deodorizers - Drackett Co.
FRESH 'N EASY - Deodorizers - Spartan Chemical Co., Inc.
FRESH 'N EASY - Food products - Modami Services Inc.
FRESH 'N EASY - Pet products - Superior Brands Inc.
FRESH-N-FANCY - Housewares - Tupperware Co.
FRESH 'N FIT - Food products - Fresh 'N Fit Inc.
FRESH 'N FLORAL - Wallcoverings - Authentic Reproductions
FRESH 'N FRAGRANT - Deodorizers - Carolina Exchange/Greenleaf Inc.
FRESH N' FREE - Mouthwashes - Geritrex Corp.
FRESH ' N FRUITY - Deodorizers - Coughlan Products Corp.
FRESH-N-GOOD - Tomato pastes and sauces - Putnam County Canning Co.
FRESH N' LIGHT - Milk - Pet Dairy
FRESH 'N' MINTY - Mouthwashes - Marietta Corp.
FRESH N' NATURAL - Fruit drinks–bottled or canned - Citrus World Inc.
FRESH 'N PURE - Fruit drinks–bottled or canned - Everfresh Beverages, Inc.
FRESH N' TASTY - Juices - Eau Claire Packing Co.
FRESH N UP - Health care products - Rockline Industries Inc.
FRESH N' VAC - Cleaning preparations–carpet and rug - AmeriPlus Inc.
FRESH NEST - Pet products - Green Pet Products, Inc.
FRESH-O-LATOR - Food containers - Community Coffee Co., Inc.
FRESH PACKS - Meats–luncheon - Dial Corp.
FRESH PACT - Vegetables–frozen - Patterson Frozen Foods, Inc.
FRESH PAK - Cleaning preparations - Bausch & Lomb Inc.
FRESH PAK - Nuts–salted, roasted, cooked, or canned - Quality Packaging Inc.
FRESH-PAK - Pickles - Green Bay Foods Co.
FRESH PAST RIBBONS - Pasta - Ribbons Pasta Co.
FRESH PET - Pet products - Pets Smellfree Inc.
FRESH PINE - Cleaning preparations - White Cap Inc.
FRESH PLACE - Food products - Del Monte Corp.
FRESH PLUS MOUTHWASH - Mouthwashes - Blue Cross Laboratories Inc.
FRESH POPPY - Lipstick ☆ - Cosrich Inc.
FRESH PRODUCE - Men's sportswear ☆ - Levi Strauss & Co.
FRESH PRODUCE SPORTSWEAR - Apparel and accessories - Fresh Produce Sportswear, Inc.
FRESH QUEST CORPORATION - Electronic equipment - Fresh Quest Corp.

FRESH QUEST PRODUCE - Fruit and vegetable markets - Fresh Quest General Partnership
FRESH SAMANTHA - Juices - Fresh Samantha Inc.
FRESH-SCENT - Cleaning preparations ☆ - Bissell Inc.
FRESH SCENT - Colognes - Kim Laube & Co. Inc.
FRESH SCENT - Deodorizers ☆ - Blue Cross Laboratories Inc.
FRESH SCENT - Hair care products - Helene Curtis Industries Inc.
FRESH SCENT CLOROX - Bleach - Clorox Co.
FRESH SCENTS - Cleaning preparations - Stanley Home Products Inc.
FRESH-SEAL - Plastics film - Gray & Co.
FRESH SEASON - Fruits–pickled or brined - Fresh Daily Produce, Inc.
FRESH SELECT - Food products - Lindy's Pre-Pak Carrots
FRESH SERVE - Whipping machines - Leland Limited Inc.
FRESH SMILE - Toothpaste - Healthco International Inc.
FRESH SPOTS - Cosmetics - Schering-Plough Healthcare Products
FRESH SQUEEZED - Toiletries - Water Resources International, Inc.
FRESH SQUEEZED WATER - Water purification systems - Water Resources International, Inc.
FRESH START - Apparel and accessories - Oxford Industries, Inc.
FRESH START - Cleaning preparations - Hillyard Enterprises, Inc.
FRESH START - Detergents - Colgate-Palmolive Co.
FRESH START - Paper–tissue - Monaco Import/Export Inc.
FRESH START SUPER ENERGY PLUS - Vitamins and nutritional supplements - Fresh Start Vitamin Co. (Pacific Packaging Concepts Inc.)
FRESH START SUPER LIFE STRESS 'N ENERGY PACK - Vitamins and nutritional supplements - Fresh Start Vitamin Co. (Pacific Packaging Concepts Inc.)
FRESH STARTS - Flowers, plants, and seeds - Frank's Nursery & Crafts, Inc.
FRESH STARTS III - Wallpaper - Essex Wallcoveringss
FRESH STATE GARDEN SPINACH - Fruits and vegetables - State Garden Celery Co., Inc.
FRESH STEP - Pet products - Clorox Co.
FRESH STEP - Shoe accessories - Schering-Plough Healthcare Products
FRESH STEP - Synthetic turf - Instant Turf Industries Inc.
FRESH-STIK - Deodorants–personal - Willert Home Products, Inc.
FRESH STROKE - Paints - Pratt & Lambert, Inc.
FRESH STUFF - Footwear - Shoe Carnival, Inc.
FRESH STYLE - Wallpaper - Sanitas Wallcoverings
FRESH SURFACE - Cosmetics - Beaute, Inc.
FRESH SURROUNDINGS - Wallpaper - Charles Barone Inc.
FRESH TANGERINE - Juices ☆ - Odwalla, Inc.
FRESH TASTE OF THE NORTHWEST, THE - Fruit juice drinks - Bakerview Farms
FRESH THE MUSIC LIBRARY - Recording label - Charles Lowndes Conquest and Wesley E. Talbot Partnership
FRESH THREADZ - Apparel–men's - Arpex Group Inc.
FRESH TOPS - Containers - Rubbermaid Inc.
FRESH TOUCH - Paints - Royal Lustre Brands
FRESH TRADITIONS - Wallpaper ☆ - Schooner Prints Inc.
FRESH TRAN PLUS - Animal feed - Cenex/Land O'Lakes AG Services
FRESH-UP - Deodorizers ☆ - Aladdin Industries, Inc.
FRESH VALUES - Electronic equipment - Dominick's Finer Foods, Inc.
FRESH WATER - Food products ☆ - Sea Harvest Packing Co.
FRESH WIND - Cordage and twine ☆ - Winchester-Auburn Mills Inc.
FRESH WONDERS - Apparel–women's - Olga Co.
FRESH20 FLUSH - Toilets–portable - Polyjohn Enterprises Corp.
FRESHAIR - Hair dryer - Questech International, Inc.
FRESHAIR - Skin care products ☆ - Hess Hair Milk Laboratories Inc.
FRESHAIRE - Clothes-drying product - Jack-Post Corp.
FRESHAVE - Shaving preparations - Donald B. Feinsod M.D.
FRESHCAFE - Coffee - Segundo Martin
FRESHE - Food products - Golden Pantry West Inc.
FRESHE - Pharmaceutical preparations - Richardson Labs, Inc.
FRESHELL - Deodorizers - Drackett Co.
FRESHEN AIRE - Housewares - Amcor Group Ltd.
FRESHEN-UP - Chewing gum - American Chicle Co.
FRESHEN UP - Deodorizers - Brulin & Co., Inc.
FRESHEN UP - Skin care products ☆ - Roberts Research Laboratories, Inc.
FRESHEN UP - Wallpaper - York Wall Coverings Inc.
FRESHER - Seafood products–fresh or frozen - Coldwater Seafood Corp.
FRESHER THAN FRESH - Fish–fresh or frozen - Starboard Inc.
FRESHER THAN FRESH - Vegetables–frozen ☆ - VIP Sales Co. Inc.
FRESHERS - Confections - Dansig Inc.
FRESHETTE - Health care products - International Sani-Fem Co.
FRESHETTE - Health care products - WorkAbles for Women
FRESHFRUIT - Candy ☆ - American Chicle Co.

☆ = Now out of production

FRESHGARD - Sanitary napkins - Kimberly-Clark Corp.

FRESHIE - Grocery stores - Food Services of America, Inc.

FRESHIE - Musical instrument accessories ☆ - Selmer Co. Inc.

FRESHIE - Nuts–salted, roasted, cooked, or canned - Nut Bar Co. Inc.

FRESHJIVE - Apparel and accessories - Fresh Jive Manufacturing, Inc.

FRESHKIN - Beauty cleansers - James River Corp.

FRESHLIKE - Salads–prepackaged - Green Giant Co.

FRESHLIKE - Vegetables–frozen - Dean Foods Vegetable Co.

FRESHLIKE BLENDS - Vegetables–frozen - Dean Foods Vegetable Co.

FRESHLIKE PASTA COMBO'S - Frozen foods - Dean Foods Vegetable Co.

FRESHLITE - Vegetables–canned - Dean Foods Vegetable Co.

FRESHLOOK COLOR ENHANCERS - Contact lenses - Wesley-Jessen Corp.

FRESHLY CUT IN TEXAS - Fruits and vegetables - Cafeteria Operators, L.P.

FRESHLY PICKED LONG STEM NOSES - Candy - Cute Candy Corp.

FRESHLY ROASTED GOURMET COFFEE FILTER BREW - Coffee - Barrie House Coffee Co., Inc.

FRESHMAKER, THE - Candy - Van Melle Inc.

FRESHMAN - Brassieres (Bras) ☆ - Lovable Co.

FRESHMAN - Electronic equipment ☆ - Hamilton Electronics Corp.

FRESHMAN - Guitars ☆ - Guild Music Corp.

FRESHMAN - Urinals–enameled - Kohler Co.

FRESHMATES - Containers - Shoot the Moon Products, Inc.

FRESHMINT - Candy ☆ - American Chicle Co.

FRESHMIST - Humidifiers - Field Controls Co.

FRESHMOR - Air purification systems ☆ - Medo Industries, Inc.

FRESHMOUTH - See PROPOLIS

FRESH'N CRUSTY - Breads - Rich Products Corp.

FRESH'N FROSTY - Confections - Rich Products Corp.

FRESH'N SQUEEZE - Juice extracting devices - FMC Corp.

FRESH'NER - Cleaning preparations - AmeriPlus Inc.

FRESHNESS - Cleaning preparations–carpet and rug - Castex Industries Inc.

FRESHNESS - Salad dressings–bottled - Nestle USA

FRESHNESS FIRST - Skin care products ☆ - Avon Products, Inc.

FRESHNESS IS FROZEN IN, THE - Chickens - Continental Grain Co.

FRESHNESS SAVER - Food products - Kraft Foods, Inc.

FRESHNESS YOU CAN SEE - Containers - Eagle Affiliates, Inc.

FRESHPAC-4 - Bags–plastic - Vanguard Plastics, Inc.

FRESHPOT - Coffee makers–electric - Freshpot Corp.

FRESHSIDES - Fruits and vegetables - Albert Fisher Holdings, Inc.

FRESHSTEEL - Paints - OEM Paints, Inc.

FRESHTABLES - Fruits and vegetables ☆ - Pillsbury Co.

FRESHTHING - Vacuum cleaners and accessories ☆ - Home Care Industries, Inc.

FRESHWATER - Recording label - Artifex Records Inc.

FRESHWATER FORMULA ONE - Pet products - Ocean Nutrition Corp.

FRESHWATER FORMULA TWO - Pet products - Ocean Nutrition Corp.

FRESHWITE - Lighting equipment - LTG Ltd.

FRESHWORLD FARMS - Food products - FreshWorld Farms Inc.

FRESHZIP - Bags–plastic - Minigrip Inc.

FRESJA - Perfumes - Fresja-Interlam Inc.

FRESKEETO - Mayonnaise - Freskeeto Frozen Foods Inc.

FRESKITO - Food products machinery - Florida Carib Fishery Inc.

FRESKOLA - Beverages–carbonated - Freskola Corp.

FRESNEL - Lenses–optical - Fresnel Technologies Inc.

FRESNO - Apparel and accessories - Caldor Corp.

FRESNO - Floor coverings–carpet and rugs - Customweave Carpets Inc.

FRESNO - Wallpaper ☆ - Wolf-Gordon Inc.

FRESNO FALCONS - Apparel and accessories - Sports-R-Us, Inc.

FRESSENCE - Onions ☆ - General Mills, Inc.

FRESTECH - Lenses–optical - Fresnel Technologies Inc.

FRETIC - Blinds–venetian - Carnegie

FRETLESS - Recording label ☆ - Rounder Records Corp.

FRETMASTER - Guitars - Dean Markley Strings, Inc.

FRETONE - Nautical instruments ☆ - Fiamm Technologies

FRETSLING - Musical instrument accessories - Washburn International

FRETZ - Jewelry - Fretz Goldsmiths

FREUD - Tools–power-driven - Freud USA, Inc.

FREUDENMACHER - Beverages–alcohol - Nor-Glo Import Co.

FREUND - Food products - American Bakeries Co.

FREY - Wines - Frey Vineyards Ltd.

FREZ-825 - Televisions - Projectapix-II

FREZ-SHAKE - Milk–malted - Juice Services Inc.

FREZZI - Battery chargers - Frezzolini Electronics, Inc.

FREZZI-MAX - Batteries - Frezzolini Electronics, Inc.

FREZZI MINI-FILL - Photographic equipment - Frezzolini Electronics, Inc.

FREZZI ON-BOARD - Batteries - Frezzolini Electronics, Inc.

FREZZI-PAG - Batteries - Frezzolini Electronics, Inc.

FREZZOLINI - Power switching equipment - Frezzolini Electronics, Inc.

FRI-AL - Shortening - Interstate Foods Corp.

FRI-BEST - Shortening ☆ - Florida Shortening Corp.

FRI-PATS - Food products - Worthington Foods Inc.

FRIAR FREDDIE - Greeting cards - Norcross Inc.

FRIAR TUCK - Food products machinery ☆ - Fort Lupton Canning Co.

FRIAR VINEYARDS - Wine - Italian and French Wine Co. of Buffalo Inc.

FRIARICO - Jewelry - Frank Rifas Co.

FRIBBIT FROG - Toys–stuffed - Russ Berrie and Co., Inc.

FRIBBLE - Games ☆ - Warren Industries Inc.

FRIBBLE - Ice cream - Hershey Foods Corp.

FRIBBLE - Toys - Tonka Corp.

FRIBOURG & TREYER - Cigarettes - G.A. Georgopulo & Co. Inc.

FRICHIK - Food products - Worthington Foods Inc.

FRICK - Saws–power - Albright Saw Co., Inc.

FRICK GALLAGHER - Containers–metal ☆ - Frick-Gallagher Manufacturing Co.

FRICK WINERY - Wines - Frick Winery

FRICKER'S RESTAURANTS - Sauces - Fricker's Progressive Concepts, Inc.

FRICKIN' CHICKEN - Food products - Frick Bros. I, Inc.

FRICKLED PICKLES - Pickles - Genny's Diner & Pub, Inc.

FRICO - Cheese - Holland-American Importing Co. Inc.

FRICTION - Footwear - Skechers USA, Inc.

FRICTION BAIL - Mining equipment - Eastern Co.

FRICTION FREE PUSH BACK - Washers–metal - TurnaSure LLC

FRICTION FUNSTERS - Toys–stuffed ☆ - Fun World Inc.

FRICTION-GRIP - Floor coverings - American Floor Products Co. Inc.

FRICTION GRIP - Propellers - Outboard Marine Corp.

FRICTION-LOK - Construction equipment - Jennmar Corp.

FRICTION MASTER - Disk brake pads - Ezon Products, Inc.

FRICTION POUR LE BAIN - Skin care products - Revlon Consumer Products Corp.

FRICTION PROOFING - Oils–lubricating - Wynn Oil Co.

FRICTION-SHIELD - Lubricants - Coastal Distributing, Inc.

FRICTION TILT - Photographic equipment ☆ - Uhler Cine Machine Co.

FRICTIONEZE - Motor vehicle parts and accessories - Sunland Refining Corp.

FRICTIONITE - Stones–synthetic ☆ - Perfecto Products Co.

FRICTIONTECH - Automotive parts and accessories - Echlin Inc.

FRIDA - Footwear - Ample Footware Corp.

FRIDAY - Telephone answering machines ☆ - Bogen Communications, Inc.

FRIDAY - Vegetables–canned - Chiquita Processed Food, LLC

FRIDAY HARBOR - Salmon–smoked, salted, dried, or pickled - J.J. Theodore Inc.

FRIDAY NIGHT FLAVAS - Broadcasting stations–radio - Baka Boyz Productions, Inc.

FRIDAY SCOTCH, THE - Beverages–alcohol - William Grant & Sons, Inc.

FRIDAY SOLUTION - Shirts - Stein Mart, Inc.

FRIDGE CONTROL - Paper - Artistic Greetings, Inc.

FRIDGE CUBE - Deodorizers - RPM Industries Inc. (Dewitt Plastics Div.)

FRIDGE FRAME-UPS - Frames–picture ☆ - ME Enterprises

FRIDGE FREE - Milk ☆ - Gossner Foods, Inc.

FRIDGE-FREEZER PACK - Baking powder - Church and Dwight Co. Inc.

FRIDGE FRESH - Deodorizers - Surco Products Inc.

FRIDGE FUN! - Frames–picture - International Designs, Inc.

FRIDGE KIDS - Greeting cards - August Highland Group Inc.

FRIDGE-N-LIGHTER - Cigarette lighters - Carl Seeger Henry and Steven Toce Partnership

FRIDGE RACK - Containers ☆ - Spacemaster Home Products

FRIDGE STIX - Magnets - Fridge Strips, Inc.

FRIDGECALENDAR - Magnetic calendar boards - Lockermate Corp.

FRIDGEFOTOS - Frames–picture - J.B. Goodhouse Inc.

FRIDGEKEYKASE - Clutter holders - Lockermate Corp.

FRIDGEMEMOBOARD - Magnetic bulletin board - Lockermate Corp.

FRIDLEY - Stationery ☆ - Coronet General Corp.

FRIED - Audio equipment - Fried Products Corp.

FRIEDA GRATZON - Jewelry - Frieda Gratzon

FRIEDA'S - Chili peppers–powdered ☆ - Frieda's, Inc.

FRIEDEL - Chocolate candy - Westdale Foods Co.

FRIEDER - Cigars - House of Windsor Inc.

FRIEDERICH ENGELHARDT - Wines - Guild Wineries

FRIEDLAND - Drapery hardware - Ralph Friedland and Brothers Inc.

FRIEDMAN - Xylophones - Marimba Productions Inc.

FRIEDRICH - Air conditioning equipment - Friedrich Air Conditioning Co.

FRIEDRICH WILHELM GYMNASIUM - Wines - Seagram's Chateau & Estate Wines Co.

☆ = Now out of production

FRIEDRICHS WORLD COFFEES - Coffee - Friedrichs World Coffees

FRIEL - Vegetables–canned - S.E.W. Friel

FRIEMANIT - Apparel–children's - Friemanit Corp.

FRIEM'S - Artists' materials - A.I. Friedman Inc.

FRIEND 2 FRIEND - Catalogs - Bendy Irawan

FRIEND BEAR - Toys - Those Characters from Cleveland, Inc.

FRIEND LINKS - Notebooks and notepads - Je Di Associates, Inc.

FRIEND OF THE EARTH - Bags–plastic - Holland Beauty Flower & Bulb Corp.

FRIEND OF THE FAMILY, A - Toys - Spalding & Evenflo Companies, Inc.

FRIEND SHIP - Toys - Mattel, Inc.

FRIEND TETRAPLOID PERENNIAL - Flowers, plants, and seeds - Jacklin Seed

FRIEND TREE - Trees - Silkey & Roehl Partnership

FRIENDLIEST SHEETS IN THE WORLD, THE - Linen - Danaher Sheets & Co.

FRIENDLY - Ice cream - Hershey Foods Corp.

FRIENDLY 7, THE - Vitamins and nutritional supplements - Empower Net, LLC

FRIENDLY BEARS - Games - Master Creative Teaching Associates, Inc.

FRIENDLY BENDIES - Toys ☆ - Imperial Toy Corp.

FRIENDLY CLAY - Clay–modeling - American Art Clay Co. Inc.

FRIENDLY CLUB - Hats ☆ - Bee Hat Co.

FRIENDLY CONNECTIONS - Health care products - NeuroLogix Systems Ltd.

FRIENDLY DONUT MAN - Bakery products - Prestige American Foods

FRIENDLY FACES - Toys - Tonka Corp.

FRIENDLY FARM - Educational materials - Learning Resources, Inc.

FRIENDLY FARMS - Ice cream ☆ - Drigg's Dairy Farms Inc.

FRIENDLY FLESHER, THE - Tools - Hionis Taxidermy Supply

FRIENDLY FOAM - Packaging–foam - Richter Manufacturing Corp.

FRIENDLY FOREST - Wallpaper ☆ - Priss Prints Inc.

FRIENDLY FOSSILS - Novelty items - Ram Products

FRIENDLY FRAME - Toys - Tot Inc.

FRIENDLY FRIVAL HOUND & HER BEST BONE, THE - Toys–stuffed - Frivals n Friends

FRIENDLY FROG - Toys - Gerber Products Co.

FRIENDLY FROSTY - Toys–stuffed - Fun World Inc.

FRIENDLY JUG, THE - Pet products - A & M Pet Products Inc.

FRIENDLY PADDED MAILERS - Envelopes - Richter Manufacturing Corp.

FRIENDLY PAINTER - Brushes–paint - Wooster Brush Co.

FRIENDLY PLASTIC - Artists' materials - American Art Clay Co. Inc.

FRIENDLY SERVE - Automotive repair shops - Mobil Oil Corp.

FRIENDLY SYSTEMS - Pet products - Friendly Systems, Inc.

FRIENDLY TO THE ENVIRONMENT - Barbecue grills - Safari Industries

FRIENDLY VILLAGE - Dinnerware–glass - Johnson Brothers, USA, Inc.

FRIENDLY VILLAGE - Dishes–china - Waterford Wedgewood USA, Inc.

FRIENDLY YELLOW PAGES, THE - Telephone directories - Associated Publishing Co.

FRIENDLYWARE - Computer software - Friendlysoft Inc.

FRIENDLYWARE ARCADE - Computer software - Friendlysoft Inc.

FRIENDLYWRITER - Computer software - Friendlysoft Inc.

FRIEND'S - Baked beans–canned - Pet Inc.

FRIENDS - Fabrics - Friends & Co.

FRIENDS & COMPANY - Pet products - Friends & Co. Pet Products, Inc.

FRIENDS AND NEIGHBORS - Wallpaper - Belmont Wallcoverings

FRIENDS AT WORK - Games ☆ - Milton Bradley Co.

FRIENDS FOR LIFE - Toys - Trinkets-N-Things, Ltd.

FRIENDS FOREVER - Dolls - Friends Forever

FRIENDS FOREVER - Dolls - Russ Berrie and Co., Inc.

FRIENDS FOREVER - Teas - Celestial Seasonings, Inc.

FRIENDS FROM FOREIGN LANDS - Dolls - Uneeda Doll Co., Inc.

FRIENDS IN FITNESS - Consulting services - Christine D. Sare

FRIENDS OF GARLIC - Salad dressing - Photi Foods Inc.

FRIENDS OF THE ENVIRONMENT - Toys - Environmental Preservation, Inc.

FRIENDS OF THE FAMILY - Greeting cards - Recycled Paper Products, Inc.

FRIENDS OF THE FOREST - Stationery - Environmental Preservation, Inc.

FRIENDS UNITED FOR WORLD STYLE - Jeans–children's - Gitano Licensing, Ltd.

FRIENDS UNITED PRESS - Publisher's imprints - Friends United Press

FRIENDSHIP - Dairy products - Friendship Food Products Inc.

FRIENDSHIP - Drinking straws - Sansom, Inc.

FRIENDSHIP - Floor coverings–carpet and rugs - Trans-Ocean Import Co. Inc.

FRIENDSHIP - Furniture ☆ - Moosehead Manufacturing Co.

FRIENDSHIP - Ships–sailing vessels - Jarvis Newman Boats

FRIENDSHIP - Trailers–travel ☆ - Shasta Industries Inc.

FRIENDSHIP - Wood products ☆ - Spaulding & Frost Co. Inc.

FRIENDSHIP I - Wallpaper - Advance Wallcoverings

FRIENDSHIP COLLECTION - Toilets–porcelain - Friendship Designs

FRIENDSHIP DAIRY FARMERS - Cheese - Dairy Fresh Products Co.

FRIENDSHIP DESIGNS - Toilets–porcelain - Friendship Designs

FRIENDSHIP DESIGNS II - Toilets–porcelain - Friendship Designs

FRIENDSHIP DESIGNS III - Toilets–porcelain - Friendship Designs

FRIENDSHIP GARLAND - Flowers–artificial - Audria's Crafts

FRIENDSHIP INNS - Hotels and motels - Choice Hotels International Inc.

FRIENDSHIP IS ALWAYS IN SEASON - Calendars ☆ - American Greetings Corp.

FRIENDSHIP LIGHT DELITE - Sour cream ☆ - Friendship Food Products Inc.

FRIENDSHIP N' FRUIT - Cottage cheese ☆ - Friendship Food Products Inc.

FRIENDSHIP STUDIOS - Paper ☆ - Artistic Greetings, Inc.

FRIENDSHIP TREE - Greeting cards ☆ - American Greetings Corp.

FRIENDTABULOUS - T-shirts–men's - Daniel M. Rhodes

FRIEZE - Floor coverings–carpet and rugs - Collins & Aikman Corp.

FRIEZE - Floor coverings–carpet and rugs ☆ - Regal Rugs Inc.

FRIEZE - Wallpaper - Koroseal Wallcoverings

FRIEZE, THE - Ice cream - World's Greatest Ice Cream Co., Inc.

FRIGATE - Fabrics - Dan River Inc.

FRIGATE NETWORKS - Computers - Charles S. Slater

FRIGHT BITE - Toys ☆ - Those Characters from Cleveland, Inc.

FRIGHT BITES - Candy - Brach and Brock Confections Inc.

FRIGHT FACE - Toys - Tonka Corp.

FRIGHT FIGHTER - Toys–automobiles - Mattel, Inc.

FRIGHT NITE - Games - Universal Manufacturing Co., Inc.

FRIGHT RIDERS - Toys–automobiles - Mattel, Inc.

FRIGHT STUFF - Novelty items - Spencer Gifts, Inc.

FRIGHT SWITCH - Novelty items - Paper Magic Group Inc.

FRIGHT WRITES - Markers–felt-tip - Liqui-Mark

FRIGHT ZONE - Toys–erector sets - Mattel, Inc.

FRIGHTFUL FLYERS - Novelty items - Russ Berrie and Co., Inc.

FRIGI-FOAM - Insulating materials - White Consolidated Industries, Inc.

FRIGI-QUIET - Lubricants - BG Products Inc.

FRIGI-TEMP - Refrigerators - Frigibar Industries Inc.

FRIGID - Fans–attic - Frigid Products Inc.

FRIGID-BLOK - Laboratory apparatus - Lab-Line Instruments, Inc.

FRIGID FOOD - Vegetables–frozen - Frigid Food Products Inc.

FRIGID FREEZE - Meat products–beef ☆ - Frigid Freeze Foods Inc./Monarch Foods

FRIGID TESTER - Novelty items - Adams Apple Distributing L.P.

FRIGID UNITS - Refrigerators - Frigid Units, Inc.

FRIGID VEGETABLES - Food products machinery - Frigid Food Products Inc.

FRIGID ZONE - Food products - Alaskan Glacier Seafoods

FRIGIDAIRE - Refrigerators - White Consolidated Industries, Inc.

FRIGIDCOIL - Compressors–gas - Yihc, Inc.

FRIGIDEGS - Eggs - Frigid Food Products Inc.

FRIGIDFRUITS - Fruits–frozen - Frigid Food Products Inc.

FRIGIDSEA - Seafood products–fresh or frozen - Fishery Products International USA

FRIGIES - Infant product ☆ - Binky-Griptight Co.

FRIGITONE - Antifreeze - Bridgestone/Firestone, Inc.

FRIGO - Cheese - Frigo Cheese Corp.

FRIGO FARMS - Cheese - Frigo Cheese Corp.

FRIGORO - Food products ☆ - Darik Enterprises Inc.

FRILICORN - Toys–stuffed - Frivals n Friends

FRILIGOAT - Toys–stuffed - Frivals n Friends

FRILION - Toys–stuffed - Frivals n Friends

FRILIPHANT - Toys–stuffed - Frivals n Friends

FRILL FRILL - Hair care products - Andre Fantasies Inc.

FRILLA - Crackers - R.W. Frookies Inc.

FRILLE - Jewelry - Steven A. Rosendorf

FRILLIKINS - Apparel–women's ☆ - Blue Swan Outline Corp.

FRILLS AND FANTASY - Dolls - Mattel, Inc.

FRILLS-N-FLUFF - Hair care products - Andre Fantasies Inc.

FRILLS 'N LACE - Hair care products - Russ Berrie and Co., Inc.

FRILUFFALO - Toys–stuffed - Frivals n Friends

FRIMATOR - Skin care products - Nemectron Skin Care Inc.

FRINGE BENEFITS - Apparel and accessories - Salant/Manhattan Industries

FRINGE COLORING - Hair coloring preparations - Helene Curtis Industries Inc.

FRINGE CONNECTION, THE - Fringe - Ellen S. Holt & Associates

F'RINSTANCE - Frames–eyeglass - Liberty Optical Manufacturing Co.

FRIO GRANDE - Ice cream - Wells' Dairy, Inc.

FRIO TEXAS - Beverages–malt - Frio Brewing Co.

FRIOBIT - Food products machinery - Frionor USA Inc.

FRIOCHIP - Seafood products–canned or cured ☆ - Frionor USA Inc.

FRIODUR - Cutlery - J.A. Henckels Zwillingswerk Inc.

FRIOFLAKE - Food products machinery - Frionor USA Inc.

FRIONOR - Fish–fresh or frozen - Frionor USA Inc.

FRIPS BOARD - Paper - Frits H. Emmerik
FRIS - Beverages–alcohol - Hiram Walker & Sons, Inc.
FRISBEE - Pet products - Nylabone Products
FRISBEE - Toys - Wham-O Manufacturing Co.
FRISBEE FLYING DISCS - Pet products - T.F.H. Publications, Inc.
FRISBEE GRIPPER - Toys - Mattel, Inc.
FRISBEE POCKET PRO - Toys ☆ - Wham-O Manufacturing Co.
FRISBEE VISION - Sporting goods - Mattel, Inc.
FRISBY - Fishing tackle - Sutton Co.
FRISBY'S - Frozen foods - Moran Foods, Inc.
FRISCO - Cabinets - Marsh Furniture Co.
FRISCO - Chimes - Nutone Inc.
FRISCO - Firearms, accessories, and parts - Welsh Sporting Goods Corp. (Boyt Div.)
FRISCO - Fruits and vegetables - Merrill Farms
FRISCO - Herring–smoked, salted, dried, or pickled - Haram-Christensen Corp.
FRISCO - Paints - Lee Paint & Varnish Co.
FRISCO - Sandwiches–prepackaged - Hardee's Food Systems, Inc.
FRISCO - Skin care products - Frances Denney
FRISCO - Wines ☆ - Bardenheier Wine Cellars
FRISCO-FIXX - Hair care products - Rescue Marketing Group
FRISCO SHIV - Cutlery ☆ - Gerber Legendary Blades
FRISCO VEGETABLES SINCE 1933 - Fruits and vegetables - Merrill Farms
FRISCODENT - Toothpaste - Frances Denney
FRISCOLOGNE - Skin care products - Frances Denney
FRISCOOL - Skin care products - Frances Denney
FRISIA - Candy - Wilkinson-Spitz Ltd.
FRISK SUGAR FREE MINTS - Candy - Gerrit J. Verburg Co.
FRISKEE FEEDER - Pet products - Ross Products Inc.
FRISKETFILM - Adhesives and sealants ☆ - Hunt Manufacturing Co.
FRISKIES - Pet products - Nestle USA
FRISKIES BUFFET - Cat food - Nestle USA
FRISKIES SENIOR - Cat food - Nestle USA
FRISKO JEENS - Jeans–women's ☆ - Lee Apparel Co. Inc.
FRISKY - Toys–stuffed ☆ - Russ Berrie and Co., Inc.
FRISKY FIDO - Dolls - Goebel United States
FRISKY FROG - Toys - Fisher-Price, Inc.
FRISKY PUPS WITH COMFY BASKET - Toys–stuffed - Tonka Corp.
FRISPS - Crackers - R.W. Frookies Inc.
FRISSON - Wines - Remy Martin Amerique Inc.
FRITO-LAY - Snack foods - Frito-Lay, Inc.
FRITO-LAY INDY - Toys–electronic - Bird Bromiticous Inc.
FRITOLA - Laxatives - Pinus Medicine Co.
FRITOS - Corn chips - Frito-Lay, Inc.
FRITOS MINI-WHEELS - Toys–electronic - Bird Bromiticous Inc.
FRITSCH - Food products ☆ - Liberty Richter Inc.
FRITTER KING - Meat products–pork - Whitaker Foods Inc.
FRITWARE - Laboratory apparatus - Bel-Art Products, Inc.
FRITZ - Aquatic pharmacuetical preparations - Fritz Industries, Inc.
FRITZ CELLARS - Wines - Fritz Cellars
FRITZ GOES TO SCHOOL - Computer software ☆ - Gessler Publishing Co., Inc.
FRITZ GUARD - Aquatic pharmacuetical preparations - Fritz Industries, Inc.
FRITZ SPRITZ - Hair care products - Cheveux Inc.
FRITZI - Apparel stores–sports - Fritzi California
FRITZI CALIFORNIA - Apparel stores–sports - Fritzi California
FRITZI PETITES - Apparel stores–sports - Fritzi California
FRITZI PLUS - Apparel and accessories - Fritzi California
FRITZIE FRESH - Candy - Fritz Co., Inc.
FRITZTILE - Floor coverings - Fritz Industries, Inc.
FRITZYME - Aquatic pharmacuetical preparations - Fritz Industries, Inc.
FRIULI - Sorbet - Friuli Sorbet, Inc.
FRIVAL HOUND - Toys–stuffed - Frivals n Friends
FRIVALS - Toys–stuffed - Frivals n Friends
FRIVOLETTE - Girdles - Lily of France Inc.
FRIVOLI - Yarn ☆ - JCA, Inc.
FRIVOLOUS - Yarn ☆ - Joseph Galler Inc.
FRIZ FREE - Hair care products ☆ - Gefden International Inc.
FRIZETTE - Yarn ☆ - Henry's Attic
FRIZZ BE GONE - Hair care products - Image Laboratories, Inc.
FRIZZ BE GONE - Hair care products - Modern Research Laboratories
FRIZZ CONTROL - Hair care products - Clairol Inc.
FRIZZ FREE - Hair care products - Gold Medal Hair Products Inc.
FRIZZ OUT - Hair care products - Conair Corp.
FRIZZ REMEDY - Hair care products - Alleghany Pharmacal Corp.

FRIZZ-SOLVER & SHINE ENHANCER - Hair care products - Alberto-Culver Co.
FRIZZLERS - Meat products–pork - Visionary Design, Inc.
FRIZZLES - Dolls ☆ - Uneeda Doll Co., Inc.
FRIZZS - Fishing lures - Hofmanns Lures
FRIZZY BEAR - Toys–stuffed - Russ Berrie and Co., Inc.
FRIZZY LOVE - Greeting cards ☆ - Fran Mar Greeting cards Ltd.
FRIZZZZ CONTROL - Hair care products - Posner Laboratories Inc.
FRK - Cleaning preparations - Roebic Laboratories Inc.
FRM - Lubricating oils ☆ - Shell Oil Co.
FRO MOLD - Bathroom accessories - Frohock-Stewart Inc.
FROEHLICH FOTO - Photographic equipment ☆ - Mamiya America Corp.
FROEHLICH FOTOVIDEO - Photographic equipment ☆ - Mamiya America Corp.
FROEZERT - Yogurt–frozen - Froezert USA Inc.
FROG - Games ☆ - Carrom Co.
FROG - Recording label - Bellaire Record Sales
FROG - Toys–automobiles ☆ - Roadmaster Corp.
FROG - Water purification systems - King Technology, Inc.
FROG A LA PEELE - Health care products ☆ - Myra Hogan
FROG BOX - Chests–wood ☆ - Little Tikes Co.
FROG HOOKS - Ramps - Sternmoor Inc.
FROG HOPPER - Amusement rides - S & S Power, Inc.
FROG HORN - Marine rigging ☆ - Woolsey Marine Industries
FROG LEG RANCH - Food products machinery - Frog Leg Ranch
FROG LIGHT UP - Toys - Steven Manufacturing Co.
FROG MAP - Maps - Frog Map, Inc.
FROG MICRO - Computers - Sales & Marketing Assistance Group
FROG NINJAZORD - Toys–automobiles - Saban Entertainment, Inc.
FROG POND - Apparel stores–children's - Frog Pond Kids Inc.
FROG, THE - Toilet seats - Tumble Forms, Inc.
FROG WISDOM - Patterns–clothing - Ann's Cottage
FROG WORK RECORDS - Recording label - Lite Album Publishing Co.
FROGBALL - Apparel and accessories - Earth Air Water Wear, Inc.
FROGBALL - Balls - Llumar Star Kites Inc.
FROGBALL - Balls - Spectra Star Kites
FROGFUR - Hair care products - Redken Laboratories, Inc.
FROGGER - Computer software ☆ - Sierra On-Line, Inc.
FROGGIE - Housewares - Sew What
FROGGIE RIDE-EM - Toys ☆ - Steven Manufacturing Co.
FROGGIE'S - Yogurt–frozen - Froggie's Frozen Yogurt Inc.
FROGGY - Floating chlorine dispenser ☆ - Utikem Products
FROGHIDE - Extension cords - General Cable Corp.
FROGISM FAMILY RECOVERY ONGOING GROWTH - Apparel and accessories - Frog Promotions
FROGLEGS - Toys–stuffed - Dakin Inc.
FROGMAN - Watches - Croton Watch Co., Inc.
FROGMORE - Toys–stuffed ☆ - Gund, Inc.
FROGS & TOADS - Kaleidoscopes - Gemini Kaleidoscopes
FROG'S LEAP - Wines - Frog's Leap Winery
FROGS LEAP - Wines - Frog's Leap Winery
FROGSKIN FORMULA - Sunblocks - Solar Gear Inc.
FROGSKINS - Eyeglasses - Oakley, Inc.
FROHOCK - Bathroom accessories - Frohock-Stewart Inc.
FROLIC - Beverages–carbonated - Shasta Beverages, Inc.
FROLIC - Clocks - General Time Corp. (Westclox/Seth Thomas Div.)
FROLIC - Computer software ☆ - Wright Line Inc.
FROLIC - Fabrics ☆ - Greenwood Mills Inc.
FROLIC - Hosiery ☆ - Parke-Davis
FROLIC - Motor vehicles–motor homes ☆ - Coachmen Industries, Inc.
FROLIC - Trailers–travel ☆ - Shasta Industries Inc.
FROLIC - Yarn - National Spinning Co., Inc.
FROLIC - Yarn ☆ - William Unger & Co. Inc.
FROLIC CURLY POPS - Candy - Eddyleon Chocolate Co. Inc.
FROLIC SHIPWRECK ALE - Beverages–malt - Mendocino Brewing Co., Inc.
FROLICS - Footwear - Wolverine World Wide, Inc.
FROLICTIME - Novelty items ☆ - Superior Balloon Co.
FROLIE - Girdles - H.F. Robbins
FROM A CHILD'S HEART - Figurines - Waco Products Corp.
FROM A LIFETIME OF GOLF - Apparel and accessories - Golden Bear International, Inc.
FROM AMERICA...WITH LOVE - Giftware - Branches
FROM ARIZONA...WITH LOVE - Giftware - Branches
FROM CALIFORNIA...WITH LOVE - Giftware - Branches
FROM COLORADO...WITH LOVE - Giftware - Branches
FROM CONNECTICUT...WITH LOVE - Giftware - Branches

☆ = Now out of production

FROM COUNTRY INNS - Furniture ☆ - Harden Furniture Co. Inc.

FROM FARM HOUSE TO YOUR HOUSE - Food products - Paradise Farm Organics, Inc.

FROM FLORIDA...WITH LOVE - Giftware - Branches

FROM GENERATION TO GENERATION - Video production - Financial Innovations, Inc.

FROM HAWAII...WITH LOVE - Giftware - Branches

FROM IOWA...WITH LOVE - Giftware - Branches

FROM KANSAS...WITH LOVE - Giftware - Branches

FROM MAINE...WITH LOVE - Giftware - Branches

FROM MASSACHUSETTS...WITH LOVE - Giftware - Branches

FROM ME TO YOU BEARS - Toys–stuffed - Russ Berrie and Co., Inc.

FROM MICHIGAN...WITH LOVE - Giftware - Branches

FROM MINNESOTA...WITH LOVE - Giftware - Branches

FROM MISSOURI...WITH LOVE - Giftware - Branches

FROM NEBRASKA...WITH LOVE - Giftware - Branches

FROM NEW HAMPSHIRE...WITH LOVE - Giftware - Branches

FROM NORTH DAKOTA...WITH LOVE - Giftware - Branches

FROM OUR GANG TO YOURS - Pizzas–frozen - A.M. Gilardi and Sons, Inc.

FROM OUR GROVES TO YOU! - Juices - R & Z Ventures, Inc.

FROM OUR KITCHEN TO YOURS - Frozen foods - Chicago Brothers, Inc.

FROM OUR WINDOW - Wallpaper - Mt. Diablo Hand Prints Inc.

FROM PACK TO POWDER - Snowshoes ☆ - Wing Enterprises, Inc.

FROM PANIC TO POWER! - Video production - Midwest Center for Stress and Anxiety, Inc.

FROM SCIENCE TO SOLUTIONS - Video production - Science Applications International Corp.

FROM SOUTH DAKOTA...WITH LOVE - Giftware - Branches

FROM THE - Apparel and accessories - Metropolis LLC

FROM THE 3! - Apparel and accessories - Mark A. Levine and Trent Tucker

FROM THE ATTIC - Christmas tree ornaments ☆ - Giordano Art, Ltd.

FROM THE DIAMOND BAR RANCH CANNONBALL 484 BBQ RIB SAUCE - Barbecue sauce - Logos Group

FROM THE FOUR CORNERS - Furniture - Thomasville Furniture Industries Inc.

FROM THE GARDEN - Soap - Gianna Rose

FROM THE GARDEN GATE - Calendars ☆ - American Greetings Corp.

FROM THE HEART - Wallpaper - Market House

FROM THE KITCHENS OF KIM - Candy - Kim's Chocolate

FROM THE SUN, WIND AND SEA - Salt - Cargill, Inc.

FROM THE YEAST TO THE GREATEST - Bakery products - Nelle's Bread Box, Inc.

FROM TX WITH LOVE - Stationery - Texan House Inc.

FROM VERMONT...WITH LOVE - Giftware - Branches

FROM WISCONSIN...WITH LOVE - Giftware - Branches

FROMAGE - Floor coverings–carpet and rugs ☆ - Robertex Associates Inc.

FROMAGE DE L'ABBE - Cheese - Walker Foods

FROMAGERIES BEL - Cheese - Fromageries Bel, Inc.

FROMAGES DE LA FRANCE - Thread - WesekPalley Tile Inc.

FROMAGETTE - Cheese ☆ - T. Marzetti Co.

FROMAGG - Macaroni - Galaxy Foods Co.

FROMED - Bathroom accessories - Frohock-Stewart Inc.

FROMEZ - Cheese ☆ - Swissrose International Inc.

FROMIX - Analgesics - Bruce M. Frome

FROMM - Hair care products - Marianna Imports, Inc.

FROMM - Pet products - Fromm Family Foods, Inc.

FROMM - Skin care products - Fromm Industries

FROMMER GUIDES - Publisher's imprints - Simon & Schuster, Inc.

FROMME'S FINEST - Coffee - Cowan & Fransman

FRONIER POLI-VOID - Adhesives and sealants - Stegmeier Corp.

FRONT - Apparel and accessories - Bruce D. Wakefield

FRONT - Computer hardware - Nimax

FRONT & CENTER - Shaving preparations ☆ - Luzier Personalized Cosmetics, Inc.

FRONT COVER - Apparel and accessories - Front Cover Inc.

FRONT DESK - Computer software - Integrity Solutions, Inc.

FRONT DESK - Computer software - JWP Telecom, Inc.

FRONT DESK INC. - Furniture stores - Front Desk, Inc.

FRONT DRAW - Tools - Monadnock Lifetime Products, Inc.

FRONT ENDER - Toys–automobiles - Mattel, Inc.

FRONT-EZE - Brassieres (Bras) - Bi-Flex International

FRONT FEMME - Apparel and accessories - Front Corp.

FRONT FIRST - Apparel and accessories - Front First Designs, Inc.

FRONT HALL - Recording label - Front Hall Enterprises Inc.

FRONT HOMME TECH - Apparel and accessories - Front Corp.

FRONT LINE - Apparel and accessories ☆ - Edison Brothers Stores, Inc.

FRONT LINE - Floor coverings–carpet and rugs ☆ - Columbus Mills, Inc.

FRONT-LINE - Heating equipment - Emerson Electric Co.

FRONT LINE - Lawn mowers - Ransomes-Cushman-Ryan

FRONT LINE - Video games - Taito America Corp.

FRONT 'N CENTER - Girdles - Wacoal America Inc.

FRONT NINE - Golfing equipment - Sun Mountain Sports, Inc.

FRONT PAGE - Computer software - Arrays Inc./Continental Software

FRONT PAGE NEWS - Greeting cards ☆ - Thought Factory

FRONT PORCH - Garden furniture–rattan - Lloyd/Flanders Industries

FRONT RANGE MERRELL - Footwear–athletic - Karhu USA Inc.

FRONT ROW - Figurines - Playing Mantis

FRONT ROW - Furniture - Barfield Furniture Inc.

FRONT ROW - Furniture ☆ - Bassett Furniture Industries, Inc.

FRONT ROW - Recording label - Domino Ltd.

FRONT ROW ENTERTAINMENT - Recording label - Front Row Entertainment, Inc.

FRONT ROW ENTERTAINMENT INC - Recording label - Front Row Entertainment, Inc.

FRONT ROW SEATS - Chairs–wood - Krueger International, Inc.

FRONT ROW.HOME THEATER SEATING COLLECTION - Furniture–upholstered - Barfield Furniture Inc.

FRONT RUNNER - Bicycles ☆ - Roadmaster Corp.

FRONT RUNNER - Fishing lures - Custom Craft Building & Renovation, Inc.

FRONT RUNNER - Fishing lures ☆ - Hildebrandt Corp.

FRONT ST. PUBLISHING - Computer software - U.S. Gold Inc.

FRONT STREET - Wainscotting - Georgia-Pacific Corp.

FRONT STREET PUBLISHING - Computer software - U.S. Gold Inc.

FRONTENAC - Watches - Hampden Corp.

FRONTERIA - Liquors - Hughes Markets Inc.

FRONTIER - Bicycles - Roadmaster Corp.

FRONTIER - Computer software - Gametek, Inc.

FRONTIER - Floor coverings ☆ - Harris-Tarkett, Inc.

FRONTIER - Floor coverings–carpet and rugs ☆ - Regal Rugs Inc.

FRONTIER - Floor coverings–tile ☆ - Kepcor, Inc./SSI Tiles

FRONTIER - Flour–blended ☆ - Stevens Industries Inc.

FRONTIER - Flowers, plants, and seeds - Frontier Grass Seed Co.

FRONTIER - Knives–pocket - Imperial Schrade Corp.

FRONTIER - Paper ☆ - Orchids Paper Products, Inc.

FRONTIER - Pharmaceutical preparations - Zidrep Laboratories

FRONTIER - Powerboat ☆ - Boston Whaler, Inc.

FRONTIER - Recording label - Heritage Records

FRONTIER - Spices and extracts - Frontier Soups

FRONTIER BOUND - Food products - New Frontier Foods

FRONTIER DAYS - Puzzles - Hasbro, Inc.

FRONTIER FLYER - Motor vehicles–motor homes - Cruise America, Inc.

FRONTIER FOODS - Rice - New Frontier Foods

FRONTIER FRICASSEE - Barbecue sauce - Andrew Williams

FRONTIER GIRL - Women's apparel - India Garments Inc.

FRONTIER JAMBOREE - Recording label - Stardust/Wizard/Doss Records

FRONTIER KETTLE - Cooking equipment–household - Tomlinson Industries

FRONTIER OUTERWEAR - Apparel–athletic - A-Ten USA, Inc.

FRONTIER PREMIUM - Beverages–malt - Frontier Cooperative Herbs

FRONTIER SERIES - Belts–apparel - Lyntone Belts Inc.

FRONTIER TECHNOLOGIES - Computer software - Frontier Technologies Corp.

FRONTIER, THE - Revolvers ☆ - Colt's Manufacturing Co. Inc.

FRONTIER WOMAN - Dolls ☆ - Effanbee Doll Corp.

FRONTIERE DIJON - Mustard - Lin-Lex Enterprises, Inc.

FRONTIERSMAN - Personal defense products - Security Equipment Corp.

FRONTLAWN - Fabrics - Dan River Inc.

FRONTLINE - Chemicals–photographic - Kappler Safety Group

FRONTLINE - Golfing equipment - Golfsmith International Inc.

FRONTLINE - Motor vehicles–ambulances - Emergency One, Inc.

FRONTLINE - Recording label - Benson Music Group

FRONTLINE - Video production - Ergometrics and Applied Personnel Research, Inc.

FRONTLINE KIDS - Recording label - Frontline Records

FRONTRUNNER 90 - Heaters–gas - Goettl Air Conditioning Inc.

FRONTRUNNERS - Toys ☆ - Testor Corp.

FRONTS & BACKS MEMORY - Games ☆ - Milton Bradley Co.

FRONTURA - Automotive parts and accessories ☆ - Lancaster Colony Automotive Group

FRONTURA PLUSH - Automotive parts and accessories ☆ - Lancaster Colony Automotive Group

FRONTYARD - Trees - Bailey Nurseries, Inc.

FROOKAROONS - Cookies - R.W. Frookies Inc.

☆ = Now out of production

FROOKIE - Cookies - Delicious Brands, Inc.
FROOKIE - Cookies - R.W. Frookies Inc.
FROOKITAS - Tortilla chips - R.W. Frookies Inc.
FROOKWICH - Confectioneries - R.W. Frookies Inc.
FROOT HOG - Candy bars - Stanico, Inc.
FROOT LOOPS - Cereal - Kellogg Co.
FROOTFETTI - Candy ☆ - Sunline Brands
FROOTY CONES - Ice cream cones - Sweetheart Cup Co. Inc.
FROOZBERRY - Beverages - Fresh Stop, Inc.
FROSH - Beverages–carbonated - Faygo Beverages, Inc.
FROST - Dinnerware–glass ☆ - Nikko Ceramics Inc.
FROST - Flower pots–earthenware - Syndicate Sales, Inc.
FROST - Wines - Renwood Winery, Inc.
FROST 8/80 - Whiskey ☆ - Brown-Forman Corp.
FROST & GLOW - Hair care products - Revlon Consumer Products Corp.
FROST & TIP - Hair coloring preparations - Clairol Inc.
FROST-BALLS - Chewing gum - Stanico, Inc.
FROST-BLANKET - Automotive parts and accessories ☆ - Ame Consumer
  Products Corp.
FROST BROS. - Apparel and accessories - Frost Bros. Inc.
FROST CLEAR - Refrigerators - White Consolidated Industries, Inc.
FROST CRAFT - Vegetables–frozen - Pitsweet Inc.
FROST FIRE - Fabrics - Fab. Industries Inc.
FROST FIRE - Rings–jewelry - Artcarved Inc.
FROST FIRE - Wines - Breitenbach Wine Cellars
FROST FLEX - Cups–plastic - WNA Comet
FROST FLOWER - Floor coverings - Tarkett, Inc.
FROST FREE LATCH - Fencing–gates and posts - Master Halco Inc.
FROST GUARD - Windows–vinyl - Texas Aluminum Industries Inc.
FROST IT HOT - Frosting ☆ - Pillsbury Co.
FROST KING - Apparel and accessories - I. Spiewak and Sons Inc.
FROST KING - Ice boxes–household - Richmond Cedar Works Manufacturing
  Corp.
FROST KING - Insulating materials - Thermwell Products Co. Inc.
FROST LITE - Glass products - Globe-Amerada Glass Co.
FROST-MAGNET - Refrigerators - Amana Refrigeration Inc.
FROST MINT - Candy - Andes Candies Inc.
FROST-OFF - Automotive parts and accessories - Merix Chemical Co.
FROST-PAK - Coolers–electric - RMF/DLO Group, Inc.
FROST-PARCH - Leather–parchment - Parsons Paper Co.
FROST PROOF - Apparel and accessories - Commander Garment Co.
FROST QUEEN - Freezers ☆ - Rangaire
FROST RIPE - Food products - Griffin Orchard
FROST SENTRY - Hardware - Emerson-Quiet Kool Co.
FROST STOPPERS - Gloves - Wells Lamont Corp.
FROST T. BEAR - Toys–stuffed ☆ - Dakin Inc.
FROST-TONE - Envelopes–paper - Georgia-Pacific Corp.
FROST-TONE - Tiles–ceramic ☆ - Huntington/Pacific Ceramics Inc.
FROST-TONE - Yarn - Lily Craft Products
FROSTA - Toys - Mattel, Inc.
FROSTAR - Frozen yogurt - J & J Snack Foods Corp.
FROSTBEATERS - Gloves - Fownes Brothers & Co., Inc.
FROSTBITE - Ice cream - McDonald Dairy Co.
FROSTBITES - Giftware - Roman, Inc.
FROSTCOATS - Veterinary nutritional supplements - Moorman Manufacturing
  Co.
FROSTEA - Teas - Lipton Investments, Inc.
FROSTED ASTERS ON BLUE - Glassware–household ☆ - Fenton Art Glass
  Co.
FROSTED BLONDE - Floor coverings–carpet and rugs - Glen Eden Wool
  Carpets
FROSTED BRAN - Cereal ☆ - Kellogg Co.
FROSTED CHEERIOS - Cereal - General Mills, Inc.
FROSTED CORN BURST - Cereal ☆ - General Mills, Inc.
FROSTED CORN FLAKES - Cereal - Barbara's Bakery, Inc.
FROSTED EMBROIDERIES - Apparel–women's - Warnaco Inc.
FROSTED FLANNEL - Window shades ☆ - Superior Shade & Blind Co. Inc.
FROSTED FLOWER - Brassieres (Bras) ☆ - Lovable Co.
FROSTED FRAMES - Giftware ☆ - U.S. Fiberglass Inc.
FROSTED FRUIT O'S - Cereal - Malt-O-Meal Co.
FROSTED FUNNIES - Cereal ☆ - Barbara's Bakery, Inc.
FROSTED IMAGES - Doors–glass - Therma-Tru Corp.
FROSTED LIGHTS - Hair care products - Clairol Inc.
FROSTED MINI SPOONERS - Cereal - Malt-O-Meal Co.
FROSTED MINI-WHEATS - Cereal - Kellogg Co.
FROSTED MOONS - Cereal - Jasper Foods, Inc.

FROSTED POPS - Food products - Tom's Foods Inc.
FROSTED RICE CHEX JUNIORS - Cereal - Ralston Purina Co.
FROSTED ROLLS - Cereal - Jasper Foods, Inc.
FROSTED SATIN 'N' LACE - Apparel stores–women's - Warnaco Inc.
FROSTED SHAKE - Food products ☆ - Borden, Inc.
FROSTED VIOLETS - Christmas tree ornaments - Cracker Box Inc.
FROSTED WHEAT-FULS - Cereal - Malt-O-Meal Co.
FROSTED WHEAT SQUARES - Cereal - Nabisco Foods Group
FROSTEMP - Air purification systems - Wynn's Climate Systems Inc.
FROSTEX - See GLAMOUR
FROSTEX - Heaters–kerosene - Raynet Corp.
FROSTFERN - Glass products ☆ - Spectrum Glass Co.
FROSTFIRE - Christmas tree ornaments - Cracker Box Inc.
FROSTI-LEMON - Soap - Georgia-Pacific Corp.
FROSTICCINO - Coffee - Coffee Masters, Inc.
FROSTIE - Beverages–carbonated - Monarch Co., Inc.
FROSTIN' - Frosting ☆ - Hershey Foods Corp.
FROSTIN PRIDE - Desserts - Presto Food Products, Inc.
FROSTING PLUS - Hair coloring preparations - Helene Curtis Industries Inc.
FROSTING SUPREME - Frosting ☆ - Pillsbury Co.
FROSTLINE - Food products - Grain Processing Corp.
FROSTLINE - Ice cream–powdered - Precision Foods, Inc.
FROSTLINE - Snow tools - Jack-Post Corp.
FROSTLING - Lipsticks - Revlon Consumer Products Corp.
FROSTLITE - Food products ☆ - TKI Foods, Inc.
FROSTLITE - Leather–vellum - Andrews/Nelson/Whitehead
FROSTPOINT - Fabrics - Dan River Inc.
FROSTWORK - Doors–glass - Sterling Plumbing Group Inc.
FROSTY - Analgesics - Schein Pharmaceutical Inc.
FROSTY - Guns - Sullivan Manufacturing & Sales Corp.
FROSTY - Ice chests–plastic - Glacier Ware Inc.
FROSTY - Ice scraper ☆ - Clean-Rite Products Co.
FROSTY - Seafood products–fresh or frozen ☆ - Flag/Westbay Seafood
  Brokers
FROSTY - Toys - Tonka Corp.
FROSTY - Toys–stuffed ☆ - Gund, Inc.
FROSTY ACRE - Pies–frozen - Herold & Miller Inc.
FROSTY ACRES - Pies–frozen - Frosty Acres Brands Inc.
FROSTY BANANA - Fruits–frozen - Affy Tapple Inc.
FROSTY BUNS RUNNING CLUB - Apparel and accessories - Robert J.
  Moeller
FROSTY DEVIL - Snack foods ☆ - Drake Bakeries, Inc.
FROSTY ETCU - Novelty items–paper - Chartpak
FROSTY FARE - Pies–frozen - Frosty Acres Brands Inc.
FROSTY FRIENDS - Toys–stuffed - Fun World Inc.
FROSTY FRUIT SENSATION!, A - Beverages - Parrot Ice Drink Products of
  America, Inc.
FROSTY FUR - Dolls - Mattel, Inc.
FROSTY KANDY KAKES - Bakery products - Tasty Baking Co.
FROSTY MORN - Christmas tree ornaments - Cracker Box Inc.
FROSTY-NO-SHOWS - Underwear and nightwear - Maidenform Inc.
FROSTY O'S - Cereal ☆ - General Mills, Inc.
FROSTY O'SHIVERS - Confections - Dansig Inc.
FROSTY PANNE - Fabrics - Symphony Fabrics Corp.
FROSTY PAWS - Pet products - Associated Ice Cream
FROSTY RAYS - Yarn - Rainbow Gallery, Inc.
FROSTY ROULITE - Hair care products - Roux Laboratories, Inc.
FROSTY SEAS - Seafood products–canned or cured - Frosty Acres Brands
  Inc.
FROSTY SEAS - Seafood products–fresh or frozen - Carrington Foods Co.
FROSTY-SNOW - Christmas tree ornaments - Union Wadding Co.
FROSTY SNOWMEN - Ice cream - Steve's Homemade Ice Cream Inc.
FROSTY SPRINGS - Water–bottled or canned - F.A.B., Inc.
FROSTY THE SNOWMAN - Giftware ☆ - Enesco Corp.
FROSTY THE SNOWMAN - Watches - Genender International, Inc.
FROSTY WELLITE - Hair care products - Wella Corp. (Consumer Products
  Div.)
FROTH-TEX - Paints ☆ - DecoArt, Inc.
FROU-FROU - Apparel–women's - Bi-Flex International
FROU-FROU - Toys–stuffed ☆ - Dakin Inc.
FROWN CLOWN - Dolls - TCA Ground Inc.
FROWNIES - Wrinkle remover - B & P Co.
FROX - Televisions - Frox Inc.
FROXX - Apparel–women's - Shyan, Inc.
FROYSTERS - Crackers - R.W. Frookies Inc.
FROZ FRUIT CO., THE - Fruits–frozen - The Froz Fruit Co.

☆ = Now out of production

FROZEE - Beverages–carbonated - Smoothie King Franchises, Inc.

FROZEN ASSETS BY PATRICIAN - Apparel stores–men's - Patrician Imports, Inc.

FROZEN AVOCADO PULP - Food products - Hofert Trading Co.

FROZEN BAKERY PRAIRIE PRIDE DELI PRODUCTS - Bakery products– frozen - Drayton Foods, LLC

FROZEN BEAR - Coffee - Coffee Consultants, Inc.

FROZEN CHERRY SMASH - Soft drinks - FCB Syrups, Inc.

FROZEN COLOMBO YOGURT - Yogurt–frozen - General Mills, Inc.

FROZEN EXPLOSION! - Beverages–alcohol - Brice Foods, Inc.

FROZEN FAVORITES - Desserts - Trustees of America's Drive-In Trust

FROZEN HARVEST GET TOGETHERS - Vegetables–frozen - Green Giant Co.

FROZEN HEAT - Cutlery - Robeson Industries

FROZEN JOY - Fruit pops–frozen - Garden of Eatin', Inc.

FROZEN LAVA - Jewelry ☆ - Hobe Cie. Ltd.

FROZEN MATES - Candy ☆ - Leaf, Inc.

FROZEN MOMENTS - Sculptures - Passage Investments, Inc.

FROZEN-RITE - Breads–frozen - Bridgford Foods Corp.

FROZEN ROSE - Beverages–alcohol - Elmar Manufacturing Co.

FROZEN SINGLES - Food products ☆ - Hormel Foods Corp.

FROZFRUIT - Food products - Paleta International

FROZFRUIT - Yogurt–frozen - Frozfruit Corp.

FRP - Paneling - Marlite

FRP - Plastics–laminated - Desco Industries Inc.

F.R.S. - Bicycles - Marin Mountain Bikes, Inc.

FRS - Shingles–asphalt or tar - Celotex Corp.

FRUBARS - Snack foods - Heartland Health Foods

FRUBET - Ice cream - TLC Trademark Co.

FRUCTABS-XL-19 - Vitamins and nutritional supplements ☆ - Great Life Laboratories Inc.

FRUCTALL - Fructose - Caleb Laboratories Inc.

FRUEHAUF - Trailers–travel - Fruehauf Trailer Corp.

FRUGAL GOURMET - Kitchen utensils–enameled - Robinson Knife & Fiddlers Plastics

FRUGALUME - Lighting fixtures - Voigt Lighting Industries Inc.

FRUIT-A-BURST - Chewing gum - American Chicle Co.

FRUIT AND ALMOND - Teas - R.C. Bigelow, Inc.

FRUIT AND CREAM - Candy ☆ - Van Melle Inc.

FRUIT & CREAM - Cereal - Quaker Oats Co.

FRUIT & FIBRE - Bakery products - Entenmann's Inc.

FRUIT & FITNESS - Cookies - Health Valley Food

FRUIT & OAT BRAN CRUNCH - Cereal ☆ - Edward & Sons Trading Co., Inc.

FRUIT & SPICE BOWS - Candy - M-B Candies Inc.

FRUIT & YOGURT - Yogurt - Swissrose International Inc.

FRUIT & YOGURT CREME BISCUITS - Cookies - Nabisco Foods Group

FRUIT-AT-THE-BOTTOM - Yogurt ☆ - Knudsen Dairy Products

FRUIT BAKES - Snack foods - Health Valley Food

FRUIT BALL ROLLS - Candy - Nabisco Foods Group

FRUIT BASKET - Candy - Brock Candy Co. Inc.

FRUIT BASKET - Clocks - General Time Corp. (Westclox/Seth Thomas Div.)

FRUIT BASKET - Dinnerware–glass - Metlox Pottery Shoppe

FRUIT BASKET - Fruits–dried - Dole Dried Fruit & Nut Co.

FRUIT BELT - Honey - Fruit Belt Products

FRUIT BITES - Snack foods - Sovex Foods, Inc.

FRUIT BLAST - Chewing gum - Leaf, Inc.

FRUIT BLEND - Health care products - Ion Laboratories Inc.

FRUIT BLENDS - Fruit drinks–bottled or canned - Del Monte Corp.

FRUIT BOMBS - Candy ☆ - Beacon Sweets, Inc.

FRUIT-BONE - Pet food - T.F.H. Publications, Inc.

FRUIT BOOSTERS - Snack foods - McKee Foods Corp.

FRUIT BOUQUET - Dinnerware - Mesa International

FRUIT BREAK - Snake bite kits ☆ - Van Melle Inc.

FRUIT BRUTE - Cereal ☆ - General Mills, Inc.

FRUIT BUD - Juices - Quality Kitchen Corp.

FRUIT BUDDIES - Fruits–canned - Amazing Beverages, Inc.

FRUIT BY THE FOOT - Fruits–candied - General Mills, Inc.

FRUIT C - Vitamins and nutritional supplements - Freeda Vitamins Inc.

FRUIT CENTERS - Cookies - Health Valley Food

FRUIT CHEWS - Candy ☆ - Van Melle Inc.

FRUIT CHEWS - Pet products - JungleTalk Inc.

FRUIT CHILL - Desserts ☆ - DCA Food Industries, Inc.

FRUIT CIRCUS - Fruits–dried - Dolefam Corp.

FRUIT CLASSICS - Food products - Gerber Products Co.

FRUIT COCKTAIL - Candy - Sweet Candy Co.

FRUIT COCKTAIL - Dinnerware–glass ☆ - Johnson Brothers, USA, Inc.

FRUIT COCKTAIL IMPERIALS - Candy - Ferrara Pan Candy Co., Inc.

FRUIT CORNERS - Snack foods - General Mills, Inc.

FRUIT COUNTRY - Desserts ☆ - Curtice-Burns Foods, Inc.

FRUIT CRISPS - Food products - Epicure Foods Inc.

FRUIT CRISPS - Fruits–dried ☆ - Oregon Freeze Dry Inc.

FRUIT CRUNCH - Yogurt - Friendship Food Products Inc.

FRUIT CURLS - Cereal - Stokely-Van Camp, Inc.

FRUIT DE JOUR - Housewares - Shafford Co. Inc.

FRUIT DELIGHT - Bird feeds - L/M Animal Farms, Inc.

FRUIT DELIGHT - Cookies - Nabisco Foods Group

FRUIT DELIGHT - Giftware - World of Porcelain & Glassware

FRUIT DELIGHTS - Candy - Liberty Orchards Co., Inc.

FRUIT D'LITE - Desserts ☆ - Rose International

FRUIT DOG CHEW - Pet food - T.F.H. Publications, Inc.

FRUIT DOODLES - Cakes ☆ - Drake Bakeries, Inc.

FRUIT DREAM - Teas - Harris Tea Co.

FRUIT DROPS - Candy - Judson-Atkinson Candies

FRUIT-E-O'S - Cereal - New Morn, Inc.

FRUIT-E-O'S - Cereal - New Morning

FRUIT ELEGANCE - Jacks–hand-operated - Royal Harvest Co.

FRUIT ESSENCE - Vitamins and nutritional supplements - Great Life Laboratories Inc.

FRUIT-EZE - Vitamins and nutritional supplements - Fruit-Eze Inc.

FRUIT FANTASY - Fruit butters ☆ - Sarabeth's Kitchen

FRUIT FARE - Bird feeds - Petland, Inc.

FRUIT FIBER - Yogurt - Darigold, Inc.

FRUIT FLASHES - Candy - Wal-Mart Stores Inc.

FRUIT FLIPS - Cookies - Fantasy Cookie Co.

FRUIT FONDUE - Chocolate bars - That's My Favorite Inc.

FRUIT FONDUES - Candy - Ben Myerson Candy Co.

FRUIT FRAPPE - Spoons ☆ - Gessner Products Co. Inc.

FRUIT-FRESH - Chemical preparations - Alltrista Corp.

FRUIT FRUIT FRUIT - Fruits–pickled or brined - Harry and David Inc.

FRUIT FULL OG - Salad dressings–bottled - Berry Best Farm

FRUIT FUNNIES - Candy - Farley Candy Co.

FRUIT GALAXY - Fruits–dried - Vacu-Dry Co.

FRUIT GARDEN - Housewares ☆ - Himark Enterprises Inc.

FRUIT GARDEN - Tableware–china ☆ - Villeroy and Boch Tableware Ltd.

FRUIT GEMS - Candy - Ben Myerson Candy Co.

FRUIT GEYSER - Fruit drinks–bottled or canned - Christopher Michael Vance

FRUIT GLOSSIES - Lip balm - Arthur Matney Co., Inc.

FRUIT GOURMAND - Jams and jellies - ABA Management & Development Inc.

FRUIT-GUARD - Insecticides - Security Products Co.

FRUIT HEADS - Chewing gum - Philadelphia Chewing Gum Corp.

FRUIT HELPER - Desserts ☆ - General Mills, Inc.

FRUIT-IN-GEL CUP - Snack foods - Del Monte Corp.

FRUIT INTEGRATION - Fruit drinks–bottled or canned - Coca-Cola Co.

FRUIT ISLANDS - Cereal - Ralston Purina Co.

FRUIT JAMMERS - Candy fruit snacks - McKee Foods Corp.

FRUIT JUICE SWEETENED CORN FLAKES - Cereal - Barbara's Bakery, Inc.

FRUIT JUICEES - Fruit pops–frozen ☆ - Coca-Cola Co.

FRUIT JUICER - Juice extracting devices ☆ - Dazey Corp.

FRUIT JUMBOS - Cookies - Health Valley Food

FRUIT KEG - Beverages - Comstock Michigan Fruit

FRUIT-KIST - Ice cream - Al-Rite Fruits & Syrups

FRUIT LOWCOOM - Candy ☆ - Gimbel Brothers Inc.

FRUIT MARKET - Chewing gum - Leaf, Inc.

FRUIT MATE - Food products ☆ - General Mills, Inc.

FRUIT MIST - Beverages–carbonated - BCB USA Corp.

FRUIT MOOS - Food products ☆ - Dannon Co., Inc.

FRUIT MOUNTAIN - Candy ☆ - Amurol Confections Co.

FRUIT 'N APPLE - Beverages ☆ - Tree Top, Inc.

FRUIT 'N BERRIES - Teas ☆ - R.C. Bigelow, Inc.

FRUIT 'N BERRY - Beverages ☆ - Tree Top, Inc.

FRUIT 'N BERRY BLEND - Bird feeds - Wagner Bros. Feed Corp.

FRUIT 'N CHERRY - Beverages ☆ - Tree Top, Inc.

FRUIT 'N CITRUS - Beverages ☆ - Tree Top, Inc.

FRUIT 'N CREAM - Snack foods - Dole Food Co., Inc.

FRUIT 'N CREME DELIGHT - Food products - Conagra, Inc.

FRUIT N CRUST - Food products - Cutie Pie Corp.

FRUIT 'N DANISH - Pastries - Sara Lee Corp.

FRUIT-N-FLAVOR - Fruit pie mixes - J.W. Allen & Co.

FRUIT N FLAVOR - Pet products - Picture Perfect Parrot

FRUIT N' FLAX - Vitamins and nutritional supplements - Tishcon Corp.

FRUIT 'N GRAPE - Beverages ☆ - Tree Top, Inc.

FRUIT N NUT - Candy bars ☆ - Nestle USA

FRUIT 'N NUT - Fruits–dried - Glico Harmony Foods Corp.

FRUIT NIBBLES - Candy - Banner Candy Manufacturing Corp.

FRUIT OF THE EARTH - Vitamins and nutritional supplements - Fruit of the Earth, Inc.

FRUIT OF THE LAND - Vitamins and nutritional supplements - Energen Products Inc.

FRUIT OF THE LOOM - Fabrics–linen ☆ - West Point-Pepperell Inc.

FRUIT OF THE LOOM - Infant product - Dundee Mills, Inc.

FRUIT OF THE LOOM - Underwear and nightwear - Fruit of the Loom Inc.

FRUIT OF THE ROOM - Deodorizers - K.P. Distributors Inc.

FRUIT OF THE WOODS - Wines ☆ - Three Lakes Winery

FRUIT ON THE BOTTOM - Yogurt - Mystic Lake Dairy Inc.

FRUIT ON THE BOTTOM - Yogurt - Yoplait USA Inc.

FRUIT OVALS - Cereal - Jasper Foods, Inc.

FRUIT PAKS - Snack foods - Mott's Inc.

FRUIT PARADE - Fruit snack - Ferrara Pan Candy Co., Inc.

FRUIT PARADE - Snack foods - Lipton Investments, Inc.

FRUIT PARTY - Beverages–carbonated - Time Beverages

FRUIT PASTRIE - Snack foods ☆ - Frito-Lay, Inc.

FRUIT PATCH - Fruits–canned - Cherry Central Cooperative Inc.

FRUIT PERFECT - Pancakes–frozen - John Labatt Foods

FRUIT POPPIN'S - Popcorn - Popcorn Explosion Inc.

FRUIT POPS - Candy - Rosemary Candy Co.

FRUIT PUNCH - Chewing gum ☆ - Clark Gum Co.

FRUIT PUNCH STIX - Candy - Leaf, Inc.

FRUIT PUNCH SUPERSTICK - Chewing gum ☆ - Clark Gum Co.

FRUIT QUENCHERS - Ice cream - Image Brands, Inc.

FRUIT RANCHERS - Candy - Leaf, Inc.

FRUIT ROLL-UPS - Snack foods - General Mills, Inc.

FRUIT ROLL-UPS HOT COLORS - Snack foods - General Mills, Inc.

FRUIT ROLL UPS YOGURT - Yogurt - Yoplait USA Inc.

FRUIT ROX - Snack foods - Lipton Investments, Inc.

FRUIT SAMPLER - Dinnerware–glass ☆ - Johnson Brothers, USA, Inc.

FRUIT SCOOPS - Ice cream - Nestle USA

FRUIT SENSATIONS - Candy - S.L. Kaye Co., Inc.

FRUIT SHAKE - Musical instruments - Remo, Inc.

FRUIT SHAPE-UPS - Fruit pops–frozen - J & J Snack Foods Corp.

FRUIT SINGLES - Fruits–frozen - Wawona Frozen Foods, Inc.

FRUIT SLICES - Yogurt - Old Home Foods Inc.

FRUIT SMOOTHIE - Puddings–canned - Del Monte Corp.

FRUIT SNACK - Snack foods - Sovex Foods, Inc.

FRUIT SNACK FARLEY - Snack foods - Farley Candy Co.

FRUIT SNACKERS - Candy - Brock Candy Co. Inc.

FRUIT SNACKERS CHILDREN'S CLASSICS - Candy - Brock Candy Co. Inc.

FRUIT SNACKS - Candy - Farley Candy Co.

FRUIT SNAX ENERGY BARS - Vitamins and nutritional supplements - NutriBiotic

FRUIT SOURS - Candy - Nabisco Foods Group

FRUIT SPINS - Cereal - Wal-Mart Stores Inc.

FRUIT SPLITS - Beverages–carbonated - Shasta Beverages, Inc.

FRUIT SPOONABLES - Snack foods - Ocean Spray Cranberries Inc.

FRUIT SQUEEZERS - Juices - Jel Sert Co.

FRUIT STAND - Fruit drinks–bottled or canned - California Foods Corp.

FRUIT STAND - Snack foods - California Pie Co., Inc.

FRUIT STIX - Chewing gum - Philadelphia Chewing Gum Corp.

FRUIT STOP - Fruits and vegetables - Comstock Michigan Fruit

FRUIT STREET - Juices - Nabisco Foods Group

FRUIT STRING THING - Snack foods - General Mills, Inc.

FRUIT STRIPE - Chewing gum - Planters LifeSavers Co.

FRUIT SUPREMES - Snack foods - Lipton Investments, Inc.

FRUIT TEA - Teas - Life Extension International, Inc.

FRUIT TEAS - Teas–herbal - San Francisco Herb & Natural Food Co.

FRUIT TEAZER - Juices - Knudsen & Sons Inc.

FRUIT TELLA - Candy ☆ - Van Melle Inc.

FRUIT TREATS - Fruits–canned ☆ - Mott's Inc.

FRUIT TREE - Housewares - Basket Master Inc.

FRUIT TROOP - Snack foods ☆ - Cemac Foods Corp.

FRUIT TROPICALS - Candy - Liberty Orchards Co., Inc.

FRUIT TWIRLS - Cereal - Grist Mill Co.

FRUIT VEG ACTIVES - Vitamins and nutritional supplements - Makers of Kal, Inc.

FRUIT WAVES - Candy - American Chicle Co.

FRUIT WAVES - Candy - Warner-Lambert Co.

FRUIT WHEATS - Cereal - Nabisco Foods Group

FRUIT WRINKLES - Snack foods - General Mills, Inc.

FRUIT-ZEES - Fruits–candied - Natural Products Corp.

FRUIT ZOOP - Beverages - The Sqwincher Corp.

FRUITABLES - Candy - R.W. Frookies Inc.

FRUIT*A*BURST - Chewing gum - Warner-Lambert Co.

FRUITAGE - Desserts - J.M. Smucker Co.

FRUITAMAX - Candy - Excel Mass Merchandiser, Inc.

FRUITART CHEWS - Candy ☆ - Sunline Brands

FRUITASTIK - Salads–prepackaged - Remlik Foods Inc.

FRUITATIONS - Fruits–frozen - J.R. Wood Inc.

FRUITBERRY - Deodorants–personal ☆ - Physician Sales & Service

FRUITCAKE - Christmas tree ornaments - Cracker Box Inc.

FRUITCAL - Food products - Procter & Gamble Co.

FRUITECH - Cosmetics - Douglas G. Hamilton

FRUITEL - Juices - Amstell, Inc.

FRUITFUL - Fruits–canned - Tree of Life, Inc.

FRUITFUL - Hair care products - Avanza Corp.

FRUITFUL - Jams and jellies - Gourmet Award Foods

FRUITFUL - Juices–frozen - Damon Industries

FRUITFUL BRAN - Cereal - Kellogg Co.

FRUITFULL - Fruit pops–frozen - Happy & Healthy Products, Inc.

FRUITFULL - Jams and jellies - Berry Best Farm

FRUITFULLY AMAZING - Juices - Ginger Group, Ltd.

FRUITIE BEARS - Candy - Pronatura, Inc.

FRUITIE PIES - Toys–stuffed ☆ - Fun World Inc.

FRUITIE TOOTIE TWISTS - Candy - Atkinson Candy Co.

FRUITINE - Food products - Beatrice Cos. Inc.

FRUITINS' - Cookies - R.W. Frookies Inc.

FRUITINS - Cookies - Next Step

FRUITION - Skin care products - Estee Corp.

FRUITLAND - Jams and jellies - Krier Foods Inc.

FRUIT'N JUICE - Juices–frozen - Dole Food Co., Inc.

FRUITOLA! - Frozen dessert - Edy's Grand Ice Cream Inc.

FRUITONIC - Vitamins and nutritional supplements - Genesis Merchandisers Inc.

FRUITOPIA - Fruit drinks–bottled or canned - Coca-Cola Co.

FRUITOPIAN LIFE - Fruit drinks–bottled or canned - Coca-Cola Co.

FRUITOPS - Confections - Homestyle Foods

FRUITOSOMES - Moisturizers - Beautycology Inc.

FRUITPLEX - Health care products - Healthwatchers System

FRUITREATS - Snack foods - Chiquita Brands, Inc.

FRUITS - Candy - Ce De Candy Inc.

FRUITS AND FLOWERS - Wallcovering - Brewster Wallcovering Co.

FRUITS & FLOWERS - Wallpaper ☆ - Andover Wallcovering

FRUITS BASKET DELIGHT - Tiles–ceramic - Monarch Tile Inc.

FRUITS FOR ALL SEASONS - Kitchenware–earthenware - Arnart Imports Inc.

FRUITS OF LIFE - Dinnerware–glass - Lenox, Inc.

FRUITS OF THE FOREST - Food products - Southern Sun Trading, Inc.

FRUITS ON FIRE - Candy - Nabisco Foods Group

FRUITSENG - Juices - Maine Naturals, Inc.

FRUITSICLE - Ice cream - Good Humor Corp.

FRUITSLUSH - Fruit pops–frozen - Lipton Investments, Inc.

FRUITSOURCE - Vitamins and nutritional supplements - Advanced Ingredients, Inc.

FRUITSWEET - Cookies ☆ - New Life Bakery Inc.

FRUITSWEETS - Fruits–dried - Madera Enterprises Inc.

FRUITWICH - Cookies - Hain Pure Food Co. Inc.

FRUITY FRUITS - Toys–stuffed - Heritage Mint, Ltd.

FRUITY MARSHMALLOW KRISPIES - Cereal - Kellogg Co.

FRUITY PUNCH - Barbara's Bakery, Inc.

FRUITY YUMMY MUMMY - Cereal - General Mills, Inc.

FRUITZER - Beverages–carbonated ☆ - Ginseng Up Corp.

FRUIZLE - Milk - Doctor's Associates, Inc.

FRUJELE - Candy - Wal-Mart Stores Inc.

FRUMARESSA - Seafood products–fresh or frozen ☆ - Pocasset Seafoods Inc.

FRUMPKINS - Dolls - Tuss Inc.

FRUMPS - Apparel and accessories - JVRS Associates, Inc.

FRUNCH - Snack foods - Waymouth Farms Inc.

FRUSTRATE - Pesticides–agricultural - Biosys, Inc.

FRUSTRATED - Apparel stores–sports - David Smith

FRUSTRATION BALL - Games - Rose Art Industries, Inc.

FRUSTRATORS - Toys - Hirsch Co.

FRUTABS - Pharmaceutical preparations - Pfanstiehl Laboratories Inc.

FRUTE-SHO - Food products - Fruitcrown Products Corp.

FRUTECH - Oils–essential - Frutech International Corp.

FRUTEE POP - Candy ☆ - S.L. Kaye Co., Inc.

FRUTI-PROTEIN - Cosmetics ☆ - Majestic Drug Co., Inc.

☆ = Now out of production

FRUTICENE - Fruits–canned - Lyons-Magnus Inc.

FRUTIOS - Candy - Brock Candy Co. Inc.

FRUTSTIX - Ice cream - Frut Stix

FRUTTA FRESCA - Earthenware - Seymour Mann Inc.

FRUTTATA - Food products ☆ - Mesa International

FRUTTI TUB - Jams and jellies - Le Belle Suisse

FRUTTICCINO - Confections - California Fresh Yogurt Inc.

FRY ALL - Kitchen appliances - Hamilton Beach/Proctor-Silex Inc.

FRY CHOPPER - Toys–automobiles - Mattel, Inc.

FRY CRISP - Automotive parts and accessories ☆ - AIFCO Co.

FRY-DEE - Shortening - Humko Products

FRY FACTORY - Cooking equipment–household - Fry Factory, Inc.

FRY-IT - Shortening - Supreme Oil Co.

FRY-KING - Griddles–electric ☆ - Bremer Manufacturing Co. Inc.

FRY KING - Shortening - Interstate Foods Corp.

FRY KRISP - Food products machinery - Fry Krisp Food Products

FRY 'N' GOLD - Shortening - Mallet and Co.

FRY PERFECT - Food products - John Labatt Foods

FRY PLUS + - Food products - Rich-Seapak Corp.

FRY 'R BAKE - Pans - E-Z-Por Corp.

FRY RITE - Frozen potatoes - Interstate Potato Packers

FRY SHIELD - Food products - Kerry Ingredients Inc.

FRY STICKS - Food products ☆ - Worthington Foods Inc.

FRY WELL - Shortening - Mallet and Co.

FRYBABY - Kitchen appliances - National Presto Industries, Inc.

FRYBRANT - Brassieres (Bras) - Cameo Coutures

FRYDADDY - Kitchen appliances - National Presto Industries, Inc.

FRYDAY CLUB - Apparel and accessories - Fryday Club, Inc.

FRYDENLUND - Beverages–malt ☆ - Safeway Stores Inc.

FRYE - Boots - Frye Co.

FRYE - Paper–carbon - Frye Copysystems Inc.

FRYED HYDE - Pet products - Gimborn U.S., Inc.

FRYENE - Shortening ☆ - Swift Edible Oil Co.

FRYER KIST - Food products - Gold Kist Inc.

FRYES MEASURE MILL - Wood products - E.B. Frye & Son Inc.

FRYFLEX - Hoses - Goodyear Tire & Rubber Co.

FRYIN' MAGIC - Seasonings - Little Crow Foods

FRYLIGHT - Food products - Sunlight Foods Inc.

FRYMAX - Food products - Procter & Gamble Co.

FRYMAX CANOLA SUPREME - Food products - Procter & Gamble Co.

FRYO - Shortening - Kraft Food Ingredients Corp.

FRYPRESS - Apparel and accessories ☆ - Horace Small Apparel Co.

FRY'S ELECTRONICS - Electronic equipment - Fry's Electronics, Inc.

FRYZ - Meat products–beef - Zartic, Inc.

FS - Dairy products - Farmers Store Co.

FS - Hose end repair kits - National Welders Supply Co. Inc.

FS - Wines ☆ - Frank Sutton & Co.

FS-1 - Guitars - Dimarzio, Inc.

FS ACTION! SCENERY - Computer software - Abacus Software, Inc.

FS FLIGHT BAG - Computer software - Abacus Software, Inc.

FS FLIGHT DECK-BLUE ANGELS ED. - Computer software - Abacus Software, Inc.

FS PLUS - Computers - SCI Systems, Inc.

FS PRO - Computer software - Info Systems of N.C., Inc.

FS PRO MARKETPLACE - Computer software - Info Systems of N.C., Inc.

FS98 TRICKS OF THE TRADE - Computer software - Abacus Software, Inc.

FS1000 - Bicycles - Sears, Roebuck and Co.

FSE - Electrical equipment - Tracer Construction Co.

FSI - Computer storage devices - Financial Software, Inc.

FSI - Frozen foods - Frozen Specialties, Inc.

FSI - Sporting goods - Funsport International Inc.

FSI FUEL BUSTER - Fire extinguishing compositions - Fire Spread Inhibitor, Inc.

FSM PANTHEON - Recording label - Random House, Inc.

FSR - Recording label - Fidelity Sound Recordings

FSR - Stain removers - Davis Instruments Corp.

FSR - Tires - Bridgestone/Firestone, Inc.

FSS - Furniture–upholstered - Frank Scerbo & Sons Inc.

FST - Bicycles ☆ - Raleigh USA Bicycle Co.

F.S.T. - Fishing lures - Triple Teazer Co.

F.S.T. - Fishing lures - Yakima Bait Co.

FST - Medical apparatus - Fine Science Tools (USA), Inc.

FST - Televisions - Toshiba America Consumer Products, Inc. (Consumer Products Business Sector)

FST-14 - Tractors–lawn - White Outdoor Products Inc.

FSW - Food containers - Feldman & Co. Inc.

FSX - Bicycles ☆ - Raleigh USA Bicycle Co.

FT - Computer software - Harris Corp.

FT - Hair care products ☆ - Gem Inc.

F.T. LTD. - Apparel–women's - Focus Apparel Group Inc.

FT-SPARC - Computer software - Sparc International, Inc.

FTC - Apparel and accessories - FTC Skate Shop

F.T.C. - Office supplies ☆ - Globe-Weis

FTC - Semiconductors - Frontec Corp.

F.T.D. - Starch–edible ☆ - CPC International Inc.

FTE AUTOMOTIVE - Automotive parts and accessories - Echlin Inc.

FTH - Jewelry - M. Fabrikant & Sons

FTI BIOPHARMA - Vitamins and nutritional supplements - Formula Technology Inc.

FTJ - Jewelry - Todisco Jewelry Inc.

FTK BLUEPINCH LAMPS - Lighting equipment - Lowel-Light Manufacturing Inc.

FTNY - Apparel and accessories - Lolly Togs, Ltd.

FTP - Metals - Fayette Tubular Products, Inc.

FTP - Pipes - Fayette Tubular Products, Inc.

FTPD NLM - Computer software - Murkworks, Inc.

FTR - Lighting equipment - Duro-Test Corp.

FTR - Pencils - Dixon Ticonderoga Co.

FTSPARC - Computers - Sparc International, Inc.

FTW - Apparel and accessories - Mark L. Thomas

FTX - Apparel and accessories - Cobarr Creative Marketing, Inc.

FU DA - Apparel and accessories - Fu Da International Ltd.

FU JIN - Wines - Papagni Vineyards

FU-KI - Wines - Monsieur Henri Wines Ltd.

FU WEAR - Apparel and accessories - Kevin J. Fulginiti

F.U.B.U. - Apparel and accessories - J. Alexander Martin

FUCEL - Antibiotics - Westwood-Squibb Pharmaceuticals, Inc.

FUCHS - Electronic equipment - Fuchs Systems, Inc.

FUCHS - Toothbrushes - Lotus Brands Inc.

FUCHS AND MOEHR - Pianos - Hanseatic Overseas Trading Inc.

FUCHS EKOTEC - Toothbrushes - Lotus Brands Inc.

FUCINI - Liquors - Transamerica Wine Corp.

FUDE, THE - Brushes–paint - Boko-Undo USA Inc.

FUDGE BOWL - Cookies - Mother's Cake & Cookie Co.

FUDGE BROWNIE, THE - Cakes–mixes - Boston Brownie Co., Inc.

FUDGE CLASSICS - Cookies - President Baking Co., Inc.

FUDGE DOMINOES - Cookies ☆ - Keebler Co.

FUDGE FANCIES - Confections ☆ - Good Humor Corp.

FUDGE FARM - Candy - Fudge Farms, Inc.

FUDGE FAVORITES - Cookies - Nabisco Holdings Corp.

FUDGE JUMBLES - Desserts ☆ - Pillsbury Co.

FUDGE N' STUFF - Confections ☆ - Good Humor Corp.

FUDGE SHOPPE - Cookies - Keebler Co.

FUDGE ZIGGITY - Food products - Presentime Food Co.

FUDGECO - Fudge - H.C. Brill Co., Inc.

FUDGETOWN - Cookies - Sunshine/Salerno Inc.

FUDGIE BEAR - Candy - Chocolate House, Inc.

FUDGIE FILBERT SMACKER - Snack foods - Betty Lou's Inc.

FUDGIE PUMPKIN - Candy - Chocolate House, Inc.

FUDGIE RABBIT - Candy - Chocolate House, Inc.

FUDGIOS - Desserts - Yohay Baking Co. Inc.

FUDGSICLE - Ice cream - Good Humor Corp.

FUDGSTIX - Ice milk - TLC Trademark Co.

FUDGSTIX LITE - Ice cream - Frut Stix

FUDR - Pharmaceutical preparations - Roche Laboratories

FUEG AZUL - Harmonicas - Hohner Inc.

FUEGO - Doors - United Dominion Industries, Inc.

FUEGO - Motor vehicles - Renault Inc.

FUEGO - Strollers–baby - Inglesina Baby Ltd.

FUEGOS - Floor coverings–carpet and rugs ☆ - Eurotex Inc.

FUEL - Apparel and accessories - Fuel Clothing Co.

FUEL BUSTER - Fire extinguishing compositions - Fire Spread Inhibitor, Inc.

FUEL-CAT - Conduits - Fuel-Cat, Inc.

FUEL CELL, THE - Chemical preparations - American Symbolic Corp.

FUEL-DRI - Chemical preparations - Dewatering Systems International, Inc.

FUEL FIGHTER - Tires - Bridgestone/Firestone, Inc.

FUEL FOR MEN - Colognes - Donna Karan Co.

FUEL FOR THOUGHT - Vitamins and nutritional supplements - Natural Organics, Inc.

FUEL FRESH - Automotive parts and accessories - Fuel Fresh, Inc.

FUEL GUARD - Gauge for gas grills and tanks ☆ - Cooper Instrument Corp.

FUEL LOGIC - Computer software - Prophesy Transportation Software, Inc.

☆ = Now out of production

FUEL MATE PLUS - Fuel additives - Conklin Co., Inc.
FUEL MUSCLE - Fuel additives - Engine Muscle
FUEL PREPORATOR - Machine parts - Charles L. Ekstam
FUEL RIGHT - Fuel additives - Fairville Products, Inc.
FUEL SAFE - Fuel additives ☆ - Gold Eagle Co.
FUEL-SAVER - Carburetors - Outboard Marine Corp.
FUEL SAVER - Cooking equipment–commercial - Pitco Frialator, Inc.
FUEL SAVER - Thermostats - Quad Six Inc.
FUEL SENTRY - Barbecues and grills ☆ - Sunbeam Outdoor Products Inc.
FUEL SMART - Computer software - Software Assurance Corp.
FUEL TAX BUDDY - Computer software - Applied Arts Limited
FUEL-TRAP - Fuel systems–motor vehicle - Racer Components, Inc.
FUELCOM SYSTEM - Measuring instruments - Flowdata, Inc.
FUELETTES - Fuel additives - Home Fuels Corp.
FUELFLO - Chemical preparations - Stewart-Hall Chemical Corp.
FUELING/RIVERA - Motor vehicle parts and accessories - Rivera Engineering, Inc.
FUELING TALKER - Electronic equipment - Advanced Information Systems (A.I.S.), LLC
FUELMASTER 21 - Heat pumps - Lennox Industries Inc.
FUELTONE - Fuel additives ☆ - Tempo Chemical Co. Inc.
FUELTOOL - Fuel additives - MFB International, Ltd.
FUELTRAK - Computer storage devices - Universal Control Systems, Ltd.
FUELVAULT - Concrete products - Cretex Companies, Inc.
FUENTES - Recording label - Miami Records & Distributing Corp.
FUERST BISMARCK - Beverages–alcohol - Niche Marketing Corp.
FUFFS - Toys–stuffed ☆ - Russ Berrie and Co., Inc.
FUGBUG! - Insect repellent ☆ - Biodex Medical Systems Inc.
FUGGLIES FOR THE BEAUTIFUL PEOPLE - Apparel and accessories - Sylvia Fernandez-Palmer
FUGITIVE - Measuring instruments - Fugitive Emission Control, Inc.
FUGITIVE POPE - Recording label - Barry Conley
FUGU - Computer software - Fugu Ltd.
FUGUE - Tables–wood ☆ - Howe Furniture Corp.
FUJI - Guitars ☆ - Philadelphia Music Co. Inc.
FUJI - Musical instruments ☆ - National Artcraft Co.
FUJI - Photographic equipment - Fuji Photo Film USA Inc.
FUJI - Sporting goods - Fuji America, Inc.
FUJI - Tiles–ceramic - Porcelanite, Inc.
FUJI CERAM - Tableware–china ☆ - Nancy Calhoun Inc.
FUJI FOODS U.S. - Meat products - Fuji Foods U.S., Inc.
FUJI KING - Fruits and vegetables - Sales King International
FUJI SEAS - Jewelry–costume ☆ - Danecraft, Inc.
FUJI TENS - Health care products - Altoona Medical Supply
FUJIBLOC - Artists' materials ☆ - Winsor & Newton
FUJICHROME - Film - Fuji Photo Film USA Inc.
FUJICHROME PROFESSIONAL - Film - Fuji Photo Film USA Inc.
FUJICOLOR HR - Film ☆ - Fuji Photo Film USA Inc.
FUJICOLOR QUICKSNAP - Cameras - Fuji Photo Film USA Inc.
FUJICOLOR SUPER HR - Film - Fuji Photo Film USA Inc.
FUJIMOTO - Aquariums–household - Fujimoto Aquariums Inc.
FUJINAR - Photographic equipment - Fuji Photo Film USA Inc.
FUJINON - Binoculars - Weems & Plath, Inc.
FUJINON - Photographic equipment - Fuji Photo Film USA Inc.
FUJISTONE - Dinnerware–glass - Sango Co. Ltd. (Sango USA Div.)
FUJITSU - Electrical equipment - Fujitsu General America Inc.
FUJITSU-GENERAL - Televisions ☆ - Fujitsu General America Inc.
FUJITSU TEN - Stereos - Fujitsu Ten Corp. of America
FUJIYAMA - Fabrics–tapestry ☆ - Coloroll Inc.
FUKIEN - House furnishings - McSin Oriental Import Co.
FUL-FIL - Paints ☆ - Fuller-O'Brien Paints Inc.
FUL-FLO - Paints - Fuller-O'Brien Paints Inc.
FUL-FLOATING - Bicycles - Schwinn Cycling & Fitness Inc.
FUL-GLO - Ophthalmic goods - Barnes-Hind Inc.
FUL-GLO - Pharmaceutical preparations - Akorn Inc.
FUL-O-FRUIT - Desserts - Dawn Food Products Inc.
FUL-O-TENE - Paints ☆ - Fulton Co.
FUL-PRUF - Paints - Fuller-O'Brien Paints Inc.
FUL-RIPE - Fruits–dried - Paramount Farms Inc.
FUL-SCREEN - Paints - Fuller-O'Brien Paints Inc.
FUL-SEAL - Glass–flat - Downey Glass
FUL-SHIELD - Paints ☆ - Fuller-O'Brien Paints Inc.
FUL-STAIN - Paints - Fuller-O'Brien Paints Inc.
FUL-TEMP - Glass–flat - Downey Glass
FUL-THIK - Insulating materials - Manville/Schuller
FUL-VALU - Meat products–poultry - Sleepy Eye Foods

FUL VALUE - Disinfectants - Patterson Laboratories Inc.
FUL-VUE - Cleaning preparations - Patterson Laboratories Inc.
FULCOLOR - Paints - Fuller-O'Brien Paints Inc.
FULCRUM - Apparel and accessories - Crystal Brands Inc.
FULCRUM - Fishing tackle ☆ - Johnson Worldwide Associates, Inc.
FULCRUM - Furniture ☆ - EAC Integrated Furniture Solutions
FULCRUMATIC - Beds–metal - HARD Manufacturing Co. Inc.
FULFILL - Pet products - Ralston Purina Co.
FULFILLMENT - Underwear and nightwear - NCC Industries, Inc.
FULFLAVOR - Chocolate syrup - J. Hungerford Smith Co.
FULFLAVOR - Food products - Flavorland Foods Inc.
FULFYL - Hair care products - Amethyst Investment Group, Inc.
FULL-BAC - Insecticides - Platte Chemical Co.
FULL BARREL - Bats–baseball - Hillerich & Bradsby Co.
FULL BEAUTY - Brassieres (Bras) ☆ - Lovable Co.
FULL-BEE PLUS C - Pharmaceutical - American Hygienic Laboratories Inc.
FULL BOND - Latex - Tec Inc.
FULL BORE - Boots - Full Bore - Cycle Lines USA
FULL BORE - Oils–lubricating - Ralph T. Flanagan
FULL-BUSTED, NOT FULL-FIGURE - Brassieres (Bras) - NCC Industries, Inc.
FULL CAGE - Sporting goods - Schutt Manufacturing Co.
FULL CIRCLE - Apparel and accessories - Full Circle Clothing, Inc.
FULL CIRCLE - Brushes–paint - Wooster Brush Co.
FULL CIRCLE FEEDBACK - Computer software - Towers, Perrin, Forster & Crosby, Inc.
FULL CIRCLE PADDING - Exercising equipment - Full Circle Padding
FULL CIRCLES - Brassieres (Bras) ☆ - Carnival Creations
FULL-COMFORT - Brassieres (Bras) - Warnaco Inc.
FULL CONTACT - Computer software - Field Integration Technology, Inc.
FULL COURT - Footwear–athletic - KangaROOS USA Inc.
FULL COURT - Trading cards and stamps - ANCO Collector Supplies, Inc.
FULL COVERAGE N.Y. - Apparel–women's - Jaxi's Inc.
FULL CYCLE - Bags–trash - Quality Transparent Bag, Inc.
FULL-EX - Fire extinguishers - Ansul, Inc.
FULL F/X EXPOSURE - Apparel–men's - Santana Ltd.
FULL FASHION PLAYERS - Apparel stores–lingerie - R & B Industries, Inc.
FULL FEND - Boats - Docker Marine
FULL FLATTERY - Brassieres (Bras) - Olga Co.
FULL FLEX - Floor coverings–tile - Tec Inc.
FULL FLEX VALET - Computer peripheral equipment - MicroComputer Accessories Inc.
FULL FLOAT VALET - Computer terminals - Rubbermaid Inc.
FULL FLOATER - Motorcycles - Suzuki of America Automotive Corp.
FULL FORCE - Golf clubs - Prostar L.P.
FULL FREEDOM - Apparel–women's ☆ - Crown Foundations Inc.
FULL-HAND - Cleaning preparations - Fuller Brush Co.
FULL HOUSE - Computer software - Gunter C. Mayer
FULL LIFE - Health journals - Informative Amenities Inc.
FULL LINE CONCEPT - Machinery - Dynamic Air, Inc.
FULL METAL JACKET - Bullets - Olin Corp. (Winchester Div.)
FULL METAL JACKET - Eyeglasses - Oakley, Inc.
FULL METAL JACKET - Knives–hunting - Hardin Bros.
FULL METAL JACKET-ENCAPSULATED - Bullets - Olin Corp. (Winchester Div.)
FULL METAL JACKET—RIFLE - Bullets - Olin Corp. (Winchester Div.)
FULL MOON - Computer software - Full Moon Software Inc.
FULL MOON - Recording label - Jazz Composer's Orchestra Association Inc.
FULL OF ALMONDS - Candy ☆ - Annabelle Candy Co. Inc.
FULL OF SHIRT - T-shirts–men's - Keith Richard Kulesza
FULL O'LIFE - Vitamins and nutritional supplements - Full O'Life Foods
FULL-ON - Men's and women's sportswear - Marino Brothers Studio
FULL POTENTIAL - Cosmetics - Clinique Laboratories, Inc.
FULL POWER - Computer peripheral equipment - Oscar Fonseca
FULL POWER - Electrical equipment - General Cable Corp.
FULL-RED - Tomato pastes and sauces - Stanislaus Food Products Co.
FULL SAIL - Apparel and accessories - Full Sail Recorders, Inc.
FULL SAIL ALE - Alcoholic beverage - B.C. Marketing Concepts Inc.
FULL SAIL CENTER FOR THE RECORDING ARTS - Publisher's imprints - Full Sail Recorders, Inc.
FULL SAIL REAL WORLD EDUCATION - Publisher's imprints - Full Sail Recorders, Inc.
FULL SECURITY - Fire extinguishers - Figgie Licensing Corp.
FULL SER-CLE - Food products - US Foodservice
FULL SET - Floor coverings–tile - Tec Inc.
FULL SET PLUS - Floor coverings–tile - Tec Inc.
FULL SHOT - Trading cards - Topps Co., Inc.

☆ = Now out of production

FULL SHRED - Musical instrument accessories - Seymour Duncan Pickups

FULL SPECTRUM - Vitamins and nutritional supplements - Solgar Vitamin and Herb Co., Inc.

FULL SPECTRUM ECHINACEA - Vitamins and nutritional supplements - Planetary Formulas

FULL SPECTRUM MAITAKE - Vitamins and nutritional supplements - Planetary Formulas

FULL-SPECTRUM POLARIZED LIGHTING - Lighting fixtures - Daniel Karpen

FULL SPECTRUM REISHI - Vitamins and nutritional supplements - Planetary Formulas

FULL SPECTRUM SHIITAKE - Vitamins and nutritional supplements - Planetary Formulas

FULL SPEED - Cigarettes - R.J. Reynolds Tobacco Co.

FULL STRINGER - Fertilizers - Green-Sol, Inc.

FULL SUSPENSION PALE ALE - Beverages—malt - Salt Lake Brewing Co., L.C.

FULL TACK - Adhesives and sealants ☆ - Tec Inc.

FULL THROTTLE - Fuel additives - Engine Muscle

FULL THROTTLE - Life vests, jackets, etc - Full Throttle Flotation Inc.

FULL THROTTLE - Skis - Nash Manufacturing Inc.

FULL THROTTLE - Sporting goods - Full Throttle Apparel Co.

FULL TILT! - Computer software - Maxis, Inc.

FULL-TIME FAMILIES - Calendars ☆ - American Greetings Corp.

FULL VALUE - Food products - Semple Co.

FULL-VIEW - Housewares - Endicott-Seymour of Ann Arbor

FULL-VIEW - Office supplies - Office Products Inc.

FULL-VIEW PRINTING - Envelopes - Quality Park Products Co.

FULL-VUE - Mirrors - Spilo/Mehaz Worldwide

FULL-WAVE - Marine rigging - Outboard Marine Corp.

FULL WAY SEACOX - Toilets—portable ☆ - Wilcox-Crittenden

FULLA PERM - Hair care products - Alaion Products Inc.

FULLA WAVES - Hair care products - Alaion Products Inc.

FULLBACK - Motor vehicles—construction - Wagner Mining and Construction Equipment Co.

FULLBACK - Recliners - Sears, Roebuck and Co.

FULLBLOOM - Pet products - Petcare Industries Inc.

FULLCLEAN - Detergents - Fuller Brush Co.

FULLCOURT - Computer software - Justice Systems, Inc.

FULLCOURT - Shoes - Trans-World Shoe Import Corp.

FULLER - Cleaning preparations - Fuller Brush Co.

FULLER - Drill bits - Flounder Bay Boat Lumber Co.

FULLER BRIKARIER - Tools - Goldblatt Tool Co.

FULLER-O'BRIEN - Paints - Fuller-O'Brien Paints Inc.

FULLER SHIELD - Surgical supplies - Birchwood Laboratories, Inc.

FULLERGLO - Paints - Fuller-O'Brien Paints Inc.

FULLERGRIPT - Brushes - Fuller Brush Co.

FULLERS ESB - Beverages—malt - Grolsch Importers Inc.

FULLERS LONDON PRIDE - Beverages—malt - Grolsch Importers Inc.

FULLERTON - Artists' materials - MacPherson Sales Co.

FULLERTON - Fabrics - QST Industries, Inc.

FULLERTON - Musical instruments - N.H.F. Musical Merchandise Corp.

FULLFIELD - Binoculars - Burris Co., Inc.

FULLFILL - Hair care products ☆ - Protege Corp.

FULLJET - Nozzles - Spraying Systems Co.

FULLMER - Lumber - Fullmer Lumber Co.

FULL'N PRETTY - Bras - Lovable Co.

FULL'N SOFT - Hair curlers ☆ - Sunbeam-Oster Household Products

FULLPRESS - Computer software - Xinet, Inc.

FULLSPACE - Shelving units—wood - Lundia

FULLTIME - Audio equipment ☆ - DCM Corp.

FULLVIDEO - Computer hardware - Digital Equipment Corp.

FULLY ASSEMBLED MOTORS & TRANSMISSIONS FOR MOTORCYCLE. - Motorcycle parts and accessories - Video Manuals

FULLY FIELD - Apparel and accessories - Cambodia Resource International Inc.

FULLY LLOYDS' COOKED BARBEQUE COMPANY - Meat products - Lloyd's Food Products, Inc.

FULLY LOADED - Beverages - Coca-Cola Co.

FULLY LOADED - Golfing equipment - TourEdge Golf Manufacturing Inc.

FULLY RADICAL - Recording label - CORE Entertainment Corp.

FULLY STRAPPED, ALWAYS PACKED - Games - Mayfair Games, Inc.

FULMER - Motorcycles - Arthur Fulmer Co.

FULSOL - Cleaning preparations - Fuller Brush Co.

FULTA PUCCINELLIA DISTANS - Flowers, plants, and seeds - Jacklin Seed

FULTON - Mail boxes - Fulton Corp.

FULTON - Mops ☆ - Helen Keller Services for the Blind

FULTON - Paints - Fulton Co.

FULTON - Trailers—boat - Fulton Manufacturing Corp.

FULTON SQUARE - Floor coverings - Congoleum Corp.

FULTON VALLEY FARMS - Poultry - Fulton Processors Inc.

FULTRON - Audio equipment - Arthur Fulmer Co.

FULVI - Cheese - Sini Fulvi USA Inc.

FULVICIN - Veterinary pharmaceutical preparations - Schering-Plough Animal Health

FULVICIN P/G - Pharmaceutical preparations - Schering-Plough Healthcare Products

FULVICIN-U/F - Pharmaceutical preparations - Schering-Plough Healthcare Products

FUMARAL SPANCAP - Pharmaceutical preparations ☆ - Vortech Pharmaceuticals

FUMARCEE - Vitamins and nutritional supplements ☆ - Legere Pharmaceuticals Inc.

FUMARITIN - Vitamins and nutritional supplements - Oxford Laboratories Inc.

FUMAS - Cigars ☆ - Moro Cigar Co.

FUMASORB - Vitamins and nutritional supplements - Milance Laboratories Inc.

FUMATINIC - Pharmaceutical preparations - Laser Inc.

FUMBLE FREE - Audio equipment - Comp General Corp.

FUMBLES - Toys—stuffed - Gund, Inc.

FUME BUSTER - Ventilation equipment - Thomas Harry Anderson

FUME-GATOR - Air conditioning equipment - United Air Specialists, Inc.

FUME-GATOR, THE - Air purification systems - United Air Specialists, Inc.

FUME-TECH - Respirators - Uvex Safety LLC

FUMEE - Cosmetics - Lancome

FUMEO - Electronics equipment - Marty Bahn & Co.

FUMEO - Projectors—photographic - Xetron

FUMERATON - Pharmaceutical preparations ☆ - U.S. Ethicals Inc.

FUMERIN - Pharmaceutical preparations ☆ - Laser Inc.

FUMERON B FORTE - Pharmaceutical preparations ☆ - U.S. Ethicals Inc.

FUMEX - Pharmaceutical preparations ☆ - Consolidated Midland Corp.

FUMIDE - Health care products ☆ - Everett Laboratories Inc.

FUMIGATOR - Insecticides - S.C. Johnson & Son, Inc.

FUN - Chewing gum - Philadelphia Chewing Gum Corp.

FUN - Cosmetics - Pentech International Inc.

FUN - Floor coverings—carpet and rugs - Glen Eden Wool Carpets

FUN - Recording label - Jazz Composer's Orchestra Association Inc.

FUN-A-ROUND - Infant product ☆ - Phoenix Prams Inc.

FUN & FANTASY - Binders - K & M Co.

FUN-AND-FITNESS FRAME - Playground equipment - Wonderline

FUN & FUNCTIONAL - Thimbles - JHB International Inc.

FUN & MAGIC CENTER - Toys - Umsi Inc.

FUN & MAGIC THROUGH SCIENCE - Toys - Revell-Monogram, Inc.

FUN & MUD II - Tires - Winston and Winston Tire Co.

FUN & SPORT - Yarn ☆ - Joseph Galler Inc.

FUN ART - Toys - Placo Products Co.

FUN AT THE PLAYGROUND! - Games - Addison-Wesley Publishing Co.

FUN-BALL POPS - Candy ☆ - Tootsie Roll Industries, Inc.

FUN BALLS - Balls - Mantua/Cosom Sporting Goods

FUN BAR - Candy ☆ - Brown & Haley

FUN BEADS - Candy - R.L. Albert & Son, Inc.

FUN BIKINIS - Apparel—men's - Comme-Ci Comme-Ca Ltd.

FUN BIRD - Boats—motor - Thompson Boat Co.

FUN BITES - Meat products—poultry - Tyson Holding Co.

FUN BLOOD - Toys—stuffed - Fun World Inc.

FUN BOGGAN - Bobsleds and toboggans - Concept Products Inc.

FUN BOX - Confections - Good Humor Corp.

FUN BREAD - Bakery products - George's Original Fun Foods, Inc.

FUN BUBBLES - Toys - Mattel, Inc.

FUN BUNCH, THE - Toys—stuffed ☆ - Fun World Inc.

FUN BUNNI BY JUDI - Figurines - JRD Art Inc.

FUN BUTTON - Toys ☆ - Imperial Toy Corp.

FUN BY THE NUMBERS - Games - Cadaco Div.

FUN CARDS - Greeting cards - Joli Greeting Card Co.

FUN CHIPS - Confections - Richardson Brands

FUN CHUMS - Toys - Advanced Design Concepts Inc.

FUN CITY - Computer software - SourceView Software International

FUN CITY - Footwear - Harvard Enterprises Inc.

FUN CITY - Recording label - Jazz Composer's Orchestra Association Inc.

FUN CLIP - Novelty items - Guardsman Products, Inc.

FUN COMPANY, THE - Toys ☆ - Arden Corp.

FUN CONNECTIONS - Apparel and accessories - J.C. Penney Co., Inc.

FUN DECK - Boats—pontoons - Riviera Cruiser

FUN DECKER - Boats - H & H Molded Products

FUN DIMENSIONS - Glue–household or industrial - Elmer's Investments, Inc.
FUN DIP - Candy - Sunline Brands
FUN DISHES - Tableware–earthenware - Anacapa Corp.
FUN-DO - Napkins–fabric ☆ - Sportsline
FUN-DOH - Clay–modeling ☆ - Strombecker Corp.
FUN DOUGH - Clay–modeling - Rose Art Industries, Inc.
FUN-E - Recording label - Bellaire Record Sales
FUN FACES - Costumes - Russ Berrie and Co., Inc.
FUN FACTORY - Stationery - Fun Factory, Inc.
FUN FACTORY - Toys–models - Kenner Products
FUN FAIR - Toys - Mattel, Inc.
FUN FARM - Toys–stuffed - Dakin Inc.
FUN FASHIONS - Footwear - Olem Shoe Corp.
FUN, FAST, & CHEAP! - Publisher's imprints - International Data Group, Inc.
FUN FAXX - Paper - Ira H. Wexter
FUN FIGURES - Toys - Tonka Corp.
FUN FILLIES PONIES - Novelty items - Totsy Manufacturing Co., Inc.
FUN FINGER - Food products ☆ - Plantation Foods, Inc.
FUN FIRST - Toys - Creative Designs International
FUN FISH - Pet products - Lynco Pet Products Inc.
FUN FLAGS - Paper–gift wrap ☆ - Kalan Inc.
FUN FLEET - Housewares - Tupperware Co.
FUN FLIGHT - Aircraft–airplanes - Fun Flight Inc.
FUN FLINGS - Confetti - Flutter Fetti Inc.
FUN FOAM - Craft supplies - Westrim Crafts
FUN FOIL - Artists' materials - Quincrafts Corp.
FUN FOLDS ORIGINAL STUFF - Wallets - Funfolds
FUN FOOD FRAME - Containers - Pseudios Artistic Edibles
FUN FOR ONE - Pizzas–frozen - McCain Ellio's Foods, Inc.
FUN FOR THE ROAD - Games - Highlights for Children, Inc.
FUN FORMS - Pet products - Pets International, Ltd.
FUN FOUNTAIN - Toys ☆ - Wham-O Manufacturing Co.
FUN FOUNTAINS - Fountains ☆ - National Artcraft Co.
FUN FRAME - Games ☆ - Western Publishing Co., Inc.
FUN FRIEND - Toys–stuffed - Mars, Inc.
FUN FRIENDS - Toys - Fisher-Price, Inc.
FUN FRIENDS - Toys–stuffed ☆ - Dakin Inc.
FUN FRUIT - Candy - R.L. Albert & Son, Inc.
FUN FRUITS - Snack foods - Lipton Investments, Inc.
FUN FUN ENTERTAINMENT GOLF CADDIETTES GC EST. 1996 - Athletic associations - Fun Fun Entertainment
FUN FUNCTIONAL - Office supplies - Rubbermaid Inc.
FUN GAB - Fabrics–gabardine ☆ - Greenwood Mills Inc.
FUN GALS - Underwear and nightwear - Fruit of the Loom Inc.
FUN GHOUL !S - Apparel and accessories - LJM Creations
FUN GLASSES - Children's card games - International Games
FUN GRAPHICS - Apparel and accessories - Fun Graphics T's, Inc.
FUN GROUP, THE - Trading cards and stamps - Fun Group, Inc.
FUN GUN - Housewares - Hutzler Manufacturing Co.
FUN HAIR - Wigs - Eva Gabor International, Ltd.
FUN HOG - Apparel and accessories - William E. Plyler
FUN HOUSE - Games - Williams Electronics Games, Inc.
FUN HOUSE - Games ☆ - Pressman Toy Corp.
FUN HOUSE MAZE - Computer software ☆ - Sunburst Communications, Inc.
FUN ICE - Housewares - Munchkin, Inc.
FUN IN THE MAKING - Toys - Natural Science Industries, Ltd.
FUN IN THE SUN - Candy - Palm Springs Candy Co.
FUN IN THE SUN - Cosmetics ☆ - Prince Matchabelli
FUN IN THE SUN - Flowers, plants, and seeds - Florists' Transworld Delivery Association, Inc.
FUN IN THE SUN - Toys - Imperial Toy Corp.
FUN IN THE SUN - Toys ☆ - Libby Lee Toys Inc.
FUN-IN-THE-TUB - Floating soap dish and soap ☆ - Cosrich Inc.
FUN IN THE TUB - Puzzles ☆ - Straight Edge Inc.
FUN IS BUILT IN, THE - Tableware–plastic - Eagle Affiliates, Inc.
FUN ISLAND - Pool floats - Intex Recreation Corp.
FUN KART - Motorcycles ☆ - Certified Parts Corp.
FUN-L-FLO - Bottles–glass - Product Images, Inc.
FUN-L-HOOP - Sporting goods - Spiderball, Inc.
FUN LINE - Sporting goods - Bishop Freeman Co.
FUN MACHINE - Pens - National Pen Co.
FUN-MATES - Vitamins and nutritional supplements ☆ - Vitarine Pharmaceuticals Inc.
FUN MOVER - Motor vehicles–motor homes - Cruise America, Inc.
FUN 'N' ACTIVE - Dolls - Meritus Industries, Inc.
FUN 'N EASY - Musical instrument accessories ☆ - Hal Leonard Corp.

FUN N' FANCY - Hair care products - Russ Berrie and Co., Inc.
FUN N' FITNESS - Key rings - Russ Berrie and Co., Inc.
FUN 'N FITNESS - Playground equipment ☆ - Game Time, Inc.
FUN 'N FLOSS - Pet products - Jack Brenner Investments, Inc.
FUN 'N FRESH - Deodorants–personal - Bertsherm Products Inc.
FUN 'N FROLIC - Underwear and nightwear - Bestform Foundations, Inc.
FUN N' FROSTY - Milk–flavored - Farmland Dairies Inc.
FUN N FRUITY - Pet products - Picture Perfect Parrot
FUN N' GAMES - Computer software - Nilesh S. Shah
FUN 'N GAMES - Fruits–dried - General Mills, Inc.
FUN 'N GAMES - Game machines - Marketing Insights, Inc.-Frank Luppino Jr., and Associates
FUN 'N GAMES - Office supplies - Avery Dennison Corp.
FUN N' MOTION - Apparel and accessories - Fun N' Motion, Inc.
FUN-NELS - Pet products - Pets International, Ltd.
FUN ON THE FARM - Toys - Happiness Express Inc.
FUN ON WHEELS - Games ☆ - Milton Bradley Co.
FUN PAD - Office supplies - Artistic Office Products
FUN PADS - Stationery - Playmore Inc. Publishers
FUN PAINT - Paints - Insilco Corp.
FUN PAINTER - Brushes–paint - Rich Art Color Co., Inc.
FUN PAINTS - Water colors - Rich Art Color Co., Inc.
FUN PAK - Cereal - Kellogg Co.
FUN PAL - Toys - Fun Pal Design Corp.
FUN PALS - Underwear and nightwear - Fruit of the Loom Inc.
FUN PANTS - House furnishings - Dan River Inc.
FUN PARK KIDS - Dolls - Meritus Industries, Inc.
FUN PET - Air purification systems ☆ - Medo Industries, Inc.
FUN PHONES - Toys - Mattel, Inc.
FUN PLANES - Toys–airplanes - Paul K. Guillow Inc.
FUN PLUM - Lipsticks - Honey & Spice Toiletries
FUN-PRINTS - Paper–toweling - Procter & Gamble Co.
FUN PUN - Stickers, note pads, key tags - Securitag Corp.
FUN-PUPPETS - Puppets ☆ - Dakin Inc.
FUN RACER - Toys–stuffed - Fun World Inc.
FUN RAISER - Publisher's imprints - Entertainer Dinner Club of the South Inc.
FUN RIDE - Toys - DGI/Buki
FUN SAVER - Cameras - Eastman Kodak Co.
FUN SEED FOR KIDS - Flowers, plants, and seeds - W. Atlee Burpee and Co.
FUN SENSE - Deodorizers - 1 Mark Consumer Products, Inc.
FUN SET - Furniture ☆ - Cosco, Inc.
FUN SHAPES - Meat products–poultry - Perdue Holdings, Inc.
FUN SHAPES - Turkeys - Perdue Farms Inc.
FUN SHIRTS USA - Shirts–polo - Pennshire Shirt Corp.
FUN SHOP - Novelty items - D. Robbins & Co. Inc.
FUN SHOT - Cameras - Salado Sales, Inc.
FUN SNAP - Cameras - Nashua Photo Inc.
FUN SOAP - Soap - Chase Holding Co. Inc.
FUN SPIRIT - Apparel and accessories - Kmart Properties, Inc.
FUN SPLASH - Pool floats - Intex Recreation Corp.
FUN SPUN - Yarn - Melrose Yarn Co. Inc.
FUN SQUEEZE - Hobby kits ☆ - Crown Art Products
FUN STARTERS - Toys - Fisher-Price, Inc.
FUN STATION - Apparel–children's - Pacific Teaze
FUN STIKS - Hobby kits - Santa's Best
FUN STIX - Pet products - Mass-Appeal Inc.
FUN STOR - Paper products - Union Camp Corp. (Fine Paper Division)
FUN STUFF - Bicycles ☆ - Huffy Corp.
FUN STUFF - Candy - Confex Inc.
FUN STUFF - Toys - Jak-Pak Inc.
FUN STUFF V - Wallpaper ☆ - Imperial Wallcoverings, Inc.
FUN-TAK - Adhesives and sealants - Dap Products Inc.
FUN TEES - Apparel and accessories - Fun-Tees, Inc.
FUN TIME - Novelty items - United Mask & Novelty Co.
FUN-TIME - Party favors - Sansom, Inc.
FUN TIME - Publisher's imprints - Heian International Inc.
FUN TIME - Tableware–earthenware - Anacapa Corp.
FUN TIME LIVE - Apparel and accessories - Fun Time Live, Inc.
FUN TIME PIZZA - Pizzas–frozen - Fun Time Pizza Corp.
FUN-TO-DRESS - Dolls - Mattel, Inc.
FUN-TO-GO PLAY CENTER - Toys - Fisher-Price, Inc.
FUN-TO-KNOW - Toys - Trend Enterprises, Inc.
FUN TO PAINT - Artists' materials - Plaid Enterprises, Inc.
FUN TONGUE - Medical apparatus - George Hopper
FUN-TOON - Boats–pontoons - Muncie Metal Spinning Inc.
FUN! TOPS - Confections - Signature Brands, LLC

☆ = Now out of production

FUN TOUCH 2 - Cameras ☆ - Nikon Inc.
FUN TUB - Hot tubs–fiberglass - Medallion Swim Pool Co., Inc.
FUN TUBE - Tubes–plastic - Bridgestone/Firestone, Inc.
FUN-TURNS - Puzzles - American Model and Pattern Co.
FUN-VAC - Vacuum cleaners and accessories–commercial - Sta-Rite
   Industries Inc.
FUN WITH ART - Computer software - Epyx Inc.
FUN WITH DIRECTIONS - Computer software - Learning Well
FUN WITH FOOD - Toys - Fisher-Price, Inc.
FUN WITH GUM - Chewing gum - Philadelphia Chewing Gum Corp.
FUN WITH MUSIC - Computer software - Epyx Inc.
FUN WITH STICKS - Craft supplies - Milton Bradley Co.
FUN WITH SUMS - Games - Leisure Learning Products
FUN WITH WORDS - Computer software - SourceView Software International
FUN WORKS - Apparel - Frank M. Scurlock
FUN-WRITER - Office accessories - Ralphco, Inc.
FUN ZONE - Chewing gum - Philadelphia Chewing Gum Corp.
FUNANIMALS - Pet products - Classic Products
FUNANIMALS - Puppets ☆ - Gund, Inc.
FUNBALL - Pencil sharpeners ☆ - Empire Berol USA
FUNBRELLA - Umbrellas - Playskool, Inc.
FUNBUILDER - Playground equipment - Yards of Fun of America Inc.
FUNBUNCH - Computer software - Unicorn Software
FUNBURST - Toys - Tonka Corp.
FUNCARDS - Publisher's imprints - Biscard Corp.
FUNCHASER - Motor vehicles–motor homes ☆ - Hi-Lo Trailer Co. Inc.
FUNCILS - Office supplies ☆ - Faber-Castell Corp.
FUNCOLOR ANIMALS - Pottery ☆ - Rubens Originals
FUNCOURT - Balls–basketball - Emmons Enterprises, Inc.
FUNCTION - Clocks - General Time Corp. (Westclox/Seth Thomas Div.)
FUNCTION GAME - Computer software ☆ - Queue Inc.
FUNCTIONAL HARMONY: BASIC CHORDS - Computer software - Electronic
   Courseware Systems Inc.
FUNCTIONPAC - Computer software - International Business Machines Corp.
FUNCTIONS - Furniture–upholstered ☆ - Selig Manufacturing Co.
FUNCYCLE - Bicycles - Trailmate Inc.
FUND RAISER - Banks–commercial - Fund$Raiser Cyberzine
FUND WRAPS - Gift wrap - Fundwraps Inc.
FUNDADOR - Brandy - Domecq Importers Inc.
FUNDAMENTAL - Recording label - Jazz Composer's Orchestra Association
   Inc.
FUNDAMENTAL FRETLESS - Musical instrument accessories - Seymour
   Duncan Pickups
FUNDAMENTAL FUN FOR EVERYONE - Amusement parks - Leaps &
   Bounds, Inc.
FUNDAMENTALS - Floor coverings–carpet and rugs - Mannington Carpets,
   Inc.
FUNDAMENTALS - Frames–eyeglass - Kenmark Optical Co.
FUNDAMENTALS - Furniture - Eisen Brothers Inc.
FUNDAMENTALS - Health care products ☆ - Avon Products, Inc.
FUNDAMENTALS - Luggage - Paris Presents Ltd.
FUNDAMENTALS - Novelty items - Fundamentals Inc.
FUNDAMENTALS - Wallcoverings - Sinclair Wallcovering
FUNDAMENTALS OF A MODEL SWING - Computer software - Parsons
   Technology, Inc.
FUNDAMENTALS OF PHYSICAL SCIENCE - Computer software - Orange
   Cherry Software
FUNDAMENTALS SKIN CARE - Skin care products - Rosen Ingberman
   Group, Inc.
FUNDAMIDDLES - Snack foods - General Mills, Inc.
FUNDANGLES - Jewelry ☆ - Libby Lee Toys Inc.
FUNDANGO! - Apparel–women's - Wacoal America Inc.
FUNDANGO - Ophthalmic goods - Foremost Optical Products
FUNDAWEAR - Apparel and accessories - Regal Industrial Products, Inc.
FUNDAY CARTOONS - Games ☆ - Warren Industries Inc.
FUNDAZZLE - Playground equipment and toys - Little Fun Station, Inc.
FUNDCONNECT - Consulting services - Painewebber Inc.
FUNDERFUL - Greeting cards - Norcross Inc.
FUNDERWEAR - Paints–artists' - Duncan Enterprises
FUND'MENTALS - Pencils ☆ - Sanford Corp.
FUNDOR - Toys–models - Express Interiors Corp.
FUNDPRO - Computer software - Manhattan Analytics, Inc.
FUNDRAISERS - Toys–banks - Agent Andy Inc.
FUNDRAISING SOLUTIONS - Coupons - Fundraising Solutions, Inc.
FUNDSERIES - Computer software - Compusense Inc.
FUNDSMITH - Consulting services - Bowne & Co., Inc.

FUNDTECH - Computer software - Arius Technology
FUNDUCATION - Greeting cards - Lion King, Inc.
FUNDUSCEIN - Prescription drug - Iolab Pharmaceuticals
FUNDWORX - Computer software - R.R. Donnelley & Sons Co.
FUNDY FAMILY CHRONICLES, THE - Recording label - Salt of the Earth, Inc.
FUNFACE - Toys ☆ - Gerber Products Co.
FUNFEET - Dolls - Cal Themes Inc.
FUNFETTI - Frosting - Pillsbury Co.
FUNFIL - Fibers–polyester - Putnam Co., Inc.
FUNFINDER - Games - Rand McNally & Co.
FUNFLOWER - Toys–stuffed - Fisher-Price, Inc.
FUNFLY - Toy - GCI Products
FUNFULL - Games - Centsable Toys Inc.
FUNFURNITURE - Furniture - WKK Corp
FUNG-AWAY - Insecticides - Green Light Co.
FUNG-O - Fungicides - Cramer Products Inc.
FUNG-O-SCRIP - Fungicides ☆ - Scrip-Physician Supply Co.
FUNGA-BATH - See SEPTIDERM-V
FUNGA-ZEMA - See SEPTIDERM-V
FUNGACETIN - Pharmaceutical preparations - Blair Laboratories Inc.
FUNGAL NAIL RECOVERY - Nail care products - Del Pharmaceuticals, Inc.
FUNGEX - Fungicides - Anitox Corp.
FUNGI-CENE - Pharmaceutical preparations ☆ - Reese Chemical Co.
FUNGI-GARD - Fungicides - Security Products Co.
FUNGI GUARD - Disinfectants - Altaire Pharmaceuticals, Inc.
FUNGI-NAIL - Antifungal nail treatment - Kramer Laboratories Inc.
FUNGI-NOT - Fungicides ☆ - Nott Manufacturing Co. Inc.
FUNGI-REX - Pharmaceutical preparations - Rexall Nutritional Products Inc.
FUNGI STOP - Pet products ☆ - Tetra Sales USA
FUNGICIDE SINGLES - Fungicides - Gulfstream Home & Garden Inc.
FUNGICIN - Pharmaceutical preparations - Pharmex Inc.
FUNGICURE - Pharmaceutical preparations - Alva-Amco Pharmacal Co.
FUNGIDEX - Veterinary pharmaceutical preparations ☆ - SmithKline Beecham
   Animal Health Products
FUNGINEX - Fungicides - Chevron Chemical Co.
FUNGISAN - Pet products - Tomlyn Products
FUNGISEAL - Paints ☆ - Monsanto Co.
FUNGISHIELD - Chemicals - Ecologel USA, Inc.
FUNGISOF - Pet products - Natra Pet Inc.
FUNGIZIN - Pet products - Aquatic Biotechnologies Inc.
FUNGIZONE - Pharmaceutical preparations - Bristol-Myers Squibb Co.
FUNGLASSES - Novelty items–paper - Ottenheimer Publishers, Inc.
FUNGLE'S - Food products - Co. of Gnoles, Inc.
FUNGLE'S FUN FOODS - Frozen foods - Co. of Gnoles, Inc.
FUNGO BAT - Toys–banks ☆ - A.J. Renzi Plastic Corp.
FUNGOID - Pharmaceutical preparations - Pedinol Pharmacal Inc.
FUNGOTIC - Pharmaceutical preparations ☆ - ICN Pharmaceuticals Inc.
FUNGUS AMONG US - Fruits and vegetables - Fungus Among Us Inc.
FUNGUS-AWAY - Pharmaceutical preparations ☆ - Lamoon Products, Inc.
FUNGUS CARE - Aquariums–household - Jungle Laboratories Corp.
FUNGUS CLEAR - Aquariums–household - Jungle Laboratories Corp.
FUNGUS CURE - Pet products - Aquarium Pharmaceuticals, Inc.
FUNGUS-EASE - Chemical preparations - Mydor Industries Inc.
FUNGUS ELIMINATOR - Aquariums–household - Jungle Laboratories Corp.
FUNGUS GUARD - Aquariums–household - Jungle Laboratories Corp.
FUNGUS HUMUNGUS - Toys - Mattel, Inc.
FUNGUS M.D. - Pharmaceutical preparations ☆ - Orly International Inc.
FUNGUS STOP - Pharmaceutical preparations - Life Works, Inc.
FUNGUSBUSTER - Shingles–asphalt or tar - Certainteed Corp. (Roofing
   Products Group)
FUNGUSIDE - Paints ☆ - PPG Industries, Inc.
FUNGUSOFF - Fungicides - Weco Products Inc.
FUNIMALS - Candy - Pennsylvania Dutch Candies
FUNIMALS - Erasers - Diener Industries Inc.
FUNISHINGS BY JENA HALL - Housewares - Jena Hall Designs, Ltd.
FUNITOS - Snack foods - Barrel O' Fun Inc.
FUNK & WAGNALLS - Publisher's imprints - Funk & Wagnalls
FUNKTIONAL - Jewelry - Karl Wahl
FUNKTOWN - Recording label - Ichiban Records, Inc.
FUNKY DIVA - Apparel–women's - Deborah Hossack-Hendrix
FUNKY FANTASY - Fireworks - Ingram Enterprises, Inc.
FUNKY FILMS - Plastics film - Grafix Plastics
FUNKY FLOWERS - Toys - Mattel, Inc.
FUNKY FOOD COVERS - Containers - Funky Food Covers, Inc.
FUNKY FRUIT - Lip balms - Sun Pharmaceuticals Corp.
FUNKY FRUIT PUNCH - Juices - Chiquita Brands, Inc.

FUNKY FUR - Notebooks and notepads - Norcom Inc.
FUN'L TUN'L - Sporting goods - Natural Science Industries, Ltd.
FUNLAB - Toys ✩ - Revell-Monogram, Inc.
FUNLAND - Candy ✩ - Shenandoah Candy Co. L.L.C.
FUNLAWN - Flowers, plants, and seeds - Jonathan Green, Inc.
FUNLINE - T.K.O.
FUNLINER - Greeting cards - Norcross Inc.
FUNLITE - Trailers–travel - Hi-Lo Trailer Co. Inc.
FUNLOVERS - Apparel and accessories - L & L Wings, Inc.
FUNMAKER - Trailers–travel ✩ - Hi-Lo Trailer Co. Inc.
FUNMALLOWS - Marshmallows - Kraft Food Ingredients Corp.
FUNMATE - Containers–insulated - Igloo Products Corp.
FUN'N SUN WEEKEND - Paper–writing - California Association of Flower Growers & Shippers
FUNNEL CAKE FACTORY, THE - Snack foods - J & J Snack Foods Corp.
FUNNEL JET - Machine parts - Nitrous Oxide Systems, Inc.
FUNNEL POUCH - Scientific apparatus - Hyclone Laboratories, Inc.
FUNNELCAN - Gas tanks–motor vehicle - Five Star Plastics Inc.
FUNNOODLE - Toys - James P. O'Rourke
FUNNY - Dolls - Alexander Doll Co. Inc.
FUNNY BIKE, THE - Bicycles - Ross Bicycles USA, Ltd.
FUNNY BONE - Pet chews - Items Inc.
FUNNY BONES - Cakes - Drake Bakeries, Inc.
FUNNY BONES - Games ✩ - Parker Brothers
FUNNY BONES - Stationery - The Rytex Co.
FUNNY BONES - Toys–stuffed - Mary Meyer Corp.
FUNNY BUMPERS - Decals and transfers - Prismatix Decal
FUNNY BUNNIES - Chocolate candy - Superior Fruit & Confections
FUNNY BUNNIES - Toys–stuffed ✩ - Fun World Inc.
FUNNY BUNNY - Candy ✩ - Keppel's Inc.
FUNNY BUNNY - Toys - Imperial Toy Corp.
FUNNY BUNNY PASTA - Pasta - Buckeye Beans & Herbs, Inc.
FUNNY BUSINESS - Posters - Sandhill Arts Publishing Co.
FUNNY CARD, A - Greeting cards - Pawprints Greeting Cards
FUNNY CHEW-CHEWS - Vitamins and nutritional supplements - Health Products Corp.
FUNNY COLOR FOAM - Soap - Cac Industries, Inc.
FUNNY COLOR FOAM - Soap - Creative Aerosol Corp.
FUNNY EXPRESSIONS - Apparel - Funny Expressions, Inc.
FUNNY FACE - Beverages–carbonated ✩ - Pillsbury Co.
FUNNY FACE - Candy - Glenn Confections Inc.
FUNNY FACE - Infant product ✩ - Sassy Inc.
FUNNY FACE - Toys - Milton Bradley Co.
FUNNY FACES - Candy ✩ - Asher Candy Co.
FUNNY FACES - Cosmetics - Spearhead Industries Inc.
FUNNY FARM - Publisher's imprints - Auto Book Press
FUNNY FARM BOOKS - Publisher's imprints - Coda Publications
FUNNY FARMACEUTICALS - Candy - Papel Freelance, Inc.
FUNNY FARMACEUTICALS - Candy - Weaver Inc.
FUNNY FLOATS - Swimming pools - Recreonics, Inc.
FUNNY FLOWERS - Apparel–women's - House of Ronnie, Inc.
FUNNY FRIENDS - Paper goods - James River Corp.
FUNNY FRIENDS - Toys–stuffed - Jennifer Mazur
FUNNY FRUIT FACES - Computer software - Seven Hills Software
FUNNY FUNDS - Novelty items - Doc's Apothecary
FUNNY GIRL - Jeans–women's ✩ - Salant/Manhattan Industries
FUNNY MONEY - Toys–automobiles - Mattel, Inc.
FUNNY-SIDE UP - Games - Play-Tech, Inc.
FUNNY STUFF - Greeting cards ✩ - Argus Communications
FUNNY THOUGHTS - Novelty items - West Coast Wood Specialties
FUNNY TRAIN - Card game - International Games
FUNNYBONES - Wallpaper - Gear Holdings, Inc.
FUNNYCASE - Pillowcases ✩ - West Point-Pepperell Inc.
FUNPACK - Paper napkins - James River Corp.
FUNPAK - Computer software ✩ - Videx, Inc.
FUNRIDER - Toys–automobiles - Mattel, Inc.
FUNRING - Jewelry - Kurt Wayne Inc.
FUNROOF - Motor vehicle parts and accessories - Donmar Enterprises Inc.
FUNSA - Automotive parts and accessories - Funsa Tire Shop Corp.
FUNSATIONAL - Novelty items - Pioneer Balloon Co.
FUNSAVER - Cameras - Eastman Kodak Co.
FUNSHINE - Fabrics–linen ✩ - Maytex Mills
FUNSHINE - Hobby kits - Greene Plastics Corp.
FUNSHINE - Toys - Samuel Lowe Co.
FUNSHINE BEAR - Toys - Those Characters from Cleveland, Inc.
FUNSHIP - Boats–pontoons ✩ - Marathon Boat Group, Inc.

FUNSHOP - Books–comic - Georgia Davis
FUNSNAX - Cookies - Pure's Food Specialities Inc.
FUNSPORT - Automotive parts and accessories - Donmar Enterprises Inc.
FUNSPORT - Helmets–athletic - Girano Products USA, Inc.
FUNSTER - Toys–airplanes - Hobby Lobby International Inc.
FUNSTIKS - Labels ✩ - Century Marketing Corp.
FUNSTUFF-N.Y. - Clothing - Funstuff N.Y.
FUNTACTIC GAMES - Games - Funtactic Games, Inc.
FUNTANS - Footwear - Morse Shoe, Inc.
FUNTASIA III - Stationery - Funtasia III
FUNTASTIC - Cakes–mixes - Standlee's Cake & Party Shop Inc.
FUNTASTIC - Magnets - Selfix, Inc.
FUNTASTIC - Ophthalmic goods - Foremost Optical Products
FUNTASTIC - Spices and extracts - David Michael & Co.
FUNTASTIC FISH STICKS - Fish–fresh or frozen - Conagra, Inc.
FUNTASTICS - Confetti - Kofco Inc.
FUNTASTIK - Apparel–children's - Funtastik Inc.
FUNTIME - Cameras - Eastman Kodak Co.
FUNTIME - Timers–appliance ✩ - Lifetime Hoan Corp.
FUNTIME - Trailers–travel - Skylark Industries Inc.
FUNTIME BARBIE - Dolls - Mattel, Inc.
FUNTIME BATH ARCH - Infant product - Century Products Co.
FUNTIME CLOCK - Dolls - Mattel, Inc.
FUNTIME KALEIDOSCOPE - Novelty items - Steven Manufacturing Co.
FUNVIEW - Automotive parts and accessories - Donmar Enterprises Inc.
FUNWAGON - Trailers–travel - Wells Cargo Inc.
FUNWALKER - Footwear - Propet USA, Inc.
FUNYUNS - Snack foods - Frito-Lay, Inc.
FUNZIE FARM - Slippers - Gerber Products Co.
FUNZIES - Slippers - Gerber Products Co.
FUR-A-LURE - Knitting machines - Peter Freund Knitting Mills
FUR BALL CARDS - Greeting cards - Brandywine Ltd
FUR BALL FRENZY - Pet products - Paws Taylor Made
FUR BUSTER - Cleaning tool - Cynthia Barnett Ltd.
FUR FOAM - Cleaning preparations - Beaumont Products, Inc.
FUR-SO-FRESH - Shampoos - Conagra, Inc.
FUR-TEX - Cases–musical instrument ✩ - Distex Corp.
FURA-AEROSOL - Pet products - Farnam Cos. Inc.
FURA-CURE - Water treating compounds - Silco Pet Products
FURA-DRESSING - Veterinary pharmaceutical preparations - Farnam Cos. Inc.
FURA-OINTMENT - Veterinary pharmaceutical preparations - Farnam Cos. Inc.
FURA-SWET - Health care products - Frye Co.
FURABASE - Pet products ✩ - Mardel Laboratories, Inc.
FURACIN - Antibiotics - Norwich-Eaton Pharmaceuticals
FURACIN - Veterinary pharmaceutical preparations - SmithKline Beecham Animal Health Products
FURACORT - Veterinary pharmaceutical preparations ✩ - SmithKline Beecham Animal Health Products
FURACYN - Pet products ✩ - Aquatronics-Filtronics
FURADAN - Herbicides - FMC Corp.
FURADANTIN - Antibiotics - Norwich-Eaton Pharmaceuticals
FURADEX - Veterinary pharmaceutical preparations ✩ - SmithKline Beecham Animal Health Products
FURALAN - Pharmaceutical preparations - Lannett Co. Inc.
FURALL - Veterinary pharmaceutical preparations - Farnam Cos. Inc.
FURALLA - Fabrics ✩ - West Point-Pepperell Inc.
FURALOID - Aquariums–household ✩ - Jungle Laboratories Corp.
FURAN - Pharmaceutical preparations ✩ - American Urologicals Inc.
FURAN-2 - Veterinary pharmaceutical preparations - Aquarium Pharmaceuticals, Inc.
FURANACE - Water treating compounds - Aquarium Products Inc.
FURAREX - Pharmaceutical preparations - C.S. Ruckstuhl Co. Inc.
FURATOIN - Pharmaceutical preparations ✩ - Vortech Pharmaceuticals
FURATON - Pharmaceutical preparations - H.R. Cenci Laboratories Inc.
FURAZITE - Pet products - Mardel Laboratories, Inc.
FURAZONE-GREEN - Veterinary pharmaceutical preparations - Dyna Pet Inc.
FURAZONE-LIGHT - Veterinary pharmaceutical preparations - Dyna Pet Inc.
FURBULOUS - Crocheted and knitted items - Brookshire Knitting Mills Inc.
FURECOL - Adhesives and sealants - Ashland Oil, Inc.
FURI - Alarm systems–burglar - Furi-Audio & Security
FURI - Insulating materials - Owens Corning
FURIO - Flatware - Dayton Hudson Corp.
FURIOUS - Apparel–athletic - Furious Designs, Ltd.
FURLED FLAG - Apparel - Corning Inc.
FURLOTTI - Wines - Agencias Intermares
FURMAN - Amplifiers–musical instrument - Bob White Associates

✩ = Now out of production

FURMAN - Audio equipment - Furman Sound, Inc.
FURMAN - Food products - Furman Foods, Inc.
FURMANO'S - Food products - Furman Foods, Inc.
FURMAN'S FAMILY FARM - Fruits and vegetables - Furman Foods, Inc.
FURMONT - Traps–animal - Fuhrman Diversified
FURNALOID - Lacquers ☆ - Steelcote Manufacturing Corp.
FURNANCE CEMENT - Adhesives and sealants - Comstar International Inc. (IPC Div.)
FURNEX - Chimney - Stephen D. McLaughlin
FURNITEX - Fabrics - Car Del
FURNITINT - Enamels ☆ - Steelcote Manufacturing Corp.
FURNITURE ACCENTS - Hardware ☆ - Amerock Corp.
FURNITURE BY KHOURY - Furniture–wood ☆ - Khoury, Inc.
FURNITURE CARE - Furniture polish and wax - Apple Polishes Inc.
FURNITURE COSMETICS - Furniture - Weiman Co.
FURNITURE CRAFTSMEN - Furniture - Broyhill Furniture Industries, Inc.
FURNITURE CREAM POLISH - Polishing rouge - Analab Inc.
FURNITURE DOCTOR - Cleaning preparations–upholstery - J.N.T. Manufacturing Co. Inc.
FURNITURE FACIAL, THE - Housewares - KozaK Auto Drywash Inc.
FURNITURE FIRST - Furniture - Furniture First Cooperative, Inc.
FURNITURE FLOATERS - Furniture ☆ - Expanded Technologies Corp.
FURNITURE GLIDES - Furniture - Expanded Technologies Corp.
FURNITURE GUYS, THE - Shirts - Edward Feldman
FURNITURE KOZY - House furnishings - Decorite, Inc.
FURNITURE MAGIC - Furniture polish and wax - Magic American Corp.
FURNITURE MAKERS - Wood products ☆ - Gerber Industries Inc.
FURNITURE PAOLI - Furniture - Paoli, Inc.
FURNITURE SKATE, THE - Housewares - Renovisions, Inc.
FURNIVALS - Dinnerware–glass ☆ - S.P. Skinner Co. Inc.
FURNIWARD - Luggage - Furniward Co.
FUROMIDE - Pharmaceutical preparations - Hyrex Pharmaceuticals
FURON - Pharmaceutical preparations ☆ - Lexis Laboratories Inc.
FURON - Valves–intake - Furon Co.
FURONATAL - Pharmaceutical preparations ☆ - Lexis Laboratories Inc.
FURONATAL FA - Pharmaceutical preparations - Lexis Laboratories Inc.
FUROPLEX - Pet products - Aquatrol, Inc.
FURORE - Yarn ☆ - Joseph Galler Inc.
FUROSE - Pharmaceutical preparations ☆ - B.F. Ascher & Co. Inc.
FUROXONE - Antibiotics - Norwich-Eaton Pharmaceuticals
FURRARRI - Pet products - R.C. Steele Co.
FURRARRI - Pet products ☆ - Dogloo Inc.
FURREVER FRIENDS - Toys–stuffed - Kenner Products
FURRIERE - Handwork supplies - Bernat Yarn & Craft Corp.
FURROW V CLOSER - Agricultural machinery - Schaffert Manufacturing Co., Inc.
FURROWS - Window coverings ☆ - Vertilux-Louverlux Inc.
FURR'S - Laxatives ☆ - Washington Homeopathic Products
FURR'S PROTEIN - Beef - Furr's Cafeterias Inc.
FURRSOFT - Fabrics–broadcloth - Collins & Aikman Corp.
FURRY BONE - Pet chews - Items Inc.
FURRY FLUFF CORSAGE - Toys–stuffed ☆ - Fun World Inc.
FURRY FOLK - Puppets - Folkmanis Inc.
FURRY FRIENDS - Animal feeds - O.H. Kruse Grain and Milling Corp.
FURRY FRIENDS - Greeting cards - Amberley Greeting Card Co.
FURRY FRIENDS - Infant product ☆ - Edison Industries Inc.
FURRY FUNZ - Pet products ☆ - Pets International, Ltd.
FURS FOR FEET - Footwear - Wolverine World Wide, Inc.
FURSEW - Thread - New Bedford Thread Co. Inc.
FURSKINS - Toys–stuffed - Original Appalachian Artworks, Inc.
FURST - Stainless steel ☆ - Villeroy and Boch Tableware Ltd.
FURST & MOONEY - Handbags - Ronald Furst
FURST PUCKLER - Chocolate bars ☆ - C. & J. Willenborg Inc.
FURSTENBERG PILSENER - Beverages–malt ☆ - Guinness Import Co.
FURSTITCH - Thread ☆ - American & Efird, Inc.
FURSURE - Greeting cards - Fursure Enterprises Inc.
FURTADO'S - Meat products–beef - North End Provision Co. Inc.
FURY - Apparel and accessories - Northern Indiana Basketball Corp.
FURY - Archery equipment - Martin Archery Inc.
FURY - Boats–motor - Century Boat Co.
FURY - Darts and dart games - Dart Mart Inc.
FURY - Footwear - Angel-Etts of California, Inc.
FURY - Guitars - Peavey Electronics Corp.
FURY - Knives–pocket - Joy Enterprises
FURY - Lawn mowers - Alamo Group

FURY - Motor vehicles–automobiles ☆ - Chrysler Corp. (Chrysler-Plymouth Div.)
FURY - Scooters–children's - Peg Perego USA Inc.
FURY - Vacuum cleaners and accessories - Yard Vac Products, Inc.
FURY IN THE WEST - Games ☆ - Avalon Hill Game Co.
FURY3 - Computer software - Microsoft Corp.
FUSALLOY - Metals - Coating Applications, Inc.
FUSARO - Jewelry - Fusaro Jewelry Co. Inc.
FUSCEL - Antibiotics - Westwood-Squibb Pharmaceuticals, Inc.
FUSE 'N BIND - Fabric binding - Freudenberg Nonwovens Apparel Division
FUSE 'N FOLD - Fabric binding - Freudenberg Nonwovens Apparel Division
FUSE, THE - Golfing equipment - Acushnet Co.
FUSECOTE - Soldering equipment - Union Carbide Corp. (Industrial Chemicals Div.)
FUSED GOLD - Gilding liquid - Barrack's Industries Inc.
FUSEGUARD - Fuses–electric - AVX Corp.
FUSELON - Thread ☆ - United Thread Mills Corp.
FUSETRON - Fuses - Cooper Industries, Inc.
FUSHION TIP - Sporting goods ☆ - Outdoor Technologies Group
FUSI-KNIT - Fabrics - Handler Textile Corp.
FUSION - Bathing suits ☆ - Jantzen Inc.
FUSION - Bicycles - Kent International Inc.
FUSION - Bicycles - Rocky Mountain Bicycle Co. Ltd.
FUSION - Bicycles ☆ - Raleigh USA Bicycle Co.
FUSION - Boats–kayaks - Wave Sports, Inc.
FUSION - Chairs–upholstered - Cramer Inc.
FUSION - Chemical preparations - Agassi Enterprises, Inc.
FUSION - Fishing tackle ☆ - Johnson Worldwide Associates, Inc.
FUSION - Floor cleaning equipment - Clarke Industries, Inc.
FUSION - Furniture - Haworth, Inc.
FUSION - Furniture–upholstered ☆ - Mersman Furniture Co.
FUSION - Skates–roller - Rollerblade, Inc.
FUSION - Stereos - Onkyo USA Corp.
FUSION - Tiles–ceramic ☆ - Laufen Ceramic Tile
FUSION - Wallpaper - Capital Carousel Inc.
FUSION - Watches - Cooper & Co., Inc.
FUSION - Wines - Bully Hill Vineyards, Inc.
FUSION 4000 - Electronic equipment - Seal Products Inc.
FUSION CD - Computer peripheral equipment - Media Vision Technology Inc.
FUSION FINISH - Hardboard siding - ABT Co., Inc.
FUSION 'FIRE - Lighting equipment - High End Systems, Inc.
FUSION-PLUS - Hair care products - Cheveux Inc.
FUSIONART - Figurines ☆ - Shube's Manufacturing, Inc.
FUSIONKOTE - Paint ☆ - Iowa Paint Manufacturing Co. Inc.
FUSIONLIGHTING - Lamps - Fusion Lighting, Inc.
FUSIONTRED - Paint product ☆ - Iowa Paint Manufacturing Co. Inc.
FUSITAL - Hardware - Valli & Colombo USA Inc.
FUSO - Bicycles - Dave Moulton Bicycles
FUSO - Health care products - Mitsubishi Fuso Truck of America Inc.
FUSON - Heating equipment - Meyercord Co.
FUSOR - Adhesives and sealants - Lord Corp. (Chemical Products Div.)
FUSOR - Chemical preparations - Lord Corp.
FUSS-FREE FIT - Patterns–clothing ☆ - Simplicity Pattern Co., Inc.
FUSS 'N GIGGLE - Dolls - Mattel, Inc.
FUSSY - Candy - Whitmans Candies, Inc.
FUSSY - Cleaning preparations–household - Mission Kleensweep Products, Inc.
FUSTAT - Fuses - Cooper Industries, Inc.
FUSUS - Lubricating oils - Shell Oil Co.
FUT-WARMER - Heating equipment - Easy Heat Inc.
FUTAJI - Electrical equipment - Duracom USA Corp.
FUTAJI - House furnishings - Inimex Corp.
FUTGOL - Sporting goods - Jorge Castillo
FUTONIA - Furniture - Le Futon
FUTORIAN - Furniture ☆ - Mohasco Corp.
FUTRASLIM - Frosting - Nader Agha
FUTREX - Medical apparatus - Futrex, Inc.
FUTREX 5000 - Health-care products ☆ - Jackson Enterprises Inc.
FUTUR 2000 - Floor coverings ☆ - Tarkett, Inc.
FUTUR-FORM - Manicure preparations - Creative Nail Design, Inc.
FUTUR-MATIC - Drafting supplies - Mayline/Hamilton
FUTURA - Adhesives and sealants - W.R. Meadows Inc.
FUTURA - Artists' materials ☆ - Plasticoid Manufacturing Inc.
FUTURA - Bathroom accessories - Franklin Brass Manufacturing Co.
FUTURA - Bathroom fixtures ☆ - Melard Manufacturing Corp.
FUTURA - Bicycles - Ross Bicycles USA, Ltd.

☆ = Now out of production

FUTURA - Binders - Master-Craft Corp.
FUTURA - Blenders - Waring Products Div.
FUTURA - Boats - Zodiac of North America
FUTURA - Boats–motor ☆ - Glastron Boats
FUTURA - Cabinets - Scott Manufacturing, Inc.
FUTURA - Cabinets–wood - Parcraft Distinctive Cabinetry
FUTURA - Cement - W.R. Meadows, Inc.
FUTURA - Cooking equipment–household - West Bend Co.
FUTURA - Craft supplies - Montrose Products Inc.
FUTURA - Electronic equipment - Computerized Elevator Control Corp.
FUTURA - Eyeglasses - Uvex Safety LLC
FUTURA - Fans–electric - Dan's Fan City
FUTURA - Floor coverings - Azrock Commercial Flooring
FUTURA - Floor coverings - Congoleum Corp.
FUTURA - Floor coverings–carpet and rugs - Mohawk Industries Inc.
FUTURA - Floor coverings–carpet and rugs ☆ - Dorsett Carpet Mills Inc.
FUTURA - Frames–picture ☆ - Art Americana
FUTURA - Furniture–metal ☆ - Samsonite Furniture Co. (Consumer Products Div.)
FUTURA - Guitars - Westheimer Corp.
FUTURA - Heating equipment - Slant/Fin Corp.
FUTURA - Ice chests–plastic - General Foam Plastics Corp.
FUTURA - Implants–surgical - Arthronics Inc.
FUTURA - Loudspeakers - International Jensen Inc.
FUTURA - Mattresses and box springs - Ohio Mattress Co.
FUTURA - Moldings–plaster of paris - Futura Home Products
FUTURA - Motor vehicles–automobiles ☆ - Ford Motor Co.
FUTURA - Office supplies - Master Caster Co.
FUTURA - Paper–bond ☆ - Parsons Paper Co.
FUTURA - Paper–crepe ☆ - Creative Expressions Group
FUTURA - Paper–gummed - Park Sherman
FUTURA - Rings–jewelry - Artcarved Inc.
FUTURA - Skates–roller - Seneca Sports, Inc.
FUTURA - Switches–electric - Carlon
FUTURA - Tables–wood ☆ - Quaker Industries Ltd.
FUTURA - Trailers–travel - Juno Industries Inc.
FUTURA - Vacuum cleaners and accessories - The Hoover Co.
FUTURA - Watches - Fada Industries Inc.
FUTURA - Water purification systems - Quality Water Engineering, Inc.
FUTURA FASHION TONES - Pigments–paint ☆ - Lilly Perfection Paint
FUTURA IV - Flag poles - Annin and Co.
FUTURA PLAZA - Computer programming services - Global Network Exchange, Inc.
FUTURA Y - Paper–photographic ☆ - Luminos Photo Corp.
FUTURAC - Varnishes - Lilly Perfection Paint
FUTURALOC - Electronic equipment - CCL Security Products
FUTURAMA - Accordions - Bennett Music School Inc.
FUTURAMA - Floor coverings–carpet and rugs ☆ - American Excelsior Co.
FUTURAMIC - Electronic equipment - Rollei of America Inc.
FUTURE - Electronic equipment - Future Network Inc.
FUTURE - Floor waxes - S.C. Johnson & Son, Inc.
FUTURE - Furniture - Lane Upholstery (Venture Furniture Div.)
FUTURE - Recording label - Dharma Records
FUTURE CONCEALERSTIK - Cosmetics - Pentech International Inc.
FUTURE CRAFT - Cooking utensils–aluminum - West Bend Co.
FUTURE ENTERTAINMENT - Recording label - MCA Universal Studios
FUTURE FLOOD - Floodlights - RAB Electric
FUTURE FOCUS - Food products - Future Focus International Ltd.
FUTURE FOODS - Toothpaste - Future Foods
FUTURE FORCE - Exercising equipment - American Athletic Inc.
FUTURE FOREST DECAF - Coffee - Frontier Cooperative Herbs
FUTURE FORM - Apparel–women's - Newton Manufacturing Corp.
FUTURE FRAMES - Frames–picture - Ray Perkins
FUTURE GRAPHICS - Inks–duplicating - Future Graphics, Inc.
FUTURE IN PRINT, THE - Computer software - MusicWriter Inc.
FUTURE INTERESTS MATE - Publisher's imprints - Little, Brown and Co., Inc.
FUTURE KLEEN - Cleaning preparations - Maid Easy, LLC
FUTURE LAWN - Synthetic turf - Instant Turf Industries Inc.
FUTURE LEAN - Animal feeds - Hormel Foods Corp.
FUTURE LEATHERS - Watchbands–leather - Vogue Watch Strap Creations
FUTURE OF KNIFE COLLECTING, THE - Fruits and vegetables ☆ - United Cutlery Corp.
FUTURE OLYMPIAN! - Bottles–plastic - United States Olympic Committee
FUTURE ONE - Computer software - Networld.Com, Inc.
FUTURE PAST - Cosmetics - Del Pharmaceuticals, Inc.
FUTURE PERFECT - Skin care products - Estee Lauder Inc.

FUTURE PERFECT: CHOC./VAN - Vitamins and nutritional supplements - Body Wise International, Inc.
FUTURE PRIMITIVE - Pins–jewelry - Future Primitive Designs Ltd.
FUTURE PROGRESSION RECORDS - Recording label - Guy L. Martin
FUTURE REFLECTIONS - Floor waxes - S.C. Johnson & Son, Inc.
FUTURE SHELL - Gasoline ☆ - Shell Oil Co.
FUTURE SHOCK - Bicycles - Specialized Bicycle Components, Inc.
FUTURE SHOCK - Computer software - Media Technology Ltd.
FUTURE STARS OF RACING - Advertising agencies - Miniature Motorsports, Inc.
FUTURE STEP - Floor coverings–carpet and rugs - Galaxy Carpet Mills Inc.
FUTURE STORIES JGAME - Games - Talicor Inc.
FUTURE TRIM - Skin care products - Cote International Inc.
FUTURE VISION - Computer software - Future Visionary, Inc.
FUTURE WAVE - Hair care products ☆ - Image Laboratories, Inc.
FUTUREBIOTICS - Health care products - Futurebiotics
FUTUREBODIES - Health care products - Future Bodies of America, Inc.
FUTUREDRIVE - Electronic equipment - Rhinestahl Corp.
FUTUREGLOSS II - Adhesives and sealants - Tivian Laboratories Inc.
FUTUREHERB EXTRACTS - Health care products - Futurebiotics
FUTUREKIDS - Educational materials - Futurekids, Inc.
FUTUREMART - Vitamins and nutritional supplements - Fred Salisbury and Jayne Jochec, Both U.S. Citizens, AS the Trustees of Minae' Products
FUTURES - Video production - Foundation for Advancements in Science & Education
FUTURESHOW - Health care products - National Home Health Care Exposition
FUTURESPORTS - Health care products - Futurebiotics
FUTURESTAR - Meters–water - Futurestar Corp.
FUTURETEL - Computer software - Futuretel, Inc.
FUTURIA - Computer software - Unicorn Software
FUTURISTIC - Cleaning preparations–carpet and rug ☆ - Promaster
FUTURISTIC 2000 - Microphones - K & S Distributors of Musical Merchandise, Inc.
FUTURITY - Body lotion - A-Veda Corp.
FUTURITY - Floor coverings–carpet and rugs ☆ - Karastan-Bigelow Inc.
FUTURITY - Hair care products - Helene Curtis Industries Inc.
FUTURITY - Musical instrument accessories - French American Reeds Manufacturing
FUTURITY - Watches - Gruen Marketing Corp.
FUTURMILL - Machine tools - Devlieg-Bullard Services Group
FUTURO - Bandages–orthopedic - Kendall Co.
FUTURO - Braces–orthopedic - Smith & Nephew Inc. (Rehabilitation Div.)
FUTURO - Furniture ☆ - Stanley Furniture Co. Inc.
FUTURO SPORT - Bandages–orthopedic - Kendall Co.
FUTUROCITY - Paper - Mead Corp.
FUTURUS - Mats - Matworks
FUZBY - Toys–stuffed ☆ - Gund, Inc.
FUZION - Film - Photran Corp.
FUZZ-A-WAY - Razor blades - Cadie Products Corp.
FUZZ BEAR - Toys–stuffed - Dakin Inc.
FUZZ BUTTON - Electrical equipment - TWP, Inc.
FUZZ-E-GRUB - Fishing lures - Lindy Little Joe Inc.
FUZZ FINDER - Dusters - Lois Noyes California Unusuals
FUZZ FLYER - Toys - Play Visions
FUZZ OFF - Housewares - Calyn Co.
FUZZ SPORT - Toys - Franklin Sports, Inc.
FUZZ, THE - Yarn ☆ - National Spinning Co., Inc.
FUZZBUCKET'S FRITTERS - Dog food - Diamonds in the Ruff
FUZZBUSTER - Communications equipment–mobile - Electrolert Inc.
FUZZE - Musical instrument accessories - Humes & Berg Manufacturing Co. Inc.
FUZZIE WUZZIES - Novelty items - Russ Berrie and Co., Inc.
FUZZIWIGS - Apparel and accessories - Rocky Mountain Chocolate Factory, Inc.
FUZZNIK - Toys–stuffed ☆ - Fun World Inc.
FUZZY - Posters - Western Graphics Corp.
FUZZY - Shoes - Footwear International Corp.
FUZZY B - Paper products - Lisa Frank, Inc.
FUZZY BEAR - Footwear - San Shoe Trading Corp.
FUZZY BUGGER - Recording label - Fuzzy Bugger Records
FUZZY DICE - Cleaning preparations ☆ - Scentex Inc.
FUZZY DUSTER - Brooms - Empire Brushes, Inc.
FUZZY FEET - Exercising equipment - Brittoys
FUZZY FIDO - Novelty items - Roberta H. Olsen
FUZZY FRAME - Frames–picture - Bryan A. Werlemann
FUZZY FREAK - Toys - On the Ball

☆ = Now out of production

FUZZY FRIENDS - Greeting cards - American Greetings Corp.
FUZZY LOVE - Greeting cards ☆ - Fran Mar Greeting cards Ltd.
FUZZY MOUSE - Puppets - David T of Hawaii
FUZZY NAVEL - Cakes ☆ - Awrey Bakeries, Inc.
FUZZY POSTERS - Posters - Western Graphics Corp.
FUZZY PUMPER - Toys - Tonka Corp.
FUZZY WUZZY - Bags ☆ - Commonwealth Toy and Novelty Co. Inc.
FUZZY WUZZY - Pet products - Teddy Pets
FUZZY ZOELLER - Apparel and accessories - Zoeller, Inc.
FUZZY'S - Animal feed supplements - Stevens Industries Inc.
FUZZYSP - Computer software - Neuralware, Inc.
FV-2000 - Computer hardware - Flight Visions, Inc.
FVA - Measuring instruments - Dantec Measurement Technology Inc.
FVI - Computer peripheral equipment ☆ - Micro Processor Systems, Inc.
FVO - Food products ☆ - Mercantile Food Co.
FVR C-P - Veterinary pharmaceutical preparations - Schering-Plough Animal Health
FW - Apparel and accessories - Let's Play Too, Inc.
FW - Games - Frederick-Willys Inc.
FW - Inks - Steig Products
FW FANNY WRAPPER - Pharmaceutical preparations - Fanny Ramirez
F.W. STEEL - Automotive parts and accessories - American Coastal Distribution
FWB - Enamels ☆ - Everseal International Sales Co. Inc.
F.W.D. - Bacon ☆ - Dold Foods Inc.
FWD - Motor vehicles - FWD Corp.
FWG - Jewelry–precious - Far West Gem & Gold
FWP - Recording label - Fred Weinberg Productions Inc.
FX - Golfing equipment - Ram Golf Corp.
FX - Machinery - Kelley Co., Inc.
FX - Paints ☆ - Multicolor Specialties Inc.
FX - Toys–trains - Digitrax, Inc.
FX - Welding equipment - International Systems and Technology Inc.
FX - Wheelchairs ☆ - Everest and Jennings International Ltd.
FX-2 - Electrical equipment - Component Equipment Co., Inc.
FX-2 - Electronic equipment ☆ - AVL
FX-10 - Sod and grass plugs - Florida Sod Growers Cooperative, Inc.
FX-80 - Printers–computer ☆ - Epson America, Inc.
FX FIGHTER - Video games - GTE Service Corp.
FX FISHING EXPEDITIONS - Apparel and accessories - Ronnie Kovach's Outdoor Expeditions, Inc.

FX MASTER - Toys - Mattel, Inc.
F.X. SMITH'S TUSCARURA - Cigars - F.X. Smiths Sons Co.
FX-XTRA - Steel products - A. Finkl & Sons Co.
FXL - Recording label - FXL Sound Studios
FXLINK - Computer software - Citibank, NA
FXNET - Computer software - Quotron Systems Inc.
FXRACK - Electronic equipment - Efxx Products Co.
FY-TON - Toys ☆ - ERTL Co., Inc.
FYARESTOR - Fire extinguishing compositions - Witco Corp.
FYBRANTA - Vitamins and nutritional supplements ☆ - Norgine Laboratories Inc.
FYBRGLASS - Erasers - Eraser Co. Inc.
FYCONTROL - Computer software - Pillar Corp.
#L'FYEO - Jewelry - Otocraft
FYFE & DRUM - Beverages–malt ☆ - Genesee Brewing Co., Inc.
FYFFES - Food products - Chiquita Brands, Inc.
FYI - Computer software - Identitech Inc.
FYI 3000 - Computer software ☆ - FYI Inc.
FYI 3000 PLUS - Computer software - FYI Inc.
FYLKING - Flowers, plants, and seeds - Jacklin Seed
FYN - Lacquers - Fyn Paint & Lacquer Co. Inc.
FYN-LUX - Enamels - Fyn Paint & Lacquer Co. Inc.
FYNE FRY - Food products - Sunnyland Refining Co.
FYNE WRAP - Paper ☆ - Arrow Industries, Inc.
FYNKLEEN - Paints ☆ - Fyn Paint & Lacquer Co. Inc.
FYNKOTE - Paints - Fyn Paint & Lacquer Co. Inc.
FYNLITE - Enamels - Fyn Paint & Lacquer Co. Inc.
FYNSPRAY - Pumps - South Pacific Associates
FYPLAN - Computer software - Pillar Corp.
FYR-FYTER - Fire extinguishers - Kidde Safety
FYR-GARD - Wood products - Niedermeyer-Martin Co.
FYR-KOTE - Paints - Morris Paint & Varnish Co.
FYR-PRUF - Thread - Threads USA Div.
FYRE-FREE - Chemical preparations - Ake Safety Equipment, Inc.
FYRE-KART - Fireplace equipment ☆ - Meteor Inc.
FYRE LITE - Fireplace logs–treated - Wescott Associates, Inc.
FYRE-WATCH - Fire extinguishers - Kidde Safety
FYRE WERKS - Yarn - Rainbow Gallery, Inc.
FYREX - Paper - Grant Wilson Inc.
FYRNETICS - Smoke detectors - Kidde Safety
FYSHSANDWYCH - Apparel and accessories - Next Year's News, Inc.
FZ - Polishing rouge ☆ - Flitz International Ltd.

G

Addresses and phone numbers for the companies cited in the brands below
are available in the Company Listings section immediately following the brands listings.

G - Apparel and accessories - Gang Peace
G - Apparel–athletic - Goodbody, Inc.
G - Boots ☆ - Miura Sports Inc.
G - Desk sets - Combex, Inc.
G - Fruits and vegetables - Giumarra Brothers Fruit Co.
G - Games - Ben H. Lightfoot
G - Handbags - Ganson Ltd.
G - Health care products - American Generics Inc.
G - Jewelry - Garden Jewelry Manufacturing Corp.
G - Meat products–beef - Granada Corp.
G - Mirrors - Gardner Mirror Corp.
G - Musical instrument accessories - Gulbransen, Inc.
G - Paints - George X. Shui
G - Pet products - Gimborn U.S., Inc.
G - Pharmaceutical preparations - Greenstone Ltd.
G - Silverware - Gemco Ware, Inc.
G - Trading cards and stamps - Green Bay Packers, Inc.
G-1 - Pharmaceutical preparations ☆ - Roberts/Hauck Pharmaceuticals Inc.
G 2 - Computer hardware - Computer Products, Inc.
G-2 - Frames–eyeglass - Rozin Optical Export Corp.
G-2 - Pharmaceutical preparations ☆ - Roberts/Hauck Pharmaceuticals Inc.
G-3 - Boats–motor ☆ - Larson Boat Div.
G-3 - Pharmaceutical preparations ☆ - Roberts/Hauck Pharmaceuticals Inc.
G 5 - Vacuum cleaners and accessories–commercial - Scott Fetzer Co.
G-6 - Fishing tackle - Gudebrod, Inc.
G-9G - Sporting goods - G-96 Products Co. Inc.
G-10N - Paint sprayers - Wagner Spray Tech Corp.
G-12 - Apparel–women's - Nuvogue Creations
G 12-1 - Adhesives and sealants - W.J. Ruscoe Co.
G-71 SUPER-VUE - Headboards - Spring Window Fashions Division, Inc.
G-71 SUPERVUE - Blinds–vertical - Spring Window Fashions Division, Inc.
G 100'S - Skates–roller - On Wheels Roller Skates
G-200-LT - Projectors–photographic ☆ - Da-Lite Screen Co. Inc.
G-7901 - Electronic equipment - Da-Tel Research Co., Inc.
G-8945 - Electronic equipment - Da-Tel Research Co., Inc.
G-9700 - Electronic equipment - Da-Tel Research Co., Inc.
G. A. PFRETZSCHNER - Violins - Ideal Musical Merchandise Co.
G. A. RIVERS - Apparel and accessories - Riverside Manufacturing Co.
G. A. SCHMITT - Wines - Maison Jomere Ltd.
G & A - Fruits and vegetables - G & A Produce Sales, Inc.
G & B - Garden equipment ☆ - Gilbert and Bennett Manufacturing Co.
G & G - Guitars - G & G Music Accessories
G & K - Health care products - G & K Creations Inc.
G & K - Wood products - Giles and Kendall Inc.
G & L - Guitars - G & L Music Sales Inc.
G & S - Skateboards - Gordon & Smith Inc.
G & W - Analgesics - G and W Laboratories Inc.
G & W - Food products - Beatrice Cos. Inc.
G B - Jewelry - Gallery Byzantium, Inc.
G. B. S. - Apparel and accessories - Gary Schwartz
G. BRUTINI - Boots - Harbor Footwear Group Ltd.
G CASUALS - Apparel–athletic - G Apparels Inc.
G-CLARON - Lenses - Schneider Optics, Inc.
G-COATE 20 - Cleaning preparations - Harris Research, Inc.
G-CON - Pipes - Reflange, Inc.
G. D. EHRET - Posters - One-of-a-Kind Workshop

G. D. T. - Rice - Gia Dong Market
G DENMARK - Apparel and accessories - A. G. S. of Hanover Inc.
G DEPOT MANAGER - Computer software - General Programming Holdings Inc.
G E-GARD - Locks–door - Truth Hardware Corp.
G. E. RUDISCHHAUSER - Paper–carbon - Dental Articulating Paper Co. Inc.
G E T T - Apparel and accessories - Sparko Fashions Inc.
G. EDISON ELECTRONICA - Electronic equipment repair shops - Hatzlachh Supply Inc.
G. F. HEBERLEIN - Violins - Ideal Musical Merchandise Co.
G-FAMS - Computer software - Derek Consulting, Inc.
G-FLEX - Games - Kulite Tungsten Corp.
G-FLOAT - Skin care products ☆ - Sween Corp.
G-FORCE - Boats–motor - G-Force High Tech
G-FORCE - Skates–roller - Rollerball International Inc.
G-FORCE - Toys - Mattel, Inc.
G FUNK MUSIC - Recording label - Warren Griffin
G G G G - Computer hardware - Graphic Systems Technology, Inc.
G-G TUSSIN - Cough medicines ☆ - Vitarine Pharmaceuticals Inc.
+G +GACOSIA - Wheels–motor vehicle - Gacosia (USA) Corp.
G. GALVANI - Neckties - Spiegel, Inc.
G GARLAND - Adhesives and sealants - Garland Co., Inc.
G GEEZER GEAR - Apparel and accessories - Geezer Gear, Inc.
G GEMCO - Food processors - Gemco Ware, Inc.
G GIACCA SPORT - Apparel–athletic - Junior Gallery Ltd.
G GLOBAL SPECIALTIES - Computer software - Interplex Electronics Inc.
G GLORUNNER - Apparel and accessories - Denson Industries, Inc.
G GODAX - Tobacco products - Campbell Tobacco Rehandling Co. Inc.
G GOODWAY - Electrical appliances - Goodway Electrical Co. (USA), Inc.
G GPC - Food products - Grain Processing Corp.
G GROOVETOWN - Recording label - BMG Music
G. H. BASS - Footwear - G.H. Bass and Co.
G. H. MUMM & CIE. - Beverages–alcohol - Seagram's Chateau & Estate Wines Co.
G HERBS - Spices and extracts - G's Seasoning Co.
G-II - Housewares - Fort Howard Corp.
G-III POWER - Vacuum cleaners and accessories - The Hoover Co.
G. J. CAHN - Neckties - G.J. Cahn Neckwear Inc.
G. K. HALL & CO. - Publisher's imprints - Twayne Publishers
G LALO - Stationery - Exclair Inc.
G-LAM - Glass–safety - California Glass Bending Co.
G-LINK - Electronic equipment - Gemstar Development Corp.
G-LIXIR - Pharmaceutical preparations ☆ - Roberts/Hauck Pharmaceuticals Inc.
G-LOX - Hardware - Gee Manufacturing Co. Inc.
G-LOX MARINE - Sporting goods - Gee Manufacturing Co. Inc.
G-M - Pharmaceutical preparations - Wait-Cahill Co.
G-MAX - Automotive parts and accessories - Packard Motor Car Co.
G. MORRIS LTD. - Footwear - G. Morris Ltd., Inc.
G. MUELLER - Flutes ☆ - St. Louis Music Supply Co.
G-MYCIN - Pharmaceutical preparations - Bolan Pharmaceutical Inc.
G-MYTICIN - Pharmaceutical preparations - Pedinol Pharmacal Inc.
G-N-S - Fertilizers - Sims Agricultural Products Co.
G-NOME - Computer peripheral equipment - 7th Level, Inc.
G NOTE - Paper products - Rutherford & Associates II, Ltd.
G/O-PRO - Computer software - Resources Engineering Systems, Inc.
G OMNI GEAR - Transmission equipment–industrial - Omni Usa, Inc.

G-P GYPSUM PRODUCTS - Gypsum products - Georgia-Pacific Corp.

G-P LAM - Wood products - Georgia-Pacific Corp.

G-P PLUS - Plywood - Georgia-Pacific Corp.

G-P TRUCK LINER - Plywood - Georgia-Pacific Corp.

G-PRO - Coatings - Bat Technologies, Inc.

G-RECILLIN-T - Pharmaceutical preparations ☆ - Solvay Pharmaceuticals Inc.

G-RING - Dental equipment - Garrison Dental Solutions, LLC

G-ROCK - Shoes - Harbor Footwear Group Ltd.

G-S-CLASSIC - Apparel—men's ☆ - Munsingwear, Inc.

G. SCHIRMER INC./ASSOCIATED MUSIC PUBLISHERS INC. - Publisher's imprints - MacMillan Publishing Co. Inc.

G-SERIES - Electronic equipment - Fairchild Industries, Inc.

G SOUP - Soups—canned - Giant Food, Inc.

G-SOX - Pharmaceutical preparations ☆ - Scrip-Physician Supply Co.

G-SPOT - Apparel and accessories - G-Spot Clothing Co.

G-SPOTTER - Vibrators - Uniquity

G-T - Fishing tackle - Gudebrod, Inc.

G T - Hair care products - Johnson Products Co., Inc.

G/T QUALIFIER S - Tires - Dunlop Tire Corp.

G-TOR - Modems - Kantronics Co., Inc.

G/TRAC - Motor vehicle parts and accessories - Steeda Autosports Inc.

G/T'S - Candy ☆ - Good Taste Products, Inc.

G/T'S 3 PAC CHOCOLATE GOLF BALLS - Candy - Good Taste Products, Inc.

G/T'S 51 OLD FASHIONED CANDY - Candy - Good Taste Products, Inc.

G/T'S 101 OLD FASHIONED CANDY - Candy - Good Taste Products, Inc.

G/T'S BUCKET OF BALLS - Candy - Good Taste Products, Inc.

G-TUBE - Health care products - Entech Inc./Enteral Technology

G-TUBE - Research—scientific - Bio Plas, Inc.

G-U-M - Pharmaceutical preparations - John O.Butler Co.

G. VETTER - Beverages—alcohol - Joseph Gies Import

G-VOX BRIDGE - Computer software - Lyrrus Inc.

G VUILLEUMIER - Watches - Hampden Corp.

G. WASHINGTON'S - Broth and food seasoning - American Home Food Products Inc.

G WAX - Cleaning preparations - Chem-Pak Inc.

G WEAR - Apparel and accessories - Robert Jr. Anastario, Jr.

G WHEELS - Apparel and accessories - Gail Wheeler

G. WHISKERS - Cat food - Martha White Foods Inc.

G-WHIZ - Veterinary nutritional supplements - Millennium Lawns, Inc.

G. WIZ - Footwear - D. Myers and Sons Inc.

G. W!LL!KERS! - Apparel—women's - G. Willikers, Inc.

G. ZANIBON - Music—sheet ☆ - GSP

G-ZERO - Recording label - Global Zero L.P.

G1 - Amplifiers—musical instrument ☆ - Pearce Amplification Ltd.

G2 - Amplifiers—musical instrument - Pearce Amplification Ltd.

G2 - Helmets—athletic - Troxel-West

G2 WEAPON - Sporting goods - O'Brien International

G3 - Binoculars - ITT Defense, Inc.

G3/G3E - Lighting equipment - Fox Lite Inc.

G3 REVENGE - Sporting goods - O'Brien International

G4 - Golfing equipment ☆ - Aldila, Inc.

G4 - Vacuum cleaners and accessories - Scott Fetzer Co.

G5 - Medical apparatus - General Physiotherapy, Inc.

G5 - Vacuum cleaners and accessories - Scott Fetzer Co.

G5 MINIMYTE - Office machines - Danka Industries Inc.

G7 - Sweaters - Krome Industries, Inc.

G24 - Motor vehicles—automobiles ☆ - DaimlerChrysler

G119 SA - Rubber—vulcanized - Goodyear Tire & Rubber Co.

G291 UNISTEEL - Tires - Goodyear Tire & Rubber Co.

G314 UNISTEEL - Tires - Goodyear Tire & Rubber Co.

G328 UNISTEEL - Tires - Goodyear Tire & Rubber Co.

G357 UNISTEEL - Tires—automobile - Goodyear Tire & Rubber Co.

G362 UNISTEEL - Tires - Goodyear Tire & Rubber Co.

G391 UNISTEEL - Tires - Goodyear Tire & Rubber Co.

G500S - Audio equipment - ADA Signal Processors Inc.

G1500 - Paint thinners - Glyptal Inc.

G4000 - Jackets—women's - Kmart Corp.

GA - Video games - Sega of America, Inc.

GA-LITE - Candles ☆ - Candle-Lite Co.

GA-ZEE-BO - Motorcycle parts and accessories - Dowco, Inc.

GAARDEN - Dinnerware—glass ☆ - Dansk International Designs, Ltd.

GABA 375 - Vitamins and nutritional supplements - M.M.R.C., Ltd. Co.

GABAR - Bathing suits - Gabar Inc.

GABAR II - Bathing suits - Gabar Inc.

GABARIELE - Shampoos - Sun-Tec Group, Inc.

GABBANELLI - Accordions - Gabbanelli Accordions & Imports LLC

GABBEH - Floor coverings—carpet and rugs - Foreign Accents

GABBIFONE - Telescopes - Teleconcepts Inc.

GABBING GHOULS - Pins—jewelry - Russ Berrie and Co., Inc.

GABBRIELE - Leather goods - Itapel, Inc.

GABBY GORILLA - Toys—stuffed ☆ - Dakin Inc.

GABBY'S - Wigs ☆ - Eva Gabor International, Ltd.

GABELLAN - Spices and extracts - Herbert Marmorek & Son, Inc.

GABEL'S - Cosmetics ☆ - Gabel's Cosmetics Inc.

GABES - Finishing agents ☆ - Hertron International Inc.

GABILA'S - Food products - Gabila & Sons Manufacturing Inc.

GABLE MASTER - Ventilation equipment - Mid-America Building Products Corp.

GABLES - Tents - Gale Group Inc.

GABOR DESIGNS - Bar fixtures—metal - Marion Manufacturing Co. Inc.

GABRADAN - Fabrics - Dan River Inc.

GABRIEL - Alarm systems - Gabriel Medical, Inc.

GABRIEL - Chairs—wood ☆ - Krueger International, Inc.

GABRIEL - Clocks ☆ - Robertshaw Controls Co.

GABRIEL - Earthenware - Swedish Products Inc. (Sojo Inc.)

GABRIEL - Shock absorbers—motor vehicle - Gabriel Ride Control Products Div.

GABRIEL - Toys—stuffed - CBS Toys

GABRIEL ALIGNE - Wine - Attiki Imports & Distributors

GABRIEL & ROSE - Cereal - David's Goodbatter

GABRIEL EDITIONS - Stationery - Gabriel Group

GABRIEL FLEURINES - Wines - Prestige Wine Corp.

GABRIEL KNIGHT: SINS OF THE FATHERS - Games - Sierra On-Line, Inc.

GABRIEL STEVENS - Jewelry - Ultralite International Corp.

GABRIELA SABATINI - Colognes - Frances Denney

GABRIELE Y CAROLINE - Wines - Smith & Hook Winery

GABRIELEEN - Hair care products ☆ - Fromm Industries

GABRIELI WEAVING - Religious articles - Israeli Accents

GABRIELLA - Chocolate candy - Bell'amore Imports Inc.

GABRIELLA - Teas - Vendors Exchange International, Inc.

GABRIELLA TORELLI - Crocheted and knitted items - M. Gabriella Torelli

GABRIELLA VINEYARDS - Wines - Sabrina Importers Ltd.

GABRIELLE - Apparel and accessories - Gimbel Brothers Inc.

GABRIELLE - Clocks ☆ - Ridgeway Clock Co.

GABRIELLE - Dolls - Uneeda Doll Co., Inc.

GABRIELLE - Dolls ☆ - Effanbee Doll Corp.

GABRIELLE - Giftware ☆ - Gorham Inc.

GABRIELLE - Shampoos ☆ - Majestic Drug Co., Inc.

GABRIELLE - Skin care products - Gabrielle, Inc.

GABRIELLE BACALL - Leather - Enger-Kress Co.

GABRIELLE DESIGNS - Toys ☆ - Tide-Rider Inc.

GABSTRETCH - Crocheted and knitted items - Garland Knitting Mills

GABY - Skin care products - Gaby Inc.

GACO - Sealing compounds - Gates Engineering Co. Inc.

GAD-ABOUTS - Apparel—athletic - Bassett-Walker Inc.

GADABOUT - Boats—motor ☆ - Alumacraft Boat Co.

GADABOUT - Mopeds - Marina Mobili Inc.

GADCO - Doors—garage - General American Door Co.

G.A.D.D. - Games - Douglas E. Yingling

GADDARD MANOR - Furniture - Singer Furniture Co.

GADG-IT BAG - Bags - Lefkowitz and Santangelo Co.

GADGET GEAR BOX - Toys - Tonka Corp.

GADGET TWINS - Toys - Gametek, Inc.

GADGETS - Shoes ☆ - Edison Brothers Stores, Inc.

GADITANA - Cigarettes - Dosal Tobacco Corp.

GADJIT - Bird feeders - Mcnaughton Inc.

GADO - Glass products ☆ - Crystal International Corp.

GADO GADO PEANUT SAUCE MIX - Sauces - Cinnabar Specialty Foods, Inc./Neera's Products

GADOL - Apparel and accessories - Gadol Embroidery

GADOLITE - Diagnostic substances - Pharmacyclics, Inc.

GADROON - Dishes—earthenware ☆ - Gorham Inc.

GADROON IMPERIAL - Dishes—earthenware ☆ - Royal China & Porcelain Companies Inc.

GADSDEN - Coffee - Max Packaging Co.

GAEBEL - Rulers—wood - Arthur H. Gaebel Inc.

GAEL ROMING - Giftware - Gael's Gallery

GAELIC MIXTURE - Tobacco products - Faber, Coe & Gregg Inc.

GAEL'S GALLERY - Giftware - Gael's Gallery

GAETA - Olive oil - A & A Food Products Corp.

GAETA - Olive oil ☆ - Fred Montesi Super Markets

☆ = Now out of production

GAETANO - Liquors - Gaetano Specialties Ltd.
GAETANO & BARTEAU - Mustard - Dean & Deluca Inc.
GAF - Floor coverings ☆ - Tarkett, Inc.
GAF - Roofing materials–clay - GAF Corp.
GAF - Toys - Great American Fun Corp.
GAFCARD - Tarpaulins - GAF Corp.
GAFFA - CD storage device - International Marketing and Partner
GAFFER - Fishing tackle - Best Tackle Manufacturing Co.
GAFFERS & SATTLER - Air conditioning equipment - Gaffers & Sattler Inc.
GAFFERS G&S SATTLER - Stoves–gas - Maytag Corp.
GAFGLAS - Roofing materials–clay - GAF Corp.
GAFSTAR - Floor coverings ☆ - Tarkett, Inc.
GAFTEMP - Roofing materials–clay - GAF Corp.
GAFTEX - Polyvinyl sheets - GAF Corp.
GAFTITE - Roofing materials–clay - GAF Corp.
GAFWARE - Computer software - GAF Corp.
GAG TAG - Patches, insignia, and emblems ☆ - Best Emblem & Insignia Co. Inc.
GAGE - Food products - Vincent Food Industries Inc.
GAGEPACK - Computer software - Productivity-Quality Systems Inc.
GAGEPORT - Computer hardware - Gagetalker Corp.
GAGGLE OF GHOSTS - Giftware - Delfino Products Inc.
GAGLIANO - Recording label - Northeastern Records
GAGLIARDI - Meat extracts - Gagliardi Bros. Inc.
GAGLIARDO DIFFUSIONE SRL - Wines - Tempo Imports Ltd.
GAGLINE - Games - Carol Turley Hines
GAGNE - Wallpaper - Gagne Wallcovering, Inc.
GAI - Jewelry - Gelin & Abaci, Inc.
GAIA - Computer software - Gaia Software, Inc.
GAIA - Watches - Telux-Pioneer Inc.
GAIA GLOBAL AUTOMATED INFORMATION ACCESS - Computer software - Patricia Mathis
GAIARAMA - Toys - Aranieda's Dreams, Inc.
GAIA'S CAFE - Grain products–rice - Barbara E. Dawson
GAIETTA - Candy ☆ - Perugina Chocolate & Confections Inc.
GAIETY - Cookies - Nabisco Foods Group
GAIETY - Watches - Bulova Corp.
GAIL GIBSON - Handbags - Kadin Brothers Inc.
GAIL GRISI - Stencils - Gail Grisi Stenciling Inc.
GAIL'S HANDI-CAPPER - Sporting goods - Gail D'oca
GAIN - Detergents - Procter & Gamble Co.
GAIN BRAIN - Audio equipment - Valley Audio Products, Inc.
GAIN TRACKS - Shoes - Tingley Rubber Corp.
GAINER - Fertilizers - Smith & Ardussi, Inc.
GAINER'S - Food products - Pioneer Food Sales Inc.
GAINERS - Footwear ☆ - Strength Systems, Inc.
GAINERS EDGE - Vitamins and nutritional supplements - Nutri Science Inc.
GAINER'S EDGE - Vitamins and nutritional supplements - Vitamin Research Products Inc.
GAINER'S FUEL 1000 - Vitamins and nutritional supplements - Twinlab
GAINER'S FUEL 2500 - Vitamins and nutritional supplements - Twinlab
GAINES REPTILES - Agricultural products - Gaines Reptiles, Inc.
GAINEY - Wines ☆ - William Grant & Sons, Inc.
GAINMOMENTUM - Computer software - Gain Technology Inc.
GAINOR MEDICAL - Medical apparatus - Gainor Medical U.S.A. Inc.
GAINSBOROUGH - Artists' materials - M. Grumbacher Inc.
GAINSBOROUGH - Dishes–earthenware - Royal China & Porcelain Companies Inc.
GAINSBOROUGH - Furniture - Tomlinson of High Point Inc.
GAINSBOROUGH - Paints–artists' - Koh-I-Noor, Inc.
GAINSBOROUGH - Paper–bond - Fox River Paper Co.
GAINSBOROUGH - Paper–writing - Simpson Paper Co.
GAINSBOROUGH & HAWKE - Skin care products - Twincraft Inc.
GAINSEEKER - Computer software - Hertzler Systems Inc.
GAINTWIST - Ammunition - Gaintwist Barrel Co.
GAIT LOCK SYSTEM - Braces–orthopedic - Smith & Nephew DonJoy Inc.
GAITERMAN - Sporting goods - Ski Accessories Co.
GAITERS - Luggage - SGI Inc.
GAITWAY - Treadmills ☆ - Kistler Instrument Corp.
GAK - Toys - Viacom International Inc.
GAKKEN - Projectors–photographic - Imperial Impressions
GAL - Colognes - Brandy Harvest
GAL - Leather goods - Great American Leatherworks Inc.
GAL DESIGNS - Jewelry - Gem Appraisers Laboratory Ltd.
GAL-TEX - Food products ☆ - Grasso Foods Inc.
GAL-VAN-ITO - Paints - Masury Paint Co.

GALA - Clocks - General Time Corp. (Westclox/Seth Thomas Div.)
GALA - Dinnerware–glass - Cyclamen Studio
GALA - Dinnerware–glass ☆ - Nikko Ceramics Inc.
GALA - Fabrics - Graniteville Co.
GALA - Floor coverings - Congoleum Corp.
GALA - Footwear–athletic - Head Sports USA
GALA - Glassware–household - Oneida Ltd.
GALA - Glassware–household - Owens-Illinois Inc. (Libbey Div.)
GALA - Paper towels and napkins - James River Corp.
GALA - Pizzas–mixes - VanEerden Distribution Co.
GALA - Puddings–mixes - Yofarm Corp.
GALA! - Stationery - Royal Imprints Corp.
GALA - Wallpaper - Capital Carousel Inc.
GALA DAY - Pickles - W.B. Roddenbery Co., Inc.
GALA HOLIDAY - Greeting cards - Royal Imprints Corp.
GALA KING - Fruits and vegetables - Sales King International
GALA LIGHTS - Lamps - General Electric Co.
GALA MOOD - Floor coverings–carpet and rugs ☆ - Walter Carpet Mills
GALA NATURALS - Vitamins and nutritional supplements - Reliance Vitamin Co. Inc.
GALA PARTY - Awnings - Denver Tent Co.
GALACTIBITE - Toys - Mattel, Inc.
GALACTIC - Cameras - Eastman Kodak Co.
GALACTIC ATTACK - Computer software ☆ - Sir-Tech Software, Inc.
GALACTIC GRAPE - Fruit drinks–bottled or canned - Green Spot Packaging, Inc.
GALACTIC GREY - Cosmetics ☆ - Noxell Corp.
GALACTIC MAGELLAN - Computer software ☆ - Krell Software Corp.
GALACTIC MARAUDERS - Posters - Jay Wheatley
GALACTIC ODYSSEY - Games - David Odessey
GALACTIC SPORTS AMERICA - Croquet sets - Anodizing, Inc.
GALACTIC TAXI - Toys–models ☆ - Estes Industries
GALACTICA - Computer software - Artel Communications Corp.
GALACTICA - Floor coverings–carpet and rugs ☆ - Mannington Carpets, Inc.
GALACTICA - Footwear–athletic - L.A. Gear, Inc.
GALACTICA - Furniture ☆ - Bassett Furniture Industries, Inc.
GALACTIMYTES - Toys - Mattel, Inc.
GALACTOSAMINE HCL - Pharmaceutical preparations - Pfanstiehl Laboratories Inc.
GALACTOSE - Pharmaceutical preparations ☆ - Harvey Laboratories Inc.
GALAHAD - Computer software - Adobe Systems Inc.
GALAHAD - Watches - Bulova Corp.
GALAHAD - Waterproof outerwear - Distributors Service Corp.
GALAN - Cabinets - Galan Manufacturing Co.
GALANT - Motor vehicles–automobiles - Mitsubishi Motor Sales of America Inc.
GALANTE - Cosmetics - Gloria Shavel Inc.
GALANTERIE - Cookies ☆ - Pillsbury Co.
GALANTINES - Food products - Marcel & Henri Charcuterie Francaise
GALAPA GUS - Toys–stuffed ☆ - Gund, Inc.
GALAPO - Apparel and accessories - B.H.B. Corp.
GALASSO/ECM - Recording label - Jazz Composer's Orchestra Association Inc.
GALASUPREME - Trees - Nick L. Davis
GALATEE - Skin care products - Lancome
GALATIC CONFLICT - Games - Flying Buffalo Inc.
GALATOR THE PROTECTOR - Costumes - McCain Ellio's Foods, Inc.
GALAX - Paints ☆ - Missouri Paint & Varnish Co.
GALAXIA - Floor coverings–tile - Porcelanite, Inc.
GALAXIAN - Games - Hasbro, Inc.
GALAXIAN 2 - Toys ☆ - Placo Products Co.
GALAXIE - Blenders - Sunbeam-Oster Household Products
GALAXIE - Floor coverings ☆ - National Floor Products Co., Inc.
GALAXIE - Floor coverings–carpet and rugs ☆ - Capel, Inc.
GALAXIE - Furniture - Weiman Co.
GALAXIE - Hair care products - Galaxie Sales of America
GALAXIE - Hardware ☆ - Amerock Corp.
GALAXIE - Housewares - Radiant-Systems
GALAXIE - Insect repellents - Flowtron Outdoor Products
GALAXIE - Jewelry - House of Commans Inc.
GALAXIE - Motor vehicles–automobiles ☆ - Ford Motor Co.
GALAXIE - Truck cabs - Galaxie Corp.
GALAXIE - Typewriters - Smith Corona Corp.
GALAXIE - Watches - Elgin Watch Co.
GALAXIE 500 - Motor vehicles–automobiles ☆ - Ford Motor Co.
GALAXIE HANDPRINTS - Wallpaper - Galaxie Handprints

☆ = Now out of production

GALAXIS - Bathroom fixtures ☆ - Aqua Glass Corp.
GALAXIS - Wallpaper - Bayview Wallcoverings
GALAXIS II - Wallpaper - Bayview Wallcoverings
GALAXIS III - Wallpaper - Bayview Wallcoverings
GALAXOLIDE - Oils–essential - International Flavors & Fragrances Inc.
GALAXY - Aircraft - Galaxy Aerospace Corp.
GALAXY - Apparel and accessories ☆ - Willson/Dalloz Safety
GALAXY - Audio equipment - Galaxy Audio
GALAXY - Blinds–venetian ☆ - Kenney Manufacturing Co.
GALAXY - Blood pressure apparatus - Graham-Field Inc.
GALAXY - Boats ☆ - Metalmast Marine
GALAXY - Boats–motor - Infinity Power Boat Repair
GALAXY - Cheese - Dairy Fresh Products Co.
GALAXY - Cigarettes - Philip Morris Companies Inc.
GALAXY - Cleaning preparations–household - Colgate-Palmolive Co.
GALAXY - Compasses–gyroscopic - Rule Industries, Inc.
GALAXY - Computer software - A.C. Nielsen Co.
GALAXY - Dinnerware–glass - Metlox Pottery Shoppe
GALAXY - Dinnerware–glass - Trend Pacific Inc.
GALAXY - Dog food - Fromm Family Foods, Inc.
GALAXY - Drums–musical instruments - LP Music Group
GALAXY - Electronic equipment - Daktronics Inc.
GALAXY - Electronic equipment - Telex Communications, Inc.
GALAXY - Exercising equipment ☆ - American Athletic Inc.
GALAXY - Fabrics ☆ - Greenwood Mills Inc.
GALAXY - Fans–electric ☆ - Lasko Metal Products Inc.
GALAXY - Fencing–chain link - Reeves Southeastern Corp.
GALAXY - Floor coverings - American Floor Products Co. Inc.
GALAXY - Floor coverings - Azrock Commercial Flooring
GALAXY - Floor coverings–carpet and rugs - Galaxy Carpet Mills Inc.
GALAXY - Floor coverings–carpet and rugs ☆ - Burtco Enterprises Inc.
GALAXY - Floor coverings–carpet and rugs ☆ - Trans-Ocean Import Co. Inc.
GALAXY - Flowers, plants, and seeds - W. Atlee Burpee and Co.
GALAXY - Flowers, plants, and seeds - Turf-Seed, Inc.
GALAXY - Frames–picture - Russ Berrie and Co., Inc.
GALAXY - Furniture - American Furniture Co. Inc.
GALAXY - Furniture - Hammary Furniture Co. Inc.
GALAXY - Furniture ☆ - Bassett Furniture Industries, Inc.
GALAXY - Furniture–upholstered ☆ - Mersman Furniture Co.
GALAXY - Games ☆ - Avalon Hill Game Co.
GALAXY - Garden equipment ☆ - Lambert Manufacturing Corp.
GALAXY - Garment hangers - Carlisle Plastics, Inc.
GALAXY - Golfing equipment - Climax Clothing Industries, Inc.
GALAXY - Greeting cards ☆ - American Artists Group Inc.
GALAXY - Hair care products - Sebring Products Inc.
GALAXY - Hair care products - Ellen Voss
GALAXY - Heating equipment - Slant/Fin Corp.
GALAXY - Jewelry - Jacoby-Bender Inc.
GALAXY - Jewelry - Sun Fashion Designs Inc.
GALAXY - Lamp bulbs–incandescent ☆ - Diamond F Corp.
GALAXY - Lighting fixtures - Galaxy Electrical Manufacturing, Inc.
GALAXY - Luggage - Airway Industries, Inc.
GALAXY - Medical apparatus - Galileo Corp.
GALAXY - Musical instrument accessories - Dimarzio, Inc.
GALAXY - Ophthalmic goods ☆ - Luxottica
GALAXY - Paints - Perry & Derrick Co.
GALAXY - Paints ☆ - DecoArt, Inc.
GALAXY - Paper–gift wrap ☆ - CPS Corp.
GALAXY - Paper–writing - Butler Paper Co.
GALAXY - Phonographs - Fantasy Inc.
GALAXY - Pipe cleaners - Binford Products, Inc.
GALAXY - Rings–jewelry - Artcarved Inc.
GALAXY - Safety caps ☆ - Granet Inc.
GALAXY - Spices and extracts - CRC
GALAXY - Sporting goods ☆ - Texas Recreation Corp.
GALAXY - Telescopes and microscopes - B-R Importing Co. Inc.
GALAXY - Television equipment - Blonder-Tongue Laboratories Inc.
GALAXY - Thread ☆ - Blumenthal/Lansing Co.
GALAXY - Toilets–porcelain - Crane Plumbing/Fiat Products
GALAXY - Trailers–travel - Starcraft Corp.
GALAXY - Vegetables–canned - Oxford Corp.
GALAXY - Veterinary pharmaceutical preparations - Schering-Plough Animal Health
GALAXY - Wallpaper ☆ - Schooner Prints Inc.
GALAXY - Whiskey - Joseph E. Seagram & Sons, Inc.
GALAXY - Window coverings - Levolor Inc.

GALAXY 2000 - Chairs–plastic - Base Comfort, Inc.
GALAXY A GO GO - Dolls - Mattel, Inc.
GALAXY BOOKS - Publisher's imprints - Oxford University Press Inc.
GALAXY COMMAND - Games - Brown and Bigelow Inc.
GALAXY CREATIONS - Jewelry - Galaxy Creations
GALAXY DINER - Apparel and accessories - JB's Restaurants, Inc.
GALAXY EXPLORER - Infant product ☆ - Century Products Co.
GALAXY FIGHTERS - Toys ☆ - Jak-Pak Inc.
GALAXY FLYER - Bicycles - Western Auto Supply Co.
GALAXY GANG, THE - Dolls - Milande Corp.
GALAXY I - Cutlery - Robinson Knife & Fiddlers Plastics
GALAXY II - Cutlery - Robinson Knife & Fiddlers Plastics
GALAXY II - Furniture ☆ - Bassett Furniture Industries, Inc.
GALAXY MATH COURSEWARE PLUS - Recording label - Random House, Inc.
GALAXY MATH FACTS - Recording label - Random House, Inc.
GALAXY NAIL PRODUCTS OF THE FUTURE - Nail care products - Galaxy Nail Products of the Future, Inc.
GALAXY PEARL - Jewelry - Ears-R-In Inc.
GALAXY REVISITED - Christmas tree ornaments - Cracker Box Inc.
GALAXY TRUCK & TRACTOR - Tires - Galaxy Tire & Wheel, Inc.
GALAXY WASH - Apparel and accessories - Marinos California Inc.
GALAXY WHIRL - Playground equipment - Miracle Recreation Equipment Co.
GALBANI - Cheese - Swissrose International Inc.
GALBRAITH - Nautical instruments - Marine Electric Systems Inc.
GALCO - Chronographs ☆ - Smith Time Inc.
GALCO - Firearms, accessories, and parts - Richard N. Gallagher
GALE - Motors–outboard - Outboard Marine Corp.
GALE - Musical instrument accessories ☆ - Bay Woodwind Mouthpieces
GALE - Ophthalmic goods - Styl-Rite Optical Manufacturing Co., Inc.
GALE AND GREGORY - Musical instrument accessories - Bay Woodwind Mouthpieces
GALE ART - Dinnerware–glass ☆ - Kenro Inc.
GALE FORCE - Apparel and accessories - Gayle Dephilippis
GALE FORCE - Ships–sailing vessels - John Kaiser Associates Inc.
GALE FORCE - Sporting goods - Gale Force Technologies Inc.
GALE GOULD - Apparel–women's - Anne Klein & Co.
GALE HAYMAN BEVERLY HILLS - Cosmetics - La Parfumerie Inc.
GALE HAYMAN BEVERLY HILLS MAN - Perfumes - La Parfumerie Inc.
GALE RESEARCH - Publisher's imprints - The Gale Group
GALE-SOBEL - Uniforms–tailored - Gale-Sobel Co.
GALENA - Floor coverings–carpet and rugs ☆ - Galaxy Carpet Mills Inc.
GALENA GIFT GALLERY - Giftware - Cotter & Co.
GALENAMINE - Health care products ☆ - Halsey Drug Co. Inc.
GALERIA - Furniture - Haworth, Inc.
GALERIA - Paints–artists' - Winsor & Newton
GALERIE BRAUN - Posters - Graphic Arts Unltd. Inc.
GALERIE WATARI JAPAN - Postcards - Fotofolio Inc.
GALET - Floor coverings–carpet and rugs ☆ - Regal Rugs Inc.
GALEY AND LORD - Fabrics - Galey and Lord Inc.
GALIANO - Musical instruments ☆ - Meisel Music Inc.
GALICE PLASTER - Wallcovering - Galice, Inc.
GALIEN JET - Hydrotherapy equipment - Setma, Inc.
GALIL - Boots - Moteng International, Inc.
GALIL - Food products - Empire Kosher Poultry Inc.
GALIL - Meat products–poultry ☆ - Hebrew Foods Inc.
GALILEA - Clocks - Sarut Inc.
GALILEO - Computer software - S3 Inc.
GALILEO - Computer software ☆ - Krell Software Corp.
GALILEO - Cosmetics ☆ - P.S. Pibbs Inc.
GALILEO - Dental equipment - Tec Ventures, Inc.
GALILEO - Electronic equipment - Galileo Corp.
GALILEO - Exercising equipment - Trotter Inc.
GALILEO - Magnifiers and microscopes - Discipline Marketing Inc.
GALILEO - Mattresses - Ohio Mattress Co.
GALILEO - Meat products–beef - Galileo-Capri Salami Inc.
GALILEO - Pet products - Nylabone Products
GALILEO - Pet products - T.F.H. Publications, Inc.
GALILEO - Pizzas–frozen - Sara Lee Corp.
GALILEO - Semiconductors - Galileo Technology, Inc.
GALILEO - Thermometers - La Crosse-McCormick
GALILEO ELECTRO-OPTICS - Electrical industrial apparatus ☆ - Galileo Corp.
GALINA - Dressing gowns - Galina-Bouquet Inc.
GALINA - Ophthalmic goods - Swank Optical
GALINA BOUQUET - Dressing gowns - Galina-Bouquet Inc.
GALITAINE - Lenses–optical ☆ - Ambassador Eyewear Group

☆ = Now out of production

GALIXY GROWTH CHAIR - Medical apparatus ✩ - Ortho-Kinetics, Inc.
GALJ - Jewelry - Baguette Unlimited, Inc.
GALL BLADDER - Health care products - Ion Laboratories Inc.
GALL-CHOL - Pharmaceutical preparations - T. Prowell Estate
GALLAGHER & BURTON - Whiskey - Four Roses Distillers Co.
GALLAGHERS - Cigars - M. Marsh & Son
GALLAHER'S LATAKIA - Tobacco products - Faber, Coe & Gregg Inc.
GALLANT - Clocks - General Time Corp. (Westclox/Seth Thomas Div.)
GALLANT - Floor coverings—carpet and rugs ✩ - Interloom Ltd.
GALLANT - Food products - SD Fisheries Enterprises Inc.
GALLANT - Frames—eyeglass - Zylo Ware Corp.
GALLANT - Lipsticks ✩ - Shiseido Cosmetics (America) Ltd.
GALLANT - Luggage - Samsonite Corp.
GALLANT - Pet products ✩ - Staff Supermarket Associates, Inc.
GALLANT - Thread ✩ - Coats and Clark Inc.
GALLANT GAL - Frames—eyeglass - Zylo Ware Corp.
GALLANT GATORS - Greeting cards - A + A
GALLANT GREETINGS - Greeting cards - Gallant Greetings Corp.
GALLANT GREETINGS KEYPERS - Key rings ✩ - Gallant Greetings Corp.
GALLANT LAD - Frames—eyeglass - Zylo Ware Corp.
GALLANT MAN - Frames—eyeglass - Zylo Ware Corp.
GALLANTES - Cigars - General Cigar Co., Inc.
GALLANTRY - Floor coverings—carpet and rugs - Robertex Associates Inc.
GALLANTRY - Floor coverings—carpet and rugs ✩ - Karastan-Bigelow Inc.
GALLANTRY - Floor coverings—carpet and rugs ✩ - Kelly Group Inc.
GALLANTRY ACCENTS - Floor coverings—carpet and rugs ✩ - Karastan-Bigelow Inc.
GALLATIN - Floor coverings—carpet and rugs - Bloomsburg Carpet Industries
GALLATIN - Mobile homes - Wick Building Systems Inc. (Manufactured Home Div./North)
GALLAXY - Flatware - Couzon USA
GALLAXY - Toys - Childcraft Education Corp.
GALLAY - Apparel—women's - MGRR, Inc.
GALLE - Floor coverings—carpet and rugs ✩ - Hollytex Carpet Mills Inc.
GALLEANO - Wines - Galleano Winery Inc.
GALLEN BEAR - Apparel and accessories - Warnaco Inc.
GALLENKAMP - Shoes - Hills Department Store Co.
GALLEON - Sinks—metal - Kohler Co.
GALLEONS OF GLORY - Computer software ✩ - Broderbund Software, Inc.
GALLER - Yarn - Joseph Galler Inc.
GALLERIA - Bathroom fixtures - American Standard Inc.
GALLERIA - Boots - Galleria Footwear Ltd. Inc.
GALLERIA - Cabinets—wood - Decora
GALLERIA - Candlesticks ✩ - Carolina Designs Ltd.
GALLERIA - Ceramic wall tile - Interceramic Inc.
GALLERIA - Dinnerware—glass - WMF/USA
GALLERIA - Electric lighting equipment - Fullerton Corp.
GALLERIA - Eyeglasses - Martin-Copeland Eyewear Corp.
GALLERIA - Fans—electric - Waban Inc.
GALLERIA - Floor coverings—carpet and rugs ✩ - American Carpet Mills
GALLERIA - Floor coverings—carpet and rugs ✩ - Mannington Carpets, Inc.
GALLERIA - Floor coverings—carpet and rugs ✩ - World Carpets, Inc.
GALLERIA - Flower pots—plastic - Krueger International, Inc.
GALLERIA - Flowers, plants, and seeds - Ball Horticultural Co.
GALLERIA - Frames—picture - Ammak Manufacturing Corp.
GALLERIA - Glassware—household ✩ - Toscany Imports Ltd.
GALLERIA - Scissors—hand-operated - Acme United Corp.
GALLERIA - Tiles—ceramic ✩ - Laufen Ceramic Tile
GALLERIA - Wallcovering - The Creative Edge, Inc.
GALLERIA FLOORS - Flooring—hardwood - Superior Products, Inc.
GALLERIA LONE STAR LIMITED, THE - Apparel and accessories - Galleria, Inc.
GALLERIA LUCIDO - Mirrors - Empire Art Products Co., Inc.
GALLERIA STONEWEAR - Ceramic tile ✩ - Integrity Tile Co.
GALLERIA WALLS - Wallcoverings - Designtex Fabrics Inc.
GALLERY - Apparel—children's - Young Gallery Ltd.
GALLERY - Ashtrays—glass ✩ - Akay Corp.
GALLERY - Bulletin boards—cork - K & M Co.
GALLERY - Candy ✩ - R.M. Palmer Co.
GALLERY - Dinnerware—glass ✩ - WMF/USA
GALLERY - Fireplaces ✩ - Thomas Industries Inc.
GALLERY - Floor coverings—carpet and rugs - Dan River Inc.
GALLERY - Floor coverings—carpet and rugs ✩ - Len Dal Carpets
GALLERY - Frames—eyeglass - Kenmark Optical Co.
GALLERY - Furniture - Boling Co.
GALLERY - Greeting cards ✩ - Chase Collection, Inc.

GALLERY - Hardware - National Manufacturing Co.
GALLERY - Hardware ✩ - Amerock Corp.
GALLERY - Lighting fixtures - Visador Co.
GALLERY - Pens - National Pen Co.
GALLERY - Photo albums - Eastman Kodak Co.
GALLERY - Puzzles - Hasbro, Inc.
GALLERY - Puzzles ✩ - Milton Bradley Co.
GALLERY - Refrigerators - White Consolidated Industries, Inc.
GALLERY - Tiles—ceramic ✩ - Epro Inc.
GALLERY - Varnishes - Perry & Derrick Co.
GALLERY - Wallpaper - Morton Jonap Co. Inc.
GALLERY - Wallpaper - Surface Industries Inc.
GALLERY 2 - Figurines - Schmid Inc.
GALLERY 66 - Statuary ✩ - Artisan House Inc.
GALLERY 100 - Paper - Rising Paper, Division of Fox River Paper Co.
GALLERY ART COLLECTION - Statuary - General Foam Plastics Corp.
GALLERY ART GLASS OF CALIFORNIA - Lighting fixtures ✩ - Root Candle Co.
GALLERY BRICK - Floor coverings—tile ✩ - National Floor Products Co., Inc.
GALLERY BY HAGGAR, THE - Apparel and accessories - Haggar Corp.
GALLERY CLIPS - Frames—picture - Gallery Clips Co.
GALLERY CLIPS - Hardware - Moore Push-Pin Co.
GALLERY COLLECTION - Flatware ✩ - National Housewares
GALLERY COLLECTION - Furniture ✩ - Hooker Furniture Corp.
GALLERY COLLECTION - Toys - Lloyderson Dolls & Toys
GALLERY COLLECTION, THE - Posters ✩ - New York Graphic Society Publishing Group
GALLERY COLLECTION, THE - Christmas cards - Prudent Publishing Co.
GALLERY COLLECTIONS - Cosmetics ✩ - Noxell Corp.
GALLERY COLLECTIONS - Dinnerware ✩ - Sakura Inc.
GALLERY DESIGNS - Tiles—ceramic ✩ - Monarch Tile Inc.
GALLERY EDITION - Novelty items—paper - Antioch Publishing Co.
GALLERY FILMS - Motion picture distributors—prerecorded - Gallery Films, Inc.
GALLERY GLASS - Artists' materials - Plaid Enterprises, Inc.
GALLERY GREETINGS - Greeting cards - Gibson Greetings, Inc.
GALLERY II - Recording label - Playback Records
GALLERY IMPRESSIONS - Skin care products - Imagination & Co.
GALLERY MATS - Mat boards - Onyx Mat Board
GALLERY MATS SUPREME - Mat boards ✩ - Onyx Mat Board
GALLERY MINIATURES - Novelty items ✩ - Evergreen Press
GALLERY OF COLORS - Paints ✩ - Montgomery Ward & Co. Inc.
GALLERY OF HORSES - Greeting cards - Leanin' Tree Inc.
GALLERY OF THE WEST - Greeting cards - Leanin' Tree Inc.
GALLERY ONE - Dyes and pigments - Engelhard Corp.
GALLERY OPAQUES - Pottery products - Duncan Enterprises
GALLERY RAIL - Hardware ✩ - Amerock Corp.
GALLERY SERIES - Door mats - Royal Rubber & Manufacturing Co.
GALLERY SERIES - Furniture - Nucraft Furniture Co.
GALLERY SERIES - Hobby kits - Craft House Corp.
GALLERY SERIES - Tiles—ceramic - Monarch Tile Inc.
GALLERY SPEC - Frames—eyeglass - May Optical Co. Inc.
GALLERY, THE - Glassware—household ✩ - Anchor Hocking Glass, Inc.
GALLERYWALL - Fabrics - Interials Inc.
GALLERYWALL - Frames—picture - Jeanmarie Gallery
GALLET - Chronographs ✩ - Smith Time Inc.
GALLEY - Cleaning preparations - Sterling Winthrop Inc.
GALLEY - Food products ✩ - Rowena's Gourmet Foods Inc.
GALLEY HEAT - Epoxy coatings - Sterling-Clark-Lurton Corp.
GALLEY MATE - Pressure vessels - Raritan Engineering Co. Inc.
GALLEY PRESS - Publisher's imprints ✩ - Smithmark Publishers
GALLI - Musical instrument accessories - Lo Duca Bros. Musical Instruments Inc.
GALLIA - Housewares - May Department Stores Co.
GALLIANO - Beverages—alcohol - Remy Amerique Inc.
GALLIKER DAIRY - Milk - Galliker Dairy Co. Inc.
GALLIPOT - Pharmaceutical preparations - Gallipot, Inc.
GALLIVARE - Beverages - Arctic Icewater
GALLO - Cigars ✩ - Avanti Cigar Co.
GALLO - Food products - Homestead Ravioli Co.
GALLO - Recording label - Organ Literature Foundation
GALLO - Statuary - Gallo Pewter Sculptures Corp.
GALLO - Wines - Ernest and Julio Gallo Winery
GALLO & GALLILEO - Meat products—beef - Gallo Salame Inc.
GALLO LIVINGSTON CELLARS - Wines - Ernest and Julio Gallo Winery

✩ = Now out of production

GALLO LIVINGSTON CELLARS SINCE 1933 PREMIUM SELECT - Wines - E. & J. Gallo Winery

GALLO SALAME - Meat products–beef - Gallo Salame Inc.

GALLO SONOMA - Wines - Ernest and Julio Gallo Winery

GALLO WINERY - Bottles–glass - Gallo Glass Co.

GALLOCRAFT - Pet products - Gallo Manufacturing Co.

GALLON - Eggs - Almark Inc.

GALLON-SPENSER - Health care products - Apothecary Products, Inc.

GALLOP - Games - Kadon Enterprises Inc.

GALLOP - Toys–models ☆ - Cox Products Inc.

GALLOP 'N GLIDE - Playground equipment - Wonderline

GALLOPING GARLIC - Spices and extracts - Jodie's Kitchen Inc.

GALLOPING GOURMET - Knife sharpeners - Wilbur Freifeld

GALLOWAY II - Wallpaper ☆ - Koroseal Wallcoverings

GALLOWAY WEST - Dairy products - Galloway-West Co.

GALL'S GEAR - Apparel and accessories - Gall's Inc.

GALOOB - Games - Lewis Galoob Toys, Inc.

GALOPECTIN - Pharmaceutical preparations ☆ - Wesley Pharmacal Co. Inc.

GALORE - Floor coverings–carpet and rugs ☆ - Columbus Mills, Inc.

GALORE - Perfumes - Monteil Paris

GALOTTA - Accordions - Castiglione Accordion

GALT CREW - Apparel and accessories - Galt Sand Co.

GALT SAND - Sweatshirts - Galt Sand Co.

GALTECH - Apparel and accessories - Galtech Computer Corp.

GALTEE - Earthenware ☆ - Waterford Wedgwood USA, Inc.

GALV-A-GARD - Garden equipment - Gilbert and Bennett Manufacturing Co.

GALV-A-GRIP - Paints - Dap Products Inc.

GALV-A-TECH III - Hardware - Stanley-Bostitch Inc.

GALV-ALUM - Paints - Dunn Edwards Corp.

GALVA-BOND - Paint primer - Iowa Paint Manufacturing Co. Inc.

GALVA-ETCH - Paints - Dunn Edwards Corp.

GALVA-GUARD - Paints - Vanguard Paints & Finishes Inc.

GALVA-LEX - Paints - Kentucky Paint Manufacturing Co.

GALVA-MATE - Paint primer - Zynolyte Products Co.

GALVA-SELE - Paints ☆ - Waterlox Coatings Corp.

GALVA-TEX - Paints - Valspar Corp.

GALVA TRUSS - Construction equipment - Angeles Metal Systems

GALVA WASH - Adhesives and sealants - Sinclair Paint Co.

GALVA-WHITE - Paints - Colony Paints Div.

GALVABEAD - Drywall corner bead - Bostwick Steel Lath Co.

GALVACOR - Metals - Illinois Tool Works Inc.

GALVACORNER - External corner bead for drywall - Bostwick Steel Lath Co.

GALVACOTE - Paint removers - Farwest Paint Manufacturing Co. Inc.

GALVAHIDE - Paints ☆ - PPG Industries, Inc.

GALVALINE - Shelving units–metal - Storex Division

GALVALUME - Playground equipment ☆ - Hedstrom Corp.

GALVANAID - Paint - American Paints

GALVANI - Footwear - Antenori Footwear Inc.

GALVANODE - Paints - Briner Paint Manufacturing Co. Inc.

GALVAPREP - Adhesives and sealants - Parker & Amchem

GALVAPRIME - Paints ☆ - Dunn Edwards Corp.

GALVAREX - Paints - Hanley Paint Manufacturing Co. Inc.

GALVASEAL - Varnishes - Lubrizol Corp.

GALVASTUD - Drywall metal screw studs - Bostwick Steel Lath Co.

GALVATRACK - Drywall metal screw track - Bostwick Steel Lath Co.

GALVAX - Rustproofing compounds - Alvin Products Inc.

GALVEST - Paints - Empire Blended Products Co.

GALVETCH - Paints - Triangle Coatings Inc.

GALVICON - Finishing agents - Pratt & Lambert United, Inc.

GALVIKLING - Paints - Graham Paint and Varnish Co.

GALVINOLEUM - Finishing agents - Rust-Oleum Corp.

GALVITE - Hardware - Sherwin-Williams Automotive Finishes Corp.

GALVO - Paints - Dozier & Gay Paint Co.

GALVOCOAT - Paints - Hempel Coatings USA Inc.

GALVOLITE - Paints ☆ - Atlas Chemical Co.

GALVOSIL - Paints - Hempel Coatings USA Inc.

GALVZINC - Paints - OEM Paints, Inc.

GALWAY - Floor coverings–carpet and rugs - Patrick Carpet Mills

GALWAY - Frames–eyeglass - Pathway Optical Prods.

GALWAY - House furnishings ☆ - Burwood Products Co.

GALWAY - Yarn - Plymouth Yarn Co.

GALWAY BAY - Floor coverings–carpet and rugs ☆ - Karastan-Bigelow Inc.

GALWAY TECHNOLOGIES, INC - Computer software - Galway Technologies, Inc.

GAM - Caulking guns - Great American Marketing, Inc.

GAM ENTERPRISES - Paper products - Sy Gam Enterprises, Inc.

GAMA - Computers - Gama Computers, Inc.

GAMA - Fabrics - Interface, Inc.

GAMA-DMG - Vitamins and nutritional supplements - Great Life Laboratories Inc.

GAMAR PICTURE VARNISH - Varnishes - Gamblin Artists Colors Co.

GAMBARELLI - Tiles–ceramic - United Ceramic Tile Corp.

GAMBELINI - Syrup - National Fruit Flavor Co.

GAMBI - Frames–eyeglass - May Optical Co. Inc.

GAMBI GIRLS - Apparel–children's - Gambella Industries, Inc.

GAMBIA - Floor coverings–carpet and rugs ☆ - Columbus Mills, Inc.

GAMBILLS - Food products - Beatrice Cos. Inc.

GAMBINA - Beverages–alcohol - Castiglione Imports

GAMBINA - Dolls - C.V. Gambina Inc.

GAMBIT - Books–comic - Marvel Entertainment Group, Inc.

GAMBIT - Publisher's imprints - Gambit Inc. Publishers

GAMBIT SERIES - Audio equipment - G Prime Limited

GAMBLE - Musical instrument accessories ☆ - Crest Audio Inc.

GAMBLE & HUFF - Recording label - Gamble Huff Music Productions

GAMBLER - Apparel and accessories - Kenny Rogers Productions

GAMBLER - Cigarette paper - Republic Tobacco L.P.

GAMBLER - Cigars - E. Regensburg & Sons

GAMBLER - Eyeglasses - Art-Craft Optical Co.

GAMBLER - Games ☆ - Parker Brothers

GAMBLER - Perfumes - Quintessence Inc.

GAMBLER MUSK - Shaving preparations - Quintessence Inc.

GAMBLER'S CHOICE BLACKJACK - Games - Steven A. Schorr

GAMBLER'S EXCUSE - Paper - MRM Entertainment Inc.

GAMBLING DARTS - Games ☆ - Ben Cooper Inc.

GAMBOGI RANCH - Wines - Deloach Vineyards

GAMBOL - Floor coverings–carpet and rugs ☆ - Regal Rugs Inc.

GAMBOLEERS - Shoes - Manistee Inc.

GAMBRELLE - Ophthalmic goods ☆ - Luxottica

GAMBRINUS - Wines - Beauvignot International Inc.

GAME - Apparel and accessories - Winston Manufacturing Corp.

GAME BABIES - Games - Tyco Industries, Inc.

GAME BALL - Apparel and accessories - Insana-Tee's

GAME BIRD - Fruits and vegetables ☆ - Peshastin Fruit Growers Association

GAME BIRDS - Dinnerware–glass ☆ - Johnson Brothers, USA, Inc.

GAME BOY - Video games - Nintendo of America Inc.

GAME BOY POCKET - Games - Nintendo of America Inc.

GAME BREAKERS - Trading cards and stamps - Score Board Holding Corp.

GAME BUSTER GET A CLUE! - Publisher's imprints - Prima Communications, Inc.

GAME CAT - Footwear–athletic - Puma Inc.

GAME CHEST - Games ☆ - Carrom Co.

GAME COCK - Animal feeds - Bluebonnet Milling Co.

GAME COUNTRY - Fishing tackle - Data Signal Inc.

GAME DAY - Sausages - Hormel Foods Corp.

GAME DECOR - Games ☆ - S.J. Miller Co.

GAME-DESIGN - Games - Drybranch Inc./Sport Design

GAME EAR - Amplifiers - Walker's (Game Ear), Inc.

GAME EAR II AFT - Amplifiers - Walker's (Game Ear), Inc.

GAME FACE - Apparel–athletic - Game Face Inc.

GAME FACES - Skin care products - Team Dynamics

GAME FACES - Trading cards and stamps - Upper Deck Co.

GAME FOR ANYTHING - Underwear and nightwear - Maidenform Inc.

GAME GEAR - Sporting goods - Pete Rickard Inc.

GAME GENIE - Games - Lewis Galoob Toys, Inc.

GAME GETTER - Guns - Marble Arms Corp.

GAME GIRL - Video games - Nintendo of America Inc.

GAME HEAD - Computer software - Pacific Hitech, Inc.

GAME LAB - Shirts - Viacom International Inc.

GAME LIGHT PLUS - Video equipment - Curtis Manufacturing Co., Inc.

GAME LINK - Video games - Nintendo of America Inc.

GAME LORDS - Computer software - Dream Quest Games, Ltd.

GAME MACHINE, THE - Games - Reuben B. Klamer

GAME MAKER - Computer software - Activision, Inc.

GAME MAKER - Game machines - Bally Gaming International, Inc.

GAME MAKER - Games - Little Kenny Publications Inc.

GAME MASTER - Eyeglasses - Art-Craft Optical Co.

GAME OF GO - Games ☆ - Milton Bradley Co.

GAME OF GOOD COOKING, THE - Games - Avalon Hill Game Co.

GAME OF LAW SCHOOL, THE - Games - Charles Game Concepts, Inc.

GAME OF LIFE, THE - Games - Milton Bradley Co.

GAME OF NATIONS, THE - Games - Franklin Merchandising Co.

GAME OF POST OFFICE, THE - Games - Cathy Anderson

☆ = Now out of production

GAME OF SOLOMON - Games - Kadon Enterprises Inc.

GAME OF THE LABYRINTH, THE - Games - Kadon Enterprises Inc.

GAME OF THE STATES - Games - Milton Bradley Co.

GAME OF TRIVIA - Games - Avalon Hill Game Co.

GAME OF Y - Games - Kadon Enterprises Inc.

GAME POINT - Archery equipment - Pro Line Co.

GAME POINT - Lenses–optical - Ditto Industries Inc.

GAME POWER FOR PHONICS PLUS - Computer software - Spin-A-Test Publishing Co.

GAME PRESERVES - Toys - T.J.K. Sales Inc.

GAME RECYCLERS - Video games - Movies and Games 4 Sale, LP

GAME REFUGE, INC. - Computer software - Game Refuge, Inc.

GAME SAK - Cases–plastic - Ryka Associates, Inc.

GAME SHOW, THE - Computer software - Advanced Ideas

GAME SHOW, THE - Game machines - Midway Manufacturing Co.

GAME SNAPS - Brackets - Vertical Designs Inc.

GAME SOCKS - Socks - Ridgeview Inc.

GAME TAME - Meat sauces - Allegro Fine Foods, Inc.

GAME TAMERS - Toys - Fun Factory, Inc.

GAME TIME - Playground equipment - Game Time, Inc.

GAME TIME PASTA - Pasta - Buckeye Beans & Herbs, Inc.

GAME TIME TOUGHIES - Dolls - Russ Berrie and Co., Inc.

GAME TOTE - Game machines - Ryka Associates, Inc.

GAME TRACKER, THE - Tools–hand-operated - Game Tracker, Inc.

GAME WAVE - Circuit boards - Orchid Technology

GAME WINNER, THE - Sporting goods - Regent Sports Corp.

GAME WITHIN THE GAME, THE - Sporting goods - Banner Strategies

GAME WORN JERSEYS - Novelty items - Sports Novelties Co.

GAME YOU CAN'T GET ENOUGH OF, THE - Games - Hasbro, Inc.

GAME ZIPPER - Knives–hunting - United Cutlery Corp.

GAMEBIT - Tools–hand-operated - Feinblanking Limited, Inc.

GAMECARD 3 AUTOMATIC - Computer peripheral equipment - Joystick Technologies (CH Products Division)

GAMECARD 3 AUTOMATIC - Electronic equipment - CH Products Div.

GAMECOCK - Food products - W.B. Roddenbery Co., Inc.

GAMECOCK - Sardines–canned ☆ - Stinson Seafood Co.

GAMECRAFT - Sporting goods - Sport Supply Group, Inc.

GAMEFISHER - Boats–motor - Sears, Roebuck and Co.

GAMEGEN - Computer software - Multigen Inc.

GAMEGETTER - Sporting goods - Easton Aluminum Inc.

GAMEKEEPER - Computers - Bally Gaming International, Inc.

GAMEKEEPER - Knives–pocket - Queen Cutlery Co.

GAMEL - Ophthalmic goods - Rozin Optical Export Corp.

GAMELLI - Coffee makers–electric - Sara Lee Corp.

GAMELON - Computer software - Menai Corp.

GAMEMAKER - Game machines - Bally Gaming International, Inc.

GAMEMASTER - Ammunition ☆ - Remington Arms Co., Inc.

GAMEMASTER - Games - Avalon Hill Game Co.

GAMEMASTER KNIFE - Knives–hunting - Jeffrey Paul Hendrickson

GAMEMASTER'S PACK - Games - Mayfair Games, Inc.

GAMEMILL - Computer software - Andrew Gelfand

GAMEPAK - Computer software ☆ - Zephyr Services

GAMEPLAN - Frames–eyeglass - Liberty Optical Manufacturing Co.

GAMEPLAYERTV - Computers - Aitech International Corp.

GAMEPOINT - Game machines - Bally Gaming International, Inc.

GAMER - Sporting goods - Gear 2000, Ltd.

GAMES 4 ALL - Game kits - Jerry A. Stebing

GAMES FOR GROWING - Educational games - International Games

GAMES GIRLS PLAY - Calendars - Coastline Entertainment Production

GAMES OF NEVADA - Video games - Mikohn Gaming Corp.

GAMES PEOPLE PLAY, THE - Games - Tibbits International

GAMES THAT TEACH THE MIND TO THINK - Puzzles - Rex Games, Inc.

GAMESCAN - Computer hardware - Telescan Systems, Inc.

GAMESCAPE - Toys - Geo-Hex

GAMESCIENCE - Games - Gamescience

GAMESHOOTER - Food products ☆ - Belleville Shoe Manufacturing Co.

GAMESMANSHIP - Frames–eyeglass - Zylo Ware Corp.

GAMESTAR - Computer peripheral equipment - DynaPoint Inc.

GAMESTER - Sporting goods ☆ - Martin Reel Co.

GAMESTICK - Computer peripheral equipment - Joystick Technologies (CH Products Division)

GAMETECH - Trade Associations - Gem Communications, Inc.

GAMETEK CINEMA - Recording label - Gametek, Inc.

GAMETIME - Playing cards ☆ - United States Playing Card Co.

GAMEVIEW - Computer software - Scorequest, Inc.

GAMEWARMER - Apparel–athletic - Majestic Athletic Wear, Ltd.

GAMEWINNERS - Trading cards and stamps - Pinnacle Brands, Inc.

GAMEWIZARDS - Computer software - Gamewizards, Inc.

GAMEWRIGHT - Games - Gamewright, Inc.

GAMFUSION - Filters–industrial - Gam Products, Inc.

GAMIN - Frames–eyeglass - May Optical Co. Inc.

GAMINE - Hosiery–women's - Easton International

GAMING A K Q J 10 - Video games - Arachnid, Inc.

GAMING SERVICES INTERNATIONAL - Game machines - Gaming Services International

GAMINI RODNIVIRA - Giftware - Reco International Corp.

GAMLA - Wines - Kedem Royal Wine Corp.

GAMLA - Wines - Royal Wine Corp.

GAMM - Popcorn - Julius Gamm Co. Inc.

GAMM ORYZANOL PLUS - Health care products ☆ - Nature Health

GAMMA - Bottles–plastic - American National Can Co.

GAMMA - Doors–metal - United Dominion Industries, Inc.

GAMMA - Electronics equipment - RTI Research Technology International

GAMMA - Guitars - N.H.F. Musical Merchandise Corp.

GAMMA - Health care products - Pharmaceutical Innovations

GAMMA - Ophthalmic goods - Rozin Optical Export Corp.

GAMMA - Ophthalmic goods ☆ - Luxottica

GAMMA - Paints - M. Grumbacher Inc.

GAMMA - Partitions–wood - Advanced Equipment Corp.

GAMMA - Sporting goods - Century Sports Inc.

GAMMA - Sporting goods - Ferrari Importing Co.

GAMMA - Sporting goods - Georgia's Tennis

GAMMA - Toys–models ☆ - Estes Industries

GAMMA 500 - Health care products - Above All Health Inc.

GAMMA BOLIC - Health care products - Sports Research Corp.

GAMMA EPA - Vitamins and nutritional supplements ☆ - Optimal Nutrients

GAMMA-GUARD - Sporting goods - Gamma Sports

GAMMA OIL - Pharmaceutical preparations ☆ - Optimal Nutrients

GAMMA PLEX - Health care products - Anabol Naturals

GAMMA PLUS - Furniture - Haworth, Inc.

GAMMA PLUS - Photographic chemicals - Alta Photographic Inc.

GAMMA RANGE - Paints ☆ - M. Grumbacher Inc.

GAMMA-RUFF - Sporting goods - Gamma Sports

GAMMA SEAL LID, THE - Containers–plastic - Gamma Plastics, Inc.

GAMMA-SORPTION - Pharmaceutical preparations ☆ - Bricker Laboratories

GAMMA SYSTEM - Sporting goods - Gamma Sports

GAMMA UNIVERSE - Computer software - Gamma Productions, Inc.

GAMMA WORLD - Games ☆ - Tsr, Inc.

GAMMACLEAN - Cleaning preparations - Applied Radiant Energy Corp.

GAMMAFRAC - Vitamins and nutritional supplements - Source Naturals

GAMMAGEE - Pharmaceutical preparations ☆ - Merck & Co., Inc. (Merck Research Laboratories)

GAMMAGRAPH - Computer hardware - Gammagraphx, Inc.

GAMMALLOY - Floor coverings - Applied Radiant Energy Corp.

GAMMAPAR - Floor coverings - Applied Radiant Energy Corp.

GAMMAPLANK - Floor coverings - Applied Radiant Energy Corp.

GAMMAR - Pharmaceutical preparations ☆ - Armour Pharmaceutical Co.

GAMMARAUDERS - Games ☆ - Tsr, Inc.

GAMMASOL - Stains - Applied Radiant Energy Corp.

GAMMASTRIP - Floor coverings - Applied Radiant Energy Corp.

GAMMATILE - Floor coverings ☆ - Applied Radiant Energy Corp.

GAMMAX - Paper products - Labelon Corp.

GAMMEL DANSK BITTERS - Beverages–alcohol - Jim Beam Brands Co.

GAMMEX - Medical apparatus - Gammex, Inc.

GAMMEX RMI - Medical apparatus - Gammex, Inc.

GAMMON - Floor coverings–carpet and rugs - Helios Carpets

GAMMON REEL - Surveying machinery - Gammon Reel, Inc.

GAMORREAN GUARD - Soap - Lucasfilm Ltd.

GAMPI TORINOKO - Artists' materials - Andrews/Nelson/Whitehead

GAMULIN RH - Pharmaceutical preparations ☆ - Parke-Davis

GAMUTGAUGE - Computer software - Candela, Ltd.

GANATREX - Pharmaceutical preparations ☆ - Marion Merrell Dow

GANCIA - Wines - Paterno Imports, Ltd.

GANDER MOUNTAIN - Apparel and accessories - Gander Mountain, Inc.

GANDER, THE - Embossing plates - Devin-Adair Co. Inc.

G&H - Metals - G & H Products Corp.

GANDHI - Food products - Indian Foods Co.

GANDY - Pool tables - Macon Manufacturing

GANDY DANCER - Book ends - S.J. Miller Co.

GANDY QUALITY CHECK - Dairy products - Dean Foods Co.

GANDYS - Dairy products - Gandys Dairies Inc.

GANELES ORIGINALS - Greeting cards - Ganeles Hebrew Cards

GANESH & CO. - Publisher's imprint - Auromere Inc.
GANG GREEN - Candy - Doug Johnson, Inc.
GANG-LAM - Wood products - Mitek Industries Inc.
GANG-LAMLUMINATED - Lumber - Louisiana-Pacific Corp.
GANG LOCK, THE - Locking mechanism - Feterl Manufacturing Co.
GANG NAIL - Hardware - Mitek Industries Inc.
GANG PEACE - Apparel and accessories - Gang Peace
GANG WAY - Apparel and accessories - Paul Blessington
GANGBUSTERS - Games ☆ - Tsr, Inc.
GANGCHEN CARPETS - Floor coverings–carpet and rugs - Innerasia Trading Co. Inc.
GANGI - Vegetables–canned - Gangi Bros. Packing Co.
GANGSTA BOOTY - Cosmetics - Hard Candy, Inc.
GANGSTERS - Games - Avalon Hill Game Co.
GANGWAY - Fabrics - Greenwood Mills Inc.
GANICIN - Paints - E.I. Dupont de Nemours and Co.
GANJA - Apparel and accessories - John S. Woodward
GANNETT MEDIA TECHNOLOGIES INTERNATIONAL - Computer software - Gannett Co., Inc.
GANNON - Paper products - Gannon Design & Packaging, Inc.
GANNON PACKAGING - Paper bags - Gannon Packaging, Inc.
GANPHEN - Pharmaceutical preparations ☆ - Solvay Pharmaceuticals Inc.
GANSON - Apparel and accessories - Ganson Ltd.
GANT - Apparel and accessories - Phillips-Van Heusen Corp.
GANT - Apparel–men's - Gant Inc.
GANT - Belts–apparel - Palm Beach Co., Inc.
GANT - Frames–eyeglass - Marine Optical, Inc.
GANT - Shirts - Crystal Apparel, Inc.
GANT GAITHER - Umbrellas - Shedrain Corp.
GANT PERRIN - Footwear - Magnes Sales Co. Inc.
GANTANOL - Antibiotics - Roche Laboratories
GANTER-WILKIES - Apparel and accessories - Andmore Sportswear Corp.
GANTNER - Bathing suits - Tighe Industries Inc.
GANTRISIN - Antibiotics - Roche Laboratories
GANYMEDE SOFTWARE - Computer software - Ganymede Software, Inc.
GAO ONG DIA - Rice - Sung Ly International Corp.
GAP - Electrical equipment - G.A.P. Antenna Products
GAP - Giftware - Great American Products Inc.
GAP - Stationery - Gap Inc.
GAP - Sunglasses - GPC U.C (Delaware), Inc.
GAP - Tote bags, duffle bags, backpacks, bike bags, and handbags - GPS, Inc.
GAP-A-RO - Fittings–cast iron - Paul L. Taylor
GAP ATHLETIC - Apparel and accessories - GPS, Inc.
GAP/GUARD - Weather stripping - Mile High Garage Door Seal Inc.
GAP-IT - Plumbing fixtures–enameled - Paul L. Taylor
GAP KIDS - Sunglasses - GPS, Inc.
GAP SCENTS - Hair care products - GPS, Inc.
GAP SCENTS - Perfumes - Gap Inc.
GAP SUN - Sunblocks - Gps, Inc.
G.A.P. TABLETS - Vitamins and nutritional supplements - Freeda Vitamins Inc.
GAP, THE - Apparel and accessories - Gap Inc.
GAP WRENCH - Tools - Lowell Corp.
GAPKIDS - Apparel–children's - Gap Inc.
GAPOXIO - Putties - Martin Carbone Inc.
GAPPER - Computer software - Queue Inc.
GAPSCENTS - Hair care products - Gap Inc.
GAPSEAL - Chemical preparations - J.V. Manufacturing Co., Inc.
GAPSTER - Spark plugs - Great Neck Saw Manufacturers, Inc.
GAR - Toys - Tonka Corp.
GAR & T - Pharmaceutical preparations - Saunders Distributors Inc.
GAR-CHEEZY - Pizzas–frozen - Nation Pizza Products L.P.
GAR-LE - Salad dressings–bottled ☆ - Henri's Food Products Co. Inc.
GAR-LITE - Vitamins and nutritional supplements - Natural Organics, Inc.
GAR-LU - Food products - Heise's Wausau Farms
GARA - Wheels–motor vehicle - Veldman's Equipment, Inc.
GARA-BOTTOM - Hardware - Portaseal Inc.
GARA-PAL - Infared heaters - Sun Technology Corp.
GARAFLEX - Plastics–laminated - Alphagary Corp.
GARAGE - Trailers–travel - Adams Vacation Trailer Manufacturing Inc.
GARAGE GARD - Lighting fixtures - General Electric Co.
GARAGE MAGIC - Cleaning preparations–household - Magic American Corp.
GARAGE MATE - Shelving units–plastic - GarageMate Inc.
GARAGE PLUS - Furniture - Do+Able Products, Inc.
GARAGE-PRO - Drills–hand-operated - Warshawsky & Co.
GARAGE PROTECTOR - Alarm systems–burglar - Qualitas Manufacturing, Inc.

GARAGE SEAL - Weather stripping - W.J. Dennis & Co.
GARAGE WORKS - Shelving units–metal - Garageworks, Inc.
GARALAN - Abrasive products - SIA America
GARAMYCIN - Antibiotics - Schering-Plough Healthcare Products
GARAN - Apparel and accessories - Garan, Inc.
GARAN ADVANTAGE - Apparel and accessories - Garan, Inc.
GARAN BY MARITA - Apparel–women's - Garan, Inc.
GARAN MAN, THE - Apparel–men's - Garan, Inc.
GARAN MOUNTAIN LION - Apparel and accessories - Garan, Inc.
GARANIMALS - Apparel–children's - Garan, Inc.
GARANT - Garden equipment - Ames Lawn & Garden Tool Co.
GARANT - Health care products ☆ - Invacare Corp.
GARASEAL - Hardware - Portaseal Inc.
GARASONE - Pharmaceutical preparations - Schering-Plough Healthcare Products
G.A.R.B. LTD. - Apparel and accessories - Frederick Atkins, Inc.
GARB-O-FLAKES - Deodorizers - Surco Products Inc.
GARBAGE - Jewelry - Stephen M. Smith
GARBAGE CAN-DY - Candy - Topps Co., Inc.
GARBAGE COLLECTION - Apparel and accessories - Garbage Collection
GARBAGE GARD - Hardware ☆ - Velcro USA Inc. (Consumer Products Div.)
GARBAGEMATE - Garbage bags - North American Plastics & Chemical Co.
GARBAGIO - Apparel–children's ☆ - Mark Trouser Inc.
GARBER SPIN & GRIN - Filters–fuel - Gar-Ber Filters Inc.
GARBO - Deodorizers ☆ - Roccorp, Inc.
GARBO - Ophthalmic goods - Styl-Rite Optical Manufacturing Co., Inc.
GARCI - Blinds–vertical - Coast to Coast Window Covering Fabricators Inc.
GARCIA - Food products - Garcia Canning Co., Inc.
GARCIA ALL NATURAL - Tortillas - R.W. Garcia
GARCIA AUTHENTIC BLUE CORN - Tortillas - R.W. Garcia
GARCIA AUTHENTIC SALSA BLUE CORN - Tortillas - R.W. Garcia
GARCIA GRANDE - Cigars ☆ - House of Windsor Inc.
GARCIA PINTO BEAN AND WHITE CORN - Tortillas - R.W. Garcia
GARCIA Y VEGA - Cigars - General Cigar Co., Inc.
GARCIA Y VEGA MADURA - Cigars - General Cigar Co., Inc.
GARCIA Y VEGA WHIFFS - Cigars - General Cigar Co., Inc.
GARCIA'S - Bean sprouts - Garcia Canning Co., Inc.
GARCIA'S - Food products - Garcia's Restaurants
GARCIA'S MEXICAN RESTAURANTS - Food products - Famous Restaurants Inc.
GARCINIA CAMBOGIA EXTRACT - Vitamins and nutritional supplements - Vitamin Research Products Inc.
GARCINIA CHI - Vitamins and nutritional supplements - Nature's Sunshine Products, Inc.
GARCINIA PLUS - Vitamins and nutritional supplements - Source Naturals
GARCITRIC GOLD - Spices and extracts - Renaissance Herbs, Inc.
GARCO - Tables–wood - Garco Manufacturing Co.
GARD - Cleaning preparations - Nash Finch Super Food Services, Inc.
GARD - Lubricants - Gard Corp.
GARD - Rubber–molded - W.H. Salisbury & Co.
GARD-A-MATIC - Microphones ☆ - Shure Brothers, Inc.
GARD-BAR - Files–tools - Flotron
GARD-LITE - Glass–safety - Buchmin Industries
GARD/MORE - Waterproofing compounds - Bickmore, Inc.
GARD-N-ERS - Gloves–work ☆ - Jomac Products Inc.
GARD 'N PEG - Garden equipment - Dalen Products Inc.
GARD-N-YARD - Garden equipment - Ariens Co.
GARD 'N YARD - Gloves–work - Pioneer Industrial Products Co.
GARD PLATE - Footwear–men's - Chippewa Shoe Co.
GARD SEAL - Sealing devices - W.H. Salisbury & Co.
GARD TOE - Footwear–men's - Chippewa Shoe Co.
GARDALL - Safes - Edward W. Baroody
GARDCO - Lighting fixtures - Thomas Industries Inc.
GARDCUT - Lubricants - Gard Corp.
GARDE - Adhesives and sealants - Apple Polishes Inc.
GARDEN - Breads ☆ - Natural Ovens of Manitowoc Inc.
GARDEN - Floor coverings–carpet and rugs ☆ - Regal Rugs Inc.
GARDEN - Hardware - Seal Rite Windows
GARDEN - Paper–tissue - Wisconsin Tissue Mills Inc.
GARDEN - Rope ☆ - Samson Cordage Works
GARDEN - Soap ☆ - Caswell-Massey Co. Ltd.
GARDEN - Tiles–ceramic ☆ - Monarch Tile Inc.
GARDEN & ORCHARD FOODS - Cookies - RCB Baking Co.
GARDEN & ORCHARD FOODS - Food products - RDO Specialty Foods Co.
GARDEN ANGEL COLLECTION - Stationery - Heartprint Inc.

☆ = Now out of production

GARDEN APT. - Floor coverings–carpet and rugs ☆ - Hollytex Carpet Mills Inc.

GARDEN ARMOIRE - Garden furniture–wood - Garden Armoires

GARDEN ART - Garden equipment - Uniflame, Inc.

GARDEN BOSS - Garden tools pouch - Portable Products, Inc.

GARDEN BOTANICA - Beauty-services franchise - Garden Botanika, Inc.

GARDEN BOTANIKA - Candles - Garden Botanika, Inc.

GARDEN BOTANIKA - Cosmetics - American Body Care, Inc.

GARDEN BOTANIKA NATURAL COLOR - Cosmetics - Garden Botanika, Inc.

GARDEN BOUQUET - Floor coverings–carpet and rugs ☆ - Couristan Inc.

GARDEN BUDDY - Garden equipment - Boonslick Industries, Inc.

GARDEN CADDY - Garden equipment - Lambert Manufacturing Corp.

GARDEN CENTER - Glass–window - General Aluminum Co.

GARDEN CHARM - Fruits–canned - Big Star Food Stores

GARDEN CHICK'N - Food products - Wholesome & Hearty Foods, Inc.

GARDEN CITY - Wallpaper ☆ - James Seeman Studios

GARDEN CLAW - Garden equipment - Faultless Starch/Bon Ami Co.

GARDEN CLUB - Candlesticks - Beagle Manufacturing Co. Inc.

GARDEN CLUB - Flower pots–earthenware - Dorothy Biddle Service

GARDEN CLUB - Food products - Clements Food Co. Inc.

GARDEN CLUB - Housewares ☆ - Van Guard Studios of North Carolina

GARDEN COLLECTION - Fabrics–tapestry ☆ - Coloroll Inc.

GARDEN COLLECTION - Vases–glass - Syndicate Sales, Inc.

GARDEN COVE - Wallpaper - J. Josephson, Inc.

GARDEN CREST - Food products - Safie Bros. Pickle Co.

GARDEN CREST - Salad dressings–bottled - Quality Food Centers, Inc.

GARDEN CRISPS - Crackers - Nabisco Foods Group

GARDEN CRITTERS - Apparel–women's - Nap, Inc.

GARDEN DANCE - Housewares - Amoco Fabrics and Fibers Co.

GARDEN DE LUXE - Wines - Gallup Sales Co. Inc.

GARDEN DELIGHT - Pizzas–frozen - Blaisdell Foods

GARDEN DELIGHT - Vegetables–frozen - Frosty Acres Brands Inc.

GARDEN DIP - Dairy products - Dean Foods Co.

GARDEN DOOR - Doors–screen - Temple Products Inc.

GARDEN DUST - Pesticides–household - Bonide Products, Inc.

GARDEN EARTH - Publisher's imprints - University of Georgia Research Foundation, Inc.

GARDEN ESTATES - Linen - Dayton Hudson Corp.

GARDEN FAIRE - Decals and transfers - Rubbermaid Inc.

GARDEN FARE - Food products - McCormick & Co., Inc.

GARDEN FESTIVAL - Wallpaper ☆ - Mayfair Wallcoverings

GARDEN FLOWERS - Wallpaper - Pickhardt & Siebert USA Inc.

GARDEN FOUNTAIN - Wallcovering - Wall Trends, Inc.

GARDEN FRESH - Cleaning preparations - Garden Fresh Inc.

GARDEN FRESH - Food products - Allen Canning Co.

GARDEN FRESH - Food products - Axelrod Distributors

GARDEN FRESH - Fruits and vegetables - Interfrost, Inc.

GARDEN FRESH - Ribbons - Bedford Industries, Inc.

GARDEN FRESH - Soap - J.R. Carlson Laboratories Inc.

GARDEN FROST - Spices and extracts - Gilroy Foods Inc.

GARDEN GAL - Toys - Tonka Corp.

GARDEN GALLERIES - Building materials - Paul Edward Riha

GARDEN GALLERY - Apparel–women's - Specialty Department Stores, Inc.

GARDEN GALS - Garden equipment - Garden Pals, Inc.

GARDEN GANG - Garden furniture ☆ - Stone City Products Inc.

GARDEN-GARD - Garden equipment ☆ - Dare Products Inc.

GARDEN GATE - Floor coverings–carpet and rugs - Milliken & Co. Inc.

GARDEN GATE - Food products - Northwest Cold Pack Co.

GARDEN GATE - Gates–ornamental - Royal Cathay Trading Co.

GARDEN GATE - Tableware–china ☆ - Lenox, Inc.

GARDEN GATE - Wallpaper ☆ - Sanitas Wallcoverings

GARDEN GAZEBO - Floor coverings–carpet and rugs - Regal Rugs Inc.

GARDEN GEMS - Pet products - Ameriguard Corp.

GARDEN GEYSERS - Sprinklers–lawn - UniteDesign

GARDEN GIFTS - Wallpaper - Gencorp Inc.

GARDEN GIGGLYS - Flowers, plants, and seeds - Applewood Seed & Garden Group

GARDEN GLORIES - Flowers–artificial - Goebel Art GmbH

GARDEN GLORIES - Flowers–artificial - Goebel United States

GARDEN GOBLINS - Garden equipment - Cobraco Manufacturing, Inc.

GARDEN GOLD - Fertilizers - Gold Kist Inc.

GARDEN GOODNESS - Raisins - North Coast Processing

GARDEN-GOURMET - Food products - Garden Gourmet Rokeach Corp.

GARDEN GOURMET - Vegetables–canned - Green Giant Co.

GARDEN GRAIN PATTIE - Meat products - Specialty Foods Investment Co.

GARDEN GREATS GREENHOUSE - Garden equipment - Carefree Garden Products

GARDEN GROVE - Floor coverings ☆ - Congoleum Corp.

GARDEN GROVE - Juices - Vim Corp.

GARDEN GROWN - Fruits and vegetables ☆ - J.R. Simplot Co.

GARDEN GUN - Garden equipment - The Fountainhead Group, Inc.

GARDEN HARVEST - Cookware - Corning Inc.

GARDEN HARVEST - Kitchenware–earthenware - Arnart Imports Inc.

GARDEN HERB TRISCUIT - Cookies - Nabisco Foods Group

GARDEN HOUSE - Tents - Gale Group Inc.

GARDEN ISLE - Floor coverings–carpet and rugs - Mohawk Carpet Corp.

GARDEN KING - Garden equipment - The Fountainhead Group, Inc.

GARDEN LANE - Beef - Hoekstra Meat Co.

GARDEN LEADER - Flowers, plants, and seeds - Grimes Seed Co.

GARDEN LEADER - Flowers, plants, and seeds - G.S. Grimes Seeds

GARDEN-LIFE - Fertilizers - Science Products Co. Inc.

GARDEN LIFE - Wallpaper ☆ - Eisenhart Wallcoverings Co.

GARDEN LITE - Electrical equipment - Gem Electric Manufacturing Co. Inc.

GARDEN LITE, THE - Lamps - Lamplight Farms, Inc.

GARDEN-MADE - Skin care products - Ellen Sinclair Davies

GARDEN MAGIC - Floor coverings - Mannington Resilient Floors

GARDEN MAGIC - Soil–potting - Michigan Peat Co.

GARDEN MARK - Soil–potting - Ashland Oil, Inc.

GARDEN MARK - Tools–garden ☆ - Montgomery Ward & Co. Inc.

GARDEN MARVEL - Fertilizers - Plant Marvel Laboratories

GARDEN MASTER - Aprons–leather - Custom Leathercraft Manufacturing

GARDEN MASTER - Computer software - SourceView Software International

GARDEN MASTER - Gasoline - Pro Hardware Inc.

GARDEN MATE - Fertilizers - Greenview Lawn & Garden Products

GARDEN MEADOW - Deodorizers - Kiwi Brands, Inc.

GARDEN-MEASURE - Garden equipment - Science Products Co. Inc.

GARDEN MEDLEY - Glassware–household - Crest Studios

GARDEN MELODY - Deodorizers - Tsumura International Inc.

GARDEN MIST - Deodorizers - Dial Corp.

GARDEN MUSES - Teas–herbal - P.J.'s USA, Inc.

GARDEN N' HOME - Fertilizers - Reliance Plastic & Chemical Corp.

GARDEN OF DREAMS - Wallpaper - Capital Carousel Inc.

GARDEN OF EATIN' - Food products - Garden of Eatin', Inc.

GARDEN OF EDEN - Floor coverings–carpet and rugs - Karastan-Bigelow Inc.

GARDEN OF EDEN - Flowers–artificial - European Imports of California Inc.

GARDEN OF EDEN - Musical instrument accessories - Sottile Manufacturing Co.

GARDEN OF EDEN - Skin care products - Garden of Eden, Inc.

GARDEN OF EDEN EXCITATION TEA - Teas and food flavoring - Fred G. Farago

GARDEN OF EDEN MEDITATION TEA - Teas - Fred G. Farago

GARDEN OF EDEN TEMPTATION TEA - Tea - Fred G. Farago

GARDEN OF GOOD EATIN', A - Spices and extracts - To Market to Market

GARDEN OF GOOD THINGS, A - Crock pots - Rival Manufacturing Co.

GARDEN OF LOVE - Giftware - Russ Berrie and Co., Inc.

GARDEN OF NATURE - Skin care products ☆ - Para Laboratories Inc.

GARDEN OF READIN', THE - Recording label - Prescott Entertainment, Inc.

GARDEN OF THE GODS SEASONINGS - Seasonings - Garden of the Gods Seasonings, Inc.

GARDEN PALS - Tools–garden - Garden Pals, Inc.

GARDEN PANTRY, THE - Catalogs - Garden Pantry, Inc.

GARDEN PARK - Furniture–wood ☆ - Flanders Industries Inc.

GARDEN PARTY - Christmas tree ornaments - Cracker Box Inc.

GARDEN PARTY - Dinnerware–glass - Johnson Brothers, USA, Inc.

GARDEN PARTY - Dolls ☆ - Effanbee Doll Corp.

GARDEN PARTY - Floor coverings–carpet and rugs ☆ - Columbus Mills, Inc.

GARDEN PARTY - Greeting cards - Thought Factory

GARDEN PARTY - Tableware–china - Pfaltzgraff Investment Co.

GARDEN PARTY - Tableware–china ☆ - Lenox, Inc.

GARDEN PARTY - Toys - Tonka Corp.

GARDEN PARTY - Wallcoverings ☆ - Arthur Sanderson and Sons North America Ltd.

GARDEN PASTA - Pasta - Kozy Shack Inc.

GARDEN PATCH FASHIONS - Dolls ☆ - Totsy Manufacturing Co., Inc.

GARDEN PATH - Air freshener - Dial Corp.

GARDEN PATH - Canned mushrooms - L.K. Bowman & Co. Inc.

GARDEN PATH - Flatware ☆ - Lifetime Hoan Corp.

GARDEN PATH - Floor coverings–carpet and rugs ☆ - Regal Rugs Inc.

GARDEN PATH - Floor coverings–carpet and rugs ☆ - Trans-Ocean Import Co. Inc.

GARDEN PATH - Wallpaper ☆ - Warner Co.

☆ = Now out of production

GARDEN PEWTER - Glassware–household ☆ - Garden Silversmiths Ltd.
GARDEN PICT - Fruits and vegetables - Comstock Michigan Fruit
GARDEN PLANNER - Computer software - Parsons Technology, Inc.
GARDEN PORTRAIT - Dinnerware - Corning Inc.
GARDEN PRIDE - Lawn mowers - Southland Mower Corp.
GARDEN PRIDE - Vegetables–frozen - Patterson Frozen Foods, Inc.
GARDEN PRINT - Napkins ☆ - James River Corp.
GARDEN PRO, THE - Tools - Jural Manufacturing Co.
GARDEN PROFESSOR - Insecticides - Green Light Co.
GARDEN PROTECTOR - Electrical equipment - North Central Plastics Inc.
GARDEN QUEEN - Benches–wood ☆ - Cardinal Home Products
GARDEN QUEEN - Hoses - Colorite Plastic Co.
GARDEN RAILWAY CO. - Toys–trains - Garden Railway Co.
GARDEN RETREAT - Wallcovering - Gencorp Inc.
GARDEN REVERIE - Wallpaper - B. Berger Co.
GARDEN RIDE - Frames–picture - Terragrafics Inc.
GARDEN ROMANCE, A - Wallpaper - Pickhardt & Siebert USA Inc.
GARDEN ROMANTICS - Wallcoverings - Sherman & Associates International
GARDEN ROW - Dinnerware ☆ - Corning Inc.
GARDEN ROW ZIPPER - Tools–garden - Pro Inc.
GARDEN SCENE - Flowers–artificial - Duraco Products Inc.
GARDEN SCOOT - Garden furniture - Master Manufacturing Co.
GARDEN SEASONS - Food products - Chattahoochee Foods
GARDEN SEAT - Furniture - Algoma Net Co.
GARDEN SHOP SPECIAL - Soil–potting ☆ - Millburn Peat Co. Inc.
GARDEN SNAKES - Tools–hand-operated - True Temper Hardware Co.
GARDEN SOUP COMPANY - Soups–canned - Bunker Hill Foods
GARDEN SPIRALS - Pasta - Gioia Macaroni Co. Inc.
GARDEN SPLENDOR - Colognes - Miracle Coatings
GARDEN SPOT - Hardware - Herr & Co. Inc.
GARDEN SPOT - Vegetables–canned - Pandora Canning Co.
GARDEN SPOTS - Footwear - Lowell Shoe, Inc.
GARDEN SPOTS ALL DAY COMFORT - Footwear - Lowell Shoe, Inc.
GARDEN STAR - Tillers–rotary - Ardisam, Inc.
GARDEN STATE - Floor coverings ☆ - Congoleum Corp.
GARDEN STATE - Fruits–frozen - Garden State Packing Co. Inc.
GARDEN STATE - Jams and jellies - Berry Best Farm
GARDEN STATE - Limestone products - Medusa Minerals Co.
GARDEN STATE DESIGN - Wallpaper - Fidelity Industries, Inc.
GARDEN TEA PARTY - Flowers, plants, and seeds - White Swan, Ltd.
GARDEN TERRACE - Garden equipment - Cobraco Manufacturing, Inc.
GARDEN, THE - Potpourri - Countryside Fragrances Inc.
GARDEN, THE - Containers - Madison Square Garden Corp.
GARDEN THUNDER - Fertilizers - Natural Earth Technologies, Inc.
GARDEN TIME - Garden equipment - Far West Forests
GARDEN TIME - Wallpaper - Chapters Wallcoverings
GARDEN TIPS - Gloves - Marmon Holdings, Inc.
GARDEN-TONE - Flowers, plants, and seeds - Espoma Co.
GARDEN TOURIST, THE - Publisher's imprints - Lois G. Rosenfeld
GARDEN TREASURES - Lighting fixtures - Special Lite Products Co. Inc.
GARDEN VALLEY - Bird feeds - United Pacific Mills
GARDEN VALLEY - Food products - Tri Valley Growers, Inc.
GARDEN VALLEY - Pet food - Kaytee Products Inc.
GARDEN VARIETEAS - Tea kettles–nonelectric - M. Kamenstein, Inc.
GARDEN VEGE-PATTIES - Meat products - Specialty Foods Investment Co.
GARDEN VEGETABLE - Omelette mix - Second Nature
GARDEN VEGGIES & GREENS - Vitamins and nutritional supplements - Highland Laboratories
GARDEN VIEW, A - Wallpaper - Sterling Prints
GARDEN WAY - Garden equipment - Garden Way Inc.
GARDEN WAY - Publisher's imprints - National Plan Service
GARDEN WEASEL - Garden equipment - Faultless Starch/Bon Ami Co.
GARDEN WHITE - Housewares - Himark Enterprises Inc.
GARDEN WINDOW - Windows - International Window Corp.
GARDEN WONDER - Vitamins and nutritional supplements - Vital Food Sources, Inc.
GARDEN WORKBENCH - Computer software - Horticopia, Inc.
GARDENA - Floor coverings ☆ - Congoleum Corp.
GARDENA - Fruits and vegetables - Chiquita Brands, Inc.
GARDENA - Vegetables–canned - Chiquita Processed Food, LLC
GARDENARIUM - Statuary - Massarelli's Lawn Ornaments, Inc.
GARDENBURGER - Food products - Wholesome & Hearty Foods, Inc.
GARDENBURGER MEXI - Food products - Wholesome & Hearty Foods, Inc.
GARDENBURGER SUB - Food products - Wholesome & Hearty Foods, Inc.
GARDENBURGER VEGGIE - Food products - Wholesome & Hearty Foods, Inc.

GARDENCARE - Skin care products - S.A.N. Associates, Inc.
GARDENCOURT - Cabinets ☆ - H.J. Scheirich Co.
GARDENDOG - Meat products - Wholesome & Hearty Foods, Inc.
GARDENELLA - Furniture–metal - Telescope Casual Furniture Inc.
GARDENELLA SLING COLLECTION - Furniture–metal - Telescope Casual Furniture Inc.
GARDENER'S BEST - Fertilizers–nitrogenous - Gardener's Supply Co.
GARDENER'S CHOICE - Gloves - Marmon Holdings, Inc.
GARDENER'S CHRONICLE - Wallpaper - Piedmont Collections
GARDENERS CHRONICLE, A - Wallpaper ☆ - Old Deerfield Fabrics Inc.
GARDENER'S MEDITATIONS - Ornamental products–glass - Patsico
GARDENER'S PLANTERS MIX - Fertilizers - Kellogg Supply, Inc.
GARDENERS PRIDE - Soil–potting - Millburn Peat Co. Inc.
GARDENERS SOFTWIST - Bakery products - Gardener Baking Co.
GARDENER'S TEA BAG - Teas - Gardener's Tea Bag Co.
GARDENGOYLES - Statuary - Design Toscano, Inc.
GARDENIA - Bathtubs–enameled - Lasco Products Group
GARDENIA - Cheese - Gardenia Foods
GARDENIA - Colognes - Old 97 Co.
GARDENIA - Footwear - Eliot Co. Inc.
GARDENIA ORCHIDEA - Tiles–ceramic - Maxsam Sales, Inc.
GARDENIA PASSION - Potpourri - Countryside Fragrances Inc.
GARDENIN' PRETTY - Dolls - Mattel, Inc.
GARDENING ANGEL - Flowers, plants, and seeds - Treasures & Trinkets, Inc.
GARDENING ON THE WING - Flowers, plants, and seeds - Puget Sound Seed Co.
GARDENS AMERICA - Flowers, plants, and seeds - Gardens America Inc.
GARDENS & GROVES - Cosmetics - Candle Corp. of America
GARDEN'S CHOICE - Pickles - Chas. F. Cates & Sons Inc.
GARDENS TO GO - Flowers, plants, and seeds - White Swan, Ltd.
GARDENSAUSAGE - Food products - Wholesome & Hearty Foods, Inc.
GARDENSCAPES - Garden equipment - Hills Department Store Co.
GARDENSIDE - Furniture–wood - Gardenside International Ltd.
GARDENSIDE - Vegetables–frozen - Safeway Stores Inc.
GARDENSONG - Pet products - Opus Inc.
GARDENSPIRITS - Towels - Lois Bender Design
GARDENSTEAK - Food products - Wholesome & Hearty Foods, Inc.
GARDENTACO - Food products ☆ - Wholesome & Hearty Foods, Inc.
GARDENVIEW - Doors–garage - Taylor Building Products Co.
GARDEVATOR - Rakes - Ansan Industries Ltd.
GARDEX - Locks–door - Dexter Lock
GARDFLEET - Lubricants - Gard Corp.
GARDGEAR - Lubricants - Gard Corp.
GARDGLAS - Glass products - Enyart Industries Inc.
GARDIAN - Insulating materials - Southern Manufacturing, Inc.
GARDINETTES - Gloves–work ☆ - Pioneer Industrial Products Co.
GARDINIERA - Olives–pickled or brined - Krinos Foods, Inc.
GARDISETTE - Window coverings - L.S. Roberts Drapery Co.
GARDLINK - Television equipment - Gardiner Communications Corp.
GARD'N AIDS - Fertilizers ☆ - T & T Industries Inc.
GARD'N GARD - Chemical preparations - G.F. Wright Steel & Wire Co.
GARDNER - Electrical equipment - GB Electrical Inc.
GARDNER - Mirrors - Gardner Mirror Corp.
GARDNER-DENVER - Pneumatic tools - Cooper Industries, Inc.
GARDNER PARDNER - Computer software - Lila M. Mcateer
GARDNER-VAIL - Hardware - Blaine Window Hardware Inc.
GARDNER'S - Pet products - The Crab Connection
GARDNERS COTTAGE - Furniture - Bassett Furniture Industries, Inc.
GARDONE - Glassware–household - Oneida Ltd.
GARDOX - Adhesives and sealants - W.R. Meadows Inc.
GARDS - Aprons - Handgards Inc.
GARDSTAR - Insecticides - Y-Tex Corp.
GARDSTAR PLUS - Insecticides - Y-Tex Corp.
GARDUNO'S - Beverages–alcohol - Tortilla, Inc.
GARDVIS - Lubricants - Gard Corp.
GARDWAY - Lubricants - Gard Corp.
GARDZ - Apparel and accessories - Gardz Patent Co.
GARE - Paints–artists' - Gare Inc.
GARED - Sporting goods - Gared Sports, Inc.
GARED MASTER 3000 - Sporting goods - Gared Sports, Inc.
GARELICK - Medical apparatus - Garelick Manufacturing Co.
GARELICK FARMS - Milk - Garelick Farms, Inc.
GARELLI - Mopeds - Agrati-Garelli Corp. of America
GARFIELD - Air purification systems - Medo Industries, Inc.
GARFIELD - Bathroom accessories ☆ - Ransburg Accessories Inc.
GARFIELD - Candy - Amurol Confections Co.

☆ = Now out of production

GARFIELD - Flour–blended - Acme-Evans/A.D.M. Milling Co.
GARFIELD - Frames–eyeglass ☆ - Universal/Univis Inc.
GARFIELD - Games ☆ - Ben Cooper Inc.
GARFIELD - Games ☆ - Parker Brothers
GARFIELD - Giftware ☆ - Enesco Corp.
GARFIELD - Hobby kits - Distinctive Design
GARFIELD - Housewares - Terragrafics Inc.
GARFIELD - Kites - Spectra Star Kites
GARFIELD - Laxatives - Alvin Last Inc.
GARFIELD - Lunch boxes - Thermos Co.
GARFIELD - Music–sheet ☆ - Centerstream Publications
GARFIELD - Novelty items–paper ☆ - Unique Industries, Inc.
GARFIELD - Ophthalmic goods - Foremost Optical Products
GARFIELD - Pharmaceutical preparations ☆ - Oakhurst Co.
GARFIELD - Pianos - Schaff Piano Supply Co.
GARFIELD - Playing cards - United States Playing Card Co.
GARFIELD - Puzzles ☆ - Milton Bradley Co.
GARFIELD - Skates–roller ☆ - National Sporting Goods Corp.
GARFIELD - Sporting goods ☆ - AC International
GARFIELD - Tires - Coker Tire Inc.
GARFIELD - Toothbrushes - John O.Butler Co.
GARFIELD - Toys - Deka Plastics Inc.
GARFIELD - Toys - Tyco Toys
GARFIELD - Toys–stuffed - Dakin Inc.
GARFIELD - Wallpaper ☆ - Priss Prints Inc.
GARFIELD - Watches - E. Gluck Corp.
GARFIELD - Watches - Morris W. Weiler Corp.
GARFIELD & CO. - Toys–stuffed - Dakin Inc.
GARFIELD & FRIENDS - Snack foods - General Mills, Inc.
GARFIELD ART CENTER - Toys ☆ - Coloron Industries
GARFIELD BACK TO SCHOOL - Toys–stuffed - Dakin Inc.
GARFIELD BIRTHDAY BAGS - Toys–stuffed - Dakin Inc.
GARFIELD BIRTHDAY STACKABLE - Figurines - Dakin Inc.
GARFIELD BORN TO PARTY - T-shirts–men's - Dakin Inc.
GARFIELD CHIEF - Toys–stuffed - Dakin Inc.
GARFIELD CHRISTMAS - Air purification systems ☆ - Medo Industries, Inc.
GARFIELD COMPANION - Computer software ☆ - SRA/McGraw-Hill (Div. of The McGraw-Hill Companies)
GARFIELD EASTER BONNET - Toys–stuffed - Dakin Inc.
GARFIELD EXPRESSIONS - Toys–stuffed - Dakin Inc.
GARFIELD FAT CAT FUNNIES - Snack foods - General Mills, Inc.
GARFIELD FOR BABIES - Wallpaper ☆ - Priss Prints Inc.
GARFIELD GOOSE - T-shirts–men's - WGN Continental Broadcasting Co.
GARFIELD GREETINGS STACKABLES - Figurines - Dakin Inc.
GARFIELD GRRR - Toys–stuffed - Dakin Inc.
GARFIELD HANGING OUT - Toys–stuffed - Dakin Inc.
GARFIELD HAPPY BIRTHDAY - T-shirts–children's - Dakin Inc.
GARFIELD HERE RABBIT - Toys–stuffed - Dakin Inc.
GARFIELD I DON'T NEED THIS - Toys–stuffed - Dakin Inc.
GARFIELD ICE SCRAPER - Toys–stuffed - Dakin Inc.
GARFIELD JITTER CRITTER - Toys–stuffed - Dakin Inc.
GARFIELD KOOL KAT - Toys–stuffed - Dakin Inc.
GARFIELD LIFE IN THE FAST LANE - Toys–stuffed - Dakin Inc.
GARFIELD LIMITED EDITION - Toys–stuffed - Dakin Inc.
GARFIELD LOVE ME - Toys–stuffed - Dakin Inc.
GARFIELD MY FAVORITE SLIPPERS - Toys–stuffed - Dakin Inc.
GARFIELD/NFL - Air purification systems ☆ - Medo Industries, Inc.
GARFIELD PARTY ANIMAL - T-shirts–men's - Dakin Inc.
GARFIELD PAWS - Chewing gum ☆ - Amurol Confections Co.
GARFIELD PIZZA O'S - Pasta - Campbell Soup Co.
GARFIELD SPAGHETTI ATTACK - Toys–stuffed - Dakin Inc.
GARFIELD STRIPES - Chewing gum ☆ - Amurol Confections Co.
GARFIELD STUCK ON YOU - Toys–stuffed - Dakin Inc.
GARFIELD TRIVIA - Computer software ☆ - SRA/McGraw-Hill (Div. of The McGraw-Hill Companies)
GARFIELD WHO ME? - Toys–stuffed - Dakin Inc.
GARFIELD YEAR OF THE PARTY - T-shirts–men's - Dakin Inc.
GARFLOR - Cleaning preparations - National Purity Inc.
GARGIULO LP - Fruits and vegetables - Gargiulo, L.P.
GARGLE-AID - Health care products - Tec Laboratories, Inc.
GARGLE-ALOE - Pharmaceutical preparations - Jess Clarke & Sons Inc.
GARGLEAID - Pharmaceutical preparations - Tec Laboratories, Inc.
GARGOYLE - Cigars - Gargoyle Cigar Co., Ltd.
GARGOYLE - Toys - Tonka Corp.
GARGOYLES - Sunglasses - Gargoyles Inc.
GARGOYLES - Toys - Walt Disney Co.

GARGOYLES STUDIO - Frames–picture - Gargoyles Studio
GARI-TONIC - Health care products - Halsey Drug Co. Inc.
GARIBALDI - Apparel and accessories - Amos Aharoni
GARIBALDI & BRUNS SUPERIOR CUT - Jewelry–precious - Fink's Jewelers Inc.
GARIBALDI & BRUNS SUPERIOR QUALITY - Jewelry–precious - Fink's Jewelers Inc.
GARIELE - Frames–eyeglass - May Optical Co. Inc.
GARIOCH - Beverages–alcohol - White Rock Distilleries Inc.
GARITA - Insect repellents - Et Products, Inc.
GARITABS - Health care products - Halsey Drug Co. Inc.
GARKUT - Abrasive products ☆ - SIA America
GARL-ACTION - Vitamins and nutritional supplements - Action Labs, Inc.
GARLAND - Crocheted and knitted items - Garland Knitting Mills
GARLAND - Dinnerware–glass - Nikko Ceramics Inc.
GARLAND - Floor coverings–carpet and rugs ☆ - Regal Rugs Inc.
GARLAND - Kitchenware–china - H. Wittur & Co.
GARLAND - Paper–toweling ☆ - Fort Howard Corp.
GARLAND - Recording label - DCC Compact Classics, Inc.
GARLAND - Rings–jewelry - Artcarved Inc.
GARLAND - Roofing materials - Garland Co., Inc.
GARLAND - Toilets–enameled - Kohler Co.
GARLAND BUNNY - Toys–stuffed - Dakin Inc.
GARLAND CIRCLETTES - Lighters - Colibri Inc.
GARLAND CROWN - Dishes–china ☆ - Denby USA Limited
GARLAND-DECOR - Drapery hardware - Repcon International, Inc.
GARLAND DRAKE - Skin care products - Major/Advance International
GARLAND DRAKE - Wigs - Garland Drake International
GARLAND HOMES - Log cabins–prefabricated - Bitterroot Precut Inc.
GARLAND RANCH - Wines - Chateau Julien
GARLAND RANCH - Wines - House of Burgundy Inc.
GARLAND-TEEN - Crocheted and knitted items - Garland Knitting Mills
GARLAND VINE - Bedding–linen - Dan River Inc.
GARLANDER - Crocheted and knitted items - Garland Knitting Mills
GARLANDS - Fabrics - Gretchen Bellinger Inc.
GARLANDS - Wallpaper ☆ - Imperial Wallcoverings, Inc.
GARLCAL 50-PLUS - Vitamins and nutritional supplements - Pure-Gar
GARLI GARNI - Seasonings - Garlic Festival Foods
GARLI GHETTI - Spaghetti - Garlic Festival Foods
GARLIC BREAD SUPREME - Seasonings - Tone Brothers, Inc.
GARLIC CRAB, THE - Sterilizing chambers - Garlic Crab Corp.
GARLIC EXPRESS - Housewares - Better Mousetraps, Inc.
GARLIC EXPRESSIONS - Salad dressings–bottled - Larmar Foods
GARLIC EXTRACT - Vitamins and nutritional supplements - Vitamin Research Products Inc.
GARLIC FESTIVAL - Seasonings - Garlic Festival Foods
GARLIC FESTIVAL - Seasonings - Randan Corp.
GARLIC GALORE - Salad dressings–bottled ☆ - Santa Barbara Olive Co.
GARLIC GALORE - Spices and extracts - Jodie's Kitchen Inc.
GARLIC, GLORIOUS GARLIC - Food products - Golden Whisk Pasta Partners
GARLIC GOLD - Vitamins and nutritional supplements - Schiff Products, Inc.
GARLIC GORO - Seasonings - Randan Corp.
GARLIC LOVERS' - Mustard - Rising Sun Farms, Inc.
GARLIC LOVER'S SALUTE - Seasonings - Flavorbank
GARLIC MIST - Oils–edible - Par-Way Group
GARLIC MIST - Oils–edible - Tryson Co.
GARLIC 'N ONION CRISSCUT FRIES - Vegetables–frozen ☆ - Lamb-Weston, Inc.
GARLIC 'N SPICE - Food products - Golden Whisk Pasta Partners
GARLIC OF EATIN' - Spices and extracts - To Market to Market
GARLIC PLUS - Vitamins and nutritional supplements - Modern Products, Inc.
GARLIC-POWER - Vitamins and nutritional supplements - Natur-Pharma, Inc.
GARLIC SPREADS - Food products - McCormick & Co., Inc.
GARLIC TAMS - Crackers - B. Manischewitz Co.
GARLICELL - Vitamins and nutritional supplements - Source Naturals
GARLICHROME - Vitamins and nutritional supplements - Home Health Products, Inc.
GARLICIN - Vitamins and nutritional supplements - Nature's Way Products, Inc.
GARLIMAX - Vitamins and nutritional supplements - Performance Labs Inc.
GARLINASE 4000 - Vitamins and nutritional supplements - Enzymatic Therapy, Inc.
GARLIPHANTS - Vitamins and nutritional supplements - Pure-Gar
GARLISAN - Vitamins and nutritional supplements - Nature's Way Products, Inc.
GARLITECH - Vitamins and nutritional supplements - Global Marketing Associates, Inc.

☆ = Now out of production

GARLO-TIME - Pharmaceutical preparations - Nutrition Headquarters, Inc.
GARMENT BAG VALET - Garment hangers - Arnold E. Gast
GARMENT WORKS, THE - Apparel–men's - Jay Garment Co.
GARMISCH - Sporting goods ☆ - Sport Obermeyer Ltd.
GARNAY - Jewelry - Garnay Inc.
GARNER - Food products - T.W. Garner Food Co.
GARNERS - Jams and jellies - T.W. Garner Food Co.
GARNET - Cosmetics ☆ - Spilo/Mehaz Worldwide
GARNET - Flatware - Denby USA Limited
GARNET - Recording label ☆ - Michele Audio Corp.
GARNET - Watches - Elgin Watch Co.
GARNET - Wines - Bully Hill Vineyards, Inc.
GARNET HILL - Bedspreads - Garnet Hill Inc.
GARNET RIBBON - Lipsticks - Estee Lauder Inc.
GAROFALO - Food products - Bel Canto Fancy Foods Ltd.
GAROFOLI - Wines - Kobrand Corp.
GAROLINI - Footwear–women's - United States Shoe Corp.
GARON - Epoxy - Garon Products Inc.
GARON - Giftware - Aaron Stern Inc.
GARON DE-ICER - Deicing fluid - Garon Products Inc.
GARON-GLO - Floor waxes - Garon Products Inc.
GARON GRABBERS & PICK-UP PACK - Tools - Garon Products Inc.
GARON PLUG - Cement - Garon Products Inc.
GARON PROTECTOR - Electric lighting equipment - Garon Products Inc.
GARON TREDS - Adhesives and sealants - Garon Products Inc.
GARONITE - Cement - Garon Products Inc.
GARRAFA MESTRE - Packaging materials - Mead Corp.
GARRAFEIRA - Wines - Admiral Wine Merchants
GARRAPINADAS - Snack foods - La Luna
GARRARD - Phonographs - Garrard USA
GARRARD - Video tapes–blank - Service Merchandise Co. Inc.
GARRETT - Furniture - Counterpoint
GARRETT - Motor vehicle parts and accessories - Alliedsignal Inc.
GARRETT - Ophthalmic goods - Styl-Rite Optical Manufacturing Co., Inc.
GARRETT POPCORN SHOPS - Popcorn - Caramelcrisp Corp.
GARRETT'S - Educational equipment - Brodhead-Garrett Co.
GARRI KATZ - Giftware - Reco International Corp.
GARRICK ANDERSON - Apparel–men's - Garrick Anderson Sartorial Ltd.
GARRISON - Cigarettes - Brown & Williamson Tobacco Corp.
GARRISON - Floor coverings–carpet and rugs - Coronet Carpets Inc.
GARRISON - Floor coverings–carpet and rugs ☆ - Karastan-Bigelow Inc.
GARRISON - Locks–door - American Lock & Supply, Inc.
GARRITY - Flashlights - Garrity Industries
GARRY'S - Cleaning preparations - Garry Laboratories Inc.
GARRY'S OF CALIFORNIA - Fruits–dried - Garry Packing Inc.
GARRY'S ROYAL SATIN - Cleaning preparations - Garry Laboratories Inc.
GARSEN - Wallpaper - Koroseal Wallcoverings
GARSITE - Fuel systems–aircraft - Garsite, Inc.
GARTEK PRO - Computer software - Gartek Technologies, Inc.
GARTERS GONE - Apparel and accessories ☆ - Warnaco Inc.
GARTH WEAR - Apparel - Blue Rose, Inc.
GARTHBOND CONCENTRATE - Chemical preparations - Gourdie Products Co. Inc.
GARUDA - Tents - Dana Design Ltd.
GARUDA - Tents - K2 Inc.
GARUDA CLOTHIER - Apparel and accessories - Garuda Clothier, Inc.
GARVENS - Scales–industrial - Hi-Speed Checkweigher Co., Inc.
GARVEY - Labels–paper - National Sales Co.
GARY - Safes - Allied Gary International
GARY FATINO'S SIGNATURE GOURMET PIZZA - Pizzas–mixes - Gary Fatino's Pizza L.C.
GARY FISHER - Bicycles - Fisher Mountain Bikes
GARY GAIL - Handbags, belts, etc. - Dallas Handbag Co.
GARY GEAR - Transmission equipment–motor vehicle - Anchored Corp.
GARY GERARD - Hair care products - Gary Gerard Inc.
GARY JENKINS - Paint sets–hobby - Martin F. Weber Co.
GARY #ORRELL HEREFORDS - Agricultural products - Gary Orrell Herefords
GARY PATTERSON COLLECTION - Greeting cards - Thought Factory
GARY PLAYER - Golfing equipment - Northwestern Golf Co.
GARY PLAYER - Golfing equipment ☆ - Ram Golf Corp.
GARY SUGAL - Musical instruments - Sugal Mouthpieces, Inc.
GARY'S - Nuts–salted, roasted, cooked, or canned - Jimbo's Jumbos Inc.
GARY'S GOURMET BURGER - Turkeys - Cooper's Turkey Place, Inc.
GARYS LEATHER - Desk sets - Gary's Leather Creations
GARY'S OF CALIFORNIA - Leather goods - Gary's Leather Creations
GARZA - Food products - E. De La Garza Inc.

GAS - Sporting goods - Basic Skateboards
G.A.S. - Tools–hand-operated - Transworld Products, Inc.
GAS-A-JUST - Shock absorbers–motor vehicle - KYB Corp. of America
GAS & GO - Toys - Fisher-Price, Inc.
GAS-BAN - Pharmaceutical preparations - Roberts/Hauck Pharmaceuticals Inc.
GAS BARONESS - Fireplaces ☆ - Malm Fireplaces Inc.
GAS BLAST - Fuel additives - Berryman Products Inc.
GAS BLASTERS - Toy cars - Intex Recreation Corp.
GAS BREAKER - Valves–industrial - UMAC Inc.
GAS BUBBLE BEADS - Fishing lures - John Ciulla
GAS CAP EASY TWIST - Wrenches - Ray G. Rhoton
GAS CASK - Gasoline ☆ - Eagle Manufacturing Co. Inc.
GAS CONTROLLER - Kilns - Ped Technologies, Inc.
GAS GLOVES - Gloves - Totes, Inc.
GAS GRIP - Handles–plastic - Dack Products International
GAS GRIP DACK PRODUCTS INT'L, INC. - Nozzles - Dack Products International
GAS-KART - Racks - Jarke Corp.
GAS LEAK DETECTOR - Chemical preparations - Highside Chemicals Inc.
GAS-MAGNUM - Shock absorbers–motor vehicle - Monroe Auto Equipment Co.
GAS-MATE - Portable fuel container ☆ - Attwood Corp.
GAS-MATIC - Shock absorbers–motor vehicle - Monroe Auto Equipment Co.
GAS-MATIC IMPORT - Shock absorbers–motor vehicle - Monroe Auto Equipment Co.
GAS MISER - Tires - Montgomery Ward & Co. Inc.
GAS-O-HAUL - Automotive parts and accessories - Gas-O-Haul, Inc.
GAS PILL, THE - Fuel conditioner - American Symbolic Corp.
GAS PLASMA - Computers–personal - National Micro Systems Inc.
GAS PUMP VALET - Automotive parts and accessories - Molor Products Co.
GAS-RAK - Racks - Jarke Corp.
GAS-RYDER - Shock absorbers–motor vehicle - Gabriel Ride Control Products Div.
GAS-RYDER LT - Shock absorbers–motor vehicle - Gabriel Ride Control Products Div.
GAS SCAN - Tanks–gas - Attwood Corp.
GAS SENTRY - Hardware - Stanley Solar & Stove Inc.
GAS-STOR - Containers–metal - Haz-Stor Co.
GAS SYSTEM INTERRUPT - Safety products ☆ - R.W. Lyall & Co., Inc.
GAS THEFT LOK - Alarm systems ☆ - Anes Electronics Burglar Alarm Systems
GAS-TITE - Housewares - Vaughan Manufacturing Co. Inc.
GAS WALKER - Containers - Tempo Products Co.
GAS-X - Antacids - Sandoz Pharmaceuticals Corp.
GASALIA - Pharmaceutical preparations - Boiron Inc.
GASAVER - Chemical preparations - Angus Chemical Co.
GASB GOVERNMENTAL ACCOUNTING RESEARCH SYSTEM - Computer software - Financial Accounting Foundation
GASBADGE - Electronic equipment - Industrial Scientific Corp.
GASCHY - Wines ☆ - Bercut-Vandervoort & Co.
GASDIA - Pipes ☆ - Federal Process Co.
GASENSHI - Artists' materials - Andrews/Nelson/Whitehead
GASENTRY - Hardware - Pelco Industries Inc.
GASEX - Lubricating oils ☆ - Shell Oil Co.
GASHOPPER - Engines–motor vehicle - Palmer Industries
GASJET - Air purification systems - Ion Systems
GASK-IT - Adhesives and sealants - Unival Corp.
GASKA TAPE - Tape–adhesive - Gaska Tape, Inc.
GASKET CASE-T - T-shirts–men's - Chums Ltd.
GASKET EATER - Tools - Frederickseal, Inc.
GASKET ELIMINATOR - Automotive parts and accessories - Loctite Corp.
GASKET ELIMINATOR 504 - Adhesives and sealants - Loctite Corp.
GASKET ELIMINATOR 510 - Adhesives and sealants - Loctite Corp.
GASKET ELIMINATOR 515 - Adhesives and sealants - Loctite Corp.
GASKET ELIMINATOR 518 - Adhesives and sealants - Loctite Corp.
GASKET-LOCK - Moldings–plaster of paris - Dayton Superior Corp.
GASKETS IN A TUB - Gaskets - Dap Products Inc.
GASLIGHT - Wood products - Georgia-Pacific Corp.
GASLINK - Computer peripheral equipment - Scott Specialty Gases, Inc.
GASLITE - Furniture ☆ - Singer Furniture Co.
GASLITE - Lighting fixtures–gas - Preway Industries Inc.
GASLOW - Meters–gas - Modern Home Products Corp.
GAS'M - Pesticides–agricultural ☆ - Roccorp, Inc.
GASMASTER - Electrical equipment - Design-Rite, Inc.
GASMASTER - Gas machinery - Gasmaster International, Inc.
GASOILA - Adhesives and sealants - Federal Process Co.

GASOILA-100 - Adhesives and sealants - Federal Process Co.

GASOILA-NT - Adhesives and sealants - Federal Process Co.

GASOILA SOFT-SET - Adhesives and sealants - Federal Process Co.

GASOLINE - Apparel and accessories - Jeanjer, Ltd.

GASOLINE - Brushes–paint - Corona Brushes Inc.

GASOLINE ALLEY - Recording label - MCA Universal Studios

GASOLINE WATER ZORB - Gasoline - Marine Development & Research Corp.

GASP - Artists' materials - Star Parts Inc.

GASP - Computer software - Attest Systems, Inc.

GASP KING - Artists' materials - Star Parts Inc.

GASPAC - Machine parts - BW/IP International, Inc.

GASPACHI - Boating equipment and accessories - Ocean Kayak, Inc.

GASPANO - Wines - Ferrara Winery

GASPAR - Meat products–cured ✩ - Galaxy Food Brokers

GASPARO - Recording label - Gasparo Records

GASPAR'S - Sausages - Gaspar's Sausage Co., Inc.

GASPEE - Frames–eyeglass ✩ - Universal/Univis Inc.

GASPETTE - Artists' materials - Star Parts Inc.

GASQUET - Seafood products–canned or cured ✩ - Tsar Nicoulai Caviar

GASSANE - Apparel and accessories - Gassane Tailors, Inc.

GASSEAL - Pet products - Mariculture Technologies International Inc.

GASSER, THE - Gasoline ✩ - Eagle Manufacturing Co. Inc.

GASSERS - Shock absorbers–motor vehicle - Works Performance Products

GASSERS - Toys–models ✩ - Cox Products Inc.

GASTALDINO - Breads - Liberty Richter Inc.

GASTECH - Machinery - Automotive Plastic Technologies, Inc.

GASTIX - Sharpening tool - Great American Tool Co., Inc.

GASTOMINS - Pharmaceutical preparations ✩ - Wesley Pharmacal Co. Inc.

GASTON - Thread - Threads USA Div.

GASTON DE LAGRANGE - Beverages–alcohol - Bacardi Imports Inc.

GASTRALSAN - Vitamins and nutritional supplements - Dolisos America, Inc.

GASTRICAL - Pharmaceutical preparations ✩ - U.S. Ethicals Inc.

GASTRICARE - Vitamins and nutritional supplements - Ayurvedic Concepts Ltd.

GASTRO-GNOMES - Novelty items–paper - Gastro-Gnomes, Inc.

GASTRO-MAGIC - Pharmaceutical preparations ✩ - Hunt Products Inc.

GASTRO-TRAC - Medical apparatus ✩ - Biosearch Medical Products Inc.

GASTROGRAFIN - Pharmaceutical preparations - Bristol-Myers Squibb Co.

GASTROMARK - Diagnostic substances - Mallinckrodt Medical, Inc.

GASTRONAL - Pharmaceutical preparations - Medical Arts Laboratories Inc.

GASTROPAL - Pharmaceutical preparations - Fernando Palafox, Sr.

GASTROSED - Pharmaceutical preparations - Roberts/Hauck Pharmaceuticals Inc.

GASTROSOOTHE - Health care products - Enzymatic Therapy, Inc.

GASWOOL - Kilns - A.C. Leadbetter & Son, Inc.

GASWORKS - Computer software - Russell C. Martin

GAT PRECISION - Computer software and data - Global Advanced Technology Corp.

GATA ORGANIC - Fertilizers - NW Organic Products Inc.

GATE - Computer software - Seven Hills Software

GATE ENSEMBLE - Computer software - Cadence Design Systems, Inc.

GATE GARD - Automotive parts and accessories - Storall Inc.

GATE KEEPER - Gas machinery - Aeronex, Inc.

GATE OPERATORS - Electronic equipment - Metropolitan Supply Inc.

GATE-TECH - Gate-opening mechanism - Embassy Gates Associates LP

GATEHOUSE - Figurines ✩ - Rawcliffe Corp.

GATEHOUSE - Wainscotting - Georgia-Pacific Corp.

GATEHOUSE - Wallpaper - K.M.L. Industries

GATEHOUSE 3RD EDITION - Wallcovering - Colortree Designs

GATEHOUSE 4TH EDITION - Wallcovering - Colortree Designs

GATEHOUSE 4TH EDITION - Wallpaper ✩ - Eisenhart Wallcoverings Co.

GATEHOUSE COLLECTION - Wallcovering ✩ - Colortree Designs

GATEHOUSE SECOND EDITION - Wallcovering ✩ - Colortree Designs

GATES - Automotive parts and accessories - Gates Rubber Co. (Automotive Aftermarket/Hardware Sales Div.)

GATES - Bakery products - Gates Management, Inc.

GATES - Gloves - Gates Gloves

GATES - Sporting goods - Parkway Systems

GATESTAR - Computers - Roger Dale White

GATEVIEW - Computer software - Proteon, Inc.

GATEWAY - Computers–personal - Gateway 2000, Inc.

GATEWAY - Floor coverings–carpet and rugs - Atlas Carpet Mills Inc.

GATEWAY - Floor coverings–carpet and rugs - Burlington House Carpets

GATEWAY - Infant product - Matchbox Toys USA

GATEWAY - Infant product ✩ - Century Products Co.

GATEWAY - Luggage - York Luggage Co.

GATEWAY - Luggage ✩ - Gateway Travelware

GATEWAY - Occasional tables ✩ - JDI Group, Inc.

GATEWAY - Prefabricated buildings–wood - Champion Enterprises Inc.

GATEWAY - Recording label - Rite Record Productions Inc.

GATEWAY - Salad dressings–bottled - Mrs. Clark's Foods

GATEWAY - Snack foods - Gateway Candy Corp.

GATEWAY 1.5-C - Communications equipment - Brooks Fiber Properties, Inc.

GATEWAY 45-C - Communications equipment - Brooks Fiber Properties, Inc.

GATEWAY 2000 - Computers - Gateway 2000, Inc.

GATEWAY AMSAFE - Eyes–glass - Gateway Amsafe Inc.

GATEWAY CASUALS - Men's apparel - Interco Inc.

GATEWAY COLLECTION - Apparel and accessories ✩ - Modern Jacket Co. Inc.

GATEWAY DL - Communications equipment - Brooks Fiber Properties, Inc.

GATEWAY FRACT - Communications equipment - Brooks Fiber Properties, Inc.

GATEWAY STORY, A - Compact discs–prerecorded - Texas Caviar, Inc.

GATEWAY TRACING - Artists' materials - Bee Paper Co. Inc.

GATEWAY2000 S O L O - Computers–personal - Gateway 2000, Inc.

GATEWAYS - Greeting cards - Sunrise Publications, Inc.

GATEX - Audio equipment - Valley Audio Products, Inc.

GATHANE - Machine parts - GIW Industries Inc.

GATHER ALL - Mops - Golden Star Inc.

GATHER VITALITY - Health care products - East Earth Herb Inc.

GATHERETTE - Office supplies - Wirth International Inc.

GATHERETTE COLLATOR - Office supplies - Wirth International Inc.

GATHERING HOUSE - Beds–wood - La-Z-Boy Chair Co.

GATHERING WINDS - Food products - Allied Old English, Inc.

GATHERINGS - Dinnerware–glass - Libbey Glass Inc.

GATI - Cat food - Cargill, Inc.

GATO - Computer software ✩ - Spectrum Holobyte, Inc.

GATO - Wines - Shaw-Ross International Importers

GATOR - Beverages–malt - Florida Brewing Co.

GATOR - Bicycles ✩ - Hunt-Wilde Corp.

GATOR - Boats–motor ✩ - Cobia Boat Co.

GATOR - Coatings - Morton International Inc. (Morton Salt Div.)

GATOR - Exercising equipment - Gator Industries, Inc.

GATOR - Fertilizers - Howard Fertilizer Co., Inc.

GATOR - Grass seed - International Seeds, Inc.

GATOR - Jewelry - Jacoby-Bender Inc.

GATOR - Knives–butcher - Fiskars Inc.

GATOR - Plugs–ear ✩ - Eleventh Hour Manufacturing

GATOR - Sporting goods - Gator Sports Inc.

GATOR-AID - Asphalt patching compound - Allstates Coatings Co., Inc.

GATOR ANT BAIT - Insecticides ✩ - Eleventh Hour Manufacturing

GATOR BAIT - Spices and extracts - Gator Bait

GATOR BAR - Candy bars - Quaker Oats Co.

GATOR BLADE - Saw blades - Greenlee Textron Inc.

GATOR BLADES - Tools–garden - Fiskars Inc.

GATOR BUNS - Sporting goods - Gator Sports Inc.

GATOR DELITES - Alligator meat - Ernesto Nunez

GATOR-FLEECE EARS - Sporting goods - Gator Sports Inc.

GATOR-FLEECE FACE - Sporting goods - Gator Sports Inc.

GATOR GATES - Gates–dam - Gator Dock & Marine, Inc.

GATOR GOLF - Games - Hasbro, Inc.

GATOR-GRIP - Bags - Durasol Drug & Chemical Co.

GATOR-GRIP - Electrical equipment - General Electric Co.

GATOR-GRIP - Gloves–work - Pioneer Industrial Products Co.

GATOR GRIP - Musical instrument accessories - Dunlop Manufacturing, Inc.

GATOR GRIP - Sporting goods - Endslip Products Co.

GATOR GRIP - Tools ✩ - Tel-O-Post Co.

GATOR GRIP GASKETS - Gaskets - Frederickseal, Inc.

GATOR GRIPS - Slippers - Totes, Inc.

GATOR HAMMOCK GATOR SAUCE - Sauces - Samuel T. Taylor

GATOR HIDE - Frames–picture - Framemica Co.

GATOR HIDE SHEET - Sheet metal products - Frederickseal, Inc.

GATOR HYDE - Flags - National Banner Co., Inc.

GATOR-HYDE - Paints - Somay Products Inc.

GATOR METER - Thermometers - Aquacide

GATOR MOP - Mops - Libman Co.

GATOR MOUNT - Boating equipment and accessories - Zebco Corp.

GATOR NET - Motor vehicle parts and accessories - Saddleman, Inc.

GATOR-PLY - Furniture–wood - International Paper (Decorative Products Division)

GATOR PRO - Vitamins and nutritional supplements - Quaker Oats Co.

✩ = Now out of production

GATOR ROACH HIVES - Insecticides ☆ - Eleventh Hour Manufacturing

GATOR SERRATER - Knives–hunting - Fiskars Inc.

GATOR SHOES - Footwear - Etc. of Henderson, Inc.

GATOR SNAPS - Toys - China Pyrotechnics, Inc.

GATOR SOX - Socks - Gator Sports Inc.

GATOR SPOONS - Fishing lures - Lindy Little Joe Inc.

GATOR-SPORT SOX - Socks - Gator Sports Inc.

GATOR, THE - Agricultural mowers - Vermeer Manufacturing Co.

GATORADE - Vitamins and nutritional supplements - Quaker Oats Co.

GATORADE FROST - Beverages - Stokely-Van Camp, Inc.

GATORADE LIGHT - Vitamins and nutritional supplements - Quaker Oats Co.

GATORADE SPORTS SCIENCE - Beverages - Stokely-Van Camp, Inc.

GATORADE THIRST QUENCHER - Beverages - Stokely-Van Camp, Inc.

GATORBACK - Tires - Goodyear Tire & Rubber Co.

GATORBACKS - Shoe soles - Etc. of Henderson, Inc.

GATORBAR - Hats - Stokely-Van Camp, Inc.

GATORCEL - Signboards - International Paper Co.

GATORFOAM - Artists' materials - International Paper (Decorative Products Division)

GATORGUM - Vitamins and nutritional supplements - Thompson and Formby

GATORPLATE - Finishing agents - Kemlite Co., Inc.

GATORPOLY - Boating equipment and accessories - Ultra Poly, Inc.

GATORS - Hair care products - Buttercut Shear Co.

GATORS - Ophthalmic goods - Hilsinger Corp.

GATORSHIELD-LITE - Hardware - Allied Tube & Conduit Corp.

GATORVAC - Garden equipment - WCI Outdoor Products, Inc.

GATSBY - Dinnerware ☆ - Corning Inc.

GATSBY - Eyeglasses - Bausch & Lomb Inc.

GATSBY - Frames–eyeglass - May Optical Co. Inc.

GATSBY - Life preservers - Stearns Manufacturing Co.

GATSBY - Whirlpools - Gatsby Spas Inc.

GATWICK - Floor coverings ☆ - Bruce Hardwood Floors

GATWICK - Floor coverings–carpet and rugs - Whitecrest Carpet Mills

GAUCHO - Attache cases - Airway Industries, Inc.

GAUCHO - Bicycles - Columbia Manufacturing Inc.

GAUCHO - Cookies - Sunshine/Salerno Inc.

GAUCHO - Fencing–steel - Bekaert Corp. (Wire & Wire Products Div.)

GAUCHO - Frames–eyeglass - Hoya Corp. USA

GAUCHO - Guitars - WMI Corp.

GAUCHO - Jewelry ☆ - Hirsch Speidel Inc.

GAUCHO - Meat products–canned - Gaucho Food Products Inc.

GAUCHO - Scooters–children's - Peg Perego USA Inc.

GAUCHO 4 X 4 - Scooters–children's ☆ - Peg Perego USA Inc.

GAUCHO BELT - Toys - Milton Bradley Co.

GAUER - Snow skis - GSI, Inc.

GAUGE - Glass products - Kaufman Glass Co.

GAUGE GARB - Apparel and accessories - Galan Lauland Designs, Inc.

GAUGE-GUARD - Health care products - Equi-Tron Inc.

GAUGE GUARD - Medical apparatus - Erie Medical (Div. of Ocenco Incorporated)

GAUGE-O-KNIT - Rulers–metal - Scandinavian House Imports Inc.

GAUGE, THE - Pianos - Ford Piano Supply Co.

GAULOISE - Perfumes - Henry Calisher Inc.

GAULOISE - Tobacco products - G.A. Georgopulo & Co. Inc.

GAULTIER - Beverages–alcohol ☆ - Nor-Glo Import Co.

GAUNTLET - Floor coverings–carpet and rugs ☆ - Karastan-Bigelow Inc.

GAUNTLET - Ships–sailing vessels - Cape Cod Shipbuilding Co.

GAUNTLET - Sporting goods - Marty Gilman Inc.

GAUNTLET - Video games - Atari Games Corp.

GAUSS - Amplifiers ☆ - Gauss Div.

G.A.U.S.S. GALACTIC ASSOCIATION UNIVERSITIES SCHOLARS STUDENTS - Apparel–athletic - Marc Howard International, Inc.

GAUTIER COGNAC - Beverages–alcohol - Marie Brizard Wines & Spirits, USA

GAUZE + - Medical and surgical gauze - United Foam Plastics Corp.

GAUZTEX - Health care products - General Bandages Inc.

GAVEL - Eyeglasses - Martin-Copeland Eyewear Corp.

GAVEL SOFTWARE - Computer software - Gavel Software

GAVELS - Toys - Carrom Co.

GAVET ADF ART DIRECTOR FORMULA - Hair care products - Ian Gavet

GAVI - Electronic equipment - General Audio-Visual Inc.

GAVI - Wines - Kobrand Corp.

GAVICIDE - Insecticides - PureGro Co.

GAVICIDE - Pesticides–agricultural - Crop Production Services Inc.

GAVICIDE-C - Insecticides - PureGro Co.

GAVILAN - Beverages–alcohol - David Sherman Corp.

GAVILAN - Liquors - Foreign Vintages Inc.

GAVILAN - Wines - Chalone Wine Group Ltd.

GAVIN - Antennas - Gavin Electronics

GAVIN - Ophthalmic goods ☆ - Luxottica

GAVINA - Coffee - F. Gavina and Sons Inc.

GAVIOTA - Bathing suits ☆ - Sirena Apparel Group Inc.

GAVISCON - Antacids - Marion Merrell Dow

GAVISCON - Health care products - SmithKline Beecham Consumer Healthcare

GAVOTTE - Frames–eyeglass - Hudson Optical Corp.

GAWITH APRICOT - Snuff - James B. Russell Inc.

GAWKERS - Apparel–women's - Ralph J. Berger

GAWLER PARK - Food products ☆ - Europa Foods Ltd.

GAY 90 MATS - Mat boards - Callen Photo Mount Corp.

GAY-90'S - Bakery products - Flowers Bakeries (West Virginia Div.)

GAY 90S - Ice cream - Borden, Inc.

GAY 90'S - Pianos - Universal Player Piano Co.

GAY BAR - Chocolate bars - Linda Grishman Chocolates, Inc.

GAY BOUQUET - Soap - Dial Corp.

GAY DECEIVER - Apparel and accessories ☆ - Warnaco Inc.

GAY FRERES - Jewelry - Nina Ricci Jewelry-Pierre Balmain

GAY GAL - Eyeglasses - Art-Craft Optical Co.

GAY LADY - Eyeglasses - Art-Craft Optical Co.

GAY NINETIES - Doilies - U.S. Lace Paper Works Inc.

GAY NINETIES - Dolls ☆ - Effanbee Doll Corp.

GAY NINETIES - Marshmallows - D.F. Stauffer Biscuit Co., Inc.

GAY NOTE - Paper–gift wrap ☆ - Plus Mark Inc.

GAY PAREE - Apparel–women's - Lady Marlene

GAY PAREE - Dolls ☆ - Effanbee Doll Corp.

GAY PARISIENNE - Dolls - Mattel, Inc.

GAY PRIDE APPAREL - Apparel and accessories - Sheila Evangeline Roberts

GAY PRINCESS - Eyeglasses - Art-Craft Optical Co.

GAY SECRET - Skin care products ☆ - T.N. Dickinson Co.

GAY SPORTS - Apparel - Gary David Johnson

GAY STEP - Hosiery - Virginia Maid Hosiery Mills Inc.

GAY TIME - Frames–eyeglass - Pathway Optical Prods.

GAY TOP - Eyeglasses - Art-Craft Optical Co.

GAY TOP - Hair care products - Helene Curtis Industries Inc.

GAY YELLOW PAGES - Telephone directories - Gay & Lesbian Yellow Pages, Inc.

GAYANNEE - Fabrics–silk - Cailor SA

GAYCHROME - High chairs - Gaychrome

GAYCUROME - Cooking equipment–commercial - Central Specialties

GAYDON - Drapery hardware - Pawley Co.

GAYELORD HAUSER - Seasonings - Modern Products, Inc.

GAYETY - Ophthalmic goods - Styl-Rite Optical Manufacturing Co., Inc.

GAYETY - Paper - Plainwell Tissue

GAYLA - Beverages - Tom Thumb Stores, Inc.

GAYLA - Combs ☆ - Morris-Flamingo Inc.

GAYLA - Hair care products - Gaylord Products Inc.

GAYLA - Kites - Gayla Industries Inc.

GAYLA - Ophthalmic goods - Swank Optical

GAYLAFLEX - Kites - Gayla Industries Inc.

GAYLAKNIT - Crocheted and knitted items - Garland Knitting Mills

GAYLORD - Food products - Frank's Food Mart

GAYLORE - Beverages–alcohol - Vintwood International Ltd.

GAYLORS - Hairpins - Gaylord Products Inc.

GAYMEBIRDS - Food products ☆ - Pierce Foods Corp.

GAYMODE - Hosiery - J.C. Penney Co., Inc.

GAYO ASUL - Cheese - Webeco Foods Inc.

GAYPET - Pet products ☆ - Franklin Laboratories

GAZE-O-GRAMS - Posters - Visual Reality Graphics

GAZEBO - Awnings - Gale Group Inc.

GAZEBO - Chocolate syrup - Chocolate Lace

GAZEBO - Fabrics - Cecil Saydah Co.

GAZEBO - Floor coverings–carpet and rugs - Barrett Carpet Mills Inc.

GAZEBO - Floor coverings–carpet and rugs - Coronet Carpets Inc.

GAZEBO - Glassware–household ☆ - Crisa Corp.

GAZEBO - Servingware, giftware - Indiana Glass Co.

GAZEBO - Tableware–china - Pfaltzgraff Investment Co.

GAZEBO - Wallpaper - Payne Fabrics

GAZEBO BLEND - Coffee - Starbucks Corp.

GAZEBO GARLAND - Tableware–china ☆ - Pfaltzgraff Investment Co.

GAZEBO ROOM - Salad dressings–bottled - Best Dressed Associates, Inc.

GAZELA VINHO VERDE - Wines - Sogrape USA Inc.

GAZELLE - Archery equipment ☆ - Martin Archery Inc.

GAZELLE - Athletic shoes - Converse Inc.
GAZELLE - Bicycles - Columbia Manufacturing Inc.
GAZELLE - Candy - Edward D. Jamron
GAZELLE - Gloves - David & Young Co., Inc.
GAZELLE - Health care products - Snug Seat, Inc.
GAZELLE - Staplers - ACCO USA, Inc.
GAZELLE II - Shoes–athletic ☆ - Titleist & Foot-Joy Worldwide
GAZETTE - Pencils ☆ - National Pen & Pencil Co.
GAZILLIONAIRE - Computer software - Lavamind
GAZINTA - Boxes–corrugated paperboard ☆ - Martin Carbone Inc.
GAZON - Floor coverings–carpet and rugs - V & B Carpet
GAZZINI - Tiles–ceramic - Federal Tile Imports Inc.
GAZZOLA MONTE REGALE - Pasta - Lettieri
GB - Cosmetics - Garden Botanika, Inc.
GB - Musical instruments - On-Site Music Group
GB - Recording label - Blue Rose, Inc.
GB - Relishes - Green Boys Foods
GB - Rivets–metal - G.B. Dupont Co., Inc.
GB - Thread - Belding Heminway Co. Inc.
G.B. FELD - Pennants ☆ - Flags International Inc.
GB GAMEBREAKER - Apparel and accessories - Gamebreaker
GB GIORGIO BRUTINI - Footwear - Harbor Footwear Group Ltd.
GB GLENNON BITTAN - Apparel and accessories - Glennon Bittan Group, Inc.
GB GOOD BEDROOMS - Furniture - Finegood Holdings, Inc.
GB PREP - Laxatives - Purdue Frederick Co.
GB-STAT - Computer software - New England Software Inc.
GBA WATER MASTER - Computer software - George Butler Associates, Inc.
G.B.B. - Golfing equipment - Callaway Golf Co.
GBC - Containers - Greif Bros. Corp. (Norco Div.)
GBC - Television equipment - CCTV Corp./GBC
GBC DIAMOND - Plastics–laminated - General Binding Corp.
GBC DOCUSEAL - Electronic equipment - General Binding Corp.
GBD - Nuts and bolts - G.B. Dupont Co., Inc.
GBI - Computers ☆ - G B Insturments, Inc.
G.B.M. - Apparel and accessories - Garan Services Corp.
GBP - Recording label - Rustron Music Productions
GBS - Computer software - Xiox Corp.
G.B.S. - Pharmaceutical preparations ☆ - Forest Pharmaceuticals Inc.
GBSII - Computer software ☆ - Cyma Systems, Inc.
GBX - Footwear - Harbor Footwear Group Ltd.
GC - Audio equipment - GC Thorsen, Inc.
GC - Computers - DTK Computer Inc.
GC - Jewelry - Geometric Co.
GC - Metals - General Casting Co.
GC - Toys - Empire Industries
GC-100 - Cleaning preparations ☆ - Davis-Howland Oil Corp.
GC AMERICA - Motor homes, camper vans, etc. - Gulf Stream Coach Inc.
G.C. BOND - Chemical preparations - GC Thorsen, Inc.
GC GAZZELLE CIAMPI - Apparel and accessories - Gazzelle Champy
G.C. SPORTS - Apparel stores–sports - Gotcha Covered
G.C. TEMPO & SONS - Wines - Tempo Imports Ltd.
GC TOOL - Tools–hand-operated - GC Thorsen, Inc.
GC VALVES - Valves - Components for Automation, Inc.
GC30 - Rackets–tennis - Spalding Sports Worldwide
GCC - Electrical equipment ☆ - General Cable Corp.
GCC - Jewelry–precious - GCC
GCC - Printers–computer - Graphline, Inc.
GCD - Golfing equipment - Ben Hogan Co.
GCF - Machinery - Good Clean Fun, Inc.
GCI THE FORCE. .IN CONTROL - Computer peripheral equipment - Geometric Controls Inc.
GCJ - Jewelry - Gold Craft Jewelry Corp.
GCK - Jewelry - Gold Creek Black Hills Gold Ltd. Inc.
GCN INTERNATIONAL - Shirts–polo - Global Commerce Network
GCO - Recording label - Jody Record Corp.
GCP - Computer software - Telxon Corp.
GCP - Glass products - Owens-Illinois Inc. (Libbey Div.)
GCP - Shampoos - Care-Tech Laboratories Inc.
GCR - Computers - Gary C. Robinson
GCR-5 - Chemical preparations - Amspec Chemical Corp.
GCRJ 86B4U - Costumes - McCain Ellio's Foods, Inc.
GCS - Computer software - Incircuit Development Corp.
GCS - Gloves - Grandoe Corp.
GCS GLOVE COMPONENT SYSTEM - Gloves - Grandoe Corp.
GCUE - Balls–billiard - Dart Mart Inc.
GCW - Jewelry - Goldcraft West Inc.

GD - Apparel and accessories - Grateful Dead Merchandising, Inc.
GD - Frames–picture - Graphik Dimensions Ltd.
GD - Lighting fixtures–airport - Dove Products Inc.
GDA - Caps–baseball - Kenneth Taylor
G'DAY - Teas–herbal - Melaleuca, Inc.
GDC - Computer software - General Datacomm, Inc.
GDC - Jewelry - Georgia Diamond Corp.
GDC - Medical apparatus - Target Therapeutics, Inc.
GDC APEX - Communications equipment - General Datacomm, Inc.
GDCT - Guitars - Jong Wook Ko
GDD - Golfing equipment - Lisco, Inc.
GDE SYSTEMS, INC. - Computer peripheral equipment - Gde Systems, Inc.
GDF - Posters - Graphique De France, Ltd.
GDI - Computer software - Garg Data International, Inc.
GDL - Lubricants - Shanco, Inc.
GDL-POWER - Vitamins ☆ - Nature's Herbs
GDS - Medical apparatus - GDS Technology Inc.
GE - Computer software - General Electric Co.
GE - Kitchen appliances - General Electric Co.
GE-FERON - Vitamins and nutritional supplements - Viva America Marketing, Inc.
GE-MARC - Electrical equipment - General Electric Co.
GE-MARC V-E - Radios - General Electric Co.
GE-NET TMX - Electrical equipment - General Electric Co.
GE-OXY 132 - Vitamins and nutritional supplements - Global Marketing Associates, Inc.
GE POWER CONTROLS - Circuit breakers - General Electric Co.
GE SILICONE SEAL - Adhesives and sealants - General Electric Co.
GE TARGET - Medical apparatus - General Electric Co.
GEAR - Flowers–artificial - Gear Holdings, Inc.
GEAR - Infant product ☆ - S. Schwab Co., Inc.
GEAR - Luggage ☆ - Pierre Cardin Electronique
GEAR - Recording label - Statiras Records
GEAR 2000 - Sporting goods - Gear 2000, Ltd.
GEAR: AMERICAN COUNTRY KIDS II - Wallpaper ☆ - Imperial Wallcoverings, Inc.
GEAR: AMERICAN COUNTRY LIFE II - Wallpaper - Imperial Wallcoverings, Inc.
GEAR: AMERICAN COUNTRY MANOR - Wallpaper - Imperial Wallcoverings, Inc.
GEAR: AMERICAN COUNTRY STENCIL - Wallpaper ☆ - Imperial Wallcoverings, Inc.
GEAR: AMERICA'S HOMELAND - Wallpaper ☆ - Imperial Wallcoverings, Inc.
GEAR BAGS - Handbags ☆ - Pyramid Handbags, Inc.
GEAR BEACH - Blankets - Gear Holdings, Inc.
GEAR BEAR BOOKS - Publisher's imprints - Grosset & Dunlap Inc.
GEAR: CITY GRAPHICS - Wallpaper ☆ - Imperial Wallcoverings, Inc.
GEAR: CITY GRAPHICS AND COUNTRY PLAIDS - Wallpaper ☆ - Imperial Wallcoverings, Inc.
GEAR: COUNTRY - Wallpaper ☆ - Imperial Wallcoverings, Inc.
GEAR COUSIN - Toys–stuffed ☆ - Gund, Inc.
GEAR DIMENSIONALS - Wallpaper ☆ - Imperial Wallcoverings, Inc.
GEAR FOR SPORTS - Apparel–athletic - Winning Ways Inc.
GEAR GRIP - Tools–hand-operated - Gear Grip Inc.
GEAR KEEPER - Sporting goods - Hammerhead Industries, Inc.
GEAR KIDS - House furnishings - Gear Holdings, Inc.
GEAR LOVES KIDS - Floor coverings–carpet and rugs - Trans-Ocean Import Co. Inc.
GEAR MASTER - Lubricants - LPS Laboratories, Inc.
GEAR-MOLY - Lubricants - Pacific Lubricants
GEAR ROLLER HOCKEY - Apparel–athletic - Gear International Trading Co.
GEAR UP! - Bicycle-storage systems - IMS Enterprises Inc.
GEAR-WIZARD - Computer software - Emerson Electric Co.
GEAR WORKS - Video games - Sony Electronic Publishing Co.
GEARBOX - Protective Clothing - Haro Designs, Inc.
GEARBOX - Sporting goods - Chisco, Inc.
GEARCHARGER - Automotive parts and accessories - Vortech Engineering, Inc.
GEARING UP - Apparel–children's - J.C. Penney Co., Inc.
GEARNET - Computer software - M & M Precision Systems Corp.
GEAROPE - Lubricants - Kano Laboratories Inc.
GEARS IN MOTION - Toys - Natural Science Industries, Ltd.
GEARTEK - Pumps - Hydraulic Analysis, Inc. (Geartek Division)
GEARWEAR - Apparel and accessories - Gear Holdings, Inc.
GEARWORKS - Musical instruments - XL Specialty Percussion
GEARY'S PALE ALE - Beverages–malt - D.L. Geary Brewing Co.

GEAUGA SPRINGS - Water–bottled or canned - Minnehaha Spring Water Co.
GEBAUER - Anesthetics ☆ - Gebauer Co.
GEBAUER 114 - Anesthetics ☆ - Gebauer Co.
GEBAUER ETHYL CHLORIDE - Anesthetics - Gebauer Co.
GEBAUER SPRAY AND STRETCH - Anesthetics - Gebauer Co.
GEBAUER'S - Pharmaceutical preparations - Gebauer Co.
GEBERIT - Plumbing fixtures - Geberit Manufacturing Inc.
GEBHARDT - Chili–canned - Hunt-Wesson, Inc.
GEBR. ALEXANDER - Musical instruments - Custom Music Co.
GECAL - Computers - General Electric Co.
GECEL - Sporting goods ☆ - Ballco Products Inc.
GECIL - Pharmaceutical preparations - Geneva Generics Inc.
GECKO - Apparel–men's - Gecko Trading Co.
GECKO - Computer software - Gecko Software
GECKO - Kites - Hi-Flier Manufacturing Co.
GECO - Electrical equipment - General Electric Co.
GECO - Sporting goods - Gerry Cosby & Co., Inc.
GED - Machinery - Glass Equipment Development, Inc.
GED FOR IBM & APPLE - Computer software - Krell Software Corp.
GEDANIA - Glassware–household - Whitehurst Imports
GEDI - Cheese ☆ - Crystal Food Import Corp.
GEDIFA - Yarn - Knitting Fever Inc.
GEDNEY - Pickles - M.A. Gedney Co.
GEDNEY - Watches - Bulova Corp.
GEDNEY COMPANY, THE - Belts–apparel - Hat Attack, Inc.
GEE - Frames–picture ☆ - Acme Frame Products, Inc.
GEE - Milk ☆ - Gossner Foods, Inc.
GEE-GEE - Pharmaceutical preparations - JMI-Canton Pharmaceuticals
GEE KIDS - Eyeglasses - Gruen Marketing Corp.
GEE O BALL - Sporting goods - Poly Enterprises
GEE WHIZ - Computer software - Direct Business Technologies, Inc.
GEE YOUR HAIR SMELLS TERRIFIC - Hair care products - Andrew Jergens Co.
GEECO - Garden equipment - Kinsman Co. Inc.
GEEDLE LINK - Computer software - Intellicom International, Inc.
GEEGEE - Apparel–women's - Milaca Mills, Inc.
GEEK SQUAD - Apparel and accessories - Geek Squad, Inc.
GEEKPORT - Computer hardware - BE Inc.
GEEKS - Candy - Sherman's Confections, Inc.
GEEPER-CREEPER - Toys - Tonka Corp.
GEE'S - Fish nets - Cuba Specialty Manufacturing Co.
GEET GOVINDA - Perfumes - R. Expo (USA) Ltd.
GEFDEN - Hair care products - Gefden International Inc.
GEFDEN NUCLEIC ACID - Hair care products - Gefden International Inc.
GEFDEN WHEAT HAIR CARE COLLECTION - Hair care products - Gefden International Inc.
GEFFEN - Recording label - Geffen Records, Inc.
GEFFEN - Recording label - Warner Bros. Records Inc.
GEFLE PORSLIN - Earthenware - Swedish Products Inc. (Sojo Inc.)
GEFU - Housewares stores - SCI Scandicrafts Inc.
GEGA - Recording label ☆ - Worldtone Music Inc.
GEHA DUPLEX - Paper–carbon - Robert F. De Castro, Inc.
GEHL'S - Coffee - Gehl's Guernsey Farms Inc.
GEHO - Pumps–water - Baker Hughes Inc.
GEI - Glass–window - Gorell Enterprises, Inc.
GEI - Rulers–wood - GEI International Inc.
GEI - Windows - Gorell Enterprises, Inc.
GEI CONTROLLERS - Appliance parts ☆ - Gas Energy Inc.
GEIER - Sausages - Haram-Christensen Corp.
GEIGEL - Paints - Geigel Co.
GEIGER - Apparel and accessories - Geiger of Austria Inc.
GEIGER - Office furniture–metal - Geiger International, Inc.
GEIGER BRICKEL - Furniture - Geiger International, Inc.
GEIMINI GORGONZOLA - Food products - Crystal Food Import Corp.
GEISERS - Snack foods - Borden, Inc.
GEISHA - Food products - Nozaki America Inc.
GEISHA - Scissors–hand-operated - Arius-Eickert Co. Inc.
GEISHA BLUE - Dinnerware–glass ☆ - Royal China & Porcelain Companies Inc.
GEISHA NAIL - Cosmetics - American International Industries
GEISLER - Pet shops - Sergeant's Pet Products, Inc.
GEISSER - Cutlery - Markuse Corp.
GEKKEIKAN - Wines - Sidney Frank Importing Co., Inc.
GEKRA - Copper products ☆ - Charles Zahn-Import Merchant
GEL - Paints - M. Grumbacher Inc.
GEL - Spices and extracts - Maple Leaf Foods Inc.

GEL-12 - Pharmaceutical preparations - Medical Chemical Corp.
GEL-120 - Footwear - Asics Tiger Corp.
GEL 2000 - Hair care products - Garcoa Labs/Vitamin Classics
GEL-AIRE - Deodorizers - Surco Products Inc.
GEL & GLOSS - Hair care products ☆ - Stanley Fay Co.
GEL BASE/GEL BLOT - Computer software - UVP Inc.
GEL BOOMERANGS - Boomerangs - Gel Boomerangs
GEL/CELL - Batteries - Johnson Controls Inc.
GEL CLEAN - Ophthalmic goods - Barnes-Hind Inc.
GEL-COAT MATCH N PATCH - Fabrics - Fibre Glass-Evercoat Co. Inc.
GEL DELICATO - Cosmetics - Princess Marcella Borghese, Inc.
GEL-EEZ - Computer peripheral equipment - Case Logic, Inc.
GEL-EEZE - Medical apparatus - Mastex Industries, Inc.
GEL GELE - Hair care products - Raymac Corp. Hair & Skin Technology
GEL-GLOSS - Housewares - TR Industries
GEL GRILL & OVEN CLEANER - Cleaning preparations–household - KC Products, Inc. (Sharon D. Spence)
GEL-IT - Hair care products - Waverly Beauty Products
GEL-KOTE - Antacids ☆ - Nutrition Control Products
GEL-LET - Deodorizers - Surco Products Inc.
GEL-LITE - Mattresses - Kap Industries, Inc.
GEL MASTER - Batteries - Exide Corp.
GEL NAILS - Cosmetics - Cosmar Corp.
GEL NAILS - Sculptured-nail kit - Jonel Inc.
GEL NATUREL - Skin care products - Rene Furterer
GEL NET - Hair care products ☆ - Palm Beach Beauty Products
GEL-OFF - American International Industries
GEL-OUT - Cleaning preparations–household - Environmental Biotech, Inc.
GEL POWER - Batteries - Concorde Battery Corp.
GEL-PRO - Computer software - Media Cybernetics, L.P.
GEL SEAL II - Adhesives and sealants - Outboard Marine Corp.
GEL-SEQ - Computer software - UVP Inc.
GEL SET - Hair care products ☆ - Palm Beach Beauty Products
GEL SET DEVELOPER - Cosmetics - American International Industries
GEL SHELL - Medical apparatus - Smith & Nephew Inc. (Rehabilitation Div.)
GEL SNACK CUP - Gelatin - Del Monte Corp.
GEL-SOLES - Shoe accessories - Pittsburgh Plastics Manufacturing, Inc.
GEL-SOLV - Cleaning products - Bane-Clene Corp.
GEL-STAT - Cleaning preparations - Geritrex Corp.
GEL STIMULANTE - Skin care products - Reviva Laboratories
GEL-SYTE - Medical apparatus - Baxter International Inc.
GEL-T - Health care products - HealthFLEX Inc.
GEL-TAC - Adhesives and sealants - PCI Paper Conversions, Inc.
GEL-TAC - Tape–adhesive - Paper Conversions Inc.
GEL-TECH - Batteries - East Penn Manufacturing Co., Inc.
GEL TIPS - Pharmaceutical preparations ☆ - Dixon-Shane Inc.
GEL TREAT - Gelatin - Kozy Shack Inc.
GEL TROPICAL - Sunblocks - Biotropics Natural Suncare, Inc.
GEL-U-SLEEP SERIES III - Mattresses - Mason Medical Products
GEL WHITE - Dental compounds - Temrex Corp.
GEL-WRITER - Pens - Gillette Co.
GELA DELIGHT - Food products - Moran Foods, Inc.
GELAMAL - Health care products - Halsey Drug Co. Inc.
GELANDE - Apparel and accessories - Sport USA, Inc.
GELAQUA - Hair care products - Image Laboratories, Inc.
GELARE - Ice cream ☆ - Borden, Inc.
GELATIN-FOR-NAILS - Nail care products - Pharmex Inc.
GELATO - Hair care products - KMS Research Inc.
GELATO AMARE - Ice cream/yogurt shop franchise - Gelato Amare
GELAVE - Hair care products - Playtex Beauty Care, Inc.
GELAZZE - Skin care products - Nemesis Inc.
GELB - Pet products - Nekton USA Inc.
GELBOND - Manicure preparations - Creative Nail Design, Inc.
GELCOHOL - Pharmaceutical preparations - Lyphomed Inc.
GELCOID - Pharmaceutical preparations ☆ - JMI-Canton Pharmaceuticals
GELCORT-H - Pharmaceutical preparations ☆ - Econo Med Pharmaceuticals Inc.
GELEE - Hair care products - Alberto-Culver Co.
GELEE COIFFANTE - Skin care products - La Coupe
GELEE EUROPEAN - Hair care products - Alberto-Culver Co.
GELEMMS - Pharmaceutical preparations ☆ - C.O. Truxton Inc.
GELFAND - Sporting goods ☆ - Powell Skateboards
GELFILM - Pharmaceutical preparations - Upjohn Co.
GELFOAM - Pharmaceutical preparations - Upjohn Co.
GELFOM - Orthopedic products - Chase Ergonomics Inc.
GELGUARD - Adhesives and sealants - Raychem Corp.

☆ = Now out of production

GELISSIMA - Hair care products - Modafini Inc.

GELITE - Food products - Golden Select Foods Co.

GELL ROLL LIGHTNING - Pens - Sakura of America

GELLE - Hair care products - Vidal Sassoon Inc.

GELLE - Skin care products - Orjene Natural Cosmetics

GELLO - Jewelry - Snails Italian Jewelry Co.

GELLO THREADS - Computer software - Lavelle Associates Inc.

GELLOTEEN - Hair care products - Redmond Products, Inc.

GELLY - Hair care products - Image Laboratories, Inc.

GELLY-BEES - Vitamins and nutritional supplements - Nikken USA, Ltd.

GELLY MIST - Hair care products - Image Laboratories, Inc.

GELLY ROLL - Pens - Sakura of America

GELMASTER - Pumps - Welch Vacuum Technology, Inc.

GELMATCH - Computer software - UVP Inc.

GELMATIC - Adhesives and sealants - Loctite Corp.

GELOCAST - Bandages - Beiersdorf Inc.

GELOMINS - Vitamins and nutritional supplements ☆ - Vita-Fore Products Co.

GELONE - Batteries - Ample Technology

GELOOZE - Snack foods - General Mills, Inc.

GELOSO - Tape recorders ☆ - Paso Sound Products Inc.

GELOTION - Hair care products - Action Environmental Products

GELOX - Pharmaceutical preparations ☆ - Xttrium Laboratories Inc.

GELOY - Resins–synthetic - General Electric Co.

GELPAC - Water treating compounds - General Environmental Science Corp.

GELPLUS - Hair care products - Hayashi for Hair Inc.

GELPRINT - Apparel and accessories - Geltman Industries

GELSEMINE HCL - Pharmaceutical preparations - City Chemical Corp.

GELSENTIAL - Hair care products - U.K. Abba Products, Inc.

GELSON'S - Food products - Gelson's Markets

GELSPAS - Pharmaceutical preparations - Goldline Laboratories, Inc.

GELSTAR - Batteries - Batteries, Inc.

GELSTATION - Power supply apparatus - Fotodyne Inc.

GELTABS - Pharmaceutical preparations ☆ - Upjohn Co.

GELTEX - Pharmaceutical preparations - Geltex Pharmaceuticals, Inc.

GELTHOTIC - Shoe insoles - Michael Kendall

GELUENT - Pharmaceutical preparations ☆ - Legere Pharmaceuticals Inc.

GELUMINA - Antacid - American Pharmaceutical Co.

GELUSIL - Antacids - Warner-Wellcome

GELUTEX - Pharmaceutical preparations ☆ - Veratex Group

GELWHIP - Hair care products - Image Laboratories, Inc.

GELWORKS - Computer software - UVP Inc.

GEM - Audio equipment ☆ - Sumiko Inc.

GEM - Bait ☆ - Siberian Salmon Egg Co.

GEM - Barbecues and grills ☆ - Ferro Corp.

GEM - Blades and razors - American Safety Razor Co.

GEM - Capacitors - General Electric Co.

GEM - Computer peripheral equipment - Michael Chian-Sun Wu

GEM - Computer software ☆ - Novell, Inc.

GEM - Daters - Consolidated Stamp Manufacturing Co. Inc.

GEM - Drafting supplies ☆ - Mayline/Hamilton

GEM - Erasers - Dixon Ticonderoga Co.

GEM - Extension cords - Gem Electric Manufacturing Co. Inc.

GEM - Food products - Western Farmers Association

GEM - Frames–eyeglass - Rozin Optical Export Corp.

GEM - Games - Gamescience

GEM - Guitars - N.H.F. Musical Merchandise Corp.

GEM - Hair care products ☆ - Hess Hair Milk Laboratories Inc.

GEM - Handles–wood - Hartwell Brothers Handle Co.

GEM - Hardware - Gem Products, Inc.

GEM - Hearing aids, now out of production - Audiotone, Inc.

GEM - Housewares - O-Cedar/Vining Household Products Co.

GEM - Lettuce - Tanimura & Antle, Inc.

GEM - Locks–padlocks - Fort Lock Corp.

GEM - Musical instruments - General Electro Music Corp.

GEM - Nail care products - London International U.S. Holdings

GEM - Office supplies - McGill Inc.

GEM - Organs ☆ - Ionic Industries Inc.

GEM - Oriental rugs - Couristan Inc.

GEM - Paints - Buten Paint & Wallpaper

GEM - Paper clips - Noesting Inc.

GEM - Perfumes - Van Cleef & Arpels, Inc.

GEM - Pharmaceutical preparations - Hybridon, Inc.

GEM - Plumbing fixtures - Sloan Valve Co.

GEM - Pumps - Sea Spike Marine Supply Co. Inc.

GEM - Safety products - Gem Safety Corp.

GEM - Salad dressings–bottled - L. Lacagnina & Sons

GEM - Sawdust - Gem Shavings & Sawdust Co.

GEM - Skates–roller - Out of Line Sports, Inc.

GEM - Stencils and carbon paper ☆ - American Coated Products Inc.

GEM - Strollers–baby - Combi International Corp.

GEM - Trays ☆ - Knobler International Ltd.

GEM - Vacuum pumps and parts - Welch Vacuum Technology, Inc.

GEM - Water treating compounds - Thermaco, Inc.

GEM - Work shoes - Interco Inc.

GEM I - Capacitors - General Electric Co.

GEM II - Capacitors - General Electric Co.

GEM-2 - Electrical equipment - Sloan Valve Co.

GEM III - Capacitors - General Electric Co.

GEM-300 - Radar systems and equipment - Geophysical Survey Systems, Inc.

GEM & JEWELRY CLEANER - Cleaning preparations - Blitz Manufacturing Co., Inc.

GEM-ART - Jewelry - Victor Corp.

GEM ARTISANS, LTD. - Jewelry - Gem Artisans, Ltd.

GEM BATTERY-POWERED RING CUTTER - Tools–hand-operated - Michael W. Mooney

GEM BLADES - Razor blades - American Safety Razor Co.

GEM BLUE STAR BLADES - Razor blades - American Safety Razor Co.

GEM-BRITE - Cleaning preparations - Arem, Inc.

GEM CASE - Jewelry - Weingeroff Enterprises, Inc.

GEM-CHROME - Kitchen utensils–aluminum - Gemco Ware, Inc.

GEM COAT - Cooking utensils–aluminum - West Bend Co.

GEM CONTOUR II RAZOR - Razor blades - American Safety Razor Co.

GEM DANDIES - Jewelry–costume - Capitol Novelty Co.

GEM-DANDY - Apparel and accessories - Gem-Dandy, Inc.

GEM DANDY - Cooking equipment–household - Alabama Manufacturing Co.

GEM FLEX - Aeronautical instruments - Gemaire Distributors, Inc.

GEM-FLEX - Jewelry - Jacoby-Bender Inc.

GEM FRIENDS - Toys–stuffed - Russ Berrie and Co., Inc.

GEM GEMS - Candy ☆ - Leaf, Inc.

GEM GUARDS - Bumpers–motor vehicle - Gem Manufacturing Corp.

GEM ICE - Jewelry - Jewelry Direct, Ltd.

GEM JIVE - Games ☆ - Yomega Corp.

GEM-LAC - Paints - Sherwin-Williams Automotive Finishes Corp.

GEM LAVA ROX - Garden equipment ☆ - Ferro Corp.

GEM LOK - Jewelry–precious - Gemveto Jewelry Co. Inc.

GEM-MAJOR - Fuses–electric - Gem Electric Manufacturing Co. Inc.

GEM MASTER II - Machinery - Fac-Ette Manufacturing, Inc.

GEM OF THE OCEAN - Sponges - Delby System

GEM OF THE SEA - Seafood products–canned or cured ☆ - Gulf King Seafood Co.

GEM-ON-GEM - Rings–jewelry - Feature Enterprises

GEM-REZ - Finishing agents - Joli Plastics & Chemical Corp.

GEM-SAKE - Jewelry - Phillip Silverstein-Phil Jewelers

GEM SAQ - Bags - Curator

GEM SR. - Nail clippers ☆ - London International U.S. Holdings

GEM SET - Hobby kits ☆ - Greene Plastics Corp.

GEM SONIC - Cleaning preparations - Standard Products Corp.

GEM SOUND - Lamps - Gem Sound Corp.

GEM SPORT - Truck bodies ☆ - Gem Top Manufacturing Inc.

GEM STAR - Jewelers' findings ☆ - Signpress Corp.

GEM STONE - Ophthalmic goods - Fidelity Case Corp.

GEM SYSTEM GUESTROOM ENERGY MANAGEMENT SYSTEM - Alarm systems - Enermetrix Corp.

GEM-TAC - Adhesives and sealants - Beacon Chemical Co. Inc.

GEM TILT-A-BED - Furniture - Gem Products, Inc.

GEM-TONE - Keys - Curtis Industries Inc.

GEM TOP - Truck bodies ☆ - Gem Top Manufacturing Inc.

GEM WORKSHOP - Toys–blocks - Natural Science Industries, Ltd.

GEM WORLD CREATIONS - Jewelry–costume - Four Winds Trading Co.

GEMA - Adhesives and sealants - Gema Import & Export Corp.

GEMACO - Playing cards - Gemaco Playing Card Co.

GEMATIC - Hardware - Fort Lock Corp.

GEMBALL - Vending machines - Snyder Jewelers, Inc.

GEMBO - Fruits–dried - Honway International Co.

GEMBRITE - Cleaning preparations - Gembrite Corp.

GEMCARV - Novelty items ☆ - Walker and Zanger Inc.

GEMCO - Gasoline - Tesoro Petroleum Corp.

GEMCO - Hardware - Goodloe E. Moore Inc.

GEMCO - Housewares - Gemco Ware, Inc.

GEMCO - Trimmings–fabric ☆ - Gem-Dandy, Inc.

GEMCOAT - Lacquers - Gemini Coatings, Inc.

GEMCOR - Pharmaceutical preparations ☆ - Upsher-Smith Laboratories, Inc.

☆ = Now out of production

GEMEINHARDT - Flutes - Gemeinhardt Co., Inc.
GEMELLI - Shoes ✩ - S. Goldberg and Co. Inc.
GEMELLI - Wines - Martin and Macfarlane, Inc.
GEMELLO'S - Wines - Obester Winery
GEMELLO'S ANNIVERSARY - Wines - Obester Winery
GEMEX - Glassware–household - Gemco Ware, Inc.
GEMEX - Jewelry - Jacoby-Bender Inc.
GEMFOIL - Capacitors - General Electric Co.
GEMI - Lamps - General Electric Co.
GEMIGLO - Wood stains - Gemini Coatings, Inc.
GEMILLI - Apparel–women's - Twin Era Ltd.
GEMINESSE - Cosmetics - Max Factor & Co.
GEMINI - See **VERSA**
GEMINI - Abrasive products - Norton Co.
GEMINI - Artists' materials - Andrews/Nelson/Whitehead
GEMINI - Artists' materials - Keuffel & Esser Co.
GEMINI - Bicycles - Columbia Manufacturing Inc.
GEMINI - Boats–motor - Dolphin Boats Ltd.
GEMINI - Computer software - Bayer Corp.
GEMINI - Drills–electric - Waukesha Cutting Tools, Inc.
GEMINI - Electronic equipment - Gemini Industries, Inc.
GEMINI - Faucets - Sterling Plumbing Group Inc.
GEMINI - Floor coverings–carpet and rugs ✩ - Regal Rugs Inc.
GEMINI - Food products ✩ - Bascoms Corp.
GEMINI - Furniture ✩ - Bassett Furniture Industries, Inc.
GEMINI - Furniture ✩ - Bernhardt Industries
GEMINI - Giftware - Gemini Gems
GEMINI - Hair care products - Wella Corp. (Consumer Products Div.)
GEMINI - Health care products - Smith and Davis Manufacturing Co.
GEMINI - Herbicides - E.I. Dupont de Nemours and Co.
GEMINI - Laboratory apparatus - Robbins Scientific Corp.
GEMINI - Lamps - General Electric Co.
GEMINI - Lawn mowers - Lambert Manufacturing Corp.
GEMINI - Navigational instruments - Rule Industries, Inc.
GEMINI - Paper - Willmann Paper Co., Inc.
GEMINI - Projectors–photographic ✩ - Star Parts Inc.
GEMINI - Refrigerators - White Consolidated Industries, Inc.
GEMINI - Security locks - Kaba High Security Locks Corp.
GEMINI - Ships–sailing vessels - Cape Cod Shipbuilding Co.
GEMINI - Ships–sailing vessels - Hood Sailmakers Inc. (Hood Yacht Systems Div.)
GEMINI - Skis ✩ - Nash Manufacturing Inc.
GEMINI - Sporting goods - Mattel, Inc.
GEMINI - Sporting goods ✩ - Aldila, Inc.
GEMINI - Stools–wood ✩ - Krueger International, Inc.
GEMINI - Stoves–wood-burning - Appalachian Stove & Fabricators, Inc.
GEMINI - Strollers–baby - Aprica Kassai USA Inc.
GEMINI - Strollers–baby ✩ - Welsh Co.
GEMINI - Tables–wood - Mitchell Manufacturing Co.
GEMINI - Teas–herbal - Calvin Thornton
GEMINI - Telescopes ✩ - Steven Manufacturing Co.
GEMINI - Tents ✩ - Coleman Co., Inc.
GEMINI - Tires–automobile - Jetzon/Telstar Tire
GEMINI - Vacuum cleaners and accessories ✩ - Bissell Inc.
GEMINI - Valves - Parker & Harper Companies, Inc.
GEMINI - Vinyl - Ohline Corp.
GEMINI - Watches - Bulova Corp.
GEMINI - Water purification systems - Roberts
GEMINI - Water treating compounds - Aquarium Products Inc.
GEMINI - Wet suits–rubber ✩ - Parkway Systems
GEMINI - Wheelchairs - Medline, Industries, Inc.
GEMINI - Whirlpool-bath pumps - ITT Marlow
GEMINI - Wine - Unique Wines, Inc.
GEMINI - Wood and metal finishes - Gemini Coatings, Inc.
GEMINI - Yarn - Henry's Attic
GEMINI 3000 - Ships–sailing vessels ✩ - Performance Cruising Inc.
GEMINI G.E.L. - Artists' materials - Gemini G.E.L.
GEMINI HOUSE - Jewelry ✩ - Litton Systems, Inc. (Airtron Division)
GEMINI III - Trays–photographic ✩ - Creatron Inc.
GEMINI MOULD MADE - Paper - Strathmore Paper Co.
GEMINI PLUS - Whirlpool bath pumps - ITT Marlow
GEMINI SPECS - Kaleidoscopes - Gemini Kaleidoscopes
GEMINI TITAN - Toys–models ✩ - Estes Industries
GEMITATION - Craft supplies - Tivian Laboratories Inc.
GEMITE - Plaster–wallboard - Premier Pools, Inc.
GEMKOR-003T - Jewelry - Gemkor Inc.

GEMLINE - Appliance parts - General Electric Co.
GEMLITE - Lighting fixtures - Lava-Simplex Internationale
GEMLITES - Lighting fixtures - Gem Electric Manufacturing Co. Inc.
GEMLUX - Marine hardware - Gem Products, Inc.
GEMMA - Shortening - Gem Packing Corp.
GEMME - Floor coverings–tile - Bisazza Mosaico
GEMNI - Floor coverings–carpet and rugs ✩ - Mannington Carpets, Inc.
GEMNISYN - Analgesics - Rhone-Poulenc Rorer Pharmaceuticals Inc.
GEMNISYN - Analgesics ✩ - Schwarz Pharma
GEMOCITE - Beads - Greene Plastics Corp.
GEMONIL - Pharmaceutical preparations - Abbott Laboratories
GEMPIRE - Clocks - GWI Corp.
GEMPOS - Computer software - Gemini Industries, Inc.
GEMPUTTER - Golfing equipment - Barker & Co.
GEMS - Candy - Salem's Old Fashioned Candies Inc.
GEMS OF JOY - Jewelry ✩ - Allan A. Goldman Inc.
GEMS OF THE FOREST - Toys–blocks - T.C. Timber/Habermaass Corp.
GEMSPRITT - Jewelry - Combine International, Inc.
GEMSTAR - Computer software - SourceView Software International
GEMSTAR - Pesticides–agricultural - Crop Genetics International Corp.
GEMSTAR - Publisher's imprints - Gemstar Development Corp.
GEMSTONE - Bird feeders - Perky-Pet Products Co.
GEMSTONE - Colognes ✩ - Avon Products, Inc.
GEMSTONE - Cooking equipment–household - Nordic Ware
GEMSTONE - Fabrics - Superior Shade & Blind Co. Inc.
GEMSTONE - Floor coverings–carpet and rugs - Queen Carpet Corp.
GEMSTONE - Floor coverings–carpet and rugs ✩ - American Carpet Mills
GEMSTONE - Floor coverings–carpet and rugs ✩ - Porter Carpet Mills Inc.
GEMSTONE - Fountains - Anna-Perenna Inc.
GEMSTONE - Furniture ✩ - Bassett Furniture Industries, Inc.
GEMSTONE - Globes ✩ - Trippensee Corp.
GEMSTONE - Mirrors ✩ - Hoyne Industries Inc.
GEMSTONE - Pet collars - Leatherite-Nylorite Manufacturing Inc.
GEMSTONE - Tiles–ceramic - W.W. Henry Co.
GEMSTONE - Watches - Benjamin E. Woomer
GEMSTONE ANIMAL CIRCUS - Figurines ✩ - Opal Supply Inc.
GEMSTONE GIRLS - Toys ✩ - Jak-Pak Inc.
GEMSTONE MAGIC - Artists' materials - Polymerics, Inc.
GEMSTONE PANORAMA - Jewelry - Jacmel Jewelry Inc.
GEMSTONE REGISTRY, THE - Jewelry - The Diamond Registry
GEMSTONES - Games - Mayfair Games, Inc.
GEMTEK - Automotive parts and accessories - Salesco Manufacturing Inc.
GEMTEX - Sanders and grinders - Spirakut Products
GEMTIME - Watches - QVC, Inc.
GEMTONE - Glassware–household - Federal Glass
GEMTONES - Pens - Sheaffer Holdings Inc.
GEMTRO - Pharmaceutical preparations - Eli Lilly and Co.
GEMTRONICS - Sporting goods ✩ - Gladding Braided Products Inc.
GEMUTLICHKEIT - Apparel and food products - German Fest Milwaukee, Inc.
GEMVAR - Capacitors - General Electric Co.
GEMVISION - Computer hardware - Jeffrey L. High
GEMWAND - Tools–hand-operated - International Bullion & Metal Brokers (USA) Inc.
GEMWOOD BY WOODS OF COLOR - Jewelry–costume - Silver Fetish Co.
GEMZ - Pens - Pentech International Inc.
GEMZAR - Pharmaceutical preparations - Eli Lilly and Co.
GEMZONE - Jewelry–precious - Snickelways, Inc.
GEN. - See also **GENERAL**
GEN - Paint finish - E.I. Dupont de Nemours and Co.
GEN-A-COAT - Veterinary pharmaceutical preparations - Nickers International Ltd.
GEN-A-HORSE - Veterinary pharmaceutical preparations - Nickers International Ltd.
GEN-A-RATE - Computer software - PRC Corp.
GEN-D-PHEN - Cough medicines - Goldline Laboratories, Inc.
GEN. DOUGLAS MAC ARTHUR - Games ✩ - A.R.C. Toys Inc.
GEN-E-VITE - Veterinary pharmaceutical preparations - Nickers International Ltd.
GEN FLYTE - Balls–golf ✩ - Gencorp Inc.
GEN-GARD - Veterinary pharmaceutical preparations - Agri Laboratories, Ltd.
GEN. GEO. S. PATTON - Games ✩ - A.R.C. Toys Inc.
GEN-PREP - Health care products - Goldline Laboratories, Inc.
GEN-X - Electrical apparatus - Advanced Power Conversions, Inc.
GEN-XENE - Pharmaceutical preparations - Alra Laboratories, Inc.
GEN7 SOFTWARE - Computer software ✩ - Synergistic Consultants, Inc.
GENA - Cosmetics - Research Council of Make-Up Artists Inc.

✩ = Now out of production

GENA - Manicure preparations - Gena Laboratories Inc.

GENABID - Pharmaceutical preparations - Goldline Laboratories, Inc.

GENAC - Pharmaceutical preparations - Goldline Laboratories, Inc.

GENAC OPTICS - Electronic equipment - Gamla Enterprises NA Inc.

GENACED - Pharmaceutical preparations - Goldline Laboratories, Inc.

GENACOL - Pharmaceutical preparations - Goldline Laboratories, Inc.

GENACOTE - Pharmaceutical preparations - Goldline Laboratories, Inc.

GENADE - Pharmaceutical preparations ☆ - Goldline Laboratories, Inc.

GENAGESIC - Pharmaceutical preparations - Goldline Laboratories, Inc.

GENAHIST - Cough medicines - Goldline Laboratories, Inc.

GENALAC - Pharmaceutical preparations - Goldline Laboratories, Inc.

GENALG - Pharmaceutical preparations - Goldline Laboratories, Inc.

GENALUDE - Pharmaceutical preparations - Goldline Laboratories, Inc.

GENAMIN - Pharmaceutical preparations - Goldline Laboratories, Inc.

GENAPAP - Pharmaceutical preparations - Goldline Laboratories, Inc.

GENAPAP-C - Pharmaceutical preparations - Goldline Laboratories, Inc.

GENAPAX - Pharmaceutical preparations ☆ - Key Pharmaceuticals Inc.

GENAPHED - Pharmaceutical preparations - Goldline Laboratories, Inc.

GENAPHED PLUS - Pharmaceutical preparations - Goldline Laboratories, Inc.

GENARCO - Spotlights - George R. Snell Associates, Inc.

GENAREG - Pharmaceutical preparations - Goldline Laboratories, Inc.

GENA'S PRIDE - Footwear - Stonewell International

GENASAL - Pharmaceutical preparations - Goldline Laboratories, Inc.

GENASEC - Pharmaceutical preparations - Goldline Laboratories, Inc.

GENASOFT - Pharmaceutical preparations - Goldline Laboratories, Inc.

GENASOFT PLUS - Pharmaceutical preparations - Goldline Laboratories, Inc.

GENASONE - Pharmaceutical preparations - Goldline Laboratories, Inc.

GENASPOR - Pharmaceutical preparations - Goldline Laboratories, Inc.

GENASTHMA - Pharmaceutical preparations - Goldline Laboratories, Inc.

GENASYME - Pharmaceutical preparations - Goldline Laboratories, Inc.

GENASYS - Motor vehicles–automobiles - Genasys L.C.

GENATAP - Cough medicines - Goldline Laboratories, Inc.

GENATON - Pharmaceutical preparations - Goldline Laboratories, Inc.

GENATUSS - Pharmaceutical preparations - Goldline Laboratories, Inc.

GENATUSS DM - Pharmaceutical preparations - Goldline Laboratories, Inc.

GENAVE-100 - Marine rigging - Genave-NRC

GENAVOX - Electronic equipment - Excelsior Accordions Inc.

GENBER - Juices - Cranberry Products Inc.

GENBER - Knives - Rothco Inc.

GENCALC 600 - Pharmaceutical preparations - Goldline Laboratories, Inc.

GENCAT - Computer software - Electric Power Research Institute Inc.

GENCO - Combs - Fromm Industries

GENCO - Oils–lubricating - Genovese Drug Stores, Inc.

GENCO - Olive oil - A & J Cheese Co., Inc.

GENCOLD - Pharmaceutical preparations - Goldline Laboratories, Inc.

GENCOUGH - Pharmaceutical preparations - Goldline Laboratories, Inc.

GENCOUGH-D - Pharmaceutical preparations - Goldline Laboratories, Inc.

GENCRYL - Latex - Gencorp Inc.

GENDAC - Integrated microcircuits - Integrated Circuit Systems, Inc.

GENDAI - Music–sheet - GSP

GENDANE - Pharmaceutical preparations - Goldline Laboratories, Inc.

GENDARME - Colognes - Gendarme Cologne for Men

GENDECON - Pharmaceutical preparations - Goldline Laboratories, Inc.

GENDER CHOICE - Pharmaceutical preparations - Pro Care Industries Ltd.

GENDER ETHNICITY SEXUAL ORIENTATION CLASS CULTURE FOREIGN BORN RACE DISABILITIES - Educational materials - Onolee Zwicke

GENDER ONE - Cosmetics - Belcam Inc.

GENDEX GXP - Photographic equipment - Dentsply International Inc.

GENDRON - Crutches - Gendron Inc.

GENE - Apparel and accessories - Quality Inc.

GENE BLILEY - Stationery - Gene Bliley Stationery

GENE IMAGES - Chemical preparations - United States Biochemical Corp.

GENE MACHINE - Computer software - Queue Inc.

GENE MCDONALD - Wallpaper - Gene McDonald

GENE MCDONALD XX - Wallpaper - Gene McDonald

GENE-METRE - Hair care products - Gene-Metre Professional Salon Products

GENE MEYER - Apparel–men's - Eugene F. Meyer, III

GENE PROFILE ASSAY - Computer software - Xenometrix, Inc.

GENE-RATOR - Sporting goods - Hokkaido-Karate Equipment Manufacturing Co.

GENE SUMMERS ARCHIVES - Posters - Domino Ltd.

GENE SUMMERS INTERNATIONAL - Publisher's imprints - Domino Ltd.

GENE SWEEP - Electronic equipment - Hoefer Scientific Instruments

GENEALOGY - Paper–bond ☆ - Fox River Paper Co.

GENEBS - Pharmaceutical preparations - Goldline Laboratories, Inc.

GENECELLE - Skin care products - Fallien, Ltd.

GENEFLORA - Dietary supplement - Sabinsa Corp.

GENEGUARD - Flowers, plants, and seeds - Sanford Scientific, Inc.

GENEMATE - Diagnostic substances - Intermountain Scientific Corp.

GENEPRO - Computer software - Genepro, Inc.

GENERA MARBLE - Floor coverings - Azrock Commercial Flooring

GENERAC-NAGANO - Engines–marine - Generac Corp.

GENERAL - See also GEN.

GENERAL - Antifreeze - General Petroleum Inc.

GENERAL - Brooms ☆ - W.E. Kautenberg Co.

GENERAL - Cans–metal - Behrens Inc.

GENERAL - Clocks - General Time Corp. (Westclox/Seth Thomas Div.)

GENERAL - Industrial machinery - General Floorcraft Inc.

GENERAL - Laces–boot and shoe - General Shoelace Co. Inc.

GENERAL - Pipes - Missouri Meerschaum Co.

GENERAL - Printing presses - Becmar Corp.

GENERAL - Sporting goods - Gear 2000, Ltd.

GENERAL - Stationery - Superior Marking Equipment Co.

GENERAL - Tape–adhesive - General Tape Corp.

GENERAL - Thread - Belding Heminway Co. Inc.

GENERAL - Tires–automobile - General Tire, Inc.

GENERAL - Tools–hand-operated - General Tools Manufacturing Co. Inc.

GENERAL - Trailers–travel - General Trailer Manufacturing & Distributing Inc.

GENERAL - Watches - Bulova Corp.

GENERAL ADMISSION - Computer software - Microleague Multimedia, Inc.

GENERAL BOOKS - Publisher's imprints - Aglow Publications

GENERAL BUSTER O'CASEY - Toys - Mattel, Inc.

GENERAL CABLE - Electrical equipment - General Cable Corp.

GENERAL CHAOS - Computer software - Electronic Arts Inc.

GENERAL CHEMICAL ISO 9002 - Chemical preparations - General Chemical Corp.

GENERAL COATINGS - Paints - General Coating Technologies, Inc.

GENERAL COLD - Air conditioning equipment - General Cold Corp.

GENERAL CONTROL - Garden equipment - Lawn & Garden Supply Co.

GENERAL CONTROLS - Valves - ITT Corp.

GENERAL CURE - Pet products - Aquarium Pharmaceuticals, Inc.

GENERAL DISASTER - Toys - Tonka Corp.

GENERAL ELECTRIC - Lamp bulbs–incandescent - General Electric Co.

GENERAL FINDINGS - Pens–fountain - General Findings

GENERAL IVAR - Toys - Saban Entertainment, Inc.

GENERAL MADINE - Toys - Lucasfilm Ltd.

GENERAL MAGIC - Telephone apparatus - General Magic, Inc.

GENERAL MEATS - Meat products–beef - Nathan Schweitzer & Co.

GENERAL/MG - Tools - General Tools Manufacturing Co. Inc.

GENERAL MILLS - Food products - General Mills, Inc.

GENERAL MILLS - Infant product - La Rue International, Inc.

GENERAL/NATIONAL - Tools - General Tools Manufacturing Co. Inc.

GENERAL NIFEL - Toys - Mattel, Inc.

GENERAL NUTRITION - Vitamins and nutritional supplements - General Nutrition Inc.

GENERAL PENCIL - Pencils - General Pencil Co.

GENERAL RIB STREET - Tires - Continental General Tire, Inc.

GENERAL S. CROW SUPERIOR TO ALL KERNELS - Popcorn - Tree of Life, Inc.

GENERAL SHALE BRICK - Bricks - General Shale Products Corp.

GENERAL SLICING - Slicing machines - Standex International Corp.

GENERAL SOUND - Televisions - General Sound Co. Ltd.

GENERAL STEEL - Hardware ☆ - Leslie-Locke, Inc.

GENERAL STORE - Glassware–household ☆ - Anchor Hocking Glass, Inc.

GENERAL SUPPLY - Apparel–women's - Frederick Atkins, Inc.

GENERAL TECHNOLOGIES, INC. - Ducts–metal - General Technologies, Inc.

GENERAL TERRY MILLS OF N.Y. - Towels - General Sales Co.

GENERAL, THE - Clocks - Delfino Products Inc.

GENERAL TIRE CHEVY CAMARO - Toys–electronic - Bird Bromiticous Inc.

GENERAL WORDS & MUSIC CO. - Publisher's imprints - Neil A. Kjos Music Co.

GENERALS - Cigarettes - Philip Morris Companies Inc.

GENERAL'S - Pencils - General Pencil Co.

GENERATION - Blankets - Fieldcrest Cannon, Inc.

GENERATION - Chemical preparations - Parkway Research Corp.

GENERATION - Cooking utensils–aluminum - West Bend Co.

GENERATION - Dishes–earthenware - Dansk International Designs, Ltd.

GENERATION - Floor coverings–carpet and rugs ☆ - Blue Ridge Carpet Mills

GENERATION - Furniture - Lane Co. Inc.

GENERATION - Guitars - Peavey Electronics Corp.

GENERATION - Health care products - Medisense, Inc.

GENERATION - Watches - Style Asia Inc.

GENERATION 2 - Smoke detectors - Generation II Smoke Detector Inc.

GENERATION 3 THE NEXT GENERATION IN CAR CHEMISTRY - Cleaning preparations - Generation3 Car Chemistry, Inc.

GENERATION 7 FRIES - Vegetables–frozen - Lamb-Weston, Inc.

GENERATION '90 - Furniture ☆ - Singer Furniture Co.

GENERATION 2000 - Apparel–children's - Caldor Corp.

GENERATION 2000 - Watches - Invasion Time Corp.

GENERATION AHEAD, A - Firearms, accessories, and parts ☆ - Modern Muzzle Loading, Inc.

GENERATION AMERICA - Women's apparel - United Pacific Apparel (USA), Inc.

GENERATION GAP - Cleaning preparations–carpet and rug - Harris Research, Inc.

GENERATION II - Drums–musical instruments - LP Music Group

GENERATION II - Paper–tissue - Fort Howard Corp.

GENERATION III - Audio equipment - American Acoustics

GENERATION III - Containers - Rotocast Plastic Products

GENERATION III - Fabrics–tapestry ☆ - Coloroll Inc.

GENERATION III - Furniture ☆ - Bassett Furniture Industries, Inc.

GENERATION III - Lockers–metal - Equipto

GENERATION III - Whipped topping–frozen - Cream Products Co. Inc.

GENERATION RECORDS - Records, CDs, and cassette tapes - Generation Records, Inc.

GENERATION SERIES II - Filters–water - Doughboy Recreational Inc.

GENERATION X - Apparel and accessories - Bugle Boy Industries, Inc.

GENERATION X - Books–comic - Marvel Entertainment Group, Inc.

GENERATION X - Colognes - Gangi International

GENERATION X - Toys - Marvel Characters, Inc.

GENERATIONS - Computer software - Gary Dean Stark

GENERATIONS - Computer software - Voicetek Corp.

GENERATIONS - Cookies - Image Brands, Inc.

GENERATIONS - Furniture - Vaughan Furniture Co. Inc.

GENERATIONS - Insurance agencies–life - Van Kampen American Capital Distributors, Inc.

GENERATIONS - Siding - Owens Corning

GENERATIONS KLINGON BIRD OF PREY - Toys–models - ERTL Co., Inc.

GENERATIONS OF COLOR - Flowers, plants, and seeds - Zelenka Nursery, Inc.

GENERATIONS U.S.S. ENTERPRISE B - Toys–models - ERTL Co., Inc.

GENERATIONS U.S.S. ENTERPRISE NCC-17010 - Toys–models - ERTL Co., Inc.

GENERATIVE TRANSACTIONS - Computer software - Creative Thinking Inc.

GENERATOR ASSOCIATE - Computer software - Environmental Support Solutions, Inc.

GENERBON - Pharmaceutical preparations - Goldline Laboratories, Inc.

GENERENE - Cough medicines ☆ - Goldline Laboratories, Inc.

GENERET - Pharmaceutical preparations - Goldline Laboratories, Inc.

GENERIC - Tobacco–chewing or smoking - Sterling Tobacco Co.

GENERICARE - Pharmaceutical preparations - Circa Pharmaceuticals, Inc.

GENERICO - Torches - Generic Equipment Co., Inc.

GENEROID - Automotive parts and accessories - Rockwell International Corp.

GENEROUS - Cosmetics - Trimerica Trading Co.

GENERRA - Apparel and accessories - Generra Sportswear

GENERRA - Dresses–women's - Generra Co.

GENERRA - Frames–eyeglass - Kenmark Optical Co.

GENERRA - Shoes - Atsco Footwear Inc.

GENERRA - Shoes - Street Cars

GENES - Recording label - Adelphi Records Inc.

GENESA - Pharmaceutical preparations - Gensia, Inc.

GENESCAN - Computer software - Applied Biosystems Inc.

GENESEE - Beverages–malt - Genesee Brewing Co., Inc.

GENESEE 12 HORSE - Beverages–malt ☆ - Genesee Brewing Co., Inc.

GENESEE CREAM - Beverages–malt - Genesee Brewing Co., Inc.

GENESEE CREAM LIGHT - Beverages–malt ☆ - Genesee Brewing Co., Inc.

GENESEE LIGHT - Beverages–malt - Genesee Brewing Co., Inc.

GENESEE NA - Beverages–malt - Genesee Brewing Co., Inc.

GENESEO SPRING BOCK - Beverages–malt - Genesee Brewing Co., Inc.

GENESEQ - Computer peripheral equipment - Oxford Molecular Group

GENESIS - Bathroom fixtures - Price Pfister Co.

GENESIS - Bicycles - Ross Bicycles USA, Ltd.

GENESIS - Blankets–electric - Sunbeam-Oster Household Products

GENESIS - Blinds–venetian - Kenney Manufacturing Co.

GENESIS - Books–comic - Malibu Comics Entertainment, Inc.

GENESIS - Cabinets–metal - Krueger International, Inc.

GENESIS - Cleaning preparations–carpet and rug - National Brands, Inc.

GENESIS - Coatings - Sherwin-Williams Automotive Finishes Corp.

GENESIS - Coats–laboratory - Fibrotek Industries, Inc.

GENESIS - Computer peripheral equipment - Amrplus Partners

GENESIS - Deodorizers - Technical Concepts, L.P.

GENESIS - Electronic equipment - AVL

GENESIS - Floor coverings–carpet and rugs - Amoco Fabrics and Fibers Co.

GENESIS - Fruits and vegetables - Sierra Vista Packing Co. Inc.

GENESIS - Furniture ☆ - Bassett Furniture Industries, Inc.

GENESIS - Games - Sega of America, Inc.

GENESIS - Hardware - ARO Corp.

GENESIS - Hearing aids - Qualitone

GENESIS - Home-health-care products - Intromark Inc.

GENESIS - Internal combustion engines–stationary - Clark Material Handling Co.

GENESIS - Kitchenware–earthenware - Arita Sales Co. Inc.

GENESIS - Lighting fixtures - Casablanca Fan Co.

GENESIS - Luggage - American Tourister, Inc.

GENESIS - Machine tools - American Rescue Technology Inc.

GENESIS - Machinery - General Binding Corp.

GENESIS - Manufactured homes - Redman Industries, Inc.

GENESIS - Notebooks and notepads - Roaring Spring Blank Book Co.

GENESIS - Ophthalmic apparatus - Surgin Surgical Instrumentation, Inc.

GENESIS - Paints - Duron, Inc.

GENESIS - Paper–toweling - Burton Medical Products Corp.

GENESIS - Photographic equipment - Eastman Kodak Co.

GENESIS - Rackets–tennis - Head Sports USA

GENESIS - Radio communications equipment - Motorola, Inc. (Land Mobile Products Sector)

GENESIS - Recording label - Crystal Records Inc.

GENESIS - Retaining walls - Tensar Corp.

GENESIS - Safety products - Point Blank Body Armor, L.P.

GENESIS - Skin care products - Veeco Manufacturing Co.

GENESIS - Sporting goods - Seneca Sports, Inc.

GENESIS - Statuary - Starlite Originals, Inc.

GENESIS - Tanks–water - Berkshire Marketing Inc.

GENESIS - Telescopes - Tele Vue Optics Inc.

GENESIS - Tents ☆ - Coleman Co., Inc.

GENESIS - Tires–automobile - Jetzon/Telstar Tire

GENESIS - Toys–trains - Digitrax, Inc.

GENESIS - Wallpaper - Seabrook Wallcoverings, Inc.

GENESIS - Watches - Temlex/Jupiter Watch Corp.

GENESIS - Water treating compounds - Aquarium Products Inc.

GENESIS - Windows–plastic - Certainteed Corp. (Roofing Products Group)

GENESIS 2 - Laboratory apparatus - Chief Automotive Systems, Inc.

GENESIS AQUAMARK - Markers–felt-tip ☆ - Sakura of America

GENESIS AQUARIUS - Markers–felt-tip ☆ - Sakura of America

GENESIS BY DELTA - Automotive parts and accessories - Housep Joe Naldjian

GENESIS COLLECTION - Furniture–upholstered - Hickory Hill Furniture Corp.

GENESIS COMPOSITES - Bicycles - Genesis Composites, Inc.

GENESIS HEAT-CELL - Electric heaters - Cotter & Co.

GENESIS II - Skin care products - Genesis II USA

GENESIS MO - Computers - Daystar Digital, Inc.

GENESIS OXY - Skin-care products - Matrix Health Products, Inc.

GENESIS PRC - Skates–roller - Seneca Sports, Inc.

GENESIS SYSTEM - Electrical equipment - Sun Industries, Inc.

GENESIS TELESYSTEM - Telephones - At&T Corp.

GENESIS WAITER CORKSCREW - Housewares - Franmara Co. Inc.

GENESIS WAY, THE - Recording label - Genesis Way, Inc.

GENESIS XL - Skates–roller - Seneca Sports, Inc.

GENESOLV - Cleaning preparations - Tech Spray, Inc.

GENESPORT - Sporting goods - Hokkaido-Karate Equipment Manufacturing Co.

GENESPRINTER - Laboratory equipment - Fotodyne Inc.

GENESTRA - Floor coverings–carpet and rugs - Alexander Smith Carpets

GENESUN - Seafood products–canned or cured ☆ - Winchester Bay Seafood Inc.

GENESYS - Computer software - CFI Proservices, Inc.

GENESYS - Electronic equipment - Asinc, Inc.

GENESYS - Generators - Magnetek Inc.

GENESYS - Photographic equipment - Vicon Industries Inc.

GENESYS 2 - Machinery - Praxair Distributors

GENET - Cabinets ☆ - Marsh Furniture Co.

GENETIC BUILDER - Livestock feed additives - Miller Co. Inc.

GENETIC CONNECTIONS - Computer software - Sonters Publishing, Inc.

GENETIC POTENTIAL THROUGH NUTRITION - Vitamins and nutritional supplements - Metagenics, Inc.

☆ = Now out of production

GENETIVAC - Veterinary pharmaceutical preparations - Schering-Plough Animal Health

GENETRON - Motor vehicle parts and accessories - Alliedsignal Inc.

GENEVA - Audio equipment - Geneva Group of Cos. Inc.

GENEVA - Cabinets–wood - UltraCraft Co.

GENEVA - Cigarettes - Brown & Williamson Tobacco Corp.

GENEVA - Computer software - Apple Computer Inc.

GENEVA - Computers–personal ☆ - Epson America, Inc.

GENEVA - Cookies - Pepperidge Farm Inc.

GENEVA - Dishes–china - Pickard Inc.

GENEVA - Flowers–artificial - European Imports of California Inc.

GENEVA - Gin ☆ - Jim Beam Brands Co.

GENEVA - Glassware–household ☆ - Lenox Crystal, Inc.

GENEVA - Pet products - Aspen Pet Products

GENEVA - Pharmaceutical preparations ☆ - Armenpharm Ltd.

GENEVA - Prefabricated buildings–wood - Florian Greenhouses, Inc.

GENEVA - Watches - Lucerne Time

GENEVA BUSINESS MANAGEMENT SYSTEMS - Computer software - Geneva Systems, Inc.

GENEVA COURT - Floor coverings ☆ - Congoleum Corp.

GENEVA CRYSTAL COLLECTION - Glassware–household - Combex, Inc.

GENEVA CUSHION - Furniture - Tropitone Furniture Co. Inc.

GENEVA GENERICS - Pharmaceutical preparations - Geneva Generics Inc.

GENEVA LIMITED EDITIONS - Watches - La Marque Watch Co. Inc.

GENEVA SLING - Furniture - Tropitone Furniture Co. Inc.

GENEVAX - Pharmaceutical preparations - Apollon, Inc.

GENEVAX-HIV - Pharmaceutical preparations - Apollon, Inc.

GENEVE - Watches - Heather Classics Inc.

GENEVIEVE - Dolls ☆ - Effanbee Doll Corp.

GENEVIEVE - Jewelry - Pakula & Co.

GENEVIEVE'S - Greeting cards - Mclaughlin Paper Co., Inc.

GENEVOX - Recording label - Sunday School Board of the Southern Baptist Convention

GENEWARE - Biochemicals - Biosource Genetics Corp.

GENEX - Pharmaceutical preparations - Goldline Laboratories, Inc.

GENEX - Welding equipment - GenEx Ltd.

GENFAST - Hardware - Gencorp Inc.

GENFIBER - Pharmaceutical preparations - Goldline Laboratories, Inc.

GENFLEX - Conduits - General Cable Industries, Inc.

GENGHIS KHAN - Fireworks - Great Grizzly, Inc.

GENI U.S. - Video games - B & N Companies, Inc.

GENIE - Apparel–women's - Randi Foundations Inc.

GENIE - Bicycles - Ross Bicycles USA, Ltd.

GENIE - Cleaning preparations–carpet and rug - Majestic Industries Inc.

GENIE - Clocks ☆ - Robertshaw Controls Co.

GENIE - Cosmetics - Burmax Co. Inc.

GENIE - Door openers–electronic - The Genie Co.

GENIE - Electronic equipment - General Electric Co.

GENIE - Exercising equipment - Physical Fitness Inc.

GENIE - Hair care products - Major/Advance International

GENIE - Handbags - Trina/Genie

GENIE - Incense - Genie Co. Inc.

GENIE - Lawn mowers ☆ - Hoffco Inc.

GENIE - Organs–musical instrument - Lowrey Organ Co.

GENIE - Personal telephones - American Telecommunications Corp.

GENIE - Vacuum cleaners and accessories - Gmi Holdings, Inc.

GENIE - Wigs - Paula Young

GENIE AFTER-BATH MAGIC - Pet-grooming product - B-Elegant Products

GENIE BOTTLES - Containers–glass - Genie Bottles, Inc.

GENIE CLEAN - Pet products - Next to Nature

GENIE GATEKEEPER - Door openers–electronic - The Genie Co.

GENIE MAGIC - Pet product - B-Elegant Products

GENIE PRODUCTS - Underwear and nightwear - Carmen Foundations Inc.

GENIE RECHARG - Batteries - The Genie Co.

GENIE SUPER SLUSHER - Ice making machinery ☆ - Flambeau Products Corp.

GENIE VAPORIZER - Air purification systems ☆ - Medo Industries, Inc.

GENII - Dolls - Effanbee Doll Corp.

GENII - Lamps - Swiss Harmony Inc.

GENIS SYSTEM, THE - Tools–hand-operated - Termax Corp.

GENISIS - Pharmaceutical preparations ☆ - Organon Inc.

GENISYS - Computers - Genisys Micro Concept International, Inc.

GENITE - Pharmaceutical preparations - Goldline Laboratories, Inc.

GENITRAC - Herbal products - Maharishi Ayur-Ved Products International, Inc.

GENIUS - Door openers–electronic - The Genie Co.

GENIUS - Electronic equipment - General Electric Co.

GENIUS - Fabrics–broadcloth - Collins & Aikman Corp.

GENIUS - Games - Wry Idea Co.

GENIUS - Irons–electric - Matsushita Electric Corp. of America

GENIUS - Ovens–microwave - Matsushita Consumer Electronics Co.

GENIUS - Recording label - Rough Trade Inc.

GENIUS - Watches and clocks - Sharp International Corp.

GENIUS - Water purification systems - Sears, Roebuck and Co.

GENIUS BLOOD PRODUCTIONS - Computer storage devices–optical - Paul Douglas Catchings

GENIUS, THE - Ovens–microwave - Matsushita Electric Corp. of America

GENIUSERIES - Toys–models - Tamiya America, Inc.

GENKENE - Cables - General Cable Corp.

GENKI - Shoes - Genki USA

GENLIFE FOOD SUPPLEMENTS - Vitamins and nutritional supplements - Genesis Way, Inc.

GENMAR - Boats–motor - Lund Boat Co.

GENMAT - Computer peripheral equipment - General Materials Management

GENMAX - Computer software - Reliance Electric Co.

GENNA - Pharmaceutical preparations - Goldline Laboratories, Inc.

GENNET - Computer software - Genesys Software Systems, Inc.

GENNIN - Pharmaceutical preparations - Goldline Laboratories, Inc.

GENNY - Beverages–malt - Genesee Brewing Co., Inc.

GENNY - Colognes - Frances Denney

GENNY - Handbags - Jerry Kohn Inc.

GENNY ICE - Beverages–malt - Genesee Brewing Co., Inc.

GENNY ICE BEER - Beverages–malt - Genesee Brewing Co., Inc.

GENNY OCCHIALI - Ophthalmic goods ☆ - Luxottica

GENNY RED LAGER - Beverages–malt - Genesee Brewing Co., Inc.

GENNY SMITH BOOKS - Publisher's imprints ☆ - William Kaufmann, Inc.

GENNY SUMMER BREW - Beverages–malt - Genesee Brewing Co., Inc.

GENNY WINTER BREW - Beverages–malt - Genesee Brewing Co., Inc.

GENO - Frames–eyeglass - U.S. Optical Frame Co.

GENOA - Computer peripheral equipment - Genoa Systems Corp.

GENOA - Furniture ☆ - Bassett Furniture Industries, Inc.

GENOA - Meat products–pork - Agar Supply Co. Inc.

GENOA & GRIFFIN - Wallpaper ☆ - Osborne & Little

GENOCO - Fuel additives ☆ - Ashland Oil, Inc.

GENOGRIP - Hardware - Genova Products Inc.

GENOMAX - Barley - Southern States Cooperative Inc.

GENOME - Computer software - Softronics Inc.

GENOPTIC SOP - Ophthalmic goods - Allergan, Inc.

GENORA - Pharmaceutical preparations - Rugby Laboratories Inc.

GENOSCOPOLAMINE - Pharmaceutical preparations - Consolidated Midland Corp.

GENOSTREN - Pharmaceutical preparations ☆ - Coast Laboratories Inc.

GENOTROPIN - Pharmaceutical preparations - Pharmacia Inc.

GENOVA - Computer software - PSW Technologies, Inc.

GENOVA - Food products - Van Camp Seafood Co. Inc.

GENOVA - Hardware - Genova Products Inc.

GENOVA TUNNO - Tuna–canned - Ralston Purina Co.

GENOWELD - Adhesives and sealants ☆ - Genova Products Inc.

GENPLUS MANAGED CARE - Apparel and accessories - Genplus Managed Care, Inc.

GENPRIL - Pharmaceutical preparations - Goldline Laboratories, Inc.

GENPRIN - Pharmaceutical preparations - Goldline Laboratories, Inc.

GENRE - Apparel–women's - D.N.S. Inc.

GENREF - Computer storage devices–optical - Biological Abstracts Inc.

GENSAN - Pharmaceutical preparations - Goldline Laboratories, Inc.

GENSE - Flatware - Scan-Agent

GENSEPTIC MOUSSE - Skin care products - Gencare Inc.

GENSLIM C/F - Pharmaceutical preparations - Goldline Laboratories, Inc.

GENSTAR - Computer hardware - Genesis Integrated Systems Inc.

GENSTAR - Floor coverings–carpet and rugs - General Floor Carpet & Mechanic Supply, Inc.

GENSTAR - Telephone apparatus - GTE Airfone Inc.

GENT-L-KARE - Health care products - Premium Plastics, Inc.

GENT-L-KATCH - Medical apparatus - Premium Plastics, Inc.

GENT-L-KLAVE - Medical apparatus - Premium Plastics, Inc.

GENT-L-KLEEN - Cleaning preparations - Gent-L-Kleen Products Inc.

GENT-L-SHAVE - Skin care products - Framesi USA/Roffler Industries Inc.

GENT-L-SORB - Medical apparatus ☆ - Premium Plastics, Inc.

GENTACIDIN - Prescription ophthalmic - Iolab Pharmaceuticals

GENTAGLYDE - Veterinary pharmaceutical preparations - American Home Products Corp.

GENTAK - Pharmaceutical preparations - Akorn Inc.

GENTAPLEX - Vitamins and nutritional supplements - Liptis Laboratories, Inc.

GENTAVED - Veterinary pharmaceutical preparations - Vedco, Inc.

GENTAVISION - Pharmaceutical preparations - Coopervision Pharmaceuticals, Inc.

GENTAX - Hair care products - Green Foods

GENTEAL - Ophthalmic goods - Ciba-Geigy Corp.

GENTEC - Mixers–concrete - Gentec Equipment Co.

GENTEEL - Prophylactics ☆ - Home Care Products Inc.

GENTEK - Antacids - L. Perrigo Co.

GENTELL - Skin care products - Gentell, Inc.

GENTESSA - Floor coverings–carpet and rugs ☆ - Callaway Carpets

GENTEX - Audio equipment - Gentex Corp.

GENTIAN BALANCING NIGHT CREME - Skin care products - Blackmores

GENTIL BEBE - Apparel–children's ☆ - Poron Ltd.

GENTILHOMME - Watches - Jaeger-Le Coultre SA

GENTILI - Apparel and accessories ☆ - Eagle Knitting Mills Inc.

GENTIOBIOSE-B - Pharmaceutical preparations - City Chemical Corp.

GENTISIC ACID - Pharmaceutical preparations - City Chemical Corp.

GENTLAX - Laxatives - Purdue Frederick Co.

GENTLE - Health care products - Apothecary Products, Inc.

GENTLE - Iodine ☆ - Farnam Cos. Inc.

GENTLE - Skin care products - Excelcis

GENTLE AIR - Dryers–hair - Belson Products

GENTLE BEN'S BREWING COMPANY - Beverages–malt - Firehouse Brewing Co.

GENTLE BLOCK - Skin care products - Procter & Gamble Co.

GENTLE BLONDE - Hair care products ☆ - Roux Laboratories, Inc.

GENTLE BLUE - Electrodes - Uni-Patch

GENTLE BODY - Shampoos - Mennen Co.

GENTLE BRUSH, THE - Hair care products - Goody Products, Inc.

GENTLE C-250 - Vitamins and nutritional supplements - Twinlab

GENTLE C-2500 - Vitamins and nutritional supplements - Twinlab

GENTLE CARE - Hair care products ☆ - Wella Corp. (Consumer Products Div.)

GENTLE-CLEANSE - Laxatives ☆ - Nature's Herbs

GENTLE COLOR - Cosmetics - Almay Inc.

GENTLE COLOR - Hair coloring preparations - Roux Laboratories, Inc.

GENTLE CONDITIONING - Shampoos - Johnson & Johnson

GENTLE CREAM - Skin care products - Geritrex Corp.

GENTLE CREATIONS - Novelty items–paper ☆ - Antioch Publishing Co.

GENTLE CURLS - Hair curlers - Windmere Corp.

GENTLE CYCLE - Hair care products - Helene Curtis Industries Inc.

GENTLE DIFFERENCE - Hair care products - Wella Corp. (Consumer Products Div.)

GENTLE EARTH - Cleaning preparations - Impact/Gentle Earth, Ltd.

GENTLE EFFECTS - Dryers–hair - Belson Products

GENTLE EFFECTS - Dryers–hair - Windmere Corp.

GENTLE EXPRESSIONS - Figurines - Cast Art Industries, Inc.

GENTLE FEELINGS - Floor coverings–carpet and rugs - Karastan-Bigelow Inc.

GENTLE FELS - Detergents - Dial Corp.

GENTLE FLO - Nozzles - H.B. Sherman Manufacturing Co.

GENTLE-FLOW - Lawn mowers - Thompson Manufacturing Co.

GENTLE GEL - Cosmetics - Almay Inc.

GENTLE GEL - Health care products - Pharmaceutical Innovations

GENTLE GENTLE MASCARA - Cosmetics - Janet Sartin, Inc.

GENTLE GLIDE - Tampons - Playtex Beauty Care, Inc.

GENTLE HEARTS - Greeting cards - American Greetings Corp.

GENTLE IMAGES - Giftware - Russ Berrie and Co., Inc.

GENTLE IRON - Vitamins and nutritional supplements - Solgar Vitamin and Herb Co., Inc.

GENTLE JOGGER - Exercising equipment - Battle Creek Equipment Co.

GENTLE-LAMB - Polishing cloths - Eller Manufacturing Co. Inc.

GENTLE-LAX - Veterinary pharmaceutical preparations - Nickers International Ltd.

GENTLE LAX-A-PET - Veterinary pharmaceutical preparations - Nickers International Ltd.

GENTLE LOVE - Giftware - Sangray Corp.

GENTLE MAGIC - Pet products ☆ - Bramton Co.

GENTLE MOMENT - Floor coverings–carpet and rugs - Monticello Carpet Mills

GENTLE MOON - Furniture–children's - American Pacific Enterprises, Inc.

GENTLE NATURE - Laxatives - Sandoz Pharmaceuticals Corp.

GENTLE NIGHT - Vitamins and nutritional supplements - Ethical Nutrients

GENTLE ORANGE - Teas–herbal - Lipton Investments, Inc.

GENTLE PERSUASION - Recording label - Essex Entertainment Inc.

GENTLE PERSUASION - Wallpaper - CSE Designs

GENTLE PINK - Dish detergent - James Austin Co.

GENTLE PURSUASION - Hair care products - Zotos International Inc.

GENTLE RAIN - Hoses - Melnor Inc.

GENTLE RAIN - Skin care products - Sween Corp.

GENTLE REFLECTIONS - Giftware - Russ Berrie and Co., Inc.

GENTLE SOLES - Footwear - Loop Shoes, Inc.

GENTLE SPORT CO., THE - Apparel and accessories - Gentle Sport Co.

GENTLE-STEP - Manicure preparations - Professional Foot Care Products Inc.

GENTLE TEMP - Thermometers - Omron Healthcare, Inc.

GENTLE THOUGHTS - Greeting cards ☆ - Stevenson Industries Inc.

GENTLE TOUCH - Adhesives and sealants - E.R. Squibb & Sons, Inc.

GENTLE TOUCH - Contact lenses - Quanterron, Inc.

GENTLE TOUCH - Paper - Plainwell Tissue

GENTLE TOUCH - Pet products - Gentle Touch Corp.

GENTLE TOUCH - Shampoos - Andrew Jergens Co.

GENTLE TOUCH - Washcloths - Scott Paper Co.

GENTLE TREATMENT - Cosmetics - Johnson Products Co., Inc.

GENTLE WIND - Recording label - Conarch Productions

GENTLE WISDOM - Greeting cards ☆ - American Greetings Corp.

GENTLE WORLD OF BESSIE PEASE GUTMANN, THE - Giftware ☆ - Enesco Corp.

GENTLEJET - Medical apparatus - HMI Industries Inc.

GENTLEMAN - Frames–eyeglass ☆ - Universal/Univis Inc.

GENTLEMAN II - Liquors ☆ - A. Smith Bowman Distillery Inc.

GENTLEMAN B.U.M. - Apparel–men's - Chauvin International Ltd.

GENTLEMAN JACK - Whiskey - Brown-Forman Corp.

GENTLEMAN JIM'S - Apparel - Jim Diamond Sales Representatives

GENTLEMAN'S CLUB - Wallpaper - Seabrook Wallcoverings, Inc.

GENTLEMAN'S PREFERENCE - Spices and extracts - Scentex Inc.

GENTLEMAN'S PRIDE - Skin care products - Aloe Vera of America, Inc.

GENTLEMEN'S CHOICE - Wallpaper ☆ - Andover Wallcovering

GENTLEMEN'S CHOICE - Wallpaper ☆ - Bob Mitchell Designs

GENTLEMEN'S CLUB - Stationery ☆ - Pratt & Austin Co.

GENTLEMEN'S JOURNLE - Wallpaper - Quality House Wallcoverings

GENTLEMEN'S LADY - Apparel and accessories - Edison Brothers Stores, Inc.

GENTLY - Paper–toilet - Western Family Foods, Inc.

GENTLY LILAC - Nail care products - Cosmair Inc.

GENTOCIN - Veterinary pharmaceutical preparations ☆ - Schering-Plough Animal Health

GENTRAN:BASIC - Computer peripheral equipment - Sterling Software, Inc.

GENTRAN:CONTROL - Computer software - Sterling Software, Inc.

GENTRAN:DATAGUARD - Computer software - Sterling Software, Inc.

GENTRAN:PLUS - Computer software - Sterling Software, Inc.

GENTRAN:REALTIME - Computer software - Sterling Software, Inc.

GENTRAN:VIEWPOINT - Computer software - Sterling Software, Inc.

GENTRONICS - Sporting goods ☆ - Gladding Braided Products Inc.

GENTRY - Apparel and accessories - Gentry Inc.

GENTRY - Apparel and accessories ☆ - J.C. Penney Co., Inc.

GENTRY - Cabinets - Grandview Products Co.

GENTRY - Cabinets–wood - Decora

GENTRY - Chairs–metal - Steelcase Inc.

GENTRY - Dog food - Blue Seal Feeds Inc.

GENTRY - Floor coverings–carpet and rugs - Alexander Smith Carpets

GENTRY - Floor coverings–carpet and rugs ☆ - Regal Rugs Inc.

GENTRY - Giftware ☆ - Gorham Inc.

GENTRY - Motor vehicle parts and accessories - Leer Inc.

GENTRY II - Wigs - Paula Young

GENU-RANGER - Orthopedic products - Bird & Cronin, Inc.

GENUIMEDI - Health care products - Medi USA L.P.

GENUINE - Almond pastes ☆ - Henry Heide, Inc.

GENUINE ALPINE COLLECTION - Apparel and accessories - Recognition Apparel Group, Inc.

GENUINE ANTIQUE PERSON - Novelty items - Laid Back Enterprises, Inc.

GENUINE ARTICLE, THE - Fudge - Fudge

GENUINE CHEVROLET - Motor vehicle parts and accessories - General Motors Corp.

GENUINE COLLECTION - Candy - Ethel M. Chocolates, Inc.

GENUINE COTTONS - Apparel and accessories - Oshkosh B'gosh, Inc.

GENUINE DRAFT LIGHT - Beer - Miller Brewing Co.

GENUINE GEAR - Apparel–children's - M & L International, Inc.

GENUINE GOAT'S BREATH BOCK MICRO BEER - Beverages–malt - T.L.C., Inc.

GENUINE GOTOH - Musical instrument accessories ☆ - Dunlop Manufacturing, Inc.

GENUINE INCENSE-CEDAR A RENEWABLE RESOURCE - Pencils - P & M Cedar Products

GENUINE KING B NATURALLY SMOKED - Food products - King B Jerky

☆ = Now out of production

GENUINE LAND - Soil–potting - Andyland Concepts Inc.

GENUINE MERCHANDISE - Apparel - Major League Baseball Properties, Inc.

GENUINE MINT, THE - Candy - Usher Candy Co. Inc.

GENUINE N-ZIMES - Vitamins and nutritional supplements - National Enzyme Co. Inc.

GENUINE PALM BEACH - Apparel and accessories - Palm Beach Co., Inc.

GENUINE PARTFINDER - Computer software - Maxserv, Inc.

GENUINE PRESSBOARD - Binders - Fiber Mark, Inc.

GENUINE SATIVA HEMP WEAR - Apparel and accessories - Sativa Hempwear

GENUINE SONOMA JEAN COMPANY - Handbags - Kohl's Department Stores, Inc.

GENUINE SPANISH FOR SPANISH SPEAKERS - Publisher's imprints - Fernandez USA Publishing Co., Inc.

GENUINE TIMBERLODGE TIMBER LAGER PREMIUM - Beverages–malt - Timber Lodge Steakhouse, Inc.

GENUINE 'X-ERS - Apparel and accessories - Harman's Special T's

GENUINESTUFF - Apparel - Outerstuff, Ltd.

GENUS - Apparel and accessories - American Marketing Industries Inc.

GENUS FINISH - Window coverings - Levolor Inc.

GENUWOOD - Flooring–hardwood - Permagrain Products, Inc.

GENVIEW - Computer software - Genesee Survey Services, Inc.

GENX - Apparel and accessories - Spring Ford Knitting Co., Inc.

GENYA - Cordage and twine - Harco Co.

GENZYME - Pharmaceutical preparations - Genzyme Corp.

GEO - Dinnerware–glass ☆ - Cyclamen Studio

GEO - Footwear - Wolverine World Wide, Inc.

GEO - Frames–picture - Recyco

GEO - Motor vehicles–automobiles - General Motors Corp.

GEO - Novelty items - Pioneer Balloon Co.

GEO - Office supplies - Scripto-Tokai Corp.

GEO ART - Artists' materials - Geographics Inc.

GEO/CAD - Computer software - RJN Computer Services, Inc.

GEO-CD - Compact discs–prerecorded - Digital Geographical Systems, Inc.

GEO CUBE - Occasional tables ☆ - JDI Group, Inc.

GEO/DERBY USA GAME - Games - Talicor Inc.

GEO-DISC - Audio equipment ☆ - Mobile Fidelity Sound Lab

GEO-DRILL - Drills–electric - Camco International Inc.

GEO-EZ - Heat pumps - Climate Master, Inc.

GEO-FLOWER - Floor coverings–carpet and rugs - Milliken & Co. Inc.

GEO FORM - Floor coverings–carpet and rugs - Callaway Carpets

GEO-LAC - Paints - Pratt & Lambert, Inc.

GEO-LENE - Thread - Threads USA Div.

GEO-MATT - Health care products - Span-America Medical Systems, Inc.

GEO-MATTRESS - Mattresses - Span-America Medical Systems, Inc.

GEO-POINT - Floor coverings–carpet and rugs - Milliken & Co. Inc.

GEO PRINT - Hair care products - Andre Fantasies Inc.

GEO-RAGS - Apparel–children's - Awear Inc.

GEO-RIB - Wallpaper ☆ - Koroseal Wallcoverings

GEO SAT LV - Toys–models ☆ - Estes Industries

GEO SAVER - Paper–toilet - Adprom Corp.

GEO SCOPE - Toys - Uncle Milton Industries Inc.

GEO SHAPES - Exercising equipment - American Athletic Inc.

GEO SHAPES - Games - Talicor Inc.

GEO-SPHERE: EARTH - Computer software - Mind Play

GEO-STAC-N/C - Computer software - Comprep Corp.

GEO-SYN - Thread - Threads USA Div.

GEO-TAPE - Audio equipment ☆ - Mobile Fidelity Sound Lab

GEO-TEK - Toys - Maryland Toy Corp.

GEO-TEX - Thread - Threads USA Div.

GEO TEXTURES - Wallpaper - Sellers & Josephson

GEO TEXTURES 3 - Wallpaper - Sellers & Josephson

GEO TEXTURES IV - Wallpaper ☆ - Wall Fashion Inc.

GEO-THERMAL - Heat pumps - Climate Master, Inc.

GEO-TRENDS - Floor coverings–carpet and rugs - Trend Carpet

GEO-TRIVIA - Publisher's imprints - Rand McNally & Co.

GEO-WIZ - Toys - Intelligent Ideas, Inc.

GEO WORM - Toys - Playskool, Inc.

GEO-ZINC - Vitamins and nutritional supplements - Integrated Health, Inc.

GEOAMI - Packaging–paper - Geopax, Ltd.

GEOART - Computer software ☆ - Ventura Educational Systems

GEOBEE - Computer storage devices–optical - National Geographic Society

GEOBLADE - Skates–roller ☆ - Rollerblade, Inc.

GEOBOARDS - Artists' materials - Geographics Inc.

GEOBOND - Coatings - Geobond International, Inc.

GEOBRIGHTS - Paper ☆ - Wausau Paper Mills Co.

GEOCALC - Computer software - Blue Marble Geographics

GEOCEM - Bathtubs–concrete ☆ - Lehigh Portland Cement Co.

GEOCENTRE - Computer software - Distribution Sciences, Inc.

GEOCILLIN - Antibiotics - J.B. Roerig & Co.

GEOCLASSICS - Floor coverings–carpet and rugs - Whitecrest Carpet Mills

GEOCLING - Artists' materials - Geographics Inc.

GEOCODER - Computer software - Geoaccess, Inc.

GEOCOUSTIC - Glass products - Pittsburgh Corning Corp.

GEOCUBE - Computer software - Schlumberger Technology Corp.

GEOCUSHION - Liners and covers–pond, pit, and landfill - Clem Environmental Corp.

GEOCYCLE - Paper - Georgia-Pacific Corp.

GEODEMX - Computer software ☆ - Geodemx Corp.

GEODESIC CLIMBER - Playground equipment - Miracle Recreation Equipment Co.

GEODESSENCE - Deodorizers - Origins Natural Resources Inc.

GEODISTRICT - Computer software - Geographic Data Technology Inc.

GEODOME - Tents - Coleman Co., Inc.

GEOENERGY - Air purification systems - Geoenergy International Corp.

GEOFFREY AMMAN - Wallets - Service Merchandise Co. Inc.

GEOFFREY B. CHOCOLATIER - Chocolate candy - Geoffrey Boehm Chocolates Inc.

GEOFFREY BEENE - Apparel and accessories ☆ - Swirl II Ltd.

GEOFFREY BEENE - Apparel–children's - Fishman and Tobin Inc.

GEOFFREY BEENE - Apparel–men's - Phillips-Van Heusen Corp.

GEOFFREY BEENE - Attache cases - H.I.T. Industries, Ltd.

GEOFFREY BEENE - Colognes - Geoffrey Beene Inc.

GEOFFREY BEENE - Neckties - Randa Corp.

GEOFFREY BEENE - Perfumes - Sanofi Beaute Inc.

GEOFFREY BEENE - Scarves ☆ - Jewel Case Inc.

GEOFFREY BEENE - Watches - Gruen Marketing Corp.

GEOFFREY BEENE FOR MEN - Apparel–men's - Joseph and Feiss Co.

GEOFFREY SCOTT - Apparel and accessories - Cleve Shirtmakers Inc.

GEOFFREY STEVEN - Crocheted and knitted items - Havenshire Knitwear Co. Inc.

GEOFFREY VALENTINE - Knitting machines - Northeast Knitting Mills Inc.

GEOFIBERS - Fibers–synthetic - Synthetic Industries, Inc.

GEOFLEX - Pipes–plastic - Environ Products, Inc.

GEOFORECASTER - Computer software - Inforum, Inc.

GEOFORM - Floor coverings–carpet and rugs - Milliken & Co. Inc.

GEOFRAME - Computer software - Schlumberger Technology Corp.

GEOGARD - Roof topcoat - Republic Powdered Metals, Inc.

GEOGENIUS - Computer software - E-8 Publications, Inc.

GEOGRAPHIC CALCULATOR, THE - Computer software - Blue Marble Geographics

GEOGRAPHIC EXPLORER, THE - Computer software - Blue Marble Geographics

GEOGRAPHIC OPTION (GO) PLAN - Communications equipment - Nynex Corp.

GEOGRAPHIC ROOTS - Map - Geographic Roots Inc.

GEOGRAPHIC TRACKER, THE - Computer software - Blue Marble Geographics

GEOGRAPHIC TRANSFORMER, THE - Computer software - Blue Marble Geographics

GEOGRAPHIC TRANSLATOR, THE - Computer software - Blue Marble Geographics

GEOGRAPHIC VIEW, THE - Computer software ☆ - Blue Marble Geographics

GEOGRAPHICS - Uniforms–tailored - Gale-Sobel Co.

GEOGRAPHY ADVENTURE: USA - Computer software - Southwest Edpsych Services Inc.

GEOGRAPHY ON FILE - Publisher's imprints - Facts on File Inc.

GEOGRAPHY SEARCH - Computer software - Tom Snyder Productions, Inc.

GEOGRAPHY SMART - Publisher's imprints - Princeton Review Publishing, LLC

GEOGUARD - Fabricated metal products - Materials International, Inc.

GEOKIDS - Video production - National Geographic Society

GEOLAY - Roofing materials - National Shelter Products, Inc.

GEOLOOP - Amusement rides - Binary Arts Corp.

GEOM - Clocks, watches, and chronometers - Louis M. Schukar and Associates

GEOMAGIC - Computer peripheral equipment - Raindrop Geomagic, Inc.

GEOMAGIC 8'S - Signs - Geographics Inc.

GEOMANCER - Books–comic - Voyager Communications Inc.

GEOMASTER - Computer software - Geographic Software Specialists, Inc.

GEOMASTER - Drafting supplies - Staedtler, Inc.

GEOMEDIA - Computer software - Intergraph Corp.

☆ = Now out of production

GEOMETALS - Wallcoverings - Worldwalls International Inc.
GEOMETREX - Puzzles - Rex Games, Inc.
GEOMETRIC - Floor coverings - American Floor Products Co. Inc.
GEOMETRIC - Floor coverings–carpet and rugs - Regal Rugs Inc.
GEOMETRIC - Hobby kits - Extra Special Products Corp.
GEOMETRIC - Kites ☆ - Hi-Flier Manufacturing Co.
GEOMETRIC MODELING LANGUAGE - Computer software - AGA Computer Services Inc.
GEOMETRIC SUPPOSER, THE - Computer software ☆ - Sunburst Communications, Inc.
GEOMETRICA - Toilets–enameled - Kohler Co.
GEOMETRICKS - Hair care products - Conair Corp.
GEOMETRICS - Erasers - Diener Industries Inc.
GEOMETRICS - Floor coverings–carpet and rugs - LaVelle Textile Marketing Inc.
GEOMETRICS - Glass products ☆ - Fenton Art Glass Co.
GEOMETRICS - Wallpaper ☆ - Bolta Wallcoverings
GEOMETRICS & TEXTURES - Fabrics–tapestry ☆ - Coloroll Inc.
GEOMETRIX - Floor coverings–carpet and rugs ☆ - J and J Industries Inc.
GEOMETRIX - Furniture ☆ - Lane Co. Inc.
GEOMETRIX - Hardware ☆ - Amerock Corp.
GEOMETRIX - Nail-care product - Cosrich Inc.
GEOMETRIX - Rulers–metal - Acme United Corp.
GEOMETRIX - Wallpaper - K.M.L. Industries
GEOMETRIX - Wallpaper ☆ - Manuscreens
GEOMETRIX II - Wallpaper - J. Josephson, Inc.
GEOMETRIX II - Wallpaper - Manuscreens
GEOMETRY CONCEPTS - Computer software - Ventura Educational Systems
GEOMETRY MASTER - Computer software - SourceView Software International
GEOMETRY TOOLKIT - Computer software - Ventura Educational Systems
GEOMINS - Vitamins and nutritional supplements - Integrated Health, Inc.
GEOMIX - Concrete–mixture - American Geodesics, Inc.
GEONETWORKS - Computer software - Geoaccess, Inc.
GEOPAK - Computer software - Bentley Systems, Inc.
GEOPAPER - Stationery - Geographics Inc.
GEOPEDIA - Computer software - Encyclopaedia Britannica Inc.
GEOPEN - Pharmaceutical preparations - J.B. Roerig & Co.
GEOPHIL - Steel springs–railroad - Needlecraft Industries
GEOPLAQUE - Signs - Geographics Inc.
GEOPRECISION - Computer peripheral equipment - Erdas, Inc.
GEOPUBLISH - Computer software - GeoWorks
GEOPURE - Pumps - Continental Water & Environmental, Inc.
GEOQUEST - Game - Tutor Corp.
GEOQUIP - Agricultural machinery - Geoquip Inc.
GEORG MOLDOW - Calendars - Bergquists
GEORGCO - Adhesives and sealants - Carolee Trifon
GEORGE - Apparel and accessories - George Co.
GEORGE - Computer software - Queue Inc.
GEORGE AND MARTHA - Flatware - Westmorland Sterling, Inc.
GEORGE BARBIER - Posters - One-of-a-Kind Workshop
GEORGE BARNES - Guitars ☆ - Guild Music Corp.
GEORGE BUTLER OF SHEFFELD - Denby USA Limited
GEORGE DENNIS - Musical instrument accessories - European Crafts/USA
GEORGE DICKEL TENNESSEE - Whiskey - Schenley Industries Inc.
GEORGE GERSHWIN - Recording label - Gershwin Enterprises
GEORGE GOLDFEIN - Giftware - George Goldfein
GEORGE GROSS - Apparel–women's - Mosaic Designs Inc.
GEORGE HORNSBY'S - Beverages–alcohol - Ernest and Julio Gallo Winery
GEORGE HORNSBY'S PUBDRAFTS - Beverages–alcohol - Ernest and Julio Gallo Winery
GEORGE JONES - Pet products - Sunshine Mills Inc.
GEORGE KOVACS - Lamps - George Kovacs Lighting Inc.
GEORGE LIQUOR AMERICAN - Shirts - Spumco, Inc.
GEORGE L'S - Guitars - L & L Sales Co. Inc.
GEORGE LUCK - Puzzles - Kingdom Puzzles
GEORGE LYNCH SCREAMIN' DEMON - Musical instrument accessories - Seymour Duncan Pickups
GEORGE MACHADO - Apparel–men's - Superba, Inc.
GEORGE MASON UNIVERSITY - Apparel and accessories - George Mason University
GEORGE MASON UNIVERSITY PATRIOTS - Games - George Mason University
GEORGE MASON UNIVERSITY PATRIOTS GMU - Games - George Mason University
GEORGE MATHIS - Artists' materials - Friday House

GEORGE O'BRIEN COLLECTION - Giftware - Woodmere China Inc.
GEORGE R. BULLITT COLLECTION - Furniture ☆ - J. Kenneth Zahn
GEORGE STANLEY - Stationery - Mara-Mi, Inc.
GEORGE STECK - Pianos - Aeolian Pianos Inc.
GEORGE WASHINGTON - Cutlery - Carvel Hall Inc.
GEORGE WASHINGTON - Tobacco products ☆ - R.J. Reynolds Tobacco Co.
GEORGE WASHINGTON CHERRY - Water–bottled or canned - Sparkling American
GEORGE WASHINGTON VANDERBILT - Wines ☆ - Biltmore Co.
GEORGEO'S - Ice - Georgeo's Water Ice Inc.
GEORGE'S 90% ALOE HERBAL RUB-DOWN - Health care products - Warren Laboratories Inc.
GEORGE'S ALWAYS ACTIVE - Health care products - Warren Laboratories Inc.
GEORGES BANK - Seafood products–fresh or frozen - John Mantia & Sons Inc.
GEORGES BOYER - Giftware - C'ports Inc.
GEORGES BRIARD DESIGNS - Giftware - Georges Briard Designs
GEORGES BRUCK - Meat products–canned - Greentree Packing Co.
GEORGES DUBOEUF - Wines - Winesellers Ltd.
GEORGES DUNAY - Wines - Blair Importers Ltd.
GEORGE'S MAGIC MIX - Flowers, plants, and seeds - G.R. Robinson Co.
GEORGES MARCEAU - Beverages–alcohol - Nor-Glo Import Co.
GEORGES MARCIANO - Eyeglasses - Guess?, Inc.
GEORGES MARCIANO - Postcards - MSK Marciano, Inc.
GEORGE'S RED - Food products ☆ - Blissfield Canning Co. Inc.
GEORGES SHOAL - Food products - Acushnet Fish Corp.
GEORGES VESSELLE - Wines ☆ - Pellegrini Bros. Wines Inc.
GEORGETOWN - Cabinets - Marsh Furniture Co.
GEORGETOWN - Cabinets ☆ - Schuler Corp.
GEORGETOWN - Candles - Lumi-Lite Candle Co. Inc.
GEORGETOWN - Clocks - General Time Corp. (Westclox/Seth Thomas Div.)
GEORGETOWN - Dinnerware–glass - Salem China Co.
GEORGETOWN - Flatware - Gorham Inc.
GEORGETOWN - Flatware - Wallace International Silversmiths, Inc.
GEORGETOWN - Floor coverings - Congoleum Corp.
GEORGETOWN - Floor coverings - Teak International
GEORGETOWN - Floor coverings–carpet and rugs - Barrett Carpet Mills Inc.
GEORGETOWN - Floor coverings–carpet and rugs ☆ - Colonial Mills Inc.
GEORGETOWN - Floor coverings–carpet and rugs ☆ - Mannington Carpets, Inc.
GEORGETOWN - Flowers, plants, and seeds - Jacklin Seed
GEORGETOWN - Frames–eyeglass - U.S. Optical Frame Co.
GEORGETOWN - Furniture - Lane Co. Inc.
GEORGETOWN - Furniture - Singer Furniture Co.
GEORGETOWN - Furniture ☆ - Hammary Furniture Co. Inc.
GEORGETOWN - Occasional tables - JDI Group, Inc.
GEORGETOWN - Paints - Muralo Co. Inc.
GEORGETOWN - Rings–jewelry - Artcarved Inc.
GEORGETOWN - Tableware–china ☆ - Lenox, Inc.
GEORGETOWN - Tableware–plastic - Federal Glass
GEORGETOWN - Tiles–ceramic - Franciscan by Johnson Brothers, USA, Inc.
GEORGETOWN - Windows–storm - Caradco
GEORGETOWN AMERICANA - Dinnerware–glass - Salem China Co.
GEORGETOWN COLLECTION - Bathroom fixtures - Price Pfister Co.
GEORGETOWN COLLECTION - Bedding–linen - Poly-Commodity Corp.
GEORGETOWN COLLECTION - Furniture ☆ - Kincaid Furniture Co. Inc.
GEORGETOWN COLLECTION, THE - Eyeglasses - Eye Deals Eyewear
GEORGETOWN FARM PURE BISON - Meat products - Edgar Bronfman
GEORGETOWN FLORAL - Dinnerware–glass - Salem China Co.
GEORGETOWN GALLERIES - Publisher's imprints - Unique Selling Propositions Inc.
GEORGETOWN HOUSE - Paper–writing ☆ - The Rytex Co.
GEORGETOWN LANDING - Furniture ☆ - Cochrane Furniture Co. Inc.
GEORGETOWN LANDING - Furniture ☆ - Sumter Cabinet Co., Inc.
GEORGETOWN SQUARE - Furniture ☆ - Bassett Furniture Industries, Inc.
GEORGETOWNE - Cabinets ☆ - Yorktowne Inc.
GEORGETOWNE - Fabrics - Dan River Inc.
GEORGETTE - Blinds–vertical - Kingdom Vertical Blinds Manufacturing Inc.
GEORGETTE - Dolls - Goldberger Doll Manufacture Co.
GEORGETTE - Wallpaper - Seabrook Wallcoverings, Inc.
GEORGI - Calendars - Sormani Inc.
GEORGI - Hats - Bierner and Son Inc.
GEORGIA - Beverages–alcohol - Consolidated Distilled Products Inc.
GEORGIA - Coffee ☆ - Coca-Cola Co.
GEORGIA - Cookies - Campbell Taggart Inc.

☆ = Now out of production

GEORGIA - Water–bottled or canned - Georgia Mountain Water Inc.
GEORGIA BELLE - Fruits and vegetables - Pomona Products Co.
GEORGIA BOOTS - Boots - Georgia Boot Inc.
GEORGIA BOY - Nuts–salted, roasted, cooked, or canned - Casey's Food & Nut Processors
GEORGIA-CHINTZ - Dinnerware–glass ☆ - Clayson Co.
GEORGIA GIANTS - Boots - Georgia Boot Inc.
GEORGIA GOLD - Food products - Cherokee Products Co.
GEORGIA MAID - Pickles - W.B. Roddenbery Co., Inc.
GEORGIA MARBLE - Marble products - Georgia Marble Co.
GEORGIA-PACIFIC - Lumber - Georgia-Pacific Corp.
GEORGIA PEACH - Beverages - Logret Import & Export Co.
GEORGIA QUALITY - Vegetables–canned ☆ - McCall Farms Inc.
GEORGIA RED - Vegetables–canned - Cherokee Products Co.
GEORGIA SISAL - Floor coverings–carpet and rugs - Burtco Enterprises Inc.
GEORGIA STAR - Sausages - Lowell Packing Co.
GEORGIA YUMMMS - Sauces - Yums Unlimited, Inc.
GEORGIAN - Audio equipment ☆ - Electro-Voice, Inc.
GEORGIAN - Cooking utensils–earthenware ☆ - Anchor Hocking Glass, Inc.
GEORGIAN - Floor coverings ☆ - Congoleum Corp.
GEORGIAN - Floor coverings–carpet and rugs - West Point-Pepperell Mill Store
GEORGIAN - Glassware–household - Dalzell-Viking
GEORGIAN - Glassware–household - Owens-Illinois Inc. (Libbey Div.)
GEORGIAN - Glassware–household ☆ - Lotus Glass Co.
GEORGIAN - Holloware - Corbell & Co.
GEORGIAN - House furnishings - Link-Taylor Corp.
GEORGIAN - House furnishings ☆ - Lexington Furniture Industries, Inc.
GEORGIAN - Mirrors ☆ - Donghia Furniture Co. Ltd.
GEORGIAN - Paper–toilet - Georgia-Pacific Corp.
GEORGIAN - Silver products - Kirk & Matz Ltd.
GEORGIAN BAY - Whiskey ☆ - Paramount Distillers Inc.
GEORGIAN COLLECTION - Giftware - Lenox, Inc.
GEORGIAN COLONY - Cabinets - Master Woodworks Kitchen Studio
GEORGIAN COURT - Furniture - Ethan Allen Finance Corp.
GEORGIAN COURT - Furniture - Ethan Allen, Inc.
GEORGIAN COURT - Tableware–china ☆ - Lenox, Inc.
GEORGIAN HALL - Furniture - Mersman Furniture Co.
GEORGIAN MANNERS - Wallpaper - Sellers & Josephson
GEORGIAN MANOR - Dishes–china - Pickard Inc.
GEORGIAN MANOR - Furniture ☆ - Fancher Furniture Co. Inc.
GEORGIAN MANOR - House furnishings ☆ - Lexington Furniture Industries, Inc.
GEORGIAN SHELL - Tableware–china - Lenox, Inc.
GEORGIAN TERRACE - Furniture - Tomlinson of High Point Inc.
GEORGIANA - Tableware–china ☆ - Lenox, Inc.
GEORGIANA ILLUSTRATIONS - Greeting cards - Georgiana Illustrations
GEORGIA'S APPLE BLOSSOM - Toiletries - Annabelle's Inc.
GEORGIA'S TENNIS - Sporting goods - Georgia's Tennis
GEORGIE - Apparel and accessories - Salant/Manhattan Industries
GEORGIE - Frames–eyeglass - U.S. Optical Frame Co.
GEORGIE BOY - Onions - SPADA enterprise, ltd.
GEORGIE GIRL - Apparel and accessories - Georgie Girl Inc.
GEORGIO GIANNI - Men's apparel - Caravelle Pour Homme Ltd.
GEORGIO MARTINI - Footwear - Conjac Inc.
GEORGIO'S - Cheese ☆ - Heluva Good Cheese Inc.
GEORGIOS - Sweaters - Gillman Knitwear Co.
GEOROM - CDROMS on geophysics topics - Society of Exploration Geophysicists
GEOSAFARI - Computer software - Educational Insights, Inc.
GEOSAT - Computer software - Graphinfo, Inc.
GEOSCORE - Medical apparatus - Del Mar Avionics
GEOSCREEN - Lighting fixtures ☆ - Thomas Lighting (Accent Division)
GEOSEEDER - Agricultural machinery - Geoquip Inc.
GEOSELECT - Computer software - Hydrosphere Data Products, Inc.
GEOSET - Diamond powder - General Electric Co.
GEOSHAPES - Games - John D. Kerlinger
GEOSIGN - Stick-on letters - Geographics Inc.
GEOSPAN - Prefabricated buildings–wood - American Geodesics, Inc.
GEOSPATIAL INFORMATION MANAGER - Computer software - Intergraph Corp.
GEOSTAT - Computer software - Retail Information Systems Inc.
GEOSTENCIL - Stencils - Geographics Inc.
GEOSTENCILS - Stencils - Geographics Inc.
GEOSTOCK - Signs - Geographics Inc.
GEOSTONE - Fireplace equipment ☆ - Majestic Co.

GEOSTRAT - Computer software - Cogniseis Development, Inc.
GEOSYNTHETICS PLUS - Construction equipment - SLT North America, Inc.
GEOSYSTEM - Dishwashing compounds - Ecolab Inc.
GEOTAG - Computer software - Lanex Corp.
GEOTAPE - Tape–adhesive - Geographics Inc.
GEOTECH - Adhesives and sealants - Akemi, Inc.
GEOTEK - Radio communications equipment - Geotek Communications, Inc.
GEOTMS - Computer software - Des Lauriers & Associates, Inc.
GEOTOGRAPHY - Games - Geotography, Inc.
GEOTREK - Computer software - Geotrek Corp.
GEOTRON - Floor coverings–carpet and rugs ☆ - Mohawk Carpet Corp.
GEOTYPE - Stencils - Geographics Inc.
GEOVIEW - Computer software - Blue Marble Geographics
GEOVIEW LT - Computer software - Blue Marble Geographics
GEOVOTER - Computer software - Map Applications, Inc.
GEOWARE - Computer software - Geoware, Inc.
GEOWIZARD - Computer software ☆ - Geodemx Corp.
GEOWORKS BINDERY - Computer software - GeoWorks
GEPE - Photographic equipment - H.P. Marketing Corp.
GEPEG - Plastics - General Electric Co.
GEPPEDDO - Dolls - Axis Corp.
GER-O-FOAM - Analgesics ☆ - Geriatric Pharmaceutical Corp.
GERA-V-PLUS - Pharmaceutical - American Laboratories Inc.
GERACIN - Pharmaceutical preparations ☆ - Lunsco Inc.
GERADINO - Perfumes - Eurostar Corp.
GERAHELTH TABS - Vitamins and nutritional supplements - Health Products Corp.
GERALD VERRIER - Darts and dart games - Dart Mart Inc.
GERALDINE - Toys–stuffed ☆ - Russ Berrie and Co., Inc.
GERALDINE'S - Snack foods - Bodacious Food Co.
GERANIUM - Nail care products - Cosmair Inc.
GERANIUM - Tableware–china - Villeroy and Boch Tableware Ltd.
GERARD - Cheese ☆ - Bongrain Cheese USA
GERARD ALEXANDRE - Cosmetics - Marie-France Andreani
GERARD BY PEGE - Apparel and accessories - Pege Partners Inc.
GERARD PELLHAM - Pet products - Gerard-Pellham Co.
GERARDO DI NOLA MACCHERONI NAPOLETANI - Pasta - Zia Dora, Inc.
GERARDO JEREZ - Clothing - Gerardo Jerez Corp.
GERARD'S LE SORBET - Fruit pops–frozen - High's Ice Cream Corp.
GERATIC - Pharmaceutical preparations ☆ - Keene Pharmaceuticals Inc.
GERAVITE - Pharmaceutical preparations - Roberts/Hauck Pharmaceuticals Inc.
GERAZOLE - Pharmaceutical preparations ☆ - C.O. Truxton Inc.
GERBEAUD - Honey - Paprikas Weiss Importer
GERBER - Baby foods - Gerber Products Co.
GERBER - Cutlery - Gerber Legendary Blades
GERBER - Infant product - La Rue International, Inc.
GERBER - Plumbing fixtures–metal - Gerber Plumbing Fixtures Corp.
GERBER EDGE - Machinery - Gerber Scientific, Inc.
GERBER GRADUATES - Baby foods - Gerber Products Co.
GERBERLEGS - Furniture–wood - Gerber Industries Inc.
GERBERT - Floor coverings–linoleum - Gerbert Ltd.
GERBRO - Food products - Savon Food Co.
GERDA SPILLMAN - Skin care products - Mar-Riche Enterprises Inc.
GERDAU - Furniture ☆ - Techport Inc.
GERDOX - Bouillon cubes ☆ - Dean & Deluca Inc.
GERE-DYNE - Vitamins and nutritional supplements ☆ - Dr. Peter Fahrney & Sons Co.
GERELAINE - Cheese - Swiss American Import Co.
GERELMA - Artists' materials - Riebe's Artist Materials Inc.
GEREMY ROSE - Health care products - New Moon Extracts, Inc.
GERI - Skin care products - Geritrex Corp.
GERI-BATH - Skin care products - Geritrex Corp.
GERI-BATH II - Skin care products - Geritrex Corp.
GERI-BOB - Vitamins and nutritional supplements - Scot-Tussin Pharmacal Co.
GERI-CAL - Vitamins and nutritional supplements - Gides-NuLife Inc.
GERI-CARE - Health care products - Geri-Care Products, LLC
GERI-CBO - Skin care products - Geritrex Corp.
GERI-DEIMAL - Pharmaceutical preparations - Boyle & Co.
GERI-DYNE - Disinfectants - Geritrex Corp.
GERI-FREEDA - Vitamins and nutritional supplements - Freeda Vitamins Inc.
GERI-G - Pharmaceutical preparations ☆ - Geneva Generics Inc.
GERI GEL TAR SHAMPOO - Hair care products - Geritrex Corp.
GERI-GEN - Pharmaceutical preparations - General Nutrition Inc.
GERI GERARD - Apparel–women's - Geri Gerard Ltd.
GERI-LAV - Skin care products ☆ - Geritrex Corp.

GERI-LAV II - Deodorizers - Geritrex Corp.

GERI MOORE - Vitamins and nutritional supplements ☆ - Moore Medical Corp.

GERI-PAR - Pharmaceutical preparations - Parmed Pharmaceuticals, Inc.

GERI-PLUS - Disinfectants - Geritrex Corp.

GERI-PRIDE - Pharmaceutical preparations - Nature's Bounty, Inc.

GERI-PROTECT - Skin care products - Geritrex Corp.

GERI-RINSE FREE - Hair care products - Geritrex Corp.

GERI-SALVE - Health care products ☆ - Geritrex Corp.

GERI-SAN DET - Disinfectants - Geritrex Corp.

GERI-SHAMPOO WITH SHEA BUTTER - Hair care products - Geritrex Corp.

GERI-SILK - Skin care products - Geritrex Corp.

GERI-SOFT - Skin care products - Geritrex Corp.

GERI-TOGS, INC. - Apparel and accessories - Geri-Togs, Inc.

GERI-V-CAPS - Pharmaceutical preparations - C.S. Ruckstuhl Co. Inc.

GERI-VITAL - Skin care products - Mana Products, Inc.

GERI-WASH - Skin care products - Geritrex Corp.

GERIACTICE - Orthopedic products ☆ - JSB Orthotics Inc.

GERIAMIC - Pharmaceutical preparations ☆ - Vortech Pharmaceuticals

GERIATRICAPS - Pharmaceutical - IDE-Interstate Inc.

GERIATRO-B - Pharmaceutical preparations - Medical Chemical Corp.

GERIATROPLEX - Pharmaceutical preparations ☆ - Morton Pharmaceuticals Inc.

GERIAVIT - Vitamins and nutritional supplements - Lustol Co.

GERIAVIT PHARMATON - Vitamins and nutritional supplements - Natureworks Inc.

GERIBAG - Bags–laundry - Prevent Products, Inc.

GERIBAND - Hats - Gerriann C. Meandro

GERIBITS - Veterinary pharmaceutical preparations - SmithKline Beecham Animal Health Products

GERIBOMS - Pharmaceutical preparations ☆ - JMI-Canton Pharmaceuticals

GERIDIUM - Pharmaceutical preparations - Goldline Laboratories, Inc.

GERIFORM - Pharmaceutical preparations - Blair Pharmacal

GERIFORT PLUS - Pharmaceutical - American Pharmaceutical Co.

GERIGRIP - Gloves - Prevent Products, Inc.

GERILETS - Pharmaceutical preparations - Abbott Laboratories

GERILIQUID - Pharmaceutical preparations ☆ - Key Pharmaceuticals Inc.

GERILITE - Pharmaceutical preparations ☆ - Vitarine Pharmaceuticals Inc.

GERILIX - Pharmaceutical preparations ☆ - Lunsco Inc.

GERIM - Veterinary pharmaceutical preparations - Nutra-Vet Research Corp.

GERIMAL - Pharmaceutical preparations - Rugby Laboratories Inc.

GERIMAX - Pharmacies - Gerimed, Inc.

GERIMED - Vitamins and nutritional supplements - Fielding Pharmaceutical Co.

GERIMEND - Skin care products - Derma Rx Corp.

GERIMOUSE - Computer peripheral equipment - STASH, Inc.

GERINATS - Pharmaceutical preparations ☆ - Saron Pharmacal Corp.

GERINATS-H - Pharmaceutical preparations ☆ - Saron Pharmacal Corp.

GERINEED - Pharmaceutical preparations - Hanlon Drug Products

GERING - Hoses - Colorite Plastic Co.

GERIO-DIET - Pet products - Triumph Pet Industries, Inc.

GERIOT - Pharmaceutical preparations - Goldline Laboratories, Inc.

GERIOUX - Flatware - Rego China/THC Systems

GERIPLEX - Vitamins and nutritional supplements ☆ - Parke-Davis

GERIRON - Pharmaceutical preparations ☆ - Legere Pharmaceuticals Inc.

GERISEV - Prescription drug - American Hygienic Laboratories Inc.

GERISTONE - Pharmaceutical preparations ☆ - U.S. Ethicals Inc.

GERITA - Kitchen cabinets–metal - Hy-Systems, Inc.

GERITOL - Vitamins and nutritional supplements - SmithKline Beecham Consumer Healthcare

GERITOL COMPLETE - Vitamins and nutritional supplements - SmithKline Beecham Consumer Healthcare

GERITOL COMPLETE - Vitamins and nutritional supplements - Smithkline Beecham Corp.

GERITOL EXTEND - Vitamins and nutritional supplements - SmithKline Beecham Consumer Healthcare

GERITOL MEGA-VITAMINS - Vitamins and nutritional supplements ☆ - Smithkline Beecham Corp.

GERITOL TONIC - Pharmaceutical preparations - Smithkline Beecham Corp.

GERITONIC - Pharmaceutical preparations - Geriatric Pharmaceutical Corp.

GERITRIN - Pharmaceutical preparations - Vita-Fore Products Co.

GERIX - Vitamins and nutritional supplements - Abbott Laboratories

GERIZYME - Pharmaceutical preparations ☆ - Upjohn Co.

GERLAND - Brandy - Leonard Kreusch Inc.

GERM BUSTERS - Bags–plastic - J.M. Sales Inc.

GERM EX - Wheat germ - Green Foods

GERM-FIGHTER - Wastebaskets - United Marketing, Inc.

GERM-FIGHTER RIGID PLASTIC LINERS - Wastebaskets - United Receptacle Inc.

GERM GUARD - Cleaning preparations - Canton Industries, Inc.

GERM GUARD - Telephone apparatus - Sutton Products Inc.

GERM KILL - Disinfectants - Conair Corp.

GERM-MYCYDYL - Fungicides - Projectapix-II

GERM STOPPER - Bags–trash - Germ Stopper Inc.

GERM TERMINATOR, THE - Disinfectants - Knight Marketing Corp.

GERM-X - Disinfectants - Vi-Jon Laboratories, Inc.

GERMA TAN - Sporting goods - Mueller Sports Medicine Inc.

GERMACK - Nuts–salted, roasted, cooked, or canned - Germack Pistachio Co.

GERMAIN - Bedding–linen - Dan River Inc.

GERMAINE DE CAPUCCINI - Skin care products - Germaine De Capuccini USA Inc.

GERMAINE MONTEIL - Cosmetics ☆ - Monteil Paris

GERMAIN'S TRAIN-ETTS - Trellises ☆ - T & T Industries Inc.

GERMAN BROT - Breads - Charles Freihofer Baking Co.

GERMAN FEST - Breads - German Fest Milwaukee, Inc.

GERMAN GLASSBLOWER, THE - Christmas tree ornaments ☆ - Biedermann & Sons Inc.

GERMAN HARD ROLLS - Rolls–dinner ☆ - Natural Ovens of Manitowoc Inc.

GERMAN NOW! - Computer software - Transparent Language, Inc.

GERMAN THE EASY WAY - Computer software - Gessler Publishing Co., Inc.

GERMAN VILLAGE - Food products - German Village Products Inc.

GERMAN WINE PROFESSOR, THE - Computer software - E-8 Publications, Inc.

GERMANIA - Herb tea ☆ - Benjamin Ansehl Co.

GERMANIA - Saddles - Thornhill Enterprises, Inc.

GERMANTOWN - Cabinets - Belwood Inc.

GERMANTOWN - Yarn - Brunswick Yarns

GERMANY ROTTWEILER GEAR EXPECT RESPECT - Boots - Kelvin C. McRae

GERMARREST - Antiseptics - Healthsafe Environmental, Inc.

GERMAX - Oxygen ☆ - Natrol, Inc.

GERMBUSTER - Welcon

GERMEX - Veterinary pharmaceutical preparations - Solvay Animal Health, Inc.

GERMGARD - Filters–air - Southern Environmental Products

GERMICIN - Pharmaceutical preparations - Consolidated Midland Corp.

GERMINATOR - Liners and covers–pond, pit, and landfill - Reemay, Inc.

GERMISAN - Pharmaceutical preparations ☆ - Barre-National, Inc.

GERMISOLVE - Disinfectant - Continental Chemical Corp.

GERMKILL - Sterilizing chambers - Vortex Innerspace Products Inc.

GERMOTOX - Disinfectants - Pioneer Manufacturing Co.

GERMWIPES - Antiseptics ☆ - NutriBiotic

GERODISC - Locomotives - ASHA Corp.

GEROLSTEINER - Water–mineral - Kreiner Imports

GERONAR - Photographic equipment ☆ - H.P. Marketing Corp.

GERONAR-WA - Photographic equipment - Berkey Marketing Cos.

GERONIMO - Boats - Glen-L Marine Designs

GERONIMO - Games - Avalon Hill Game Co.

GERONIMO - Sauces - Public Label Brands, Inc.

GERONIMO - Shoes - Harbor Footwear Group Ltd.

GERONIMO - Wallpaper - Pantasote Inc. (Wallcovering Div.)

GERONIMO BY STEPHEN DIGERONIMO - Apparel and accessories - Stephen Digeronimo, Inc.

GEROPLAST - Pencils ☆ - Faber-Castell Corp.

GEROTON-E - Vitamins and nutritional supplements - Winning Laboratories Corp.

GEROVICAP - Teas–herbal - Gerovicap Pharmaceutical Corp.

GERRARD BANDING AND SEALS - Fabricated metal products - Pabco Metals Corp.

GERRARD PAB-BANDS - Fabricated metal products - Pabco Metals Corp.

GERRI'S - Nail care products - Gerri's Professional Nail Products, Inc.

GERRIT'S - Candy - Gerrit J. Verburg Co.

GERRY - Apparel and accessories - Gerry Sportswear Corp.

GERRY - Infant product ☆ - Gerry Baby Products Co.

GERRY A LA MODE - Strollers–baby - Gerry Baby Products Co.

GERRY BABY SAFETRONICS - Infant product - Gerry Baby Products Co.

GERRY BEAR 3 - Infant product ☆ - Gerry Baby Products Co.

GERRY BIG BATH - Infant product - Gerry Baby Products Co.

GERRY COSBY - Apparel–athletic - Gerry Cosby & Co., Inc.

GERRY COSMOPOLITAN - Bags ☆ - Gerry Baby Products Co.

GERRY CUB CUDDLE - Infant product ☆ - Gerry Baby Products Co.

GERRY DOUBLE CARE - Bags ☆ - Gerry Baby Products Co.

GERRY DOUBLE GUARD - Infant product - Gerry Baby Products Co.

☆ = Now out of production

GERRY DOUBLE TAKE - Strollers–baby ☆ - Gerry Baby Products Co.
GERRY ESCORT - Infant product - Gerry Baby Products Co.
GERRY EXPRESS - Strollers–baby ☆ - Gerry Baby Products Co.
GERRY FIRST MEALS - High chairs - Gerry Baby Products Co.
GERRY FLIP-TOP - Buckets–plastic - Gerry Baby Products Co.
GERRY FOLDING 40 - Toys - Gerry Baby Products Co.
GERRY FOOTHOLD - Infant product - Gerry Baby Products Co.
GERRY FUTURE - Infant product ☆ - Gerry Baby Products Co.
GERRY GO ROUND - Strollers–baby ☆ - Gerry Baby Products Co.
GERRY GRAND STAND - Stools–wood ☆ - Gerry Baby Products Co.
GERRY GUARDIAN - Infant product - Gerry Baby Products Co.
GERRY HOLIDAY - Strollers–baby ☆ - Gerry Baby Products Co.
GERRY K-TECH - Infant product - Gerry Baby Products Co.
GERRY KIDDIE SEAT - Infant product - Gerry Baby Products Co.
GERRY MEAL TIMES - High chairs - Gerry Baby Products Co.
GERRY OF CALIFORNIA - Bathing suits - Wior Corp.
GERRY POCKET ROCKET - Strollers–baby ☆ - Gerry Baby Products Co.
GERRY SIXPACK - Infant product ☆ - Gerry Baby Products Co.
GERRY TWO YEARS - Infant product - Gerry Baby Products Co.
GERRY ULTRA SOFT - Infant product ☆ - Gerry Baby Products Co.
GERRY VOYAGER - Infant product ☆ - Gerry Baby Products Co.
GERRY WALK-THRU - Infant product - Gerry Baby Products Co.
GERRY ZEPHYR - Strollers–baby ☆ - Gerry Baby Products Co.
GERRY'S COLLECTIBLES - Christmas tree ornaments - Gerry's Creations Inc.
GERRY'S CREATIONS - Jewelry–costume - Gerry's Creations Inc.
GERSHWIN - Music–sheet - Gershwin Enterprises
GERSON - Paint dryers - Louis M. Gerson Co. Inc.
GERST - Beverages–malt - Evansville Brewing Co.
GERSTEL BRAN - Beverages–malt - Barton Brands, Ltd.
GERSTMAYER - Greeting cards - H. George Caspari Inc.
GERSTNER - Chests–wood - H. Gerstner & Sons
GERSTUNG - Exercising equipment - Gerstung/Gym-Thing Inc.
GERSTUNG AIR BASE - Exercising equipment - Gerstung/Gym-Thing Inc.
GERTIE - Balls - Small World Toys
GERTNER AUDIO - Loudspeakers - Stephen James Gertner, Jr.
GERTRUDE - Toys–stuffed ☆ - Gund, Inc.
GERTRUDE HAWK CHOCOLATES - Candy - Gertrude Hawks Chocolate Inc.
GERTRUDES - Shoes - Crawford Shoe & Garment Manufacturing
GERTRUDE'S PUZZLES - Computer software ☆ - Gessler Publishing Co., Inc.
GERTRUDE'S SECRETS - Computer software ☆ - Gessler Publishing Co., Inc.
GERTRUDE'S SECRETS - Computer software ☆ - The Learning Co., Inc.
GERVAIS-PENARD - Watches - Hampden Corp.
GERWIN - Hardware - H.B. Ives
GERZ - Glassware–household - Bavaria Importers Inc.
GES - Chemical preparations - Environmental Biotech, Inc.
GES-LINE - Giftware - Gessner Products Co. Inc.
GES-SNUFF - Ashtrays–glass - Gessner Products Co. Inc.
GES-TWIST - Giftware ☆ - Gessner Products Co. Inc.
GESCAN - Computer software ☆ - Sas Institute Inc.
GESCO DIALY-NATE - Medical apparatus - Utah Medical Products, Inc.
GESCO HEMO-NATE - Medical apparatus - Utah Medical Products, Inc.
GESCO HEMO-TAP - Medical apparatus - Utah Medical Products, Inc.
GESCO MYELO-NATE - Medical apparatus - Utah Medical Products, Inc.
GESCO NUTRI-CATH - Medical apparatus - Utah Medical Products, Inc.
GESCO PALA-NATE - Medical apparatus - Utah Medical Products, Inc.
GESCO THORA-CATH - Medical apparatus - Utah Medical Products, Inc.
GESCO UMBILI-CATH - Medical apparatus - Utah Medical Products, Inc.
GESCO URI-CATH - Medical apparatus - Utah Medical Products, Inc.
GESHMAKA - Sauerkraut ☆ - Rea-D-Pack Foods Inc.
GESPA - Yarn ☆ - William Unger & Co. Inc.
GESSNER - Housewares - Gessner Products Co. Inc.
GESSO-PAQUE - Paints ☆ - Old World Art
GEST-AID - Pet products - Rael Co.
GESTATION - Recording label - Soundmasters Studio
GESTEROL - Pharmaceutical preparations ☆ - Forest Pharmaceuticals Inc.
GESTONEED - Pharmaceutical preparations - Hanlon Drug Products
GESTSMOOTH - Hair care products - Attitudes Unltd.
GESTURE - Floor coverings–carpet and rugs ☆ - Blue Ridge Carpet Mills
GESTUREGLOVE - Computer hardware - Virtual Technologies
GESTURES - Apparel–women's - China Trade & Research, Inc.
GESTURES - Wallpaper - Capital Carousel Inc.
GESTY LOOK - Cigars - Gesty Trading & Manufacturing Corp.
GET! - Computer software ☆ - Everex Systems, Inc.
GET A CLU! - Novelty items - Douglas Gan and James Gordon Partnership
GET A CLUE FIND A NEW REALITY - Apparel and accessories - Lyceum Communications Inc.

GET A GRIP! - Concrete repair products - Brink's Manufacturing Co., Inc.
GET A GRIP - Dental equipment - Jeffrey D. Hempel
GET-A-GRIP - Hooks - Shepherd Industries, Inc.
GET A GRIP - Pliers - Channellock, Inc.
GET A GRIP ON YOUR GAME - Sports rackets and accessories - Tacki-Mac Grips, Inc.
GET A GRIPP - Bottles–glass - Get a Gripp II, Inc.
GET A LIFE - Video production - Vocational Video, Inc.
GET ALONG GANG - Publisher's imprints - Scholastic Inc.
GET ALONG GANG - Puzzles - Playskool, Inc.
GET AWAY - Repellent - Intagra, Inc.
GET AWAY BEAR - Toys–stuffed - Russ Berrie and Co., Inc.
GET BENT - Apparel and accessories - North Atlantic Group Inc.
GET BIG - Vitamins and nutritional supplements - Dener Management Inc.
GET BSH - Apparel and accessories - Scott P. McGraw
GET BUFF - Apparel and accessories - Kevin S. Pinson
GET-CLAIM - Computer software - Med-Link Technologies Inc.
GET CUP CRAZY - Apparel–women's - National Hockey League
GET DOWN - Musical instrument accessories ☆ - Fredrico Percussion
GET EVEN - Games - Patricio Baca
GET EVEN - Shoe insoles - Career Footwear Corp.
GET EXTREME - Apparel and accessories - Pel Industries, Inc.
GET FLEECED AUTHENTIC RUGGED OUTERWEAR - Apparel and accessories - Get Fleeced
GET GLOWING - Cosmetics - Dolly Parton Inc.
GET GOING - Body wash - Matrix Essentials, Inc.
GET HAPPY - Jewelry ☆ - Imperial Toy Corp.
GET-IN - Golfing equipment - Karsten Manufacturing Corp.
GET IN THE WIND - T-shirts–men's - Brian W. Lawrence
GET INVOLVED - Notebooks and notepads - Get Involved, Inc.
GET-IT! A WINNING FORMULA! - Recording label - Sonnett International
GET IT BEFORE YOU LOSE IT - Exercising equipment - Pro-Innovative Concepts, Inc.
GET IT DONE - Notebooks and notepads ☆ - Southworth Co.
GET IT MOVIN! - Office supplies - Master Caster Co.
GET IT ON! - Sporting goods - Kenneth J. Benoit
GET IT RIGHT, FROM THE KITCHEN. - Coleslaw - Sara Lee Corp.
GET-IT-RIGHT POSTERS - Posters - Clement Communications Inc.
GET KLEEN - Fuel additives - K & W Products
GET MOVING - Apparel and accessories ☆ - Warnaco Inc.
GET-O-BALL - Games - Michael Patrick Sullivan
GET OFF ME - Hats - Get Off Me Wear, Inc.
GET OFF MY ASPHALT - Apparel and accessories - Out W Designs, LLC
GET OFF MY BACK - Games ☆ - Tyco Toys
GET OFF MY GARDEN - Annato extract ☆ - Security Products Co.
GET OFF MY GARDEN - Pet products - Farnam Cos. Inc.
GET OFF MY PLANTS - Pet products - Farnam Cos. Inc.
GET ON THE BALL - Exercising equipment - Fitness Quest Inc.
GET ORGANIZED - Computer software ☆ - Electronic Arts Inc.
GET OUT AND STAY OUT - Apparel and accessories - W.L. Gore & Associates, Inc.
GET OUT THERE - Wheelchairs - Quickie Designs Inc.
GET OUT WHILE YOU CAN - Backpacks - Jansport Apparel Corp.
GET OVER IT! - Apparel and accessories - Strasburg, Inc.
GET PAID - Apparel and accessories - Pro Athlete in Development
GET REAL - Apparel–athletic - Logo 7 Inc.
GET REAL - Greeting cards - First Concept Corp.
GET ROLLIN'! THE GAME - Games - Shelly Schoenberger
GET SERIOUS - Bicycles - Columbia Manufacturing Inc.
GET SERIOUS! - Stain removers - Van Charles Laboratories
GET SET - Computer software - Educational Testing Service
GET SET - Hair care products - Alberto-Culver Co.
GET SET - Starch–laundry - Bond Adhesives Co.
GET SET TO LEARN! - Computer peripheral equipment - Creative Wonders, LLC
GET SMART - Apparel and accessories - CBS Inc.
GET SMART - Binders - ACCO USA, Inc.
GET SMART - Vitamins and nutritional supplements - Natural Organics, Inc.
G.E.T. S.M.A.R.T. GREAT EDUCATIONAL TRAINING IN SCIENCE, MATH AND ROBOTIC TECHNO - Educational materials - Creative Learning Association, Inc.
GET SMART WITH IDG BOOKS! - Bags–duffel - International Data Group, Inc.
GET SMOOTH - Hair care products - Image Laboratories, Inc.
GET SOLE - Shoes - Famolare Inc.
GET SOLID - Apparel–athletic - Dennis K. Rodman

GET SOME - Apparel and accessories - Tim Newcomb
GET SPOILED - Apparel and accessories - Maran, Inc.
GET STAR - Video games - Taito America Corp.
GET STARTED - Skin care products - Origins Natural Resources Inc.
GET THE MESSAGE - Signs ☆ - Securitag Corp.
GET THERE - Footwear - Famolare Inc.
GET TO THE POINT - Computer software ☆ - Sunburst Communications, Inc.
GET TWISTED - Pretzels - Portland Pretzel Co.
GET UP - Shoes - Famolare Inc.
GET UP & GLOW - Clocks - Seiko Corp. of America
GET-UP-N-GO - Apparel–women's - Sanmark-Stardust Inc.
GET-UPS 'N GO - Dolls - Mattel, Inc.
GET USED - Apparel and accessories - Title Jeans Wear Inc.
GET WAXED - Candles - Get Waxed Franchising, Inc.
GET WELL - Cookies - Creative Cookie Inc. (American Dream Enterprises)
GET WELL BELL - Novelty items - Foytt Industries
GET WET - Apparel and accessories - Downing Hawaii
GET WET CUSTOM SWIMWEAR - Bathing suits - Get Wet Custom Swimwear
GET WICKED TONIGHT - Apparel and accessories - Pete's Brewing Co.
GET WILD ABOUT ANIMALS - Pet products ☆ - Kal Kan Foods, Inc.
GET WITH THE PROGRAM - Jewelry - J.D.M. Import Co., Inc.
GET YOUR AFFAIRS IN ORDER - Computer software - Compu-Tations Inc.
GET YOUR JUICES FLOWING - Fruit drinks–bottled or canned ☆ - Coca-Cola Co.
GETA GRIP - Razors - Douglas A. Pick
GETAWAY - Computer software - Epyx Inc.
GETAWAY - Cooking equipment–household ☆ - Mirro Corp.
GETAWAY BAG - Travel accessories - American Guard-It Manufacturing Co. Inc.
GETAWAY, THE - Games - Williams Electronics Games, Inc.
GETEK - Electrical equipment - General Electric Co.
GETS-IT - Pharmaceutical preparations - Oakhurst Co.
GETTELFINGER - Popcorn - Preston Farms, L.P.
GETTIN' BIGGER BEARS - Toys ☆ - American Greetings Corp.
GETTIN' PRETTY BEAUTY BOUTIQUE - Toys–stuffed - CBS Toys
GETTING EVEN - Skin care products - Frances Denney
GETTING FIT - Video production - Donna Aucoin
GETTING GOING - Computer software - Dow Jones and Co. Inc.
GETTING STARTED WITH BASIC - Computer software ☆ - SRA/McGraw-Hill (Div. of The McGraw-Hill Companies)
GETTING STARTED WITH LOGO - Computer software ☆ - SRA/McGraw-Hill (Div. of The McGraw-Hill Companies)
GETTING TO KNOW YOU ...BETTER - Games - Games Partnership Ltd., Inc.
GETTLEMAN - Beer - Miller Brewing Co.
GETTY - Hardware - Blaine Window Hardware Inc.
GETTY - Hardware - Merit Metal Products Corp.
GETTY - Petroleum - Getty Petroleum Marketing, Inc.
GETTY PROVENANCE INDEX, THE - Recording label - Getty Information Institute
GETTY TEDDY - Toys–stuffed - Russ Berrie and Co., Inc.
GETTYSBURG - Cabinets–metal - American Woodmark Corp.
GETTYSBURG - Flowers, plants, and seeds - Jonathan Green, Inc.
GETTYSBURG - Games - Avalon Hill Game Co.
GETTYSBURG - Pottery products - Henriksen Imports Inc.
GETZEN - Musical instruments - Getzen Co.
GETZIT - Skin care products - Goa Laboratories
G.E.V. - Games - Steve Jackson Games Inc.
GEVALIA - Coffee - Kraft Food Ingredients Corp.
GEVALIA KAFFE - Coffee - Gevalia Kaffe Import Service
GEVEREX - Pharmaceutical preparations - C.S. Ruckstuhl Co. Inc.
GEVIDERM - Skin care products - Geviderm, Inc.
GEVIZOL - Pharmaceutical preparations ☆ - Saron Pharmacal Corp.
GEVRABON - Vitamins and nutritional supplements - Lederle Laboratories
GEVRAL - Pharmaceutical preparations - Lederle Laboratories
GEWA - Printers–computer - Zygo Industries Inc.
GEWA & JAEGER - Cases–musical instrument - Ideal Musical Merchandise Co.
GEWURZ TRAMINER - Wines - Chicama Vineyards
GEXCO - Sporting goods - Gexco Enterprises
GEXCO BALL PICKUP BASKET - Sporting goods - Gexco Enterprises
GEXCO NEOPRENE SUPPORTS - Sporting goods - Gexco Enterprises
GEXCO TENNIS ELBOW GUARD - Sporting goods - Gexco Enterprises
GEYER'S - Beverages–malt - Geyer Bros. Brewing Co.
GEYSER - Apparel and accessories - Geyser International, Inc.
GEYSER - Pumps - Simer Pump Co.
GEYSER - Water–bottled or canned - Christopher Michael Vance

GEYSER LEGENDARY SPRING WATER - Water–bottled or canned - Water Star Bottling
GEYSER PEAK - Wines - Geyser Peak Winery
GEYSGRVILLE - Wines - Ridge Vineyards Inc.
GEZE - Sporting goods - Elan-Monark
GEZI - Cooking utensils–enameled ☆ - Reston Lloyd Ltd.
GEZIP - Electrical equipment - General Electric Co.
GF - Bandages–surgical - Graham-Field Inc.
GF - Fabrics - Guilford Mills, Inc.
GF - Lighting equipment ☆ - Fox Lite Inc.
GF - Toners - Radiant Color Div.
GF - Water purification systems - General Filter Co.
GF - Water purification systems - General Filter Co.
GF1 - Floor coverings - L.D. Brinkman & Co. Inc.
GFC - Gauging instruments - Savant Measurement Corp.
GFC - Meats - GFI America, Inc.
GFC AMERICA - Meat - GFI America, Inc.
GFE - Lighting equipment ☆ - Fox Lite Inc.
GFI - Electronic equipment - General Signal Corp.
GFI - Eyeglasses - Goat Eyewear
GFI - Floor coverings–carpet and rugs - General Felt Industries, Inc.
GFI - Food products - Beatrice Cos. Inc.
GFI - Jewelry - Gold Force International Ltd.
GFL - Handbags - DFS Group Ltd.
GFR - Chemical preparations - Ulano Corp.
GFS GATEWAY FREIGHT SERVICES - Freight cars–locomotive - Gateway Freight Services
GFS PLUS - Computer software - Gordon Food Service, Inc.
G.F.S. SORCERESS - Games ☆ - Avalon Hill Game Co.
GFX - Skates–roller - Rollerball International Inc.
GG - Mirrors - Gardner Mirror Corp.
GG - Recording label - Guts & Grace Records, Inc.
GG - Video production - Kideo Productions, Inc.
GG - Wallets - Gucci America, Inc.
GG-CEN - Cold remedies - Central Pharmaceutical Inc.
GGG - Bags–duffel - Group III International Ltd.
GGG - Meat products - J. Gerber & Co., Inc.
GGG CLOTHES - Apparel–men's - Andre Romanelli, Inc.
GG'S - Biscuits - Seckinger-Lee Co.
GGS - Chairs–folding - Mulholland Positioning Systems Inc.
GG'S - Manicure preparations - GG's Nail Systems
GGX - Computer hardware - Gammagraphx, Inc.
GH - Paint sprayers - Graco Inc.
G.H. ACTION - Vitamins and nutritional supplements - Natural Organics, Inc.
G.H. BASS & CO. - Footwear - G.H. Bass and Co.
GH DESIGNS - Apparel and accessories - International Designer Accessories
GH ENHANCERS - Vitamins and nutritional supplements - Healthy 'N Fit Nutritionals
G.H. EVE - Health care products - Above All Health Inc.
GH MEDICAL INC - Medical apparatus - GH Medical, Inc.
G.H. MORNING - Health care products - Above All Health Inc.
G.H. RELEASE - Vitamins and nutritional supplements - Natural Organics, Inc.
GH RELEASERS - Vitamins and nutritional supplements - Anabol Naturals
GH3X - Health care products - Healthwatchers System
GH1000 - Vitamins and nutritional supplements - Iron Curtain Labs Inc.
GHB - Labels–paper - Jazzology-GHB Records
GHB - Lighting equipment - General Electric Co.
GHC - Hair care products - Watkins Inc.
GHEE JAR - Food products - Mike Hudson Distributing Inc.
GHENGIS - Floor coverings–carpet and rugs ☆ - Trans-Ocean Import Co. Inc.
GHENT - Wallcoverings - Stretchwall Fabrics Co.
GHETTO BLEU - Clothing - Davindar Singh Dhillon
GHETTO BLOCKERS - Sunglasses - Blublocker Corp.
GHIA - See **MUSTANG GHIA**
GHIACCIO - Colognes - Jovito F. Javier
GHIOTTINI - Cookies ☆ - Liberty Richter Inc.
GHIRARDELLI - Chocolate candy - Ghirardelli Chocolate Co.
GHIRARDELLI - Chocolate candy - Naron Candy Co. Inc.
GHIRARDELLI - Chocolate milk - Lund Distribution, Inc.
GHIRARDELLI - Ice cream - Eskimo Pie Corp.
GHIRARDELLI CLASSICO - Confections - Ghirardelli Chocolate Co.
GHOST - Computers–personal - Gimix Inc.
GHOST - Hunting equipment - Patton Crafted Products, Inc.
GHOST - Motor vehicle parts and accessories ☆ - Bell Sports Corp.
GHOST - Musical instrument accessories ☆ - Selmer Co. Inc.
GHOST - Soccer equipment - Brine Inc.

☆ = Now out of production

GHOST BATTALION - Toys - Jasman, Inc.
GHOST BUSTERS - Cereal - Ralston Purina Co.
GHOST BUSTERS SLIMER SLIMERY - Candy ☆ - Maramor Candy Co.
GHOST DANCE - Video production - Ghost Dance Productions
GHOST GLOVE - Skin care products ☆ - Heyer Inc.
GHOST IN THE HOUSE, THE - Electronic equipment ☆ - Texas Instruments Inc.
GHOST MINNOW - Fishing tackle - Horizon Lure Co.
GHOST MUNCHERS - Candy ☆ - R.M. Palmer Co.
GHOST MYST - Perfumes - Coty Inc.
GHOST SERIES TX - Microphones - CCS International Ltd.
GHOST WARRIORS - Toys - Tonka Corp.
GHOST WRITER - Markers–felt-tip - General Pencil Co.
GHOST WRITER - Markers–felt-tip - Sanford Corp.
GHOST WRITER - Video production - Children's Television Workshop
GHOSTBUSTERS - Candy ☆ - Alma-Leo USA Inc.
GHOSTBUSTERS - Computer software - Activision, Inc.
GHOSTBUSTERS - Games ☆ - Ben Cooper Inc.
GHOSTBUSTERS II - Candy ☆ - Topps Co., Inc.
GHOSTBUSTERS SLIMER - Chewing gum ☆ - Amurol Confections Co.
GHOSTDUSTER - Erasers - Quartet Manufacturing Co.
GHOSTLY GRAMMAR - Computer software - Unicorn Software
GHOSTS - Candy - Glenn Confections Inc.
GHOSTS! - Games ☆ - Milton Bradley Co.
GHOSTS - Publisher's imprints - Philip Makanna
GHOSTS 'N GOBLINS - Video games - Taito America Corp.
GHOSTSTRIKER X-16 - Toys–automobiles - Hasbro, Inc.
GHOSTWRITER - Computer software - Precedent Systems, Inc.
GHOULERY - Costumes - Spearhead Industries Inc.
GHOULERY JEWELRY - Jewelry - Paper Magic Group Inc.
GHOULISH GOODIES - Candy - Russ Berrie and Co., Inc.
GHS - Musical instrument accessories - GHS Strings
GHURKA COLLECTION, THE - Leather goods - TGL Corp.
GI - Can openers–electric - J.W. Speaker Corp.
GI - Colognes - Express, Inc.
G.I. - Footwear - Vans, Inc.
G.I. - Inks - Mark Master Inc.
GI - Thread - Belding Heminway Co. Inc.
G.I. ANVIL OF VICTORY - Games - Avalon Hill Game Co.
G.I. CLEANSE - Vitamins and nutritional supplements ☆ - Ethical Nutrients
GI GI - Fishing tackle - Truline Glass Rod Manufacturing Co.
GI-GI - Greeting cards - Gallant Greetings Corp.
GI INTRUDER - Sporting goods - O'Brien International
G.I. JOE - Bags–duffel ☆ - A.D. Sutton & Sons Inc.
G.I. JOE - Bathroom accessories ☆ - Tsumura International Inc.
G.I. JOE - Candy ☆ - Maramor Candy Co.
GI JOE - Computer software - Epyx Inc.
GI JOE - Games ☆ - Ben Cooper Inc.
G.I. JOE - Puzzles ☆ - Milton Bradley Co.
G.I. JOE - Tents ☆ - Intex Recreation Corp.
G.I. JOE - Toys - Hasbro, Inc.
GI JOE - Toys - Playtime Corp.
GI JOE - Toys ☆ - Tyco Toys
G.I. JOE - Wallpaper ☆ - Priss Prints Inc.
G.I. JOE ACTION STARS - Cereal - Ralston Purina Co.
G.I. JOE COMMANDO ATTACK - Games ☆ - Milton Bradley Co.
G.I. JOE EXTREME - Toys - Hasbro, Inc.
G.I. STOGIES - Chewing gum ☆ - Leaf, Inc.
G.I. TIME - Watches - Webster Watch Co. Associates
GIA - Apparel–women's - E. Greenwald & Sons Inc.
GIA LENS - Lenses–optical - American Polylite, Inc.
GIACCA - Apparel–children's - Young Gallery Ltd.
GIACOBAZZI - Fruit drinks–bottled or canned - American Marketing Team
GIALLI - Pasta ☆ - Dean & Deluca Inc.
GIAM BELLI - Apparel and accessories - Damon Creations Inc.
GIAN CARLO LAMBERTI - Apparel–men's - D & L, Inc.
GIAN FRANCO LOTTI - Apparel and accessories ☆ - Italian Classics Inc.
GIAN MARIO - Neckties ☆ - Carl Neckwear Co. Inc.
GIAN-SCALA - Accordions ☆ - Petosa Accordions Inc.
GIANA - Jewelry - Jojak, Inc.
GIANCARLO IMPIGLIA STUDIO - Posters - Giancarlo Impiglia Studio
GIANCARLO ROMANO - Jewelry - Tuxacco, Inc.
GIANDUIA - Chocolate candy - Perugina Chocolate & Confections Inc.
GIANDUJOT - Confections - Ferrero U.S.A Inc.
GIANELLI - Apparel and accessories - Neema Clothing, Ltd.
GIANELLI - Sausages - G. & L. Davis Meat Co.

GIANFRANCO FERRE - Apparel–women's - Ultimo
GIANFRANCO FERRE - Colognes - Gary Farn Ltd.
GIANFRANCO FERRE - Scarves - Jerry Kohn Inc.
GIANFRANCO FERRE LUNETTES - Sunglasses - Solargenics
GIANFRANCO RUFFINI - Apparel–athletic - Ruffini Sportswear
GIANFRANCO RUFFINI ITALY - Apparel and accessories - Gianfranco Ruffini
GIANNA - Apparel–women's - Gianna Inc.
GIANNA ROSE - Housewares - Gianna Rose
GIANNI - Apparel–women's - Gianni Sport Ltd.
GIANNI - Spaghetti sauces - Ventre Packing Co. Inc.
GIANNI BRAVO - Footwear - Gianni Bravo Inc.
GIANNI GAGLIANDO - Wines - Tyfield Importers
GIANNI MANZONI - Apparel–men's - Alpetora Imports Inc.
GIANNI VERSACE - Floor coverings–tile - Finetex Co. Inc.
GIANNI VERSACE - Hosiery - Kartex International Cos. Inc.
GIANNINA - Coffee makers–electric - Zyliss USA Inc.
GIANNIZZERRA MCDLIII GRUPPO OTTOMANO - Apparel and accessories - Gruppo Ottomano, Ltd.
GIANNONE - Pasta - Giannone Products
GIANOLA - Food products - Sara Lee Corp.
GIANPINI - Watches - GianPini Inc.
GIANPINI G - Pens–fountain - GianPini Inc.
GIANT - Bait - Siberian Salmon Egg Co.
GIANT - Bicycles - Giant Bicycle, Inc.
GIANT - Brushes - Corona Brushes Inc.
GIANT - Fruit drinks–bottled or canned - Golden Gem Growers Inc.
GIANT - Games - Scramb-L-Gram, Inc.
GIANT - Gasoline - Giant Industries Inc.
GIANT - Greeting cards - Gibson Greetings, Inc.
GIANT - Hardware - Tel-O-Post Co.
GIANT - Ice chests–plastic - Igloo Products Corp.
GIANT - Meats–luncheon - Circle K Corp.
GIANT - Pencil sharpeners - Empire Berol USA
GIANT - Propylene ☆ - Coleman Co., Inc.
GIANT - Recording label - Benson Music Group
GIANT - Shoes - Sam Brilliant Sporto
GIANT - Sporting goods - Weber Industries Inc.
GIANT - Staplers - ACCO USA, Inc.
GIANT - Tires ☆ - Cooper Tire & Rubber Co.
GIANT AMAZING BUBBLE GUM THING - Confections - Steve's Homemade Ice Cream Inc.
GIANT AMAZING COOKIE THING - Confections - Steve's Homemade Ice Cream Inc.
GIANT AMAZING CRUNCH THING - Confections - Steve's Homemade Ice Cream Inc.
GIANT BANQUET - Pet products - Aquatrol, Inc.
GIANT BARREL OF MONKEYS - Games - Lakeside Games
GIANT BITES - Ice cream - Nestle USA
GIANT BLOCKS - Toys–blocks ☆ - Little Tikes Co.
GIANT BOOK, THE - Photo albums ☆ - Esselte Corp.
GIANT BUG DEMON - Squeegees - Laitner Brush Co.
GIANT BUMPKIN FACE - Candy - R.M. Palmer Co.
GIANT CAESAR - Food products - Little Caesar Enterprises, Inc.
GIANT CANES - Candy - Bobs Candies Inc.
GIANT COOTIE - Games ☆ - Milton Bradley Co.
GIANT CRUNCHY - Food products ☆ - Pro-Portion Industries
GIANT DANDY - Paper clips - Noesting Inc.
GIANT DESTROYER, THE - Rodenticide - Atlas Chemical Corp.
GIANT EAGLE - Publisher's imprints - Giant Eagle, Inc. (By Itself and Through Related Companies)
GIANT FOOTSTEPS - Playground equipment - Wonderline
GIANT GEM - Paper clips - Noesting Inc.
GIANT GRILLERS - Seafood products–fresh or frozen - Minn-Con Marketing
GIANT GYRO - Gyroscopes - Steven Manufacturing Co.
GIANT HARVESTER - Food products - Nation's Foodservice, Inc.
GIANT IMAGES - Advertising balloons - Giant Images International, Inc.
GIANT JEAN - Apparel and accessories - J. Crew Inc.
GIANT JR. - Greeting cards - Gibson Greetings, Inc.
GIANT KILLER - Apparel and accessories - Giant Killer, Inc.
GIANT KILLER - Fishing lures - Sheldons', Inc.
GIANT MARCEL - Paper clips - Noesting Inc.
GIANT NOW AND LATER - Candy - Phoenix Confections Inc.
GIANT OLD MAID - Games - Warren Industries Inc.
GIANT OOGIES - Confections - Boomer's Oogies
GIANT PIXY STIX - Candy - Sunline Brands
GIANT PURITAN GEM - Crochet thread ☆ - Susan Bates Inc.

GIANT RECORDS - Recording label ☆ - Zondervan Publishing House

GIANT RIP-OFF - Carpet- and tile-removal equipment - Inventive Manufacturing

GIANT ROCK-A-STACK - Toys - Fisher-Price, Inc.

GIANT S-O - Binders ☆ - Stationers Loose Leaf Co.

GIANT SAUCER-TOSSER - Toys - Concept Products Inc.

GIANT SONIC ROBOT - Toys - Mike's Train House, Inc.

GIANT STEP - Fertilizers - Doggett Corp.

GIANT SWEET - Onions - Fort Boise Produce Co.

GIANT TANDEM - Fishing lures - Lindy Little Joe Inc.

GIANT TINKLE CRINKLE - Toys–stuffed - Gund, Inc.

GIANT TWISTS - Candy - Swizzels Matlow (USA) Ltd.

GIANT TWIZZLERS - Licorice - Y & S Candies Inc.

GIANT WORLD - Computer software ☆ - Gessler Publishing Co., Inc.

GIANTARTS - Candy - Sunline Brands

GIANTS - Games - Mayfair Games, Inc.

GIARDANI - Footwear - Mystic Corp.

GIARDINELLI - Brass products - American Music Group Ltd.

GIARDINELLI - Musical instruments - Giardinelli Band Instrument Co.

GIARDINI DI MONTECATINI - Perfumes - Revlon Consumer Products Corp.

GIARDINO - Dishes–china - Pasmantier Co. Inc.

GIARDINO FRESCO - Food products - Williamsburg Canning Co.

GIARROUSSO - Apparel and accessories ☆ - Edison Brothers Stores, Inc.

GIASOL - Pharmaceutical preparations ☆ - Ulmer Pharmacal Co.

GIB-U-LANT - Flowers, plants, and seeds - Mylen Co.

GIBAL - Footwear - Footlinks/CEJ Corp.

GIBALTER-TELESCOPE MOUNT - Telescopes - Tele Vue Optics Inc.

GIBB - Ships–sailing vessels - Gibb Yachting Equipment Co.

GIBBEX - Measuring instruments - Griffin Corp.

GIBBONS - Beverages–malt - Lion Brewery, Inc.

GIBBS - Computer software - Gibbs System Inc.

GIBBS - Gasoline - Glen-mor Oil

GIBBS - Post hole diggers–hand-operated - Seymour Manufacturing Co.,Inc.

GIBBS - Preserved foods–canned - Hanover Foods Corp.

GIBBS - Stools–wood - Gibbs Manufacturing Co.

GIBBS SYSTEM, THE - Computer software - Gibbs System Inc.

GIBCLOSER - Pet products - Reilor Inc.

GIBCO AROMATIC CEDAR - Lumber - Gibco Services Inc.

GIBCO BRL - Laboratory apparatus - Life Technologies, Inc.

GIBECK - Medical apparatus - Gibeck, Inc.

GIBEX - Recording label - Jazz Composer's Orchestra Association Inc.

GIBOR - Thread ☆ - Soltex International Inc.

GIBRALTAR - Clocks - General Time Corp. (Westclox/Seth Thomas Div.)

GIBRALTAR - Concrete products - Gibraltar National Corp.

GIBRALTAR - Counter tops–plastic - Ralph Wilson Plastics Co.

GIBRALTAR - Drums–musical instruments - Kaman Music Corp.

GIBRALTAR - Easels - Art Supply & Instrument Co.

GIBRALTAR - Fabrics - Gretchen Bellinger Inc.

GIBRALTAR - Fabrics - Greenwood Mills Inc.

GIBRALTAR - Floor coverings - Mannington Resilient Floors

GIBRALTAR - Floor coverings–carpet and rugs - Coronet Carpets Inc.

GIBRALTAR - Floor coverings–carpet and rugs - Couristan Inc.

GIBRALTAR - Floor coverings–carpet and rugs ☆ - Blue Ridge Carpet Mills

GIBRALTAR - Floor coverings–carpet and rugs ☆ - Robertex Associates Inc.

GIBRALTAR - Flour–blended - Stevens Industries Inc.

GIBRALTAR - Furniture - Koning Machine and Tool Co.

GIBRALTAR - Furniture–public buildings ☆ - Fleetwood Furniture Co.

GIBRALTAR - Microscopes - Burleigh Instruments, Inc.

GIBRALTAR II - Fabrics–twill - Greenwood Mills Inc.

GIBRALTAR III - Floor coverings–carpet and rugs ☆ - Heuga USA

GIBRALTER - Floor coverings–carpet and rugs ☆ - Kelly Group Inc.

GIBRALTER - Glassware–household - Owens-Illinois Inc. (Libbey Div.)

GIBRALTER - Musical instrument accessories - C. Bruno & Son Inc.

GIBRALTER - Safes - Meilink Safe Co.

GIBRALTER - Shelving units–metal - Hirsh Co.

GIBRALTER - Wallpaper ☆ - Wall-Pride Inc.

GIBRALTER - Watches - Hampden Corp.

GIBSON - Books–blank - C.R. Gibson Co.

GIBSON - Greeting cards - Gibson Greetings, Inc.

GIBSON - Musical instrument accessories - Gibson Strings & Accessories

GIBSON - Refrigerators - White Consolidated Industries, Inc.

GIBSON - Ships - Gibson Fiberglass Products Inc.

GIBSON - Sinks–metal - Kohler Co.

GIBSON - Vegetables–canned - Kent Canning Co.

GIBSON - Wines - Gibson Wine Co.

GIBSON GIRL - Dolls ☆ - Effanbee Doll Corp.

GIBSON GIRL - Electronic equipment - Benjamin Electroproducts Inc. (Robins Div.)

GIBSON GIRLS - Posters - One-of-a-Kind Workshop

GIBSON HOLDERS - Easels - Gibson Holders, Inc.

GIBSON-HOMANS PRO'S CHOICE - Roofing materials - Gibson-Homans Co.

GIBSON HOUSEWARES - Housewares - Gibson Overseas Inc.

GIBSON MONA-STEEL - Musical instrument accessories - Gibson Strings & Accessories

GIBSON MUSICAL TIES - Neckties - Global Neckwear Marketing Inc.

GIBSON TUBE G - Tubes–steel - Gibson Tube, Inc.

GIBSON VINEYARDS - Wines - Gibson Wine Co.

GIBSON WHITE PHEASANT - Wines - Gibson Wine Co.

GIBSONBURG - Vegetables–canned - Gibsonburg Canning Co. Inc.

GIBSON'S GOURMET RANCH - Meat products–beef - Price Co.

GIDDY GATOR - Puppets - Dakin Inc.

GIDDY-UP - Toys - Denny Scopellite

GIDDYUP - Computer software - Adobe Systems Inc.

GIDDYUP - Toys - Mattel, Inc.

GIDDYUP THANGS - Computer software - Adobe Systems Inc.

GIDEBETA - Vitamins and nutritional supplements - Gides-NuLife Inc.

GIDEON - Apparel and accessories - Salant/Manhattan Industries

GIEN - Tableware–china ☆ - Rochard

GIESEE - Cosmetics - Giesee International

GIESELLMANN & WILLI - Chocolate candy - John Sommer Inc.

GIESEN - Cosmetics - Morris-Flamingo Inc.

GIEVES & HAWKES - Apparel–men's - Hartmarx Corp.

GIFFORD'S - Ice cream - Gifford's Famous Ice Cream

GIFT - Recording label - Track America

GIFT BEAR-ER - Toys–stuffed - Trina, Inc.

GIFT CREATIONS - Jewelry - Gift Creations, Inc.

GIFT-DESIGN - Giftware - Drybranch Inc./Sport Design

GIFT FOR YOU, A - Flowers, plants, and seeds - Plant Promotions, Inc.

GIFT FROM THE AGES, A - Vitamins and nutritional supplements - Benchmark USA, Inc.

GIFT FROM THE ENVIRONMENT, A - Paper–gift wrap - Earthelp Inc.

GIFT GIVING - Dolls - Mattel, Inc.

GIFT GREETERS - Paper mills - Olivia Mullin

GIFT HUGGERS - Toys–stuffed - Princess Soft Toys

GIFT IN A BALLOON - Novelty items - Classy Wrap

GIFT MAKER - Computer software - Austin-Brett, Inc.

GIFT MATES - Paper–gift wrap - Sangamon Co.

GIFT MATES - Towels - Stevens Linen Associates Inc.

GIFT-N-GREETING - Greeting cards - Arnold S. Silling

GIFT 'N GREETING - Novelty items - Franklin Mint

GIFT 'N' GREETING - Paper–gift wrap - Norcross Inc.

GIFT OF BRAN - Oils–edible - Select Origins Inc.

GIFT OF CREATION, A - Bottled spring water - Gentleman Jim's, Inc.

GIFT OF GOLD - Candy - McDonald Candy Co. Inc.

GIFT OF LIFE - Skin care products - Para Laboratories Inc.

GIFT OF LIFE ENZYMES, THE - Vitamins and nutritional supplements - Kristopher Vanoeveren

GIFT OF NATURE - Food products - Mitsui Foods Inc.

GIFT OF THE MAGI - Candles - Empire Manufacturing Co.

GIFT OF THE SEA - Food products - Mitsui & Co. Inc.

GIFT OF THE THREE WISE MEN - Soap ☆ - Carolina Designs Ltd.

GIFT OF TIME, A - Greeting cards - M.S. Strong, LLC

GIFT REGALOS - Furniture ☆ - J. Kenneth Zahn

GIFT SHIRTIFICATE - Forms–preprinted - Color My World, Inc.

GIFT SLEEVES - Paper–gift wrap - Annette Austin

GIFT TOTE - Spices and extracts - Jodie's Kitchen Inc.

GIFT WARES - Hobby kits - Janlynn Corp.

GIFT WRAP EXPRESS - Bags–plastic - Kellock Co. Inc.

GIFT WRAPPED HEART, THE - Jewelry - Stuller Settings, Inc.

GIFTABLES - Jewelry - Jacmel Jewelry Inc.

GIFTABLES - Jewelry - Tubular Steel Inc.

GIFTCO - Housewares - Giftco Inc.

GIFTEA - Teas - Chinese Native Products

GIFTED - Toys - Friday Saturday Sunday, Inc.

GIFTED & TALENTED - Publisher's imprints - Lowell House

GIFTED BAGS - Paper–gift wrap - The Gifted Line

GIFTED BOXES - Boxes - The Gifted Line

GIFTED CARDS - Greeting cards - The Gifted Line

GIFTED GREETINGS - Giftware ☆ - Enesco Corp.

GIFTED LINE, THE - Apparel and accessories - The Gifted Line

GIFTED PORTFOLIOS - File folders - The Gifted Line

GIFTED STICKERS - Stationery - The Gifted Line

☆ = Now out of production

GIFTED TAGS - Paper–gift wrap ☆ - The Gifted Line
GIFTED WRAP - Paper–gift wrap - The Gifted Line
GIFTEES - Flowers, plants, and seeds - Better World Enterprises, Inc.
GIFTGO - Recording label - Charles L. Cleek
GIFTING - Giftware - L.E. Smith Glass Co.
GIFTINS - Containers–plastic - Pacad, Inc.
GIFTIQUE - Bath product, shampoo, fragrances, etc. - Cosrich Inc.
GIFTMARKS - Giftware ☆ - Quality Artworks Inc.
GIFTPRINTS - Posters - Kimball Concepts Ltd.
GIFTS BY SERAD - Ice buckets - Shelton-Ware Corp.
GIFTS FOR THE BODY - Confections - Devine Foods, Inc.
GIFTS FROM THE SEA - Novelty items - RDE Imports
GIFTS FROM THE SEA - Seafood products–fresh or frozen - Lobsters Inc.
GIFTS OF THE MAGI, THE - Incense - Bayou Blending Co., Inc.
GIFTS OF THE SPIRIT - Greeting cards - Hallmark Cards Inc.
GIFTWARE SUITE - Crystal giftware - Swarovski Retail Management Inc.
GIFTWOOD - Furniture–wood - Hansen Industries Inc. (Nevco Div.)
GIFTWORKS CHRONICLE BOOKS - Publisher's imprints - Chronicle Publishing Co.
GIFTWRAP COMPANY OF AMERICA, THE - Paper–gift wrap - Gift Wrap Co.
GIFTWRAPS BY ARTISTS - Paper–gift wrap - Harry N. Abrams Inc.
GIG - Musical instrument accessories - Meisel Music Inc.
GIGA-ROM - Computer storage devices–optical - Quantum Leap Technologies, Inc.
GIGABAND - Electronic circuits - Applied Micro Circuits Corp.
GIGACUBE - Computers - Microway, Inc.
GIGAFRAME - Computer hardware - Fibronics International, Inc.
GIGAHUB - Computer hardware - Fibronics International, Inc.
GIGANTIC - Ice chests–plastic - Coleman Co., Inc.
GIGANTISAUR - Toys - Mattel, Inc.
GIGANTOR - Games - Creatif Licensing Corp.
GIGANTOR - Video production - Entercolor Technologies Corp.
GIGAROUTER - Computer peripheral equipment - Netstar, Inc.
GIGASTAR - Computer software - Gigalabs, Inc.
GIGASWITCH - Computer peripheral equipment - Digital Equipment Corp.
GIGAVIEW - Computer software - Gigalabs, Inc.
GIGBAGS - Cases–musical instrument ☆ - Dimarzio, Inc.
GIGETTE INC. - Apparel–women's - Elias Sayour Co.
GIGEX - Electronic equipment - V-Cast, Inc.
GIGGLE - Chewing gum - Fleer Corp.
GIGGLE - Decals and transfers ☆ - Creative Expressions Group
GIGGLE BUNNY - Novelty items - Those Characters from Cleveland, Inc.
GIGGLE E. BEAR - Toys - Fran Goldman Associates, Inc.
GIGGLE GOLF - Golfing equipment - Golfsmith International Inc.
GIGGLE HEADS - Costumes - Paper Magic Group Inc.
GIGGLE-OO - Playground equipment - Wonderline
GIGGLE POPS - Desserts - Crowley Frozen Desserts Inc.
GIGGLE WIGGLE - Games - Milton Bradley Co.
GIGGLEBONE GANG - Computer software - Headbone Interactive, Inc.
GIGGLES - Cookies - Nabisco Foods Group
GIGGLES - Diapers–disposable - Weyerhaeuser Co.
GIGGLES - Dolls - Russ Berrie and Co., Inc.
GIGGLES - Dolls - Well-Made Toy Manufacturing Corp.
GIGGLES - Wallpaper - Frankford Wallcoverings Inc.
GIGGLES AND KISSES - Dolls - Tyco Toys
GIGGLES 'N BOWS - Dolls - Mattel, Inc.
GIGGLES TO GO - Greeting cards - Current, Inc.
GIGGL'IN GRAPE - Chewing gum - Fleer Corp.
GIGI - Animal feeds - Bush Brothers and Co.
GIGI - Computer software - Digital Equipment Corp.
GIGI - Dinnerware–glass - Metlox Pottery Shoppe
GIGI - Dolls ☆ - Effanbee Doll Corp.
GIGI - Frames–eyeglass - Rozin Optical Export Corp.
GIGI - Hair care products - American International Industries
GIGI - Housewares - Clinton Manufacturing
GIGI - Skin care products - Gigi Laboratories
GIGI - Underwear and nightwear - Bestform Foundations, Inc.
GIGLIO ROSSO - Apparel and accessories - Raphael Shaya
GIGPACS - Cases–musical instrument - Deg Music Products Inc.
GIL-BILT - Woodworking machinery - Gilliom Manufacturing Co.
GIL-GLO - Adhesives and sealants - Missouri Paint & Varnish Co.
GIL-GUARD - Paints - Gilman Co. Inc.
GIL-KOTE - Paints - Gilman Co. Inc.
GIL-LAC - Paints - Gilman Co. Inc.
GIL MARINE - Engines–marine - Ohio Associated Enterprises, Inc.
GIL-POXY - Paints - Gilman Co. Inc.

GIL-SAND - Adhesives and sealants - Gilman Co. Inc.
GIL-SOLV - Paints - Gilman Co. Inc.
GIL-SPAK - Paints - Gilman Co. Inc.
GIL-STRIP - Paints - Gilman Co. Inc.
GIL-THANE - Paints - Gilman Co. Inc.
GIL-TREAD - Paints - Gilman Co. Inc.
GILA-DUCT - Electrical equipment - Tamaqua Cable Products Corp.
GILA-GRAPHICS - Auto supply stores ☆ - Courtaulds Performance Plus
GILA MONSTER - Beverages–malt - Trader Joe's Co.
GILA MONSTER - Toys–automobiles - Tonka Corp.
GILA RIVER - See **SUNSHINE**
GILARDI CLASSICS - Food products - A.M. Gilardi and Sons, Inc.
GILARDI'S - Food products - A.M. Gilardi and Sons, Inc.
GILARDI'S FOCACIA - Food products - A.M. Gilardi and Sons, Inc.
GILBERT - Hosiery–men's - S.L. Gilbert Co.
GILBERT - Paper–writing - Gilbert Paper Co.
GILBERT - Toys–stuffed - CBS Toys
GILBERT & CLARK - Publisher's imprints - Amereon Ltd.
GILBERT & MILLER - Pens - Perfect Pen Corp.
GILBERT DAYMAKER - Lighting fixtures - Hubbell Lighting, Inc. (Lighting Div.)
GILBERT ORCHARDS - Food products - Gilbert Orchards Inc.
GILBERT TWIN BEAM DROP - Lighting fixtures - Hubbell Lighting, Inc. (Lighting Div.)
GILBERTIE'S - Deodorizers - Gilbertie's Herb Gardens, Inc.
GILBERT'S - Beverages–alcohol - M.S. Walker Inc./Seacoast
GILBERT'S - Giftware ☆ - Gilbert Stone Enterprises Inc.
GILBEY'S - Beverages–alcohol - Jim Beam Brands Co.
GILBEY'S LACOUR PAVILLON - Wines ☆ - Dreyfus Ashby Inc.
GILCA - Cheese - Fromark
GILCHRIST & SOAMES - Toiletries - Gilchrist & Soames
GILCLEAR - Paper - Gilbert Paper Co.
GILCO - Novelty items - E.R. Gilligan Chain Co.
GILCOLITE - Chains - E.R. Gilligan Chain Co.
GILCOR - Display unit parts - Giltspur Inc.
GILCREST LAID - Paper–writing - Gilbert Paper Co.
GILD-IT - Waxes–mineral - Floquil-Polly S Color Corp.
GILDA - Crackers - Fancy Foods of Virginia Inc.
GILDA - Watches - Bulova Corp.
GILDA MARX - Apparel and accessories - Gilda Marx Inc.
GILDA MARX SPORT - Apparel–athletic - Gilda Marx Inc.
GILDED CAGE - Wallpaper ☆ - Winfield Design Associates, Inc.
GILDED CLASSICS - Wallpaper - J. Josephson, Inc.
GILDED COLLECTION - Cosmetics - Max Factor & Co.
GILDED TRELLIS SERIES, THE - Furniture - BBA Holdings
GILDMORE - Artists' materials ☆ - M. Grumbacher Inc.
GILES - Cooking equipment–commercial - Giles Enterprises, Inc.
GILFORD - Sinks–metal - Kohler Co.
GILFRANCO - Cigars - Gilfranco Cigar Co.
GILI - Publisher's imprints - Rizzoli International Publications Inc.
GILKA KUMMEL - Beverages–alcohol - Sidney Frank Importing Co., Inc.
GILL - Musical instruments - Barclay Music
GILLCORE - Motor vehicle parts and accessories - M.C. Gill Corp.
GILLES - Yogurt–frozen - Gilles Frozen Custard
GILLES GOURMET - Yogurt–frozen - Gilles Frozen Custard
GILLESPIE - Fans–electric - Fasco Industries Inc. (Consumer Products Div.)
GILLESPIE - Varnishes - Klean-Strip
GILLESPIE CLEAN & WAX YOUR WOOD FLOORS - Floor waxes - Klean-Strip
GILLESPIE CLEAN YOUR WOOD FLOORS - Floor waxes - Klean-Strip
GILLETTE - Apparel and accessories - Sandra Gillette
GILLETTE - Milk - Gillette Dairy
GILLETTE - Pens - Gillette Co.
GILLETTE - Tires ☆ - Uniroyal Goodrich Tire Co.
GILLETTE FOAMY - Shaving preparations - Gillette Co.
GILLETTE SENSOR SPORT - Shaving preparations - Gillette Co.
GILLETTE SERIES - Shaving preparations - Gillette Co.
GILLETTO - Frozen desserts - Nebraska Dairies, Inc.
GILLEY'S - Apparel and accessories - Mickey Gilley Interests, Inc.
GILLI-YUMS - Candy - Gilliam Candy Co. Inc. (Gilliam Candy Brands)
GILLIAM - Candy - Gilliam Candy Brands
GILLIAN - Apparel - St. Gillian Sportswear Ltd.
GILLIAN - Apparel–women's - Zachar Ltd.
GILLIAN - Toys - Mattel, Inc.
GILLIARD - Wines - Dreyfus Ashby Inc.
GILLIES - Apparel and accessories - McCrory Corp.
GILLIES - Coffee - Gillies Coffee Co.

GILLIGAN & O'MALLEY - Apparel–men's - Craftex Creations Inc.
GILLINDER - Glass products - Gillinder Brothers Inc.
GILLMANIA - Greeting cards - American Greetings Corp.
GILLNETTER'S DELIGHT - Wines - Shallon Winery
GILLNETTERSBEST - Salmon–smoked, salted, dried, or pickled - Peter Pan Seafoods, Inc.
GILLOCK - Publisher's imprints - Willis Music Co.
GILL'S - Coffee - James G. Gill Co. Inc.
GILL'S GOLDEN BLEND - Coffee - James G. Gill Co. Inc.
GILL'S HOTEL SPECIAL - Coffee - James G. Gill Co. Inc.
GILLS ONIONS WHOLE PEELED DICED - Onions - Gills Onions
GILL'S RED BAG - Coffee - James G. Gill Co. Inc.
GILLY - Toys–stuffed - Russ Berrie and Co., Inc.
GILLYGALOO NOOK AND CRANNY - Food products - Spank Products
GILMAN - Paints - Gilman Co. Inc.
GILMORE - Popcorn - Moran Foods, Inc.
GILMOUR - Tools–garden - Gilmour Manufacturing Co.
GILPA - Pet products - Gilpa
GILPLEX - Paints - Gilman Co. Inc.
GILROY - Food products - Gilroy Foods Inc.
GILROY - Wines - Thomas Kruse Winery
GILROY FARMS - Food products - McCormick & Co., Inc.
GILROY FARMS - Seasonings - Mojave Foods Corp.
GILROY FOODS - Spices and seasonings - Gilroy Foods Inc.
GILROY GARLIC FESTIVAL - Publisher's imprints - Gilroy Garlic Festival Association, Inc.
GILSALUME - Paints ☆ - United Gilsonite Laboratories
GILSDORF - Health care products - Entech Inc./Enteral Technology
GILSON - Garden equipment ☆ - Lawn-Boy
GILT EDGE - Dairy products - Gilt Edge Farms Inc.
GILT EDGE - Jewelry ☆ - Hirsch Speidel Inc.
GILT EDGE - Paints - United Hardware
GILWAY - Sugar–granulated, refined, or powdered - Gilway Co. Ltd.
GIMBALS FRUIT LOWCOOM - Candy ☆ - Gimbel Brothers Inc.
GIMBEL - Window coverings - Vertical Blind Factory
GIMBELINE - Window coverings - J. Gimbel Inc.
GIMBELS - Mattresses - Gimbel Brothers Inc.
GIMBORN - Pet products - Gimborn U.S., Inc.
GIMINI - Cameras - Eastman Kodak Co.
GIMIX - Computers–personal - Gimix Inc.
GIMLET - Sinks–metal - Kohler Co.
GIMME - Golfing equipment - Tru-Line Usa, Inc.
GIMME - Hair care products - Helene Curtis Industries Inc.
GIMME 5 - Game machines - Bally Gaming International, Inc.
GIMME 5 - Games - Tyco Toys
GIMME A BREAK - Video game - Bally Sente Inc.
GIMME BODY - Hair care products - Helene Curtis Industries Inc.
GIMME CURL - Hair care products - Helene Curtis Industries Inc.
GIMME DAT - Apparel and accessories - Gimme Dat
GIMME FIVE - Hosiery–women's ☆ - Fischer Hosiery Co.
GIMME FIVE - Jewelry - Sunstone Imports, Inc.
GIMME GIMME GUMM GANG - Chewing gum - Anthony Schirripa
GIMME LEAN - Food products - Lightlife Foods, Inc.
GIMMICK - Apparel–men's - Montgomery Ward & Co. Inc.
GIMMIE D'CRICKET - Live-bait container - Ideal Manufacturing Inc.
GIMP - Pharmaceutical preparations - Link Chemical Co.
GIN - Health care products - Medical Molding Corp. of America
GIN-ACTION - Vitamins and nutritional supplements - Action Labs, Inc.
GIN BLOSSOMS - Posters - Gin Blossoms Partnership
GIN-CHIA - Vitamins and nutritional supplements - Aloe Vera of America, Inc.
GIN-GARL - Vitamins and nutritional supplements - Action Labs, Inc.
GIN KING - Computer software - Software Toolworks, Inc.
GIN RUMMY - Computer software - Manhattan Software
GIN-ZING - Vitamins and nutritional supplements - Leiner Health Products Inc.
GINA - Computer software - California State University Institute
GINA - Floor coverings–carpet and rugs ☆ - Regal Rugs Inc.
GINA - Shoes–athletic - Coast Shoes Inc.
GINA FARRO - Apparel–athletic - Pierre Cardin Electronique
GINA GABRIEL - Coats - Ronlee Apparel Co.
GINA LINA'S - Meat products–beef - Quaker Maid Meats Inc.
GINA MARIE - Cheese ☆ - Leprino Foods
GINA PETERS - Apparel and accessories - Kellwood Co.
GINA PETERS AND DESIGN - Apparel and accessories - Kellwood Co.
GINA PETERS SPORT AND DESIGN - Apparel and accessories - Kellwood Co.
GINA SOFTOYS - Toys–stuffed - C & H Toy of America, Inc.

GINCOR - Aquariums–household - Ginger, Inc.
GINERGY SUPPLEMENT - Vitamins and nutritional supplements - Basic Organics, Inc.
GINGA PLEX - Vitamins and nutritional supplements - Natural Organics, Inc.
GINGAFILL - Dental compounds - Cosmedent, Inc.
GINGER - Bathroom accessories - Gusa
GINGER - Dinnerware ☆ - Corning Inc.
GINGER - Dolls - Mattel, Inc.
GINGER - Pet products - Ginger, Inc.
GINGER - Toys–stuffed ☆ - Gund, Inc.
GINGER - Wigs ☆ - Paula Young
GINGER AID - Teas–herbal - Traditional Medicinals, Inc.
GINGER COOLER - Juices ☆ - Knudsen & Sons Inc.
GINGER EXTRACT - Vitamins and nutritional supplements - Vitamin Research Products Inc.
GINGER GOLD - Trees - Adams County Nursery Inc.
GINGER GRAHAMS - Cereal - New Morn, Inc.
GINGER KIDS - Bakery products - Ginger Kids, Inc.
GINGER KRISPY - Candy - See's Candy Shops, Inc.
GINGER PEACHY - Hair- and skin-care products, fragrance, etc. - Benjamin Ansehl Co.
GINGER PEAR - Teas - Eastern Shore Tea Co.
GINGER PINEAPPLE CHUTNEY - Seasonings - Cinnabar Specialty Foods, Inc./Neera's Products
GINGER PUPPY - Toys–stuffed - Russ Berrie and Co., Inc.
GINGER ROOT - Shampoos - S.C. Johnson & Son, Inc.
GINGER ROSE - Cosmetics - Lancome
GINGER/SPICE/CURRY - Spices and extracts - To Market to Market
GINGER THE CAT - Computer software - SourceView Software International
GINGER TREE III - Wallpaper ☆ - Ginger Tree Designs
GINGER TREE IV - Wallpaper ☆ - Ginger Tree Designs
GINGER TWIST - Soap - Crabtree & Evelyn, Ltd.
GINGER TWIST - Teas - Lipton Investments, Inc.
GINGER WONDER SYRUP - Syrup - New Moon Extracts, Inc.
GINGER ZAPS - Cookies ☆ - Nanak's Gourmet Cookies
GINGERAFFE - Toys–stuffed ☆ - Gund, Inc.
GINGERAID - Vitamins and nutritional supplements - Enzymatic Therapy, Inc.
GINGERALL - Vitamins and nutritional supplements - Enzymatic Therapy, Inc.
GINGERBREAD - Wallpaper ☆ - Ginger Tree Designs
GINGERBREAD COLLECTION, THE - Christmas tree ornaments - Lawton Nutrition Services, Inc.
GINGERBREAD CONSTRUCTION CO., THE - Cookies - Gingerbread Construction Co. Inc.
GINGERBREAD FAMILY, THE - Jewelry - Julia Diller
GINGERBREAD MAN - Games ☆ - Milton Bradley Co.
GINGERBREAD MEN - Ice cream - Steve's Homemade Ice Cream Inc.
GINGERED HONEY - Lipsticks - Estee Lauder Inc.
GINGERKIDS - Doughnuts–mixes - Country Home Creations, Inc.
GINGERLY - Lipsticks ☆ - Honey & Spice Toiletries
GINGERMAN - Teas - Eastern Shore Tea Co.
GINGETTE - Apparel–women's - Hooper Associates Ltd.
GINGHAM - Dinnerware–glass ☆ - Nikko Ceramics Inc.
GINGHAM - Floor coverings–carpet and rugs ☆ - Regal Rugs Inc.
GINGHAM - Food products - Certified Grocers of California, Ltd.
GINGHAM - Infant product ☆ - Edison Industries Inc.
GINGHAM - Soap - Bath & Body Works, Inc.
GINGHAM GIRL - Flour–blended - ADM Milling Co.
GINGHAM GOOSE - Craft supplies ☆ - VIP/VIP Crafts
GINGHAM TIME - Clocks - General Time Corp. (Westclox/Seth Thomas Div.)
GINGI-CARE - Mouthwashes - Peri-Oral Dental Products, Inc.
GINGIKNIT - Dental equipment - Van R Dental Products Corp.
GINGINKGO - Vitamins and nutritional supplements - Botalia
GINGISS - Tuxedo rental shops - Gingiss International Inc.
GINGKO 1000 - Food products - Laci Le Beau Corp.
GINGKO-GO! - Vitamins and nutritional supplements - Kyolic/Wakunaga
GINGKO-GO - Vitamins and nutritional supplements - Wakunaga of America Co., Ltd.
GINGKO TREE - Wallpaper ☆ - Textile Wallcoverings International Ltd.
GINI - Computer software - Donald T. Knight
GINJIKOMI - Beverages–malt ☆ - Sapporo USA Inc.
GINJO KABAYABURI - Beverages–malt ☆ - Suntory International Corp.
GINK-O 100 - Vitamins and nutritional supplements - Barth's Nutra Products
GINKAI - Vitamins and nutritional supplements - Lichtwer Pharma U.S., Inc.
GINKALERT - Vitamins and nutritional supplements - Solaray
GINKGO - Pharmaceutical preparations - Mericon Industries Inc.
GINKGO-24 - Vitamins and nutritional supplements - Source Naturals

☆ = Now out of production

GINKGO BILOBA - Health care products - Above All Health Inc.

GINKGO BILOBA - Vitamins and nutritional supplements - Natrol, Inc.

GINKGO BILOBA - Vitamins and nutritional supplements - Reese Chemical Co.

GINKGO BILOBA EXTRACT - Vitamins and nutritional supplements - Vitamin Research Products Inc.

GINKGO BOOSTER - Vitamins and nutritional supplements - United Vitamin Manufacturing Corp.

GINKGO-COMBO - Health care products - Nature's Plus

GINKGO MIND - Vitamins and nutritional supplements - Evan Nutraceuticals, Inc.

GINKGO PLUS - Dietary supplements - Key Products Co.

GINKGOLD - Vitamins and nutritional supplements - Nature's Way Products, Inc.

GINKGOVIT - Vitamins and nutritional supplements - Rueckert Pharmaceutical Co.

GINKO BILOBA PLUS - Vitamins and nutritional supplements - Action Labs, Inc.

GINKOLA - Vitamins and nutritional supplements - Vitamin Classics, Inc.

GINKOS - Cereal - New Morn, Inc.

GINNIE JOHANSEN - Apparel and accessories - Ginnie Johansen Designs Inc.

GINNIE LOU - Hairpins - Sta-Rite Ginnie Lou Inc.

GINNY - Dolls - Dakin Inc.

GINNY - Dolls - Vogue Doll Co., Inc.

GINNY - Dolls - The Vogue Doll Co., Inc.

GINNY - Sponges - Delby System

GINNY BABY - Dolls - Vogue Dolls Inc.

GINNY DEER - Sponges - Delby System

GINNY FROM FAR-AWAY LANDS - Dolls - Vogue Dolls Inc.

GINNY THE PRETTY WHITE DOE - Sponges - Delby System

GINNYKUB - Games ☆ - Pressman Toy Corp.

GINNY'S FARM - Glass products ☆ - United China and Glass Co.

GINO - Handbags - Etra Handbags Inc.

GINO CAPPELI - Apparel–men's - Nulook Fashions Menswear Inc.

GINO D - Shoes - Donato Marrone Ltd.

GINO DI BALTI - Apparel–men's - Wm. B. Kessler Inc.

GINO DI GIORGIO - Apparel and accessories - Comint Leather Goods Inc.

GINO FABRINI - Apparel and accessories - Wilk Shirt Corp.

GINO FAILLI - Vinegar ☆ - Liberty Richter Inc.

GINO FIRENZ - Socks - Sockyard Co. Inc.

GINO FRANCO - P. Peugeot/Viva Time

GINO FRANCO - Watches - Viva Time Corp.

GINO MANETTI - Jewelry–precious - H.K. Schaeffer & Co.

GINO MORGANTI - Footwear - E.F. Shoes, Inc.

GINO NICCI - Footwear–women's - Mariando International Inc.

GINO PAOLI - Apparel–men's - National Service Industries, Inc.

GINO PAOLI - Leather and sheep-lined clothing - Excelled Sheepskin Leather Inc.

GINO POLLI - Clocks - Hooty Enterprises

GINO POMPEII - Neckties ☆ - Randa Corp.

GINO ZANETTI - Handbags - American Angel Corp.

GINO'S - Pizzas–frozen - Avanti Foods Co.

GINO'S - Prepared sandwiches - J & J Food Service

GINO'S - Salad dressings–bottled - Gino's Restaurant & Lounge Inc.

GINOSAR - Health care products - AGAR USA Inc.

GINSA-MAX - Vitamins and nutritional supplements - Makers of Kal, Inc.

GINSAI - Vitamins and nutritional supplements - Lichtwer Pharma U.S., Inc.

GINSANA - Vitamins and nutritional supplements - Sunsource Health Products Inc.

GINSAVENA - Health care products ☆ - Bioforce of America Ltd.

GINSENG - Cigarettes - West Park Tobacco Inc.

GINSENG BLAST - Vitamins and nutritional supplements - CVC Specialties

GINSENG CHEWS - Candy - Herbal Home Products

GINSENG COOLER - Juices ☆ - Knudsen & Sons Inc.

GINSENG CRUNCH - Cereal - New Morn, Inc.

GINSENG D - Beverages–carbonated ☆ - Ginseng Up Corp.

GINSENG EXTRA - Beverages–carbonated - Ginseng Up Corp.

GINSENG EXTRACTS - Vitamins and nutritional supplements - Vitamin Research Products Inc.

GINSENG FRESH - Vitamins and nutritional supplements - Progenix Corp.

GINSENG PLUS - Teas–herbal - Celestial Seasonings, Inc.

GINSENG-POWER - Health care products ☆ - Nature's Herbs

GINSENG POWER+ - Teas - Satori Fine Herbals

GINSENG POWER MAX - Vitamins and nutritional supplements - Action Labs, Inc.

GINSENG RUSH - Soft drinks - Corr's Natural Beverages Inc.

GINSENG STRESS FORMULA - Health care products - Pacific BioLogic Inc.

GINSENG UP - Beverages–carbonated - Ginseng Up Corp.

GINSENGFRESH AMERICAN - Teas - Connex Enterprises Inc.

GINSENSE - Vitamins and nutritional supplements - Spectrum Wholesale International, Inc.

GINSEY CUSH 'N SOFT - Toilet seats ☆ - Ginsey Industries, Inc.

GINSTAMINA - Vitamins and nutritional supplements - Rexall Sundown, Inc.

GINSU - Cutlery - Douglas/Quikut

GINSU - Knives - Scott Fetzer Co.

GINSU CLASSIC - Knives - Scott Fetzer Co.

GINSU PROFESSIONAL - Knives - Scott Fetzer Co.

GINSUN - Vitamins and nutritional supplements - Nature's Way Products, Inc.

GINTEX - Chemical preparations - Cotton Conditioners Inc.

GINTY - Golfing equipment - Stan Thompson Golf Club Inc.

GINVY - Pharmaceutical preparations ☆ - L.T. York Co.

GINZA - Hair care products - Conair Corp.

GINZA - Steel springs–railroad - Needlecraft Industries

GINZA-PLUS - Vitamins and nutritional supplements - Irwin Naturals

GIO - Cosmetics ☆ - Cassidy Inc.

GIO - Jewelry - Giovanni Jewelry Co.

GIO - Perfumes - Cosmair Inc.

GIO ALBERTOLLI - Apparel–men's - Comtrade, Inc.

GIOCOMELLI PIZZA - Pizzas–frozen - Giocomelli Foods Inc.

GIOGIO CARNEVALE - Beverages–alcohol ☆ - Connolly & Co. Inc.

GIOIA - Pasta - Gioia Macaroni Co. Inc.

GIOIA LUISA - Liqueurs - Chris Payne International

GIOLLI - Belts, handbags, etc. - Bobtron International Inc.

GIONELLI - Liquors - United States Distilled Products Co.

GIORDAN SANTA CLAUS - Stationery - Giordano Art, Ltd.

GIORDANNO - Whirlpools - Lasco Products Group

GIORDANO - Footwear - Leo's Dancewear, Inc.

GIORDANO - Paper products - Giordano Art, Ltd.

GIORDANO - Watches - Invasion Time Corp.

GIORDANO OPTIKS - Eyeglasses - Continental Accessory Corp.

GIORDONNO - Footwear - Conjac Inc.

GIORGIO - Bags - Giorgio Beverly Hills, Inc.

GIORGIO - Colognes - Giorgio Beverly Hills

GIORGIO - Flatware - Wallace International Silversmiths, Inc.

GIORGIO - Mushrooms - Giorgio Foods Inc.

GIORGIO - Ophthalmic goods - Luxottica

GIORGIO - Wallpaper ☆ - Lawrence Wallcoverings

GIORGIO II - Wallpaper ☆ - Winfield Design Associates, Inc.

GIORGIO ARMANI - Colognes - Cosmair Inc.

GIORGIO ARMANI - Leather goods - Italian Classics Inc.

GIORGIO ARMANI OCCHIALI - Ophthalmic goods ☆ - Luxottica

GIORGIO BERNINI - Briefcases - Service Merchandise Co. Inc.

GIORGIO BEVERLY HILLS - Frames–eyeglass - Giorgio Beverly Hills

GIORGIO BEVERLY HILLS - Handbags - Giorgio Beverly Hills, Inc.

GIORGIO BEVERLY HILLS LITE NATURAL SPRAY - Perfumes - Procter & Gamble Co.

GIORGIO BOTTAZZI - Apparel–men's - James Edmond, Inc.

GIORGIO BRUTINI - Footwear–men's - Harbor Footwear Group Ltd.

GIORGIO CELLINI - Handbags - American Angel Corp.

GIORGIO DI MARCO - Frames–eyeglass - Ambassador Eyewear Group

GIORGIO MORANDI - Apparel and accessories - Giorgio Morandi, Inc.

GIORGIO RED - Colognes - Procter & Gamble Co.

GIORGIO VINCENTE - Frames–eyeglass - National Vision Associates, Ltd.

GIORGIO'S BEVERLY HILLS TAN - Suntan lotions - Giorgio Beverly Hills

GIORNO POETRY - Recording label - Jazz Composer's Orchestra Association Inc.

GIOS - Bicycles - Gios America Co.

GIOVA - Pasta - Giova Food International Inc.

GIOVANE - Wines - Hilton Commercial Group Inc.

GIOVANI'S - Syrup - Inventory Auditors Inc.

GIOVANNA CORRETI - Shoes - Frederick Atkins, Inc.

GIOVANNI - Food products - Acme Food Specialties Inc.

GIOVANNI - Food products ☆ - Giovanni Foods

GIOVANNI - Jeans–women's - K.S. Trading Corp.

GIOVANNI - Wines - Richard Adlai Corp.

GIOVANNI PIRANESI - Posters - One-of-a-Kind Workshop

GIOVANNI SERIES BY BORO - Kitchen cabinets and vanities - Legeis Corp.

GIOVANNI UOMO - Apparel–men's - Comtrade, Inc.

GIOVANNI'S - Food products - Giovanni's Appetizing Food Products

GIPPER GORILLA - Toys–stuffed - Russ Berrie and Co., Inc.

GIPSY - Pet products - Strongheart Products, Inc.

GIPSY - Thread - Threads USA Div.

GIRA-TAZOS - Games - Recot, Inc.
GIRAF - Beverages–malt ✩ - Heaven Hill Distilleries, Inc.
GIRAFFE - Apparel–women's - Jones Apparel Group Inc.
GIRAFFE - Bicycles - Schwinn Cycling & Fitness Inc.
GIRAFFE - Candy - Tpl, Inc.
GIRAFFE - Health care products - Snug Seat, Inc.
GIRAFFE - Lighting fixtures - Swivelier Co. Inc.
GIRAFFE - Perfumes - FMG/Tsumara Medical
GIRAFFE - Tools–pruning - Winmark Co.
GIRAFFE DESIGNS - Frames–picture - Avant Modes
GIRAFFE-FARE - Pet products - Reliable Protein Products
GIRAFFE RIDE 'EM - Toys ✩ - Steven Manufacturing Co.
GIRAFFITI - Apparel–children's - Miniworld
GIRALDA - Olive oil - Specialty Food & Beverage Sales Inc.
GIRARD - Cheese - Dairy Fresh Products Co.
GIRARD - Wines - Girard Winery Inc.
GIRARD SPRING - Water–bottled or canned - Girard Spring Water Co.
GIRARD SUNWEAR - Sunglasses - Quest Eyewear Inc.
GIRARD THE GIRAFFE - Furniture–children's - Maze Inc.
GIRARD WINERY - Wines - Girard Winery Inc.
GIRARDI - Tiles–terrazzo - Imperial Tile and Marble Corp.
GIRARD'S - Food products - Girard's Fine Foods Inc.
GIRARD'S - Salad dressings–bottled - T. Marzetti Co.
GIRARD'S WILDE RASPBERRY - Salad dressings–bottled - T. Marzetti Co.
GIRAUDON - Footwear - French Dressing Inc.
GIRBAUD - Apparel and accessories - V.F. Corp.
GIRDLE FOR 2 - Girdles - Nuvogue Creations
GIRDLETTE - Thread ✩ - SCT Yarns Inc.
GIRDSLAX - Women's sportswear - Koret North America
GIRL BRAND - Rice - Connell Co.
GIRL FRIDAY - Leather goods - St. Thomas Inc.
GIRL FRIDAY - Ribbons - Eaton Allen Ko-Rec-Type Corp.
GIRL GAMES - Computer software - Girl Games, Inc.
GIRL GLO - Colognes ✩ - Avon Products, Inc.
GIRL PRIDE - Apparel–women's - Alexis M. Colker
GIRL-RILLA - Apparel and accessories - Janine Rose Farinelli
GIRL SCOUTS - Apparel and accessories - Girl Scouts of the United States of America
GIRL SKATEBOARD - Skateboards - Girl Skateboard Co., Inc.
GIRL TALK - Games ✩ - Western Publishing Co., Inc.
GIRL TRAPS - Novelty items - Doc's Apothecary
GIRL WATCHER - Panty hose - Lincolnwood Merchandising Co. Inc.
GIRL WATCHERS - Eyeglasses ✩ - Carter-Wallace, Inc.
GIRLETTE - Apparel–women's - Lily of France Inc.
GIRLFRIEND - Computer software - Aivr Corp.
GIRLFRIENDS - Dolls - Meritus Industries, Inc.
GIRLHOOD JOURNEYS - Dolls - Girlhood Journeys, Inc.
GIRLIE - Apparel–children's - Buster Brown Apparel Inc.
GIRLING - Brakes–motor vehicle - Lucas Service
GIRL'S BEST FRIEND, A - Apparel and accessories ✩ - Glamorise Foundations Inc.
GIRLS CAN DO ANYTHING! - Apparel and accessories - Co. of Women Inc.
GIRL'S CLUB - Computer software - Philips Interactive Media of America
GIRL'S CLUB - Dolls and accessories - Kid Kore International Ltd.
GIRL'S FRIEND - Apparel–women's - Wacoal America Inc.
GIRLS OF CANBY HALL, THE - Publisher's imprints - Scholastic Inc.
GIRLS OF THE GAME - Apparel–women's - Sassi, Inc.
GIRLS ON THE GO - Jewelry–costume - Wal-Mart Stores Inc.
GIRLS ON THE GO - Toys - Libby Lee Toys Inc.
GIRLS, THE - Deodorizers - Surco Products Inc.
GIRLS WILL BE GIRLS - Wallpaper - James Seeman Studios
GIRLS!GIRLS!GIRLS! - Air purification systems - Medo Industries, Inc.
GIRLSTUFF - Toiletries - Thais Zoe
GIRLY THINGS - Apparel–women's - Andrew D. Howell
GIRO - Beverages–alcohol ✩ - Domecq Importers Inc.
GIRO AEROHEAD - Helmets–athletic ✩ - Giro Sport Design
GIRO HAMMERHEAD - Incubators–laboratory ✩ - Giro Sport Design
GIRO PROCAP - Helmets–athletic ✩ - Giro Sport Design
GIRO PROLIGHT - Helmets–athletic ✩ - Giro Sport Design
GIRO WEATHER WARRIOR - Helmets–athletic ✩ - Giro Sport Design
GIRO WINSKIN - Helmets–athletic ✩ - Giro Sport Design
GIROUX - Beverages - Romanoff International Inc.
GIRSYSTEM - Computer peripheral equipment - Industrial Computer Source
GIRVES - Food products - Brown Derby, Inc.
GIS MAGIC - Computer software - Science Applications International Corp.
GISELLE - Dolls ✩ - Effanbee Doll Corp.

GISELLE - Footwear - Rod-Man Children's Footwear Corp.
GISELLE - Furniture ✩ - Stanley Furniture Co. Inc.
GISELLE - Wigs - Helene Curtis Industries Inc.
GISELLE - Yarn ✩ - JCA, Inc.
GISLAVED - Tires - Private Brands Ltd.
GISLAVED TIVES - Food products - Products-from-Sweden Inc.
GISLIB - Computer software - Devplan, Inc.
GISTATION - Computer software - Clinical Information Advantages, Inc.
GISTEX - Spices and extracts - Gist-Brocades Food Ingredients Inc.
GIT BIZZY! - Sportswear - Gregoire Enterprises Inc.
GIT-ROT - Hardware - Boatlife Inc.
GIT-RUST - Hardware - Boatlife Inc.
GIT UM - Dust cloths - Las-Stik Manufacturing Co.
GITA - Ophthalmic goods - Swank Optical
GITALIGIN - Pharmaceutical preparations - Schering-Plough Healthcare Products
GITANA - Crackers - Nabisco Foods Group
GITANE - Cigarettes - G.A. Georgopulo & Co. Inc.
GITANO - Apparel and accessories - Orit Imports Inc.
GITANO - Handbags - Bagland
GITANO - Hosiery - Bangle Brothers Inc.
GITANO - Housewares - SCI Scandicrafts Inc.
GITANO - Pens - Gitano Licensing, Ltd.
GITANO - Skin care products ✩ - English Mist Ltd.
GITANO - Socks - Renfro Corp.
GITANO - Umbrellas ✩ - Gila Products LLC
GITANO - Watches - A.K.S. Timewear
GITANO - Watches - Fada Industries Inc.
GITANO AMERICAN MADE - Slacks–women's - Gitano Fashions Ltd.
GITANO-CODE-18 - Apparel stores–sports - E.J. Gitano Inc.
GITANO HIKERS - Footwear - Gitano Licensing, Ltd.
GITANO LIGHTWEIGHTS - Umbrellas - E.J. Gitano Inc.
GITS-IT-LIQUID CORN REMOVER - Health care products - Woolfoam Corp.
GITTIN' OFF ZERO - Apparel and accessories - Gittin' Off Zero
GITTIS - Vitamins and nutritional supplements - Milupa Co.
GITZO - Photographic equipment - Bogen Photo Corp.
GITZO - Tripods–photographic ✩ - Heitz Service Corp.
GIULIANO - Food products - Giulianos' Specialty Foods
GIULIETTI - Accordions - Giulietti Accordion Corp.
GIULIO - Ophthalmic goods ✩ - Luxottica
GIUMARRA - Wines - Giumarra Vineyards
GIUNTI - Wines - Tyfield Importers
GIURLANI - Olive oil - StarFine Foods, Inc.
GIUSEPPE - Apparel–men's - Jodamo International Ltd.
GIUSEPPE MASCARELLO - Wines - Classic Wine Imports Inc.
GIUSEPPE POMODOR - Food products - Mrs. Mazzula's
GIUSEPPE UOMO - Apparel–men's - Jodamo International Ltd.
GIUSEPPE'S - Pizzas–frozen - Armato's Pizza Co.
GIUSEPPE'S ORIGINAL SAUSAGE - Sausages - Giuseppe's Original Sausage Co.
GIUSEPPI - Statuary - Joseph A. Avarista
GIV - Aircraft–airplanes - Gulfstream Aerospace Corp.
GIVA - Skin care products - Waverly Beauty Products
GIVALDI - Leather goods - Attaches International
GIVALEX - Pharmaceutical preparations ✩ - Norgine Laboratories Inc.
GIVE - Frames–eyeglass - May Optical Co. Inc.
GIVE - Jeans–children's ✩ - Jonbil Inc.
GIVE-A-SHOW - Projectors–photographic - Kenner Products
GIVE-AND-TAKE - Apparel–men's - J. Schoeneman Inc.
GIVE & TAKE - Games - CBS Toys
GIVE & TAKE - Hair care products - Helene Curtis Industries Inc.
GIVE MEMORIES - Jewelry - Simon Golub & Sons Inc.
GIVE-N-GO - Fabrics - Guilford Mills, Inc.
GIVENCHY - Apparel–men's - Hartz & Co., Inc.
GIVENCHY - Belts–apparel - Senix Group
GIVENCHY - Dinnerware–plastic ✩ - Grainware Co.
GIVENCHY - Greeting cards ✩ - Brett-Forer Greetings Inc.
GIVENCHY - Handbags ✩ - Koret Inc.
GIVENCHY - Hosiery - Pennaco Hosiery Inc.
GIVENCHY - Hosiery–men's - Keepers International
GIVENCHY - Luggage - Kingport International Corp.
GIVENCHY - Shoes ✩ - Schwartz & Benjamin Inc.
GIVENCHY - Umbrellas ✩ - English Mist Ltd.
GIVENCHY - Watches - Gruen Marketing Corp.
GIVENCHY BIARRITZ - Frames–eyeglass ✩ - Universal/Univis Inc.
GIVENCHY CANNES - Frames–eyeglass ✩ - Universal/Univis Inc.

✩ = Now out of production

GIVENCHY CONCORDE - Frames—eyeglass ☆ - Universal/Univis Inc.

GIVENCHY CRAVATES - Neckties - Carter & Holmes

GIVENCHY DEAUVILLE - Frames—eyeglass ☆ - Universal/Univis Inc.

GIVENCHY DUCHESS - Frames—eyeglass ☆ - Universal/Univis Inc.

GIVENCHY ELOQUENCY - Frames—eyeglass ☆ - Universal/Univis Inc.

GIVENCHY GENTLEMAN - Colognes - Parfums Givenchy, Inc.

GIVENCHY GRANDE SPORT - Frames—eyeglass ☆ - Universal/Univis Inc.

GIVENCHY I - Frames—eyeglass ☆ - Universal/Univis Inc.

GIVENCHY III - Perfumes - Parfums Givenchy, Inc.

GIVENCHY LADY - Frames—eyeglass ☆ - Universal/Univis Inc.

GIVENCHY LANDAU - Frames—eyeglass ☆ - Universal/Univis Inc.

GIVENCHY LORD - Frames—eyeglass ☆ - Universal/Univis Inc.

GIVENCHY LYON - Frames—eyeglass ☆ - Universal/Univis Inc.

GIVENCHY MARQUIS - Frames—eyeglass ☆ - Universal/Univis Inc.

GIVENCHY MONACO - Frames—eyeglass ☆ - Universal/Univis Inc.

GIVENCHY MONTE CARLO - Frames—eyeglass ☆ - Universal/Univis Inc.

GIVENCHY REGENT - Frames—eyeglass ☆ - Universal/Univis Inc.

GIVENCHY REGINE - Frames—eyeglass ☆ - Universal/Univis Inc.

GIVENCHY ST. TROPEZ - Frames—eyeglass ☆ - Universal/Univis Inc.

GIVENCHY SOLAIRE - Sunglasses - B. Robinson Sunglasses

GIVENCHY SPORT - Frames—eyeglass ☆ - Universal/Univis Inc.

GIVENCHY SUPRA SPORT - Frames—eyeglass ☆ - Universal/Univis Inc.

GIVENCHY TRIOMPHE - Frames—eyeglass ☆ - Universal/Univis Inc.

GIVERNY - Floor coverings—carpet and rugs - Masland Corp.

GIVING NATURE - Eggs - John R. Baker

GIZA - Cigarettes - G.A. Georgopulo & Co. Inc.

GIZA - Floor coverings—carpet and rugs - Couristan Inc.

GIZMO - Shaving preparations - Gillette Co.

GIZMO 32 - Tools—boring - Thirty-Three Enterprises, Inc.

GIZMOS - Games - Pressman Toy Corp.

GIZMO'S - Pet products - RBC Enterprises

GIZMOS 98 - Computer software - Play Inc.

GIZMOS & GADGETS! - Computer software - The Learning Co., Inc.

GIZMOZ - Watches - Timex Corp.

GIZZMO - Electronic equipment - Woods Industries, Inc.

GIZZMO'S HOME ENTERTAINMENT - Electronic equipment - Woods Industries, Inc.

GJ GERARDO JEREZ - Clothing - Gerardo Jerez Corp.

GJP - Recording label - Rustron Music Productions

G.K. - Laxative - American Hygienic Laboratories Inc.

GK CHLORO GOLD - Fungicides - Gold Kist Inc.

GK SIL-SPREAD - Chemical preparations - Gold Kist Inc.

GKG - Audio equipment - Kolorama Distributing Co. Inc.

GKI - Lighting fixtures - New England Pottery Co., Inc.

GL-2 - Adhesives and sealants - Gordon Laboratories

GL-7 - Adhesives and sealants - Gordon Laboratories

GL-10 - Glue—household or industrial - Clark Craft Boat Co.

GL-15 - Boats - Clark Craft Boat Co.

GL-350 DRYWALL REPLACEMENT SYSTEM - Partitions—metal - Gravity Lock Systems, Inc.

GL2 - Fishing tackle - G. Loomis, Inc.

GL10 - Motor vehicles—automobiles - Subaru of America, Inc.

GLA - Vitamins and nutritional supplements - Vitamin Research Products Inc.

GLACE - Blinds—vertical - Tontine/VyTech Industries Inc.

GLACE - Craft supplies - Stanislaus Imports, Inc.

GLACE - Floor coverings—carpet and rugs - Collins & Aikman Corp.

GLACE - Food products ☆ - Continental Food Corp.

GLACE - Frames—eyeglass - May Optical Co., Inc.

GLACE - Tiles—ceramic - Huntington/Pacific Ceramics Inc.

GLACE LINE - Tiles—ceramic - Huntington/Pacific Ceramics Inc.

GLACE SUNGOLD - Lipsticks - Cosmair Inc.

GLACEAU - Water—bottled or canned - Glacier Water Co. Inc.

GLACEE - Shoes - Intershoe Inc.

GLACEX - Thread ☆ - Perfect Thread Co. Inc.

GLACIA - Candy - Perugina Chocolate & Confections Inc.

GLACIAL - Bowls ☆ - Lenox Crystal, Inc.

GLACIAL - Salt - Aldon Industries Inc.

GLACIAL FRESH - Hair care products - Alaska Glacier Products

GLACIAL GEL - Pharmaceutical preparations - Lyphomed Inc.

GLACIAL GYP - Flowers, plants, and seeds - Selecta Farms, Inc.

GLACIAL MARBLE - Floor coverings - Mannington Resilient Floors

GLACIALS - Beverages—carbonated - Juba Beverages Corp.

GLACIER - Apparel—athletic - Swan Enterprises, Inc.

GLACIER - Ashtrays—glass - Mandala Productions

GLACIER - Bathroom accessories ☆ - KLR Products, Inc.

GLACIER - Blinds—vertical - Steelwood Extruding Corp.

GLACIER - Cabinets - Alpine Cabinet Co.

GLACIER - Cabinets - Imperial Cabinets Inc.

GLACIER - Cabinets - Schrock

GLACIER - Colognes - Quintessence Inc.

GLACIER - Cosmetics ☆ - Alpine Crafts Co. Inc.

GLACIER - Crocheted and knitted items ☆ - Schuessler Knitting Mills Inc.

GLACIER - Flatware - Washington Forge Inc.

GLACIER - Floor coverings—tile - ECC International

GLACIER - Fruits and vegetables - J.R. Wood Inc.

GLACIER - Giftware - World of Porcelain & Glassware

GLACIER - Glassware—household - Federal Glass

GLACIER - Glassware—household ☆ - WMF/USA

GLACIER - Hair care products - Belson Products

GLACIER - Ice - Wetco

GLACIER - Lipsticks ☆ - Elysee Scientific Cosmetic Co.

GLACIER - Tiles—ceiling - USG Interiors, Inc.

GLACIER - Vegetables—frozen - Gerawan Foods Inc.

GLACIER - Water—bottled or canned - Glacier Water Co. Inc.

GLACIER BAY - Beverages—alcohol ☆ - Century Importers Inc.

GLACIER BAY - Door frames - Canyon Creek Cabinet Co.

GLACIER BAY - Seafood products—fresh or frozen - Glacier Bay Food Co. Inc.

GLACIER CLUB - Ice cream - Borden, Inc.

GLACIER CREME - Yogurt - Matanuska Maid Dairy

GLACIER FOODS - Fruits—frozen - Glacier Foods

GLACIER FRESH - Water—mineral - Wetco

GLACIER GLOVE - Gloves - Swan Enterprises, Inc.

GLACIER-GRIP - Tires ☆ - Cooper Tire & Rubber Co.

GLACIER-GUARD - Antifreeze - Multi-Line Enterprises Inc.

GLACIER II - Preservative - Archer Daniels Midland Co.

GLACIER ISLANDS - Food products machinery - M & E Manufacturing Co., Inc.

GLACIER LAKE - Footwear - Kenai River Imports, Inc.

GLACIER MELT - Deicing fluid - Cargill Salt

GLACIER MELT - Salt - Cargill, Inc.

GLACIER METALWORKING FLUIDS BY MONSANTO - Lubricants - Monsanto Co.

GLACIER MOUNTAIN PRODUCTS INC. - Fruit drink bases and flavors - R.T. Marketing, Inc.

GLACIER PAK & DESIGN - Cartons—paperboard - Georgia-Pacific Corp.

GLACIER PEAK FROZEN YOGURT - Yogurt—frozen - Brice Foods, Inc.

GLACIER PITCHER - Containers - David Mark Meneo

GLACIER POINT - Bicycles - Dynacraft Industries Inc.

GLACIER POINT - Dinnerware—glass ☆ - Lenox, Inc.

GLACIER PURE - Water purification systems - Farberware Inc.

GLACIER ROSE - Dishes—china - Taylor, Smith & Taylor Co.

GLACIER RUN - Water—mineral - Northeast Marketing Group, Inc.

GLACIER SEAL - Puppets - Dakin Inc.

GLACIER TRACKS - Shoes - Tingley Rubber Corp.

GLACIER VALLEY - Water—bottled or canned - Natural Country Farms Inc.

GLACIER WARE - Ice chests—plastic ☆ - Glacier Ware Inc.

GLACIER'S EDGE - Apparel—athletic - Fred Meyer, Inc.

GLAD - Bags—trash - First Brands Corp.

GLAD-A-BOB - Sleds - Paris Co. Inc.

GLAD-A-BOGGAN - Bobsleds and toboggans - Paris Co. Inc.

GLAD CORN - Snack foods - G.E.F., Inc.

GLAD DRAWSTRING - Bags—trash - First Brands Corp.

GLAD HANDLE-TIE - Bags—trash - First Brands Corp.

GLAD HANDS - Gloves - Ross Laboratories

GLAD-LOCK - Bags—plastic - First Brands Corp.

GLAD PAD - Cleaning preparations - Swiss-Tex Inc.

GLAD RAGS - Markers—felt-tip ☆ - Sanford Corp.

GLAD RAGS - T-shirts—women's - Prelude Designs

GLAD RAGS RECOVERY CREATIONS - Greeting cards - Gene Williamson

GLAD TIDINGS - Frames—eyeglass - May Optical Co. Inc.

GLAD TIDINGS - Invitations - Glad Tidings Inc.

GLAD WAGS - Dog food - Beatrice Cos. Inc.

GLADDER'S - Bakery products - Gladder's Gourmet Cookies, Inc.

GLADDING - Sporting goods - Gladding Braided Products Inc.

GLADDING DEL-REY - Trailers—travel - Gladding Del-Rey

GLADDING/HEDLUND - Sporting goods ☆ - Gladding Braided Products Inc.

GLADDING-SOUTH BEND - Sporting goods ☆ - Gladding Braided Products Inc.

GLADE - Deodorizers - S.C. Johnson & Son, Inc.

GLADE - Flowers, plants, and seeds - Jacklin Seed

GLADE BASICS - Deodorizers - S.C. Johnson & Son, Inc.

☆ = Now out of production

GLADE CLIP-ONS - Deodorizers - S.C. Johnson & Son, Inc.
GLADE CREEK - Furniture ☆ - Singer Furniture Co.
GLADE LIGHT - Deodorizers - S.C. Johnson & Son, Inc.
GLADE PLUG INS FOR LARGE ROOMS - Deodorizers - S.C. Johnson & Son, Inc.
GLADE SMOKE AWAY - Deodorizers - S.C. Johnson & Son, Inc.
GLADE SPRING ORCHARD - Deodorizers - S.C. Johnson & Son, Inc.
GLADE'S - Candy - Glade Taffy Town, Inc.
GLADIATOR - Apparel and accessories - Neema Clothing, Ltd.
GLADIATOR - Apparel–athletic - Jobst Institute Inc.
GLADIATOR - Batteries - Exide Corp.
GLADIATOR - Boats - MCP Inc.
GLADIATOR - Bricks - A.P. Green Industries Inc.
GLADIATOR - Computer peripheral equipment - MTI Technology Corp.
GLADIATOR - Computer software - Vernalwood Realty Trust
GLADIATOR - Doors–metal - Jeld-Wen, Inc.
GLADIATOR - Floor coverings–carpet and rugs - Galaxy Carpet Mills Inc.
GLADIATOR - Floor coverings–carpet and rugs ☆ - Blue Ridge Carpet Mills
GLADIATOR - Furniture - Conover Chair Co. Inc.
GLADIATOR - Games - Avalon Hill Game Co.
GLADIATOR - Pencils ☆ - Staedtler, Inc.
GLADIATOR - Thread ☆ - Perfect Thread Co. Inc.
GLADIATOR - Video games - Taito America Corp.
GLADIATOR - Wastebaskets - F.H. Lawson Co.
GLADIATOR - Wet suits–rubber - Overton's Inc.
GLADIOLA - Food products - Beatrice Cos. Inc.
GLADLINE - Fishing tackle ☆ - Gladding Braided Products Inc.
GLADLY - Toys - Playskool, Inc.
GLADSTONE - Cigars - House of Windsor Inc.
GLADSTONE - Fabrics - Uniroyal Engineered Products
GLADSTONE - Frames–eyeglass - Hudson Optical Corp.
GLADWIN 113 - Wines - Heritage Wine Cellars
GLADWYNE - Frames–eyeglass ☆ - Universal/Univis Inc.
GLADYL - Fishing tackle ☆ - Gladding Braided Products Inc.
GLADYS - Frames–eyeglass - Rozin Optical Export Corp.
GLADYS AND FRIENDS - Greeting cards - AGC, Inc.
GLADYS AND FRIENDS - Greeting cards - American Greetings Corp.
GLAESEL - Musical instrument accessories ☆ - Selmer Co. Inc.
GLAM-R - Aprons ☆ - United Plastic Products
GLAM-R-TRED - Stair treads ☆ - Ace Rubber Products Inc.
GLAMA-GOLD - Frames–eyeglass - Hudson Optical Corp.
GLAMA-LOPE - Envelopes - CTI Paper Co., Inc.
GLAMA NATURAL - Paper–transfer - CTI Paper Co., Inc.
GLAMARBLE - Plastics - Dimensional Plastics Corp.
GLAMIRROR - Mirrors ☆ - Trepte Wire and Metal Works
GLAMOR - Beverages–carbonated - Canada Dry Corp.
GLAMOR - Paints - Jones Blair Co.
GLAMOR ALL - Sponges - Acme Sponge & Chamois Co., Inc.
GLAMOR-GARDS - Gloves ☆ - Brookville Glove Manufacturing Co.
GLAMOR LADY - Eyeglasses - Art-Craft Optical Co.
GLAMOR-LITE - Eyeglasses - Art-Craft Optical Co.
GLAMOR-TEX - Apparel and accessories - Glamorise Foundations Inc.
GLAMOR-TROL - Apparel and accessories - Glamorise Foundations Inc.
GLAMOR-X - Apparel and accessories - Glamorise Foundations Inc.
GLAMORAMA - Frames–eyeglass - Hudson Optical Corp.
GLAMORENE - Cleaning preparations–carpet and rug - Airwick Industries
GLAMORENE - Cleaning preparations–carpet and rug - Benckiser Consumer Products Inc.
GLAMORISE - Apparel and accessories - Glamorise Foundations Inc.
GLAMORISE - Eyeglasses - Art-Craft Optical Co.
GLAMORIZER'S - Cosmetics - Glamorizer's, Inc.
GLAMOROUS GREEN - Kites ☆ - Hi-Flier Manufacturing Co.
GLAMOUR - Dairy products - Mid-America Dairymen Inc. Southern Div.
GLAMOUR - Darts and dart games - Dart World Inc.
GLAMOUR - Floor coverings–carpet and rugs ☆ - American Carpet Mills
GLAMOUR - Footwear - Glamour Footwear
GLAMOUR - Hair care products ☆ - Morris-Flamingo Inc.
GLAMOUR - Hair care products ☆ - Select Brands
GLAMOUR - Jewelry - Richton International Corp.
GLAMOUR - Ophthalmic goods ☆ - Luxottica
GLAMOUR - Perfume, etc. - Bourjois Inc.
GLAMOUR BAND - Cosmetics ☆ - N.B. Cohen Co.
GLAMOUR BEACH - Bicycles - Huffy Corp.
GLAMOUR BLONDES - Hair care products - Revlon Consumer Products Corp.
GLAMOUR BRA - Brassieres (Bras) - Lane Bryant, Inc.
GLAMOUR BY EDEN - Wedding gowns - Eden Bridals, Inc.

GLAMOUR CURL - Curling irons–electric - Telebrands Corp.
GLAMOUR DUST - Paints ☆ - DecoArt, Inc.
GLAMOUR FRAME - Frames–eyeglass - Hudson Optical Corp.
GLAMOUR GARTERS - Novelty items ☆ - Hortense B. Hewitt Inc.
GLAMOUR GIRL - Bicycles - Dynacraft Industries Inc.
GLAMOUR GIRL - Boats–motor - Anchorage Inc.
GLAMOUR GIRL - Cosmetics - Worldwide Cosmetics
GLAMOUR GIRL - Frames–eyeglass ☆ - Universal/Univis Inc.
GLAMOUR GIRL - Jewelry–costume ☆ - Komor Manufacturing
GLAMOUR GIRL MAKE OVER BEAUTY CENTER - Games ☆ - A.R.C. Toys Inc.
GLAMOUR GIRLS - Computer storage devices - Arch Interactive, Inc.
GLAMOUR GLITTER - Paints ☆ - DecoArt, Inc.
GLAMOUR-GLO - Apparel–women's - Exquisite Form Industries
GLAMOUR GOOP - Toy modeling materials - Toymax Inc.
GLAMOUR HOUSE - Cosmetics - Glamour House Products Inc.
GLAMOUR KIT - Leather goods - St. Thomas Inc.
GLAMOUR KITS SCOOPLES - Pet products - Waverly Mineral Products Co.
GLAMOUR KITTY - Pet products - Waverly Mineral Products Co.
GLAMOUR LIFT - Cosmetics - Spilo/Mehaz Worldwide
GLAMOUR LIGHTS - Hair care products - Revlon Consumer Products Corp.
GLAMOUR ORIGINALS - Women's shoes ☆ - Consolidated Shoe Co., Inc.
GLAMOUR PET TOGS - Pet products - Ben Richter Co.
GLAMOUR PUSS - Cat food - Heinz Pet Products Co.
GLAMOUR PUSS - Dolls - Dantzer, Inc.
GLAMOUR/REST - Bathroom accessories - Better Sleep, Inc.
GLAMOUR ROUNDS - Frames–eyeglass - May Optical Co. Inc.
GLAMOUR SHOTS - Portrait studios - Glamour Shots
GLAMOUR STYLE - Bicycles ☆ - Huffy Corp.
GLAMOUR TEEN - Apparel–women's - Wacoal America Inc.
GLAMOUR TEEN - Dolls - Carole A. Lenz
GLAMOUR-TEX - Hair care products ☆ - Hess Hair Milk Laboratories Inc.
GLAMOUR THIN - Health care products ☆ - Halsey Drug Co. Inc.
GLAMOUR TONE - Skin care products - Goubaud
GLAMOUR-VUE - Lenses–optical - Ditto Industries Inc.
GLAMOUR-WARE - Serving carts ☆ - Quaker Industries Ltd.
GLAMOUR WRAP - Hair care products - Glamour, Inc.
GLAMOUR-WYRE - Brassieres (Bras) - Edith Lances Corp.
GLAMOURESQUE - Floor coverings–carpet and rugs - World Carpets, Inc.
GLAMOURESQUE - Floor coverings–carpet and rugs ☆ - Zenith Carpets
GLAMOURETTE - Gloves–rubber - Duracraft Corp.
GLAMOURFORM - Bathroom fixtures - Dimensional Plastics Corp.
GLAMOURGLAS - Glass products - Dimensional Plastics Corp.
GLAMOURGLUV - Gloves ☆ - Brookville Glove Manufacturing Co.
GLAMOURLINE - Window coverings - Vertical Blind Factory
GLANCE - Belts, hair accessories, and jewelry - Sun Ban Fashions
GLANCE - Clocks - General Time Corp. (Westclox/Seth Thomas Div.)
GLANCE - Shampoos - Colgate-Palmolive Co.
GLANCES - Occasional tables - JDI Group, Inc.
GLAND-CAPS - Vitamins and nutritional supplements - Solaray
GLANDOSANE - Health care products - Fresenius Pharma
GLANDULIN - Vitamins and nutritional supplements - Winning Laboratories Corp.
GLANOGEN - Vitamins and nutritional supplements - Great Life Laboratories Inc.
GLANOLIN - Health care products - Abkit, Inc.
GLANTE CLASSICS - Women's apparel - Glenda Agee
GLANTRI - Games - Tsr, Inc.
GLANVILLE PUBLISHERS INC. - Publisher's imprints - Oceana Publications Inc.
GLARE-BAN - Lenses–optical - Ditto Industries Inc.
GLARE-BAN LENS - Lighting fixtures - Voigt Lighting Industries Inc.
GLARE-BAR - Lenses–optical - American Polarizers Inc.
GLARE CARE - Computer programming services - ACCO USA, Inc.
GLARE CARE - Office supplies - Mead Corp.
GLARE DEFENDER - Adhesives and sealants - Optical Coating Laboratory Inc.–Santa Rosa Div.
GLARE DROPS - Pharmaceutical preparations - Ergovision, Inc.
GLARE FREE - Lenses–optical - Bell Optical Laboratories, Inc.
GLARE/GUARD - Reflectors–optical - Optical Coating Laboratory Inc.–Santa Rosa Div.
GLARE-OUT - Chemical preparations - Lil-Tec Laboratories, Inc.
GLARE-PROOF - Lenses–optical - Ditto Industries Inc.
GLARE-STOP - Ophthalmic goods - Styl-Rite Optical Manufacturing Co., Inc.
GLARE STOPPER - Automotive parts and accessories - Allied Plastics
GLAREBAN LITE - Computer peripheral equipment - Denton Vacuum, Inc.

☆ = Now out of production

GLAREBUSTER - Office supplies ☆ - Ames Safety Envelope Co.

GLAREDEFENDER - Electrical equipment - Optical Coating Laboratory Inc.–Santa Rosa Div.

GLAREFIGHTER, THE - Lighting equipment - General Electric Co.

GLARESHIELD - Electronic equipment - Brandons Inc.

GLARESTOP - Computer peripheral equipment - Texwipe Co. LLC

GLARO - Office furniture–metal - Glaro Inc.

GLAROS - Liquors - Paramount Distillers Inc.

GLAS BOUTIQUE - Glassware–household - Oneida Ltd.

GLAS-CAME - Doors–glass - Pease Industries, Inc.

GLAS-CLEAR - Office supplies - Alvin and Co. Inc.

GLAS GALERIE - Giftware ☆ - W.M.F. of America Inc.

GLAS-KLEN - Cleaning preparations–window - Jefco Laboratories, Inc.

GLAS/LITE - Sporting goods ☆ - Plas-Steel Products Inc.

GLAS MATE - Antennas - Wintenna Inc.

GLAS MESH COMPANY - Pipes–plastic - E. Davis Bogle

GLAS-PATCH - Cement - Garon Products Inc.

GLAS-SHEEN - Skin care products - Rudolph International, Inc.

GLAS-SNAP - Glass products ☆ - Corning Inc.

GLAS-STAR - Sporting goods - Outboard Marine Corp.

GLAS-STICK - Office supplies - Wesco Industries Inc.

GLAS STOP - Office supplies ☆ - Sainberg and Co. Inc.

GLASBAKE - Cooking utensils–glass - Jeannette Corp.

GLASBED - Firearms, accessories, and parts - Brownells, Inc.

GLASBED - Firearms, accessories, and parts ☆ - Anderson Manufacturing Co.

GLASBORD - Fiberboard - Kemlite Co., Inc.

GLASCLENE - Glass products ☆ - Tempo Chemical Co. Inc.

GLASCO - Vending machines - Unidynamics Corp.

GLASCOAT - Firearms, accessories, and parts ☆ - Anderson Manufacturing Co.

GLASCOAT - Furniture - Cherry Grove, Inc.

GLASCOTE - Asphalt felts and coatings ☆ - Gibson-Homans Co.

GLASCOTER - Adhesives and sealants ☆ - Pettit Paint Co. Inc.

GLASCRETE - Furniture - Dura Art Stone

GLASCRETE - Mortars–clay ☆ - Custom Building Products

GLASER - Pickles - Green Bay Foods Co.

GLASER DESIGNS SAN FRANCISCO - Leather goods - Glaser Designs Inc.

GLASGLO - Glass–stained - Glass House Studio Inc.

GLASGLU - Adhesives and sealants ☆ - L.B. Allen Co. Inc.

GLASGOW - Floor coverings–carpet and rugs - Atlas Carpet Mills Inc.

GLASGOW - Wallpaper - Koroseal Wallcoverings

GLASGOW PLACE - Floor coverings–carpet and rugs - Atlas Carpet Mills Inc.

GLASGOW ROSE - Dinnerware–glass ☆ - Cyclamen Studio

GLASHEEN - Detergents - Advance Cleaning Products Inc.

GLASHOUSE - Skylights - United Skys, Inc.

GLASKERAMIK - Giftware - Superlux Ltd.

GLASLOCK - Shingles - Owens Corning

GLASMASTER - Antennas - Valor Enterprises, Inc.

GLASMESH - Hardware ☆ - Bondex International Inc.

GLASMO - Thread - Belding Heminway Co. Inc.

GLASMO TEE - Thread - Belding Heminway Co. Inc.

GLASNOST - Games - Gini Graham Scott

GLASPRAY - Firearms, accessories, and parts ☆ - Anderson Manufacturing Co.

GLASS - Food products machinery ☆ - SCI Scandicrafts Inc.

GLASS - Recording label - Butler Video Productions

GLASS ACT - Glassware–household ☆ - L.E. Smith Glass Co.

GLASS AMERICA - Glassware–household - Moderne Glass Co., Inc.

GLASS & MORE - Cleaning preparations–window ☆ - Blue Cross Laboratories Inc.

GLASS ART - Fiberglass panels ☆ - Auburn Plastic Engineering

GLASS BARON - Figurines - Glass Baron, Inc.

GLASS-BASE - Shingles - Tamko Roofing Products, Inc.

GLASS BRITE - Cleaning preparations–window - Blue Cross Laboratories Inc.

GLASS BY GLASS - Glassware–household - Glass by Glass Co.

GLASS CADDY, THE - Glass sample carrying case ☆ - Arch Specs, Inc.

GLASS CARTOONS - Figurines - The Glass People Inc.

GLASS CEILING . SHATTER IT!, THE - Jewelry–costume - Susan L. Harris

GLASS CLEAR - Insulating materials ☆ - Pacur Inc.

GLASS COMPANY - Cutting boards - Chase Collection, Inc.

GLASS CORE - Insulating materials ☆ - Manville/Schuller

GLASS CREATIONS COLLECTION - Glassware–household - Owens-Illinois Inc. (Libbey Div.)

GLASS CRYSTALS - Glass products - Emix Corp.

GLASS-DEK - Epoxy coatings - L.D. Sterns Corp.

GLASS EATER - Trash compactors–household - Compactall Inc.

GLASS FILTER PLUS - Computer peripheral equipment - Curtis Manufacturing Co., Inc.

GLASS-GARD - Novelty items - Seron Manufacturing Co.

GLASS GARDEN - Vases - Frog Prince Inc.

GLASS GEMS - Pet products - National Display Materials

GLASS GLAZE - Insecticides - Loctite Corp.

GLASS GLEAM 3 - Cleaning preparations–window - Titan Laboratories

GLASS GLEAM 7 - Cleaning preparations–window - Titan Laboratories

GLASS-GLO - Cleaning preparations–window ☆ - Paxon Manufacturing Co.

GLASS GRAPHITE MASTER - Golfing equipment ☆ - Aldila, Inc.

GLASS GROOM - Cleaning preparations–window - Viking Manufacturing Co. Inc.

GLASS GUARD - Motor vehicle parts and accessories - Transit Care, Inc.

GLASS HOLD - Adhesives and sealants - National Artcraft Co.

GLASS KEEPER - Apparel and accessories ☆ - Park Sherman

GLASS KING - Washboards - National Washboard Co.

GLASS KOTE - Finishing agents - Carolyn's Crafts

GLASS LIGHTS - Candles - A Touch of Elegance

GLASS-LITES - Candles - Federal Glass

GLASS MAGIC - Detergents - RCN Products Inc.

GLASS MASK - Paints - Wagner Spray Tech Corp.

GLASS-MATE - Signs - Effron Sales

GLASS-MATE - Soap - Embassy Rug & Upholstery Cleaning Co. Inc.

GLASS MATES - Cleaning preparations–window - L & F Consumer Products

GLASS MATES - Cleaning preparations–window - Linden Corp.

GLASS MENAGERIE - Ornamental products–glass - J. Kenneth Zahn

GLASS MOUNT 800 - Antennas - Childs Corp.

GLASS MOUNTAIN QUARRY - Wines - Markham Vineyards

GLASS-O-NET - Plastics film - Warp Bros.

GLASS OF SPAIN - Vases - Knobler International Ltd.

GLASS PAC - Cleaning preparations–window - PortionPac Chemical Corp.

GLASS PAK - Containers - Glass-Pak, Inc.

GLASS PAK - Tape–adhesive - Central Products Co.

GLASS-PERK, THE - Coffee makers–electric - Gemco Ware, Inc.

GLASS PLUS - Cleaning preparations–window - Dowbrands L.P.

GLASS PLUS - Musical instruments - Remle Musical Products Inc.

GLASS-PORE - Pumps ☆ - Aquaculture Research/Environmental Associates Inc.

GLASS RENU - Cleaning preparations–household - Auto Specialty Products, Inc.

GLASS RIDGE - Wines - Geerlings & Wade, Inc.

GLASS-SEAL - Shingles - Tamko Roofing Products, Inc.

GLASS-SEAL AR - Shingles - Tamko Roofing Products, Inc.

GLASS SHOP - Glassware–household ☆ - Lancaster Colony Corp.

GLASS SLIPPER - Christmas tree ornaments - Cracker Box Inc.

GLASS-STIK - Plastic sheet - Rescue Innovation, Inc.

GLASS-VIEW - Stoves–wood-burning - Russo Products Inc.

GLASS WAX - Floor waxers–household - Reckitt & Colman, Inc.

GLASS-WEAVE - Plastics film - Warp Bros.

GLASS WING - Educational materials - Joanne Sales

GLASS WRAP - Doors - Morgan Products Ltd.

GLASSBLAST - Glass products - Glass Recycling, Inc.

GLASSBLOWER - Glass products - Corning Inc.

GLASSBOND - Sporting goods - Outdoor Technologies Group

GLASSCOTE - Chemical preparations - Woolsey Marine Industries

GLASSCRAFT - Glass products - Binswanger Glass Co. (Glasscraft Div.)

GLASSCRAFT - Trays - Houze Glass Corp.

GLASSEAL - Tape–adhesive - Central Products Co.

GLASSEEZ - Glass-cleaning towels - Jacone Distributors Inc.

GLASSENE - Cleaning preparations–household - Care-Tech Laboratories Inc.

GLASSER - Musical instrument accessories - International Violin Co. Ltd.

GLASSER - Violins - Glasser Manufacturing Co. Inc.

GLASSEXPORT - Giftware - Superlux Ltd.

GLASSFYRE - Fireplace equipment - Thomas Industries Inc. (Portland Willamette Div.)

GLASSFYRE - Fireplace screens - Portland Willamette

GLASSGUARD - Shingles–asphalt or tar - Certainteed Corp. (Roofing Products Group)

GLASSHIELD - Insulating materials ☆ - Manville/Schuller

GLASSHOUSE - Glass products ☆ - Westminster Trading Corp.

GLASSI HONI GLAZE - Frosting - Brokay Products Inc.

GLASSIC ART - Glass products ☆ - Poly-Optical Products, Inc.

GLASSICS - Jars–glass - Federal Glass

GLASSING FACTORY, THE - Sporting goods - West Wind Sailboards

GLASSIPS - Straws–drinking - Spir-it Inc.

GLASSIQUE COLLECTION - Glassware–household - Owens-Illinois Inc. (Libbey Div.)
GLASSIT - Motor vehicle parts and accessories - BASF Corp.
GLASSKOTER - Paintbrushes, rollers - Corona Brushes Inc.
GLASSMARX - Crayons ☆ - Walbuck Crayon Co., Inc.
GLASSMASTER - Alarm systems–burglar - Litton Security Systems
GLASSMASTER - Boats–motor - Glassmaster Co.
GLASSMASTER - Cleaning preparations - Mega Manufacturing Co. Inc.
GLASSMASTER - Shingles - Atlas Roofing Corp.
GLASSMOLD - Artists' materials - Creek-Turn Inc. (Ceramic Supply Div.)
GLASSO - Motor vehicle parts and accessories - BASF Corp.
GLASSOCRYL - Motor vehicle parts and accessories - BASF Corp.
GLASSODUR - Motor vehicle parts and accessories - BASF Corp.
GLASSOHYD - Motor vehicle parts and accessories - BASF Corp.
GLASSOLUTION - Cleaning preparations–window - Burnishine Products
GLASSOMAX - Motor vehicle parts and accessories - BASF Corp.
GLASSPAR - Boats–motor ☆ - Larson Boat Div.
GLASSPLANT - Glass products ☆ - Corning Inc.
GLASSPLAX - Awards, plaques and medals - Stephen Ryan Tortomasi
GLASSRITE - Pencils ☆ - Faber-Castell Corp.
GLASSSTARS - Decals and transfers - Screen Stars Safety Corp.
GLASSTEEL - Glass–tempered - Colonial Mirror and Glass Corp.
GLASSTEX - Shingles–asphalt or tar - Certainteed Corp. (Roofing Products Group)
GLASSTEX - Tape–adhesive ☆ - Central Products Co.
GLASSTEX - Thread - Advance Thread Corp.
GLASSTEX - Tires ☆ - Uniroyal Goodrich Tire Co.
GLASSWALLS - Prefabricated buildings–wood - Mon-Ray, Inc.
GLASSWEB - Tape–adhesive - Central Products Co.
GLASSWORKS - Doors–glass - Kohler Co.
GLASTAR - Tools - D & L Stained Glass Supply, Inc.
GLASTEX - Boats–motor - Glastex Co.
GLASTEX - Computer peripheral equipment - Vytech Industries, Inc.
GLASTEX - Window coverings - Duratex Inc.
GLASTIQUE - Blinds–vertical ☆ - Tontine/VyTech Industries Inc.
GLASTIX - Bar fixtures–plastic - Spir-it Inc.
GLASTON - Floor coverings–carpet and rugs - Atlas Carpet Mills Inc.
GLASTONBURY - Clocks ☆ - General Time Corp. (Westclox/Seth Thomas Div.)
GLASTONBURY - Fireplace equipment - Majestic Co.
GLASTRON - Boats–motor - Glastron Boats
GLASTRON/CARLSON - Boats–motor - Glastron Boats
GLASTRON/CONROY - Boats–motor ☆ - Glastron Boats
GLASURIT - Motor vehicle parts and accessories - BASF Corp.
GLAUCOMA—SCOPE - Medical instruments - Ophthalmic Imaging Systems
GLAUCON - Ophthalmic goods - Alcon Laboratories, Inc.
GLAUCTABS - Pharmaceutical preparations - Akorn Inc.
GLAX - Cleaning preparations - RTW International Corp.
GLAYVA - Cordials - Marie Brizard Wines & Spirits, USA
GLAZ-A-WAY - Artists' materials - Momentum Graphics
GLAZE - Hair care products - Gefden International Inc.
GLAZE - Paints - American Art Clay Co. Inc.
GLAZE - Paints - Pen Paints Inc.
GLAZE - Waxes–sealing - Airosol Co. Inc.
GLAZE A PIE - Pies–fresh - Concord Foods Inc.
GLAZE ALL - Cleaning preparations - Rukin Industries Inc.
GLAZE-COAT - Putties - Fibre Glass-Evercoat Co. Inc.
GLAZE COAT II - Adhesives and sealants - Titan Corp.
GLAZE-CREST - Tiles–ceiling ☆ - Artcrest Products Co. Inc.
GLAZE-GARD - Car care preparations - Automotive International, Inc.
GLAZE GLASS CRAFT - Glass–stained ☆ - Beagle Manufacturing Co. Inc.
GLAZE-IT - Cleaning preparations ☆ - Knight Marketing Corp.
GLAZE-IT - Glue–household or industrial - Binney & Smith Inc.
GLAZE-IT - Hair care products - Waverly Beauty Products
GLAZE-N-GROW - Nail care products - Gabel Holding Co. Inc.
GLAZE POP - Food products - Gold Medal Products Co.
GLAZE-TEX - Christmas tree ornaments - Union Wadding Co.
GLAZE-TUFF - Window coverings - Elmer's Products, Inc.
GLAZED GLASS - Nail care products - Backscratchers, Inc.
GLAZED MINI BONES - Dog food - Vitakraft Pet Products Co., Inc.
GLAZED MORESCA - Floor coverings–tile ☆ - Kentile Floors Inc.
GLAZED PECANS - Food products - Mrs. Powell's Gourmet Pecans
GLAZED SCHLEMMERTOPF - Cooking utensils–enameled - Reston Lloyd Ltd.
GLAZED TIERRA - Floor coverings–tile - Kentile Floors Inc.
GLAZEDOR - Doors–wood - Panelfold Inc.

GLAZEINE - Pastries ☆ - Food Ingredients Manufacturing Co.
GLAZENAMEL - Enamels ☆ - Atlas Chemical Co.
GLAZETONES - Tiles–ceramic ☆ - American Olean Tile Co.
GLAZIN' IMAGES - Tiles–ceramic - Tile Art
GLAZIN' RAISIN - Pretzels - Auntie Anne's, Inc.
GLAZINE - Varnishes - United Hardware
GLAZRITE - Putties ☆ - Biddle Co.
GLAZROC - Paints - Rock Paint & Chemical Co.
GLAZTILE - Paneling - ABT Co., Inc.
GLAZY BONE - Pet chews - Items Inc.
GLB - Lighting equipment - General Electric Co.
GLB - Thread - Belding Heminway Co. Inc.
GLC - Lenses–optical - Gentex Corp.
GLC - Motor vehicles–automobiles ☆ - Mazda Motor of America Inc.
GLC100 - Computers - Total Control Products, Inc.
GLEAM - Floor finishing machines–commercial - Mercury Floor Machines Inc.
GLEAM - Paper–gift wrap - American Greetings Corp.
GLEAM - Shortening - Kraft Food Ingredients Corp.
GLEAM-LITES - Christmas tree lights - Dependable Electric Manufacturing Co.
GLEAM TEAM - Toys–automobiles - Mattel, Inc.
GLEAMING SKIN - Cosmetics - Signature Club A Ltd.
GLEAMING STAR - Floor coverings–carpet and rugs ☆ - Callaway Carpets
GLEAM'N SHREDS - Novelty items - Beistle Co.
GLEAM'N STREAMERS - Novelty items - Beistle Co.
GLEAM'N TWIRL - Novelty items - Beistle Co.
GLEAM'N WRAP - Paper–gift wrap - Beistle Co.
GLEAMO - Sealing compounds - PLC
GLEAN - Herbicides - E.I. Dupont de Nemours and Co.
GLEAN BAG 100% RECYCLED GB, THE - Bags–paper - LinPac, Inc.
GLEAN BINDER - Binders - LinPac, Inc.
GLEAN BOX - Boxes–corrugated paperboard - LinPac, Inc.
GLEAN BOX 100% RECYCLED GB, THE - Boxes–corrugated paperboard - LinPac, Inc.
GLEAN-TECH - Adhesives and sealants - Jules J. Fryoux
GLEANER - Toys–automobiles - Agco Corp.
GLEANONS - Toys - Mattel, Inc.
GLEASH - Pet collars - George Landis
GLED - Musical instrument accessories ☆ - Five Star Entertainment
GLEE - Beverages–carbonated - Malone and Hyde Inc.
GLEE - Skin care products - Helene Curtis Industries Inc.
GLEE CLUB - Musical instruments - C. Bruno & Son Inc.
GLEEM - Paint - Wheeler's Paints
GLEEM - Paints ☆ - Dutch Boy Group
GLEEM - Toothpaste - Procter & Gamble Co.
GLEEM COLORSCOPE - Paints ☆ - Dutch Boy Group
GLEEM II - Toothpaste - Procter & Gamble Co.
GLEEMERS - Cosmetics - MNI Products Inc.
GLEISSNER - Musical instrument accessories - International Violin Co. Ltd.
GLEMBY - Pharmaceutical preparations - Glemby Co. Inc.
GLEME - Cleaning preparations–window - Claire Manufacturing Co.
GLEN - Beverages–alcohol - White Rock Distilleries Inc.
GLEN - Hair-cutting shears - B.W. Boyd Shears Inc.
GLEN - Shoes - Glen Shoe Co. Inc.
GLEN ABBEY - Bathtubs–enameled - Lyons Industries Inc.
GLEN AFTON - Fruits and vegetables - Rinehart Orchards Inc.
GLEN ALBYN - Beverages–malt - European Beverage Co., Inc.
GLEN ARBOR - Candles - Hanna's Potpourri Specialties, Inc.
GLEN ARBOR - Playground equipment - Coleman Co., Inc.
GLEN BUDINE - Liquors - Leonard Kreusch, Inc.
GLEN BURNIE - Floor coverings ☆ - Tarkett, Inc.
GLEN CANDAM - Beverages–malt - European Beverage Co., Inc.
GLEN CLOVA SCOTCH - Beverages–alcohol - Marie Brizard Wines & Spirits, USA
GLEN COURT - Floor coverings–carpet and rugs - Alexander Smith Carpets
GLEN COVE - Fabrics–tapestry - Comark Wallcoverings
GLEN COVE - Floor coverings - Bruce Hardwood Floors
GLEN COVE - Furniture ☆ - Bassett Furniture Industries, Inc.
GLEN COVE - Wallpaper ☆ - Thomas Strahan Wallcoverings
GLEN EAGLE - Floor coverings–carpet and rugs ☆ - Customweave Carpets Inc.
GLEN ECHO - Floor coverings–carpet and rugs - Barrett Carpet Mills Inc.
GLEN ELLEN - Wines - Glen Ellen Winery
GLEN ELLEN - Wines - IDV Wines (Beaulieu Vineyard)
GLEN FALLS - Sinks–metal - Kohler Co.
GLEN GALLERY - Stationery - Fragrances of Ireland Accent on Irish Wares Ltd.

☆ = Now out of production

GLEN GATE - Apparel–athletic - Swingster Co.
GLEN-GERY - Bricks - Glen-Gery Corp.
GLEN HAVEN - Floor coverings–carpet and rugs - Galaxy Carpet Mills Inc.
GLEN HEATHER - Floor coverings–carpet and rugs - Mohawk Carpet Corp.
GLEN HEATHER - Floor coverings–carpet and rugs ✰ - Karastan-Bigelow Inc.
GLEN-JOE - Food products - Glen-Joe Inc.
GLEN-L - Boats - Glen-L Marine Designs
GLEN LAKE - Food products - Triple D Orchards Inc.
GLEN LOATES - Artists' materials - Nature Incentives USA
GLEN MHOR - Beverages–malt - European Beverage Co., Inc.
GLEN MILLS - Grindstones - Glen Mills Inc.
GLEN MORAY - Beverages–alcohol - Blair Importers Ltd.
GLEN MORAY - Whiskey ✰ - Marie Brizard Wines & Spirits, USA
GLEN MORAY - Whiskey ✰ - David Sherman Corp.
GLEN OAK - Furniture - Cochrane Furniture Co. Inc.
GLEN OAK - Lumber - Glen Oak Lumber and Milling Inc.
GLEN OAKS - Floor coverings–carpet and rugs - Gulistan Carpet Inc.
GLEN OAKS - Furniture ✰ - Hooker Furniture Corp.
GLEN OAKS - Slacks–men's - Glen Oaks Industries Inc.
GLEN OAKS - Wallpaper - Newmarket Designs Ltd.
GLEN OAKS - Wallpaper ✰ - Tattersalls
GLEN OAKS - Wines ✰ - Louis M. Martini Corp.
GLEN OAKS - Yogurt - Glen Oaks Farms
GLEN PARK - Tomato pastes and sauces - Federated Foods Inc.
GLEN RAVEN - Hosiery–women's - Glen Raven Mills Inc.
GLEN ROSE - Wallpaper - Capital Carousel Inc.
GLEN-SLEEVE - Bandages - Glenwood LLC
GLEN SUMMIT - Water–bottled or canned - Glen Summit Springs Water
GLEN-TECH - Fabrics - Glen Raven Mills Inc.
GLEN, THE - Shirts - Watkins Glen International, Inc.
GLEN TOUCH - Yarn - Glen Raven Mills Inc.
GLEN YORK - Blouses–women's ✰ - Salant/Manhattan Industries
GLENAIRE - Goggles - Glendale Protective Technologies Inc.
GLENARA - Fabric stores - Glenoit Mills Inc.
GLENART - Apparel–men's ✰ - Goodstein Bros. & Co. Inc.
GLENAURA - Fabrics - Glenoit Mills Inc.
GLENBEIGH - Wallpaper ✰ - Wallquest, Inc.
GLENBROOK - Candy - Nabisco Foods Group
GLENBROOK - Floor coverings - Congoleum Corp.
GLENBROOK - Lumber - Georgia-Pacific Corp.
GLENBROOK - Trailers–travel - Fleetwood Enterprises, Inc.
GLENBROOK - Wines - B. Cribari & Sons Winery
GLENBROOK ICE-FLOE - Fountains–drinking - Kohler Co.
GLENBROOKE - Apparel–women's ✰ - J.C. Penney Co., Inc.
GLENBURGIE - Beverages–malt - European Beverage Co., Inc.
GLENCANNON - Yarn ✰ - Caron International Inc.
GLENCO - Shoe accessories - Glencairn Manufacturing Co.
GLENCO STAR - Refrigerators - Glenco Star Corp.
GLENCOE - Dinnerware–glass - Franciscan by Johnson Brothers, USA, Inc.
GLENCOE - Floor coverings - Congoleum Corp.
GLENCOE - Food products - Glencoe Butter and Produce Association
GLENCOE - Publisher's imprints - McGraw-Hill Companies, Inc.
GLENCOE PUBLISHING CO. INC. - Publisher's imprints - MacMillan Publishing Co. Inc.
GLENCRAFT - Wallpaper ✰ - Imperial Wallcoverings, Inc.
GLENCREE - Earthenware ✰ - Waterford Wedgewood USA, Inc.
GLENDALE - Beverages - Wetterau Inc.
GLENDALE - Bicycles - Kent International Inc.
GLENDALE - Clocks - Ridgeway Clock Co.
GLENDALE - Easels - Anco Wood Specialties Inc.
GLENDALE - Furniture ✰ - Broyhill Furniture Industries, Inc.
GLENDALE - Hardware - Pease Industries, Inc.
GLENDALE - Manufactured homes - Redman Industries, Inc.
GLENDALE - Paints ✰ - Dehart Paint & Varnish Co.
GLENDALE - Thread - Threads USA Div.
GLENDORA - Floor coverings–carpet and rugs ✰ - Walter Carpet Mills
GLENDRONACH, THE - Beverages–alcohol - Hiram Walker & Sons, Inc.
GLENDROSTEN - Liquors - Leonard Kreusch, Inc.
GLENDURA - Wallpaper ✰ - Imperial Wallcoverings, Inc.
GLENEAGLE - Goggles - Glendale Protective Technologies Inc.
GLENEAGLES - Apparel and accessories - Hartmarx Corp.
GLENFARCLAS - Whiskey - Barton Brands, Ltd.
GLENFARCLASS-GLENLIVET - Beverages–malt - European Beverage Co., Inc.
GLENFIDDICH - Liquors - William Grant & Sons, Inc.
GLENFIELD - Guns ✰ - Marlin Firearms Co.

GLENFIELD FARMS - Milk - Wholesale Service Brands, Inc.
GLENFORRES - Whiskey - European Beverage Co., Inc.
GLENGARD - Goggles - Glendale Protective Technologies Inc.
GLENGARIOCH - Liquors ✰ - European Beverage Co., Inc.
GLENGARRIFF - Earthenware ✰ - Waterford Wedgewood USA, Inc.
GLENGATE - Apparel and accessories - Glengate Apparel Inc.
GLENGOYNE - Whiskey - Paterno Imports, Ltd.
GLENGUARD ICE-FLOE - Fountains–drinking - Kohler Co.
GLENHAVEN - Beverages–alcohol ✰ - Maison Jomere Ltd.
GLENHOLLOW - Wallpaper - Seabrook Wallcoverings, Inc.
GLENKEITH - Beverages–malt - European Beverage Co., Inc.
GLENLIVET - Beverages–malt - European Beverage Co., Inc.
GLENLIVET - Liquors - House of Seagram
GLENLIVET SINGLE, THE - Liquors - House of Seagram
GLENLOCHY - Beverages–malt - European Beverage Co., Inc.
GLENMAR - Paper–writing - Kurtz Bros. Inc.
GLENMARK - Food products - Glenmark Industries, Ltd.
GLENMARK - Whiskey - Distilled Trading International
GLENMARK FRESH ORIGINALS - Food products - Glenmark Industries, Ltd.
GLENMERE - Tables–wood ✰ - Anco Wood Specialties Inc.
GLENMERE - Teas - Harris Milford & Co., Inc.
GLENMONT - Cabinets - Yorktowne Inc.
GLENMORANGIE - Whiskey - Schieffelin and Somerset Co.
GLENMORE - Earthenware ✰ - Waterford Wedgewood USA, Inc.
GLENMORE - Liquors - Canandaigua Wine Co. Inc.
GLENMORE - Thread - Threads USA Div.
GLENN DOMAN - Recording label - Glenn Doman
GLENN MELLO - Candy - Glenn Confections Inc.
GLENN ST. STUDIO, THE - Fabrics - Malden Mills Industries, Inc.
GLENNA'S ORIGINAL JAMALADE - Jams and jellies - Glenna E. Hazelwood
GLENNEL - Compounding material - Dunnington Co.
GLENNON BITTAN - Apparel and accessories - Glennon Bittan Group, Inc.
GLENNTEX - Fabrics - Scan Lines Inc.
GLENNVEL - Leather–vellum - Scan Lines Inc.
GLENNWOOD - Cribs–wood ✰ - Welsh Co.
GLENNY'S - Snack foods - Glenn Foods Inc.
GLENNY'S FAT-FREE - Food products - Glenn Foods Inc.
GLENOAK - Furniture - Chromcraft Corp.
GLENOIT - Fabric stores - Glenoit Mills Inc.
GLENOLA NOOKIES - Snack foods - Glenn Foods Inc.
GLENORA - Dinnerware ✰ - Corning Inc.
GLENORA - Wines - Glenora Wine Cellars, Inc.
GLENRAY - Food products machinery - Tomlinson Industries
GLENROSE - Wallpaper - Morton Jonap Co. Inc.
GLENROTHES - Beverages–malt - European Beverage Co., Inc.
GLEN'S KINDLIN' - Fireplace logs–treated - Clemens Co.
GLENSHIRE - Apparel–men's ✰ - J.C. Penney Co., Inc.
GLENSIDE - Canned vegetables - American Stores Co.
GLENSITE - Goggles - Glendale Protective Technologies Inc.
GLENSTONE - Floor coverings–carpet and rugs - Conquest Carpet Mills Inc.
GLENSTONE - Furniture ✰ - Bassett Furniture Industries, Inc.
GLENSTYLE - Wallpaper ✰ - Imperial Wallcoverings, Inc.
GLENTAUCHERS - Beverages–malt - European Beverage Co., Inc.
GLENTEX - Apparel and accessories - Glentex Corp.
GLENTOUCH - Yarn - Glen Raven Mills Inc.
GLENTROMIE HIGHLAND - Whiskey ✰ - Sazerac Co. Inc.
GLENTWOOD - Floor coverings–carpet and rugs - Karastan-Bigelow Inc.
GLENVALE - Beverages–alcohol - Carradale Import Co.
GLENVIEW - Cabinets - American Woodmark Corp.
GLENVIEW - Lamps - Stiffel Co.
GLENWELD - Goggles ✰ - Glendale Protective Technologies Inc.
GLENWOOD - Product description unknown - Wood Bros. Inc.
GLENWOOD - Cider - Thomas Manning
GLENWOOD - Dinnerware–glass ✰ - Reston Lloyd Ltd.
GLENWOOD - Drapery rods - Kirsch Co.
GLENWOOD - Furniture - Dinaire Corp.
GLENWOOD - Giftware ✰ - Gorham Inc.
GLENWOOD - Glassware–household - Durand International
GLENWOOD - Housewares - Amana Refrigeration Inc.
GLENWOOD - Underwear and nightwear - Munsingwear, Inc.
GLENWOOD - Wood products ✰ - Anco Wood Specialties Inc.
GLENWOOD COURT - Furniture ✰ - Bassett Furniture Industries, Inc.
GLENWOOD II - Cabinets–wood ✰ - Kitchen Kompact Inc.
GLENWOOD-INGLEWOOD - Water bottles–rubber - Glenwood-Inglewood Co.
GLENWOOD INN - Syrup ✰ - Food Producers International Inc.
GLENWOOD SPRINGS - Wines - Mark West Vineyards

✰ = Now out of production

GLETSCHERPRISE - Snuff - James B. Russell Inc.
GLH GREAT LITTLE HARP - Harmonicas - Hohner Inc.
GLI INTERNATIONAL - Measuring instruments - Great Lakes Instruments, Inc.
GLICINE - Yarn ☆ - William Unger & Co. Inc.
GLID-COOL - Paints - Glidden Co.
GLID-CRETE - Paints - Glidden Co.
GLID GUARD - Paints - Glidden Co.
GLID-O-MATIC - Brushes–paint - Baker Brush Co. Inc.
GLID-SEAL - Paints ☆ - Glidden Co.
GLID-SET - Paints ☆ - Glidden Co.
GLID-STRIP - Paints - Glidden Co.
GLID-THANE ONE - Paints - Glidden Co.
GLID-TONE - Paints - Glidden Co.
GLIDA-PUCK - Hockey equipment - Life Industries Inc.
GLIDAIR - Paints ☆ - Glidden Co.
GLIDDEN - Paints - Glidden Co.
GLIDDEN BEST SELLERS - Wallpaper ☆ - Glidden Co.
GLIDDENCOAT - Paints - Glidden Co.
GLIDDENSPAR - Paints ☆ - Glidden Co.
GLIDE - Health care products - W.L. Gore & Associates, Inc.
GLIDE - Lip balms - L.T. Laboratories
GLIDE - Paints - Jones Blair Co.
GLIDE - Paints - Sophir Morris Paint
GLIDE - Shoes - Up-Front Footwear, Inc.
GLIDE - Skin care products - Barrows Pharmacal Inc.
GLIDE-A-MIRROR - Doors–glass ☆ - PPG Industries, Inc.
GLIDE & DECAY - Musical instrument accessories - EJE Research Corp.
GLIDE ARCH - Binders - Boorum & Pease Co.
GLIDE-EASE - Paints - Spencer-Adams Paint Co. Inc.
GLIDE-FREE - Inks - Formulabs, Inc.
GLIDE-LOCK 180 - Easels and easel holders - James-Howard Co.
GLIDE-ON - Paints - Glidden Co.
GLIDE-ON - Paper clips ☆ - Noesting Inc.
GLIDE ON - Trailers–boat - Soaring Industries Inc.
GLIDE RAIL - Bathroom fixtures - Alsons Corp.
GLIDE RIDER - Bicycles - Emory Manufacturing Co.
GLIDE RITE - Floor waxes - Burnishine Products
GLIDE-STAR - Fixtures ☆ - Prest-On Co.
GLIDE THROUGH - Hair care products - Roberts Research Laboratories, Inc.
GLIDEFIT - Insulating materials - Amesbury Group Inc.
GLIDEMASTER - Window frames ☆ - Biltbest Windows
GLIDEPOINT - Computer peripheral equipment - Humphrey Systems
GLIDEPOINT - Computer software - Cirque Corp.
GLIDER - Artists' materials - Stangren Co.
GLIDER - Office accessories - Montisa Office Furniture
GLIDER - Paints - Schulte Paint & Lacquer Manufacturing Co., Inc.
GLIDER - Strollers–baby - Graco Children's Products
GLIDER - Thread ☆ - SCT Yarns Inc.
GLIDER II - Medical apparatus - Trademark Corp.
GLIDER-RIDER - Playground equipment - Wonderline
GLIDER SHADE - Window shades - Comfortex Corp.
GLIDER, THE - Hair care products - Helene Curtis Industries Inc.
GLIDER, THE - Vacuum cleaners and accessories–commercial - Lomart Industries
GLIDEX - Telephone apparatus - General Communications Products Inc.
GLIDEXPRESS - Irons–electric - Black & Decker Corp.
GLIDING LINERS - Cosmetics - Sassaby Inc.
GLIDOMATIC - Lead products ☆ - Koh-I-Noor, Inc.
GLIDRAULIC - Hardware ☆ - Illinois Lock Co.
GLIDVAR - Paints ☆ - Glidden Co.
GLIFX - Signs - Glifx, Inc.
GLIM-R - Floor finishing machines–commercial ☆ - Foy-Johnston Inc.
GLIM-R - Varnishes - Perry & Derrick Co.
GLIMMA - Glassware–household - Swedish Products Inc. (Sojo Inc.)
GLIMMAIRE - Apparel–men's ☆ - Michaels/Stern & Co. Inc.
GLIMMER - Dolls - Mattel, Inc.
GLIMMER - Water treating compounds - PPG Industries, Inc.
GLIMMER - Yarn ☆ - Caron International Inc.
GLIMMER - Yarn ☆ - William Unger & Co. Inc.
GLIMMERSILK - Fabric - Warren Leasing, Inc.
GLIMMERSTICKS - Cosmetics - Avon Products, Inc.
GLIMPSE - Computer software - Pixar
GLINTS - Hair coloring preparations - Clairol Inc.
GLIS - Starch–laundry - L & F Consumer Products
GLIS N - Hair care products - Roux Laboratories, Inc.
GLISADE - Detergents - L & F Consumer Products

GLISANDA - Apparel and accessories - Vanity Fair Mills Inc.
GLISSADE - Apparel - Glissade Products
GLISSADE - Sporting goods - James R. Gerlach
GLISSTIPS - Pens - Hedra Inc.
GLISTEN - Frames–eyeglass ☆ - Universal/Univis Inc.
GLISTEN - Toilets–porcelain - Sterling Plumbing Group Inc.
GLISTENS - Candy - Farley Candy Co.
GLISTER - Mouthwashes - Amway Corp.
GLIST'N - Hair care products - Revlon Consumer Products Corp.
GLIT - Cleaning preparations–window - Kano Laboratories Inc.
GLIT - Sponges - Glit, Inc.
GLIT MAT - Mats–grass, reed, and jute - Glit, Inc.
GLIT SAND - Sanders and grinders - Glit, Inc.
GLIT-STIK - Tools–hand-operated - Glit, Inc.
GLITCH - Figurines - Nord Advertising Associates
GLITCH GRABBER - Electronic equipment ☆ - GC Thorsen, Inc.
GLITCH GRABBER PLUS - Electronic equipment ☆ - GC Thorsen, Inc.
GLITCH MASTER - Electrical equipment - New Concepts Technology
GLITTER - Bandages - American White Cross, Inc.
GLITTER - Craft supplies ☆ - Walco Linck Co.
GLITTER - Floor coverings - Congoleum Corp.
GLITTER - Paints - Long Island Paint & Chemical Co.
GLITTER - Paints - Tulip Productions
GLITTER - Paper–gummed ☆ - Park Sherman
GLITTER - Yarn ☆ - Caron International Inc.
GLITTER & GLOW - Dolls - Mattel, Inc.
GLITTER AND SAND CREATIONS - Handicraft kit - Quincrafts Corp.
GLITTER ART - Craft supplies ☆ - Strombecker Corp.
GLITTER BEACH - Dolls - Mattel, Inc.
GLITTER BOX - Apparel trimmings - Glitter International, Inc.
GLITTER BRITE - Craft supplies ☆ - Walco Linck Co.
GLITTER-BRITE - Paints - Xonex International, Inc.
GLITTER CRITTERS - Novelty items - Paper Magic Group Inc.
GLITTER EEL - Fishing lures - Uncle Josh Bait Co.
GLITTER EGGS - Novelty items - Easter Unltd. Inc.
GLITTER ESSENCE - Jewelry, cosmetics - Glitter Essence Corp.
GLITTER FROG - Fishing lures - Uncle Josh Bait Co.
GLITTER GEMS - Toys - Binney & Smith Inc.
GLITTER GLAMOUR GOOP - Toys - Toymax Inc.
GLITTER-GLO - American International Industries
GLITTER GLO - Craft supplies - Ben Cooper Inc.
GLITTER GLOBE - Lamp bulbs–fluorescent - Duro-Test Corp.
GLITTER GLOVE - Chewing gum ☆ - Fleer Corp.
GLITTER GLUE - Craft supplies ☆ - Walco Linck Co.
GLITTER GREETERS - Novelty items - Paper Magic Group Inc.
GLITTER-HEART - Telephone directories - Heart Cards
GLITTER ISLAND - Toys - Mattel, Inc.
GLITTER JAFAR - Novelty items - Paper Magic Group Inc.
GLITTER KNIT - Yarn - Lion Brand Yarn Co.
GLITTER-KOTE - Varnishes ☆ - Sherwin-Williams Automotive Finishes Corp.
GLITTER LITE - Lighting fixtures ☆ - Lava-Simplex Internationale
GLITTER LOOKS - Hobby kits - Tri-Chem Inc.
GLITTER MAGIC - Craft supplies ☆ - Walco Linck Co.
GLITTER MAGIC - Yarn - Lion Brand Yarn Co.
GLITTER 'N GROW - Dolls - Mattel, Inc.
GLITTER PLAQUES - Giftware - Kage Co. Inc.
GLITTER PORK - Fishing lures - Uncle Josh Bait Co.
GLITTER STICKERS - Toys ☆ - Henry Gordy International Inc.
GLITTER SUPER BAIT - Bait - Siberian Salmon Egg Co.
GLITTER SURPRISE - Toys - Mattel, Inc.
GLITTER TIPS - Cosmetics ☆ - London International U.S. Holdings
GLITTER-TONE - Posters ☆ - Milton Bradley Co.
GLITTER WEBBING - Pigments–metallic - Carnival Arts, Inc.
GLITTERATOR - Toys - Tiger Electronics, Inc.
GLITTERCOAT - Paints - Morton International Inc. (Morton Salt Div.)
GLITTERDOMES - Giftware - Roman, Inc.
GLITTERFOIL - Gold products - M. Swift and Sons Inc.
GLITTERING GHOULS - Novelty items - Paper Magic Group Inc.
GLITTERING GOLDFISH IN FRESHWATER POOL - Toys - Tonka Corp.
GLITTERLOCKS - Dolls - Mattel, Inc.
GLITTERON - Thread - Belding Heminway Co. Inc.
GLITTERTEX - Christmas tree ornaments - Santa's Best
GLITTERWRAP - Giftware - Glitterwrap Inc.
GLITZ - Craft supplies - Glitz Inc.
GLITZ - Ophthalmic goods - Foremost Optical Products
GLITZ & GLAMOUR - Bicycles - Dynacraft Industries Inc.

☆ = Now out of production

GLITZ IT! - Craft supplies - Glitz Inc.
GLITZY GEAR - Paint sets–hobby ☆ - Tulip Productions
GLIZY - Hosiery ☆ - M.A. Rabinowitz Corp.
GLM - Condiments ☆ - G.L. Mezzetta Inc.
GLM - Microphones - Crown International, Inc.
GLM - Rackets–tennis - Wilson Sporting Goods Co.
GLO - Food products ☆ - Hanover Foods Corp.
GLO - Pet products - John Ewing Co.
GLO - Recording label - Jody Record Corp.
GLO-BAND - Toys - Allied Toy Co.
GLO-BLASTERS! - Paper - Miami Valley Paper Co. Inc.
GLO-BOARD - Artists' materials - Southern States Marketing, Inc.
GLO-BRITE - Paints - Vogart Crafts Corp.
GLO-BRITE - Pet products - Glo-Marr Products Inc.
GLO-COAT - Floor waxes - S.C. Johnson & Son, Inc.
GLO COAT - Pet products - Natra Pet Inc.
GLO-COPTER - Toys–airplanes - Hobie Enterprises, Inc.
GLO CREME - Finishing agents ☆ - Tulip Productions
GLO CURL - Ribbons - Gaylord Specialties Corp.
GLO-DADDY - Fishing lures - Michael P. Rogan
GLO-DOODLER SLATE - Games - Colorforms
GLO . DOT - Archery equipment - Truglo, Inc.
GLO-EZE - Sporting goods - Almetek Industries, Inc.
GLO-FETCH - Balls–rubber - Rockywoods, Inc.
GLO-FLECTOR - Lighting fixtures - Trimble House Corp.
GLO-FLEX - Floor coverings ☆ - Congoleum Corp.
GLO-FLEX - Tape–adhesive - American Ingenuity, Inc.
GLO-FLO - Hobby kits ☆ - Hazel Pearson Handicrafts
GLO-GETTER - Fishing lures - Maurine Industries Inc.
GLO GLUV - Gloves - Granet Inc.
GLO-GRAIN - Ribbons ☆ - Paperwork Ltd.
GLO HEDD-HUNTER - Sporting goods ☆ - James Heddon's Sons
GLO-HIPS - Signboards - Pace Industries, Inc.
GLO-KLEEN - Paint removers ☆ - Monsey Products Co.
GLO-KLEN - Fireplace equipment - Conserve-a-Therm Co. Inc.
GLO KNIT - Yarn ☆ - Lion Brand Yarn Co.
GLO-LINKS - Toys - Allied Toy Co.
GLO-LON - Hosiery - Dan River Inc.
GLO-LUSTRE - Enamels ☆ - Sherwin-Williams Automotive Finishes Corp.
GLO-MARR - Pet products - Glo-Marr Products Inc.
GLO-MASTER - Signs - Mid-America Building Products Corp.
GLO-MAX - Awnings - Styleline
GLO-MAX - Cables–fiber optic - Glo-Max Fiber Optics System, Inc.
GLO-MESH - Sponges - Glit, Inc.
GLO-MOR - Charcoal - Arrow Industries, Inc.
GLO 'N GO - Lamps - Playskool Baby Inc.
GLO NITE - Coatings - BASF Corp.
GLO NOTES - Paper - Miami Valley Paper Co. Inc.
GLO-PLUGS - Plugs–ear - Karlen Manufacturing, Inc.
GLO-PRO - Floor finishing machines–commercial - United Floor Machine Co.
GLO-RING - Tools - Eraser Co. Inc.
GLO-RITE - Crayons ☆ - Milton Bradley Co.
GLO-RITE - Inks–lithographic - Momentum Graphics
GLO-RITER - Games - Colorforms
GLO-SEL - Pharmaceutical preparations - Syosset Laboratories Inc.
GLO-SHEEN - Pet products - Glo-Marr Products Inc.
GLO-STICKYS - Paper - Miami Valley Paper Co. Inc.
GLO-STRIP - Floor coverings–tile - R.C.A. Rubber Co.
GLO TADPOLLY - Sporting goods - James Heddon's Sons
GLO-TEL - Chemical preparations - E.I. Dupont de Nemours and Co.
GLO-THERM - Thermometers - Taylor Environmental Instruments
GLO-TIP - Medical apparatus - Wilson-Cook Medical Inc.
GLO TO SLEEP - Wallpaper ☆ - Kingfisher Wallcoverings
GLO TONE - Ribbons - Gaylord Specialties Corp.
GLO-TONE - Yarn - Lily Craft Products
GLO-TONES - Tiles–ceramic - H & R Johnson Inc.
GLO-TRAC - Coatings - Garon Products Inc.
GLO-TRODE - Health care products - Medical Science Products Inc.
GLO WARM - Fireplaces - Rinnai America Corp.
GLO WORM LIGHT & LEARN - Games ☆ - Milton Bradley Co.
GLO-WORMS - Candy - Ferrara Pan Candy Co., Inc.
GLO WORM'S MUSICAL DREAMWORLD - Toys - Playskool, Inc.
GLO YO - Toys ☆ - Airko Manufacturing Co.
GLOBAL - Cigarettes - Global Shipping Corp.
GLOBAL - Cooking equipment–household - New Era Co.
GLOBAL - Dryers–commercial - American Dryer Inc.

GLOBAL - Food products - Global Produce Corp.
GLOBAL - Food products - Reede International Seafood Corp.
GLOBAL - Games - Eric M. Heermann
GLOBAL - Pet products - Pets Pacifica Inc.
GLOBAL - Sporting goods - Vision Sports Holding Corp.
GLOBAL - Umbrellas - Darwell Import Co. Inc.
GLOBAL ACCESS - Educational materials - Penton Overseas, Inc.
GLOBAL ACTIONS - Security brokers - Telesphere Corp.
GLOBAL ASSAULT FORCE - Toys - Davis Brothers & Madison Ltd.
GLOBAL BALANCE - Cleaning preparations - Allan Benjamin
GLOBAL BRAIN - Computer software - First Financial Resources, Inc.
GLOBAL BRAIN - Video production - Global Brain, Inc.
GLOBAL CARPET - Floor coverings–carpet and rugs - Durfee's Inc.
GLOBAL CASUAL - Apparel and accessories - Kinney Shoe Corp.
GLOBAL CHURCH GROWTH - Publisher's imprints ☆ - William Carey Library
GLOBAL COLORS - Markers–felt-tip - Liqui-Mark
GLOBAL CONQUEST - Computer software - Microprose Software, Inc.
GLOBAL CONSENSUS, INC - Computer software - Global Consensus, Inc.
GLOBAL COOLER - Ice chests - Polyset Products, Inc.
GLOBAL DATA MANAGER - Computer software - World Game Institute
GLOBAL DELIGHTS - Food products - Caribbean Products Ltd.
GLOBAL DIVERSITY GAME - Games - Quality Education Development, Inc.
GLOBAL DOUBLE OVAL - Vitamins and nutritional supplements - Global Marketing Associates, Inc.
GLOBAL DRIVETRAIN - Transmissions–motor vehicle - Truck Parts Co.
GLOBAL EFFECT - Apparel and accessories - Sheer Joy Corp.
GLOBAL ELEPHANT - Rice - Tong Enterprises Inc.
GLOBAL EXPEDITION - Apparel–men's - Price Co.
GLOBAL EXPEDITIONS - Floor coverings–tile - Interface, Inc.
GLOBAL EXPLORER - Computer program - Delorme Publishing Co., Inc.
GLOBAL EXPLORER SW 2000 - Radios–citizens' band - Electrobrand, Inc.
GLOBAL EXPRESS ATLAS-SERIES - Computer software - Orange Cherry Software
GLOBAL EXPRESS ATLAS-U.S. - Computer software - Orange Cherry Software
GLOBAL EXPRESS ATLAS-WORLD - Computer software - Orange Cherry Software
GLOBAL GOLF - Publisher's imprints ☆ - Flagpin Productions
GLOBAL GOURMET - Publisher's imprints - Lowell House
GLOBAL GREEN - Apparel and accessories - Global Green, Inc.
GLOBAL GRILL - Meat products - Hudson Foods, Inc.
GLOBAL HORIZON INTERCHANGE - Computer software - State Street Boston Corp.
GLOBAL IMAGE - Televisions ☆ - Avnet, Inc.
GLOBAL INNOVATOR OF SMART PRODUCTS - Sonar systems and equipment - Saturn Electronics & Engineering, Inc.
GLOBAL LAB COLOR - Computer software - Data Translation, Inc.
GLOBAL LAB IMAGE - Computer software - Data Translation, Inc.
GLOBAL LOGISTICS 2000+ - Computer programs - Dymax Systems Inc.
GLOBAL-MID SOUTH - Hardware - Blaine Window Hardware Inc.
GLOBAL MUSICON - Recording label - Global Records & Tapes
GLOBAL NUTRITION, LTD - Vitamins and nutritional supplements - Global Nutrition, Ltd.
GLOBAL OUTLOOK, THE - Publisher's imprints - RGB Associates, Inc.
GLOBAL PACIFIC - Recording label - Global Pacific Records
GLOBAL PET - Pet products - Global Pet Products Inc.
GLOBAL PM - Computer software - AT&T Global Information Solutions
GLOBAL PORTFOLIO SYSTEM - Computer software - Belvedere Financial Systems, Inc.
GLOBAL PRODUCTION SERVICES - Motion picture distributors–prerecorded - Global Production Services
GLOBAL PROTECTION CORP. - Condoms - Global Protection Corp.
GLOBAL R.E.S.C.U.E. - Apparel and accessories - Michael Sloan & Associates
GLOBAL SATELLITE - Recording label - Global Records & Tapes
GLOBAL SCENTS - Perfumes - Lorann Oils, Inc.
GLOBAL SOLUTIONS - Artists' materials - Global Solutions, Inc.
GLOBAL SPORTS LEGENDS - Awards, plaques and medals - Global Recognition, Inc.
GLOBAL STUDIES - Publisher's imprints - Dushkin Publishing Group Inc.
GLOBAL SURVIVAL - Games - Vision Quest Enterprises, Inc.
GLOBAL TELEMEDIX - Computer terminals - William S. Kazman
GLOBAL TEXT - Computer peripheral equipment - Hewlett-Packard Co.
GLOBAL TEXTURES - Wallpaper - Royson's Corp.
GLOBAL TRADING - Fruits–frozen - Global Trading Inc.
GLOBAL TRENDS - Caps–baseball - Dorfman-Pacific Co. Inc.
GLOBAL USA - Computer systems - Global Computer Network, Inc.

☆ = Now out of production

GLOBAL VANTAGE - Computer storage devices–optical - McGraw-Hill Companies, Inc.
GLOBAL VIBES - Apparel and accessories - Yamo Designs
GLOBAL VIDEOPHONE STANDARD GVS - Videophones - At&T Corp.
GLOBAL VILLAGE - Recording label - Joseph Nicoletti Music Co.
GLOBAL VISION - Sunglasses - Wright Products Co.
GLOBAL VISUAL LIBRARY - Computer software - Geosphere Project
GLOBAL WARMERS - Beverages–alcohol - Happy Guests International, Inc.
GLOBAL WARMING - Apparel–children's - Terri Peck
GLOBAL WORSTEDS - Apparel–men's - J. Schoeneman Inc.
GLOBAL WRAP - Plastics–laminated - Global Wrap and Services, Inc.
GLOBAL YACHTS - Jackets - Global Yachts International, Inc.
GLOBAL ZERO - Video production - Global Zero L.P.
GLOBAL ZONE - Apparel–women's - Weekend Exercise Co., Inc.
GLOBALBEST - Jackets–leather - Global Impex Enterprises Inc.
GLOBALCENTER - Computer software - Global Village Communication, Inc.
GLOBALFILE - Office supplies - American Trading and Production Corp.
GLOBALFIND - Computer software - Stierer Group, Inc.
GLOBALINK - Computer software - Globalink, Inc.
GLOBALINK THE TRANSLATION COMPANY - Computer software - Globalink, Inc.
GLOBALPAK - Containers–plastic - Elco Textron Inc.
GLOBALSYNC - Switches–electric - NEC Technologies, Inc.
GLOBALTALK - Computer software - Lexicon Branding, Inc.
GLOBALTEK - Vacuum cleaners and accessories - Globaltek International Corp.
GLOBALVIEW - Computer software - Xerox Corp.
GLOBALVISION - Computer software and accessories - Electronic Publishing Group, Inc.
GLOBALWARE - Computer software - International Documentation
GLOBANDS - Novelty items - Inspiration Corp.
GLOBE - Bicycles - Ross Bicycles USA, Ltd.
GLOBE - Brushes–paint - Corona Brushes Inc.
GLOBE - Dairy products - Globe Extracts Inc.
GLOBE - Food products - Curtice-Burns Foods, Inc.
GLOBE - Office machines - Distinctive Business Machines
GLOBE - Paints - Schulte Paint & Lacquer Manufacturing Co., Inc.
GLOBE - Pencils ☆ - Faber-Castell Corp.
GLOBE - Skates–roller - Globe United Inc.
GLOBE - Spices and extracts - Borthwicks Flavors USA, Inc.
GLOBE - Thread - United Thread Mills Corp.
GLOBE 25 - Shingles–asphalt or tar - Globe Building Materials Inc.
GLOBE A-1 - Macaroni - Western Globe Products Inc.
GLOBE-ALUME - Siding–metal ☆ - Globe Building Materials Inc.
GLOBE & BANNER DESIGN - Toys - Wonderline
GLOBE BASE III - Shingles–asphalt or tar - Globe Building Materials Inc.
GLOBE CAP & BASE - Shingles–asphalt or tar - Globe Building Materials Inc.
GLOBE-GUARD - Office supplies ☆ - Globe-Weis
GLOBE MASTER - Paints - Schulte Paint & Lacquer Manufacturing Co., Inc.
GLOBE MOSAICS - Ceramic tile - Integrity Tile Co.
GLOBE/PEQUOT PRESS, THE - Publisher's imprints - Globe/Pequot Press
GLOBE SEALS - Shingles–asphalt or tar - Globe Building Materials Inc.
GLOBE SPIN - Games - Tuxedo Toys
GLOBE STAR - Computer peripheral equipment - Globe Star Innovations, Ltd.
GLOBE TEX - Paints - Schulte Paint & Lacquer Manufacturing Co., Inc.
GLOBE TIME - Clocks - Delfino Products Inc.
GLOBE TROTTER - Containers–insulated ☆ - Aladdin Industries, Inc.
GLOBE TROTTER - Trailers–travel - Airstream Inc.
GLOBE TROTTER - Watches - Hampden Corp.
GLOBE TROTTER, THE - Garment bag - American Flyer
GLOBE-WARE - Tables–wood ☆ - Quaker Industries Ltd.
GLOBE-WEIS - Office supplies - ATAPCO Office Products Group
GLOBEBRIGHT - Christmas tree lights - Noma International, Inc.
GLOBEE - Hobby kits - Twinn-K Hobbies Inc.
GLOBELITES - Lighting equipment - Duro-Lite Lamps Inc.
GLOBELL - Hair care products - Globell Inc.
GLOBEMASTER - Compasses–magnetic - E.S. Ritchie & Sons Inc.
GLOBEMASTER - Globes - Replogle Globes Inc.
GLOBESAVER - Air conditioning equipment - National Refrigeration and Air Conditioning Products, Inc.
GLOBESHOTS - Compact discs–prerecorded ☆ - Digital Wisdom, Inc.
GLOBETROTTER - Artists' materials - Bee Paper Co. Inc.
GLOBETROTTER - Computer software - SourceView Software International
GLOBETROTTER - Pet products - Petland, Inc.
GLOBETROTTER - Utility knives - Buck Knives, Inc.
GLOBIX - Computer software - Infomag Software Systems Inc.

GLOCK - Pistols and holsters - Glock Inc.
GLODO - Shortening - Procter & Gamble Co.
GLOLITE - Christmas tree lights ☆ - Noma International, Inc.
GLOMAR - Lamp bulbs - Satco Products, Inc.
GLOMATI - Marble products - Globe Marble & Tile Inc.
GLOMATI BAGNO - Marble products - Globe Marble & Tile Inc.
GLOMERIX - Floor coverings–tile ☆ - Mannington Carpets, Inc.
GLOMITT - Gloves - Fox River Mills, Inc.
GLOO - Adhesives and sealants - Vibe Records Inc.
GLOOMIES - Dolls - Mattel, Inc.
GLOP - Adhesives and sealants - Carborundum Abrasives North America
GLOP - Candy - Catco, Inc.
GLOPPETS - Puppets - Animal Fair Inc.
GLORANTHA - Games ☆ - Avalon Hill Game Co.
GLORANTHA BESTIARY - Games - Avalon Hill Game Co.
GLORI-WOOD - Finishing agents ☆ - Masury Paint Co.
GLORIA - Accordions - Italo-American Accordion Manufacturing Co.
GLORIA - Floor coverings–carpet and rugs - Gloria of America Inc.
GLORIA - Glassware–household ☆ - Lotus Glass Co.
GLORIA - Hair care products - Lever Brothers Co. Inc.
GLORIA - Mail boxes - Gordon Associates
GLORIA - Skin care products ☆ - Robinette Inc.
GLORIA - Tools–garden - Qualcast USA
GLORIA - Watches - Bulova Corp.
GLORIA - Yarn - William Unger & Co. Inc.
GLORIA BAKER - Toys - Tonka Corp.
GLORIA CABRERA - Hair care products - Gloria Cabrera International Inc.
GLORIA DIEHL BOOK CLUB SELECTION - Publisher's imprints - Book Margins, Inc.
GLORIA EHRET LOUISVILLE - Golfing equipment ☆ - Hillerich & Bradsby Co.
GLORIA FERRER - Wines - Freixenet USA
GLORIA JEAN'S GOURMET COFFEES - Beverages - Gloria Jean's Gourmet Coffees Corp.
GLORIA MARSHALL FIGURE SALON - Physical fitness centers - Gloria Marshall Figure Salons Ltd.
GLORIA MUNDE - Cosmetics - Gloria Munde International
GLORIA RAE - Novelty items - Lady Love
GLORIA SAMPLE - Food products - Gloria Sample
GLORIA SPECIAL - Stationery - H.T. Herbert Co. Inc.
GLORIA SWANSON - Dresses–women's - Anne Klein & Co.
GLORIA VANDERBILT - Apparel and accessories - G.V. Trademark Investments Ltd.
GLORIA VANDERBILT - Apparel and accessories - Regent International Corp.
GLORIA VANDERBILT - Apparel–men's ☆ - Castle Neckwear Inc.
GLORIA VANDERBILT - Belts–apparel - Circa Corp.
GLORIA VANDERBILT - Chocolate candy ☆ - Houston Foods Co.
GLORIA VANDERBILT - Footwear - Fisher Camuto Corp.
GLORIA VANDERBILT - Footwear–women's - E.S. Originals, Inc.
GLORIA VANDERBILT - Leather goods - RGA Accessories Inc.
GLORIA VANDERBILT - Luggage - Pierre Cardin Electronique
GLORIA VANDERBILT - Perfumes - Cosmair Inc.
GLORIA VANDERBILT - Watches - Fada Industries Inc.
GLORIA VANDERBILT COLLECTION - Frames–eyeglass - Zylo Ware Corp.
GLORIA VANDERBILT FOR JONATHAN LOGAN - Dresses–women's ☆ - Jonathan Logan Inc.
GLORIA VANDERBILT SPORT - Bags–cosmetic - G.V. Licensing Inc.
GLORIAGRAPE - Fruits and vegetables - Marglo Products Corp.
GLORIAMELON - Fruits and vegetables - Marglo Products Corp.
GLORIANA - Recording label - Gloriana, Inc.
GLORIANNA - Footwear ☆ - Consolidated Shoe Co., Inc.
GLORIANT - Toiletries - Benjamin Ansehl Co.
GLORIA'S - Cakes–mixes - Gloria's Kitchen
GLORIES ON GREY - Dinnerware–glass - Lenox, Inc.
GLORIETTA - Fruits–canned - Tri Valley Growers, Inc.
GLORIETTA - Vegetables–canned - S & W Fine Foods, Inc.
GLORIETTE - Dinnerware–glass - WMF/USA
GLORIFIED - Rings–jewelry - Feature Enterprises
GLORIOSA - Fabrics - Rosebar Textile Co.
GLORIOUS - Floor coverings - Aladdin Mills, Inc.
GLORIOUS - Perfumes - Cosmair Inc.
GLORIOUS - Wines - Fred Bofird Co.
GLORIOUS BREAD - Breads - Natural Ovens of Manitowoc Inc.
GLORIOUS CHRISTMAS - Figurines - International House Inc.
GLORIOUS GARDENS - Toiletries - Alwin Enterprises International, Inc.
GLORIOUS GLITTERS - Paints ☆ - DecoArt, Inc.
GLORIOUS GRAYS - Hair coloring preparations - Clairol Inc.

☆ = Now out of production

GLORIOUS MUSIC - Recording label - Integrity Music, Inc.
GLORIUS - Jewelry - J.C. Penney Co., Inc.
GLORY - Cigarettes - Tobacco Alternative Inc.
GLORY - Cleaning preparations–carpet and rug - S.C. Johnson & Son, Inc.
GLORY - Floor coverings–carpet and rugs - Barrett Carpet Mills Inc.
GLORY - Rings–jewelry - Artcarved Inc.
GLORY BE! - Calendars ☆ - American Greetings Corp.
GLORY BEE - Bedding–linen - Morning Glory Products
GLORY BIRD - Toys - Mattel, Inc.
GLORY FIELDS - Colognes - Glory Fields Inc.
GLORY FILL - Bedding–linen - Morning Glory Products
GLORY FOODS - Vegetables–pickled or brined - Glory Foods Inc.
GLORY HELMET - Helmets–athletic - Lubinsky & Associates, Inc.
GLORY HOLE - Fishing tackle - Mickey Jacobs, Inc.
GLORY HOUSE - Publisher's imprints - Glory Yau-Huai Tsai
GLORY ROSE - Toilets–enameled - Kohler Co.
GLORY TORCHES - Fireworks - Ingram Enterprises, Inc.
GLORYBEE - Honey - Glorybee Food Inc.
GLOSPAN - Fibers–synthetic - Globe Manufacturing Co.
GLOSS - Cleaning preparations ☆ - Knight Marketing Corp.
GLOSS-8 - Hair care products - J. Strickland & Co.
GLOSS BOSS - Cleaning preparations–household - Pullman/Holt Corp.
GLOSS BOSS, THE - Nail care products ☆ - Noxell Corp.
GLOSS BUILDER - Finishing agents - Calgon Vestal Laboratories
GLOSS LAC - Varnishes - Bridges Smith & Co.
GLOSS MASTER - Floor waxers–household - Southwest Manufacturers & Distributors, Inc.
GLOSS TONE - Tiles–ceramic - Huntington/Pacific Ceramics Inc.
GLOSS-WASH - Automotive parts and accessories - Tuff-Kote Dinol Inc.
GLOSSE - Lipsticks - Revlon Consumer Products Corp.
GLOSSER - Nail care products - Orly International Inc.
GLOSSIES - Apparel–women's - Lily of France Inc.
GLOSSIFIER - Hair care products - Matrix Essentials, Inc.
GLOSSIFYER OIL SPRAY - Hair care products ☆ - Summit Laboratories
GLOSSIMO - Hair care products - Framesi USA/Roffler Industries Inc.
GLOSSINE - Hair care products - Madame C.J. Walker Inc.
GLOSSING - Shampoos - Jheri Redding Products Inc.
GLOSSIQUE - Perfumes - Cosmair Inc.
GLOSS'N TOSS - Cleaning preparations ☆ - S.C. Johnson & Son, Inc.
GLOSSOMAT - Photographic equipment ☆ - Charles Beseler Co.
GLOSSOVERS - Cosmetics - Sassaby Inc.
GLOSSTONE - Pet products - Clifford W. Estes Co. Inc.
GLOSSY COAT - Pet products - Zema Corp.
GLOSTHANE - Finishing agents - Daly's Inc.
GLOSTORA - Hair care products - Sterling Winthrop Inc.
GLOUCESTER - Dishes–earthenware ☆ - Royal China & Porcelain Companies Inc.
GLOUCESTER - Floor coverings–carpet and rugs ☆ - Karastan-Bigelow Inc.
GLOUCESTER - Paints ☆ - Rule Industries, Inc.
GLOUCESTER - Seafood products–fresh or frozen - Fishery Products International USA
GLOUCESTER BY BOSTON - Clocks ☆ - Chelsea Clock Co. Inc.
GLOUCESTER FISHERMAN - Boats - Nautical Boats Ltd.
GLOV-ETT - Shoes - Dodson-Fisher Co.
GLOV ETT - Shoes - Kettle Moraine Shoe Corp.
GLOVABLE - Toys - Liberty International Development, Inc.
GLOVE BOY - Gloves - Glove Boy
GLOVE BUTTER - Health care products - Bowman Manufacturing Co. Inc.
GLOVE CONNECTION - Gloves - Becker Glove International, Inc.
GLOVE CONNECTION BY BECKER - Gloves - Becker Glove International, Inc.
GLOVE COTE - Skin care products - Fibre Glass-Evercoat Co. Inc.
GLOVE-EASE - Shorts–women's ☆ - J. Steiner Imports Inc.
GLOVE-FREE - Labels–paper - Uarco Inc.
GLOVE-HER - Prophylactics - LTC Products, Inc.
GLOVE-IN-A-JAR - Skin care products - Cadet Laboratories
GLOVE KID - Peanut butter ☆ - C.F. Sauer Co.
GLOVE 'N CARE - Cosmetics - Essential Dental Systems, Inc.
GLOVE-SOX - Gloves–work ☆ - Tufco Technologies Inc.
GLOVE, THE - Personal defense products - Carol Kerns
GLOVE, THE - Sporting goods - Terradyne, Ltd.
GLOVEAL - Shoes - Clinic Shoe Co.
GLOVEMATE - Deodorants–personal - Buchanan, Inc.
GLOVE'N CARE - Skin care products - Essential Dental Systems, Inc.
GLOVERALL OF LONDON - Coats - Frank L. Savage Imports Inc.
GLOVES IN A BOTTLE - Skin care products - Gloves In A Bottle, Inc.

GLOVETEX - Health care products - American Health Products Corp.
GLOW - Cleaning preparations ☆ - Vibe Records Inc.
GLOW - Cleaning preparations–household - J. Goddard & Sons
GLOW - Gift shops - Spencer Gifts, Inc.
GLOW - Ophthalmic goods - Foremost Optical Products
GLOW - Shampoos - Beautymasters
GLOW - Soft drink - Bottlers International Ltd.
GLOW & GLITTER - Shoes - Polly of California
GLOW BELL BOTTLE - Pet products - Novalek, Inc.
GLOW BRITES - Laces–boot and shoe ☆ - Mitchellace Inc.
GLOW CUBE 100 SERIES - Electronic equipment - Daktronics Inc.
GLOW CUBE CUSTOM - Electronic equipment - Daktronics Inc.
GLOW CUBE LINE DISPLAYS - Electronic equipment - Daktronics Inc.
GLOW GEAR - Safety products - Mcinternational
GLOW GLASSES - Glow-in-the-dark eyeglasses - Cuddlewear Inc.
GLOW GRIP - Flashlights - Brinkmann Corp.
GLOW IMPERIAL - Toys - Duncan Toys Co.
GLOW-IN-THE-DARK - Giftware ☆ - Cleo Inc.
GLOW IN THE DARK - Hobby kits - Hinkle Easter Products
GLOW-IN-THE-DARK - Paints - American Art Clay Co. Inc.
GLOW IN THE DARK KOOSH - Toys - Oddzon Products, Inc.
GLOW MAX - Paper–writing - Riverside Paper Corp.
GLOW 'N DARK FACES - Toys–stuffed - Fun World Inc.
GLOW-N-GLITTER - Fishing lures - Magic Products, Inc.
GLOW 'N TELL - Tape–adhesive - Vascutech Inc.
GLOW-ON - Cosmetics - Preview Products
GLOW PAINT - Coatings - Seal-Krete Inc.
GLOW PLASTI-GOOP - Toys - Toymax Inc.
GLOW POWER - Crayons - Playstation Inc.
GLOW STICK - Novelty items - Omniglow Corp.
GLOW STICS - Pens - Bic Corp.
GLOW-TIES - Yarn ☆ - Stephen Lawrence Co.
GLOW TONE - Envelopes - Western States Envelope Co.
GLOW TRACKER - Chemical preparations - Foundry Laboratories, Inc.
GLOW-TRAP - Fishing lures - Sports Design and Development, Inc.
GLOWALOONS - Aircraft–balloons - Tillotson Rubber Co.
GLOWARANG - Boomerangs - Ozwest Imports, Inc.
GLOWATCH - Watches - M.Z. Berger & Co. Inc.
GLOWBALLS - Novelty items - Wescosa Inc.
GLOWEE - Dolls - Mattel, Inc.
GLOWFLIES - Fishing nets - U.S. Tackle Corp.
GLOWFLOR - Floor coverings ☆ - Congoleum Corp.
GLOWING CRIMSON - Lipsticks ☆ - Honey & Spice Toiletries
GLOWING EMBER - Pet products - Tomlyn Products
GLOWING FINISH - Cosmetics ☆ - Coty Inc.
GLOWING STAR - Floor coverings–carpet and rugs - Mohawk Carpet Corp.
GLOWING STAR - Food products - US Foodservice
GLOWING TOUCH - Skin care products - Sunshine Products
GLOWLINE - Medical apparatus - B. Braun Medical Inc. (Burron Cardiovascular Division)
GLOW'N FACES - Toys - Spearhead Industries Inc.
GLOWORM - Fishing lures ☆ - Creme Lure Co.
GLOWSAN - Cleaning equipment - Restortek, Inc.
GLOWTION - Skin care products - Charles Revson Inc.
GLOWY - Computer software - Hartley Courseware Inc.
GLOZE - Hair care products - Mahdeen Laboratory
GLP - Containers - Great Lakes Packaging Corp.
GLR - Traction apparatus–medical - Camp, Inc.
GLR FASTENERS - Hardware - GLR Fasteners, Inc.
GLS GRACE LEWIS STUDIO - Wallpaper - Gagne Wallcovering, Inc.
GLT - Golfing equipment - Aldila, Inc.
GLT - Motor vehicles–automobiles ☆ - Volvo Cars of North America Inc.
GLT TRACTION II - Tires - General Tire, Inc.
GLT TRACTION 78 - Tires–automobile - General Tire, Inc.
GLU-BIRD - Glue–household or industrial - Dap Products Inc.
GLU-BOY - Glue–household or industrial - Dap Products Inc.
GLU-DOWN - Wood flooring - Standard Plywood Inc.
GLU 'N TUK - Machinery - R.A. Jones & Co. Inc.
GLU-RIFIC! - Glue ☆ - Itoya of America, Ltd.
GLUCAGON - Pharmaceutical preparations - Eli Lilly and Co.
GLUCAHERB - Vitamins and nutritional supplements ☆ - J.R. Carlson Laboratories Inc.
GLUCAMIDE - Pharmaceutical preparations ☆ - Lemmon Co.
G'LUCKS - Greeting cards - Wilmer Graphics Inc.
GLUCO BALANCE - Vitamins and nutritional supplements ☆ - Ethical Nutrients
GLUCO-FEDRIN - Cold remedies ☆ - Parke-Davis

GLUCO-SEC - Vitamins and nutritional supplements ☆ - Great Life Laboratories Inc.

GLUCOCARE - Vitamins and nutritional supplements - Ayurvedic Concepts Ltd.

GLUCOFACTS - Computer software - Miles Inc.

GLUCOLORS - Glue–household or industrial - Elmer's Products, Inc.

GLUCOMANMAN - Health care products - Natrol, Inc.

GLUCOMAR - Vitamins and nutritional supplements ☆ - Marlop Pharmaceuticals Inc.

GLUCOMETER 3 - Blood-glucose meter - Polymer Technology International

GLUCOMETER ELITE - Pharmaceuticals - Miles Inc.

GLUCOMETER ENCORE - Diagnostic apparatus - Miles Inc.

GLUCOMETER II - Blood-glucose meter - Polymer Technology International

GLUCOMETER SYSTEM - Medical apparatus - Miles Inc.

GLUCOMINE - Vitamins and nutritional supplements - Body Wise International, Inc.

GLUCONASE - Vitamins and nutritional supplements - Nutraceutical Research Labs, Inc.

GLUCORON - Pharmaceutical preparations ☆ - Lemmon Co.

GLUCOSAMEND - Vitamins and nutritional supplements - Source Naturals

GLUCOSAMINE COMPLEX - Vitamins and nutritional supplements - Vitamin Research Products Inc.

GLUCOSAMINE PLUS CHONDROITIN - Vitamins and nutritional supplements - Reese Chemical Co.

GLUCOSTAT - Computer software - Glucoware

GLUCOSTAT - Herbal products - Maharishi Ayur-Ved Products International, Inc.

GLUCOTROL XL - Pharmaceutical preparations - Pfizer Inc.

GLUCOVITE - Pharmaceutical preparations ☆ - Pal-Pak Inc.

GLUCOWARE - Computer software - Glucoware

GLUCURONOLACTONE - Pharmaceutical preparations - City Chemical Corp.

GLUE ALL - Glue–household or industrial - Elmer's Products, Inc.

GLUE & GO - Nail care products - International Beauty Design, Inc.

GLUE APPLICATORS - Hardware - The Centro Co. Inc.

GLUE BUDDY - Adhesives and sealants - Sashco Inc.

GLUE-FAST - Glue–household or industrial - Glue-Fast Equipment Co. Inc.

GLUE FIX 3000 - Guns - Steinel America Inc.

GLUE FOLDER - Machinery - Glue-Fold, Inc.

GLUE MARKER - Office supplies - Uchida of America Corp.

GLUE-OCTOPUS - Toys - Applied Elastomerics, Inc.

GLUE OFF - Cosmetics - American International Industries

GLUE-ON - Glue–household or industrial - Dap Products Inc.

GLUE PETS - Glue–household or industrial - Super Glue Corp.

GLUE-SEA-ANEMONE - Toys - Applied Elastomerics, Inc.

GLUE STIC - Adhesives and sealants - Avery Dennison Corp.

GLUEFROG - Toys - Applied Elastomerics, Inc.

GLUEMATIC - Adhesives and sealants - Loctite Corp.

GLUERITE - Glue–household or industrial - Glue-Fast Equipment Co. Inc.

GLUESLUG - Toys - Applied Elastomerics, Inc.

GLUG GLUG TUG - Toys ☆ - Steven Manufacturing Co.

GLUKOR - Pharmaceutical preparations - Hyrex Pharmaceuticals

GLUNZ CELLARS - Wines - Louis Glunz Inc.

GLUPLICATOR - Glue–household or industrial - Slomons Laboratories Inc.

GLUTAIN - Pharmaceutical preparations - Lanpar Co.

GLUTAMAX - Vitamins and nutritional supplements - Ultimate Nutrition Products, Inc.

GLUTAMINE B-C - Health care products - Resurrection Laboratories

GLUTAMINE FUEL - Vitamins and nutritional supplements - Twinlab

GLUTAMINE PRESERVATION SYSTEM - Vitamins and nutritional supplements - Experimental & Applied Sciences, Inc.

GLUTANAC - Vitamins and nutritional supplements - James Franckelton

GLUTARALDEHYDE - Pharmaceutical preparations - City Chemical Corp.

GLUTATHIONE - Pharmaceutical preparations - City Chemical Corp.

GLUTATHIONE-C - Health care products - Health Maintenance Programs Inc.

GLUTATHIONE-FORTE - Vitamins and nutritional supplements - Health Maintenance Programs Inc.

GLUTATHIONE-HEALTH PACKS - Vitamins and nutritional supplements - Health Maintenance Programs Inc.

GLUTE MASTER - Exercising equipment - Fitness Warehouse, Inc.

GLUTILITY - Computer software - Softblox Inc.

GLUTOFAC - Vitamins and nutritional supplements - Kenwood Laboratories Inc.

GLUTOL - Pharmaceutical preparations - Paddock Laboratories Inc.

GLUTOLIN - Pharmaceutical preparations ☆ - American Hygienic Laboratories Inc.

GLUTOLINE - Paints - Key Products Inc.

GLUTOSE - Pharmaceutical preparations - Paddock Laboratories Inc.

GLUTOSE-15 - Pharmaceutical preparations - Paddock Laboratories Inc.

GLUVIT - Epoxy - Travaco Laboratories Inc.

GLV - Jewelry–precious - Gregory Lynn Villalobos

GLX - Fishing tackle - G. Loomis, Inc.

GLY-ADEX - Lotions - Lynwood Laboratories

GLY-AIR - Air purification systems ☆ - LaSalle Marketing Corp.

GLY-JENE - Skin care products ☆ - Orjene Natural Cosmetics

GLY-JUVA - Skin care products - Dermcente Noire, Inc.

GLY-MIRACLE - Skin care products - Palm Beach Beauty Products

GLY-OXIDE - Antiseptics - Marion Merrell Dow

GLY-OXIDE - Health care products - SmithKline Beecham Consumer Healthcare

GLY SILICONE GREASE - Silicon products - Travaco Laboratories Inc.

GLY SILK - Skin care products - M.D. Dermaceuticals, Inc.

GLY SPRAY - Lubricants ☆ - Travaco Laboratories Inc.

GLYATE - Cough medicines - Geneva Generics Inc.

GLYATUSS - Pharmaceutical preparations ☆ - Dixon-Shane Inc.

GLYBRON - Pharmaceutical preparations ☆ - Rugby Laboratories Inc.

GLYCATE - Pharmaceutical preparations ☆ - Forest Pharmaceuticals Inc.

GLYCAUROL - Pharmaceutical preparations ☆ - Vita-Fore Products Co.

GLYCEL - Skin care products ☆ - Alfin Fragrances Inc.

GLYCEMIC FACTORS - Vitamins - Country Life

GLYCER-X - Hair care products - Dena Corp.

GLYCERALDEHYDE - Pharmaceutical preparations - City Chemical Corp.

GLYCERYL-T - Pharmaceutical preparations - Rugby Laboratories Inc.

GLYCICAL - Antacids ☆ - Cameron Medical Corp.

GLYCINE - Lipsticks - Lancome

GLYCINE - Pharmaceutical preparations - City Chemical Corp.

GLYCINE - Vases - Durand International

GLYCINE CAPS - Vitamins and nutritional supplements - M.M.R.C., Ltd. Co.

GLYCINE POWDER - Vitamins and nutritional supplements - M.M.R.C., Ltd. Co.

GLYCO-ACTIVE - Pharmaceutical preparations - Rexall Sundown, Inc.

GLYCO-CARBS - Vitamins and nutritional supplements - JBN Enterprises, Inc.

GLYCO-PEPPERMINT - Skin care products - Scentsabilities, Inc.

GLYCO-THYMOLINE - Mouthwashes - Kress & Owen Co.

GLYCOBAR - Vitamins and nutritional supplements - Nu Skin International, Inc.

GLYCOCHROM - Chromatographs - Bio-Rad Laboratories, Inc.

GLYCOFED - Pharmaceutical preparations - Pal-Pak Inc.

GLYCOFORM-D - Skin care products - Glycoform-D, Inc.

GLYCOFRUIT TREATMENT - Skin care products - Paul Penders Co. Inc.

GLYCOLACTIC - Skin care products - Abbe Cosmetic Group International, Inc.

GLYCOLIGHTEN - Skin care products - Abbe Cosmetic Group International, Inc.

GLYCOLIQUE - Skin care products - Marcor Labs Inc.

GLYCOLIQUE - Skin care products ☆ - Reviva Laboratories

GLYCOLS - Pharmaceutical preparations ☆ - JMI-Canton Pharmaceuticals

GLYCOPHEN - Pharmaceutical preparations ☆ - Rugby Laboratories Inc.

GLYCOPHENE - Pharmaceutical preparations ☆ - Rush & Hebble Co. Inc.

GLYCOPLEX - Vitamins and nutritional supplements - The Lifestar Millennium, Inc.

GLYCOTONE - Pharmaceutical preparations ☆ - Wesley Pharmacal Co. Inc.

GLYCOTRAK - Diagnostic apparatus ☆ - Seradyn, Inc.

GLYCOTUSS - Pharmaceutical preparations ☆ - Pal-Pak Inc.

GLYCOTUSS-DM - Pharmaceutical preparations - Pal-Pak Inc.

GLYCYLGLYCINE - Pharmaceutical preparations - Pfanstiehl Laboratories Inc.

GLYD-LOC - File folders ☆ - Smead Manufacturing Co.

GLYDE - Hair care products - Image Laboratories, Inc.

GLYDEINE - Cough medicines - Geneva Generics Inc.

GLYDER - Electric lighting equipment - Lutron Electronics Co., Inc.

GLYDER - Safety products - D B Industries, Inc.

GLYDEX - Hardware ☆ - Hunt Manufacturing Co.

GLYDM - Cough medicines - Geneva Generics Inc.

GLYKON - Teas–herbal - Metabolic Formulations, Inc.

GLYLACTRUS - Skin care products - Wilma Schumann International, Inc.

GLYNASE/PRESSTAB - Pharmaceutical preparations - Upjohn Co.

GLYNAZAN - Cough medicines ☆ - Schering-Plough Healthcare Products

GLYNDA TURLEY - Frames–picture - Glynda Turley Prints Inc.

GLYNDA TURLEY COLLECTION, THE - Pillows - Glynda Turley Prints Inc.

GLYPHIC - Computer software - Glyphic Technology

GLYPHIX - Games - Frank Ciofalo

GLYPLEX - Hair care products - Watkins Inc.

GLYPRO-L - Shampoos - Redken Laboratories, Inc.

GLYPROGENIC - Hair care products - Redken Laboratories, Inc.

GLYPTEX - Enamels - Porter Paint Co.

GLYROL - Prescription drug - CooperVision Inc.

☆ = Now out of production

GLYSALIX - Skin care products - Topix Pharmaceuticals, Inc.

GLYSENNID - Pharmaceutical preparations - Dorsey Laboratories

GLYSIRENA - Soap ☆ - Tropical Soap Co.

GLYSOL 400 - Pharmaceutical preparations - Cytosol Laboratories, Inc.

GLYSOL 500 - Pharmaceutical preparations - Cytosol Laboratories, Inc.

GLYSYN-KOTE - Paints - Delaware Valley Paint Co.

GLYTABS - Pharmaceutical preparations - Pharmics Inc.

GLYTINIC - Pharmaceutical preparations - Boyle & Co.

GLYTONE - Skin care products - C&M Pharmacal, Inc.

GLYTRATE - Skin care products - Keene Distributors, Inc.

GLYTUSS - Pharmaceutical preparations - Merz Inc.

GLYVERA - Skin-care products - Creative Laboratories Inc.

GM - Chemical preparations - Landmark Exterior Restoration, Inc.

GM - Jewelry - Aftacast Inc.

GM - Jewelry–precious - Golden Moon Inc.

GM - Paint sprayers - Graco Inc.

GM 66 - Flour–blended ☆ - General Mills, Inc.

GM 2000 SELECTION - Wines ☆ - Maison Jomere Ltd.

GM II - Skates–roller - Chicago Roller Skate Co.

GM PARTS - Apparel–men's - Spire of California

GM RESTORATION PARTS - Motor vehicle parts and accessories - General Motors Corp.

GM ULTRALITE - Toys–automobiles - General Motors Corp.

GMA - Brakes–motor vehicle - Rivera Engineering, Inc.

GMA - Jewelry - GMA Inc.

GMAT FOR IBM & APPLE - Computer software - Krell Software Corp.

GMAX - Circuit boards - General Scanning Inc.

GMC - Amplifiers–musical instrument ☆ - Grossman Music Corp.

GMC TRUCK - Motor vehicles–trucks - General Motors Corp.

GMD - Pharmaceutical preparations - Columbia Drug Co. Inc.

GMF - Tools–garden - Qualcast USA

GMI - Electronic equipment - The Genie Co.

GMK - Teas–herbal - Metabolic Formulations, Inc.

GMLA - Apparel and accessories - Georges Marciano

GMP 1ST - Computer software - GMP Institute

GMP GOOD MANUFACTURING PRACTICE - Food processors - Stason Industrial Corp.

GMP LABELING - Printed labels - GMP Labeling, Inc.

GMP TUTOR - Computer software - Vectech, Inc.

GMS - Boats–motor ☆ - Glassmaster Co.

GMS - Drums–musical instruments ☆ - Paiste America, Inc.

GMSURF - Apparel and accessories - Marble Sportswear, Inc.

GMT - Floor coverings–tile - GMT Floor Tile Inc.

GMT-MASTER - Watches - Rolex Watch USA, Inc.

GMUNDNER KERAMIK - Dishes–earthenware - Landhaus Inc.

GMX - Computers–personal - Gimix Inc.

GMX - Water treating compounds - GMX Corp.

GN-1 - Flowers, plants, and seeds - Great White Shark Enterprises, Inc.

GNARLY GOLF - Computer software - Compton's NewMedia

GNARLY SURFIN' 'TOOS - Toys - Mattel, Inc.

GNASH - Toys - Mattel, Inc.

GNAWHIDE - Pet products ☆ - Pets International, Ltd.

GNAWSOME - Pet products - Farnam Cos. Inc.

GNN - Computer software - O'Reilly & Associates, Inc.

GNOCCHITELLI - Pasta - CLD Corp.

GNOME - Posters - Aegis Entertainment, Inc.

GNOME - Toys–models - Estes Industries

GNOMIE - Toys–stuffed - Renee Pierro

GNOMIN - Dolls - Kenneth Patrizzi

GNOSIS - Computer software - Deskin Research Group

GNOSSOS - Computer software - Gnossos Software, Inc.

GNP - Amplifiers - GNP Audio Video Inc.

GNP - Health care products - Guadalupe Natural Productions Inc.

GNP CRESCENDO - Recording label - GNP Crescendo Record Co. Inc.

GNU - Apparel and accessories - Csoc Holdings, Inc.

GNU - Apparel–men's - McCrory Corp.

GO - Cameras ☆ - Olympus America Inc.

GO - Computer software - Go Corp.

GO! - Fruits–dried - International Harvest

GO - Games ☆ - Avalon Hill Game Co.

GO - Oils–lubricating - Ashland Inc.

GO - Recording label - Billy Baker & Associates

GO 4 IT - Recording label - Megalodon Enterprises Inc.

GO AHEAD - Candy bars ☆ - Nestle USA

GO AHEADS - Incontinence products - George Disposables

GO-ALL - Novelty items - Creatnetics

GO AWAY - Insecticides ☆ - Demert & Dougherty, Inc.

GO AWAY EVIL - Deodorizers - M. & A. Amateau Inc.

GO-B-TWEENS - Snack foods - Pepsico, Inc.

GO BANANAS - Sleds - Emsco Inc.

GO-BE - Bottles–plastic - Fastrak Systems, Inc.

GO BERSERK! - Apparel and accessories - G Industries, Inc.

GO-BETWEEN - Health care products - Lactona Corp.

GO-BETWEEN - Housewares - Tupperware Co.

GO BETWEEN - Padding–foam - Jade Industries Inc.

GO BIG - Apparel and accessories - Go Big, Co.

GO BIKES - Bicycles ☆ - Hedstrom Corp.

GO-BOLT - Metals - Go-Bolt, Inc.

GO BOTS - Dishes–plastic - Deka Plastics Inc.

GO CAMERA - Cameras ☆ - Olympus America Inc.

GO CUP - Dishes–plastic ☆ - Thermos Co.

GO-EVERYWHERE - Patterns–clothing ☆ - Simplicity Pattern Co., Inc.

GO EZ - Hardware - Houck Industries Inc.

GO-FER - Motorcycles ☆ - Suzuki of America Automotive Corp.

GO-FER - Welding equipment - Weld Tooling Corp.

GO FETCH - Pet products - Classic Products

GO FIGURE THE PROBLEM-SOLVING TOOLKIT - Computer software - Twisted Logic

GO FONE - Audio equipment - Technidyne

GO FOR BROKE - Games ☆ - Milton Bradley Co.

GO-FOR-IT - Kites ☆ - Hi-Flier Manufacturing Co.

GO FOR IT - Shoes - Cypress Shoes

GO FOR IT! - Toys–stuffed - Dakin Inc.

GO FOR THE BRONZE - Cosmetics - Revlon Consumer Products Corp.

GO FOR THE GREEN - Beverages–malt - Anheuser-Busch Companies Inc.

GO-FOR-THE-MAX - Health care products ☆ - Foodscience Laboratories Inc.

GO-GET-IT - Fishing lures - G.L.D. Products, Inc.

GO-GETTER - Fishing lures - Hildebrandt Corp.

GO-GETTER - Tires ☆ - Cooper Tire & Rubber Co.

GO-GIRL - Hosiery–children's ☆ - Fieldcrest Cannon, Inc.

GO GLO, A - Clocks - Indiglo Corp.

GO-GO - Beverage containers - Little Kids, Inc.

GO-GO - Electronic equipment - Timely Products

GO-GO - Toys - Brumberger Co. Inc.

GO-GO - Underwear and nightwear - Youthcraft-Charmfit

GO-GO BELLS - Musical instrument accessories - Fredrico Percussion

GO-GO DOG - Pet products - Century Craft Industries

GO! GO! DOUGH - Clay–modeling - Hasbro, Inc.

GO GO GEARS - Toys - Playskool, Inc.

GO-GO GUITAR - Toys - Brumberger Co. Inc.

GO GO MY WALKING PUP - Toys–stuffed - Hasbro, Inc.

GO-GO PET - Pet products - Century Craft Industries

GO GO SPARKLER - Musical instrument accessories - Sottile Manufacturing Co.

GO! GO! WORMS - Games - Hasbro, Inc.

GO-GO'S - Pasta - Hanover Foods Corp.

GO GOYA - Spices and extracts - Goya Foods, Inc.

GO GREEN - Tape–adhesive - Manco, Inc.

GO HYANG - Rice - Comet Rice, Inc.

GO IN STYLE - Dolls - Mattel, Inc.

GO-JO - Soap - Go-Jo Industries Inc.

GO-KOOLER - Ice chests - Weber Plastics Inc.

GO LIGHTLY - Candy - Golightly Candy Co.

GO LITE - Audio equipment - Recoton Corp.

GO MAIL - Computer software - Go Corp.

GO MART - Antifreeze - Go-Mart, Inc.

GO-MAX - Pet products - Farnam Cos. Inc.

GO MEDIA COMPANIES - Video production - Goco, Inc.

G.O. METRIC - Kites - Gayla Industries Inc.

GO MIX - Fuel additives ☆ - Ashland Oil, Inc.

GO 'N' GROW - Infant product ☆ - Dolly, Inc.

GO NATURAL - Floor coverings–carpet and rugs ☆ - Gulistan Carpet Inc.

GO NATURAL STRIPES - Floor coverings–carpet and rugs ☆ - Gulistan Carpet Inc.

GO OVERBOARD - Cosmetics - Cosmair Inc.

GO-PACKS - Fruit drinks–bottled or canned ☆ - Lykes Services Co.

GO-PAK! - Bags - Go-Pak! Llc

GO-PED - Scooters–motorized - Motoboard International

GO-PED - Scooters–motorized - Patmont Motor Werks

GO-PHER BROKE - Sportswear - Go-Pher Broke

GO POP A CORK - Apparel and accessories ☆ - Westport Rivers Vineyard & Winery

GO-QUAD - Scooters–motorized - Patmont Motor Werks

GO RHINO! - Motor vehicle parts and accessories - California Aluminium Products Co.

GO-ROLL-A-GORILLA - Games - Toyvision, Inc.

GO SAIL - Paper products - Cruise World Travel

GO SHAMPOO - Hair care products - Framesi USA/Roffler Industries Inc.

GO SHIRT - Apparel and accessories - L'Zinger International

GO-SHOW - Electronic equipment - General Audio-Visual Inc.

GO SKATES - Skates–roller - On Wheels Roller Skates

GO, SPOT, GO - Cleaning preparations–upholstery - Go Spot Go Partnership

GO STRAIGHT - Hair curlers - Conair Corp.

GO TO THE HEAD OF THE CLASS - Games - Milton Bradley Co.

GO TOGETHER REDS - Lipstick and nail polish ✩ - Cosrich Inc.

GO-TOGETHERS - Apparel–women's ✩ - Manhattan International

GO TRIKES - Tricycles ✩ - Hedstrom Corp.

G.O. VARJA - Wines - Pellegrini Bros. Wines Inc.

GO VICKI! - Apparel–women's - Decorp Inc.

GO WARE TRAVEL SOUL - Maps - Go Ware Travel

GO WEST - Cosmetics ✩ - Noxell Corp.

GO WILD - Colognes - Mem Co., Inc.

GO WITH THE FLOW - Cleaning preparations - S.C. Johnson & Son, Inc.

GO WITH THE FLOW - Footwear - Nu-Technologies, Inc.

GO-YO - Sporting goods - Leading Edge, Inc.

GOA PLASTER - Wallcovering - Galice, Inc.

GOAL - Computer software ✩ - Knowledge Adventure

GOAL - Electronic game - Jaleco USA, Inc.

GOAL - Hair care products - Helene Curtis Industries Inc.

GOAL - Vitamins and nutritional supplements - Goal Nutrition Inc.

GOAL - Wines - Smith & Hook Winery

GOAL-D - Electrical equipment - Pak, Inc.

GOAL EATER - Toys ✩ - Those Characters from Cleveland, Inc.

GOAL LINE ENVIRONMENTAL TECHNOLOGIES - Automotive parts and accessories - Sunlaw Energy Corp.

GOAL SEEKER - Computer software - Brown Bag Software Inc.

GOAL! SNACKS - Bakery products - Flowers Family Bakeries, Inc.

GOAL STORM - Computer storage devices–optical - Konami (America) Inc.

GOALIE - Games ✩ - Pacific Game Co.

GOALIE II - Flowers, plants, and seeds - Jacklin Seed

GOALIE GHOST - Video game - Bally Sente Inc.

GOALINE DARTS - Games - Glen S. Tolson

GOALMASTER - Computer software - Federated Investors, Inc.

GOALPOSTERS - Posters - Quest Your Best, Inc.

GOALSETTER - Sporting goods - Goalsetter Systems

GOALTRAK - Computer software - Paradigm Shifts, Inc.

GOALWATCHER - Computer software - Spantec, Inc.

GOAT - Eyeglasses - Goat Eyewear

G.O.A.T. - Snowmobiles - Timemasters, Inc.

GOAT - Snowmobiles - Timemasters, Inc.

GOAT CLAW - Sporting goods ✩ - Ramer Products, Ltd.

GOAT DESIGN - Apparel and accessories - Mazama Store, Inc.

GOAT IN A BIRD SUIT - Recording label - Jazz Composer's Orchestra Association Inc.

GOAT WHITE - Wines - Bully Hill Vineyards, Inc.

GOAT'S MILK & HONEY - Toiletries - Caswell-Massey Co. Ltd.

GOATZARELLA - Dairy products ✩ - Skyhill Napa Valley Farms, Inc.

GOBABIES - Infant product - TigerRed Enterprises

GOBAR - Computer software - Clinical Multiphase Research, Inc.

GOBBLE - Pharmaceutical preparations - W.W. Grainger, Inc.

GOBBLE AND CHOP - Paper cutters - I.D.A.B. Inc.

GOBBLE BALL - Toys–stuffed - Commonwealth Toy and Novelty Co. Inc.

GOBBLE D. GLU - Candy ✩ - Zeebs Enterprises, Inc.

GOBBLE GATOR - Games - Toyvision, Inc.

GOBBLE POPS - Candy - Russ Berrie and Co., Inc.

GOBBLE UP - Turkey product - Iowa Turkey Products, Inc.

GOBBLE UP - Turkeys - Midwest Turkey Hatchery, Inc.

GOBBLEDY-GOOP - Nail care products - Palm Beach Laboratories Co.

GOBBLEDYGOOK - Game - Stardom Co. Ltd.

GOBBLEKNOBS - Giftware - Russ Berrie and Co., Inc.

GOBBLER CALL - Sporting goods - Penn's Woods Products Inc.

GOBBLER-GETTER - Sporting goods - Camp-Cap Products

GOBBLERS - Food products ✩ - Shelton's Poultry, Inc.

GOBBLES THE CRAZY EATING GOAT - Toys–stuffed ✩ - Kenner Products

GOBBLESTIX - Turkeys - Jerome Foods Inc.

GOBELIN - Fabrics–tapestry - Corona Decor Co.

GOBELIN - Frames–picture - M & M Associates Ltd.

GOBI - Solar energy collectors - Heliodyne Inc.

GOBLIN - Toys–models ✩ - Estes Industries

GOBLIN GOODIES - Decorations - Bleyer Industries (Peoria Plastics Div.)

GOBLIN GUIDES - Hobby kits - Kama, Inc.

GOBO - Toys - Jim Henson Productions, Inc.

GOBOT POWER SUITS - Toys - Tonka Corp.

GOBOT PUZZLER - Toys - Tonka Corp.

GOBOTRON - Toys - Tonka Corp.

GOBOTS - Toys - Tonka Corp.

GOBOTS - Toys ✩ - Coloron Industries

GOBSTOPPER - Candy - Willy Wonka Brands

GOBSTOPPER EGGS - Candy ✩ - Willy Wonka Brands

GOC - Jewelry - Gems One Corp.

GOCABULARY - Video games - Tesco Research, Inc.

GOD BLESS YOU DOLLS, THE - Dolls - C. Ashley's Expression

GOD BLESS YOUR BONES - Novelty items - David L. Clark

GOD IS KING - Apparel and accessories - Lauri Andrea Kaye

GOD OF FORTUNE - Rice - Wu Chu Trading Corp.

GODA - Fish–fresh or frozen - Haram-Christensen Corp.

GODAIKIN - Toys–electronic ✩ - Bandai America Inc.

GODCHAUX - Food products - Godchaux-Henderson Sugar Co. Inc.

GODDARD - Valves–industrial - Webstone Co. Inc.

GODDARD MANOR - Furniture - Singer Furniture Co.

GODDARDS - Cleaning preparations–household - J. Goddard & Sons

GODDESS - Brassieres (Bras) - Goddess Bra

GODDESS - Brushes–hair ✩ - Phillips Brush Corp.

GODDESS - Jewelry - Goddess Jewelry Manufacturing Co.

GODDESS - Olives–pickled or brined - V.M. Calderon Inc.

GODDESS - Pencils - General Pencil Co.

GODDESS - Salt - Nancy B. Watson's Potions

GODDESS - Skin care products - Goddess Co.

GODDESS - Watches - Bulova Corp.

GODDESS BLENDS - Oils–essential - Elizabeth Van Buren Aromatherapy

GODDESS COLLECTION - Novelty items - Co. of Women Inc.

GODDESS G - Perfumes - Parfum de Coeur Ltd.

GODDESS OF FORTUNE - Deodorizers - Aromax Scented Products

GODDESS OF TIME - Watches - Bulova Corp.

GODDETTE - Brassieres (Bras) - Goddess Bra

GODEFROY - Hair care products - Bradco Products Inc.

GODET - Beverages–alcohol - Paddington Corp.

GODET - Wines - European Beverage Co., Inc.

GODI - Herring–smoked, salted, dried, or pickled ✩ - Haram-Christensen Corp.

GODINE COUNTRY CLASSICS - Publisher's imprints - David R. Godine Publisher Inc.

GODINE STORYTELLERS - Publisher's imprints - David R. Godine Publisher Inc.

GODINGER - House furnishings - Godinger Silver Art Ltd.

GODINGER SILVER ART - Giftware - Godinger Silver Art Ltd.

GODIVA - Coffee - Godiva Chocolatier, Inc.

GODIVA - Food products - Godiva Chocolatier

GODIVA - Frames–eyeglass - Rozin Optical Export Corp.

GODPARENT - Jewelry - Kirchner Corp.

GOD'S IN HIS HEAVEN - Greeting cards - American Greetings Corp.

GODS OF GLORANTHA - Games - Avalon Hill Game Co.

GODS PROMISES - Magnets - Rainfall Inc.

GOD'S SHELF - Shelving units–wood - Dorothy Jackie Hurst

GODS WHOLE EARTH - Vitamins and nutritional supplements - Holy Bible Gospel Ministry of The Body of Christ, Yeshua, of the Holy Land,

GODZILLA - Video production - Toho Co., Ltd.

GOEBEL - Beverages–malt - The Stroh Brewery Co.

GOEBEL - Figurines - Goebel of North America

GOEBEL CRYSTAL - Giftware ✩ - Goebel of North America

GOEBEL DOLLS - Dolls - Goebel of North America

GOEBEL GIFTS - Figurines - Goebel of North America

GOEBEL LIGHT - Beverages–malt - The Stroh Brewery Co.

GOEBEL MINIATURES - Figurines - Goebel of North America

GOELITZ - Candy - Naron Candy Co. Inc.

GOELITZ CONFECTIONS - Candy - Herman Goelitz Candy Co., Inc.

GOELITZ FRUIT SNACKS - Snack food - Herman Goelitz Candy Co., Inc.

GOELITZ GUMMI - Candy - Herman Goelitz Candy Co., Inc.

GOEMAR - Agricultural products - Goemar International & Agrimar

GOERLICH - Mufflers–motor vehicle - Goerlich's

GOERLICH 1 - Mufflers–motor vehicle - AP Parts

GOERLICH'S - Motor vehicle parts and accessories - AP Parts

GOERZ - Lenses–photographic ✩ - Schneider Optics, Inc.

GOES - Office supplies - Goes Lithographing Co.

✩ = Now out of production

GOES TO COLLEGE - Dolls - Diversified Educational Services, Inc.

GOESSER - Beverages–malt ☆ - Stanley Stawski Distributing Co.

GOETSCHMANN G 8585 AV - Photographic equipment - Mamiya America Corp.

GOETZ - Beverages–malt ☆ - Pearl Brewing Co.

GOETZ PALE - Beverages–malt - Pearl Brewing Co.

GOETZE'S OLD FASHIONED CARAMEL APPLE STICK - Candy - Goetze's Candy Co., Inc.

GOFAST - Bicycle parts and accessories - Mady International Inc.

GOFAST - Computer software - US Software

GOFAX - Fax machines - Gofax Inc.

GOFER - Computer software - Microlytics Inc.

GOFER - Tables–metal - Tyke Corp.

GOFF - Cat food - Consolidated Pet Industries

GOGETTER - Sporting goods - Chesal Golf

GOGGLE BANDS - Crocheted and knitted items ☆ - Reliable of Milwaukee

GOGGLE-EYE - Fishing lures - Boone Bait Co. Inc.

GOGGLE GATOR - Cases–eyeglass - Gator Sports Inc.

GOGGLEMATE - Goggles–safety - Spot Safety Products, Inc.

GOGGS - Goggles - Fairfield Line, Inc.

GOGOPOGOP - Hobby kits - Rapco

GOH SERIES - Garment hangers - Batts, Inc.

GOING BANANAS - Greeting cards - American Greetings Corp.

GOING FIRST CLASS - Floor coverings–carpet and rugs ☆ - Calladium & Marglen

GOING FISHIN' - Fishing tackle - R & R Tackle Manufacturing

GOING GOING GONE - Girdles - Preferred Foundations

GOING GREAT - Floor coverings–carpet and rugs - Alexander Smith Carpets

GOING HOME - House furnishings - Lexington Furniture Industries, Inc.

GOING HOME - Recording label - Monroe Institute

GOING INTERNATIONAL - Video production - Griggs Productions Inc.

GOING PLACES - Floor coverings–carpet and rugs - Calladium & Marglen

GOING PLACES - Floor coverings–carpet and rugs - Lees Carpets

GOING PLACES - Hosiery - Van Raalte Gloves

GOING PLACES - Luggage ☆ - Mercury Luggage Manufacturing Co.

GOING PLACES - Wallpaper ☆ - Pantasote Inc. (Wallcovering Div.)

GOING PLACES WITH BARCO - Uniforms–tailored ☆ - Barco of California

GOING TO GRANDMA'S - Luggage - Mercury Luggage Manufacturing Co.

GOJ - Jewelry - Sterling Inc.

GOJOEGO - Publisher's imprints - Joseph F. Dzialo

GOJU-KAI - Sports clubs - Norimi Gosei Yamaguchi

GOKEY - Sporting goods - Orvis Gokey Co.

GOKO - Photographic equipment ☆ - Mamiya America Corp.

GOL BON - Meat products–canned - Zartic, Inc.

GOL-PAK - Food products ☆ - Gol-Pak Corp.

GOLA - Accordions - Hohner Inc.

GOLAN - Knives - Golan Designs, Inc.

GOLBON - Coffee - Park Corp.

GOLBON - Food products - Golbon

GOLBON - Meat products–beef - Melson Meat Co. Inc.

GOLCONDA - Perfumes - Classic Fragrances Ltd.

GOLD - Beverages–malt ☆ - Pabst Brewing Co.

GOLD - Darts and dart games - Dart Mart Inc.

GOLD - Film - Eastman Kodak Co.

GOLD - Games ☆ - Avalon Hill Game Co.

GOLD - Hair care products - Sebring Products Inc.

GOLD - Handbags ☆ - Great American Leatherworks Inc.

GOLD - Medical apparatus - Baxter International Inc.

GOLD - Modems - Global Village Communication, Inc.

GOLD - Oils–lubricating - Sunmarks, Inc.

GOLD - Snack foods - Namar Co.

GOLD - Sporting goods - Ashaway Line & Twine Manufacturing Co.

GOLD - Trading cards - Star International Inc.

GOLD - Trailers–travel - Alfa Leisure, Inc.

GOLD 20 - Recording label - Gay 90's Village Inc.

GOLD 2000 - Beverages–alcohol - Gaetano Specialties Ltd.

GOLD ACCENT - Dishes–china ☆ - Pickard Inc.

GOLD AERO - Electron tubes - Gold Aero, Inc.

GOLD AM - Soap - Georgia-Pacific Corp.

GOLD & BLACK - Cigarettes - G.A. Georgopulo & Co. Inc.

GOLD & BLACK DRYER 1800W - Dryers–hair - Dubl Duck/Jet Set Inc.

GOLD & GOOD - Pancakes–mixes - Roland Industries Inc.

GOLD & LACE - Dolls - Mattel, Inc.

GOLD & MILD - Tobacco products - John Middleton Inc.

GOLD & OAK - Bathroom fixtures - Melard Manufacturing Corp.

GOLD ARROW - Footwear - Ambassador Shoe Corp.

GOLD AWARD - Thread - Van Waters and Rogers Inc.

GOLD AWARD - Toys ☆ - Duncan Toys Co.

GOLD BABY GOLDFISH FOOD - Pet products - Hikari Sales USA Inc.

GOLD BAND - Hardware - Esmet, Inc.

GOLD BAND - Meat products–beef - Armour Swift-Eckrich

GOLD BAND - Tableware ☆ - Corning Inc.

GOLD BANNER - Meat products–beef - Julian Freirich Food

GOLD BAROQUE - Dishes–china - Pickard Inc.

GOLD BARS - Candy ☆ - Confex Inc.

GOLD BEAUTY - Brooms - Hanset Brothers Inc.

GOLD BELL - Brandy ☆ - Oak Ridge Vineyards

GOLD BELT - Motorcycles - Gold Belt Line Inc.

GOLD BLEND - Coffee - Nestle Beverage Co.

GOLD BOAT - Fish–canned or cured - I. Epstein & Sons Inc.

GOLD BOND - Adhesives and sealants - National Gypsum Co.

GOLD BOND - Health care products - Gold Bond Pharmaceutical Corp.

GOLD BOND - Lubricating oils - Warren Distribution, Inc.

GOLD BOND - Mattresses - Standard Mattress Co.

GOLD BOND - Salad dressings–bottled - Ventura Foods

GOLD BOND - Shortening - Humko Products

GOLD BOND - Skin care products - Signal Investment & Management Co.

GOLD BOND - Tires ☆ - Bridgestone/Firestone, Inc.

GOLD BOND - Trading cards and stamps - Gold Bond Stamp Co.

GOLD BOND MEDICATED CREAM - Skin care products - Martin Himmel Inc.

GOLD BOND MEDICATED POWDER - Skin care products - Martin Himmel Inc.

GOLD BOOK - Greeting cards ☆ - Paper Magic Group Inc.

GOLD BOUNTY - Glassware–household - Owens-Illinois Inc. (Libbey Div.)

GOLD BOX - Talcum powders - Specialty Products Co.

GOLD-BOY - Masonry bits - Intercontinental Machinery Co.

GOLD BRACELET - Dishes–china - Pickard Inc.

GOLD BRAID - Rope - Wellington Leisure Products, Inc.

GOLD BRASS - Darts and dart games - Dart Mart Inc.

GOLD BRICK - Candy - Elmer Candy Corp.

GOLD-BRITE - Enamels - T.J. Ronan Paint Corp.

GOLD BROCADE - Glass–leaded - Seneca Glass Co.

GOLD BUCKLE BRISKET SAUCE - Meat sauces - Allegro Fine Foods, Inc.

GOLD BUG - Cages–wire - Global Pet Products Inc.

GOLD BUG - Pillows - Gold Inc.

GOLD BULLION - Jewelry ☆ - Hirsch Speidel Inc.

GOLD CANYON CALIFORNIA - Wines - Kautz Vineyards, Inc.

GOLD CAPS - Cat food - Cornucopia Express

GOLD CARD, THE - Trading cards and stamps - David Chobat

GOLD CARE - Aquariums–household - Jungle Laboratories Corp.

GOLD CARMEL - Flatware ☆ - Wallace International Silversmiths, Inc.

GOLD CASTLE/CYPRESS - Recording label - Capitol-EMI Music Inc.

GOLD CAT EDITION - Automotive accessories - Roman Chariot, Inc.

GOLD CHIEF - Housewares - Brown Stove Works Inc.

GOLD CHIP - Floor coverings ☆ - Congoleum Corp.

GOLD CHLORIDE - Pharmaceutical preparations - City Chemical Corp.

GOLD CHOICE - Coffee - Cain's Coffee Co.

GOLD CIRCLE COIN - Prophylactics - Durex Consumer Products

GOLD CLAD - Watches - Bulova Corp.

GOLD CLASP - Envelopes–paper ☆ - Editions Ltd.

GOLD CLASSIC - Clippers–barber - Marianna Imports, Inc.

GOLD CLASSIC - Cooking utensils–aluminum - Health Craft, Inc.

GOLD CLASSIC - Golfing equipment - Golfsmith International Inc.

GOLD CLASSIC COLLECTION - Chocolate candy - Perugina Chocolate & Confections Inc.

GOLD CLUB - Vegetables–frozen ☆ - Norpac Services, Inc.

GOLD COAST - Apparel and accessories - Bi-Rite Corp.

GOLD COAST - Cigarettes - R.J. Reynolds Tobacco Co.

GOLD COAST - Floor coverings - Mannington Resilient Floors

GOLD COAST - Floor coverings–carpet and rugs ☆ - Bellbridge Carpets

GOLD COAST - Floor coverings–carpet and rugs ☆ - Customweave Carpets Inc.

GOLD COAST - Recording label - Ripete Music Group

GOLD COAST - Seafood products–fresh or frozen - C.A. Curtze Co.

GOLD COAST - Shrimp–fresh or frozen - International Market Brands, Inc.

GOLD COAST - Vegetables–frozen - Bellingham Frozen Foods

GOLD COAST BLEND - Coffee - Starbucks Corp.

GOLD COAST LAGER - Beverages–malt ☆ - Pete's Brewing Co.

GOLD COAST PISTACHIOS - Nuts–salted, roasted, cooked, or canned - Gold Coast Pistachios, Inc.

GOLD COAT - Pens - Sanford Corp.

GOLD COIN - Food products - Cudahy Co.

GOLD COIN - Syrup - Sunset Food & Beverage Corp.
GOLD COLLECTION - Ice cream - Crowley Foods, Inc.
GOLD CORE - Thread - Elmore-Pisgah, Inc.
GOLD CORN - Food products - Hughes Markets Inc.
GOLD-COTE - Cleaning preparations–household - J.N.T. Manufacturing Co. Inc.
GOLD COUNTRY - Bird feeds - B.C.A. Products
GOLD COW - Butter - O-AT-KA Milk Products Cooperative Inc.
GOLD CRAFT - Brushes–paint - Elder & Jenks, Inc.
GOLD CREEK - Snack foods - Quality Food Centers, Inc.
GOLD CREEK CELLARS - Wines - Haviland Vintners
GOLD CREST - Bicycles - Columbia Manufacturing Inc.
GOLD CREST - Bond paper - Copco Papers Inc.
GOLD CREST - Brushes–paint - H & G Industries
GOLD CREST - Floor coverings–tile ☆ - National Floor Products Co., Inc.
GOLD CREST - Food products - The Kroger Co.
GOLD CREST - Office supplies ☆ - Ames Supply Co.
GOLD CREST - Paints - Blue Ribbon Paint Co.
GOLD CREST - Pipes–tobacco - S.M. Frank & Co. Inc. (Kaywoodie-Yello-Bole-Medico)
GOLD CREST - Sauces - Hudson Industries, Inc.
GOLD CREST - Turkeys - Armour Swift-Eckrich
GOLD CREST - Vitamins and nutritional supplements - American Vitamin Products, Inc.
GOLD CREST FOR HER - Apparel–women's - Bugle Boy Industries, Inc.
GOLD CREST FOR MEN - Apparel–men's - Bugle Boy Industries, Inc.
GOLD CROWN - Candy ☆ - F.B. Washburn Candy Corp.
GOLD CROWN - Cordials - White Rock Distilleries Inc.
GOLD CROWN - Crocheted and knitted items - Le Roy Knitted Sportswear Inc.
GOLD CROWN - Gasoline ☆ - Amoco Oil Co.
GOLD CROWN - Leather goods - AR Accessories Group Inc.
GOLD CROWN - Musical instruments - White Eagle Rawhide Manufacturing Co.
GOLD CROWN - Nameplates–engraved - Sargent-Sowell Co.
GOLD CROWN - Sporting goods ☆ - Brunswick Corp.
GOLD CROWN - Stationery - Fay Paper Products Inc.
GOLD CROWN - Tape recorders ☆ - Crown International, Inc.
GOLD CROWN - Whiskey - Montebello Brands, Inc.
GOLD CROWN III - Sporting goods - Brunswick Corp.
GOLD CROWN PREMIUM - Beverages–malt - Jones Brewing Co.
GOLD CUP - Breads–mixes - L. Karp & Sons, Inc.
GOLD CUP - Pet product - Consolidated Seed & Pet Inc.
GOLD CUP - Prunes ☆ - Sanofi Bio-Industries Inc.
GOLD CUP - Sporting goods - Seaway Importing Co.
GOLD CUP - Sporting goods ☆ - National Sporting Goods Corp.
GOLD CUP NATIONAL MATCH - Pistols - Colt's Manufacturing Co. Inc.
GOLD DAHLIA - Dinnerware–glass ☆ - Metlox Pottery Shoppe
GOLD DIAMOND - Tobacco–chewing or smoking - United States Tobacco Co.
GOLD DIGGER - Fruits and vegetables - Gold Digger Apple Inc.
GOLD DOLLAR - Vinegar - Burgie Industries Inc.
GOLD DOT - Bullets - Blount, Inc.
GOLD DOT - Saw blades - Heinemann Saw Corp.
GOLD DRAGON - Saw blades - Sandvik Saws & Tools
GOLD DROPS - Key rings - Specialty Sales Inc.
GOLD DROPS - Wines - Transamerica Wine Corp.
GOLD DUST - Christmas tree ornaments - Cracker Box Inc.
GOLD DUST - Clippers–barber ☆ - Sunbeam-Oster Household Products
GOLD DUST - Fertilizers - Star Nursery, Inc.
GOLD DUST - Finishing agents ☆ - Carnival Arts, Inc.
GOLD DUST - Gypsum products - Domtar Gypsum Inc.
GOLD DUST - Gypsum products - Georgia-Pacific Corp.
GOLD DUST - Lipsticks ☆ - Honey & Spice Toiletries
GOLD DUST - Liquors - United States Distilled Products Co.
GOLD DUST - Pottery products - Duncan Enterprises
GOLD DUST - Recording label - Gold Dust Records
GOLD DUST PIZZA EXPRESS - Food products - Gold Dust Express Co.
GOLD DUSTER - Motor vehicles–automobiles ☆ - Chrysler Corp. (Chrysler-Plymouth Div.)
GOLD EAGLE - Cleaning preparations–window - Gold Eagle Co.
GOLD EAGLE - Golfing equipment - Sport Supply Group, Inc.
GOLD EAGLE - Sporting goods ☆ - Wright & McGill Co.
GOLD EAGLE II - Sporting goods ☆ - Wright & McGill Co.
GOLD EDGE PRO - Cutlery - Regent Sheffield, Ltd.
GOLD EDITION - Candy - Farley Candy Co.
GOLD EDITION - Toys–models - Top Flite Models
GOLD EFFECTS - Electroplating machine - Gold Effects, Inc.

GOLD ENCHANTRESS - Flatware ☆ - Wallace International Silversmiths, Inc.
GOLD-ENS - Electronic equipment - Recoton Corp.
GOLD ESSENTIALS - Lipsticks - Maybelline Co.
GOLD FEATHER - Dinnerware–glass - Royal China & Porcelain Companies Inc.
GOLD FIBRE - Paper–writing - Ampad Corp.
GOLD-FINGERS - Meat products–poultry - Pierce Foods Corp.
GOLD FIRE - Sporting goods ☆ - Gold Eagle/Arnold Palmer
GOLD FIX - Aquariums–household - Jungle Laboratories Corp.
GOLD FLAKE - Cigarettes - American Tobacco Co.
GOLD FLAME - Fuel additives - Farmers Petroleum Cooperative, Inc.
GOLD-FLEX - Jewelry - Simon Golub & Sons Inc.
GOLD FLYER - Bicycles - Ross Bicycles USA, Ltd.
GOLD FOX - Sporting goods - FTM Sports
GOLD GALAXY - Hair care products - Sebring Products Inc.
GOLD GEAR - Exhaust systems–motor vehicle - Superior Industries International, Inc.
GOLD GETTER - Skin care products ☆ - F.W. Engels Inc.
GOLD-GUARD - Insulating materials - Plymouth Foam Products
GOLD-GUARD - Sporting goods - Trace Athletic Corp.
GOLD GUARD PLUS - Oils–lubricating - Conklin Co., Inc.
GOLD HEART - Flour–blended - ConAgra Grain Co.
GOLD HILL - Fruits–canned - Rogue River Packing Corp.
GOLD HILL - Recording label - Vision Records Inc.
GOLD HORIZON - Dishes–china - Pickard Inc.
GOLD ICE - Hair care products - Fromm Industries
GOLD ICE - Scissors–hand-operated - F.W. Engels Inc.
GOLD IN MOTION - Jewelry–precious - James P. Farley
GOLD INN - Food products - Mission-Harlingen Canning Co.
GOLD ITALIA - Jewelry - American Foreign Trade Inc.
GOLD JACKS - Giftware - Russ Berrie and Co., Inc.
GOLD JUBILEE - Dolls - Mattel, Inc.
GOLD JULIET - Dishes–china ☆ - Pickard Inc.
GOLD KEG - Beverages–malt ☆ - Labatt Importers Inc.
GOLD KEY - Publisher's imprints - Western Publishing Co., Inc.
GOLD KIST - Food products - Gold Kist Inc.
GOLD-KOTER - Cleaning preparations - Mega Manufacturing Co. Inc.
GOLD LABEL - Apparel–women's - Town Fashions
GOLD LABEL - Bedding–linen - Fieldcrest Cannon, Inc.
GOLD LABEL - Breads - Campbell Taggart Inc.
GOLD LABEL - Cleaning preparations - DL/Banite
GOLD LABEL - Concrete products - Fosroc Inc.
GOLD LABEL - Desserts - Northville Laboratories Inc. (Jogue Inc.)
GOLD LABEL - Dog food - Pet Products Plus
GOLD LABEL - Ducks - Maple Leaf Farms Inc.
GOLD LABEL - Floor waxes - Chemifax
GOLD LABEL - Garden equipment - H.B. Sherman Manufacturing Co.
GOLD LABEL - Health care products - Creative Laboratories Inc.
GOLD LABEL - Health care products ☆ - McZand Herbal, Inc.
GOLD LABEL - Ice cream ☆ - Roney-Oatman Inc.
GOLD LABEL - Jams and jellies - Mountain Maid Gourmet Jelly
GOLD LABEL - Paper–carbon - A.B. Dick Co.
GOLD LABEL - Salad dressings–bottled - Sunlight Foods Inc.
GOLD LABEL - Seasonings ☆ - Sigma Quality Foods Corp.
GOLD LABEL - Soups–canned ☆ - Campbell Soup Co.
GOLD LABEL - Thread - Cincinnati Thread Co.
GOLD LABEL - Vegetables–canned - Gerawan Foods Inc.
GOLD LABEL - Vegetables–frozen - Norpac Services, Inc.
GOLD LABEL - Vitamins and nutritional supplements - Solgar Vitamin and Herb Co., Inc.
GOLD LABEL BOTANICALS - Health care products - McZand Herbal, Inc.
GOLD LABEL CEDAR FENCING - Cedar fencing - Caffall Brothers Forest Products, Inc.
GOLD LABEL CEDAR LUMBER - Building materials - Caffall Brothers Forest Products, Inc.
GOLD LABEL OLD VIENNA - Fish–canned or cured - I. Rokeach and Sons Inc.
GOLD LANCE - Giftware ☆ - Towle Silversmiths
GOLD LEAF - Food products - Tyson Foods Inc.
GOLD LEAF - Seafood products–fresh or frozen - New England Fish Co.
GOLD LEAF - Wallpaper - Wallpaper Imports Inc.
GOLD LEAF - Wines - Warner Vineyards Inc.
GOLD LEAF PORCELAIN - Dishes–china - Mikasa Co.
GOLD LINE - Candy - Bobs Candies Inc.
GOLD LINE - Computers–personal - Gold Line Connectors Inc.
GOLD LINE - Office supplies - Esselte Corp.

☆ = Now out of production

GOLD LINE - Pagers - Motorola, Inc. (Land Mobile Products Sector)

GOLD LINE - Radios–citizens' band - Motorola, Inc.

GOLD LINE - Tape–adhesive - Capitol Adhesives Inc.

GOLD LINE - Thermometers - Popper & Sons Inc.

GOLD LINE - Tools - Ames Taping Tool Systems Co.

GOLD LINE - Vegetables–frozen - Hanover Foods Corp.

GOLD LOTUS - Flatware - Wallace International Silversmiths, Inc.

GOLD LOW ALCOHOL - Beverages–malt ☆ - Pabst Brewing Co.

GOLD LUCK - Game machines - Autotote Systems, Inc.

GOLD-LUX - Handles–metal - Goipar, Inc.

GOLD MAGIC - Cosmetics - Ardell International Inc.

GOLD MAGIC - Hair care products - American International Industries

GOLD MARQUE ARTIST SERIES - Hobby kits - Bell Ceramics, Inc.

GOLD MASTER - Artists' materials - Robert Simmons Inc.

GOLD MEASURE - Nuts–salted, roasted, cooked, or canned - Planters LifeSavers Co.

GOLD MEDAL - Ammunition - Federal Cartridge Co.

GOLD MEDAL - Antiseptics ☆ - Pfeiffer Pharmaceuticals Inc.

GOLD MEDAL - Bicycles - Columbia Manufacturing Inc.

GOLD MEDAL - Eyeglasses ☆ - Cable Car Eyeware

GOLD MEDAL - Faucets - Great Lakes Marketing of Michigan Inc.

GOLD MEDAL - Firearms, accessories, and parts - Federal-Hoffman, Inc.

GOLD MEDAL - Firearms, accessories, and parts ☆ - Blount International, Inc. (Sporting Equipment Group)

GOLD MEDAL - Fishing tackle - Penn Fishing Tackle Manufacturing Co.

GOLD MEDAL - Flour–blended - General Mills, Inc.

GOLD MEDAL - Furniture - Gold Medal Inc.

GOLD MEDAL - Health care products - Carolina Products Inc.

GOLD MEDAL - Jewelry ☆ - Fantasy Diamond Corp.

GOLD MEDAL - Juices - S. Martinelli and Co.

GOLD MEDAL - Juices ☆ - Heinke's Inc.

GOLD MEDAL - Ladders–metal - Patent Construction Systems

GOLD MEDAL - Ladders–metal ☆ - Werner Co.

GOLD MEDAL - Macaroni ☆ - Pastamania

GOLD MEDAL - Mayonnaise - C.F. Sauer Co.

GOLD MEDAL - Paint rollers - Arsco International Inc.

GOLD MEDAL - Processed meats - Aesquivel Corp. of California

GOLD MEDAL - Saxophones - Ideal Musical Merchandise Co.

GOLD MEDAL - Spices and extracts - American Laboratories, Inc.

GOLD MEDAL - Sporting goods - Gold Medal Recreational Products

GOLD MEDAL - Twine - Blue Mountain Industries, Inc.

GOLD MEDAL - Twine - Seattle Marine & Fishing Supply Co.

GOLD MEDAL - Water–bottled or canned - All-American Bottling Corp.

GOLD MEDAL - Window shades - C-Mor Co.

GOLD MEDAL BABY - Dolls - Gata Box Ltd.

GOLD MEDAL GRIPPERS - Toy cars ☆ - Intex Recreation Corp.

GOLD MEDAL LINE - Cheese - Crystal Food Import Corp.

GOLD MEDAL PETS - Pet products - Cardinal Laboratories, Inc.

GOLD MEDAL TIOGA - Ladders–metal - Gold Medal Ladder Co.

GOLD MEDAL ULTRAMATCH - Firearms, accessories, and parts - Federal-Hoffman, Inc.

GOLD MEDALIST - Archery equipment - Hoyt

GOLD MEDALIST - Boats–canoes - Coleman Co., Inc.

GOLD MEDALIST - Sealing compounds - Hillyard Enterprises, Inc.

GOLD MEDALLION - Clocks - Ansonia Clock Co. Inc.

GOLD MEDALLION - Computer software - Gold Medallion Software Inc.

GOLD MEDALLION - Fishing tackle - Zebco Corp.

GOLD MERIDIAN - Seafood products–fresh or frozen - Meridian Products

GOLD MERIDIAN - Seafood products–fresh or frozen - Meridian Products, Inc.

GOLD MINES - Jewelry - Norman T. Kanel Corp.

GOLD MIST - Dinnerware–glass ☆ - Lenox, Inc.

GOLD MIST - Glassware–household ☆ - Lenox Crystal, Inc.

GOLD MOGUL - Banjos - OME Co. Inc.

GOLD MONARCH - Banjos - OME Co. Inc.

GOLD MONTEREY - Flatware - Wallace International Silversmiths, Inc.

GOLD N BAKE - Dairy products ☆ - DMV USA Inc.

GOLD N BITS - Dog food - Buckeye Feed Mills, Inc.

GOLD-N-BRAID - Rope ☆ - Samson Cordage Works

GOLD N' CRUST - Food products ☆ - Adolph's Ltd.

GOLD 'N FLU - Food products - Herbs of China Ltd.

GOLD-N-FRESH - Food products - Seaboard Farms of Athens Inc.

GOLD N' FRI - Shortening - Florida Shortening Corp.

GOLD N' GLOW - Candles ☆ - Empire Manufacturing Co.

GOLD 'N HOT - Dryers–hair - Windmere Corp.

GOLD 'N HOT - Hair care products - Belson Products

GOLD N KIBBLE - Dog food - MFA Inc.

GOLD-N-KOTE - Insulating materials ☆ - GS Roofing Products Co.

GOLD-N-KOTE - Roofing materials–concrete ☆ - Flintkote Co.

GOLD-N-LINE - Recoil pads, butt plates, and spacers - Pachmayr Ltd.

GOLD 'N LITE - Cheese ☆ - Hormel Foods Corp.

GOLD 'N NATURAL - Sugar–granulated, refined, or powdered - Savannah Foods and Industries Inc.

GOLD N PRO - Dog food - MFA Inc.

GOLD N PUPPY - Dog food - MFA Inc.

GOLD N PURE - Beverages - Tropicana Products, Inc.

GOLD N RICH - Dog food - MFA Inc.

GOLD N/S - Darts and dart games - Dart Mart Inc.

GOLD N' SILVER - Greeting cards - Regency Thermographers Inc.

GOLD-N-SOFT - Margarine ☆ - Borden Food Service

GOLD-N-SWEET - Food products - Wilsey Foods, Inc.

GOLD N' VELVET - Candles ☆ - Empire Manufacturing Co.

GOLD 'N WHITE - Vegetables–canned - Stokely USA, Inc.

GOLD NECTAR - Beverages–malt - Humboldt Brewing Co.

GOLD NUGGET - Animal feeds - Louis E. Fite

GOLD NUGGET - Cheese - Nelson-Ricks Creamery Co.

GOLD NUGGET - Christmas tree ornaments - Cracker Box Inc.

GOLD NUGGET - Meat products–beef - Sigman Meat Co. Inc.

GOLD NUGGET - Polishing cloths - S.M. Arnold Inc.

GOLD NUGGET - Wines - Amador Foothill Winery

GOLD NUGGETS - Recording label - Ripete Music Group

GOLD NUT - Food products ☆ - Gold Kist Inc.

GOLD-O-MINT - Liquors ☆ - House of Seagram

GOLD-OFF - Artists' materials - Etchall Co.

GOLD OLD APRICOT - Mustard - Silver Palate Kitchen

GOLD-OOMED - Pet products - Tetra Sales USA

GOLD OUT - Shampoos - Colorful Products Corp.

GOLD PACK - Vitamins and nutritional supplements - Golden Pride-Rawleigh, Inc.

GOLD PERFORMANCE - Trading cards and stamps - Allstar Marketing Corp.

GOLD PFEIL - Leather goods - Italian Classics Inc.

GOLD PIECE - Fruits and vegetables - Gold Rush Produce, Inc.

GOLD PLATE - Meat products–poultry - Jerome Foods Inc.

GOLD PLATE - Recording label ☆ - Amherst Records

GOLD PLUS - Hardware - Allpro Corp.

GOLD-POINT - Sporting goods - Schutt Manufacturing Co.

GOLD POINT/ADVANT-EDGE - Orthodontic equipment - TP Orthodontics, Inc.

GOLD PREMIUM - Vegetables–frozen - Inn Foods, Inc.

GOLD PREMIUM - Video tapes–blank - Shape Inc.

GOLD PRO - Hair care products - Gold Medal Hair Products Inc.

GOLD/PRO - Paints - Allpro Corp.

GOLD PURE - Seasonings ☆ - Gold Pure Food Products Inc.

GOLD RANGER - Toys - Saban Entertainment, Inc.

GOLD RAZOR EDGE - Scissors–hand-operated - F.W. Engels Inc.

GOLD RESERVE - Footwear ☆ - E.S. Originals, Inc.

GOLD RESERVE - Rum - Bacardi Imports Inc.

GOLD RETRIEVER - Mining equipment ☆ - Anderson Manufacturing Co.

GOLD RIBBON - Food products ☆ - Wallabout Meat Packing Co.

GOLD RIBBON - Hams - Hatfield, Inc.

GOLD RIBBON - Popcorn ☆ - TV Time Foods Inc.

GOLD RIBBON KAKEBAKE - Shortening ☆ - Swift Edible Oil Co.

GOLD RIBBON VREAMAY - Shortening ☆ - Swift Edible Oil Co.

GOLD RING - Drums–musical instruments ☆ - Pearl Corp.

GOLD RIVER - Snuff - American Maize-Products Co.

GOLD RIVER - Tobacco products - Swisher International, Inc.

GOLD ROAST - Coffee - Cameron Coffee Co. Inc.

GOLD RUNNER - Footwear–athletic - KangaROOS USA Inc.

GOLD RUSH - Bicycles - Easy Racers Inc.

GOLD RUSH - Candy ☆ - Topps Co., Inc.

GOLD RUSH - Ice cream - Vroman Foods Inc.

GOLD RUSH - Machinery - Sunkist Growers Inc.

GOLD RUSH - Machinery - Sunkist Growers, Inc.

GOLD RUSH - Sunglasses - Wal-Mart Stores Inc.

GOLD RUSH - Toys–models - GHQ

GOLD RUSH - Trading cards and stamps - Pinnacle Brands, Inc.

GOLD RUSH 14 - Yarn - Rainbow Gallery, Inc.

GOLD RUSH JAM - Jams and jellies - Mountain Maid Gourmet Jelly

GOLD SASH - Brushes–paint - Corona Brushes Inc.

GOLD SCOPE - Archery equipment - Golden Key Futura, Inc.

GOLD SEAL - Aircraft parts - Teledyne Industries Inc.

GOLD SEAL - Beverages–alcohol - Canandaigua Wine Co. Inc.

GOLD SEAL - Clamps–hose - Murray Corp.

GOLD SEAL - Drapery hardware - Kirsch Co.

GOLD SEAL - Footwear–athletic - Gold Seal Rubber Co.
GOLD SEAL - Furniture ☆ - H. Wilson Co.
GOLD SEAL - Ice cream - Crowley Foods, Inc.
GOLD SEAL - Musical instrument accessories - Harptone
GOLD SEAL - Paints - Buten Paint & Wallpaper
GOLD SEAL - Publisher's imprints - Western Skyways, Inc.
GOLD SEAL - Recording label - RCA Records
GOLD SEAL - Salmon–smoked, salted, dried, or pickled - Specialty Seafoods
GOLD SEAL - Socks - Sockyard Co. Inc.
GOLD SEAL - Thread - Sebro Thread Corp.
GOLD SEAL - Tiles–ceramic - Congoleum Corp.
GOLD SEAL - Wines - Gold Seal Vineyards Inc.
GOLD SEAL CATAWBA - Wines - Joseph E. Seagram & Sons, Inc.
GOLD SELECTA - Seafood products–fresh or frozen - Selecta Seafoods, Inc.
GOLD SENSATION - Dolls - Mattel, Inc.
GOLD SERIES - Basketball backboards ☆ - Lifetime Products, Inc.
GOLD SERIES - Brushes–paint - Allpro Corp.
GOLD SERIES - Curling irons–electric - Helen of Troy Corp.
GOLD SERIES - Insecticides - Bengal Chemical, Inc.
GOLD SERIES - Perfumes - Genesis International Distribution Inc.
GOLD SHAFT, THE - Golfing equipment - Golfsmith International Inc.
GOLD SHIELD - Nuts–salted, roasted, cooked, or canned - Pacific Foods Inc.
GOLD SHIELD BABY ARMOR - Skin care products - David M. Mayer
GOLD SHIELD SKIN ARMOR - Skin care products - David M. Mayer
GOLD SIGNATURE - Golfing equipment ☆ - Northwestern Golf Co.
GOLD SOLUTION, THE - Cleaning preparations - Sheffield Plate Polish Co. Ltd.
GOLD SOUND - Recording label - Casino Record Inc.
GOLD SPIRAL - Glassware–household - Owens-Illinois Inc. (Libbey Div.)
GOLD SPOT - Games - Trade Products, Inc.
GOLD SPOT - Vitamins and nutritional supplements - Tishcon Corp.
GOLD SPOT DAIRY - Milk - Highland Dairy
GOLD STANDARD - Dental products - Myron International Inc.
GOLD STANDARD - Food products - New England Fish Co.
GOLD STANDARD - Motor vehicle parts and accessories - Budge Industries, Inc.
GOLD STANDARD - Pens - Craft Supplies USA
GOLD STANDARD - Trading cards and stamps - Collector's Club, Inc.
GOLD STAR - Aircraft engines - West Star Aviation, Inc.
GOLD STAR - Canvas–artists' - Wolsey Co.
GOLD STAR - Coffee - Gold Star Coffee Co. Inc.
GOLD STAR - Dryers–hair - Helene Curtis Industries Inc.
GOLD STAR - Food products - Northern Star Co.
GOLD STAR - Goggles–safety - Cabot Safety Intermediate Corp.
GOLD STAR - Nuts–salted, roasted, cooked, or canned - Nut Bar Co. Inc.
GOLD STAR - Pet products - Merrick's Inc.
GOLD-STAR - Van bodies - Morgan Trailer Manufacturing. Co.
GOLD STAR-PREAMPS - Amplifiers ☆ - Winegard Co.
GOLD STAR REMANUFACTURED ENGINE - Engines - West Star Aviation, Inc.
GOLD STRAND - Aluminum products - Root Corp. (New York Wire Div.)
GOLD STRIKE - Beverages–alcohol - William Grant & Sons, Inc.
GOLD STRIKE - Cordage and twine - Wellington Leisure Products, Inc.
GOLD SWEPE - Brooms - Hamburg Broom Works Inc.
GOLD SYSTEM - Floor coverings - Congoleum Corp.
GOLD TEE - Footwear - Ambassador Shoe Corp.
GOLD TEST - Tiles–ceramic - Louis Goldey Co. Inc.
GOLD-TIP - Artists' materials ☆ - Binney & Smith Inc.
GOLD TIP - Glass products - Fletcher-Terry Co.
GOLD TIP - Vegetables–canned - Taormina Co.
GOLD TOE - Hosiery - GAKM Resources Corp.
GOLD TOE - Socks - Great American Knitting Mills
GOLD TOE CLASSIC - Hosiery - GAKM Resources Corp.
GOLD TONE - Coffee fillers - Golden Brew Inc.
GOLD TOP - Adhesives and sealants - Super-Tek Products Inc.
GOLD TOP - Batteries - General Electric Co.
GOLD TOP - Bottles–glass - Capitol Novelty Co.
GOLD TOP - Lanterns–kerosene - Coleman Co., Inc.
GOLD TOUCH - Chemical preparations - Gold Touch, Inc.
GOLD TRACK IV/DSP - Automated welding system - Dimetrics Inc.
GOLD TRIM - Brushes–paint - Corona Brushes Inc.
GOLD VEIN - Floor coverings ☆ - Congoleum Corp.
GOLD VET - Veterinary nutritional supplements - Landco
GOLD VET HYPO-K - Vitamins and nutritional supplements - Landco
GOLD WANRIKI - Vitamins and nutritional supplements - Winning Laboratories Corp.

GOLD WHEEL - Seafood products–fresh or frozen - Alpine International
GOLD WINES - Glassware–household - Ceraglass Inc.
GOLD WING - Fishing lures - Hildebrandt Corp.
GOLD WRITE - Pigments ☆ - Martin F. Weber Co.
GOLDARIUM - Lighting equipment - Cosmedico Light, Inc.
GOLDBAR - Jewelry - Goldbar Manufacturing Corp.
GOLDBERG - Film/tape reels - J and R Film Co. Inc.
GOLDBERGER - Dolls - Goldberger Doll Manufacture Co.
GOLDBLATT - Brushes - Stanley Works
GOLDBLOX - Jewelry - Color Merchants, Inc.
GOLDBRICK - Cheese - Beatrice Cheese Co.
GOLDBUG - Phonographs ☆ - Kevek Speaker Technology
GOLDCAST II - Sporting goods - Daiwa Corp.
GOLDCHEM - Agricultural products - Westmark AG Group, Inc.
GOLDCO - Conveyors - Goldco Industries, Inc.
GOLDCOAST - Greeting cards - Amberley Greeting Card Co.
GOLDCORE - Air cushions - Select Comfort Corp.
GOLDCRAFT - Watches - Bulova Corp.
GOLDCREST - Paper–bond - Saxon Paper Co.
GOLDDIGGERS - Food products ☆ - Pierre Frozen Foods Inc.
GOLDEDGE - Cosmetics ☆ - Dubl Duck/Jet Set Inc.
GOLDEN - Ammunition - Remington Arms Co., Inc.
GOLDEN - Apparel and accessories - Piedmont Industries Inc.
GOLDEN - Bakery products ☆ - Old Fashioned Kitchen Inc.
GOLDEN - Beverages - Atlas Bottling Co.
GOLDEN - Cheese - Golden Cheese Co. of California
GOLDEN - Food products - Maloney Seafood Corp.
GOLDEN - Food products - Union Foods
GOLDEN - Fruits and vegetables - International Golden Foods, Inc.
GOLDEN - Gasoline ☆ - J. & L. Oil Inc.
GOLDEN - Glassware–household - Avitra Corp.
GOLDEN - Greeting cards - Gibson Greetings, Inc.
GOLDEN - Juices - Nestle Beverage Co.
GOLDEN - Nuts–salted, roasted, cooked, or canned - Gulf Farms Inc.
GOLDEN - Pet products - Golden West Bird Farm Inc.
GOLDEN - Pianos ☆ - Strydel Inc.
GOLDEN - Sugar–granulated, refined, or powdered - Montgomery Sugar
GOLDEN 18 - Dog food - Shawnee Milling Co.
GOLDEN 49ER - Giftware ☆ - W.M.F. of America Inc.
GOLDEN A5 - Clippers–barber - Sunbeam-Oster Household Products
GOLDEN ACRE - Turkeys - Wampler Foods Inc.
GOLDEN ADRIA - Flatware ☆ - Gorham Inc.
GOLDEN AEGEAN WEAVE - Flatware - Wallace International Silversmiths, Inc.
GOLDEN AFTERNOON - Wallpaper ☆ - Imperial Wallcoverings, Inc.
GOLDEN AGAVE - Beverages–alcohol - American Stores Co.
GOLDEN AGE - Beverages–carbonated - Shasta Beverages, Inc.
GOLDEN AGE - Rice - Bunn Capitol Co.
GOLDEN AGE - Veterinary nutritional supplements - Dr. Goodpet
GOLDEN AGE - Wallpaper ☆ - Winfield Design Associates, Inc.
GOLDEN AGE COLLECTION - Publisher's imprints - Maier Group Inc.
GOLDEN AGE OF BASEBALL, THE - Chessboards - Bradford Exchange, Ltd.
GOLDEN AGE SPLENDER - Fabrics - Piedmont Collections
GOLDEN ALBUM - Greeting cards - American Artists Group Inc.
GOLDEN ALLURE - Watches - Bulova Corp.
GOLDEN ALMOND - Candy - Hershey Chocolate USA
GOLDEN ALMOND - Jewelry - Almond Jewelers Inc.
GOLDEN ALMOND SOLITAIRES - Candy - Hershey Chocolate USA
GOLDEN A.M. - Apparel–athletic - A.M. Player, Inc.
GOLDEN AMERICAN - Putties - Spectro Oils of America
GOLDEN ANCHOR - Rice - Viet Wah Trading Corp.
GOLDEN ANNIVERSARY - Beverages–malt - Genesee Brewing Co., Inc.
GOLDEN APPLE - Nail care products - Cosmair Inc.
GOLDEN APPLES - Fabrics - Gretchen Bellinger Inc.
GOLDEN ARCHIVES COLLECTION - Greeting cards ☆ - Evergreen Press
GOLDEN ARIEL - Flatware - Reed and Barton Corp.
GOLDEN ARMOR - Jewelry - Jacoby-Bender Inc.
GOLDEN ARROW - Bicycles ☆ - Roadmaster Corp.
GOLDEN ARROW - Golfing equipment - Golfsmith International Inc.
GOLDEN ARROW - Pens ☆ - Parker Pen USA
GOLDEN ARTESIA - Flatware - Pfaltzgraff Investment Co.
GOLDEN ARTIST COLORS - Paints–artists' - Golden Artist Colors, Inc.
GOLDEN ASH - Tobacco–chewing or smoking - Amar Blends Co.
GOLDEN ASHMONT - Flatware - Reed and Barton Corp.
GOLDEN AUTUMN - Colognes ☆ - Prince Matchabelli
GOLDEN AUTUMN - Jewelry ☆ - Hirsch Speidel Inc.

☆ = Now out of production

GOLDEN AWARD - Oils–edible - Bunge Foods Corp.

GOLDEN BALANCE - Cheese - Golden Cheese Co. of California

GOLDEN BALM - Analgesics - Teamup International, Inc.

GOLDEN BAQUETTE - Jewelry - Jacoby-Bender Inc.

GOLDEN BAR - Cheese - Farmers Cheese Co.

GOLDEN BARREL - Food products - Good Food Inc.

GOLDEN BARREL SYRUP - Pies–frozen - Good Food Inc.

GOLDEN BATCH - Cookies - Heritage Wafers Ltd.

GOLDEN BEAR - Apparel and accessories - Warnaco Inc.

GOLDEN BEAR - Backpacks - United Merchandising Corp.

GOLDEN BEAR - Beverages–malt - Golden Pacific Brewing Co., Inc.

GOLDEN BEAR - Beverages–malt - Charles Rixford

GOLDEN BEAR - Golfing equipment - Brunswick Corp.

GOLDEN BEAR - Oils–lubricating - Witco Corp.

GOLDEN BEAR - Pet products - Loos and Co. Inc.

GOLDEN BEAR - Toys - Brittoys

GOLDEN BEAUTY - Flowers, plants, and seeds - Proven Winners

GOLDEN BEAUTY - Jewelry - Golden Beauty Wedding Rings, Inc.

GOLDEN BELL - Tiles–ceramic - Golden Bell USA Co.

GOLDEN BELLE - Food products - Van Den Bergh Foods Co.

GOLDEN BELT - Staples - Stanley-Bostitch Inc.

GOLDEN BLAZE - Hair coloring preparations - Cosmair Inc.

GOLDEN BLEND - Dog food - Sunshine Mills Inc.

GOLDEN BLEND - Underwear and nightwear ☆ - Fruit of the Loom Inc.

GOLDEN BLOSSOM - Honey - John Paton Inc.

GOLDEN BLOSSOM - Shampoos ☆ - Texas Best Unlimited, LP

GOLDEN BOBBIN - Sewing machines–household - VWS Inc.

GOLDEN BOMBAY - Flatware ☆ - Lifetime Hoan Corp.

GOLDEN BOND - Cooking equipment–household ☆ - Nordic Ware

GOLDEN BOOK 'N TAPE - Publisher's imprints - Western Publishing Co., Inc.

GOLDEN BOOKS - Publisher's imprints - Western Publishing Co., Inc.

GOLDEN BOOKS INTERACTIVE - Computer software - Western Publishing Co., Inc.

GOLDEN BOOKS WITH SOUND - Toys–electronic - Western Publishing Co., Inc.

GOLDEN BOUNTY - Vitamins and nutritional supplements - Bristol-Myers Squibb Co.

GOLDEN BOWL - Fruits and vegetables - Limoneira Co.

GOLDEN BOY - Recording label - Golden Boy Records

GOLDEN BOY BRAND - Food products - Lien Hoa Food Corp.

GOLDEN BOY JAZZ - Recording label - Golden Boy Records

GOLDEN BRAND - Oils–edible - Wilson Foods Corp.

GOLDEN BREED - Apparel–men's - Richton International Corp.

GOLDEN BREED - Apparel–men's - Hisao Yamada

GOLDEN BREW - Coffee - Park Corp.

GOLDEN BRILLIANCE - Jewelry - William Schneider Inc.

GOLDEN BRITE - Cleaning preparations - Leon Supply Co.

GOLDEN BROCADE - Flatware - Gorham Inc.

GOLDEN BROWN - Food products ☆ - Grasso Foods Inc.

GOLDEN BROWN - Sausages - Jones Dairy Farm

GOLDEN BUCKEYE - Brushes–paint - Wooster Brush Co.

GOLDEN BUSY BOOKS - Publisher's imprints - Western Publishing Co., Inc.

GOLDEN BUTTER - Food products ☆ - Curtice-Burns Foods, Inc.

GOLDEN BUTTERFLY - Giftware - Arnart Imports Inc.

GOLDEN C - Juices - Carolina Products Inc.

GOLDEN CAD - Paints - Easthill Group, Inc.

GOLDEN CALIFORNIA - Cheese - Golden Cheese Co. of California

GOLDEN CALIFORNIA - Skin care products - Golden California Co. Inc.

GOLDEN CALVERT - Flatware ☆ - Kirk Stieff Co.

GOLDEN CAMEOS - Stationery - Burgoyne Inc./Curtis Swann

GOLDEN CAR SONGS - Games - Western Publishing Co., Inc.

GOLDEN CAROUSEL - Agricultural products - Bailey Nurseries, Inc.

GOLDEN CASHEWS - Candy - Golden Triangle Import/Export Corp.

GOLDEN CAT - Casters - Golden Cat Corp.

GOLDEN CAVALIER - Lighters - Colibri Inc.

GOLDEN CHAMPION - Jewelry - Jacoby-Bender Inc.

GOLDEN CHARDONNAY - Flatware - Reed and Barton Corp.

GOLDEN CHASSIS - Lubricants - Quaker State Oil Refining Corp.

GOLDEN CHILE - Seafood products–fresh or frozen ☆ - Pocasset Seafoods Inc.

GOLDEN CHIP - Margarine - Miami Margarine Co. Inc.

GOLDEN CHOICE - Coffee - Gourmet's Choice Coffee Inc.

GOLDEN CHOICE - Dog food - Wells Pet Foods Co.

GOLDEN CHOICE - Meat products–poultry - Golden Choice Co.

GOLDEN CHOICE FOODS - Snack foods - Golden Choice Foods Corp.

GOLDEN CHORD - Jewelry ☆ - Hirsch Speidel Inc.

GOLDEN CIRCLE - Jewelry - Jacoby-Bender Inc.

GOLDEN CIRCLE - Leather goods - AR Accessories Group Inc.

GOLDEN CIRCLE SPORTS - Archery equipment - Archer Sports Inc.

GOLDEN CITRUS - Fruit drinks–bottled or canned - McCain Citrus, Inc.

GOLDEN CLASP - Neckties - A. Schreter & Sons Co. Inc.

GOLDEN CLASSIC - Barbecues and grills - Thermos Co.

GOLDEN CLASSIC - Clocks - General Time Corp. (Westclox/Seth Thomas Div.)

GOLDEN CLASSICS - Soups–canned - Campbell Soup Co.

GOLDEN CLIPPER - Watches - Bulova Corp.

GOLDEN CLUB - Giftware ☆ - Papel Freelance, Inc.

GOLDEN COAST - Floor coverings–carpet and rugs - Golden Bell USA Co.

GOLDEN COAT - Food products - Original Trenton Cracker Co.

GOLDEN COBRA - Game machines - Ramparts Inc.

GOLDEN COIN - Jewelry - Jacoby-Bender Inc.

GOLDEN COLA - Beverages–carbonated - Cadbury Beverages Inc.

GOLDEN COLLECTION, THE - Candy - Hershey Chocolate USA

GOLDEN COLLECTION, THE - Quilts - Vip Far-East Corp.

GOLDEN COMFORT - Health care products - Lakon Herbals Inc.

GOLDEN COMMPASS - Computer programs - Creative Systems Programming Corp.

GOLDEN COPLEY - Flatware - Reed and Barton Corp.

GOLDEN CORN FLY - Fishing lures - Joe's Flies

GOLDEN CORN NUGGETS - Cereal - Malt-O-Meal Co.

GOLDEN COVE - Floor coverings–carpet and rugs ☆ - Royalweve Carpet Mills

GOLDEN COW - Meat products–beef - Bay World Trading, Ltd.

GOLDEN COZY - Publisher's imprints - Western Publishing Co., Inc.

GOLDEN CRANE - Vitamins and nutritional supplements - Ethical Nutrients

GOLDEN CRAYON GO ROUND - Games ☆ - Western Publishing Co., Inc.

GOLDEN CREME - Dairy products - Certified Grocers of California, Ltd.

GOLDEN CREME - Moisturizing and analgesic creams - Relief, Inc.

GOLDEN CRESCENDO - Flatware - Reed and Barton Corp.

GOLDEN CRESCENT - Paints - Gulf States Paint Co.

GOLDEN CREST - Flour–blended ☆ - Western Star Mill Co.

GOLDEN CRINKLES - Vegetables–frozen - Ore-Ida Foods, Inc.

GOLDEN CRISP - Bacon - Patrick Cudahy Inc.

GOLDEN CRISP - Potato chips - Bachman Co.

GOLDEN CRISP - Snack foods ☆ - Wyandot, Inc.

GOLDEN CROSSROADS - Flatware - Pfaltzgraff Investment Co.

GOLDEN CROWN - Food products ☆ - Interstate Restaurant Supply Co.

GOLDEN CROWN - Fruit drinks–bottled or canned - McCain Citrus, Inc.

GOLDEN CROWN - Giftware - Ebeling and Reuss Co.

GOLDEN CROWN - Lemonade - Cliffstar Corp.

GOLDEN CROWN - Medical apparatus - Nelkin/Piper Health Products

GOLDEN CROWN - Photographic equipment - General Electric Co.

GOLDEN CROWN ROYALE - Cutlery ☆ - Lifetime Hoan Corp.

GOLDEN CRUNCHIES - Candy ☆ - Gilliam Candy Co. Inc. (Gilliam Candy Brands)

GOLDEN CRUST - Food products - Shawnee Milling Co.

GOLDEN CUP - Coffee - Golden Cup Coffee

GOLDEN CURE - Meat products - Lykes Bros., Inc.

GOLDEN D - Oils–lubricating - Cenex

GOLDEN D BRAND - Frankfurters - Golden D Brand Meats, Inc.

GOLDEN DAIRY - Milk - KDK Inc.

GOLDEN DANDY - Brushes–paint - Wooster Brush Co.

GOLDEN DANISH - Tobacco products - Lane Ltd.

GOLDEN DANUBE - Flatware - Gorham Inc.

GOLDEN DAYS - Candy - Bobs Candies Inc.

GOLDEN DAYS - Floor coverings–carpet and rugs ☆ - Downs Carpet Co. Inc.

GOLDEN DAYS - Food products - H.J. Heinz Co.

GOLDEN DAYS - Incense ☆ - Olfactory Corp.

GOLDEN DAYS - Vitamins and nutritional supplements - Synergy Plus

GOLDEN DEER - Footwear - Conjac Inc.

GOLDEN DEER BRAND - Food products - Great Year Import Co., Inc.

GOLDEN DELIGHT - Beverages–carbonated - New England Dairies Inc.

GOLDEN DELIGHT - Food products - Florida Dynamic Marketing Concepts

GOLDEN DELIGHT - Juices - Givaudan Rare Flavors

GOLDEN DELIGHT - Waffles–frozen ☆ - Roman Meal Co.

GOLDEN DELIGHTS - Potato chips - Curtice-Burns Foods, Inc.

GOLDEN DELTA - Watches ☆ - Swiss Army Brands, Ltd.

GOLDEN DELUXE - Greeting cards - Creative Card Co.

GOLDEN DELUXE - Meat products - GFI America, Inc.

GOLDEN DESERT - Trees - Handy Nursery Co.

GOLDEN DEW - Shampoos - Like Me Products Co. Inc.

GOLDEN DIJON - Potato chips - Recot, Inc.

GOLDEN DIPT - Food products - Golden Dipt Co.
GOLDEN DIPT - Spices and extracts - McCormick & Co., Inc.
GOLDEN DOOR - Meat products–poultry ☆ - Cagle's Inc.
GOLDEN DOT - Fishing tackle ☆ - Gladding Braided Products Inc.
GOLDEN DRAGON - Food products - Associated Fruit Co.
GOLDEN DRAGON - Fruits–canned - Skookum Packers Association Inc.
GOLDEN DRAGONS - Fruits and vegetables - Gold Coast Packing, Inc.
GOLDEN DREAM - Dolls - Mattel, Inc.
GOLDEN DREAMS - Bedding–linen - Hollander Home Fashions Inc.
GOLDEN DREAMS - Christmas tree ornaments - Cracker Box Inc.
GOLDEN DUKE - Pipes–tobacco - Dr. Grabow Pre-Smoked Pipes Inc.
GOLDEN DUSTERS - Fabrics - Erikson Nonwoven Textiles Inc.
GOLDEN E - Shampoos - Golden California Co. Inc.
GOLDEN EAGLE - Archery equipment - Golden Eagle Archery
GOLDEN EAGLE - Bicycles - Ross Bicycles USA, Ltd.
GOLDEN EAGLE - Cutlery - Ginkgo International Ltd.
GOLDEN EAGLE - Flour–blended - House-Autry Mills, Inc.
GOLDEN EAGLE - Flowers, plants, and seeds - Spring Hill Nurseries Co.
GOLDEN EAGLE - Pencils - Empire Berol USA
GOLDEN EAGLE - Sporting goods ☆ - Outboard Marine Corp.
GOLDEN EAGLE - Sporting goods ☆ - Richardson Sports Inc.
GOLDEN EAGLE - Syrup - Golden Eagle Syrup Co. Inc.
GOLDEN EAGLE - Tobacco products - 1776 Tobacco Co.
GOLDEN EAGLE - Watches - Bulova Corp.
GOLDEN EAGLE ACIER NOIR - Cutlery - Ginkgo International Ltd.
GOLDEN EAGLE HERBAL CHEW - Tobacco–chewing or smoking - Coltsfoot
GOLDEN EARTH - Food products - Golden Earth Herbs
GOLDEN EASY READER, A - Publisher's imprints ☆ - Western Publishing Co., Inc.
GOLDEN ECHO - Tableware–china - Pfaltzgraff Investment Co.
GOLDEN EDGE - Artists' materials - M. Grumbacher Inc.
GOLDEN ELEGANCE - Flatware - Salem China Co.
GOLDEN ELEGANCE - Flatware ☆ - Gorham Inc.
GOLDEN ELEGANCE - Giftware - Enesco Corp.
GOLDEN EMBASSY SCROLL - Flatware - Rogers, Lunt and Bowlen Co.
GOLDEN EMPRESS - Giftware - Arnart Imports Inc.
GOLDEN ENERGIZER - Animal feeds - Manna Pro Corp.
GOLDEN ERA - Greeting cards - Fink & Co.
GOLDEN ERA - Musical instruments - C.F. Martin & Co., Inc.
GOLDEN ESTATE - Prefabricated buildings–wood - Golden West Homes
GOLDEN EVENING - Dolls - Mattel, Inc.
GOLDEN EXTRACT - Skin care products - Flori Roberts Inc.
GOLDEN EYE MAKER, THE - Eye makeup kits ☆ - Cosrich Inc.
GOLDEN FACETED BEADS - Jewelry - Aurafin Corp.
GOLDEN FALCON - Bicycles - Ross Bicycles USA, Ltd.
GOLDEN FALCON - Tires - Bridgestone/Firestone, Inc.
GOLDEN FAMILY - Breads - Entenmann's Inc.
GOLDEN FANCY - Candy ☆ - Pet Inc. (Whitman's Chocolates Div.)
GOLDEN FARMS - Food products - Beatrice Cos. Inc.
GOLDEN FEET - Cosmetics ☆ - Nature's Answer (Bio Botanica)
GOLDEN FIVE STAR - Rifles - Redfield Co.
GOLDEN FLAIR - Shortening - Kraft Food Ingredients Corp.
GOLDEN FLAKE - Snack foods - Golden Enterprises Inc.
GOLDEN FLAME - Fireplace logs–treated - Gold Kist Inc.
GOLDEN FLAME, THE - Fireplaces - Heat-N-Glo Fireplace Products, Inc.
GOLDEN FLAVOR - Batter and bakery mixes - DCA Food Industries, Inc.
GOLDEN FLAVOR - Food products - Northern Star Co.
GOLDEN FLAX ON COBALT - Giftware ☆ - Fenton Art Glass Co.
GOLDEN FLEECE - Apparel and accessories - Brooks Brothers, Inc.
GOLDEN FLEECE - Apparel and accessories - I. Spiewak and Sons Inc.
GOLDEN FLEECE - Polishing cloths - S.M. Arnold Inc.
GOLDEN FLEECE COLLECTION, THE - Colognes - Brooks Brothers, Inc.
GOLDEN FLEET - Seafood products–fresh or frozen - Singleton Seafood Co.
GOLDEN FLO - Paint rollers - Wooster Brush Co.
GOLDEN FLOWER CHINESE HERBS - Vitamins and nutritional supplements - Golden Flower Chinese Herbs, Inc.
GOLDEN FLOWER GARDEN - Flatware ☆ - Stanley Roberts, Inc.
GOLDEN FLUTED SCROLL - Flatware - Reed and Barton Corp.
GOLDEN FOOD - Coffee - Golden Cup Coffee
GOLDEN FOOD - Food products - Wei-Chuan U.S.A., Inc.
GOLDEN FRENCH - Baskets–steel - Golden French Imports
GOLDEN FRESH - Food products - President Global Corp.
GOLDEN FRESH - Juices ☆ - Treesweet Products Co.
GOLDEN FRIES - Vegetables–frozen - Ore-Ida Foods, Inc.
GOLDEN FRUIT - Cookies - Sunshine Biscuits, Inc.

GOLDEN FRUIT OF THE LOOM - Underwear and nightwear ☆ - Fruit of the Loom Inc.
GOLDEN FRY - Vegetables–frozen - McCain Foods Inc.
GOLDEN GABLE - Jewelry - Jacoby-Bender Inc.
GOLDEN GALLON - Milk - Golden Gallon Inc.
GOLDEN GAMES - Games ☆ - Western Publishing Co., Inc.
GOLDEN GARDEN - Dinnerware–glass ☆ - Metlox Pottery Shoppe
GOLDEN GARDEN - Housewares - Great American Fun Corp.
GOLDEN GATE - Aquarium accessories - Kordon
GOLDEN GATE - Aquarium accessories - Novalek, Inc.
GOLDEN GATE - Beverages–malt - Golden Pacific Brewing Co., Inc.
GOLDEN GATE - Cider - Napa Valley Wines
GOLDEN GATE - Floor coverings–carpet and rugs - Cabin Crafts Carpets
GOLDEN GATE - Floor coverings–carpet and rugs ☆ - Blue Ridge Carpet Mills
GOLDEN GATE - Flour–blended ☆ - General Mills, Inc.
GOLDEN GATE - Olives–canned - StarFine Foods, Inc.
GOLDEN GATE - Paints ☆ - Dunn Edwards Corp.
GOLDEN GATE - Seafood products–fresh or frozen - Golden Gate Seafood Inc.
GOLDEN GATE - Tableware–china ☆ - Lenox, Inc.
GOLDEN GATE - Tobacco–chewing or smoking - G.A. Georgopulo & Co. Inc.
GOLDEN GATE PARK - Floor coverings–carpet and rugs ☆ - Hollytex Carpet Mills Inc.
GOLDEN GATE PARK 30 - Floor coverings–carpet and rugs ☆ - Hollytex Carpet Mills Inc.
GOLDEN GATE PARK 40 - Floor coverings–carpet and rugs ☆ - Hollytex Carpet Mills Inc.
GOLDEN GATOR - Jewelry - Jacoby-Bender Inc.
GOLDEN GEAR - Dolls - Mattel, Inc.
GOLDEN GEM - Fruit drinks–bottled or canned - Golden Gem Growers Inc.
GOLDEN GIANTS - Publisher's imprints - Walter J. Black Inc.
GOLDEN GIFT - Candy - Pangburn Candy Co.
GOLDEN GIRL - Balls–golf - Hansberger Precision Golf Worldwide
GOLDEN GIRL - Golfing equipment - Ram Golf Corp.
GOLDEN GIRL - Hair care products - Gold Medal Hair Products Inc.
GOLDEN GIRL - Watches - Hampden Corp.
GOLDEN GIRL AND THE GUARDIANS OF THE GEMSTONES - Games ☆ - Parker Brothers
GOLDEN GIRLS - Dolls ☆ - Lewis Galoob Toys, Inc.
GOLDEN GLEN - Rings–jewelry - Artcarved Inc.
GOLDEN GLENWOOD - Giftware ☆ - Gorham Inc.
GOLDEN GLIDE - Blinds–vertical - Kaleidoscope Industries Inc.
GOLDEN-GLIDE - Stairway lift ☆ - Access Industries, Inc.
GOLDEN GLINT - Hair preparation ☆ - Benjamin Ansehl Co.
GOLDEN GLITTER - Toys - Tonka Corp.
GOLDEN GLO - Ammonia ☆ - Erbrich Products Co. Inc.
GOLDEN GLO - Brushes–paint - Wooster Brush Co.
GOLDEN GLO - Meat products–poultry - Jerome Foods Inc.
GOLDEN GLORY - Candy - James P. Linette Inc.
GOLDEN GLORY - Dinnerware–glass - Federal Glass
GOLDEN GLOVES - Sporting goods - Shield Manufacturing Inc.
GOLDEN GLOW - Beverages–malt ☆ - Joseph Huber Brewing Co., Inc.
GOLDEN GLOW - Fabrics–polyester - BASF Corp.
GOLDEN GLOW - Fireplaces - Majestic Co.
GOLDEN GLOW - Food products ☆ - Curtice-Burns Foods, Inc.
GOLDEN GLOW - Margarine - Lever Brothers Co. Inc.
GOLDEN GLOW - Vinegar - Vintage Foods Inc.
GOLDEN GOBLET - Fruits and vegetables - Firmenich Inc.
GOLDEN GODDESS - Watches - Bulova Corp.
GOLDEN GOLIATH - Flowers, plants, and seeds ☆ - Akin Seed Co.
GOLDEN GOOD VIBES - Housewares - David Patrick Marion
GOLDEN GOODNESS - Beverages–carbonated - Cadbury Beverages Inc.
GOLDEN GOODNESS - Fruit juice concentrates - James R. Keller
GOLDEN GOODNESS - Meat products–poultry ☆ - Harrison Poultry Inc.
GOLDEN GOOSE - Games - Smethport Specialty Co.
GOLDEN GOOSE BY DANIEL YOUNG - Coats–men's - Daniel Young International Corp.
GOLDEN GORHAM SHELL - Flatware ☆ - Gorham Inc.
GOLDEN GOURMET - Food products - Sysco Food Services
GOLDEN GOURMETS - Novelty items–stitched - A + A
GOLDEN GOURMETS, THE - Greeting cards - A + A
GOLDEN GRAB-IT - Gloves - Edmont
GOLDEN GRAHAMS - Cereal - General Mills, Inc.
GOLDEN GRAIN - See **DAIRY GOLD**
GOLDEN GRAIN - Food products ☆ - Golden Grain Co.

☆ = Now out of production

GOLDEN GRAIN - Liquors - Canandaigua Wine Co. Inc.

GOLDEN GRAIN - Tobacco products - Brown & Williamson Tobacco Corp.

GOLDEN GRANDE BAROQUE - Flatware - Wallace International Silversmiths, Inc.

GOLDEN GRAPE - Blown glassware ☆ - Indiana Glass Co.

GOLDEN GRAPE ESTATE - Wines - PRP Wine International, Inc.

GOLDEN GRAPES - Glassware—household - Ceraglass Inc.

GOLDEN GREEN HERB - Teas - Traditional Medicinals, Inc.

GOLDEN GREETINGS - Dolls - Mattel, Inc.

GOLDEN GREETINGS - Giftware - Wald Designs Acrylic Idea Factory

GOLDEN GRIDDLE - Syrup - CPC International Inc.

GOLDEN GRIP - Tools - Fuller Tool Co. Inc.

GOLDEN GRIPPER - Gloves ☆ - Distributors Service Corp.

GOLDEN GRIT - Cigars - A.J. Golden Inc.

GOLDEN GRITS - Hominy - Quaker Oats Co.

GOLDEN GROVE - Food processors - Vim Corp.

GOLDEN GUERNSEY - Milk - Golden Guernsey Dairy Cooperative

GOLDEN GUIDES - Publisher's imprints - Western Publishing Co., Inc.

GOLDEN GUILD - Puzzles - Western Publishing Co., Inc.

GOLDEN GULF - Seafood products—canned or cured ☆ - Gulf King Seafood Co.

GOLDEN HADDIE - Food products - Gulf Pacific Seafood, Inc.

GOLDEN HALO - Christmas tree ornaments - Cracker Box Inc.

GOLDEN HARVEST - Adhesives and sealants - Golden Harvest Adhesives

GOLDEN HARVEST - Adhesives and sealants - Roman Adhesives, Inc.

GOLDEN HARVEST - Beverages ☆ - Veryfine Products, Inc.

GOLDEN HARVEST - Bird feeds - Handley Corp.

GOLDEN HARVEST - Crackers - PFP Speciality Foods Inc.

GOLDEN HARVEST - Dinnerware—glass - Federal Glass

GOLDEN HARVEST - Jewelry ☆ - Hirsch Speidel Inc.

GOLDEN HARVEST - Noodles - Vesley Foods Inc.

GOLDEN HARVEST - Shrimp—fresh or frozen - Pan American Seafood, Inc.

GOLDEN HARVEST COLLECTION - Jams and jellies - Knott's Berry Farm

GOLDEN HAWK - Bicycles - Ross Bicycles USA, Ltd.

GOLDEN HAWK - Golfing equipment - Golfsmith International Inc.

GOLDEN HAWK - Watches - Bulova Corp.

GOLDEN HEALING - Health care products - Equinox Botanicals, Inc.

GOLDEN HEARTH - Bakery products - National Baking Div.

GOLDEN HEIRLOOM - Dinnerware—glass ☆ - Shafford Co. Inc.

GOLDEN HENNA - Lipsticks - Cosmair Inc.

GOLDEN HERB - Meat products—poultry - Shoney's, Inc.

GOLDEN HERITAGE - Jewelry ☆ - Pakula & Co.

GOLDEN HI-CRU - Shirts - Sara Lee Knit Products Inc.

GOLDEN HIBISCUS - Preserved foods—prepackaged - Liberty House, Inc.

GOLDEN HILL - Juices ☆ - Holly Hill Fruit Products Co.

GOLDEN HILLS - Wines - Pedrizzetti Winery

GOLDEN HOLLY - Juices - Holly Hill Fruit Products Co.

GOLDEN HOMES - Prefabricated buildings—wood - Golden West Homes

GOLDEN HORIZON - Glassware—household - Gorham Inc.

GOLDEN HORSE - Pet food - Gold Kist Inc.

GOLDEN HOUR - Agricultural products - Kraft-Holleb Foodservice

GOLDEN HOUR - Candy - Gordon's Markets

GOLDEN HOUR - Clocks ☆ - Jefferson Electric Co.

GOLDEN HOUSE - Apparel—men's - J. Schoeneman Inc.

GOLDEN-HUED GIFTWARE - Giftware ☆ - Gorham Inc.

GOLDEN III - Chocolate bars - Hershey Chocolate USA

GOLDEN ILLUSIONS - Jewelry—precious - International Importers and Liquidators, Inc.

GOLDEN IMAGE - Window coverings - Golden Image Inc.

GOLDEN IMAGES - Christmas tree ornaments - Cracker Box Inc.

GOLDEN IRIS - Food products - Scrivner, Inc.

GOLDEN ISLE - Sweaters - Harper Shirt Co.

GOLDEN ISLE - Vegetables—canned - Kent Canning Co.

GOLDEN ISLE HOT RODDER - Bicycles - Ross Bicycles USA, Ltd.

GOLDEN ISLES - Wood products - Georgia-Pacific Corp.

GOLDEN JERSEY - Milk - Hygeia Dairy Co.

GOLDEN JET - Bicycles - Ross Bicycles USA, Ltd.

GOLDEN JET - Insecticides - Claire Manufacturing Co.

GOLDEN KENNEL - Animal feeds - Golden Sun Feeds, Inc.

GOLDEN KERNEL STADIUM PEANUTS - Nuts—salted, roasted, cooked, or canned - A.L. Schutzman Co., Inc.

GOLDEN KEY - Jewelry - Pakula & Co.

GOLDEN KEY - Milk—canned or powdered - Pet Inc.

GOLDEN KING - Watches - Hampden Corp.

GOLDEN KITCHEN - Food products ☆ - Golden Valley Microwave Foods, Inc.

GOLDEN KNIGHT - Apparel—men's - Central-Samuels Inc.

GOLDEN KNIGHT - Jewelry ☆ - Hirsch Speidel Inc.

GOLDEN KNIGHT - Toiletries - Benjamin Ansehl Co.

GOLDEN KOLA - Beverages—carbonated - Visa, Inc.

GOLDEN KRUST - Bakery products - W.E. Long Co.

GOLDEN KRUST PATTIES - Food products - Golden Krust Patties, Inc.

GOLDEN LADLE - Cakes—mixes - L. Karp & Sons, Inc.

GOLDEN LAGER - Beverages—malt ☆ - Adolph Coors Co.

GOLDEN LASSIE - Golfing equipment - Ram Golf Corp.

GOLDEN LAUREL - Nuts—salted, roasted, cooked, or canned - Gulf Farms Inc.

GOLDEN LEAF - Breads - Athens Foods

GOLDEN LEAF - Cosmetics - Lancome

GOLDEN LEAF - Fertilizers - UAP/Ga AG Chem Inc.

GOLDEN LEAN - Meats—luncheon ☆ - John Morrell & Co.

GOLDEN LEGACY - Flatware - Gorham Inc.

GOLDEN LEGENDS - Trading cards and stamps - Megacards, Inc.

GOLDEN LEGS - Hosiery - Goldstone Hosiery Co.

GOLDEN LEMONADE - Lemonade - Givaudan Rare Flavors

GOLDEN LIFE - Health care products - Esteem Products Ltd.

GOLDEN LIFESAVER - Tires ☆ - Uniroyal Goodrich Tire Co.

GOLDEN LINE - Bicycles - Murray, Inc.

GOLDEN LINE, THE - Bronze products - Saxton Industrial Inc.

GOLDEN LINKS - Jewelry ☆ - Hirsch Speidel Inc.

GOLDEN-LITE - Bird feeds - L/M Animal Farms, Inc.

GOLDEN LITES - Codfish—smoked, salted, dried, or pickled - Viking Seafoods Inc.

GOLDEN LITTLE SUPER SHAPE BOOK, A - Publisher's imprints - Golden Books Publishing Co., Inc.

GOLDEN LOCKE - Hair-care products - Amethyst Investment Group, Inc.

GOLDEN LONGWOOD - Flatware - Reed and Barton Corp.

GOLDEN LOOK - Jewelry - Kramer Jewelry Creations Inc.

GOLDEN LOOK-LOOK BOOKS - Publisher's imprints - Western Publishing Co., Inc.

GOLDEN LORELEI - Glassware—household ☆ - ACC

GOLDEN LOTUS - Flatware - Wallace International Silversmiths, Inc.

GOLDEN MACHINES - Toys - Mattel, Inc.

GOLDEN MAGIC - Bakery products - Daylight Corp.

GOLDEN MAID - Margarine - Miami Margarine Co. Inc.

GOLDEN MANSION - Mobile homes - Golden West Homes

GOLDEN MAPLE NUT - Food products - Breadshop's Natural Foods

GOLDEN MARK - Tires - Universal Cooperative Inc.

GOLDEN MEADOW - Honey - Miller's Honey Co.

GOLDEN MEADOW - Rings—jewelry - Artcarved Inc.

GOLDEN MEAL - Breads—mixes - Roland Industries Inc.

GOLDEN MELODY - Harmonicas - Hohner Inc.

GOLDEN MELON BUD - Flatware - Gorham Inc.

GOLDEN MEMORIES - Figurines - Lladro USA, Inc.

GOLDEN MEMORIES - Lighting fixtures ☆ - Meyda Tiffany Inc.

GOLDEN MINUTE - Clocks - Jefferson Electric Co.

GOLDEN MIST - Christmas tree ornaments - Cracker Box Inc.

GOLDEN MIST - Margarine - Kraft Food Ingredients Corp.

GOLDEN MIST - Seafood products—fresh or frozen - New England Fish Co.

GOLDEN MIX - Candy - Storck USA L.P.

GOLDEN MIX - Pancakes—mixes - Little Crow Foods

GOLDEN MIXTURE - Tobacco products - Lane Ltd.

GOLDEN MOMENT - Floor coverings—carpet and rugs - Trend Carpet

GOLDEN MOMENTS - Floor coverings—carpet and rugs - Columbus Mills, Inc.

GOLDEN MOMENTS - Food products - Hanover Direct Inc.

GOLDEN MOMENTS - Jewelry - International Bullion & Metal Brokers (USA) Inc.

GOLDEN MOMENTS - Trophies—metal - Robarkajon Enterprises, Inc.

GOLDEN MOON - Food products ☆ - Seafood Enterprises Inc.

GOLDEN MORN - Rings—jewelry - Artcarved Inc.

GOLDEN MULTICRISPS - Snack foods - Old Dutch Foods, Inc.

GOLDEN MUSIC - Recording label - Western Publishing Co., Inc.

GOLDEN MYSTERY PUZZLE?, A - Games ☆ - Western Publishing Co., Inc.

GOLDEN NAPTIME TALE, A - Publisher's imprints - Western Publishing Co., Inc.

GOLDEN NATURE ESL - Eggs - Stevens Industries Inc.

GOLDEN NECK - Seafood products—fresh or frozen - American Mussel Harvesters Inc.

GOLDEN NECTAR - Honey - Europa Foods Ltd.

GOLDEN NECTAR - Honey - Liberty Richter Inc.

GOLDEN NESTLING - Pet products - Golden West Bird Farm Inc.

GOLDEN NIP - Food products - Procter & Gamble Co.

GOLDEN NIP - Juices - Ben Hill Griffin, Inc.

GOLDEN NORTH - Fish–fresh or frozen - Togiak Fisheries Inc.
GOLDEN NOTES - Stationery - Burgoyne Inc./Curtis Swann
GOLDEN NOUGAT - Confections - Imperial Nougat Co.
GOLDEN NUGGET - Bait - Siberian Salmon Egg Co.
GOLDEN NUGGET - Brushes–paint - Joseph Lieberman & Sons, Inc.
GOLDEN NUGGET - Candy - Hershey Chocolate USA
GOLDEN NUGGET - Candy ☆ - Annabelle Candy Co. Inc.
GOLDEN NUGGET - Dog food - Darigold, Inc.
GOLDEN NUGGET - Gloves - Granet Inc.
GOLDEN NUGGET - Nuts–salted, roasted, cooked, or canned - Los Angeles Nut House
GOLDEN NUGGET LAS VEGAS - Apparel and accessories - Gnlv, Corp.
GOLDEN NUGGETS - Snack foods - Betty Lou's Inc.
GOLDEN NUGGETS - Vitamins and nutritional supplements - Royal Kingdom Enterprises Inc.
GOLDEN O - Food products - Diamond E Packers
GOLDEN OAK - Bathroom accessories - Franklin Brass Manufacturing Co.
GOLDEN OAK - Dishes–china - Viletta China Co.
GOLDEN OAK - Frames–picture - Structural Industries
GOLDEN OAK - Housewares ☆ - Doranne
GOLDEN OAK - Liquors - Hughes Markets Inc.
GOLDEN OAK - Sporting goods ☆ - Brunswick Corp.
GOLDEN OAKS - Furniture ☆ - Broyhill Furniture Industries, Inc.
GOLDEN OAKS - Furniture–upholstered - River Oaks Furniture, Inc.
GOLDEN OAKS - Wines - Mark West Vineyards
GOLDEN OIL - Shortening ☆ - Swift Edible Oil Co.
GOLDEN OLDIES - Computer software - Software Toolworks, Inc.
GOLDEN OLDIES - Recording label - Original Sound Record Co. Inc.
GOLDEN OLDIES - Toys–models - ERTL Co., Inc.
GOLDEN ONION - Bagels - B. Manischewitz Co.
GOLDEN OPPORTUNITY - Jewelry - Spec Imports, Inc.
GOLDEN PAC - Snack foods - Golden Pac Foods
GOLDEN PALACE - Rice - American Rice, Inc.
GOLDEN PALACE - Rice - Comet American Marketing
GOLDEN PALETTE - Paints - M. Grumbacher Inc.
GOLDEN PALETTE - Paints–artists' - Koh-I-Noor, Inc.
GOLDEN PANTRY - Bakery products - Van Den Bergh Foods Co.
GOLDEN PATTIES - Vegetables–frozen - Ore-Ida Foods, Inc.
GOLDEN PAWS - Linen - White Swan, Ltd.
GOLDEN PEACE (PIECE), THE - Greeting cards - Marilynn S Perry
GOLDEN PEAKS DAIRY - Milk - Golden Peaks Dairy
GOLDEN PEARL - Rice - Rice Growers of California
GOLDEN PEARLS - Pottery products - Duncan Enterprises
GOLDEN PEARLS - Vitamins and nutritional supplements - Royal Kingdom Enterprises Inc.
GOLDEN PECAN - Candy bars - Hershey Chocolate USA
GOLDEN PECAN - Cocoa–powders or mixes - Coffee Bean International, Inc.
GOLDEN PENNY - Jewelry - Jacoby-Bender Inc.
GOLDEN PETALS - Jewelry ☆ - Hirsch Speidel Inc.
GOLDEN PETITE - Watches ☆ - SMH (US) Inc.
GOLDEN PHEASANT - Beverages–alcohol - Stawski Distributing Co., Inc.
GOLDEN PHEASANT - Candy ☆ - Gimbel Brothers Inc.
GOLDEN PHEASANT BEER - Beverages–malt - Stanley Stawski Distributing Co.
GOLDEN PINE - Cabinets–wood ☆ - Kemper
GOLDEN PINE CONES - Giftware ☆ - Fenton Art Glass Co.
GOLDEN PLACENTA - Hair care products - Palm Beach Beauty Products
GOLDEN PLAINS - Meat products ☆ - Omaha Steaks International
GOLDEN PLAYER - Apparel and accessories - A.M. Inc.
GOLDEN POND - Food products - Gold Kist Inc.
GOLDEN POND - Furniture - Universal Flooring
GOLDEN POP - Popcorn - Borden, Inc.
GOLDEN POWER STAFF - Toys–guns - Saban Entertainment, Inc.
GOLDEN POWER SYSTEMS - Electrical equipment - Golden Systems, Inc.
GOLDEN PRAIRIE - Beverages–malt - Golden Prairie Brewing Co.
GOLDEN PRAIRIE - Food products - American Foods Group
GOLDEN PRECISION - Clippers–barber - Sunbeam-Oster Household Products
GOLDEN PREMIER PUZZLE, A - Games ☆ - Western Publishing Co., Inc.
GOLDEN PREMIUM - Candy - Hershey Chocolate USA
GOLDEN PRESS BOOKS - Publisher's imprints - Western Publishing Co., Inc.
GOLDEN PRIDE - Gold products - Kohinoor Diamond Corp.
GOLDEN PRINCESS - Food products - Choctaw Maid Farms Inc.
GOLDEN PROMISE - Beverages–malt - Thames America Trading Co. Ltd.
GOLDEN PROMISE - Rings–jewelry - Artcarved Inc.
GOLDEN PROVIDENCE - Flatware - Pfaltzgraff Investment Co.

GOLDEN PUFFS - Cereal - Malt-O-Meal Co.
GOLDEN Q - Watches - Timex Corp.
GOLDEN QUALITY - Cleaning preparations ☆ - Banner Mat Inc.
GOLDEN QUALITY BEDDING ORIGINAL - Linen - Golden Sheet Manufacturing A.A. Corp
GOLDEN QUEEN - Watches - Hampden Corp.
GOLDEN R - Shrimp–canned or cured ☆ - Reuther's Seafood Co. Inc.
GOLDEN R SUPREME - Shrimp–canned or cured - Reuther's Seafood Co. Inc.
GOLDEN RAM - Bicycles - Columbia Manufacturing Inc.
GOLDEN RAM - Golfing equipment - Ram Golf Corp.
GOLDEN RANSOM - Vitamins and nutritional supplements - Royal Kingdom Enterprises Inc.
GOLDEN RATIO - Jewelry–precious - Frank P. Klauda
GOLDEN REFLECTIONS - Cosmetics - Elizabeth Arden Inc.
GOLDEN REGAL - See FIN-NOR
GOLDEN RELIEF - Pharmaceutical preparations - Brown Manufacturing Co.
GOLDEN RETRIEVER - Footwear–men's - B.B. Walker Co.
GOLDEN RETRIEVER - Hand tool - Edward D. Corboy, Jr.
GOLDEN REY - Food products - US Foodservice
GOLDEN RHAPSODY - Flatware ☆ - Utica Cutlery Co.
GOLDEN RIBBON - Lighters - Colibri Inc.
GOLDEN RIBBON EDGE - Flatware - Gorham Inc.
GOLDEN RIDGE - Honey - Norsland Kitchens
GOLDEN RIDGES - Potato chips - Bachman Co.
GOLDEN RINGCAKE - Cakes - Creative Bakers Inc.
GOLDEN ROAST - Coffee ☆ - Try Coffee Group Ltd.
GOLDEN ROCKET - Bicycles - Ross Bicycles USA, Ltd.
GOLDEN ROCKET - Oakum - Ace Jute Packing Co.
GOLDEN ROD - Christmas tree ornaments - Cracker Box Inc.
GOLDEN ROD - Curling irons–electric ☆ - Spilo/Mehaz Worldwide
GOLDEN ROD - Paper ☆ - Mead Corp.
GOLDEN ROLLER - Golfing equipment - Golfsmith International Inc.
GOLDEN ROMANCE OF THE SEA - Flatware - Wallace International Silversmiths, Inc.
GOLDEN RONDELLE - Glassware–household - Gorham Inc.
GOLDEN ROOT - Skin care products - Golden California Co. Inc.
GOLDEN ROSE - Glassware–household - ACC
GOLDEN ROSE POINT - Flatware - Wallace International Silversmiths, Inc.
GOLDEN ROSECLIFF - Flatware - Reed and Barton Corp.
GOLDEN ROYAL - Milk - Schepps-Foremost, Inc.
GOLDEN ROYAL SCOT - Projection screens - Brumberger Co. Inc.
GOLDEN RULE - Brooms - Fluffo Mop & Broom Co. Inc.
GOLDEN RULE - Clocks - General Time Corp. (Westclox/Seth Thomas Div.)
GOLDEN RULE - Machinery - S. Morantz Inc.
GOLDEN RULE - Vegetables–frozen - Crosetti Frozen Foods Inc.
GOLDEN RULE IN CONTROL, THE - Transducers - Fairchild Industrial Products Co.
GOLDEN RULE, THE - Jewelry - Ralph D. Funkhouser
GOLDEN RUNNER - Footwear–athletic - KangaROOS USA Inc.
GOLDEN SAGE - Cosmetics - Lancome
GOLDEN ST. MORITZ - Cutlery ☆ - Lifetime Hoan Corp.
GOLDEN SALVE, THE - Skin care products - Equinox Botanicals, Inc.
GOLDEN SAND DUNE - Tableware–china - Lenox, Inc.
GOLDEN SATELLITE - Televisions ☆ - Quasar Co.
GOLDEN SAUTE - Rice - Lipton Investments, Inc.
GOLDEN SCEPTRE - Salmon–smoked, salted, dried, or pickled ☆ - Trident Seafoods Corp.
GOLDEN SCROLL - Dinnerware–glass ☆ - Metlox Pottery Shoppe
GOLDEN SEAFARE - Flatware - Reed and Barton Corp.
GOLDEN SEAL - Flour–blended - Ross Industries Inc.
GOLDEN SEAL - Roofing materials–clay - Carlisle Corp.
GOLDEN SEAL ROOT - Hair care products - Holistic Laboratories
GOLDEN SEEK 'N' SOUND - Toys - Western Publishing Co., Inc.
GOLDEN SELENE - Flatware - Kirk Stieff Co.
GOLDEN SERIES - Recording label - Marsal Productions Inc.
GOLDEN SET - Hair care products - Raymac Corp. Hair & Skin Technology
GOLDEN SETH - Clocks ☆ - General Time Corp. (Westclox/Seth Thomas Div.)
GOLDEN SHADOW - Watches ☆ - Holzerwatch Co. Inc.
GOLDEN SHADOWS - Perfumes - Evyan Perfumes Inc.
GOLDEN SHANANDOAH - Flatware - Wallace International Silversmiths, Inc.
GOLDEN SHELL - Cooking utensils–earthenware ☆ - Anchor Hocking Glass, Inc.
GOLDEN SHELL - Cutlery ☆ - Lifetime Hoan Corp.
GOLDEN SHELL - Lubricants - Shell Oil Co.
GOLDEN SHIELD - Recording label - Rite Record Productions Inc.

☆ = Now out of production

GOLDEN SHILLING - Jewelry - Jacoby-Bender Inc.

GOLDEN SHORE - Salmon–smoked, salted, dried, or pickled ☆ - Trident Seafoods Corp.

GOLDEN SHORE - Seafood products–fresh or frozen - King & Prince Seafood Corp.

GOLDEN SIXTIES - Watches - Hampden Corp.

GOLDEN SKILLET - Food franchise - Golden Skillet Cos.

GOLDEN SLEEP - Bedding - Ohio Mattress Co.

GOLDEN SLIM TEA - Teas - Golden Border, Inc.

GOLDEN SMACKERS - Snack foods - Betty Lou's Inc.

GOLDEN SMOKED - Meat products–beef - Bob Ostrow Co.

GOLDEN SONG - Bird feeds - Gold Kist Inc.

GOLDEN SOUL - Recording label - Sonic Arts Corp.

GOLDEN SOUND - Computer software - Denny T. Huang

GOLDEN SOUND STORY BOOKS - Publisher's imprints - Western Publishing Co., Inc.

GOLDEN SPIKE, THE - Toys–trains - Bachmann Industries Inc.

GOLDEN SPIRAL - Musical instrument accessories - J. D'Addario & Co. Inc.

GOLDEN SPIRE - Flatware - Reed and Barton Corp.

GOLDEN SPIRITS - Beverages–alcohol - Joseph E. Seagram & Sons, Inc.

GOLDEN SPLIT TOP - Breads - American Bakeries Co.

GOLDEN SPRED - Margarine ☆ - Borden Food Service

GOLDEN SPRIG - Flour–blended - Cahokia Flour Co.

GOLDEN SPRING BUD - Flatware ☆ - Gorham Inc.

GOLDEN SPRINGS - Juices - Sinton Dairy Foods Co. Inc.

GOLDEN SPUD - Food products - Nestle USA

GOLDEN SQUIRE - Flatware - Gorham Inc.

GOLDEN STAG - Lenses–optical ☆ - Bausch & Lomb Inc.

GOLDEN STAR - Food products - Conagra, Inc.

GOLDEN STAR - Food products - Golden Star Trading Co., Inc.

GOLDEN STAR - Polishing rouge ☆ - Golden Star Inc.

GOLDEN STAR - Seafood products–fresh or frozen - Alpine International

GOLDEN STAR READER, A - Publisher's imprints ☆ - Western Publishing Co., Inc.

GOLDEN STATE - Food products - Golden State Packers

GOLDEN STATE - Fruits–frozen - New West Foods Inc.

GOLDEN STATE - Leather and sheep-lined clothing - Fred Roth Associates

GOLDEN STATE - Milk - Golden State Foods Corp.

GOLDEN STATE - Mobile homes - Kit Manufacturing Co.

GOLDEN STATE - Motor oil - Specialty Oil Co. Inc.

GOLDEN STATE - Nuts–salted, roasted, cooked, or canned - Blue Diamond Growers

GOLDEN STATE - Vinegar - Walker Foods Inc.

GOLDEN STATE VINTERS - Wines - HDT Importers Inc.

GOLDEN STATE VINTNERS - Wines - Golden State Vintners

GOLDEN STATEMENTS - Jewelry - Almond Jewelers Inc.

GOLDEN STRAD - Musical instruments - Boosey & Hawkes Buffet Crampon USA

GOLDEN STREAM - Snack foods - Golden Stream Quality Foods

GOLDEN SUFI CENTER, THE - Recording label - Golden Sufi Center

GOLDEN SUGAR PUFFS - Cereal - Malt-O-Meal Co.

GOLDEN SUN - Animal feeds - Golden Sun Feeds, Inc.

GOLDEN SUN - Juices - S & D Coffee, Inc.

GOLDEN SUN - Skin care products - Golden Sun Vitamins

GOLDEN SUN - Suntan lotions - Estee Lauder Inc.

GOLDEN SUN - Watches - Shube's Manufacturing, Inc.

GOLDEN SUN MAGIC - Lipsticks - Pavion Ltd.

GOLDEN SUN MEATY CHUNKS - Animal feeds - Golden Sun Feeds, Inc.

GOLDEN SUNBURST - Pet products - Carlson Speciality Seeds, Inc.

GOLDEN SUNNING - Suntan lotions - Estee Lauder Inc.

GOLDEN SUNRISE - Mobile homes ☆ - Kit Manufacturing Co.

GOLDEN SUNSET - Ashtrays–glass ☆ - Advertisers Publishing Co.

GOLDEN SUNSET - Glass products - Westmoreland Glass Co.

GOLDEN SUNSET - Glassware–household - Gorham Inc.

GOLDEN SUNSET - Glassware–household - Lenox, Inc.

GOLDEN SUNSHINE - Fish–fresh or frozen - Kent Sea arms Corp.

GOLDEN SUPERFRIES - Vegetables–frozen - McCain Foods Inc.

GOLDEN SUPERIOR - Musical instrument accessories - E. & O. Mari Inc.

GOLDEN SUPREME - Cosmetics - Morris-Flamingo Inc.

GOLDEN SUPREME - Curling irons–electric - Marianna Imports, Inc.

GOLDEN SUZY - Glassware–household - ACC

GOLDEN SWIRL - Flatware - Gorham Inc.

GOLDEN SWIRL - Yogurt–frozen - Golden Swirl

GOLDEN TAKE-A-LOOK BOOK, A - Publisher's imprints - Western Publishing Co., Inc.

GOLDEN TAKLON TOLE - Brushes–paint ☆ - Winsor & Newton

GOLDEN TALKING TALES - Publisher's imprints - Western Publishing Co., Inc.

GOLDEN TAN - Suntan lotions ☆ - Carter-Wallace, Inc.

GOLDEN TANNING BLEND - Suntan lotions - Sun Pharmaceuticals Corp.

GOLDEN TEMPLAR - Jewelry ☆ - Hirsch Speidel Inc.

GOLDEN TEMPLE - Cereal - Golden Temple Natural Foods Bakery

GOLDEN TEMPLE - Rice - International Multifoods Corp.

GOLDEN TEQUILA POPPERS - Snack foods - Anchor Food Products, Inc.

GOLDEN THREAD - Apparel–men's - Brill Bros. Inc.

GOLDEN THREAD - Rings–jewelry - Artcarved Inc.

GOLDEN THYME - Lipsticks - Pfizer Inc.

GOLDEN TIGER - Chinese foods - Chinese Food Processing Corp.

GOLDEN TIGER - Frozen foods - Windsor Quality Food Co. Ltd.

GOLDEN TIGER - Gloves - Champion Glove Manufacturing Co.

GOLDEN TOFFEE CRUNCH - Snack foods - Sovex Foods, Inc.

GOLDEN-TONE - Electric-guitar pick-ups - International Music Corp.

GOLDEN-TONE - Musical instrument accessories - E. & O. Mari Inc.

GOLDEN TONE - Musical instruments - Hyer Percussion Products

GOLDEN TOP - Vegetable oil - Ventura Foods LLC (Lou Ana Division)

GOLDEN TOUCH - Automotive repair shops - Gold Eagle Co.

GOLDEN TOUCH - Blinds–vertical - Louverdrape Inc.

GOLDEN TOUCH - Computer software - Pars Electronics, Inc.

GOLDEN TOUCH - Cookware coating - Boyle-Midway

GOLDEN TOUCH - Fabrics–polyester - BASF Corp.

GOLDEN TOUCH - Hair care products - Belson Products

GOLDEN TOUCH - Inks - Parker Pen USA

GOLDEN TOUCH - Paints - United Coatings, Inc.

GOLDEN TOUCH - Paper ☆ - Munford Inc.

GOLDEN TOUCH - Skin care products - Weeks & Leo Co. Inc.

GOLDEN TOUCH, THE - Ophthalmic goods - Embassy Creations Inc.

GOLDEN TOUCH, THE - Florists - Faster-Form Corp.

GOLDEN TOWNSEND - Giftware - Gorham Inc.

GOLDEN TRANSITION I - Vitamins and nutritional supplements - Maharishi Ayurveda Products International Inc.

GOLDEN TRANSITION II - Vitamins and nutritional supplements - Maharishi Ayurveda Products International Inc.

GOLDEN TREASURE - Rings–jewelry - Samuel Aaron Inc.

GOLDEN TREASURE - Watches - Bulova Corp.

GOLDEN TREASURES - Cologne and necklace ☆ - Cosrich Inc.

GOLDEN TRELLIS - Dinnerware–glass - Nikko Ceramics Inc.

GOLDEN TRELLIS - Dinnerware–glass - Royal China & Porcelain Companies Inc.

GOLDEN TRI-CUT - Tools - Klein Tools Inc.

GOLDEN TROPICS - Food products - Golden Tropics, Ltd.

GOLDEN TURK - Food products - K & O Foods

GOLDEN TURTLE - Shrimp–canned or cured - Jimyko, Inc.

GOLDEN TWIST - Rings–jewelry - Artcarved Inc.

GOLDEN USA - Chocolate candy - Maxfield Candy Co.

GOLDEN V - Apparel and accessories - Piedmont Industries Inc.

GOLDEN VALLEY - Dinnerware–glass ☆ - Royal China & Porcelain Companies Inc.

GOLDEN VALLEY - Food products - Nash-Finch Co.

GOLDEN VALLEY - Food products ☆ - Golden Valley Microwave Foods, Inc.

GOLDEN VALLEY - Vitamins and nutritional supplements ☆ - Pharmavite Corp.

GOLDEN VALLEY FARMS - Sandwiches–prepackaged - Golden Valley Farms Commodity Group, Inc.

GOLDEN VALUE - Mattresses - Simmons USA

GOLDEN VANILLA - Candy - Golden Triangle Import/Export Corp.

GOLDEN-VEE - Frames–eyeglass - Hudson Optical Corp.

GOLDEN VEIL - Skin care products - Goubaud

GOLDEN VELVET - Cheese - Land O'Lakes Inc.

GOLDEN VELVET - Paints - C.M. Athey Paint Co.

GOLDEN VERY EASY READER, A - Publisher's imprints - Western Publishing Co., Inc.

GOLDEN VIEW - Televisions ☆ - Quasar Co.

GOLDEN VINEYARDS - Wines ☆ - Giumarra Vineyards

GOLDEN VISTA - Flatware - Gorham Inc.

GOLDEN VOICE - Dietary and nutritional supplements - Tea Garden Products, Inc.

GOLDEN-VU - Cooking equipment–household - Thermos Co.

GOLDEN-WAVE - Pretzels - Dan Dee Pretzel & Potato Chip Co.

GOLDEN WEAVE - Rings–jewelry - Artcarved Inc.

GOLDEN WEDDING - Cigars ☆ - Phillies Cigar Co.

GOLDEN WEIL - Cheese ☆ - Swiss American Import Co.

GOLDEN WEST - Flour–blended - Central Milling Co.

☆ = Now out of production

GOLDEN WEST - Mobile homes - Golden West Homes

GOLDEN WEST - Publisher's imprints - Golden West Books

GOLDEN WEST FOODS - Food products - Golden West Foods Inc.

GOLDEN WEST MOTORSPORTS - Sports clubs - Golden West Cinema Supply

GOLDEN WHEAT GERM - Shampoos - Demert & Dougherty, Inc.

GOLDEN WHEEL - Giftware - Golden Wheel Creations

GOLDEN WILDERNESS - Water–mineral - Clasped Hands Inc.

GOLDEN WING - Frames–eyeglass - May Optical Co. Inc.

GOLDEN WINSLOW - Flatware - Kirk Stieff Co.

GOLDEN WISP - Jewelry - Jacoby-Bender Inc.

GOLDEN WOODBRIDGE - Flatware - Reed and Barton Corp.

GOLDEN WREATH - Tableware–china ☆ - Lenox, Inc.

GOLDEN WREATHTRIEVER - Greeting cards - Fursure Enterprises Inc.

GOLDEN YEARS - Furniture ☆ - Bassett Furniture Industries, Inc.

GOLDEN YEARS - Vitamins and nutritional supplements - Natural Organics, Inc.

GOLDEN ZYL - Frames–eyeglass - May Optical Co. Inc.

GOLDENACEA - Vitamins and nutritional supplements - Botalia

GOLDENAIRE - Clocks ☆ - General Time Corp. (Westclox/Seth Thomas Div.)

GOLDENBRAU - Beverages–malt ☆ - Eastern Brewing Corp.

GOLDENCREST - Cabinets - Oxford Furniture Corp.

GOLDENER OKTOBER/VILLA SACHSEN - Wines - C & B Vintage Cellars

GOLDENEYE - Frames–eyeglass - Liberty Optical Manufacturing Co.

GOLDENEYE - Ships–sailing vessels - Cape Cod Shipbuilding Co.

GOLDENEYE - Trailers–travel ☆ - Mallard Coach

GOLDENFEAST - Pet products - Barnwood Enterprises Inc.

GOLDENHAGEN - Cheese - Swissrose International Inc.

GOLDENKRAFT - File folders - Ameriforms Inc.

GOLDENLINE - Apparel and accessories - Wilson Brothers

GOLDENROD - Christmas tree ornaments - Cracker Box Inc.

GOLDENROD - Construction equipment - Dutton-Lainson Co.

GOLDENROD - Dehumidifiers - Buenger Enterprises

GOLDENROD - Frames–eyeglass - Liberty Optical Manufacturing Co.

GOLDENROD - Fruits and vegetables - Perham Fruit Corp.

GOLDEN'S - Games - Golden's Magic Wand

GOLDEN'S BLUE RIBBON - Cigars - H.L. Neff & Co. Inc.

GOLDEN'S MAGIC WAND - Costumes - Golden's Magic Wand

GOLDENSEAL - Health care products - Country Comfort

GOLDENSEAL CPX - Health care products ☆ - Nature's Herbs

GOLDENSTRAND - Fabrics - Greenwood Mills Inc.

GOLDENTONE - Musical instrument accessories ☆ - Selmer Co. Inc.

GOLDENTONES, THE - Recording label - Bigmom Productions, Ltd.

GOLDENTOUCH - Product description unknown - Wright and Lato Inc.

GOLDENTREE - Publisher's imprints - Harlan Davidson Inc.

GOLDENTRENDS - Flowers, plants, and seeds - Flower Trading Corp.

GOLDENVALE - Cheese - Peacock Foods Inc.

GOLDENVILLA - Manufactured homes ☆ - Bonnavilla Homes

GOLDENWARM - Fireplace equipment - Vermont Castings, Inc.

GOLDERN LEAVES - Floor coverings–carpet and rugs ☆ - Capel, Inc.

GOLDETTE - Jewelry - Circle Jewelry Products Inc.

GOLDFILTER - Coffee makers–electric - Salton/Maxim Housewares, Inc.

GOLDFINCH - Frames–eyeglass ☆ - Universal/Univis Inc.

GOLDFINGER - Boats–motor ☆ - Hobie Cat Co.

GOLDFINGER - Frames–eyeglass - Pathway Optical Prods.

GOLDFINGER - Musical instrument accessories ☆ - Herco Products

GOLDFINGER ADVENTURE - Games - Avalon Hill Game Co.

GOLDFINGER II - Games - Avalon Hill Game Co.

GOLDFINGERS - Candy - Nellson Candies Inc.

GOLDFINGERS - Candy ☆ - Leaf, Inc.

GOLDFINGERS - Hair care products - Cosmair Inc.

GOLDFINGERS - Manicure preparations - Customcraft Nails Inc.

GOLDFINGER'S - Seasonings - Ark Restaurant

GOLDFINKS - Candy ☆ - Leaf, Inc.

GOLDFISH - Crackers - Pepperidge Farm Inc.

GOLDFISH FUNGUS ELIMINATOR - Aquariums–household - Jungle Laboratories Corp.

GOLDFISH ICK GUARD - Aquariums–household - Jungle Laboratories Corp.

GOLDFISH LIFE - Aquariums–household - Jungle Laboratories Corp.

GOLDFISH PARASITE GUARD - Aquariums–household - Jungle Laboratories Corp.

GOLDFISH SALT - Aquariums–household - Jungle Laboratories Corp.

GOLDFISH STAPLE FOOD - Fish food - Jungle Laboratories Corp.

GOLDFISH START - Aquariums–household - Jungle Laboratories Corp.

GOLDFISH STARTER FOOD - Fish food - Jungle Laboratories Corp.

GOLDFISH T.E.N. - Fish food - Wardley Corp.

GOLDFLEX - Fertilizers ☆ - Anchor Swan

GOLDGUARD - Motor vehicle parts and accessories - Rally Accessories, Inc.

GOLDHAWKE - Recording label - MCA Universal Studios

GOLDIBEAR - Toys–stuffed ☆ - Gund, Inc.

GOLDIE - Fish–fresh or frozen ☆ - Slade Gorton and Co. Inc.

GOLDIE - Frames–eyeglass ☆ - Universal/Univis Inc.

GOLDIE GOLDEN RETRIEVER - Toys–stuffed - Russ Berrie and Co., Inc.

GOLDIGGERS - Apparel and accessories - Mamiye Brothers, Inc.

GOLDILOCKS - Air purification systems - Safe Air LLC

GOLDILOCKS - Apparel and accessories - Citywide Garments

GOLDILOCKS - Combs - Krest Products Corp.

GOLDILOCKS - Frames–eyeglass - May Optical Co. Inc.

GOLDILOCKS - Pet products - Loos and Co. Inc.

GOLDILOCKS AND THE THREE BEARS - Games - Cadaco Div.

GOLDILOCKS AND THE THREE BEARS - Games - Rapid Mounting and Finishing Co.

GOLDILOCKS AND THE THREE BEARS - Toys–stuffed ☆ - Toy Works, Inc.

GOLDINA - Baking chocolate ☆ - Liberty Richter Inc.

GOLDING FARMS GOLDEN STEAK SAUCE - Sauces - Golding Farms Foods, Inc.

GOLDIN'S - Food products - Goldin Pickle Co. Inc.

GOLDIN'S PIK-L-PAK - Pickles - Goldin Pickle Co. Inc.

GOLDISC - Recording label - Timeless Entertainment Corp.

GOLDLEAF - Cosmetics - Rubigo Cosmetics Inc.

GOLDLEAF AND HYDRANGEA - Skin care products - Thymes Limited

GOLDLEAF FINISHES - Paints - Sheffield Bronze Paint Corp.

GOLDLEX - Canned foods - Summit Import Corp.

GOLDLINE - Audio equipment ☆ - Bob White Associates

GOLDLINE - Climate-control product - Independent Energy Inc. (Goldline Controls Div.)

GOLDLINE - Cough medicines - Goldline Laboratories, Inc.

GOLDLINE - Rope ☆ - Columbian Rope Co.

GOLDLINE - Vacuum cleaners and accessories–commercial - Sta-Rite Industries Inc.

GOLDLINE II - Rope - Columbian Rope Co.

GOLDLINERS - Office supplies ☆ - JM Co.

GOLDLINK - Audio equipment - American Trading and Production Corp.

GOLDLINK - Computer software - Goldleaf Technologies Inc.

GOLDLINK - Connectors–electronic - Atlas/Soundolier

GOLDLON - Rope - Tubbs Cordage Co.

GOLDMAN - Jewelry - Frederick Goldman, Inc.

GOLDMARK - Agricultural products - Westmark AG Group, Inc.

GOLDMARK - Boxes–corrugated paperboard - Mason Box Co. Inc.

GOLDMARK - Frames–eyeglass - Hudson Optical Corp.

GOLDMARK - Motor vehicle parts and accessories - ADAP DBA Auto Palace

GOLDMASTER - Electronic equipment ☆ - White's Electronics, Inc.

GOLDMASTER - Eyeglasses - Martin-Copeland Eyewear Corp.

GOLDMEDAL - Pet products - Tetra Sales USA

GOLDMINE - Frames–picture - Framemica Co.

GOLDMINER - Breads - Pioneer French Baking Co., Inc.

GOLD'N BRANDS - Food products ☆ - Old Fashioned Kitchen Inc.

GOLD'N CRAFT - Ornamental products–metal ☆ - Zell Co.

GOLD'N CRISPY - Waffle irons - Sunbeam-Oster Household Products

GOLD'N GRAINS - Breads - Kotarides Baking Co., Inc.

GOLD'N PAN 7 GRIDDLE - Vegetable shortening - Supreme Oil Co.

GOLD'N PLUMP PREMIUM SELECTS - Meat products–poultry - Gold'n Plump Poultry, Inc.

GOLD'N PRIDE - Onions - Fort Boise Produce Co.

GOLD'N QUICK - Food products - Golden Dipt Co.

GOLD'N SWEET - Onions - Fort Boise Produce Co.

GOLDNET - Computer software - Goldleaf Technologies Inc.

GOLD'N'SPICE - Food products - Brakebush Brothers Inc.

GOLDNUGGET - Veterinary pharmaceutical preparations - Immunomed Corp.

GOLDPAK - Bags–storage - Accurate Flannel Bag Co.

GOLDPLY - Plywood ☆ - Fibreboard Corp.

GOLDPOINT - Fishing tackle - Outdoor Technologies Group

GOLDPOINT - Pens - Marketex Corp.

GOLDRING - Phonographs - Import Audio

GOLDRITE - Pigments ☆ - Martin F. Weber Co.

GOLDRUSH - Breads - Cal-Gar Corp.

GOLD'S - Mustard - Gold Pure Food Products Inc.

GOLD'S GYM - Apparel–athletic - Gold's Gym Enterprises Inc.

GOLD'S GYM - Bags - Sirco International Corp.

GOLD'S GYM ACCESSORIES - Exercising equipment - CSA, Inc.

GOLD'S GYM BENCHES - Exercising equipment - CSA, Inc.

GOLD'S STEPPER 2000 - Exercise equipment - CSA, Inc.

☆ = Now out of production

GOLDSCHLAGER - Beverages–alcohol - Paddington Corp.
GOLDSPUN - Noodles - Vesley Foods Inc.
GOLDSPUN ROSE - Cosmetics ☆ - Sally Hansen
GOLDSPUN SMOKE - Cosmetics - Lancome
GOLDS'S - Vegetable seasonings - Harvest States Cooperatives
GOLDSTAR - Automotive parts and accessories - Carfel Inc.
GOLDSTAR - Electronic equipment ☆ - Fidelitone Inc.
GOLDSTAR - Electronics stores - Goldstar Electronics International Inc.
GOLDSTONE - Paints - Triangle Coatings Inc.
GOLDSTONE - Pottery products ☆ - Duncan Enterprises
GOLDSWINGER - Frames–eyeglass - Liberty Optical Manufacturing Co.
GOLDTIP - Brushes–paint ☆ - DecoArt, Inc.
GOLDTONE - Jewelry - American Foreign Trade Inc.
GOLDTONE CLASP - Envelopes–paper - Specialty Envelopes Inc.
GOLDUP - Rice - Pexco, Inc.
GOLDUST - Fabrics–broadcloth - Detroit Popcorn Co.
GOLDUST - Recording label - Goldust Records Co.
GOLDUST - Toys - Titan Sports, Inc.
GOLDWASSER - Liquors - Adamba Imports International Inc.
GOLDWATER - Footwear - Gold Water Industries Inc.
GOLDWATER'S TASTE OF THE SOUTHWEST - Barbecue sauce -
 Goldwater's Foods of Arizona
GOLDWAX - Recording label - Goldwax Record Co. Inc.
GOLDWELL - Hair care products - GOLDWELL Cosmetics (USA) Inc.
GOLDWYN - Ophthalmic goods - Styl-Rite Optical Manufacturing Co., Inc.
GOLDY - Pet products ☆ - Sera Aquaristik USA Inc.
GOLDY'S - Dairy equipment - G & G Specialty Foods, Inc.
GOLDY'S GOURMET - Food products - G & G Specialty Foods, Inc.
GOLETTE - Accordions - Hohner Inc.
GOLF - Flowers, plants, and seeds ☆ - NK Lawn & Garden Co.
GOLF - Motor vehicles–automobiles - Volkswagen of America Inc.
GOLF - Pencils - Empire Berol USA
GOLF - Pencils - Musgrave Pencil Co. Inc.
GOLF 21 - Golf equipment - Golf 21, Inc.
GOLF-AGE - Sportswear - Daewoo International (America) Corp.
GOLF-AIDE - Food products - Horizon Worldwide Export Corp.
GOLF ALLEY - Golfing equipment - Golf Alley of Kansas, LLC
GOLF AMERICA - Apparel–athletic - Stuart M. Lucas
GOLF AMERICA - Computer software - Richard M. Wilbur
GOLF AMERICANA - Frames–picture - Flagpin Productions
GOLF AND TENNIS CARPET COLLECTION - Floor coverings–carpet and
 rugs - Burtco Enterprises Inc.
GOLF ARCADE - Games - Tonka Corp.
GOLF BALLS - Candy ☆ - Leaf, Inc.
GOLF CAFETERIA - Golfing equipment - Superior Golf, Inc.
GOLF CARDS - Playing cards - Novelti Playing Cards
GOLF CHANNEL, THE - Stationery - TGC, Inc.
GOLF CHUMS - Toys - Advanced Design Concepts Inc.
GOLF CLASSIC/BATTLING BUGS - Computer software ☆ - Milliken
 Publishing Co. (Computer Software Div.)
GOLF CLASSICS - Golfing equipment - British American Imports
GOLF CLUB - Giftware - Papel Freelance, Inc.
GOLF CLUB - Golfing equipment - Golf Club Liquidation Centers
GOLF CLUB INTERNATIONAL - Apparel and accessories - Tropical
 Sportswear International Corp.
GOLF CLUB LIQUIDATION CENTERS - Golfing equipment - Golf Club
 Liquidation Centers
GOLF COURSES - Glassware–household - Ceraglass Inc.
GOLF DAY - Sporting goods - Golf Day Products Inc.
GOLF DESIGN - Golfing equipment - Golf Design USA
GOLF DRIVEMETER - Sporting goods - Hed-Line, Inc.
GOLF EAGLE EYE 70 - Sporting goods - Ranging Inc.
GOLF EQUIPMENT PROFESSIONALS OF AMERICA - Golfing equipment -
 Golf Equipment Professionals of America, Inc.
GOLF FANTASY - Calendars - Las Vegas Discount Golf & Tennis, Inc.
GOLF FOR WOMEN - Golfing equipment - Meredith Corp.
GOLF GADGET - Sporting goods - Milano Offshore Manufacturing Inc.
GOLF GAL - Apparel–women's - Vermont Sports Apparel Inc.
GOLF GODS - Golfing equipment - Grandinetti's, Inc.
GOLF GUARD - Luggage - Woodstream Corp.
GOLF GUY - Apparel–men's - Vermont Sports Apparel Inc.
GOLF GUZZLER - Golfing equipment - Korex Corp.
GOLF HOUSE COLLECTION - Golfing equipment - United States Golf
 Association
GOLF HYPNOSIS - Recording label - Golf Hypnosis
GOLF III - Motor vehicles–automobiles - Volkswagen of America Inc.

GOLF-IN-KNIT - Apparel–men's ☆ - Brill Bros. Inc.
GOLF LIES - Apparel and accessories - John D. Stanton
GOLF MAN - Apparel and accessories ☆ - Super Products, Inc.
GOLF MAX - Herbal products - Roger H. Schnur
GOLF MEMORIES INC. - Calendars - Golf Memories Inc.
GOLF OFF - Sporting goods ☆ - Chesal Golf
GOLF OR DIE - Hats - Rebel-Wear
GOLF POKER - Golfing equipment - Shannon-Winters Ltd. Inc.
GOLF POKER DISCARDS - Golfing equipment - Shannon-Winters Ltd. Inc.
GOLF POWER - Golfing equipment - Besco USA
GOLF PRIDE - Golfing equipment - Eaton Corp. (Golf Grip Div.)
GOLF PRO - Knives - Precise International/Wenger
GOLF PRO - Ophthalmic goods - Foremost Optical Products
GOLF PRO X10 RAZOR - Razors - C.A. Daniels & Co.
GOLF PUNK - Apparel and accessories - Cigar, LLC
GOLF PUNK GIRL - Apparel and accessories - Cigar, LLC
GOLF REPUBLIC - Apparel–athletic - Patrick Perez Pernia
GOLF RITE - Apparel–athletic - Match Play of Pinehurst
GOLF ROAD MAP - Maps - Fore Better Golf, Inc.
GOLF SCIENCE - Golfing equipment - Ernst F. Sturm
GOLF SIMS. - See PRO PLAYGOLF
GOLF SKOS - Footwear–athletic ☆ - Allen-Edmonds Shoe Corp.
GOLF STAR IDAHO NON-CREEPING - Flowers, plants, and seeds - Jacklin
 Seed
GOLF STICK, THE - Golfing equipment - River Sharpe, Inc.
GOLF STIX - Golfing equipment - Golf Stix, Inc.
GOLF SWING TRAINER - Golfing equipment - Gasperoni International
GOLF TEE, THE - Towels - DMC Designs Corp.
GOLF - THE FINAL ROUND - Computer storage devices–optical - Konami
 (America) Inc.
GOLF THING, THE - Golfing equipment - Golf Thing, Inc.
GOLF TOURNAMENT - Computer software - Scobra Software Solutions, Ltd.
GOLF XPRESS - Golf carts - Electric Mobility Corp.
GOLFAIDE - Manicure preparations - W.E. Bassett Co.
GOLFBALL - Desk sets - Crystal Promotions Ltd.
GOLFCREST - Golfing equipment - Lipphardt & Associates
GOLFER - Eyeglasses - Art-Craft Optical Co.
GOLFER TEDDY - Toys–stuffed - Dakin Inc.
GOLFER, THE - Deodorizers ☆ - Car-Freshner Corp.
GOLFERCISE - Video production - Timothy D. Conwell
GOLFERS - Cigar boxes–wood - Consolidated Cigar Corp.
GOLFER'S CLASSIC INVITATIONAL - Sweaters - Affinity Group Marketing,
 Inc.
GOLFER'S DEFENSE - Sunblocks - Randall Products International
GOLFERS EDGE - Sporting goods - Unique Sports Products Inc.
GOLFER'S GIZMO - Golfing equipment - Koala-T, Inc.
GOLFER'S GOPHER - Golfing equipment - A & A Properties, Inc.
GOLFERS-PAK - Sporting goods - Chesal Golf
GOLFER'S PREFERRED - Sporting goods - Paragon Products Inc.
GOLFER'S TOOL BELT, THE - Golfing equipment - William M. Mcguigan
GOLFHAWK - Golfing equipment - Golfsmith International Inc.
GOLFIC - Golfing equipment - John T. Slager
GOLFING GIZMO - Games ☆ - Cathay International
GOLFING MOMENT - Figurines - Aus-Ben Studios
GOLFING THE WORLD - Trading cards and stamps - Bradley J. Bennett
GOLFINGLY YOURS - Posters - Historic Golf Prints, Inc.
GOLFLEECE - Golfing equipment - Sun Mountain Sports, Inc.
GOLFLIX - Projectors–photographic - Golflix Inc.
GOLF'N SOL - Skin care products - Caribbean Pacific International, Inc.
GOLFOMAT - Golfing equipment - Golfomat Corp.
GOLFONE - Telephones–cellular - Be In Touch Inc.
GOLFOUNDRY - Golfing equipment - Besco USA
GOLFRITE - Golfing equipment - Golfrite Inc.
GOLF'S MOST SOLID INVESTMENT - Golfing equipment - TourEdge Golf
 Manufacturing Inc.
GOLFSHOTS - Balls–golf - Jiss Corp.
GOLFSMITH - Golfing equipment - Golfsmith International Inc.
GOLFSTER - Motor vehicles - Ransomes-Cushman-Ryan
GOLFSTIR - Bar fixtures–plastic - Spir-it Inc.
GOLFTEK - Computer software - Golftek, Inc.
GOLFTOONS - Apparel and accessories - Howard Ziehm
GOLFWEAR FOR AMERICA'S GAME - Apparel–athletic - Stuart M. Lucas
GOLFWORKS, THE - Golfing equipment - Ralph Maltby Enterprises Inc.
GOLFZILLA - Apparel - Zilla, Inc.
GOLIAN CASTRO PRODUCTIONS - Recording label - Deborah Golian Castro
GOLIATH - Brushes - Robert Simmons Inc.

☆ = Now out of production

GOLIATH - Frames–eyeglass - Hudson Optical Corp.
GOLIATH - Furniture - Bean Station Furniture Factory Inc.
GOLIATH - Golfing equipment - Dunlop Slazenger Corp.
GOLIATH - Harmonicas - Hohner Inc.
GOLIATH - Pencils - Faber-Castell Corp.
GOLIATH - Sporting goods - Lisco, Inc.
GOLIATH - Staplers - ACCO USA, Inc.
GOLIATH - Toys - Tonka Corp.
GOLIATH JAW BREAKERS - Candy ☆ - Willy Wonka Brands
GOLINK - Communications equipment - Tatung Telecom Corp.
GOLLIPOPS - Candy - Gollipops Inc.
GOLLY WHOMPERS - Caramel corn ☆ - Iroquois Popcorn Co. Inc.
GOLLY WHOPPER - Flags - Plastics Research and Development Co.
GOLO - Power winch - Cordem Corp.
GOLORAK - Needlework supplies ☆ - Susan Bates Inc.
GOMASIO - Salt - Maranatha! Natural Foods
GOMCO - Medical apparatus - Allied Healthcare Products Inc.
GOMECOL - Pharmaceutical preparations ☆ - C.O. Truxton Inc.
GOMES - Meat products–pork - Galileo-Capri Salami Inc.
GOMEZ - Costumes - Paramount Pictures Corp.
GOMMAGE VEGETAL - Skin care products - Ella Bache Inc.
GOMO - Jewelry–precious - James P. Farley
GOMOZO - Laxatives - Dr. Peter Fahrney & Sons Co.
GOMUSIC - Recording label - Harvard Research Group, Inc.
GON - Cleaning preparations - X-I-M Products Inc.
GON BOPS - Drums–musical instruments - Gon Bops of California
GONADOPLEX - Pharmaceutical preparations ☆ - Wesley Pharmacal Co. Inc.
GONAK - Pharmaceutical preparations - Akorn Inc.
GONATRIN-L - Pharmaceutical preparations - G.O. Spanner Inc.
GONDOLA - Fishing lures ☆ - Hildebrandt Corp.
GONDOLA - Food products - Tosi Trading Co.
GONDOLA - Footwear–men's - L.B. Evans' Son Co.
GONDOLA - Pasta - Gondola Foods of New England
GONE - Cleaning preparations - Enviro-Chem Inc.
GONE AWAY - Nail care products - Lamoon Products, Inc.
GONE BALLISTIC - Apparel and accessories - Gone Ballistic of Florida
GONE BEARNANAS - Toys–stuffed - Gone Bearnanas
GONE BUGGIN' - Games - Hasbro, Inc.
GONE DADDY - Shirts - Northern Produce Co./Mushrooms Inc.
GONE FISHING - Sweatshirts - Arroyo Grande USA
GONE GATOR RECORDS - Recording label - Tom Petty
GONE RACIN' U.S.A. - Apparel and accessories - Terence D. Thomson
GONE TO THE DOGS - Pet products - Gone to the Dogs
GONE TROPPO - Jams, jellies and fruit preserves - Irene D. Doyle
GONE WITH THE WIND - Giftware ☆ - Enesco Corp.
GONE WITH THE WIND COLLECTION - Dolls - World Doll Inc.
GONE WITH THE WIND COLLECTION - Figurines - Dave Grossman Creations Inc.
GONESH - Incense - Genie Co. Inc.
GONESH - Novelty items - Gonesh Incense Co.
GONFLEE - Skin care products - Lendan USA Co.
GONGA - Toys–stuffed - Russ Berrie and Co., Inc.
GONIC - Pharmaceutical preparations - Roberts/Hauck Pharmaceuticals Inc.
GONIOSCOPIC PRISM SOL - Ophthalmic goods - Alcon Laboratories, Inc.
GONIOSOL - Ophthalmic pharmaceutical - Iolab Pharmaceuticals
GONNELLA - Bakery products - Gonnella Baking Co.
GONODOSYN-M - Vitamins and nutritional supplements - Great Life Laboratories Inc.
GONOSTAT - Diagnostic substances - Sierra Diagnostics, Inc.
GONOSTICON DRI-DOT - Pharmaceutical preparations ☆ - Organon Inc.
GONZ-O RING - Footwear - Deckers Outdoor Corp.
GONZALES - Food products - Gonzales Products Co. Inc.
GONZALES CHORIZO - Sausages ☆ - J & B Sausage Co., Inc.
GONZALEZ BYASS - Beverages–alcohol - Sunbelt Beverage Corp.
GONZO - Bicycles - Bur-Gon Corp.
GONZO GORILLA - Toys–stuffed - Russ Berrie and Co., Inc.
GONZO PET HAIR LIFTER, THE - Pet products - Gonzo Corp.
GONZO SAFARI - Archery equipment ☆ - Martin Archery Inc.
GONZO SCREEN CLEANER, THE - Sponges - Gonzo Corp.
GONZO WONDER SPONGE, THE - Sponges - Gonzo Corp.
GOO - Adhesives and sealants - Hobsco Inc.
GOO - Adhesives and sealants - Wm. K. Walthers Inc.
GOO - Hair care products - Revlon Consumer Products Corp.
GOO FISH - Toys - Saban Entertainment, Inc.
GOO GONE - Cleaning preparations - Magic American Corp.
GOO GOO - Frames–eyeglass - Hudson Optical Corp.

GOO GOO CLUSTERS - Candy - Standard Candy Co. Inc.
GOO GOO GORILLA - Toys–stuffed - Dakin Inc.
GOO GOO MONKEY - Puppets - Dakin Inc.
GOO GOO PEANUT BUTTER - Candy - Standard Candy Co. Inc.
GOO GOO PUPPY - Toys–stuffed - Dakin Inc.
GOO GOO SUPREME - Candy - Standard Candy Co. Inc.
GOO GOO TEDDY - Toys–stuffed - Dakin Inc.
GOOBER - Toys–stuffed ☆ - Gund, Inc.
GOOBER PEA - Apparel and accessories - Janice M. Jacobson
GOOBER-UP - Ice cream ☆ - Nestle USA
GOOBERS - Candy - Nestle USA
GOOCH - Veterinary pharmaceutical preparations ☆ - SuperSweet Feed
GOOCHERS - Blankets - Gooch, Inc.
GOOCH'S BEST - Flour–blended - ADM Milling Co.
GOOD - Candy - L.C. Good Candy Co. Inc.
GOOD - Food products - Good Food Inc.
GOOD - Rope - Good Automatic Windlass Inc.
GOOD ADVICE - Paints - Premier Coatings, Inc.
GOOD-AIRE - Deodorizers - L & F Consumer Products
GOOD & PLENTY - Candy - Leaf, Inc.
GOOD & SIMPLE - Food products - Fairest Made Foods, Inc.
GOOD AS GOLD - Eyeglasses - Martin-Copeland Eyewear Corp.
GOOD AS GOLD - Incense - Genie Co. Inc.
GOOD BIRD - Pet products - Candin Charter Corp.
GOOD BLOSSOM - Food products - Good Source, Inc.
GOOD BOOKKEEPER, THE - Book ends - Dress Rite Forms
GOOD BOY - Computer software - Pet Supply Imports Inc.
GOOD BOY - Pet products - Lambert-Kay
GOOD BREATH - Veterinary pharmaceutical preparations - Dr. Goodpet
GOOD BUDDIES - Fruit drinks–bottled or canned - Green Spot Packaging, Inc.
GOOD BUDDY - Bicycles - Columbia Manufacturing Inc.
GOOD BUDDY - Candy bars - A.M. Marketing Inc.
GOOD BUY MR. CHIPS - Pet treats - Items Inc.
GOOD-BY TANGLES - Pet products - Four Paws Products Ltd.
GOOD-BY WRINKLES - Skin care products - William R. Hansen
GOOD-BYE DRY - Pet products - Lambert-Kay
GOOD-BYE ODOR - Deodorizers - Guardsman Products, Inc.
GOOD-BYE SPLATTERS - Paint removers - Pro Power, Inc.
GOOD-BYE SPLATTERS SUPER REMOVER - Paint removers - Pro Power, Inc.
GOOD BYE WEEDS - Garden equipment - Cobraco Manufacturing, Inc.
GOOD CARAMEL - Desserts ☆ - Natural Nectar Corp.
GOOD CATCH! - Apparel and accessories - Good Catch
GOOD CATCH - Postcards - Fotofolio Inc.
GOOD CHOICE - Food products - Butler Wholesale Products
GOOD CHOICE - Pharmaceutical preparations - Vi-Jon Laboratories, Inc.
GOOD CLEAN FUN - Sportswear - Good Clean Fun
GOOD CLEAN FUN - Toiletries - Smith & Vandiver, Inc.
GOOD COMPANY - Floor coverings–carpet and rugs - Lees Carpets
GOOD COMPANY - Wallpaper - Bayview Wallcoverings
GOOD COMPANY II - Wallpaper - Bayview Wallcoverings
GOOD COOK - Kitchen utensils–aluminum - Bradshaw International Inc.
GOOD COOK QUALITY BY DESIGN - Kitchen utensils–aluminum - Bradshaw International Inc.
GOOD DEAL - Eyeglasses - Martin-Copeland Eyewear Corp.
GOOD DOG - Pet products - Petland, Inc.
GOOD DOG FARMS - Fruits and vegetables - Produce Exchange, Inc.
GOOD EARTH - Floor coverings–carpet and rugs ☆ - Masland Corp.
GOOD EARTH - Giftware - Arnart Imports Inc.
GOOD EARTH - Nurseries and garden stores - Great Neck Saw Manufacturers, Inc.
GOOD EARTH - Pottery products - Good Earth Corp.
GOOD EARTH - Teas–herbal - Good Earth Products
GOOD EARTH GINSENG - Teas–herbal - Good Earth Products
GOOD EARTH GREEN - Teas–herbal - Good Earth Products
GOOD FEELING - Floor coverings–carpet and rugs - Lees Carpets
GOOD FELLAS - Apparel - Isaac Morris Ltd.
GOOD FOOT - Skin care products - Samlo
GOOD FOOTIN' - Canes - Sure Foot Inc.
GOOD FOR NOTHING CHEST, THE - Novelty items - Paul Kurtz, Inc.
GOOD FOR OUR WORLD GREAT FOR YOUR HAIR - Hair care products - Joico Laboratories, Inc.
GOOD FOR WHAT ALES YOU - Apparel and accessories - Salt Lake Brewing Co., L.C.
GOOD FOR YOU ! - Bakery products - Guttenplan's

☆ = Now out of production

GOOD FOR YOU - Frames–eyeglass - May Optical Co. Inc.

GOOD FOR YOU! - Milk - Southern Belle Dairy Co.

GOOD FOR YOU AMERICA - Food and vitamin supplements - Good for You America, Inc.

GOOD FOR YOU BAGELS! - Bakery products–frozen - Guttenplan's

GOOD FOR YOU BREAD! - Breads - Guttenplan's

GOOD FOR YOU ROLLS! - Breads - Guttenplan's

GOOD FOR YOUR LIPS - Hair care products - Revlon Consumer Products Corp.

GOOD FOR YOUR SKIN - Skin care products - Revlon Consumer Products Corp.

GOOD FORTUNE - Candles - Tops Malibu

GOOD FORTUNE - Rice - Rice Growers of California

GOOD FORTUNE - Snack foods - Leland Voeltz

GOOD FORTUNE - Wallcovering - Wall Trends, Inc.

GOOD FORTUNE PANDA - Toys–stuffed - Russ Berrie and Co., Inc.

GOOD FRIEND - Bird feeds - Kellogg Inc.

GOOD FRIENDS & NEIGHBORS - Toys–stuffed ✩ - Russ Berrie and Co., Inc.

GOOD G'DONNE - Liquors ✩ - Kedem Royal Wine Corp.

GOOD GNOMEN - Gold products - Replaform Corp.

GOOD GRAVY - Towels ✩ - Arden Corp.

GOOD GREIF - Apparel–athletic ✩ - High Point Knitting Inc.

GOOD GRIPS - Flatware - OXO International

GOOD GRIPS - Kitchen cabinets–metal - General Housewares Corp.

GOOD GULF - Gasoline - Chevron Corp.

GOOD GUYS - Apparel and accessories - Siegfried & Parzifal, Inc.

GOOD GUYS - Frames–eyeglass - May Optical Co. Inc.

GOOD GUYS & BAD GUYS - Candy - Leaf, Inc.

GOOD GUYS WEAR BLACK - Apparel and accessories - Chicago White Sox, Ltd.

GOOD HAIR - Vitamins and nutritional supplements - Century Systems Inc.

GOOD HAIR DAY - Recording label - Direct Response Television, Inc.

GOOD HARBOR VINEYARDS - Wines - Good Harbor Vineyards

GOOD HARVEST - Food products - Burns Philp Food Inc.

GOOD HEALTH - Beverages–carbonated - Canada Dry Corp.

GOOD HEALTH - Cheese - Miller's Cheese Corp.

GOOD HEALTH - Health care products - Ross Laboratories

GOOD HEALTH - Jewelry - Tiara Corp.

GOOD HEALTH! - Juices - Winning Solutions Inc./Miracle of Aloe

GOOD HEALTH - Pharmaceutical preparations - Pennex Products

GOOD HEALTH - Snack foods - Good Health Natural Foods

GOOD HEALTH CHEESE ALTERNATIVE, THE - Cheese - P.J. Lisac & Associates, Inc.

GOOD HEALTH GUIDES - Publisher's imprints - Keats Publishing Co.

GOOD HEALTH HABITS - Computer software - Right on Programs

GOOD HEARTH - Breads - Ralston Purina Co.

GOOD HEAVENS! - Games - Ampersand Press

GOOD HEAVENS - Underwear and nightwear - Silvil Corp.

GOOD HELP - Cooking equipment–household ✩ - Farberware Inc.

GOOD HORSE SCENTS - Pet products ✩ - Vital Nutrition Products

GOOD HOUSEKEEPING - Housewares - Stirling-Everest Champion Inventrol

GOOD HOUSEKEEPING - Publisher's imprints - Hearst Corp.

GOOD HUMOR - Greeting cards - Kalan Inc.

GOOD HUMOR - Ice cream - Good Humor Corp.

GOOD HUMOR - Ophthalmic goods - Embassy Creations Inc.

GOOD HUMOR BARS - Desk sets - Crystal Products Corp.

GOOD HUMOR FEAST - Frozen foods - Good Humor Corp.

GOOD HUMOR FEAST - Ice cream - Good Humor Corp.

GOOD-I-KINS - Crocheted and knitted items - La Femme Knitting Mills Inc.

GOOD IDEA - Frames–eyeglass - Hudson Optical Corp.

GOOD IDEAS - Skateboards - Good Ideas Enterprises Inc.

GOOD IMPRESSIONS - Hosiery - Holt Hosiery Mills, Inc.

GOOD KNIGHT - Toys - Tonka Corp.

GOOD LAD - Apparel–children's - Good Lad Co.

GOOD LIE - Apparel and accessories - Christopher S Mcnulty

GOOD LIFE - Beverages - Weider Health and Fitness

GOOD LIFE - Cosmetics - Good Life, Inc.

GOOD LIFE - Floor coverings–carpet and rugs - Queen Carpet Corp.

GOOD LIFE - Frames–eyeglass - U.S. Optical Frame Co.

GOOD LIFE, THE - Water–bottled or canned - Berkshire Beverage Corp.

GOOD LIFE, THE - Wallpaper ✩ - Capital Carousel Inc.

GOOD LIFE, THE - Checkbooks - DRB Holdings, Inc.

GOOD LIFE, THE - Floor coverings–carpet and rugs - Mohawk Industries Inc.

GOOD LOAF - Flour–blended - Southeastern Mills Inc.

GOOD LOOK - Frames–eyeglass - May Optical Co. Inc.

GOOD LOOK - Paper–photographic - Eastman Kodak Co.

GOOD LOOKIN' - Butter - Butterball Farms

GOOD LOOKING GOLF - Video production - Gotellit, Inc.

GOOD LOOKS - Apparel and accessories - Spencer Industries Inc.

GOOD LUCK - Gloves - Good Luck Glove Co.

GOOD LUCK - Margarine - Lever Brothers Co. Inc.

GOOD LUCK - Soil–potting ✩ - Millburn Peat Co. Inc.

GOOD LUCK COLLECTION - Figurines ✩ - Reco International Corp.

GOOD LUCK GOLF BALL - Christmas tree ornaments - Prosperity Tree International

GOOD LUCK KNOCKING BLOCK - Novelty items - Wry Idea Co.

GOOD MEALS - Preserved foods–prepackaged - Melanie Peskett

GOOD MEASURE - Apparel stores–lingerie - Goddess Bra

GOOD MEASURE - Detergents ✩ - Monarch Crown Corp.

GOOD MEWS - Cat food - Ralston Purina Co.

GOOD MEWS - Pet products - Stutzman Environmental Products

GOOD MOOD - Dishes–earthenware - Monaco Import/Export Inc.

GOOD MOOD - Teas - Vermont Tea & Maple

GOOD MORNING - Cereal ✩ - New England Natural Bakers Inc.

GOOD MORNING - House furnishings - Dan River Inc.

GOOD MORNING - Kitchen appliances ✩ - National Housewares

GOOD MORNING - Pharmaceutical preparations ✩ - Naturade Inc.

GOOD MORNING - Teas - San Francisco Herb & Natural Food Co.

GOOD MORNING - Vitamins and nutritional supplements ✩ - Fibertone Co.

GOOD MORNING - Wallpaper ✩ - Decorative Coverings Inc.

GOOD MORNING II - Fabrics–tapestry - Comark Wallcoverings

GOOD MORNING USA - Fabrics–tapestry ✩ - Coloroll Inc.

GOOD MORNINGS - Egg substitutes - Willamette Egg Farms

GOOD MOVE - Floor coverings–carpet and rugs ✩ - Masland Corp.

GOOD 'N BED - Medical apparatus - Roloke Co.

GOOD 'N BUTTERY - Biscuits - Pillsbury Co.

GOOD 'N CLEAN - Cleaning preparations ✩ - Foremost Chemicals Inc.

GOOD-N-FAST - Food products ✩ - Schwan's Sales Enterprises, Inc.

GOOD 'N FRUITY - Candy - Leaf, Inc.

GOOD 'N HOT - Candy - Leaf, Inc.

GOOD 'N PLENTY - Floor coverings ✩ - Congoleum Corp.

GOOD 'N PLENTY - Pet products - Four Paws Products Ltd.

GOOD N' PUDDIN - Confections ✩ - Good Humor Corp.

GOOD 'N QUICK - Egg substitutes - Wilcox Family Farms Inc.

GOOD 'N' QUICK - Soups–canned - Ryt-Way Industries, Inc.

GOOD N' READY - Sandwiches - Country Lane Foods Inc.

GOOD 'N TASTY - Food products - State Fair Foods, Inc.

GOOD 'N TUFF - Bags–trash - Maynard Plastics

GOOD 'N WHOLESOME - Food products ✩ - Tyson Foods Inc.

GOOD NATURE - Baby foods - Nestle USA

GOOD NATURE - Skin care products ✩ - Bonne Bell, Inc.

GOOD NEIGHBOR - Fencing–wood - Machalk Enterprises Inc.

GOOD NEIGHBOR PHARMACY - Razor blades - Bergen Brunswig Corp.

GOOD NEIGHBOR SERIES - Manufactured homes - Redman Industries, Inc.

GOOD NEIGHBORS - Wallpaper ✩ - Decorative Coverings Inc.

GOOD NEWS - Apparel and accessories ✩ - Warnaco Inc.

GOOD NEWS - Apparel–children's - Agabang USA, Inc.

GOOD NEWS - Candy - Ben Myerson Candy Co.

GOOD NEWS - Cereal ✩ - General Mills, Inc.

GOOD NEWS - Eyeglasses - Martin-Copeland Eyewear Corp.

GOOD NEWS - Floor coverings–carpet and rugs - Barrett Carpet Mills Inc.

GOOD NEWS - Recording label - Word, Inc.

GOOD NEWS - Shaving preparations - Gillette Co.

GOOD NEWS - Toys–stuffed ✩ - Gund, Inc.

GOOD NEWS EGGS - Eggs - Hamilton Farm Bureau

GOOD NEWS GANG, THE - Toys–stuffed ✩ - Fun World Inc.

GOOD NEWS LIL' BEAR - Toys–stuffed ✩ - Gund, Inc.

GOOD NEWS REUSED - Building insulation - Cellulose Marketing Council

GOOD NIGHT - Shirts - Chums Ltd.

GOOD NIGHT FORTUNE - Chocolate candy - Lanco Corp.

GOOD NIGHT SLEEP TIGHT - Wallpaper - Gencorp Inc.

GOOD-NITE - Health care products ✩ - Nature's Herbs

GOOD-NITE TEDDY - Dolls - Takara USA Corp.

GOOD OL' BILL'S - Cookies ✩ - Fort Biscuit Co.

GOOD OL' BOY'S - Beverages–malt - Strobe & Associates, Inc.

GOOD 'OL DAYS - Clocks ✩ - General Time Corp. (Westclox/Seth Thomas Div.)

GOOD OLD BEARS, THE - Toys - Barbara Englant

GOOD OLD DAYS - Food products - Good Old Days Foods Inc.

GOOD OLD DAYS - Puzzles ✩ - Milton Bradley Co.

GOOD OLD RED - Toys - Tonka Corp.

GOOD OLD TIMES - Beverages–carbonated - Canada Dry Corp.

GOOD ONE - Motor vehicle parts and accessories - Vern's Cycle

GOOD OWNERS, GREAT DOGS - Video production - Family Dog Distribution Inc.

GOOD PAL - Candy ☆ - Brady Enterprises Inc.

GOOD PENNYWORTH PRESS - Paper–book - Norman D. Rodger

GOOD PICKENS - Fruits–canned - Cashmere Fruit Exchange

GOOD RIDDANCE - Pet products - Zema Corp.

GOOD RIDE CLUB - Apparel and accessories - Hardwear Clothing

GOOD SAMARITAN HEALING OINTMENT - Pharmaceutical preparations - Good Samaritan Laboratories, Inc.

GOOD SCENTS - Bags–trash - Maynard Plastics

GOOD SCENTS - Pet products - Petland, Inc.

GOOD SEASONS - Salad dressings–mixes - Kraft Foods, Inc.

GOOD SENSATIONS - Health care products - Sunbeam-Oster Household Products

GOOD SENSE - Bags–plastic - Chelsea Industries Inc.

GOOD SENSE - Bags–plastic - Webster Industries

GOOD SENSE - Floor coverings–carpet and rugs - Calladium & Marglen

GOOD SENSE - Publisher's imprints - Greenworld Enterprises, Inc.

GOOD SENSE - Skin care products - L. Perrigo Co.

GOOD SERVINGS - Meat product - Jac Pac Foods

GOOD SHEPHERD - Cereal - Sovex Foods, Inc.

GOOD SOUND - Recording label - DTA

GOOD SPIRITS - Food products - United Citrus Products Corp.

GOOD SPORT - Frames–eyeglass - May Optical Co. Inc.

GOOD SQUEEZE - Pens - Tops Pen Co.

GOOD START - Baby foods - Nestle USA

GOOD START - Pet products - Walco International, Inc.

GOOD START - Toys - Tonka Corp.

GOOD STUFF - Chemical preparations - Evans Manufacturing

GOOD STUFF - Fabrics–polyester - Stearns Technical Textiles Co.

GOOD STUFF - Hair care products - Modern Research Laboratories

GOOD-SUM - Vegetables–canned - Furman Foods, Inc.

GOOD TASTE - Cookies - Banner Biscuit Co. Inc.

GOOD TASTE - Floor coverings ☆ - Aladdin Mills, Inc.

GOOD TASTE - Food products - New Era Canning Co.

GOOD TASTE IS CLEAR, THE - Honey - Roso Honey, Inc.

GOOD TECH - Adhesives and sealants - Nationwide Chemical Coating Manufacturers, Inc.

GOOD THING - Toys - Good Things International, Inc.

GOOD THINGS - Fish–fresh or frozen - King Oscar Inc.

GOOD TIME - Ophthalmic goods - Embassy Creations Inc.

GOOD TIME CHEERS - Beverages - Silver Palate Kitchen

GOOD TIME JAZZ - Musical sound recordings - Fantasy Inc.

GOOD-TIME SIGNS - Paper products ☆ - Woodstock Wire, Inc.

GOOD TIMES - Chili sauce - Kraft Foods, Inc.

GOOD TIMES - Floor coverings–carpet and rugs - Kelly Group Inc.

GOOD TIMES - Food products - Cap's Italian Foods Inc.

GOOD TIMES - Sporting goods - Good Times Intelligence Agency, Inc.

GOOD TIMES AMERICA - Photo albums ☆ - Webway, Inc.

GOOD TO TOUCH - Cosmetics - Mennen Co.

GOOD TORCH - Novelty items ☆ - Chase Collection, Inc.

GOOD VALUE - Toothbrushes - Milor

GOOD VENTURE - Food products ☆ - Darik Enterprises Inc.

GOOD VIBES - Giftware - Pollenex Corp.

GOOD VIBES - Mallets ☆ - Selmer Co. Inc.

GOOD VIBRATIONS - Beds–wood ☆ - Waterworth

GOOD VIBRATIONS - Bicycles ☆ - Huffy Corp.

GOOD VIBRATIONS - Plaster–wallboard - Compositite Inc.

GOOD WISHES BEARS - Toys–stuffed - Russ Berrie and Co., Inc.

GOOD WITCH - Dolls - Effanbee Doll Corp.

GOOD WOOD - Wood products - Julie Pomerantz Inc.

GOOD WORK CLOTHES - Apparel - Spiegel, Inc.

GOOD YEAR - Fruits and vegetables ☆ - Mazo-Lerch Co. Inc.

GOOD YEAR - Wallpaper ☆ - Budeke's Paint

GOODBEAR - Toys - Noland Four Creative Services, Inc.

GOODBERRY'S - Custard–frozen - Goodberry's Creamery, Inc.

GOODBOY - Golfing equipment - Macdougall & Co.

GOODBY MR. CHIP - Games ☆ - Parker Brothers

GOODBYE MOSS - Roofing materials - All American Metal Products

GOODBYE WEEDS - Chemical preparations - Cobraco Manufacturing, Inc.

GOODCOOK ULTRA SERIES - Kitchen utensils–aluminum - Bradshaw International Inc.

GOODE - Cots–metal - E-Z Sales & Manufacturing, Inc.

GOODE - Sporting goods - S.A.C. Industries, Inc.

GOODE-READY - Wines - Murphy-Goode Estate Winery

GOODEAL - Vehicle parts - Goodeal Discount Transmissions, Inc.

GOODEBODIES - Toiletries - Goodebodies Natural Investments, Inc.

GOODEEZ - Brassieres (Bras) - Wacoal America Inc.

GOODELL - Paint removers - Chicago Cutlery Manufacturing Inc.

GOODFORM - Food products - Goodform Hanger Co. Inc.

GOODFORM II - Chairs–metal - GF Office Furniture Ltd.

GOODFRIEND'S - Coffee - Goodfriend's Vintage Organic Coffee and Estate Tea, Inc.

GOODFRIEND'S ESTATE TEA - Teas - Goodfriend's Vintage Organic Coffee and Estate Tea, Inc.

GOODHEALTH - Health care products - Abbott Laboratories

GOODHEALTH - Health care products - Abbott Laboratories

GOODHUE'S - Food products - Goodhue's Inc.

GOODIE - Recording label - Fee Bee Record Co.

GOODIER'S - Skin care products - Goodier Co. Inc.

GOODIES GAME, THE - Games ☆ - Warren Industries Inc.

GOODKIND - Pens - Ian Forrest Lebauer

GOODLIFE - Pet products - United Pacific Mills

GOODLUCK BEAR - Toys - Those Characters from Cleveland, Inc.

GOODMAN - Hydrogen peroxide - Larkspur Group Inc.

GOODMAN - Noodles - Paramount Macaroni Co. Inc.

GOODMAN'S - Crackers - G.M.B. Enterprises Inc.

GOODMAN'S - Pasta - Borden, Inc.

GOODMARK - Food products ☆ - Goodmark Foods, Inc.

GOODMARK - Motor vehicle parts and accessories - Goodmark Industries, Inc.

GOODNEST - Health care products - Dayton Hudson Corp.

GOODNIGHT - Pharmaceutical preparations ☆ - Quantum, Inc.

GOODNIGHT - Sportswear, loungewear - Charles Goodnight Inc.

GOODNIGHT AMERICA - Apparel - Charles Goodnight Inc.

GOODNIGHT MOON - Toys–stuffed - Eden LLC

GOODNITES - Cellulose plastics materials - Kimberly-Clark Corp.

GOODNUFF - Nuts–salted, roasted, cooked, or canned - Aster Nut Products Co. Inc.

GOODRICH - Audio equipment - Goodrich Sound Co.

GOODRICH - Epoxy - W.J. Ruscoe Co.

GOODRICH - Rubber bands - B.F. Goodrich Co.

GOODRICH - Watches - Hampden Corp.

GOODRICH DAIRY - Milk - Goodrich Dairy

GOOD'S - Horseradish - Silver Spring Gardens Inc.

GOOD'S - Tar - James Good Co.

GOODSHOW - Frames–eyeglass - Hudson Optical Corp.

GOODSLEEP - Pharmaceutical preparations ☆ - Quantum, Inc.

GOODSPORT - Apparel and accessories - Determined Productions, Inc.

GOODTIME - Musical instrument accessories - Pro-Mark Corp.

GOODTIMES - Video production - Goodtimes Home Video Corp.

GOODWILL - Fencing–wood - Machalk Enterprises Inc.

GOODWILL AMBASSADORS - Greeting cards - Burgoyne Inc./Curtis Swann

GOODWIND'S - Kites - Goodwin's Kites at The Gasworks Park Kite Shop

GOODWINOL - Veterinary pharmaceutical preparations - Goodwinol Products Corp.

GOODWIN'S - Housewares - Goodwin Co.

GOODWRENCH - Footwear - E.S. Originals, Inc.

GOODY - Hair care products - Goody Products, Inc.

GOODY - Ophthalmic goods - Foremost Optical Products

GOODY GOODY - Cartons–paperboard - Collector's Gallery

GOODY-GOODY - Food products ☆ - Erbrich Products Co. Inc.

GOODY GOODY GUMDROPS - Food - Marvin J. Rosenblum

GOODY TIPTOES - Dolls - Frederick Warne & Co., Inc.

GOODY TWO CHEWS - Pet products - Ralston Purina Co.

GOODY TWO-SHOES - Apparel and accessories - Atlas Trading Associates, Inc.

GOODY TWO SHOES - Candy, cereal and snacks - Marvin J. Rosenblum

GOODYEAR - Erasers ☆ - Faber-Castell Corp.

GOODYEAR - Tires - Goodyear Tire & Rubber Co.

GOODYEAR ALUMA-TAPE - Roofing materials–concrete - Consolidated Coatings Corp.

GOODYEAR ALUMA-TEK - Adhesives and sealants - Consolidated Coatings Corp.

GOODYEAR AQUATRED - Tires - Goodyear Tire & Rubber Co.

GOODYEAR BLACK RUBBER KOTE - Adhesives and sealants - Consolidated Coatings Corp.

GOODYEAR PLASTI-GLAS CEMENT - Adhesives and sealants - Consolidated Coatings Corp.

GOODYEAR POLY-CON - Roofing materials–concrete - Consolidated Coatings Corp.

☆ = Now out of production

GOODYEAR ROOF RESATURANT 701 - Adhesives and sealants - Consolidated Coatings Corp.

GOODYEAR TIRE CENTER - Automotive repair shops - Goodyear Tire & Rubber Co.

GOODY'S - Pharmaceutical preparations - Goody's Manufacturing Corp.

GOODYSACKS - Toys–stuffed ☆ - Fun World Inc.

GOOEY BUTTER - Cakes - Hazelwood Farms

GOOEY GLUE GEL - Glue–household or industrial - Elmer's Investments, Inc.

GOOEY LOUIE - Games - Pressman Toy Corp.

GOOF BALLS - Candy - Leaf, Inc.

GOOF OFF - HOME Product - Atlanta Sundries Inc.

GOOF OFF - Office supplies - Repeat-O-Type Manufacturing Corp.

GOOF OFF - Paint removers - Guardsman Products, Inc.

GOOF-OFF KIT - Signs - Wry Idea Co.

GOOF PROOF - Decals and transfers - Stahls' Inc.

GOOF PROOF - Decals and transfers - Transfer Express, Inc.

GOOF-PROOF - Wigs - Revlon General Wig Manufacturers, Inc.

GOOFBALL CLOWNS - Toys ☆ - Those Characters from Cleveland, Inc.

GOOFBALL FRIENDS - Stuffed toys ☆ - American Greetings Corp.

GOOFLES - Toys - Mattel, Inc.

GOOFLESS - Binders - Bind-It Corp.

GOOFPASTE - Candy - Zeebs Enterprises, Inc.

GOOFPROOF - Glue–household or industrial - Arlan Art Products

GOOFY - Wallpaper ☆ - Priss Prints Inc.

GOOFY FACES - Chocolate candy - Superior Fruit & Confections

GOOFY FACES - Toys - Tonka Corp.

GOOFY GHERKINS - Pickles - Green Bay Foods Co.

GOOFY GOBLINS - Candy ☆ - R.M. Palmer Co.

GOOFY PUTTY - Novelty items ☆ - S.S. Adams Co.

GOOFY ROOF - Shirts - Barbara D. Foster

GOOFY WALKER - Toys - Tonka Corp.

GOOFY'S GOOF BALLS - Candy ☆ - American Candy Co.

GOOGLES - Vehicle window screens - Auto-Shade Inc.

GOOGOL - Teas - Satori Fine Herbals

GOOKIE - Ice cream ☆ - Beitzell and Co. Inc.

GOONEY BEARS - Candy ☆ - Brock Candy Co. Inc.

GOONY TUNES - Toys–stuffed ☆ - Gund, Inc.

GOOP - Soap - Critzas Industries Inc.

GOOP - Toys - Toymax Inc.

GOORIN BROS. - Apparel stores–sports - Goorin Bros. Inc.

GOOSE - Robes - Woods

GOOSE - Video production - Nalpak Video Sales, Inc.

GOOSE AND THE GOLDEN EGG - Publisher's imprints - Covey Leadership Center, Inc.

GOOSE BUMPS - Chewing gum - Fleer Corp.

GOOSE CREEK - Wines - Goosecross Cellars, Inc.

GOOSE EGGS - Candy - New England Confectionery Co.

GOOSE GUN - Guns ☆ - Armsport Inc.

GOOSE ISLAND - Beverages–malt - Gibc, Inc.

GOOSE ISLAND HONKER'S ALE CRAFT BREWED & BOTTLE CONDITIONED CHICAGO, ILLINOIS - Beverages - Gibc, Inc.

GOOSE!, THE - Hitches–trailer - Reese Products, Inc.

GOOSEBERRY - Teas - Royal Gardens Tea

GOOSEBERRY BUZZ - Jams and jellies - Mountain Maid Gourmet Jelly

GOOSEBERRY FARM I - Wallpaper ☆ - Imperial Wallcoverings, Inc.

GOOSEBERRY FARMS - Fruits and vegetables - Gooseberry Farms, Inc.

GOOSEBUMPS - Apparel and accessories - Goosebumps Products, Inc.

GOOSEBUMPS - Video production - Parachute Press, Inc.

GOOSENECK TRAILER MFG. CO. INC. - Trailers–industrial - Gooseneck Trailer Manufacturing Co., Inc.

GOP ELEPHANT - Toys–stuffed - Dakin Inc.

GOPHA-RID - Pesticides–household - Bell Laboratories Inc.

GOPHER - Wallets ☆ - Smead Manufacturing Co.

GOPHER BAIT I - Rodenticides - C.J. Martin Co.

GOPHER BAIT II - Rodenticides - C.J. Martin Co.

GOPHER GASSER - Pesticides–household - Dexol Industries

GOPHER GETTER - Rodenticides ☆ - Woodstream Corp.

GOPHER GREENS - Games - Ben H. Lightfoot

GOPHER SPORT - Sporting goods - Prophet Corp.

GORABBIT - Toys–stuffed - Wendell L. Stephens

GORAL - Food products - King George Packing Co. Inc.

GORALIN - Skin care products - Coronet International

GORAM - Tires - Major Tires Corp.

GORATOR - Pumps - Dorr-Oliver Inc.

GORBUNNY - Toys–stuffed - Wendell L. Stephens

GORDANNE - Clocks - N.S. Gustin Co.

GORDET - Oboes - Ben Storch Corp.

GORDGE - Cases–musical instrument - Ideal Musical Merchandise Co.

GORDIE - Apparel and accessories - Rockaway Beach Surf Shop Inc.

GORDINI - Goggles - Gordini U.S.A. Inc.

GORDINI - Motor vehicles ☆ - Renault Inc.

GORDO-POOL - Chemical preparations - Gordon Laboratories

GORDO-VITE - See **VITE A**

GORDOBALM - Lotions - Gordon Laboratories

GORDOCHOM - Nail care products - Gordon Laboratories

GORDOFILM - Pharmaceutical preparations - Gordon Laboratories

GORDOGESIC - Pharmaceutical preparations - Gordon Laboratories

GORDOMATIC - Skin care products - Gordon Laboratories

GORDON - Hardware - Gordon Associates

GORDON - Horseshoes - Queen City Forging Co.

GORDON - Ophthalmic goods ☆ - Luxottica

GORDON - Pharmaceutical preparations - Gordon Laboratories

GORDON - Wines ☆ - Kobrand Corp.

GORDON ALLAN - Luggage - Commercial Sewing, Inc.

GORDON & FERGUSON NECKWEAR - Neckties - Gordon & Ferguson of Delaware, Inc.

GORDON AND SMITH - Apparel and accessories - Gayle Gordon

GORDON BIERSCH GARLIC FRIES - Food products - Gordon Biersch Brewing Co., Inc.

GORDON FRASER - Giftware ☆ - Gorham Inc.

GORDON FRASER - Greeting cards ☆ - Gordon Fraser Inc.

GORDON FRASER - Music boxes ☆ - Schmid Inc.

GORDON SPIN-ON - Horseshoes - Queen City Forging Co.

GORDON'S - Corn chips ☆ - Sunshine Biscuits, Inc.

GORDON'S - Food products - Gourmet Specialties

GORDONS - Potato chips ☆ - Hiland Potato Chip Co.

GORDONS - Toys–automobiles - Toy Truck Lines, Inc.

GORDON'S - Vodka - Schenley Industries Inc.

GORDON'S ANTIBACTERIAL - Soap - Gordon Laboratories

GORDON'S BAT RACK - Furniture–children's - Maze Inc.

GORDON'S NO. 5 - Pharmaceutical preparations - Gordon Laboratories

GORDON'S UREA - Pharmaceutical preparations - Gordon Laboratories

GORDONSTOUN - House furnishings - Dan River Inc.

GORDOPHENE - Pharmaceutical preparations - Gordon Laboratories

GORDY - Recording label - Motown Record Co. L.P.

GORDY-MITE - Toys ☆ - Henry Gordy International Inc.

GORDYS - Food products - Gordy's Inc.

GORE - Medical apparatus - W.L. Gore & Associates, Inc.

GORE-FLIGHT - Cables–coaxial - W.L. Gore & Associates, Inc.

GORE-ILLA - Toys - Mattel, Inc.

GORE JAW - Toys - Tonka Corp.

GORE-NO STAT - Filters–industrial - W.L. Gore & Associates, Inc.

GORE-SELECT - Plastics–laminated - W. L. Gore & Associates, Inc.

GORE-SHIELD - Gaskets - W.L. Gore & Associates, Inc.

GORE SMOOTHER - Surgical supplies - W.L. Gore & Associates, Inc.

GORE-SORBER - Vaporizers - W. L. Gore & Associates, Inc.

GORE-TEX - Hats - W.L. Gore & Associates, Inc.

GORE-TEX ALL-WEATHER - Ventilation equipment - W.L. Gore & Associates, Inc.

GORE-TEX BEST DEFENSE - Apparel and accessories - W.L. Gore & Associates, Inc.

GORE-TEX COMFORT COOL - Apparel and accessories - W.L. Gore & Associates, Inc.

GORE-TEX FLEX - Gloves - W.L. Gore & Associates, Inc.

GORE-TEX HEAVYWEIGHT - Filters–industrial - W.L. Gore & Associates, Inc.

GORE-TEX PRE-VENT - Filters–air - W.L. Gore & Associates, Inc.

GORE-TRET - Computers - W.L. Gore & Associates, Inc.

GORE WINDSTOPPER - Fabrics - W.L. Gore & Associates, Inc.

GORF - Games - Hasbro, Inc.

GORGE CLASSIC - Fresh fruits - Duckwall-Pooley Fruit Co.

GORGEOUS - Ophthalmic goods ☆ - Luxottica

GORGEOUS - T-shirts–men's - Gregory S. Higgins

GORGEOUS GOTHICS - Cosmetics - Del Pharmaceuticals, Inc.

GORGEOUS GRAPE - Lipsticks ☆ - Honey & Spice Toiletries

GORGON - Cables–steel - Kryptonite Corp.

GORGY - Clocks - Franklin Instrument Co. Inc.

GORHAM - Giftware - Gorham Inc.

GORHAM-REIZART - Giftware ☆ - Gorham Inc.

GORHAM SHELL - Flatware - Gorham Inc.

GORHAMCRAFT - Flatware ☆ - Gorham Inc.

GORILLA - Amplifiers - Evets Corp.

GORILLA - Amplifiers - Gorilla, Inc.

GORILLA - Amplifiers - Pignose Industries
GORILLA - Floor coverings - Etc. of Henderson, Inc.
GORILLA - Hoses - Goodyear Tire & Rubber Co.
GORILLA - Lawn mowers - Alamo Industrial
GORILLA - Motor vehicle parts and accessories - Amcor Industries, Inc.
GORILLA - Motor vehicle parts and accessories - Bell Sports Corp.
GORILLA - Paints - Pen Paints Inc.
GORILLA - Pet products - IVC Corp.
GORILLA - Safety products - Snug Seat, Inc.
GORILLA - Shoes - Carolina Shoe Co.
GORILLA - Skin care products - Schnapp Enterprises Inc.
GORILLA - Toys - Centuri Corp.
GORILLA BAGS - Luggage ☆ - American Tourister, Inc.
GORILLA BAR - Confections - Famous Pacific Dessert Co.
GORILLA DECAF - Coffee - Organic Coffee Co., Inc.
GORILLA GARLIC - Spices and extracts - Drake Foods, Inc.
GORILLA GOAL - Balls–basketball - Hydra Rib, Inc.
GORILLA-GOAL - Sporting goods - Sorensen-Christian Industries Inc.
GORILLA GOURMET - Spices and extracts - Drake Foods, Inc.
GORILLA GRABBER - Toys - Empire Industries
GORILLA GREASE - Skin care products - Caribbean Connection
GORILLA GREASE - Suntan lotions - ALB, Inc.
GORILLA GRIP - Fabric binding - Stahls' Inc.
GORILLA KNUCKLES - Candy - Jason & Son
GORILLA NET - Netting - B & J Martin, Inc.
GORILLA NITRO - Vitamins and nutritional supplements - Vitol Health Products
GORILLA RIB - Glass products - BP Chemicals Inc. (Filon Products Div.)
GORILLA SILVERBACK - Beverages–malt ☆ - Greentree Group, Inc.
GORILLA VANILLA - Spices and extracts - David Michael & Co.
GORILLA WEAR - Apparel and accessories - Gorilla Wear Inc.
GORILLABAND - Saw blades ☆ - Sandvik Saws & Tools
GORILLATALK - Computer software - Gorilla Systems Corp.
GORKI - Vodka - Standard Distillers Products Inc.
GORKY - Liquors - United States Distilled Products Co.
GORMAN - Containers - Sabhi, Inc.
GORMEL - Skin care products - Gordon Laboratories
GORO GORILLA - Toys–stuffed - Dakin Inc.
GORP - Consulting services - Greer Consulting Services, Inc.
GORRBO GORILLA - Toys–stuffed - Russ Berrie and Co., Inc.
GORSUCH LTD. - Candles - Gorsuch Ltd.
GORSUCH SCARISBRICK PUBLISHERS - Publisher's imprints - Gorsuch Scarisbrick Publishers
GORTON'S - Seafood products–fresh or frozen - Gorton Group
GORTON'S OF GLOUCESTER - Seafood products–fresh or frozen - Gorton Group
GORTON'S SELECT - Fish–fresh or frozen - Gorton Group
GOSCH - Seafood products–fresh or frozen - Kreiner Imports
GOSEN - Sporting goods - Century Sports Inc.
GOSEN - Sporting goods - Rocky Mountain Sports
GOSEN PRO FORM - Sporting goods - Century Sports Inc.
GOSHAWK - Eyeglasses - Art-Craft Optical Co.
GOSHEN - Furniture–metal ☆ - Gleason Industrial Products
GOSHIKI - Pet products - Novalek, Inc.
GOSLING - Food products - Mid-America Potato Co.
GOSLING TAPES SEW EASY - Fabric tapes - William E. Wright
GOSLING'S BLACK SEAL RUM - Rum - Marie Brizard Wines & Spirits, USA
GOSPEARL - Recording label - Atlanta International Record Co. Inc.
GOSPEL CITY - Recording label - Bollman International Records
GOSPEL GEAR - Apparel and accessories - FCF Enterprises Inc.
GOSPEL GEMS - Business cards - Challenge Card Co.
GOSPEL IN ART, THE - Posters - Friberg Fine Art Prints
GOSPEL JUBILEE - Recording label - Scorpio Enterprises Inc.
GOSPEL SPIRIT, THE - Tape recorders–cassette - Sony Music Entertainment Inc.
GOSPELCISE - Exercising equipment - Dove Productions Inc.
GOSPO CENTRIC - Computer software - Gospocentric
GOSS FLUSH - Hardware ☆ - J.W. Goss Co.
GOSSAMER - Cosmetics - Panco Ltd.
GOSSAMER - Fabric softeners - Puritan-Churchill Chemical Co.
GOSSAMER BAY - Wines - E. & J. Gallo Winery
GOSSAMER SHEER COLLECTION - Fabrics - Guilford Mills, Inc.
GOSSAMER WINGS - Fabrics–tapestry ☆ - Christopher Prints
GOSSARD ANSWER - Girdles - Crown Foundations Inc.
GOSSEMER STEEL - Wallpaper - RJF International Corp.
GOSSEN - Molding compounds–plastics - Gossen Corp.
GOSSEN - Photographic equipment - Bogen Photo Corp.

GOSSIP - Ophthalmic goods - Styl-Rite Optical Manufacturing Co., Inc.
GOSSNER - Cheese - Gossner Foods, Inc.
GOSSNER FOODS - Cheese - Gossner Foods, Inc.
GOSTELRADIO - Recording label ☆ - Mobile Fidelity Sound Lab
GOSYSTEM 2 - Computer storage devices - Computer Language Research Inc.
GOT A MINUTE - Games ☆ - Milton Bradley Co.
GOT BALLS - Apparel and accessories - Got Balls & Got Marbles, Inc.
GOT 'CHA! - Games ☆ - Milton Bradley Co.
G.O.T. FRIES - Snack foods - Golden Choice Foods Corp.
GOT THE HANDLE ON MESQUITE - Charcoal - Bill Lord
GOTAMINE - Pharmaceutical preparations - Vita Elixir Co. Inc.
GOTCHA - Alarm systems - Gotcha Sportswear Inc.
GOTCHA - Apparel and accessories - Munsingwear, Inc.
GOTCHA - Candy - Zeebs Enterprises, Inc.
GOTCHA - Cleaning equipment - Minuteman International, Inc.
GOTCHA! - Dolls - Effanbee Doll Corp.
GOTCHA - Floodlights - RAB Electric
GOTCHA - Office furniture–plastic - Rose Displays, Ltd.
GOTCHA COVERED - Product description unknown - Scott Paper Co.
GOTCHA COVERED - Apparel stores–sports - Gotcha Covered
GOTCHA COVERED - Musical instrument accessories ☆ - L.A. Sax Co.
GOTCHA DAY - Greeting cards - Craig Widrig
GOTCHA DRY - Dryers–hair ☆ - Philips Electronics North America Corp.
GOTCHA! FRAUD DETECTIVE - Computer software - Nicholas Bredimus
GOTCHA GUN - Dryers–hair ☆ - Philips Electronics North America Corp.
GOTCHAS - Candy - McDonald Candy Co. Inc.
GOTEBORGS KEX - Biscuits - A.V. Olsson Trading Co., Inc.
GOTHAM - Apparel stores–sports ☆ - Gotham Knitting Mills
GOTHAM - Bathroom fixtures - Crane Plumbing/Fiat Products
GOTHAM - Cables - G Prime Limited
GOTHAM - Clocks ☆ - General Time Corp. (Westclox/Seth Thomas Div.)
GOTHAM - Crayons ☆ - Binney & Smith Inc.
GOTHAM - Floor coverings ☆ - Congoleum Corp.
GOTHAM - Floor coverings–carpet and rugs ☆ - J and J Industries Inc.
GOTHAM - Footwear - Gotham Shoe Manufacturing Co.
GOTHAM - Frames–eyeglass - May Optical Co. Inc.
GOTHAM - Lighting fixtures - National Service Industries, Inc.
GOTHAM - Rings–jewelry - Feature Enterprises
GOTHAM - Twine - A.W. Archer Co. Inc.
GOTHAM - Underwear and nightwear ☆ - L.V. Myles
GOTHAM - Watches - Nicolet International Inc.
GOTHAM LIBRARY, THE - Publisher's imprints ☆ - New York University Press
GOTHAMATIC - Rings–jewelry - Feature Enterprises
GOTHIC - Chessboards - Pacific Game Co.
GOTHIC - Crayons - Sargent Art, Inc.
GOTHIC - Floor coverings–carpet and rugs ☆ - World Carpets, Inc.
GOTHIC - Frames–eyeglass - Pathway Optical Prods.
GOTHIC - Paints - Amsterdam Color Works Inc.
GOTHIC - Recording label - Gothic Records Inc.
GOTHIC - Shoes - E.F. Shoes, Inc.
GOTICA - Tiles–ceramic ☆ - Federal Tile Imports Inc.
GOTOWN - Recording label - Kilgore Records Co.
GOTT - Ice chests–plastic - Rubbermaid Inc.
GOTT ESCORT - Jars–plastic ☆ - Rubbermaid Inc.
GOTT ESCORT EXTRA - Jars–plastic ☆ - Rubbermaid Inc.
GOTT GRIPPER - See BOUNCER
GOTT SPORTCOOLER - Ice chests–plastic - Rubbermaid Inc.
GOTT-TO-GO - Ice chests–plastic ☆ - Rubbermaid Inc.
GOTTA - Cosmetics ☆ - S.R. Droescher Inc.
GOTTA - Pet products - Grah & Plumacher USA
GOTTA DANCE - Christmas tree ornaments - Cracker Box Inc.
GOTTA GETTA GUND GANG - Toys–stuffed - Gund, Inc.
GOTTA GO - Toilets–portable - James Edward McNamara
GOTTA GO POTTY - Toilet seats - Century Products Co.
GOTTALOTTA - Bakery products - Lone Star Consolidated Foods, Inc.
GOTTENA - Bakery products ☆ - C. & J. Willenborg Inc.
GOTTEX - Apparel and accessories - Gottex Industries Inc.
GOTTEX - Sunglasses - 3R Optics/Gottex Eyewear
GOTTEX - Watches - Bienne Time Corp.
GOTTEX MENS - Bathing suits - Gottex Industries Inc.
GOTTFRIED - Health care products - Gottfried Medical Inc.
GOTTHARD SCHUSTER - Musical instrument accessories ☆ - Scherl & Roth Inc.
GOTTSCHALK - Cleaning preparations–household - Gottschalk Metal Sponge Sales Corp.

☆ = Now out of production

GOTU KOLA EXTRACT - Vitamins and nutritional supplements - Vitamin Research Products Inc.

GOTZ - Biscuits - Kreiner Imports

GOTZ - Food products - George C. Brown's Biscuits & Confections

GOUARINI - Frozen foods - Made in France

GOUBAUD DE PARIS - Skin care products - Goubaud

GOUCHO - Trailers–travel ☆ - Serro Travel Trailer Co. Inc.

GOUDA - Apparel and accessories - Gouda Inc.

GOUDY - Ophthalmic goods - Styl-Rite Optical Manufacturing Co., Inc.

GOUGE-GARD - Adhesives and sealants - Creative Football Concepts, Inc.

GOULD - Drapery hardware - Worldwide Window Treatments

GOULDS - Water purification systems - Goulds Pumps, Inc.

GOULISH GREETINGS - Ornamental products–glass - Russ Berrie and Co., Inc.

GOURDSKET - Containers - Wanda Jane Baker

GOURM-EGG - Food products - Ralston Purina Co.

GOURMAND - Food products - Gourmand Inc.

GOURMANDISE - Cheese ☆ - Bongrain Cheese USA

GOURMASE - Pharmaceutical preparations ☆ - Solvay Pharmaceuticals Inc.

GOURMAZE - Food products - Brown Seed Farms

GOURMAZING FOODS INC. - Sauces - Gourmazing Foods Inc.

GOURMET - Bakery products ☆ - Parco Foods, Inc.

GOURMET - Bird feeds - Reinders, Inc.

GOURMET - Cakes - French Accent

GOURMET - Cakes - Mr. Dan's Gourmet Pound Cakes

GOURMET - Cutlery - J.A. Henckels Zwillingswerk Inc.

GOURMET - Cutlery ☆ - Lifetime Hoan Corp.

GOURMET - Cutting boards - Fleet Manufacturing Co., Inc.

GOURMET - Dinnerware–glass - Royal China & Porcelain Companies Inc.

GOURMET - Dishes–earthenware - Hadley Pottery Co. Inc.

GOURMET - Dishes–earthenware ☆ - Denby USA Limited

GOURMET - Dishes–plastic ☆ - Kaz Business Systems Inc.

GOURMET - Food products - Alpineaire Foods

GOURMET - Food products - American Connoisseur

GOURMET - Food products - Moon Shine Trading Co.

GOURMET - Frames–eyeglass - Hudson Optical Corp.

GOURMET - Fruits and vegetables - Stanley Orchards Sales Inc.

GOURMET - Garden equipment - Carefree Garden Products

GOURMET - Glass–leaded - Seneca Glass Co.

GOURMET - Glassware–household - Owens-Illinois Inc. (Libbey Div.)

GOURMET - Hams - Lykes Bros. Inc. (Meat Packing Div.)

GOURMET - House furnishings - Montgomery Ward & Co. Inc.

GOURMET - Meat products–poultry - Snowball Foods, Inc.

GOURMET - Nuts–candied ☆ - Sycamore Creek Co. (INARI, Ltd.)

GOURMET - Pasta - Gourmet's Fresh Pasta Inc.

GOURMET - Pepper - Young's Market Co.

GOURMET - Pet products - Gimborn U.S., Inc.

GOURMET - Salads–prepackaged ☆ - Green County of Wisconsin

GOURMET - Salt and pepper mills - William Bounds, Ltd.

GOURMET - Sinks–metal - Elkay Manufacturing Co.

GOURMET - Spices and extracts - Mel-O-Gold

GOURMET - Stoves ☆ - Leigh

GOURMET - Teas ☆ - Traditional Medicinals, Inc.

GOURMET - Wallpaper ☆ - Kingfisher Wallcoverings

GOURMET ALL AMERICAN - Chocolate candy - Maxfield Candy Co.

GOURMET ALL THE WAY - Candy - Billy Burden

GOURMET ALLEY - Noodles - Alpine International

GOURMET AMERICAN - Roast beef, corned beef, and pastrami - Royal Quality Foods, Inc.

GOURMET AT PLAY - Mustard - California Style Gourmet

GOURMET AWARD - Flatware - Tree of Life, Inc.

GOURMET AWARD - Food products - Godiva Chocolatier

GOURMET AWARD - Food products - Gourmet Award Foods

GOURMET BANDED - Dinnerware–glass ☆ - Metlox Pottery Shoppe

GOURMET BOUQUET - Confections - Coast Novelty Manufacturing Co.

GOURMET BRAND - Fruits and vegetables - Corrin

GOURMET BREW - Spices and extracts - Virginia Dare Extract Co., Inc.

GOURMET CAJUN FOODS - Food products - Creoles' Inc.

GOURMET CANES - Candy - Asher Candy Co.

GOURMET CHEDDAR - Cheese - Sargento Cheese Co. Inc.

GOURMET CHEF - Cooking equipment–household - GSW Jackes-Evans Manufacturing Co.

GOURMET CHEW - Pet products ☆ - Pets International, Ltd.

GOURMET CHOCOLATE BARS - Candy - Home of the Hebert Candies, Inc.

GOURMET CHOICE - Food products - Erbrich Products Co. Inc.

GOURMET CHOICE - Food products - Gourmet Choice

GOURMET CHOLINE COOLER - Vitamins and nutritional supplements ☆ - Vitamin Research Products Inc.

GOURMET CLUB - Food products - Gourmet Club Corp.

GOURMET CLUB - Shrimp - Continental Seafoods Inc.

GOURMET COFFEE HOSPITALITY CENTER - Coffee - Boyd Coffee Co.

GOURMET COLLECTION - Cooking equipment–household ☆ - Kraftware Corp. (Morgan Div.)

GOURMET COLLECTION - Sinks–metal - Elkay Manufacturing Co.

GOURMET COMPUTER COOKBOOK - Computer software - Electronic Courseware Systems Inc.

GOURMET CUISINE - Soups–mixes ☆ - Caltex Trading, Inc.

GOURMET DELI - Bagels - Western Bagel Baking Corp.

GOURMET DELI VITO'S MARKET - Food products - Vito's Gourmet Market, Inc.

GOURMET DELIGHT - Cooking equipment–household - Robert D. Murray & Associates

GOURMET DELIGHT - Fruits and vegetables - Roland Marketing Inc.

GOURMET DELIGHT'S - Mustards - Cortina Corp.

GOURMET DELITE - Meat products–poultry ☆ - Louis Rich Co.

GOURMET DIETER - Teas - Satori Fine Herbals

GOURMET DINNER ROLLS - Rolls–dinner - Natural Ovens of Manitowoc Inc.

GOURMET DISHES - Pet products - Rolf C. Hagen (USA) Corp.

GOURMET FAVORITES - Corned beef - Bessin Corp.

GOURMET FRANCE - Food products - Continental Food Corp.

GOURMET FRANCIAS - Food products ☆ - Crystal Food Import Corp.

GOURMET FREDDIE'S - Cabbage rolls - RDS Specialty Meats Inc.

GOURMET FRESH - Health care products - Quong Hop & Co.

GOURMET GALLERY - Housewares stores - Barth-Dreyfuss of California

GOURMET GARDEN - Pet products ☆ - Penn-Plax, Inc.

GOURMET GARDENS - Jams and jellies - EasTex Farms

GOURMET GARLIC DELITE - Margarine - Don Pietro's Gourmet Food Products, Inc.

GOURMET GOLD - Candy ☆ - F.B. Washburn Candy Corp.

GOURMET GOLD - Food products - Merkt Cheese Co., Inc.

GOURMET GOLD - Seasonings - Randan Corp.

GOURMET GOLD - Vegetables–frozen ☆ - Lamb-Weston, Inc.

GOURMET GRAPHICS - Pigments–paint - Leshner Corp.

GOURMET GREENS - Greeting cards ☆ - Applewood Seed & Garden Group

GOURMET GRILL - Charcoal - Longs Drug Stores Corp.

GOURMET GRILLER RIBS - Meat products - Farmland Foods, Inc.

GOURMET GROUND - Coffee - Sara Lee Corp.

GOURMET GUBAS - Nuts–salted, roasted, cooked, or canned - Sopakco Foods

GOURMET HARVEST - Food products - American Culinary Foods, Inc.

GOURMET HOUSE - Rice - Gourmet House Inc.

GOURMET INTERNATIONAL - Food products - International Foods Retort Co.

GOURMET INTERNATIONAL - Meat products–beef - Mann's International Meat Specialties Inc.

GOURMET ITALIANO - Giftware - Doranne

GOURMET JUNK FOOD - Candy ☆ - Harry London's Candies Inc.

GOURMET KERNELS - Popcorn - Royale International

GOURMET KITCHEN - Food products - Kozy Shack Inc.

GOURMET LID, THE - Containers–plastic - Sweetheart Cup Co. Inc.

GOURMET LITE - Meat products–canned - Dietz & Watson

GOURMET MARKET - Wines ☆ - Bully Hill Vineyards, Inc.

GOURMET MARKETPLACE - Catalogs - Hickory Farms, Inc.

GOURMET NATURALLY - Food products - Abco Laboratories, Inc.

GOURMET NATURALS - Teas–herbal - Gourmet Naturals

GOURMET NUT CENTER - Nuts–salted, roasted, cooked, or canned ☆ - Dole Dried Fruit & Nut Co.

GOURMET OUTDOOR KITCHEN - Barbecues and grills - Prochef, Inc.

GOURMET PARISIAN - Vinegar ☆ - Crystal Food Import Corp.

GOURMET PEANUTS - Candy - American Chewing Gum Inc.

GOURMET PET - Animal feeds - Gourmet Pet Division

GOURMET PRIDE - Soups–canned - Superior Brands

GOURMET QUARTS - Ice cream - Friendly Ice Cream Corp.

GOURMET RECIPE - Meat products–poultry - Hudson Foods, Inc.

GOURMET RESERVES - Food products - Alpineaire Foods

GOURMET-ROAST - Meat products–poultry - Hester Industries, Inc.

GOURMET SALADS - Food products - Gourmet Salads

GOURMET SEAFOOD - Seafood products–fresh or frozen - O'Donnell-Usen Fisheries Corp.

GOURMET SELECTED - Chocolate candy - Maxfield Candy Co.

GOURMET SLIM - Dinners–frozen - All American Gourmet Co.

GOURMET SNACKIN' SAUCE - Snack foods - Amazing Grazing, Inc.

GOURMET SOFT - Yogurt–frozen - Mrs. Fields Development Corp.

☆ = Now out of production

GOURMET SORBETTO - Confections - Mama Tish's Italian Specialties, Inc.
GOURMET SPECIAL BLEND - Spices and extracts - Finest Kind Spices
GOURMET SPICE - Spices and extracts ☆ - McSteven's
GOURMET TABLE - Food products - A.F.I. Food Service Distributors Inc.
GOURMET, THE - Stoves - Amana Refrigeration Inc.
GOURMET, THE - Puzzles ☆ - International Polygonics Ltd.
GOURMET, THE - Food products - Matlaw's Food Products Inc.
GOURMET TO GO - Food products ☆ - Creoles' Inc.
GOURMET TO GO - Meat products - Hot 'n Spicey, Inc.
GOURMET TOUCH - Salad dressings–mixes - Slyman's Lebanese Foods
GOURMET TREE - Cookies ☆ - Fox Run Craftsmen
GOURMET VILLAGE - Food products - Chase Collection, Inc.
GOURMET VINAIGRETTE - Salad dressings–bottled - American Connoisseur
GOURMET WEIGH - Kitchen utensils–enameled - Metrokane
GOURMETFRESH - Meat and grain entrees/side dishes - Alfresh Foods, Inc.
GOURMET'S CHOICE - Coffee - Gourmet's Choice Coffee Inc.
GOURMET'S CHOICE - Cooking utensils–enameled - Mazel Co. L.P.
GOURMET'S CHOICE, THE - Cutting boards - Zanger Co.
GOURMET'S FINEST BRAND - Dinners–frozen - Alfresh Foods, Inc.
GOURMET...THE NATURAL WAY - Coffee - Nature's Finest Products Inc.
GOURMUTT - Dog food - Woofy Products LLC
GOV. - See also GOVERNOR
GOVBOND - Computer software - Horizon Real-Time Systems, Inc.
GOVENAIR - Air conditioning equipment - Commercial Environmental Systems
GOVERNESS - Eyeglasses - Art-Craft Optical Co.
GOVERNMENT MODEL - Firearms, accessories, and parts - New Colt Holding Corp.
GOVERNMENT TECHNOLOGY - Publisher's imprints - GMW Communications, Inc.
GOVERNOR - See also GOV.
GOVERNOR - Mobile homes ☆ - Wescon Products Co.
GOVERNOR - Thread - Threads USA Div.
GOVERNOR - Watches - Gruen Marketing Corp.
GOVERNOR CLINTON - Glassware–household - Owens-Illinois Inc. (Libbey Div.)
GOVERNOR PHILLIP - Wines ☆ - David Sherman Corp.
GOVERNOR WINTHROP - Hardware ☆ - Amerock Corp.
GOVERNOR'S CLUB - Whiskey - David Sherman Corp.
GOVERNOR'S OAK - Furniture - Kincaid Furniture Co. Inc.
GOVERNOR'S OAK K - Furniture - La-Z-Boy Chair Co.
GOVERNOR'S PATH - Floor coverings–carpet and rugs ☆ - Bloomsburg Carpet Industries
GOVERNOR'S ROW - Floor coverings–carpet and rugs - Evans-Black Carpet Mills
GOVERNORS VILLAGE - Real estate agencies - Governors Club LP
GOVREPO - Computer software - Horizon Real-Time Systems, Inc.
GOWAN - Pesticides–agricultural - Gowan Co.
GOWANDA - Automotive parts and accessories - Gowanda Electronics Corp.
GOWER - Musical instrument accessories - G. Leblanc Corp.
GOWI - Toys - Small World Toys
GOWRITE - Computer software - Go Corp.
GOWRON - Toys - Paramount Pictures Corp.
GOYA - Artists' materials - Andrews/Nelson/Whitehead
GOYA - Beverages–carbonated - Ancel Products Inc.
GOYA - Cigarettes - G.A. Georgopulo & Co. Inc.
GOYA - Floor coverings ☆ - Congoleum Corp.
GOYA - Jewelry - Goya Foods, Inc.
GOYA - Milk - Farmland Dairies Inc.
GOYA - Musical instruments - C.F. Martin & Co., Inc.
GOYA - Wood products ☆ - Homasote Co.
GOYA HELADO CLASSICO - Ice cream - Goya Foods, Inc.
GOYU - Artists' materials - Andrews/Nelson/Whitehead
GOZAN - Toys–automobiles - Victor M. Bulgarelli Associates Inc.
GOZIO - Tricycles - Dean J. Rettger
GP - Oils–lubricating - Castoleum Corp.
G.P. - Paper ☆ - Howard Paper Mills Inc.
GP - Pet products - Art J. Jones Corp.
GP - Recording label - GP Records & Tapes
GP - Resins–polymer - Georgia-Pacific Corp.
GP-1 - Sunglasses - Bolle' America, Inc.
GP-2 - Vitamins and nutritional supplements - Sports One, Inc.
GP 20 - Pigments–organic - South Pacific Corp.
GP 76 - Frames–eyeglass ☆ - Universal/Univis Inc.
GP-100 - Revolvers - Sturm, Ruger & Co., Inc.
GP & DESIGN - Plywood - Georgia-Pacific Corp.
GP DESIGNS - Jewelry - Gem Platinum Manufacturing Co.

GP GENUINE BEVELED GLASS & MIRROR - Awards, plaques and medals - Stephen Ryan Tortomasi
GP GUARDPACK - Bags–paper - Cavert Wire Co. Inc.
GP N.S.I. BOARD & DESIGN - Cartons–paperboard - Georgia-Pacific Corp.
GP PLANNER & DESIGN - Computer software - Georgia-Pacific Corp.
GP PLUS - Audio equipment - Telequest Inc.
GP SORENSEN - Automotive parts and accessories - Standard Motor Products, Inc.
G.P.8 PLUS - Concrete products - Bartron Corp.
GP350 - Radio communications equipment - Motorola, Inc. (Land Mobile Products Sector)
GPA - Computer software - Alza Corp.
GPC - Chemical preparations - Grain Processing Corp.
GPC - Cigarettes - Brown & Williamson Tobacco Corp.
GPH MUSIC - Recording label - Gospel Publishing House
GPL - Tools ☆ - Dayco Products, Inc.
GPL II - Cartons–paperboard - Georgia-Pacific Corp.
GPM - Jewelry - Gem Platinum Manufacturing Co.
GPR - Safety equipment - General Scientific Equipment Co.
GPRI - Resins–polymer - Georgia-Pacific Corp.
GPRT - Recording label - GP Records & Tapes
G.P.S. - Apparel and accessories - Sportailor Inc.
GPS - Archery equipment ☆ - Bear Archery Inc.
GPS - Computer software - Belvedere Financial Systems, Inc.
GPS - Generators–gas - Surface Combustion, Inc.
GPS - Navigational instruments - Lowrance Electronics, Inc.
GPS - Shortening - Florida Shortening Corp.
GPS-5 - Navigational instruments - Ray Jefferson
GPS COMMANDER - Navigational instruments - Magellan Corp.
GPS EDGE - Computer peripheral equipment - Green Pasture Software, Inc.
GPS EXTENSION - Antennas - Avcom of Virginia Inc.
GPS TOTAL STATION - Electronic equipment - Trimble Navigation Ltd.
GPS TRAILBLAZER - Electrical equipment - Magellan Systems Corp.
GPX - Paper–bond - Saxon Nuco Inc.
GPX - Toys–electronic - Gran Prix Electronics
GPX DIESEL COATINGS - Machine parts - General Plasma Inc.
GPX GLASSPROTEX - Doors–metal - O'Keeffe's, Inc.
GQ EXPRESS COURIER - Courier services–air - Gq Express Courier, Inc.
GR-2 - Shock absorbers–motor vehicle - KYB Corp. of America
GR 20 - Rackets–tennis - Spalding Sports Worldwide
GR-REAT 'N EASY - Cleaning preparations - Herbert Stanley Co.
GR TECHNOLOGIES - Computer software - Genrad, Inc.
GR8 PLTS - Key rings - Imagine
GRA-NITTLE - Snack foods ☆ - Sovex Foods, Inc.
GRAB-4-IT - Bowl sets ☆ - Corning Inc.
GRAB-A-BAG - Toys - Henry Gordy International Inc.
GRAB A BRUSH - Paint brushes - United Coatings Inc.
GRAB-A-GRAND - Game machines - Sigma Game Inc.
GRAB-A-MEAL - Cookware, servingware ☆ - Corning Inc.
GRAB-A-RAG - Paper - Scott Paper Co.
GRAB A TAN - Suntan lotions - Key West Aloe Inc.
GRAB A TAN PLUS - Suntan lotions - Key West Aloe Inc.
GRAB BAG - Leather - Enger-Kress Co.
GRAB BAG - Sporting goods - Marty Gilman Inc.
GRAB BAGS - Snack foods - Frito-Lay, Inc.
GRAB 'EMS - Toys–stuffed ☆ - Century Products Co.
GRAB HOLD - Glue–household or industrial - National Artcraft Co.
GRAB-IT - Computer software ☆ - UVP Inc.
GRAB-IT - Cookware, bakeware, servingware, etc. - Corning Inc.
GRAB-IT - Floor coverings–carpet and rugs - E.R. Carpenter Co.
GRAB IT - Floor coverings–carpet and rugs - Omalon
GRAB-IT - Gloves–work - Edmont
GRAB-ME - Rope - W.T. Ayres & Associates
GRAB MY GUTZ - Toys–stuffed - Rumpus Corp.
GRAB ON - Pens - Grab-On Products
GRAB ON MAXI - Bicycle parts and accessories - Grab-On Products
GRAB ON MTN - Bicycle parts and accessories - Grab-On Products
GRABBA GORILLA - Toys–stuffed - Dakin Inc.
GRABBER - Adhesives and sealants - Chemray Coatings Corp.
GRABBER - Bicycles - Sears, Roebuck and Co.
GRABBER - Fasteners–hook and eye - VSI Fasteners, Inc.
GRABBER - Footwear - Iron Age Corp.
GRABBER - Games - Nationsbank of North Carolina, N.A.
GRABBER - Golfing equipment - DBA Products Co.
GRABBER - Health care products - Temco Health Care
GRABBER - Tape–adhesive - Seam Master Industry

☆ = Now out of production

GRABBER - Tires–automobile - General Tire, Inc.
GRABBER & RETREEVER - Tools ☆ - MJR Industries, Inc.
GRABBER AP - Tires–automobile - General Tire, Inc.
GRABBER AT - Tires–automobile - General Tire, Inc.
GRABBER-CONE - Safety products - Traffix Devices
GRABBER FQ - Belts–industrial - Advanced Belt Technology
GRABBER JR., THE - Hardware - Securitag Corp.
GRABBER LT - Tires–automobile - General Tire, Inc.
GRABBER MT - Tires–automobile - General Tire, Inc.
GRABBER ROCKER, THE - Machinery - John Wagner Associates Inc.
GRABBER, THE - Mats - Roope Corp.
GRABBER, THE - Hardware - Securitag Corp.
GRABBER, THE - Glue–household or industrial - Super Glue Corp.
GRABBER-TUBE - Safety products - Traffix Devices
GRABBER ZOO - Hardware - Securitag Corp.
GRABBERS - Discount coupon cards - Jesco, Inc.
GRABBERS - Food products ☆ - Bodin Foods Inc.
GRABBERS - Musical instrument accessories - Gibson Strings & Accessories
GRABBERS, THE - Electrical equipment - Kinetics Ltd.
GRABBIN' GRASSHOPPERS - Games - Tyco Toys
GRABBIT - Games - Centsable Toys Inc.
GRABBIT - Games ☆ - Milton Bradley Co.
GRABBIT RABBIT - Infant product - Hugger Bugger Corp.
GRABBITS - Toys - Tonka Corp.
GRABB'R - Anchors - Barrett Manufacturing Co.
GRABELL - Lamps - H. Grabell & Sons
GRABER - Blinds–vertical - Vertical Blind Factory
GRABER - Drapery hardware - Endisco Supply Co.
GRABER - Drapery hardware ☆ - Spring Window Fashions Division, Inc.
GRABER - Food products - C.C. Graber Co.
GRABER & BALI - Window coverings - ESI
GRABER II - Blinds–vertical ☆ - Spring Window Fashions Division, Inc.
GRABER MINI-BLINDS - Blinds–venetian ☆ - Bamboo Abbott Florida Corp.
GRABER PLEATED SHADES - Window shades ☆ - Bamboo Abbott Florida Corp.
GRABER VERTICAL BLINDS - Blinds–venetian ☆ - Bamboo Abbott Florida Corp.
GRABERLITE - Blinds–vertical - Spring Window Fashions Division, Inc.
GRABFAB - Wall fabric for display ☆ - Brewster Corp.
GRABIT - Skin care products - J. Frey Enterprises Inc.
GRAC-EASE - Medical apparatus - Miltex Instrument Co., Inc.
GRACE - Apparel–children's - Grace Co.
GRACE - Audio equipment ☆ - Sumiko Inc.
GRACE - Bedding–linen - Dan River Inc.
GRACE - Combs ☆ - Fromm Industries
GRACE - Dishes–china - Pickard Inc.
GRACE - Frames–eyeglass - Rozin Optical Export Corp.
GRACE - Glass–leaded - Seneca Glass Co.
GRACE - Phonographic needles - GNP Audio Video Inc.
GRACE - Rings–jewelry - Artcarved Inc.
GRACE - Rulers–wood - W.R. Grace & Co.
GRACE - Tableware–china - Lenox, Inc.
GRACE - Teas - Grace Tea Co. Ltd.
GRACE - Watches - Bulova Corp.
GRACE A DICE PLAY 21 - Games - Felipe V. Velez
GRACE A. RUSH - Food products - Grace A. Rush Inc.
GRACE DAVISON - Chemical preparations - W.R. Grace & Co.
GRACE GRAPE - Dolls - Mattel, Inc.
GRACE NET - Computer software - W.R. Grace & Co.
GRACE RUSH - Bakery products - Mille Lacs M.P. Co., Inc.
GRACE RUSH - Chocolate candy - Scott's, Inc.
GRACE RUSH - Food products - Mille Lacs Maple Products Corp.
GRACE SPICE COMPANY - Spices and extracts - Gelov Enterprises, Inc.
GRACE-WAIST - Girdles - Latex Foundations Co. Inc.
GRACEFIELD - Floor coverings ☆ - Congoleum Corp.
GRACEFORM - Girdles - H.F. Robbins
GRACEFUL - Ophthalmic goods - Foremost Optical Products
GRACEFUL ARM - Garden equipment - Presto Galaxy Suction Cups Inc.
GRACEFUL DRAPE - Hair care products - Andre Fantasies Inc.
GRACEFUL LAMB - Toys–stuffed - Dakin Inc.
GRACEFUL SPENDOR - Floor coverings–carpet and rugs - Monticello Carpet Mills
GRACEFUL WAY - Floor coverings–carpet and rugs - Mohawk Carpet Corp.
GRACELAND - Floor coverings–carpet and rugs - Barrett Carpet Mills Inc.
GRACELAND - Recording label - Frontline Records

GRACELAND - Wines - Elvis Presley Enterprises Inc.
GRACELETTE - Girdles - Bonwit Teller & Co.
GRACELINE DESIGN INC. - Magnetic media - Graceline Design Inc.
GRACELINE DESIGN INCORPORATED - Magnetic tape–blank - Graceline Design Inc.
GRACIAS - Food products - Comstock Michigan Fruit
GRACIAS - Food products - Curtice-Burns Foods, Inc.
GRACIE - Frames–eyeglass ☆ - Vanity Optical Manufacturing Co. Inc.
GRACIE - Musical instrument accessories - Gracie Enterprises (Gracie Stands Div.)
GRACIE BEAR - Toys–stuffed - Russ Berrie and Co., Inc.
GRACIE SQUARE - Bicycles - Ross Bicycles USA, Ltd.
GRACIES - Apparel stores–lingerie - H.F. Robbins
GRACIE'S GRAND SAMPLER - Dog food - Three Dog Bakery, Inc.
GRACIE'S LOVE POTION - Teas–herbal - Susan K. Dunsmore
GRACILE - Corsets ☆ - Strouse, Adler Co.
GRACIOUS - Bedding–linen ☆ - Dan River Inc.
GRACIOUS - Ophthalmic goods ☆ - Luxottica
GRACIOUS DINING - Food products - Idle Wild Farm
GRACIOUS GREETINGS - Greeting cards - Gracious Greetings, Inc.
GRACIOUS LADY - Eyeglasses - Art-Craft Optical Co.
GRACIOUS LIFE - Floor coverings–carpet and rugs ☆ - Lees Carpets
GRACIOUS LIVING - Floor coverings–carpet and rugs - Queen Carpet Corp.
GRACIOUS LIVING - Floor coverings–carpet and rugs - Roxbury Carpet Co.
GRACIOUS LIVING - Steel ☆ - Regal Ware, Inc.
GRACIOUS LIVING - Wallpaper - Warner Co.
GRACIOUS TOUCH - Floor coverings–carpet and rugs - Milliken & Co. Inc.
GRACO - Maraschino cherries ☆ - Gray & Co.
GRACO - Paint sprayers - Graco Inc.
GRAD - Golfing equipment - Mizuno Corp. of America
GRAD - Paper - Mead Corp.
GRADCO - Publisher's imprints - Graphic Arts Development Co.
GRADE A - Ribbons–inked - Phillips Ribbon & Carbon Co.
GRADE A - Wet mops ☆ - American Textile Products Co.
GRADE LEVEL ART - Publisher's imprints - Johanna Hansen Whisman
GRADE LEVEL EVALUATION - Computer program - Tudor Publishing Co.
GRADE-O-MAT - Photographic equipment ☆ - Charles Beseler Co.
GRADE REPORTER - Computer software ☆ - Cross Educational Software Inc.
GRADEBOOK 2000 - Computer software - Electronic Gradebook, L.P.
GRADEBOOK DELUXE - Computer software ☆ - Edusoft
GRADEKEEPER - Computer software - Daniel Ethier
GRADEMASTER - Agricultural machinery - Odenberg Engineering Inc.
GRADEMASTER - Motor vehicles–construction - Badger Equipment Co.
GRADIANCE - Dinnerware–glass ☆ - Nikko Ceramics Inc.
GRADIENT - Bicycles - Klein Bicycle Corp.
GRADIENT - Computer software - Gradient Technologies Inc.
GRADIOSO - Cookies ☆ - Bahlsen Inc.
GRADIUS III - Video games - Nintendo of America Inc.
GRADO - Audio equipment - Grado Laboratories
GRADTRACKER - Computer software - Peterson's Guides, Inc.
GRADUAL GREY - Hair coloring preparations - Bristol-Myers Squibb Co.
GRADUATE - Brassieres (Bras) ☆ - Lovable Co.
GRADUATE - Eyeglasses - Martin-Copeland Eyewear Corp.
GRADUATE - Fathometers - Rule Industries, Inc.
GRADUATE - Floor coverings–carpet and rugs - Kelly Group Inc.
GRADUATE - Floor coverings–carpet and rugs ☆ - J and J Industries Inc.
GRADUATE - Footwear - Toddler University
GRADUATE - Furniture - Omni International Inc.
GRADUATE - Medical apparatus ☆ - Lossing Orthopedic Co.
GRADUATE - Sewing machines–household ☆ - Singer Co.
GRADUATE - Stationery - Springfield Tablet Co.
GRADUATE MANAGEMENT ADMISSION COUNCIL - Computer programs - Graduate Management Admission Council
GRADUATES - Cigars ☆ - National Cigar Corp.
GRADUATES, THE - Toys–stuffed - Fun World Inc.
GRADUATES VARIETY - Baby foods - Gerber Products Co.
GRADUATION - Dolls - Mattel, Inc.
GRADUATION - Recording label - Graduation Records Inc.
GRADY - Saddles - Thornhill Enterprises, Inc.
GRADY - Shoes ☆ - Allen-Edmonds Shoe Corp.
GRAF - Photographic equipment ☆ - R.T.S. Inc.
GRAF BARRIER - Coatings - Jay Bee Paint Co.
GRAF-SLIDE - Musical instrument accessories ☆ - Micro Musical Products Corp.
GRAF STIK - Sporting goods ☆ - Shakespeare Fishing Tackle
GRAFCO - Flooring–hardwood - Grafco Hardwood Floors Inc.

GRAFCO - Hair care products - Graham-Field Inc.
GRAFCO MULTI MATTRESS - Mattresses - Graham-Field Inc.
GRAFEETIES - Shoe accessories - Grafeeties Co. Internt'l Inc.
GRAFF FIRE - Sporting goods ☆ - Gold Eagle/Arnold Palmer
GRAFFIC TRAFFIC - Toys–automobiles - Matchbox Toys USA
GRAFFIT - Paper - Gamescience
GRAFFITEES - Golfing equipment - SPL International, Inc.
GRAFFITI - Apparel and accessories - Roba, Inc.
GRAFFITI - Apparel and accessories - World Trading Inc.
GRAFFITI - Artists' materials - Fredrix Artist Canvas Inc.
GRAFFITI - Cameras - Eastman Kodak Co.
GRAFFITI - Computer software - Palm Computing, Inc.
GRAFFITI - Frames–eyeglass ☆ - Universal/Univis Inc.
GRAFFITI - Letterpress plates - Tara Materials Inc.
GRAFFITI - Pens - Scripto-Tokai Corp.
GRAFFITI - Pet products - Century Craft Industries
GRAFFITI BAG - Artists' materials - Food For Thought Inc.
GRAFFITI BARRIER - Coatings - Seal-Krete Inc.
GRAFFITI BEACH - Apparel–men's - Graffiti Beach
GRAFFITI BLASTER - Cleaning preparations - Fred Smith Adhesives, Inc.
GRAFFITI BRIGADE REMOVER - Chemical remover - Genesis Coatings, Inc.
GRAFFITI FREE - Paint removers - Enviro-Northeast Sales Corp.
GRAFFITI GREETINGS - Greeting cards ☆ - Thought Factory
GRAFFITI GUARD - Housewares - Moisture Guard Systems
GRAFFITI MELT GENESIS COATINGS - Sealant - Genesis Coatings, Inc.
GRAFFITI NAILWRITER - Cosmetics - Chesebrough-Pond's USA Co.
GRAFFITI OFF - Graffiti remover - Construction Adhesives Co.
GRAFFITI-SHIELD - Paint removers - Decratrend Corp.
GRAFFITI SOLUTION SYSTEM - Paints - American Polymer Corp.
GRAFFITI SOUND - Sound equipment - Helix Electronics, Inc.
GRAFFITI TERMINATOR REMOVER - Cleaning preparations - Genesis Coatings, Inc.
GRAFFITI WIPE - Cleaning preparations - Fred Smith Adhesives, Inc.
GRAFFITO - Floor coverings–carpet and rugs ☆ - Mannington Carpets, Inc.
GRAFFITTI - Recording label - Johnny Angel Music Entertainment
GRAFFIX - Floor coverings - Congoleum Corp.
GRAFI - Athletic footwear - Contax Sports Inc.
GRAFIK EYE - Electric lighting equipment - Lutron Electronics Co., Inc.
GRAFIT - Goggles–safety ☆ - Sellstrom Manufacturing Co.
GRAFITE TECH - Bicycle accessories ☆ - Corso Bicycle Distributor Inc.
GRAFIX - Apparel and accessories - Signal Knitwear Co.
GRAFIX - Artists' materials - Grafix Plastics
GRAFIX - Laser recorder - Information International, Inc.
GRAFIX - Socks - Ben Berger LLC.
GRAFIX - Timepieces - Chrysalid Group, Inc.
GRAFIX SPORT - Apparel–children's ☆ - Bruxton Shirt Co.
GRAFIZE - Lubricants - Reardon Products
GRAFKETTE - Health care products ☆ - Graham-Field Inc.
GRAFLEX - Leather–glove - Bali Leathers, Inc.
GRAFLEX XL - Fishing tackle - South Bend Sporting Goods Inc.
GRAFLITE - Sporting goods - Shakespeare Fishing Tackle
GRAFOS - Metals - Mor L. Mayer
GRAFSMAN - Computer software - Soft-Tek International, Inc.
GRAFSONIC - Electronic equipment - Telex Communications, Inc.
GRAFTCYTE - Pharmaceutical preparations - Procyte Corp.
GRAFTEX - Tape–adhesive ☆ - Fiber Mark, Inc.
GRAFTLON - Cooking equipment–household - Birmingham Stove & Range Co.
GRAFTON VILLAGE CHEESE CO. - Cheese - Grafton Village Cheese Co., Inc.
GRAFTONITE - Musical instrument accessories - Rico International
GRAHAM - Audio equipment ☆ - Telequest Inc.
GRAHAM - Cotton–sterilized - Marianna Imports, Inc.
GRAHAM - Pumps–vacuum - Graham Corp.
GRAHAM - Wines ☆ - European Beverage Co., Inc.
GRAHAM & GUNN - Apparel–men's - Hartmarx Corp.
GRAHAM BITES - Crackers - Nabisco Foods Group
GRAHAM CHEX - Cereal - Ralston Purina Co.
GRAHAM CRACKER DELIGHT - Ice cream - Melanie Lane Farms, Inc.
GRAHAM CRACKER KIDS COLLECTION, THE - Invitations - Desktop Depot, Inc.
GRAHAM-FIELD - Bandages - Graham-Field Inc.
GRAHAM MAID - Crackers - Nabisco Foods Group
GRAHAM MANUFACTURING CO., INC. - Condensers - Graham Corp.
GRAHAM SELECTS - Crackers - Keebler Co.
GRAHAM SMITH AT KANGOL - Hats - Kangol Inc.

GRAHAMS - Crackers - Richmond Baking Co.
GRAHAMTASTIC - Crackers - Nabisco Holdings Corp.
GRAHAMY BEARS - Crackers ☆ - Sunshine Biscuits, Inc.
GRAHM CREW - Wines ☆ - Bonny Doon Winery Inc.
GRAIL - Books–comic - Aegis Entertainment, Inc.
GRAIN & SALT SOCIETY - Salt - Grain & Salt Society, Inc.
GRAIN BELT - Beverages–malt - The Stroh Brewery Co.
GRAIN BELT GOLDEN - Beverages–malt - Minnesota Brewing Co.
GRAIN BELT GOLDEN LIGHT - Beverages–malt - Minnesota Brewing Co.
GRAIN BELT PREMIUM - Beverages–malt - Minnesota Brewing Co.
GRAIN BELT PREMIUM LIGHT - Beverages–malt - Minnesota Brewing Co.
GRAIN-BIN, THE - Breads - Grain-Bin Bakers Ltd.
GRAIN DAMPER - Machinery - Baker Built Products Inc.
GRAIN KITCHEN, THE - Food products - The Grain Kitchen
GRAIN LAND - Cereal ☆ - Golden Temple Natural Foods Bakery
GRAIN MILLERS - Food products - Grain Millers, Inc.
GRAIN 'N STAIN - Varnishes ☆ - Old World Art
GRAIN O LAKES - Rice ☆ - Gourmet House Inc.
GRAIN-PERFECT - Pigments–paint - Chemical Coatings, Inc.
GRAIN PREP - Chemical preparations - Agrichem, Inc.
GRAIN PUMP - Grain conveyor - Hutchinson/Mayrath
GRAIN-RITE - Envelopes - Niagara Envelope Co., Inc.
GRAIN-TEX - Siding–metal ☆ - Aluminum Co. of America
GRAIN-TONE - Wood products ☆ - Anchor Sales Corp.
GRAIN-TRAK - Computer hardware - Micro-Trak Systems, Inc.
GRAINDANCE - Food products - Amberwave Foods
GRAINFIELDS - Cereal - Weetabix Co., Inc.
GRAINGER - Computer software - W.W. Grainger, Inc.
GRAINGERS - Snack foods ☆ - Borden, Inc.
GRAINOLA - Breads ☆ - Schmidt Baking Co., Inc.
GRAINS KEEPER - Golfing equipment - Applied Design Technology, Ltd.
GRAINS PLUS - Food products - GP Foods International, Inc.
GRAINSTAY - Cereal ☆ - Arrowhead Mills, Inc.
GRAINSTORM - Bakery products - Bagelmania Bakery, Inc.
GRAINSWORTH - Bakery products - Food For Life Baking Co.
GRAINWARE - Dinnerware–plastic - Grainware Co.
GRAINY GARLIC - Mustard ☆ - Cortina Corp.
GRAIT, THE - Restraints–patient - Heelbo Inc.
GRALE BOOSTERS - Publisher's imprints - Lowell House
GRAM DADDY - Food products - Southland Corp.
GRAM-MATCHED - Golfing equipment - William L. Cornelius
GRAM-O-LECI - Vitamins and nutritional supplements - Freeda Vitamins Inc.
GRAMARCY - Computer software - Robert L. Nicolai
GRAMAVISION - Recording label - Polygram Records, Inc.
GRAMAVISION - Recording label - Rykodisc Inc.
GRAMBY FARMS - Soups–mixes - Somerset Soup Works, Inc.
GRAMDA'S PATCHOULI - Soap - Grandpa Brands Co.
GRAMELLI - Shorts–men's - Go-Pro Ltd.
GRAMERCY - Hudson Optical Corp.
GRAMERCY - Accordions, guitars, amplifiers - Atlas Accordions Inc.
GRAMERCY - Artists' materials - Hilb Art & Drafting Inc.
GRAMERCY - Bedding–linen - Sufolla Industries Inc.
GRAMERCY - Floor coverings ☆ - Kentile Floors Inc.
GRAMERCY - Furniture ☆ - Lane Co. Inc.
GRAMERCY - Tableware–china ☆ - Lenox, Inc.
GRAMERCY - Wallpaper - FSC Wallcoverings
GRAMERCY PARK - Bicycles - Ross Bicycles USA, Ltd.
GRAMERCY PARK - Boxes - Carolina Manufacturing Inc.
GRAMERCY PARK - Dolls ☆ - Effanbee Doll Corp.
GRAMERCY PARK - Floor coverings–carpet and rugs - Atlas Carpet Mills Inc.
GRAMERCY PARK - Floor coverings–carpet and rugs ☆ - Walter Carpet Mills
GRAMERCY PARK - Wallpaper ☆ - Wolf-Gordon Inc.
GRAMINANTE - Fertilizers - Alquimia Laboratories, Inc.
GRAMMA ANNA'S - Snack foods - Orchard Crest Farms
GRAMMA REDMOND'S AUSSIE NATURAL - Hair care products - Redmond Products, Inc.
GRAMMAN - Boats–motor - Outboard Marine Corp.
GRAMMAR BASEBALL - Computer software - Gamco Industries Inc.
GRAMMAR EXAMINER, THE - Computer peripheral equipment - Compton's NewMedia
GRAMMAR GAMES - Computer software ☆ - Knowledge Adventure
GRAMMAR GIRL - Frames–eyeglass ☆ - Universal/Univis Inc.
GRAMMAR GREMLINS - Computer software ☆ - Knowledge Adventure
GRAMMAR MASTERY - Computer software - American Language Academy Inc.

☆ = Now out of production

GRAMMAR PATHS - Computer software ☆ - SRA/McGraw-Hill (Div. of The McGraw-Hill Companies)

GRAMMAR-RIGHT SYSTEM 1 - Typewriters - Smith Corona Corp.

GRAMMAR ROCK - Video tapes–blank - ABC Inc.

GRAMMAR SMART - Magazines - Princeton Review Publishing, LLC

GRAMMAR-WHAT BIG TEETH YOU HAVE - Computer software - Krell Software Corp.

GRAMMAR YOU MEANT TO LEARN - Educational materials - Better Communications, Inc.

GRAMMATIK - Computer software ☆ - Digital Marketing Corp.

GRAMMERCY SQUARE - Furniture - Universal Flooring

GRAMMY - Optical scanners–computer - Tart Optical

GRAMMY - Recording label - National Academy of Recording Arts & Sciences, Inc.

GRAMMY'S - Snack foods - Keystone Food Products

GRAMOPHONE -

GRAMOPHONE - Recording label - Gramophone Records Co. of the USA

GRAMPA'S DEER SUCKER - Hunting equipment - Grampa's Inc.

GRAMPIL SKI GLOVES - Gloves - Fabry Glove & Mitten Co.

GRAMPS TEEL - Banjos - Here Inc.

GRAMS - Computer software - Galactic Industries Corp.

GRAMS/32 - Computer software - Galactic Industries Corp.

GRAMS/386 - Computer software - Galactic Industries Corp.

GRAMWICH - Ice cream - Melanie Lane Farms, Inc.

GRAN - Gelato - Gran Gelato

GRAN 500 - Bicycles - Kent International Inc.

GRAN BATEAU - Boats–motor ☆ - Cruisers

GRAN BISCOTTI BOILED HAM - Hams - Crystal Food Import Corp.

GRAN CHAMPION - Tires - Bridgestone/Firestone, Inc.

GRAN CODORNIU - Wines - Codorniu USA Inc.

GRAN CONCOR - Bicycles - Kent International Inc.

GRAN CONDAL - Wines - Blair Importers Ltd.

GRAN CORNICHE - Furniture ☆ - Lane Co. Inc.

GRAN DUQUE D'ALBA - Brandy - Blair Importers Ltd.

GRAN EMYCO - Footwear–men's - Univshoe Inc.

GRAN EUROSPORT - Bicycles - Ross Bicycles USA, Ltd.

GRAN FLEX BY EMYCO - Footwear ☆ - Univshoe Inc.

GRAN FURY - Motor vehicles–automobiles ☆ - DaimlerChrysler

GRAN GUSTO SPANISH SHERRY - Vinegar - Europa Foods Ltd.

GRAN LOOP - Floor coverings–carpet and rugs - Alliance Industries Inc.

GRAN MARNIE'S - Money scoops - Marne A. Glass

GRAN-NOODLES - Snack foods - Everfresh Foods Corp.

GRAN PARADISO - Dishes–china - Viletta China Co.

GRAN PRIX - Bathroom fixtures ☆ - Crane Plumbing/Fiat Products

GRAN PRIX - Bicycles ☆ - Raleigh USA Bicycle Co.

GRAN PRIX - Glassware–household ☆ - Crisa Corp.

GRAN PRIX - Scooters ☆ - Italjet USA

GRAN PRIX - Toys–electronic - Gran Prix Electronics

GRAN ROYAL - Flatware - International Silver Co.

GRAN SPORT - Bicycles ☆ - Raleigh USA Bicycle Co.

GRAN SPORT - Boats - Wellcraft Marine Corp.

GRAN SPORT - Ships - Sutphen Marine Corp.

GRAN SPRINT - Bicycles - Kent International Inc.

GRAN STAND - Guitars ☆ - Music People Inc.

GRAN STAND, THE - Electronic equipment - Screen Works

GRAN TECH - Footwear–men's - Universal Shoe Inc.

GRAN TORINO - Liquors - House of Seagram

GRAN TORINO - Motor vehicles–automobiles ☆ - Ford Motor Co.

GRAN TORINO SQUIRE - Motor vehicles–automobiles ☆ - Ford Motor Co.

GRAN TORRES - Beverages–alcohol - Joseph E. Seagram & Sons, Inc.

GRAN TOUR - Bicycles - Ross Bicycles USA, Ltd.

GRAN TOUR - Shirts - Texfi Industries, Inc.

GRAN TOURIST - Bicycles - Ross Bicycles USA, Ltd.

GRAN TURISMO - Motor vehicles–automobiles ☆ - Alfa Romeo Distributors of North America

GRAN VAL - Wines ☆ - Clos du Val Wine Co. Ltd.

GRAN VELOUR - Floor coverings–carpet and rugs - Alliance Industries Inc.

GRANAAT - Floor coverings–carpet and rugs ☆ - Eurotex Inc.

GRANADA - Apparel–men's ☆ - Michaels/Stern & Co. Inc.

GRANADA - Audio equipment - Granada Electronics Corp.

GRANADA - Boats - Glen-L Marine Designs

GRANADA - Cigar boxes–wood ☆ - Consolidated Cigar Corp.

GRANADA - Fabrics - Uniroyal Engineered Products

GRANADA - Floor coverings - Congoleum Corp.

GRANADA - Floor coverings–carpet and rugs - Foreign Accents

GRANADA - Floor coverings–carpet and rugs ☆ - Eurotex Inc.

GRANADA - Food products - Kold Kist Brands Inc.

GRANADA - Frames–eyeglass ☆ - Universal/Univis Inc.

GRANADA - Furniture - Pavilion/Sunburst Furniture

GRANADA - Glassware–household ☆ - Lenox Crystal, Inc.

GRANADA - Guitars - J.M. Sahlein Music Co. Inc.

GRANADA - Liquors ☆ - SPAR Inc.

GRANADA - Mops ☆ - Helen Keller Services for the Blind

GRANADA - Motor vehicles–automobiles ☆ - Ford Motor Co.

GRANADA - Recording label - Creav Inc. USA

GRANADA - Rice - Producers Rice Mill, Inc.

GRANADA - Rings–jewelry - Artcarved Inc.

GRANADA - Ships–sailing vessels - Scandinavian Yachts

GRANADA - Tableware–china ☆ - Villeroy and Boch Tableware Ltd.

GRANADA - Thread - Threads USA Div.

GRANADA - Trailers–travel ☆ - Hop-Cap Inc.

GRANADA - Vegetables–canned - Gangi Bros. Packing Co.

GRANADA - Weather tracking equipment ☆ - Bausch & Lomb Inc.

GRANADA - Windows–storm - Duo-Temp

GRANADA FRESHNESS GUARANTEE - Meat products–beef - Granada Corp.

GRANADA REGATTA - Ships–sailing vessels - Scandinavian Yachts

GRANADO - Rum - House of Seagram

GRANAGE - Floor coverings–tile ☆ - Vida Mosaic Co. Inc.

GRANARY HARVEST - Bird feeds - Handley Corp.

GRANARY OAK - Flooring–hardwood - Mountain Lumber Co., Inc.

GRANAT - Jewelry - Zale Corp.

GRANATA - Wines - Wiederkehr Wine Cellars Inc.

GRANBURGER - Food products - Worthington Foods Inc.

GRANBY - Floor coverings ☆ - Tarkett, Inc.

GRANCELLI - Fruit drinks–bottled or canned - Natural Juice Manufacturing Co.

GRANCOURT - Footwear - K-Swiss Inc.

GRAND - Apparel and accessories - Fab. Industries Inc.

GRAND - Brushes–paint - Corona Brushes Inc.

GRAND - Computers - Grand Junction Networks, Inc.

GRAND - Food containers - Farmhouse Foods

GRAND - Fruits and vegetables - Orchard Foods

GRAND - Outdoor and casual furniture, wicker baskets, bathroom accessories, etc. - Grand Basket Co. Inc.

GRAND - Puzzles - Milton Bradley Co.

GRAND - Trumpets - N.H.F. Musical Merchandise Corp.

GRAND AFFAIR - Floor coverings–carpet and rugs - Mohawk Carpet Corp.

GRAND AIR - Motor vehicle parts and accessories - Cricket Camper Manufacturing Co.

GRAND AM - Motor vehicles–automobiles - General Motors Corp. (Pontiac/GMC Div.)

GRAND ARTIST - Banjos - OME Co. Inc.

GRAND ATRIUM - Mats - Matworks

GRAND AWARD - Cigars - E. Regensburg & Sons

GRAND AWARD - Cosmetics - Demert & Dougherty, Inc.

GRAND AWARD - Floor coverings–carpet and rugs ☆ - American Carpet Mills

GRAND AWARD - Greeting cards - Paper Magic Group Inc.

GRAND AWARD - Lenses–optical - Ditto Industries Inc.

GRAND AWARD, SLOAN - Greeting cards - Grand Award

GRAND AWARDS - Floor coverings–carpet and rugs - Roxbury Carpet Co.

GRAND BAHAMA - Furniture–wood ☆ - Flanders Industries Inc.

GRAND BAHAMAS - Floor coverings–carpet and rugs ☆ - Masland Corp.

GRAND BANKS OUTFITTERS - Apparel–men's - Harper Shirt Co.

GRAND BARRON - Floor coverings–carpet and rugs - Mohawk Carpet Corp.

GRAND BASKET, THE - Candy - Home of the Hebert Candies, Inc.

GRAND BAY - Seafood products–fresh or frozen - Gulf City Fisheries Inc.

GRAND BAYOU - Seafood products–fresh or frozen - Gorton Group

GRAND BEER - Glassware–household - Durand International

GRAND BERNARD - Beverages–alcohol ☆ - Stimson Lane Vineyards & Estates

GRAND BUCHE - Cheese - Swissrose International Inc.

GRAND CAMEMBERT - Cheese - Bongrain Cheese USA

GRAND CANYON - Campers - American Sterling Corp.

GRAND CANYON - Floor coverings–carpet and rugs ☆ - Southern Carpet Mills

GRAND CANYON - Furniture - Lane Upholstery (Venture Furniture Div.)

GRAND CANYON - Jams and jellies - Mountain Maid Gourmet Jelly

GRAND CANYON BEER - Beverages–alcohol - Grand Canyon Beer Brewing Co.

GRAND CANYON RAFTERS - Novelty items ☆ - Arizona Fall League, Inc.

GRAND CANYON RAILWAY - Glassware–household - Grand Canyon Railway Inc.

GRAND CARAVAN - Motor vehicles - Chrysler Corp. (Dodge Car Div.)

GRAND CARGO - Wallpaper - Charles Barone Inc.

GRAND CASINO GULFPORT MISSISSIPPI - Apparel and accessories - Grand Casinos Inc.

GRAND CAYMAN CHEESECAKE - Yogurt–frozen - Alta-Dena Certified Dairy, Inc.

GRAND CENTRAL BAKING COMPANY - Bakery products - Grand Central Bakery, Inc.

GRAND CHALET - Cabinets - Grandview Products Co.

GRAND CHAMP - Pet products - Montana Pet Foods

GRAND CHAMPAGNE - Glassware–household - Durand International

GRAND CHAMPION - Floor coverings–carpet and rugs - Evans-Black Carpet Mills

GRAND CHAMPION - Hair care products - Conair Corp.

GRAND CHAMPION - Pet products - B & T National Distributors Inc.

GRAND CHAMPION - Pet products - Farnam Cos. Inc.

GRAND CHAMPION - Video games - Taito America Corp.

GRAND CHAMPION RANCH PRODUCTS - Agricultural products - Grand Champion Ranch Products, Inc.

GRAND CHATEAU - Glassware–household - Durand International

LE GRAND CHENEAU - Wines - Sunbelt Beverage Corp.

GRAND CHEROKEE - Motor vehicles–jeeps - DaimlerChrysler

GRAND CLASSIC - Floor coverings–carpet and rugs - Mohawk Carpet Corp.

GRAND CLASSICS - Beverages–carbonated - Grand Union Co.

GRAND COLLECTION - Food products - Weight Watchers International, Inc.

GRAND COLONIAL - Flatware - Wallace International Silversmiths, Inc.

GRAND CONCERT - Musical instrument accessories - Rico International

GRAND CONTURA - Furniture ✪ - Cosco, Inc.

GRAND CORNICHE - Wallpaper ✪ - Wallquest, Inc.

GRAND COUNTRY - Footwear–athletic - Grand Imports, Inc.

GRAND COURT - Floor coverings - Mannington Resilient Floors

GRAND CREATION - Floor coverings–carpet and rugs ✪ - World Carpets, Inc.

GRAND CREST - Fruits and vegetables - Orchard Foods

GRAND CROSSING PRODUCTS OF DISTINCTION - Furniture - Catherine A. Lunenschloss

GRAND CRU - Beverages–malt - Grand Cru

GRAND CRU - Cigars - Villazon and Co.

GRAND CRU - Glassware–household ✪ - Lancaster Colony Corp.

GRAND CRU - Wines ✪ - House of Burgundy Inc.

GRAND CRU CHABLIS - Wines ✪ - Kobrand Corp.

GRAND CRU GEWURZTRAMINER BRAND & RIESLING SCHOENENBURG - Wines ✪ - Kobrand Corp.

GRAND CRU VINEYARDS - Wines - Bronco Wine Co.

GRAND CRU VINEYARDS - Wines - Grand Cru Vineyards

GRAND CUISINE - Mats - Matworks

GRAND CUSTOM - Seat covers - Grand Auto Inc.

GRAND DEBUT - Floor coverings–carpet and rugs - Monticello Carpet Mills

GRAND DELIGHTS - Ice cream - Dreyer's Grand Ice Cream, Inc.

GRAND DESIGN - Floor coverings–carpet and rugs ✪ - Richmond Carpet Mills

GRAND DESIGNER - Hair care products ✪ - Designer's Edge International

GRAND DIPLOMAT - Floor coverings–carpet and rugs - Milliken & Co. Inc.

GRAND DOOR - Doors–metal - Albany International Corp.

GRAND DUC - Wines ✪ - Weibel Vineyards

GRAND DUCHESS - Christmas tree ornaments - Cracker Box Inc.

GRAND DUKE - Christmas tree ornaments - Cracker Box Inc.

GRAND DUKE - Mattresses - Mattress Discounters Corp.

GRAND DUKE - Pipes–tobacco - Dr. Grabow Pre-Smoked Pipes Inc.

GRAND DUO - Cosmetics - Monteil Paris

GRAND ELEGANCE - Wallpaper - Pantasote Inc. (Wallcovering Div.)

GRAND ELEGENCE - Wallpaper - Pantasote Inc. (Wallcovering Div.)

GRAND EMBRACE - Pillows - Pacific Coast Feather Co.

GRAND ENTRANCE - Brassieres (Bras) - Lovable Co.

GRAND ENTRANCE - Floor coverings–carpet and rugs - LaVelle Textile Marketing Inc.

GRAND ENTRY - Floor coverings–carpet and rugs ✪ - Karastan-Bigelow Inc.

GRAND EVENT - Floor coverings–carpet and rugs - Columbus Mills, Inc.

GRAND EXEC - Pens - Accutec Inc.

GRAND EXPLORER - Seats–automobile - Cosco, Inc.

GRAND EXPRESSIONS - Wallpaper ✪ - Wallquest, Inc.

GRAND FINAL - Floor coverings–carpet and rugs - Whitecrest Carpet Mills

GRAND FINALE - Candy - Grand Finale Confections

GRAND FINALE - Hair care products - Faberge Co.

GRAND FINALE PLAISIRS - Candy ✪ - Grand Finale Confections

GRAND FLAGSHIP - Motor vehicles–automobiles - Chicago Armor & Limousine Manufacturingcorporation

GRAND FLEURI-VAN GOGH - Perfumes - Alfin Fragrances Inc.

GRAND FLEURON - Wines ✪ - Pellegrini Bros. Wines Inc.

GRAND FLORAL - Floor coverings–carpet and rugs - Trans-Ocean Import Co. Inc.

GRAND FUNK RAILROAD - Recording label - Grand Funk Railroad Co.

GRAND GOURMET - Dog food - Nestle USA

GRAND GOURMET - Knives–carving - Meijer, Inc.

GRAND HALL - Furniture ✪ - Bassett Furniture Industries, Inc.

GRAND HAVEN - Furniture–wood - Flexsteel Industries Inc.

GRAND HOTEL - Floor coverings–carpet and rugs ✪ - Royalweve Carpet Mills

GRAND HOTEL - Ice cream - Grand Hotel Co.

GRAND HUNTER - Boots - Hunter Footwear, Inc.

GRAND ILLUSION - Floor coverings–carpet and rugs ✪ - Cabin Crafts Carpets

GRAND ILLUSION - Jewelry - Marvella Inc.

GRAND ILLUSION - Underwear and nightwear - Maidenform Inc.

GRAND ILLUSION - Wallpaper ✪ - Winfield Design Associates, Inc.

GRAND IMPERIAL EAGLE - Sporting goods ✪ - Wright & McGill Co.

GRAND IMPRESSIONS - Floor coverings–carpet and rugs - Lees Carpets

GRAND IMPRESSIONS - Furniture - Broyhill Furniture Industries, Inc.

GRAND IMPRESSIONS - Wallpaper - Piedmont Collections

GRAND INTEGRA - Stereos ✪ - Onkyo USA Corp.

GRAND ISLAND - Rum ✪ - Paramount Distillers Inc.

GRAND ISLE - Floor coverings–carpet and rugs - Criterion Mills Inc.

GRAND ISLE - Garden furniture–metal - Lloyd/Flanders Industries

GRAND ISLE - Sinks–porcelain - Mansfield Plumbing Products, Inc.

GRAND ISLE COLLECTION - Furniture - Cardinal American Corp.

GRAND JEAN CO. - Apparel and accessories - Sights Denim Systems, Inc.

GRAND JUNCTION - Computers, computer hardware and Computer software - Grand Junction Networks, Inc.

GRAND JUNCTION - Jackets - Paul Davril Inc.

GRAND JUNCTION NETWORKS - Computers - Grand Junction Networks, Inc.

GRAND KNITTING - Crocheted and knitted items - Grand Knitting Mills, Inc.

GRAND KOLINSKI - Nail care products - Opi Products, Inc.

GRAND LADY - Hosiery - Rice Hosiery Corp.

GRAND LE MANS - Motor vehicles–automobiles ✪ - General Motors Corp. (Pontiac/GMC Div.)

GRAND LEGACY - Furniture - American Drew

GRAND LIFE SEITAN - Food products - Sweet Earth Natural Foods

GRAND LODGE - Motor vehicles–motor homes ✪ - Avco Aerostructures Inc.

GRAND LODGE F. & A.M. OF FLORIDA - Jewelry - Most Worshipful Grand Lodge of Free And Accepted Masons of Florida

GRAND LUSTER - Christmas tree ornaments - Union Wadding Co.

GRAND LUXURY - Floor coverings–carpet and rugs - Mohawk Carpet Corp.

GRAND LUXUS - Bicycles - Murray, Inc.

GRAND LYON - Catsup - Marketing Ventures of America, Inc.

GRAND MACNISH - Whiskey - Jas. Barclay & Co. Ltd.

GRAND MANNER - Towels - Fieldcrest Cannon, Inc.

GRAND MANOR - Fans–electric - Montgomery Ward & Co. Inc.

GRAND MANOR - Floor coverings–carpet and rugs ✪ - Galaxy Carpet Mills Inc.

GRAND MANOR - Floor coverings–carpet and rugs ✪ - World Carpets, Inc.

GRAND MANOR - Furniture–upholstered - Grand Manor Furniture, Inc.

GRAND MANOR - Shingles–asphalt or tar - Certainteed Corp. (Roofing Products Group)

GRAND MARNIER - Food products ✪ - Cuisine Perel Corp.

GRAND MARNIER PECANS - Food products - Mrs. Powell's Gourmet Pecans

GRAND MARQUE - Pens - Accutec Inc.

GRAND MARQUIS - Motor vehicles–automobiles - Ford Motor Co. (Lincoln-Mercury Div.)

GRAND MARQUIS - Motor vehicles–motor homes - Beaver Coaches Inc.

GRAND MARSHALL - Labels–paper - King Walk Inc.

GRAND MASTER - Dietary food, vitamin, and mineral supplements - Nutrition for Life International, Inc.

GRAND MASTER - Electronics equipment - Ampex Corp.

GRAND MASTER - Floor coverings–carpet and rugs - Lees Carpets

GRAND MASTER - Games - Brown and Bigelow Inc.

GRAND MASTER - Leather–chamois - Acme Sponge & Chamois Co., Inc.

GRAND MASTERS - Floor coverings–carpet and rugs ✪ - Royalweve Carpet Mills

GRAND MASTERS - Lamps - Meyda Tiffany Inc.

GRAND MASTERS - Neckties - Allyn St. George International, Inc.

✪ = Now out of production

GRAND MAW BEAR - Toys–stuffed ✮ - Dakin Inc.
GRAND MEADOW - Margarine - Moran Foods, Inc.
GRAND MEISTER - Meat products–beef - Schweigert Foods
GRAND-MERE - Dolls ✮ - Effanbee Doll Corp.
GRAND MERIDIEN - Glassware–household - Durand International
GRAND MILIEU - Wallpaper - Greeff Fabrics Inc.
GRAND MOGUL - Banjos - OME Co. Inc.
GRAND MONDE - Floor coverings–carpet and rugs - Dan River Inc.
GRAND NADOR - Liquors ✮ - European Beverage Co., Inc.
GRAND NATIONAL - Fencing–chain link - Common Sense Fence
GRAND NATIONAL - Tires ✮ - Bridgestone/Firestone, Inc.
GRAND NATIONAL - Toys ✮ - ERTL Co., Inc.
GRAND NICA - Cigars - Central America Tobacco Corp.
GRAND NOBLESSE - Glassware–household - Durand International
GRAND NOBLESSE - Watches - Madison Sales Corp.
GRAND OCCASIONS - Hosiery - Aire Hosiery Inc.
GRAND 'OL FLAG SHIRT COMPANY, THE - Shirts - Warnaco Inc.
GRAND OLD CHESS - Food products - Antique Mall & Crown
GRAND OLD PARR - Whiskey - Peartree Imports Inc.
GRAND OLD PARTY - Novelty items - Republican National Committee
GRAND OPENING - Boxes - Climax Manufacturing Co. Inc.
GRAND OPENING - Corkscrews ✮ - Franmara Co. Inc.
GRAND OPENING - Floor coverings–carpet and rugs - Mohawk Carpet Corp.
GRAND OPENING II - Wallpaper - Dunridge Industries Inc.
GRAND OPENINGS - Greeting cards - Sunrise Publications, Inc.
GRAND OPULENCE - Floor coverings–carpet and rugs - Downs Carpet Co. Inc.
GRAND-PAK - Fruits and vegetables - Grand View Heights Citrus Association
GRAND PALACE - Floor coverings - Mannington Resilient Floors
GRAND PAN - Pizzas–mixes - Pizza Hut Inc.
GRAND PANAX - Wines - Holmbru, Ltd.
GRAND PARQUET - Floor coverings–carpet and rugs - Roxbury Carpet Co.
GRAND PASSAGE - Wood products - Georgia-Pacific Corp.
GRAND PAW BEAR - Toys–stuffed ✮ - Dakin Inc.
GRAND PEAK - Bicycles ✮ - Huffy Corp.
GRAND PECAN BALL - Ice cream - Grand Hotel Co.
GRAND PERFORMANCE - Floor coverings–carpet and rugs - Lees Carpets
GRAND PERFORMANCE - Floor coverings–carpet and rugs ✮ - Downs Carpet Co. Inc.
GRAND PLAZA - Luggage - Amway Corp.
GRAND POP ICE STICKS - Candy - Leonhardt Inc.
GRAND PORTAGE CLOTHING - Apparel and accessories - Marvin Smith & Son Inc.
GRAND PRAIRIE - Bicycles ✮ - Huffy Corp.
GRAND PREMIER - Mattresses - Colgate Mattress Co.
GRAND PREMIO - Cigars - General Cigar Co., Inc.
GRAND PREMIUM - Nuts–salted, roasted, cooked, or canned - Grand Union Co.
GRAND PRESHRUNKS - Mops - Piedmont Mop Co.
GRAND PRIX - Audio equipment ✮ - Telequest Inc.
GRAND PRIX - Beverages–malt ✮ - Labatt Importers Inc.
GRAND PRIX - Bottle openers - Crossbow Inc.
GRAND PRIX - Brandy - M.S. Walker Inc./Seacoast
GRAND PRIX - Cigars - General Cigar Co., Inc.
GRAND PRIX - Cocoa–powders or mixes - Givaudan Rare Flavors
GRAND PRIX - Computer software - Activision, Inc.
GRAND PRIX - Electronic equipment - GAF Corp.
GRAND PRIX - Food products ✮ - VIP Sales Co. Inc.
GRAND PRIX - Fruits and vegetables - Stanley Orchards Sales Inc.
GRAND PRIX - Games - S. Alden Inc.
GRAND PRIX - Giftware - Accutec Inc.
GRAND PRIX - Guitars - Tamarkin Co.
GRAND PRIX - Jewelry - Kaspar & Esh Inc.
GRAND PRIX - Melamine product - Boonton Molding Co. Inc.
GRAND PRIX - Motor vehicles–automobiles - General Motors Corp. (Pontiac/GMC Div.)
GRAND PRIX - Oils–lubricating - Castrol, Inc.
GRAND PRIX - Pens - National Pen & Pencil Co.
GRAND PRIX - Pipes–tobacco - Bradbery Briar Pipe Corp.
GRAND PRIX - Play map - Integra Toys, Inc.
GRAND PRIX - Ribbons - Berwick Industries, Inc.
GRAND PRIX - Sunglasses - Leisure Time Products, Inc.
GRAND PRIX - Tiles–ceramic - Porcelanite, Inc.
GRAND PRIX - Tires - TBC Corp.
GRAND PRIX - Toys - Tyco Toys
GRAND PRIX - Underwear and nightwear - Youthcraft-Charmfit

GRAND PRIX JUMPERS - Candy - Harbor Sweets Inc.
GRAND PRIX PIZZA - Food products - Grand Prix Pizza
GRAND PRIZE - Game machines - Sigma Game Inc.
GRAND PRIZE - Hair care products - Helene Curtis Industries Inc.
GRAND PRIZE - Recording label - Soundwaves Records
GRAND PRO - Boats–motor - Glastex Co.
GRAND PROCESSIONAL - Floor coverings–carpet and rugs ✮ - World Carpets, Inc.
GRAND PROMINADE - Floor coverings–carpet and rugs ✮ - Cabin Crafts Carpets
GRAND RAID - Boats - Zodiac of North America
GRAND RAPIDS - Hardware - Blaine Window Hardware Inc.
GRAND RAPIDS - Musical instruments ✮ - Barclay Music
GRAND RAPIDS - Vacuum cleaners and accessories ✮ - Bissell Inc.
GRAND RAPIDS GRIFFINS - Apparel and accessories - West Michigan Hockey, Inc.
GRAND RAPIDS HOOPS - Advertising posters - Grand Rapids Hoops, Ltd.
GRAND RAPIDS INTERNATIONAL PUBLICATIONS - Publisher's imprints ✮ - Kregel Publications & Bookstores
GRAND REGENCY - Furniture ✮ - Stanley Furniture Co. Inc.
GRAND RENNAISANCE - Banjos - OME Co. Inc.
GRAND REVEIL - Alarm watches - Jaeger-Le Coultre SA
GRAND RIVER BOOKS - Publisher's imprints - Omnigraphics Inc.
GRAND RIVER VINEYARD - Wines - Grand River Wine Co.
GRAND ROSSO - Tomato pastes and sauces - P & L Imports, Inc.
GRAND ROYAL - Video production - Grand Royal Records, Inc.
GRAND ROYAL VELVET - Floor coverings–carpet and rugs - Calladium & Marglen
GRAND SALAMI - Food products - Heid Meat Service & Catering Ltd.
GRAND SATIN - Frames–picture - Framemica Co.
GRAND/SECURITY - Chains - Grand Auto Inc.
GRAND SEQUOIA - Shingles - Building Materials Corp. of America
GRAND SIECBE - Floor coverings - Parquet de France Inc.
GRAND SINHUE - Fabrics ✮ - Charter Fabrics Inc.
GRAND SLAM - Ammunition - Blount International, Inc. (Sporting Equipment Group)
GRAND SLAM - Apparel–men's - Munsingwear, Inc.
GRAND SLAM - Candy bars - Hershey Chocolate USA
GRAND SLAM - Cleaning preparations - Vibe Records Inc.
GRAND SLAM - Coffee - Thanksgiving Coffee Co.
GRAND SLAM - Fishing tackle - Hi-Seas Industries, Inc.
GRAND SLAM - Floor coverings–carpet and rugs ✮ - Len Dal Carpets
GRAND SLAM - Floor waxes - S.C. Johnson & Son, Inc.
GRAND SLAM - Food products - Denny's Inc.
GRAND SLAM - Food products ✮ - Pierre Frozen Foods Inc.
GRAND SLAM - Golfing equipment - Hillerich & Bradsby Co.
GRAND SLAM - Pizzas–frozen ✮ - Mr. Z's Fund Raising Corp.
GRAND SLAM - Sandwiches–prepackaged - Gourmet Programs Inc.
GRAND SLAM - Trading card kits - ANCO Collector Supplies, Inc.
GRAND SLAM BASEBALL - Computer software - Cosmi Corp.
GRAND SLAM BRIDGE - Computer software - Electronic Arts Inc.
GRAND SLAM GOLF - Apparel and accessories - Munsingwear, Inc.
GRAND SLAM POKER - Game tables - Essex Holdings, Ltd.
GRAND SLAM TOUR - Apparel–men's - Munsingwear, Inc.
GRAND SLAMM - Loudspeakers - Wilson Audio Specialties, Inc.
GRAND SLAMM - Recording label - I.R.S. Records
GRAND SLAMMER - Candy - Pennsylvania Dutch Candies
GRAND-SLAMMER I - Amplifiers ✮ - CSI/Speco
GRAND-SLAMMER II - Amplifiers ✮ - CSI/Speco
GRAND SOIR - Fabrics ✮ - Charter Fabrics Inc.
GRAND SPIRIT - Tires - TBC Corp.
GRAND SPORT - Bicycles - Columbia Manufacturing Inc.
GRAND SPORT - Motor vehicles–automobiles ✮ - General Motors Corp. (Buick Motor Div.)
GRAND SPORT - Seat covers - Saddleman, Inc.
GRAND SPORT - Tires–motorcycle - Sport Tracks Co.
GRAND SPORT CLASSIC - Bicycles - Columbia Manufacturing Inc.
GRAND SPORT PREMIER - Bicycles - Columbia Manufacturing Inc.
GRAND STAND - Office supplies - Rubbermaid Commercial Products Inc.
GRAND STAND, THE - Music stands - Hal Leonard Corp.
GRAND STANDS, THE - Collectible trading cards - ANCO Collector Supplies, Inc.
GRAND STATEMENT - Floor coverings–carpet and rugs ✮ - Karastan-Bigelow Inc.
GRAND STICK - Musical instruments - Stick Enterprises, Inc.
GRAND SUMMIT - Awnings - E-Z Sales & Manufacturing, Inc.

✮ = Now out of production

GRAND SUZETTE - Beverages–alcohol - Consolidated Distilled Products Inc.
GRAND TANS - Puzzles - Kadon Enterprises Inc.
GRAND TARGHEE - Apparel and accessories - Takson Down Manufacturing Inc.
GRAND TERRACE - Wallcovering ☆ - Fashon Wallcoverings
GRAND TETON - Blankets - Pendleton
GRAND TETON - Campers - American Sterling Corp.
GRAND TETON - Cheese - Nelson-Ricks Creamery Co.
GRAND TETON ALPINE WATER - Water–bottled or canned - H20h!, LLC
GRAND TETONS - Floor coverings–carpet and rugs ☆ - Royalweve Carpet Mills
GRAND THEATRE - Wines - World Wide Wine and Spirits Inc.
GRAND TIER - Christmas tree ornaments - Cracker Box Inc.
GRAND TIER - Tableware–china - Lenox, Inc.
GRAND TIERRA - Ceramic wall tile - Interceramic Inc.
GRAND TITANIUM - Golfing equipment - Golfsmith International Inc.
GRAND TOAST - Cheese - Swissrose International Inc.
GRAND TOUCH - Floor coverings–carpet and rugs ☆ - Gulistan Carpet Inc.
GRAND TOUR - Furniture - CTH/Sherrill Occasional
GRAND TOUR - Furniture ☆ - Hammary Furniture Co. Inc.
GRAND TOUR - House furnishings - Lexington Furniture Industries, Inc.
GRAND TOUR - Luggage - Airway Industries, Inc.
GRAND TOUR - Medical apparatus - Guardian Products Inc.
GRAND TOUR - Wallcovering - Gilford Co.
GRAND TOUR - Wallpaper - Seabrook Wallcoverings, Inc.
GRAND TOUR COLLECTION - Giftware - Waterford Wedgewood USA, Inc.
GRAND TOURING - Bicycles - Columbia Manufacturing Inc.
GRAND TOURISM - Boats ☆ - Zodiac of North America
GRAND TOWER OF TREATS - Food products - Harry and David Inc.
GRAND TRADITION - Cutlery ☆ - Lifetime Hoan Corp.
GRAND TRADITION - Floor coverings–carpet and rugs - Calladium & Marglen
GRAND TRADITION - Floor coverings–carpet and rugs - Galaxy Carpet Mills Inc.
GRAND TRADITION - Floor coverings–carpet and rugs ☆ - Lees Carpets
GRAND TRADITION - Mattresses - Richards Quality Bedding
GRAND TRADITIONS - Furniture ☆ - Stanley Furniture Co. Inc.
GRAND TRADITIONS - Wallpaper - Fine Art Wallcoverings Ltd.
GRAND TRAVERSE - Fruits–canned - Cherry Central Cooperative Inc.
GRAND TRAVERSE VINEYARDS - Wines - Chateau Grand Traverse Ltd.
GRAND UNION - Food products - Grand Union Co.
GRAND UNION - Seafood products–fresh or frozen ☆ - Singleton Seafood Co.
GRAND UNION USDA CHOICE A CUT ABOVE - Meat products–beef - Grand Union Co.
GRAND VENETIAN - Flatware ☆ - Wallace International Silversmiths, Inc.
GRAND VICTORIAN - Flatware - Wallace International Silversmiths, Inc.
GRAND VIEW - Windows - Georgia-Pacific Corp.
GRAND VILLA - Recreational vehicle dealers - Foretravel Inc.
GRAND VILLE - Motor vehicles–automobiles ☆ - General Motors Corp. (Pontiac/GMC Div.)
GRAND VIN - Glassware–household - Durand International
GRAND VISION - Computer software - Dobbs-Stanford Corp.
GRAND VOYAGER - Motor vehicles - Chrysler Corp. (Chrysler-Plymouth Div.)
GRAND WAGONEER - Motor vehicles–jeeps ☆ - DaimlerChrysler
GRANDADDY'S - Snack foods - Wyandot, Inc.
GRANDAGON - Photographic equipment - H.P. Marketing Corp.
GRANDBEAM - Roofing materials - Gentek Building Products, Inc.
GRANDBEAM THE NEXT GENERATION - Roofing materials - Gentek Building Products, Inc.
GRANDCO - Sandals - Grand Overseas Inc.
GRANDE - Sasaki
GRANDE - Bakery products - Awrey Bakeries, Inc.
GRANDE - Beverages–carbonated - Florida Brewing Co.
GRANDE - Boats–motor - Century Boat Co.
GRANDE - Cheese - Grande Cheese Co.
GRANDE - Floor coverings–carpet and rugs ☆ - Regal Rugs Inc.
GRANDE - Glassware–household - Owens-Illinois Inc. (Libbey Div.)
GRANDE - Luggage - Universal Trav-ler Inc.
GRANDE - Tires - Bridgestone/Firestone, Inc.
GRANDE - Wallpaper - Koroseal Wallcoverings
GRANDE - Wines - Honeywood Winery
GRANDE 70 - Tires ☆ - Bridgestone/Firestone, Inc.
GRANDE AFFAIR - Floor coverings–carpet and rugs - Masterpiece Finishing Co.
GRANDE ARTISTE-NOBLET - Clarinets - G. Leblanc Corp.
GRANDE BAROQUE - Dinnerware - Wallace International Silversmiths, Inc.
GRANDE BEAD - Handbags ☆ - Lumured Corp.

GRANDE BRAND CHEDDAR - Cheese - Grande Cheese Co.
GRANDE BRAND CHEDDAR BLEND - Cheese - Grande Cheese Co.
GRANDE BRAND PROVOLONE BOCCINI STYLE - Cheese - Grande Cheese Co.
GRANDE BRAND PROVOLONE PROVOLETTINE STYLE - Cheese - Grande Cheese Co.
GRANDE BRAND PROVOLONE SALAMINI STYLE - Cheese - Grande Cheese Co.
GRANDE BUFFET - Serving carts ☆ - National Housewares
GRANDE BY DINGO - Footwear - Acme Boot Co., Inc.
GRANDE CANTINA - Wines - Laird and Co.
GRANDE CARDINALE - Wines - Leonard Kreusch Inc.
GRANDE CHANDELLE - Candles - Colonial Candle of Cape Cod
GRANDE CLASSICS - Food products - Norpac Services, Inc.
GRANDE CLASSIQUE - Window coverings - Del Mar Window Coverings
GRANDE CLASSIQUE - Window frames - Home Entertainment & Decor Systems Inc.
GRANDE CORNICHE - Wallcoverings - Worldwalls International Inc.
GRANDE CRANBERRY - Wines - Honeywood Winery
GRANDE CUISINE - Food products - Idle Wild Farm
GRANDE CUISINE - Housewares - Williams-Sonoma, Inc.
GRANDE CUSTOM INGREDIENTS GROUP - Lactose - Grande Cheese Co.
GRANDE DAME - Fabrics - Gretchen Bellinger Inc.
GRANDE DEUR - Chocolate candy - Grand Deur Chocolates, Inc.
GRANDE DINNERS - Food products ☆ - Anheuser-Busch Companies Inc.
GRANDE EPOQUE NAPOLEON III - Brandy - Shaw-Ross International Importers
GRANDE EXPRESS - Seats–automobile - Wise Co., Inc.
GRANDE GOURMET - Meat products–poultry - Hester Industries, Inc.
GRANDE ITALIA - Coffee - Inter-Continental Imports
GRANDE MANIA - Lamps–wall - Light Inc.
GRANDE MARQUE - Skin care products ☆ - Hirsch Speidel Inc.
GRANDE PEACH - Wines - Honeywood Winery
GRANDE RASPBERRY - Wines - Honeywood Winery
GRANDE RENNAISANCE - Silverware - Reed and Barton Corp.
GRANDE REVERENCE - Coffee - Executive Coffee Service Co.
GRANDE SOURCE - Beverages - Vittel Imports USA Inc.
GRANDE SPORT - Seat covers - Alco Manufacturing Co. Inc.
GRANDE VELVET - Floor coverings–carpet and rugs ☆ - Royalweve Carpet Mills
GRANDE VOX - Accordions - Colombo & Sons Accordion Co.
GRANDE XL - Boats–motor - Century Boat Co.
GRANDEAIR - Pharmaceutical preparations - Pulsair Inc.
GRANDEAU - Floor coverings–carpet and rugs ☆ - World Carpets, Inc.
GRANDECKER - Boats–fishing - Anchor Industries Inc.
GRANDEE - Cabinets - Del Mar Cabinets
GRANDEE - Cigars ☆ - General Cigar Co., Inc.
GRANDEE - Olives–canned - Vlasic Foods Inc.
GRANDEE - Paper - Strathmore Paper Co.
GRANDEE - Rings–jewelry - Artcarved Inc.
GRANDELLE - Candles ☆ - Colonial Candle of Cape Cod
GRANDES DAMES - Dolls ☆ - Effanbee Doll Corp.
GRANDEST FLEET, THE - Video games - Quantum Quality Productions, Inc.
GRANDEUR - Cutlery ☆ - National Housewares
GRANDEUR - Dishes–china ☆ - Pickard Inc.
GRANDEUR - Floor coverings - Congoleum Corp.
GRANDEUR - Floor coverings–carpet and rugs - Calladium & Marglen
GRANDEUR - Furniture ☆ - Bassett Furniture Industries, Inc.
GRANDEUR - Glass–leaded - Seneca Glass Co.
GRANDEUR - Glassware–household - Lenox, Inc.
GRANDEUR - Jewelry - Jacoby-Bender Inc.
GRANDEUR - Mats - Majestic Mat Co.
GRANDEUR - Rings–jewelry - Artcarved Inc.
GRANDEUR NOEL - Ornamental products–glass - Wal-Mart Stores Inc.
GRANDFIELD LANDMARK - Siding–metal - Armor Bond Building Products, Inc.
GRANDFIELD TRADITION - Siding–metal - Armor Bond Building Products, Inc.
GRANDI GROOM - Housewares - Groom Industries, Inc.
GRANDI VOCI - Recording label - Random House, Inc.
GRANDIAL - Wines ☆ - Alimar & Cie. Inc.
GRANDIN HILL - Cabinets - Nutone Inc.
GRANDIN SPARKLING WINES - Wines - Marie Brizard Wines & Spirits, USA
GRANDIOSE - Floor coverings–carpet and rugs - Philadelphia Carpets
GRANDIOSO - Cigars - G.A. Georgopulo & Co. Inc.
GRANDITOS - Snack foods - Grande Foods, Inc.

☆ = Now out of production

GRANDKID - Pillows - Pacific Coast Feather Co.

GRANDMA - Greeting cards ☆ - Evergreen Press

GRANDMA BINKS - Candy ☆ - R.M. Palmer Co.

GRANDMA BROWN'S - Food products - Grandma Brown's Beans Inc.

GRANDMA BRYAN - Salads–prepackaged ☆ - Supreme Foods Inc.

GRANDMA EMILIES - Breads - Grandma Emilie Brown, Inc.

GRANDMA GEBHARD - Food products - Grandma Gebhard

GRANDMA GIBBLE'S OLD FASHIONED HOME STYLE - Popcorn - Consolidated Snacks, Inc.

GRANDMA GOLDE - Cookies - Hills of Westchester Inc.

GRANDMA GOODWINS - Potato chips - Granny Goose Foods, Inc.

GRANDMA HEART - Dolls - Mattel, Inc.

GRANDMA IN ALL LANGUAGES - Jewelry - Avon Products, Inc.

GRANDMA K'S - Hams - Kowalski Sausage Co. Inc.

GRANDMA LOUELLA'S - Barbecue sauce - Gina Cawthern

GRANDMA MOSES - Giftware ☆ - Bernard W. Bernthal Inc.

GRANDMA PFEIFFERS - Cakes ☆ - Goebel of North America

GRANDMA ROSA'S - Skin care products - Mazzarella Direct Marketing Inc.

GRANDMA ROSIE'S - Food products ☆ - Ruiz Food Products Inc.

GRANDMA SHEARER'S - Food products - Shearer's Foods, Inc.

GRANDMA STEPHEN'S - Candy - J.B.R, Inc.

GRANDMA STEPHENS CHOCOLATES - Coffee - Coffee & Tea Ltd.

GRANDMA SYCAMORE'S HOME MAID BREAD - Bakery products - Leland Sycamore

GRANDMA UTZ'S - Potato chips - UTZ Quality Foods Inc.

GRANDMA'S - Cookies - Frito-Lay, Inc.

GRANDMA'S - Food products - I. Rokeach and Sons Inc.

GRANDMA'S - Molasses - Mott's Inc.

GRANDMA'S - Pasta - Food City USA Inc.

GRANDMA'S - Soap - Grandpa Brands Co.

GRANDMA'S BEAR LAKE - Fruits and vegetables - Price Family Partnership

GRANDMA'S BEST CROCHET THREAD - Thread - Caron International Inc.

GRANDMA'S BROOCH - Christmas tree ornaments - Cracker Box Inc.

GRANDMA'S CLASSIC - Snack foods - Barrel O' Fun Inc.

GRANDMA'S COMFORT-ME - Lotions - Grandpa Brands Co.

GRANDMA'S COUNTRY KITCHEN - Spices and extracts ☆ - Scentex Inc.

GRANDMA'S FANCY - Soap - Grandpa Brands Co.

GRANDMA'S FANCY LUXURY - Soap - Grandpa Brands Co.

GRANDMA'S HOMESTYLE - Pasta - Food City USA Inc.

GRANDMA'S HOUSE - Computer software - Queue Inc.

GRANDMA'S MARSHMALLOW BABIES - Toys - Playskool, Inc.

GRANDMA'S MOLASSES UNSULPHURED MILD FLAVOR THE SURPRISE NATURAL SWEETENER - Molasses - Mott's Inc.

GRANDMA'S OLD FASHIONED - Soap - Grandpa Brands Co.

GRANDMA'S REMEDIES - Pharmaceutical preparations - Park Laboratory Co., Inc.

GRANDMA'S TRUNK - Games - Brown and Bigelow Inc.

GRANDMA'S TUMMY MINT - Teas–herbal - Celestial Seasonings, Inc.

GRANDMASTER - Flowers, plants, and seeds - Cascade International Seed Co.

GRANDMASTER - Paint brushes and rollers - Adams Brush Manufacturing Co., Inc.

GRANDMASTER - Sporting goods - Set Tennis Co.

GRANDMASTER CHESS - Computer software - Capstone Software

GRANDMASTER CHESS DELUXE - Computer software - Capstone Software

GRANDMERE - Food products ☆ - Commerce Foods Inc.

GRANDMERE - Wines - Renwood Winery, Inc.

GRANDMOTHER JOSHUA - Food products - Beatrice Cos. Inc.

GRANDMOTHER'S - Jams and jellies - Whipple Co.

GRANDMOTHER'S FLOWER GARDEN - Craft supplies ☆ - VIP/VIP Crafts

GRANDO - Jewelry - Grando, Inc.

GRANDOE - Gloves - Grandoe Corp.

GRANDOE GOLD - Gloves - Grandoe Corp.

GRANDPA BASIL - Toys–stuffed ☆ - Gund, Inc.

GRANDPA CAP'S TONIC - Vitamins and nutritional supplements - Polam Wholesale Inc.

GRANDPA CAPS TONIC - Vitamins and nutritional supplements ☆ - Reese Chemical Co.

GRANDPA CHARLIES - Food products ☆ - Chas. Hollenbach Inc.

GRANDPA GIBBLES - Potato chips - Nibble with Gibble's Inc.

GRANDPA GIBBLE'S SLOW COOKED POTATO CHIPS - Potato chips - Consolidated Snacks, Inc.

GRANDPA HEART - Dolls - Mattel, Inc.

GRANDPA JOHN'S - Snack foods - Beatrice Cos. Inc.

GRANDPA JOHN'S PORK CRACKLINS - Pork rinds - Rudolph Foods Co.

GRANDPA MEIER'S - Wines - Meier's Wine Cellars Inc.

GRANDPA TALES - Computer software - Capitol Multimedia, Inc.

GRANDPARENTING BY GRACE - Publisher's imprints - Sunday School Board of the Southern Baptist Convention

GRANDPARENTS, YOU ARE SPECIAL - Recording label ☆ - Christian Children's Associates, Inc.

GRANDPA'S - Soap - Grandpa Brands Co.

GRANDPA'S CRAFTS - Puzzles - Ibssl, Inc.

GRANDPA'S FAVORITE - Food products - Grandpa's Favorite Manufacturing

GRANDPA'S FAVORITE SCONE MIX - Desserts - Grandpa's Favorite Manufacturing

GRANDPA'S ORIGINAL - Cakes - O'Wayne Enterprises, Inc.

GRANDPA'S RECORDS - Recording label - Oakridge Music Recording Service

GRANDPERE - Wines - Renwood Winery, Inc.

GRANDPERE'S - Cheese - Swissrose International Inc.

GRANDPLANNER - Calendars - Krapf Business Systems, Inc.

GRANDRIB - Siding–metal - Alcan Aluminum Corp. Alcan Building Products Div.

GRANDRIVER - Golf clubs - Austad Co.

GRANDS - Biscuits - Pillsbury Co.

GRANDSTAND - Apparel and accessories ☆ - Lacy Corp.

GRANDSTAND - Apparel stores–uniforms - David W. McConnell

GRANDSTAND - Electronic equipment - Screen Works

GRANDSTAND - Golfing equipment - Voit Corp.

GRANDSTAND - Hunting equipment - Paul Meeks

GRANDSTAND - Office supplies - Rubbermaid Inc.

GRANDTIQUE - Blinds–venetian - Bamboo Abbott Florida Corp.

GRANDTONE - Guitars - Harptone

GRANDTREK - Tires - Dunlop Tire Corp.

GRANDUCA - Beverages–alcohol ☆ - Kobrand Corp.

GRANDURA - Luggage - United States Luggage Corp.

GRANDVIEW - Artists' materials - Glenview Products Inc.

GRANDVIEW - Computer software - Symantec Corp.

GRANDVIEW - Floor coverings - Congoleum Corp.

GRANDVIEW - Manufactured homes - Redman Industries, Inc.

GRANDVIEW - Trailers–travel ☆ - Fleetwood Enterprises, Inc.

GRANDVIEW - Window coverings - Skagfield Corp.

GRANDY'S - Food products - Sea Harvest Packing Co.

GRANECON - Gloves - Granet Inc.

GRANEER - Fabrics - Greenwood Mills Inc.

GRANELLI ICE - Syrup - Frozen Dessert Concepts Inc.

GRANERA - Bird feeds ☆ - Lafeber Co.

GRANESE - Cheese - Rosenbergers Dairies Inc.

GRANET - Gloves - Granet Inc.

GRANETTE - Floor coverings–carpet and rugs ☆ - Downs Carpet Co. Inc.

GRANFLEX - Gloves - Granet Inc.

GRANFORNO - Breads - Source Atlantique

GRANGALA - Liquors - Disusa Imports Co.

GRANGER - Apparel–men's ☆ - Berkley Shirt Co. Inc.

GRANGER - Floor coverings–carpet and rugs - Chembond

GRANGER - Sporting goods - Wright & McGill Co.

GRANGER - Tobacco products - Swedish Math North America Inc.

GRANGER ANTHOLOGY, THE - Publisher's imprints ☆ - Roth Publishing Inc.

GRANGER IMARI - Dinnerware–glass ☆ - Royal China & Porcelain Companies Inc.

GRANGER IMPERIAL - Sporting goods ☆ - Wright & McGill Co.

GRANGER MEDALLION - Sporting goods - Wright & McGill Co.

GRANGER OCEAN - Sporting goods - Wright & McGill Co.

GRANGER POETRY LIBRARY - Publisher's imprints ☆ - Roth Publishing Inc.

GRANGER SELECT - Tobacco–chewing or smoking - Swedish Math North America Inc.

GRANGET SCULPTURES - Figurines ☆ - Goebel of North America

GRANICOAT - Polymermatrix - Safas Corp.

GRANIT - Floor coverings - Tarkett, Inc.

GRANIT ELITE - Floor coverings - Tarkett, Inc.

GRANITA GLACE - Beverages - Tetley Inc.

GRANITE - Apparel and accessories - RHG Ltd.

GRANITE - Dinnerware–glass ☆ - Lenox, Inc.

GRANITE - Floor coverings - Congoleum Corp.

GRANITE - Floor coverings - National Floor Products Co., Inc.

GRANITE - Floor coverings–carpet and rugs - Hartford Carpet Mills

GRANITE - Floor coverings–tile - Kentile Floors Inc.

GRANITE - Floor coverings–tile - Robbins Interior Surface Inc.

GRANITE - Frames–picture - North American Enclosures Inc.

GRANITE - Recording label - Granite Records & Tapes

GRANITE - Thread - Threads USA Div.

GRANITE - Toys - Tonka Corp.

GRANITE - Water–bottled or canned - Granite Spring Water Co.
GRANITE 5 - ITW Ramset/Red Head
GRANITE 24 - Floor coverings–carpet and rugs ☆ - Cumberland Mills Inc.
GRANITE BLOCKS - Drums–musical instruments - LP Music Group
GRANITE COLLECTION - Cooking utensils–aluminum - Himark Enterprises Inc.
GRANITE CREEK TANNERY - Footwear - JBI, Inc.
GRANITE DE FRUTTA - Watches ☆ - Swatch Watch USA
GRANITE EXTRAORDINAIRE - Wallpaper - Snap & Sell Corp.
GRANITE FILL 2000 - Building materials - Arizona Cultured Stone Products, Inc.
GRANITE GARDEN - Glassware–household - Great American Fun Corp.
GRANITE-LIKE - Enamels - Perry & Derrick Co.
GRANITE MUSIC CORP. - Recording label - Criterion Music Corp.
GRANITE RIDGE - Apparel and accessories - Sundventures, Inc.
GRANITE RIDGE - Swimming pools - Doughboy Recreational Inc.
GRANITE RIDGE - Swimming pools - Hoffinger Industries, Inc.
GRANITE RIDGE - Wines - Cannon Wines Ltd.
GRANITE ROSE - Floor coverings - Mannington Resilient Floors
GRANITE RUN - Floor coverings - Mannington Resilient Floors
GRANITE SPRINGS - Wines - Granite Springs Winery
GRANITE WARE - Cookware - General Housewares Corp.
GRANITEWARE - See CERAMIC ON STEEL
GRANITEX - Binders ☆ - Jacob North Printing Co. Inc.
GRANITEX - Concrete products - Devoe & Raynolds Co.
GRANITEX - Marble products ☆ - Maxsam Sales, Inc.
GRANITI - Tiles–ceramic - American Marazzi Tile, Inc.
GRANITO - Coffee - Granito Coffee Works, Inc.
GRANITO - Dinnerware ☆ - Corning Inc.
GRANITO - Floor coverings ☆ - National Floor Products Co., Inc.
GRANITO - Floor coverings–tile - Porcelanite, Inc.
GRANITO - Tiles–ceramic - KPT Inc.
GRANITONES - Tiles–ceramic ☆ - American Olean Tile Co.
GRANMASTER - Sporting goods - Wellington Leisure Products, Inc.
GRAN'MERE'S GARLIC DRESSING - Food products - Select Origins Inc.
GRANNICK'S BITTER APPLE - Pet products - Grannick's Bitter Apple Co.
GRANNING - Truck air suspension systems - Fluidrive Inc.
GRANNY - Dinnerware–plastic - Plastics Manufacturing Co.
GRANNY - Food products - I. Rokeach and Sons Inc.
GRANNY BONES - Pet products - K.C. Pharmacal Inc.
GRANNY BOOZER'S - Whipped topping–frozen - Margaret Van Der Blom Sapp
GRANNY DELL'S - Candy - Old Dominion Peanut Inc.
GRANNY ELLA'S - Cookies - Moran Foods, Inc.
GRANNY GATOR'S - Barbecue sauce - Granny Gator's Specialty Foods, Inc.
GRANNY GOOD - Bakery products - Specialty Bakers, Inc.
GRANNY GOOSE - Snack foods - Granny Goose Foods Inc.
GRANNY GOOSE - Snack foods - Granny Goose Foods, Inc.
GRANNY GOOSE RIPPLES - Potato chips - Granny Goose Foods Inc.
GRANNY HOOVER'S - Pasta - Winter Gardens Salad Co.
GRANNY LOCK'S LIL' TYKES - Rocking chairs - Oak Land Furn. Manufacturing, Inc.
GRANNY MAC - Candy - McDonald Candy Co. Inc.
GRANNY SHAKERS - Housewares ☆ - Gemco Ware, Inc.
GRANNY SMITH - Linen - Notra Trading, Inc.
GRANNYGOOD PIES - Pies–fresh ☆ - Specialty Bakers Inc.
GRANNYKINS - Dolls - Uneeda Doll Co., Inc.
GRANNY'S - Bakery products–frozen - Bubbles Baking Co.
GRANNY'S - Cutlery - Imperial Schrade Corp.
GRANNY'S - Food containers - Farmhouse Foods
GRANNY'S - Wines - Monarch Wine Co. of Georgia
GRANNY'S BLOOMER - Fertilizers - Security Products Co.
GRANNY'S CHOICE - Juices - Natural Country Juice Products, Inc.
GRANNY'S CORNER - Dolls ☆ - Effanbee Doll Corp.
GRANNY'S GOODIES - Snack foods - Joshua D. Frey
GRANNY'S GOURMET GOODIES - Bakery products - Bubbles Baking Co.
GRANNY'S MELON BUCKETS - Apparel and accessories - Granny's Melon Buckets, Inc.
GRANNY'S PICTURE PAK - Hobby kits ☆ - Polyform Products Inc.
GRANNY'S TARTJACK GRANNY SMITH - Liqueurs - Joseph E. Seagram & Sons, Inc.
GRANNYWORLD - Recording label - Delman/Rosen Design Group, Inc.
GRANOBLE - Floor coverings–carpet and rugs - Bloomsburg Carpet Industries
GRANOLA BITES - Snack foods - General Mills, Inc.
GRANOLA CHEWS - Food products - Honeypot Treats

GRANOLA CRUNCH - Pet products - RHB Enterprises
GRANOLA KITCHENS - Snack foods - Granola Kitchen Inc.
GRANOLA MUNCHIES - Snack foods ☆ - Hershey Import Co. Inc.
GRANOLA NUTS - Snack foods ☆ - Anacon Foods Co.
GRANOLA SPECIAL - Cookies - Biscotti Cookie
GRANOLA'S - Cereal - Golden Temple Natural Foods Bakery
GRANOLENE - Animal feeds - Evergreen Mills Inc.
GRAN'PA DON'S - Meat products–beef - Pioneer Food Sales Inc.
GRANPAPPY - Kitchen appliances - National Presto Industries, Inc.
GRANPAW'S DOGGIE COOKIES - Dog food - DOCA USA, Inc.
GRANPAW'S GRANOLA BONE - Dog food - DOCA USA, Inc.
GRANPAW'S MINI-BITES - Dog food - DOCA USA, Inc.
GRANPAW'S MUTT MINTS - Dog food - DOCA USA, Inc.
GRANPAW'S POOCH PLEASERS - Dog food - DOCA USA, Inc.
GRANSPORT - Sporting goods - Wellington Leisure Products, Inc.
GRANSTONE - Wallpaper - ICI Americas Inc.
GRANT - See DYNA-CARE
GRANT - Greeting cards ☆ - Century Engraving & Embossing Co.
GRANT - Hardware - Hettich America L.P.
GRANT - Watches - Page Jewelers
GRANT ADMINISTRATOR - Computer software - Dyna-Quest Technologies, Inc.
GRANT HOWARD - Glassware–household - Glassware International Inc.
GRANT PARK - Bicycles - Ross Bicycles USA, Ltd.
GRANT SMITH - Wines - Joseph Victori Wines, Inc.
GRANTFINDER - Computer software - Cambridge Fund Raising Association
GRANTHAM - Dryers–household - Rosco Machinery Co., Inc.
GRANTON - Footwear–children's - Granton Shoe Imports
GRANT'S - Beverages–malt ☆ - Yakima Brewing & Malting Co.
GRANTS - Garden equipment - Lawn & Garden Supply Co.
GRANTS - Liquors - William Grant & Sons, Inc.
GRANT'S - Pet products - Grant Laboratories
GRANT'S - Soups–canned - C. & J. Willenborg Inc.
GRANT'S CELTIC - Beverages–malt ☆ - Yakima Brewing & Malting Co.
GRANTS DATABASE, THE - Computer software - Oryx Press, Inc.
GRANT'S FARM - Breads - Campbell Taggart Inc.
GRANT'S FARM - Candy - Anheuser-Busch Companies Inc.
GRANT'S FARM ESSENTIALS - Bakery products - Anheuser-Busch Companies Inc.
GRANT'S GRAND SLAM - Beverages–malt ☆ - Yakima Brewing & Malting Co.
GRANT'S IMPERIAL - Beverages–malt ☆ - Yakima Brewing & Malting Co.
GRANT'S INDIA - Beverages–malt ☆ - Yakima Brewing & Malting Co.
GRANTS OF DUNDEE - Jams and jellies - Europa Foods Ltd.
GRANTS ROYAL - Liquors - William Grant & Sons, Inc.
GRANT'S SCOTTISH - Beverages–malt ☆ - Yakima Brewing & Malting Co.
GRANT'S SPRINGBOK - Beverages–malt ☆ - Yakima Brewing & Malting Co.
GRANT'S WEIS - Beverages–malt ☆ - Yakima Brewing & Malting Co.
GRANT'S YAKIMA - Beverages ☆ - Yakima Brewing & Malting Co.
GRANU MED - Pharmaceutical preparations - Rugby Laboratories Inc.
GRANUBOR - Fertilizers - U.S. Borax Inc.
GRANUER - Floor coverings–carpet and rugs ☆ - J.L. Benson Co.
GRANUFACTIN - Pharmaceutical preparations - Johnson & Johnson
GRANUFLO - Pharmaceutical preparations - Fresenius USA, Inc.
GRANULA-4 - Cleaning preparations–household - L & F Consumer Products
GRANULAIRE - Floor coverings - Mannington Resilient Floors
GRANULAR - Flour–blended - King of Potatoes Inc.
GRANULEX - Pharmaceutical preparations - Dow B. Hickam Inc.
GRANULIME - Lime and gypsum ☆ - AMPEL Corp.
GRANULITE - Fertilizers - Wheelabrator Clean Water Systems Inc.
GRANULON - Hardware - Formica Corp.
GRANUMAG - Powdered magnesia - Premier Services Corp.
GRANUSEAL - Food products - Givaudan Roure
GRANUTEC - Pharmaceutical preparations - Granutec Inc.
GRANUTIRE TIRE REDUCTION SYSTEM - Machinery - Granutech Environmental Systems, Inc.
GRANVELOUR - Floor coverings–carpet and rugs - Mohawk Industries Inc.
GRANVIA - Wallpaper - Textile Wallcoverings International Ltd.
GRANVILLA - Furniture–metal ☆ - Telescope Casual Furniture Inc.
GRANVILLE - Computer software - Gessler Publishing Co., Inc.
GRANVILLE - Cookies - Sunshine/Salerno Inc.
GRANVILLE - Desks - Boling Co.
GRANVILLE - Dishes–china - Waterford Wedgwood USA, Inc.
GRANVILLE - Floor coverings - Mannington Resilient Floors
GRANVILLE - Lighting fixtures - Holophane Corp.
GRANVILLE - Manufactured homes - Redman Industries, Inc.

☆ = Now out of production

GRANVILLE SQUARE - Floor coverings–carpet and rugs - Gulistan Carpet Inc.

GRAO VASCO - Beverages–alcohol - Sogrape USA Inc.

GRAPE - Recording label - The Pegasus Group, Inc.

GRAPE-A-GO-GO B'GUM - Chewing gum ☆ - R.L. Albert & Son, Inc.

GRAPE APE - Chewing gum ☆ - Amurol Confections Co.

GRAPE ARBOR - Housewares - Himark Enterprises Inc.

GRAPE BEYOND - Fruit drinks–bottled or canned ☆ - Coca-Cola Co.

GRAPE BEYOND, THE - Beverages - Coca-Cola Co.

GRAPE BOWER - Dinnerware ☆ - Corning Inc.

GRAPE ESCAPE - Fruits and vegetables - Kings River Ranch

GRAPE-GRAPE - Juices - Pokka, Inc.

GRAPE ICE - Dolls - Mattel, Inc.

GRAPE-ITS - Candy ☆ - Donruss Co.

GRAPE JILL - Fruit drinks–bottled or canned ☆ - Yakima Valley Grape Producers Inc.

GRAPE JILLY - Dolls - Mattel, Inc.

GRAPE LIGHT - Beverages - Hansen Beverage Co.

GRAPE LIGHTS - Hardware - Mark F. Grape

GRAPE MOONS - Candy - American Chewing Gum Inc.

GRAPE NETWERK - Sporting goods - Vision Sports Holding Corp.

GRAPE PARFAIT - Lipsticks - Honey & Spice Toiletries

GRAPE SEED EXTRACT - Vitamins and nutritional supplements - Vitamin Research Products Inc.

GRAPE SOURS - Candy - Judson-Atkinson Candies

GRAPE STIX - Candy - Leaf, Inc.

GRAPE VALLEY - Juices ☆ - Warner Vineyards Inc.

GRAPE VINE - Beverages–alcohol - Monarch Wine Co.

GRAPE VINE WINERY - Wines - Grape Vine Winery

GRAPE WAY - Juices - Nabisco Foods Group

GRAPE WHIPS - Candy - American Licorice Co.

GRAPEFRUIT - Skin care products - American Image

GRAPEFRUIT 60 - Vitamins and nutritional supplements - Head Start Vitamin Products

GRAPEFRUIT GREETINGS - Greeting cards - Cushman & Pearl Co.

GRAPEFUL - Beverages - White Rock Products Corp.

GRAPEHEAD - Candy - Ferrara Pan Candy Co., Inc.

GRAPELEAF - Foil–aluminum - Highland Supply Corp.

GRAPELETS - Candy - Liberty Orchards Co., Inc.

GRAPEMIST - Grape juices - International Marketing Services Inc.

GRAPES LA ROMA - Plastics ☆ - Fry Plastics International Inc. (O)

GRAPES OF BATH - Soap - Casper Silva, Inc.

GRAPES OF FRATH - Games - Decipher Inc.

GRAPESKINS - Insulating materials ☆ - Life-Link International, Inc.

GRAPETOWN - Turkeys - Sunday House Foods Inc.

GRAPETTE - Beverages–carbonated - Grapette International

GRAPEVINE - Hair coloring preparations - Cosmair Inc.

GRAPEVINE - Tableware–earthenware - Pfaltzgraff Investment Co.

GRAPEVINE - Wallpaper ☆ - Ginger Tree Designs

GRAPEVINE KNITS - Apparel and accessories ☆ - Sally Gee Inc.

GRAPEVINE, THE - Beverages–alcohol - Monarch Wine Co.

GRAPEVINE WINE CELLARS - Wines - Monarch Wine Co.

GRAPEY - Chewing gum - Philadelphia Chewing Gum Corp.

GRAPH-A-CATOR - Lubricants ☆ - Panef Corp.

GRAPH-A-MATIC - Office supplies ☆ - Victor Systems & Equipment Co.

GRAPH & MATE - Computer software ☆ - DacEasy Inc.

GRAPH ART - Greeting cards - American Artists Group Inc.

GRAPH BUILDER - Publisher's imprints - Harcourt Brace & Co.

GRAPH CLUB, THE - Computer software - Tom Snyder Productions, Inc.

GRAPH-EASE + - Computer software - Ventura Educational Systems

GRAPH EDITOR TOOLKIT - Computer software - Tom Sawyer Software Corp.

GRAPH-IN-THE-BOX - Computer software - New England Software Inc.

GRAPH-IN-THE-BOX ANALYTIC - Computer software - New England Software Inc.

GRAPH-IN-THE-BOX EXECUTIVE - Computer software - New England Software Inc.

GRAPH-IN-THE-BOX RELEASE 2 - Computer software - New England Software Inc.

GRAPH-IT - Cross-stitch graphing system - Nancy Claytor Designs

GRAPH LAYOUT TOOLKIT - Computer software - Tom Sawyer Software Corp.

GRAPH-TEK - Chemical preparations - Graphic Technologies, Inc.

GRAPH TEX - Floor coverings–carpet and rugs ☆ - Playfield International Inc.

GRAPHATECH - Packaging–foam - RM Engineered Products, Inc.

GRAPHATHERM - Packaging–foam - RM Engineered Products, Inc.

GRAPHEASY - Computer software - Speakeasy Computing Corp.

GRAPHER - Computer software - Golden Software, Inc.

GRAPHIC - Floor coverings - Congoleum Corp.

GRAPHIC - Floor coverings–carpet and rugs - Alliance Industries Inc.

GRAPHIC - Mats - JCH International Inc.

GRAPHIC - Ophthalmic goods - Foremost Optical Products

GRAPHIC ALERT - Signs - Lab Safety Supply, Inc.

GRAPHIC-ART - Office supplies - Alvin and Co. Inc.

GRAPHIC ARTS - Artists' materials - M. Grumbacher Inc.

GRAPHIC CONNECTION - Stationery - Pratt & Austin Co.

GRAPHIC DESIGNS - Floor coverings–carpet and rugs - Philadelphia Carpets

GRAPHIC DISPLAY SYSTEMS - Display cases–wood - Graphic Display Systems

GRAPHIC ENTERPRISES INC - Photocopy machines - Graphic Enterprises of Ohio, Inc.

GRAPHIC GAMES GALORE - Computer software - Recreational Mathemagical Software

GRAPHIC GREETINGS - Greeting cards - Recycled Paper Products, Inc.

GRAPHIC IMPACT - Software - Generic Software, Inc.

GRAPHIC IMPRESSIONS - Floor coverings–carpet and rugs - Philadelphia Carpets

GRAPHIC IMPRINTS - Invitations - C'est Papier Inc.

GRAPHIC LEARNING - Educational materials - Abrams and Co. Publishers Inc.

GRAPHIC NEEDLE - Craft supplies - Ports of Scandinavia Inc.

GRAPHIC PROGRAMMER, THE - Computer software - AV Systems Inc.

GRAPHIC REVOLUTIONS - Signs - Clearr Corp.

GRAPHIC SERIES - Duplicating machines - Graphic Communications Corp.

GRAPHIC SERIES - Paper products - Georgia-Pacific Corp.

GRAPHIC SERIES, THE - Office supplies - Georgia-Pacific Corp.

GRAPHIC SHOP - Computer software - Mastersoft, Inc.

GRAPHIC SOURCE - Publisher's imprints - Graphic Products Corp.

GRAPHIC-STANDARD - Artists' materials - Graphic-Standard Instruments Co.

GRAPHIC TILES - Tiles–ceramic - Kimberly Enterprises Inc.

GRAPHIC TOOLKIT - Artists' materials ☆ - Graphic Products Corp.

GRAPHIC TRAFFIC - Apparel and accessories - Graphic Traffic Inc.

GRAPHIC TRAFFIC - Paper ☆ - Stuart Hall Co., Inc.

GRAPHIC UTILITIES - Inks - Graphic Utilities, Inc.

GRAPHIC-VISION - Cameras–video - Panels & Controls Corp.

GRAPHIC WOOD - Building materials - Entol Industries Inc.

GRAPHICA - Wood products - Georgia-Pacific Corp.

GRAPHICAL DESIGNER - Computer software - Advanced Software Technologies Inc.

GRAPHICO - Cosmetics - Revlon Consumer Products Corp.

GRAPHICRAFT - Artists' materials - Graphicraft

GRAPHICRAFT - Computer software - Commodore Business Machines Inc.

GRAPHICS - Floor coverings–carpet and rugs ☆ - Blue Ridge Carpet Mills

GRAPHICS - Tiles–ceramic - Porcelanite, Inc.

GRAPHICS ARE EASY - Computer software - Electronic Courseware Systems Inc.

GRAPHICS BASIC - Computer software - SourceView Software International

GRAPHICS CONVERTER GOLD - Computer software - IMSI

GRAPHICS DEPARTMENT - Computer software ☆ - Quality Computers and Applications

GRAPHICS 'N GLYPHS - Hardware ☆ - Scott Sign Systems, Inc.

GRAPHICS PEOPLE LOVE TO TOUCH - Fabrics - High Voltage Graphics, Inc.

GRAPHICS STUDIO, THE - Computer software - Accolade Inc.

GRAPHICS TIPS - Computer software - Locus Systems

GRAPHICS VISUALIZATION & USABILITY CENTER - Research–educational - Georgia Tech Research Corp.

GRAPHICUTILITIES - Inks - Graphic Utilities, Inc.

GRAPHICWEAVE - Paper products - Georgia-Pacific Corp.

GRAPHICWORKS 1.1 - Computer software - Mindscape Software Inc.

GRAPHICWRITER III - Computer software - Seven Hills Software

GRAPHIKORE - Sign panels - Baltek Corp.

GRAPHING EQUATIONS - Computer software ☆ - Sunburst Communications, Inc.

GRAPHIQUE KITS - Hobby kits - Extension Inc.

GRAPHIS - Wallpaper ☆ - Marburg Wallcoverings Inc.

GRAPHISOTE - Paints ☆ - Nowstar

GRAPHIT - Computer software - Control Automation Inc.

GRAPHITE - Apparel–men's - Specialty Retailers, Inc.

GRAPHITE - Bathroom fixtures - Kohler Co.

GRAPHITE - Exercising equipment - American Athletic Inc.

GRAPHITE - Recording label - Granite Records & Tapes

GRAPHITE - Sporting goods - Wright & McGill Co.

GRAPHITE 95 - Rackets–tennis - Spalding Sports Worldwide

GRAPHITE 100 - Fishing tackle ☆ - South Bend Sporting Goods Inc.
GRAPHITE 999 - Fishing tackle - South Bend Sporting Goods Inc.
GRAPHITE MASTER - Rackets–tennis - Head Sports USA
GRAPHITE PLUS - Fishing tackle ☆ - South Bend Sporting Goods Inc.
GRAPHITE PROFESSIONAL - Rackets–tennis - Head Sports USA
GRAPHITE PROJECT - Golfing equipment - Golfsmith International Inc.
GRAPHITE SOFTWARE - Computer software - Graphite Software, Inc.
GRAPHITEX SUPER - Sports rackets and accessories - Winn, Inc.
GRAPHITRACK - Computer software - Mars, Inc.
GRAPHIX - Apparel and accessories ☆ - Jasper Textiles Inc.
GRAPHIX - Tape–adhesive - Main Tape Co. Inc.
GRAPHLINE - Printing trades machinery - Graphline, Inc.
GRAPHLITE - Construction equipment - Neptco Inc.
GRAPHO GLAS - Gaskets - Rutland Products
GRAPHPAD PRISM - Computer software - GraphPad Software Inc.
GRAPHPOWER - Computer software - Ventura Educational Systems
GRAPHS - Craft supplies - Marion Dove Werth
GRAPHTECH - Sporting goods - Prince Manufacturing Inc.
GRAPHUS - Artists' materials ☆ - Dick Blick Co.
GRAPILLON/OBI - Juices - H.J. Gasser Specialty Foods
GRAPINE - Vitamins and nutritional supplements - Nature's Sunshine Products, Inc.
GRAPPA DI BRUNELLO - Wines - Banfi Vintners
GRAPPA DI ORNELLAIA - Beverages–alcohol - Kobrand Corp.
GRAPPA DI SASSICAIA - Beverages–alcohol - Kobrand Corp.
GRAPPA EXTRA - Wines - Palm Bay Imports, Inc.
GRAPPA JULIA - Brandy - Disusa Imports Co.
GRAPPA RUTA CANDOLINI - Beverages–alcohol - Carillon Importers Ltd.
GRAPPARITA - Beverages–alcohol - Dallesa, Inc.
GRAPPLE - Fruit drinks–bottled or canned - Jerry Lee Soll
GRAPPLE - Games ☆ - Parker Brothers
GRAPPLER - Tires - Montgomery Ward & Co. Inc.
GRAPPLER - Tools ☆ - Virtual Industries, Inc.
GRAPPLER E'LIRE - Tires ☆ - Montgomery Ward & Co. Inc.
GRAPPOLINI - Food products - Bel Canto Fancy Foods Ltd.
GRASMERE COLLECTION - Wallpaper ☆ - Richard E. Thibaut, Inc.
GRASON-STADLER - Medical apparatus - Grason-Stadler, Inc.
GRASP - Adhesives and sealants - Mantrose-Haeuser Co. Inc.
GRASP 'N SQUEEZE ME - Toys ☆ - Gerber Products Co.
GRASS - Mats ☆ - Ludlow Composites Corp.
GRASS-B-GON - Herbicides - Chevron Chemical Co.
GRASS CADDY - Motor vehicles - Ransomes-Cushman-Ryan
GRASS CLOTH CONNECTION, THE - Wallpaper - Snap & Sell Corp.
GRASS CROPPER - Nurseries and garden stores ☆ - Granet Inc.
GRASS-FAST - Garden equipment - Dalen Products Inc.
GRASS GETTER - Garden equipment ☆ - Montgomery Ward & Co. Inc.
GRASS HANDLER - Garden equipment ☆ - J.C. Penney Co., Inc.
GRASS KING - Mowers ☆ - Alamo Industrial
GRASS MAGIC - Grass seed - Alljack & Co.
GRASS MOUNTAIN - Recording label - Ridge Runner
GRASS OIL - Perfumes - Quintessence Inc.
GRASS-OUT! - Herbicides - Dexol Industries
GRASS PLUS - Animal feeds - Buckeye Feed Mills, Inc.
GRASS POPPER - Toys ☆ - Steven Manufacturing Co.
GRASS RAGGS - Apparel–women's - G.M.L.A., Inc.
GRASS RECORDS - Recording label - Grass Entertainment Group Inc.
GRASS ROOTS COLLECTION - Apparel and accessories ☆ - Terramar Sports Worldwide, Ltd.
GRASS STOP - Garden equipment - Nichols-Homeshield Inc.
GRASS TEX - Christmas tree ornaments ☆ - Union Wadding Co.
GRASS-TO-GO - Floor coverings–carpet and rugs - Habitat International Inc.
GRASSBUGGY - Garden equipment - Elkhart Cases Inc.
GRASSCLOTH & WEAVES - Wallpaper - Seabrook Wallcoverings, Inc.
GRASSCRETE - Tools–garden - Bomanite Corp.
GRASSE - Colognes - Brandy Harvest
GRASSGUY - Novelty items - Ontel Products Corp.
GRASSHOPPER - Fertilizers - Geo. W. McGuire Co. Inc.
GRASSHOPPER - Fragrance ☆ - Cosrich Inc.
GRASSHOPPER - Luggage - Airway Industries, Inc.
GRASSHOPPER - Toys - Processed Plastic Co.
GRASSHOPPER - Wallpaper ☆ - Ginger Tree Designs
GRASSHOPPER PIE - Ice cream - H.P. Hood & Sons Inc.
GRASSHOPPERS - Cookies - Keebler Co.
GRASSHOPPERS - Footwear - Sr Holdings, Inc.
GRASSHOPPERS - Footwear - Stride Rite Corp.
GRASSL - Beverages–alcohol - Dieter Steinmann Inc.

GRASSLAND - Butter - Grassland Dairy Products, Inc.
GRASSMAN - Novelty items - Grass People, Inc.
GRASSO - Food products - Grasso Foods Inc.
GRASSSAVER - Food products - Garmon Corp.
GRASSY CREEK CRITTERS - Decorative accessories ☆ - Aus-Ben Studios
GRATE-N-SHRED - Housewares - RonCo Inc.
GRATE SHAKES - Bowls - Felknor International Inc.
GRATE WISCON - Cheese - Wisconsin Corp.
GRATEBAKED - Bakery products - Lewis Bakeries, Inc.
GRATEFUL GEESE - Novelty items - Possible Dreams, Ltd.
GRATEFUL HEAD, THE - Medical apparatus - Moberg Research, Inc.
GRATEFUL NATION REMEMBERS 1941-1945 E, A - Awards, plaques and medals - Department of the Army
GRATER 'N BOWL - Housewares - Hutzler Manufacturing Co.
GRATIEN & MEYER - Wines - Seagram's Chateau & Estate Wines Co.
GRATIFIER - Hearing aids - Dyn-Aura Engineering Laboratories Inc.
GRATLOCH - Medical equipment - Thomas A. Graziano
GRATONNI'S - Food products - Grace Culinary Systems Inc.
GRATUITY WALLET - Novelty items - Tawn Chi & Associates Inc.
GRATUNE - Tiles–ceramic ☆ - Huntington/Pacific Ceramics Inc.
GRAU - Automotive parts and accessories - Echlin Inc.
GRAUADO - Rum - Joseph E. Seagram & Sons, Inc.
GRAVE DANGER - Games - Pressman Toy Corp.
GRAVE YARD SHIFT - Giftware - Russ Berrie and Co., Inc.
GRAVEL - Chewing gum ☆ - Leaf, Inc.
GRAVEL - Footwear - Vans, Inc.
GRAVEL KING - Toys - Tonka Corp.
GRAVEL-LOCK - Adhesives and sealants - Atlas Chemical Co.
GRAVEL SAVER - Construction equipment - Tensar Corp.
GRAVEL VAC - Cleaning preparations - Penn-Plax, Inc.
GRAVEL WASH - Aquariums–household - Jungle Laboratories Corp.
GRAVELGUARD - Pet products - Penn-Plax, Inc.
GRAVELLE - Floor coverings ☆ - Kentile Floors Inc.
GRAVELLY MEADOW - Wines - Diamond Creek Vineyards
GRAVELSTONE - Wines - Brown-Forman Corp.
GRAVELY - Nurseries and garden stores - Gravely International Inc.
GRAVENHURST - Music–sheet - Jeree Records
GRAVER STUDIO - Apparel–women's - Susan Graver Sportswear
GRAVES - Boats - Marblehead Boatyard Associates
GRAVES DESIGN - Watches - Markuse Corp.
GRAVESTONE ARTWEAR - Apparel and accessories - Gravestone Artwear
GRAVETIAN - Wallpaper - Capital Carousel Inc.
GRAVEX - Recording label - International Record Corp.
GRAVEYARD GHOULIES - Toys - Toymax Inc.
GRAVIGEN - Pharmaceutical preparations ☆ - Bluco Inc.
GRAVIMERIK - Packaging machines - Merrick Industries Inc.
GRAVINEED - Pharmaceutical preparations - Hanlon Drug Products
GRAVIT-EYE - Medical apparatus - Sellstrom Manufacturing Co.
GRAVITATE - Apparel and accessories - F 40 California, Inc.
GRAVITATION - Games - Pacific Game Co.
GRAVITRON - Exercising equipment - Stairmaster Sports/Medical Products, Inc.
GRAVITRON - Toys - Tedco Inc.
GRAVITY - Apparel and accessories - Gravity Graphics, Inc.
GRAVITY - Cosmetics - Pfizer Inc.
GRAVITY - Men's fragrance - Coty Inc.
GRAVITY - Recording label - Matthew E. Zekala
GRAVITY ACTIVATED SPORTS - Apparel and accessories - Gravity Activated Sports, Inc.
GRAVITY BALANCE - Golfing equipment - Palm Springs Golf Co. Inc.
GRAVITY BOOTS - Exercising equipment - STL International, Inc.
GRAVITY FORCE - Apparel and accessories - Gravity Active Wear, Inc.
GRAVITY FREE - Apparel and accessories - Ira Josephs
GRAVITY GLIDE - Chairs–upholstered - Franklin Corp.
GRAVITY LOCK SYSTEMS - Building materials - Gravity Lock Systems, Inc.
GRAVITY PLUS - Chemical preparations - Midwest Industrial Supply, Inc.
GRAVITY RIDER - Exercising equipment - Fitness Solutions, Inc.
GRAVITY RINGS - Toys - Aqua-Leisure Industries, Inc.
GRAVITYFLO - Pharmaceutical preparations - Speakman Co.
GRAVOFLEX - Embossing machines - New Hermes Inc.
GRAVOPLY - Embossing machines - New Hermes Inc.
GRAVURA - Floor coverings ☆ - Kentile Floors Inc.
GRAVURE - Floor coverings–carpet and rugs - Criterion Mills Inc.
GRAVY DELIGHT - Dog food - Sunshine Mills Inc.
GRAVY GALORE - Pet products - Sunshine Mills Inc.
GRAVY GOURMET - Gravy - Bruce Foods Corp.

☆ = Now out of production

GRAVY MAGIC - Food products ✩ - General Mills, Inc.
GRAVY MASTER - Food products - Gravymaster Inc.
GRAVY QUIK - Gravy - Specialty Foods Investment Co.
GRAVY-SKIMMER - Cooking utensils–stoneware - East Hampton Industries Inc.
GRAVY TRAIN - Dog food - Heinz Pet Products Co.
GRAY - Sporting goods - Pompanette Inc.
GRAY AUDOGRAPH - Dictating machines ✩ - Lanier Voice Products
GRAY AWAY - Hair coloring preparations ✩ - Lusan Inc.
GRAY BE GONE - Hair care products - Trionics Systems Corp.
GRAY BY CROSS - Pens - Mark Cross Inc.
GRAY CRICKETS - Fishing lures - Armstrong's Cricket Farm
GRAY EAGLE - Sporting goods ✩ - Wright & McGill Co.
GRAY E.T.C. - Dictating machines ✩ - Lanier Voice Products
GRAY HILLS - Dinnerware–glass ✩ - WMF/USA
GRAY LADY - Watches - Bulova Corp.
GRAY MAGIC - Cosmetics - Ardell International Inc.
GRAY MAGIC - Hair care products - American International Industries
GRAY MATTER - Brakes–bicycle - Dia-Compe USA, Inc.
GRAY NO MORE - Hair care products - Gold Medal Hair Products Inc.
GRAY PHONAUDOGRAPH - Dictating machines ✩ - Lanier Voice Products
GRAY-SEAL - Paints - Progress Paint Manufacturing Co.
GRAY SHARE - Computer software - Apple Computer Inc.
GRAY TAPER-EDGE - Erasers ✩ - Bright Boy Abrasives
GRAYBEARD - Apparel and accessories - Donald Julius Mitchell, Sr.
GRAYBILLS - Milk - Wengerts Dairy Inc.
GRAYFITE - Sporting goods ✩ - Outdoor Technologies Group
GRAYHALL - Wines - European Beverage Co., Inc.
GRAYHIDE - Gloves - Jomac Products Inc.
GRAYLEDGE FARMS - Food products - Grayledge Farms
GRAYLINE - Business forms ✩ - ACCO USA, Inc.
GRAYLINE - Housewares - Grayline Housewares
GRAYLINE - Motor vehicle parts and accessories - Airtech
GRAYLYN - Floor coverings–carpet and rugs - Monticello Carpet Mills
GRAYPOINT - Erasers ✩ - Bright Boy Abrasives
GRAYRAL - Food products - Glass Inc.
GRAYS - Sporting goods - Cran Barry Inc.
GRAYS BY GARY WASSERMAN - Apparel–men's - Genesco Inc.
GRAYS BY GARY WASSERMAN - Apparel–men's - Greif Cos.
GRAYS HARBOR - Watches - QVC, Inc.
GRAYS OF CAMBRIDGE - Sporting goods - Cran Barry Inc.
GRAYSHARE - Computer software - Apple Computer Inc.
GRAYSKULL - Toys - Mattel, Inc.
GRAYSLAKE MALLOBASE - Gelatin - Grayslake Gelatin Co.
GRAYSLAKE SUPER QUALITY - Gelatin - Grayslake Gelatin Co.
GRAYSMARSH FARM - Food products - Graysmarsh Farm
GRAYSON - Floor coverings–carpet and rugs - Mannington Carpets, Inc.
GRAYSON - Margarine ✩ - Kraft Food Ingredients Corp.
GRAYSON - Shoes - Allen-Edmonds Shoe Corp.
GRAYSON - Water–bottled or canned - Grayson Mountain Water Co.
GRAYSON CELLARS - Wines - The Beverage Source Inc.
GRAYSPEED - Artists' materials ✩ - M. Grumbacher Inc.
GRAYSTONE - Dinnerware–glass ✩ - Royal China & Porcelain Companies Inc.
GRAYTONE - Artists' materials - M. Grumbacher Inc.
GRAYWORKS - Computer software - Logitech, Inc.
GRAZE N HAY - Animal feeds ✩ - AgriBioTech, Inc.
GRAZIA - Jewelry - National Chain Co.
GRAZIANO'S FRESH PRODUCE SINCE 1904 - Fruits and vegetables - Graziano Produce Co.
GRAZIOSI - Wines - Leonard Kreusch Inc.
GRAZOR - Garden equipment - Billy Goat Industries Inc.
GRB20 - Rackets–tennis - Spalding Sports Worldwide
GRC - Fertilizers - Dynacast
GRC - Ribbons–inked - General Ribbon Corp.
GRD - Machinery - International GRD Inc.
GRE - Computer software - Educational Testing Service
GRE FOR IBM & APPLE - Computer software - Krell Software Corp.
GRE SA WAY - Cleaning preparations - Altona Specialties
GRE-SOLVENT - Cleaning preparations ✩ - Mione Manufacturing Co.
GREAS - Computer software - Pacific Sierra Research Corp.
GREAS-OFF - Housewares ✩ - Chase Products Co.
GREAS-TUF - Cleaning preparations - Delta Biological Products Inc.
GREASE - Hair care products - Sebastian International, Inc.
GREASE - Shoes - Glen Shoe Co. Inc.
GREANSE AWAY - Cleaning preparations–carpet and rug - Promaster

GREASE BAG - Bicycle parts and accessories - John Stephen Reynolds
GREASE BUSTER - Adhesives and sealants - Federal Process Co.
GREASE CLENE - Cleaning preparations ✩ - Klean-Strip
GREASE CUT - Degreaser - Comstar International Inc. (IPC Div.)
GREASE-EM - Lubricants - Kadee Quality Products
GREASE FIGHTER PLUS - Cleaning preparations ✩ - Malco Products, Inc.
GREASE GRABBER - Cleaning preparations - Knight Marketing Corp.
GREASE GUARD - Bicycles - Wilderness Trail Bikes Inc.
GREASE GUARD - Protective coating - Ecolab Inc.
GREASE-KLEN - Cleaning preparations ✩ - Permite Corp.
GREASE MONKEY - Filters–industrial - Brook Industries, Inc.
GREASE -N- STUFF - Containers - Barry W. Vandiver
GREASE PLUG - Saxophones - Miracle Music
GREASE POLICE - All purpose cleaners - Strategic Direct Marketing, Inc.
GREASE RELIEF - Cleaning preparations - Dowbrands L.P.
GREASE-SOLVE - Cleaning preparations - Nyco Products Co.
GREASE, THE - Musical instrument accessories ✩ - Musichem
GREASED LIGHTNING GL3000 - Lubricating oils - Ramco-USA, Inc.
GREASEFREE - Cleaning equipment - Texwipe Co. LLC
GREASEMASTER - Lotions - TMT Services Corp.
GREASEPIT - Toys - Brentwood Television Funnies, Inc.
GREASESTRIP PLUS - Cleaning preparations - Ecolab Inc.
GREASGO - Cleaning preparations ✩ - Tempo Chemical Co. Inc.
GREASOFF - Cleaning preparations - Kleer Flo Co. Inc.
GREAT! - Apparel and accessories - Daniel Lee Smigrod
GREAT - Computer software - Law Enforcement Communication Network
GREAT! - Shirts - Great!
GREAT 7 - Stickers - Great Seven Trading Inc.
GREAT 8 - Fasteners–hook and eye ✩ - Universal Fasteners Inc.
GREAT 28 - Cereal - General Mills, Inc.
GREAT ADDITIONS - Desserts - Pillsbury Co.
GREAT ADVENTURES - Computer software ✩ - Knowledge Adventure
GREAT ADVENTURES - Infant product - Lisco, Inc.
GREAT ADVENTURES - Toys - Fisher-Price, Inc.
GREAT AIRPLANES - Toys–airplanes - Paul K. Guillow Inc.
GREAT AMERICAN - Food products - Great American Foods
GREAT AMERICAN - Fruits and vegetables - MBG Marketing
GREAT AMERICAN - Fruits and vegetables - Westin Inc.
GREAT AMERICAN - Games - Flagpin Productions
GREAT AMERICAN - Glassware–household - Rhinehart Glass
GREAT AMERICAN - Puzzles - Great American Puzzle Factory Inc.
GREAT AMERICAN - Salad dressings–bottled ✩ - Caesar Cardini Foods
GREAT AMERICAN - Seafood products–fresh or frozen ✩ - Ewarts Frozen Foods
GREAT AMERICAN - Soups–canned - H.J. Heinz Co.
GREAT AMERICAN - Toys ✩ - Hi-Flier Manufacturing Co.
GREAT AMERICAN - Water–bottled or canned - Aquapenn Spring Water Co., Inc.
GREAT AMERICAN AUCTION GAME - Games ✩ - Western Publishing Co., Inc.
GREAT AMERICAN AUDIO - Recording label - Great American Audio Corp.
GREAT AMERICAN BAGEL - Bagels - Great American Bagel, Inc.
GREAT AMERICAN BUCKLE CO. - Apparel and accessories - Great American Products Inc.
GREAT AMERICAN CAUSES - Calendars - Steve Cram & Associates, Inc.
GREAT AMERICAN CHILE MADNESS - Food products - Pecos Valley Spice Co.
GREAT AMERICAN COMBINATIONS - Dinners–frozen - Green Giant Co.
GREAT AMERICAN COOKIES - Bakery products - Great American Cookie Co., Inc.
GREAT AMERICAN COOKOUT - Linen - Town & Country Linen Corp.
GREAT AMERICAN CROSS-COUNTRY ROAD RACE - Computer software - Activision, Inc.
GREAT AMERICAN DIET, THE - Vitamins and nutritional supplements - GLQ Inc.
GREAT AMERICAN EATING CARD - Cookies - Great American Cookie Co., Inc.
GREAT AMERICAN FARMS - Fruits and vegetables - Van Buren County Fruit Exchange
GREAT AMERICAN FUN - Toys and games - Great American Fun Corp.
GREAT AMERICAN HEROES - Trading cards and stamps - Great American Pastime Inc.
GREAT AMERICAN HITS - Wallpaper - Imperial Wallcoverings, Inc.
GREAT AMERICAN HOME COLLECTION - Floor coverings–carpet and rugs ✩ - Karastan-Bigelow Inc.

✩ = Now out of production

GREAT AMERICAN HOMEMAKER, THE - Manufactured homes - Redman Industries, Inc.

GREAT AMERICAN KIDS STARRING THE PURPLEBALLOON PLAYERS - Recording label - Great American Audio Corp.

GREAT AMERICAN KITCHEN & BATH 2, THE - Wallpaper ☆ - Kingfisher Wallcoverings

GREAT AMERICAN KITCHEN, THE - Wallpaper ☆ - Kingfisher Wallcoverings

GREAT AMERICAN LEATHERWORKS - Belts, handbags, etc. - Marco Avane

GREAT AMERICAN LOOKS - Eyeglasses - Pan Optics, Inc.

GREAT! AMERICAN OAK - Desks - Cowden Metal Specialties, Inc.

GREAT AMERICAN OAK - Furniture–wood - Cowden Metal Specialties, Inc.

GREAT AMERICAN OPTION - Wigs, hair-care products - International Hairgoods Inc.

GREAT AMERICAN ORIGINALS - Shirts - Century Place Inc.

GREAT AMERICAN PERM, THE - Hair care products - Systems by Marfonzo

GREAT AMERICAN PIT STOP COMPETITION - Advertising agencies - Group Five Sales, Inc.

GREAT AMERICAN POPCORN MACHINE - Popcorn poppers ☆ - Sunbeam-Oster Household Products

GREAT AMERICAN PUZZLE FACTORY - Puzzles - Great American Puzzle Factory Inc.

GREAT AMERICAN SING-ALONG, THE - Recording label - MMO Music Group Inc.

GREAT AMERICAN SOFTWARE - Computer software - Great American Software Inc.

GREAT AMERICAN SONG MACHINE - Recording label - Spanda Records

GREAT ATLANTIC SHIRT COMPANY - Apparel and accessories - Spring Ford Knitting Co., Inc.

GREAT AWAKENING, THE - Electronic equipment - Thomson Consumer Electronics, Inc.

GREAT AWAKENINGS - Pillows - Kmart Corp.

GREAT BAKED - Cookies - Acme Food Specialties Inc.

GREAT BAKES - Breads–mixes - DCA Food Industries, Inc.

GREAT BALLS OF FIRE - Candy - Creative Confection Concepts, Inc.

GREAT BALLS OF FIRE - Candy ☆ - Glenn Confections Inc.

GREAT BALLS OF FIRE - Fireworks - Red Rocket Fireworks Co., Inc.

GREAT BARRIER - Apparel and accessories - Outback Trading Co. Ltd.

GREAT BARRIER LADDER, THE - Ladders–plastic - Lomart Industries

GREAT BAY - Wrenches - Gregory Fossella

GREAT BAY LACE COMPANY - Linen - Great Bay Lace Co., Inc.

GREAT BEAR - Auto-repair franchise - Great Bear Automotive Centers Inc.

GREAT BEAR - Computer software - Great Bear Technology Inc.

GREAT BEAR - Water–bottled or canned - Great Bear Spring Co.

GREAT BEAR - Water–mineral - Perrier Group of America Inc.

GREAT BEGINNINGS - Meat products–canned - Hormel Foods Corp.

GREAT BICYCLE RACE, THE - Games - Addison-Wesley Publishing Co.

GREAT BIG BERTHA - Golfing equipment - Callaway Golf Co.

GREAT BIG PARADE GAME - Toys - Hasbro, Inc.

GREAT BLOCK - Brake parts - Raybestos/Brake Parts Inc.

GREAT BODY - Hair care products ☆ - Clairol Inc.

GREAT BODY GAINERS - Diet supplement - Great Earth International Inc.

GREAT BRANDS-LOW PRICES-NICE FOLKS - Housewares - Best Brands Plus, Inc.

GREAT BREATH - Candy - Pharmavite Corp.

GREAT BRUSH - Curling irons–electric - Helene Curtis Industries Inc.

GREAT BUCKIN FOOD - Glassware–household - Lettuce Entertain You Enterprises

GREAT B.U.T.T. - T-shirts–men's - MSW Distributor

GREAT CAESAR - Salad dressings–bottled - Johnny's Enterprises Inc.

GREAT CAMPAIGN - Furniture - Taylor-Ramsey Corp.

GREAT CARE - Curling irons–electric - Helene Curtis Industries Inc.

GREAT CHANGE - Hair care products - Helene Curtis Industries Inc.

GREAT CHEESES OF FRANCE - Cheese - Schratter Foods Inc.

GREAT CHEFS - Publisher's imprints - GCI Inc. (Great Chefs Television/ Publishing Div.)

GREAT CHICAGO PIZZA COMPANY - Food products - Vienna Sausage Manufacturing Co.

GREAT CHOCOLATE CHIP COOKIES - Cookies - Nature's Warehouse Inc.

GREAT CHOCOLATE COVER-UP, THE - Chocolate sauce - Sara Brook Desserts Inc.

GREAT CIRCLE - Computer software - Geodesic Systems, Inc.

GREAT COAT - Paints - Montgomery Ward & Co. Inc.

GREAT COCONUT - Confections - Nabisco Foods Group

GREAT CONNECTIONS - Apparel and accessories - J.C. Penney Co., Inc.

GREAT COOKERY, THE - Cheese - Bruder Dairy Products Co.

GREAT COOKIE, THE - Cookies - Great Cookie Ltd.

GREAT CREATION - Vitamins and nutritional supplements - Tea Garden Products, Inc.

GREAT CREATOR, THE - Computer software - Professor Corp.

GREAT CRISPS! - Crackers - Nabisco Foods Group

GREAT CURL - Curling irons–electric - Helene Curtis Industries Inc.

GREAT DANE - Cheese - Chesman Inc.

GREAT DANE - Musical instrument accessories - Trophy Music Co.

GREAT DANE - Pipes - Missouri Meerschaum Co.

GREAT DATE - Apparel–women's - Wacoal America Inc.

GREAT DATE - Dolls - Mattel, Inc.

GREAT DATES - Toys - Tonka Corp.

GREAT DAY - Apparel stores–lingerie - Goddess Bra

GREAT DAY - Floor coverings–carpet and rugs - Quaker Inc.

GREAT DAY - Fruit drinks–bottled or canned - Soda Mate Enterprises Inc.

GREAT DAY - Hair coloring preparations - Clairol Inc.

GREAT DAY/AM - Vitamins and nutritional supplements - Nikken Inc.

GREAT DAY AT THE RACES, A - Computer software - Philips Interactive Media of America

GREAT DESIRE - Floor coverings–carpet and rugs ☆ - World Carpets, Inc.

GREAT DISHES - Cookware - Regal Ware, Inc.

GREAT DIVIDE - Building materials–asbestos - Champion International Corp.

GREAT DIVIDE GD - Recording label - Great Divide Inc.

GREAT DOWN HILL SKI GAME, THE - Games - Franklin Merchandising Co.

GREAT DRAGON - Vitamins and nutritional supplements - Ethical Nutrients

GREAT DRY - Curling irons–electric - Helene Curtis Industries Inc.

GREAT EASTERN SUN - Teas - Great Eastern Sun Trading Co. Inc.

GREAT EGG - Food products ☆ - Sunnyfresh Inc.

GREAT EGG-SPECTATIONS - Novelty goods - Kristen DeLamar

GREAT EGGSCAPE, THE - Eggs - Wakefern Food Corp.

GREAT EGGSPECTATIONS - Food products - Topco Associates, Inc.

GREAT ENCLOSURE - Weather stripping ☆ - Oatey Co.

GREAT ENDING - Hair care products - Helene Curtis Industries Inc.

GREAT ENTERTAINER, THE - Cheese - Bruder Dairy Products Co.

GREAT EVENT - Floor coverings–carpet and rugs ☆ - Galaxy Carpet Mills Inc.

GREAT EXPECTATIONS - Beauty shops - Great Expectations Precision Haircutters

GREAT EXPECTATIONS - Floor coverings–carpet and rugs ☆ - Cabin Crafts Carpets

GREAT EXPECTATIONS - Recording label - I AM Records

GREAT EYE SHOW, THE - Eye-makeup kits ☆ - Cosrich Inc.

GREAT FACE MAKER, THE - Makeup kits ☆ - Cosrich Inc.

GREAT FACT GAME, THE - Computer software - Southwest Edpsych Services Inc.

GREAT FEELING - Wigs - Revlon General Wig Manufacturers, Inc.

GREAT FEELING - Wigs - Roux Laboratories, Inc.

GREAT FEELING NEW BREED - Hair care products - Revlon Consumer Products Corp.

GREAT FINISH - Cosmetics - Maybelline Co.

GREAT FINISHES - Paints - Ace Hardware Corp.

GREAT FIT, A - Brassieres (Bras) - Playtex Apparel, Inc.

GREAT FLIPPO - Toys–stuffed - Animal Fair Inc.

GREAT FLOSS - Candy - Great Western Products Inc.

GREAT FOOD IN A FLASH - Ovens–microwave - Quadlux, Inc.

GREAT FOOTWEAR FOR THE GREAT OUTDOORS - Footwear - Dunham Boot Makers

GREAT FORMATION - Cosmetics - Chem Spray Aerosols Inc.

GREAT FUDGE - Fudge - Nabisco Foods Group

GREAT GAME COMPANY - Easels ☆ - I.J.E. Inc.

GREAT GATSBEAR - Toys–stuffed ☆ - Gund, Inc.

GREAT GIFTS - Publisher's imprints - Cowles Creative Publishing, Inc.

GREAT GLASS - Glass–stained - Plaid Enterprises, Inc.

GREAT-GO-TOGETHERS - Skirts–girls' ☆ - R. & M. Kaufmann

GREAT GOLIATHS - Candy ☆ - Willy Wonka Brands

GREAT GRAND POP ICE STICKS - Candy - Leonhardt Inc.

GREAT GRANOLA - Cereal - Natural Ovens of Manitowoc Inc.

GREAT GRAPE APE - Chewing gum ☆ - Amurol Confections Co.

GREAT GRAPEFRUIT DIET - Health care products - Futurebiotics

GREAT GRAPHIC ORIGINALS - Giftware ☆ - Great Graphic Originals

GREAT GRASSCLOTHS OF CHINA - Wallpaper - K.M.L. Industries

GREAT GRAVY - Astringents - Agway Country Foods Inc.

GREAT GREEN - Garden equipment - Garden Pals, Inc.

GREAT GREETINGS - Giftware - Wald Designs Acrylic Idea Factory

GREAT GREETINGS - Greeting cards - P.S. Greetings

GREAT GRID - Cooking equipment–household - Thermos Co.

GREAT GRILLSBY - Meat products - Glenmark Industries, Ltd.

☆ = Now out of production

GREAT GRIP - Artists' materials - Rose Art Industries, Inc.

GREAT GRIP - Tools - Great Neck Saw Manufacturers, Inc.

GREAT GRIZZLY - Fireworks - Great Grizzly, Inc.

GREAT GUMBALL GAME, THE - Games - Warren Industries Inc.

GREAT GUN - Curling irons–electric - Helene Curtis Industries Inc.

GREAT GURIANOS - Video games - Taito America Corp.

GREAT GUSTO - Chili–canned - Pacific Valley Foods

GREAT HAIR - Vitamins and nutritional supplements - Val Vasilef Vital Products, Inc.

GREAT HALL - Furniture ☆ - Virginia House Furniture Corp.

GREAT HARVEST BREAD CO. - Bakery products - Great Harvest Franchising, Inc.

GREAT HILL ROAD COLLECTION, THE - Furniture - Riverside Furniture Corp.

GREAT HYMNS OF FAITH - Publisher's imprints - Carlsongs of America Inc.

GREAT IDEA COLLECTION - Dinnerware–plastic - Grainware Co.

GREAT ILLUSTRATED CLASSICS - Publisher's imprints - Playmore Inc. Publishers

GREAT IMPRESSIONS - Cosmetics - Chem Spray Aerosols Inc.

GREAT IMPRESSIONS - Food products - PFP Speciality Foods Inc.

GREAT IMPRESSIONS - Salad dressings–bottled - American Specialty Foods Inc.

GREAT JONES - Recording label - Island Records Inc.

GREAT LADY - Perfumes - Evyan Perfumes Inc.

GREAT LAKE - Beverages–malt - Kalamazoo Brewing Co., Inc.

GREAT LAKES - Charcoal - Imperial Products Corp.

GREAT LAKES - Corn, soybean, and alfalfa seed - Great Lakes Hybrids, Inc.

GREAT LAKES - Footwear - Wolverine World Wide, Inc.

GREAT LAKES - Fruits and vegetables - MBG Marketing

GREAT LAKES - Furniture - Algoma Net Co.

GREAT LAKES - Honey ☆ - Hubbard Beef Supply

GREAT LAKES - Lighting equipment–aircraft ☆ - Dove Foods

GREAT LAKES - Pretzels - Great Lakes Pretzel Co.

GREAT LAKES - Recording label - Casino Record Inc.

GREAT LAKES - Sugar–granulated, refined, or powdered - Savannah Foods and Industries Inc.

GREAT LAKES - Water purification systems - Aquatic Eco-Systems, Inc.

GREAT LAKES ADVISORS - Banks–commercial - Great Lakes Advisors, Inc.

GREAT LAKES BFE - Chemical preparations - Great Lakes Chemical Corp.

GREAT LAKES BOOKS - Publisher's imprints - Wayne State University Press

GREAT LAKES DBS - Chemical preparations - Great Lakes Chemical Corp.

GREAT LAKES HAMMOCKS - Hammocks - Gleason Corp.

GREAT LAKES NAVY - Hammocks - Algoma Net Co.

GREAT LAKES PACKAGING CORPORATION - Packaging–paper - Great Lakes Packaging Corp.

GREAT LAKES SPECIAL - Boats–motor ☆ - Sport-Craft Inc.

GREAT LAKES TFP - Chemical preparations - Great Lakes Chemical Corp.

GREAT LAKES TRADING CO. - Apparel and accessories - Wolverine World Wide, Inc.

GREAT LASH - Cosmetics - Maybelline Co.

GREAT LEAP'N LENTILS - Soups–canned - Buckeye Beans & Herbs, Inc.

GREAT LENGTHS - Bathing suits - Apparel Ventures, Inc.

GREAT LENGTHS - Pillows - American Fiber Industries Corp.

GREAT LENGTHS - Shelving units–metal - Lee Rowan Co.

GREAT LIFE - Paints - Martin-Senour Co.

GREAT LIFE - Toiletries - Parfum de Coeur Ltd.

GREAT LINE - Cosmetics - Maybelline Co.

GREAT LIP - Cosmetics - Maybelline Co.

GREAT LIP - Lipsticks - Maybelline Intermediate Co.

GREAT LITE WHALE, THE - Cookies - Fleetwood Snacks Inc.

GREAT LITTLE DESSERTS - Food products - Conagra, Inc.

GREAT LITTLE WORD GAME, THE - Games - Hasbro, Inc.

GREAT LIVES - Publisher's imprints - Charles Scribner's Sons

GREAT LOOKS - Underwear and nightwear ☆ - Fruit of the Loom Inc.

GREAT MAINE TO CALIFORNIA RACE, THE - Computer software ☆ - Spinnaker Software Corp.

GREAT MISTAKES - Apparel–athletic - East Coast Trading Co. Inc.

GREAT MOMENTS IN GOLFING - Statues - Aus-Ben Studios

GREAT MOMENTS IN HISTORY - Dolls ☆ - Effanbee Doll Corp.

GREAT MOMENTS IN LITERATURE - Dolls ☆ - Effanbee Doll Corp.

GREAT MOMENTS IN MUSIC - Dolls ☆ - Effanbee Doll Corp.

GREAT MOMENTS IN SPORTS - Dolls ☆ - Effanbee Doll Corp.

GREAT MOMENTS IN TELEVISION - Dolls ☆ - Effanbee Doll Corp.

GREAT MONSTER PARTY, THE - Electronic equipment ☆ - Texas Instruments Inc.

GREAT MORNINGS - Wallpaper ☆ - Andover Wallcovering

GREAT MORNINGS II - Wallpaper ☆ - Andover Wallcovering

GREAT MORNINGS III - Wallpaper - Andover Wallcovering

GREAT MOVES - Consulting services - Argonaut Relocation Services LLC

GREAT NATURE - Apples - G & G Orchards

GREAT NECK - Tools - Great Neck Saw Manufacturers, Inc.

GREAT NEWS - Apparel–women's - Wacoal America Inc.

GREAT NEWS - Paints - United Coatings, Inc.

GREAT NORTHERN - Cereal - Nieland Marketing, Inc.

GREAT NORTHERN - Shoes - Interco Inc.

GREAT NORTHERN ARTS - Recording label - Broadbeach Records

GREAT NORTHWEST - Apparel–men's - Fred Meyer, Inc.

GREAT NORTHWEST RECORD COMPANY - Compact discs–prerecorded - Great Northwest Productions

GREAT NUMBER CHASE, THE - Computer software ☆ - Milliken Publishing Co. (Computer Software Div.)

GREAT NUT - Ice cream - Taste the Tropics, Inc.

GREAT NUT FUDGE - Fudge - Nabisco Foods Group

GREAT OAK - Cases–vanity - Doors Inc.

GREAT OAK - Water–bottled or canned - Great Oak Spring Water

GREAT OAKS - Recording label - John Hughes

GREAT ONES, THE - Curling irons–electric - Helene Curtis Industries Inc.

GREAT OUTDOORS - Apparel and accessories ☆ - Gordon & Ferguson of Delaware, Inc.

GREAT OUTDOORS - Floor coverings–carpet and rugs ☆ - Playfield International Inc.

GREAT OUTDOORS - Food products - Edlin Sales

GREAT OUTDOORS - Lighting fixtures - Big Beam Emergency Systems Inc.

GREAT OUTDOORS PUBLISHING CO. - Publisher's imprints - Great Outdoors Publishing Co.

GREAT PAPERS! - Stationery - Taylor Corp.

GREAT PATTERN MIX-UP - Crocheted and knitted items - Winston Manufacturing Corp.

GREAT PERFORMERS - Respirators - Respironics, Inc.

GREAT PET - Pet products - Art J. Jones Corp.

GREAT PHONE CARD 19, THE - Telephone accessories - Centerpiece Communications, Inc.

GREAT PIG - Toys–banks - A.J. Renzi Plastic Corp.

GREAT PLAINS - Agricultural machinery - Great Plains Manufacturing, Inc.

GREAT PLAINS - Shoes - Federated Department Stores, Inc.

GREAT PLAINS - Vitamins and nutritional supplements - Yerba Prima, Inc.

GREAT PLAINS DYNAMICS - Computer software - Great Plains Software Inc.

GREAT PLAINS FOODS - Meat products - Great Plains Foods Co.

GREAT PLANES - Toys–airplanes - Hobbico Inc.

GREAT PLATE - Trays ☆ - Kenro Inc.

GREAT POP - Popcorn - Great Western Products Inc.

GREAT POSSIBILITIES - Magazines - Georgia-Pacific Corp.

GREAT PRETENDERS - Perfumes ☆ - Spilo/Mehaz Worldwide

GREAT PRINT - Kraft linerboard - Georgia-Pacific Corp.

GREAT PROTECTOR - Locks–padlocks - Cycle Products Co.

GREAT PROTECTOR, THE - Vitamins and nutritional supplements - Tea Garden Products, Inc.

GREAT PROVIDENCE BREWING CO., THE - Apparel and accessories - Great Providence Brewing Co.

GREAT PUT ON, THE - Meat sauces ☆ - Nalley's Fine Foods

GREAT PYRAMID, THE - Pet products - Aquarium Pharmaceuticals, Inc.

GREAT RAILS - Toys–trains - Life-Like Products Inc.

GREAT RANDOM SHAKES - Siding - ABT Co., Inc.

GREAT RECIPE - Food products ☆ - Uncle Ben's, Inc.

GREAT RECIPES - Food products - Great Recipes, Inc.

GREAT RED - Wines - St. Julian Wine Co.

GREAT RIVER MARKET COOPERATIVE OF GROWERS AND FOOD ARTISANS - Fruits and vegetables - Alyson's Apple Orchard Inc.

GREAT RIVER WINERY - Wines - Windsor Vineyards & Great River Winery

GREAT ROOM BY COUNTRY COACH - Motor vehicles–motor homes ☆ - Country Coach, Inc.

GREAT SAFES - Safes - Empire Safe Co. Inc.

GREAT SCAPES - Flagstones - Best Block Co.

GREAT SCENTS - Deodorizers - Dial Corp.

GREAT SCOT - Coffee - Great Scott Inc.

GREAT SCOT - Golfing equipment - Tommy Armour Golf Co.

GREAT SCOTT - Baked beans–canned ☆ - Marshfield Foods

GREAT SEAL OF FLORIDA INTERNATIONAL UNIVERSITY FIU SPES SCIENTIA FACULTAS 1965 - Jewelry - Florida International University

GREAT SEX IN A BOTTLE - Vitamins and nutritional supplements - Shana Shoblaska

GREAT SHAKES - Beverages–carbonated - Worldwide Beverage Co.

GREAT SHAKES - Medical apparatus ☆ - Wahl Clipper Corp.

GREAT SHAKES - Novelty items - Securitag Corp.

GREAT SHAPE - Cosmetics - Revlon Consumer Products Corp.

GREAT SHAPE - Dairy products - Maola Milk and Ice Cream Co.

GREAT SHAPE - Health care products ☆ - Futurebiotics

GREAT SHAPE BARBIE - Dolls - Mattel, Inc.

GREAT SHAPES - Calendars ☆ - American Greetings Corp.

GREAT SHAPES - Hosiery - Kayser-Roth Corp.

GREAT SHAPES - Trimmings–metal - Wolverine Technologies

GREAT SHOTS - Golfing equipment - Marvin I. Nelson

GREAT SKOTT - Candy - Great Skott Foods, Inc.

GREAT SMOKY GLAZED - Candles - Great Smoky Mt Candle Co.

GREAT SOUTHERN - Paints - Diamond/Kuhn Paint Co.

GREAT SOUTHERN - Recording label - Great Southern Record Co. Inc.

GREAT SOUTHERN - Seafood products–fresh or frozen ☆ - Central Seaway Co.

GREAT SOUTHERN BBQ - Publisher's imprints - GCI Inc. (Great Chefs Television/Publishing Div.)

GREAT SOUTHERN SAUCE COMPANY - Sauces - Crecorp, Inc.

GREAT SOUTHWEST TACO CO., THE - Food products - H & M Foods Systems Co., Inc.

GREAT SPACE RACE, THE - Computer software - Hartley Courseware Inc.

GREAT SPIRIT & LITTLE SPIRIT - Toys–stuffed ☆ - Gund, Inc.

GREAT START - Computer software - Houghton Mifflin Co.

GREAT STARTS - Food products - Campbell Soup Co.

GREAT STATES - Lawn mowers - Great States Corp.

GREAT STUF - Belts–apparel - Great Stuf International Inc.

GREAT STUFF - Analgesics - Hobe Labs Inc.

GREAT STUFF - Sealant - Insta-Foam Products, Inc.

GREAT SUEDE - Fabrics–broadcloth ☆ - Collins & Aikman Corp.

GREAT SUNBELT - Fruits and vegetables - MBG Marketing

GREAT SWEATS - Sportswear ☆ - Levi Strauss & Co.

GREAT SWORDSMAN - Video games - Taito America Corp.

GREAT TASTE - Water purification systems - Marigny Corp.

GREAT TASTE! GREAT PRICE PIZZA!PIZZA! - Food products - Little Caesar Enterprises, Inc.

GREAT TASTE OF GOOD HEALTH, THE - Pancakes–mixes - Conagra, Inc.

GREAT TASTING - Health care products - Yampa Valley Products

GREAT TEACHERS LIBRARY - Recording label - Brenzel Publishing, Inc.

GREAT TEAS OF BRITAIN - Teas–herbal ☆ - Chase Collection, Inc.

GREAT TEAS OF CHINA, THE - Teas ☆ - First Colony Coffee and Tea Co. Inc.

GREAT TEX - Glass–stained - Plaid Enterprises, Inc.

GREAT THINGS - Candy - ACB/Richard Watson

GREAT THREADS - Apparel and accessories - Great Threads, Inc.

GREAT TIME MACHINE - Electrical equipment ☆ - Quasar Co.

GREAT TIMES - Apparel and accessories - Kellwood Co.

GREAT TIMES - Apparel–women's - Sally Gee Inc.

GREAT TRAIN STORE, THE - Apparel - Great Train Store Partners L.P.

GREAT-TREE - Wines ☆ - Bully Hill Vineyards, Inc.

GREAT VALLEY - Food products - Castle Food Products

GREAT VALU$ - Housewares - McKesson Home Health Care

GREAT VARIETY, A - Recording label - Jay Jay Record & Tape Co.

GREAT VIBES - Vibrators ☆ - Dubl Duck/Jet Set Inc.

GREAT VIBRATIONS - Plumbing fixtures–metal - ONDINE From Interbath

GREAT VILLAINS COLLECTION - Dolls - Mattel, Inc.

GREAT WALL - Beverages–alcohol - Monarch Wine Co.

GREAT WALL - Floor coverings–tile ☆ - Shep Brown Associates Inc.

GREAT WALL - Skin care products - Great Wall International Inc.

GREAT WALL - Wallpaper - Wall Fabrics Inc.

GREAT WALL BRAND - Pharmaceutical preparations - So's USA Co., Inc.

GREAT WALL ST. FORTUNE HUNT, THE - Toys–electronic ☆ - Philips Consumer Electronics Co.

GREAT WALL TEXTURE COLLECTION, THE - Wallpaper - Wall Fabrics Inc.

GREAT WALLS - Motor vehicle parts and accessories - ASC Columbus

GREAT WAY - Skin care products - Vitamin Power Inc.

GREAT WEAR - Cosmetics - Intellectual Property Holding Co.

GREAT WEEKEND - Dolls - Mattel, Inc.

GREAT WEST ENDS - Recording label - Vandor Motion Pictures, Phonorecords & Music Publishing Group

GREAT WESTERN - Apparel and accessories ☆ - Hartmarx Corp.

GREAT WESTERN - Beverages–alcohol - Canandaigua Wine Co. Inc.

GREAT WESTERN - Wines - Great Western Winery

GREAT WESTERN BAR - Candy ☆ - Henry Heide, Inc.

GREAT WESTERN FINER FOODS - Food products ☆ - American Home Food Products Inc.

GREAT WESTERN SHOOT-OUT - Computer peripheral equipment - Compton's NewMedia

GREAT WHITE - Cleaning preparations - Coast Distribution System

GREAT WHITE - Golfing equipment - Tiger Shark Golf Inc.

GREAT WHITE - Paper - Union Camp Corp. (Fine Paper Division)

GREAT WHITE - Wines - St. Julian Wine Co.

GREAT WHITE BEER - Beverages–malt - Table Bluff Brewing, Inc.

GREAT WHITE SHARK - Electrical industrial apparatus - DBNA Trademarks Holding Inc.

GREAT WHITE, THE - Backpacks - Sea World, Inc.

GREAT WHITES - Snack food ☆ - Cornnuts Inc.

GREAT WOMEN - Playing cards - Miriam Hipsh

GREAT WOODS - Wainscotting - Georgia-Pacific Corp.

GREAT WORKS OF NOBLE ARTS - Figurines - Noble Arts Inc.

GREATDIVIDE - Dinnerware–plastic ☆ - Oak Hill Industries Corp.

GREATEFUL DEAD - Apparel–children's - Grateful Dead Merchandising

GREATER EXPECTATIONS - Floor coverings–carpet and rugs - Cabin Crafts Carpets

GREATER FREEDOM - Pet products - Pet-Eze

GREATER GOOD COMPANY, THE - Beeswax - Greater Good Co.

GREATER MAGIC VIDEO LIBRARY, THE - Video production - Joe Stevens

GREATER THAN - Shirts - Greater Than, Inc.

GREATEST GAME ON DIRT - Novelty items - Arkansas Travelers Baseball Club, Inc.

GREATEST GAMES EVER PLAYED - Games - Jax Ltd.

GREATEST STORIES EVER TOLD - Containers - Home Interiors & Gifts, Inc.

GREATEST, THE - Audio equipment - Marketing Insights, Inc.-Frank Luppino Jr., and Associates

GREATFRUIT - Vitamins and nutritional supplements - Head Start Vitamin Products

GREATHOUSE - Furniture - Romweber Co.

GREATHOUSE - Furniture - Vaughan Furniture Co. Inc.

GREATLAND - Fruit drinks–bottled or canned - Dayton Hudson Corp.

GREATLINK - Computer peripheral equipment - Greatlink International, Inc.

GREATNESS STARTS UNDERNEATH - Apparel–athletic - Sports Image, Inc.

GREATPLATE - Dinnerware–plastic ☆ - Oak Hill Industries Corp.

GREATSHAPES - Exercising equipment - Foam Design Consumer Products Inc.

GREBEX - Health care products - Polam Wholesale Inc.

GRECIAN CLOCKS - Giftware - Waterford Wedgewood USA, Inc.

GRECIAN CRYSTAL - Wallpaper - Maya Romanoff Corp.

GRECIAN DELIGHT - Food products - GDF, Inc.

GRECIAN FORMULA 16 - Hair coloring preparations - Combe Inc.

GRECIAN LILAC - Nail care products - Cosmair Inc.

GRECIAN LITE - Chimes ☆ - Nutone Inc.

GRECIAN MARBLES - Floor coverings ☆ - Kentile Floors Inc.

GRECIAN PLUS - Hair coloring preparations - Combe Inc.

GRECIAN TRECO - Girdles - H.F. Robbins

GRECIAN WALL - Wallpaper ☆ - Maya Romanoff Corp.

GRECO - Flatware - Couzon USA

GRECO - Paints ☆ - Triple G Coatings Inc.

GRECO COLORS - Flatware - Couzon USA

GRECOPHON - Recording label - Fiesta Record Co. Inc.

GRECOS - Cigars - Faber, Coe & Gregg Inc.

GREE - Wire products - B.G. Electronics, Inc.

GREEBRIER PARK - Furniture–wood - Ficks Reed Co. Inc.

GREED - Apparel and accessories - Greed, Inc.

GREED GIRL - Apparel–women's - Greed, Inc.

GREEFF - Wallpaper - FSC Wallcoverings

GREEFF - Wallpaper - Greeff Fabrics Inc.

GREEK BATH - Bathtubs–enameled - Kohler Co.

GREEK CLASSICS - Food products - Casbah/Sahara Natural Foods Inc.

GREEK CUSTOM ARCHERY - Archery equipment - Archer Sports Inc.

GREEK FLAG - Olive oil - John's Import Foods, Inc.

GREEK GOURMET THE BEST FROM GREECE - Olive oil - Greek Gourmet, Ltd.

GREEK GUIDE - Publisher's imprints - Greek Directories, Inc.

GREEK ISLES - Floor coverings–carpet and rugs ☆ - Customweave Carpets Inc.

GREEK KEY BORDER - Floor coverings–carpet and rugs - Bloomsburg Carpet Industries

GREEK MAID - Underwear and nightwear - Younkers Inc.

GREEK PAGES, THE - Telephone directories - Bernstein Group, Inc.

GREEK SHELL - Frames–picture ☆ - Lenox, Inc.

GREEK SKY - Olive oil - John's Import Foods, Inc.

GREEK TEMPLE - Floor coverings - Mannington Resilient Floors

☆ = Now out of production

GREEK TUTOR - Computer software - Parsons Technology, Inc.

GREEK VILLAGE - Fruits and vegetables - Patrick Michael Mullen

GREEK VILLAGE - Olive oil - Greek Village Imports, Ltd.

GREEK WREATH - Floor coverings—carpet and rugs - Daltonian Carpet & Cushion Inc.

GREEKTOOS - Novelty items - Lowell Schlenker

GREELY SQUARE - Floor coverings ☆ - Tarkett, Inc.

GREEN - Ball bearings - Green Ball Bearing Co.

GREEN - Dinnerware - Corning Inc.

GREEN 3 - Cleaning preparations ☆ - Iron Out, Inc.

GREEN-AGAIN - Fertilizers - Weatherly Consumer Products, Inc.

GREEN AGE - Machinery - Grapar Corp.

GREEN AIR - Deodorizers - Waterbury Companies, Inc.

GREEN APE - Men's chore gloves - Boss Manufacturing Co.

GREEN APPLE - Cosmetics - Sebastian International, Inc.

GREEN APPLE - Teas - Eastern Shore Tea Co.

GREEN APPLES - Jeans—women's ☆ - Gabriel Manufacturing Co.

GREEN ARROW - Golfing equipment - Brandell Products, Inc.

GREEN-BAK - Garden equipment - Lawn & Garden Supply Co.

GREEN BAMBOO - Dinnerware—glass ☆ - Royal China & Porcelain Companies Inc.

GREEN BAY - Vegetables—frozen ☆ - Dean Foods Vegetable Co.

GREEN BAY GAMBLERS - Publisher's imprints - Stauffacher Hockey Club, LLC

GREEN BAY KIDZ CLUB - Playground equipment - Kidz Manufacturing Co., Inc.

GREEN BEAUTY - Pickles ☆ - Green Bay Foods Co.

GREEN BELT - Fertilizers - AFS, Inc.

GREEN BIRD - Dishes—earthenware ☆ - Hadley Pottery Co. Inc.

GREEN BLASTER - Drain pipe cleaners - J.C. Whitlam Manufacturing Co.

GREEN BOOK - Wallpaper - Gene McDonald

GREEN BOSS - Housewares ☆ - Amaza Laboratories Inc.

GREEN BOYS - Food products - Green Boys Foods

GREEN BRIAR - Gloves - Brookville Glove Manufacturing Co.

GREEN BROTHERS APPLE HILLS - Fruits and vegetables - Green Brothers Apple Hills

GREEN BULLET - Microphones - Shure Brothers, Inc.

GREEN CARDS - Greeting cards - Green Cards

GREEN CLAY - Hair care products ☆ - Nature de France

GREEN CLEAN - Detergents ☆ - Edward & Sons Trading Co., Inc.

GREEN CLEANER - Cleaning preparations - Hartco Inc.

GREEN COMFORT - Health care products - Lakon Herbals Inc.

GREEN CORE - Tape—adhesive - Central Products Co.

GREEN COTTON - Fabrics ☆ - Seventh Generation Wholesale Inc.

GREEN COUNTY - Snack foods - ACB/Richard Watson

GREEN CRACKED - Olives—pickled or brined - Krinos Foods, Inc.

GREEN CREST - Fungicides - Roussel-Uclaf Corp.

GREEN CROWN - Cottonseed oil—edible ☆ - CPC International Inc.

GREEN CUISINE - Vegetables—canned - Sunnyland Foods Inc.

GREEN DAY - Paper products - Green Day, Inc.

GREEN DEVIL - Food products ☆ - Trappey's Fine Foods Inc.

GREEN DIET EAZE - Diet aid - Country Life

GREEN DOG - Recording label - Green Dog Productions

GREEN DOLPHIN - Recording label - Jeree Records

GREEN DOT - Balls - Worth Inc.

GREEN DOT - Fishing tackle - Mason Tackle Co.

GREEN DRAGON - Coffee - Mills Coffee Roasting Co.

GREEN DRAGON - Food products ☆ - Trappey's Fine Foods Inc.

GREEN DRAGON - Seafood products—canned or cured - Gulf Food Products Co.

GREEN EAGLE - Golfing equipment - Green Eagle, Inc.

GREEN EARTH - Lamp bulbs—fluorescent - Cogenfax

GREEN EARTH - Pet products - Boswell R & D Inc.

GREEN EARTH - Tools—pruning - Arett Sales Corp.

GREEN EARTH CARDS - Greeting cards ☆ - Applewood Seed & Garden Group

GREEN EARTH NATURAL - Pet products - Boswell R & D Inc.

GREEN-EDGE - Filing cabinets—metal ☆ - Hedges Manufacturing Co.

GREEN EGGS AND HAM - Games - Dr. Seuss Enterprises, L.P.

GREEN ENERGY - See **CHI ENERGY**

GREEN ENERGY - Computer peripheral equipment - Mag Innovision, Inc.

GREEN ENERGY - Vitamins and nutritional supplements - Pines International, Inc.

GREEN ESSENCE - Juices - Green Foods

GREEN EXPLORER - Computer software - Microbase, Inc.

GREEN FARM HARVEST - Teas—herbal - Green Farm Herb Products

GREEN FIELDS - Note books - Leather Loft Stores, Inc.

GREEN FIRE - Sporting goods ☆ - Gold Eagle/Arnold Palmer

GREEN FLAG - Trading cards and stamps - ANCO Collector Supplies, Inc.

GREEN FLAKE PLUS - Pet products - Aquatronics-Filtronics

GREEN-FLEX - Garden equipment - Garden Pals, Inc.

GREEN FOOD CONCENTRATES - Health care products - Futurebiotics

GREEN FOREST - Paper - Fort Howard Corp.

GREEN FORTUNE - Vitamins and nutritional supplements - Earthrise Trading Co.

GREEN FRAMER DECORATIVE FINE ART ACCESSORIES, THE - Paper—stencil - Green Framer

GREEN FROG - Gloves - Good Luck Glove Co.

GREEN GALAXIE - Dinnerware—glass ☆ - Nikko Ceramics Inc.

GREEN-GARD - Electrical equipment - GB Electrical Inc.

GREEN GARDEN - Salad dressings—bottled - Green Garden Food Products, Inc.

GREEN GARDEN - Sprinklers—lawn - Green Garden Inc.

GREEN GARDEN GATE - Publisher's imprints - Cynthia Torp and Mary Dennis Kannapell Partnership

GREEN GENE - Cement - Rectorseal Corp.

GREEN GENIE - Cleaning preparations—household - Petrolon Management, Inc.

GREEN GHOST - Toys - Tonka Corp.

GREEN GIANT - Food products - Green Giant Co.

GREEN GIANT - Kitchen utensils—aluminum - Lifetime Hoan Corp.

GREEN GIANT - Vegetables—canned - Pillsbury Co.

GREEN GIANT CREATE-A-MEAL - Pasta - Pillsbury Co.

GREEN GIANT FRESH - Fruits and vegetables - New Corn Co.

GREEN GIANT SOMETHING SPECIAL! - Vegetables—canned ☆ - Green Giant Co.

GREEN GLAZE - Earthenware ☆ - Waterford Wedgewood USA, Inc.

GREEN GLEAM - Polishing rouge - John Henry Co.

GREEN-GLO - Housewares - California Wheatgrass Sprouter Co.

GREEN GLOBS'S GRAPHING EQUATIONS - Computer software - Sunburst Communications, Inc.

GREEN GLOW - Erasers ☆ - Bright Boy Abrasives

GREEN GODDESS - Salad dressings—bottled - Kraft Food Ingredients Corp.

GREEN GORILLA, THE - Apparel—athletic - James M. Thompson

GREEN GRASS - Tools—garden - Gilmour Manufacturing Co.

GREEN GREEN - Fertilizers - Greenview Lawn & Garden Products

GREEN GREETINGS - Greeting cards ☆ - Applewood Seed & Garden Group

GREEN-GRO - Lawn mowers - Tee & Gee Sales

GREEN GUIDE FOR OFF-HIGHWAY TRUCKS & TRAILERS - Publisher's imprints - K-III Directory Corp.

GREEN GURU - Food products - Deep Foods, Inc.

GREEN HAVENS - Garden equipment ☆ - The Coleman Co.

GREEN HILL - Compact discs—prerecorded - Chapel Music Group, Inc.

GREEN HILL - Food products - Saramar Corp.

GREEN HILL - Trailers—travel - Fleetwood Enterprises, Inc.

GREEN HORNET, THE - Video production - Green Hornet, Inc.

GREEN HUNTER AV - Toys—automobiles - Saban Entertainment, Inc.

GREEN HUNTER BEETLEBORG - Toys - Saban Entertainment, Inc.

GREEN ICE - Flowers, plants, and seeds - Monrovia Nursery Co.

GREEN IRON - Agricultural machinery - May-Wes Manufacturing, Inc.

GREEN ISLAND FARMS - Fruits and vegetables - Purcell International

GREEN JAY ARITHMETIC - Computer software ☆ - Quality Educational Designs Inc.

GREEN-JOYS - Shoes—athletic - Acushnet Co.

GREEN-JOYS - Shoes—athletic - Titleist & Foot-Joy Worldwide

GREEN KAMUT - Juices - Green Kamut

GREEN KNIGHT - Handles—wood - Hartwell Brothers Handle Co.

GREEN LABEL - Floor coverings - Congoleum Corp.

GREEN LABEL - Paper - Labelon Corp.

GREEN LABEL - Paper—carbon - A.B. Dick Co.

GREEN LABEL FAX PAPER - Paper - Labelon Corp.

GREEN LAKE - Food products - Valyu Pak Foods Inc.

GREEN LAKE - Hams - Green Lake Meats Inc.

GREEN LANTERN CORPS - Games ☆ - Mayfair Games, Inc.

GREEN LEAF - Fertilizers - Valu Home Centers, Inc.

GREEN LEAF - Hair care products - Bonat Inc.

GREEN LEAF - Health care products - Guy O'Neill Co.

GREEN-LEAF - Paper - Robert F. De Castro, Inc.

GREEN LEAF - Stationery - Stuart Hall Co., Inc.

GREEN LEAF - Teas ☆ - Wahyet Inc.

GREEN LEAF HERBS - Vitamins and nutritional supplements - All Natural Products, Inc.

GREEN LIGHT - Garden equipment - Lawn & Garden Supply Co.
GREEN LIGHT COMPANY - Insecticides - Green Light Co.
GREEN LINE - Cement - W.R. Meadows Inc.
GREEN LINE - Electrical equipment - Finney Co.
GREEN LINE - Paper - Rittenhouse Paper Co.
GREEN-LINE - Yarn - Tahki Imports Ltd.
GREEN LINE PREMIUM - Tape–adhesive - Capitol Adhesives Inc.
GREEN LINNET - Recording label - Green Linnet Records Inc.
GREEN LINNET RECORDS - Recording label - Green Linnet Records Inc.
GREEN-LITE - Packaging–paper - Damage Prevention Products Corp.
GREEN LYTE - Vitamins and nutritional supplements - Ameri-Pac, Inc.
GREEN MACHINE - Pumps–water ☆ - Edson Corp.
GREEN MACHINE - Tools - Homelite, Inc.
GREEN MACHINE, THE - Garden equipment - Mark Macline Inc.
GREEN MAGIC - Vitamins and nutritional supplements ☆ - Quantum, Inc.
GREEN MAGMA - Juices - Green Foods
GREEN MATH - Computer hardware - LC Technology, Inc.
GREEN MEADOW - Detergents - Hannaford Brothers Co.
GREEN MEADOWS - Butter - Hannaford Brothers Co.
GREEN MEADOWS - Food products - Richard A. Shaw Inc.
GREEN MEADOWS - Health care products - Energen Products Inc.
GREEN MEADOWS - Tools–hand-operated - Test-Rite Products Corp.
GREEN MENU - Recording label - Henry Jerome Music Inc.
GREEN MILL - Candy - Jianas Brothers Packaging Co.
GREEN MINT - Cleaning preparations–carpet and rug - Block Drug Co., Inc.
GREEN MIRACLE - Vitamins and nutritional supplements - Ultimate Living International, Inc.
GREEN MIRROR - Coatings - Lilly Industries, Inc.
GREEN MIST - Glassware–household ☆ - Lenox Crystal, Inc.
GREEN MONSTER - Apparel and accessories - Agostino D'Angelo
GREEN MOO-MIX - Flowers, plants, and seeds - Akin Seed Co.
GREEN MT. - Veterinary pharmaceutical preparations - Dairy Association Co. Inc.
GREEN MOUNTAIN - Coffee - Green Mountain Coffee Roasters, Inc.
GREEN MOUNTAIN - Firearms, accessories, and parts - Green Mountain Rifle Barrel Co., Inc.
GREEN MOUNTAIN - Food products - Cabot Creamery Cooperative, Inc.
GREEN MOUNTAIN - Health care products - Futurebiotics
GREEN MOUNTAIN - Paper–construction - Cascade School Supplies
GREEN MOUNTAIN - Water–bottled or canned - Green Mountain Springs
GREEN MOUNTAIN BEARS, THE - Toys–stuffed - Mary Meyer Corp.
GREEN MOUNTAIN BLEU - Cheese - Sugarbush Farm
GREEN MOUNTAIN COFFEE ROASTERS - Coffee - Green Mountain Coffee Roasters, Inc.
GREEN MOUNTAIN INN - Furniture - Jamestown Sterling
GREEN MOUNTAIN JACK - Cheese - Sugarbush Farm
GREEN MOUNTAIN TWIST - Teas - Vermont Tea & Maple
GREEN MUNK - Chore gloves - Boss Manufacturing Co.
GREEN NATURE - Teas–herbal - Korean Ginseng Products Co., Ltd.
GREEN O'COP BOTTOM - Paints - Valspar Corp.
GREEN OUT - Shampoos - Colorful Products Corp.
GREEN PARK INN - Furniture - Lane Upholstery (Venture Furniture Div.)
GREEN PARK PRESS - Books - Mississippi Valley Publishing, Corp.
GREEN PEPPER - Patterns–clothing - Lite Speed of Oregon
GREEN PHARMACY, THE - Vitamins and nutritional supplements - Green Pharmacy, Inc.
GREEN PILLAR - Flowers, plants, and seeds - Newplant Associates
GREEN PLANET HARMONY ON EARTH - Apparel and accessories - Green Planet, Inc.
GREEN POWER - Batteries - Eveready Battery Co., Inc.
GREEN POWER - Fertilizers - Greenview Lawn & Garden Products
GREEN PRENE - Gloves–safety - Edmont
GREEN PRIDE - Flowers, plants, and seeds - Garfield Williamson, Inc.
GREEN REFILL - Hair care products - Clairol Inc.
GREEN RIBBON - Seasonings - Flavormatic Industries Inc.
GREEN RIVER - Beverages–carbonated - Green River Corp.
GREEN RIVER - Floor coverings - Green River Lumber Inc.
GREEN RIVER - Paper–bond - Esleeck Manufacturing Co., Inc.
GREEN RIVER WORKS - Cutlery - Russell Harrington Cutlery, Inc.
GREEN ROMANCE - Tableware–china ☆ - Villeroy and Boch Tableware Ltd.
GREEN SATIN GLOVE - Soap - Harley Chemicals
GREEN SCENES - Flowers–artificial - Amlings Flowerland
GREEN SEAL - Belts–automotive - Goodyear Tire & Rubber Co.
GREEN SEAL - Lighting fixtures - Green Seal, Inc.
GREEN SERIES - Lawn mowers - Toro Co.
GREEN SHADOW - Glassware–household ☆ - Lenox Crystal, Inc.

GREEN SHIELD - Automotive oils - Quaker State Oil Refining Corp.
GREEN SHIELD - Coatings - Sherwin-Williams Automotive Finishes Corp.
GREEN SLIME - Chewing gum - Viacom International Inc.
GREEN SMITH - Meat products - Smith's Food & Drug Centers, Inc.
GREEN SMITH SMITH'S FOOD & DRUG CENTERS - Pharmacies - Smith's Food & Drug Centers, Inc.
GREEN SOAP - Pharmaceutical preparations - Century Pharmaceuticals Inc.
GREEN-SOL - Plant growth regulators - Green-Sol, Inc.
GREEN SOLUTION, THE - Paper products - Clark Material Handling Co.
GREEN SPOT - Food products ☆ - Agripac, Inc.
GREEN SPOT - Fruit drinks–bottled or canned - Green Spot Packaging, Inc.
GREEN SPRING - Milk - Green Spring Dairy Inc.
GREEN STAR - Food products - Weis Markets Inc.
GREEN START - Fertilizers - Greenview Lawn & Garden Products
GREEN STRIPE - Floor waxes - Butcher Co.
GREEN STUFF - Nutritional supplements - Gary Null & Associates, Inc.
GREEN STUFF - Pharmaceutical preparations - Aloe Gator Suncare Co.
GREEN SUPREME - Flowers, plants, and seeds - Wax Co., Inc.
GREEN SUPREME - Vitamins and nutritional supplements - Ultra Life Products Inc.
GREEN SWEEP - Chemicals - Ossian, Inc.
GREEN-T PFC - Fertilizers - Plant Food Co., Inc.
GREEN TAG - Food products ☆ - Dole Food Co., Inc.
GREEN TAG - Gypsum products - Georgia-Pacific Corp.
GREEN TEA - Teas–herbal - M.I.M.T. Corp. of USA
GREEN TEA - Vitamins and nutritional supplements - Reese Chemical Co.
GREEN TEA EXTRACT - Vitamins and nutritional supplements - Vitamin Research Products Inc.
GREEN TEA PRODUCTS - Health care products - Head Shampoo, Inc.
GREEN TEAM - Flowers, plants, and seeds - Seed Corp. of America
GREEN TEE - Socks - Synergy Enterprises Inc.
GREEN THUMB - Gloves - Becton, Dickinson and Co.
GREEN THUMB - Lawn and garden chemicals and equipment - Cotter & Co.
GREEN THUMB - Soil–potting - Millburn Peat Co. Inc.
GREEN THUMB - Spices and extracts ☆ - De Choix Specialty Foods Co.
GREEN THUNDER - Soap - Mione Manufacturing Co.
GREEN TIGER - Crocheted and knitted items - Heritage Sportswear
GREEN TIGER - Greeting cards - Green Tiger Press
GREEN TIGER - Health care products - East Earth Herb Inc.
GREEN TINGLEBERRY - Candy - Phoenix Confections Inc.
GREEN TOMALILLO SALSA - Sauces - Guiltless Gourmet, Inc.
GREEN TOMORROW - Vitamins and nutritional supplements - Hachi Jo Island Corp.
GREEN TOUCH - Gloves - Good Luck Glove Co.
GREEN TRADING U.S.A. - Dolls - Green Trading USA Corp.
GREEN TREAT - Water treating compounds - United Chemical Corp.
GREEN TREE - Fruits and vegetables - C & S Wholesale Grocers, Inc.
GREEN TREE - Meats–luncheon - M.H. Greenebaum Inc.
GREEN TREE - Recording label ☆ - Rounder Records Corp.
GREEN TURTLE - Food products - Green Turtle Cannery
GREEN-UP - Fertilizers - Jonathan Green, Inc.
GREEN UP - Flowers, plants, and seeds ☆ - Security Products Co.
GREEN VALLEY - Dishwashing compounds - Conopco, Inc.
GREEN VALLEY - Swimming pools ☆ - Doughboy Recreational Inc.
GREEN VALLEY - Vegetables–canned - Chiquita Processed Food, LLC
GREEN VALLEY - Vitamins and nutritional supplements ☆ - Pharmavite Corp.
GREEN VALLEY - Wines - Galleano Winery Inc.
GREEN VALLEY VINEYARDS - Wines - Green Valley Vineyards
GREEN VASE - Trees, stem cuttings, etc. - Treesearch
GREEN VINE - Soap - GPS, Inc.
GREEN WASHING - Detergents ☆ - Edward & Sons Trading Co., Inc.
GREEN WATER CONTROL - Pet products ☆ - Aquatronics-Filtronics
GREEN WAY SYSTEMS - Containers - Richard Green
GREEN WILLOW - Publisher's imprints - William Morrow and Co. Inc.
GREEN WOOD MUSK - Fragrance, now out of production - Cosrich Inc.
GREEN WORLD DISCOVERY - Horticultural product - J.T. Inman Co. Inc.
GREEN X - Tires - Michelin Tire Corp.
GREEN ZONE - Motors - Magnetek, Inc.
GREENADES - Chewing gum - Zeebs Enterprises, Inc.
GREENALL'S - Gin - Paterno Imports, Ltd.
GREENSAVER - Switchboards–power - William E. Lynch
GREENBACK - Banks–commercial - NTS, Inc.
GREENBACK - Fishing tackle - Ashaway Line & Twine Manufacturing Co.
GREENBAN - Insecticides - Greenban
GREENBERG - Publisher's imprints - Kalmbach Publishing Co.
GREENBERRY'S - Coffee - Greenberry's Coffee & Tea Co.

☆ = Now out of production

GREENBRIAR - Bicycles - Columbia Manufacturing Inc.
GREENBRIAR - Cabinets ☆ - Medallion Kitchens of Minnesota Inc.
GREENBRIAR - Floor coverings–carpet and rugs - Regal Rugs Inc.
GREENBRIAR - Garden equipment - Liberty Distributors Group
GREENBRIAR - Hardware - Alside Div.
GREENBRIAR - Stationery ☆ - Evergreen Press
GREENBRIAR - Vans–conversion - Coachmen Industries, Inc.
GREENBRIAR FARMS - Water–mineral - Absopure Water Co.
GREENBRIAR III - See +ENDURA SUPREME
GREENBRIAR IV - Siding - Associated Materials, Inc.
GREENBRIER - Dishes–china ☆ - Pickard Inc.
GREENBRIER - Floor coverings ☆ - Congoleum Corp.
GREENBRIER - Furniture - Pilliod Co.
GREENBRIER - Furniture ☆ - Mersman Furniture Co.
GREENBRIER - Glassware–household - Federal Glass
GREENBRIER - House furnishings ☆ - Kellwood Co.
GREENBRIER - Tobacco products - John Middleton Inc.
GREENBRIER - Water–mineral - CSX Hotels, Inc.
GREENBRIER STUDIOS - Placemats - Bright of America Inc.
GREENCASTLE SOAP - Soap - Greencastle Inc.
GREENCO MAID - Apparel–women's - E. Greenwald & Sons Inc.
GREENCOOL - Chemical preparations - Greencool Washington Inc.
GREENCOOL CFC FREE & ENERGY SAVING REFRIGERANTS - Chemical
  preparations - Greencool Washington Inc.
GREENE KING - Beverages–malt - Wolfgang Morandell Import
GREENE KING ABBOT ALE - Beverages–malt - Thames America Trading
  Co. Ltd.
GREENE VALLEY - Flowers, plants, and seeds - Page Seed Co.
GREENEARTH CONTAINERS - Containers–trash - Project Together We
  Stand, Inc.
GREENER PASTURES - Bedding–linen - Dan River Inc.
GREENER PASTURES - Computer software - Charlie A. Webb
GREENERY, THE - Lawn mowers ☆ - Mr. Chain
GREENERY TO GO! - Flowers - International Flower Imports, Inc.
GREENE'S - Fish–fresh or frozen - Blue Lakes Trout Farm Inc.
GREENE'S FARM - Food products - Stokes/Ellis Foods
GREENE'S MINERAL PASTE - Cleaning preparations–household ☆ - J.A.
  Wright & Co.
GREENEVILLE PRESS - Greeting cards - American Greetings Corp.
GREENEX - Aquatic pharmacuetical preparations ☆ - Aquatronics-Filtronics
GREENEX - Chemical preparations - Yajou USA, Inc.
GREENFIELD - Cabinets - Yorktowne Inc.
GREENFIELD - Food products - Greenfield Noodle & Specialty
GREENFIELD - Mobile homes ☆ - Wick Building Systems Inc. (Manufactured
  Home Div./North)
GREENFIELD - Tableware–china ☆ - Lenox, Inc.
GREENFIELD BOOKS - Publisher's imprints - Pierian Press
GREENFIELD CARRYALL - Sporting goods - Greenfield Industries, Inc.
GREENFIELD EASYSTAND - Bike stand - Greenfield Industries, Inc.
GREENFIELD HEALTHY FOODS - Bakery products - Greenfield Healthy
  Foods Co.
GREENFIELD INDUSTRIES - Tools–power-driven - Greenfield Industries Inc.
GREENFIELD MANOR - Clocks ☆ - SMH (US) Inc.
GREENFIELD STABILIZER - Bicycles - Greenfield Industries, Inc.
GREENFIELD VILLAGE - Furniture - A. Brandt Co. Inc.
GREENFIELD VILLAGE - Wallpaper - S.M. Hexter Co.
GREENFIRE - Chili–canned - Drew-More Inc.
GREENGENE - Flowers, plants, and seeds - Sanford Scientific, Inc.
GREENGOODS - Apparel and accessories - Smith & Hawken, Ltd.
GREENGRO - Fruits and vegetables - Lawrence Turner Co., Inc.
GREENGUARD - Coatings - W.W. Henry Co.
GREENHAVEN - Beverages–alcohol - European Beverage Co., Inc.
GREENHAYS - Recording label - Flying Fish Records Inc.
GREENHORN - Greeting cards - Hourglass Editions
GREENHOUSE - Garden equipment ☆ - Rockline Industries Inc.
GREENHOUSE - Wallpaper - Seabrook Wallcoverings, Inc.
GREENHOUSE SUPER - Paint - Continental Products Co.
GREENHOUSE, THE - Garden furniture - French & Pacific Trading Corp.
GREENHOUSE, THE - Cosmetics - Greenhouse Spa, Inc.
GREENIE - Apparel - Greenie, A Prodigy Group, Inc.
GREENIE THE SMOKE EATING GENIE - Oils–vulcanized - Enviro-Dynamics
  Inc.
GREENKEEPER - Electronic equipment - Toro Co.
GREENLAND - Shrimp–fresh or frozen ☆ - Gourmet Club Corp.
GREENLEAF - Flowers, plants, and seeds - Elk Mound Feed and Farm Supply,
  Inc.

GREENLEAF & WHITTIER - Candles - Tsumura International Inc.
GREENLEAF SOFTWARE - Computer software - Greenleaf Software Inc.
GREENLEAVES - Shoes - C. & J. Clark America, Inc.
GREENLESS - Fluxes–welding and soldering ☆ - S.O.S. Products Co., Inc.
GREENLIFTER - Office supplies - Oliner Fibre Co. Inc.
GREENLIGHT - Computer software - Elan Associates (GreenLight Software
  Division)
GREENLINE - Apparel and accessories - Glint Inc.
GREENLINE - Office supplies - Wescosa Inc.
GREENLINKS - Fertilizers - Tyler Enterprises of Elwood Inc.
GREENMARK - Cleaning preparations - Topco Associates, Inc.
GREENMASTER - Tires–airplane - Greenball Corp.
GREENOL - Fertilizers - Chevron Chemical Co.
GREENPAK - Adhesives and sealants - NPD Corp.
GREENPATCH - Flowers, plants, and seeds - Jonathan Green, Inc.
GREENPATCH BOOK, A - Publisher's imprints - Harcourt Brace & Co.
GREENPATCH GANG, THE - Books–comic - Harcourt Brace & Co.
GREENPATCH KIDS - Publisher's imprints - Harcourt Brace & Co.
GREENPEACE - Recording label - Would'n Shoe Records
GREENPEACE BLEND - Coffee - Frontier Cooperative Herbs
GREENPORT - Marine rigging - Wm. J. Mills & Co.
GREENROOM, THE - Apparel and accessories - Rich Pavel
GREENS - Computer software - Microprose Software, Inc.
GREEN'S - Paints - Green Products Co.
GREENS KEEPER - Cooking equipment–household - Rubbermaid Inc.
GREENS PLUS - Vitamins and nutritional supplements ☆ - Naturade Inc.
GREEN'S SECRET AGENT - Cleaning preparations - Green Products Co.
GREENSAIRE - Aerator - Ransomes-Cushman-Ryan
GREENSAVER - Aerator - Ransomes-Cushman-Ryan
GREENSAVER - Stationery - Paper Corp. of America
GREENSBORO DYNAMO - Apparel and accessories - Greensboro Dynamo,
  Inc.
GREENSBORO DYNAMO IFC - Apparel and accessories - Greensboro
  Dynamo, Inc.
GREENSCHOICE - Soil testing kits - Premier Environmental Products, Inc.
GREENSIDE RECORDS - Recording label - Tony Mendoza
GREENSKAPES - Garden furniture–wood - Greenskapes
GREENSKEEPER - Garden equipment ☆ - Specialty Manufacturing Co.
GREENSKEEPER - Shoes - Genesco Inc.
GREENSLEEVES - Plastics - Matt Haggstrom
GREENSPEC - Fertilizers - Greenway Services, Inc.
GREENSPEED METER - Golfing equipment - Palm Beach Plastics Inc.
GREENSPLEX - Lawn mowers - Ransomes-Cushman-Ryan
GREENSPOT - Sporting goods - Cortland Line Co., Inc.
GREENSPRING DAIRY - Milk - Johanna Foods, Inc.
GREENSPROUTS - Artificial foliage - Charcon Florals
GREENSTONE - Pharmaceutical preparations - Greenstone Ltd.
GREENSTONE - Pharmaceutical preparations - Upjohn Co.
GREENSTONE WINERY - Wines - Greenstone Winery
GREENSTREET - Apparel–women's - Orbit Industries, Inc.
GREENSWARD - Fertilizers - Tyler Enterprises of Elwood Inc.
GREENSWEEPER - Rakes - Ames Lawn & Garden Tool Co.
GREENTECH - Fertilizers - Greenway Services, Inc.
GREENTREE - Computer software - Aspen Tree Software, Inc.
GREENTREE - Frames–picture - M.W. Carr & Co. Inc.
GREENVIEW - Fertilizers - Lebanon Seaboard Corp.
GREENWARE TECHNOLOGIES - Computer peripheral equipment -
  Greenware Technologies, L.P.
GREENWEAR - Sweaters - Westbury Knitwear Co. Inc.
GREENWICH - Clocks - General Time Corp. (Westclox/Seth Thomas Div.)
GREENWICH - Dinnerware - Denby USA Limited
GREENWICH - Dinnerware–glass ☆ - Lenox, Inc.
GREENWICH - Easels - Anco Wood Specialties Inc.
GREENWICH - Floor coverings ☆ - Congoleum Corp.
GREENWICH - Food products - Tyson Foods Inc.
GREENWICH - Frames–eyeglass ☆ - Universal/Univis Inc.
GREENWICH - Toilets–enameled - Kohler Co.
GREENWICH COLLECTION - Furniture - Decorative Crafts
GREENWICH VILLAGE - Coffee - First Colony Coffee and Tea Co. Inc.
GREENWICH VILLAGE - Wallcoverings - Ben Rose Ltd.
GREENWICH WORKSHOP CHAPBOOK - Publisher's imprints - Greenwich
  Workshop, Inc.
GREENWICH WORKSHOP CLASSICS - Posters - Greenwich Workshop, Inc.
GREENWICH WORKSHOP, THE - Statuary - Greenwich Workshop, Inc.
GREENWILLOW BOOKS - Publisher's imprints - William Morrow and Co. Inc.
GREENWOOD - Easels ☆ - Anco Wood Specialties Inc.

☆ = Now out of production

GREENWOOD - Fabrics - Greenwood Mills Inc.
GREENWOOD - Furniture–wood - Calder Manufacturing Co.
GREENWOOD - Water–bottled or canned - Greenwood Springs Water
GREENWOOD PRESERVATIVE - Paints - Chilton Paint Co.
GREENWOOD RIDGE VINEYARDS - Wines - Greenwood Ridge Vineyards
GREENWOOD'S - Food products - Curtice-Burns Foods, Inc.
GREER - Fruits–canned - Jones Brothers Canning Co.
GREER'S - Food products - Autry Greer and Sons Inc.
GREER'S - Hair curlers - Greer's Hair Replacement Co.
GREETEES - Greeting cards - Duck Press
GREETER - Chimes ☆ - Nutone Inc.
GREETING ART - Posters - Noteworthy
GREETING BOX - Publisher's imprints - Opine Consultants
GREETING CARD BANNER - Paper–rolls - Life Lines, Inc.
GREETING CARD PACKAGING - Giftware - Contemporary Inc.
GREETING DISC, THE - Compact discs–prerecorded - ANS Records Inc.
GREETING GAMES - Greeting cards with games ☆ - American Publishing Corp.
GREETING MONSTERS - Toys–stuffed - Sandra Boynton
GREETING MUG, THE - Novelty items ☆ - Papel Freelance, Inc.
GREETING SCENTS - Greeting cards - Great Northwestern Greeting Seed Co.
GREETING SEEDS - Greeting cards - Great Northwestern Greeting Seed Co.
GREETING STICKERS - Paper–gummed ☆ - Moderne Card Co. Inc.
GREETING SUDS - Greeting cards - Great Northwestern Greeting Seed Co.
GREETING TEAS - Greeting cards - Great Northwestern Greeting Seed Co.
GREETING TREE AND GREETER, THE - Stationery - Peg Brenner Associates
GREETING U - Greeting cards - American Greetings Corp.
GREETINGPADS - Dishcloths ☆ - Now Designs
GREETINGRAM - Greeting cards - Roberta Edwina Madison
GREETINGS - Computer software - Parsons Technology, Inc.
GREETINGS - Lenses–magnifying - C. Bennett Scopes Inc.
GREETINGS BY GLYNDA - Greeting cards - Glynda Turley Prints Inc.
GREETINGS FROM TINSEL TOWN - Greeting cards ☆ - Remigraphics, State of the Heart
GREETINGS FROM YOUR COMPUTER - Computer software - Softtech Animation, Inc.
GREETINGS INC. - Greeting cards - Norcross Inc.
GREETINGS OF THE FUTURE - Storage-container/time capsules ☆ - Dan M. Adler
GREETINGS THAT GROW - Flowers, plants, and seeds - Applewood Seed & Garden Group
GREET'N PATCH - Greeting cards ☆ - Best Emblem & Insignia Co. Inc.
GREEVER'S - Veterinary pharmaceutical preparations - Greever's
GREG - Ophthalmic goods - Rozin Optical Export Corp.
GREG BELL - Outerwear - Ronlee Apparel Co.
GREG LEMOND - Bicycle parts and accessories - Greg Lemond
GREG MATTHEWS - Novelty items - Greg Matthews by Oggeiti
GREG 'N BRAD - Fruits–canned - Greg Orchards & Produce Inc.
GREG NORMAN - Apparel and accessories - Great White Shark Enterprises, Inc.
GREG PACK - Beverages–carbonated - Gregory Packaging Inc.
GREGG PRESS, THE - Publisher's imprints - Gregg Press
GREGG'S BANQUET - Syrup - Borden Food Service
GREGOR - Boats–motor - Gregor Boat Co.
GREGORIUS - Stringed instruments - Jim Atlas Cymbal Works
GREGORY - Musical instrument accessories ☆ - Rico International
GREGORY - Sporting goods - Bianchi International
GREGORY AND ME - Recording label - Kideo Productions, Inc.
GREGORY DESIGNS - Clothing - Focus Apparel Group Inc.
GREGORY MASTER - Musical instrument accessories - Nova Reed Corp.
GREGORY'S - Fertilizers - Gregory General Farms
GREGORYS - Perfumes - Givaudan-Roure Corp.
GREIF - Apparel–men's - Greif Cos.
GREIF NEW YORK - Apparel–men's - Greif Cos.
GREIF STUDIO - Apparel–men's - Greif Cos.
GREIGE - Cosmetics - Lancome
GREISINGER MEATS - Meat products - Crystal Food Import Corp.
GREMLIN - Bicycles - Schwinn Cycling & Fitness Inc.
GREMLIN - Guitars - Midco International
GREMLIN - Motor vehicles ☆ - DaimlerChrysler
GREMLIN - Musical instruments - Here Inc.
GREMLIN GREEN - Fishing lures - Water Gremlin Co.
GREMLINS - Candy - Brown & Haley
GREMLINS - Candy ☆ - Topps Co., Inc.
GREMLINS - Cereal - Ralston Purina Co.
GREMLINS - Giftware - Warner Bros. Inc.

GREMLINS 2 - Candy - Topps Co., Inc.
GREMLINS 2 - Watches ☆ - Genender International, Inc.
GREN-DOUCHETTES - Pharmaceutical preparations - American Hygienic Laboratories Inc.
GRENACHE - Wines - Seagram's Chateau & Estate Wines Co.
GRENADA - Milk–canned or powdered - Barber's Grenada Farms Inc.
GRENADA - Shoes ☆ - Allen-Edmonds Shoe Corp.
GRENADA AND ORLEANS - Liquors - SPAR Inc.
GRENADE - Hair care products - Grenade Inc.
GRENADE - Veterinary pharmaceutical preparations - Schering-Plough Animal Health
GRENADIER - Candy - Grandma Wheaton
GRENADIER - Crocheted and knitted items ☆ - Harwood Companies Inc.
GRENADIER - Fabrics - Dan River Inc.
GRENADIER - Figurines - Grenadier Models
GRENADIER - Floor coverings–carpet and rugs ☆ - Kelly Group Inc.
GRENADIER - Floor coverings–carpet and rugs ☆ - Porter Carpet Mills Inc.
GRENADIER - Tires - Bridgestone/Firestone, Inc.
GRENADIER - Vodka ☆ - Frank Sutton & Co.
GRENADIER HALL - Floor coverings–carpet and rugs ☆ - Downs Carpet Co. Inc.
GRENADIERS - Cigar boxes–wood - Consolidated Cigar Corp.
GRENADINE - Ships–sailing vessels ☆ - Hulls Unlimited East Inc.
GRENALD'S - Pharmaceutical preparations - American Hygienic Laboratories Inc.
GRENE - Breads - Haram-Christensen Corp.
GRENOBLE - Bicycles - Murray, Inc.
GRENOBLE - Floor coverings - Mannington Resilient Floors
GRENOBLE - Furniture ☆ - Union National Inc.
GRENOBLE - Rings–jewelry - Artcarved Inc.
GRENOBLE - Window coverings ☆ - Vertilux-Louverlux Inc.
GRENOUILLEAU - Beverages–alcohol - Ginday Imports Ltd.
GRENSON - Footwear–men's - Baker-Benjes, Inc.
GRENZQUELL - Beverages–malt ☆ - Pabst Brewing Co.
GREPA - Infants' products - International Imports
GREPSI - Soft drinks - Joel Bruce Nadler
GRES CATALAN - Terra-cotta tile - Integrity Tile Co.
GRES D ELBA - Tiles–ceramic ☆ - United Ceramic Tile Corp.
GRESAILLE - Dinnerware–glass - Arita Sales Co. Inc.
GRESHAM HALL - Floor coverings ☆ - Tarkett, Inc.
GRETA - Glassware–household ☆ - Dansk International Designs, Ltd.
GRETA - Ophthalmic goods - Rozin Optical Export Corp.
GRETA GRAPE - Toys - Mattel, Inc.
GRETA'S - Food products - Gourmet Specialties
GRETCHEN - Greeting cards - American Greetings Corp.
GRETCHEN BELLINGER - Fabrics - Gretchen Bellinger Inc.
GRETEL - Dolls - Effanbee Doll Corp.
GRETSCH - Musical instruments ☆ - Fred Gretsch Enterprises
GRETSCH-GLADSTONE - Drums–musical instruments ☆ - Fred Gretsch Enterprises
GRETTA - Pencils - J.R. Moon Pencil Co., Inc.
GRETTO - Recording label - Moss Music Group Inc.
GRETZELS - Pretzels - Gretzels Inc.
GREY ARC - Gloves - Knoxville Glove Co.
GREY BAND - Dinnerware–glass ☆ - Lenox, Inc.
GREY BOOK - Wallpaper - Gene McDonald
GREY BRUSHSTROKES - Dinnerware–glass ☆ - Lenox, Inc.
GREY CORE - Tape–adhesive - Central Products Co.
GREY EYE GLANCES - Recording label - Sojourn Hills, Inc.
GREY FLANNEL - Colognes - Geoffrey Beene Inc.
GREY FLANNEL - Colognes - Sanofi Beaute Inc.
GREY FOX - Sleeping bags - Coleman Co., Inc.
GREY FOX - Sporting goods - FTM Sports
GREY GHOST - Bicycles - Schwinn Cycling & Fitness Inc.
GREY GOOSE - Beverages–alcohol - Sidney Frank Importing Co., Inc.
GREY HAWK - Golfing equipment - Golfsmith International Inc.
GREY HAWK - Toys–models ☆ - Estes Industries
GREY HUB - Machine parts - Grey Hub Trolley Wheel Co.
GREY MATTER - Recording label - Jazz Composer's Orchestra Association Inc.
GREY OWL - Hobby kits - Grey Owl Indian Craft Co. Inc.
GREY OWL - Rice - Grey Owl Foods
GREY PINSTRIPES - Dinnerware–glass ☆ - Lenox, Inc.
GREY POUPON - Food products - Nabisco Holdings Corp.
GREY POUPON - Mustard - Nabisco Foods Group
GREY POUPON PARISIAN - Mustard - Nabisco Foods Group

☆ = Now out of production

GREY-ROCK - Automotive parts and accessories - Echlin Inc.

GREY-ROCK - Brake parts - Raybestos/Brake Parts Inc.

GREY-TECH COLLECTION, THE - Aluminum compounds ☆ - Regal Ware, Inc.

GREY TONE CLASSICS - Greeting cards - Grey Tone Classics Publications

GREY WATER ODOR CONTROL - Deodorizers - Thetford Corp.

GREYFOX SYSTEMS - Electronic equipment - Jennison Greyfox Systems, Inc.

GREYHAWK - Golfing equipment - Golfsmith International Inc.

GREYHAWK - Publisher's imprints ☆ - Tsr, Inc.

GREYHOUND - Bicycles - Ross Bicycles USA, Ltd.

GREYHOUND - Pet products - Berolina Imports

GREYHOUND - Skates–roller ☆ - Lancaster Toy Co.

GREYHOUNDS - Gloves - Jomac Products Inc.

GREYHOUNDS BY M & H - Footwear - M & H Shoes Inc.

GREYLAWN - Stationery ☆ - Crane & Co. Inc.

GREYLINE - Computers - Total Control Products, Inc.

GREYLOCK - Paper–bond - Cascade School Supplies

GREY'S - Cigarettes - Faber, Coe & Gregg Inc.

GREYSTOKE - Wallpaper - Kirk-Brummel

GREYSTONE - Dishes–earthenware ☆ - Denby USA Limited

GREYSTONE - Fabrics–wool - Worcester Co.

GREYSTONE - Shorts–men's - Amiken, Inc.

GREYSTONE - Tools–power-driven - Meijer, Inc.

GREZ-OFF - Degreasing solvents - Knight Marketing Corp.

GRF - Computers - Ascend Communications, Inc.

GRF 1000 - Fishing rods - Cortland Line Co., Inc.

GRG RECORDS - Recording label - Gabriella Productions Unlimited, Inc.

GRGICH HILLS - Wines - Grgich Hills Cellar

GRI-GLYCALC - Computer software - Gas Research Institute

GRI-HAPCALC - Computer software - Gas Research Institute

GRIBBIT - Games ☆ - Milton Bradley Co.

G.R.I.D. - Shoes - Hyde Athletic Industries Inc.

GRID 1520 - Computers–personal - Grid Systems Corp.

GRID CUTTER - Bicycles - Roadmaster Corp.

GRID-LOC - Floor coverings–carpet and rugs - Couristan Inc.

GRID-LOCK - Aircraft parts - Tolo, Inc.

GRID-LOCK - Fencing–gates and posts - Mapes Industries Inc.

GRID MAGIC - Hobby kits - Eastern Wire Products Co.

GRID RUNNER - Computer software - Virgin Interactive Entertainment, Inc.

GRID-SET - Adhesives and sealants - Interface, Inc.

GRID-SHIELD - Insulating materials - Schuller International, Inc.

GRID, THE - Synthesizers–musical instrument - Stick Enterprises, Inc.

GRID VIEW - Medical apparatus - Computerized Imaging Reference Systems, Inc.

GRID WORKS - Patterns–clothing - A.G.S., Inc.

GRIDBOARD - Paper products - Mafcote Industries, Inc.

GRIDBOARD - Plastics - Gridcore Systems International, Inc.

GRIDCASE 1520 - Computers–personal - Grid Systems Corp.

GRIDCORE INSIDE! - Building materials - Noble Franklin Corp.

GRIDD - Toys - Mattel, Inc.

GRIDDERS - Computer software - Tetragon, Inc.

GRIDDLE KING - Cooking equipment–household - Nordic Ware

GRIDDLE KING - Shortening - Miami Margarine Co. Inc.

GRIDDLE LITE - Pancakes–mixes ☆ - Arrowhead Mills, Inc.

GRIDDLE QUEEN - Cooking equipment–household ☆ - Nordic Ware

GRIDDLE TIME - Bakery products - Martha White Foods Inc.

GRIDIRON - Balls–football - Markwort Sporting Goods Co.

GRIDIRON - Ophthalmic goods - Foremost Optical Products

GRIDIRON CLUB, THE - Apparel–athletic - Bosa, Inc.

GRIDIRON GEAR - Apparel and accessories - H.H. Cutler Co.

GRIDIRON SKILLS - Trading cards and stamps - Score Group, Inc.

GRID'L-TOP - Barbecues and grills - Thermos Co.

GRIDLITE PLUS - Computers–personal - Grid Systems Corp.

GRIDLITER - Lighting fixtures - Hubbell Lighting, Inc. (Lighting Div.)

GRIDLOC - Synthetic turf - Instant Turf Industries Inc.

GRIDLOCK - Blocks–concrete - Westblock Products, Inc.

GRIDLOCK - Games - CBS Toys

GRIDLOCK - Games - Little Harbor Corp.

GRIDLOCK - Mats - Majestic Mat Co.

GRIDLOCK - Shoes - Kotoni Trading Inc.

GRIDLUX - Lighting fixtures - Hubbell Lighting, Inc. (Lighting Div.)

GRIDPLAN - Computer software - Grid Systems Corp.

GRIDPOINT - Floor coverings–carpet and rugs ☆ - J and J Industries Inc.

GRIDSTONE - Gypsum products - National Gypsum Co.

GRIDWORK - Floor coverings–carpet and rugs - J and J Industries Inc.

GRIDWORKS - Metals - Liberty Diversified Industries Inc.

GRIF-FLEX - Floor mats for vehicles - Bobby F. Griffin, Inc.

GRIFF-COAT - Coating ☆ - Griffolyn Co. Inc. (Reef Industries, Inc.)

GRIFFEN - Bicycles - Tony Free

GRIFFIN - Helmets–athletic - Canstar Sports USA

GRIFFIN - Kites - Condor Kite Co.

GRIFFIN - Knives - Arthur H. Gaebel Inc.

GRIFFIN - Paints - Winsor & Newton

GRIFFIN - Pesticides–agricultural - Griffin Corp.

GRIFFIN - Shoe accessories - Boyle-Midway

GRIFFIN - Shoe polish - Hickory Industries, Inc.

GRIFFIN - Wallpaper - Koroseal Wallcoverings

GRIFFIN B. HARDY - Dairy products ☆ - Sinton Dairy Foods Co. Inc.

GRIFFIN MEDICAL PRODUCTS - Linen - Griffin Medical Products, Inc.

GRIFFIN MUSIC - Compact discs–prerecorded - Feedback, Inc.

GRIFFIN - ST.JAMES - Jewelry - Mary Ann Paul

GRIFFIN SPORT - Fishing tackle - Ashaway Line & Twine Manufacturing Co.

GRIFFIN THUNDERZORD - Toys - Saban Entertainment, Inc.

GRIFFIN VINEYARD - Wines - Hop Kiln Winery

GRIFFINS - Cookies - Masterpeace Food Imports

GRIFFIN'S - Food products - Griffin Food Co.

GRIFFITH GOLD - Fuel pipes–motor vehicle - Griffith Oil Co., Inc.

GRIFFITH GRAY FOR ST. JOHN - Apparel–women's - St. John Knits, Inc.

GRIFFO - Barbecues and grills - Griffo Products Inc.

GRIFFOLYN - Polyvinyl sheets - Griffolyn Co. Inc. (Reef Industries, Inc.)

GRIFFON - Apparel and accessories ☆ - Genesco Inc.

GRIFFON - Cutlery - Griffon Cutlery Co.

GRIFFON - Paper–writing ☆ - Keuffel & Esser Co.

GRIFFS - Health care products ☆ - REVELATION LLC

GRIFHOLD - Tools–hand-operated - Griffin Manufacturing Co. Inc.

GRIFO - Wines - Orion Imports Ltd.

GRIFO-GEN - Vitamins and nutritional supplements - Gourmet Mushrooms Inc.

GRIFULVIN V - Pharmaceutical preparations - Ortho Pharmaceutical Corp.

GRIGIOPERLA - Perfumes - La Parfumerie Inc.

GRILL-A-MATIC - Cooking equipment–household - West Bend Co.

GRILL AMERICA - Barbecues and grills - Maverick Industries, Inc.

GRILL BITS - Dog food - Heinz Pet Products Co.

GRILL BRITE - Housewares - Alwin Products

GRILL CHEF - Cooking equipment–household - GSW Jackes-Evans Manufacturing Co.

GRILL CRAZY - Grocery stores - TAV Brands, Inc.

GRILL CREATIONS - Seasonings - Burns Philp Food Inc.

GRILL-ETTE - Barbecues and grills ☆ - Jenn-Air Corp.

GRILL FLAVOR - Spices and extracts - Kraft Food Ingredients Corp.

GRILL GOURMET - Meat products–poultry - Pierce Foods Corp.

GRILL GREAT - Food products - Jewel Food Stores Inc.

GRILL GREATS - Barbecues and grills - Du-Co Ceramics Co. Inc.

GRILL-GUIDE - Thermometers - Taylor Environmental Instruments

GRILL HAPPY - Seasonings - Peterson Concessions, Inc.

GRILL LITE 21 - Fish–fresh or frozen - Trident Seafoods Corp.

GRILL MATES - Seasonings - McCormick & Co., Inc.

GRILL MATES - Seasonings - Pacific Foods Inc.

GRILL 'N SEAR - Cookware - Williams-Sonoma, Inc.

GRILL-NU - Grill degreaser - Keromate Products Inc.

GRILL PAC - Camping products - Lindy Little Joe Inc.

GRILL PERFECT - Bacon - Hormel Foods Corp.

GRILL PLUS - Sauces - Creehan's Market Inc.

GRILL RAK BY DECKMATE - Brackets - GCHM Enterprises, Inc.

GRILL-RITE - Fireplace equipment ☆ - Thermo-Rite Manufacturing Co.

GRILL SEEKERS - Meat products–beef - Hannaford Brothers Co.

GRILL STIX - Pet food ☆ - Star-Kist Foods, Inc.

GRILL STUFF EVERYTHING BUT THE STEAK - Brushes - Mr. Bar-B-Q, Inc.

GRILL-T - Valves - Richard L. Diehl

GRILL!, THE - Barbecues and grills - Start International, Inc.

GRILL TIME - Charcoal - Royal Oak Enterprises, Inc.

GRILL TO ORDER - Barbecue sauce - Swiss American Import Co.

G'RILLA BREST II - Food products - Hester Industries, Inc.

G'RILLAS II - Meat products–poultry - Pierce Foods Corp.

GRILLBASA - Sausages - Joseph Decosta Inc.

GRILLE - Wallpaper ☆ - Maya Romanoff Corp.

GRILLE, FRENCH CRISP TOAST - Food products - Jaret Specialties Inc.

GRILLED AND FILLED - Food products - Janson's Foods Inc.

GRILLED DOGGIE - Pet products - Gimborn U.S., Inc.

GRILLER, THE - Kitchen appliances ☆ - Regal Ware, Inc.

GRILLERIE - Barbecues and grills - Toastmaster Inc.

GRILLERS - Food products - Worthington Foods Inc.

GRILLER'S WORLD - Barbecue and grill accessories - Grillers' World, Inc.

GRILLFRIEND - Cleaning preparations - ACS Industries Inc.
GRILLIN CHEF - Cooking appliances - Dazey Corp.
GRILLING BROCHURE - Publisher's imprints - National Turkey Federation
GRILLI'S - Beverages–carbonated - Grilli's Beverages
GRILLMASTER - Barbecues and grills - Sunbeam Outdoor Products Inc.
GRILLMASTER - Barbecues and grills - United States Pumice Co.
GRILLMASTER - Frankfurters - Hygrade Food Products Corp.
GRILLWORKS - Cooking equipment–household - General Housewares Corp.
GRIM CREEPER - Toys - Mattel, Inc.
GRIM REAPER - Golfing equipment ☆ - John Rouzee Green Co., Inc.
GRIM WOOD - Heating pads–electric - Chromalox
GRIMBERGEN - Beverages–malt - Thames America Trading Co. Ltd.
GRIME AWAY - Cleaning preparations - Turtle Wax, Inc.
GRIME BUSTER - Cleaning preparations - Comstar International Inc. (IPC Div.)
GRIME GRABBER - Cleaning preparations - Gent-L-Kleen Products Inc.
GRIME-OUT - Cleaning preparations ☆ - Elcal Enterprises Ltd.
GRIME POWER - Soap ☆ - Demert & Dougherty, Inc.
GRIME SOLVER, THE - Health care products - Barcolene Inc.
GRIME STOPPERS - Socks - Viking Technology Inc.
GRIMEBLASTER - Tools–hand-operated - Gilmour Manufacturing Co.
GRIMECA BRAKE COMPONENTS - Cosmopolitan Motors Inc.
GRIMEFIGHTERS - Mops - Suburbanite Industries
GRIMES - Meat products–poultry - Pennfield Farms
GRIMES AEROSPACE - Aircraft parts - Grimes Aerospace Co.
GRIMESOLV - Housewares - Stewart-Hall Chemical Corp.
GRIMLOCK - Toys - Hasbro, Inc.
GRIMMWAY - Vegetables–frozen - Grimmway Frozen Foods
GRIMMWAY FARMS - Fruits and vegetables - Grimmway Enterprises, Inc.
GRIMMY - Giftware ☆ - Enesco Corp.
GRIMOIRE - Role-playing-game accessories - Fasa Corp.
GRIMSKULL - Toys - Landmark Entertainment Group
GRIMTOOTH'S - Games - Flying Buffalo Inc.
GRIN AND GRAB IT - Garters - Russ Berrie and Co., Inc.
GRIN BEARER RAZOR - Razors - C.A. Daniels & Co.
GRIN BINS - Containers - Springs Industries, Inc.
GRIN PINS - Pins–jewelry - Pleasant Co.
GRIN REAPER - Greeting cards - Woodbridge Press Publishing Co.
GRIND-A-WAY - Grinders - Robinson Knife & Fiddlers Plastics
GRIND-ALL - Garbage disposal units–household - Emerson Electric Co.
GRIND-AWAY - Cleaning preparations–carpet and rug - Flo-Pac Corp.
GRIND INDUSTRIES - Apparel and accessories - Grind Industries
GRIND KING - Sporting goods - Donald D. Cassel
GRIND MASTER - Grinders - Gillies Coffee Co.
GRIND MAX - Grinders - Genesis Materials International
GRIND-N-JOINT - Tools - Granberg International
GRIND-O-FLEX - Abrasive products - Merit Abrasive Products, Inc.
GRIND-O-MAT - Kitchen appliances - Rival Manufacturing Co.
GRIND-O-MATIC - Kitchen appliances - Rival Manufacturing Co.
GRIND-R-GUIDE - Tools - Granberg International
GRIND-R-KIT - Tools ☆ - Granberg International
GRINDELIA - Pharmaceutical preparations - Sherwood Laboratories Inc.
GRINDER - Skin care products - Rudolph International, Inc.
GRINDER, THE - Skin care products - Sogo Inc.
GRINDEROO - Baby-food grinder - International Design Manufacturing Inc.
GRINDMASTER - Coffee - First Colony Coffee and Tea Co. Inc.
GRINDMAX - Industrial machinery - Genesis Materials International
GRINDRITE - Grinders - Ski Tuner Manufacturing, Inc.
GRINDSTONE CAFE - Cream–canned or powdered - Vsa, Inc.
GRINGO - Recording label - TMC Productions
GRINGO PREMIUM BEER - Beverages–malt - Gringo Companies Inc.
GRINGO'S BURRITOS - Food products ☆ - VIP Sales Co. Inc.
GRINIBBLES - Greeting cards - Elizabeth Charles, Inc.
GRINNELL GLOVES - Gloves ☆ - DeLong Sportswear Inc.
GRINNER - Meat products - Oscar Mayer Foods Corp.
GRINNLY BEAR - Greeting cards - Morehead, Inc.
GRINZING - Cheese - Crystal Food Import Corp.
GRIOT - Recording label - Jazz Composer's Orchestra Association Inc.
GRIOT'S GARAGE - Auto cleaning products - Griot's Garage
GRIP - Frames–picture ☆ - A.P.F. Master Framemaker
GRIP - Pencils–mechanical - Yasutomo
GRIP - Sporting goods - Grip Inc.
GRIP - Wallpaper - Conros Corp.
GRIP-A-TAC - Rackets–tennis - Gexco Enterprises
GRIP-ALL - Adhesives and sealants - Clamp-All Corp.
GRIP-ALL - Skin care products - Hess Hair Milk Laboratories Inc.
GRIP/ALL - Tools ☆ - Walton March

GRIP & GO - Limestone products - Medusa Minerals Co.
GRIP AND SEAL - Sealing compounds - Coronado Paint Co.
GRIP BAND - Sporting goods - Unique Sports Products Inc.
GRIP CHECK - Gloves–leather - Ajay Leisure Products Inc.
GRIP-CLAMP - Tools–machine - Aladdin Engineering & Manufacturing, Inc.
GRIP CLIP - Clamps - Paine Co.
GRIP/CLIP - Health care products - Maddak Inc.
GRIP COAT - Adhesives and sealants - Garon Products Inc.
GRIP COUNTER - Exercising equipment ☆ - Precise International/Wenger
GRIP-CRETE - Paints - Waterlox Coatings Corp.
GRIP DECK - Paints - Fuller-O'Brien Paints Inc.
GRIP EASY-STRIP - Adhesives and sealants - Mantrose-Haeuser Co. Inc.
GRIP FAST - Hobby kits - Time Saver Tool Corp.
GRIP FIT - Pet products - Decker Manufacturing Co.
GRIP FLEX - Gloves - Mizuno Golf Co.
GRIP-IT - Signs - Joseph Struhl Co., Inc.
GRIP-IT - Tools - Klein Tools Inc.
GRIP-ITS - Housewares - Selfix, Inc.
GRIP-KOTE - Rubber–synthetic - Marine Development & Research Corp.
GRIP-LIP - Flower pots–plastic - Nursery Supplies West Inc.
GRIP-LOC - Adhesives and sealants - Grip Rip, Inc.
GRIP-LOCK - Automotive parts and accessories ☆ - Lancaster Colony Automotive Group
GRIP-LOCK - Bathroom accessories - Kinkead/Tub/Shower Doors
GRIP-LOCK SYSTEM - Luggage - Hartmann Luggage Co.
GRIP-LOK - Bags ☆ - Canover Industries Inc.
GRIP-LOK - Doors–metal - Pioneer Industries
GRIP MASTER - Bowling balls - Master Industries Inc.
GRIP-MASTER - Fertilizers ☆ - Luster Leaf Products Inc.
GRIP-MAT - Mats - Warp Bros.
GRIP MODELED AFTER THE F-4 PHANTOM. - See **PFCS-PRO FLIGHT CONTROL SYSTEM**
GRIP N' LIFT - Gloves - Ulico
GRIP-N-STICK - Adhesives and sealants - Panelmatch
GRIP-ON - Paints - Martin Paint Stores
GRIP-ON - Pliers - Anglo American Enterprises Corp.
GRIP RIP ELIMINATOR, THE - Medical apparatus - Quality Medical and Sports, Inc.
GRIP RITE - Handles–rubber - Americo Manufacturing Co. Inc.
GRIP-RITE - Pencils - Hoyle Products Inc.
GRIP-RITE - Screws - Prime Source Building Products, Inc.
GRIP-RITE COLLATED FASTENERS - Staples - Prime Source Building Products, Inc.
GRIP ROCK - Floor coverings - Matrix Engineering Inc.
GRIP ROPE - Exercising equipment ☆ - Precise International/Wenger
GRIP-SEAL - Envelopes - Westvaco Corp.
GRIP SHIFT - Bicycles - Raleigh USA Bicycle Co.
GRIP SHIFT - Sporting goods - Sram Corp.
GRIP SHIFT CAT-1 - Sporting goods - Sram Corp.
GRIP SKINS - Rackets–tennis ☆ - Gexco Enterprises
GRIP SPINTITE - Wrenches - Stevens Walden Inc.
GRIP-STAT - Mats - Tenex Corp.
GRIP-STIK - Hair care products - Rescue Marketing Group
GRIP STIX - Pliers - Zoo Plastix LLP
GRIP STRIP - Floor coverings - Capitol Adhesives Inc.
GRIP STRIP - Floor coverings - Johnsonite Flooring Products
GRIP-STRIP - Office supplies - JM Co.
GRIP STRIPS - Stationery - Edwards Creative Products, Inc.
GRIP-SUR - Epoxy coatings - Garon Products Inc.
GRIP, THE - Razors - William Hudson & Associates
GRIP TIGHT - Handtools - Alltrade Inc.
GRIP-TIGHT - Hardware - Erco Manufacturing Co.
GRIP TIP - Handles–wood - Wooster Brush Co.
GRIP TITE - Archery equipment - Saunders Archery Co.
GRIP TITE - Bottle caps - Vaughan Manufacturing Co. Inc.
GRIP-TITE - Decals and transfers - Rubbermaid Inc.
GRIP-TITE - Shelving units–wood ☆ - Quaker Industries Ltd.
GRIP-TRAC - Metals - Morton Manufacturing Co.
GRIP TREAD - Tires - Goodyear Tire & Rubber Co.
GRIP-TUTH HAIRTAINER - Hair care products - Cardinal Comb & Brush
GRIP-WOOD - Wood adhesive - Devcon Consumer Products (ITW Devcon)
GRIP-X - Exercising equipment - Alimed, Inc.
GRIPALLOY - Paints - Tenax Finishing Product
GRIPBOND - Paints - Davis Paint Co.
GRIPCLAD - Hardware ☆ - Sherwin-Williams Automotive Finishes Corp.
GRIPDEX - Index clips and hangers - Atlas Vertical Filing Systems

☆ = Now out of production

GRIPE-TITE - Mops - Zephyr Manufacturing Co.

GRIP*EASE - Rehabilitation centers - Prism Enterprises, Inc.

GRIPEEE - Hockey equipment - Jeffrey T. Gessner

GRIPEEZ - Stationery - ACCO USA, Inc.

GRIPERIFIC - Footwear - Kobacker Co.

GRIPEX SR - Pharmaceutical preparations - A.J. Bart

GRIPFAST - Mops ☆ - Helen Keller Services for the Blind

GRIPFIT - Hardware - General Wire Spring Co.

GRIPHOIST - Hoists - Griphoist Inc.

GRIPIT - Tool boxes - Geerpres Wringer Co.

GRIPLATE - Hardware ☆ - Sherwin-Williams Automotive Finishes Corp.

GRIPLOCK - Key rings - Reutlinger USA

GRIPLOCK - Pliers - Channellock, Inc.

GRIPLOX - Paints - Cloverleaf Paint & Varnish

GRIPMASTER - Tools–hand-operated - Clark National Products Inc.

GRIPMATE - Clamps - Disstim Corp.

GRIPO - Varnishes - Barrett Varnish Co.

GRIPON - Electrical equipment - McGill Manufacturing Co. Inc.

GRIPPA - Seafood products–fresh or frozen - BG Lobster & Shrimp Corp.

GRIPPA SUPREME - Seafood products–fresh or frozen - BG Lobster & Shrimp Corp.

GRIPPER - Ball-point pens - Itoya of America, Ltd.

GRIPPER - Bottles–glass - The Stroh Brewery Co.

GRIPPER - Containers–insulated - Get a Gripp II, Inc.

GRIPPER - Housewares - Selfix, Inc.

GRIPPER - Lighting fixtures - Point Electric

GRIPPER - Mats - Tenex Corp.

GRIPPER - Motor vehicle parts and accessories - Crown Products

GRIPPER - Pipes–plastic - Workman Developments, Inc.

GRIPPER - Shock absorbers–motor vehicle ☆ - Monroe Auto Equipment Co.

GRIPPER - Zippers - Scovill Inc.

GRIPPER CLIPS - Hardware - Gibson Good Tools Inc.

GRIPPER EDGE - Office supplies - Mead Corp.

GRIPPER I - Tool boxes - Center Products Inc.

GRIPPER-LOC - Antislip rug treatment - American Non-Slip Products

GRIPPER TAG - Office supplies - Richard Wade Whittington

GRIPPER, THE - Housewares - Getagrip, Inc.

GRIPPER, THE - Jewelry ☆ - Hirsch Speidel Inc.

GRIPPER, THE - Pet products - KT Hodges

GRIPPER, THE - Shoe accessories - Moore & Nosewiczs, LLC

GRIPPER, THE - Wigs - Penthouse for Men

GRIPPER, THE - Plastics - Plastic Safety Systems, Inc.

GRIPPER, THE - Garment hangers - Selfix, Inc.

GRIPPER TREAD - Floor coverings–carpet and rugs - Superior American Plastics Co.

GRIPPER XL - Gift pen/pencil set - Itoya of America, Ltd.

GRIPPERS - Cosmetics - Comare Corp.

GRIPPERS - Filing cabinets–metal - Hedges Manufacturing Co.

GRIPPERS - Tape–adhesive - Seam Master Industry

GRIPPERS - Toy vehicles - Intex Recreation Corp.

GRIPPERS - Wheelchairs - Genesis Composites, Inc.

GRIPPERWEB - Cordage and twine - American Cord & Webbing Co., Inc.

GRIPPIT - Adhesives and sealants - Sanford Corp.

GRIPPIT - Game machines - Micro Manufacturing, Inc.

GRIPPIT - Screws - Equality Screw Co. Inc.

GRIPPITS - Toys–stuffed ☆ - Mighty Star Inc. (Special Effects Div.)

GRIPPO - Garment hangers - L.M. Leathers' Sons

GRIPS - Tools - Wells Lamont Corp.

GRIPS - Trading cards and stamps - Score Group, Inc.

GRIPS-ALL - Envelopes - Westvaco Corp.

GRIPS-ALL - Paints ☆ - Dutch Boy Group

GRIPSAN - Tools–power-driven - Dico Products Corp.

GRIPSTER - Knives - Hunt Manufacturing Co.

GRIPTAPE - Adhesive-backed felt - Aetna Felt Corp.

GRIPTEC - Golfing equipment - GTI Manufacturing, Inc.

GRIPTEX - Adhesives and sealants - Adhesive Products, Inc.

GRIPTEX - Vinyl coated fabrics - Sargent Cycle Products

GRIPTITE - Drill bits - A.T. & G. Co., Inc.

GRIPTITE - Housewares - Shelby Standard Inc.

GRIPWELD - Adhesives and sealants - Adhesive Products, Inc.

GRIPWORKS - Sporting goods - Sinclair & Rush, Inc.

GRIPZ - Adhesives and sealants - Absolute Coatings Inc.

GRIPZ - Sunglasses - Skyline Northwest Corp.

GRIPZ - Tools–hand-operated - Fit Enterprises

GRIPZIN - Hardware - Star Anchors & Fasteners

GRIS - Hair care products ☆ - Framesi USA/Roffler Industries Inc.

GRIS-PEG - Skin care products - Allergan, Inc.

GRISACTIN - Antibiotics - Wyeth-Ayerst Laboratories

GRISAILLE - Floor coverings–carpet and rugs ☆ - Customweave Carpets Inc.

GRISCER - Kitchen appliances - Kitchen-Quip Inc.

GRISHUNA - Beef ☆ - Liberty Richter Inc.

GRISK COFFEE CO. - Coffee - Brisk Coffee Co.

GRISKO - Shoes–athletic - Victoria's Dance-Theatrical Supply

GRISSE - Skin care products - Lendan USA Co.

GRISSIN BON - Cookies - Bri-AL, Inc.

GRISSOM'S HOME BAKED GOODNESS - Bakery products - Moran Foods, Inc.

GRIST MILL - Granola bars - Grist Mill Co.

GRIST MILL BRICK - Floor coverings ☆ - Tarkett, Inc.

GRISTLE - Toys - Hasbro, Inc.

GRISWOLD - Cooking utensils–enameled ☆ - General Housewares Corp.

GRISWOLD - Electronic equipment - Neumade Products Corp.

GRIT - Recording label ☆ - Alshire International Inc.

GRIT-GRABBER - Mats ☆ - Ludlow Composites Corp.

GRIT HOG - Machinery - Balcon, Inc.

GRIT-LIFE - Paper–sand - Credo Co.

GRIT-ON - Adhesives and sealants - Garon Products Inc.

GRITMEISTER - Water purification systems - Hycor Corp.

GRIVEL - Sporting goods - Climb High Inc.

GRIZZA LEE BEAR - Toys–stuffed - Destiny Designs, Inc.

GRIZZELDA - Toys–stuffed ☆ - Gund, Inc.

GRIZZLE CHEW - Pet products - Classic Products

GRIZZLES - Toys–stuffed - Russ Berrie and Co., Inc.

GRIZZLIES - Granola bars - Wildtime Foods

GRIZZLIES - Shoes - Interco Inc.

GRIZZLIES BRAND - Cereal - DCF Inc.

GRIZZLIES, THE - Hobby kits - Grizzlies

GRIZZLOR - Toys - Mattel, Inc.

GRIZZLY - Apparel and accessories ☆ - North By Northeast

GRIZZLY - Beverages–malt ☆ - Van Munching and Co. Inc.

GRIZZLY - Brake parts - Ferodo America Inc.

GRIZZLY - Cleaning supplies ☆ - American Textile Products Co.

GRIZZLY - Coffee - Coffee Traders, Inc.

GRIZZLY - Cots–metal - E-Z Sales & Manufacturing, Inc.

GRIZZLY - Electronic equipment - Loma Technologies Inc.

GRIZZLY - Generators–electric - Clarke Mosquito Equipment, Inc.

GRIZZLY - Hoses - Dayco Products, Inc.

GRIZZLY - Knives–hunting ☆ - Cole Consumer Products Inc.

GRIZZLY - Skates–roller - Grizzly Gear, Inc.

GRIZZLY - Sporting goods ☆ - Bear Archery Inc.

GRIZZLY - Stoves–wood-burning - Derco Inc.

GRIZZLY - Thermostats - Kirkhill Inc.

GRIZZLY - Tools - Klein Tools Inc.

GRIZZLY - Varnishes - Behr Process Corp.

GRIZZLY - Watches - Grizzly Knife & Tackle, Inc.

GRIZZLY BEAR - Firearms, accessories, and parts - Markesbery Muzzle Loaders, Inc.

GRIZZLY BEAR - Toys–stuffed - Dakin Inc.

GRIZZLY CHOMPS - Snack cakes - Interstate Brands Corp.

GRIZZLY GEAR - Hoists - Craig Products, Inc.

GRIZZLY GEAR - Skates–roller - Grizzly Gear, Inc.

GRIZZLY PEAK TRADING COMPANY - Apparel and accessories - Jon A. Carlson

GRK - Musical instrument accessories - GRK Manufacturing

GRM - Roofing materials–clay - W.R. Grace & Co.

G.R.M. - Veterinary pharmaceutical preparations - Nutra-Vet Research Corp.

GRO-250 - Machine parts - Creco's Machine Shop, Inc.

GRO-A-LONG - Nail care products - Mimi's Discount Beauty Supply

GRO A SAURUS - Household planters - F.G.C. International Inc.

GRO A TROLL - Flower pots–earthenware - F.G.C. International Inc.

GRO & SHO - Lamps - General Electric Co.

GRO-BELOW - Fertilizers - Golden Cat Corp.

GRO BEST - Fertilizers - Alljack & Co.

GRO-BRICK - Chemical preparations - Crystal Co.

GRO-CART - Furniture - Benjamin Jay Harman

GRO-COATED - Flowers, plants, and seeds - Akin Seed Co.

GRO-CUP - Apparel–women's - Wacoal America Inc.

GRO-DEC - Pharmaceutical preparations - Group Drug Service Inc.

GRO-HARD - Pharmaceutical preparations - Group Drug Service Inc.

GRO-LIFE - Lighting fixtures - Lights of America Inc.

GRO-LITE - Lighting fixtures ☆ - Prestigeline Inc.

GRO LUX - Lighting equipment - GTE Corp.

☆ = Now out of production

GRO-MATO - Trays - Hanover Companies
GRO * MOR WAND SEEDER - Machinery - Thomas M. Morin
GRO 'N WIN - Animal feed supplements - Buckeye Feed Mills, Inc.
GRO-NATURAL - Pharmaceutical preparations - Group Drug Service Inc.
GRO-NET - Fertilizers - Ross Daniels Inc.
GRO-POWER - Flowers, plants, and seeds - Akin Seed Co.
GRO-QUICK - Chemical preparations - Wrap-On Co. Inc.
GRO-SET FOR LITTLEST ANGELS - Apparel–women's - Wacoal America Inc.
GRO-STAKES - Fertilizers - Ross Daniels Inc.
GRO-TEK - Adhesives and sealants - Oremor International, Inc.
GRO-THRU - Garden equipment - Kinsman Co. Inc.
GRO-TONE - Fertilizers - Vigoro Industries, Inc.
GRO-TUBE - Garden equipment ☆ - Siemer Milling Co.
GRO-TUFF - Garden equipment - Silver Creek Supply, Inc.
GRO-WELL - Fertilizers - J. & L. Adikes Inc.
GROBOSKI - Motor vehicle parts and accessories - Highland Group
GROBOT - Electronic equipment - Reinard C. Delp
GROCERS CHOICE - Fruits–dried - Lever Brothers Co. Inc.
GROCER'S PRIDE - Food products ☆ - Richfood (Pennsylvania Division)
GROCERY GRIP - Health care products - Maddak Inc.
GROCERY SACHS - Bags–canvas - Sachs Brothers Inc.
GROCO - Resins–synthetic - Groco Specialty Coatings Co.
GRODIES - Hobby kits ☆ - Testor Corp.
GROENDYK - Rubber–molded - Groendyk Manufacturing Co., Inc.
GROENDYK MANUFACTURING CO., INC. - Rubber–synthetic - Groendyk Manufacturing Co., Inc.
GROENLAND - Apparel and accessories ☆ - Alpine Crafts Co. Inc.
GROGANIC - Fertilizers - Northwest Chemical Corp.
GROGRAIN - Floor coverings–carpet and rugs ☆ - Karastan-Bigelow Inc.
GROJEAN - Biscuits ☆ - Liberty Richter Inc.
GROLAND - Fertilizer - Agri-Urban Inc.
GROLIER MULTI-MEDIA ENCYCLOPEDIA, THE - Publisher's imprints - Grolier Electronic Publishing, Inc.
GROLSCH - Beverages–malt - Grolsch Importers Inc.
GROMES - Dolls - Growing Heads Ltd.
GROMME ENDANGERED SPECIES - Posters - Stanton & Lee
GROMME MASTER PRINTS - Posters - Stanton & Lee
GROMME-MCARTHUR COLLECTION - Posters - Stanton & Lee
GROMMES & ULLRICH - Beverages–alcohol - Consolidated Distilled Products Inc.
GRONDONA - Biscuits ☆ - Liberty Richter Inc.
GROOM - Watches - Gruen Marketing Corp.
GROOM A COMB - Pet products ☆ - Dubl Duck/Jet Set Inc.
GROOM-A-LABEL - Pet products - Barkleigh Productions, Inc.
GROOM-A-LEASH - Pet products ☆ - Barkleigh Productions, Inc.
GROOM-AID - Pet products - Natra Pet Inc.
GROOM AID - Veterinary pharmaceutical preparations - Evsco Pharmaceuticals
GROOM & GLOW - Pet products - Carter-Wallace, Inc.
GROOM CLIPPER - Pet products - Andis Co.
GROOM MASTER - Agricultural machinery - Ransomes-Cushman-Ryan
GROOM 'N FLEA - Pet products - Hogil Pharmaceutical Corp.
GROOM 'N SET - Pet products ☆ - Gerard-Pellham Co.
GROOM-O-NIZER - Pet products - Du-Zee Products
GROOM-UP - Cosmetics - Circle of Beauty, Inc.
GROOMA - Pet products - White Horse Trading Co., Inc.
GROOMASTER - Pet products - Classic Products
GROOMAX - Pet products - Sporting Dog Specialties, Inc.
GROOMER - Cosmetics ☆ - Dubl Duck/Jet Set Inc.
GROOMER - Electrical equipment ☆ - Toastmaster Inc.
GROOMER 8000 - Clippers–barber ☆ - Sunbeam-Oster Household Products
GROOMER MAGIC - Pet products ☆ - Gerard-Pellham Co.
GROOMER TO GROOMER - Magazines - Barkleigh Productions, Inc.
GROOMERS - Pet products - Professional Pet Products
GROOMERS CHOICE - Pet products - Stylist Wear
GROOMERS CHOICE - Pet products ☆ - Fromm Industries
GROOMERS EDGE - Pet products - Double K Industries, Inc.
GROOMER'S HELPER - Pet products ☆ - Farnam Cos. Inc.
GROOMERS SECRET - Nail care products - W3 Marketing Corp.
GROOMER'S SUCCESS - Pet products - Marianna Imports, Inc.
GROOMER'S TOUCH - Pet products - Four Paws Products Ltd.
GROOMERS WIZARD - Pet products - Tomlyn Products
GROOMING GEAR - Skin care products - Amway Corp.
GROOMING MACHINE, THE - Pet products - Edemco Dryers Inc.
GROOMING POWDER - Pet products - Crowne Royale, Ltd.
GROOMING PRETTY - Dolls - Mattel, Inc.

GROOMING TIME - Pet products - Classic Products
GROOMOGRAMS - Pet products - Barkleigh Productions, Inc.
GROOMSMAN - Razors - Wahl Clipper Corp.
GROOMWAGON - Pet products - Rapid Electric/R & R Manufacturing
GROOMY GROOMY - Hair care products - Wee Talk, Inc.
GROOP-CHUTE - Sporting goods - Fabrication Enterprises
GROOSUMS - Toys–stuffed - Fun World Inc.
GROOVE - Bicycles - Gyan S. Uppal
GROOVE - Recording label - Extra Sensory Productions
GROOVE BLOCKS - Drums–musical instruments - LP Music Group
GROOVE DOWN - Recording label - Kenneth Taylor
GROOVE DOWN APPAREL - Apparel and accessories - Kenneth Taylor
GROOVE-E-SWING - Golfing equipment - Brandell Products, Inc.
GROOVE-EZE - Cartons–paperboard - Anderson & Middleton Co.
GROOVE LOX - Tools - Fuller Tool Co. Inc.
GROOVE PAK - Musical instrument accessories - Sam Ash Music Corp.
GROOVE PERCUSSION - Musical instruments - Sam Ash Music Corp.
GROOVE PLUG - Audio equipment - Sam Ash Music Corp.
GROOVE SOUND - Recording label - Musicor Records Inc.
GROOVE SWEEPER - Electronic equipment - Benjamin Electroproducts Inc. (Robins Div.)
GROOVE THING: A VISUAL JAM - Computer software - Big Top Productions Inc.
GROOVE TUBES - Audio equipment - Groove Tubes
GROOVED ASCOT - Tires ☆ - Bridgestone/Firestone, Inc.
GROOVEGRIP - Tools–hand-operated - Genesis Materials International
GROOVEMASTER - Electronic equipment - Stanton Magnetics Inc.
GROOVERS - Musical instrument accessories ☆ - Selmer Co. Inc.
GROOVIDEX - Machine tools - Threading Systems Inc.
GROOVIE LITES - Novelty lights - IMS Corp.
GROOVIN' - Apparel and accessories - Label Marketing International Inc.
GROOVIN' GRAPE - Juices - Chiquita Brands, Inc.
GROOVY - Fabrics ☆ - Greenwood Mills Inc.
GROOVY GRAPE - Candy - American Chewing Gum Inc.
GROOVY GRAPEFRUIT - Toiletries - GPS, Inc.
GROOVY GRAPES - Plastics ☆ - Fry Plastics International Inc. (O)
GROOVY LONGBOARDS - Apparel and accessories - Ron Friedman
GROPOINT - Floor coverings–carpet and rugs ☆ - Karastan-Bigelow Inc.
GROSFILLEX - Garden furniture - Grosfillex Inc.
GROSOLI - Vinegar - New Horizon
GROSS - Food products - R. Gross Dairy Dinners Inc.
GROSS BUSTERS - Candy - Bee International
GROSS-ERIES - Toys - Toymax Inc.
GROSS FOURRE - Cookies - Kedem Food Products Co.
GROSS NATIONAL PRODUCT - Broadcasting stations–television - GNP Productions, Inc.
GROSS OUTS - Bandages - Good Marketing, Inc.
GROSS PATISSERIE - Cookies - Kedem Food Products Co.
GROSS WEAR - Apparel–men's - Almo Industries, Inc.
GROSSFACTS - Calendars - BCDM Publishing
GROSSINGER - Bakery products - Allied Bakers Co.
GROSSINGER'S - Cream ☆ - MPS Marketing Services Inc.
GROSSLOCKNER 5'S - Cigars - G.A. Georgopulo & Co. Inc.
GROSSMAN PUBLISHERS - Publisher's imprints - Penguin USA
GROSSOLOGY - Publisher's imprints - Addison Wesley Longman, Inc.
GROSSVILLE HIGH SCHOOL - Chewing gum - Fleer Corp.
GROSVENOR - Furniture - Tomlinson of High Point Inc.
GROSVENOR - Slippers - Wolverine World Wide, Inc.
GROSVENOR CLASSIC - Footwear - Tru-Stitch Footwear (Div. of Wolverine World Wide)
GROSVENOR OF LONDON - Perfumes ☆ - Chase Collection, Inc.
GROSVENOR SQUARE CLASSICS - Footwear - Tru-Stitch Footwear (Div. of Wolverine World Wide)
GROTEC - Herbicides - Lawn & Garden Supply Co.
GROTECH - Machinery - Southlane Maintenance Co., Inc.
GROTON INN - Furniture - A. Brandt Co. Inc.
GROTTO - Shower rods - Trayco, Inc.
GROUCH - Crocheted and knitted items ☆ - Munsingwear, Inc.
GROUCH CONTROL PILLS - Candy - Marsyl Inc. (Marsyl Enterprises, Inc.)
GROUCHO MARX - Dolls - Goldberger Doll Manufacture Co.
GROUCHO MARX - Dolls ☆ - Effanbee Doll Corp.
GROUCHO PUDDY - Greeting cards - Fursure Enterprises Inc.
GROUCHY - Pens - Pentech International Inc.
GROUND BASE - Exercising equipment - Hammer Corp.
GROUND BREAK - Electronic equipment - General Electric Co.
GROUND BUSTER - Tires–motorcycle - Greenball Corp.

☆ = Now out of production

GROUND CENTRAL STATION - Meat products - D & W Food Centers, Inc.
GROUND CONTROL - Bicycles ☆ - Kent International Inc.
GROUND COVER - Wallcoverings - Ben Rose Ltd.
GROUND EFFECTS - Vans–conversion - Prodesign of Indiana Inc.
GROUND GAINER - Shoes - Sam Brilliant Sporto
GROUND GOURMET - Dog food - Nestle USA
GROUND GRIP - Tires - Bridgestone/Firestone, Inc.
GROUND GRIPPER - Household appliance stores - Emerson Electric Co.
GROUND GRIPPER - Shoes - Premier Brands of America
GROUND GUARD - Computer software - Electronic Marine Systems, Inc.
GROUND HANG - Tires - Denman Tire Corp.
GROUND HOG - Hardware - Len Smith
GROUND MONITOR - Electronic equipment - Trinetics Inc.
GROUND PICK - Fabrics - Greenwood Mills Inc.
GROUND PROBE - Electrical equipment - Core Industries Inc.
GROUND ROUND - Machine parts - Fenner Drives
GROUND RUNNER - Pet products - T.E. Scott Inc.
GROUND SUPPORT PRODUCTS CORP. - Hardware - Ground Support Products Corp.
GROUND TRACKER - Toys - Hasbro, Inc.
GROUND TROOPS - Toys - Mattel, Inc.
GROUND TURKEY BROCHURE - Publisher's imprints - National Turkey Federation
GROUND WOUND ROUND - Guitars - Dean Markley Strings, Inc.
GROUND ZERO TEXAS - Video games - Sega of America, Inc.
GROUNDBREAKERS LANDSCAPING TOOLS - Landscaping hand tools - Vaughan & Bushnell Manufacturing Co.
GROUNDCLEAR - Herbicides - Monsanto Co.
GROUNDER - Pet products - Roccorp, Inc.
GROUNDGAINER - Tires ☆ - J.C. Penney Co., Inc.
GROUNDGUARD - Sporting goods - Stearns Manufacturing Co.
GROUNDHOG SANDSCREW - Spikes - William H. Ward, Jr.
GROUNDS AND BORDERS - Wallpaper - Christopher Hyland
GROUNDS FOR INDEPENDENCE - Coffee - Richard Saunders International, Inc.
GROUNDS FOR SUCCESS - Coffee - Jollie Sales, Ltd.
GROUNDSKEEPER - See **SPECTRA-DELUXE**
GROUNDSKEEPER - Hardware - Reemay, Inc.
GROUNDSKEEPER - Mats - Ludlow Composites Corp.
GROUNDWORKS - Computer software - Mindworks Interactive, Inc.
GROUP - Recording label - Cexton Entertainment Group
GROUP 7 - Motor vehicle parts and accessories - Purolator Products Co.
GROUP 64 - Office furniture–metal - Joyce International Inc.
GROUP 450 - Photographic equipment - Norman Enterprises Inc.
GROUP F - Desks ☆ - Joyce International Inc.
GROUP III - Luggage - Group III International Ltd.
GROUP LOGIC, INC. - Computer software - Group Logic
GROUP PACK - Computer software - Lotus Development Corp.
GROUP TECHNOLOGIES - Computer hardware - Group Technologies Corp.
GROUP USA - Jewelry - First Trading Corp.
GROUPBASE - Computer storage devices - Fluor Corp.
GROUPE THERAPY - Apparel and accessories - Groupe Therapy
GROUPER - Communications equipment - Digital Ocean, Inc.
GROUPER - Photographic equipment ☆ - Wess Plastic
GROUPIES - Giftware - Metalco Industries Inc.
GROUPSHOW - Photographic equipment - Hudson Photographic Industries Inc.
GROUPWARE KERNEL - Computer software - Crosswise Corp.
GROUPWARE STANDARD, THE - Computer software - Lotus Development Corp.
GROUT GUARD - Grout release - Klein & Co.
GROUT-WELL - Grouting material - Wyo-Ben Inc.
GROUTITE - Plastics - Fluoro Plastics Inc.
GROUTRENEW - Grout cleaner and protectant - Slipsafe Professional Products, Inc.
GROUTS-OFF - Cleaning preparations - Applied Polymers of America Inc.
GROVA - Crackers ☆ - A.V. Olsson Trading Co., Inc.
GROVCO - Window frames - Grovco Sales Co. Inc.
GROVE - Construction equipment - Grove Products Inc.
GROVE FRESH - Juices - Eau Claire Packing Co.
GROVE MANLIFT - Platforms–cargo - Kidde Industries, Inc.
GROVE PARK - Clocks - General Time Corp. (Westclox/Seth Thomas Div.)
GROVE PARK - Floor coverings–carpet and rugs - Wunda Weve Carpet Co.
GROVE PARK - Furniture - Lane Co. Inc.
GROVE PARK - Furniture ☆ - Bassett Furniture Industries, Inc.
GROVE PARK - Wallpaper - Seabrook Wallcoverings, Inc.
GROVE PRESS - Publisher's imprints - ∑ Grove/Atlantic, Inc.

GROVE QUEEN - Food products - Tropicana Products, Inc.
GROVE STREET - Wines - Belvedere Winery
GROVE SWEET - Juices - Citrus Service, Inc.
GROVER - Frames–eyeglass - Rozin Optical Export Corp.
GROVER - Horns–motor vehicle - Grover Products Co.
GROVER - Musical instrument accessories - Grover/Trophy Musical Products Inc.
GROVER - Toys - Jim Henson Productions, Inc.
GROVER CDR - Ophthalmic goods - Rozin Optical Export Corp.
GROVER GULCH - Wines - Grover Gulch Winery
GROVER'S CORNERS - Bedding–linen - Dan River Inc.
GROVES - Beverages - White Rock Products Corp.
GROVES - Milk - Groves Dairy Inc.
GROVESTAND - Juices - Tropicana Products, Inc.
GROVNER SQUARE - Floor coverings ☆ - Tarkett, Inc.
GROW - Fertilizers ☆ - W. Atlee Burpee and Co.
GROW - Vitamins and nutritional supplements ☆ - Ethical Nutrients
GROW 10 - Nail care products - Revlon Consumer Products Corp.
GROW A FROG - Games - Three Rivers Amphibian Inc.
GROW AID - Hair care products - Samlo
GROW ALONG SHAPES 'N SONGS - Toys - Mattel, Inc.
GROW AMERICA - Publisher's imprints - O. Ames Co.
GROW & SEASON - Flowers, plants, and seeds - W. Atlee Burpee and Co.
GROW & TELL - Toys - Aquapore Moisture Systems, Inc.
GROW AS YOU GO - Panty hose - Leading Lady Companies Inc.
GROW-COLT - Pet products - Farnam Cos. Inc.
GROW-CUFF - Shirts - Celebrity International, Inc.
GROW-FINISH 65, A - Animal feeds - Carl S. Akey Inc.
GROW GREEN - Lawn mowers - Thompson Manufacturing Co.
GROW GUARD - Fencing–plastic - Subcon Products, Inc.
GROW HOUSE - Prefabricated buildings–wood - Gardener's Supply Co.
GROW-IT - Aquatic pharmacuetical preparations - Aquatronics-Filtronics
GROW IT - Prefabricated buildings–metal - Cover-It, Inc.
GROW MATE - Pottery products - Grow Mate
GROW-N-GLOW - Pet products - Merrick's Inc.
GROW PARTNER - Fertilizers - Ampel, Corp.
GROW SMART - Fertilizers - Chas H. Lilly Co.
GROW STRONG - Nail care products - Cosmair Inc.
GROW TEN - Nail care products - Revlon Consumer Products Corp.
GROW THICKER! - Nail care products - Cosmair Inc.
GROW TO PRO - Sporting goods - Fisher-Price, Inc.
GROW WITH US - Flower pots–earthenware - Duraco Products Inc.
GROW YOUR OWN - Apparel and accessories - Grow Your Own, Inc.
GROWANOTE - Greeting cards - Green Field Paper Co.
GROWCO - Adhesives and sealants - National Aerosol Products Co.
GROWCO - Paints - Growco Aerosol
GROWEATHER - Weather tracking equipment - Davis Instruments Corp.
GROWER - Jojoba oil - J & J Jojoba
GROWER PRIDE - Fruit and vegetable markets - Fruit Growers Marketing Association
GROWER SELECT - Flowers, plants, and seeds - Ball Horticultural Co.
GROWER TESTED, GROWER ENDORSED - Fertilizers - Agrotech, Inc.
GROWERS - Beverages–alcohol - Golden State Vintners
GROWERS - Juices - Lemon-X Corp.
GROWER'S - Wines - Bully Hill Vineyards, Inc.
GROWER'S - Wines ☆ - Golden State Vintners
GROWERS 6-PAK - Beverages ☆ - Hawkhaven Greenhouse Int'l.
GROWERS' BLEND - Fruit drinks–bottled or canned - Sunkist Growers Inc.
GROWER'S CHOICE - Fertilizers - Northwest Chemical Corp.
GROWERS FANCY - Juices - Lemon-X Corp.
GROWERS' RESERVE - Juices - Ocean Spray Cranberries Inc.
GROWIN' UPS - Archery equipment - Playskool Baby Inc.
GROWING FOR AMERICA - Flowers, plants, and seeds - Flynn Rainbow Nurseries Inc.
GROWING FUN - Toys - Mattel, Inc.
GROWING HEALTHY - Baby food products - Growing Healthy Inc.
GROWING INVESTMENTS LIBERTY IN GOD WE TRUST - Flowers, plants, and seeds - David Mackenzie
GROWING ROOM - Furniture–children's - Gerry Wood Products
GROWING RUBBER TREE - Novelty items - Global Giggles
GROWING UP - Figurines ☆ - Enesco Corp.
GROWING UP - Toys - Brass Key, Inc.
GROWING UP GREAT - Toys - Brass Key, Inc.
GROWING UP SMARTER - Computer software - Tele-Story
GROWING UP WITH VASSARETTE - Socks - Vanity Fair, Inc.
GROWING UP WITH VASSARETTE - Underwear and nightwear - V.F. Corp.

GROWING UP WITH WALL-TEX - Fabrics–tapestry ☆ - Columbus Coated Fabrics Co.

GROWING WILD PLUS - Wallpaper - Charterhouse Ltd.

GROWING WITH MATHEMATICS - Recording label - Carringbush, Inc.

GROWL TOWEL - Towels - John Kevin Homsey

GROWN 4U - Fruits and vegetables - R.A. Rasmussen & Sons, Inc.

GROWN BY MONTEREY AT AROMAS - Flowers, plants, and seeds - 3-Way Farms Inc.

GROW'N SHOW - Fertilizers - Dynacast

GROWN THE BETTER WAY - Agricultural products - Monsanto Co.

GROWN UP BEARS - Toys–stuffed - British American Imports

GROWPARTNER - Fertilizers - AMPEL Corp.

GROWPARTNER PLUS - Fertilizers - AMPEL Corp.

GROWTH - Dog food - Ralston Purina Co.

GROWTH - Paper products - Georgia-Pacific Corp.

GROWTH - Pharmaceutical preparations - Bricker Laboratories

GROWTH ENDERS - Herbicides - Burlington Bio-Medical & Scientific Corp.

GROWTH FACTOR-2000 - Nail care products - Rothschild Transdermal Technologies Inc.

GROWTH GUIDANCE SYSTEM - Health care products - Mulholland Positioning Systems Inc.

GROWTH PHASE - Vitamins and nutritional supplements ☆ - Makers of Kal, Inc.

GROWTH-PLUS - Pharmaceutical preparations - Bricker Laboratories

GROWTH PLUS - Shampoos ☆ - Rel-Eeze/JDM Enterprises

GROWTHWARE - Computer software - Ashford Software

GROWTTH - Apparel and accessories - Freudenberg-Nok General Partnership

GROWZONE, INC. - Flower pots–earthenware - Growzone, Inc.

GROZYME - Soil–potting - AgroPlus Inc.

GRREAT CHOICE - Pet food - Petstuff, Inc.

GRRIP - Adhesives and sealants - Bond Adhesives Co.

GRRIP - Air conditioning equipment - Hercules Chemical Co. Inc.

GRRIP - Tools - Remington Arms Co., Inc.

GRRIP-LITE - Adhesives and sealants - Hercules Chemical Co. Inc.

GRRR - Puzzles ☆ - Parker Brothers

GRRR - Recording label - Word, Inc.

GRRR - Toys - Mattel, Inc.

GRRR-NOLA TREATS - Granola bars ☆ - Barbara's Bakery, Inc.

GRRRAVY - Dog food - Ralston Purina Co.

GRRRIP, THE - Pet products - Crowd Pleaser Pet Products

GRRRS TIGER - Puppets - Dakin Inc.

GRS - Computer software - Automated Archives, Inc.

GRS/GRG - Brake parts - Raybestos/Brake Parts Inc.

GRT - Apparel–athletic - Columbia Sportswear Co.

GRUB BEATER - Pesticides–household - Bonide Products, Inc.

GRUB-HIDE - Fishing lures - Five Star Manufacturing, Inc.

GRUB RUB - Seasonings - Gordon Specialty Foods, Inc.

GRUB STOPPER - Insecticides - Seacoast Laboratories Inc.

GRUB TOX - Pesticides–household - Bonide Products, Inc.

GRUBBY'S - Apparel and accessories - Patty Grubbs

GRUBEX - Herbicides - OMS Investments, Inc.

GRUBSTAKE - Banjos - OME Co. Inc.

GRUEN - Watches - Gruen Marketing Corp.

GRUEN PRECISION - Watches - Gruen Precision, Inc.

GRUENMATIC - Watches - Gruen Marketing Corp.

GRUESOME TWOSOME - Toys - Francis W. Shaw

GRUET'AGE - Flavored popped popcorn - Gruet'age

GRUHN - Guitars - Gruhn Guitars, Inc.

GRUMBACHER - Paints–artists' - Koh-I-Noor, Inc.

GRUMBLE BEE - Toys - Saban Entertainment, Inc.

GRUMMAN - Boats - Grumman Data Systems Corp.

GRUMMAN - Boats–canoes ☆ - Marathon Boat Group, Inc.

GRUMMAN SUNSTREAM - Solar energy collectors - Grumman Energy Systems Co.

GRUMPLIN - Dolls - Mattel, Inc.

GRUMPY BEAR - Toys - Those Characters from Cleveland, Inc.

GRUMPY GRAPE - Juices - General Mills, Inc.

GRUMTINE - Turpentine - M. Grumbacher Inc.

GRUNDENS OF SWEDEN - Apparel and accessories - Cofish International Inc.

GRUNDIG - Razors–electric - Parks Products Inc.

GRUNDIG - Tape players - Las Electronics East Inc.

GRUNDO-AIR - Compressors–air - TT Technologies, Inc.

GRUNDO-OIL - Lubricating oils - TT Technologies, Inc.

GRUNDOBURST - Machinery - TT Technologies, Inc.

GRUNDOWINCH - Winches - TT Technologies, Inc.

GRUNE & STRATTON - Publisher's imprints - W.B. Saunders Co.

GRUNERT - Refrigerators - Marine Air Systems Inc.

GRUNGE - Novelty items–paper - Aegis Entertainment, Inc.

GRUNGE BUSTER THE CHAMP - Cleaning preparations ☆ - Klean-Strip

GRUNGE GUNK - Hair care products - BodyFX Co.

GRUNGIES - Footwear - Shore Enterprises, Inc.

GRUNGY - Leather - Prime Tanning Co., Inc.

GRUNGY BUNGY - Rubber–extruded - Rubber Recovery Partnership

GRUNT - Costumes - McCain Ellio's Foods, Inc.

GRUNT - Recording label - RCA Records

GRUNTWEAR - Apparel and accessories - David Pierpont and Dustin Yates

GRUTZMACHER - Beverages–alcohol - Carradale Import Co.

GRUV - Apparel and accessories - Andrew Allen Rubin

GRUVLOK - Couplings - Grinnell Corp.

GRW FASTENER EXCHANGE - Hardware products - James H. Miller

GRX-FOAM DRESSING - Health care products - Geritrex Corp.

GRX-HYDROGEL DRESSING - Health care products - Geritrex Corp.

GRX-PETROLATUM GAUZE - Health care products - Geritrex Corp.

GRX-SALINE GAUZE - Health care products - Geritrex Corp.

GRX-SPLIT FOAM DRESSING - Health care products - Geritrex Corp.

GRX-WOUND GEL SYRINGE - Health care products - Geritrex Corp.

GRYPHON BOOKS - Publisher's imprints - Omnigraphics Inc.

GRYPROC - Screws - C. Itoh Building Products

GS - Jewelry - Gold Spectrum, Ltd. Inc.

GS - Roofing materials - GS Roofing Products Co.

GS - Thread - Belding Heminway Co. Inc.

GS-27 - Automotive parts and accessories - National Express, Inc.

GS-500 - Vitamins and nutritional supplements - Enzymatic Therapy, Inc.

GS 2000 - Golfing equipment - Golfsmith International Inc.

GS ADD-ON - Glassware–household - Morton Glass Works Inc.

G'S BEST - Food products - Ginsberg's

GS-FIORANO - Tires - Goodyear Tire & Rubber Co.

GS SPORT - Pharmaceutical preparations - Starter Galt, Inc.

GSA - Electronic equipment - George R. Snell Associates, Inc.

GSA - Giftware - Godinger Silver Art Ltd.

GSA GS KING - Vitamins and nutritional supplements - Paul H. Paek

GSC - Food products - Chazy Orchards Inc.

GSE - Jewelry–precious - G.S.E. Jewelry, Inc.

G'SELL - Wines - G'sell Wine Negociants

GSF - Food products - Golden Specialty Foods Inc.

G.S.F. - Pharmaceutical preparations ☆ - American Hygienic Laboratories Inc.

GSI - Bins - Grain Systems, Inc.

GSI - Fabrics ☆ - Fibers and Fabrics of Georgia Inc.

GSI - Footwear - G.S.I. Ltd.

GSI - Game machines - Gaming Services International

GSI - Medical apparatus - Grason-Stadler, Inc.

GSI - Publisher's imprints - Psychological Dimensions Inc.

GSIC - Semiconductors - Cree Research, Inc.

G.S.J. - Jewelry - Gold Stone Jewelry Corp.

GSL - Computer devices - Computer Products, Inc.

GSL - Salt - North American Salt Co.

GSL - Skin care products ☆ - Elysee Scientific Cosmetic Co.

GSL-4 - Chemical preparations - Energy Additives, Inc.

GSM - Motor vehicle parts and accessories - Summit Industries, Inc.

GSM GLOBAL SECURITIES MANAGER - Computer software - Sungard Investment Ventures, Inc.

GSN SEED - Flowers, plants, and seeds - California Valley Seed Co.

GSO - Oils–edible - The Lifestar Millennium, Inc.

GSP/KAMEI RECORDINGS - Recording label - GSP

GSP RECORDINGS - Recording label - GSP

GSP STRINGS - Musical instrument accessories - GSP

GSPJAZ - Recording label - GSP

GSR - Pipes–plastic - R. & G. Sloane Manufacturing Co. Inc.

GSR - Tires - Bridgestone/Firestone, Inc.

GSS-10 - Paints - American Polymer Corp.

GST - Hoses - Dayco Products, Inc.

GSX-145 - Printers–computer - Citizen America Corp.

GT - Bicycles - GT Bicycles Inc.

GT - Boats–motor ☆ - Glastron Boats

GT - Cleaning preparations - Roebic Laboratories Inc.

GT - Clocks - GTC Properties Inc.

GT - Computer software - GT Interactive Software Corp.

GT - Electrical equipment - Groove Tubes

GT - Garden equipment ☆ - Homelite, Inc.

GT - Golfing equipment - Aldila, Inc.

GT - Machine tools - Baker Hughes Inc.

GT - Motor vehicle parts and accessories ☆ - Dunham Bush, Inc.

☆ = Now out of production

GT - Trailers–travel - Gladding Del-Rey

GT - Vans–conversion - Starcraft Corp.

G.T. - Wines ☆ - Vose Vineyards

GT - Wire - Gas Tech, Inc.

GT-1 - Oils–lubricating - Witco Corp.

GT 2 - Boats - Nautical Boats Ltd.

GT-5 - Motor vehicles–automobiles - Toyota Motor Sales USA Inc.

GT-8 - Waxes–mineral - Knight Marketing Corp.

GT 1000 - Infant product - Graco Children's Products

GT ALL TERRA - Bicycles - GT Bicycles Inc.

GT BICYCLES - Bicycles and bicycles structural parts - GT Bicycles Inc.

GT CLEEN-RITE - Degreasing solvents - State Chemical Manufacturing Co.

GT COUPE - Toys - Tonka Corp.

GT FOR MEN - Hair-care products - Johnson Products Co., Inc.

GT GOOD TABLES - Tables–wood - Finegood Holdings, Inc.

G.T. HUGGER - Footwear - Brooks Shoe Inc.

GT II SPORT GRIP - Steering mechanisms–motor vehicle - Superior Industries International, Inc.

GT-LMA - Brake fluids - Castrol, Inc.

GT V6 - Motor vehicles–automobiles ☆ - Alfa Romeo Distributors of North America

GT VELOCE - Motor vehicles–automobiles ☆ - Alfa Romeo Distributors of North America

GT90 - Toys - Ford Motor Co.

GTA - Computers - Vas, Inc.

GTA - Dog food - GTA Feeds

GTA IV - Computers - Vas, Inc.

GTA V - Computers - Vas, Inc.

GTC - Recreational vehicle dealers ☆ - Foretravel Inc.

GTC FORMULA - Vitamins - Bronson Pharmaceuticals

GTE - Photographic equipment - GTE Corp.

GTF - Vitamins and nutritional supplements - Makers of Kal, Inc.

GTG - Recording label - Global Talent Guild, Inc.

G.T.H. - Headbands - Golf & Tennis Headwear Co.

GTI - Ducts–metal - General Technologies, Inc.

GTI - Motor vehicles–automobiles - Volkswagen of America Inc.

GTI - Paper products - Graphic Technology, Inc.

GTI 25 - Sporting goods - Donnay USA

GTI JUNGNER - Grinders - Grinding Technology, Inc.

GTI PAT - Diagnostic substances - Genetic Testing Institute, Inc.

GTI SUPER LEVEL WIND - Fishing tackle - Penn Fishing Tackle Manufacturing Co.

GTK - Electronic equipment - Moor Electronics Inc.

GTKL II - Electronic equipment - Moor Electronics Inc.

GTM - Machinery - Brown & Co., Inc.

GTM - Machinery - Engineering Developments Co. Inc.

GTM - Pillows - Mildred E. Scott

GTMASTER - Computer software - Thermoflow, Inc.

GTO - Bicycles - Bridgestone/Firestone, Inc.

GTO - Motor vehicles–automobiles ☆ - General Motors Corp. (Pontiac/GMC Div.)

GTP NISSAN - Toys–models - Cox Products Inc.

GTPRO - Computer software - Thermoflow, Inc.

GTR - Electrical equipment - General Electric Co.

GTR - Jewelry - Samuel Aaron Inc.

GTS - Apparel and accessories - Garan Services Corp.

GTS - Heating equipment - GTS Energy, Inc.

GTS - Humidifiers - Dri-Steem Humidifier Co.

GTS ENERGY - Heating equipment - GTS Energy, Inc.

GTS SCHMIDT - Hand tools - George T. Schmidt Inc.

GTT - Apparel and accessories - G.T.T. Partnership

GTT-124 - Fuel additive - Turnkey Application Programs

GTW - Men's sportswear - Dino DiMilano Corp.

GTW - Recording label - Jazz Composer's Orchestra Association Inc.

GTX - Guitars ☆ - Kaman Music Corp.

GTX - Motor vehicles–automobiles ☆ - Chrysler Corp. (Chrysler-Plymouth Div.)

GTX - Oils–lubricating - Castrol, Inc.

GTX - Powerboat/runabout ☆ - Boston Whaler, Inc.

GTX - Rubber–vulcanized - Game Time, Inc.

GTX 25 - Sporting goods - Donnay USA

GTX IMAGE CAD - Computer software - GTX Corp.

GTX IMAGE CAD PLUS - Computer software - GTX Corp.

GTX IMAGE CAD PLUS W/ICR - Computer software - GTX Corp.

GTX IMAGE EDIT - Computer software - GTX Corp.

GTX OSR - Computer software - GTX Corp.

GTX RASTER CAD - Computer software - GTX Corp.

GTX RASTER CAD PLUS - Computer software - GTX Corp.

GTX RASTER CAD PLUS W/ICR - Computer software - GTX Corp.

GU FAST FOOD FOR ATHLETES - Food products - Advanced Food Concepts

GU-ON DECOUPAGE - Artists' materials - Natcol Crafts & Hobbies

GUAC DUST - Spices and extracts - Cajun Dust, LLC

GUADALAJARA - Floor coverings - Mannington Resilient Floors

GUADALUPE VALLEY - Wines - Guadalupe Valley Winery

GUAI-SUDO - Pharmaceutical preparations - MD Pharmaceutical, Inc.

GUAIACOLATE - Pharmaceutical preparations - Medical Chemical Corp.

GUAIAMEN - Analgesics - Lannett Co. Inc.

GUAIDEX - Cough medicines ☆ - JMI-Canton Pharmaceuticals

GUAIFED - Pharmaceutical preparations - Muro Pharmaceuticals Inc.

GUAIFED-PD - Pharmaceutical preparations - Muro Pharmaceuticals Inc.

GUAIMAX-D - Cold remedies - Central Pharmaceutical Inc.

GUAITAB - Pharmaceutical preparations ☆ - Muro Pharmaceuticals Inc.

GUAJILLO - Chili peppers–powdered ☆ - Frieda's, Inc.

GUAJIRO - Recording label - Guajiro Records Inc.

GUALINO - Breadsticks, cookies - Euromark Inc.

GUANAJA 1502 - Chocolate candy - Seyco Products Co. Inc.

GUANIDINE - Pharmaceutical preparations - Key Pharmaceuticals Inc.

GUAPI O/S - Computer software - Kevin Sharp Enterprises, Inc.

GUAR GUM - Vitamins and nutritional supplements - Natrol, Inc.

GUAR OPTIMUM POTENCY - Health care products ☆ - Nature's Way Products, Inc.

GUARANA ENERGIZER - Vitamins and nutritional supplements - Source Naturals

GUARANTEE - Paints - Schulte Paint & Lacquer Manufacturing Co., Inc.

GUARANTEE - Pet products - La Pet Foods

GUARANTEED - Lamp bulbs - Marvel Lighting Corp.

GUARANTEED COMFORT - Underwear and nightwear - Warnaco Inc.

GUARANTEED FOR GOOD - Paper - Beaverprints, Inc.

GUARANTEED FROZEN AT SEA - Seafood products–fresh or frozen - American Factory Trawler Association

GUARANTEED GASOLINE - Gasoline - Quiktrip Corp.

GUARANTEED-R SYSTEM - Insulating materials - Rockwool Industries Inc.

GUARANTEED START - Batteries - Johnson Controls Inc.

GUARANTEED-TO-FIT - Mattress pads - Pillowtex Corp.

GUARANTEED TO LAST - Windows–vinyl - Home Improvement Supply Co., Inc.

GUARANTEED TO RUST - Bells - Wind Works Inc.

GUARANTEEING REVENUE RESULTS - Educational materials - Sales Management Systems, Inc.

GUARD - Chemicals–photographic - Merix Chemical Co.

GUARD - Fabrics–tapestry ☆ - Columbus Coated Fabrics Co.

GUARD - Wallpaper - Borden, Inc.

GUARD-AC - Machinery - MTE Corp.

GUARD-AIRE - Shoes - Record Industrial Co.

GUARD ALERT - Alarm - Red Alert Corp.

GUARD & B.O.P - Hoses - Hose Master, Inc.

GUARD ANSWERS - Fabrics–tapestry - Columbus Coated Fabrics Co.

GUARD BORDER COLLECTION - Fabrics–tapestry - Columbus Coated Fabrics Co.

GUARD-COAT - Paints - Vanguard Paints & Finishes Inc.

GUARD D-8 - Firefighting apparatus - Thomas John Ruzich

GUARD-DISC - Chromatography columns - Sarasep Inc.

GUARD DOG - Lighting fixtures - Leen & Associates, Inc.

GUARD-DOGS - Goggles–safety - Parmelee Industries, Inc.

GUARD-DOGS - Goggles–safety - U.S. Safety Corp.

GUARD GRAND TRADITIONS - Fabrics–tapestry - Columbus Coated Fabrics Co.

GUARD GRIP - Mattress pads - Louisville Bedding Co.

GUARD HARMONY - Fabrics–tapestry - Columbus Coated Fabrics Co.

GUARD HOUSE - Caulking compounds - Glidden Co.

GUARD-IT - Locks–door - M.A.G. Engineering & Manufacturing Co. Inc.

GUARD-IT - Luggage, etc. - American Guard-It Manufacturing Co. Inc.

GUARD LANDSCAPES - Fabrics–tapestry - Columbus Coated Fabrics Co.

GUARD LINE - Paints - Vanguard Paints & Finishes Inc.

GUARD MASTER - Alarm systems - Ultimate Products, Ltd.

GUARD MASTER - Housewares - Seymour Housewares Corp.

GUARD N GRO - Garden equipment ☆ - Harrison-Hoge Industries Inc.

GUARD NUT - Hardware - GNI

GUARD PLUS - Wallcovering - BDH Two, Inc.

GUARD QUICKSHIP - Fabrics–tapestry - Columbus Coated Fabrics Co.

GUARD RENOVATIONS - Fabrics–tapestry - Columbus Coated Fabrics Co.

GUARD RUG - Shampoos ☆ - Bissell Inc.

GUARD SELECTIONS - Fabrics–tapestry - Columbus Coated Fabrics Co.

☆ = Now out of production

GUARD-TEX - Tape–adhesive - General Bandages Inc.
GUARD-TOP - Asphalt felts and coatings - Garon Products Inc.
GUARD TYPE I - Fabrics–tapestry - Columbus Coated Fabrics Co.
GUARD-WEL - Infant product ☆ - Welsh Co.
GUARD WOOD - Finishing agents - Sinclair Paint Co.
GUARD-YOURSELF - Windows–plastic - National Stove Works Inc.
GUARDAL - Vitamins and nutritional supplements - Morton Pharmaceuticals Inc.
GUARDDOG - Measuring and dispensing pumps - ITT Industries, Inc.
GUARDETTE - Watch attachment - Jacoby-Bender Inc.
GUARDEX - Water treating compounds - Bio-Lab, Inc.
GUARDFATHER - Air conditioning equipment - Herco Products
GUARDIAN - Air conditioning equipment - Evcon Industries, Inc.
GUARDIAN - Bathtubs–enameled - Kohler Co.
GUARDIAN - Bicycles - Graber Products, Inc.
GUARDIAN - Bicycles - Ross Bicycles USA, Ltd.
GUARDIAN - Boating equipment and accessories - Attwood Corp.
GUARDIAN - Cases–cigar - Vigilant Inc.
GUARDIAN - Chemical preparations - Unit Chemical Corp.
GUARDIAN - Cigars - Faber, Coe & Gregg Inc.
GUARDIAN - Communications equipment–satellite - Dictaphone Corp.
GUARDIAN - Computer hardware - Raymond Engineering Inc.
GUARDIAN - Computer peripheral equipment - Raritan Computer, Inc.
GUARDIAN - Contact lenses - Evans Case Co.
GUARDIAN - Crutches - Guardian Products, Inc.
GUARDIAN - Cutlery - Gerber Legendary Blades
GUARDIAN - Deicing fluid - North American Salt Co.
GUARDIAN - Doors–garage - McKee Door, Inc.
GUARDIAN - Dryers–hair - Marianna Imports, Inc.
GUARDIAN - Electrical equipment - Ratelco, Inc.
GUARDIAN - Electrical equipment ☆ - General Cable Corp.
GUARDIAN - Fencing–steel ☆ - CF and I Steel L.P.
GUARDIAN - Film-exposure meter - General Electric Co.
GUARDIAN - Floor coverings–carpet and rugs - Collins & Aikman Corp.
GUARDIAN - Floor coverings–carpet and rugs - Playfield International Inc.
GUARDIAN - Gates–ornamental ☆ - Paris Co. Inc.
GUARDIAN - Goggles–safety ☆ - U.S. Safety Corp.
GUARDIAN - Headphones ☆ - Hamilton Electronics Corp.
GUARDIAN - Health care products - Sunrise Medical Inc.
GUARDIAN - Heating equipment - Yukon Energy Corp.
GUARDIAN - Housewares - Georgia-Pacific Corp.
GUARDIAN - Infant product - Test-Rite Products Corp.
GUARDIAN - Lawn mowers - Toro Co.
GUARDIAN - Lighting equipment - Dura Electric Lamp Co. Inc.
GUARDIAN - Lighting equipment - Standard-Keil Hardware Manufacturing Co.
GUARDIAN - Lockers–metal - Penco Products Div.
GUARDIAN - Luggage - Samsonite Corp.
GUARDIAN - Mats - Matworks
GUARDIAN - Paints ☆ - Colony Paints Div.
GUARDIAN - Playthings - Babcock Industries Inc. (Babcock Control Group)
GUARDIAN - Pumps - Duriron Co. Inc.
GUARDIAN - Pumps - Saginaw Pump Manufacturing Co.
GUARDIAN - Pumps ☆ - Dunham Bush, Inc.
GUARDIAN - Refuse systems - Hyde Products Inc.
GUARDIAN - Safes - Diebold Inc.
GUARDIAN - Safety products - Mattson Spray Equipment Inc.
GUARDIAN - Self-defense spray - PWP, Inc.
GUARDIAN - Siding–insulating - Simpson Timber Co.
GUARDIAN - Skin care products - Lloyd George Associates
GUARDIAN - Sporting goods - Basketball Products International Inc.
GUARDIAN - Sporting goods - Brimms Inc.
GUARDIAN - Sporting goods - Shield Manufacturing Inc.
GUARDIAN - Tablecloths - Ohio Table Pad Co.
GUARDIAN - Video games - Taito America Corp.
GUARDIAN - Wallets - Enger-Kress Co.
GUARDIAN - Windows–storm - Caradco
GUARDIAN ANGEL - Bookmarks - Treasures & Trinkets, Inc.
GUARDIAN ANGEL - Crocheted and knitted items - Collins & Aikman Corp.
GUARDIAN ANGEL - Dolls - Heaven's Corner, Inc.
GUARDIAN ANGEL - Paper - Mactac Inc. (Packaging Closures Systems Div.)
GUARDIAN ANGEL - Pins–jewelry ☆ - Papel Freelance, Inc.
GUARDIAN ANGELS - Giftware - Fenton Art Glass Co.
GUARDIAN BLOCK - Blocks–paving - Guardian Plastics Inc.
GUARDIAN CARRIER - Containers - Sweetheart Cup Co. Inc.
GUARDIAN CLASP - Envelopes - Union Envelope Co.
GUARDIAN DNA - Medical apparatus - Alpha Stainless, Inc.

GUARDIAN FIRM-LOCK - Locks–door - Briggs Co.
GUARDIAN GEL - Skin care products - Guardian Angel Health Care Products, Inc.
GUARDIAN KNIGHT - Heating equipment - Heat Controller Inc.
GUARDIAN LION, THE - Health care products - Guardian Products Inc.
GUARDIAN MOUNT - Fabrics - Bacon Felt Co. Inc.
GUARDIAN NO-WAX - Floor coverings ☆ - Tarkett, Inc.
GUARDIAN POWER - Air purification systems - Gateway Pacific Corp.
GUARDIAN POWER - Tools - Buffalo Tool
GUARDIAN SAFETY - Glass–flat - Guardian Industries Corp. (Architectural Glass Div.)
GUARDIAN SCREEN - Fireplace equipment - Schaefer Co.
GUARDIAN, THE - Consulting services - Guardian Life Insurance Co. of America
GUARDIAN TILTER - Window coverings - Levolor Inc.
GUARDIAN WAR - Computer software - Matsushita Electric Corp. of America
GUARDIANS - Waterproof footwear ☆ - Kaysam Corp. of America
GUARDIANS OF INFINITY - Computer software ☆ - Microprose Software, Inc.
GUARDIANS, THE - Vitamins and nutritional supplements - Sundown Vitamins, Inc.
GUARDIAQ - Measuring instruments - Gaztech International Corp.
GUARDION - Water purification systems - Sensible Technologies, Inc.
GUARDION - Water treating compounds - Baker Hughes Inc.
GUARDLITE - Window shades - C-Mor Co.
GUARDMAIL - Computer software - Secureware, Inc.
GUARDMASTER - Housewares - Lear Siegler Seymour Corp.
GUARDMATIC - Tools–power-driven - DBNA Trademarks Holding Inc.
GUARD'N CAT - Garden equipment - Dalen Products Inc.
GUARDOL - Oils–lubricating - Unocal Corp.
GUARDS - Gloves–rubber - Guards Corp.
GUARDS - Prophylactics - Boston Medical Corp.
GUARDSEAL - Concrete repair products - Polymer Plastic Corp.
GUARDSMAN - Bathroom fixtures ☆ - Melard Manufacturing Corp.
GUARDSMAN - Bicycles - Ross Bicycles USA, Ltd.
GUARDSMAN - Cigars - Consolidated Cigar Corp.
GUARDSMAN - Doors–metal - Clopay Millwork
GUARDSMAN - Enamels - Columbia Paint Inc.
GUARDSMAN - Floor coverings–carpet and rugs ☆ - Kelly Group Inc.
GUARDSMAN - Furniture polish and wax - Guardsman Products, Inc.
GUARDSMAN - Leather goods - St. Thomas Inc.
GUARDSMAN - Luggage ☆ - Platt Luggage Inc.
GUARDSMAN - Musical instruments - GRK Manufacturing
GUARDSMAN - Pipes–tobacco ☆ - S.M. Frank & Co. Inc. (Kaywoodie-Yello-Bole-Medico)
GUARDSMAN - Revolvers ☆ - Harrington & Richardson Inc.
GUARDSMAN - Shingles - Manville/Schuller
GUARDSMAN - Television equipment - Blonder-Tongue Laboratories Inc.
GUARDSMAN - Thread - Van Waters and Rogers Inc.
GUARDSMAN - Tool boxes - Merriam Manufacturing Co. Inc.
GUARDSMAN - Vacuum cleaners and accessories - The Hoover Co.
GUARDSMAN - Weather stripping - National Guard Products Inc.
GUARDSMAN HERITAGE - Furniture polish and wax - Guardsman Products, Inc.
GUARDSMAN OUTDOOR RECEPTACLES - Wastebaskets - United Receptacle Inc.
GUARDSMAN, THE - Binders - Angler's Roslyn Group Ltd.
GUARDSMAN WOODPRO - Paints - Guardsman Products, Inc.
GUARDSMEN - Desks - Vanguard Corp.
GUARDSWITCH - Electronics equipment - Sentrol Inc.
GUARDSWOOD - Paints - Gray Seal Paint Manufacturing Co. Inc.
GUARDTECH - Alarm systems - Guard Tech Industries, Inc.
GUARDWARE - Hardware ☆ - Stanley Hardware Div.
GUARSOL - Pharmaceutical preparations - Western Research Laboratories
GUARTEC - Chewing gum ☆ - General Mills, Inc.
GUASTI - Wines - Beaver Wine Co.
GUAVA BEACH - Clothing - Guava Beach
GUAVA KAI - Jams and jellies - C Brewer Co. Limited
GUAVA PASSION - Food products - Cascadian Farm, Inc.
GUBBLE BUM - Chewing gum - Philadelphia Chewing Gum Corp.
GUBBLO - Tiles–ceramic - TJ Imports
GUBELIN - Watches - Gubelin Inc.
GUBOR - Chocolate candy ☆ - Bahlsen Inc.
GUCCI - Handbags - Gucci America Inc.
GUCCI ACCENTI - Toiletries - Gucci America, Inc.
GUCCI EYEWEAR - Sunglasses - Solargenics
GUCCI NOBILE - Colognes - Frances Denney

☆ = Now out of production

GUCCI NO. 1 - Colognes - Frances Denney
GUCCI NO. 3 - Colognes - Frances Denney
GUCCI POUR HOMME - Colognes - Frances Denney
GUCO - Rulers—metal - Guedon Co.
GUDE - Thread - Gudebrod, Inc.
GUDE-DAY - Thread ☆ - Gudebrod, Inc.
GUDE-STITCH - Thread ☆ - Gudebrod, Inc.
GUDEBROD - Thread - Gudebrod, Inc.
GUDEGRADE - Thread ☆ - Gudebrod, Inc.
GUDERIAN - Games - Avalon Hill Game Co.
GUDEWIND - Thread ☆ - Gudebrod, Inc.
GUDI - Bedding—linen - Michael Friedman Corp.
GUDRUN - Confections - Morris National Inc.
GUDULUP - Chewing gum - Pepsico, Inc.
GUDY-O - Adhesives and sealants - Interlam Inc.
GUELI - Water—bottled or canned - Gueli Spring Water Co.
GUENOC - Wines - Guenoc & Langtry Estate Vineyards and Winery
GUEPARD - Perfumes - Classic Fragrances Ltd.
GUEPARD HOMME - Perfumes - Classic Fragrances Ltd.
GUERLAIN - Skin care products - Guerlain Inc.
GUERNSEY BEL - Syrup - Guernsey Dell, Inc.
GUERNSEY DELL - Syrup - Guernsey Dell, Inc.
GUERNSEY FARMS - Dairy products - Guernsey Farms Dairy
GUERNSEY POTTERY - Novelty items ☆ - Chase Collection, Inc.
GUERNSEY'S GIFT - Cheese - Guernsey's Gift Marketing Association
GUERRERO - Sporting goods ☆ - Powell Skateboards
GUERRINI - Accordions - Castiglione Accordion
GUESS? - Apparel and accessories - Bonnie Doon
GUESS? - Apparel and accessories - Guess?, Inc.
GUESS - Watches - Timex Corp.
GUESS ACTIVEWEAR - Apparel and accessories - Guess?, Inc.
GUESS ATHLETIC - Watches - Guess?, Inc.
GUESS COLLECTION - Apparel and accessories - Guess?, Inc.
GUESS INNERWEAR - Underwear and nightwear - Guess?, Inc.
GUESS IT - Playing cards - Aristoplay, Ltd.
GUESS JEANS U.S.A. - Apparel and accessories - Guess?, Inc.
GUESS KIDS - Apparel—children's - Guess?, Inc.
GUESS MY RULE - Computer software ☆ - Queue Inc.
GUESS USA - Apparel and accessories - Guess?, Inc.
GUESS WHO? - Crocheted and knitted items - Winston Manufacturing Corp.
GUESS WHO? - Games - Milton Bradley Co.
GUESS WORD - Games - Smethport Specialty Co.
GUESSTURES - Games - Milton Bradley Co.
GUEST - T-shirts—men's - Needlecraft Industries
GUEST BEDS - Sofabeds - England/Corsair, Inc.
GUEST-GUARD - Eyeglasses - Sellstrom Manufacturing Co.
GUEST HOUSE - Floor coverings—carpet and rugs - Milliken & Co. Inc.
GUEST-O-PEDIC - Mattresses - Dynasty Consolidated Industries, Inc.
GUEST OF HONOR - Floor coverings—carpet and rugs - Lees Carpets
GUEST QUALITY - Food products ☆ - Hanover Foods Corp.
GUEST QUARTERS - Hotels and motels - Guest Quarters Hotel L.P.
GUEST RANCH - Paper—tissue - Georgia-Pacific Corp.
GUEST STACKER - Chairs - Corry Hiebert
GUESTBOOK - Computer storage devices—magnetic - Plainfield's Place, Ltd.
GUESTHOME PRINTS - Wallpaper - Eisenhart Wallcoverings Co.
GUESTSERVICES - Computer software - Servidyne Systems, Inc.
GUESTSTACKER - Chairs—metal - Hon Co.
GUESTWORKS - Electronic equipment - Lucent Technologies Inc.
GUFFY - Toys—stuffed ☆ - Toy Works, Inc.
GUFI - Computer software - Isec, Inc.
GUFI - Computer software - Isec, Inc.
GUFS, THE - Apparel and accessories - Red Submarine Records, Ltd.
GUGGACIN COMPLEX - Vitamins and nutritional supplements - Vitamin Shoppe Industries Inc.
GUGGENHEIM MUSEUM - Jewelry - Solomon R. Guggenheim Foundation
GUGGENHEIM MUSEUM - Postcards - Fotofolio Inc.
GUGGENHEIM MUSEUM PUBLICATIONS - Publisher's imprints - Rizzoli International Publications Inc.
GUGGUL RAJ - Vitamins and nutritional supplements - Planetary Formulas
GUGLIELMO - Wines - Emilio Guglielmo Winery
GUGULIPID EXTRACT - Vitamins and nutritional supplements - Vitamin Research Products Inc.
GUIA CAMPH - Analgesics - Dorsey Laboratories
GUIAMID - Pharmaceutical preparations ☆ - Vangard Labs Inc.
GUIAPHED - Pharmaceutical preparations - Barre-National, Inc.
GUIATEX - Pharmaceutical preparations ☆ - Scrip-Physician Supply Co.

GUIATUSCON - Pharmaceutical preparations - Consolidated Midland Corp.
GUIATUSS - Pharmaceutical preparations - Barre-National, Inc.
GUIDA - Water—bottled or canned - Guida's Seibert Dairy
GUIDA-SEIBERT - Milk - Guida's Seibert Dairy
GUIDABENE BY BERNARDO - Footwear—women's - Bernardo Brands
GUIDE - Boats—canoes - Old Town Canoe Co.
GUIDE - Boats—canoes ☆ - Sawyer Composite Products
GUIDE - Coatings, etc. - Continental Products Co.
GUIDE - Lighting equipment—automotive - General Motors Corp. (Fisher Guide Div.)
GUIDE - Recording label - Bellaire Record Sales
GUIDE - Sights—gun - Williams Gun Sight Co.
GUIDE-A-KNIFE - Cutlery ☆ - Lifetime Hoan Corp.
GUIDE-BRITE - Reflectors—optical - Thayer Systems, Inc.
GUIDE DRIL - Drills—mining - UTILX Corp.
GUIDE EXPRESS - Computer software - Federal National Mortgage Association
GUIDE GRIP - Tires - Bridgestone/Firestone, Inc.
GUIDE-LINE - Artists' materials - Fluorographic Services Inc.
GUIDE LINE - Limestone products - Medusa Minerals Co.
GUIDE-LINE - Office supplies - Alvin and Co. Inc.
GUIDE-LINED - Electronic equipment - LTV Steel Co. Inc.
GUIDE-LINER - Automotive parts and accessories - K-Line Industries
GUIDE-MASTER - Knives - Imperial Schrade Corp.
GUIDE MASTER - Refueling (in flight) equipment—aircraft - Hannay Reels
GUIDE MATIC - Lighting equipment—automotive - General Motors Corp. (Fisher Guide Div.)
GUIDE-O-FOLDER - File folders ☆ - Gussco Manufacturing Inc.
GUIDE-RITE - Steel products - B-Line Systems, Inc.
GUIDE SERIES - Camping products - Coleman Co., Inc.
GUIDE SERIES - Waterproof outerwear - Gordon & Ferguson of Delaware, Inc.
GUIDE SPECIAL - Boats - Tracker Marine Corp.
GUIDE SPECIAL - Boats—canoes ☆ - Sawyer Composite Products
GUIDE-TECH - Compasses—magnetic - Cobbs Manufacturing Co.
GUIDE-TRACE - Electronic equipment - GAF Corp.
GUIDE WRITE - Posters ☆ - Fiber Mark, Inc.
GUIDEBACK - Sporting goods - Marty Gilman Inc.
GUIDEBOAT - Boats—motor ☆ - Alumacraft Boat Co.
GUIDEBOAT - Fabrics - Gretchen Bellinger Inc.
GUIDED - Vitamins and nutritional supplements - Schiff Products, Inc.
GUIDED-INPUT - Computer software - Trinitech Systems, Inc.
GUIDED READER - Projector, filmstrips, and computer software ☆ - Instructional/Communications Technology Inc.
GUIDED READER PLAYMATE - Cassette player ☆ - Instructional/Communications Technology Inc.
GUIDELINE - Drafting supplies - Pickett Industries
GUIDELINE - Fishing tackle - H.K. International
GUIDELINE - Floor coverings—carpet and rugs ☆ - Blue Ridge Carpet Mills
GUIDELINE - Floor coverings—carpet and rugs ☆ - Walter Carpet Mills
GUIDELINE - Paperboard - W.W. Holes Manufacturing
GUIDELINES - Computer software - GTE Telecommunications Services Inc.
GUIDELITE - Lighting fixtures - Guidelite, Inc.
GUIDEPOSTS FIND - Publisher's imprints - Guideposts Associates, Inc.
GUIDESTAR - Electronic equipment - Delco Electronics Corp.
GUIDEWEAR - Coats - Cabela's Inc.
GUIDEX - Research—educational - Centaur Records
GUIDEX TYPE II PRESSBOARD - Pressboard - Fiber Mark, Inc.
GUIDING GODDESS GAME, THE - Games - Techniart Inc.
GUIDING HEART - Jewelry - Sandberg & Sikorski Diamond Corp.
GUIDISC - Computer storage devices—optical - CD Technology, Inc.
GUIDO - Food products ☆ - Borden, Inc.
GUIDON - Motor vehicle parts and accessories - Rigid Form, Inc.
GUIDON - Motor vehicles—motor homes - Guidon Truck Covers
GUIDO'S - Confections - Good Humor Corp.
GUIDO'S - Food products - Ateeco, Inc.
GUIDO'S SERIOUS SAUCE PASADENA - Barbecue sauce - Guido's International Foods, LLC
GUIDR-FLEX - Bumpers—motor vehicle - General Motors Corp. (Fisher Guide Div.)
GUIL-GLO - Fabrics - Guilford Mills, Inc.
GUIL KNITS - Fabrics - Guilford Mills, Inc.
GUILANA - Fabrics - Guilford Mills, Inc.
GUILCOTE - Fabrics - Guilford Mills, Inc.
GUILD - Brandy - Guild Wineries
GUILD - Guitars - Guild Music Corp.
GUILD - Watches - Gruen Marketing Corp.

☆ = Now out of production

GUILD BLUE RIBBON - Wines - Guild Wineries
GUILD HOUSE - Candles - American Greetings Corp.
GUILD SELECTIONS - Wallpaper ☆ - Gilman Wallcoverings
GUILD, THE - Shirts–polo - Jockeys' Guild, Inc.
GUILDCRAFT - Floor coverings–carpet and rugs - Karastan-Bigelow Inc.
GUILDCRAFT - Metals - Fabcraft Inc.
GUILDCRAFT - Scissors–hand-operated ☆ - National Housewares
GUILDCRAFT - Watches - Gruen Marketing Corp.
GUILDHALL - Floor coverings ☆ - Congoleum Corp.
GUILDHALL - Floor coverings–carpet and rugs ☆ - Karastan-Bigelow Inc.
GUILDHOUSE COLLECTION - Furniture - National/Mt. Airy Furniture
GUILDITE - Watches - Gruen Marketing Corp.
GUILDMARK - Floor coverings–carpet and rugs ☆ - Karastan-Bigelow Inc.
GUILDPOINT - Floor coverings–carpet and rugs - Karastan-Bigelow Inc.
GUILDWORKS - Kites - Guildworks Flight Studio
GUILDWORKS FLIGHT STUDIO - Kites - Guildworks Flight Studio
GUILFORD - Books–blank - Keith Clark Inc.
GUILFORD - Furniture - Boling Co.
GUILFORD GOLD - Books–blank ☆ - Keith Clark Inc.
GUILFORD HOUSE - Fabrics - Guilford Mills, Inc.
GUILFORD HOUSE - Window coverings - Norman Lacoff & Associates Inc.
GUILFORD PHARMACEUTICALS - Pharmaceutical preparations - Guilford Pharmaceuticals Inc.
GUILFORD TAVERN - Furniture ☆ - Bassett Furniture Industries, Inc.
GUILFORD'S DYNASTY ONE - Fabrics - Guilford Mills, Inc.
GUILFORD'S HEAVEN CLOTH - Fabrics - Guilford Mills, Inc.
GUILFORD'S VELTERRA - Fabrics - Guilford Mills, Inc.
GUILLORY'S - Rice - Gourmet America
GUILLOT - Beverages–alcohol ☆ - Winesellers Ltd.
GUILLOW'S - Wood products - Paul K. Guillow Inc.
GUILOY - Toys–models ☆ - Reeves International, Inc.
GUILSUEDE - Fabrics - Guilford Mills, Inc.
GUILT - Cosmetics - Territory Ahead
GUILT FREE - Confections - Yarnell Ice Cream Co., Inc.
GUILTEC - Fabrics - Guilford Mills, Inc.
GUILTLESS GOURMET - Food products - Guiltless Gourmet, Inc.
GUILTLESS INDULGENCE - Cookies - Cookietree Bakeries
GUIMAR - Footwear ☆ - Conjac Inc.
GUINAN - Toys - Paramount Pictures Corp.
GUINEA PIG GOURMET - Animal feeds - Kellogg Inc.
GUINEA PIG NIBBLETS - Animal feeds - Bluebonnet Milling Co.
GUINEVERE - Dolls ☆ - Effanbee Doll Corp.
GUINEVERE - Watches - Bulova Corp.
GUINNESS EXTRA - Beverages–malt - Guinness Import Co.
GUINNESS GAME OF WORLD RECORDS, THE - Games ☆ - Parker Brothers
GUINNESS GOLD - Beverages–malt - Guinness Import Co.
GUINTI - Beverages–alcohol - Arthur G. Lombardi & Son
GUIOSAN - Pharmaceutical preparations ☆ - Pal-Pak Inc.
GUISEPE ARMANI - Figurines - Miller Import Corp.
GUISTERY FORTIS - Pharmaceutical preparations - JMI-Canton Pharmaceuticals
GUISTI - Postcards - Fotofolio Inc.
GUITAR CLEAN - Guitar-polishing cloth - Jan-Mar Industries
GUITAR GLO - Musical instrument accessories - McMillan Music Co.
GUITAR GRIMOIRE, THE - Publisher's imprints - Metatron Inc.
GUITAR HYPERFORMANCE PRODUCTS - Amplifiers–musical instrument - Korg USA
GUITAR MIC - Musical instrument accessories - P.A. Products
GUITAR RECORDINGS - Recording label - Guitar Recordings, Inc.
GUITAR RECORDINGS CLASSIC CUTS - Recording label - Guitar Recordings, Inc.
GUITAR SOLO PUBLICATIONS - Music–sheet - GSP
GUITAR TALK - Apparel - Dean Sanderson and Peter Cowley Partnership
GUITAR WIZARDS - Musical instrument accessories - Dimarzio, Inc.
GUITARAK - Musical instrument accessories ☆ - Gracie Enterprises (Gracie Stands Div.)
GUITARISTICS - Computer software ☆ - Dr. T's Music Software Inc.
GUITARMAKER'S CONNECTION - Musical instrument accessories - C.F. Martin & Co., Inc.
GUITARO - Guitars ☆ - Oscar Schmidt International Inc.
GUITTARD - Baking chocolate - Guittard Chocolate Corp.
GULABI ALWARDI - Teas–herbal - M.I.M.T. Corp. of USA
GULABI BAROOTI - Teas–herbal - M.I.M.T. Corp. of USA
GULABI KALMI - Teas–herbal - M.I.M.T. Corp. of USA
GULATI - Giftware ☆ - J. Kenneth Zahn
GULBRANSEN - Musical instrument accessories - Gulbransen, Inc.

GULCH STEPPER - Toys–automobiles - Mattel, Inc.
GULCO - Reflectors–vehicular ☆ - Bright Star Industries Inc.
GULD MARIE - Cookies - A.V. Olsson Trading Co., Inc.
GULDEN'S - Mustard - American Home Food Products Inc.
GULDEN'S DIABLO - Mustard - American Home Food Products Inc.
GULF - Aquariums–household - Weco Products Inc.
GULF - Frozen foods - Ocean Duke Corp.
GULF - Fruits–dried - Lawnelson Corp.
GULF - Petroleum - Chevron Corp.
GULF - Salt - United Salt Corp.
GULF - Ships–sailing vessels - Capital Yachts Inc.
GULF - Thread - Cincinnati Thread Co.
GULF BEAUTIES - Seafood products–fresh or frozen - St. Joseph Fisheries
GULF BELLE - Seafood products–canned or cured ☆ - Southland Canning & Packing Co. Inc.
GULF BEST - Seafood products–fresh or frozen - Gulf City Fisheries Inc.
GULF BOTTOM COMPOUND - Paints - Diamond/Kuhn Paint Co.
GULF BOULEVARD - Wallpaper - Richard E. Thibaut, Inc.
GULF BREEZE - Honey - Bessonet Bee Co. Inc.
GULF BREEZE - Shrimp–fresh or frozen - King Midas Quality Seafood Co.
GULF BREEZE - Skin care products - American Salon Products
GULF BREEZES - Skin care products - Softsoap Enterprises, Inc.
GULF CENTRAL - Seafood products–canned or cured - Gulf Central Seafoods
GULF CITY - Seafood products–fresh or frozen - Gulf City Fisheries Inc.
GULF CITY SEAFOODS - Seafood products–fresh or frozen - Gulf City Fisheries Inc.
GULF CLASSIC - Seafood products–fresh or frozen - L.M. Sandler & Sons, Inc.
GULF CLUB - Shrimp - Continental Seafoods Inc.
GULF COAST - Oils–lubricating - R.I. Marketing Inc.
GULF CREST - Gasoline - Chevron Corp.
GULF CREST - Seafood products–fresh or frozen - Dejean Packing Co.
GULF CREST - Seafood products–fresh or frozen - Southern Belle Frozen Foods Inc.
GULF FINEST - Shrimp - Alpha Seafood Enterprises Inc.
GULF FORCE - Fireworks - American Promotional Events, Inc.
GULF KING - Seafood products–fresh or frozen - Gulf King Seafood Co.
GULF KING PREMIUM - Seafood products–fresh or frozen - Gulf King Seafood Co.
GULF KING SEAFOOD - Seafood products–fresh or frozen - Gulf King Seafood Co.
GULF KIST - Seafood products–fresh or frozen - Southern Shell Fish Co.
GULF-KOTE - Paints - Gulf Paint & Chemical Co.
GULF LIGHT - Lighter fluid - Boyle-Midway
GULF LITE - Lighter fluid - Chevron Corp.
GULF MERIDIAN - Seafood products–fresh or frozen - Meridian Products
GULF-MEX - Seafood products–fresh or frozen - QF Inc.
GULF NO-NOX - Gasoline - Chevron Corp.
GULF PORT - Floor coverings–carpet and rugs ☆ - Porter Carpet Mills Inc.
GULF PUBLISHING CO. - Publisher's imprints - Gulf Publishing Co. (Book & Div.)
GULF SHORE BOAT - Deicing fluid ☆ - Cargill Salt
GULF STAR - Seafood products–canned or cured - Gulf Central Seafoods
GULF STAR - Shrimp–fresh or frozen - Weems Brothers Seafood Co.
GULF STATES - Paints - Gulf States Paint Co.
GULF STATES OVENABLES - Containers–paper - Gulf States Paper Corp.
GULF STATES VEP - Paints - Gulf States Paint Co.
GULF STREAM - Recreational vehicles - Gulf Stream Coach Inc.
GULF STREAM - Seafood products–fresh or frozen - King & Prince Seafood Corp.
GULF STREAM PROSTI-BREW - Pharmaceutical preparations - Twin Laboratories, Inc.
GULF STRIKE - Games - Avalon Hill Game Co.
GULF SUPER - Gasoline - Chevron Corp.
GULF TRADERS - Men's woven shirts - Specialty Department Stores, Inc.
GULF TREASURE - Food products - Wally Sea Products Corp.
GULFBREEZE - Fabrics–tapestry - Comark Wallcoverings
GULFCOMP - Computer peripheral equipment - Gulfstream Aerospace Corp.
GULFGAS - Gasoline ☆ - Warren Petroleum Co.
GULFLUBE - Oils–lubricating - Chevron Corp.
GULFPHOS - Finishing agents - Gulf States Paint Co.
GULFPORT - Motor vehicles–motor homes ☆ - Honey Recreational Vehicles Inc.
GULFPRIDE - Oils–lubricating - Chevron Corp.
GULFSTREAM - Aquariums–household - Gulfstream Tropical Aquarium

☆ = Now out of production

GULFSTREAM - Aquariums–household - Marine Metal Products
GULFSTREAM - Awnings - John Boyle & Co., Inc.
GULFSTREAM - Boats - Marlin Products
GULFSTREAM - Boats–houseboats ☆ - Bluewater
GULFSTREAM - Boats–motor - Glassmaster Co.
GULFSTREAM - Boats–motor - Grady-White Boats, Inc.
GULFSTREAM - Boats–motor - H & H Molded Products
GULFSTREAM - Boats–motor ☆ - Cobia Boat Co.
GULFSTREAM - Pet products - Nelson Manufacturing Co.
GULFSTREAM - Whirlpools - Plastic Creations Inc.
GULFSTREAM IV-SP - Aircraft–airplanes - Gulfstream Aerospace Corp.
GULFSTREAM SHARES - Banks–commercial - Gulfstream Aerospace Corp.
GULFSTREAM SPORT PALM BEACH - Sportswear - Saul Brothers and Co. Inc.
GULFSTREAM V - Aircraft–airplanes - Gulfstream Aerospace Corp.
GULFTECH - Computer software - Gulfstream Industries Inc.
GULFWAX - Waxes–paraffin - Chevron Corp.
GULFWINDS - Boats–motor ☆ - Cobia Boat Co.
GULI'S - Beads - Ramodi's
GULISTAN - Floor coverings–carpet and rugs - Gulistan Carpet Inc.
GULISTAN CARPET - Floor coverings–carpet and rugs - Gulistan Carpet Inc.
GULL - Boats–motor ☆ - Old Town Canoe Co.
GULL - Clocks ☆ - General Time Corp. (Westclox/Seth Thomas Div.)
GULL - Water purification systems - Coughlan Products Corp.
GULL LAKE - Furniture - Homecrest Industries Inc.
GULLIVER - Leather goods - Stebco Products Corp.
GULLIVER - Toys–stuffed ☆ - Gund, Inc.
GULLIVER BOOKS - Publisher's imprints - Harcourt Brace & Co.
GULLIVER PERSONAL TRAVEL ASSISTANT - Computer software - True North, Inc.
GULLIVER'S GARDEN - Flowers, plants, and seeds - White Swan, Ltd.
GULLY - Toys - Tonka Corp.
GULLY TRANSPORTATION - Freight cars–locomotive - Gully Transportation, Inc.
GULLYWASHER - Filters–water - Aqua-Net, Inc.
GULP/FRENZY - Computer software - Milliken Publishing Co. (Computer Software Div.)
GULPY - Toys - Philip B. Fleet
GULTA MIND - Vitamins and nutritional supplements - Natural Organics, Inc.
GULTON ELECTRIC - Cigarette lighters - Gulton Industries Inc.
G-U-M - Toothbrushes - John O.Butler Co.
GUM ACACIA - Health care products - Hugh J. Meeter & Associates
GUM-AID - Dental compounds - Reliance Dental Manufacturing Co.
GUM BALLS - Jewelry - Lawrence Jewelry Co.
GUM-BESTOS - Air conditioning equipment ☆ - Grant Wilson Inc.
GUM CHASER - Cleaning preparations - Gold Eagle Co.
GUM CHOMPERS - Candy - Foreign Candy Co. Inc.
GUM CHUPS - Candy ☆ - Uniconfis Corp.
GUM DINGER - Candy - Brach and Brock Confections Inc.
GUM DROP - Crocheted and knitted items - Alpha Mills Corp.
GUM DROP - Dolls ☆ - Effanbee Doll Corp.
GUM DROPS - Footwear - J. Baker Inc.
GUM-GO - Cleaning preparations - Hillyard Enterprises, Inc.
GUM GUYS - Sporting goods - Tonka Corp.
GUM 'N POWDER - Candy - Glenn Confections Inc.
GUM-SOLVE - Cleaning preparations - Penray Companies, Inc.
GUM TIME - Chewing gum - R.L. Albert & Son, Inc.
GUM-TITE PILLS - Hardware ☆ - Seal-O-Matic Corp.
GUM TO GO - Chewing gum - Leon Bush Manufacturing, Inc.
GUM ZAPPER - Tools–power-driven - American Information Marketing, Inc.
GUM-ZOR - Pharmaceutical preparations - Church and Dwight Co. Inc.
GUMABALL - Pet products - Nylabone Products
GUMABONE - Pet products - T.F.H. Publications, Inc.
GUMABONE - Veterinary pharmaceutical preparations - Nylabone Products
GUMADISC - Pet products - Nylabone Products
GUMAKNOT - Pet products - Nylabone Products
GUMARING - Pet products - Nylabone Products
GUMBERRIES - Candy ☆ - Topps Co., Inc.
GUMBITTY - Toys ☆ - Roseart Inc.
GUMBO - Putties - Midland Chicago Corp.
GUMBO POT - Housewares ☆ - General Housewares Corp.
GUMBY - Candy - Glenn Confections Inc.
GUMBY - Toys - Lakeside Games
GUMBY & POKEY - Candy - Zaloom Brothers Co. of New Jersey
GUMBY & POKEY - Toys - Lakeside Games
GUMBY AND POKEY - Toys - Playskool, Inc.

GUMBY SUPER-FLEX - Toys - Lakeside Games
GUMBY'S PAL POKEY - Toys - Lakeside Games
GUMDROP - Christmas tree ornaments - Cracker Box Inc.
GUMDROP - Pet products - Coastal Pet Products, Inc.
GUMDROP - Toys - Eugene Doll & Novelty Co. Inc.
GUMDROP BUNNY - Toys–stuffed - Russ Berrie and Co., Inc.
GUMGUM - Chewing gum ☆ - Makers of Kal, Inc.
GUMI - Jewelry–costume - Design Circle Ltd.
GUMMALLOS - Candy - Dae Julie, Inc.
GUMMI APPLE O'S - Candy - Trolli, Inc.
GUMMI BEANS - Candy ☆ - Golightly Candy Co.
GUMMI BERRY JUICE - Fruit drinks–bottled or canned - Bradley Candy Manufacturing Co.
GUMMI CHUMS - Candy ☆ - L.E.G. Inc.
GUMMI DYENOSAURS - Candy ☆ - Trolli, Inc.
GUMMI FRUITS - Candy - Stark Candy Co.
GUMMI-FUN - Candy - Uniconfis Corp.
GUMMI GHOSTS - Candy - Stark Candy Co.
GUMMI HEARTS - Candy - Koppers Chocolate Specialty Co. Inc.
GUMMI KARZ - Candy - Zeebs Enterprises, Inc.
GUMMI MELON PATCH - Candy - Trolli, Inc.
GUMMI MOUSE - Candy ☆ - Gerrit J. Verburg Co.
GUMMI NEON BEARS & SQUIGGLES - Candy - Trolli, Inc.
GUMMI ORANGE GROVE - Candy ☆ - Trolli, Inc.
GUMMI PEACHIES - Candy - Trolli, Inc.
GUMMI PIZZA - Candy - Euro-American Brands Inc.
GUMMI SAURUS - Candy ☆ - L.E.G. Inc.
GUMMI SAVERS - Candy - Nabisco Foods Group
GUMMI SAVERS - Candy - Planters LifeSavers Co.
GUMMI SOUR BRITECRAWLERS - Candy - Trolli, Inc.
GUMMI-SQUIGGLES - Candy - Trolli, Inc.
GUMMI STRAWBERRY PUFFS - Candy - Trolli, Inc.
GUMMI SUPER LOOPS - Candy ☆ - Trolli, Inc.
GUMMI TARANTULA - Candy ☆ - Gerrit J. Verburg Co.
GUMMI TROLLS - Candy ☆ - Trolli, Inc.
GUMMIES - Bicycle parts and accessories - Serfus, Inc.
GUMMIJUJYS - Candy - Henry Heide, Inc.
GUMMIJUJYS - Candy - Ph. Wunderle Inc.
GUMMY BEARS - Candy - Ferrara Pan Candy Co., Inc.
GUMMY BEARS & FRIENDS - Candy - Homestead, Inc.
GUMMY BEARS & HEARTS - Candy - Homestead, Inc.
GUMMY CHERRIES - Candy - Ferrara Pan Candy Co., Inc.
GUMMY CRUNCHERS - Candy - R.L. Products Corp.
GUMMY DINOSAURS - Candy - Ferrara Pan Candy Co., Inc.
GUMMY DOLPHINS - Candy - Ferrara Pan Candy Co., Inc.
GUMMY FRUIT COCKTAIL - Candy - Ferrara Pan Candy Co., Inc.
GUMMY GLO-WORMS - Candy - Ferrara Pan Candy Co., Inc.
GUMMY MELLOS - Candy - Ferrara Pan Candy Co., Inc.
GUMMY MELLOS - Candy ☆ - Foreign Candy Co. Inc.
GUMMY MUMMIES - Candy - Fleer Corp.
GUMMY NERDS - Candy - Willy Wonka Brands
GUMMY PINK GRAPEFRUIT - Candy - Ferrara Pan Candy Co., Inc.
GUMMY SQUIRMS - Candy - Brock Candy Co. Inc.
GUMMY STRAWBERRIES - Candy - Ferrara Pan Candy Co., Inc.
GUMMY WABBITS - Candy ☆ - C. & J. Willenborg Inc.
GUMMY WORMS - Candy - Ferrara Pan Candy Co., Inc.
GUMNIKS - Candy ☆ - Topps Co., Inc.
GUMOUT CARB & FUEL INJECTOR CLEANER - Cleaning preparations - Pennzoil Co. (Gumout Div.)
GUMOUT JET SPRAY CARB & CHOKE CLEANER - Cleaning preparations - Pennzoil Co. (Gumout Div.)
GUMOUT TUNE UP SPRAY FOR FUEL INJECTED ENGINES - Automotive parts and accessories - Pennzoil Co. (Gumout Div.)
GUMPUTER - Chewing gum - Amurol Confections Co.
GUMPY - Candy - William A. Mogush
GUMPY JIG - Fishing lures - Bomber Bait Co.
GUMPY'S FARM - Housewares - Gumpy's Farm, Inc.
GUMSHOE - Shoes - Barnes & Flanagan, Inc.
GUMZILLA - Toys - Basic Fun, Inc.
GUN-A-MATIC - Guns - Test-Rite Products Corp.
GUN BLUE - Lubricants - G-96 Products Co. Inc.
GUN BOOT - Rifles - Kolpin Manufacturing, Inc.
GUN-COAT - Lubricants - Fluoramics Inc.
GUN DOG HOUSE DOOR - Pet products - Gun Dog House Door Co.
GUN DRY - Chemical preparations - Vapor Products
GUN FIGHTERS - Video games - Konami (America) Inc.

GUN GRINNER - Toys–guns - Mattel, Inc.
GUN GUARD - Guns - Doskocil Manufacturing Co., Inc.
GUN GUM - Chewing gum - Murray-Allen International Inc.
GUN-HO - Racks ☆ - Pedro Cos. (Pedro Manufacturing Div.)
GUN HUGGER - Guns ☆ - Doskocil Manufacturing Co., Inc.
GUN NAC - Computer software - Nexoft Corp.
GUN SAV'R - Lubricants - Chem-Pak Inc.
GUN SCRUBBER - Sporting goods - Birchwood Casey
GUN SHIELD - Apparel and accessories - Bob Allen Sportswear
GUN SLINGER - Electrical equipment - GB Electrical Inc.
GUN SLINGER - Toys–automobiles - Mattel, Inc.
GUN SOCK - Sporting goods - East-Tenn Mills Inc.
GUN WRAP - Firearms, accessories, and parts - Fibre Wrap Inc.
GUNCHAPS - Firearms, accessories, and parts - Kane Products, Inc.
GUND - Toys–stuffed - Gund, Inc.
GUND CHEER - Toys–stuffed - Gund, Inc.
GUNDAM 0079 - Video games - Presto Studios, Inc.
GUNDELSHEIM - Catsup - American Marketing Team
GUNDELSHEIM - Sauerkraut - Haram-Christensen Corp.
GUNDERBEAR - Toys–stuffed ☆ - Gund, Inc.
GUNDFRIENDS - Toys–stuffed ☆ - Gund, Inc.
GUNDLACH - Tools - Beno J. Gundlach Co.
GUNDLACH BUNDSCHU - Wines - Gundlach-Bundschu Winery
GUNDY - Toys–stuffed - Gund, Inc.
GUNFIGHT AT OK CORRAL - Games ☆ - CBS Toys
GUNFLINT - Varnishes, colors in oil - American Paints
GUNFORCE - Computer software - IREM America Corp.
GUNG HO - Boats - Glen-L Marine Designs
GUNG HO - Food products - Gung Ho Corp.
GUNG HO - Games - Avalon Hill Game Co.
GUNGA DIN - Portable water fountain - B & G Equipment Co.
GUNJET - Paint sprayers - Spraying Systems Co.
GUNK - Cleaning preparations - Radiator Specialty Co.
GUNK B-O-P - Cleaning preparations - Radiator Specialty Co.
GUNK G-P - Cleaning preparations - Radiator Specialty Co.
GUNK NEO-MET - Cleaning preparations - Radiator Specialty Co.
GUNK SOLVE - Enamel and epoxy stripper - Tivian Laboratories Inc.
GUNMAR - Recording label - Jazz Composer's Orchestra Association Inc.
GUNMASTER - Cases - Delta Consolidated Industries, Inc.
GUNNACHUCK - Apparel and accessories - Gunnachuck itizens
GUNNAR - Craft supplies - Ports of Scandinavia Inc.
GUNNARSSON - Wood products - Swedish Products Inc. (Sojo Inc.)
GUNNE SAX - Apparel–women's - Jessica McClintock Inc.
GUNNEL-GARD - Rubber–molded - W.H. Salisbury & Co.
GUNNER - Firearms, accessories, and parts - Welsh Sporting Goods Corp. (Boyt Div.)
GUNNER'S - Teas - Eastern Shore Tea Co.
GUNNERS - Toys–automobiles - Mattel, Inc.
GUNNERS GUIDE - Firearms, accessories, and parts ☆ - Marble Arms Corp.
GUNNISON BLACK CANYON - Apparel and accessories - Masterpiece Apparel, Inc.
GUNNUR - Rifles - Conetrol Scope Mounts
GUNNY SKINZ - Apparel and accessories - B.B.G.B., Inc.
GUNNYR - Toys - Tonka Corp.
GUNPOWDER PEARL PINHEAD GREEN - Teas - Grace Tea Co. Ltd.
GUNS N ROSES - Recording label - Guns N' Roses
GUNS OF AUGUST - Games - Avalon Hill Game Co.
GUNS OF FORT DEFIANCE - Games ☆ - Avalon Hill Game Co.
GUNSHELL - Packaging–paper - C.L. Downey Co.
GUNSHIP - Computer software ☆ - Microprose Software, Inc.
GUNSLICK - Sporting goods - Outers Laboratories Inc.
GUNSLINGER - Floor coverings–carpet and rugs - Sweetwater Carpet Corp.
GUNSLINGER - Games ☆ - Avalon Hill Game Co.
GUNSLINGER - Sunglasses - Face 2 Face Corp.
GUNSLINGER RECORDS - Recording label - Gunslinger Records, Inc.
GUNSLINGER, THE - Sporting goods - GB Electrical Inc.
GUNSLINGER, THE - Hunting equipment - JRH Sport Industries, Inc.
GUNSMITH SERVICES HANDGUNS - Firearms, accessories, and parts - Evolution Gun Works
GUNSMOKE - Cigarettes - Star Tobacco Corp.
GUNSMOKE - Recording label - Gunsmoke Entertainment Inc.
GUNSMOKE - Trading cards and stamps - CBS Inc.
GUNSTON HALL - Food products - Janney-Marshall Co.
GUNTEX - Paints - Sherwin-Williams Automotive Finishes Corp.
GUNTHER EXTRA/BUILD - Adhesives and sealants - C. Gunther Co.
GUNTHER R. GRANGET - Statuary ☆ - WMF/USA

GUNTHER ULTRA/BOND - Adhesives and sealants - C. Gunther Co.
GUNTHER'S CASTLE - Hardware - Werner Co.
GUNTRUM - Wines - Sogrape USA Inc.
GUP-PEA - Publisher's imprints - Creative Excellence, Inc.
GUPPIES - Crackers - Prepco
GUPPY - Aquarium thermometers ☆ - American Thermometer Co.
GUPPY GEAR - Scuba diving equipment - Marine Sports Designs, Inc.
GUPPY GILLS - Sporting goods - Marine Sports Designs, Inc.
GUPPY GOGGLES - Sporting goods - Marine Sports Designs, Inc.
GUPTA - Computer software - Gupta Corp.
GUPWEAR - Apparel and accessories - Gupwear
GURD'S - Beverages–carbonated - Procter & Gamble Co.
GURGLER - Fishing lures - Paul Warner Industries
GURGLIN GUTZ - Games - 4 Kidz, Inc.
GURIAN - Apparel–women's - Anne Klein & Co.
GURIMUR - Wallcovering - The Creative Edge, Inc.
GURKEE'S - Footwear - Gurkee's International, Inc.
GURKHA - Skin care products - Wharton Shober
GURLEY'S GOLDEN RECIPE - Nuts–salted, roasted, cooked, or canned - Consolidated Biscuit Co.
GURPS - Games - Steve Jackson Games Inc.
GURTNER - Food products - De Choix Specialty Foods Co.
GURU - Data loggers - Micro Data Base Systems Inc.
GURU MINI BIDI - Cigarettes - G.A. Georgopulo & Co. Inc.
GUS - See NICKEL ROCKERS
GUS - Medical apparatus - Guardian Products Inc.
GUS GUTZ - Toys–stuffed - Rumpus Corp.
GUS THE WALRUS - Toys - Fisher-Price, Inc.
GUSANO GRANDE - Beverages–alcohol - Consolidated Distilled Products Inc.
GUSANO ROJO - Beverages–alcohol - Barton Brands, Ltd.
GUSDORF - Furniture - Gusdorf Corp.
GUSHER - Beverages–carbonated - Coastal Corp.
GUSHER - Pumps ☆ - Imtra Corp.
GUSHERS - Snack foods - General Mills, Inc.
GUSHIN RUSH - Snack foods - General Mills, Inc.
GUSSCO - Index cards - Gussco Manufacturing Inc.
GUSSIES - Apparel stores–lingerie - Formfit Rogers
GUSTAFSONS DAIRY - Milk - Gustafsons Dairy Inc.
GUSTALAC - Antacids ☆ - Geriatric Pharmaceutical Corp.
GUSTASE - Pharmaceutical preparations - Geriatric Pharmaceutical Corp.
GUSTASE PLUS - Pharmaceutical preparations - Geriatric Pharmaceutical Corp.
GUSTAV - Glassware–household - Dansk International Designs, Ltd.
GUSTAV - Glassware–household - Denby USA Limited
GUSTAV - Recording label - Jazz Composer's Orchestra Association Inc.
GUSTAV PRAGER - Musical instrument accessories ☆ - Scherl & Roth Inc.
GUSTAV WERNER - Beverages–malt - Old European Brewery Co.
GUSTAVE AUGUST FICKER - Violins - William Lewis & Son
GUSTAVE LORENTZ - Wines - World Shippers & Importers
GUSTAVE NIEBAUM - Wines - Heublein, Inc.
GUSTIFROLLI - Cookies - Commerce Foods Inc.
GUSTMASTER - Weather tracking equipment - Maximum Inc.
GUSTO - Apparel and accessories ☆ - Italian Classics Inc.
GUSTO - Glassware–household ☆ - Dansk International Designs, Ltd.
GUSTO - Meat products–cured - Burke Marketing Corp.
GUSTO - Meat products–pork - Gusto Packing Co., Inc.
GUSTO - Paper - John Hofmeister & Son, Inc.
GUSTO - Recording label - Gusto Records Inc.
GUSTO'S HEARTLAND - Meat products–pork - Gusto Packing Co., Inc.
GUT Z GATOR - Toys - NSL
GUTENBERG - Artists' materials - Andrews/Nelson/Whitehead
GUTENBERG - Computer software ☆ - Gessler Publishing Co., Inc.
GUTEX - Sports rackets and accessories - Winn, Inc.
GUTH - Lighting fixtures - Guth Lighting
GUTHION - Insecticides - Bayer Corp. (Agriculture Div.)
GUTIERS - Men's suits and blazers - International Clothing of Florida Inc.
GUTITE - Sports rackets and accessories - Winn, Inc.
GUTITE SPIN - Sports rackets and accessories - Winn, Inc.
GUTLON - Sporting goods ☆ - Winn, Inc.
GUTS & GRACE RECORDS - Recording label - Guts & Grace Records, Inc.
GUTSIE - Sports rackets and accessories - Gexco Enterprises
GUTSY LADY - Apparel–women's - Kellwood Co.
GUTTA-GARDS - Gutters–plastic - Colonial Iron Works Inc.
GUTTA PERCHA - Paints ☆ - PPG Industries, Inc.
GUTTENBAR - Sandwiches–prepackaged - Suzannah Farms
GUTTER ARMOR - Eaves - Seamless International, Inc.

☆ = Now out of production

GUTTER BLASTER - Cleaning preparations - Gordon Charles Associates
GUTTER DOWNSPOUT - Cleaning preparations - Alumin-Nu Corp.
GUTTER FINGERS - Gutters–metal - Chapiewsky's Inc.
GUTTER GROOMER - Cleaning equipment - Carroll E. Dietle Revocable Living Trust
GUTTER GUARD - Gutters–metal - Mortite Inc.
GUTTER KING - Gutters–metal - Elda, Inc.
GUTTER PRO - Gutters–metal - E. Wayne Anglin
GUTTER SHIELD - Finishing agents - Rust-Oleum Corp.
GUTTER-TITE - Adhesives and sealants ✰ - Macco Adhesives
GUTTER TOPPER - Gutters–metal - J.O.Y. Enterprises
GUTTERSNIPE - Housewares - Perfex Corp.
GUTZ - Adhesives and sealants - Camco Paints Inc.
GUV'NOR - Health care products ✰ - Avon Products, Inc.
GUY - Colognes - Brandy Harvest
GUY - Handbags - S.C. Import & Export Ltd.
GUY - Snack foods ✰ - Borden, Inc.
GUY-A-WIRE - Wire - Anchor Wire Corp.
GUY BUFFET COLLECTION - Paper products - Diversified Car Leasing
GUY CHAUMONT - Wines - Chartrand Imports
GUY DE BARJAC - Beverages–alcohol - Wine House Ltd.
GUY DEGRENNE - Steel products - Zrike Co. Inc.
GUY GORILLA - Toys–stuffed - Dakin Inc.
GUY HAWKINS - Clarinet and saxophone mouthpieces - J.J. Babbitt Co. Inc.
GUY LAROCHE - Apparel and accessories ✰ - Genesco Inc.
GUY LAROCHE - Hosiery–women's - Magnolia Hosiery Mill Inc.
GUY LAROCHE - Neckties - Dunleigh Tuxton Inc.
GUY LAROCHE - Perfumes - Lancome
GUY LAROCHE - Sunglasses - Status Eyes Ltd.
GUY RENNE - Musical instruments ✰ - Hershman Musical Instrument
GUY ROULOT - Wines - Parliament Import Co.
GUYDEN - Recording label - Universal Record
GUY'S - Food products - Guy's Foods Inc.
GUYS & DOLLS - Dolls - Authentic Models, Inc.
GUYS 'N DOLLS - Cosmetics - Revlon Consumer Products Corp.
GUY'S SHOES - Clothing ✰ - Garrison Keillor
GUYS SPORTSWEAR, THE - Apparel and accessories ✰ - Oshkosh B'gosh, Inc.
GUY'S TEA - Teas - Lalith D. Paranavitana
GUYSON CORP. FLEXBEAD - Cleaning preparations - Guyson Corp. of USA
GUYSON METALBEAD - Chemical preparations - Guyson Corp. of USA
G.U.Y.Z. - Apparel and accessories - Gimmie International, Inc.
GUZZLER - Mops - O-Cedar/Vining Household Products Co.
GUZZLER - Pumps - Bosworth Co.
GUZZLER, THE - Automotive parts and accessories - Pingel Enterprise, Inc.
GUZZLER, THE - Mats - Superior Manufacturing Group/Notrax Floor Matting
GV - Apparel–athletic - G.V. Licensing Inc.
GV - Draperies - Gloria Vanderbilt Home Furnishings Inc.
GV - Laboratory apparatus - General Valve Corp.
GV - Personal-care shower - Interbath, Inc.
GV 350 - Medical apparatus - Biomedical Life Systems, Inc.
GV GOVERNORS VILLAGE - Real estate agencies - Governors Club LP
G.V. HOMEOPATHIC REMEDIES - Herbal beverages - Ellon Bach USA Inc.
GVC - Electronics equipment - Grass Valley Group Inc.
GVE - Fresh vegetables - Growers Vegetable
GVG - Pet products ✰ - Sera Aquaristik USA Inc.
GVP-100 - Leather–parchment - West Carrollton Parchment Co.
GVS - Pharmaceutical preparations ✰ - Savage Laboratories Inc.
GW - Jewelry - Gemworks Inc.
GW - Pizzas–frozen - Frozen Specialties, Inc.
GW - Plastics - GW Plastics, Inc.
GW - Rings–jewelry - Feature Enterprises
GW - Sugar–granulated, refined, or powdered - Great Western Sugar Co.
GW 1 - Aquariums–household - Vortex Innerspace Products Inc.
G.W. BARTLETT CO. - Luggage - G.W. Bartlett Co., Inc.
GW GEM - Construction equipment rental services - GW Associates, Inc.
GW MASTER - Tripods–photographic ✰ - Edixa Camera Co.
GW PARAGON - Tools–hand-operated - Garrett Wade Co., Inc.
GW PARAMOUNT - Tripods–photographic ✰ - Edixa Camera Co.
GW PREVENT - Chemical preparations - Great Western Chemical Co.
GWALTNEY - Meats–luncheon - Gwaltney of Smithfield Ltd.
GWALTNEY'S OLDE SMITHFIELD - Meats–luncheon - Gwaltney of Smithfield Ltd.
GWCOM - Computer peripheral equipment - GWCOM, Inc.
GWEN N' BARRETT - Toys ✰ - Silvestri Corp.
GWENDOLYN GOOSE - Toys–stuffed - Dakin Inc.

GWENOID - Pharmaceutical preparations - Sargeant Acnoid Pharmaceutical Co.
GWETZLI'S - Bakery products - New Life Bakery Inc.
GWILDOR - Toys - Mattel, Inc.
GWONK - Toys ✰ - Those Characters from Cleveland, Inc.
GWR - Rings–jewelry - Feature Enterprises
GWT - Aquariums–household - Great Western Trading Co., Inc.
GWV - Wines - Biltmore Estate Wine Co.
GX - Apparel and accessories - Vision Marketing, Inc.
GX - Jewelry - Rope Chain Enterprises
GX-GRIP - Rackets–racquetball - Gexco Enterprises
GXO - Lamps - Voltarc Technologies, Inc.
GYLANPHEN - Pharmaceutical preparations - Lannett Co. Inc.
GYM - Colognes - Brandy Harvest
GYM - Sporting goods - Bob O'Leary Sports Science
GYM DANDIES - Toys–stuffed - Russ Berrie and Co., Inc.
GYM-DANDY - Mats - Ludlow Composites Corp.
GYM-DANDY - Playground equipment - Wonderline
GYM DANDY! - Video production - Thomas & Partners Co., Inc.
GYM DOLLIES - Toys - Mattel, Inc.
GYM FRESH-NER - Deodorizers - Cramer Products Inc.
GYM GEAR - Apparel and accessories - American Argo Corp.
GYM-IN-ONE - Exercising equipment ✰ - Maximus Fitness Products
GYM-KIN - Apparel–athletic - Elite Sportswear L.P.
GYM LOCKER - Candy ✰ - Fleer Corp.
GYM RAT - Apparel and accessories - Gym Rat, Inc.
GYM-RINGS - Pet products - Pyramid Bird Toys
GYM-RUNNER - Floor coverings - American Floor Products Co. Inc.
GYM-SCHOLAR - Luggage - Universal Trav-ler Inc.
GYM SEAT - Exercising equipment - Evenflo Co.
GYM SHOE - Floor waxes - Basic Coatings, Inc.
GYM TECH - Playground equipment - Hedstrom Corp.
GYM-THING - Exercising equipment - Gerstung/Gym-Thing Inc.
GYM TRAX - Mats - Superior Manufacturing Group/Notrax Floor Matting
GYMBABY - Apparel–children's - Gymboree Corp.
GYMBOARDS - Advertising agencies - Network Event Theater, Inc.
GYMBOREE - Apparel and accessories - Gymboree Corp.
GYMBUBBLES - Toys - Gymboree Corp.
GYMESYL - Vitamins - Natur-Pharma, Inc.
GYMFINITY - Infant product - Today's Kids Inc.
GYMFLOR ELITE - Floor coverings - Tarkett, Inc.
GYMKID - Play equipment - Gymboree Corp.
GYMNAST - Mattresses - Bemco Associates, Inc.
GYMNASTS, THE - Publisher's imprints - Scholastic Inc.
GYMNEMA SYLVESTRE - Vitamins and nutritional supplements - Natrol, Inc.
GYMNEMA SYLVESTRE EXTRACT - Vitamins and nutritional supplements - Vitamin Research Products Inc.
GYMNIT - Apparel–women's - David Guy Kubowitz
GYMPAC - Sporting goods - Diversified Products Corp.
GYMPAC 6200 - Sporting goods - Diversified Products Corp.
GYMPHLEX - Shorts–men's - Rugby & Soccer Supply
GYMSEAL - Varnishes - McCloskey Corp.
GYMSPIN - Play equipment - Gymboree Corp.
GYMSTIK - Exercising equipment - Dan Kropp
GYMSTONES - Games and puzzles - Heno Head, Jr.
GYMTILE - Floor coverings–tile - Pawling Corp. (Standard Products Div.)
GYMTIPS FOR KIDS ON THE GROW - Dolls - Gymboree Corp.
GYMTRACKS - Footwear - Gymboree Corp.
GYMTUBES - Play equipment - Gymboree Corp.
GYNE-LOTRIMIN - Pharmaceutical preparations - Schering-Plough Healthcare Products
GYNE-MOISTRIN - Pharmaceutical preparations - Schering-Plough Healthcare Products
GYNE SULF - Health care products - G and W Laboratories Inc.
GYNECORT - Health care products - Combe Inc.
GYNEPATH - Surgical instruments - Ovamed Corp.
GYNERGEN - Pharmaceutical preparations - Sandoz Pharmaceuticals Corp.
GYNETONE - Pharmaceutical preparations - Schering-Plough Healthcare Products
GYNOGEN - Analgesics - Forest Pharmaceuticals Inc.
GYNOL II - Pharmaceutical preparations - Ortho Pharmaceutical Corp.
GYNOREST - Pharmaceutical preparations - Westwood-Squibb Pharmaceuticals, Inc.
GYNSEPTIC - Pharmaceutical preparations - Sporicidin International
GYP-C-JACK - Tools - Goldblatt Tool Co.
GYP-CRETE - Gypsum products - Maxxon Corp.

✰ = Now out of production

GYP-CRETE 2000 - Gypsum products - Maxxon Corp.
GYP-GRIP - Screws - Georgia-Pacific Corp.
GYP SYN - Fertilizers–nitrogenous - Reuse Technology, Inc.
GYPROC - Gypsum products - Georgia-Pacific Corp.
GYPSI JIG - Fishing tackle - Northland Fishing Tackle, Inc.
GYPSIES - Footwear - A.G.S. of Hanover Inc.
GYPSOLITE - Gypsum products - National Gypsum Co.
GYPSONITE - Fiberboard - Furman Lumber Inc.
GYPSY - Apparel–women's - Berlei USA
GYPSY - Boats - Glen-L Marine Designs
GYPSY - Chemical preparations - Coastal Industries Inc.
GYPSY - Dishes–earthenware ☆ - Denby USA Limited
GYPSY - Games ☆ - Avalon Hill Game Co.
GYPSY BALM - Perfumes - Gianna Rose
GYPSY BAND - Girdles - Formflex Foundations Inc.
GYPSY CAB - Salad dressings–bottled - Gypsy Enterprises, Inc.
GYPSY COLD CARE - Teas–herbal - Traditional Medicinals, Inc.
GYPSY DREAMS - Jewelry ☆ - Jody Coyote, Inc.
GYPSY FIRE - Christmas tree ornaments - Cracker Box Inc.
GYPSY LASH - Cosmetics - Worldwide Cosmetics
GYPSY WITCH - Playing cards - United States Playing Card Co.
GYPSYS & THIEVES - Apparel - Luis Pulido
GYPTEX - Gypsum products - Georgia-Pacific Corp.
GYRACER - Toys–automobiles - Mattel, Inc.
GYRALITE - Lighting fixtures - Hubbell Lighting, Inc. (Lighting Div.)
GYRLZ N F/X - Recording label - Digital Prisoner Records
GYRO - Computer hardware - Intelligent Resources Integrated Systems, Inc.
GYRO - Dryers–hair - Magic Distributing Ltd.
GYRO - Floor-scrubbing machine ☆ - Advance Machine Co.
GYRO - Girdles - Formflex Foundations Inc.
GYRO - Shaving preparations - Gillette Co.

GYRO - Sporting goods - O'Brien International
GYRO - Toys–airplanes ☆ - Victor Stanzel and Co.
GYRO BRUSH - Curling irons–electric ☆ - Helen of Troy Corp.
GYRO CYCLES - Toys–automobiles - Mattel, Inc.
GYRO I - Bowling balls - Ebonite International, Inc.
GYRO-JUMP - Exercising equipment - Excel, The Exercise Co.
GYRO-LITE - Lighting fixtures - Swivelier Co. Inc.
GYRO-LUX - Lighting fixtures - Swivelier Co. Inc.
GYRO-MATIC - Globes - Replogle Globes Inc.
GYRO-PAC - Abrasive products ☆ - Norton Co.
GYRO WINDFEATHER - Weather vanes ☆ - Woolsey Marine Industries
GYRO WRAP - Restaurant franchise - Gyro Wrap, Inc.
GYROC - Toys–models ☆ - Estes Industries
GYROCAM - Photographic equipment - Aerial Films, Inc.
GYROENGINE - Medical apparatus - Gyration Inc.
GYROLL - Sporting goods - Mike Stewart Inc.
GYROMAZE - Games ☆ - Kenner Products
GYROMIXER - Mixers - Fluid Management
GYROMOUNT - Photographic equipment - NTT Enterprises, Inc.
GYRON - Camera platform - E.F. Nettmann & Associates, Inc.
GYRONIMO - Toys - Mattel, Inc.
GYROPOD - Photographic equipment - NTT Enterprises, Inc.
GYROS - Toys - Tedco Inc.
GYROS CLASSIC, THE - Meat products - Grecian Delight Foods, Inc.
GYROSCOPE - Recording label - Caroline Records, Inc.
GYROSCOPIC-BALANCE - Furnaces–industrial ☆ - Arrowhead Environmental Control
GYROTONIC EXPANSION SYSTEM - Exercise equipment and apparatus - Gyrotonic Sales Corp.
GYROTONIC LINEA NOVA - Exercising equipment ☆ - Gyrotonic Sales Corp.
GYRUS - Computer software - Gyrus Systems Inc.

☆ = Now out of production

H

Addresses and phone numbers for the companies cited in the brands below
are available in the Company Listings section immediately following the brands listings.

H - Ammunition ☆ - Olin Corp. (Winchester Div.)
H - Apparel and accessories - Hickory Baseball, Inc.
H - Apparel and accessories - Marketforce
H - Apparel–athletic - Hooter Sportswear Inc.
H - Apparel–women's - Chermisqui Novak & Hoenscheidt Inc.
H - Beverages–malt - Anheuser-Busch Companies Inc.
H - Insecticides - Airosol Co. Inc.
H - Jewelry - Caretta Inc.
H - Jewelry - Hamilton Jewelers Inc.
H - Jewelry - Hidalgo Corp.
H - Jewelry–precious - Hannoush Jewelers
H - Metal goods - Holnam Inc.
H - Motor vehicles - Holiday Rambler Corp.
H - Protective apparel - Harvey's Skindiving Supply, Inc.
H - Sporting goods - Hansen Sports, Inc.
H - Sportswear and dinnerware - Virginia Hot Springs Inc.
H - Tools ☆ - Hannay Reels
H - Typewriters - Smith Corona Corp.
H-2 OFF - Paints - Klee Chemical Coatings
H-4Z - Novelty items - PC Manufacturing Corp.
H-20 MULTPROBE - Computer software - Hydrolab Corp.
H-101 - Deodorizers - Hillyard Enterprises, Inc.
H-330 - Tires - Bridgestone/Firestone, Inc.
H-A - Helmets–metal - Accessory Distributors Inc.
H. A. CALAHAN - Cleaning preparations - Davis Instruments Corp.
H A USA LEATHER - Apparel and accessories - Damien JP Senkir
H AMERICAN HEROES - Film - Arthur Elgort Ltd.
H & A - Rope - Hooven Allison
H & B - Thread - Belding Heminway Co. Inc.
H & C - Paints - FLR Paints Inc.
H & G - Tools - Cleveland Twist Drill Co.
#H & G STUDIOS - Music boxes - H & G Studio Inc.
H & H - Bakery products - H & H Bakery & Restaurant Inc.
H & H - Enamels - Lasting Paints Inc.
H & H - Gin - United States Distilled Products Co.
H & H - Pastries ☆ - Henry Heide, Inc.
H & H - Shotguns - Fie Corp.
H & H JR. - Food products - McLane Southern Grocery Distribution
H & L - Health care products ☆ - Alconox Inc.
H & L - Jewelry - H & L Wholesale Jewelry, Inc.
H & M - Publisher's imprints - Himalayan Publishers
H & M - Syrup - Herold & Miller Inc.
H & N - Seafood - H & N Fish Co.
H & N FISH CO. - Seafood - H & N Fish Co.
H & R - Coffee - Chock Full O'Nuts Corp.
H & R - Food products ☆ - Pillsbury Co.
H & R - Guns ☆ - Harrington & Richardson Inc.
H & R BLOCK - Accounting services - H & R Block, Inc.
H & R JOHNSON - Tiles–ceramic - H & R Johnson Inc.
H & R REISING - Guns ☆ - Harrington & Richardson Inc.
H & S - Bakery products - H and S Bakery Inc.
H & T - Infant product - Chase Holding Co. Inc.
H & W BATH LINE, THE - Bathroom accessories ☆ - Liette International Ltd.
H-B - Cigarettes - G.A. Georgopulo & Co. Inc.
H-B - Cough drops ☆ - F.B. Washburn Candy Corp.
H-B - Glass–safety - Marsco Manufacturing Co.

H. B. FULLER - Paints - H.B. Fuller Co. (North American Adhesives, Sealants and Coatings Group)
H. B. HELLER - Underwear and nightwear - Spencer Supports Ltd.
H. B. SCOTTS - Chewing tobacco - Conwood Co. L.P.
H-BAR-C RANCHWEAR - Apparel–men's - Halpern & Christenfeld Inc.
H BAR H - Floor waxes - D.J. Mead, Hubbs & Howe Co.
H BLUE O - Apparel and accessories - John M. Caldwell Distributing Co. Inc.
H. BUESCHE BRASS - Hardware - Avondale Distributors Inc.
H-CLIP - Hardware - Teco/Lumberlok
H. COUF - Musical instrument accessories - Armstrong Woodwinds
H COURT OFFICIAL - Apparel and accessories - Douglas Allan Witkop
H-CREST SYMBOL - Appliance parts - General Electric Co.
H-D - Aircraft repairing services - Heli-Dyne Systems, Inc.
H-D 240 - Motorcycle engine oil - Harley-Davidson, Inc.
H-D SILICONE - Lubricants - CRC Chemicals USA/Siloo
H DOUBLE HATTER - Apparel stores–millinery - Get-A-Head
H-E-B - Beverages–carbonated - H.E. Butt Grocery Co.
H-E-B RICH & LITE - Ice cream - H.E. Butt Grocery Co.
H-E-B SPORTS QUENCHER - Fruit drinks–bottled or canned - H.E. Butt Grocery Co.
H E L I U M AUTHENTIQUE - Apparel and accessories - A.I.J.J. Enterprises, Inc.
H E M A ENTERPRISES, INC. - Tools–hand-operated - Hema Enterprises, Inc.
H-FACT - Crane parts - Manitowoc Co. Inc.
H FACTOR - Apparel and accessories - MS&H Inc.
H. FIEHN - Musical instruments ☆ - Fred Gretsch Enterprises
H GRAND HARVEST - Food products - Golden Lyon Investment, Inc.
H GRAYS - Apparel and accessories - Negro Leagues Baseball Museum, Inc.
H-GROW - Shampoos - Green Foods
H-GUN - Paint sprayers - Speeflo Manufacturing Corp.
H-H-BROWN SCUBALINED - Footwear ☆ - H.H. Brown Shoe Co., Inc.
H HALSTEAD - Metallic tubing - Halstead Industries Inc.
H HANES - Computer software - Sara Lee Corp.
+H +HARGER - Electrical equipment - Harger Lightning Protection, Inc.
H HARVEY - Windows–storm - Harvey Industries, Inc.
H HEAVE - Footwear–athletic - Virginia G. Pettibone
H HERCULES - Automotive bumpers - Hercules Bumpers Inc.
H HINGED - Apparel and accessories - Lee Lottes and Jeff Venanzi Partnership
H HIRSHFIELD'S - Caulking compounds - Hirshfield's, Inc.
H HIRSHFIELDS - Paints - Hirshfield's, Inc.
H HOLLOWAY - Bedspreads - Holloway Group, Inc.
H HOLLYWELL - Paper products - Hollywell, Inc.
H-HOUR - Toys ☆ - War House
H HUFFY - Bicycles - Huffy Corp.
H HYGENIC - Rubber–molded - Hygenic Corp.
H-I - Fishing lures - Horrocks-Ibbotson Co.
H-I-N-T/COM - Electronic equipment - Earmark Inc.
H-I-P - Chewing gum ☆ - Leaf, Inc.
H. J. WOOD & SON - Glassware–household ☆ - Crownford Giftware Co. Inc.
H. KRULL - Brushes ☆ - Walker and Zanger Inc.
H L BIS NEW YORK - Apparel–women's - Go On Sportswear USA Ltd.
H. L. HUBBELL - Clocks ☆ - Burwood Products Co.
H/M - Bacterial vaccines - Triple F, Inc.
H. M. ABERNATHY - Coats–women's - Hit or Miss Inc.

☆ = Now out of production

973

H-M-F - Apparel–men's - HMF, Inc.
H. M. GOUSHA - Publisher's imprints - Simon & Schuster, Inc.
H. M. QUACKENBUSH - Nutcrackers - H.M. Quackenbush Inc.
H-O HOT GRANOLA - Cereal - GFA Brands Inc.
H OF C - Jewelry - House of Commans Inc.
H. ORITSKY - Apparel–men's - Hartmarx Corp.
H-P FORTIFIER - Animal feeds ☆ - Agri-King Inc.
H-PANTOTEN - Health care products - Healthwatchers System
H-R - Lubricants - Carter-Wallace, Inc.
H/R ARTYPE - Artists' materials - Artype Inc.
H R BRITE - Steel - J. Rubin & Co.
H. R. WILHELM - Musical instrument accessories - M & M Distributing Co.
H-REFLEX TECHNOLOGY TRI-PHASIC MODALITY - Electronic nerve stimulator - Frank G. Hine
H S - Vitamins and nutritional supplements - Herbal Science International Inc.
H. SALT SEAFOOD RESTAURANTS - Restaurants–fast food ☆ - H. Salt Seafood Restaurants
H. SCHICKER - Musical-instrument bows ☆ - International Violin Co. Ltd.
H-SCRIBE - Ambulatory monitors - Mortara Instrument, Inc.
H-SERIES - Filing cabinets–metal - Haskell of Pittsburgh, Inc.
H-SPECIAL - Brooms - Hamburg Broom Works Inc.
H-SPIDER - Apparel–men's - H-Spider, Inc.
H-STRUT - Building materials–asbestos - Haydon Corp.
H-T - Food products - Harris-Teeter Inc.
H THE HOUSE - Catalogs - Active Sports, Inc.
H-TUBE LITE - Lighting equipment ☆ - SOS Lighting Devices
H. UPMANN - Cigar boxes–wood - Consolidated Cigar Corp.
H. UPMANN - Cigarettes - G.A. Georgopulo & Co. Inc.
H. UPMANN APERITIFS - Cigars - Cuban Cigar Brands, NV
H.-V.-B. - Pharmaceutical preparations ☆ - JMI-Canton Pharmaceuticals
H. W. CARTER & SONS - Work clothes - H.W. Carter & Sons Inc.
H. W. CARTER'S - Apparel–men's - Smart Style Industries Inc.
H. W. POWERS - Candy ☆ - Powers Pharmaceutical Corp.
H0 GO - Leather goods - Unlimited Solutions
H1 F1 - Dryers–hair ☆ - Sunbeam-Oster Household Products
H1 H.L GOOD FOOD INC. MASTER SAUCE - Sauces - H.L. Good Food, Inc.
H2 GO - Water purification systems - H2 Go, Inc.
H2 OIL BASE - Paints - William Zinsser & Co. Inc.
H2 PRO - Boats–canoes ☆ - Old Town Canoe Co.
H2NO - Adhesives and sealants - Patagonia, Inc.
H2NO - Housewares - Amcor Group Ltd.
H2NO LIGHT - Adhesives and sealants - Patagonia, Inc.
H2NO PLUS - Adhesives and sealants - Patagonia, Inc.
H2NO STORM - Adhesives and sealants - Patagonia, Inc.
H2O - Apparel–men's - Bugle Boy Industries, Inc.
H2O - Fabrics ☆ - West Point-Pepperell Inc.
H2O - Finishing agents - Master Products Inc.
H2O - Furniture - Avant Industries
H2O - Paint - Vogel Paint and Wax Co., Inc.
H2O+ - Water–bottled or canned - Aqua Lyte Corp.
H2O - Water–bottled or canned - Hubinger Co.
-H2O PILL - Vitamins and nutritional supplements - JBN Enterprises, Inc.
H2O PRO - Oils–lubricating - Joseph Mario Donnolo, III
H2O WORKS - Exercising equipment - Hedstrom Corp.
H2OFF - Varnish removers - Savogran Co.
H2OFF - Vitamins and nutritional supplements - Alleghany Pharmacal Corp.
H2OH! - Beverages–carbonated - Pepsico, Inc.
H2ONLY - Water purification systems - Servapure Co.
H2OPTIX - Eyeglasses - Solar-Mates Sunglasses
H2OUT - Vitamins and nutritional supplements - Barth-Spencer Corp.
H2SO4 - Cleaning preparations - Noco Co.
H4C - Apparel - Carl David Harry
H20 - Apparel and accessories - Arnold Sing-Huat Yew
H20 - Varnishes - Vogel Paint and Wax Co., Inc.
H20 - Water–bottled or canned - Suntory Water Group. Inc.
H20 PLUS HYDROGELS - Skin care products - H2O Plus, L.P.
H20-PRO - Filters–water - Vickers, Inc.
H20 WORKS - Sporting goods - Hedstrom Corp.
H20DYSSEA - Scuba diving equipment - PIC International Inc.
H20FF - Skin care products - Slipp-Nott Corp.
H20'IRISH - Water–bottled or canned - Aqua-Pac, Inc.
H47 - Jewelry - N.Y. 47th St. Jewelry, Inc.
HA BASICS - Apparel and accessories - Hanna Andersson Corp.
HA RA - Food products - Inn Foods, Inc.
HA SURFSIDE - Recording label - Hawaii Calls Inc.
HAAGEN-DAZS - Beverages–alcohol ☆ - Hiram Walker & Sons, Inc.

HAAGEN-DAZS - Ice cream - Haagen-Dazs Co. Inc.
HAAGEN-DAZS - Ice cream - Pillsbury Co.
HAAGEN DAZS SORBET - Ice cream - Haagen-Dazs Co. Inc.
HAAKE-BECK - Beverages–malt - Dribeck Importers, Inc.
HAAKE BECK NON-ALCOHOLIC - Beverages–malt - Beck's North America
HAARMANN - Vinegar - Haarmann Vinegar & Pickle Co.
HAARSWIRL - Hair care products - Arius-Eickert Co. Inc.
HAAS - Bakery products - Haas Baking Co.
HAAS - Brushes - St. Lawrence Sales Inc.
HAAS - Cabinets - Haas Cabinet Co. Inc.
HAAS - Candy - Chiodo Candy Co.
HAAS - Fruit and vegetable markets - Haas Fruit Co. Inc.
HAAS - Pickles ☆ - Holland-American Importing Co. Inc.
HAAS & DERST - Cigars - G.A. Georgopulo & Co. Inc.
HAB - Beverages–malt - Kalsec, Inc.
HAB - Jewelry - Hab Tool, Inc.
HABA - Toys–blocks - T.C. Timber/Habermaass Corp.
HABADEX - Computer software - Haba Systems
HABAN MANUFACTURING, INC. - Lawn mowers - Haban Manufacturing, Inc.
HABAND - Apparel and accessories - Haband Co.
HABANERO - Barbecue sauce - Robb's Ribs
HABANERO - Chili peppers–powdered ☆ - Frieda's, Inc.
HABANERO - Computer peripheral equipment - Board of Trustees of the University of Illinois
HABANERO - Food products - Sauces & Salsas, Ltd.
HABANERO - Jams and jellies - Coyote Cocina
HABANITA - Colognes ☆ - Gary Farn Ltd.
HABANTA - Perfumes ☆ - Classic Fragrances Ltd.
HABATAT WILDERNESS - Apparel and accessories - Diversified Enterprises, Inc.
HABAWORD - Computer software - Haba Systems
HABBA TREES - Pet products - Zoo Med Laboratories, Inc.
HABBERSETT - Sausages - Jones Dairy Farm
HABDRYL - Pharmaceutical preparations ☆ - JMI-Canton Pharmaceuticals
HABER - Computer software ☆ - CONDUIT
HABER-TECH - Computer software - Queue Inc.
HABERDASHERY - Apparel–women's - Leslie Fay Companies Inc.
HABERLINE - Musical instruments - David Wexler & Co.
HABERO - Spices and extracts - La Mexicana, Inc.
HABERSHAM - Clocks ☆ - General Time Corp. (Westclox/Seth Thomas Div.)
HABERSHAM PLANTATION EST. 1972 - Furniture - Habersham Plantation
HABERSHAM ROAD - Apparel and accessories ☆ - Edison Brothers Stores, Inc.
HABERULE - Gauging instruments - Arthur Brown and Bros. Inc.
HABIBI - Skin care products - Goubaud
HABILE - Skin care products - Goubaud
HABIT - Housewares - Cello Chemical Co.
HABIT BREAKER - Pet products - Bramton Co.
HABIT BREAKER, THE - Health care products - Health Your Way, Inc.
HABIT I - Skin care products - Bare Essentials
HABIT II - Skin care products - Bare Essentials
HABIT III - Skin care products - Bare Essentials
HABIT-NIP - Pet products ☆ - Roccorp, Inc.
HABIT ROUGE - Perfumes - Guerlain Inc.
HABITANT - Fencing–wood - Machalk Enterprises Inc.
HABITAT - Computer software - Treacyfaces Inc.
HABITAT - Curtains–shower - Kohler Co.
HABITAT - Floor coverings–carpet and rugs - Habitat International Inc.
HABITAT - House furnishings ☆ - Lexington Furniture Industries, Inc.
HABITAT - Pet products - Novalek, Inc.
HABITAT - Tiles–ceramic - Monarch Tile Inc.
HABITAT - Trays - Vincent Lippe Co.
HABITAT:EARTH - Toys - Play Visions
HABITAT II - Fishing tackle - Frabill Inc.
HABITAT MASTERBATH - Curtains–shower - Kohler Co.
HABITAT SERIES - Telephone equipment - Protel, Inc.
HABITAT V - Fishing tackle - Frabill Inc.
HABITRAIL - Pet products - Rolf C. Hagen (USA) Corp.
HABITREE - Pet products - Lava Enterprises
HABITROL - Smoking-cessation aid - Basel Pharmaceuticals
HABITS - Apparel–women's ☆ - Palm Beach Co., Inc.
HABLAMOS ESPANOL - Video cassettes - Eurotel Inc.
HABOND - Cement - Hastings Plastics Co.
HABRIL - Mixers - Fluid Management
HABUTEE PRINTS - Fabrics - Burlington House Fabrics Group
HAC - Apparel–athletic - Hampton Athletic Club Inc.

☆ = Now out of production

HAC GROUP - Motor vehicle dealers - Half-A-Car-Co.
HAC32 - Computer peripheral equipment - Hughes Aircraft Co.
HACCP GUARDIAN - Housewares - Georgia-Pacific Corp.
HACIENDA - Dinnerware–glass - Franciscan by Johnson Brothers, USA, Inc.
HACIENDA - Fans–electric ☆ - Nutone Inc.
HACIENDA - Floor coverings–carpet and rugs ☆ - Kelly Group Inc.
HACIENDA - Flour–blended ☆ - Central Milling Co.
HACIENDA - Food products - Alex Foods, Inc.
HACIENDA - Food products ☆ - Nalley's Fine Foods
HACIENDA - Tiles–ceramic ☆ - H & R Johnson Inc.
HACIENDA - Wallpaper - Seabrook Wallcoverings, Inc.
HACIENDA - Window coverings - 3 Day Blinds, Inc.
HACIENDA - Wines - Hacienda Wine Cellars Inc.
HACIENDA GOLD - Dinnerware–glass - Franciscan by Johnson Brothers, USA, Inc.
HACIENDA GREEN - Dinnerware–glass - Franciscan by Johnson Brothers, USA, Inc.
HACIENDA MONASTERIO - Wines - European Beverage Co., Inc.
HACIENDA WINE CELLARS - Wines - Bronco Wine Co.
HACK DEVIL - Tools - Warren Tool Group
HACKENSACK - Wire products - Carolina Steel and Wire Corp.
HACKER - Toys - Tonka Corp.
HACKER DEADBOLT - Computer software - Xiox Corp.
HACKER NATION - Paper - Leo Carroll
HACKER PREVENTER - Computer storage devices - Xiox Corp.
HACKER-PSCHORR - Beverages–malt - The Stroh Brewery Co.
HACKER TRACKER - Computer software - Xiox Corp.
HACKLES - Combs - Robert Main & Sons Inc.
HACKMAN - Housewares - Hackman Tabletop Inc.
HACKMASTER J - Saw blades ☆ - American Saw & Manufacturing Co.
HACKMASTER R - Saw blades ☆ - American Saw & Manufacturing Co.
HACKMASTER V - Hacksaw blades ☆ - American Saw & Manufacturing Co.
HACKNEY - Motor vehicles–trucks - Hackney & Sons, Inc.
HACKNEY - Recording label - LBI
HACKY SACK - Toys - Wham-O Manufacturing Co.
HACOL - Pigments - Hastings Plastics Co.
HAD-A-SNAIL - Water treating compounds - Aquarium Products Inc.
HADABUG - Insecticides ☆ - Walco Linck Co.
HADANY - Brass religious articles ☆ - Israeli Accents
HADAR - Food products ☆ - Greenfield Noodle & Specialty
HADAS KOSHER - Meat products–poultry ☆ - Empire Kosher Poultry Inc.
HADASSIM - Wines - Gibson Wine Co.
HADCO - Finishing agents - PLC
HADCO - Lighting fixtures - Hadco
HADDAR - Food products - Erba Food Products Inc.
HADDINGTON FARMS - Chocolate candy - Cherrydale Farms Inc.
HADDOCK - Food products - Holland-American Importing Co. Inc.
HADDON HALL - Cigars - Swisher International, Inc.
HADDON HALL - Floor coverings - Harris-Tarkett, Inc.
HADDON HALL - Floor coverings - Teak International
HADDON HALL - Floor coverings ☆ - Bruce Hardwood Floors
HADDON HALL - Floor coverings ☆ - Robbins Inc.
HADDON HALL - Floor waxes - Twi-Laq Industries Inc.
HADDON HALL - Furniture - Lane Co. Inc.
HADDON HALL - Furniture ☆ - Bernhardt Industries
HADDON HOUSE - Food products - Tidelands Sales Co. Inc.
HADDON HOUSE - Pickles - Haddon House Food Products Inc.
HADDONFIELD - Fireplace equipment ☆ - Majestic Co.
HADDONFIELD - Floor coverings - Mannington Resilient Floors
HADDONFIELD - Floor coverings–carpet and rugs ☆ - Lees Carpets
HADELAND OF NORWAY - Giftware - Royal Copenhagen Porcelain Inc.
HADER - Blood pressure apparatus - Intermedix Medical Products Corp.
HADJI BEY'S - Candy ☆ - Bewley Irish Imports
HADLEIGH MANOR - Furniture ☆ - Henredon Furniture Industries Inc.
HADLEY - Apparel and accessories - Hadley
HADLEY - Bedding–linen - Dan River Inc.
HADLEY - Food products - Hadley Fruit Orchards, Inc.
HADLEY - Tableware–china ☆ - Lenox, Inc.
HADLEY - Watchbands–leather - Hadley Roma Corp.
HADLEY - Watches - Bulova Corp.
HADLEY FRUIT ORCHARDS - Beverages - Hadley Fruit Orchards, Inc.
HADLEY HALL - Wallpaper ☆ - Imperial Wallcoverings, Inc.
HADLEY HOUSE PLATES - Giftware - Viking Import House Inc.
HADLEY POTTERY - Pottery - H. George Caspari Inc.
HADLEY ROMA - Watchbands–base metal - Roma Industries
HADLEY'S PRESTIGE - Wines - Hadley Fruit Orchards, Inc.

HADON HALL - Stationery ☆ - Pratt & Austin Co.
HADRIAN - Glass products - Decora Imports Inc.
HADRIAN - Navigational instruments ☆ - Brookes & Gatehouse Inc.
HAEGER - Giftware - Haeger Potteries
HAEGER FLORAL - Giftware - Haeger Potteries
HAEGER POTTERIES, THE - Giftware - Haeger Potteries
HAELAN 951 - Vitamins and nutritional supplements - Haelan Products, Inc.
HAEMOLANCE - Chronimed Inc.
HAER - Hair care products - Nature Products
HAEUSER - Varnishes - Mantrose-Haeuser Co. Inc.
HAFFENREFFER - Beverages–malt - Falstaff Brewing Corp.
HAFI - Chemical preparations - Penray Companies, Inc.
HAFI - Jams and jellies - Haram-Christensen Corp.
HAFLE VINEYARDS - Wines - Hafle Vineyards
HAFLER - Audio equipment - Hafler Co.
HAFLEX - Molding compounds–plastics - Hastings Plastics Co.
HAFNER PRESS - Publisher's imprints - MacMillan Publishing Co. Inc.
HAFNER VINEYARDS - Wines - Hafner Winery
HAFNIA - Flatware - Yamazaki Tableware Inc.
HAFNIA - Hams ☆ - Jack Greenberg Inc.
HAGA - Jacklin Seed
HAGAFEN - Wines - Hagafen Cellars
HAGAMAN - Floor coverings–carpet and rugs - Hagaman Industries Inc.
HAGAN - Skis - Climb High Inc.
HAGAR LE TERRIBLE - Computer software - Gessler Publishing Co., Inc.
HAGARON-PEEL - Chemical preparations ☆ - Yasutomo
HAGEN - Pet products - Rolf C. Hagen (USA) Corp.
HAGEN - Sporting goods - Wilson Sporting Goods Co.
HAGEN HOUSE - Mayonnaise - Hagen House
HAGEN-RENAKER - Figurines - Hagen-Renaker Inc.
HAGER - Hardware - Hager Hinge Co.
HAGERTY - Finishing agents - W.J. Hagerty & Sons Ltd. Inc.
HAGERTY FOODS - Food products - Hagerty Foods, Inc.
HAGGAR - Apparel–men's - Haggar Corp.
HAGGAR - Neckties - MMG Corp.
HAGGAR - Underwear and nightwear - Tugaloo River Boxer Co.
HAGGAR WRINKLE-FREE COTTONS - Slacks–men's - Haggar Apparel Co.
HAGLET - Maps - Hagstrom Map Co., Inc.
HAGSTROM MAP CO. - Maps and atlases - American Map Corp.
HAHLON - Brushes - Hahl Filaments, Inc.
HAHN - Jewelry - Hahn Watch & Jewelry Co.
HAHN - Nurseries and garden stores ☆ - Gravely International Inc.
HAHN AND HENNE - Giftware ☆ - Charles Zahn-Import Merchant
HAHN ESTATES - Wines - Smith & Hook Winery
HAHN ESTATES - Wines ☆ - House of Burgundy Inc.
HAHN SHOES - Shoe stores - United States Shoe Corp.
HAHNEL - Photographic equipment ☆ - Argraph Corp. (Samigon Div.)
HAHNENKAMM - Sweaters - Hagemeister-Lert Inc.
HAHN'S - Cakes - Hahn's Old Fashioned Cake
HAHT SOFTWARE - Computer software - Haht Software, Inc.
HAHTSITE - Computer software - Haht Software, Inc.
HAHVUD LAMPPOST - Greeting cards - Originals by Maris (O.B.M. Publishing)
HAI - Computer peripheral equipment - Home Automation, Inc.
HAI HOCHO - Knives - Cold Steel Inc.
HAI KARATE - Colognes - Pfizer Inc.
HAI OMNI - Computer hardware - Home Automation, Inc.
HAID - Clocks ☆ - Coehler-Coptex Co.
HAIGHT COVERTSIDE - Wines - Haight Vineyard
HAIGHT VINEYARD - Wines - Haight Vineyard
HAIKU - Teas ☆ - Great Eastern Sun Trading Co. Inc.
HAIKU HOUSES COUNTRY HOUSES OF 16TH CENTURY JAPAN - Prefabricated buildings–wood - Gordon R. Steen
HAIKU JAPANESE TEAS - Teas - Great Eastern Sun Trading Co. Inc.
HAIL RAGNER - Furniture–wood ☆ - Gold Medal Inc.
HAIL/SAFE - Marine rigging ☆ - Ray Jefferson
HAILGUARD HAG ENTERPRISES - Air conditioning equipment - Richard D. Dickinson
HAILWOOD - Milk - Hailwood Inc.
HAIN - Health care products - Hain Pure Food Co. Inc.
HAIN NATURALS - Food products - Hain Pure Food Co. Inc.
HAIN PURE FOODS - Crackers - Hain Pure Foods Co. Inc.
HAINES - Seafood products–canned or cured ☆ - Coast Seafoods Co.
HAINES BROS. - Pianos - Aeolian Pianos Inc.
HAINES HUNTER - Boats–motor - Outboard Marine Corp.
HAIR ADDITION - Hair-replacement product - International Hairgoods Inc.
HAIR ALIVE - Hair care products - Moore Beauty Inc.

HAIR AND NAILS - Vitamins and nutritional supplements - Hall Laboratories, Inc.

HAIR & NOW - Vitamins and nutritional supplements ☆ - Head Start Vitamin Products

HAIR APPAREL - Hair care products - Hair Apparel, Inc.

HAIR ARRANGER - Hair care products - Cooper Products, Inc.

HAIR AT REST - Hair care products - Paul Brown Salon & Spa

HAIR-AWAY - Depilatories ☆ - Spilo/Mehaz Worldwide

HAIR BACK - Hair care products - B.C. Cosmaceuticals, Inc.

HAIR BAND-IT - Hair care products - Lee Innovations, Inc.

HAIR BEAR - Toys - Smethport Specialty Co.

HAIR BEAR BUNCH - Pet products - Precious Paws

HAIR BEAUTIFIER - Hair care products - Aristocrat Hairseptic Co.

HAIR BEYOND REPAIR - Hair care products - Nature's Design Ltd.

HAIR BOOSTER - Hair care products - Nature's Bounty, Inc.

HAIR BRILLIANCE - Vitamins and nutritional supplements - Evan Nutraceuticals, Inc.

HAIR CANDY - Hair care products - Focus 21 International Inc.

HAIR CEMENT - Hair care products ☆ - Roberts Research Laboratories, Inc.

HAIR CHARMS - Barrettes - Mattel, Inc.

HAIR CLEARIFIER - Hair care products - Scruples Professional Salon Products, Inc.

HAIR CLUB FOR WOMEN - Beauty shops - Hair Club for Men Ltd.

HAIR COMPONENTS - Hair-care products - Interface

HAIR CONSTRUCTION - Brushes–hair - Helen of Troy Corp.

HAIR COUNTRY - Hair curlers - Burmax Co. Inc.

HAIR CRAFT - Hair coloring preparations - Stylors Inc.

HAIR CRIMPER, THE - Curling irons–electric - Helene Curtis Industries Inc.

HAIR DEFENSE - Hair care products - Colgate-Palmolive Co.

HAIR DESIGNER - Curling irons–electric - Helene Curtis Industries Inc.

HAIR DISC - Hair care products - Mane Inc.

HAIR-DO HARRIET - Toys - Smethport Specialty Co.

HAIR DOCTOR - Hair care products - Tangler-Wrangler Inc.

HAIR DOODLES - Hair care products - Goody Products, Inc.

HAIR ENERGIZED - Hair care products - Nu-Tress Laboratories Inc.

HAIR ENERGY - Hair care products - Mahdeen Laboratory

HAIR ENERGY - Hair care products ☆ - Advanced Research Laboratories

HAIR-EPIL - Skin care products - Bioswiss Cosmetics USA

HAIR EPOXY - Hair care products ☆ - Advanced Research Laboratories

HAIR ESSENTIALS - Hair care products - Andre Fantasies Inc.

HAIR ESSENTIALS - Shampoos - Neill Corp.

HAIR ESSENTIALS II - Hair care products - Andre Fantasies Inc.

HAIR FACTORS - Hair care products - Twinlab

HAIR FAIR - Barrettes ☆ - Pakula & Co.

HAIR FITNESS - Hair care products - Jeannie Maxon

HAIR FIXER, THE - Hair care products - Cosmair Inc.

HAIR FIXX - Hair care products - Mahdeen Laboratory

HAIR-FLAIR - Hair care products - Russ Berrie and Co., Inc.

HAIR FLEX - Brushes–hair - GCP, Inc.

HAIR FOOD FOR ROOTS - Hair care products - Ampro Industries, Inc.

HAIR FORMULA PLUS - Hair care products - EHA Laboratories

HAIR FUN - Dolls - Mattel, Inc.

HAIR GENIE - Leather–chamois - Lloyd Lapidus

HAIR-GLO - Hair care products - Murray's Worldwide Inc.

HAIR GOES - Depilatories - CCA Industries, Inc.

HAIR GRIP - Hair care products - Raynauld Creations, Inc.

HAIR HANDLER - Hair care products - Major International Inc.

HAIR HELPER - Health care products - Above All Health Inc.

HAIR HOOK UP - Hairpins - Hair Hook Ups

HAIR HOOPS - Hair curlers - Hair Hoops, Inc.

HAIR HUES - Hair coloring preparations - Helene Curtis Industries Inc.

HAIR HUGGER - Headbands - M & T Bank

HAIR IN A PINCH - Wigs - Look of Love International

HAIR IN ACTION - Hair care products - Roberts Research Laboratories, Inc.

HAIR INSTANT - Hair care products - Nu-Tress Laboratories Inc.

HAIR-IT-IS - Wigs - Revlon General Wig Manufacturers, Inc.

HAIR JEWELZ - Hair accessories - Trenz Inc.

HAIR KISS - Hair-texturizing shears - B.W. Boyd Shears Inc.

HAIR KITE - Hairpins - Claire's Boutiques, Inc.

HAIR LIFE - Hair care products - Nature's Design Ltd.

HAIR LIFT - Combs - Comare Corp.

HAIR LIFTER - Hair care products ☆ - Advanced Research Laboratories

HAIR LOVERS - Hair care products - Hobe Labs Inc.

HAIR MAGIC - Wigs - Revlon General Wig Manufacturers, Inc.

HAIR MANAGEMENT FOR MEN - Shampoos - Conair Corp.

HAIR MASK - Hair care products - Chesebrough-Pond's USA Co.

HAIR MASK - Hair care products - Reviva Laboratories

HAIR MAX - Dolls - Gata Box Ltd.

HAIR MONI'S - Hair accessories - Moni International, Inc.

HAIR MUSCLE - Hair care products ☆ - Modern Research Laboratories

HAIR/NAILS/SKIN SUPPORT - Health care products - Healthwatchers System

HAIR NATURAL - Hair care products - Nu-Tress Laboratories Inc.

HAIR-O-GOLD - Hair care products - Larkspur Group Inc.

HAIR OFF - Depilatories - CCA Industries, Inc.

HAIR PARADE - Wigs - Eva Gabor International, Ltd.

HAIR PARADISE - Hair care products - Redmond Products, Inc.

HAIR PATTERNS BY BERNI - Hair care products - Bernadine A. Marcotte

HAIR PERFORMERS - Beauty shops - Hair Performers

HAIR PIK - Combs - Comare Corp.

HAIR POLISH - Hair care products - Sacha International

HAIR PROTECTOR BRUSH - Hair brushes - Alkinco

HAIR-PROTEIN PACK - Hair care products - Nu-Tress Laboratories Inc.

HAIR RAISER - Coffee - Caribbean Coffee Co.

HAIR RAISERS - Hair care products - Hair Raisers Inc.

HAIR RECOVERY COMPLEXE - Hair care products - La Coupe

HAIR REPAIR - Hair care products - St. Ives Laboratories, Inc.

HAIR REPARE - Hair care products - Rex Research Laboratories

HAIR REPLACEMENT SYSTEMS - Hairstyling franchise, no longer in business - Hairbuilders

HAIR SALAD - Hair care products - Redmond Products, Inc.

HAIR SALVATION - Hair care products - Keystone Laboratories Inc.

HAIR SAVER - Hair care products - Bretney Corp.

HAIR SAVER - Hair care products - Palm Beach Beauty Products

HAIR SAVER - Pet products - Custom Cable Co.

HAIR SAVER - Shampoos - Gold Medal Hair Products Inc.

HAIR SCIENCE - Hair care products - Alberto-Culver Co.

HAIR SCULPT - Hair care products - Mahdeen Laboratory

HAIR, SKIN & NAILS - Health care products - Futurebiotics

HAIR SLIDE - Hair care products - M & T Bank

HAIR SNARE - Plumbing fixtures–metal - Faucet-Queens Inc.

HAIR-SNARE - Tools - Edward O'Malley Valve Co.

HAIR SO BEAUTIFUL - Hair care products - Nature Clean, Inc.

HAIR SO NEW - Hair care products - Clairol Inc.

HAIR SPA - Hair care products - Regis Corp.

HAIR SPARKS - Wigs - Look of Love International

HAIR SPECIFICS - Hair care products - Helene Curtis Industries Inc.

HAIR-STOP BREAK - Hair care products - Nu-Tress Laboratories Inc.

HAIR STRATE - Hair care products ☆ - Summit Laboratories

HAIR STRENGTH 10 - Hair care products - Bonat Inc.

HAIR SUCCESS - Hair care products - E.T. Browne Drug Co. Inc.

HAIR SUPER SETTER - Hair care products - Nu-Tress Laboratories Inc.

HAIR TAMER - Hair care products - Pro-Capa Products Inc.

HAIR TAMER PLUS - Pet products - Tomlyn Products

HAIR THERAPY - Hair care products - Miriam Collins - Palm Beach Laboratories Co.

HAIR THERAPY - Shampoos - Palm Beach Beauty Products

HAIR THERMAL - Hair care products - Nu-Tress Laboratories Inc.

HAIR TO GO - Hair care products - Helene Curtis Industries Inc.

HAIR TO HAIR - Shampoos - Stanley Fay Co.

HAIR TOOL - Hair care products ☆ - Philips Electronics North America Corp.

HAIR TOP - Hair care products - Bae & Bae Partnership

HAIR TOYS - Hair care products - Focus 21 International Inc.

HAIR TRIP - Hair care products - Everybody Ltd.

HAIR TRIX - Wigs ☆ - Eva Gabor International, Ltd.

HAIR T'S - Hair care products - Bill Whitten

HAIR VITE-SUPER - Hair care products - Michigan Pharmaceutical

HAIR ZAPPER - Hair care products - Gillette Co.

HAIR ZONE - Hair care products ☆ - Palm Beach Beauty Products

HAIR ZOO - Hair care products - Hair Zoo

HAIRABOU - Fly-fishing material - International Hairgoods Inc.

HAIRALL - Vitamins and nutritional supplements ☆ - Fibertone Co.

HAIRAMINS - Hair care products - Cosmetics International

HAIRART - Wigs - Hairart Inc.

HAIRAZZ - Hair care products - Moore Beauty Inc.

HAIRBALL REMEDY - Pet products - Helmac Products Corp.

HAIRBERRY - Shampoos - Apollo Products, Inc.

HAIRBUILDERS - Hairstyling franchise - Hairbuilders

HAIRCARE SHOPS - Razor blades - City Looks International

HAIRCO - Hair care products - Lawrence D. Gaynor

HAIRCRAFTERS - Beauty shops - Great Expectations Precision Haircutters

HAIRDINI - Hair care products - Angelhair, Ltd.

HAIREVER - Hair care products - Home Health Products, Inc.

☆ = Now out of production

HAIRFORCE - Hair care products - Kenra Laboratories, Inc.

HAIRFX - Hair care products - BodyFX Co.

HAIRGO - Pet products - Aaronco Grooming Products

HAIRGO - Pet products - Aaronco Pet Products, Inc.

HAIRLOOM TREASURES - Containers - Karen Walsh

HAIRMOSTAT - Pet products - Aaronco Grooming Products

HAIROBICS - Hair care products - Hair Research X Inc.

HAIRPEDIC - Infant product - Nurserytyme Products/Doppelt Industries

HAIRPIN HOLDERS - Flower pots–earthenware - Blue Ribbon Flower Holder Co.

HAIRPLUS - Clip-in hair extensions, hairpieces, etc. - International Hairgoods Inc.

HAIRS LOOKING AT YOU - Novelty items ☆ - Jobar International Inc./Bibi Products

HAIRSEPTIC - Hair care products - Aristocrat Hairseptic Co.

HAIRSETTERS - Hair care products - Clairol Inc.

HAIRSTYX - Hair care products - Mebco Industries, Inc.

HAIRTEX - Hair care products - Intra-America Beauty Network

HAIRTIQUES - Hair care products - Nailtiques Cosmetic Corp.

HAIRTWISTERS - Hairpins - A. Eickert Co., Inc.

HAIRWARE - Hair care products - Spilo/Mehaz Worldwide

HAIRWORKS PLUS - Hair care products - Hairworks Plus Inc.

HAIRY HARRY - Furs–artificial - Leister Game Co. Inc.

HAIRY HURLERS - Balls - Cadaco Div.

HAIRY SCARY - Costumes - Paper Magic Group Inc.

HAK - Agricultural products - Holland-American Importing Co. Inc.

HAKES - Health care products - Cyrus D. Hakes

HAKOTEV - Publisher's imprints - Software Systems East

HAKSYS - Computer software - Jemeng Soh

HAKUTSURU - Wines - Dreyfus Ashby Inc.

HAL-20 - Electronic equipment - AudioControl

HAL-100 - Electronic equipment - AudioControl

HAL GENIC - Health care products ☆ - Sage Products

HAL LEONARD - Musical instrument accessories ☆ - Hal Leonard Corp.

HALA - Floor coverings–carpet and rugs - Customweave Carpets Inc.

HALARC - Lamps - General Electric Co.

HALAZONE - Water purification systems - Abbott Laboratories

HALCION - Pharmaceutical preparations - Upjohn Co.

HALCO - Cooking utensils–aluminum - Harold Leonard & Co. Inc.

HALCO - Furniture–restaurant - Hale Engineering Co., Inc.

HALCONORM - Cooking utensils–aluminum - Harold Leonard & Co. Inc.

HALCOWARE - Cooking utensils–aluminum - Harold Leonard & Co. Inc.

HALCYON - Desks ☆ - Domore/DO3

HALCYON - Food products ☆ - Curtice-Burns Foods, Inc.

HALCYON - Navigational instruments - Brookes & Gatehouse Inc.

HALCYON GARDENS - Seeds–salted, roasted, cooked, or canned - Kingfisher Inc.

HALCYON HOUSE - Publisher's imprints - National Book Co.

HALCYON VICTORIAN - Greeting cards ☆ - Chase Collection, Inc.

HALD - Markers–felt-tip ☆ - Faber-Castell Corp.

HALDOL - Pharmaceutical preparations - McNeil Pharmaceuticals

HALDRONE - Pharmaceutical preparations ☆ - Eli Lilly and Co.

HALE - Piano tools - American Piano Supply Co.

HALE - Pianos - Tuners Supply Co. Inc.

HALE ELECTRO - Musical instrument accessories - Tuners Supply Co. Inc.

HALE SECURITY PET DOOR - Doors–metal - Seymour B. Hale, Jr.

HALE SIGHT-O-TUNER - Musical instrument accessories - Tuners Supply Co. Inc.

HALENA - Dishes–china ☆ - Gorham Inc.

HALENOL - Health care products - Halsey Drug Co. Inc.

HALERCOL - Pharmaceutical preparations - Roberts/Hauck Pharmaceuticals Inc.

HALES - Audio equipment - Hales Design Group, Inc.

HALE'S - Beverages–malt - Hale's Ales Ltd.

HALEX - Darts and dart games ☆ - Dart World Inc.

HALEY - Apparel and accessories - Sport-Haley, Inc.

HALEY'S M-O - Pharmaceutical preparations - Bayer Corp. (Consumer Care Div.)

HALEY'S WHITETAIL FARM - Pet products - Richard L. Haley

HALF-A-CROWN - Frames–eyeglass - Hudson Optical Corp.

HALF-A-MILLION - Eyeglasses - Martin-Copeland Eyewear Corp.

HALF & HALF - Beverages–carbonated - Canada Dry Corp.

HALF & HALF - Cream - Country Lake Foods Inc.

HALF & HALF - Hair care products - Helene Curtis Industries Inc.

HALF & HALF - Sporting goods - Mueller Sports Medicine Inc.

HALF AND HALF - Tobacco and cigarettes - American Tobacco Co.

HALF & HALF - Tobacco products - Swedish Math North America Inc.

HALF & HALF ROPE - Rope - Pigeon Mountain Industries, Inc.

HALF BAKED IDEAS - Pipes–tobacco - Adam Scott Greenwald

HALF BREED - Antennas - Valor Enterprises, Inc.

HALF-BREED - Hats - Manny Gammage's Texas Hatters, Inc.

HALF CAB - Footwear - Vans, Inc.

HALF CAF - Coffee - Thanksgiving Coffee Co.

HALF CORD - Craft supplies - Synthetic Textiles Inc.

HALF COURT - Shoes - Trans-World Shoe Import Corp.

HALF-DEE - Ophthalmic goods ☆ - Luxottica

HALF DOME - Water–distilled - Markstein Importers

HALF-DOZEN COUSINS, THE - Toys - Hasbro, Inc.

HALF EAGLE - Eyeglasses - Martin-Copeland Eyewear Corp.

HALF-EYE - Frames–eyeglass - May Optical Co. Inc.

HALF-FLEX - Ophthalmic goods - Vista Optical Corp.

HALF GALLON - Hats ☆ - Stetson Hat Co. Inc.

HALF HI - Frames–eyeglass - Pathway Optical Prods.

HALF-LITE - Frames–eyeglass - Hudson Optical Corp.

HALF MILE HAILER - Audio equipment - Perma Power Electronics Inc.

HALF MOON - Pencils ☆ - Staedtler, Inc.

HALF MOON BAY - Apparel–athletic - Irving B. Reder & Co.

HALF MOON BOOK, A - Children's books - Simon & Schuster, Inc.

HALF MOON FRUIT PUNCH - Beverages–carbonated - Archibald Bros. Fine Beverages, Inc.

HALF-N-HALF - Mats, matting ☆ - American Floor Products Co. Inc.

HALF NOTE JAZZ - Recording label - Athena Productions

HALF NOTES - Notebooks and notepads - Galison Books

HALF OUNCER - Frames–eyeglass - May Optical Co. Inc.

HALF PAST - Eyeglasses - Martin-Copeland Eyewear Corp.

HALF PINT - Clippers–barber - Wahl Clipper Corp.

HALF PINT - Dolls ☆ - Effanbee Doll Corp.

HALF PINT - Frames–eyeglass - May Optical Co. Inc.

HALF PINT - Infant product - Market Visions International

HALF PINT - Piggy bank ☆ - Bower Manufacturing Co. Inc.

HALF-PINT - Strollers–baby - Phoenix Prams Inc.

HALF PINT - Toys–stuffed ☆ - Gund, Inc.

HALF PINT & TAG ALONG - Giftware - Brushcreek Creative Co.

HALF PINTS - Toys–stuffed - Kamar International Inc.

HALF POUNDER - Candy ☆ - Bobs Candies Inc.

HALF ROUND - Musical instrument accessories - J. D'Addario & Co. Inc.

HALF SNAP - Roofing materials - Structall Building Systems, Inc.

HALF SPEC - Frames–eyeglass - U.S. Optical Frame Co.

HALF-SPEC - Ophthalmic goods ☆ - Luxottica

HALF SPECS - Ophthalmic goods - Foremost Optical Products

HALF THE SALT - Pickles - Vlasic Foods Inc.

HALF THE SALT - Potato chips - Laura Scudder's

HALF TIME - Chemical preparations - Alco Industries, Inc.

HALF TIME - Cigarettes - Gesty Trading & Manufacturing Corp.

HALF TIME - Cleaning preparations - Twi-Laq Industries Inc.

HALF-TIME - Meat products–poultry - Cuddy Farms, Inc.

HALF TIME - Pet products - Arn Industries, Inc.

HALF TRACK - Garment racks - Barbara D. Arner

HALF TRAK - Toys - Tonka Corp.

HALF VU - Ophthalmic goods - Foremost Optical Products

HALF-WIT - Sporting goods - Weber Industries Inc.

HALFAN - Pharmaceutical preparations - Smithkline Beecham Corp.

HALFASPHEARE - Eyeglasses - Martin-Copeland Eyewear Corp.

HALFBACK - Frames–eyeglass ☆ - Universal/Univis Inc.

HALFBACK - Furniture - Kensington Microware Ltd.

HALFPENNY - Ophthalmic goods - Swank Optical

HALFPRICE PASSPORT - Coupons - CUC Publishing, Inc.

HALFPRIN - Analgesics - Atlantic Licensing Corp.

HALFTIME - Audio equipment ☆ - DCM Corp.

HALFTIME - Eyeglasses - Martin-Copeland Eyewear Corp.

HALFTIME BATTLIN' BANDS - Computer software - CBS Software

HALIFAX - Blinds–venetian ☆ - Hunter Douglas, Inc.

HALIFAX - Ceiling tile ☆ - Conwed Plastics

HALIFAX - Furniture - Boling Co.

HALIFAX - Furniture - White Furniture Co.

HALIFAX - Pillows - Pillowtex Corp.

HALIFAX - Wallpaper ☆ - Wolf-Gordon Inc.

HALIFAX HALL - Furniture ☆ - Singer Furniture Co.

HALIFAX OAK COLLECTION - Dining room furniture - Daystrom Furniture Inc.

HALIGRAM - Paper products - Interscan Corp.

HALIMETER - Medical apparatus - Interscan Corp.

HALITE - Chemical preparations - Akzo America Inc.

☆ = Now out of production

HALITE - Floodlights - RAB Electric
HALITE - Floodlights - Rab Electric Manufacturing, Inc.
HALITE WINTER-MELT - Deicing fluid - Cargill Salt
HALL - Dishes–china - Hall China Co.
HALL - Health care products - Hall Laboratories, Inc.
HALL COMPANY, THE - Switches–electric - Hall Co. (Scrollcraft Div.)
HALL OF FAME - Chili–canned - Bay Area Merchandising Co., Inc.
HALL OF FAME - Colognes - Parfum de Coeur Ltd.
HALL OF FAME - Eyeglasses - Art-Craft Optical Co.
HALL OF FAME - Greeting cards ☆ - Artistic Greetings, Inc.
HALL OF FAME - Music–sheet - Gramophone Records Co. of the USA
HALL OF FAME - Recording label - Hope International
HALL OF FAME - Toys ☆ - A.J. Renzi Plastic Corp.
HALL OF FAME SPORT - Apparel–men's - Hall of Fame Enterprises
HALL OF FAMER - Apparel–men's - Hall of Fame Enterprises
HALL OF FAMERS - Recording label - Hard Hat Records
HALL OF FRAMES - Giftware - Medford Monument Co.
HALL RIVER PREMIUM SOCKS - Hosiery - Kilgore Hosiery Inc.
HALL SUPER-CERAM - Dishes–earthenware - Hall China Co.
HALLANDALE - Floor coverings - Mannington Resilient Floors
HALLANDALE - Floor coverings–carpet and rugs - Lees Carpets
HALLBERG RASSY - Ships–sailing vessels - Hallberg Rassy Yachts
HALLBROOK - Lighting fixtures - Holophane Corp.
HALLCO - Sporting goods - Hall Co. (Scrollcraft Div.)
HALLELUJAH - Cleaning preparations–household - Canton Industries, Inc.
HALLELUJAH FROM ISRAEL - Greeting cards - Dona Greetin Cards Inc.
HALLER - Clocks - Staufen Studio
HALLET & DAVIS - Pianos - Aeolian Pianos Inc.
HALLETT - Aircraft parts - Champion Aviation Products
HALLEY'S COMET - Frames–eyeglass ☆ - Universal/Univis Inc.
HALLEY'S COMET - Kites - Gayla Industries Inc.
HALLEY'S COMET - Video games - Taito America Corp.
HALLEY'S COMET LOCATOR - Computer software - SourceView Software International
HALLEY'S TAIL - Toys–models ☆ - Estes Industries
HALLKRAFT - Dishes–earthenware - Mikasa Co.
HALLMADE - Insulating materials - Medford Monument Co.
HALLMARK - Artists' materials - Shiva Inc.
HALLMARK - Brushes–paint - E-Z Paintr Corp.
HALLMARK - Cabinets - Quality Cabinets
HALLMARK - Cabinets - Yorktowne Inc.
HALLMARK - Candles - Empire Manufacturing Co.
HALLMARK - Christmas tree ornaments - Cracker Box Inc.
HALLMARK - Cigarettes - Brown & Williamson Tobacco Corp.
HALLMARK - Clocks ☆ - SMH (US) Inc.
HALLMARK - Crocheted and knitted items ☆ - Roosevelt Mills Inc.
HALLMARK - Desks - Haskell of Pittsburgh, Inc.
HALLMARK - Fireplace equipment - Robert H. Peterson Co.
HALLMARK - Flatware - Utica Cutlery Co.
HALLMARK - Furniture ☆ - Bassett Furniture Industries, Inc.
HALLMARK - Furniture ☆ - Singer Furniture Co.
HALLMARK - Greeting cards - Hallmark Cards Inc.
HALLMARK - Hardware ☆ - Shower Shield
HALLMARK - Health care products - Sunrise Medical
HALLMARK - Infant product - Mount Vernon Mills Inc.
HALLMARK - Manufactured homes - Redman Industries, Inc.
HALLMARK - Mattresses ☆ - Kingsdown, Inc.
HALLMARK - Medical apparatus - Hallmark Orthopedic Co.
HALLMARK - Musical instruments ☆ - Barclay Music
HALLMARK - Neckties - MMG Corp.
HALLMARK - Paints - Nationwide Research Corp.
HALLMARK - Recreational vehicles - International Vehicle Corp.
HALLMARK - Seafood products–fresh or frozen - California Shellfish Co. Inc.
HALLMARK - Tires - Hallmark Tire & Rubber Co.
HALLMARK - Tires - Kelly-Springfield Tire Co.
HALLMARK - Vegetables–canned ☆ - Hunt Products Inc.
HALLMARK - Watches - Elgin Watch Co.
HALLMARK - Wood products - Caradco
HALLMARK II - Floor coverings–carpet and rugs ☆ - Mannington Carpets, Inc.
HALLMARK/AMBASSADOR - Apparel–men's - Sanmark-Stardust Inc.
HALLMARK BUSINESS EXPRESSIONS - Greeting cards - Hallmark Cards Inc.
HALLMARK FLOWERS - Flowers, plants, and seeds - Hallmark Cards Inc.
HALLMARK GOLD - Dishes–china - Gorham Inc.
HALLMARK HALL OF FAME - Recording label - Hallmark Licensing, Inc.
HALLMARK PLATINUM - Dishes–china - Gorham Inc.

HALLMARK QUALITY - Seafood products–fresh or frozen - Hallmark Fisheries
HALLMARK SHANGLE - Shingles–asphalt or tar - Certainteed Corp. (Roofing Products Group)
HALLOBAG - Bags–storage - Printmark Industries Inc.
HALLOCAPE - Novelty items - Printmark Industries, Inc.
HALLOW-WEE-ONES - Costumes - Disguise Inc.
HALLOWED GROUND - Trading cards and stamps - American Legacy Trading Co.
HALLOWEEN - Apparel and accessories - Coen-Bakker USA Ltd.
HALLOWEEN - Flowers, plants, and seeds - Panamerican Seed
HALLOWEEN CONCEPTS - Costumes - Rubie's Costume Co., Inc.
HALLOWEEN FX - Cosmetics - Cinema Secrets Inc.
HALLOWEEN-GLOW - Novelty items–paper - Romar Enterprises Ltd.
HALLOWEEN HAUNTER, THE - Toys - Mark L. Chutick
HALLOWEEN HI-LITES - Candles - Russ Berrie and Co., Inc.
HALLOWEEN HOUSE - Plastics - Ades Imports Inc.
HALLOWEEN ON ICE - Recording label - Proserv, Inc.
HALLOWEEN OREOS - Cookies - Nabisco Foods Group
HALLOWEEN SHADE - Lamp shades–fabric ☆ - Vista Solutions Inc.
HALLOWEEN SPOOKS - Candy - Rosemary Candy Co.
HALLOWEEN WORLD - Novelty items–paper - Kurt S. Adler Inc.
HALLOWEEN YARD - Bags–trash - Kenley Corp.
HALLOWEENKIDS - Dolls - Santa's Best
HALLOWEENKINS - Dolls - Santa's Best
HALLOWEENY BEANIES - Giftware - Russ Berrie and Co., Inc.
HALLOWELL - Lockers–metal - List Industries Inc. (Hallowell Div.)
HALLS - Candy - American Chicle Co.
HALL'S - Cheese - Silver Foods Corp.
HALLS - Commercial printing - Business Records Corp.
HALL'S - Food products - Hallman International, Inc.
HALLS AND ALL - Wallpaper - Sanitas Wallcoverings
HALLS-PLUS - Candy - American Chicle Co.
HALLS SUGAR FREE - Cough drops - American Chicle Co.
HALLS VITAMIN C - Cough drops - American Chicle Co.
HALLSTICK - Electronic equipment - Elweco, Inc.
HALLWAG - Maps - Rand McNally & Co.
HALLWAY INTERNATIONAL - Recording label - Hallways to Fame Productions Inc.
HALLWOOD - Potato flakes - John W. Taylor Packing Co. Inc.
HALLY - Toys–stuffed ☆ - Gund, Inc.
HALLY CALLER - Sporting goods - Joe Hall's Shooting Products Inc.
HALMATIC - Boats ☆ - Wells Yachts Inc.
HALMODE PETITES - Apparel and accessories - Kellwood Co.
HALMODE PLUS - Apparel and accessories - Kellwood Co.
HALO - Candles ☆ - Will & Baumer, Inc.
HALO - Computer software - Media Cybernetics, L.P.
HALO - Electronic equipment - HD Electric Co.
HALO - Fabrics–ticking - Hickory Springs Manufacturing Co.
HALO - Face shields ☆ - U.S. Safety Corp.
HALO - Flatware ☆ - Lotus Glass Co.
HALO - Footwear - Wolverine World Wide, Inc.
HALO - Frames–eyeglass ☆ - Universal/Univis Inc.
HALO - Hair care products - Colgate-Palmolive Co.
HALO - Infant product - American Baby Concepts
HALO - Lighting - Cooper Industries, Inc.
HALO - Ornamental products–glass - W and F Products Inc.
HALO - Pet products - Applause for Healthy Pets
HALO - Recording label - Mark Five Sandcastle
HALO - Rope - Wellington Leisure Products, Inc.
HALO BLUE - Kitchenware–china - H. Wittur & Co.
HALO HOLLYS - Moldings–plaster of paris ☆ - DecoArt, Inc.
HALO LIGHT - Mirrors - Windmere Corp.
HALO LUSTER - Christmas tree ornaments - Union Wadding Co.
HALO TWIN - Automotive parts and accessories - Subaru of America, Inc.
HALOBEX T - Health care products - Halsey Drug Co. Inc.
HALOCATOR - Electrical equipment - A.W. Sperry Instruments, Inc.
HALOCOL - Health care products ☆ - Halsey Drug Co. Inc.
HALODENT - Denture cleaners - Halsey Drug Co. Inc.
HALODRIN - Pharmaceutical preparations - Upjohn Co.
HALOFED - Health care products - Halsey Drug Co. Inc.
HALOG - Pharmaceutical preparations - Bristol-Myers Squibb Co.
HALOGAN - Health care products - Halsey Drug Co. Inc.
HALOGEN SAFE - Lamps - Angelo Brothers Co.
HALOGENGOLD - Motor vehicle parts and accessories - Cooper Industries, Inc.

☆ = Now out of production

HALOGUARD - Safety products - Thermal Gas Systems, Inc.

HALORTRON - Pharmaceutical preparations - Vita Elixir Co. Inc.

HALOS - Apparel and accessories - Marco Delli

HALOTESTIN - Pharmaceutical preparations - Upjohn Co.

HALOTUSSIN - Health care products - Halsey Drug Co. Inc.

HALOX - Water purification systems - The Halox Co.

HALPER BROTHERS - Apparel and accessories - Halper Brothers Inc.

HAL'S PALS - Dolls - Mattel, Inc.

HALSA - Hair care products - Dep Corp.

HALSAVE - Computer software - Najeeba Enterprises, Inc.

HALSEY - Housewares ☆ - Lipper International Inc.

HALSEY COLLECTION, THE - Apparel and accessories - Halsey Fashion Imports, Inc.

HALSINGBORG - Dishes–china - Viletta China Co.

HALSTEAD BAY - Wallpaper - Sherburne Ewing Wallcovering Co.

HALSTEAD HANDY COILS - Plumbing fixtures–metal - Halstead Industries Inc.

HALSTON - Cosmetics ☆ - Halston Borghese Inc. (North America Div.)

HALSTON - Footwear–women's ☆ - United States Shoe Corp.

HALSTON - Perfumes - Revlon Consumer Products Corp.

HALSTON 101 - Perfumes ☆ - Halston Borghese Inc. (North America Div.)

HALSTON TOUCH, THE - Floor coverings–carpet and rugs ☆ - Karastan-Bigelow Inc.

HALT - Analgesics - Halt Enterprises, Inc.

HALT! - Fencing–steel - Universal Cooperative Inc.

HALT - Finishing agents ☆ - Woolsey Marine Industries

HALT - Locks–padlocks - Assa High Security Locks

HALT - Pesticides–household - ARI

HALT - Self-defense spray - Clifford W. Lynch

HALTERNATE - Apparel–women's - Blue Bay Inc.

HALTINGEN - Skin care products - Hanah Beauty & Health Inc.

HALTON - Ventilation equipment - Halton Co.

HALTRAN - Pharmaceutical preparations ☆ - Upjohn Co.

HALTS - Fertilizers - Scotts Co. (Organics Business Group)

HALTS PLUS - Fertilizers - Scotts Co. (Organics Business Group)

HALTS-RUST - Paints ☆ - Steelcote Manufacturing Corp.

HALTZ - Stain removers ☆ - Finnaren & Haley Inc.

HALTZ II - Paints ☆ - Finnaren & Haley Inc.

HALU - Shutters–wood - Catalina Shading Systems Inc.

HALU-HALU - Sauces - Mary Rose, Inc.

HALVIES - Frames–eyeglass ☆ - Universal/Univis Inc.

HAM & EGGS - Apparel and accessories - Ham & Eggs

HAM CARVER - Food products - Boston Chicken, Inc.

HAM-ON-BACON - Meat products–pork - Schaller & Weber

HAM ROYALE - Meat products–cured - Agar Food Products Co.

HAM-SEM - Recording label ☆ - Mr. Wonderful Productions Inc.

HAM STICKS - Antennas - Wintenna Inc.

HAMADA - Coffee - Hamada

HAMAGI - Recording label - Jazz Composer's Orchestra Association Inc.

HAMAMELIS LEAF - Pharmaceutical preparations - Sherwood Laboratories Inc.

HAMAMILIS - Skin care products - Bioforce of America Ltd.

HAMAXE - Axes - E-Z Sales & Manufacturing, Inc.

HAMBASSADOR - Meat products–pork - Agar Food Products Co.

HAMBERDOG - Food products - Archer Daniels Midland Co.

HAMBERG - Flatware ☆ - Washington Forge Inc.

HAMBLETONIAN - Apparel and accessories - Hambletonian Society, Inc.

HAMBLY - Calendars - Hambly Studios

HAMBURG - Dishes–china ☆ - Royal China & Porcelain Companies Inc.

HAMBURG - Watches - Elgin Watch Co.

HAMBURGER HELPER - Food products - General Mills, Inc.

HAMBURGER PARTNER - Food products ☆ - Super Valu Inc.

HAMBURGERS - Apparel–women's - Phillips-Van Heusen Corp.

HAMCO - Apparel–children's - Hamco, Inc.

HAMDEN - Sinks–porcelain - Jameco Industries, Inc.

HAMDEN COURT - Floor coverings–carpet and rugs ☆ - Lees Carpets

HAMER - Guitars - Hamer Guitars

HAMER - Guitars - Kaman Music Corp.

HAMER'S HOT ONES - Wood products - Hamer Pellet Fuel Co.

HAMEX - Orthopedic products - Thomas L. Brady

HAMFLEXOR - Exercise equipment - Flex Equipment Inc.

HAMHOLDER - Hams - June Tailor Inc.

HAMILTON - Apparel–women's - Hamilton Manufacturing Inc.

HAMILTON - Artists' materials - Hamilton Industries

HAMILTON - Bakery products - Hamilton Home Bakery

HAMILTON - Bakery products - Hamilton Meat Pies Co., Inc.

HAMILTON - Bicycles - Ross Bicycles USA, Ltd.

HAMILTON - Bowls ☆ - Lenox Crystal, Inc.

HAMILTON - Crocheted and knitted items - M and M Woolen Co. Inc.

HAMILTON - Floor coverings - Congoleum Corp.

HAMILTON - Floor coverings–carpet and rugs - Karastan-Bigelow Inc.

HAMILTON - Floor coverings–carpet and rugs ☆ - Masland Corp.

HAMILTON - Frames–eyeglass ☆ - Universal/Univis Inc.

HAMILTON - Furniture - Hamilton Sorter Co. Inc.

HAMILTON - Hardware - Baldwin Hardware Corp.

HAMILTON - Mirrors ☆ - Hamilton Glass Products Inc.

HAMILTON - Music boxes - Krauth & Benninghofen Inc.

HAMILTON - Musical instruments ☆ - Grossman Music Corp.

HAMILTON - Office supplies - Da-Lite Screen Co. Inc.

HAMILTON - Pet products - Hamilton Products Inc.

HAMILTON - Pianos - Baldwin Piano & Organ Co.

HAMILTON - Playing cards - United States Playing Card Co.

HAMILTON - Stereos - Hamilton Electronics Corp.

HAMILTON - Tableware–china - Lenox, Inc.

HAMILTON - Washing machines–household ☆ - White Consolidated Industries, Inc.

HAMILTON - Watches ☆ - SMH (US) Inc.

HAMILTON - Wheels - Hamilton Caster & Manufacturing Co.

HAMILTON ADAMS - Fabrics - Hamilton Adams Imports Ltd.

HAMILTON BEACH - Kitchen appliances - Hamilton Beach/Proctor-Silex Inc.

HAMILTON CARPET MILLS - Floor coverings–carpet and rugs - Aladdin Mills, Inc.

HAMILTON COLLECTION - Giftware - Viking Import House Inc.

HAMILTON COURT III - Floor coverings–carpet and rugs - Barrett Carpet Mills Inc.

HAMILTON ELECTRIC - Air conditioning equipment - Goodman Manufacturing Co., L.P.

HAMILTON ESTATES - Wines - Geerlings & Wade, Inc.

HAMILTON GIFTS LTD. - Glassware–household ☆ - Enesco Corp.

HAMILTON HALL - Furniture–wood - Johnston-Tombigbee

HAMILTON HOUSE - Fabrics–tapestry ☆ - Coloroll Inc.

HAMILTON HOUSE - Furniture - Hammary Furniture Co. Inc.

HAMILTON HOUSE - House furnishings - Lexington Furniture Industries, Inc.

HAMILTON MANOR - Coats - Frederick Atkins, Inc.

HAMILTON PARK - Siding–insulating - Certainteed Corp. (Roofing Products Group)

HAMILTON PHARMA - Pharmaceutical preparations - Hamilton Pharma, Inc.

HAMILTON SILK - Mattresses - Simmons USA

HAMILTON SQUARE - Furniture ☆ - Bassett Furniture Industries, Inc.

HAMILTON-WRENN - Furniture–upholstered - Southwood Furniture Corp.

HAMILTON'S - Pork - Sf Investments, Inc.

HAMILTON'S CHOICE - Furniture - CTH/Sherrill Occasional

HAMLET - Glassware–household - Crisa Corp.

HAMLET - Hams - Fischer Packing Co.

HAMLET - Pencils ☆ - Faber-Castell Corp.

HAMLET - Prefabricated buildings–metal - Arrow Group Industries

HAMLET - Tools–hand-operated - James Edwin Harper, Jr.

HAMLEY - Saddles - Hamley & Co.

HAMLEY KIT, THE - Rope - Hamley & Co.

HAMM BONE - Pet products - Hill Top Enterprises

HAMMACHER SCHLEMMER - Sporting goods - Hammacher Schlemmer & Co.

HAMMAR - Boating equipment and accessories - Datrex Inc.

HAMMARY - Furniture - Hammary Furniture Co. Inc.

HAMMEN - Labels–gummed - Hammen Co.

HAMMER - Bats–baseball - Easton Aluminum Inc.

HAMMER - Beverages–carbonated - Canada Dry Corp.

HAMMER - Boats - Baja Marine Corp.

HAMMER - Dolls - Mattel, Inc.

HAMMER - Golfing equipment - Triumph Golf Co.

HAMMER - Knives–pocket ☆ - Imperial Schrade Corp.

HAMMER - Metals - Mor L. Mayer

HAMMER - Sporting goods - E-Z Gard Industries, Inc.

HAMMER - Sporting goods - Wasp Archery Products, Inc.

HAMMER - Toys - Tyco Toys

HAMMER & LACE - Recording label - Polygram Records, Inc.

HAMMER AWAY - Toys - Montgomery Schoolhouse

HAMMER-CAPSULE - Chemical preparations - Rawlplug Co., Inc.

HAMMER DRIVE - Construction equipment - Rawlplug Co., Inc.

HAMMER GEL - Vitamins and nutritional supplements - Brian David Frank

HAMMER-GLENN PRODUCTIONS - Video production - W. Glenn McKeown

HAMMER HEAD - Auto parts - Rugged Trail, Inc.

HAMMER-HEAD - Knives–putty - Hyde Manufacturing Co.

HAMMER-IN - Hardware - Dynacast

HAMMER KNIFE - Lawn mowers - Alamo Group

HAMMER-LAK - Finishing agents - Lenmar Inc.

HAMMER OF THE GODS - Video games - New World Computing Inc.

HAMMER-SCREW - Fabricated metal products - Rawlplug Co., Inc.

HAMMER SNOWBOARDS - Snowboards - Raichle Molitor USA, Inc.

HAMMER SYSTEM - Sporting goods - Wilson Sporting Goods Co.

HAMMER, THE - Balls - Seneca Sports, Inc.

HAMMER, THE - Exercising equipment - Vital Form Inc.

HAMMER VOLLEYBALL - Balls - Seneca Sports, Inc.

HAMMERCRAFT - Cooking equipment–household - Jacksonville Manufacturing

HAMMERCRAFT - Hinges - Liberty Hardware Manufacturing Corp.

HAMMERED - Glass products - AFG Industries Inc. (Glass Group Div.)

HAMMERED ANTIQUE - Flatware - Towle Silversmiths

HAMMERED SPOONS - Fishing lures - Hopkins Fishing Lures Co. Inc.

HAMMERFANG - Eyeglasses - Oakley, Inc.

HAMMERHEAD - Audio equipment - ADA Signal Processors Inc.

HAMMERHEAD - Boats - Hammerhead Corp.

HAMMERHEAD - Boats–fishing - Lanness K. McKee & Co.

HAMMERHEAD - Computer software - 1-2-3 Ideas Inc.

HAMMERHEAD - Fishing lures ☆ - Fred Arbogast Co. Inc.

HAMMERHEAD - Golfing equipment - Barley Mill Pub, Inc.

HAMMERHEAD - Golfing equipment - Tiger Shark Golf Inc.

HAMMERHEAD - Knives–pocket ☆ - W.R. Case & Sons Cutlery Co.

HAMMERHEAD - Video games - Playfair Shuffleboard Co., Inc.

HAMMERHEAD RED - Beverages–alcohol - Hops Grill & Bar, Inc.

HAMMERIN' HARRY - Computer software - IREM America Corp.

HAMMERLAST - Sports rackets and accessories - Wilson Sporting Goods Co.

HAMMERLI - Firearms, accessories, and parts ☆ - Beeman Precision Airguns

HAMMERLOCK - Locks–padlocks - Hammerlock Industries, Inc.

HAMMERLOCK - Tools–power-driven - Power Tool Holders Inc.

HAMMERLOK - Hardware - Columbus Mckinnon Corp.

HAMMERMARK - Paints - Tenax Finishing Product

HAMMERMILL - Paper - International Paper Co.

HAMMERON - Toys - Saban Entertainment, Inc.

HAMMERPROOF - Tools - Fuller Tool Co. Inc.

HAMMERS - Ophthalmic goods ☆ - Oakley, Inc.

HAMMER'S SLAMMERS - Games ☆ - Mayfair Games, Inc.

HAMMERSLEY - Giftware - Salem China Co.

HAMMERSLEY OF ENGLAND - Apparel and accessories - Alexandre of England, Inc.

HAMMERTAILS - Fishing lures - Hopkins Fishing Lures Co. Inc.

HAMMERTEC - Sporting goods - Wilson Sporting Goods Co.

HAMMERTONE - Cleaning preparations–carpet and rug - Sterling Plumbing Group Inc.

HAMMERTONE - Finishing agents ☆ - Samuel Cabot Inc.

HAMMERTONE - Housewares ☆ - Doranne

HAMMETTS - Artists' materials - J.L. Hammett Co.

HAMMIG - Piccolos - West Music Co., Inc.

HAMMO - Cosmetics - Hammo Inc.

HAMMOCK - Food products - Lake Region Pack Association

HAMMOCK HIDEAWAY - Toys - Mattel, Inc.

HAMMOCK STROLLER - Hammocks - The HammockSource

HAMMOCKMASTER - Hammocks - Stanton's Quills

HAMMOND - Maps - Hammond Inc.

HAMMOND'S N-SOL - Pharmaceutical preparations - Brown Manufacturing Co.

HAMMONS PRODUCTS - Nuts–salted, roasted, cooked, or canned - Hammons Products Co.

HAMMONTON PARK - Apparel–men's - Wm. B. Kessler Inc.

HAMM'S - Beverages–malt - Pabst Brewing Co.

HAMM'S - Veterinary pharmaceutical preparations - Hamm Supply Co., Inc.

HAMM'S NA - Beverages - Pabst Brewing Co.

HAMM'S SPECIAL LIGHT - Beverages–malt - Pabst Brewing Co.

HAMMY'S 'JAMMYS - Apparel and accessories - Hamwear, Inc.

HAMP SHIRES - Footwear–women's - Salvatrice Shoe Inc.

HAMPCO - Apparel and accessories - Hampton Industries, Inc.

HAMPDEN - Beverages–malt - Piel Bros. Ltd.

HAMPDEN - Footwear–men's - L.B. Evans' Son Co.

HAMPDEN - Paper cutters ☆ - Milton Bradley Co.

HAMPDEN - Watches - Hampden Corp.

HAMPER - Detergents - R.T. Ertle Associates Inc.

HAMPER AID - Deodorizers ☆ - Noble Pine Products Co.

HAMPER GUARD - Deodorizers ☆ - Frank J. Curran-Esquire Chemical Co.

HAMPSHIRE - Beverages–alcohol - Jenkins Spirits Corp., Ltd.

HAMPSHIRE - Cabinets ☆ - Nutone Inc.

HAMPSHIRE - Clocks ☆ - General Time Corp. (Westclox/Seth Thomas Div.)

HAMPSHIRE - Dinnerware–glass - Franciscan by Johnson Brothers, USA, Inc.

HAMPSHIRE - Floor coverings–carpet and rugs ☆ - Regal Rugs Inc.

HAMPSHIRE - Floor coverings–carpet and rugs - Stanton Carpet Corp.

HAMPSHIRE - Frames–eyeglass - May Optical Co. Inc.

HAMPSHIRE - Frames–picture - Terragrafics Inc.

HAMPSHIRE - Greeting cards ☆ - Doehla Greeting Cards Inc.

HAMPSHIRE - Hardware - Emhart Inc.

HAMPSHIRE - Sour cream - Knudsen Dairy Products

HAMPSHIRE - Tableware–china ☆ - Lenox, Inc.

HAMPSHIRE - Wallpaper ☆ - Wolf-Gordon Inc.

HAMPSHIRE DE LUXE - Stationery ☆ - Pratt & Austin Co.

HAMPSHIRE DUTCH LAP - Hardware - Alside Div.

HAMPSHIRE HALL - Kitchenware–china - Charles Zahn-Import Merchant

HAMPSHIRE HOUSE - Floor coverings - Mannington Resilient Floors

HAMPSHIRE HOUSE - Floor coverings–carpet and rugs - Colonial Mills Inc.

HAMPSHIRE HOUSE - Stationery - Pratt & Austin Co.

HAMPSHIRE LTD. - Crocheted and knitted items ☆ - Hampshire Hosiery, Inc.

HAMPSHIRE PEWTER - Giftware - Hampshire Pewter Co.

HAMPSHIRE SPECIAL - Beverages–malt - D.L. Geary Brewing Co.

HAMPSHIRE SPRINGS - Water–bottled or canned - Castle Springs L.P.

HAMPSHIRE STUDIO - Sweaters - Hampshire Designers, Inc.

HAMPSHIRES - Shoes - Athlone Industries Inc.

HAMPSTEAD - Cabinets - Marsh Furniture Co.

HAMPSTEAD - Furniture ☆ - Bassett Furniture Industries, Inc.

HAMPTON - Apparel and accessories - Authentic Imports Inc.

HAMPTON - Artists' materials - Bee Paper Co. Inc.

HAMPTON - Boats–motor - Hampton Shipyards/Hampton Boat Sales Ltd.

HAMPTON - Boats–motor - Larson Boat Div.

HAMPTON - Brass products - Robert D. Murray & Associates

HAMPTON - Cabinets - American Woodmark Corp.

HAMPTON - Cabinets - Canyon Creek Cabinet Co.

HAMPTON - Cabinets - Formitex Inc.

HAMPTON - Cabinets - Western Cabinet & Millwork Inc.

HAMPTON - Chimes - Nutone Inc.

HAMPTON - Dinnerware–glass - Nikko Ceramics Inc.

HAMPTON - Dishes–china - Midland Enterprises Inc.

HAMPTON - Fabrics - Greenwood Mills Inc.

HAMPTON - Flatware - Royal Silver Manufacturing Co. Inc.

HAMPTON - Floor coverings ☆ - Bruce Hardwood Floors

HAMPTON - Floor coverings–carpet and rugs ☆ - Regal Rugs Inc.

HAMPTON - Frames–eyeglass - U.S. Optical Frame Co.

HAMPTON - Furniture–wood - Ficks Reed Co. Inc.

HAMPTON - Greeting cards - Hampton Greeting Card Co.

HAMPTON - Ice buckets ☆ - Lenox Crystal, Inc.

HAMPTON - Kitchen, vanity, and bathroom cabinets - IXL Furniture Co. Inc.

HAMPTON - Locks–padlocks - Hampton International

HAMPTON - Luggage - Montgomery Ward & Co. Inc.

HAMPTON - Mattresses - Stearns & Foster Bedding Co.

HAMPTON - Pianos - Story & Clark Piano Co.

HAMPTON - Publisher's imprints ☆ - Rand McNally & Co.

HAMPTON - Rings–jewelry - Artcarved Inc.

HAMPTON - Robes - Hampton Industries, Inc.

HAMPTON - Ships–sailing vessels - HODRA

HAMPTON - Shirts - Donnkenny Inc.

HAMPTON - Shoes ☆ - Allen-Edmonds Shoe Corp.

HAMPTON - Stationery - Royal Imprints Corp.

HAMPTON - Tableware–china - Pfaltzgraff Investment Co.

HAMPTON - Toilets–enameled - Kohler Co.

HAMPTON - Transmitting apparatus - Hampton Power Products, Inc.

HAMPTON - Underwear and nightwear - Youthcraft-Charmfit

HAMPTON - Wallpaper - Capital Carousel Inc.

HAMPTON BAY - Furniture - Athens Furniture Industries Inc.

HAMPTON BAY - Wallpaper - Magic Appliques Inc.

HAMPTON BRASS - Giftware - Hampton Brass

HAMPTON BREAD COMPANY LTD., THE - Food products - Hampton Bread Co., Ltd.

HAMPTON-BROWN - Recording label - Hampton-Brown Co., Inc.

HAMPTON COLLECTION, THE - Furniture - Riverside Furniture Corp.

HAMPTON COURT - Barometers ☆ - Airguide Instrument Co.

HAMPTON COURT - Floor coverings - Mannington Resilient Floors

HAMPTON COURT - Floor coverings–carpet and rugs - Galaxy Carpet Mills Inc.

HAMPTON COURT - Floor coverings–carpet and rugs - Glen Eden Wool Carpets

☆ = Now out of production

HAMPTON COURT - Floor coverings–carpet and rugs ☆ - Downs Carpet Co. Inc.

HAMPTON COURT - Furniture - Stanley Furniture Co. Inc.

HAMPTON COURT - Furniture ☆ - Bassett Furniture Industries, Inc.

HAMPTON COURT - Silverware - Reed and Barton Corp.

HAMPTON COURT - Wallpaper - B. Berger Co.

HAMPTON COURT - Wallpaper - Capital Carousel Inc.

HAMPTON COURT - Wallpaper - Christopher Hyland

HAMPTON COURT II - Wallpaper ☆ - Ashford House

HAMPTON FALLS - Water–bottled or canned - Twin Mountain Spring Water Co., Inc.

HAMPTON FITNESS PRODUCTS - Weightlifting equipment - Hampton Fitness Products

HAMPTON GIRL - Apparel and accessories - Hampton Industries, Inc.

HAMPTON HALL - Giftware - Noritake Co. Inc.

HAMPTON HILL - Floor coverings–carpet and rugs - Mohawk Carpet Corp.

HAMPTON HOUSE - Floor coverings–carpet and rugs ☆ - Lees Carpets

HAMPTON HOUSE - Furniture ☆ - Bernhardt Industries

HAMPTON HOUSE - Furniture–upholstered - Norwalk Furniture Corp.

HAMPTON III - Siding - Variform, Inc.

HAMPTON MANOR - Vegetables–frozen ☆ - Lamb-Weston, Inc.

HAMPTON OAKS - Furniture - Lane Co. Inc.

HAMPTON PARK - Furniture - Singer Furniture Co.

HAMPTON PARK EXECUTIVES - Footwear–men's - B. Levy & Son

HAMPTON PEAK - Wines - European Beverage Co., Inc.

HAMPTON PLUM - Beverages–alcohol ☆ - White Rock Products Corp.

HAMPTON SQUARE - Furniture ☆ - Sumter Cabinet Co., Inc.

HAMPTON, THE - Fencing–plastic - Nebraska Plastics, Inc.

HAMPTONE - Paints ☆ - Hampton Paint Manufacturing Co.

HAMPTONS II, THE - Wallpaper - Magic Appliques Inc.

HAMPTONS, THE - Wallpaper - Magic Appliques Inc.

HAMRTWIST - Tools - Star Anchors & Fasteners

HAMS PETER - Milk - Dairy Fresh Corp.

HAMSHIRE HOUSE INTERNATIONAL - Lamps - Flashco

HAMSTER BITES - Pet products - Pets International, Ltd.

HAMSTER CITY - Pet products - Petrapport, Inc.

HAMSTER HAVEN - Pet products - Next to Nature

HAMSTER HEALTH CLUB - Cages–wire - Blue Ribbon Pet Products, Inc.

HAMSTER HIDEAWAY - Pet products - Zoo Med Laboratories, Inc.

HAMSTER HOME - Pet products ☆ - Circle K Industries Inc.

HAMSTRA - Teas - H. Hamstra & Co.

HAMTASTIC - Meat products–pork - Harper's Country Hams

HAMTRAC - Pet products - Pets International, Ltd.

HAMTRACTOR - Exercise equipment - Flex Equipment Inc.

HAN - Candy - Han Trading Corp.

HAN - Electronic equipment - Il Shin International Inc.

HAN - Jewelry - Helen Andrews, Inc.

HAN BAN DO - Wallpaper - Capital Carousel Inc.

HAN BAN DO - Wallpaper - Textile Wallcoverings International Ltd.

HAN-D - Cleaning preparations - Cresset Chemical Co.

HAN-D-JET - Bathroom accessories ☆ - Dazey Corp.

HAN-D-MADE - Carts ☆ - Steelworks, Inc.

HAN-D-PAK - Bags–paper - Brown Paper Goods Co.

HAN-D-RUB - Tools - New England Carbide

HAN-DEE - Leather - Eller Manufacturing Co. Inc.

HAN-DEE PADS - Cleaning preparations - Swiss-Tex Inc.

HAN-DEFENDER - Housewares - Trinity Marketing Inc.

HAN-DY - Storage and furniture units - Plywood Components Inc.

HAN FENG - Jewelry - Han Feng Fashions Inc.

HAN SOLO VINYL FIGURE - Toys - ERTL Co., Inc.

HAN-SUDS - Cleaning preparations–household ☆ - Peerless Chemical Co. Inc.

HANA - Computer storage devices - Hana USA, Inc.

HANA BAY - Apparel and accessories - Michael Gerald Ltd.

HANABEE - Steel springs–railroad - Needlecraft Industries

HANAH SILK - Fabrics–silk - Hanah Jane Exley

HANAKO - Hair clippers–veterinary - Major International Inc.

HANALEI - Floor coverings–carpet and rugs ☆ - Customweave Carpets Inc.

HANAN'S - Whipped topping–frozen - Hanan Products Co., Inc.

HANATABA - Bedding–linen - Dan River Inc.

HANCOCK - Floor coverings - Bruce Hardwood Floors

HANCOCK - Frames–eyeglass - May Optical Co. Inc.

HANCOCK - Milk - Hancock County Creamery

HANCOCK - Paints - Hancock Paint & Varnish Co.

HANCOCK - Tableware–china - Lenox, Inc.

HANCOCK - Thread ☆ - Perfect Thread Co. Inc.

HANCOCK - Valves–industrial - Dresser Industries, Inc.

HANCOCK PEANUT COMPANY - Nuts–salted, roasted, cooked, or canned - Morven Partners, LP

HANCOCK SHAKER VILLAGE - Pottery ☆ - Hartstone Inc.

HANCOCK SQUARE - Floor coverings ☆ - Congoleum Corp.

HANCOCK SQUARE - Furniture ☆ - Bassett Furniture Industries, Inc.

HANCOCK'S RESERVE SINGLE BARREL - Liquors - Sazerac Co. Inc.

HANCOCK'S SINGLE BARREL RESERVE - Beverages–alcohol - R.H. Farms Inc.

HANCOLITE - Paint removers - Handschy Industries Inc.

HAND-AIDE - Skin care products ☆ - Beauty Aids Inc.

HAND & NAIL THERAPY - Skin care products - Del Pharmaceuticals, Inc.

HAND BUOYS - Exercising equipment - Hydro-Fit, Inc.

HAND CARE - Gloves–work - Pioneer Industrial Products Co.

HAND CARE - Housewares - Magla Products Inc.

HAND CLEANER - Cleaning preparations - Black Swan Manufacturing Co.

HAND CLEANER 38 - Cleaning preparations - Titan Laboratories

HAND-CLENE - Cleaning preparations ☆ - Flo-Pac Corp.

HAND CRAFTED LUMIERES - Candles - D'Adant and Sons Inc.

HAND CUTS - Mat boards - Callen Photo Mount Corp.

HAND-D TEAR - Tape–adhesive - PDM Adhesives Corp.

HAND-E-DRY - Bowling balls - Master Industries Inc.

HAND EASY - Photographic equipment - Pic-Mount Corp. (Seary Manufacturing Div.)

HAND-EEZ - Abrasive products ☆ - Carborundum Abrasives North America

HAND GRENADE - Syrup - Tropical Isle, Inc.

HAND-GRIP - Staplers - Bates Manufacturing Co.

HAND GROOM - Paint and wallpaper cleaners - Mantrose-Haeuser Co. Inc.

HAND-GUARD - Pet products - Four Paws Products Ltd.

HAND GYM - Health care products - Maddak Inc.

HAND HELPER - Health care products - Meddev Corp.

HAND HELPERS - Gloves - Magla Products Inc.

HAND HUGGERS - Pens - Sanford Corp.

HAND KLEEN - Cleaning preparations - Handschy Industries Inc.

HAND-L-HOLD - Housewares - Bassick Casters

HAND-LER - Timers–appliance - Volk Enterprises, Inc.

HAND-MARBLED - Paper–gift wrap ☆ - Stephen Lawrence Co.

HAND-MASKER - Novelty items - PC Manufacturing Corp.

HAND-MATE - Impact absorbing band - Fergie Glove, Inc.

HAND-ME-OUTS - Candy - Farley Candy Co.

HAND 'N' BRUSH - Garment hangers–wood - Lois Noyes California Unusuals

HAND 'N NAIL - Skin care products ☆ - Para Laboratories Inc.

HAND N SCRATCH - Pet products - Booda Products, Inc.

HAND-O-PUMP II - Pumps ☆ - Monogram Sanitation Co.

HAND PADDLES - Swimming pools - Recreonics, Inc.

HAND PAINTED MURALS - Wallpaper - Capital Carousel Inc.

HAND PERFECTING TREATMENT - Cosmetics - Estee Lauder Inc.

HAND SANDER - Abrasive products - Allway Tools Inc.

HAND SAVER - Skin care products - Delore International

HAND SAVER - Skin care products ☆ - Cadet Laboratories

HAND SHAPE - Skin care products ☆ - Warner-Lambert Co.

HAND-SPUN - Candy ☆ - New England Confectionery Co.

HAND STANDS - Apparel–children's ☆ - Eagle Knitting Mills Inc.

HAND-TEK - Surgical gloves - Boyd Medical & Safety Supplies, Inc.

HAND-TIED BARRETTE, THE - Barrettes - Bead Weaver Ltd.

HAND-TITE LITE - Tools–power-driven - Jacobs Chuck Technology Corp.

HAND TO HAND ROLLA HOCKEY - Toys - Goods Manufacturers International

HAND TO HAND SPEED HOCKEY - Garage door openers - Mjci Corp.

HAND TYPE - Housewares ☆ - Regional Respotary

HAND-UP SCAN - Medical apparatus - Sherry Hunt Jancik

HAND VAC - Vacuum cleaners and accessories - Royal Appliance Manufacturing Co.

H.A.N.D. WEAR U.S.A. - Apparel and accessories - Bill Vitanyi

HAND WORKABLE - Epoxy ☆ - Martin Carbone Inc.

HAND WROUGHT I - Wallpaper - Patterson Piazza

HAND WROUGHT II - Wallpaper - Patterson Piazza

HAND-Y BUDDY - Toys - Gerber Products Co.

HAND-Y PAL - Toys - Gerber Products Co.

HAND-Y-SHAG - Sporting goods - Chesal Golf

HAND-Y TEES - Apparel and accessories - Access Wear Plus, Inc.

HANDAID - Gloves–safety - Michael Litman

HANDAID - Skin care products ☆ - Christine Valmy, Inc.

HANDAIDE - Health care products - Omron Healthcare, Inc.

HANDALL - Firearms, accessories, and parts - Hogue Grips

HANDCRAFT - Furniture - Mersman Furniture Co.

HANDCRAFT - Tiles–ceramic ☆ - Wenczel Tile Co.

HANDCRAFT BY PILGRIM - Glass products - Pilgrim Glass Corp.
HANDCRAFTED BY NICE PEOPLE - Novelty items - Paul Hoge Creations, Inc.
HANDCRAFTERS - Looms - Nasco Handcrafters
HANDCRAFTS FOR THE HOME - Containers ☆ - Our Secret, Ltd.
HANDCYCLE - Motor vehicles - Palmer Industries
HANDEASE - Medical apparatus - American Health Specialties Inc.
HANDEE - Podiatric product - Aetna Felt Corp.
HANDEE - Rope ☆ - Wellington Leisure Products, Inc.
HANDEE - Tools - Sandusky-Chicago Abrasive Wheel Co.
HANDEE BEND - Nozzles - Milton Industries Inc.
HANDEE HITCH - Hardware - ITT Jabsco
HANDEE-HOOKS - Hooks - Tyz-All Plastics Inc.
HANDEE INTERNATIONAL - Teas - Handee International
HANDEE RAM ROD - Tools–plumbing - Moen Inc.
HANDEEVEST - Dental compounds - Dentex Research Development, Inc.
HANDEL & METTLER - Wines ☆ - Oak Ridge Vineyards
HANDEMONIUM - Puppets - Barry Gordemer
HANDEZE - Medical apparatus - Dome Publishing Co., Inc.
HANDEZE - Splints ☆ - D'mannco, Inc.
H&G STUDIOS PLATES & MUSIC BOXES - Figurines - Viking Import House Inc.
HANDGARDS - Bags–plastic - Handgards, Inc.
HANDGARDS - Gloves - Handgards Inc.
HANDGLIDER - Computer peripheral equipment - John A. Gelardi, Anthony Gelardi and Leonard Goldman Partnership
HANDGUN - Nozzles - Williams Fire & Hazard Control, Inc.
H&H - Bagels - Fourth Toro Family LP
H&H - Herring–smoked, salted, dried, or pickled - Adamba Imports International Inc.
H&H - Nail care products - H & H Products
HANDHUGGERS - Office supplies - Empire Berol USA
HANDI - Housewares - Selfix, Inc.
HANDI - Mops - Royal Maid Association for the Blind Inc.
HANDI - Tools–hand-operated - Gilmour Manufacturing Co.
HANDI - Tricycles ☆ - GT Bicycles Inc.
HANDI AID - Publisher's imprints ☆ - Rosen Publishing Group & Pelion Press
HANDI-BACK - Chairs–folding - Algoma Net Co.
HANDI-BACK - Hammocks - Gleason Corp.
HANDI-BAG - Bags ☆ - Stebco Products Corp.
HANDI-BAG - Bags–plastic - Webster Industries
HANDI BAR - Food products - Dolphin Dispensers
HANDI-BAR - Giftware ☆ - Iron-A-Way, Inc.
HANDI-BAR - Tools ☆ - True Temper Hardware Co.
HANDI BOTTLE - Infant product - Just for Baby Inc.
HANDI-BOY - Ice chests - Handi-Boy, Inc.
HANDI-BRIK - Bricks - Gloria Enterprises Inc.
HANDI-BRIK - Bricks ☆ - Glen-Gery Corp.
HANDI BRUSH - Fabric brush - Groom Industries, Inc.
HANDI-CAN - Containers–trash - F.H. Lawson Co.
HANDI-CARI - Cases–vanity ☆ - Jacob North Printing Co. Inc.
HANDI-CLAMP - Medical apparatus - Handi-Ramp Inc.
HANDI CLAMP - Timers–appliance - Volk Enterprises, Inc.
HANDI-CLEAN - Photoengraving machines - Leedall Products Manufacturing Co.
HANDI-CLIP - Staplers - Markwell Manufacturing Co. Inc.
HANDI CRETE - Paints - Quikrete Cos.
HANDI-CUFF - Cuffs–hand - Tyton Corp.
HANDI-CUT - Fabrics ☆ - Dan River Inc.
HANDI-ENCLOSURE - Health care products - Cheney Co. Inc.
HANDI-FILE - Filing cabinets–metal - Fesco Plastics Corp.
HANDI-FILE - Office furniture–metal - Joyce International Inc.
HANDI-FINDER - Electronic equipment - Robert A. Leskovec
HANDI-FLARE - Lanterns–kerosene ☆ - Dorco Manufacturing Inc.
HANDI-FLOOR TRYM - Tiles–ceramic - Futura Home Products
HANDI FLY-CONTROL - Tools–garden - Gilmour Manufacturing Co.
HANDI-FRAME - Frames–picture ☆ - Futura Home Products
HANDI-GARD - Adhesives and sealants ☆ - Gibson-Homans Co.
HANDI-GLAZE - Putties ☆ - Gibson-Homans Co.
HANDI-GRIP - Health care products - Maddak Inc.
HANDI-GRIPS - Cameras ☆ - Yashica Inc.
HANDI GROMMET KIT - Hardware - Lord & Hodge, Inc.
HANDI-GUARD - Health care products - Cheney Co. Inc.
HANDI-HAMPER - Bags–laundry - Clairson International Corp.
HANDI HEET - Tools - Smith Equipment
HANDI-HELPER - Scrapers ☆ - Royal Maid Association for the Blind Inc.

HANDI-HOLD - Spray bottle - Intex Chemical Inc.
HANDI HOLDER - Milk - Evlo Plastics Inc.
HANDI-HOLDERS - Serving carts - Tomlinson Industries
HANDI HOME-LIFT - Health care products - Cheney Co. Inc.
HANDI-KART - Wheelchairs - AM Scooters
HANDI KEY - Key rings ☆ - Hill Security Products
HANDI-KIT - Ophthalmic goods - Karlen Manufacturing, Inc.
HANDI-KLEEN - Motor vehicle parts and accessories - Graymills Corp.
HANDI-KUTTER - Knives–pocket - Handi-Kutter Inc.
HANDI-LAV - Hardware - Masco Corp. (Plumbing Products Div.)
HANDI-LEASH - Pet products - Roccorp, Inc.
HANDI-LENS - Lenses–magnifying - Ultra-Optix Inc.
HANDI LEVER SLIM - Handles–metal - Extend, Inc.
HANDI-LIFT - Health care products - Cheney Co. Inc.
HANDI-LINER - Dental floss - Mizzy Inc.
HANDI-LOC - File folders - Angler's Roslyn Group Ltd.
HANDI-LUBE - Lubricants ☆ - SAFCO Corp.
HANDI-LUNCHES - Food products - Kraft Food Ingredients Corp.
HANDI-MAID - Cleaning preparations - Penn Jersey Paper Co.
HANDI-MAID - Cleaning preparations–window ☆ - Royal Maid Association for the Blind Inc.
HANDI-MAN - Brushes–paint - E-Z Paintr Corp.
HANDI MATES - Apparel and accessories - A.C. Weber & Co. Inc.
HANDI-MATIC - Office machines - Mead-Hatcher, Inc.
HANDI-MEASURE - Garden equipment - Science Products Co. Inc.
HANDI MOVE - Health care products - T.F. Herceg Inc.
HANDI PAC - Hardware ☆ - Phifer Wire Products Inc.
HANDI PACKS - Office supplies - Wallace Computer Services, Inc.
HANDI-PADS - Fabrics - Veratec
HANDI-PAK - Cereal - Kellogg Co.
HANDI-PAN - Housewares - Toastmaster Inc.
HANDI-PAN - Pans - Royal Maid Association for the Blind Inc.
HANDI-PENS - Pens - Rolamech Inc.
HANDI-PIN - Pins–safety - Lindgren, Phoenix Niesley
HANDI-PRESS - Housewares - Iron-A-Way, Inc.
HANDI PROLIFT - Health care products - Cheney Co. Inc.
HANDI-PUTTI - Putties ☆ - Gibson-Homans Co.
HANDI-RAMP - Medical apparatus - Handi-Ramp Inc.
HANDI-RAMP - Ramps - E-Quest, Inc.
HANDI-REACH-HANDLE - Garden equipment - Dramm Corp.
HANDI ROLL IT - Hardware - Shur-Line Inc.
HANDI-ROLLER - See **PAINT 'N ROLL**
HANDI ROLLS - Hardware - Keystone-Seneca Wire Cloth Co.
HANDI-SCOOP - Pet products - Nel-Rich Products Inc.
HANDI-SCOPE - Lenses–magnifying ☆ - Buhl Optical Co.
HANDI-SCRUB - Soap - Georgia-Pacific Corp.
HANDI-SEAL - Putties ☆ - Gibson-Homans Co.
HANDI-SET - Plates–paper - Beach Products
HANDI-SHELF - Hardware ☆ - Futura Home Products
HANDI-SILL - Weather stripping - Futura Home Products
HANDI-SLEDGE - Tools ☆ - True Temper Hardware Co.
HANDI-SLIDE - Motor vehicle parts and accessories - Rocky Mountain Technology Engineering Corp.
HANDI-SNACKS - Snack foods - Kraft Foods, Inc.
HANDI-SOUND - Electronic equipment ☆ - Fleetwood Furniture Co.
HANDI SPARK - Barbecues and grills ☆ - Meteor Inc.
HANDI-SPRAY - Bathroom fixtures - Alsons Corp.
HANDI-SQUEEZE - Bottles–plastic - Lynd Properties Inc.
HANDI SQUEEZE - Mops - Lighthouse Industries
HANDI STANDS - Photographic equipment ☆ - L.F. Deardorff & Sons Inc.
HANDI-STEEL MILL - Hardware - American Industrial Products Co.
HANDI-STRIP - Hardware - Senco Products, Inc.
HANDI-SWEEP - Housewares ☆ - Normark Corp.
HANDI-TAB - Drafting supplies - Pierce Business Products Inc.
HANDI TACKER - Adhesives and sealants - Super Glue Corp.
HANDI-TACKER - Health care products - Maddak Inc.
HANDI-TAPE - Weather stripping ☆ - Futura Home Products
HANDI TOTE - Luggage - Samsonite Corp.
HANDI-TRACK - Weather stripping - Futura Home Products
HANDI-TRAKS - Medical apparatus - Handi-Ramp Inc.
HANDI-TRAY - Trays - Goody Products, Inc.
HANDI-TRUSS - Roofing materials–clay ☆ - O.D. Funk Co.
HANDI-TRYM - Moldings–plaster of paris - Colotrym
HANDI-TUBE - Adhesives and sealants ☆ - Willert Home Products, Inc.
HANDI VAC - Hardware - The Genie Co.
HANDI-VAC - Tools–hand-operated - Virtual Industries, Inc.

☆ = Now out of production

HANDI WALL - Brushes–paint - E-Z Paintr Corp.

HANDI-WALL TRYM - Moldings–plaster of paris - Futura Home Products

HANDI-WASH - Cleaning preparations - Fort Lauderdale Distributing Co.

HANDI WHISK - Brooms - Royal Maid Association for the Blind Inc.

HANDI WIPES - Towels - Colgate-Palmolive Co.

HANDI-WIRE - Hardware - Anchor Wire Corp.

HANDI-WRAP - Plastics film - Dowbrands L.P.

HANDI-WRAP COLORS - Plastics film - Dowbrands L.P.

HANDI-ZAP - Adhesives and sealants - Pacer Technology

HANDIART FOR CREATIVE TEACHERS - Computer software ☆ - Ventura Educational Systems

HANDICAP - Ammunition ☆ - Remington Arms Co., Inc.

HANDICARE - Health care products - Inbrand Corp.

HANDICARE - Plumbing fixtures - National Fiber Glass Products

HANDICOMM - Toilets–porcelain - Mansfield Plumbing Products, Inc.

HANDICRAFT - Plywood - Georgia-Pacific Corp.

HANDICRAFTER - Welding equipment ☆ - Controls Corp. of America

HANDIE-TALKIE - Radios - Motorola, Inc. (Land Mobile Products Sector)

HANDIES - Gloves - Oak Technical Inc.

HANDIFOLD - Paper–toweling - Fort Howard Corp.

HANDIFORM - Insulating materials - Foil-Ray Inc.

HANDIHEAD II - Toilets–portable ☆ - Monogram Sanitation Co.

HANDILITE - Lanterns–kerosene ☆ - Dorco Manufacturing Inc.

HANDIOIL - Lubricants - Health-Tech, Inc.

HANDIPAK - Insulating materials - Manville/Schuller

HANDIPT - Candles - Colonial Candle of Cape Cod

HANDIPUL - Pulleys–industrial ☆ - Steelgrip Tools Inc.

HANDISAX - Bags–paper - Chase Bag Co.

HANDISOL - Medical apparatus - National Biological Corp.

HANDISPENSER - Labeling machinery - Trade Aid Supply Co.

HANDISTAND - Racks - Peco Manufacturing Co. Inc.

HANDISWEET - Semiconductors - Fasweet Co.

HANDIVAC I - Vacuum cleaners and accessories ☆ - The Hoover Co.

HANDIWIRE - Wire - Diamond Wire & Cable Co.

HANDIWOOD - Veneer ☆ - Flexible Materials Inc.

HANDIWORKS - Gloves–rubber - Safeskin Corp.

HANDKERCHIEF HOUSE - Handkerchiefs - British American Imports

HANDKEY - Electronics - Recognition Systems, Inc.

HANDKIND - Apparel and accessories - Kirk Martensen

HANDKRAFT - Sporting goods - Weber Industries Inc.

HANDLE GRAPHICS - Computer software - Mathworks, Inc.

HANDLE HELPER - Handles–plastic - Handle Helper, L.P.

HANDLE IT - Cookware - Frieling USA, Inc.

HANDLE-IT - Garden tool accessories - Intromark Inc.

HANDLE-IT - Health care products - Maddak Inc.

HANDLE LINER - Liners and covers–pond, pit, and landfill - Avantage Group Inc.

HANDLE ON HISTORY - Bags–paper - Handle on History Inc.

HANDLE SAVER, THE - Tools - Ultimate Tool Group

HANDLE, THE - Cameras - Eastman Kodak Co.

HANDLE WALL SAVER - Recliners - Action Industries Inc.

HANDLE WITH CARE - Cosmetics - Origins Natural Resources Inc.

HANDLE WITH CARE - Footwear - Bennett Importing, Inc.

HANDLE2 - Cameras - Eastman Kodak Co.

HANDLEBAR - Frames–eyeglass - Liberty Optical Manufacturing Co.

HANDLELOCK - Fabrics–polyethylene - Burdick & Jackson, Inc.

HANDLER - Pet products - PLM Handles Inc.

HANDLER - Shock absorbers–motor vehicle ☆ - Monroe Auto Equipment Co.

HANDLER - Waste collection materials - PM Industries Inc.

HANDLER, THE - Shampoos - Gillette Co.

HANDLER'S CHOICE - Pet products - Pet Products Plus

HANDLERS, THE - Microphones - Paso Sound Products Inc.

HANDLET - Jewelry - Thea L. Loch

HANDMACHER - Women's suits - Country Miss Inc.

HANDMADE - Trade journals - George Little Management, Inc.

HANDMADE CREATIONS - Toys–stuffed - Handmade Creations Inc.

HANDMADE TO BE HANDED DOWN - Baskets–wood - Longaberger Co.

HANDMOLD METRICS - Floor coverings–tile ☆ - Kepcor, Inc./SSI Tiles

HANDNIB - Scissors–hand-operated - Heinrich Co.

HANDOM - Gloves–rubber - Shell Containers, Inc.

HANDPAINTED COUNTRY - Wallpaper - Andover Wallcovering

HANDPAINTED EFFECTS - Wallpaper - Bayview Wallcoverings

HANDPAINTED SILKS - Cosmetics - Yves St. Laurent Parfum Corp.

HANDPICKED FROM THE WORLD'S FINEST FARMS - Olive oil - Friendly Fruit, Inc.

HANDPRINT SIGNATURE - Greeting cards - Paula Carlson

HANDPRINTS - Greeting cards - Handprints

HANDRO FOR MEN - Apparel and accessories - Slumbertogs Inc.

HANDS AROUND THE WORLD: HUMANITY CELEBRATES THE MILLENNIUM - Broadcasting stations–cable television - Pan-Amour Entertainment, Inc.

HAND'S BEST FRIEND - Gloves ☆ - Wolverine World Wide, Inc.

HANDS DOWN - Games - CBS Toys

HANDS DOWN - Games - Milton Bradley Co.

HANDS DOWN - Shirts - Charles Lang

HANDS DOWN - Telephone apparatus - Rubbermaid Commercial Products Inc.

HANDS FREE - Containers–trash - Toter, Inc.

HANDS-FREE - Coolers–electric - Elkay Manufacturing Co.

HANDS FREE - Hunting equipment - Adventure Game Calls

HANDS FREE WRENCH - Tools–hand-operated - Newington Corp.

HANDS HICKORY - Musical instrument accessories - Pro-Mark Corp.

HANDS-O-KLEEN - Housewares - J.C. Whitlam Manufacturing Co.

HANDS OFF - Bathroom fixtures - Earl C. Brown

HANDS OFF - Toys–electronic - Mattel, Inc.

HANDS OFF! - Video production - Golden Sky Productions, Inc.

HANDS ON - Cleaning preparations - State Chemical Manufacturing Co.

HANDS ON - Gloves–safety - Edmont

HANDS ON - Wallpaper - Armor & Tabler

HANDS-ON ELECTRONICS - Computer software ☆ - Ventura Educational Systems

HANDS-ON HEALTH - Medical apparatus - American Cyanamid Co.

HANDS ON LEARNING - Video production - Learn PC, Inc.

HANDS-ON MATH VOLUME 2 - Computer software - Ventura Educational Systems

HANDS-ON MATH VOLUME 3 - Computer software - Ventura Educational Systems

HANDS-ON MATH VOLUME I - Computer software - Ventura Educational Systems

HANDS PLUS - Skin care products - Stanley Home Products Inc.

HANDSAVER - Gloves–rubber - Playtex Beauty Care, Inc.

HANDSDOWN - Paper–toweling - Kimberly-Clark Corp.

HANDSHAKE-EMULATION - Computer software - Andrew Corp.

HANDSHOWER - Faucets - Kallista Inc.

HANDSOFF - Telephones - Otis Elevator Co.

HANDSOME - Frames–eyeglass - Zylo Ware Corp.

HANDSOME DAN - Tobacco–chewing or smoking ☆ - Philip Morris Companies Inc.

HANDSOME MAN - Frames–eyeglass - Zylo Ware Corp.

HANDSPRINGS PUPPET BOX - Hobby kits - Craft World International Inc.

HANDSTANDS - Apparel–children's - J.C. Penney Co., Inc.

HANDSTRAPS - Pamphlets - Handstraps Co.

HANDSTRETCHED - Pizzas–mixes - KT Kitchens

HANDWASH - Electronic equipment - General Electric Co.

HANDWEAVING BY RUTH - Leather goods - Ruth N. Campbell

HANDWRITER, THE - Computer software ☆ - Communication Intelligence Corp.

HANDY - Brushes - Wright-Bernet

HANDY - Brushes–paint - Pettit Paint Co. Inc.

HANDY - Chalk - U.S. Crayon Co.

HANDY - Cleaning preparations - Cadet Laboratories

HANDY - Crab meat–fresh - John T. Handy Co. Inc.

HANDY - Hardware - Handy Hardware Wholesale Inc.

HANDY - Insecticides - H.D. Hudson Manufacturing Co.

HANDY - Kitchen appliances - Black & Decker Corp.

HANDY - Knives - Spectrum Razor Tools

HANDY - Knives–pocket - Handy Twine Knife Co.

HANDY - Ledgers - Garrett & Massie Inc.

HANDY - Meat products–pork - Hygrade Food Products Corp.

HANDY - Motor vehicle parts and accessories - Chrysler Corp. (Introl Div.)

HANDY - Office supplies - Chaselle Inc.

HANDY - Pet products ☆ - Dandy Products Inc.

HANDY - Plywood - Harbor Sales Co.

HANDY - Polishing rouge ☆ - Golden Star Inc.

HANDY - Projection screens ☆ - Da-Lite Screen Co. Inc.

HANDY - Saws–power - Allway Tools Inc.

HANDY - Tape measures ☆ - Keuffel & Esser Co.

HANDY A - Stencils - Ideal Stencil Machine and Tape Co.

HANDY ANDY - Brooms - Perfex Corp.

HANDY ANDY - Detergents - Lever Brothers Co. Inc.

HANDY ANDY - Gloves - Wells Lamont Corp.

HANDY ANDY - Toys - Revell-Monogram, Inc.

HANDY ANDY'S HENHOUSE - Candy ☆ - R.M. Palmer Co.

HANDY ANVIL - Anvils - James F. Johnson
HANDY ART - Paints - Rock Paint Distributing Corp.
HANDY B - Stencils ✩ - Ideal Stencil Machine and Tape Co.
HANDY-BAR - Tools - Estwing Manufacturing Co.
HANDY BEAR - Toys - Discovery Toys, Inc.
HANDY BEAVER - Cleaning preparations - Scott Paper Co.
HANDY BELT - Tool belts - Portable Products, Inc.
HANDY BIN - Cabinets ✩ - Akro-Mils Inc.
HANDY BOY - Heaters–space - Spectrum Infrared Inc.
HANDY BOY - Pumps - ITT Jabsco
HANDY BOY - Video game toy - Nintendo of America Inc.
HANDY BUDDY - Leather goods - Marcor, Inc.
HANDY BUFFER - Tools–power-driven - Black & Decker Corp.
HANDY C - Stencils - Ideal Stencil Machine and Tape Co.
HANDY CAN - Lubricants ✩ - Magic American Corp.
HANDY CAT - Ships–sailing vessels ✩ - Newport Shipyards (Cape Dory Div.)
HANDY CHAIR - High chairs - Handy Chair Corp.
HANDY CHOPPER - Kitchen appliances - Black & Decker Corp.
HANDY-CLEAN - Gloves–rubber - Red Steer Glove Co.
HANDY-CLEAN - Skin care products ✩ - Pettit Paint Co. Inc.
HANDY CLOTH - Tools–garden - King Cotton Cordage Co.
HANDY CONE - Safety products - Michael V. Johnson
HANDY COPIER - Duplicating machines - Sharp Electronics Corp.
HANDY CRAFT PAK - Toys - Fitzgerald Enterprises Inc.
HANDY-CRATE - Containers - Monoflo International Inc.
HANDY CUTTER LINE - Tools–hand-operated - Spectrum Razor Tools
HANDY-DAN - Cooking equipment–household - Birmingham Stove & Range Co.
HANDY-DANDY - Apparel and accessories - Mamiye Brothers, Inc.
HANDY DANDY - Electrical equipment ✩ - Burnworth Tester Co.
HANDY DANDY - Feather dusters - Texas Feathers Inc.
HANDY DANDY - Housewares - Alwin Products
HANDY DECK - Wood products ✩ - Handy Home Products
HANDY DOT - Containers - Telesis Marketing Team, Inc.
HANDY DRIVER - Screw drivers - Black & Decker Corp.
HANDY-EDGE - Stone products - Handy-Stone Corp.
HANDY EDGE - Tools–hand-operated - Pilgrim Designs, Inc.
HANDY FILL - Seasonings - McCormick & Co., Inc.
HANDY FOLIO MUSIC CO. - Music–sheet ✩ - T.S. Denison and Co.
HANDY GIRLS - Toys - Handy Girls Inc.
HANDY GREEN - Garden equipment - Scotts Co. (Organics Business Group)
HANDY HAMPER - Hampers ✩ - Burlington Basket Co. Inc.
HANDY HANDS - Tools - Wells Lamont Corp.
HANDY-HANG UPS - Hardware - Androck Hardware Corp.
HANDY HANGERS - Framing supplies - Tom Kedzie Projects
HANDY HANGERS - Hardware ✩ - John L. Chaney Instrument Co.
HANDY HARRY - Paints–artists' ✩ - A. Flohr Co. Inc.
HANDY HEAT - Electrical equipment - Cox and Co. Inc.
HANDY HELPERS - Towels - Revere Mills, Inc.
HANDY HOLDERS - Ophthalmic goods - Hilsinger Corp.
HANDY HOME HELPERS - Polishing equipment–jewelry - Fox Run Craftsmen
HANDY HOOKER - Knives - Pacific Handy Cutter Inc.
HANDY HOOKER - Knives - Spectrum Razor Tools
HANDY HOOKS - Crochet hooks - Accento Plastic Manufacturing Inc.
HANDY-HOOKS - Wood products ✩ - Knape and Vogt Manufacturing Co.
HANDY HUTS - Wood products - Handy Home Products
HANDY-JACK - Knives–pocket ✩ - Colonial Knife Co. Inc.
HANDY JUICER - Kitchen appliances - Black & Decker Corp.
HANDY KIT - Housewares - Groom Industries, Inc.
HANDY LIFT - Machinery - Louis Berkman Co.
HANDY LINE - Fasteners–hook and eye - Rockford Products Corp. (International Group)
HANDY-LITE - Electrical equipment - Acme Battery Manufacturing Co.
HANDY-LOCK - Locks–padlocks - C. Sherman Johnson Co. Inc.
HANDY-MAN - Lamp bulbs–fluorescent - Regent Lighting Corp. (Consumer Products Div.)
HANDY-MAN - Lubricants - Witco Corp.
HANDY MAN - Rope - Crow Rope Industries LLC
HANDY-MARKER - Crayons - U.S. Crayon Co.
HANDY MIXER - Housewares - Black & Decker Corp.
HANDY-MIXER - Juices - Sunkist Growers Inc.
HANDY PAC - Vegetables–frozen - McCain Foods Inc.
HANDY-PAC - Wire - General Cable Corp.
HANDY PACK - Novelty items - Reed Productions
HANDY PACK - Paper–sand - Norton Co.
HANDY PACKS - Hardware - Bulldog Home Hardware

HANDY PAK - Office supplies ✩ - Avery Label Systems
HANDY-PAK - Roofing material - Continental Materials Co.
HANDY-PAK - Welding equipment - Controls Corp. of America
HANDY PAN - Pans - California Flexrake Corp.
HANDY PANTIES - Apparel–women's - Comfy Corp.
HANDY PATCH - Hardware ✩ - Bondex International Inc.
HANDY PICKER UPPER - Pet shops - Dunwishin Enterprises
HANDY POP 'N SERVE - Popcorn poppers - Black & Decker Corp.
HANDY PRO - Compressors–air - Ames Department Stores, Inc.
HANDY ROLL - Tools - Norton Co.
HANDY SAFETY POINT - Knives - Pacific Handy Cutter Inc.
HANDY SHARP - Tools–hand-operated - All Rite Products, Inc.
HANDY SHAVER - Razors–electric ✩ - Duracell Co. USA
HANDY-SHIELD - Insulating materials - Plumberex Specialty Products, Inc.
HANDY SHORTCUT - Food processors - Black & Decker Corp.
HANDY SIGN - Signs - Mike V. Johnson
HANDY SLENDERBLENDER - Blenders - Black & Decker Corp.
HANDY SLICE 'N SHRED - Food processors - Black & Decker Corp.
HANDY SOAKER - Garden equipment - H.B. Sherman Manufacturing Co.
HANDY SPRAY - Inks - Ideal Stencil Machine and Tape Co.
HANDY SPRAY - Nozzles - H.B. Sherman Manufacturing Co.
HANDY STEAMER - Kitchen appliances - Black & Decker Corp.
HANDY STEAMER PLUS - Kitchen appliances - Black & Decker Corp.
HANDY STITCH - Sewing machines–household - Singer Co.
HANDY STONE - Stone products - Handy-Stone Corp.
HANDY-STRAPS - Hardware ✩ - General Wire Spring Co.
HANDY-SUPER - Chalk - U.S. Crayon Co.
HANDY-TAB - Automotive parts and accessories - Roderick G. Rohrberg
HANDY TABLES - Furniture - Vaughan Manufacturing Co. Inc.
HANDY-TEMP - Thermometers - Taylor Environmental Instruments
HANDY-TIES - Rope ✩ - Outdoor Technologies Group
HANDY-TOOLS - Tools - Sequence (USA) Co. Ltd.
HANDY WAY - Farm machinery - Spyker Spreader Works
HANDYBLENDER - Blenders - Black & Decker Corp.
HANDYBLENDER II - Blenders - Black & Decker Corp.
HANDYBOY - Tools - Diamond/Triangle Tool Group Inc.
HANDYCAM - Cameras–video - Sony Corp. of America
HANDYCAM PRO - Cameras–video - Sony Corp. of America
HANDYCAPPER - Containers–insulated - Vanderbuilt LLC
HANDYCHECK - Electrical equipment - Midland Manufacturing Corp.
HANDYCHOPPER - Kitchen appliances - Black & Decker Corp.
HANDYDRIVER - Screw drivers - Black & Decker Corp.
HANDYFILE - Cabinets–metal ✩ - Esselte Corp.
HANDYGEAR - Aprons–leather - McGuire-Nicholas Co., Inc.
HANDYKNIFE - Knives–electric - Black & Decker Corp.
HANDYLECTRIC - Tools–power-driven - General Wire Spring Co.
HANDYMAN - Automotive parts and accessories - Bloomfield Manufacturing Co.
HANDYMAN - First aid kits - National Patent Medical
HANDYMAN - Knives - Precise International/Wenger
HANDYMAN JR. - Toys - Diversified Specialists, Inc.
HANDYMASTER - Heaters–space - Desa International, Inc.
HANDYMATE - Lighting fixtures - Point Electric
HANDYMIXER - Kitchen appliances - Black & Decker Corp.
HANDYOPENER - Kitchen appliances - Black & Decker Corp.
HANDYPOST - Garden equipment - Universal Industrial Products Co.
HANDYSOUND - Musical instrument accessories - Yamaha Corp. of America
HANDYSWITCH - Electrical equipment ✩ - McMillan Design Inc.
HANDYTRADE - Giftware - Handy Trading Co. Of America
HANDYXPRESS - Irons–electric - Black & Decker Corp.
HANES - Apparel and accessories - Sara Lee Knit Products Inc.
HANES - Draperies - Hanes Fabrics Co.
HANES - Hosiery - Sara Lee Corp.
HANES ABSOLUTELY ULTRA SHEER - Hosiery - Sara Lee Corp.
HANES ALIVE - Hosiery - Sara Lee Corp.
HANES HEAVYWEIGHT - Apparel and accessories - Sara Lee Corp.
HANES HER WAY - Rocking horses - Sara Lee Corp.
HANES HER WAY - Underwear and nightwear - Sara Lee Knit Products Inc.
HANES HER WAY ACTIVEWEAR - Women's apparel - Sara Lee Corp.
HANES HER WAY FOR GIRLS - Apparel–children's - Sara Lee Knit Products Inc.
HANES HER WAY SIGNATURE COLLECTION - Apparel–women's - Sara Lee Corp.
HANES OTHERWEAR - Apparel and accessories - Sara Lee Corp.
HANES PRINTABLES - Underwear and nightwear - Sara Lee Knit Products Inc.

✩ = Now out of production

HANES SIGNATURE COLLECTION - Apparel and accessories - Sara Lee Corp.

HANES TOO - Hosiery - Sara Lee Corp.

HANESPORTS - Uniforms–athletic - Sara Lee Knit Products Inc.

HANFORD COURT - Floor coverings–carpet and rugs - Hollytex Carpet Mills Inc.

HANFORD FORGE - Tableware–plastic ✩ - Washington Forge Inc.

HANFORD'S - Veterinary pharmaceutical preparations - G.C. Hanford Manufacturing Co.

HANG-A-HOOK - Storage space extenders ✩ - Invention Marketing Inc.

HANG-A-LONG FIRE ENGINE - Toys ✩ - Combi International Corp.

HANG A PLAK - Plastics - Deep Flex Plastic Molds Inc.

HANG-A-PLANT - Fertilizers ✩ - Stanley Hardware Div.

HANG-A-REF - Binders - Dennison National Co.

HANG-A-THING - Hardware - True Temper Hardware Co.

HANG-A-TING - Hardware - Custom Tapes, Inc.

HANG-A-TING OR TWO - Hardware - Custom Tapes, Inc.

HANG-ABOUT BUDDIES - Toys–stuffed ✩ - Fun World Inc.

HANG ALL - Garment hangers - World Hangers, Inc.

HANG-ALL - Housewares - Ricker Co.

HANG AROUND - Key rings ✩ - Ramco Arts

HANG AROUNDS - Greeting cards - Gillette Designs

HANG AROUNDS - Toys ✩ - Imperial Toy Corp.

HANG-EM-ALL - Meters–water - Aqua-Trol Corp.

HANG-EM HIGH - Metal racks - Ward Enterprises

HANG-EZ - Garment hangers–wood - Michael Kazel

HANG FUNG TAI - Ginseng tea - Hang Fung Tai Ginseng Inc.

HANG GLIDER - Luggage - Boyt L.P.

HANG GLIDER - Thread - Lewis Threads Inc.

HANG IN THERE - Apparel and accessories - Tom Togs of Carolina, Inc.

HANG IN THERE! - Figurines - Nancy Engle

HANG IN THERE - Greeting cards - American Greetings Corp.

HANG-IT - Hooks ✩ - Willert Home Products, Inc.

HANG IT ALL - Artists' materials - Artistic Office Products

HANG-IT-ALL - Doors–glass - June Tailor Inc.

HANG-IT-ALL - Garden equipment - Cardinal Home Products

HANG IT ALL - Hardware - Magna Visual, Inc.

HANG-IT-ALL - Hooks - Lucia Eames Demetrios

HANG-IT-ALL - Lawn mowers ✩ - Mr. Chain

HANG-IT-ALL - Luggage - York Luggage Co.

HANG-IT-ALL - Wire - South Hill Ventures

HANG-IT UP - Hooks - Woodcraft Manufacturing Co.

HANG IT UP - Suspenders - Clifton Enterprises

HANG IT UP! - Wall hangings - Kinsella Designs, Inc.

HANG MASTER - Housewares - David McHugh

HANG-MOR - Garment hangers - David E. Sharp

HANG N HOOKS - Hooks ✩ - Alger Creations Inc.

HANG 'N SLIDE - Cutting boards - Designs by Alice, Inc.

HANG-N-STOR - Hardware - Steel City Corp.

HANG 'N STUFF - Christmas tree ornaments - Santa's Best

HANG-N-TAGS - Labels–paper - John Henry Co.

HANG-O-BRACKET - Fasteners–hook and eye - Hobby Hill Inc.

HANG-O-LITE - Lighting equipment - Hobby Hill Inc.

HANG-ON - Plastics ✩ - Efson Inc.

HANG OUTS - Deodorizers - California Scents

HANG-PAK - Candles - Columbia Wax Products Inc.

HANG R PAK - Garment racks–metal - Viator Products Corp.

HANG SIX - Display racks - Kingery/Rodriguez Partnership

HANG STUFF - Hardware - Steel City Corp.

HANG-TAB - Plastics - Effron Sales

HANG TANG - File folders - Duo Tang, Inc.

HANG TEN - Apparel and accessories - Sigallo Ltd.

HANG TEN - Footwear - Home Court International, Ltd.

HANG TEN - Surfboards - Hang Ten International

HANG THE MOON ART - Scarves - Cynthia E. MacCollum

HANG-TIGHT - Office supplies - Wescosa Inc.

HANG TIME - Basketball equipment - Lifetime Products, Inc.

HANG TIME - Chewing gum ✩ - Amurol Confections Co.

HANG TIME - Cleaning preparations - Apter Industries, Inc.

HANG TRASH - Housewares - Abel Kameona Hokoana, Jr.

HANG TUBE - Tubes–plastic - VisiPak

HANG TUFF - Clocks - Creative Leisure Inc.

HANG TUFF - Hardware ✩ - Steel City Corp.

HANG UP - Children's hangers - Bridgeman Enterprises

HANG-UP - Lighting fixtures - Swivelier Co. Inc.

HANG-UP - Tables–wood ✩ - Quaker Industries Ltd.

HANG-UP VAC - Vacuum cleaners and accessories - Shop Vac Corp.

HANG-UPS - Brackets - Crawford Products Inc.

HANG UPS - Cleaning preparations - AmeriPlus Inc.

HANG UPS - Exercising equipment - STL International, Inc.

HANG UPS - Greeting cards - Russ Berrie and Co., Inc.

HANG-UPS - Housewares - Co.'s Coming Inc.

HANG-UPS - Jewelry ✩ - Hirsch Speidel Inc.

HANG UPS - Pharmaceutical preparations - Scentex Inc.

HANG-UPS - Plaque and picture hangers - Ed Clarke Co.

HANG-UPS - Stationery - Kristin Elliott Inc.

HANG-UPS - Toys - Extension Inc.

HANG-UPS HANGER - Housewares - Molor Products Co.

HANG-WELL - Drapery hardware - Hang-Well Corp.

HANG YOUR HEART - Cardboard cutouts - American Heart Association New York State Affiliate, Inc.

HANGABLES, THE - Kitchen utensils–aluminum - Bonny Products Inc.

HANGAROO - Paper products - Cox Research and Technology, Inc.

HANGAWAYS - Luggage - Ventura Travelware Inc.

HANG'EM - Fixtures–plastic - LSP Specialty Products Co.

HANGER-GUARD - Pet products - Novalek, Inc.

HANGER HELPER - Closet organizers ✩ - Duchess Royale Inc.

HANGER PAK - Tubes–plastic - VisiPak

HANGER SPOUT - Adhesives and sealants - Stay-Tite Products Co. Inc.

HANGERMATE - Anchors - Elco Industries, Inc.

HANGEROOS - Bags - E-Z-Por Corp.

HANGIN' GUM - Chewing gum - Amurol Confections Co.

HANGIN' ON THE RIM - Apparel - Sun Sportswear, Inc.

HANGING BY A THREAD - Frames–picture - Patricia Kutza

HANGING GARDENS - Aquariums–household - Pets International, Ltd.

HANGING GARDENS - Flowers, plants, and seeds ✩ - Fry Plastics International Inc. (O)

HANGING GARDENS - Giftware ✩ - Avon Products, Inc.

HANGING HORRIBLES - Toys–stuffed - Fun World Inc.

HANGING HORRORS - Pencils - Russ Berrie and Co., Inc.

HANGING HORRORS TISSUE DECORATIONS - Novelty items - Paper Magic Group Inc.

HANGING LOOSE - Jackets - York East Merchandise, Inc.

HANGIT - Office supplies ✩ - Evans International Inc.

HANGMAN - Framing supplies - Tom Kedzie Projects

HANGMAN - Games - Milton Bradley Co.

HANGMAN - Recording label - Echo Records Inc.

HANGMAN - Video games - Atari Games Corp.

HANGOVER - Furniture - Aaron Luebke

HANGOVER FORMULA - Vitamins and nutritional supplements - Source Naturals

HANGOVER HELPER - Homeopathic remedies - Hangover Helper, Inc.

HANGOVER HELPER - Pharmaceutical preparations - Mankind Research Unltd. Inc.

HANGTIME - Shoes–athletic - Wilson Sporting Goods Co.

HANGTIME - Sporting goods - Lifetime Products, Inc.

HANGTIME SPORTSWEAR - Apparel–athletic - Hangtime

HANGTIMER - Timers–appliance ✩ - Healthometer

HANGTOWN - Wines - Boeger Winery Inc.

HANGUP, THE - Hardware ✩ - Lois Noyes California Unusuals

HANHART - Clocks - Eric Armin Inc.

HANIMEX - Cameras - Vivitar Corp.

HANIPLEX - Pharmaceutical preparations - Hanlon Drug Products

HANITA - Tools - Solcoor Inc.

HANITECH ONE OF A KIND - Pagers - Hanitech, Inc.

HANJET - Garden equipment ✩ - Solo, Inc.

HANK - Ophthalmic goods ✩ - Luxotica

HANK AARON BASEBALL TRAINER - Games ✩ - CBS Toys

HANK AARON-BAT & BALL SET - Games ✩ - CBS Toys

HANK AARON BLASTER BAT - Games ✩ - CBS Toys

HANK & HAL'S - Water–bottled or canned - United Artists Theatre Circuit, Inc.

HANK MOCKEL - Greeting cards - Henry R. Mockel's

HANK ROBERTS - Fishing lures - Fred Arbogast Co. Inc.

HANK THE COWDOG - Games - Texas Monthly Inc.

HANKEY BANNISTER - Liquors - Canandaigua Wine Co. Inc.

HANKEY BANNISTER - Whiskey - Peerless Importers Inc.

HANKIE-PANKIE - Toys - Creatnetics

HANKIES - Facial tissues - Marcal Paper Mills, Inc.

HANKINS - Ships–sailing vessels - Charles Hankins

HANKINS SEASKIFF - Boats–motor - Charles Hankins

HANKO - Bedding–linen - Dan River Inc.

HANKOOK - Tires - Hankook Tire America Corp.

HANKOW BATCHELOR - Teas - Gilbey's International

HANK'S CHEESECAKES - Pastries - Hank's Cheesecakes

HANKSCRAFT - Vaporizers ☆ - Sunrise Medical (Respiratory Products Division)

HANKY PANKY - Candy ☆ - Bachman Co.

HANKY PANKY - Cookies - Sunshine/Salerno Inc.

HANKY PANKYS - Greeting cards ☆ - Cathay International

HANKY PANTS - Underwear and nightwear - Bestform Foundations, Inc.

HANMI - Wallpaper - Kev Don Industries Inc.

HANNA BARBERA - Bop bags, inflatable beds, tent sets - Intex Recreation Corp.

HANNA PDQ - Resins—synthetic - M.A. Hanna Co.

HANNAFORD - Fabric softeners - Hannaford Brothers Co.

HANNAH - Computer software - Secureware, Inc.

HANNAH - Greeting cards - Andrea S. Liss

HANNAH - Tableware—china - Lenox, Inc.

HANNAH - Whirlpools - Jason International, Inc.

HANNAH & HER SCISSORS - Hair care products - Hannah & Her Scissors, Inc.

HANNAH & HOGG - Beverages—alcohol - Consolidated Distilled Products Inc.

HANNAH'S HELPER - Sponges - Glit, Inc.

HANNAROOS - Apparel and accessories - H.E.M., Inc.

HANNA'S - Candles - Hanna's Potpourri Specialties, Inc.

HANNA'S - Food products ☆ - Kroeger Herb Products Co. Inc.

HANNI - Fabrics ☆ - Decorative Aides Co. Inc.

HANNIBAL - Brushes—paint - Corona Brushes Inc.

HANNIBAL - Recording label - Rykodisc Inc.

HANNIBAL - Recording label - Sounds-Vision Music

HANNIBAL, THE - Fencing—plastic - Nebraska Plastics, Inc.

HANNIBAL'S - Coffee - Hannibal's Coffee Co.

HANNILASE - Chemical preparations - Christian Hansen's Laboratory Inc.

HANNOUSH JEWELERS - Jewelry - Hannoush Jewelers

HANNOVER - Fabrics - Gretchen Bellinger Inc.

HANNOVER - Harpsichords - Carl Dudash Harpsichords

HANNS KORNELL - Wines - Larkmead-Kornell Champagne Cellars

HANOVER - Cabinets ☆ - American Woodmark Corp.

HANOVER - Cookies - Bahlsen Inc.

HANOVER - Floor coverings - Mannington Resilient Floors

HANOVER - Floor coverings—carpet and rugs - Dan River Inc.

HANOVER - Floor coverings—carpet and rugs ☆ - Atlas Carpet Mills Inc.

HANOVER - Food products - Hanover Foods Corp.

HANOVER - Footwear—men's - C. & J. Clark America, Inc.

HANOVER - Frames—eyeglass ☆ - Universal/Univis Inc.

HANOVER - Furniture ☆ - Bassett Furniture Industries, Inc.

HANOVER - Glassware—household ☆ - Lenox Crystal, Inc.

HANOVER - Packing and oakum - Ace Jute Packing Co.

HANOVER - Pens - Hanover Pen Corp.

HANOVER - Pretzels - Nittany Corp.

HANOVER - Sporting goods - Fairfield Line, Inc.

HANOVER BEAR - Toys—stuffed - Russ Berrie and Co., Inc.

HANOVER CLUB - Beverages—carbonated ☆ - The Atlantic Beverage Group, USA, Inc.

HANOVER COLLECTION - Furniture - National/Mt. Airy Furniture

HANOVER FARMS - Food products - Nittany Corp.

HANOVER FARMS - Pies—frozen - Hanover Foods Corp.

HANOVER HEIRLOOMS - Tables—wood - Leisters Furniture Inc.

HANOVER HOME BRAND - Snack foods - UTZ Quality Foods Inc.

HANOVER HOUSE - Cigars ☆ - House of Windsor Inc.

HANOVER HOUSE - Hardware - Hanover Direct Inc.

HANOVER PARK - Dinnerware—glass ☆ - Lenox, Inc.

HANOVER SIERRA CASUALS - Footwear - C. & J. Clark America, Inc.

HANOVER SLATE - Floor coverings—tile - Kentile Floors Inc.

HANOVIA - Coatings - Engelhard Corp.

HANOVIA - Floor coverings - Mannington Resilient Floors

HANRO U.S.A. - Underwear and nightwear - Slumbertogs Inc.

HANS - Medical apparatus ☆ - Ortho-Kinetics, Inc.

HANS BOERSMA - Food products - Liberty Richter Inc.

HANS BRINKER - Dolls ☆ - Effanbee Doll Corp.

HANS BRINKER - Figurines ☆ - Coehler-Coptex Co.

HANS CHRISTIAN ANDERSEN - Toys - Creative Characters, Inc.

HANS-CUFF - Toys - Tonka Corp.

HANS FEIN - Sausages - Furr's Cafeterias Inc.

HANS HAUSER - Guitars - European Crafts/USA

HANS HOYER - Musical instruments - Hanseatic Overseas Trading Inc.

HANS JURGEN - Pickles - Frank Brunckhorst Co., LP

HANS LONG - Beverages—alcohol ☆ - AHD Vinter's Ltd.

HAN'S NATURAL HONEY LOQUAT - Cough medicines - Prince of Peace Enterprises Inc.

HANS SCHILLER - Violins - Deltex Music Corp.

HANS SCHUSTER - Musical instruments - Kaman Music Corp.

HANS WIEDERKEHR - Wines - Wiederkehr Wine Cellars Inc.

HANSA BRANTA - Apparel and accessories - Stearns Manufacturing Co.

HANSAMIN - Teas—herbal - Korean Ginseng Products Co., Ltd.

HANSBERG - Beverages—malt - Dover Vineyards Inc.

HANSCO - Office supplies ☆ - C.H. Hanson Co.

HANSCOM - Frames—eyeglass - May Optical Co. Inc.

HANSEL - Dolls - Effanbee Doll Corp.

HANSEL & GRETA - Fabrics - Dan River Inc.

HANSEL & GRETEL - Cheese ☆ - MD Foods USA Inc.

HANSEL & GRETEL - Meat products—canned - Hansel 'n Gretel Brand, Inc.

HANSEL & GRETEL AND THE ENCHANTED CASTLE - Computer software - Terraglyph Interactive, LP

HANSEN - Cheese - Skandia Foods Inc.

HANSEN - Chewing gum ☆ - R.L. Albert & Son, Inc.

HANSEN - Recording label - DTA

HANSEN - Trays - Scandia Specialties Inc.

HANSEN ISLAND - Fudge - Redco Foods Inc.

HANSEN LITES - Fruit drinks—bottled or canned - Hansen Beverage Co.

HANSEN NORGE - Fish—canned or cured ☆ - Hansen Caviar Co.

HANSEN SLED - Sleds - Viking Imports, Inc.

HANSEN STURM - Fish—canned or cured - Hansen Caviar Co.

HANSEN'S - Water—bottled or canned - Calistoga Mineral Water Co.

HANSEN'S - Yogurt - Christian Hansen's Laboratory Inc.

HANSENS DAIRY - Milk - Hansen's Dairy Inc.

HANSEN'S PET SYSTEMS HPS - Shampoos - Mason Distributing

HANSMANN'S - Flour—blended - Hansmann's Mills Inc.

HANSOLAR - Heaters—solar - Hanson Energy Products

HANSOM - Apparel—men's ☆ - Carl Neckwear Co. Inc.

HANSON - Boots - Hanson Industries Inc.

HANSON - Drill presses - Illinois Fastening Systems

HANSON - Drills—hand-operated - Buehler Scope Mounts (Maynard P. Buehler Inc.)

HANSON - Scales—bathroom ☆ - Sunbeam-Oster Household Products

HANSON - Tools - American Tool Companies Inc.

HANSON - Towels - Hanson Textile Co.

HANSSON-FLEMMING - Signal flares ☆ - Datrex Inc.

HANSSON PYROTECH - Signal flares - Datrex Inc.

HANUTA - Candy - Ferrero U.S.A Inc.

HANVER, THE - Fencing—plastic - Nebraska Plastics, Inc.

HANZ OFF SOCCER GEAR - Apparel—athletic - Robert E. Biallas

HANZELL VINEYARDS - Wines - Hanzell Vineyards

HAP - Dolls - Mattel, Inc.

HAP - Hair care products - Frances Denney

HAPCO FARMS - Fruits and vegetables - Hapco Farms, Inc.

HAPEX - Epoxy - Hastings Plastics Co.

HAPI - Frames—eyeglass - May Optical Co. Inc.

HAPLA - Splints - Smith & Nephew Inc. (Rehabilitation Div.)

HAPLAS - Moldings—plaster of paris - Hastings Plastics Co.

HAPOL - Resins—synthetic - Hastings Plastics Co.

HAPP - Apparel and accessories - Oxford Industries, Inc.

HAPPEE CARE - Combs - World Trend Inc.

HAPPEE TEETH - Toothbrushes - World Trend Inc.

HAPPENING - Recording label - Jazz Composer's Orchestra Association Inc.

HAPPENING HAIR - Dolls - Mattel, Inc.

HAPPENING HAIR COLLECTION - Toys - Mattel, Inc.

HAPPENING III - Wallpaper - Dunridge Industries Inc.

HAPPENING IV - Wallpaper - Dunridge Industries Inc.

HAPPENING IV - Wallpaper - K.M.L. Industries

HAPPENINGS - Dresses—women's ☆ - Huntington Industries Inc.

HAPPENINGS - Games - Meyers List Inc.

HAPPENSTANCE - Apparel—women's - Anne Klein & Co.

HAPPENSTANCE - Pigments ☆ - Pomegranate Publications

HAPPI RETURNS - Toys—stuffed - CBS Toys

HAPPIDAZE - Trees - Willet N. Wandell

HAPPIES - Diapers—disposable - Confab, Inc.

HAPPIJAC - Automotive parts and accessories - Recreation Systems Inc.

HAPPILY - Toys ☆ - Playskool, Inc.

HAPPILY EVER AFTER - Wallpaper - Andover Wallcovering

HAPPINESS - Air purification systems ☆ - Medo Industries, Inc.

HAPPINESS - Breads - Natural Ovens of Manitowoc Inc.

HAPPINESS - Frames—eyeglass - Hudson Optical Corp.

HAPPINESS - Games ☆ - Milton Bradley Co.

☆ = Now out of production

HAPPINESS - Greeting cards - Happiness Inc.
HAPPINESS - Hair coloring preparations - Clairol Inc.
HAPPINESS - Rings–jewelry - Artcarved Inc.
HAPPINESS BABY CLUB - Toys - Happiness Express Inc.
HAPPINESS BABY PEEKABOO - Dolls - Happiness Express Inc.
HAPPINESS BY DAY - Hosiery ☆ - Mayer/Berkshire Corp.
HAPPINESS BY NIGHT - Hosiery ☆ - Mayer/Berkshire Corp.
HAPPINESS CLOWN - Toys–stuffed ☆ - Dakin Inc.
HAPPINESS METER - Toys - Life Equations Inc.
HAPPINESS PEN-PAK - Stationery - Happiness Inc.
HAPPINESS PINK - Juices - Bully Hill Vineyards, Inc.
HAPPINESS RED - Processed foods - Tai Wing Hong Importer, Inc.
HAPPU - Cooking utensils–stoneware ☆ - Otagiri Mercantile Co. Inc.
HAPPY - Apparel and accessories - Eric John Boyd
HAPPY - Baby carriers, backpacks, etc. - International Design Manufacturing Inc.
HAPPY - Colognes - Brandy Harvest
HAPPY - Dog food - Products Carousel Inc.
HAPPY - Milk - Taylor All Star Dairy
HAPPY - Skin care products - Fashion Two Twenty Inc.
HAPPY & JOY - Giftware ☆ - Brushcreek Creative Co.
HAPPY ANNIVERSARY - Glassware–household - Rezler & Howell Co.
HAPPY APPLE - Toys - Fisher-Price, Inc.
HAPPY BABY - Dolls - Horsman
HAPPY BABY - Health care products - Omron Healthcare, Inc.
HAPPY BABY - Infant product ☆ - Gerry Baby Products Co.
HAPPY BABY - Recording label - Perleberg Publisher, Inc.
HAPPY BAKER - Food processors - Wapato Fruit Products Inc.
HAPPY BAKER - Jams and jellies ☆ - Happy Baker Products
HAPPY BAKERZ - Breads - Ahurmazda, Inc.
HAPPY BATH SALTS - Bath salts - Mark Juarez
HAPPY BIRTHDAY! - Chocolate bars - Celebration Chocolates, Inc.
HAPPY BIRTHDAY - Dolls - Mattel, Inc.
HAPPY BIRTHDAY BABY - Toys - Eugene Doll & Novelty Co. Inc.
HAPPY BODY LOTION - Lotions - Mark Juarez
HAPPY BREATH - Pet products - Lambert-Kay
HAPPY BUBBLE BATH - Skin care products - Mark Juarez
HAPPY BUG - Toys - Barval Toys Inc.
HAPPY CABANA - Playpens–wood - Lisco, Inc.
HAPPY CAMPER - Candy - Leaf, Inc.
HAPPY CAMPER - Playpens–metal - Evenflo Co.
HAPPY CAMPER - Popcorn - Tanton Enterprises
HAPPY CAMPER - Seasonings ☆ - El Paso Chili Co.
HAPPY CAMPER - Skin care products - West Coast Products, Inc.
HAPPY CAMPER - Vitamins and nutritional supplements - Natural Balance, Inc.
HAPPY CAMPER - Vitamins and nutritional supplements - Caroline Owens
HAPPY CAMPER BASSINET - Playpens–metal - Lisco, Inc.
HAPPY CAMPER DELUXE - Infant product - Lisco, Inc.
HAPPY CAMPERS - Candy - Blueberry Confections, Inc.
HAPPY CAPS - Plastics - Accento Plastic Manufacturing Inc.
HAPPY CAR - Toys ☆ - Combi International Corp.
HAPPY CAT - Cat food - Ralston Purina Co.
HAPPY CHAP - Eyeglasses - Art-Craft Optical Co.
HAPPY CLAM - Toys ☆ - Gerber Products Co.
HAPPY CLEAN - Cleaning preparations–household - Miavana Wholesale Co.
HAPPY CLOTHES - Apparel–children's - Happy Clothes
HAPPY CLOWN - Toys–stuffed ☆ - Gund, Inc.
HAPPY COLAS - Candy - Haribo of America Inc.
HAPPY COW - Fertilizers - Gardner Manufacturing Co.
HAPPY DAWN - Rope ☆ - Wellington Leisure Products, Inc.
HAPPY DAY - Frames–eyeglass - Pathway Optical Prods.
HAPPY DAY BOOKS - Publisher's imprints - Standard Publishing Co.
HAPPY DAY MUSIC CO. - Publisher's imprints - The Keene Music Group
HAPPY DAY POPS - Candy - Helms Candy Manufacturing Co. Inc.
HAPPY DAYS - Bedding–linen - Dan River Inc.
HAPPY DAYS - Cereal - Amway Corp.
HAPPY DAYS - Games ☆ - Parker Brothers
HAPPY DAYS - Pharmaceutical preparations - Only Natural, Inc.
HAPPY DAYS - Tobacco–chewing or smoking - United States Tobacco Co.
HAPPY DAZE - Floor coverings–carpet and rugs - Sheridan Carpet Mills
HAPPY DOG - Dog food - Ralston Purina Co.
HAPPY DOUGH 2 GO - Craft supplies - Absorene Manufacturing Co.
HAPPY DREAMS - Recording label - Mark E. Davis
HAPPY DRYS - Diapers–disposable - Weyerhaeuser Co.
HAPPY ELEPHANT - Toys ☆ - Gerber Products Co.

HAPPY EYE PILLOW - Pillows - Mark Juarez
HAPPY EYES - Frames–eyeglass - Pathway Optical Prods.
HAPPY FACE - Candy - Rosemary Candy Co.
HAPPY FACE - Frames–eyeglass ☆ - Universal/Univis Inc.
HAPPY FACE - Frames–picture - Russ Berrie and Co., Inc.
HAPPY FACE - Skin care products - Gillette Co.
HAPPY FACE - Toys–stuffed - Dan-Dee International Ltd.
HAPPY FAMILY - Breast pump - International Design Manufacturing Inc.
HAPPY FAMILY - Games ☆ - Milton Bradley Co.
HAPPY FEET - Dolls - Mattel, Inc.
HAPPY FEET - Foot baths - Salton/Maxim Housewares, Inc.
HAPPY FEET - Infant product ☆ - Ming Ta Supply
HAPPY FEET - Mats - Majestic Mat Co.
HAPPY FEET - Pet products - DD Pet Products Inc.
HAPPY FEET - Pharmaceutical preparations - Williams Laboratory
HAPPY FINGERS - Skin care products - Evans International Inc.
HAPPY FLOWER - Toys–stuffed ☆ - Gund, Inc.
HAPPY FRUIT - Gelatin - Mama Tish's Italian Specialties, Inc.
HAPPY-GO-LIGHTLY - Footwear–women's - P.W. Minor & Son Inc.
HAPPY GO LIGHTY - Greeting cards - Gibson Greetings, Inc.
HAPPY GO LUCKY - Greeting cards - Gibson Greetings, Inc.
HAPPY HAIR - Hair care products - Faberge Co.
HAPPY HAND - Desk sets - Richard Low
HAPPY HAND - Gloves - Midwest Glove Co.
HAPPY HANDS - Hobby kits ☆ - Accent Studios Inc.
HAPPY HANDS - Housewares - Oak Rubber Co.
HAPPY HANG-UPS - Garment hangers ☆ - Mactac Inc. (Packaging Closures Systems Div.)
HAPPY HANUKKAH! - Chocolate bars - Celebration Chocolates, Inc.
HAPPY HARRY'S - Pharmaceutical preparations - Happy Harry's, Inc.
HAPPY HAUNTERS - Toys - Russ Berrie and Co., Inc.
HAPPY HEART - Food products - TKI Foods, Inc.
HAPPY HEARTS - Chewing gum - Fleer Corp.
HAPPY HEARTS - Greeting cards - Current, Inc.
HAPPY HEARTS - Toys–stuffed - Fun World Inc.
HAPPY HEATHER - Dolls - Mattel, Inc.
HAPPY HELPER - Cooking equipment–household - Imperial Schrade Corp.
HAPPY HERBERT'S - Snack foods - Happy Herbert's Food Co., Inc.
HAPPY HERMIT BEACH CONDO - Pet products - The Crab Connection
HAPPY HERMIT BUNGALOW - Pet products - The Crab Connection
HAPPY HERMIT CLIMBING HOUSE - Pet products - The Crab Connection
HAPPY HERMIT HIDEAWAY - Pet products - The Crab Connection
HAPPY HERMIT HUT - Pet products - The Crab Connection
HAPPY HERMIT TRAVELING SHACK - Pet products - The Crab Connection
HAPPY HIDEAWAY - Dolls - Mattel, Inc.
HAPPY HIKERS - Shoes - Interco Inc.
HAPPY HIPPO TUB - Dolls - Goldberger Doll Manufacture Co.
HAPPY HOBO - Toys ☆ - Gerber Products Co.
HAPPY HOLIDAY - Christmas seals, favors, and decorations ☆ - Attleboro Printing & Embossing
HAPPY HOLIDAY - Christmas tree ornaments - Cracker Box Inc.
HAPPY HOLIDAYS - Cakes ☆ - Lifetime Hoan Corp.
HAPPY HOLIDAYS - Dinnerware–glass - Nikko Ceramics Inc.
HAPPY HOLIDAYS - Dolls - Mattel, Inc.
HAPPY HOME - Bedding–linen - Dan River Inc.
HAPPY HOME - Dresses–women's ☆ - Huntington Industries Inc.
HAPPY HOME - Frankfurters - Sanderson Farms Inc.
HAPPY HOME - Spices and extracts - Southern Flavoring Co.
HAPPY HOME HIDEOUT - Toys–stuffed - Lewis Galoob Toys, Inc.
HAPPY HOOPS - Toys - Fisher-Price, Inc.
HAPPY HOPPERS - Infant product ☆ - Welsh Co.
HAPPY HOPSTER - Toys–stuffed - Dan-Dee International Ltd.
HAPPY HORN - Toys - A.J. Renzi Plastic Corp.
HAPPY HOROSCOPES - Chewing gum - Philadelphia Chewing Gum Corp.
HAPPY HORSE - Fertilizers - Gardner Manufacturing Co.
HAPPY HORSES - Toys - Mattel, Inc.
HAPPY HOSE - Diagnostic apparatus - Instrumentation Northwest, Inc.
HAPPY HOUND - Pet products - Crown Products Co.
HAPPY HOUR - Bar fixtures–wood - Prorose Inc.
HAPPY HOUR - Floor coverings–carpet and rugs ☆ - Alexander Smith Carpets
HAPPY HOUR - Seafood products–fresh or frozen - Alaska Beachcomber Seafoods
HAPPY HOUR - Snack foods - Original Trenton Cracker Co.
HAPPY HOUR MUSIC - Recording label - Happy Hour Music
HAPPY HOURS - Boats - Glen-L Marine Designs

☆ = Now out of production

HAPPY HUES - Paints ☆ - Adelphi Coatings Co.
HAPPY HUGGIE BUNNY - Toys–stuffed - Spearhead Industries Inc.
HAPPY JACK - Syrup - Doxsee Food Corp.
HAPPY JACK - Veterinary pharmaceutical preparations ☆ - Happy Jack, Inc.
HAPPY JIM - Tobacco products - House of Windsor Inc.
HAPPY JOSE - Food products - Schwan's Sales Enterprises, Inc.
HAPPY KAPPY - Dolls - Patricia F. Kussin
HAPPY KAT - Eyeglasses - Goat Eyewear
HAPPY KAT - Pet products - K.C. Pharmacal Inc.
HAPPY KIDS - Apparel–children's - Happy Kids Ltd.
HAPPY KIDS - Pickles - W.B. Roddenbery Co., Inc.
HAPPY KITTEN - Cat food - Ralston Purina Co.
HAPPY LAND - Food products - Frank S. Oliver & Son
HAPPY LANDINGS - Frames–eyeglass - May Optical Co. Inc.
HAPPY LEGS - Apparel–women's - Happy Legs Inc.
HAPPY LITTLE ONE IN HER HIGH CHAIR - Dolls - Goldberger Doll Manufacture Co.
HAPPY LITTLE TRAIN - Games ☆ - Milton Bradley Co.
HAPPY LOTTO - Card/board game - SEC Co.
HAPPY MASSAGE OIL - Oils–essential - Mark Juarez
HAPPY MASSAGER - Medical apparatus - Tender Loving Things Inc.
HAPPY MEDIUM, THE - Paper products - Pratt Industries (USA), Inc.
HAPPY MEMORIES TODDLER COLLECTION - Dolls - Heritage Mint, Ltd.
HAPPY NAP - Fabrics - Guilford Mills, Inc.
HAPPY NEW YEAR - Dolls - Mattel, Inc.
HAPPY ONE - Underwear and nightwear - Holly Bra of California
HAPPY PAPER - Computer storage devices–optical - Tropus, Inc.
HAPPY PEOPLE - Underwear and nightwear - L.V. Myles
HAPPY POPS - Candy - D.E. Manufacturing Co.
HAPPY PUMPER - Toys ☆ - Little Tikes Co.
HAPPY PUPS WITH COZY PUPHOUSE - Toys–stuffed - Tonka Corp.
HAPPY QUADRUPEDS - Housewares ☆ - Doranne
HAPPY RABBIT - Infant product ☆ - Welsh Co.
HAPPY RATTLES - Infant product - Playskool Baby Inc.
HAPPY RETURN - Floor coverings–carpet and rugs ☆ - Gulistan Carpet Inc.
HAPPY SAM - Gloves - Midwest Glove Co.
HAPPY SCHNAPPS COMBO 100 PROOF - Apparel and accessories - Rich Krueger
HAPPY SHAPES - Cereal - Gilster-Mary Lee Corp.
HAPPY SHOWER CREAM - Skin care products - Mark Juarez
HAPPY SHOWER GEL - Skin care products - Mark Juarez
HAPPY SLEEPER - Mattresses - Happy Sleeper Mattress Factories Inc.
HAPPY SMILE KAMAKAZE - Beverages–alcohol - Kasser Laird Distilling Co.
HAPPY SOCKS - Hosiery - Adams-Millis Corp.
HAPPY STEPPERS - Shoes - Clinic Shoe Co.
HAPPY STICK-A-DOOS - Toys ☆ - Imperial Toy Corp.
HAPPY STONES - Pharmaceutical preparations - Williams Laboratory
HAPPY STRAP, THE - Apparel and accessories - Brazabra Corp.
HAPPY STRIPS - Bandages - Kendall Co.
HAPPY TACKS - Hardware ☆ - American Tack & Hardware Co., Inc.
HAPPY TAFFY - Candy ☆ - Classic Caramel Co.
HAPPY TAILS - Dog food - Whimsey Inc.
HAPPY TALES - Footwear ☆ - E.S. Originals, Inc.
HAPPY TALK - Ophthalmic goods - Embassy Creations Inc.
HAPPY TEA - Teas–herbal - Celestial Seasonings, Inc.
HAPPY TEDDY - Toys–stuffed ☆ - Gund, Inc.
HAPPY TEETHERS - Infant product - Playskool Baby Inc.
HAPPY THINGS - Patterns–clothing - Happy Things
HAPPY TIME - See JOGGLESIME
HAPPY TIME - Floor coverings–carpet and rugs ☆ - Regal Rugs Inc.
HAPPY TIME - Fruit and vegetable markets - Frigid Food Products Inc.
HAPPY TIME - Greeting cards - Happiness Inc.
HAPPY TIME - Ice cream - Certified Grocers of California, Ltd.
HAPPY TIME - Infant product - Marlin Toy Products Inc.
HAPPY TIME - Plastics - F.S. Sales & Manufacturing Inc.
HAPPY-TIME - Vitamins and nutritional supplements - Frances Denney
HAPPY TO BE ME - Dolls - High Self Esteem Toy Corp.
HAPPY TOES - Shoes - Conaway-Winter Inc.
HAPPY TOES - Skin care products - Mark Juarez
HAPPY TOM - Spices and extracts ☆ - Jodie's Kitchen Inc.
HAPPY TRAILS - Apparel and accessories - Fred C. Gilbert
HAPPY TRAILS - Infant product ☆ - Ming Ta Supply
HAPPY TRAILS - Meat products - Huisken Meat Center, Inc.
HAPPY TRAILS CLUB - Toys - Sky Kids Inc.
HAPPY TRAVELER - Skin care products - Celeste Co. Inc.
HAPPY TURTLES - Toys - Gerber Products Co.

HAPPY TYME - Apparel - Beverly D. Wilson
HAPPY TYME - Toys–stuffed ☆ - Gund, Inc.
HAPPY VALE - Bakery products ☆ - Martha White Foods Inc.
HAPPY VALLEY - Frames–eyeglass - Zylo Ware Corp.
HAPPY VALLEY - Wines ☆ - Kolln Vineyards (O)
HAPPY WADDLER - Toys–stuffed - Fun World Inc.
HAPPY WALKER - Pet products - Amtek Pet Behavior Products
HAPPY WALKER - Pet products - R.C. Steele Co.
HAPPYFEET - Paper–toweling - Cross Country Paper Products, Inc.
HAPPYMATH - Educational materials - Gail R. Bernard
HAPPYSACKS - Novelty items–paper - Oriental Trading Co., Inc.
HAPPYTIZERS - Frozen foods - Dewey's Foods Inc.
HAPUNA - Golfing equipment - South Kohala Resort Corp.
HAPUNA BEACH PRINCE HOTEL MAUNA KEA RESORT - Hats - South Kohala Resort Corp.
HAPUNA GOLF COURSE - Apparel and accessories - South Kohala Resort Corp.
HAQUA - Water–bottled or canned - Custom Water Systems, Inc.
HAR-SEAL - Windows–storm ☆ - Harbor Sales Co.
HAR-SIGNS - Signs - Har-Signs
HAR-VEY - Hardware ☆ - Nichols-Homeshield Inc.
HARADA - Antennas - Harada Industry of America Inc.
HARAM-CHRISTENSEN - Cooking utensils–aluminum ☆ - Haram-Christensen Corp.
HARAPLATE - Dishes–china ☆ - Baum Bros. Imports Inc.
HARASSER FLASHER - Pins–jewelry - Snow's at Birmingham
HARBAL NAIL SOAK - Cosmetics - Nu Skin International, Inc.
HARBINGER - Books–comic - Voyager Communications Inc.
HARBINGER - Exercise equipment - Harbinger
HARBINGER HOUSE - Publisher's imprints - Harbinger House Inc.
HARBISONS - Food products - Southland Corp.
HARBOR - Apparel and accessories - Roxanne Swim Suits Co. Inc.
HARBOR - Brooms - Harbor Manufacturing
HARBOR - Footwear–men's ☆ - Harbor Footwear Group Ltd.
HARBOR - Luggage - Samsonite Corp.
HARBOR - Occasional tables ☆ - JDI Group, Inc.
HARBOR - Paper–toweling - Von Drehle Corp.
HARBOR - Thread - New Bedford Thread Co.
HARBOR - Wood products - Harbor Sales Co.
HARBOR 1 - Apparel and accessories - Williamson-Dickie Manufacturing Co.
HARBOR BANKS - Seafood products–fresh or frozen - JP Foodservice, Inc.
HARBOR BAR - Ice cream - Harbor Foods
HARBOR BAY - Floor coverings–carpet and rugs ☆ - Masland Corp.
HARBOR BAY - Furniture ☆ - Bassett Furniture Industries, Inc.
HARBOR BAY CASUALS - Apparel and accessories - JBI, Inc.
HARBOR BAY CLOTHING COMPANY - Apparel and accessories - JBI, Inc.
HARBOR BELL - Seafood products–fresh or frozen - Harbor Bell Inc.
HARBOR BRAVEL - Seafood products–canned or cured - Tampa Maid Seafoods, Inc.
HARBOR CLUB COLLECTION - Handbags - Sabina Handbag Inc.
HARBOR COVE - Floor coverings–carpet and rugs - Tuftex Carpet Mills, Inc.
HARBOR FANFARE, INC. - Frozen foods - Harbor Fanfare, Inc.
HARBOR HILL - Floor coverings - Congoleum Corp.
HARBOR HOUSE - Apparel and accessories - American Classics Sportswear, Inc.
HARBOR HOUSE SEAFOOD - Seafood products–fresh or frozen - Harbor House Seafood, Inc.
HARBOR LANDING - Footwear–athletic - Wal-Mart Stores Inc.
HARBOR LIGHT - Watches - QVC, Inc.
HARBOR LIGHTS - Candy - Harbor Sweets Inc.
HARBOR LIGHTS - Cosmetics ☆ - Redken Laboratories, Inc.
HARBOR LIGHTS - Floor coverings–carpet and rugs - Coronet Carpets Inc.
HARBOR LIGHTS - Floor coverings–carpet and rugs - J and J Industries Inc.
HARBOR LIGHTS - Wines - Bully Hill Vineyards, Inc.
HARBOR MASTER - Apparel and accessories - Misty Harbor Properties
HARBOR MASTER - Apparel–men's - United Merchants and Manufacturers Inc.
HARBOR MASTER - Boats - Boating Corp. of America
HARBOR MASTER - Brushes–paint - Cotter & Co.
HARBOR MASTER - Furniture - Lane Upholstery (Venture Furniture Div.)
HARBOR MIST - Floor coverings - Congoleum Corp.
HARBOR OAK - Furniture ☆ - U.S. Furniture Industries Inc.
HARBOR PINE - Furniture ☆ - Kincaid Furniture Co. Inc.
HARBOR POINT - Furniture ☆ - Bassett Furniture Industries, Inc.
HARBOR POINTE - Floor coverings–carpet and rugs - Alexander Smith Carpets

☆ = Now out of production

HARBOR POINTE - Hardware ☆ - Alside Div.

HARBOR RIDGE - Floor coverings–carpet and rugs ☆ - Customweave Carpets Inc.

HARBOR ROAD - Apparel and accessories ☆ - Warnaco Inc.

HARBOR SIDE - Apparel–children's - Marshall Field's

HARBOR SIDE - Floor coverings - Mannington Resilient Floors

HARBOR SPRINGS - Trailers–travel - Fleetwood Enterprises, Inc.

HARBOR SPRINGS - Wainscotting - Georgia-Pacific Corp.

HARBOR SPRINGS - Water–bottled or canned - Harbor Springs Water Co.

HARBOR SUPER MARINE - Wood products - Harbor Sales Co.

HARBOR TOWN - Indoor-outdoor carpet - Instant Turf Industries Inc.

HARBOR TOWN BY HUSH PUPPIES - Footwear - Hush Puppies Co.

HARBOR VIEW SNACKS - Snack foods - Star Snacks Co. Inc.

HARBOR WINERY - Wines - Harbor Winery

HARBORLIGHT - Computer software - Harbor Software, Inc.

HARBORMASTER - Boats - Glen-L Marine Designs

HARBORMASTER - Clocks - Maximum Inc.

HARBORSIDE - Floor coverings–carpet and rugs - Karastan-Bigelow Inc.

HARBORSIDE - Scarves, neckwear - Wilmarth Co. Inc.

HARBORSIDE GRAPHICS - Apparel and accessories - Harborside Enterprises Ltd.

HARBORWEAVE - Wallpaper - Koroseal Wallcoverings

HARBOUR - Bedding–linen - Dan River Inc.

HARBOUR - Floor coverings–carpet and rugs ☆ - Mannington Carpets, Inc.

HARBOUR CASUALS - Apparel and accessories - Harbour Casuals

HARBOUR CREATIONS - Furniture - United Stationers Inc.

HARBOUR DESIGNS - Wallpaper - J.M. Lynne Co. Inc.

HARBOUR LEAGUE - Giftware - Albert E. Price, Inc.

HARBOUR LIGHTS - Figurines - Harbour Lights

HARBOUR LIGHTS - Floor coverings–carpet and rugs ☆ - Catalina Carpet Mills Inc.

HARBOUR LIGHTS - Floor coverings–carpet and rugs ☆ - Galaxy Carpet Mills Inc.

HARBOUR POINTE - Furniture - Lyon-Shaw Inc.

HARBOUR SHELL - Flatware ☆ - Kirk Stieff Co.

HARBOUR STAR - Seafood products–fresh or frozen - Impex Shrimp & Fish Co.

HARBOUR TOWNE - Furniture ☆ - Hammary Furniture Co. Inc.

HARBOURITE - Stucco - Synthetic Industries, Inc.

HARC - Hearing aids - Harc Mercantile Ltd.

HARC - Remote control devices - Super Star Technology, Inc.

HARCO - Adhesives and sealants - Harco Chemical Coatings Inc.

HARCO - Cleaning equipment ☆ - Harley Chemicals

HARCO - Deodorants–personal - Harvey Co. Inc.

HARCO - Valves - Harco Manufacturing, Inc.

HARCOURT - Floor coverings–carpet and rugs ☆ - Kelly Group Inc.

HARCOURT BRACE - Games - Harcourt Brace & Co.

HARCOURT BRACE - Publisher's imprints - Harcourt Brace Jovanovich, Inc.

HARCOURT PRESS, THE - Educational materials - Harcourt Brace & Co.

HARCOURT STITCH - Frames–picture - Terragrafics Inc.

HARD - Beds–metal - HARD Manufacturing Co. Inc.

HARD & FAST - Nail care products ☆ - Roberts Research Laboratories, Inc.

HARD ARKANSAS - Tools - Norton Co.

HARD AS NAILS - Cosmetics - Sally Hansen

HARD AS NAILS W/NYLON - Cosmetics - Sally Hansen

HARD ATTACK - Drums–musical instruments - Tucson Wholesale Music

HARD-BAK - Siding–insulating - Edco Products Inc.

HARD BODIES - Ice chests–plastic - Igloo Products Corp.

HARD BODY - Railroad transportation–passenger - MLO Products, Inc.

HARD BODY - Toys - Tootsietoy

HARD BODY AMERICA WEST - Toys - Tootsietoy

HARD BODY COLLECTABLES - Toys - Strombecker Corp.

HARD BODY CONSTRUCTION COMPANY - Toys - Tootsietoy

HARD BODY COOL CRUISERS - Toys - Tootsietoy

HARD BODY FAST PAC - Toys - Tootsietoy

HARD BODY GAINER 3600 - Railroad transportation–passenger - MLO Products, Inc.

HARD BODY HITZHUPS - Toys - Tootsietoy

HARD BODY MOMMY DOLL - Dolls - Tootsietoy

HARD BODY SPEEDSTERS - Toys - Tootsietoy

HARD BOILED - Books–comic - Frank Miller, Inc.

HARD BUCK RODEO CO. - Apparel and accessories - Wyoming West Designs

HARD CARDS - Games - Hard Cards

HARD COPY - Markers–felt-tip - Liqui-Mark

HARD COPY PLUS - Markers - Liqui-Mark

HARD CORE - Archery equipment - Pro Line Co.

HARD CORE - Balls - Brine Inc.

HARD CORE - Balls - Sports Licensing, Inc.

HARD CORE - Dental composite material - Pulpdent Corp.

HARD-CORE - Hunting equipment - Wildlife Research Center, Inc.

HARD CORE - Nail hardener - Cosmetic Arts Inc.

HARD COURT - Balls - Franklin Sports, Inc.

HARD COURT - Balls - Mikasa Sports

HARD COURT - Footwear–athletic - Puma Inc.

HARD DRIVE - Shoes–athletic - Wilson Sporting Goods Co.

HARD DRIVER OIL FILTERS - Filters–oil - Old World Industries, Inc.

HARD DRIVES INTERNATIONAL - Computer peripheral equipment - Insight Direct, Inc.

HARD DRIVIN' - Computer software - Atari Games Corp.

HARD FAST - Vitamins and nutritional supplements - Universal Nutritional Systems

HARD HAT - Antennas - Alliance Telecommunications Corp.

HARD HAT - Apparel–men's - Jonbil Inc.

HARD HAT - Finishing agents - Rust-Oleum Corp.

HARD HAT - Health care products - Handicapped Driving Systems Inc.

HARD HAT - Knives–pocket - Hard Hat Inc.

HARD HAT - Leather - Prime Tanning Co., Inc.

HARD HAT - Recording label - Hard Hat Records

HARD HAT - Trailers - TCF Manufacturing, Inc.

HARD HAT CONTRACTORS - Toys - Nylint Toy Corp.

HARD HAT LEATHER WORKS - Belts–apparel - Hard Hat Inc.

HARD-HEAD - Drill bits - Relton Corp.

HARD HORIZONS - Adhesives and sealants ☆ - Pettit Paint Co. Inc.

HARD HULL - Boats–kayaks - Rotocast Plastic Products

HARD KNOCKIN ROCKIN RING - Toys - Mattel, Inc.

HARD KNOX MAIL BOX - Mail boxes - Charles R. McMillion

HARD LINER - Automotive parts and accessories - Vehicle Protection, Inc.

HARD-MASTER - Gloves–work - Magid Manufacturing Co. Inc.

HARD NOSE - Pens - Gillette Co.

HARD NOSE - Shoes - J.C. Penney Co., Inc.

HARD-NOX - Lighting fixtures - Progress Lighting Inc.

HARD RIDER - Watches - Ankuo International, Corp.

HARD ROCK - Chemical preparations - Slipsafe International, Inc.

HARD ROCK - Floor coverings–carpet and rugs - Quaker Inc.

HARD ROCK CAFE - Apparel and accessories - Hard Rock Cafe Licensing Corp.

HARD ROCK HOLD - Hair care products - Gold Medal Hair Products Inc.

HARD ROCK HOTEL - Apparel and accessories - Hard Rock Cafe Licensing Corp.

HARD ROCK HOTEL - Jackets - Hard Rock Cafe Licensing Corp.

HARD ROCKIN' STEEL - Musical instrument accessories - E. & O. Mari Inc.

HARD ROCKS - Musical instrument accessories ☆ - Music Accessories Manufacturing Co. Inc.

HARD STEP - Lighting fixtures ☆ - Hubbell Lighting, Inc. (Lighting Div.)

HARD TAIL - Apparel - Hard Trail

HARD TAIL - Bicycles - Western Auto Supply Co.

HARD TIP - Saw blades ☆ - Heinemann Saw Corp.

HARD TO FIND SPECIALTY PRODUCTS - Machine parts - VSI Fasteners, Inc.

HARD-TO-HANG 3500 - Adhesives and sealants - Brod-Dugan Co./Sherwin Williams Co.

HARD TO RESIST - Hair care products - Redken Laboratories, Inc.

HARD TO RESIST - Varnishes - Parks Corp.

HARD-TUFF 56 - Electrodes - Alloy Rods Global, Inc.

HARD-WALL SYSTEM, THE - Insulating materials ☆ - Premix-Marbletite Manufacturing Co.

HARD WAY, THE - T-shirts–men's - Soccer Post International Franchise Corp.

HARD WEAR - Jewelry - Marc F. Wiegand

HARD WIRE - Cables–steel - Kryptonite Corp.

HARDANGER - Giftware ☆ - Henriksen Imports Inc.

HARDASNAILS - Paints ☆ - D.I.Y. Products

HARDBAG - Cases–musical instrument - Hardbag Musical Instrument Cases

HARDBALL - Apparel - Hardball Apparel, Inc.

HARDBALL - Games - Accolade Inc.

HARDBALL RECORDS - Records, cassette tapes, and compact discs - Line Drive Productions, Inc.

HARDBODY - Hair care products - Image Laboratories, Inc.

HARDBODY BY MID-USA - Motorcycles - Mid-USA Cycle Parts, Inc.

HARDBODY FITNESS BAR - Exercising equipment - Hardbody Fitness Systems

HARDCARD II XL 50 - Computer storage devices - Plus Development Corp.

HARDCARD II XL 105 - Computer peripheral equipment - Plus Development Corp.

HARDCASTLE & MC CORMICK - Toys–automobiles ☆ - ERTL Co., Inc.

HARDCORE - Wines - Boston Beer Co. LP

HARDCORE PURE AMERICAN MUSCLE - Apparel and accessories - Palco, Inc.

HARDCORE SOCCER - Apparel and accessories - Borneo Group, Inc.

HARDCORE SURF - Apparel and accessories - Hardcore Surf Designs

HARDCORE UNDERGROUND - Apparel - Chris Carmichael

HARDCORE USA - Apparel–athletic - B.T. Industries, Inc.

HARDEE - Sporting goods - Weber Industries Inc.

HARDEE'S - Restaurants–fast food - Hardee's Food Systems, Inc.

HARDEE'S LI'L CHEF - Sandwiches–prepackaged - Hardee's Food Systems, Inc.

HARDELOT - Furniture - Pilliod Co.

HARDEN - Computer software - Harden Industries Inc.

HARDEN GALLERIES - Furniture–upholstered ☆ - Harden Furniture Co. Inc.

HARDEN HOUSE - Furniture–upholstered ☆ - Harden Furniture Co. Inc.

HARDEN TRADITIONS - Furniture–upholstered ☆ - Harden Furniture Co. Inc.

HARDENED THROUGHOUT - Moldings and trim - PCS Co.

HARDGEAR - Sporting goods - Kellwood Co.

HARDGLASS - Tape–adhesive - C.H.B. Industries Inc.

HARDGRIP - Floor coverings ☆ - Champion International Corp.

HARDHAT BRIGADE - Hats - Vincent J. Nolan

HARDHEAD FLAIR - Pens - Paper Mate Co.

HARDI-TAINER - Containers–plastic ☆ - Hardigg Industries, Inc.

HARDIACKER - Tiles–ceramic - James Hardie Building Products Inc.

HARDIES - Chewing gum - Finnfoods Div.

HARDIGG CASES - Containers–shipping - Hardigg Industries, Inc.

HARDIN MARINE - Engines–marine - Hardin Marine Inc.

HARDING'S - Corned beef - John P. Harding Market Co.

HARDINS GOLD LABEL - Breads - Campbell Taggart Inc.

HARDIWEAVE - Apparel–men's ☆ - Michaels/Stern & Co. Inc.

HARDKORE - Exercising equipment - Douglas E. Brendle

HARDKORE - Sunglasses - Hardkore, Inc.

HARDKORE EQUIPMENT - Apparel and accessories - Douglas E. Brendle

HARDLESS SOFTWARE - Computer software ☆ - John L. Stewart

HARDLINE - Computer software - Virgin Interactive Entertainment, Inc.

HARDLY - Recording label - Third Story Recording Inc.

HARDMAN - Pianos - Aeolian Pianos Inc.

HARDROLLS - Metals - Shenango Furnace Co.

HARDTAIL - Bicycles - Security Bicycle Accessories, Inc.

HARDTICKET ENTERTAINMENT - Recording label - Musicmasters

HARDTREDS - Wallpaper ☆ - Blumenthal

HARDWALL - Modular building system - Downing Displays Inc.

HARDWARE - Books–comic - DC Comics

HARDWARE - Tools - Chickasaw Handle Co. Inc.

HARDWARE HANDBOOK - Games ☆ - Mayfair Games, Inc.

HARDWARE HOUSE - Housewares - Moore-Handley Inc.

HARDWARE JUNCTION - Hardware - Hardware Junction, Inc.

HARDWARE/SOFTWARE INFORMATION GUIDE - Publisher's imprints - Parsons Technology, Inc.

HARDWATER FAUCETS - Faucets - Gerber Plumbing Fixtures Corp.

HARDWEAR - Fabrics - Designtex Fabrics, Inc.

HARDWEAR - Floor coverings–carpet and rugs - Masland Carpets, Inc.

HARDWEAR - Jeans - Levi Strauss & Co.

HARDWEAR - Tools - Swan Handle Corp.

HARDWEAR - Watches ☆ - Swatch Watch USA

HARDWEIGHER - Scales - Pennsylvania Scale Co.

HARDWICK - Apparel and accessories - Hardwick Clothes Inc.

HARDWICK - Furniture ☆ - Athens Furniture Industries Inc.

HARDWICK - Stoves - Hardwick Stove Co.

HARDWICK HALL - Furniture - Hooker Furniture Corp.

HARDWICKE - Dinnerware–glass - Franciscan by Johnson Brothers, USA, Inc.

HARDWOOD - Racks - J.K. Adams Co. Inc.

HARDWOOD HEAT - Wood products ☆ - Hamer Pellet Fuel Co.

HARDWORLD - Leather goods - Karelitz International, Inc.

HARDY - Dolls - Goldberger Doll Manufacture Co.

HARDY - Shoes - Genesco Inc.

HARDY AMIES - Apparel and accessories - Neema Clothing, Ltd.

HARDY AMIES - Apparel–men's - Berkley Shirt Co. Inc.

HARDY BOYS - Publisher's imprints - Grosset & Dunlap Inc.

HARE BALLS - Dolls - Susan Sona

HARE BIZ - Apparel and accessories - Denise Curatolo

HARE BRAINED HOBBIES - Hobby kits - Rabbit Ears Productions, Inc.

HARE RAZOR - Razors - C.A. Daniels & Co.

HARE, THE - Apparel–children's - Montgomery Ward & Co. Inc.

HAREABOU - Toys–stuffed - Corrington's Alaskan Ivory, Ltd.

HAREDINI - Toys–stuffed ☆ - Fun World Inc.

HARELINE - Greeting cards - Susan Zimmerman

HAREM - Underwear and nightwear - Bestform Foundations, Inc.

HAREM PLUSH - Floor coverings - Glenoit Mills Inc.

HARESPRAY - Dolls - Susan Sona

HARFLEUR - Rings–jewelry - Artcarved Inc.

HARGATE - Insecticides - Mylen Co.

HARGRAVE - Chisels - Warren Tool Group

HARGROVE - Food products - Brechet and Richter Co.

HARI CHESTS - Wigs - Chicago Hair Good Inc.

HARI-E - Appliques ☆ - Activa Products Inc.

HARI KARI - Insecticides - Lynwood Laboratories, Inc.

HARIAN CREATIVE AWARDS - Publisher's imprints - Harian Creative Press-Books

HARIAN CREATIVE BOOKS - Publisher's imprints - Harian Creative Press-Books

HARIAN CREATIVE PRESS - Publisher's imprints - Harian Creative Press-Books

HARIBO - Candy - Acme Food Specialties Inc.

HARIBO - Chocolate candy - Naron Candy Co. Inc.

HARIBO DINOSOURS - Candy ☆ - Haribo of America Inc.

HARIBO GOLD-BEARS - Candy - Haribo of America Inc.

HARILELA'S - Apparel and accessories - Harilela (America) Inc.

HARISSA - Spices and extracts - Europa Foods Ltd.

HARKEN - Boating equipment and accessories - Harken, Inc.

HARKEN - Ships - Harken Yacht Fittings

HARKEN DRIVE - Engines–marine - Harken Yacht Fittings

HARKEN HAND HOLD - Ships–sailing vessels - Harken Yacht Fittings

HARKER'S COMPLETES YOUR MENU - Food products - Harker's Distribution Inc.

HARKER'S HOMESTYLE - Dinners–frozen ☆ - Harker's Distribution Inc.

HARLAN - Wines - Harlan Winery

HARLEM TEXTILE WORKS - Tablecloths - Harlem Textile Works

HARLEM YOUTH NEWSPAPER - Paper–newsprint - Black Media Foundation, Inc.

HARLEQUIN - Dinnerware - Denby USA Limited

HARLEQUIN - Floor coverings–carpet and rugs - Daltonian Carpet & Cushion Inc.

HARLEQUIN - Floor coverings–carpet and rugs - Foreign Accents

HARLEQUIN - Frames–eyeglass - Zylo Ware Corp.

HARLEQUIN - Glassware–household ☆ - Kraftware Corp. (Morgan Div.)

HARLEQUIN - Jewelry ☆ - K & M Associates

HARLEQUINS - Sofabeds - Flexsteel Industries Inc.

HARLEQUINS - Tiles–ceramic - Latco Products

HARLES JOURDAN - Footwear–women's ☆ - Charles Jourdan

HARLEY - Apparel and accessories - Harley-Davidson, Inc.

HARLEY - Flatware - Wallace International Silversmiths, Inc.

HARLEY - Inks - E.L. Harley Inc.

HARLEY - Sandwiches–prepackaged - H-D Michigan, Inc.

HARLEY - Wallpaper ☆ - Wolf-Gordon Inc.

HARLEY BEACH CLEANER - Machine parts - Glenmac Inc.

HARLEY DAVIDSON - Apparel and accessories - Jay Garment Co.

HARLEY-DAVIDSON - Cigarettes - Lorillard Tobacco Co.

HARLEY DAVIDSON - Dolls ☆ - Applause, Inc.

HARLEY DAVIDSON - Footwear–athletic ☆ - E.S. Originals, Inc.

HARLEY DAVIDSON - Kites - Hi-Flier Manufacturing Co.

HARLEY-DAVIDSON - Knives–pocket - United Cutlery Corp.

HARLEY-DAVIDSON - Motorcycles - Harley-Davidson, Inc.

HARLEY-DAVIDSON - Watches - Bulova Corp.

HARLEY DAVIDSON CAFE - Apparel and accessories - H-D Michigan, Inc.

HARLEY-DAVIDSON SKY-FLIER - Kites - Hi-Flier Manufacturing Co.

HARLEY-DAVIDSON USA - Apparel and accessories - Harley-Davidson, Inc.

HARLEY HOG - Sandwiches–prepackaged - H-D Michigan, Inc.

HARLEY HOTELS - Hotels and motels - Harley Hotels Inc.

HARLEY RAKE - Machine parts - Glenmac Inc.

HARLEY STREET - Floor coverings–carpet and rugs - Patcraft Mills Inc.

HARLEY'S OIL SOAP - Cleaning preparations - Harley Chemicals

HARLINGER DUTCH - Tiles–ceramic - Amsterdam Corp.

HARLO - Watches - Centric Corp.

HARLOC - Doors - Harloc, Inc.

HARLOW - Apparel–women's - Jezebel-Renee of Hollywood

HARLOW - Floor coverings–carpet and rugs ☆ - Masland Corp.

HARLOW GOLD ACCENT - Flatware - Yamazaki Tableware Inc.

☆ = Now out of production

H.A.R.M. - Trading cards and stamps - Aegis Entertainment, Inc.
HARMALINE - Pharmaceutical preparations ☆ - City Chemical Corp.
HARMAN-KARDON - Audio equipment - Harman Consumer Group
HARMEN - Tools—woodworking - Harmen Co. Inc.
HARMER'S CHARACTER JUGS - Containers - Andrew D. Darvas Inc.
HARMINE - Pharmaceutical preparations ☆ - City Chemical Corp.
HARMLESS - Paper clips - Noesting Inc.
HARMON - Musical instrument accessories - Carpenter Co.
HARMON AUTOGLASS - Glass products - Apogee Enterprises, Inc.
HARMONA - Accordions - Castiglione Accordion
HARMONETTA - Harmonicas - Hohner Inc.
HARMONIA - Faucets - Kallista Inc.
HARMONIA - Glassware—household ☆ - St. Gobain International Glassware
HARMONIA - Recording label - Apon Record Co., Inc.
HARMONIA MUNDI - Recording label ☆ - Apon Record Co., Inc.
HARMONIA MUNDI ACOUSTICA - Audio equipment - G Prime Limited
HARMONIC - Water—bottled or canned - Harmonics International, LLC
HARMONIC GUARD - Computer peripheral equipment - Trans-Coil Inc.
HARMONIC LYRE, THE - Chimes - Now & Zen, Inc.
HARMONIC-O - Saw blades - Clemson Brothers Inc.
HARMONIC PERCOLATOR - Music-effect devices - InterFax Inc.
HARMONIC PROGRESSIONS - Computer software - Electronic Courseware Systems Inc.
HARMONIC SPECTRUM CONTROL - Hearing aids - Qualitone
HARMONIC SYSTEMS INCORPORATED - Communications equipment - PNC Associates, Inc.
HARMONIC SYSTEMS, INC. - Communications equipment - PNC Associates, Inc.
HARMONICA-STYLE - Harmonicas - William Kratt Co.
HARMONIE - Vases - Durand International
HARMONIES - Wallpaper ☆ - Capital Carousel Inc.
HARMONIES IN COLOR - Wallpaper ☆ - Pickhardt & Siebert USA Inc.
HARMONIES IN COLOR - Wallpaper ☆ - Southport
HARMONIEUSE - Yarn ☆ - Joseph Galler Inc.
HARMONIKIDS - Harmonicas - Hohner Inc.
HARMONIQUE - Vitamins and nutritional supplements - Earthrise Trading Co.
HARMONIZE - Floor coverings—carpet and rugs - J and J Industries Inc.
HARMONIZE II - Floor coverings—carpet and rugs - J and J Industries Inc.
HARMONIZER - Coatings - Sherwin-Williams Automotive Finishes Corp.
HARMONIZER - Electronic equipment - Eventide Inc.
HARMONIZER - Exercising equipment - L.C. Harmonizer
HARMONIZER - Vitamins and nutritional supplements - Irvin H. Miller
HARMONIZERS - Tiles—ceramic - Monarch Tile Inc.
HARMONY - See **FLOTATION FAMILY**
HARMONY - Animal feeds - Harmony Products, Inc.
HARMONY - Bathtubs—enameled - Arjo-Century Inc.
HARMONY - Bathtubs—enameled - Kohler Co.
HARMONY - Boats - Clark Craft Boat Co.
HARMONY - Cabinets - Schrock
HARMONY - Cabinets—wood - Decora
HARMONY - Chimes - Nutone Inc.
HARMONY - Clocks - General Time Corp. (Westclox/Seth Thomas Div.)
HARMONY - Computer software - Radisson Hotels International Inc.
HARMONY - Copper compounds ☆ - Regal Ware, Inc.
HARMONY - Cribs—wood ☆ - Cosco, Inc.
HARMONY - Dinnerware—glass ☆ - WMF/USA
HARMONY - Doors—storm - Canyon Creek Cabinet Co.
HARMONY - Floor coverings - Mannington Resilient Floors
HARMONY - Floor coverings—carpet and rugs - Colonial Mills Inc.
HARMONY - Floor coverings—carpet and rugs - Mohawk Carpet Corp.
HARMONY - Floor coverings—carpet and rugs ☆ - Blue Ridge Carpet Mills
HARMONY - Floor coverings—carpet and rugs ☆ - Orian Rugs Inc.
HARMONY - Floor coverings—carpet and rugs ☆ - Royalweve Carpet Mills
HARMONY - Food products - Dairy Fresh Products Co.
HARMONY - Fruits—dried - Glico Harmony Foods Corp.
HARMONY - Furniture ☆ - Bassett Furniture Industries, Inc.
HARMONY - Furniture—metal - Samsonite Furniture Co. (Consumer Products Div.)
HARMONY - Giftware - Block China Co.
HARMONY - Glassware—household - Owens-Illinois Inc. (Libbey Div.)
HARMONY - Glassware—household ☆ - Lotus Glass Co.
HARMONY - Glassware—household ☆ - Oneida Ltd.
HARMONY - Guitars ☆ - Heritage Industries
HARMONY - Hardware - Alumax Aluminum Corp.
HARMONY - Hardware ☆ - Amerock Corp.
HARMONY - Heat pumps - Lennox Industries Inc.

HARMONY - Herbicides - E.I. Dupont de Nemours and Co.
HARMONY - Incense - Lotus Brands Inc.
HARMONY - Invitations - Classic Thermographers Ltd.
HARMONY - Jewelry - Meyer Jewelry Co.
HARMONY - Occasional tables ☆ - JDI Group, Inc.
HARMONY - Paper - M. Grumbacher Inc.
HARMONY - Paper—bond - Mead Corp.
HARMONY - Pet products - Golden Pond Inc.
HARMONY - Pet products - Harmony Fastening Systems Inc.
HARMONY - Recorded music - Sony Music Entertainment Inc.
HARMONY - Recording label - Sound Image Entertainment Inc.
HARMONY - Ribbons - Vaban Ribbons International
HARMONY - Rings—jewelry - Artcarved Inc.
HARMONY - Scissors—hand-operated - F.W. Engels Inc.
HARMONY - Starch—laundry - Ingersoll & Associates
HARMONY - Telescopes - Northern Telecom, Inc.
HARMONY - Tiles—ceramic - H & R Johnson Inc.
HARMONY - Vacuum cleaners and accessories - Amway Corp.
HARMONY - Wallpaper - Singer Wallcoverings, Inc.
HARMONY - Wood products - Scott Paper Co.
HARMONY BAY - Coffee - Comfort Foods, Inc.
HARMONY BEAR - Toys—stuffed - Fun World Inc.
HARMONY BOOKS - Publisher's imprints - Crown Publishers Inc.
HARMONY BY JACK PRINCE - Dinnerware—glass - Block China Co.
HARMONY CAVE - Floor coverings—carpet and rugs - Capel, Inc.
HARMONY COURT - Floor coverings ☆ - Congoleum Corp.
HARMONY FARMS - Food products ☆ - Agway Country Foods Inc.
HARMONY GROVE - Figurines - Peebles Inc.
HARMONY HARP SEAL - Toys—stuffed - Dakin Inc.
HARMONY HOUSE - Floor coverings—carpet and rugs - Evans-Black Carpet Mills
HARMONY HOUSE - Processed foods - Volume Sales Producers, Inc.
HARMONY KINGDOM - Figurines - Hereafter, Inc.
HARMONY OF BRAZIL - Cosmetics - Guerlain Inc.
HARMONY OF FLORIDA - Cosmetics - Guerlain Inc.
HARMONY PLUS - Musical instrument accessories - Lowrey Organ Co.
HARMONY QUEEN - Harmonicas - Hohner Inc.
HARMONY SNACKS - Nuts—salted, roasted, cooked, or canned - Glico Harmony Foods Corp.
HARMONY SYSTEM, THE - Containers—glass - Comar, Inc.
HARMONY TOY - Games - Harmony Toy Ltd.
HARMONYL - Pharmaceutical preparations - Abbott Laboratories
HARMOPHONE - Organs—musical instrument ☆ - St. Louis Music Supply Co.
HARNELL - Sporting goods ☆ - Gladding Braided Products Inc.
HARNESS - Harnesses - Michael Bianco Inc.
HARNESS - Herbicides - Monsanto Co.
HARNESS HEROES - Trading cards and stamps - Harness Horse Youth Foundation Inc.
HARNESS HOUSE - Leather goods ☆ - Salant/Manhattan Industries
HARNESS KINGS - Fishing tackle - Paul Warner Industries
HARNIK - Signs - Har-Signs
HARNISCH - Nautical instruments ☆ - Watrous & Co. Inc.
HARO - Bicycles - Haro Marketing Corp.
HAROFORM - Fabrics - Harodite Finishing Co. Inc.
HAROLD - Doors—storm - Quaker Window Products Co.
HAROLD - Toys—stuffed - Russ Berrie and Co., Inc.
HAROLD POWELL - Apparel and accessories - Harold's Stores, Inc.
HAROLD REASON - Women's shoes - G. Morris Ltd., Inc.
HAROLON - Fabrics - Harodite Finishing Co. Inc.
HAROT - Food products ☆ - Empire Kosher Poultry Inc.
HAROWE - Health care products - Fasco Industries Inc.
HARP JACK - Harmonicas - Jack Bryson Bowden
HARP LAGER - Beverages—malt - Guinness Import Co.
HARPBODIES - Cases—eyeglass - California Optical Leather Inc.
HARPER - Tools ☆ - Neilson Wheel Co. Inc.
HARPER CAROUSEL - Publisher's imprints - Harper Junior Books Group
HARPER I CAN READ BOOKS - Publisher's imprints - Harper Junior Books Group
HARPER JUNIOR BOOKS - Publisher's imprints - Harper Junior Books Group
HARPER KEYPOINT - Publisher's imprints - Harper Junior Books Group
HARPER SPOTLIGHT - Publisher's imprints - Harpercollins Publishers Inc.
HARPER TROPHY - Publisher's imprints - Harper Junior Books Group
HARPER TROPHY I CAN READ BOOKS - Publisher's imprints - Harper Junior Books Group
HARPER TROPHY LET'S-READ-AND-FIND-OUT - Publisher's imprints - Harper Junior Books Group

☆ = Now out of production

HARPERCOLLINS - Publisher's imprints - Harpercollins Publishers Inc.

HARPERPRISM - Publisher's imprints - Harpercollins Publishers Inc.

HARPER'S - Leather–rawhide - Harper Leather Goods Manufacturing Co.

HARPER'S BAZAAR - Frames–eyeglass - Zylo Ware Corp.

HARPER'S BAZAAR - Publisher's imprints - Hearst Corp.

HARPER'S FARE - Paper–gift wrap ☆ - Zondervan Publishing House

HARPERS FERRY - Rifles–pellet - Euroarms of America

HARPER'S PREMIUM - Leather–rawhide - Harper Leather Goods Manufacturing Co.

HARPETH - Apparel and accessories ☆ - Genesco Inc.

HARPOON - Golf clubs - King Par Corp.

HARPOON - Insecticides - Tree Technology Systems, Inc.

HARPOON - Medical equipment - Arthrotek, Inc.

HARPOON - Seafood products–canned or cured ☆ - Bumble Bee Seafoods, Inc.

HARPOON - Toys–models ☆ - Estes Industries

HARPO'S - Salad dressings–bottled - Trombetta & Youngs Enterprises Ltd.

HARPTONE - Cases–musical instrument - Harptone

HARRIER - Brushes–paint - Allpro Corp.

HARRIER - Electronic equipment - Brookes & Gatehouse Inc.

HARRIET MASTER SPUN - Yarn - Harriet & Henderson Yarns, Inc.

HARRIET ROYCE - Hosiery - Royce Hosiery Mills Inc.

HARRIET'S - Hummus - Harriet Foods

HARRIETT OF ATLANTA - Stationery ☆ - Compac Industries Inc.

HARRINGTON - Floor coverings ☆ - Congoleum Corp.

HARRINGTON - Tools–hand-operated - Harrington Tools Inc.

HARRINGTON - Watches - Bulova Corp.

HARRINGTON & RICHARDSON - Guns ☆ - Harrington & Richardson Inc.

HARRINGTON HOUSE - Floor coverings - Mannington Resilient Floors

HARRINGTON'S HOT IRISH - Mustard - Michael Harrington

HARRIS - Apparel and accessories - Union Manufacturing Co.

HARRIS - Boats–pontoons - Harris-Kayot Inc.

HARRIS - Crab meat–canned or cured - Borden, Inc.

HARRIS - Electronics equipment - Harris Corp.

HARRIS - Floor coverings - Harris-Tarkett, Inc.

HARRIS - Laboratory apparatus - Revco Scientific, Inc.

HARRIS - Lamps - Harris Industries

HARRIS - Lamps - Harris Lamps Co.

HARRIS - Paints ☆ - Devoe & Raynolds Co.

HARRIS - Sporting goods ☆ - Powell Skateboards

HARRIS - Stamps–hand - H.E. Harris & Co.

HARRIS & MALLOW - Clocks - Harris & Mallow Products

HARRIS-MARCUS - Lamps - Harris Lamps Co.

HARRIS MASTERWORK - Photo albums - H.E. Harris & Co.

HARRIS NAVIGATOR - Computer peripheral equipment - Harris Waste Management Group, Inc.

HARRIS TEETER FAST & FRESH KITCHENS - Salads–prepackaged - Harris Teeter, Inc.

HARRIS TWEED - Floor coverings–carpet and rugs ☆ - Concord/Aldon Industries Inc.

HARRISBURG DAIRY - Milk - Harrisburg Dairies Inc.

HARRISON - Musical instrument accessories - Harrison-Hurtz Enterprises Inc.

HARRISON - Oils–edible - De Medici Imports Ltd.

HARRISON - Tableware–china ☆ - Lenox, Inc.

HARRISON & TAYLOR - Shirts - Pacific Teaze

HARRISON BROS. - Silver products - Kirk & Matz Ltd.

HARRISON FILM CHANGING TENTS - Tents - Camera Essentials

HARRISON FISHER - Posters - One-of-a-Kind Workshop

HARRISON GOLDEN GOODNESS - Meat products–poultry - Harrison Poultry Inc.

HARRISON-HOGE - Fishing lures - Harrison-Hoge Industries Inc.

HARRISON HOUND - Toys–stuffed - Animal Fair Inc.

HARRISON HOUSE - Wallpaper ☆ - Winfield Design Associates, Inc.

HARRISON LIFETIME LIMITED WARRANTY - Golfing equipment - Harrison Sports, Inc.

HARRISON PARK - Floor coverings–carpet and rugs - Cabin Crafts Carpets

HARRISON PRO 2.5 - Golfing equipment - Harrison Sports, Inc.

HARRISON'S BIRD DIETS - Bird feeds - HBD, Inc.

HARRISON'S COUNTRY STORE - Plates–copper ☆ - H & G Studio Inc.

HARRODS - Cigarettes - G.A. Georgopulo & Co. Inc.

HARROGATE - Dinnerware–glass ☆ - Royal China & Porcelain Companies Inc.

HARROGATE - Floor coverings–carpet and rugs - Hartford Carpet Mills

HARROGATE - Floor coverings–carpet and rugs ☆ - Patcraft Mills Inc.

HARROGATE - Wallpaper - Seabrook Wallcoverings, Inc.

HARROLD - Tools - Harrold Tool Co.

HARROWS - Sporting goods - Collette Manufacturing Co.

HARROWS QUADRO - Darts and dart games ☆ - Dart World Inc.

HARRY - Toys - Bien Productions, Inc.

HARRY - Toys–stuffed ☆ - Russ Berrie and Co., Inc.

HARRY AND DAVID - Food products - Harry and David Inc.

HARRY & ME - Apparel–children's - Baylis Brothers Inc.

HARRY GLANTZ - Musical instrument accessories ☆ - Charles Colin Music Publishers

HARRY H. BELL & SONS - Food products - Harry H. Bell and Sons Inc.

HARRY HEARTHROB - Toys–stuffed ☆ - Gund, Inc.

HARRY HOUND - Toys–stuffed - Dakin Inc.

HARRY LONDON'S - Chocolate candy - Harry London's Candies Inc.

HARRY THE CLOWN - Toys - Smethport Specialty Co.

HARRY W. SMITH - Giftware - Barnstable Originals

HARRY WHO - Apparel–women's - Mosaic Designs Inc.

HARRY'S - Fish–fresh or frozen - Harry's Farmers Market, Inc.

HARRY'S - Salsas - Harry's Premium Snacks

HARRY'S BEST - Pet food - Alpha-Lac, Inc.

HARRY'S BIG & TALL - Apparel–men's - Edison Brothers Stores, Inc.

HARRY'S CRESTVIEW GROVES - Fruits and vegetables - Standex International Corp.

HARRY'S PREMIUM SNACKS - Potato chips - Original Hampton Potato Chip Co.

HARSAX - Prefabricated buildings–wood - All American Homes Inc.

HARSCOURT - Floor coverings - Tarkett, Inc.

HARSTO - Safes - Boston Lock & Safe Co.

HART - Fireplace equipment - Jack-Post Corp.

HART - Fruits–canned - Stokely USA, Inc.

HART - Sporting goods - Hart Ski Manufacturing Co.

HART - Vegetables–canned - Chiquita Processed Food, LLC

HART - Video production - Wilbur N. Ischie

HART 2-BY TURNER - Tools–hand-operated - Hart Tool Co., Inc.

HART & COOLEY - Air conditioning equipment - Hart and Cooley Inc.

HART & HOLM COLLECTION - Cutlery - Test-Rite Products Corp.

HART BREWERY & PUB - Beverages–malt - Hart Brewing, Inc.

HART BREWING - Beer and ales - Hart Brewing, Inc.

HART SCHAFFNER & MARX - Waterproof outerwear - Hartmarx Corp.

HART SPORT WHEELS - Wheels–motor vehicle - D. Christopher Hart

HART WINERY - Wines - Hart Winery

HARTCO - Floor coverings - Hartco Wood Flooring

HARTCO AMERICAN PRIDE - Flooring–hardwood - Tibbals Flooring Co.

HARTCO GUARD - Floor waxes - Hartco Wood Flooring

HARTCO TOTAL CARE - Floor waxes - Hartco Wood Flooring

HARTER I/F - Furniture ☆ - Harter

HARTER INTERNATIONAL COLLECTION - Furniture ☆ - Harter

HARTER NB - Furniture ☆ - Harter

HARTER/STAND - Furniture ☆ - Harter

HARTER TASK - Furniture - Harter

HARTERMARTINSTOLL - Furniture ☆ - Harter

HARTEX - Floor coverings–carpet and rugs - Leggett & Platt/Hartex

HARTEX - Food products - H.E. Butt Grocery Co.

HARTFORD - Bicycles - Columbia Manufacturing Inc.

HARTFORD - Cabinets - Imperial Cabinet Co. Inc.

HARTFORD - Floor coverings ☆ - Bruce Hardwood Floors

HARTFORD - Floor coverings–carpet and rugs ☆ - Royalweve Carpet Mills

HARTFORD - Plumbing fixtures–metal - Sterline Manufacturing Corp.

HARTFORD - Vegetables–canned - Hartford Packing Co. Inc.

HARTFORD COURT - Wines - Kendall Jackson Winery, Ltd.

HARTFORD HOUSE - Furniture - Habersham Hearth Inc.

HARTFORD OAK - Cabinets - Del Mar Cabinets

HARTING - Cabinets - Harting Enterprises

HARTING GRANGE - Publisher's imprints - Caledonia Press

HARTJES - Ski suits–children's - Swix Sport USA, Inc.

HARTKE - Audio equipment - Samson Technologies Inc.

HARTLAND - Figurines - USA Hartland Inc.

HARTLAND - Floor coverings–carpet and rugs ☆ - Mandate-Dawn Carpet Mills

HARTLAND - Furniture - Universal Flooring

HARTLAND - Toys–models ☆ - Steven Manufacturing Co.

HARTLEY - Brandy - Heublein, Inc.

HARTLEY - Liquors - Canandaigua Wine Co. Inc.

HARTLEY - Pens - Hartley Co.

HARTLEY - Preserved foods–prepackaged ☆ - FCW Imports

HARTLEY & GIBSON'S - Wines - Jack Poust & Co. Inc.

HARTLEY PARKERS - Beverages–alcohol - Star Liquor Imports Inc.

HARTLEY'S - Syrup - H & H Products Co.

☆ = Now out of production

HARTLEY'S FLAVORBURST - Syrup - H & H Products Co.

HARTLEY'S WILD WHIPPLE - Beverages–carbonated ☆ - H & H Products Co.

HARTMANN - Luggage - Hartmann Luggage Co.

HARTOG - Apparel–men's - Media Industries

HARTOGLASS - Windows–screen - Hartwig-Hartoglass Inc.

HARTOLITE - Insulating materials - Hartwig-Hartoglass Inc.

HARTOLUME - Insulating materials ☆ - Hartwig-Hartoglass Inc.

HARTOP - Cement - Hartline Products Co. Inc.

HARTOPANE - Insulating materials - Hartwig-Hartoglass Inc.

HARTORAY - Insulating materials - Hartwig-Hartoglass Inc.

HARTS - Milk ☆ - T.G. Lee Foods Inc.

HART'S - Seeds–salted, roasted, cooked, or canned - Chas. C. Hart Seed Co.

HARTSELL - Publisher's imprints - Willis Music Co.

HARTSFIELD - Floor coverings–carpet and rugs ☆ - Quaker Inc.

HARTSTONE - Dinnerware–glass - Hartstone Inc.

HARTSTONE HOME FRAGRANCE COLLECTION - Giftware - Hartstone Inc.

HARTSTRINGS BABY - Apparel–children's - Hartstrings, Inc.

HARTVILLE TOUR BASKET - Baskets–wood - Longaberger Co.

HARTWELL - Shirts ☆ - Hartwell Garment Co.

HARTWELL HOUSE - Tableware–china - Lenox, Inc.

HARTZ - Pet products - Hartz Mountain Corp.

HARTZ & CO. - Apparel–men's - Hartz & Co., Inc.

HARTZ MOUNTAIN - Pet products - Hartz Mountain Corp.

HARUBANG - Seafood products–fresh or frozen - Nishimoto Trading Co. Ltd.

HARVADE - Plant growth regulators - Uniroyal Chemical Co. Inc. (Crop Protection Div.)

HARVADINE - Pharmaceutical preparations - Harvey Laboratories Inc.

HARVAPLEX - Pharmaceutical preparations - Harvey Laboratories Inc.

HARVARD - Basketball, table tennis, dart equipment, and pool and game tables - Indian Industries Inc.

HARVARD - Bed frames - L & P Property Management Co.

HARVARD - Beverages–malt - Piel Bros. Ltd.

HARVARD - Bicycles - Columbia Manufacturing Inc.

HARVARD - Brushes–paint - Rubberset Co.

HARVARD - Computer software - Software Publishing Corp.

HARVARD - Confectionery, nuts - American Nut & Chocolate Co.

HARVARD - Cribs–wood ☆ - Welsh Co.

HARVARD - Cutlery and tableware - Cotter & Co.

HARVARD - Dinnerware–glass - Royal China & Porcelain Companies Inc.

HARVARD - Filters–industrial - Harvard Corp.

HARVARD - Floor coverings–carpet and rugs - Atlas Carpet Mills Inc.

HARVARD - Frames–eyeglass - U.S. Optical Frame Co.

HARVARD - Frames–eyeglass - Universal/Univis Inc.

HARVARD - Jewelry - President and Fellows of Harvard College

HARVARD - Ladders–metal ☆ - John S. Tilley Ladders Co. Inc.

HARVARD - Office furniture–wood - Anderson Desk Inc.

HARVARD - Plumbing and well supplies - American Granby Inc.

HARVARD - Safes - Boston Lock & Safe Co.

HARVARD CHARTXL - Computer software - Software Publishing Corp.

HARVARD DRAW - Computer software - Software Publishing Corp.

HARVARD GEOGRAPHICS - Computer software ☆ - Software Publishing Corp.

HARVARD GRAPHICS - Computer software - Software Publishing Corp.

HARVARD GRAPHICS ADVISOR - Computer software - Software Publishing Corp.

HARVARD HALL - Floor coverings–carpet and rugs ☆ - Downs Carpet Co. Inc.

HARVARD HOUSE - House furnishings - Designer's Den Inc.

HARVARD MONTAGE - Computer software - Software Publishing Corp.

HARVARD PROJECT MANAGER - Computer software - Software Publishing Corp.

HARVARD SPOTLIGHT - Computer software - Software Publishing Corp.

HARVARD SQUARE - Floor coverings–carpet and rugs ☆ - Mohawk Carpet Corp.

HARVARD SQUARE - Office supplies - Brooks Drug, Inc.

HARVARD SQUARE - Wallpaper ☆ - Pickhardt & Siebert USA Inc.

HARVARD TRAIL - Bicycles ☆ - Huffy Corp.

HARVATROPIN - Pharmaceutical preparations ☆ - Harvey Laboratories Inc.

HARVE BENARD - Apparel and accessories - Harve Benard Ltd.

HARVELL - Office supplies - Ballonoff Home Products

HARVEST - Bacon ☆ - Dold Foods Inc.

HARVEST - Bird feeds - Stanford Seed Co.

HARVEST - Cabinets - Karman Kitchens Inc.

HARVEST - Cabinets ☆ - Merillat Industries, Inc.

HARVEST - Cereal - National Oats Co. Inc.

HARVEST - Computer software - InterFax Inc.

HARVEST - Dishes–earthenware - Louisville Stoneware Co.

HARVEST - Floor coverings–carpet and rugs - Foreign Accents

HARVEST - Food products - Pet Inc.

HARVEST - Fruit and vegetable markets - J.P. Sullivan & Co.

HARVEST - Furniture ☆ - Kincaid Furniture Co. Inc.

HARVEST - Glassware–household - Dansk International Designs, Ltd.

HARVEST - Glassware–household ☆ - Lancaster Colony Corp.

HARVEST - Hardware ☆ - Amerock Corp.

HARVEST - Honey - Harvest Foods

HARVEST - Housewares - Doranne

HARVEST - Meat products–beef - Ohio Packing Co.

HARVEST - Oils–illuminating ☆ - Lamplight Farms, Inc.

HARVEST - Pencils - Musgrave Pencil Co. Inc.

HARVEST - Pet food - Harvest Industries, Inc.

HARVEST - Pet products - Lyric Pet Bird Food

HARVEST - Recording label - Eddie Crook Co.

HARVEST - Rice - Producers Rice Mill, Inc.

HARVEST - Tableware–china ☆ - Lenox, Inc.

HARVEST - Wines - Meredyth Vineyard

HARVEST - Wood products - Georgia-Pacific Corp.

HARVEST AMBER - Cooking utensils–earthenware ☆ - Anchor Hocking Glass, Inc.

HARVEST BEST 100 - Juices–frozen ☆ - Park Corp.

HARVEST BLEND - Juices - Welch Foods Inc.

HARVEST BLEND - Rice - Rice Growers of California

HARVEST BLOSSOM - Flour–blended ☆ - Safeway Stores Inc.

HARVEST BLUE - Dishes–earthenware - Portmeirion USA

HARVEST CHERRY - Cough drops - Warner-Lambert Co.

HARVEST CHOICE - Juices - Wagner Excello Foods Inc.

HARVEST CLASSIC - Milk - Auburn Dairy Products, Inc.

HARVEST COLLECTION - Bedding–linen - Perfect Fit Industries, Inc.

HARVEST COLLECTION - Furniture ☆ - Virginia House Furniture Corp.

HARVEST COLLECTION - Hobby kits - Craft World International Inc.

HARVEST CRISPS - Crackers - Nabisco Foods Group

HARVEST CRUNCH - Cereal - Quaker Oats Co.

HARVEST DAY - Food products - American Stores Co.

HARVEST DELIGHT - Food products ☆ - Dawn Food Products Inc.

HARVEST DELIGHT - Popcorn - National Oats Co. Inc.

HARVEST FAIR - Bakeware - Corning Inc.

HARVEST FEAST COOKING SET - Toys - Mattel, Inc.

HARVEST FESTIVAL - Magnets - Russ Berrie and Co., Inc.

HARVEST FIELDS - Dried fruits and vegetables - East Indies Coffee & Tea Co.

HARVEST FIELDS - Giftware - Enesco Corp.

HARVEST FRESH - Fruits and vegetables - Pillsbury Co.

HARVEST FRESH - Juices - Daily Juice Products Inc.

HARVEST GLORY - Fruits and vegetables - Desert Harvest, Ltd.

HARVEST GOLD - Christmas tree ornaments - Cracker Box Inc.

HARVEST GOLD - Food products - Carmine Foods Inc.

HARVEST GOLD - Seeds–salted, roasted, cooked, or canned - Pocahontas Foods USA Inc.

HARVEST GOLD - Tobacco products - Faber, Coe & Gregg Inc.

HARVEST GOLD - Vitamins and nutritional supplements - Hillestad International, Inc.

HARVEST-GUARD - Garden equipment - Dalen Products Inc.

HARVEST/HBJ - Publisher's imprints - Harcourt Brace & Co.

HARVEST HEARTS - Candy ☆ - Nellson Candies Inc.

HARVEST HILL - Furniture–upholstered ☆ - Webb Furniture Enterprises Inc.

HARVEST HILL - Wine coolers ☆ - Canandaigua Wine Co. Inc.

HARVEST HOLIDAY - Food products - Mrs. Ressler's Food Products Co.

HARVEST HOME - Dinnerware ☆ - Corning Inc.

HARVEST HOME - Publisher's imprints - Stephen Greene Press

HARVEST HOME - Wallpaper - Gencorp Inc.

HARVEST KING - Handles–wood - Crook-Miller Co.

HARVEST LANE - Food products ☆ - PFP Speciality Foods Inc.

HARVEST LIGHT - Food products ☆ - Northern Soy

HARVEST LITTER - Agricultural products - Northwest Pet Products, Inc.

HARVEST MAID - Purifiers - Norwalk Sales & Service

HARVEST MOON - Flour–blended - Cahokia Flour Co.

HARVEST MOON - Food products - Seneca Foods Corp.

HARVEST MOON - Jams and jellies - Tree of Life, Inc.

HARVEST NOODLE - Soups–mixes - Lipton Investments, Inc.

HARVEST OAK - Furniture ☆ - Bassett Furniture Industries, Inc.

HARVEST OAK COLLECTION - House furnishings ☆ - Lea Industries Inc.

HARVEST OF JOHNNY WILDSEED, THE - Flowers, plants, and seeds - Wildseed Farms

HARVEST OF NATURE - Cookies ☆ - PFP Speciality Foods Inc.
HARVEST OF THE SEA - Seafood products–fresh or frozen - Ore-Cal Corp.
HARVEST OF VALUES - Vitamins and nutritional supplements - Hillestad International, Inc.
HARVEST PACK - Vegetables–frozen - Packers' Marketing Inc.
HARVEST PARTNERS - Electrical equipment - American Cyanamid Co.
HARVEST PEAR - Beverages–alcohol ☆ - Jim Beam Brands Co.
HARVEST PINE - Furniture ☆ - Brill Manufacturing Co.
HARVEST PRIDE - Bakery products - Quiktrip Corp.
HARVEST PRIDE - Food products - Shuksan Frozen Foods Inc.
HARVEST PURE - Fruit drinks–bottled or canned - Tropical Pleasures, Inc.
HARVEST QUEEN - Food products ☆ - Super Valu Inc.
HARVEST RECIPE - Breads - Roman Meal Co.
HARVEST RIDGE - Breads - Interstate Brands Corp.
HARVEST ROSE - Dinnerware–glass ☆ - Royal China & Porcelain Companies Inc.
HARVEST SALAD - Food products - Bob Evans Farms Inc.
HARVEST SAVOR - Dehydrating equipment - Vita-Mix Corp.
HARVEST SEASON - Spices and extracts - Moran Foods, Inc.
HARVEST SQUARE - Furniture - Universal Flooring
HARVEST TIME - Cider - Readington Farms
HARVEST TIME - Clocks - General Time Corp. (Westclox/Seth Thomas Div.)
HARVEST TIME - Giftware - United China and Glass Co.
HARVEST TIME - Potato flakes - Superior Frozen Vegetables Inc.
HARVEST TIME BROWN - Dinnerware–glass ☆ - Johnson Brothers, USA, Inc.
HARVEST TOWER OF TREATS - Food products - Harry and David Inc.
HARVEST VALUE - Fruits–canned - JP Foodservice, Inc.
HARVEST VEGETABLE - Cookware - Mesa International
HARVEST WHEAT - Crackers ☆ - Keebler Co.
HARVESTER - Brushes–hair - Wright-Bernet
HARVESTER - Cigar boxes–wood - Consolidated Cigar Corp.
HARVESTER - Kitchenware–earthenware - Arnart Imports Inc.
HARVESTERS - Crackers ☆ - Keebler Co.
HARVESTTIME - Deodorizers - Marlen Manufacturing & Developing Co.
HARVESTYME - Tools–hand-operated - Windquest International Asia Pacific Operations, Inc.
HARVEY CARTOON - Puzzles ☆ - Warren Industries Inc.
HARVEY CLASSICS - Books–comic - Harvey Comics Entertainment, Inc.
HARVEY CLASSICS RICHIE RICH - Books–comic - Harvey Comics Entertainment, Inc.
HARVEY COLLECTIBLES - Books–comic - Harvey Comics Entertainment, Inc.
HARVEY GENE'S - Cleaning preparations - Harvey Gene, Inc.
HARVEY HOUSE - Publisher's imprints - Harvey House
HARVEY KNOX KINGDOM - Figurines ☆ - Goebel of North America
HARVEY MASON SIGNATURE - Musical instruments - Vic Firth Inc.
HARVEY PENICK CLASSIC LADY - Golfing equipment - Golfsmith International Inc.
HARVEY PENICK CLASSIC PLAYER - Golfing equipment - Golfsmith International Inc.
HARVEY PENICK FUTURE CLASSIC - Golfing equipment - Golfsmith International Inc.
HARVEY PENICK MASTER - Golfing equipment - Golfsmith International Inc.
HARVEY PENICK PLUS - Golfing equipment - Golfsmith International Inc.
HARVEY PENICK PROFESSIONAL - Golfing equipment - Golfsmith International Inc.
HARVEY'S - Apparel - Harvey's Skindiving Supply, Inc.
HARVEY'S - Giftware - Q.E.D. Industries
HARVEY'S - Health care products - First Aids Inc.
HARVEY'S - Whiskey - Shaw-Ross International Importers
HARVEY'S 1000 SCALE & RUST REMOVER - Cleaning preparations - Harvey Universal Inc.
HARVEY'S BIO 520 - Chemical preparations - Harvey Universal Inc.
HARVEY'S BRISTOL CREAM - Beverages–alcohol - Hiram Walker & Sons, Inc.
HARVEY'S GEL RUST REMOVER - Cleaning preparations - Harvey Universal Inc.
HARVEY'S RUST SHIELD 2000 - Rustproof coating - Harvey Universal Inc.
HARVEYTOONS - Books–comic - Harvey Comics Entertainment, Inc.
HARVIN - Candlesticks ☆ - Virginia Metalcrafters Inc.
HARVIX - Pharmaceutical preparations ☆ - Harvey Laboratories Inc.
HARVY - Canes - Harvy Surgical Supply Corp.
HARWALD - Electronics equipment - RTI Research Technology International
HARWOOD - Apparel and accessories - Harwood Companies Inc.
HARWOOD - Floor coverings–carpet and rugs ☆ - Patcraft Mills Inc.

HARWOOD - Sinks–porcelain - Vance Industries Inc.
HARWOOD - Sporting goods - MacGregor Sport Products Inc.
HARWOOD - Tables–wood - Anco Wood Specialties Inc.
HARWOOD - Whiskey - Heaven Hill Distilleries, Inc.
HARY DARY - Apparel and accessories - Hary Dary International
HARZER HAND KAESE - Cheese - Swissrose International Inc.
HAS - Vitamins and nutritional supplements - Nature's Way Products, Inc.
HASBRO - Toys - Hasbro, Inc.
HASCH PLATTEN - Recording label - Jazz Composer's Orchestra Association Inc.
HASCO - Switches–electric - Hasco Components International Corp.
HASE PURE SHINE - Hair care products - Alleghany Pharmacal Corp.
HASENBURG - Beverages–alcohol - Joseph Gies Import
HASH HOUSE - Corned beef - Henry J's Hashtime-USA
HASHANI - Wallpaper - Steven Stanley Designs
HASHANI II - Wallpaper - Steven Stanley Designs
HASI HESTER COLLECTION - Furniture - Tomlinson of High Point Inc.
HASK - Hair care products ☆ - Alleghany Pharmacal Corp.
HASK PLACENTA - Cosmetics ☆ - Alleghany Pharmacal Corp.
HASKELL - Office furniture–wood - Haskell of Pittsburgh, Inc.
HASKELL'S HEAVYPACK - Agricultural products - Heavypack Inc.
HASLOV - Glassware–household - Crystal Clear Importing Co. Inc.
HASLUM - Greeting cards - H. George Caspari Inc.
HASNA - Skin care products - Pro Cap
HASP - Pharmaceutical preparations ☆ - Merz Inc.
HASPEL - Apparel and accessories - Neema Clothing, Ltd.
HASPEL - Apparel–men's - Haspel Brothers Inc.
HASPLOCK - Hardware ☆ - Master Lock Co.
HASQA-WARE - Flatware - HSQA Corp.
HASSCAD - Computer software - Sanders Firesoft Inc.
HASSELBLAD - Photographic equipment - Victor Hasselblad Inc.
HASSELBLAD 205TCC - Cameras - Victor Hasselblad Inc.
HASSLE-FREE - Computer peripheral equipment - ASP Computer Products Inc.
HASSLE FREE MEALS - Meat products - Hormel Foods Corp.
HASSLEFREE - Flowers, plants, and seeds - Centerton Nursery, Inc.
HASSON 360 SERIES - Medical apparatus - Cook Urological Inc.
HASTI-HOE - Hoes ☆ - Yard Marvel Manufacturing Co. Inc.
HASTINGS - Apparel–men's - HSSI, Inc.
HASTINGS - Automotive parts and accessories - Hastings Manufacturing Co.
HASTINGS - Dishes–china ☆ - WMF/USA
HASTINGS - Pianos ☆ - Kaman Music Corp.
HASTINGS - Tools–machine - Hastings Manufacturing Corp.
HASTINGS BRAND - Filters–air ☆ - Hastings Manufacturing Co.
HASTINGS TRADITIONS - Apparel–men's - General Electric Capital Corp.
HASTY HEARTH - Dinners–frozen - Conagra, Inc.
HAT ART - Recording label - Jazz Composer's Orchestra Association Inc.
HAT ATTACK - Hats - Hat Attack, Inc.
HAT BOX LEARNING SERIES - Games - Encore Technical Resources Inc.
HAT BUNNY - Toys–stuffed ☆ - Fun World Inc.
HAT-COR - Ammunition - Blount International, Inc. (Sporting Equipment Group)
HAT CREEK - Seafood products–fresh or frozen - Napa Valley Trading Co.
HAT CREEK FISH - Fish–canned or cured - Napa Valley Trading Co.
HAT-IN-RING - Bicycles - Schwinn Cycling & Fitness Inc.
HAT SHACK, THE - Hats - Lid Co.
HAT TRAP - Boxes–hat - Coppers Ltd.
HAT TRICK - Bakery products - International Schmidt-Cannon
HAT TRICK - Cookies - Schmidt-Cannon, Inc.
HAT TRICK - Game machines - Bally Gaming International, Inc.
HAT TRICK - Herbicides - Northwest Chemical Corp.
HAT TRICK - Sporting goods - Ray F. Miller
HAT TRICK - Video game - Bally Sente Inc.
HAT WORKS, THE - Hats - Comfort Cushion Mills, Inc.
HATBOX - Vacuum cleaners and accessories–commercial - Kent Co.
HATBOX DOLLS - Toys - Merry Andrews Toys Inc.
HATCH - Recording label - Would'n Shoe Records
HATCH POPPER - Toys–automobiles - Mattel, Inc.
HATCH-TOP - Cases–musical instrument - M & M Distributing Co.
HATCHBACK - Converters–electric - Johnson Matthey Inc.
HATCHER - Pet products - Aquarium Products Inc.
HATCHERS - Apparel–athletic - Cran Barry Inc.
HATCHET - Archery equipment - Bear Archery Inc.
HATCHET HARNESS - Fishing lures - Lindy Little Joe Inc.
HATCHETT, THE - Boots - Art Stone Theatrical Corp.
HATCHGARD - Veterinary pharmaceutical preparations - Intervet, Inc.
HATCHLINGS - Toys - Russ Berrie and Co., Inc.

☆ = Now out of production

HATFIELD - Archery equipment - Martin Archery Inc.
HATFIELD - Meat products - Hqm, Ltd.
HATFIELD - Meat products–beef - Hatfield, Inc.
HATFIELD PENNSYLVANIA DUTCH STYLE - Meat products - HGM, Ltd.
HATHANE - Foam rubber - Hastings Plastics Co.
HATHAWAY - Floor coverings–carpet and rugs - Burlington House Carpets
HATHAWAY - Leather goods - Noymer Leather and Gifts Ltd.
HATHAWAY - Neckties - Randa Corp.
HATHAWAY - Shirts - C.F. Hathaway Co.
HATHAWAY GOLF - Apparel–men's - Warnaco Inc.
HATHUT - Recording label - Creav Inc. USA
HATIS - Hearing aids - Phoenix Management, Inc.
HATLEY COVE - Wallpaper ☆ - Wallquest, Inc.
HATLEY SQUARE - Wallpaper ☆ - Glidden Co.
HATLINE - Hats - Rodin Industries Inc.
HATQUARTERS USA - Hats - Henschel Manufacturing Co.
HATRACK - Toys–stuffed ☆ - Gund, Inc.
HATS INCREDIBLE - Hats - Raymond B. Balee
HATS OFF - Paper–gift wrap ☆ - American Greetings Corp.
HATS OFF - Sunscreen - Premier Sunscreens, Inc.
HATSAX - Apparel and accessories - Incandescent Innovations Inc.
HATSUYUKI - Beverages–malt - Wine of Japan Import Inc.
HATTARAS - Shingles–asphalt or tar - Certainteed Corp. (Roofing Products Group)
HATTARAS - Siding–insulating - Champion International Corp.
HATTERAS - Boats - Genmar Industries Inc.
HATTERAS - Cabinets - Marsh Furniture Co.
HATTERAS - Dinnerware–glass ☆ - Lenox, Inc.
HATTERAS - Floor coverings–carpet and rugs - Mannington Carpets, Inc.
HATTERAS - Furniture - Pilliod Co.
HATTERAS - Garden furniture–rattan - Lloyd/Flanders Industries
HATTERAS - Hammocks - The HammockSource
HATTERAS - Ships–sailing vessels - Hatteras Yachts
HATTIE HIPPO TOY BOX - Chests–wood ☆ - Little Tikes Co.
HATTIE HOLIDAY - Dolls ☆ - Effanbee Doll Corp.
HATTIE'S CHICKEN SHACK - Chickens - Christel Baker
HATUEY - Beverages–malt - Florida Brewing Co.
HATUEY MALTA - Beverages–carbonated - Florida Brewing Co.
HATZI-MICHLAIS - Wine - Attiki Imports & Distributors
HAUBER - Apparel–women's - Hooper Associates Ltd.
HAUCK - Pharmaceutical preparations ☆ - Roberts/Hauck Pharmaceuticals Inc.
HAUDECOEUR - Food products ☆ - Europa Foods Ltd.
HAUGIN'S FARM - Food products ☆ - Schwan's Sales Enterprises, Inc.
HAUL ICE - Apparel and accessories - Grady J. Shaw
HAUL MASTER - Tires - Uniroyal Goodrich Tire Co.
HAUL-RITE - Boat trailers - B & M Manufacturing Co.
HAUL ROAD DUST CONTROL - Chemical preparations - Midwest Industrial Supply, Inc.
HAUL-STAR - Industrial machinery ☆ - Daka Corp.
HAULAMATIC - Winches ☆ - Bosworth Co.
HAULAWAY STORAGE CONTAINERS - Containers–metal - C R & R Inc.
HAULIN - Trailers - I Corp.
HAULMARK - Trailers - Mobile Structures, Inc.
HAULPAK - Motor vehicles–trucks - Komatsu America International Co.
HAULSTAR - Tires ☆ - Ashland Oil, Inc.
HAULSTER - Motor vehicles - Ransomes-Cushman-Ryan
HAUNT - Insecticides - Uncle Sam Chemical Co., Inc.
HAUNT-N-EYES - Novelty items - National Artcraft Co.
HAUNT-N-LIGHTS - Novelty items - National Artcraft Co.
HAUNT-N-PLAY - Novelty items - National Artcraft Co.
HAUNT, THE - Games ☆ - Mayfair Games, Inc.
HAUNTED HEADSTONE - Games - Tiger Electronics, Inc.
HAUNTED HIGHWAY - Toys - Tyco Industries, Inc.
HAUNTED HOUSE - Candy - Fleer Corp.
HAUNTED HOUSE - Costumes - Rubie's Costume Co., Inc.
HAUNTED HOUSE - Games - Smethport Specialty Co.
HAUNTED HOUSE MULTIMEDIA - Computer software - Haunted House Multimedia
HAUNTED HOUSE MYSTERY BANK - Toys - Brumberger Co. Inc.
HAUNTED ISLAND - Computer software - Knowledge Adventure, Inc.
HAUNTED RUINS, THE - Games - Avalon Hill Game Co.
HAUPIA - Food products - Noh Foods International
HAUPTMANN - Cigars - National Cigar Corp.
HAUPTNER - Pet products - Berolina Imports
HAUS OF FRANZ - Wines - Francis A. Bonanno, Inc.
HAUSER - Broth - Modern Products, Inc.

HAUSER CHOCOLATIER - Chocolate candy - Hauser Foods Inc.
HAUST - Biscuits - Holland-American Importing Co. Inc.
HAUST - Pastries ☆ - Liberty Richter Inc.
HAUSWALD'S - Breads - Schmidt Baking Co., Inc.
HAUT CHIC - Wallpaper - K.M.L. Industries
HAUTE 4U - Paints ☆ - Carnival Arts, Inc.
HAUTE CANINE - Pet products - L. Coffey Ltd.
HAUTE CELLARS - Wines - Great Thinks
HAUTE CHIC - Wallcoverings - Cork Products Co. Inc.
HAUTE COLOURS - Paints - Carnival Arts, Inc.
HAUTE CUISINE NON-STICK CAST ALUMINUM BY LE CREUSET - Cookware ☆ - Le Creuset of America, Inc.
HAUTE FELINE - Pet products - L. Coffey Ltd.
HAUTE GLACE - Hair care products - Peter Hantz Co.
HAUTE LUXE - Toilets–porcelain ☆ - Jolie Papier
HAUTE LUXE - Wallpaper ☆ - Capital Carousel Inc.
HAUTE NATURE - Fabric - Ecosport, Inc.
HAUTE ROUTE - Handbags - Esprit De Corp.
HAUTE STUFF BY BARRY WELLS - Neckties - TBAC-Prince Gardner Inc.
HAUTEFORT - Vases - Durand International
HAUZE - Glass products - Houze Glass Corp.
HAV-A-BALL - Golfing equipment - Warren Andersen Associates Inc.
HAV-A-HANK - Handkerchiefs - Carolina Manufacturing Inc.
HAV-A-TAMPA - Cigars - Havatampa Inc.
HAV-A-TAMPA JEWEL - Cigars - Havatampa Inc.
HAVABALL - Barbecues and grills - James A. Bethel, Jr.
HAVABAR - Ice cream - Hav-A-Bar, Inc.
HAVAHART - Traps–animal - Woodstream Corp.
HAVAHART LITTER RIDDER - Pet products - Woodstream Corp.
HAVANA - Beverages - North American Beverage Corp.
HAVANA - Cigarettes - Nat Sherman, Inc.
HAVANA - Colognes - Aramis Inc.
HAVANA - Floor coverings–carpet and rugs - Foreign Accents
HAVANA BANANA - Apparel and accessories - Craig Paul Miller
HAVANA BANANA - Food products - Star Kay White, Inc.
HAVANA BAY COMPANY - Apparel and accessories - Yellow Rose Financial Corp.
HAVANA HEAT - Fireworks - Ingram Enterprises, Inc.
HAVANA OVALS - Cigarettes - Nat Sherman, Inc.
HAVE A BLAST! - Apparel–women's - Tony Marterie & Associates
HAVE A CHEESE BALL - Food products - Bon Melange Inc.
HAVE A CROOK - Cigars ☆ - T.E. Brooks & Co.
HAVE A HEART - Candy ☆ - Good Taste Products, Inc.
HAVE A HEART - Confections - Maredy Corp.
HAVE-A-MAID - Housewares - RonCo Inc.
HAVE A NICE DAY - Mats–rattan - Golden Star Inc.
HAVE A SQUARE EGG! - Eggs - Olesky Enterprises International, Inc.
HAVE A SWEET - Cigars - T.E. Brooks & Co.
HAVE-A-TRAY - Health care products - Maddak Inc.
HAVE CASE-WILL TRAVEL - Toys - Natural Science Industries, Ltd.
HAVE FUN! - Food products - Oh Boy! Oberto
HAVE MERCY - Apparel–women's - Syndicate Sales, Inc.
HAVEGARD - Pet products - Havegard Farm Inc.
HAVEMEYER - Wines - Bercut-Vandervoort & Co.
HAVEN - Banks–commercial - Haven Capital Management, Inc.
HAVEN - Recording label - Tuneworks Records Inc.
HAVEN - Tools - Klein Tools Inc.
HAVEN GROVES - Food products - Fantasy Blankebaer
HAVEN RIDGE - Floor coverings–carpet and rugs ☆ - Walter Carpet Mills
HAVENS - Bird feeds - Duncraft, Inc.
HAVENSHIRE - Hosiery - Havenshire Knitwear Co. Inc.
HAVERFORD - Cabinets ☆ - Nutone Inc.
HAVERFORD HALL - Tableware–china - Lenox, Inc.
HAVERHILL - Cabinets - H.J. Scheirich Co.
HAVERHILL - Cabinets ☆ - American Woodmark Corp.
HAVERHILL - Floor coverings - Mannington Resilient Floors
HAVERHILL - Floor coverings–carpet and rugs - Leggett & Platt/Hartex
HAVI - Candles - Hackman Tabletop Inc.
HAVILAND - Candy ☆ - Haviland Candy Inc.
HAVILAND - Chemical preparations ☆ - Haviland Consumer Products, Inc.
HAVILAND - Chocolate candy - New England Confectionery Co.
HAVILAND - Floor coverings–carpet and rugs ☆ - Masland Corp.
HAVILAND - Wines - Haviland Vintners
HAVILAND LIMOGES - Housewares - Haviland Limoges
HAVOC - Rodenticides - Hacco, Inc./Loveland Industries, Inc.

☆ = Now out of production

HAVOC - Veterinary pharmaceutical preparations - Schering-Plough Animal Health

HAVOC BRUTE - Veterinary pharmaceutical preparations - Schering-Plough Animal Health

HAVOC CHUNKS WITH RAPIDO BAIT SYSTEM - Rodenticides - Hacco, Inc./ Loveland Industries, Inc.

HAVOKWARE - Computer software - Havokware LLC

HAVOLINE - Filters—oil - Texaco, Inc.

HAVOLINE - Petroleum - Texaco Lubricants Co.

HAVOLINE FORMULA 3 - Petroleum - Texaco Lubricants Co.

HAWAII - Footwear—women's - Hawaii Shoe Co.

HAWAII - Sweatshirts - Flavors of Hawaii Inc.

HAWAII - Window shades ☆ - Colony Shade Co.

HAWAII 2O - Water—bottled or canned - Rudy H. Ahrens

HAWAII AND SONS - Clocks - Jewel-Time Co.

HAWAII AT HOME - Housewares - Paul Marshall Products L.P.

HAWAII BEACHY - T-shirts—men's - Honolulu T-Shirt Co.

HAWAII CALLS - Recording label - Hawaii Calls Inc.

HAWAII CANDY - Cookies - Hawaii Candy Inc.

HAWAII CANE - Syrup - Hamakua Sugar Co. Inc.

HAWAII COUNTY - Apparel—men's - Sportailor Inc.

HAWAII FIVE-O - Apparel and accessories - CBS Inc.

HAWAII KAI - Floor coverings—carpet and rugs ☆ - J.L. Benson Co.

HAWAII PRINT - Fabrics - G. Von Hamm Textiles Inc.

HAWAII REAL ESTATE CENTRAL - Real estate agencies - Honolulu Board of Realtors

HAWAII VISITORS BUREAU - Apparel and accessories - Hawai'i Visitors and Convention Bureau

HAWAII WINTER BASEBALL - Apparel and accessories - Hawaii Winter Baseball, Inc.

HAWAIIAN - Candles - Aloha Candle Manufacturing Co. Inc.

HAWAIIAN - Fishing lures - Sunset Line and Twine Co.

HAWAIIAN - Hammocks - E-Z Sales & Manufacturing, Inc.

HAWAIIAN - Water bottles—rubber - Connelly Skis, Inc.

HAWAIIAN - Water—mineral - Hawaiian Water Partners

HAWAIIAN ANGEL - Coffee - Hawaiian Angel Coffee Co.

HAWAIIAN BARBECUE - Nuts—salted, roasted, cooked, or canned - Mauna Loa Macadamia Nut Corp.

HAWAIIAN BATIK - Floor coverings—carpet and rugs ☆ - Evans-Black Carpet Mills

HAWAIIAN BIRD CANDY - Bird feeds - Kevin Andrews

HAWAIIAN BISCOTTI BY KELI MIA - Cookies - Kelimia Mednick

HAWAIIAN BLADES - Shirts - Hawaiian Blades, Inc.

HAWAIIAN BLEND - Shampoos - Mahdeen Laboratory

HAWAIIAN BLOSSOM - Candles - Aloha Candle Manufacturing Co. Inc.

HAWAIIAN BLUE - Cosmetics - Langer Hawaii Corp.

HAWAIIAN BREEZE - Fans—electric - Wholesale Ceiling Fans Inc.

HAWAIIAN CLASSIC CLOTHING COMPANY - Apparel and accessories - Happy Shirts, Inc.

HAWAIIAN COLORS - Cosmetics - Wilshire Group Inc.

HAWAIIAN CORAL - Floor coverings - Congoleum Corp.

HAWAIIAN CROSS - Fruits—canned ☆ - Maui Pineapple Co.

HAWAIIAN DELIGHT - Candy - DFS Group Ltd.

HAWAIIAN DELIGHT - Fireworks - American Promotional Events, Inc.

HAWAIIAN DELIGHT - Food products ☆ - Essential Products Co. Inc.

HAWAIIAN DELIGHTS - Pet products - Pink Parrot

HAWAIIAN FASHIONS BY CARLTON - Shoes - Classic Sales Inc.

HAWAIIAN FLOATING - Candles - Aloha Candle Manufacturing Co. Inc.

HAWAIIAN FUN - Dolls - Mattel, Inc.

HAWAIIAN GOLD - Fruit drinks—bottled or canned - Maui Pineapple Co.

HAWAIIAN HAPPY HOUR - Housewares - Aloha Candle Manufacturing Co. Inc.

HAWAIIAN HOLIDAY - Dinnerware—glass - Noritake Co. Inc.

HAWAIIAN HOLIDAY - Toys - Tonka Corp.

HAWAIIAN HOST - Chocolate candy - Hawaiian Host Inc.

HAWAIIAN HULA - Salad dressings—bottled - Rainbow of Tastes Hawaii

HAWAIIAN ICE - Beverages—carbonated ☆ - Canandaigua Wine Co. Inc.

HAWAIIAN ICE PARTY - Toys - Mattel, Inc.

HAWAIIAN ISLAND - Salad dressings—bottled - Hawaiian Island Spice

HAWAIIAN ISLAND CRISP - Cookies - Hawaii Candy Inc.

HAWAIIAN ISLAND POPS - Candy ☆ - Amurol Confections Co.

HAWAIIAN ISLE - Beverages—alcohol ☆ - Consolidated Distilled Products Inc.

HAWAIIAN JULEP - Fruit drink - Hawaiian Julep, Inc.

HAWAIIAN KETTLE - Potato chips ☆ - Anheuser-Busch Companies Inc.

HAWAIIAN KNIGHTS - Publisher's imprints - Hard Hat Records

HAWAIIAN LEGENDS - Apparel and accessories - Design Tees Hawaii Inc.

HAWAIIAN LITES - Candles ☆ - Will & Baumer, Inc.

HAWAIIAN LUAU LITES - Candles ☆ - Aloha Candle Manufacturing Co. Inc.

HAWAIIAN MAGIC - Cosmetics - Wilshire Group Inc.

HAWAIIAN ODYSSEY - Computer software - SubLogic Corp.

HAWAIIAN OHANA - Jams and jellies - Hawaiian Ohana Food, Ltd.

HAWAIIAN PASSION - Barbecue sauce - Hawaiian Plantations Inc.

HAWAIIAN PLANTATIONS - Food products - Hawaiian Plantations Inc.

HAWAIIAN PRINCESS - Toys - Milton Bradley Co.

HAWAIIAN PRO DESIGNS - Sporting goods - Hawaiian Pro Designs

HAWAIIAN PRODUCE CO. - Towels - Aloha Candle Manufacturing Co. Inc.

HAWAIIAN PUNCH - Fruit drinks—bottled or canned - Nabisco Foods Group

HAWAIIAN PUNCH DODGE DAYTONA - Toys—electronic - Bird Bromiticous Inc.

HAWAIIAN PUNCH LITE - Fruit drinks—bottled or canned - Nabisco Foods Group

HAWAIIAN PUNCH TYPHOON BLASTERS - Fruit drinks—bottled or canned - Procter & Gamble Co.

HAWAIIAN RAINBOW INTERLINE FARE - Air transportation—passengers - Hawaiian Airlines, Inc.

HAWAIIAN ROYALES - Apparel and accessories - Hard Hat Records

HAWAIIAN SALROSE - Teas - Hawaiian Tropical Teas Inc.

HAWAIIAN SILKY - Hair care products - Green Acre

HAWAIIAN SPICY CHICKEN - Seasonings - Noh Foods International

HAWAIIAN SPOON - Fishing lures - Fred Arbogast Co. Inc.

HAWAIIAN STAR - Fruits—canned ☆ - Maui Pineapple Co.

HAWAIIAN STYLE - Apparel—men's - Local Motion, Inc.

HAWAIIAN STYLE BAND - Tapes, compact discs, and records - Wade Cambern

HAWAIIAN SUN - Food products - Hawaiian Sun Products Inc.

HAWAIIAN SUNDAE - Ice cream - United Dairy Farmers Inc.

HAWAIIAN SUNRISE - Juices - Chiquita Brands, Inc.

HAWAIIAN SUNSET - Floor coverings—carpet and rugs ☆ - Customweave Carpets Inc.

HAWAIIAN SUNSET - Floor coverings—carpet and rugs ☆ - Zenith Carpets

HAWAIIAN TAN - Sunblocks - Caribia, Cosmetic Research Laboratories Inc.

HAWAIIAN TEXTILES - Fabrics - G. Von Hamm Textiles Inc.

HAWAIIAN TREATS PARTY - Dolls - Mattel, Inc.

HAWAIIAN TROPIC - Apparel—children's ☆ - Backflips

HAWAIIAN TROPIC - Skin care products - Tanning Research Laboratories Inc.

HAWAIIAN VISTA - Floor coverings—carpet and rugs ☆ - Karastan-Bigelow Inc.

HAWAIIAN WHITE GINGER - Colognes ☆ - Avon Products, Inc.

HAWAIIAN WIGGLER - Fishing lures - Fred Arbogast Co. Inc.

HAWAIIAN WOODROSE - Candles ☆ - Aloha Candle Manufacturing Co. Inc.

HAWAIICE - Kitchen appliances - Back to Basics Products Inc.

HAWAII'S FAVORITE - Bottle caps - Yick Lung Co., Inc.

HAWAII'S FINEST SHAVE ICE - Food products - Gold Medal Products Co.

HAWAII'S OWN - Fruit drinks—bottled or canned - Hawaiian Juice Industries Ltd.

HAWAII'S OWN PARADISE PUNCH - Juices - Hawaiian Juice Industries Ltd.

HAWES - Furniture polish - American Home Products Corp.

HAWES WENSLEORLE - Food products - Crystal Food Import Corp.

HAWESTA - Fish—fresh or frozen - Haram-Christensen Corp.

HAWG - Motor vehicle parts and accessories ☆ - Custom Chrome, Inc.

HAWG BOSS - Fishing lures - Yakima Bait Co.

HAWG DAWG - Fishing lures - Snag Proof Manufacturing, Inc.

HAWG HACKLE WORM - Fishing lures - Magic Products, Inc.

HAWG HUNTER - Apparel and accessories - Don P. Roccoforte

HAWG-LY - Fishing lures - Lawrence P. Davidson

HAWG PEN GRAND CHAMPION FORMULA 1 - Barbecue sauce and seasoning - All American Bar-B-Que Co., Inc.

HAWG TIES - Dog food ☆ - Petsations Pet Products

HAWIE - Hardware - Hawie Manufacturing Co.

HAWIIAN SECRETS - Hair curlers - Hawaiian Secrets International Inc.

HAWK - Archery equipment - Saunders Archery Co.

HAWK - Audio equipment - Shahinian Acoustics Ltd.

HAWK - Automotive parts and accessories - Hop-Cap Inc.

HAWK - Automotive parts and accessories - Lancaster Colony Automotive Group

HAWK - Bicycles ☆ - Roadmaster Corp.

HAWK - Boats—fishing ☆ - C-G Industries Inc.

HAWK - Boats—motor - Glastex Co.

HAWK - Boats—motor ☆ - Skeeter Products Inc.

HAWK - Calculators ☆ - Brookes & Gatehouse Inc.

HAWK - Colognes - Mennen Co.

HAWK - Computer peripheral equipment - American Gage and Machine Co.

☆ = Now out of production

HAWK - Disk drives–computer - Seagate Technology, Inc.
HAWK - Electronic equipment ☆ - Moor Electronics Inc.
HAWK - Fire extinguishers - Hawk International, Inc.
HAWK - Golfing equipment - Allied Golf Co.
HAWK - Knives–pocket - Queen Cutlery Co.
HAWK - Motor vehicles - Ransomes-Cushman-Ryan
HAWK - Shoes–athletic ☆ - Brookfield Athletic Co. Inc.
HAWK - Sporting goods ☆ - Powell Skateboards
HAWK - Telephone apparatus ☆ - RF Communications Div.
HAWK - Toys–guns ☆ - Ray Plastic Inc.
HAWK - Trailers–travel - Jayco Inc.
HAWK - Trailers–truck ☆ - Sun-Lite Inc.
HAWK 747 - Luggage ☆ - Shalam Imports Inc.
HAWK 800 - Rug cleaning machines–commercial ☆ - Castex Industries Inc.
HAWK ARTS INTERNATIONAL RECORDS - Recording label - Hawk Arts Co.
HAWK CREST - Wines - Stag's Leap Wine Cellars
HAWK DUAL 8 - Projectors–photographic ☆ - Edixa Camera Co.
HAWK EYE - Golfing equipment - Golfsmith International Inc.
HAWK-EYE - Motor vehicle parts and accessories - Rosco, Inc.
HAWK EYE - Sporting goods - Brinkmann Corp.
HAWK I - Skis ☆ - Nash Manufacturing Inc.
HAWK MISSILE LAUNCHER - Toys - Tyco Toys
HAWK MODULE - Audio equipment - Shahinian Acoustics Ltd.
HAWK MOUNTAIN - Footwear - Hawk Mountain Trading Co.
HAWK MOUNTAIN - Shirts - Wrights Knitwear Corp.
HAWK PRO - Bicycles ☆ - Roadmaster Corp.
HAWK QUILL - Pens ☆ - Hunt Manufacturing Co.
HAWKBUCKER - Musical instrument accessories - Seymour Duncan Pickups
HAWKEN - Chewing tobacco - Conwood Co. L.P.
HAWKEN - Rifles - Thompson/Center Arms
HAWKEN SHOP, THE - Tools–hand-operated - Hawken Shop
HAWKES - Glass products - Tiffin Glass Co. Inc.
HAWKEYE - Automotive parts and accessories ☆ - Optronics Inc.
HAWKEYE - Baskets–wood - Burlington Basket Co. Inc.
HAWKEYE - Bicycles - Columbia Manufacturing Inc.
HAWKEYE - Cameras - Eastman Kodak Co.
HAWKEYE - Computer software - Number Nine Visual Technology Corp.
HAWKEYE - Electrical testing instruments - Veris Industries, Inc.
HAWKEYE - Firearms, accessories, and parts - Welsh Sporting Goods Corp. (Boyt Div.)
HAWKEYE - Footwear–men's - Acme Boot Co., Inc.
HAWKEYE - Golfing equipment - Golfsmith International Inc.
HAWKEYE - Ladders–metal - John S. Tilley Ladders Co. Inc.
HAWKEYE - Medical apparatus - Linvatec Corp.
HAWKEYE - Revolvers - Sturm, Ruger & Co., Inc.
HAWKEYE - Tools - Sands Level & Tool
HAWKEYE - Toys–models - Estes Industries
HAWKEYE - Transmitting apparatus ☆ - VDO Pak Batteries
HAWKHAVEN - Food products - Hawkhaven Greenhouse Int'l.
HAWKHEAD - Automotive parts and accessories - Hawkhead Automotive Inc.
HAWKINS - Brushes ☆ - Mill Rose Co.
HAWKINS - Candy ☆ - Morla Corp.
HAWKINS GUIDE - Publisher's imprints - Blue Green Publishing, Inc.
HAWKMOON - Games - Chaosium Inc.
HAWKSLEY & WIGHT - Apparel–women's - Hart Schaffner & Marx
HAWLEY - Bicycles - Hawley Co. Inc.
HAWORTH - Furniture - Haworth, Inc.
HAWORTH DESIGNS - Apparel and accessories - Haworth Designs
HAWTHORN - Sporting goods - Brunswick Corp.
HAWTHORN BERRY TINCTURE - Tofu - Polam Wholesale Inc.
HAWTHORN BOOKS - Publisher's imprints - E.P. Dutton Inc.
HAWTHORN EXTRACT - Vitamins and nutritional supplements - Vitamin Research Products Inc.
HAWTHORN INN - Fabrics–tapestry ☆ - Coloroll Inc.
HAWTHORN MELLODY - Dairy products - Hawthorn Mellody Inc.
HAWTHORN-POWER - Vitamins and nutritional supplements ☆ - Nature's Herbs
HAWTHORNE - Apparel and accessories - Libertyville Saddle Shop, Inc.
HAWTHORNE - Artists' materials - J.L. Hammett Co.
HAWTHORNE - Belts–money - Kohler Co.
HAWTHORNE - Cabinets - Yorktowne Inc.
HAWTHORNE - Clocks ☆ - General Time Corp. (Westclox/Seth Thomas Div.)
HAWTHORNE - Dishes–china - Viletta China Co.
HAWTHORNE - Firearms, accessories, and parts ☆ - Montgomery Ward & Co. Inc.
HAWTHORNE - Floor coverings–carpet and rugs ☆ - Masland Corp.

HAWTHORNE - Flour–blended ☆ - Ross Industries Inc.
HAWTHORNE - Water–mineral - Hawthorne Spring Water
HAWTHORNE - Wood products - Georgia-Pacific Corp.
HAWTHORNE HILL - Comforters - American Pacific Enterprises, Inc.
HAWTHORNE HOUSE - Preserved foods–canned - Hamady Bros. Food Markets
HAWTHORNE PORCHLIGHT COLLECTIONS - Figurines - Hawthorne Architectural Register, Ltd.
HAY DAY - Colognes ☆ - Avon Products, Inc.
HAY FEVER - Pharmaceutical preparations ☆ - Boiron Inc.
HAY FEVER AIDE - Pharmaceutical preparations - Boericke & Tafel
HAY-GARD - Tarpaulins - Xton, Inc.
HAY-SHEDD - Agricultural chemicals - Vigortone AG Products Inc.
HAYASHI - Apparel–athletic - Pioneer Interstate, Inc.
HAYASHI - Hair care products - Hayashi for Hair Inc.
HAYAT - Water–bottled or canned - Holsa Inc.
HAYDEN - Automotive parts and accessories - Hayden Inc.
HAYDEN - Housewares - Scott Fetzer Co.
HAYDEN BAY - Cabinets–wood - Huggy Bear's Cupboards, Inc.
HAYDEN HOUSE - Food products - Tyson Foods Inc.
HAYDEN'S - Skin care products - Robinson Laboratories Inc.
HAYDRAN - Health care products ☆ - Halsey Drug Co. Inc.
HAYES - Automotive parts and accessories - Echlin Inc.
HAYES - Tools - Great Neck Saw Manufacturers, Inc.
HAYES - Trailers–truck ☆ - EBM'
HAYES PARKER - Figurines - Hayes Parker
HAYES SMARTCOM II - Communications equipment–satellite - Hayes Microcomputer Products Inc.
HAYES WHEELS - Wheels–motor vehicle - Hayes Wheels International, Inc.
HAYESCONNECT - Computer software - Hayes Microcomputer Products Inc.
HAYFEBROL - Pharmaceutical preparations - Scot-Tussin Pharmacal Co.
HAYFLOWERPILLOW - Health care products - European Skin & Haircare
HAYKING II ORCHARDGRASS - Flowers, plants, and seeds - Jacklin Seed
HAYK'S TRIANGLE - Mayonnaise - Stache Foods
HAYLE - Artists' materials - Andrews/Nelson/Whitehead
HAYLITT - Bedding–linen - Dan River Inc.
HAYMAKER - Apparel–women's - Crystal Brands Inc.
HAYMAKER - Farm machinery - Worksaver, Inc.
HAYMAKER - Footwear - Tog Shop, Inc.
HAYMAN - Musical instruments - Dallas Music Industries Ltd.
HAYMARKET - Cheese - Chesman Inc.
HAYMARKET - Fabrics–tapestry ☆ - Coloroll Inc.
HAYMARKET SQUARE - Floor coverings - Mannington Resilient Floors
HAYNES - Fabrics–velvet - Majestic Mills Inc.
HAYNES - Flutes - William S. Haynes Co.
HAYNES-SCHWELM - Flutes - Enzo Pizzi
HAYPRESS PASTA CO. - Food products - Cowan & Fransman
HAYRIDE II: SUMMER PICNIC - Wallpaper ☆ - Imperial Wallcoverings, Inc.
HAYSMA - Pharmaceutical preparations - Haysma Co. Inc.
HAYSTACK - Toys–stuffed - Mary Meyer Corp.
HAYSTAX - Candy ☆ - Earl's Candy Co.
HAYWARD - Tobacco products - Lane Ltd.
HAYWARD - Watches - Bulova Corp.
HAYWARDS MILITARY - Pickles - British Wholesale Imports
HAYWOOD - Clocks - General Time Corp. (Westclox/Seth Thomas Div.)
HAYWOOD - Wines - Buena Vista Winery, Inc.
HAYWOOD - Wines - Los Chamizal Winery
HAYWOOD ESTATE ZINFANDEL - Wines - Buena Vista Winery, Inc.
HAYWORTH - Glassware–household ☆ - Lenox Crystal, Inc.
HAYWORTH - Tableware–china - Lenox, Inc.
HAZ-CAM - Video equipment - Spectrum Dynamics
HAZ-MAT - Coveralls - Distributors Service Corp.
HAZ-MAT - Sporting goods - Donald D. Cassel
HAZ-VAULT - Prefabricated buildings–metal - Haz-Stor Co.
HAZAN - Postcards - Fotofolio Inc.
HAZARD GUARD - Apparel and accessories - Durafab Inc.
HAZARD/GUARD PLUS - Apparel and accessories - Durafab Inc.
HAZARD HUT - Prefabricated buildings–wood - ENPAC Corp.
HAZARD MASTER - Umbrellas - Haas-Jordan Co.
HAZARDGARD - Air conditioning equipment - Friedrich Air Conditioning Co.
HAZCAD APEX ENVIRONMENTAL, INC. - Computer software ☆ - Apex Environmental, Inc.
HAZCAO - Computer software - Apex Environmental, Inc.
HAZEBUSTER - Computer software - VayTek, Inc.
HAZEL - Attache cases - Hazel Inc.
HAZEL - Fruits–canned - National Tea Co.

☆ = Now out of production

HAZEL - Housewares ☆ - Scio Pottery Co.

HAZEL - Paper–bond - Goes Lithographing Co.

HAZEL - Watches - Bulova Corp.

HAZEL BISHOP - Cosmetics - Hazel Bishop International

HAZEL FRESH - Cleaning preparations - W.L. Young Inc.

HAZEL GROVE - Wallpaper - Seabrook Wallcoverings, Inc.

HAZELCREEK CLOTHING COMPANY - Apparel and accessories - T.C. Lyle, Inc.

HAZELESSENCE - Cosmetics - T.N. Dickinson Co.

HAZELETS - Health care products - T.N. Dickinson Co.

HAZELNUT MELTAWAY GENEVAS - Candy - Home of the Hebert Candies, Inc.

HAZELNUT 'N HONEY - Candy - Doug Johnson, Inc.

HAZEL'S - Hobby kits - Jessies Hobbies & Crafts

HAZEL'S - Novelty items–paper - Roman Arts

HAZELTINE - Apparel and accessories - Hazeltine National Golf Club

HAZELTINE NATIONAL GOLF CLUB - Apparel and accessories - Hazeltine National Golf Club

HAZELWOOD FARMS - Food products - Wetterau Inc.

HAZEN'S NOTCH SPRING - Teas - Vermont Tea & Maple

HAZLE - Novelty items ☆ - Chase Collection, Inc.

HAZLETON BROS. - Pianos - Kohler & Campbell Inc.

HAZMAT - Apparel and accessories - CSP Apparel, Inc.

HAZMAT - Computer software - Bureau of Dangerous Goods, Ltd.

HAZMAX - Paper products - Georgia-Pacific Corp.

HAZOGEL - Pharmaceutical preparations - Nortech Laboratories

HAZORB - Cleaning preparations - Hazorb Inc.

HAZPROFILE - Computer software - Petroleum Information Corp.

HAZRESPONSE - Chemical preparations - Spill 911, Inc.

HAZSEARCH - Computer software - Petroleum Information Corp.

HAZSOFT - Computer software - Resource Compliance, Inc.

HAZTAINER - Containers–plastic - Hardigg Industries, Inc.

HAZTRAC - Computer software - Hoes Engineering, Inc.

HAZWOPER KITS - Educational materials - Marcom Group, Ltd.

HAZY - Film - General Electric Co.

HB - Ammunition - Olin Corp. (Winchester Div.)

HB - Grinders - Jimei Tools, Inc.

HB - Recording label - Hampton-Brown Co., Inc.

H.B. - Skin care products - H.B. Accessories

HB - Tools–hand-operated - H B Carbide Co., Inc.

H.B. 15 - Animal feed supplements - Farnam Cos. Inc.

H.B. CHOCOLATES - Chocolate candy - Roth & Liebmann Inc.

HB/HENRIOT - Pottery - Quimper Faience Inc.

H.B. INTIMATE - Underwear and nightwear - Spencer Supports Ltd.

HB200 - Musical instrument accessories - Music Accessories Manufacturing Co. Inc.

HBK - Flowers, plants, and seeds - Hornbeck Seed Co., Inc.

HBO - Hats - Time Warner Entertainment Co., L.P.

HBP - Apparel and accessories - Mark A. Rasmussen

HBP - Pharmaceutical preparations ☆ - Saron Pharmacal Corp.

HBR - Machinery - HBR Industries Inc.

HBS HOME BUYERS SERVICE - Computer software - MBS Real Estate Services, Inc.

HBSI CALIBER - Computer software - HBS International, Inc.

HBW - Plumbing fixtures - Harrington Brass Works Ltd. Inc.

HBX - Audio equipment - HBX International, Inc.

HBX - Plywood - Linnton Plywood Association

HC - Apparel and accessories - Houndstooth Clothing Co., Inc.

HC - Auto and machine parts - Hadady Corp.

HC - Cleaning preparations - Hydro-Chem Systems, Inc.

HC - Jewelry - College of the Holy Cross

HC - Pharmaceutical preparations - C&M Pharmacal, Inc.

HC - Pharmaceutical preparations ☆ - Saron Pharmacal Corp.

HC - Shampoos - Highpoint Chemicals Inc.

HC/2 - Computer peripheral equipment - General Scanning Inc.

HC-5 - Paper–resinous - Luminos Photo Corp.

HC-22A - Air conditioning equipment - Oz Technology, Inc.

HC-110 - Photographic equipment - Eastman Kodak Co.

H.C. DELUXE - Musical-instrument strings and accessories - Howard Core & Co. Inc.

HC DERMA-PAX - Health care products - Recsei Laboratories

HC-FORM - Pharmaceutical preparations ☆ - Recsei Laboratories

HC FORMULA - Hair care products - Mastey De Paris

HC FORMULA + B5 - Skin care products - Mastey De Paris

HC THE BOURBON HERITAGE COLLECTION - Liquors - United Distillers of North America

HCC - Ammunition - Hansen Cartridge Co.

HCC: HME - Computer software - Healthcare Computer Corp.

HCC: NURSE - Computer software - Healthcare Computer Corp.

HCC PAR EXCELLENCE - Cheese ☆ - Haram-Christensen Corp.

HCF - Beverages–malt - Kalsec, Inc.

HCG BEST-SLIDE MONOCLONAL II - Pharmaceutical preparations - Wampole Laboratories Div.

HCG URINE CONTROL SET - Pharmaceutical preparations - Wampole Laboratories Div.

HCH 81 PLUS - Plastics–laminated ☆ - HCH Associates Inc.

HCL ADVANTAGE - Chemical preparations - Great Lakes Biochemical Co., Inc.

HCM - Bicycles - Giant Bicycle, Inc.

HCP - Tools–power-driven - Lako Tool and Manufacturing Co. Inc.

HCT MAMA - Breads - Rosie's Fine Foods Inc.

HCV - Antibiotics - Saron Pharmacal Corp.

HD - Apparel and accessories - Harley-Davidson, Inc.

HD - Cases–musical instrument - HD Electric Co.

HD-28 - Floor coverings–carpet and rugs ☆ - Mohawk Carpet Corp.

HD-50 - Concrete products - Dayton Superior Corp.

H.D. DEGREASER - Cleaning preparations - Analab Inc.

HD-DOMS/OSQL - Computer software - HyperDesk Corp.

HD HEAVY DUTY - Machinery - Broan Manufacturing Co., Inc.

HD (HIGH DYNAMIC) - Audio equipment - ESS Laboratory Inc.

HD-PRO - Audio equipment - TDK Electronics Corp.

HD40 - Gloves–rubber ☆ - Granet Inc.

H.D.C. - Degreasing solvents ☆ - Paxon Manufacturing Co.

HDCD - Audio equipment - Pacific Microsonics, Inc.

HDH - Phonographs ☆ - Fantasy Inc.

HDM PLUS - Electrical equipment - Teradyne, Inc.

HDMI - High density packaging - Hughes Aircraft Co.

H.D.O. - Plywood - Harbor Sales Co.

HDO - Sunglasses - Oakley, Inc.

HDP - Fuel additives ☆ - Demert & Dougherty, Inc.

HDR - Frames–eyeglass - Hoya Corp. USA

HDR - Hair care products - Revlon Consumer Products Corp.

HDT - Oils–lubricating - Getty Petroleum Marketing, Inc.

HDX - Magnetic tape–blank - Tomei Industries (America), Inc.

HDX BACKBOARD - Medical equipment - Life Support Products Inc.

HE - Filters–air - Hendee Enterprises, Inc.

HE - Floor coverings–carpet and rugs - Beaulieu of America, Inc.

HE - Jewelry - E.B. Harvey and Co., Inc.

HE - Medical apparatus - Health Enterprises, Inc.

HE 600 HEPA AIR CLEANER - Deodorizers ☆ - Vaportek, Inc.

HE MAKES ME BLUSH - Cosmetics - Cosmedic Concepts, Inc.

HE-MAN - Bacon ☆ - Dold Foods Inc.

HE-MAN - Erasers - Bright Boy Abrasives

HE-MAN - Toys - Mattel, Inc.

HEA - Reflectors–optical - Optical Coating Laboratory Inc.–Santa Rosa Div.

HEAD - Shampoos - Head Shampoo, Inc.

HEAD - Sporting goods - Head Sports USA

HEAD AID - Vitamins and nutritional supplements - Planetary Formulas

HEAD & CHEST - Cold remedies - Procter & Gamble Co.

HEAD & SHOULDERS - Shampoos - Procter & Gamble Co.

HEAD BALLS - Balls - Catco, Inc.

HEAD BANGER - Bicycles ☆ - Huffy Corp.

HEAD BOYS - Apparel and accessories - American Argo Corp.

HEAD BUTTING ROBOGOAT - Toys - Saban Entertainment, Inc.

HEAD CAPS - Analgesics ☆ - Oakmont Investments Co.

HEAD CASE - Hats - Leo R. Estopare

HEAD CHUNK - Recording label - Head Chunk Records

HEAD CUFF - Instruments for Research and Industry, I2R Inc.

HEAD DONUT - Instruments for Research and Industry, I2R Inc.

HEAD FORE COVER - Toys–automobiles - Eugene I. Helm

HEAD GAMES - Games - Head Games, Unlimited

HEAD GEAR - Condoms - Byron H. Butler, Jr.

HEAD GIRLS - Apparel and accessories - American Argo Corp.

HEAD-GUARD - Rackets–tennis - Head Sports USA

HEAD HOG - Beverages–malt - Head Hog Beer

HEAD HONCHOS - Novelty items - Paul A. Scheeler

HEAD-KNITS - Crocheted and knitted items - Reliable of Milwaukee

HEAD LASER - Flashlights - Ezekiel S. Carter

HEAD LIGHTS - Crocheted and knitted items ☆ - Schuessler Knitting Mills Inc.

HEAD LINER - Computer software ☆ - Zephyr Services

HEAD-LITE - Lighting equipment–bicycles ☆ - Wonder Corp. of America

HEAD LOCK - Musical instrument accessories ☆ - Selmer Co. Inc.

HEAD MASTER - Clocks ☆ - SMH (US) Inc.

HEAD-MATE - Toilets–portable - Wilcox-Crittenden

HEAD OIL - Musical instrument accessories ☆ - LP Music Group

HEAD ON - Hair care products - Alleghany Pharmacal Corp.

HEAD OVER HEELS - Footwear - Cardinal Shoe Corp.

HEAD OVER HEELS - Perfumes - Helen of Troy Corp.

HEAD OVER HEELS - Sporting goods - Sport Fun, Inc.

HEAD REST - Herbal products - Boutique Alternare, Inc.

HEAD SCENTS - Deodorizers - Toys Etc., Inc.

HEAD SHOK - Bicycle parts and accessories - Cannondale Corp.

HEAD START - Fishing lures - Wanabe Outdoors, Inc.

HEAD START - Oils–lubricating - Conklin Co., Inc.

HEAD START - Textbooks - Warner Bros. Publications

HEAD START - Vitamins and nutritional supplements - Head Start Vitamin Products

HEAD START HELSINKI FORMULA - Hair care products - Head Start Vitamin Products

HEAD STRONG - Hair care products - Gold Medal Hair Products Inc.

HEAD-TO-HEAD - Trading cards and stamps - Score Group, Inc.

HEAD TO HEAD SPORTS - Toys–electronic - Hasbro, Inc.

HEAD TO HEEL - Medical apparatus - USMS, Inc.

HEAD TO TAIL - Pet products - Lassie Pet Products

HEAD-TO-TOE - Shampoos ☆ - Sanitek Products Inc.

HEAD VEST - Hats - Bruce Adams

HEAD WRYTER - Golfing equipment - Plawood Mormac Corp.

HEADA-HAIR - Hair preparation - House of Zizaco Inc.

HEADACHE - Games - CBS Toys

HEADACHE BAND - Pharmaceutical preparations - Nutrience Inc.

HEADAIDE - Pharmaceutical preparations - Boericke & Tafel

HEADAIDE - Teas - Merz Apothecary Inc.

HEADBANGER - FISH LURES - Fishing lures - Hildebrandt Corp.

HEADBOARD HUGGER - Beds–hospital - Maxwell Products

HEADCRAFT - Wigs - Headcraft Manufacturing Corp.

HEADFIRST - Labels–paper - K-Tel International, Inc.

HEADGASKET - Visors - Life-Link International, Inc.

HEADHUGGER, THE - Wigs - Penthouse for Men

HEADHUNTER STORMTROOPER - Toys - Hasbro, Inc.

HEADHUNTERS HH - Eyeglasses - John P. Saik

HEADJAMMER - Amplifiers - Gibson Guitar Corp.

HEADJAMMERS - Amplifiers–musical instrument - Gibson Strings & Accessories

HEADKEEPER - Musical instrument accessories - Silver St. Inc.

HEADLAND - Golfing equipment - MacGregor Golf Co.

HEADLAND BICYCLE ACCESSORIES - Bicycle accessories - Headland Bicycle Accessories

HEADLIGHT-D-10 - Lamps ☆ - Luxo Corp.

HEADLINE - Agricultural products - BASF Corp.

HEADLINE - Banners - Micropore, Inc.

HEADLINE - Cigar boxes–wood - Consolidated Cigar Corp.

HEADLINE - Deodorizers - Pettibone Laboratories Inc.

HEADLINE AUDIO - Audio equipment - Prince Corp.

HEADLINE HARRY AND THE GREAT PAPER RACE - Computer software ☆ - Knowledge Adventure

HEADLINER - Electronic equipment - Bell & Howell Co.

HEADLINER - Floor coverings - Mannington Resilient Floors

HEADLINER - Floor coverings–carpet and rugs ☆ - Calladium & Marglen

HEADLINER - Floor waxes - National Chemsearch Corp.

HEADLINER - Hair care products - Helene Curtis Industries Inc.

HEADLINER - Headbands - Seirus Innovative Accessories, Inc.

HEADLINER - Wigs - Designs for Comfort Inc.

HEADLINER - Writing product - Binney & Smith Inc.

HEADLINERS - Apparel and accessories - Venture Stores, Inc.

HEADLINERS - Beads - Greene Plastics Corp.

HEADLINERS - Caps–baseball - California Headwear, Inc.

HEADLINERS - Combs ☆ - Ace Comb Co. Inc.

HEADLINERS - Glassware–household - Ceraglass Inc.

HEADLINERS PORTRAIT SCULPTURE - Statuary - Gary Carson

HEADLINERS SPORT - Apparel and accessories - Venture Stores, Inc.

HEADLINES BY H.I.S. - Apparel–men's - H.I.S. Sportswear

HEADLITE - Lamps ☆ - Prestigeline Inc.

HEADLITES - Barrettes ☆ - Adrian Perrault Jewelers

HEADLOCK - Hardware - Hickory Springs Manufacturing Co.

HEADLOCK - Helmets–athletic - American Recreation Co., Inc.

HEADLOCK - Toys–automobiles - Mattel, Inc.

HEADLONG - Colognes ☆ - Avon Products, Inc.

HEADRESS - Hair care products - Nexxus Products Co.

HEADRIN EXTRA-STRENGTH PAIN RELIEVER - Photo albums - Reese Chemical Co.

HEADS AND TAILS - Bicycle seat covers - Schnaubelt Shorts, Inc.

HEADS 'N TAILS - Fishing lures - Earl L. Lewis

HEADS 'N TAILS - Games - Smethport Specialty Co.

HEAD'S RITE - Infant product - Pansy Ellen Products, Inc.

HEADS UP - Food products - Robert L. Schilling

HEADS UP - Games ☆ - Milton Bradley Co.

HEADS UP - Hair care products - Gillette Co.

HEADS-UP - Life preservers - Stearns Manufacturing Co.

HEADS UP - Medical apparatus - Spencer Supports Ltd.

HEADS UP - Pins–jewelry - Fotoball USA Inc.

HEADS UP - Toys - Gold Inc.

HEADS UP - Trading cards and stamps - Topps Co., Inc.

HEADS UP TENT, THE - Sporting goods - Kellwood Co.

HEADSPACE - Computer software - Headspace, Inc.

HEADSPORT - Apparel and accessories - American Argo Corp.

HEADSTART - Brushes–hair - I. Sekine Co. Inc.

HEADSTART - Computers–personal ☆ - Philips Business Systems Co.

HEADSTART - Garden equipment ☆ - Fearing Manufacturing Co. Inc.

HEADSTART EXPLORER - Computers–personal ☆ - Philips Business Systems Co.

HEADSTART III - Computers–personal ☆ - Philips Business Systems Co.

HEADSTRONG - Educational materials - Denver Osteopathic Foundation

HEADSTRONG - Helmets–athletic - Wolverine World Wide, Inc.

HEADSTRONG - Shaving preparations - All American Brush Manufacturing Corp.

HEADSTRONG HELMETS - Helmets–athletic - Renaissance Marketing, Inc.

HEADTOG - Headwear - Colorado Contract Cut and Sew

HEADTRIP - Cameras–video - Headtrip, Inc.

HEADWAVES - Eyeglasses - E-M International

HEADWAY - Hats - Headway International Inc.

HEADWAY - Pillows - Perfect Fit Industries, Inc.

HEADWAY TECHNOLOGIES - Computer peripheral equipment - Headway Technologies, Inc.

HEADWINDS - Helmets–athletic - Cycle Products Co.

HEADWIPES - Cleaning preparations ☆ - Auto Cellular Systems

HEADZYME - Sewage treatment equipment - Marine Development & Research Corp.

HEAL AID PLUS - Pharmaceutical preparations - Reese Chemical Co.

HEAL PAD - Medical apparatus - Roho, Inc.

HEAL-RITE - Chemical preparations - Nott Manufacturing Co. Inc.

HEAL THE WORLD - Recording label - Heal the World Foundation

HEALEY - Thermostats - Stanley G. Flagg & Co.

HEALING ADVANTAGE - Medical devices - Amei Technologies Inc.

HEALING GARDEN, THE - Colognes - Coty US Inc.

HEALING HEARTS - Pillows - Kane Enterprises

HEALING LIGHT - Candles - Madu Lamar, Inc.

HEALING SHOE - Health care products ☆ - Meiller Co.

HEALING THROUGH HAPPINESS - Toys - Mcdonald's Corp.

HEALING TRENDS/STARS - Humphrey Systems

HEALITE - Footwear - John A Zeffer

HEALON - Pharmaceutical preparations - Kabi Pharmacia Inc.

HEALOX - Skin care products ☆ - Majestic Drug Co., Inc.

HEALTH - Copper compounds ☆ - Regal Ware, Inc.

HEALTH - Fish–fresh or frozen - Abramo Fish Co. Inc.

HEALTH-AGE - Water–mineral - Coastal Healthcare

HEALTH-AIDE - Computer software - Programming Technology Inc.

HEALTH AIDE - Juices - L and A Juice Co. Inc.

HEALTH AIRE - Air purification systems - Pollenex Corp.

HEALTH ALERT - Computer software - Stratecision, Inc.

HEALTH AND FITNESS - Calendars - Moe Sanford Photography

HEALTH & FITNESS OPTIONS - Directories - VV Publishing Corp.

HEALTH & OUR BODIES - Computer software - Right on Programs

HEALTH & WHOLENESS - Health care products - Maharishi Ayur-Ved Products International, Inc.

HEALTH AT HOME - Heating pads–electric - Sunbeam Corp.

HEALTH BAR - Food products ☆ - Knudsen Dairy Products

HEALTH BEST - Snack foods - Health Best Distributors Inc.

HEALTH BLEND - Dietary pet food - Colgate-Palmolive Co.

HEALTH BRANDS - Pharmaceutical preparations - Republic Drug Co. Inc.

HEALTH BUILDER - Exercising equipment - Battle Creek Equipment Co.

HEALTH CARE - Skin care products - Recreations

HEALTH CAREPOSTERS - Educational materials - Clement Communications Inc.

HEALTH CHECK - Cheese - Milk House Cheese Corp.

HEALTH CHECK - Pharmaceutical preparations - Technical Chemicals and Products, Inc.

HEALTH CLEANSE - Vitamins and nutritional supplements - Bioenergy Nutrient's Inc.

HEALTH CLUB - Dairy products - Crowley Foods, Inc.

HEALTH CLUB - Giftware - Pollenex Corp.

HEALTH CLUB STEPPER - Exercising equipment - American Direct Marketing, Inc.

HEALTH COMFORT - Mattresses - Spring Air Bedding Inc.

HEALTH CRAFT - Blenders - Health Craft, Inc.

HEALTH DEFENSE - Vitamins and nutritional supplements - Healthcare Laboratories, Inc.

HEALTH DIET LIFE - Food products - US Foodservice

HEALTH-DRI - Underwear and nightwear - Health-Dri Systems, Inc.

HEALTH EPA - Health care products - Health Products Corp.

HEALTH EXPRESS - Vitamins and nutritional supplements ☆ - Nature's Way Products, Inc.

HEALTH FARMS - Bagel crisps, chips, etc. - International Baking Co.

HEALTH FIRST - Food products ☆ - Bodin Foods Inc.

HEALTH FOODS PLUS - Food products - Bertae Health Specialties Inc.

HEALTH FROM THE HIVE - Vitamins and nutritional supplements - La Parfumerie Inc.

HEALTH FROM THE SUN - Oils–essential - Oakmont Investments Co.

HEALTH GAIN - Vitamins and nutritional supplements - Metagenics, Inc.

HEALTH GUARD - Skin care products - Kutol Products Co.

HEALTH GUIDES - Calendars - St. Joseph Medical Center of Fort Wayne Inc.

HEALTH HERO - Video games - Raya Systems, Inc.

HEALTH IS WEALTH - Snack foods - Snowball Foods, Inc.

HEALTH JOURNEYS - Recording label - Image Paths, Inc.

HEALTH LINE - Cough medicines - Eckerd Corp.

HEALTH LINE - Egg product - Papetti's Hygrade Egg Products, Inc.

HEALTH LINK - Soap - Barrow Riddell & Associates

HEALTH LITE - Sandwiches–prepackaged - E.A. Sween Co.

HEALTH MATE - Juices - Wagner Excello Foods Inc.

HEALTH MAX - Vitamins and nutritional supplements - Vitamin Classics, Inc.

HEALTH-MOR - Vacuum cleaners and accessories - Health-Mor Inc.

HEALTH NUGGETS - Cereal - Breadshop's Natural Foods

HEALTH NUT - Apparel and accessories - Michael John Kent

HEALTH/NUTRITION - Publisher's imprints - Keats Publishing Co.

HEALTH O METER - Medical apparatus - Health O Meter, Inc.

HEALTH O METER - Scales–bathroom - Healthometer

HEALTH OFFICIAL MASCOT, THE - Jewelry - Rene J. Espinosa

HEALTH-PAK - Medical kits - Health-Pak Inc.

HEALTH PREVIEW - Computer software ☆ - CarePoint Analytics Inc.

HEALTH PRO - Pharmaceutical preparations - Nirvana Labs

HEALTH PROTECTION - Vitamins and nutritional supplements ☆ - Schiff Products, Inc.

HEALTH PROTECTOR - Vitamins and nutritional supplements ☆ - Schiff Products, Inc.

HEALTH-RAY - Food products ☆ - Countrymark Cooperative, Inc.

HEALTH RESPONSE SYSTEM 3000 - Computer peripheral equipment - Johnson & Johnson

HEALTH RICH - Snack foods - Country Grown Foods

HEALTH RIGHT - Bagels - Tryum Corp.

HEALTH RIZER, THE - Furniture - A-1 Manufacturing Corp.

HEALTH RX - Pharmaceutical preparations - Able Laboratories Inc.

HEALTH SALUD REACTIVITY REACTIVIDAD FLAMMABILITY INFLAMMABLIDAD - Cleaning preparations - IVAX Industries, Inc.

HEALTH SELECTIONS - Food products - Hormel Foods Corp.

HEALTH SHEEN - Pet products - RHB Enterprises

HEALTH SHIELD - Gloves–rubber - Safeskin Corp.

HEALTH SIGH - Diagnostic apparatus - Immuchem Technology, Inc.

HEALTH SPA - Cosmetics - Ray Hayes Inc.

HEALTH STONE - Mattresses - Hwan Sang Kim

HEALTH STRIDE - Footwear ☆ - E.S. Originals, Inc.

HEALTH SUMMIT - Snack foods - Pharmavite Corp.

HEALTH SUPPORT - Medical apparatus - Carolon Co.

HEALTH TABS - Vitamins and nutritional supplements - MDR Fitness Corp.

HEALTH TEA - Teas - Modern Tea Packers

HEALTH TECH - Exercising equipment - Formula Ventures

HEALTH-TECH - Watches - Advance Watch Co. Ltd.

HEALTH-TEX - Apparel–children's - Health-Tex Inc.

HEALTH-TEX - Apparel–children's - Oneita Industries Inc.

HEALTH TIME - Cheese ☆ - Leprino Foods

HEALTH TIME - Soups–canned - I. Rokeach and Sons Inc.

HEALTH TRAK - Socks - Railroad Sock, Inc.

HEALTH TWINS - Health care products - Pacific Genesis Inc.

HEALTH VALLEY - Food products - Health Valley Food

HEALTH VEGGI-LEAN - Vitamins and nutritional supplements - Food Innovations International, Inc.

HEALTH WALKER - Treadmills - Battle Creek Equipment Co.

HEALTH WATCH - Safety products - Health Watch, Inc.

HEALTH WORKS - Hair care products ☆ - Smithkline Beecham Corp.

HEALTHAIRE - Health care products - Healthdyne Technologies, Inc.

HEALTHCAIR - Medical apparatus - Squire-Cogswell Co.

HEALTHCARE NATURALS - Health care products ☆ - Nature's Herbs

HEALTHCARE PROFESSIONAL PLANNER - Calendars - Pindar Publications Ltd.

HEALTHCOMMAND - Computer software - Stratecision, Inc.

HEALTHCREST - Pharmaceutical preparations - Roc E. Gantt

HEALTHDESK - Computer software - HealthDesk Corp.

HEALTHEES - Apparel–women's - Bi-Flex International

HEALTHFIRST - Pharmaceutical preparations - Healthfirst Corp.

HEALTHFIT - Computer software - ARA Human Factors

HEALTHFLOW - Bottles–plastic - Johnson & Johnson

HEALTHFUL CREATIONS - Seafood products–fresh or frozen - Schwan's Sales Enterprises, Inc.

HEALTHGARD - Vitamins and nutritional supplements - Miles Inc.

HEALTHGUARD - Ophthalmic goods - Bausch & Lomb Pharmaceuticals, Inc.

HEALTHGUARD - Water filters - Healthguard, Inc.

HEALTHGUARDE - Disinfectants - Timaru Technology Group

HEALTHGUIDE - Computer software - Staywell Health Management Systems Inc.

HEALTHIER BALANCE FOR A HEALTHIER PET, A - Pet food - Colgate-Palmolive Co.

HEALTHIER CHOICE CARPETS & CUSHIONS - Floor coverings–carpet and rugs - Healthier Choice Carpets & Cushions, Inc.

HEALTHIER EATING MADE EASY - Publisher's imprints - Pillsbury Co.

HEALTHIER EGG, THE - Eggs - Nabisco Foods Group

HEALTHIER JUNK FOOD, THE - Cakes - Healthier Junk Food Co. Inc.

HEALTHIEST STORY EVER TOLD, THE - Apparel and accessories - Joseph P. Piechota

HEALTHKIST - Juices - Daily Juice Products Inc.

HEALTHKNIT - Underwear and nightwear - Stanwood Corp.

HEALTHLINE - Inhalers - Healthline Medical

HEALTHLINK - Alarms–personal - Guardtech Industries Inc.

HEALTHLITE SYSTEM - Health care products - Healthwatchers System

HEALTHMAPS - Computer software - Towers, Perrin, Forster & Crosby, Inc.

HEALTHMARK - Medical apparatus - Healthmark Industries Co.

HEALTHMASTER - Computer peripheral equipment - Healthmaster, Inc.

HEALTHMASTER - Computer software - SourceView Software International

HEALTHMASTER - Exercising equipment - Roadmaster Corp.

HEALTHMATE - Calendars - Kathleen R. De Remer

HEALTHMATE - Stethoscopes - Prestige Medical Corp.

HEALTHMAX - Exercise equipment - Willabee & Ward

HEALTHOBJECTS - Computer software - Healthobjects, Inc.

HEALTHOMETER - Scales–bathroom - Healthometer

HEALTHPAK - Meat products–beef - Gorges Foodservice, Inc.

HEALTHPOINT - Pharmaceutical preparations - DPT Laboratories Inc.

HEALTHQUEST - Athletic associations - Clemson Fitness, Inc.

HEALTHRICH FARMS - Meat products–poultry - Ostrich Producers Coop of the Mid-West

HEALTHSAFE - Skin care products - Americare Health Products

HEALTHSEAL COLLECTION - Fabrics - Mayer-Paetz, Inc.

HEALTHSOFT - Computer software - Healthsoft, Inc.

HEALTHSOUNDS - Recording label - Santa Rosa Health Care, Inc.

HEALTHSPEC - Paints - Sherwin-Williams Automotive Finishes Corp.

HEALTHSTAR - Vitamins and nutritional supplements - Sportstar Health & Fitness

HEALTHSTAR MEDICAL SAVINGS CARD - Identification tags - Healthstar Managed Care Corp.

HEALTHSTEP - Computer software - Staywell Health Management Systems Inc.

HEALTHSUITE - Computer peripheral equipment - Ram Technologies, Inc.

HEALTHTEAM - Health care products - Graham-Field Inc.

HEALTHTEAM ADVANTAGE - Computer software - Healthteam Management Services, Inc.

HEALTHTEC ADHESIVES - Adhesive - Healthtec Adhesives, Inc.

HEALTHTEX - Backpacks - Healthtex Apparel Corp.

HEALTHTRAC - Medical apparatus - Lossing Orthopedic Co.

HEALTHTRIM - Vitamins and nutritional supplements - Nu Skin International, Inc.

☆ = Now out of production

HEALTHWALKER - Footwear–athletic ☆ - Nike, Inc.
HEALTHWARD BOUND - Apparel and accessories - Brooke K. Summers
HEALTHWATCH - Computer software - IVI Publishing, Inc.
HEALTHWAY - Teas–herbal - Makers of Kal, Inc.
HEALTHWISE - Dairy products - Roberts Dairy Co.
HEALTHWISE - Food products - Indian Summer
HEALTHWISE - Toiletries - Scientific Hygiene, Inc.
HEALTHWORLD - Gauze–surgical - Dermpak International
HEALTHY - Skin care products - Action Laboratories Inc.
HEALTHY 1 - Confections - Marilyn M. Stucker
HEALTHY ACHIEVERS - Video production - Human Kinetics Publishers, Inc.
HEALTHY ADVANTAGE - Dairy products - Country Lake Foods Inc.
HEALTHY & FLAVORFUL - Meats–luncheon - Bryan Foods, Inc.
HEALTHY ANSWER - Food products - Holten Meat, Inc.
HEALTHY APPETITE ENTREE - Dinners–frozen - Mrs. Gooch's Natural Food Markets Inc.
HEALTHY ATTITUDE - Apparel–women's - Oshman's Sporting Goods Inc.
HEALTHY BACK BAG - Bags–canvas - Ameribag, Inc.
HEALTHY BALANCE - Dinners–frozen - Conagra, Inc.
HEALTHY BODIES - Beverages - Healthy Bodies, Inc.
HEALTHY BY DESIGN - Food products - Morton Scott, Ltd.
HEALTHY BY DESIGN - Pillows - Pacific Coast Feather Co.
HEALTHY CALLING - Telephone apparatus - P.H. White, Jr.
HEALTHY CAT - Cat food ☆ - Prepco
HEALTHY CHIPS - Cookies - Health Valley Food
HEALTHY CHOICE - Food products - Conagra, Inc.
HEALTHY CHOICE - Food products - Hunt-Wesson, Inc.
HEALTHY CHOICE FROM KELLOGG'S - Cereal - Kellogg Co.
HEALTHY CLASSICS - Soups–canned - Progresso Quality Foods
HEALTHY COLLECTION - Motor vehicles–jeeps - Health Valley Food
HEALTHY CREATIONS - Ice cream - Schwan's Sales Enterprises, Inc.
HEALTHY CREATIONS - Pretzels - Maxim Marketing Corp.
HEALTHY CRUNCH - Cereal - Health Valley Food
HEALTHY DELIGHT - Beverages - Goya Foods, Inc.
HEALTHY DOG - Dog food ☆ - Prepco
HEALTHY EDGE, THE - Food products - Food for Health Co., Inc.
HEALTHY FACE - Health care products ☆ - Avon Products, Inc.
HEALTHY FAMILY WHITE BREAD - Breads - Flowers Family Bakeries, Inc.
HEALTHY FAST - Vitamins and nutritional supplements - Tishcon Corp.
HEALTHY FAVORITES - Cheese - Kraft Foods, Inc.
HEALTHY FAVORITES - Meats–luncheon - Oscar Mayer Foods Corp.
HEALTHY FRUIT CENTERS - Cookies - Health Valley Food
HEALTHY GOURMET - Candy ☆ - Queen Bee Gardens
HEALTHY GOURMET, THE - Barbecues and grills - Harris & Mallow Products
HEALTHY GRAHAMS - Cookies - Health Valley Food
HEALTHY GRAINFOODS - Grain products–flour - Harold W. Zukerman
HEALTHY GREENS - Vitamins and natural food supplements - M.K. Health Food Distributors, Inc.
HEALTHY GREENS - Vitamins and nutritional supplements - Premier Pet Products, Inc.
HEALTHY HABIT - Fruits and vegetables - Kern Ridge Growers, Inc.
HEALTHY HABITS - Food products ☆ - Healthwatchers System
HEALTHY HAIR - Pharmaceutical preparations - Vita Plus Industries Inc.
HEALTHY HAIR - Shampoos - Vitamin Research Products Inc.
HEALTHY HANDS - Skin care products - P.J. Maxwell Co., Inc.
HEALTHY HARVEST - Cleaning preparations - Healthy Harvest, Inc.
HEALTHY HARVEST - Pet food - Ralston Purina Co.
HEALTHY HEART - Bakery products - Elaine & Lisa's Inc.
HEALTHY HEART - Vitamins and nutritional supplements - Re-Vita Manufacturing Co., Inc.
HEALTHY HOOF - Nail care products - Gena Laboratories Inc.
HEALTHY HOT POTATOES - Snack foods - Health Valley Food
HEALTHY HOUR - Watches - Healthy Hour Project
HEALTHY KITCHEN - Cookware - Progressive International Corp.
HEALTHY LAFFS - Greeting cards ☆ - Duck Press
HEALTHY LIFE - Bakery products - Lewis Bakeries, Inc.
HEALTHY LIFESTYLE - Cooking equipment–household - Eagle Affiliates, Inc.
HEALTHY LIFESTYLE CUISINE - Food products - Sierra Sunset Inc.
HEALTHY MALE - Vitamins and nutritional supplements - Re-Vita Manufacturing Co., Inc.
HEALTHY MASSAGE - Video production - V.I.E.W. Video Inc.
HEALTHY MORN - Egg substitutes - Papetti's Hygrade Egg Products, Inc.
HEALTHY O - Cereal - Health Valley Food
HEALTHY OCEAN - Seafood products–fresh or frozen - Gulf King Seafood Co.
HEALTHY ORDER - Preserved foods–prepackaged - Brenda Lowry

HEALTHY ORIGINS - Vitamins and nutritional supplements - Eby Sales, Inc.
HEALTHY OVEN - Bakery goods, and mixes - Simply Sarah's
HEALTHY OVEN - Bakery products - Healthy Oven, Inc.
HEALTHY PET - Pet products - Re-Vita Manufacturing Co., Inc.
HEALTHY PLANET PRODUCTS - Gift shops - Healthy Planet Products, Inc.
HEALTHY PLANTS HEALTHY PLANET - Tools - Fiskars Inc.
HEALTHY POCKETS - Breads–frozen - General American Foods Manufacturing Corp.
HEALTHY POP - Popcorn - American Pop Corn Co.
HEALTHY RECIPES - Food products - Novartis Nutrition Corp.
HEALTHY REQUEST - Soups–canned - Campbell Soup Co.
HEALTHY ROMAN FAT FREE PIZZA - Pizzas–frozen - Healthy Roman, Inc.
HEALTHY SAUCE - Sauces - Colavita USA, Inc.
HEALTHY SENSATION - Salad dressings–bottled - Lipton Investments, Inc.
HEALTHY SNACK TO GROW ON, A - Cheese - Frigo Cheese Corp.
HEALTHY SNACKS WITH A TWIST - Cooking equipment–household - Kitchen Connection Inc.
HEALTHY SOIL HEALTHY PLANTS HEALTHY PEOPLE - Vegetables–pickled or brined - Jacobs Farm/Del Cabo Inc.
HEALTHY SOLUTIONS - Floor coverings–carpet and rugs - Queen Carpet Corp.
HEALTHY SOLUTIONS PLUS+ - Hair care products - J.M. Products, Inc.
HEALTHY SUNRISE - Breakfast sausage - Richard Pryor
HEALTHY SWEETS - Candy - Natural Foods Inc.
HEALTHY THOUGHTS - Greeting cards - Compuvisuals
HEALTHY TIME - Cooking equipment–household - Metrokane
HEALTHY TREASURES - Food products - Mrs. Paul's Kitchens Inc.
HEALTHY TREATS - Snack foods - Grist Mill Co.
HEALTHY TREND - Beverages - United Restaurant Equipment, Inc.
HEALTHY TRESSES FOR MEN AND WOMEN - Vitamins and nutritional supplements - Scott Pierce, Inc.
HEALTHY TRINITY - Vitamins and nutritional supplements - Natren Inc.
HEALTHY USA - Food products - Pocahontas Foods USA Inc.
HEALTHY WEALTHY AND WISE - Fruits and vegetables - L.P. Sharyland
HEALTHYBAKE-28 - Seafood products–fresh or frozen - Fishery Products International USA
HEALTHYCOTE - Pet care products - Kent Integrated Scientific Systems, Inc.
HEALTHYPC - Computer software - Symantec Corp.
HEAPAGENT - Computer software - MicroQuill Software Publishing Inc.
HEAPWITE - Enamels - Hancock Paint & Varnish Co.
HEAR-EZE - Office supplies - IDL Manufacturing & Sales Corp.
HEAR GEAR - Telephone apparatus - Recoton Corp.
HEAR-HEAR - Health care products - Fleetwood Co.
HEAR! HEAR! - Publisher's imprints - Western Publishing Co., Inc.
HEAR-RING - Telephones - Specialized Audio Engineering
HEAR TODAY...PLAY TOMORROW - Computer software - Electronic Courseware Systems Inc.
HEAR TRONICS - Hearing aids - Hear Tronics
HEAR YE, HEAR YE, HEAR YE CLEARLY - Communications equipment - Primeco Personal Communications, LP
HEARALL - Plugs–ear - Comprehensive Assessment Services, Inc.
HEARGEAR - Hearing aids - Beltone Electronics Corp.
HEARING AID EXPRESS - Hearing aids - Mark Brumback
HEARING AID SAVER - Headphones - Westone Laboratories Inc.
HEARING HELPER - Electronic equipment - New England Security Inc.
HEARING MASTERS - Hearing aids - Hearing Masters, Inc.
HEARING POWER - Batteries - John Willemsen Corp.
HEARING THE HOMONYMS - Computer software - Right on Programs
HEARLOVE - Greeting cards - Stanyan Record Co.
HEARPHONE - Audio equipment - Technical Exhibits Corp.
HEARSAY - Game - International Games
HEART - Air purification systems - Medo Industries, Inc.
HEART - Bathroom accessories ☆ - Better Sleep, Inc.
HEART - Fencing–plastic - Southern Sales & Marketing Group, Inc.
HEART - Glassware–household - Svend Jensen of Denmark Inc.
HEART - Ice cream - Lipton Investments, Inc.
HEART - Paper goods ☆ - Nicolaus Paper Inc.
HEART - Shampoos - Gillette Co.
HEART ADVENTURE, THE - Exercising equipment - Sport Supply Group, Inc.
HEART & HAND - Publisher's imprints ☆ - Harold Shaw Publishers
HEART AND HAND - Stationery - Christmas Tree Shops, Inc.
HEART & SOUL - Food products - L.T. Plant, Inc.
HEART BABYBELL - Toys–stuffed ☆ - Gund, Inc.
HEART BEAT - See SMART BEAT
HEART BEAT - Margarine - Fitness Foods, Inc.
HEART BEATS - Key rings - Russ Berrie and Co., Inc.

☆ = Now out of production

HEART BRAND PULLMAN-WA MOSCOW-IDA THE HEART OF THE PEA AND LENTIL INDUSTRY - Fruits and vegetables - P.S. Southern, Inc.

HEART BUD - Frames–picture - Terragrafics Inc.

HEART CARE - Vitamins and nutritional supplements - Nature's Way Products, Inc.

HEART CLOVER - Canned foods - C. Itoh & Co. America Inc.

HEART COLLECTION - Giftware - Lenox, Inc.

HEART DE-LITE - Candles ☆ - Candle-Lite Co.

HEART DELIGHTS FOR THE GOLDEN YEARS - Books - Lighten Up Enterprises

HEART DOODLES - Apparel and accessories - Kids to Parents

HEART FOOD CAPS - Pharmaceutical preparations - Heart Foods Co., Inc.

HEART FOR BEARS - Figurines - Teresa Lynn Zanetti

HEART-GARD - Chest protector - S & M Human Performance Products, Inc.

HEART GEMS - Magnets - Russ Berrie and Co., Inc.

HEART GLANDULAR PLUS - Vitamins and nutritional supplements - Ethical Nutrients

HEART GLITTER - Greeting cards - Heart Cards

HEART HEALTHY - Salad dressings–bottled - HVR Co.

HEART ISSUES - Publisher's imprints - Aglow Publications

HEART-KLIPS - Paper clips - Baumgarten's

HEART LINE - Cheese - Masters Gallery Foods Inc.

HEART LOCK - Rings–jewelry - Feature Enterprises

HEART LOVERS - Food products ☆ - TKI Foods, Inc.

HEART MATE - Food products - American Laboratories, Inc.

HEART NOTES - Novelty items–paper ☆ - Agent Andy Inc.

HEART O' CALIFORNIA - Food products - Sacramento Foods

HEART-O-HICKORY - Charcoal ☆ - Kingsford Co.

HEART OF AFRICA - Computer software ☆ - Electronic Arts Inc.

HEART OF AMERICA - Finishing agents - Dap Products Inc.

HEART OF AMERICA - Flour–blended - Stevens Industries Inc.

HEART OF AMERICA - Meat products–beef - Wiloma Corp.

HEART OF AMERICAN - Paints - Schering-Plough Healthcare Products

HEART OF BALSAM - Hair care products - Helene Curtis Industries Inc.

HEART OF FLORIDA - Citrus products - B.C. Cook & Sons Enterprises Inc.

HEART OF GOLD - Candy - Hearts & Flowers Candy Co.

HEART OF GOLD - Dolls - Mattel, Inc.

HEART OF GOLD - Rings–jewelry - Artcarved Inc.

HEART OF HEALTH - Health care products - Bios

HEART-OF-PINK - Shingles - Owens Corning

HEART OF ROCA - See **ALMOND ROCA**

HEART OF STONE - Mountaineering clothing, outerwear - Black Diamond Equipment, Ltd.

HEART OF TEXAS - Pet products - Tank's-a-Lot Inc.

HEART-OF-THE-CAMP - Stoves–gas ☆ - Fatsco

HEART OF THE COUNTRY - Kitchen appliances ☆ - National Housewares

HEART OF THE LAND - Fruits and vegetables - Heartland Harvest, Inc.

HEART OF THE MAELSTROM - Computer software - Sir-Tech Software, Inc.

HEART OF THE WEST - Flour–blended - Stevens Industries Inc.

HEART OF THE WEST - Greeting cards - Leanin' Tree Inc.

HEART OF THE WEST - Jewelry - Carlisle Jewelry Co., Inc.

HEART OF UTAH - Juices ☆ - Stevens Canning Co.

HEART OF VERMONT - Food products - Cherry Hill Cannery Inc.

HEART OF VIRGINIA - Agricultural products - Ronald W. Harvey and Co.

HEART OF WISCONSIN - Cheese - Wisconsin Cheeseman, Inc.

HEART OF WORSHIP - Recording label - Jubilee Communications Inc.

HEART O'MAGUEY - Sweetener, syrup ☆ - Botanical Products

HEART ON - Jewelry - Aveo Inc.

HEART PACK - Food products - Snyder Communications, L.P.

HEART PILLOW - Medical apparatus - Shumsky Enterprises, Inc.

HEART POPS - Candy - Spangler Candy Co.

HEART QI - Health care products - East Earth Herb Inc.

HEART SCIENCE - Vitamins and nutritional supplements - Source Naturals

HEART SMART - Health care products - Health Products Corp.

HEART SMART POPCORN, THE - Popcorn - Kernel Pops USA Inc.

HEART SONG - Oils–essential - Frontier Cooperative Herbs

HEART SONG PETS - Toys–stuffed - Fun World Inc.

HEART SPEEDOMETER - Heart monitors ☆ - Polar Electro Inc.

HEART STOPPERS - Candy - Fleer Corp.

HEART STRINGS - Toys - Malibu Fun Stuffed, Inc.

HEART STYLE - Bicycles - Huffy Corp.

HEART-T-HEART - Greeting cards - National Card 'n Gift Co.

HEART THROB - Air purification systems - Medo Industries, Inc.

HEART THROB - Flowers, plants, and seeds - Don Schmidt Nursery, Inc.

HEART THROB - Jewelry - Hobe Cie. Ltd.

HEART-THROB - Plush toys - Plush Creations, Inc.

HEART-THROB BEAR - Toys–stuffed - Dakin Inc.

HEART-THROBS - Chocolate candy - Superior Fruit & Confections

HEART THROBS - Cookies - Sunshine Treats, Inc.

HEART THROBS - Pet products - Vo-Toys Inc.

HEART TO HEART - Apparel–women's - Julius Corn & Co.

HEART-TO-HEART - Backpacks - Infantino, Inc.

HEART TO HEART - Candy - Ethel M. Chocolates, Inc.

HEART TO HEART - Erasers - Russ Berrie and Co., Inc.

HEART TO HEART - Figurines - EuropAmerica Inc.

HEART TO HEART - Greeting cards - Heart to Heart

HEART TO HEART - Infant product ☆ - Cosco, Inc.

HEART TO HEART - Jewelry - Jackmail Jewelry Inc.

HEART TO HEART EXPRESSIONS - Greeting cards - Heartfelt Greetings Inc.

HEART-TOONS - Candy - R.M. Palmer Co.

HEART-TREX - Analgesics - Otis Clapp & Son Inc.

HEART-TREX - Pharmaceutical preparations - Buffington

HEART TUGS - Figurines - Cast Art Industries, Inc.

HEART TUGS - Music boxes - Danko Graphics, Inc.

HEART TWIRLS - Writing instruments - Impact International Inc.

HEART WARMERS - Toys–stuffed - Russ Berrie and Co., Inc.

HEART WATABALL - Frames–picture - Delfino Products Inc.

HEART WATCH - Medical apparatus - Instromedix, Inc.

HEART WATCH - Vitamins and nutritional supplements ☆ - ICN Pharmaceuticals Inc.

HEART WRENCH - Novelty items - William W. Cloud

HEARTBASE - Computer software - Sir Americas, Inc.

HEARTBEAT - Brassieres (Bras) - Wacoal America Inc.

HEARTBEAT - Colognes - Max Factor & Co.

HEARTBEAT - Jewelry - Barr Enterprises Inc.

HEARTBEAT - Recording label - Rounder Records Corp.

HEARTBEAT PERSONAL TRAINER - Video games - Heartbeat Corp.

HEARTBEAT STETHOSCOPE - Stethoscopes ☆ - Kenner Products

HEARTBEAT TOY, THE - Toys–stuffed - Bijou Enterprises Inc.

HEARTBEEPS - Computer software - Lindy Enterprises, Inc.

HEARTBOOK - Binders - Mercy Hospital of Pittsburgh

HEARTBREAK - Apparel and accessories ☆ - Edison Brothers Stores, Inc.

HEARTBREAK - Computer software - SourceView Software International

HEARTBREAK HOTEL - Matches - Elvis Presley Enterprises Inc.

HEARTBREAKER - Amplifiers - Mesa/Boogie Ltd.

HEARTBREAKERS - Candy - Willy Wonka Brands

HEARTCARE - Vitamins and nutritional supplements - Ayurvedic Concepts Ltd.

HEARTCRAFT - Hobby kits - Tulip Productions

HEARTCRAFT - Jewelry - Ostbye & Anderson, Inc.

HEARTCRAFT COLLECTION - Toys–stuffed - Russ Berrie and Co., Inc.

HEARTFELT AUDIO - Audio equipment - Heartfelt Audio, Inc.

HEARTFELT COLLECTION - Novelty items–paper - Heartfelt, Inc.

HEARTFELT EXPRESSIONS - Furniture - Heartland International Inc.

HEARTFIRE ROMANCE - Publisher's imprints - Kensington Publishing Corp.

HEARTGARD-30 - Veterinary pharmaceutical preparations - Merck & Co., Inc. (Merck Agvet Division)

HEARTH & HOME - Deodorizers - Lumi-Lite Candle Co. Inc.

HEARTH & HOME - Greeting cards - Current, Inc.

HEARTH & HOME - Wallpaper - Seabrook Wallcoverings, Inc.

HEARTH AND HOME DESIGNS - Dinnerware - Hearth and Home Design

HEARTH & SKILLET - Food products - Pioneer Flour Mills

HEARTH-BAKED - Breads - Amoroso's Baking Co. Inc.

HEARTH BAKED - Pizzas–mixes - Metz Baking Co.

HEARTH CLUB - Baking powder - Rumford Co.

HEARTH CONES - Flowers, plants, and seeds - Tennessee Gold Inc.

HEARTH CRAFT - Fireplace equipment - Hearth Craft

HEARTH CRAFT - Infant product ☆ - Graco Children's Products

HEARTH ESSENTIALS - Fireplace equipment - Duraflame, Inc.

HEARTH EXPRESS - Meat products - Hearth Express, Inc.

HEARTH FARMS - Bread and rolls - Cotton Bros. Baking Co. Inc.

HEARTH FARMS - Breads - Stroehmann Bakeries Inc.

HEARTH-FLO - Stoves–wood-burning - GSW Jackes-Evans Manufacturing Co.

HEARTH-GLO - Stoves–wood-burning - GSW Jackes-Evans Manufacturing Co.

HEARTH HONEY - Meat products - Boston Chicken, Inc.

HEARTH-LIGHT - Candles - Empire Manufacturing Co.

HEARTH LIGHT - Tools - Venture Stores, Inc.

HEARTH MATE - Controls–heating systems - C & D Distributors Inc.

HEARTH PAK - Fireplace equipment - GSW Jackes-Evans Manufacturing Co.

HEARTH SHINE LUMINARY - Candles - Candle Corp. of America

HEARTH SIDE - Fireplace logs–treated - Forest Technology Corp.

☆ = Now out of production

HEARTH WARMER - Portable electric heater - Therm Technology Corp.
HEARTH WITCH - Dolls ☆ - Effanbee Doll Corp.
HEARTHBREAD - Breads - Hearthbread Bakehouse, Inc.
HEARTHGLOW - Floor coverings–carpet and rugs - Whitecrest Carpet Mills
HEARTHGLOW - Glassware–household ☆ - Gorham Inc.
HEARTHMASTER - Hard woods - Southeastern Natural Energies, Inc.
HEARTHORN - Vitamins and nutritional supplements - Solaray
HEARTHROBS - Greeting cards - American Greetings Corp.
HEARTHSHIELD - Stoves ☆ - Heatsafe
HEARTHSIDE - Cabinets - Yorktowne Inc.
HEARTHSIDE - Colognes ☆ - Avon Products, Inc.
HEARTHSIDE - Floor coverings ☆ - Congoleum Corp.
HEARTHSIDE - Furniture - Hooker Furniture Corp.
HEARTHSIDE - Furniture ☆ - Brill Manufacturing Co.
HEARTHSIDE - Lumber - Georgia-Pacific Corp.
HEARTHSIDE - Towels ☆ - Stevens Linen Associates Inc.
HEARTHSIDE COLLECTION - Furniture–factory ☆ - Clayton Marcus Co. Inc.
HEARTHSIDE IRONSTONE - Dinnerware–glass ☆ - Homer Laughlin China Co.
HEARTHSIDE SIMMER - Perfumes - Tennessee Gold Inc.
HEARTHSIDE VILLAGE - Giftware - Bradlees Stores, Inc.
HEARTHSTAR - Fireplaces - Superior Fireplace Co.
HEARTHSTEAD - Floor coverings - Congoleum Corp.
HEARTHSTEAD - Shingles–asphalt or tar - Certainteed Corp. (Roofing Products Group)
HEARTHSTONE - Dinnerware–glass ☆ - Block China Co.
HEARTHSTONE - Finishing agents ☆ - Flintkote Co.
HEARTHSTONE - Floor coverings–carpet and rugs ☆ - Kelly Group Inc.
HEARTHSTONE - Furniture - Hooker Furniture Corp.
HEARTHSTONE - Furniture ☆ - Broyhill Furniture Industries, Inc.
HEARTHSTONE - Hams - Sara Lee Corp.
HEARTHSTONE - Paints ☆ - GS Roofing Products Co.
HEARTHSTONE - Wood products - Weyerhaeuser Co.
HEARTHSTONE 26 - Floor coverings–carpet and rugs ☆ - Cumberland Mills Inc.
HEARTHSTONE OVENS - Pet products - Penn-Plax, Inc.
HEARTHSTONE PHOENIX - Stoves–wood-burning - N.H.C., Inc.
HEARTHSTONE STERLING - Heating stoves - N.H.C., Inc.
HEARTHWARMER - Fireplaces ☆ - Superior Fireplace Co.
HEARTHWINDOW - Glass–flat - Corning Inc.
HEARTKISS - Fruit drinks–bottled or canned - DNE World Fruit Sales
HEARTLAND - Baskets - Longaberger Co.
HEARTLAND - Bedroom furniture - Impact Furniture
HEARTLAND - Cabinets - Aristokraft, Inc.
HEARTLAND - Cabinets - Fieldstone Cabinetry
HEARTLAND - Cabinets - Riviera Cabinets Inc.
HEARTLAND - Cereal - Pet Inc.
HEARTLAND - Cutlery ☆ - Lifetime Hoan Corp.
HEARTLAND - Dinnerware - International China Corp.
HEARTLAND - Floor coverings–carpet and rugs ☆ - Regal Rugs Inc.
HEARTLAND - Floor coverings–carpet and rugs ☆ - Whitecrest Carpet Mills
HEARTLAND - Footwear - Heartland Shoe Co.
HEARTLAND - Furniture - Heartland Futons & Fibers, Inc.
HEARTLAND - Furniture - National/Mt. Airy Furniture
HEARTLAND - Furniture - Tell City Chair Co.
HEARTLAND - Furniture ☆ - Bassett Furniture Industries, Inc.
HEARTLAND - Glassware–household - Owens-Illinois Inc. (Libbey Div.)
HEARTLAND - Health care products - Heartland Health Foods
HEARTLAND - Jewelry - Shube's Manufacturing, Inc.
HEARTLAND - Pasta - American Italian Pasta Co.
HEARTLAND - Tiles–ceramic ☆ - Huntington/Pacific Ceramics Inc.
HEARTLAND - Toys - Heartland Homes Inc.
HEARTLAND - Wallpaper - Benchmark Preferred Wallcoverings
HEARTLAND - Water–bottled or canned ☆ - Hinckley & Schmitt (Bottled Water Group)
HEARTLAND ALMANAC - Calendars ☆ - American Greetings Corp.
HEARTLAND BREWERY REAL BEER - Glassware–household - Heartland Brewery, Inc.
HEARTLAND BUNNY - Giftware - Dakin Inc.
HEARTLAND BUNNY DECOUPAGE EGGS - Toys–blocks - Dakin Inc.
HEARTLAND COLLECTIONS - Clocks - Sunbeam Corp.
HEARTLAND COMPANY LTD., THE - Apparel - Heartland Co. Ltd.
HEARTLAND HARVEST - Fruits and vegetables - Heartland Harvest, Inc.
HEARTLAND INTERNATIONAL - Furniture - Heartland International Inc.
HEARTLAND LABS - Cleaning preparations–household - A & V, Inc.
HEARTLAND OF AMERICA - Candy - Eddyleon Chocolate Co. Inc.

HEARTLAND SAMPLERS - Paper–writing - Heartland Samplers Inc.
HEARTLAND WEISS - Beer - Chicago Brewing Co.
HEARTLAND'S BEST - Eggs - Dad's Products
HEARTLETTE - Brassieres (Bras) ☆ - Lovable Co.
HEARTLINE - Electrodes - Burdick, Inc.
HEARTLINE - Exercising equipment - Heartline Fitness Products, Inc.
HEARTLINE - Greeting cards - Hallmark Cards Inc.
HEARTLINE - Underwear and nightwear ☆ - Lovable Co.
HEARTLITES - Novelty items–paper ☆ - Antioch Publishing Co.
HEARTMATE - Exercising equipment - Heartmate
HEARTMATES - Dolls - Mark Alan Reuther
HEARTMATES - Jewelry - Theresa A. Jansen
HEARTMATH DISCOVERY PROGRAM - Computer software - The HeartMath System
HEARTMINDER - Heart monitors ☆ - Polar Electro Inc.
HEARTPAK - Blood derivatives - Cryolife, Inc.
HEARTPLANK - Wood products - Nordic American Corp.
HEARTPRINT - Medical apparatus - Del Mar Avionics
HEARTPRINT - Posters - Heartprint Inc.
HEARTRAK XL - Audio equipment - Universal Medical, Inc.
HEARTRING - Hair care products ☆ - Arius-Eickert Co. Inc.
HEARTS - Apparel stores–children's ☆ - D. Glasgow & Sons Inc.
HEARTS - Bakeware - Corning Inc.
HEARTS - Candy - Sunline Brands
HEARTS - Cheese - World's Best Cheeses, Inc.
HEARTS - Floor coverings–carpet and rugs - Regal Rugs Inc.
HEARTS - Games ☆ - Warren Industries Inc.
HEARTS - Glassware–household - Durand International
HEARTS & BOWS - Linen - Lillian Vernon Corp.
HEARTS & CRAFTS - Artists' materials - E.K. Success Ltd.
HEARTS AND FLOWERS - Apparel–children's - Meijer, Inc.
HEARTS AND FLOWERS - Candy - Scott's, Inc.
HEARTS & FLOWERS - Dinnerware–glass - Cyclamen Studio
HEARTS & FLOWERS - Dinnerware–glass ☆ - Johnson Brothers, USA, Inc.
HEARTS AND FLOWERS - Dolls - Goldberger Doll Manufacture Co.
HEARTS & FLOWERS - Flowers, plants, and seeds - Florists' Transworld Delivery Association, Inc.
HEARTS AND FLOWERS - Glassware–household ☆ - Fenton Art Glass Co.
HEARTS & FLOWERS - Wallpaper - Sanitas Wallcoverings
HEARTS & STARS - Colognes - Parfum de Coeur Ltd.
HEARTS & VINE - Floor coverings–carpet and rugs ☆ - Regal Rugs Inc.
HEARTS BAR - Candy ☆ - Good Taste Products, Inc.
HEARTS BY YARD - Toys–stuffed - Russ Berrie and Co., Inc.
HEART'S CHOICE - Food products - Fiesta Foods, Inc.
HEART'S DELIGHT - Floor coverings–carpet and rugs - Eagle Carpets Inc.
HEART'S DELIGHT - Juices - Nestle Beverage Co.
HEART'S DELIGHT - Pet products ☆ - Central Soya Co. Inc.
HEART'S DELIGHT - Underwear and nightwear - Lovable Co.
HEARTS DELIGHTS - Toys–stuffed ☆ - Fun World Inc.
HEARTS DESIRE - Bedroom furniture - Impact Furniture
HEART'S DESIRE - Floor coverings–carpet and rugs - Monticello Carpet Mills
HEART'S DESIRES - Signs - Charlotte Holland
HEART'S D'LITE - Cheese ☆ - Rose International
HEARTS GALORE - Clocks - General Time Corp. (Westclox/Seth Thomas Div.)
HEARTS, HEARTS, HEARTS - Greeting cards - American Greetings Corp.
HEARTS IN BLOOM - Paper–gift wrap ☆ - American Greetings Corp.
HEARTS IN SONG - Dolls - Georgetown Collection, Inc.
HEARTS 'N GEESE - Glassware–household - Durand International
HEARTS OF CAULIFLOWER - Fruits and vegetables - Mann Packing Co., Inc.
HEARTS OF CORN - Grits - National Oats Co. Inc.
HEARTS OF SCONE - Bakery products - American Bran Stand, Inc.
HEARTS OF SPACE - Recording label - Hearts of Space Inc.
HEARTS OF TEAL - Strollers–baby - MTS Products
HEARTS ON FIRE - Jewelry–precious - Di-Star, Ltd.
HEARTS, STARS & STUFF - Toys - Imperial Toy Corp.
HEARTS WOOD - Wines - Delicato Vineyards
HEARTS&HANDS M - Sweatshirts - Mcdonald's Corp.
HEARTSAVER - Ladders–metal - White Metal Rolling & Stamping Corp.
HEARTSAVER - Orthopedic products - Wolverine World Wide, Inc.
HEARTSCENT - Air fresheners - California Fragrance Co.
HEARTSONGS - Jewelry - Heartsongs
HEARTSTEPS - Greeting cards - HeartSteps
HEARTSTRINGS - Stencils ☆ - Slomons Laboratories Inc.
HEARTSTRINGS - Underwear and nightwear - Maidenform Inc.
HEARTSTRINGS - Wallpaper ☆ - Pelican Prints

HEARTSURE - Vitamins and nutritional supplements - Nature's Way Products, Inc.
HEARTSWOOD - Wines ☆ - Winequest
HEARTTHROB - Games ☆ - Milton Bradley Co.
HEARTTHROB - Mufflers—motor vehicle - Crow River Exhaust Manufacturing Co.
HEARTTHROB BEAR - Figurines ☆ - Fenton Art Glass Co.
HEARTVIEW - Computer software - Heartware, Inc.
HEARTWARE STORE - Health care products - Omron Healthcare, Inc.
HEARTWARMER - Vitamins and nutritional supplements - Kroeger Herb Products Co. Inc.
HEARTWARMERS - Toys—stuffed - American Greetings Corp.
HEARTWATCH - Heart monitors ☆ - Polar Electro Inc.
HEARTWATCHERS - Computer software - Heart Watchers International Inc.
HEARTWISE - See **FIBERWISE**
HEARTWOOD - Window coverings - Joanna Western Mills Co.
HEARTWOOD - Wood products - Weyerhaeuser Co.
HEARTWOOD & DESIGN - Paper products - Georgia-Pacific Corp.
HEARTY - Food products - Hearty-Virginia Inc.
HEARTY - Soups—mixes - Lipton Investments, Inc.
HEARTY & NATURAL - Food products - Springhill Farm Foods, Inc.
HEARTY CHEWS - Dog food - Ralston Purina Co.
HEARTY CHOICE - Pet food - Texas Farm Products Co.
HEARTY CLASSICS - Food products - Wis-Pak Foods, Inc.
HEARTY DINNER - Pet products - Eagle Products, Inc.
HEARTY DINNERS - Cat food - Heinz Pet Products Co.
HEARTY FARE - Food products - Conagra, Inc.
HEARTY FEAST - Dog food ☆ - Kal Kan Foods, Inc.
HEARTY FRUIT - Pastries - Sara Lee Corp.
HEARTY GRAINS - Food products - Pillsbury Co.
HEARTY HANDFULS - Breads—frozen - Conagra, Inc.
HEARTY HELPINGS - Food products - Hormel Foods Corp.
HEARTY KITCHEN - Meat products—poultry - Universal Food Marketing Inc.
HEARTY LIFE - Bakery products - Lewis Bakeries, Inc.
HEARTY LIFE - Cereal - Sovex Foods, Inc.
HEARTY LIFE NATURAL FOODS - Cereal - Sovex Foods, Inc.
HEARTY MEAL - Food products ☆ - Seymour Canning Co.
HEARTY NUT - Breads - Charles Freihofer Baking Co.
HEARTY PORTIONS - Frozen foods - Stouffer Foods Corp.
HEARTY SANDWICH ROLLS - Bagels ☆ - Natural Ovens of Manitowoc Inc.
HEARTY STYLE - Frozen entrees - American Home Food Products Inc.
HEARTY WEST - Salad dressings—bottled ☆ - Hunt-Wesson, Inc.
HEARTZONE - Medical apparatus - Bodyshaping, Inc.
HEAT-A-GRATE - Fireplace equipment - Woodmack Products Inc.
HEAT-A-LAMP - Heaters—space - Nutone Inc.
HEAT-A-LITES - Heaters—space - Nutone Inc.
HEAT-A-MARK - Inks - Matthews International Corp.
HEAT-A-MATIC - Heating equipment - E.C. Geiger, Inc.
HEAT-A-RAMA - Cosmetics ☆ - Worldwide Cosmetics
HEAT-A-THON - Heating equipment - Frahm Enterprises Inc.
HEAT-A-VENTLIGHTS - Heaters—space - Nutone Inc.
HEAT-A-VENTS - Heaters—space - Nutone Inc.
HEAT AND CONTROL - Scales, food processors, etc. - Heat and Control Inc.
HEAT-AND-SERVE - Soups—canned - Hain Pure Food Co. Inc.
HEAT-BAN - Paints - Jones Blair Co.
HEAT-BASE 700 - Radiators—furnace - Haydon Corp.
HEAT BATTERY - Batteries - O.E.M. Products Inc.
HEAT BELT, THE - Heating equipment - Eugene B. Ross
HEAT BROTHERS - Milk - Seegers Dairy Inc.
HEAT-COOL - Air conditioning equipment ☆ - General Electric Co.
HEAT CREAM - Skin care products - Set-N-Me-Free Aloe Vera Co.
HEAT DEFIER II - Gloves - Jomac Products Inc.
HEAT DEMON - Heaters—space - Desa International, Inc.
HEAT DISH - Kitchen appliances - National Presto Industries, Inc.
HEAT EXPRESS PLUS - Heaters—space - Duracraft Corp.
HEAT FINS - Thermostats ☆ - Oatey Co.
HEAT FLOW - Gloves - Fairfield Line, Inc.
HEAT FURNACE - Heaters—space - Duracraft Corp.
HEAT GARD - Gloves - Brookville Glove Manufacturing Co.
HEAT GUARD - Batteries - Exide Corp.
HEAT GUARD - Hair care products ☆ - Stanley Fay Co.
HEAT GUARD - Kitchen appliances - Black & Decker Corp.
HEAT GUARD - Vitamins and nutritional supplements - Mission Pharmacal Co.
HEAT GUN, THE - Radiofrequency measuring equipment - Roger F. Kershaw
HEAT-HOUSER - Tractors - Burch Manufacturing Co. Inc.
HEAT-IT - Oils—illuminating - Heat-It Manufacturing, Inc.

HEAT IT & EAT IT - Food products - Sweet Earth Natural Foods
HEAT-KART - Lamps - DriQuik, Inc.
HEAT-KING - Housewares - Pro Hardware Inc.
HEAT MACHINE - Air conditioning equipment - Carrier Corp.
HEAT-MAGNET - Electrical equipment - Phillips & Temro Industries Inc.
HEAT MASTER - Heating equipment - Holmes Products, Corp.
HEAT MAX - Pans - Anchor Hocking Glass, Inc.
HEAT MIRROR - Glass—window - Southwall Technologies Inc.
HEAT MIRROR - Windows—storm - Hurd Millwork Co. Inc.
HEAT MIRROR PLUS - Glass—window - Southwall Technologies Inc.
HEAT 'N BRUSH - Fabrics - Sew-Art International
HEAT 'N DRY - Hair care products - William Marvy Co., Inc.
HEAT 'N' EAT - Cookware - Corning Inc.
HEAT 'N EAT - Sausages - Owens Country Sausage Inc.
HEAT 'N SERVE - Biscuits - Bridgford Foods Corp.
HEAT 'N SHOOT - Hockey equipment - Christian Brothers, Inc.
HEAT 'N STRIP - Hardware - Black & Decker Corp.
HEAT OFF - Deodorizers - Krueger Enterprises
HEAT-POWER - Heaters—gas - Holmes Products, Corp.
HEAT PROTECTOR - Batteries ☆ - TBC Corp.
HEAT PUMP HELPER - Pumps - Tri-County Better Home Heat Council, Inc.
HEAT-R-FAN - Fans—electric - Tensor Corp.
HEAT-RAY - Lamps - Philips Lighting Co.
HEAT RAY - Motor vehicle parts and accessories - Diesel Research & Development Corp.
HEAT READY - Thread ☆ - Perfect Thread Co. Inc.
HEAT-REM - Paints - Chemray Coatings Corp.
HEAT RESISTOR - Batteries ☆ - TBC Corp.
HEAT SAFE - Hair care products - Neutrogena Corp.
HEAT SAVER - Heating equipment ☆ - Oatey Co.
HEAT SAVER - Insulating materials - Easy Heat Inc.
HEAT-SAVER - Trays - Eagle Glass Products
HEAT SCREEN - Fireplace equipment - Sears, Roebuck and Co.
HEAT-SEAL STIK - Epoxy - La-Co Industries, Inc.
HEAT SEALER - Bags—plastic - Saket Co.
HEAT SEEKER - Toys - Tonka Corp.
HEAT SENTRY - Attic ventilators - Cool Attic
HEAT SHEET - Bedding—linen - Dynamic Development
HEAT SHIELD - Hair care products - Hair Institute
HEAT SHOCK - Bicycles - Roadmaster Corp.
HEAT SMART - Computer software - Aerco International, Inc.
HEAT STATION - Coffee makers—electric - Windmere Corp.
HEAT STOP - Electrical equipment - Ohmite Manufacturing Co.
HEAT STREAM - Electrical equipment - Arvin Industries Inc.
HEAT STREAM - Heaters—space - Adobe Air Inc.
HEAT SWEEP - Heaters—space - Adobe Air Inc.
HEAT-TETTES - Health care products - H & L Concepts Inc.
HEAT TO GO - Heaters—space - Sunbeam-Oster Household Products
HEAT TOOL - Pens - Uchida of America Corp.
HEAT-TOWER - Heaters—gas - Holmes Products, Corp.
HEAT TRACE - Computer software - Russell C. Martin
HEAT TRANSFER FLUIDS - Chemical preparations - Consolidated Recycling Co, Inc.
HEAT-TREATED - Glassware—household - Owens-Illinois Inc. (Libbey Div.)
HEAT TUNNEL, THE - Heaters—space - Tatung Co. of America Inc.
HEAT-TYTE - Cement - J.C. Whitlam Manufacturing Co.
HEAT WAVE - Bicycles - Murray, Inc.
HEAT WAVE - Christmas tree ornaments - Cracker Box Inc.
HEAT WAVE - Flowers, plants, and seeds - Loft's Seed Inc.
HEAT-WAVE - Heaters—space - Rolf C. Hagen (USA) Corp.
HEAT WAVE - Pumps—water - Aqua Cal, Inc.
HEAT WAVE PADDLE BALL - Game - Maui Toys
HEAT WAVES - Pens - Bic Corp.
HEAT WORKS - Hardware - Black & Decker Corp.
HEAT X - Pet products - National Scent Co.
HEAT-ZONE - Radiators—furnace - Haydon Corp.
HEATAB - Vitamins and nutritional supplements - Hillestad International, Inc.
HEATABLES - Decals and transfers - Rubbermaid Inc.
HEATBLASTER - Heating equipment - Holmes Products, Corp.
HEATBLOK - Gloves - Jomac Products Inc.
HEATBUSTER - Motor vehicle parts and accessories - Go/Dan Industries
HEATCANNON - Heating equipment ☆ - National Presto Industries, Inc.
HEATCARE - Hair care products - Playtex Beauty Care, Inc.
HEATER - Eyeglasses - Oakley, Inc.
HEATER - Golfing equipment - Tommy Armour Golf Co.
HEATER KITS - Heating equipment - Safety Technology International, Inc.

☆ = Now out of production

HEATERMEALS - Food products - Zestotherm Inc.

H'EATERY - Kitchen appliances ☆ - Hamilton Beach/Proctor-Silex Inc.

HEATFORM - Fireplaces - Superior Fireplace Co.

HEATH - Cakes - Heath Manufacturing Co.

HEATH - Candy - Leaf, Inc.

HEATH - Cookies - Delicious Cookies

HEATH - Electronic equipment ☆ - Heath Co.

HEATH - Ice cream - Nestle USA

HEATH & HEATHER - Teas - Blue Mountain Imports Inc.

HEATH AND HEATHER - Teas - Fancy Foods of Virginia Inc.

HEATH & HEATHER - Teas–herbal - Chase Collection, Inc.

HEATH SENSATIONS - Candy - Leaf, Inc.

HEATH SUNDAE - Ice cream ☆ - Eskimo Pie Corp.

HEATHANDLER - Batteries - Sears, Roebuck and Co.

HEATHCLIFF - Fabrics - Dan River Inc.

HEATHCLIFF - Toys - Knickerbocker Toy Co. Inc.

HEATHCLIFF & SPIKE - Pet products ☆ - St. Jon Pet Care Products Inc.

HEATHCOTE - Crocheted and knitted items ☆ - Hampshire Hosiery, Inc.

HEATHCOTE & IVORY - Bath salts ☆ - Chase Collection, Inc.

HEATHER - Bicycles - Sears, Roebuck and Co.

HEATHER - Cabinets - Merillat Industries, Inc.

HEATHER - Christmas tree ornaments - Cracker Box Inc.

HEATHER - Deodorants–personal - Whitehall Laboratories

HEATHER - Dinnerware ☆ - Corning Inc.

HEATHER - Dinnerware–glass ☆ - Nikko Ceramics Inc.

HEATHER - Flatware - Utica Cutlery Co.

HEATHER - Floor coverings–carpet and rugs - Barrett Carpet Mills Inc.

HEATHER - Floor coverings–carpet and rugs - Mohawk Carpet Corp.

HEATHER - Fruits and vegetables ☆ - Idaho Fruit Sales Inc.

HEATHER - Nail care products - Cosmair Inc.

HEATHER - Novelty items ☆ - Royal Cathay Trading Co.

HEATHER - Shoes ☆ - Daniel Green Co.

HEATHER - Wigs - Jean Paree Weegs Inc.

HEATHER & TWEED - Apparel–men's - TJX Companies, Inc.

HEATHER BAY - Floor coverings–carpet and rugs - Evans-Black Carpet Mills

HEATHER BRAID - Twine - Geo. B. Carpenter Co.

HEATHER CHECK - Floor coverings–carpet and rugs - Karastan-Bigelow Inc.

HEATHER CREAM - Liqueurs - Canandaigua Wine Co. Inc.

HEATHER FLECK - Floor coverings–carpet and rugs - Karastan-Bigelow Inc.

HEATHER GLEN - Floor coverings–carpet and rugs - Dorsett Carpet Mills Inc.

HEATHER-GLEN - Scarves, neckwear - Calzeat & Co. Ltd.

HEATHER GLENN - Mattresses - Kingsdown, Inc.

HEATHER GRAY - Apparel and accessories - Breton Industries

HEATHER HILL - Floor coverings–carpet and rugs ☆ - Lees Carpets

HEATHER HILL - Wallpaper - S.M. Hexter Co.

HEATHER HILL - Wallpaper ☆ - Fairwinds Studio

HEATHER HILL - Wood products - Georgia-Pacific Corp.

HEATHER HILL II - Wallpaper ☆ - Fairwinds Studio

HEATHER ISLAND - Floor coverings ☆ - Congoleum Corp.

HEATHER LANE - Apparel–women's - Synari, Ltd.

HEATHER MOOR - Mattresses - Kingsdown, Inc.

HEATHER ON THE HILL - Christmas tree ornaments - Cracker Box Inc.

HEATHER POINT/STRIPE - Floor coverings–carpet and rugs ☆ - Criterion Mills Inc.

HEATHER SET - Fibers–nylon - Mohawk Carpet Corp.

HEATHER THE HIPPO - Furniture–children's - Maze Inc.

HEATHER TRACE - Floor coverings–carpet and rugs - Evans-Black Carpet Mills

HEATHERBLEND - Yarn ☆ - Brunswick Yarns

HEATHERBROWN - Floor coverings–tile - Shep Brown Associates Inc.

HEATHERCRAFT - Floor coverings–carpet and rugs - Walter Carpet Mills

HEATHERCROME - Apparel–men's - Michaels/Stern & Co. Inc.

HEATHERDOWNS - Furniture - Pilliod Co.

HEATHERING HEIGHTS - Fabrics–velvet - Dan River Inc.

HEATHERLOC - Floor coverings–carpet and rugs - Patrick Carpet Mills

HEATHERLUX - Floor coverings–carpet and rugs - Sheridan Carpet Mills

HEATHERTEK - Floor coverings–carpet and rugs ☆ - World Carpets, Inc.

HEATHERTON - Floor coverings–carpet and rugs ☆ - Columbus Mills, Inc.

HEATHERTON - Floor coverings–carpet and rugs ☆ - Mannington Carpets, Inc.

HEATHERTONE - Floor coverings - Congoleum Corp.

HEATHERTONE - Furniture–upholstered ☆ - Samsonite Corp.

HEATHERTUFT II - Floor coverings–carpet and rugs ☆ - Callaway Carpets

HEATHERWOOD - Floor coverings–carpet and rugs - Coronet Carpets Inc.

HEATHERWOOD - Fruit drinks–bottled or canned - Peninsular Products Co./Heatherwood Farms Co.

HEATHKIT - Educational materials ☆ - Heath Co.

HEATHKIT BOONIE BIKE - Scooters–motorized ☆ - Heath Co.

HEATHROE - Apparel–men's ☆ - Goodstein Bros. & Co. Inc.

HEATHROW - Floor coverings–carpet and rugs - Whitecrest Carpet Mills

HEATH'S - Playing cards - Robert Heath

HEATHWORKS - Kitchen utensils–aluminum ☆ - Lifetime Hoan Corp.

HEATHY KIDS - Vitamins and nutritional supplements - Marlyn Nutraceuticals, Inc.

HEATILATOR - Fireplaces - Heatilator Inc.

HEATING EDGE BASEBOARD HEAT, THE - Radiators–furnace - Yankee Resources Corp.

HEATLOG - Heaters–aircraft - Toastmaster Inc.

HEATMAPS - Computer software - Neovision Hypersystems, Inc.

HEATMASTER - Finishing agents - Dap Products Inc.

HEATMASTER - Fireplace logs–treated - Heatmaster, Inc.

HEATMASTER - Heaters–motor vehicle - MasterForce Inc.

HEATMASTER - Heaters–swimming pool - Hayward Industries Inc.

HEAT'N EAT - Biscuits ☆ - Pillsbury Co.

HEATPLACE - Fireplaces ☆ - Superior Fireplace Co.

HEATRAP - Apparel and accessories - Gordini USA Inc.

HEATREST - Heating pads–electric ☆ - Vornado Air Circulation Systems Inc.

HEATRIM - Radiators–furnace - Bel-Aire Sales Corp.

HEATRITE - Furnaces–electric ☆ - Nordyne Inc.

HEATRITE - Photographic equipment ☆ - Testrite Instrument Co. Inc.

HEATROL - Electrolyte diagnostic agents ☆ - Otis Clapp & Son Inc.

HEAT'S ON - Hair care products - Helene Curtis Industries Inc.

HEAT'S-ON - Housewares - Franzus Co. Inc.

HEATS-ON - Veterinary pharmaceutical preparations ☆ - Zirin Laboratories International

HEATSAFE - Hair care products - Neutrogena Corp.

HEATSAFE - Stoves ☆ - Heatsafe

HEATSAFE FIBRESEAL - Gaskets - Heatsafe

HEATSEEKER - Computer software - Marketstrategies, Inc.

HEATSHIELD - Fabrics - Parvin Manufacturing Co.

HEATWARE - Containers - Sevko, Inc.

HEATWATCH - Electronic equipment - DDX, Inc.

HEATWAVE - Barbecues and grills - W.C. Bradley Co., Inc.

HEATWAVE - Housewares - Niche Marketing, Inc.

HEATWAVE - Ovens–microwave ☆ - Quasar Co.

HEATWICK - Audio equipment - Electro-Voice, Inc.

HEATWORKS - Hair care products - Revlon-Realistic Professional Products Inc.

HEAV-N-LINE - Life preservers - UK Sailmakers

HEAVEN - Candles - Gps, Inc.

HEAVEN - Health care products - Superior Trading Co.

HEAVEN - Ice cream - Nestle USA

HEAVEN & EARTH - Computer software - Publishing International

HEAVEN & EARTH - Health care products - Frontier Products

HEAVEN HEART - Dolls - Mattel, Inc.

HEAVEN HILL - Beverages–alcohol - Heaven Hill Distilleries, Inc.

HEAVEN INTERNATIONAL - Apparel–women's - Her Style Inc.

HEAVEN KIDS - Apparel–children's - R & H Designs, Inc.

HEAVEN KNOWS - Dolls - Heaven Knows Inc.

HEAVEN ON EARTH - Toys - Heaven on Earth, Inc.

HEAVEN SCENT - Cookies - Heaven Scent Natural Foods

HEAVEN SENT - Christmas tree ornaments - Cracker Box Inc.

HEAVEN SENT - Colognes - Mem Co., Inc.

HEAVEN SENT - Dolls ☆ - Effanbee Doll Corp.

HEAVEN SENT DISTRIBUTING - Toys–stuffed - Heaven Sent Distributing, Inc.

HEAVEN SERIES - Computer storage devices - Most Significant Bits

HEAVENLY - Cribs–wood ☆ - Welsh Co.

HEAVENLY - Hair care products - Helene Curtis Industries Inc.

HEAVENLY - Rings–jewelry ☆ - Artcarved Inc.

HEAVENLY - Sauces - Rowena's Gourmet Foods Inc.

HEAVENLY 7'S - Games - International Gamco, Inc.

HEAVENLY ANGEL - Glassware–household - Fenton Art Glass Co.

HEAVENLY ANGEL - Jewelry - Plaza Jewelry, Inc.

HEAVENLY ANGEL - Lighting equipment - General Electric Co.

HEAVENLY ANGELS - Figurines - Potpourri Designs

HEAVENLY BABY - Dolls - Horsman

HEAVENLY BLUE - Dinnerware–glass ☆ - Nikko Ceramics Inc.

HEAVENLY BODY - Hair care products - Tussy Cosmetics Inc.

HEAVENLY BRA - Apparel–women's - Jezebel-Renee of Hollywood

HEAVENLY CHOCO - Rolls–dinner ☆ - Natural Ovens of Manitowoc Inc.

HEAVENLY COMFORT - Footwear–women's - Argyris Inc.

HEAVENLY CONFECTIONS - Candy - Farley Candy Co.
HEAVENLY CURL, THE - Exercise equipment - Ellen R. Rusk
HEAVENLY DELIGHT - Snack foods ☆ - Hershey Import Co. Inc.
HEAVENLY DREAM - Bedding–linen - Pillowtex Corp.
HEAVENLY DREAMERS - Greeting cards - Gallant Greetings Corp.
HEAVENLY FUN - Catalogs - Georgia-Pacific Corp.
HEAVENLY GINSENGS - Health care products - East Earth Herb Inc.
HEAVENLY GOLF - Games - Golf Gifts, Inc.
HEAVENLY HAIR - Hair care products - Protege Corp.
HEAVENLY HAM - Hams - Paradise Foods, Inc.
HEAVENLY HARP CO. - Decorations - Heavenly Harp
HEAVENLY HASH - Candy - Elmer Candy Corp.
HEAVENLY HASH - Candy - Visitation Home Made Candies
HEAVENLY HAWAIIAN - Rolls–dinner ☆ - Natural Ovens of Manitowoc Inc.
HEAVENLY HEAT - Food products - Gib's Classics, Inc.
HEAVENLY HOLIDAYS - Dolls - Mattel, Inc.
HEAVENLY HOLSTEIN - Ice cream ☆ - Country Fresh Dairy
HEAVENLY HUES - Paints - DecoArt, Inc.
HEAVENLY NEST - Pet products ☆ - Black Sheep Inc.
HEAVENLY NIGHT - Fabrics - Guilford Mills, Inc.
HEAVENLY NUT BAR - Candy ☆ - Visitation Home Made Candies
HEAVENLY PLUSH - Floor coverings–carpet and rugs ☆ - Galaxy Carpet Mills Inc.
HEAVENLY SCENTS - Skin care products - Liberty Natural Products
HEAVENLY SCENTSATIONS - Deodorizers - Heavenly Scentsations, Inc.
HEAVENLY SEVEN, THE - Publisher's imprints - Melissa Deal Forth
HEAVENLY STAR - Floor coverings–carpet and rugs ☆ - World Carpets, Inc.
HEAVENLY STAR - Floor coverings–carpet and rugs ☆ - Zenith Carpets
HEAVENLY STEP - Slippers - Thorp Direct Sales, Inc.
HEAVENLY TEETHER - Infant product - Mattel, Inc.
HEAVENLY WEIGHTWALKING - Exercising equipment - Blaine Wasel Sell
HEAVEN'S ESSENCE - Pharmaceutical preparations - Philip R. Ricker
HEAVENS HAABITS - Christmas tree ornaments - Art Mill, Inc.
HEAVEN'S HELPER - Apparel–women's - Jezebel-Renee of Hollywood
HEAVEN'S LITTLE HELPERS - Giftware - Bradford Exchange, Ltd.
HEAVEN'S SAKE - Checkbooks - Checks in the Mail, Inc.
HEAVEN'S TOUCH - Floor coverings–carpet and rugs - Evans-Black Carpet Mills
HEAVEN'S UNOFFICIAL GREETINGS - Greeting cards - Dayspring Cards
HEAVENWOOD - Golf clubs - Callaway Golf Co.
HEAVIER THAN WATER LUBRICANT - Lubricants - Castoleum Corp.
HEAVIES - Containers–trash - Victor Stanley, Inc.
HEAVIES, THE - Amplifiers ☆ - CSI/Speco
HEAVY ARTILLERY - Toys - Hasbro, Inc.
HEAVY CUTTER - Welding equipment - Controls Corp. of America
HEAVY-DUTI - Bicycles - Schwinn Cycling & Fitness Inc.
HEAVY DUTY - Cleaning preparations - DL/Banite
HEAVY DUTY - Flowers, plants, and seeds - D. Landreth Seed Co.
HEAVY DUTY - Paints - Hirshfield's Paint Manufacturing
HEAVY DUTY - Pet products - Novalek, Inc.
HEAVY DUTY - Windshields–plastic ☆ - National Cycle Inc.
HEAVY DUTY AMERICA - Fuel additives - HD America, Inc.
HEAVY DUTY WAX - Wax removers - Analab Inc.
HEAVY GRIP - Cement - Elmer's Products, Inc.
HEAVY HAULER - Toys–automobiles - Processed Plastic Co.
HEAVY HAULER - Toys–trains - Life-Like Products Inc.
HEAVY HAULERS - Toys–automobiles - K-Line
HEAVY HITTER - Cleaning preparations - W.W. Grainger, Inc.
HEAVY HITTER - Game machines ☆ - WMS Gaming Inc.
HEAVY JAM - Recording label - Terock Records
HEAVY MECHANIC - Ladders–metal - Davidson Ladders Inc.
HEAVY METAL - Chairs–metal - Clarin Corp.
HEAVY METAL - Exercising equipment - Universal Gym Equipment, Inc.
HEAVY METAL - Games - American Game Caps
HEAVY METAL - Musical instrument accessories - Heavy Metal Strings
HEAVY METAL - Pencils - National Pen & Pencil Co.
HEAVY METAL - School supplies - Rudell Design
HEAVY METAL - Shirts - Metal Mammoth, Inc.
HEAVY METAL MAMA - Toys - Tonka Corp.
HEAVY METALS - Paints ☆ - DecoArt, Inc.
HEAVY METALS LIGHT - Paints ☆ - DecoArt, Inc.
HEAVY ROPE - Sporting goods - Strength Systems, Inc.
HEAVY SHREDDIN - Computer software ☆ - Parker Brothers
HEAVY SILVER - Hoses - Action Technology Co.
HEAVY TRAFFIC - Cleaning preparations–carpet and rug - Playtex Beauty Care, Inc.

HEAVY TRAFFIC - Flowers, plants, and seeds - Jonathan Green, Inc.
HEAVY TREAD - Ladders–wood - John S. Tilley Ladders Co. Inc.
HEAVY UNIT - Apparel and accessories - James Chien Ho
HEAVY WEIGHT - Detergents - Dar-Lin Products Inc.
HEAVY WEIGHTS - Men's leather-palm gloves - Boss Manufacturing Co.
HEAVYHANDS - Weightlifting equipment - SLM Inc.
HEAVYHEAD - Bats–baseball - Markwort Sporting Goods Co.
HEAVYPACK - Fruits and vegetables - Gold Digger Apple Inc.
HEAVYWEAR - Apparel and accessories - Michael R. Knopp
HEAVYWEIGHT - Pet products - Penn-Plax, Inc.
HEAVYWEIGHT - Vegetables–frozen - Bryd Harvest Inc.
HEAVYWEIGHT CHAMPION, THE - Golfing equipment - Bobby Grace Golf Design, Inc.
HEAVYWEIGHT GAINER 900 - Vitamins and nutritional supplements - Champion Nutrition
HEAVYWEIGHTS - Cooking equipment–household ☆ - Nordic Ware
HEAVYWEIGHTS - Footwear - Import Systems International Inc.
HEAVYWEIGHTS, THE - Toys–trains - K-Line
HEB-CORT - Ophthalmic goods ☆ - Barnes-Hind Inc.
HEBERT - Candy - Hebert Candies Inc.
HEBREW NATIONAL - Meat products–poultry - Hebrew Foods Inc.
HEBREW PUBLISHING CO. - Publisher's imprints - Hebrew Publishing Co.
HEBREW TUTOR - Computer software - Parsons Technology, Inc.
HEBREWMERLIN - Office supplies - Varitronic Systems, Inc.
HEBRON - Computer storage devices–magnetic - Payne Loving Trust
HEBRON - Furniture - Moosehead Manufacturing Co.
HEBRON - Pharmaceutical preparations - Harvey Laboratories Inc.
HECEK-BIEBRICH - Musical instruments - Custom Music Co.
HECK CELLARS - Wines - F. Korbel and Bros. Inc.
HECK 'ER CHECKER - Games - Jack Gasnick, The Virtuous Locksmith
HECKER PASS WINERY - Wines - Hecker Pass Winery
HECKERS - Flour–blended - Uhlmann Co.
HECKERT - Machinery - WMW Machinery Co., Inc.
HECKLE AND JECKLE - Apparel and accessories - Viacom International Inc.
HECKLER BRAU - Beverages–malt - Heckler Brewing Co. Inc.
HECKMAN - Food products - Chas. F. Cates & Sons Inc.
HECO - Audio equipment - Bell & Howell Co.
HECO - Circuit breakers - Heinemann Electric Co.
HECO - Clocks - Coehler-Coptex Co.
HECON - Computers - Hecon Corp.
HECTA - Sonar systems and equipment - Brookes & Gatehouse Inc.
HECTOR & HOLLYHOCK - Chocolate candy - Superior Fruit & Confections
HECTOR RABBIT - Candy - Brock Candy Co. Inc.
HED - Audio equipment ☆ - Cerwin-Vega Inc.
HEDAR - Nail care products ☆ - Arius-Eickert Co. Inc.
HEDBEDS - Motor vehicle parts and accessories - Talus Corp.
HEDCO - Medical travel cases - Hedco Inc.
HEDD-HUNTER - Sporting goods ☆ - James Heddon's Sons
HEDD PLUG - Fishing lures - James Heddon's Sons
HEDDA FEATHERS - Cleaning equipment - Sunshine Industries Inc.
HEDGE - Paints ☆ - Impervious Paint Industries Ltd.
HEDGE HOG - Tools–pruning - Black & Decker Corp.
HEDGE-TRIM - Garden equipment - Science Products Co. Inc.
HEDGEROW HOUSE - Artists' materials - Hedgerow House Publishing Co. Inc.
HEDGES - Games - Rhea Bradford
HEDGES - Heating equipment ☆ - Bradford-White Corp.
HEDGREN - Bags - Sirco International Corp.
HEDIS - Publisher's imprints - National Committee for Quality Assurance
HEDONISM - Apparel and accessories - Comme-Ci Comme-Ca Ltd.
HEDRICK - Beverages–malt - Piel Bros. Ltd.
HEDROCEL - Medical apparatus - Implex Corp.
HEDRON - Glass products - Pittsburgh Corning Corp.
HEDSTROM - Toys - Hedstrom Corp.
HEDULIN - Pharmaceutical preparations ☆ - Marion Merrell Dow
HEDY KNITS - Crocheted and knitted items - Hedy Knits of California
HEEE HAW - Beverages–carbonated - A.J. Canfield Co.
HEEKSUEDE - Fabrics–cotton - Heeksuede Inc.
HEEL BONE - Sporting goods ☆ - Powell Skateboards
HEEL-EASE - Mattresses - Anatomic Concepts, Inc.
HEEL FLY - Rope - Robert Callaway
HEEL FREE - Medical apparatus - Alimed, Inc.
HEEL GUARD - Footwear accessories - Schering-Plough Healthcare Products
HEEL LATCH - Women's shoes - Interco Inc.
HEEL LOCK - Health care products - Boehringer Mannheim Corp.
HEEL SNUGS - Footwear - Professional Product Research, Inc.

☆ = Now out of production

HEEL SOFTENING CREAM - Pharmaceutical preparations - Jess Clarke & Sons Inc.
HEELBO - Bandages–orthopedic - Heelbo Inc.
HEELER, THE - Inflatable cushions - Twenty-First Century Products Inc.
HEELOCK - Hosiery ☆ - Chipman-Union Inc.
HEELS DOWN - Shoes - Miller Harness Co., Inc.
HEELSTAT - Electrical equipment - Walter G. Legge Co., Inc.
HEERING - Beverages–alcohol - Blair Importers Ltd.
HEET - Chemical preparations - Gold Eagle Co.
HEET - Fuel additives - Demert & Dougherty, Inc.
HEET - Pharmaceutical preparations - Whitehall Laboratories
HEET ALL SEASON DIESEL FLO - Antifreeze ☆ - Demert & Dougherty, Inc.
HEET AVEL - Fuel additives - Demert & Dougherty, Inc.
HEET PLUS - Fuel additives - Demert & Dougherty, Inc.
HEETMASTER - Aquariums–household - Eugene G. Danner Manufacturing Inc.
HEETMASTER - Heating equipment - Aeroil Products Co. Inc.
HEF-T - T-shirts–men's - Tee Jays Manufacturing Co., Inc.
HEF-T 100 - Apparel and accessories - Tee Jays Manufacturing Co., Inc.
HEF-T-CLEAN - Cleaning preparations - Microtron Abrasives, Inc.
HEF-T-PAD - Electrical equipment ☆ - Hefco Plastics Inc.
HEFCO PLASTICS - Molding compounds–plastics ☆ - Hefco Plastics Inc.
HEFF WEISS - Beverages–malt - Sprecher Brewing Co. Inc.
HEFFELFLOPPER - Candy - R.M. Palmer Co.
HEFFERN - Jewelry - Elleard B. Heffern, Inc.
HEFLIN - Hardware - Heflin Steel Supply Co.
HEFNER/TEX-FLEX - Air conditioning equipment ☆ - Hefco Plastics Inc.
HEFTEE - Gloves - Brookville Glove Manufacturing Co.
HEFTEE BLUE H.D. - Degreasing solvents - Analab Inc.
HEFTI-RIB - Siding–metal - Alcan Aluminum Corp. Alcan Building Products Div.
HEFTY - Bags–plastic - Mobil Chemical Co. Plastics Div.
HEFTY - Floor coverings–carpet and rugs ☆ - Columbus Mills, Inc.
HEFTY - Office supplies ☆ - Lee Products Co.
HEFTY BASICS - Bags–plastic - Mobil Chemical Co. Plastics Div.
HEFTY CINCH SAK - Bags–plastic ☆ - Mobil Chemical Co. Plastics Div.
HEFTY HANDLE SAK - Bags–trash - Mobil Chemical Co. Plastics Div.
HEFTY-LEFTY - Stationery - Stuart Hall Co., Inc.
HEFTY LUSTRA - Packaging–paper ☆ - Mobil Chemical Co. Plastics Div.
HEFTY MAGENTA - Plates–paper ☆ - Mobil Chemical Co. Plastics Div.
HEFTY-MARK - Office supplies ☆ - Faber-Castell Corp.
HEFTY ONEZIP - Bags–plastic - Mobil Chemical Co. Plastics Div.
HEFTY RECORDS - Video tapes–blank - John Hughes, III
HEFTY SPRING BOUQUET - Bags–plastic - Mobil Chemical Co. Plastics Div.
HEFTY TABS - Office supplies - Lee Products Co.
HEGA - Food products - General Spice
HEGER'S ALTERNATIVE - Pet products - South St. Paul Feed Inc.
HEGG & HEGG - Seafood products–canned or cured - Hegg and Hegg Smoked Salmon
HEGO - Colognes ☆ - L.T. Products Ltd.
HEI - Computer software - Education Achievement Corp.
HEI HOME EDUCATION, INC. - Computer software - Education Achievement Corp.
HEIAN'S - Publisher's imprints - Heian International Inc.
HEIBAO - Dentifrices - Pacific Trade Alliance, Inc.
HEICO - Chemicals–photographic - Brandess Kalt Aetna
HEIDE - Candy - Henry Heide, Inc.
HEIDE OF COPENHAGEN - Glassware–household ☆ - Svend Jensen of Denmark Inc.
HEIDE SOUR - Candy - Ph. Wunderle Inc.
HEIDEL - Food products - George C. Brown's Biscuits & Confections
HEIDEL HOUSE - Cheese ☆ - Heidel House Famous Foods Inc.
HEIDELBERG - Beverages–malt - The Stroh Brewery Co.
HEIDELBERG - Breads - Holsum Bakery Inc.
HEIDELBERG - Musical instruments ☆ - Grossman Music Corp.
HEIDI - Cheese - Heidi's Cheese Products
HEIDI - Crocheted and knitted items - Ekay Knitting Mills Inc.
HEIDI - Dolls - Russ Berrie and Co., Inc.
HEIDI - Dolls ☆ - Effanbee Doll Corp.
HEIDI - Girdles - Swisstex Co.
HEIDI HEFFELFLOPPER - Candy - R.M. Palmer Co.
HEIDI-HO - Girdles - Swisstex Co.
HEIDI LAMB - Toys–stuffed - Dakin Inc.
HEIDI'S GOURMET CAKES - Bakeries - Heidi's Pastry, Inc.
HEIDIS HOUSE - Computer software - Andover Productions, Inc.
HEID'S OF WI - Meat products–beef - Heid Meat Service & Catering Ltd.

HEIDSIECK MONOPOLE - Wines - Seagram's Chateau & Estate Wines Co.
HEIFETZ - Pickles - Heifetz Pickling Co.
HEIGHT OF STYLE - Wallpaper ☆ - Imperial Wallcoverings, Inc.
HEIGHTS SQUARE - Floor coverings - Congoleum Corp.
HEIGHTSTOWN - Fireplace equipment - Majestic Co.
HEIKES FARMS FINEST - Food products - Heikes Produce, Inc.
HEIKES SELECT - Fruits–frozen - Heikes Produce, Inc.
HEIL - Heating and cooling systems - Inter-City Products Corp. (USA)
HEIL-OEL - Health care products - Dr. Peter Fahrney & Sons Co.
HEILEMANS OLD STYLE CLASSIC DRAFT COOL BREWED COLD-FILTERED BEER - Beverages–malt - G. Heileman Brewing Co., Inc.
HEILEX - Plastics - Heil Process Equipment Corp.
HEIMER - Musical instrument accessories - Westheimer Corp.
HEIN GERICKE - Apparel and accessories - Intersport Fashions West
HEINEKEN - Beverages–malt - Van Munching and Co. Inc.
HEINEMAN KITCHENS - Bakery products ☆ - Super Valu Inc.
HEINEMANN-STERN - Food products - Mike Hudson Distributing Inc.
HEINEMANN - Circuit breakers - Heinemann Electric Co.
HEINEMANN'S - Bakery products - Heinemann's Inc.
HEINEMANS - Wines - Heineman Winery
HEINE'S - Tobacco pouches - Sutliff Tobacco Co.
HEINES'S - Tobacco pouches - Consolidated Cigar Corp.
HEINIE-HURTIN' HOT - Food products - Ingleby Farms, Inc.
HEINI'S - Cheese - Bunker Hill Cheese Co., Inc.
HEINKE'S - Juices - Heinke's Inc.
HEINLE - Food products - Serv-Agen Corp.
HEINRICH GRIP MASTER - Tools - Heinrich Co.
HEINRICHSHAUS - Wines - Heinrichshaus Vineyards & Winery
HEINS - Hardware - H. Behlen & Bro. Inc.
HEINS - Honey - PureFoods
HEINS OREGON TRAIL - Honey - PureFoods
HEINZ - Calendars - Success Business Industries, Inc.
HEINZ - Food products - H.J. Heinz Co.
HEINZ DEEP FRIES - Food products - H.J. Heinz Co.
HEINZ HOMESTYLE - Gravy - H.J. Heinz Co.
HEINZ HOMESTYLE RECIPES - Baby foods - H.J. Heinz Co.
HEINZ LET'S EAT - Gravy - H.J. Heinz Co.
HEINZ MATHAI - Glassware–household - Whitehurst Imports
HEINZ SELECT - Barbecue sauce - H.J. Heinz Co.
HEINZ SELF SIZZLING DEEP FRIES - Vegetables–frozen - Ore-Ida Foods, Inc.
HEINZ SIMPLE GOODNESS - Baby foods - H.J. Heinz Co.
HEINZE CHOCOLATES - Candy ☆ - R.L. Albert & Son, Inc.
HEIRBORNE - Recording label - Eagle Mountain International Church
HEIRESS - Flatware - General Mills, Inc.
HEIRESS - Floor coverings–carpet and rugs - Edgecrest Carpet Mills
HEIRESS - Floor coverings–carpet and rugs ☆ - Callaway Carpets
HEIRESS - Rings–jewelry - Artcarved Inc.
HEIRESS - Soap - SBS Products, Inc.
HEIRESS - Tableware–china ☆ - Lenox, Inc.
HEIRESS OF TIME - Watches - Bulova Corp.
HEIRLOOM - Aluminum foil laminates - Highland Supply Corp.
HEIRLOOM - Candles - W and F Products Inc.
HEIRLOOM - Chimes ☆ - Nutone Inc.
HEIRLOOM - Clocks - Overocean Clock Co. Inc.
HEIRLOOM - Craft supplies - Lok-Box Inc.
HEIRLOOM - Curtains - A.L. Ellis Inc.
HEIRLOOM - Dinnerware–glass ☆ - Henriksen Imports Inc.
HEIRLOOM - Dishes–china - Pickard Inc.
HEIRLOOM - Dolls ☆ - Schmid Inc.
HEIRLOOM - Fertilizers ☆ - Anchor Swan
HEIRLOOM - Flatware - Oneida Ltd.
HEIRLOOM - Floor coverings ☆ - Congoleum Corp.
HEIRLOOM - Floor coverings–carpet and rugs ☆ - J and J Industries Inc.
HEIRLOOM - Floor coverings–carpet and rugs ☆ - Regal Rugs Inc.
HEIRLOOM - Frames–picture ☆ - Intercraft Industries
HEIRLOOM - Furniture - Ethan Allen, Inc.
HEIRLOOM - Furniture - Link-Taylor Corp.
HEIRLOOM - Furniture ☆ - Cosco, Inc.
HEIRLOOM - Furniture–children's - Child Craft Industries Inc.
HEIRLOOM - Garden furniture–rattan - Lloyd/Flanders Industries
HEIRLOOM - Giftware - C.M. Paula Co.
HEIRLOOM - Glass–leaded - Seneca Glass Co.
HEIRLOOM - Globes - Replogle Globes Inc.
HEIRLOOM - Greeting cards - Sunrise Publications, Inc.
HEIRLOOM - Hobby kits ☆ - Craft World International Inc.

HEIRLOOM - Lamps - Lamplight Farms, Inc.
HEIRLOOM - Manicure preparations - W.E. Bassett Co.
HEIRLOOM - Pans - Anchor Hocking Glass, Inc.
HEIRLOOM - Photo albums ☆ - Webway, Inc.
HEIRLOOM - Publisher's imprints - Heirloom Bible Publications
HEIRLOOM - Salad dressings–mixes - Gens Du Monde, LLC
HEIRLOOM - Tableware–china - Pfaltzgraff Investment Co.
HEIRLOOM - Toys - Montgomery Schoolhouse
HEIRLOOM - Varnishes - McCloskey Corp.
HEIRLOOM - Vases–stone - Heirloom, Inc.
HEIRLOOM - Watches - Bulova Corp.
HEIRLOOM - Wood products - Independent Stave Co. Inc.
HEIRLOOM - Yarn ☆ - Caron International Inc.
HEIRLOOM 73 - Jewelry, watches - Vintage Creations Inc.
HEIRLOOM BY VIRGINIA HOUSE - Furniture - Virginia House Furniture Corp.
HEIRLOOM CHERRY - Furniture - Virginia House Furniture Corp.
HEIRLOOM CHRISTMAS - Christmas tree ornaments - Seasonal Specialties Electrics, Inc.
HEIRLOOM COLLECTABLES - Occasional furniture ☆ - American Drew
HEIRLOOM COLLECTION - Figurines - Lenox, Inc.
HEIRLOOM COLLECTION - Infant product - Judi's Orijinals
HEIRLOOM COLLECTION - Jewelry–costume - Import Ltd.
HEIRLOOM EDITIONS - Dishes–china - Heirloom Editions Ltd.
HEIRLOOM EDITIONS LTD - Bells - Heirloom Editions Ltd.
HEIRLOOM ELEGANCE - Craft supplies ☆ - Woodline Products Inc.
HEIRLOOM GALLERY - Furniture - Pilliod Co.
HEIRLOOM GARDENS - Flowers, plants, and seeds ☆ - ABRA Inc.
HEIRLOOM GOLD HOLDER - Ophthalmic goods - Karlen Manufacturing, Inc.
HEIRLOOM LACE COLLECTION, THE - Pillows - L. Kee & Co., Inc.
HEIRLOOM MAHOGANY - Furniture - Lexington Furniture Industries, Inc.
HEIRLOOM MAHOGANY-OLDE WORLD - House furnishings - Lexington Furniture Industries, Inc.
HEIRLOOM-NEEDLECRAFT - Hobby kits - Heirloom Needlecraft Inc.
HEIRLOOM OAK - Furniture - Virginia House Furniture Corp.
HEIRLOOM OAK COLLECTION - Furniture ☆ - Evenflo Juvenile Furniture Co.
HEIRLOOM PRINTS - Fabrics - Ely and Walker Co.
HEIRLOOM STENCIL - Floor coverings–carpet and rugs - Capel, Inc.
HEIRLOOM, THE - Oboes - Dovre Inc.
HEIRLOOM VICTORIAN - House furnishings - Lexington Furniture Industries, Inc.
HEIRLOOMS - Furniture - Pulaski Furniture Corp.
HEIRLOOMS - Tiles–ceramic - Latco Products
HEIRLOOMS BY HERITAGE - Furniture - Drexel Heritage Furnishings, Inc.
HEIROPHANT - Candles - Merrill-West Publishing
HEIRWOOD - Shutters–wood - Heirwood Shutters Inc.
HEISKELL'S - Soap ☆ - J.H. Guild Co. Inc.
HEISTAD - Vegetables–canned ☆ - Haram-Christensen Corp.
HEITMAN RED H - Food products - Heitman Poultry Co.
HEITZ CELLAR - Wines - Heitz Wine Cellars
HEIWA - Photographic equipment - Lenmar Enterprises, Inc.
HEKTO - Ribbons–inked ☆ - Heyer Inc.
HEKTO-PRINTER - Duplicating machines ☆ - Heyer Inc.
HEKTOGRAPH - Duplicating machines ☆ - Heyer Inc.
HEL - Jewelry–costume - Howard Eldon Ltd.
HELANCA - Rings–jewelry - Artcarved Inc.
HELANCA PETITES - Apparel–women's - Wacoal America Inc.
HELARIOUS - Flatware - Anacapa Corp.
HELASANA - Health care products - JUZO
HELASTIC - Health care products - JUZO
HELBROS - Watches - Helbros International
HELD - Sporting goods - Gill Sports Equipment, Inc.
HELDERBERG TRACE - Publisher's imprints ☆ - Whitston Publishing Co.
HELDON - Jewelry–costume - Howard Eldon Ltd.
HELEN EDWARD USA - Apparel–women's - X & C International, Inc.
HELEN LEE - Cosmetics - New Concept Cosmetics Inc.
HELEN NYLAND BRIDAL SERVICES - Giftware - Bride Has Whispered Services
HELEN OF ST. MORITZ - Cosmetics - Helen of St. Moritz
HELEN OF TROY - Apparel–women's - Sanmark-Stardust Inc.
HELEN OF TROY - Dryers–hair - Marianna Imports, Inc.
HELEN OF TROY - Shampoos ☆ - Helen of Troy Corp.
HELEN WEBBER II: EARTHSONG - Wallpaper ☆ - Sterling Prints
HELEN ZACHARY - Candy ☆ - Zachary Confections Inc.
HELENA - Children's apparel - Ingamia Inc.
HELENA - Clocks ☆ - Ridgeway Clock Co.
HELENA - Floor coverings - Mannington Resilient Floors

HELENA - Glassware–household - ACC
HELENA - Insecticides - Lawn & Garden Supply Co.
HELENA - Rings–jewelry - Artcarved Inc.
HELENA-RUBINSTEIN - Sunglasses - L'Amy Inc.
HELENE - Dinnerware–glass ☆ - Cyclamen Studio
HELENE - Floor coverings–carpet and rugs - Eligere Carpets
HELENE BY BAMBOO - Apparel–women's - Bamboo Inc.
HELENE CURTIS - Hair care products - Helene Curtis Industries Inc.
HELENE CURTIS ORGANICS - Hair care products - Helene Curtis, Inc.
HELENOR - Wire - Helenor Industries
HELFRANCE - Combs - Accessories International
HELGA - Apparel–women's - Walter Oppenheimer
HELGA - Glass–leaded - Seneca Glass Co.
HELGA VAN DYKE - Skin care products - Helga Van Dyke Skin Care
HELGN'S TROPICAL EXOTICS - Food products - Blue Mountain Imports Inc.
HELGRAMITE - Fishing tackle - Schumann's Fly Fish Kit Co.
HELI-CAM USA - Motion picture distributors–prerecorded - Blue Water Production Co., Inc.
HELI-CUT - Machine tools - Union Butterfield Corp.
HELI-FOIL - Sails - Harken, Inc.
HELI-NUT - Metal fasteners - Emhart Inc.
HELI-SEP - Machinery - World Water Systems, Inc.
HELI-VAC - Rope - Columbian Rope Co.
HELIBOLT - Anchors - ESC Industries
HELICAL PIER - Hardware - Emerson Electric Co.
HELICAT - Toys–models - Estes Industries
HELICLEAN - Pumps–water - Hycor Corp.
HELICLEAN PLUS - Water purification systems - Hycor Corp.
HELICON - Water purification systems - Hycor Corp.
HELICOPTER - Apparel–women's - MJM Group Inc.
HELICOPTER - Deodorizers - American Auto Accessories, Inc.
HELICORE - Musical instrument accessories - J. D'Addario & Co. Inc.
HELICROWN - Transmission equipment–industrial - Bayside Controls, Inc.
HELIDYN - Pumps–vacuum ☆ - Danielson Vacuum Products, Inc.
HELIKON CLOCK - Accordions - Castiglione Accordion
HELILOK - Machine parts - Esco Corp.
HELIN - Fishing lures - Yakima Bait Co.
HELIO - Aircraft - Helio Enterprises, Inc.
HELIO - Colognes - Caswell-Massey Co. Ltd.
HELIO COPTER - Toys–models - Estes Industries
HELIO COURIER - Aircraft - Helio Enterprises, Inc.
HELIO-FLO - Controls–heating systems - Heliodyne Inc.
HELIO-PAK - Heaters–solar - Heliodyne Inc.
HELIOCOL - Solar energy collectors - Heliocol USA, Inc.
HELIODERM - Skin care products - California SunCare, Inc.
HELIOLITE - Glass products ☆ - HGP Industries Inc.
HELIOMARINE - Cosmetics ☆ - Sothys USA Inc.
HELIOPAN - Photographic equipment - H.P. Marketing Corp.
HELIOS - Bathroom accessories - Kohler Co.
HELIOS - Clothing - Ocean Front Enterprises
HELIOS - Computers - ACMA Computers Inc.
HELIOS - Flatware - Yamazaki Tableware Inc.
HELIOS - Machine tools - Strippit, Inc.
HELIOS - Photographic equipment - Keuffel & Esser Co.
HELIOS - Sunglasses - Gargoyles Inc.
HELIOS DESIGN COMPANY - Housewares - Graceann Warn
HELIOTHERAPHY INTENSIFIER - Skin care products - California SunCare, Inc.
HELIOTHERAPY - Skin care products - California SunCare, Inc.
HELIOTHERAPY HYDRATION COMPLEX - Skin care products - California SunCare, Inc.
HELIOTHERAPY MAXIMIZER - Skin care products - California SunCare, Inc.
HELIOTROPE - Garden furniture - Heliotrope LLC
HELIOTROPIC SPRAY GEL - Skin care products - California SunCare, Inc.
HELISIEVE PLUS - Water purification systems - Hycor Corp.
HELIUM HOPPERS - Novelty items - Beistle Co.
HELIVS - Bicycle parts and accessories - Windstream Power Systems Inc.
HELIX - Audio equipment - Pro-Co. Sound Co. Inc.
HELIX - Chairs–upholstered - United Chair Co., Inc.
HELIX - Computer software - Odesta Corp.
HELIX - Conveyors - Prab Robots, Inc.
HELIX - Hair care products - Lotus Brands Inc.
HELIX - Hearing aids - Starkey Labs Inc.
HELIX - Skin care products - California SunCare, Inc.
HELIX - Sporting goods ☆ - Prince Sports Group, Inc.
HELIX & ALTIMA - Lighting fixtures - Lucifer Lighting Co.

☆ = Now out of production

HELIX INTERACTIVE PRODUCTIONS - Computer software - Helix Interactive Productions, Inc.

HELIX PV - Solar energy collectors - Heliodyne Inc.

HELIX VMX - Computer software - Odesta Corp.

HELIXATE - Pharmaceutical preparations - Armour Pharmaceutical Co.

HELL ACROSS TEXAS - Dips–sour cream based - Jardine's Texas Foods

HELL CAT - Boats - Glen-L Marine Designs

HELL CAT - Toys–models - Comet Montrose Ltd.

HELL FOR STOUT - Nuts and bolts - Scott Investment Partners

HELL IN A JAR - Spices and extracts - Pure Spice Products

HELL ON THE RED - Barbecue sauce - Hell on the Red Inc.

HELL OR HIGHWATER - Apparel and accessories - Dana Martinson

HELLACIOUS ACRES - Wines - Eberlina

HELLACIOUS HASH - Spices and extracts - Star Kay White, Inc.

HELLAPENO - Jams and jellies - Gib's Classics, Inc.

HELLAS - Candy - Finnfoods Div.

HELLAS - Glass products ☆ - Avitra Corp.

HELLAS - Licorice - Pennsylvania Dutch Candies

HELLBANERO FIRE - Sauces - Gib's Classics, Inc.

HELLBENDER - Beverages–malt - Ronald D. Young

HELLBENDER - Flags - Plastics Research and Development Co.

HELLCAB - Computer software - Pepe Moreno

HELLCAT - Ammunition ☆ - Remington Arms Co., Inc.

HELLCAT - Apparel and accessories - No Fear, Inc.

HELLCAT - Flags - Plastics Research and Development Co.

HELLCAT - Motorcycles - Confederate Motorcycles Co.

HELLEMA - Bakery products - H. Hamstra & Co.

HELLEMA - Cookies - Westdale Foods Co.

HELLEMANN - Floor coverings ☆ - Omega Pattern Works, Inc.

HELLEMANN - Floor coverings ☆ - Tek Stil Concepts Inc.

HELLEMCA - Tiles–ceramic - American Marazzi Tile, Inc.

HELLENBRAND - Water treating compounds - Hellenbrand Water Conditioners Inc.

HELLENIC - Hardware ☆ - Amerock Corp.

HELLENIC HOUSE - Apparel–athletic - Universal Enterprises

HELLER - Bowls - Heller Inc.

HELLER - Fruits and vegetables - Heller Brothers Packing Corp.

HELLER'S - Candy ☆ - Powers Pharmaceutical Corp.

HELLFIRE - Alarm systems - Harrison Electronic Systems Inc.

HELLFIRE GOLD - Alarm systems - Harrison Electronic Systems Inc.

HELLMANN'S - Mayonnaise - CPC International Inc.

HELLMANN'S LOW FAT - Mayonnaise - CPC International Inc.

HELLO - Hats - Chums Ltd.

HELLO - Recording label - Stark Records & Tape Co.

HELLO AGAIN - Housewares - Bammental Wallcoverings Inc.

HELLO APPLE - Computer software - AV Systems Inc.

HELLO BERET - Hats - Chums Ltd.

HELLO BRIAN - Women's apparel - SU Enterprise Corp.

HELLO COLA - Beverages–carbonated - Hello Cola Co.

HELLO COLOR - Toys - Tonka Corp.

HELLO DOLLY - Dollies–industrial - Albert E. Price, Inc.

HELLO HAWAII - Apparel and accessories - Black & Black Inc.

HELLO KITTY - Paper–writing - Sanrio Inc.

HELLO KITTY - Socks - High Point Knitting Inc.

HELLO MATH READER - Publisher's imprints - Scholastic Inc.

HELLO READER - Publisher's imprints - Scholastic Inc.

HELLO STRAWBERRY SHORTCAKE - Toy telephones, now out of production - American Greetings Corp.

HELLO THERE - Chairs–wood ☆ - Krueger International, Inc.

HELLOSET - Telephone apparatus - Hello Direct

HELLOWEAR - Apparel and accessories - Chums Ltd.

HELLRAISER - Fishing lures - Plastics Research and Development Co.

HELLS BELLS - Games - Universal Manufacturing Co., Inc.

HELLS CANYON - Fruits and vegetables ☆ - Idaho Fruit Sales Inc.

HELLS FLAME EGGS - Fishing lures - Brown Bear Bait Co.

HELL'S HIGHWAY - Games - Avalon Hill Game Co.

HELLSLAYER - Publisher's imprints - Aegis Entertainment, Inc.

HELLSTRIKE - Posters - Aegis Entertainment, Inc.

HELLY-TECH - Waterproof outerwear - Helly-Hansen Inc.

HELM - Toys - Playtime Corp.

HELMA B. - Cosmetics - Alo Pro of Chicago Inc.

HELMAC - House furnishings - Helmac Products Corp.

HELMET HAT - Caps–baseball - Louisville Manufacturing

HELMET HEAD - Helmets–athletic - Paradise Productions

HELMITTS - Helmets–athletic - Melinda Brown Baraty

HELMS - Candy - Helms Candy Manufacturing Co. Inc.

HELMSLEY - Tableware–china ☆ - Lenox, Inc.

HELMSMAN - Clocks - General Time Corp. (Westclox/Seth Thomas Div.)

HELMSMAN - Compasses–magnetic - E.S. Ritchie & Sons Inc.

HELMSMAN - Lighters - Park Lane Associates Inc.

HELMSTAR - Automatic pilots - Brookes & Gatehouse Inc.

HELMUFS - Apparel and accessories - Bryan D. Gordon

HELMUT - Insulating materials - Vesmont Management Group, Inc.

HELMUT MAYER - Violins - Ideal Musical Merchandise Co.

HELMVIT - Veterinary nutritional supplements - Helm New York Chemical Corp.

HELNWEIN - Posters ☆ - Icart Vendor Graphics Inc.

HELO - Saunas - Cedarbrook Sauna Inc.

HELOISE'S MOST HELPFUL HINT - Cleaning preparations–household - Pronce K. Cruse

HELOR - Adhesives and sealants - Epoxy Coatings Co.

H.E.L.P. - Air filters - Rick L. Chapman

H.E.L.P. - Alarm systems - Alert Companion Inc.

HELP - Electronic equipment - Thomson Consumer Electronics, Inc.

H.E.L.P. - Filters–air - Air Kontrol Inc.

HELP - Nautical instruments ☆ - Davis Instruments Corp.

HELP-10 - Nail-care product - International Beauty Design, Inc.

HELP EVER - HURT NEVER - Apparel and accessories - House of Blues Brands Corp.

HELP HANDLES - Linen - Angela Niemeyer

H.E.L.P. MACHINES - Toys–automobiles - Mattel, Inc.

HELP MATE - Cleaning preparations–household - Chemspec, Inc.

HELP MATE - Cleaning supplies - American Textile Products Co.

HELP MATE - Health care products - Maddak Inc.

HELP-MATE - Rust removers ☆ - Strathmore Products, Inc.

HELP-MATE - Vacuum cleaners and accessories - The Hoover Co.

HELP-MATE - Veterinary pharmaceutical preparations - Intervet, Inc.

HELP ME - Alarm systems - Winner International Corp.

HELP PAK - Food products - Star Food Processing, Inc.

HELP TO HTML - Computer software - Blue Sky Software Corp.

HELP-TO-SOURCE - Computer software - Blue Sky Software Corp.

HELP-TO-WORD - Computer software - Blue Sky Software Corp.

HELP YOURSELF! - Computer software - Softlogic Solutions, Inc.

HELP YOURSELF - Computer software - Softlogic Solutions, Inc.

HELP2HTML - Computer software - Blue Sky Software Corp.

H.E.L.P.A. - Filters–air - Air Kontrol Inc.

HELPBREEZE - Computer software - Solutionsoft

HELPER - Leather–chamois - KozaK Auto Drywash Inc.

HELPFUL - Brushes–paint ☆ - PPG Industries, Inc.

HELPING HAND - Food products - General Mills, Inc.

HELPING HAND - Glue–household or industrial - Faucet-Queens, Inc.

HELPING HAND - Paper - Scott Paper Co.

HELPING HAND - Tools–hand-operated - Faucet-Queens Inc.

HELPING HANDS - Skin care products ☆ - Care-Tech Laboratories Inc.

HELPING OUR PLANET'S ECOLOGY - Paper ☆ - Orchids Paper Products, Inc.

HELPING PRESERVE OUR FORESTS - Paper–tissue - Fort Howard Corp.

HELPLINE - Health care products - Omni Group Inc.

HELPLINK - Telephones - Delaware Capital Formation Inc.

HELPMATE - Cleaning preparations–carpet and rug - Chemspec, Inc.

HELPMATE - Computer software - General Electric Co.

HELPMATE - Tools–hand-operated - Victor Automotive Products, Inc.

HELPME - Computer software - California Software Products Inc.

HELPS - Cough medicines - Luden's Inc.

HELPS - Licorice ☆ - Y & S Candies Inc.

HELPTEL - Telephones–cellular - Lindsay Communications, Inc.

HELSINKI - Bedding–linen - Dan River Inc.

HELSINKI - Floor coverings–carpet and rugs - Artistic Rugs Inc.

HELSPONT - Toys - Aegis Entertainment, Inc.

HELTER - Tires - Cheng Shin Rubber USA, Inc.

HELTH-A-DAY - Health care products - Health Products Corp.

HELTH HAIR - Hair care products - Health Products Corp.

HELTH-HEAD - Vitamins and nutritional supplements - Health Products Corp.

HELTHBEE - Vitamins and nutritional supplements - Health Products Corp.

HELUVA GOOD - Cheese - Heluva Good Cheese Inc.

HELVETICA - Rings–jewelry - Artcarved Inc.

HELWAN - Firearms, accessories, and parts - International Armament Corp.

HELYX - Concrete products - Hillwood Manufacturing Co.

HEL'Z A POPPIN - Meat products–beef - Paisano Food Products Inc.

HEL'Z A POPPIN - Meats - Cousins Foods Ltd.

HELZBERG DIAMONDS, DIAMONDS, DIAMONDS - Jewelry–precious - Helzbergs Diamond Shops Inc.

HELZBERG LIMITED EDITION - Jewelry - Helzbergs Diamond Shops Inc.

HEM-BATH - Cosmetics - Newton Laboratories Inc.

HEM-LINE - Computer software - New Century Information Services, Inc.

HEM-N-TRIM - Craft supplies - Prym Dritz Corp.

HEM-O-LOCK - Medical apparatus - Edward Weck & Co. Inc.

HEM-SORT - Motor vehicle parts and accessories - NBS Trucking, Inc.

HEMA-COMBISTIX - Chemical preparations - Miles Inc.

HEMA-LARDON - Pharmaceutical preparations - Lardon Laboratories

HEMABATE - Pharmaceutical preparations - Upjohn Co.

HEMAFERRIN - Pharmaceutical preparations - Western Research Laboratories

HEMAFLO 2 - Medical apparatus ☆ - Camp, Inc.

HEMAGLO - Pharmaceutical preparations - Seatrace Co.

HEMALIQUID - Pharmaceutical preparations ☆ - Ulmer Pharmacal Co.

HEMAMAN - Refrigerators - Jewett Refrigerator Co., Inc.

HEMAN - Mustard - Keller Food Products Co.

HEMANA BANANA - Food products - Bob White Organization

HEMANEED - Pharmaceutical preparations - Hanlon Drug Products

HEMAPROMPT - Medical apparatus - Robert Schreiber

HEMASHIELD - Medical apparatus - Meadox Medicals, Inc.

HEMASPAN - Pharmaceutical preparations - Bock Pharmacal Co.

HEMASSIST - Medical apparatus - Baxter International Inc.

HEMASTIX - Chemical preparations - Miles Inc.

HEMATEST - Chemical preparations - Miles Inc.

HEMATOL - Pharmaceutical preparations ☆ - Pharm-A-Lab

HEMATOVALS - Pharmaceutical preparations ☆ - Ulmer Pharmacal Co.

HEMATRAN - Pharmaceutical preparations ☆ - Roberts/Hauck Pharmaceuticals Inc.

HEMATROL - Veterinary pharmaceutical preparations ☆ - Schering-Plough Animal Health

HEMATRON - Pharmaceutical preparations ☆ - U.S. Ethicals Inc.

HEMATROPIN - Pharmaceutical preparations ☆ - Roberts/Hauck Pharmaceuticals Inc.

HEMAWIPE - Diagnostic substances - Medtek, LLC

HEMAWIPE - Health care products - Labeltape Meditect Inc.

HEMAX - Pharmaceutical - Elanex Pharmaceuticals, Inc.

HEMBOBS - Thread - Belding Heminway Co. Inc.

HEMCO - Lighting equipment - Home Equipment Manufacturing Co.

HEMCO - Thread ☆ - Belding Heminway Co. Inc.

HEMCO SHELF HARDWARE - Hardware - Home Equipment Manufacturing Co.

HEMET - Health care products - Halsey Drug Co. Inc.

HEMEX - Glassware–household - Owens-Illinois Inc. (Libbey Div.)

HEMI - Footwear - Vans, Inc.

HEMI - Housewares ☆ - Shepherd Products U.S. Inc.

HEMI-AMBULATOR - Health care products - Temco Health Care

HEMI-C - Pharmaceutical preparations ☆ - Jones Medical Industries, Inc. (Medical Div.)

HEMI FOOT-STOP - Exercising equipment - Lisa Sattler

HEMINGWAY - Chocolate candy - Hemingway Chocolate Co.

HEMINGWAY - Wallpaper - Doshi Wallcoveringss Inc.

HEMINGWAY BROS. 960 NEW BEDFORD, MASS. - Toys–automobiles - Toy Truck Lines, Inc.

HEMINGWAY COLLECTION, THE - Posters - Stanton & Lee

HEMINGWAY POINT - Handkerchiefs - Kmart Properties, Inc.

HEMINWAY - Thread - Belding Heminway Co. Inc.

HEMISPHERE - Apparel and accessories ☆ - Gap Inc.

HEMISPHERE - Mirrors - Vincent Lippe Co.

HEMISPHERE - Wallpaper - Imperial Wallcoverings, Inc.

HEMISPHERES - Jewelry - Tracy J. Priest, Jr.

HEMISPHONICS - Recording label - Progressive Awareness Research, Inc.

HEMKUNT BOOKS - Publisher's imprint - Auromere Inc.

HEMLAST - Housewares - Gustin-Kramer Co.

HEMLOCK - Paper–bond ☆ - Pengad, Inc.

HEMLOCK SPINNERS - Fishing tackle - Sutton Co.

HEMMA PLEX - Vitamins and nutritional supplements - Natural Organics, Inc.

HEMO - Food products ☆ - Borden, Inc.

HEMO-CLEAN - Pharmaceutical preparations - Business Medical Supply, Inc.

HEMO-LIV - Health care products ☆ - Kay Pharmacal Co. Inc.

HEMOCAINE - Pharmaceutical preparations - Roberts/Hauck Pharmaceuticals Inc.

HEMOCARE - Vitamins and nutritional supplements - Ayurvedic Concepts Ltd.

HEMOCCULT - Health care products ☆ - SmithKline Beecham Consumer Healthcare

HEMOCYTE - Pharmaceutical preparations - U.S. Pharmaceutical Corp.

HEMOCYTE-C - Pharmaceutical preparations - U.S. Pharmaceutical Corp.

HEMOCYTE-F - Pharmaceutical preparations - U.S. Pharmaceutical Corp.

HEMOCYTE-F ELIXER - Pharmaceutical preparations - U.S. Pharmaceutical Corp.

HEMOCYTE PLUS - Vitamins and nutritional supplements - U.S. Pharmaceutical Corp.

HEMODYNE - Pharmaceutical preparations ☆ - Wesley Pharmacal Co. Inc.

HEMOFERIN - Veterinary pharmaceutical preparations - Gerard-Pellham Co.

HEMOFLEX - Medical apparatus - Viskase Corp.

HEMOFORM - Pharmaceutical preparations - G.O. Spanner Inc.

HEMOGEN - Vitamins and nutritional supplements ☆ - Fibertone Co.

HEMOID - Hemorrhoid treatment - American Laboratories Inc.

HEMOLIANCE - Pharmaceutical preparations - MLA/Ortho Hemostatis

HEMOPLEXIC - Pharmaceutical preparations ☆ - Morton Pharmaceuticals Inc.

HEMOR-AID 3 - Pharmaceutical preparations - Norstar Consumer Products Co., Inc.

HEMOREX - Skin care products - Derma Rx Corp.

HEMORID - Pharmaceutical preparations - Thompson Medical Co., Inc.

HEMORRHOID TABLETS & SUPPOSITORIES - Pharmaceutical preparations - Boiron Inc.

HEMORRHOIDAL CARE SPECIALIST, THE - Pharmaceutical preparations - American Home Products Corp.

HEMORRODIL - Pharmaceutical preparations - Tarmac Products Inc.

HEMORROINTMENT - Health care products - Thornton-Minor McCleary Ointment Co.

HEMORRZ - Pharmaceutical preparations - Au Pharmaceuticals Inc.

HEMOSEV - Pharmaceutical preparations ☆ - American Hygienic Laboratories Inc.

HEMOSTATIC ERASER - Medical apparatus - Mentor O & O Inc.

HEMOSTATIX - Medical apparatus - Telegenix, Inc.

HEMOTEMP - Health care products - Biosynergy Inc.

HEMOTEMP II - Health care products - Biosynergy Inc.

HEMOTINIC PLUS - Pharmaceutical preparations ☆ - Vitarine Pharmaceuticals Inc.

HEMOTONIC - Veterinary pharmaceutical preparations - Equest, Inc. (Saratoga Veterinary Products, Co.)

HEMOVAC - Medical apparatus - Zimmer, Inc.

HEMOZYME - Pharmaceutical preparations - Barrows Pharmacal Inc.

HEMP - Furniture - Hemp Boards Inc.

HEMP BALM - Medical apparatus - Gerry C. Shapiro

HEMP GOLF - Golfing equipment - Cobarr Creative Marketing, Inc.

HEMP HOP - Apparel and accessories - Hemp Hop Enterprises

HEMP NOW - Apparel–men's - Two Star Dog

HEMP PEDALER - Lubricants - Hemp Pedaler Co.

HEMP-RELLA - Cheese - Rose Enterprises Ltd.

HEMP RELLA - Food products - Rella Good Cheese Co.

HEMP RELLA - Food products - Rose International

HEMP SPORTS - Apparel and accessories - Cobarr Creative Marketing, Inc.

HEMPADUR - Paints - Hempel Coatings USA Inc.

HEMPALIN - Paints - Hempel Coatings USA Inc.

HEMPANYL - Paints - Hempel Coatings USA Inc.

HEMPATHANE - Paints - Hempel Coatings USA Inc.

HEMPATONE - Paints - Hempel Coatings USA Inc.

HEMPCOT - Yarn - Hemp Textiles International

HEMPEH - Food products - Rella Good Cheese Co.

HEMPEH - Food products - Rose International

HEMPINOL - Paints - Hempel Coatings USA Inc.

HEMPNUT - Food products - Rella Good Cheese Co.

HEMPREP - Health care products - G and W Laboratories Inc.

HEMPRESSIONS - Apparel–men's - Richard Dale Lippard

HEMPSTEAD BRICK - Floor coverings - Congoleum Corp.

HEMPTEX - Hemp - Hemp Textiles International

HEMPWOL - Yarn - Hemp Textiles International

HEMPY'S - Apparel and accessories - Earthwise Enterprise

HEMPZ - Shoes - Heavenly Hemp, Inc.

HEMRIL-HC - Pharmaceutical preparations - Upsher-Smith Laboratories, Inc.

HEMS - Computer software - EQ2, Inc.

HEMSHIRE - Thread - Threads USA Div.

HEMSLEY - Floor coverings - Tarkett, Inc.

HEMSLEY - Floor coverings–carpet and rugs ☆ - Customweave Carpets Inc.

HEMSOID BELL - Pharmaceutical preparations - Hollings-Smith Co. Inc.

HEMUCRYL - Paints - Hempel Coatings USA Inc.

HEN & ROOSTER - Knives–pocket - A.G. Russell Knives Inc.

HEN-'N-HEAT - Sporting goods - Camp-Cap Products

HENA - Teas - Hena Inc.

HENARA - Hair care products ☆ - Miracle Exclusives Inc.

HENCKELS - Cutlery - J.A. Henckels Zwillingswerk Inc.

HENCKELS INTERNATIONAL - Cutlery - J.A. Henckels Zwillingswerk Inc.

☆ = Now out of production

HENCOL - Switches–electric - Cole Hersee Co.

HENDEE - Filters–air - Hendee Enterprises, Inc.

HENDERSON - Bicycles - Schwinn Cycling & Fitness Inc.

HENDERSON - Food products - Zartic, Inc.

HENDERSON - Tools–garden - Kinco Manufacturing Co.

HENDERSONVILLE - Recording label - Terock Records

HENDLER'S - Ice cream ☆ - Borden, Inc.

HENDRICK END PAPERS COLLECTION - Wallcoverings - Ben Rose Ltd.

HENDRICKS, THE - Publisher's imprints - City Guide Magazine

HENDRICKSON - Canes ☆ - Otto Bock Orthopedic Industry Inc.

HENDRICKSON - Fishing lures - Thomas and Thomas Rodmakers Inc.

HENDRIES - Yogurt–frozen - H.P. Hood & Sons Inc.

HENDRY - Office accessories - Hendry Mechanical Works

HENDRY - Pet products - Prevue Metal Products Inc.

HENDRY X - Pet products - Prevue Metal Products Inc.

HENGIST - Windmills ☆ - Brookes & Gatehouse Inc.

HENGSTENBERG - Pickles - C. & J. Willenborg Inc.

HENGSTENBERG - Vegetables–pickled or brined - Haram-Christensen Corp.

HENKELL AND SOHNLEIN - Beverages–alcohol - Paterno Imports, Ltd.

HENLAN - Hair care products - Quimby & Co.

HENLEY - Wallpaper - Surface Industries Inc.

HENLEY COLLECTION BY EASTPAK - Luggage - Eastpak

HENNA - Hair care products - Avigal Henna

HENNA DIFFERENCE, THE - Hair care products - Helene Curtis Industries Inc.

HENNA ESSENCE - Hair care products - Helene Curtis Industries Inc.

HENNA-GLO - Hair care products ☆ - Jerant Co. Inc.

HENNA GOLD - Hair care products - ShiKai Natural Body Care Products, Inc.

HENNA HI-LIGHTS - Hair care products - Jason Natural Products, Inc.

HENNA 'N PLACENTA - Hair care products ☆ - Alleghany Pharmacal Corp.

HENNA - PROTEIN LINE - Hair care products - Roberts Research Laboratories, Inc.

HENNA SAN - Hair coloring preparations - Alvin Last Inc.

HENNA TONE - Hair care products ☆ - Jason Natural Products, Inc.

HENNACARE - Hair-care products - Cabot Laboratories Inc.

HENNAGIZER - Hair care products - Helene Curtis Industries Inc.

HENNALUCENT - American International Industries

HENNALUCENT - Hair care products - Ardell International Inc.

HENNESSY - Apparel–men's - Phillips-Van Heusen Corp.

HENNESSY - Brandy - Schieffelin and Somerset Co.

HENNESSY - Neckties ☆ - Randa Corp.

HENNESSY MARTINI - Beverages–alcohol - Schieffelin & Co.

HENNIEZE - Water–mineral ☆ - HDT Importers Inc.

HENNING KOPPEL - Tableware–china - Royal Copenhagen Porcelain Inc.

HENNINGER - Beverages–malt - Barton Brands, Ltd.

HENNINGSEN - Food products - Henningsen Foods Inc.

HENNY PEN - Dog food - Allied Foods Inc.

HENOMINT - Pharmaceutical preparations ☆ - JMI-Canton Pharmaceuticals

HENOTAL - Pharmaceutical preparations ☆ - JMI-Canton Pharmaceuticals

HENREDON - Furniture - Henredon Furniture Industries Inc.

HENREDON REGISTRY - Furniture–upholstered - Henredon Furniture Industries Inc.

HENRI - Food products - Sar-A-Lee Inc.

HENRI - Vinyl - Henri Studio, Inc.

HENRI ABELE - Wines - Freixenet USA

HENRI BENDEL - Hair care products - Bendelco, Inc.

HENRI BOUCHE - Musical instruments - Goodman Music Corp.

HENRI CHRISTIAN - Apparel–athletic - Pedigree USA Inc.

HENRI DE BOISSEAU - Wines ☆ - European Beverage Co., Inc.

HENRI HUTIN - Cheese - Fromark

HENRI HUTIN BELLETOILE - Cheese - Fromark

HENRI IV - Cheese ☆ - Bongrain Cheese USA

HENRI LEGER - Wines ☆ - Alimar & Cie. Inc.

HENRI-LIMOUZY - Beverages–alcohol ☆ - Victoire Imports Co.

HENRI-LLOYD - Waterproof outerwear - Mariner Resource Corp.

HENRI LYON - Wines ☆ - Alimar & Cie. Inc.

HENRI MARCHANT - Beverages–alcohol - Canandaigua Wine Co. Inc.

HENRI MARCHANT - Wines - Gold Seal Vineyards Inc.

HENRI NESTLE - Chocolate bars - Nestle USA

HENRI PIROT - Giftware - Merchandisers Association Inc.

HENRI PORTIER, PARIS - Fabrics - Leimtex Corp.

HENRI SAVARD - Wines - Sidney Frank Importing Co., Inc.

HENRI SELMER - Musical instruments ☆ - Selmer Co. Inc.

HENRI (THE NAVIGATOR) - Computer software - Genasys II, Inc.

HENRI WATER GARDENING - Filters–water - Henri Studio, Inc.

HENRI WINTERMAN - Cigars - G.A. Georgopulo & Co. Inc.

HENRI ZALZER - Musical instruments - Fred Gretsch Enterprises

HENRIKSEN - Glassware–household ☆ - Henriksen Imports Inc.

HENRIQUEST HENRIQUES - Wines ☆ - Wilson Daniels Ltd.

HENRI'S - Salad dressings–bottled - Henri's Food Products Co. Inc.

HENRI'S FRONTIER FRENCH - Salad dressings–bottled - Henri's Food Products Co. Inc.

HENRI'S LIGHT TAS-TEE - Salad dressings–bottled - Henri's Food Products Co. Inc.

HENRI'S SALAD DRESSING - Salad dressings–bottled - Henri's Food Products Co. Inc.

HENRI'S TAS-TEE - Salad dressings–bottled - Henri's Food Products Co. Inc.

HENRI'S YOGOWHIP - Salad dressings–bottled - Henri's Food Products Co. Inc.

HENRY - Computer software - Tiger Electronics, Inc.

HENRY - Floor coverings - Virginia Hardwood Co.

HENRY - Toys–stuffed ☆ - Gund, Inc.

HENRY - Wines - Scott Henry's Winery

HENRY & GORDON BEHRENWALD - Honey ☆ - Gordon & Henry Behrenwald

HENRY CALVIN - Wallpaper - K.M.L. Industries

HENRY CLAY - Cigar boxes–wood - Consolidated Cigar Corp.

HENRY COEHLER - Clocks - Coehler-Coptex Co.

HENRY CYCLE - Posters - John Lemmon Films Inc.

HENRY F. MILLER - Pianos - Aeolian Pianos Inc.

HENRY FIELD - Fertilizers - Gurney Seed & Nursery Corp.

HENRY FORD MUSEUM REPRODUCTIONS - Giftware - Woodbury Pewterers Inc.

HENRY GRETHEL - Hosiery–men's - Camp Hosiery

HENRY GRETHEL - Sunglasses ☆ - International Tropic-Cal Inc. (I SKI Div.)

HENRY GRETHEL - Umbrellas ☆ - Shaw Creations Inc.

HENRY GRETHEL - Waterproof outerwear - Hartmarx Corp.

HENRY HIPPO - Toys - Fisher-Price, Inc.

HENRY HOLT - Publisher's imprints - Henry Holt and Co.

HENRY HOLT MYSTERY, A - Publisher's imprints - Henry Holt and Co.

HENRY J'S - Corned beef - Henry J's Hashtime-USA

HENRY LINK - Furniture ☆ - Masco Corp.

HENRY MARGU - Wigs - Henry Margu, Inc.

HENRY MARGU'S GEMZ - Wigs - Henry Margu, Inc.

HENRY MCKENNA - Liquors - Heaven Hill Distilleries, Inc.

HENRY O - Boats - Taylor Manufacturing Inc.

HENRY PETROLEUM - Consulting services - Henry Petroleum Corp.

HENRY PHILLIPE - Cordials - Paramount Distillers Inc.

HENRY POURCELLE - Musical instruments - C. Bruno & Son Inc.

HENRY R. MOCKEL - Posters - Henry R. Mockel's

HENRY RIES - Greeting cards - American Artists Group Inc.

+HENRY +ROSENFELD LUGGAGE - Luggage - Badanco Enterprises, Inc.

HENRY SCHEIN - Dental equipment - Henry Schein, Inc.

HENRY STROBEL - Musical instrument accessories - International Violin Co. Ltd.

HENRY WAKE - Musical instrument accessories - International Violin Co. Ltd.

HENRY WATSON'S - Pottery - Hartstone Inc.

HENRY WEINARD'S PRIVATE RESERVE LIGHT - Beverages–malt - The Stroh Brewery Co.

HENRY WEINARD'S ROOT BEER - Beverages–carbonated - The Stroh Brewery Co.

HENRY WEINARD'S VANILLA CREAM - Beverages–carbonated - The Stroh Brewery Co.

HENRY WEINHARD'S PRIVATE RESERVE - Beverages–malt - The Stroh Brewery Co.

HENRY WEINHARD'S PRIVATE RESERVE DARK - Beverages–malt - The Stroh Brewery Co.

HENRYETTE - Nail care products ☆ - RH Cosmetics Corp.

HENRY'S - Mushrooms - H.K. Canning Inc.

HENRY'S - Skin care products - Henry Beauty Imports Inc.

HENRY'S BLEND - Coffee - House of Coffee

HEN'S CRISPEANUTS - Nuts–salted, roasted, cooked, or canned - S & H Foods

HEN'S HARVEST - Eggs - Almark Inc.

HENSCHEL - Drafting supplies ☆ - Canson-Talens Inc.

HENSHALL - Sporting goods - Weber Industries Inc.

HENSON - Underwear and nightwear - Henson-Kickernick Inc.

HENTEX - Food products - Henningsen Foods Inc.

HEP - Beverages–carbonated ☆ - Universal Flavor USA

HEP-B-GAMMAGEE - Pharmaceutical preparations - Merck & Co., Inc. (Merck Research Laboratories)

HEP FORTE - Vitamins and nutritional supplements - Marlyn Co. Inc.

HEP KAT - Deodorizers ☆ - Car-Freshner Corp.

HEP SPINNER - Fishing lures - James Heddon's Sons

☆ = Now out of production

HEPA - Respirators - Uvex Safety LLC

HEPA-CHOL - Pharmaceutical preparations ☆ - Keene Pharmaceuticals Inc.

HEPA-CLEAR - Air purification systems - Slant/Fin Corp.

HEPA-DESICOL - Pharmaceutical preparations ☆ - Parke-Davis

HEPA EVENLY SAVER - Filters–air - HEPA Corp.

HEPA-MAX - Filters–air - HEPA Corp.

HEPA PLEAT II - Filters–air - HEPA Corp.

HEPA-PLUS - Filters–air - HEPA Corp.

HEPA SEP - Filters–air - HEPA Corp.

HEPACARE - Air purification systems - Hepacare Corp.

HEPACOL - Pharmaceutical preparations ☆ - C.O. Truxton Inc.

HEPACRON PUREAIR ZONE - Air purification systems - VBM Corp.

HEPADIN - Vitamins and nutritional supplements ☆ - Vita-Fore Products Co.

HEPAFERRON - Pharmaceutical preparations ☆ - U.S. Ethicals Inc.

HEPANAIRE - Cleaning preparations - Summit Hill Laboratories

HEPANE-LS - Pharmaceutical preparations - Medical Chemical Corp.

HEPARPLEX - Pharmaceutical preparations ☆ - U.S. Ethicals Inc.

HEPARTCO - Sealing devices - Hepco

HEPATA CARE - Vitamins and nutritional supplements - Maharishi Ayurveda Products International Inc.

HEPATA CARE, JR. - Vitamins and nutritional supplements - Maharishi Ayurveda Products International Inc.

HEPATAHERB - Vitamins and nutritional supplements ☆ - J.R. Carlson Laboratories Inc.

HEPATO-PURE - Vitamins and nutritional supplements - Planetary Formulas

HEPATOGEN - Vitamins and nutritional supplements - Vitamin Research Products Inc.

HEPATOSCREEN - Medical apparatus - Dorn C. Cook

HEPATROPHIN PMG - Vitamins and nutritional supplements - Standard Process Inc.

HEPBURN - Food products - Hepburn Orchards Inc.

HEPBURN'S BROADCAST CONNECTION - Computer software - Hepburn's Broadcast Connection

HEPCAT - Recording label - Sounds-Vision Music

HEPFOMIN - Pharmaceutical preparations ☆ - Keene Pharmaceuticals Inc.

HEPICEBRIN - Pharmaceutical preparations - Eli Lilly and Co.

HE+ - Video games - Jasco Products Co. Inc.

HEPP-IRON - Pharmaceutical preparations ☆ - Norgine Laboratories Inc.

HEPPNER - Audio equipment - Heppner Manufacturing Co.

HEPRON - Pharmaceutical preparations ☆ - Norgine Laboratories Inc.

HEPTALAC - Pharmaceutical preparations - Copley Pharmaceutical, Inc.

HEPTAVAX-B - Vaccines - Merck & Co., Inc. (Merck Research Laboratories)

HEPTUNA - Pharmaceutical preparations - J.B. Roerig & Co.

HEPTUNA PLUS - Pharmaceutical preparations - J.B. Roerig & Co.

HER DRYNESS - Diapers–disposable - Associated Hygienic Products

HER EXCELLENCY - Watches - Bulova Corp.

HER FATHER'S BUSINESS - Greeting cards - Sherri P. Richards

HER FIRST - Toys - Libby Lee Toys Inc.

HER GAME 2. - Apparel and accessories - Her Game 2, Inc.

HER H - Hosiery - Ellis Hosiery Mills, Inc.

HER HIGHNESS - Dryers–hair - Helene Curtis Industries Inc.

HER MAJESTY - Apparel and accessories - Heckler Manufacturing & Investment Group Inc.

HER MAJESTY - Apparel–children's - Her Majesty Industries Inc.

HER MAJESTY - Floor coverings–carpet and rugs - Lees Carpets

HER MAJESTY - Floor coverings–carpet and rugs ☆ - American Carpet Mills

HER PRETTINESS - Health care products ☆ - Avon Products, Inc.

HER STYLE - Skirts–girls' - Her Style Inc.

HERA - Sport watches - Jaeger-Le Coultre SA

HERACLES - Vases - Durand International

HERALD - Cigarettes - Brown & Williamson Tobacco Corp.

HERALD - Dinnerware–glass ☆ - Salem China Co.

HERALD - Floor coverings–carpet and rugs - Patrick Carpet Mills

HERALD - Recording label - Caroline Records, Inc.

HERALD HOUSE - Publisher's imprints - Herald House

HERALD PRESS - Publisher's imprints - Herald Press

HERALD SCRIPTURE LIBRARY - See FRANCISCAN HERALD PRESS

HERALD SQUARE - Finishing agents ☆ - Flintkote Co.

HERALD SQUARE - Floor coverings - Mannington Resilient Floors

HERALD SQUARE - Handles–metal - Weslock National, Inc.

HERALD SQUARE - Hardware - A.J.P. Weslock Industries Co.

HERALD SQUARE - Paints ☆ - GS Roofing Products Co.

HERALDRY - Floor coverings - Mannington Resilient Floors

HERALDRY HOUSE - Jewelry - CJC Holdings, Inc.

HERB - Frames–eyeglass - Rozin Optical Export Corp.

HERB - Toys–stuffed ☆ - Gund, Inc.

HERB ALCHEMY - Herbal products - Foodscience Laboratories Inc.

HERB ALCHEMY EXTRACTS - Pharmaceutical preparations - Foodscience Corp.

HERB & SPICE GOURMET - Spices and extracts - Finest Kind Spices

HERB-ART - Artists' materials - H.T. Herbert Co. Inc.

HERB CLASSICS - Salad dressings–bottled - Lipton Investments, Inc.

HERB FARM - Vinegar - Bittersweet Herb Farm

HERB GARDEN - Hair- and skin-care products, fragrance, etc. - Benjamin Ansehl Co.

HERB GARDEN - Salad dressings–bottled ☆ - Nalley's Fine Foods

HERB GARDEN SOF-POT - Flowers, plants, and seeds - Applewood Seed & Garden Group

HERB GATHERING - Cosmetics - Holiday Magic Inc.

HERB GC - Jewelry - Herbert Goldberg Co., Inc.

HERB-LAX - Vitamins and nutritional supplements - Shaklee Corp.

HERB LIFE - Publisher's imprints - Edward Maldonado

HERB MAGIC - Food products - Reily Foods

HERB MASTERS' ORIGINAL FORMULAS, THE - Health care products - Nature's Herbs

HERB 'N GOURMET - Food products - Herb 'n Gourmet, Inc.

HERB NURSERY - Seeds–salted, roasted, cooked, or canned - Kingfisher Inc.

HERB OX REAL HERBS REAL FLAVOR - Bouillon cubes - Hormel Foods Corp.

HERB PATCH - Flowers, plants, and seeds - Amturf

HERB RUBS - Seasonings - Companion Group

HERB SHOP, THE - Herbal products - Christopher Enterprises Inc.

HERBA CHOLINE - Vitamins and nutritional supplements - Natur-Pharma, Inc.

HERBA-FED - Pharmaceutical preparations ☆ - Traditional Medicinals, Inc.

HERBA HYDROXY - Skin care products - Cal Trade

HERBA-MUNE - Health care products - Bio-Research Laboratories

HERBA-TUSSIN - Teas–herbal - Traditional Medicinals, Inc.

HERBA-VITES - Vitamins and nutritional supplements - Natur-Pharma, Inc.

HERBACOL - Cough medicines - Home Health Products, Inc.

HERBACOY - Vitamins and nutritional supplements - Herbacoy Natural Products Inc.

HERBACURE - Vitamins and nutritional supplements - Herbacure Natural Supplements Inc.

HERBADASHERY - Food products - Eli Dicklich and Barbara Dicklich

HERBADE - Vitamins and nutritional supplements - Tishcon Corp.

HERBADERM - Vitamins and nutritional supplements - Planetary Formulas

HERBAFLEX - Vitamins and nutritional supplements ☆ - Green Farm Herb Products

HERBAL - Skin care products - Herb Products Co.

HERBAL ALLERGY FORMULA - Vitamins and nutritional supplements - Vitamin Research Products Inc.

HERBAL AMBROSIA - Vitamins and nutritional supplements - New Moon Extracts, Inc.

HERBAL ANIMAL - Pet products ☆ - Natural Animal Health Products, Inc.

HERBAL BLADDER FORMULA - Vitamins and nutritional supplements - Matrix Health Products, Inc.

HERBAL BODYWORKS - Health care products - New Age Creations/Herbal Bodyworks

HERBAL BOUQUET - Seasonings - Modern Products, Inc.

HERBAL BOUQUET - Toiletries - Blue Cross Laboratories Inc.

HERBAL-C - Teas ☆ - Traditional Medicinals, Inc.

HERBAL C COMPLEX - Health care products - Futurebiotics

HERBAL CALCIUM RICH - Pharmaceutical preparations - Maharishi Ayurveda Products International Inc.

HERBAL CALM - Nail care products - Health Products Corp.

HERBAL CHOICE - Pharmaceutical preparations - Botalia

HERBAL CLASSICS - Vitamins and nutritional supplements - Vitamin Classics, Inc.

HERBAL CLEAN - Vitamins and nutritional supplements - BNG Enterprises, Inc.

HERBAL CLEANSE - Vitamins and nutritional supplements - Maharishi Ayurveda Products International Inc.

HERBAL COMFORT - Skin care products - Sunshine Products

HERBAL COMFORT - Teas - Celestial Seasonings, Inc.

HERBAL CONCEPTS - Vitamins and nutritional supplements - Herbal Concepts Inc.

HERBAL CURIO - Vitamins and nutritional supplements - Vital Energy

HERBAL DEEPCLEAN - Cosmetics - Revlon Consumer Products Corp.

HERBAL DEFENSE FORMULA - Vitamins and nutritional supplements ☆ - Jones Pharma Inc.

HERBAL EASE - Vitamins and nutritional supplements - Bioenergy Nutrient's Inc.

☆ = Now out of production

HERBAL EDGE, THE - Vitamins and nutritional supplements - Nanci Corp. International

HERBAL ESSENCE - Hair care products - Clairol Inc.

HERBAL ESSENCES - Hair care products - Clairol Inc.

HERBAL EXTRAS - Vitamins and nutritional supplements - Rainbow Light Nutritional Systems, Inc.

HERBAL FEMALE FORMULA - Vitamins and nutritional supplements - Matrix Health Products, Inc.

HERBAL FORMULA FOR MEN - Vitamins and nutritional supplements ☆ - Vitamin Research Products Inc.

HERBAL FORMULA FOR WOMEN - Vitamins and nutritional supplements - Vitamin Research Products Inc.

HERBAL GARDEN - Herbal products - Vitamin Power Inc.

HERBAL GARDEN BIJOUX DE BAIN - Skin care products - Savonnerie, Inc.

HERBAL GOLD - Cigarettes - Alternative Cigarettes, Inc.

HERBAL GUARD - Pet products - Revere Manufacturing

HERBAL HARMONY - Health care products - Futurebiotics

HERBAL HARMONY - Vitamins and nutritional supplements - Pdk Labs, Inc.

HERBAL HARVEST - Health care products - Nature's Bounty, Inc.

HERBAL HARVEST INC. - Vitamins and nutritional supplements - Design Visualization Services, Inc.

HERBAL HOME - Health care products - Herbal Home Products

HERBAL HOUSE QUALITY GARDENS, INC. - Fruits and vegetables - Herbal House Quality Gardens, Inc.

HERBAL IRON RICH - Pharmaceutical preparations - Maharishi Ayurveda Products International Inc.

HERBAL LITE - Hair care products - Gold Medal Hair Products Inc.

HERBAL-LITE - Teas–herbal ☆ - Traditional Medicinals, Inc.

HERBAL MAGIC - Skin care products - Home Health Products, Inc.

HERBAL MEDLEY - Shampoos - Anasazi Salon System, Inc.

HERBAL MELANGE - Health care products - Norimoor Co.

HERBAL METAPHORS - Skin care products - Thymes Limited

HERBAL MINERAL - Vitamins and nutritional supplements ☆ - Nature's Way Products, Inc.

HERBAL MINTS - Candy - Lotte USA Inc.

HERBAL MIST - Sprayers - Blue Cross Laboratories Inc.

HERBAL MIST - Vitamins and nutritional supplements - McZand Herbal, Inc.

HERBAL-NATURAL - Shampoos - Kim Laube & Co. Inc.

HERBAL OASIS - Vitamins and nutritional supplements - Organic Diversions, Inc.

HERBAL OIL - Skin care products - Fanie International

HERBAL PAIN AWAY-ROLL ON - Skin care products - Victoria Vogue, Inc.

HERBAL PERFORMANCE - Skin care products - Alessio International

HERBAL PHARMA-C - Teas–herbal ☆ - Traditional Medicinals, Inc.

HERBAL PILLOW - Health care products ☆ - European Skin & Haircare

HERBAL PLASMA - Skin care products - Earth Science Inc.

HERBAL POWER - Vitamins and nutritional supplements - Herbal Power Inc.

HERBAL REMETEAS - Teas–herbal - Twin Laboratories, Inc.

HERBAL RISING - Vitamins and nutritional supplements - Planetary Formulas

HERBAL SAVVY - Health care products - Country Comfort

HERBAL SECRETS - Salad dressings–bottled - El Molino Mills

HERBAL SENSE - Sporting goods - Camp-Cap Products

HERBAL SERENITY - Beauty aids - BC International Cosmetics & Image Services, Inc.

HERBAL SKIN & COAT RUB - Pet products - Nala Barry Laboratories

HERBAL SLEEP - Teas–herbal - Health Products Corp.

HERBAL SLEEP - Vitamins and nutritional supplements - Vitamin Research Products Inc.

HERBAL SLIM - Vitamins and nutritional supplements - Nature's Way Products, Inc.

HERBAL SLUMBER - Vitamins and nutritional supplements - Natural Balance, Inc.

HERBAL SOFT - Skin care products - Gena Laboratories Inc.

HERBAL SOLUTIONS - Vitamins and nutritional supplements - Natural Organics, Inc.

HERBAL SOOTHE I - Herbal products - Maharishi Ayurveda Products International Inc.

HERBAL SOOTHE II - Cosmetics - Maharishi Ayurveda Products International Inc.

HERBAL SPA - Skin care products ☆ - ABRA Inc.

HERBAL SPA - Skin care products ☆ - Nu-Tress Laboratories Inc.

HERBAL SPRINGS - Skin care products - Shaklee Corp.

HERBAL SURGE - Homeopathic remedies - Enzymatic Therapy, Inc.

HERBAL SYNERGY - Skin care products - Andrew Easton Co.

HERBAL TAME - Hair care products - Gold Medal Hair Products Inc.

HERBAL TECHNOLOGIES - Vitamins and nutritional supplements - Natural Organics, Inc.

HERBAL-THIN - Vitamins and nutritional supplements - Day Enterprises

HERBAL TRADITIONS - Health care products - Christopher Enterprises Inc.

HERBAL UP - Vitamins and nutritional supplements - Nature's Way Products, Inc.

HERBAL VAPORS - Health care products - Simmons Handcrafts

HERBAL VERBAL - Greeting cards - Continnuus

HERBAL VITALITY - Herbal products - Beauticontrol Cosmetics Inc.

HERBAL WONDER - Hair care products ☆ - Leading Man & Woman

HERBAL YUTH - Vitamins and nutritional supplements - Grand Stone Corp.

HERBALAB - Vitamins and nutritional supplements - Montana Naturals Int'l. Inc.

HERBALANCE I - Vitamins and nutritional supplements - Vitamin Research Products Inc.

HERBALANCE II - Vitamins and nutritional supplements - Vitamin Research Products Inc.

HERBALANIMALS ORGANICALLY GROWN - Pillows - Herbalanimals, Inc.

HERBALENZA - Vitamins and nutritional supplements ☆ - Nature's Way Products, Inc.

HERBALEZE - Analgesics - Golden Pride-Rawleigh, Inc.

HERBALGEST - Vitamins and nutritional supplements - 4 Health, Inc.

HERBALHIGH - Herbal products - Longevity Network, Ltd.

HERBALIFE - Skin care products - Herbalife International, Inc.

HERBALIST, THE - Computer software - Hopkins Technology LLC

HERBALIST'S COLLECTION, THE - Flowers, plants, and seeds ☆ - Applewood Seed & Garden Group

HERBALMUNE - Vitamins and nutritional supplements - Lotus Brands Inc.

HERBALOCK - Seasonings - Kalsec, Inc.

HERBALOX - Seasonings - Kalsec, Inc.

HERBALOZENGE - Vitamins and nutritional supplements - McZand Herbal, Inc.

HERBALPRIME - Vitamins and nutritional supplements - Frankie Avalon Products, Inc.

HERBALTINE - Teas–herbal - Herb Products Co.

HERBALVEDIC - Health care products - Auroma International Inc.

HERBALVEDIC AYURVEDIC - Health care products - Ayurherbal Corp.

HERBAMARE - Seasonings - Bioforce of America Ltd.

HERBANARIO - Herbal products - Suzanne Silvia Designs

HERBARICH - Hair care products - Revlon Consumer Products Corp.

HERBARY GARDENS - Sachets - Andre Richard

HERBASAURS - Vitamins and nutritional supplements - Lifetrends International

HERBASAURS - Vitamins and nutritional supplements - Nature's Sunshine Products, Inc.

HERBASHIELD - Sprayers - Specialty AG Equipment, Inc.

HERBASHIELD - Vitamins and nutritional supplements - Natural Organics, Inc.

HERBCARE - Food products - Kanpo Imports, Inc.

HERBCLOT - Skin care products - Applewood Acres, Inc.

HERBCRAFT - Apparel and accessories - Crowntuft Manufacturing Corp.

HERBCRAFT - Apparel and accessories - Kellwood Co.

HERBCRAFT - Spices and extracts - Starwest Botanicals Inc.

HERBCRAFT II - Apparel and accessories - Kellwood Co.

HERBE ROYALE - Spices and extracts - Rose Spice, Inc.

HERBEMONT - Wines - Val Verde Winery

HERBERT STANLEY - Cleaning preparations - Herbert Stanley Co.

HERBERT TAREYTON - Cigarettes, tobacco - American Tobacco Co.

HERBESSENCE - Hair and skin-care products - Imaging By BMD, Inc.

HERBGELS - Vitamins and nutritional supplements - R.P. Scherer Corp.

HERBI-FARE - Pet products - Reliable Protein Products

HERBI GRAY, HANDWEAVER - Giftware - Herbi Gray Handweaver

HERBICIDE EXPRESS - Pesticides–agricultural - Crop Production Services Inc.

HERBICIDE SINGLES - Herbicides - Gulfstream Home & Garden Inc.

HERBIE - Bandages - American White Cross, Inc.

HERBIE - Fireworks - South Carolina Distributors, Inc.

HERBIMMUNE - Vitamins and nutritional supplements - Lotus Brands Inc.

HERBISSIMO - Perfumes - Dana Perfumes Corp.

HERBIT - Spices and extracts - Presco Food Seasonings Inc.

HERBITROL - Hair care products - Haztec Inc.

HERBKO - Games - Herbko International, Inc.

HERBOFIT - Vitamins and nutritional supplements - Tishcon Corp.

HERBOGEST - Vitamins and nutritional supplements - Tishcon Corp.

HERBOLD - Toiletries - Alvin Last Inc.

HERBOMINERAL - Bathing powder - Auromere Inc.

HERBOQUIL - Vitamins and nutritional supplements - Tishcon Corp.

HERBOSOM - Vitamins and nutritional supplements - Tishcon Corp.

☆ = Now out of production

HERBOZYME - Vitamins and nutritional supplements - Tishcon Corp.
HERBRUCK FROZEN FRIED - Food products - Herbruck Poultry Ranch
HERBRUCK'S - Cheese - Herbruck's Country Counter
HERBRUCK'S - Eggs - Herbruck Poultry Ranch
HERB'S - Food products - Bet-Del Foods, Inc.
HERB'S - Pasta - Schmidt Noodle Co.
HERBS & SPICE - Deodorants–personal - Jason Natural Products, Inc.
HERBS & SPICES - Dinnerware–glass ✩ - Shafford Co. Inc.
HERBS FOR HEALTH - Food products - Golden Gate Herb Research
HERBS OF SHAKESPEARE, THE - Flowers, plants, and seeds ✩ - Applewood Seed & Garden Group
HERBS OF THE VALLEY - Mustard - Napa Valley Mustard
HERBS OF TUSCANY - Spices and extracts - Deirdre Andrews
HERBS OF YESTERDAY FOR TODAY - Publisher's imprints - Ten Talents Distributors
HERB'S PARTY SALSA - Vegetables–dried - Bet-Del Foods, Inc.
HERBSAINT LIQUEUR D'ANIS - Liquors - Sazerac Co. Inc.
HERBSPIRIN - Health care products - Healthwatchers System
HERC - Golf clubs - Austad Co.
HERC-ALLOY - Chains - Columbus Mckinnon Corp.
HERC STORMSAILOR - Toys - Mattel, Inc.
HERCO - Hardware - Herr & Co. Inc.
HERCO - Lamps ✩ - Herco Lighting Co.
HERCO - Musical instrument accessories - Herco Products
HERCOLITE - Hydrocarbon resins - Hercules Inc.
HERCULAIR - Shoe soles - Jones & Vining Inc.
HERCULEAN - Trunks - General Fibre Products Inc.
HERCULENE - Film - Keuffel & Esser Co.
HERCULENS - Ophthalmic goods ✩ - Vision Ease
HERCULES - Accordions, guitars, amplifiers - Atlas Accordions Inc.
HERCULES - Adhesives and sealants ✩ - Seal-O-Matic Corp.
HERCULES - Automotive parts and accessories - Hercules Service Corp.
HERCULES - Beverages–malt - Wolfgang D. Morandell
HERCULES - Bicycles ✩ - Roadmaster Corp.
HERCULES - Boats - Glen-L Marine Designs
HERCULES - Boats–pontoons - Boatel Marine, Inc.
HERCULES - Brooms - Hamburg Broom Works Inc.
HERCULES - Combs - Spilo/Mehaz Worldwide
HERCULES - Cording - U.S. Line Co.
HERCULES - Electronic equipment - The Genie Co.
HERCULES - Exercising equipment - York Barbell Co., Inc.
HERCULES - Fabrics - Greenwood Mills Inc.
HERCULES - Flatware ✩ - Mundial Inc.
HERCULES - Floor finishing machines–commercial - Mercury Floor Machines Inc.
HERCULES - Footwear - S. Goldberg and Co. Inc.
HERCULES - Garden equipment - Seymour Manufacturing Co.,Inc.
HERCULES - Garden equipment - True Temper Hardware Co.
HERCULES - Garden equipment ✩ - Union Fork and Hoe Co.
HERCULES - Handles–wood - Turner, Day and Woolworth Handle Corp.
HERCULES - Hooks - Andiamo Inc.
HERCULES - Hoses - HBD Industries, Inc.
HERCULES - Hot tubs–fiberglass - Litehouse Products Inc.
HERCULES - Lighting fixtures ✩ - Hubbell Lighting, Inc. (Lighting Div.)
HERCULES - Navigational instruments - Brookes & Gatehouse Inc.
HERCULES - Office supplies - R.A. Stewart Superior
HERCULES - Ophthalmic goods ✩ - Luxottica
HERCULES - Pet products - Nylabone Products
HERCULES - Pet products - T.F.H. Publications, Inc.
HERCULES - Pharmaceutical preparations - Drug Package Inc.
HERCULES - Safes - Meilink Safe Co.
HERCULES - Sealing devices - Stahls' Inc.
HERCULES - Siding–metal - Granite City Steel Co.
HERCULES - Sporting goods - Carron Net Co. Inc.
HERCULES - Thread ✩ - Susan Bates Inc.
HERCULES - Tires–automobile - Hercules Tire & Rubber Co.
HERCULES - Toys–automobiles - Nikko America, Inc.
HERCULES - Toys–models - Estes Industries
HERCULES - Wet mops - Bouras Mop Manufacturing Co.
HERCULES 190 - Navigational instruments - Brookes & Gatehouse Inc.
HERCULES 290 - Navigational instruments - Brookes & Gatehouse Inc.
HERCULES GRAPHICS STATION CARD - Computers–mainframe - Hercules Computer Technology Inc.
HERCULES MAT - Building materials–concrete - Strata Products (USA), Inc.
HERCULES, THE - Ice chests–plastic - Life-Like Products Inc.
HERCULES-TRIAX - Cables - Cable Design Technologies, Inc.

HERCULEX II - Fabrics–coated - Herculite Products, Inc.
HERCULIFE - Wire - Belton Industries Inc.
HERCULINE - Cordage and twine - Pacific Strapping, Inc.
HERCULIS - Anchors - Barrett Manufacturing Co.
HERCULITE - Glass products - PPG Industries, Inc.
HERCULITE - Luggage - Universal Trav-ler Inc.
HERCULITE - Swimming pools - William Tricker Inc.
HERCULITE K - Glass–safety - PPG Industries, Inc.
HERCULOCK - Locks–padlocks - ILCO Unican Corp.
HERCULOG - Monitors–electronic - MSI Crane & Equipment Co., Inc.
HERCULON - Fabrics - Pure Culture Products
HERCULUG - Tires–automobile ✩ - Hercules Tire & Rubber Co.
HERCULUME - Doors–glass ✩ - Showerlux USA
HERCULUX - Lighting fixtures - Kenall Manufacturing Co.
HERCULYTE - Luggage - United States Luggage Corp.
HERCUMILE - Tires–automobile - Hercules Tire & Rubber Co.
HERCUPOWER - Automotive parts and accessories ✩ - Hercules Tire & Rubber Co.
HERCUROCK - Ophthalmic goods - Styl-Rite Optical Manufacturing Co., Inc.
HERCURON - Luggage - United States Luggage Corp.
HERCUVIT - Glass products ✩ - PPG Industries, Inc.
HERD HANDLER - Sporting goods ✩ - Penn's Woods Products Inc.
HERD PRO A DAIRY HERD MONITOR SOFTWARE - Computer peripheral equipment - Frederick G. Austin
HERD, THE - Figurines - Marty Sculpture
HERD-VAC - Vaccines - Oxford Veterinary Laboratories, Inc.
HERD YOUR HORSES! - Games - Aristoplay, Ltd.
HERDGUARD - Veterinary pharmaceutical preparations - Schering Corp.
HERDIM - Musical instrument accessories - International Violin Co. Ltd.
HERE & NOW - Brassieres (Bras) - Lovable Co.
HERE & NOW - Frames–eyeglass - Liberty Optical Manufacturing Co.
HERE COME THE CLOWNS - Craft supplies ✩ - VIP/VIP Crafts
HERE COME THE CLOWNS - Dolls ✩ - Effanbee Doll Corp.
HERE COMES SANTA - Chocolate candy - Superior Fruit & Confections
HERE COMES SANTA - Christmas tree ornaments - Cracker Box Inc.
HERE COMES THE BRIDE - Games - Talicor Inc.
HERE DEER! - Sporting goods - Sugar Valley Products, Inc.
HERE KITTY - Pet products - Petland, Inc.
HERE SHE IS - Stationery - Leslie McMurchie
HEREDITY DOG - Computer software - Queue Inc.
HEREFORD - Food products - Tupman Thurlow Co. Inc.
HEREFORD - Saddles - Tex Tan Western Co. of Yoakum, Inc.
HEREND - Dishes–china - Martin's Herend Imports Inc.
HERE'S BEAUTY - Colognes ✩ - Avon Products, Inc.
HERE'S HOWE - Nuts–salted, roasted, cooked, or canned - Geo. J. Howe Co. Inc.
HERE'S HOWE - Video production - Power Play International, Inc.
HERE'S LOOKING AT YOU - Mirrors - Fabulous Forgeries Ltd.
HERE'S MY HEART - Colognes ✩ - Avon Products, Inc.
HERE'S MY HEART - Wallpaper ✩ - Warner Co.
HERETIC - Computer software - Raven Software Corp.
HERFF JONES - Jewelry - Herff Jones Inc.
HERFORDER - Floor coverings - Tek Stil Concepts Inc.
HERGA - Canvas–artists' ✩ - Winsor & Newton
HERGO - Furniture - Hergo Ergonomic Support Systems, Inc.
HERGONIZED - Furniture - Hergo Ergonomic Support Systems, Inc.
HERIBA - Musical instrument accessories - Midco International
HERING - Apparel and accessories - Hering North America Inc.
HERING - Harmonicas - Importoys
HERITAGE - See **MR. HORACE SMALL HERITAGE COLLECTION**
HERITAGE - Apparel and accessories - Palm Beach Co., Inc.
HERITAGE - Apparel–athletic - Heritage Sportswear
HERITAGE - Bedding–linen - Dan River Inc.
HERITAGE - Bicycles - Columbia Manufacturing Inc.
HERITAGE - Blown glassware - Indiana Glass Co.
HERITAGE - Boats–motor - Glassmaster Co.
HERITAGE - Boats–motor - Thompson Boat Co.
HERITAGE - Boats–pontoons - Harris-Kayot Inc.
HERITAGE - Books–blank - C.R. Gibson Co.
HERITAGE - Bricks ✩ - Roxite Fiberglass
HERITAGE - Building materials - Texas Aluminum Industries Inc.
HERITAGE - Burial vaults–concrete - Greenwood Plastics Industries, Inc.
HERITAGE - Cabinets - Karman Kitchens Inc.
HERITAGE - Cabinets - Quality Cabinets
HERITAGE - Cabinets - Scott Manufacturing, Inc.
HERITAGE - Cabinets–wood - Decora

✩ = Now out of production

HERITAGE - Candles - Carolina Designs Ltd.
HERITAGE - Candles ☆ - Muench-Kreuzer Candle Co.
HERITAGE - Candy ☆ - Fine Products Co. Inc.
HERITAGE - Chimes - Nutone Inc.
HERITAGE - Cigarettes - Lorillard Tobacco Co.
HERITAGE - Clocks - Freeman Products, Inc.
HERITAGE - Clocks - Heritage International
HERITAGE - Clocks - Simplex Time Recorder Co.
HERITAGE - Cooking utensils–enameled - Jacksonville Manufacturing
HERITAGE - Cribs–wood ☆ - Welsh Co.
HERITAGE - Dinnerware–glass ☆ - Johnson Brothers, USA, Inc.
HERITAGE - Dolls - Oglala Sioux Products Inc.
HERITAGE - Doughnuts–mixes - Dawn Food Products Inc.
HERITAGE - Drapery hardware - Kirsch Co.
HERITAGE - Electronics equipment - International Audio Inc.
HERITAGE - Exercising equipment ☆ - Little River Marine Co.
HERITAGE - Fireplace equipment - Jack-Post Corp.
HERITAGE - Fireplace equipment - Vogelzang International Corp.
HERITAGE - Fishing lures - Thomas and Thomas Rodmakers Inc.
HERITAGE - Floor coverings–carpet and rugs - Capel, Inc.
HERITAGE - Floor coverings–carpet and rugs - Coronet Carpets Inc.
HERITAGE - Floor coverings–carpet and rugs - Karastan-Bigelow Inc.
HERITAGE - Floor coverings–carpet and rugs ☆ - Bellbridge Carpets
HERITAGE - Floor coverings–carpet and rugs ☆ - Regal Rugs Inc.
HERITAGE - Floor coverings–carpet and rugs ☆ - Royalweve Carpet Mills
HERITAGE - Flooring–hardwood - Memphis Hardwood Flooring Co.
HERITAGE - Flour–blended - Acme-Evans/A.D.M. Milling Co.
HERITAGE - Footwear ☆ - Seaway Importing Co.
HERITAGE - Frames–picture - Holson Burnes Group
HERITAGE - Furniture - Drexel Heritage Furnishings, Inc.
HERITAGE - Furniture - Pilliod Co.
HERITAGE - Furniture - Universal Flooring
HERITAGE - Furniture ☆ - Bassett Furniture Industries, Inc.
HERITAGE - Furniture ☆ - Gerry Wood Products
HERITAGE - Garden equipment - Austram, Inc.
HERITAGE - Giftware - Wing Industries Inc.
HERITAGE - Giftware ☆ - Gorham Inc.
HERITAGE - Glassware–household - Crystal Clear Importing Co. Inc.
HERITAGE - Glassware–household - Princess House, Inc.
HERITAGE - Glassware–household - L.E. Smith Glass Co.
HERITAGE - Glassware–household ☆ - Colony Glass
HERITAGE - Glassware–household ☆ - Lotus Glass Co.
HERITAGE - Greeting cards - American Artists Group Inc.
HERITAGE - Hams - Carando Inc.
HERITAGE - Hardware - Dynacast
HERITAGE - Hardware - National Lock Hardware
HERITAGE - Hardware - Rixson Firemark Inc.
HERITAGE - Hearing aids - G.N. Danavox Inc.
HERITAGE - Heaters–kerosene - Sunbeam-Oster Household Products
HERITAGE - Hobby kits ☆ - Craft World International Inc.
HERITAGE - Hoses - Anchor Swan
HERITAGE - Housewares - Kirkhill Inc.
HERITAGE - Housewares ☆ - Lamplight Farms, Inc.
HERITAGE - Iron - Gilpin Inc.
HERITAGE - Jewelry - Jacoby-Bender Inc.
HERITAGE - Jewelry, class rings - CJC Holdings, Inc.
HERITAGE - Kitchen appliances ☆ - Caloric Corp.
HERITAGE - Knives–carving - Kimco International Inc.
HERITAGE - Knives–pocket ☆ - Imperial Schrade Corp.
HERITAGE - Lace - Heritage Imports, Inc.
HERITAGE - Leather goods - Enger-Kress Co.
HERITAGE - Molding compounds–plastics ☆ - Gossen Corp.
HERITAGE - Musical instruments ☆ - Armstrong Woodwinds
HERITAGE - Novelty items–paper ☆ - Antioch Publishing Co.
HERITAGE - Occasional tables - JDI Group, Inc.
HERITAGE - Paintbrushes - Corona Brushes Inc.
HERITAGE - Paints - Paragon Paint & Varnish Corp.
HERITAGE - Paper - Gulf States Paper Corp.
HERITAGE - Pens - Quill Co. Inc.
HERITAGE - Pens ☆ - Parker Pen USA
HERITAGE - Pet food - Farmland Industries Inc.
HERITAGE - Plumbing fittings - American Standard Inc.
HERITAGE - Pool tables - International Billiards Inc.
HERITAGE - Posters ☆ - Crownford Giftware Co. Inc.
HERITAGE - Prefabricated buildings–wood - Heritage Homes Inc.
HERITAGE - Recording label - Heritage Records

HERITAGE - Recording label - TMA Records
HERITAGE - Rings–jewelry - Artcarved Inc.
HERITAGE - Sandwiches–prepackaged - H-D Michigan, Inc.
HERITAGE - Shingles - Tamko Roofing Products, Inc.
HERITAGE - Siding–insulating - Nichols-Homeshield Inc.
HERITAGE - Skin care products - Crawford Group, Inc.
HERITAGE - Skin care products - Guerlain Inc.
HERITAGE - Skin care products - Heritage Store Inc.
HERITAGE - Sporting goods ☆ - Brunswick Corp.
HERITAGE - Stain - Interstate Paint Corp.
HERITAGE - Tableware–china - Pfaltzgraff Investment Co.
HERITAGE - Tea kettles–nonelectric ☆ - Revere Ware Corp.
HERITAGE - Telescopes - Northern Telecom, Inc.
HERITAGE - Tiles–ceramic ☆ - KPT Inc.
HERITAGE - Toilets–enameled - Kohler Co.
HERITAGE - Trees - Heritage Trees, Inc.
HERITAGE - Vacuum cleaners and accessories ☆ - Bissell Inc.
HERITAGE - Wallpaper - Payne Fabrics
HERITAGE - Wallpaper ☆ - Koroseal Wallcoverings
HERITAGE - Water purification systems - Springsoft International Inc.
HERITAGE - Wheelchairs - Jaken Co., Inc.
HERITAGE - Window shades - Caradco
HERITAGE - Wines - Heritage Wine Cellars
HERITAGE - Wines - House of Burgundy Inc.
HERITAGE - Wines - Sebastiani Vineyards, Inc.
HERITAGE 25 - Shingles - Tamko Roofing Products, Inc.
HERITAGE 25AR - Shingles - Tamko Roofing Products, Inc.
HERITAGE 30 - Shingles - Tamko Roofing Products, Inc.
HERITAGE 30AR - Shingles - Tamko Roofing Products, Inc.
HERITAGE 40 - Shingles - Tamko Roofing Products, Inc.
HERITAGE 40AR - Shingles - Tamko Roofing Products, Inc.
HERITAGE BARNS - Frames–picture - Reynolds Building Systems Inc.
(Heritage Barns Div.)
HERITAGE BRASS - Hardware - Amerock Corp.
HERITAGE BRASS - Hardware - Newell Operating Co.
HERITAGE BRASS ARTISANS - Lamps - Fabcraft Inc.
HERITAGE BY SMITH - Glassware–household - L.E. Smith Glass Co.
HERITAGE COLLECTION - Candy - Home of the Hebert Candies, Inc.
HERITAGE COLLECTION - Giftware - Lenox, Inc.
HERITAGE COLLECTION - Hobby kits - JCA, Inc.
HERITAGE COLLECTION - Pet products - Vidmark Entertainment Inc.
HERITAGE COLLECTION - Tiles–ceramic - Huntington/Pacific Ceramics Inc.
HERITAGE COLLECTION - Trading cards and stamps - Family Line an Allison
Greetings Co. Inc.
HERITAGE COLLECTION, THE - Tableware–plastic - Dinex International, Inc.
HERITAGE COLLECTION, THE - Moldings–plaster of paris - Reliance
Industries Inc.
HERITAGE COLLECTIONS - Fabrics–brocade ☆ - Clark Imports Inc.
HERITAGE COLLECTIONS, LTD., THE - Christmas tree ornaments - Heritage
Collections Ltd.
HERITAGE COMMON - Tiles–facing - Design Brick Products Inc.
HERITAGE COMPACT HOTPOINT - Air conditioning equipment ☆ - General
Electric Co.
HERITAGE EDITION - Sprinklers–lawn - Melnor Inc.
HERITAGE FARM - Food products - Heritage Farm Market
HERITAGE GALLERY - Floor coverings ☆ - Tarkett, Inc.
HERITAGE GIFTS - Leather - Action Gift Line
HERITAGE GLEN - Dinnerware–glass - Lenox, Inc.
HERITAGE GREEN - Glassware–household ☆ - Fenton Art Glass Co.
HERITAGE HEARTH - Breads–mixes - Roland Industries Inc.
HERITAGE HILL - Furniture - Bassett Furniture Industries, Inc.
HERITAGE HILLS II - Floor coverings–carpet and rugs - Evans-Black Carpet
Mills
HERITAGE HIP AND RIDGE - Shingles - Tamko Roofing Products, Inc.
HERITAGE HOME FASHIONS - Linen - Tuckaseigee Mills, Inc.
HERITAGE HOUSE - Beverages–alcohol - Riser Foods Inc.
HERITAGE HOUSE - Floor coverings - Tobin Manufacturing Co.
HERITAGE HOUSE - Food products - Dominick's Finer Foods, Inc.
HERITAGE HOUSE - Furniture, water-bed accessories, etc. - Contract Design
HERITAGE HOUSE - Wallpaper - Mobile Paint Manufacturing Co.
HERITAGE HOUSE - Wines - Monarch Wine Co. of Georgia
HERITAGE HOUSE DESIGNS - Wallcovering - Key Wallcoverings, Inc.
HERITAGE II - Dining room furniture ☆ - John Boos and Co. Inc.
HERITAGE II - Shingles - Tamko Roofing Products, Inc.
HERITAGE LEATHERS - Leather goods - Enger-Kress Co.
HERITAGE LITE - Breads - Earthgrains/Waldensian Bakerie

☆ = Now out of production

HERITAGE M30 - Shingles - Tamko Roofing Products, Inc.
HERITAGE M40 - Shingles - Tamko Roofing Products, Inc.
HERITAGE MASTERS COLLECTION - Giftware - Imperial Crystal and China Inc.
HERITAGE MEMORIAL - Frames–picture - Sandol Enterprises, Inc.
HERITAGE OAK - Bathroom fixtures ☆ - Artesian Industries
HERITAGE PARK - Floor coverings–carpet and rugs ☆ - Hollytex Carpet Mills Inc.
HERITAGE PEWTER - Glassware–household - Heritage Metalworks
HERITAGE POINTE - Motor vehicles–motor homes ☆ - Fleetwood Enterprises, Inc.
HERITAGE PREMIUM SHADOWTONE SERIES - Shingles–asphalt or tar - Tamko Roofing Products, Inc.
HERITAGE PRINTS - Wallpaper - Tattersalls
HERITAGE RIB - Floor coverings–carpet and rugs - Superior Manufacturing Group/Notrax Floor Matting
HERITAGE RIDGE PACK - Roofing materials - Tamko Roofing Products, Inc.
HERITAGE SAFE COMPANY - Safe deposit boxes - Heritage Safe Co., Inc.
HERITAGE SALMON - Fish–fresh or frozen - Heritage Salmon Co., Inc.
HERITAGE SQUARE - Floor coverings - Bruce Hardwood Floors
HERITAGE SWISS STIX - Cheese - Heidi's Cheese Products
HERITAGE, THE - Musical instruments - Heritage Guitar, Inc.
HERITAGE TILE COLLECTION - Tiles–ceramic - Epro Inc.
HERITAGE U.S.A. - Sweaters - Signal Knitwear Co.
HERITAGE VILLAGE - Wallpaper - Sanitas Wallcoverings
HERITAGE VILLAGE COLLECTION - Figurines - Department 56 Inc.
HERITAGE VINEYARDS - Wines - Heritage Vineyards
HERITAGE WHITE - Dishes–china - Waterford Wedgewood USA, Inc.
HERITAGE'S - Dairy products - Heritage's Dairy Stores
HERITGE M25 - Shingles - Tamko Roofing Products, Inc.
HERITIERS GUILBAUD - Wines - House of Burgundy Inc.
HERIZ - Floor coverings–carpet and rugs - Capel, Inc.
HERKIMER COLD PACK - Cheese - Original Herkimer County Cheese Co. Inc.
HERKO - Computer hardware - Douglas Herko
HERKULES - Apparel and accessories - Michael A. Jackson
HERLAG - Furniture - Kettler International Inc.
HERLOCHER'S - Mustard - Del Grosso Foods Inc.
HERM. SPRENGER - Pet collars - Berolina Imports
HERM. SPRENGER - Pet products - Haber's Export Agencies
HERMAL - Skin care products - Center Laboratories/Hermal Dermatology Group
HERMAN - Footwear - Joseph M. Herman Shoe Co.
HERMAN COLLECTION - Figurines - Waco Products Corp.
HERMAN GEIST - Dresses–women's - Sage Design, Inc.
HERMAN GOELITZ - Candy - Herman Goelitz Candy Co., Inc.
HERMAN JOSEPH'S - Beverages–malt - Adolph Coors Co.
HERMAN JOSEPH'S 1868 - Beverages–malt ☆ - Adolph Coors Co.
HERMAN JOSEPH'S LIGHT - Beverages–malt ☆ - Adolph Coors Co.
HERMAN JOSEPH'S ORIGINAL DRAFT - Beverages–malt ☆ - Adolph Coors Co.
HERMAN KAY - Coats–women's - Herman Kay Co., Inc.
HERMAN KRESS ORIGINALS - Girdles - Character Foundations Inc.
HERMAN MILLER - Furniture - Herman Miller, Inc.
HERMANN - Toys–stuffed - Fagan International
HERMANN BEYER - Musical instruments - United Musical Instruments USA Inc.
HERMANN HIRSCH USA - Watchbands–leather - Hirsch USA Inc.
HERMANN J. WIEMER - Wines - Hermann J. Wiemer Vineyard
HERMANN LOWENDALL - Violins - Ideal Musical Merchandise Co.
HERMANNHOF - Wines - Hermannhof
HERMANN'S - Water–bottled or canned - Herrmann's Water
HERMANS - Boots - Joseph M. Herman Shoe Co.
HERMAN'S - Salad dressings–bottled - Kosto Food Products Co.
HERMANS - Sauces - Global Gourmet
HERMCO - Pet products - Hermco Worldwide Trading Inc.
HERMES - Floor coverings–carpet and rugs ☆ - Hollytex Carpet Mills Inc.
HERMES - Marine rigging ☆ - Brookes & Gatehouse Inc.
HERMES - Musical instrument accessories - Prestini Reed Corp.
HERMES - Recording label - Nimbus Records Ltd.
HERMET - Labels–fabric - La-Co Industries, Inc.
HERMETIC ADVANTAGE - Electronic equipment - Pacific Coast Technologies
HERMI ODLE - Toys - Lucasfilm Ltd.
HERMIS - Brushes–paint - Rubberset Co.
HERMITAGE - Cabinets ☆ - Yorktowne Inc.
HERMITAGE - Floor coverings ☆ - Robbins Inc.

HERMITAGE - Food products - Robert Orr-Sysco Food Services Co.
HERMITAGE - Furniture - A.A. Laun Furniture Co.
HERMITAGE - Furniture - Pilliod Co.
HERMITAGE - Lumber - Georgia-Pacific Corp.
HERMITAGE - Pencils - Musgrave Pencil Co. Inc.
HERMITAGE BURN-O - Gasoline - Robert Orr-Sysco Food Services Co.
HERMITAGE FARMS - Deodorizers - Lumi-Lite Candle Co. Inc.
HERMITAGE HOUSE - Furniture - Cochrane Furniture Co. Inc.
HERMITAGE I - Furniture ☆ - Hammary Furniture Co. Inc.
HERMITAGE OAK - Floor coverings - National Floor Products Co., Inc.
HERMITAGE POTTERY - Pottery products - Loomco International
HERMITEX - Cleaning equipment - Hermitage Industries, Inc.
HERMLE - Clocks - Black Forest Imports, Inc.
HERMON PRESS - Publisher's imprints - Sepher-Hermon Press, Inc.
HERMOSA - Fans–electric - Casablanca Fan Co.
HERMOSA - Floor coverings–carpet and rugs - Tuftex Carpet Mills, Inc.
HERMOSA MILLS - Bedding–linen - Custom Designs
HERMTEX - Toys - Westminster Sports
HERNIA-GUARD - Health care products - Bell-Horn
HERNKE - Food products - Dairy Fresh Products Co.
HERNON - Adhesives and sealants - Davis-Howland Oil Corp.
HERO - Antennas–satellite ☆ - Hero Communications
HERO - Cleaning preparations–household - Enforcer Products Inc.
HERO - Colognes - Prince Matchabelli
H.E.R.O. - Computer software - Activision, Inc.
HERO - Dog food - Ralston Purina Co.
HERO - Floor coverings–carpet and rugs - Mica Inc.
HERO - Frames–eyeglass - Zylo Ware Corp.
HERO - Toys - Tonka Corp.
HERO - Toys–musical - Darwell Import Co. Inc.
HERO 1 - Robots–industrial ☆ - Heath Co.
HERO ARTS - Stationery - Hero Arts Rubber Stamps Inc.
HERO BY NIGHT - Computer software - Azeroth Inc.
HERO CAPS - Novelty items ☆ - Marvel Entertainment Group, Inc.
HERO HURLERS - Toys - Trendmasters, Inc.
HERO JR. - Robots–industrial ☆ - Heath Co.
HERO QUEST - Games - Milton Bradley Co.
HERO ROSTI - Potato flakes - Source Atlantique
HERO SUPER 7 - Antennas–satellite ☆ - Hero Communications
HERO SUPER-TENNAS - Antennas–satellite - Hero Communications
HERO SWISS - Jams and jellies - Source Atlantique
HERO SYSTEM - Game - Hero Games
HEROES IN ACTION - Toys - Mattel, Inc.
HEROES INC. - Publisher's imprints - Ballantine Books Inc.
HEROES OF ASFAR - Games - Artistically Inclined
HEROES OF BASEBALL - Trading cards and stamps - Upper Deck Co.
HEROES OF MIGHT AND MAGIC - Computer software - New World Computing Inc.
HEROES OF RACING - Trading cards and stamps - Press Pass
HEROES ONLY USA - Sandals ☆ - Earth & Ocean Sports, Inc.
HEROHEADS - Novelty items - Lakeside Games
HEROIC CAT PACK - Toys–automobiles - Mattel, Inc.
HEROIC FANTASY - Games - Flying Buffalo Inc.
HEROIC WARRIORS - Toys - Mattel, Inc.
HEROINE - Frames–eyeglass - Zylo Ware Corp.
HEROIX - Computer software ☆ - Heroix Corp.
HEROLD - Combs ☆ - S.R. Droescher Inc.
HERON - Boats–kayaks - Old Town Canoe Co.
HERON - Brushes - Wright-Bernet
HERON - Fishing tackle - P/S Engineering and Manufacturing Co.
HERON - Mats - Tepromark International Inc.
HERON AEROLITE - Binoculars ☆ - Swift Instruments, Inc.
HERON BAY - Apparel–athletic - Clothesmakers, Inc.
HERON HILL - Wines - Heron Hill Vineyards Inc.
HERON ST. - Compact discs–prerecorded - Heron St. Co.
HEROS - Candy - American Chewing Gum Inc.
HEROS - Toys - Darda Inc. USA
HEROX - Fabrics–nylon - E.I. Dupont de Nemours and Co.
HERP-EX - Pharmaceutical preparations ☆ - Abana Pharmaceuticals, Inc.
HERP HABITAT - Pet products - Terrarium Art
HERP HOME - Pet products - Valentine Equipment Co.
HERP X - Vitamins and nutritional supplements - Kroeger Herb Products Co. Inc.
HERPAMINE - Pharmaceutical preparations - Alva-Amco Pharmacal Co.
HERPATAT - Pet products - Pets & Things

☆ = Now out of production

HERPCARE - Veterinary pharmaceutical preparations - Mardel Laboratories, Inc.

HERPECIN-L - Lip balms ☆ - Campbell Laboratories Inc.

HERPESALVE - Lip balms ☆ - Campbell Laboratories Inc.

HERPETOCULTURAL LIBRARY SERIES - Publisher's imprints - Advanced Vivarium Systems, Inc.

HERPETROL - Pharmaceutical preparations - Alva-Amco Pharmacal Co.

HERPEZYME - Health care products ☆ - Kay Pharmacal Co. Inc.

HERPILYN - OTC - Pharmaceutical preparations - Enzymatic Therapy, Inc.

HERPLEX LIQUIFILM - Ophthalmic goods ☆ - Allergan, Inc.

HERPTIVITE - Vitamins and nutritional supplements - Rep-Cal Research Labs

HERR FIEND - Toys - Tonka Corp.

HERRADURA - Liquors - House of Seagram

HERRENBRAU - Beverages–malt - Wolfgang Morandell Import

HERRESHOFF - Ships–sailing vessels - Cape Cod Shipbuilding Co.

HERRICK STONE PRODUCTIONS - Recording label - Moseka Records & Tapes

HERRING-HALL-MARVIN - Safes ☆ - Meilink Safe Co.

HERRING PLUS - Fishing lures - Yakima Bait Co.

HERRINGBLOCK - Flooring–parquet - Memphis Hardwood Flooring Co.

HERRINGBLOK - Floor coverings ☆ - Bruce Hardwood Floors

HERRINGBONE - Floor coverings ☆ - Robbins Inc.

HERRINGBONE - Rope - Williamsport Wirerope Works, Inc.

HERRINGBONE - Wallpaper ☆ - Carey Lind Designs

HERRING'S HUNT - Dishes–earthenware - Royal China & Porcelain Companies Inc.

HERRINGSTRIP - Floor coverings - Bruce Hardwood Floors

HERRINGSTRIP - Flooring–hardwood - Triangle Pacific Corp. (Cabinet Division)

HERRMANN - Noodles - Haram-Christensen Corp.

HERR'S - Food products - Herr Foods Inc.

HERRUD - Meat products–beef - Thorn Apple Valley Inc.

HERS - Health care products - Ayurherbal Corp.

HERS - Health care products - Davol Inc.

HERS - Shaving preparations - Medtech Laboratories Inc.

HERSCHEL WALKER - Sporting goods - Franklin Sports, Inc.

HERSELF THE ELF - Greeting cards - American Greetings Corp.

HERSELF THE ELF - Greeting cards - Those Characters from Cleveland, Inc.

HERSELF, THE ELF WILD BERRY - Cosmetics ☆ - Bonne Bell, Inc.

HERSEY CUSTOM - Shoes - Hersey Custom Shoe Co.

HERSEY DPS PLUS - Shoes–athletic - Hersey Custom Shoe Co.

HERSEY ORIGINAL PLUS - Shoes–athletic - Hersey Custom Shoe Co.

HERSEY TR - Shoes–athletic - Hersey Custom Shoe Co.

HERSHEY - Food products ☆ - Health is Wealth

HERSHEY - Food products ☆ - Williams Foods Inc.

HERSHEY - Handkerchiefs ☆ - Carolina Manufacturing Inc.

HERSHEY-ETS - Candy - Hershey Chocolate USA

HERSHEY FREE - Tapioca - Hershey Foods Corp.

HERSHEY PASTELS - Beverages - Hershey Foods Corp.

HERSHEY SUPER SHAKE - Candy - Hershey Foods Corp.

HERSHEYPARK FRANKS - Frankfurters - Herco Inc.

HERSHEY'S - Beverages–carbonated - Dr. Pepper/Seven Up, Inc.

HERSHEY'S - Candy - Hershey Chocolate USA

HERSHEY'S - Coconut–shredded - Hershey Foods Corp.

HERSHEY'S - Popcorn - Homestead, Inc.

HERSHEY'S CHOCOLATE COVERED MARSHMALLOWEGG - Candy - Homestead, Inc.

HERSHEY'S CHOCOLATE DRINK - Beverages - Hershey Foods Corp.

HERSHEY'S COOKIES - Cookies - Hershey Foods Corp.

HERSHEY'S HOT COCOA DUTCH CHOCOLATE COLLECTION - Cocoa–powders or mixes - Homestead, Inc.

HERSHEY'S HUGS - Chocolate candy - Homestead, Inc.

HERSHEY'S HUGS WITH ALMONDS - Candy - Hershey Foods Corp.

HERSHEY'S HUGS'N KISSES - Chocolate candy - Homestead, Inc.

HERSHEY'S KISS BEAR - Toys–stuffed - K.B. Brothers Inc.

HERSHEY'S KISSES - Candy - Hershey Chocolate USA

HERSHEY'S LOW FAT MILK BOXES - Chocolate milk - Hershey Chocolate USA

HERSHEY'S MILK CHOCOLATE COVERED CARAMEL & PEANUT EGG - Candy - Homestead, Inc.

HERSHEY'S MINIATURES - Candy - Hershey Chocolate USA

HERSHEY'S PEPPERMINT PATTIES - Chocolate bars - Hershey Foods Corp.

HERSHEY'S SNACK BOX - Candy - Homestead, Inc.

HERTHA - Ophthalmic goods ☆ - Luxottica

HERTRO-BOND - Cement - Hertron International Inc.

HERTRO-CLEAN - Cleaning preparations - Hertron International Inc.

HERTRO-KOTE - Sealing compounds ☆ - Hertron International Inc.

HERTRO-LITE - Sealing compounds ☆ - Hertron International Inc.

HERVEX - Musical instrument accessories - Herco Products

HERVIC - Photographic equipment - Hervic Corp.

HERVIC AMBASSADOR - Cases–camera - Hervic Corp.

HERVIC/COMFORTSTRAP - Photographic equipment - Hervic Corp.

HERVIC HYDROFLUID JR. - Tripods–photographic ☆ - Hervic Corp.

HERVIC/MINETTE - Photographic equipment - Hervic Corp.

HERVIC/ZEUS - Projection screens ☆ - Hervic Corp.

HERZOG - Rope - American Manufacturing Co. Inc.

HERZOG SELECTION - Wines - Kedem Royal Wine Corp.

HERZOG SELECTION - Wines - Royal Wine Corp.

HES BIC - Pharmaceutical preparations ☆ - Kenyon Drug Co. Inc.

HESCO - Stencils - H.E. Smith Co.

HESIOD - Computer software - Massachusetts Institute of Technology

HESITATION - Eyeglasses - Martin-Copeland Eyewear Corp.

HESPER-C - Pharmaceutical preparations - Marion Merrell Dow

HESS - Hair care products - Hess Hair Milk Laboratories Inc.

HESS - Petroleum products - Amerada Hess Corp.

HESS MACHINE INTERNATIONAL - Medical apparatus - Hess Machine Co.

HESS PREMIUM DIESEL - Petroleum - Amerada Hess Corp.

HESSE - Frames–eyeglass ☆ - Universal/Univis Inc.

HESSMER & WERCKER - Wire - Helenor Industries

HESSTON - Toys - Agco Corp.

HESTER - Dolls ☆ - Effanbee Doll Corp.

HESTER - Food products machinery - Freskeeto Frozen Foods Inc.

HESTERIA - Recording label - Jazz Composer's Orchestra Association Inc.

HESTIA - Marine rigging ☆ - Brookes & Gatehouse Inc.

HESTRON - Glass products ☆ - PPG Industries, Inc.

HET LUILEKKERLAND BV - Food products ☆ - Vincent Food Industries Inc.

HETACIN-K - Veterinary pharmaceutical preparations - Bristol-Myers Squibb Co.

HETHER - Ophthalmic goods - Rozin Optical Export Corp.

HETTY - Teas–herbal - Hetty Enterprise USA Inc.

HETTY FAIR - Olives–canned - Hetty Fair Foods Co.

HEUBLEIN - Beverages–alcohol - Heublein, Inc.

HEUCK - Kitchen gadgets - Cook Things

HEUER - Watches - Tag-Heuer Time & Electronics Corp.

HEUGAFELT - Floor coverings–carpet and rugs ☆ - Heuga USA

HEUGAFLOR - Floor coverings–carpet and rugs ☆ - Heuga USA

HEUGALAINE - Floor coverings–carpet and rugs ☆ - Heuga USA

HEUGALUX - Floor coverings–carpet and rugs ☆ - Heuga USA

HEUL - Bakery products - Holland-American Importing Co. Inc.

HEURISTECH PRESS - Publisher's imprints ☆ - William Kaufmann, Inc.

HEURTIER - Projectors–photographic ☆ - Hervic Corp.

HEVI-DUTI - Envelopes - Western States Envelope Co.

HEVI-DUTY - Freezers - Revco Scientific, Inc.

HEVI-WRITE - Pencils ☆ - Faber-Castell Corp.

HEVIDUTY - Brushes–paint ☆ - PPG Industries, Inc.

HEVIWATE CHAMPION - Lighting fixtures - Acme-Lite Manufacturing Co.

HEVY - Gloves - Boss Manufacturing Co.

HEWITT - Soap - Hewitt Soap Co., Inc.

HEWLETT-PACKARD - Computers–personal - Hewlett-Packard Co.

HEX - Frames–eyeglass - Hudson Optical Corp.

HEX - Games - Dean T. Layton

HEX - Honey - R.B. Swan & Son

HEX-A-VITAL - Pet products - Aquatronics-Filtronics

HEX-CRIMP - Tools - Quick Cable Corp.

HEX-L - Keys - Eklind Tool Co.

HEX-LOK - Electrical equipment - GB Electrical Inc.

HEX-O-GRAM - Games - Lakeside Games

HEX-ON - Deodorizers - Sween Corp.

HEX-ON LIGHT - Deodorizers - Sween Corp.

HEX-VENT - Tiles–ceiling ☆ - Artcrest Products Co. Inc.

HEX WEDGE - Cosmetics - Karlen Manufacturing, Inc.

HEX-WIK - Soldering equipment - Hexacon Electric Co.

HEXA-BETALIN - Pharmaceutical preparations - Eli Lilly and Co.

HEXA-CAT - Ships–sailing vessels - Harken Yacht Fittings

HEXA-FOAM - Pharmaceutical preparations - IBA Inc.

HEXA-RATCHET - Ships–sailing vessels - Harken Yacht Fittings

HEXABAMATE - Pharmaceutical preparations - Rugby Laboratories Inc.

HEXACHROME - Inks - Pantone, Inc.

HEXACORT - Pharmaceutical preparations ☆ - C.O. Truxton Inc.

HEXACREST - Pharmaceutical preparations ☆ - Nutrition Control Products

HEXADROL - Pharmaceutical preparations - Organon Inc.

☆ = Now out of production

1017

HEXAGLOT - Communications equipment–mobile - Fidelity Electronics International Inc.
HEXAGON - Glassware–household ☆ - Oneida Ltd.
HEXAGON - Housewares - Blue Magic Products Inc.
HEXAGON - Optical scanners–computer - Tart Optical
HEXAGONY - Games ☆ - Avalon Hill Game Co.
HEXAGUARD - Cushions - Foamex LP
HEXALITE - Footwear - Reebok International Ltd.
HEXALOL - Pharmaceutical preparations ☆ - Central Pharmaceutical Inc.
HEXAMIT - Pet products ☆ - Aquatronics-Filtronics
HEXAROUND - Aquariums–household - Midwest Tropical Inc.
HEXAROUND - Pencils ☆ - Faber-Castell Corp.
HEXAROUND TOWER - Aquariums–household - Midwest Tropical Inc.
HEXASEPT - Skin care products - Medical Chemical Corp.
HEXAWIPE - Cleaning equipment - Contec, Inc.
HEXBITS - Hardware - Eazypower Corp.
HEXCEL - Sporting goods - Hanson Industries Inc.
HEXCOLUMN - Audio equipment - Paso Sound Products Inc.
HEXDAM - Computer software - Engineering Analysis, Inc.
HEXEN - Games - Raven Software Corp.
HEXENKESSEL - Copper products ☆ - Charles Zahn-Import Merchant
HEXERCISER - Exercising equipment ☆ - Gerstung/Gym-Thing Inc.
HEXICASE - Ophthalmic goods - Barnes-Hind Inc.
HEXIE - Sugar–granulated, refined, or powdered - Hexagon Co.
HEXISPLIT - Computer peripheral equipment - Communications Specialties, Inc.
HEXIT - Paper - Gamescience
HEXIT KNOB - Doors–metal - Robert Leonard, Jr.
HEXMOZAIX - Puzzles - Kadon Enterprises Inc.
HEXMOZAIX JR - Puzzles - Kadon Enterprises Inc.
HEXNUT - Puzzles - Kadon Enterprises Inc.
HEXNUT, JR. - Puzzles - Kadon Enterprises Inc.
HEXO - Erasers ☆ - Bright Boy Abrasives
HEXO-CLEANER - Erasers ☆ - Bright Boy Abrasives
HEXOL - Disinfectants - Hexol Inc.
HEXPIN - Sanders and grinders - Pearl Abrasive Co.
HEXSIGN - Toilets–enameled - Kohler Co.
HEXTEND - Pharmaceutical preparations - Biotime, Inc.
HEXTER - Toys–stuffed - Kamar International Inc.
HEXTER - Wallpaper - S.M. Hexter Co.
HEXTER'S - Wallpaper - Charles Otto Wallpapers
HEXVIEW - Ophthalmic goods - Styl-Rite Optical Manufacturing Co., Inc.
HEY DAY - Brassieres (Bras) - Wacoal America Inc.
HEY DAY - Floor coverings–carpet and rugs ☆ - Galaxy Carpet Mills Inc.
HEY DIDDLE - Kites ☆ - Hi-Flier Manufacturing Co.
HEY-DUDE - Shirts - C-Mrk, Inc.
HEY EWE - Slippers - Acorn
HEY-GIRL! - Frames–eyeglass - Liberty Optical Manufacturing Co.
HEY GIRL! - Greeting cards - Kersten Bros. Studios
HEY-MAN - Apparel–men's - C-Mrk, Inc.
HEY MAN - Chewing gum - Philadelphia Chewing Gum Corp.
HEY! SAILOR - Footwear - Masterpeace Footwear
HEY TAXI - Games ☆ - Milton Bradley Co.
HEY, THAT'S ME! - Greeting cards - AGC, Inc.
HEY THAT'S ME - Greeting cards - American Greetings Corp.
HEYBEL SANE - Pharmaceutical preparations - Enzymatic Therapy, Inc.
HEYCLIP - Clamps - Heyco Products, Inc.
HEYCO - Tools–hand-operated - Heyco Products, Inc.
HEYCO-FLEX - Connectors–electrical - Heyco Products, Inc.
HEYCONNECTOR - Connectors–electrical ☆ - Heyco Products, Inc.
HEYDAY - Cookies - Nabisco Foods Group
HEYDAY - Recording label - Rough Trade Inc.
HEYDEN-RAY - Frames–picture - House of Heydenryk Jr. Inc.
HEYDENRYK'S - Frames–picture - House of Heydenryk Jr. Inc.
HEYE-WEYES - Frames–eyeglass - May Optical Co. Inc.
HEYER SCHULTE NEURO CARE - Medical apparatus - Heyer-Schulte Neurocare, LP
HEYGILL - Cleaning preparations–household - Thornton White Group
HEYJO - Apparel and accessories - Georges Marciano
HEYM - Rifles and shotguns - Continental Arms Corp.
HEYMAN - Coffee - Globe Extracts Inc.
HEYWARD HOUSE - Lamps - Thornton White Group
HF - Caps–baseball - Here's Fred Golf Co., Inc.
H.F. - Pharmaceutical preparations - Specialty Products Co.
HF - Suits–men's - Hickey-Freeman Co. Inc.
HF - Valves - Hydraforce, Inc.

HFA - Stoves–wood-burning - Rohn
HFB - Jewelry - H.F. Barrows Co.
HFC - Paper–thermoplastics coated ☆ - Unnatural Resources Inc.
HFC-2000 - Computer hardware - At&T Corp.
HFC VERTREL - Cleaning preparations - Tech Spray, Inc.
HFP POLYNESIA - Shoes - Classic Sales Inc.
HG-SIV - Particulate absorbents - UOP
HGH AM+ - See **G.H. MORNING**
HGH PM+ - See **G.H. EVE**
HGNY - Women's clothing - Karizma Inc.
HGO.NET - Computer software - Hgo Technology, Inc.
HGP - Contact-lens solution - CooperVision Inc.
HGP - Polishes - State Chemical Manufacturing Co.
HGR - Jewelry - House of Grafstein Ltd.
H.G.V. - Fruits and vegetables - Marglo Products Corp.
HGX MERCURY DECONTAMINANT - Cleaning preparations - Acton Technologies Inc.
HH - Gold products - H H Gold, Inc.
HH - Toys ☆ - Those Characters from Cleveland, Inc.
HH HEAD HONCHOS - Novelty items - Paul A. Scheeler
HH SCOTT - Computer peripheral equipment ☆ - Emerson Radio Corp.
HH SERIES - Elevators - Montgomery Kone Inc.
H.H.C. FUN FACTORY - Apparel and accessories - H.H. Cutler Co.
HHE - Frames–eyeglass - Hoya Corp. USA
HHS - Jewelry - Harry Solomon Co.
HI - Greeting cards ☆ - Amberley Greeting Card Co.
HI - Hair care products - Hair Institute
HI - Hardware - Sequentia Inc. (Reinforced Plastics Div.)
HI - Pet products - Nishiki Koi USA Inc.
HI - Toys–stuffed - Universal Tradewinds, Inc.
HI! 5 BISCUITS! - Dog food - D & K Inc.
HI 18 - Cigarettes ☆ - Nat Sherman, Inc.
HI-A - Brassieres (Bras) ☆ - Marja Foundations
HI ACID - Fertilizers - Plant Marvel Laboratories
HI-ACRES - Juices–frozen ☆ - Hi-Acres Inc.
HI-ALERT - Alarm systems - Frasier Products, Inc.
HI & DRI - Health care products - Revlon Consumer Products Corp.
HI & LOIS - Publisher's imprints - Comicana Inc.
HI & MITEY - High chairs - Bilt-Rite Juvenile Products
HI-ARC - Faucets - Elkay Manufacturing Co.
HI BALL - Furniture–children's - Maze Inc.
HI-BAN - Pet products - Hill Manufacturing Co. Inc.
HI-BAR - Frames–eyeglass ☆ - Universal/Univis Inc.
HI-BAR - Hardware - Lee Co.
HI-BEAM - Electronic equipment - Bell & Howell Co.
HI BEAM - Markers–felt-tip - Pentech International Inc.
HI BEAMS - Footwear ☆ - E.S. Originals, Inc.
HI-BEE - Veterinary product ☆ - Zirin Laboratories International
HI-BEE - Vitamins and nutritional supplements ☆ - Vortech Pharmaceuticals
HI-BEE PLUS - Vitamins and nutritional supplements ☆ - Vortech Pharmaceuticals
HI BLITE - Recording label - Creav Inc. USA
HI-BOND - Hardware ☆ - Keystone Steel & Wire Co.
HI-BOR - Wood products - U.S. Borax Inc.
HI-BOUNCE - Balls ☆ - Strombecker Corp.
HI-BOY - Motor vehicles–trucks - Rotec Industries, Inc.
HI BOY - Pumps - Hilo Industries
HI-BOY - Tripods–photographic - QuickSet International Inc.
HI BRAND - Dinners–frozen - Design Foods
HI-BRAU - Beverages–malt - Joseph Huber Brewing Co., Inc.
HI-BREAK - Circuit breakers - General Electric Co.
HI-BRIDGE - Frames–eyeglass - Pathway Optical Prods.
HI-BRITE - Artists' materials - Shannon Luminous Materials Inc.
HI BRITE - Chemical preparations - Coastal Industries Inc.
HI-BRITE - Paper–writing - Champion International Corp.
HI BROWS - Greeting cards - American Greetings Corp.
HI-BUILD - See **POOLPOXY HI-BILD**
HI-BUILD - Varnishes - Pettit Paint Co. Inc.
HI-BULK - Fishing lines - Cortland Line Co., Inc.
HI-BULK - Paper–tissue - Paper Service Ltd.
HI-BUV-ALL - Food products - Butler Trading Co. Inc.
HI-C - Capacitors - General Electric Co.
HI-C - Frames–eyeglass - May Optical Co. Inc.
HI-C - Juices - Coca-Cola Co.
HI-C 100 - Fruit drinks–bottled or canned - Coca-Cola Co.
HI-C HULA COOLER - Fruit drinks–bottled or canned - Coca-Cola Co.

☆ = Now out of production

HI C PLEX - Vitamins and nutritional supplements - Naturally Vitamin Supplements Inc.

HI-C READY-TO-SERVE - Fruit drinks—bottled or canned - Coca-Cola Co.

HI-CALCIUM - Milk - Borden, Inc.

HI-CALIBRE - Vitamins and nutritional supplements - Frankie Avalon Products, Inc.

HI-CAP - Pumps - Wilcox-Crittenden

HI-CEE - Veterinary pharmaceutical preparations ☆ - Zirin Laboratories International

HI-CEL - Machinery - Carver, Inc.

HI-CLASS - Pet food ☆ - American Stores Co.

HI-CO - Food products - ACB/Richard Watson

HI-COMP - Car audio equipment - Audiovox Corp.

HI-CONTRAST - Hair care products - Sebastian International, Inc.

HI-COR - Pharmaceutical preparations - C&M Pharmacal, Inc.

HI-CORT - Prescription drug ☆ - Blaine Co. Inc.

HI-CORT N - Ointment ☆ - Blaine Co. Inc.

HI-COUNT - Paper—toweling - Kimberly-Clark Corp.

HI-COUNT - Seeds—salted, roasted, cooked, or canned - Golden Peanut Co.

HI-COUNTRY - Juices - Hi-Country Foods Corp.

HI-COUNTRY - Meat products—beef - Hi Country Beef Jerky

HI-CRAFT - Envelopes - Pen-Tab Industries

HI CRAFT - Pet products - Berolina Imports

HI-CRU - Apparel—athletic - Sara Lee Knit Products Inc.

HI D - Cables - Conquest Sound Inc.

HI-D - Fishing tackle - Minnesota Mining & Manufacturing Co.

HI-D - Health care products ☆ - Sammons Preston

HI-D-HO - Candy ☆ - Henry Heide, Inc.

HI-D-LIPO - Vitamins and nutritional supplements ☆ - Freeda Vitamins Inc.

HI DAK - Flour—blended ☆ - Western Star Mill Co.

HI DAK HI GLUTEN - Flour - Inland Mills Co.

HI-DESIGN - Health care products - Temco Health Care

HI-DIVE - Underwear and nightwear - Youthcraft-Charmfit

HI DIVES - Apparel and accessories - M & L International, Inc.

HI DRAFT - Pens - Summagraphics Corp.

HI DRI - Cleaning preparations—household - Waverly Mineral Products Co.

HI-DRI - Paper—toweling - Kimberly-Clark Corp.

HI DRI - Varnishes ☆ - Mantrose-Haeuser Co. Inc.

HI-DROP - Ophthalmic goods - Sola Optical USA, Inc.

HI-DRUM - Racks - Jarke Corp.

HI-DX - Hardware - HDI/Hardware Designers Inc.

HI-DYE - Dyes and pigments ☆ - Aleene's

HI-E - Heaters—swimming pool - Teledyne Laars

HI-E - Veterinary pharmaceutical preparations ☆ - Zirin Laboratories International

HI-ENERGY - Drums—musical instruments - Aquarian Accessories Corp.

HI-ENERGY - Granola bars ☆ - Knudsen & Sons Inc.

HI-ENERGY - Hair care products - Raymac Corp. Hair & Skin Technology

HI ENHANCE - Girdles - Lily of France Inc.

HI-ENHANCE 21 - Apparel—women's - Lily of France Inc.

HI-F - Capacitors - General Electric Co.

HI-FI - Apparel and accessories - Sean Barger

HI-FI - Audio equipment - TDK Electronics Corp.

HI-FI - Correction fluid - Eaton Allen Ko-Rec-Type Corp.

HI-FI - Paints - Quartet Manufacturing Co.

HI-FI - Paints ☆ - Masury Paint Co.

HI-FI - Pet products - Rolf C. Hagen (USA) Corp.

HI FI - Recording label - Everest Record Group

HI-FI - Rope - Wellington Leisure Products, Inc.

HI-FI - Shortening - Supreme Oil Co.

HI FI - Underwear and nightwear ☆ - Elegante Foundations Inc.

HI-FI - Watches - Hampden Corp.

HI-FI BASS - Musical instrument accessories ☆ - Gibson Strings & Accessories

HI FI HI GLUTEN - Flour - Inland Mills Co.

HI FI/LIFE - Recording label - Everest Record Group

HI-FIRE - Water heaters—household - Lochinvar Corp.

HI FI'S - Crackers - Vista Bakery, Inc.

HI FIVE SPORTS - Towels - Revere Mills, Inc.

HI-FLAG - Fishing tackle - U.S. Line Co.

HI-FLAKE - Shortening - Patrick Cudahy Inc.

HI-FLASH - Cleaning preparations - Uncle Sam Chemical Co., Inc.

HI-FLEX - Electronic equipment - Shure Brothers, Inc.

HI-FLEX - Roofing materials - Taracorp Evans, Inc.

HI-FLIER - Frames—eyeglass - May Optical Co. Inc.

HI-FLIER - Kites ☆ - Hi-Flier Manufacturing Co.

HI-FLO - Water filtration system - Culligan International Co.

HI-FLOW - Exhaust systems—motor vehicle - Sand Mountain Rod Shop, Inc.

HI-FLYER - Pet products - Colony Pet Goods

HI FOAM - Skin care products - Waverly Beauty Products

HI-FORM - Foil—aluminum ☆ - International Paper Co.

HI-FORM - Ointment ☆ - Blaine Co. Inc.

HI-FRAME - Racks - Jarke Corp.

HI-FRIES - Vegetables—frozen ☆ - Lamb-Weston, Inc.

HI-FY - Fuel additives - Ashland Oil, Inc.

HI-FYLON - Fabrics - Advance Group

HI-G - Pharmaceutical preparations - Enzyme Process Co. Inc.

HI-G - Watches ☆ - SMH (US) Inc.

HI-GAIN - Amplifiers—musical instrument ☆ - Seymour Duncan Pickups

HI GAIN - Flashlights - Diamond Light

HI-GAIN E.Q. - Amplifiers—musical instrument ☆ - Seymour Duncan Pickups

HI-GAIN HYBRID - Amplifiers—musical instrument ☆ - Seymour Duncan Pickups

HI-GAIN +6 - Amplifiers—musical instrument ☆ - Seymour Duncan Pickups

HI-GARD - Tape—masking - Ivex Corp.

HI GEAR - Frames—eyeglass - May Optical Co. Inc.

HI-GENIC - Cleaning preparations—household - IVAX Industries, Inc.

HI-GINA - Health care products - Ridon Group Inc.

HI GLAZE - Tiles—ceramic ☆ - Halstead International

HI GLIDE - Plotters—computer - Summagraphics Corp.

HI GLOSS - Cleaning preparations ☆ - Knight Marketing Corp.

HI-GLOSS - Coatings - Garon Products Inc.

HI GLOSS - Epoxy coatings - Epoxy Coatings Co.

HI GLOSS - Food products - L. Karp & Sons, Inc.

HI-GLOSS - Hair care products - Hayashi for Hair Inc.

HI GLOSS - Nail care products - Worldwide Cosmetics

HI-GLOSS - Paints ☆ - Klean-Strip

HI-GRADE - Oils—lubricating - Quaker State Oil Refining Corp.

HI-GRADE - Pencils - Reliance Pen & Pencil Corp.

HI-GRADE DAIRY - Milk - Hi-Grade Dairy

HI-GROWTH KOI FOOD - Pet products - Hikari Sales USA Inc.

HI GUARD - Sanitary napkins - Kimberly-Clark Corp.

HI-HANGERS - Hardware - Wilderness Naturals Marketing Co.

HI-HAT - Eyeglasses - Art-Craft Optical Co.

HI-HAT - Ribbons—inked - Phillips Process Co. Inc.

HI-HEAT - Bunsen burners - Indianapolis Dental Specialty Co., Inc.

HI-HEAT - Finishing agents - Dap Products Inc.

HI-HEAT - Housewares - Plastics, Inc. (Anchor Hocking Plastics)

#HI HEAT IT - Tools - Ranger Industries

HI-HI JINX - Girdles - Vanity Corset Co. Inc.

HI HI STAR - Medical apparatus - Health Images, Inc.

HI-HIDE - Paints - Porter Paint Co.

HI HO - Crackers - Sunshine Biscuits, Inc.

HI HO DINO - Toys—stuffed - Great American Fun Corp.

HI HO SANTA - Christmas tree ornaments - Giordano Art, Ltd.

HI HO SILVER.AWAY - Barbecue sauce - Silver Palate Kitchen

HI HONEY - Candy - Honey Acres Inc.

HI-HOSE - Water sprinklers - Hi-Hose Inc.

HI IMPACT - Ammunition - Olin Corp. (Winchester Div.)

HI-IMPACT - Gypsum products - National Gypsum Co.

HI IMPACT - Pens - Sanford Corp.

HI-JACKER - Fishing nets - Four Rivers Tackle Co.

HI-JACKER - Shock absorbers—motor vehicle - Gabriel Ride Control Products Div.

HI-JINKS - Crocheted and knitted items ☆ - Gotham Knitting Mills

HI JOHN - See COMFORT SEAT

HI-K - Veterinary pharmaceutical preparations ☆ - Zirin Laboratories International

HI K KOLA - Beverages—carbonated - Alacer Co.

HI KIDS - Knit goods - Infanta Knitting Mills

HI! KOREAN - Computer software - Arumehsoft, Inc.

HI-KOVITE - Vitamins and nutritional supplements - Freeda Vitamins Inc.

HI-LAG - Electrical equipment - Ware Fuse Corp.

HI-LAND - Milk - Hiland Dairy Co.

HI-LAND - Sporting goods ☆ - Maurice Sporting Goods, Inc.

HI LASSIE - Fabrics—taffetas - Rosebar Textile Co.

HI-LASTIC - Electronic equipment - MacWhyte Co.

HI-LEAN - Medicated livestock feed - Hubbard Milling Co.

HI-LETHOL - Veterinary pharmaceutical preparations ☆ - Vineland Laboratories Inc.

HI LI - Apparel—men's ☆ - Alpha Mills Corp.

HI-LI - Frames—eyeglass - Hudson Optical Corp.

HI-LI - Toys - The Hi-Li Co.

☆ = Now out of production

HI-LI SCOOP - Games - Mantua/Cosom Sporting Goods
HI LIFE - Computer software - Sai Software Consultants, Inc.
HI LIFE - Eyeglasses - Art-Craft Optical Co.
HI-LIFE - Machine tools - SPS Technologies, Inc.
HI-LIFE - Pet products ☆ - Pet Life Foods Inc.
HI-LIFE JAWS - Machine parts - Esco Corp.
HI-LIFT - Jacks–hydraulic - Bloomfield Manufacturing Co.
HI-LIGHT - Lamps - Cannon Products Inc.
HI LIGHTS - Jewelry–costume - McKesson Home Health Care
HI-LINE - Chairs–folding ☆ - Cramer Inc.
HI-LINE - Electronics equipment - Hi-Line Electric Co., Inc.
HI-LINE - Eyelets–shoe and boot - American Mineral Gift Co.
HI-LINE - Girdles - Swisstex Co.
HI-LINE - Mat boards - Crescent Cardboard Co.
HI-LINE - Paper–toilet - Georgia-Pacific Corp.
HI-LINE - Shoe soles ☆ - Leather Factory Inc.
HI-LINE - Tools - Lufkin Rule Co.
HI-LINE BY PAPER MATE - Pens - Paper Mate Co.
HI-LINER - Markers–felt-tip - Micropoint Inc.
HI-LINOLEUM - Floor coverings–linoleum - Lucky America Inc.
HI-LITE - Bags–trash - Health-Ex Corp.
HI-LITE - Eyeglasses - Phillips Lens Co.
HI-LITE - Furniture polish - Intex Chemical Inc.
HI-LITE - Glass products - D & L Stained Glass Supply, Inc.
HI-LITE - Lamps ☆ - Eagle Electric Manufacturing Co., Inc.
HI-LITE - Leather–chamois - KozaK Auto Drywash Inc.
HI-LITE - Lighting fixtures - National Artcraft Co.
HI-LITE - Manicure preparations - Hi-Lite Cosmetics Inc.
HI LITE - Paints - Sophir Morris Paint
HI-LITE - Pet products - Eagle Beauty Laboratories Inc.
HI-LITE - Projectors–photographic ☆ - Buhl Optical Co.
HI-LITE - Recording label - Blue Gem Records
HI-LITE - Thermometers - Taylor Environmental Instruments
HI-LITE - Toys–models - Centuri Corp.
HI-LITE - Toys–models - Estes Industries
HI-LITE 7 - Manicure preparations - Hi-Lite Cosmetics Inc.
HI-LITE WRAPS - Hair care products - W.R. Rayson Co., Inc.
HI-LITER - Markers–felt-tip - Avery Dennison Corp.
HI-LITER - Spotlights - Rollei of America Inc.
HI-LITES - Fruits–dried - California Hi-Lites, Inc.
HI-LITES - Pet products - Hi-Lites Distribution
HI/LO - Automobile fluids - Hi-Lo Auto Supply, L.P.
HI-LO - Bicycles - Columbia Manufacturing Inc.
HI-LO - Chairs–upholstered ☆ - La-Z-Boy Chair Co.
HI-LO - Furniture - Penta Associates
HI-LO - Garden equipment - Parker Sweeper Co.
HI-LO - Gloves - Midwest Glove Co.
HI-LO - Glue–household or industrial - H.B. Fuller Co. (North American Adhesives, Sealants and Coatings Group)
HI-LO - Hardware - Elco Industries, Inc.
HI/LO - Health care products - W.A. Baum Co. Inc.
HI-LO - Health care products ☆ - Sammons Preston
HI-LO - Hobby kits - Edna Looney Products
HI-LO - Labels–paper - Cel-U-Dex Corp.
HI/LO - Lighting equipment - Thomas Industries Inc.
HI-LO - Macaroni ☆ - Pastamania
HI-LO - Matting ☆ - American Floor Products Co. Inc.
HI-LO - Musical instruments - Vic Firth Inc.
HI-LO - Office supplies - Service Tool & Die Co.
HI-LO - Poultry feeds - Grain Systems, Inc.
HI-LO - Racks ☆ - William Hodges & Co.
HI-LO - Ships ☆ - Bay Manufacturing
HI-LO - Sporting goods - Cardinal Home Products
HI-LO - Switches–electric - Pass & Seymour, Inc.
HI-LO - Tables–metal - Walker and Zanger Inc.
HI-LO - Trailers–travel - Hi-Lo Trailer Co. Inc.
HI-LO - Wheels - Hamilton Caster & Manufacturing Co.
HI-LO BALANCE - Health care products - Alta Health Products
HI/LO BOOKS - Publisher's imprints ☆ - Bantam Doubleday Dell Publishing Group, Inc.
HI-LO LITTLE INCH - Lighting fixtures - Alkco Lighting Co.
HI LO NO - Games - Hi-Lo-No Inc.
HI-LO PENETRAY - Lighting equipment - Philips Lighting Co.
HI-LOFT - Fabrics - Fairfield Processing Corp.
HI-LOFT - Iron products - June Tailor Inc.
HI-LOO - Health care products - ETAC USA Inc.

HI-LOW - Tables–metal - H. Wilson Co.
HI-LOW - Water purification systems - Penn-Plax, Inc.
HI-LOW WITCHERY - Apparel–women's - Exquisite Form Industries
HI-LUME - Electric lighting equipment - Lutron Electronics Co., Inc.
HI-LUSTER - Paints - Triangle Coatings Inc.
HI-LUSTRE - Cleaning preparations - Hi-Lustre Products Inc.
HI-LUSTRE - Hair coloring preparations ☆ - Ladds-Nessler Co. Inc.
HI LUSTRE - Solder - L.B. Allen Co. Inc.
HI-LUX - Frames–eyeglass - Hoya Corp. USA
HI MARK - Paper–carbon ☆ - Frye Copysystems Inc.
HI-MATIC - Photographic equipment - Eastman Kodak Co.
HI MEDIUM LOW - Recording label - Praise Hymn, Inc.
HI-META - Hair care products - Shear World International
HI-MILER - Belts–automotive - Goodyear Tire & Rubber Co.
HI MINUS - Frames–eyeglass - May Optical Co. Inc.
HI-MIRROR - Mirrors - Orient Glass Inc.
HI-MOD - Thread - Atlantic Thread and Supply Co. Inc.
HI-MOD - Thread - Signal Thread Co. Inc.
HI MODE - Headphones - Unisar, Inc.
HI-MODEL - Chairs–folding ☆ - Cramer Inc.
HI-MOUNT - Frames–eyeglass - Zylo Ware Corp.
HI MOUNTAIN - Seasonings - Hi Mountain Jerky Inc.
HI MOUNTAIN JERKY - Seasonings - Hi Mountain Jerky Inc.
HI-N-DRI - Boats ☆ - Teledyne Aero-Cal
HI 'N' DRI - Marine elevator - Atlantic Boatlifts Inc.
HI-N-DRY - Mats - Roope Corp.
HI-NATE 90 - Vitamins and nutritional supplements - Highland Packaging Co.
HI NORTH - Food products - Seward Fisheries
HI-NOTE - Ophthalmic goods - Foremost Optical Products
HI OPAKE - Paper–writing - Champion International Corp.
HI-OUTPUT - Lamps - Philips Lighting Co.
HI-PALS - Boots - Wellco Enterprises Inc.
HI-PEN - Pesticides–agricultural - Van Diest Supply Co.
HI-PER - Hoses - Goodyear Tire & Rubber Co.
HI-PERFORMANCE - Clamps - Breeze Industrial Products
HI-PERFORMANCE - Drums–musical instruments - Aquarian Accessories Corp.
HI-PERFORMANCE - Shelving units–metal - Penco Products Div.
HI-PET - Floor coverings–linoleum - Lucky America Inc.
H.I. PETITES - Dresses–women's - Huntington Industries Inc.
HI PIETRO - Fruits and vegetables - Pasquinelli Produce Co.
HI PINE - Cleaning preparations - Analab Inc.
HI PLANE SMOOTH CUT - Tobacco products ☆ - House of Edgeworth
HI-PLANER - Sport tubes - Intex Recreation Corp.
HI POCKETS - Vests–men's - Maxim Sorbents Inc.
HI-POINT - Brooms ☆ - Lighthouse Industries
HI POINT - Fabrics - School Apparel, Inc.
HI-POINT - Motor vehicle parts and accessories - Hi-Point Racing Products
HI POINT - Pet products - Shawnee Milling Co.
HI-POINT - Sports rackets and accessories - Victor Sports
HI-POLY - Juices - Sunkist Growers Inc.
HI-POLYMER - Pencils - Pentel of America, Ltd.
HI-POP - Popcorn - Manley Inc.
HI-POWER - Ammunition - Federal Cartridge Co.
HI-POWER - Grinders - Sandusky-Chicago Abrasive Wheel Co.
HI-POWER - Insecticides - Chevron Chemical Co.
HI-POWER - Lighting equipment ☆ - Photogenic Machine Co.
HI POWER - Rope - Wellington Leisure Products, Inc.
HI-POWER - Skin care products - Frances Denney
HI POWER - Underwear and nightwear ☆ - Lovable Co.
HI-POWER - Water heaters–household - Lochinvar Corp.
HI POWER II - Belts–automotive - Gates Rubber Co. (Automotive Aftermarket/ Hardware Sales Div.)
HI PRAIZE - Horseradish - Brede Inc.
HI-PRO - Alarm systems - Crimestopper Security Products Inc.
HI-PRO - Animal feeds - Friona Industries, LP
HI PRO - Cereal ☆ - General Mills, Inc.
HI-PRO - Dog food - Bailes Pet Food Co. Inc.
HI PRO - Dog food - Darigold, Inc.
HI-PRO - Motor vehicle parts and accessories - Coast Distribution System
HI PRO - Sporting goods - Hi Products
HI-PRO - Wallpaper - Wallquest, Inc.
HI PRO PAC - Hair care products - New Concepts for Beauty Inc.
HI-PRO-PAC - Hair care products - Roberts Research Laboratories, Inc.
HI PRO PAK - Skin care products ☆ - B & B Distributors
HI-PRO PLUS - Dog food - Inorex Inc.

☆ = Now out of production

HI PRO PLUS - Pet food - Texas Farm Products Co.
HI-PROTEIN - Food products - York Barbell Co., Inc.
HI-PROTEIN - Milk - Borden, Inc.
HI-Q - Food products - New Horizon Education, Inc.
HI-Q - Games - CBS Toys
HI Q - Pigments–paint - Tru-Test Manufacturing
HI-Q - Pipes - Hancor Inc.
HI-Q - Recording label - Fortune & Hi-Q Records
HI QUALITY BISCUIT - Bakery products - Dawn Food Products Inc.
HI-QUARTZ - Frames–eyeglass - Hoya Corp. USA
HI-R-BLEND - Shortening - Florida Shortening Corp.
HI-R MASONRY WALL SYSTEM - Building materials - Concrete Block Insulating Systems, Inc.
HI-R-PLUS - Shortening - Florida Shortening Corp.
HI-RAM INTAKE MANIFOLDS - Manifolds–motor vehicle - Weiand Automotive Industries
HI-RANGER - Construction equipment - Utility Equipment Co., Inc.
HI-RECOVERY - Water heaters–household - Quiet Automatic Burner Corp.
HI-REV - Automotive parts and accessories - Marvel Oil Co. Inc.
HI-RIB - Floor coverings - Ludlow Composites Corp.
HI RIB - Floor coverings - Pawling Corp. (Standard Products Div.)
HI-RIDER - Bicycles ☆ - Roadmaster Corp.
HI RIDER - Boats - Glen-L Marine Designs
HI-RIDER - Seats–automobile - Kolcraft Enterprises, Inc.
HI-RISE - Bookcases–wood ☆ - Jesse Jones Box Corp.
HI-RISE - Faucets - Sterling Plumbing Group Inc.
HI-RISE - Furniture ☆ - Hedstrom Corp.
HI RISE - Padding–foam ☆ - Foamex LP
HI-RISE - Swimming pools - Home & Roam Leisure Products, Inc.
HI-RISE - Toilet seats - Magnolia Products
HI-RISE - Toys - Hasbro, Inc.
HI RISE - Windows - Continental Aluminum Products Co. Inc.
HI-RISE BALLOONS - Toys - Wilhite Wholesale Inc.
HI-RISER - Apparel–athletic - Top Comfo Athletic Sox Inc.
HI RIZ - Flour–blended - Acme-Evans/A.D.M. Milling Co.
HI ROLLER - Golfing equipment - U.S. Precision Inc.
HI-ROLLER - Pens - Pentel of America, Ltd.
HI-ROLLER - Strollers–baby ☆ - Welsh Co.
HI-SAF - Ice cream - Frozen Desserts Co.
HI-SAFF - Oils–edible - Hain Pure Food Co. Inc.
HI-SCALE - Connectors–electrical ☆ - Heyco Products, Inc.
HI-SCORE BOWLING - Games - Smethport Specialty Co.
HI-SEAS - Fishing lures - Hi-Seas Industries, Inc.
HI-SEE - Frames–eyeglass - May Optical Co. Inc.
HI-SHEEN - Enamels - Jones Blair Co.
HI-SHINE - Cleaning preparations - R.M. Hollingshead Corp.
HI-SHINE - Hair care products - Hayashi for Hair Inc.
HI SHINE - Pet products - Carfore Ltd.
HI SHOCK - Hot tubs–plastic ☆ - Coleman Spas
HI-SHOK - Ammunition - Federal Cartridge Co.
HI SIERRA - Footwear–men's ☆ - Belleville Shoe Manufacturing Co.
HI-SIERRA - Wood products ☆ - States Industries Inc.
HI SIERRA'S - Glass products ☆ - Globe Building Materials Inc.
HI-SKOR - Gunpowder ☆ - E.I. Dupont de Nemours and Co.
HI-SKORE - Pencils ☆ - Faber-Castell Corp.
HI SLIDE - Swimming pools - General Foam Plastics Corp.
HI SOCIETY - Floor coverings–carpet and rugs ☆ - Fieldturf & Carpet Inc.
HI-SPEC - Adhesives and sealants - W.R. Meadows Inc.
HI-SPEED - Ammunition - Remington Arms Co., Inc.
HI-SPEED - Pet products - Oscar Enterprises Inc.
HI-SPEED - Photographic equipment ☆ - Edwal Scientific Products Corp.
HI-SPEED - Pumps–water - Sandpiper
HI-SPEED - Staples - Staplex Co.
HI-SPEED - Welding equipment - Dockson Corp.
HI-SPEED LOTTERY ROLLER - Stamps–hand - GB Products International Corp.
HI SPIRITS - Frames–eyeglass - May Optical Co. Inc.
HI-SPOT - Beverages–carbonated - Canada Dry Corp.
HI-SPOT - Tools - Dykem Co.
HI-STAINER - Laboratory apparatus - Innovation Instruments, Inc.
HI STAT - Polyvinyl sheets - Catalina Coating and Plastics, Inc.
HI-STEPPER - Apparel stores–lingerie - Goddess Bra
HI STRENGTH - Resins–acetal ☆ - Fibre Glass-Evercoat Co. Inc.
HI STRESS - Vitamins and nutritional supplements - Source Naturals
HI STYLE - Bicycles - Rand International, Inc.
HI-STYLE - Dry erase boards - Quartet Manufacturing Co.

HI STYLE - Eyeglasses - Art-Craft Optical Co.
HI-STYLE - Paints - Touraine Paints Inc.
HI-T DEGREASOL - Degreasing solvents - Kleer Flo Co. Inc.
HI-TAC TACTICAL GEAR - Apparel and accessories - Brigade Quartermasters Ltd.
HI-TACK - Adhesives and sealants - Pres-On Merchandising Corp.
HI TAILS - Deodorizers ☆ - Car-Freshner Corp.
HI-TAK - Adhesives and sealants - Microscale Industries Inc.
HI-TAN - Lamp bulbs–fluorescent - Kosmedico, Inc.
HI TANK - Tanks–gas ☆ - Bettcher Manufacturing Corp.
HI-TAPER - Luggage ☆ - American Tourister, Inc.
HI-TEC - Adhesives and sealants - Mechanic's Helper, Inc.
HI-TEC - Fireplaces - Preway Industries Inc.
HI-TEC - Footwear - Hi-Tec Sports USA Inc.
HI-TEC CELLULAR - Telephone accessories - Amcell Corp.
HI-TECH - Archery equipment - Wasp Archery Products, Inc.
HI-TECH - Drafting supplies ☆ - Plan Hold Corp.
HI-TECH - Floor coverings ☆ - Tarkett, Inc.
HI-TECH - Hair care products - Belson Products
HI TECH - Office furniture–metal - Luxor
HI-TECH - Paint rollers - Great American Marketing, Inc.
HI-TECH - Paints - Seymour of Sycamore Inc.
HI-TECH - Pens - Alexander Manufacturing Co.
HI-TECH - Pet products - Trendco Inc.
HI-TECH - Power switching equipment - Hi-Tech Systems
HI-TECH - Shelving units–metal - List Industries Inc. (Hallowell Div.)
HI-TECH - Tape–adhesive - Permacel
HI-TECH - Toys–automobiles - Bird Bromiticous Inc.
HI-TECH - Toys–electronic ☆ - Polk's Model Craft Hobbies, Inc.
HI-TECH - Vinyl - Collins & Aikman Corp.
HI-TECH - Wallpaper - Wallpaper Imports Inc.
HI-TECH 2000 - Beauty shop equipment - Flowery Beauty Products, Inc.
HI TECH PLUS - Cartons–paperboard - F-P Mkt. Inc.
HI TECH VINYLS VOL. V. - Wallpaper - Wallpaper Imports Inc.
HI-TEK - Computers–keypunch - NMB Technologies Inc. (Hi-Tek Div.)
HI-TEK - Cosmetics - Tek Products, Inc.
HI-TEK - Electronic equipment ☆ - Bogen Communications, Inc.
HI TEK - Floor coverings ☆ - Azrock Commercial Flooring
HI-TEK - Floor coverings–carpet and rugs ☆ - Customweave Carpets Inc.
HI-TEK PLUS - Photographic solutions - Alta Photographic Inc.
HI-TEL - Telephone apparatus - Wal South Inc.
HI-TEMP - Antifreeze - Gold Eagle Co.
HI TEMP - Knives - RonCo Inc.
HI-TEMP - Lubricants - Texas Refinery Corp. (Lubricants Div.)
HI-TEMP - Markers–felt-tip - Empire Berol USA
HI-TEMP - Paints - M.A. Bruder & Sons Inc.
HI-TEMP - Pipes–copper ☆ - Genova Products Inc.
HI-TEMP RTV - Adhesives and sealants - Loctite Corp.
HI-TEN - Automotive parts and accessories - Rite Autotronics Corp.
HI-TENN - Thread - Signal Thread Co. Inc.
HI-TENSION - Frames–eyeglass - Pathway Optical Prods.
HI-TEST - Heels–boot and shoe - L. Karno & Co.
HI-TEST - Thread - Cincinnati Thread Co.
HI-TEX - Cleaning preparations–carpet and rug - Coastal Industries Inc.
HI-TEX - Novelty items - CTI Industries Corp.
HI TEX - Yarn - Dixie Yarns, Inc.
HI THERE - Shoes - Famolare Inc.
HI TIDE - Shrimp - International Seafood Traders
HI-TILT - Marine rigging - Outboard Marine Corp.
HI-TIME - Frames–eyeglass - Pathway Optical Prods.
HI-TIMERS - Postcards ☆ - Gallant Greetings Corp.
HI-TINT - Paints - Day-Glo Color Corp.
HI-TOP - Electrical equipment - Matsushita Consumer Electronics Co.
HI-TOP - Frames–eyeglass - Pathway Optical Prods.
HI-TOP CONVOLUTE - Wheelchairs - Mason Medical Products
HI-TOR - Pet products - Triumph Pet Industries, Inc.
HI-TORK PORTABLE - Mixers–concrete - Philadelphia Mixers Corp.
HI-TORQUE - Clamps - Breeze Industrial Products
HI-TORQUE - Clamps–metal - Clamp-All Corp.
HI TORQUE - Motors–automotive - IMI Performance Products
HI-TORQUE APPROACH - Medical devices - Advanced Cardiovascular Systems, Inc.
HI-TORQUE BALANCE - Medical apparatus - Advanced Cardiovascular Systems, Inc.
HI-TORQUE STANDARD - Medical apparatus - Advanced Cardiovascular Systems, Inc.

HI-TRAC - Golfing equipment - Daiwa Corp.
HI-TRACK - Frames–picture - Farr Co.
HI-TRAFFIC - Floor waxes ☆ - Hako Minuteman Inc.
HI-TREND - Frames–eyeglass - Hudson Optical Corp.
HI-TUSS DM - Antihistamine preparations - Highland Packaging Co.
HI-UGNAW - Vitamins and nutritional supplements - Omega Nutrition USA Inc.
HI UP - Shoes - Famolare Inc.
HI VAL - Computer hardware - Hi-Val, Inc.
HI-VAL - Gasoline - Mobil Oil Corp.
HI-VALUE - Brushes–paint - E-Z Paintr Corp.
HI-VALUE - Cooking utensils–aluminum ☆ - Mirro Corp.
HI-VALUE - Food products - C-B Drug Co.
HI-VALUE - Fretted instruments ☆ - International Music Corp.
HI VALUE - Silicon products - Kirkhill Rubber Co.
HI-VEGI-LIP - Vitamins and nutritional supplements - Freeda Vitamins Inc.
HI-VI - Pet products - Strongheart Products, Inc.
HI-VIS - Containers–plastic - Ropak Corp.
HI-VIS - Lubricants - Outboard Marine Corp.
HI VIS - Sporting goods ☆ - Outdoor Technologies Group
HI-VITE - Veterinary pharmaceutical preparations - Evsco Pharmaceuticals
HI-VIZ - Fishing lures ☆ - Den Manufacturing Co.
HI-VIZ - Measuring instruments - Cooper Industries, Inc.
HI-VIZ - Pigments - Lawter International Inc.
HI-VIZ - Safety products - Conspicuity Inc.
HI VOLT - Automotive parts and accessories - Wynn Oil Co.
HI-WAISTER - Girdles - Cupid Foundations Inc.
HI-WALL - Health care products ☆ - Sammons Preston
HI-WATER - Adhesives and sealants - Epoxy Coatings Co.
HI-WAY DRAG - Tools - Lufkin Rule Co.
HI-WEST - Food products - Western Farmers Association
HI WEST - Vegetables–frozen - Pacific Valley Foods
HI-Y - Agricultural products - Hubbard Farms, Inc.
HI Y - Girdles - Beverly Vogue Co.
HI-Z - Voltmeters - Ross Engineering Corp.
HI ZINC - Paints - Tresco Paint Co. Inc.
HI8 - Tape recorders–video - Sony Corp. of America
HIALEAH - Fabrics - Dan River Inc.
HIALEAH - Whirlpools - Lasco Products Group
HIATUS - Apparel and accessories - Sunburst Products Inc.
HIAWATHA - Fabrics - Gretchen Bellinger Inc.
HIAWATHA - Footwear - Hiawatha Shoe Co.
HIAWATHA - Pickles - M.A. Gedney Co.
HIAWATHA - Sporting goods - Gamble-Skogmo Inc.
HIAWATHA - Vegetables–canned - Freemont Co.
HIBACHI GRILL - Sauces - Hormel Foods Corp.
HIBARI - Frames–eyeglass - May Optical Co. Inc.
HIBASE - Computer software - Equisoft, Inc.
HIBBEN KNIVES - Knives - United Cutlery Corp.
HIBEL - Paper products - Hibel Studio, Inc.
HIBEL LAURELS - Posters - Edna Hibel Studio
HIBEL L'IMAGE - Giftware - Edna Hibel Studio
HIBEL MUSEUM - Stationery - Edna Hibel Studio
HIBEL STUDIO - Giftware - Edna Hibel Studio
HIBEL VERTU - Giftware - Edna Hibel Studio
HIBERNATION - Waterbeds and accessories - Big Sur Waterbeds, Inc.
HIBERNATION COMBINATION - Beds–metal - Big Sur Waterbeds, Inc.
HIBERNIA - Earthenware ☆ - Waterford Wedgewood USA, Inc.
HIBICLENS - Cleaning preparations - Zeneca Inc.
HIBISCUS - Dinnerware - Corning Inc.
HIBISCUS - Furniture ☆ - Tropitone Furniture Co. Inc.
HIBISCUS - Giftware ☆ - Gorham Inc.
HIBISCUS - Giftware ☆ - World of Porcelain & Glassware
HIBISCUS PUNCH - Teas–herbal - San Francisco Herb & Natural Food Co.
HIBISCUS STRIPE - Bedding–linen - Dan River Inc.
HIBISTAT - Cleaning preparations - Zeneca Inc.
HIBITANE - Pharmaceutical preparations ☆ - Zeneca Inc.
HIBO - Eyeglasses - Art-Craft Optical Co.
HIC - Helmets–athletic - Hong Jin Crown America, Inc.
HIC - Tableware–china - Harold Import Co. Inc.
HIC-O-REE - Cheese - Cheese Smokers Inc.
HICAP - Fuses - Cooper Industries, Inc.
HICCUPPIN' HOT SAUCE - Sauces - Ford's Fancy Foods
HICKETY PICKETY - Games ☆ - Parker Brothers
HICKEY-FREEMAN - Apparel–men's - Hickey-Freeman Co. Inc.
HICKEY-FREEMAN CUSTOMIZED - Apparel–men's - Hickey-Freeman Co. Inc.

HICKEY GRIPPER - Printing trades machinery - Republic Roller Corp.
HICKOK - Leather goods - Tandy Brands Accessories Inc.
HICKORY - Handles–wood - Fleischmann Handle Co.
HICKORY - Laces–boot and shoe ☆ - Hickory Industries, Inc.
HICKORY - Recording label - Acuff-Rose Music Publishing, Inc.
HICKORY - Tobacco products - John Middleton Inc.
HICKORY & TWEED - Apparel and accessories - Hickory & Tweed, Inc.
HICKORY CHIEF - Handles–wood - Sequatchie Handle Works Inc.
HICKORY CRAWDADS - Apparel and accessories - Hickory Baseball, Inc.
HICKORY DICKORY DOCK - Watches - Kessler Marketing Group, Inc.
HICKORY FARMS - Food products - Hickory Farms, Inc.
HICKORY FARMS HAM STICK - Food products - Hickory Farms, Inc.
HICKORY FARMS TURKEY STICK - Food products - Hickory Farms, Inc.
HICKORY HAMS - Hams - Hickory Hams Inc.
HICKORY HARVEST - Fruits–dried - Hickory Harvest Foods
HICKORY HILL - Hams - Armour Swift-Eckrich
HICKORY HILL - Trailers–travel - Fleetwood Enterprises, Inc.
HICKORY HOLLOW - Hams - Land O Frost Inc.
HICKORY HOUSE - Barbecue sauce ☆ - Bridgeford Foods (Superior Div.)
HICKORY HOUSE - Sausages - Schweigert Foods
HICKORY HOUSE COLLECTION - Furniture–upholstered - Hickory Hill Furniture Corp.
HICKORY MAID - Meat product - Nagel Inc.
HICKORY MANOR - Cabinets ☆ - Aristokraft, Inc.
HICKORY 'N HONEY - Hams - Suzannah Farms
HICKORY RIDGE - Apparel and accessories - Neuville Industries Inc.
HICKORY SMOKE - Meat sauces ☆ - Allegro Fine Foods, Inc.
HICKORY SPECIALTIES - Charcoal - Bob Evans Farms Inc.
HICKORY SPRINGS - Furniture - Hickory Springs Manufacturing Co.
HICKORY TAVERN - Furniture–upholstered - Hickory Tavern Furniture
HICKORY VALLEY - Flowers–artificial - Vincent Lippe Co.
HICKORY WHITE CO. - Furniture - Hickory White Co.
HICKORYCRAFT - Furniture - Hickorycraft Inc.
HICKORYHOT! - Gravy ☆ - Durkee French Foods
HICKORYMARK - Furniture - Cherry Grove, Inc.
HICKS, THE - Playing cards - Universal Manufacturing Co., Inc.
HICKS WITH STICKS - Apparel and accessories - Mobile Press Register, Inc.
HICOM - Telephone apparatus ☆ - RF Communications Div.
HICON - Lenses–optical - Capo, Inc.
HICROLOY - Saw blades - Heinemann Saw Corp.
HIDA - Data loggers - Health Industry Distributors Association
HIDALGO - Ceramic tile ☆ - Integrity Tile Co.
HIDALGO COLLECTION - Tiles–ceramic - Huntington/Pacific Ceramics Inc.
HIDDEN AGENDA - Apparel and accessories - I. Spiewak and Sons Inc.
HIDDEN AGENDA - Tote bags and waist packs - Mist Inc.
HIDDEN CELLARS - Wines - Hidden Cellars Winery Inc.
HIDDEN COMFORT - Apparel–women's - E. Greenwald & Sons Inc.
HIDDEN COMFORT - Shoe accessories - Schering-Plough Healthcare Products
HIDDEN CROSS - Underwear and nightwear - Lovable Co.
HIDDEN DIFFERENCE - Pajamas–women's - Vanity Fair, Inc.
HIDDEN DIMENSIONS - Paper products - Daniel J. Dyckman
HIDDEN EAR - Hearing aids - Qualitone
HIDDEN EDGE - Self-defense spray - Defenders Network, Inc.
HIDDEN EYES - Eyeglasses - Opti-Ray, Inc.
HIDDEN FENCE II - Pet products - Waters Research Co.
HIDDEN FIRE - Cigarette lighters - Bowers Lighter Co.
HIDDEN GLIDES - Dressers–wood - American Woodmark Corp.
HIDDEN GOLD - Dolls - Mattel, Inc.
HIDDEN GREENS - Golf equipment - Burch L. Schleisner
HIDDEN HARDWARE - Holsters ☆ - Bianchi International
HIDDEN HEART - Apparel and accessories - Hidden Heart
HIDDEN HEART BEAR - Dolls - Mattel, Inc.
HIDDEN HEROES - Artists' materials - Louis G. Bowles, Jr.
HIDDEN HINGE - Cabinets - American Woodmark Corp.
HIDDEN HUE - Chemical preparations - Minnesota Mining & Manufacturing Co.
HIDDEN IMAGES - Toys - Betallic, Inc.
HIDDEN LAKES - Furniture ☆ - Bassett Furniture Industries, Inc.
HIDDEN MAGIC - Hair care products - Procter & Gamble Co.
HIDDEN MEANING - Recording label - Jazz Composer's Orchestra Association Inc.
HIDDEN POWER - Toys - Tonka Corp.
HIDDEN SECRET - Sunglasses - Esther Fuhrman Designs, Ltd.
HIDDEN SECRETS - Womens undergarments - Inner Secrets, Inc.
HIDDEN SPRING - Water–bottled or canned - Vermont Pure Holdings, Ltd.

☆ = Now out of production

HIDDEN SPRINGS - Floor coverings–carpet and rugs ☆ - Downs Carpet Co. Inc.

HIDDEN SPRINGS WINERY - Wines - Hidden Springs Winery

HIDDEN SUN, THE - Toys - Hasbro, Inc.

HIDDEN SURPRISES - Bicycles ☆ - Huffy Corp.

HIDDEN TALENTS - Games - Pressman Toy Corp.

HIDDEN TOY - Computer software - Laureate Learning Systems Inc.

HIDDEN TREASURE MYSTERIES - Jigsaw puzzle - Lombard Marketing, Inc.

HIDDEN TREASURE OF MAUI, THE - Coffee - AMFAC/JMB Hawaii, Inc.

HIDDEN TREASURES - Cereal - General Mills, Inc.

HIDDEN TREASURES - Floor coverings–carpet and rugs - Gulistan Carpet Inc.

HIDDEN TREASURES - Publisher's imprints - Hidden Treasures, Inc.

HIDDEN VALLEY - Dishes–china - Taylor, Smith & Taylor Co.

HIDDEN VALLEY - Floor coverings–carpet and rugs - Criterion Mills Inc.

HIDDEN VALLEY - Food products - Hidden Valley Ranch

HIDDEN VALLEY - Furniture - Pilliod Co.

HIDDEN VALLEY RANCH - Food products - HVR Co.

HIDDEN VALLEY RANCH - Salad dressings–mixes - Hidden Valley Ranch

HIDDEN VILLA RANCH - Dairy products - Luberski, Inc.

HIDDEN WORLD - Recording label - Joanne Bernice McDonough

HIDDEN YEARS - Books–comic - Warp Graphics, Inc.

HIDDENBROOKE - Dishes–china - Misawa Homes of America, Inc.

HIDE-A-BASE - Heating equipment - Embassy Industries Inc.

HIDE-A-BED - Sofas - Simmons USA

HIDE-A-BOARD - Furniture - Mead-Hatcher, Inc.

HIDE-A-CHAIR - Furniture - Bush Industries, Inc.

HIDE A DISC - Dentifrices - Surco Products Inc.

HIDE-A-DRAWER - Shelving units–wood - Hirsh Co.

HIDE-A-HOOK - Fishing tackle ☆ - Hypark Specialty Co., Inc.

HIDE-A-LINE - Rope - Nutone Inc.

HIDE-A-LITE - Lighting fixtures - Progress Lighting Inc.

HIDE-A-MARK - Stencils - Krylon/Dupli-Color

HIDE A PAKS - Candy - Brock Candy Co. Inc.

HIDE-A-REST - Air beds - Intex Recreation Corp.

HIDE-A-REST - Sofabeds - Super Sagless Corp.

HIDE A SAFE - Luggage - Ronde

HIDE-A-SPEC - Frames–eyeglass - Hudson Optical Corp.

HIDE-A-SPRAY - Paints ☆ - PPG Industries, Inc.

HIDE-A-SWITCH - Fixtures–plastic ☆ - Grandpa Brand Co. (Par Beverage Co.)

HIDE-A-TENNA - Automotive accessories - Interdynamics, Inc.

HIDE-A-VECTOR - Heating equipment - Embassy Industries Inc.

HIDE-A-VENT - Aluminum products - N.H. Rudeen Co.

HIDE-A-VENT - Heating vents - Georgia-Pacific Corp.

HIDE-A-WAL - Paints ☆ - Foy-Johnston Inc.

HIDE-A-WALL - Paints - Perry & Derrick Co.

HIDE-A-WAND - Toys - Strombecker Corp.

HIDE-A-WAY - Combs - Comare Corp.

HIDE-A-WAY - Housewares - Willert Home Products, Inc.

HIDE-A-WAY - Paper - Spectrum Industries Inc.

HIDE-A-WAY - Pet product - ISE Inc.

HIDE-A-WAY - Socks - Leininger Mills Inc.

HIDE-A-WAY EGGS - Candy - Brock Candy Co. Inc.

HIDE-A-WAYS - Footwear–men's - L.B. Evans' Son Co.

HIDE ALL - Paints - C.M. Athey Paint Co.

HIDE ALL - Paints - Hirshfield's Paint Manufacturing

HIDE-ALL - Paints - Standard Brands Paint Co.

HIDE AND GO SEEK - Games - Smethport Specialty Co.

HIDE AND SEEK - Games - Universal Manufacturing Co., Inc.

HIDE & SEEK SCIENCE - Publisher's imprints - Chardiet Unlimited Inc.

HIDE-AWAY - Motor vehicle parts and accessories - Curtis Tractor Cab Inc.

HIDE AWAY - Trailers–travel - Sun-Lite Inc.

HIDE BEHIND - Apparel and accessories - Barbara Ann Diskin

HIDE-IT - Cosmetics - Nu-Nails

HIDE-N-RIDE - Antennas - Wintenna Inc.

HIDE 'N SEEK - Floor coverings–carpet and rugs - Trend Carpet

HIDE N' SEEK - Pet products - Boomer Ball

HIDE 'N SEEK - Underwear and nightwear ☆ - Lovable Co.

HIDE N' SLEEK - Cosmetics - RH Cosmetics Corp.

HIDE 'N SLEEP - Play tents - Springs Industries, Inc.

HIDE 'N SQUEAK - Games - Hasbro, Inc.

HIDE-N-STORE - Hardware - Heinz J. Smirmaul

HIDE 'N' THIEF - Games ☆ - Western Publishing Co., Inc.

HIDE-O-PAQUE - Enamels - Commercial Chemical Co. Inc.

HIDE THOSE WIRES - Moldings and trim - Tellure Marketing & Distribution, Inc.

HIDE UM' HUNTER - Fabrics - Brell Mar Products, Inc.

HIDE YOUR DOUGH - Product for hiding valuables, now out of production - Iwasaki Images of America

HIDEAWAY - Chests–wood - Little Tikes Co.

HIDEAWAY - Chimes - Nutone Inc.

HIDEAWAY - Jewelry ☆ - Hirsch Speidel Inc.

HIDEAWAY - Skin care products - Mana Products, Inc.

HIDEAWAY - Sporting goods - Camp-Cap Products

HIDEAWAY BEAR - Dolls - Mattel, Inc.

HIDEAWAY CREAM - Cosmetics - Madeleine Mono Ltd.

HIDEAWAY HANDSIDE TRUCK - Trailers–travel ☆ - Sun-Lite Inc.

HIDEAWAY HOOD - Crocheted and knitted items ☆ - Reliable of Milwaukee

HIDEAWAY WORKBENCH - Work benches - Crawford Products Inc.

HIDEAWAYS - Toys - Indiana Tool, Inc.

HIDE'N SEAL - Paints - Mantrose-Haeuser Co. Inc.

HIDE'N SNEAKS - Footwear ☆ - Talus Corp.

HIDEOUSLY DEFORMED CREATURES OF SUPERHUMAN SIZE AND STRENGTH - Toys - Troma, Inc.

HIDEOUT - Communications equipment - Whitaker Corp.

HIDEOUT - Fabrics - Highland Industries Inc.

HIDEOUT - Fishing tackle - Frabill Inc.

HIDES ANYTHING - Cosmetics - Monteil Paris

HIDESIGN - Leather - Hide Design of America Inc.

HIDEX - Paints ☆ - Watson-Standard Co.

HIDEY-HOLE - Toys - Novalek, Inc.

HIDG - Jewelry - Hacker Jewelers Designers & Goldsmiths,Inc.

HIDING PLACE - Pet products ☆ - Tetra Sales USA

HIDROMAR - Pharmaceutical preparations ☆ - Marlop Pharmaceuticals Inc.

HIDROVITALEN - Skin care products - Lendan USA Co.

HIDUCT - Primers - BASF Corp.

HIEL DE VACA - Soap - Crusellas & Compania Inc.

HIELIABRINE - Skin care products - Nailtex Inc.

HIENZ - Food products ☆ - Needlecraft Industries

HIERARCH - Floor coverings–carpet and rugs ☆ - Patcraft Mills Inc.

HIFI II - Pet products - Rolf C. Hagen (USA) Corp.

HI!FINANCE - Computer software - Aatrix Software Inc.

HIFLEX - Doughnuts–mixes - Mallet and Co.

HIFLEX - Steel products - Brainard Strapping

HIFLOAT - Life preservers - Wildwater Designs Ltd.

HIFOCALS - Eyeglass accessories - Joe Buser

HIG DURABLE - Office supplies - Globe-Weis

HIGBEE - Machinery - Dry-Tab Package Sealer Co.

HIGBEE BUTTON - Cording - Novelty Cord and Tassel Co. Inc.

HIGGINS - Computer software - Higgins Group

HIGGINS - Inks - Faber-Castell Corp.

HIGGINS - Toys–stuffed ☆ - Gund, Inc.

HIGGINS AMERICAN - Inks ☆ - Faber-Castell Corp.

HIGGINS BOLDSTROKE - Pens ☆ - Faber-Castell Corp.

HIGGS - Health care products - Carex Health Products Inc.

HIGH 5 - Cereal ☆ - Barbara's Bakery, Inc.

HIGH 5 SPORTSWEAR - Apparel - High 5 Sportswear, Inc.

HIGH ACHIEVER - Wallcovering - Jonathan E. Collins

HIGH ADVENTURE - Floor coverings–carpet and rugs ☆ - Gulistan Carpet Inc.

HIGH ADVENTURE - Games - Tsr, Inc.

HIGH ALPINE - Apparel and accessories - High Sierra, Ltd.

HIGH ALTITUDE FORMULA - Pharmaceutical preparations - John Mikkelsen

HIGH APPALACHIAN HIGH QUALITY EST. 1988 - Food products - High Appalachian Limited Liability Co.

HIGH BALL - Games ☆ - Norton Co.

HIGH BANKS THE SPEEDWAY TRIVIA GAME - Games - Richard Scott Trevisan

HIGH-BEAM - Fabrics - Performance Textiles, Inc.

HIGH BRANCH - Garden equipment - Green Mountain Products Inc.

HIGH BROW - Cosmetics - Sassaby Inc.

HIGH BUILD - Adhesives and sealants - Bonakemi USA, Inc.

HIGH-CAL-D - Pharmaceutical preparations ☆ - Scrip-Physician Supply Co.

HIGH CALIBER PRODUCTIONS - Video tapes - High Caliber Productions, Inc.

HIGH CAPACITY - Soap - Georgia-Pacific Corp.

HIGH CHAIR KIDS - Toys–stuffed - Fun World Inc.

HIGH-CLEAN - Cleaning equipment - Clean ESD Products, Inc.

HIGH CONCURRENCY OBJECT - Computer software - Ontos, Inc,

HIGH COUNTRY - Binoculars - Tasco Sales, Inc.

HIGH COUNTRY - Faucets - Kohler Co.

HIGH COUNTRY - Firearms, accessories, and parts - Welsh Sporting Goods Corp. (Boyt Div.)

HIGH COUNTRY - Floor coverings–carpet and rugs ☆ - Quaker Inc.

HIGH COUNTRY - Sporting goods ☆ - Rocky Mountain Sports

HIGH COUNTRY - Sports apparel and accessories ☆ - Dionysian Inc. (Jacobs Div.)

HIGH COUNTRY - Swimming pools ☆ - Doughboy Recreational Inc.

HIGH COUNTRY - Trees–artificial - Ann C. Thompson

HIGH COUNTRY - Wallpaper - Mt. Diablo Hand Prints Inc.

HIGH COUNTRY COLLECTION - Furniture–upholstered - Hickory Hill Furniture Corp.

HIGH COUNTRY HUNTER - Knives–hunting ☆ - Camillus Cutlery Co.

HIGH COUNTRY MONTANA POKER - Game machines - Dynamo Corp.

HIGH COUNTRY OAK - Furniture ☆ - A. Brandt Co. Inc.

HIGH DEFINITION - Hair care products - Scruples Professional Salon Products, Inc.

HIGH DEFINITION - Shingles–shakes - Elk Corp. of Dallas

HIGH DEFINITION OPTICS - Eyeglasses - Oakley, Inc.

HIGH DENSITY - Cosmetics - Charles of the Ritz Group Ltd.

HIGH DENSITY RECYCLED PLASTIC - Plastics - Ronald Krueger

HIGH DESERT - Shampoos - Medical Auditing Services, Inc.

HIGH DESERT - Vitamins and nutritional supplements - CC Pollen Co.

HIGH DESERT MILD - Beverages–alcohol - Deschutes Brewery

HIGH DESERT SOFTWARE - Computer software - High Desert Software, Inc.

HIGH DESIGN - Shingles - Herbert Malarkey Roofing Co.

HIGH DR. - Apparel and accessories - Todd Number 1

HIGH EFFICIENCY COOKWARE - Cooking equipment–household - Nordic Ware

HIGH EFFICIENCY II - Heaters–gas - Modine Manufacturing Co.

HIGH END SYSTEMS - Chemical preparations - High End Systems, Inc.

HIGH ENDURANCE - Deodorants–personal - Shulton, Inc.

HIGH ENERGY - Health care products - Natural Laboratories Corp.

HIGH ENERGY - Pet products - Shawnee Milling Co.

HIGH ENERGY - Teas - Seelect, Inc.

HIGH ENERGY - Telephones - Conair Corp.

HIGH ENERGY EDGE, THE - Publisher's imprints - Hume Financial Services Inc.

HIGH ENERGY MEDICINE - Vitamins and nutritional supplements - King Bio Pharmaceuticals, Inc.

HIGH ESTEEM - Wallpaper - Unique Wall Fashions Inc.

HIGH EXPECTATIONS - Floor coverings–carpet and rugs - World Carpets, Inc.

HIGH FALLS - Beverages–malt - Genesee Brewing Co., Inc.

HIGH FASHION - Bicycles - Dynacraft Industries Inc.

HIGH FASHION - Floor coverings–carpet and rugs ☆ - Callaway Carpets

HIGH-FASHION - Ribbons - Papercraft Corp.

HIGH FIDELITY - Floor coverings–carpet and rugs - Roxbury Carpet Co.

HIGH FIVE - Deodorants–personal - Bertsherm Products Inc.

HIGH FIVES - Game machines - Bally Gaming International, Inc.

HIGH FLANGE SEAL - Weather stripping - KEL-EEZ

HIGH FLEX - Gypsum products - National Gypsum Co.

HIGH FLEX ZONE - Golfing equipment - Lisco, Inc.

HIGH FLIGHT - Bicycles - Murray, Inc.

HIGH FLIGHT - Cologne - Sumar Medical Services, Inc.

HIGH-FLO - Automotive parts and accessories - Edelbrock Corp.

HIGH-FLYER - Eyeglasses - Uvex Safety LLC

HIGH FLYING FRIED CHICKEN - Preserved foods–prepackaged - Conagra, Inc.

HIGH-FORM - Fireplaces ☆ - Superior Fireplace Co.

HIGH FREQUENCY - Kites ☆ - Hi-Flier Manufacturing Co.

HIGH GAIN - Labels - Epsen Hillmer Graphics Co.

HIGH GATE LTD. - Apparel–women's - Frederick Atkins, Inc.

HIGH GEAR - Apparel–women's - Duet Creations Inc.

HIGH GEAR - Camping products - Jeffrey O. Phillips

HIGH GEAR - Trading cards and stamps - Wheels Racing, Inc.

HIGH GEAR RODEO - Trading cards and stamps - Wheels Racing, Inc.

HIGH GLOSS - Automotive parts and accessories - Turtle Wax, Inc.

HIGH GLOSS - Blinds–venetian - Kenney Manufacturing Co.

HIGH GLOSS - Horseshoes ☆ - Farnam Cos. Inc.

HIGH GLOSS - Underwear and nightwear - Lovable Co.

HIGH GRADE - Apparel and accessories - Pendleton

HIGH GRADE - Paints - Dean and Barry Co.

HIGH HAIR - Hair care products - Wella Corp. (Consumer Products Div.)

HIGH HAND - Games ☆ - Milton Bradley Co.

HIGH HATS - Window coverings - Curtron Curtain Inc.

HIGH HEAT - Cleaning preparations - Viking Manufacturing Co. Inc.

HIGH HEAT - Crayons - Dixon Ticonderoga Co.

HIGH HIDE - Lacquers - Dunn Edwards Corp.

HIGH-HIDE - Paints - Somay Products Inc.

HIGH HILL FARMS - Sauces ☆ - Chelten House Products Inc.

HIGH HONORS - Brassieres (Bras) ☆ - Lovable Co.

HIGH HOPES - Floor coverings–carpet and rugs - Trend Carpet

HIGH IMPACT - Bags–duffel - Gary Gaines, Inc.

HIGH IMPACT - Games - Gamescience

HIGH IMPACT - Games - Williams Electronics Games, Inc.

HIGH IMPACT - Trading cards and stamps - Impel Marketing Inc.

HIGH IMPACT COLORS - Cosmetics - Almay Inc.

HIGH IMPACT FLAVORS - Seasonings - Flavor & Fragrance Specialties Inc.

HIGH IMPACT SYSTEM - Roofing materials - Hydro Seal Coatings Co., Inc.

HIGH IMPULSE - Toys–models - Estes Industries

HIGH INTENSITY - Apparel and accessories - Mercantile Stores Co., Inc.

HIGH IQ - Hair care products - Revlon-Realistic Professional Products Inc.

HIGH-JET - Electronic equipment - The Fogmaster Corp.

HIGH JINKS - Bicycles - Murray, Inc.

HIGH LIFE - Beverages–malt - Miller Brewing Co.

HIGH LIFE - Salad dressings–bottled - Ventura Foods

HIGH + LIGHT - Hair care products - Trionics Systems Corp.

HIGH-LIGHT - Window coverings - Window Quilt

HIGH LIMB - Garden equipment - Green Mountain Products Inc.

HIGH-LINE - Photographic equipment - Eastman Kodak Co.

HIGH LINER - Seafood products–fresh or frozen ☆ - National Sea Products U.S. Corp.

HIGH-LITE - Vacuum cleaners and accessories - Bissell Inc.

HIGH LOFT - Soap - Pacific Coast Feather Co.

HIGH-M - Bakery mixes - International Multifoods Corp.

HIGH MANOR - Floor coverings–carpet and rugs - Patcraft Mills Inc.

HIGH MEADOWS - Ice cream - Fancy Foods of Virginia Inc.

HIGH MODULUS - Fabrics–sailcloth - Challenge Sailcloth

HIGH MOUNTAIN - Luggage - Shalam Imports Inc.

HIGH-MOUNTAIN COLA - Beverages - Logret Import & Export Co.

HIGH NOON - Floor coverings–carpet and rugs ☆ - Colonial Mills Inc.

HIGH NOON - Floor coverings–carpet and rugs ☆ - Zenith Carpets

HIGH NOON - Furniture - Bean Station Furniture Factory Inc.

HIGH NOON - Lumber - Georgia-Pacific Corp.

HIGH NOON SALOON AND RIB JOINT - Barbecue sauce - O'Egans, Inc.

HIGH NUTRIENT - Hair care products - Bonat Inc.

HIGH NUTRITION - Breakfast cereal - Weetabix Co., Inc.

HIGH ON SPEED - Apparel and accessories - Wiseguy Racing and Design

HIGH PERFORMANCE - Air purification systems - Medo Industries, Inc.

HIGH PERFORMANCE - Cables - Transparent Audio Marketing, Inc.

HIGH PERFORMANCE - Colognes ☆ - Avon Products, Inc.

HIGH-PERFORMANCE - Pharmaceutical preparations - Light Force Inc.

HIGH PERFORMANCE - Recording label - Jazz Composer's Orchestra Association Inc.

HIGH PERFORMANCE GOLF - Computer software - Holden Production Group, Inc.

HIGH PERFORMANCE HYGIENE - Toiletries - Advanced Health Products, LLC

HIGH PERFORMING TEACHER, THE - Video production - Canter and Associates, Inc.

HIGH PLAINS - Food products - Burlington Marketing Corp.

HIGH PLAINS SPORTER - Rifles ☆ - Thompson/Center Arms

HIGH POINT - Chairs–wood - High Point Furniture Industries

HIGH POINT - Cigar boxes–wood ☆ - Consolidated Cigar Corp.

HIGH POINT - Coffee - Procter & Gamble Co.

HIGH POINT - Door locks - Weiser Lock Corp.

HIGH POINT - Floor coverings–carpet and rugs ☆ - Cumberland Mills Inc.

HIGH POINT - Floor coverings–carpet and rugs ☆ - Porter Carpet Mills Inc.

HIGH POINT - Socks - High Point Knitting Inc.

HIGH POINT FURNITURE INDUSTRIES - Furniture - High Point Furniture Industries

HIGH POINT HOME FASHIONS - Linen - Notra Trading, Inc.

HIGH-PORE - Pet products ☆ - Penn-Plax, Inc.

HIGH POWER - Electronic equipment - Dukane Corp.

HIGH POWER - Projection screens - Da-Lite Screen Co. Inc.

HIGH PRAISE - Floor coverings–carpet and rugs ☆ - Gulistan Carpet Inc.

HIGH PRESSURE - Brooms - American Water Broom Co.

HIGH-PRO - Glass products - Bellco Glass Inc.

HIGH-PRO - Pet products - Strongheart Products, Inc.

HIGH PRODUCTIVITY SYSTEMS - Computer software - Seer Technologies Inc.

HIGH PROFILE - Hair care products - Peter Hantz Co.

HIGH PROFILE - Health care products - Roho, Inc.

☆ = Now out of production

HIGH PROTECTION SPF 15 - Suntan lotions - Sothys USA Inc.
HIGH PROTEIN - Pet products - Ralston Purina Co.
HIGH PULSE FOR THE BIG ACTION. - Fishing lures - Keith B. Alexander
HIGH-Q - Fabrics–cotton - Barnhardt Manufacturing Co.
HIGH-Q - Ice milk ☆ - Pet Dairy
HIGH Q - Publisher's imprints - McClanahan Book Co., Inc.
HIGH QUALITY - Recording label - Rashid Sales Co.
HIGH-RAILS - Toys–models - R. K. Enterprises
HIGH REGARD - Floor coverings–carpet and rugs - Porter Carpet Mills Inc.
HIGH RELIEF - Hair care products - European Tanning Systems Inc.
HIGH RIB - Mats ☆ - U.S. Mat & Rubber Co. Inc.
HIGH RIDGE - Jewelry ☆ - Hirsch Speidel Inc.
HIGH RIDGE - Luggage - SGI Inc.
HIGH RIDGE - Lumber - Georgia-Pacific Corp.
HIGH RISE - Dining-room furniture - American Furniture Co. Inc.
HIGH-RISE - Filing cabinets–metal - Buddy Products
HIGH RISE - Floor coverings–carpet and rugs ☆ - American Carpet Mills
HIGH-RISE - Hobby kits - Rapco
HIGH RISE CLASSIC - Dining-room furniture - American Furniture Co. Inc.
HIGH ROCKETS - Recording label - Dick Michaels Productions
HIGH ROLLER - Brushes–paint - Gerhard-Sorenson Corp.
HIGH ROLLER - Candy - Madelaine Chocolate Novelties, Inc.
HIGH ROLLER - Computer software - Mindscape Software Inc.
HIGH ROLLER - Dollies–industrial ☆ - Kelley Manufacturing Co.
HIGH ROLLERS - Housewares ☆ - Sunbeam-Oster Household Products
HIGH SEA - Seafood products–canned or cured - Robinson Canning Co. Inc.
HIGH SEAS - Apparel and accessories - H. Bernbaum Import-Export Co.
HIGH-SEAS - Apparel and accessories ☆ - Williamson-Dickie Manufacturing Co.
HIGH SEAS - Shaving preparations ☆ - S.C. Johnson & Son, Inc.
HIGH SEAS TECHNOLOGY - Communications equipment–marine - High Seas Technology, Inc.
HIGH SHINE - Hair care products - Pantresse Inc.
HIGH SHINE FAVOR - Furniture polish and wax - S.C. Johnson & Son, Inc.
HIGH SIERRA - Bicycles - Schwinn Cycling & Fitness Inc.
HIGH SIERRA - Cutlery ☆ - Washington Forge Inc.
HIGH SIERRA - Firearms, accessories, and parts - High Standard Manufacturing Corp.
HIGH SIERRA - Furniture ☆ - Bassett Furniture Industries, Inc.
HIGH SIERRA - Luggage - H. Bernbaum Import-Export Co.
HIGH SIERRA - Meat products–beef ☆ - King B Jerky
HIGH SIERRA - Seat covers - Alco Manufacturing Co. Inc.
HIGH SIERRA - Shingles–asphalt or tar ☆ - GS Roofing Products Co.
HIGH SIERRA - Wallpaper - Newmarket Designs Ltd.
HIGH SIERRA - Water–bottled or canned - Sierra Spring Water Co.
HIGH SIERRA - Wood products - National Bark Sales
HIGH SIERRA II - Swimming pools ☆ - Lomart Industries
HIGH SKORE - Sporting goods - Wa Mac Inc.
HIGH SKY - Recording label - Dick Michaels Productions
HIGH SOCIETY - Christmas tree ornaments - Cracker Box Inc.
HIGH SOCIETY - Floor coverings–carpet and rugs - Philadelphia Carpets
HIGH SOCIETY - Recording label - Diamond Communications, Inc.
HIGH SOCIETY - Wallcoverings - Ben Rose Ltd.
HIGH SOCIETY - Watches - Borel Watch Co.
HIGH SPEED - Lubricants - G-96 Products Co. Inc.
HIGH SPEED DOUBLE KOTE NT - Machinery - D & K Custom Machine Design, Inc.
HIGH SPEED GEAR - Apparel and accessories - S.I. Creations
HIGH SPEED INDUSTRIAL - Sunglasses - Ted Swiet
HIGH SPIRITS - Dog food - Darigold, Inc.
HIGH SPIRITS - Floor coverings–carpet and rugs ☆ - Galaxy Carpet Mills Inc.
HIGH SPIRITS - Floor coverings–carpet and rugs ☆ - Lees Carpets
HIGH SPIRITS - Office supplies ☆ - Evergreen Press
HIGH-STAK - Filing cabinets–wood - Fellowes Manufacturing Co.
HIGH STAKES CHALLENGE - Games - High Stakes Challenge, Inc.
HIGH STANDARD - Audio equipment - TDK Electronics Corp.
HIGH STANDARD - Firearms, accessories, and parts - High Standard Manufacturing Corp.
HIGH STANDARD - Floor coverings–carpet and rugs - Milliken & Co. Inc.
HIGH STEPPER - Toys–stuffed - Mattel, Inc.
HIGH STREET - Lighting equipment - Industrial Molding Corp.
HIGH STREET - Recording label - Windham Hill Productions Inc.
HIGH STRUNG - Apparel and accessories - High Strung Inc.
HIGH STYLE - Floor coverings–carpet and rugs - Galaxy Carpet Mills Inc.
HIGH STYLE - Skin care products - H.K. Simon Co.
HIGH STYLE - Wallpaper - Walls Alive

HIGH-TACK - Adhesives and sealants - W.J. Ruscoe Co.
HIGH TEA - Tea kettles–nonelectric - Robinson Knife & Fiddlers Plastics
HIGH TECH - Bathing suits - Authentic Fitness Corp.
HIGH TECH - Dog food - Livestock Supply Co., Inc.
HIGH TECH - Floor coverings–carpet and rugs ☆ - Mohawk Carpet Corp.
HIGH TECH - Office supplies ☆ - Springfield Tablet Co.
HIGH-TECH - Toys–guns - Imperial Toy Corp.
HIGH TECH PRODUCTS - Pet products - Biological Engineering/High Tech Pet Products
HIGH TECH RECOVER - Pharmaceutical preparations - Bricker Laboratories
HIGH TECH REPORTS - Video production - Scholastic Inc.
HIGH TECH TABS - Chemical preparations - John Girvan Co., Inc.
HIGH TEMPERATURE LININGS HTL - Building materials - High Temperature Linings
HIGH TIDE - Apparel–women's - Warnaco Inc.
HIGH TIDE - Floor coverings–carpet and rugs ☆ - Calladium & Marglen
HIGH TIDE - Floor coverings–carpet and rugs ☆ - Foreign Accents
HIGH TIDE - Seafood products–fresh or frozen - Conagra, Inc.
HIGH TIMBER - Bicycles - Schwinn Cycling & Fitness Inc.
HIGH TIMBERS - Furniture - Universal Flooring
HIGH TIME - Clocks ☆ - Hoyle Products
HIGH TIME - Floor coverings–carpet and rugs - Monticello Carpet Mills
HIGH TIME - Floor coverings–carpet and rugs ☆ - Masland Corp.
HIGH TIME - Vitamins and nutritional supplements - Country's Health
HIGH TIME RADIANT COLORS - Paints - Muralo Co. Inc.
HIGH TIMES - Watches and belts - Heller Willette Ltd.
HIGH-TOP BEAUTY SHOP - Dolls - Mattel, Inc.
HIGH-TOUCH - Facsimile equipment - Touchfax Information Systems, Inc.
HIGH TRAC - Cleaning preparations - Minuteman International, Inc.
HIGH TRACK - Adhesives and sealants - Loctite Corp.
HIGH TRAILS - Backpacks - A.D. Sutton & Sons Inc.
HIGH VALLEY FARM - Meat products–cured - Hickory Baked Foods
HIGH VELOCITY - Ammunition - Remington Arms Co., Inc.
HIGH VELOCITY - Hair care products - Concentrics Inc.
HIGH VELOCITY - Safety products - U.S. Armor Corp.
HIGH VELOCITY COMPRESSION DR. - Loudspeakers - Polk Investment Corp.
HIGH VISIBILITY - Floor coverings–carpet and rugs - Karastan-Bigelow Inc.
HIGH VISTA - Wallpaper ☆ - Fidelity Industries, Inc.
HIGH VOLTAGE - Footwear ☆ - Margaret Gerald
HIGH VOLTAGE - Vitamins and nutritional supplements - American Body Building Products, Inc.
HIGH-VOLTAGE VIOLET - Cosmetics - Elizabeth Arden Inc.
HIGH VOLUME - Hair-care products - Mebco Industries, Inc.
HIGH VOLUME - Hair care products - Pantresse Inc.
HIGH WATER - Recording label - High Water Recording Co.
HIGH WATER ENERGY FOR YOUR SOUL - Beverages–carbonated - Hans P. Lammersdorf
HIGH WIRE - Wallcovering - Capital Carousel Inc.
HIGH WIRE - Wallpaper - Academy Handprints Ltd.
HIGH-X - Lenses–optical - X-Cel Optical Co.
HIGH YIELD - Coffee - Nestle Beverage Co.
HIGH YIELD - Floor coverings–carpet and rugs ☆ - Columbus Mills, Inc.
HIGH YIELD 500, THE - Computer software - Knowledge Exchange Inc.
HIGHBOY - Wastebaskets - F.H. Lawson Co.
HIGHBRIDGE - Water–bottled or canned - Highbridge Spring Water
HIGHBRIDGE CLASSICS - Recording label - Highbridge Co.
HIGHBRIDGE SPRINGS - Water–bottled or canned - Highbridge Spring Water
HIGHBRIGHT - Audio equipment - Hughes Aircraft Co.
HIGHCAL90PLUS - Lime products - Highcal Pellet Lime, L.P.
HIGHCLIFF - Toilets–enameled - Kohler Co.
HIGHCREST - Bathroom fixtures - Kohler Co.
HIGHCROFT - Food products - Associated Fruit Co.
HIGHCULTURE - Yogurt–frozen - Greater Pacific Foods, Inc.
HIGHER ALTITUDE HIGHER ATTITUDE - Apparel and accessories - Martin P. Connelly
HIGHER & HIGHER - Hair care products - Helene Curtis Industries Inc.
HIGHER & HIGHER - Hair care products - Trionics Systems Corp.
HIGHER GROUND - Jackets - William S. Jackson
HIGHER GROUND - Wallpaper - Tony Putnam Inc.
HIGHER LEVEL - Apparel and accessories - Higher Level Manufacturing, Inc.
HIGHER MIND - Vitamins and nutritional supplements - Source Naturals
HIGHER OCTAVE - Recording label - Higher Octave Music, Inc.
HIGHER SOURCE RECORDS - Recording label - Higher Source Records, Inc.
HIGHEST QUALITY - Paints - Perry & Derrick Co.
HIGHFALLS - Beverages–malt - Genesee Brewing Co., Inc.
HIGHFLO - Hardware - Genova Products Inc.

☆ = Now out of production

HIGHFLYER - Goggles–safety - Uvex Safety LLC

HIGHGAIN VOLUME - Amplifiers–musical instrument - Dunlop Manufacturing, Inc.

HIGHGAR FARMS - Vitamins and nutritional supplements - Pure-Gar

HIGHLAND - Blankets–electric ☆ - Sunbeam-Oster Household Products

HIGHLAND - Brushes–paint ☆ - PPG Industries, Inc.

HIGHLAND - Cabinets - Aristokraft, Inc.

HIGHLAND - Cabinets - Wellborn Cabinet, Inc.

HIGHLAND - Candles ☆ - Candle Mill

HIGHLAND - Coffee - Tradewell Stores Inc.

HIGHLAND - Floor coverings–carpet and rugs - Galaxy Carpet Mills Inc.

HIGHLAND - Floor coverings–carpet and rugs - Regal Rugs Inc.

HIGHLAND - Fruits and vegetables ☆ - Marley Orchards Corp.

HIGHLAND - Liquors - Canandaigua Wine Co. Inc.

HIGHLAND - Pharmaceutical preparations - Highland Packaging Co.

HIGHLAND - Scarves, neckwear - Calzeat & Co. Ltd.

HIGHLAND - Stationery ☆ - Berkshire Stationery Inc.

HIGHLAND - Tape–adhesive - Minnesota Mining & Manufacturing Co.

HIGHLAND - Tobacco products ☆ - Lane Ltd.

HIGHLAND - Toilets–porcelain - Mansfield Plumbing Products, Inc.

HIGHLAND - Wallpaper ☆ - Wall-Pride Inc.

HIGHLAND - Wire - Highland Supply Corp.

HIGHLAND - Yarn ☆ - JCA, Inc.

HIGHLAND/ASTORIA/SEASIDE - Flowers, plants, and seeds - Jacklin Seed

HIGHLAND BEEFALO FARMS - Meat products–beef - Highland Beefalo Farms, Inc.

HIGHLAND BOOKS - Publisher's imprints - Berkley Publishing Corp.

HIGHLAND CREEK - Shoes - Rack Room Shoes, Inc.

HIGHLAND DANBY - Marble products - Carl Schilling Stoneworks

HIGHLAND DM - Antihistamine preparations - Highland Packaging Co.

HIGHLAND HARPS - Accordions - Castiglione Accordion

HIGHLAND HC - Cough medicines - Highland Packaging Co.

HIGHLAND HEATHER - Floor coverings–carpet and rugs ☆ - Karastan-Bigelow Inc.

HIGHLAND HEATHERS - Yarn ☆ - Caron International Inc.

HIGHLAND HICKORY - Lumber - Georgia-Pacific Corp.

HIGHLAND HILL - Apparel and accessories - Wal-Mart Stores Inc.

HIGHLAND HISTINE-D - Pharmaceutical preparations - Highland Packaging Co.

HIGHLAND HOUSE - Mattresses ☆ - Kingsdown, Inc.

HIGHLAND KNITS - Sweaters ☆ - Moriarty Hat and Sweater Co.

HIGHLAND MANOR - Wall covering sample books - Seabrook Wallcoverings, Inc.

HIGHLAND MANOR - Wines - Highland Manor Winery

HIGHLAND MEADOWS - Furniture - Pilliod Co.

HIGHLAND MIST - Beverages–alcohol - Barton Brands, Ltd.

HIGHLAND PARK - Apparel and accessories - Montgomery Ward & Co. Inc.

HIGHLAND PARK - Beverages–malt - European Beverage Co., Inc.

HIGHLAND PARK - Furniture - Pilliod Co.

HIGHLAND PARK - Trailers–travel - Fleetwood Enterprises, Inc.

HIGHLAND PIPER - Liquors - Paramount Distillers Inc.

HIGHLAND PLUSH - Floor coverings–carpet and rugs - Mohawk Carpet Corp.

HIGHLAND POINT - Floor coverings–carpet and rugs ☆ - Playfield International Inc.

HIGHLAND ROGUE - Beverages–alcohol - Alimar & Cie. Inc.

HIGHLAND ROMAN ARCH - Cabinets - Aristokraft, Inc.

HIGHLAND SPICE - Yarn ☆ - Caron International Inc.

HIGHLAND SUEDE - Floor coverings–carpet and rugs - Mohawk Carpet Corp.

HIGHLAND TEDDY - Toys - Russ Berrie and Co., Inc.

HIGHLAND TWEED II - Floor coverings–carpet and rugs ☆ - Playfield International Inc.

HIGHLANDER - Balls–golf - Highlander Co.

HIGHLANDER - Beverages–malt - Rainier Brewing Co.

HIGHLANDER - Bicycles - Bike Line Corp.

HIGHLANDER - Cabinets - Prestige Inc.

HIGHLANDER - Floor coverings–carpet and rugs ☆ - Kelly Group Inc.

HIGHLANDER - Floor coverings–carpet and rugs ☆ - Mannington Carpets, Inc.

HIGHLANDER - Floor coverings–carpet and rugs ☆ - Olympic Carpets Inc.

HIGHLANDER - Handkerchiefs ☆ - Carolina Manufacturing Inc.

HIGHLANDER - Ophthalmic goods - Fidelity Case Corp.

HIGHLANDER - Paper–gift wrap - Highland Supply Corp.

HIGHLANDER - Shelving units–metal - List Industries Inc. (Hallowell Div.)

HIGHLANDER AND LORD - Whiskey - Majestic Distilling Co.

HIGHLANDER BOWIE - Knives ☆ - United Cutlery Corp.

HIGHLANDER PLAID - Floor coverings–carpet and rugs ☆ - Downs Carpet Co. Inc.

HIGHLANDER SUPERSTICK - Golfing equipment - Highlander Co.

HIGHLANDS - Desk sets - Kentucky Woodcrafts Co. Inc.

HIGHLANDS - Floor coverings–carpet and rugs ☆ - Dorsett Carpet Mills Inc.

HIGHLANDS - Furniture ☆ - Virginia House Furniture Corp.

HIGHLANDS - Shingles–asphalt or tar - Certainteed Corp. (Roofing Products Group)

HIGHLANDS - Silverware - Reed and Barton Corp.

HIGHLANDS CALIFORNIA - Wines - Kautz Vineyards, Inc.

HIGHLANDS FLAIR - Blinds–venetian ☆ - Hunter Douglas, Inc.

HIGHLANDS ICED COFFEE - Coffee - Target Flavors, Inc.

HIGHLIGHT - Floor coverings - Congoleum Corp.

HIGHLIGHT - Floor coverings–carpet and rugs - Coronet Carpets Inc.

HIGHLIGHT - Grass seed ☆ - International Seeds, Inc.

HIGHLIGHT - Mats - Matworks

HIGHLIGHT - Rings–jewelry - Artcarved Inc.

HIGHLIGHT - Sporting goods ☆ - Allsop, Inc.

HIGHLIGHT - Window coverings ☆ - Courtaulds Performance Plus

HIGHLIGHT ADVANTAGE - Analyzers–amino acid - General Electric Co.

HIGHLIGHTER - Markers ☆ - American Coated Products Inc.

HIGHLIGHTER TAPE - Tape–adhesive - Lee Products Co.

HIGHLIGHTS - Apparel–women's - Olga Co.

HIGHLIGHTS - Barrettes - American Greetings Corp.

HIGHLIGHTS - Hair care products - Andre Fantasies Inc.

HIGHLIGHTS - Mirrors ☆ - Sunbeam-Oster Household Products

HIGHLIGHTS - Wallpaper - Capital Carousel Inc.

HIGHLIGHTS - Wallpaper ☆ - Horizon Wallcoverings

HIGHLIGHTS - Window shades - Kirsch Co.

HIGHLIGHTS COLLECTION - Paper–gift wrap - Sopp America Inc.

HIGHLINE - Toilets–enameled - Kohler Co.

HIGHLINER, THE - Footwear - West Coast Shoe Co.

HIGHLITE - Cleaning preparations ☆ - Oakite Products, Inc.

HIGHLOPHANE - Aluminum foil wrap - Highland Supply Corp.

HIGHMOUNT - Novelty items - M.B. Daniels & Co. Inc.

HIGHPOINT - Furniture - K.M.L. Industries

HIGHPOINT - Shampoos - Highpoint Chemicals Inc.

HIGHREACH LEARNING - Educational materials - Highreach Learning, Inc.

HIGHRISE - Floor coverings–carpet and rugs ☆ - Hollytex Carpet Mills Inc.

HIGHS - Ice cream - Kay's Ice Cream

HIGH'S - Milk - Highs of Baltimore Inc.

HIGHSTYLE - Mouldings, door frames, building adhesive, etc. - Focal Point Inc.

HIGHTONE - Recording label - HighTone Records

HIGHTREE - Tape recorders - Hightree Media Corp.

HIGHWALL - Containers - Perstorp Xytec Inc.

HIGHWAY - Apparel–women's - Louise Paris, Ltd.

HIGHWAY - Cigarettes - R.J. Reynolds Tobacco Co.

HIGHWAY - Fruits and vegetables ☆ - Safeway Stores Inc.

HIGHWAY - Gasoline - Highway Oil Inc.

HIGHWAY 2000 - Games ☆ - Gamescience

HIGHWAY BUILDERS - Toys–automobiles - Mattel, Inc.

HIGHWAY DUMP TRUCK - Toys - Fisher-Price, Inc.

HIGHWAY HAULER - Toys–automobiles - Mattel, Inc.

HIGHWAY HEAT - Toys–automobiles - Mattel, Inc.

HIGHWAY HELP - Emergency road signs - Intromark Inc.

HIGHWAY HELPER - Signs - Highway Helper, Inc.

HIGHWAY MASTER - Coatings - American Stone Mix

HIGHWAY PATROL - Toy rescue set ☆ - Intex Recreation Corp.

HIGHWAY PATROL - Tricycles ☆ - Peg Perego USA Inc.

HIGHWAY PATROLMAN - Revolvers - Smith & Wesson Corp.

HIGHWAYMAN - Radios–citizens' band - Royal Sound Co. Inc.

HIJAX - Toys–models - Estes Industries

HIJET - Motor vehicles - Daihatsu America Inc.

HIJIN - Cosmetics - Pacific Corp. of America

HIKARI - Hair care products - Hikari Products Inc.

HIKARI - Jewelry - Hikari Southsea Pearl Co. Inc.

HIKARI - Musical instruments - C. Bruno & Son Inc.

HIKARI FREEZE DRIED BLOOD WORMS - Pet products - Hikari Sales USA Inc.

HIKARI FREEZE DRIED BRINE SHRIMP - Pet products - Hikari Sales USA Inc.

HIKARI FREEZE DRIED TUBIFEX WORMS - Pet products - Hikari Sales USA Inc.

HIKARI FREEZE DRIED TUBILINA - Pet products - Hikari Sales USA Inc.

HIKARI GOLD KOI FOOD - Pet products - Hikari Sales USA Inc.

HIKARI STAPLE KOI FOOD - Pet products - Hikari Sales USA Inc.

☆ = Now out of production

HIKARI TROPICAL ALGAE WAFERS - Pet products - Hikari Sales USA Inc.

HIKARI TROPICAL BETTA BIO-GOLD - Pet products - Hikari Sales USA Inc.

HIKARI TROPICAL DISCUS RED ENHANCER - Pet products - Hikari Sales USA Inc.

HIKARI TROPICAL FANCY GUPPY PET - Pet products - Hikari Sales USA Inc.

HIKARI TROPICAL FOOD STICKS - Pet products - Hikari Sales USA Inc.

HIKARI TROPICAL MARINE -A- - Pet products - Hikari Sales USA Inc.

HIKARI TROPICAL MICRO PELLETS - Pet products - Hikari Sales USA Inc.

HIKARI TROPICAL SINKING CARNIVORE - Pet products - Hikari Sales USA Inc.

HIKARI TROPICAL SINKING WAFERS - Pet products - Hikari Sales USA Inc.

HIKARI TROPICAL TURTLE STICKS - Pet products - Hikari Sales USA Inc.

HIKE - Pharmaceutical preparations - Walker Pharmacal Co.

HIKE A BIKE - Bicycle parts and accessories - Hike A Bike

HIKE-A-POOSE - Infant product ☆ - Pearson Archery

HIKE BIKE - Bicycles - Columbia Manufacturing Inc.

HIKE 'N ROLL - Infant product - Lisco, Inc.

HIKE-TOO - Furniture - Tyke Corp.

HIKEMASTER - Cases–camera - SP Systems/Saratons

HIKER BUDDY - Apparel–athletic - Marcor, Inc.

HIKERS - Ophthalmic goods - Karlen Manufacturing, Inc.

HIKER'S DELIGHT - Snack foods - A.L. Schutzman Co., Inc.

HIKING STIK - Marine rigging ☆ - Windline Marine

HIKINI - Underwear and nightwear - Henson-Kickernick Inc.

HIL-AIRE II - Deodorizers - Hillyard Enterprises, Inc.

HIL-FOAM - Cleaning preparations–carpet and rug - Hillyard Enterprises, Inc.

HIL-GLO - Cleaning preparations - Hillyard Enterprises, Inc.

HIL-MIST - Mops - Hillyard Enterprises, Inc.

HIL-PHENE II - Disinfectants - Hillyard Enterprises, Inc.

HIL-SHEEN - Floor waxes - Hillyard Enterprises, Inc.

HIL-TEX - Sealing compounds - Hillyard Enterprises, Inc.

HIL-TREAT - Cleaning preparations - Hillyard Enterprises, Inc.

HILAIRE - Olive oil ☆ - Liberty Richter Inc.

HILAIRE EXTRA VIRGIN OLIVE OIL - Oils–edible - Europa Foods Ltd.

HILAND - Snack foods - Hiland Potato Chip Co.

HILAND OLD RECIPE - Ice cream - Highland Dairy

HILAND PARK - Trailers–travel ☆ - Coachmen Industries, Inc.

HILAND ROBERTS - Ice cream - Roberts Dairy Co.

HILANDER - Trailers–travel ☆ - Serro Travel Trailer Co. Inc.

HILARIOUS - Computer software - Optimum Resource, Inc.

HILARY - Flatware - Yamazaki Tableware Inc.

HILARY - Floor coverings ☆ - Tarkett, Inc.

HILARY GIFFORD - Scarves, neckwear - Hilyer Inc.

HILARY GOLD ACCENT - Flatware - Yamazaki Tableware Inc.

HILBERG - Food products - National Marketing Inc.

HILBUN - Chickens ☆ - Continental Grain Co.

HILCO - Cleaning preparations ☆ - Hillyard Enterprises, Inc.

HILCO TECHNOLOGIES - Computer software - Hilco Technologies, Inc.

HILCONA - Preserved foods–dried - Ernest L. Fischel Co.

HILDA - Hardware - Gordon Associates

HILDABE - Artists' materials - Riebe's Artist Materials Inc.

HILDEBRANDT SPINNERS - Fishing lures - Hildebrandt Corp.

HILDICK - Brandy - Laird and Co.

HILDRETH & HERRICKS - Apparel–men's - Wearwolf Group Ltd.

HILEX - Cleaning preparations - Hilex Co.

HILEX - Eyeglasses - Hudson Universal Ltd.

HILGAR - Floor coverings–carpet and rugs - Rugby Rugs Inc.

HILGER - Hearing-aid product - American Overseas Trading Corp.

HILIGHT - Windows–plastic - Roto Frank of America Inc.

HILINE - Computer software - TransCal Corp.

HILITE - Computer storage devices - Computer Products Center, Inc.

HILITE - Lamp bulbs–incandescent - Angelo Brothers Co.

HILITE 18 - Floor finish - Continental Chemical Corp.

HILITE-A-PLANT - Lighting equipment - Holmes Products, Corp.

HILITE U.S.A. - Computer peripheral equipment - Computer Products Center, Inc.

HILITER - Medical apparatus - INRAD, Inc.

HILL - Bags–duffel - Grant Hill

HILL - Garden equipment - Seymour Manufacturing Co.,Inc.

HILL & ARCHER - Apparel and accessories - Montgomery Ward & Co. Inc.

HILL & DALE - Eggs - C.H. James and Co.

HILL & HILL - Whiskey - Jim Beam Brands Co.

HILL AND WANG - Publisher's imprints - Farrar, Straus and Giroux Inc.

HILL-BILLY POLITICS - Watches - Mark A. Rasmussen

HILL BULLY - Toys - Tonka Corp.

HILL CAT - Bicycles - Murray, Inc.

HILL CHAMP - Bicycles - Columbia Manufacturing Inc.

HILL CLIMBER - Toys–automobiles - Mattel, Inc.

HILL COUNTRY - Meat products–poultry - Night Hawk Foods Inc. (Frozen Foods Div.)

HILL COUNTRY - Turkeys - Sunday House Foods Inc.

HILL COUNTRY - Wines - Guadalupe Valley Winery

HILL COUNTRY CLOTHIERS - Women's sportswear - Focus Apparel Group Inc.

HILL COUNTRY COOLER - Medical apparatus - Home Chiropractic

HILL COUNTRY SOAP COMPANY - Soap - Surrey, Inc.

HILL HIKER - Bicycles - Columbia Manufacturing Inc.

HILL HOBO - Bicycles - Columbia Manufacturing Inc.

HILL HOLDER - Automotive parts and accessories - Gjovik Enterprises

HILL HUMP - Agricultural machinery - Decker Manufacturing Co.

HILL MED - Medical apparatus - Hill-Med, Inc.

HILL RAZER - Bicycles - Raleigh USA Bicycle Co.

HILL-SHADE - Pharmaceutical preparations - Hill Dermaceuticals

HILL STEPHENS - Coffee - Chock Full O'Nuts Corp.

HILL, THE - Games - Stephan Daubney

HILL, THE - Shoes–athletic - Fila USA, Inc.

HILL TOP - Agricultural products - Highland Fruit Growers Inc.

HILLANDALE - Cigarettes - All Service, Inc.

HILLARY - Rings–jewelry - Artcarved Inc.

HILLARY - Sporting goods - Kellwood Co.

HILLARY HORSE - Dolls - A + A

HILLARY JEAN NAY - Dolls - Meritus Industries, Inc.

HILLARY PAIGE - Hair care products - Parisian, Inc.

HILLARY SLIDE BRACELET - Jewelry - Towne Silversmith, Inc.

HILLBERG - Food products ☆ - Pierre Frozen Foods Inc.

HILLBILLY - Baked goods - Interstate Brands Corp.

HILLBILLY - Bicycles - Columbia Manufacturing Inc.

HILLBILLY - Jeans–men's - Master Industries Corp.

HILLBILLY HICKS - Playing cards - Universal Manufacturing Co., Inc.

HILLBROOK - Floor coverings ☆ - Congoleum Corp.

HILLCO - Ice cream - H.G. Hill Stores Inc.

HILLCRAFT - Jewelry - Hillcraft Jewelry Co. Inc.

HILLCREST - Floor coverings - Tarkett, Inc.

HILLCREST - Floor coverings–carpet and rugs - Philadelphia Carpets

HILLCREST - Floor coverings–carpet and rugs ☆ - Daltonian Carpet & Cushion Inc.

HILLCREST - Furniture ☆ - Tell City Chair Co.

HILLCREST - Linen - Hillcrest International, Inc.

HILLCREST - Mobile homes - Skyline Corp.

HILLCREST - Pipes–tobacco - Dr. Grabow Pre-Smoked Pipes Inc.

HILLCREST - Trailers–travel ☆ - Kit Manufacturing Co.

HILLCREST - Vegetables–frozen - Chase Farms Inc.

HILLCREST - Water–bottled or canned - Hillcrest Spring Water Inc.

HILLCREST - Wines - Hillcrest Vineyard

HILLCREST ORCHARDS - Cider - Hillcrest Orchards Inc.

HILLCREST VINEYARD - Wines - Hillcrest Vineyard

HILLE - Bakery products - Holland-American Importing Co. Inc.

HILLENDALE - Furniture - Universal Flooring

HILLHOLDER - Automotive parts and accessories - Subaru of America, Inc.

HILLMAN - Nuts and bolts - SDI Partners I, L.P.

HILLMAN'S D COMPOUND - Pharmaceutical preparations - Hillman Pharmaceutical Co.

HILLMASTER - Combines–agricultural - Rahco Environmental Services

HILLQUIST - Electronic equipment - Hillquist Inc.

HILL'S - Pet products - Geo. W. Hill and Co., Inc.

HILL'S - Pet products - Hill's Pet Nutrition Inc.

HILLS AND VALLEYS - Colognes - Pfizer Inc.

HILLS BROTHERS - Coffee - Nestle Beverage Co.

HILLS OF WAYNE - Food products - Hopkins of Sodus Inc.

HILLS OF WESTCHESTER - Candy - Hills of Westchester Inc.

HILLSBOROR - Shoes ☆ - Allen-Edmonds Shoe Corp.

HILLSBOROUGH - Furniture - Universal Flooring

HILLSDALE - Benches–metal - Artesian Industries

HILLSDALE - Fruits and vegetables - Valley View Packing Co., Inc.

HILLSDALE - Luggage - Samsonite Corp.

HILLSDALE - Paper ☆ - Fox River Paper Co.

HILLSHIRE FARM - Meat products–beef - Hillshire Farm Co.

HILLSHIRE FARM CRACKER TOPPERS - Meat products - Saramar Corp.

HILLSHIRE FARMS LIGHT ENCOUNTER - Frankfurters - Hillshire Farm Co.

HILLSHIRE GOLDEN HERITAGE - Hams - Sara Lee Corp.

HILLSHIRE LITE - Sausages - Hillshire Farm Co.

HILLSIDE - Coffee - Hillside Coffee Inc.
HILLSIDE - Floor coverings–carpet and rugs ☆ - Gulistan Carpet Inc.
HILLSIDE - Plywood - Georgia-Pacific Corp.
HILLSIDE - Recording label ☆ - Nationwide Sound Distributors
HILLSIDE HOUSE - Statuary ☆ - Hillside House of Originals
HILLSIDE ORIGINALS - Statuary ☆ - Hillside House of Originals
HILLSIDE SELECT - Wines - Shafer Vineyards Inc.
HILLSMITH ESTATES - Wines - Liquest International Corp.
HILLTAK - Recording label - Atlantic Records
HILLTOP - Fabrics - Greenwood Mills Inc.
HILLTOP - Food products ☆ - Gold Kist Inc.
HILLTOP - Fruits–frozen - Haines City Citrus Growers Association
HILLTOP - Mail boxes - Leigh
HILLTOP - Recording label ☆ - Nationwide Sound Distributors
HILLTOP GARDENS - Cosmetics - Hilltop Gardens
HILLTOP GOLD - Fruits–frozen - Haines City Citrus Growers Association
HILLTOP HEARTH - Cookies - JP Foodservice, Inc.
HILLTOP HOUSE - House furnishings - Dan River Inc.
HILLTOP ORCHARD - Fruits and vegetables - Mike Norinsberg Manufacturing Inc.
HILLTOP PLUS - Fabrics - Greenwood Mills Inc.
HILLTOPPER - Motor vehicles - Hilltop RV & Sports Center
HILLVIEW - Recording label - Heath & Associates
HILLWARE - Bowls - Hillside Metal Ware Co.
HILLWARE - Springform cake pans - Cook Things
HILLWOOD - Fasteners–hook and eye - Hillwood Manufacturing Co.
HILLWOOD - Synthesizers–musical instrument ☆ - St. Louis Music Supply Co.
HILLY - Toys–stuffed ☆ - Gund, Inc.
HILLYARD - Disinfectants - Hillyard Enterprises, Inc.
HILMAR - Cheese - R.W. Zant Co.
HILO - Boats–motor ☆ - Larson Boat Div.
HILO - Hardware ☆ - Frantz Manufacturing Co.
HILO - Mops - Perfex Corp.
HILO - Pet products - Roccorp, Inc.
HILO - Potato chips - Atebara Potato Chips Co.
HILO - Sporting goods - Tel-O-Post Co.
HILO - Thread - Threads USA Div.
HILO - Ukuleles - Kaman Music Corp.
HILO DIP - Pet products - Roccorp, Inc.
HILO HATTIE - Preserved foods–prepackaged - Pomare, Ltd.
HILOX - Skin care products - Takara Belmont USA, Inc.
HILSHIRE FARM - Food products - Hillshire Farm Co.
HILTARY - Cutlery - Beads & More
HILTI - Tools - Hilti Inc.
HILTON - Brushes–paint ☆ - PPG Industries, Inc.
HILTON - Crocheted and knitted items - Hilton Sportswear Inc.
HILTON - Hotels and motels - Hilton Hotels Corp.
HILTON - Pipes–tobacco - Bradberry Briar Pipe Corp.
HILTON - Sewing machines–household - VWS Inc.
HILTON - Trailers–travel ☆ - Hop-Cap Inc.
HILTON CORPORATE CASUALS - Apparel and accessories - K2 Inc.
HILTON GARDEN INNS - Hotels and motels - Hilton Hotels Corp.
HILTON HEAD - Apparel and accessories ☆ - Umbro USA
HILTON HEAD GOLF CLUB - Apparel and accessories - Nash Stores, Inc.
HILTON SUITES - Hotels and motels - Hilton Hotels Corp.
HILTON WIDE-ANGLE 180 - Audio equipment - Hilton Family Trust
HILTON'S - Oysters–canned or cured ☆ - Coast Seafoods Co.
HILTON'S WILLAPOINT - Oysters–canned or cured - Coast Seafoods Co.
HILUX - Medical uniforms - First Medical Infection Control Associates, Inc.
HIM II - Apparel–men's ☆ - Gem-Dandy, Inc.
HIMALAYA - Computers - Tandem Computers Inc.
HIMALAYA - Playing cards - Charles A. Wilkins
HIMALAYA - Shoes - Carolina Shoe Co.
HIMALAYAN - Sporting goods - Pearson Archery
HIMALAYAN - Watches - Questech International, Inc.
HIMALAYAN INSTITUTE - Publisher's imprints - Himalayan Publishers
HIMALAYAN PUBLISHERS - Publisher's imprints - Himalayan Publishers
HIMALAYAS, THE - Apparel and accessories - Donald Matheheson
HIMCO - Aluminum products - Leed Himmel Industries Inc.
HIMED - Dental compounds - Hitemco Medical Applications, Inc.
HIMMEL - Motors - American Contex Corp.
HIMS - Computers - Hims Inc.
HIMSELF THE ELF - Greeting cards - American Greetings Corp.
HI'N DRI - Dehumidifiers - Viking Manufacturing Co. Inc.
HINANO - Beverages–malt ☆ - Hawaiian Water Partners
HINCKLEY - Boats - The Hinckley Co.

HINCKLEY & SCHMITT - Water–bottled or canned - Hinckley & Schmitt (Bottled Water Group)
HINCKLEY HORSESHOE - Life preservers - The Hinckley Co.
HIND - Apparel–athletic - Hind, Inc.
HIND PERFORMANCE - Apparel–athletic - Hind, Inc.
HINDER - Veterinary pharmaceutical preparations - Pace International Corp.
HINDES - Pet products - Berolina Imports
HINDLEY - Hardware - Hindley Manufacturing Co. Inc.
HINDOSTONE - Nail care products - Marianna Imports, Inc.
HINDQUARTERS - Jeans–men's - Hindquarters Inc.
HINDS HONEY - Skin care products - Sterling Winthrop Inc.
HINDSIGHT - Bicycle parts and accessories - Schwinn Cycling & Fitness Inc.
HINDSIGHT - Recording label - Welk Music Group
HINDSIGHT - Underwear and nightwear ☆ - Lovable Co.
HINDUSHEEN - Hair care products - Eden Beauty Products
HINDUSTAN - Floor coverings ☆ - Teak International
HINE - Brandy - United Distillers of North America
HINE - Wines - European Beverage Co., Inc.
HINES - Hardware - New England Lock and Hardware Co.
HINES CO., THE - Recording label - J. Hines Co., Inc.
HINES CO. WHERE THE SONG BEGAN, THE - Recording label - J. Hines Co., Inc.
HINES LEAF DESIGN - Flowers, plants, and seeds - Weyerhaeuser Co.
HINEY - Wines - River Edge Winery
HINEY WINE - Novelty items - Dorsey & Donnelly Enterprises
HINGA SHTAK - Vitamins and nutritional supplements - Planetary Formulas
HINGE-FLEX - Circuit boards - Sheldahl, Inc.
HINGE-IT - Hinges - Hinge-It Corp.
HINGETOP - Bins - Tucker Housewares Inc.
HINGHAM - Cabinets - American Woodmark Corp.
HINJBOARD - Packaging–paper - Protostar Packaging Inc.
HINKEL - Electrical equipment - Arizona Institute of Electrolysis
HINKLE BROTHERS - Apparel and accessories - Hinkle Brothers, Inc.
HINKLE EGGS EASY - Hobby kits ☆ - Hinkle Easter Products
HINKLE PAINT BY NUMBER - Hobby kits ☆ - Hinkle Easter Products
HINKLE SCRAMBLIN EGGS - Hobby kits ☆ - Hinkle Easter Products
HINKLE'S - Hobby kits ☆ - Hinkle Easter Products
HINKLE'S DONUTS - Doughnuts - Hinkle's Donuts of Toledo Inc.
HINKLEY AFTER HOURS - Lighting fixtures - Hinkley Lighting, Inc.
HINKLEY'S SOUTHWEST - Lighting equipment - Light Inc.
HINKY-FOODS - Food products - Hinky Dinky Stores
HINMAN VINEYARDS - Wines - Briggs Hill Investments, Inc.
HINMAN VINEYARDS - Wines - Hinman Vineyards
HINODE - Rice - Rice Growers of California
HINODE CALIFORNIA BROWN - Rice - Rice Growers of California
HINODE CALIFORNIA WHITE - Rice - Rice Growers of California
HINODE FIESTA RECIPE - Rice - Rice Growers of California
HINODE SOUTHERN RECIPE - Rice - Rice Growers of California
HINOICHI - Food products - House Foods America Corp.
HINOKI - Hair care products - Hayashi for Hair Inc.
HINOMOTO - Food products - Hinomoto Corp.
HINOTE - Computers–personal - Digital Equipment Corp.
HINSDALE - Shoes - Allen-Edmonds Shoe Corp.
HINSDILLS - Office supplies ☆ - Boorum & Pease Co.
HINSON - Lighting fixtures - Dorothy Horne Hinson Inc.
HINSON - Wallpaper - Hinson & Co.
HINSON ANTHOLOGY - Wallpaper - Hinson & Co.
HINSON STRIPES - Fabrics - Hinson & Co.
HINT! - Computer software - Edusoft, LC
HINT - Electronic equipment - Hint Corp.
HINT & HUNT - Computer software - SRA/McGraw-Hill (Div. of The McGraw-Hill Companies)
HINT CARDS - Greeting cards - Wry Idea Co.
HINT OF MINT - Cigarettes - Nat Sherman, Inc.
HINT OF MUSK - Health care products - C.B. Fleet Co. Inc.
HINT OF SPRING - Deodorizers ☆ - Whink Products Co.
HINZERLING - Wines - Wallfam Inc.
HIO-STAR - Vegetables–canned - Heskett Foods
HIOXIDE - Hair care products - Highpoint Chemicals Inc.
HIP - Computer storage devices–optical - Center for Image Processing in Education, Inc.
HIP - Greeting cards ☆ - Moderne Card Co. Inc.
H.I.P. - Pharmaceutical preparations ☆ - Hyrex Pharmaceuticals
HIP 5 - Floor coverings–tile - Mannington Mills, Inc.
HIP BOP - Recording label - Silva Screen Records America, Inc.
HIP CADDIE - Golfing equipment - Daniel T. Melillo

HIP-EZE - Underwear and nightwear - Bestform Foundations, Inc.
HIP FIVE - Floor coverings–tile - Mannington Mills, Inc.
HIP GARD - Sporting goods - Fem Gard Inc.
HIP-GRIP - Firearms, accessories, and parts - Barami Corp.
HIP GRIP - Underwear and nightwear ☆ - B.V.D. Co. Inc.
HIP HAIR WEAR - Hobby kits - Lisa Frank, Inc.
HIP HIDER - Bathing suits - Patricia Byrnes Kane
HIP HOP - Bicycles ☆ - Huffy Corp.
HIP HOP - Socks - HipHop Hosiery & Design
HIP-HOP COLLEGE - Apparel and accessories - Jordan Enterprises, Inc.
HIP HOP EXPRESSIONS - Greeting cards - Linda Serina Phoenix
HIP HOP POPCORN - Popcorn - James A. Lindsay
HIP-HUGGER - Girdles ☆ - Kellogg Industries Inc.
HIP HUGGER - Laundry tubs–plastic - Rubbermaid Inc.
HIP HUGGERS - Bags - Kane Products, Inc.
HIP HUGGERS - Games - Smethport Specialty Co.
HIP KEY, THE - Magazines - Younique Youth
HIP-LETS - Panty hose ☆ - West Point-Pepperell Inc.
HIP MASTER - Building materials - Mid-America Building Products Corp.
HIP MATE - Apparel–women's - Wacoal America Inc.
HIP MEISTER - Apparel–women's - Lovable Co.
HIP POCKET - Audio equipment - Technidyne
HIP POCKET - Cosmetics - Burmax Co. Inc.
HIP POCKET GUIDE - Publisher's imprints ☆ - And/Or Press
HIP TUNES - Radios - Sun Coast Merchandise Corp.
HIPAD - Electronic equipment - Houston Instrument
HIPBONE - Toys - Tonka Corp.
HIPCO - Flashlights - Hipwell Manufacturing Co.
HIPER - Computer software - Ford Investor Services, Inc.
HIPERLOAD FOR VSAM - Computer software - Softworks Inc.
HIPERSTATION - Computer software - Compuware Corp.
HIPERTHANE - Cables - Peterson Systems International, Inc.
HIPFIX - Medical apparatus - Med-Tec, Inc.
HIPHUGGER - Braces–orthopedic - Chase Ergonomics Inc.
HIPIRIN - Pharmaceutical preparations ☆ - Blaine Co. Inc.
HIPKIDS - Apparel and accessories - Diane Ruth Ramsey
HIPLOT - Electronic equipment ☆ - Houston Instrument
HIPLOT - Plotters–computer - Summagraphics Corp.
HIPMOLD - Underwear and nightwear - Youthcraft-Charmfit
HIPOLE - Garden equipment - Pini Lipski & Associates
HIPOLITE - Marshmallows ☆ - Little Crow Foods
HIPOTEST - Vitamins and nutritional supplements - Marlop Pharmaceuticals Inc.
HIPOVITES - Vitamins and nutritional supplements ☆ - Vita-Fore Products Co.
HIPOXY-2000 - Epoxy - Powell Electrical Manufacturing Co.
HIPPIE - Toys–electronic - Jack Gasnick, The Virtuous Locksmith
HIPPIE WIPE - Paper–toweling - Cleveland Cotton Products Co.
HIPPITY-HOP-POP - Chocolate candy - Superior Fruit & Confections
HIPPITY HOPS - Figurines - Henri Studio, Inc.
HIPPO - Rice - Broussard Rice Mill Inc.
HIPPO BLOWER - Tools ☆ - Shop Vac Corp.
HIPPO-CLIP - Electronic equipment - Mueller Electric Co.
HIPPO HAMPER - Housewares stores - With Design in Mind
HIPPO HIDE - Gloves - Granet Inc.
HIPPO HIDE - Sporting goods - Rip Flag
HIPPO HINGE - Plugs–electric - General Electric Co.
HIPPO HYDRAULIC COMPACTOR - Machine tools - JB Development, Inc.
HIPPO SINK - Toys - Tyco Toys
HIPPO-VAC - Vacuum cleaners and accessories - Shop Vac Corp.
HIPPO WHEEL - Toys - Fisher-Price, Inc.
HIPPOCRAS - Beverages ☆ - Chase Collection, Inc.
HIPPOPOTAMYTH - Figurines - Marjorie Sarnat & Associates, Inc.
HIPPOSCISSIUS - Paper cutters - Acme United Corp.
HIPREX - Pharmaceutical preparations - Marion Merrell Dow
HIPROMIN - Fish food - Longlife Pet Products
HIPSHOT - Musical instrument accessories - Hipshot Music Products
HIPSHOT - Vacuum cleaners and accessories–commercial - Kent Co.
HIPSLENDA - Underwear and nightwear - Youthcraft-Charmfit
HIPSTER - Apparel–women's - Wacoal America Inc.
HIPSTER - Bicycles - Columbia Manufacturing Inc.
HIPSTER - Cosmetics ☆ - Spilo/Mehaz Worldwide
HIPSTER - Handbags - Wilson Designers
HIPSTER - Leather goods - St. Thomas Inc.
HIPSTICK - Apparel–women's - Wacoal America Inc.
HIPTEX - Fabrics - Evin Industries USA Ltd.
HIRAM WALKER - Beverages–alcohol - Hiram Walker & Sons, Inc.

HIRED HAND - Jacks–hydraulic - Bloomfield Manufacturing Co.
HIRERIGHT - Computer software - Dynanet, Inc.
HIRES - Beverages–carbonated - Dr. Pepper/Seven Up, Inc.
HIRES - Root beer–bottled or canned - Schweppes USA Ltd.
HIRIDER - Health care products - Falcon Rehabilitation Products Inc.
HIRO LIFT - Escalators - Hiro Lift USA Inc.
HIRO TAKA - Toys - Tonka Corp.
HIROKO - Hair clippers–veterinary - Major International Inc.
HIROKO MOTO - Apparel and accessories - Galix Shops Inc.
HIROTA - Banners - Darwell Import Co. Inc.
HIRSBRUNNER - Musical instruments - Custom Music Co.
HIRSCH - Jewelry - Hirsch USA Inc.
HIRSCH WEIS - Apparel–men's - Authentic Fitness Corp.
HIRSCHCO - Toys–electronic - Hirsch Co.
HIRSCHL & BENDHEIM - Pipes ☆ - Missouri Meerschaum Co.
HIRSCHMANN - Antennas - Walter Odemer Co. Inc.
HIRSCHMANN - Audio equipment - Richard Hirschmann of America Inc.
HIRSH SHELF HELP - Shelving units–metal - Hirsh Co.
HIRSHLINE - Shelving units–metal ☆ - Hirsh Co.
HIRT - Machinery - SRV, Inc.
HIRULOG - Pharmaceutical preparations - Biogen Inc.
H.I.S. - Apparel–athletic - H.I.S. Sportswear
H.I.S. - Apparel–men's - Chic by H.I.S. Inc.
H.I.S. - Footwear–men's - Chic by H.I.S. Licensing Corp.
HIS & HER - Hair care products - U.S. Custom Hair Works
HIS AND HER CUTICLE - Wigs - His & Her Hair Goods Co.
HIS AND HERS - Cabinets - Vinotemp International
HIS DRYNESS - Diapers–disposable - Associated Hygienic Products
HIS EXCELLENCY - Watches - Bulova Corp.
H.I.S. FOR MEN - Apparel and accessories - H.I.S. Sportswear
HIS HIGHNESS - Watches - Bulova Corp.
HIS MAJESTY - Dinnerware–glass ☆ - Johnson Brothers, USA, Inc.
HIS MATES' SELECTIONS - Greeting cards ☆ - Royal Imprints Corp.
HIS N HERS - Fishing nets - Four Rivers Tackle Co.
HIS NIBS - Fabrics - Dan River Inc.
HISAFE - Safes - United Video Network, Inc.
HISAKO - Hair clippers–veterinary - Major International Inc.
HISAR - Radar systems and equipment - Hughes Aircraft Co.
HIS.BIND - Chemical preparations - Novagen, Inc.
HISCATABS - Pharmaceutical preparations ☆ - Ulmer Pharmacal Co.
HISERPIA - Tranquilizers ☆ - JMI-Canton Pharmaceuticals
HISITE - Dental compounds - Ultradent Products, Inc.
HISMANAL - Antihistamine - Janssen Pharmaceutica Inc.
HISO - Yarn - Dixie Yarns, Inc.
HISPANA - Giftware ☆ - Gorham Inc.
HISPANIA - Giftware - Zaphir USA Distribution Corp.
HISPANO - Guitars - European Crafts/USA
HISPRIL SPANSULE - Antihistamine preparations - Smithkline Beecham Corp.
HISSS 'N HERS - Toys–stuffed - Dakin Inc.
HIST-A-CORT-E - Antihistamine preparations ☆ - Miles Inc.
HIST-DRIST MLT - Pharmaceutical preparations - Global Pharmaceutical Corp.
HIST-FIVE - Pharmaceutical preparations ☆ - Cumberland Pharmacal Co. Inc.
HISTA-CALMA - Pharmaceutical preparations ☆ - Rexall Nutritional Products Inc.
HISTA-CLOPANE - Pharmaceutical preparations ☆ - Eli Lilly and Co.
HISTA-COMPOUND NO. 5 - Pharmaceutical preparations ☆ - Vortech Pharmaceuticals
HISTA-DERFULE - Analgesics ☆ - Forest Pharmaceuticals Inc.
HISTA-PHEN - Pharmaceutical preparations ☆ - Recsei Laboratories
HISTA TABS - Health care products - Leiner Health Products Inc.
HISTA-TROCHES - Pharmaceutical preparations ☆ - Barre-National, Inc.
HISTA-VADRIN - Pharmaceutical preparations - Schering-Plough Healthcare Products
HISTA-VENT - Pharmaceutical preparations - KV Pharmaceutical Co.
HISTA-ZINC - Vitamins and nutritional supplements ☆ - Integrated Health, Inc.
HISTABID - Pharmaceutical preparations - Glaxo Wellcome Inc.
HISTABS - Pharmaceutical preparations ☆ - U.S. Ethicals Inc.
HISTACON - Pharmaceutical preparations - Marsh-Emory Laboratories
HISTADERM - Pharmaceutical preparations ☆ - U.S. Ethicals Inc.
HISTADEX - Pharmaceutical preparations - Harvey Laboratories Inc.
HISTADYL - Antihistamine preparations - Eli Lilly and Co.
HISTAFED - Prescription drug - Iodent Co.
HIS.TAG - Chemical preparations - Novagen, Inc.
HISTAGESIC - Pharmaceutical preparations - JMI-Canton Pharmaceuticals
HISTAJECT - Pharmaceutical preparations ☆ - Merz Inc.
HISTALET - Pharmaceutical preparations - Solvay Pharmaceuticals Inc.

☆ = Now out of production

HISTALOG - Pharmaceutical preparations ☆ - Eli Lilly and Co.
HISTAMIC - Pharmaceutical preparations - Lexis Laboratories Inc.
HISTAPHEN C & D - Cough medicines ☆ - Chase Laboratories Inc.
HISTAPLEX - Pharmaceutical preparations ☆ - Global Pharmaceutical Corp.
HISTAPLEX II - Antihistamine preparations - Global Pharmaceutical Corp.
HISTAPRIN - Cold remedies - Pharmex Inc.
HISTAREST - Vitamins and nutritional supplements - Neutraceutical Research Labs, Inc.
HISTASPAN - Pharmaceutical preparations ☆ - Rhone-Poulenc Rorer Pharmaceuticals Inc.
HISTATAB PLUS - Pharmaceutical preparations - Century Pharmaceuticals Inc.
HISTATAPP - Pharmaceutical preparations ☆ - Upsher-Smith Laboratories, Inc.
HISTCODIN - Pharmaceutical preparations - C.O. Truxton Inc.
HISTEC - Pharmaceutical preparations ☆ - C.S. Ruckstuhl Co. Inc.
HISTENOL-FORTE - Analgesics - Zee Medical Inc.
HISTERONE - Pharmaceutical preparations - Roberts/Hauck Pharmaceuticals Inc.
HISTI LAIN - Vitamins and nutritional supplements - Natural Organics, Inc.
HISTI VITE - Vitamins and nutritional supplements - Natural Organics, Inc.
HISTINEX - Cold remedies - KV Pharmaceutical Co.
HISTIVITE-D - Cough medicines ☆ - Vitarine Pharmaceuticals Inc.
HISTO-CLEAR - Chemical preparations - National Diagnostics
HISTOGRADE - Containers–plastic - Trend Scientific, Inc.
HISTOMAP - Maps - Rand McNally & Co.
HISTOPLASMIN - Pharmaceutical preparations - Parke-Davis
HISTOR-D - Pharmaceutical preparations - Roberts/Hauck Pharmaceuticals Inc.
HISTORAL - Pharmaceutical preparations - I.C.P. Pharmaceuticals
HISTOREST - Pharmaceutical preparations ☆ - JMI-Canton Pharmaceuticals
HISTORIC AMERICA - Calendars - National Trust for Historic Preservation in the United States
HISTORIC AMERICA - Dinnerware–glass ☆ - Johnson Brothers, USA, Inc.
HISTORIC AMERICA - Wallpaper - Sterling Prints
HISTORIC CHARLESTON - Giftware - Virginia Metalcrafters Inc.
HISTORIC CHARLESTON - Towels - Stevens Linen Associates Inc.
HISTORIC CHARLESTON PAPERS - Wallpaper - Scalamandre Silks Inc.
HISTORIC CHARM - Furniture - Bassett Furniture Industries, Inc.
HISTORIC COLLECTION - Wood products - Masonite Corp.
HISTORIC COLORS OF PHILADELPHIA - Paints - Finnaren & Haley Inc.
HISTORIC DEERFIELD MUSEUM - Wallpaper - Greeff Fabrics Inc.
HISTORIC GARDEN - Flowers, plants, and seeds - D. Landreth Seed Co.
HISTORIC HEART PINE - Wood products - Mountain Lumber Co., Inc.
HISTORIC HOMES OF AMERICA - Wallpaper - Capital Carousel Inc.
HISTORIC HOMES OF AMERICA - Wallpaper - Richard E. Thibaut, Inc.
HISTORIC LANDSCAPE - Flowers, plants, and seeds - D. Landreth Seed Co.
HISTORIC LIGHTING - Lighting fixtures - Fredrick Ramond Inc.
HISTORIC NATHCEZ REPRODUCTIONS - Dinnerware - Eastern Shore Trading Co.
HISTORIC NEWPORT - Brass products - Virginia Metalcrafters Inc.
HISTORIC NEWPORT RHODE ISLAND - Jams and jellies - Preservation Society of Newport County
HISTORIC TIMEKEEPERS - Cleaning preparations–household - Historic Timekeepers, Inc.
HISTORICA - Novelty items - Davis Hartwell
HISTORICAL - Recording label - Biograph Records Inc.
HISTORICAL ARTS AND CASTING - Art councils - Historical Arts & Casting, Inc.
HISTORICAL COLLECTION - Siding - Associated Materials, Inc.
HISTORICAL JAMES RIVER PLANTATION - Furniture - Hickory Chair Co.
HISTORICAL LOUVER - Ventilation equipment - Ida A. Lavoie
HISTORICAL RESEARCH CENTER, THE - Paper products - Historical Research Center, Inc.
HISTORIOGRAPH - Computer software - Commsoft
HISTORIOGRAPH 2 - Computer software - Commsoft
HISTORY - Recording label - AudioLoft Recording Studios
HISTORY COLLECTION - Computer software - SourceView Software International
HISTORY HAPPENS - Recording label - Arthur B. Rouse
HISTORY IN WOOD - Toys–airplanes - History In Wood Inc.
HISTORY, IT BECOMES YOU. - Jewelry - Michael Monahan
HISTORY OF FLIGHT - Toys - Natural Science Industries, Ltd.
HISTORY OF TIME - Toys - Natural Science Industries, Ltd.
HISTORY SAFARI - Educational materials - Educational Insights, Inc.
HISTORYBASE - Computer software - Fluor Corp.
HISTOSAL - Health care products - Ferndale Laboratories, Inc.
HISTREY - Pharmaceutical preparations ☆ - JMI-Canton Pharmaceuticals

HISTUSSINOL - Pharmaceutical preparations ☆ - Bock Pharmacal Co.
HISTYLE - Bulletin boards–cork - Davson Inc.
H.I.T. - Attache cases ☆ - H.C. Meyers Co.
HIT - Biscuits - Bahlsen Inc.
HIT - Clocks - Heritage International
HIT - Frames–eyeglass - Hoya Corp. USA
H.I.T. - Golfing equipment - King Par Corp.
HIT 17 - Playing cards - Kenneth Touroo
HIT BATH RENEWAL - Cleaning preparations–household - Miavana Wholesale Co.
HIT EM HARD - Apparel and accessories - Commander Garment Co.
HIT HARD - Apparel–athletic - Saul Y. Avelar
HIT-KING - Pizzas–frozen - Pete Rose Enterprises, Inc.
HIT LABEL - Apparel–children's ☆ - Umbro USA
HIT ME AGAIN - Balls–golf - D.H. Hutson Enterprises, Inc.
HIT N MISS - Games ☆ - Milton Bradley Co.
HIT 'N RUN - Game machines - Bally Gaming International, Inc.
HIT PARADE - Apparel–men's - St. Tropez Ltd.
HIT PARADE - Harmonicas - William Kratt Co.
HIT THE BALL ALICE - Books–comic - Dane H. Collins
HIT THE SPOT - Video production - Peter Pan Industries
HIT THE TRAIL - Beverages–malt - Long Trail Brewing Co.
HITACHI - Audio equipment - Hitachi Home Electronics America Inc.
HITACHI - Massage tool - Jackson Enterprises Inc.
HITCH ALIGN - Automotive parts and accessories - Gary Howard
HITCH HAND - Automotive parts and accessories - Name of Corp.: Happy Hollow, Inc.
HITCH-HIKER - Bicycles - Graber Products, Inc.
HITCH-HIKER - Infant product - Nurturtech
HITCH HIKER - Toys - Tonka Corp.
HITCH HIKER GLIDER - Toys–models ☆ - Estes Industries
HITCH-LOCK - Locks for tow-behind trailers - Flip-Lock II, Inc.
HITCH-N-SWEEP - Garden equipment - Parker Sweeper Co.
HITCH-QUICK - Sporting goods - Schwinn Cycling & Fitness Inc.
HITCH-UPS - Toys - Strombecker Corp.
HITCH WITCH - Hitches–trailer - C.M. Support, Inc.
HITCH WORLD - Car and truck hitches - Amerco Inc.
HITCHBALL - Hitches–trailer - Big Boy Products Inc.
HITCHCOCK - Beverages - Tropicana Products, Inc.
HITCHCOCK - Furniture - Hitchcock Chair Co. Inc.
HITCHHIKER - Bicycle parts and accessories - Tri Industries, Inc.
HITCHHIKER - Envelopes - Marvin Envelope & Paper Co.
HITCHHIKER 5TH WHEEL - Trailers–travel - Nu-Wa Industries Inc.
HITCHHIKER II - Trailers–travel - Custom Campers Inc.
HITCHHIKERS - Fishing accessories - Tru Turn, Inc.
HITCHHIKER'S GUIDE TO THE GALAXY, THE - Computer software - Activision, Inc.
HITCHIKERS - Shoes - Clinic Shoe Co.
HITCHING POST - Hardware - Projectapix-II
HITCHKIT - Hitches–trailer - Big Boy Products Inc.
HITCHLIFT - Wheelchairs - AM Scooters
HITCO - Tools–garden - Hardware & Industrial Tool Co., Inc.
HITE-A-MATIC - Musical instrument accessories - GRK Manufacturing
HITE-RITE - Springs–mechanical - Breeze & Angell
HITEC - Polyethylene sheets - Compression Polymers Group
HITECH - Batteries - East Penn Manufacturing Co., Inc.
HITECH - Communications equipment - Hitech Corp.
HITECH BLENDS - Wallcoverings - Cork Products Co. Inc.
HITECSOFT - Computer software ☆ - Integrated Medical System
HITEMP - Insulating materials - Hitemp Insulation Products, Inc.
HITEMP - Smokeless powder - Hercules Inc.
HITIE - Anchors - Securtech Co.
HITLER'S WAR - Games - Avalon Hill Game Co.
HITLINE - Recording label - Victori Promotions & Marketing Inc.
HITO-AJI - Rice - California Pacific Rice Milling, Ltd.
HITOP - Vinyl laminated fabrics - Highland Industries Inc.
HITOR-II - Epoxy - Cambridge Tile Manufacturing Co.
HITRAID - Computer storage devices - Hitachi America, Ltd.
HITRAN - Transformers–electric - Hitran Corp.
HITRATE - Fuel additives - Klotz Special Formula Products, Inc.
H.I.T.S. - Computer software - Datamaxx Applied Technologies, Inc.
HITS FOR YOUR HEART - Greeting cards - Bare Wall Productions Inc.
HITSCHLER - Confections ☆ - C. & J. Willenborg Inc.
HITSVILLE - Recording label - Motown Record Co. L.P.
HITTERS CLUB - T-shirts–men's - National Football League Properties, Inc.
HITTIN HARD - Recording label - Black Diamond Records, Inc.

☆ = Now out of production

HITTING TOWEL - Toys - Uniquity

HITWARE - Computer software ☆ - Hal Leonard Corp.

HIVAL - Illuminated signs - Cummings Inc.

H.I.V.E. - Games ☆ - Mayfair Games, Inc.

HIVE, THE - Apparel and accessories - Steve Varasteh

HIVID - Video equipment - NEC Technologies, Inc.

HIVIZ - Apparel and accessories - Conspicuity Inc.

HIWAY EXPRESS - Furniture - Wise Co., Inc.

HIWAY-WIPE - Paper–toweling - Georgia-Pacific Corp.

HIWAYS & BYWAYS - Toys - Lewis Galoob Toys, Inc.

HIWIRE - Musical-instrument accessories - Tropical Music and Pro Audio

HIWOLFIA - Pharmaceutical preparations ☆ - JMI-Canton Pharmaceuticals

HIZYME - Flour–blended ☆ - Central Soya Co. Inc.

HJ - Computer software - Herff Jones Inc.

HJ - Pet food - Mutual Group USA, Inc.

HJ LIGHT - Beverages–malt ☆ - Adolph Coors Co.

HJB - Dental compounds - Harry J. Bosworth Co.

HK - Caulking compounds - W.P. Hickman Systems

HK - Jewelry - Harriette Klepper

HK - Pet products - Nishiki Koi USA Inc.

HK - Sewing machines–household - Emil Katz & Co.

HK - Wheat–flour or meal - Cereal Ingredients, Inc.

HK-1 - Clothing - Evergreen International Aviation Inc.

HK-10 - Wheat–flour or meal - Cereal Ingredients, Inc.

HK-60 - Tools - Hot Tools Inc.

HKA - Sweaters - Gillman Knitwear Co.

HKE - Recording label - The Pegasus Group, Inc.

HKK - Chains - HKK Chain Corp.

HKM - Jewelry - H.K. Mallak Inc.

H.K.P. - Hair care products - Joico Laboratories, Inc.

HL - Bicycles - HL USA

HL - Boats–motor - Starcraft Corp.

HL - Floor coverings–carpet and rugs - Gloria of America Inc.

HL - Lamps - Hamilton Lamp Corp.

H.L. - Photographic equipment - Aristo Grid Lamp Products Inc.

HL-3168 PREMIUM HI-LO - Lubricants - Kerr-McGee Chemical Corp.

HL HOLIDAY LUMINATIONS INC. - Lighting fixtures - Holiday Luminations Inc.

HL320 - Computers–personal - Hitachi Home Electronics America Inc.

HLAVACEK - Accordions - Castiglione Accordion

HLD - Lighting fixtures - Hubbell Lighting, Inc. (Lighting Div.)

H.L.F. - Vegetable oil - Humko Products

HLH - Pharmaceutical preparations ☆ - Hunt Products Inc.

HLP - Computer software - E. David & Associates

HLT - Nuts and bolts - Hi-Shear Corp.

HM - Housewares - Hutzler Manufacturing Co.

HM-03 - Measuring instruments - Humidial Corp.

HM-30 SUPERLITE - Golfing equipment - Aldila, Inc.

HM-35 - Golfing equipment - Aldila, Inc.

HM-40 - Golfing equipment - Aldila, Inc.

HM2 - Apparel and accessories - Triform, Inc.

HME NEWS - Publisher's imprints - United Publications, Inc.

HMF - Gasoline - Shell Oil Co.

HMG - Fishing tackle - Fenwick

HMG - Lasers - HMG Photonics, Inc.

HMH - Cigars - Playboy Enterprises, Inc.

HMI - Aquariums–household - Hawaiian Marine Imports Inc.

HMI COLLECTION - Apparel and accessories - Heritage Marketing, Inc.

HMI METALLOGEN - Electronic equipment - George R. Snell Associates, Inc.

HMK - Cleaning preparations - HMK Stone Care System

HMR VINEYARDS - Wines - HMR Ltd.

HMS - Electrical equipment - Komatsu Dresser Co.

HMS - Lighting fixtures–street - Holophane Corp.

HMS - Ships–sailing vessels - International Marine

HMS - Software - Network Compatibility Group Inc.

HMS - Surgical supplies - Hospital Marketing Service Inc.

HMS LIQUIFILM - Ophthalmic goods - Allergan, Inc.

HMSA - Laser systems–medical - Hitachi Medical Systems America, Inc.

HMT - Fishing lures - Thomas and Thomas Rodmakers Inc.

HMT - Machinery - Hot Melt Technologies

HMWS - Computer storage devices - Fluor Corp.

HN - Sachets - Hillhouse Naturals Farm

HN - T-shirts–men's - Hyden Corp.

HNC - Hair care products - Paul Mazzotta Inc.

HNK - Lighting fixtures - Swivelier Co. Inc.

HNW VINEYARDS - Wines ☆ - Honig Vineyard & Winery

HNX - Generators–gas - Surface Combustion, Inc.

HO - Apparel–athletic - HO Sports Inc.

HO HO - Toys ☆ - Strombecker Corp.

HO HO - Toys–stuffed ☆ - Russ Berrie and Co., Inc.

HO HO HO! A LOT OF PILLOW - Pillows - Pillowtex Corp.

HO HO HOLIDAY RICE KRISPIES - Cereal ☆ - Kellogg Co.

HO! HO! HOT ROD - Toys - Mattel, Inc.

HO HO'S - Snack cakes - Interstate Brands Corp.

HO-KA - Food products - Kauffman Poultry Farms Inc.

HO KING - Fruits and vegetables - Tay Shing Corp.

HO-MAI - Food products - Ocean-Wide Food Industries Inc.

HO MED - Tool boxes - Homak Manufacturing Co. Inc.

HO TAI - Food products - Wei-Chuan U.S.A., Inc.

HO TAI'S SPICY PEANUT - Sauces - Golden Whisk Pasta Partners

HO YAN HOR - Teas–herbal - Overseas Factor Corp.

HO-ZONE - Greeting cards - Renaissance Greeting Cards Inc.

HOAGIE WORKS - Sandwiches–prepackaged - Wild Goose Holding Co., Inc.

HOAN - Housewares - Southbury Manufacturing Corp.

HOAN - Tools–hand-operated - Hoan Products Ltd.

HOAX - Apparel - Pacific Sunwear of California Inc.

HOB - Jewelry - House of Bangles Inc.

HOB - Recording label - Essex Entertainment Inc.

H.O.B. - Sporting goods - Weber Industries Inc.

HOB-E-TAC ADHESIVE - Hobby kits - Osment Models, Inc.

HOB-NAIL II - Mats - Proffitt Manufacturing Co.

HOB-NOB - Shirts - Jean Zenier

HOB-NOB - Tools - Wells Lamont Corp.

HOBACARE - Cosmetics - Boston Jojoba Co., Inc.

HOBACK GLEN - Wines - European Beverage Co., Inc.

HOBART M. CABLE - Pianos - QRS Music Rolls, Inc.

HOBBIES - Apparel and accessories - Lorch Co.

HOBBIES & IDEAS - Stationery products - Mead Corp.

HOBBIT INSPIRED - Posters - Fairfax Prints Ltd.

HOBBY - Cameras - Eastman Kodak Co.

HOBBY - Harmonicas - Hohner Inc.

HOBBY - Paint sprayers - W.R. Brown Co.

HOBBY - Tripods–photographic ☆ - QuickSet International Inc.

HOBBY - Vegetables–frozen - Lakeside Packing Co.

HOBBY - Yarn ☆ - Lion Brand Yarn Co.

HOBBY-ART - Paint sets–hobby ☆ - Canson-Talens Inc.

HOBBY CORNER - Computer software - Save on Software

HOBBY HORSE - Christmas tree ornaments - Cracker Box Inc.

HOBBY HORSE - Infant product - Michael Friedman Corp.

HOBBY JEANS - Apparel and accessories - Smith & Weber Co.

HOBBY KIDS - Yarn - Tahki Imports Ltd.

HOBBY NOBBY - Fabrics - Dan River Inc.

HOBBY-OPTICALS - Hobby kits ☆ - Poly-Optical Products, Inc.

HOBBY-PAC - Photographic equipment - Eastman Kodak Co.

HOBBY PAINTERS - Paint sets–hobby - Martin F. Weber Co.

HOBBY PLASTER - Artists' materials - Rutland Products

HOBBY QUEST MERCHANTS FOR THE IMAGINATION! - Games - Hobby Quest, Inc.

HOBBY STRIP - Adhesives and sealants ☆ - Loctite Corp.

HOBBY WRAP - Tools - OK Industries Inc.

HOBBYAIR - Air purification systems - Fastech Corp.

HOBBYCRAFT - Brushes–paint - Baker Brush Co. Inc.

HOBBYCRAFT - Toys ☆ - Coloron Industries

HOBBYIST - Artists' materials - Solo-Horton Brush Co.

HOBBYIST - Pet products - Aquarium Pharmaceuticals, Inc.

HOBBYIST - Tools - Esselte Corp.

HOBBYIST'S CHOICE - Aquarium accessories - Oceanic Systems, Inc.

HOBBYLITE - Lamps - Luxo Corp.

HOBBYPOXY FORMULA 4 - Epoxy - Pettit Paint Co. Inc.

HOBCO - Brake parts - Britton of Southport Inc.

HOBE - Fruits and vegetables - Becker Holding Corp.

HOBE - Jewelry - Hobe Cie. Ltd.

HOBE GROVES - Fruits and vegetables - Becker Holding Corp.

HOBEY BAKER MEMORIAL AWARD - Apparel–athletic - Hobey Baker Memorial Award Foundation

HOBGOBLIN - Musical instruments - Here Inc.

HOBIE - Bathing suits - Manhattan Beachwear, Inc.

HOBIE - Ships–sailing vessels - Hobie Cat Co.

HOBIE - Skateboards - Nash Manufacturing Inc.

HOBIE - Skis - Hobie Designs, Inc.

HOBIE CAT - Ships–sailing vessels - Hobie Cat Co.

HOBIE HAWK - Toys–models - Midwest Products Co. Inc.

HOBIE HOT STICK - Nautical instruments - Hobie Cat Co.

HOBIE MAGIC - Ships–sailing vessels - Hobie Cat Co.
HOBIE MONO-CAT - Ships–sailing vessels ☆ - Hobie Cat Co.
HOBIE ONE - Ships–sailing vessels - Hobie Cat Co.
HOBIE POWER SKIFF - Boats–motor - Hobie Cat Co.
HOBIE TRIFOILER - Ships–sailing vessels ☆ - Hobie Cat Co.
HOBIE'S - Soups–canned - Hobies Inc.
HOBNAIL - Blinds–venetian ☆ - Hunter Douglas, Inc.
HOBNAIL - Floor coverings–carpet and rugs - Mohawk Carpet Corp.
HOBNAIL - Floor coverings–carpet and rugs - Royal Rubber & Manufacturing Co.
HOBNAIL - Floor coverings–carpet and rugs ☆ - Playfield International Inc.
HOBNAIL - Mats - JCH International Inc.
HOBNOB - Bar fixtures–plastic - Spir-it Inc.
HOBO - Apparel - North Beach Leather International Inc.
HOBO - Data loggers - Onset Computer Corp.
HOBO - Ice chests–plastic ☆ - Coleman Co., Inc.
HOBO CHEWS GELLS - Candy - Murray-Allen International Inc.
HOBO INTERNATIONAL - Handbags - Ray Enterprises of Chesapeake Walk, Inc.
HOBS - Insecticides ☆ - Walco Linck Co.
HOBSON - Bicycles - JB Two Corp.
HOCHI 88 - Tools - Quali-Kraft International Inc.
HOCHLAND - Yarn - Tahki Imports Ltd.
HOCK SHOP - Games ☆ - Western Publishing Co., Inc.
HOCKANUM - Fabrics–wool ☆ - West Point-Pepperell Inc.
HOCKEY - Candy - Topps Co., Inc.
HOCKEY DOG - Dog food - Golden Ball & Son Corp.
HOCKEY ESSENTIALS - Apparel–athletic - Up in the Air, Inc.
HOCKEY HOODS - Crocheted and knitted items ☆ - Reliable of Milwaukee
HOCKEY HOUNDS - T-shirts–men's - Michael B. Lange
HOCKEY JOCKEY - Sporting goods - Markwort Sporting Goods Co.
HOCKEY NUTS - Nuts–salted, roasted, cooked, or canned - Clem Snacks, Inc.
HOCKEY PLUS - Apparel and accessories - Hockey Plus Inc.
HOCKEY SCOUT - Computer software - Forem Associates
HOCKEY TODAY - Trading cards and stamps - Treat Entertainment, Inc.
HOCKEYBLADE - Skates–roller ☆ - Rollerblade, Inc.
HOCKEYMAN - Apparel and accessories - Scott-Stegemeyer
HOCKEYSTIC - Bar fixtures–plastic - Spir-it Inc.
HOCKS - Hearing aids - Hocks Laboratories
HOCUS-FOCUS - Giftware - S.J. Miller Co.
HOCUS POCUS - Games - Apogee Software Ltd.
HOCUS POCUS - Novelty items - S.S. Adams Co.
HOCUS POCUS - Wallpaper - Jack Foley Associates Inc.
HOCUS POCUS - Wallpaper ☆ - W.H.S. Lloyd
HODAKA - Motorcycles ☆ - Pabatco
HODGE PODGE - Computer software - Dynacomp Inc.
HODGEY BEARS - Posters - Hodgey Bears Inc.
HODGSON MILL - Food products - Hodgson Mill
HODGSON MILL - Pasta - Pastamania
HOE - Underwear and nightwear - Hoe Fong Co.
HOE-MATIC - Garden equipment - Olympia Industrial Inc.
HOE-MATIC - Tools–garden - Village Blacksmith
HOEBOY - Garden equipment - Tradewinds Inc.
HO,ECREST - Shingles - Aluminum Co. of America
HOEDOWN - Cultivators–agricultural - Faultless Starch/Bon Ami Co.
HOEDOWN - Food products ☆ - Pierce Foods Corp.
HOEDOWNS - Cookies - Sunshine/Salerno Inc.
HOEGAARDEN - Beverages–malt - Labatt Importers Inc.
HOEGH - Pet products - Hoegh Industries Inc.
HOEI - Pet products - Pets Pacifica Inc.
HOEKSTRA - Meat products–beef - Hoekstra Meat Co.
HOENES - Clocks - Black Forest Imports, Inc.
HOE'S - Food products ☆ - Liberty Richter Inc.
HOF - Footwear - K-Swiss Inc.
HOF-BRAU - Beverages–alcohol ☆ - Falstaff Brewing Corp.
HOF FOODS - Frozen foods - Wilton Foods Inc.
HOF HAUS - Hams - John Hofmeister & Son, Inc.
HOF TEXTILES - Yarn - Hof Textiles, Inc.
HOFA CERTIFIED ORGANIC - Apparel and accessories - Hawaii Organic Farmers Association
HOFBAUER BLEIKRISTALLGLASWERKE - Toys–automobiles - O'Neill Importing Corp.
HOFBRAU BIER - Beverages–malt ☆ - Hudepohl-Schoenling Brewing Co.
HOFBRAU KASE - Cheese - Roth Kase USA, Ltd.
HOFERT - Christmas tree lights - J. Hofert Co.

HOFFCO - Lawn mowers ☆ - Hoffco Inc.
HOFFCO - Shoe polish - Harri Hoffmann Co. Inc.
HOFFGUARD - Coatings - ITT Industries, Inc.
HOFFMAN - Cheese - Dairy Fresh Products Co.
HOFFMAN - Crocheted and knitted items - Hoffman Mills Inc.
HOFFMAN - Heating equipment ☆ - Bradford-White Corp.
HOFFMAN - Pressing machines–commercial - Hoffman/New Yorker, Inc.
HOFFMAN BROS. - Chickens - Markel-Johnson Poultry Co.
HOFFMAN BROTHERS - Meat products–beef - Hoffman Brothers Packing Co. Inc.
HOFFMAN HOUSE - Glassware–household - Owens-Illinois Inc. (Libbey Div.)
HOFFMAN HOUSE - Salad dressings–bottled - Green Bay Foods Co.
HOFFMANN - Food products ☆ - C. & J. Willenborg Inc.
HOFFMAN'S - Food products - York Barbell Co., Inc.
HOFFRITZ - Cutlery - Hoffritz International
HOFFRITZ - Cutlery - Lifetime Hoan Corp.
HOFFY - Meat products–beef - Hoffman Brothers Packing Co. Inc.
HOFKASE - Cheese - Beatrice Cheese Co.
HOFLITE - Hams - John Hofmeister & Son, Inc.
HOFNAR - Cigars - Gesty Trading & Manufacturing Corp.
HOFNER - Guitars - Multivox/Sorkin Music Co. Inc.
HOG - Motor vehicle parts and accessories - Harley-Davidson, Inc.
HOG CALL - Soap - Mark A. Sloan
HOG CLUB - Sandwiches–prepackaged - H-D Michigan, Inc.
HOG HEAVEN - Giftware - Russ Berrie and Co., Inc.
HOG HUGS PIG - Toys–stuffed - Russ Berrie and Co., Inc.
HOG ISLAND - Seafood products–fresh or frozen - Hog Island Oyster Co., Inc.
HOG MAX - Pet products - Destron Fearing Corp.
HOG-N-RICH KOLEAN - Veterinary nutritional supplements - Vita Plus Corp.
HOG TUFF - Agricultural products - Osborne Industries Inc.
HOG WILD - Barbecue sauce - Ashman Distributing Co.
HOGAN - Golfing equipment - Ben Hogan Co.
HOGAN EDGE - Golfing equipment - Ben Hogan Co.
HOGAN H40 - Golfing equipment - Ben Hogan Co.
HOGANS - Breads–mixes - Bewley Irish Imports
HOGARIN - Toys - F.A.O. Schwarz
HOGEYE - Recording label ☆ - Flying Fish Records Inc.
HOGGER - Tools - LRH Enterprises Inc.
HOGGIES - Apparel and accessories - Green Planet, Inc.
HOGGIN' DOGG - Stationery - Melissa Ann Freeman and Virginia Van Diepen Partnership
HOGLAND - Recording label - Hogland Entertainment Inc.
HOGS AND KISSES - Figurines - Brennan Studio Inc.
HOG'S BREATH - Beverages–malt ☆ - Greentree Group, Inc.
HOGUA - Water–bottled or canned - Aqua-Pac, Inc.
HOGUE - Food products - Castle Food Products
HOGUE - Wines - Hogue Cellars, Ltd.
HOGUE CELLARS, THE - Wines - Hogue Cellars, Ltd.
HOGUE FARMS - Carrots - International Marketing Services Inc.
HOGUE FARMS - Vegetables–pickled or brined - Gilway Co. Ltd.
HOGWASH - Bags–laundry - Hog Wild!
HOHMONICA - Harmonicas - Hohner Inc.
HOHNER - Accordions - Castiglione Accordion
HOHNER - Harmonicas - Hohner Inc.
HOHNER INTERNATIONAL - Harmonicas - Hohner Inc.
HOHNER MUSIKLAND - Toys–musical - Hohner Inc.
HOHNER ORGAPHON - Harmonicas - Hohner Inc.
HOHNER PROFESSIONAL - Guitars - Hohner Inc.
HOHNER VOX - Harmonicas - Hohner Inc.
HOHNERPHONE - Harmonicas - Hohner Inc.
HOHNER'S WORLD OF MUSIC - Musical instruments - Hohner Inc.
HOI - Overseas Operations Inc.
HOIST AHOY - Hoists - Terek Inc.
HOIST DIAMOND GYM - Exercising equipment - Fitness Warehouse, Inc.
HOJA - Men's cologne - L.H. Ollins, Jr., Inc.
HOJO - Beverages–carbonated - Howard Johnson Co.
HOKAN - Food products - Gourmet America
HOKANSON - Computer software - D.E. Hokanson, Inc.
HOKE - Metal valves and fittings - Hoke Inc.
HOKEE - Fruits and vegetables - Fresh Pack Inc.
HOKEY POKEY - Snack foods - Midwest/Northern, Inc.
HOKKAIDO FISHERIES - Food products - Mitsubishi International Corp.
HOKO - Chocolate drink - Bottlers International Ltd.
HOKTRONIKS - Personal-computer systems and software - Auto Office Co.
HOKULE'A - Apparel and accessories - Hawaii Maritime Center

☆ = Now out of production

HOKULO TIMOTHY - Flowers, plants, and seeds - Jacklin Seed
HOKUS POKUS - Sleeping bags - Kellwood Co.
HOKUSEN TIMOTHY - Flowers, plants, and seeds - Jacklin Seed
HOKUSHIN - Projectors–photographic - Rangertone Research Inc.
HOL-DEX - Labels–paper - Cel-U-Dex Corp.
HOL-DOW - Clamps - Disstim Corp.
HOL-GRAIN - Crackers - Parco Foods, Inc.
HOL-GRAIN - Food products - Conrad Rice Mill Inc.
HOL-HI - Balls–golf ✩ - Wilson Sporting Goods Co.
HOL-HUGGER - Hardware ✩ - Hilti Inc.
HOLA! - Apparel and accessories - Jose L. Musa
HOLBOLL - Figurines - Odin Ltd.-Scan Am Imports Inc.
HOLBROOK - Apparel–men's - Oxford Industries, Inc.
HOLBROOK - Shoes - Allen-Edmonds Shoe Corp.
HOLD - Cough medicines - Smithkline Beecham Corp.
HOLD - Hair care products - Chem Spray Aerosols Inc.
HOLD-18 - Floor waxes ✩ - Sanitek Products Inc.
HOLD 2000 - Tape players–cassette - Robert Christensen
HOLD-A-BRUSH - Paints ✩ - Leaktite Corp.
HOLD-A-NUT - Magnet - Anthony D. Williams
HOLD ALL - Rope - American Tack & Hardware Co., Inc.
HOLD & BAKE - Biscuits–mixes - Southeastern Mills Inc.
HOLD AND CLEAN - Hair care products - Gillette Co.
HOLD & MOLD - Cosmetics - Sebastian International, Inc.
HOLD-E-ZEE - Screw drivers - Channellock, Inc.
HOLD 'EM - Agricultural machinery - Decker Manufacturing Co.
HOLD EVERYTHING - Tote bags, carry-on luggage - Jameslee Corp.
HOLD-EZ - Notebooks and notepads ✩ - Newell Office Products
HOLD FAST - Hair care products - Concentrics Inc.
HOLD-FAST - Wire - Holdwire America, Inc.
HOLD GUARD - Pet products - Novalek, Inc.
HOLD-IT! - Adhesives and sealants - Endslip Products Co.
HOLD IT! - Barrettes - Hold It! Hair Accessories, Inc.
HOLD IT - Concrete products - Set Consumer Products Inc.
HOLD-IT - Cup or can holder ✩ - Docker Marine
HOLD-IT - Electronic equipment - Madison Equipment Co.
HOLD IT - Fasteners–hook and eye - Curtis Industries Inc.
HOLD IT - Hair care products - Helene Curtis Industries Inc.
HOLD-IT - Hair care products - Jerant Co. Inc.
HOLD-IT - Plastics ✩ - Vaportek, Inc.
HOLD-IT - Security devices - Aztec Security Products
HOLD-IT - Sporting goods - IFM Industries
HOLD IT ALL - Tools ✩ - Hirsh Co.
HOLD-ITS - Office supplies - Tyz-All Plastics Inc.
HOLD ME SOFT - Dolls ✩ - Intex Recreation Corp.
HOLD-ME-TIGHT - Toys - J & G Toys
HOLD 'N' FLOSS - Dental compounds - Molor Products Co.
HOLD N' FOLD - Office supplies - Charles Leonard Inc.
HOLD 'N HANDS - Toys - Mattel, Inc.
HOLD-N-SHEEN - Cosmetics - Johnson Products Co., Inc.
HOLD ON TO YOUR HAT - Dolls - Mattel, Inc.
HOLD-RITE - Automotive parts and accessories - Manlee Industries Inc.
HOLD STIX - Chopsticks - Sidney Shapiro
HOLD THAT THOUGHT - Audio equipment - Comp General Corp.
HOLD THE FAT! - Food products - Just Help Yourself Food Co.
HOLD THE MUSTARD - Postcards ✩ - Fotofolio Inc.
HOLD TIGHT - Hair care products - Revlon Consumer Products Corp.
HOLD TIGHT - Hoses ✩ - Melnor Inc.
HOLD-TITE - Adhesives and sealants - L.D. Sterns Corp.
HOLD-TITE - Cleaning preparations ✩ - Klean-Strip
HOLD-TITE - Flexible magnets for household use - Quikey Manufacturing Co. Inc.
HOLD-TITE - Paints - Davis Paint Co.
HOLD-UP - Adhesives and sealants - Lepage's, Inc.
HOLD-UP - Brackets - John Daly
HOLD UP - Hair care products - Mahdeen Laboratory
HOLD-UP - Office supplies - Ghent Manufacturing Inc.
HOLD UP - Squash and badminton replacement grip - Babolat
HOLD-UP - Suspenders - Hold-Up Suspender Co.
HOLD-UP, THE - Shelving units–plastic ✩ - Syroco
HOLD-VAC - Tools–hand-operated - Virtual Industries, Inc.
HOLD YOUR HORSES - Games - World Wide Press, Inc.
HOLD YOUR OWN - Dinnerware–plastic - Grainware Co.
HOLD-ZIT - Automotive parts and accessories - Radiator Specialty Co.
HOLDALL - Mattresses - Del Astra Industries Inc.
HOLDEEZ - Garment racks–metal ✩ - A.J. Ganz Co. Inc.

HOLDEN - Photographic equipment - J.B. Holden Co.
HOLDENS - Cleaning preparations - J.W.W. Holden Inc.
HOLDER FOLDERS - Binders - Colad Group Inc.
HOLDER, THE - Office supplies - Metra Inc.
HOLDETOTE - Liquid containers - Image Maker Enterprises
HOLDEX - Water treating compounds - Jungle Laboratories Corp.
HOLDFAST - Adhesives and sealants - Aquarium Systems, Inc.
HOLDFAST - Brushes–paint ✩ - PPG Industries, Inc.
HOLDFAST - Cordage and twine ✩ - Winchester-Auburn Mills Inc.
HOLDFAST - Hardware - Metalcrafters
HOLDFAST - Hardware - St. Louis Hardware Manufacturing Co.
HOLDFAST - Health care products - Maddak Inc.
HOLDFAST - Ships–sailing vessels - Lewmar Marine Inc.
HOLDFAST - Traps–animal - Woodstream Corp.
HOLDIN'-EASY - Prosthetic apparatus - Mark One Healthcare Products Inc.
HOLDING - Cosmetics - Johnson Products Co., Inc.
HOLDING COMPANY, THE - Garden equipment - Cobraco Manufacturing, Inc.
HOLDING TANK KLEEN - Cleaning preparations - G.G. Bean Inc.
HOLDING YOUR WORLD TOGETHER - Tape–adhesive - Manco, Inc.
HOLDIT! - Adhesives and sealants - Cardinal Products
HOLDIT - Adhesives and sealants - Faber-Castell Corp.
HOLD'N IRON SET - Hair care products - Hair Institute
HOLDON - Hair care products - Brocato International
HOLDSTER - Electronic-equipment carrier - Naymark Communications Inc.
HOLDSTER BAG - Leather goods ✩ - AR Accessories Group Inc.
HOLDTIGHT - Padding–foam - Vantage Industries Inc.
HOLDTITE - Twine - Malow Corp.
HOLDUPS - Racks - Epic Products Inc.
HOLDZ - Skin care products - Sequel Products Inc.
HOLDZIT - Tool boxes - Adventures Northwest Limited
HOLE-E-SMOKED - Cheese - Churny Co., Inc.
HOLE GANG, THE - Doughnuts - PBI Proballs Inc.
HOLE HAWGS - Tools - Milwaukee Electric Tool Corp.
HOLE-IN-ONE - Agricultural products - Fresh Pacific Fruit & Vegetable, Inc.
HOLE IN ONE - Floor coverings–carpet and rugs - Mohawk Carpet Corp.
HOLE-IN-ONE! - Games - S.J. Miller Co.
HOLE IN ONE - Glassware–household ✩ - Crest Studios
HOLE IN ONE - Toys ✩ - A.J. Renzi Plastic Corp.
HOLE IN ONE - Toys–electronic - Bally Manufacturing Corp.
HOLE-IN-ONE BASKETBALL - Balls–basketball - Marvin E. Palmquist
HOLE-IN-THE-HANDLE - Knives–electric - Hamilton Beach/Proctor-Silex Inc.
HOLE IN THE HEAD - Golfing equipment - Callaway Golf Co.
HOLE IN THE WALL GANG - Giftware - Kurt S. Adler Inc.
HOLE-IS-ONE - Hobby kits - Extra Special Products Corp.
HOLE-MASTER - Saws–power - Misener Manufacturing Co. Inc.
HOLE-N-HEAD GUARD - Aquariums–household - Jungle Laboratories Corp.
HOLE 'N ONE - Golfing equipment - Dennco, Inc.
HOLE 'N ONE - Pet products - American Cat Emporium
HOLE-SHOOTER - Tools–power-driven - Milwaukee Electric Tool Corp.
HOLE SOCKET - Hand tools - Scot Tools Inc.
HOLEPROOF - Hosiery - Kayser-Roth Corp.
HOLEY CARDS - Forms–preprinted - Dress Rite Forms
HOLGATE - Toys - Holgate Toy Co.
HOLGUN - Drills–electric - Black & Decker Corp.
HOLI-DEER - Ornamental products–glass - Russ Berrie and Co., Inc.
HOLIDAY - Apparel and accessories - Fidelity Sportswear Co.
HOLIDAY - Apparel–men's ✩ - Cross Country Clothes
HOLIDAY - Bags–plastic - Mobil Chemical Co. Plastics Div.
HOLIDAY - Barbecues and grills ✩ - Southland Mower Corp.
HOLIDAY - Beverages - Universal Flavor USA
HOLIDAY - Beverages–malt ✩ - Joseph Huber Brewing Co., Inc.
HOLIDAY - Binoculars ✩ - Swift Instruments, Inc.
HOLIDAY - Boats ✩ - Clark Craft Boat Co.
HOLIDAY - Boats–lifeboats - Reeves Brothers Inc.
HOLIDAY - Boats–motor ✩ - Carver Boat Corp.
HOLIDAY - Boats–motor ✩ - Cobia Boat Co.
HOLIDAY - Boats–motor ✩ - Cruisers
HOLIDAY - Chocolate candy - Eddyleon Chocolate Co. Inc.
HOLIDAY - Containers–plastic - Plastican, Inc.
HOLIDAY - Cooking equipment–household - Jacksonville Manufacturing
HOLIDAY - Cooking equipment–household ✩ - Mirro Corp.
HOLIDAY - Cosmetics ✩ - Duart Industries Ltd.
HOLIDAY - Cutlery - Burrell Cutlery Co. Inc.
HOLIDAY - Deodorizers - Mcauley's, Inc.
HOLIDAY - Dinnerware–glass ✩ - Kenro Inc.
HOLIDAY - Exercising equipment ✩ - American Athletic Inc.

HOLIDAY - Flatware - Reed and Barton Corp.
HOLIDAY - Flatware - Kirk Stieff Co.
HOLIDAY - Floor coverings - Congoleum Corp.
HOLIDAY - Floor coverings–carpet and rugs ☆ - Robertex Associates Inc.
HOLIDAY - Flowers–artificial - C & C Florists Supplies Inc.
HOLIDAY - Food products - Bar S Food Co. Inc.
HOLIDAY - Food products - Cudahy Co.
HOLIDAY - Food products - Old Neighborhood Foods
HOLIDAY - Freezers - Lowe's Companies Inc.
HOLIDAY - Furniture ☆ - Lea Industries Inc.
HOLIDAY - Games ☆ - A.R.C. Toys Inc.
HOLIDAY - Glassware–household ☆ - Lenox Crystal, Inc.
HOLIDAY - Hobby kits - Liberty Distributors Group
HOLIDAY - Hobby kits ☆ - Blumenthal/Lansing Co.
HOLIDAY - Insecticides - Boyle-Midway
HOLIDAY - Jewelry - Jacoby-Bender Inc.
HOLIDAY - Luggage - Monarch Luggage Co., Inc.
HOLIDAY - Molasses - Allied Old English, Inc.
HOLIDAY - Pens - Gillette Co.
HOLIDAY - Pet products - Colgate-Palmolive Co.
HOLIDAY - Pet products - Farnam Cos. Inc.
HOLIDAY - Pickles - Chas. F. Cates & Sons Inc.
HOLIDAY - Pickles - Green Bay Foods Co.
HOLIDAY - Playing cards ☆ - Case Stationery Co. Inc.
HOLIDAY - Pottery products ☆ - Western Stoneware
HOLIDAY - Rings–jewelry ☆ - Artcarved Inc.
HOLIDAY - Roach traps - American Home Products Corp.
HOLIDAY - Steel products - S-B Manufacturing Co. Ltd.
HOLIDAY - Tableware–china - Lenox, Inc.
HOLIDAY - Tents - Coleman Co., Inc.
HOLIDAY - Tires - Bridgestone/Firestone, Inc.
HOLIDAY - Tobacco products - House of Edgeworth
HOLIDAY - Tobacco products - Lane Ltd.
HOLIDAY - Trailers–travel - Holiday Rambler Corp.
HOLIDAY - Underwear and nightwear ☆ - Lovable Co.
HOLIDAY - Watches - Bulova Corp.
HOLIDAY - Watches - Hampden Corp.
HOLIDAY - Window frames - Yale Ogron Manufacturing Co. Inc.
HOLIDAY ACCENT - Cooking equipment–household - Jacksonville Manufacturing
HOLIDAY ACCENT - Giftware - Lenox, Inc.
HOLIDAY ACCENTS - Electric lighting equipment - Ames Department Stores, Inc.
HOLIDAY BABY - Dolls - Mattel, Inc.
HOLIDAY BARBIE - Dolls - Mattel, Inc.
HOLIDAY BEAR - Greeting cards ☆ - Fun World Inc.
HOLIDAY BERRY - Housewares - S.C. Johnson & Son, Inc.
HOLIDAY BLEND - Coffee - Caravali Coffees, Inc.
HOLIDAY BLEND - Coffee - Java City
HOLIDAY BOUTIQUE - Buttons - JHB International Inc.
HOLIDAY BOUTIQUE - Salt and pepper sets, candle holders, etc. - Action Industries Inc.
HOLIDAY BRIGHTS - Lighting equipment - Collins International Co., Ltd.
HOLIDAY BY RUBBERMAID - Garden furniture ☆ - Rubbermaid-Allibert Inc.
HOLIDAY CAROL-OKY - Recording label - John Schmidt and Brian Spillane Partnership
HOLIDAY CAROLER - Dolls - Mattel, Inc.
HOLIDAY CAROUSEL - Christmas tree ornaments - Mr. Christmas, Inc.
HOLIDAY CHEER JELLY - Jams and jellies - Mountain Maid Gourmet Jelly
HOLIDAY CHEER STARTS HERE - Candy ☆ - R.M. Palmer Co.
HOLIDAY CLASSICS - Novelty items - Holiday Classics
HOLIDAY CLUB - Furniture ☆ - Tel-O-Post Co.
HOLIDAY CLUB - Furniture–wood - Cardinal Home Products
HOLIDAY COLLECTIBLES - Wood products - Jennings Decoy Co.
HOLIDAY COLLECTION - Greeting cards - Royal Stationery Co.
HOLIDAY COLLECTION - Hobby kits - Craft World International Inc.
HOLIDAY COLORAMA - Guitars ☆ - International Music Corp.
HOLIDAY CREATIONS - Giftware - Holiday Creations, Inc.
HOLIDAY CROWN GOLD - Posters - Holiday Export-Import
HOLIDAY CROWN SILVER - Posters - Holiday Export-Import
HOLIDAY DESIGN KIT - Computer software - Parsons Technology, Inc.
HOLIDAY DOOR CHIMES - Decorations - Noma International, Inc.
HOLIDAY DREAMS - Dolls - Mattel, Inc.
HOLIDAY ESCENTIALS - Spices and extracts - Scentex Inc.
HOLIDAY EXPRESS - Glassware–household - Durand International
HOLIDAY EXPRESSIONS - Ceramic figurines - Collins International Co., Ltd.

HOLIDAY FAIR - Handbags - Holiday Fair, Inc.
HOLIDAY FEEDERS - Animal feeds - Blue Ribbon Pet Products, Inc.
HOLIDAY FIESTA - Tires - Bridgestone/Firestone, Inc.
HOLIDAY FIESTA - Underwear and nightwear - Youthcraft-Charmfit
HOLIDAY FOGGER - Insecticide - American Home Products Corp.
HOLIDAY FRUIT - Christmas tree ornaments - Lenox, Inc.
HOLIDAY GLITTER - Greeting cards - Stephen Lawrence Co.
HOLIDAY GREEN - Glassware–household ☆ - Fenton Art Glass Co.
HOLIDAY HANG 'EMS - Wire products - Beagle Manufacturing Co. Inc.
HOLIDAY HEART & HOME - Pasta - Buckeye Beans & Herbs, Inc.
HOLIDAY HELPER - Dolls - Jubilee Mold Co.
HOLIDAY HELPERS - Craft supplies - VIP/VIP Crafts
HOLIDAY HELPERS - File folders - Duo Tang, Inc.
HOLIDAY HELPERS - Garment hangers - Miller Studio
HOLIDAY HIGHLIGHTS - Ornamental products–glass - Russ Berrie and Co., Inc.
HOLIDAY HILL - Christmas tree stands - Heinrich Industries
HOLIDAY HOLLY - Dolls - Caldor Corp.
HOLIDAY HOMERUN - Collectible trading cards - ANCO Collector Supplies, Inc.
HOLIDAY HOSTESS - Dinnerware–glass - Fairwinds Inc.
HOLIDAY HOSTESS - Dinnerware–glass - Tienshan, Inc.
HOLIDAY HOSTESS - Dolls - Mattel, Inc.
HOLIDAY HOT WHEELS - Toys - Mattel, Inc.
HOLIDAY HOUSE - Publisher's imprints - Holiday House Inc.
HOLIDAY HOUSEWARES - Containers - Holiday Housewares, Inc.
HOLIDAY HUGGABLES - Toys–stuffed - Fun World Inc.
HOLIDAY INN - Hotels and motels - Holiday Inns, Inc.
HOLIDAY INN CROWNE PLAZA - Hotels and motels - Holiday Inns, Inc.
HOLIDAY INN TRAV-L-PARKS - Campgrounds - Holiday Inns, Inc.
HOLIDAY JEWEL - Dolls - Mattel, Inc.
HOLIDAY KITTIES - Dolls - Mattel, Inc.
HOLIDAY KRINGLES - Food products - Bake-Line Products Inc.
HOLIDAY LANE - Figurines - Federated Department Stores, Inc.
HOLIDAY MAGIC - Christmas tree ornaments - Cracker Box Inc.
HOLIDAY MAGNETS - Magnets ☆ - United Design Corp.
HOLIDAY MELODIES - Coffee - Saramar Corp.
HOLIDAY MEMORIES - Toys - Mattel, Inc.
HOLIDAY MINIATURES - Toys ☆ - Knickerbocker Toy Co. Inc.
HOLIDAY MINT GREEN - Shampoos ☆ - Duart Industries Ltd.
HOLIDAY NOG - Eggnog - Vitamilk Dairy
HOLIDAY OCCASIONS - Christmas tree ornaments - Wilton Co.
HOLIDAY OVERSHADE - Lamp shades–fabric ☆ - Vista Solutions Inc.
HOLIDAY PINE - Deodorizers - S.C. Johnson & Son, Inc.
HOLIDAY POOLS - Swimming pools - Melcher Manufacturing Co. Inc.
HOLIDAY PORCELAIN BARBIE COLLECTION - Dolls - Mattel, Inc.
HOLIDAY PUPPIES - Dolls - Mattel, Inc.
HOLIDAY PUPS - Toys–stuffed - Fun World Inc.
HOLIDAY RAMBLER - Motor vehicles - Holiday Rambler Corp.
HOLIDAY RAMBLER CLUB - Motor vehicles–motor homes - Holiday Rambler Corp.
HOLIDAY RAMBLER IMPERIAL - Motor vehicles–motor homes - Holiday Rambler Corp.
HOLIDAY RAMBLER PARK ESTATE - Trailers–travel ☆ - Holiday Rambler Corp.
HOLIDAY RAMBLER PRESIDENTIAL - Motor vehicles–motor homes ☆ - Holiday Rambler Corp.
HOLIDAY RAMBLER STATESMAN - Motor vehicles–motor homes ☆ - Holiday Rambler Corp.
HOLIDAY RAMBLETTE - Motor vehicles–motor homes ☆ - Holiday Rambler Corp.
HOLIDAY RICE KRISPIES - Snack foods ☆ - Kellogg Co.
HOLIDAY ROYAL - Pickles - Freestone Pickle Co. Inc.
HOLIDAY SCENICS - Postcards - Schellmark, Inc. (Netlaunch, Inc. Division)
HOLIDAY SCENTSABLES - Christmas tree ornaments - Hercon Laboratories Corp.
HOLIDAY SENSATION - Dolls - Mattel, Inc.
HOLIDAY SKATERS - Christmas tree ornaments - Mr. Christmas, Inc.
HOLIDAY SPECIALTREES - Trees - Holiday Specialtrees
HOLIDAY SPICE - Oils–essential - Countryside Fragrances Inc.
HOLIDAY SPICE - Perfumes - Tennessee Gold Inc.
HOLIDAY SPIRIT - Floor coverings–carpet and rugs - Mohawk Carpet Corp.
HOLIDAY SPLENDOR - Cleaning preparations - Miracle Coatings
HOLIDAY SWINGERS - Ornamental products–glass - Russ Berrie and Co., Inc.
HOLIDAY TIME - Tablecloths - Straubel Paper Co.

☆ = Now out of production

HOLIDAY TOY SHOP - Toys - Mattel, Inc.
HOLIDAY TRADITION - Popcorn - Hyman Products Inc.
HOLIDAY TREASURES - Ornamental products–glass - Russ Berrie and Co., Inc.
HOLIDAY TRIMS - Christmas tree ornaments - Holiday Trims Inc.
HOLIDAY TRINKETS - Cookies - Stella D'Oro Biscuit Co. Inc.
HOLIDAY VACATIONER - Trailers–travel ☆ - Holiday Rambler Corp.
HOLIDAY WISHES - Dolls - Mattel, Inc.
HOLIDAY WISHES COLLECTION - Christmas tree ornaments - Lenox, Inc.
HOLIDAY WORKSHOP - Novelty items - International Silver Co.
HOLIDAYS - Apparel and accessories - CBK Ltd. Inc.
HOLIDAYS - Candy - Mars, Inc.
HOLIDAYS - Giftware - Himark Enterprises Inc.
HOLIDAYS TO REMEMBER - Deodorizers - Norpak Companies Ltd.
HOLISTICA - Pharmaceutical preparations - Grifair Co.
HOLISTICA - Vitamins and nutritional supplements ☆ - Miracle Exclusives Inc.
HOLLAENDER - Pipes - Hollaender Manufacturing Co.
HOLLAND - Cakes - Holland Honey Cake Co.
HOLLAND - Floor coverings ☆ - Kentile Floors Inc.
HOLLAND - Food products - Wood Bros. Inc.
HOLLAND - Hydraulic pumps - Holland Pump Manufacturing, Inc.
HOLLAND - Moldings–plaster of paris - Holland Mold Inc.
HOLLAND - Pottery products - Erie Tool Works
HOLLAND - Thread - Belding Heminway Co. Inc.
HOLLAND - Wallpaper ☆ - Maharam Vertical Surfaces
HOLLAND-AMERICAN - Earthenware - Holland-American Importing Co. Inc.
HOLLAND COLLECTION - Wallpaper - Maharam Vertical Surfaces
HOLLAND DAIRY - Milk - Holland Dairies Inc.
HOLLAND DAYS - Floor coverings–carpet and rugs - Artistic Rugs Inc.
HOLLAND FARM - Cheese - White Clover Dairy Inc.
HOLLAND GLORY - Chocolate candy - W.L.M. Bensdorp Co.
HOLLAND HALL - Ice cream - Grand Union Co.
HOLLAND HARVEST COLLECTION - Flowers–artificial ☆ - Mangelsen's (VDI)
HOLLAND HI PROFILE - Mattresses - Richards Quality Bedding
HOLLAND HOUSE - Beverages - Mott's Inc.
HOLLAND HOUSE - Canned luncheon meat - J & M Universal Sales Co.
HOLLAND IRISIAN GIRL - Cheese - Jacques F. Weber Co.
HOLLAND PEDIC - Pillows - Hollander Home Fashions Inc.
HOLLAND POND HUSH - Teas - Vermont Tea & Maple
HOLLAND POTTERY - Cooking equipment–household ☆ - Loroman Co.
HOLLAND QUEEN - Cheese - Beatrice Cheese Co.
HOLLAND RUSK - Breads - Nabisco Foods Group
HOLLAND SPORT - Leather goods - Holland Sport
HOLLANDALE - Margarine ☆ - Kraft Food Ingredients Corp.
HOLLANDAMMER - Cheese - Webeco Foods Inc.
HOLLANDER - Beverages–malt - G.W. Kent, Inc.
HOLLANDIA - Cookies - Advanced Marketing & Sales
HOLLANDIA DAIRY - Milk - Hollandia Dairy
HOLLDON - Cosmetics - Morris-Flamingo Inc.
HOLLENBACH - Sausages - Chas. Hollenbach Inc.
HOLLEN'S - Food products - Sona and Hollen Foods Inc.
HOLLENS GOURMET - Sauces - Sona and Hollen Foods Inc.
HOLLER - Games - Dollsandreams
HOLLER'S CALIFORNIA STYLE - Vegetables–canned - Holler's
HOLLEX - Glass products - Owens Corning Fiberglass Technology Inc.
HOLLEY - Carburetors - Coltec Industries Inc.
HOLLEY - Pocket knives - Tennessee River Valley Knife Association Inc.
HOLLEYRIPE - Food products - Tripifoods Inc.
HOLLI - Recording label - Candy Records
HOLLI-GRO - Fertilizers - Erth-Rite, Inc.
HOLLINGSHEAD - Cleaning preparations - R.M. Hollingshead Corp.
HOLLINGTON - Chairs–metal - Herman Miller, Inc.
HOLLIPOPS - Candy - Russ Berrie and Co., Inc.
HOLLIS - Seat frames–automobile ☆ - Hollis Co.
HOLLISTER - Sinks–metal - Kohler Co.
HOLLMARK - Thread - Belding Heminway Co. Inc.
HOLLOFIL - Fibers–synthetic - E.I. Dupont de Nemours and Co.
HOLLOFOAM - Fiberfill - E.I. Dupont de Nemours and Co.
HOLLOHAZA - Giftware - Schildkraut Giftware Corp.
HOLLOHAZA PORCELAIN FACTORY - Dinnerware–glass - M & M Associates Ltd.
HOLLOLOFT - Fiber - E.I. Dupont de Nemours and Co.
HOLLOMAX - Bedding items - E.I. Dupont de Nemours and Co.
HOLLOPLUMP - Bedding–linen - E.I. Dupont de Nemours and Co.
HOLLOREST - Bedding items - E.I. Dupont de Nemours and Co.

HOLLOW CORE - Health care products - Med Foam
HOLLOW-FLEX - Hearing aids - Starkey Labs Inc.
HOLLOW LEGIONS - Games - Avalon Hill Game Co.
HOLLOW POINT BOATTAIL - Bullets - Olin Corp. (Winchester Div.)
HOLLOW POINT BULLET - Bullets - Olin Corp. (Winchester Div.)
HOLLOW SOFT POINT - Bullets - Olin Corp. (Winchester Div.)
HOLLOW TREE - Ice cream cones - Illinois Baking Co.
HOLLOWARM - Housewares - E.I. Dupont de Nemours and Co.
HOLLOWAY HOUSE - Food products ☆ - Pillsbury Co.
HOLLOWBODY - Recording label - Sundazed Music
HOLLOWJET - Nozzles - Spraying Systems Co.
HOLLOWOOD - Sporting goods ☆ - Gill Sports Equipment, Inc.
HOLLY - Christmas tree ornaments - J. Hofert Co.
HOLLY - Dinnerware–glass ☆ - Nikko Ceramics Inc.
HOLLY - Frames–eyeglass - Rozin Optical Export Corp.
HOLLY - Furnaces–electric ☆ - Nordyne Inc.
HOLLY - Housewares - Scio Pottery Co.
HOLLY - Milk - Holly Milk Cooperative
HOLLY - Nuts–salted, roasted, cooked, or canned ☆ - Southern Frozen Foods Inc.
HOLLY - Sugar–granulated, refined, or powdered - Imperial Holly Corp.
HOLLY - Toys–stuffed ☆ - Gund, Inc.
HOLLY - Wall fasteners - MKT Fastening, LLC
HOLLY & IVY - Dishes–earthenware - Portmeirion USA
HOLLY & SPRUCE - Dinnerware–glass - Taylor, Smith & Taylor Co.
HOLLY & THE IVY, THE - Dinnerware - Federated Department Stores, Inc.
HOLLY ANNA - Office supplies - Staver Westport Inc.
HOLLY BABE - Hobby kits - Morehead, Inc.
HOLLY BABES - Giftware ☆ - Enesco Corp.
HOLLY BEARIES - Figurines - Kurt S. Adler Inc.
HOLLY BEAUTY - Food products ☆ - Hanover Foods Corp.
HOLLY BERRIES - Candy - Leaf, Inc.
HOLLY CANES - Candy - Bobs Candies Inc.
HOLLY CHEER - Glassware–household - Durand International
HOLLY-CO-ED - Underwear and nightwear - Holly Bra of California
HOLLY CREST - Food products - Mille Lacs Maple Products Corp.
HOLLY DAYS - Dinnerware ☆ - Corning Inc.
HOLLY FARMS - Food products - Tyson Foods Inc.
HOLLY FARMS TIME TRIMMER - Food products - Tyson Foods Inc.
HOLLY GLASS - Christmas tree ornaments - J. Hofert Co.
HOLLY GREENE - Housewares - Marilee Pearson
HOLLY HEDGEHOG AND HER FRIENDS - Recording label - Taylor-Allwine Associates, Inc.
HOLLY HILL - Fruits and vegetables - Woodmont Orchards Inc.
HOLLY HILL - Furniture - Homecrest Industries Inc.
HOLLY HILL - Juices - Holly Hill Fruit Products Co.
HOLLY HILL - Water–mineral - Holly Hill Distributing Inc.
HOLLY HILL - Wood products - Georgia-Pacific Corp.
HOLLY HILL COLLECTION - Placemats ☆ - Bright of America Inc.
HOLLY HOBBIE - Dolls - Knickerbocker Toy Co. Inc.
HOLLY HOBBIE - Furniture - American Toy & Furniture Co.
HOLLY HOBBIE - Garment hangers ☆ - Mactac Inc. (Packaging Closures Systems Div.)
HOLLY HOBBIE - Giftware - Designers Collection
HOLLY HOBBIE - Greeting cards ☆ - American Greetings Corp.
HOLLY HOBBIE - Novelty items - Those Characters from Cleveland, Inc.
HOLLY HOBBIE - Toys - Chilton-Globe, Inc.
HOLLY JOY - Tableware–earthenware - Pfaltzgraff Investment Co.
HOLLY LIGHT - Christmas tree lights - Dependable Electric Manufacturing Co.
HOLLY MATRON - Underwear and nightwear - Holly Bra of California
HOLLY MINE - Dolls - Well-Made Toy Manufacturing Corp.
HOLLY MISS - Underwear and nightwear - Holly Bra of California
HOLLY-N-BERRY - Glassware–household - Crisa Corp.
HOLLY-OPTICALS - Christmas tree ornaments ☆ - Poly-Optical Products, Inc.
HOLLY-POLLY - Steel springs–railroad - Needlecraft Industries
HOLLY RIBBONS - Dinnerware–glass - Royal China & Porcelain Companies Inc.
HOLLY RIDGE - Desserts - Holly Ridge Foods Inc.
HOLLY SPIN - Underwear and nightwear - Holly Bra of California
HOLLY SPRINGS - Furniture ☆ - Bassett Furniture Industries, Inc.
HOLLY-TONE - Flowers, plants, and seeds - Espoma Co.
HOLLY TREE - Figurines - Service Merchandise Co. Inc.
HOLLY TREE - Housewares - Service Merchandise Co., Inc.
HOLLY TWIST - Cording - Pepperell Braiding Co. Inc.
HOLLYBEARY U.S.A. - Figurines - May Department Stores Co.

HOLLYBERRY HOLIDAY - Sachets Bath Crystals - Country Lane Enterprises Inc.
HOLLYCARE - Fertilizers - Jonathan Green, Inc.
HOLLYCROSS - Christmas tree ornaments - Inspired Ornaments
HOLLYDALE - Floor coverings ☆ - Congoleum Corp.
HOLLDENE ESTATE - Wines - Beverage America, Inc.
HOLLYHILL - Floor coverings - Congoleum Corp.
HOLLYHOCK - Flour–blended - Martha White Foods Inc.
HOLLYHOCK HOUSE - Jewelry - Friends of Hollyhock House Inc.
HOLLYKINS - Magnets - Pathfinder Productions Inc.
HOLLYPARK - Apparel–athletic - Monarch Knit and Sportswear Inc.
HOLLYRIDGE - Floor coverings–carpet and rugs ☆ - Gulistan Carpet Inc.
HOLLY'S - Bathroom accessories ☆ - Designers Collection
HOLLYSHIRE PLACE - Figurines - Seasonal Specialties Electrics, Inc.
HOLLYSPUN - Crocheted and knitted items - Garland Knitting Mills
HOLLYTEX - Fabrics - Ahlstrom Filtration Inc. Industrial Products Group
HOLLYTEX - Floor coverings–carpet and rugs - L.D. Brinkman & Co. Inc.
HOLLYTREE - Floor coverings–carpet and rugs - Gulistan Carpet Inc.
HOLLYWEB - Fabrics ☆ - Ahlstrom Filtration Inc. Industrial Products Group
HOLLYWEIRD MAXY WAX - Recording label ☆ - Mystic Records
HOLLYWOOD - Audio equipment - Hollywood Sound Labs
HOLLYWOOD - Bicycles - Hollywood Engineering Inc.
HOLLYWOOD - Bicycles - Schwinn Cycling & Fitness Inc.
HOLLYWOOD - Breads - American Bakeries Co.
HOLLYWOOD - Breads–mixes - Elam's
HOLLYWOOD - Cabinets ☆ - Nutone Inc.
HOLLYWOOD - Candy - Leaf, Inc.
HOLLYWOOD - Desk sets ☆ - Marnay Sales & Manufacturing Co. Inc.
HOLLYWOOD - Food products - Hollywood Health Foods
HOLLYWOOD - Food products - Pet Inc.
HOLLYWOOD - Furniture ☆ - Tropitone Furniture Co. Inc.
HOLLYWOOD - Glassware–household - Crisa Corp.
HOLLYWOOD - Guitars ☆ - International Music Corp.
HOLLYWOOD - Hair care products - Scolding Locks Corp.
HOLLYWOOD - Musical instrument accessories - European Crafts/USA
HOLLYWOOD - Olive oil - Hollywood Foods
HOLLYWOOD - Popcorn - Great Western Products Inc.
HOLLYWOOD - Publisher's imprints - Hollywood Chamber of Commerce
HOLLYWOOD - Recording label - Hollywood Records of California
HOLLYWOOD - Tables–metal - Stainless Steel Products
HOLLYWOOD - Watches - Gruen Marketing Corp.
HOLLYWOOD - Wigs ☆ - Paula Young
HOLLYWOOD - Window coverings - Vertilux-Louverlux Inc.
HOLLYWOOD ATHLETIC CLUB - T-shirts–men's - Hollywood Athletic Club Licensing Corp.
HOLLYWOOD BABE - Cosmetics - Hollywood Babe Inc.
HOLLYWOOD BEAR - Stationery - Lisa Frank, Inc.
HOLLYWOOD BIG SHOT - Hair care products - Rescue Marketing Group
HOLLYWOOD BITES - Broadcasting stations–radio - SJS Entertainment Corp.
HOLLYWOOD BRITE - Dental preparations - J.K. Sales
HOLLYWOOD BUMPER - Infant product ☆ - Century Products Co.
HOLLYWOOD CASINO - Hotels and motels - Hollywood Casino Corp.
HOLLYWOOD CONNECTION, THE - Apparel and accessories - Travilla Inc.
HOLLYWOOD CUP - Coffee substitutes - Cal-Leaf Health Products Inc.
HOLLYWOOD DELICACIES - Food products - California Citrus Processors
HOLLYWOOD FASHION GIRL - Dolls ☆ - Imperial Toy Corp.
HOLLYWOOD/FX - Binoculars - Tiffen Manufacturing Corp.
HOLLYWOOD FX MASTERS - Toys - Mattel, Inc.
HOLLYWOOD GIN - Computer software - Manhattan Software
HOLLYWOOD HAIR - Dolls - Mattel, Inc.
HOLLYWOOD HANDOUTS - Advertising agencies - Spectra Products, Inc.
HOLLYWOOD HEADBANDS - Hairpins - Sta-Rite Ginnie Lou Inc.
HOLLYWOOD HEALTH HUNZA - Food products ☆ - Hollywood Health Foods
HOLLYWOOD HIGH - Computer software - Theatrix Interactive, Inc.
HOLLYWOOD HIGH - Games - Decipher Inc.
HOLLYWOOD HOUNDS - Toys–stuffed - Cultural Exchange Corp.
HOLLYWOOD ILLUSIONS - Costumes - Spencer Gifts, Inc.
HOLLYWOOD LEGENDS COLLECTION - Dolls - Mattel, Inc.
HOLLYWOOD-LITE - Lighting fixtures ☆ - Prestigeline Inc.
HOLLYWOOD MAGIC - Cosmetics and skin-care products - House of Westmore, Inc.
HOLLYWOOD MEMORIES - Toys - Hot Properties, Inc.
HOLLYWOOD MICKEY & MINNIE - Cosmetics - Cosrich Inc.
HOLLYWOOD MOVIE THEATRE - Toys - Brumberger Co. Inc.
HOLLYWOOD NIGHTS - Apparel and accessories - Breton Industries
HOLLYWOOD POP - Popcorn - Titan Management Corp.

HOLLYWOOD POP POPCORN - Popcorn - Titan Management Corp.
HOLLYWOOD PREMIERE - Dolls - Mattel, Inc.
HOLLYWOOD PREMIERE OF POWAR AND GREEDE, THE - Games - Decipher Inc.
HOLLYWOOD SHOWCASE - Greeting cards ☆ - Regency Thermographers Inc.
HOLLYWOOD SOUND - Audio speakers - Hollywood Sound Labs
HOLLYWOOD SPA, THE - Apparel and accessories - John Ferry
HOLLYWOOD SQUARES - Games ☆ - Milton Bradley Co.
HOLLYWOOD STAR - Dolls - Imperial Toy Corp.
HOLLYWOOD STARS - Dog food - J.R.B. Foods, Inc.
HOLLYWOOD STIK'S - Antennas - Wintenna Inc.
HOLLYWOOD STOCK EXCHANGE - Games - HSX, Holdings, Inc.
HOLLYWOOD-STRIP - Lighting equipment - Lowel-Light Manufacturing Inc.
HOLLYWOOD TRIMS - Fabric stores - Amjacs Interwest Inc.
HOLLYWOOD UNIFORMS - Hair care products - Spilo/Mehaz Worldwide
HOLLYWOOD WAX MUSEUM - Key rings - Hollywood Wax Museum, Inc.
HOLLYWOODS - Dolls - Tonka Corp.
HOLLYWOOD'S GOLDEN AGE - Recording label - Twentieth Century Fox Film Corp.
HOLLYWOOD'S LEGENDS - Stationery - Reed Productions
HOLLYWOOD'S REEL SCHEPEEL FOR YOUNGSTARS - Games - Game Geste, Inc.
HOLLYWOOD'S REEL SCHPEEL - Games - Game Geste, Inc.
HOLLYWOOD'S ULTIMATE SPECIAL EFFECT - Apparel and accessories - Bodylines Inc.
HOLLYWORD - Computer software - Simon Skill Systems, Inc.
HOLLYWREATH - Housewares - Amoco Fabrics and Fibers Co.
HOLMAN - Motor vehicles - Holman Enterprises
HOLMEGAARD - Giftware - Royal Copenhagen Porcelain Inc.
HOLMES - Amplifiers–musical instrument - On-Site Music Group
HOLMES - Computer software - On-Line Information Networks
HOLMES - Doors–garage - Holmes-Hally Industries
HOLMES - Glass products - T.J. Holmes Co.
HOLMES - Lamps - Holmes Products, Corp.
HOLMES - Winches - Century Wrecker Corp.
HOLMES & EDWARDS - Paints - Insilco Corp.
HOLMES & EDWARDS - Silverware - International Silver Co.
HOLMES APPLE FARM - Pies–fresh - Rich Products Corp.
HOLMSPRAY - Atomizers - T.J. Holmes Co.
HOLO CLEAR - Computer software - Transfer Print Foils, Inc.
HOLO-FLITE - Heating equipment - Svedala Industries, Inc.
HOLO-KNURL - Hardware - Holo-Krome Co.
HOLO-SEAL - Hardware - Holo-Krome Co.
HOLO SIGHT - Sights–gun - Eotech, Inc.
HOLO-TORC - Hardware - Holo-Krome Co.
HOLOCATOR - Golfer's training aid - United Ventures Inc.
HOLOCOMM SYSTEMS - Lighting equipment - Holocomm Systems, Inc.
HOLOFIBER - Cables–fiber optic - Physical Optics Corp.
HOLOFLEX - Electrical equipment - Holophane Corp.
HOLOFRACTION - Foil–tin - Holopak Technologies, Inc.
HOLOGRAM - Games - Hologram Ventures
HOLOJAM - Trading cards and stamps - Upper Deck Co.
HOLOKROME - Hardware - Holo-Krome Co.
HOLOPAK - Paper - Holopak Technologies, Inc.
HOLOPHANE LEADER IN LIGHTING SOLUTIONS - Lighting fixtures - Holophane Corp.
HOLOPHANE NAVIGATOR SERIES LIFE SAFETY PRODUCTS - Lighting fixtures - Holophane Corp.
HOLOPIX - Trading cards and stamps - Fleer Corp.
HOLOSCOPE - Toys ☆ - Small World Toys
HOLOSCREEN - Projection screens - Kaiser Optical Systems, Inc.
HOLOTEX - Fabrics - Imagen Holography, Inc.
HOLOVET II - Wallpaper ☆ - Wall Fashion Inc.
HOLSON - Photo albums - Holson Co.
HOLSON BURNES - Frames–picture - Holson Burnes Group
HOLSTED - Glassware–household - Dansk International Designs, Ltd.
HOLSTEIN COW PIES - Chocolate candy ☆ - Tom and Sally's Handmade Chocolates, Inc.
HOLSTEIN DESIGN - Computer software - Ellen Horowitz
HOLSTON - Flooring–hardwood - Harris-Tarkett, Inc.
HOLSUM - Breads - Holsum Bakers
HOLSUM - Breads - W.E. Long Co.-Independent Bakers' Cooperative
HOLSUM - Food products - Golden Pantry West Inc.
HOLSUM - Macaroni ☆ - Pastamania
HOLSUM - Mayonnaise - Ventura Foods

☆ = Now out of production

HOLSUM - Pet products - United Grocers Inc.
HOLT - Chemical preparations - Challenger Manufacturing, Inc.
HOLT IT - Screws - Ames Taping Tool Systems Co.
HOLTEN - Food products - Holten Meat, Inc.
HOLTER MONITORING - Medical apparatus - Del Mar Avionics
HOLTEREXPRESS - Medical apparatus - Del Mar Avionics
HOLTHE - Giftware ☆ - Henriksen Imports Inc.
HOLTINK - Fabric dye - Holt Manufacturing Co. Inc.
HOLTITE - Brushes–paint ☆ - PPG Industries, Inc.
HOLTON - Musical instrument accessories - G. Leblanc Corp.
HOLTON TST - Musical instrument accessories - G. Leblanc Corp.
HOLTS - Leather–chamois ☆ - Bloch/New England, Inc.
HOLUBARZ - Sporting goods - North Face
HOLUSION - House furnishings - Nvision Grafix, Inc.
HOLVOET 2 - Wallpaper - Textile Wallcoverings International Ltd.
HOLY - Candy - Allied International Corp.
HOLY BARBARIANS - Recording label - Ian Astbury
HOLY BIBLE GOSPEL MUSIC - Recording label - Holy Bible Gospel Ministry of The Body of Christ, Yeshua, of the Holy Land,
HOLY COW - Beverages ☆ - Vess Beverages Inc.
HOLY COW! - Beverages–malt - Big Dog's Hospitality Group, Inc.
HOLY COW! - Dog food ☆ - Merrick Petfoods Inc.
HOLY COW - Meat products–beef ☆ - Pierce Foods Corp.
HOLY COW - Puppets - Dakin Inc.
HOLY COW - Toys–stuffed ☆ - Gund, Inc.
HOLY GRAIL NUT BROWN ALE - Beverages–malt - Oldenberg Brewing Co.
HOLY SMOKE - Charcoal - El Paso Chili Co.
HOLY SMOKE - Perfumes - Caswell-Massey Co. Ltd.
HOLYOKE - Rings–jewelry - Artcarved
HOLYOKE - Tableware–china - Lenox, Inc.
HOLYOKE - Water–distilled - Holyoke Distilled Water Co. Inc.
HOLYWOOD BASES - Sporting goods - Schutt Manufacturing Co.
HOLZ-EM - Dust-mop heads ☆ - American Textile Products Co.
HOLZIN - Hardware - Star Anchors & Fasteners
HOMA - Seeds–salted, roasted, cooked, or canned - Homa Co.
HOMACO - Communications equipment–mobile - Homaco Inc.
HOMADE - Seasonings ☆ - Sona and Hollen Foods Inc.
HOMADE CHILI SAUCE - Chili sauce - Sona and Hollen Foods Inc.
HOMADE COCKTAIL SAUCE - Food products - Sona and Hollen Foods Inc.
HOMADE SWEET & SOUR SAUCE - Food products - Sona and Hollen Foods Inc.
HOMAGANIZED BAKON - Bacon - Micromatic Inc.
HOMAGE - Furniture - Architectural Textiles USA Inc.
HOMAGE PRESS - Printed materials - Zero Sum Press, Inc.
HOMAGE STUDIOS - Printed material - Zero Sum Press, Inc.
HOMAK - Tool boxes - Homak Manufacturing Co. Inc.
HOMART - Hardware - Sears, Roebuck and Co.
HOMASOTE - Floor coverings - Homasote Co.
HOMASOTE 4-WAY - Floor coverings - Homasote Co.
HOMAT MEDI - Health care products ☆ - Mulholland Positioning Systems Inc.
HOMATROPINE HYDROBROMIDE - Ophthalmic prescription drug - Iolab Pharmaceuticals
HOMBRE - Hair care products - Grayson O. Group
HOMBRE - Revolvers - Fie Corp.
HOMBRES - Shoes - Bob Le Vine Shoe Sales
HOMBURG - Hams - Walker Foods
HOME - Brushes–paint - Rubberset Co.
HOME - Fire extinguishers - Kidde Safety
HOME - Paperboard - Home Stores Inc.
HOME - Recording label - Credence Records
HOME - Thread - Threads USA Div.
HOME - Vegetables–canned - Home Canning Co.
HOME ACCENTS - Furniture - Belk Stores Services, Inc.
HOME ACCOUNTANT - Computer software - Arrays Inc./Continental Software
HOME ADVANTAGE - Cleaning preparations - ChemPlus
HOME AGAIN - Electronic equipment - Schering Corp.
HOME AGAIN - Wallpaper - Lin-Gor Wallcoverings
HOME AIDE - Washboards ☆ - Columbus Washboard Co.
HOME AIDS - Fabrics - Dyno Merchandise
HOME ALONE - Apparel–children's - Twentieth Century Fox Film Corp.
HOME ALONE - Computer software ☆ - Capstone Software
HOME ALONE 2 - Computer software - Capstone Software
HOME ALONE COLORING BOOK - Computer software - Capstone Software
HOME AND ABROAD - Handbags - Home and Abroad, Inc.
HOME & AWAY - Forms–preprinted - Dataprint, Inc.
HOME & FAMILY - Air purification systems - Regina Meade Management, Inc.

HOME & GARDEN - Fruits and vegetables - Market Wholesale Grocery Co.
HOME & GARDEN SHOWPLACE - Fertilizers - Servistar Corp.
HOME & HEARTH - Windows - Parco Manufacturing, Inc.
HOME & HOBBY - Office accessories - Brother International Corp.
HOME & HOBBY LUBRICANT PROTECTANT - Lubricants - International Lubrication Laboratories, Inc.
HOME & ROAM - Infant product - Baby Trend Inc.
HOME & TRAVEL - Iron - Franzus Co. Inc.
HOME & YARD - Pet products - HTZ Investment Corp.
HOME AROMA - Sachets - Natural Products Corp.
HOME-ART OF HOLLAND - House furnishings ☆ - S.P. Skinner Co. Inc.
HOME AT LAST - Bedding–linen - Springs Industries, Inc.
HOME ATTENDANT - Alarm systems - Pittway Corp.
HOME/AUTO LANTERN - Lanterns–electric - Brinkmann Lighting Products
HOME BAKE SHOP - Bakery products–frozen - Conagra, Inc.
HOME BAKED - Bakery products - Home Baked Group, Inc.
HOME-BAKED TASTE BY THE SPOONFUL! - Cereal - General Mills, Inc.
HOME BAKERY - Kitchen appliances - Matsushita Consumer Electronics Co.
HOME BASICS - Cabinets - White Consolidated Industries, Inc.
HOME BASICS - Towels - R & R Textile Mills, Inc.
HOME BAZAAR, THE - Housewares - Frederick Atkins, Inc.
HOME BEAUTIFUL - Dishes–china - Mikasa Co.
HOME BEAUTY - Flowers, plants, and seeds - Seaboard Seed Co.
HOME BEST - Cleaning preparations–household - Wetterau Inc.
HOME BILI LIGHT - Health care products - Physician Engineered Products
HOME BOYS - Potato chips - Home Boys Inc.
HOME BREW PUB - Beverages–malt - Glenn Henry Martin
HOME BRITE - Lighting fixtures - International Lighting Manufacturing Co.
HOME BROWNS - Vegetables–frozen ☆ - Lamb-Weston, Inc.
HOME BUDDY - File folders - Creative Learning Products Inc.
HOME BUDGETER - Computer software - SourceView Software International
HOME BUYERS BIBLE - Publisher's imprints - Bennett A. Fletcher
HOME BUYERS CLUB - Real estate agencies - Jeffrey Brummitt
HOME BUYERS' COMPANION - Computer software ☆ - Parsons Technology, Inc.
HOME CARE - Paints ☆ - Devoe & Raynolds Co.
HOME CARE - Vacuum cleaners and accessories - Home Care Industries, Inc.
HOME CARE HELPERS - Caulking compounds - W.J. Dennis & Co.
HOME CHOICE - Paints - Buten Paint & Wallpaper
HOME CHURCH WORSHIP A MINISTRY OF HOME CHURCH MINISTRIES - Electronic equipment - Home Church Ministries
HOME CINEMA DESIGNS - Furniture - Benchmark Industries, Inc.
HOME CINEMA MADE EASY - Loudspeakers - Bose Corp.
HOME CITY ICE - Ice - Home City Ice Co.
HOME CLASSIC - Appliances - Li-Fong Industrial Co. Ltd.
HOME COAT - Plaster–wallboard - Max Products Corp.
HOME COFFEE ROASTERS' SOCIETY - Coffee - Jeff Strode
HOME COLOURS - Lamps - Alexander Julian, Inc.
HOME COMFORT - Medical apparatus - Physicians Appliance Co.
HOME COMFORT - Recording label ☆ - Ray Lawrence Ltd.
HOME COMFORT - Window shades - Deborah Bliss
HOME COMING - Wallpaper - Lin-Gor Wallcoverings
HOME COOKIN - Glassware–household - Meijer, Inc.
HOME COOKIN' - Soups–canned - Campbell Soup Co.
HOME-COST - Notebooks and notepads - Lorenz J. Schwager
HOME COUNTRY - Rice - Falcon Rice Mill Inc.
HOME COUTURE - Housewares - Marcie Vesel Bronkar
HOME CRAFTED TOYS - Toys - Homecrafters Manufacturing Corp.
HOME CREATIONS - Lamps - Meijer, Inc.
HOME CRISPS - Potato chips - Groff's Snack-Food
HOME CYCLE - Exercising equipment - Tunturi, Inc.
HOME DAIRIES - Dairy products - Dairigold Inc.
HOME DEC IN-A-SEC - Craft supplies - Mccall Pattern Co.
HOME DECOR - Fabrics - Ramallah, Inc.
HOME DECOR - Lamps ☆ - Poly-Optical Products, Inc.
HOME DECOR - Paints - Nu-Brite Chemical Co. Inc.
HOME DECOR - Stamps–hand - Personal Stamp Exchange
HOME DECORATING INSTITUTE COUNTRY CRAFTS COLLECTION, THE - Publisher's imprints - Cy Decosse Inc.
HOME DECORATOR - House furnishings - Miller Studio
HOME DECORATOR - Paints - Martin-Senour Co.
HOME DECORATORS COLLECTION - Housewares stores - Home Decorators Collection, Inc.
HOME DELIGHT - Floor coverings–carpet and rugs - Gulistan Carpet Inc.
HOME DELIGHT - Nuts–salted, roasted, cooked, or canned - Sunshine Pecan Co.

HOME DESIGN - Siding–insulating - Heartland Building Products Inc.
HOME DESIGN 3D - Computer software - Expert Software Inc.
HOME DIAGNOSTICS - Air purification systems - Purisys Inc.
HOME DINING SELECTIONS - Food products - Aspen Foods, a division of Koch Poultry
HOME DYNAMICS - Video tapes–blank - Rodale Press, Inc.
HOME EFFECTS FX - Linen - Crown Crafts, Inc.
HOME ENTERTAINER - Microphones - Shure Brothers, Inc.
HOME ESCENTIALS - Spices and extracts - Scentex Inc.
HOME ESSENTIALS - Computer software - Microsoft Corp.
HOME ESSENTIALS & BEYOND - Serving carts - Home Essentials & Beyond, Inc.
HOME FASHIONED FAVORITES - Candy - Russell Stover Candies, Inc.
HOME FIELD - Video tapes–blank - Home Court Productions Inc.
HOME FINDER SYSTEMS - Software - Home Finder Systems
HOME FINISHES - Paints - United Coatings, Inc.
HOME FIRE SHIELD, THE - Safety products - ANTHEM Inc.
HOME FIREMAN, THE - Fire extinguishers - Safehome Industries, Inc.
HOME FOR CHRISTMAS - Christmas tree ornaments - Creative Home Collections Inc.
HOME FOR THE HOLIDAYS - Craft supplies ☆ - VIP/VIP Crafts
HOME FOR THE HOLIDAYS - Dinnerware - Meiwa USA, Ltd.
HOME FOR THE HOLIDAYS - Towels - Revere Mills, Inc.
HOME FOUNDATIONS - Carpeting - Shaw Industries Inc.
HOME FRAGRANCE CENTER - Sachets - Natural Products Corp.
HOME FREE - Filters–air - Airguard Industries, Inc.
HOME FREE - Pet products - R.C. Steele Co.
HOME FRIES - Potato chips - Wise Foods
HOME FURNISHINGS COUNCIL - Furniture - Home Furnishings Council Inc.
HOME GAME - Frankfurters - Cher-Make Sausage Co.
HOME GARD - Locks–door - Truth Hardware Corp.
HOME GARDEN - Fruits and vegetables ☆ - Market Wholesale Grocery Co.
HOME GLOW - Floor coverings–carpet and rugs - Alexander Smith Carpets
HOME GROWN - Apparel and accessories - Chester County Sportswear Co. Inc.
HOME GROWN - Garden equipment ☆ - Uncle Milton Industries Inc.
HOME GROWN HYDRO-FARMS - Fruits and vegetables - Beth Ann Goldman
HOME GROWN THREADZ - T-shirts–men's - Home Grown Threadz, Inc.
HOME GUARD - Ashtrays–glass ☆ - Frank J. Curran-Esquire Chemical Co.
HOME GUARD - Electrical equipment - EFI Electronics Corp.
HOME GUARD - Locks–door - M-P Corp.
HOME GUARD - Paints ☆ - Atlas Chemical Co.
HOME HARBOR - Seafood products–fresh or frozen - Home Harbor Seafoods Inc.
HOME HEALTH - Cooking equipment–commercial - Alabama Manufacturing Co.
HOME HEALTH PRO - Health care products - Sandata Inc.
HOME HEARTH - Breads - Nabisco Foods Group
HOME HELPERS - Cleaning preparations - Frances Denney
HOME HELPERS - File folders - Duo Tang, Inc.
HOME HELPERS - Hosiery - Magla Products Inc.
HOME HERITAGE STATIONERY - Stationery - Cathy Wragg
HOME IMPRESSIONS - Bars–steel - HMI Industries Inc.
HOME IMPROVEMENT - Tools–hand-operated - Walt Disney Co.
HOME IMPROVEMENT KIT - Candy - Annedore's Fine Chocolates, Ltd.
HOME INFANT WARMER - Health care products - Physician Engineered Products
HOME INNOVATIONS BY GABRIELLE - Bathroom accessories - Home Innovations Inc.
HOME, JAMES! - Skin care products - Return of Home James!, Inc.
HOME JUICE - Fruit drinks–bottled or canned - Home Juice Co.
HOME KAIR - Medical apparatus - Kinetic Concepts, Inc.
HOME KIST - Crackers - Vista Bakery, Inc.
HOME KIT & CABOODLE - First aid kits - Economic Alliance Corp.
HOME LIBRARY CATALOGER - Computer software - Right on Programs
HOME LIFE - Paints - Proctor Paint & Varnish Co. Inc.
HOME LIVING - Lamps - Fishers Big Wheel, Inc.
HOME LOAN WIZARD - Computer software - Countrywide Funding Corp.
HOME MADE - Cigars - Swisher International, Inc.
HOME-MADE, MADE EASY! - Bakery products - Anna Lena's Cranberry Products, Inc.
HOME MAID - Fruit drinks–bottled or canned - Florida Home Juice Co.
HOME MAID - Molasses - Crompton and Knowles Corp.
HOME MARK - Floor coverings–carpet and rugs - Shaw Industries Inc.
HOME-MARK - Furniture–upholstered - Statesville Chair Co. Inc.
HOME MASSUESE - Massage products - Wahl Clipper Corp.

HOME MATES - Placemats - Stevens Linen Associates Inc.
HOME MATTERS - Video production - Discovery Communications, Inc.
HOME-MECH - Tools - Mayes Brothers Tool Manufacturing
HOME MEDIC - Cleaning preparations - CMC Inc.
HOME MEDICAL ADVISOR PRO - Computer storage devices–optical - Pixel Perfect Inc.
HOME MISER - Meters–gas - Home Integrated Technologies, Inc.
HOME 'N AUTO - Sponges - S.M. Arnold Inc.
HOME-N-AWAY - Coffee makers–electric - Metal Ware Corp.
HOME 'N AWAY - Games - Cadaco Div.
HOME 'N CAR PACK - Flashlights - Dorcy International, Inc.
HOME NATURALS - Towels - Excello Ltd.
HOME OF OPTICAL ILLUSIONARY ART - Posters - Manifestations Inc.
HOME OF QUALITY - Desserts - Calip Dairies, Inc.
HOME OF THE BOSTON RED SOX FENWAY PARK - Apparel and accessories - Boston Red Sox Baseball Club L.P.
HOME OF THE DOME - Tents - Creative Energies Inc.
HOME OF THE HAPPY AUTO PARTS - Motor vehicle parts and accessories - Jimmie's Auto Parts, Inc.
HOME OF THE HOCKEY DOCTOR, THE - Sporting goods - Edward Mrozowski
HOME OF THE LITTLE INDIAN - Boxes - Sheboygan Paper Box Co.
HOME OFFICE - Computer software ☆ - Spectrum Universal
HOME OFFICE - Furniture - Harden Furniture Co. Inc.
HOME OFFICE - Furniture ☆ - Lexington Furniture Industries, Inc.
HOME ON THE GO - Toys - Mattel, Inc.
HOME ON THE RANGE - Kitchen utensils–aluminum - Amco Corp.
HOME ON THE RANGE - Wallpaper ☆ - Imperial Wallcoverings, Inc.
HOME ORGANIZER - Computer software - Tandy Corp.
HOME ORGANIZER'S CHOICE - Shelving - InterMetro Industries Corp.
HOME OVEN - Clay–modeling ☆ - Duncan Enterprises
HOME OWNER - Brushes–paint - E-Z Paintr Corp.
HOME OWNERS - Pet products - Excel-Mineral Co. Inc.
HOME PAK - Fasteners–hook and eye - VSI Fasteners, Inc.
HOME-PERFECTED - Flour–blended ☆ - General Mills, Inc.
HOME PHONE - Compact discs–prerecorded - Pro CD Inc.
HOME PHONE COMPANION - Paper products - Riverside Solutions
HOME PHONE PAD - Paper products - Riverside Solutions
HOME PLACES ALL THROUGH THE HOUSE - Wallcovering - Fashon Wallcoverings
HOME PLANNERS - Publisher's imprints - Home Planners Inc.
HOME PLATE - Apparel and accessories - Pan Am Knitwear, Inc.
HOME PLAY - Sporting goods - Schutt Manufacturing Co.
HOME PLUMBER - Plumbing fittings - Brass Craft Manufacturing Co.
HOME PLUS H+ - Containers–plastic - Siong Sing Tan
HOME PRETTY - Dolls - Mattel, Inc.
HOME PRIDE - Bread - Interstate Brands Corp.
HOME PRIDE - Breads - Interstate Brands Co. - Licensing Co.
HOME PRIDE - Faucets - Sisco, Inc.
HOME PRIDE HEARTY - Breads - Interstate Brands Corp.
HOME PRIDE WHITE GRAIN - Bread - Interstate Brands Corp.
HOME PRO - Cleaning preparations - Specialty Chemical Resources, Inc.
HOME-PRO - Containers - Stack-On Products Co.
HOME PRO - Water dispensers - Alaska Fish Fertilizer Co.
HOME PRO LINE, THE - Silicon products - General Electric Co.
HOME REFEREE KIT - Sporting goods - Amanda Moseley
HOME REMEDIES - Computer software - Parsons Technology, Inc.
HOME ROCK ENTERTAINMENT - Puzzles - Worldwide Games, Inc.
HOME RUN - Chewing gum - Philadelphia Chewing Gum Corp.
HOME RUN - Cigarettes ☆ - Liggett Group Inc.
HOME RUN - Collectible trading cards - ANCO Collector Supplies, Inc.
HOME RUN - Confections - Tuscan
HOME RUN - Eyeglasses - Dioptics Medical Products, Inc.
HOME RUN - Food products - Little Caesar Enterprises, Inc.
HOME RUN - Fruits and vegetables - Edward Pitsch Produce Inc.
HOME RUN - Games - Smethport Specialty Co.
HOME RUN - Pasta - Buckeye Beans & Herbs, Inc.
HOME RUN - Video games - Atari Games Corp.
HOME RUN INN - Pizzas–frozen - Home Run Inn Frozen Foods
HOME RUN SNACKS - Bakery products - California Pie Co., Inc.
HOME-RUN TALL - Flowers, plants, and seeds - Seed Corp. of America
HOME SACHET - Deodorizers ☆ - American Air Filter International (Replacement Filter Products)
HOME SAFE - Apparel stores–sports - Face Guards Inc.
HOME SAFE - Shutters–wood - Qualitas Manufacturing, Inc.
HOME SAVER - Paints - Sophir Morris Paint

☆ = Now out of production

HOME-SAVER SHUTTERS - Shutters–metal - Prime Marketing Group, Inc.

HOME SECURITY INSURANCE INVENTORY - Computer software - Right on Programs

HOME SOURCE - Tiles–ceramic - Dal-Tile Corp.

HOME SPAS - Bedding–linen - Dan River Inc.

HOME SPRINGS - Water purification systems - Stone Mountain Water Co.

HOME SPUN - Housewares ☆ - King Cotton Cordage Co.

HOME STATEMENTS - Tablecloths - Fashion Industries Inc.

HOME STRETCH - Apparel and accessories - Russ Togs Inc.

HOME STRETCH - Games ☆ - Milton Bradley Co.

HOME STUFF - Cookware - Home Stuff Co., Inc.

HOME STYLE - Breads - Cole's Quality Foods, Inc.

HOME STYLE - Chili sauce - John's Chili Parlor

HOME STYLE - Food products - Coloma Frozen Foods Inc.

HOME STYLE - Food products - Home Style Foods Inc.

HOME STYLE - Onions - Delicious Foods Co.

HOME STYLE - Sandwiches–prepackaged - E.A. Sween Co.

HOME-STYLE - Sausages ☆ - Pacific Westcoast Foods

HOME STYLE - Teas - Snapple Beverage Corp.

HOME STYLE FUDGE - Fudge - Nabisco Foods Group

HOME STYLER - Clippers–barber - Wahl Clipper Corp.

HOME STYLER - Paints - Martin-Senour Co.

HOME SUITE - Pet products - Circle K Industries Inc.

HOME SURVIVAL TOOLKIT - Computer software - Books That Work

HOME SWEET HOME - Fabrics–tapestry ☆ - Coloroll Inc.

HOME, SWEET HOME - Games - J. Hermes

HOME SWEET HOME - Linen - Notra Trading, Inc.

HOME SWEET HOME - Ribbons - Fabric Barn

HOME SWEET HOME - Ribbons - Jay Keegan

HOME SWEET HOME GOURMET COOKIES - Cookies - Home Sweet Home Gourmet Cookies

HOME TEAM - Lighting fixtures - Spartus Corp.

HOME TEAM ADVANTAGE - Clothing - Nutmeg Mills, Inc.

HOME TECH - Audio equipment - Dana Innovations

HOME THEATER SYNERGY - Audio equipment - International Super Store Connection, Inc.

HOME THEATRE - Electronic equipment - Thomson Consumer Electronics, Inc.

HOME THERAPA - Candles - Hanna's Potpourri Specialties, Inc.

HOME-TIES - Twine - January and Wood Co. Inc.

HOME TIPS - Paper–newsprint - Barcharts, Inc.

HOME TOWN - Milk - Roberts Hometown Dairy

HOME TOWN COLLECTION, THE - Paper products - National Association of Professional Baseball Leagues, Inc.

HOME TRADITIONS - Lamps - L. Kee & Co., Inc.

HOME TRIM - Clippers–barber - Sunbeam-Oster Household Products

HOME TWEET HOME - Bird feeders - Home Tweet Home

HOME TWISTER - Yarn ☆ - Knitting Fever Inc.

HOME-UTILITY - Tools ☆ - Black & Decker Corp.

HOME VENTORY - Computer software - Zephyr Services

HOME VISITOR 7 14 34 35 57 66 - Snack foods - Zachary Shalvarjian

HOME-VUE - Lighting fixtures - Lithonia Lighting

HOME WEAVE - Hosiery ☆ - Paul Lavitt Mills, Inc.

HOME WORKPLAN - Educational materials - Fournier Learning Strategies

HOME WORKS - Electronic equipment - Zenith Electronics Corp.

HOME ZOO - Play map - Integra Toys, Inc.

HOMEADVANTAGE - Computer peripheral equipment - Logicon Syscon, Inc.

HOMEAGAIN - Data loggers - Schering Corp.

HOMEBAKE - Pizzas–mixes - HomeBake Pizza Shoppes Inc.

HOMEBEST - Film - Wetterau Inc.

HOMEBEST - Housewares - Super Valu Inc.

HOMEBOUND STUDIOS - Figurines - Homebound Studios

HOMEBOY - Jewelry - Resource Enterprises Collective, Inc.

HOMEBRAIN - Electrical equipment - Hypertek, Inc.

HOMEBUILDERS COUPLES SERIES - Publisher's imprints - Campus Crusade for Christ, Inc.

HOMEBUILDERS, THE - School supplies - Georgia-Pacific Corp.

HOMEBUYER - Real estate agencies - Robert Takeda Blake

HOMECARE - Apparel–children's ☆ - Mount Vernon Mills Inc.

HOMECARE - Computer software - Infomed

HOMECARE - Electrical equipment - Gordon's Markets

HOMECARE PAC - Home-health-care products - Infomed

HOMECHECK - Medical apparatus ☆ - Penox Technologies Inc.

HOMECHOICE - Bathroom accessories - Lenape Products Co., Inc.

HOMECHOICE - Home health care products - Baxter International Inc.

HOMECLOSE - Banks–commercial - Mcpinto & Associates, Inc.

HOMECOMING - Floor coverings ☆ - Tarkett, Inc.

HOMECOMING - Furniture - Thomasville Furniture Industries Inc.

HOMECOMING - Recording label - Aztec Corp.

HOMECOMING - Wallpaper ☆ - Pantasote Inc. (Wallcovering Div.)

HOMECOMING KIT - Bird cages - Petland, Inc.

HOMECOMING QUEEN - Dolls - Mattel, Inc.

HOMECRAFT - Construction equipment ☆ - Homecraft Corp.

HOMECRAFT - Floor coverings–carpet and rugs - Cabin Crafts Carpets

HOMECRAFT - Hardware - Dynacast

HOMECRAFT - Windows–storm - Duo-Temp

HOMECRAFT - Wood products ☆ - States Industries Inc.

HOMECRAFT - Yarn ☆ - January and Wood Co. Inc.

HOMECREST - Cabinets - HomeCrest Corp.

HOMEDCO - Pharmaceutical preparations - Homedco, Inc.

HOMEDEFENSE - Insecticides - Monsanto Co.

HOMEFILE - File folders - Financial Advantage Inc.

HOMEFILER - Computer software - Software Innovations, Inc.

HOMEFIRE COAL-PAK - Charcoal - Homefire Inc.

HOMEFOAM - Foam rubber ☆ - Voltek Inc.

HOMEFOLKS - Food products - Allen Canning Co.

HOMEFONE - Telephones ☆ - TIE Communications Inc.

HOMEFRONT - Electrical equipment - Wal-Mart Stores Inc.

HOMEFRONT - Siding - Amerimark Building Products, Inc.

HOMEGAME - Frankfurters - Cher-Make Sausage Co.

HOMEGARD - Paints - Sampson Coatings Inc.

HOMEGROWN - Bicycles - Schwinn Cycling & Fitness Inc.

HOMEGROWN BEEF PREMIUM BEEF - Meat products - Homegrown, Inc.

HOMEGROWN VIDEO - Recording label - Frontier Media, Inc.

HOMEHEALTH SOLUTION, THE - Computer software - Healthcare Automation Inc.

HOMELAND - Food products - Hormel Foods Corp.

HOMELAND - Recording label - Homeland Recording & Publishing

HOMELAND - Siding - Heartland Building Products Inc.

HOMELAWN - Flowers, plants, and seeds - NK Lawn & Garden Co.

HOMELESS ANGEL, THE - Christmas tree ornaments - Ford's Produce Co., Inc.

HOMELIFE - Caulking compounds - Leech Products Inc.

HOMELINE - Circuit breakers - Square D Co.

HOMELINE - Envelopes ☆ - Westvaco Corp.

HOMELINE - Heating equipment - Rheem Manufacturing Co.

HOMELINE - Telephone answering machines - Homeline of Virginia, Inc.

HOMELINK - Electrical equipment - Prince Corp.

HOMELITE - Lawn mowers - Homelite, Inc.

HOMELITE - Tools–power-driven - Textron Inc.

HOMEMADE - Frozen yogurt novelties - United Dairy Farmers Inc.

HOMEMADE BRAND - Ice cream - United Dairy Farmers Inc.

HOMEMADE CANDY - Candy - Hooper's Chocolates

HOMEMADES - Candy ☆ - Price Candy Co. Inc.

HOMEMAIL - Computer software - SL Software, Inc.

HOMEMAKER - Furniture - Bean Station Furniture Factory Inc.

HOMEMAKER - Sofabeds ☆ - Aireloom Bedding Co.

HOMEMAKER'S CHOICE - Hardware - Dynacast

HOMEMATE - Remote control devices - Lamson & Sessions Co.

HOMEO PET - Homeopathic remedies - Washington Homeopathic Products

HOMEODENT - Toothpaste - Boiron Inc.

HOMEOENERGETICS - Vitamins and nutritional supplements - Apex Energetics Inc.

HOMEOPATHY WORKS - Homeopathic remedies - Washington Homeopathic Products

HOMEOPET - Pet products - Natural Animal Health Products, Inc.

HOMEOVITICS - Vitamins and nutritional supplements - HVS Laboratories

HOMEOWNERS ASSOCIATION DIRECTORS' SURVIVAL KIT - Computer software - George B. Markle

HOMEOWNERS CHOICE - Paints - Sherwin-Williams Automotive Finishes Corp.

HOMEOWNER'S CHOICE - Tools–hand-operated - Harbor Sales Co.

HOMEPLACE - Furniture ☆ - Athens Furniture Industries Inc.

HOMEPLACES - Wallpaper - Gencorp Inc.

HOMEPLACES CLASSIC ELEGANCE - Wallcovering - Fashon Wallcoverings

HOMEPLACES COTTAGE EDITION - Wallcovering - Fashon Wallcoverings

HOMEPLACES OLDER KIDS - Wallcovering - Fashon Wallcoverings

HOMEPLACES SOFT CONTEMPORARY - Wallcovering - Fashon Wallcoverings

HOMEPLACES SOPHISTICATED - Wallcovering - Fashon Wallcoverings

HOMEPLACES TRADITIONAL - Wallcovering - Fashon Wallcoverings

HOMEPLACES WEEKEND RETREAT - Wallcovering - Fashon Wallcoverings

HOMEPORT - Wallpaper - China Seas Inc.
HOMEPOURRI - Giftware ☆ - Tsumura International Inc.
HOMEPRINTS - Recording label - Visual Coordination by Carole Talbott, Inc.
HOMEPRO - Clippers–barber - Wahl Clipper Corp.
HOMEPROFILE - Computer software - Transamerica Intellitech, Inc.
HOMEPUMP - Health care products - Block Medical, Inc.
HOMEPUMP - Vitamins and nutritional supplements - Mcgaw, Inc.
HOMEPUMP ECLIPSE - Surgical instruments - Block Medical, Inc.
HOMEQUEST - Grinders - Jessup Manufacturing Co.
HOMEQUEST II - Floor coverings–carpet and rugs - Prestige Mills Inc.
HOMER - Golfing equipment ☆ - Henry-Griffitts, Inc.
HOMER - Jewelry, watches - Disegno Collection
HOMER CLOWN - Dolls ☆ - Effanbee Doll Corp.
HOMER FINE FOODS - Food products - Christopher Brookes Distinctive Foods
HOMER/HERON - Sporting goods - Brookes & Gatehouse Inc.
HOMER LAUGHLIN - Dishes–china - Homer Laughlin China Co.
HOMER SMITH - Seafood products–fresh or frozen - BG Lobster & Shrimp Corp.
HOMEROOM - Publisher's imprints - Scholastic Inc.
HOMERX - Vascular compression stockings and pumps - Kendall Co.
HOMES CONSTRUCTION SERVICE - Construction equipment rental services - Mankind Research Unltd. Inc.
HOMES WITH A SILVER LINING - Prefabricated buildings–metal - Angeles Metal Systems
HOMES WIZARD - Computer software - Oz Software Inc.
HOMESAFE - Adhesives and sealants ☆ - Champion International Corp.
HOMESCAPES - Wallpaper - Chapters Wallcoverings
HOMESEAL - Plastics film - Foamseal, Inc.
HOMESEAL N.A.I.S. - Adhesives and sealants - Foamseal, Inc.
HOMESELECT - Carpets - E.I. Dupont de Nemours and Co.
HOMESENSE - Electrical equipment - Homesense Corp.
HOMESHIELD - Construction equipment ☆ - Nichols-Homeshield Inc.
HOMESIDE - Building materials–concrete - Amerimark Building Products, Inc.
HOMESPOT - Food products - Blue Anchor Inc.
HOMESPUN - Clocks - General Time Corp. (Westclox/Seth Thomas Div.)
HOMESPUN - Dinnerware–glass - Nikko Ceramics Inc.
HOMESPUN - Dishes–china - Taylor, Smith & Taylor Co.
HOMESPUN - Fabrics–tapestry - Art Metal-U.S. Corp.
HOMESPUN - Floor coverings–carpet and rugs - Capel, Inc.
HOMESPUN - Floor coverings–carpet and rugs - Langhorne Carpet Co. Inc.
HOMESPUN - Floor coverings–carpet and rugs - Southern Carpet Mills
HOMESPUN - Floor coverings–carpet and rugs - Whitecrest Carpet Mills
HOMESPUN - Floor coverings–carpet and rugs ☆ - Columbus Mills, Inc.
HOMESPUN - Hosiery - Rudin & Roth Inc.
HOMESPUN - Napkins–paper - Erving Paper Mills
HOMESPUN - Stencils - Plaid Enterprises, Inc.
HOMESPUN - Wallpaper - United Wallcoverings
HOMESPUN - Wood products - Champion International Corp.
HOMESPUN - Yarn - Lion Brand Yarn Co.
HOMESPUN COLORS - Cosmetics ☆ - Noxell Corp.
HOMESPUN CREATIONS - Toys–stuffed - Dan-Dee International Ltd.
HOMESPUN LOVE - Magnets - Russ Berrie and Co., Inc.
HOMESPUN MAZURKAS - Cookies - Homespun Foods Inc.
HOMESPUN PLACEMATS - Placemats - Tara Handcrafts
HOMESPUN SHAKER - House furnishings - Lexington Furniture Industries, Inc.
HOMESPUN TAPES - Recording label - Homespun Tapes Inc.
HOMESPUN TREASURES - Giftware - Russ Berrie and Co., Inc.
HOMESTAKE MINING COMPANY HMC - Gold products - Homestake Mining Co.
HOMESTAR - Fans–electric - Homestead Products
HOMESTAR - Windows - Homestar Industries, Inc.
HOMESTEAD - Bakeware ☆ - Corning Inc.
HOMESTEAD - Barbecues and grills - Prochef, Inc.
HOMESTEAD - Bedding–linen - Whiting Manufacturing Co. Inc.
HOMESTEAD - Building supplies - J & W Fence Supply Co. Inc.
HOMESTEAD - Cabinets - Merillat Industries, Inc.
HOMESTEAD - Candles - Country Candle Co., Inc.
HOMESTEAD - Candy - Helms Candy Manufacturing Co. Inc.
HOMESTEAD - Ceramic kitchenware ☆ - Knobler International Ltd.
HOMESTEAD - Clocks - General Time Corp. (Westclox/Seth Thomas Div.)
HOMESTEAD - Dolls ☆ - Caron International Inc.
HOMESTEAD - Doors–metal - Pease Industries, Inc.
HOMESTEAD - Doors–storm - Vantage Products Inc.
HOMESTEAD - Fertilizers - Greenview Lawn & Garden Products
HOMESTEAD - Fireplace equipment - Seymour Manufacturing Co.,Inc.
HOMESTEAD - Floor coverings - Bruce Hardwood Floors

HOMESTEAD - Floor coverings - Mannington Resilient Floors
HOMESTEAD - Floor coverings–carpet and rugs - Cabin Crafts Carpets
HOMESTEAD - Floor coverings–carpet and rugs ☆ - Rugby Rugs Inc.
HOMESTEAD - Furniture ☆ - Universal Flooring
HOMESTEAD - Furniture–wood - Design Line Cabinets
HOMESTEAD - Garden equipment ☆ - Parker Sweeper Co.
HOMESTEAD - Glassware–household ☆ - Fenton Art Glass Co.
HOMESTEAD - Heaters–kerosene - Sunbeam-Oster Household Products
HOMESTEAD - Housewares ☆ - Doranne
HOMESTEAD - Lamps ☆ - Lamplight Farms, Inc.
HOMESTEAD - Meats–luncheon - John Liber & Co. Inc.
HOMESTEAD - Melamine product - Boonton Molding Co. Inc.
HOMESTEAD - Milk ☆ - Land O' Lakes, Inc. (Fluid Dairy Division)
HOMESTEAD - Paper–toweling - Grand Union Co.
HOMESTEAD - Ravioli–canned - Homestead Ravioli Co.
HOMESTEAD - Recording label - County Records
HOMESTEAD - Stains - Distribution America, Inc.
HOMESTEAD - Tiles–ceramic ☆ - Wenczel Tile Co.
HOMESTEAD - Trailers–travel ☆ - Carriage, Inc.
HOMESTEAD - Wines - Ehrle Bros. Inc.
HOMESTEAD COLLECTION - Furniture - Sligh Furniture Co.
HOMESTEAD GALLEY RAIL - Hardware - Marley Mouldings Inc.
HOMESTEAD LIFE COLLECTION - Figurines - W.C. Owen Inc.
HOMESTEAD MILLS - Flour–blended - Homestead Mills
HOMESTEAD PARTNERS, THE - Construction equipment - Homestead Partners, Inc.
HOMESTEAD PINE - Furniture - Vaughan Furniture Co. Inc.
HOMESTEAD PROVINCIAL - Dinnerware–glass - Metlox Pottery Shoppe
HOMESTEAD SUGAR HOUSE - Candy - Homestead Products (Homestead Sugar Division)
HOMESTEADER - Motor vehicles–motor homes - K & S Manufacturing Inc.
HOMESTEADER - Soups–frozen ☆ - John Labatt Foods
HOMESTEADER - Tool boxes - Universal Cooperative Inc.
HOMESTEADERS - Stoves ☆ - Martin Industries, Inc.
HOMESTRETCH - Apparel and accessories - Sutton Shirt Corp.
HOMESTRETCH - Computer software - Iwn, Inc.
HOMESTYLE - Bakery products - Pan-O-Gold Baking Co.
HOMESTYLE - Bedding–linen - Dan River Inc.
HOMESTYLE - Beverages - Logret Import & Export Co.
HOMESTYLE - Confections - Sara Lee Corp.
HOMESTYLE - Floor coverings–carpet and rugs - Mohawk Carpet Corp.
HOMESTYLE - Food products - Best Foods/Mueller Co.
HOMESTYLE - Food products - General Mills, Inc.
HOMESTYLE - Food products - Homestyle Foods
HOMESTYLE - Food products - Tyson Foods Inc.
HOMESTYLE - Fruit butters - J.M. Smucker Co.
HOMESTYLE - Glassware–household - Libbey Glass Inc.
HOMESTYLE - Glassware–household - Owens-Illinois Inc. (Libbey Div.)
HOMESTYLE - Ice cream - Maplehurst Farms Inc.
HOMESTYLE - Ice cream - Purity Dairies, Inc.
HOMESTYLE - Juices - Tropicana Products, Inc.
HOMESTYLE - Kitchen appliances - West Bend Co.
HOMESTYLE - Snack foods ☆ - Wyandot, Inc.
HOMESTYLE - Soups–mixes - Lipton Investments, Inc.
HOMESTYLE - Soups–mixes - Nile Spice Foods Inc.
HOMESTYLE - Towels - Shavel Associates, Inc.
HOMESTYLE - Trailers–travel ☆ - Shasta Industries Inc.
HOMESTYLE CHUNKY - Food products - Pet Inc.
HOMESTYLE COLLECTION - Cookies - Archway Cookie Inc.
HOMESTYLE HAMBURGER HELPER - Food products - General Mills, Inc.
HOMESTYLE HELPER - Food products - General Mills, Inc.
HOMESTYLE NATURALS - Soups–canned - Westbrae Natural Foods, Inc.
HOMESTYLE SEPARATES - Food products - Hunt-Wesson, Inc.
HOMESTYLES - Furniture - Ernst Home Center Inc.
HOMESTYLES - Occasional furniture ☆ - JDI Group, Inc.
HOMESTYLES - Slippers - Supreme Slipper Manufacturing Co., Inc.
HOMESTYLES - Wallpaper - Warner Co.
HOMETASTING - Gravy - Del Monte Corp.
HOMETER, THE - Meters–electric ☆ - Schelling Manufacturing Corp.
HOMETLE - Mobile homes - Skyline Corp.
HOMETOWN - Bakery products - Flowers Industries Inc.
HOMETOWN - Building materials–asbestos - Champion International Corp.
HOMETOWN - Lumber - Georgia-Pacific Corp.
HOMETOWN - Pasta - Hometown
HOMETOWN - Recording label - Homeland Recording & Publishing
HOMETOWN - Underwear and nightwear - J.E. Morgan Knitting Mills

☆ = Now out of production

HOMETOWN AMERICA - Puzzles - Warren Industries Inc.

HOMETOWN AMERICA 2 PACK - Puzzles - Warren Industries Inc.

HOMETOWN BUNNIES - Chocolate candy - Superior Fruit & Confections

HOMETOWN CLASSICS - Food products ☆ - R.L. Products Corp.

HOMETOWN FINISHES - Paints - United Coatings, Inc.

HOMETOWN HEROES - Trading cards - Score Group, Inc.

HOMETOWN HOLIDAYS - Figurines - Noma International, Inc.

HOMETOWN STARS - Cereal - Carlisle Cereal Co.

HOMETOWN TREES - Trees - IGA Inc.

HOMETOWNE COLLECTION - Furniture ☆ - Berkline Corp.

HOMETRAC - Medical apparatus - Saunders Group

HOMETRENDS - Linen - Wal-Mart Stores Inc.

HOMEVIEW - Computer software - Whitaker Corp.

HOMEVU - Computer software - Netlight Systems, Inc.

HOMEVUE - Computers - Homevue Health Systems, Inc.

HOMEWAITER 75 - Dumbwaiter - Inclinator Co. of America

HOMEWARD BOUND - Candlesticks ☆ - Carolina Designs Ltd.

HOMEWARD BOUND - Pet products - R.A.F. Trading Inc.

HOMEWATCH HOLIDAY SAFETY - Broadcasting stations–cable television - Scripps Howard Broadcasting

HOMEWATER - Filters–water - Value Direct Filtration Systems, Inc.

HOMEWAY - Construction equipment - Homeway Corp.

HOMEWERK - Desks - Orman Grubb Co.

HOMEWIRE - Wire–copper - Southwire Co.

HOMEWOOD - Doors–glass - Malta Co.

HOMEWOOD - Doors–metal - Jeld-Wen, Inc.

HOMEWOOD - Furniture - Dinaire Corp.

HOMEWOOD COLLECTION - Furniture ☆ - Evenflo Juvenile Furniture Co.

HOMEWORD - Computer software - Sierra On-Line, Inc.

HOMEWORK COLLECTOR - Computer software - Worthington Publishing Co., Inc.

HOMEWORK HELPERS - Computer software - Queue Inc.

HOMEWORK TOOL BOX - School supplies - Wanda M. Reynolds and William J. Reynolds Partnership

HOMEWORK WITHOUT TEARS - Video production - Canter and Associates, Inc.

HOMEWORKER - Computer software ☆ - Knowledge Adventure

HOMEWORKS - Computer software - Paradygn Concepts Inc.

HOMEWORKS - Electrical equipment - Lutron Electronics Co., Inc.

HOMEWORKS - Furniture - Sligh Furniture Co.

HOMEWORKS - Glassware–household - Toscany Imports Ltd.

HOMEWORKS - Office furniture–plastic - Rubbermaid Office Products Inc.

HOMEWORKS UNLIMITED - Clocks - Sligh Furniture Co.

HOMEWORLD - Computer software ☆ - Legend Entertainment Co.

HOMEWORLD - Dinnerware–glass - Stanley Roberts, Inc.

HOMEWRECKER - Tools - Cepco Tool Co.

HOMEWRITE - Computer peripheral equipment - Logicon Syscon, Inc.

HOMEWURKS - Knives - Fiskars Inc.

HOMEX 300 - Sealing compounds - Homasote Co.

HOMEY D. CLOWN - Computer software - Capstone Software

HOMGRON DESIGNS - T-shirts–men's - Homgron Designs

HOMICEBRIN - Vitamins and nutritional supplements - Eli Lilly and Co.

HOMIES - T-shirts–men's - Gonzales Graphics, Inc.

HOMKO - Garden equipment - Minstar Inc.

HOMMUS FACTORY INC., THE - Food products - Hommus Factory Inc.

HOMO-FERRUM - Beverages ☆ - Standard Homeopathic Co., Inc.

HOMO-TET - Pharmaceutical preparations ☆ - Savage Laboratories Inc.

HOMOCYSTEINE DEFENSE - Health care products - Healthwatchers System

HOMOGEN - Pharmaceutical preparations ☆ - Wesley Pharmacal Co. Inc.

HOMOGENE-S - Pharmaceutical preparations - G.O. Spanner Inc.

HOMOGENITE - Fertilizers - Howard Fertilizer Co., Inc.

HOMONYM HEROES - Electronic equipment ☆ - Texas Instruments Inc.

HOMS - Office supplies - Douglas Homs Corp.

HOMS DIAL-A-PHRASE - Office supplies - Douglas Homs Corp.

HON - Bicycles ☆ - Toppertown Inc.

HON - Office furniture–metal - Hon Co.

HON-E-WAX - Cosmetics ☆ - Jason Natural Products, Inc.

HONAN - Floor coverings–carpet and rugs ☆ - Trans-Ocean Import Co. Inc.

HONAY HILL FARMS - Yogurt - Alpine Distribution Services

HONCHO - Fabrics - Dan River Inc.

HONCHO - Fabrics–twill - Greenwood Mills Inc.

HONCHO - Food products - Jardine's Texas Foods

HONCHO - Furniture - Bassick Casters

HONCHO - Motorcycles ☆ - Suzuki of America Automotive Corp.

HONCHO - Wigs ☆ - Jean Paree Weegs Inc.

HONCHO - Wire products - Kaspar Wire Works, Inc.

HONCHO DEFENDER - Furniture - Bassick Casters

HONCHO GRANDE - Beverages–alcohol - Yellow Rose Brewing Co

HONCHORITA - Beverages–alcohol - Houlihan's Restaurants, Inc.

HONDA - Motor vehicles - American Honda Motor Co. Inc. (Acura Div.)

HONDASHI - Food products - Ajinomoto USA, Inc.

HONDIUS - Maps ☆ - Replogle Globes Inc.

HONDO - Bicycles - Columbia Manufacturing Inc.

HONDO - Boots - Hondo Boots

HONDO - Fretted instruments - International Music Corp.

HONDO - Guitars - MBT International, Inc.

HONDU-RICA - Sour cream - Zamorano Enterprises, Inc.

HONEE - Skin care products - American International Industries

HONEE - Skin care products - Gigi Laboratories

HONEE SWEET - Food products ☆ - W.B. Roddenbery Co., Inc.

HONEES - Candy - Andre Prost Inc.

HONEST - Snuff - Conwood Co. L.P.

HONEST DINER - Coffee - Diner, Inc.

HONEST JOHN - Cement - Rectorseal Corp.

HONEST JOHN - Toys–models - Cox Products Inc.

HONEST JOHN - Toys–models ☆ - Estes Industries

HONEST LONG CUT - Tobacco - American Tobacco Co.

HONEST-TO-GOODNESS.GOODNESS DUTCH KITCHEN - Sausages - Dutch Packing Co.

HONESTLY FRESH SQUEEZED - Juices - Vero Beach Groves Inc.

HONESTY - Cosmetics - Jean Philippe Fragrances, Inc.

HONEY - Candy ☆ - Perugina Chocolate & Confections Inc.

HONEY - Cereal - Ralston Purina Co.

HONEY - Fudge - Honey House

HONEY - Motor vehicles–motor homes ☆ - Honey Recreational Vehicles Inc.

HONEY - Publisher's imprints - Country Bazaar-Publishing

HONEY - Toys - Giordano Art, Ltd.

HONEY - Toys - Mattel, Inc.

HONEY - Wines - Olympic Cellars

HONEY - Yarn - National Spinning Co., Inc.

HONEY ACRES - Honey - Honey Acres Inc.

HONEY ALMOND - Deodorants–personal - Bertsherm Products Inc.

HONEY ALMOND - Shampoos - Demert & Dougherty, Inc.

HONEY ALMOND OATIOS - Cereal - New Morning

HONEY & GOLD - Pet products - Carlson Speciality Seeds, Inc.

HONEY & NUT TOASTED OATS - Breakfast cereal - Malt-O-Meal Co.

HONEY & SPICE - Cosmetics - Honey & Spice Toiletries

HONEY B - Crocheted and knitted items - Beldoch Industries Corp.

HONEY-B-ANISE - Hair care products - Henry Thayer Co.

HONEY BABY - Crocheted and knitted items - Beldoch Industries Corp.

HONEY BEAR - Apparel–children's - Bomark Group Inc.

HONEY BEAR - Bicycles - Murray, Inc.

HONEY BEAR - Pet products - Precious Paws

HONEY BEAR - Puppets - Russ Berrie and Co., Inc.

HONEY BEAR - Puzzles ☆ - Warren Industries Inc.

HONEY BEARS - Christmas tree ornaments - Prosperity Tree International

HONEY BEE - Bicycles - Columbia Manufacturing Inc.

HONEY BEE - Cabinets - Bee Cabinet Corp.

HONEY BEE - Food products - Mid-America Potato Co.

HONEY BEE - Motor vehicles–automobiles ☆ - Nissan Motor Corp. USA

HONEY BEE - Recording label - Freko Records

HONEY BEE - Sporting goods - Jobe Ski Corp.

HONEY BOY - Honey - Barkman Honey Co. Inc.

HONEY BRAN - Cereal - Ralston Purina Co.

HONEY BROSIA - Skin care products - Goubaud

HONEY BUG - Apparel–children's - Blue Bird Knitwear Co.

HONEY BUN - Dolls ☆ - Effanbee Doll Corp.

HONEY BUN - Food products - Nabisco Foods Group

HONEY BUN BEAR - Toys–stuffed ☆ - Dakin Inc.

HONEY BUNCH - Toys–stuffed ☆ - Fun World Inc.

HONEY BUNCHES OF OATS - Cereal - Kraft Foods, Inc.

HONEY BUNNY - Greeting cards - Norcross Inc.

HONEY BUNNY - Toys–stuffed ☆ - Fun World Inc.

HONEY CLENZ - Hair care products - Image Laboratories, Inc.

HONEY COMB - Pizza crust - Joe Corbi's Wholesale Pizza Inc.

HONEY-COMBE-FOME - Cleaning preparations - Swiss-Tex Inc.

HONEY CORDIALS - Food products - Oregon Apiaries

HONEY CREEK - Cheese - Dairy Fresh Products Co.

HONEY CREEK - Furniture - Arbek Furniture Manufacturing Inc.

HONEY CREST - Tobacco–chewing or smoking - Amar Blends Co.

HONEY CREST - Turkeys - Lee Harris Farms, Inc.

HONEY CRUNCH STARS - Cereal - Barbara's Bakery, Inc.

HONEY CRUNCHERS - Candy - Nabisco Foods Group
HONEY DEW - Beverages–carbonated - Monarch Co., Inc.
HONEY DEW - Food products - Brechet and Richter Co.
HONEY DEW - Tobacco–chewing or smoking - Gesty Trading & Manufacturing Corp.
HONEY DEW DOUGHNUTS - Doughnuts - Honey Dewassociates, Inc.
HONEY-DIPT - Food products - Pierce Foods Corp.
HONEY-DRI SPRINKLE - Honey ☆ - Miller's Honey Co.
HONEY ESSENCE - Candy - Queen Bee Gardens
HONEY FACTORY, THE - Computer software - CBS Software
HONEY FLUFF - Honey - Howland's Honey
HONEY FROSTED FLAKES - Cereal - New Morning
HONEY FROSTED FLAKES-FLAX/OMEGA3 - Cereal - New Morn, Inc.
HONEY FROSTED WHEATIES - Cereal - General Mills, Inc.
HONEY GLOW - Varnish, paintbrushes - Corona Brushes Inc.
HONEY GOLD - Cereal - General Mills, Inc.
HONEY GOLD - Cooking equipment–household ☆ - General Housewares Corp.
HONEY GOLD BEANS - Snack foods ☆ - Robison Ranch
HONEY GOLD WHEATIES - Cereal - General Mills, Inc.
HONEY GONE NUTS - Food products - Breadshop's Natural Foods
HONEY GRAHAM CRACKERS - Crackers - New Morning
HONEY GRAHAM MINI-BITES - Cereal - New Morn, Inc.
HONEY GRAHAMS - Cereal - New Morn, Inc.
HONEY GRAHAMS - Crackers - R.W. Frookies Inc.
HONEY GRAIN - Breads - Campbell Taggart Inc.
HONEY GRAIN - Breads - Flowers Bakeries
HONEY GROVE - Food products - White Villa Famous Foods
HONEY GROVE - Furniture ☆ - Singer Furniture Co.
HONEY HILL FARMS AVARI CREME GLACE - Desserts - Honey Hill Farms Frozen Yogurt
HONEY HIVE MIXTURE - Tobacco products - Shepherd Tobacco Co.
HONEY HOOKERS - Cookies - Dainty Cookies Inc.
HONEY HOUSE, THE - Honey - Honey House Enterprises, Inc.
HONEY HUGGIE BUNNY - Toys–stuffed - Spearhead Industries Inc.
HONEY JUMBOS - Cookies - Health Valley Food
HONEY KANES - Honey - Universal Products Co.
HONEY KISSED - Mustard - American Specialty Foods Inc.
HONEY LEMON - Teas - Eastern Shore Tea Co.
HONEY LOVIN'S - Food products - Health Valley Food
HONEY MAID - Crackers - Nabisco Foods Group
HONEY MAKER - Coveralls - Mann Lake, Ltd.
HONEY MESQUITE - Fireplace logs–treated - Buck Creek Mesquite
HONEY MINI - Motor vehicles–motor homes ☆ - Honey Recreational Vehicles Inc.
HONEY MINTS - Candy - Honey Acres Inc.
HONEY MONEY - Candy - Pangburn Candy Co.
HONEY MONEY - Furniture–wood - Everett Marmont Enterprises
HONEY-N-ALMOND OATIOS - Cereal - New Morn, Inc.
HONEY NOTES - Stationery - Brenda W. King
HONEY NUGGETS - Cereal - Niblack
HONEY NUT CHEERIOS - Cereal - General Mills, Inc.
HONEY-NUT SPINS - Cereal - Wal-Mart Stores Inc.
HONEY OAT HOOPS - Cereal - Kraft, Inc.
HONEY-PEANUT POWER - Food products - Weider Health and Fitness
HONEY POT - Health care products - Autumn-Harp, Inc.
HONEY POT MIXTURE - Tobacco products - Shepherd Tobacco Co.
HONEY POT TOP - Toys - Marlin Toy Products Inc.
HONEY PUFFED KASHI - Cereal - Kashi Co.
HONEY RITE - Crackers - Keebler Co.
HONEY ROSE - Fruits and vegetables - Rose Valley Group, Inc.
HONEY ROYALE - Food products ☆ - Beehive Botanicals Inc.
HONEY SILK - Health care products - Beehive Botanicals Inc.
HONEY SMOKE - Tobacco products - Sterling Tobacco Co.
HONEY SQUEAKS - Toys–stuffed - Dakin Inc.
HONEY STUNG - Food products - Tyson Foods Inc.
HONEY SUCKERS - Candy ☆ - Helms Candy Manufacturing Co. Inc.
HONEY SWEET - Fruits and vegetables - Comstock Michigan Fruit
HONEY TAFEE - Candy - McAlpine Associates
HONEY TOUCHED - Food products - Brakebush Brothers Inc.
HONEY TREETOT - Toys - Tonka Corp.
HONEY TRI-FOLD - Calendars - Risto Inc.
HONEY V - Breads - American Bakeries Co.
HONEY VALLEY FARMS - Meat products–canned - Hansel 'n Gretel Brand, Inc.

HONEY YOU'RE TERRIFIC - Salad dressings–bottled - Johnny's Enterprises Inc.
HONEYBAKED HAM COMPANY, THE - Paper products - HBH L.P.
HONEYBARS - Pet products - 8 in 1 Pet Products Inc.
HONEYBEA - Novelty items - Gale Bartlett Nemec
HONEYBEAR - Syrup ☆ - Honeypot Treats
HONEYBEARS - Candy - Beehive Botanicals Inc.
HONEYBEE - Lenses–optical - Designs for Vision, Inc.
HONEYBEE 'N MESSAGE BEAR - Toys–stuffed ☆ - Fun World Inc.
HONEYBEE TREE - Games ☆ - Parker Brothers
HONEYBEES - Jewelry - Charlotte NBA Limited
HONEYBEES - Jewelry - George Swim Sports, Inc.
HONEYBELLES - Dolls - Goldberger Doll Manufacture Co.
HONEYBROOK - Pipes - National Briar Pipe Co.
HONEYBROOK - Syrup - Good Food Inc.
HONEYBUN - Hair care products ☆ - Leon J.A. Buchheit Inc.
HONEYBUNCH - Toys - Lisco, Inc.
HONEYBUNCH - Toys–stuffed ☆ - Gund, Inc.
HONEYCOMB - Candles ☆ - Candle-Lite Co.
HONEYCOMB - Cooking equipment–household ☆ - General Housewares Corp.
HONEYCOMB - Dinnerware–glass ☆ - Block China Co.
HONEYCOMB - Display cases–plastic - Ovadia Corp.
HONEYCOMB - Fabrics - Gretchen Bellinger Inc.
HONEYCOMB - Fabrics - Texwipe Co. LLC
HONEYCOMB - Floor coverings–carpet and rugs - Trend Carpet
HONEYCOMB - Lamps ☆ - Lamplight Farms, Inc.
HONEYCOMB - Pet products - Aaronco Grooming Products
HONEYCOMB FOIL - Foil–aluminum - Bagcraft Corp. of America
HONEYCOMB GOLD - Glassware–household - Owens-Illinois Inc. (Libbey Div.)
HONEYCOMB JUMPERS - Sporting goods - O'Brien International
HONEYCOMB SINGLE TRICK - Sporting goods - O'Brien International
HONEYCOMBE - Dehumidifiers - Cargocaire Engineering Corp.
HONEYCOMBERS - Craft supplies - Milton Bradley Co.
HONEYCOMBS - Pet products - Aaronco Pet Products, Inc.
HONEYCUP - Mustard - Liberty Richter Inc.
HONEYDEW - Dinnerware ☆ - Corning Inc.
HONEYDEW - Food products ☆ - Red Wing Co., Inc.
HONEYDEW - Tobacco–chewing or smoking - James B. Russell Inc.
HONEYDEW BEAR - Toys–stuffed - Russ Berrie and Co., Inc.
HONEYED GINGER-GARLIC - Sauces - Golden Whisk Pasta Partners
HONEYFOAM - Hair- and skin-care products, fragrance, etc. - Benjamin Ansehl Co.
HONEYGRILLED CHICKEN - Sandwiches–prepackaged - Checkers Drive-In Restaurants Inc.
HONEYKIST - Meat products–poultry - Gold Kist Inc.
HONEYLOVE COLLECTION - Greeting cards - American Greetings Corp.
HONEYLOVE FRIENDS - Calendars - American Greetings Corp.
HONEYLOVE TEDDY BEARS - Greeting cards - American Greetings Corp.
HONEYMAN HAND TRUCKS - Dollies–industrial - Harco Products, Inc.
HONEYMOON - Floor coverings–carpet and rugs ☆ - Masland Corp.
HONEYMOON - Teas–herbal - Yellow Emperor Inc.
HONEY'N NUT - Pet products - L/M Animal Farms, Inc.
HONEYPOT - Candles - Creighton Cutts
HONEYPOT - Candy bars - Honeypot Treats
HONEYROSE - Cigarettes ☆ - James B. Russell Inc.
HONEYROSE - Herbal products - Fmali Herb Co.
HONEYSAURUS - Bicycles - Raleigh USA Bicycle Co.
HONEYSTIX - Honey - Beehive Botanicals Inc.
HONEYSUCKLE - Colognes ☆ - Avon Products, Inc.
HONEYSUCKLE - Dinnerware–glass ☆ - Royal China & Porcelain Companies Inc.
HONEYSUCKLE - Floor coverings–carpet and rugs - Capel, Inc.
HONEYSUCKLE - Meat products–poultry - Stevens Industries Inc.
HONEYSUCKLE - Perfumes - Tennessee Gold Inc.
HONEYSUCKLE - Wallpaper - Koroseal Wallcoverings
HONEYSUCKLE GOLD - Meat products–poultry ☆ - Stevens Industries Inc.
HONEYSUCKLE HOLLOW - Frames–picture - May Department Stores Co.
HONEYSUCKLE PEACH - Wines - Honeywood Winery
HONEYSUCKLE PINE - Clocks ☆ - General Time Corp. (Westclox/Seth Thomas Div.)
HONEYSUCKLE ROSE - Hair and skin-care products - Aubrey Organics, Inc.
HONEYSUCKLE STRAWS - Candy ☆ - Russell Stover Candies, Inc.
HONEYSUCKLE WHITE - Meat products–poultry - Stevens Industries Inc.
HONEYSUCKLE WHITE TURKEY GRAVY MIX - Gravy - Williams Foods Inc.

☆ = Now out of production

HONEYSWEET - Cereal - Breadshop's Natural Foods

HONEYSWEET - Pretzels ☆ - Barbara's Bakery, Inc.

HONEYTIP - Manicure preparations - Creative Nail Design, Inc.

HONEYWEAVE - Blankets - Pillowtex Corp.

HONEYWELL - Electronic equipment - Honeywell Inc.

HONEYWELL AUTO/STROBONAR 110 - Electronic equipment - Rollei of America Inc.

HONEYWOOD - Jams and jellies - Honeywood Winery

HONG KONG BLEND - Frozen foods - Patterson Frozen Foods, Inc.

HONG KONG DIM SUM - Food products - Ming's Supermarket, Inc.

HONG KONG GORILLA - Toys - Imperial Toy Corp.

HONG KONG RECORDS - Recording label - John Keaney

HONIES - Cakes ☆ - Nature's Hearth

HONIG - Food products - Holland-American Importing Co. Inc.

HONIG CELLARS - Wines - Honig Vineyard & Winery

HONKERS - Cosmetics - Paper Magic Group Inc.

HONKER'S ALE - Beverages—malt - Gibc, Inc.

HONOLULU ACADEMY OF ARTS - Postcards - Fotofolio Inc.

HONOLULU MARATHON - Apparel and accessories - Honolulu Marathon Association

HONOMOTO - Jewelry - Honora Jewelry Corp.

HONOR - Confections ☆ - Central Carolina Grocers Inc.

HONOR - Dog food - Gimborn U.S., Inc.

HONOR - Jewelry ☆ - Fantasy Diamond Corp.

HONOR - Office furniture—metal ☆ - Hon Co.

HONOR-BILT - Photo albums ☆ - H.E. Harris & Co.

HONOR CRAFT - Copper compounds ☆ - Regal Ware, Inc.

HONOR ROLL - Floor coverings—carpet and rugs - Barrett Carpet Mills Inc.

HONOR ROLL - Floor coverings—carpet and rugs ☆ - Playfield International Inc.

HONOR ROLL - Pencils - National Pen & Pencil Co.

HONOR YOUR ROOTS - Hair care products - Keystone Laboratories Inc.

HONORABLE TOFU - Tofu - Garden of Eatin', Inc.

HONORE - Rings—jewelry - Artcarved Inc.

HONORS - Cutlery - Dayton Hudson Corp.

HONORS - Games - Charles H. Vogt

HONORS - Golf equipment - Golf Day Products Inc.

HONORVEND - Wire products - Kaspar Wire Works, Inc.

HONOUR CORPS - Slacks ☆ - Horace Small Apparel Co.

HONOURS - Golfing equipment - Slotline Golf

HONOURS - Vodka ☆ - Majestic Distilling Co.

HON'S BUNS - Bakery products - Honie Ann Peacock

HONWOOD - Office furniture—metal ☆ - Hon Co.

HONY - Jewelry - Harris Originals of New York, Inc.

HOO HUNG WOO - Games - Decipher Inc.

HOO-NOBS - Fishing lures - Area Rule Engineering Inc.

HOOCH - Apparel and accessories - Wildwest Trading Co., Inc.

HOOCHIE COOCHIE - Sauces - Red Hot & Blue Restaurants, Inc.

HOOCHY - Sporting goods - Weber Industries Inc.

HOOD - Ships—sailing vessels - Hood Sailmakers Inc. (Hood Yacht Systems Div.)

HOOD - Ships—sailing vessels ☆ - Lyman-Morse Boatbuilding Co. Inc.

HOOD - Tires - Uniroyal Goodrich Tire Co.

HOOD - Yogurt—frozen - H.P. Hood & Sons Inc.

HOOD BASHER - Toys—automobiles - Mattel, Inc.

HOOD FREE - Cottage cheese - H.P. Hood & Sons Inc.

HOOD GEMS - Automotive parts and accessories - Gem Manufacturing Corp.

HOOD HOOP - Basketball equipment - Rimball Marketing and Development, Inc.

HOOD LIGHT - Cottage cheese - H.P. Hood & Sons Inc.

HOOD LYMAN - Ships—sailing vessels ☆ - Lyman-Morse Boatbuilding Co. Inc.

HOOD NATURAL BLENDERS - Juices - H.P. Hood & Sons Inc.

HOOD RIVER - Candy - Hood River Candy Co.

HOOD SELECT - Fruit drinks—bottled or canned - H.P. Hood & Sons Inc.

HOOD SOK - Apparel and accessories - Spray Sok Co. Inc.

HOODAT - Hats - Aerobox Athletic Enterprises, Inc.

HOODLUM - Apparel and accessories - No Fear, Inc.

HOODS - Hair coloring preparations - Lusan Inc.

HOODSPORT - Wines - Hoodsport Winery

HOODWINK - Apparel and accessories - Hoodwink Apparel Co.

HOODWINK - Ashtrays—glass - Vohann of California Inc.

HOODWINK - Games ☆ - Milton Bradley Co.

HOODWINKS - Ice cream - H.P. Hood & Sons Inc.

HOODY'S - Snack foods - Hoody Corp.

HOODY'S FRESH PACK SNACKS - Snack foods - Hoody Corp.

HOODY'S HEARTY & HANDY - See **HOODY'S FRESH PACK SNACKS**

HOOF BEAT SOFTWARE - Computer software - Delca Corp.

HOOF BLACK - Veterinary pharmaceutical preparations - Farnam Cos. Inc.

HOOF HOOF HOORAY - Nail care products - Cut-Heal Animal Care Products, Inc.

HOOF-IT - Adhesives and sealants - HIMG

HOOF LACQUER - Nail care products - Gena Laboratories Inc.

HOOF MARVEL - Veterinary pharmaceutical preparations - HMCO

HOOF 'N FOOT TREATMENT - Nail care products - Lancelot Marketing Services, Inc.

HOOF QUENCHER - Veterinary pharmaceutical preparations - W.F. Young, Inc.

HOOF SAVER - Veterinary pharmaceutical preparations - Farnam Cos. Inc.

HOOF TO NAILS - Cosmetics - Aloe Advantage Inc.

HOOFLEX - Veterinary pharmaceutical preparations - W.F. Young, Inc.

HOOFMAKER, THE - Veterinary pharmaceutical preparations - Straight Arrow Products, Inc.

HOOGIE'S PRO C.A.D. - Detergents - Hoogies, Inc.

HOOGIE'S PRO SEAL - Adhesives and sealants - Hoogies, Inc.

HOOGIE'S PRO-SEEK - Detergents - Hoogies, Inc.

HOOHOBBERS - Apparel—children's - Tyke Corp.

HOOIE STICK - Toys - Gregory Landerer

HOOK - Chemical preparations - Nutrite Corp.

HOOK - Games - Primos, Inc.

HOOK - Recording label - Fred Rice Productions

HOOK - Seafood products—fresh or frozen - Central Seaway Co.

HOOK - Toys - Tri-Star Pictures Inc.

HOOK A BOOK - Publisher's imprints - Reader's Digest Association, Inc.

HOOK & LADDER - Chili—canned - Cincinnati Recipe Inc.

HOOK AND PILE - Electronic equipment - Ohio Flock-Cote Co.

HOOK AND SHELVE - Hooks ☆ - Knape and Vogt Manufacturing Co.

HOOK-AWN - Hooks - Randall G. Williams

HOOK-EYE - Automotive repair shops—glass - Gold Glass Group Corp.

HOOK-FAB - Bulletin boards—cork - Claridge Products and Equipment Inc.

HOOK-FLEX - Fasteners—hook and eye - North and Judd Inc.

HOOK GENIE - Fishing tackle - Fishing Pro Products, Inc.

HOOK HOOD - Sporting goods - Leonard P. Weiss

HOOK-IT - Hooks - Outrigger, Inc.

HOOK-IT - Hooks ☆ - A.J. Ganz Co. Inc.

HOOK LINE AND SINKER - Wallpaper ☆ - Imperial Wallcoverings, Inc.

HOOK LOCK - Hooks - Southtec, Inc.

HOOK-LOK - Locks—padlocks - Santa Cruz Industries, Inc.

HOOK-MATE - Hooks - Beckson Marine Inc.

HOOK-N-GO - Truck bodies - Galion Dump Bodies, Inc.

HOOK RITE - Fishing lures - William H. McWethy, Jr.

HOOK SUIT - Clothing - J.G. Hook, Inc.

HOOKED - Games - Patrick S. Wilson

HOOKED ON GOLF - Calendars ☆ - American Greetings Corp.

HOOKED ON PHONICS - Educational products - Gateway Educational Products, Ltd.

HOOKED ON SUNSHINE - Wallpaper - Artisan Handprints Inc.

HOOKEEZ - Hooks ☆ - Willert Home Products, Inc.

HOOK'EMS - Hooks - VSI Fasteners, Inc.

HOOKER - Anchors - Rule Industries, Inc.

HOOKER - Anchors - Tie Down, Inc.

HOOKER - Boats—motor - Glastex Co.

HOOKER - Boats—motor ☆ - Snark Boats

HOOKER - Lawn mowers - Way Easy, Inc.

HOOKER - Paints - Graham Paint and Varnish Co.

HOOKERS - Novelty items - Tracy Miller

HOOKEY - Games - Cadaco Div.

HOOK'N HANG - Hooks - Disstim Corp.

HOOK'N RIG - Fishing tackle - Tonka Lures Inc.

HOOK'N RIG'R PROBE - Fishing tackle - Tonka Lures Inc.

HOOKOVER - Toys ☆ - Trend Enterprises, Inc.

HOOKS - Dolls - Mattel, Inc.

HOOK'S LINES & INKERS - Stamps—hand - Gary R. Hook

HOOKS 'N RAILS - Hardware - James D. Hermann

HOOKS 'N RAILS - Hooks ☆ - Earth Stove Inc.

HOOKSETTER - Fishing tackle - Fenwick

HOOKSPORT - Apparel and accessories - J.G. Hook, Inc.

HOOKWEAR - Apparel and accessories - J.G. Hook, Inc.

HOOLA COUPE - Infant product ☆ - Century Products Co.

HOOLA EGGS - Candy ☆ - Leaf, Inc.

HOOLIGAN - Clothes - Hooligan

HOOLIGAN - Tools - Paratech Inc.

HOONOSE - Fishing tackle - Tru Turn, Inc.

HOOP-A-WHEEL - Toys - G.M. Inc.
HOOP BREAK - Toys - Pepsico, Inc.
HOOP CROQUET - Games - Electro-Mech Inc.
HOOP CROWN - Sporting goods - Paul J. Mahoney
HOOP HAT - Hats - Set the Curve, Inc.
HOOP HOCKEY - Games - Electro-Mech Inc.
HOOP HYSTERIA - Games - Sigler and Flanders, Inc.
HOOP-IT-UP - Apparel and accessories - Streetball Partners, Inc.
HOOP LOGIC - Apparel and accessories - James Daids
HOOP 'N HOLD - Toys - Kel-Gar, Inc.
HOOP QUEST H Q - Apparel–athletic - Gardus Tate
HOOP SCOOP - Publisher's imprints - Hoop Scoop, Inc.
HOOP STAR - Balls–basketball - Collette Manufacturing Co.
HOOP STIK - Traps–animal - Fuhrman Diversified
HOOP SUPREMACY - Bicycles - Graber Products, Inc.
HOOPAHOLICS - Apparel and accessories - Steven Hawes
HOOPEE DOOPS - Candy - Hooper's Chocolates
HOOPER - Apparel–women's - Hooper Associates Ltd.
HOOPER - Wines ☆ - European Beverage Co., Inc.
HOOPER ALLEY - Apparel and accessories - Todd Number 1
HOOPER HANDLE - Housewares - Merrick Industries Inc.
HOOPER THE HOUND - Colognes ☆ - Avon Products, Inc.
HOOPLAS - Crackers ☆ - Keebler Co.
HOOPLETS - Jewelry - Leach & Garner Co.
HOOPS FEST - Apparel and accessories - Missouri Valley Conference
HOOPS IN THE HEARTLAND - Apparel and accessories - Missouri Valley Conference
HOOPS IN THE HOOD - Apparel and accessories - Ethnos Enterprises
HOOPS TEDDY - Toys–stuffed - Russ Berrie and Co., Inc.
HOOPS THE GYM - Apparel–athletic - Hoops, Inc.
HOOPSTER - Footwear - L.A. Gear, Inc.
HOOSAC - Paper–construction - Cascade School Supplies
HOOSIER - See **STAR**
HOOSIER - Ballet slippers - Hoosier Bat Co., Inc.
HOOSIER - Water–bottled or canned - Hinckley & Schmitt (Bottled Water Group)
HOOSIER - Wire products - Jesco Industries, Inc.
HOOSIER RED LAGER - Beverages–alcohol - Evansville Brewing Co.
HOOSIER STAR - Tools - O.P. Link Handle Co. Inc.
HOOSIER SWEETS - Fruits–canned - Curtice-Burns Foods, Inc.
HOOSTER - Candy bars - Special Preparations Co.
HOOSTER-BOOSTER - Candy bars - Special Preparations Co.
HOOTENANNY - Musical instrument accessories - Sottile Manufacturing Co.
HOOTLUM - Recording label - Macola Record Group Inc.
HOOTON - Cocoa–powders or mixes - Hooton Chocolate Co.
HOOTY-HOO - Apparel and accessories - Paul Tonelli
HOOV-R-LINE - Tools–plumbing - Moen Inc.
HOOVE - Toys - Mattel, Inc.
HOOVEN & ALLISON - Twine - Geo. B. Carpenter Co.
HOOVER - Vacuum cleaners and accessories - The Hoover Co.
HOOX - Brackets - Gary E. Blessing
HOP - Jewelry - Rainbow Gems
H.O.P. - Pet products - House of Pets
HOP-ABOUT BUNNY - Toys–stuffed - Fun World Inc.
HOP & SKIPPY'S LANGUAGE ISLAND - Computer software - Gessler Publishing Co., Inc.
HOP CAP - Automotive parts and accessories - Hop-Cap Inc.
HOP CAT - Automotive parts and accessories ☆ - Toppertown Inc.
HOP HEAD - Beverages - Thomas Defazio, Jr.
HOP-INS - Apparel and accessories ☆ - Barad & Co.
HOP KILN WINERY - Wines - Hop Kiln Winery
HOP 'N HAMPER - Hampers - Mattel, Inc.
HOP SACK - Fabrics - Dan River Inc.
HOP-SYN - Paper - Hop Industries Corp.
HOPALONE - Oils–edible - Kalsec, Inc.
HOPALONG FTP - Computer software - Rapidata Systems, Inc.
HOPCAID - Fertilizers - Mapco Inc.
HOPE - Bedding–linen - West Point-Pepperell Inc.
HOPE - Beverages–malt - Hope Brewing Corp.
HOPE - Game - Robert C. Selby
HOPE - Toys–stuffed - Jolly U.S.A., Inc.
HOPE - Wigs ☆ - Paula Young
HOPE DIAMOND CHOCOLATE, THE - Chocolate candy - Big Gems
HOPE IMAGING - Photographic equipment - Hope Imaging Corp.
HOPE IN A BOTTLE - Skin care products - Philosophy, Inc.
HOPE IN A JAR - Skin care products - Cosmedic Concepts, Inc.

HOPE LITE - Beverages–malt - Hope Brewing Corp.
HOPE ON A ROPE - Massage products - Transpan Products, Inc.
HOPE PHARMACEUTICALS - Pharmaceutical preparations - Hope Pharmaceuticals
HOPE SAFE-T-BAR - Brakes–motor vehicle - Maintenance-Free Brakes, Inc.
HOPE YOU GET LUCKY! - Chocolate candy - Harry London's Candies Inc.
HOPECHEST - Wallpaper ☆ - Eisenhart Wallcoverings Co.
HOPECHEST II - Wallpaper ☆ - Eisenhart Wallcoverings Co.
HOPECHEST III - Wallpaper ☆ - Eisenhart Wallcoverings Co.
HOPE'S - Chemical preparations - Hope Co., Inc.
HOPES - Hardware - Blaine Window Hardware Inc.
HOPE'S - Window frames - Hope's Architectural Products, Inc.
HOPE'S COUNTRY FRESH COOKIES - Cookies - Country Fresh Batter, Inc.
HOPE'S PERFECT GLOSS - Cleaning preparations - Hope Co., Inc.
HOPEWELL - Dresses–women's ☆ - Jonathan Logan Inc.
HOPEWELL STORES - Audio tapes–blank - Hopewell Enterprises
HOPF - Guitars ☆ - Dauphin Co.
HOPF - Zithers - Hanseatic Overseas Trading Inc.
HOPFENPERLE - Paints - Omni Industries
HOPI - Clocks ☆ - General Time Corp. (Westclox/Seth Thomas Div.)
HOPI - Floor coverings - American Floor Products Co. Inc.
HOPI - Floor coverings–carpet and rugs - Masland Corp.
HOPI - Floor coverings–carpet and rugs - Regal Rugs Inc.
HOPI - Frames–picture - Terragrafics Inc.
HOPI HUNTER - Archery equipment - Rollin Wilson Co. Inc.
HOPKINS - Food products - Hopkins of Sodus Inc.
HOPKINS - Furniture - Hopkins Manufacturing Corp.
HOPKINS EGYPTIAN - Cosmetics - Chicago Hair Good Inc.
HOPKINS VINEYARD - Wines - Hopkins Vineyard
HOPLER - Wines - Admiral Wine Merchants
HOPPE - Cookies - Jaret Specialties Inc.
HOPPER - Bags–trash ☆ - North American Plastics Corp.
HOPPER - Furniture - Haworth, Inc.
HOPPER - Games - House of Packaging, Inc.
HOPPER - Motor vehicle parts and accessories - Delta Consolidated Industries, Inc.
HOPPER - Paper products - Georgia-Pacific Corp.
HOPPER - Tools–hand-operated - W.M.T. Co.
HOPPER - Toys–stuffed - Dakin Inc.
HOPPER CREEK WINERY - Wines - Hidden Canyon Vineyard
HOPPER INC. - Oxygen - Air Liquide America Corp.
HOPPERGUARD - Alfalfa - Land O'Lakes, Inc.
HOPPERLINE, THE - Toys–models - Fashioncraft-Excello
HOPPERS - Toys–stuffed ☆ - Fun World Inc.
HOPPES - Firearms, accessories, and parts - Hoppe's
HOPPIN' CHECKERS - Games - Hasbro, Inc.
HOPPIN POPS - Candy - Impact Confections, Inc.
HOPPING - Beverages–carbonated - Hopping Bottling Co. Inc.
HOPPITY DONALD DUCK - Toys ☆ - Sun Products Corp. (Wellington)
HOPPITY HOP - Toys - Sun Products Corp. (Wellington)
HOPPITY HOP - Toys - Wellington Leisure Products, Inc.
HOPPITY HOP FRUIT BALLS - Toys ☆ - Sun Products Corp. (Wellington)
HOPPITY HORSE - Toys ☆ - Sun Products Corp. (Wellington)
HOPPITY MICKEY MOUSE - Toys ☆ - Sun Products Corp. (Wellington)
HOPPITY TOT - Toys - Wellington Leisure Products, Inc.
HOPPITY TOT - Toys ☆ - Sun Products Corp. (Wellington)
HOPPY BEAR PAW - Hardware - Hopkins Manufacturing Corp.
HOPPY BUNNY - Toys–stuffed - Russ Berrie and Co., Inc.
HOPPY CLAUS - Beverages–malt - Technically Leading Consultants Co.
HOPPY FACE - Beverages–malt - Technically Leading Consultants Co.
HOPPY KANGAROO - Toys–stuffed ☆ - Gund, Inc.
HOPPY SPRINGS - Beverages–malt - Technically Leading Consultants Co.
HOPPY ULTIMATE - Hardware - Hopkins Manufacturing Corp.
HOPSCOTCH - Floor coverings–carpet and rugs - Galaxy Carpet Mills Inc.
HOPSCOTCH - Tableware–china - Pfaltzgraff Investment Co.
HOPSCOTCH BLUE - Dishes–china - Waterford Wedgewood USA, Inc.
HOPSTEINER - Seeds–salted, roasted, cooked, or canned - S.S. Steiner Inc.
HOPTIK - Optical machinery - Hoptik
HOR-SHU - Braces–orthopedic - Surgical Appliance Industries, Inc.
HORA - Food products - Pocahontas Foods USA Inc.
HORABE - Guitars - JTG of Nashville
HORACE H. HEFFELFLOPPER - Candy - R.M. Palmer Co.
HORACE SMALL - Apparel and accessories - Horace Small Apparel Co.
HORATIO - Toys–stuffed ☆ - Gund, Inc.
HORCHATA CRUISIN COOL - Ice cream - Royale International
HORDAK - Toys - Mattel, Inc.

☆ = Now out of production

HORDE, THE - Video games - Crystal Dynamics, Inc.

HORDE TROOPER - Toys - Mattel, Inc.

HORIZON - Air conditioning equipment - American Standard Inc.

HORIZON - Apparel and accessories - Bolle' America, Inc.

HORIZON - Apparel and accessories - Pat Fashions Industries Inc.

HORIZON - Ashtrays–glass - Durand International

HORIZON - Audio equipment - Horizon Music, Inc.

HORIZON - Audio equipment ☆ - Pyle Industries Inc.

HORIZON - Bathroom accessories - Chemcraft

HORIZON - Binders - Standard Duplicating Machines Corp.

HORIZON - Boats–motor - Four Winns Inc.

HORIZON - Brushes - Corona Brushes Inc.

HORIZON - Cabinets - Merillat Industries, Inc.

HORIZON - Chairs–folding - E-Z Sales & Manufacturing, Inc.

HORIZON - Computer software - Chemware, Inc.

HORIZON - Dishes–china - Pickard Inc.

HORIZON - Doors–storm - Canyon Creek Cabinet Co.

HORIZON - Electrical building control systems - THORN Automated Systems Inc.

HORIZON - Electronics equipment - Grass Valley Group Inc.

HORIZON - Fireplace equipment - Hearth Craft

HORIZON - Fishing tackle ☆ - Horizon Lure Co.

HORIZON - Floor coverings - American Floor Products Co. Inc.

HORIZON - Floor coverings–carpet and rugs - Regal Rugs Inc.

HORIZON - Floor coverings–carpet and rugs ☆ - Capel, Inc.

HORIZON - Furniture - Singer Furniture Co.

HORIZON - Furniture ☆ - Bassett Furniture Industries, Inc.

HORIZON - Furniture ☆ - Boling Co.

HORIZON - Furniture ☆ - Halcyon Inc.

HORIZON - Glassware–household ☆ - Lenox Crystal, Inc.

HORIZON - Hair-cutting shears - B.W. Boyd Shears Inc.

HORIZON - Hardware ☆ - Leslie-Locke, Inc.

HORIZON - Hearing aids - Rexton Inc.

HORIZON - History, art, and archaeology books - American Heritage

HORIZON - Hot tubs–plastic - Coleman Spas

HORIZON - Jewelry - Gold Lance Inc.

HORIZON - Manufactured homes - Redman Industries, Inc.

HORIZON - Massage products - Everett Associates Inc.

HORIZON - Medical apparatus - Mentor O & O Inc.

HORIZON - Medical apparatus - Sunrise Medical (Respiratory Products Division)

HORIZON - Microscopes - Burleigh Instruments, Inc.

HORIZON - Motor vehicles–automobiles ☆ - Chrysler Corp. (Chrysler-Plymouth Div.)

HORIZON - Navigational instruments - Brookes & Gatehouse Inc.

HORIZON - Occasional tables ☆ - JDI Group, Inc.

HORIZON - Pumps - Mcgaw, Inc.

HORIZON - Radios - Standard Communications Corp.

HORIZON - Recording label - Blue Wave Records

HORIZON - Recreational vehicles - International Vehicle Corp.

HORIZON - Rope ☆ - Geo. B. Carpenter Co.

HORIZON - Serving carts ☆ - National Housewares

HORIZON - Shelving units–metal - Knape and Vogt Manufacturing Co.

HORIZON - Skates–roller - Rollerblade, Inc.

HORIZON - Telephones - At&T Corp.

HORIZON - Tiles–ceramic - Cambridge Tile Manufacturing Co.

HORIZON - Trailers–travel - Leader Enterprises

HORIZON - Vacuum cleaners and accessories - Tacony Corp.

HORIZON - Wallpaper ☆ - Carlton-Metro Wallcoverings

HORIZON - Water–bottled or canned - Deer Park Spring Water Inc.

HORIZON - Weighing device - Terraillon Corp.

HORIZON - Wheels ☆ - Faultless Caster Co.

HORIZON - Window coverings - ESI

HORIZON - Window coverings - Tachikawa USA Inc.

HORIZON 1280 - Computer software - Truevision, Inc.

HORIZON 2000 - Pumps - Bennett Pump Co.

HORIZON 4060X - Laboratory apparatus - General Signal Corp.

HORIZON 4080X - Laboratory apparatus - General Signal Corp.

HORIZON 4085X - Electronic equipment - General Signal Corp.

HORIZON ARCH - Doors–storm - Canyon Creek Cabinet Co.

HORIZON CARAVEL - Publisher's imprints - Harper & Row Publishers Inc.

HORIZON DESIGNS INC. - Bags–cosmetic - Horizon Designs Inc.

HORIZON HERBS - Flowers, plants, and seeds - Horizon Herbs

HORIZON MODULAR INFUSION SYSTEM - Pumps - Mcgaw, Inc.

HORIZON OF HOPE - Baskets–wood - Longaberger Co.

HORIZON PHARMACEUTICAL - Pharmaceutical preparations - Horizon Pharmaceutical Corp.

HORIZON PINK - Lipsticks - Cosmair Inc.

HORIZON SERIES - Computer software - Macola, Inc.

HORIZON SHANGLE - Shingles–asphalt or tar - Certainteed Corp. (Roofing Products Group)

HORIZON, THE - Oboes - Dovre Inc.

HORIZON WEST - Wallpaper ☆ - London Lamps & Decor Accessories

HORIZONLINE - Computer software - Truevision, Inc.

HORIZONLITE - Windows–plastic - O'Keeffe's, Inc.

HORIZONS - Adhesives and sealants ☆ - Pettit Paint Co. Inc.

HORIZONS - Bathroom fixtures ☆ - Artesian Industries

HORIZONS - Bicycles - Roadmaster Corp.

HORIZONS - Footwear - Brown Shoe Co.

HORIZONS - Furniture - Hammary Furniture Co. Inc.

HORIZONS - Furniture–wood ☆ - Ficks Reed Co. Inc.

HORIZONS - Handbags - Tandem Imports Corp.

HORIZONS - Wallpaper - Taylor Wallcoverings Inc.

HORIZONS - Window coverings - Tempo Industries Inc.

HORIZONS 2 - Adhesives and sealants ☆ - Pettit Paint Co. Inc.

HORIZONS EAST - Furniture ☆ - Davis Cabinet Co.

HORIZON'S EDGE - Wines - Horizon Wines

HORIZONS PINE PRODUCTIONS - Furniture–wood - NJT-Horizon Inc.

HORIZONS TECHNOLOGY - Computer software and hardware - Horizons Technology, Inc.

HORIZONSHADE - Windows–plastic - O'Keeffe's, Inc.

HORIZONTAL - Lighting equipment - ProLight

HORIZONTAL TRANSFER - Insecticides - Ecoscience Corp.

HORIZONTE - Figurines ☆ - Artists of the World

HORIZONTI-FILE - Filing cabinets–metal - Buddy Products

HORIZONVAULT - Windows–plastic - O'Keeffe's, Inc.

HORIZONVENT - Windows–plastic - O'Keeffe's, Inc.

HORLEY - Skin care products ☆ - Houbigant, Inc.

HORLICKS - Beverages–malt ☆ - Gilway Co. Ltd.

HORLUCK'S - Ice cream - Darigold, Inc.

HORMEL - Containers - Hormel Corp.

HORMEL - Giftware - H.C. Meyers Co.

HORMEL - Meat products - Hormel Foods Corp.

HORMEL CHILI - Chili–canned - Hormel Foods Corp.

HORMEL QUICK MEAL - Food products - Hormel Foods Corp.

HORMELICATESSEN - Food products - Hormel Foods Corp.

HORMEX - Rooting powders and liquid - Brooker Chemical Corp.

HORMONIN - Hormone preparations ☆ - Carnick Laboratories Inc.

HORMOVITE - Pharmaceutical preparations ☆ - U.S. Ethicals Inc.

HORMOX - Pharmaceutical preparations ☆ - Parmed Pharmaceuticals, Inc.

HORMS - Vitamins and nutritional supplements - Vitamin Institute

HORN - Desk sets ☆ - W.C. Horn

HORN - Floor coverings–carpet and rugs ☆ - Hollytex Carpet Mills Inc.

HORN - Sealing compounds - A.C. Horn Co.

HORN - Waterproofing compounds ☆ - Sequa Corp.

HORN 240 - Sealing compounds - A.C. Horn Co.

HORN CLAMP - See **SPINREEL**

HORN GARD - Cleaning preparations - Chem-Pak Inc.

HORN HEAD - Toys ☆ - Those Characters from Cleveland, Inc.

HORN OF PLENTY - Fruits–canned - Schreiber Foods International, Inc.

HORN OF PLENTY - Furniture - H.W. Hull & Sons Inc.

HORN OF ROLAND - Games ☆ - Avalon Hill Game Co.

HORNADY - Ammunition - Hornady Manufacturing Co.

HORNBOARD - Sealing compounds - A.C. Horn Co.

HORNBRO - Health care products - Bell-Horn

HORNER - Floor coverings - Horner Flooring Co. Inc.

HORNET - Alarm systems - Directed Electronics, Inc.

HORNET - Archery equipment ☆ - Martin Archery Inc.

HORNET - Bicycles - Schwinn Cycling & Fitness Inc.

HORNET - Boats–motor ☆ - Commander Marine

HORNET - Cleaning preparations - Whitco Inc.

HORNET - Motor vehicles ☆ - DaimlerChrysler

HORNET - Paint sprayers - Binks Manufacturing Co.

HORNET - Thread - Threads USA Div.

HORNET - Toys - Imperial Toy Corp.

HORNET - Toys - Tonka Corp.

HORNET - Toys–models - Estes Industries

HORNET - Trailers–travel - Damon Corp.

HORNET - Vacuum cleaners and accessories - The Hoover Co.

HORNET 4 - Boats - Brookes & Gatehouse Inc.

HORNET III - Boats–motor ☆ - Donzi Marine Corp.

☆ = Now out of production

HORNET SPORTABOUT - Motor vehicles ☆ - DaimlerChrysler
HORNFLEX - Sealing compounds - A.C. Horn Co.
HORNFOAM - Sealing compounds - A.C. Horn Co.
HORNICK BROTHERS - Decoys ☆ - Stoney Point Decoys Ltd.
HORNIMAN'S - Teas - Young's Market Co.
HORNITOS - Beverages–alcohol ☆ - Domecq Importers Inc.
HORNOLITH - Sealing compounds - A.C. Horn Co.
HORNSBY'S - Beverages–alcohol - Ernest and Julio Gallo Winery
HORNSEA - Housewares ☆ - Zrike Co. Inc.
HORNWELD - Sealing compounds - A.C. Horn Co.
HORNY GATOR - Beverages–alcohol - Tropical Isle, Inc.
HORNY TESTER - Novelty items - Adams Apple Distributing L.P.
HORNY TOAD ACTIVEWEAR - Apparel and accessories - GMS Holding, Inc.
HOROSCOPE BOARD GAME, THE - Games - Robert L.J. Swinton
HOROSCOPICS - Computer software - Zephyr Services
HOROWITZ-MARGARETEN - Food products - Margareten Enterprises
HORRG - Dolls - Mattel, Inc.
HORRIBLES - Toys - Dyno Merchandise
HORRIBLY GOOD ROOT BEER - Beverages–carbonated - New Century Beverage Co.
HORROCKS-IBBOTSON - Fishing lures - Horrocks-Ibbotson Co.
HORROR POPS - Candy - Fleer Corp.
HORROR STORIES - Toys - Tonka Corp.
HORRORS OF NORTH AMERICA - Games - Mayfair Games, Inc.
HORRORS OF SCHOOL, THE - Stationery ☆ - Scentex Inc.
HORS D'OEUVRES - Pet products - Rolf C. Hagen (USA) Corp.
HORS D'OEUVRES FACTORY, THE - Kosher food products - Aristocrat International Corp.
HORSA - Boats ☆ - Brookes & Gatehouse Inc.
HORSE - Candy - Tpl, Inc.
HORSE - Tiles–asphalt - Garden Way Inc.
HORSE-A-ROUNDS - Pet products - Dale Distributing
HORSE BACK - Leather goods - American Saddlery, Inc.
HORSE COUNTRY - Fencing materials - Stockton, Inc.
HORSE GUARD - Veterinary nutritional supplements - Horse Guard Inc.
HORSE LOVER - Gloves - Unika International Inc.
HORSE MASTER - Blankets–horse - Libertyville Saddle Shop, Inc.
HORSE-N-AROUND - Cages–wire - Hoff Fabrication
HORSE SENSE - Games - John F. Kamenar
HORSE SHOW - Games - Gamewright, Inc.
HORSE SHOW WORLD - Writing product ☆ - Binney & Smith Inc.
HORSE SPORTS - Gravy - Horseman's Financial Group
HORSE TEETH - Candy - Glenn Confections Inc.
HORSE TENDER - Horse bits - Bernard T. Jenson
HORSE TO HUMAN - Cosmetics - Cut-Heal Animal Care Products, Inc.
HORSE TREATS - Animal feed supplements - Farnam Cos. Inc.
HORSEHEAD - Giftware ☆ - A.M. Designs
HORSEHEAD - Tires - Bridgestone/Firestone, Inc.
HORSEMAN'S BOOT SHIELD - Waterproofing compounds - W.F. Young, Inc.
HORSEMAN'S ONE STEP - Cleaning preparations - W.F. Young, Inc.
HORSEPOWER FOR THE TURNS - Automotive parts and accessories - Eibach Springs, Inc.
HORSESHOE - Fruits and vegetables - V.H. Azhderian & Co., Inc.
HORSESHOE HARNESS - Nautical instruments - Defender Industries
HORSESHOES - Footwear–athletic - Karman Western Apparel
HORSESOCKS - Socks - Karman Western Apparel
HORSESPURS - Apparel and accessories - Karman Western Apparel
HORSETAIL - Pharmaceutical preparations - William P. Canale
HORSMAN - Dolls - Horsman
HORST GRUNERT - Cellos ☆ - St. Louis Music Supply Co.
HORT-I-GREEN - Fertilizers ☆ - Agway Country Foods Inc.
HORTEN'S MIDWEST FARMS - Food products - Southland Corp.
HORTI-PERL - Insulating materials - Redco II
HORTICOLA - Artichokes–canned - Caragol, Esformes & Phelan Corp.
HORTICOPIA - Computer software - Horticopia, Inc.
HORTIS OP IS - Computer software - J. Mendoza Gardens Inc.
HORTISCULPTURES - Statuary - Brastoff Designs Inc.
HORTIWOOL - Garden equipment - Rockwool Industries Inc.
HORTON - Archery equipment - Horton Manufacturing Co. Inc.
HORTON - Brake parts - Horton Holdings, Inc.
HORTON - Coffee - McCullough/Horton Coffee Co. Inc.
HORTON - Toys–stuffed - Russ Berrie and Co., Inc.
HORTON BLACK RUM CAKE - Bakery products - Europa Foods Ltd.
HORTON VINEYARDS - Wines - Horton Vineyards Inc.
HORTSON - Projectors–photographic ☆ - Xetron
HORTUS GROUP - Flowers, plants, and seeds - Hans A. Gerritsen

HOSANNA! - Recording label - Integrity Music, Inc.
HOSANNA! MUSIC - Recording label - Integrity Music, Inc.
HOSANNA MUSIC - Recording label - Sparrow Corp.
HOSE HANDLER - Handles–plastic - Odyssey Systems
HOSE HANGOUT - Garden equipment - Custom Plastics Inc.
HOSE HANGOUT JR. - Garden equipment - Custom Plastics Inc.
HOSE HIDERS - Garden equipment - Emsco Inc.
HOSE KING - Hoses - Ames Lawn & Garden Tool Co.
HOSE LINKS - Hoses - Action Technology Co.
HOSE MANAGER - Carts - Melnor Inc.
HOSE MASTER - Flexible metal hoses - Hose Master, Inc.
HOSE MENDER - Tools–garden - Gilmour Manufacturing Co.
HOSE MINDER - Hoses - Melnor Inc.
HOSE MOLE - Tools–hand-operated - Slautterback Corp.
HOSE REEL - Swimming pools - Recreonics, Inc.
HOSEHANDLER - Garden equipment - Custom Plastics Inc.
HOSEMASTER - Tools–garden - Gilmour Manufacturing Co.
HOSEMOBILE - Garden equipment - Custom Plastics Inc.
HOSESAVER - Hoses - K. Scott Miller
HOSHO - Artists' materials - Andrews/Nelson/Whitehead
HOSIERY CARE - Detergents - Kleen Chemical Manufacturing Co.
HOSIERY MATE - Detergents - Kleen Chemical Manufacturing Co.
HOSKINS CREEK TABLE COMPANY - Furniture - John B. Vaughan III
HOSKOFF - Cough medicines - Frye Co.
HOSOI ROCKET - Skateboards - Santa Cruz Skateboards
HOSOKAWA OHBAN - Artists' materials - Andrews/Nelson/Whitehead
HOSPI-GARD - Air purification systems - Envirco Corp.
HOSPI-LOTION - Skin care products ☆ - Ulmer Pharmacal Co.
HOSPICE - Decals and transfers - Hospice Seal
HOSPICES DE BEAUNE - Wines - Finest Wines Inc.
HOSPITAL - Candy ☆ - F.B. Washburn Candy Corp.
HOSPITAL LAND - Games ☆ - Franciscan Health System of Cincinnati Inc.
HOSPITALITY - Food products - Gilster-Mary Lee Corp.
HOSPITALITY - Glass–leaded - Seneca Glass Co.
HOSPITALITY - Glassware–household - Owens-Illinois Inc. (Libbey Div.)
HOSPITALITY - Melamine product - Boonton Molding Co. Inc.
HOSPITALITY - Tables–wood - Howe Furniture Corp.
HOSPITALITY - Wallcoverings - Intex Plastics Sales Co. (Wallcovering Div.)
HOSPITALITY & HEALTHCARE - Wallpaper - Rigo Wallcoverings Inc.
HOSPITALITY COLLECTION - Bathroom accessories - Jado Bathroom and Hardware Manufacturing Corp.
HOSPITALITY SKILLS TRAINING SERIES - Publisher's imprints - Educational Institute of the American Hotel & Motel Association
HOSPITAL'S CHOICE - Disinfectant - Heartland Corp.
HOSS SAUCE - Suntan lotions - Dale Hansen
HOSS SAUCE - Suntan lotions - Hoss Sauce
HOSS SLAUGHTER - Toys - Tonka Corp.
HOST - Beverages–alcohol - M.S. Walker Inc./Seacoast
HOST - Cleaning preparations–carpet and rug - Host/Racine Industries Inc.
HOST DELIGHT - Food products - S.S. Piers
HOST PRESENTER - Computer software - Novell, Inc.
HOSTEL - Tents - Coleman Co., Inc.
HOSTESS - Bakery products - Interstate Brands Corp.
HOSTESS - Floor coverings–carpet and rugs ☆ - Barrett Carpet Mills Inc.
HOSTESS - Food products - Everfresh Foods Corp.
HOSTESS - Food products - Hooper's Chocolates
HOSTESS - Hams - Armour Swift-Eckrich
HOSTESS - Health care products - JUZO
HOSTESS - Housewares - Knobler International Ltd.
HOSTESS - Plumbing fixtures–enameled - Watercare Corp.
HOSTESS - Thread - Threads USA Div.
HOSTESS - Whipped topping–powdered ☆ - Presto Food Products, Inc.
HOSTESS - Wines ☆ - Tenner Brothers Inc.
HOSTESS BAKERY SELECT - Cookies - Interstate Brands Corp.
HOSTESS CHOICE - Fabrics–linen - Maytex Mills
HOSTESS COLLECTION, THE - Servingware - Cornwall Industries Inc.
HOSTESS HELPER - Knives–carving - Wallace International Silversmiths, Inc.
HOSTESS KOOKIES - Cookies - Interstate Brands Corp.
HOSTESS LIGHTS - Snack cakes - Interstate Brands Corp.
HOSTESS O'S - Doughnuts - Interstate Brands Corp.
HOSTESS SETS - Glassware–household - Owens-Illinois Inc. (Libbey Div.)
HOSTESS TIGER TAILS - Cakes - Interstate Brands Co. - Licensing Co.
HOSTETSS BASKET - Candy - Home of the Hebert Candies, Inc.
HOSTSCAPE - Computer software - Platinum Technology, Inc.
HOT - Computer software - Xtree Co.
HOT - Mops - Rubbermaid Commercial Products Inc.

☆ = Now out of production

HOT - Ophthalmic goods - Foremost Optical Products
HOT - Perfumes - Revlon Consumer Products Corp.
HOT! - Suntan lotions - ETS, Inc.
HOT 40 - Computers - Telescan Systems, Inc.
HOT AIR BALLOON - Bedding–linen ☆ - Welsh Co.
HOT AIR BALLOONS - Erasers - Diener Industries Inc.
HOT AIR BALLOONS - Kites - Hi-Flier Manufacturing Co.
HOT & COLD - Health care products - Rinz-L-O Pillow Co.
HOT & HONEY - Sauces - Kelly Paul French
HOT & SAFE - Heaters–space - Patton Electric Co. Inc.
HOT & SPICY WINGLETS - Snack foods - Conagra, Inc.
HOT & WILD - Post cards - Philip Mattes
HOT-AS-A-PIXEL - Meat products–poultry - Hester Industries, Inc.
HOT ASH BOX - Boxes - Medallion Swim Pool Co., Inc.
HOT-B - Toys–electronic - Hot-B USA Inc.
HOT BACKUP - Transmitting apparatus - Rosemount Inc.
HOT BANNANA - Apparel–children's - Hot Bannana Kids Co.
HOT BANQUET - Pickles - Nalley's Fine Foods
HOT BASKET - Trays–warming - Salton/Maxim Housewares, Inc.
HOT BAT - Bats–baseball ☆ - Hillerich & Bradsby Co.
HOT BIRD - Toys - Mattel, Inc.
HOT BITES - Food products - Conagra, Inc.
HOT BLADE - Automotive parts and accessories - Dewey G. Holland
HOT BLAST - Stoves - United States Stove Co. Inc.
HOT BLOCK - Pet products - Tetra Sales USA
HOT BLOCKS - Computer software - Gary Marince
HOT BLOCKS - Tiles–ceramic - Corning Inc.
HOT BODIES - Toys–automobiles - Carter Brothers Manufacturing Co., Inc.
HOT BODYZ - Apparel and accessories - Hot Bodyz
HOT BOOTS - Fabrics - Dan River Inc.
HOT BOTTOM - Coatings - Barnacle Ban Corp.
HOT BOTTOM - Evaporation apparatus–laboratory - Power Plant Service Inc.
HOT BOX - Electrical equipment - GB Electrical Inc.
HOT BOX - Electronic equipment - Cardone Industries, Inc.
HOT BOX - Fishing tackle - Zebco Corp.
HOT BOX - Heaters–motor vehicle - South Wind Corp.
HOT BRIGHT - Toys ☆ - Coloron Industries
HOT-BRITE COLORS - Toys - Empire of Carolina Inc.
HOT BRUSH - Skin care products - La Coupe
HOT BUNS - Kitchen appliances - Wintenna Inc.
HOT BUTTERED SOUL - Recording label - MCA Universal Studios
HOT-C-POPS - Candy - Helms Candy Manufacturing Co. Inc.
HOT CABS - Audio equipment - KICS USA
HOT CAKES - Apparel stores–sports ☆ - Kombi Ltd.
HOT CAKES - Shoes ☆ - World Import Co. Inc.
HOT CARAMEL - Lipsticks - Honey & Spice Toiletries
HOT CARGO - Apparel and accessories - Wemco, Inc.
HOT CATS - Pet products - Full Circle Herb Co.
HOT CATS - Seafood products–fresh or frozen - Iceland Seafood Corp.
HOT CD - Video games - PointGroup Corp.
HOT CHA CHA - Food products - La Paloma Foods
HOT CHA CHA! - Molasses - Allied Old English, Inc.
HOT-CHAPS - Apparel and accessories - Hot-Shot Products Co.
HOT CHAR - Charcoal - Cotter & Co.
HOT CHERRY - Lipsticks ☆ - Honey & Spice Toiletries
HOT CHILLYS - Apparel and accessories - Hot Chillys Inc.
HOT CHILLYS - Apparel and accessories - Guy Wells & Co., Inc.
HOT CHIPS! - Food products ☆ - J.R. Simplot Co.
HOT CHIX BUFFALO WING SAUCE - Sauces - Hot Chix
HOT CHIX EXTRA HOT BBQ SAUCE - Sauces - Hot Chix
HOT CHIX EXTRA HOT WING SAUCE - Sauces - Hot Chix
HOT CHOCOLATE FINE CHOCOLATE THAT BITES BACK - Chocolate candy - Taste Teasers
HOT CHOCOLATES - Cookies - Jill's One Smart Cookie Inc.
HOT CHOICE - Vending machines - KRH Thermal Systems
HOT CHU - Chewing gum - Philadelphia Chewing Gum Corp.
HOT CINNAMON SCREAMERS - Candy - Sconza Candy Co.
HOT CINOMON - Candy - Nabisco Foods Group
HOT CLIPS - Paper clips - Acco World Corp.
HOT CO-COW - Cocoa–powders or mixes - E. Rosen Co.
HOT COFFEE COOL PLANET RECYCLE - Coffee - Coffee & Tea Market, Inc.
HOT COLE - Bathing suits - Authentic Fitness Corp.
HOT COLES - Bathing suits - Cole of California Inc.
HOT COLORS - Skin care products ☆ - Cosmetic Firsts Ltd.
HOT COLORS - Snack foods - General Mills, Inc.
HOT + COOL - Bags - Prince Lionheart, Inc.

HOT COOLER - Apparel and accessories - Premier Equity Inc.
HOT COTTON - Apparel and accessories - Marc Wear
HOT COUNTRY NIGHTS - Apparel and accessories - Dick Clark Productions Inc.
HOT COVERS - Book covers - Kittrich Corp.
HOT CUFFS - Slippers - Totes, Inc.
HOT CURLER - Brushes–hair - Phillips Brush Corp.
HOT CUTS - Cheese, meat ☆ - Bryan Foods, Inc.
HOT DAMN - Apparel–women's - Stonefish, Inc.
HOT DAMN - Beverages–alcohol - Jim Beam Brands Co.
HOT DANCIN' - T-shirts–children's - Mattel, Inc.
HOT DATE - Broadcasting stations–television - Karin-Maria K. Winkelhorn
HOT/DERM - Skin care products - Fox Pharmacal Inc.
HOT DESK - Computer software - Smith Micro Software, Inc.
HOT DIET - Vitamins and nutritional supplements - Country's Health
HOT DIGGITY - Food products machinery - Gold Medal Products Co.
HOT-DIGGITY - Food products ☆ - Pierre Frozen Foods Inc.
HOT-DO - Hair care products - Gillette Co.
HOT DOG - Bicycles - Dynacraft Industries Inc.
HOT DOG - Toys–stuffed ☆ - Gund, Inc.
HOT DOG CENTRAL - Restaurants–fast food - Dairy Mart Convenience Stores, Inc.
HOT DOG LOVERS HOT DOG - Frankfurters - Vienna Sausage Manufacturing Co.
HOT DOG STAND: THE WORKS - Computer software - Sunburst Communications, Inc.
HOT DOGGER - Kitchen appliances - National Presto Industries, Inc.
HOT DOGS - Apparel–children's - Mcgregor Corp.
HOT DOGS - Chewing gum - Leaf, Inc.
HOT DOT - Audio equipment ☆ - Barcus-Berry Inc.
HOT DOTS - Bedding–linen - Dan River Inc.
HOT DOTS - Fabrics ☆ - Greenwood Mills Inc.
HOT DOTS - Leather goods ☆ - Design Circle Ltd.
HOT DOTS - Markers–felt-tip - Tulip Productions
HOT DOTS - Trimmings–fabric - Meadowbrook Inventions Inc.
HOT ESPRESSO - Lipsticks ☆ - Honey & Spice Toiletries
HOT FEET - Footwear - Alta Products Corp.
HOT FILE - Office supplies - Rubbermaid Office Products Inc.
HOT FILL - Clothing insulations - Dionysian Inc. (Jacobs Div.)
HOT FINGERS - Dryers–hair - Windmere Corp.
HOT-FINGERS - Seasonings ☆ - Pierce Foods Corp.
HOT FINGERS DIFFUSER - Dryers–hair - Nino Originals
HOT FOOT - Apparel and accessories - Fair Haven Industries Inc.
HOT FOOT - Shoes - Edwards Creative Products, Inc.
HOT FUDGE - Lipsticks ☆ - Honey & Spice Toiletries
HOT FUN - Apparel and accessories - Hot Fun, Inc.
HOT GARLIC PECANS - Food products - Mrs. Powell's Gourmet Pecans
HOT GEAR - Sports apparel, accessories, and equipment - Dionysian Inc. (Jacobs Div.)
HOT GOLD - Liqueurs - Mango Bottling, Inc.
HOT GRILLS - Barbecues and grills - The Companion Group
HOT GRIP - Medical apparatus - Prism Enterprises, Inc.
HOT GRIZZLIES - Cashews - MT OSO Trading Co.
HOT HAND - Apparel and accessories - William V. Schulkin
HOT HAND - Dryers–hair - Conair Corp.
HOT HAND - Health care products - Maddak Inc.
HOT HANDS - Apparel and accessories - Hypark Specialty Co., Inc.
HOT HEAD - Crocheted and knitted items - Fair Haven Industries Inc.
HOT HEAD - Photographic equipment - Egripment USA, Inc.
HOT HEADS - Razors - Conair Corp.
HOT HEELS - Shoes - Imxco Sales Inc.
HOT HIP & COUNTRY - Shirts - Debra Sue Maffett
HOT HOLDER - Trivets ☆ - Interdesign, Inc.
HOT HOT CAJUN - Nuts–salted, roasted, cooked, or canned ☆ - Sonne Laboratories
HOT HOT HOT - Sauces - Victoria's Treasure Inc.
HOT HOUSE - Mushrooms - Purcell International
HOT HUBS SERIES - Toys–automobiles - Mattel, Inc.
HOT ICE - Candy ☆ - Leaf, Inc.
HOT ICE - Jewelry–costume - Hot Ice Inc.
HOT ICE - Trophies–metal - Alenite, L.P.
HOT JAVA - Computer software - Sun Microsystems, Inc.
HOT JOTS - Pens - Faber-Castell Corp.
HOT KNOTS - Pretzels - J & J Snack Foods Corp.
HOT LASHES - Cosmetics - Alexandra McMullen
HOT LAVA - Sporting goods ☆ - O'Brien International

☆ = Now out of production

HOT LEAD - Firearms - Cold Steel Inc.

HOT LEAD - Musical instrument accessories - Seymour Duncan Pickups

HOT LEAD FOR TELE - Musical instrument accessories - Seymour Duncan Pickups

HOT LICKS - Candy - Russ Berrie and Co., Inc.

HOT LICKS - Lotions - Beyond All Expectations

HOT LICKS - Recording label - Hot Licks Productions Inc.

HOT LINE - Bicycles ☆ - Hedstrom Corp.

HOT LINE - Bicycles ☆ - Roadmaster Corp.

HOT LINER - Pens ☆ - Paper Mate Co.

HOT LINES - Wallpaper - Riverside Silkscreen

HOT LIPS - Audio equipment - Telequest Inc.

HOT LIPS - Candy - Glenn Confections Inc.

HOT LIPS - Chocolate candy - Harry London's Candies Inc.

HOT-LIPS - Food products - Pierce Foods Corp.

HOT LIPS - Games - International Gamco, Inc.

HOT LIPS - Lipsticks - Preview Products

HOT LIPS PIZZA - Pizzas–frozen - Hot Lips Pizza, Inc.

HOT LIQUIDS BRING RELIEF - Teas–herbal - Traditional Medicinals, Inc.

HOT LITE - Flashlights - Garrity Industries

HOT LITES - Pens - Bic Corp.

HOT LITTLE DEVILS - Candy - E. Rosen Co.

HOT LOOKS - Bicycles - Huffy Corp.

HOT LOOKS - Dolls - Mattel, Inc.

HOT LOOKS INTERNATIONAL, INC. - Hair care products - Hot Looks International, Inc.

HOT LULU'S - Medical apparatus - Luanne Jordan

HOT LUNCH - Dinners–frozen - Kraft Foods, Inc.

HOT MAMAS - Ravioli–canned - Homestead Ravioli Co.

HOT MELT - Glue–household or industrial - FPC Corp.

HOT METAL - Harmonicas - Hohner Inc.

HOT MIC - Microphones - Undersea Systems International, Inc.

HOT MIST - Cleaning preparations–carpet and rug - Windsor Wax Co. Inc.

HOT MITT - Gloves - Fair Haven Industries Inc.

HOT MITTS - Mittens - Hot Mitts, Inc.

HOT MIX - Food products - Deep Foods, Inc.

HOT MONEY B'GUM - Chewing gum ☆ - R.L. Albert & Son, Inc.

HOT MUSIC FOR COOL NIGHTS - Recording label - Capitol Records, Inc.

HOT 'N BRITE - Hobby kits - Rose Art Industries, Inc.

HOT 'N CHUNKY - Sauces - Gold Pure Food Products Inc.

HOT-N'-COLD - Cups–paper ☆ - Royal Paper Products Inc.

HOT-N-COLDPOPS - Candy - Helms Candy Manufacturing Co. Inc.

HOT 'N COOL - Adhesives and sealants - Atlan Plastics Inc.

HOT-N-COOLER - Ice chests–plastic - General Foam Plastics Corp.

HOT 'N' FRESH - Doughs–frozen - Campbell Taggart Inc.

HOT 'N GOOD - Bread and muffins - Aldi Inc.

HOT-'N-HANDY - Heaters–gas - Holmes Products, Corp.

HOT 'N SNAPPY - Condiment - Miss Scarlett

HOT 'N SOUR ROWDIES - Candy - Herman Goelitz Candy Co., Inc.

HOT 'N SPICY - Chickens - Conagra, Inc.

HOT 'N SPICY - Meat products–cured - Dial Corp.

HOT 'N SPICY - Salt - Lawry's Foods Inc.

HOT 'N STEAMY - Irons–electric ☆ - Hamilton Beach/Proctor-Silex Inc.

HOT-N-STICKY - Tires–automobile - Max-Trac Tire Co.

HOT-N-TOT - Barbecue sauce ☆ - E.H. Wright Co. Inc.

HOT 'N TOT - Fishing lures - Storm Manufacturing Co.

HOT 'N TOT PYGMY - Fishing lures - Storm Manufacturing Co.

HOT 'N WET - Electronic equipment ☆ - Rayex Corp.

HOT 'N ZESTY COUNTRY SAUSAGE - Sausages - Johnsonville Sausage, Inc.

HOT NAILS - Nail care products - Hotlocks Hair Care International

HOT NAILS - Toys - Larami Limited, Inc.

HOT NEON - Cameras - Keystone Camera Corp.

HOT NIPS - Pet products - Full Circle Herb Co.

HOT NOTES - Pasta - Hanover Foods Corp.

HOT NUMBERS - Apparel and accessories - Gym Rat, Inc.

HOT NUMBERS - Office supplies ☆ - Faber-Castell Corp.

HOT OFF THE PRESS - Fabrics - Gretchen Bellinger Inc.

HOT OIL - Pet products - Rich Health

HOT ONE - Adhesives and sealants - Stahls' Inc.

HOT ONE - Batteries - Exide Corp.

HOT ONE, THE - Bathroom accessories - Better Sleep, Inc.

HOT ONE, THE - Balls–golf - Bost Enterprises, Inc.

HOT ONE, THE - Heaters–space - Cadet Manufacturing Co.

HOT ONE, THE - Shaving preparations - Gillette Co.

HOT ONE, THE - Cups–plastic ☆ - Nyman Manufacturing Co.

HOT ONE, THE - Pet products - Rapid Electric/R & R Manufacturing

HOT ONES - Key rings - Union Pen Co.

HOT ONES - Office furniture–metal - K & M Co.

HOT OR MILD? - Backpacks - Taco Bell Corp.

HOT PACKS - Trading cards and stamps - Fleer Corp.

HOT PAD - Musical instrument accessories - Silver St. Inc.

HOT PADS - Stationery ☆ - Gallant Greetings Corp.

HOT PAGES - Computer software - Prentice-Hall, Inc.

HOT PAIR - Footwear–women's - Verden Imports Co. Ltd.

HOT PANS - Water colors ☆ - Sanford Corp.

HOT PANTS - Colognes ☆ - Pfizer Inc.

HOT PANTS - Pet products - Dr. Goodpet

HOT PARTY SERVER - Trays–warming ☆ - Salton/Maxim Housewares, Inc.

HOT PEPPER - Floor coverings–carpet and rugs ☆ - Mohawk Carpet Corp.

HOT PEPPERS - Candy - Haribo of America Inc.

HOT PICKUP - Musical instrument accessories - Seymour Duncan Pickups

HOT PICKUP FOR P-BASS - Musical instrument accessories ☆ - Seymour Duncan Pickups

HOT PICKUP FOR STRAT - Musical instrument accessories ☆ - Seymour Duncan Pickups

HOT PINK - Cleaning preparations - Chem Lab Products, Inc.

HOT PIX - Cameras - Ansco Photo-Optical Products Corp.

HOT PLATE - Dehumidifiers - Heat Pipe Technology Inc.

HOT POCKETS - See THE ORGANIZER

HOT POCKETS - Frozen foods - Chef America, Inc.

HOT POCKITS - Sporting goods - Sports Access/America

HOT POINT - Electrical testing instruments - Omega Engineering, Inc.

HOT POLY - Heating pads–electric - Briskheat Corp.

HOT POPS - Candy ☆ - American Candy Co.

HOT POPS - Confections ☆ - Creative Flavors

HOT POPS - Popcorn - Ash Enterprises, Inc.

HOT POT - Cooking equipment–household - West Bend Co.

HOT POT - Puppets - Robin A. Merritt

HOT POT HEAT 'N SERVER - Cooking equipment–household - West Bend Co.

HOT-POT-POURRI - Incense ☆ - Applewood Seed & Garden Group

HOT POTATO - Games ☆ - Parker Brothers

HOT POTATOES - Stamps–hand - Mary Benagh O'Neil

HOT POTS - Dishcloths - Boston Warehouse Trading Corp.

HOT POTS - Perfumes - Tennessee Gold Inc.

HOT POWER - Cleaning preparations - Comstar International Inc. (IPC Div.)

HOT PRO - Dryers–hair ☆ - Sunbeam-Oster Household Products

HOT PUFF - Hair care products - Helene Curtis Industries Inc.

HOT PURPLE - Lipsticks ☆ - Honey & Spice Toiletries

HOT PURSUIT - Apparel–children's - Dobie Industries Inc.

HOT-R-COLD - Health care products - Arthur Blank and Co. Inc.

HOT-R-COLD - Lacquers - V.J. Dolan & Co. Inc.

HOT R' COLD - Pharmaceutical preparations - Tetra Medical Supply Corp.

HOT RACK - Office supplies - Rubbermaid Office Products Inc.

HOT RAILS - Musical instrument accessories - Seymour Duncan Pickups

HOT RAILS FOR TELE - Musical instrument accessories ☆ - Seymour Duncan Pickups

HOT RED EGGS - Fishing lures - Brown Bear Bait Co.

HOT RHYTHM - Musical instrument accessories - Seymour Duncan Pickups

HOT RHYTHM FOR TELE - Musical instrument accessories ☆ - Seymour Duncan Pickups

HOT RINGS - Candy - Nabisco Foods Group

HOT RINGS - Candy - Nabisco Holdings Corp.

HOT ROCK - Footwear - Tristar International Footwear, Ltd.

HOT ROCKIN' - Toys–automobiles - Mattel, Inc.

HOT ROCKS - Candy ☆ - Leaf, Inc.

HOT ROCKS - Heating pads–electric - Renee S. Kimmel

HOT ROCKS - Novelty items ☆ - Cal Themes Inc.

HOT ROD - Boats - Glen-L Marine Designs

HOT ROD - Curling irons–electric - Spilo/Mehaz Worldwide

HOT ROD - Ophthalmic goods - Foremost Optical Products

HOT ROD - Radio communications equipment - Francis Industries Inc.

HOT ROD - Toys - Steven Manufacturing Co.

HOT ROD BOB - Salad dressings–bottled - Special Edition Foods, Inc.

HOT ROD NOSTALGIA - Catalogs - Hot Rod Nostalgia

HOT ROD RACERS - Toys–automobiles - Matchbox Toys USA

HOT ROD ROADSTER - Toys - Fisher-Price, Inc.

HOT RODS - Heating equipment - Occunomix International Inc.

HOT RODS - Musical instrument accessories - Pro-Mark Corp.

HOT RODS - Novelty items - Deja Vu Enterprises

HOT RODS - Pistons - Hot Rods Motorcycle & Auto Parts Corp.

☆ = Now out of production

HOT ROLLED BRITE - Metals - J. Rubin & Co.
HOT ROUNDS - Musical instrument accessories - G & L Music Sales Inc.
HOT ROX - Jewelry - Marshal T. Simpson
HOT SANDWICH TOPPERS - Food products - Conagra, Inc.
HOT SAUCE - Health care products - Universal Nutritional Systems
HOT SAUCE - Waxes–mineral - Hertel & Co. Inc.
HOT SAUCE FROM HELL - Sauces - Southwest Specialty Foods
HOT SCOT - Golfing equipment - Tommy Armour Golf Co.
HOT SCOT - Heaters–space - Ritchie Industries, Inc.
HOT SEAT - Bicycles - Wild Side West Inc.
HOT SEAT - Gloves - Fair Haven Industries Inc.
HOT SEAT - Toys–automobiles ☆ - Roadmaster Corp.
HOT SEAT - Video games - Power to the 10th Inc.
HOT SEAT MATE - Firearms, accessories, and parts - Fair Haven Industries Inc.
HOT SECRET - Food products - General Mills, Inc.
HOT SECRET - Paper–book - Tadeusz Wajda
HOT SEVENS - Game machines - Sigma Game Inc.
HOT SEX - Beverages–alcohol - Chatam International Inc.
HOT SHAPES - Bathing suits - Gardner Park, Inc.
HOT SHEWS - Nuts–salted, roasted, cooked, or canned - George's Inc.
HOT SHIFT - Automotive parts and accessories - Hurst Performance Inc.
HOT SHINE - Hair care products - Roberts Research Laboratories, Inc.
HOT SHOT - Adhesives and sealants - Gibson-Homans Co. (Sealant Technology)
HOT SHOT - Automotive parts and accessories - Spray Products Corp.
HOT SHOT - Bicycles - Kent International Inc.
HOT SHOT - Cleaning preparations–household - W.W. Grainger, Inc.
HOT SHOT - Coffee makers–electric - Sunbeam-Oster Household Products
HOT-SHOT - Dental equipment - E & D Dental Products, Inc.
HOT SHOT - Evaporation apparatus–laboratory - Power Plant Service Inc.
HOT SHOT - Fireworks - American Promotional Events, Inc.
HOT SHOT - Floor coverings–carpet and rugs - Evans-Black Carpet Mills
HOT SHOT - Food products - Universal Packers Corp.
HOT SHOT - Games - Munro Games Inc.
HOT SHOT - Gasoline ☆ - Wynn Oil Co.
HOT SHOT - Hair care products - Conair Corp.
HOT SHOT - Hardware ☆ - Keystone Steel & Wire Co.
HOT SHOT - Lighters - Cricket Lighters
HOT SHOT - Motor vehicle parts and accessories - Durimex Inc.
HOT-SHOT - Novelty items - Kolcraft Enterprises, Inc.
HOT SHOT - Photographic equipment - Egripment USA, Inc.
HOT SHOT - Sporting goods - Head Sports USA
HOT SHOT - Sports rackets and accessories - Gexco Enterprises
HOT SHOT - Tools–power-driven - General Wire Spring Co.
HOT SHOT - Toys - Tonka Corp.
HOT SHOT - Trays ☆ - Eagle Glass Products
HOT SHOT - Vacuum cleaners and accessories ☆ - The Eureka Co.
HOT SHOT BASKETBALL - Games - Milton Bradley Co.
HOT SHOT BELT - Exercising equipment - Kytec Innovative Sports Equipment
HOT SHOT SCHNAPPS - Cordials - David Sherman Corp.
HOT SHOT VEST - Exercising equipment - Kytec Innovative Sports Equipment
HOT SHOTS - Apparel–children's - Hot Shots Inc.
HOT SHOTS - Cameras - Sakar International Inc.
HOT SHOTS - Chemical preparations - Frank Miller and Sons Inc.
HOT SHOTS - Dryers–hair - S.C. Johnson & Son, Inc.
HOT-SHOTS - Electrical equipment - Hot-Shot Products Co.
HOT SHOTS - Frames–picture - Russ Berrie and Co., Inc.
HOT SHOTS - Greeting cards ☆ - American Greetings Corp.
HOT SHOTS - Musical instrument accessories - MBT International, Inc.
HOT SHOTS - Paints ☆ - DecoArt, Inc.
HOT SHOTS - Toys–airplanes - Comet Montrose Ltd.
HOT SHOTS ATHLETIC APPAREL - Uniforms–athletic - Victor Hernandez
HOT SHOTS INDOOR BEACH VOLLEYBALL CLUB - Apparel and accessories - IBF, Inc.
HOT SICILIAN - Food products - Pometta's Italian Salsa
HOT SILVER - Hair care products - Belson Products
HOT SILVER - Office supplies - Securitag Corp.
HOT SINGLES - Computer software - Adobe Systems Inc.
HOT SIX - Hair and skin care products - Bronner Bros. Manufacturing Co., Inc.
HOT SKINS - Clothing - Hot Skins Bodywear International, Inc.
HOT SKINS - Sporting goods - O'Brien International
HOT SNOWBOARDS - Snowboards - Raichle Molitor USA, Inc.
HOT SOLOS - Cheese and sauce - Land O'Lakes Inc.
HOT SOX - Gloves - Fair Haven Industries Inc.
HOT SOX - Hosiery - Hot Sox Co. Inc. Ralph Lauren Hosiery Div.

HOT SOX - Skates–ice - Northern Skate Gear LLC
HOT SPARKS - Candy - Banner Candy Manufacturing Corp.
HOT SPARKS - Hair coloring preparations - Cosmair Inc.
HOT SPICE - Floor coverings–carpet and rugs ☆ - Mohawk Carpet Corp.
HOT SPICED VIENNESE - Coffee - Coffee Beanery Ltd.
HOT SPICES - Apparel and accessories - Toppe California Inc.
HOT SPOT - Audio equipment - Galaxy Audio
HOT SPOT - Fishing lures - Lindy Little Joe Inc.
HOT SPOT - Heating equipment - Colgate-Palmolive Co.
HOT SPOT - Markers–felt-tip - Pentech International Inc.
HOT SPOT - Soldering equipment - Bell Group, Inc.
HOT SPOT - Spas - Watkins Manufacturing Corp.
HOT SPOT - Spotlights - Lectro Science, Inc.
HOT SPOT - Veterinary pharmaceutical preparations - Vital Nutrition Products
HOT SPOT THE ANYWHERE ANYTIME TUB - Hot tubs–fiberglass - Watkins Manufacturing Corp.
HOT SPOTS - Food products - Hines-Park Foods Inc.
HOT SPOTS - Jewelry ☆ - A.J. Ganz Co. Inc.
HOT SPOTS - Recording label - Zapset, Inc.
HOT SPOTS! - Snack foods - Cindy's Bite-Size Bakery
HOT SPOTS - Sunblocks - Autumn-Harp, Inc.
HOT SPOTS FOR TOTS - Sunblocks - Autumn-Harp, Inc.
HOT SPOTTER - Labels–paper - Robin Groth
HOT SPRING - Bathroom accessories - Watkins Manufacturing Corp.
HOT SPRINGS HOT - Catsup - Kerwin S. Koerper
HOT SPRINGS SHOWER - Bathroom fixtures - Pacific Spirit Corp.
HOT SPRINGS SPA - Hot tubs–fiberglass - Masco Corp.
HOT SPRINT - Automotive parts and accessories ☆ - Lancaster Colony Automotive Group
HOT SPURS - Socks - Hotspurs Ltd.
HOT STEAK - Heaters–space - Sunbeam-Oster Household Products
HOT STIC - Pens - Bic Corp.
HOT STK - Heaters–kerosene - Webb Enterprises Inc.
HOT STOCKS - Toy vehicles - Matchbox Toys USA
HOT STRIDES - Toys ☆ - A.R.C. Toys Inc.
HOT STUFF - Air purification systems ☆ - Medo Industries, Inc.
HOT STUFF - Analgesics - Mueller Sports Medicine Inc.
HOT STUFF - Books–comic - Harvey Comics Entertainment, Inc.
HOT-STUFF - Candy ☆ - Chex Co.
HOT STUFF - Chewing gum ☆ - Fleer Corp.
HOT STUFF - Coffee makers–electric - Philips Electronics North America Corp.
HOT STUFF - Dolls - Mattel, Inc.
HOT STUFF - Fishing tackle - Creme Lure Co.
HOT STUFF - Floor coverings–carpet and rugs ☆ - Carpet Crafts Inc.
HOT STUFF - Frames–picture - Russ Berrie and Co., Inc.
HOT STUFF - Fuel additives - Index Industries Inc.
HOT STUFF - Gloves - Knoxville Glove Co.
HOT STUFF - Heaters–space - Enerco Technical Products
HOT STUFF - Perfumes - Caswell-Massey Co. Ltd.
HOT STUFF - Pizzas–frozen - Schwan's Sales Enterprises, Inc.
HOT STUFF - Sauce - American Natural Foods Inc.
HOT STUFF - Sausages - Johnsonville Sausage, Inc.
HOT STUFF - Seasonings - Silver Palate Kitchen
HOT STUFF - Self-defense sprays - Advanced Defense Technologies, Inc.
HOT STUFF - Toys - Imperial Toy Corp.
HOT STUFF BEARS - Toys–stuffed ☆ - Fun World Inc.
HOT STUFF DEVIL - Toys–stuffed - Russ Berrie and Co., Inc.
HOT STUFF PIZZA - Pizzas–frozen - Hot Stuff Food Systems, Inc.
HOT STUFF SERIES - Heating equipment - Mr. Heater Corp.
HOT STUFF STICK - Analgesics - Mueller Sports Medicine Inc.
HOT STUFF, THE - Chemical preparations - Milazzo Industries Inc.
HOT STUFF'N - Apparel–athletic ☆ - Reliable of Milwaukee
HOT STYLE - Bicycles ☆ - Huffy Corp.
HOT STYLER - Brushes–hair - Phillips Brush Corp.
HOT SURPRISE - Toys - Taco Bell Corp.
HOT TAMALE - Apparel and accessories - Elaine Siegel
HOT TAMALES - Candy - Just Born Inc.
HOT TAPES - Lighters - Park Lane Associates, Inc.
HOT TERM - Computer software - Telecorp Systems Inc.
HOT THAI - Salad dressings–bottled - Cuisine Perel Corp.
HOT THANGS - Meat products - Sysco Corp.
HOT-TIE - Electrical equipment - Exide Electronics Corp.
HOT TIMES - Dolls - Mattel, Inc.
HOT TIPS - Automotive parts and accessories - Hedman Hedders
HOT TIPS - Computer software - Kinetic Effects Inc.

☆ = Now out of production

HOT TIPS - Hair care products - Trimco International
HOT TIPS - Postcards - Lakewood Publications Acquisition Corp.
HOT-TIPZ - Gloves - Aris Isotoner Inc.
HOT TIRE PEELERS - Toys–automobiles - Imperial Toy Corp.
HOT TOAST - Lipstick ☆ - Cosrich Inc.
HOT TOMATA - Beverages–alcohol - Hiram Walker & Sons, Inc.
HOT TOOL - Tools - Hot Tools Inc.
HOT TOOLS - Hair care products - Helen of Troy Corp.
HOT TOP, THE - Containers ☆ - Warner-Lambert Co.
HOT TOPPER - Kitchen appliances - National Presto Industries, Inc.
HOT-TOT - Kitchen appliances ☆ - National Presto Industries, Inc.
HOT TOTS - Dolls - Feber N.A., Inc.
HOT TOTS - Vegetables–frozen - Ore-Ida Foods, Inc.
HOT TOUCH - Machine parts - Republic Roller Corp.
HOT TRACKS - Apparel and accessories - J.C. Penney Co., Inc.
HOT TRAX - Toys–automobiles - Empire Industries
HOT TUB - Health care products ☆ - Sunbeam-Oster Household Products
HOT TUB - Office supplies - Rubbermaid Office Products Inc.
HOT TUB POXY - Epoxy - Permalite Plastics Corp.
HOT TUBE - Electrical equipment - GB Electrical Inc.
HOT TUBE - Evaporation apparatus–laboratory - Power Plant Service Inc.
HOT TUBE - Water heaters–household - Daka Corp.
HOT TWIRLING CURLS - Hair care products - Cosmair Inc.
HOT VAC - Soldering equipment - Eldon Industries Inc. (Ungar Div.)
HOT VIBES - Health care products ☆ - Dubl Duck/Jet Set Inc.
HOT VOLTAGE - Apparel and accessories - United Merchandising Corp.
HOT WALL - Posters - Off-The-Wall
HOT WATER - Bathing suits - Sirena Apparel Group Inc.
HOT WATER MACHWE - Plumbing fixtures–metal - Elkay Manufacturing Co.
HOT WATT - Amplifiers–radio - Evets Corp.
HOT WAX - Candles - Hot Wax Works
HOT WAX - Recording label - Edward J. Holland, Jr.
HOT WAX WORKS - Greeting cards - Hot Wax Works
HOT WHEELS - Candy ☆ - Clark Gum Co.
HOT WHEELS - Computer software - Epyx Inc.
HOT WHEELS - Footwear ☆ - Pagoda Trading Co.
HOT WHEELS - Potato chips - Groff's Snack-Food
HOT WHEELS - Shoes - Sidney Rich Associates Inc.
HOT WHEELS - Toys–automobiles - Mattel, Inc.
HOT WHEELS - Wheelchairs ☆ - Everest and Jennings International Ltd.
HOT WHEELS 500 - Toys - Mattel, Inc.
HOT WHEELS ADVENTURES - Toys - Mattel, Inc.
HOT WHEELS COLLECTIBLES - Toys - Mattel, Inc.
HOT WHEELS TATTOOS - Decals and transfers - Philadelphia Chewing Gum Corp.
HOT WILD - Barbecue sauce - Ashman Distributing Co.
HOT WINGS - Meat products–poultry - KFC Corp.
HOT WIRES - Cables - Music People Inc.
HOT YELLOW - Nail care products - Pavion Ltd.
HOT YOGA - Video production - Baptiste Power Yoga Institute, Inc.
HOT-Z - Golfing equipment - Arnold Palmer Golf Co.
HOT ZIGGETY - Skin care products ☆ - Pro Star Salon Products
HOT ZINX - Suntan lotions - Del Pharmaceuticals, Inc.
HOTABLE - Serving carts - Salton/Maxim Housewares, Inc.
HOTAI - Incense ☆ - Candle Corp. of America
HOTAS - Video games - Thrustmaster, Inc.
HOTBALL - Hockey equipment - Shield Manufacturing Inc.
HOTBLADE - Hockey equipment - Shield Manufacturing Inc.
HOTBOX - Audio equipment - Whirlwind Music Distributors, Inc.
HOTBUTTONS - Computer software - Computer Concepts Corp.
HOTDIJ - Computer software - Geocomp, Ltd.
HOTDISK - Computer software - Smith Micro Software, Inc.
HOTDOCS - Computer software - Capsoft Development Corp.
HOTDOGGER - Apparel and accessories ☆ - Kellwood Co.
HOTDOT - Sights–gun - Emerging Technologies Inc.
HOTEL BAR - Butter - Hotel Bar Foods Inc.
HOTEL BEL-AIR - Skin care products - Sazale (Bel-Air) GP Corp.
HOTEL COMPUSYSTEM - Computer software - Mai Systems Corp.
HOTEL INFORMATION SYSTEMS - Computer software - Hotel Information Systems
HOTEL MEXICO - Apparel and accessories - SDK Investments, Inc.
HOTEL SPECIAL - Seasonings - Silver Foods Corp.
HOTEL TWIN DOLPHIN - Apparel and accessories - Twin Dolphin
HOTELS - Games - Milton Bradley Co.
HOTELSTAT - Thermostats - PSG Limited , LLC
HOTELVIEW - Computer software - Hotelview Corp.

HOTFINGER - Office supplies - Bedol International Group, Inc.
HOTFINGERS - Apparel - Marmon Holdings, Inc.
HOTFINGERS - Gloves - Promark
HOTFOOT - Machinery - Corrugated Gear and Sprocket, Inc.
HOTHIGHS - Meat products–poultry - Designer Foods, Inc.
HOTKAPS - Garden equipment ☆ - T & T Industries Inc.
HOTLANTA - Food products - Jardine's Texas Foods
HOTLANTA - Recording label - Hottrax Records
HOTLANTA - Sauces ☆ - Texxstar Resources (USA), Inc.
HOTLICKS - Apparel - Hotlicks Franchise Marketing Inc.
HOTLICKS - Musical instrument accessories - Dunlop Manufacturing, Inc.
HOTLINE - Apparel and accessories - Hotline USA
HOTLINE - Floor coverings–carpet and rugs - Coronet Carpets Inc.
HOTLINE - Hand tool kit - Creative Craftsmen Co., Inc.
HOTLINE - Stationery, ring binders, portfolios, etc. - S.I. Jacobson Manufacturing Co.
HOTLINE - Television equipment - Zenith Electronics Corp.
HOTLINE - Valves - Erie Controls
HOTLINER - Pens - Gillette Co.
HOTLINES - Wallcoverings - Penthouse Wallcoverings Ltd.
HOTLOCKS - Hair care products - Hotlocks Hair Care International
HOT'N FOAMY - Cleaning preparations - Takeo Enterprises Corp.
HOT'N HANDY - Cooking equipment–household ☆ - West Bend Co.
HOT'N STEAMY - Hair curlers - Windmere Corp.
HOT'N TOASTY - Kitchen appliances - Sunbeam-Oster Household Products
HOT'N TOT FLASH - Fishing lures - Storm Manufacturing Co.
HOTPACK - Clay–kiln ☆ - Hotpack Co.
HOTPAINT - Solar energy collectors - Vegetable Factory, Inc. (Sunbeam Structures Div.)
HOTPLATE-WITH-THE-BRAIN - Hotplates - Capitol Products Co.
HOTPLOT - Computer software - Mentor Graphics Corp.
HOTPOINT - Appliance parts - General Electric Co.
HOTPOINT - Stoves - Hotpoint
HOTPOP - Popcorn - Golden Valley Microwave Foods, Inc.
HOTPORTS - Computer software - Lawrence Jewelry Co.
HOTPOTZ - Musical instrument accessories - Dunlop Manufacturing, Inc.
HOTRAY - Trays–warming - Salton/Maxim Housewares, Inc.
HOTROCKS - Barbecues and grills - Far West Forests
HOTROD - Barbecues and grills - American Wyott Corp.
HOTRONIX - Adhesives and sealants - Stahls' Inc.
HOTS - Educational materials - Thinking with Computers, Inc.
HOTS - Footwear–children's - Richman Gordman Stores Inc.
HOTS - Paper–toilet - Georgia-Pacific Corp.
HOTS-MATH - Publisher's imprints - Thinking with Computers, Inc.
HOTSHOT - Eyeglasses - Art-Craft Optical Co.
HOTSHOT - Fireplace equipment ☆ - Earth Stove Inc.
HOTSHOTS - Notebooks and notepads ☆ - Union Camp Corp. (Fine Paper Division)
HOTSIE TOTSIES - Candy - Ash Enterprises, Inc.
HOTSILKS - Apparel and accessories - Sports Specialists Limited
HOTSLEEVE - Sporting goods - William Getz Corp.
HOTSOCKETS - Computer software - Ensodex, Inc.
HOTSPOT - Tools–hand-operated - Clauss Cutlery Co.
HOTSTART 20 - Laboratory apparatus - Molecular Bio-Products, Inc.
HOTSTART 50 - Laboratory apparatus - Molecular Bio-Products, Inc.
HOTSTART 100 - Laboratory apparatus - Molecular Bio-Products, Inc.
HOTSTICK - Hockey equipment - Shield Manufacturing Inc.
HOTSTIK - Fishing tackle ☆ - Fenwick
HOTSTREAM - Water heaters–household - S.A.B.H. U.S. Water Heaters
HOTSTUFF - Apparel and accessories - Jays Industries Inc.
HOTSTUFF - Gloves - WorkAbles for Women
HOTSY - Medical apparatus - Denver Splint Co., Inc.
HOTSYNC - Computer peripheral equipment - Palm Computing, Inc.
HOTSYS - Computer software - Jemeng Soh
HOTT ROD - Heating equipment - Terri Bremer
HOTTER THAN HELL CHILE MADNESS - Food products - Pecos Valley Spice Co.
HOTTEST THING GOING, THE - Thermostats - Tempco Electric Heater Corp.
HOTTLE - Glass products - Jeannette Corp.
HOTTLE BOTTLE - Glassware–household - Gemco Ware, Inc.
HOTTRAX - Recording label - Hottrax Records
HOTTRAX DMT - Audio tapes–blank - Hottrax Records
HOTWALL - Wallpaper - 4 Every Wall
HOTWIPE - Cleaning preparations - Newhouse Specialty Co., Inc.
HOTZ - Computer software - Hotz Corp.
HOTZ - Harmonicas - Hohner Inc.

☆ = Now out of production

HOTZ - Writing instruments - Pentech International Inc.
HOTZ-4-U - Sauces - Hotz-4-U, Inc.
HOTZ PLAYER - Computer software - Hotz Corp.
HOTZ TRANSLATOR - Musical instruments - Hotz Corp.
HOUBIGANT - Perfumes - Houbigant, Inc.
HOUCHENS - Food products - Houchens Industries, Inc.
HOUCHENS FAMILY TRADITIONS - Meat products - Houchens Industries, Inc.
HOUCK'S - Furniture polish and wax - Delhi Chemicals Inc.
HOUDINI - Toys - Evenflo Co.
HOUDINI RABBIT - Toys–stuffed - Russ Berrie and Co., Inc.
HOUFLEX - Wire - Houston Wire and Cable Co.
HOUGHTO-KOTE - Paints ✩ - E.F. Houghton & Co.
HOUGHTON - Floor coverings ✩ - Azrock Commercial Flooring
HOUGHTON MIFFLIN CO. - Publisher's imprints - Houghton Mifflin Co.
HOUGHTON MIFFLIN EDUCATION PLACE - Educational materials - Houghton Mifflin Co.
HOUKA STYLE - Apparel and accessories - Julio Robert Bardavid
HOULE'S - Dog food - E.J. Houle Inc.
HOULES - Fabrics ✩ - Sidney Davis Fabrics
HOULE'S EXPANDED - Dog food - E.J. Houle Inc.
HOULIHAN'S - Food products - Houlihan's Restaurants, Inc.
HOULIHAN'S - Furniture ✩ - Pulaski Furniture Corp.
HOULTON FARMS - Milk - Houlton Farms Dairy
HOUMA - Food products - Blum & Bergeron Inc.
HOUN' DAWG - Dog food - Lipscomb Feed
HOUN' PUP - Dog food - Lipscomb Feed
HOUND - Marine rigging ✩ - Brookes & Gatehouse Inc.
HOUND-DOG - Sandwiches–prepackaged - Southeast Food Systems, Inc.
HOUND DOG - Toys–banks - A.J. Renzi Plastic Corp.
HOUND DOG CHRISTMAS - Toys - Trendmasters, Inc.
HOUND DOG GANG, THE - Crackers - D.F. Stauffer Biscuit Co., Inc.
HOUND DOGGIE - Toys - Gerber Products Co.
HOUND LOUNGER - Pet products - Elaine T. Tinsley
HOUND SURROUND - Fencing–chain link - Master Halco Inc.
HOUNDAWG - Pet products - O.D. Funk Co.
HOUNDOG - Grass seed - International Seeds, Inc.
HOUNDS AND JACKALS - Games - Pyram Enterprises, Inc.
HOUND'S HARVEST - Pet products - Dale Distributing
HOUND'S ROUNDS - Pet products - Dale Distributing
HOUNDSTOOTH - Floor coverings–carpet and rugs ✩ - Regal Rugs Inc.
HOUNDSTOOTH - Wallpaper ✩ - Carey Lind Designs
HOUNDSTOOTH CLOTHING CO. - Apparel and accessories - Michael Baker
HOUR AFTER HOUR - Deodorants–personal - Colgate-Palmolive Co.
HOUR GLASS - Frames–eyeglass - Liberty Optical Manufacturing Co.
HOUR SEALER - Paints - Lilly Perfection Paint
HOUR VARNISH - Varnishes ✩ - McCloskey Corp.
HOURGLASS - Bathing suits - Great American Industries Inc. (Robby Len Fashions Divison.)
HOURGLASS - Floor coverings ✩ - Congoleum Corp.
HOURGLASS - Puzzles - Milton Bradley Co.
HOURGLASS BATH - Bathtubs–enameled - Kohler Co.
HOURGLASS EDITIONS - Greeting cards - Hourglass Editions
HOURGLASS FOREBODY - Sporting goods - O'Brien International
HOURGLASS JEWELRY CLEANING KIT - Cleaning equipment - Ultronics
HOURGLASS LOOK - Dolls ✩ - Effanbee Doll Corp.
HOURLY RATES - Computer software - Cost Research
HOURS LONGER - Cosmetics - Del Pharmaceuticals, Inc.
HOUSE - Window shades - John M. Sanders
HOUSE A ROCK'N - Video games - Sigma Game Inc.
HOUSE AIDE - Bags–paper - Electric Sweeper Service Co.
HOUSE & FARM - Tableware–earthenware - Anacapa Corp.
HOUSE & HOME - Scissors–hand-operated - Meijer, Inc.
HOUSE & TRIM - Paints - Hirshfield's Paint Manufacturing
HOUSE & WALL WASH - Cleaning preparations–household - Enviro-Chem Inc.
HOUSE-AUTRY - Flour–blended - House-Autry Mills, Inc.
HOUSE BEAUTIFUL - Publisher's imprints - Hearst Corp.
HOUSE/CASA - Computer software ✩ - Laureate Learning Systems Inc.
HOUSE COAT - Paints ✩ - Montgomery Ward & Co. Inc.
HOUSE DOCTOR, THE - Video production - Robert C. Yapp Jr.
HOUSE/GARD - Paints - Valspar Corp.
HOUSE GUARD - Paints - Hirshfield's Paint Manufacturing
HOUSE HOSE, THE - Sprinklers–lawn - Sunbeam-Oster Household Products
HOUSE IN BLOOM - Fertilizers ✩ - Pfizer Inc.
HOUSE IN THE HAMPTONS, A - Wallpaper ✩ - Raintree Designs Inc.

HOUSE JAM - Recording label - Gamble Huff Music Productions
HOUSE KEEPERS - Pet products ✩ - Ranpak Corp.
HOUSE-KOTE - Paints - Proko Industries Inc.
HOUSE LONDON BROIL - Barbecue sauce - Ashman Distributing Co.
HOUSE-MATES - Hardware - Crown Bolt, Inc.
HOUSE MOUSE - Health care products - St. John's Herb Garden Inc.
HOUSE-MOUSE DESIGNS - Stationery - House-Mouse Designs, Inc.
HOUSE 'N HOBBY - Gloves - Brookville Glove Manufacturing Co.
HOUSE O' WEENIES - Frankfurters - Marathon Enterprises, Inc.
HOUSE ODOR KLEEN - Deodorizers - G.G. Bean Inc.
HOUSE OF AULSEBROOKS - Food products ✩ - Masterpeace Food Imports
HOUSE OF BAUER, THE - Candy - Glico Harmony Foods Corp.
HOUSE OF BAUER, THE - Chocolate candy - Price Candy Co. Inc.
HOUSE OF BAZZINI - Snack foods - A.L. Bazzini Co. Inc.
HOUSE OF BEAUTY - Wallpaper ✩ - Eisenhart Wallcoverings Co.
HOUSE OF BLUES - Hats - House of Blues Brands Corp.
HOUSE OF CARDS - Playing cards - Lucia Eames Demetrios
HOUSE OF CARDS - Trading cards and stamps - Treat Entertainment, Inc.
HOUSE OF CHRISTIANA, THE - Apparel and accessories - Maner's, Inc.
HOUSE OF COLORS - Thread - Threads USA Div.
HOUSE OF COPPER - Hobby kits - Extra Special Products Corp.
HOUSE OF COUPONS - Coupons - House of Coupons, Inc.
HOUSE OF COVERS - Binders - Histacount Corp.
HOUSE OF DORCHESTER - Chocolate candy - Christopher Brookes Distinctive Foods
HOUSE OF EGGROLL - Food products - Pioneer Food Sales Inc.
HOUSE OF FABRICS - Fabrics–broadcloth - Collins & Aikman Corp.
HOUSE OF FLAVORS, THE - Spices and extracts - Marion-Kay-Reidco Inc.
HOUSE OF FUDGE - Fudge - House of Fudge
HOUSE OF FULLER - Cleaning preparations - Fuller Brush Co.
HOUSE OF GIULIANI - Jewelry ✩ - Harry Burke
HOUSE OF GOLD - Dairy products - Frigo Cheese Corp.
HOUSE OF GUEST - Fruits–canned ✩ - A. Camacho Inc.
HOUSE OF GUITARS - Recording label - Mirror Records Inc.
HOUSE OF HAMPTON - Skin care products ✩ - T.N. Dickinson Co.
HOUSE OF HASENFRATZ - Giftware - House of Hasenfratz
HOUSE OF HATTEN - Giftware - Vincent Lippe Co.
HOUSE OF HEMP - Cloth - Canvasmaker, Inc.
HOUSE OF HERBS - Seasonings - House of Herbs Inc.
HOUSE OF JOSEPH - Nature plaques - Aus-Ben Studios
HOUSE OF KASSER - Beverages–alcohol - Kasser Laird Distilling Co.
HOUSE OF KOLOR - Paints - House of Kolor, Inc.
HOUSE OF LANCASTER - Cigars ✩ - House of Windsor Inc.
HOUSE OF LEE - Food products - Lee Kum Kee Inc.
HOUSE OF LITZ - Figurines ✩ - Charles Zahn-Import Merchant
HOUSE OF LORD - Whiskey - European Beverage Co., Inc.
HOUSE OF LORDS - Food products - Martin Gillet and Co. Inc.
HOUSE OF LORDS - Ophthalmic goods - Embassy Creations Inc.
HOUSE OF LORDS - Tobacco products - Lane Ltd.
HOUSE OF LUMBER - Apparel and accessories - Ronald J. Stefancin, Jr.
HOUSE OF MARI - Musical instruments - E. & O. Mari Inc.
HOUSE OF MARION - Bar fixtures–metal - Marion Manufacturing Co. Inc.
HOUSE OF MILNER - Jewelry - House of Milner
HOUSE OF MUIRHEAD - Whiskey ✩ - Marie Brizard Wines & Spirits, USA
HOUSE OF NAPKINS - Party goods ✩ - American Greetings Corp.
HOUSE OF NISBET - Toys–blocks - Dakin Inc.
HOUSE OF ORANGE - Recording label - Universal Record
HOUSE OF PAINTINGS, THE - Posters - Andrew Kolb and Son Ltd.
HOUSE OF PAPER - Paper party goods ✩ - American Greetings Corp.
HOUSE OF PARISIAN LUNETTES - Frames–eyeglass - Continental Trading Co. Inc.
HOUSE OF PARLIAMENT - Food products - Lea and Perrins Inc.
HOUSE OF PRILL - Cutlery - House of Prill Inc.
HOUSE OF RAND - Lamps - House of Rand
HOUSE OF RONNIE - Apparel–children's - House of Ronnie, Inc.
HOUSE OF SEAGRAM - Beverages–alcohol - Joseph E. Seagram & Sons, Inc.
HOUSE OF SECRETS - Books–comic - DC Comics
HOUSE OF SHINDLER - Meat products–beef - House of Shindler Inc.
HOUSE OF SISSOKO - Artists' materials - House of Sissoko, Inc.
HOUSE OF STUART - Beverages–alcohol - Barton Brands, Ltd.
HOUSE OF STUART - Liquors - Canandaigua Wine Co. Inc.
HOUSE OF THALLER, INC. - Food products - House of Thaller, Inc.
HOUSE OF THE MOUSE - Pet products - R.A.F. Trading Inc.
HOUSE OF TROY - Lamps - GRK Manufacturing
HOUSE OF TROY - Lighting fixtures - House of Troy Inc.

HOUSE OF TSANG - Oils—edible - House of Tsang Ltd.

HOUSE OF TSANG BANGKOK PADANG PEANUT SAUCE - Vegetable sauces - Universal Trading Industries

HOUSE OF TSANG MANDARIN - Sauces - Universal Trading Industries

HOUSE OF TSANG SAIGON SIZZLE - Sauces - House of Tsang Ltd.

HOUSE OF TUNG - Oils—edible - Hyman Products Inc.

HOUSE OF VISION - Ophthalmic goods - Benson Optical Co., Inc.

HOUSE OF WALSH - Apparel and accessories - Willmott Services, Inc.

HOUSE OF WINDSOR - Cigars - House of Windsor Inc.

HOUSE OF WINDSOR - Wallpaper ☆ - Brewster Wallcovering Co.

HOUSE OF YAKITORI - Food products - Greens & Powder, Ltd.

HOUSE OF YORK - Bedspreads - Rose York Sales, Inc.

HOUSE RECIPE - Food products - Sysco Food Services

HOUSE RECIPE - Tomato pastes and sauces - Sysco Corp.

HOUSE STORAGE - Trunks - Seward Luggage Co.

HOUSE THAT QUALITY BUILT, THE - Insulating tape - Schnee-Morehead, Inc.

HOUSE THAT ROCK BUILT, THE - Apparel and accessories - Rock and Roll Hall of Fame and Museum, Inc.

HOUSE, THE - Catalogs - Active Sports, Inc.

HOUSE, THE - Computer software - Gessler Publishing Co., Inc.

HOUSE WORKS - Adhesives and sealants - Loctite Corp.

HOUSE WORKS - Glue—household or industrial - Loctite Corp.

HOUSEBREAK - Pet products - National Scent Co.

HOUSEBREAK HELPERS - Pet products - Teach Your Pet Inc.

HOUSECALL - Computer software - Pratt Medical Inc.

HOUSECOAT - Paints - Hirshfield's Paint Manufacturing

HOUSEHOLD 500 - Mops - Lighthouse Industries

HOUSEHOLD DELIGHT - Cleaning preparations ☆ - Certified Grocers Midwest Inc.

HOUSEHOLD GOOP - Adhesives and sealants - Eclectic Products Inc.

HOUSEHOLD INSTITUTE - Cooking utensils—enameled - Jacksonville Manufacturing

HOUSEHOLDR - Buckets—plastic - MacCourt Products Inc.

HOUSEKEEPER - Vacuum cleaners and accessories - Regina Co.

HOUSEKEEPER DELUXE - Sewing machines—household - VWS Inc.

HOUSEKEEPER PLUS - Vacuum cleaners and accessories - Regina Co.

HOUSEKEEPING CUBE - Toys - Learning Products Inc.

HOUSEMASTER - Filters—water - Housemaster of America, Inc.

HOUSEMIX - Apparel and accessories - Quick & Easy Inc.

HOUSEPLANT - Magazines - HousePlant Inc.

HOUSEPLANT INSECT CONTROL - Insecticides - Security Products Co.

HOUSE'S - Corn—flour or meal - House-Autry Mills, Inc.

HOUSESAVER - Paints - Mautz Paint Co.

HOUSEWARES BY BEACON - Housewares - Beacon Products Corp.

HOUSEWARES FOR HEALTH - Kitchen utensils—aluminum - Back to Basics Products Inc.

HOUSEWARMERS - Candles, candlemaking product ☆ - Corning Inc.

HOUSEWARMERS - Pigments—paint - Leshner Corp.

HOUSEWARMING SURPRISE - Toys - Tonka Corp.

HOUSING MANAGEMENT SYSTEM - Computer software - Network Compatibility Group Inc.

HOUSTON - Frames—eyeglass - Pathway Optical Prods.

HOUSTON AEROS - Backpacks - Southwest Ice Enterprises, Inc.

HOUSTON FOODS - Giftware - Houston Foods Co.

HOUSTON HALO - Traction apparatus—medical ☆ - Camp, Inc.

HOUSTON ROCKETS - Trading cards and stamps - Rocket Ball, Ltd.

HOUSTON VII - Floor coverings—carpet and rugs - Milliken & Co. Inc.

HOUSTON WHEAT - Beverages—malt - 2426 Dunstan, L.C.

HOUSTON WHEAT - Beverages—malt - Village Brewery

HOUSTON WHOLESALE JEWELERS - Jewelry - Houston Wholesale Jewelers, Inc.

HOUSTONIAN - Hair care products - Perfector Products

HOUSTON'S LEADING INFORMATION SOURCE - Paper—newsprint - Hearst Corp.

HOUSTY - Footwear ☆ - French Dressing Inc.

HOUVA II - Medical apparatus - National Biological Corp.

HOUZE ART - Glass products - Houze Glass Corp.

HOUZE LO-TRAN - Glass products ☆ - Houze Glass Corp.

HOVER COVER - Manhole covers - Universal Valve Co., Inc.

HOVER COVER - Swimming pool covers - Hover Cover

HOVERVELDT - Shoes ☆ - Clarks of England Inc.

HOVI RAE - Floor tiles - Allstate Rubber Corp.

HOVOCO - Ophthalmic goods - Benson Optical Co., Inc.

HOVOTEX - Hardware - Ambassador Industries

HOVOWIPE - Cleaning equipment - Hollingsworth & Vose Co.

HOW ABOUT A NICE GAME OF CHESS - Computer software ☆ - Odesta Corp.

HOW CAN IT BE SO SOUR! - Candy - Sherman's Confections, Inc.

HOW DO YOU SPELL RELIEF? - Pharmaceutical preparations - Warner-Lambert Co.

HOW DRY I AM - Apparel—athletic - Reliable of Milwaukee

HOW-ELL DOR - Doors—garage - Howell Manufacturing Co.

HOW LOVELY - Floor coverings—carpet and rugs - Alexander Smith Carpets

HOW LOVELY - Frames—picture - Terragrafics Inc.

HOW RED - Fruits and vegetables - Sun World International

HOW SWEET IT IS - Mouthwashes - American Hygienic Laboratories Inc.

HOW TO BE PERFECT - Video games - Great Bear Technology Inc.

HOW TO COLLECT STAMPS - Paper—gummed - Treat Entertainment, Inc.

HOW TO DO EVERYTHING—BETTER! - Games - Gamescience

HOW TO DRAW - Publisher's imprints - Kidsbooks, Inc.

HOW TO GET AN A IN LIFE - Publisher's imprints - Dudeck Group

HOW TO HOST A MURDER - Games - Decipher Inc.

HOW TO HOST A MYSTERY - Games - Decipher Inc.

HOW TO HOST A ROMANTIC EVENING - Games ☆ - Decipher Inc.

HOW TO HOST A TEEN MYSTERY - Games - Decipher Inc.

HOW TO MAKE RETIREMENT A NEW ADVENTURE - Recording label - Pacific Institute Inc.

HOW TO MOVE HANDBOOK - Publisher's imprints - Computing!

HOW TO RETIRE RICH - Video production - Moss Adams L.L.P.

HOW TO ROCK CLIMB - Publisher's imprints - Chockstone Press, Inc.

HOW TO TALK MORTGAGE TALK - Publisher's imprints - Computing!

HOW WEATHER WORKS - Computer software - Orange Cherry Software

HOW WINNERS PLAY THE GAME - Bags—duffel - Hillerich & Bradsby Co.

HOWA - Firearms, accessories, and parts - International Armament Corp.

HOWARD - Clocks - Follett Time Recording Co. Inc.

HOWARD - Dinnerware—glass - Royal China & Porcelain Companies Inc.

HOWARD - Fans—electric - Howard Industries Inc.

HOWARD - Hardware ☆ - Alexander-Roberts Co.

HOWARD - Ladders—metal - Howard Manufacturing Co.

HOWARD - Ophthalmic goods - Styl-Rite Optical Manufacturing Co., Inc.

HOWARD - Paper ☆ - Howard Paper Mills Inc.

HOWARD - Pianos - Baldwin Piano & Organ Co.

HOWARD - Syrup - Howard Foods Inc.

HOWARD BOND - Paper - Howard Paper Mills Inc.

HOWARD BOUND HAZELNUT - Coffee - Frontier Cooperative Herbs

HOWARD CAPITOL - Paper ☆ - Howard Paper Mills Inc.

HOWARD HOUSE - Fruits and vegetables - Biggers Brothers Inc.

HOWARD HUGE - Toys - William Hoest Enterprises, Inc.

HOWARD IMPORTS - Leather goods - Howard Imports

HOWARD JOHNSON'S - Flowers, plants, and seeds - Howard Johnson's Enterprises, Inc.

HOWARD KAPLAN - Dolls ☆ - Schmid Inc.

HOWARD LEDGER - Paper - Howard Paper Mills Inc.

HOWARD LINEN - Paper - Howard Paper Mills Inc.

HOWARD LINEN - Paper—bond - Fox River Paper Co.

HOWARD MANOR - Mobile homes - Western Homes Corp.

HOWARD MILLER - Clocks - Howard Miller Clock Co.

HOWARD OUTDOOR RECEPTACLES - Wastebaskets - United Receptacle Inc.

HOWARD SWAN - Posters - Graphic Arts Unltd. Inc.

HOWARD TEXT & COVER - Paper - Howard Paper Mills Inc.

HOWARD WOLF - Apparel—women's - Howard B. Wolf Inc.

HOWARD'S - Greeting cards ☆ - Regency Thermographers Inc.

HOWARD'S - Relishes - Howard Foods Inc.

HOWATT HUNTER - Archery equipment - Martin Archery Inc.

HOWCO - Hobby kits - R.B. Howell Co.

HOWDA DESIGNZ - Novelty items - Howda Designz, Inc.

HOWDAH - Fabrics - Dan River Inc.

HOWDY - Beverages—carbonated ☆ - Dr. Pepper/Seven Up, Inc.

HOWDY - Computer software - Alta Vista Corp.

HOWDY DOODY - Dolls - Goldberger Doll Manufacture Co.

HOWDY THE TALKING PONY - Toys—stuffed - Mattel, Inc.

HOWE - Coffee - Geo. J. Howe Co. Inc.

HOWE - Water—distilled ☆ - Howe Water Corp.

HOWE BRICK - Floor coverings - Tarkett, Inc.

HOWEL - Towels - Big Orange Sports Service

HOWELITE - Varnishes ☆ - Thibaut & Walker Co. Inc.

HOWELL - Food products ☆ - Custom Food Products Inc.

HOWELL - Pet products - Berolina Imports

HOWELL BEGINNER'S GUIDE - Publisher's imprints - Howell Book House Inc.

HOWEL'S - Root beer—bottled or canned - Julep Co.

☆ = Now out of production

HOWEVER - Colognes ☆ - Avon Products, Inc.

HOWFOAM - Tablecloths ☆ - Howe Furniture Corp.

HOWITZER - Golfing equipment - Titleist & Foot-Joy Worldwide

HOWLAND - Recording label - Jazz Composer's Orchestra Association Inc.

HOWLAND SPRINGS - Water–bottled or canned - Howland Springs Water Co.

HOWLER - Balls - Oddzon Products, Inc.

HOWLIN' COYOTE - Dinners–frozen - Paradise Kitchens Inc.

HOWLIN' HOT - Sauces - Rogers and Jones Corp.

HOWLIN' HOWIE'S - Apparel and accessories - Howlin Howies, Inc.

HOWLIN' JALAPENO - Pretzels - Pretzelmaker, Inc.

HOWLITE - Tablecloths - Howe Furniture Corp.

HOWMATIC - Tables–metal ☆ - Howe Furniture Corp.

HOWMET - Awnings ☆ - Alcan Aluminum Corp. Alcan Building Products Div.

HOWRED - Fruits and vegetables ☆ - Sun World International

HOW'S MY DRIVING? - Vending machines - National Automatic Merchandising Association

HOWTEX - Sweaters - Binghamton Knitting Co.

HOY BROS. - Seafood products–fresh or frozen - Newport Shrimp Co.

HOYA - Cameras - Uniphot Corp.

HOYA - Dinnerware–glass - Mikasa Co.

HOYA - Fabrics - Dan River Inc.

HOYA 99 - Frames–eyeglass - Hoya Corp. USA

HOYATRON - Frames–eyeglass - Hoya Corp. USA

HOYLE - Games - Hoyle Products

HOYO DE MONTERREY - Cigars - Danby-Palicio

HOYPOLOI - Apparel and accessories - Ronald M. Hoy

HOYT/HARKEN - Boats–motor - Harken Yacht Fittings

HOYT HARP SCREENS - Hardware - Hoyt Wire Cloth Co.

HOYT'S - Hair care products - J. Strickland & Co.

HP - Electronic equipment - Hewlett-Packard Co.

HP - Food products - Lea and Perrins Inc.

HP - Gloves–leather - Jean Hauser

HP - Pharmaceutical preparations - Healthpoint Medical Ltd.

HP - Shrimp–fresh or frozen - Harrison Pierce & Co. Inc.

HP - Vinegar and condiments - International Marketing Services Inc.

HP - Wallpaper - Gloria Alexander Designs

HP - Water bottles–rubber - Connelly Skis, Inc.

HP-01 - Watches ☆ - Hewlett-Packard Co.

HP-2 - Automotive parts and accessories - Marson Creative Fastener Group

HP-7 - Pumps - Root Equipment Corp.

HP 7 - Toys–electronic - Tyco Toys

H.P. 19 - Cosmetics - Redken Laboratories, Inc.

HP-21 - Sporting goods ☆ - General Sportcraft Co. Ltd.

HP 110 - Computers–personal - Hewlett-Packard Co.

HP 150 - Computers–personal - Hewlett-Packard Co.

HP 910 - Generators–electric - Clarke Mosquito Equipment, Inc.

HP 2000 - Tires - Bridgestone/Firestone, Inc.

HP 9000 - Cleaning preparations–upholstery - Kelmort Trading & Co. Ltd.

HP ADVANCENET - Computer software - Hewlett-Packard Co.

HP AGENT - Hair care products - U-Do-It Beauty Products

HP BOOKS - Publisher's imprints - Price Stern Sloan Inc.

HP BUSINESS CONSULTANT - Calculators - Hewlett-Packard Co.

HP CHEMSTATION - Computer software - Hewlett-Packard Co.

HP COMBI-PLAN - Photographic equipment - H.P. Marketing Corp.

HP CRITERION - Exercising equipment - Hooker Industries, Inc.

HP FILE SERVER - Computer software - Hewlett-Packard Co.

HP FOR MEN - Socks - High Point Knitting Inc.

HP HALDIRAM'S - Snack foods - California Certified Import-Export

HP HEIKES PRODUCE, INC. FAMOUS FROZEN FRUITS - Fruits–frozen - Heikes Produce, Inc.

HP INFORMATION ACCESS - Computer software - Hewlett-Packard Co.

HP INTEGRAL - Computers–personal - Hewlett-Packard Co.

HP LE TOUR - Bicycles - Schwinn Cycling & Fitness Inc.

H.P. MUGS - Pet products - Hamilton Products Inc.

HP OMNISHARE CONFERENCER - Office equipment - At&T Corp.

HP PROSHIELD - Pharmaceutical preparations - DPT Laboratories Inc.

HP QUIETJET - Printers–computer - Hewlett-Packard Co.

HP RACING - Motor vehicle parts and accessories - Hi-Point Racing Products

HP RESOURCE SHARING - Computer software - Hewlett-Packard Co.

HP SCANJET - Computer peripheral equipment - Hewlett-Packard Co.

HP SPORTS TOURING - Bicycles - Schwinn Cycling & Fitness Inc.

HP VECTRA - Computers–personal - Hewlett-Packard Co.

HP VECTRA LS - Computers–personal - Hewlett-Packard Co.

HP2 - Golf balls - Acushnet Co.

HP3 - Hair care products - Ardell International Inc.

HP5 PLUS - Film - ILFORD Photo Corp.

HPC - Pens - Hanover Pen Corp.

HPC-1 - Contact lenses - Conforma Contact Lenses

HPC MEDX - Medical apparatus - Hanover Pen Corp.

HPC TACKLE - Fishing tackle - Hick Plastics Co. Inc.

HPCD - Medical apparatus - Kensey Nash Corp.

HPCMAN - Computer software - Infosys Corp.

HPI - Electronic equipment - Hudson Photographic Industries Inc.

HPL - Hardware - Hi-Shear Corp.

HPL 9000 - Sporting goods - AMF Bowling Worldwide

HPL 9000 HIGH PERFORMANCE LANES - Sporting goods - AMF Bowling Worldwide

HPL ALLIANCE - Sporting goods - AMF Bowling Worldwide

HPL INTEGRA - Sporting goods - AMF Bowling Worldwide

HPM - Lubricants - Cyprus Metals Co.

HPM - Mouthwashes - Heritage Store Inc.

HPO - Fabrics - Guilford Mills, Inc.

HPO - Lubricants - Ashland Oil, Inc.

HPO HOLOGRAPHY PRESSES ON - Film - Janice Wingeier Bussard

HPOWER - Motorcycles - Dimer International Group, Inc.

HPR - Adhesives and sealants - Courtaulds Performance Films Inc.

HPR - Tires ☆ - Bridgestone/Firestone, Inc.

HPS - Medical apparatus - Harvey Professional Supply Co. Inc.

HPS GOLD - Computer software - DHI Computing Service, Inc.

HPS SLIDER - Door frames - Kawneer Co., Inc.

HPT - Whipped topping–frozen - Hanan Products Co., Inc.

HPV - Vitamins and nutritional supplements - Summa Pharmaceutical Laboratories Inc.

HPX - Automobile parts - SDI Operating Partners

HQ - Filter line dryers and motors - Inter-City Products Corp. (USA)

HQ - Tape players–video - Sima Products Corp.

HQ - Thermostats - Heil-Quaker Corp.

HQ - Video tapes–blank - Fuji Photo Film USA Inc.

HQ-HI-QUA - Sporting goods - Hi-Qua Sports

HQ ISO 9000 REGISTERED HEATCRAFT QUALITY - Refrigerators - Heatcraft Inc.

H.Q. STUDIO - Apparel–women's - Lamonts Apparel Inc.

H.Q.C. - Pharmaceutical preparations ☆ - ICN Pharmaceuticals Inc.

HQI MATCHMAKER - Computer software - Healthcare Quality Insights, Inc.

HQI VALIDATA - Computer software - Healthcare Quality Insights, Inc.

HQP - Inks - Sun Chemical Corp.

HR - Carpet cleaner - American Home Products Corp.

HR - Fluid power pumps - McCrometer, Inc.

HR - Motor vehicles–motor homes - Holiday Rambler Corp.

HR - Sails - Windsurfing International Inc.

HR-1 - Pliers - ACCO USA, Inc.

HR-120 - Metals - Haynes International, Inc.

HR-2000 - Cleaning preparations - Hillyard Enterprises, Inc.

HR DIRECT - Calendars - Career Dynamics, Inc.

HR EDGE - Computer software - Wyatt Co.

HR EVENTS - Computer software - Blake E. Allen

HR HELENA RUBINSTEIN ROUGE FOREVER - Costumes - Parbel

HR HELENA RUBINSTEIN SUBLIMESCENCE - Skin care products - Parbel

HR MASTERS - Hair care products - Rescue Marketing Group

HR NAVIGATOR - Software - Automating Peripherals, Inc.

HR STREAM - Computer software - Dun and Bradstreet Software Services, Inc.

HR VISION - Computer software - Sas Institute Inc.

H.R. WE CARE - Toys–blocks - H.R. We Care & Sons

HRA - Computer software - Hoffmann Research Associates, Inc.

HRAF PRESS - Publisher's imprints - Human Relations Area Files Inc.

HRC - Automotive parts and accessories ☆ - Household Research Corp.

H.R.C. - Paper - Historical Research Center, Inc.

H.R.D. - Beverages–alcohol - Hood River Distillers Inc.

HRD THE VINCENT HRD CO LTD. STEVENAGE HERTS - Apparel and accessories - Egl 1, Inc.

HRH - Frames–eyeglass - Zylo Ware Corp.

H.R.H. - Linen - Hosel & Ackerson, Inc.

H.R.H. - Paints - Eaglo Paint & Varnish Corp.

HRLINE - Coaxial transmission lines - Andrew Corp.

HRM - Hair-care products - Amethyst Investment Group, Inc.

HRM - Hobby kits - Educational Products Co.

HRP - Filters–water - Sta-Rite Industries Inc.

HRP - Photographic equipment - Eastman Kodak Co.

HRR - Water purification systems - USFilter-Stranco

HRS - Apparel and accessories - SRH Productions

H.R.S. - Drafting supplies - Koh-I-Noor, Inc.

☆ = Now out of production

H.R.S. - Musical instrument accessories - E. & O. Mari Inc.
HRS - Phonographs ☆ - Fantasy Inc.
HRSOFT, INC. - Computer software - Corporate University, Inc.
HRT - Projectiles–jet propulsion - Smith Corona Corp.
HRV - Honey/rum/vanilla flavor - American Flavor & Fragrance Corp.
HRW - Recording label - Harcourt Brace & Co.
HRW MULTIMEDIA CURRICULUM SYSTEMS - Educational materials - Harcourt Brace & Co.
HS - Jewelry - Hoover & Strong, Inc.
HS - T-shirts–women's - Earl E. Rayfield
HS - Tiles–mosaic ☆ - Federal Tile Imports Inc.
HS 1 - Guitars - Dimarzio, Inc.
HS-2 - Musical instrument accessories - Dimarzio, Inc.
HS-2C - Electrodes - Alloy Rods Global, Inc.
HS-3 - Musical instrument accessories - Dimarzio, Inc.
HS-7 - Welding equipment - Alloy Rods Global, Inc.
HS-9 - Housewares ☆ - Amaza Laboratories Inc.
HS-65 - Housewares ☆ - Amaza Laboratories Inc.
HS-65W - Electrodes - Alloy Rods Global, Inc.
H.S. ARCHERY - Archery equipment - Hunter's Specialties, Inc.
H.S. CALLS - Hunting equipment - Hunter's Specialties, Inc.
H.S. CAMO - Cosmetics - Hunter's Specialties, Inc.
H.S. ELK - Hunting equipment - Hunter's Specialties, Inc.
HS HUNT SAVER SIGHT SYSTEM - Firearms, accessories, and parts - Gun Doctor
HS HYDROSTIX - Apparel and accessories - Hydro Stix Inc.
H.S. NEED - Pharmaceutical preparations - Hanlon Drug Products
H.S. PENTA - Finishing agents - PSR Co.
H.S. SCENTS - Hunting equipment - Hunter's Specialties, Inc.
HS SERIES - Pumps - Gorman-Rupp Co.
HS SOLO - Paint - BASF Corp.
H.S. STRUT - Hunting equipment - Hunter's Specialties, Inc.
H.S. STRUT STRUT - Video production - Hunter's Specialties, Inc.
H.S. TRASK AMERICAN BISON AUTHENTIC FOOTWEAR BOZEMAN MONTANA - Apparel and accessories - H.S. Trask & Co.
H.S. WATERFOWL - Hunting equipment - Hunter's Specialties, Inc.
HSA - Audio equipment - Price Master Corp.
HSC - Computer software - HSC Software
HSC - Glue–household or industrial - Highland Supply Corp.
HSC HIGHLAND SUPPLY CORP. FOIL AND FILMCONVERTERS - Glue–household or industrial - Highland Supply Corp.
HSDTST - Computer hardware - Applied Data Sciences Inc.
HSG - Office furniture–metal ☆ - Hon Co.
HSI - Hearing aids - Hearing Services Inc.
HSI-TUO - Infant product - T.C. International Inc.
HSINCHU GARDENS - Giftware - Ebeling and Reuss Co.
HSM - Golfing equipment - Bobby Grace Golf Design, Inc.
HSM - Pumps–water - ITT Industries, Inc.
HSMC - Cranes - MSI Crane & Equipment Co., Inc.
HSO SZYMANSKI SURFBOARDS USA - Surfboards - Szymanski Surfboards
HSP - Adhesives and sealants - HSP International, Inc.
HSP - Cabinets–metal - Horizon Steel Products Inc.
HSPICE - Computer software - Meta-Software, Inc.
HSQ - Business forms - Health Outcomes Institute
H.S.S. - Pharmaceutical preparations ☆ - Legere Pharmaceuticals Inc.
HSSC - Filters–industrial - Otis Engineering Corp.
H.S.SCENTS - Hunting equipment - Hunter's Specialties, Inc.
HSSD - Smoke detectors - Kidde-Fenwal, Inc.
HSSI - Computer peripheral equipment - Cisco Systems, Inc.
HST - Nuts and bolts - Hi-Shear Corp.
HSV.TAG - Chemical preparations - Novagen, Inc.
HT - Bags–trash ☆ - Holiday Trims Inc.
HT - Chemical preparations - Monsanto Co.
HT - Exercising equipment - Schwinn Cycling & Fitness Inc.
H.T. - Golfing equipment ☆ - Wilson Sporting Goods Co.
HT - Thread - Gudebrod, Inc.
HT 20 - Veterinary nutritional supplements - Vita Flex Nutrition Co., Inc.
HT 1600 - Paints ☆ - United Gilsonite Laboratories
HT & NY - Jewelry - H & T Goldman Inc.
H.T. #CHITTUM & CO. - Clothing - H.T. Chittum, Inc.
HT ONE - Headsets–telephone - GN Netcom Inc.
H.T. PRO - Aerobic footwear ☆ - Autry Industries Inc.
HT PROFILNINE - Pharmaceutical preparations - Alpha Therapeutic Corp.
HT+400 - Vitamins and nutritional supplements - R. Day Enterprises, Inc.
HTB - Furniture - HTB Contemporary Designs
HTB - Thread - Belding Heminway Co. Inc.

H.T.C. - Sporting goods - Bike Athletic Co.
HTI - Broadcasting stations–television - Schorr Communications, Inc.
HTM - Jewelry - H.T. Manufacturing Inc.
HTM-SPECTRA - Computer software - Hamilton-Thorn Research
HTML BUILDER - Computer software - Flfsoft, Inc.
HTO - Thread - Belding Heminway Co. Inc.
H:1 - Computer software - E. David & Associates
HTP - Agricultural products - American Products Enterprises
HTP CALM - Vitamins and nutritional supplements - Natural Balance, Inc.
HTPIO - Vitamins and nutritional supplements - M.M.R.C., Ltd. Co.
HTRF - Computer peripheral equipment - Packard Instrument Co., Inc.
HTS - Automotive parts and accessories - Standard Motor Products, Inc.
HTS - Exercise equipment ☆ - CSA, Inc.
HTS - Heating equipment - Rampe Manufacturing Co.
HTS - Jewelry - Hill's Indian Jewelry Shop Inc.
HTS - Microphones ☆ - Shure Brothers, Inc.
HTS - Pumps - High Temperature Systems, Inc.
HTS - Sporting goods - Hurricane Sports, Inc.
HTS - Thread - Belding Heminway Co. Inc.
HTS MONITOR - Antennas - Recoton Corp.
HU-HU - Frames–eyeglass - Hudson Optical Corp.
HU-KWA - Teas - Mark T. Wendell Co.
HUADONG TSING TAO - Wines - Blair Importers Ltd.
HUALIN - Tires - Aoyama International Inc.
HUANG - Musical instruments - Huang, Inc.
HUB - Pens - Hub Pen Co. Inc.
HUB - Publisher's imprints - The Porter Revocable Family Trust
HUB - Seeds–salted, roasted, cooked, or canned - O.J. Childs Seed Co.
HUB-A-LARM - Alarm systems - Preco Inc.
HUB-BUB - Frames–eyeglass - Liberty Optical Manufacturing Co.
HUB-SHARK - Tools–hand-operated - Oldforge Tools Corp.
HUB STATES - Insecticides - Hub States Corp.
HUBBA-BUBBA - Beverages–carbonated - A.J. Canfield Co.
HUBBA BUBBA - Chewing gum - Amurol Confections Co.
HUBBA CUB - Stationery - Lisa Frank, Inc.
HUBBARD - Flour–blended - Hubbard Milling Co.
HUBBARD - Meat products–beef - Hubbard Beef Supply
HUBBARD - Paper ☆ - Silver Leaf Paper Co.
HUBBARD HOUSE - Food products - Hubbard Milling Co.
HUBBARD PRESS - Publisher's imprints ☆ - Rand McNally & Co.
HUBBARD SPECIAL - Flour–blended - Hubbard Milling Co.
HUBBARD'S - Seafood products–fresh or frozen - A.W. Woodfield & Son
HUBBELL - Tools–hand-operated - Hubbell Inc.
HUBBELL - Wire products - Hubbell Electrical Products
HUBBELL GARD - Chemical preparations - Hubbell Lighting, Inc. (Lighting Div.)
HUBBELL QUALITY - Sausages ☆ - J & B Sausage Co., Inc.
HUBBELL SEAL - Chemical preparations - Hubbell Lighting, Inc. (Lighting Div.)
HUBBELL-TROL - Lighting fixtures - Hubbell Lighting, Inc. (Lighting Div.)
HUBBELLITE - Lighting fixtures - Hubbell Lighting, Inc. (Lighting Div.)
HUBCAPS - Novelty items–paper ☆ - Western Publishing Co., Inc.
HUBCO - Toys–blocks - Hub Manufacturing Co. Inc.
HUBE - Exercising equipment - Thomas M. Crevar
HUBEI - Mats–grass, reed, and jute - Darwell Import Co. Inc.
HUBER - Beverages–malt - Joseph Huber Brewing Co., Inc.
HUBER BOCK - Beverages–malt - Joseph Huber Brewing Co., Inc.
HUBER ORCHARD - Wines - Huber Orchard Winery
HUBER'S SALAD BOY - Fruits–frozen - Olympia Frosted Foods
HUBINGER - Syrup - Hubinger Co.
HUBLINK - Computer hardware - Hublink, Inc.
HUBNER - Bath salts - Baudelaire Inc.
HUBPM - Computer software - 3DV Technology, Inc.
HUBS - Nuts–salted, roasted, cooked, or canned - Hubbard Peanut
HUBSCO - Pesticides–agricultural - Hub States Corp.
HUBU - Computer software - Electronic Vision International, Inc.
HUBWAY - Computer hardware - ASP Computer Products Inc.
HUCK FINN - Boats - Glen-L Marine Designs
HUCK FINN - Eyeglasses - Art-Craft Optical Co.
HUCK-SPIN - Tools–hand-operated - Huck International, Inc.
HUCKLE BUCKLE - Eyeglasses - Art-Craft Optical Co.
HUCKLEBERRY - Stoneware dinnerware - Iron Mountain Stoneware Inc.
HUCKLEBERRY FEMME - Greeting cards - Debra A. Schrodt
HUCKLEBERRY FINN - Dolls ☆ - Effanbee Doll Corp.
HUCKLEBERRY FINN - Fruits–canned - Hartford Farm Supply Inc.
HUCKLEBERRY HOUND - Kites ☆ - Hi-Flier Manufacturing Co.
HUCKLEBERRY HOUND PUNCHO - Toys - Hasbro, Inc.

　　　　　　　　　　　　　　　　　　　　　　　　　☆ = Now out of production

HUCKLEBERRY MOUNTAIN - Jams and jellies - Huckleberry Mountain

HUCKLEBERRY SCRIM - Apparel with needlepoint designs - Innovations Design

HUCKLEBERRYBASKETS LTD. - Gift baskets - Huckleberrybaskets Ltd.

HUCKSTER - Ophthalmic goods - Styl-Rite Optical Manufacturing Co., Inc.

HUD - Colognes ✿ - Avon Products, Inc.

HUD - Oils–lubricating - Hudson Handy Stop

HUDBAR - Frames–eyeglass - Hudson Optical Corp.

HUDCO - Bacon - White Packing Co., Inc.

HUDDLES - Toys–stuffed - Tudor Inc.

HUDDLES - Toys–stuffed ✿ - Gund, Inc.

HUDEPOHL - Beverages–malt ✿ - Hudepohl-Schoenling Brewing Co.

HUDEPOHL 14-K - Beverages–malt ✿ - Hudepohl-Schoenling Brewing Co.

HUDEPOHL DELIGHT - Beverages–malt - Hudepohl-Schoenling Brewing Co.

HUDEPOHL GOLD - Beverages–malt ✿ - Hudepohl-Schoenling Brewing Co.

HUDEPOHL JUBILEE 100 - Beverages–malt - Hudepohl-Schoenling Brewing Co.

HUDMAN - Frames–eyeglass - Hudson Optical Corp.

HUDSET - Frames–eyeglass - Hudson Optical Corp.

HUDSON - Bicycles - Columbia Manufacturing Inc.

HUDSON - Figurines - Lance Corp.

HUDSON - Food preparation machines - Hudson Butcher Supply Co., Inc.

HUDSON - Food products ✿ - Curtice-Burns Foods, Inc.

HUDSON - Frames–eyeglass - Hudson Optical Corp.

HUDSON - Gasoline - Hudson Handy Stop

HUDSON - Gloves - Hudson Glove Corp.

HUDSON - Gloves–work - Avon Glove Corp.

HUDSON - Hardware - Gordon Associates

HUDSON - Herbicides - Lawn & Garden Supply Co.

HUDSON - Insecticides - H.D. Hudson Manufacturing Co.

HUDSON - Ladders–wood - John S. Tilley Ladders Co. Inc.

HUDSON - Paper–carbon - Kores Nordic USA Corp.

HUDSON - Paper–toweling - Georgia-Pacific Corp.

HUDSON - Skin care products - Hudson Corp.

HUDSON - Toilets–enameled - Kohler Co.

HUDSON - Vegetables–canned - S.E.W. Friel

HUDSON - Window shades - Hudson Venetian Blind Service

HUDSON BAY - Liquors - Sidney Frank Importing Co., Inc.

HUDSON BAY KNIFE & TOOL WORKS - Knives–hunting - Cold Steel Inc.

HUDSON BAY MILLING CO. - Breads - Metz Baking Co.

HUDSON BLUE - Vegetables–canned - S.E.W. Friel

HUDSON CANYON - Recording label - Celluloid Records

HUDSON HILLS PRESS - Publisher's imprints - Rizzoli International Publications Inc.

HUDSON PEWTER - Figurines - Lance Corp.

HUDSON PRIDE - Juices ✿ - Hudson Valley Apple Products Co. Inc.

HUDSON QUARRY - Floor coverings - Tarkett, Inc.

HUDSON RCI - Health care products - Hudson Respiratory Care Inc.

HUDSON RED - Vegetables–canned - S.E.W. Friel

HUDSON RIVER - Furniture ✿ - Kincaid Furniture Co. Inc.

HUDSON VALLEY - Beverages–carbonated ✿ - Brooklyn Bottling Corp.

HUDSON VALLEY - Furniture ✿ - Mersman Furniture Co.

HUDSON VALLEY - Meat products–poultry - Made in France

HUDSON VALLEY - Pet products - Pet Products, Inc.

HUDSON VALLEY BEEF RAWHIDE - Leather–rawhide - Pet Products, Inc.

HUDSON VALLEY COLLECTION - Furniture - Harden Furniture Co. Inc.

HUDSON VALLEY GARLIC FESTIVAL - T-shirts–women's - Kiwanis Club of Saugerties N.Y.

HUDSON VAN DAM - Recording label - Celluloid Records

HUDSONJERSEY STAMATO SANITATION - Garbage disposal units–commercial - Hudson Jersey Sanitation Co.

HUDSON'S BAY DEMERARA - Rum - House of Seagram

HUDSON'S GOURMET - Food products - Dayton Hudson Corp.

HUDSON'S TOTAL CONTROL - Computer software and manuals - Hudson Control Group Inc.

HUDTANE - Gasoline - Hudson Handy Stop

HUDVAL - Food products - Hudson Valley Apple Products Co. Inc.

HUDY BOLD - Beverages–malt - Hudepohl-Schoenling Brewing Co.

HUDZYL - Frames–eyeglass - Hudson Optical Corp.

HUE - Games ✿ - Mayfair Games, Inc.

HUE - Hosiery - Hue Legwear

HUE - Tights–stockings - Kayser-Roth Corp.

HUE M - Hosiery - Moskal & Chilewich Inc.

HUE M - Hosiery–women's - Hue Legwear

HUE-NIQUE - Frames–eyeglass - Liberty Optical Manufacturing Co.

HUE Q - Hosiery - Hue Legwear

HUE-VU - Welcon

HUELLER - Musical instruments - Custom Music Co.

HUEPPE - Shower stalls–plastic - Masco Corp.

HUES - Frames–eyeglass - Zylo Ware Corp.

HUES 'N' BREWS - Housewares - Herman Dodge & Son Inc.

HUEY - Lenses–optical - Ditto Industries Inc.

HUEY COBRA - Toys - Fisher-Price, Inc.

HUFCOR - Doors - Hufcor Inc.

HUFF & PUFF - Dog food - Huff & Puff Pet Foods Inc.

HUFF AND PUFF - Publisher's imprints ✿ - Warren Publishing House, Inc.

HUFFNPUFFIN - Exercising equipment - Huff N Puffin, Inc.

HUFFY - Ophthalmic goods - Embassy Creations Inc.

HUFFY 314 - Bicycles ✿ - Huffy Corp.

HUFFY BLADES - Bicycles - Huffy Corp.

HUFFY ONE ON ONE - Electronic equipment - Huffy Corp.

HUFFY SPORTS - Sporting goods ✿ - Huffy Corp.

HUFFY TRIKES - Tricycles ✿ - The Coleman Co.

HUFFY TUFF - Sporting goods - Huffy Corp.

HUFTEC - Veterinary supplies - Huftec, Inc.

HUG - Pillows - Hug's Marketing, Inc.

HUG, A - Novelty items - St. Clair & Co.

HUG-A-BODIES - Artists' materials - Decorator and Craft Corp.

HUG-A-HEARTS - Toys–stuffed - Fun World Inc.

HUG-A-LUG - Nuts and bolts - Aluminum Co. of America

HUG-A-MOCS - Crocheted and knitted items ✿ - Reliable of Milwaukee

HUG-A-PAL PLUSH - Stuffed animals - Hugga Plush Creations and H.P. Creations

HUG-A-RUG - Floor coverings–carpet and rugs - Custom Tapes, Inc.

HUG A TOT - Toys–stuffed - T & H, Inc.

HUG-ABLES - Pillows - Theresa J. Woodruff

HUG-AND-HOLD - Apparel and accessories ✿ - Strouse, Adler Co.

HUG & KISSES - Apparel–women's - Cupid Foundations Inc.

HUG BLANKET - Blankets - Peggy M. Hunter

HUG BUG - Apparel and accessories - Indiana Knitwear Corp.

HUG BUGS - Dolls - Jeff Swift

HUG ME - Bags–canvas - Im-Ex Around The World

HUG-ME - Infant product ✿ - Binky-Griptight Co.

HUG-MEES - Handbags - Dover Handbag Corp.

HUG 'N HOLD TWIN - Dolls - Mattel, Inc.

HUG N' SNIFF - Dolls - Uneeda Doll Co., Ltd.

HUG-N-SOF - Toys–stuffed - Douglas Co. Inc.

HUG N TALK - Toys–stuffed - Video Technology U.S. Inc.

HUG N'STUFF - Dolls - Uneeda Doll Co., Inc.

HUG STRIPE - Apparel stores–lingerie - Formflex Foundations Inc.

HUG-THE-CEILING - Fans–electric - Nutone Inc.

HUG TIGHT - Infant product - Mattel, Inc.

HUG-WAIST - Girdles - Youthcraft-Charmfit

HUGABUG - Toys–stuffed ✿ - Gund, Inc.

HUGABUN - Apparel and accessories - Intertech Corp.

HUGBUNDLE - Greeting cards - Robert G. Phipps

HUGE - Vitamins and nutritional supplements ✿ - Nature's Way Products, Inc.

HUGE SPORTSWEAR - Apparel and accessories - Huge Sportswear, Inc.

HUGG-A-PLANET - Pillows - Hugg-A-Planet

HUGG-A-PLANET - Stuffed toys - XTC Products Inc.

HUGG-A-STAR - Toys - Hugg-A-Planet

HUGG-A-WORLD - Pillows - Hugg-A-Planet

HUGG-AMERICA - Pillows - Hugg-A-Planet

HUGG-L-O - Gustave Rick Rinz

HUGG-L-O - Pillows - Rinz-L-O Pillow Co.

HUGG-THE-EARTH - Pillows - Hugg-A-Planet

HUGGA BUNCH - Bathroom accessories ✿ - Tsumura International Inc.

HUGGA BUNCH - Dishes–plastic - Deka Plastics Inc.

HUGGA BUNCH - Dolls - Kenner Products

HUGGA BUNCH - Footwear ✿ - Mercury International Trading Corp.

HUGGA BUNCH - Games ✿ - Parker Brothers

HUGGA BUNNY - Toys–stuffed - Fun World Inc.

HUGGA RACK - Cooking equipment–household - Martin Industries, Inc.

HUGGABEAR - Publisher's imprints - Impact Confections, Inc.

HUGGABLE LOVEABLE MOMMI - Dolls - Jo Anne Nightingale

HUGGABLE SCRUBS - Medical uniforms - Trademark Corp.

HUGGABLES - Dolls ✿ - Effanbee Doll Corp.

HUGGAGE - Containers - Delta Consolidated Industries, Inc.

HUGGAGE - Luggage - Cindy R. Meyers

HUGGAPUFFS - Toys–stuffed - DCN Industries Inc.

HUGGER - Corkscrews - Franmara Co. Inc.

HUGGER - Hooks - US 261 Corp.

HUGGER - Infant product ☆ - Cosco, Inc.
HUGGER - Ophthalmic goods - Embassy Creations Inc.
HUGGER - Pet products - O'Donnell Industries Inc.
HUGGER - Socks - Moretz Hosiery Mills Inc.
HUGGER - Toys–automobiles ☆ - Roadmaster Corp.
HUGGER - Wet mops ☆ - American Textile Products Co.
HUGGER BACK - High chairs ☆ - Cosco, Inc.
HUGGER DUO-BACK - Office furniture–plastic - Grahl Industries, Inc.
HUGGERS - Pans ☆ - General Housewares Corp.
HUGGIES - Diapers–disposable - Kimberly-Clark Corp.
HUGGIES - Puzzles ☆ - Milton Bradley Co.
HUGGIES - Toys–stuffed - Kamar International Inc.
HUGGIES NATURAL CARE - Washboards - Kimberly-Clark Corp.
HUGGIES SUPREME - Diapers–disposable - Kimberly-Clark Corp.
HUGGIES ULTRATRIM - Diapers–disposable - Kimberly-Clark Corp.
HUGGIN' ARMS - Infant product - Marlena Asher
HUGGIN CLEAN - Pet products - Lambert-Kay
HUGGINS - Coffee ☆ - Coca-Cola Co.
HUGGLES BEAR - Toys–stuffed - Russ Berrie and Co., Inc.
HUGGUMS - Dolls - Alexander Doll Co. Inc.
HUGGY - Jewelry - Jordan Meryl, Inc.
HUGGY BEAR - Toys–stuffed - Rodtom Enterprises
HUGGY BEAR - Toys–stuffed ☆ - Dakin Inc.
HUGGY BEAR - Toys–stuffed ☆ - Gund, Inc.
HUGGY BEARS - Toys–stuffed - Russ Berrie and Co., Inc.
HUGGY BEAR'S CUPBOARDS - Cabinets - Huggy Bear's Cupboards, Inc.
HUGGY BUNNY - Toys–stuffed - Dakin Inc.
HUGGY STYLETTE - Dolls - Golden Ribbon Playthings Inc.
HUGGY TUB - Infant product - Century Products Co.
HUGGY TUGGY - Toys–models ☆ - Century Products Co.
HUGGYBEAN - Dolls - Golden Ribbon Playthings Inc.
HUGH BANNER - Sporting goods - Climb High Inc.
HUGH HEFNER - Cigars - Playboy Enterprises, Inc.
HUGHES - Food products - Hughes Markets Inc.
HUGHES - Pennants - Flags International Inc.
HUGHES FLYING BOAT - Apparel - Evergreen International Aviation Inc.
HUGLI - Bouillon cubes - EFCO Importers
HUGLIGHT - Toys - Mattel, Inc.
HUGO - Clay–modeling - Sculpture House Inc.
HUGO - Colognes - Giorgio Beverly Hills
HUGO - Publisher's imprints - Littlefield, Adams & Co.
HUGO BOSS - Colognes - Procter & Gamble Co.
HUGO MAXX - Watches - Hugo Maxx Inc.
HUGO THE UNICORN - Toys ☆ - Mego Financial Corp.
HUGO'S CELLAR - Wines - Hugo's Cellar-Glenoak Hills Winery
HUGO'S MUSIC - Recording label - Jazz Composer's Orchestra Association Inc.
HUGS - Candy - Hershey Chocolate USA
HUGS - Candy - Homestead, Inc.
HUGS 'N' DREAMS - Dolls - Heaven Knows Inc.
HUGS N' KISSES - Toys–automobiles - Roadmaster Corp.
HUGS 'N KISSES - Wallpaper - Atlas Wallpaper & Paint Co.
HUGS + STITCHES - Patterns–clothing ☆ - Simplicity Pattern Co., Inc.
HUGS TO YOU - Toys–stuffed - Heart to Heart
HUGSTER - Pillows - Michelle M. Fanto-Chan
HUGSTER - Underwear and nightwear - Youthcraft-Charmfit
HUGSTERS - Bags ☆ - Commonwealth Toy and Novelty Co. Inc.
HUGSTICKS - Juices - Daily Juice Products Inc.
HUGUENIN - Watches ☆ - SMH (US) Inc.
HUH - Recording label - Warner Music Enterprises Inc.
HUI NALU CANOE CLUB HAWAII 1908 HN - Apparel and accessories - Hui Nalu O Hawaii
HUI O HE'E NALU N. SHORE, O'AHU - Labels–gummed - Da Hui, Inc.
HUICHICA HILLS - Wines - Robert Mondavi Winery
HUILE - Suntan lotions ☆ - Sothys USA Inc.
HUILE VITALE - Cosmetics - Christian Dior Perfumes Corp.
HUILERIES DU BERRY - Oils–edible - Dean & Deluca Inc.
HUILES ESSENTIELLES - Skin care products - Mastey De Paris
HUISKEN - Meat products - Huisken Meat Center, Inc.
HUIT - Underwear and nightwear - M.A. Rabinowitz Corp.
HUIXING - Building materials - USA Huixing Stone, Inc.
HUK A POO - Apparel–children's - D. Stone Industries, Inc.
HUK-A-POO FOR GIRLS - Apparel–children's - Charles Greenberg & Sons Inc.
HUL-IT - Machinery - E. Kaiser Fabrication Inc.
HULA - Apparel–athletic - Timerica Inc.

HULA - Recording label - Hawaii Calls Inc.
HULA BEAR - Apparel and accessories - Woolson Spice Co., Inc.
HULA DANCER - Fishing lures ☆ - Fred Arbogast Co. Inc.
HULA FRUITS - Breakfast cereal - Amway Corp.
HULA HOOP - Toys - Wham-O Manufacturing Co.
HULA-KAI - Candy ☆ - Annabelle Candy Co. Inc.
HULA LU - Musical instrument accessories - J.M. Sahlein Music Co. Inc.
HULA MOON - Apparel stores–sports - Surf Line Hawaii, Ltd.
HULA PANTY - Underwear and nightwear ☆ - Elegante Foundations Inc.
HULA PIE - Ice cream - T.S. Enterprises, Inc.
HULA POPPER - Fishing lures - Fred Arbogast Co. Inc.
HULA PUNCH - Chewing gum ☆ - Fleer Corp.
HULA RECORDS INTERNATIONAL - Recording label - Hawaii Calls Inc.
HULA SKIRTS - Fishing lures - Fred Arbogast Co. Inc.
HULA-TEASER - Fishing lures - Fred Arbogast Co. Inc.
HULK SKID STEER - Tires–automobile - Galaxy Tire & Wheel, Inc.
HULK, THE - Bop bags ☆ - Intex Recreation Corp.
HULL - Brushes–paint - Corona Brushes Inc.
HULL - Gasoline - Hull Oil Co.
HULL CLEAN - Boats ☆ - Docker Marine
HULL-GARD - Boats - N.A. Taylor Co. Inc.
HULL LIGHT - Lighting equipment–boat and ship - Barnegat Light
HULL O'UA - Cleaning preparations - Viking Manufacturing Co. Inc.
HULLABALOO - Frames–eyeglass - Hudson Optical Corp.
HULLSAVR - Ramps - Bill D. Laue
HULLTEK - Paints ☆ - PPG Industries, Inc.
HULTGREN & SAMPERTON - Wines - Hultgren & Samperton
HUM-A-ZOO - Toys–musical - Trophy Music Co.
HUM-BAR - Kites ☆ - Gayla Industries Inc.
HUM-BURGER - Sandwiches–prepackaged - Hamburger Station
HUM-DINGER - Meat products–poultry - Pierce Foods Corp.
HUM-I-DRI - Dehumidifiers - Lionel Industries Inc.
HUM-PHABET - Housewares - Arts Uniq', Inc.
HUMAFAC - Pharmaceutical preparations ☆ - Parke-Davis
HUMALOG - Insulin - Eli Lilly and Co.
HUMAN - Apparel–men's - Jerrold Anthony Dollwet Partnership
HUMAN CANNONBALL - Video games - Atari Games Corp.
HUMAN CODE - Computer software - Human Code, Inc.
HUMAN COMPUTER - Computer peripheral equipment - John A. Lim
HUMAN ENERGY AT WORK - Video production - Griggs Productions Inc.
HUMAN-I-TEES - Posters - Human-I-Tees, Inc.
HUMAN NATURE - Vitamins and nutritional supplements - Rexall Sundown, Inc.
HUMAN POTENTIAL RISES TO NEW HEIGHTS WHEN THE MIND AND BODY WORK IN UNISON - Electronic equipment - Cognitech Corp.
HUMAN SCENT BUSTER - Deodorizers - Ole Time Woodsman
HUMAN SPIRIT, THE - Apparel - Brooks Sports, Inc.
HUMAN TRIBE - Paper products - Designs for Education, Inc.
HUMAN WEAPON - Posters - Donald T. Albrecht
HUMANATOMY - Publisher's imprints - Tim Peters and Co., Inc.
HUMANATONE - Musical instruments - Fred Gretsch Enterprises
HUMANE - Garden equipment - Seymour Manufacturing Co.,Inc.
HUMANE HARVEST - Eggs - Chino Valley Ranchers
HUMANE SOCIETY OF THE UNITED STATES - Greeting cards ☆ - Healthy Planet Products, Inc.
HUMANIST CLASSICS - Publisher's imprints - Bandanna Books
HUMANITY - Books–comic - Anthony Masino
HUMANTONE - Musical instrument accessories - Trophy Music Co.
HUMATIN - Pharmaceutical preparations - Parke-Davis
HUMATRIX - Medical apparatus - Care-Tech Laboratories Inc.
HUMAX - Agricultural products - JH Biotech, Inc.
HUMBOLDT - Beverages–malt - Humboldt Brewing Co.
HUMBOLDT - Milk - Humboldt Creamery Association
HUMBOLDT - Seafood products–fresh or frozen - Pacific Choice Seafoods
HUMBOLDT - Water–distilled - Humboldt Springs Water Co.
HUMBOLDT BREWING CO. GOLD RUSH EXTRA PALE ALE - Beverages–malt - Humboldt Brewing Co.
HUMBUCKER FROM HELL - Guitars - Dimarzio, Inc.
HUMCO - Pharmaceutical preparations - Humco
HUMCO - Recording label - Horttor Universal Music Co.
HUMDINGER - Musical instruments - S.J. Miller Co.
HUMDINGER - Paint sprayers - Binks Manufacturing Co.
HUME AID - Fertilizers - Phoenix Agricultural Group Inc.
HUMECTAN - Hair care products - Chasalco Inc.
HUMECTANT 9 - Hair care products ☆ - Roberts Research Laboratories, Inc.
HUMECTRESS - Hair care products - Nexxus Products Co.

☆ = Now out of production

HUMEGON - Pharmaceutical preparations - Organon Inc.
HUMES & BERG - Musical instrument accessories - Humes & Berg Manufacturing Co. Inc.
HUMI-HEAT - Cabinets - Wilder Manufacturing Co., Inc.
HUMI-JAR - Glassware—household ✩ - Owens-Illinois Inc. (Libbey Div.)
HUMIBID - Pharmaceutical preparations - Adams Laboratories Inc.
HUMID-A-MIST - Controls—heating systems - Galmar Enterprises Inc.
HUMID-AIRE - Humidifiers - Adams Manufacturing Co.
HUMID KING - Air conditioning equipment ✩ - Skuttle Manufacturing Co.
HUMID QUEEN - Air conditioning equipment ✩ - Skuttle Manufacturing Co.
HUMIDEX - Chemical preparations - Stewart-Hall Chemical Corp.
HUMIDI-CASE - Cases—musical instrument - M & M Distributing Co.
HUMIDI-CLEAR - Vaporizers ✩ - Sunrise Medical (Respiratory Products Division)
HUMIDI-GUARD - Musical instrument accessories - M & M Distributing Co.
HUMIDI-TECH - Humidifiers - Dri-Steem Humidifier Co.
HUMIDIBELT - Humidifer accessories - RPS Products Inc.
HUMIDICLEAN - Humidifier/vaporizer-scale dissolver - RPS Products Inc.
HUMIDICON - Hair care products - Jheri Redding Products Inc.
HUMIDIFIER HELPER - Water purification systems - Whink Products Co.
HUMIDIFIER KLEEN - Cleaning preparations - G.G. Bean Inc.
HUMIDIGROW - Air purification systems - Kaz Business Systems Inc.
HUMIDIGUIDE - Thermometers - Taylor Environmental Instruments
HUMIDIMATIC - Humidifiers - Hamilton Home Products Inc.
HUMIDIPACK - Humidifiers - Armstrong International, Inc.
HUMIDIPAD - Humidifier evaporation pads - RPS Products Inc.
HUMIDIPAK - Tobacco products ✩ - S.M. Frank & Co. Inc. (Kaywoodie-Yello-Bole-Medico)
HUMIDISET - Appliance parts - Duracraft Corp.
HUMIDISPRAY - Health care products - Lennox Industries Inc.
HUMIDIVE - Scuba diving equipment - Weh, Inc.
HUMIDIWHEEL - Health care products - Lennox Industries Inc.
HUMIDIWICK - Humidifier filters - RPS Products Inc.
HUMIDOR FACTORY, LTD., THE - Cases—cigar - Humidor Factory, Ltd.
HUMILAC - Skin care products - Allerderm Inc.
HUMIST - Pharmaceutical preparations - Schering-Plough Healthcare Products
HUMISTAT - Musical instrument accessories - David Wexler & Co.
HUMITAR - Musical instrument accessories ✩ - Dean Markley Strings, Inc.
HUMITRODE - Health care products - Neuromedics
HUMKO - Vegetable oil - Humko Products
HUMKOTE - Butter - Humko Products
HUMM...BLE GAME - Games - Talicor Inc.
HUMMEL SPRING - Water—bottled or canned - Hummel Spring Corp.
HUMMER - Motor vehicles - AM General Corp.
HUMMER - Paper punches - Bates Manufacturing Co.
HUMMER - Sporting goods - A & T Ski Co. Inc.
HUMMER - Sporting goods - Grand Slam USA
HUMMER - Tools ✩ - Thor Power Tools
HUMMER - Toys - Tonka Corp.
HUMMER HAWGS - Fishing lures - Li'l Hummer Lures
HUMMER PLUS - Brushes - Droll Yankees, Inc.
HUMMERS - Abrasive products - M.K. Morse Co.
HUMMERS - Footwear ✩ - Tru-Stitch Footwear (Div. of Wolverine World Wide)
HUMMER'S GALORE - Bird feeders - Bacon Products Corp.
HUMMIN' BIRD - Beverages—malt - Spring Garden Brewing Co.
HUMMING BIRDS - Dishes—china - Waterford Wedgewood USA, Inc.
HUMMINGBIRD - Dinnerware ✩ - Corning Inc.
HUMMINGBIRD - Games - Ampersand Press
HUMMINGBIRD - Musical instruments - Gibson Guitar Corp.
HUMMINGBIRD - Recording label - Hummingbird Productions, Inc.
HUMMINGBIRD - Recording label - Jazz Composer's Orchestra Association Inc.
HUMMINGBIRD - Trailers—truck ✩ - Sun-Lite Inc.
HUMMINGBIRD - Wallpaper - Warner Co.
HUMMINGBIRD II - Wallpaper - Warner Co.
HUMMY-BIRD BAR - Pet products - Hummingbird Heaven
HUMMZINGER - Office furniture—metal - Aspects Inc.
HUMONITOR - Humidity-monitoring device - Multiform Desiccants Inc.
HUMORESK - Greeting cards - Gibson Greetings, Inc.
HUMORESQUE - Floor coverings—carpet and rugs ✩ - Alexander Smith Carpets
HUMOROUS BONE - Pet chews - Items Inc.
HUMORSOL - Pharmaceutical preparations - Merck & Co., Inc. (Merck Research Laboratories)
HUMOUR A LA CARTE - Postcards ✩ - Fotofolio Inc.
HUMPHREE - Musical instrument accessories - Adder Plus Corp.

HUMPHREY - Gas machinery - Humphrey Products Co.
HUMPHREY - Toys—stuffed ✩ - Gund, Inc.
HUMPHREY ACUITUS - Medical apparatus - Humphrey Systems
HUMPHREY AND HILLARY HEFFELFLOPPER - Candy - R.M. Palmer Co.
HUMPHREY ATLAS - Medical apparatus - Humphrey Systems
HUMPHREY AUTOMATIC REFRACTOR/KERATOMETER - Medical apparatus - Humphrey Systems
HUMPHREY BOGART - Apparel and accessories - Bogart Inc.
HUMPHREY BUGKILLER - Insecticides - Value Line Laboratories
HUMPHREY FDT - Medical apparatus - Humphrey Systems
HUMPHREY FIELD ANALYZER - Medical apparatus - Humphrey Systems
HUMPHREY LENS ANALYZER - Medical apparatus - Humphrey Systems
HUMPHREY OPTICAL COHERENCE TOMOGRAPHY SCANNER - Medical apparatus - Humphrey Systems
HUMPHREY THE DINOSAUR - Hampers - Rubbermaid Inc.
HUMPHREYS - Pharmaceutical preparations - Humphreys Pharmacal Inc.
HUMPS - Candy ✩ - Brock Candy Co. Inc.
HUMPTY DUMPTY - Candy ✩ - Glade Taffy Town, Inc.
HUMPTY DUMPTY - Dolls - Effanbee Doll Corp.
HUMPTY DUMPTY - Food products - Humpty Dumpty Potato Chip Co.
HUMPTY DUMPTY - Food products - Papetti's Hygrade Egg Products, Inc.
HUMPTY-DUMPTY - Fruits and vegetables - Orchard Foods
HUMPTY DUMPTY - Games ✩ - Tyco Toys
HUMPTY DUMPTY - Hosiery—children's - Sanda Hosiery Mills Inc.
HUMPTY DUMPTY - Leather goods - AR Accessories Group Inc.
HUMPTY DUMPTY - Salmon—smoked, salted, dried, or pickled - Peter Pan Seafoods, Inc.
HUMPTY DUMPTY - Thermometers ✩ - Sell-O Manufacturing Inc.
HUMPTY DUMPTY - Toys - Maryland Toy Corp.
HUMS - Aircraft parts - Teledyne Industries Inc.
HUMULIN - Insulin - Eli Lilly and Co.
HUMUS - Hunting equipment - Patton Crafted Products, Inc.
HUMUS - Toilets—portable - Water Conservation Systems Inc.
HUMUS-80 - Toilets—enameled ✩ - Ecos/Water Conservation System Inc.
HUMVEE - Motor vehicles - AM General Corp.
HUNAN - Food products - Lo-An/Florida Inc.
HUNAN SMOKEHUT - Sauces - Hormel Foods Corp.
HUNCHBACK OF NOTRE DAME - Dinnerware - Disney Enterprises, Inc.
HUND-N-FLOCKEN - Dog food - Solid Gold Holistic Animal/Equine Nutrition Center
HUNDRED DAYS BATTLES - Games ✩ - Avalon Hill Game Co.
HUNGARIAN - Flour—blended - ConAgra Grain Co.
HUNGER BUSTERS .STOP HUNGER BEFORE IT STARTS - Vitamins and nutritional supplements - Barbara Cooper Enterprises, Inc.
HUNGER CRUNCHERS - Snack foods - Spicer's International Inc.
HUNGER FILLER - Breads - Natural Ovens of Manitowoc Inc.
HUNGER-TAMER - Appetite suppressant ✩ - Vigor Co.
HUNGREX - Health care products - CCA Industries, Inc.
HUNGREX - Vitamins and nutritional supplements - Alleghany Pharmacal Corp.
HUNGREX PLUS - Health care products - CCA Industries, Inc.
HUNGRIZZLY - Toys - Texas Dairy Queen Operators' Council
HUNGRY BACTERIA - Chemical preparations - Osprey Biotechnics, Inc.
HUNGRY DAWG - Apparel and accessories ✩ - Joy Athletic, Inc.
HUNGRY HOUND - Pet products - Shawnee Milling Co.
HUNGRY HUNGRY HIPPOS - Games - Milton Bradley Co.
HUNGRY JACK - Flour—blended - Pillsbury Co.
HUNGRY JACK BISCUIT GRAVY MIX - Gravy - Williams Foods Inc.
HUNGRY JACK BROWN GRAVY MIX - Gravy - Williams Foods Inc.
HUNGRY JACK CHICKEN GRAVY MIX - Gravy - Williams Foods Inc.
HUNGRY MAN - Dinners—frozen - Campbell Soup Co.
HUNGRY? WHY WAIT? - Candy - Mars, Inc.
HUNK - Pillows - Pacific Coast Feather Co.
HUNKERS - Shoes - Lisa Lee
HUNKEY DOREY - Candy - Sterling Candy Corp.
HUNKS O' CHUNX - Dog food - Jim Dandy Co.
HUNKS OF HISTORY, THE - Calendars - Kathleen Manning
HUNKY DORY - Boats - Glen-L Marine Designs
HUNKY-DORY - House furnishings - Buckler's Inc.
HUNNICUT - Tobacco—chewing or smoking - Sterling Tobacco Co.
HUNT - Pens - Hunt Manufacturing Co.
HUNT - Photographic equipment - OCG
HUNT & BROADHURST - Stationery ✩ - Chase Collection, Inc.
HUNT-BOND - Archery equipment - Saunders Archery Co.
HUNT CLUB - Apparel and accessories - J.C. Penney Co., Inc.
HUNT CLUB - Jewelry - R.F. Simmons Co.
HUNT CLUB OAK - Lumber - Georgia-Pacific Corp.

✩ = Now out of production

HUNT COUNTRY - Furniture - Lane Co. Inc.
HUNT COUNTRY - Juices - Hunt Country Vineyards
HUNT COUNTRY VINEYARDS - Wines - Hunt Country Vineyards
HUNT FOR RED OCTOBER, THE - Jewelry - Paramount Pictures Corp.
HUNT FOR THE HUNGRY - Meat products–beef - Building A Better America
HUNT LYMAN - Boats–motor ☆ - Lyman-Morse Boatbuilding Co. Inc.
HUNT MARCKWALD'S HICKORY SMOKE RECIPE - Barbecue sauce - Marketing Group
HUNT MARCKWALD'S ORIGINAL RECIPE - Barbecue sauce - Marketing Group
HUNT MASTERS - Computer software - N-TK (Entertainment Technology), Inc.
HUNT MEADOW - Apparel - Woods & Gray, Ltd.
HUNT MIDWEST RIP RAPTOR - Stone products - Hunt Midwest Mining, Inc.
HUNT, THE - Cosmetics - Carolina Designs Ltd.
HUNT THE RUT - T-shirts–men's - Jarod D. Wenrick
HUNT-WESSON - Food products ☆ - Hunt-Wesson, Inc.
HUNTCLIFF - Apparel–men's - Oxford Industries, Inc.
HUNTCLIFF - Floor coverings–carpet and rugs - Mohawk Industries Inc.
HUNTCLOTH - Fabrics - Squires Hightech
HUNTER - Bicycles - American Cycle Group
HUNTER - Boat dealers - Brookes & Gatehouse Inc.
HUNTER - Boats–canoes - Old Town Canoe Co.
HUNTER - Chairs–wood - Gunlocke Co.
HUNTER - Cheese - Hunter, Walton and Co. Inc.
HUNTER - Cigars ☆ - Swisher International, Inc.
HUNTER - Fans–electric ☆ - Hunter Fan Co.
HUNTER - Golfing equipment - All American Golf Sales, Inc.
HUNTER - Meat products–beef - John Morrell & Co.
HUNTER - Milk - Hunters Jersey Farms Inc.
HUNTER - Mops - Piedmont Mop Co.
HUNTER - Motor vehicles–motor homes ☆ - Honey Recreational Vehicles Inc.
HUNTER - Pet products - Valhoma Industries Inc.
HUNTER - Ships–sailing vessels - Hunter Marine Corp.
HUNTER - Tools ☆ - Danaher Tool Group
HUNTER - Toys - Tonka Corp.
HUNTER - Whiskey - Four Roses Distillers Co.
HUNTER 1886 LIMITED EDITION - Fans–electric - Hunter Fan Co.
HUNTER ALL NATURAL - Ice cream - Harris-Teeter Inc.
HUNTER & LORDS - Apparel–men's - John H. Daniel Co.
HUNTER CARLTON - Fans–electric - Hunter Fan Co.
HUNTER CLAW - Toys - Saban Entertainment, Inc.
HUNTER DOUGLAS - Blinds–venetian - California Textiles Inc.
HUNTER DOUGLAS - Blinds–venetian - Hunter Douglas, Inc.
HUNTER DOUGLAS - Window coverings - Hunter Douglas Intermountain Fabrication Inc.
HUNTER DOUGLAS - Window coverings - Vertical Blind Factory
HUNTER DOUGLAS - Window shades - A & E Blind & Awning Co.
HUNTER ESTATE, THE - Wallpaper - Seabrook Wallcoverings, Inc.
HUNTER FARMS - Ice cream - Harris-Teeter Inc.
HUNTER HAIG - Apparel–men's - Palm Beach Co., Inc.
HUNTER HALF - Trailers–travel ☆ - Beaver Coaches Inc.
HUNTER HILL - Shirts - Wilson Brothers
HUNTER MARK II - Binoculars ☆ - Swift Instruments, Inc.
HUNTER ODOR KLEEN - Deodorizers - G.G. Bean Inc.
HUNTER ORIGINAL - Fans–electric - Hunter Fan Co.
HUNTER SAFE - Hunting equipment - Sunburst Co. Inc.
HUNTER SPORTS - Glassware–household - Hunter Manufacturing Group, Inc.
HUNTER, THE - Gloves - Dakota Corp.
HUNTERDON FARMS - Food products - Original Trenton Cracker Co.
HUNTERLIFT - Platforms–cargo - Thomas P. Clark
HUNTERS - Dog food - Buckeye Feed Mills, Inc.
HUNTER'S - Food products - H.B. Hunter Co.
HUNTER'S - Wines ☆ - Prestige Wine Imports Corp.
HUNTER'S ASSET - Hunting equipment - Two River Products
HUNTER'S BLIND - Detergents - Camp-Cap Products
HUNTER'S BUDDY - Tape recorders - Joe L. Castagno
HUNTERS' CHOICE - Dog food - Jim Dandy Co.
HUNTER'S CHOICE - Dog food - Tjdc, Inc.
HUNTER'S CHOICE - Gloves - Fairfield Line, Inc.
HUNTERS CHOICE - Gloves - Good Luck Glove Co.
HUNTER'S CHOICE - Soap - Windau Enterprises, Inc.
HUNTER'S COURT - Furniture ☆ - Kincaid Furniture Co. Inc.
HUNTERS FIELD - Gloves - D & H Products Co.
HUNTER'S HOLLOW - Wallpaper - Old Stone Mill
HUNTER'S POINT - Floor coverings–carpet and rugs - Evans-Black Carpet Mills

HUNTERS POINTE - Wallpaper - Surface Industries Inc.
HUNTER'S PRIDE - Dog food - Dobosco Inc.
HUNTER'S PRIDE - Dog food - Stevens Industries Inc.
HUNTER'S RUN - Furniture - Kincaid Furniture Co. Inc.
HUNTER'S SPECIAL - Knives ☆ - Tru-Balance Knife Co.
HUNTER'S SPECIALTIES - Sporting goods ☆ - Rothco Inc.
HUNTERSPOINTE - Cabinets - Fieldstone Cabinetry
HUNTIN CRUISER - Pet products - HME Enterprises, Inc.
HUNTIN FEVER - Clothing - Michigan Outdoor Products, Inc.
HUNTING - Binoculars - Pioneer Marketing & Research, Inc.
HUNTING CLUB - Furniture ☆ - Bassett Furniture Industries, Inc.
HUNTING HILLS - Furniture - Pilliod Co.
HUNTING HORN - Apparel and accessories - Edison Brothers Stores, Inc.
HUNTING RIDGE - Furniture ☆ - Hooker Furniture Corp.
HUNTING SCENES - Dinnerware–glass - Franciscan by Johnson Brothers, USA, Inc.
HUNTING WORLD EXPLORA - Luggage - Hunting World, Inc.
HUNTING WORLD SAFARI - Luggage - Hunting World, Inc.
HUNTING Z - Binoculars - Pioneer Marketing & Research, Inc.
HUNTINGDON - Furniture ☆ - Bassett Furniture Industries, Inc.
HUNTINGTON - Cabinets - H.J. Scheirich Co.
HUNTINGTON - Cabinets - Yorktowne Inc.
HUNTINGTON - Cabinets ☆ - Medallion Kitchens of Minnesota Inc.
HUNTINGTON - Cleaning preparations - Ecolab Inc.
HUNTINGTON - Clocks - Ridgeway Clock Co.
HUNTINGTON - Dishes–china ☆ - Gorham Inc.
HUNTINGTON - Floor coverings–carpet and rugs - Artistic Rugs Inc.
HUNTINGTON - Floor coverings–carpet and rugs ☆ - Royalweve Carpet Mills
HUNTINGTON - Frames–picture - Intercraft Industries
HUNTINGTON - Furniture - Universal Flooring
HUNTINGTON - Furniture ☆ - Broyhill Furniture Industries, Inc.
HUNTINGTON - Glassware–household - Cambro Manufacturing Co.
HUNTINGTON - Locks–door - Weiser Lock Corp.
HUNTINGTON - Office furniture–wood - Herman Miller, Inc.
HUNTINGTON - Prefabricated buildings–wood - Champion Enterprises Inc.
HUNTINGTON - Rings–jewelry - Artcarved Inc.
HUNTINGTON - Wallpaper ☆ - Wolf-Gordon Inc.
HUNTINGTON BRONZES - Statuary - E.M.I. Inc.
HUNTINGTON CLOTHIERS & SHIRTMAKERS - Jewelry - Huntington Clothiers
HUNTINGTON CLUB - Floor coverings–carpet and rugs - Whitecrest Carpet Mills
HUNTINGTON GARDEN - Furniture - Tropitone Furniture Co. Inc.
HUNTINGTON HARE - Toys–stuffed - Russ Berrie and Co., Inc.
HUNTINGTON ORIGINALS - Figurines - E.M.I. Inc.
HUNTINGTON PLANK - Floor coverings - Robbins Inc.
HUNTINGTON RIDGE - Hosiery - Wal-Mart Stores Inc.
HUNTINGTON SQUARE - Floor coverings - Congoleum Corp.
HUNTLEIGH - Occasional tables - JDI Group, Inc.
HUNTLEY - Furniture ☆ - Thomasville Furniture Industries Inc.
HUNTLEY - Uniforms–tailored ☆ - Angelica Uniform Group
HUNTMASTER-2000 - Archery equipment - Golden Key Futura, Inc.
HUNT'S - Food products - Hunt-Wesson, Inc.
HUNT'S - Wines - Canada Dry Corp.
HUNT'S ALL NATURAL - Sauces ☆ - Hunt-Wesson, Inc.
HUNT'S CHOICE-CUT - Food products - Hunt-Wesson, Inc.
HUNT'S HOMESTYLE - Food products ☆ - Hunt-Wesson, Inc.
HUNT'S HOT & SPICY - Barbecue sauce ☆ - Hunt-Wesson, Inc.
HUNT'S LIGHT - Barbecue sauce ☆ - Hunt-Wesson, Inc.
HUNT'S MAYA - Tomato pastes and sauces - Hunt-Wesson, Inc.
HUNT'S OPEN RANGE - Sauces ☆ - Hunt-Wesson, Inc.
HUNT'S POINT - Sunglasses - Eddie Bauer Inc.
HUNT'S READY - Tomato pastes and sauces ☆ - Hunt-Wesson, Inc.
HUNTSMAN - Archery equipment - Bear Archery Inc.
HUNTSMAN - Bicycles - Ross Bicycles USA, Ltd.
HUNTSMAN - Boats–canoes - Sawyer Composite Products
HUNTSMAN - Firearms, accessories, and parts - Welsh Sporting Goods Corp. (Boyt Div.)
HUNTSMAN - Shotguns ☆ - Harrington & Richardson Inc.
HUNTSMAN - Stoves–wood-burning - Martin Industries, Inc.
HUNTSVILLE - Floor coverings–carpet and rugs ☆ - World Carpets, Inc.
HUNTSVILLE - Flowers, plants, and seeds - Jacklin Seed
HUNTUR - Rifles - Conetrol Scope Mounts
HUNZA - Food products ☆ - Hain Pure Food Co. Inc.
HUOT - Hardware - Huot Manufacturing Co.
HUPFELD - Pianos - Hanseatic Overseas Trading Inc.

☆ = Now out of production

HUPPEN - Cookies ☆ - Albert Uster Imports Inc.

HURD - Food products - M.G. Hurd & Sons Inc.

HURD - Windows and doors - Continental Aluminum Products Co. Inc.

HURDLE HOP - Toys - Twinson Co.

HURDLER - Screws - C. Itoh Building Products

HURDY-GURDY - Confections - Hurdy-Gurdy International, Ltd.

HURI-DEK - Construction machinery ☆ - Peter G. Murray

HURLEY - Filters—water - Hurley Chicago Co. Inc.

HURLEY - Ships—sailing vessels ☆ - Dockrell Yachts Ltd.

HURLEY EAGLE - Filters—water - Hurley Chicago Co. Inc.

HURLEY III - Filters—water - Hurley Chicago Co. Inc.

HURLEY NOVUS - Filters—water - Hurley Chicago Co. Inc.

HURLEY NOVUS II - Filters—water - Hurley Chicago Co. Inc.

HURLEY RAIN - Filters—water - Hurley Chicago Co. Inc.

HURON - Automotive parts and accessories - Huron Products, Inc.

HURON - Bicycles ☆ - Raleigh USA Bicycle Co.

HURON - Boats - Glen-L Marine Designs

HURON - Fencing—wood - Machalk Enterprises Inc.

HURON - Paper—bond - Port Huron Paper Co.

HURON FARMS - Fruits—frozen - Decatur Fruit Co.

HURON SHORES - Honey - William H. Munyon

HURRI-CLEAN - Cleaning preparations - Webb Chemical Co. Inc.

HURRI HOT - Hudson Standard Corp.

HURRICAINE - Anesthetics - Beutlich L.P. Pharmaceuticals

HURRICANE - Archery equipment - Pro Line Co.

HURRICANE - Beverages - J.L. Franklin & Co.

HURRICANE - Bicycles - Schwinn Cycling & Fitness Inc.

HURRICANE - Boats - Clark Craft Boat Co.

HURRICANE - Boats—motor - H & H Molded Products

HURRICANE - Boats—motor ☆ - Godfrey Marine Co.

HURRICANE - Brushes—paint - Allpro Corp.

HURRICANE - Colognes ☆ - Avon Products, Inc.

HURRICANE - Compressors—air - Air Compressor Products, Inc.

HURRICANE - Darts and dart games - Dart World Inc.

HURRICANE - Garden equipment - Parker Sweeper Co.

HURRICANE - Golfing equipment - Hurricane Sports, Inc.

HURRICANE - Hoses - M & W Hydraulics, Inc.

HURRICANE - Markers—felt-tip - Mark Master Inc.

HURRICANE - Matches - Davis Instruments Corp.

HURRICANE - Motor vehicles—motor homes - Thor Tech, Inc.

HURRICANE - Soccer equipment - Spalding Sports Worldwide

HURRICANE - Tape—adhesive - Hurricane Tape, Inc.

HURRICANE - Toys - Tonka Corp.

HURRICANE - Toys—airplanes - Cox Products Inc.

HURRICANE - Valves - I.S.I. Fluid Power, Inc.

HURRICANE - Wines - Chicama Vineyards

HURRICANE ALERT - Shutters—metal - Hurricane Alert, Inc.

HURRICANE GUARD - Metal window shutters - International Gate Corp.

HURRICANE HARDWARE - Brackets - Ronald C. Winger

HURRICANE HOCKEY GAME - Games ☆ - CBS Toys

HURRICANE HOMER - Cement - Rectorseal Corp.

HURRICANE MALT LIQUOR - Beverages—malt - Anheuser-Busch Companies Inc.

HURRICANE POWER - Electronic equipment - Miyako America, Inc.

HURRICANE-READY - Doors—garage - Raynor Manufacturing Co.

HURRICANE REEF - Shirts - Miami Brewing Co.

HURRICANE RIDERS - Sweat pants - Chums Ltd.

HURRICANE SHADES - Glassware—household ☆ - Fenton Art Glass Co.

HURRICANE SLIDE - Playground equipment - Miracle Recreation Equipment Co.

HURRICANE SUBMERSIBLE ASPIRATING AERATOR - Water purification systems - Aeromix Systems, Inc.

HURRICANE SYSTEMS - Computer hardware - Software Brokers of America, Inc.

HURRICANE TOP - Sweatshirts - Chums Ltd.

HURRICANE TRACKING SYSTEM - Sporting goods - Hurricane Sports, Inc.

HURRICANE WALKERS - Shorts—men's - Chums Ltd.

HURRICANES - Dolls - Dic Animation City, Inc.

HURRICANES - Novelty items—paper ☆ - Unique Industries, Inc.

HURR'S - Ice cream - Hurr's Convenience Inc.

HURRY HOME - Games - Red Lion Corp.

HURRY UP - Nail care products - Finger Mates Inc.

HURRYCLEAN - Garden equipment - Yard Vac Products, Inc.

HURST - Automotive parts and accessories - Echlin Inc.

HURST PLOTTER - Marine rigging - Brookes & Gatehouse Inc.

HURST'S BERRY FARM - Fruit and vegetable markets - Hurst's Berry Farm, Inc.

HUS-KEY - Key rings - West Coast Chain Manufacturing Co.

HUSCA - Footwear - K-Swiss Inc.

HUSCH - Wines - Husch Vineyards

HUSH - Audio equipment - Rocktron Corp.

HUSH - Cables - Conquest Sound Inc.

HUSH - Dryers—hair - Helene Curtis Industries Inc.

HUSH - Pet products - ID Store

HUSH-A-BY - Mattresses ☆ - Welsh Co.

HUSH-A-BYE - Apparel and accessories - Tom Togs of Carolina, Inc.

HUSH-A-MATIC - Electronic equipment - GAF Corp.

HUSH I - Pet products - Rolf C. Hagen (USA) Corp.

HUSH MUFFS - Apparel and accessories - Wolverine World Wide, Inc.

HUSH PUMPS - Pet products - Rolf C. Hagen (USA) Corp.

HUSH PUPPIES - Leather goods - Wolverine World Wide, Inc.

HUSH PUPPIES - Shoes - Coleman

HUSH PUPPIES ATHLEISURE - Footwear—athletic ☆ - Wolverine World Wide, Inc.

HUSH PUPPY - Pet products - Biological Engineering/High Tech Pet Products

HUSH-STEP - Floor coverings ☆ - Pawling Corp. (Standard Products Div.)

HUSH SYSTEMS - Audio equipment - Rocktron Corp.

HUSH-TEX - Finishing agents ☆ - Dunn Edwards Corp.

HUSHABYE - Apparel and accessories - Vanity Fair Mills Inc.

HUSHBOARD - Fiberboard - Georgia-Pacific Corp.

HUSHCOAT - Coatings - Kohler Co.

HUSHED HUES - Bathing suits - Catalina

HUSHED ROSE - Nail care products - Cosmair Inc.

HUSHER - Musical instrument accessories - ignazus P. Oliveri

HUSHFLO - Tanks—water - Plumb Shop

HUSHLITE - Glass products - Laminated Glass Corp.

HUSHMASTER - Infant product - Binky-Griptight Co.

HUSHPUPPIES EYEWEAR - Frames—eyeglass - Kenmark Optical Co.

HUSHPUPPIES PUPS - Frames—eyeglass - Kenmark Optical Co.

HUSHPUPPIES SUN EYEWEAR - Sunglasses - Kenmark Optical Co.

HUSHTONE - Tiles—ceiling - Lamvin Inc.

HUSKEE - Apparel and accessories - Keezer Manufacturing Co. Inc.

HUSKEES - Chests—wood - Life-Like Products Inc.

HUSKER DU - Memory game ☆ - Regina Products Inc.

HUSKI - Hardware - CCL Security Products

HUSKI KNITS - Apparel—athletic ☆ - Moriarty Hat and Sweater Co.

HUSKIE HHH - Hammers - IPC Industries, Inc.

HUSKIE HYDRAULIC HAMMERS - Hammers - IPC Industries, Inc.

HUSKIE PUPS - Moccasins - Wolverine World Wide, Inc.

HUSKIES - Apparel and accessories - Board of Control of Michigan Technological University

HUSKIES - Socks - Adams-Millis Corp.

HUSKY - Apparel and accessories - Adtees Corp.

HUSKY - Bags—trash - Poly-America, Inc.

HUSKY - Bicycles - Ross Bicycles USA, Ltd.

HUSKY - Bottle openers ☆ - Alexander Manufacturing Co.

HUSKY - Brooms - Lighthouse Industries

HUSKY - Cordage and twine ☆ - Winchester-Auburn Mills Inc.

HUSKY - Cylinders - Compact Air Products, Inc.

HUSKY - Door frames - Kawneer Co., Inc.

HUSKY - Electronic equipment - QuickSet International Inc.

HUSKY - Fishing lures - Normark Corp.

HUSKY - Floor coverings—carpet and rugs - Conquest Carpet Mills Inc.

HUSKY - Fruits—canned - Chief Tonasket Growers

HUSKY - Hardware - Shelburne Corp.

HUSKY - Heating equipment - Yukon Energy Corp.

HUSKY - Hydrotherapy equipment - Deconna Ice Cream

HUSKY - Ladders—plastic - John S. Tilley Ladders Co. Inc.

HUSKY - Machinery - Flow International Corp.

HUSKY - Paint rollers - Rubberset Co.

HUSKY - Paper—bond - Weyerhaeuser Co.

HUSKY - Pencils - Empire Berol USA

HUSKY - Pet products - Strongheart Products, Inc.

HUSKY - Rifles - Tradewinds Inc.

HUSKY - Tape—masking - Malow Corp.

HUSKY - Tool boxes - Stanley Works

HUSKY - Tools ☆ - Litton Industries Inc. (New Britain Tool Div.)

HUSKY - Tools—garden - Gilmour Manufacturing Co.

HUSKY - Toys—automobiles - Nylint Toy Corp.

HUSKY-BRONCO - Shovels - Ames Lawn & Garden Tool Co.

HUSKY DEVLE - Fishing lures - Eppinger Manufacturing Co.

☆ = Now out of production

HUSKY HELPERS - Toys–automobiles - Fisher-Price, Inc.
HUSKY JON - Boats - O.M.C. Aluminum Boat Group
HUSKY-MUSKY - Fishing tackle - Frabill Inc.
HUSKY VAC - Vacuum cleaners and accessories - VWS Inc.
HUSKYLOCK - Sewing machines–household - VWS Inc.
HUSMAN - Snack foods - Curtice-Burns Foods, Inc.
HUSMOR - Fish–fresh or frozen - Haram-Christensen Corp.
HUSQUVARNA - Sewing machines–household - VWS Inc.
HUSQVARNA - Motorcycles - Cagiva of North America
HUSQVARNA - Rifles ☆ - Tradewinds Inc.
HUSQVARNA - Saws–chain - Husqvarna Forest & Garden Co.
HUSQVARNA-EMBROIDERY - Computer software - VWS Inc.
HUSQVARNA EMBROIDERY-CUSTOMIZING SYSTEM - Sewing machines–
    household - VWS Inc.
HUSQVARNA EMBROIDERY-DIGITIZING SYSTEM - Sewing machines–
    household - VWS Inc.
HUSQVARNA EMBROIDERY-LIBRARY OF DESIGNS - Publisher's imprints -
    VWS Inc.
HUSS - Food products ☆ - Melson Meat Co. Inc.
HUSSARD - Glassware–household - Durand International
HUSSMAN & HAHN - Fish–canned or cured - Acme Food Specialties Inc.
HUSSONG'S - Beverages–malt - Montezuma Imports Inc.
HUSSONG'S AGAVE - Beverages–alcohol - Mccormick Distilling Co., Inc.
HUSSY - Apparel–women's - Steven Hughes
HUSTLER - Boats - O.M.C. Aluminum Boat Group
HUSTLER - Brackets - Goldblatt Tool Co.
HUSTLER - Communications equipment–mobile - Hustler Inc.
HUSTLER - Fishing lures ☆ - Fred Arbogast Co. Inc.
HUSTLER - Game tables - Minnesota Fats Billiard Factory Inc.
HUSTLER - Motorcycles ☆ - Suzuki of America Automotive Corp.
HUSTLER - Motors–outboard ☆ - Outboard Marine Corp.
HUSTLER MX - Bicycles ☆ - Muskin Leisure Products Inc.
HUSTLER STATE - Apparel and accessories - Kenneth L. Jackson
HUSTLIN' HEN - Sporting goods - William T. White, Jr.
HUSTLIN' HOSS - Toys - Tonka Corp.
HUT SCUFF - Slippers - Acorn
HUTCH - Sporting goods - Fuqua Industries Inc.
HUTCH - Uniforms–athletic - Hutch Sports USA Inc.
HUTCHHOUSE - Bakery products - Gardner Merchant Food Service Inc.
HUTCHINGS & HARDING - Leather - Bloch/New England, Inc.
HUTCHINSON & ROSS - Publisher's imprints - Van Nostrand Reinhold Inc.
HUTH - Tube benders - International Parts Corp.
HUTSCHENREUTHER - Dishes–china ☆ - WMF/USA
HUTTERBAUER - Meat products–beef - Western State Sales
HUTTON - Antennas - Hutton Communications
HUTTON - Furniture - Hutton Furniture Co.
HUXTABLE - Food products - Huxtable Comestibles
HUZZAH - Wines - Peaceful Bend Vineyard
HV-SH - Locks–door - Powerbrace Corp.
HVAC AIR FILTER - Filters–air - Air Kontrol Inc.
HVAC COIL CLEANER - Cleaning preparations - Air Kontrol Inc.
HVAP - Food products - Hudson Valley Apple Products Co. Inc.
HVD - Skin care products - Helga Van Dyke Skin Care
HVO - Vegetable oil - Florida Shortening Corp.
HVP - Animal feeds - Moorman Manufacturing Co.
HW - Aquariums–household - Hawaiian Marine Imports Inc.
HW - Jewelry - Harry Winston, Inc.
HW - Tomato pastes and sauces ☆ - Hunt-Wesson, Inc.
HW-BIO-ELEMENTS - Aquariums–household - Hawaiian Marine Imports Inc.
H.W. CARTER & SONS VINTAGE SINCE 1859 - Apparel and accessories -
    Four M. Industries, Inc.
HW-FERROPLANT - Aquariums–household - Hawaiian Marine Imports Inc.
HW-MARINEMIX - Aquariums–household - Hawaiian Marine Imports Inc.
HW-ODINEX - Aquariums–household - Hawaiian Marine Imports Inc.
HWD - Forklifts - Clark Material Handling Co.
H.W.F. - Cigars - Finck Cigar Co.
HWI - Hardware - Hardware Wholesalers, Inc.
HWP - Springs–mechanical - L & P Property Management Co.
HWY. - Brake fluids - Warren Oil Co., Inc.
HX - Electronic equipment - Halex/Scott Fetzer Co.
HX - Generators - Surface Combustion, Inc.
HY - Steel products - Pacific Plus International Inc.
HY-50 - Veterinary pharmaceutical preparations - G P Associates, Inc.
HY-BIO - Vitamins and nutritional supplements - Solgar Vitamin and Herb Co.,
    Inc.
HY-BUTE/60 - Insulating materials - General Electric Co.

HY-C - Vitamins and nutritional supplements - Solgar Vitamin and Herb Co.,
    Inc.
HY-CASE - Bars–steel - A.M. Castle & Co.
HY-D - Veterinary nutritional supplements - Amoco Bioproducts Corp.
HY-DERV - Sour cream - Cream Products Co. Inc.
HY-DRO-SOL - Fuel-tank water absorber - Vibe Records Inc.
HY-FLOW - Coatings - Lilly Industries, Inc.
HY-FLOW - Contact-lens solution - CooperVision Inc.
HY-GAIN - Antennas - Telex Communications, Inc.
HY-GESTRONE 2X - Pharmaceutical preparations - Pasadena Research
    Laboratories, Inc.
HY-GLO - Signs - Hy-Ko Products Co.
HY GLOW - Christmas tree lights ☆ - Noma International, Inc.
HY-GRADE - Skin care products - Hy-Grade Laboratories
HY-GRADE - Stationery ☆ - Springfield Tablet Co.
HY-GRO - Fertilizers ☆ - Plantabbs Products
HY-HATT - Popcorn - Doreen D. Key
HY-KLAS - Food products ☆ - Kovac's Affiliated Super Foods
HY-KO-LITE - Signs - Hy-Ko Products Co.
HY-KWALITY - Handles–wood - Sequatchie Handle Works Inc.
HY-LEA - Thread - Blue Mountain Industries, Inc.
HY LITE COPY - Highlight pen - Barouh Eaton Allen Corp.
HY-LO - Containers–insulated ☆ - Aladdin Industries, Inc.
HY LO - Denture cleaners - Scheu Products Co. Inc.
HY-LUX - Enamels - Ellis Paint Co.
HY-LYTER - Trailers–travel - Moeller Products Co. Inc.
HY-MARK - Apparel and accessories - Needlecraft Industries
HY-MAST - Pharmaceutical preparations - Pharmacia & Upjohn Co.
HY-MO-DEE - Steel springs–railroad - Needlecraft Industries
HY O'LAND - Food products - President Global Corp.
HY-PACK - Filters–water - Beckart Environmental, Inc.
HY-PHEN - Pharmaceutical preparations - B.F. Ascher & Co. Inc.
HY/PILE - Floor waxers–household ☆ - Royal Maid Association for the Blind
    Inc.
HY-POINT DAIRY - Milk - Hy-Point Dairy Farms
HY POWER - Bowling balls - Carmen Salvino Inc.
HY POWER - Meat products–canned - Kelly Foods Inc.
HY-Q - Pharmaceutical preparations - Mill-Mark Pharmaceuticals Inc.
HY-RANGE - Musical instrument accessories - Rudy Muck Musical Instruments
HY-RATION - Pet products - Eagle Products, Inc.
HY-SHEEP - Sporting goods - Century Sports Inc.
HY-SILTONE - Paper–gift wrap ☆ - Gift Wrap Co.
HY-SMOKE - Spices and extracts - Baltimore Spice, Inc.
HY-SPEED 500 - Concrete products - Garon Products Inc.
HY STOR - Batteries - Ergenics, Inc.
HY-STYLE - Paper–gift wrap - Gift Wrap Co.
HY-T - Belts–automotive - Goodyear Tire & Rubber Co.
HY TEK - Bicycles - Hunt-Wilde Corp.
HY-TEMP - Shortening ☆ - Swift Edible Oil Co.
HY-TENSIL - Siding–insulating - Nichols-Homeshield Inc.
HY-TEST - Men's shoes - Interco Inc.
HY-TEST - Scissors–hand-operated ☆ - Acme United Corp.
HY-TEST - Shoes - Wolverine World Wide, Inc.
HY-TEX - Paper–toilet - Fort Howard Corp.
HY-THERM - Insulating materials–foam - Celotex Corp.
HY TRAK - Construction equipment - TRAK International Inc.
HY-TROUS - Fertilizers - Skat Co.
HY-V - Apparel and accessories - Max Wiener & Co., Inc.
HY VALLEY - Fruits and vegetables - Hansen Fruit & Cold Storage Co., Inc.
HY VAN - Spices and extracts - E.A. Weber & Co.
HY VAN SUPREME - Spices and extracts - E.A. Weber & Co.
HY VEE - Food products - Hy-Vee Food Stores Inc.
HY-YEST - Yeast - Quest International Flavors & Food Ingredients Co.
HY1 - Health care products - Pacific BioLogic Inc.
HYAGEN - Cleaning preparations - Miami Products & Chemical Co.
HYAK WALL - Blocks–concrete - Eldorado Stone Corp.
HYALYN - Housewares - Van Guard Studios of North Carolina
HYANNIS - Bedding–linen - Dan River Inc.
HYANNIS - Clocks - General Time Corp. (Westclox/Seth Thomas Div.)
HYANNIS - Floor coverings - Mannington Resilient Floors
HYANNIS - Yarn ☆ - Caron International Inc.
HYASORB - Antibiotics ☆ - Key Pharmaceuticals Inc.
HYATMET - Pharmaceutical preparations ☆ - Legere Pharmaceuticals Inc.
HYATT - Hotels and motels - Hyatt International Corp.
HYATT VACATION CLUB - Real estate agencies - Hyatt International Corp.
HYAZIDE - Pharmaceutical preparations ☆ - Hyrex Pharmaceuticals

☆ = Now out of production

HYBEC - Pharmaceutical - American Laboratories Inc.

HYBEPHEN - Pharmaceutical preparations ☆ - Smithkline Beecham Corp.

HYBOLIN-DECANOATE - Pharmaceutical preparations - Hyrex Pharmaceuticals

HYBOND - Adhesives and sealants - Pratt & Lambert, Inc. (Specialty Products Div.)

HYBRID - Cases–musical instrument - Hybrid Cases

HYBRID - Eyeglasses - Oakley, Inc.

HYBRID - Faucets - Sterling Plumbing Group Inc.

HYBRID - Filters–industrial - Porous Media Corp.

HYBRID - Hair coloring preparations - Matrix Essentials, Inc.

HYBRID - Recording label - Hybrid Records

HYBRID - Wallpaper - Quality House Inc.

HYBRID 141A7 - Musical instrument accessories - Musichem

HYBRID 2000 - Faucets - Sterling Plumbing Group Inc.

HYBRIDON - Diagnostic substances - Hybridon, Inc.

HYBRIDOVEN - Laboratory apparatus - USA/Scientific Plastics, Inc.

HYBRIDUR - Binders - Air Products and Chemicals, Inc.

HYBRINETICS - Lighting equipment - Hybrinetics Inc. (Aladdin Products Div.)

HYBRISHAKE - Laboratory apparatus - Thomas Scientific

HYBUR - Food products - Ambassador Seafoods Inc.

HYCASTE - Hardware - Premax L.P.

HYCEL - Skin care products - Surface Solutions Inc.

HYCO-PAP - Pharmaceutical preparations - Lunsco Inc.

HYCO SERIES 70 - Motor vehicle parts and accessories - Dana Corp.

HYCOAT - Pharmaceutical preparations - Hymed Group Corp.

HYCODAN - Pharmaceutical preparations - Du Pont Pharmaceuticals

HYCOFF - Cough medicines - Saron Pharmacal Corp.

HYCOFF A-NN - Antihistamine preparations - Saron Pharmacal Corp.

HYCOFF-X - Cough medicines - Saron Pharmacal Corp.

HYCOL - Bakery products ☆ - Dykem Co.

HYCOMAR - Pharmaceutical preparations ☆ - Marlop Pharmaceuticals Inc.

HYCOMINE - Cough medicines - Du Pont Pharmaceuticals

HYCOPHEN - Pharmaceutical preparations - H.R. Cenci Laboratories Inc.

HYCORT - Health care products - Everett Laboratories Inc.

HYCORT - Pharmaceutical preparations ☆ - ICN Pharmaceuticals Inc.

HYCOTUSS - Health care products - Du Pont Pharmaceuticals

HYCRON - Gloves–work - Edmont

HYCRYL - Coatings - Rudd Co. Inc.

HYCURE - Pharmaceutical preparations - Hymed Group Corp.

HYCURE - Pharmaceutical preparations - The Hymed Group Corp.

HYCURE GEL - Pharmaceutical preparations - Hymed Group Corp.

HYDAPIPE - Bathroom fixtures - Symmons Industries Inc.

HYDATE - Watches ☆ - Merit Watch Co. Inc.

HYDE - Bird feeders - Hyde's Birdfeeder, Inc.

HYDE - Knives–putty - Hyde Manufacturing Co.

HYDE - Marine rigging ☆ - Hyde Products Inc.

HYDE - Shoes ☆ - Hyde Athletic Industries Inc.

HYDE & SEEK - Wallpaper - Illuminations Wallcoverings & Fabrics Inc.

HYDE-CAST - Plastics - A.L. Hyde Co.

HYDE OIL - Lubricants - McCollister & Co.

HYDE PARK - Agricultural products - Hyde Park Products, Inc.

HYDE PARK - Bakery products–frozen ☆ - Herold & Miller Inc.

HYDE PARK - Cabinets–wood ☆ - Kemper

HYDE PARK - Cigars - General Cigar Co., Inc.

HYDE PARK - Desk sets ☆ - L.E. Mason Co.

HYDE PARK - Dishes–china ☆ - Royal China & Porcelain Companies Inc.

HYDE PARK - Dolls ☆ - Effanbee Doll Corp.

HYDE PARK - Floor coverings ☆ - Tarkett, Inc.

HYDE PARK - Floor coverings–carpet and rugs - Atlas Carpet Mills Inc.

HYDE PARK - Floor coverings–carpet and rugs - Glen Eden Wool Carpets

HYDE PARK - Floor coverings–carpet and rugs ☆ - Regal Rugs Inc.

HYDE PARK - Floor coverings–carpet and rugs ☆ - World Carpets, Inc.

HYDE PARK - Food products - Malone and Hyde Inc.

HYDE PARK - Furniture ☆ - Hammary Furniture Co. Inc.

HYDE PARK - Furniture ☆ - Lane Co. Inc.

HYDE PARK - Furniture–wood ☆ - Ficks Reed Co. Inc.

HYDE PARK - Garden equipment - Edmond J. Lang

HYDE PARK - Pillows - Hollander Home Fashions Inc.

HYDE PARK - Shirts - Lands' End Inc.

HYDE PARK - Watches - Hope Industries Inc.

HYDE PARK STAINLESS - Cutlery - Burrell Cutlery Co. Inc.

HYDE STREET - Floor coverings–carpet and rugs ☆ - Hollytex Carpet Mills Inc.

HYDE-WOOD - Knives–putty - Hyde Manufacturing Co.

HYDELTRA-T.B.A. - Pharmaceutical preparations - Merck & Co., Inc. (Merck Research Laboratories)

HYDELTRASOL - Pharmaceutical preparations - Merck & Co., Inc. (Merck Research Laboratories)

HYDELTRONE - Veterinary pharmaceutical preparations ☆ - Merck & Co., Inc. (Merck Agvet Division)

HYDEOWS - Filters–oil - Hyde Products Inc.

HYDERGINE - Pharmaceutical preparations - Sandoz Pharmaceuticals Corp.

HYDE'S - Candy - Hyde's Northwest Candy Inc.

HYDETOS - Filters–oil - Hyde Products Inc.

HYDEXTRAN - Pharmaceutical preparations ☆ - Hyrex Pharmaceuticals

HYDLAR - Plastics - A.L. Hyde Co.

HYDOCAINE - Pharmaceutical preparations - Wesley Pharmacal Co. Inc.

HYDOL - Paints - Blue Ribbon Paint Co.

HYDORIL - Pharmaceutical preparations - H.R. Cenci Laboratories Inc.

HYDRA - Circuit boards - Lsi Logic Corp.

HYDRA - Computer software - Bear, Stearns & Co. Inc.

HYDRA - Electrical testing instruments - Vitel, Inc.

HYDRA - Guitars ☆ - Peavey Electronics Corp.

HYDRA - Sponges - Hydra Sponge Co., Inc.

HYDRA 330 - Ships–sailing vessels - Brookes & Gatehouse Inc.

HYDRA-BALANCE - Skin care products - Lancome

HYDRA BASS - Boats–fishing - Glasstream Boats Inc.

HYDRA BED - Truck beds - Triple C Manufacturing, Inc.

HYDRA-BULLET - Industrial machinery - Hydra-Stop, Inc.

HYDRA CLEAN - Paint sprayers - Graco Inc.

HYDRA CLEANSE - Skin care products - Gary E. Loest

HYDRA/DAMP - Hydraulic shock absorbers - Anchor-Darling Industries Inc.

HYDRA-DIOR - Cosmetics - Christian Dior Perfumes Corp.

HYDRA-DRILL - Drills–electric - Houston Engineers, Inc.

HYDRA-FLAT - Paints ☆ - Briner Paint Manufacturing Co. Inc.

HYDRA FORCE - Machinery - A.O. Smith Harvestore Products, Inc.

HYDRA FUEL - Vitamins and nutritional supplements - Twinlab

HYDRA-GEN - Generators–power ☆ - Mercantile Manufacturing Co. Inc.

HYDRA-GUN - Garden equipment - H.D. Hudson Manufacturing Co.

HYDRA-HEADBOARD - Motor vehicle parts and accessories - Keith W. Billotte

HYDRA-JET - Industrial machinery - Hydra-Stop, Inc.

HYDRA-KIT - Ophthalmic goods ☆ - Barnes-Hind Inc.

HYDRA-KNIT - Crocheted and knitted items - Puritan Sportswear Corp.

HYDRA-LOK - Hardware - Predator Industries, Inc.

HYDRA-LON - Machine parts - HPS Inc.

HYDRA-LYTE - Glucose ☆ - Endovations Inc.

HYDRA M - Paint sprayers - Speeflo Manufacturing Corp.

HYDRA-MAG - Pharmaceutical preparations ☆ - Pal-Pak Inc.

HYDRA-MAT II - Ophthalmic goods - Barnes-Hind Inc.

HYDRA-MAX - Gun stocks - Adience Inc.

HYDRA-MIX - Machinery - Air-O-Lator Corp.

HYDRA-MOIST - Manicure preparations ☆ - Avon Products, Inc.

HYDRA-MOTIVE - Sponges - Hydra Sponge Co., Inc.

HYDRA PERFECTE - Cosmetics - Cosmair Inc.

HYDRA-PLUS - Gun stocks - Adience Inc.

HYDRA-POWER - Treadmills - Hewitt-Robins Corp. (Conveyor Div.)

HYDRA PRO - Paint sprayers - Speeflo Manufacturing Corp.

HYDRA Q - Hair care products - Image Laboratories, Inc.

HYDRA-RIB - Sporting goods - Sorensen-Christian Industries Inc.

HYDRA SAVER - Medical apparatus - Del Mar Avionics

HYDRA SET - Medical apparatus - Del Mar Avionics

HYDRA-SHOK - Ammunition - Federal Cartridge Co.

HYDRA-SLIDE - Door openers–electronic ☆ - Ronan & Kunzl Inc.

HYDRA SOAR - Garden tools - Robert D. Newman

HYDRA-SPORTS - Boats–motor - Outboard Marine Corp.

HYDRA SPRAY L.A. - Pharmaceutical preparations ☆ - Vortech Pharmaceuticals

HYDRA STAR - Cosmetics - Parfums Christian Dior U.S. Corp.

HYDRA-STAR - Skin care products - Christian Dior Perfumes Corp.

HYDRA-STAR - Sweeteners–artificial - Bunge Foods Corp.

HYDRA SUEDE - Apparel and accessories - InSport International Inc.

HYDRA-SYSTEME LEVRES - Lip moisturizer - Chanel Inc.

HYDRA-TENSIONER MARK II - Ships–sailing vessels - Rudolph E. Krueger Co.

HYDRA-TUG - Motor vehicles - Rayco Manufacturing, Inc.

HYDRA-TURN - Industrial machinery - Hydra-Stop, Inc.

HYDRA-VALVE KLEEN - Cleaning preparations - CRC Chemicals USA/Siloo

HYDRA-WAY - Lubricating oils - Texaco, Inc.

HYDRA-WIPE - Leather–chamois - Hydra Sponge Co., Inc.

HYDRABACK - Bathing suits ☆ - Ocean Pool Co.

☆ = Now out of production

HYDRABASE - Pharmaceutical preparations ☆ - Summers Laboratories Inc.
HYDRACHARGE - Food products ☆ - Natural Balance, Inc.
HYDRACHLORSERPINE - Pharmaceutical preparations - David A. Rosow Inc.
HYDRACISER - Exercising equipment - Tim H. Elliott
HYDRACREME - Cosmetics - Lancome
HYDRACREME - Skin care products - Gary E. Loest
HYDRAFILM - Cosmetics - Chanel Inc.
HYDRAFINE - Chemical preparations - J.M. Huber Corp.
HYDRAFIRM - Skin care products - Mana Products, Inc.
HYDRAFITNESS - Exchangers–heat - Maxxim Medical Inc.
HYDRAFLEX - Hoses - Hose Master, Inc.
HYDRAFLIGHT - Archery equipment - Charles O. Waller
HYDRAFLOR - Fertilizers - Floralife, Inc.
HYDRAFORCE - Valves - Hydraforce, Inc.
HYDRAFUSE - Hair care products - Amethyst Investment Group, Inc.
HYDRAGARD - Lubricants - Gard Corp.
HYDRALAST - Bathroom fixtures ☆ - Acorn Manufacturing Co., Inc.
HYDRALEN - Skin care products - Lendan USA Co.
HYDRALIN - Pharmaceutical preparations ☆ - Dixon-Shane Inc.
HYDRALINE - Waterproofing compounds - Universal Protective Coatings
HYDRALONE - Food products - Kalsec, Inc.
HYDRALT - Finishing agents ☆ - Flintkote Co.
HYDRALT - Paints ☆ - GS Roofing Products Co.
HYDRALYN - Pharmaceutical preparations ☆ - Kenyon Drug Co. Inc.
HYDRAMAX - Paint sprayers - Speeflo Manufacturing Corp.
HYDRAMINE - Pharmaceutical preparations - Barre-National, Inc.
HYDRAN - Hydraulic oil - Fina Oil and Chemical Co.
HYDRANGEA - Baskets–wood ☆ - Royal Cathay Trading Co.
HYDRANGEA - Bedding–linen - Dan River Inc.
HYDRAPASS - Machinery - Gnesys, Inc.
HYDRAPATCH - Cement ☆ - Blackthorn, Inc.
HYDRAPLEX - Enamels - Strathmore Products, Inc.
HYDRAPLEX - Hair care products - Paul Mazzotta Inc.
HYDRAPRENE - Cosmetic applicators - Wood Corp.
HYDRASAND - Filters–water - Andritz Sprout-Bauer, Inc.
HYDRASERP - Pharmaceutical preparations - Armenpharm Ltd.
HYDRASET - Concrete products - W.R. Meadows Inc.
HYDRASPERSE - Massage products - Innovative Biosciences Corp.
HYDRASTAR - Perfumes - Christian Dior Perfumes Corp.
HYDRASTON - Pharmaceutical preparations - Herb Products Co.
HYDRASWASH - Hair care products - Tressa, Inc.
HYDRATE - Pharmaceutical preparations - Hyrex Pharmaceuticals
HYDRATE OR DIE - Water bottles–rubber - Fastrak Systems Inc.
HYDRATEIN - Hair-care products - Alberto-Culver Co.
HYDRATING TANNING LOTION SPF 4 - Suntan lotions - Sothys USA Inc.
HYDRATION-PLUS - Cosmetics - Clarins USA Inc.
HYDRATOOLS - Computer software - Ramss, Inc.
HYDRAULIC BOOM MOWERS - Lawn mowers - Alamo Industrial
HYDRAULIC MODEL - Computer software - Ramss, Inc.
HYDRAVAC - Cleaning preparations ☆ - Hydravac Corp.
HYDRAWAY - Drainboards - Monsanto Co.
HYDRAWEDGE - Laboratory apparatus - Duffers Scientific Inc.
HYDRAWLIK - Office supplies - Hydrawlik Co.
HYDREA - Pharmaceutical preparations - Bristol-Myers Squibb Co.
HYDREFINER - Water purification systems - RainSoft Water Conditioning Co.
HYDRELT - Pharmaceutical preparations ☆ - ICN Pharmaceuticals Inc.
HYDREX - Chemical preparations - Wearco LLC
HYDRI - Paints - Republic Powdered Metals, Inc.
HYDRID - Apparel and accessories - Dawson International Holdings (USA), Inc.
HYDRINATE - Pharmaceutical preparations - Barre-National, Inc.
HYDRISALIC GEL - Health care products - Pedinol Pharmacal Inc.
HYDRISINOL - Pharmaceutical preparations - Pedinol Pharmacal Inc.
HYDRISOLIC GEL - Health care products - Pedinol Pharmacal Inc.
HYDRIX - Cosmetics - Lancome
HYDRO - Laparoscope - Circon Corp.
HYDRO - Shoes - Fine International Footwear Inc.
HYDRO 15 - Lawn mowers - Alamo Industrial
HYDRO 2000 - Tires - General Tire, Inc.
HYDRO-AID - Water treating compounds - Albano & Hamilton Manufacturing Corp.
HYDRO-AIR II - Pumps–water - ITT Jabsco
HYDRO-BAFFLES - Drains - Geotechnical Marine Corp.
HYDRO BAZOOKA - Toy sporting equipment - Tonka Corp.
HYDRO-BIKES - Boats - Hydro-Bikes Inc.
HYDRO-BILEIN - Pharmaceutical preparations ☆ - Abbott Laboratories
HYDRO-BLOCK - Paints - Adelphi Coatings Co.

HYDRO-CARE - Cosmetics - Cassidy Inc.
HYDRO-CHEM SYSTEMS - Cleaning preparations - Hydro-Chem Systems, Inc.
HYDRO-CHIL - Kitchen appliances - Multiplex Co., Inc.
HYDRO-CHLOR - Pharmaceutical preparations ☆ - Vortech Pharmaceuticals
HYDRO-CLAD - Paints - Standard Paint Co.
HYDRO CLEAN - RBP Chemical Corp.
HYDRO CLEAN - Coffee makers–electric - Hamilton Beach/Proctor-Silex Inc.
HYDRO CLEAN - Degreasing solvents - Ecotech Enterprises, Inc.
HYDRO-CLEAN - Pet products - Tetra Sales USA
HYDRO-CLEAN DELUXE - Pet products - Tetra Sales USA
HYDRO-CLEAN, JR. - Pet products - Tetra Sales USA
HYDRO-CLEAN PROFESSIONAL - Pet products - Tetra Sales USA
HYDRO-CLEAN REGULAR - Pet products - Tetra Sales USA
HYDRO CLEAR - Pharmaceutical preparations - Miles Inc.
HYDRO-COAT - Engravers' plates - Revere Graphic Products, Inc.
HYDRO-COBEX - Pharmaceutical preparations - Pasadena Research Laboratories, Inc.
HYDRO COLORS - Cement - Tamms Industries Co.
HYDRO COMMAND - Housewares ☆ - Amana Refrigeration Inc.
HYDRO-CREPE - Packaging–paper - National Packaging Services Corp.
HYDRO-CRYSTI-12 - Pharmaceutical preparations - Roberts/Hauck Pharmaceuticals Inc.
HYDRO-CYCLE - Medical apparatus - Hydro-Cycle
HYDRO-D - Health care products - Halsey Drug Co. Inc.
HYDRO DYNAMICS - Fabrics–linen - Hydro Dynamics Inc.
HYDRO-EASE - Air mattresses - Mason Medical Products
HYDRO-ERGOLOID - Pharmaceutical preparations - Schein Pharmaceutical Inc.
HYDRO FEED - Fertilizers - Plant Marvel Laboratories
HYDRO-FIL - Sealing compounds - C.M. Athey Paint Co.
HYDRO-FILL - Pet products ☆ - Tetra Sales USA
HYDRO-FILM - Plastic sheets - Flex-O-Glass, Inc.
HYDRO-FILM - Sporting goods ☆ - Shakespeare Fishing Tackle
HYDRO FILTER - Fabrics - Hydroflo System, Inc.
HYDRO FLEECE - Apparel and accessories - Browning Manufacturing Co.
HYDRO FLIGHT - Fittings–cast iron - Phoenix Forging Co., Inc.
HYDRO-FLO SYSTEMS - Machinery - Rock Tool and Machine Co. Inc.
HYDRO-FLOAT - Health care products - Med Foam
HYDRO FLOW - Printing trades machinery - Chase Elastomer Corp.
HYDRO FORM - Beds–wood - Classic Corp.
HYDRO-FORM GEL - Hair care products - Peter Hantz Co.
HYDRO-GEAR - Machine parts - Hydro-Gear LP
HYDRO GLASS - Dental compounds - Savage Precision Dental Laboratory, Inc.
HYDRO GLAZE - Enamels - Mautz Paint Co.
HYDRO-GLAZE - Hair care products - Matrix Essentials, Inc.
HYDRO GOLD - Dental compounds - Savage Precision Dental Laboratory, Inc.
HYDRO GREENHOUSE - Garden equipment - Uncle Milton Industries Inc.
HYDRO-GRIP - Paints - Tenax Finishing Product
HYDRO-GUARD - Gloves - Fairfield Line, Inc.
HYDRO GUARD - Thread - Belding Heminway Co. Inc.
HYDRO GUARD - Tires ☆ - Kelly-Springfield Tire Co.
HYDRO HALT - Paints - C.M. Athey Paint Co.
HYDRO-HIST - Health care products ☆ - Ferndale Laboratories, Inc.
HYDRO HOODS - Filters–air - Hydro Hoods Corp.
HYDRO-HOTPAK - Heating pads–electric - Logan Inc.
HYDRO KOTE - Paints - M.A. Bruder & Sons Inc.
HYDRO-LASTIC - Paints - M.A. Bruder & Sons Inc.
HYDRO LAX - Health care products ☆ - Sunbeam-Oster Household Products
HYDRO LIGHT - Skin care products - Dorothy Gray Cosmetics Ltd.
HYDRO-LITH - Chemical preparations - Clearwater, Inc.
HYDRO-LOK PLUS - Floor coverings–carpet and rugs - Masland Carpets, Inc.
HYDRO-LOX - Finishing agents ☆ - Dunn Edwards Corp.
HYDRO-LUBE - Lubricating oils ☆ - Proton Engineering Inc.
HYDRO MAG - Antacids - Schein Pharmaceutical Inc.
HYDRO MARKER - Pencils - Empire Berol USA
HYDRO-MATE - Water heaters–household ☆ - Hydrotherm
HYDRO-MATIC - Sporting goods - Court & Slope Inc.
HYDRO-MINERALI - Skin care products - Revlon Consumer Products Corp.
HYDRO-MIST - Lubrication equipment–industrial - Aetna Manufacturing Co.
HYDRO PAR - Pharmaceutical preparations - Parmed Pharmaceuticals, Inc.
HYDRO-PLUG - Waterproofing compounds - Camp Co. Inc.
HYDRO-PLUS - Hair care products - Gene-Metre Professional Salon Products
HYDRO POWER PAK - Industrial machinery - Iraal, Inc.
HYDRO-PRIME - Paints - M.A. Bruder & Sons Inc.
HYDRO-PRO - Dental equipment - Whitestone LLC

☆ = Now out of production

HYDRO-PROOFER - Waterproofing compounds - Advanced Adhesives Technology

HYDRO-PULSE - Drain pipe cleaners - Viking Engineering Inc.

HYDRO-PULSE - Hot-water boilers ☆ - Hydrotherm

HYDRO PULSE - Toys - Larami Limited, Inc.

HYDRO-PURE - Pet products - Oscar Enterprises Inc.

HYDRO-Q - Skin care products - K'Arsan Corp.

HYDRO-QUEST - Chemical preparations - Aqua Clear Industries Inc.

HYDRO-RINSE - Water treating compounds - Water Resources International, Inc.

HYDRO-SAFE - Aquariums–household - Marine Environment/Aqua Craft

HYDRO-SAVAGE - Cleaning equipment - Pressure Cleaning International, Inc.

HYDRO-SEAL - Paints - Sherwin-Williams Automotive Finishes Corp.

HYDRO SEEDING SPECIAL - Fertilizers - Plant Marvel Laboratories

HYDRO-SET - Spa control device - Len Gordon Co.

HYDRO-SHIELD - Footwear - Rockport Co. Inc.

HYDRO-SHIELD - Toys–guns - Diversified Specialists, Inc.

HYDRO SHOOTER - Toys–guns - LCD International

HYDRO-SHUR - Paints - Grow Group, Inc.

HYDRO SLIDE - Toys - Kransco Manufacturing Inc.

HYDRO SORB - Chemical preparations - Hydrotex, Inc.

HYDRO-SPONGE - Pet products - Aquarium Technology Inc.

HYDRO-SPOT - Paints - Nelson Paint Co., Inc.

HYDRO SQUADRON - Toys–guns - Meritus Industries, Inc.

HYDRO-STONE - Cement - United States Gypsum Co.

HYDRO STRIKE - Toys - Pressman Toy Corp.

HYDRO-STRUT - Metals–liquid - Hydro-Craft, Inc.

HYDRO-SURG - Medical apparatus - American Hydro-Surgical Instruments, Inc.

HYDRO-SWEEP - Brooms ☆ - Dazey Corp.

HYDRO SWEEP - Cleaning equipment - Florida Pool Products, Inc.

HYDRO-TECH - Doors–glass - Contractors Wardrobe, Inc.

HYDRO TECH - Waterproof outerwear - Browning Manufacturing Co.

HYDRO-TEX - Housewares - Hydro-Tex Corp.

HYDRO-TEX - Pharmaceutical preparations - Syosset Laboratories Inc.

HYDRO/THERM - Hair care products ☆ - Image Laboratories, Inc.

HYDRO-THERMAL - Heating equipment - Hydro-Thermal Corp.

HYDRO TOOLS - Pool cleaning equipment - Hydro Tools, Inc.

HYDRO TORPEDOES - Toy sporting equipment - Tonka Corp.

HYDRO TRACK - Exercising equipment - Conray, Inc.

HYDRO TRIM - Enamels - Lilly Perfection Paint

HYDRO-TURF - Boats - Pacific Creations Inc.

HYDRO-VAC - Boating equipment and accessories - W.H. Salisbury & Co.

HYDRO-VAC - Pet products - Tetra Sales USA

HYDRO VENGER - Toys–automobiles - Jeff D. Myers

HYDRO-VENT - Catalysts - W.R. Grace & Co.

HYDRO-WHIRL - Toilets–enameled - Kohler Co.

HYDRO WING - Golfing equipment - Confidence Golf, Inc.

HYDRO WOVEN - Fabrics–linen - Hydro Dynamics Inc.

HYDRO WRAP - Insulating materials - Hydroflo System, Inc.

HYDRO-Z-50 - Pharmaceutical preparations ☆ - Merz Inc.

HYDROAIR - Pet products ☆ - Aquatronics-Filtronics

HYDROBAK - Backpacks - Fastrak Systems, Inc.

HYDROBATH - Bathroom fixtures ☆ - Shower-Rite Corp.

HYDROBEXAN - Pharmaceutical preparations ☆ - Keene Pharmaceuticals Inc.

HYDROBICS - Exercising equipment - Hydrobics Products

HYDROBOLIC WATER LAUNCHER - Toys - Water Sports, Inc.

HYDROBOT - Electronic equipment - Reinard C. Delp

HYDROBROM - Chemical preparations - Alden Leeds Corp.

HYDROBUILD - Waterproofing compounds - Devoe & Raynolds Co.

HYDROCAL - Cement - United States Gypsum Co.

HYDROCARBON - Apparel and accessories - Goldenwood International, Inc.

HYDROCARE - Spas–home - Gatsby Spas Inc.

HYDROCAT - Machinery - Flow International Corp.

HYDROCERIN - Skin care products - Geritrex Corp.

HYDROCET - Analgesics - Carnick Laboratories Inc.

HYDROCHAIR - Furniture - Hydra Chair Corp.

HYDROCHLOR - Pharmaceutical preparations - Legere Pharmaceuticals Inc.

HYDROCHLORULAN - Pharmaceutical preparations - Lannett Co. Inc.

HYDROCIL - Pharmaceutical preparations - Solvay Pharmaceuticals Inc.

HYDROCLEAN - Cleaning preparations–carpet and rug ☆ - Douglas/Quikut

HYDROCLEAR DIAMOND CLASS COMPRESSOR FLUID - Automotive parts and accessories - Conoco Inc.

HYDROCOAT - Surgical instruments - Zimmer, Inc.

HYDROCOLLATOR - Health care products - Chattanooga Group, Inc.

HYDROCORTISONE LOTION 1% - Pharmaceutical preparations - Mericon Industries Inc.

HYDROCORTISONE PET LOTION 1/2% - Veterinary pharmaceutical preparations - Mericon Industries Inc.

HYDROCORTONE - Pharmaceutical preparations - Merck & Co., Inc. (Merck Research Laboratories)

HYDROCOT - Pharmaceutical preparations - C.O. Truxton Inc.

HYDROCOTE - Finishing agents - Hydrocote Co., Inc.

HYDROCOTE POLYSHIELD - Coatings - Hydrocote Co., Inc.

HYDROCREAM - Pharmaceutical preparations - Paddock Laboratories Inc.

HYDROCURVE II - Ophthalmic goods - Barnes-Hind Inc.

HYDROCUSHION - Health care products ☆ - International Healthcare Products

HYDROCUT - Nurseries and garden stores - American Roller Bushing Corp.

HYDROCYCLONE - Machinery - Ingersoll-Rand Co.

HYDRODAN - Pharmaceutical preparations ☆ - Jones Medical Industries, Inc. (Medical Div.)

HYDRODERM - Bandages - Wilshire Technologies, Inc.

HYDRODIURIL - Diuretics - Merck & Co., Inc. (Merck Research Laboratories)

HYDRODUCT DRAINSHIELD - Drains - W.R. Grace & Co.

HYDRODYNE - Boats–motor - Midwestern Industries Corp.

HYDROESSENCE - Cosmetics - Phytochem, Inc.

HYDROFILM - Waterproofing compounds - Devoe & Raynolds Co.

HYDROFIT - Denture materials - Recigno Laboratories, Inc.

HYDROFLEX - Medical apparatus ☆ - Biosearch Medical Products Inc.

HYDROFLEX - Paints - Lox Systems Inc.

HYDROFLEX - Primers - Tremco Inc.

HYDROFLEX - Water dispensers - Treg C. Bradley

HYDROFLEX - Waterproofing compounds - Devoe & Raynolds Co.

HYDROFLO - Lighting fixtures–underwater - Hydroflex, Inc.

HYDROFLO - Machine parts - Magniflo Corp.

HYDROFLOW - Cleaning preparations–carpet and rug ☆ - Douglas/Quikut

HYDROFLOW - Filters–industrial - Hydroflow, Inc.

HYDROFLOW - Footwear - Brooks Sports, Inc.

HYDROFLOW - Footwear - Wolverine World Wide, Inc.

HYDROFOAM - Foam rubber - Plastomer Corp.

HYDROFOAM - Footwear - Faytex Corp.

HYDROFORCE - Boats - Anchor Industries, Inc.

HYDROFORM - Pharmaceutical preparations ☆ - Jones Medical Industries, Inc. (Medical Div.)

HYDROGARD - Health care products - Marquest Medical Products Inc.

HYDROGAUZE - Medical apparatus - NDM Acquisition Corp.

HYDROGEAR - Headbands - Marketforce

HYDROGESIC - Pharmaceutical preparations - Edwards Pharmaceuticals, Inc.

HYDROGLASS - Filters–oil - Central Illinois Manufacturing

HYDROGLASS SYSTEMS - Coatings - G & S Technology, Inc.

HYDROGLOSS - Inks - Sun Chemical Corp.

HYDROGREEN - Garden equipment - Uncle Milton Industries Inc.

HYDROGROWTH - Fertilizers - Hydro Growth Technology, Inc.

HYDROHOIST - Hardware - Hydrohoist International, Inc.

HYDROJET - Water heaters–household - Bradford-White Corp.

HYDROKOLL - Aquariums–household - Hawaiian Marine Imports Inc.

HYDROKRAFT - Inks–letterpress - Sun Chemical Corp.

HYDROLAC - Skin care products - Dome Cosmetics

HYDROLASTIC - Waterproofing compounds - Devoe & Raynolds Co.

HYDROLATUM - Pharmaceutical preparations - Denison Pharmaceuticals, Inc.

HYDROLIC JUMP - Apparel and accessories - Goldenwood International, Inc.

HYDROLIFTS - Boats ☆ - Marine Muffler Corp.

HYDROLIGHT - Waxes–mineral - Ocean Pacific Sunwear Ltd.

HYDROLINE - Floor finishing machines–commercial ☆ - Basic Coatings, Inc.

HYDROLINE SPOTCLEAN - Solvents ☆ - Basic Coatings, Inc.

HYDROLOAD - Beverages ☆ - ICN Pharmaceuticals Inc.

HYDROLOC SEAL - Bathroom fixtures - Kohler Co.

HYDROLON - Apparel and accessories - Collins & Aikman Corp.

HYDROLOSE - Laxatives ☆ - Upjohn Co.

HYDROLUX - Paints - Tenax Finishing Product

HYDROMAL - Pharmaceutical preparations ☆ - Roberts/Hauck Pharmaceuticals Inc.

HYDROMARINE - Wood products - Harbor Sales Co.

HYDROMATE - Computer software - Ramss, Inc.

HYDROMATE - Electrical equipment - Softub, Inc.

HYDROMATE - Paints - Valspar Corp.

HYDROMAX - Health care products - Halsey Drug Co. Inc.

HYDROMAX 90 - Conveyors - Atotech Usa Inc.

HYDROMENT - Tile grout, sealing materials, etc. - Bostik Inc.

HYDROMENT 428 - Flexible grout - Bostik Inc.

HYDROMENT 3600 - Wall-tile mastic ☆ - Bostik Inc.

HYDROMENT 7001 - Adhesives and sealants - Bostik Inc.
HYDROMENT REMOVE - Cleaning preparations - Bostik Inc.
HYDROMENT SINGLE-STEP - Latex mortars ☆ - Bostik Inc.
HYDROMENT ULTRA-SET - Waterproofing agent, etc ☆ - Bostik Inc.
HYDROMER - Medical apparatus - Biosearch Medical Products Inc.
HYDROMET - Tiles—ceramic - Capitol Tile Import Co.
HYDROMEX - Building materials - Hydromex, Inc.
HYDROMITE - Casting plaster - United States Gypsum Co.
HYDROMIX - Fertilizers ☆ - Doggett Corp.
HYDRON - Pigments—paint - Scott Paint Corp.
HYDRON - Skin care products - Dento-Med Industries, Inc.
HYDRON - Skin care products - Hydron Technologies, Inc.
HYDRON - Toys - Mattel, Inc.
HYDRON MODULE - Heat pumps - Millbrook Hutterian Brethren Inc.
HYDRONAUTICS - Luggage - Nautica Enterprises Inc.
HYDRONIC - Marine rigging ☆ - Hydronic Corp.
HYDRONICS - Coolers—electric - Marine Air Systems Inc.
HYDROPANE - Health care products - Halsey Drug Co. Inc.
HYDROPAR - Photographic equipment - Hydroflex, Inc.
HYDROPATCH - Paints - Devoe & Raynolds Co.
HYDROPEDES INSOLES - Shoe insoles - Hydropedes Insoles
HYDROPEL - Pharmaceutical preparations - C&M Pharmacal, Inc.
HYDROPHED - Pharmaceutical preparations - Rugby Laboratories Inc.
HYDROPHEN - Pharmaceutical preparations - Rugby Laboratories Inc.
HYDROPHILLIC OINTMENT - Skin care products - Geritrex Corp.
HYDROPHOR OINTMENT - Skin care products - Geritrex Corp.
HYDROPLEX - Hair care products - Helene Curtis Industries Inc.
HYDROPOD - Boats - North American Fiberglass Corp.
HYDROPRES - Pharmaceutical preparations - Merck & Co., Inc. (Merck Research Laboratories)
HYDROPRIME - Sealing compounds - Devoe & Raynolds Co.
HYDROPRIN - Pharmaceutical preparations - H.R. Cenci Laboratories Inc.
HYDROPRO - Health care products - Marketforce
HYDROPROTECTIVE FACTORS - Lotions - Avon Products, Inc.
HYDROPTIMALE - Skin care products - Sothys USA Inc.
HYDROPULSE - Machinery - George Fischer Foundry Systems, Inc.
HYDROPURGE - Cleaning preparations - Gage Products Co.
HYDROQUINONE - Pharmaceutical preparations - City Chemical Corp.
HYDRORAM - Pet products ☆ - Aquatronics-Filtronics
HYDROREX - Pharmaceutical preparations - C.S. Ruckstuhl Co. Inc.
HYDROSAFE - Water treating compounds - Hydrosafe Environmental Systems Inc.
HYDROSAL - Stencils - Hydrosal Co.
HYDROSEAL - Machinery - Baker Hughes Inc.
HYDROSEALER - Sealing compounds - Devoe & Raynolds Co.
HYDROSELL - Automotive parts and accessories - G.M.B. Battery Inc.
HYDROSERAPZINE - Pharmaceutical preparations - Goldline Laboratories, Inc.
HYDROSERPALAN - Pharmaceutical preparations - Lannett Co. Inc.
HYDROSHIELD - Coatings - HK Research Corp.
HYDROSKIN - Pharmaceutical preparations - Rugby Laboratories Inc.
HYDROSMART - Containers - Codisys Corp.
HYDROSONE - Pharmaceutical preparations - C.S. Ruckstuhl Co. Inc.
HYDROSONIC - Massage products - SRT, Inc.
HYDROSOYWRAP - Inks - Sun Chemical Corp.
HYDROSPAN - Caulking compounds - Edison Coatings, Inc.
HYDROSPORT - Bottles—glass - Julie Parnell
HYDROSTAR - Hydrogen - Praxair Technology, Inc.
HYDROSTICK - Primers - Duron, Inc.
HYDROSTIM - Electrodes - Uni-Patch
HYDROSTORM - Pumps—water - Caretaker Systems Inc.
HYDROSWEEP - Swimming pools - Hayward Pool Products Inc.
HYDROTAIL - Fishing tackle - Lunker City Fishing Specialties
HYDROTAINER - Boxes - Georgia-Pacific Corp.
HYDROTECH - Boats—kayaks - Rocky Mountain Trading, Inc.
HYDROTECH - Water treating compounds - Bio-Lab, Inc.
HYDROTENSIN-50 - Pharmaceutical preparations ☆ - Merz Inc.
HYDROTEX - Paints - Tenax Finishing Product
HYDROTEX - Tools - Goldblatt Tool Co.
HYDROTHANE - Paints - American Marine Coatings, Inc.
HYDROTHERM - Surgical supplies - Pelton Shepherd Industries
HYDROTHRUSTOR - Pet products ☆ - Aquatronics-Filtronics
HYDROTIC - Pharmaceutical preparations ☆ - Legere Pharmaceuticals Inc.
HYDROTIE - Neckties - Marketforce
HYDROTILE - Epoxy coatings - Standard Paint Co.
HYDROTILE - Heating equipment - Dunham Bush, Inc.
HYDROTRACK - Measuring instruments - Rk2, Inc.

HYDROTRACK - Medical apparatus - Ferno Washington, Inc.
HYDROTRAILER - Hardware - Mark Doherty
HYDROTREAD - Sporting goods - O'Brien International
HYDROTROPINE - Pharmaceutical preparations - Rugby Laboratories Inc.
HYDROVENGER - Toys—automobiles - Modern Thought Combine
HYDROVIEW - Lenses—optical - Storz Instrument Co.
HYDROVITA - Cosmetics - Dr. Babor Natural Cosmetics
HYDROVUE - Lenses—optical - O.S.I. Corp.
HYDROWRAP - Tape—adhesive - Argosy International (USA), Inc.
HYDROX - Beverages—carbonated ☆ - Certified Grocers Midwest Inc.
HYDROX - Cookies - Sunshine Biscuits, Inc.
HYDROX - Water purification systems - Oxidation Systems, Inc.
HYDROXACEN - Pharmaceutical preparations ☆ - Central Pharmaceutical Inc.
HYDROXIAL DIMENSION - Implants—surgical - Kirschner Medical Corp.
HYDROXOCOBALAMIN - Veterinary pharmaceutical preparations ☆ - New England Serum Co.
HYDROXY - Epoxy - Lilly Perfection Paint
HYDROXY B-12 - Pharmaceutical preparations - C.S. Ruckstuhl Co. Inc.
HYDROXY GOLD PLUS - Skin care products - Creative Laboratories Inc.
HYDROXYCAL - Vitamins and nutritional supplements - Great Life Laboratories Inc.
HYDROXYLVENT - Medical apparatus - Smith & Nephew Richards, Inc.
HYDROXYZINE - Health care products - Kay Pharmacal Co. Inc.
HYDRQULIC FLEX-WING MOWERS - Lawn mowers - Alamo Industrial
HYDRUS - Electronic equipment - Multi Products Co.
HYDRUS - Paints—artists' - Salis International, Inc.
HYDRY - Adhesives and sealants - F.H. Von Damm Inc.
HYDRYLLIN - Antihistamine preparations ☆ - G. D. Searle & Co.
HYE DELITES - Crackers - Hye Quality Bakery
HYE ROLLER - Breads - Hye Quality Bakery
HYER - Boots - Mahan Western Industries
HYFAB - Plastics film - Fabrite Laminating Corp.
HYFLEX - Paper—coated - REXAM DSI
HYFRE-VAC - Medical apparatus - Birtcher Medical Systems Inc.
HYGA-COLOR - Chalk - Dixon Ticonderoga Co.
HYGEA - Paper—toweling - Nice-Pak Products, Inc.
HYGEA FLUSH - Toilet-bowl cleaner - Continental Chemical Corp.
HYGEAIRE - Air purification systems - Atlantic Ultraviolet Corp.
HYGEENY - Toothbrushes - John D. Blue
HYGEIA - Dairy products - Hygeia Dairy Co.
HYGEIA - Deodorizers - Hygeia Products Inc.
HYGEIA - Infant product - Drug Plastic and Glass Co.
HYGEIA DAIRY - Milk - Hygeia Dairy Co.
HYGEL - Artists' materials - M. Grumbacher Inc.
HYGEL - Paints—artists' - Koh-I-Noor, Inc.
HYGENAIRE - Disinfectants - Hygenaire (Hygenaire, Inc.)
HYGENIA - Health care products - Nature's Own Inc.
HYGENIA - Health care products - VMC Corp.
HYGENIC PHONE CLEANER - Cleaning preparations - Lee Products Co.
HYGENIE - Machinery - Intertech
HYGENIUS - Electronic equipment - S.C. Johnson & Son, Inc.
HYGIA - Hydrotherapy equipment - Setma, Inc.
HYGIEIA - Chalk - Dixon Ticonderoga Co.
HYGIENE - Skin care products - Hygiene Industries
HYGIENE PLUS - Plumbing fixtures - Shopping Center Review Inc.
HYGIENE PLUS THE AUTOMATIC SOLUTION - Plumbing fixtures - Shopping Center Review Inc.
HYGIENIC ELEGANCE - Skin care products - Backscratchers, Inc.
HYGIENIKIT - Medical apparatus - Ameda/Egnell Corp.
HYGLICERON B - Veterinary pharmaceutical preparations - Nutra-Vet Research Corp.
HYGLO - Paper clips - American Pin & Fastener Corp.
HYGO PORT - Toilets—portable - Bella Hygo-Port, Inc.
HYGRADE - Automotive parts and accessories - Standard Motor Products, Inc.
HYGRADE - Bait ☆ - Siberian Salmon Egg Co.
HYGRADE - Daters and numberers - Consolidated Stamp Manufacturing Co. Inc.
HYGRADE - Food products - Hygrade Food Products Corp.
HYGRADE - Hobby kits - Grossman Stamp Co. Inc.
HYGROHEIERS - Weather tracking equipment - Watrous & Co. Inc.
HYGROTON - Pharmaceutical preparations - Rhone-Poulenc Rorer Pharmaceuticals Inc.
HYJET - Bidets - Seahorse International Corp.
HYJO - Frames—picture - Fredrix Artist Canvas Inc.
HYKRO - Pet products - Vo-Toys Inc.
HYLAND - Animal feeds - Hyland Co.

☆ = Now out of production

HYLAND KIDS - Food products - Cowiche Growers Inc.

HYLAND'S - Cough medicines - P. & S. Laboratories Inc.

HYLAND'S - Infant product - Standard Homeopathic Co., Inc.

HYLARON - Hair care products - Mahdeen Laboratory

HYLATE - Pharmaceutical preparations ☆ - Hyrex Pharmaceuticals

HYLENE - Yarns - Harris Yarns, Inc.

HYLITE - Sporting goods - Oceanic

HYLITE - Thread - Belding Heminway Co. Inc.

HYLITES - Tiles–ceramic - Dal-Tile Corp.

HYLIVER PLUS - Pharmaceutical preparations - Hyrex Pharmaceuticals

HYLOGRIP - Adhesives and sealants ☆ - AE Clevite Inc.

HYLOMAR - Adhesives and sealants - AE Clevite Inc.

HYLOPLATE SURFAS-KOTER - Chalk ☆ - Quartet Manufacturing Co.

HYLOREL - Health care products - Fisons Corp.

HYLOSIL - Adhesives and sealants ☆ - AE Clevite Inc.

HYLTON HOUSE - Furniture - Eastern Sleep Products Co.

HYLUMED - Research–biological - Genzyme Corp.

HYLUNIA THERAPEUTIC CARE FOR SKIN - Skin care products - Hylunia International Inc.

HYLUTIN - Pharmaceutical preparations - Hyrex Pharmaceuticals

HYLYNE - Dental compounds - Darby Dental Supply Co., Inc.

HYLYT - Pet products - DVM Pharmaceuticals, Inc.

HYLYTE - Hardware - Marley Mouldings Inc.

HYMAN HOUSE - Floor coverings–carpet and rugs - Lewis Hyman, Inc.

HYMED - Skin care products - US Advanced Medical Research Inc.

HYMETIC - Pharmaceutical preparations ☆ - Hyrex Pharmaceuticals

HYMONT - Bathroom fixtures - Crane Plumbing/Fiat Products

HY'N DRY - Whipped topping–frozen - Cream Products Co. Inc.

HYNAP - Napkins–fabric - Fort Howard Corp.

HYNAUTIC - Marine rigging - Hynautic Inc.

HYNET - Computer software - Hynet Technologies

HYONATOL - Barbituates ☆ - JMI-Canton Pharmaceuticals

HYOSOPHEN - Pharmaceutical preparations - Rugby Laboratories Inc.

HYP - Apparel and accessories - HYP

HYP - Watches - Hypnotic Hats, Ltd.

HYPA GLAZE - Polishes - Paul Chao

HYPAC - Machinery - Compaction America, Inc.

HYPACK - Computer software - Coastal Oceanographics, Inc.

HYPACT SR03-VHMW - Plastics - King Plastic Corp.

HYPACT SR12-UHMW - Plastics - King Plastic Corp.

HYPALLERGIC - Orthodontic equipment - MASEL

HYPALON - Rubber–synthetic - E.I. Dupont de Nemours and Co.

HYPAQUE-CYSTO - Pharmaceutical preparations - Winthrop Pharmaceuticals

HYPAROTIN - Pharmaceutical preparations - Cutter Laboratories

HYPE - Apparel–women's - Harkham Industries, Inc.

HYPE - Recording label - Bee Jay Recording Studios

HYPEADELIC - Apparel - Benkel Manufacturing Co.

HYPEDREAMZ - Video production - Hypedreamz Inc.

HYPEEL - Flowers, plants, and seeds - Petoseed Co., Inc.

HYPER - Golfing equipment - Active Sport Products Inc.

HYPER - Paper–bond - Riverside Paper Corp.

HYPER 8 - Bicycles - Huffy Corp.

HYPER AIR - Skates–roller - Bravo Corp.

HYPER ASPHERIC - Lenses–optical - Signet Armorlite, Inc.

HYPER-BACKGAMMON - Computer peripheral equipment - American Rare Coin Trading Group

HYPER BENDERVAC - Swimming pools - Recreonics, Inc.

HYPER COMIX - Computer software - P.C. Comix, Inc.

HYPER CONCENTRATE - Cleaning preparations - Turtle Wax, Inc.

HYPER CONVERTER - Computer software - PC Video Conversion

HYPER-CUBE - Toys - Concept Products Inc.

HYPER D - Pharmaceutical preparations - Biosepra Inc.

HYPER DA - Computer software - Symmetry Corp.

HYPER ENDS - Bar ends for bikes - Answer Products Inc.

HYPER FLEX - Fishing lures - KG Enterprise, Inc.

HYPER FOAM - Hair care products - Helene Curtis Industries Inc.

HYPER/FORMANCE - Toys - Tonka Corp.

HYPER GLOSS PERFORMER - Floor waxers–household - Southwest Manufacturers & Distributors, Inc.

HYPER GRIP - Toys - Tonka Corp.

HYPER GRUB - Fishing lures - KG Enterprise, Inc.

HYPER-HUMUS - Garden equipment - Hyper-Humus Co.

HYPER-LITE - Golfing equipment - TourEdge Golf Manufacturing Inc.

HYPER-LITE - Life preservers - Safariland Ltd., Inc.

HYPER-LITE - Lighting equipment - Leon Friday

HYPER LITE - Sporting goods - HO Sports Inc.

HYPER-RAP - Plastics - Ark-Plas Products, Inc.

HYPER REALITY - Games - Tsr, Inc.

HYPER-RIDGE - Microphones - Shure Brothers, Inc.

HYPER-SOLV - Vitamins and nutritional supplements - Tishcon Corp.

HYPER STRIPE - Food products - Good Humor Corp.

HYPER STUDIO GS - Computer software - Roger Wagner Publishing Inc.

HYPER-TET - Pharmaceutical preparations - Cutter Laboratories

HYPER-TONER - Pigments–paint - Accurate Coatings & Dispersions, Inc.

HYPER TWISTER - Toys–automobiles - Mattel, Inc.

HYPER VALUE CLUBPACK - Food products - Marketing Management, Inc.

HYPER VIPER - Toys–airplanes - Cox Products Inc.

HYPER WALK - Sporting goods - Bravo Corp.

HYPER YOURDON - Computer software - CGI Systems, Inc.

HYPERACTIVE - Apparel - MJN Productions

HYPERACTIVE - Gloves - Active Sport Products Inc.

HYPERACTIVE - Wheels - Cannondale Corp.

HYPERARCHIVE - Computer hardware - Rogan Medical Systems, Inc.

HYPERB - Pens - Pentel of America, Ltd.

HYPERBEAM - now out of production - Konami (America) Inc.

HYPERBRAKE - Machine parts - Janel Hydro Co.

HYPERCARD - Computer software - Apple Computer Inc.

HYPERCARD COURSE-IN-A-BOX - Computer software - Ventura Educational Systems

HYPERCARD PROJECTS BUNDLE - Computer software - Ventura Educational Systems

HYPERCARD PROJECTS FOR KIDS - Computer software - Ventura Educational Systems

HYPERCARD PROJECTS FOR LANGUAGE ARTS - Computer software - Ventura Educational Systems

HYPERCARD PROJECTS FOR MATH-COMPUTER SOFTWARE - Computer software - Ventura Educational Systems

HYPERCARD PROJECTS FOR MULTICULTURAL - Ventura Educational Systems

HYPERCARD PROJECTS FOR TEACHERS - Computer software - Ventura Educational Systems

HYPERCASE - Computer software - Kenneth E. Kendall

HYPERCELL - Computer software - Digalog Corp.

HYPERCHARGE - Computer software - Kinetic Computing Inc.

HYPERCLEAN - Pillows - Pacific Coast Feather Co.

HYPERCOILS - Automotive parts and accessories - Hyperco, Inc.

HYPERCUBED - Communications equipment–satellite - Spacecom Systems, Inc.

HYPERCYCLES - Toys–automobiles - Mattel, Inc.

HYPERCYL - Machine parts - Aries Engineering Co., Inc.

HYPERDAT - Audio equipment - APS Technologies

HYPERDOS - Computer software - Leading Technology Inc.

HYPERDRIVE - Computer software - Paperwise Inc.

HYPERDRIVERS - Toys - Tonka Corp.

HYPERETIC - Pharmaceutical preparations ☆ - ICN Pharmaceuticals Inc.

HYPERFIBER - Dietary supplement - Humanetics Corp.

HYPERFIRM - Brakes–motorcycle - Earl's Supply Co.

HYPERFLEX - Cosmetics - Ladyfingers

HYPERFLEX - Medical device - Linvatec Corp.

HYPERFLOW - Fuel systems–motor vehicle - Cutler Induction Systems, Inc.

HYPERFORMANCE - Apparel and accessories - Hyperformance

HYPERFORMANCE - Paints - Kansas Paint & Color Co.

HYPERFORMER - Computer software - Mcgaw, Inc.

HYPERGEAR - Apparel and accessories - Coronet Group, Inc.

HYPERGUARD - Computer software - Hilgraeve Inc.

HYPERGUARD - Paints - Kansas Paint & Color Co.

HYPERHELP - Computer software - Bristol Technology, Inc.

HYPERION - Electric lighting equipment - Lutron Electronics Co., Inc.

HYPERION - Toys–models ☆ - Estes Industries

HYPERION PRESS - Photographic portfolios - Hyperion Press Ltd.

HYPERION SOFTWARE - Computer software - Hyperion Software Corp.

HYPERISAN - Health care products - Bioforce of America Ltd.

HYPERKRYL - Paints - Kansas Paint & Color Co.

HYPERLITE - Bicycle parts and accessories - Answer Products Inc.

HYPERLYTE - Toys–guns - Mattel, Inc.

HYPERMAN - Computer software - New Learning Project, Inc.

HYPERMAPPING - Computer software - Barbara L. Barros

HYPERMATRIX - Computer software - Expert Object Corp.

HYPERMEDIA ONLINE - Computer software - Hypermedia Online, Inc.

HYPERNET - Construction equipment - SLT North America, Inc.

HYPERPACS - Computer peripheral equipment - Rogan Medical Systems, Inc.

HYPERPLOT - Computer software - Pinebush Technologies, Inc.

☆ = Now out of production

HYPERPULSE - Oxygen tents - Stephenson Industries Inc.
HYPERREALITY - Games - Tsr, Inc.
HYPERSEAL - Swimming pools - Hunting Industrial Coatings
HYPERSED - Pharmaceutical preparations - Econo Med Pharmaceuticals Inc.
HYPERSERP - Pharmaceutical preparations ☆ - ICN Pharmaceuticals Inc.
HYPERSHIELD - Paints - Kansas Paint & Color Co.
HYPERSLICK - Paints - Kansas Paint & Color Co.
HYPERSONIC - Toys - Azrak-Hamway International, Inc.
HYPERSONIC - Toys–automobiles ☆ - Imperial Toy Corp.
HYPERSONIC 4WD BULLET CAR - Toys–automobiles ☆ - Imperial Toy Corp.
HYPERSORB - Pet products ☆ - Seachem Laboratories
HYPERSPARC - Computers - Sparc International, Inc.
HYPERSPARSE - Computer software - Kenan Systems Corp.
HYPERSPEED - Computer peripheral equipment - Hyperspeed Technologies Inc.
HYPERSPEED - Computer software - Microprose Software, Inc.
HYPERSPERSE - Chemical preparations - D.W. Walker & Associates, Inc.
HYPERSTACKS - Computer software - Apple Computer Inc.
HYPERSTAT - Pharmaceutical preparations - Schering-Plough Healthcare Products
HYPERSTATION - Computer hardware - Ross Technology, Inc.
HYPERSTONE HEIST, THE - Computer software ☆ - Konami (America) Inc.
HYPERSTUDY - Computer manuals - Compuco, Inc.
HYPERSUITE - Computer software - Hyperlynx, Inc.
HYPERSYNC - Computer peripheral equipment - Star-Gate Technologies, Inc.
HYPERTABS - Pharmaceutical preparations ☆ - JMI-Canton Pharmaceuticals
HYPERTALK - Computer software - Apple Computer Inc.
HYPERTECH - Electronic equipment - Hypertech, Inc.
HYPERTEK - Rockets - Environmental Aerosciences Corp.
HYPERTHANE - Paints - Kansas Paint & Color Co.
HYPERTWIST - Fishing lures - Lures Missouri, Inc.
HYPERTYPER - Computer software - Digital Marketing Corp.
HYPERVAX+ - Vaccines - Univax Biologics Inc.
HYPERWHITE - Paints - Kansas Paint & Color Co.
HYPHED - Pharmaceutical preparations ☆ - Lunsco Inc.
HYPLAR - Paints - M. Grumbacher Inc.
HYPLAR SUPREME - Brushes–paint - M. Grumbacher Inc.
HYPLEX - Finishing agents - Rudd Co. Inc.
HYPLEZ - Varnishes - Gilbert Spruance Co.
HYPLICATOR - Tools - Engis Corp.
HYPNALDYNE - Pharmaceutical preparations ☆ - Vortech Pharmaceuticals
HYPNEU - Computer software - Bardyne, Inc.
HYPNO - Aquariums–household - Jungle Laboratories Corp.
HYPNOTIC POISON - Perfumes - Parfums Christian Dior U.S. Corp.
HYPNOTIZE - Apparel and accessories - Hypnotize, Inc.
HYPO-50 - Vitamins and nutritional supplements - Thompson Nutritional Products
HYPO-ACID - Garden equipment ☆ - Scotts Co. (Organics Business Group)
HYPO-ADE - Health care products - Enzymatic Therapy, Inc.
HYPO-ALLERGENIC COTTONELLE - Paper–toilet - Scott Paper Co.
HYPO-CLEAR - Cleaning preparations - Bausch & Lomb Inc.
HYPO-GEN - Water purification systems - Capital Controls Co.
HYPO PLEX - Vitamins and nutritional supplements - Natural Organics, Inc.
HYPO SHIELD - Earring backings - Fashion Solutions USA Inc.
HYPOGLY-C-MINS - Health care products ☆ - Futurebiotics
HYPOGLYCIL - Health care products - Futurebiotics
HYPOID - Lubricants - Fiske Brothers Refining Co. (Lubriplate Div.)
HYPOLET - Health care products - British-American Medical Inc.
HYPOLEX - Mattress pads - B.G. Industries Inc.
HYPOMINS - Vitamins and nutritional supplements - Pasadena Research Laboratories, Inc.
HYPONEX - Garden equipment - Scotts Co. (Organics Business Group)

HYPORT - Cooking equipment–household ☆ - Clayson Co.
HYPOTEARS - Lubricating eyedrops - Iolab Pharmaceuticals
HYPOTHALAMUS PMG - Vitamins and nutritional supplements - Standard Process Inc.
HYPOTULTRA - Measuring instruments - Associated Research, Inc.
HYPOWR - Gelatin - Vyse Gelatin Co.
HYPOY C - Oils–lubricating - Castrol, Inc.
HYPRESSURE JENNY - Cleaning preparations - Jenny Products, Inc.
HYPREZ FIVE-STAR - Abrasive products - Engineered Transitions Co. Inc.
HYPRFROG - Computer software - Cross Educational Software Inc.
HYPRO - Paper ☆ - M. Grumbacher Inc.
HYPRO - Pumps - Hypro Corp.
HYPROGEST - Pharmaceutical preparations ☆ - Keene Pharmaceuticals Inc.
HYPROPAQ - Medical apparatus - Thermionics Corp.
HYPROVAL - Pharmaceutical preparations ☆ - Solvay Pharmaceuticals Inc.
HYPTRAN - Pharmaceutical preparations ☆ - Wallace Laboratories
HYPURE - Agricultural products - Isolab, Inc.
HYRAX - Recording label - Jazz Composer's Orchestra Association Inc.
HYREX-105 - Pharmaceutical preparations ☆ - Hyrex Pharmaceuticals
HYREXIN - Pharmaceutical preparations - Hyrex Pharmaceuticals
HYROCAIN - Pharmaceutical - American Pharmaceutical Co.
HYROXON - Health care products - Kay Pharmacal Co. Inc.
HYRYZ - Shortening - Karlshamns USA Inc.
HY'S - Food products ☆ - World Finer Foods, Inc.
HYSCORBIC PLUS - Pharmaceutical preparations - Bock Pharmacal Co.
HYSEN - Electronic equipment - General Electric Co.
HYSEP - Toothpaste - Bioglobe Tech. Inc.
HYSER - Pharmaceutical preparations ☆ - Legere Pharmaceuticals Inc.
HYSERPLUS - Pharmaceutical preparations ☆ - Legere Pharmaceuticals Inc.
HYSKON - Pharmaceutical preparations - Kabi Pharmacia Inc.
HYSLO - Paints - M. Grumbacher Inc.
HYSOL - Paints ☆ - Tenax Finishing Product
HYSONE - Pharmaceutical preparations - Roberts/Hauck Pharmaceuticals Inc.
HYSORB - Bandages - Hymedix International, Inc.
HYSTER - Forklifts - Hyster Co.
HYSTEROSYS - Catheters - Ovamed
HYST'RY MYST'RY HOUSE - Publisher's imprints - Hyst'ry Myst'ry House
HYSYNAL - Tubes–surgical - Hygenic Corp.
HYTAKEROL - Pharmaceutical preparations - Winthrop Pharmaceuticals
HYTEN - Fibers–synthetic - E.I. Dupont de Nemours and Co.
HYTENNAS - Antennas - Hytennas, Inc.
HYTEST - Flowers, plants, and seeds - Stanford Seed Co.
HYTINIC - Pharmaceutical preparations - Hyrex Pharmaceuticals
HYTON - Crocheted and knitted items - Veratec
HYTONE - Ceiling panels - Celotex Corp.
HYTONE - Paper–writing - Mead Corp.
HYTONE - Pharmaceutical preparations - Dermik Laboratories Inc.
HYTROL - Conveyors - Hytrol Conveyor Co., Inc.
HYTRON - Detergents - Stearns Packaging Corp.
HYTROPHEN - Pharmaceutical preparations ☆ - Wesley Pharmacal Co. Inc.
HYTROUS - Garden equipment - Hytrous/Flash Sales Inc.
HYTUSS - Pharmaceutical preparations - Hyrex Pharmaceuticals
HYTUSS-2X - Pharmaceutical preparations - Hyrex Pharmaceuticals
HYTUSSIN - Pharmaceutical preparations - H.R. Cenci Laboratories Inc.
HYUNDAI - Guitars - MBT International, Inc.
HYUNDAI - Motor vehicles–automobiles ☆ - Hyundai Motor America
HYUNDAI - Pianos - North American Music Inc.
HYVAR X - Herbicides - E.I. Dupont de Nemours and Co.
HYWARE - Pet products ☆ - Berolina Imports
HYWAY - Signs - Stello Products Inc.
HYWAY WAREHOUSING, INC. - Lighting equipment - Hyway Warehousing, Inc.
HYZINE - Pharmaceutical preparations - Hyrex Pharmaceuticals
H!ZONE - Computer software - WizardWorks Group Inc.

I

Addresses and phone numbers for the companies cited in the brands below
are available in the Company Listings section immediately following the brands listings.

I - Apparel and accessories - I-Golf Co.

I - Computer hardware - Integrated Micro Solutions, Inc.

I - Cosmetics ☆ - Nutri/System L.P.

I - Medical apparatus - Indigo Medical, Inc.

I - Recording label - Left Bank Records Inc.

I-4 - Apparel and accessories - Alan L. Hamilton

I-80 EXPRESSWAY - Toys–erector sets - Little Tikes Co.

I 100 - Auger bits - Irwin Co.

I 585 - Scissors–hand-operated - F.W. Engels Inc.

I AM A READ ME, COLOR ME BOOK. - Publisher's imprints - Clarine L. Morris

I AM FINE - Respirators - I Am Fine, Inc.

I AM LOVED - Jewelry - Helzbergs Diamond Shops Inc.

I AM MUSIC OF THE SPHERES - Prerecorded audio tapes - Saint Germain Foundation

I AM SHEE - Recording label - Jazz Composer's Orchestra Association Inc.

I & A - Septic tanks–metal - Hancor Inc.

I/B/E/S - Computer software - I/B/E/S International

I BAGELS - Meats and processed foods - I Love Bagels, Inc.

I BELIEVE - Publisher's imprints ☆ - Wm. B. Eerdmans Publishing Co.

I BELONG TO ME! - Buttons - Peoplehood Products and Properties

I-BOMB - Insecticides - Plant Marvel Laboratories

I-BOY - Games - Toy Works, Inc.

I BRANDS - Apparel and accessories - Dave Behar

I-BRIDGE - Computer software - I-Kinetics, Inc.

I BUONATAVOLA - Cheese - Sini Fulvi USA Inc.

I-C COLLECTIONS - Underwear and nightwear - ICM

I-C GOLD - Wallcovering - Parex, Inc.

I CAFE BUSTELO - Coffee - Tetley USA Inc.

I CAME TO PLAY AND I'LL BEAT YOU EVERY TIME! - Apparel and accessories - G Industries, Inc.

I CAN BAKE - Cookie mix - Pelican Bay Ltd. Inc.

I CAN BAKE MUFFINS - Muffin mixes - Pelican Bay Ltd. Inc.

I CAN BREATHE! - Apparel and accessories - I Can Breathe! Inc.

I-CAN-DO-IT - Hobby kits - Cascade Fibers Co.

I CAN DO IT! - Publisher's imprints - Gruner Jahr Printing & Publishing Co.

I CAN DO IT - Toys ☆ - Trend Enterprises, Inc.

I CAN LEARN - Educational materials - JRL Enterprises, Inc.

I CAN TIE MY SHOES - Footwear–children's - James Stanfield and Co., Inc.

I CAN'T BELIEVE I'M DEAD - Apparel and accessories - Westpac Products Co. Inc.

I CAN'T BELIEVE IT'S NOT BUTTER - Margarine - Van Den Bergh Foods Co.

I CAN'T BELIEVE IT'S YOGURT - Yogurt–frozen - Brice Foods, Inc.

I CAN'T BELIEVE IT'S YOGURT - Yogurt–frozen - I Can't Believe It's Yogurt Inc.

I CHING FORTUNE - Beverages–carbonated - Fred G. Farago

I-CHOMP - Toys–models - Mattel, Inc.

I-CLEAN - Paper products - Insignia Systems, Inc.

I COWBOYS OUTWEST - Western apparel - Karman Western Apparel

I-D - Health care products - Gregg Haskell

I D E A IRON DUCK EXTRICATION APPARATUS - Medical apparatus - Fleming Industries, Inc.

I. D. KIDS - Furniture–children's - American Sleepcenters, Inc.

I-DEAL - Bags–plastic - Inteplast Group Ltd.

I DEAL CARDWEAR - Apparel and accessories - I Deal Cardwear

I. DEARS - Dolls - Cindy Raye Stewart

I DESERVE IT! - Candy - I Deserve It Inc.

I DIE FOR YOU - Apparel–women's - Ikeddi Enterprises Inc.

I DIVE! - Apparel and accessories - Dave Behar

I DO - Housewares - Van Horn Hayward

I DO DOWNTOWN - Credit institutions - Downtown Cincinnati Development Inc.

I DONE SNAPPED RECORDS - Recording label - Freddie Echols, Jr.

I DUNK!BASKETBALLS - Apparel and accessories - Dave Behar

I FED THE PROP SHARK - Shirts - Nautical Toys International, Inc.

I FIND - Trays - Sturdy Manufacturing Co.

I FISH! - Apparel and accessories - Dave Behar

I FLY! - Apparel and accessories - Dave Behar

I FORM - Paper products - Intouch Group, Inc.

I GEAR - Computer peripheral equipment - Unified Research Laboratories, Inc.

I-GENE - Straws–drinking - Johnstown Manufacturing, Inc.

I-GLASS - Glassware–household ☆ - Hackman Tabletop Inc.

I GOT A BOOBOO - Apparel–children's - Laura S. Cleminson

I GRANDI INTERPRETI - Recording label - Music and Arts Programs of America Inc.

I HATE - Greeting cards - Crane Hill Publishers, Inc.

I HAVE A SOLUTION - Insurance agencies–health - Integrated Healthcare Auditing and Services, Inc.

I-HELIX - Hoses - Action Technology Co.

I HIKE! - Apparel stores–sports - Dave Behar

I III V - Skin care products - Beautycology Inc.

IMMUNODIAGNOSTICS, INC. - Pharmaceutical preparations - Immunodiagnostics, Inc.

I INSO - Computer software - INSO Corp.

I INVINCIBLE - Furniture - Invincible Metal Furniture Co.

I IZOD - Balls–golf - Crystal Brands Inc.

I KID-YOU-NOT - Maps - American Map Corp.

I KID-YOU-NOT NO TURN R - Maps - American Map Corp.

I-KNOW-HOW - Footwear - Toddler University

I KNOW IT'S HERE SOMEWHERE! - Computer software ☆ - Spinnaker Software Corp.

I KRAVE - Jewelry - Edwin B. Cutshall

I-LAB - Inks - I - Lab Corp.

I. LAYTON - Bedding–linen - Layton Home Fashions

I LEATHER - Footwear–women's - Taj K Imports, Inc.

I-LID - Health care products - Sherman Pharmaceuticals, Inc.

I-LINE - Circuit breakers - Square D Co.

I-LINER - Artists' materials - Stangren Co.

I-LINER - Cosmetics - Revlon Consumer Products Corp.

I LOVE ALL PEOPLE - Apparel and accessories - Gloria Claiborne and Sheila Y. Sims Partnership

I LOVE AMERICA - Toys–stuffed ☆ - Russ Berrie and Co., Inc.

I LOVE BORDERS - Wallpaper ☆ - Imperial Wallcoverings, Inc.

I LOVE DOUBLE CHEX - Cereal - Ralston Purina Co.

I LOVE IT! - Frames–picture - Terragrafics Inc.

I LOVE IT AND I'M LEAVING IT TO MY CHILDREN - Bags–canvas - Caray, Inc.

I LOVE IT IN COFFEE - Candy - Loveable Chocolates

I LOVE JESUS - Air purification systems - Medo Industries, Inc.

I LOVE LEMON - Teas–herbal - R.C. Bigelow, Inc.

I LOVE LIFE - Air purification systems ☆ - Medo Industries, Inc.

I LOVE LUCY - Games - Talicor Inc.

I LOVE MY DOG - Pet products - Rawcliffe Corp.

I LOVE MY PUPPY - Pet products - Ozark Honey-Dew Farms, Inc.

I LOVE NY - Coffee - Fairwinds Gourmet Coffee Co. Inc.

I LOVE SCHIFF - Vitamins and nutritional supplements - Schiff Products, Inc.

I LOVE SCHOOL - Kites ☆ - Hi-Flier Manufacturing Co.

I LOVE SCIENCE! - Publisher's imprints - Advantage/Aurora Publications

I LOVE THE WAY YOU TAKE CARE OF ME - Infant product - Spectrum Juvenile Products Inc.

I LOVE THIS GAME - Apparel and accessories - NBA Properties, Inc.

I LOVE THIS STUFF! NBA - Apparel and accessories - NBA Properties, Inc.

I LOVE THIS TEAM - Apparel and accessories - NBA Properties, Inc.

I LOVE U - Vitamins and nutritional supplements - Banner-Pharmacaps Inc. (Advanced Nutritional Technology Division)

I LOVE YOU - Candy - Kencraft, Inc.

I LOVE YOU BABY - Dolls - Horsman

I LOVE YOU FROM THE BOTTOM OF MY HEART - Candy - Cute Candy Corp.

I LOVE YOU IN THE SKY, BUTTERFLY - Computer software - Hartley Courseware Inc.

I-LYA - Apparel and accessories - Inter-Lake Yachting Association

I M P - Chemical preparations - Miles Inc.

I-MAGIC - Computer software - SP Enterprises, Inc.

I-MAIL - Computer software - Computer Solutions International, Inc.

I MALTA INDIA LIGHT - Beverages - Cerveceria India, Inc.

I MANN ALLIGATORS - Toys - All American Toy Co.

I-MARK - Motor vehicles–automobiles ☆ - American Isuzu Motors Inc.

I-MARK - Pens - American National Supply, Inc.

I MY DADDY - Apparel–children's - Power Clothing Inc.

I MY PET - Toys - Phoenix Worldwide, Inc.

I-N-T INTERCEPTORS - Toys - Tonka Corp.

I NATURAL COSMETICS - Beauty-services franchise - I Natural Cosmetics

I NEED A GOOD BUY - Office furniture–wood - Krueger International, Inc.

I NY - Christmas tree ornaments and decorations - New York State Department of Economic Development

I/O - Audio equipment ☆ - Galaxy Audio

I/O 8+ - Electronic equipment - Specialix, Inc.

I/O EXPRESS - Computer software - Executive Software International, Inc.

I/O PORT SYSTEM - Computer peripheral equipment - Ansan Industries Ltd.

I/O SYSTEM ONE - Electronic equipment - Input/Output Inc.

I/O SYSTEM TWO - Electronics equipment - Input/Output Inc.

I/O WORKS - Computer software - Vme Microsystems International Corp.

I/O4 - Electronic equipment - Specialix, Inc.

I ONLY WEAR RED ONE DAY A YEAR - Shirts - Tortoize Productions, Inc.

I ORLANDO - Apparel and accessories - Central Florida Investments, Inc.

I PICOLI AMICI - Cookies - Commerce Foods Inc.

I PLAY - Diapers–cloth - Family Clubhouse

I-PLUS - Vitamins and nutritional supplements - Enrich Corp.

I-POWERADMIN - Computer software - Unified Research Laboratories, Inc.

I PRESUME - Greeting cards - Hourglass Editions

I PRIMI D'ITALIA - Pasta - James Ferrara

I-PROXY - Computer peripheral equipment - Unified Research Laboratories, Inc.

I RELISH YOU - Relishes - Lin-Lex Enterprises, Inc.

I REMEMBER WHAT I SEE - Computer hardware - Pixel, Inc.

I-REST - Pillows - Pacific Spirit Corp.

I-RINSE - Health care products - Sherman Pharmaceuticals, Inc.

I RUN! R A C E S - Apparel and accessories - Dave Behar

I SCREAM - Candy ☆ - Van Melle Inc.

I-SCREAM - Games - Lakeside Games

I SCREAM SANDWICH - Cookies - Sunshine/Salerno Inc.

I SCREAMS'N YOU SCREAMS - Cookies - Nabisco Foods Group

I-SCRUB - Eyelid cleanser - CooperVision Inc.

I-SEDRIN - Cold remedies ☆ - Eli Lilly and Co.

I-SEE-ME - Cribs–wood ☆ - Welsh Co.

I SEE YOU - Jewelry - Genis International, Inc.

I-SEE-YOU - Publisher's imprints - McClanahan Book Co., Inc.

I SEND YOU - Greeting cards - Green Tiger Press

I SHELIN BY SHELIN - Ophthalmic goods - Shelin International Enterprises, Inc.

I/SITE - Electronic equipment - CSI Control Systems International, Inc.

I-SITE - Veterinary pharmaceutical preparations - Agri Laboratories, Ltd.

I SKI - Eyeglasses - International Tropic-Cal Inc. (I SKI Div.)

I SKI - Sunglasses - Outlook Eyewear Co.

I SLAM, THEREFORE I AM. - Calendars - Cullman Ventures Inc.

I SLUG DRUGS - Apparel and accessories - Peoplehood Products and Properties

I-SMASH - Toys–models - Mattel, Inc.

I. SOAR - Toys - Mattel, Inc.

I SOCCER I PASTA - Pasta - Fortune Macaroni Co.

I-SOYALAC - Baby foods - Mt. Vernon Foods

I-SPEAR - Surgical supplies - Alcon Laboratories, Inc.

I-STAT - Diagnostic apparatus - I-Stat Corp.

I STEAM CONE - Boating equipment and accessories - Alan M. Simon

I-STEPS - Computer software - Pacific Environmental Services Inc.

I-STOMP - Toys–models - Mattel, Inc.

I. TATTOLI - Food products - Bel Canto Fancy Foods Ltd.

I TOURNAMENT NO. 1 - Badminton equipment - Rackets International (Racket Sports Div.)

I-TRATE - Pharmaceutical preparations - Vista Laboratories Inc.

I-TRAX - Computer storage devices–optical - Aix Entertainment, Inc.

I V ONE - Paper punches - I.V. One, Inc.

I VISOR - Computer software - Unified Research Laboratories, Inc.

I-VITA - Vitamins and nutritional supplements - Nutrition Enterprises

I. W. HARPER - Whiskey - Schenley Industries Inc.

I WALK! - Apparel and accessories - Dave Behar

I WANT TO READ - Video production - Learning Research, Inc.

I WEAR IT FOR ME - Nail care products ☆ - Nina International, Inc.

I WILL - Seafood products–fresh or frozen - Noon Hour Food Products

I WISH IT WERE SNOWING - Umbrellas - Ski Euipment Electronics, Inc.

I XENTAUR - Meters–gas - Xentaur Corp.

I-Z PATCHED - Concrete products - Century Chemical Co.

I2R - Medical apparatus - Instruments for Research and Industry, I2R Inc.

I2S - Medical apparatus - Biomedix, Inc.

I3 - Apparel - Leslie Cornish

I3 - Communications equipment - Intek Information, Inc.

I3 - Computers - Interactive International Inc.

I486 - Computers–micro - Intel Corp.

I860 - Computer software - Intel Corp.

I.A.B. - Apparel and accessories - Standard Paints Inc.

IAC - Computer peripheral equipment - Group 1 Software, Inc.

IAM - Flowers, plants, and seeds - Ronald G. Iverson

IAMBIC - Computer software - Tambic Software

IAMIN - Pharmaceutical preparations - Procyte Corp.

IAMIN-IB - Pharmaceutical preparations - Procyte Corp.

IAMIN-VET - Pharmaceutical preparations - Procyte Corp.

IAMOND RING - Puzzles - Kadon Enterprises Inc.

IAMS - Dog food - Iams Co.

IAMS LESS ACTIVE - Dog food - Iams Co.

IAMS NATURAL - Pet products - Iams Co.

IAN - Freight cars–locomotive - Ian International

IAN CRAWFORD - Wallpaper - Ian Crawford Ltd.

IAN CRAWFORD III - Wallpaper - Ian Crawford Ltd.

IAPMO T - Tanks–water - International Association of Plumbing and Mechanical Officials

IAQ - Air and water purification units - IAQ, Inc.

I.A.S. - Floor coverings–carpet and rugs - Olympic Carpets Inc.

IASYS - Electronic equipment - AudioControl

I.A.T. MICRO ZYME - Fertilizers - Integrated Agri-Tech, Inc.

IAUS - Publisher's imprints - Rizzoli International Publications Inc.

IB - Fans–electric - Illinois Blower, Inc.

I.B. BLACKMAN - Apparel and accessories - Benson O. Williams, Jr.

IBA - Electronic equipment - Leica USA Inc.

IBAM COINS - Candy ☆ - R.L. Albert & Son, Inc.

IBANEZ - Guitars - Hoshino USA Inc.

IBANK - Computer hardware - Ibank Systems, Inc.

IBBERSON - Knives–pocket - Gibb Yachting Equipment Co.

IBBOTSON FUND STRATEGIST - Computer software - Ibbotson Associates

IBBS - Communications equipment–marine - System Software Services

IBC - Beverages–carbonated - Dr. Pepper/Seven Up, Inc.

IBC - Mattresses - IBC Group, Inc.

IBDU - Fertilizers - Vigoro Industries, Inc.

IBDU - Fertilizers–nitrogenous - Lebanon Seaboard Corp.

IBERET - Pharmaceutical preparations - Abbott Laboratories

IBERIA - Floor coverings - Mannington Resilient Floors

IBERIA - Food products - Joseph Victori Wines Inc.

IBERIA - Wood products ☆ - Homasote Co.

IBERLATE - Pharmaceutical preparations ☆ - Abbott Laboratories

IBEROL - Pharmaceutical preparations - Abbott Laboratories

IBEX - Bicycles - MV International Corp.

IBEX - Boots ☆ - Liberty Mountain Sports

IBEX - Computer peripheral equipment - Ibex Inc.

IBEX - Fabric for hygienic products - Springs Canada, Inc.

IBEX - Footwear - Garrison Industries

☆ = Now out of production

IBEX - Insecticides - Walco Linck Co.

IBEX - Musical instrument accessories - International Violin Co. Ltd.

IBEX - Musical instrument accessories - Metropolitan Music Co.

IBEX THERAPEUTIC - See PARVLEX

IBG - Fish–fresh or frozen - I.B.G. (Florida) Inc.

IBG - Prefabricated buildings–metal ☆ - Roper Corp.

IBI - Industrial machinery - International Bearings, Inc.

IBICO - Calculators - Ibico Inc.

IBIIS - Computer software - Iffland Kavanagh Waterbury, P.C.

IBIS - Blinds–venetian ☆ - Hunter Douglas, Inc.

I.B.I.S - Computer software - Alchemical Medicine Research & Technology Association

IBIS - Golfing equipment - Hurricane Sports, Inc.

IBIS - Sunglasses ☆ - Corning Inc.

IBIS - Watches - Donald J. Gavin

IBIZA - Floor coverings–carpet and rugs - Couristan Inc.

IBIZA - Window coverings ☆ - Vertilux-Louverlux Inc.

IBM - Computers - International Business Machines Corp.

IBM PC CONVERTIBLE - Computers - International Business Machines Corp.

IBOB 9000 - Computer peripheral equipment - Micro Processor Systems, Inc.

IBOLD - Cigars - National Cigar Corp.

IBOX - Electronic equipment - Japan Computer International, Inc.

IBP - Food products - IBP Inc.

IBP SUPREME - Hams - IBP Inc.

IBREN - Pharmaceutical preparations - Econo Med Pharmaceuticals Inc.

IBROKER - Computer peripheral equipment - Intelligent Brokerage, Inc.

I.B.S. - Lip balms - Frances Denney

IBS - Medical apparatus - Interproduct Inc.

IBT - Film - Eastman Kodak Co.

IBTIZ - Cleaning preparations - IBTIZ Inc.

IBU - Recording label - Jazz Composer's Orchestra Association Inc.

IBUGESIC - Analgesics - Tishcon Corp.

IBUPRIN - Vitamins and nutritional supplements ☆ - Thompson Medical Co., Inc.

IBUPROFEN-200 - Pharmaceutical preparations - Reese Chemical Co.

IBUPROFEN PMR - Pharmaceutical preparations - Reese Chemical Co.

IC - Amplifiers–musical instrument ☆ - Seymour Duncan Pickups

IC - Boats - Intex Recreation Corp.

I.C. - Food products ☆ - Seneca Foods Corp.

IC - Hair care products - Fantasia Industries Corp.

I.C. - Hooks ☆ - Trademark Corp.

IC - Paints - Inorganic Coatings, Inc.

IC - Polyvinyl sheets - Intex Plastics Corp.

I.C. - Soap - Cramer Products Inc.

IC-110 - Epoxy - Club Kit Inc.

IC 531 - Paints - Inorganic Coatings, Inc.

I.C. CHIPS - Chocolate candy - Infotime International, Inc.

IC CRAFTSMAN - Computer software - Cooper & Chyan Technology, Inc.

I.C. GOLDEN LAGER - Beverages–malt - Pittsburgh Brewing Co.

I.C. INTENSIVE CARE - Pet products ☆ - Aquatronics-Filtronics

IC NIKKOR - Photographic equipment - Nikon Inc.

I.C. SPECS PURVEYOR OF FINE EYEWEAR - Eyeglasses - I.C. Spec's, Inc.

I.C. TEA COOLER - Beverages–alcohol - Pittsburgh Brewing Co.

I.C. TIPS - Dental equipment - Jim Samp

I.C.2 - Lighting equipment - Cornerstone/Clearlight

ICA - Spices - Ingredients Corp. of America

ICAPS PLUS - Nutritional supplement - La Haye Laboratories Inc.

ICAR-10 - Insulating materials–foam - Insulation Corp. of America

ICAREX - Fabrics - Daniel Prentice

ICARO - Bathtubs–enameled - Americh Corp.

ICART - Posters - Icart Vendor Graphics Inc.

ICARUS - Computer software - SourceView Software International

ICARUS - Dishes–china - Waterford Wedgewood USA, Inc.

ICARUS - Toys–models ☆ - Estes Industries

ICARUS 2000 - Computer software - Icarus Corp.

ICARUS WORLD ISSUES - Publisher's imprints - Rosen Publishing Group & Pelion Press

ICAS - Machinery - ENDEVCO Corp.

ICAT COMMERCE ONLINE - Computer software - iCat

ICAT SYSTEMS, INC. - Pharmaceutical preparations - ICAT Systems, Inc.

ICC - Glassware–household - Imperial Crystal and China Inc.

I.C.C. - Soap - Imperial Manufacturing Co. Inc.

ICC INTERNATIONAL - Electrical equipment - Industrial Commutator Corp.

ICC TECHNOLOGIES - Ventilation equipment - Icc Technologies, Inc.

ICCI - Machine parts - ICCI

ICCP - Electrical equipment - ICCP, LLC

ICD - Hardware - Innovative Concrete Design Corp.

ICE - Beverages - Talking Rain Beverage Co. Inc.

I.C.E. - Bicycles - XLM Corp.

ICE - Computer terminals - Planar Systems, Inc.

ICE - Denture materials - Implant Innovations, Inc.

ICE - Food products - Southern Retailers Inc.

ICE - Glassware–household ☆ - Lenox Crystal, Inc.

I.C.E. - Hair care products - Joico Laboratories, Inc.

ICE - Packaging–blisterwrap - Curwood, Inc.

ICE - Pharmaceutical preparations - Sepracor Inc.

ICE - Radios - Sun Coast Merchandise Corp.

ICE - Sporting goods - Expedition Trading Co., L.C.

ICE - Stoneware dinnerware - Iron Mountain Stoneware Inc.

ICE 1 - Footwear - Mercury International Trading Corp.

ICE AGE - Water–bottled or canned - Golden Brands Marketing

ICE AGE - Water–bottled or canned - Today Products Inc.

ICE-AID - Health care products - Reliable Plastics

ICE ALERT - Road-condition monitor ☆ - American Thermometer Co.

ICE & EASY - Cookies - Parco Foods, Inc.

ICE AND FIRE - Computer software - Zombie, LLC

ICE ATTACK - Chemical preparations - Frank Miller and Sons Inc.

ICE AWAY - Cleaning preparations–window - Kafko International Ltd.

ICE AWAY - Deicing fluid - Vibe Records Inc.

ICE BASKET - Ice chests–plastic - Coleman Co., Inc.

ICE BAY - Gloves - Swan Enterprises, Inc.

ICE BEAN - Food products - Barricini Foods Inc.

ICE BITER - Tires ☆ - Bridgestone/Firestone, Inc.

ICE BLENDED - Coffee - International Coffee & Tea, Inc.

ICE BLOCK - Building materials - Wam, Inc.

ICE BLUE - Apparel–athletic ☆ - Skea Ltd.

ICE BLUE - Christmas tree ornaments - Cracker Box Inc.

ICE BLUE - Polysheeting - Up North Plastics Inc.

ICE BOKS - Hardware ☆ - Amerock Corp.

ICE BOX - Beverages–alcohol - White Rock Distilleries Inc.

ICE BOX ART - Greeting cards - Constance C. King

ICE BOX SPORTSWEAR - Apparel–athletic - Ice-Box T's, Inc.

ICE BREAKER - Scrapers - Wescon Products Co.

ICE BREAKERS - Chewing gum - Nabisco Brands Co.

ICE BREAKERS - Chewing gum - Nabisco Foods Group

ICE BREAKERS - Chewing gum - Nabisco Holdings Corp.

ICE BREAKERS - Gloves - Grandoe Corp.

ICE CAP - Hair care products - Graham Webb International

ICE CASTLES - Christmas tree ornaments - Cracker Box Inc.

ICE-CEL - Hydrophones - Dunham Bush, Inc.

ICE CLIPPER - Tools–hand-operated - Hopkins Manufacturing Corp.

ICE COLD BEER - Video games ☆ - Taito America Corp.

ICE CORE - Bottles–plastic - AC International

ICE CREAM - Toys - Village Toys

ICE CREAM - Yarn ☆ - Joseph Galler Inc.

ICE CREAM CONE - Kites ☆ - Hi-Flier Manufacturing Co.

ICE CREAM CONE - Skates–roller ☆ - National Sporting Goods Corp.

ICE CREAM CONES - Cereal - General Mills, Inc.

ICE CREAM DIPS - Candy - Philadelphia Chewing Gum Corp.

ICE CREAM DIXIES - Paper cups - James River Corp.

ICE CREAM FAVORITES - Cookies - PF Brands, Inc.

ICE CREAM FLAVORS - Candy - Ph. Wunderle Inc.

ICE CREAM GUM - Candy ☆ - American Chicle Co.

ICE CREAM HEADACHE - Apparel and accessories - Kevin L. Staab

ICE CREAM MAKER - Toys - Tyco Toys

ICE CREAM MAKES YOU PRETTY - Ice cream cones - Henry's Ice Cream, Inc.

ICE CREAM-ON-A-STICK - Confections ☆ - Good Humor Corp.

ICE CREAM PALES - Skin care products - Schering-Plough Healthcare Products

ICE CREAM PARLOR - Ice making machinery - Waring Products Div.

ICE CREAM PARLOR - Lipsticks ☆ - Tinkerbell

ICE CREAM PARLOR II - Ice making machinery - Waring Products Div.

ICE CREAM PARLOR TASTE - Ice cream - Kraft Foods, Inc.

ICE CREAM PLUS - Ice cream - John Edgar Boggan

ICE CREAM SALOON - Confections - Ice Cream Saloon

ICE CREAM SHOPPE - Toys - Mattel, Inc.

ICE CRYSTALS - Aquariums–household - Pets International, Ltd.

ICE CRYSTALS - Bath salts - Helene Curtis Industries Inc.

ICE CUBE - Metal ice storage container - Post-Harvest Technologies, Inc.

ICE CUBE, THE - Paperboard–corrugated - Inland Container Corp.

ICE CUBES - Candy - R.L. Albert & Son, Inc.

ICE-CURE - Chemical preparations - State Chemical Manufacturing Co.
ICE-CUTTER - Crocheted and knitted items ☆ - Puritan Sportswear Corp.
ICE DANCE PRINCESS - Doll - Tonka Corp.
ICE DEVICE - Tools–hand-operated - Blitz USA Inc.
ICE DROPS - Pharmaceutical preparations - Oralabs, Inc.
ICE DROPS - Pharmaceutical preparations - Oralabs, Inc.
ICE-E-POPS - Molding compounds–plastics ☆ - Flambeau Products Corp.
ICE ELVES - Games ☆ - Mayfair Games, Inc.
ICE ERASER - Deicing fluid - Conagra, Inc.
ICE EXPLORER - Fishing tackle - Frabill Inc.
ICE EXPRESS - Fishing tackle ☆ - Frabill Inc.
ICE FIGHTER PLUS - Deicing fluid - Morgro Chemical Co.
ICE FOG - Christmas tree ornaments - Cracker Box Inc.
ICE FORMATIONS - Hair care products - John Amico Expressive Hair Care Products
ICE-FREE - Fishing tackle - Mason Tackle Co.
ICE-FREE CONVEYOR - Chemical preparations - Midwest Industrial Supply, Inc.
ICE-FREE SWITCH - Chemical preparations - Midwest Industrial Supply, Inc.
ICE GALLERY - Trading cards and stamps - Upper Deck Co.
ICE GATOR - Shirts - Walt Disney Co.
ICE GROOVE - Bicycles ☆ - Huffy Corp.
ICE GUARD - Chemical preparations - Ossian, Inc.
ICE HOCKEY IN HARLEM - Apparel and accessories - Ice Hockey in Harlem Inc.
ICE HOUSE - Liquors ☆ - Gaetano Specialties Ltd.
ICE: ICE CONTROL EDGE - Sporting goods - Edbert E.L. Dittmar
ICE IT NICE - Cooking equipment–household ☆ - Nordic Ware
ICE JEWELRY - Jewelry - Shari Lynn Mizrahi
ICE KING - Antifreeze ☆ - Conoco Inc.
ICE KINGS - Trading cards and stamps - Ice Kings, Inc.
ICE LUSTER - Christmas tree ornaments - Union Wadding Co.
ICE MAN - Beverages–malt - Pabst Brewing Co.
ICE MAN - Lunch boxes - Metrokane
ICE-MAN BUCKETS - Ice buckets - Elmar Manufacturing Co.
ICE MASTER - Deicing fluid - North American Salt Co.
ICE-MASTER - Ice cream–powdered - Morris & Associates
ICE MAT - Health care products - Reliable Plastics
ICE MAT - Ice chests–plastic - Igloo Products Corp.
ICE MELTERS THAT WORK - Chemical preparations - Ossian, Inc.
ICE MINT - Pharmaceutical preparations - Westwood-Squibb Pharmaceuticals, Inc.
ICE MIST - Hair care products - Joico Laboratories, Inc.
ICE MOUNTAIN - Water–bottled or canned - Perrier Group of America Inc.
ICE MOUNTAIN - Water–bottled or canned - Poland Spring Bottling Co.
ICE 'N COLD - Ice chests–plastic - Glacier Ware Inc.
ICE-N-EASY - Frosting - J.W. Allen & Co.
ICE-N-EASY - Ice chests - Krieg Boys Ice Corp.
ICE 'N WATER - Refrigerators - Amana Refrigeration Inc.
ICE N'FIL - Food products - Rich Products Corp.
ICE-NO-MOR - Deicing fluid - E.C. Grow Inc.
ICE-O-BOT - Machinery - Laroche Chemicals Inc.
ICE-O-LATER - Deicing fluid - North American Salt Co.
ICE-O-MAT - Kitchen appliances - Rival Manufacturing Co.
ICE-O-MATIC - Kitchen appliances - Rival Manufacturing Co.
ICE-OFF - Cleaning preparations - Kay Chemical Co.
ICE-OFF - Deicing fluid - CRC Chemicals USA/Siloo
ICE OPTIONS - Jewelry - MBM Co., Inc.
ICE-PAD - Health care products - Reliable Plastics
ICE PAIN GEL - Analgesics - Health Products Corp.
ICE-PAK - Computer software - International Consulting and Education,Inc.
ICE PAKS - Pharmaceutical preparations - Paks Drugs Inc.
ICE PALACE - Christmas tree ornaments - Cracker Box Inc.
ICE PALACE - Floor coverings–carpet and rugs ☆ - World Carpets, Inc.
ICE PILOTS PENSACOLA - Apparel and accessories - Pensacola Professional Hockey Club, Inc.
ICE PIRATES - Apparel and accessories - Robert Andrew Wagenhoffer
ICE PLANET 2002 - Toys–blocks - Lego Systems Inc.
ICE POINT - Apparel and accessories - Specialty Sports Ltd.
ICE POP - Beverages - Mackie International, Inc.
ICE PROBE - Coolers–electric - Coolworks, Inc.
ICE QUEEN - Scissors–hand-operated - F.W. Engels Inc.
ICE RANGER - Fishing tackle - Frabill Inc.
ICE-REM - Chemical preparations - Malco Products, Inc.
ICE-REM SUPER - Chemical preparations - Malco Products, Inc.
ICE R.O.M. - Medical apparatus - Dura*Kold Corp.

ICE RUNNER - Footwear - Sure Foot Corp.
ICE SCREAM MACHINE - Toys - Tyco Industries, Inc.
ICE SCULPTURES - Kitchen appliances - Carlisle Foodservice Products, Inc.
ICE SHIELD - Cleaning preparations–window - Kafko International Ltd.
ICE SHUTTLE - Fishing tackle - Frabill Inc.
ICE SLICER - Deicing fluid - Redmond Clay & Salt Co.
ICE STICKS - Candy - Leonhardt Inc.
ICE STUDIO - Computer peripheral equipment - Microtek International Development Systems Division, Inc.
ICE T - Toys–automobiles - Mattel, Inc.
ICE TAPE - Bandages - Medical Sea Pak. Co.
ICE TEA EXPRESS - Iced tea–bottled or canned - Farberware Inc.
ICE TEASERS - Iced tea–bottled or canned - Nestle Beverage Co.
ICE TEMPERED - Scissors–hand-operated - F.W. Engels Inc.
ICE THAW - Ice melter - Pioneer Manufacturing Co.
ICE TICKLE - Confections - California Snack Foods, Inc.
ICE TICKLE - Toys - Mattel, Inc.
ICE-T'S - Scissors–hand-operated - Together Everyone Achieves More Associates, Inc.
ICE TUPS - Housewares - Tupperware Co.
ICE-WEAR - Apparel and accessories - Almax Sportswear Corp.
ICE WRAP BY BODIPAX - Medical apparatus - ZTSB Corp.
ICE3 - Tanks–storage - Post-Harvest Technologies, Inc.
ICEARCTIC - Caviar - Gourmet America
ICEBAK - Containers–insulated - Fastrak Systems, Inc.
ICEBANK - Air conditioning equipment - Calmac Manufacturing Corp.
ICEBERG - Bedding–linen - Dan River Inc.
ICEBERG - Cheese - Swissrose International Inc.
ICEBERG - Christmas tree ornaments - Cracker Box Inc.
ICEBERG - Food products - CPC Best Foods
ICEBERG - Storage units - Storage Technology Corp.
ICEBERG 100'S - Cigarettes - American Tobacco Co.
ICEBERGS - Candy ☆ - Sweet Candy Co.
ICEBERGS - Games ☆ - Tsr, Inc.
ICEBLOCK - Paints - Triangle Coatings Inc.
ICEBOX - Microscopes–electron - Zilog, Inc.
ICEBOX BAKEABLES - Bakery products - Batchbakers LLC
ICEBOX BAKERS - Doughs–frozen - Batchbakers LLC
ICEBOX BUDDIES - Hobby shops - Point Concepts Design, Inc.
ICEBOX, THE - Ice chests–plastic - Igloo Products Corp.
ICEBRAND - Tuna–canned - Associated Sea Fisheries
ICEBREAKER - Batteries - Northern Automotive Corp.
ICEBREAKERS - Toys - Play Visions
ICECO - Electronics equipment - International Cinema Equipment Co.
ICECREAMNOW - Bakery machines ☆ - National Presto Industries, Inc.
ICED ANIMALS - Cookies - Keebler Co.
ICED COPPER - Giftware ☆ - European Imports of California Inc.
ICED COTTON - Underwear and nightwear - Warnaco Inc.
ICED DELIGHT - Teas–herbal - Celestial Seasonings, Inc.
ICED FUDGE RIPPLE - Coffee - Coffee Beanery Ltd.
ICED GOLD - Iced tea–bottled or canned - Tetley Inc.
ICED HOUSE - Crackers - Vista Bakery, Inc.
ICED LILAC - Cosmetics - Lancome
ICED POINSETTIA - Glassware–household ☆ - Fenton Art Glass Co.
ICED SATIN - Underwear and nightwear - Warnaco Inc.
ICED SILK - Yarn - Collins & Aikman Corp.
ICED TEA POT, THE - Iced tea–bottled or canned - Mr. Coffee, Inc.
ICED TEE MUG - Beverages - Leah Palmer-Anderson Design Inc.
ICED T'S - Shirts - Colleen & Co. Inc.
ICEE - Bicycle parts and accessories - Icee of America, Inc.
ICEE - Snack foods - J & J Snack Foods Corp.
ICEE COLDEST DRINK IN TOWN - Bags–duffel - Icee of America, Inc.
ICEE IT'S CHILLIN' - Beverages - Icee of America, Inc.
ICEFIRE - Recording label - Vandor Motion Pictures, Phonorecords & Music Publishing Group
ICEFLOE - Salmon–smoked, salted, dried, or pickled - Tidewater Packing Co.
ICEHOUSE - Beverages–malt - Miller Brewing Co.
ICELAND BREEZE - Astringents - Master Chemical Co.
ICELAND HARVEST - Seafood products–fresh or frozen - Ocean Harvest Corp.
ICELAND SEAS - Seafood products–fresh or frozen ☆ - Pocasset Seafoods Inc.
ICELAND WATERS - Seafood products–canned or cured - King Oscar Inc.
ICELANDIA PURE - Water–bottled or canned - Icelandia Pure, Inc.
ICELANDIC - Seafood products–fresh or frozen - Coldwater Seafood Corp.
ICELANDIC - Seafood products–fresh or frozen - Pocasset Seafoods Inc.

☆ = Now out of production

ICELANDIC - Yarn - Brunswick Yarns
ICELANDICAS - Seafood products–fresh or frozen - Pocasset Seafoods Inc.
ICELINE - Rope - Tubbs Cordage Co.
ICEMAN - Computer hardware - Embedded Performance Inc.
ICEMAN - Computer software - Pixar
ICEMASTER - Electronic equipment - Metalink Corp.
ICEMAX - Chemical preparations - Highside Chemicals Inc.
ICEMINT - Candy - Clasen Quality Coating Inc.
ICEMULE - Ice chests - James E. Collie
ICEOLATER - Refreeze bottles - Diversified Recycling Systems
ICEPLUS - Computer peripheral equipment - Planar Systems, Inc.
ICEPRO - Sporting goods - Icepro, Ltd.
ICER-ETTES - Ice making machinery - Raritan Engineering Co. Inc.
ICESKI - Coolers - S.E. Design
ICEUR - Containers–insulated - Wine Jacket Partners, L.P.
ICEWARE - Containers–insulated - Aladdin Industries, Inc.
ICEWOOL - Yarn ☆ - JCA, Inc.
ICEX - Health care products ☆ - E. Fougera & Co. Inc.
ICEY D - Food products - ICD Group Inc.
ICEY LEMON SPICE - Teas ☆ - Romanoff International Inc.
ICG - Publisher's imprints - Intercultural Group Inc.
ICH CURE - Pet products - Aquatrol, Inc.
ICHI - Games - Michael Alan Gotlieb
ICHIBAN - Hair care products - J.A. Fleuridas Co.
ICHIBAN - Recording label - Ichiban Records, Inc.
ICHIMATSU - Artists' materials - Andrews/Nelson/Whitehead
ICHTHYOL - Pharmaceutical preparations ☆ - Stiefel Laboratories, Inc.
ICHTHYS CROSS - Jewelry - Simplex Diam Inc.
ICI - Toiletries - Coty US Inc.
ICICLE - Glassware–household ☆ - Lenox Crystal, Inc.
ICICLE - Seafood products–fresh or frozen - Icicle Seafoods, Inc.
ICICLE KINGDOM - Giftware ☆ - Fenton Art Glass Co.
ICICLE MINT - Christmas tree ornaments - Cracker Box Inc.
ICICLE SNOW - Paints - Duncan Enterprises
ICICLES - Underwear and nightwear - Jockey International, Inc.
ICIES - Candy ☆ - Leaf, Inc.
ICING - Chemical preparations - Alco Industries, Inc.
ICING - Collectible trading cards - ANCO Collector Supplies, Inc.
ICING - Computer software - International Business Machines Corp.
ICIS - Jewelry - Isis Inc.
ICK CARE - Aquariums–household - Jungle Laboratories Corp.
ICK CLEAR - Aquariums–household - Jungle Laboratories Corp.
ICK-EASE - Chemical preparations - Mydor Industries Inc.
ICK GUARD - Aquariums–household - Jungle Laboratories Corp.
ICK GUARD II - Aquariums–household - Jungle Laboratories Corp.
ICKIS - Toys - Mattel, Inc.
ICKY STICKY - Cosmetics - Top Ten Cosmetics, Inc.
ICLAIRS - Frozen foods - Anthony Feola
ICLE - Publisher's imprints - New Jersey Institute for Continuing Legal Education
ICM - Food product - Interocean Inc.
ICM - Sporting goods - Canstar Sports USA
ICON - Belts, gloves, sunglasses, etc. - Mimex
ICON - Books–comic - DC Comics
ICON - Flatware - Yamazaki Tableware Inc.
ICON - Furniture - ICON International, Inc.
ICON - Golfing equipment - Plop Golf Co.
ICON - Guitars - Roscoe Guitars
ICON - Recording label - Jazz Composer's Orchestra Association Inc.
ICON - Sewing machines–household - Clearwater Precision Instruments Co.
ICON - Veterinary pharmaceutical preparations - IBA Inc.
ICON EXPRESS - Computer software - American Computer Technologies, Inc.
ICON GOLD ACCENT - Flatware - Yamazaki Tableware Inc.
ICON-O-CLASSIC - Guitars - Roscoe Guitars
ICON PERSONAL SEMINARS - Computer software - Icon Associates, Inc.
ICON PRODUCTIONS - Recording label - Icon Productions, Inc.
ICON SYSTEMS INC - Computer software - Icon Systems, Inc.
ICON UNIVERSAL INSERTS - Building materials - Concrete Block Insulating Systems, Inc.
ICON-VERT - Computer software - International Computer Operating Networks, Inc.
ICONAGE - Artists' materials - Beach Co.
ICONDRAW - Computer software - ASB Inc. WinSoft Div.
ICONIC - Furniture ☆ - Altec Lansing Consumer Products
ICONIC QUERY - Computer software - IntelligenceWare Inc.
ICONMOVER - Computer peripheral equipment ☆ - CE Software, Inc.

ICONPEELER - Computer software - Philips Media Inc.
ICONS - Frames–picture - Atlantic Optical Co., Inc.
ICONTERM - Computer peripheral equipment - Na Nutec Corp.
ICONTROL - Computer software - ICONtrol Inc.
ICONZ - Apparel and accessories - Iconz Inc.
ICOS - Pharmaceutical preparations - Icos Corp.
ICOSA-TRIAD - Puzzles - Kadon Enterprises Inc.
ICOSAHEDRON - Balls - Voit Corp.
ICPI - Bandages–surgical - Infection Control Products, Inc.
ICS - Cordage and twine - Incomex, Inc.
ICS - Publisher's imprints - ICS Intangibles Holding Co.
ICS JET CLEAN - Cleaning preparations - Paul E. Leonard
ICS LEARNING SYSTEMS - Computer software - ICS Intangibles Holding Co.
ICT GOLD - Veterinary pharmaceutical preparations - Synbiotics Corp.
ICT GOLD FELV - Pharmaceutical preparations - Synbiotics Corp.
ICT GOLD HW - Veterinary pharmaceutical preparations - Synbiotics Corp.
ICT INTERNATIONAL CARBIDE TOOL - Tools - Rogers Tool Works, Inc.
ICTOSTIX - Chemical preparations ☆ - Miles Inc.
ICTOTEST - Chemical preparations - Miles Inc.
I.C.U. - Apparel–athletic - 20/20 Sport Inc.
I.C.U. - Cosmetics - Salon Sciences Inc.
ICUBE - Puzzles - Derek H. Chan
I.C.U.'S CREATE-A-PLATE - Novelty items - Illuminating Cars Uniquely, Ltd
I.C.U.'S DESIGN-A-PLATE - Novelty items - Illuminating Cars Uniquely, Ltd
I.C.U.'S ILLUM-A-PLATE - Novelty items - Illuminating Cars Uniquely, Ltd
ICW - Custom wheels - Itco Tire Co.
ICW - Golfing equipment - Taylor Made Golf Co. Inc.
ICY - Vodka ☆ - Brown-Forman Corp.
ICY BEVERAGES - Iced tea–bottled or canned - Swiss Natural Foods, Inc.
ICY BLUE - Veterinary pharmaceutical preparations - Straight Arrow Products, Inc.
ICY CAPE - Salmon–smoked, salted, dried, or pickled - Wards Cove Packing Co.
ICY-FROST - Confections ☆ - Good Humor Corp.
ICY-GALS - Toys - Tonka Corp.
ICY HOT - Health care products - Procter & Gamble Co.
ICY HOT CHILL STICK - Analgesics - Chattem Inc.
ICY POINT - Salmon–smoked, salted, dried, or pickled - Ocean Beauty Seafood, Inc.
ICY SPICY COLA - Beverages ☆ - Golden Brands Marketing
ICY VELVET - Cosmetics - Delby System
ICY WATERS - Herring–smoked, salted, dried, or pickled - Lyon Food Products Inc.
ICYBAY - Ice cream - General Container Co. of Michigan, Inc.
ICYBAY - Seafood products–fresh or frozen - Slade Gorton and Co. Inc.
ICYCLE - Food products - Seward Fisheries
ICYCLE - Ice chests - Second Star Ventures, Inc.
ICYMINT - Candy - Oralabs, Inc.
ID + - Electronic equipment - Jenrik Marketing Group Inc.
ID - Giftware and religious articles - Israel Designs
ID - Ink and inkless reagents - Identicator Corp.
ID-II - Photographic equipment - ILFORD Photo Corp.
I.D. 50 - Pharmaceutical preparations ☆ - Solvay Pharmaceuticals Inc.
ID 4000 - Electronics equipment - Polaroid Corp.
ID BOUTIGA - Apparel and accessories - Ray Strauss Unlimited Inc.
ID CARDSCAN - Computer software - Identicator Corp.
ID COLLECTION - Watches - I.D. Enterprises
ID EXPRESS - Computer software - Goddard Technology Corp.
ID INC SOFTWARE - Computer software - ID Software, Inc.
ID LIGHT - Lighting equipment - Lowel-Light Manufacturing Inc.
I.D. LITE - Signs - I.D. Lite, Inc.
ID LOGIC - Broadcast receivers - PRS Corp.
I.D. MARKETING CHILD I.D. KIT - Identification tags - Jon Leon Girod
ID MATCHER - Computer software and hardware - Identicator Corp.
I.D. MATRIX - Computers - International Data Matrix Inc.
I'D RATHER BE - Giftware - Russ Berrie and Co., Inc.
I'D RATHER BE SKINNY DIPPING - Apparel and accessories - Adam Starchild
I'D RATHER LATHER - Shampoos - Mennen Co.
ID TECH - Measuring instruments - ID Tech, Inc.
ID TELEPHONE - Telephones - Sony Electronics Inc.
ID TITANIUM - Watches - I.D. Enterprises
ID4 INDEPENDENCE DAY - Computer peripheral equipment - Twentieth Century Fox Film Corp.
I.D.A. - Beverages–malt - Chatham Imports, Inc.
IDA - Publisher's imprints - International Development Association
IDA-GEM - Milk - Dairigold Inc.

IDA GOLD - Food products - Ore-Ida Foods, Inc.
IDA GRAE - Cosmetics - Ida Grae Cosmetics
IDA TREAT - Food products - Universal Frozen Foods Co.
IDAC - Radio communications equipment - Stanford Telecommunications Inc.
IDAHO - Frames–eyeglass - Rozin Optical Export Corp.
IDAHO COUNTRY - Milk - Idaho Country Milk
IDAHO NATURALLY - Potato flakes - Magic Valley Foods Inc.
IDAHO ORIGINAL RECIPE - Food products ☆ - Universal Frozen Foods Co.
IDAHO PACIFIC - Food products - Idaho Pacific Corp.
IDAHO RUSS - Potato chips - Country Crisp Food
IDAHO SPUD - Candy - Idaho Candy Co.
IDAHO SUPREME - Potato flakes - Idaho Supreme Potatoes Inc.
IDAHO VALLEY - Vegetables–frozen - Ore-Ida Foods, Inc.
IDAHOAN - Potato flakes - Idahoan Foods Inc.
IDAHOAN REAL - Potato flakes - Clement Bros.
IDAHO'S BEST - Food products - Rim View Trout Co.
IDAPI - Computer software - Borland International, Inc.
IDARON - Metals - I.D.A.R., Inc.
IDA'S - Aluminum products - Dale Ray Shaw
I.D.C. - Sunglasses - Michel Loubiere
IDDINGS - Paints - Rosco Laboratories Inc.
IDDON IT FUNNY? - Greeting cards - American Greetings Corp.
IDDY BIDDY - Brooms - O-Cedar/Vining Household Products Co.
IDDY BITS - Figurines ☆ - E.M.I. Inc.
IDE - Jukebox - International Data Engineering, Inc.
IDE/AS - Computer software - Lockheed Martin Corp.
IDE-TAG - Stencils - Ideal Stencil Machine and Tape Co.
IDEA - Giftware - H.C. Meyers Co.
IDEA-A-DAY - Hobby kits - Highlights for Children, Inc.
IDEA CAPSULE - Tape recorders–cassette ☆ - Philips Business Systems Co.
IDEA CHANNEL, THE - Recording label - Idea Channel, Inc.
IDEA INVASION - Computer software - SRA/McGraw-Hill (Div. of The McGraw-Hill Companies)
IDEA MACHINE - Dictating machines ☆ - Philips Business Systems Co.
IDEA MEDIA - Recording label - Evan A. Smith
IDEA NAPKINS - Napkins–paper - Idea Group
IDEA SHAPER - Computer software - Jostens Learning Corp.
IDEABOARD - Wood products - North Douglas Wood Products
IDEACOMM CLIENT - Computer hardware - I.D.E. Corp.
IDEACOMM MAINFRAME CLIENT - Computer hardware - I.D.E. Corp.
IDEACOMM MIDRANGE CLIENT - Computer hardware - I.D.E. Corp.
IDEAHUB - Computer software - I.D.E. Corp.
IDEAL - Artists' materials - American Blueprint Co. Inc.
IDEAL - Awnings–metal - Texas Aluminum Industries Inc.
IDEAL - Baked goods - Interstate Brands Corp.
IDEAL - Bicycles - Columbia Manufacturing Inc.
IDEAL - Clamps - American Granby Inc.
IDEAL - Cleaning preparations–window - W.J. Dennis & Co.
IDEAL - Clothespins - Forster Inc.
IDEAL - Cocoa–powders or mixes - Wilbur Chocolate Co. Inc.
IDEAL - Computer software - Softeasy Software, Inc.
IDEAL - Film - M & R Marking Systems, Inc.
IDEAL - Floor coverings–carpet and rugs ☆ - World Carpets, Inc.
IDEAL - Food containers - Purity Products Inc.
IDEAL - Games - CBS Toys
IDEAL - Gun stocks - Lyman Products Corp.
IDEAL - Hardware - Baker Manufacturing Co.
IDEAL - Health care products - Salter Labs
IDEAL - Lighter fluid - R.M. Hollingshead Corp.
IDEAL - Lighting equipment - Dura Electric Lamp Co. Inc.
IDEAL - Meat products–pork - Ideal Sausage Inc.
IDEAL - Musical instruments - Fender Musical Instruments
IDEAL - Office supplies - Ameriforms Inc.
IDEAL - Office supplies ☆ - Esselte Corp.
IDEAL - Office supplies ☆ - Faber-Castell Corp.
IDEAL - Office supplies ☆ - Mayline/Hamilton
IDEAL - Oils–lubricating - Lyondell Petrochemical Co.
IDEAL - Paint rollers - Great American Marketing, Inc.
IDEAL - Paper clips - Noesting Inc.
IDEAL - Paper–bond - United Stationers Inc.
IDEAL - Pencils - Ideal Metal Products Co. Inc.
IDEAL - Pet food - Doane Products Co.
IDEAL - Pet food - Inorex Inc.
IDEAL - Photo albums - J.L. Hanson Co.
IDEAL - Recording label - Record-Rama Sound Archives
IDEAL - Rice ☆ - La Cena Fine Foods Inc.

IDEAL - Salmon–smoked, salted, dried, or pickled - Northern Products Corp.
IDEAL - Snack foods - Nabisco Foods Group
IDEAL - Stencils - Ideal Stencil Machine and Tape Co.
IDEAL - Tools–soldering - Esico Triton
IDEAL - Trailers–travel - Alfa Leisure, Inc.
IDEAL - Windows–plastic ☆ - Certainteed Corp. (Roofing Products Group)
IDEAL 18 - Boats–skiffs - Shumway Yacht Sales
IDEAL CAMBRAY - Fabrics–cotton - Dan River Inc.
IDEAL CHOICE - Dinnerware–plastic - Nyman Manufacturing Co.
IDEAL DOOR - Doors–garage - Clopay Building Products Co., Inc.
IDEAL ENVIRONMENTAL - Lockers–metal - Containment Consultants Inc.
IDEAL-EYES - Mascara-remover pads - American Hygienic Laboratories Inc.
IDEAL FINISH - Varnishes - Master Products Inc.
IDEAL FINISH - Wood stains - Vogel Paint and Wax Co., Inc.
IDEAL FLOR - Flowers–artificial - C & C Florists Supplies Inc.
IDEAL GROW & GO - Pet food - Inorex Inc.
IDEAL HEALTH AIDS - Veterinary pharmaceutical preparations - Immunomed Corp.
IDEAL INSTRUMENTS - Veterinary medical equipment - Immunomed Corp.
IDEAL MARK - Markers–felt-tip - Ideal Stencil Machine and Tape Co.
IDEAL ORIGINALS - Figurines - Ideal Originals
IDEAL PEDESTAL PLASTIC - Pedestals–plastic - Snap & Sell Corp.
IDEAL QUALITYBILT - Windows–storm - Ideal Co.
IDEAL SOLUTION, THE - Cash registers - Lipman USA, Inc.
IDEAL-STANDARD - Plumbing fixtures - American Standard Inc.
IDEAL STENCIL - Pens - Ideal Stencil Machine and Tape Co.
IDEAL SUPER SLIM - Pet food - Inorex Inc.
IDEAL TEAM - Video production - Alternative Visions, Inc.
IDEAL WALL DECOR - Figurines ☆ - Ideal Originals
IDEALINE - Lighters ☆ - Latama Inc.
IDEALITE - Photographic equipment - Richard Manufacturing Co.
IDEALITES - Bags–plastic - Comic Conservation Co.
IDEALOGIC/3 - Office supplies - Ideal Stencil Machine and Tape Co.
IDEALS - Cigar boxes–wood - Consolidated Cigar Corp.
IDEALS - Publisher's imprints - Ideals Publishing Co.
IDEAS - Writing product - Island Pen Manufacturing Corp.
IDEAS FOR THE WAY YOU LIVE - Banks–commercial - Barnett Banks, Inc.
IDEAS INSPIRED BY PARENTS - Deodorizers - The First Years Inc.
IDEAS ON HOLD - Recording label - Sandra Levy
IDEAWORKS - Flowers, plants, and seeds - John Henry Co.
IDEAWORKS INC. - Vacuum cleaners and accessories - Ideaworks, Inc.
I.DEEZ BY PETER BRAMS - Jewelry - Peter Brams Designs, Ltd.
IDEF TOOLS - Computer software - Wizdom Systems, Inc.
IDEFINE-0 - Computer software - Wizdom Systems, Inc.
IDEFINE-1X - Computer software - Wizdom Systems, Inc.
IDEK - Mechanical pencils - San Antonio Association for the Blind
IDENAL - Prescription drug - IDE-Interstate Inc.
IDENT-A-CHECK - Checkbooks - Jason D. Wallis
IDENT-A-GUEST - Key rings - Luey Laughlin
IDENT-A-PATCH - Gloves ☆ - Fairfield Line, Inc.
IDENT-A-VET OF AMERICA, INC. - Decals and transfers - Ident-A-Vet of America, Inc.
IDENT-I-LITE - Signs - Weber Enterprises Inc.
IDENT-O-FILM - Electronics equipment - RTI Research Technology International
IDENT-O-SPINE - File folders - Angler's Roslyn Group Ltd.
IDENT TAG - Tracking device - I. Elliott Wallace
IDENTA-SEALS - Labels–gummed - John Henry Co.
IDENTI-CASE - Luggage - United States Luggage Corp.
IDENTI-CHECK - Diagnostic substances ☆ - Warner-Lambert Co.
IDENTI-DOSE - Pharmaceutical preparations - Eli Lilly and Co.
IDENTI-KIT - Computer software - Smith & Wesson Corp.
IDENTI-KIT III - Computer software - Smith & Wesson Corp.
IDENTI-PEN - Pens - Sakura of America
IDENTI-VIEW - Solar optical filters - JMB, Inc.
IDENTI-VUE - Envelopes - Tension Envelope Corp.
IDENTICOLLAR - Pet collars - Mona R. Massaro
IDENTICULT - Diagnostic apparatus - Prepared Media Laboratories, Inc.
IDENTIFIER - Computer software - Ultrapointe Corp.
IDENTIFIER - Leather goods - AR Accessories Group Inc.
IDENTIFIER - Medical apparatus - Arizona E.M.S. Products, Inc.
IDENTIFILE - Cartons–paperboard - Ames Safety Envelope Co.
IDENTIFIOR - Medical apparatus - USMS, Inc.
IDENTIFY YOURSELF - Jewelry - Drozd & Drozd Enterprises Inc.
IDENTIPLATE - Machinery - Telesis Technologies, Inc.
IDENTIPLATES - Signs - Scott Sign Systems, Inc.

☆ = Now out of production

IDENTISCAN - Electronic equipment - Accu-Time Systems, Inc.
IDENTISNAPS - Fasteners–snap - Mona R. Massaro
IDENTITAGS - Identification tags - Image Group Inc.
IDENTITY - Computers - Integrated Resource Group Inc.
IDENTITY - Display cases–plastic - Hamilton Fixture Co.
IDENTITY - Jackets - Swingster Co.
IDENTITY - Paper–rolls - Georgia-Pacific Corp.
IDENTITY APPAREL - Shirts - Omni Services, Inc.
IDENTITY APPAREL - Uniforms–tailored - Barco of California
IDENTIVOICE-2000 - Electronics equipment - Electronic Warfare Associates, Inc.
IDENTO DESIGN - Bags–paper - Bagcraft Corp. of America
IDF - Iridescent diffraction foil - Diffraction Co.
I.D.F.M. - Apparel and accessories ☆ - Fox-Knapp Inc.
I.D.G. - Apparel–women's - H.L. Miller and Son, Inc.
IDGAME - Computer software ☆ - CONDUIT
IDG'S INTROGRAPHIC SERIES - Publisher's imprints - International Data Group, Inc.
IDI - Dryers–hair - Helene Curtis Industries Inc.
IDI - Jewelry - International Diamond Importers Inc.
IDI - Scuba diving equipment - Kaiser Continental Rubber and Sales Inc.
IDI PERSHIELD - Medical apparatus - Pershield, Inc.
IDIBIB - Recording label - Jazz Composer's Orchestra Association Inc.
IDIO SYNCRATIC - Recording label - Jazz Composer's Orchestra Association Inc.
IDIOM - Computer peripheral equipment - Chadwyck-Healey, Inc.
IDIS - Computer software - PC-Plus Communications Lp
IDITAROD - Ice cream - Iditarod Trail Committee, Inc.
IDITAROD/YUKON - Pet products - Rae's Harness Shop
IDL - Clocks - IDL Manufacturing & Sales Corp.
IDL-655 - Electronic equipment - Peavey Electronics Corp.
IDL-TRODAT - Office supplies - IDL Manufacturing & Sales Corp.
I.D.L.A. - Watches - I.D. Enterprises
IDLE-TIME - Trailers–travel - Allen Camper Manufacturing Co. Inc.
IDLE WILD FARM - Food products - Idle Wild Farm
IDLERS - Recording label - Warlock Records
IDLERS BY FLORSHEIM - Men's shoes - Interco Inc.
IDLEWILD - Apparel and accessories - Summit Resources, Inc.
IDLEWILD - Floor coverings–carpet and rugs ☆ - World Carpets, Inc.
IDLEWOOD - Furniture ☆ - Hedstrom Corp.
IDM - Hardware - Inductametals Corp.
IDN - Vitamins and nutritional supplements - Nu Skin International, Inc.
IDNX - Electronic equipment - Network Equipment Technologies Inc.
IDO PARCORT - Pharmaceutical preparations - Parmed Pharmaceuticals, Inc.
IDOL - Candy ☆ - Mars, Inc.
IDOL EYES - Cosmetics - Pavion Ltd.
IDOL EYES - Cosmetics ☆ - Jason Natural Products, Inc.
IDOL MAKER - Ophthalmic goods - Foremost Optical Products
I.D.OLOGY - Alarm systems - Orion Systems, Inc.
IDOLS - Trading cards and stamps - Score Group, Inc.
IDP - Automotive parts and accessories - Ingersoll-Dresser Pump Co.
ID'R PLUS - Electronic equipment - Tempo Research Corp.
IDROX - Hair care products - Framesi USA/Roffler Industries Inc.
IDS - Office supplies - Mod-Systems Inc.
IDT - Apparel and accessories - I.D.T. Worldwide Inc.
IDT - Blackboards - Greensteel Inc.
I.D.T. - Pharmaceutical preparations ☆ - Hyrex Pharmaceuticals
IDWARE - Computer hardware - Polaroid Corp.
IDYLLE - Wallpaper ☆ - Marburg Wallcoverings Inc.
IDYLLWILD - Furniture ☆ - Landes Manufacturing Co.
IE - Computer hardware - IE Associates, Inc.
IE - Jewelry - International Emco Gem Inc.
IE: EXPERT - Computer software - Information Engineering Systems Corp.
I.E. FARS - Computer software - Computer Data Systems, Inc.
I.E. NIKE - Footwear–athletic ☆ - Nike, Inc.
IEC: INTELLIGENT ENERGY CORPORATION - Controls–air conditioning systems - Intelligent Energy Corp.
IED - Computer peripheral equipment - Innovative Electronic Designs, Inc.
IED - Sound equipment - Innovative Electronic Designs, Inc.
IEEE SYMBOL LIBRARIES - Computer software ☆ - IMSI
IEG 14K - Jewelry - IEG Sales Co. Inc.
I.E.I. - Apparel–women's - I.E. Industries Fashions, Inc.
IEM - Computer peripheral equipment - International Electronic Machinery, Inc.
I.E.M. FURNITURE - Furniture - Good Value Furniture Corp.
IEPRO - Computer software - Bruce Alter
IEPS - Electrical equipment - iEPS Electronic Inc.

IES - Measuring instruments - Instrumentation and Engineering Services, Inc.
IES - Medical equipment and instruments - Arthrotek, Inc.
IF - Apparel and accessories - If Fashion, Inc.
IF - Caulking compounds - Insta-Foam Products, Inc.
IF. - Computer software - Leep Technology, Inc.
IF - Shoes - Interco Inc.
IF-4000 - Health care products - Wholesale Medical Import
I.F. & S. - Thread - Cincinnati Thread Co.
IF GAME, THE - Games - RJE Games Inc.
IF I ONLY HAVE NINE LIVES, LET ME SPEND THEM ALL WITH YOU - Figurines - Marjorie Sarnat & Associates, Inc.
IF IT'S NOT JURASSIC PARK, IT'S EXTINCT! - T-shirts–children's - Amblin' Entertainment, Inc.
IF/SO - Computer software - Forerunner Systems, Inc.
IF YOU CARE - Paper - A.V. Olsson Trading Co., Inc.
IF YOU CARE - Paper products - Jaret Specialties Inc.
IF YOU DARE - Lipsticks ☆ - A.R. Winarick Inc.
IFC - Snack foods - Indian Foods Co.
IFC-FLOWERS THAT DAZZLE - Flowers, plants, and seeds - International Floral Corp.
IFCO - Furniture - International Fixture & Furniture Corp.
IFF FIRE-ROAST FLAVOR - Spices and extracts - International Flavors & Fragrances Inc.
IFFUSIONS - Skin care products - International Flavors & Fragrances Inc.
IFI - Prerecorded videotapes - Industrial Fasteners Institute
IFI STANDARD - Printed materials ☆ - Industrial Fasteners Institute
IFL LIBRARY OF CRIME CLASSICS - Publisher's imprints - International Polygonics Ltd.
IFO CASCADE - Toilets–enameled - Ecos/Water Conservation System Inc.
IFORCE.DLL - Computer software - Immersion Human Interface Corp.
IFP - Oils–edible - International Food Products Corp.
IFS - Computer software ☆ - CONDUIT
IFS - Fruits and vegetables ☆ - Idaho Fruit Sales Inc.
IFT FOOD EXPO - Advertising agencies - Institute of Food Technologists
IG - Apparel and accessories - Iron Generation, LLC
IG-LO - Antifreeze - Ashland Oil, Inc.
IG-PRIME - Chemical preparations - Novagen, Inc.
IG SUITE - Computer peripheral equipment - Oxford Molecular Group
IGA - Food products - IGA Inc.
IGA - Shotguns - Stoeger Industries
I.G.A. - Wallpaper - I. Gottlieb & Associates
I.G.A. TEXTILES VOL. 2 - Wallpaper ☆ - I. Gottlieb & Associates
IGAS - Adhesives and sealants ☆ - Sika Corp.
IGC - Product description unknown - Somfy Systems Inc.
IGCA - Toys–electronic - Innovative Gaming Corp. of America
IGEM - Controllers, sensors and actuators - Woodward Governor Co.
IGES/LIB - Computer software ☆ - International TechneGroup Inc.
IGES/WORKS - Computer software - International TechneGroup Inc.
IGF - Olives–canned - M.I. Industries, Inc.
IGGIES - Ice chests–plastic - Igloo Products Corp.
IGGY'S - Bakery products - Iggy's Bread Ltd.
IGI - Chemical preparations - International Group
IGI MENS - Men's apparel - India Garments Inc.
IGLOO - First aid kits ☆ - Apothecary Products, Inc.
IGLOO - Ice chests–plastic - Igloo Products Corp.
IGLOO ICE - Ice chests–plastic - Igloo Products Corp.
IGLOO ROOF AND WALL SYSTEMS - Prefabricated buildings–metal ☆ - Pavilion/Sunburst Furniture
IGLOOBED - Beds–wood - Markko International, Inc.
IGLOOS - Crocheted and knitted items - Schuessler Knitting Mills Inc.
IGM - Marble tile, granite, travertine, and slate - International Granite & Marble Corp.
IGN - Dental equipment - Ariel West Inc.
IGNITER - Guitars - Heritage Industries
IGOFLEUR - Hair care products - Schwarzkopf Inc.
IGOR THE INVISIBLE - Vodka - Joseph E. Seagram & Sons, Inc.
IGORA - Hair care products - Schwarzkopf Inc.
IGORA VARIO BLONDE - Hair care products - Schwarzkopf Inc.
IGOR'S - Food products - Continental Delight/Ore-Ida
IGOR'S PIROSHKI - Preserved foods–prepackaged - Ore-Ida Foods, Inc.
IGOR'S POCKET - Frozen foods - Ore-Ida Foods, Inc.
IGP - Computer software and hardware - Printronix, Inc.
IGP/AUTO LABEL MAPPING - Computer software - Printronix, Inc.
IGR PLUS - Pet products - Zoecon Corp.
IGRIP - Computer software - Deneb Robotics, Inc.
IGS - Golfing equipment - Pro Kennex, Inc.

☆ = Now out of production

IGS-II - Vitamins and nutritional supplements - Lifetrends International
IGS-II - Vitamins and nutritional supplements - Lifetrends International
IGT - Integrated circuits - Integrated Telecom Technology Inc.
IGUAN ARIUM - Pet products - Zoo Med Laboratories, Inc.
IGUANA - Iced tea - Iguana Bay
IGUANA DON - Jewelry ☆ - Snake Creek Manufacturing Co., Inc.
IGUANA DONNA - Apparel–children's - Snake Creek Manufacturing Co., Inc.
IGUANA ENTERTAINMENT - Computer software - Iguana Entertainment, Inc.
IGUANA MAN - Fireworks - American Promotional Events, Inc.
IGUANA PUNCHO - Pet products - Zoo Med Laboratories, Inc.
IH - See INTERNATIONAL
IHI - Wigs - International Hairgoods Inc.
IHK - Sporting equipment - IHK International Corp.
IHS - Jewelry - College of the Holy Cross
IHS - Recording label - LVW Entertainment
IHS EXCHANGES - Computer software - International Health Services, Inc.
II - Apparel and accessories - Indians, Inc.
II BOSCO - Wines - Francis A. Bonanno, Inc.
II GIANGIO - Wines - Francis A. Bonanno, Inc.
II INTEGRATED INFORMATION TECHNOLOGY-INC. - Computer software - Integrated Information Technology Inc.
III FINGERS SOFTWARE - Computer software - William McDonald
III INTERACTIVE INNOVATIONS, INC. - Targets - Interactive Innovations, Inc.
IIS INTELLECT - Computer software - Integrated Information Services, Inc.
IITAS - Game machines - Video Lottery Technologies, Inc.
IIYAMA VISIONMASTER - Monitors–electronic - iiyama North America, Inc.
IJ - Fabrics - Dan River Inc.
IJ70-17A - Firearms, accessories, and parts - B-West Imports, Inc.
IJAM - Computer software - Medior Inc.
IJM - Jewelry - International Jewelry Marketing, Inc.
IK - Jewelry - I. Kurgan and Co. Inc.
IK IPOCORK - Floor coverings–tile - Ipocork Ltd.
IKARI - Barbecues and grills ☆ - Precise International/Wenger
IKAROS - Signal flares - Datrex Inc.
IKAT - Apparel–athletic - Ikat Sportwear
IKAT - Floor coverings–carpet and rugs ☆ - Regal Rugs Inc.
IKAT - Wallpaper ☆ - Blumenthal
IKFO - File folders - Angler's Roslyn Group Ltd.
I.K.L. - Sweaters - IKL International, Inc.
IKO - Medical apparatus - Indiana Brace Co., Inc.
IKON - Chemical preparations - Jonathan Shelley Nimitz
IKON - Hair care products - Major International Inc.
IKORA - Giftware ☆ - W.M.F. of America Inc.
IKS - Apparel–athletic - Moriarty Hat and Sweater Co.
IKS STIKS - Sporting goods ☆ - Moriarty Hat and Sweater Co.
IL BISONTE - Paper–kraft - E. Bolan Inc.
IL CAMPIONE - Cheese - Arpin Dairy Inc.
IL CASTELLO - Cookies - Bell'amore Imports Inc.
IL CHEF - Pizzas–mixes ☆ - Supreme Foods Inc.
IL CLASSICO - Coffee - S & W Fine Foods, Inc.
IL CLASSICO DI CALIFORNIA - Wines - California Olive Oil Corp.
IL DUOMO DI MILANO - Food products - Crystal Food Import Corp.
IL FARO - Cheese - Arthur Schuman Inc.
IL FLORENTINO - Wines - Joseph E. Seagram & Sons, Inc.
IL FORNAIO - Olive oil - Il Fornaio America Corp.
IL GIARDINO - Cheese - Swissrose International Inc.
IL GREPPONE MAZZI - Beverages–alcohol - Kobrand Corp.
IL HWA - Food products - Il HWA American Corp.
IL-MAKIAGE - Cosmetics - IL-Makiage
IL MEE - Food products - California Pacific Rice Milling, Ltd.
IL MIGLIOR - Food products - Tri Valley Growers, Inc.
IL NUMERO UNO - Food products - De Choix Specialty Foods Co.
IL NUMERO UNO - Meat product - Galaxy Trading Co.
IL PALIO - Wines - Martin and Macfarlane, Inc.
IL PASTELLO - Wallcoverings - Cork Products Co. Inc.
IL POGGIOLO - Beverages–alcohol - Trebon Wine & Spirit Corp.
IL PRIMO - Coffee makers–electric - Robert Krups North America
IL RE - Food products ☆ - Flagship Foods Inc.
IL TASSO - Beverages–alcohol - Vias Imports Ltd.
IL TOSCANO - Sauces - 10 Toscano, Inc.
ILA - Projectors–photographic - Hughes-JVC Technology Corp.
ILANA - Bedding–linen - Dan River Inc.
ILANA - Underwear and nightwear - Youthcraft-Charmfit
ILAND EXPRESS - Fishing lures - Tournament Tackle, Inc.
ILAND PRO - Fishing lures - Tournament Tackle, Inc.
ILAND SAILURE - Fishing lures - Tournament Tackle, Inc.

ILANDER - Fishing lures - Tournament Tackle, Inc.
ILANIT-OLAMTOV - Satin-finish glassware - Israeli Accents
ILANTEC - Computers - Palo Alto Design Group Inc.
ILASHCOMB - Combs - S.R. Droescher Inc.
ILASTRONE - Pharmaceutical preparations ☆ - Coast Laboratories Inc.
ILC 90 - Chemicals–photographic - Brandess Kalt Aetna
ILCHESTER - Cheese - Swissrose International Inc.
ILCO - Locks–padlocks - ILCO Unican Corp.
ILE DE FRANCE - Cheese - Schratter Import
ILE DE FRANCE - Cookies - Liberty Richter Inc.
ILE DE FRANCE COUSCOUS - Starch–edible - Europa Foods Ltd.
ILEX - Photographic equipment ☆ - Ilex Optical Co. Inc.
ILEXTIGMAT - Photographic equipment ☆ - Ilex Optical Co. Inc.
ILFOBROM - Paper–photographic - ILFORD Photo Corp.
ILFOBROM GALERIE FB - Paper–photographic - ILFORD Photo Corp.
ILFOCHROME CLASSIC - Paper–photographic - ILFORD Photo Corp.
ILFOCOLOR DELUXE RA IK - Paper–photographic - ILFORD Photo Corp.
ILFORD - Photographic equipment - ILFORD Photo Corp.
ILFOSPEED 2000 - Chemical preparations - ILFORD Photo Corp.
ILFOSPEED RC - Paper–photographic - ILFORD Photo Corp.
ILFOTEC - Chemical preparations - ILFORD Photo Corp.
ILIAS LA LAOUNIS - Jewelry - Ilias La Laounis
ILIASKA SPECIAL - Fishing lures - Thomas and Thomas Rodmakers Inc.
ILISE STEVENS - Apparel–women's - Kellwood Co.
ILIXCO - Fabrics–muslin - Ilixco, Inc.
I'LL BITE - See NATURE'S OWN
I'LL DRINK TO THAT - Giftware - Russ Berrie and Co., Inc.
ILLEGAL LENGTHS - Cosmetics - Maybelline Co.
ILLEGAL WHEELS - Toy vehicles - Tonka Corp.
ILLEGALE - Perfumes - Houbigant, Inc.
ILLES - Spices and extracts - The Illes Co.
ILLINI BOOKS - Publisher's imprints - University of Illinois Press
ILLINOIS - Hair care products - Fromm Industries
ILLINOIS - Locks–door - Illinois Lock Co.
ILLINOIS - Watches ☆ - SMH (US) Inc.
ILLINOIS CALIFORNIA EXPRESS - Toys - Toy Truck Lines, Inc.
ILLINOIS CEMENT CO. - Cement - Centex Corp.
ILLINOIS FRUIT & PRODUCE - Food products - Bernardi Italian Foods Co.
ILLINOIS PRAIRIE - Soups–canned - Frontier Soups
ILLINOIS PROUD! - Beverages–carbonated - Hondo Inc.
ILLOGICAL ZOO SOCIETY - Jewelry - C.A. Daniels & Co.
ILLUM-N-ART - Lighting equipment ☆ - Creative Concepts
ILLUMA - Electronics equipment - Bencher Inc.
ILLUMASEAL - Meters–electric - Datcon Instrument Co.
ILLUME-SET - Jewelry - Pe Jay Creations Ltd.
ILLUMI-BOARD - Clipboards - G. B. Invedyne Inc.
ILLUMIN8 - Video production - Illumin8, Inc.
ILLUMINATE - Cleaning preparations - Malter International Corp.
ILLUMINATE - Computer software - Lamb & Co., Inc.
ILLUMINATI - Games - Steve Jackson Games Inc.
ILLUMINATI - Recording label - Driftwood Records
ILLUMINATION INNOVATION - Lighting fixtures - Angelo Brothers Co.
ILLUMINATIONS - Floor coverings–carpet and rugs ☆ - Karastan-Bigelow Inc.
ILLUMINATIONS - Frames–picture - Greenbrier Collection
ILLUMINATIONS - Prefabricated buildings–metal - Millenium Design Corp.
ILLUMINATOR - Floor finishing machines–commercial - Pioneer/Eclipse Corp.
ILLUMINATOR - Photography equipment - F.J. Westcott Co.
ILLUMINEE - Jewelry cleaner - Intromark Inc.
ILLUMINEE DU MONDE - Candles - Illuminee Du Monde, Ltd.
ILLUMINEE DU MONDE, LTD - Candles - Illuminee Du Monde, Ltd.
ILLUMINESCENCE - Floor coverings–carpet and rugs ☆ - Cabin Crafts Carpets
ILLUMITEX - Coatings - Coronado Paint Co.
ILLUMITEX - Vinyl ☆ - United Textile & Supply Co.
ILLUMITRAN - Photographic equipment ☆ - Bogen Photo Corp.
ILLUSION - Amplifiers - International Jensen Inc.
ILLUSION - Blankets–electric ☆ - Sunbeam-Oster Household Products
ILLUSION - Cosmetics - Elizabeth Arden Inc.
ILLUSION - Curtains–shower ☆ - Kleinert's Inc.
ILLUSION - Dishes–china - Pickard Inc.
ILLUSION - Drapery hardware - Kirsch Co.
ILLUSION - Floor coverings ☆ - Toli International
ILLUSION - Floor coverings–carpet and rugs ☆ - Regal Rugs Inc.
ILLUSION - Floor finish - Intex Chemical Inc.
ILLUSION - Furniture - Hammary Furniture Co. Inc.
ILLUSION - Glassware–household - Federal Glass

☆ = Now out of production

ILLUSION - Novelty items - Western Enterprises
ILLUSION - Rings–jewelry - Artcarved Inc.
ILLUSION - Telescopes - WildeWood Creative Products Inc.
ILLUSION - Underwear and nightwear ✰ - Youthform Co.
ILLUSION - Vases ✰ - Lenox Crystal, Inc.
ILLUSION - Wood products - Weyerhaeuser Co.
ILLUSION COMFORT-SEAL - Mattresses - Schottenstein Stores Corp.
ILLUSION OF BEAUTIFUL - Perfumes - L'Illusion Fragrance
ILLUSION OF CHANEL NO. 5 - Perfumes - L'Illusion Fragrance
ILLUSION OF ETERNITY - Perfumes - L'Illusion Fragrance
ILLUSION OF GIORGIO - Perfumes - L'Illusion Fragrance
ILLUSION OF LIZ CLAIBORNE - Perfumes - L'Illusion Fragrance
ILLUSION OF OBSESSION - Perfumes - L'Illusion Fragrance
ILLUSION OF OPIUM - Perfumes - L'Illusion Fragrance
ILLUSION OF OSCAR DE LA RENTA - Perfumes - L'Illusion Fragrance
ILLUSION OF PASSION - Perfumes - L'Illusion Fragrance
ILLUSION OF POISON - Perfumes - L'Illusion Fragrance
ILLUSION OF RED - Perfumes - L'Illusion Fragrance
ILLUSION OF SHALIMAR - Perfumes - L'Illusion Fragrance
ILLUSION OF WHITE LINEN - Perfumes - L'Illusion Fragrance
ILLUSION OF WHITE SHOULDERS - Perfumes - L'Illusion Fragrance
ILLUSIONAIRE - Jewelry ✰ - Jewelry Corp. of America, Inc.
ILLUSIONE - Containers - John Henry Co.
ILLUSIONS - Air purification systems - Medo Industries, Inc.
ILLUSIONS - Bearings–motor vehicle - Focus 21 International Inc.
ILLUSIONS - Bicycles - Murray, Inc.
ILLUSIONS - Blinds–vertical - Tontine/VyTech Industries Inc.
ILLUSIONS - Cabinets - Zenith Products Corp.
ILLUSIONS - Christmas tree ornaments - Cracker Box Inc.
ILLUSIONS - Faucets ✰ - Chicago Faucet Co.
ILLUSIONS - Floor coverings–carpet and rugs - Criterion Mills Inc.
ILLUSIONS - Floor coverings–carpet and rugs ✰ - Fieldturf & Carpet Inc.
ILLUSIONS - Lighting fixtures - Waban Inc.
ILLUSIONS - Pens - Bic Corp.
ILLUSIONS - Wallcovering - Capital Carousel Inc.
ILLUSIONS - Wallpaper - Academy Handprints Ltd.
ILLUSIONS - Wallpaper - Carlton-Metro Wallcoverings
ILLUSIONS - Wallpaper - Robert Crowder & Co.
ILLUSIONS - Wallpaper - Rigo Wallcoverings Inc.
ILLUSIONS - Wastebaskets ✰ - Witt Co.
ILLUSIONS BY CATALINA - Bathing suits - CCC Acquisition Corp.
ILLUSIONS COLLECTION, THE - Plumbing fixtures - Chicago Faucet Co.
ILLUSIONS EAST - Furniture ✰ - Lane Co. Inc.
ILLUSIONS I - Furniture - Weiman Co.
ILLUSIONS II - Furniture - Weiman Co.
ILLUSTRA - Computer software - Montage Software, Inc.
ILLUSTRATED BARTSCH, THE - Publisher's imprints - Abaris Books Inc.
ILLUSTRATED INTERACTIVE - Computer software - ITP Licensing Corp.
ILLUSTRATIONS - Floor coverings–carpet and rugs - Mohawk Carpet Corp.
ILLUSTRATIONS REMEMBERED - Posters - Illustrations Remembered, Inc.
ILLUSTRATOR - Lighting fixtures ✰ - Hubbell Lighting, Inc. (Lighting Div.)
ILLUSTRATOR - Pens - Illustrator Pen Products Inc.
ILLUSTRATOR - Projectors–photographic - Radmar Inc.
ILLUSTRAVOX - Electronic equipment - Telex Communications, Inc.
ILLUSTRIOUS - Cleaning preparations - Puritan-Churchill Chemical Co.
ILLY - Coffee - Lund Distribution, Inc.
ILMA - Bedding–linen - Dan River Inc.
ILMARI - Jewelry - John Kresten Jespersen
ILONA - Cosmetics - Ilona, Inc.
ILOSONE - Pharmaceutical preparations - Dista Products Co.
ILOTYCIN - Pharmaceutical preparations - Dista Products Co.
ILOTYCIN GLUCEPTATE - Antibiotics - Eli Lilly and Co.
ILR - Computer software - Intersolv, Inc.
I.L.S. - Computer software - Interactive Lighting Showrooms, Inc.
ILS - Motor vehicle parts and accessories - Mobile-Tech, Corp.
ILSA - Ceramic tile - Integrity Tile Co.
ILSA - Tiles–ceramic - Federal Tile Imports Inc.
ILSON - Bathroom accessories - I. Levy Sons Inc.
ILTS - Computer peripheral equipment - International Lottery & Totalizator Systems, Inc.
I.L.X. - Pharmaceutical preparations - Kenwood Laboratories Inc.
ILX CONSTRUCTION TRAINING - Computer software - Xactware Information Services, Inc.
ILX XACTIMATE CONCEPTS - Computer software - Xactware Information Services, Inc.
IM - Electronic equipment - Intellimedia Corp.

IM - Hardware - International Marine Holdings, Inc.
I'M... - Identification tags - Ashner Specialties, Inc.
I'M . . . - Labels–paper - Ashner Specialties, Inc.
IM - Vitamins and nutritional supplements - Eleva, Inc.
IM 18 - Apparel–women's - Nuvogue Creations
IM-2000 - Electronic equipment - Food Automation - Service Techniques, Inc.
I'M A ——— BABY - Apparel and accessories - Russell Mende
I'M A BEDBUG - Novelty items - Russ Berrie and Co., Inc.
I'M A BIG KID NOW - Apparel and accessories - Kimberly-Clark Corp.
I'M A CHEERLEADER - Pompon - James Industries, Inc.
I'M A LITTLE TEA POT - Tea kettles–nonelectric ✰ - General Housewares Corp.
I'M A LOVE BUG - Toys–stuffed - Russ Berrie and Co., Inc.
I'M A NOGGIN - Apparel–athletic - I'm a Noggin Sportswear, Inc.
I'M A PART OF THE HEALING - Bracelets - Vietnam Veterans Aid Foundation
I'M A PRECIOUS CREATION - Children's clothing - Michelle Jensen & Co.
I'M A PRINCESS - Apparel and accessories - Jacques Moret, Inc.
I'M A RECYCLER - Recycling containers, posters, buttons, etc. - Diversified Recycling Systems
I'M AN ECO MANIAC - Publisher's imprints - Howard F. Wathen
I.M. BIGG - Diapers–disposable - Kimberly-Clark Corp.
I.M. GOLFER - Apparel and accessories - Pivot Rules, Inc.
IM INTENSE MOMENTS - Apparel and accessories - Guillermo Goni
I'M MOVING! JUNIOR CHANGE OF ADDRESS KIT - Greeting cards - Three Wishes, Inc.
IM NUTRIENTS - Vitamins and nutritional supplements - J.R. Carlson Laboratories Inc.
I'M ONLINE @ - Stationery - Social Etceteras
I.M. ORGANIZED - Cabinets - Clairson International Corp.
I'M REVERSIBLE - Totes - Coordinated Products Corp.
I'M SCARED CLOTHING FOR THE SPINELESS - Apparel and accessories - James Mark Young
I'M THE BOSS - Calendars ✰ - American Greetings Corp.
I'M THE GREATEST - Fruits–dried - Wilkinson-Spitz Ltd.
I'M THE MAN - Apparel and accessories - Robert Luis Cabico
IMA - Audio equipment ✰ - Spectra Merchandising International, Inc.
IMA - Computer software - Information Management Associates, Inc.
IMA BRASS - Giftware - International Mercantile
IMAC - Chemical preparations - Chevron Chemical Co.
IMAC - Computer peripheral equipment - Digi International Inc.
IMAC - Measuring instruments - ABB Power T&D Co. Inc.
IMAC - Paints - Imac
IMACOM - Computer software - T. Jason Chou
IMAG - Electronic equipment - Conductus, Inc.
IMAGE - Apparel–children's - Jay-Zee Inc.
IMAGE - Audio equipment ✰ - Yorkville Sound
IMAGE - Books–comic - Image Comics, Inc.
IMAGE - Cabinets ✰ - Marsh Furniture Co.
IMAGE - Computers - NEC Technologies, Inc.
IMAGE - Cooking equipment–household ✰ - Regal Ware, Inc.
IMAGE - Dinnerware–glass - Arita Sales Co. Inc.
IMAGE - Dinnerware–glass ✰ - Svend Jensen of Denmark Inc.
IMAGE - Envelopes–paper - John Henry Co.
IMAGE - Exercising equipment - Icon Health & Fitness, Inc.
IMAGE - Faucets - Sterling Plumbing Group Inc.
IMAGE - Flatware - Couzon USA
IMAGE - Floor coverings - Domco Industries Ltd.
IMAGE - Floor coverings–carpet and rugs - Image Industries, Inc.
IMAGE - Floor coverings–carpet and rugs ✰ - Ebsco Carpet Mills
IMAGE - Floor coverings–carpet and rugs ✰ - Regal Rugs Inc.
IMAGE - Furniture - Lane Co. Inc.
IMAGE - Furniture–upholstered ✰ - Bassett Furniture Industries, Inc.
IMAGE - Games ✰ - Avalon Hill Game Co.
IMAGE - Glassware - Indiana Glass Co.
IMAGE - Glassware–household - Federal Glass
IMAGE - Hair care products - Image Laboratories, Inc.
IMAGE - Hearing aids ✰ - Magnatone Hearing Aid Corp.
IMAGE - Helmets–athletic - Bell Sports Corp.
IMAGE - Machinery - Seal Products Inc.
IMAGE - Music–sheet - TRF Production Music Libraries
IMAGE - Padding–foam - Image Carpets Inc.
IMAGE - Paints - Hy-Klas Paints Inc.
IMAGE - Paper–coated - Butler Paper Co.
IMAGE - Publisher's imprints - Bantam Doubleday Dell Publishing Group, Inc.
IMAGE - Seasonings - Flavorite Laboratories Inc.
IMAGE - Switches - Continental Telephone Corp.

✰ = Now out of production

IMAGE - Synthetic turf - Instant Turf Industries Inc.

IMAGE - Thread - Threads USA Div.

IMAGE - Vacuum cleaners and accessories–commercial - Clarke Industries, Inc.

IMAGE 21 - Computer software - Identitech Inc.

IMAGE 76 - Furniture ☆ - Kincaid Furniture Co. Inc.

IMAGE 1500 - Office supplies - Rubbermaid Office Products Inc.

IMAGE ALBUM - Computer software - Parsons Technology, Inc.

IMAGE AMPLIFIER - Electronic equipment ☆ - Buhl Optical Co.

IMAGE BLENDER - Electronics equipment - RMF Products Inc.

IMAGE BOOKS - Publisher's imprints - Bantam Doubleday Dell Publishing Group, Inc.

IMAGE BUILDER - Golf-swing training mirrors ☆ - Dennco, Inc.

IMAGE BUILDER, THE - Food products - Martin Gillet and Co. Inc.

IMAGE CAP - Novelty items - Images International Direct Sales Corp.

IMAGE COUTURE - Eyeglasses ☆ - Windsor Optical Inc.

IMAGE CRAFTS - Stationery - Color Associates Inc.

IMAGE DB - Computer software - Integrated Software

IMAGE DESIGN - Magnets ☆ - Giftware Objectdesign, Inc.

IMAGE EDITION - Computer software - TDF Technologies, Inc.

IMAGE GUARD - Coatings - Sureguard, Inc.

IMAGE HANDLER - Computer hardware - Lead Technologies, Inc.

IMAGE INDEPENDENCE - Computer software - Elastic Reality, Inc.

IMAGE INKS - Paper–transfer - Image Inks Co.

IMAGE INLAY - Jewelry - CJC Holdings, Inc.

IMAGE INTERNATIONAL - Watches - Image International

IMAGE-LINK - Computer software - Eastman Kodak Co.

IMAGE-LOK - Electronic equipment - Telex Communications, Inc.

IMAGE MAGIC - Paper products - Eastman Kodak Co.

IMAGE MAKER - Computer software - Electronic Courseware Systems Inc.

IMAGE MAKER - Hair care products - Helene Curtis Industries Inc.

IMAGE MAKER - Medical apparatus - Hill Rom, Inc.

IMAGE MAKER - Photographic equipment ☆ - Omega/Arkay

IMAGE MAKERS - Sunglasses - Bonneau Co.

IMAGE MATS - Mats - Ludlow Composites Corp.

IMAGE MOUNTER - Photographic equipment ☆ - Omega/Arkay

IMAGE NOW - Computer software - Genesis Software, Inc.

IMAGE OBJECTS - Computer software - Watermark Software Inc.

IMAGE OF YOUTH - Brassieres (Bras) - Milady Brassiere & Corset Co., Inc.

IMAGE PERFECT - Frames–picture - Zuel Co. Inc.

IMAGE PLUS - Dental equipment - Micro Select

IMAGE PLUS - Floor waxes - Selig Co. Inc.

IMAGE PLUS - Office supplies - AVAS Corp.

IMAGE PLUS - Ribbons–inked - Jaypar Industries Inc.

IMAGE PRO - Photographic equipment ☆ - Omega/Arkay

IMAGE QUEST - Computer software ☆ - Mouse Systems Corp.

IMAGE-SAFE - Tiles–ceiling - Inter-County Building Materials Corp.

IMAGE SEAL - Paper - Standard Register Co.

IMAGE SERVER - Printers–computer - QMS, Inc.

IMAGE SMITH - Computer software - Philips Media Inc.

IMAGE STATION - Printers–computer - QMS, Inc.

IMAGE STREET ELECTRONIC PRINT SHOP - Computer software - Moore Business Forms, Inc.

IMAGE SUPPORT PLUS - Tripods–photographic - Davis & Sanford Co. Inc.

IMAGE TECH - Photographic equipment - Image Technology International, Inc.

IMAGE TERMINAL - Electronics equipment - Image Data Corp.

IMAGE TRANSLATOR - Video-cassette recorders - Instant Replay, Inc.

IMAGE UP - Computer software - Greg Merriman

IMAGE VAULT - Compact discs–prerecorded - Digital Impact

IMAGE WEAR - Apparel and accessories - Workwear Corp. Inc.

IMAGE WIZARD - Computer software ☆ - Imageware Software, Inc.

IMAGE WORKS - Apparel and accessories - Image Works, Inc.

IMAGE WRITER - Printers–computer - Apple Computer Inc.

IMAGE WRITER II - Printers–computer - Apple Computer Inc.

IMAGE-X 70 - Dental equipment - AFP Imaging Corp.

IMAGE XPERT - High resolution printers - Xerographics Laser Images Corp.

IMAGEBASIC - Computer software - Diamond Head Software, Inc.

IMAGEBIND - Paper products - Imagebind, LLC

IMAGECOM - Electronic equipment - Paso Sound Products Inc.

IMAGECOMMANDER - Computer software - Jasc Software, Inc.

IMAGECONTROLS - Computer software - Kofax Image Products, Inc.

IMAGEDISC - Recording label - Image Premastering Services, Ltd.

IMAGEEXTENDER - Computer software - Genesys Corp.

IMAGEFIND - Computer software - Genesys Corp.

IMAGEGUARD - Mirrors - Sureguard, Inc.

IMAGELAN - Computer peripheral equipment - Advanced Technology Laboratories, Inc.

IMAGELINK - Film - Eastman Kodak Co.

IMAGEMAKER - Computer storage devices - Microtech Conversion Systems

IMAGEMAKER - Hair care products - Global Imaging Inc.

IMAGEMAN - Computer software - Data Techniques Inc.

IMAGEMASTER - Audio equipment ☆ - DCM Corp.

IMAGEMASTER - Electronic equipment - Eastman Kodak Co.

IMAGEMASTER - Portable overhead projectors - Audiscan Products Co.

IMAGEMATE - Facsimile paper - Murata Bus Systems Inc.

IMAGEMATE - Photographic equipment - Eastman Kodak Co.

IMAGEMIND - Computer software - John F. Cruz

IMAGEMOVER - Computer software - Information Management Consultants Inc. (IMC)

IMAGEPAK - Surveillance equipment - Pelco

IMAGEPERFECT - Cosmetics - Jackie Brown, Inc.

IMAGEPOINT - Cameras–video - Photometrics Ltd.

IMAGEPOINT - Ultrasonic scanning devices - Hewlett-Packard Co.

IMAGEPRINT - Photographic equipment - Polaroid Corp.

IMAGEPRO - Liquid crystal displays - Dukane Corp.

IMAGEPRO - Printers–computer - Spring Point Corp.

IMAGERY - Computer software - Imagery Software, Inc.

IMAGERY - Floor coverings–carpet and rugs - Mohawk Industries Inc.

IMAGERY - Floor coverings–carpet and rugs ☆ - Blue Ridge Carpet Mills

IMAGERY - Floor coverings–carpet and rugs ☆ - J and J Industries Inc.

IMAGERY - Wallpaper - Manuscreens

IMAGERY - Wines - Glen Ellen Winery

IMAGERY I - Wallpaper ☆ - J. Josephson, Inc.

IMAGE'S - Apparel–women's - Jezebel-Renee of Hollywood

IMAGES - Bathroom fixtures - Artesian Industries

IMAGES - Bedding–linen - C.S. Brooks Canada Inc.

IMAGES - Bedroom furniture - American Furniture Co. Inc.

IMAGES - Calendars - Keith Clark Inc.

IMAGES - Dinnerware - Corning Inc.

IMAGES - Dishes–earthenware - Mug Shanty

IMAGES - Fabrics–tapestry ☆ - Coloroll Inc.

IMAGES - Floor coverings - Mannington Resilient Floors

IMAGES - Floor coverings - Tarkett, Inc.

IMAGES - Floor coverings–carpet and rugs ☆ - Galaxy Carpet Mills Inc.

IMAGES - Frames–eyeglass ☆ - Universal/Univis Inc.

IMAGES - Furniture ☆ - Lexington Furniture Industries, Inc.

IMAGES - Furniture–wood ☆ - Ficks Reed Co. Inc.

IMAGES - Glassware–household - Majestic Gifts

IMAGES - Glassware–household - Owens-Illinois Inc. (Libbey Div.)

IMAGES - Greeting cards - Paramount Cards Inc.

IMAGES - Hair care products ☆ - Cassidy Inc.

IMAGES - Hardware - Baldwin Hardware Corp.

IMAGES - Occasional tables - JDI Group, Inc.

IMAGES - Posters ☆ - Hambly Studios

IMAGES - Publisher's imprints - Armament Systems and Procedures, Inc.

IMAGES - Tableware–china ☆ - Pfaltzgraff Investment Co.

IMAGES - Tiles–ceramic - Porcelanite, Inc.

IMAGES - Wallpaper - Robert Crowder & Co.

IMAGES & FEATURE STRIPS - Tiles–ceramic - Porcelanite, Inc.

IMAGES & IDEAS - Posters - Empire State Studios Corp.

IMAGES ARTCAPS - Toys - Images International Direct Sales Corp.

IMAGES BY FOREVER YOURS - Gowns - Forever Yours International Corp.

IMAGES CHANGE - Wallpaper ☆ - Gagne Wallcovering, Inc.

IMAGES OF AMERICA - Fabrics–tapestry - Comark Wallcoverings

IMAGES OF AMERICA - Wallpaper ☆ - Thomas Strahan Wallcoverings

IMAGES OF CHRISTMAS - Figurines - Heartprint Inc.

IMAGES OF TIME - Infant plaster-mold kit - Intromark Inc.

IMAGESAFE - Checkbooks - Clarke American Checks, Inc.

IMAGESETTER - Skin care products - Images International

IMAGESOURCE - Toners - Eastman Kodak Co.

IMAGESPEED - Computer software - Digital Technology International

IMAGESPEED - Computer software - Digital Technology International

IMAGESTATION - Computer software - Yale Graphics

IMAGETECH - Advertising agencies - Imagetech Communications, Inc.

IMAGE*TMS - Communications equipment - General Datacomm, Inc.

IMAGETOOLS - Computer software - Intelligent Resources Integrated Systems, Inc.

IMAGETRAC - Computer hardware - Southern Computer Systems, Inc.

IMAGETTES - Greeting cards - Paramount Cards Inc.

IMAGEVOX - Telephone answering machines - George Ferrara

IMAGEWORKS - Computer software - PCI Remote Sensing Corp.

☆ = Now out of production

IMAGEWORX - Pagers - Pagenet
IMAGEXPO - Computer software - Group Logic
IMAGI FOAM - Craft supplies - Mangelsen's
IMAGIC BAKON CRUMBLES - Bacon - PMS Foods
IMAGICIAN - Lighting equipment - Cornerstone/Clearlight
IMAGIFOAM - Foam rubber - Mangelsen's (VDI)
IMAGIIX - Artists' materials - Imagiix, Inc.
IMAGIIX KIDS - Infant product - Imagiix, Inc.
IMAGIMAKER SERIES - Computer peripheral equipment - Broderbund
    Software, Inc.
IMAGIN - Floor coverings - Armstrong World Industries, Inc.
IMAGINAIRE - Wallpaper - Pickhardt & Siebert USA Inc.
IMAGINARIES - Educational materials - Kemper Enterprises, Inc.
IMAGINART - Educational materials - Imaginart International, Inc.
IMAGINARY - Recording label - Imaginary Entertainment Corp.
IMAGINARY ROAD - Recording label - Big Wisdom, Inc.
IMAGINATION - Apparel–women's - Wacoal America Inc.
IMAGINATION - Binders ☆ - ACCO USA, Inc.
IMAGINATION - Christmas tree ornaments - Cracker Box Inc.
IMAGINATION - Computer peripheral equipment - Krikorian Miller Associates,
    Inc.
IMAGINATION - Floor coverings–carpet and rugs ☆ - Lees Carpets
IMAGINATION - Frames–eyeglass ☆ - Universal/Univis Inc.
IMAGINATION - Glassware–household - Durand International
IMAGINATION - Rings–jewelry - Artcarved Inc.
IMAGINATION - Telescopes - Northern Telecom, Inc.
IMAGINATION - Wallpaper - Bayview Wallcoverings
IMAGINATION - Wallpaper ☆ - Mirage Wallcovering Co.
IMAGINATION BEAR - Toys - Brass Key, Inc.
IMAGINATION BUNNY - Toys - Brass Key, Inc.
IMAGINATION GALLERY - Paper–bond - Micro Format, Inc.
IMAGINATION K & B - Wallpaper - Andover Wallcovering
IMAGINATION KIT - Games - Little Thinker
IMAGINATION PILOTS - Compact discs–prerecorded - Imagination Pilots
IMAGINATION SERIES - Tiles–ceiling - La Crosse Acoustical Tile, Inc.
    (Interior Systems)
IMAGINATION ZONE - Floor coverings–carpet and rugs - Studio RTA, Inc.
IMAGINATION ZONE, THE - Toys - O.T. Group, Inc.
IMAGINATIONERY - Stationery - Lisa Frank, Inc.
IMAGINATIONS - House furnishings - Lexington Furniture Industries, Inc.
IMAGINE - Computer software - Imagination Software, Inc.
IMAGINE - Wallpaper - MGA/Palais
IMAGINE - Yarn - Lion Brand Yarn Co.
IMAGINE AUTOWARP - Computer software - Erdas, Inc.
IMAGINE IT - Wallpaper ☆ - Gilford Corp.
IMAGINE NATURAL PUDDING SNACKS - Puddings–canned - Imagine
    Foods Inc.
IMAGINE NO LIMITS - Electronic equipment - McCaw Cellular
    Communications, Inc.
IMAGINE THAT! - Computer software - Imagine That, Inc.
IMAGINE THAT! - Posters - Trend Enterprises, Inc.
IMAGINE THE POSSIBILITIES - Computer software - Imagination Software,
    Inc.
IMAGINE VISTA - Computer software - Erdas, Inc.
IMAGINE WHAT WE CAN DO TOGETHER - Organs–musical instrument -
    Corning Inc.
IMAGINELAND - Recording label - Chaparral Entertainment, Inc.
IMAGINERY DELI - Sandwiches–prepackaged - Essential Foods Inc. (O)
IMAGINET - Toys - Staver Westport Inc.
IMAGINETICS - Toys ☆ - Revell-Monogram, Inc.
IMAGING AMERICA - Film - Donald Charles Warren
IMAGINGS - Greeting cards ☆ - American Greetings Corp.
IMAGINIT BASEBALL FEDERATION - Apparel and accessories - Silverman
    Group, Inc.
IMAGINOPOLIS - Computer software - Microsoft Corp.
IMAGIO - Apparel–women's - Hit or Miss Inc.
IMAGIO - Cosmetics - Beauty for All Seasons Inc.
IMAGIZER - Electronics equipment - AZTEK Inc.
IMAGO - Recording label - Imago Group Inc.
IMAGON - Photographic equipment - H.P. Marketing Corp.
IMAGYN - Medical apparatus - Imagyn Medical Tech., Inc.
IMAI - Toys–models ☆ - Minicraft Models Inc.
IMAKE VIP TEST TOOL 2000 - Computer software - Imake Software &
    Services, Inc.
IMAN - Cosmetics - Color Me Beautiful, Inc.
IMANI - Blinds–venetian ☆ - Hunter Douglas, Inc.

IMANI - Dolls - Olmec Toys, Inc.
IMAR X - Pharmaceutical preparations - Imarx Pharmaceutical Corp.
IMARI - Colognes - Avon Products, Inc.
IMARI - Statuary ☆ - Eastern Shore Trading Co.
IMARI GARDEN - Dinnerware–glass - Nikko Ceramics Inc.
IMATHINATION - Recording label - S & J Products International, Inc.
IMATRONIC - Electronics equipment ☆ - RMF Products Inc.
IMAVATE - Pharmaceutical preparations ☆ - A.H. Robins Co. Inc.
IMAX EARTHENWARE COLLECTION - Pottery - Imax
IMAX GALVANIZED TIN COLLECTION - Pottery - Imax
IMAX WORLDWIDE IMPORTS - Copper products - Imax
IMAZE - Computer software - BlumbergExcelsior, Inc.
IMBAC - Hardware - Aluplast Roll Shutter Systems Inc.
IMBE - Computer software - Digital Voice Systems, Inc.
IMBIANCO - Wines - Viansa Winery and Marketplace
IMBIBER BEADS - Chemical preparations - Imbibitive Technologies Corp.
IMBICOLL - Laxatives ☆ - Upjohn Co.
IMBUE - Hair care products - Concentrics Inc.
IMC - Cabinets ☆ - H. Wilson Co.
IMC - Recording label - Refuge Music Group
IMC AGRICO - Fertilizers - IMC-Agrico Co.
IMD - Golfing equipment ☆ - Ben Hogan Co.
IMDUR - Pharmaceutical preparations - Key Pharmaceuticals Inc.
IMEDEEN - Skin care products ☆ - Scandinavian Natural Health & Beauty
    Products, Inc.
IMERMAN - Apparel–children's - Jonathan Logan Inc.
IMEX - Toy model kits - Imex Model Co., Inc.
IMF - Paints - Buten Paint & Wallpaper
IMFERON - Health care products ☆ - Fisons Corp.
IMG - Gloves–rubber - International Manufacturing Group, Inc.
IMG - Nail care products - Jewels by IMG Inc.
IMG INTERNATIONAL TOUR TENNIS - Video games - International
    Management, Inc.
IMGTM - Nail care products - Jewels by IMG Inc.
IMI - Building materials - Irving Materials, Inc.
IMI COMBI ENTERTAINMENT - Marine stereos and accessories ☆ -
    International Marine Industries
IMI-CORN - Flowers, plants, and seeds - American Cyanamid Co.
IMI ISOMAT - Spars and hardware - International Marine Industries
IMI JIMI - Apparel and accessories - Thomas E. Hollar
I.M.I.M. - Apparel and accessories - Happy Guests International, Inc.
IMITATIONS EXCELLENTIA IMITATIO - Jewelry - Replicas, Inc.
IMLAR - Finishing agents - E.I. Dupont de Nemours and Co.
IMLAY - Mushrooms - Four H. Corp.
IMLOGIX - Medical apparatus - Visiplex Instruments Corp.
IMMA COLATA - Apparel and accessories - Ariela & Associates, Inc.
IMMACULATE - Recording label - Immaculate Records
IMMACULATE CONFECTION - Desserts - Stache Foods
IMMACULATE CONSUMPTION - Coffee - Little River Trading Co., Inc.
IMMACULATE SUSPENSION - Audio equipment - Marketing Insights, Inc.-
    Frank Luppino Jr., and Associates
IMMAGINARE - Lighting fixtures - Angelo Brothers Co.
IMMEDIA - Hair care products - Tressa, Inc.
IMMEDIATE - Computer software - Media Marketing, Inc.
IMMEDIATE GRATIFICATIONS - Fruits–dried - Immediate Gratifications, Inc.
IMMEDIATE RECORDS - Recording label - TNA Records
IMMEDIATELY VISIBLE - Cosmetics - Rachel Perry, Inc.
IMMENCILS - Cosmetics - Lancome
IMMERSADESK - Augers - Board of Trustees of the University of Illinois
IMMERSE-A-MATIC - Kitchen appliances ☆ - Hamilton Beach/Proctor-Silex Inc.
IMMERSION+ - Recording label - Penton Overseas, Inc.
IMMERSION CORP - Computer peripheral equipment - Immersion Human
    Interface Corp.
IMMERSION PROBE - Computer hardware - Immersion Human Interface Corp.
IMMERSO-JET - Machinery - Ransohoff Co.
IMMI - Automotive parts and accessories - Indiana Mills & Manufacturing, Inc.
IMMI - Motorcycles - Indian Motorcycle Manufacturing, Inc.
IMMIX - Office accessories - Lifetrax Inc.
IMMIX - Video and television production equipment - Carlton International Corp.
IMMOBILE-ICER - Medical apparatus - Dura*Kold Corp.
IMMOLIN - Pharmaceutical preparations - Schmid Laboratories
IMMORTAL - Frames–eyeglass - Pathway Optical Prods.
IMMORTAL - Games - Precedence Publishing, Inc.
IMMORTALITEA - Teas–herbal - Fun Optics Inc.
IMMTHER - Pharmaceutical preparations - Endorex Corp. Immunotherapeutics
IMMU-BAC - Animal feeds - Protocol Products, Inc.

IMMU-G - Pharmaceutical preparations ☆ - Parke-Davis

IMMU-START - Veterinary pharmaceutical preparations - Imu-Tek Animal Health, Inc.

IMMU-STRESS - Vitamins and nutritional supplements - Health Care Investors Inc.

IMMU-TETANUS - Pharmaceutical preparations ☆ - Parke-Davis

IMMUCAN - Vitamins and nutritional supplements - Bio San Laboratories Inc.

IMMUCELL - Vitamins and nutritional supplements - Molecule 2000, LLC

IMMUGLOBIN - Pharmaceutical preparations ☆ - Savage Laboratories Inc.

IMMUNACEA - Health care products - Christopher Enterprises Inc.

IMMUNACTIN - Pharmaceutical preparations - Natural Organics, Inc.

IMMUNAGE - Skin care products - Elizabeth Arden Inc.

IMMUNAID - Vitamins and nutritional supplements - Nature's Way Products, Inc.

IMMUNE ACE - Vitamins and nutritional supplements - Natural Organics, Inc.

IMMUNE BOOSTER - Health care products - Life Force Nutrition

IMMUNE LIFE - Health care products - Esteem Products Ltd.

IMMUNE MAX - Vitamins and nutritional supplements - Vitamin Research Products Inc.

IMMUNE SYSTEM AND CHINESE HERBS - Publisher's imprints - Tsung Corp.

IMMUNECTAR - Vitamins and nutritional supplements - Nature's Plus

IMMUNENE - Vitamins and nutritional supplements - Bioenergy Nutrient's Inc.

IMMUNEX - Pharmaceutical preparations - Immunex Corp.

IMMUNEX CRP - Pharmaceutical preparations - Wampole Laboratories Div.

IMMUNIGEN - Vitamins and nutritional supplements - Pharmaceutical Technologies, Inc.

IMMUNISCIENCE - Skin care products - Sothys USA Inc.

IMMUNITEA - Teas–herbal - Unitea Herbs

IMMUNITY - Recording label - Bee Jay Recording Studios

IMMUNIZATION ALERT - Computer software - Kenneth R. Dardick

IMMUNO-32 - Animal feed supplements - Jorgensen Laboratories, Inc.

IMMUNO-PLEX - Health care products ☆ - Enzymatic Therapy, Inc.

IMMUNOCARE - Vitamins and nutritional supplements - Ayurvedic Concepts Ltd.

IMMUNOCOLOR - Pharmaceutical preparations - Cytocolor, Inc.

IMMUNOFIN - Vitamins and nutritional supplements - Lane Labs-USA, Inc.

IMMUNOFORCE - Pharmaceutical preparations ☆ - Bioforce of America Ltd.

IMMUNOGEN - Health care products ☆ - Pacific BioLogic Inc.

IMMUNOMEDICS - Diagnostic substances - Immunomedics, Inc.

IMMUNOQUEST - Pharmaceutical preparations - Blake Laboratories Corp.

IMMUNOSCAN - Medical apparatus - Baxter International Inc.

IMMUNOVAC - Vaccines ☆ - Parke-Davis

IMMUREGEN - Food products - Mankind Research Unltd. Inc.

IMMUSTIM - Veterinary nutritional supplements - Immudyne, Inc.

IMMUSYN C - Pharmaceutical preparations - Maurice A. Minuto

IMMUTABS - Vitamins and nutritional supplements - Health Products Corp.

IMMUVIT - Vitamins and nutritional supplements - Rueckert Pharmaceutical Co.

IMNET IMAGE ENGINE - Computer software - Imnet Systems, Inc.

IMO - Food products - Merico Inc.

IMO - Sour cream - Rod's Food Products Inc.

IMO - Toiletries - Jonathan International, Inc.

IMO AND THE KING - Computer software ☆ - Knowledge Adventure

IMODIUM - Antidiarrheal - Janssen Pharmaceutica Inc.

IMODIUM - Health care products ☆ - McNeil Consumer Products Co.

IMODIUM A-D - Health care products - McNeil Consumer Products Co.

IMOLA - Ceramic tile ☆ - Integrity Tile Co.

IMOLA - Tiles–ceramic - Maxsam Sales, Inc.

IMO'S - Seasonings - Imo's Franchising, Inc.

IMP - Boats - Glen-L Marine Designs

IMP - Boats–motor - Sea Environments International, Inc.

IMP - Computer accessory - MicroMed Systems Inc.

IMP - Medical apparatus - Innovative Medical Products, Inc.

IMP - Ophthalmic goods - Styl-Rite Optical Manufacturing Co., Inc.

IMP - Slippers ☆ - Daniel Green Co.

IMP INDUSTRIAL MARKET PLACE - Paper–newsprint - Industrial Market Place, Inc.

IMP KITS - Games - Wff'n Proof Learning Games Associates

IMP ORIGINALS - Apparel–children's - IMP Originals Inc.

IMP POSTERS - Posters - Imp Posters

IMP2 - Musical instrument accessories - Whirlwind Music Distributors, Inc.

IMPAC - Lumber - North Pacific Lumber Co.

IMPAC - Motor vehicles–trucks - Central Tank of Oklahoma, Inc.

IMPAC 3 - Health care products - Med Covers Inc.

IMPACA - Crocheted and knitted items ☆ - Puritan Sportswear Corp.

IMPACCT - Computer software - Arrington Travel Center Inc.

IMPACDOR - Doors–wood - E.S. Robbins Corp.

IMPACK - Air conditioning equipment - American Standard Inc.

IMPACSAFE - Electronic equipment repair shops - Ministor Peripherals Corp.

IMPACT - Bicycles - Schwinn Cycling & Fitness Inc.

IMPACT - Boats - Boston Whaler, Inc.

IMPACT - Cleaning preparations - E.I. Dupont de Nemours and Co.

IMPACT - Computer software - Admit Computer Services Inc.

IMPACT - Computer software - Impact Technologies Group, Inc.

IMPACT - Computer software - Microtime Inc.

IMPACT - Computer software - Westhaven Services Co.

IMPACT - Drums–musical instruments - Impact Industries Inc.

IMPACT - Fabrics - Dan River Inc.

IMPACT - Fabrics - Greenwood Mills Inc.

IMPACT - Floor coverings - Durable Corp.

IMPACT - Floor coverings–carpet and rugs - Philadelphia Carpets

IMPACT - Floor coverings–carpet and rugs - Wunda Weve Carpet Co.

IMPACT - Floor coverings–carpet and rugs ☆ - Regal Rugs Inc.

IMPACT - Floor waxes - Basic Coatings, Inc.

IMPACT - Frames–eyeglass - Pathway Optical Prods.

IMPACT - Furniture ☆ - Bassett Furniture Industries, Inc.

IMPACT - Furniture–wood - Flexsteel Industries Inc.

IMPACT - Guitars - Peavey Electronics Corp.

IMPACT - Hair care products - Helene Curtis Industries Inc.

IMPACT - Machine parts - Barber-Colman Co.

IMPACT - Machinery - Keith Manufacturing Co.

IMPACT - Markers–felt-tip - Sanford Corp.

IMPACT - Nail care products - Procter & Gamble Co.

IMPACT - Novelty items - Oak Rubber Co.

IMPACT - Paper ☆ - Finch, Pruyn and Co.

IMPACT - Paper–carbon - Frye Copysystems Inc.

IMPACT - Pet products - 3-D Investment, Inc.

IMPACT - Photographic equipment - Sinar-Bron Inc.

IMPACT - Plates–plastic - Impact

IMPACT - Postcards ☆ - Transworld Visions

IMPACT - Recording label - Benson Music Group

IMPACT - Recording label - Homeland Recording & Publishing

IMPACT - Seasonings - Edlong Corp.

IMPACT - Slacks–men's - Kalikow Bros. Inc.

IMPACT - Spectrometers - Nicolet Instrument Corp.

IMPACT - Sporting goods - Lifetime Products, Inc.

IMPACT - Sporting goods - Schutt Manufacturing Co.

IMPACT - Sporting goods - Spalding Sports Worldwide

IMPACT - Tools–machine - Okuma America

IMPACT - Wallpaper - Brewster Wallcovering Co.

IMPACT - Wheelchairs - Kareco International Inc.

IMPACT 1 - Guitars - Peavey Electronics Corp.

IMPACT 2 - Guitars - Peavey Electronics Corp.

IMPACT:3C - Computer software - Computer Concepts Corp.

IMPACT 26 - Floor coverings–carpet and rugs - Diamond Carpet Mills Inc.

IMPACT 2000 - Aircraft parts - Plastic Fabricating Co., Inc.

IMPACT 2000 - Door jambs and moldings ☆ - Contact Lumber Co.

IMPACT II - Welding alloys - SDI Operating Partners

IMPACT METAL STUD EATER - Saws–power - John Wagner Associates Inc.

IMPACT ONE - Sporting goods - Voit Corp.

IMPACT OPTICS - Eyeglasses and protective lenses - Wesley A. Kemp

IMPACT-P - Chemical preparations - Environmental Dynamics, Inc.

IMPACT RPR CARD TEST - Pharmaceutical preparations - Wampole Laboratories Div.

IMPACT RUBELLA - Diagnostic test - Carter-Wallace, Inc.

IMPACT SELLING - Recording label - The Brooks Group

IMPACT SPORTS - T-shirts–men's - Impact Sports Inc.

IMPACT SYSTEM - Roofing materials - Hydro Seal Coatings Co., Inc.

IMPACT TOY, INC. - Toys - Impact Toy, Inc.

IMPACTAIRE - Infant product - Jack Gasnick, The Virtuous Locksmith

IMPACTEK - Foam rubber - Frelonic/Division of Dertek Corp.

IMPACTO - Tools - Universal Products International

IMPACTO EVANGELISTICO - Video production - Movimiento Misionero Mundial, Inc.

IMPACTS - Shoes ☆ - Sidney Rich Associates Inc.

IMPACTWARE - Computer software - Optimum Configuration, Inc.

IMPAK - Photo albums - Pakon, Inc.

IMPALA - Apparel and accessories - Impala Mills

IMPALA - Archery equipment ☆ - Martin Archery Inc.

IMPALA - Computer modems - Omron Office Automation Products Inc.

IMPALA - Fabrics - Guilford Mills, Inc.

IMPALA - Floor coverings–carpet and rugs - Ashley Commercial Carpets

IMPALA - Footwear - Vans, Inc.

☆ = Now out of production

IMPALA - Lenses–optical - Kelley & Hueber
IMPALA - Motor vehicles - General Motors Corp. (Chevrolet Motor Div.)
IMPALA - Trailers–travel - Travel Line Enterprises Inc.
IMPALA - Wheelchairs - Pin Dot Products
IMPALA CARESSA - Upholstery leather - American Leather Manufacturing Co.
IMPALA JEANS - Apparel and accessories - Peter Kavehzadeh
IMPALA RECORDS - Recording label - Record-Rama Sound Archives
IMPART - T-shirts–men's - Impart, Inc.
IMPAX - Hammers - Nupla Corp.
IMPAX - Telephone apparatus - DSC Communications Corp.
IMPAX SUPPLY - Bags–duffel - Impax Supply
IMPECCABLE - Colognes ☆ - Avon Products, Inc.
IMPECCABLE - Frames–eyeglass - Hudson Optical Corp.
IMPEDANCE PNEUMOGRAPH MONITOR - Medical apparatus - Nellcor Puritan Bennett
IMPEDE - Insect repellents ☆ - Landco
IMPELLAIR - Aquarium accessories - Aquarium Systems, Inc.
IMPELLIST - Paints–artists' - Sakura Color Products of America, Inc.
IMPELLIST WATERCOLORS - Artists' materials - Sakura of America
IMPENETRA - Security glass - American Glass Products Co.
IMPERAMAR - Floor coverings–carpet and rugs - Couristan Inc.
IMPERATIVE - Floor coverings–carpet and rugs - Mohawk Industries Inc.
IMPERATIVE - Frames–eyeglass ☆ - Universal/Univis Inc.
IMPERATOR - Harmonicas - Hohner Inc.
IMPERATOR - Thread - Threads USA Div.
IMPERATOR - Wines ☆ - Batavia Wine Cellars Inc.
IMPEREAL - Bakery products - Lotus Manufacturing Co.
IMPERIA - Bread crumbs - Imperia Foods Inc.
IMPERIA - Dinnerware–glass ☆ - WMF/USA
IMPERIA - Figurines ☆ - Himark Enterprises Inc.
IMPERIA - Guitars - European Crafts/USA
IMPERIA - Hardware ☆ - Amerock Corp.
IMPERIAL - Aluminum compounds ☆ - Regal Ware, Inc.
IMPERIAL - Aluminum sliding windows - International Aluminum Corp.
IMPERIAL - Apparel and accessories - Imperial Knitting Co. Inc.
IMPERIAL - Bathroom fixtures - Melard Manufacturing Corp.
IMPERIAL - Belts, hair accessories, jewelry, etc. - David Geoffrey Accessories
IMPERIAL - Beverages–malt - European Beverage Co., Inc.
IMPERIAL - Bicycles - Columbia Manufacturing Inc.
IMPERIAL - Binders - Boorum & Pease Co.
IMPERIAL - Boats ☆ - Clark Craft Boat Co.
IMPERIAL - Boats–motor - Midwestern Industries Corp.
IMPERIAL - Boats–motor - Penn Yan Boats Inc.
IMPERIAL - Boats–motor ☆ - Regal Marine Industries Inc.
IMPERIAL - Boats–motor ☆ - Sport-Craft Inc.
IMPERIAL - Brackets - Southern Imperial Inc.
IMPERIAL - Brushes–hair ☆ - Phillips Brush Corp.
IMPERIAL - Buckets–plastic - Imperial Paint Applicators Ltd.
IMPERIAL - Cabinets - Claridge Products and Equipment Inc.
IMPERIAL - Candy - Vernell's Fine Candies
IMPERIAL - Chairs–upholstered - Alladin Plastics Inc.
IMPERIAL - Charcoal - Hubbard's Imperial Inc.
IMPERIAL - Chemical preparations - Wilson Imperial Co.
IMPERIAL - Chocolate candy - Brock Candy Co. Inc.
IMPERIAL - Cleaning preparations–carpet and rug ☆ - Bissell Inc.
IMPERIAL - Combs - Ace Comb Co. Inc.
IMPERIAL - Cutlery - Imperial Schrade Corp.
IMPERIAL - Dairy products - Imperial Frozen Novelties Inc.
IMPERIAL - Detergents - Imperial Manufacturing Co. Inc.
IMPERIAL - Dining room furniture - Imperial Manufacturing Co.
IMPERIAL - Directories ☆ - Hoyle Products
IMPERIAL - Dishcloths - Robertson-Ceco Corp.
IMPERIAL - Dishes–china ☆ - Royal China & Porcelain Companies Inc.
IMPERIAL - Door frames - Dunbarton Corp.
IMPERIAL - Doors–garage - Temple Products Inc.
IMPERIAL - Doors–wood - Maywood Inc.
IMPERIAL - Drapery hardware - Kenney Manufacturing Co.
IMPERIAL - Easels - Anco Wood Specialties Inc.
IMPERIAL - Easels ☆ - Winsor & Newton
IMPERIAL - Fabrics–broadcloth - Spechler-Vogel
IMPERIAL - Faucets - Kallista Inc.
IMPERIAL - Firearms, accessories, and parts - High Standard Manufacturing Corp.
IMPERIAL - Fireplace equipment - Vogelzang International Corp.
IMPERIAL - Flatware ☆ - National Housewares
IMPERIAL - Floor coverings ☆ - Hartco Wood Flooring

IMPERIAL - Food products - Imperial Foods
IMPERIAL - Furnaces–electric - Rheem Manufacturing Co.
IMPERIAL - Furniture - Simon Corp.
IMPERIAL - Gasoline - Exxon Corp.
IMPERIAL - Gasoline - Imperial Refineries Corp.
IMPERIAL - Gasoline ☆ - United Oil
IMPERIAL - Glassware–household - Imperial Crystal and China Inc.
IMPERIAL - Glassware–household - Oneida Ltd.
IMPERIAL - Glassware–household ☆ - Lenox Crystal, Inc.
IMPERIAL - Globes - Geo. F. Cram Co.
IMPERIAL - Gloves - Champion Glove Manufacturing Co.
IMPERIAL - Gloves–rubber - Schmid Laboratories
IMPERIAL - Greeting cards - Masterpiece Studios Inc.
IMPERIAL - Hardware - Alumax Aluminum Corp.
IMPERIAL - Hardware - Hardware Supply Co.
IMPERIAL - Hats - Imperial Headwear Inc.
IMPERIAL - Hearing aids - Audiotone, Inc.
IMPERIAL - Housewares - Brown Stove Works Inc.
IMPERIAL - Infant product ☆ - Century Products Co.
IMPERIAL - Jewelry - Imperial Pearl Syndicate Inc.
IMPERIAL - Kitchen and bathroom cabinets - IXL Furniture Co. Inc.
IMPERIAL - Lighting fixtures - Hubbell Lighting, Inc. (Lighting Div.)
IMPERIAL - Liquors - Canandaigua Wine Co. Inc.
IMPERIAL - Luggage - United States Luggage Corp.
IMPERIAL - Margarine - Lever Brothers Co. Inc.
IMPERIAL - Marine rigging - Imperial Marine Equipment Inc.
IMPERIAL - Mats - U.S. Mat & Rubber Co. Inc.
IMPERIAL - Mirrors - Windmere Corp.
IMPERIAL - Mops ☆ - Royal Maid Association for the Blind Inc.
IMPERIAL - Motor vehicles–automobiles ☆ - Chrysler Corp. (Chrysler-Plymouth Div.)
IMPERIAL - Motor vehicles–motor homes ☆ - Beaver Coaches Inc.
IMPERIAL - Musical instrument accessories - Grover/Trophy Musical Products Inc.
IMPERIAL - Musical instrument accessories - G. Leblanc Corp.
IMPERIAL - Musical instruments - Boosey & Hawkes Buffet Crampon USA
IMPERIAL - Office supplies ☆ - Esselte Corp.
IMPERIAL - Paint sprayers - Karmichael Industries Inc.
IMPERIAL - Paints - United States Gypsum Co.
IMPERIAL - Paints ☆ - Imperial Hardware Co.
IMPERIAL - Paper - Strathmore Paper Co.
IMPERIAL - Pens ☆ - Sheaffer Inc.
IMPERIAL - Pharmaceutical preparations - Heritage Store Inc.
IMPERIAL - Pipes–tobacco - S.M. Frank & Co. Inc. (Kaywoodie-Yello-Bole-Medico)
IMPERIAL - Playing cards ☆ - United States Playing Card Co.
IMPERIAL - Plumbing fixtures–metal ☆ - Moen Inc.
IMPERIAL - Projectors–photographic - Toshiba America Medical Systems Inc.
IMPERIAL - Saddles - St. Lawrence Sales Inc.
IMPERIAL - Salt - Leslie Salt Co.
IMPERIAL - Scales–industrial - Triner Scale and Manufacturing Co. Inc.
IMPERIAL - Shortening ☆ - Swift Edible Oil Co.
IMPERIAL - Skates–ice - Life Industries Inc.
IMPERIAL - Skin care products - Crown Health Equipment Co.
IMPERIAL - Soldering equipment - Eldon Industries Inc. (Ungar Div.)
IMPERIAL - Sports rackets and accessories - Victor Sports
IMPERIAL - Steel - St. Paul Corrugating Co.
IMPERIAL - Sugar–granulated, refined, or powdered - Imperial Sugar Co.
IMPERIAL - Tablecloths - Imperial Childrens Wear Inc.
IMPERIAL - Tableware–china ☆ - Lenox, Inc.
IMPERIAL - Talcum powders - Luzenac America Inc.
IMPERIAL - Tiles–terrazzo - Imperial Tile and Marble Corp.
IMPERIAL - Tires ☆ - Bridgestone/Firestone, Inc.
IMPERIAL - Toilets–portable ☆ - Wilcox-Crittenden
IMPERIAL - Toys - Criterion Co.
IMPERIAL - Toys - Duncan Toys Co.
IMPERIAL - Toys - Flambeau Products Corp.
IMPERIAL - Trailers–travel - Franklin Coach Co.
IMPERIAL - Trays - Wescosa Inc.
IMPERIAL - Trees–artificial - General Foam Plastics Corp.
IMPERIAL - Uniforms–academic - Ottenheimer and Co. Inc.
IMPERIAL - Vacuum cleaners and accessories - The Eureka Co.
IMPERIAL - Valves - American Granby Inc.
IMPERIAL - Wallpaper - Imperial Wallcoverings, Inc.
IMPERIAL - Wallpaper ☆ - Fabricut Inc.
IMPERAL - Watches - Nicolet International Inc.

☆ = Now out of production

IMPERIAL - Watches - North American Watch Corp.
IMPERIAL - Waxes–mineral - Minnesota Mining & Manufacturing Co.
IMPERIAL - Window coverings - Conso Products Co.
IMPERIAL - Windows - International Window Corp.
IMPERIAL - Wine ☆ - Batavia Wine Cellars Inc.
IMPERIAL - Wines - Patriarche Pere & Fils
IMPERIAL - Wire - Mid-States Wire
IMPERIAL - Wire products ☆ - Hanover Wire Cloth
IMPERIAL 400 - Hotels and motels - Imperial Hotels Corp.
IMPERIAL 500 - Dishwashers–household - Whirlpool Properties, Inc.
IMPERIAL 2000 - Teas–herbal - Min Tong Herbs, Inc.
IMPERIAL BEACH - Furniture - Singer Furniture Co.
IMPERIAL BLOCK - Mats, matting ☆ - American Floor Products Co. Inc.
IMPERIAL BLUE - Dinnerware - Denby USA Limited
IMPERIAL BOND - Envelopes ☆ - Quality Park Products Co.
IMPERIAL BOND - Floor coverings–carpet and rugs - Barrett Carpet Mills Inc.
IMPERIAL BRASS - Pens - Sheaffer Inc.
IMPERIAL BY HAGGAR - Apparel and accessories - Haggar Corp.
IMPERIAL CAROUSEL - Fireplaces - Malm Fireplaces Inc.
IMPERIAL CASEMENT - Window frames ☆ - Biltbest Windows
IMPERIAL CLUTCH - Handbags - St. Thomas Inc.
IMPERIAL COLLECTION BATH - Medical apparatus - Lumex, Inc.
IMPERIAL COLLECTION C.F. HATHAWAY - Apparel–men's - Warnaco Inc.
IMPERIAL COLLECTION, THE - Greeting cards - One Write Systems, Inc.
IMPERIAL COMFORT - Mattresses - Kingsdown, Inc.
IMPERIAL CORONAS - Cigars ☆ - J.C. Newman Cigar Co.
IMPERIAL COTTON - Linen - Shula Wardinon, Inc.
IMPERIAL COURT - Floor coverings - Mannington Resilient Floors
IMPERIAL COURT - Floor coverings–carpet and rugs - Mohawk Carpet Corp.
IMPERIAL COURT - Furniture - Collingwood Furniture
IMPERIAL CROWN - Christmas tree ornaments - Cracker Box Inc.
IMPERIAL CROWN - Furniture - Imperial of Morristown Inc.
IMPERIAL DANBY - Marble products - Carl Schilling Stoneworks
IMPERIAL DELIGHT - Food products - Van Den Bergh Foods Co.
IMPERIAL DRAGON SOFTWARE - Computer software - Timothy Paul Driver
IMPERIAL DUETS - Jewelry - Imperial-Deltah Inc.
IMPERIAL DYNASTY - Floor coverings–carpet and rugs - Cabin Crafts Carpets
IMPERIAL DYNASTY - Floor coverings–carpet and rugs - Walter Carpet Mills
IMPERIAL DYNASTY - Food products - Sysco Corp.
IMPERIAL DYNASTY - Giftware - Seymour Mann Inc.
IMPERIAL EAGLE - Sporting goods - Wright & McGill Co.
IMPERIAL EDITION - Furniture ☆ - Bassett Furniture Industries, Inc.
IMPERIAL ELITE - Hair curlers - Burmax Co. Inc.
IMPERIAL ELITE - Strollers–baby - Aprica Kassai USA Inc.
IMPERIAL ELIXIR - Vitamins and nutritional supplements - Ginseng Co.
IMPERIAL EMPIRE - Furniture ☆ - Bassett Furniture Industries, Inc.
IMPERIAL FALCON - Tires - Bridgestone/Firestone, Inc.
IMPERIAL FLAVORS - See **FANTASY BLANKE BAER**
IMPERIAL FORGE - Tools ☆ - Imperial Hardware Corp.
IMPERIAL GARDENS - Craft supplies ☆ - VIP/VIP Crafts
IMPERIAL GARDENS - Wallpaper - Charles Barone Inc.
IMPERIAL GUARD - Games ☆ - Gamescience
IMPERIAL GUARD II - Games ☆ - Gamescience
IMPERIAL HEIGHTS - Cabinets - Imperial Cabinets Inc.
IMPERIAL HOLLY - Sugar–granulated, refined, or powdered - Imperial Holly Corp.
IMPERIAL HOUSE PRESENTS - Recording label - Imperial Schrade Corp.
IMPERIAL II - Dining-room furniture - American Furniture Co. Inc.
IMPERIAL INN - Furniture ☆ - Bassett Furniture Industries, Inc.
IMPERIAL ISLE - Corned beef - Berns & Koppstein
IMPERIAL JADE - Dinnerware–glass ☆ - Wallace International Silversmiths, Inc.
IMPERIAL JEWELRY CO. - Jewelry - Weingeroff Enterprises, Inc.
IMPERIAL KITCHENS - Pasta - Fred's Frozen Foods Inc.
IMPERIAL LEATHER - Soap - Dial Corp.
IMPERIAL LIFESTYLES - Bedspreads - Imperial Wallcoverings, Inc.
IMPERIAL LIGHT - Margarine - Lever Brothers Co. Inc.
IMPERIAL LINK - Link mats ☆ - American Floor Products Co. Inc.
IMPERIAL LINK - Mats - Superior Manufacturing Group/Notrax Floor Matting
IMPERIAL MAJESTY - Floor coverings–carpet and rugs - Cabin Crafts Carpets
IMPERIAL MAJESTY - Floor coverings–carpet and rugs - Walter Carpet Mills
IMPERIAL MANDARIN - Caviar - Tsar Nicoulai Caviar
IMPERIAL MANOR - Floor coverings–carpet and rugs - Mohawk Carpet Corp.
IMPERIAL MAPS - Publisher's imprints ☆ - Rand McNally & Co.

IMPERIAL MARK I - Office supplies ☆ - Bates Manufacturing Co.
IMPERIAL MICROWARE - Copper compounds ☆ - Regal Ware, Inc.
IMPERIAL MING - Floor coverings–carpet and rugs ☆ - Couristan Inc.
IMPERIAL/MORRISTOWN - Furniture - Imperial of Morristown Inc.
IMPERIAL OCEANIC - Cases–vanity ☆ - Rod Caddy Industries
IMPERIAL PALOMINO - Pipes–tobacco ☆ - S.M. Frank & Co. Inc. (Kaywoodie-Yello-Bole-Medico)
IMPERIAL PEACOCK - Giftware - Arnart Imports Inc.
IMPERIAL POPLIN - Fabrics–poplin - Minnetonka Mills Inc.
IMPERIAL PRIDE - Shrimp–fresh or frozen - Florida Sea Inc.
IMPERIAL PURSUIT - Computer software - Lucasarts Entertainment Co.
IMPERIAL QUALITY - Footwear - Interco Inc.
IMPERIAL RAINWARE - Eaves ☆ - Alcan Aluminum Corp. Alcan Building Products Div.
IMPERIAL RAPID BRUSH - Paint and wallpaper cleaners - Wilson Imperial Co.
IMPERIAL REDUCER - Floor coverings - Dexter Corp. (Mercer Plastics Div.)
IMPERIAL REGENCY - Dishes–china ☆ - Richard-Stephen Co.
IMPERIAL RESERVE - Wines ☆ - Canandaigua Wine Co. Inc.
IMPERIAL-RETRO - Doors–metal - United Dominion Industries, Inc.
IMPERIAL RIB - Garden equipment - American Building Components Co.
IMPERIAL SABEL - Coats–fur - Martin Paswall Inc.
IMPERIAL SAVORY SQUEEZE - Oils–edible - Van Den Bergh Foods Co.
IMPERIAL SPIN TOP - Toys - Duncan Toys Co.
IMPERIAL SPLENDOR - Cosmetics ☆ - Shiseido Cosmetics (America) Ltd.
IMPERIAL STAR - Jewelry - Tiara Corp.
IMPERIAL STONE - Jewelry - Imperial Stone Ltd.
IMPERIAL STORMTROOPER - Publisher's imprints - Lucasfilm Ltd.
IMPERIAL-STYLE - Shutters–wood ☆ - Kingsford Building Products
IMPERIAL SUPREME - Dairy products - Lever Brothers Co. Inc.
IMPERIAL SUPREME - Mattresses - Schottenstein Stores Corp.
IMPERIAL TRADITION - Floor coverings–carpet and rugs - Cabin Crafts Carpets
IMPERIAL TRADITION - Floor coverings–carpet and rugs - West Point-Pepperell Mill Store
IMPERIAL TWIST - Mats - Ludlow Composites Corp.
IMPERIAL UNDERGROUND SPRINKLER CO. - Sprinklers–lawn - Imperial Underground Sprinkler Co.
IMPERIAL VELOUR - Floor coverings–carpet and rugs - Couristan Inc.
IMPERIAL VELVET - Paints - Sophir Morris Paint
IMPERIAL WATER WASH - Paint and wallpaper cleaners - Wilson Imperial Co.
IMPERIAL WHITETAIL MAGNET MIX - Animal feed supplements - Whitetail Institute of North America, Inc.
IMPERIAL XL - Bait - Siberian Salmon Egg Co.
IMPERIALE - Fabrics ☆ - Gretchen Bellinger Inc.
IMPERIALE - Vegetable oil - Catania-Spagna Corp.
IMPERIALES - Cigars - House of Windsor Inc.
IMPERIALISM - Computer software - Strategic Simulations, Inc.
IMPERIUM - Remote control devices - Teledyne Brown Engineering Co.
IMPERLUX - Glassware–household - Imperial Crystal and China Inc.
IMPERO - Dishes–china - Pasmantier Co. Inc.
IMPERVA - Tiles–ceramic - Summitville Tiles, Inc.
IMPERVEX - Paints - Benjamin Moore & Co.
IMPERVI-KOAT - Waterproofing compounds - Universal Protective Coatings
IMPERVIA - Doors - Jeld-Wen, Inc.
IMPERVIOUS - Paints - Impervious Paint Industries Ltd.
IMPERVITITE - Floor patch - Pioneer Manufacturing Co.
IMPERVO - Bricks ☆ - Glen-Gery Corp.
IMPERVO - Varnishes - Benjamin Moore & Co.
IMPETUOUS - Floor coverings–carpet and rugs ☆ - Columbus Mills, Inc.
IMPETUS - Tires–automobile - Holsa Inc.
IMPEX - Cheese - Lactoprot USA, Inc.
IMPEX - Exercising equipment - Impex Inc.
IMPEX - Fire extinguishing compositions - United American, Inc.
IMPEX - Golfing equipment - Hireko Trading Co., Inc.
IMPEX - Watches ☆ - Delta Impex Watch Corp.
IMPI - Colognes - Fragranhaus
IMPICS - Computer software - Impics Computer Solutions
IMPIGLIA - Posters - Icart Vendor Graphics Inc.
IMPKO - Novelty items - Trench-Impko
IMPLAN - Computer integrated systems design services - Professional Laboratory Service
IMPLANT CAP SHEET - Dental compounds - THM Biomedical, Inc.
IMPLATOME - Medical apparatus - Soredex-Finndent, Inc.
IMPLEX CORP. - Orthopedic products - Implex Corp.
IMPLICIT - Lenses–optical - Ditto Industries Inc.
IMPLIED - Lenses–optical - Ditto Industries Inc.

☆ = Now out of production

IMPLUS - Medical apparatus - Implus Corp.

IMPLUS-C - Hormone preparations - Ivy Laboratories, Inc.

IMPLUS EZ1 - Medical apparatus - Ivy Laboratories, Inc.

IMPO - Shoes - Impo International Inc.

IMPO - Tiles–ceramic - Impo Glaztile Inc.

IMPORT - Thread - Threads USA Div.

IMPORT COLLECTION - Furniture - Weiman Co.

IMPORT LTD. - Jewelry–costume - Import Ltd.

IMPORT TRADE - Wallpaper - Tattersalls

IMPORTANCE OF PLACE, THE - Computer software - Rand McNally & Co.

IMPORTANTE - Apparel and accessories - Pier Connection

IMPORTED LINENS - Wallpaper - Advance Wallcoverings

IMPORTED SILVER TEQUILA PATRON - Beverages–alcohol - St. Maarten Spirits, Ltd.

IMPORTINA - Hats - Commodore Hats Corp.

IMPORTS INTERNATIONAL - Frames–eyeglass ☆ - Universal/Univis Inc.

IMPOSSIBLE! - Apparel and accessories - Greenfield International, Inc.

IMPOSSIBLE - Recording label - Jazz Composer's Orchestra Association Inc.

IMPOSSIBLES - Puzzles - Lombard Marketing, Inc.

IMPOSTER, THE - Musical instrument accessories - Silver St. Inc.

IMPOSTERS - Recording label - Imposter Mark

IMPOWER - Computer software - Imaginitis Interactive, Inc.

IMPOZE - Apparel and housewares - DMC Designs Corp.

IMPRA CARBOFLO - Medical apparatus - Impra, Inc.

IMPRA DISTAFLO - Medical apparatus - Impra, Inc.

IMPRA-MIX - Dental equipment - Darby Dental Supply Co., Inc.

IMPRA VENAFLO - Medical apparatus - Impra, Inc.

IMPREGON - Infant product - Fleming & Co.

IMPREGUM - Dental equipment - Premier Dental Products Co.

IMPRESARIO - Artists' materials - Loew-Cornell Inc.

IMPRESARIO - Computer software - Ideas, Inc.

IMPRESARIO - Floor coverings–carpet and rugs - Mohawk Industries Inc.

IMPRESS - Cleaning preparations ☆ - Dick Blick Co.

IMPRESS - Computer software - QMS, Inc.

IMPRESS - Soap - SBS Products, Inc.

IMPRESS - Stamps–hand - Impress Rubber Stamps

IMPRESS - Stamps–hand - Tsukineko, Inc.

IMPRESS II - Printing trades machinery - Pioneer Balloon Co.

IMPRESS GRAPHICS - Posters - Donald Art Co.

IMPRESSA DIGITAL LABEL & DECAL PRESS - Printers–computer - Fargo Electronics Inc.

IMPRESSABLE - Paper - Artistic Greetings, Inc.

IMPRESSION - Doors–wood - Composite Door Industries, Inc.

IMPRESSION - Floor coverings–carpet and rugs - Patrick Carpet Mills

IMPRESSION - Furniture ☆ - White Furniture Co.

IMPRESSION - Mortars–clay ☆ - Custom Building Products

IMPRESSION - Rings–jewelry - Artcarved Inc.

IMPRESSION - Telephones - Comdial Corp.

IMPRESSION - Trailers–travel - Fleetwood Enterprises, Inc.

IMPRESSION - Wallpaper - David & Dash

IMPRESSION MAKER - Office machines - General Binding Corp.

IMPRESSIONABLE - Floor coverings–carpet and rugs - Downs Carpet Co. Inc.

IMPRESSIONISM - Floor coverings–carpet and rugs ☆ - Karastan-Bigelow Inc.

IMPRESSIONIST - Eyeglasses - Martin-Copeland Eyewear Corp.

IMPRESSIONIST - Mats–rattan - Golden Star Inc.

IMPRESSIONS - Artists' materials - Carolina Pad and Paper Co.

IMPRESSIONS - Bags–cosmetic - A.J. Siris Products Corp.

IMPRESSIONS - Bathing suits - Ocean Pool Co.

IMPRESSIONS - Briefcases ☆ - U.S. Luggage & Leather Products

IMPRESSIONS - Cases–eyeglass - California Optical Leather Inc.

IMPRESSIONS - Counter tops–laminated ☆ - International Paper (Decorative Products Division)

IMPRESSIONS - Cutlery ☆ - Lifetime Hoan Corp.

IMPRESSIONS - Dinnerware - Corning Inc.

IMPRESSIONS - Dinnerware–glass ☆ - Arita Sales Co. Inc.

IMPRESSIONS - Fencing–plastic - Reeves Southeastern Corp.

IMPRESSIONS - Floor coverings ☆ - Bellbridge Carpets

IMPRESSIONS - Floor coverings–carpet and rugs - Burtco Enterprises Inc.

IMPRESSIONS - Floor coverings–carpet and rugs - Carpet Crafts Inc.

IMPRESSIONS - Floor coverings–carpet and rugs - Couristan Inc.

IMPRESSIONS - Floor coverings–carpet and rugs - Customweave Carpets Inc.

IMPRESSIONS - Floor coverings–carpet and rugs - Masland Corp.

IMPRESSIONS - Floor coverings–carpet and rugs - Walter Carpet Mills

IMPRESSIONS - Floor coverings–carpet and rugs ☆ - Bloomsburg Carpet Industries

IMPRESSIONS - Floor coverings–carpet and rugs ☆ - Regal Rugs Inc.

IMPRESSIONS - Floor coverings–carpet and rugs ☆ - Royalweve Carpet Mills

IMPRESSIONS - Frames–eyeglass - Zylo Ware Corp.

IMPRESSIONS - Furniture - Bassett Furniture Industries, Inc.

IMPRESSIONS - Furniture ☆ - Lane Co. Inc.

IMPRESSIONS - Garden furniture–rattan - Lloyd/Flanders Industries

IMPRESSIONS - Glassware–household - Crisa Corp.

IMPRESSIONS - Greeting cards - Renaissance Greeting Cards Inc.

IMPRESSIONS - Hair care products - Conair Corp.

IMPRESSIONS - Hair care products - Fromm Industries

IMPRESSIONS - Incense ☆ - Chase Collection, Inc.

IMPRESSIONS - Luggage - Ventura Travelware Inc.

IMPRESSIONS - Magnetic tape–blank - Northword Press, Inc.

IMPRESSIONS - Shoes ☆ - Oomphies Inc.

IMPRESSIONS - Swimming pools - Doughboy Recreational Inc.

IMPRESSIONS - Swimming pools - Hoffinger Industries, Inc.

IMPRESSIONS - Tiles–ceramic - KPT Inc.

IMPRESSIONS - Tiles–ceramic ☆ - Wenczel Tile Co.

IMPRESSIONS - Wallpaper - Capital Carousel Inc.

IMPRESSIONS - Wallpaper ☆ - ICI Americas Inc.

IMPRESSIONS - Wallpaper ☆ - Walldesigns

IMPRESSIONS - Wiring devices - Pass & Seymour, Inc.

IMPRESSIONS - Yarn - Caron Collection

IMPRESSIONS II - Tiles–ceramic - KPT Inc.

IMPRESSIONS II - Tiles–ceramic ☆ - Wenczel Tile Co.

IMPRESSIONS COLLECTION, THE - Floor coverings - Congoleum Corp.

IMPRESSIONS HART SCHAFFNER & MARX - Apparel–men's - Hart Schaffner & Marx

IMPRESSIONS OF CALIFORNIA - Apparel–women's - Brasking, Inc.

IMPRESSIONS OF SPRING - Toys–stuffed - Dakin Inc.

IMPRESSIONS PLUS - Paints - Duron, Inc.

IMPRESSIONS SERIES - Display cases–wood - Structural Concepts Corp.

IMPRESSIVE - Floor coverings–carpet and rugs - Queen Carpet Corp.

IMPRESSIVE - Floor coverings–carpet and rugs - World Carpets, Inc.

IMPRESSIVE - Floor coverings–carpet and rugs ☆ - Customweave Carpets Inc.

IMPRESSIVES - Plastic letters and numbers ☆ - Cole Consumer Products Inc.

IMPRESSO - Apparel–women's - Artwin, Inc.

IMPRESSOR - Eyeglasses - Martin-Copeland Eyewear Corp.

IMPRESTO - Stamps–hand - Sanford Corp.

IMPREVU - Perfume, talc, bath oil, etc ☆ - Coty Inc.

IMPREZ - Pens - Lodis Corp.

IMPREZA - Automotive parts and accessories - Subaru of America, Inc.

IMPREZZIV - Bags–paper - Imprezziv

IMPRINT - Mats - Matworks

IMPRINT RECORDS - Recording label - Veritas Music Entertainment, Inc.

IMPRINTATIONS - Stationery - Fairchild Art

IMPRINTS - Fabrics–tapestry ☆ - Columbus Coated Fabrics Co.

IMPRINTS - School supplies - Newell Office Products

IMPRO-BRITE - Cleaning preparations–carpet and rug - Imperial Manufacturing Co. Inc.

IMPRO-CLEAN - Cleaning preparations–carpet and rug - Imperial Manufacturing Co. Inc.

IMPROFLEX - Containers - Weyerhaeuser Co.

IMPROMPTU - Apparel–women's - Oxford Industries, Inc.

IMPROMPTU - Dinners–frozen - All American Gourmet Co.

IMPROMPTU - Eyeglasses - Art-Craft Optical Co.

IMPROMPTU - Furniture - CTH/Sherrill Occasional

IMPROMPTU - Glassware–household - Owens-Illinois Inc. (Libbey Div.)

IMPROMPTU - Glassware–household - Lenox Crystal, Inc.

IMPROMPTU - Wallpaper - Richard E. Thibaut, Inc.

IMPROMPTU - Wallpaper ☆ - Capital Carousel Inc.

IMPRONTA - Tiles–ceramic - Los Angeles Tile Co., Inc.

IMPRONTA - Tiles–ceramic ☆ - Maxsam Sales, Inc.

IMPROV - Colognes - Herbalife International, Inc.

IMPROV - Furniture - Haworth, Inc.

IMPROV - Jewelry - Providence Importing Co.

IMPROVE - Hair care products - Gabel's Cosmetics Inc.

IMPROVE YOUR CONNECTIONS - Electrical equipment - Konnektech

IMPROVED GEM - Paper clips - Noesting Inc.

IMPROVED HEDD - Fishing lures ☆ - James Heddon's Sons

IMPROVISATIONS - Wallpaper ☆ - Morton Jonap Co. Inc.

IMPROWET - Detergents - Imperial Manufacturing Co. Inc.

IMPRUV 349 - Adhesives and sealants - Loctite Corp.

☆ = Now out of production

IMPRUV 363 - Adhesives and sealants - Loctite Corp.
IMPRUV 365 - Adhesives and sealants - Loctite Corp.
IMPRUV 366 - Adhesives and sealants - Loctite Corp.
IMPTECH IMPROVEMENT TECHNOLOGIES - Computer software - Improvement Technologies, LLC
IMPULS - Printers–computer - Impuls I.D.Systems, Inc.
IMPULSE - Audio equipment ☆ - Russ Jones Marketing
IMPULSE - Bicycles ☆ - Raleigh USA Bicycle Co.
IMPULSE - Bicycles ☆ - Roadmaster Corp.
IMPULSE - Colognes - Lever Brothers Co. Inc.
IMPULSE - Cups–plastic - Dart Container Corp.
IMPULSE - Cymbals - Avedis Zildjian Co.
IMPULSE - Exercising equipment - Excel, The Exercise Co.
IMPULSE - Eyeglasses - Art-Craft Optical Co.
IMPULSE - Floor coverings–carpet and rugs - Trend Carpet
IMPULSE - Floor coverings–carpet and rugs ☆ - Regal Rugs Inc.
IMPULSE - Furniture - Edward Hostmann, Inc.
IMPULSE - Golfing equipment - Triumph Golf Co.
IMPULSE - Hearing aids - Omni Hearing Systems
IMPULSE - Motor vehicles–automobiles - American Isuzu Motors Inc.
IMPULSE - Pipes–tobacco ☆ - S.M. Frank & Co. Inc. (Kaywoodie-Yello-Bole-Medico)
IMPULSE - Recording label - MCA Universal Studios
IMPULSE - Sailboat - Impulse Marine
IMPULSE - Skin care products - Impulse Inc.
IMPULSE - Sporting goods - O'Brien International
IMPULSE - Sporting goods - Wellington Leisure Products, Inc.
IMPULSE - Sports rackets and accessories - Gexco Enterprises
IMPULSE - Tools–power-driven - ITW Paslode
IMPULSE - Toys–models - Estes Industries
IMPULSE - Wheelchairs ☆ - Everest and Jennings International Ltd.
IMPULSE DESIGNS - Artists' materials - Tac Holdings, Inc.
IMPULSE LURES - Fishing lures - Classic Manufacturing Co., Inc.
IMPULSE SO HOT! - Perfumes - Conopco, Inc.
IMPULSIVE - Glass–optical - Welling International
IMPULSOR - Bicycles - Roadmaster Corp.
IMPUZZABLES - Puzzles - Lakeside Games
IMPYRO - Thread - Signal Thread Co. Inc.
IMPZ - Chewing gum - Duo Delights, Inc.
IMRAY - Navigational instruments - Weems & Plath, Inc.
IMRELON - Synthetic fiber - Edith Imre Hair Fashions Inc.
IMRS FORMS - Computer software - IMRS Operations Inc.
IMS - See **ASCOM HASLER**
IMS - Electronic equipment - The Berquist Co.
IMS - Medical apparatus - International Medical Systems, Inc.
IMS - Tables–wood ☆ - Howe Furniture Corp.
IMS CS/2 - Computer software - International Business Machines Corp.
IMS SMARTMAP - Computer peripheral equipment - Lowrance Electronics, Inc.
IMSI - Computer software and peripherals - IMSI
IMSI MOUSE - Computer software - IMSI
IMSI PUBLISHER - Computer software - IMSI
IMSL - Mathematical and statistical software - IMSL Inc.
IMSTATION - Computer software - Clinical Information Advantages, Inc.
IMSYS INJURY MANAGEMENT SYSTEMS - Medical apparatus - World Class Technologies, Inc.
IMT - Video-production equipment - Interactive Media Technologies Inc.
IMTECH CLASSIC - Electronic equipment - Imtech International, Inc.
IMTECH ULTRA - Electrical equipment - Imtech International, Inc.
IMTEX - Medical apparatus - Joseph Petito
IMTEXT - Computer terminals - Imtech International, Inc.
IMTN - Computer peripheral equipment - DSC Communications Corp.
IMTRA - Lighting equipment–boat and ship - Imtra Corp.
IMTX - Computer peripheral device - Interactive Media Technologies Inc.
IMU-GEN - Health care products - Alta Health Products
IMUNIVY - Health care products ☆ - Kay Pharmacal Co. Inc.
IMUNOAK - Pharmaceutical preparations ☆ - E.D. Bullard Co.
IMURAN - Pharmaceutical preparations - Burroughs Wellcome Co.
IMUREGEN - Vitamins and nutritional supplements - Mankind Research Unltd. Inc.
IMVBIRD - Medical apparatus - Bird Products Corp.
IMX - Computer software - Instromedix, Inc.
IMX - Golfing equipment - G. Loomis, Inc.
IN - Health care products ☆ - Ingersoll & Associates
IN - Pet-food supplement - American Lecithin Co. Inc.
IN - Stationery ☆ - Mead Corp.
IN-A-CARD - Fabrics - Dan River Inc.

IN A FLASH - Ovens–microwave - Quadlux, Inc.
IN A GENTLE MANOR - Wallpaper ☆ - Wiffle Hill Studio
IN A JAM - Spices and extracts - To Market to Market
IN A JAR - Educational materials - Attitude Matters, Inc.
IN A JIFFY - Frozen foods - Moran Foods, Inc.
IN ADVANCE - Apparel–women's - Kellwood Co.
IN & AROUND - Publisher's imprints - In & Around Brochures, Inc.
IN-BE-TWEEN COURTWEAR - Apparel–athletic - In-Be-Tween Courtwear
IN BETWEEN - Apparel–women's - Exquisite Form Industries
IN BETWEEN - Deodorizers - Sunshine Products, Inc.
IN-BETWEEN - Publisher's imprints ☆ - Antioch Publishing Co.
IN-BETWEEN - Skin care products - Sogo Inc.
IN BOCCA AL LUPO - Photo albums - Daniela Coutcher
IN BOUNDS - Underwear and nightwear - Jockey International, Inc.
IN BRIEF - Briefcases - Belle Cadeaux Inc.
IN CAHOOTS - Patterns–clothing - In Cahoots
IN CASA - Wallpaper ☆ - Wallquest, Inc.
IN CASE - Attache, cosmetic bag, eyeglass case, etc. - In Case Inc.
IN CHARGE - Computer software - Spitfire Software
IN CHARGE - Frames–eyeglass - Liberty Optical Manufacturing Co.
IN CHOCOLATE - Chocolate candy - In Chocolate, Inc.
IN COMMAND - Computer software - Celltech Cellular Information Systems, Inc.
IN COMMAND - Frames–eyeglass - Liberty Optical Manufacturing Co.
IN CONDITION - Hair care products - Andre Fantasies Inc.
IN CONTROL - Computer software - Attain Corp.
IN CONTROL - Panty hose - Mayer/Berkshire Corp.
IN CONTROL - Video tapes–blank - Health Products Marketing Inc.
IN-CREDIBLE! - Adhesives and sealants - Convenience Products Inc.
IN-CROWD - Frames–eyeglass - Liberty Optical Manufacturing Co.
IN CROWD - Men's and boys' outerwear - Celebration Imports Inc.
IN DANGER - Apparel and accessories - Modern Thought Combine
IN DEMAND - Apparel–women's - In Demand Clothing, Inc.
IN-DEPTH - Hair care products - Wella Corp. (Consumer Products Div.)
IN DEPTH - Plastics - Lady Squire Colors
IN DEPTH - Shampoos - Key West Aloe Inc.
IN DETAIL - Underwear and nightwear - J.C. Penney Co., Inc.
IN-DEX - Directories ☆ - Hoyle Products
IN-DOORS - Cabinets - Facelifters Home Systems Inc.
IN-EFFECT - Recording label - Relativity/Combat/In-Effect
IN EXCESS - Apparel and accessories - In Excess Corp.
IN FACT - Toys–electronic - Interactive Network, Inc.
IN FASHION - Floor coverings–carpet and rugs ☆ - Lees Carpets
IN FASHION - Wallpaper - K.M.L. Industries
IN FASHION - Wallpaper ☆ - Wallquest, Inc.
IN FAUX - Wallcovering - Fidelity Industries, Inc.
IN FAUX - Wallpaper ☆ - Wallquest, Inc.
IN FLIGHT - Sunglasses - Sungold Enterprises Ltd.
IN-FLITE - Frames–eyeglass - May Optical Co. Inc.
IN FLU - Vitamins and nutritional supplements - Kroeger Herb Products Co. Inc.
IN FLYTE - Vitamins and nutritional supplements - Intelligent Nutrition Systems
IN FOCUS - Computer software - In Focus Systems, Inc.
IN FOCUS - Floor coverings–carpet and rugs ☆ - Masland Corp.
IN FOCUS - Frames–eyeglass - May Optical Co. Inc.
IN-FORCER - Air conditioning equipment - Tjernlund Products Inc.
IN-FORCER - Screwdrivers - Ingersoll-Rand Co.
IN-FORM - Apparel–women's - Exquisite Form Industries
IN-FORMATION - Hair care products - Helene Curtis Industries Inc.
IN FURN O - Fireplaces ☆ - American Road Equipment Co.
I.N. GEAR - Toys - Wild Planet Toys, Inc.
IN GOOD COMPANY - Wallpaper - Pantasote Inc. (Wallcovering Div.)
IN GOOD HANDS BY ESPRIT - Apparel and accessories ☆ - Esprit De Corp.
IN GROOVE - Recording label - Soulstreet Records Inc.
IN-GROUP - Apparel–women's - Exquisite Form Industries
IN-GROUP - Eyeglasses - Martin-Copeland Eyewear Corp.
IN HIS TIME - Software - Colonnade Technologies, Inc.
IN HOME - Furniture repair shops - Bjip, Inc.
IN HOT PURSUIT - Games ☆ - Mayfair Games, Inc.
IN JAIL JUST VISITING - Game - Tonka Corp.
IN-KEEPERS - Glassware–household - Owens-Illinois Inc. (Libbey Div.)
IN-KNIT - Sweaters - Bash Knits Inc.
IN-KOTE - Enamels ☆ - Kelly-Moore Paint Co. Inc.
IN-LINE - Display cases–metal - Displaymor Manufacturing Co.
IN-LINE - Electronic equipment - Electric and Gas Technology Inc.
IN LINE - Office supplies - Mead Corp.
IN-LINE - Sporting goods - Diversified Innovations

IN LINE HEAD - Needles–sewing ☆ - Coats and Clark Inc.

IN LINE HEAD - Needlework supplies ☆ - Susan Bates Inc.

IN-MAJIC - Fireplace equipment ☆ - Majestic Co.

IN MANY WAYS - Colognes ☆ - Avon Products, Inc.

IN-MOLDED SWITCH - Switches–electric - Bergquist Co.

IN MY ROOM - Furniture–children's ☆ - Child Craft Industries Inc.

IN MY THOUGHTS...IN MY HEART - Greeting cards - American Greetings Corp.

IN-N-OUT BURGER - Restaurants–fast food - In-N-Out Burgers

IN ONE - Golfing equipment - In One Corp.

IN ORDER - Computer programs - Sharpened Software, Inc.

IN OTHER WORDS - Games - Spokadena Enterprises Inc.

IN OTHER WORDS. - Greeting cards - Teresa V. Woodward

IN PASSION - Wallpaper ☆ - Wallquest, Inc.

IN PLACE - Cosmetics ☆ - Gefden International Inc.

IN PLANTS - Chemical preparations - McCalla Co.

IN PROCESS - Health care products - J.R. Porter Associates Inc.

IN SEARCH OF - Computer software - Estes Industries

IN SEARCH OF THE MOST AMAZING THING - Computer software ☆ - Gessler Publishing Co., Inc.

IN SEARCH OF UNICORNS - Wallpaper - Kirk-Brummel

IN-SEASON - Footwear - Montgomery Ward & Co. Inc.

IN SHAPE - Frames–eyeglass - Hudson Optical Corp.

IN-SHAPE - Sporting goods - In-Shape International, Inc.

IN-SIDER - Windows–storm ☆ - Plaskolite Inc.

IN-SIGHT - File folders - Ames Safety Envelope Co.

IN SIGHT IN MIND IN ORDER CARD MINDERS - Business cards - Amerifun Products

IN-SIGHTER - Golfing equipment - Sports Enhancement Associates, Inc.

IN SILICO - Computer software - World Information Networks Corp.

IN-SINK-ERATOR - Household appliance stores - Emerson Electric Co.

IN-SOL-THERM - Doors–storm - Calder Manufacturing Co.

IN-SORT - Computer hardware - M.A.I.L. Code Inc.

IN SOUND - Recording label ☆ - Accent Records

IN SPA RATION BATH SYSTEM FOR ALL-OVER BODY RELAXATION - Spas - In*Spa*Ration

IN-STAT ANALYST - Computer software - Information Management Systems, Inc.

IN-STEP - Children's shoes - In-Step Footwear Inc.

IN-STEP - Frames–eyeglass ☆ - Universal/Univis Inc.

IN STEP - Hosiery - Paul Lavitt Mills, Inc.

IN STITCHES - Note cards and gift bags ☆ - Mccall Pattern Co.

IN STOCK - Apparel and accessories - Robert Stock Designs, Inc.

IN STYLE - Magazines - Time Inc.

IN STYLE - Ophthalmic goods - Foremost Optical Products

IN STYLE AND IN TOUCH - Pager services - Source One Wireless, Inc.

IN SYNC - Computer software - In Sync Corp.

IN SYNC MEDIA SERVICES - Broadcasting stations–television - In Sync Productions, Inc. Ta in Sync Media Services

IN THE 1ST DEGREE - Computer software - Broderbund Software, Inc.

IN THE BAG - Magnets - Russ Berrie and Co., Inc.

IN THE BEGINNING - Recording label - CCC of America, Inc.

IN THE BOWEN MANOR - Wallcoverings ☆ - Louis W. Bowen

IN THE BUFF - Skin care products - Cosmedic Concepts, Inc.

IN-THE-BUFF - Sponges - Zane Products Inc.

IN THE CHIPS - Fencing–gates and posts - T.J. Bohme

IN THE CHIPS - Ice-cream sandwich - Cool-A-Coo Ice Cream

IN THE CITY - Apparel–women's - California Swimwear Co., Inc.

IN THE CLEAR - Skin care products - Ilona, Inc.

IN THE DARK - Toys - Tonka Corp.

IN THE GARDEN - Dolls - Seymour Mann Inc.

IN THE HUDDLE - Video games - Interactive Network, Inc.

IN THE LIMELIGHT - Christmas tree ornaments - Cracker Box Inc.

IN THE MIDST OF MY HEART IS A GARDEN - Apparel and accessories - VS Designs

IN THE MOOD - Floor coverings–carpet and rugs - Mohawk Carpet Corp.

IN THE MOOD - Floor coverings–carpet and rugs - Tuftex Carpet Mills, Inc.

IN THE PAINT - Trading cards and stamps - Treat Entertainment, Inc.

IN THE PAINT BASKETBALL GEAR - Apparel and accessories - Nancy Kahn Designs, Inc.

IN THE PICTURE - Cameras–video ☆ - Visionary Products, Inc.

IN THE PICTURE - Game - Intempo Toys L.P.

IN-THE-PINK - Lipsticks ☆ - Honey & Spice Toiletries

IN THE PINK! - Pet food - Tammy Dunahoo

IN THE SHADE - Bathing suits - Jonah's Fashion Inc.

IN THE SHOWER - Hair care products ∑ Key West Aloe Inc.

IN THE STARS - Novelty items - Papel Freelance, Inc.

IN THE WILD - Broadcasting stations–television - Commonwealth Productions, Inc.

IN THE WILD - Shirts - Demco Group

IN THE WIND - Colognes ☆ - Avon Products, Inc.

IN THE ZONE - Publisher's imprints - JM Perry Corp.

IN TIME WITH STYLE - Watches - Hampden Corp.

IN-TO-IT BY SPEIDEL - Jewelry - Hirsch Speidel Inc.

IN-TO-IT BY SPEIDEL - Watches - Textron Inc.

IN TOUCH - Computer software - LifeScan Inc.

IN TOUCH - Floor coverings–carpet and rugs ☆ - Callaway Carpets

IN TOUCH - Greeting cards - American Greetings Corp.

IN TOUCH - Hair coloring preparations - Stylors Inc.

IN-TOWN - Frames–eyeglass - Liberty Optical Manufacturing Co.

IN-TRACK - Computer software - F.M.E. Corp.

IN-TRAY - Recipe cards ☆ - Uncle Ben's, Inc.

IN TREADS - Socks - Russell National Sport Socks

IN TUNE - Socks - Pine Hosiery Mills, Inc.

IN-VENT - Cleaning preparations - Dial Corp.

IN-VENT - Ventilation equipment - G.S. Blodgett Corp.

IN-VEST-MENTS - Jewelry - Dillard Department Stores Inc.

IN-VIGOR-OL - Vitamins and nutritional supplements - Sundown Vitamins, Inc.

IN-VISION - Office supplies - Alperstein Brothers, Inc.

IN-VIZ-EEZ - Apparel–women's - Nuvogue Creations

IN-WEAR - Women's apparel - In-Wear/Matinique Inc.

IN-WEG - Plumbing fixtures - J. Fletcher Creamer & Son, Inc.

IN XCESS - Sporting goods - Lisco, Inc.

IN YOUR FACE - Apparel–athletic - Nancy Kahn Designs, Inc.

IN YOUR FACE - Video games - Jaleco USA, Inc.

IN YOUR FACE CARDS - Greeting cards - In Your Face Cards

IN-Z-IT - Luggage - Jinwoong Inc.

IN3 - Computer software - Command Corp., Inc.

INA/ANDREWS - Ball bearings - Ina Bearing Co., Inc.

INA CAROL - Dresses–women's - Carolina Maid Products Inc.

INACTIN - Chemical preparations - Research Biochemicals International

INAKA MUGI - Miso - American Miso Co.

INAPSINE - Tranquilizer - Janssen Pharmaceutica Inc.

INASTONE - Tiles–ceramic - Kowa Texas Inc.

INAUGURATION - Eyeglasses - Art-Craft Optical Co.

INBASKET - Sign boards - Eagle Window & Door Inc.

INBETWEENS - Snack food - Just Help Yourself Food Co.

INBRAND - Underwear and nightwear - Inbrand Corp.

INCA - Cigarettes - G.A. Georgopulo & Co., Inc.

INCA - Computer software ☆ - Spinnaker Software Corp.

INCA - Floor coverings - American Floor Products Co. Inc.

INCA - Floor coverings–carpet and rugs ☆ - Regal Rugs Inc.

INCA - Hardware - Inca Corp.

INCA - Heating equipment ☆ - Kalglo Electronics Co. Inc.

INCA - Pallets - Inca Presswood-Pallets, Ltd.

INCA - Paper ☆ - Hunt Manufacturing Co.

INCA - Pottery - Royal Cathay Trading Co.

INCA - Woodworking machinery - Injecta Machinery Corp.

INCA GOLD - Toilet-bowl deodorizer - Inca Corp.

INCA PALLETTE - Wallpaper - Kirk-Brummel

INCA PISCO - Beverages–alcohol ☆ - Marie Brizard Wines & Spirits, USA

INCA PISCO BRANDY - Brandy - Marie Brizard Wines & Spirits, USA

INCAFLEX - Giftware - Wyler Sales Corp.

INCAP - Computer peripheral equipment - Incap

INCASE - Computer software - Electronic Data Systems Corp.

INCENDO - Paper products - Harry R. McClellan

INCENSE MATCH, THE - Incense - Lois Noyes California Unusuals

INCENSE MOON - Colognes - Parfum de Coeur Ltd.

INCENTIVE - Floor coverings–carpet and rugs ☆ - Hollytex Carpet Mills Inc.

INCENTIVE - Floor coverings–carpet and rugs ☆ - World Carpets, Inc.

INCENTIVE - Recording label - Incentive Productions

INCH BY INCH - Skin care products - Inch by Inch International Inc.

INCH BY INCH - Skin care products - John J. Savas

INCH-WELL - Measuring instruments - Paste-Well Corp.

INCHEQUE - Medical apparatus - Minnesota Mining & Manufacturing Co.

INCHWORM - Motors - Burleigh Instruments, Inc.

INCHWORM - Publisher's imprints - Pauloa Hawaii Ltd.

INCIDENT - Frames–eyeglass ☆ - Universal/Univis Inc.

INCINERATOR - Toys - Hasbro, Inc.

INCINOMITE - Heating equipment - Midco International Inc.

INCISOR - Tires - Cheng Shin Rubber USA, Inc.

INCLIN-ATOR - Electric stair elevators for home use - Inclinator Co. of America

☆ = Now out of production

INCLINATION - Lenses–optical - Ditto Industries Inc.
INCLINATIONS - Apparel and accessories - Wildlife Sportswear, Inc.
INCLINE YOUR SPINE - Sporting goods - Jansen Ent. Inc.
INCLINETTE - Electric stair climber - Inclinator Co. of America
INCLITRACK - Computer software - Xitech Corp.
INCOGNEATO! - Glassware–household - Mad Dog Productions Inc.
INCOGNITIALS - Games - Thomas H. Benton
INCOGNITO - Apparel - Holiday Togs, Inc.
INCOGNITO - Colognes - Noxell Corp.
INCOGNITO - Eyeglasses - Incognito Inc.
INCOGNITO - Frames–eyeglass - Zylo Ware Corp.
INCOGNITO - Pet products - Compass Marketing
INCOLAC - Sealing compounds - Dap Products Inc.
INCOLAY - Giftware - Incolay Studios Inc.
INCOLITE - Giftware - Incolay Studios Inc.
INCOMING - Golfing equipment - Striker Golf Club Co. Inc.
INCOMMAND - Computer peripheral equipment - Ring King Visibles, Inc.
INCOMPARABLE - Eyeglasses - Art-Craft Optical Co.
INCOMPARABLE CASHMERE - Apparel and accessories - Saks Fifth Avenue
INCON - Computer software - SRI International
INCONCERT - Computer software - Xerox Corp.
INCONDITION LIPBLUSH - Cosmetics - Noxell Corp.
INCONT-AID KIT - Skin care products - Care-Tech Laboratories Inc.
INCONT-ALERT - Electrical signalling detector - Innovation Products Unlimited, Inc.
INCONTEXT - Computer software - Xerox Corp.
INCONTICARE - Health care products ☆ - Graham-Field Inc.
INCONTINAIDE - Vitamins and nutritional supplements - Amrion, Inc.
INCONTINENT KLEEN - Deodorizers - G.G. Bean Inc.
INCONTROL - Heart monitors - Incontrol Inc.
INCOPESCA - Food products - Liberty Fish Co.
INCOR - Cement - Lone Star Industries Inc.
INC.PLAN - Computer programs - Goldhirsh Group, Inc.
INCOTAX - Tax-service franchise - Incotax Systems Inc.
INCOTEC - Chemical preparations - Incotec Integrated Coating and Seed Technology, Inc.
INCOTEC WCA-8P - Coatings - Innovative Coatings Technology Corp.
INCRE-LITE - Electronic equipment - Bell & Howell Co.
INCREASE - Recording label - Increase Inc.
INCREATIONS - Wallpaper ☆ - Wallquest, Inc.
INCREDA-MEAL - Vitamins and nutritional supplements - Increda-Meal Corp.
INCREDI-MIX - Toys - Toymax Inc.
INCREDIBELL - Bicycle parts and accessories - Mirrycle Corp.
INCREDIBITES - Snack foods - General Mills, Inc.
INCREDIBLE - Artists' materials - Grafix Plastics
INCREDIBLE - Dermatological preparations - R. Bruce Parker
INCREDIBLE - Floor coverings–carpet and rugs - Galaxy Carpet Mills Inc.
INCREDIBLE - Hair care products - Helene Curtis Industries Inc.
INCREDIBLE - Lenses–optical - Ditto Industries Inc.
INCREDIBLE ACCESSORIES - Furniture - O'Sullivan Industries, Inc.
INCREDIBLE BLUE MASK, THE - Skin care products - Max Factor & Co.
INCREDIBLE BRAIN BUGGY, THE - Toys - Tonka Corp.
INCREDIBLE BULK, THE - Crocheted and knitted items - Schuessler Knitting Mills Inc.
INCREDIBLE BUT TRUE - Computer software - Orange Cherry Software
INCREDIBLE CAR FACTORY - Toys - Toymax Inc.
INCREDIBLE COMPONENTS - Office furniture–wood - O'Sullivan Industries, Inc.
INCREDIBLE CRASH DUMMIES, THE - Toys - Tyco Toys
INCREDIBLE DESSERT DECORATOR - Whipped topping–frozen - Rich Products Corp.
INCREDIBLE EDIBLE - Food products - Natural Nectar Corp.
INCREDIBLE EDIBLE PRETZEL, THE - Pretzels ☆ - New England Pretzel & Popcorn Co.
INCREDIBLE EDIBLE RADICAL CAT, THE - Leather goods - Scott Wolcott
INCREDIBLE EDIBLES - Toys - Mattel, Inc.
INCREDIBLE ENERGY & WATER SAVERS, THE - Plumbing fixtures–enameled - Resources Park
INCREDIBLE ENERGY SAVERS, THE - Weather stripping ☆ - Resources Park
INCREDIBLE EUROPA, THE - Bathroom accessories - Resources Park
INCREDIBLE HEAD, THE - Plumbing fixtures–enameled - Resources Park
INCREDIBLE HULK - Hobby kits - Rapco
INCREDIBLE HULK, THE - Games ☆ - CBS Toys
INCREDIBLE HULK, THE - Books–comic - Marvel Entertainment Group, Inc.
INCREDIBLE ICE CREAM MACHINE, THE - Health care products ☆ - Tawn Ltd.

INCREDIBLE LABORATORY, THE - Computer software - Sunburst Communications, Inc.
INCREDIBLE LENGTHS - Cosmetics - Avon Products, Inc.
INCREDIBLE MACHINE - Computer software - Sierra On-Line, Inc.
INCREDIBLE SHOWER MACHINE - Bathroom accessories - Colgate-Palmolive Co.
INCREDIBLE SHRINK FIT WINDOW KIT, THE - Windows–storm - Resources Park
INCREDIBLE SHRINKING TABLE, THE - Tables–metal ☆ - L.E. Mason Co.
INCREDIBLE SOAP MACHINE - Bathroom accessories - Colgate-Palmolive Co.
INCREDIBLE SODA MACHINE - Soda fountains - Frank M. Baroudi
INCREDIBLE UNIVERSE - Apparel and accessories - Tandy Corp.
INCREDIBLES - Snack foods - Frito-Lay, Inc.
INCREDIBLY DELICIOUS - Snake bite kits ☆ - Natural Nectar Corp.
INCREDIBLY EDIBLE DELITES - Fruits and vegetables - Incredibly Edible Delites Inc.
INCREDIBLY GREAT - Cookies - Interbake Foods Inc.
INCREDIBRA - Apparel–women's - Lovable Co.
INCREDIBUBBLE BOMBER - Novelty items - Fordick Corp.
INCREDICOAT - Paints - Sherwin-Williams Automotive Finishes Corp.
INCREDIGRIP - Gloves - Colt Gloves KC, Inc.
INCREDIGRIP GLOVES - Gloves - Colt Gloves KC, Inc.
INCREDISUPPORT - Braces–orthopedic - Colt Gloves KC, Inc.
INCREDIT - Computer software - Credit Management Solutions, Inc.
INCREMEG - Computer equipment - Mountaingate Data Systems, Inc.
INCREMIN - Vitamins and nutritional supplements - Lederle Laboratories
INCS-64 - Computers - Western Telematic Inc.
INCU-STAGE - Heating equipment - Lab-Line Instruments, Inc.
INCUBATOR!, THE - Computer software - Type Solutions Inc.
INCUBUS - T-shirts–men's - Incubus
INCUNABULA - Games ☆ - Avalon Hill Game Co.
IND/COM - Cleaning preparations - Hydrite Chemical Co.
IND-X - Fire extinguishers - Ansul, Inc.
INDAG - Floor coverings - Minnesota Mining & Manufacturing Co.
INDAR - Teas - Liberty Richter Inc.
INDAR BLENDED & SCENTED TEA - Teas - Europa Foods Ltd.
INDASS - Knobs–porcelain ☆ - Dutch Products & Supply Co.
INDATA SYSTEMS - Magnetic recording equipment - Industrial Data Entry Automation Systems, Inc.
INDCO - Cleaning preparations ☆ - Hastings Plastics Co.
INDECENT - Perfumes - Mahender M. Sabhnani
INDECOR - Lamps - Indecor Inc.
INDEED - Frames–eyeglass - Liberty Optical Manufacturing Co.
INDEED BY HILTON - Crocheted and knitted items - Hilton Sportswear Inc.
INDELIBLO - Paints - Muralo Co. Inc.
INDELICATO PRIVATE STOCK - Wines - Delicato Vineyards
INDELIPRINT - Marking kits - Consolidated Stamp Manufacturing Co. Inc.
INDELOGRAPH - Pencils - Reliance Pen & Pencil Corp.
INDENT-A-MARK - Inks - Matthews International Corp.
INDENTER, THE - Hardware - Eazypower Corp.
INDENTOR - Toys–automobiles - Mattel, Inc.
INDEO - Computer hardware and software - Intel Corp.
INDEPENDENCE - Boats–motor - Independence Marine Resources
INDEPENDENCE - Boilers–gas - Burnham Corp.
INDEPENDENCE - Cabinets - Saco Industries Inc.
INDEPENDENCE - Computer software - Seven Hills Software
INDEPENDENCE - Elevators - Delaware Capital Formation Inc.
INDEPENDENCE - Exercising equipment - Spirit Manufacturing Co. Inc.
INDEPENDENCE - Eyeglasses - Art-Craft Optical Co.
INDEPENDENCE - Motor vehicles - Palmer Industries
INDEPENDENCE II - Furniture ☆ - Broyhill Furniture Industries, Inc.
INDEPENDENCE HALL - Flowers, plants, and seeds - D. Landreth Seed Co.
INDEPENDENCE OAK COLLECTION - Furniture ☆ - Universal Flooring
INDEPENDENCE PRESS - Publisher's imprints - Herald House
INDEPENDENCE SHANGLE - Shingles–asphalt or tar - Certainteed Corp. (Roofing Products Group)
INDEPENDENCE SQUARE - Exercising equipment - Guynes Design, Inc.
INDEPENDENCE SQUARE - Furniture ☆ - Bassett Furniture Industries, Inc.
INDEPENDENT - Fruit product - Independent Food Processors Corp.
INDEPENDENT - Fruits and vegetables - Washington Fruit & Produce Co.
INDEPENDENT - Office supplies - R.A. Stewart Superior
INDEPENDENT - Publisher's imprints - Independent, Inc.
INDEPENDENT - Skateboards - Santa Cruz Skateboards
INDEPENDENT - Thread - Threads USA Div.
INDEPENDENT DAIRY - Milk, ice cream - Independent Dairy Inc.

☆ = Now out of production

INDEPENDENT LIFESTYLE - Dinnerware - Knarf Nob, Inc.
INDEPENDENT LIVING - See LIVING RAMP
INDEPENDENT LIVING AIDS - Health care products - Barrier Free Lifts, Inc.
INDEPENDENT PET CO-OP INCORPORATED INPET'S CHOICE - Animal feeds - Independent Pet Co-Op Inc.
INDEPENDENT PROJECT - Recording label - Chameleon Music Group Inc.
INDEPENDENTS' CHOICE - Cold remedies - Gulf Distribution Inc.
INDEPENDENT'S CHOICE - Cookies - IGA Inc.
INDEPENDENTS V - Furniture ☆ - Bernhardt Industries
INDERAL - Pharmaceutical preparations - Wyeth-Ayerst Laboratories
INDERIDE - Pharmaceutical preparations - Wyeth-Ayerst Laboratories
INDESTRUCTA POND - Garden equipment - Henri Studio, Inc.
INDESTRUCTA POND WATER GARDEN - Plastics - Henri Studio, Inc.
INDESTRUCTO - Labels–paper - Maco Tag and Label Inc.
INDEX - Apparel and accessories - Kellwood Co.
INDEX - Apparel–women's ☆ - En Chante
INDEX - Disinfectants ☆ - Hilex Co.
INDEX - Floor coverings–carpet and rugs ☆ - J and J Industries Inc.
INDEX - Multivitamin - IDE-Interstate Inc.
INDEX - Paints - Bridges Smith & Co.
INDEX - Wallpaper ☆ - Gilford Corp.
INDEX 8 - Eyeglasses - Phillips Lens Co.
INDEX EXPRESS - Office supplies - McBee Loose Leaf Binders
INDEX II - Floor coverings–carpet and rugs - Walter Carpet Mills
INDEX INTEGRATED DESIGN EFFICIENCY EXAMINATION - Computer software - Criterion, Inc.
INDEX-IT - Leather goods - St. Thomas Inc.
INDEX MAKER - Labels–paper - Avery Dennison Corp.
INDEX TRADER - Computer software - Stockmasters, Inc.
INDEX WOMEN BY MELROSE - Apparel and accessories - Kellwood Co.
INDEXTRA - Labels–paper - American Trading and Production Corp.
INDEXX - Toys - Mattel, Inc.
IND$FILE - Computer software - Proginet Corp.
INDI-PEP - Vegetable sauces - Trappey's Fine Foods Inc.
INDIA - Abrasive products - Norton Co.
INDIA - Brushes–paint - Corona Brushes Inc.
INDIA - Cocoa–powders or mixes - W.L.M. Bensdorp Co.
INDIA - Erasers ☆ - Bright Boy Abrasives
INDIA - Games - Milton Bradley Co.
INDIA - Incense ☆ - Genie Co. Inc.
INDIA - Soap ☆ - Caswell-Massey Co. Ltd.
INDIA - Thread - Threads USA Div.
INDIA DE RES - Food products - Ninfa's Inc.
INDIA EXPRESS - Water–bottled or canned - Procter & Gamble Co.
INDIA JEWELRY PALACE - Handcrafted jewelry and gifts - India Jewelry & Gifts Inc.
INDIA NAVIGATION - Recording label - Jazz Composer's Orchestra Association Inc.
INDIA OFFICE - Artists' materials ☆ - Andrews/Nelson/Whitehead
INDIA OVEN - Barbecues and grills - India Oven of America, Inc.
INDIA TEMPLE - Incense - Excelsior Incense Works
INDIA TREE - Spices and extracts - India Tree Gourmet Spices & Specialities
INDIA ZEPHYR - Pajamas–men's - Knothe Corp.
INDIACRAFTS - Oils–essential - Excelsior Incense Works
INDIAN - Apparel stores–sports - Goodman Knitting Co. Inc.
INDIAN - Archery equipment - Indian Industries Inc.
INDIAN - Corn chips - Borden, Inc.
INDIAN - Envelopes - Massachusetts Envelope Co.
INDIAN - Fire extinguishers - The Fountainhead Group, Inc.
INDIAN - Flints ☆ - Red Devil Products Inc.
INDIAN - Motor vehicles–motor homes - Winnebago Industries, Inc.
INDIAN - Motorcycle parts and accessories - Indian Motorcycle Supply, Inc.
INDIAN - Paper ☆ - National Printfast
INDIAN - Pencils ☆ - Faber-Castell Corp.
INDIAN - Snack foods - Zenobia Co.
INDIAN - Sporting goods - Ole Time Woodsman
INDIAN BANJA - Handbags - Pacific Connections of California, Inc.
INDIAN CAMP - Jackets - Livingston Sports, Corp.
INDIAN CHEF - Bakery products - American Trading Corp. of N.Y.
INDIAN CREEK - Metals - Sibley Industries, Inc.
INDIAN CREEK - Wines - Navarro Vineyards and Winery
INDIAN CREEK WINERY - Wines - Navarro Vineyards and Winery
INDIAN DEER - Fruit ☆ - Florida Fresh
INDIAN DOE URINE - Sporting goods - Ole Time Woodsman
INDIAN EARTH - Cosmetics - Spilo/Mehaz Worldwide
INDIAN EYES BULLET - Cosmetics - Madeleine Mono Ltd.

INDIAN FEAST - Dishes–china - Mikasa Co.
INDIAN FIRE - Tools - O.P. Link Handle Co. Inc.
INDIAN FIRE TRAIL - Bicycles - Marin Mountain Bikes, Inc.
INDIAN GARDEN - Wallpaper ☆ - Sandpiper Studios
INDIAN GRILL - Food products - Green Bay Foods Co.
INDIAN HEAD - Automotive parts and accessories - Loctite Corp.
INDIAN HEAD - Cigars ☆ - Tropical Tobacco, Inc.
INDIAN HEAD - Corn–flour or meal - Wilkins-Rogers Inc.
INDIAN HEAD - Dairy products - Tripifoods Inc.
INDIAN HEAD - Water ☆ - Yosemite Water Co.
INDIAN HEMP - Hair care products - Valmor Products Co.
INDIAN HERITAGE - Bathroom fixtures - Kohler Co.
INDIAN HUSKS - Vitamins and nutritional supplements - Freeda Vitamins Inc.
INDIAN JUTE WEAVE - Wallpaper - Flexi-Wall Systems
INDIAN LINE - Floor coverings–carpet and rugs ☆ - Sponge-Cushion Inc.
INDIAN MAID - Food products - Land O'Lakes Inc.
INDIAN MUSK - Skin care products - Renee A. Gabet
INDIAN MYSORE - Coffee - Longbottom Coffee and Tea
INDIAN NIGHTS - Perfumes - Conopco, Inc.
INDIAN PAINT PONY - Toys–stuffed - Dakin Inc.
INDIAN PONY - Hair care products ☆ - Fromm Industries
INDIAN PRINCESS - Jewelry - Carlisle Jewelry Co., Inc.
INDIAN RIVER SELECT - Juices - Freshco, Ltd.
INDIAN SAND - Floor waxes - Chemifax
INDIAN SCOUT - Toys ☆ - Rollin Wilson Co. Inc.
INDIAN SPIRIT - Deodorizers - E. Davis Inc.
INDIAN SPRING - Water - Indian Spring Water Co.
INDIAN SPRINGS VINEYARDS - Wines - Indian Springs Vineyards
INDIAN STAG - Knives–hunting ☆ - Camillus Cutlery Co.
INDIAN STONECRAFT - Knives–pocket ☆ - Camillus Cutlery Co.
INDIAN SUMMER - African violets, accessories - Holtkamp Greenhouses Inc.
INDIAN SUMMER - Beverages–carbonated - Indian Summer, Inc.
INDIAN SUMMER - Cooking utensils–enameled ☆ - Herman Dodge & Son Inc.
INDIAN SUMMER - Dinnerware ☆ - Corning Inc.
INDIAN SUMMER - Food products - RHM Holdings (USA) Inc.
INDIAN SUMMER - Tableware–china ☆ - Villeroy and Boch Tableware Ltd.
INDIAN SUMMER - Toys - Tonka Corp.
INDIAN SUMMER - Wallcoverings - Cork Products Co. Inc.
INDIAN SUMMER GOLF & COUNTRY CLUB - Golfing equipment - Indian Summer Partnership
INDIAN TEMPLE - Incense - Vedanta Press
INDIAN TERRITORY - Novelty items - Indian Territory, Inc.
INDIAN TRAIL - Fruits–frozen - Green Bay Foods Co.
INDIAN TRAILS - Blueberries ☆ - Adkin Blue Ribbon Packing Co.
INDIAN TREE - Dishes–earthenware - Royal China & Porcelain Companies Inc.
INDIAN TREE - Pottery ☆ - Charles Zahn-Import Merchant
INDIAN TREE CORAL - Dinnerware–glass - Franciscan by Johnson Brothers, USA, Inc.
INDIAN VALLEY - Non-alcoholic wines, fruit juices - Folk-Lore Natural Foods Inc.
INDIAN WAR DANCE - Educational materials - Twinson Co.
INDIAN WHEAT - Cooking utensils–aluminum ☆ - General Housewares Corp.
INDIANA - Cash boxes - Indiana Cash Drawer Co.
INDIANA FARMLAND HARVEST - Soups–canned - Frontier Soups
INDIANA JONES - Apparel and accessories - Lucasfilm Ltd.
INDIANA JONES - Apparel–athletic ☆ - Cooper Sportswear Manufacturing Co., Inc.
INDIANA JONES CLASSIC - Novelty items - Lucasfilm Ltd.
INDIANA KING - Food products - Ray Brothers and Noble Canning Inc.
INDIANA MAID - Housewares - O-Cedar/Vining Household Products Co.
INDIANA MILLS - Straps, seat belts, etc. - Indiana Mills & Manufacturing, Inc.
INDIANA PROUD! - Beverages–carbonated - Hondo Inc.
INDIANA SLIMS - Cigars - James B. Russell Inc.
INDIANA VENEER PRODUCTS INC. - Wood products - Harris-Tarkett, Inc.
INDIANAPOLIS MOTOR SPEEDWAY - Apparel and accessories - Indianapolis Motor Speedway Corp.
INDIANAPOLIS MOTOR SPEEDWAY BRICKYARD 400 AUGUST 7, 1999 - Apparel and accessories - Indianapolis Motor Speedway Corp.
INDIANA'S FAVORITE - Food products ☆ - Eaton Foods Inc.
INDIANA'S FINEST - Food products ☆ - Red Gold Inc.
INDIANHEAD - Tools - Chickasaw Handle Co. Inc.
INDIANOLA - Fish–fresh or frozen - Clegg Shrimp Co. Inc.
INDIANWEAVE - Desk blotters - James River Corp.
INDICARD - Medical apparatus - American Home Products Corp.

☆ = Now out of production

INDICATENS - Computer software - MicroStim Inc.

INDICATION - Floor coverings–carpet and rugs - Heuga USA

INDICATIONS - Apparel–women's - Cheerful International Corp.

INDICATOR - Paper–carbon ☆ - Eaton Allen Ko-Rec-Type Corp.

INDICATOR - Thread ☆ - SCT Yarns Inc.

INDICO II - Fishing equipment - Indico, Inc.

INDIECITA - Yarn - Plymouth Yarn Co.

INDIES - Dinnerware–glass ☆ - Johnson Brothers, USA, Inc.

INDIES GOLD - Rings–jewelry - Artcarved Inc.

INDIGITA - Computer software - Indigita Corp.

INDIGLO - Clocks - Timex Corp.

INDIGLO - Watches - Indiglo Corp.

INDIGO - Bathroom accessories - Baldwin Hardware Corp.

INDIGO - Dinnerware ☆ - Corning Inc.

INDIGO - Dinnerware–glass ☆ - Metlox Pottery Shoppe

INDIGO - Dishes–china - Waterford Wedgwood USA, Inc.

INDIGO - Exhaust systems–motor vehicle - Richard D. Moore

INDIGO - Food products - Alix Kenagy Carson

INDIGO - Health care products - Dorothy Gray Cosmetics Ltd.

INDIGO - Lighting fixtures - Hubbell Lighting, Inc. (Lighting Div.)

INDIGO - Scooters–motorized - Joerns Healthcare, Inc.

INDIGO - Wallpaper - Warner Co.

INDIGO BAY - Bathing suits - A.H. Schreiber Co.

INDIGO BOOKS - Publisher's imprints - Alexander Stoddard Inc.

INDIGO CREEK - Apparel and accessories - I. Goldberg Management Corp.

INDIGO HAND - Apparel and accessories - Origin America, LLC

INDIGO ICE - Christmas tree ornaments - Cracker Box Inc.

INDIGO ME - Apparel and accessories - Forgotten Woman

INDIGO-PLUS - Fabrics ☆ - Cone Mills Corp.

INDIGOBLUES - Apparel and accessories - Slick Too Corp.

INDIO - Fabrics - Charter Fabrics Inc.

INDIO - Pharmaceutical preparations - Vartex Pharmaceuticals Inc.

INDIPRENEURIAL - Recording label - Carolyn Corbin, Inc.

INDIRA - Snack foods - Indian Foods Co.

INDIRECTOR - Lighting fixtures ☆ - Hubbell Lighting, Inc. (Lighting Div.)

INDISCREET - Ophthalmic goods - Styl-Rite Optical Manufacturing Co., Inc.

INDISPENSABLE DISPENSER, THE - Toothpaste - Liette International Ltd.

INDISQUISE - Novelty items - Rubie's Costume Co., Inc.

INDIVIDUALIST - Fishing lures - Thomas and Thomas Rodmakers Inc.

INDIVIDUALITY - Floor coverings–carpet and rugs ☆ - Lees Carpets

INDIVIDUALITY - Jewelry - Hobe Cie. Ltd.

INDIVIDUALLY MATCH SHAFTS - Golfing equipment - Penley Sports, LLC

INDIVIDUALLY YOURS - Furniture - Universal Flooring

INDIVIJEWELS - Jewelry - National Findings, Inc.

INDIVISUALS - Sunglasses - Racing Visions Inc.

INDIX - Computer software - Emerging Technology Consultants Inc.

INDO - Finishing agents ☆ - Dap Products Inc.

INDO - Seasonings - Modern Products, Inc.

INDO-EUROPEAN - Vegetables–canned - Indo-European Foods, Inc.

INDO-LEMMON - Pharmaceutical preparations ☆ - Lemmon Co.

INDO-PERSIAN - Floor coverings–carpet and rugs - Couristan Inc.

INDOCHINE - Apparel and accessories - Kan Hollend Acquisitions

INDOCHINE - Bathing suits ☆ - Jantzen Inc.

INDOCIN - Pharmaceutical preparations - Merck & Co., Inc. (Merck Research Laboratories)

INDOGESIC - Pharmaceutical preparations - Century Pharmaceuticals Inc.

INDOLA - Hair care products - Indola North America

INDOMUNE - Pharmaceutical - Greenwich Pharmaceuticals Inc.

INDOOR AIR QUALITY ADHESIVE TESTING PROGRAM - Adhesives and sealants - The Carpet and Rug Institute

INDOOR AIR QUALITY CARPET TESTING PROGRAM - Adhesives and sealants - The Carpet and Rug Institute

INDOOR AIR QUALITY CUSHION TESTING PROGRAM - Adhesives and sealants - The Carpet and Rug Institute

INDOOR OASIS - Exercising equipment - Quick Tech., Inc.

INDOOR-OUTDOOR - Bells - Bevin Brothers Manufacturing Co.

INDOOR/OUTDOOR - Suntan lotions ☆ - Carter-Wallace, Inc.

INDOOR REFRACTOPACK - Lighting fixtures - Holophane Corp.

INDORLITE - Paints - Adelphi Coatings Co.

INDOTHANE - Finishing agents - Dap Products Inc.

INDOX GOLDEN TONE - Electric-guitar pick-ups ☆ - International Music Corp.

INDRA - Floor coverings–carpet and rugs ☆ - Hollytex Carpet Mills Inc.

INDRA - Skin care products - Aveda Corp.

INDRAMIC - Waxes–paraffin - LaSalle Marketing Corp.

INDRAPET - Petroleum - LaSalle Marketing Corp.

INDRAWAX - Waxes–paraffin - LaSalle Marketing Corp.

INDUBRONZ - Paints - Finnaren & Haley Inc.

INDUCE - Chemicals - Helena Chemical Co.

INDUCOTE - Lacquers ☆ - Finnaren & Haley Inc.

INDUCT-A-CORE - Pans - All-Clad Metalcrafters Inc.

INDUCTROL - Regulators–voltage - General Electric Co.

INDULGE - Artificial sweetener - Sysco Corp.

INDULGE - Snack foods - Indulge Snacks

INDULGENCE - Floor coverings–carpet and rugs - Regal Rugs Inc.

INDULGENCE - Floor coverings–carpet and rugs ☆ - Royalweve Carpet Mills

INDULGENCE WITH CONSCIENCE - Vitamins and nutritional supplements - Ultimate Life, Inc.

INDULGENT - Cookies ☆ - Sunshine Biscuits, Inc.

INDULIN - Chemical preparations - Westvaco Corp.

INDUR-ON - Pillows - American Fiber Industries Corp.

INDURA - Finishing agents ☆ - Finnaren & Haley Inc.

INDURACRYL - Adhesives and sealants ☆ - Induron Coatings Inc.

INDURALL - Adhesives and sealants ☆ - Induron Coatings Inc.

INDURAMASTIC - Adhesives and sealants - Induron Coatings Inc.

INDURATABS - Office supplies ☆ - Samsill Corp.

INDURETHANE - Adhesives and sealants - Induron Coatings Inc.

INDURLUX - Adhesives and sealants - Induron Coatings Inc.

INDURON - Adhesives and sealants - Induron Coatings Inc.

INDURUST - Adhesives and sealants - Induron Coatings Inc.

INDUSCRIPT - Computer storage devices–magnetic - Payne Loving Trust

INDUSPARQUET - Floor coverings - BR 111 Imports & Exports, Inc.

INDUSTRAPANEL - Particle board - Georgia-Pacific Corp.

INDUSTREX - Glass products - AFG Industries Inc. (Glass Group Div.)

INDUSTREX - Paints ☆ - Glidden Co.

INDUSTRIAL CHOICE - Cleaning preparations - Huish Detergents, Inc.

INDUSTRIAL COMPUTER SOURCE - Computer peripheral equipment - Industrial Computer Source

INDUSTRIAL CONTROL - Cleaning preparations - Clean Control Corp.

INDUSTRIAL CUSHION STEP - Mats - Ludlow Composites Corp.

INDUSTRIAL EDGE - Disinfectant - Industrial Edge USA

INDUSTRIAL ELECTRIC WIRE AND CABLE INC. - Wire cable - Industrial Electric Wire and Cable, Inc.

INDUSTRIAL FLOOR SEALER - Coatings - Seal-Krete Inc.

INDUSTRIAL HEALTH 2000 - Business software - Software 2000, Inc.

INDUSTRIAL PARK - Floor coverings–carpet and rugs ☆ - Hollytex Carpet Mills Inc.

INDUSTRIAL PERFORMANCE COATINGS - Paints - KCI Coatings, Inc.

INDUSTRIAL RAGS - Apparel and accessories - Maurices Inc.

INDUSTRIAL STRENGTH - Computer peripheral equipment - Chase Ergonomics Inc.

INDUSTRIAL SURF DESIGNS - Apparel and accessories - Eric Kincaide Williams

INDUSTRIAL TOUGH - Bags–plastic - Mobil Oil Corp.

INDUSTRIEVER - Filing cabinets–metal - Kardex Systems, Inc.

INDUSTRILINE - Woodworking equipment - Industriline Co.

INDUSTROCLEAN - Cleaning preparations - Amway Corp.

INDUSTRY CONNECTION - Computer software - Industry Connection, Inc.

INDUSTRY CONNECTION, THE - Computer software - Industry Connection, Inc.

INDUSTRY WORKS IN LEHIGH SAFETY SHOES - Safety products - Lehigh Safety Shoe Co.

INDUSTRYNET - Computer software - Franklin McKee Corp.

INDY - Motorcycles ☆ - Suzuki of America Automotive Corp.

INDY - Skateboards - Santa Cruz Skateboards

INDY AL - Candy ☆ - R.M. Palmer Co.

INDY CAR - Toys–models - Cox Products Inc.

INDY HEAT - Video games - Leland Corp.

INDY KNIT - Apparel and accessories - Indiana Knitwear Corp.

INDY MATIC - Automotive parts and accessories - Hurst Performance Inc.

INDY QUALIFIER - Automotive parts and accessories - Hurst Performance Inc.

INDY RACING LEAGUE - Apparel stores–men's - Indianapolis Motor Speedway Corp.

INDY SELECT - Shock absorbers–motor vehicle - Polaris Industries Partners LP

INDY SSA - Automotive parts and accessories - Hurst Performance Inc.

INDY TURBO - Toys–automobiles - Tyco Toys

INDY WAGEN - Automotive parts and accessories - Hurst Performance Inc.

INERAL - Hair care products - Cosmair Inc.

INERGEN - Chemical preparations - Wormald U.S., Inc.

INERGEN - Fire extinguishers - Ansul, Inc.

INERGI - Recording label ☆ - Nationwide Sound Distributors

INERTIA - Sports Apparel and tote bags - Shopko Stores, Inc.

☆ = Now out of production

INERTIA - Trailers - Real Trailers Inc.

INERTIA BALANCE SYSTEM, THE - Golfing equipment - Wheatley Golf Inc.

INERTIAL - Golfing equipment - Slotline Golf

INET - Telecommunication software - Inet

INET/IX - Computer software - Micro Computer Systems, Inc.

INETIX - Computer software - Micro Computer Systems, Inc.

INEXOL - Paints ☆ - Everseal International Sales Co. Inc.

INEXPAC - Seafood products–fresh or frozen - Southeast Foods Inc.

INEXPRESS - Children's handbags - Jaclyn, Inc.

INF PLUS - Medical apparatus - Medserv Group, Inc.

INFA-MATION CENTER - Infant product - G.W. DMKA Inc./Best Days Inc.

INFA-TRI-SOL - Pharmaceutical preparations ☆ - Vita-Fore Products Co.

INFACAPS A & D - Vitamins and nutritional supplements - Lannett Co. Inc.

INFADATA - Infant product ☆ - Healthdyne Technologies, Inc.

INFADORM - Pharmaceutical preparations ☆ - Solvay Pharmaceuticals Inc.

INFAL-POLY-SOL - Pharmaceutical preparations ☆ - Vita-Fore Products Co.

INFANSEAT - Infant product ☆ - Evenflo Co.

INFANT AIRLINES - Toys–automobiles ☆ - Roadmaster Corp.

INFANT CARE - Vitamins and nutritional supplements - Twinlab

INFANT CARRIER PLAY CENTER - Infant product - Summer Infant Products Inc.

INFANT GRIP - Infant product - Ansa Co. Inc.

INFANT LOVE SEAT - Infant product - Century Products Co.

INFANT SHADE - Infant product - Margo A. Garrand

INFANT STIM - Infant product - Wimmer-Ferguson Inc.

INFANT SWADDLER, THE - Bedding–linen - Comfort Silkie Co. Inc.

INFANTA - Knit goods - Infanta Knitting Mills

INFANTASTIC LULLABYES - Video production - V.I.E.W. Video Inc.

INFANTI - Furniture - Infanti Chair Manufacturing Corp.

INFANTOL - Pharmaceutical preparations ☆ - Schering-Plough Healthcare Products

INFANTS' PRODUCTS - Sporting goods - Lisco, Inc.

INFANTSEA - Infant product - Ben Kiester

INFATUATION - Fabrics - Guilford Mills, Inc.

INFATUATION - Floor coverings–carpet and rugs - Monticello Carpet Mills

INFATUATION - Wallpaper - Seabrook Wallcoverings, Inc.

INFECTA GUARD - Veterinary product - Fearing Manufacturing Co. Inc.

INFECTIOUS DISEASE - Pharmaceutical preparations - Wampole Laboratories Div.

INFECTIOUS DISEASES IN CLINICAL PRACTICE - Journals - Waverly, Inc.

INFECTIOUS RECORDS - Recording label - Infectious Records, Inc.

INFEP - Computer peripheral equipment - International Network of Film and Entertainment Professionals, Inc.

INFER - Colognes - Eurostar Corp.

INFER - Pharmaceutical preparations ☆ - Wesley Pharmacal Co. Inc.

INFERGEN - Pharmaceutical preparations - Amgen Inc.

INFERNO - Batteries - East Penn Manufacturing Co., Inc.

INFERNO - Toys - Hasbro, Inc.

INFERNO - Vitamins and nutritional supplements - American Body Building Products, Inc.

INFERNO-LITE - Glass products - Globe-Amerada Glass Co.

INFERNO WINGS - Food products - Brakebush Brothers Inc.

INFERNOTTO - Wines - Shaw-Ross International Importers

INFI LUX - Mattresses - Angel Echevarria Co. Inc.

INFIDEL - Computer software ☆ - Activision, Inc.

INFIELD - Computer software - Pf1 Corp.

INFILTRATION - Apparel and accessories ☆ - Edison Brothers Stores, Inc.

INFILTRATOR - Computer software - Mindscape Software Inc.

INFINATOR - Electronic equipment ☆ - Heitz Service Corp.

INFINI - Cabinets - Schrock

INFINI - Sunglasses - Sunglass Originals Inc.

INFINICAP - Capacitors - Peter J. Moncrieff

INFINIFONT - Computer software - ElseWare Corp.

INFINIQUE - Floor coverings–carpet and rugs ☆ - Customweave Carpets Inc.

INFINIT - Vitamins and nutritional supplements - Image Solutions Inc.

INFINIT-INDEXER - Machine parts - Quincy Technologies Inc.

INFINITE - Clarinets - G. Leblanc Corp.

INFINITE - Floor coverings - Aladdin Mills, Inc.

INFINITE - Floor coverings–carpet and rugs - World Carpets, Inc.

INFINITE' - Hair care products - Pyramid Enterprises

INFINITE CONTROL - Hair care products - Naturelle, Inc.

INFINITE CURL - Curling irons–electric - Helene Curtis Industries Inc.

INFINITE FOCUS - Binoculars ☆ - Swift Instruments, Inc.

INFINITE II - Floor coverings–carpet and rugs ☆ - Regal Rugs Inc.

INFINITE PRO - Dryers–hair - Helene Curtis Industries Inc.

INFINITE QUALITY - Shampoos - Infinite Quality, Inc.

INFINITE QUALITY IQ - Hair care products - Infinite Quality, Inc.

INFINITE RECALL - Computer software - Byte Ideas

INFINITE VOGUE - Jewelry - Infinite Vogue, Inc.

INFINITEX - Building materials ☆ - Dryvit Systems, Inc.

INFINITI - Computer peripheral equipment - Chyron Corp.

INFINITI - Computer peripheral equipment - Microstar Computer Technology Inc.

INFINITI - Cosmetics - Pro Finish USA, Ltd.

INFINITI - Dietary supplement - L & S Research Corp.

INFINITI - Fans–electric - Hunter Fan Co.

INFINITI - Fishing tackle - South Bend Sporting Goods Inc.

INFINITI - Medical apparatus - Cordis Corp.

INFINITI - Motor vehicles–automobiles - Nissan Motor Corp. USA

INFINITI - Transmitting apparatus - Detector Electronics Corp.

INFINITI G20 - Motor vehicles–automobiles - Nissan Motor Corp. USA

INFINITI I30 - Motor vehicles–automobiles - Nissan Motor Corp. USA

INFINITI J30 - Motor vehicles–automobiles - Nissan Motor Corp. USA

INFINITI Q45 - Motor vehicles–automobiles - Nissan Motor Corp. USA

INFINITY - Golden Star Inc.

INFINITY - Alarm systems–burglar - Trionics Corp.

INFINITY - Audio equipment - Infinity Systems, Inc.

INFINITY - Belts–industrial - Appleton Mills

INFINITY - Bicycles - Ace Tool & Engineering Co.

INFINITY - Building materials - Dryvit Systems, Inc.

INFINITY - Building materials - Interstitial Systems

INFINITY - Cameras ☆ - Olympus America Inc.

INFINITY - Display cases–plastic - Ovadia Corp.

INFINITY - Doors–storm - Canyon Creek Cabinet Co.

INFINITY - Endoscopic equipment - Galileo Corp.

INFINITY - Fish hooks - VMC, Inc.

INFINITY - Floor coverings - Compass Concepts

INFINITY - Floor coverings–carpet and rugs - Alliance Industries Inc.

INFINITY - Floor coverings–carpet and rugs - Calladium & Marglen

INFINITY - Floor coverings–carpet and rugs - Playfield International Inc.

INFINITY - Floor coverings–carpet and rugs ☆ - Criterion Mills Inc.

INFINITY - Furniture - Brown Jordan Co.

INFINITY - Furniture - Vaughan Furniture Co. Inc.

INFINITY - Furniture ☆ - Hammary Furniture Co. Inc.

INFINITY - Furniture ☆ - Singer Furniture Co.

INFINITY - Furniture ☆ - Stanley Furniture Co. Inc.

INFINITY - Glassware–household - Majestic Gifts

INFINITY - Gloves - F.F.F. Enterprises, Inc.

INFINITY - Hair care products - Samlo

INFINITY - Hair-replacement product ☆ - International Hairgoods Inc.

INFINITY - House furnishings ☆ - Lea Industries Inc.

INFINITY - Jewelry - Pepi Kelman Inc.

INFINITY - Lighting equipment - Meteor Light & Sound Co.

INFINITY - Luggage - Airway Industries, Inc.

INFINITY - Mattresses - Spring Air Bedding Inc.

INFINITY - Meters–electric - Newport Electronic, Inc.

INFINITY - Motor vehicles–motor homes - Thor Tech, Inc.

INFINITY - Occasional tables - JDI Group, Inc.

INFINITY - Recording label - Billy Baker & Associates

INFINITY - Teas - Satori Fine Herbals

INFINITY - Wallcoverings - Atrium Industries Inc.

INFINITY - Watches - Sigma Impex Inc.

INFINITY - Water heaters–household - S.A.B.H. U.S. Water Heaters

INFINITY - Wheelchairs ☆ - Activeaid Inc.

INFINITY 8 - Wallpaper - Pantasote Inc. (Wallcovering Div.)

INFINITY 2000 - Funeral services - EFH, Inc.

INFINITY ACOUSTIC 10 - Audio equipment - Infinity Systems, Inc.

INFINITY AVITA - Exercising equipment - Formula Ventures

INFINITY BATH - Bathtubs–enameled - Kohler Co.

INFINITY BEAM - Lasers - Laser Fantasy International, Inc.

INFINITY FASTENERS INCORPORATED - Nuts and bolts - Infinity Fasteners, Inc.

INFINITY GROUP - Game machines - Infinity Group, Inc.

INFINITY HI-LITE - Cameras - Olympus America Inc.

INFINITY HYPER-OIL - Lubricating oils - Engineered Polymer Research, Inc.

INFINITY JR. - See NEW INFINITY JR.

INFINITY MINI - Cameras - Olympus America Inc.

INFINITY PLUS - Golden Star Inc.

INFINITY PRO - Soccer equipment - Brine Inc.

INFINITY S - Cameras ☆ - Olympus America Inc.

INFINITY SERIES - Recording label - Scarlet Records Inc.

INFINITY STYLUS - Cameras ☆ - Olympus America Inc.

INFINITY STYLUS ZOOM - Cameras ☆ - Olympus America Inc.
INFINITY SUPER ZZIPPER - Apparel and accessories - Zzip Designs
INFINITY SUPERZOOM - See INFINITY SUPERZOOM 330
INFINITY SUPERZOOM 330 - Cameras ☆ - Olympus America Inc.
INFINITY SUPERZOOM 3000 - Cameras ☆ - Olympus America Inc.
INFINITY TECHNOLOGY - Soccer equipment - Brine Inc.
INFINITY TELE - Cameras ☆ - Olympus America Inc.
INFINITY TWIN - Cameras ☆ - Olympus America Inc.
INFINITY TWIST - Mops - Golden Star Inc.
INFINITY WAR, THE - Publisher's imprints ☆ - Marvel Entertainment Group, Inc.
INFINITY WORLD - Fertilizers - Byotron Technical Ltd.
INFINITY ZOOM - See INFINITY ZOOM 200
INFINITY ZOOM 200 - Cameras ☆ - Olympus America Inc.
INFINITY ZOOM 210 - Cameras ☆ - Olympus America Inc.
INFINITY ZOOM 220 PANORAMA - Cameras ☆ - Olympus America Inc.
INFINITY ZOOM 230 - Cameras ☆ - Olympus America Inc.
INFINITY ZOOM 2000 - Cameras - Olympus America Inc.
INFINIUM - Computer software - Software 2000, Inc.
INFINOX - Guitars ☆ - JTG of Nashville
INFLAM-ACTIN - Vitamins and nutritional supplements - Natural Organics, Inc.
INFLAMASE - Prescription ophthalmic - Iolab Pharmaceuticals
INFLAMASE FORTE - Prescription ophthalmic - Iolab Pharmaceuticals
INFLATABLE BOOSTER SEAT - Infant product - Children on the Go, Inc.
INFLATABLE FLYER - Sleds - Paris Co. Inc.
INFLATABLE FUN - Kites - Gayla Industries Inc.
INFLATABLE GIFTWARE - Giftware - Air Packaging Technologies Inc.
INFLATABLE GREETINGS - Novelty items - Gibson Greetings, Inc.
INFLATE-ALL - Compressors–air - Coleman Co., Inc.
INFLATE-O-GRAMS - Greeting cards - Ron B. Liebermann
INFLATOY - Toys - Alvimar Manufacturing Co. Inc.
INFLATROL - Vitamins and nutritional supplements - Amrion, Inc.
INFLAZYME FORTE - Health care products - American Biologics
INFLECTIONS - Colognes ☆ - Avon Products, Inc.
INFLOOR HEATING SYSTEMS - Heating equipment - Maxxon Corp.
INFLUAFORCE - Pharmaceutical preparations ☆ - Bioforce of America Ltd.
INFLUENCE - Golfing equipment - Echelon, Golf Inc.
INFLUENCE - Paper–writing - Champion International Corp.
INFLUENCES - Fabrics–tapestry ☆ - Columbus Coated Fabrics Co.
INFLUX - Hair care products - American International Industries
INFO - Stationery ☆ - Mead Corp.
INFO-ACTIVE - Computer storage devices–optical - Bell Atlantic Network Services, Inc.
INFO BLITZ - Computer peripheral equipment - New Media Corp.
INFO DIRECT - Computer software - Donaldson Lufkin & Jenrette Securities Corp.
INFO-EXPRESS - Computer peripheral equipment - EFA Corp. of America
INFO-LINE DIARIES - Publisher's imprints - Per Annum, Inc.
INFO-LINK - Computer software - Eastman Kodak Co.
INFO-MAC - Computer storage devices–optical - Pacific Hitech, Inc.
INFO MODELER 1.5 - Computer software - Asymetrix Corp.
INFO MORPH - Computer software - Advantageware, Inc.
INFO PAD - Computers - Amherst International Enterprises Co.
INFO-PAK - Adhesives and sealants - Loctite Corp.
INFO REST, THE - Computer peripheral equipment - Colorado Compensation Insurance Authority
INFO TEE - T-shirts - Blue Hen Graphics
INFO TO GO - Computer software - Third-Wave Technologies, Inc.
INFO USA - Apparel–women's - Jean St. Germain, Inc.
INFOACCESSORIES - Advertising agencies - American College of Cardiology
INFOADVISOR - Computer software - Platinum Technology, Inc.
INFOALLIANCE - Computer software ☆ - Software Publishing Corp.
INFOARK - Computer software - First Step Research, Inc.
INFOASSISTANT - Computer software - Asymetrix Corp.
INFOCARD - Office supplies - Transkrit
INFOCASE - Carrying case for notebook computers - Infocase Inc.
INFOCOM - Electronic equipment - Dictaphone Corp.
INFODEX - Computer storage devices - Lloyd W. Raymond
INFODEX - Computers - Planned Technologies Ltd.
INFODRIVE - Computer peripheral equipment - Virtual Microsystems Inc.
INFODYNAMICS - Computer software - Infodynamics, Inc.
INFOEDGE - Recording label - Infoedge, Inc.
INFOEXPRESS - Computer hardware - EFA Corp. of America
INFOGOLD - Computer software - Everware Technology Co.
INFOHUB - Publisher's imprints - Trinzic Corp.
INFOIMAGE - Computer software - Unisys Corp.

INFOKID - Identification tags - Debra Slater
INFOLABEL - Labels–paper - Continental Dataforms
INFOLDERS - Sunglasses ☆ - Placo Products Co.
INFOLERT - Identification tags - Gay Yellen-Rams
INFOLINE - Electronic equipment - Daktronics Inc.
INFOLIO - Computer hardware - PI Systems Corp.
INFOMAIL - Telecommunications software - Digital Sound Corp.
INFOMAKER - Computer software - Powersoft Corp.
INFOMED - Identification tags - RJS Manufacturing Corp.
INFOMEDIA - Computer peripheral equipment - Infomedia Microelectronics, Inc.
INFOMINE - Computer software - Softeasy Software, Inc.
INFOMODELER - Computer software - Asymetrix Corp.
INFONET - Electronic equipment - Daktronics Inc.
INFOONCALL - Computer software - Taiwan Trading Center, Inc.
INFOPEDIA - Computer software - Future Vision Holding, Inc.
INFOPHARM - Computer peripheral equipment - Medi-Promotions, Inc.
INFOPLANET - Electronics stores - Infoplanet Voice & Data, Inc.
INFOPLUS - Computer software - Setpoint Inc.
INFOPOINT - Computer software - CA Management Inc.
INFOPORT - Connectors–electronic - Whitaker Corp.
INFORM - Computer software - Howell Training Co.
INFORM - Computer software - Peerless Systems, Inc.
INFORM - Monitors–electronic - Pacific Bank Technology, Inc.
INFORM & CONSENT - Computer software - In/Form Software, Inc.
INFORM RX - Pharmaceutical preparations - Diversified Pharmaceutical Services, Inc.
INFORMAL ELEGANCE - Greeting cards - Norcross Inc.
INFORMALS - Glassware–household - Owens-Illinois Inc. (Libbey Div.)
INFORMANIAC, THE - Computer software - E-8 Publications, Inc.
INFORMATION BAR - Office supplies - Rubbermaid Office Products Inc.
INFORMATION BUILDERS - Computer software - Information Builders, Inc.
INFORMATION CATALOG, THE - Catalogs - Find/SVP Inc.
INFORMATION DELIVERY SERVICE - Computer software - Mse Corp.
INFORMATION FINDER - Computer software - World Book, Inc.
INFORMATION INTEGRITY - Computer software - Unitech Systems Inc.
INFORMATION MASTERPLAN - Computer software - Cohr Inc.
INFORMATION ON THE MOVE - Electronic equipment - Motorola, Inc. (Land Mobile Products Sector)
INFORMATION PLEASE, INC. - Boxes - Information Please, Inc.
INFORMATION PLUS - Educational materials - Information Aids, Inc.
INFORMATION PROTECTORS - Slicing machines - Heyer Inc.
INFORMATION SUPER HIGHWAY - T-shirts–men's - Marketing by Design, Inc.
INFORMATION SUPERHIGHWAY - Telephones - Columbia Telecommunications Group Inc.
INFORMATION WAREHOUSE - Computer software - International Business Machines Corp.
INFORMED - Prerecorded video cassette tapes and disks - Informed, Inc.
INFORMER - Computer software - Essential Software Co., Inc.
INFORMETRICS - Computer software - F. Jay Holland
INFORMTEAM - Computer software - Scopus Technology, Inc.
INFOSAFE IMAGING - Computer software - Infosafe Systems, Inc.
INFOSAIC - Computer software - Computer Language Research Inc.
INFOSCAN - Health care products - James Goforth
INFOSEAL - Office supplies - Transkrit
INFOSERVER - Computer storage devices - Digital Equipment Corp.
INFOSESSION - Computer software - Platinum Technology, Inc.
INFOSETTES - Audio equipment - MCP Davisound
INFOSHARE - Computer software - Notis Systems, Inc.
INFOSHOW - Electronic equipment repair shops - Felknor International Inc.
INFOSITE - Computer hardware - LCC Inc.
INFOSORT - Computer hardware - Wisconsin Manufacturers and Commerce Service Corp.
INFOSTAAR - Home-health-care products - Infomed
INFOSTAR - Data communication equipment - Vodavi, Inc.
INFOSTATION - Computer software - VTLS, Inc.
INFOSYNC - Computer software - Infosync Corp.
INFOTAG - Labels–paper - Infosight Corp.
INFOTEST - Electronic equipment - Leviton Manufacturing Co., Inc.
INFOTHEK - Computer software - Informatik, Inc.
INFOTRACK - Computer peripheral equipment - E-Systems, Inc.
INFOTRAVEL - Computer software - Bell Atlantic Corp.
INFOTREND - Computer software - Infotrend, Inc.
INFOTRUST - Computer software - Ellington Duval Inc.
INFOTRUST TELCO - Communications equipment - Infotrust Telco
INFOTYME - Computer storage devices - R.L. Polk & Co.

☆ = Now out of production

INFOVAX-ID - Labels–gummed - American Home Products Corp.

INFOWATCH - Computer peripheral equipment - Syntellect, Inc.

INFOWAVE SIGHT, SOUND AND TOUCH - Computer peripheral equipment - Joseph L. Stern

INFOWAY - Computer software - Tandem Computers Inc.

INFOWORLD - Publisher's imprints - International Data Group, Inc.

INFOZAP - Computer software - Collegeview Partnership

INFRA-CAINE - Skin care products - Pharmex Inc.

INFRA-GUARD - Goggles–safety - Sellstrom Manufacturing Co.

INFRA HEAT - Medical apparatus - Nelkin/Piper Health Products

INFRA-RAY - Stoves - Amana Refrigeration Inc.

INFRA-RED - Health care products - Sunbeam-Oster Household Products

INFRA-RED ATTACK - Fireworks - American Promotional Events, Inc.

INFRA-RED ATTACK - Fireworks - China Pyrotechnics, Inc.

INFRA SHOWER - Lamps - Nemectron-Belmont Inc.

INFRA-STAT - Heaters–space - Desa International, Inc.

INFRA-TOUCH - Clutches–industrial - Access Unlimited

INFRABAND - Infrared filters - Optical Coating Laboratory Inc.–Santa Rosa Div.

INFRACAL - Measuring instruments - Wilks Enterprise, Inc.

INFRACAM - Cameras–video - Inframetrics, Inc.

INFRADURA - Welding equipment - Uvex Safety LLC

INFRALITE - Lighting fixtures - Kirlin Co.

INFRALUX - Health care products - Infralux International

INFRAMIX - Asphalt - Robert S. Marino

INFRANALYSIS - Cameras - Computational Systems Inc.

INFRAPAK - Packaging machines - New Infra Pak, Inc.

INFRAPRO - Thermometers - Cole-Parmer Instrument Co.

INFRARAIL - Thermostats - Ircon, Inc.

INFRARED - Nail care products - Cosmair Inc.

INFRARUB - Pharmaceutical preparations - Whitehall Laboratories

INFRASCOPE - Microscopes - Barnes Engineering Co.

INFRASOUND - Headphones - Arkon Resources Inc.

INFRASTOP - Glass products - Crystal International Corp.

INFRAVIB - Health care products - Infralux International

INFRAVISION - Cameras - Gabriel Medical, Inc.

INFU-SURG - Medical apparatus - Ethox Corp.

INFUMED - Health care products - MedFusion Systems Inc.

INFUSE-A-KIT - Medical apparatus - Strato/Infusaid Inc.

INFUSION - Skin care products - Professional Services Institute

INFUSION - Vitamins and nutritional supplements - Nature's Best Inc.

INFUSIUM - Hair care products - Clairol Inc.

INFUSIUM 23 - Hair care products - Duart Industries Ltd.

INGA - Glassware–household - Svend Jensen of Denmark Inc.

INGAGE - Computer software - AG Communication Systems Corp.

INGE - Jewelry–precious - Rare Things

INGE-GLAS COLLECTION - Christmas tree ornaments - Old World Christmas

INGEAR - Bags–duffel - Ingear Corp.

INGEBORG'S - Confections - Brent V. Pedersen

INGELURE - Knit goods ☆ - Three by Three

INGENIOUS - Office supplies - InteliDesign Products Inc.

INGENTO - Paper cutters - Quartet Manufacturing Co.

INGENUE - Dolls ☆ - Effanbee Doll Corp.

INGENUE - Floor coverings–carpet and rugs ☆ - Hollytex Carpet Mills Inc.

INGENUE - Rings–jewelry - Artcarved Inc.

INGENUE - Underwear and nightwear - Spirite Industries Inc.

INGENUE BY SPIRITE - Foundation garments–women's - Spirite Industries Inc.

INGER K - Jewelry–precious - Inger Kleckner

INGERSOLL - Watches - Timex Corp.

INGERSOLL HIGH VELOCITY - Machinery - Ingersoll Milling Machine Co.

INGERSOLL-RAND - Power tools - Ingersoll-Rand Co.

INGIE - Looms ☆ - Northfield Loom

INGLEBROOK - Cabinets ☆ - Decora

INGLEBY FARMS - Food products - Ingleby Farms, Inc.

INGLEHOFFER - Sauces - Beaverton Foods

INGLENOOK - Wine - Canandaigua Wine Co. Inc.

INGLES LA FORMA FACIL - Recording label - Paul Wayne White

INGLESIDE - Furniture - Cochrane Furniture Co. Inc.

INGLESIDE - Wines - Ingleside Plantation Winery

INGOT - Cakes - EMAC International, Inc.

INGOT - Flatware ☆ - Dansk International Designs, Ltd.

INGRAHAM - Clocks - Toastmaster Inc.

INGRAHAM SINCE 1831 - Clocks - Toastmaster Inc.

INGRAIN - Vinyl - All Pro Building Products Inc.

INGRAM MICRO - Computer stores - Ingram Industries Inc.

INGRAM'S I.Q.U. - Skin care products ☆ - Campbell Laboratories Inc.

INGREDIENT FINDEX - Computer software - Hopkins Technology LLC

INGREDIENTS FOR SUCCESS - Dyes–food - Bunge Foods Corp.

INGRES - Artists' materials - Bee Paper Co. Inc.

INGRES - Paper - Canson-Talens Inc.

INGRES ANTIQUE - Artists' materials - Andrews/Nelson/Whitehead

INGRID - Dinnerware–glass ☆ - Svend Jensen of Denmark Inc.

INGROWN - Files–tools - Professional Product Research, Inc.

INGUA - Jewelry–costume - A & G Manufacturing Co.

INH - Antibiotics - Ciba-Geigy Corp.

INHAL-AID - Inhalers ☆ - Key Pharmaceuticals Inc.

INHALATIONS - Deodorizers - Origins Natural Resources Inc.

INHERIT - Computer software - Business Center Alternatives, Inc.

INHERITANCE - Blankets - Faribault Woolen Mill Co.

INHERITANCE - Floor coverings–carpet and rugs ☆ - Karastan-Bigelow Inc.

INHERITANCE - Furniture ☆ - Broyhill Furniture Industries, Inc.

INHERITANCE - Wallpaper ☆ - Glidden Co.

INHIBATE - Water treating compounds - Empirical Technologies Corp.

INHIBITIZED - Paints - Kansas Paint & Color Co.

INHIBITOL - Vitamins and nutritional supplements - Natural Balance, Inc.

INHIBITOR, THE - Cleaning preparations–carpet and rug - Queen Carpet Corp.

INHOLTRA - Vitamins and nutritional supplements - Inholtra Inc.

INHOUSE - Skateboards - Jeffrey Madrid

INI EDIT - Computer software - Spinoza Limited

INITALITE - Lighters - Spraz Co.

INITIA - Vitamins and nutritional supplements ☆ - Parke-Davis

INITIAL - Paper–bond ☆ - Park Sherman

INITIAL MATS - Floor coverings - Devon Corp.

INITIALLY YOURS - Key rings - Russ Berrie and Co., Inc.

INITIALS - Lamps - DLZ

INITIALS - Stationery ☆ - Berkshire Stationery Inc.

INITIATE - Floor coverings–carpet and rugs ☆ - Mohawk Carpet Corp.

INITIATE - Fungicides - Loveland Industries, Inc.

INITIATIVE - Floor coverings–carpet and rugs ☆ - Hollytex Carpet Mills Inc.

INITIATOR - Medical apparatus - B. Braun Medical Inc.

INITIATOR - Water treating compounds - Bio-Lab, Inc.

INITIO - Computer software - Initio Corp.

INJA - Fabrics - Dan River Inc.

INJECT ALLOY - Machine parts - Remington Arms Co., Inc.

INJECT-ASSIST - Medical apparatus - Apothecary Products, Inc.

INJECT-EASE - Medical apparatus - Palco Laboratories

INJECTIDRY - Dryers–household - Ernest J. Storrer

INJECTION BREWING - Coffee - Keurig, Inc.

INJECTO-CLEAN - Cleaning preparations - Kleer Flo Co. Inc.

INJECTO-LUBE - Tools - Taylor Environmental Instruments

INJECTOR - Razor blades - Schick/Wilkinson

INJECTOR STING - Chemical preparations - Hastings Manufacturing Co.

INJECTROL - Cook Vascular Inc.

INJEX - Oils–lubricating - Phillips Petroleum Co.

INJOY - Recording label - Injoy, Inc.

INJOY LIFE CLUB - Recording label - Injoy, Inc.

INJURED RESERVE - Apparel–athletic - Injured Reserve, Inc.

INJURY MANAGEMENT SYSTEM - Braces–orthopedic - World Class Technologies, Inc.

INJURY TABS - Vitamins and nutritional supplements - Ethical Nutrients

INJUSA - Bicycles - Victor M. Bulgarelli Associates Inc.

INK A BINK - Apparel–children's - China Trade & Research, Inc.

INK BLOTZ - Games ☆ - Decipher Inc.

INK CZAR - Inks - Pacific Poly Crafts, Inc.

INK DESOLVER - Cleaning preparations - Van Son Holland Ink Corp. of America

INK EAU - Pencils ☆ - Faber-Castell Corp.

INK FLOW - Ribbons–inked - Phillips Process Co. Inc.

INK-IT! - Computer software - Planning Works, Inc.

INK JET SELECT - Paper products - S.D. Warren Co.

INK LINK - Computer software - Ink Link Software

INK LOAD - Cleaning equipment - Thomas R. Lucenta

INK-N-TROL - Pens - Universal Fountain Pen & Pencil Co.

INK NO MOR - Stain removers - Like Me Products Co. Inc.

INK OFF - Stain removers - Cadie Products Corp.

INK ON PAPER - Artists' materials - Food For Thought Inc.

INK-OUT - Pens - Mark-Tex Corp.

INK SOURCE - Cleaning preparations - Videojet Systems International Inc.

INK-STIK - Pens - Micropoint Inc.

INK-STIK 'N' HOLDER - Pens - Micropoint Inc.

INK STONE - Stamps–hand - Rubberstampede Partnership
INK STORES INC - Ink - Ink Stores Inc.
INKA - Glassware–household ☆ - WMF/USA
INKABLE WHITE - Artists' materials - Steig Products
INKADINX - Apparel–children's - Kellwood Co.
INKFINDER - Computer storage devices–magnetic - Aha! Software Corp.
INKIT - Inks - Smith Corona Corp.
INKJET - Ink - Inkjet, Inc.
INKJET & DESIGN - Paper products - Georgia-Pacific Corp.
INKJETXCEL - Paper products - Georgia-Pacific Corp.
INKLESS INK JET, THE - Computer printers - Lasertechnics, Inc.
INKLINGS - Jewelry - Erwin Pearl Inc.
INKLINGS - Stamps–hand - Highlights for Children, Inc.
INKMASTER - Chemical preparations - Rhone-Poulenc Specialty Chemicals Co.
INKMASTER - Inks - Inkmaster, Ltd.
INKO - Artists' materials - Screen Process Supplies Manufacturing Co.
INKODYE - Dyes and pigments - Screen Process Supplies Manufacturing Co.
INKOKO - Floor coverings - Merida Meridian, Inc.
INKOR - Cooking utensils–aluminum - West Bend Co.
INKPLUS - Inks - NewGen Imaging Systems Corp.
INKPROCESSOR - Computer software - Aha! Software Corp.
INKS - Hardware - Ideal Stencil Machine and Tape Co.
INKSHRINK - Computer software - Communication Intelligence Corp.
INKSTONE - Inks - Rubber Stampede
INKSWELL - Stamp pads - Independent Ink Inc.
INKTRONIC - Telephones - At&T Corp.
INKUM'S - Stamps–hand - Clearsnap, Inc.
INKWEL - Printers–computer - Triton Digital Imaging Systems, Inc.
INKWRAP - Computer software - Aha! Software Corp.
INKWRITER - Computer software - Aha! Software Corp.
INKY DINKS - Pens - National Pen & Pencil Co.
INKYDINK NOTES - Stationery - Other Mother Co.
INKYDINKS - Novelty items - Other Mother Co.
INLAID - Scissors–hand-operated - Wiss-Cooper Tools
INLAND - Steel products - Corteo Industries Inc.
INLAND - Tools - D & L Stained Glass Supply, Inc.
INLAND GLASS - Giftware ☆ - Jacksonville Manufacturing
INLAND SPECIAL - Flour - Inland Mills Co.
INLAND SPRING - Flour - Inland Mills Co.
INLAND VALLEY - Food products - Universal Frozen Foods Co.
INLAND'S - Flour - Inland Mills Co.
INLAYCORE - Floor coverings - Colmar Industries, Inc.
INLEX - Computer software - Data Research Associates, Inc.
INLINE - Bicycles - Seattle Bike Supply, Inc.
INLINE - Building materials - Hoffman
INLINE WEAR - Apparel and accessories - Inline Wear
INLOC - Adhesives and sealants - Staple Sewing Aids Corp.
INMAN - Sterling giftware - J.T. Inman Co. Inc.
INMASS - Computer software - Stratford Group, Inc.
INMATE - Boats–motor ☆ - Checkmate Boats Inc.
INMAX - Computers - Megamax, Inc.
INN AT LITTLE WASHINGTON, THE - Apparel and accessories - Inn at Little Washington
INN COMFORT COLLECTION - Comforters - Pacific Coast Feather Co.
INN-KEEPER - Seafood products–fresh or frozen - Eat-All Frozen Food Co.
INN MAID - Noodles - Inn Maid Products Inc.
INN PERLE - Cheese - Swissrose International Inc.
INN ROOM - Cups–plastic ☆ - WNA Comet
INN SHAPE - Mattresses - Ther-A-Pedic Sleep Products Inc.
INN SHOP, THE - Apparel–men's - J.C. Penney Co., Inc.
INN SIGNS - Pottery ☆ - Charles Zahn-Import Merchant
INN SOCIETY - Wallpaper - Benchmark Preferred Wallcoverings
INN TATERS - Vegetables–frozen ☆ - J.R. Simplot Co.
INN TEXTURES - Wallcoverings - Flexcell Wallcoverings
INN, THE - Food products - Inn Foods, Inc.
INN WISCONSIN TRAVEL - Publisher's imprints - I.S.T.P., Inc.
INNCREDIBLE KIDS - Pizzas–mixes - Pizza Inn, Inc.
INNER - Greeting cards ☆ - Amberley Greeting Card Co.
INNER BEAUTY - Hot sauce - Inner Beauty Inc.
INNER BEAUTY - Sauces - Last Resort, Inc.
INNER BEAUTY - Underwear and nightwear - Liberty Enterprises Groups Inc.
INNER-BELTED - Ammunition ☆ - Remington Arms Co., Inc.
INNER CARE - Hair care products - Afam Concept, Inc.
INNER CIRCLE - Floor coverings–carpet and rugs - Criterion Mills Inc.
INNER CIRCLE - Floor coverings–carpet and rugs ☆ - Masland Corp.

INNER CITY - Recording label ☆ - MMO Music Group Inc.
INNER-DRY - Gloves - Glove Source, Inc.
INNER FORCE SPORTSTONIC - Teas–herbal - Yellow Emperor Inc.
INNER FRAME - Knives–pocket - Walter W. Collins
INNER G - Food products ☆ - Love Natural Foods
INNER-GLOW - Candles - Gibson Greetings, Inc.
INNER-GLOW - Figurines - Aurora Art Inc.
INNER HARBOR - Apparel and accessories - Inner Harbor, Inc.
INNER-INSUR - Health care products - Earthnet
INNER-KLEEN - Cleaning preparations - Tuff-Kote Dinol Inc.
INNER-KOTE - Cleaning preparations - Tuff-Kote Dinol Inc.
INNER LIGHT RESOURCES - Wallet cards, charts, and booklets - Inner Light Resources Inc.
INNER-LIP - Health care products - Maddak Inc.
INNER LITE - Hair coloring preparations - Helene Curtis Industries Inc.
INNER-LITE - Ornamental products–glass - Gordon Huether
INNER LOCK - Drums–musical instruments - Drum Workshop, Inc.
INNER MOODS - Candles - Candle-Lite Co.
INNER NATURE - Hair coloring preparations - Helene Curtis Industries Inc.
INNER NATURE EXTRA - Hair care products - Helene Curtis Industries Inc.
INNER PURR - Compact discs–prerecorded - Imaginer Communications, Inc.
INNER REALM - Colognes - Erox Corp.
INNER RING, THE - Apparel and accessories - Rudy Gonzalez
INNER-SEAL - Storm windows ☆ - Continental Aluminum Products Co. Inc.
INNER-SEAL - Weather stripping - W.J. Dennis & Co.
INNER-SEALOCK - Envelopes ☆ - Quality Park Products Co.
INNER SECRET - Hair care products - Professional Services Institute
INNER SHEARS - Scissors–hand-operated - Helene Curtis Industries Inc.
INNER SOLUTIONS - Vitamins and nutritional supplements - Inner Solutions, Inc.
INNER SPIRIT - Recording label - Wilson Okulolo Inc.
INNER STATEMENTS - Mugs - Russ Berrie and Co., Inc.
INNER STRENGTH - Hair care products ☆ - Avon Products, Inc.
INNER STRENGTH - Pharmaceutical preparations - Metagenics, Inc.
INNER STRENGTH - Vitamins and nutritional supplements - Ethical Nutrients
INNER STRUCTURE - Vitamins and nutritional supplements - Hall Laboratories, Inc.
INNER TUBE - Audio equipment - MCP Davisound
INNER WORLD - Girls' lingerie and sleepwear - Inner World Inc.
INNER ZONE - Apparel–children's - Parigi Clothing Corp.
INNERBODYWORKS - Computer storage devices–optical - Tom Snyder Productions, Inc.
INNERCARE - Pharmaceutical preparations - American Pharmacal Inc.
INNERCLEAN - Laxatives - Alvin Last Inc.
INNERDYNE - Medical apparatus - Innerdyne Medical, Inc.
INNEREYE - Games - Pear, Inc.
INNERFACE - Signs - Innerface Architectural Signage, Inc.
INNERGIZE - Beverages - Reliv' International, Inc.
INNERGY - Vitamins and nutritional supplements - Natural Balance, Inc.
INNERHEALTH HERBS - Vitamins and nutritional supplements - Michael's Naturopatic Products
INNERKEY - Electronics equipment - Intelock Technologies
INNERLOC - Archery equipment - Dennis E. Sullivan
INNERMAST - Marine rigging - General Boats Corp.
INNERMOST NATURE FOR MEN - Vitamins and nutritional supplements - Reese Chemical Co.
INNERSILK - Hair care products ☆ - Advanced Research Laboratories
INNERSPACE - Containers–metal - Innerspace Corp.
INNERSPACE - Personal-communications product - Innerspace Power Supply Corp.
INNERTABS - Laxatives - Alvin Last Inc.
INNERTALK - Recording label - Progressive Awareness Research, Inc.
INNERTHANE - Wheelchairs - American Airless
INNERWEAR - Apparel and accessories ☆ - Terramar Sports Worldwide, Ltd.
INNERWOOL - Fabrics–broadcloth ☆ - William Carter Co.
INNING - Giftware ☆ - Avon Products, Inc.
INNISBROOK - Floor coverings–carpet and rugs - Patcraft Mills Inc.
INNISBROOK - Furniture - Pilliod Co.
INNISBROOK CHAMPIONSHIP COURSE - Computer software - Access Software Inc.
INNISFAIL - Earthenware ☆ - Waterford Wedgewood USA, Inc.
INNISFAIL COLLECTION - Apparel and accessories - Innisfail
INNISFREE - Shirts - Individualized Shirts
INNISFREE - Wines - Joseph Phelps Vineyards
INNI'Z - Underwear and nightwear - Saramar Corp.
INNKEEPER - Meat products–beef - Ottman & Co.

☆ = Now out of production

INNKEEPER LINENS - Bedding–linen - J. Abouchar & Sons, Inc.
INNKEEPERS - Pretzels - Snyder of Berlin
INNKEEPERS BREW - Breads - Southern Roots
INNKEEPER'S CHOICE - Pretzels - Curtice-Burns Foods, Inc.
INNKEEPER'S COFFEE - Coffee - Brisk Coffee Co.
INNKEEPERS, THE - Ashtrays–glass ☆ - Frank J. Curran-Esquire Chemical Co.
INNOCENCE - Dolls ☆ - Effanbee Doll Corp.
INNOCENCE - Footwear - Shoe Carnival, Inc.
INNOCENCE - Furniture - Stanley Furniture Co. Inc.
INNOCENCE - House furnishings ☆ - Kellwood Co.
INNOCENCE - Rings–jewelry - Artcarved Inc.
INNOCENCE - Tableware–china ☆ - Pfaltzgraff Investment Co.
INNOCENTS - Brassieres (Bras) - Lovable Co.
INNOCENTS - Figurines ☆ - E.M.I. Inc.
INNOCRON - Watches - Innovative Time Corp.
INNOFLUOR - Pharmaceutical preparations - Oxis International, Inc.
INNOGEL PLUS - Hair care products - Hogil Pharmaceutical Corp.
INNOMAX - Water-bed frames, mattresses, and heaters - Innomax Corp.
INNOMED - Pharmaceutical preparations - Hogil Pharmaceutical Corp.
INNOMETALX - Aluminum compounds - Aluminum Co. of America
INNOPET VETERINARIAN FORMULA - Dog food - Innopet Brands Corp.
INNOTECH - Audio systems - Innotech Corp.
INNOTECH - Scientific apparatus - Innotech, Inc.
INNOV - Computer software - Innov Corp.
INNOVA - Animal feeds - Natura Pet Products, Inc.
INNOVA - Bicycles - Giant Bicycle, Inc.
INNOVA - Fans–electric - Hunter Fan Co.
INNOVA - Wallpaper - Norwall Wallcoverings
INNOVA RECORDINGS - Recording label - Minnesota Composers Forum
INNOVAR - Analgesic tranquilizer, anesthetic - Janssen Pharmaceutica Inc.
INNOVASIVE DEVICES, INC. - Surgical instruments - Innovasive Devices, Inc.
INNOVATE WITH C.A.R.E. PROFILE - Publisher's imprints - Carlson Learning Co.
INNOVATECH CORPORATION - Computer software - Innovatech Corp.
INNOVATION - Apparel and accessories - Edison Brothers Stores, Inc.
INNOVATION - Ashtrays–glass - Federal Glass
INNOVATION - Floor coverings - Congoleum Corp.
INNOVATION - Floor coverings–carpet and rugs - Patrick Carpet Mills
INNOVATION - Floor coverings–carpet and rugs - Whitecrest Carpet Mills
INNOVATION - Floor coverings–carpet and rugs ☆ - Kelly Group Inc.
INNOVATION - Tires–automobile - Jetzon/Telstar Tire
INNOVATION - Underwear and nightwear - Maidenform Inc.
INNOVATION - Vacuum cleaners and accessories - The Hoover Co.
INNOVATION - Video equipment - Gerrold General Instrument Corp.
INNOVATION - Video game - Ultimate Game Club, Ltd.
INNOVATION II - Floor coverings–carpet and rugs - Patrick Carpet Mills
INNOVATION AT LIGHTSPEED - Fabrics - Imagen Holography, Inc.
INNOVATION AT WORK - Paper–toilet - Scott Paper Co.
INNOVATION BEYOND IMAGINATION - Office machines - Sanyo Fisher (USA) Corp.
INNOVATION JUMP-START - Computer software - Workflow Technologies, Inc.
INNOVATION-LINE - Electrical equipment - Innovation Industries, Inc.
INNOVATION TEAM PROJECT - Computer software - Workflow Technologies, Inc.
INNOVATIONS - Blinds–venetian ☆ - Hunter Douglas, Inc.
INNOVATIONS - Dinnerware–glass ☆ - Nikko Ceramics Inc.
INNOVATIONS - Faucets - Masco Corp. (Plumbing Products Div.)
INNOVATIONS - Footwear–women's - United States Shoe Corp.
INNOVATIONS - Furniture–wood - Flexsteel Industries Inc.
INNOVATIONS - Housewares - Cornwall Industries Inc.
INNOVATIONS - Incontinence product - E-Z Fit Inc.
INNOVATIONS - Scales - Counselor Co.
INNOVATIONS EXPERIENCING LITERATURE IN THE CLASSROOM - Publisher's imprints - Scholastic Inc.
INNOVATIONS IN ACRYLIC - Furniture ☆ - Akko Inc.
INNOVATIONS IN LIGHT - Candleholders - Indiana Glass Co.
INNOVATIVE - Food products - Innovative Foods Inc.
INNOVATIVE - Packaging machines - Innovative Machinery Co.
INNOVATIVE AUDIO - Audio equipment - Steven G. Bell
INNOVATIVE COMMUNICATIONS - Recording label - Chameleon Music Group Inc.
INNOVATIVE CONCEPTS - Computer accessories - Innovative Concepts Inc.
INNOVATIVE COOKING ENTERPRISES I.C.E., INC. ANCHORAGE, ALASKA - Publisher's imprints - Innovative Cooking Enterprises

INNOVATIVE EDGE - Telephones - Cincinnati Microwave, Inc.
INNOVATIVE FITNESS PRODUCTS - Racks - Innovative Fitness Products
INNOVATIVE FLAVORS - WORLDWIDE - Chemical preparations - Edlong Corp.
INNOVATIVE KITCHENS - Cabinets, countertops, etc. - Innovative Companies Inc.
INNOVATIVE LEARNING PUBLICATIONS - Educational materials - Addison-Wesley Publishing Co.
INNOVATIVE-MATCH - Computer software - Innovative Systems, Inc.
INNOVATIVE SCREEN TECHNOLOGY - Vibrators - Innovative Screen Technology, LLC
INNOVATIVE SOFTWARE - Computer software - Innovative Software Development Co.
INNOVATIVE SURGICAL - Surgical instruments - Innovative Surgical, Inc.
INNOVATIVE TIME - Watches and clocks - Innovative Time Corp.
INNOVATIVE VETERINARY DIETS - Animal feeds - Nature's Recipe
INNOVATIVE WIRL - Wire products - Jesco Industries, Inc.
INNOVATOR - Air conditioning equipment - Lennox Industries Inc.
INNOVATOR - Apparel–men's ☆ - Michaels/Stern & Co. Inc.
INNOVATOR - Bathtubs–enameled - Lyons Industries Inc.
INNOVATOR - Bicycles ☆ - Hedstrom Corp.
INNOVATOR - Electronics equipment - Instructional Industries Inc.
INNOVATOR - Furniture–upholstered ☆ - Mersman Furniture Co.
INNOVATOR - Grinders - Portec Inc.
INNOVATOR - Hardware - Shepherd Products U.S. Inc.
INNOVATOR - Medical apparatus - Del Mar Avionics
INNOVATOR - Motor vehicles–trucks - McNeilus Truck and Manufacturing, Inc.
INNOVATOR - Pet products - Dogloo Inc.
INNOVATOR - Plants - Greiling Farms, Inc.
INNOVATORS - Hardware - HDI/Hardware Designers Inc.
INNOVENTIONS - Electronic equipment - Innoventions, Inc.
INNOVISIONS - Greeting cards - InnoVisions Inc.
INNOVONICS - Computer hardware - Innovonics, Inc.
INNS OF CALIFORNIA - Wallpaper - Greeff Fabrics Inc.
INNS OF CAPE MAY - Wallpaper - E.C. Carter
INNS OF CAPE MAY - Wallpaper - Greeff Fabrics Inc.
INNSBRAU - Beverages–malt - Fuhrmann & Schmidt Brewing Co.
INNSBRUCK - Beverages–malt - Renfroe Co. Inc.
INNSBRUCK - Cabinets - Quality Cabinets
INNSBRUCK - Cabinets ☆ - Medallion Kitchens of Minnesota Inc.
INNSBRUCK - Hosiery - Wigwam Mills Inc.
INNSBRUCK - Tableware–plastic ☆ - Washington Forge Inc.
INNUENDO - Wallpaper ☆ - Camelot Design Studios
INNUNISCIENCE - Skin care products - Sothys USA Inc.
INNURCO - Fish food - William Tricker Inc.
INNUWINDOW - Department stores - Jeffrey-Ellen Corp.
INNY - Jewelry - International Import Corp.
INOCRAFT - X-ray apparatus - A & S Trading
INOFOOD - Snack foods - Churny Co., Inc.
INOMACHI - Artists' materials - Andrews/Nelson/Whitehead
INOSEPTIC - Mouthwashes - Claflin Co.
INOSEPTOL - Mouthwashes - Claflin Co.
INOSINE 750 - Health care products - Above All Health Inc.
INOSINE PLUS - Health care products - Nature Health
INOSINE + - Vitamins and nutritional supplements ☆ - Makers of Kal, Inc.
INOSITOL - Vitamins and nutritional supplements - Freeda Vitamins Inc.
INOTON - Health care products ☆ - E. Fougera & Co. Inc.
INOUI - Cosmetics - Shiseido Cosmetics (America) Ltd.
INOVA - Chemical preparations - Inova Diagnostics, Inc.
INOVAR - Varnishes ☆ - PPG Industries, Inc.
INOX - Electronic equipment - Enox Technologies, Inc.
INOX - Needles–sewing - Scandinavian House Imports Inc.
INOX - Tableware–china ☆ - Robinson Knife & Fiddlers Plastics
INPERSON - Computer software - Silicon Graphics, Inc.
INPERSPECTIVE - Computer software - Integral Systems Inc.
INPESCA - Shrimp–canned or cured ☆ - Darik Enterprises Inc.
INPOSITION - Electronic equipment - DK&A, Inc.
INPOWER - Computer software - Integral Systems Inc.
INPRINT - Office machines - A.B. Dick Co.
INPROVE - Wood fillers - Unique Products, Inc.
INPUT - Health care products - Celeste Co. Inc.
INPUT - Surgical instruments - C.R. Bard, Inc.
INQUE ADVANCED PERSONAL INFORMATION MANAGER - Paper products - Process Management, Inc.
INQUEST - Chemical preparations - Ohmicron Technology, Inc.

☆ = Now out of production

INQUIRY - Computer software - Parsons, McKee, Sommers and Co.
INQUIRY SYSTEM - Computer software - FormAtion Technologies Inc.
I.N.R. - Electrical equipment ☆ - C.T.I. Audio Inc.
INRAD - Medical apparatus - INRAD, Inc.
INRAIL - Computer software - Intergraph Corp.
INRES - Computer peripheral equipment - Inres (USA), Inc.
INS SCRIBE - Computer software - Insmark, Inc.
INS-TENT - Tents - Springbok Corp.
INSALCOR - Insulating materials ☆ - Thermal Ceramics Inc.
INSANITY - Sauces - Dave's Gourmet
INSCAN - X-ray apparatus - Thermedics Detection Inc.
INSCAPE - Flowers, plants, and seeds - Weyerhaeuser Co.
INSCAPES - Wallpaper - Soni Wallace Designs Ltd.
INSCITE - Electrical equipment - Saporito & Associates, Inc.
INSCRIBE - Computers - Inscribe, Inc.
INSCRIPTIONTILE - Tiles–ceramic - Recognition Resources
INSEACO - Seafood products–fresh or frozen - Interocean Seafoods Co.
INSECT MASTER - Insecticides - Surco Products Inc.
INSECT-OFF - Insecticides - Natural Laboratories Corp.
INSECT SHOOO - Pet products ☆ - Natural Animal Health Products, Inc.
INSECT WORLD, THE - Computer software - Ventura Educational Systems
INSECTAPE - Insecticides - Hercon Environmental Corp.
INSECTICIDE SINGLES - Insecticides - Gulfstream Home & Garden Inc.
INSECTO - Insecticides - Natural Insecto Products, Inc.
INSECTO - Lighting equipment - Philips Lighting Co.
INSECTOCUTOR - Insecticides - Devpro Machine Inc. (Insectocutor Div.)
INSECTOJET - Nozzles - Spraying Systems Co.
INSECTS UP CLOSE - Pet products - Educational Insights, Inc.
INSEL - Siding–insulating ☆ - Aluminum Co. of America
INSELBRIC - Siding–metal ☆ - Aluminum Co. of America
INSENSE - Colognes - Parfums Givenchy, Inc.
INSERT - Paper–writing - Champion International Corp.
INSERT A FOOT - Health care products ☆ - Sammons Preston
INSERTABLE, THE - Binders - Samsill Corp.
INSERTABLES - Window coverings ☆ - Hunter Douglas, Inc.
INSERTAWARD - Frames–picture - G. Neil Companies
INSESSION - Computer software - Insession, Inc.
INSGIFT - Computer software - Insmark, Inc.
INSGIFT - Computer software - Insmark Insurance Services
INSHAPE - Vitamins and nutritional supplements - Integrity International, Inc.
INSIDE ADVANTAGE, THE - Computer peripheral equipment - Radisys Corp.
INSIDE EDGE - Ski apparel - Inside Edge
INSIDE FLEA RELIEF - Veterinary pharmaceutical preparations - Dr. Goodpet
INSIDE HELP - Apparel and accessories ☆ - Warnaco Inc.
INSIDE INFORMATION - Computer software - Microlytics Inc.
INSIDE JOB - Cleaning preparations - Top Brass Metal, Inc.
INSIDE LANE - Exercising equipment ☆ - Exercycle Corp.
INSIDE MOVES - Games ☆ - Parker Brothers
INSIDE OUT - Apparel and accessories - Sets Design Inc.
INSIDE-OUT - Paints - Burgess Fobes Paint Co.
INSIDE OUT - Skin care products - Ilona, Inc.
INSIDE OUT - Vitamins and nutritional supplements - Ontrend Enterprises, Inc.
INSIDE-OUT SPOUT - Packaging machines - Nimco Corp.
INSIDE/OUTSIDE - Enamels ☆ - PPG Industries, Inc.
INSIDE-OUTSIDE PUZZLES - Puzzles - Straight Edge Inc.
INSIDE SECRET - Vitamins and nutritional supplements - Windmill Marketing Services, Inc.
INSIDE STORY - Apparel–women's - Cupid Foundations Inc.
INSIDE STORY LITE - Apparel–women's - Cupid Foundations Inc.
INSIDE THE LINES - Apparel–athletic - Majestic Athletic Wear, Ltd.
INSIDE TIPS - Gloves - Marmon Holdings, Inc.
INSIDE TRACK - Exercising equipment - Pollenex Corp.
INSIDENTAL - Toothbrushes - Vortex Inc.
INSIDER - Audio equipment - Barcus-Berry Inc.
INSIDER - Lighting equipment - Falcon Eye Inc.
INSIDER GOLD - Footwear–men's - L.B. Evans' Son Co.
INSIDER, THE - Windows–storm ☆ - Plaskolite Inc.
INSIDERS - Aircraft–balloons - Anagram International, Inc.
INSIDERS - Fabrics - Milliken & Co. Inc.
INSIDERS - Luggage - Glaser Designs Inc.
INSIDETRAK - Computer software - Solutions by Computer Inc.
INSIGHT - Automotive parts and accessories - Nolan Brown Inc.
INSIGHT - Chemical preparations - WTT, Inc.
INSIGHT - Cleaning preparations - Now Products, Inc.
INSIGHT - Computer peripheral equipment - Insight Direct, Inc.
INSIGHT - Computer software - American Sigma, Inc.

INSIGHT - Computer software - Rational
INSIGHT - Computer storage devices–optical - Luna Imaging, Inc.
INSIGHT - Fireplaces ☆ - Thomas Industries Inc.
INSIGHT - Floor coverings–carpet and rugs ☆ - Criterion Mills Inc.
INSIGHT - Flower pots–plastic - Vista Products, Inc.
INSIGHT - Frames–picture ☆ - Structural Industries
INSIGHT - Medical device - Applied Urology Inc.
INSIGHT - Publisher's imprints - Simon & Schuster, Inc.
INSIGHT - Recording label - Nightingale-Conant Corp.
INSIGHT - Surgical supplies - Microtek Medical, Inc.
INSIGHT - Tape recorders–cassette ☆ - Lanier Voice Products
INSIGHT/AM - Computer software - Alpha Microsystems
INSIGHT BOOKS - Publisher's imprint - News World Communications Inc.
INSIGHT EXPERT - Computer software - Peachtree Software Inc.
INSIGHT LINKS - Computer software - Peachtree Software Inc.
INSIGHT SOLUTIONS - Computer software - Gabriel Groner
INSIGHTS - Computer software - Pavilion Technologies, Inc.
INSIGHTS - Greeting cards ☆ - American Greetings Corp.
INSIGHTS - Sunglasses - Capo, Inc.
INSIGHTS - Video production - American Isuzu Motors Inc.
INSIGNIA - Doors–vinyl - Jeld-Wen, Inc.
INSIGNIA - Faucets - T & S Brass and Bronze Works, Inc.
INSIGNIA - Pens - Parker Pen USA
INSIGNIA COLLECTION - Drapery rods - Springs Industries, Inc.
INSINUATION - Fabrics - Dan River Inc.
INSIST - Cleaning preparations - Ecolab Inc.
INSITE EDGE - Computer software - James M. Sweet
INSITE PERIPHERALS - Disk drives–computer - Insite Peripherals, Inc.
INSITEC - Measuring instruments - Malvern/Insitec, Inc.
INSITEVISION - Pharmaceutical preparations - InSite Vision Inc.
INSL-KOTE - Paints ☆ - Devoe & Raynolds Co.
INSL-THANE - Paints and coatings - Insl-X Products Corp.
INSL-TILE - Paints and coatings - Insl-X Products Corp.
INSL-TRON - Paints and coatings - Insl-X Products Corp.
INSLIDE - Sporting goods - M.J.E. Enterprises, Inc.
INSMARK PROPOSAL SYSTEM - Computer software - Insmark, Inc.
INSNET - Computer software - National Council on Compensation Insurance, Inc.
INSO - Computer software - INSO Corp.
INSOL - Plastics - Western Waterproofing Co. Inc.
INSOL-8 - Windows–storm - Hurd Millwork Co. Inc.
INSOMAWAY - Health care products - Advantage Life Products Inc.
INSORB - Hair care products - John Amico Expressive Hair Care Products
INSOUCIANCE - Beverages–alcohol - Thomas Kruse Winery
INSOURCE - Computer software - Computer Language Research Inc.
INSOURCE - Computer storage devices–optical - Nils Publishing Co.
INSOURCE SOFTWARE SOLUTIONS - Computer software - Insource Software Solutions, Inc.
INSPEC - Computer software - Hoechst Celanese Corp.
INSPECT-O-FILM - Electronics equipment - RTI Research Technology International
INSPECTA SHIELD - Hardware - Park Wylie Distributors
INSPECTACAM - Cameras - Sonora Manufacturing Group
INSPECTASCOPE - Microscopes - Learning Things Inc.
INSPECTOR - Insecticides - Whitmire Research Laboratories, Inc.
INSPECTOR CROSS - Games ☆ - Lombard Marketing, Inc.
INSPECTOR GADGET - Games ☆ - Milton Bradley Co.
INSPECTOR GADGET - Toys - Coloron Industries
INSPECTOR GADGET - Toys ☆ - Jak-Pak Inc.
INSPECTOR PC - Computer software - Highpoint Technologies, Inc.
INSPECTOR, THE - Measuring instruments - A.A. Jansson, Inc.
INSPIRAL - Underwear and nightwear - NCC Industries, Inc.
INSPIRATE Y ESCRIBE - Greeting cards - Joche Davila Studio
INSPIRATION - Apparel and accessories - Edison Brothers Stores, Inc.
INSPIRATION - Bathroom fixtures ☆ - International Paper (Decorative Products Division)
INSPIRATION - Bedding–linen - Whiting Manufacturing Co. Inc.
INSPIRATION - Clocks - General Time Corp. (Westclox/Seth Thomas Div.)
INSPIRATION - Cosmetics - Fame International Inc.
INSPIRATION - Dryers–hair ☆ - P.S. Pibbs Inc.
INSPIRATION - Floor coverings - Congoleum Corp.
INSPIRATION - Floor coverings–carpet and rugs - Cabin Crafts Carpets
INSPIRATION - Floor coverings–carpet and rugs - Lees Carpets
INSPIRATION - Glassware–household - Crisa Corp.
INSPIRATION - Housewares - Wal-Mart Stores Inc.
INSPIRATION - Jewelry - Fantasy Diamond Corp.

☆ = Now out of production

INSPIRATION - Wallpaper - Illuminations Wallcoverings & Fabrics Inc.

INSPIRATION - Window coverings - Levolor Inc.

INSPIRATION BY WARNACO - Apparel and accessories ☆ - Warnaco Inc.

INSPIRATION HEALTHDYNE - Medical equipment - Healthdyne Technologies, Inc.

INSPIRATIONAL COLLECTION - Giftware - Arnart Imports Inc.

INSPIRATIONAL FEELINGS - Glassware–household - Papel Freelance, Inc.

INSPIRATIONAL MOMENTS - Novelty items - Russ Berrie and Co., Inc.

INSPIRATIONAL PARCHMENT - Greeting cards - Norcross Inc.

INSPIRATIONAL PLAQUES - Novelty items ☆ - Sell-O Manufacturing Inc.

INSPIRATIONAL POETRY - Greeting cards ☆ - Amberley Greeting Card Co.

INSPIRATIONAL THOUGHTS - Magnets - Russ Berrie and Co., Inc.

INSPIRATIONAL TREASURES - Publisher's imprints ☆ - Warner Press, Inc.

INSPIRATIONAL VICTORIA - Greeting cards ☆ - Amberley Greeting Card Co.

INSPIRATIONS - Books–blank - Thomas Nelson, Inc.

INSPIRATIONS - Floor coverings - Mannington Resilient Floors

INSPIRATIONS - Floor coverings–carpet and rugs ☆ - World Carpets, Inc.

INSPIRATIONS - Food products - Brakebush Brothers Inc.

INSPIRATIONS - Footwear - D. Myers and Sons Inc.

INSPIRATIONS - Ice cream, frozen yogurt - Edy's Grand Ice Cream Inc.

INSPIRATIONS - Publisher's imprints - Silhouette Books

INSPIRATIONS - Wallcoverings - Scancelli Prints, Inc.

INSPIRATIONS - Wallpaper - Judscott Handprints Ltd.

INSPIRATIONS - Wallpaper - K.M.L. Industries

INSPIRATIONS - Wigs - Revlon General Wig Manufacturers, Inc.

INSPIRATIONS BY CHASE - Invitations - Chase

INSPIRATIONS THOMAS/NELSON GIFTS - Notebooks and notepads - Thomas Nelson, Inc.

INSPIRE - Perfumes - Avon Products, Inc.

INSPIRE BOOK - Publisher's imprints ☆ - Himalayan Publishers

INSPIREASE - Inhalers - Key Pharmaceuticals Inc.

INSPIRED BY TRADITION - Wallcovering - Gencorp Inc.

INSPIRED FIELDS - Floor coverings - Mannington Resilient Floors

INSPIRED TOASTS - Glass products - Co. of Women Inc.

INSPIRED TOASTS II - Glass products - Co. of Women Inc.

INSPIRON - Oxygen concentrators ☆ - Specialty Health Care Products Inc.

INSPIRX - Spirometers ☆ - Specialty Health Care Products Inc.

INSPORE - Monitors–electronic ☆ - Trimline Medical Products Corp.

INSPORT - Apparel and accessories - InSport International Inc.

INST-A-MATIC - Furniture - Leggett & Platt/Hartex

INST-AWARD - Frames–picture - Time-Frame Inc.

INSTA-BACK - Fixtures - Prest-On Co.

INSTA-BAKE - Bakery products - Hodgson Mill

INSTA-BASKET - Baskets–wood - Premier Manufacturing Corp.

INSTA-BLEND - Blenders - Hamilton Beach/Proctor-Silex Inc.

INSTA-BREWER - Product description unknown - Boonton Molding Co. Inc.

INSTA-BROIL - Housewares - Amana Refrigeration Inc.

INSTA-BUILD - Hair care products - Wella Corp. (Consumer Products Div.)

INSTA-CARROT - Vegetables–dried - Gilroy Foods Inc.

INSTA-CAST - Plastics - Douglas & Sturgess

INSTA-CLEAR - Water treating compounds ☆ - Aquatronics-Filtronics

INSTA CLEAR - Windshields–glass - Ford Motor Co. (Glass Div.)

INSTA-CLING - Window shades - Auto-Shade Inc.

INSTA-CLIP - Lighting fixtures - Coleman Co., Inc.

INSTA-COLD - Pharmaceutical preparations - Tetra Medical Supply Corp.

INSTA-COM - Amplifiers–public address ☆ - Fasco Industries Inc. (Consumer Products Div.)

INSTA-CONNECT - Audio equipment - Recoton Corp.

INSTA-CORE - Tires - Trojan Tire Core, Inc.

INSTA COUPLE - Hoses - Goodyear Tire & Rubber Co.

INSTA-COVER - Office supplies - Lion Office Products, Inc.

INSTA-CURE - Glue–household or industrial - Bob Smith Industries

INSTA-DRI - Paints - Allstates Coatings Co., Inc.

INSTA DRY - Stationery - Diagraph Corp.

INSTA-FAST - Elevators - Columbia Elevator Products Co., Inc.

INSTA-FILL - Pet products - Novalek, Inc.

INSTA-FIT - Jewelry - C & G Jewelers

INSTA FIX - Chemical preparations - NEO-FLO Inc.

INSTA-FLAG - Signs - Fasteners for Retail, Inc.

INSTA-FOAM - Hearing aids - Environmental Acoustical Research Inc.

INSTA-GLUCOSE - Pharmaceutical preparations - ICN Pharmaceuticals Inc.

INSTA GRAINS - Grain products–oats - Briess Industries Inc.

INSTA-GRIP - Chemical preparations - Insta-Foam Products, Inc.

INSTA-GROUP - Alarm systems - Baker Industries, Inc.

INSTA-HEAT - Containers - Insta-Heat, Inc.

INSTA-HEAT - Water heaters–household - Franzus Co. Inc.

INSTA-HITCH - Hitches–trailer - Reese Products, Inc.

INSTA-HOT - Pharmaceutical preparations - Tetra Medical Supply Corp.

INSTA-HUT - Tents - Klein Tools Inc.

INSTA-JEL - Desserts - Nabisco Foods Group

INSTA-LITE - Lighting fixtures - National Service Industries, Inc.

INSTA-LOAD - Electronic equipment - Telex Communications, Inc.

INSTA LOCK - Screws - Goodyear Tire & Rubber Co.

INSTA-LUBE - Electrical equipment - GB Electrical Inc.

INSTA-LUBE - Lubricants - Applied Power Inc.

INSTA-MAGIC - Photo albums ☆ - JM Co.

INSTA-MARKER - Stationery - Diagraph Corp.

INSTA-MATCH - Lighters - Duraflame, Inc.

INSTA-MATIC - Ovens–microwave ☆ - Quasar Co.

INSTA-MOLD - Chemical preparations - Activa Products Inc.

INSTA-MOLD - Hearing aids - Environmental Acoustical Research Inc.

INSTA NAIL DRI - Skin care products - Allercare Inc.

INSTA NEG - Chemical preparations - NEO-FLO Inc.

INSTA-PAK - Electronic equipment - Instrument Specialists, Inc.

INSTA-PANES - Window frames ☆ - Mansion Industries Inc.

INSTA-PAY - Computer software - Cheque-Mate International, Inc.

INSTA-PLAQUE - Artists' materials - Artistic Office Products

INSTA PULSE - Exercising equipment ☆ - Maximus Fitness Products

INSTA-PULSE - Medical apparatus - Biosig Instruments Inc.

INSTA-PUMP - Athletic footwear - Reebok International Ltd.

INSTA-RAMP - Pickup-truck loading ramp - Universal Industrial Products Co.

INSTA-READ - Thermometers - Component Design Northwest, Inc.

INSTA RINSE - Plumbing fixtures–metal - Moen Inc.

INSTA-SCHEDULE - Computer software - Scheduling Resources Group

INSTA-SEAL - Hair care products - Wella Corp. (Consumer Products Div.)

INSTA SEAL - Weather stripping - KEL-EEZ

INSTA-SET - Chemical preparations - Bob Smith Industries

INSTA-SET - Watches - Elgin Watch Co.

INSTA SHADE - Tents - Enviroworks

INSTA-SHAPE - Trees–artificial - Mr. Christmas, Inc.

INSTA-SHELF - Closet organizers - Premier Manufacturing Corp.

INSTA-SHIELD - Golfing equipment - B. B. S., Inc.

INSTA-SHOWER - Toiletries - William G. Cooke

INSTA SWEET - Coffee - NSI Sweeteners, Inc.

INSTA SWEET - Sweeteners–artificial - Necta Sweeet Inc.

INSTA-TARG-PAC - Targets ☆ - Lyman Products Corp.

INSTA-TEST - Paints - Urbco Products Inc.

INSTA TRAK - Chemical preparations - Prestone Products Corp.

INSTA-TRIM - Sporting goods - Boat Leveler Manufacturing Co.

INSTA-TRIM - Vitamins and nutritional supplements - Alleghany Pharmacal Corp.

INSTA-TUNE - Auto-repair franchise - Insta-Tune Auto Tune-Ups

INSTA-VAC - Swimming pool/spa/hot tub suction-pump cleaner - Karma Corp.

INSTA-VALVE - Industrial machinery - Hydra-Stop, Inc.

INSTA-WIPE - Scouring pads ☆ - Beverly Manufacturing Corp.

INSTA-WRAP - Skin care products - Rudolph International, Inc.

INSTACACHE - Computer peripheral equipment - National Cachecard Co.

INSTACOOL - Pharmaceutical preparations - Procter & Gamble Co.

INSTACORP - Computer software - Corporate Agents, Inc,

INSTACRETE - Epoxy - Polymeric Systems, Inc.

INSTACURE - Hair care products - Matrix Essentials, Inc.

INSTADRY - Polishes - Turtle Wax, Inc.

INSTAFAX - Photographic equipment - Eastman Kodak Co.

INSTAFIND - Belts–automotive - Goodyear Tire & Rubber Co.

INSTAFINISH - Artists' materials - Avant Inc.

INSTAFIT - Pet doors - Pet-Eze

INSTAFLAM - Stoves ☆ - Wonder Corp. of America

INSTAFLOOR - Flooring–hardwood - Lignotrade International

INSTAFLOW - Water purification systems - Bel-Aire Sales Corp.

INSTAFREEZE - Pharmaceutical preparations ☆ - Century Pharmaceuticals Inc.

INSTAFUSION - Shampoos - Fantasia Industries Corp.

INSTAGARD - Medical apparatus - Baxter International Inc.

INSTAGLO - Letterpress plates ☆ - Insta Lettering Machine Co., Inc.

INSTAGLOW - Housewares - Amana Refrigeration Inc.

INSTAGRAPHIC - Cameras - Eastman Kodak Co.

INSTAJUST - Braces–orthopedic - Slim-Ez Mr. America Manufacturing, Inc.

INSTAJUST - Metals - Anvil American, Inc.

INSTAKEY - Keys - Instakey Lock Corp.

INSTAL-A-PIER - Do-it-yourself pier and accessories - Indiana Galvanizing & Manufacturing Co.

INSTALBUM - Photo albums - Hudson Photographic Industries Inc.

INSTALEAD - Hobby kits ☆ - Bendix Mouldings Inc.
INSTALITE - Cooking equipment–household - Thermos Co.
INSTALITE THE NIGHT - Watches - E. Gluck Corp.
INSTALL-A-LOCK - Locks–door - M.A.G. Engineering & Manufacturing Co. Inc.
INSTALL SERIES - Microphones - Sam Ash Music Corp.
INSTALLER FRIENDLY - Floor coverings–tile - Tarkett, Inc.
INSTALLERS' SERVICE WAREHOUSE - Automotive parts and accessories - A.P.S., Inc.
INSTALLSHIELD - Computer software - Stirling Technologies, Inc.
INSTALLWIZARD - Computer software - Jetstream Software, Inc.
INSTALOAD - Trailers - Welding Co. of America
INSTAMASH - Potato flakes - Idahoan Foods Inc.
INSTAMATCH - Fireplace equipment - Duraflame, Inc.
INSTAMATIC - Cameras - Eastman Kodak Co.
INSTAMATIC - Meters–electric - AMI Medical Electronics Inc.
INSTAMATIC - Paint rollers ☆ - Arsco International Inc.
INSTAMATIC CALENDAR - Watches - Movado Time Corp.
INSTAMATIC DUO - Meters–electric - AMI Medical Electronics Inc.
INSTAMATIC PH - Meters–electric - AMI Medical Electronics Inc.
INSTAMELT - Salt - Hartline Products Co. Inc.
INSTANBUL - Floor coverings–carpet and rugs ☆ - Regal Rugs Inc.
INSTANT - Candles ☆ - W and F Products Inc.
INSTANT - Coatings - Sherwin-Williams Automotive Finishes Corp.
INSTANT ACTION FIRMER - Skin care products - Monteil Paris
INSTANT AIRPLANE MAKER - Computer software - Abacus Software, Inc.
INSTANT-ALGAE R - Fertilizers - Marine World
INSTANT ANALYST - Computer software - PERSONICS Corp.
INSTANT ARCHES - Arch supports - S.L.R. Foot Products, Inc.
INSTANT ART CENTER - Artists' materials ☆ - M. Grumbacher Inc.
INSTANT BEAUTY - Hair coloring preparations - Clairol Inc.
INSTANT BOUND - Office supplies - Esselte Corp.
INSTANT BREAKFAST - Food products - Nestle USA
INSTANT BROWS - Tape–adhesive - Joan Halpern
INSTANT BUILDINGS - Artists' materials - Wm. K. Walthers Inc.
INSTANT-C - Computer software - Rational Systems Inc.
INSTANT CANDLE BEADS - Candles - Smith & Vandiver, Inc.
INSTANT CASH - Novelty items - Doc's Apothecary
INSTANT CLEAVAGE PUSH-UP - Brassieres (Bras) - Leisure Acquisition, Inc.
INSTANT-COLOR - Paint sets–hobby ☆ - Loctite Corp.
INSTANT COMFORT - Shoe soles - Secondwind Products Inc.
INSTANT COOKIES - Cooking equipment–household ☆ - Nordic Ware
INSTANT DATABASE - Computer software - Asymetrix Corp.
INSTANT DECHLOR - Pet products - Weco Products Inc.
INSTANT DIP COSTUME - Cleaning preparations - Casabar
INSTANT DIP FINE - Cleaning preparations - Casabar
INSTANT DRAWER - Office supplies - Rubbermaid Inc.
INSTANT DRESSING - Apparel stores–lingerie - Formfit Rogers
INSTANT ETHERNET - Circuit boards–printed - Intl. Corp.
INSTANT EXPERT - Recording label - Steven A. Devore
INSTANT FASHION - Patterns–clothing - Butterick Co. Inc.
INSTANT FELS - Soap - Dial Corp.
INSTANT FIGURE - Apparel–women's ☆ - Bali Co. Inc.
INSTANT FILE - Stationery - George A. Arkwright
INSTANT FINISH - Nail enamel - Estee Lauder Inc.
INSTANT FIT - Slacks–women's - Counterparts Sportswear, Inc.
INSTANT FLANGER - Electronic equipment - Eventide Inc.
INSTANT-FLOW - Water heaters–household - Chronomite Laboratories Inc.
INSTANT FLOWER GARDEN - Flowers, plants, and seeds - Telamerica Media Inc.
INSTANT FRAME IT - Frames–picture ☆ - Structural Industries
INSTANT FREEZE - Hair care products - Redmond Products, Inc.
INSTANT FRESH - Chemical preparations - Star Brite
INSTANT FUN - Music–sheet - Mitchell Video Productions
INSTANT FURNITURE - Furniture ☆ - Gerber Industries Inc.
INSTANT-FUSION - Adhesives and sealants - Repair-It Industries Inc.
INSTANT GARDEN - Flowers, plants, and seeds ☆ - Sprout-Ease Co.
INSTANT-GLOW - Clocks - Spartus Corp.
INSTANT GRIP - Sporting goods - Sta-Dry Chemical Co.
INSTANT GROOM - Pet products ☆ - Spellman & Zenon Products Corp.
INSTANT GROOMER - Cosmetics - Sebastian International, Inc.
INSTANT GUTS! - Recording label - Big Mouth Publications
INSTANT HAIR EXTENSIONS - Wigs - Jean Paree Weegs Inc.
INSTANT HAIR PLUS - Cosmetics - Entre-Nous Fragrances Ltd.
INSTANT HANGUPS - Curtains - Everfast Inc.
INSTANT HEET - Fuel additives ☆ - Demert & Dougherty, Inc.

INSTANT HEROES - Paper products - MSL America Corp.
INSTANT HORIZONS - Artists' materials - Wm. K. Walthers Inc.
INSTANT ICER - Glassware–household - Dynamic Classics Ltd.
INSTANT INDIA - Sauces and seasonings - Preferred Brands Inc.
INSTANT INDIA BOMBAY SPICE & SOUR TAMARIND - Food products - India Spice
INSTANT INSANITY - Puzzles ☆ - Parker Brothers
INSTANT ISDN - Computer software - Netaccess, Inc.
INSTANT-JEL - Jams and jellies - H.C. Brill Co., Inc.
INSTANT KEYBOARD FUN I - Computer software ☆ - Electronic Courseware Systems Inc.
INSTANT LANDSCAPE - Synthetic turf - Instant Turf Industries Inc.
INSTANT LETTERING - Decals and transfers - Letraset USA Inc.
INSTANT LIFE - Novelty items - Transcience Corp.
INSTANT LIGHT - Barbecues and grills - E-Z-Por Corp.
INSTANT LUNCH - Soups–mixes - Maruchan Inc.
INSTANT LUNCH - Vitamins and nutritional supplements - Shamrock Foods Co.
INSTANT MAID - Food products - Jewel Food Stores Inc.
INSTANT MEND - Hair care products - Redmond Products, Inc.
INSTANT MILLIONAIRE - Novelty items–paper - Michael Edward Robak
INSTANT MOUNT - Photo albums ☆ - Jobar International Inc./Bibi Products
INSTANT MUSIC - Computer software - Electronic Arts Inc.
INSTANT MUSIC: IT'S ONLY ROCK 'N' ROLL - Computer software - Electronic Arts Inc.
INSTANT NAIL GLUE - Manicure preparations - Lee Pharmaceuticals
INSTANT NAIL STRENGTH - Skin care products - Fanie International
INSTANT NUZINC - Paints - OEM Paints, Inc.
INSTANT OCEAN - Salt - Aquarium Systems, Inc.
INSTANT PATCH - Roofing materials–concrete - Tremco Inc.
INSTANT PETS - Novelty items - Dynamic Development
INSTANT PLANT - Novelty items - Dynamic Development
INSTANT PLEASURE - Computer software - Martin Shawn Inc.
INSTANT POWER - Glue–household or industrial - Versachem Corp.
INSTANT PREPLAY - Sporting goods - Neon Shirtworks
INSTANT PRO - Cameras - Minolta Corp.
INSTANT PROGRAMMER - Controllers - Gemstar Development Corp.
INSTANT PROTEIN - Vitamins and nutritional supplements - Shaklee Corp.
INSTANT RECALL - Electronic equipment ☆ - J.L. Cooper Electronics
INSTANT REPLAY - Floor waxes - Brulin & Co., Inc.
INSTANT REPLAY - Furniture–upholstered ☆ - Harden Furniture Co. Inc.
INSTANT REPLAY - Hair care products - Hayashi for Hair Inc.
INSTANT ROAD REPAIR - Concrete repair products - Safety Lights Co.
INSTANT SCREEN - Frames–picture ☆ - Tyz-All Plastics Inc.
INSTANT SEAL - Sealing compounds - Kentucky Paint Manufacturing Co.
INSTANT SHINE - Cleaning preparations - Star Brite
INSTANT SHINE - Hair care products - Redmond Products, Inc.
INSTANT SMOOTHING - Cosmetics - Yves St. Laurent Parfum Corp.
INSTANT-SOFT - Fabrics - Dan River Inc.
INSTANT SOUPBREAK - Soups–mixes - Mayacamas Fine Foods, Inc.
INSTANT SPANISH - Computer software - Bilingual Software Co.
INSTANT SPELLER - Electronic equipment - Dennison National Co.
INSTANT START UV - Lamps–ultraviolet - Online Energy, Inc.
INSTANT STENCIL - Thermal stencils - American Coated Products Inc.
INSTANT-STIK - Labels–gummed - Maco Tag and Label Inc.
INSTANT SUMMER TAN - Suntan lotions ☆ - Carter-Wallace, Inc.
INSTANT-TEMP - Water heaters–household - Chronomite Laboratories Inc.
INSTANT TRACTION - Automotive parts and accessories ☆ - Turtle Wax, Inc.
INSTANT T'S - Computer peripheral equipment - A.I. Ketcher Corp.
INSTANT TURF - Synthetic turf - Instant Turf Industries Inc.
INSTANT TURF 2400 - Indoor-outdoor turf - Instant Turf Industries Inc.
INSTANT TURF 6000 - Indoor-outdoor turf - Instant Turf Industries Inc.
INSTANT-USE - Floor coverings ☆ - Fluoro Plastics Inc.
INSTANT WALL BEAUTY - Wallpaper - Lin-Gor Wallcoverings
INSTANT WALL MAGIC - Wallpaper - Lin-Gor Wallcoverings
INSTANT-WAY - Scales–industrial - Arkfeld Manufacturing & Distributing Co.
INSTANT-WELD - Adhesives and sealants - Oneida Electronics Manufacturing Co. Inc.
INSTANT WHIP - Hair care products - Clairol Inc.
INSTANT WHIP LADY CLAIROL - Hair care products - Clairol Inc.
INSTANTAN - Tanning agents - Professional Aids Corp.
INSTANTBLEND - Cream - Instantwhip Foods Inc.
INSTANTEA - Teas ☆ - Redco Foods Inc.
INSTANTEX - Decals and transfers - Letraset USA Inc.
INSTANTIMAGE - Computer software - Avery Dennison Corp.
INSTANTINA - Teas ☆ - Chase Collection, Inc.

☆ = Now out of production

INSTANTOP - Pickup caps - Instantop Inc.
INSTANTRF - Computer software - Nettech Systems, Inc.
INSTANTRON - Epilator - Instantron Co. Inc.
INSTANTWATER COLOR - Markers–felt-tip - Dixon Ticonderoga Co.
INSTANTWHIP - Whipped toppings, dressings, creamers - Instantwhip-Chicago Inc.
INSTANTWHIP - Whipping cream - Instantwhip Foods Inc.
INSTAPAK - Packaging–paper - Sealed Air Corp.
INSTAPANE - Glass–window - Capitol Glass and Aluminum Corp.
INSTAPANEL - Pet products - Pet-Eze
INSTAPERM - Construction equipment rental services - Mankind Research Unltd. Inc.
INSTAPURE - Health care products - Teledyne Water Pik
INSTAROK - Cement - Metalcrete Industries Inc.
INSTASAFE - Anti-slip preparation - Slipsafe Professional Products, Inc.
INSTASEAL - Plugs–ear - Cabot Safety Intermediate Corp.
INSTASHADE - Windows–plastic ☆ - Carefree of Colorado
INSTASHEETER - Packaging–paper - Sealed Air Corp.
INSTASWITCH - Computer software - Digital Pictures, Inc.
INSTAT - Computer software - GraphPad Software Inc.
INSTATACK - Paneling - Real Trailers Inc.
INSTATEAR - Film - Favorite Plastics Corp.
INSTATECH - Cameras - Eastman Kodak Co.
INSTATRACE - Electrodes - Conmed Andover Medical, Inc.
INSTATRAK - Medical apparatus - Visualization Technology, Inc.
INSTAVISION - Binoculars - Bausch & Lomb Inc.
INSTAVISION - Electronics equipment - Ampex Corp.
INSTAWALL - Wallpaper - PCI Industries Inc.
INSTCAFE - Coffee - Allied International Corp.
INSTEAD - Medical apparatus - Ultrafem, Inc.
INSTEAD - Vitamins and nutritional supplements - Christopher Enterprises Inc.
INSTEAD OF SALT - Seasonings - Health Valley Food
INSTEC - Computer software - Insurance Information Technologies, Inc.
INSTED - Computer software - Thaerocomp Technical Corp.
INSTED O'LEAD - Chemical preparations - Bardahl Manufacturing Corp.
INSTEEL - Furniture - AA Mine Service, Inc.
INSTENT - Cheese puffs - Instent Inc.
INSTEP - Shoes - Hyde Athletic Industries Inc.
INSTI-KLEAN - Cleaning preparations - Sysco Food Services
INSTIBEAM - Alarm systems - Electronic Security Products of California
INSTIDESK - Computer storage devices - Commscan, Inc.
INSTIGATORS - Shoes ☆ - Edison Brothers Stores, Inc.
INSTINCT - Automotive parts and accessories - Cheng Shin Rubber USA, Inc.
INSTINCT - Computer software - Kinetic Systems Corp.
INSTINCT - Golfing equipment - Triumph Golf Co.
INSTINCT - Medical apparatus - Cordis Endovascular Systems, Inc.
INSTINCT - Recording label - Instinct Records Corp.
INSTINCT AMBIEMT - Recording label - Instinct Records Corp.
INSTINCT CORPORATION - Computer software - Instinct Corp.
INSTINCT JAZZ - Recording label - Instinct Records Corp.
INSTINCT RECORDS - Recording label - Instinct Records Corp.
INSTINCTIVE PAYROLL - Computer software - Robert M. Gossett
INSTINCTIVES - Shoes - Cypress Shoes
INSTINCTS - Bathing suits - Bendigo International Inc.
INSTITUTE SWISS - Skin care products - FMG/Tsumara Medical
INSTITUTE SWISS - Toiletries - Guest Supply Inc.
INSTO - Paints - Valspar Corp.
INSTO CHLOR - Water treating compounds - Jungle Laboratories Corp.
INSTOEMATIC - Brakes–motor vehicle - Hamilton Caster & Manufacturing Co.
INSTON - Office supplies - Universal Paper Goods Co.
INSTORELINK - Computer software - STR, Inc.
INSTRU-MINT - Musical instrument accessories ☆ - McMillan Music Co.
INSTRUCT-O-MATIC - Electronic equipment - Apollo Audiovisual Inc.
INSTRUCTABLE - Desks - Fleetwood Furniture Co.
INSTRUCTERN - Furniture - Fleetwood Furniture Co.
INSTRUCTIONAL WORKBENCH - Computer software - At&T Corp.
INSTRUCTOR - Electronic equipment - Telex Communications, Inc.
INSTRUCTOR - Golfing equipment - Royal Grip, Inc.
INSTRUCTOR - Sports apparel - Reebok International Ltd.
INSTRUCTORBOOK - Publisher's imprints - Sports Instructors, Inc.
INSTRUCTOR'S CHOICE, THE - Sporting goods - Underwater Diving Inc.
INSTRUMENT MANAGERS - Computer software ☆ - Performance Products Inc.
INSTRUMENTAL - Computer software - Instrumental, Inc.
INSTRUMENTAL - Floor coverings–carpet and rugs ☆ - Karastan-Bigelow Inc.
INSTRUMENTALITIES - Lamps - GRK Manufacturing

INSTRUMENTS FOR RESEARCH AND INDUSTRY - Laboratory equipment - Instruments for Research and Industry, I2R Inc.
INSTY-DRIVE - Tools–power-driven - James L. Wienhold
INSTY-NOTES - Adhesive notes - Insty Prints Inc.
INSTY-PRINTS - Printing and photocopying franchise - Insty Prints Inc.
INSTY-STAMP - Stamps–hand ☆ - Carolina Marking Devices, Inc.
INSTYDOSE - Pharmaceutical preparations - Medique Products
INSU-LINER - Refrigerators - Amana Refrigeration Inc.
INSUL - Sleeping bags - Coleman Co., Inc.
INSUL-AID - Paints - Glidden Co.
INSUL-AIR - Swimming pool covers - St. John Manufacturing Co., Inc.
INSUL-BAIT - Fishing lures - Frabill Inc.
INSUL-BAR-BUS-SYSTEM - Electronic equipment - General Electric Co.
INSUL-BLAZE - Paints - Glidden Co.
INSUL-COOL - Medical apparatus - Apothecary Products, Inc.
INSUL CORE - Doors–wood - Rubbair Door
INSUL-CUBE - Insulating materials - Guardian Industries Corp. (Architectural Glass Div.)
INSUL-DECK - Wood products - Texas Aluminum Industries Inc.
INSUL-DOOR - Pet products - Insul-House
INSUL DOR - Doors–glass - Acorn Window Systems Inc.
INSUL-DRAIN - Drainboards - UC Industries, Inc.
INSUL-ELE - Medical apparatus ☆ - Apothecary Products, Inc.
INSUL-EZE - Health care products - Apothecary Products, Inc.
INSUL-EZE - Medical apparatus - Palco Laboratories
INSUL-FLUE - Ventilation equipment - Bernard Dalsin Manufacturing
INSUL-GARD - Insulating materials ☆ - Sto-Cote Products Inc.
INSUL-GARD - Ventilation equipment - N.H. Rudeen Co.
INSUL-GLASS - Glass products - Burton Enterprises Inc.
INSUL-LINER - Insulating materials - Z-Flex U.S. Inc.
INSUL-LITE - Tanks–steel - We-Mac Manufacturing Co.
INSUL-PANEL - Insulation - Insul-Board
INSUL-QUICK - Insulating materials - Owens Corning
INSUL-SAFE - Insulating materials - Certainteed Corp. (Roofing Products Group)
INSUL-SEAL - Conduits–electrical - Ravenhorst Concrete Products, Inc.
INSUL-SHIELD - Insulating materials - Manville/Schuller
INSUL-SHIELD - Insulating materials - Nichols-Homeshield Inc.
INSUL-SHIELD - Insulating materials - Schuller International, Inc.
INSUL-TEX - Paints - Chemex Paint & Coatings Inc.
INSUL-TILT - Windows–storm - Caldwell Manufacturing Co.
INSUL-TOTE - Bags - Palco Laboratories
INSUL-TOTE JUNIOR - Bags - Palco Laboratories
INSUL-TRAC - Curtains ☆ - Anderson Fabrics Inc.
INSUL-VENT - Tubes–steel - Z-Flex U.S. Inc.
INSUL WAL - Window frames - Acorn Window Systems Inc.
INSUL-WRAP - Insulating materials - Ultra Industries/Polycel Products
INSULA - Insulating materials - Floral Glass & Mirror Inc.
INSULA-DOME SKYHATCH - Skylights - Insula-Dome Skylights
INSULAIR - Containers - Insulair, Inc.
INSULARC - Insulating materials - Franklin Fibre-Lamitex Corp.
INSULATARD - Insulin - Novo Nordisk Pharmaceuticals Inc.
INSULATE - Chemicals to inhibit plant frost - Monterey Chemical Co. Inc.
INSULATE - Cough medicines - Mayer Laboratories, Inc.
INSULATION - Cosmetics - Estee Lauder Inc.
INSULATOR - Cleaning preparations–upholstery - Production Chemical Manufacturing, Inc.
INSULATOR - Doors–storm ☆ - Gerkin Windows & Doors
INSULATOR - Kitchen appliances - Carlisle Foodservice Products, Inc.
INSULATOR BY MAXWELL, THE - Computer software - Maxwell Systems Inc.
INSULATOR, THE - Window shades - Newell Window Furnishing Co.
INSULAYER - Soft-sided insulated products - Diversified Recycling Systems
INSULAYMENT III - Insulating materials ☆ - Simplex Products Div.
INSULBOND - Adhesives and sealants - Henry Co.
INSULCOAT - Paints - Somay Products Inc.
INSULECTRIC - Paints - Standard T Chemical Co. Inc.
INSULEZE - Insulation kits - Templeton Coal Co. Inc.
INSUL*FILM - Window coverings - Courtaulds Performance Plus
INSULFRAX - Insulating materials - Carborundum Co.
INSULGLAZE - Adhesives and sealants - Biddle Co.
INSULIGHT - Jackets - Tomen Apparel Group Inc.
INSULIN-COOL - Medical apparatus ☆ - Apothecary Products, Inc.
INSULIN PROTECTOR - Medical apparatus - Medicool Inc.
INSULINER - Bathroom fixtures - Kohler Co.
INSULITE - Bathroom accessories - Insulite Inc.
INSULITE - Fabrics–cotton - Arthur Kahn Co. Inc.

☆ = Now out of production

INSULKIT - Leather goods - Robert H. Gregory
INSULKNIT - Crocheted and knitted items ☆ - Roosevelt Mills Inc.
INSULKOTE - Coatings - Manville/Schuller
INSULKOTE - Coatings - Nationwide Chemical Coating Manufacturers, Inc.
INSULMAT - Pet products ☆ - Pet-Eze
INSULOCK - Building materials - Williams Panel Bricks Inc.
INSULOFT DOWN - Fibers–synthetic - United Feather & Down Inc.
INSULPANE - Glass–illuminating - Croft Metals Inc.
INSULPINK - Insulating materials - Owens Corning Fiberglass Technology Inc.
INSULROCK - Construction equipment ☆ - Flintkote Co.
INSULROCK - Insulating materials ☆ - GS Roofing Products Co.
INSULSTACK - Blocks–chimney - Heatilator Inc.
INSULTHERM - Apparel and accessories - Magnum Sportswear, Inc.
INSULUX - Paints - Wyckoff Paint & Wallpaper Co.
INSURANCE - Detergents - Calgon Vestal Laboratories
INSURANCE - Skin-care products - California SunCare, Inc.
INSURANCE CONNECTOR - Computer software - Brand Software, Inc.
INSURANCE DIMENSIONS - Computer software - Insurance Information Technologies, Inc.
INSURANCE FORMULA - Vitamins - Bronson Pharmaceuticals
INSURE - Automotive parts and accessories - Pirelli Power Transmission Corp.
INSURE++ - Computer software - Parasoft Corp.
INSURE HERBAL - Vitamins and nutritional supplements - McZand Herbal, Inc.
INSURLCE 2000 - Water purification systems - Everpure Inc.
INSURLCE 3000 - Water purification systems - Everpure Inc.
INSWOOL - Insulation fibers - A.P. Green Industries Inc.
INSYNC - Computer hardware - Mantech Systems Corp.
INSYNC - Computer software - Di Biasio & Edgington, Inc.
INT 4000 - Communications equipment ☆ - NEC America, Inc.
INTA - Recording label - International Trademark Association, Inc.
INTAC - Lubricating oils - Intac Automotive Products Inc.
INTACEPT - Health care products ☆ - Abkit, Inc.
INTACRYL - Awnings - Rainbow Awnings
INTACT - Computer software - ASCI
INTACT - Health care products - C.R. Bard, Inc.
INTAGLIO - Cosmetics - Research Institute for Plastic, Cosmetic and Reconstructive Surgery, Inc.
INTAGLIO - Flatware - Reed and Barton Corp.
INTAGLIO - Floor coverings–carpet and rugs - Sweetwater Carpet Corp.
INTAGLIO - Glass products ☆ - Pittsburgh Corning Corp.
INTAGLIO - Shoes - Edison Brothers Stores, Inc.
INTAGLIO - Wallpaper - Capital Carousel Inc.
INTAGLIO - Watches - Tiffany and Co.
INTAKES - Computer software - Compass Systems Corp.
INTAL - Health care products - Fisons Corp.
INTALINE - Construction equipment - Alcan Aluminum Corp. Alcan Building Products Div.
INTAMATE ENERGIZER - Vitamins and nutritional supplements - Beso Biological Research Center, Inc.
INTANGIBLE - Colognes ☆ - Avon Products, Inc.
INTANGIBLE - Publisher's imprints - Intangible Publications, Inc.
INTANGIBLES - Wallpaper - Charles Barone Inc.
INTARSIA - Faucets - Gerber Plumbing Fixtures Corp.
INTARSIA - Floor coverings–carpet and rugs - Atlas Carpet Mills Inc.
INTASEDOL - Pharmaceutical preparations ☆ - ICN Pharmaceuticals Inc.
INTEC - Vitamins and dietary food supplements - Intec Laboratories
INTECH - Golfing equipment - Knight Golf, Inc.
INTECH EDM - Chemical preparations - Intech Technology Corp.
INTECLEAR - Resins–acrylic - World-Pak Corp.
INTEDUR - Resins–acrylic - World-Pak Corp.
INTEFOAM - Resins–acrylic - World-Pak Corp.
INTEGER ARCADE - Computer software ☆ - Queue Inc.
INTEGRA - Fans–electric - HPI Inc.
INTEGRA - Floor coverings–carpet and rugs - Whitecrest Carpet Mills
INTEGRA - Goggles–safety - Pyramex Safety Products, Inc.
INTEGRA - Machine parts - Fluoroware, Inc.
INTEGRA - Motor vehicles–automobiles - American Honda Motor Co. Inc. (Acura Div.)
INTEGRA - Plastics film - DRG Medical Packaging, Inc.
INTEGRA - Stereos - Onkyo USA Corp.
INTEGRA - Tables–metal - Alvin and Co. Inc.
INTEGRA - Tents - Kellwood Co.
INTEGRA - Upholstered furniture - Integra
INTEGRA - Water heaters–household - S.A.B.H. U.S. Water Heaters
INTEGRA TEAR - Plastics - Curwood, Inc.

INTEGRA WINBEEP - Computer software - Integra Technology International, Inc.
INTEGRAL - Adhesives in film form - Dow Chemical Co.
INTEGRAL - Disk drives–computer - Integral Peripherals Inc.
INTEGRAL - Golfing equipment - Taylor Made Golf Co. Inc.
INTEGRAL - Implants–surgical - Biomet, Inc.
INTEGRAL DNA - Skin care products - Catherine Atzen
INTEGRAL PERIPHERALS - Computers - Integral Peripherals Inc.
INTEGRAL TECHNOLOGIES - Computer software - Integral Technologies, Inc.
INTEGRAL THREADLOC - Medical apparatus - Calcitek, Inc.
INTEGRAL WALL - Partitions–wood - Dowcraft Corp.
INTEGRALE - Health care products - C.R. Bard, Inc.
INTEGRALOCK - Locks–door - Sargent Manufacturing Co.
INTEGRAPERF - Packaging–blisterwrap - Curwood, Inc.
INTEGRATE - Furniture–wood ☆ - Recyco
INTEGRATED - Golfing equipment - Pro Kennex, Inc.
INTEGRATED - Mailing machines ☆ - Transkrit
INTEGRATED DECISION MANAGER - Computer software - Servantis Systems, Inc.
INTEGRATED FABRIC RESOURCE - Boats - Holland Awning Co.
INTEGRATED HEALTH SYSTEMS - Computer storage devices - Integrated Health Systems Inc.
INTEGRATED LANGUAGE ENVIRONMENT - Computer software - International Business Machines Corp.
INTEGRATED PROTECTION SYSTEMS - Computer software - Beckwith Electric Co.
INTEGRATED QUALITY DYNAMICS - Computer software - Integrated Quality Dynamics, Inc.
INTEGRATED SERVICES INC. - Computer software - Integrated Services, Inc.
INTEGRATED SOLUTIONS - Computer software - Hart Information Services, Inc.
INTEGRATED TOE STOP CHASSIS - Sporting goods - Seneca Sports, Inc.
INTEGRATION SPECIALISTS, INC. - Computer hardware - Integration Specialists, Inc.
INTEGRATION WORKS - Computer software - Data Integration Solutions Corp.
INTEGRATOR - Computer software - ITP Licensing Corp.
INTEGRATOR - Controls–heating systems - Teletrol Systems Inc.
INTEGRATOR - Kitchen appliances - Carlisle Foodservice Products, Inc.
INTEGRATOR, THE - Furniture - Motorola, Inc. (Land Mobile Products Sector)
INTEGRATRAK - Computer software - Integratrak, Inc.
INTEGREATER EXPRESS - Computer software - National Education Training Group, Inc.
INTEGRITEST - Measuring instruments - Millipore Corp.
INTEGRITY - Bedding–linen ☆ - Dan River Inc.
INTEGRITY - Coffee makers–electric - Bloomfield Industries Inc.
INTEGRITY - Cooking equipment–household - Nordic Ware
INTEGRITY - Fabrics - Greenwood Mills Inc.
INTEGRITY - Floor coverings–carpet and rugs - Patrick Carpet Mills
INTEGRITY - Floor coverings–carpet and rugs - Queen Carpet Corp.
INTEGRITY - Floor coverings–carpet and rugs - S and S Mills Inc.
INTEGRITY - Hair care products - Joico Laboratories
INTEGRITY - Medical apparatus - Kirschner Medical Corp.
INTEGRITY - Paints - Valspar Corp.
INTEGRITY - Thread - Threads USA Div.
INTEGRITY - Windows - Marvin Lumber and Cedar Co.
INTEGRITY FLOOR GASKET - Gaskets - Shadwell Co., Inc.
INTEGRITY MUSIC - Recording label - Sparrow Corp.
INTEGRITY PET PRODUCTS - Pet food - Animal Supply Co.
INTEGRIX - Computers–mainframe - Integrix Inc.
INTEKON - Computer software - Mikon Systems, Inc.
INTEL - Computers–personal - Intel Corp.
INTEL-A-KEY - Motor vehicle parts and accessories - Roger D. Taylor
INTEL PROSHARE - Computer hardware - Intel Corp.
INTELE-MODEM - Telephones–text - Ultratec, Inc.
INTELE-TYPE - Telephones–text ☆ - Ultratec, Inc.
INTELEK-PRO - Industrial machinery - Signet Scientific Co.
INTELEVISION - Television equipment - Spruce Run Technologies, Inc.
INTELEX - Exercising equipment - Proform Fitness Products, Inc.
INTELI POWER 9000 - Converters–electric - Progressive Dynamics, Inc.
INTELI POWER 9100 - Generators–battery charging - Progressive Dynamics, Inc.
INTELIQUEST - Educational materials - Steven A. Devore
INTELISWITCH - Electrical equipment - Watt Stopper Inc.
INTELITIMER - Lighting equipment - Watt Stopper Inc.
INTELL-A-CHECK - Computer software - Intell-A-Check Corp.
INTELLAGENT - Computer peripheral equipment - Genesis 2000, Inc.

☆ = Now out of production

INTELLAGENT CONTROL - Computer software - Veritas Technologies, Inc.
INTELLAMATIC - Battery chargers - Associated Equipment Corp.
INTELLBELL - Weightlifting equipment - Intellbell, Inc.
INTELLECT - Computer software - Clearwave Communications, Inc.
INTELLECT - Controls–heating systems - Intelligent Energy Corp.
INTELLECTUAL ATTACHE, THE - Briefcases - Monarch Luggage Co., Inc.
INTELLECTUAL MULTIMEDIA - Computer software - Graphic M*I*S, LLC
INTELLECTUAL PURSUITS - Computer software - Hartley Courseware Inc.
INTELLEDGE - Advertising agencies - Intelledge Corp.
INTELLI-GATE - Remote control devices - Integrated Security Systems Inc.
INTELLI-PHONE - Telephones ☆ - Universal Security Instruments Inc.
INTELLI-READER - Computers - Destron/Idi, Inc.
INTELLI-TEXT DESIGNER - Computer software - KnowledgePoint
INTELLI-TYPE - Computer software - Electronic Arts Inc.
INTELLIBAR - Printers–computer - NEC Technologies, Inc.
INTELLICAM - Surveillance equipment - Intevac, Inc.
INTELLICARE - Computer software - Sunquest Information Systems, Inc.
INTELLICART - Computer hardware - Barcode Resources, Inc.
INTELLICAST - Publisher's imprints - Radyne Comstream Corp.
INTELLICAT - Computer software - United Stationers Inc.
INTELLICATH - Catheters - Interflo Medical Inc.
INTELLICELL - Batteries - Cellular Telecom Corp.
INTELLICELL - Communications equipment - Arraycomm, Inc.
INTELLICENTER - Computer software - Fujitsu Business Communication Systems,Inc.
INTELLICHARGE - Battery chargers - Motorola, Inc. (Land Mobile Products Sector)
INTELLICHARGE - Computer software - Intuit Inc.
INTELLICODE - Radio communications equipment - Gmi Holdings, Inc.
INTELLICOLOR - Computer peripheral equipment - Radius Inc.
INTELLICUT - Plastics - RDN Manufacturing Co., Inc.
INTELLIDERM - Vitamins and nutritional supplements - A-Veda Corp.
INTELLIDESK - Computer software - Intelligent Technology Group Inc.
INTELLIDESK - Computer software - System Development Co. of New Hampshire, Inc.
INTELLIDOOR - Computers - Thomson Training & Simulation, Inc.
INTELLIDRY - Dental compounds - Maytag Corp.
INTELLIEDGE - Computer software - Ohio Electronic Engravers, Inc.
INTELLIFEX - Audio equipment - Rocktron Corp.
INTELLIFINDER - Computer software - Infosoft International, Inc.
INTELLIFRAME - Computer hardware - Tektronix, Inc.
INTELLIGEN INC. - Generators–electric - Intelink Research Inc.
INTELLIGENT ACCOMPANIMENT - Computer software - Coda Music Technology, Inc.
INTELLIGENT ACCOMPANIST - Computer peripheral equipment - Coda Music Technology, Inc.
INTELLIGENT ALTERNATIVES - Consulting services - Richard M. Goldberg
INTELLIGENT BUSINESS SYSTEMS - Computer software - Intelligent Business Systems Inc.
INTELLIGENT CALLROUTER - Computer software - Geotel Communications Corp.
INTELLIGENT CEILING, THE - Wiring devices - AFC Cable Systems, Inc.
INTELLIGENT CHOICE I.C. - Beverages–carbonated - Frank A. Corsini
INTELLIGENT CHOICE IN DATA COMMUNICATIONS, THE - Communications equipment–mobile - U.S. Robotics Access Corp.
INTELLIGENT CONNECTABLE FACSIMILE, THE - Computer software - Toshiba America Information Systems, Inc.
INTELLIGENT ENERGY SAVER - Computer peripheral equipment - Unipower Corp.
INTELLIGENT FAST CHARGER - Battery chargers - Cellstar, Ltd.
INTELLIGENT FLOOR, THE - Electrical equipment - AFC Cable Systems, Inc.
INTELLIGENT FLOW METER - Meters–frequency - Curtin Matheson Scientific, Inc.
INTELLIGENT HOUSEWARES - Carts - Wire World of America, Inc.
INTELLIGENT IDEAS - Toys - Abdolreza Assadi-Lamouki
INTELLIGENT INSTRUMENTATION - Computer hardware - Intelligent Instrumentation, Inc.
INTELLIGENT LAWN FOOD - Iced tea–bottled or canned - Stern's Miracle-Gro Products, Inc.
INTELLIGENT LUBRICANTS - Automotive lubricants - Simon Petrochemicals, Inc.
INTELLIGENT NAVIGATOR - Computer software ☆ - Horizons Technology, Inc.
INTELLIGENT NO-IMPACT WORKOUT, THE - Exercising equipment - Aqua-Leisure Industries, Inc.

INTELLIGENT PAPER TO CAD SOLUTIONS - Computer software - GTX Corp.
INTELLIGENT REBUILD - Computer software ☆ - ECCS, Inc.
INTELLIGENT SERIAL INTERFACE - Computer hardware - Multi-Tech Systems, Inc.
INTELLIGENT SYSTEMS - Computers–personal - Intelligent Systems Corp.
INTELLIGENT TAN, THE - Skin care products ☆ - Holistic Products Corp.
INTELLIGENT TECHNOLOGY. - Machine parts - Haldex Corp.
INTELLIGENT TOOL FOR CARE MANAGEMENT, THE - Computer software - Health Service Affiliates, Inc.
INTELLIGENT WINDOW - Window coverings - Rockland Industries Inc.
INTELLIGENTLY QUIET - Computer software - Smith Corona Corp.
INTELLIGON - Computer software - Software AG of North America, Inc.
INTELLIGUARD 9000 - Alarm systems–burglar - Honeywell Inc.
INTELLIJECT - Medical apparatus - Medex, Inc.
INTELLILAB - Computer software - Intellidata, Inc.
INTELLIMATRIX - Machinery - Ward Holding Co., Inc.
INTELLIMEDIA - Electronic equipment - Intellimedia Corp.
INTELLIMIX - Audio equipment - Shure Brothers, Inc.
INTELLINET - Ophthalmic apparatus - Chiron Corp.
INTELLIPAINT - Computer software - Intellitools, Inc.
INTELLIPAK - Air conditioning equipment - American Standard Inc.
INTELLIPICK - Computer software - The Raymond Corp.
INTELLIPLANS - Computer software - Finally Inc.
INTELLIPOINT - Alarm systems–burglar - Honeywell Inc.
INTELLIPRO - Electronic equipment - Intellimedia Corp.
INTELLIPULL - Plastics - RDN Manufacturing Co., Inc.
INTELLIREPEATER - Radio communications equipment - Motorola, Inc. (Land Mobile Products Sector)
INTELLIROM - Computer software - Intellirom Corp.
INTELLISALES - Computer software - ESI Systems, Inc.
INTELLISCAN - Computer software - Pictronics Corp.
INTELLISCREEN - Computer software - Farallon Computing, Inc.
INTELLISCRIBE - Computer software - III G.I., Ltd.
INTELLISEEK - Computer storage devices–optical - Information Access Co.
INTELLISENSE - Alarm systems - Intellisense Security Systems Inc.
INTELLISENSE - Computer software - Microsoft Corp.
INTELLISENSE - Dishwashers–household - Maytag Corp.
INTELLISENSE - Electronic equipment - C & K Systems, Inc.
INTELLISENSE - Measuring instruments - National Draeger, Inc.
INTELLISENSE - Monitors–electronic - Crane Co.
INTELLISENSOR - Measuring instruments - Datcon Instrument Co.
INTELLISERV - Computer software - United Stationers Inc.
INTELLISERVER - Computer software - Computone Corp.
INTELLISITE - Computer software - Sirrus Internet Solutions
INTELLISIZE - Plastics - RDN Manufacturing Co., Inc.
INTELLISPEED - Machinery - Kingsbury Corp.
INTELLISTAT - Air purification systems - Simco
INTELLISYNC - Cleaning preparations - Puma Technology, Inc.
INTELLITAG - Computer software - Wordperfect Corp.
INTELLITALK - Computer software - Unicorn Engineering, Inc.
INTELLITOOLS - Compuer keyboards - Unicorn Engineering, Inc.
INTELLITRACK - Computer hardware - Intelliscan, Inc.
INTELLITRAVEL - Computer software - Automobile Club of Southern California
INTELLITUTOR - Computer software - ITP Licensing Corp.
INTELLIVISION - Electronic equipment - C & K Systems, Inc.
INTELLIVUE - Computer software - III G.I., Ltd.
INTELOCK - Locks–door - Intelock Technologies
INTELSENSE - Pumps–hydraulic - Ingersoll-Rand Co.
INTEND - Computer software - GraphPad Software Inc.
INTENN ENGINEERING, INC. - Surgical instruments - Intenn Engineering, Inc.
INTENNA - Telephones - Cobra Electronics Corp.
INTENNA 900 - Radio communications equipment - Cobra Electronics Corp.
INTENSCOLOR INTERGUARD - Medical apparatus - Impra, Inc.
INTENSE - Recording label - Frontline Records
INTENSICODER - Audio equipment ☆ - Technamics Co.
INTENSIFIER - Tools - Bowen Tools, Inc.
INTENSITY - Electronic equipment - Ronald C. Medeiros
INTENSITY - Health care products - Natural Organics, Inc.
INTENSITY - Prophylactics - Ansell Inc. (Personal Products Div.)
INTENSIVE - Hair care products - Peter Hantz Co.
INTENSIVE - Hair care products - Protege Corp.
INTENSIVE SUN DEFENSE - Sunblocks - Orjene Natural Cosmetics
INTENSIVE USE - Chairs–upholstered - Domore/DO3
INTENSIVES - Hair care products - Graham Webb International
INTENSIVES - Pharmaceutical preparations ☆ - Dermalogica Inc.

☆ = Now out of production

INTENT - Hair care products - Chenice Beverly Hills
INTENTIONS - Apparel and accessories - Eddie Haggar Ltd., Inc.
INTENTIONS - Apparel and accessories ☆ - Hartwell Garment Co.
INTEPHONE - Computer software - Intecom Inc.
INTEPRO - Containers–plastic - World-Pak Corp.
INTEQ - Surgical instruments - Linvatec Corp.
INTER-AM - Handlebars–motorcycle - Summit Industries, Inc.
INTER-CAL - Vitamins and nutritional supplements - Oxycal Laboratories, Inc.
INTER-CHECK - Computer peripheral equipment - Pelco
INTER-CONTINENTAL - Hotel chain - Inter-Continental Hotels
INTER-FEAR-ON-MAGIC - Pharmaceutical preparations - Bethurum Research & Development Inc.
INTER-GLASS - Swimming pools - American Chem-Tech Inc.
INTER-ISLAND SURF SHOP - Surfboards - Barry L. Morrison
INTER-ISLAND SURF SHOP CUSTOM HAWAII - Sporting goods - Barry L. Morrison
INTER-LOC - Siding–insulating - Weyerhaeuser Co.
INTER LOCK - Hair care products ☆ - Molina International
INTER-LOK - Doors–metal - Amweld Building Products
INTER-LUDE - Underwear and nightwear - Maidenform Inc.
INTER/PHASE - Musical instrument accessories - Adder Plus Corp.
INTER PLAY - Brassieres (Bras) ☆ - Lovable Co.
INTER RECYCLING - Machinery - Inter Recycling, Inc.
INTER-SHAPE - Apparel–women's - Champion Jogbra
INTER-TONE - Paints ☆ - Standard Brands Paint Co.
INTER-VUE - Lenses–magnifying - United States Marketing Corp.
INTER-WEAVE - Wigs ☆ - Rene of Paris Inc.
INTER-X - Computer software - Intergraph Corp.
INTERA - Health care products - Geri-Care Products, LLC
INTERA LITE - Health care products - Geri-Care Products, LLC
INTERACCESS - Modems - Electronic Information Technologies, Inc.
INTERACT - Chemical preparations - O'Neil Color and Compounding Corp.
INTERACT - Computer software - Mpact Manufacturing Systems, Inc.
INTERACT - Electrical equipment - Sola
INTERACT - Floor coverings–carpet and rugs - Walter Carpet Mills
INTERACTION - Computer software ☆ - Capstone Software
INTERACTION CALLING CARD - Telephone accessories - Interaction Solutions, Inc.
INTERACTIVE - Health care products - Innovative Medical Engineering Inc.
INTERACTIVE - Pens - Moon Products, Inc.
INTERACTIVE ARTS - Toys - Richard E. Olsen
INTERACTIVE AV - Electronic equipment ☆ - J.C. Penney Co., Inc.
INTERACTIVE BIBLIOGRAPHY - Computer software - SourceView Software International
INTERACTIVE BY DESIGN - Floor coverings–linoleum - Mannington Mills, Inc.
INTERACTIVE CATALOG - Computer software - SourceView Software International
INTERACTIVE CD-ROM TRAINING LIBRARY - Educational materials - Marcom Group, Ltd.
INTERACTIVE CLASSROOMS INC. - Computer hardware - Interactive Classrooms, Inc.
INTERACTIVE COBOL GENERATOR - Computer software - SourceView Software International
INTERACTIVE COMICS - Books–comic - Malibu Comics Entertainment, Inc.
INTERACTIVE COMMUNICATIONS TECHNOLOGIES - Computer software - Interactive Communications Technologies Inc.
INTERACTIVE COMPUTER AIDED NATURAL LEARNING - Educational materials - JRL Enterprises, Inc.
INTERACTIVE COURTROOM - Multimedia Computer software and hardware - CLE Group
INTERACTIVE DISTRIBUTION - Tape recorders–cassette - Internet Services Corp.
INTERACTIVE FLIPCHART (IFC) - Computers–mainframe - Numonics Corp.
INTERACTIVE GOAL - Soccer goals and nets - Goal Oriented Co.
INTERACTIVE I/O - Computer storage devices - Interactive I/O, Inc.
INTERACTIVE INFLATABLES INCORPORATED - Sporting goods - Interactive Inflatables, Inc.
INTERACTIVE INSANITY - Computer software - Great Bear Technology Inc.
INTERACTIVE INSTRUCTOR - Computer software - Shaws-Lawson Associates
INTERACTIVE INTELLIGENCE - Computer software - Interactive Intelligence, Inc.
INTERACTIVE MAGIC - Games - Interactive Magic, Inc.
INTERACTIVE MC - Computer software - IMRS Operations Inc.
INTERACTIVE MULTIPLAYER - Electronic equipment - 3do Co.
INTERACTIVE MUSIC WORKSTATION - Musical instruments - Korg USA

INTERACTIVE NOVA - Computer software - WGBH Educational Foundation
INTERACTIVE OPTIONS - Computer software - SourceView Software International
INTERACTIVE OUTDOORS - Computer storage devices–optical - Interactive Outdoors, Inc.
INTERACTIVE PRESENTATION MANAGER (IPM) - Computers–mainframe - Numonics Corp.
INTERACTIVE READER - Computer software - Orange Cherry Software
INTERACTIVE RESUME - Computer software - SourceView Software International
INTERACTIVE RESUME, THE - Computer software - Genesys Corp.
INTERACTIVE SAILING - Video games - SWFTE International, Ltd.
INTERACTIVE SERVER - Computer software - Interactive Inc.
INTERACTIVE STOCK - Computer software - SourceView Software International
INTERACTIVE TEXTBOOK - Video production - James McEverette Carrol
INTERACTIVE WARRANTY - Computer software - SourceView Software International
INTERACTIVE WATERPLAY - Sporting goods - Specialized Component Supply Co.
INTERACTIVE WHITEBOARD (IWB) - Computers–mainframe - Numonics Corp.
INTERACTIVEMAX - Electrical surge protectors ☆ - Panamax
INTERAGENT - Computer software - Modulus Technologies, Inc.
INTERAIMS - Sights–gun - Stoeger Industries
INTERAMERICAS - Video production - Reed Foundation
INTERARMS - Firearms, accessories, and parts - International Armament Corp.
INTERART - Greeting cards - Sunrise Publications, Inc.
INTERAUDIO BY BOSE - Loudspeakers ☆ - Bose Corp.
INTERAX - Recording label - Interax Corp.
INTERBACKUP - Computer software - Chevry
INTERBAKE DAIRY INGREDIENTS - Confections - Interbake Foods Inc.
INTERBAKE FOODS - Cookies - Interbake Foods Inc.
INTERBASE - Coatings - Sherwin-Williams Automotive Finishes Corp.
INTERBIOL - Hair care products - Hairtech International Inc.
INTER(B)LOCK - Floor coverings - Norman Kaswell
INTER(B)LOCK - Padding–foam - Kaswell & Co., Inc.
INTERBRIDGE - Computer peripheral equipment - Hayes Microcomputer Products Inc.
INTERBURNER - Oil machinery - Adams Manufacturing Co.
INTERBUZ - Computer software - Live Data Systems, Inc.
INTERCAST - Computer hardware - Intel Corp.
INTERCELL - Floor coverings - Interface, Inc.
INTERCELL - Skin care products - Reviva Laboratories
INTERCEPT - Diaphragms - Johnson & Johnson
INTERCEPT - Electronic equipment - Pelco
INTERCEPT - Insulating materials - PPG Industries, Inc.
INTERCEPT-H&G - Insecticides - Agrevo Environmental Health, Inc.
INTERCEPER - Boats ☆ - Clark Craft Boat Co.
INTERCEPTOR - Alarm systems - Astro-Guard Industries Inc.
INTERCEPTOR - Ammunition - Fiocchi of America, Inc.
INTERCEPTOR - Electrical surge protectors - Control Concepts Corp.
INTERCEPTOR - Electronics equipment - Optoelectronics, Inc.
INTERCEPTOR - Hardware - National Banner Co., Inc.
INTERCEPTOR - Pharmaceutical preparations - Ciba-Geigy Corp.
INTERCEPTOR - Sporting goods - Ektelon
INTERCEPTOR - Tires - Dunlop Tire Corp.
INTERCEPTOR - Toys–models ☆ - Estes Industries
INTERCEPTOR - Truck cabs - Travelier Industries Inc.
INTERCEPTOR - Vacuum cleaners and accessories–commercial - Gilbertson Manufacturing
INTERCEPTOR G - Toys–models - Estes Industries
INTERCERAMIC - Ceramic tile - Interceramic Inc.
INTERCESSIONS - Recording label - Intercessions Publishing, Inc.
INTERCHANGE - Humphrey Systems
INTERCHANGEABLE - Hardware - Unarco Industries Inc. Materials Handling Div.
INTERCHRON - Watches - Interchron Ltd.
INTERCLUB - Boats - Vanguard Racing Sailboats
INTERCON 50 - Electronics equipment - InterCon Systems, Inc.
INTERCONNECT - Computer software - Jack White & Co.
INTERCONNECTOR - Buttons - Herman Pearl Button Co., Inc.
INTERCONTINENTAL - Meters–water - K-5 Coatings Inc.
INTERCONTINENTAL CLASSIC BRASS - Brass specialties - American Intercontinental Trade Group Inc.
INTERCRAFT - Frames–picture - Intercraft Industries

INTERCROSS - Flowers, plants, and seeds - W-L Research, Inc.

INTERCUT - Machinery - John E. Fox, Inc.

INTERDIGITAL - Radio communications equipment - Interdigital Communications Corp.

INTERDIGITAL GLAND SCENT - Sporting goods - Ole Time Woodsman

INTERDIMENSIONAL TRUTH - Paper–newsprint - Phillip Edward Bell

INTERDYNAMICS - Electrical equipment - Interdynamics, Inc.

INTEREST VISION PRO - Computer software - Parsons Technology, Inc.

INTERFACE - Audio equipment ☆ - Electro-Voice, Inc.

INTERFACE - Computer software - Bright Star Technology Inc.

INTERFACE - Dental compounds - Interstate Dental Co. Inc.

INTERFACE - Golfing equipment - Golfsmith International Inc.

INTERFACE SOFTWARE - Computer software - Interface Software, Inc.

INTERFAX - Amplifier components - InterFax Inc.

INTERFAX - Computers - Everex Systems, Inc.

INTERFILL - Putty - Interlux Yacht Finishes

INTERFIN - Real estate agencies - Interfin Corp.

INTERFINISH - Metals - Chicago Metallic Corp.

INTERFIT - Orthopedic products - Smith & Nephew Richards, Inc.

INTERFLEX - Cabinets - Fleetwood Furniture Co.

INTERFLEX - Cushions - Roho, Inc.

INTERFLEX - Gaskets - Intertech Group, Inc.

INTERFLEX - Hoses - Hose Master, Inc.

INTERFUSE - Hair care products - Interfuse Natural Products, Inc.

INTERGATE - Computer hardware - Internet Products, Inc.

INTERGROUP - Computer software - Intergroup, Inc.

INTERIM HISTORY - Publisher's imprints ☆ - Facts on File Inc.

INTERIOR - Wallpaper ☆ - Marburg Wallcoverings Inc.

INTERIOR APPROACH - Fabrics–tapestry - Comark Wallcoverings

INTERIOR CONCEPTS - Wallpaper - Essex Wallcoveringss

INTERIOR EXPRESSIONS - Wallcoverings - Beverly Stevens Ltd.

INTERIOR/EXTERIOR - Moldings and trim - Gossen Corp.

INTERIOR IMAGES BY SALTERINI - Furniture - Sam Blount Co., Inc.

INTERIOR LANDSCAPES - Wallpaper ☆ - Eisenhart Wallcoverings Co.

INTERIOR PACKAGE PLUS - Automotive parts and accessories - Auto Accessories of America

INTERIOR SHOWCASE - Wallpaper ☆ - Imperial Wallcoverings, Inc.

INTERIOR SHOWCASE I - Wallpaper ☆ - Imperial Wallcoverings, Inc.

INTERIOR TOUCH - Wallpaper - Norwall Wallcoverings

INTERIORS - Floor coverings–carpet and rugs - Wunda Weve Carpet Co.

INTERJEWEL - Jewelry - Interjewel, Inc.

INTERKEEL - Marine rigging - John G. Alden Inc.

INTERLACE - Sinks–metal - Kohler Co.

INTERLACHEN - Apparel–rubberized - Rutland's, Inc.

INTERLACHEN - Crocheted and knitted items ☆ - Puritan Sportswear Corp.

INTERLAKE - Boats–pontoons - Customflex Inc.

INTERLAKEN - Mattresses and box springs - Ohio Mattress Co.

INTERLAM - Film coverings, adhesive backing films and adhesive tapes - Filmolux (USA) Inc.

INTERLANDI - Orthodontic equipment - Orthoband Co., Inc.

INTERLANE - Computer software - Tecom, Inc.

INTERLAST - Audio equipment - LAST Factory

INTERLAY - Paper–tissue - Paper Service Ltd.

INTERLAY 1000 - Paper–tissue - Paper Service Ltd.

INTERLAY LIGHT - Paper–tissue - Paper Service Ltd.

INTERLEAF - Electrical equipment - Illinois Tool Works Inc.

INTERLECTRIC - Scales–railroad - Isotech Laboratories Manufacturing Inc.

INTERLIBRARY LOAN CONTROL - Computer software - Right on Programs

INTERLIN - Vitamins and nutritional supplements - Oxford Laboratories Inc.

INTERLINK - Home health care products - Baxter International Inc.

INTERLINK - Tiles–ceramic - Kowa Texas Inc.

INTERLOC - Bicycles - Interloc, Inc.

INTERLOCK - Extension poles and parts - Steccone Products Co.

INTERLOCK - Faucets - Sterling Plumbing Group Inc.

INTERLOCK - Floor coverings–carpet and rugs ☆ - Regal Rugs Inc.

INTERLOCK PAD - Computer peripheral equipment - Biological Engineering/High Tech Pet Products

INTERLOCKS - Hair care products - Image Laboratories, Inc.

INTERLOK - Floor coverings–tile - Pawling Corp. (Standard Products Div.)

INTERLOOP - Fabrics - Staflex Harotex

INTERLOTT - Electronic equipment - International Lottery Inc.

INTERLUBE 292 - Chemical preparations - C.P. Hall Co.

INTERLUDE - Colognes - Frances Denney

INTERLUDE - Doors–storm - Canyon Creek Cabinet Co.

INTERLUDE - Floor coverings - Mannington Resilient Floors

INTERLUDE - Furniture - American Drew

INTERLUDE - Glassware–household - Federal Glass

INTERLUDE - Glassware–household - Owens-Illinois Inc. (Libbey Div.)

INTERLUDE - House furnishings - Liberty Vinyl Corp.

INTERLUDE - Luggage - Airway Industries, Inc.

INTERLUDE - Metals - Armstrong World Industries, Inc.

INTERLUDE - Rings–jewelry - Artcarved Inc.

INTERLUDE - Tableware–china ☆ - Lenox, Inc.

INTERLUDE - Tapestries, fabric paintings, etc. - Interlude Inc.

INTERLUDE - Toilets–enameled - Kohler Co.

INTERLUDE - Underwear and nightwear - Henson-Kickernick Inc.

INTERLUDE - Vitamins - Caroline Owens

INTERLUDE - Vitamins and nutritional supplements ☆ - Natural Balance, Inc.

INTERLUDE - Wallpaper - James Seeman Studios

INTERLUDE - Watches - North American Watch Corp.

INTERLUDE ARCH - Doors–storm - Canyon Creek Cabinet Co.

INTERLUDES - Greeting cards - Happiness Inc.

INTERLUDES - Recording label - Integrity Music, Inc.

INTERLUDES - Tiles–ceramic ☆ - Latco Products

INTERLUX - Adhesives, coatings, paints and painting accessories - Interlux Yacht Finishes

INTERMACH - Calendars - Mach 1, Inc.

INTERMASTER - File folders - Stacor Corp.

INTERMATE - Health care products - Baxter International Inc.

INTERMATIC - Electric timers and time switches - Intermatic Inc.

INTERMAX - Rivets–metal - Textron Aerospace Fasteners

INTERMEDIARY - Computer software - Carl E. Hewitt

INTERMEDIATE - Archery equipment - Pro Line Co.

INTERMEDIATE CONTROL - Compressors–air - Pneumatech, Inc.

INTERMEDIATE MATH SKILLS - Computer software - Orange Cherry Software

INTERMEZZO - Cigarettes - Gesty Trading & Manufacturing Corp.

INTERMEZZO - Dishes–china ☆ - WMF/USA

INTERMEZZO - Jewelry - Jacoby-Bender Inc.

INTERMEZZO - Rings–jewelry - Artcarved Inc.

INTERMEZZO - Yarn - William Unger & Co. Inc.

INTERMIND - Computer software - Intermind Corp.

INTERMISSION - Computer software - ICOM Simulations Inc.

INTERMISSION - Floor coverings–carpet and rugs - Milliken & Co. Inc.

INTERMISSION TIP - Cigars ☆ - National Cigar Corp.

INTERMISSIONS - Hair care products - Redmond Products, Inc.

INTERMIX - Lubricants - J. Thomas Distributors, Inc.

INTERN - Games - Avalon Hill Game Co.

INTERN-OL - Pharmaceutical preparations - Rexall Sundown, Inc.

INTERNA-RAIL - Rails–aluminum - Hollaender Manufacturing Co.

INTERNAL BREATH FRESHENER, THE - Pharmaceutical preparations - Garlic-Go USA Inc.

INTERNAL INGENUITY II - Telephone apparatus - Cobra Electronics Corp.

INTERNAL PARASITE GUARD - Aquariums–household - Jungle Laboratories Corp.

INTERNAL POWER DESIGNS - Clothing - Internal Power

INTERNAL RAIL - Automotive parts and accessories - Hurst Performance Inc.

INTERNAL SKINCARE - Vitamins and nutritional supplements - Murad Skin Research Laboratories, Inc.

INTERNATIONAL - See MASTERMARK

INTERNATIONAL - Air conditioning equipment ☆ - Nordyne Inc.

INTERNATIONAL - Aluminum sliding doors and windows - International Aluminum Corp.

INTERNATIONAL - Bicycles ☆ - Raleigh USA Bicycle Co.

INTERNATIONAL - Boats–fishing ☆ - Larson Boat Div.

INTERNATIONAL - Boats–motor ☆ - Trojan Yacht

INTERNATIONAL - Briefcases ☆ - Sun Coast Merchandise Corp.

INTERNATIONAL - Cabinets ☆ - Diamond Cabinets

INTERNATIONAL - Clippers–barber ☆ - Sunbeam-Oster Household Products

INTERNATIONAL - Confections - Sara Lee Corp.

INTERNATIONAL - Dinnerware–glass ☆ - Homer Laughlin China Co.

INTERNATIONAL - Dolls - Alexander Doll Co. Inc.

INTERNATIONAL - Door hardware - International Door Closers Inc.

INTERNATIONAL - Drums–musical instruments ☆ - Pearl Corp.

INTERNATIONAL - Fabrics–tapestry ☆ - Columbus Coated Fabrics Co.

INTERNATIONAL - Fishing tackle - Penn Fishing Tackle Manufacturing Co.

INTERNATIONAL - Flavors and flavor blends - International Bakers Services Inc.

INTERNATIONAL - Floor coverings–carpet and rugs ☆ - Atlas Carpet Mills Inc.

INTERNATIONAL - Food products ☆ - Edward & Sons Trading Co., Inc.

INTERNATIONAL - Furniture - Schnadig Corp.

INTERNATIONAL - Hardware - Blaine Window Hardware Inc.

INTERNATIONAL - Herbal products - Farmer Bros. Co.

INTERNATIONAL - Ice-cream sandwiches - International Ice Cream Corp.

INTERNATIONAL - Luggage - Hartmann Luggage Co.

INTERNATIONAL - Meat products–beef - Colonial Beef Co.

INTERNATIONAL - Motor vehicles - Airstream Inc.

INTERNATIONAL - Motor vehicles–automobiles - Navistar International Transportation Corp.

INTERNATIONAL - Oils–edible - International Food Products Corp.

INTERNATIONAL - Oils–essential - Euro International

INTERNATIONAL - Silver products ☆ - Wallace International Silversmiths, Inc.

INTERNATIONAL - Sporting goods - Pompanette Inc.

INTERNATIONAL - Sunglasses - International Tropic-Cal Inc. (I SKI Div.)

INTERNATIONAL - Tea kettles–nonelectric ☆ - National Housewares

INTERNATIONAL - Threads - International Thread Co.

INTERNATIONAL - Trailers–travel - Travel Line Enterprises Inc.

INTERNATIONAL 32 - Soccer equipment - Brine Inc.

INTERNATIONAL 1847 ROGERS BROS - Silverware - Wallace International Silversmiths, Inc.

INTERNATIONAL 8300 - Toys–electronic - Bird Bromiticous Inc.

INTERNATIONAL ABRASIVES - Abrasive products - Genesis Materials International

INTERNATIONAL ACCENTS - Seafood products–fresh or frozen - O'Donnell-Usen Fisheries Corp.

INTERNATIONAL ARCTIC PROJECT - Apparel and accessories - International Arctic Project

INTERNATIONAL ART SOCIETY - Canvas–artists' - Fabulous Forgeries Ltd.

INTERNATIONAL ASSOCIATION FOR HEALTHCARE SECURITY & SAFETY IAHSS - Computer software - International Association for Healthcare Security and Safety

INTERNATIONAL BAZAAR - Food products - International Bazaar Inc.

INTERNATIONAL BEACH CHAMP - Balls - Mikasa Sports

INTERNATIONAL BRAKE INDUSTRIES - Brakes–motor vehicle - International Brake Industries, Inc.

INTERNATIONAL BREADS - Breads ☆ - John Labatt Foods

INTERNATIONAL BRIDES - Dolls ☆ - Effanbee Doll Corp.

INTERNATIONAL CC - Audio, video, and telephone accessories - International Components Corp.

INTERNATIONAL CENTER OF PHOTOGRAPHY - Postcards - Fotofolio Inc.

INTERNATIONAL CHEF - Sauces - Masterfoods Specialities, Inc.

INTERNATIONAL CHINA - Dinnerware - International China Corp.

INTERNATIONAL CHINA - Kitchen utensils–aluminum - Reston Lloyd Ltd.

INTERNATIONAL CHOICE - Meat products–beef - Atalanta Corp.

INTERNATIONAL CHRISTIAN MEDIA - Broadcasting stations–radio - International Christian Media, Inc.

INTERNATIONAL CLASS - Balls ☆ - Mikasa Sports

INTERNATIONAL CLASSICS - Cookies - Keebler Co.

INTERNATIONAL CLASSICS - Vegetables–frozen - Norpac Services, Inc.

INTERNATIONAL CLOTHESPIN COLLECTIBLES - Hobby kits ☆ - Hazel Pearson Handicrafts

INTERNATIONAL COLLECTION - Cookies - Nabisco Foods Group

INTERNATIONAL COLLECTION - Cookies - Pepperidge Farm Inc.

INTERNATIONAL COLLECTION - Floor coverings ☆ - Azrock Commercial Flooring

INTERNATIONAL CONGRESS OF LOCAL CHURCHES - Religious organizations - Donald Dwight Meares

INTERNATIONAL CREATIVE FOODS - Seafood products–fresh or frozen ☆ - Gourmet Club Corp.

INTERNATIONAL CRYSTAL - Clocks - Wallace International Silversmiths, Inc.

INTERNATIONAL CUISINE - Food products - Diet Center, Inc.

INTERNATIONAL CULINARIA - Cookware ☆ - Corning Inc.

INTERNATIONAL DECO IMAGE - Labels–paper - International Playing Card and Label Co., Inc.

INTERNATIONAL DEEPSILVER - Silverware - Wallace International Silversmiths, Inc.

INTERNATIONAL DELI - Meat products–beef - Armour Swift-Eckrich

INTERNATIONAL DELIGHT - Cream–canned or powdered - Morningstar Group Inc.

INTERNATIONAL DELIGHT - Food products - Avoset Food Corp.

INTERNATIONAL DESIGN LIBRARY, THE - Publisher's imprints - Stemmer House Publishers Inc.

INTERNATIONAL DESIGN TEAM - Apparel and accessories - Media Industries

INTERNATIONAL DESIGNER SERIES - Hair care products - Wella Corp. (Consumer Products Div.)

INTERNATIONAL DESSERT PARTNERS - Desserts - International Dessert Partners LLC

INTERNATIONAL DIRECTIONS - Wallpaper - Wall Fabrics Inc.

INTERNATIONAL DUNES - Hotel/motel chain - International Dunes Co.

INTERNATIONAL ENTERPRISE - Boats–skiffs - Enterprise Association of the U.S.

INTERNATIONAL ENTREE - Meat products–poultry - Armour Swift-Eckrich

INTERNATIONAL EXPRESSIONS - Flatware - Wallace International Silversmiths, Inc.

INTERNATIONAL FLAVORS - Meat products–poultry ☆ - Michel's Magnifique Ltd.

INTERNATIONAL FOLKLORE - Recording label - Sound Inc.

INTERNATIONAL GENEALOGICAL INDEX - Compact discs–prerecorded - Corp. of the President of the Church of Jesus Christ of Latter-Day Saints

INTERNATIONAL GOURMET - Coffee - Lorann Oils, Inc.

INTERNATIONAL GOURMET - Olive oil - International Gourmet

INTERNATIONAL GOURMET COLLECTION - Flatware - Wallace International Silversmiths, Inc.

INTERNATIONAL GRD - Machinery - International GRD Inc.

INTERNATIONAL GRD - Oil machinery - International GRD Inc.

INTERNATIONAL GREETINGS - Greeting cards - Burgoyne Inc./Curtis Swann

INTERNATIONAL HAIRGOODS - Hair-replacement product and services - International Hairgoods Inc.

INTERNATIONAL HARVESTER - See NAVISTAR INTERNATIONAL

INTERNATIONAL HOME - Floor coverings–carpet and rugs - Trans-Ocean Import Co. Inc.

INTERNATIONAL HOUSEWARES - Housewares - International Silver Co.

INTERNATIONAL IMAGES - Floor coverings–carpet and rugs - Navan Carpets Inc.

INTERNATIONAL JEWELRY CLEANER - Cleaning equipment - International Silver Co.

INTERNATIONAL KAP ALLIANCE - Games - Treat Entertainment, Inc.

INTERNATIONAL LIGHTING - Lighting fixtures - International Lighting Manufacturing Co.

INTERNATIONAL LOGISTICS SYSTEMS, INC. - Electronic equipment - International Logistics Systems, Inc.

INTERNATIONAL LYON 18/8 COLLECTION - Flatware - Wallace International Silversmiths, Inc.

INTERNATIONAL MATCH - Rifles - Redfield Co.

INTERNATIONAL MEDICINE CENTER - Medical apparatus - Edward R. Rensimer

INTERNATIONAL MENU - Cooking utensils–aluminum - Himark Enterprises Inc.

INTERNATIONAL MINI EMPANADAS - Pastries - Dufour Pastry Kitchens Inc.

INTERNATIONAL MOD - Recording label - Soundmasters Studio

INTERNATIONAL MUSCLE U.S.A. - Apparel and accessories - KOS USA

INTERNATIONAL NO-COOK - Spaghetti sauces - Fresh Pasta Co.

INTERNATIONAL OFFSHORE - Nautical instruments - Datamarine International Inc.

INTERNATIONAL OFFSHORE - Waterproof outerwear ☆ - Helly-Hansen Inc.

INTERNATIONAL OIL - Oils–lubricating - Pinnacle Oil, Inc.

INTERNATIONAL OPERATIONS - Books–comic - Aegis Entertainment, Inc.

INTERNATIONAL OPTIMIST - Boats - Vanguard Racing Sailboats

INTERNATIONAL PARTY BOOKS - Publisher's imprints - Gibson Greetings, Inc.

INTERNATIONAL POWER TECHNOLOGIES - Electrical equipment - Power Technologies, Inc.

INTERNATIONAL POWERSYSTEMS - Electrical equipment - International Power Systems, Inc.

INTERNATIONAL PROVISION - Food products - International Provisions

INTERNATIONAL RAINBOW - Fertilizers - IMC Fertilizer Group Inc.

INTERNATIONAL ROBOTIC SYSTEMS, INC. - Boats - International Robotic Systems, Inc.

INTERNATIONAL SCENE - Apparel–women's - Character Suburbanwear, Inc.

INTERNATIONAL SELECT - Food products - Zinal, Inc.

INTERNATIONAL SOCCER - Computer software ☆ - Commodore Business Machines Inc.

INTERNATIONAL SOCK EXCHANGE - Socks - International Sock Exchange, Inc.

INTERNATIONAL SOUP CLASSICS - Soups–mixes - Lipton Investments, Inc.

INTERNATIONAL SOUP OR SAUCE - Soups–mixes - Mayacamas Fine Foods, Inc.

INTERNATIONAL SPORTING - Ammunition ☆ - Olin Corp. (Winchester Div.)

INTERNATIONAL SPORTS CLUB - Apparel and accessories ☆ - Jantzen Inc.

INTERNATIONAL STONE POLISH - Cleaning preparations - Stone Care International Inc.

INTERNATIONAL SYMBOL - Apparel–athletic - Reflective Image Inc.

☆ = Now out of production

INTERNATIONAL TEXTURES - Floor coverings–carpet and rugs ☆ - Callaway Carpets

INTERNATIONAL TEXTURES - Hair care products - Pantresse Inc.

INTERNATIONAL TIGERS - Video production - International Vision, Inc.

INTERNATIONAL TOTALIZATOR SYSTEMS, INC. - Computers - International Totalizator Systems Inc.

INTERNATIONAL TOUR - Apparel–athletic - Ski Limited Enterprises, Inc.

INTERNATIONAL TRACK & FIELD - Computer storage devices–optical - Konami (America) Inc.

INTERNATIONAL TRADE DATA NETWORK - Computer software - Bryant College

INTERNATIONAL TRADEMARK ASSOCIATION - Recording label - International Trademark Association, Inc.

INTERNATIONAL TRAVELER - Trailers–travel ☆ - Travel Line Enterprises Inc.

INTERNATIONAL TREASURES - Furniture - Lineage Home Furnishings, Inc.

INTERNATIONAL VIDEO NETWORK - Video production - Ivn Communications, Inc.

INTERNATIONAL WEATHER NETWORK, THE - Computer software - International Weather Network

INTERNATIONALE - Health care products - Prosperity Farms

INTERNATIONALEREST - Computer software - Financial Engineering Associates, Inc.

INTERNATIONALLY GENON - Wallpaper - Gencorp Polymer Products

INTERNATIONALS - Hair care products - Revlon Consumer Products Corp.

INTERNATURAL - Vitamins and nutritional supplements - Aim International, Inc.

INTERNET - Paper - Manistique Papers, Inc.

INTERNET ASSISTANT - Computer software - Microsoft Corp.

INTERNET COMMERCE - Computer software - Infosafe Systems, Inc.

INTERNET EXPLORER - Computer software - Microsoft Corp.

INTERNET HOSERY - Panty hose - Team Products

INTERNET SERVICES CORPORATION - Recording label - Internet Services Corp.

INTERNET TOOLS FOR NON-PROGRAMMERS - Computer software - Network Multimedia, Inc.

INTERNETWORK MEDIA - Computer software - Internetwork Media, Inc.

INTERNEWTS, THE - Paper products - Ivan Arnove

INTERNEXT - Computer software - Racal-Datacom, Inc.

INTEROFFICE EXPRESS - Office machines - Interoffice Express, LLC

INTERP - Computer software ☆ - CONDUIT

INTERPAGE - Pagers - Inter Page Corp.

INTERPETS - Computer peripheral equipment - Vision 21 Advertising Inc.

INTERPHOTO - Photographic equipment - SP Systems/Saratons

INTERPLAK - Toothbrushes–electric - Bausch & Lomb Inc.

INTERPLAK PLUS - Toothbrushes–electric - Bausch & Lomb Inc.

INTERPLAK VOYAGER - Toothbrushes–electric - Bausch & Lomb Inc.

INTERPLANETARY LIZARDS - Toys - Leadbelly Productions

INTERPLANETARY LIZARDS OF THE TEXAS PLAINS - Games - Creatif Licensing Corp.

INTERPLANETARY SPY - Publisher's imprints ☆ - Bantam Doubleday Dell Publishing Group, Inc.

INTERPLAY - Recording label - Interplay Records Inc.

INTERPLAY - Wallpaper ☆ - James Seeman Studios

INTERPLEX - Hair care products - Bonat Inc.

INTERPLOT - Computer software - Intergraph Corp.

INTERPOLY - Polyurethane enamels ☆ - Interlux Yacht Finishes

INTERPOSE - Computer integrated systems design services - Interpose, Inc.

INTERPRETATION - Furniture - Hooker Furniture Corp.

INTERPRETATION - Furniture ☆ - Virginia House Furniture Corp.

INTERPRETATIONS - Cosmetics - Frances Denney

INTERPRETATIONS - Floor coverings–carpet and rugs - Couristan Inc.

INTERPRETING GRAPHS - Computer software ☆ - Sunburst Communications, Inc.

INTERPRIME - Boat primer - Interlux Yacht Finishes

INTERPROTECT - Epoxy sealers and primers - Interlux Yacht Finishes

INTERQ - Computer software - Dun and Bradstreet Software Services, Inc.

INTERRACIALLY CORRECT GREETING CARDS - Greeting cards - Tracy Margaret Smith

INTERRANTE - Tomato pastes and sauces - Salvati Foods, Inc.

INTERRUPT - Insecticides - Farnam Cos. Inc.

INTERRUPTER/15 - Circuit breakers - Pass & Seymour, Inc.

INTERRUPTION STOPPER - Electronic equipment - Designtech International, Inc.

INTERSCAPE - Floor coverings ☆ - Kentile Floors Inc.

INTERSE - Eyeglasses - Cliff Weil, Inc.

INTERSECT - Computer hardware and software - Persoft, Inc.

INTERSECT - Electrical testing instruments - Reliability, Inc.

INTERSECT - Golfing equipment - Dunlop Maxfli Sports Corp.

INTERSEW - Machine parts ☆ - John E. Fox, Inc.

INTERSHARE - Computers - Intershare, Inc.

INTERSOLV - Computer hardware and software - Intersolv, Inc.

INTERSORB - Health care products - Sherwood Medical Co.

INTERSOUND - Audio equipment - Tapco

INTERSOUND - Recording label - Counter Culture

INTERSPAN - Building materials - Larsen Products Corp.

INTERSPHERE 2 - Skin care products - Sothys USA Inc.

INTERSPRAY - Polyurethane - Interlux Yacht Finishes

INTERSPUN - Fabrics ☆ - International Paper Co.

INTERSTACK - Paper - Interstate Paper Corp.

INTERSTAGE - Computer software - IA Corp.

INTERSTAR - Toys - International Playthings Inc.

INTERSTATE - Acne cleanser, analgesic balm, etc. - IDE-Interstate Inc.

INTERSTATE - Floor coverings ☆ - Aladdin Mills, Inc.

INTERSTATE - Frozen potatoes - Interstate Potato Packers

INTERSTATE - Motorcycles - American Honda Motor Co. Inc. (Acura Div.)

INTERSTATE - Play map - Integra Toys, Inc.

INTERSTATE - Tires - Oliver Rubber Co.

INTERSTATE - Toys–automobiles - Toy Truck Lines, Inc.

INTERSTATE - Window blinds and shades - Interstate Window Coverings

INTERSTATE BAG - Bags–paper - Interstate Packaging Corp.

INTERSTATE INN - Hotel/motel chain - Interstate Inns

INTERSTATE MULLET TOSS - Clothing - Flora-Bama Lounge & Package Store, Inc.

INTERSTATE TRANSMISSIONS - Automotive repair shops–transmission - Multistate Transmissions Inc.

INTERSTATER - Lawn mowers ☆ - Alamo Industrial

INTERSTELLAR PROPELLER - Hats - Interstellar Propeller

INTERTEC SYSTEMS - Automotive parts and accessories - Intertec Systems, LLC

INTERTECH - Artists' materials - Utley Co. Inc.

INTERTEX - Racks - Intertex Carousels Corp.

INTERTHANE PLUS - Polyurethane enamels - Interlux Yacht Finishes

INTERTHERM - Furnaces–electric - Nordyne Inc.

INTERTON - Hearing aids - Magnatone Hearing Aid Corp.

INTERTRIM - Boats - Intertrim Inc.

INTERTRON - Awnings - Rainbow Awnings

INTERTRON - Medical apparatus - Standex International Corp.

INTERTUBES - Socks ☆ - Kayser-Roth Corp.

INTERURBAN - Tires - Bridgestone/Firestone, Inc.

INTERVAL - Dental compounds - Temrex Corp.

INTERVAL - Fertilizer - Outdoor Equipment Co.

INTERVAL DRILLMASTER - Computer software ☆ - CONDUIT

INTERVALE - Craft supplies - Superior Knitting Co.

INTERVALE - Water - Intervale Spring Water

INTERVALS - Shampoos - Redken Laboratories, Inc.

INTERVISION - Computer software - Baker Hughes Inc.

INTERVISION - Computers - Intervision Systems, Inc.

INTERVOX - Audio and electronic equipment - International Components Corp.

INTERVUE - Computer hardware - Intergraph Corp.

INTERWAVE - Audio equipment - Advanced Micro Devices, Inc.

INTERWEAVE - Fabrics - West Point-Pepperell Inc.

INTERWEAVE - Floor coverings–carpet and rugs - Kelly Group Inc.

INTERWEAVE - Wallpaper - Koroseal Wallcoverings

INTERWELT PLUS - Fabrics–cotton - J.P. Stevens & Co. Inc. (Knit & Narrow Fabric Div.)

INTERWEVE - Floor coverings–carpet and rugs - Karastan-Bigelow Inc.

INTERWEVE HIGHLIGHTS - Floor coverings–carpet and rugs - Karastan-Bigelow Inc.

INTERWORKING LABS - Computer software - Interworking Labs

INTERWOVEN - Bathing suits - Catalina

INTERWOVEN - Socks - Kayser-Roth Corp.

INTESSERA VUEFINDER - Computer software - Intessera, LP

INTESTI-CLEANSE - Pharmaceutical preparations ☆ - Herb-Pharm

INTESTIN-KLENSE - Herbal products - Life Services Supplements, Inc.

INTESTINAL CARE - Vitamins and nutritional supplements - Ethical Nutrients

INTESTINAL CARE DF - Vitamins and nutritional supplements - Ethical Nutrients

INTESTINAL FLORA FACTORS - Vitamins and nutritional supplements - Ethical Nutrients

INTESTINALIA - Vitamins and nutritional supplements - Life Services Supplements, Inc.

☆ = Now out of production

INTESTINEX - Pharmaceutical preparations - Marin Pharmaceuticals

INTESTO-KLENZ - Dialing devices–telephone ☆ - ICN Pharmaceuticals Inc.

INTEVAC - Binoculars - Intevac, Inc.

INTEX - Decorating product - Industrial Textile Corp.

INTEX - Vinyl, water-bed mattresses, sporting goods, etc. - Intex Recreation Corp.

INTEX-TERIOR - Cleaner - Intex Chemical Inc.

INTIGIR - Computer hardware - Aero Computing, Ltd.

INTIL 970 - Blood pressure apparatus - Vanguard Racing Sailboats

INTIMA - Fabrics - Guilford Mills, Inc.

INTIMA - Recording label - Enigma Entertainment

INTIMA - Thread - Belding Heminway Co. Inc.

INTIMA - Underwear and nightwear - Saramar Corp.

INTIMACIES - Wallpaper - ICI Americas Inc.

INTIMACY - Floor coverings–carpet and rugs ☆ - S and S Mills Inc.

INTIMATE - Audio equipment ☆ - Infinity Systems, Inc.

INTIMATE - Cosmetics - Revlon Consumer Products Corp.

INTIMATE - Floor coverings–carpet and rugs - Lees Carpets

INTIMATE AFFAIR - Apparel–women's - Romance Du Jour, Inc.

INTIMATE AFTERTHOUGHTS - Greeting cards - American Greetings Corp.

INTIMATE APPROACH - Underwear and nightwear - Lewis J. Spruance

INTIMATE ATTITUDES - Underwear and nightwear - National Corset Supply House

INTIMATE CHARM - Floor coverings–carpet and rugs - Evans-Black Carpet Mills

INTIMATE COLLECTIONS - Apparel and accessories - Design Your Drawers, Inc.

INTIMATE COMFORT - Fabrics - Liberty Fabrics, Inc.

INTIMATE CONCEPTS - Apparel–women's ☆ - Chic Lingerie Co.

INTIMATE CONCEPTS - Underwear and nightwear - Kellwood Co.

INTIMATE CONNECTION - Apparel–women's - Intimate Connection, Inc.

INTIMATE FANTASY - Apparel–women's - Jade Oriental Intimate Inc.

INTIMATE INSPIRATIONS - Floor coverings–carpet and rugs ☆ - Olympic Carpets Inc.

INTIMATE MOMENTS - Greeting cards ☆ - American Greetings Corp.

INTIMATE MOOD - Floor coverings–carpet and rugs ☆ - Downs Carpet Co. Inc.

INTIMATE MOODS - Fabrics - Guilford Mills, Inc.

INTIMATE MUSK - Perfumes - Revlon Consumer Products Corp.

INTIMATE PASSION PAINT - Sauces - Allan Lyons, Inc.

INTIMATE POWER - Apparel and accessories - Juliette Horton

INTIMATE SILHOUETTES - Apparel–women's - Intima Manufacturing Corp.

INTIMATES - Tiles–ceramic ☆ - Latco Products

INTIMATES BY NICOLE - Brassieres (Bras) - A & D International Corp.

INTIMATIONS - Apparel and accessories - Warnaco Inc.

INTIME - Computer software - Intelligy Corp.

INTIME - Computer software - Radisys Corp.

INTIMIDATOR - Archery equipment - Thomas J. Grimaldi

INTIMIDATOR - Basketball shoes ☆ - Jaclar

INTIMIDATOR - Bicycles - Rand International, Inc.

INTIMIDATOR - Sporting goods - Gear 2000, Ltd.

INTIMIDATOR - Sporting goods - Lisco, Inc.

INT'L 920 - Boat dealers - Vanguard Racing Sailboats

INTO IMPROV - Games ☆ - Odin Ltd.-Scan Am Imports Inc.

INTO THE GARDEN - Calendars ☆ - American Greetings Corp.

INTO THE NET - Apparel and accessories - M Hidary & Co., Inc.

INTO THE UNKNOWN - Computer software - Focus Media Inc.

INTO THE WILD - Jewelry–costume - Phillips International Jewelry & Souvenirs Inc.

INTO THE WOODS - Candles - Origins Natural Resources Inc.

INTO THE WOODS - Furniture - Annette Atwood Design

INTODUCTION TO GEOGRAPHY - Computer software - Orange Cherry Software

INTOPIA - Computer software - Intopia, Inc.

INTOUCH - Checkbooks - Clarke American Checks, Inc.

INTOX RX - Vitamins and nutritional supplements - Vitamin Research Products Inc.

INTR-SEPTOR - Machinery - International Separation Technology, Inc.

INTRA - Hearing aids - Starkey Labs Inc.

INTRA-DRIVE - Gears - WEC Co.

INTRA-KOOL - Air conditioning equipment - Surface Combustion, Inc.

INTRA-NEUT - Hair care products - Revlon Consumer Products Corp.

INTRA PAK - Hair care products - Image Laboratories, Inc.

INTRA-QUATIC - Hair care products - Revlon Consumer Products Corp.

INTRA-SONIX - Medical apparatus - Intra-Sonix Inc.

INTRA-VYVING - Hair care products - Roux Laboratories, Inc.

INTRAAX - Automotive parts and accessories - Boler Co.

INTRACEL - Intracell Nutrition Inc.

INTRACEL - Cosmetics - Organics Corp. of America (Ambix Laboratories Div.)

INTRACELL - Health care products - Body Care Inc.

INTRACOASTAL - Boats–motor - Century Boat Co.

INTRACTION - Apparel–women's - Intraction

INTRACURE - Pet products ☆ - Robarb Inc.

INTRADAL - Health care products - Sara Lee Corp.

INTRAKERA - Hair care products - Image Laboratories, Inc.

INTRALINK - Computer hardware - Vixel Corp.

INTRALIPID - Pharmaceutical preparations - Kabi Pharmacia Inc.

INTRALOK - Adhesives and sealants - W.R. Meadows Inc.

INTRAMOIST - Hair care products - Image Laboratories, Inc.

INTRAN - Medical apparatus - Utah Medical Products, Inc.

INTRANS - Computer software - Integrity Software Solutions, Inc.

INTRAPAN - Pharmaceutical preparations ☆ - Elkins-Sinn Inc.

INTRASCAPES - Window treatments - Intrascapes

INTRASCOPIC - Surgical instruments - Sherwood Medical Co.

INTRASTRIPE - Floor coverings ☆ - Tarkett, Inc.

INTRATEC - Firearms, accessories, and parts - Intratec

INTRAVISION - Computer software - Iges Data Analysis Co.

INTRAX - Shock absorbers–motor vehicle - Intrax Suspension Technology

INTRE - Recording label - International Record Corp.

INTREC - Computer software - Intrec Software, Inc.

INTRENDS - Furniture - Walker and Zanger Inc.

INTREPID - Apparel and accessories - Manhattan International

INTREPID - Balls - Lisco, Inc.

INTREPID - Bicycles - Columbia Manufacturing Inc.

INTREPID - Bicycles - Rand International, Inc.

INTREPID - Fabrics - Dan River Inc.

INTREPID - Fabrics - Greenwood Mills Inc.

INTREPID - Floor coverings–carpet and rugs - Dorsett Carpet Mills Inc.

INTREPID - Furniture ☆ - Bassett Furniture Industries, Inc.

INTREPID - Medical products - Smith & Nephew DonJoy Inc.

INTREPID - Motor vehicles - Chrysler Corp. (Dodge Car Div.)

INTREPID - Paper–coated - Blandin Paper Co.

INTREPID - Rackets–tennis - Spalding Sports Worldwide

INTREPID - Recording label - Jazz Composer's Orchestra Association Inc.

INTREPID - Rope - Columbian Rope Co.

INTREPID - Strollers–baby ☆ - Welsh Co.

INTREPID - Tires - Goodyear Tire & Rubber Co.

INTREPID - Video equipment - Larry Ehlers & Associates, Inc.

INTREPID II - Stoves–wood-burning - Vermont Castings, Inc.

INTREX 60 - Telephones - TIE Communications, Inc.

INTRIBEX - Pharmaceutical preparations ☆ - Parke-Davis

INTRIGUE - Christmas tree ornaments - Cracker Box Inc.

INTRIGUE - Clocks - General Time Corp. (Westclox/Seth Thomas Div.)

INTRIGUE - Computer software ☆ - Spectrum Holobyte, Inc.

INTRIGUE - Dinnerware ☆ - Corning Inc.

INTRIGUE - Floor coverings - Congoleum Corp.

INTRIGUE - Floor coverings–carpet and rugs - Tuftex Carpet Mills, Inc.

INTRIGUE - Floor coverings–carpet and rugs ☆ - Downs Carpet Co. Inc.

INTRIGUE - Floor coverings–carpet and rugs ☆ - Royalweve Carpet Mills

INTRIGUE - Furniture ☆ - Bassett Furniture Industries, Inc.

INTRIGUE - Glassware–household ☆ - Lenox Crystal, Inc.

INTRIGUE - Mattresses - King Koil Licensing Co., Inc.

INTRIGUE - Prosthetic apparatus - Coloplast Corp.

INTRIGUE - Rings–jewelry - Artcarved Inc.

INTRIGUE - Wallcoverings - Beverly Stevens Ltd.

INTRIGUE - Women's shoes - International Seaway Trading Corp.

INTRIGUE BY COUNTRY COACH - Motor vehicles–buses ☆ - Country Coach, Inc.

INTRIGUE BY FOREVER YOURS - Wedding gowns - Forever Yours International Corp.

INTRIGUE TONES - Floor coverings–carpet and rugs ☆ - Karastan-Bigelow Inc.

INTRIGUING - Floor coverings–carpet and rugs - Philadelphia Carpets

INTRINASE - Pharmaceutical preparations ☆ - Upjohn Co.

INTRINSIC - Apparel–men's - In Private Inc.

INTRINSITINIC - Pharmaceutical preparations - Schein Pharmaceutical Inc.

INTRIX - Computer software - Intrix Systems Group Inc.

INTRO 80 - Furniture - Tomlinson of High Point Inc.

INTRO-SERT - Metals - Yardley Products Corp.

INTRO-TECH - Motor vehicle parts and accessories - Intromarketing, Inc.

INTROAPP - Computer software - Enrollment Technologies, Inc.

INTRODUCTION - Underwear and nightwear - Maidenform Inc.

☆ = Now out of production

INTROMARK - Games - Intromark Inc.

INTRON A - Pharmaceutical preparations - Schering-Plough Healthcare Products

INTRONICS - Power switching equipment - Intronics, Inc.

INTROSPECT - Apparel and accessories - Paul Davril Inc.

INTROSPECT - Computer software - Icon Consulting Group Inc.

INTROSPECTS - Greeting cards ☆ - American Greetings Corp.

INTROTEX - Fabrics - Guilford Mills, Inc.

INTROVIGNE'S - Breads - Angy's Tortellini Inc.

INTRUDER - Balls—golf - D.H. Hutson Enterprises, Inc.

INTRUDER - Floor coverings—carpet and rugs - Tuftex Carpet Mills, Inc.

INTRUDER - Motor vehicles—motor homes - Damon Corp.

INTRUDER - Motorcycles - Suzuki of America Automotive Corp.

INTRUDER - Powerboat ☆ - Invader Marine Inc.

INTRUST - Computer software - Michael P. Osterloh

INTUIT - Computer software - Intuit Inc.

INTUITION - Floor coverings—carpet and rugs - Patcraft Mills Inc.

INTUITION - Furniture - Thomasville Furniture Industries Inc.

INTUITIONS - Apparel and accessories - JH Collectibles Inc.

INTUITIONS - Women's sportswear - Interstyle Inc.

INTUITIVE - Floor coverings—carpet and rugs - Monticello Carpet Mills

INTUITIVE SOLUTIONS - Games - Joy Drake

INTUNE RECORDS - Recording label - Intune, Inc.

INTUNE WITH NATURE - Socks - Pine Hosiery Mills, Inc.

INTURN - Cleaning preparations—carpet and rug ☆ - Castex Industries Inc.

INVA TRAC - Health care products ☆ - Invacare Corp.

INVACARE - Health care products - Invacare Corp.

INVADE PLUS - Chemical preparations - Terra International, Inc.

INVADER - Apparel—men's ☆ - Michaels/Stern & Co. Inc.

INVADER - Batteries - Exide Corp.

INVADER - Boats—motor - American Marine Ltd.

INVADER - Fabrics—percale - Cohn-Hall-Marx Co.

INVADER - Fishing lures - Paul Warner Industries

INVADER - Fishing tackle ☆ - K-Line Industries

INVADER - Footwear—men's - L.B. Evans' Son Co.

INVADER - Insecticides - Waterbury Companies, Inc.

INVADER - Kites - Gayla Industries Inc.

INVADER - Musical instrument accessories - Seymour Duncan Pickups

INVADER - Powerboat ☆ - Invader Marine Inc.

INVADER - Skateboards ☆ - National Sporting Goods Corp.

INVADER - Sporting goods - Gear 2000, Ltd.

INVADER - Toys—automobiles - Tyco Industries, Inc.

INVADER - Watches - Fossil Inc.

INVADER BMX - Bicycles - Western Auto Supply Co.

INVADER CC - Bicycles - Western Auto Supply Co.

INVADER JR. - Sporting goods ☆ - Hedstrom Corp.

INVADER TURBO-KITE - Games - Isle Laboratories Inc.

INVADERS FROM HYPERSPACE - Toys—electronic ☆ - Philips Consumer Electronics Co.

INVALEASE - Health care products ☆ - Invacare Corp.

INVASION - Recording label - Bomp Records Inc.

INVASION OF ANZIO - Toys - Multi Toys Corp.

INVASION OF NORMANDY - Fireworks - B.J. Alan Co. Inc.

INVENT/REINVENT - Hair care products - Matrix Essentials, Inc.

INVENTION MACHINE - Computer software - Invention Machine Corp.

INVENTIONS - Games ☆ - Avalon Hill Game Co.

INVENTIONS THAT AFFECT OUR LIVES - Computer software - Orange Cherry Software

INVENTORS, THE - Games ☆ - Parker Brothers

INVENTORY COLLECTION - Booklet - Full Circle International, Ltd.

INVENTORY GROUP - Shelving units—wood - Naomi Gale Wall Systems

INVENTORY PROTECTION SYSTEMS, INC. - Recording label - Inventory Protection Systems, Inc.

INVER HOUSE - Liquors - Canandaigua Wine Co. Inc.

INVERNESS - Apparel and accessories - Caledonia Knitwear Co.

INVERNESS - Ceiling tile ☆ - Conwed Plastics

INVERNESS - Crocheted and knitted items - Puritan Sportswear Corp.

INVERNESS - Dairy products - Inverness Dairy Inc.

INVERNESS - Floor coverings ☆ - Tarkett, Inc.

INVERNESS - Floor coverings—carpet and rugs - Patcraft Mills Inc.

INVERNESS - Floor coverings—carpet and rugs - Whitecrest Carpet Mills

INVERNESS - Floor coverings—carpet and rugs ☆ - Royalweve Carpet Mills

INVERNESS - Furniture ☆ - Bassett Furniture Industries, Inc.

INVERNESS - Jewelry cleaner, shaving gel - Inverness Corp.

INVERNESS - Luggage - Samsonite Corp.

INVERNESS - Motor vehicles—motor homes - Damon Corp.

INVERRAY - Floor coverings ☆ - Congoleum Corp.

INVERSE - Giftware - Sasaki

INVERSE MIRRORING - Computer storage devices - ECCS, Inc.

INVERSINE - Pharmaceutical preparations - Merck & Co., Inc. (Merck Research Laboratories)

INVERSION - Apparel and accessories - Amtai Imports Inc.

INVERSION - Health care products - Unicare Health & Fitness Co.

INVERSION TABLE - Exercising equipment - STL International, Inc.

INVERT - Pet products - Ocean Nutrition Corp.

INVERT-A-CAP - Paints - Aervoe-Pacific Co. Inc.

INVERT-A-VOLT - Power transformers - La Marche Manufacturing Co.

INVERTASE - Pharmaceutical preparations - Pfanstiehl Laboratories Inc.

INVERTED OVERLAP - Ski boots - Rossignol Ski Co., Inc.

INVERTER-DUTY - Motors—hydraulic - Magnetek Inc.

INVERTER GRADE - Machine parts - Emerson Electric Co.

INVEST-A-COAT - Sealing compounds - Monsey Products Co.

INVEST-A-DIRT - Novelty items - Philip H. Huggins

INVEST IN YOUR VALUES - Paper—book - Career Systems, Inc.

INVESTAGE - Veterinary products - Pro-Vet Companies, Inc.

INVESTIGATOR - Computer program - University of Florida

INVESTIGATOR - Medical apparatus - Electro-Catheter Corp.

INVESTMENT - Floor coverings—carpet and rugs - Wunda Weve Carpet Co.

INVESTMENT IN EXCELLENCE - Video production - Pacific Institute Inc.

INVESTMENTS - Frames—eyeglass - Universal/Univis Inc.

INVESTOR - Floor coverings—carpet and rugs ☆ - Walter Carpet Mills

INVESTOR - Golfing equipment - Ram Golf Corp.

INVESTOR PLUS - Calculators - Calculated Industries, Inc.

INVESTOR'S CHOICE, THE - Trading cards and stamps - ANCO Collector Supplies, Inc.

INVESTOR'S HOTLINE - Recording label - Audio Alert, Inc.

INVESTRAK! - Computer software - Dean J. Hastas

INVICTA - Bicycles - Kenstone Corp. Inc.

INVICTA - Bicycles - Ross Bicycles USA, Ltd.

INVICTA - Floor coverings—carpet and rugs - Wool Merchants International Inc.

INVICTA - Golfing equipment - Dunlop Slazenger Corp.

INVICTA - Luggage - York Luggage Co.

INVICTA - Motor vehicles—automobiles ☆ - General Motors Corp. (Buick Motor Div.)

INVICTA - Recording label - James L. Roberts

INVICTA - Tires - Goodyear Tire & Rubber Co.

INVICTA - Watches - Elgin Watch Co.

INVIDEO - Computer software - Dean Friedman Productions, Inc.

INVIGORATING - Cosmetics - Dr. Babor Natural Cosmetics

INVIGORATOR - Massage products - Omron Healthcare, Inc.

INVIGORIN - Vitamins and nutritional supplements - Tishcon Corp.

INVINCIBLE - Cigars - General Cigar Co., Inc.

INVINCIBLE - Fishing tackle ☆ - Gladding Braided Products Inc.

INVINCIBLE - Floor coverings - Carpet Co-Op of America Association

INVINCIBLE - Floor coverings—carpet and rugs - Johnson's Carpets Inc.

INVINCIBLE - Frames—eyeglass - Zylo Ware Corp.

INVINCIBLE - Mops - Golden Star Inc.

INVINCIBLE - Tape measures ☆ - Keuffel & Esser Co.

INVINCIBLE - Watches - Helbros International

INVIS-A-GRO - Apparel—women's ☆ - J.C. Penney Co., Inc.

INVISA - Hearing aids - Beltone Electronics Corp.

INVISATRACE - Medical device - Andover Medical Inc.

INVISI-GARD - Fabric stores ☆ - Golden Star Inc.

INVISI-TRIM - Plastics—laminated - Sufix USA, Inc.

INVISIBANDS - Cosmetics - American International Industries

INVISIBANDS - Cosmetics - Ardell International Inc.

INVISIBLE - Apparel and accessories - Kin Hing International, Inc.

INVISIBLE - Cosmetics - Hard Candy, Inc.

INVISIBLE - Electrical fence - Invisible Fence Co. Inc.

INVISIBLE - Fans—electric - Duracraft Corp.

INVISIBLE - Health care products ☆ - Sammons Preston

INVISIBLE BAKER, THE - Bakery products - Lawrence Foods Inc.

INVISIBLE-BAND - Cosmetics - Beautee Sense Inc.

INVISIBLE BARRIER - Transmitter wire - Invisible Fence Co. Inc.

INVISIBLE BOUNDARY - Animal confinement system - Invisible Fence Co. Inc.

INVISIBLE BREAST ENHANCER - Apparel and accessories - Bodylines Inc.

INVISIBLE FENCE KNUCKLES - Pet products - Invisible Fence Co., Inc.

INVISIBLE FILTER, THE - Cigarette filters - Venturi, Inc.

INVISIBLE LINE - Notebooks and notepads - Mead Corp.

INVISIBLE LINE, THE - Educational materials - Sepler & Associates, Inc.

INVISIBLE MASK - Electrical equipment - Invisible Fence Co. Inc.

INVISIBLE POWER - Electronic equipment - Invisible Fence Co. Inc.
INVISIBLE RAFTER - Awnings ☆ - Carefree of Colorado
INVISIBLE SAFE, THE - Safes - Omega Manufacturing
INVISIBLE SHIELD - Paints - Unelko Corp.
INVISIBLE SOFTWARE - Computer software - Invisible Software Inc.
INVISIBLE TOUCH - Apparel–women's - Olga Co.
INVISIBLE TOUCH - Skin care products - Rajoc International
INVISIBLE TOUCH STEERING CONTROL - Automotive parts and accessories - New Generation Steering Control, Inc.
INVISIBLE UNIVERSE - Computer storage devices–optical - Voyager Software Corp.
INVISIBLEACH - American International Industries
INVISIBLES - Cabinets - Nutone Inc.
INVISIBLES BY ST. EVE - Underwear and nightwear - St. Eve International, Inc.
INVISICOAT - Frozen potatoes - McCain Foods Inc.
INVISICON - Electrical equipment - Adflex Solutions, Inc.
INVISIGLASS - Frames–picture - Optical Coating Laboratory Inc.–Santa Rosa Div.
INVISIMIST - Hair care products - Clairol Inc.
INVISINET - Apparel stores–lingerie - Formflex Foundations Inc.
INVISION - Video recording label - Inovision Corp.
INVISION GEAR - Apparel and accessories - Foi Industries, Inc.
INVISIPERF - Window coverings - Exeter Architectural Products, Inc.
INVISIVENT - Soffit - Wolverine Technologies
INVISO - Finishing agents ☆ - Uncle Sam Chemical Co., Inc.
INVISO - Thread - Monofilaments International Inc.
INVISO - Waterproofing compounds ☆ - Everseal International Sales Co. Inc.
INVISO-HT - Thread - Monofilaments International Inc.
INVITATION - Blankets - Pillowtex Corp.
INVITATION - Furniture–upholstered ☆ - Mersman Furniture Co.
INVITATION - Giftware ☆ - Gorham Inc.
INVITATION - Hair care products - Helene Curtis Industries Inc.
INVITATION - Nuts–salted, roasted, cooked, or canned - Blue Diamond Growers
INVITATION - Ships–sailing vessels ☆ - Bombardier Corp.
INVITATION - Toilets–enameled - Kohler Co.
INVITATION IX - Wallpaper - Norwall Wallcoverings
INVITATION XII - Wallpaper - Norwall Wallcoverings
INVITATIONAL - Floor coverings–carpet and rugs - Calladium & Marglen
INVITATIONAL - Floor coverings–carpet and rugs - West Point-Pepperell Mill Store
INVITATIONAL - Floor coverings–carpet and rugs - Wool Merchants International Inc.
INVITATIONS BY CHASE - Stationery - Chase
INVIZEES-STEP - Apparel–women's - Nuvogue Creations
INVOICE-IT - Computer software - Future Systems
INVOICEXPRESS - Communications equipment - Access Communication Systems, Inc.
INW - Diagnostic apparatus - Instrumentation Northwest, Inc.
INWALL - Hardware - Genova Products Inc.
INWHA - Jewelry ☆ - Amkor Pacific
INWO - Games - Steve Jackson Games Inc.
INWOOD - Floor coverings ☆ - Congoleum Corp.
INWOOD - Wood products ☆ - Anco Wood Specialties Inc.
INWORLD - Computer software - Inworld VR, Inc.
INYATI - Polymer coatings - Polyguard USA, Inc.
I.N.Z. - Veterinary pharmaceutical preparations - Dyna Pet Inc.
INZA ORIGINALS - Mexican art objects ☆ - Plastics Manufacturing Co.
IO INTELI OPTICS - Binoculars - Brunton Co.
IO LA PERLA - Perfumes - La Parfumerie Inc.
IO/NET - Computer peripheral equipment - Square D Co.
IO-VINE - Veterinary pharmaceutical preparations - Vineland Laboratories Inc.
IOBLETS - Pharmaceutical preparations ☆ - Chase Laboratories Inc.
IODENT - Toothpaste - Iodent Co.
IODEX - Pharmaceutical preparations - Medtech Laboratories Inc.
IODO-CHON - Mouthwashes - Pharmac Laboratories
IODO-FED - Pharmaceutical preparations ☆ - Tracy Pharmacal Co.
IODO-FIVE - Disinfectants - Cottrell, Ltd.
IODO-JEL - Pharmaceutical preparations - Pharmac Laboratories
IODO-NIACIN - Pharmaceutical preparations ☆ - Forest Pharmaceuticals Inc.
IODO-PHENO-GEL - Pharmaceutical preparations - Pharmac Laboratories
IODOACETAMIDE - Pharmaceutical preparations - City Chemical Corp.
IODOCORT - Pharmaceutical preparations ☆ - Ulmer Pharmacal Co.
IODOPUR - Water purification systems - SQM Iodine Corp., USA
IODOSORB - Filters–water - Umpqua Research Co.

IODOZYME - Chemical preparations - Symbollon Corp.
IOGONE - Pharmaceutical preparations - Nice-Pak Products, Inc.
IOK - Jewelry - Phi Theta Kappa
IOMA - Food processors - Wapsie Produce Inc.
IOMED - Medical apparatus - Iomed, Inc.
IOMEGA - Computer peripheral equipment - Iomega Corp.
ION-ALERT - Diagnostic apparatus - Kentucky Water Treatment
ION IMAGINATION - Recording label - Ion Imagination Entertainment, Inc.
ION KIDS - Sunglasses - Outlook Eyewear Co.
ION SPORT - Sunglasses - Outlook Eyewear Co.
ION SYSTEMS - Air purification systems - Ion Systems
IONA - Floor coverings–carpet and rugs - Atlas Carpet Mills Inc.
IONA - Rings–jewelry - Artcarved Inc.
IONAIR - Filters–air - Vita Craft Corp.
IONAMIN - Health care products - Fisons Corp.
IONAX - Pharmaceutical preparations - Owen/Galderma Laboratories Inc.
IONGRAFIX - Computer peripheral equipment ☆ - QMS, Inc.
IONIA - Olive oil - Yaniv Enterprises, Inc.
IONIAN - Furniture ☆ - Bassett Furniture Industries, Inc.
IONIC - Artists' materials ☆ - Keuffel & Esser Co.
IONIC - Floor coverings–carpet and rugs ☆ - World Carpets, Inc.
IONICAMERA - Visual musical display ☆ - Ionic Industries Inc.
IONICS - Water - Ionics, Inc.
IONIL - Shampoos - Owen/Galderma Laboratories Inc.
IONIL PLUS - Shampoos - Owen/Galderma Laboratories Inc.
IONPRO - Controls–heating systems - Surface Combustion, Inc.
IONPRO-IMS - Monitors–electronic - Molecular Analytics, LLC
IOPENER - Computer software - National Semiconductor Corp.
IOPHED - Pharmaceutical preparations - Marsh-Emory Laboratories
IOPHEN - Pharmaceutical preparations - Barre-National, Inc.
IOPIDINE - Health care products - Alcon Laboratories, Inc.
IORIO - Accordions - Syn-Cordion Musical Instruments Corp.
IOSEL 250 - Pharmaceutical preparations ☆ - Owen/Galderma Laboratories Inc.
IOSSO - Cleaning preparations - IOSSO Products
IOSYN - Pharmaceutical preparations - G.O. Spanner Inc.
IOTABS - Iodine - Wayne Chemical Inc.
IOTEC - Surgical instruments - Dexide, Inc.
IOTRODE - Pharmaceutical preparations - Maxxim Medical Inc.
IOTUSS - Pharmaceutical preparations - H.R. Cenci Laboratories Inc.
IOTUSS - Pharmaceutical preparations ☆ - Muro Pharmaceuticals Inc.
IOTUSS-DM - Pharmaceutical preparations ☆ - Muro Pharmaceuticals Inc.
I.O.U. - Apparel and accessories - MGRR, Inc.
IOU - Greeting cards ☆ - Fun, Inc.
IOVISION - Surgical products - Iovision, Inc.
IOWA CUBS - Paper - Chicago National League Ball Club Inc.
IOWA ELECTRONIC ELBOW - Medical apparatus - ElectroBionics Corp.
IOWA LADYFINGER - Popcorn ☆ - Select Origins Inc.
IOWA PORK SUPERB - Food products - American Foods Group
IOWA PORKBURGERS - Pork patties - American Foods Group
IOWARE - Computer software - Iomega Corp.
IOWORKS - Computer software - Vme Microsystems International Corp.
IOX - Transmitting apparatus–television - Comark Communications, Inc.
IOZ - Action figure toys - HB Production Co.
I.P. - Food products - Burke Marketing Corp.
IP MANAGER - Computer software - Process Focus Software, Inc.
IPA - Beverages–malt ☆ - Labatt Importers Inc.
IPAGARD - Epoxy - IPA Systems Inc.
IPALASTIC - Waterproof coatings - IPA Systems Inc.
IPANA - Mouthwashes - American Vitamin Products, Inc.
IPANEMA - Bathing suits - Made in Brazil Inc.
IPANEMA - Women's shoes - Ipanema Shoe Corp.
IPAPHOB - Waterproofing sealant - IPA Systems Inc.
IPC - Automotive exhaust parts - International Parts Corp.
IPC - Garment hangers ☆ - Selfix, Inc.
IPC - Machine parts - Esco Corp.
IPC - Projectors–photographic - International Cinema Equipment Co.
IPC ORGANIZER - Housewares ☆ - Selfix, Inc.
IPCLIP - Housewares - Selfix, Inc.
IPECEA - Seafood products–fresh or frozen - Demerico Corp.
IPECHAR - Pharmaceutical preparations ☆ - Colgate Oral Pharmaceuticals Inc.
IPENDENT - Mouthwashes - Heritage Store Inc.
IPEX - Computer software - Fluor Corp.
IPF - Repellent - Wisconsin Pharmacal Co. Inc.
IPG - Fruits and vegetables - Western Farmers Association
IPG - Glass–tempered - Import Products Co., Inc.

☆ = Now out of production

IPI - Automotive parts and accessories - Echlin Inc.

IPI - Pharmaceutical products - ImmunoPharmaceutics Inc.

IPI - Sporting goods - Institutional Products, Inc.

IPIN - Rice - Tawa Supermarket, Inc.

IPLUS 4 - See **SMART R**

IPM - Computer peripheral equipment - NEC Technologies, Inc.

IPM - Computer software - Interqual, Inc.

IPO - Computer hardware - Dong Sung America, Inc.

IPOCORK-WICANDER - Floor coverings–tile - Ipocork Ltd.

IPOD - Office furniture - Chrysalis Inc.

IPOWER - Computer hardware - National Semiconductor Corp.

IPPCO - Frozen potatoes - Interstate Potato Packers

IPPOLITO'S - Spaghetti - Ideal Macaroni Co.

IPPOLITO'S IDEAL PIZZOLI - Pizzas–frozen - Ideal Macaroni Co.

IPR-3 - Skin care products - CCA Industries, Inc.

IPRAX - Computer software - Iprax Corp.

IPROCESS - Computer software - Grumman Data Systems Corp.

IPROJECT - Educational materials - Panda Enterprises

IPROJR - Computer software - Ipro, Inc.

IPROSCAN - Computer software - Ipro, Inc.

IPROTRIEVE - Computer software - Ipro, Inc.

IPROTRIEVE 2000 - Computer software - Ipro, Inc.

IPS - Jewelry - Imperial-Deltah Inc.

IPS - Recording label - Jazz Composer's Orchestra Association Inc.

IPS INTERNATIONAL POWERSYSTEMS - Power switching equipment - International Power Systems, Inc.

IPS WELD-ON HOT 'R COLD - Adhesives and sealants - IPS Corp.

IPS WELD-ON POOL 'R SPA - Adhesives and sealants - IPS Corp.

IPSAB - Pharmaceutical preparations - Heritage Store Inc.

IPSATOL - Cough medicines - Kenwood Laboratories Inc.

IPSO FACTOR - Handbags, wallets, etc. - Christiane Paine Accessories

IPSPLOT - Computer software - Beckwith Electric Co.

IPU - Furniture - Innovation Products Unlimited, Inc.

IPW USA - Automotive parts and accessories - IPW Corp

IQ - Battery chargers - HM Electronics, Inc.

IQ - Circuit boards - Crown International, Inc.

IQ - Computer hardware - Gammagraphx, Inc.

I.Q. - Games - The Learning Experience Inc.

IQ - Golfing equipment - Cobra Golf Inc.

IQ - Optical machinery - Coburn Optical Industries, Inc.

IQ - Toothbrushes - Uni Lac Corp.

IQ ACCESS - Computer software - IQ Software Corp.

IQ ADMIN - Computer software - Intecom Inc.

IQ ARCADE - Games - Educational Insights, Inc.

IQ BOOKS - Computer software - Advantage KBS, Inc.

IQ INTERQUEST - Video production - Interquest Ltd.

IQ LIGHTING - Lamp bulbs - Phillips Electronics North America Corp.

IQ/MLC - Window shades - Mecho Shade Corp.

IQ PLUS - Electronic equipment - Mark O. Johnson

I.Q. PLUS - Vitamins and nutritional supplements ☆ - Vitamin Research Products Inc.

IQ/SMARTSERVER - Computer software - IQ Software Corp.

IQ SYSTEM - Computer terminals - Crown International, Inc.

IQ TESTER - Novelty items - Adams Apple Distributing L.P.

IQ UNLIMITED - Computers–personal - Video Technology U.S. Inc.

I.Q. WINDOW - Vinyl - Reynolds Metals Co.

IQ.CLEAR - Computer software - Allen Telecom Inc.

IQF - Seafood products–fresh or frozen - Gulf Central Seafoods

IQI INTERNATIONAL QUALITY INSTITUTE - Computer software - International Quality Institute

IQ.LINK - Computer peripheral equipment - Comsearch

IQS - Bags–plastic - Stone Container Corp.

IQS/3 - Water purification systems - Bruner Corp.

IQ.SIGNUM - Computer software - Allen Telecom Inc.

I.Q.S.Y. TOMAHAWK - Toys–models ☆ - Estes Industries

IQUITOS - Perfumes - Campbell & Thiselton

IQZOOM - Cameras - Pentax Corp.

IQZOOM 80E - Cameras - Pentax Corp.

IQZOOM 90-WR - Cameras - Pentax Corp.

IQZOOM 90MC - Cameras - Pentax Corp.

IQZOOM 115 - Cameras ☆ - Pentax Corp.

IQZOOM 115M - Cameras - Pentax Corp.

IQZOOM 140 - Cameras - Pentax Corp.

IQZOOM 160 - Cameras - Pentax Corp.

IQZOOM 928 - Cameras - Pentax Corp.

IQZOOM EZY - Cameras - Pentax Corp.

IR - Electronic equipment - Infrared Data Association

IR 9 - Suntan lotions ☆ - Carter-Wallace, Inc.

IR IMMORTAL RECORDS - Recording label - Immortal Entertainment

IR LINK - Electronic equipment - Galileo Corp.

I.R. VISION - Binoculars - Sakar International Inc.

IR100 - Sporting goods - Jack Martin Co.

IRA JOYCE - Apparel–athletic - Isaac Hazan & Co.

IRA ROBERTS - Giftware ☆ - Hillside House of Originals

I.R.A. SELECTOR - Computer software - SourceView Software International

IRA TRAKKER - Computer software - Advanced Information Solutions, Inc.

IRACA PALM - Baskets–wood - La Casa De Carlo

IRADICAV - Pharmaceutical preparations ☆ - Ranir Corp.

IRANI - Tea - Irani & Co.

IRATA - Cameras - Irata, Inc.

IRAUTO - Automotive parts and accessories - Echlin Inc.

IRC - Thermal imaging camera - Cincinnati Electronics Corp.

IRCON - Pharmaceutical preparations - Kenwood Laboratories Inc.

IRCON FA - Vitamins and nutritional supplements - Kenwood Laboratories Inc.

IRCOSPERSE - Lubricants - Lubrizol Corp.

IRD - Bicycles - Interloc, Inc.

IREADY - Computer software - Iready Corp.

IREGA - Wrenches - Anglo American Enterprises Corp.

IRELAND - Candy - Bewley Irish Imports

IRELAND - Coffee, tea - Ireland Coffee and Tea Inc.

IRELAND'S - Food products ☆ - American Home Food Products Inc.

IREM AMERICA - Video games - IREM America Corp.

IRENA - Glassware–household - Miller Import Corp.

IRENE - Watches - Bulova Corp.

IRENE DASH - Greeting cards ☆ - American Artists Group Inc.

IRENE GARI - Cosmetics - Fiske Industries Inc.

IRENE'S SUPER-GRIP - Glue–household or industrial - Skyline Distributing Co.

IREX - Computer software - Tech-Logic, Inc.

IREX 100 - Apparel and accessories ☆ - Bolle' America, Inc.

IREX LITE - Apparel and accessories ☆ - Bolle' America, Inc.

IRGEN - Computer software - Technology Service Corp.

IRGEN-RT - Computer software - Technology Service Corp.

IRICE - Giftware - Irving W. Rice & Co. Inc.

IRIDA - Recording label - Jazz Composer's Orchestra Association Inc.

IRIDESCENCE - Floor coverings–carpet and rugs - Collins & Aikman Corp.

IRIDESCENCE - Jewelry–costume - Phillips International Jewelry & Souvenirs Inc.

IRIDESCENCE - Recording label - Jazz Composer's Orchestra Association Inc.

IRIDESCENT - Skin care products - Takara Belmont USA, Inc.

IRIDIANCE - Hair care products - Cosmair Inc.

IRIDISC - Compact discs–prerecorded - Iridisc Digital Media

IRIDIUM - Apparel and accessories - Iridium, Inc.

IRIDIUM - Eyeglasses - Oakley, Inc.

IRIDIZED OPAL - Glassware–household ☆ - Fenton Art Glass Co.

IRIDNET - Electronic equipment - Jenoptik Infab Intrak, Inc.

IRIE BLUE - Clothing - West Indies Clothing Co.

IRIGATE - Pharmaceutical preparations - Steri-Med Inc.

IRIS - Blinds–vertical - Kingdom Vertical Blinds Manufacturing Inc.

IRIS - Chimes - Nutone Inc.

IRIS - Computer software - Federal Publications, Inc.

IRIS - Dinnerware ☆ - Corning Inc.

IRIS - Dinnerware–glass ☆ - Metlox Pottery Shoppe

IRIS - Dinnerware–glass ☆ - Nikko Ceramics Inc.

IRIS - Fabrics - Permalin Products Co.

IRIS - Flatware - Yamazaki Tableware Inc.

IRIS - Food products - Smart and Final Stores Corp.

IRIS - Glassware–household ☆ - WMF/USA

IRIS - Index cards - Cel-U-Dex Corp.

IRIS - Inks - Iris Graphics, Inc.

IRIS - Jewelry–costume - H.S. Strygler & Co. Inc.

IRIS - Paper products - Iris U.S.A. Inc.

IRIS - Tableware–china - Villeroy and Boch Tableware Ltd.

IRIS - Tiles–ceramic - Federal Tile Imports Inc.

IRIS - Tiles–ceramic - Maxsam Sales, Inc.

IRIS - Toys–models ☆ - Estes Industries

IRIS - Video production - Wright State University

IRIS - Wallpaper ☆ - Fidelity Industries, Inc.

IRIS - Watches - Bulova Corp.

IRIS 900UDX - Computer software - International Remote Imaging Systems, Inc.

IRIS AND IVY - Apparel–children's - Gerson and Gerson Inc.

☆ = Now out of production

IRIS & KITTY, INC. - Board game - Iris & Kitty Inc.

IRIS DE FETE - Perfumes - Revlon Consumer Products Corp.

IRIS FANTASY - Bedding–linen - Dan River Inc.

IRIS GOLD ACCENT - Flatware - Yamazaki Tableware Inc.

IRIS IO - Publisher's imprints - Strawberry Hill Press

IRIS MEDICAL - Medical equipment - IRIS Medical Instruments.

IRIS NOUVEAU - Floor coverings–carpet and rugs ☆ - Capel, Inc.

IRIS ON GREY - Dinnerware–glass ☆ - Lenox, Inc.

IRISH - Audio and video cassettes and accessories - Irish Magnetic Industries

IRISH - Electronics equipment - Ampex Corp.

IRISH-AMERICAN SOCIETY - Embossing plates - Devin-Adair Co. Inc.

IRISH BASICS - Floor coverings–carpet and rugs ☆ - Concepts International

IRISH BREAKFAST - Teas ☆ - R.C. Bigelow, Inc.

IRISH COFFEE - Glassware–household - World of Porcelain & Glassware

IRISH COFFEE - Glassware–household ☆ - Lenox Crystal, Inc.

IRISH CREAM MINT - Candy - Ben Myerson Candy Co.

IRISH CREAM MIST - Teas–herbal ☆ - Celestial Seasonings, Inc.

IRISH D HIGH TOAST - Snuff - Faber, Coe & Gregg Inc.

IRISH DAWN - Teas–herbal - Bewley Irish Imports

IRISH ERINSTONE - Dishes–china - Mikasa Co.

IRISH ESSENCE - Wallpaper - J. Chesterfield Studio

IRISH FLAME - Fireplace logs–treated - Haddon House Food Products Inc.

IRISH GEORGIAN SOCIETY - Wallpaper - Scalamandre Silks Inc.

IRISH GRAPE - Fruit juice ☆ - Folk-Lore Natural Foods Inc.

IRISH HAND LEATHER - Leather product - Atlas Co.

IRISH HILLS - Dairy products - Irish Hills Goat Dairy

IRISH HILLS - Fudge - Stagecoach Stop Fudge Shop

IRISH KIDS - Apparel–children's - Marianne Kinkopf

IRISH LACE - Yarn - Henry's Attic

IRISH MINVITONE - Veterinary pharmaceutical preparations - Southeastern Laboratories

IRISH MIST - Beverages–alcohol - Hiram Walker & Sons, Inc.

IRISH MIST - Perfumes - Knight Marketing Corp.

IRISH MOSS - Liquors - House of Seagram

IRISH O'GARLIC - Sausages - Johnsonville Foods Co.

IRISH PORTER - Cakes - Shamrock Foods Co.

IRISH POTCHEEN - Whiskey - Camelot Importing Co., Inc.

IRISH RIVER - Furniture ☆ - Tropitone Furniture Co. Inc.

IRISH ROVER - Boats - Marine Metals Inc.

IRISH SEA SPRAY - Salmon–smoked, salted, dried, or pickled ☆ - G.F. Higgins

IRISH SETTER - Boots - Red Wing Shoe Co. Inc.

IRISH SPRING - Soap - Colgate-Palmolive Co.

IRISH SPRING WATERFALL - Soap - Colgate-Palmolive Co.

IRISH STUDIES - Publisher's imprints - Syracuse University Press

IRISH SWIRL - Floor coverings–carpet and rugs - Reeves Brothers Inc.

IRISH TREASURE - Floor coverings–carpet and rugs ☆ - Masland Corp.

IRISH TWEED - Fabrics - Uniroyal Engineered Products

IRISH VILLAGE - Artists' materials - Joan Hurley

IRISH WHISKEY - Cakes - Shamrock Foods Co.

IRISIDENT - Computer software - Sensar, Inc.

IRISPRO - Computer software - Federal Publications, Inc.

IRISTUTOR - Computer software - Data Translation, Inc.

IRIX - Computer software - Silicon Graphics, Inc.

IRKA - Women's apparel ☆ - Irka

IRLIB - Computer software - AMX Corp.

IRLITE - Computer software - Counterpoint Systems Foundry, Inc.

IRM - Recording label - Sound Inc.

IRMA - Medical apparatus - Diametrics Medical, Inc.

IRMCO - Lubricants - International Refining & Manufacturing Co.

IRMI - Infant product ☆ - Reliance Products Corp.

IRMSTAN - Pens, desk sets, pencils - Irmstan Pen Manufacturing Co. & Enterprises

IRODEX - Pharmaceutical preparations ☆ - Keene Pharmaceuticals Inc.

IROFOL - Pharmaceutical preparations - Dayton Laboratories, Inc.

IROMIN-G - Vitamins and nutritional supplements - Mission Pharmacal Co.

IRON - Fishing tackle - Zebco Corp.

IRON - Men's fragrance - Coty Inc.

IRON - Ophthalmic goods - Foremost Optical Products

IRON-A-WAY - Ironing tables, housewares - Iron-A-Way, Inc.

IRON AGE - Footwear - Iron Age Corp.

IRON AGE MAXIMUM - Footwear - Iron Age Corp.

IRON AGE PLUS - Footwear - Iron Age Corp.

IRON AGE SPORTWORK II - Footwear - Iron Age Corp.

IRON ANGEL OF THE APOCALYPSE - Computer software - Synergy Interactive Corp.

IRON ASSAULT - Computer software - Virgin Interactive Entertainment, Inc.

IRON BULL - Exercising equipment - James Pellechia

IRON BULL - Fertilizers - OMS Investments, Inc.

IRON CARE - Cleaning preparations - Enforcer Products Inc.

IRON CITY - Beverages–malt - Pittsburgh Brewing Co.

IRON CITY COOLER - Beverages–malt - Pittsburgh Brewing Co.

IRON CITY DARK - Beverages–malt - Pittsburgh Brewing Co.

IRON CITY GOLDEN - Beverages–malt - Pittsburgh Brewing Co.

IRON CITY LIGHT - Beverages–malt - Pittsburgh Brewing Co.

IRON CLAD - Brooms - Fluffo Mop & Broom Co. Inc.

IRON CLAD - Floor coverings–carpet and rugs ☆ - Patcraft Mills Inc.

IRON CLASSICS - Iron products - Houston International Trading

IRON CURTAIN - Water treating compounds - Hellenbrand Water Conditioners Inc.

IRON CURTAIN LABS - Vitamins and nutritional supplements - Iron Curtain Labs Inc.

IRON DUCK - Sweatshirts - Iron Duck Grafix

IRON DUKE - Floor coverings–carpet and rugs - Barrett Carpet Mills Inc.

IRON DUKE - Gloves - Wells Lamont Corp.

IRON DUKE - Golfing equipment - Slotline Golf

IRON-EASE - Fabrics–cotton - Dan River Inc.

IRON EDGE - Garden equipment - Border Concepts, Inc.

IRON ETCH - Cleaning preparations - Sherwin-Williams Automotive Finishes Corp.

IRON FEATHER - Fishing tackle - Fenwick

IRON FIGHTER - Salt - Stevens Industries Inc.

IRON FIREMAN - Boilers–steam - Dunham Bush, Inc.

IRON-FOR-WOMEN - Pharmaceutical preparations - Pharmex Inc.

IRON FORCE - Calendars - Mach 1, Inc.

IRON GATE - Caviar - Caviar & Caviar Corp.

IRON GATE - Floor coverings–carpet and rugs - Trend Carpet

IRON GEAR - Apparel and accessories - World Triathlon Corp.

IRON GENERATION - Apparel and accessories - Iron Generation, LLC

IRON GLYCINATE PLUS - Vitamins and nutritional supplements - Ethical Nutrients

IRON GO - Chemical preparations ☆ - Coastal Industries Inc.

IRON GRIP - Exercising equipment - Scott J. Frasco

IRON-GRIP - Shelving units–metal - Equipto

IRON HAND - Gloves - Knoxville Glove Co.

IRON HAWK - Fishing tackle ☆ - Fenwick

IRON-HOLD - Bags–trash - North American Plastics Corp.

IRON HOOKER - Golfing equipment - Gordon Larson

IRON HORSE - Engines - Outboard Marine Corp.

IRON HORSE - Golfing equipment - Here's Fred Golf Co., Inc.

IRON HORSE - Horse bits - Lazy K Distributors Inc.

IRON HORSE - Motor vehicle parts and accessories ☆ - Saddleman, Inc.

IRON HORSE - Motors–hydraulic ☆ - Magnetek Inc.

IRON HORSE - Work benches - Hirsh Co.

IRON HORSE TRAIL - Blankets - Dewey Trading Co.

IRON HORSE VINEYARDS - Wines - Iron Horse Vineyards

IRON HORSE WORK SYSTEMS BY HIRSH - Tool boxes - Hirsh Co.

IRON IKE - Rust removers - Hercules Chemical Co. Inc.

IRON KE-MIN - Chemical preparations - Georgia-Pacific Corp.

IRON KLAW - Toys - Hasbro, Inc.

IRON LION SNOWBOARDS - Apparel and accessories - Nicholas J. Perdaris

IRON MAN - Apparel and accessories - Marvel Entertainment Group, Inc.

IRON MAN - Motors - Leeson Electric Corp.

IRON MAN - Ophthalmic goods - Foremost Optical Products

IRON-MAN AIR - Compressors–air - Ronald D. Ittner

IRON MASK - Welders' hoods - Sellstrom Manufacturing Co.

IRON MASTER - Exercising equipment ☆ - California Gym Equipment

IRON-MATE - Ironing board pads - E & M Engineering, Inc.

IRON MATES - Lighting equipment - Jimway, Inc.

IRON MEND - Fabrics - McNett Corp.

IRON MIKE - Gloves - Knoxville Glove Co.

IRON MIKE - Sporting goods - Master Pitching Machine, Inc.

IRON MOUNTAIN - Ammunition - Iron Mountain, Ltd.

IRON MOUNTAIN - Floor coverings - Aladdin Mills, Inc.

IRON MOUNTAIN - Outdoor furniture - Jack-Post Corp.

IRON MOUNTAIN - Shoes - J.P. Original Corp.

IRON MOUNTAIN - Stoneware dinnerware - Iron Mountain Stoneware Inc.

IRON MYTE - Chemical preparations - Coastal Industries Inc.

IRON-ONS - Pet products - Gimborn U.S., Inc.

IRON OUT - Rust removers ☆ - Iron Out, Inc.

IRON PLUS - Chemical preparations - Kemmer Agricultural Manufacturing Co. Inc.

☆ = Now out of production

IRON PLUS - Fertilizers - Thompson Manufacturing Co.

IRON PLUS - Vitamins and nutritional supplements - Vita-Fore Products Co.

IRON PLUS CHELATE - Fertilizers - Security Products Co.

IRON QUEST - Vitamins and nutritional supplements - Nutri-West

IRON-QUIK - Fabrics - Graniteville Co.

IRON RANGE - Beverages—malt - James Page Brewing Co., LLC

IRON ROOT - Anchors - Tie Down, Inc.

IRON SAK - Trash bags - Ironclad Inc.

IRON-SOL - Health care products - Halsey Drug Co. Inc.

IRON SOUL - Containers - Success Ware, Inc.

IRON SPIKE - Toys - Tonka Corp.

IRON STONE 24 - Floor coverings—carpet and rugs - Mohawk Carpet Corp.

IRON SURE - Vitamins and nutritional supplements ☆ - Pharmavite Corp.

IRON/TONES - Sinks—metal - Kohler Co.

IRON TOP - Toys - Tonka Corp.

IRON TUFF - Apparel and accessories - RefrigiWear Inc.

IRON VELVET - Fabrics—velvet - Guilford Mills, Inc.

IRON-VITE - Vitamins and nutritional supplements ☆ - Pharm-A-Lab

IRON WING - Safety products - D B Industries, Inc.

IRON WORKS - Candlesticks - Our Secret, Ltd.

IRON WORKS - Recording label - Azra International

IRONBOUND - Floor coverings ☆ - Robbins Inc.

IRONBOUND - Recording label ☆ - Peter Pan Industries

IRONBUTT - Exercising equipment - Slim-Ez Mr. America Manufacturing, Inc.

IRONCLAD - Floor coverings—carpet and rugs ☆ - Interloom Ltd.

IRONCLAD - Paints - Benjamin Moore & Co.

IRONCLAD - Watches - Croton Watch Co., Inc.

IRONCO-B - Pharmaceutical preparations ☆ - Pal-Pak Inc.

IRONCOAT - Epoxy coatings - Pioneer Manufacturing Co.

IRONDALE CAFE ORIGINAL WHISTLE STOP - Apparel and accessories - Ghc, Inc.

IRONDALE CAFE ORIGINAL WHISTLE STOP - Glassware—household - GHC Products, Inc.

IRONEES - Housewares - Ironees Co.

IRONEX - Pharmaceutical preparations - Legere Pharmaceuticals Inc.

IRONFINGERS - Gloves - David Frey

IRONFIX - Ironing boards - Hafele America Co.

IRONFLEX - Musical instruments ☆ - St. Louis Music Supply Co.

IRONGATE - Floor coverings—carpet and rugs - Ebsco Carpet Mills

IRONHIDE - Paints ☆ - PPG Industries, Inc.

IRONIKA - Iron products ☆ - Clinton Packaging Co.

IRONING STATION - Storage rack - Clairson International Corp.

IRONITE - Garden equipment - Lawn & Garden Supply Co.

IRONKIDS - Apparel—athletic - World Triathlon Corp.

IRONLORDS - Toys - Midgetoy

IRONLUX - Tablecloths - Mount Vernon Mills Inc.

IRONMAN - Dropcloths - Poly-America, Inc.

IRONMAN - Hardware - Crown Bolt, Inc.

IRONMAN - Sporting goods - Gridiron Enterprises, Inc.

IRONMAN - Vacuum cleaners and accessories - Oreck Corp.

IRONMAN TRIATHLON - Sportswear - World Triathlon Corp.

IRONMAN TRIATHLON CROSS TRAINING - Shirts - World Triathlon Corp.

IRONMAR - Vitamins and nutritional supplements - Marlop Pharmaceuticals Inc.

IRONMASTER - Chemical preparations - Polymerica, Inc.

IRONMASTER - Irons—electric - Sunbeam-Oster Household Products

IRONPLATE - Paint dryers - Connelly-GPM, Inc.

IRONPLY - Wood products - American Piano Service and Supply Corp.

IRONPLY - Wood products - The Piano Man

IRONQUEST - Apparel and accessories - Kingdom Life Christian Center

IRONROCK - Tiles—ceramic - Metropolitan Ceramics

IRONROCK - Tiles—ceramic - Metropolitan Industries, Inc.

IRONSIDE - Lumber - Georgia-Pacific Corp.

IRONSIDES - Chairs—metal ☆ - Cramer Inc.

IRONSIDES - Leather-palm gloves - Boss Manufacturing Co.

IRONSIDES - Ophthalmic goods - Foremost Optical Products

IRONSIDES - Security doors and burglar bars - Vanguard Manufacturing Co.

IRONSIDES - Vacuum cleaners and accessories - The Eureka Co.

IRONSIGHTER - Photographic equipment - J.B. Holden Co.

IRONSITES - Containers—trash - Victor Stanley, Inc.

IRONSKIN - Wet suits—rubber - Wellington Leisure Products, Inc.

IRONSMITH - Machinery - Tractor Supply Co.

IRONSMITH MACHINES FOR METAL - Machinery - Tractor Supply Co.

IRONSTONE - Floor coverings—carpet and rugs - Mohawk Carpet Corp.

IRONSTONE - Floor coverings—carpet and rugs ☆ - Cumberland Mills Inc.

IRONTHREAD - Sporting goods ☆ - Outdoor Technologies Group

IRONTITE - Fabrics - Stearns Technical Textiles Co.

IRONTONE PLUS - Vitamins and nutritional supplements - Nature's Concept Inc.

IRONWEAR - Ceramic tile - Integrity Tile Co.

IRONWEAR - Finishing agents - Pioneer Manufacturing Co.

IRONWEAR - Hosiery - Kayser-Roth Corp.

IRONWEVE - Hosiery - Ithaca Industries Inc.

IRONWEVE 2000 - Hosiery - Ithaca Industries Inc.

IRONWOOD - Apparel and accessories - Montgomery Ward & Co. Inc.

IRONWOOD - Building materials - Behlen Manufacturing Co.

IRONWOOD - Cutlery - Mundial Inc.

IRONWOOD - Floor coverings—carpet and rugs - Barrett Carpet Mills Inc.

IRONWOOD - Floor coverings—carpet and rugs ☆ - Royalweve Carpet Mills

IRONWOOD TRADING COMPANY - Apparel and accessories - Montgomery Ward & Co. Inc.

IRONWORKS - Curtain rods - Newell Operating Co.

IRONWORKS - Racks - Our Secret, Ltd.

IROPHOS-D - Pharmaceutical preparations - Lannett Co. Inc.

IROQUOIS - Automotive parts and accessories - Echlin Inc.

IROQUOIS - Beverages—malt - Fred Koch Brewery Inc.

IROQUOIS - Flavored popcorns and pretzels - Iroquois Popcorn Co. Inc.

IROQUOIS - Floor coverings - American Floor Products Co. Inc.

IROQUOIS - Health care products ☆ - Majestic Drug Co., Inc.

IROQUOIS - Knives - Utica Cutlery Co.

IROQUOIS - Rubber—molded - Carlisle Tire & Rubber Co.

IROQUOIS - Teas—herbal ☆ - Hays Pharmaceutical Co.

IROQUOIS BOOKS - Publisher's imprints - Syracuse University Press

IROQUOIS NATIONALS LACROSSE - Apparel and accessories - Iroquois Nationals Lacrosse

IROSPAN - Pharmaceutical preparations - Fielding Pharmaceutical Co.

IRP FARE - Computer software - R.L. Polk & Co.

IRPAK - Dryers—laboratory - Fusion UV Systems, Inc.

IRR INSTANT ROAD REPAIR - Asphalt - Safety Lights Co.

IRRCOL - Computer software - Portland Cement

IRREGULERS - Apparel—athletic ☆ - A-B Emblem Corp.

IRREPLACEABLE ARTIFACTS - Antique stores - Stardial Communications Corp.

IRRESISTABLE CHANEL - Cosmetics - Chanel Inc.

IRRESISTIBLE - Floor coverings—carpet and rugs - Durkan Patterned Carpets

IRRESISTIBLE - Perfumes - All Clubman

IRRESISTIBLE COOKIE JAR, THE - Cookies - The Basket Case

IRRESISTIBLE LACE - Apparel and accessories - Sears, Roebuck and Co.

IRRESISTIBLE STITCHABLES - Appliques ☆ - Mail Pouch

IRRESISTIBLES - Jewelry - K & M Associates

IRRESPONSIBLE - Perfumes ☆ - Tristar Corp.

IRRESTISTIBLE IMPOSTERS - Colognes - Parfum de Coeur Ltd.

IRREZESTABLES - Dinners—frozen ☆ - Stouffer Foods Corp.

IRRIBOOST - Pumps - Barrett Engineered Pumps

IRRIGATOR - Engines—diesel - Powermark Ltd.

IRRIGATOR - Hoses - Colorite Plastic Co.

IRRIGOL - Mouthwashes ☆ - Alkalol Co.

IRRITAINMENT - Recording label - Mark C. Rudolph and Fabio P. Roberti Partnership

IRRIVAC - Surgical supplies - Dexide, Inc.

IRS - Computer software - Professional Safety Consultants Inc.

IRS - Recording label - Capitol-EMI Music Inc.

IRS INNER RHYTHM SURFBOARDS - Apparel and accessories - Inner Rhythm Surf

IRS MAN, THE - Novelty items - Voodoo To You Inc.

IRS METAL - Recording label - I.R.S. Records

IRSC - Computer software - I.R.S.C., Inc.

IRSCO - Hair care products - Fromm Industries

IRT - Television equipment - Television Equipment Associates

IRTH - Napkins—paper - Wisconsin Tissue Mills Inc.

IRVING SLOANE - Musical instrument accessories - Stewart-MacDonald Manufacturing

IRVING TRADING, INC. - Herbal products - Irving Trading, Inc.

IRVING W. RICE - Giftware ☆ - Avnet, Inc.

IRVING YOUNGER AUDIO/VIDEO CLE SERIES, THE - Educational materials - Professional Education Group, Inc.

IRVINWARE - Barware, party goods, kitchen accessories, etc. - Irvinware Inc.

IRV'S - Apparel and accessories - Rack Clothing, Inc.

IRWIN - Sailing yachts - America Cruising Yacht Corp.

IRWIN - Screwdrivers, wood-boring and measuring tools - Irwin Co.

IRWIN - Tools - American Tool Companies Inc.

IRWIN-HODSON - Badges, labels, stamp pads, etc. - Irwin-Hodson Co.

☆ = Now out of production

IRWIN PROMBA - Computer software - Times Mirror Higher Education Group, Inc.
IRWINWARE - Giftware ☆ - Towle Silversmiths
IRX - Generators–gas - Surface Combustion, Inc.
IRYFIX - Health care products - C.R. Bard, Inc.
IS - Computer hardware - Intersolv, Inc.
IS - Computer software - Icon Solutions, Inc.
IS' - Puzzles ☆ - Milton Bradley Co.
IS-1 - Cameras ☆ - Olympus America Inc.
IS-3 - Cameras - Olympus America Inc.
IS-10 - Cameras ☆ - Olympus America Inc.
IS-10STYLUS - Cameras - Olympus America Inc.
IS-2000 - Golfing equipment - Impact Solutions, Inc.
IS AGENT - Computer software ☆ - Integrated Software
IS-IBC1 - Electronic equipment - D.R. Joseph, Inc.
IS INFOSONICS - Telephone apparatus - Infosonics Corp.
IS IT BY CHANCE? OR IS IT BY CHOICE? - Hair coloring preparations - Clairol Inc.
IS IT IE OR EI? - Computer software ☆ - Right on Programs
IS IT MOM? OR IS IT MUNCHKIN? - Infant product - Munchkin, Inc.
IS IT TRUE.BLONDES HAVE MORE FUN? - Hair coloring preparations - Clairol Inc.
IS/MODELER - Computer software - Intec Systems, Inc.
IS THAT A FACT - Games - Scott A. Johnson
IS2 - Automotive parts and accessories - U-Fuel, Inc.
IS8 - Tools–power-driven - Phillips Screw Co.
ISA-LOK - Containers - Aluminum Co. of America
ISAAC GELLIS - Meat products - Hebrew Foods Inc.
ISAAC HAZAN - Crocheted and knitted items - Isaac Hazan & Co.
ISAAC MIZRAHI - Belts–apparel - Isaac Mizrahi & Co.
ISAAC NEWTON - Computer software - Krell Software Corp.
ISAAC NEWTON SUPERPREMIUM - Ice cream - Hagan Ice Cream
ISAAN - Food products - Tucuru
ISABABIES - Apparel–children's - Kessner and Rabinowitz, Inc.
ISABADE - Health care products ☆ - Halsey Drug Co. Inc.
ISABEL CRISTINA - Nail care products - RBR Productions, Inc.
ISABELLA - Apparel–children's - Kessner and Rabinowitz, Inc.
ISABELLA - Furniture - Tropitone Furniture Co. Inc.
ISABELLA - Giftware ☆ - Gorham Inc.
ISABELLA - Jewelry - Hobe Cie. Ltd.
ISABELLA - Wines - Heritage Wine Cellars
ISABELLA AND GIOVANNI - Footwear - Frederick Atkins, Inc.
ISABELLA'S - Bakery products - Isabella's Bakery, Inc.
ISACS - Computers - Industry Standard Architecture Computersystems Inc.
ISADORA - Fabrics - Gretchen Bellinger Inc.
ISADORA - Fabrics ☆ - Dan River Inc.
ISADORA - Shoes - Novus, Inc.
ISAGEL - Skin care products - Sween Corp.
ISALND COTTON - Yarn - Henry's Attic
ISAMATION - Compact discs–prerecorded - Computer Solutions of Orlando, Inc.
ISAMU NOGUCHI - Lamps - Isamu Noguchi Foundation, Inc.
ISBA - Apparel–athletic ☆ - Regina Imports
ISBX - Communications equipment - Tadiran Electronic Industries, Inc.
ISC - Jewelry–precious - Pan American Diamond Corp.
ISCASTAT - Pharmaceutical preparations - Cambridge Neuroscience, Inc.
ISCH-DISH - Health care products - Embracing Concepts Inc.
ISCHIA - Toiletries - Sara Lee Corp.
ISCO - Lenses–photographic ☆ - Schneider Optics, Inc.
ISCO - Lenses–projection - Optical Radiation Corp.
ISCOLOK - Electronic equipment - Optical Radiation Corp.
ISCONAR - Lenses–photographic ☆ - Heitz Service Corp.
ISCORAMA - Electronic equipment - Optical Radiation Corp.
ISCOVAR - Electronic equipment - Optical Radiation Corp.
ISCP - Computer software - Bell Communications Research, Inc.
ISCT - Ball bearings - International Supply Co., Inc.
ISD-SAC - Publisher's imprints - Interqual, Inc.
ISE LITE - Paints ☆ - Conco Paint Co.
ISECAP - Light filters - Integrated Systems Engineering
ISECURE - Computer hardware - Intervoice LP
ISELA - Fruits and vegetables - Plantain World Corp.
(ISELI) JEAN'S DILLY - Flowers, plants, and seeds - Iseli Nursery, Inc.
ISELIN-JEFFERSON - Fabrics - Dan River Inc.
ISENBECK - Beverages–malt - Ginday Imports Ltd.
ISERE - Boats - Phoenix Products Inc.
ISERNIO'S SAUSAGE - Meat products - ISC Inc.

ISF - Filters–oil - Baker Hughes Inc.
ISFAHAN - Floor coverings–carpet and rugs - Gloria of America Inc.
ISG PRO - Envelopes - Standard Register Co.
ISGO - Fabrics–tapestry - Columbus Coated Fabrics Co.
ISHIME - Adhesives and sealants - Nittoh Tile Corp.
ISHMAEL'S SPECIAL BLEND - Spices and extracts - Ishmael Fails
ISI - Golfing equipment - Karsten Manufacturing Corp.
ISI INTERNATIONAL SYSTEMS INC. - Computer software - International Systems Inc.
ISI SKATEBOARDS - Skateboards - Watson Laminates, Inc.
ISINIS - Hair care products - Variety Imports
I.S.I.S. - Alarm systems - RGM Industries Inc.
ISIS - Alarm systems–burglar - Litton Security Systems
ISIS - Computer software - Pixel Translations, Inc.
ISIS - Computers - Triton Technology, Inc.
ISIS - Flatware - Couzon USA
ISIS - Floor coverings–carpet and rugs - Foreign Accents
ISIS - Generators–power - Holophane Corp.
ISIS - Skin-care products - Isis Industries Inc.
ISIS - Toilets–enameled - Kohler Co.
ISITREADYYET - Computer software - Plum Hall Inc.
ISK BIOSCIENCES - Pesticides–agricultural - ISK Biosciences Corp.
ISK BIOTECH - Chemical preparations - ISK Biosciences Corp.
ISL - Boats–motor - Starcraft Corp.
ISL - Lighting equipment - Art Specialty Co. Inc.
ISLA - Cosmetics - Isla Cosmetique
ISLA - Cosmetics ☆ - Spilo/Mehaz Worldwide
ISLA BAHIAI - Garden furniture - Winston Furniture Co. Inc.
ISLA VISTA - Floor coverings–carpet and rugs - Western Carpet Mills
ISLAGUARD - Electrical surge protectors - Control Concepts Corp.
ISLAMORADA - Furniture ☆ - Tropitone Furniture Co. Inc.
ISLAMORADA II - Furniture - Tropitone Furniture Co. Inc.
ISLAND - Ashtrays–glass - Frank J. Curran-Esquire Chemical Co.
ISLAND - Bicycles - Ross Bicycles USA, Ltd.
ISLAND - Boats–pontoons ☆ - Forester Boats Inc.
ISLAND - Bowls - Svend Jensen of Denmark Inc.
ISLAND - Cabinets - Vinotemp International
ISLAND - File folders ☆ - Esselte Corp.
ISLAND - Fireplaces - Majestic Co.
ISLAND - Potato chips ☆ - Barbara's Bakery, Inc.
ISLAND - Recording label - Island Records Inc.
ISLAND - Seafood products–fresh or frozen - Iceland Seafood Corp.
ISLAND - Soy sauce - Honolulu Sake Brewery Co. Ltd.
ISLAND - Tapioca - Eastern Tea Corp.
ISLAND ADVENTURE - Toys - Discovery Toys, Inc.
ISLAND BERRY - Beverages–carbonated ☆ - Canandaigua Wine Co. Inc.
ISLAND BLENDS - Fruit drinks–bottled or canned - Nabisco Foods Group
ISLAND BLOSSOM - Deodorizers - Reckitt & Colman, Inc.
ISLAND BREEZE - Bicycles - Dynacraft Industries Inc.
ISLAND BREEZE - Dinnerware - Corning Inc.
ISLAND BREEZE - Furniture ☆ - Bassett Furniture Industries, Inc.
ISLAND BREEZE - House furnishings ☆ - Florida Furniture Industries Inc.
ISLAND BREEZE COLLECTION - Giftware - Lenox, Inc.
ISLAND BREEZE RECORDS - Recording label - Island Breeze Records & Publishing Co.
ISLAND BRONZE - Suntan lotions - Roy M. Duleba, II
ISLAND CAPS - Games - Vast Marketing & Promotion
ISLAND CASINO - Recording label - Williams Entertainment Inc.
ISLAND CHANNEL, THE - Recording label - Image Video Group, Inc.
ISLAND CHIPS - Snack foods ☆ - ATGT, Inc.
ISLAND CLASSIC - Beverages - Coca-Cola Enterprises Inc.
ISLAND CLUB - Seafood - Continental Seafoods Inc.
ISLAND COTTAGE - Meat - Matlaw's Food Products Inc.
ISLAND COVE - Floor coverings–carpet and rugs ☆ - Catalina Carpet Mills Inc.
ISLAND DELITES - Ice cream - New Yorker Ice Cream Corp.
ISLAND DOG - Skin care products - Island Dog Cosmetics, Inc.
ISLAND DREAM - Floor coverings–carpet and rugs ☆ - Mohawk Carpet Corp.
ISLAND DREAMS - Skin-care products - Aquarius Trading Co.
ISLAND EARTH - Apparel and accessories - David Raymond Zappini
ISLAND FANTASY - Bath salts - Jason Natural Products, Inc.
ISLAND FARM - Vegetables–canned - Draper-King Cole Inc.
ISLAND FLOWERS - Giftware ☆ - Avon Products, Inc.
ISLAND FLOWERS - Publisher's imprints - Jeffrey J. Rosz
ISLAND FRUIT - Granola bars - Debbie's Famous Granola
ISLAND FRUIT MIX - Snack foods - A.L. Schutzman Co., Inc.

☆ = Now out of production

ISLAND FUN - Dolls - Mattel, Inc.

ISLAND G - Apparel–athletic - Island G Ltd.

ISLAND GARDENIA - Perfumes - Quintessence Inc.

ISLAND GEAR - Apparel–athletic - Carolina Stores, Inc.

ISLAND GIRL - Bicycles ☆ - Roadmaster Corp.

ISLAND GIRL - Cleaning preparations - Island Girl Laboratories

ISLAND GIRL - Rice - AC Humko Rice Specialties

ISLAND GLOW - Sunblocks - Ledimar Inc.

ISLAND GOLD - Suntan lotions - Island Gold, Inc.

ISLAND GUAVA - Juices - Ocean Spray Cranberries Inc.

ISLAND HEAT - Pepper - Helen's

ISLAND HEAT - Suntan lotions - Most Products

ISLAND HOPPER - Toys - Mattel, Inc.

ISLAND HOPPING - Office and school supplies - Climax Paper Converters Inc.

ISLAND HOUSE - House furnishings - Lea Industries Inc.

ISLAND IMAGES - Paper products - Island Images

ISLAND IMPOSITION PUBLISHER - Computer software - Island Graphics Corp.

ISLAND JIM'S - Suntan lotions - Island Jim's

ISLAND LIFE - T-shirts–women's - Clothes for Heroes Inc.

ISLAND LIGHT - Beverages–malt - Refreshawaii, Inc.

ISLAND LIME - Beverages–carbonated - Canada Dry Corp.

ISLAND MAID - Seafood products–fresh or frozen - Carver Shellfish, Inc.

ISLAND MISS - Bicycles ☆ - Huffy Corp.

ISLAND NATURALS - Hair care products - Aubrey Organics, Inc.

ISLAND NUT-N-JAVA CO. - Coffee - Island Nut-N-Java Co.

ISLAND OAK - Furniture ☆ - Hooker Furniture Corp.

ISLAND OF DR. BRAIN - Games - Sierra On-Line, Inc.

ISLAND ORIGINAL - Suntan lotions - S & G Ventures

ISLAND PACKET - Sailboat - Island Packet Yachts Inc.

ISLAND PARADISE - Toys ☆ - Hi-Flier Manufacturing Co.

ISLAND PASSION - Beverages–carbonated - David Voth

ISLAND PASSION - Fruits and vegetables - Lykes Pasco, Inc.

ISLAND PASTURE - Bells - North Country Wind Bells Inc.

ISLAND PLEASURE - Teas - John Wagner & Sons, Inc.

ISLAND PLEASURE - Teas - Wagner Gourmet Foods, Inc.

ISLAND POINTE - Apparel and accessories - Pilgrim Enterprises Inc.

ISLAND POST CAP - Fencing–wood - Hunter Corp.

ISLAND PRESS - Publisher's imprint - Island Press

ISLAND PREVIEWER - Computer software - Island Graphics Corp.

ISLAND PROFESSIONAL SERIES - Computer software - Island Graphics Corp.

ISLAND PROVISIONS - Apparel and accessories - Treasure Island Corp.

ISLAND PUP - Skin care products - Island Dog Cosmetics, Inc.

ISLAND QUEEN - Food products - Beaver Street Fisheries Inc.

ISLAND QUEEN - Food products - Shore Lobster & Shrimp Corp.

ISLAND REFLECTIONS - Tiles–ceiling - Inter-County Building Materials Corp.

ISLAND RUNNER - Boats - Island Runner Boats & Marine, Inc.

ISLAND SHADE - Apparel–athletic - Skin Research Labs, Inc.

ISLAND SORBET NON DAIRY SOFT - SERVE - Yogurt–powdered - Covington Foods Inc.

ISLAND SOUL - Apparel and accessories - Quiksilver, Inc.

ISLAND SPICE MIST - Sachets - Andre Richard

ISLAND SPORTS - Footwear–athletic - Pegasus Co.

ISLAND SUN - Fruits–canned - Purcell International

ISLAND SUN - Suntan lotions ☆ - Pharmavite Corp.

ISLAND TEASE - Iced tea–bottled or canned - Penn Traffic Co.

ISLAND TEASERS - Pet products - Pink Parrot

ISLAND THYMES - Skin care products - Thymes Limited

ISLAND TIME - Apparel and accessories - Island Time International

ISLAND TIME - Apparel–children's - Joyce C. Foster

ISLAND TRADER - Ships–sailing vessels - Marine Trading International Inc.

ISLAND TRADERS WILD & MILD, THE - Jams and jellies - Calido Chile Traders Systems, Inc.

ISLAND TRADITIONS - House furnishings - Lexington Furniture Industries, Inc.

ISLAND TREASURE - Sauces - Anjo's Imports

ISLAND TREAT - Fruit drinks–bottled or canned - Smoothie King Franchises, Inc.

ISLAND TROPICS - Beverages–alcohol - Joseph E. Seagram & Sons, Inc.

ISLAND TWIST - Apparel–women's - St. Topaz International

ISLAND VIEW - Floor coverings–carpet and rugs - Bloomsburg Carpet Industries

ISLAND WEAVES - Wallpaper - Maya Romanoff Corp.

ISLAND WORCESTER - Dishes–earthenware ☆ - Royal China & Porcelain Companies Inc.

ISLAND YEAST - Yeast - Georgia-Pacific Corp.

ISLANDCHART - Computer software - Island Graphics Corp.

ISLANDCRAFTS - Toys - Island Corp. Inc.

ISLANDER - Boats - Glen-L Marine Designs

ISLANDER - Boats–motor - Catalina Yachts Inc.

ISLANDER - Boats–motor - Glastex Corp.

ISLANDER - Boats–motor - Grady-White Boats, Inc.

ISLANDER - Boats–motor ☆ - Bluewater

ISLANDER - Boats–pontoons - Forester Boats Inc.

ISLANDER - Brushes–paint - Max C's Ceramic & Craft

ISLANDER - Cabinets ☆ - Gragg Cabinet Industries

ISLANDER - Furniture ☆ - Bassett Furniture Industries, Inc.

ISLANDER - Motor vehicles–motor homes ☆ - Georgie Boy Manufacturing, Inc.

ISLANDER - Swing sets - Island Wood Products Inc.

ISLANDER - Toilets–enameled - Kohler Co.

ISLANDER - Ukuleles ☆ - French American Reeds Manufacturing

ISLANDER BY ATS - Motor vehicles–all-terrain - American Travel Systems, Inc.

ISLANDER FLAGS OF KITTY HAWK - Fabrics–nylon - Islander Flags of Kitty Hawk, Inc.

ISLANDER SUIT - Waterproof outerwear ☆ - Helly-Hansen Inc.

ISLANDER'S CHOICE - Meat products - Robert Mangal

ISLANDIA - Floor coverings–carpet and rugs ☆ - Catalina Carpet Mills Inc.

ISLANDOLLS - Toys - Island Corp. Inc.

ISLANDPRESENTS - Computer software - Island Graphics Corp.

ISLANDS - Bath salts - Cosway Co., Inc.

ISLANDS - Food products - John's Import Foods, Inc.

ISLANDS - Furniture - Arbek Furniture Manufacturing Inc.

ISLANDS - Ships–sailing vessels - Sumner Boat Co., Inc.

ISLANDS AND IMAGES - Furniture - Pinnacle Furniture Co.

ISLANDS IN THE SEA - Shirts - Cluett, Peabody & Co.

ISLANDS OF BETA, THE - Computer software ☆ - Milliken Publishing Co. (Computer Software Div.)

ISLANDSHELLS - Seashell products - Island Corp. Inc.

ISLANDTABLE - Computer software - Island Graphics Corp.

ISLE BISCAY - Furniture - Homecrest Industries Inc.

ISLE OF COTTON - Apparel–men's - Pine State Knitwear Co.

ISLE OF GOLD - Food products - Hawaiian Sun Products Inc.

ISLE OF JURA - Liquors - Heaven Hill Distilleries, Inc.

ISLE OF MAN - Frames–eyeglass ☆ - Universal/Univis Inc.

ISLE OF SKYE - Whiskey - Parrott & Co.

ISLE OF WIGHT - Musical instrument accessories - Sottile Manufacturing Co.

ISLE ROYALE - Campers - American Sterling Corp.

ISLE ROYALE - Dinnerware–glass ☆ - Lenox, Inc.

ISLE ROYALE - Furniture - Homecrest Industries Inc.

ISLE ST. GEORGE - Wines - Meier's Wine Cellars Inc.

ISLON - Fabrics - Dan River Inc.

ISM - Safes - Empire Safe Co. Inc.

ISMALUN - Cigarettes - G.A. Georgopulo & Co. Inc.

ISMELIN - Pharmaceutical preparations - Ciba-Geigy Corp.

-ISMIST - Recording label - Ismist Recordings

ISMOTIC - Pharmaceutical preparations - Alcon Laboratories, Inc.

ISN/ADA-E - Signs - Inter Sign National, Inc.

ISN-MILLENNIUM - Heating and cooling equipment - York International Corp.

ISN'T IT DIVINE - Brassieres (Bras) - Sears, Roebuck and Co.

ISN'T THAT YOU - Optical services - Foster Grant Co. Inc.

ISO - Dishes–earthenware - ISO Associates Inc.

ISO - Pharmaceutical preparations ☆ - Richie Pharmacal Co. Inc.

ISO 400 - Photographic equipment - Vivitar Corp.

ISO 9000 - Batteries - Yuasa-Exide, Inc.

ISO-ACETAZONE - Pharmaceutical preparations - Rugby Laboratories Inc.

ISO-ASMINYL - Barbituates ☆ - Cole Pharmacal Co. Inc.

ISO-B - Vitamins and nutritional supplements - Integrated Health, Inc.

ISO-B - Vitamins and nutritional supplements - Tyson & Associates, Inc.

ISO-BEESWAX - Waxes–paraffin - Strahl & Pitsch Inc.

ISO-BID - Pharmaceutical preparations - Geriatric Pharmaceutical Corp.

ISO BIFLUX DUAL FIELDS - Musical instrument accessories - Actodyne General, Inc.

ISO-CAL 9000 - Computers - Thermo Electric Co., Inc.

ISO CARE - Pews - Nice-Pak Products, Inc.

ISO-CEPTIC - Pharmaceutical preparations - Bethurum Research & Development Inc.

ISO CISER - Exercising equipment - Paragon Images

ISO-CLAD - Paints - Briner Paint Manufacturing Co. Inc.

ISO CLOR - Swimming pools ☆ - Utikem Products

ISO-D - Pharmaceutical preparations - Dunhall Pharmaceuticals Inc.

☆ = Now out of production

ISO-FLEX - Adhesives and sealants ☆ - Master Builders Inc.
ISO-GARD - Medical equipment - Gibeck-Dryden Corp.
ISO HEET - Antifreeze - Demert & Dougherty, Inc.
ISO-LIT - Lighting equipment ☆ - Siemens Components Inc. (Optoelectronics Div.)
ISO-LO - Ophthalmic decongestant, eyewash - American Pharmaceutical Co.
ISO-MAX - Transformers–electric - Jensen Transformers, Inc.
ISO-MOUNT - Machine parts - Fort Wayne Wire Die, Inc.
ISO-NASOL - Pharmaceutical preparations - Alva-Amco Pharmacal Co.
ISO-NEB - Health care products - Hudson Respiratory Care Inc.
ISO-PAR - Pharmaceutical preparations - Parmed Pharmaceuticals, Inc.
ISO PEGS - Motor vehicle parts and accessories - KuryAkyn Holdings
ISO-PIPE - Pipes - B-Line Systems, Inc.
ISO-QUIN - Disinfectants - Cramer Products Inc.
ISO-RING - Marine rigging - Outboard Marine Corp.
ISO-SEAL - Scales–bathroom - John Chatillon & Sons
ISO-TABS-60 - Pharmaceutical preparations ☆ - Solvay Pharmaceuticals Inc.
ISO-TECK - Blinds–vertical - Vertical Blind Factory
ISO-TEQ - Chemical preparations - Baker Hughes Inc.
ISO-TIP - Tools–soldering - Wahl Clipper Corp.
ISO-TORQ - Measuring instruments - Appa Systems, Inc.
ISO-VIS - Oils–lubricating ☆ - Amoco Oil Co.
ISOBAR - Antifreeze - Fleet Wholesale Supply Co., Inc.
ISOBAR - Valves - Water Soft Inc.
ISOBUTYL - Pharmaceutical preparations - Goldline Laboratories, Inc.
ISOCAL - Pharmaceutical preparations - Bristol-Myers Squibb Co.
ISOCLEAN - Air purification systems - Envirco Corp.
ISOCLEAR - Tape–adhesive ☆ - Lectec Corp.
ISOCLOR - Health care products - Fisons Corp.
ISOCODE - Chemical preparations - Schleicher and Schuell Inc.
ISOCOM - Pharmaceutical preparations - Glenwood LLC
ISOCOR - Computer software - Isocor
ISODAMP - Insulating materials - Aearo Co.
ISODERM - Pharmaceutical preparations ☆ - U.S. Ethicals Inc.
ISODETTES - Pharmaceutical preparations - Goody's Manufacturing Corp.
ISODINE - Health care products ☆ - Blair Laboratories Inc.
ISOFAX - Computer software - BGL Development Corp.
ISOFIL - Pharmaceutical preparations ☆ - Seatrace Co.
ISOFLAP - Cushion valves - Roho, Inc.
ISOFLASH-RAPID - Cameras ☆ - Miles Inc. (Agfa Div.)
ISOFLEX - Valves–exhaust - Crosby Valve & Gage Co.
ISOFLO - Pharmaceutical preparations - Abbott Laboratories
ISOFRAME - Building materials–concrete - Isoframe Systems International, Inc.
ISOGEN COMPOUND - Pharmaceutical preparations - Rugby Laboratories Inc.
ISOGLASS - Glass–safety - Two-F Glass Armor Co., LLC
ISOGRIP - Exercising equipment - Taylor-Nathan Co., Inc.
ISOGRIP - Urethane adhesives - Ashland Oil, Inc.
ISOGRO - Hair care products - All Ways Natural Industries Inc.
ISOGUARD - Uninterruptible-power systems - AFP Transformers, Inc.
ISOHALANT - Pharmaceutical preparations ☆ - ICN Pharmaceuticals Inc.
ISOHOP - Beverages–malt - Pfizer Inc.
ISOKANE - Exercising equipment - Portable Isokinetics Inc.
ISOLA BELLA - Dishes–china - Viletta China Co.
ISOLATE - Hair care products - Redken Laboratories, Inc.
ISOLATED SHIELD MATRIX - Cables - Tara Labs, Inc.
ISOLATION - Games - Lakeside Games
ISOLATOR SYSTEM - Pharmaceutical preparations - Wampole Laboratories Div.
ISOLATOR, THE - Sporting goods - Steven R. Lawson
ISOLAY - Lighting fixtures ☆ - Hubbell Lighting, Inc. (Lighting Div.)
ISOLENE - Rubber cement - Hardman
ISOLEX - Home health care products - Baxter International Inc.
ISOLITE - Dental equipment - Cross Country Paper Products, Inc.
ISOLLYL - Pharmaceutical preparations - Rugby Laboratories Inc.
ISOLOGGER - Monitors–electronic - Zellweger Analytics, Inc.
ISOLONE - Food products - Kalsec, Inc.
ISOLOOP - Antennas - Advanced Electronic Applications Inc.
ISOLOSS - Health care products - E-A-R Specialty Composites
ISOLUTE ENV+ - Chemical preparations - International Sorbent Technology, Ltd.
ISOLUTION TOOLS FOR THE TIMES - Computer software - Edward Secrest
ISOMAN - Hair care products - J.M. Products, Inc.
ISOMAX - Microphones - Countryman Associates
ISOMAX - Tape recorders - Eastman Kodak Co.
ISOMAX - Tools–hand-operated - Eazypower Corp.

ISOMET - Tools–power-driven - Buehler Ltd.
ISOMETRIC - Apparel and accessories - Glamorise Foundations Inc.
ISOMIL - Vitamins and nutritional supplements - Ross Laboratories
ISOMILK DF-SOY FORMULA - Vitamins and nutritional supplements - Ross Laboratories
ISONEX - Aquatic pharmacuetical preparations ☆ - Aquatronics-Filtronics
ISONUTRIENTS - Vitamins and nutritional supplements - Isonutrients Corp.
ISONUTRIENTS - Vitamins and nutritional supplements - Thompson Nutritional Products
ISOPALM - Skin care products - Knight Marketing Corp.
ISOPAP - Pharmaceutical preparations ☆ - Columbia Drug Co. Inc.
ISOPHON - Amplifiers–musical instrument - Walter Odemer Co. Inc.
ISOPLUS PREPLUS - Hair care products - J.M. Products, Inc.
ISOPRIME - Laboratory apparatus - Hoefer Pharmacia Biotech Inc.
ISOPRO - Pharmaceutical preparations ☆ - Rugby Laboratories Inc.
ISOPRO - Tools–hand-operated - Eazypower Corp.
ISOPROL COMPOUND - Pharmaceutical preparations - Consolidated Midland Corp.
ISOPTIN - Pharmaceutical preparations - Knoll Pharmaceutical Co.
ISOPTO - Ophthalmic goods ☆ - Alcon Laboratories, Inc.
ISOPTO ALKALINE - Health care products - Alcon Laboratories, Inc.
ISOPTO ATROPINE - Health care products - Alcon Laboratories, Inc.
ISOPTO CARBACHOL - Health care products - Alcon Laboratories, Inc.
ISOPTO-CARPINE - Pharmaceutical preparations - Alcon Laboratories, Inc.
ISOPTO CETAMIDE - Health care products - Alcon Laboratories, Inc.
ISOPTO CETAPRED - Health care products - Alcon Laboratories, Inc.
ISOPTO FRIN - Health care products - Alcon Laboratories, Inc.
ISOPTO HOMATROPINE - Health care products - Alcon Laboratories, Inc.
ISOPTO HYOSCINE - Health care products - Alcon Laboratories, Inc.
ISOPTO PLAIN - Health care products - Alcon Laboratories, Inc.
ISOPTO TEARS - Health care products - Alcon Laboratories, Inc.
ISOPULSE - Exercising equipment - Larry Shane Harmon
ISORDIL - Pharmaceutical preparations - Wyeth-Ayerst Laboratories
ISOREG - Lamps - Magnetek Universal Manufacturing
ISOREG - Uninterruptible-power systems, etc. - AFP Transformers, Inc.
ISOROY - Plywood - Harbor Sales Co.
ISOSCELES STORAGE SYSTEM - Backpacks - Visual Impact Films Corp.
ISOSENS - Hydrophones - Innovative Transducers Inc.
ISOSHIELD - Insulating materials - Apache Products Co.
ISOSHIELD - Power system isolators - AFP Transformers, Inc.
ISOSTAT - Air purification systems - Ion Systems
ISOSTATIC - Hair care products ☆ - Cassidy Inc.
ISOSTRUT - Windows - Kawneer Co., Inc.
ISOSWEET - Corn syrup - A.E. Staley Manufacturing Co. (Industrial Marketing Div.)
ISOSYSTEM - Publisher's imprints - William F. Beiber
ISOTEC - Electronic equipment - Mescon Technologies, Inc.
ISOTECH - Scales–railroad - Isotech Laboratories Manufacturing Inc.
ISOTEIN HN - Vitamins and nutritional supplements - Novartis Nutrition Corp.
ISOTEK31 - Fertilizers - Lebanon Seaboard Corp.
ISOTONE - Gloves - Aris Isotoner Inc.
ISOTONER - Hosiery–women's - Sara Lee Corp.
ISOTONER - Hosiery–women's - Saramar Corp.
ISOTONER - Orthopedic products - Smith & Nephew Inc. (Rehabilitation Div.)
ISOTONER CLASSICS - Apparel and accessories - Saramar Corp.
ISOTONER COUNTRY - Apparel–women's - Saramar Corp.
ISOTONER-FOOT-CARE KIT - Footcare products - Saramar Corp.
ISOTONER KNITS - Apparel and accessories - Saramar Corp.
ISOTONER SPORTS CLUB - Gloves - Aris Isotoner Inc.
ISOTONER SPORTS CLUB - Socks - Saramar Corp.
ISOTONER SUBURBAN - Gloves - Saramar Corp.
ISOTONIX - Vitamins and nutritional supplements - Isotonix Corp.
ISOTOX - Chemical preparations - Chevron Chemical Co.
ISOTRATE - Pharmaceutical preparations ☆ - Roberts/Hauck Pharmaceuticals Inc.
ISOVET - Veterinary pharmaceutical preparations - Inhalon Pharmaceuticals, Inc.
ISOVET - Veterinary pharmaceutical preparations - Schering-Plough Animal Health
ISOVEX - Pharmaceutical preparations ☆ - U.S. Pharmaceutical Corp.
ISOVIBRANT - Musical instrument accessories ☆ - French American Reeds Manufacturing
ISOVUE - Pharmaceutical preparations - Bristol-Myers Squibb Co.
ISOVUE MULTIPACK - Diagnostic substances - Bracco Diagnostics Inc.
ISOWEB - Window frames - Kawneer Co., Inc.
ISOWOMAN - Hair care products - J.M. Products, Inc.

☆ = Now out of production

ISP - Jewelry - Instock Corp.

I.S.P. - Skin care products - Geritrex Corp.

ISPGDS - Circuit boards - Lattice Semiconductor Corp.

ISPHAHAN - Floor coverings - Beaulieu of America, Inc.

ISPO - Stationery - Mokiem & Julian Ind Corp.

ISPORTE - Computer hardware - Microcom Systems, Inc.

ISPY - Computer software - E. David & Associates

ISR - Engine additive - BGI

ISRA-ART - Artists' materials ✫ - Classic Oils & Portraits

ISRAEL ACADEMY OF SCIENCES & HUMANITIES - Publisher's imprints - Hebrew Publishing Co.

ISRAEL DESIGNS - Giftware - Israel Designs

ISRAEL-LITES - Greeting cards - Melodie Kleiman

ISRAELCRAFT - Greeting cards - Dona Greetin Cards Inc.

ISRAELI - Food products - I. Rokeach and Sons Inc.

ISRAELI - Pickles - Bonduel Pickling Co.

ISS - Communications equipment - William W. Baker

ISSATEX - Bedspreads - Unico Enterprises Inc.

ISSATEX COMFORT - QUALITY & DESIGN - Linen - Unico Enterprises Inc.

ISSHO - Jewelry - Mercury Ring Corp.

ISSI - Electronic equipment - Integrated Security Systems Inc.

ISSUEWEAVER - Computer software - Tower Concepts, Inc.

IST - Surgical instruments - Innovative Surgical Technology, Inc.

ISTANBUL - Christmas tree ornaments - Cracker Box Inc.

ISTANBUL - Cigars - G.A. Georgopulo & Co. Inc.

ISTANBUL - Eyeglasses - Art-Craft Optical Co.

ISTANBUL - Floor coverings ✫ - Congoleum Corp.

ISTRC SYSTEM - Tools–hand-operated - International Sports Turf Research Center, Inc.

ISTVAN BERNATH - Posters - Icart Vendor Graphics Inc.

ISU - Computer peripheral equipment - Adtran

ISU 128 - Computer peripheral equipment - Adtran

ISUPREL - Pharmaceutical preparations - Winthrop Pharmaceuticals

ISUZU - Motor vehicles–automobiles - American Isuzu Motors Inc.

ISYS - Computer software - Gtech Corp.

IT! - Beverages–carbonated - Sheetz Inc.

IT - Hair care products - Waverly Beauty Products

IT - Silicon products - Harvey-Westbury Corp.

IT AIN'T PRETTY - Artists' materials - James K. Benton

IT ALL STARTS HERE - Computer peripheral equipment - Stirling Technologies, Inc.

IT COULDN'T BE A PANTY - Apparel–women's - Newton Manufacturing Corp.

IT COULDN'T HURT - Nuts–salted, roasted, cooked, or canned - Mashuga Nuts, Inc.

IT FIGURES - Apparel–women's - Exquisite Form Industries

IT FITS, IT FITS! - Hosiery - Mayer/Berkshire Corp.

IT FROM THE PIT - Games - Hasbro, Inc.

IT JUST COMES EASY - Beverages–malt - Miller Brewing Co.

IT JUST MAKES SENSE - Pipes - NMI

IT MEANS IDEA - Advertising agencies - Eidos Marketing Communications, Inc.

IT MUST BE MAGIC - Underwear and nightwear - Vanity Fair, Inc.

IT REALLY WORKS - Brassieres (Bras) - Maidenform Inc.

IT RUNS ON THE SUN - Solar energy collectors - Vegetable Factory, Inc. (Sunbeam Structures Div.)

IT SERVICE VISION - Computer software - Sas Institute Inc.

IT SHOULD HAPPEN TO A DOG - Pet chews - Items Inc.

IT SRC - Cleaning preparations - Sun Ray Corp.

IT STARTS WITH THE RIGHT ATTITUDE - Apparel and accessories - Starter Corp.

IT STAYS - Health care products - Bell-Horn

IT WAS A VERY GOOD YEAR - Greeting cards - Kalan Inc.

IT WORKS! - Vitamins and nutritional supplements - Moneytree Management

IT WORKS FOR ME - Apparel and accessories - It Works for Me, Inc.

IT WORKS FOR ME - Pharmaceutical preparations - American Home Products Corp.

IT WORKS FOR YOU - Jewelry - Marc F. Wiegand

IT WORKS INFORMATION TECHNOLOGY - Computer software - Information Technology Works, Inc.

IT WORKS. YOU DON'T. - Fertilizers - Weatherly Consumer Products, Inc.

ITA - Trimmings–fabric ✫ - Hollcar Trading Co.

ITABS - Veterinary nutritional supplements - Ivet Laboratories, Inc.

ITACA - Window coverings - Vertilux-Louverlux Inc.

ITAHOLI - Olive oil - Bel Canto Fancy Foods Ltd.

ITAL BABY - Furniture–children's ✫ - Child Craft Industries Inc.

ITALEIMA - Confections ✫ - R.L. Albert & Son, Inc.

ITALIA - Ceramic tile ✫ - Interceramic Inc.

ITALIA - Crystal and glass - Italia Collections

ITALIA - Floor coverings–carpet and rugs - Masland Corp.

ITALIA - Furniture - Dinaire Corp.

ITALIA - Furniture–children's ✫ - Child Craft Industries Inc.

ITALIA - Glass products - Kohler Co.

ITALIA - Novelty items - RDE Imports

ITALIA - Office supplies - Esselte Corp.

ITALIA - Pasta - Italia Foods Inc.

ITALIA! - Sausages - Johnsonville Foods Co.

ITALIA - Tiles–ceramic ✫ - Dal-Tile Corp.

ITALIA - Wallpaper - Motif Designs, Inc.

ITALIA D'ORO - Coffee - Boyd Coffee Co.

ITALIA GALLERIA COLLECTION - Crystal - Italia Collections

ITALIAN BAKING COMPANY, THE - Bakery products - Italian Baking Co.

ITALIAN BEEF SANDWICH - Food products - Atlantic Richfield Co.

ITALIAN CAFE BLEND - Coffee - Brewing Market, Ltd.

ITALIAN CHEF - Pasta - Pasta USA Inc.

ITALIAN CHEF - Spaghetti sauces - Pastorelli Food Products Inc.

ITALIAN CHEF PASTA & CHEESE - Pasta - Pasta USA Inc.

ITALIAN CLASSIC SAUSAGE PIZZA - Pizzas–frozen - Godfather's Pizza, Inc.

ITALIAN COLLECTION - Cooking equipment–household ✫ - General Housewares Corp.

ITALIAN COUNTRY - Breads - La Pace Imports

ITALIAN COUNTRY ARCH - Frames–picture - Terragrafics Inc.

ITALIAN FRUIT - Dishes–china - Pasmantier Co. Inc.

ITALIAN GARDEN - Vegetables–frozen - Patterson Frozen Foods, Inc.

ITALIAN GRAFFITI - Wallpaper ✫ - Gamrod-Harman

ITALIAN HOLIDAY - Pasta - Armanino Foods of Distinction, Inc.

ITALIAN ICE - Fruits and vegetables - Agricultural Innovation & Trade Inc.

ITALIAN LA TORTA - Food products - G & G Specialty Foods, Inc.

ITALIAN MAID - Bakery products - Schinderle's Genuine Italian Maid Bakery Shop

ITALIAN MAID - Pizzas–frozen - Multi-National Food Service

ITALIAN MARBLE - Wallpaper - Thomas Ray Designs Inc.

ITALIAN MARKET - Food products - Pet Inc.

ITALIAN NACHOS - Snack foods - Cleyera Inc.

ITALIAN NOW! - Computer software - Transparent Language, Inc.

ITALIAN ORCHARD - Dinnerware ✫ - Corning Inc.

ITALIAN PASTRY - Food products - Tony's Pizza Service

ITALIAN PILLOWS - Food products - Joseph Seviroli, Inc.

ITALIAN RECIPE - Food products - Del Monte Corp.

ITALIAN REVIVAL - Barbecue sauce - Chef Papy's Foods

ITALIAN SAUSAGE PATTY - Spices and extracts - Aldo's Spices

ITALIAN SCALLION - Seasonings - Garlic Festival Foods

ITALIAN SCALLION - Seasonings - Randan Corp.

ITALIAN SHELLS - Food products - Tom's Foods Inc.

ITALIAN STYLE - Bakery products - Moose Brothers

ITALIAN STYLE - Sausages - Hillshire Farm Co.

ITALIAN SUPREME - Spaghetti sauces - Father Caserta's Italian Products

ITALIAN SWISS COLONY - Beverages–alcohol - Canandaigua Wine Co. Inc.

ITALIAN SWISS COLONY - Wines - The Beverage Source Inc.

ITALIAN TWISTER - Confections - Mazzone Enterprises Inc.

ITALIAN TWO MINUTE WONDER - Hair care products ✫ - Marianna Imports, Inc.

ITALIAN VILLA - Salad dressings–bottled - Joyce Nottingham

ITALIANA - Lenses–optical - Ditto Industries Inc.

ITALIANI - Meat products–poultry - Pierce Foods Corp.

ITALIANI/LS - Meat products–poultry - Pierce Foods Corp.

ITALIANO - Lenses–optical - Ditto Industries Inc.

ITALIANO - Luggage ✫ - Samsonite Corp.

ITALIANTI - Sausages - Johnsonville Foods Co.

ITALICA - Food products - Tee Pee Olives Inc.

ITALICA - Olive oil - Italica Imports

ITALICA CORNICHONS - Olives–canned - Tee Pee Olives Inc.

ITALICS - Footwear–women's ✫ - Johansen Brothers Shoe Co.

ITALINI - Pizzas–frozen - Smiley's Foods

ITALINI - Pizzas–frozen - Southland Corp.

ITALIO PETRANTONI - Beverages–alcohol - R.V. D'Alfonso Co.

ITALJET - Motorcycles - Italjet USA

ITALJET MOTORCYCLES - Minicycles - Cosmopolitan Motors Inc.

ITALO-AMERICAN - Accordions - Italo-American Accordion Manufacturing Co.

ITALO-AMERICAN - Ravioli–canned - Sta-Wite Inc.

ITALOLI VECCHI TEMPI - Olive oil ✫ - Lettieri

✫ = Now out of production

ITALTRIKE - Bicycles - Dollsandreams
IT&LY - Hair care products - IT&LY Hairfashion NA Inc.
ITALY'S GIFT TO THE WORLD - Beverages–alcohol - Distillerie Stock USA Ltd.
ITANCHA - Skates–roller - Alpine Tooling, Inc.
ITASCA - Motor vehicles–motor homes - Winnebago Industries, Inc.
ITASCA - Oils–lubricating - Quaker State Oil Refining Corp.
ITASCA - Shoe accessories - Itasca Systems Inc.
ITC - Computer peripheral equipment - Invincible Technologies Corp.
ITC - Leather goods - Insider Trading Co., Inc.
ITC - Spices and extracts - Crompton & Knowles Corp.
ITC - Tubes–copper - Helenor Industries
ITC HIGHLANDER - Magnetic recording equipment - International Typeface Corp.
ITCH-AID - Antipyretics - Pharmacy Girl Inc. Laboratories
ITCH-AWAY - Vitamins and nutritional supplements - Moyco Industries, Inc.
ITCH-B-GONE - Pet products - Bethurum Research & Development Inc.
ITCH-ENDER - Health care products - Urocare Products Inc.
ITCH GUARD - Pharmaceutical preparations - Jess Clarke & Sons Inc.
ITCH-GUARD - Pharmaceutical preparations - Winning Solutions Inc./Miracle of Aloe
ITCH ME NOT - Skin care products - Keller Co.
ITCH-X - Pharmaceutical preparations - B.F. Ascher & Co. Inc.
ITCHY & SCRATCHY - Watches - Twentieth Century Fox Film Corp.
ITCOB - Sporting goods - Laurin International, Inc.
ITDN - Computer software - Bryant College
ITEK - Cameras - A.B. Dick Co.
ITEK - Frames–eyeglass ✩ - Universal/Univis Inc.
ITEM-EYES - Frames–eyeglass - Liberty Optical Manufacturing Co.
ITEM INVENTORY & TRACKING - Computer software - Right on Programs
ITEM SYSTEMS - Computer software - Item Systems
ITEMISER - Electronic equipment - Ion Track Instruments, Inc.
ITEMS COLLECTION - Furniture ✩ - Lane Co. Inc.
ITEXCO - Marble products - Itexco/Marble Tiles of America
ITHACA - Firearms - Ithaca Gun Co. Inc.
ITHACA - Frames–eyeglass ✩ - Universal/Univis Inc.
ITI - Recording label - Allegiance Records Ltd.
ITI - Recording label - Spindletop Records Inc.
ITINERARY - Shirts - Kellwood Co.
ITIS - Vitamins and nutritional supplements - Great Life Laboratories Inc.
IT'LL STOP YOU COLD. - Skates–roller - Mearthane Products Corp.
I.T.M.S. - Electronic equipment - Ion Track Instruments, Inc.
ITOH - Bicycles - C. Itoh & Co. America Inc.
ITOMEN - Pasta ✩ - American Roland Food Corp.
ITONICS - Wallpaper ✩ - Wall Fashion Inc.
ITOYA - Writing instruments and accessories - Itoya of America, Ltd.
ITP - Computer hardware - Progen Technology Inc.
ITP CONCRETE WALL-INSUL - Insulating materials - Schuller International, Inc.
ITP SPORT - Apparel–athletic - Nancy Kahn Designs, Inc.
ITR - Fasteners–snap - B.F. Goodrich Co.
IT'S 2ND NATURE - Computer software - Unimax Systems Corp.
IT'S A BABY! - Cookies - Creative Cookie Inc. (American Dream Enterprises)
IT'S A BEAUTIFUL GIRL - Cigars - G.W. Van Slyke & Horton
IT'S A BEAUTIFUL TIME - Watches - Elgin Watch Co.
IT'S A BLACK THING - Health care products - Peggy L. Curry & Cobette Harper Partnership
IT'S A BOY - Apparel–children's - Kessner and Rabinowitz, Inc.
IT'S A BOY - Chewing gum - Philadelphia Chewing Gum Corp.
IT'S A BOY - Chocolate candy - Superior Fruit & Confections
IT'S A BOY - Toys–stuffed ✩ - Dakin Inc.
IT'S A BOY'S LIFE - Apparel and accessories - Parigi Ltd.
ITS A CANDY WORLD - Toys ✩ - Giordano Art, Ltd.
IT'S-A-CAT - Gloves - Knoxville Glove Co.
IT'S A CAULKER - Caulking compounds - Continental Brands Inc.
IT'S A CURIOUS LIFE - Calendars ✩ - American Greetings Corp.
IT'S A D.C. THANG - Apparel and accessories - It's a D.C. Thang
IT'S-A-DILLY - Spices and extracts - McCormick & Co., Inc.
IT'S A DOG'S LIFE - Calendars - AGC, Inc.
IT'S A DOG'S LIFE - Calendars - American Greetings Corp.
IT'S A DOOZEY IN THE KITCHEN - Kitchen utensils–enameled - Robinson Knife & Fiddlers Plastics
ITS-A-GAS - Barbecues and grills - Sunbeam Outdoor Products Inc.
IT'S A GIMMIE - Beverages–malt - Anheuser-Busch Companies Inc.
IT'S A GIRL - Candy bars - Kenneth E. Butler
IT'S A GIRL - Chewing gum - Philadelphia Chewing Gum Corp.

IT'S A GIRL - Chocolate candy - Superior Fruit & Confections
IT'S A GIRL - Toys–stuffed ✩ - Dakin Inc.
IT'S A GIRL WITHOUT NUTS - Candy bars - Kenneth E. Butler
IT'S A GRANDBABY - Candy - Harry London's Candies Inc.
IT'S A GRANDDAUGHTER - Candy - Harry London's Candies Inc.
IT'S A GRANDSON - Candy - Harry London's Candies Inc.
IT'S A HANDSOME BOY - Cigars - G.W. Van Slyke & Horton
IT'S A HIT - Baseball journal - Informative Amenities Inc.
IT'S A JUNGLE OUT THERE - Shirts - Lifeforms International, Inc.
IT'S A KEEPER - Brackets - Searcy Enterprises
IT'S A LOCKER BUDDY - Bags–storage - Bruce White
IT'S A MIXED BAG - Candy - S.L. Kaye Co., Inc.
IT'S A PIECE OF CAKE - Bakery products ✩ - Sprout Delights Inc.
IT'S A SNAP ELECTRICAL ACCESSORIES - Electrical equipment ✩ - Buchanan Construction Products, Inc.
IT'S A TIE-UP HAIRDINI - Hair curlers - Angelhair, Ltd.
IT'S A U BUN - Food products - Janson's Foods Inc.
IT'S A WIG - Wigs - It's a Wig!
IT'S A WINNER - Candy - Nabisco Foods Group
IT'S A WOMAN THING - Games - Philip Morris Inc.
IT'S A WONDERFUL LIFE - Posters - Republic Entertainment Inc.
IT'S A WONDERFUL LIFE GIFT COLLECTION - Toys–models - Cape Craftsmen, Inc.
IT'S A WRAP! REUSABLE EARTH-FRIENDLY GIFT WRAP - Fabrics - It's a Wrap
IT'S ABOUT THYME - Spices and extracts - To Market to Market
IT'S ABOUT TIME - Apparel–women's - I.E. Industries Fashions, Inc.
IT'S ABOUT TIME - Computer software ✩ - Gessler Publishing Co., Inc.
IT'S ABOUT TIME - Games - International Gamco, Inc.
IT'S ACADEMIC - Luggage - It's Academic of Illinois, Inc.
IT'S ALL ABOUT THE KIDS - Jackets - Al E. Productions
IT'S ALL IN THE HEAD - Apparel and accessories - Hypeadelic, Inc.
IT'S ALL ME - Brassieres (Bras) - Wacoal America Inc.
IT'S BEADTASTIC - Toys - Rose Art Industries, Inc.
IT'S CARESSABLE - Fabrics - Guilford Mills, Inc.
IT'S CATCHY - Games - It's Catchy Inc.
IT'S CHILLIN' ICEE ORIGINAL SINCE 1965 - Beverages–carbonated - Icee of America, Inc.
IT'S CHRISTMAS - Greeting cards - Paper Magic Group Inc.
IT'S COVERED - Housewares - Michele Ashe
IT'S CRACKERJACK! - Wallpaper - Jack Foley Associates Inc.
IT'S CRACKERJACK! - Wallpaper ✩ - W.H.S. Lloyd
IT'S CRACKERJACK! II - Wallpaper - Jack Foley Associates Inc.
IT'S CRACKERJACK! II - Wallpaper - W.H.S. Lloyd
IT'S CRUST D'LICIOUS - Pizza - Mr. Gatti's, Inc.
IT'S DE-LOVELY - Underwear and nightwear ✩ - Lovable Co.
IT'S DELICIOUS FRISKIE - Ice cream - Hall's Ice Cream, Inc.
IT'S EASY - Curtain rods - Kenney Manufacturing Co.
IT'S FAMILY TIME - Video production - Learning Through Entertainment Inc.
IT'S FOR YOU - Office paper products - Wallace Computer Services, Inc.
IT'S FUDGE - Fudge - Sweet Street
IT'S FUN - Apparel–children's - Doe Spun Inc.
IT'S FUN TYME - Toys–stuffed ✩ - Fun World Inc.
IT'S GREEK TO ME - Seasonings - Tone Brothers, Inc.
ITS HAIR AGAIN - Hair care products ✩ - Protege Corp.
IT'S HAPPENING BY VINCENT FANELLI - Footwear - New York City Shoes Inc.
IT'S HARD TO STOP A TRANE - Air-conditioner repair shops - American Standard Inc.
IT'S JUST ISSUED - Apparel and accessories - Just Issued, Inc.
IT'S KILLER - Sporting goods - Continental Sports Supply Inc.
IT'S LOVE - Novelty items ✩ - S.J. Miller Co.
IT'S MAGIC - Floor coverings–carpet and rugs - Masterpiece Finishing Co.
IT'S MAGIC - Frames–eyeglass - May Optical Co. Inc.
IT'S MAGIC! - Toy magic sets - Mannix Co., Ltd.
ITS ME - Underwear and nightwear - Rago Foundations Inc. LLC
IT'S MIGHTY FINE! - Ice cream - Byrne Dairy, Inc.
IT'S MILWAUKEE FOR ME! THE TOWN WITH A SMILE. - Apparel and accessories - Edward C. Stevens
IT'S MORPHIN TIME - Apparel–athletic - Saban Entertainment, Inc.
IT'S NATURALLY UP & COMING! - Water–mineral - Pocono Springs Co.
IT'S NEVER TOO LATE - Apparel–athletic - Jackson O. Wells
IT'S NOT A PIZZA - Food products - Fast Food Gourmet, Inc.
IT'S NOT CRAB - Seafood products–fresh or frozen ✩ - Mendel's Haymish Brand

✩ = Now out of production

IT'S NOT KOSHER FISH - Seafood products–fresh or frozen ☆ - Mendel's Haymish Brand

IT'S NOT LOBSTER - Seafood products–fresh or frozen ☆ - Mendel's Haymish Brand

IT'S NOT POPCORN - Snack foods - Premier Gourmet Products Inc.

IT'S NOT SHRIMP - Seafood products–fresh or frozen ☆ - Mendel's Haymish Brand

IT'S NOT WHAT YOU EAT, IT'S WHAT YOUR BODY ABSORBS - Vitamins and nutritional supplements - Pure Source, Inc.

IT'S ONLY MONEY - Lighter fluid ☆ - S.J. Miller Co.

IT'S ONLY NATURAL - Wallpaper ☆ - Andover Wallcovering

ITS ORGANIC NATURALLY - Hair care products - Dena Corp.

IT'S OUR NATURE - Paper - Kaulfuss Designers Inc.

IT'S OUR TIME - Sweaters - Fashion Avenue Knits Inc.

IT'S OUT! - Stain removers ☆ - Magic American Corp.

IT'S PARTY TIME - Dolls ☆ - Fun World Inc.

ITS PASTIME - Games - Universal Manufacturing Co., Inc.

IT'S POTTY TIME - Video production - Learning Through Entertainment Inc.

IT'S RAINING - Umbrellas - Gila Products LLC

IT'S RAINING CATS AND DOGS - Toys–stuffed - Dakin Inc.

IT'S REALLY SOMETHING - Apparel and accessories - Warnaco Inc.

IT'S SAND - Statuary - Sand Art of Ft. Lauderdale, Inc.

IT'S SANDSATIONAL - Artists' materials - Fasco Ltd.

IT'S SO CHEEZY - Food products - Crystal Farms Inc.

IT'S SO DAINTY - Underwear and nightwear - Maidenform Inc.

IT'S SO EASY - Barbecues and grills - Sunbeam Corp.

IT'S SO EASY IT'S SIMPLICITY - Patterns–clothing ☆ - Simplicity Pattern Co., Inc.

IT'S SO ELEGANT - Underwear and nightwear - Maidenform Inc.

IT'S SO EXTRA SPECIAL - Underwear and nightwear - Maidenform Inc.

IT'S SO IRRESISTABLE - Underwear and nightwear - Maidenform Inc.

IT'S SO LACY - Underwear and nightwear - Maidenform Inc.

IT'S SO PRETTY - Underwear and nightwear - Maidenform Inc.

IT'S STRIPED TO FIGHT - Toothpaste - Smithkline Beecham Corp.

IT'S TACORRIFIC - Restaurants–fast food ☆ - Taco John's International Inc.

IT'S THAT OTHER SAUCE - Sauces - Oinkers, Inc.

IT'S THE BERRIES - Hair care products - Helene Curtis Industries Inc.

IT'S THE BERRIES - Novelty items - Russ Berrie and Co., Inc.

IT'S THE B.E.S.T. - Cleaning preparations - Environmental Products of America, Inc.

IT'S THE COWS - Milk - Marigold Foods Inc.

IT'S THE RAGE - Novelty items - Russ Berrie and Co., Inc.

IT'S THE VEAL THING - Veal slices - It's the Veal Thing Inc.

IT'S TIME - Ophthalmic goods - Embassy Creations Inc.

IT'S TIME - Timers–appliance ☆ - Markuse Corp.

IT'S TIME TO HANG OUT - Watches - Loop

IT'S TODAY - Wallpaper ☆ - James Seeman Studios

IT'S TOUCH-LESS - Electrical equipment - Ben Veal

IT'S UP TO YOU - Apparel stores–sports - Starter Corp.

IT'S VISIBLY - Cookware - Corning Inc.

IT'S VISIBLY SUPERIOR - Glassware–household - Corning Inc.

IT'S WHAT THE PROS PLAY ON - Sporting goods - Porter Athletic Equipment Co.

IT'S WIRELESS - Office supplies - Mead Corp.

IT'S WISE TO SAY NO TO ALCOHOL - Computer software - Right on Programs

IT'S WISE TO SAY NO TO DRUGS - Computer software - Right on Programs

IT'S YOU BY WARNER'S - Apparel and accessories ☆ - Warnaco Inc.

IT'S YOUR DAY - Display units - Linda K. Engravalle

IT'SA - Food products - Customer Co.

ITSABOUTIME - Fabrics - Dan River Inc.

I.T.S.C. - Skates–roller - Seneca Sports, Inc.

ITSIE - Dolls - Annalee Mobilitee Dolls Inc.

ITSOLONG MR. FREEZE - Fruit pops–frozen ☆ - Leaf, Inc.

I.T.S.S. - Traction apparatus–medical ☆ - Lossing Orthopedic Co.

ITSY BITSY - Apparel and accessories - Itsy Bitsy, Inc.

ITSY-BITSY - Artists' materials - Stangren Co.

ITSY BITSY - Candy - Farley Candy Co.

ITSY BITSY - Double hung tapers - Lumi-Lite Candle Co. Inc.

ITSY BITSY BUDDYS - Toys - SLM Inc.

ITSY-BITSY KITTY - Toys–stuffed ☆ - Dakin Inc.

ITSY BITSY MICE WITH CHEEZY MAZE - Toys - Tonka Corp.

ITSY-BITSY TEENY-WEENY CURLS - Hair curlers ☆ - Sunbeam-Oster Household Products

I.T.T. - Fishing lures - Harville Manufacturing Co., Inc.

ITT - Goggles - ITT Corp.

ITT - Telecommunications products - Cortelco Systems Inc.

ITTALA - Glassware–household - Hackman Tabletop Inc.

ITTY BITTY - Bagels - Garden of Eatin', Inc.

ITTY BITTY - Greeting cards ☆ - Amberley Greeting Card Co.

ITTY BITTY - Lighting fixtures - Zelco Industries, Inc.

ITTY-BITTY - Pet brushes - Carter-Wallace, Inc.

ITTY BITTY - Pet products - Lambert-Kay

ITTY BITTY BLENDER - Blenders - AMS Industries Inc.

ITTY BITTY BODY BUDDY - Pillows - Hollander Home Fashions Inc.

ITTY-BITTY CANDY WADS - Candy - Kraft Food Ingredients Corp.

ITTY BITTY CRAZY KITTY - Pet products - Cardinal Laboratories, Inc.

ITTY BITTY CRITTERS - Figurines - United Design Corp.

ITTY BITTY CRYSTALS - Pet products - Zeotech Corp.

ITTY BITTY FLINTSTONES - Erasers ☆ - Diener Industries Inc.

ITTY BITTY GROLITE - Lighting fixtures - Zelco Industries, Inc.

ITTY BITTY POP N' PEEPS - Toys - Trendmasters, Inc.

ITTY BITTYS - Erasers - Diener Industries Inc.

ITVL INTERNATIONAL TAX VIDEO LIBRARY - Video production - USA Tax Videos, Inc.

ITZ - Bags–duffel - Sports, Inc.

ITZA PIE - Candy - Crown Candy Corp.

IUKA IV - Flowers, plants, and seeds - Mott Ranch, Inc.

IUP - Publisher's imprints - International Universities Press Inc.

IV GEORGES BRASS - Glass products - Kohler Co.

IV ID - Medical apparatus - Innovative Concept Development, Inc.

IV OPTION - Awards, plaques and medals - Tropar Manufacturing Co., Inc.

I.V. PRO - Medical apparatus - I.V. Pro Tek, Inc.

IV SCANNER - Measuring instruments - Shenandoah Electronic Intelligence, Inc.

I.V. SOLUTION, THE - Computer software - Healthcare Automation Inc.

IVADANTIN - Pharmaceutical preparations - Norwich-Eaton Pharmaceuticals

IVAN - Eyeglasses - Art-Craft Optical Co.

IVAN LENDL - Apparel and accessories - Adidas USA Inc.

IVAN PAYA - Hotels and motels - Motel 6 Corp.

IVAN POGUE - Glass products - Ivan Pogue Studio of Glass Sculpture

IVAN TAMAS - Wines - Parrott & Co.

IVAN TAMAS - Wines - Ivan Tamas Wineries

IVAN TAMAS VINEYARDS - Wines ☆ - Shaw-Ross International Importers

IVANA - Apparel–women's - Ivana M. Trump

IVANHOE - Clocks - Ridgeway Clock Co.

IVANHOE - Frames–eyeglass ☆ - Universal/Univis Inc.

IVANHOE - Pencils ☆ - Faber-Castell Corp.

IVANHOE - Thread - Threads USA Div.

IVANHOE - Tobacco - American Tobacco Co.

IVANHOE - Watches - Bulova Corp.

IVANKO - Sporting goods - Sta-Slim Products

IVANO - Apparel and accessories - Ivano Wear

IVAREST - Pharmaceutical preparations - Blistex Inc.

IVAR'S - Seasonings, sauces, etc. - Ivar's Inc.

IVATOS - Games - Gari Gold Kennedy

IVC - Artists' materials - International Visual Corp.

IVC - Video tapes–blank - International Video Conversions Inc.

IVC - Vitamins and nutritional supplements - Wyeth-Ayerst Laboratories

IVC 2000 - Golfing equipment - Golfsmith International Inc.

I'VE BEEN THERE - Glassware–household - Papel Freelance, Inc.

I'VE BEEN TO - Buttons - U.S. Souvenir & Novelty

I'VE GOT THE HOTS FOR YOU - Candy - Harry London's Candies Inc.

I'VE GOT THE WINNING EDGE - Apparel and accessories - Winning Edge Inc.

I'VE GOT YOUR NUMBER - Toys–electronic ☆ - Philips Consumer Electronics Co.

IVER JOHNSON - Pistols - Iver Johnson Arms Co.

IVERS & POND - Piccolos - Aeolian Pianos Inc.

IVERSEN - Bread - Iversen Baking Co.

IVES - Hardware - H.B. Ives

IVES - Wines - Bully Hill Vineyards, Inc.

IVES SIGNATURE COLLECTION - Knobs–wood - Harrow Products Inc.

IVES VALVES - Valves - Concentric, Inc.

IVET - Veterinary nutritional supplements - Ivet Laboratories, Inc.

IVETERNATION - Fishing tackle ☆ - Penn Fishing Tackle Manufacturing Co.

IVEX - Packaging–blisterwrap - Ivex Coated Products Corp.

IVEY - Lenses–optical - National Optical Co.

IVI PUBLISHING - Computer software - IVI Publishing, Inc.

IVIS - Computer software - Ivis International

IVISION - Cameras - Silicon Vision, Inc.

IVISOFT - Computer software - Ivis International

☆ = Now out of production

IVISS MANAGER - Computer software - Computer Associates International, Inc.

I.V.L. TECHNOLOGIES - Guitars - Kramer

IVLA CASUALWEAR - Apparel and accessories - Kellwood Co.

IVOCORT - Pharmaceutical preparations ☆ - Roberts/Hauck Pharmaceuticals Inc.

IVOIRE - Colognes - Frances Denney

IVOIRE CREME - Nail care products - Cosmair Inc.

IVOIRE DE BALMAIN - Cosmetics - Revlon Consumer Products Corp.

IVOIRE SOFT COVER - Cosmetics ☆ - Monteil Paris

IVOIRIZ - Rice - Connell Co.

IVOMEC - Veterinary pharmaceutical preparations - Merck & Co., Inc. (Merck Agvet Division)

IVORY - Erasers ☆ - Faber-Castell Corp.

IVORY - Needles–sewing ☆ - Knitting Fever Inc.

IVORY - Salt ☆ - Morton International Inc. (Morton Salt Div.)

IVORY - Soap - Procter & Gamble Co.

IVORY ALMOND K'NUCKLE - Popcorn - Trelay Farms, Inc.

IVORY AND PEARLS - Frames–picture - Terragrafics Inc.

IVORY CARPET - Flowers, plants, and seeds - Hines Nurseries, Inc.

IVORY CATS - Giftware ☆ - Enesco Corp.

IVORY CLUB - Seafood - Continental Seafoods Inc.

IVORY COAST - Floor coverings–carpet and rugs ☆ - Masland Corp.

IVORY COAST COLLECTION - Dining room furniture - Daystrom Furniture Inc.

IVORY COAST ULTRA SENSITIVE - Hair care products - Revlon Consumer Products Corp.

IVORY DYNASTY - Giftware - Arnart Imports Inc.

IVORY FEATHER - Flowers, plants, and seeds - Monrovia

IVORY FLAKES - Soap - Procter & Gamble Co.

IVORY FLEUR - Giftware - Arnart Imports Inc.

IVORY LACE - Colognes - Dynamite Enterprises

IVORY LACE - Frames–picture - Terragrafics Inc.

IVORY LIQUID - Detergents - Procter & Gamble Co.

IVORY MIST - Cosmetics - Lancome

IVORY MOISTURECARE - Skin care products - Procter & Gamble Co.

IVORY PALACE - Floor coverings–carpet and rugs - Barrett Carpet Mills Inc.

IVORY PALACE - Floor coverings–carpet and rugs - Itexco/Marble Tiles of America

IVORY PLACE - Floor coverings–carpet and rugs ☆ - Blue Ridge Carpet Mills

IVORY ROYALE - Cakes - Godiva Chocolatier

IVORY SNOW - Detergents - Procter & Gamble Co.

IVORY TOWER - Dishes–china - Taylor, Smith & Taylor Co.

IVORY TOWER - Publisher's imprints - Ivory Tower Publishing Inc.

IVP - Audio equipment - Electro-Voice, Inc.

IVX - Electronic equipment - Estech Systems, Inc.

IVY - Apparel and accessories - Kellwood Co.

IVY - Dinnerware–glass - Franciscan by Johnson Brothers, USA, Inc.

IVY - Footwear ☆ - Olem Shoe Corp.

IVY - Glassware–household - Crystal Clear Importing Co. Inc.

IVY - Thread - Threads USA Div.

IVY AND DESIGN - Apparel and accessories - Kellwood Co.

IVY & INNOCENCE - Figurines - Cast Art Industries, Inc.

IVY AT THE SHORE - Shirts - L.A. Desserts, Inc.

IVY-CHEX - Pharmaceutical preparations - JMI-Canton Pharmaceuticals

IVY CLING SCENES - Window decorations and stickers - Ivy Integrated Marketing Inc.

IVY CLUB - Apparel and accessories - Venture Stores, Inc.

IVY COLLECTIBLES - Apparel–women's - AJ Brandon

IVY COLLECTIONS - Apparel and accessories - Kellwood Co.

IVY COTTAGE - Stationery - Heartprint Inc.

IVY-DRY - Pharmaceutical preparations - Ivy Corp.

IVY GLEN - Furniture–upholstered ☆ - Webb Furniture Enterprises Inc.

IVY HALL - Fabrics - Dan River Inc.

IVY HALL - Ophthalmic goods - Styl-Rite Optical Manufacturing Co., Inc.

IVY HILL - Slacks - Master Industries Corp.

IVY IMPRESSIONS - Apparel and accessories - Kellwood Co.

IVY LEAGUE - Eyeglasses - Art-Craft Optical Co.

IVY LEAGUE - Floor coverings–carpet and rugs - Barrett Carpet Mills Inc.

IVY LEAGUE - Floor coverings–carpet and rugs - Olympic Carpets Inc.

IVY LEAGUE - Frames–eyeglass - U.S. Optical Frame Co.

IVY LEAGUE - Wallpaper - Imperial Wallcoverings, Inc.

IVY LEAGUE - Wood products - Champion International Corp.

IVY LEAGUE, THE - Apparel and accessories - Kellwood Co.

IVY LITE - Frames–eyeglass - U.S. Optical Frame Co.

IVY RECORDS - Recording label - Jill Holly

IVY-RID - Pharmaceutical preparations - Roberts/Hauck Pharmaceuticals Inc.

IVY SCREEN - Skin care products - SolarCare Technologies Corp.

IVY WEAR - Apparel and accessories - Kellwood Co.

IVY WEAR - Apparel–women's - AJ Brandon

IVY WORKS - Apparel–women's - AJ Brandon

IVYCARE - Computer software - Alcon Laboratories, Inc.

IWAN - Augers - Seymour Manufacturing Co.,Inc.

IWAYHOPPER - Computer hardware - Multi-Tech Systems, Inc.

IWEBCLASS - Computer software - Analytical Technologies, Inc.

IWERKS - Cameras–motion picture - Iwerks Entertainment, Inc.

IWI - Jewelry - Imperial World, Inc.

IWN - Computer software - Iwn, Inc.

IX - Microscopes - Olympus America Inc.

IX - Shock absorbers–motor vehicle - Intrax Suspension Technology

IX CHAINS - Recording label - Mainstream Records Inc.

IX CHEL - Perfumes - A-Veda Corp.

IXAI - Graphics software for personal computers - RIX SoftWorks Inc.

IXL - Chili–canned - Nalley's Fine Foods

IXL - Kitchen and vanity cabinets - IXL Furniture Co. Inc.

IXL - Lighter fluid - R.M. Hollingshead Corp.

IXL GROUP, THE - Handles–wood - IXL Manufacturing Co., Inc.

IXORA - Apparel–women's - Ixora Ltd.

IXPLUS - Computer software - Electronic Data Systems Corp.

IXSPA GOLF - Backpacks - GFI Holding Co., Inc.

IXTAPA S.P.O.R.T - Clothing - Fred C. Gilbert

IXTHOS - Digital encoders - Ixthos, Inc.

IYO - Artists' materials - Andrews/Nelson/Whitehead

IZ PATCH - Novelty items–paper - Epoca Corp.

IZANO - Apparel and accessories - Lawrence Martin and John D. Walker Partnership

IZDAS - Towels, bathrobes - Izdas Trading Co. Ltd. Inc.

IZENKLAR - Beverages–malt - Pabst Brewing Co.

IZMIR - Floor coverings–carpet and rugs ☆ - Trans-Ocean Import Co. Inc.

IZMIR/ONYX - Floor coverings–carpet and rugs ☆ - Trans-Ocean Import Co. Inc.

IZMIRA - Vodka - Paddington Corp.

IZOD - Apparel and accessories - Phillips-Van Heusen Corp.

IZOD - Sportswear - Crystal Brands Inc.

IZOD BABY - Apparel–children's - Crystal Brands Inc.

IZOD CLUB INTERNATIONAL TOUR - Apparel and accessories - Crystal Brands Inc.

IZOD KIDS - Apparel–children's - Crystal Brands Inc.

IZON - Air conditioning equipment - Izon Inc.

IZON-FLOOR - Finishing agents - Analab Inc.

IZUMI - Skin care products - Kenshin Trading

IZUMI-DAI OZONE - Fish–canned or cured - Unified Seafood Co., Inc.

IZZATSEW - Apparel and accessories - Izzatsew Inc.

IZZI - Puzzles - Binary Arts Corp.

IZZY'S - Pizza - Covalt Enterprises Inc.

☆ = Now out of production

J

Addresses and phone numbers for the companies cited in the brands below
are available in the Company Listings section immediately following the brands listings.

J - Computer peripheral equipment - Prio Corp.
J - Furniture - Jofco, Inc.
J - Gasoline - Flying J Inc.
J - Sailboat - J Boats, Inc.
J-6 MARTIN - Archery equipment - Martin Archery Inc.
J-16 - Asphalt felts and coatings - Maintenance Inc.
J-90 - Whirlpools - Jacuzzi Inc.
J 126 - Frames–eyeglass - Felix M. Mendelson Co.
J-554 - Flowers, plants, and seeds - Jacklin Seed
J-1224 - Flowers, plants, and seeds - Jacklin Seed
J. A. BACZEWSKI - Beverages–alcohol - Stanley Stawski Distributing Co.
J. A. HENCKELS - Scissors–hand-operated - J.A. Henckels Zwillingswerk Inc.
J. ALAN'S - Cleaning preparations - J. Alan Inc.
J & B - Beverages–alcohol - Paddington Corp.
J & B - Footwear - Stallion Boot Co.
J. & C. FERRARA - Jewelry - J. & C. Ferrara Co. Inc.
J. & C. FISCHER - Pianos - Aeolian Pianos Inc.
J. & D. HITE - Musical instrument accessories - Hite Mouthpieces
J & F - Suits–men's ☆ - Joseph and Feiss Co.
J. & F LURTON - Wines - Classic Wine Imports Inc.
J. & J. - Giftware - RDE Imports
J & J - Jojoba oil - J & J Jojoba
J & J - Prepared sandwiches - J & J Food Service
J & J - Shampoos - Johnson & Johnson
J & J - Tomato pastes and sauces - Gibsonburg Canning Co. Inc.
J & J - Wheels - Standex International Corp.
J & J BEE SERVICE - Honey - J & J Bee Service
J. & L. - Gasoline and motor oil - J. & L. Oil Inc.
J & M - Shoes - Genesco Inc.
J & M EAGLE SOFTEE - Shoes - Genesco Inc.
J & M PRESIDENT'S COLLECTION - Shoes - Genesco Inc.
J. & P. COATS - Needles–sewing - Coats and Clark Inc.
J. ANDRE - Brushes - J.A. Fleuridas Co.
J. #ARMENIO - Apparel and accessories - Just Suited, Inc.
J. ASHFORD - Apparel and accessories ☆ - Edison Brothers Stores, Inc.
J-B - Apparel–men's - Jonbil Inc.
J-B - Cleaning preparations - Brownells, Inc.
J B BEAN AND ASSOCIATES - Toys - Boyds Collection Ltd.
J. BALATON - Musical instrument accessories - Midco International
J BAR B - Sausages - J & B Sausage Co., Inc.
J-BAR-J - Footwear–children's - Jumping-Jacks Shoes Inc.
J. BEGG - Whiskey - Schenley Industries Inc.
J. BERTRAND WILLIAMS - Brandy ☆ - David Sherman Corp.
J. BLADES - Neckties - Cornell of California Inc.
J-BLOCK - Hardware - Vagedes Industries Inc.
J. BOISSIERE - Beverages–alcohol ☆ - Jim Beam Brands Co.
J. BOREL - Watch and jewelry supplies - Jules Borel & Co.
J. BRADLEY - Office supplies - Jonathan Bradley Pens Inc.
J. C. BOARDMAN SILVERSMITHS - Giftware ☆ - Boardman Silversmiths Inc.
J. C. FINNANZZA - Violins - Ideal Musical Merchandise Co.
J. C. KERR'S - Beverages–alcohol ☆ - Star Liquor Imports Inc.
J. C. PENNEY - Apparel and accessories - J.C. Penney Co., Inc.
J. C. RATEAU - Wines - Chartrand Imports
J. CALVANI - Apparel - John Victor Calvani
J. CAMPTON - Apparel and accessories - East End Apparel Group Ltd.
J CARDOT - Watches - Uti Time Corp.

J-CARRE - Whirlpools - Jacuzzi Inc.
J. CHISHOLM - Boots - Texas Boot Co.
J. CHISHOLM - Footwear - United States Shoe Corp.
J. CHISHOLM HANDCRAFTED BOOTS - Boots - United States Shoe Corp.
J-CLASS 1930 1937 - Apparel–men's - Nautica Enterprises Inc.
J-CLIP - Fastening tool - ITW Ramset/Red Head
J. COLET - Apparel–men's - Penn State Clothing Corp.
J-CORNER SHOWER TOWER - Whirlpools - Jacuzzi Inc.
J-D - Blinds–venetian - Halsey-Themper Co. (Mill Supply Div.)
J. D. BANCHERO - Food products - Hickory Farms, Inc.
J. DEMERE DESIGNS - Jewelry–precious - J.D.M., Inc.
J DON OF HICKORY - Furniture - Hickorycraft Inc.
J-DREAM - Whirlpools - Jacuzzi Inc.
J-DREAM II - Whirlpools - Jacuzzi Inc.
J/E - Sporting goods - Bausch & Lomb Inc.
J. E. SUGDEN - Audio equipment - Import Audio
J. E. WOLFENSBERGER - Greeting cards - H. George Caspari Inc.
J. #ELLIOTT - Hair care products - Joseph Elliott Co.
J. FLAYVORS - Footwear - Shuman Shoe Co. Inc.
J. FLEURIDAS - Hair care products - J.A. Fleuridas Co.
J-FLEX - Plumbing fixtures–metal - Jameco Industries, Inc.
J-FLEX - Sporting goods - Jim Viola Co.
J. FOREST & CO. - Apparel–children's - Jamesway Corp.
J. G. FAST - Uniforms–tailored - James G. Fast Co.
J. G. HOOK - Apparel and accessories - J.G. Hook, Inc.
J. G. HOOK - Footwear - Interco Inc.
J. G. HOOK - Umbrellas - Essex Manufacturing Inc.
J. G. HOOK: AT HOME - Wallpaper - Imperial Wallcoverings, Inc.
J. G. HOOK FOR SWIRL - Apparel and accessories ☆ - Swirl II Ltd.
J. G. HOOK: SAFE HARBOUR - Wallpaper ☆ - Imperial Wallcoverings, Inc.
J. G. HOOK: THE HUNT CLUB - Wallpaper ☆ - Imperial Wallcoverings, Inc.
J. G. HOOK: TRADITIONAL ELEGANCE - Wallpaper ☆ - Imperial Wallcoverings, Inc.
J. GRANDE - Boats–kayaks ☆ - Noah Corp.
J-GRIPPER - Gloves - Jomac Products Inc.
J H HYDRO RAIN - Electronic equipment ☆ - Hardie-Toro Irrigation
J. HERMES - Glue–household or industrial - J. Hermes
J. HIGGS - Snack foods - Moran Foods, Inc.
J. HOFERT - Christmas tree ornaments - J. Hofert Co.
J. HUGEE MINISTRIES - Recording label - Johnnie Hugee
J. HUNGERFORD SMITH'S - Syrup ☆ - J. Hungerford Smith Co.
J INTERNATIONAL - Jewelry - Jan Bell Marketing Inc.
J. J. BABBITT - Clarinet and saxophone mouthpieces - J.J. Babbitt Co. Inc.
J. J. CASSONE - Bakery products - Allied Bakers Co.
J. J. JONES - Figurines - Delfino Products Inc.
J. J. VINCENT & FILS - Wines - Frederick Wildman and Sons Ltd.
J JAN BELL PREMIERE DIAMOND COLLECTION - Jewelry - Jan Bell Marketing Inc.
J. JASMINE - Recording label - Jazz Composer's Orchestra Association Inc.
J. JAVILLIER - Wines ☆ - Chartrand Imports
J. JILL LTD. - Apparel–women's - DM Management Co.
J JIMMY - Apparel and accessories - A & J Sportswear, Corp.
+J +JULIE - Electronic equipment - Julie Associates, Inc.
J. K. ADAMS - Wood products - J.K. Adams Co. Inc.
J. K. LASSER - Publisher's imprints - Simon & Schuster, Inc.

☆ = Now out of production

1115

J. K. LASSER'S YOUR INCOME TAX - Computer software - Simon & Schuster Computer Software

J. K. LASSER'S YOUR MONEY MANAGER - Computer software - Simon & Schuster Computer Software

J. KRANT CELLARS - Wines - Geerlings & Wade, Inc.

J L - Jewelry–precious - Color Merchants, Inc.

J. L. COOMBS - Footwear - J.L. Coombs & Co. Inc.

J-LAR - Tape–adhesive - Permacel

J-LAR 910 - Tape–adhesive - Permacel

J-LAR II - Tape–adhesive - Permacel

J-LINE - Canes - Otto Bock Orthopedic Industry Inc.

J-LINE - Educational equipment - Brodhead-Garrett Co.

J. LOHR - Wines - J. Lohr Winery

J-LOK - Jitter reduction apparatus for lasers ☆ - Spectra-Physics Lasers, Inc.

J-LOY - Hardware - L.E. Jones Co., Inc.

J. LUBER AG - Housewares ☆ - Chase Collection, Inc.

J-M - Fire extinguishers ☆ - Manville/Schuller

J. M. CARROLL & CO. - Publisher's imprints - Amereon Ltd.

J M GLASSWARE - Glass–leaded - Charles Norman Inc.

J. M. HOLLANDER - Apparel and accessories - Hampton Industries, Inc.

J. M. LINTON - Musical instruments - J.M. Linton Co.

J. M. MONMOUSSEAU - Wines - Wine World Inc.

J. M. RUBIN - Gloves - Rubin Gloves Inc.

J. MACINALLY'S - Apparel - Shopko Stores, Inc.

J/MAN - Racks - J/Man LLC

J-MARK - Motor vehicle parts and accessories - JMX Inc.

J-MAS - Audio equipment - John Marovskis Audio Systems

J. MASON PRODUCTS - Strollers–baby - Ben M. Hsia Ming

J. MCLAUGHLIN - Apparel and accessories - Sea Island Clothiers Inc.

J. MONNIER - Beverages–alcohol ☆ - Diamond Wine Merchants

J. MOREAU & FILS - Wines - Frederick Wildman and Sons Ltd.

J-MOUSE - Computer peripheral equipment - Prio Corp.

J. MURPHY - Boots - Genesco Inc.

J. NORVELL - Cosmetics - Designs by Norvell Inc.

J. P. CHENET - Wines - Palm Bay Imports, Inc.

J. P. KETTLEBANGER'S - Popcorn - National Oats Co. Inc.

J. P. MOUEIX - Wines - Dreyfus Ashby Inc.

J. P. MURRAY - Rifles–pellet - Euroarms of America

J-PAD - Sporting goods - Jim Viola Co.

J. PATRICK DORE - Wines ☆ - Coastal Wine Merchants

J. PEDRONCELLI - Wines - J. Pedroncelli Winery

J/R - Hair care products - Jheri Redding Products Inc.

J/R - Sporting goods - Prince Manufacturing Inc.

J R, A - Jewelry - Reeds Corporate Services, Inc.

J. R. CARUS - Footwear–women's - J.R. Carus Inc.

J. R. EWING'S PRIVATE STOCK - Beverages–malt ☆ - Pearl Brewing Co.

J. R. JILBERT - Dairy products - John R. Jilbert Dairy Inc.

J-R-T - Apparel and accessories - Newport News, Inc.

J. RENNE - Shoes - Remac Inc.

J. RIDGE DESIGNS - Wallpaper ☆ - Wallquest, Inc.

J. RIGGINGS - Apparel–men's - Edison Brothers Stores, Inc.

J. ROCHIOLI VINEYARDS & WINERY - Wines - J. Rochioli Vineyards

J. ROGET - Wines - Canandaigua Wine Co. Inc.

J. #ROGET CHAMPAGNE - Beverages–alcohol - Canandaigua Wine Co. Inc.

J-ROLLER FINE - Pens - Zebra Pen Corp.

J-ROLLER MEDIUM - Pens - Zebra Pen Corp.

J-RULE - Scale drawing boards ☆ - Harold Cunningham & Co.

J. RUPPERT'S - Beverages–malt - The Stroh Brewery Co.

J. RUPPERT'S LIGHT - Beverages–malt - The Stroh Brewery Co.

J SAILER - Ships–sailing vessels - Johnson Boat Works

J. SCHRAM - Wines - Schramsberg Vineyards Co.

J-SERIES - Trailers–travel - Jayco Inc.

J. SETH - Neckties ☆ - Salant/Manhattan Industries

J SHINE - Chemicals - Sybron Chemical Holdings Inc.

J-SHOWER TOWER - Whirlpools - Jacuzzi Inc.

J. #SILVER CLOTHING - Apparel and accessories - Price is Right Shops, Inc.

J. SILVER CLOTHING - Apparel and accessories - Price is Right Shops, Inc.

J. STEELE - Guitars - Music Imports Ltd.

J. STONE - Apparel and accessories - Jonathan Stone Ltd.

J. T. BECKETT - Apparel–men's - J.C. Penney Co., Inc.

J. T. BUEL - Fishing lures - Eppinger Manufacturing Co.

J. T. INMAN CO. - Spoons ☆ - Whiting & Davis Co.

J. T. MCCORD'S - Restaurants–pizzerias - Pizza Inn, Inc.

J. TIRAS - Handbags - J. Tiras Classic Handbags, Inc.

J. #TRIGGS - Musical instruments - James P. Triggs

J TRIGGS - Musical instruments - James P. Triggs

J TRIMM - Apparel–men's - Cavaliero Cravats

J-VAC - Veterinary pharmaceutical preparations - Sanofi Animal Health, Inc.

J-VAP - Machinery - JWI, Inc.

J. VIDAL FLEURY - Wines - W.J. Deutsch & Sons Ltd.

J. W. DANT - Whiskey - Schenley Industries Inc.

J. W. FORD - Posters - Icart Vendor Graphics Inc.

J. W. HALL'S - Food products - Ellison Meat Co.

J. WALKEN LTD. - Slacks–men's - Stanwood Corp.

J. WALK'N - Slacks–children's - Duck Head Apparel Co., Inc.

J-WEAR - Apparel and accessories - Cyrk Inc.

J. WILE AND SONS - Wines - Golden State Vintners

J. WILKINS - Apparel–women's ☆ - Wilkins Industries Inc.

J. WILLEFORD - Kites ☆ - Gayla Industries Inc.

J. WM. DERR - Cosmetics ☆ - Fashion Express

J-WOOD - Cabinets - White Consolidated Industries, Inc.

J-WRAP - Sporting goods - Jim Viola Co.

J Z - Bird feeders - Dataware Technologies

J-Z - Medical apparatus - Jones Metal Products Co.

J5PW - Balls–football - Spalding & Evenflo Companies, Inc.

J5V - Sporting goods - Spalding Sports Worldwide

J10 - Motor vehicles–jeeps ☆ - DaimlerChrysler

J20 - Motor vehicles–jeeps ☆ - DaimlerChrysler

J316 - Apparel and accessories - USA T-Shirt & Screen Printing Co., Inc.

JA - Cigars ☆ - Avanti Cigar Co.

JA - Compact discs–prerecorded - Peter Pan Industries

JA - Gaming equipment - Gamblers General Store, Inc.

JA - Hair care products - John Amico Expressive Hair Care Products

JA-EAT-YET - Sandwiches–prepackaged - Waltham Beef & Provision Co.

JA MAI - Furniture ☆ - Lane Co. Inc.

JA-WES - Recording label - Daran Records

JA37 - Apparel–women's - Pants 'R Us

JAAFER SWEETS - Pastries - Jaafer Sweets, Inc.

JABALA - Recording label - Spanda Records

JABBA - Toys–stuffed - Gund, Inc.

JABBA THE HUTT - Shampoos - Lucasfilm Ltd.

JABEL - Rings - Jabel Ring Manufacturing Co. Inc.

JABLUM - Coffee - Fairwinds Gourmet Coffee Co. Inc.

JABON DE RUDA - Soap - Via Natura Inc.

JABRA - Electronic equipment - Jabra Corp.

JABRA EARSET - Communications equipment - Jabra Corp.

JABRO - Batteries - Jabro Batteries, Inc.

JABS USA - Apparel–athletic - Joanie Greggains

JABSCO - Pumps - ITT Jabsco

JAC - Medical apparatus - Mentor O & O Inc.

JAC-BRUSH - Containers–glass - Excel Brush Works Inc.

JAC DE PARIS - Cosmetics ☆ - Beauty Guild Inc.

JAC IN THE SAC - Jackets - Mighty-Mac

JAC-KLAMP - Battery terminal connectors - Allentech Co.

JAC-O-NET - Waterproof outerwear - Hairnet Corp. of America

JAC PAC - Meat product - Jac Pac Foods

JACADA - Computer software - Client/Server Technology, Inc.

JACARANDA - Furniture ☆ - Tropitone Furniture Co. Inc.

JACARE - Floor coverings–carpet and rugs ☆ - Columbus Mills, Inc.

JACARE - Wines - Heublein, Inc.

JACINE - Pharmaceutical - Jamco Inc.

JACK - Dolls ☆ - Effanbee Doll Corp.

JACK - Frames–eyeglass - Rozin Optical Export Corp.

JACK - Heating equipment - Yukon Energy Corp.

JACK - Tools - American Tool Companies Inc.

JACK & EDIE QUOTABLES - Greeting cards - Stevenson Industries Inc.

JACK & JANE HICKS - Soap ☆ - Carolina Designs Ltd.

JACK & JILL - Candy ☆ - Just Born Inc.

JACK & JILL - Cleaning preparations - Miami Products & Chemical Co.

JACK & JILL - Dairy products - Nash-Finch Co.

JACK AND JILL - Eyeglasses - Art-Craft Optical Co.

JACK AND JILL - Footwear - Morse Shoe, Inc.

JACK AND JILL - Games ☆ - Tyco Toys

JACK & JILL - Ice cream, frozen yogurt - Jack & Jill Ice Cream Co.

JACK & JILL - Kites ☆ - Hi-Flier Manufacturing Co.

JACK & JILL - Soap - Manhattan Products Inc.

JACK AND SPIKE - Apparel–children's - Rays Apparel, Inc.

JACK AND THE BEAN DEP - Spices and extracts - To Market to Market

JACK AND THE BEAN STALK - Frozen foods - Agripac, Inc.

JACK AND THE BEANSTALK - Computer software - Queue Inc.

JACK & THE BEANSTALK - Games - Three Rivers Amphibian Inc.

JACK ATTACK - Computer software - Jellyvision, Inc.

☆ = Now out of production

JACK BE NIMBLE - Kites ☆ - Hi-Flier Manufacturing Co.

JACK-BOT - Game machines - Williams Electronics Games, Inc.

JACK CANYON CELLARS - Wines - Geerlings & Wade, Inc.

JACK CITY - Apparel and accessories - John D. Hornke

JACK CORBETT - Sporting goods - Schutt Manufacturing Co.

JACK CREEK STEAKHOUSE - Napkins–paper - Paul Fundanish

JACK DANIEL'S - Beverages–alcohol - Co. Store

JACK DANIEL'S - Candy - Lynchburg Merchantile

JACK DANIEL'S - Mustard - Romanoff International Inc.

JACK DANIEL'S - Whiskey - Jack Daniel's Distillery

JACK DANIEL'S 1866 - Beverages–malt - Brown-Forman Corp.

JACK DANIEL'S BLACK - Whiskey - Jack Daniel's Distillery

JACK DANIEL'S CLASSIC 1866 - Beverages–malt - Jack Daniel's Distillery

JACK DANIELS COLLECTION - Furniture ☆ - Davis Cabinet Co.

JACK DANIEL'S MASTER DISTILLER - Whiskey - Jack Daniel's Distillery

JACK DANIEL'S MASTER DISTILLER TENNESSEE WHISKEY - Whiskey - Jack Daniel's Distillery

JACK DANIEL'S NATURE-GLO - Charcoal - Hickory Specialties, Inc.

JACK DANIEL'S TENNESSEE COOLER - Whiskey - Jack Daniel's Distillery

JACK FLASH - Toys–automobiles - Mattel, Inc.

JACK FROST - Antifreeze - Lowe Oil Co.

JACK FROST - Candy ☆ - Melster Candies Inc.

JACK FROST - Figurines - Marjorie Sarnat & Associates, Inc.

JACK FROST - Frames–eyeglass - Hudson Optical Corp.

JACK FROST - Fruit and vegetable markets - Jack Frost Fruit Co.

JACK FROST - Snow making machinery - Sullivan Manufacturing & Sales Corp.

JACK FROST - Sugar–granulated, refined, or powdered - Monitor Sugar Co.

JACK HAMMER - Cleaning preparations–carpet and rug - Uncle Sam Chemical Co., Inc.

JACK-IN-THE-BOX - Bedding–linen ☆ - Welsh Co.

JACK KRAMER - Sporting goods - Wilson Sporting Goods Co.

JACK KRAMER STAFF - Rackets–tennis - Wilson Sporting Goods Co.

JACK LA LANNE - Footwear - TJ International Inc.

JACK LA LANNE - Physical fitness centers - Jack La Lanne Health Spas

JACK +LALANNE - Exercising equipment - Jack Lalanne Co.

JACK LALANNE - Granola bars ☆ - Barbara's Bakery, Inc.

JACK LAWRENCE - Jeans–men's ☆ - Hindquarters Inc.

JACK LINK'S CHERRY BOMB - Meat products - C & K Industries, Inc.

JACK LINK'S PICKLED PETE - Snack foods - C & K Industries, Inc.

JACK LINK'S SNACK FOODS - Meat products - C & K Industries, Inc.

JACK LONDON HOUSE OF FERMENTATION - Wines ☆ - Vose Vineyards

JACK MCCONNELL BOUTIQUE - Hats - Aldo Hat Corp.

JACK 'N DIANE - Apparel–children's - Beyond Basics Kids, Inc.

JACK 'N JILL - Meat products–canned - Hansel 'n Gretel Brand, Inc.

JACK N JILL - Playground equipment - Miracle Recreation Equipment Co.

JACK-N-VERTERS - Power transformers - Noco Co.

JACK NICKLAUS - Apparel–athletic - Warnaco Inc.

JACK NICKLAUS - Apparel–men's - Golden Bear International, Inc.

JACK NICKLAUS - Apparel–men's - Hartmarx Corp.

JACK NICKLAUS - Sunglasses ☆ - Optique du Monde Ltd.

JACK NICKLAUS-MUIRFIELD - Golfing equipment ☆ - MacGregor Golf Co.

JACK NICKLAUS VIP - Golfing equipment - Brunswick Corp.

JACK NUTS - Fasteners - Auto Vehicle Parts Co.

JACK NUTS - Hardware - Black & Decker Corp.

JACK O' LANTERN - Candles - Columbia Wax Products Inc.

JACK-O-LANTERN - Food products ☆ - Joan of Arc Co.

JACK-O-LANTERN - Toys–stuffed ☆ - Fun World Inc.

JACK-O-LANTERNS - Snack foods - Flowers Family Bakeries, Inc.

JACK-O-MATIC - Medical apparatus - Instruments for Research and Industry, I2R Inc.

JACK-O-RITA - Beverages–alcohol - Chi-Chi's, Inc.

JACK-POST - Flag poles - Flags International Inc.

JACK POT - Beverage, now out of production - Big Red Inc.

JACK POT - Games - Crisloid Inc.

JACK POT - Rice - Falcon Rice Mill Inc.

JACK PUMPKIN - Dolls - Russ Berrie and Co., Inc.

JACK PURCELL - Footwear - Converse Inc.

JACK RABBIT - Toys - Tonka Corp.

JACK RABBIT FRAME SHOP, THE - Frames–picture - National Frame Corp.

JACK RABBIT JAVA - Coffee - Southwest Specialty Foods

JACK RABBIT PALE ALE - Beverages–malt - Carver Brewing Co.

JACK RABBITS - Toy vehicles - Intex Recreation Corp.

JACK ROGERS - Footwear–women's - Jack Rogers Inc.

JACK SEBASTIAN - Footwear - Conjac Inc.

JACK SPRAT - Shoes - JAE Holdings Inc.

JACK SPRATT - Musical instrument accessories - Jack Spratt Woodwind Shop

JACK STRAP - Footwear - Nicholas Newton

JACK STRAWS - Games ☆ - Parker Brothers

JACK TAR - Boats - Glen-L Marine Designs

JACK TAR - Mops - Zephyr Manufacturing Co.

JACK TAR - Paints - Mobile Paint Manufacturing Co.

JACK THE FLIPPER - Video games - Taito America Corp.

JACK THE GRIPPER - Posters - Foresight

JACK THE RABBIT - Toys–stuffed - Dakin Inc.

JACK THE RIPPER - Toys - Gametek, Inc.

JACK THE SAW SPECIALIST - Saws–hand-operated - American Tool Companies Inc.

JACK VALENTINE TRIM LINE - Wallpaper - K.M.L. Industries

JACK WOLFSKIN - Camping products - Johnson Worldwide Associates, Inc.

JACKAL - Footwear–athletic - Intersport Ltd.

JACKAL - Sunglasses, ophthalmic lenses and frames ☆ - Corning Inc.

JACKAL - Toys - Tonka Corp.

JACKAL RAIDER - Toys - Tonka Corp.

JACKAROO - Barbecue sauce - Eastern Foods, Inc.

JACKAROO - Meat sauces - Naturally Fresh

JACKAROO - Sauces - American Culinary Foods, Inc.

JACKASS HILL - Wines - Lee Martinelli

JACKASS VINEYARD - Wines - Lee Martinelli

JACKBY - Cheese - Swiss American Import Co.

JACKEL FARMS - Produce - Jackel Farms & Cold Storage

JACKET - Ophthalmic goods - Oakley, Inc.

JACKET ADDENDUM - Shawls - Nancy Zellmer

JACKETED HOLLOW POINT - Bullets - Olin Corp. (Winchester Div.)

JACKETRON - Valves - Keystone International Holdings Corp.

JACKETS - Eyeglasses - Oakley, Inc.

JACKHAMMER - Cleaning preparations - Butcher Co.

JACKHAMMER - Toys - Tonka Corp.

JACKIE - Dolls - Horsman

JACKIE - Ophthalmic goods - Swank Optical

JACKIE - Tomatoes - Esformes Properties

JACKIE - Wigs - Jean Paree Weegs Inc.

JACKIE COLLINS WILD - Perfumes - Sel-Leb Marketing, Inc.

JACKIE JO - Apparel and accessories - Leemor-Mahana, Inc.

JACKIE JORDAN - Apparel–women's - Jacqueline S. Snell

+JACKIE +JORDAN - Apparel–women's - Jacqueline S. Snell

JACKIE STEWART'S GRAND PRIX AUTO RACING - Games ☆ - A.R.C. Toys Inc.

JACKIE'S - Cat food - Nutritreat, Ltd.

JACKIE'S CAT SNACKS - Cat food - Nutritreat, Ltd.

JACKIE'S GIRLS - Robes - Waterbury Garment Corp.

JACKKIES - Hair care products - I. Sekine Co. Inc.

JACKKNIFE - Boats - Glen-L Marine Designs

JACKLIN - Flowers, plants, and seeds - Jacklin Seed

JACKLON - Cosmetics - Caswell-Massey Co. Ltd.

JACKMAN - Apparel–men's - Steven Kurtzman Inc.

JACKMAN MUSIC - Music–sheet - Jackman Music Corp.

JACKMASTER - Knives–pocket - Imperial Schrade Corp.

JACKNIFE - Toys–automobiles - Tyco Industries, Inc.

JACKO - Deodorizers - American Auto Accessories, Inc.

JACKO & FRIENDS - Giftware ☆ - Schmid Inc.

JACKOAT - Apparel and accessories - RefrigiWear Inc.

JACKOPIERCE - Musical instruments - Jp-Jackopierce

JACKPLUS - Saws–hand-operated - American Tool Companies Inc.

JACKPOT - Colognes - Brandy Harvest

JACKPOT - Floor coverings–carpet and rugs ☆ - Galaxy Carpet Mills Inc.

JACKPOT - Flowers, plants, and seeds - Jacklin Seed

JACKPOT - Golfing equipment - All American Golf Sales, Inc.

JACKPOT - Rice - Riceland Foods, Inc.

JACKPOT - Wallpaper - Sellers & Josephson

JACKPOT 3 - Wallpaper - Sellers & Josephson

JACKPOT BINGO - Games - World Wide Press, Inc.

JACKPOT EXPRESS - Game machines - Sigma Game Inc.

JACKPOT FACTORY, THE - Game machines - Sigma Game Inc.

JACKPOT GEMS - Jewelry–precious - Jackpot Gems, Inc.

JACKPOT JUNGLE - Game machines - IGT - North America

JACKPOT RUMMY - Games ☆ - Milton Bradley Co.

JACKPRO - Tools–hand-operated - American Tool Companies Inc.

JACKRABBIT - Drill bits - Giffin Tec Inc.

JACKS - Cigarettes - R.J. Reynolds Tobacco Co.

JACKS - Food products ☆ - Mrs. Giles Country Kitchens Inc.

JACKS - Food products ☆ - Leavenworth Fruit Co.

JACK'S - Honey - Jack's Honey Bee Products
JACKS - Photographic equipment - Penn-Daniels, Inc.
JACK'S - Pizzas–frozen - Jack's Frozen Pizza Co.
JACK'S FAVORITE - Meat products - Gourmet Game, Ltd.
JACK'S HOUSE - Computer software - Imagine Software, Inc.
JACKS HYBRID MAGIC POP - Popcorn - KBL Trading and Processing Co.
JACKS MAGIC POP - Popcorn - KBL Trading and Processing Co.
JACK'S MUNCHKINS - Cookies - Flowers Bakeries
JACK'S PATTY MELT - Sandwiches–prepackaged - Foodmaker, Inc.
JACK'S PLACE - Display racks - Reflex Corp.
JACKS PREMIUM MAGIC POP - Popcorn - KBL Trading and Processing Co.
JACKS PRIDE - Dog food - Penn-Daniels, Inc.
JACKS R BETTER - Game machines - Bally Gaming International, Inc.
JACKS SUPERIOR - Dried beans - KBL Trading and Processing Co.
JACKSON - Binders - The Union Group
JACKSON - Brushes–paint - Corona Brushes Inc.
JACKSON - Electrodes - Jackson Products, Inc.
JACKSON - Frames–eyeglass - U.S. Optical Frame Co.
JACKSON - Safety equipment - General Scientific Equipment Co.
JACKSON - Wallets - Jackson Corp.
JACKSON - Wallpaper - Capital Carousel Inc.
JACKSON - Wallpaper ☆ - Wolf-Gordon Inc.
JACKSON - Wheelbarrows, carts, lawn rollers - Jackson Manufacturing Co.
JACKSON ALL STAR - Dairy products - Jackson All Star Dairy Inc.
JACKSON CERVIPILLO - Pillows - Maxxim Medical Inc.
JACKSON CORNERS HERB FARM - Deodorizers - Aphrodisia Products
JACKSON ELECTRONICS - Musical-instrument pickups - Jackson/Charvel
JACKSON FAMILY FARMS - Fruits and vegetables - Kingsburg Apple Packers Inc.
JACKSON FAMILY JF INC. - Apparel and accessories - Jackson Family Inc.
JACKSON HEWITT - Accounting services - Jackson Hewitt Inc.
JACKSON INTERNATIONAL INC - Hardware - Jackson International, Inc.
JACKSON JILL - Underwear and nightwear - Jackson Jill, Inc.
JACKSON OF DANVILLE - Upholstered furniture - Jackson of Danville Inc.
JACKSON PECAN - Floor coverings - National Floor Products Co., Inc.
JACKSON SQUARE - Floor coverings ☆ - Bruce Hardwood Floors
JACKSON SQUARE - Furniture ☆ - Athens Furniture Industries Inc.
JACKSON SQUARE PRESS - Publisher's imprints - Pelican Publishing Co. Inc.
JACKSON WOODS COLLECTION - Giftware - Delfino Products Inc.
JACKSONLEA - Finishing agents - Jason Inc.
JACKSON'S - Ice cream - Dillon Cos. Inc.
JACKSON'S APPLE JACK - Chewing tobacco - American Maize-Products Co.
JACKSONS OF PICCADILLY - Teas - British American Imports
JACKSONS OF PICCADILLY - Teas - C. & J. Willenborg Inc.
JACKSONVILLE - Frames–eyeglass - U.S. Optical Frame Co.
JACKSTRAWS - Candy - M-B Candies Inc.
JACLAR - Athletic footwear ☆ - Jaclar
JACLYN - Cabinets - Kabom Kitchen & Bath Manufacturing
JACLYN - Frames–eyeglass - U.S. Optical Frame Co.
JACLYN - Handbags - Jaclyn, Inc.
JACLYN APPAREL - Apparel - Jaclyn, Inc.
JACLYN COLLECTIONS - Maternity suits - Jaclyn, Inc.
JACLYN HART - Apparel–women's - Dawn Joy Fashions, Inc.
JACLYN MICHELLE - Apparel–women's - Fritzi California
JACLYN PAIGE - Eyeglasses - D.O.C. Optics Corp.
JACLYN SMITH - Apparel–women's - Kmart Corp.
JACLYN SMITH - Jewelry–costume - Kmart Properties, Inc.
JACLYN T - Apparel and accessories - Fritzi California
JACLYN'S - Food products - Jaclyn's Food Products
JACLYN'S FAT FREE - Food products - Jaclyn's Food Products
JACMOR - Watches - Perfect Timing of New York, Inc.
JACO - See JACOBSON
JACOB BEST - Beverages–malt - Pabst Brewing Co.
JACOB KNOOP - Wines - Parliament Import Co.
JACOB REED'S SONS - Apparel–men's - Gushner Brothers, Inc.
JACOB SCHMIDT - Beverages–malt - The Stroh Brewery Co.
JACOB SCHMIDT LIGHT - Beverages–malt - The Stroh Brewery Co.
JACOBEAN - Dinnerware–glass ☆ - Johnson Brothers, USA, Inc.
JACOBS - Coffee - Acme Food Specialties Inc.
JACOBS - Coffee - Haram-Christensen Corp.
JACOBS - Greeting cards ☆ - Amcal Inc.
JACOBS - Sports apparel, accessories, and equipment ☆ - Dionysian Inc. (Jacobs Div.)
JACOBS - Windmills - Renewable Energy Ventures
JACOB'S CREEK - Wines ☆ - IDV Wines (Beaulieu Vineyard)

JACOBS ELECTRONICS - Automotive parts and accessories - Jacobs Electronics
JACOBS FARM - Fruits and vegetables - Jacobs Farm/Del Cabo Inc.
JACOBS SOUCHARD - Coffee ☆ - Gillies Coffee Co.
JACOBSEN - Lawn mowers ☆ - Homelite, Inc.
JACOBSEN - Machinery - Textron Inc.
JACOBSEN - Ships–sailing vessels ☆ - Canor Plarex Inc.
JACOBSEN'S - Bakery products - Log House Foods Inc.
JACOBSON - Produce - Jacobson Produce Inc.
JACOBUS - Ventilation equipment - Maid-o-Mist
JACOBUS HORNSTEINER - Musical instruments ☆ - Scherl & Roth Inc.
JACOBY-BENDER - Jewelry - Genal Strap Co. Inc.
JACOLATT - Beverages - Caffe Espress Corp.
JACOMINO - Footwear–women's - Footwear Express, Ltd.
JACOR - Jewelry - Jabel Ring Manufacturing Co. Inc.
JACOTTE - Breads - Original Parisian Bakery Inc.
JACQCAD MASTER - Computer software - Fletcher Applied Sciences, Inc.
JACQUANET - Underwear and nightwear - Kayser-Roth Corp.
JACQUARD - Paints - Rupert, Gibbon and Spider, Inc.
JACQUARD - Wallpaper - Capital Carousel Inc.
JACQUARD COLLECTION - Frames–picture - Lenox, Inc.
JACQUARD JEWELS - Wallpaper ☆ - Decor International Wallcovering Inc.
JACQUARD WEAVE - Wallpaper - Capital Carousel Inc.
JACQUARDS - Wallpaper - Bayview Wallcoverings
JACQUARDS - Wallpaper - Doshi Wallcoveringss Inc.
JACQUART - Wines - Paterno Imports, Ltd.
JACQUE ARMAND - Apparel–men's - Oxxford Clothes Inc.
JACQUE DE PARIS - Cosmetics - Jacob Aini
JACQUE TISSERAND - Musical instruments - Dekalb Musicians Supply Co. Inc.
JACQUELINE - Cosmetics - Gera Dist. Inc.
JACQUELINE - Dolls - Mattel, Inc.
JACQUELINE - Footwear–women's - Wohl Shoe Co.
JACQUELINE - Frames–eyeglass ☆ - Universal/Univis Inc.
JACQUELINE - Tableware–china ☆ - Lenox, Inc.
JACQUELINE - Whirlpools - Jason International, Inc.
JACQUELINE FERRAR - Handbags - J.C. Penney Co., Inc.
JACQUELINE KLEIN TLG - Apparel and accessories - Jacqueline P. Klein
JACQUELINE LEE - Wigs ☆ - Lacey Costume Wigs
JACQUELINE LEIGH - Skin care products - Concord Chemists
JACQUELINE PUMPKIN - Dolls - Russ Berrie and Co., Inc.
JACQUELITE - Candlesticks - Brastoff Designs Inc.
JACQUES - Ice cream - San Francisco Ice Cream Co.
JACQUES - Ophthalmic goods ☆ - Luxottica
JACQUES BELLINI CLOTHING - Apparel–men's - Andre Romanelli, Inc.
JACQUES BERNE - Apparel and accessories ☆ - Edison Brothers Stores, Inc.
JACQUES BONET - Wines - Canandaigua Wine Co. Inc.
JACQUES CARDIN - Liquors - Sidney Frank Importing Co., Inc.
JACQUES COUER - Cooking utensils–earthenware - French & Pacific Trading Corp.
JACQUES DE LOUX - Crocheted and knitted items - Jacques De Loux Inc.
JACQUES DEPAGNEUX - Wines - Frederick Wildman and Sons Ltd.
JACQUES FAREL - Watches - Universe International Inc.
JACQUES FRELIN - Wines - Chartrand Imports
JACQUES' GOURMET. - Jams and jellies - Champagne, Inc.
JACQUES JUGEAT - Cooking utensils–china ☆ - Lalique North America
JACQUES LAFLEUR - Toys - Tonka Corp.
JACQUES LEVINE - Footwear - Middletown Footwear Inc.
JACQUES MARTIN - Sunglasses - Jack Martin Co.
JACQUES MORET - Footwear ☆ - Jacques Moret, Inc.
JACQUES MORET - Handbags ☆ - Sarne Co. Inc.
JACQUES PRIEUR - Wines - Winesellers Ltd.
JACQUES REYNARD - Wines - Weibel Vineyards
JACQUES RICHE - Apparel–men's ☆ - Sampson Inc.
JACQUES VINCENT - Shoes - Fisher Camuto Corp.
JACQUESMONET KIDS - Apparel–children's - Jacques Moret, Inc.
JACQUET - Bread - Interstate Brands Corp.
JACQUIN - Cordials - Charles Jacquin et Compagnie Inc.
JACS - Apparel–rubberized - Janitor and Custodian Safety, Inc.
JACSAN - Footwear - Conjac Inc.
JACT - Apparel and accessories - Jason L. Austin, Jr. & Mike F. Metzger
JACUZZI JET CHEF - Barbecues and grills - Prochef, Inc.
JACYLN NASH ORIGINALS - Fabrics - JD Fabrics Ltd.
JADCO - Locks–padlocks - Patricia A. De Martino
JADE - Apparel and accessories - Betty Dain Creations Inc.
JADE - Brushes–hair - Fox Marketing Group, Inc.

☆ = Now out of production

JADE - Brushes–paint - Corona Brushes Inc.
JADE - Detergents - Malco Products, Inc.
JADE - Dishes–china - Waterford Wedgwood USA, Inc.
JADE - Eyeglasses - Art-Craft Optical Co.
JADE - Nail care products - Major International Inc.
JADE - Recording label - All Star Promotions
JADE - Rice - US Foodservice
JADE - Tableware–china - Villeroy and Boch Tableware Ltd.
JADE - Tape–adhesive - Jade Industries Inc.
JADE - Wallcovering - Wall Trends, Inc.
JADE - Wallpaper - Bayview Wallcoverings
JADE - Wallpaper - Capital Carousel Inc.
JADE - Wallpaper - Madison Wallcoverings
JADE - Wallpaper - Gloria Merrill Enterprises
JADE BEACH - Aquarium accessories - Kordon
JADE BEACH - Aquarium accessories - Novalek, Inc.
JADE BREEZES - Air freshener - Dial Corp.
JADE CERAMIC MID PLUS - Sporting goods ☆ - Gold Eagle/Arnold Palmer
JADE CHINA - Lamps - Kaadan Ltd.
JADE CHINESE HERBALS - Health care products - East Earth Herb Inc.
JADE EMPRESS - Vitamins and nutritional supplements - Ethical Nutrients
JADE FIRE - Sporting goods ☆ - Gold Eagle/Arnold Palmer
JADE-ITE - Glassware–household ☆ - Anchor Hocking Glass, Inc.
JADE MOUNTAIN - Flatware - Sysco Corp.
JADE OPALINE - Glassware–household ☆ - Fenton Art Glass Co.
JADE PALACE - Frozen foods - Minh Food Corp.
JADE PEARL - Glassware–household ☆ - Fenton Art Glass Co.
JADE PETAL - Pottery ☆ - Rubens Originals
JADE PHARMACY - Health care products - East Earth Herb Inc.
JADE-POLE - Antennas - Jade Products, Inc.
JADE QUEEN - Food products - Pacmarine Products Inc.
JADE SONG - Bedding–linen - Dan River Inc.
JADE TONIC - Health care products - East Earth Herb Inc.
JADE TREE - Furniture - Lane Upholstery (Venture Furniture Div.)
JADED - Hair care products - Cosmair Inc.
JADEE - Guitars ☆ - White Eagle Rawhide Manufacturing Co.
JADIS - Eyeglasses - Art-Craft Optical Co.
JADOR - Recording label - Goldband Recording Corp.
JADZIA DAX - Toys - Paramount Pictures Corp.
JAEGER - Apparel - Jaeger International
JAEGER - Apparel–men's - Hickey-Freeman Co. Inc.
JAEGER - Water purification systems - MP Pumps Inc.
JAEGER - Yarn - Susan Bates Inc.
JAEGER - Yarn - Knitting Fever Inc.
JAEGER VINEYARDS - Wines ☆ - Pellegrini Bros. Wines Inc.
JAEGERSBERG - Cheese ☆ - Webeco Foods Inc.
JAFA - Cookies ☆ - Dairy State Foods Inc.
JAFFA - Bedding–linen - Dan River Inc.
JAFFA - Beverages–alcohol - Juba Beverages Corp.
JAFFA GOLD - Juices - Source Atlantique
JAFFA JOY - Beverages - White Rock Products Corp.
JAFFELIN - Wines - Remy Martin Amerique Inc.
JAFFREY CORNER - Floor coverings - Tarkett, Inc.
JAFFRYS - Hair care products - Jaffrys Laboratories
JAFRA - Cosmetics - Jafra Cosmetics Inc.
JAFRA INTIMA - Panty hose - Jafra Cosmetics Inc.
JAG - Apparel and accessories - Jag Licensing LLC
JAG - Bathing suits - Deweese Inc.
JAG - Eyeglasses - Martin-Copeland Eyewear Corp.
JAG - Sunglasses - Sungold Enterprises Ltd.
JAG-STANG - Guitars - Fender Musical Instruments
JAG TAGS - Novelty items - Doc's Apothecary
JA'GEL - Hair care products - John Amico Expressive Hair Care Products
JAGERMEISTER - Beverages–alcohol - Sidney Frank Importing Co., Inc.
JAGGED ALLIANCE - Computer software - Sir-Tech Software, Inc.
JAGGED ALLIANCE-DEADLY GAMES - Computer software - Sir-Tech Software, Inc.
JAGGED EDGE - Apparel and accessories - Jagged Edge
JAGGED EDGE - Bicycles - Dynacraft Industries Inc.
JAGUAR - Archery equipment - Martin Archery Inc.
JAGUAR - Binoculars - Swift Instruments, Inc.
JAGUAR - Envelopes - Unisource Converting (Envelope Div.)
JAGUAR - Floor cleaning equipment - Etc. of Henderson, Inc.
JAGUAR - Floor coverings–carpet and rugs - Jade Industries Inc.
JAGUAR - Floor coverings–carpet and rugs - Patcraft Mills Inc.
JAGUAR - Flowers, plants, and seeds - Mangelsdorf Seed Co.

JAGUAR - Frames–eyeglass - Windsor Optical Inc.
JAGUAR - Glassware–household ☆ - Crisa Corp.
JAGUAR - Guitars - Fender Musical Instruments
JAGUAR - Health care products ☆ - Invacare Corp.
JAGUAR - Lawn mowers - Ransomes-Cushman-Ryan
JAGUAR - Lighters - Colibri Inc.
JAGUAR - Motor vehicles–automobiles - Jaguar Cars
JAGUAR - Scissors–hand-operated - J.A. Henckels Zwillingswerk Inc.
JAGUAR - Shoes - B. Levy & Son
JAGUAR - Tripods–photographic - Phoenix Corp. of America
JAGUAR - Video games - Atari Games Corp.
JAGUAR - Wallpaper - Cavalier Handprints Ltd.
JAGUAR - Wallpaper ☆ - Wallpaper Imports Inc.
JAGUAR - Watches - Bulova Corp.
JAGUAR 70 - Cigars ☆ - General Cigar Co., Inc.
JAGUAR JAVA - Coffee - R.A. Jackson Investment Co., Inc.
JAGUAR S - Fireworks - American Promotional Events, Inc.
JAGUNDA - Bird feeders - Droll Yankees, Inc.
JAHABOW - Suntan lotions - SunQuest Products
JAHARI - Recording label - Jazz Composer's Orchestra Association Inc.
JAHN BRACKET - Concrete products - Dayton Superior Corp.
JAHRHUNDERT - Beverages–malt - Merchant du Vin Corp.
JAI ALAI - Furniture ☆ - Tropitone Furniture Co. Inc.
JAI-LAI - Frames–eyeglass - May Optical Co. Inc.
JAI-TOSS - Toys - Biotech Corp.
JAILHOUSE CAVIAR - Food products - Jardine's Texas Foods
JAIME - Frames–eyeglass - U.S. Optical Frame Co.
J'AIME - Jewelry–precious - SKL Co. Inc.
JAIME - Terra cotta - N.S. Gustin Co.
JAIMS - Publisher's imprints - Japan-American Institute of Management Science
JAIPUIR - Frames–eyeglass - May Optical Co. Inc.
JAISEL - Apparel and accessories - Bee Flat Ltd.
JAJ - Recording label - J & J Musical Enterprises Ltd.
JAK 842 - Luggage - La Rue International, Inc.
JAK-KNIFE - Tools - Red Devil Inc.
JAK PAK - Backpacks - La Rue International, Inc.
JAK-PAK - Toys - Jak-Pak Inc.
JAKA - Hams ☆ - Jack Greenberg Inc.
JAKAL - Bicycles ☆ - Huffy Corp.
JAKARTA - Cigarettes - G.A. Georgopulo & Co. Inc.
JAKARTA - Floor coverings–carpet and rugs - Mohawk Carpet Corp.
JAKARTA - Floor coverings–carpet and rugs ☆ - Regal Rugs Inc.
JAKARTA - Floor coverings–carpet and rugs - World Carpets, Inc.
JAKARTA - Floor coverings–tile - Interface, Inc.
JAKARTA - Novelty items - Royal Cathay Trading Co.
JAKARTA - Spices and extracts - Texas Food Research, Inc.
JAKARTA CORN SILK - Cigarettes - G.A. Georgopulo & Co. Inc.
JAKARTA II - Fabrics - Interface, Inc.
JAKE - Ophthalmic goods ☆ - Luxottica
JAKE & AMOS - Fruit butters - Jake & Amos Co.
JAKE & CO. - Hosiery–men's - Paul Lavitt Mills, Inc.
JAKE & CO. - Men's and boys' underwear - Pico Manufacturing Sales Corp.
JAKE JOHNSON - Leather goods - Enger-Kress Co.
JAKE JR. - Apparel–children's - Pico Manufacturing Sales Corp.
JAKE O'S - Apparel and accessories - Oshman's Sporting Goods Inc.
JAKE ROCKWELL - Toys - Tonka Corp.
JAKE SISKO - Toys - Paramount Pictures Corp.
JAKE STUART - Shirts - Jake Stuart, Inc.
JAKE THE PLUMR - Tool boxes - Cross at the Green...Not in Between Enterprises
JAKE THE SNAKE - Novelty items ☆ - Titan Sports, Inc.
JAKELIN - Apparel–women's - Mehar International, Inc.
JAKELIN DESIGNS - Apparel–women's - Mehar International, Inc.
JAKELIN SPORT - Apparel–women's - Mehar International, Inc.
JAKE'S - Beverages–carbonated ☆ - Pepsi-Cola Co.
JAKE'S - Ice cream - Danken's Gourmet Ice Creams
JAKE'S ACHILLES HEELSAVERS - Orthopedic products - James P. Jacobson
JAKE'S COMB - Stationery ☆ - Scentex Inc.
JAKE'S DIET COLA - Beverages–carbonated - Pepsi-Cola Co.
JAKES JOKES - Joke cards - International Games
JAKE'S PIZZA - Pizzas–frozen - Jake's Pizza International Inc.
JAKKI COLOURS - Cosmetics - Jakki Colours
JAKOB - Wigs - International Hairgoods Inc.
JAKOB DEMMER - Wines - David Sherman Corp.
JAKOB WINTER - Musical instrument accessories - International Violin Co. Ltd.

☆ = Now out of production

JAKOB'S OLD WORLD - Meat products–canned - Oregon Chief Portland Provision Co.

JAKOSCOPE - Medical apparatus - Atlantis Surgical Inc.

JAKSON - Curtain rods - CHF Industries, Inc.

JAKSTRAP - Flashlight holders - Liston Concepts, Inc.

JAKTMATCH - Ammunition ☆ - Federal Cartridge Co.

JALAPEANUTS - Nuts–salted, roasted, cooked, or canned - Cajun Creole Products Inc.

JALAPENATA - Food products ☆ - Vlasic Foods Inc.

JALAPENIE WIENIES - Sausages - Elburn Market, Inc.

JALAPENO - Food products - Festin Foods

JALAPENO JEETERS - Food products - Sargento Cheese Co. Inc.

JALAPENO KETCHUP - Catsup - B-T Trading Co.

JALAPENO KETCHUP - Food products - Ingleby Farms, Inc.

JALAPENO SAM - Sauces - Unimark Group Inc.

JALEA DE JALAPENO - Jams and jellies - Ash Enterprises, Inc.

JALINC JEANS - Apparel and accessories - Terry B. Smith

JALOPY JUMP - Toys - Toymax Inc.

JALOPY JUNKER - Toys - Tonka Corp.

JALPA - Motor vehicles–automobiles ☆ - DaimlerChrysler

JALYN - Recording label - Jack Lynch Music Group

JALZINC - Siding–metal ☆ - WCI Steel Inc.

J.A.M. - Orthopedic products - Trebay Medical Corp.

JAM - Skin care products - Supre, Inc.

JAM-ALONG - Audio equipment - Power Technology

JAM AND JELLY FACTORY, THE - Jams and jellies - Rowena's Gourmet Foods Inc.

JAM BLOCK - Drums–musical instruments - LP Music Group

JAM FACTORY - Computer software - Dr. T's Music Software Inc.

JAM GYM. - T-shirts–men's - Jamnastics, Ltd.

JAM-IT - Apparel and accessories - Basketball USA, Inc.

JAM-IT - Sporting goods - Basketball Products International Inc.

JAM MAN - Audio equipment ☆ - Lexicon, Inc.

JAM ON THE RIVER - Musical instrument stores - Philadelphia Convention & Visitors Bureau

JAM PAC - Toys - Strombecker Corp.

JAM SESSION - Recording label ☆ - Ray Lawrence Ltd.

JAM SESSION - Video production - NBA Properties, Inc.

JAMA - Costumes - Rubie's Costume Co., Inc.

JAMACOLE - Giftware - James A. Cole Co. Inc.

JAMACOLOR - Plumbing fixtures–plastic - Jameco Industries, Inc.

JAMAICA - Boats - McKenzie Boat Manufacturing Co.

JAMAICA - Boats–motor ☆ - Bayliner Marine Corp.

JAMAICA - Cigars - Faber, Coe & Gregg Inc.

JAMAICA - Floor coverings–carpet and rugs ☆ - Regal Rugs Inc.

JAMAICA - Wallpaper ☆ - Winfield Design Associates, Inc.

JAMAICA - Window shades ☆ - Kenney Manufacturing Co.

JAMAICA BAY - Apparel–men's - Westbury Knitwear Co. Inc.

JAMAICA BAY - Dishes–china - Taylor, Smith & Taylor Co.

JAMAICA BEST BRAND - Jams and jellies - Jamaica Producers Marketing

JAMAICA CLUB - Rum - Black Prince Distillery, Inc.

JAMAICA COLA - Beverages–carbonated - Canada Dry Corp.

JAMAICA HELLFIRE - Food products - Rafal Spice Co.

JAMAICA JOE'S - Apparel - Jamaica Joe's Inc.

JAMAICA ME CRAZY - Beverages - Parrot Ice Drink Products of America, Inc.

JAMAICA MINTS - Candy - Nabisco Foods Group

JAMAICA MISTAKE - Salad dressings–bottled - Johnny's Enterprises Inc.

JAMAICA MOUNTAIN CHOICE - Coffee - Gillies Coffee Co.

JAMAICA RED - Wines - Bardenheier Wine Cellars

JAMAICA STYLE - Food products - Caribbean Food Delights

JAMAICA SUN - Floor coverings–carpet and rugs ☆ - Zenith Carpets

JAMAICAN - Bicycles ☆ - Bridgestone/Firestone, Inc.

JAMAICAN DIGESTI BREW - Herbal products - Twin Laboratories, Inc.

JAMAICAN GOLD LABEL - Cigars - Villco Imports Inc.

JAMAICAN JERK - Seasonings - Helen's Tropical Exotics Inc.

JAMAICAN JERK SPICE - Spices and extracts - Cinnabar Specialty Foods, Inc./Neera's Products

JAMAICAN LIME - Spices and extracts - Finest Kind Spices

JAMAICAN ME CRAZY - Sweatshirts - Ca' D'zan International, Inc.

JAMAICAN PEBBLE - Floor coverings ☆ - Congoleum Corp.

JAMAICAN PUNCH - Fruit drinks–bottled or canned ☆ - Everfresh Beverages, Inc.

JAMAICAN RED LABEL - Cigars - Villco Imports Inc.

JAMAICAN SHINE - Hair care products - Garcoa Labs/Vitamin Classics

JAMAICAN SPA DIET - Health care products - Futurebiotics

JAMAICAN STYLE DIRTY RICE MIX - Spices and extracts - Cinnabar Specialty Foods, Inc./Neera's Products

JAMAICAN WATERFALL - Housewares ☆ - Avon Products, Inc.

JAMAK FABRICATION, INC. - Motor vehicle parts and accessories - JMK International, Inc.

JAMAL - Doll - Olmec Toys, Inc.

JAMAL - Dolls - Mattel, Inc.

JAMAR - Medical apparatus - Sammons Preston

JAMAR - Nail care products ☆ - Senoret Chemical Co.

JAMARC - Recording label - Pandisc Records

JAMB-JACK - Screws - Pease Industries, Inc.

JAMB-UP - Adhesives and sealants ☆ - Macklanburg-Duncan Co.

JAMBA - Computer software - Aimtech Corp.

JAMBALAYA - Snack foods - Dayton Nut Specialties, Inc.

JAMBALAYA JACKPOT - Game machines - Sigma Game Inc.

JAMBO AFRICA - Shoes - Maryesta Carr International

JAMBOREE - Bicycles - Columbia Manufacturing Inc.

JAMBOREE - Dinnerware–glass - Nikko Ceramics Inc.

JAMBOREE - Fabrics - Dan River Inc.

JAMBOREE - Floor coverings–carpet and rugs - Cabin Crafts Carpets

JAMBOREE - Food products ☆ - Golden Valley Microwave Foods, Inc.

JAMBOREE - Footwear–athletic - New Balance Athletic Shoe, Inc.

JAMBOREE - Guitars - International Music Corp.

JAMBOREE - Jams and jellies - Nestle USA

JAMBOREE - Motor vehicles–motor homes ☆ - Fleetwood Enterprises, Inc.

JAMBOREE - Rugs - Nourison

JAMBOREE RALLYE - Motor vehicles–motor homes - Fleetwood Enterprises, Inc.

JAMBOREE SEARCHER - Motor vehicles–motor homes - Fleetwood Enterprises, Inc.

JAMBOREE USA - Apparel and accessories - Wheeling Entertainment Corp.

JAMBROS - Recording label - Third Story Recording Inc.

JAMBSEAL - Weather stripping - Gossen Corp.

JAMCO - Cod-liver oil - Jamco Inc.

JAMCO - Housewares - Trepte Wire and Metal Works

JAMECOLOR - Plumbing fixtures–metal - Jameco Industries, Inc.

JAMEE - Motor vehicles - Skyline Corp.

JAMERCO - Tools–hand-operated - Jamerco, Inc.

JAMES - Bicycles ☆ - Roadmaster Corp.

JAMES - Coffee - Peter James Coffee Ltd.

JAMES - Motor vehicle parts and accessories - Rivera Engineering, Inc.

JAMES - Paints ☆ - Crescent Bronze Powder

JAMES ALEXANDER - Pharmaceutical preparations - James Alexander Inc.

JAMES B. FAIRCHILD - Neckties - Loring-Fairchild Ltd.

JAMES BOND 007 - Games - Avalon Hill Game Co.

JAMES BOND JR. - Toys and electronics - Danjaq, Inc.

JAMES BONE THE DOG - Puppets - Kashmier Toys Corp.

JAMES BRIGHT - Photographic equipment - James Bright Backgrounds

JAMES COOK - Boats - Glen-L Marine Designs

JAMES CREEK WINERY - Wines - Newlan Vineyards & Winery Inc.

JAMES DARIO - Footwear - Leatherwork Manufacturing Co. Inc.

JAMES DEAN - Postcards ☆ - Classico San Francisco Inc.

JAMES DISCOVERS MATH - Computer software - Broderbund Software, Inc.

JAMES FOXE - Whiskey - Sazerac Co. Inc.

JAMES HALBERT - Apparel - Quetzal Enterprises, Inc.

JAMES HAMILTON INT'L WILDLIFE - Puzzles - Kingdom Puzzles

JAMES MARTIN INSIGHT - Recording label - National Education Training Group, Inc.

JAMES MICHAEL DESIGNS - Furniture–wood - CTS Products, Inc.

JAMES PAGE BREWING CO. - Apparel and accessories - James Page Brewing Co., LLC

JAMES PAPALIA - Clocks - James Papalia Studios

JAMES RIVER - Floor coverings - Applied Radiant Energy Corp.

JAMES RIVER - Meat products–cured - Smithfield Ham Products Co. Inc.

JAMES RIVER - Paper products, plastic wrap, food containers, etc. - James River Corp.

JAMES RIVER - Wallpaper - Payne Fabrics

JAMES RIVER BLENDS COMPOST - Compost - Environmental Solutions, Inc.

JAMES RIVER COLLECTION - Furniture - Lane Co. Inc.

JAMES RIVER COLLECTION, THE - Fabrics - Payne Fabrics

JAMES RIVER WINERY - Wines - La Abra Farm & Winery Inc.

JAMES ROBINSON - Flatware - James Robinson Inc.

JAMES SADLER & SONS - Tea kettles–nonelectric - Cuthbertson Imports Inc.

JAMES SCOTT - Sporting goods - Red Ball Corp.

JAMES SEEMAN STUDIOS - Wallpaper - Borden, Inc.

JAMES SEEMAN STUDIOS - Wallpaper - Sunwall of America

☆ = Now out of production

JAMES VICKS - Flowers, plants, and seeds ☆ - W. Atlee Burpee and Co.

JAMES WHITEHEAD OF LONDON - Apparel—men's - Eisenberg International Corp.

JAMESLEE - Luggage, travel accessories, etc. - Jameslee Corp.

JAMESON - Thermostats - Jameson Home Products Inc.

JAMESON - Whiskey - Joseph E. Seagram & Sons, Inc.

JAMESON 1780 SPECIAL RESERVE - Whiskey - Joseph E. Seagram & Sons, Inc.

JAMESON PARK BY HAGGAR - Apparel and accessories ☆ - Haggar Corp.

JAMESON PREMIUM - Whiskey - Joseph E. Seagram & Sons, Inc.

JAMESTOWN - Barometers - Airguide Instrument Co.

JAMESTOWN - Bathroom accessories - Franklin Brass Manufacturing Co.

JAMESTOWN - Cabinets - Del Mar Cabinets

JAMESTOWN - Cabinets ☆ - Marsh Furniture Co.

JAMESTOWN - Cooking equipment—household ☆ - Mirro Corp.

JAMESTOWN - Flatware - Reed and Barton Corp.

JAMESTOWN - Flatware - Royal Silver Manufacturing Co. Inc.

JAMESTOWN - Floor coverings ☆ - Bruce Hardwood Floors

JAMESTOWN - Floor coverings—carpet and rugs ☆ - Atlas Carpet Mills Inc.

JAMESTOWN - Floor coverings—carpet and rugs ☆ - Columbus Mills, Inc.

JAMESTOWN - Floor coverings—carpet and rugs ☆ - S and S Mills Inc.

JAMESTOWN - Frames—eyeglass - U.S. Optical Frame Co.

JAMESTOWN - Furniture - Dinaire Corp.

JAMESTOWN - Furniture ☆ - Hammary Furniture Co. Inc.

JAMESTOWN - Glass products - Pilgrim Glass Corp.

JAMESTOWN - Hardware - Harloc, Inc.

JAMESTOWN - Lamps ☆ - Lamplight Farms, Inc.

JAMESTOWN - Lounge furniture - Jamestown Lounge Co.

JAMESTOWN - Paper - Union Camp Corp. (Fine Paper Division)

JAMESTOWN - Siding—insulating - Reynolds Metals Co.

JAMESTOWN - Tablecloths - Cascade Fibers Co.

JAMESTOWN - Tea kettles—nonelectric ☆ - Revere Ware Corp.

JAMESTOWN - Toilets—enameled - Kohler Co.

JAMESTOWN-AMERICAN - Furniture - Jamestown Sterling

JAMESTOWN BRICK - Floor coverings - Congoleum Corp.

JAMESTOWN COLONY - Furniture - Henkel-Harris Co.

JAMESTOWN GOLD - Glassware—household - Mikasa Licensing, Inc.

JAMESTOWN INN - House furnishings ☆ - Lea Industries Inc.

JAMESTOWN LANDING - Furniture ☆ - Brooks Furniture Manufacturing Inc.

JAMESTOWN PLANTATION - House furnishings ☆ - Lea Industries Inc.

JAMESTOWN TRADITIONALS - Wallpaper ☆ - Imperial Wallcoverings, Inc.

JAMESTOWNE FIRESIDES - Fireplace equipment - Lewis Hyman, Inc.

JAMESTOWNE SHELVING - Shelving units—wood - Lewis Hyman, Inc.

JAMESWAY - Agricultural machinery - J-Star Industries, Inc.

JAMI - Soups—mixes - Ginsberg's

JA'MI INTERNATIONAL - Hair care products - Hair Performers

JAMIE - Belts - Campaign Belts

JAMIE - Belts—apparel - Norman M. Morris Corp.

JAMIE - Dolls - Uneeda Doll Co., Inc.

JAMIE - Floor coverings—carpet and rugs ☆ - Regal Rugs Inc.

JAMIE - Recording label - Universal Record

JAMIE - Yarn - Lion Brand Yarn Co.

JAMIE '08 - Beverages—alcohol - Sunbelt Beverage Corp.

JAMIE BABY - Yarn - Lion Brand Yarn Co.

JAMIE BONUS BUNDLE - Yarn - Lion Brand Yarn Co.

JAMIE 4 KIDS - Yarn - Lion Brand Yarn Co.

JAMIE 4 PLY - Yarn - Lion Brand Yarn Co.

JAMIE LEIGH - Underwear and nightwear - Sylray Inc.

JAMIE ON SWING - Toys—stuffed - Russ Berrie and Co., Inc.

JAMIE SCOTT - Apparel and accessories - Jamie Scott, Inc.

JAMIES - Tights—stockings ☆ - Easton International

JAMIN HOPJES - Candy - Murray-Allen International Inc.

JAMINATOR - Toys—musical - Worlds of Wonder

JAMIS - Bicycles - American Cycle Group

JAMIT - Food products - Dach Ranch

JAMMA - Footwear—athletic - Puma Inc.

JAMMER - Bicycles ☆ - Roadmaster Corp.

JAMMER - Computer software - Sound Logic, Ltd.

JAMMER - Musical instruments - VMI Industries

JAMMER - Skateboards - Santa Cruz Skateboards

JAMMER - Sporting goods - Bell Sports Corp.

JAMMER - Toys - Wham-O Manufacturing Co.

JAMMERANG - Toys - Sandeen, Inc.

JAMMERS - Binders ☆ - Union Camp Corp. (Fine Paper Division)

JAMMERS - Cookies - Auburn Farms, Inc.

JAMMERS - Toys—stuffed ☆ - Gund, Inc.

JAMMERZ - Jewelry - Jammerz

JAMMIE TIME - Toys—stuffed - Jammie Time

JAMMIES IN A JAR - Apparel and accessories - Access Wear Plus, Inc.

JAMMIN - Kites - Hi-Flier Manufacturing Co.

JAMMIN - Toys—models ☆ - Estes Industries

JAMMIN' 360 BACKFLIP - Toys - Hasbro, Inc.

JAMMIN' GIANT - Toy action figures - Tonka Corp.

JAMMIN' JOEY - Toys - Mattel, Inc.

JAMMIN' JOHNS - Toilet seats - Jammin' Johns

JAMMIN' JUMPERS - Candy - Topps Co., Inc.

JAMMIN' MUSICAL LEARNING - Recording label - Rock 'N Learn Inc.

JAMMIT - Computer software - GTE Vantage Inc.

JAM'N - Cases—musical instrument - TKL Products Corp.

JAM'N - Exercising equipment - Jam'n Fitness Corp.

JAMO - Audio equipment - Jamo Hi-Fi USA Inc.

JAMOCA - Dinnerware—glass - Franciscan by Johnson Brothers, USA, Inc.

JAMPACKER - Office supplies ☆ - JM Co.

JAMS - Bathing suits - Surf Line Hawaii, Ltd.

JAMS - Chewing gum ☆ - Amurol Confections Co.

JAMS WORLD - Apparel and accessories - Surf Line Hawaii, Ltd.

JAMSEY - Jewelry - JamSey & Co. Inc.

JAMSTAND - Toy radios - Diversified Specialists, Inc.

JAMTOWN - Games - John M. Hayden

JAMTRAX - Books—blank - Music Sales Corp.

JAMY - Juvenile product - Jamy Inc.

JAN - Projector - International Cinema Equipment Co.

JAN BELL PREMIERE DIAMOND COLLECTION - Jewelry - Jan Bell Marketing Inc.

JAN BRIGGS - Apparel—children's - Jan Briggs, Inc.

JAN FREELAND FOR BANDANNA - Toys ☆ - Bandanna

JAN HOLZMEISTER - Food products - Jay Hoyt Bakery (Sonoma Valley Cheesecake)

JAN KULIK - Musical instruments - Ideal Musical Merchandise Co.

JAN-MAR - Caps—baseball ☆ - Innovo Inc.

JAN MICHAELS - Jewelry - Jan Michaels Inc.

JAN SHACKELFORD ORIGINALS - Dolls - Jan Shackelford Originals Inc.

JAN STUART - Deodorants—personal - Jan Stuart Co.

JAN TANA - Skin care products - Jan Tana, Inc.

JAN-U-WINE - Food products - Beatrice Cos. Inc.

JANA - Recording label - Landmark Communications Group

JANACA VINEYARDS - Wines ☆ - Thomas Kruse Winery

JANA'S CLASSICS - Ready-to-bake cookie dough - Jana's Classic Cookies

JANCO - Food products - Janney-Marshall Co.

JANCO - Greenhouses, sunrooms - Janco Greenhouses

JANCYN - Plumbing-line cleaner - Jancyn Manufacturing Corp.

JANCYN MAIN LINE - Cleaner - Jancyn Manufacturing Corp.

JANDEE'S WAFFLES - Waffles—frozen - Jandee's Co., Inc.

J&H*CERT - Computer software - Johnson & Higgins

J&M - Motorcycle parts and accessories - J & M Corp.

JANDORF - Metals - ORRCO, Inc.

J&T - Computer software - J & T Associates, Inc.

J&W - Food products - J & W Ford, Inc.

JANDY - Valves—intake - Jandy Industries, Inc.

JANE - Dolls ☆ - Effanbee Doll Corp.

JANE - Perfumes - Sassaby Inc.

JANE - Pet products - Interwood Corp.

JANE & GOLDIE - Snack foods - Jane & Goldie Co., Inc.

+JANE +ASHLEY - Apparel—women's - Jeetish Imports Inc.

JANE BARRY - Leather - A & A Sales

JANE BLUSHING CHEEKS - Cosmetics - Sassaby Inc.

JANE BOOKE - Apparel—women's - Jane Booke

JANE BY SASSABY - Perfumes - Sassaby Inc.

JANE COLBY - Apparel—women's - Jane Colby Inc.

JANE CORNELL - Cosmetic and nail brushes - Jane Cornell Inc.

JANE CORNELL NAIL CENTER - Nail care products - Jane Cornell Inc.

JANE CROSS - Knit goods, scarves, and neckwear - Norman Stephen Enterprise Ltd.

JANE DOE - Sunglasses - Mountain Shades

JANE EYRE - Glass—leaded - Seneca Glass Co.

JANE LOGAN - Ice cream - Leehi Dally Dairies

JANE OIL FREE FOUNDATION - Cosmetics - Sassaby Inc.

JANE PARKER - Food products - Great Atlantic & Pacific Tea Co., Inc.

JANE PHELAN - Giftware - Jane Phelan

JANE STEWART - Candy - Salem's Old Fashioned Candies Inc.

JANE SUTTELL - Apparel and accessories - Jane Suttell

JANE YOO WEARABLE ART - Leather goods - Jane Yoo Wearable Art, Inc.

☆ = Now out of production

JANEIL - See **FUJITSU-GENERAL**
JANEL - Diamond and gold jewelry - Janel Manufacturing Co.
JANEL - Toys - Tonka Corp.
JANELL - Flowers, plants, and seeds - George W. Park Seed Co., Inc.
JANELL - Recording label - Tiki Enterprises Inc.
JANELLE MIGNON - Skin care products - Janelle Mignon Cosmetics
JANES - Seafood products–fresh or frozen - Flag/Westbay Seafood Brokers
JANE'S COMBAT STICK - Computer peripheral equipment - Joystick Technologies (CH Products Division)
JANE'S KRAZY - Salt - Haddon House Food Products Inc.
JANE'S KRAZY SEASONINGS - Seasonings - Tidelands Sales Co. Inc.
JANE'S NEW CREATIONS - Appliques - Jane P. Oliver
JANET - Dolls - Mattel, Inc.
JANET - Watches ☆ - Helbros International
JANET - Yarn ☆ - William Unger & Co. Inc.
JANET G. - Lamps - Janet G., Inc.
JANET GREESON'S THE POWER OF ONENESS TO LOSE WEIGHT AND BE LOVED FOR WHO I AM - Recording label - Janet Greeson
JANET LEE - Food products - Albertson's Inc.
JANET ROBSON - Figurines ☆ - Goebel of North America
JANET SARTIN SKIN VEIL - Cosmetics - Janet Sartin Inc.
JANET ZWEIG - Greeting cards - Enthusiastic Enterprises
JANET'S - Food products ☆ - Mrs. Giles Country Kitchens Inc.
JANETTI - Accordions - N.H.F. Musical Merchandise Corp.
JANEX - Toys - Janex Corp.
JANG STENG MEE MIXED RICE - Rice - Haitai America, Inc.
JANGLE BONES - Games - On the Ball
JANGLES - Toys–stuffed - Fun World Inc.
JANGLING BONES - Novelty items - Paper Magic Group Inc.
JANI - Nail care products - Jani & Sweet Lady Jane
JANICE - Glassware–household - ACC
JANIERO - Floor coverings - Congoleum Corp.
JANIMINE - Pharmaceutical preparations - Abbott Laboratories
JANINA - Floor coverings - Mannington Resilient Floors
JANINE - Floor coverings–carpet and rugs ☆ - Masland Corp.
JANINE COLETTE - Confections - Farley Candy Co.
JANIS - Audio equipment - John Marovskis Audio Systems
JANITOR IN A DRUM - Cleaning preparations - Dowbrands L.P.
JANITORS DEPOT - Cleaning preparations - Rug Doctor, L.P.
JANITORS DEPOT - Vacuum cleaners and accessories - Rug Doctor
JANLIBO - Beverages - Jianlibao America Ltd.
JANLYNN - Hobby kits - Janlynn Corp.
JANNCO - Automotive parts - J & N Auto Electric, Inc.
JANNEAU - Wines - Seagram's Chateau & Estate Wines Co.
JANNELL - Dolls - Lovee Doll and Toy Co. Inc.
JAN'S - Dog food - Wow-Bow Distributors Ltd.
JANS MOUNTAIN OUTFITTERS - Apparel and accessories - Jan's Ltd.
JANSPORT - Backpacks - Jansport Apparel Corp.
JANSPORT - Sports apparel, backpack equipments and outdoor gear - Jansport Inc.
JANSSEN - Pianos ☆ - Walter Piano Co.
JANTE - Shoes - Chi-Shun Associates
JANTZEN - Bathing suits - Jantzen Inc.
JANTZEN - Sporting goods - Schmid Laboratories
JANTZEN 100 - Apparel–men's ☆ - Jantzen Inc.
JANTZEN CLASSICS - Apparel–women's - Jantzen Inc.
JANTZEN GIRLS - Bathing suits - Jantzen Inc.
JANTZEN GOLD - Apparel and accessories ☆ - Jantzen Inc.
JANTZEN JRS. - Apparel and accessories ☆ - Jantzen Inc.
JANTZEN LIMITED - Apparel–men's ☆ - Jantzen Inc.
JANTZEN OPEN - Apparel–men's ☆ - Jantzen Inc.
JANTZEN PETITES - Apparel–women's - Jantzen Inc.
JANTZEN WOMEN'S - Bathing suits - Jantzen Inc.
JANUS - Awards, plaques and medals - PortionPac Chemical Corp.
JANUS - Blood derivatives - Frederick Blattner
JANUS - Computers - Intermec Corp.
JANUS - Erasers - Faber-Castell Corp.
JANUS - Fabrics - Superior Shade & Blind Co. Inc.
JANUS - Hardware - Pinpoint Fiberoptics Limited
JANUS - Publisher's imprints - Paramount Publishers
JANUS - Women's apparel - Interco Inc.
JANUS LIBRARY - Publisher's imprints - Abaris Books Inc.
JAO - Sewing machines–household - JAO Enterprises Inc.
J.A.P. - Recording label - Creav Inc. USA
JAPAN - Dinnerware–glass - Arlen China Co.
JAPAN COLLECTIBLES - Wallpaper ☆ - Maya Romanoff Corp.

JAPAN LIFE'S - Apparel and accessories - Genki USA
JAPANESE GARDEN - Clocks - General Time Corp. (Westclox/Seth Thomas Div.)
JAPANESE RICE PAPERS - Wallpaper - Wallpaper Imports Inc.
JAPANESE SHARK CARTILAGE POWDER - Vitamins and nutritional supplements - Now Foods Corp.
JAPANESE SILKY STRINGS - Wallpaper ☆ - Wallpaper Imports Inc.
JAPANESE WEEKEND - Apparel–women's - Japanese Weekend, Inc.
JAPIDEMIC - Insecticides - Fairfax Biological Laboratory
JAPONAIS - Candy bars ☆ - Brocks Candy Co.
JAPONAISE - Chocolate candy ☆ - Bahlsen Inc.
JAPONES - Chili peppers–powdered ☆ - Frieda's, Inc.
JAPONESQUE - Cosmetics - Japonesque
JAPONEX - Insecticides ☆ - Hydroponic Chemical Co. Inc.
JAPRO - Bookmarks - Auromere Inc.
JAR GAME/CHAOS, THE - Computer software ☆ - Milliken Publishing Co. (Computer Software Div.)
JAR LIGHTS - Candy - Squire Boone Caverns, Inc.
JAR, THE - Tools–garden - Sprout-Ease Co.
JARA - Toys - Saban Entertainment, Inc.
JARAR WINDOW - Windows - Jarar Window Systems, Inc.
JARAR WINDOW SYSTEMS - Windows - Jarar Window Systems, Inc.
JARDE - Musical instruments - Ardsley Musical Instrument Co.
JARDEN - Glassware–household - Lancaster Colony Corp.
JARDIN - Dinnerware–glass - Cyclamen Studio
JARDIN - Floor coverings–carpet and rugs ☆ - Regal Rugs Inc.
JARDIN - Floor coverings–carpet and rugs ☆ - Trans-Ocean Import Co. Inc.
JARDIN D'AMOUR - Health care products - Max Factor & Co.
JARDIN EN FLEUR - Wallpaper - Pickhardt & Siebert USA Inc.
JARDINE - Motor vehicle parts and accessories - Summit Industries, Inc.
JARDINE - Motorcycle and all-terrain-vehicle exhaust systems, etc. - Inter-Am Manufacturing Inc.
JARDINE - Tea kettles–nonelectric ☆ - National Housewares
JARDINIERE - Dinnerware–glass - Nikko Ceramics Inc.
JARDINIERE - Dishes–china ☆ - Gorham Inc.
JARDINIERE GREEN - Dishes–china - Waterford Wedgewood USA, Inc.
JARDINIERE YELLOW - Dishes–china - Waterford Wedgewood USA, Inc.
JARDINS DE BAGATELLE - Perfumes - Guerlain Inc.
JARDINS FRANCAIS - Tableware–china - Villeroy and Boch Tableware Ltd.
JARET - Cough drops ☆ - Jaret Specialties Inc.
JARETTA - Jewelry - Fashion Pride Inc.
JARGAR - Musical instrument accessories - Ideal Musical Merchandise Co.
JARGAR - Musical instrument accessories - International Violin Co. Ltd.
JARIT DETACH - Medical apparatus - J. Jamner Surgical Instruments, Inc.
JARIT VANGUARD - Surgical instruments - J. Jamner Surgical Instruments, Inc.
JARLSBERG - Cheese - Norseland Foods Inc.
JARMAIN - Floor coverings–carpet and rugs ☆ - Regal Rugs Inc.
JARMAN - Shoes ☆ - Jarman Shoe Co.
JARRAY - Apparel and accessories - Jarray Sportswear, Inc.
JARRET - Ophthalmic goods - Rozin Optical Export Corp.
JARRETT - Post hole diggers–hand-operated - Tradewinds Inc.
JARRITOS - Beverages - Jarritos, Inc.
JARRON - Vegetables–dried - Kelley Bean Co., Inc.
JARTS - Outdoor game - Tonka Corp.
JARU - Frames–picture - Harris Industries
JARVES - Urinals–enameled - Kohler Co.
JARVIE-FLINT - Enamels - Farwest Paint Manufacturing Co. Inc.
JARVIK 2000 - Medical apparatus - Robert Jarvik
JARVIS - Wines - Jarvis Vineyards
JARVIS & JARVIS - Casters - Young's
JARVIS-PEMCO - Wheels - Standex International Corp.
JARZEBIAK - Vodka - Adamba Imports International Inc.
JAS - Hair care products - Jean Alexander Cosmetics, Inc.
JAS. LAURENT - Apparel and accessories - Alexander Campbell, Inc.
JAS-Z GOURMET! - Beverages - Jas It Up, Ltd.
JASBA-MOSAIK - Tiles–ceramic - Amsterdam Corp.
JASBAG - Bags - Sander Designs
JASCO - Electronic equipment - Jasco Products Co. Inc.
JASCO - Fabrics - Jasco Fabrics, Inc.
JASCO - Paint removers - JASCO Chemical Corp.
JASK - Computer software - Aegis, L.P.
JASMA - Incense - Excelsior Incense Works
JASMILON - Teas - Lalith D. Paranavitana
JASMIN - Floor coverings–carpet and rugs ☆ - Trans-Ocean Import Co. Inc.
JASMIN - Footwear–women's - Jasmine Ltd.

☆ = Now out of production

JASMIN - Glassware–household - H. Wittur & Co.

JASMIN DE PROVENCE - Soap - Bourjois Ltd.

JASMIN DE PROVENCE - Soap - Crabtree & Evelyn, Ltd.

JASMIN FROSTED - Glassware–household ☆ - Villeroy and Boch Tableware Ltd.

JASMIN KIDS - Shoes - Jasmine Ltd.

JASMINE - Candlesticks ☆ - Lenox Crystal, Inc.

JASMINE - Cigarettes - Eve Holdings Inc.

JASMINE - Floor coverings–carpet and rugs - Couristan Inc.

JASMINE - Frames–eyeglass - U.S. Optical Frame Co.

JASMINE - Golfing equipment - Knight Golf, Inc.

JASMINE - Guitars - Kaman Music Corp.

JASMINE - Prophylactics - Custom Service International, Inc.

JASMINE - Rings–jewelry ☆ - Artcarved Inc.

JASMINE - Thread - Threads USA Div.

JASMINE - Toys - Tonka Corp.

JASMINE - Wallpaper - Wall Fabrics Inc.

JASMINE - Yarn - Joseph Galler Inc.

JASON - Binoculars - Bausch & Lomb Inc.

JASON - Bread crumbs - Jason Dairy Products Co. Inc.

JASON - Dollies, musical saws - Box Maker

JASON - Frames–eyeglass - U.S. Optical Frame Co.

JASON - Hydrotherapy equipment - Jason International, Inc.

JASON & SON - Snack foods - Jason & Son

JASON BROOKS - Apparel–children's - Farah Inc.

JASON CHARLES - Neckties ☆ - Charles S. Gelles & Son

JASON FLAV - Food products - Jason Dairy Products Co. Inc.

JASON GOLDEN NATURALS - Deodorants–personal ☆ - Jason Natural Products, Inc.

JASON KOLE - Coats–women's - Herman Kay Co., Inc.

JASON MATTHEWS - Shirts - Shelburne Shirt Co. Inc.

JASON MAXWELL - Apparel and accessories - Regent International Corp.

JASON NATURAL - Cosmetics - Jason Natural Products, Inc.

JASON REESE - Guitars - Shane Music Products

JASON WINTER - Teas - Genki USA

JASPE - Wallpaper - Maya Romanoff Corp.

JASPER - Auto supply stores - Jasper Engine & Transmission Exchange

JASPER - Cereal - Jasper Foods, Inc.

JASPER - Furniture - Jasper Cabinet Co.

JASPER - Sandals - Footwear International Corp.

JASPER - Toys ☆ - Volcano Woodworks

JASPER - Wallpaper - Capital Carousel Inc.

JASPER CLASSICS - Apparel and accessories ☆ - Jasper Textiles Inc.

JASPER MARINE - Engines–marine - Jasper Engine & Transmission Exchange

JASPER TOMKINS - Greeting cards - Green Tiger Press

JASPER WARE - Vases–stone - Waterford Wedgewood USA, Inc.

JASPERS - Apparel and accessories - Manhattan College

JASPER'S BISCUIT SHOPPES - Sausages - Jasper's Biscuit Shoppes, Inc.

JASPERS SUGAR BUSH - Syrup - Jaspers Sugar Bush

JASPRE SPORT - Children's clothing - Miniworld, Inc.

JASS - Recording label - Stash Records Inc.

JASSE - Cosmetics - Jasse Cosmetics

JASSIE JONES - Apparel and accessories - Wongas International Textiles, Ltd.

JASVINE - Fruits and vegetables - Jasmine Vineyards, Inc.

JATAMANSI - Hair care products ☆ - Washington Homeopathic Products

JATO - Cleaning preparations–household - L & F Consumer Products

JATO - Recording label - TMC Productions

JAUME SERRA CAVA - Wines - Leonard Kreusch Inc.

JAUME SERRA ESTATES - Wines - Leonard Kreusch Inc.

JAUNTY - Apparel–women's - Bi-Flex International

JAUS - Food products ☆ - Norganic Foods USA Inc.

JAVA - Cigars - G.W. Van Slyke & Horton

JAVA - Computer software - Sun Microsystems, Inc.

JAVA - Cookies ☆ - Bahlsen Inc.

JAVA - Flowers, plants, and seeds - Panamerican Seed

JAVA - Food products - Mitsubishi International Corp.

JAVA - Housewares - Royal Cathay Trading Co.

JAVA - Lighting fixtures - Swivelier Co. Inc.

JAVA - Pet products - Rolf C. Hagen (USA) Corp.

JAVA - Toiletries - Bourjois Inc.

JAVA BLU - Apparel and accessories - Salmor Import Export Corp.

JAVA BREAK - Vending machines - Java Break, Inc.

JAVA BREW - Coffee - Rock N Java Cafe, Inc.

JAVA CHILLER - Beverages–carbonated - Autocrat, Inc.

JAVA CITY ROASTERS OF FINE COFFEES - Glassware–household - Java City

JAVA COAST - Coffee - I Can't Believe It's Yogurt Inc.

JAVA COAST FINE COFFEES - Coffee - Brice Foods, Inc.

JAVA COOLERS - Coffee - Millstone Coffee, Inc.

JAVA DAVE'S - Coffee - Java Dave's, Inc.

JAVA DOG - Backpacks - Java Dog

JAVA EXPRESS - Coffee makers–electric - Interstate Coffee Services

JAVA JACKET - Paper products - Java Jacket

JAVA JAZZ - Coffee - Coffee Connection, Inc.

JAVA JOE'S - Coffee - Java Joe's Coffee Co. Inc.

JAVA JOLT - Jewelry - C.A. Daniels & Co.

JAVA JONES - Coffee - Java Jones, Inc.

JAVA KEY - Dishes–china - Taylor, Smith & Taylor Co.

JAVA LAVA - Candy - Lynette Cline

JAVA MAN FRESH ROASTED BEANS - Coffee - Joseph M. Seither

JAVA NOIR - Coffee - Coffee People Inc.

JAVA SHAKE - Coffee - Millstone Coffee, Inc.

JAVA-SUN COFFEE ROASTERS - Coffee - Java Sun Coffee Roasters, Inc.

JAVA SUPREMO WAWA ESPRESSO LATTE CAPPUCCINO - Coffee - Wild Goose Holding Co., Inc.

JAVA TRADING CO. - Coffee - Remark Corp.

JAVA TRIM - Beverages - Omnitrition International, Inc.

JAVAHHCCINO! - Coffee - Bruegger's Corp.

JAVAJOLT - Coffee - Ceb of Charlotte, Inc.

JAVALANCHE - Beverages - Caravali Coffees, Inc.

JAVAONE - Trade Associations - Sun Microsystems, Inc.

JAVELAN - Software - Barrister Information Systems Corp.

JAVELIN - Bicycles - King Cycles, Inc.

JAVELIN - Bicycles - Roadmaster Corp.

JAVELIN - Boats - McKenzie Boat Manufacturing Co.

JAVELIN - Computer software - Digital Technology International

JAVELIN - Cranes - Egripment USA, Inc.

JAVELIN - Floor coverings–carpet and rugs - Trend Carpet

JAVELIN - Fruits and vegetables - Pacific Earth Resources, Ltd.

JAVELIN - Motor vehicles ☆ - DaimlerChrysler

JAVELIN - Motors–outboard - Outboard Marine Corp.

JAVELIN - Paper–writing - Champion International Corp.

JAVELIN - Ships–sailing vessels - Javelin Association

JAVELIN - Toys–models ☆ - Estes Industries

JAVELIN - Watches - Timex Corp.

JAVELIN AMX - Motor vehicles ☆ - DaimlerChrysler

JAVELIN JUNIOR COMP - Sporting goods ☆ - Outboard Marine Corp.

JAVELIN MARK III - Lawn mowers ☆ - Homelite, Inc.

JAVELIN STAR-FLITE - Sporting goods ☆ - Outboard Marine Corp.

JAVELIN WEEKENDER - Sporting goods ☆ - Outboard Marine Corp.

JAVIER'S GOURMET MEXICANO - Sauces - Gush Inc.

JAVOLIS - Apparel and accessories - Michelle Chiou

JAW - Jewelry - Jarnow Corp.

JAW - Lures, nets, etc. - J & W Net Co. Inc.

JAW - Thread ☆ - Perfect Thread Co. Inc.

JAW BONE - Sporting goods ☆ - Powell Skateboards

JAW BONE JERKY - Meat products–dried - Jeanne Golden Scott

JAW BREAKER - Computer software ☆ - Sierra On-Line, Inc.

JAW BREAKERS - Candy - Ferrara Pan Candy Co., Inc.

JAW-FULS - Chewing gum - Leaf, Inc.

JAW JAMMERS - Candy ☆ - Van Melle Inc.

JAWA - Ophthalmic goods - Totes-Isotoner Corp.

JAWA CZ125 - Mopeds ☆ - Motor Bikes Import

JAWBERRIES - Candy - Donald J. Beck

JAWBOLT - Nuts and bolts - JAW Manufacturing Co.

JAWBONE - Toys - Tonka Corp.

JAWBOX - Apparel and accessories - Viewpoint International, Inc.

JAWBREAKER - Apparel and accessories - Jawbreaker

JAWBREAKER - Clippers–nail - Chaska Inc./Medihome-Doctors Podiatry

JAWBREAKER POPS - Candy - Blueberry Confections, Inc.

JAWBREAKERS - Candy - American Chewing Gum Co.

JAWCO - Tools–hand-operated - JAW Manufacturing Co.

JAWG N-BLOCK - Recording label - David J. Thomson

JAWMASTER - Crushing apparatus–laboratory - Svedala Industries, Inc.

JAWROBEAKS - Pet products - Kong Co.

JAWROBICS - Pet products - Kong Co.

JAWS - Clamps - Disston Co.

JAWS - Cleaning preparations ☆ - Swiss-Tex Inc.

JAWS - Dust-mop handles and ferrules - American Textile Products Co.

JAWS - Games ☆ - CBS Toys

☆ = Now out of production

JAWS - Locks–padlocks - S. Parker Hardware Manufacturing Corp.
JAWS - Tools–power-driven - Gutmann Cutlery Inc.
JAWS 2 - Food products - Janson's Foods Inc.
JAWS 3 - Food products - Janson's Foods Inc.
JAX - Beverages–malt - Pearl Brewing Co.
JAX - Books–comic - Midway Manufacturing Co.
JAX - Furniture - Beatrice Cos. Inc.
JAX - Games - Jax Ltd.
JAX - Snack foods - Bachman Co.
JAXERS - Underwear and nightwear - Samcaps New York Ltd.
JAXMOR - Salad dressings–bottled - Kraft Food Ingredients Corp.
JAXON - Thread - Threads USA Div.
JAXOS - Snack foods ☆ - Bachman Co.
JAY - Cushions - Jay Medical Ltd.
JAY ACTIVE - Cushions - Jay Medical Ltd.
JAY AND LAURIE - Computer software - Hartley Courseware Inc.
JAY BEE - Sporting goods - John B. Flaherty Co. Inc.
JAY-BO-DUCK - Children's books and apparel - Guy C. Grazioso
JAY BRAKE - Brakes–motor vehicle - Rivera Engineering, Inc.
JAY BRAKE - Motorcycles - Jaybrake Enterprises Inc.
JAY CARE - Cushions - Jay Medical Ltd.
JAY DEE'S - Restaurants–fast food - Darby Gas & Oil Co., Inc.
JAY DUBBS - Apparel and accessories ☆ - Edison Brothers Stores, Inc.
JAY DUO - Cushions - Jay Medical Ltd.
JAY EDWARDS - Video production - Jerry E. Fosgate
JAY-GLOSS - Cleaning preparations - Rajan Paul
JAY GS - Cushions - Jay Medical Ltd.
JAY J2 - Cushions - Jay Medical Ltd.
JAY JAY - Recording label - Jay Jay Record & Tape Co.
JAY JAY - Recording label - Kidquest, Inc.
JAY KAY - Rice - Jacob Kauffman
JAY MODULAR - Cushions - Jay Medical Ltd.
JAY PROTECTOR - Cushions - Jay Medical Ltd.
JAY SPECTRE COLLECTION, THE - Furniture–wood ☆ - Century Furniture Co.
JAY WILLFRED - Giftware - Charles Sadek and Jay Willfred Import Co.
JAY YANG CLASSICS - Wallpaper ☆ - Imperial Wallcoverings, Inc.
JAY YANG CLASSICS II - Wallpaper ☆ - Imperial Wallcoverings, Inc.
JAY YANG INTERIORS - Wallpaper ☆ - Imperial Wallcoverings, Inc.
JAY YANG INTERIORS II - Wallpaper ☆ - Imperial Wallcoverings, Inc.
JAY YANG ORIENT EXPRESS - Wallpaper - Imperial Wallcoverings, Inc.
JAYBIRD - Recording label - Guajiro Records Inc.
JAYBOW - Food products - Amende and Schultz
JAYCARDINAL - Trailers–travel - Jayco Inc.
JAYCE - Toys - Mattel, Inc.
JAYCO - Trailers–travel - Jayco Inc.
JAYCO SPORT - Apparel and accessories - Jayco Sales International, Inc.
JAYCOR WESTS - Firearms, accessories, and parts - Jaycor
JAYCRAFT - Ornamental products–metal ☆ - Shube's Manufacturing, Inc.
JAYCRANE - Trailers–travel - Jayco Inc.
JAYDEE'S NAIL FOOD - Vitamins and nutritional supplements - Center for Interior Services, Inc.
JAYDOVE - Trailers–travel - Jayco Inc.
JAYEAGLE - Trailers–travel - Jayco Inc.
JAYFINCH - Trailers–travel - Jayco Inc.
JAYHAWK - Fabrics - Greenwood Mills Inc.
JAYHAWK - Footwear ☆ - Asics Tiger Corp.
JAYHAWK - Toys–models - Estes Industries
JAYHAWK - Trailers–travel - Jayco Inc.
JAYKEEZ - Sunglasses and eyeglasses - J.W. Envisions
JAYKING - Trailers–travel - Jayco Inc.
JAYLASTIC - Sporting goods - Jaybird & Mais, Inc.
JAYMAR - Slacks–men's - Jaymar-Ruby Inc.
JAYMAR - Toys - Jaymar Specialty Co.
JAYMAR-SANSABELT - Apparel–men's - Jaymar-Ruby Inc.
JAYMAR SPORT - Apparel–men's - Jaymar-Ruby Inc.
JAYMARK - Jewelry - Jaymark Jewelry
JAYMATO - Food products - Robertet Flavors Inc.
JAYMONT MARBLE - Floor coverings ☆ - Tarkett, Inc.
JAYNE HOUSTON - Dinnerware–glass - Reusche & Co.
JAYNE'S - Veterinary pharmaceutical preparations - Sterling Winthrop Inc.
JAYPOSON - Jewelry - Jayposon Charm & Jewelry Manufacturing
JAYRON - Pharmaceutical preparations ☆ - Viobin U.S.A.
JAY'S - Food products - Robertet Flavors Inc.
JAYS - Snack foods - Jays Foods LLC
JAYSHREE - Spices and extracts - Jayshree

JAYSON - Artists' materials ☆ - Plasticoid Manufacturing Inc.
JAYSPORTSTER - Trailers–travel - Jayco Inc.
JAYSWAN - Trailers–travel - Jayco Inc.
JAYTHRUSH - Trailers–travel - Jayco Inc.
JAZ - Automotive parts and accessories - Jaz Products Inc.
JAZ - Computer storage devices - Iomega Corp.
JAZ - Watches - Seiko Corp. of America
JAZ DRIVES - Computer peripheral equipment - Iomega Corp.
JAZ-LOK - Post and pole support bases - Michael J. Jasinsky
JAZZ - Beverages–carbonated - Hampton Associates and Son, Inc.
JAZZ - Cases–eyeglass - California Optical Leather Co.
JAZZ - Computer software - Lotus Development Corp.
JAZZ - Dolls - Tonka Corp.
JAZZ - Floor coverings–carpet and rugs ☆ - Burtco Enterprises Inc.
JAZZ - Floor coverings–carpet and rugs ☆ - Galaxy Carpet Mills Inc.
JAZZ - Hair care products - Giovanni Cosmetics Inc.
JAZZ - Musical instrument accessories - Seymour Duncan Pickups
JAZZ - Paints - Van Aken International
JAZZ - Perfumes - Yves St. Laurent Parfum Corp.
JAZZ - Pet products - Doane Products Co.
JAZZ - Recording label - Hope International
JAZZ - Resin furniture - Diversified Recycling Systems
JAZZ - Shoes - Intershoe Inc.
JAZZ II - Apparel–women's - Chorus Line Corp.
JAZZ 3000 - Shoes ☆ - Hyde Athletic Industries Inc.
JAZZ ALLIANCE, THE - Recording label - Jazz Alliance, Inc.
JAZZ ANTHOLOGY - Recording label - Musidisc SA
JAZZ AT LINCOLN CENTER - Recording label - Lincoln Center for the Performing Arts, Inc.
JAZZ BY BODUM - Housewares - Bodum, Inc.
JAZZ BY COAST - Shoes–athletic ☆ - Coast Shoes Inc.
JAZZ CLUB - Beverages–alcohol - Olde St. Nick Distillery Inc.
JAZZ COLORS - Paints - Day-Glo Color Corp.
JAZZ CONNOISSEUR - Recording label - Zim Records
JAZZ ESSENCE - Recording label - Jazz Composer's Orchestra Association Inc.
JAZZ FORUM - Recording label - Jazz Composer's Orchestra Association Inc.
JAZZ GLOSS - Paints - Van Aken International
JAZZ LIONS - Recording label - Athena Productions
JAZZ MIND - Recording label ☆ - Sea Breeze Record Co.
JAZZ PLUS - Footwear ☆ - Hyde Athletic Industries Inc.
JAZZ SCHOOL - Paints - Van Aken International
JAZZ SPORT - Apparel–women's - Chorus Line Corp.
JAZZ WAG - Handkerchiefs - Southern Traditions by Betty-Jo
JAZZANNE - Recording label - Jazzand Records
JAZZE - Flowers, plants, and seeds - Panamerican Seed
JAZZED - Bicycles ☆ - Hedstrom Corp.
JAZZED UP - Dolls - Mattel, Inc.
JAZZERCISE - Exercise apparel - Weekend Exercise Co., Inc.
JAZZERCISE - Footwear - Items International Airwalk Inc.
JAZZERCISE - Socks - Moretz Hosiery Mills Inc.
JAZZI BRITE - Bicycles - Huffy Corp.
JAZZIE - Dolls - Mattel, Inc.
JAZZIEST COLORNOTES - Cosmetics ☆ - Noxell Corp.
JAZZING - Hair coloring preparations - Clairol Inc.
JAZZLAND - Phonographs - Fantasy Inc.
JAZZMAN - Clothing - Jazzman Sportswear Corp.
JAZZMASTER - Guitars - Fender Musical Instruments
JAZZOLOGY - Labels–paper - Jazzology-GHB Records
JAZZY - Jams and jellies - Fannie's Kitchen Inc.
JAZZY - Ophthalmic goods - Foremost Optical Products
JAZZY - Scooters–motorized - Pride Health Care, Inc.
JAZZY - Underwear and nightwear ☆ - Elegante Foundations Inc.
JAZZY CATS - Bicycles - Dynacraft Industries Inc.
JAZZY JACKS - Novelty items - S.J. Miller Co.
JAZZY JEANS - Dolls - Mattel, Inc.
JAZZY JELLYS - Food products - Jazzy Jellys, L.C.
JAZZY JERSEYS - Apparel and accessories - Salant/Manhattan Industries
JAZZY JEWELRY - Toys - Binney & Smith Inc.
JAZZY KOOSH - Balls ☆ - Oddzon Products, Inc.
JAZZY POCKETS - Jewelry–costume - Repcon International, Inc.
JAZZY TRAILS - Bicycles - Huffy Corp.
JAZZY TURNER - Lenses–magnifying - C. Bennett Scopes Inc.
JAZZY WHEELS - Bicycles ☆ - Huffy Corp.
JAZZY WINE - Lipsticks ☆ - Honey & Spice Toiletries
JAZZY'S GARLIC JAZZ - Food products - Golden Whisk Pasta Partners

☆ = Now out of production

JAZZZ BAND - Hearing aids - Moldex-Metric Inc.

JB - Giftware - Joseph Berland

JB - Jewelry - Jacoby-Bender Inc.

JB - Motorcycles - Jaybrake Enterprises Inc.

JB - Musical instrument accessories - Seymour Duncan Pickups

JB - Recording label ☆ - Joey Boy Records Corp.

JB-80 - Lubricants - Justice Brothers Inc.

JB COLLECTION - Apparel—women's - Fashion Initiatives

J.B. COOL - Candy - Herman Goelitz Candy Co., Inc.

J.B. HOT - Candy - Herman Goelitz Candy Co., Inc.

J.B. HUDSON - Jewelry - Facets Fine Jewelry, LLC

JB JR. FOR STRAT - Musical instrument accessories - Seymour Duncan Pickups

JB KWIK - Welding equipment - Mary L. Bonham

JB NON-IMBEDDING BORE CLEANING COMPOUND - Firearms, accessories, and parts - Brownells, Inc.

J.B. PLAYER - Guitars - MBT International, Inc.

J.B. REESE - Toys - Saban Entertainment, Inc.

J.B. #RICH - Jewelry - Anatone Jewelry Co.

J.B. SOUR - Candy - Herman Goelitz Candy Co., Inc.

JBA GUIDELINES - Computer software - Jba International Inc.

JBA VIEWFINDER - Computer software - Jba International Inc.

JBC - Jewelry - James Breski & Co., Inc.

JBF - Boats - JBF Scientific Co., Inc.

JBI - Jewelry - John Buechner Inc.

JBJ - Apparel and accessories - Oxford Industries, Inc.

JBL - Audio equipment - Harman Consumer Group

JBL - Electronics equipment - JBL Inc.

JBM - Jewelry - Jewelry by Michael, Inc.

JBN CASUALS - Apparel and accessories - JBN Enterprises Inc.

JBNI - Jewelry - Bijoux D'amour

JBR FARMS - Food products - Renfro Foods Inc.

JBSTAR - Jewelry - Jewels by Star Ltd.

JBX - Apparel and accessories - Viewpoint International, Inc.

JBX - Tape recorders—cassette - Montgomery Ward & Co. Inc.

JC - Apparel and accessories - Jupiter Coyote, Inc.

JC - Cleaning preparations—carpet and rug - Multi-Care Corp.

JC - Jewelry - Yodan Enterprises, Inc.

JC - Tools—hand-operated - Arctic Industries, Inc.

J.C. BEAR - Toys—stuffed - J.C. Penney Co., Inc.

JC GEAR - Anvils - JC Gear

JC WHITNEY - Drills—hand-operated - Warshawsky & Co.

JC30 - Adhesives and sealants - Federal Process Co.

JCA BABY - Hobby kits - JCA, Inc.

JCA WEARABLES - Hobby kits - JCA, Inc.

JCB PASSPORT MAP - Maps - JCB International Credit Card Co., Ltd.

JCCC - Jewelry - Johnson County Community College

JCF - Jewelry - J. & C. Ferrara Co. Inc.

JCFORMS - Computer software - Law Desq. Corp.

JCI - Recording label - Essex Entertainment Inc.

JCL NAVIGATOR - Computer software - Canyon Software Corp.

JCLPLUS! - Computer software - Software Engineering of America, Inc.

J.C.O.A. - Recording label - Jazz Composer's Orchestra Association Inc.

JCRC - Jewelry - Victor Corp.

JCS - Syrup - Kingston-Miami Trading

JCS-COR - Jewelry - Cordova Inc.

J.D. DROVER - Clothing - Manny Margaretis

JD FABRICS LTD. - Fabrics - JD Fabrics Ltd.

J.D. HUSSONG'S BAJA RED - Chili sauce - John D. Hussong

JD JIMMY DEAN DELI - Sandwiches—prepackaged - Saramar Corp.

JD JULIE DESIGNS - Sporting goods - Julie Designs

JD ORIGINALS - Furniture - Jackson of Danville Inc.

JD ORIGINALS - Wallpaper - Decorator and Craft Corp.

JDD - Jewelry - J.D. Dawson Co.

JDF - Recording label - Jazz Composer's Orchestra Association Inc.

JDI - Furniture - Klaussner Corporate Services, Inc.

JDI GROUP - Furniture - JDI Group, Inc.

JDL - Jewelry - Jana Designs, Ltd.

JDS - Musical instruments - Wolf Imports

J.D.'S BLEND - Tobacco—chewing or smoking - P.T.C. Brands, Inc.

J.D.'S BLEND - Tobacco—chewing or smoking - Swedish Math North America Inc.

J.D.U. - Jewelry - Jewelry Designs Unlimited Inc.

JDVISION - Computer software - Deere & Co.

JE - Watches - Yacov Yida

JE CHAMPION - Watchbands—leather - Genal Strap Co. Inc.

J.E. JAW TEASERS - Candy - American Chewing Gum Inc.

JE MARI'S - Yogurt—frozen - Je Mari's, Inc.

J.E. MORGAN - Apparel and accessories - J.E. Morgan Knitting Mills

J.E. MORGAN BODYWARMERS - Underwear - J.E. Morgan Knitting Mills

J.E. MORGAN LONG HANDLES - Underwear and nightwear - J.E. Morgan Knitting Mills

JE NE SAIS QUOI - Apparel—women's - T.A.C. Group, Inc.

JE PREMIER SERIES - Air conditioning equipment - Baltimore Aircoil Co. Inc.

JE SUIS MOI - Publisher's imprints - Dorothye B. Abraham

JE T'ADORE - Apparel—women's - Lady Ester Lingerie Corp.

JEALOUSY - Apparel—women's - SU Enterprise Corp.

JEALOUSY - Christmas tree ornaments - Cracker Box Inc.

JEALOUSY - Colognes - Del Pharmaceuticals, Inc.

JEAN - Thread ☆ - Synthetic Thread Co. Inc.

JEAN ANDRE - Apparel—men's - Wm. B. Kessler Inc.

JEAN BAPTISTE - Musical instruments - Sam Ash Music Corp.

JEAN BELL - Shirts - Jean Bell

JEAN BERGERU MADRE PERLATTA - Pipes—tobacco - Bradberry Briar Pipe Corp.

JEAN BLUE - Apparel—athletic - Stanford Trading Inc.

JEAN BOREL - Wines ☆ - Monsieur Henri Wines Ltd.

JEAN BOULAINE - Wine ☆ - Charles Jacquin et Compagnie Inc.

JEAN CACHAREL - Cosmetics - Cosmair Inc.

JEAN-CHARLES - Colognes - Frances Denney

JEAN COUNTRY - Apparel and accessories - Landmark Pants Corp.

JEAN COUTURIER - Perfumes - Classic Fragrances Ltd.

JEAN DAMION - Watches - La Marque Watch Co. Inc.

JEAN DANFLOU - Beverages—alcohol - Marie Brizard Wines & Spirits, USA

JEAN DECO - Toys ☆ - Imperial Toy Corp.

JEAN ESCALLE - Wines ☆ - Golden State Vintners

JEAN FISHER - Nuts—salted, roasted, cooked, or canned - Fisher Nut Co.

JEAN GALLER - Food products ☆ - De Choix Specialty Foods Co.

JEAN GUI - Food products ☆ - Liberty Richter Inc.

JEAN GUILLOT - Wines - European Beverage Co., Inc.

+JEAN-JACQUES +BROUSSARD - Perfumes - Difaya International, Inc.

JEAN KLEBERT - Cosmetics - Ya-Man Ltd.

JEAN KLEBERT SEPGRETO - Cosmetics - Ya-Man Ltd.

JEAN LAPERRIERE - Wine ☆ - Charles Jacquin et Compagnie Inc.

JEAN LASSALE - Watches ☆ - Seiko Corp. of America

JEAN LEON - Wines ☆ - Kobrand Corp.

JEAN LOUIS COQUET - Dinnerware—glass - Lalique North America

JEAN LOUIS PREVOST - Posters - One-of-a-Kind Workshop

JEAN LOUIS ROEHRICH - Jewelry - Jean Louis Roehrich Inc.

JEAN-LOUIS SCHERRER - Frames—eyeglass - Euro-Frames Inc.

JEAN MARIE - Toys—stuffed - Jolly U.S.A., Inc.

JEAN MARTIN - Food products - Made in France

JEAN MARTIN - Olives—canned ☆ - De Medici Imports Ltd.

JEAN MCLAIN - Wallpaper ☆ - Imperial Wallcoverings, Inc.

JEAN MICHEL - Leather goods - GSL Enterprises Inc.

JEAN NATE - Apparel and accessories - Kellwood Co.

JEAN NATE - Apparel and accessories - Revlon Consumer Products Corp.

JEAN NATE BEAUTY BUFFS - Skin care products - Revlon Consumer Products Corp.

JEAN NATE FRESH MUSK - Perfumes - Revlon Consumer Products Corp.

JEAN PATOU - Perfumes - Jean Patou, Inc.

JEAN PATOU - Scarves - Jerry Kohn Inc.

JEAN PAUL GAULTIER - Sunglasses - Optical Affairs, Inc.

JEAN-PIERRE - Bakery products - Jean-Pierre Bleger

JEAN PIERRE - Leather and sheep-lined clothing - Excelled Sheepskin Leather Inc.

JEAN-PIERRE LAMY - Sunglasses - L'Amy Inc.

JEAN-PIERRE MOUEIX - Wines - Kobrand Corp.

JEAN PIRAT - Wallpaper - Surface Industries Inc.

JEAN PIRAT - Wallpaper ☆ - Winfield Design Associates, Inc.

JEAN ST. - Apparel and accessories - Montgomery Ward & Co. Inc.

JEAN ST. GERMAIN - Jeans—women's - Jean St. Germain, Inc.

JEAN SLACKS - Slacks—men's ☆ - Haggar Corp.

JEAN TONET - Saxophones - N.H.F. Musical Merchandise Corp.

JEAN-TOP - Apparel and accessories - Pannill Knitting Co. Inc.

JEAN TWINS - Giftware ☆ - Brushcreek Creative Co.

JEAN VITAU - Jewelry - Gemveto Jewelry Co. Inc.

JEAN YVES AUDEBERT - Beverages—alcohol - Margus Co.

JEANETTE - Watches - Bulova Corp.

JEANIE - Dolls - National Association of Fashion and Accessory Designers Inc.

JEANIE RUB - Skin care products - Hess Hair Milk Laboratories Inc.

JEANINE - Footwear—women's - Shoe Works, Inc.

JEANMARIE - Paper–gift wrap - Jeanmarie Gallery
JEANNE - Corsets - John Wanamaker Inc.
JEANNE BENET - Handbags - Carryland Co.
JEANNE DURRELL - Dresses–women's - Lorch Co.
JEANNE GATINEAU - Cosmetics - Revlon Consumer Products Corp.
JEANNE ROSE HERBAL BODYWORKS - Herbal products - Jeanne Rose
JEANNE ROSE'S - Health care products - New Age Creations/Herbal
  Bodyworks
JEANNE STUART - Women's apparel - Banner Industries, Inc.
JEANNE WEST - Dresses–women's - Smoler Bros. Inc.
JEANNETTE - Glassware–household - Jeannette Corp.
JEANNIE - Stationery - Holiday Fair, Inc.
JEANNIE - Wigs - Jean Paree Weegs Inc.
JEANNIE EDMOND - Jewelry - Electro-Time
JEANNINE - Golfing equipment - Badgley Manufacturing Co. Inc.
JEANS BEANS - Dolls - Mattel, Inc.
JEANS BOOT - Shoes - Import Systems International Inc.
JEANS MACHINE - Sewing machines–household - VWS Inc.
JEANS 'N JEWELS - Toys - Mattel, Inc.
JEANS WEST - Apparel and accessories - Edison Brothers Stores, Inc.
JEANSTRAP - Watchbands–leather - Vogue Watch Strap Creations
JEANZIPS - Zippers - YKK USA Inc.
JEB-ROD - Rods–plastic - John Sterling Corp.
JEBCO - Apparel and accessories - Jebco, Inc.
JEBCO - Containers - Jebco Packaging Systems, Inc.
JEB'S - Food products - Jewel Food Stores Inc.
JECTA - Fungicides - Nisus Corp.
JECTA-MIN - Veterinary nutritional supplements - Technological
  Commercialization Transfer, Ltd.
JECTABEE - Prescription drug - American Hygienic Laboratories Inc.
JED - Jewelry - Joseph E. De Marco Inc.
JEDA - Bicycles - Schwinn Cycling & Fitness Inc.
JEDDAH - Floor coverings–carpet and rugs ☆ - Eurotex Inc.
JEDEDIAH CLAUSS & SONS - Publisher's imprints - Amereon Ltd.
JEDI - Computer storage devices - Peripherals Plus Inc.
JEDI ARENA - Video games - Lucasfilm Ltd.
JEEL - Hair care products ☆ - Duart Industries Ltd.
JEEP - Motor vehicles–jeeps - DaimlerChrysler
JEEP - Watches - Bloomfield International Inc.
JEEP-CASE - Photographic equipment ☆ - H.P. Marketing Corp.
JEEP EYEWEAR - Artists' materials - Artoptic International Corp.
JEEPERS - Candy ☆ - R.M. Palmer Co.
JEEPERS - Cereal - Stokely-Van Camp, Inc.
JEEPERS - Ophthalmic goods - Foremost Optical Products
JEEPERS BEEPERS - Apparel and accessories - Jeepers Beepers, Inc.
JEEPERS CREEPER - Mechanics' creepers - Lisle Corp.
JEEPERS CREEPERS - Apparel–children's ☆ - Brill Bros. Inc.
JEEPERS CREEPERS - Toys - Russ Berrie and Co., Inc.
JEFAZOLE - Health care products ☆ - Halsey Drug Co. Inc.
JEFCO - Cleaning preparations - Jefco Laboratories, Inc.
JEFF - Trailers–boat - Hustler Boat Trailers
JEFF GORDON - Jewelry - Jeff Gordon, Inc.
JEFF HAMILTON - Sportswear - JH Design Group
JEFF HO - Shirts - Allan Jeffrey Ho
JEFF LANTZ - Recording label - Jeff Lantz
JEFF-PRESS - Fabrics - Dan River Inc.
JEFFCO - Cosmetics - Morris-Flamingo Inc.
JEFFCO - Food products - Jenney's Frozen Foods Inc.
JEFFERIES - Accordions - Castiglione Accordion
JEFFERIES - Meat products–poultry - Jefferies Foods Co.
JEFFERIES - Socks - Jefferies Socks
JEFFERS - Pet products - Jeffers Vet Supply
JEFFERS ELECTRONICS - Electronic equipment - Jeffers Electronics Inc.
JEFFERSON - Cabinets ☆ - Mouser Kitchens Inc.
JEFFERSON - Computer software ☆ - Cambridge Educational
JEFFERSON - Cribs–metal - Evenflo Juvenile Furniture Co.
JEFFERSON - Floor coverings - Applied Radiant Energy Corp.
JEFFERSON - Floor coverings–carpet and rugs - Colonial Mills Inc.
JEFFERSON - Floor coverings–carpet and rugs - Jefferson Industries Inc.
JEFFERSON - Flowers, plants, and seeds - Jonathan Green, Inc.
JEFFERSON - Hardware - Moore-Handley Inc.
JEFFERSON - Meat products–beef - Foodbrands America, Inc.
JEFFERSON - Real estate agencies - JPI Texas Development, Inc.
JEFFERSON - Shrimp–canned or cured ☆ - Robinson Canning Co. Inc.
JEFFERSON - Silver products - Kirk Stieff Co.
JEFFERSON - Tableware–china - Lenox, Inc.

JEFFERSON - Toys–musical - Jefferson Manufacturing Co.
JEFFERSON - Toys–stuffed - Dakin Inc.
JEFFERSON COLLECTION - Furniture ☆ - Lane Co. Inc.
JEFFERSON COLLECTION - Giftware - Kirk Stieff Co.
JEFFERSON COTTON - Fabrics–cotton - Thomas William Reynolds
JEFFERSON COUNTY - Sausages - Farmland Foods, Inc.
JEFFERSON DESK COLLECTION - Giftware - Kirk Stieff Co.
JEFFERSON ELECTRIC - Clocks ☆ - Jefferson Electric Co.
JEFFERSON FABRIC - Housewares - Thomas William Reynolds
JEFFERSON FIBRE - Apparel and accessories - Thomas William Reynolds
JEFFERSON JAZZ - Tape players–cassette - Sony Music Entertainment Inc.
JEFFERSON LUXURY - Mattresses - Simmons USA
JEFFERSON MANOR - Floor coverings ☆ - Tarkett, Inc.
JEFFERSON MANOR - House furnishings - Lea Industries Inc.
JEFFERSON PINE - Furniture ☆ - Bassett Furniture Industries, Inc.
JEFFERSON SPIVEY - Knives–hunting - Jefferson Spivey
JEFFERSON, THE - Garment hangers ☆ - Selfix, Inc.
JEFFERSONIAN - Cabinets ☆ - Nutone Inc.
JEFFERSONIAN - Floor coverings ☆ - Bruce Hardwood Floors
JEFFERSONIAN - Floor coverings ☆ - Robbins Inc.
JEFFERSONIAN BOUCLE - Floor coverings–carpet and rugs ☆ - Mohawk
  Carpet Corp.
JEFFERSONIAN II - Floor coverings - Bruce Hardwood Floors
JEFFERSONIAN, THE - Pianos - Kohler & Campbell Inc.
JEFFREY ADAM COLLECTION - Cosmetics - Hydro-Tex Corp.
JEFFREY & ME - Apparel–women's - Jeffrey & Me, Inc.
JEFFREY BANKS - Apparel and accessories - Neema Clothing, Ltd.
JEFFREY BANKS - Apparel–men's - Jeffrey Banks International
JEFFREY COURT - Tiles–ceramic - Amsterdam Corp.
JEFFREY DUANE - Apparel–men's - Sadow Inc.
JEFFRON - Toys - Tonka Corp.
JEFF'S AMAZING NEW YORK - Soft drink - Egg Cream America Inc.
JEFFTREAT - Chemical preparations - Huntsman Corp.
JEFIC - Sewing machines–industrial - John E. Fox, Inc.
JEFSTEEL - Filing cabinets–metal - Jefsteel Business Equipment Corp.
JEG - Bandages - J.E. Goold & Co.
JEI - Massage tools - Jackson Enterprises Inc.
JEINS - Apparel and accessories - Jeins & Co, Inc.
JEKEL VINEYARD - Wines - Jekel Vineyard
JEL - Food products - Baker Brands
JEL-FLUX - Fluxes–welding and soldering - Hercules Chemical Co. Inc.
JEL MATE - Cushions - Encore Products Inc.
JEL 'N JAM - Jams and jellies - Kerr Group, Inc.
JEL-RING - Housewares - Tupperware Co.
JEL SERT - Food products ☆ - Jel Sert Co.
JEL-SHOOTER - Tubes–plastic - Jel-Master, Inc.
JELAN - Apparel and accessories - Screenwork, Inc.
JELCLEER - Water purification systems - First Water Filtration
JEL'D-POLY-KOTE - Finishing agents - Wood Kote Products, Inc.
JEL'D STAIN - Stains - Wood Kote Products, Inc.
JELE ROYALE - Skin care products - Nicole Research Inc.
JELL-O - Apparel–children's - Garan, Inc.
JELL-O - Yogurt - Kraft Foods, Inc.
JELL WELL - Gelatin ☆ - Safeway Stores Inc.
JELLASHEEN - Shampoos - Redken Laboratories, Inc.
JELLIES - Candy - Ferrara Pan Candy Co., Inc.
JELLISY - Shoes - Topline Imports, Inc.
JELLS - Candy ☆ - New England Confectionery Co.
JELLY APPLE - Candy ☆ - Topps Co., Inc.
JELLY BEAN - Chewing gum - Leaf, Inc.
JELLY BEAN - Tricycles ☆ - Peg Perego USA Inc.
JELLY BEAN BUNNY - Toys–stuffed - Dan-Dee International Ltd.
JELLY BEAN BUNNY - Toys–stuffed - Russ Berrie and Co., Inc.
JELLY BEAN VILLAGE - Infant product - Dundee Mills, Inc.
JELLY BEANS - Apparel–children's ☆ - ICM
JELLY BELLY - Candy - Herman Goelitz Candy Co., Inc.
JELLY BELT - Belts–apparel - Paris Accessories, Inc.
JELLY DE LITES - Candles - Empire Manufacturing Co.
JELLY DOLLS - Toys ☆ - Those Characters from Cleveland, Inc.
JELLY DROP - Toys - Eugene Doll & Novelty Co. Inc.
JELLY-EGG JIM - Candy ☆ - R.M. Palmer Co.
JELLY JEANS - Dolls ☆ - Uneeda Doll Co., Inc.
JELLY LITES - Candles - Emkay Candles
JELLY N' JAM - Apparel–children's - Renzo Co., Inc.
JELLY ROLLS - Paint rollers ☆ - Arsco International Inc.
JELLY STIX - Candy ☆ - Cap Toys, Inc.

☆ = Now out of production

JELLYBEAN - Pet products - Coastal Pet Products, Inc.
JELLYBONE - Pet products - Penn-Plax, Inc.
JELLYFISH - Candy - Richardson Brands Co.
JELLYPULL - Pet products - Penn-Plax, Inc.
JELLYROLL - Bags–canvas ✰ - J.C. Penney Co., Inc.
JELLYSTONE - Campgrounds - Leisure Systems Inc.
JELLYVISION - Computer software - Jellyvision, Inc.
JELPOP - Trays - Jel-Master, Inc.
JELSWEET - Sweeteners–artificial ✰ - Firmenich Inc.
JELTRODES - Health care products - Neuromedics
JELVYN - Skin care products - Richardson-Vicks USA
JEM - Cosmetics for children ✰ - Cosrich Inc.
JEM - Dolls - Hasbro, Inc.
JEM - Puzzles ✰ - Milton Bradley Co.
JEM CONCERT CLASH - Games ✰ - Milton Bradley Co.
JEM FASHION FLASH - Games ✰ - Milton Bradley Co.
JEM PUZZLES THAT REALLY MOVE - Puzzles ✰ - Milton Bradley Co.
JEM ROCK 'N ROMANCE - Games ✰ - Milton Bradley Co.
JEMCO - Brassieres (Bras) - Abraham & Straus/Jordan Marsh Co.
J.E.M.F. - Recording label ✰ - Arhoolie Productions Inc.
JEMIMA PUDDLE-DUCK - Frames–picture - Frederick Warne & Co., Inc.
JEMLITE - Lamps - Public Service Lamp Corp.
JEMM - Meat products–beef - Jemm Wholesale Meat Co.
JEMMS DELUX - Meat products–beef - Jemm Wholesale Meat Co.
JEMMS PURE - Meat products–beef - Jemm Wholesale Meat Co.
JEMOPTIK - Lenses–photographic ✰ - Ercona Corp.
JEN-CEL-LITE - Insulating materials - Jen Cel Lite Corp.
JEN-MI BAO SLIM TEA - Beverages - Fec Ginseng & Marine Products
JENA - Lenses–photographic - Ercona Corp.
JENA - Watches - Zell Bros.
JENA - Wedding gowns - Jena Bridals Inc.
JENA MOLLE - Gold-decorated glassware - International Bent Glass Inc.
JENAMICIN - Pharmaceutical preparations - Roberts/Hauck Pharmaceuticals Inc.
JENARD - Wines - Cannon Wines Ltd.
JENCRAFT - Window coverings - Jencraft Corp.
JENE MICHAELS - Footwear - Soft Shoe, Inc.
JENEAL - Skin care products - Jeneal International Inc.
JENEST-28 - Pharmaceutical preparations - Organon Inc.
JENGA - Games - Milton Bradley Co.
JENIFER - Wigs - Jean Paree Weegs Inc.
JENIFER & HAIDEE - Cosmetics - New Skin Research, Inc.
JENISYS - Computer peripheral equipment - Jensen Information Systems, Inc.
JENKINS - Beverages–alcohol - Jenkins Spirits Corp., Ltd.
JENKINS - Rings–jewelry - J. Jenkins Sons Co. Inc.
JENKINS REDDY MADE - Beverages–alcohol - Jenkins Spirits Corp., Ltd.
JENN-AIR - Barbecues and grills - Jenn-Air Corp.
JENN-AIR - Washing machines–household - Maytag Corp.
JENNA - Frames–eyeglass - Rozin Optical Export Corp.
JENNA - Wheelchairs - Brainwaves Design Group Inc.
JENNA-BASE - Health care products ✰ - Snug Seat, Inc.
JENNA NICOLE - Jewelry, watches - Vintage Creations Inc.
JENNI - Dolls - Uneeda Doll Co., Inc.
JENNI-PURR - Toys–stuffed ✰ - Gund, Inc.
JENNI-STEAK - Food products ✰ - Tops Meat Co. Inc.
JENNIE' FAT FREE - Cookies - Red Mill Farms Inc.
JENNIE G. - Toys - Jennie G. Sales Co. Inc.
JENNIE-O - Meat products–poultry - Jennie-O Foods, Inc.
JENNIES - Cookies - Red Mill Farms Inc.
JENNIFER - Cosmetics - Just & Nice Trading Co., Inc.
JENNIFER - Dolls - Uneeda Doll Co., Inc.
JENNIFER - Fabrics–tapestry - Comark Wallcoverings
JENNIFER - Floor coverings–carpet and rugs ✰ - Regal Rugs Inc.
JENNIFER - Frames–eyeglass - U.S. Optical Frame Co.
JENNIFER - Glassware–household ✰ - Knobler International Ltd.
JENNIFER - Toys–stuffed - Russ Berrie and Co., Inc.
JENNIFER BLAIR BY NORTHERN ISLES - Apparel and accessories ✰ - Kellwood Co.
JENNIFER BY ITS A WIG - Wigs - It's a Wig!
JENNIFER CLARKE - Apparel–athletic - Montgomery Ward & Co. Inc.
JENNIFER CONVERTIBLES - Sofabeds - Jennifer Convertibles Inc.
JENNIFER C'S - Apparel and accessories - Duckwall-Alco Stores, Inc.
JENNIFER DALE - Apparel–children's - Jennifer Dale Inc.
JENNIFER DALE FOR KIDS - Apparel–children's ✰ - Jennifer Dale Inc.
JENNIFER GEORGE BY NIGHT - Women's apparel - Jennifer George Inc.
JENNIFER GRAHAM - Leather goods ∑ Wenjen, Inc.

JENNIFER MIRYA COLLECTIONS - Underwear and nightwear - Jennifer Mirya Collections
JENNIFER MOORE - Apparel and accessories - R.H. Macy & Co.
JENNIFER ORIGINALS - Shoes - Sam Brilliant Sporto
JENNIFER SCOTT - Apparel and accessories - Regent International Corp.
JENNIFER, THE - Prefabricated buildings–wood ✰ - A-Zak Wood Specialties
JENNIFER WONG JW - Apparel–women's - Jenny Wong
JENNIKER - Ships–sailing vessels ✰ - Britton of Southport Inc.
JENNINGS - Archery equipment - Bear Archery Inc.
JENNINGS - Wooden porch swings and gliders - Jack-Post Corp.
JENNINGS COUNTY - Floor coverings–carpet and rugs ✰ - Regal Rugs Inc.
JENNINGS TEA - Teas - International Tea Co., Inc.
JENNSWING - Playground equipment - Deanna M. Eddy
JENNY - Cleaning preparations - Jenny Products, Inc.
JENNY - Detergents - Homestead Industries Inc. (Jenny Div.)
JENNY - Floor coverings–carpet and rugs ✰ - Regal Rugs Inc.
JENNY - Giftware ✰ - Enesco Corp.
JENNY - Greeting cards ✰ - American Greetings Corp.
JENNY B - Apparel–children's - Bon-Ton Trade Corp.
JENNY BROOKS - Eyeglasses - United States Shoe Corp.
JENNY BROWN - Fruit butters ✰ - National Fruit Product Co., Inc.
JENNY BUCHANAN - Jewelry - Bon-Ton Trade Corp.
JENNY FAITH - Novelty items - Atico International Inc.
JENNY JONES & BABY JOHN - Toys–stuffed ✰ - Kenner Products
JENNY LIND - Furniture - Evenflo Juvenile Furniture Co.
JENNY LIND - Infant product ✰ - Century Products Co.
JENNY LIND - Infant product ✰ - Welsh Co.
JENNY LIND - Pianos - Kohler & Campbell Inc.
JENNY LIND DEERFIELD COLLECTION - Furniture ✰ - Evenflo Juvenile Furniture Co.
JENNY TEE - Handbags - S & H Pocketbook
JENNY WREN - Wallpaper - Storeys Wallcoverings
JENNY WREN - Wallpaper ✰ - Andover Wallcovering
JENNY'S GARDEN - Wallpaper - Andover Wallcovering
JENNY'S LACE - Bedding–linen - Dan River Inc.
JENOAH - Boats–canoes ✰ - Noah Corp.
JENO'S - Food products - Jeno's Inc.
JENO'S - Food products - Pillsbury Co.
JENSEN - Apparel and accessories - Winston Manufacturing Corp.
JENSEN - Electrical equipment - Stanley Works
JENSEN - Engines - Jensen Manufacturing Co. Inc.
JENSEN - Games ✰ - Importoys
JENSEN - Stereo systems, cassette receivers, equalizers, amplifiers, CDG - International Jensen Inc.
JENSEN - Wines - Calera Wine Co.
JENSEN & JONBY - Soap ✰ - Freund-Mayer & Co. Inc.
JENSEN'S - Pens - Jensen's Inc.
JENSON - Jackets ✰ - Needlecraft Industries
JENTEX - Machinery - Central/Ats, Inc.
JENTRY - Wallpaper - Advent Industries Inc.
JEON DOBRE - Hair care products - Dobre Products Inc.
JEON PIERRE - Brushes–hair - Dona-Paul Co.
JEOPARDY - Games ✰ - Pressman Toy Corp.
JEPSON - Tools–power-driven - Illinois Fastening Systems
JEPSON VINEYARDS - Beverages–alcohol - Jepson Vineyards Ltd.
JER SHAMROCK - Onions - James E. Riley Farms Inc.
JERANTS - Hair care products ✰ - Jerant Co. Inc.
JERAY - Giftware - Breit-Boragno Inc.
JERC - Ophthalmic goods - Chums Ltd.
JERDON - Hair care products - Windmere Corp.
JERED - Toilets–enameled - Jered Brown Bros. Inc.
JEREE - Recording label - Jeree Records
JEREMIAH WEED - Liquors - Heublein, Inc.
JEREMIAH'S - Cakes ✰ - Sanders/Country Home of Michigan
JEREMY - Toys–stuffed ✰ - Dakin Inc.
JEREMY & LORD - Saddles and bridles - Libertyville Saddle Shop, Inc.
JEREMY BEAU - Apparel and accessories - Jeremy Beaux Inc.
JEREMY COBB - Apparel and accessories - Kingsport, Int'l, Inc.
JEREMY DOG - Toys–stuffed - Russ Berrie and Co., Inc.
JEREMY SLADE - Apparel–men's - Edison Brothers Stores, Inc.
JEREZ - Watches - Elgin Watch Co.
JERGA - Shirts - Native Art Trading Co.
JERGENS - Soap - Andrew Jergens Co.
JERGEN'S ADVANCED THERAPY - Cosmetics - Andrew Jergens Co.
JERGENS REFRESHING - Shampoos - Andrew Jergens Co.

JERGEN'S SHOWER-ACTIVE MOISTURIZER - Skin care products - Andrew Jergens Co.

JERGUSON - Valves - Clark-Reliance Corp.

JERI-BATH - Pharmaceutical preparations ☆ - Dermik Laboratories Inc.

JERI-LOTION - Pharmaceutical preparations ☆ - Dermik Laboratories Inc.

JERI-TAR-BATH - Bath salts ☆ - Dermik Laboratories Inc.

JERICHO AMERICA - Coffee makers–electric - Coffee Bean International, Inc.

JERICO - Transmission equipment–motor vehicle - Hemmingson Enterprises, Inc.

JERIEL - Skin care products - International Trade Unlimited of Miami, Inc.

JERIS - Hair care products - A.R. Winarick Inc.

JERIS - Toiletries - American International Industries

JERK-JIGGER - Fishing lures - Hildebrandt Corp.

JERK NUTS - Snack foods ☆ - Cinnabar Specialty Foods, Inc./Neera's Products

JERK, THE - Fishing lures - O.F. Mossberg & Sons, Inc.

JERK WEAR - Apparel and accessories - Walter M. Dill

JERKEY PUFFS - Dog food - Merrick Petfoods Inc.

JERKY BITS - Pet products - ALPO Petfoods Inc.

JERKY BONES - Dog food - Pet Center, Inc.

JERKY CHEW'M - Dog food - Hartz Mountain Corp.

JERKY FACTORY, THE - Processed meats - Tillamook Country Smoker, Inc.

JERKY SHOOTER - Cooking equipment–household - BPE Inc.

JERKY STRIPS - Dog food - Nabisco Foods Group

JERKY TREATS - Dog food - Heinz Pet Products Co.

JERKY TREATS PHILLY STEAK & CHEESE - Pet food - Star-Kist Foods, Inc.

JERMA - Recording label - Jerma Records Co. (Div. of Jerma Productions)

JERO - Beverages - Sunstar Foods Inc.

JERO - Scissors–hand-operated - Zanger Co.

JERO PROFESSIONALS - Food products - Sunstar Foods Inc.

JEROME - Food products - Empire Butter & Egg Co.

JEROME - Frames–eyeglass - U.S. Optical Frame Co.

JEROME - Music boxes - Cathay International

JEROME - Orthopedic products - Jerome Medical

JEROME ASTI - Skin care products - Ed Wyse Beauty Supply Inc.

JEROME IRISH - Whiskey - Joseph E. Seagram & Sons, Inc.

JEROME LORENTZ - Beverages–alcohol ☆ - Diamond Wine Merchants

JEROME PRIVEE - Skin-care products - Perfumania Inc.

JEROME RUSSELL - Hair care products - Jerome Russell Cosmetics, Inc.

JEROME'S CRUMBLES - Turkeys - Jerome Foods Inc.

JERRELL'S - Milk–canned or powdered - S.T. Jerrell Co.

JERROLD - Antennas - Jerrold General Instrument Corp.

JERROLD - Electronic equipment - Gerrold General Instrument Corp.

JERROLD GI GENERAL INSTRUMENT - Broadcasting equipment - Gerrold General Instrument Corp.

JERRY BLANKE - Placemats - Jersey Blanke Designs Inc.

JERRY DONAHUE MODEL - Musical instrument accessories - Seymour Duncan Pickups

JERRY-GIRAFFE - Toys–stuffed ☆ - Gund, Inc.

JERRY JAZZ MUSICIAN - Pottery products - Joe Maita

JERRY JUG - Containers - Igloo Products Corp.

JERRY LINDSEY - Jewelry - Jerry Lindsey Custom Jewelry

JERRY MCKINNIS - Sporting goods ☆ - Wright & McGill Co.

JERRY MILLER - Posters ☆ - Stevenson Industries Inc.

JERRY MILLER - Shoes - Jerry Miller Shoes Ltd.

JERRY PETS - Toys - Jerry Elsner Co. Inc.

JERRY SILVERMAN - Apparel and accessories - Warnaco Inc.

JERRY THE PHARMACIST - Computers - Innovative Enterprises International Corp.

JERRY'S - Charcoal - Jerry's Hickory Products

JERRY'S - Meat product ☆ - Indianapolis Meat Co. Inc.

JERSEY - Boats–motor - Jersey Yachts

JERSEY - Candy - S.L. Kaye Co., Inc.

JERSEY - Thread - Threads USA Div.

JERSEY CHERRIES - Candy - Henry Heide, Inc.

JERSEY CREAM - Butter ☆ - Kelley Co., Inc.

JERSEY DAIRIES - Apparel and accessories - Joseph P. Piechota

JERSEY DEVIL - Vegetable sauces - Joseph R. Ingemi

JERSEY FRUIT - Fruits–dried - Jersey Fruit Cooperative Association Inc.

JERSEY GANG, THE - Apparel–children's ☆ - Munsingwear, Inc.

JERSEY JIM'S - Beverages–malt - C.J. Jaspers, Inc.

JERSEY JIM'S BREWING COMPANY - Apparel and accessories - C.J. Jaspers, Inc.

JERSEY 'N TERRY - Fabrics–velvet - Dan River Inc.

JERSEY PRIDE - Egg substitutes - Papetti's Hygrade Egg Products, Inc.

JERSEYAN - Bicycles - Ross Bicycles USA, Ltd.

JERUSALEM - Games ☆ - Mayfair Games, Inc.

JERUSALEM - Perfumes - Raphael Glass, Inc.

JERYCO - Novelty items - M. Pressner and Co. Inc.

JERYL'S JEMS - Bakery goods - Jeryl's Jems

JERZEE - Milk–canned or powdered - Defiance Milk Products Co.

JERZEES - Apparel–athletic - Russell Athletic Div.

JES-KAY - Food products - Valley Distributing Co.

JES-TEX - Apparel stores–sports - Jesco Athletic Co.

JESARA - Jewelry - Weingeroff Enterprises, Inc.

JESCO - Wire products - Jesco Industries, Inc.

JESICA - Frames–eyeglass - Rozin Optical Export Corp.

JESICA DELUXE - Frames–eyeglass - Rozin Optical Export Corp.

JESS & LIZ - Apparel–women's - Jerell, Inc.

JESSE - Cosmetics - Berthelet Food Products

JESSE COUNTRY WESTERN - Apparel and accessories - Ben Elias Industries Corp.

JESSE ESCUE - Apparel and accessories - Jesse J. Escue

JESSE JAMES - Toys - Geronimo Productions Inc.

JESSE JAMES - Toys ☆ - Henry Gordy International Inc.

JESSE JONES - Food products ☆ - Goodmark Foods, Inc.

JESSE'S - Snack foods - Uncle Jesse's, Inc.

JESSE'S BEST - Beef - Supreme Foods Inc.

JESSE'S GIRL - Cosmetics - Boston and Pacific Marketing Inc.

JESSE'S HAVANA HONEYBACON DRESSING - Salad dressings–bottled - Jesse Foods Co.

JESSE'S ST. LOUIS BLUES CHUNKY BLUE CHEESE DRESSING - Salad dressings–bottled - Jesse Foods Co.

JESSE'S SANTA FE PEPPERCORN RANCH DRESSING - Salad dressings–bottled - Jesse Foods Co.

JESSICA - Apparel stores–lingerie - Strawbridge & Clothier

JESSICA - Dolls - Uneeda Doll Co., Inc.

JESSICA - Skin care products - Jessica Cosmetics Inc.

JESSICA - Toys–stuffed - Dakin Inc.

JESSICA - Wigs - Jean Paree Weegs Inc.

JESSICA ASH - Apparel–women's - Adorable Enterprises, Inc.

JESSICA B. - Apparel–children's - Trend Associates, Inc.

JESSICA DEAN - Jewelry - Uptons Inc.

JESSICA LEE - Cosmetics - Jessica Lee Inc.

JESSICA LYNN - Apparel–women's - Val Mode Lingerie Inc.

JESSICA MCCLINTOCK - Patterns–clothing ☆ - Simplicity Pattern Co., Inc.

JESSICA MCCLINTOCK - Women's apparel - Jessica McClintock Inc.

JESSICA RAE COLLECTION - Wallpaper - I. Gottlieb & Associates

JESSICA RYAN - Men's, women's and children's footwear - Dynasty Footwear, Ltd.

JESSICA SCOTT - Apparel–women's - Kmart Properties, Inc.

JESSICA STEVENS - Handbags - Venture Stores, Inc.

JESSIE - Toys - Tonka Corp.

JESSIE LORD - Baked goods - Country Home Bakers, Inc.

JESSUP - Recording label ☆ - Michele Audio Corp.

JESSUP - Tape–adhesive - Jessup Manufacturing Co.

JESSY & COMPANY - Stationery - Gene Bliley Stationery

JESTE - Apparel–women's - Clubhouse Marketing, Inc.

JESTER - Books–comic - Aegis Entertainment, Inc.

JESTER - Candy - Murray-Allen International Inc.

JESTER - Paper products - Crown Central Petroleum Corp.

JESTER CO., INC., THE - Dolls - Jester Co., Inc.

JESTER RAZOR - Razors - C.A. Daniels & Co.

JESTERS - Studio greeting cards ☆ - American Greetings Corp.

JESTERS WILD - Apparel and accessories - Jesters Wild

JESTICKS - Drums–musical instruments ☆ - J.D. Calato Manufacturing Inc.

JESUIS - Apparel–men's - Wemco, Inc.

JESUS CHRIST LORD - Jewelry - Paul A. Lucas and Daniel P. Lucas Partnership

JESUS IS LORD - Frames–picture - Paul A. Lucas and Daniel P. Lucas Partnership

JESUS IS THE REASON FOR THE SEASON - Paper–gift wrap - Parable Group, Inc.

JESUS LOVES ME BY BETTY CHAISSON - Giftware - Roman, Inc.

JESUS SAVES - Air purification systems - Medo Industries, Inc.

JET - Alarm systems - Jet Co., Inc.

JET - Ammunition - Remington Arms Co., Inc.

JET - Artists' materials - Stangren Co.

JET - Balls–basketball - Wilson Sporting Goods Co.

JET - Batteries - Exide Corp.

JET - Brooms - Hamburg Broom Works Inc.

JET - Chemical preparations - Airosol Co. Inc.

☆ = Now out of production

JET - Computer software - SubLogic Corp.

JET - Drums–musical instruments - N.H.F. Musical Merchandise Corp.

JET - Erasers - Faber-Castell Corp.

JET - Erasers ☆ - Bright Boy Abrasives

JET - Gasoline ☆ - Conoco Inc.

JET - Grinders ☆ - Latama Inc.

JET - Hardware - Alumatic Corp. of America

JET - Inks - Independent Ink Inc.

JET - Insecticides ☆ - Roccorp, Inc.

JET - Mops ☆ - Helen Keller Services for the Blind

JET - Nail care products - Salon Essentials

JET - Nozzles - H.B. Sherman Manufacturing Co.

JET - Paint rollers - Wooster Brush Co.

JET - Pet products - Rapid Electric/R & R Manufacturing

JET - Sports rackets and accessories ☆ - Victor Sports

JET - Starch–laundry - Barcolene Inc.

JET - Tape players–cassette - Sony Music Entertainment Inc.

JET - Tools - Chickasaw Handle Co. Inc.

JET 80 - Shingles–asphalt or tar - Bird Inc.

JET 170 - Office supplies ☆ - Ace Fastener

JET-A-LAC - Enamels - Bridges Smith & Co.

JET-A-MARK - Inks - Matthews International Corp.

JET-A-WAY - Brooms - American Water Broom Co.

JET-A-WAY - Cleaning preparations–carpet and rug - Promaster

JET AERATOR - Bathroom fixtures - Melard Manufacturing Corp.

JET AGE - Tires ☆ - Bridgestone/Firestone, Inc.

JET-AGE - Video production - Jet-Age Productions

JET-AIR - Swimming pools - Hayward Pool Products Inc.

JET AIRE - Compressors–air - Parks Products Inc.

JET-AIRE - Saw blades - Heinemann Saw Corp.

JET AIRLINER - Guitars - Fred Gretsch Enterprises

JET AMERICAN - Bicycles - Columbia Manufacturing Inc.

JET BILLIARDS - Games ☆ - Pacific Game Co.

JET-BLAC - Paints, etc ☆ - Atlantic Varnish & Paint Co. Inc.

JET-BLACK - Sealing compounds - Jet-Black Sealcoating & Repair, Inc.

JET BONNET - Hair care products - Windmere Corp.

JET-BOYS - Computer software ☆ - Accolade Inc.

JET CARE INTERNATIONAL - Cleaning preparations - Thomas Esposito

JET CAT - Boats - Glen-L Marine Designs

JET CHEF - Barbecues and grills ☆ - Jacuzzi Brothers

JET CHEF - Food products - Langlois Frozen Foods

JET CITY PALE ALE - Beverages–malt - Jet City Brewing Co.

JET CLEAN - Fuel additives - Associated Equipment Corp.

JET CLEAN - Machinery - Shasta Industries, Inc.

JET-CLIP - Plastics - DHJ Plastics (USA), Inc.

JET CLIPPER - Watches - Bulova Corp.

JET CO. - Tarpaulins - Jet Co., Inc.

JET COMPETITION - Balls–basketball - Wilson Sporting Goods Co.

JET CONNECT - Computer peripheral equipment ☆ - QMS, Inc.

JET COPTER - Toys–airplanes - Park Plastics Co.

JET-CUT - Abrasive products - Bullard Abrasives Inc.

JET CUT - Cutlery ☆ - Lifetime Hoan Corp.

JET DIAL - Sprinklers–lawn ☆ - L.R. Nelson Corp.

JET DISCS - Toys - Ray Plastic Inc.

JET DOCK - Docks - Jet Dock Systems, Inc.

JET-DOT - Inks and solvents - Independent Ink Inc.

JET DRI - Paints - Proctor Paint & Varnish Co. Inc.

JET DRIVE - Computer software - Manesh Electronics, Inc.

JET-DRIVER - Tufting machines - Tuftamatic, Inc.

JET DRY - Dishwashing compounds - Benckiser Consumer Products Inc.

JET-DRY - Dishwashing compounds - Ecolab Inc.

JET DRY - Inks - American Coated Products Inc.

JET DRY - Photographic equipment - Century Labs Inc.

JET-EDGE - Office supplies ☆ - JM Co.

JET-ERASE - Office supplies - Bee Paper Co. Inc.

JET EYE - Recording label - Jet-Eye Record Products Inc.

JET FLAME - Lighters–cigarette - Adams Apple Distributing L.P.

JET FLIGHTER - Pens ☆ - Parker Pen USA

JET FLO - Hockey equipment - Mylec, Inc.

JET FLO - Pet products - Rolf C. Hagen (USA) Corp.

JET FLO DUSTMASTER - Engine-air precleaner and aspirator - R.C. Plath Co.

JET-FRESH SEAFOOD - Seafood products–fresh or frozen - JLP International Trade, Ltd.

JET-GARD - Sealing compounds - Garon Products Inc.

JET GRIP - Tape–adhesive - Conso Products Co.

JET GUARD - Plastics–laminated - Seal Products Inc.

JET HAWK - Toys–models - Cox Products Inc.

JET-HEAD - Drill bits - Driltec, Drilling and Fastening Technics, Inc.

JET HIDE - Paints - Perry & Derrick Co.

JET HIDE - Paints ☆ - Foy-Johnston Inc.

JET-IT-OFF - Paint removers ☆ - Masury Paint Co.

JET JEL - Hair care products - Paula Payne Products Co. Inc.

JET JIVE - Bicycles - Neal Enterprises

JET JUMP - Ramps - Bayreuther Boat Yard Inc.

JET KING BUTANE CHARGERS - Battery chargers ☆ - Kidde Safety

JET KING CO2 - Battery chargers ☆ - Kidde Safety

JET LAG - Apparel–athletic - Shear Intensity

JET LIGHT - Bicycles - Columbia Manufacturing Inc.

JET LINE - Electrical equipment - GB Electrical Inc.

JET LINE - Trailers–travel ☆ - Shasta Industries Inc.

JET LINER - Dinnerware–plastic - Plastics, Inc. (Anchor Hocking Plastics)

JET-LITE - Luggage - Airway Industries, Inc.

JET LOCK - Box springs - Steadley Co.

JET LOCK - Tape–adhesive - Conso Products Co.

JET MAINLINER - Guitars - Fred Gretsch Enterprises

JET MIST - Humidifier ☆ - Hamilton Home Products Inc.

JET N SPRAY - Boats - Eckler Industries Inc.

JET-O-MATIC - Toilets–portable - Mag Aerospace Industries, Inc.

JET PAC - Luggage - Airline Textile Manufacturing Co.

JET PAC - Musical instrument accessories - Westheimer Corp.

JET PACER - Ships - Sutphen Marine Corp.

JET PACK JAB - Toys - Mattel, Inc.

JET PILOT - Toys–automobiles ☆ - Roadmaster Corp.

JET PLANES - Candy ☆ - R.L. Albert & Son, Inc.

JET-PLOT - Plotter printing paper - Dietzgen Corp.

JET POINT - Tools–power-driven - American Tool Companies Inc.

JET RAG - Apparel–athletic - Jet Rag Corp.

JET RIDER - Toys - Tyco Toys

JET-ROC - Concrete products ☆ - Maintenance Inc.

JET ROCKET - Tools ☆ - True Temper Hardware Co.

JET ROLL - Doors - Overhead Door Corp.

JET RUB - Health care products - Halsey Drug Co. Inc.

JET RYDER - Sporting goods - Wellington Leisure Products, Inc.

JET SCRIPT - Computer peripheral equipment - QMS, Inc.

JET SCRUB - Brooms - Lighthouse Industries

JET SET - Apparel and accessories - Mamiye Brothers, Inc.

JET SET - Dryers–hair ☆ - Sunbeam-Oster Household Products

JET SET - Hair care products - Flori Roberts Inc.

JET SET - Hair curlers - Olivia Garden International, Inc.

JET SET - Luggage - Standard Ohio Leasing Corp.

JET SET - Skates–roller - Globe United Inc.

JET SET - Skin care products - Dubl Duck/Jet Set Inc.

JET SET - Tools - General Wire Spring Co.

JET SET - Watches - Hampden Corp.

JET SET AIR IRON - Cosmetics - Dubl Duck/Jet Set Inc.

JET SET AIR STYLER - Hair care products - Dubl Duck/Jet Set Inc.

JET SET BOYZ - Apparel–children's - Mamiye Brothers, Inc.

JET SET COOL KIDS - Apparel ☆ - Mamiye Brothers, Inc.

JET SET JUNIOR - Apparel–women's - Wacoal America Inc.

JET SET JR. - Skates–roller - Globe United Inc.

JET-SETTER - Bathroom fixtures - Price Pfister Co.

JET SKI - Motor vehicles - Kawasaki Motors Corp. USA

JET SKI 750 ZXI - Motor vehicles - Kawasaki Motors Corp. USA

JET SLED - Toys - Mattel, Inc.

JET SOAP - Soap - Creative Products Inc. of Rossville

JET-SOL - Juices - Sunkist Growers Inc.

JET SOUNDS - Audio equipment - Jet Sound Electronics

JET-SPAR - Enamels - Kentucky Paint Manufacturing Co.

JET SPEE - Tools–garden ☆ - Gilmour Manufacturing Co.

JET-SPRAY - Paints ☆ - Lawter International Inc.

JET-SPRED II - Fertilizers - Greenview Lawn & Garden Products

JET SQUIRTER - Toys–guns - Daisy Manufacturing Co.

JET STAR - Bicycles - Columbia Manufacturing Inc.

JET STAR - Boats–motor ☆ - Lund Boat Co.

JET STAR - Kites - Gayla Industries Inc.

JET STAR - Machinery - Busch Co.

JET STAR - Vacuum cleaners and accessories - Baracuda International Corp.

JET STEPPERS - Footwear–athletic ☆ - American Athletic Shoe Co.

JET STICK - Computer peripheral equipment - Joystick Technologies (CH Products Division)

JET STREAK - Bicycles - Columbia Manufacturing Inc.

JET STREAM - Hair care products - Graham Webb International

☆ = Now out of production

JET STREAM - Hand and type cleaners - American Coated Products Inc.
JET STREAM - Jewelry - Jacoby-Bender Inc.
JET STREAM - Machinery - Steam Jet Corp.
JET STREAM - Pet products - Rolf C. Hagen (USA) Corp.
JET STREAM - Pipes - National Briar Pipe Co.
JET STREAM - Recording label - Music Enterprises Inc.
JET STREAM - Skis - Wellington Leisure Products, Inc.
JET STREEX - Toys–airplanes - Mattel, Inc.
JET STRIP - Paint and wallpaper cleaners ☆ - H.F. Staples & Co. Inc.
JET SUIT - Wet suits–rubber ☆ - Parkway Systems
JET SWEEP - Pumps - Marley Pump Co.
JET SWEEP - Water purification systems - World Wide Sports, Inc.
JET SWEEP X5 - Toys–airplanes - Mattel, Inc.
JET SWING - Wallets ☆ - Kleer-Vu Plastics Inc.
JET-TECH - Paper products - Mead Corp.
JET THREAT - Toys–airplanes - Mattel, Inc.
JET-TONE - Musical instrument accessories - Jet-Tone Inc.
JET TORCH - Torches - Bernzomatic
JET TRAINER - Skates–roller ☆ - Steven Manufacturing Co.
JET TRAX - Computer software - Lynne M. Warsaw
JET TRIO - Erasers ☆ - Bright Boy Abrasives
JET TWIN - Guitars ☆ - Fred Gretsch Enterprises
JET VAC - Vacuum cleaners and accessories - The Genie Co.
JET VIEW - Computer software - Houston Instrument
JET VOYAGER - Watches - Hampden Corp.
JET WAVE - Boats - Prodesign of Indiana Inc.
JET WAVE - Sporting goods - Nikko America, Inc.
JET WORD - Games ☆ - Milton Bradley Co.
JET X - Cleaning preparations - Master Force Marketing, Inc.
JET-X - Fire extinguishers - Ansul, Inc.
JET-X - Tools - MasterForce Inc.
JET X-PLUS - Brushes - MasterForce Inc.
JETARRAY - Printers–computer - Domino Amjet Inc.
JETAWAY - Luggage ☆ - Platt Luggage Inc.
JETBAG - Bags–cosmetic - Holiday Fair, Inc.
JETBLAK - Cement - GAF Corp.
JETBOOK - Computers - Jetta International Inc.
JETBOOT - Footwear - Philip's Group, Inc.
JETBRITE - Waxes–sealing - Baker Hughes Inc.
JETCAL 2000 - Engines - Howell Instruments, Inc.
JETCLEAN - Dishwashers–household - Maytag Corp.
JETCONNECT - Computer software - XDB Systems, Inc.
JETER - File folders - Jeter Systems Corp.
JETFAX - Electronic equipment repair shops - Jetfax, Inc.
JETFIL - Talcum powders - Luzenac America Inc.
JETFILL - Inks - Coast Oil Country Tubulars
JETFIRE - Toys–airplanes - Paul K. Guillow Inc.
JETFLO - Water purification systems - Pneumo Abex Corp.
JETFLOW - Machinery - Aluminum Co. of America
JETFORM BIZFORMS - Computer software - Jetform Corp.
JETGEAR - Containers–plastic - Samuel D. Blatt
JETGLAS - Heating equipment ☆ - Bradford-White Corp.
JETGUARD - Life preservers - Bart's Water Ski Center, Inc.
JETHRO CLOWN - Dolls ☆ - Effanbee Doll Corp.
JETHRO'S ORIGINAL SALSA - Sauces - JD Foods, Inc.
JETLAN - Computer peripheral equipment - ASP Computer Products Inc.
JETLINE - Markers–felt-tip ☆ - National Pen & Pencil Co.
JETLINER - Bicycles - Columbia Manufacturing Co.
JETLINER - Cosmetics - Revlon Consumer Products Corp.
JETLINER - Toys - Fisher-Price, Inc.
JETLOG - Computer software - Glenn R. Cox
JETMATE - Boats–motor ☆ - Checkmate Boats Inc.
JETNET - Sporting goods - Jetnet Corp.
JETO-MATIC - Toilets–portable - Monogram Sanitation Co.
JETPAK - Garden equipment - Solo, Inc.
JETPUCK - Toys - Mattel, Inc.
JETRAIL - Machinery - Tie Down, Inc.
JETRIC - Office supplies ☆ - Yasutomo
JETROLL - Doors–garage - Overhead Door Corp.
JETS - Cereal ☆ - General Mills, Inc.
JETS - Marshmallows - Kraft Foods, Inc.
JETS - Vitamins and nutritional supplements - Freeda Vitamins Inc.
JETSAILER - Boats - Westwind Yachts, Inc.
JETSERIES - Paper - Hewlett-Packard Co.
JETSET - Doors–garage - Overhead Door Corp.
JETSETTER - Curling irons–electric - Helen of Troy Corp.

JETSLIDE - Doors–garage - Overhead Door Corp.
JETSONS - Air purification systems ☆ - Medo Industries, Inc.
JETSON'S COSMIC CANDY - Candy ☆ - Warner-Lambert Co.
JETSONS, THE - Toys–stuffed ☆ - Dakin Inc.
JETSONS, THE - Apparel and accessories - Hanna-Barbera Productions, Inc.
JETSONS, THE - Games - Milton Bradley Co.
JETSPRAY - Fertilizers - Reliance Plastic & Chemical Corp.
JETSPRAY - Lacquers - H. Behlen & Bro. Inc.
JETSTAR - Floor coverings–carpet and rugs ☆ - World Carpets, Inc.
JETSTAR - Recreational vehicle dealers - Ultranautics Corp.
JETSTAR - Vacuum cleaners and accessories–commercial - Baracuda International Corp.
JETSTART - Dryers–hair ☆ - Ronson Consumer Products Corp.
JETSTEEL - Tires–automobile - General Tire, Inc.
JETSTICK - Computer peripheral equipment - Joystick Technologies (CH Products Division)
JETSTONE - Cement - W.W. Henry Co.
JETSTREAM - Bicycles - Columbia Manufacturing Inc.
JETSTREAM - Envelopes - Quality Park Products Co.
JETSTREAM - Faucets - Kallista Inc.
JETSTREAM - Golfing equipment - Golfsmith International Inc.
JETSTREAM - Sprinklers–lawn - Melnor Inc.
JETSTREAM - Synthetic turf - Instant Turf Industries Inc.
JETSTREAM - Toys–airplanes - Paul K. Guillow Inc.
JETSTREAM - Watches - Gruen Marketing Corp.
JETSTREAM 2 - Golfing equipment - Golfsmith International Inc.
JETSTREAM DOUBLE BAR - Shower rods - Kallista Inc.
JETSTREAM TOUR - Golfing equipment - Golfsmith International Inc.
JETSTREAMER - Skates–roller - National Sporting Goods Corp.
JETSUITE - Computer software - Jetfax, Inc.
JETT HEAD - Toilets–porcelain - Raritan Engineering Co. Inc.
JETTA - Motor vehicles–automobiles - Volkswagen of America Inc.
JETTACHE - Luggage ☆ - Stebco Products Corp.
JETTACIN - Cleaning preparations - Chemed Corp.
JETTE - Housewares ☆ - Dansk International Designs, Ltd.
JETTER - Thread ☆ - American & Efird, Inc.
JETTISON - Pumps - Mayfair Molded Products
JETWASH - Hoses - Jetwash Co.
JETWELT - Window coverings - Conso Products Co.
JETWIND - Boats - Sears, Roebuck and Co.
JETZEN - Footwear - L.A. Gear, Inc.
JETZON - Tires–automobile - Jetzon/Telstar Tire
JEUNE ROSE - Lipsticks - Cosmair Inc.
JEUNESSE - Dinnerware–glass - WMF/USA
JEUNESSE - Frames–eyeglass - Charmant Inc. USA
JEUNESSE - Furniture - Singer Furniture Co.
JEUNESSE - Perfumes ☆ - Luzier Personalized Cosmetics, Inc.
JEUNIQUE - Pharmaceutical preparations - Jeunique International, Inc.
JEVAL A-PEEL - Skin care products - Jeval Laboratories, Inc.
JEVERON - Pharmaceutical preparations - Parmed Pharmaceuticals, Inc.
JEWEL - Aquariums–household - O'Dell Industries
JEWEL - Artists' materials ☆ - Binney & Smith Inc.
JEWEL - Candlesticks - Libbey Glass Inc.
JEWEL - Candy ☆ - Topps Co., Inc.
JEWEL - Dishes–earthenware ☆ - Royal China & Porcelain Companies Inc.
JEWEL - Fabrics - Land Fabric Co.
JEWEL - Faucets - B & K Industries, Inc.
JEWEL - Fencing–iron ☆ - Waters Corp.
JEWEL - Fishing tackle - Jewel Industries Inc.
JEWEL - Floor coverings–carpet and rugs ☆ - American Carpet Mills
JEWEL - Floor coverings–carpet and rugs ☆ - Bloomsburg Carpet Industries
JEWEL - Floor coverings–carpet and rugs ☆ - Regal Rugs Inc.
JEWEL - Food products - American Stores Co.
JEWEL - Food products - Beatrice Cos. Inc.
JEWEL - Frames–eyeglass - Rozin Optical Export Corp.
JEWEL - Fruits and vegetables - Roche Fruit Co. Inc.
JEWEL - Handles–wood - Hartwell Brothers Handle Co.
JEWEL - Housewares - Shuford Mills Inc. (Diversified Products Division)
JEWEL - Irons–electric - Sunbeam-Oster Household Products
JEWEL - Labels–paper - Sue Records Inc.
JEWEL - Laces–boot and shoe - South Carolina Elastic Co.
JEWEL - Mops ☆ - Helen Keller Services for the Blind
JEWEL - Office supplies - Seal-O-Matic Corp.
JEWEL - Paints ☆ - KCI Coatings, Inc.
JEWEL - Pencils ☆ - Faber-Castell Corp.
JEWEL - Stationery ☆ - Mead Corp.

☆ = Now out of production

JEWEL - Thread ☆ - Premier Thread Co.
JEWEL - Tiles–ceramic - Dal-Tile Corp.
JEWEL - Toys ☆ - Duncan Toys Co.
JEWEL - Watches - Bulova Corp.
JEWEL - Yarn ☆ - Caron International Inc.
JEWEL - Yarn ☆ - William Unger & Co. Inc.
JEWEL & ONYX - Tiles–ceramic ☆ - Huntington/Pacific Ceramics Inc.
JEWEL BOX - Shoes - Edison Brothers Stores, Inc.
JEWEL BOX II - Wallpaper ☆ - David & Dash
JEWEL BOX III - Wallpaper ☆ - David & Dash
JEWEL CLEAN - Cleaning preparations - W.J. Hagerty & Sons Ltd. Inc.
JEWEL COLLECTION - Toys - Mattel, Inc.
JEWEL CREST - Floor coverings–carpet and rugs - Cabin Crafts Carpets
JEWEL CUBE - Electronic equipment - Bose Corp.
JEWEL DOUBLEQUICK - Paints ☆ - KCI Coatings, Inc.
JEWEL ESSENCE - Mattresses - Restonic Inc.
JEWEL FAIR COLLECTION, THE - Jewelry - Frank Vernon
JEWEL FASHIONS - Dolls ☆ - Totsy Manufacturing Co., Inc.
JEWEL FX - Jewelry - Ali Vahidi
JEWEL HAIR MERMAID - Dolls - Mattel, Inc.
JEWEL HOLD - Glue–household or industrial - National Artcraft Co.
JEWEL JUBILEE - Dolls - Mattel, Inc.
JEWEL KING - Jewelry - Louis Neff Inc.
JEWEL-LITE - Christmas tree lights - General Enterprises Inc.
JEWEL LO-LUSTRE - Paints ☆ - KCI Coatings, Inc.
JEWEL LOOK - Furniture - Erwin-Lambeth Inc.
JEWEL MAID - Food products - Jewel Food Stores Inc.
JEWEL MONT - Jewelry - Golden Mist Jewelry
JEWEL OF INDIA - Sauces - Victoria's Treasure Inc.
JEWEL PETS - Toys - Hasbro, Inc.
JEWEL PRINCESS - Dolls - Mattel, Inc.
JEWEL-RAY - Jewelry - Hobe Cie. Ltd.
JEWEL RENEWAL - Jewelry cleaner - Fashion Solutions USA Inc.
JEWEL ROYALE COLLECTION - Flatware ☆ - Kirk Stieff Co.
JEWEL SONG - Christmas tree ornaments - Cracker Box Inc.
JEWEL TIME - Watches - Luxury International Inc.
JEWEL TONES - Hair care products - Redmond Products, Inc.
JEWEL TONES - Wallpaper ☆ - Imperial Wallcoverings, Inc.
JEWEL TREE - Greeting cards - Norcross Inc.
JEWEL-UP - Jewelry boxes - Noemi Chaparro
JEWEL WHITE - Dishes–earthenware - Denby USA Limited
JEWELBRIGHT - Christmas tree lights - Noma International, Inc.
JEWELCAST - Jewelry - Classic Industries Inc.
JEWELED ELEGANCE - Greeting cards - Norcross Inc.
JEWELED GREETINGS - Hobby kits ☆ - Greene Plastics Corp.
JEWELED OPULENCE - Cosmetics - Del Pharmaceuticals, Inc.
JEWELERS BEST - Jewelry - Jacoby-Bender Inc.
JEWELERS FRIEND - Jewelry - Jacoby-Bender Inc.
JEWELER'S JEWELER, THE - Jewelry–precious - Oscar Heyman & Brothers, Inc.
JEWELERS OF LAS VEGAS, THE - Jewelry - Mordechai Yerushalmi
JEWELIARDS - Jewelry - True Gems, Inc.
JEWELITE - Cleaning preparations - Connoisseurs Products Corp.
JEWELITE - Lighting equipment - Leviton Manufacturing Co., Inc.
JEWELITE - Signs - Jewelite Sign Co.
JEWELITE-LETTER TRIM - Signs - Wagner Zip-Change Inc.
JEWELLED LADY - Jewelry - Jacoby-Bender Inc.
JEWELLERY WITH A MEANING - Jewelry - Alchemists, Inc.
JEWELL'S CLASSIC BOTTOMS - Apparel and accessories - Jewell's Classic Bottoms, Inc.
JEWELMONT - Jewelry - Jewelmont Corp.
JEWELOK - Buckles - Hawie Manufacturing Co.
JEWELROLL - Giftware - Accessories International
JEWELRY ACCENTS - Jewelry ☆ - Duncan Enterprises
JEWELRY BY JOSHUA - Jewelry - Jewelry by Joshua
JEWELRY-BY-THE-INCH - Jewelry - Lasting Impressions Inc.
JEWELRY CENTER, THE - Electronic equipment - Windmere Corp.
JEWELRY CONNECTION, THE - Artists' materials - Decorator and Craft Corp.
JEWELRY CREATIONS - Hobby kits - Quincrafts Corp.
JEWELRY EXCHANGE - Jewelry - Goldenwest Diamond Corp.
JEWELRY FOR GENERATIONS - Jewelry - CJC Holdings, Inc.
JEWELRY FOR THE HOME - Flowers, plants, and seeds - Eric's Exotics, Inc.
JEWELRY FUN - Dolls - Mattel, Inc.
JEWELRY ORGANIZER, THE - Display cases–plastic - Design Northwest
JEWELRY REPAIRS BY US - Jewelry stores - Jewelry Repairs by Us
JEWELRY ROUGE - Polishing cloths - Cadie Products Corp.

JEWELRY SAQ - Bags - Curator
JEWELRY SCREEN - Skin care products - Blitz Manufacturing Co., Inc.
JEWELRY SHIELD - Skin care products - M'destiny, Inc.
JEWELRY SHOP, THE - Hobby kits - Weingeroff Enterprises, Inc.
JEWELRY WORKS, THE - Jewelry - Jewelry Works Inc.
JEWELRYCRAFT - Toys ☆ - Coloron Industries
JEWELS - Dinnerware–glass - Block China Co.
JEWELS - Dolls ☆ - Effanbee Doll Corp.
JEWELS - Games - International Gamco, Inc.
JEWELS - Mats - Majestic Mat Co.
JEWELS - Underwear and nightwear - Slumbertogs Inc.
JEWELS & JEMS - Paints - Carnival Arts, Inc.
JEWELS & STONES - Wallpaper - Capital Carousel Inc.
JEWELS BLACK GOLD - Cigars - Havatampa Inc.
JEWELS BY DANSAL - Jewelry - Dansal Corp.
JEWELS BY MARINA SCHIANO - Jewelry - Schiano, Marina
JEWELS BY PARK LANE - Jewelry - Jewels by Park Lane, Inc.
JEWELS BY RAFFI - Jewelry–costume - Cinerama Jewelry Inc.
JEWELS BY RITA HELENE - Jewelry - Walter Bauman Jewelers Inc.
JEWELS FOR LIFE - Jewelry - Wet Seal Inc.
JEWELS 'N' GEMS - Apparel and accessories - Coloron Industries
JEWELS OF ASIA - Wallpaper - K.M.L. Industries
JEWELS OF LEGENDARY SPLENDOR - Jewelry - Hobe Cie. Ltd.
JEWELS OF LIGHT - Candles ☆ - Candle-Lite Co.
JEWELS OF THE HERMITAGE - Christmas tree ornaments - Cracker Box Inc.
JEWELS OF THE SEA - Cosmetics - Maybelline Co.
JEWELS SWEETS - Cigars - Havatampa Inc.
JEWELSAFE - Cases–vanity - Mautner Co. Inc.
JEWELSTAR - Toys - Mattel, Inc.
JEWELSTONES - Tiles–ceramic - Dal-Tile Corp.
JEWELTONE - Clocks - General Time Corp. (Westclox/Seth Thomas Div.)
JEWELTRIM - Jewelry - Fred Frankel & Sons Inc.
JEWISH ART - Publisher's imprints - Hebrew Publishing Co.
JEWISH FOLK ART - Calendars ☆ - Amcal Inc.
JEWISH FORTUNE COOKIES - Cookies - Creative Cookie Inc. (American Dream Enterprises)
JEWISH MOTHER'S - Soups–canned - Young's Market Co.
JEWISH PRIDE - Posters - Ethnic Pride, Inc.
JEWISH STUDIES - Publisher's imprints - Syracuse University Press
JEX - Badminton equipment - Rackets International (Racket Sports Div.)
JEX - Steel products - Williams Co.
JEZ - Apparel–women's - Jez of California
JEZ BY JUANITA RITTER - Apparel–women's - Jez of California
JEZE-BARE - Apparel–women's - Jezebel-Renee of Hollywood
JEZEBEL - Apparel–women's - Jezebel-Renee of Hollywood
JEZEBEL - Cigarettes - G.A. Georgopulo & Co. Inc.
JEZEBEL - Dolls ☆ - Effanbee Doll Corp.
JEZEBEL - Firearms, accessories, and parts - Texas Longhorn Arms, Inc.
JEZEBEL - Floor coverings–carpet and rugs - Queen Carpet Corp.
JEZLAINE - Jewelry - Jezlaine Ltd.
JEZZIE - Footwear–women's - Jezzie, L.C.
JEZZIES - Apparel–women's - Jezebel-Renee of Hollywood
JF - Apparel and accessories - Thomas William Reynolds
J.F. - Jewelry–costume - Jewelry Fashions Inc.
JF - Teas - Robertet Flavors Inc.
JF SEAL OF QUALITY - Milk - Johanna Dairies Inc.
JF WORLD - Footwear - JF World Inc.
JFA - Coveralls - Edmont
JFA - Jewelry - JFA Designs
JFAX - Computer software - Jfax Communications, Inc.
JFG - Coffee - JFG Coffee Co.
JFH - Underwear and nightwear - Jockey International, Inc.
JFIS - Steel products - Kenneth W. Hummell
JFJ WINERY - Wines - Bronco Wine Co.
JFM - Musical instrument accessories ☆ - Scherl & Roth Inc.
JFS LITIGATION WORKGROUP - Computer software - Docucon, Inc.
JFS LITIGATOR'S NOTEBOOK - Computer software - Docucon, Inc.
JFW - Valves - JFW Industries, Inc.
J.G. - Frames–eyeglass - May Optical Co. Inc.
JG - Furniture–wood - Burlington Industries, Inc.
JG - Guitars ☆ - Giulietti Accordion Corp.
JG - Jewelry - Joe R. Gluck
J.G. HOOK - Apparel - J.G. Hook, Inc.
J.G. HOOK - Footwear - J.G. Hook, Inc.
J.G. HOOK - Gloves, hats, and scarves - Hansen Knits
J.G. HOOK - Hosiery - Easton International

J.G. HOOK - Jewelry - Darlene Jewelry Manufacturing Co., Inc.
J.G. HOOK BED & BREADFAST - Wallcovering - Fashon Wallcoverings
J.G. HOOK JEANSWEAR - Apparel and accessories - J.G. Hook, Inc.
JG JACK GEORGES - Leather goods - Jack Georges Inc.
JG JOE +GIBBS RACING - Apparel and accessories - Joe Gibbs Racing, Inc.
JG PRESS - Publisher's imprints - World Publications, Inc.
JGEE J - Apparel—women's - Unlimited Avenues Inc.
JGF DISENO - Skirts—women's - JGF Diseno
J.G.HOOK - Frames—eyeglass - Pan Oceanic Eyewear, Ltd.
JH COLLECTIBLES - Apparel—women's - JH Collectibles Inc.
JHATS - Hats - Jacobson Hat Co.
JHB - Apparel and accessories - Jhane Barnes (Del.) Inc.
JHB - Buttons - JHB International Inc.
JHC - Apparel and accessories - JH Collectibles Inc.
JHERI KURL - Hair care products - Pantresse Inc.
JHERI REDDING - Hair care products - Conair Corp.
JHERI REDDING PROFESSIONAL THERATREAT - Hair care products - Conair Corp.
JHERI SHEEN - Hair care products - Nexxus Products Co.
JHIRMACK - Hair care products - Playtex Beauty Care, Inc.
JHIRMACK FABULOUSLY CLEAN - Hair care products - Maybelline Co.
JHIRMACK PLUS - Hair care products - Playtex Beauty Care, Inc.
JHIRMACK SHINE - Hair care products - Playtex Beauty Care, Inc.
JHIRMACK SILVER - Hair care products - Playtex Beauty Care, Inc.
JHIRMACK STYLING SPRITZ - Hair care products - Playtex Beauty Care, Inc.
JHIRMACK ULTIMATE HOLD - Hair care products - Playtex Beauty Care, Inc.
J.H.L. - Perfumes - Estee Lauder Inc.
JHM - Hosiery - Johnson Hosiery Mills, Inc.
JHONE BARNES - Apparel and accessories - Oxford Industries, Inc.
JHOON RHEE - Sporting goods - Hokkaido-Karate Equipment Manufacturing Co.
JHS - Syrup - J. Hungerford Smith Co.
J.I. - Fruits and vegetables - Pitsweet Inc.
JI - Jewelry - Jewelry Innovations Inc.
J.I. CASE - Toys - ERTL Co., Inc.
JI-GAN-TICS - Construction toys - James Industries, Inc.
JI-RO - Toys - Maryland Toy Corp.
JIALING - Motorcycles - Jialing Motorcycle (America) Corp.
JIAN - Rackets—tennis - Mark Wheatley
JIB AWAY - Boats - Mariner Co.
JIBBA JABBER - Toys - ERTL Co., Inc.
JIBBAJABBER - Dolls - ERTL Co., Inc.
JIBBER JABBERS! - Apparel and accessories - Rein Designs Inc.
JIBCO - Giftware - Jibco Industries Inc.
JIBFURL - Sporting goods - Blue Water Marine Inc.
JIBS - Footwear - Columbia Footwear Corp.
JIC - Glue—household or industrial - Crescent Products Co.
JICKY - Perfumes - Guerlain Inc.
JIF - Peanut butter - Procter & Gamble Co.
JIF ACTION - Chemical preparations - GC Thorsen, Inc.
JIF-SET - Gypsum products - F.H. Leinweber Co. Inc.
JIF-Y-CLEAN - Cleaning preparations - Microtron Abrasives, Inc.
JIFFCO - Vegetables—frozen - Pitsweet Inc.
JIFFI-EGG - Food products ☆ - Agway Country Foods Inc.
JIFFI-SAFE - Knives - Cosco Industries Inc.
JIFFIES - Sausages - Jones Dairy Farm
JIFFIES - Slip covers - Kayser-Roth Corp.
JIFFY - Adhesives and sealants - L.D. Sterns Corp.
JIFFY - Apparel—women's ☆ - Vermont Sports Apparel Inc.
JIFFY - Bags - Mason Box Co. Inc.
JIFFY - Bakery products - Chelsea Milling Co.
JIFFY - Brackets - Grand Haven Stamped Products Co.
JIFFY - Christmas tree stands - Michael R. Conrad
JIFFY - Drills—hand-operated - Feldmann Engineering & Manufacturing Co., Inc.
JIFFY - Electrical equipment - Eagle Electric Manufacturing Co., Inc.
JIFFY - Enamels - Jones Blair Co.
JIFFY - Food products - Conagra, Inc.
JIFFY - Garment storage bags ☆ - Neely Manufacturing Co. Inc.
JIFFY - Hair care products - Gaylord Products Inc.
JIFFY - Hardware - C & D Distributors Inc.
JIFFY - Housewares - Ballonoff Home Products
JIFFY - Key rings - Art Craft Wallets Inc.
JIFFY - Mouthwashes - Block Drug Co., Inc.
JIFFY - Packaging—paper - Sealed Air Corp.
JIFFY - Patterns—clothing ☆ - Simplicity Pattern Co., Inc.

JIFFY - Pen holders - Wescosa Inc.
JIFFY - Pet products - Beckett Corp.
JIFFY - Skin care products - Pro-Capa Products Inc.
JIFFY - Steamers—apparel - Jiffy Steamer Co.
JIFFY - Thread - Staple Sewing Aids Corp.
JIFFY - Toys—stuffed ☆ - Gund, Inc.
JIFFY - Yarn ☆ - Lion Brand Yarn Co.
JIFFY-7'S - Garden equipment - Carefree Garden Products
JIFFY ANGLE SQUARE - Hand tool - Vermont American Corp.
JIFFY BASIC - Yarn ☆ - Lion Brand Yarn Co.
JIFFY-BOND - Adhesives and sealants - Jones Blair Co.
JIFFY BONUS BUNDLE - Yarn - Lion Brand Yarn Co.
JIFFY BUDGET-PAK - Cleaning preparations - Durawool Inc.
JIFFY CHUNKY - Yarn ☆ - Lion Brand Yarn Co.
JIFFY-COVER - Plastics film - Warp Bros.
JIFFY CUT - Building materials - Wes-Cut Corp.
JIFFY-DRI - Varnishes ☆ - Nowstar
JIFFY DRY - Varnishes - Jones Blair Co.
JIFFY DRYER - Cordage and twine ☆ - Alger Creations Inc.
JIFFY FIL - Bats—baseball - Jen Cel Lite Corp.
JIFFY FLEX - Thread - Staple Sewing Aids Corp.
JIFFY FUSE - Thread - Staple Sewing Aids Corp.
JIFFY-GEMS - Jewelry - Coburn Corp.
JIFFY GRIP - Thread - Staple Sewing Aids Corp.
JIFFY-GRO - Garden equipment - Carefree Garden Products
JIFFY-GROWER - Garden equipment ☆ - Carefree Garden Products
JIFFY-GYM - Exercising equipment - Voit Corp.
JIFFY HOOK - Hardware - South Camden Iron Works
JIFFY JACK - Cheese - Mid-America Dairymen Inc. Southern Div.
JIFFY JIGSAWS - Puzzles ☆ - Parker Brothers
JIFFY-KEY - Key cases - Arch T. Dulaney
JIFFY KIT - Automotive parts and accessories - Standard Motor Products, Inc.
JIFFY MELT - Chemical preparations - Akzo Nobel Salt Inc.
JIFFY MELT - Salt ☆ - Akzo America Inc.
JIFFY-MIRACLE - Garden equipment - Carefree Garden Products
JIFFY-MIX - Garden equipment - Carefree Garden Products
JIFFY PACKER - Packaging—paper - Sealed Air Corp.
JIFFY PLEATER - Thread ☆ - Staple Sewing Aids Corp.
JIFFY POP - Popcorn - American Home Food Products Inc.
JIFFY POP KIDS, THE - Popcorn - American Home Food Products Inc.
JIFFY POP LIGHT - Popcorn - American Home Food Products Inc.
JIFFY-POTS - Flowerpots - Geo. J. Ball, Inc.
JIFFY-POTS - Garden equipment - Carefree Garden Products
JIFFY PUSH-PULL - Electrical equipment - Eagle Electric Manufacturing Co., Inc.
JIFFY RACK - Tools ☆ - Arco Products Corp.
JIFFY RIGI BAG - Packaging—paper - Sealed Air Corp.
JIFFY-RINK - Skating rinks—ice ☆ - Warp Bros.
JIFFY RIVET - Luggage - Ohio Travel Bag Manufacturing Co.
JIFFY-SEAL - Adhesives and sealants ☆ - Nowstar
JIFFY SEAL 140/60 - Waterproofing compounds - Protecto Wrap Co.
JIFFY SLATE - Braille slates ☆ - Howe Press
JIFFY SPRAY - Housewares - Unival Corp.
JIFFY SPUDS - Food products - Victory Spud Service
JIFFY-STRIPS - Garden equipment - Carefree Garden Products
JIFFY-TAGS - Pet identification tags - B-Elegant Products
JIFFY-VAR - Varnishes ☆ - Nowstar
JIFFY WAISTBAND - Thread - Staple Sewing Aids Corp.
JIFFY-WALL - Movable partitions ☆ - Yates Furniture Systems Corp.
JIFFY WRAP - Gauze—surgical - National Patent Medical
JIFFY-WRAP - Plastics film ☆ - Warp Bros.
JIFFYLITE - Envelopes - Mason Box Co. Inc.
JIFFYLITE - Packaging—paper - Sealed Air Corp.
JIG CRAWLER - Flags - Plastics Research and Development Co.
JIG FIX - Fishing lures - Billy E. Trent
JIG HELLO'S - Greeting cards - Martin Roland Auger
JIG IN A BOX - Puzzles ☆ - MonkeyPuzzle Inc.
JIG IT - Hinges - Rockler Companies, Inc.
JIG LIFT - Machinery - JLG Industries Inc.
JIG MASTER - Fishing tackle - Penn Fishing Tackle Manufacturing Co.
JIG SAW - Toys - Tonka Corp.
JIG SIZZOR - Machinery - JLG Industries Inc.
JIGGER, THE - Ice cream - Charlotte D. Allwein
JIGGER TWINS - Bar fixtures—plastic - Crossbow Inc.
JIGGLE - Toys - Concept Products Inc.
JIGGLE BELLS - Bathing suits - Group E. Ltd.

☆ = Now out of production

JIGGLE BERRY - Fruit drinks–bottled or canned ☆ - Green Spot Packaging, Inc.

JIGGLEBALL - Toys - Gerber Products Co.

JIGGLERS - Novelty items - Paper Magic Group Inc.

JIGGLERS - Yogurt - Kraft Foods, Inc.

JIGGLES - Toys–stuffed - Fun World Inc.

JIGGS DAY - Fishing lures - Day Bait Co.

JIGGY - Sporting goods - Weber Industries Inc.

JIGMIL - Machine tools and parts - DV Associates L.P.

JIGSAW MARCI - Puzzles - Joslin Photo Puzzle Co.

JIGSAW STAND-UP - Puzzles - Warren Industries Inc.

JIL SANDER - Colognes - Gary Farn Ltd.

JILAN BEUTI-NAILS - Nail care products - Premier Brands of America

JILBERE - Beauty shop equipment ☆ - JRC Products Inc.

JILDOR - Footwear - Jildor Shoes, Inc.

JILIN PRODUCTS - Vitamins and nutritional supplements - Wicsun Trading, Inc.

JILL - Dolls ☆ - Effanbee Doll Corp.

JILL - Watches - Bulova Corp.

JILL LINDBERG - Hair care products - Jill Lindberg Products Inc.

JILL MARLOWE - Apparel and accessories - High Sierra, Ltd.

JILL PAIGE ORIGINALS - Apparel–women's - Bram International Limited

JILL ROGERS - Apparel and accessories - General Fashion Corp. of New York

JILL #ROGERS - Apparel–women's - Strong Choice-New York

JILL SNEDEKER - Infant product - Baby League

JILL STUART - Knapsacks - Ron Curtis

JILL WRIGHT - Greeting cards - Recycled Paper Products, Inc.

JILLCORE - Thread - Sebro Thread Corp.

JILLIE - Athletic footwear ☆ - Autry Industries Inc.

JILL'S - Fruit drinks–bottled or canned ☆ - Yakima Valley Grape Producers Inc.

JILL'S JUNIORS - Food products - John & Jill's, Inc.

JILL'S PRIVATE COLLECTION - Apparel–athletic - General Fashion Corp. of New York

JILLSPUN - Thread - Sebro Thread Corp.

JILLY - Brushes–hair ☆ - Phillips Brush Corp.

JILLY - Candy - Lanco Corp.

JILLY - Toys–stuffed ☆ - Russ Berrie and Co., Inc.

JILLY KNITS - Apparel–women's - Mark Harrison Enterprises

JILLY MAC - Bedding–linen - Diane's Designs Inc.

JIM - Colognes - Brandy Harvest

JIM - Ophthalmic goods - Rozin Optical Export Corp.

JIM - Recording label ☆ - Homeland Recording & Publishing

JIM AND DANDY - Toys–stuffed - CBS Toys

JIM BEAM - Beverages–alcohol - Jim Beam Brands Co.

JIM BEAM 8 STAR - Whiskey ☆ - Jim Beam Brands Co.

+JIM +BEAM AMERICAN BASIC - Beverages–alcohol - Jim Beam Brands Co.

JIM BEAM & COLA - Beverages–alcohol - Jim Beam Brands Co.

JIM BEAM & GINGER ALE - Beverages–alcohol - Jim Beam Brands Co.

JIM BEAM & LEMON-LIME SODA - Beverages–alcohol - Jim Beam Brands Co.

JIM BEAM BARREL-BONDED - Beverages–alcohol ☆ - Jim Beam Brands Co.

JIM BEAM: THE NEW AMERICAN FRONTIER - Beverages–alcohol - Jim Beam Brands Co.

JIM BOWIE - Knives–carving - Knife Importers Inc.

JIM BRACKENBURY - Sporting goods - Jim Brackenbury Bows Inc.

JIM-BUOY - Marine rigging - Cal-June Inc.

JIM CRUMLEY'S - Apparel and accessories - James H. Crumley

JIM +CRUMLEY'S - Apparel and accessories - James H. Crumley

JIM CRUMLEY'S TREBARK - Fabrics - James H. Crumley

JIM DANDY - Corn–flour or meal - Martha White Foods Inc.

JIM DANDY - Handles–wood - Turner, Day and Woolworth Handle Corp.

JIM DANDY - Hardware - Barco Industries, Inc.

JIM DANDY - Musical instrument accessories - Mechanical Music Corp.

JIM DANDY - Pet products - Jim Dandy Co.

JIM DANDY - Pet products - Pillsbury Co.

JIM DANDY - Tools ☆ - True Temper Hardware Co.

JIM DANDY - Tractors ☆ - Engineering Products Co.

JIM DANDY CLASSIC DINNER - Dog food - Jim Dandy Co.

JIM DUNLOP - Musical instrument accessories - Dunlop Manufacturing, Inc.

JIM DUNLOP USA - Musical instrument accessories - Dunlop Manufacturing, Inc.

JIM-E'S OLD FASHIONED - Cakes–frozen - Jim-E's Old Fashioned Cheesecake Ltd.

JIM GRANT - Liquors - Gaetano Specialties Ltd.

JIM GRIFFITH'S - Pharmaceutical preparations - Jim Griffith Co.

JIM HENSON - Recording label - Jim Henson Productions, Inc.

JIM HENSON PRODUCTIONS - Video equipment - Jim Henson Productions, Inc.

JIM HENSON'S ANIMAL SHOW - Lunch boxes - Thermos Co.

JIM HENSON'S KERMIT COLLECTION - Notebooks and notepads - Raleigh Studios

JIM HENSON'S MUPPET BABIES - Recording label - Jim Henson Productions, Inc.

JIM HENSON'S MUPPET LEARNING KEYS - Apparel and accessories - Jim Henson Productions, Inc.

JIM HENSON'S MUPPET WORKSHOP - Hobby kits - Jim Henson Productions, Inc.

JIM HENSON'S MUPPETS - Watches - Jim Henson Productions, Inc.

JIM HJELM - Apparel–women's - Jim Hjelm a Private Collection, Inc.

JIM HJELM NEW TRADITIONS - Wedding gowns - Jim Hjelm a Private Collection, Inc.

JIM HJELM OCCASIONS - Wedding gowns - Jim Hjelm a Private Collection, Inc.

JIM KELLY - Sporting goods - Collette Manufacturing Co.

JIM KOTE - Varnishes - Selig Co. Inc.

JIM MARKHAM - Hair care products - Markham Products

JIM MARVIN - Christmas tree ornaments - Vincent Lippe Co.

JIM MAYFIELD - Boomerangs - Windsports, Inc.

JIM-PAK - Intrauterine devices - Arndt Electronics

JIM PORTER - Whiskey - Heaven Hill Distilleries, Inc.

JIM VINCENT'S RIO - Fishing tackle - Cecily C. Pearson Vincent

JIM WADE - Fruits and vegetables - Columbia Fruit Packers Inc.

JIM WALTER - Office supplies - Jim Walter Corp.

JIMAPCO MAPS TO SWEAR BY.NOT AT! - Maps - Jimapco, Inc.

JIMBLES - Toys–stuffed ☆ - Gund, Inc.

JIMBO - Food products - Village Kitchen Foods Inc.

JIMBO'S JUMBOS - Nuts–salted, roasted, cooked, or canned - Jimbo's Jumbos Inc.

JIMBO'S JUMBOS - Nuts–salted, roasted, cooked, or canned - Morven Partners, LP

JIMENEZ - Snack foods - Fiesta-Jimenez Co.

JIMI-BAR - Guitars ☆ - On-Site Music Group

+JIMI #HENDRIX - Apparel and accessories - Experience Hendrix, LLC

JIMI HENDRIX - Musical instrument accessories - Dunlop Manufacturing, Inc.

JIMINI - Toys–stuffed - Gund, Inc.

JIMINY - Ice cream topping - Homestead, Inc.

JIMI'S - Food products - Kold Kist Brands Inc.

JIMMETTES - Candy - Cocoline Chocolate Co.

JIMMIE - Handbags ☆ - Henschel Manufacturing Co.

JIMMIE CHOCS - Candy - Premier Gourmet Products Inc.

JIMMIE RAY'S - Soups–canned - Bailey's Enterprises, Inc.

JIMMIES - Candy ☆ - Just Born Inc.

JIMM'S - Pizzas–mixes - Day Food Co.

JIMMY - Motor vehicle dealers - General Motors Corp.

JIMMY - Toys–stuffed ☆ - Russ Berrie and Co., Inc.

JIMMY - Vans–conversion ☆ - Coachmen Industries, Inc.

JIMMY B. CHIN - Toys - Mattel, Inc.

JIMMY BOY - Apparel–men's - Tropical Sportswear International Corp.

JIMMY CONNORS - Footwear - Brooks Shoe Inc.

JIMMY CONNORS - Sports apparel - Converse Inc.

JIMMY DEAN - Food products - Jimmy Dean Foods Div.

JIMMY DEAN - Meat products - Saramar Corp.

JIMMY DEAN CHILI SEASONING - Seasonings - Williams Foods Inc.

JIMMY DEAN COUNTRY GRAVY MIX - Gravy - Williams Foods Inc.

+JIMMY +DEAN FLAPSTICKS - Food products - Saramar Corp.

JIMMY DEAN HEAT 'N SERVE - Preserved foods–prepackaged - Jimmy Dean Foods Div.

JIMMY DEAN HEAT'EM UP - Food products ☆ - Jimmy Dean Foods Div.

JIMMY DEAN SNACK WINGS - Meat products–poultry - Saramar Corp.

JIMMY DEAN TASTEFULS - Meats–luncheon - Jimmy Dean Foods Div.

JIMMY DURANTE - Ukuleles ☆ - Strydel Inc.

JIMMY G - Toys–stuffed - Natural 9 (USA) Co., Ltd.

JIMMY GARCIA NEW YORK - Apparel and accessories - Jimmy Garcia

JIMMY JEM'S - Confetti - Z-Barten Productions

JIMMY JEM'S - Confetti - ZBP, Inc.

JIMMY JIMMY - Apparel and accessories - A & J Sportswear Corp.

JIMMY LATIN - Apparel and accessories - Jimmy Latin Enterprises Inc.

JIMMY OF THE FUTURE - Toys - Spumco, Inc.

JIMMY THE IDIOT BOY - Paints–artists' - Spumco, Inc.

☆ = Now out of production

JIMMY Z - Apparel and accessories - Mass Transit
JIMMY'S - Candy - Arway Confections Inc.
JIMMY'S - Salad dressings–bottled - Fish House Dressings, Inc.
JIMMY'S PHILLY CHILI - Chili–canned - James G. Robinson
JIMNIE - Pencils–mechanical - Zebra Pen Corp.
JIM'S - Meat products–beef - Byron's Bar-B-Q
JIMS - Tools–power-driven - Power Tool Holders Inc.
JIM'S JUNGLE PLAY - Playground equipment - Custom Machine Interprises
JIN - Recording label - Flat Town Music Co.
JIN JIAN - Cigarettes - West Park Tobacco Inc.
JINGLE - Giftware - Russ Berrie and Co., Inc.
JINGLE BABY - Dolls - Meritus Industries, Inc.
JINGLE BABY - Dolls ☆ - Horsman
JINGLE BALLS - Ornamental products–glass - Russ Berrie and Co., Inc.
JINGLE BEARS - Ornamental products–glass - Russ Berrie and Co., Inc.
JINGLE BELL GREETER - Toys–stuffed - Great American Fun Corp.
JINGLE BELL JALOPY - Toys–automobiles - Mattel, Inc.
JINGLE BOOTS - Ornamental products–glass - Seasonal Specialties Electrics, Inc.
JINGLE CAT - Pet products - Pet Concepts
JINGLE CATS - Recording label - Jingle Cats Music
JINGLE DOG - Pet products - Pet Concepts
JINGLE JACK - Publisher's imprints - Cross at the Green...Not in Between Enterprises
JINGLE RING - Drums–musical instruments - LP Music Group
JINGLE RING - Telephone accessories - DTR Associates, LP
JINGLES - Hair care products - Jingles International
JINGLES - Recording label ☆ - Centaur Records
JINGLESAURUS - Toys - Schmidt-Cannon, Inc.
JINGO - Toys - Maryland Toy Corp.
JINJU - Wallpaper ☆ - Imperial Wallcoverings, Inc.
JINKAI - Fishing nets - U.S. Seven Oceans Inc.
JINSI - Apparel–athletic - Balamar, Inc.
JINX - Apparel and accessories - Steven Alan Lippert
JINX - Deodorizers ☆ - Coughlan Products Corp.
JINX-ODOR - Deodorizers - Neuhaus Chemical Products, Inc.
JINX-STARCH - Cleaning preparations - Neuhaus Chemical Products, Inc.
JIT ENTERPRISE SYSTEM - Computer software ☆ - Fourth Shift Corp.
JITSU - Toys - Mattel, Inc.
JITTER - Dolls - Tonka Corp.
JITTER BUG - Insecticides - W.W. Grainger, Inc.
JITTER CRITTER - Toys–stuffed - Dakin Inc.
JITTER GUARD - Computer hardware - Bytex Corp.
JITTERBUG - Apparel–children's - Specialty Department Stores, Inc.
JITTERBUG - Concrete products - Goldblatt Tool Co.
JITTERBUG - Fishing lures - Fred Arbogast Co. Inc.
JITTERS - Games ☆ - Milton Bradley Co.
JITTERSTICK - Fishing lures - Fred Arbogast Co. Inc.
JITTERY JOE'S - Coffee - Jittery Joe's, Inc.
JIVAGO - Cosmetics - Jivago, Inc.
JIVE - Bicycles - Neal Enterprises
JIVE - Recording label - Zomba Recording Corp.
JIVE GUY - Toys - Mattel, Inc.
JIVE NUTS - Bicycles - Neal Enterprises
JIVE ON - Video games - Visioneering International, Inc.
JIVE/RCA - Recording label - RCA Records
JIWA FASHIONS - Apparel and accessories - Jiwa Fashions, Inc.
JJ - Automotive parts and accessories - Jerry Jeffries
JJ - Cases–eyeglass - Jacobs Co., Inc.
J.J. - Footwear–children's - Jumping-Jacks Shoes Inc.
JJ - Musical instrument accessories ☆ - Gracie Enterprises (Gracie Stands Div.)
JJ - Plastic films - Johnson Laminating & Coating, Inc.
J.J. CRESS - Kilns - Creek-Turn Inc. (Ceramic Supply Div.)
J.J. FLATS - Breads - Best Foods Baking Group
J.J. HOBBS - Footwear - Mag Shoe Corp.
+J.J. +JAXSON - Apparel–women's - Arveebee Co. Ltd.
J.J. MAGIRK - Apparel and accessories - Breton Industries
JJ ORIGINAL FOMATIONS - Foam rubber - JJ Original Fomations, Inc.
J.J. PEPPER'S - Food products - J.J. Pepper Foods
J.J. SPORT - Apparel–children's - Jumping-Jacks Shoes Inc.
J.J. +STAR - Jewelry - Anderson Associates, Inc.
J.J. WAINWRIGHT'S SELECT - Beverages–malt - Pittsburgh Brewing Co.
JJAY - Umbrellas - J Jay Products Co.
JJI - Light fixtures - Jji Lighting Group, Inc.
JJLTD - Jewelry - Jerry's Jewelers Ltd.

JJMPAD - Computer software - JJM Design Co.
JJ'S - Bakery products - JTM Foods, Inc.
JJ'S - Fishing lures - J.J.'s Custom Lures, Inc.
JK - Apparel–women's - Lane Bryant, Inc.
JK - Tires - Stateside International Inc.
JK BAG - Candy ☆ - Jacob Kern & Sons
JKC - Jewelry - Jack Kellmer Co.
J.L. - Cosmetics - Junee Commercial Co. Inc.
J.L. ANDERSON'S - Food products - Anderson's Ham Co.
JL AUDIO - Audio equipment - JL Audio, Inc.
J.L. COLLECTION - Hand showers and faucets - Jaclo Inc.
JL KRAFT - Salad dressings–bottled - Kraft Foods, Inc.
JL4K - Jewelry - J.F. Jewelry
JLB - Colognes - Viviane Woodard Industries, Ltd.
JLC - Apparel and accessories - G-III Apparel Group, Ltd.
JLC OUTERWEAR - Apparel and accessories - G-III Apparel Group, Ltd.
JLE - Cases–cigar - Jorge L. Espinosa
JLE - Jewelry - J & L Edwards Designs
J'LEEN - Giftware - J'leen, Ltd.
J.L.I. - Recording label - J.L.I. Records
JLM VISUALS PHYSICAL GEOLOGY - Computer software - Hopkins Technology LLC
JLN USA - Handbags - Jaclyn, Inc.
JM - Binders - JM Co.
JM - Jewelry - Jerry Madison Jewelry
JM - Jewelry ☆ - S. K. VanGilder N.A. Ltd.
JM-TRUSS - Hardware - Jennmar Corp.
JMA - Percussion instruments - Island Musical Supplies
J'MAE NELL - Health care products - Steff & Stori Enterprises
JMB - Food products - Malcolm & Burtt Jacobs
JMC - Electronics equipment - Jerome Menell Co.
JMC - Women's apparel - Jessica McClintock Inc.
JME - Figurines - Jean Enos
JMF - Jewelry - J.M. Fisher Co.
JMJ - Jewelry - Jaymark Jewelry
JMJ - Jewelry - Montanari Fine Arts Jewelers Inc.
JML - Jewelry - M & L Jewelry Manufacturing Inc.
JMLA - Apparel and accessories - Breton Industries
JMR - Golf carts - JMR Corp.
JMS CABLE - Nuts and bolts - Jennmar Corp.
JN - Flowers, plants, and seeds - Jon's Nursery, Inc.
JNCO - Apparel and accessories - Revatex, Inc.
JNT - Furniture polish and wax - J.N.T. Manufacturing Co. Inc.
JNT-A - Vitamins and nutritional supplements - Lifetrends International
JNY - Apparel–women's - Jones Apparel Group Inc.
JO - Jewelry - Jack Otchis
JO - Jewelry–precious - Jonique
JO-ANN - Crocheted and knitted items - Roosevelt Mills Inc.
JO ANN - Pepper ☆ - Old Mansion Foods Inc.
JO ANN'S NUT HOUSE - Nuts–salted, roasted, cooked, or canned - Candy Candy Inc.
JO-BI FARMS - Food products - Conagra, Inc.
JO-CUR - Hair care products ☆ - Whitehall Laboratories
JO-HAN - Toys–models ☆ - CMA Marketing Corp.
JO HARDIN - Apparel–women's - Sunny South Fashions, Inc.
JO JOBA - Apparel and accessories - Huntington Industries Inc.
JO-LA - Girdles - Jo La Foundations Inc.
JO LENE - Apparel–children's - Jo Lene Co., Inc.
JO LINDA - Wigs ☆ - Jean Paree Weegs Inc.
JO SAN - Food products - World Variety Produce Inc.
JO SONJA - Artists' materials ☆ - Chroma Acrylics Inc.
JO SONJA ACRYLIC GOUACHE - Paints–artists' - Chroma Acrylics Inc.
JO SPIER - Greeting cards ☆ - American Artists Group Inc.
JOACHIM - Musical instrument accessories - Selmer Co. Inc.
JOACHIM - Violins ☆ - William Lewis & Son
JOAL - Toys - Victor M. Bulgarelli Associates Inc.
JOAN - Recording label - Jazz Composer's Orchestra Association Inc.
JOAN & DAVID - Footwear - Joan & David Helpern Inc.
JOAN & DAVID COUTURE - Footwear - Joan & David Helpern Inc.
JOAN & DAVID TOO - Footwear - Joan & David Helpern Inc.
JOAN & LEE WULFF - Apparel and accessories ☆ - Bob Allen Sportswear
JOAN & MARSHA - Clothing - San Moire Apparel Corp.
JOAN ANDREWS - Apparel–women's - Wide Pacific Development, Inc.
JOAN BARI - Apparel and accessories ☆ - Edison Brothers Stores, Inc.
JOAN BROWN - Apparel–women's ☆ - Montgomery Ward & Co. Inc.
JOAN COLLINS - Apparel–women's ☆ - Sanmark-Stardust Inc.

☆ = Now out of production

JOAN COLLINS - Frames–eyeglass - Marine Optical, Inc.
JOAN HELPERN SIGNATURE - Footwear - Joan & David Helpern Inc.
JOAN MARTIN - Apparel and accessories - Breton Industries
JOAN OF ARC - Cheese - Swissrose International Inc.
JOAN OF ARC - Vegetables–canned - Joan of Arc Co.
JOAN OF ARC - Vegetables–canned - Pillsbury Co.
JOAN OSTER - Publisher's imprints - Sunbeam-Oster Household Products
JOAN RIVERS CLASSICS COLLECTION - Jewelry - Joan Rivers Worldwide
JOAN SIMMONS - Brushes - Robert Simmons Inc.
JOAN STEELE - Apparel–women's - Lucia, Inc.
JOAN VASS U.S.A. - Apparel and accessories - Signal Knitwear Co.
JOAN WALSH ANGLUND - Giftware - Determined Productions, Inc.
JOANAMOUR - Pharmaceutical preparations - Jacob Aini
JOANAMOUR 23-23 - Hair care products - Jacob Aini
JOANIQUE - Depilatories - K.B.K. Products Inc.
JOANN - Floor coverings–carpet and rugs ☆ - Regal Rugs Inc.
JOANN SHE - Jewelry - First Import Los Angeles, Corp.
JOANNA - Glassware–household ☆ - Knobler International Ltd.
JOANNA - Tableware–china - Lenox, Inc.
JOANNA - Window coverings - Newell Window Furnishings, Inc.
JOANNA - Window shades - Joanna Western Mills Co.
JOANNA & CHARLES - Apparel and accessories - Joanna & Charles, Inc.
JOANNA VYLINE - Window coverings ☆ - Joanna Western Mills Co.
JOANNE - Apparel–women's - Newton Manufacturing Corp.
JOANNE - Statuary - Hillside House of Originals
JOANNIE - Wigs - Jean Paree Weegs Inc.
JOB - Cigarette paper - Republic Tobacco L.P.
JOB - Labels–paper - Sue Records Inc.
JOB 1 - Cleaning preparations - Moran Foods, Inc.
JOB BLEU - Cigarettes - G.A. Georgopulo & Co. Inc.
JOB BOSS - Bags - Portable Products, Inc.
JOB BOSS - Computer software - Job Boss Software, Inc.
JOB BOX - Publisher's imprints - Career Management International Inc.
JOB CART - Furniture ☆ - Cosco, Inc.
JOB FLOW - Computer software - EDP Systems, Inc.
JOB HANDLERS - Tools - Red Devil Inc.
JOB-LIGHTER - Lighting fixtures - Kenall Manufacturing Co.
JOB MANAGER - Boxes - Igloo Products Corp.
JOB-MASTER - Ladders–metal - Werner Co.
JOB MASTER - Toys ☆ - Stanley Hardware Div.
JOB PAC - Aluminum products ☆ - Phifer Wire Products Inc.
JOB POWER - Publisher's imprints - Michael B. Levine
JOB PRO - Lanterns–electric - Coleman Co., Inc.
JOB RATED - Brushes–paint - Wooster Brush Co.
JOB-REPAIR - Epoxy - Accumetric, Inc.
JOB SAVER - Gloves - Jomac Products Inc.
JOB SITE - Adhesives and sealants - Miracle Adhesives
JOB SQUAD - Paper–toweling - Scott Paper Co.
JOB TOUGH - Footwear ☆ - E.S. Originals, Inc.
JOB TOUGH JOB SMART - Tools - Portable Products, Inc.
JOB WORKS - Computer software - State of Oregon
JOBA OIL - Vegetable oil - Sun Engineering and Research Corp.
JOBAR - Housewares - Jobar International Inc./Bibi Products
JOBASE - Computer software - Gerst Software, Inc.
J.O.B.B. - Apparel and accessories - Integrity Sportswear, Inc.
JOBBER - Calculators - David L. Simmons
JOBBERS - Bathing suits - Surf Line Hawaii, Ltd.
JOBBS - Computer software - Ibex Enterprises, Inc.
JOBCAST - Job training services - Career Central Corp.
JOBE SOUND - Amplifiers - Sonic Technology Products Inc.
JOBE'S - Flowers, plants, and seeds ☆ - Weatherly Consumer Products, Inc.
JOBE'S LEAF SHINE WIPES - Flowers, plants, and seeds - Weatherly Consumer Products, Inc.
JOBE'S SPIKES - Flowers, plants, and seeds - Weatherly Consumer Products, Inc.
JOBE'S SUNSPLASH - Flowers, plants, and seeds - Weatherly Consumer Products, Inc.
JOBE'S WATER SIGNALS - Flowers, plants, and seeds - Weatherly Consumer Products, Inc.
JOBI - Scrapers - Precision West Tool and Manufacturing
JOBIN - Wood products - Alice Sturzinger Ltd.
JOBLOG - Computer software - S-Cubed Software, Inc.
JOBMASTER - Fastening tool ☆ - ITW Ramset/Red Head
JOBMASTER - Publisher's imprints - William M. Mercer, Inc.
JOBMASTER - Trash bags - United Plastic Films, Inc.
JOBMASTER, THE - Footwear - West Coast Shoe Co.

JOBMATE - Motor vehicle parts and accessories - Leer Inc.
JOBO - Dog food - Allied Foods Inc.
JOBOX - Motor vehicle parts and accessories - Delta Consolidated Industries, Inc.
JOB'S FIREMUD HOT BEAN PASTE - Vegetables–canned - Jo B's, Inc.
JOBSCAPE - Computer software - Platinum Technology, Inc.
JOBSEARCH-BREAKING THE BARRIERS - Video production - Eclecon
JOBSEARCH-THE INSIDE TRACK 2.0 - Video production - Eclecon
JOBSEARCH-THE RIGHT TRACK - Video production - Eclecon
JOBSITE - Containers - Delta Consolidated Industries, Inc.
JOBSKIN - Health care products - Jobst Institute Inc.
JOBST - Health care products ☆ - Jobst Institute Inc.
JOBST-CUSTOM - Health care products - Jobst Institute Inc.
JOBST RELIEF - See **SHEER MATERNITY**
JOBTALK - Recording label - Alan Parham, Inc.
JOC - Lotions - Vi-Jon Laboratories, Inc.
JOCHE DAVILA STUDIO - Greeting cards - Joche Davila Studio
JOCK BIRD HOMES - Cages–wire ☆ - Pets International, Ltd.
JOCK SKATEBOARDS - Skateboards - Jock Skateboards
JOCK, THE - Sport bags, luggage, travel accessories - Jameslee Corp.
JOCKETTE - Underwear and nightwear - Jockey International, Inc.
JOCKEY - Apparel and accessories - Jockey International, Inc.
JOCKEY - Brushes–hair - Wright-Bernet
JOCKEY - Dinnerware–glass - Crest Studios
JOCKEY - Health care products - Saxony Products Inc.
JOCKEY ACTIVEWEAR - Apparel–women's - Jacques Moret, Inc.
JOCKEY ATTI2DES - Apparel and accessories - Jockey International, Inc.
JOCKEY CLUB - Apparel and accessories - Jockey International, Inc.
JOCKEY CLUB - Beverages–malt ☆ - Labatt Importers Inc.
JOCKEY CLUB - Cigarettes - G.A. Georgopulo & Co. Inc.
JOCKEY CLUB - Jewelry - R.F. Simmons Co.
JOCKEY CLUB - Soap - Caswell-Massey Co. Ltd.
JOCKEY FOR HER - Underwear and nightwear - Jockey International, Inc.
JOCKEY HOLLOW VINEYARDS - Wines - Allied Management, Inc.
JOCKEY POUCH - Apparel–men's - Jockey International, Inc.
JOCKEY REPS - Underwear and nightwear - Jockey International, Inc.
JOCKEY SILKS - Underwear and nightwear - Jockey International, Inc.
JOCKEY SPORT - Underwear and nightwear - Jockey International, Inc.
JOCKEY STORE, THE - Apparel stores - Jockey International, Inc.
JOCKEY TECH - Underwear and nightwear - Jockey International, Inc.
JOCKEY ZONE - Underwear and nightwear - Jockey International, Inc.
JOCKO - Dolls - Nicholas A. Milohnic
JOCKO - Food products - China Doll, Inc.
JOCKO COMBO - Sporting goods - Patrick W. Guyer and Richard J. Guyer Partnership
JOCKS - Video production - Conwest Resources, Inc.
JOCO - Novelty items - Jaco
JODEE - Brassieres (Bras) - Jodee Bra Co.
JODHPURS II - Wallpaper - Newmarket Designs Ltd.
JODI - Cables - Four Paws Products Ltd.
JODI - Dolls - K.B. Brothers Inc.
JODI - Figurines - Gare Inc.
JODI - Mops ☆ - Daily Dryer Co. Inc.
JODI - Toys - Kid Kore International Ltd.
JODI'S - Jewelry - Ulta 3 Inc.
JODI'S PRIDE - Food products - Leon Supply Co.
JODORESQUE - Colognes - Fragranhaus
JODPHURS - Wallpaper ☆ - Newmarket Designs Ltd.
JODY - Hair care products - Jody Cosmetic Co., Ltd.
JODY - Recording label - Jody Record Corp.
JODY - Toys–stuffed ☆ - CBS Toys
JODY BERGSMA - Figurines ☆ - Reco International Corp.
JODY MARONI'S SAUSAGE KINGDOM - Sausages - Jody Maroni's Italian Sausage Kingdom, Inc.
JOE - Frames–eyeglass - Rozin Optical Export Corp.
JOE AMERICA - Apparel and accessories - Joe America Limited Liability Co.
JOE BASEBALL - Apparel and accessories - Pleasure Gift & Apparel Co.
JOE BASKETBALL - Apparel and accessories - Pleasure Gift & Apparel Co.
JOE BILL MILLER - Hats - Bierner and Son Inc.
JOE BLASCO COSMETICS - Cosmetics - Joe Blasco Enterprises, Inc.
JOE BLO - Chewing gum - Philadelphia Chewing Gum Corp.
JOE BOB GOBBLER - Giftware - Brushcreek Creative Co.
JOE BOXER - Watches - Joe Boxer Corp.
JOE BOXER - Watches - Timex Corp.
JOE BOXER BOY - Apparel and accessories - Joe Boxer Corp.
JOE BOY - Fishing lures - Joe's Flies

☆ = Now out of production

JOE BROWN - Helmets–athletic - Climb High Inc.
JOE COLLEGE - Apparel and accessories - Bentley Lingerie, Inc.
JOE FAN - Apparel and accessories - Bentley Lingerie, Inc.
JOE FEE - Recording label - Sharon Productions Inc.
JOE FOOTBALL - Apparel and accessories - Myles B. Barchas
JOE GOLFER - Video production - Raymond A. Ringwald
JOE HAMAKA - Apparel–men's - Weekendz-Off, Inc.
JOE HARDY - Toys–stuffed ☆ - Kenner Products
JOE JONES - Recording label - Sharon Productions Inc.
JOE JONES & REYNOSA BROS - Recording label - Joe Jones & the Reynosa Bros. Records
JOE KEENE MUSIC CO. - Publisher's imprints - The Keene Music Group
JOE MOMMA - Apparel and accessories - Metapro, Inc.
JOE NAKASH - Apparel–men's - Jordache Enterprises Inc.
JOE NAMATH - Sporting goods - Dynamic Classics Ltd.
JOE NAMATH - Sporting goods ☆ - Franklin Sports, Inc.
JOE NAMATH CLOTHES - Apparel–men's ☆ - Palm Beach Co., Inc.
JOE-PYE RECORDS - Recording label - Batteries Not, Inc.
JOE RACER - Apparel and accessories - Ware Enterprises, Inc.
JOE ROCKET - Apparel - Parker Bros. Motorsports Warehouse
JOE SMITH - Gloves - Midwest Glove Co.
JOE SNEAKS - Apparel–children's - Snake Creek Manufacturing Co., Inc.
JOE SOCCER - Apparel and accessories - Pleasure Gift & Apparel Co.
JOE SPORT BY WEIDER - Apparel and accessories - Weider Health and Fitness
JOE TECCE'S - Spaghetti sauces - Joe Tecce
JOE TENNIS - Apparel and accessories - Pleasure Gift & Apparel Co.
JOE THE BARMAN - Kitchen appliances ☆ - Sunbeam-Oster Household Products
JOE TOURIST - Apparel and accessories - Pleasure Gift & Apparel Co.
JOE WEIDER - Vitamins and nutritional supplements - Weider Health and Fitness
JOE WEIDER'S ANABOLIC MEGA PACK - Vitamins and nutritional supplements - Weider Health and Fitness
JOEBREAD - Breads - JoeBread Foods
JOEL - Ophthalmic goods ☆ - Luxottica
JOEL PARKER - Shoes - Joseph E. Parker
JOELLE - Dolls - Russ Berrie and Co., Inc.
JOELLE - Giftware ☆ - Gorham Inc.
JOELLE - Perfumes - Joelle, Inc.
JOELLE - Perfumes - Spice Market, Inc.
JOELLE - Toys - Tonka Corp.
JOERNS - Health care products - Sunrise Medical Inc.
JOE'S - Fishing lures - Joe's Flies
JOE'S - Food products ☆ - Deer Valley Farm
JOE'S - Mushrooms - Joe's Restaurant Inc.
JOE'S - Musical instrument accessories - Modular Sound Technology
JOE'S CITRUS BLUE HAND CLEANER - Soap - Kleen Products, Inc.
JOE'S GARAGE - Compact discs–prerecorded - Zappa Family Trust
JOE'S GOURMET COFFEE - Coffee - Joseph I. Teitlebaum
JOE'S HAWAIIAN WATER ICE - Confections - Pacific Refreshments Co., Inc.
JOE'S HELLIOUS SALSA - Food products - Teffeteller Sales
JOE'S RED ALE - Beverages–malt - Carolina Brewing Group, Inc.
JOE'S SMASHING - Recording label - Jazz Composer's Orchestra Association Inc.
JOE'S STUFF - Spices and extracts - Louisiana General Store, Inc.
JOESONS - Housewares ☆ - LaSalle Marketing Corp.
JOEY - Bicycles - Gulf Cycle Corp.
JOEY - Computer software - Joey Technologies, Inc.
JOEY - Dolls - Fisher-Price, Inc.
JOEY - Health care products - Fiberoptic Medical Products
JOEY - Recording label - Joey Records International Inc.
JOEY CHIPS - Snack foods ☆ - General Mills, Inc.
JOEY D'S - Salad dressings–bottled - Joey D and Associates
JOEY INTERNATIONAL DISCOS - Recording label - Joey Records International Inc.
JOEY PAGODA'S ORIENTAL EXPRESS - Dinners–frozen - Schwan's Sales Enterprises, Inc.
JOEY RECORDS - Recording label - Record-Rama Sound Archives
JOEY #RUSSO - Dolls - Walt Disney Co.
JOEY'S - Footwear–athletic - KangaROOS USA Inc.
JOEY'S ITALIAN COOKING - Barbecue sauce - Continental Classes
JOEY'S LUV IN EVERY BITE - Bakery products - Joseph Aihini
JOFA - Sporting goods - Reliable Racing Supply Inc.
JOFFREY - Musical instrument accessories - Jack Spratt Woodwind Shop
JOFFREY'S COFFEE & TEA CO. - Beverages - Joffrey's Coffee and Tea Co.

JOFU - Food products - Tomsun Foods Inc.
JOG-A-LITE - Sporting goods - Jog-A-Lite Inc.
JOG-A-NOGGIN - Games ☆ - CBS Toys
JOG A NOTE - Notebooks and notepads - Rufus W. Burks
JOG ABOUT - Strollers–baby - Tri Industries, Inc.
JOG-LEASH - Pet products ☆ - AD & G Enterprises
JOG N' WALK XJ-900 - Shoes–athletic - Payless Shoesource Worldwide, Inc.
JOG-O-LINE - Exercising equipment ☆ - National Sporting Goods Corp.
JOG-O-MATIC - Duplicators and supplies ☆ - Copy Plus Inc.
JOG PAD - Electronics equipment - Grass Valley Group Inc.
JOG-R - Pharmaceutical preparations ☆ - Orjene Natural Cosmetics
JOG TAG - Jewelers' findings - Republic Drug Co. Inc.
JOG TOGS - Apparel–children's - H.H. Cutler Co.
JOGABOUTS - Footwear - Mason Shoe Manufacturing Co.
JOGBRA - Apparel stores–sports - Champion Jogbra
JOGGA - Breads - Arnie's Inc.
JOGGER - Electronics equipment - Grass Valley Group Inc.
JOGGER - Health care products - Equi-Tron Inc.
JOGGER - Screws - C. Itoh Building Products
JOGGER - Strollers–baby - Racing Strollers Inc.
JOGGER PLUS - Office supplies - Primages Inc.
JOGGERHOOP - Games - Electro-Mech Inc.
JOGGERS - Staples - Automation Fastening Co.
JOGGERS CHOICE - Snack foods - Glico Harmony Foods Corp.
JOGGETTE - Strollers–baby - Motiv Sports Inc.
JOGGING IN A JUG - Fruit drinks–bottled or canned - Third Option Laboratories Inc.
JOGGING JOY - Toys - Tonka Corp.
JOGGLESIME - Apparel stores–children's - Greaten Corp.
JOGGY BAGS - Pet products - City Dog Designed Co., Inc.
JOGS - Men's footwear - Bostonian Shoe Co.
JOGS - Socks - Davis Sales
JOH. JOS. PRUM - Wines - Seagram's Chateau & Estate Wines Co.
JOHAN THE LIFE SAVER - Posters - Sonja K. Vervik
JOHANN HAUCK - Beverages–malt - Hudepohl-Schoenling Brewing Co.
JOHANN HEINRICH HAMMIG - Musical instruments - J.M. Sahlein Music Co. Inc.
JOHANNA - Eyeglasses - Art-Craft Optical Co.
JOHANNA FARMS - Milk - Johanna Foods, Inc.
JOHANNES KOHR - Stringed instruments - Howard Core & Co. Inc.
JOHANNI - Apparel–men's - Laus Apparel, Inc.
JOHANNOT - Paper - Canson-Talens Inc.
JOHANSEN - Footwear–women's - Johansen Brothers Shoe Co.
JOHANSENETTE - Footwear–women's - Johansen Brothers Shoe Co.
JOHAR - Bicycles - Johar Inc.
JOHKA FRIS - Agricultural products - Holland-American Importing Co. Inc.
JOHL - Shelving units–wood - Spacesaver Corp.
JOHN - Frames–eyeglass ☆ - Universal/Univis Inc.
JOHN A. RUTHVEN - Hobby kits - Wildlife Internationale Inc.
JOHN A. UHL - Cigars - John A. Uhl Cigar Co.
JOHN ALEXANDER - Apparel–men's - Biltwell Clothing Co. Inc.
JOHN AMICO - Hair care products - John Amico Expressive Hair Care Products
JOHN & JILL'S CHEESECAKE - Cakes - John & Jill's, Inc.
JOHN AND PRISCILLA - Flatware - Westmorland Sterling, Inc.
JOHN APEL - Jewelry - Dilaro Jewelry, Inc.
JOHN ASHFORD SPORT - Apparel and accessories - May Department Stores Co.
JOHN B. TAYLOR - Dishes–earthenware ☆ - Louisville Stoneware Co.
+JOHN +BARTLETT - Apparel and accessories - Bartlett Unlimited, Inc.
JOHN BARTLETT - Apparel and accessories - Bartlett Unlimited, Inc.
JOHN BAUER - Stationery ☆ - Merry Thoughts Inc.
JOHN BEAN - Automotive parts and accessories - Snap-On Technologies, Inc.
JOHN BEGG BLUE CAP - Whiskey - United Distillers of North America
JOHN BEGG GOLD CAP - Whiskey - United Distillers of North America
JOHN BESWICK STUDIO - Figurines - Royal Doulton-Somerset UK Ltd.
JOHN +BICKART'S - Computer software - John Bickart, Inc.
JOHN BOY - Infant product ☆ - Ming Ta Supply
JOHN BOY & BILLY ROCK & ROLL BIG SHOW - Recording label - John Boy & Billy, Inc.
JOHN BOY & BILLY ROCK & ROLL RACING - Hats - John Boy & Billy, Inc.
JOHN BULL - Beverages–malt - Associated Importers Co.
JOHN BULL - Leather–chamois - Schroeder & Tremayne, Inc.
JOHN BULL PERFUMERY POT POURRI TOILET WATER - Toiletries - Cambridge Chemists Inc.
JOHN BUNN - Medical apparatus - Preferred Medical Supply Inc.

☆ = Now out of production

JOHN BYRNE'S NEXT MEN - Books–comic - John Byrne, Inc.
JOHN C. ROBERTS - Shoes - Interco Inc.
JOHN CARLISLE OF SAN FRANCISCO - Apparel and accessories - Baguda Wear Inc.
JOHN CARVER - Cigars - M & N Cigar Manufacturing Inc.
JOHN CONTI - Coffee - John Conti Coffee Co.
JOHN COPE'S - Fruits and vegetables - John Cope's Food Products, Inc.
JOHN COTTON - Athletic footwear - John Cotton Shoe Co.
JOHN COTTON - Tobacco products - Faber, Coe & Gregg Inc.
JOHN COURAGE - Beverages–alcohol - Century Importers Inc.
JOHN COURAGE AMBER LAGER - Beverages–malt - Scottish & Newcastle Importers Co.
JOHN DEERE - Garden equipment - Deere & Co.
JOHN DELLARIA - Hair care products - Beaux Gens Beauty Supply Inc.
JOHN DERBY - Knives - Samuel Peace Inc.
JOHN DOZE - Clothing - Jeffrey Muncy
JOHN DUSTIN - Hair care products - Larry's Beauty Co.
JOHN EBEN - Shoes ☆ - Endicott Johnson Corp.
JOHN EVANS - Hair care products - John Evans Products
JOHN F. BLAIR - Publisher's imprints - John F. Blair, Publisher Inc.
JOHN F. STRATTON - Musical instrument accessories - C. Bruno & Son Inc.
JOHN FOSTER GREEN - Beverages - Compact Industries, Inc.
JOHN FREDERICS - Neckties - Dunleigh Tuxton Inc.
JOHN FREDERICS - Underwear and nightwear - Kayser-Roth Corp.
JOHN G. SHEDD AQUARIUM - Publisher's imprints - Shedd Aquarium Society
JOHN GEORGE CREATIONS - Statuary ☆ - Hillside House of Originals
JOHN GILBERT'S RIVERBOAT BRAND - Beer ☆ - Evansville Brewing Co.
JOHN GNAGY - Artists' materials - Martin F. Weber Co.
JOHN GRAVES - Meat products–beef - John Graves Food Service
JOHN GREENLEAF - Furniture - Whittier Wood Products Co.
+JOHN +GREENLEAF FURNITURE - Furniture–wood - Whittier Wood Products Co.
JOHN GRIMES - Postcards - Fotofolio Inc.
JOHN HAMPTON LTD. - Apparel–men's - Leon of Paris Co. Inc.
JOHN HANCAT - Pans - Penn-Plax, Inc.
JOHN HANCOCK - Furniture - Beatrice Cos. Inc.
JOHN HANDSCRIPT - Paper - Riverside Paper Corp.
JOHN HANDY - Whiskey - Sazerac Co. Inc.
JOHN HARDY - Apparel and accessories - John Hardy, Inc.
JOHN HARDY - Shoes - Genesco Inc.
JOHN HENRY - Apparel and accessories - Manhattan International
JOHN HENRY - Apparel and accessories - Salant/Manhattan Industries
JOHN HENRY - Apparel–men's - Farah Inc.
JOHN HENRY - Eyeglasses - International Tropic-Cal Inc. (I SKI Div.)
JOHN HENRY - Greeting cards - John Henry Co.
JOHN HENRY - Leather goods - Prince Gardner Inc.
JOHN HENRY - Pipes ☆ - Missouri Meerschaum Co.
JOHN HENRY - Tobacco–chewing or smoking - Brown & Williamson Tobacco Corp.
JOHN HENRY - Underwear and nightwear - J.E. Morgan Knitting Mills
JOHN HENRY - Underwear and nightwear - Nantucket Industries Inc.
JOHN HENRY - Wallets - Frost Bros. Enterprises, Inc.
JOHN HENRY FOR BOYS - Apparel–children's - Jay-Zee Inc.
JOHN HENRY FOR WOMEN - Apparel and accessories - John Henry for Women
JOHN HINDE LTD. - Calendars - Sormani Inc.
JOHN ISLAND - T-shirts–men's - Jeffrey J. Rosz
JOHN J MADISON - Figurines - John Madison Co. Inc.
JOHN JAQUES & SON - Games - Croquet International Ltd.
JOHN-JOHN - Sterling giftware ☆ - J.T. Inman Co. Inc.
JOHN JOHN'S - Apparel and accessories - Ramodi's
JOHN JRS. - Cigars - A.J. Golden Inc.
JOHN JUZEK - Musical instruments - Metropolitan Music Co.
JOHN KIRALY - Stationery ☆ - Key West Aloe Inc.
JOHN L. BLAIR - Suits–men's - Blair Holdings, Inc.
JOHN LABATT CLASSIC - Beverages–malt ☆ - Labatt Importers Inc.
JOHN LABATT EXTRA STOCK - Beverages–malt ☆ - Labatt Importers Inc.
JOHN LENNON - Eyeglasses - Windsor Optical Inc.
JOHN LENNON - Watches - Western Watches International
JOHN M. SMYTH - Furniture - John M. Smyth Co.
JOHN M. SMYTH'S HOMEMAKERS - Furniture - John M. Smyth Co.
JOHN MADDOCK - Dinnerware–glass - Ellis Barker Silver Co.
JOHN MAIN INSTITUTE, THE - Publisher's imprints - John Main Institute Inc.
JOHN MALLOY - Shoes - Edison Brothers Stores, Inc.
JOHN MARSHALL DIVISION - Publisher's imprints ☆ - Oceana Publications Inc.

JOHN MCCLELLAND - Figurines - Reco International Corp.
JOHN MCGIL GOLD LABEL - Whiskey - Mazeltov Beverages Import & Export, Inc.
JOHN MORLEY - Harpsichords - Peter Redstone Harpsichords
JOHN MORRELL - Meat products–beef - John Morrell & Co.
JOHN MORRELL CERTIFIED BLACK - Meat products ☆ - John Morrell & Co.
JOHN MORRELL E-Z CUT - Meats–luncheon - John Morrell & Co.
JOHN +MURROUGH - Apparel–women's - Winters and Murrough Design Group Inc.
JOHN NEWCOMBE ACTIVEWEAR - Apparel–men's - Catalina
JOHN PAUL GOEBEL - Uniforms–tailored - Gale-Sobel Co.
JOHN PAUL RICHARD - Apparel and accessories - John Paul Richard, Inc.
JOHN PEARSE - Musical instruments - Breezy Ridge Instruments
JOHN PEEL LTD. - Apparel–men's - TMG Corp.
JOHN PILGRIM - Toys - Russ Berrie and Co., Inc.
JOHN PLAYER - Beverages–alcohol ☆ - Majestic Distilling Co.
JOHN PRIMBLE - Knives–pocket - Bluegrass Cutlery Inc.
JOHN QUADE - Apparel–men's - Smart Style Industries Inc.
JOHN RIEKES - Glassware–household ☆ - Crisa Corp.
JOHN ROBERT POWERS - School franchise - Robie Enterprises
JOHN ROBERTS - Rings–jewelry - Artcarved Inc.
JOHN ROLFE - Tobacco products - Lane Ltd.
+JOHN +ROMAIN - Leather goods - Rommark Handbags, Inc.
JOHN RUSKIN - Cigars ☆ - Phillies Cigar Co.
JOHN SINCLAIR - Tobacco products - Faber, Coe & Gregg Inc.
JOHN SMITH - Footwear ☆ - Conjac Inc.
JOHN SOMERS' - Pewterware - John Somers Pewter
JOHN STERLING - Jewelry - Park Lane Associates, Inc.
JOHN STORIE'S HAWK - Boats - Vision Manufacturing, LLC
JOHN T. MCCANN'S SOFTRACK - Computer software - Integrity Software, Inc.
JOHN TROY'S NATURAL SAUCERY - Vegetable sauces - Simply Delicious, Inc.
JOHN WANAMAKER - Apparel and accessories - John Wanamaker Inc.
JOHN WAYNE-AMERICAN - Dolls ☆ - Effanbee Doll Corp.
JOHN WAYNE DUKE - Revolvers ☆ - Colt's Manufacturing Co. Inc.
JOHN WEITE - Hosiery - Keepers International
JOHN WEITZ - Apparel and accessories - Crystal Brands Inc.
JOHN WEITZ - Apparel and accessories ☆ - Host Apparel Inc.
JOHN WEITZ - Apparel–men's - Castle Neckwear Inc.
JOHN WEITZ - Belts–apparel - Humphrey's Inc.
JOHN WEITZ - Leather goods - Westport Corp.
JOHN WEITZ - Luggage ☆ - U.S. Luggage & Leather Products
JOHN WEITZ - Umbrellas - Shaw Creations Inc.
JOHN WEITZ - Watches - M.Z. Berger & Co. Inc.
JOHN WEITZ DESIGNS BY TOWNE & KING - Crocheted and knitted items - Towne & King Inc.
JOHN WEITZ FOR STORM HERO - Umbrellas - Storm Hero Umbrella Co. Inc.
JOHN WEITZ SIGNATURE - Apparel–men's - Palm Beach Co., Inc.
JOHN WEITZ SLACKS BY GLEN OAKS - Slacks–men's - Glen Oaks Industries Inc.
JOHN WHEATLEY - Sporting goods - John Wheatley
JOHN WILMAN - Fabrics–tapestry ☆ - Coloroll Inc.
JOHN WOLF - Window coverings - Lewrene Interiors
JOHN WOOD - Tanks–water - Alco Industries, Inc.
JOHN WRIGHT - Aluminum products - John Wright Co.
JOHNDOE - Frames–eyeglass - Liberty Optical Manufacturing Co.
JOHNI BOLT - Plumbing fixtures–metal - Hercules Chemical Co. Inc.
JOHNI-KLEAN - Controls–heating systems - Cobra Products Inc.
JOHNI RING - Plumbing fixtures–enameled - Hercules Chemical Co. Inc.
JOHNKE - Printers–computer - Johnke Manufacturing Co.
JOHNNIE - Lenses–optical - Ditto Industries Inc.
JOHNNIE WALKER - Beverages–alcohol - Co. Store
JOHNNIE WALKER - Footwear–men's - St. Louis Shoe Co. Inc.
JOHNNIE WALKER BLACK LABEL - Whiskey - United Distillers of North America
JOHNNIE WALKER RED LABEL - Whiskey - United Distillers of North America
JOHNNY - Lenses–optical - Ditto Industries Inc.
JOHNNY - Recording label - Freddie Records
JOHNNY 3 LEGS - Beverages–malt - Elias Reiter
JOHNNY APPLE TREATS - Candy - Ferrara Pan Candy Co., Inc.
JOHNNY APPLESEED'S VERYFINE - Cider ☆ - Veryfine Products, Inc.
JOHNNY BIRDSEED - Bird feeds - Audubon Park Co.
JOHNNY BOY - Apparel–men's - Tropical Sportswear International Corp.
JOHNNY CARSON - Apparel and accessories ☆ - Host Apparel Inc.

JOHNNY CARSON - Apparel–men's - Johnny Carson Apparel Inc.
JOHNNY CARSON - Apparel–men's - Superba, Inc.
JOHNNY CARSON - Belts–apparel ☆ - Salant/Manhattan Industries
JOHNNY CARSON - Men's footwear ☆ - Bostonian Shoe Co.
+JOHNNY +CASTAWAY - Computer software - Sierra On-Line, Inc.
JOHNNY COTTON - Apparel and accessories - Design Projects
+JOHNNY +DRUM - Whiskey - Pure Kentucky Distilling Co.
JOHNNY FOOTPAD - Plastics - Narrow Way Products
JOHNNY GRAIT - Restraints–patient - Heelbo Inc.
JOHNNY HARRIS - Sauces - Johnny Harris, Inc.
JOHNNY HARRIS FAMOUS - Barbecue sauce - Johnny Harris, Inc.
JOHNNY HEAVEN - Apparel and accessories - Johnny Devil, Inc.
JOHNNY HUSH - Plumbing fixtures–metal - Moen Inc.
JOHNNY JUMP-UP - Exercising equipment - Evenflo Co.
JOHNNY LIGHTNING - Toys - Master Cell
JOHNNY LIGHTNING - Toys–automobiles ☆ - Playing Mantis
JOHNNY MARVIN - Fretted instruments ☆ - International Music Corp.
JOHNNY-ON-THE-GO - Infant product - Century Products Co.
JOHNNY ON THE SPOT - Cleaning preparations - Cathay International
JOHNNY PLASTIC ICE - Surgical supplies - Pelton Shepherd Industries
JOHNNY PLAY CHAIR - Infant product ☆ - Century Products Co.
JOHNNY RIB - Pork - Webber Farms
JOHNNY STEP UP - Infant product ☆ - Century Products Co.
JOHNNY STOP - Plumbing fixtures–metal ☆ - Moen Inc.
JOHNNY UP - Toilet seats - Arete Enterprises, Inc.
JOHNNY WAS - Apparel–children's - Cover Design Inc.
JOHNNY WEISSMULLER - Swimming pools - Delair Group Inc.
JOHNNY WHITING - Food products - B. Sessler Co.
JOHNNY WILDSEED - Flowers, plants, and seeds - Wildseed Farms
JOHNNY WUNKOTE - Paints ☆ - Adelphi Coatings Co.
JOHNNYBILT HANDI-STEPS - Frames–picture ☆ - O.D. Funk Co.
JOHNNYBILT HANDI-TRUSS - Trusses–surgical ☆ - O.D. Funk Co.
JOHNNY'S $ - Apparel and accessories - Johnny's Sportswear, Inc.
JOHNNY'S - Food products - Willman Cookie & Nut Co.
JOHN'S - Casting slips - Ohio Ceramic Supply Inc.
JOHNS - Wines - John W. Rauner
JOHNS - Wines - Yakima River Winery Inc.
JOHN'S PASS - Seafood products–fresh or frozen - John's Pass Seafood Co.
JOHNSBURY - Clocks ☆ - General Time Corp. (Westclox/Seth Thomas Div.)
JOHNSON - Candy - Johnson Candy Co.
JOHNSON - Doors–metal - Johnson Metal Products
JOHNSON - Fishing rods - Johnson Worldwide Associates, Inc.
JOHNSON - Food products - Camino Real Foods
JOHNSON - Generators - Johnson Kart Manufacturing
JOHNSON - Heating equipment ☆ - Magic Chef Inc.
JOHNSON - Ladders–metal - Pat Johnson Manufacturing Co.
JOHNSON - Motors–outboard - Outboard Marine Corp.
JOHNSON - Radio communications equipment - E.F. Johnson Co.
JOHNSON - Ships–sailing vessels - Johnson Boat Works
JOHNSON - Sporting goods - Johnson Fishing Inc.
JOHNSON - Sporting goods - NSC Corp. (Johnson Tent Div.)
JOHNSON - Stoves - S.T. Johnson Co.
JOHNSON - Windows–screen - US Filter/Johnson Screens
JOHNSON - Wines - Frederick S. Johnson Vineyards
JOHNSON & JOHNSON - Health care products - Johnson & Johnson
JOHNSON & JOHNSON K-Y JELLY - Lubricants - Johnson & Johnson
JOHNSON & JOHNSON K-Y PLUS NONOXYNOL-9 - Pharmaceutical
    preparations - Johnson & Johnson
JOHNSON BIG WHEEL - Lawn mowers - Johnson Big Wheel Mowers, Inc.
JOHNSON BROTHERS - Dinnerware–glass - Johnson Brothers, USA, Inc.
JOHNSON ESTATE - Wines - Frederick S. Johnson Vineyards
JOHNSON-GRACE - Computer software - Johnson-Grace Co.
JOHNSON GT - Motors–outboard - Outboard Marine Corp.
JOHNSON-MIDDLEBY - Fruits–canned - Johnson-Middleby Co. (Karp's
    Manufactured Products Div.)
JOHNSON PET-DOR - Pet products - Johnson Pet-Dor Inc.
JOHNSON PET-DOR - Pet products - R.C. Steele Co.
JOHNSON RANCHES - Snack foods - Johnson Ranches
JOHNSON SILVER STAR SERIES - Motors–outboard - Outboard Marine
    Corp.
JOHNSON STROMAN TRIBE - Books–comic - Axis Comics
JOHNSON, THE - Clutches–industrial ☆ - Carlyle Johnson Machine Co.
JOHNSON TURNBULL - Wines - Johnson Turnbull Vineyards
JOHNSON ULTRA - Motors–outboard - Outboard Marine Corp.
JOHNSONIAN - Shoes ☆ - Endicott Johnson Corp.
JOHNSONITE - Floor coverings - Johnsonite Flooring Products

JOHNSON'S - Antiseptics - Martin Drug Co.
JOHNSON'S - Beverages–alcohol - United States Distilled Products Co.
JOHNSON'S - Floor coverings–carpet and rugs - Johnson's Carpets Inc.
JOHNSON'S - Floor waxes - S.C. Johnson & Son, Inc.
JOHNSON'S - Food products - Stewart's Restaurants Inc.
JOHNSON'S - Food products - Willman Cookie & Nut Co.
JOHNSON'S - Footcare products - Combe Inc.
JOHNSON'S - Health care products - Johnson & Johnson
JOHNSON'S - Syrup - Charles Johnson
JOHNSON'S - Wines - Johnson's Alexander Valley Wines
JOHNSON'S ALEXANDER VALLEY - Wines - Johnson's Alexander Valley
    Wines
JOHNSON'S ANODYNE - Health care products - Etna Products Co. Inc.
JOHNSON'S BABY - Cosmetics - Johnson & Johnson
JOHNSON'S BABY HEALTHFLOW - Infant product - Johnson & Johnson
JOHNSON'S KIDS - Hair care products - Johnson & Johnson
JOHNSON'S ODOR-EATERS - Shoe insoles - Combe Inc.
JOHNSON'S SPRITE - Fishing lures ☆ - Johnson Worldwide Associates, Inc.
JOHNSONVILLE - Meat products - Johnsonville Sausage, Inc.
JOHNSONVILLE - Sausages - Johnsonville Foods Co.
JOHNSONVILLE APPLE 'N CINNAMON - Sausages - Johnsonville Sausage,
    Inc.
JOHNSONVILLE VERMONT MAPLE SYRUP BREAKFAST SAUSAGE -
    Sausages - Johnsonville Sausage, Inc.
JOHNSTON - Apparel–children's - Johnston Inc.
JOHNSTON & MURPHY - Shoes - Genesco Inc.
JOHNSTON & MURPHY TAILORED CASUAL - Shoes - Genesco Inc.
JOHNSTON CASUALS - Furniture - Shaver-Howard Co.
JOHNSTON'S - Pizzas–mixes ☆ - Masterson Co. Inc.
JOHNSTON'S GOOD AS GOLD - Tools–garden - Johnston Seed Co.
JOHNSTON'S NO ROACH - Insecticides - Walco Linck Co.
JOI - Health care products - Joi Specialty Products Inc.
JOI - Vitamins and nutritional supplements - Sunrider Corp.
JOI-GEL - Hair care products - Joico Laboratories, Inc.
JOI-MIST - Hair care products ☆ - Joico Laboratories, Inc.
JOICO - Hair care products - Joico Laboratories, Inc.
JOICO ECO - Hair care products - Joico Laboratories, Inc.
JOIE DE LAIT - Skin care products - The Nutribath Co.
JOIGEL - Hair styling products - Joico Laboratories, Inc.
JOIKA - Meat products - Haram-Christensen Corp.
JOIKO - Sporting goods ☆ - K & S Engineering Inc.
JOIMIST - Hair care products - Joico Laboratories, Inc.
JOIN 'EMS - Toys - Toymax Inc.
JOIN THE NAVY - Hair care products - Cosmair Inc.
JOIN THE TEAM - Apparel and accessories - Kerusso Activewear, Inc.
JOINT ACTIVE SYSTEMS - Medical apparatus - Apogee Medical Products,
    Inc.
JOINT ADVENTURE - Apparel and accessories - Joint Adventure Productions,
    LLC
JOINT ADVENTURES - Quilts ☆ - Martingale & Co.
JOINT-EASE - Health care products - Natural Laboratories Corp.
JOINT-GARD - Tape–adhesive - Metallized Products Inc.
JOINT HERB - Herbal products - Natrol, Inc.
JOINT JACK - Splints - Smith & Nephew Inc. (Rehabilitation Div.)
JOINT SOLUTION - Vitamins and nutritional supplements - Highland
    Laboratories
JOINT SUPPORT COMPLEX - Vitamins and nutritional supplements - Horizon
    Worldwide Export Corp.
JOINT VENTURE - Floor coverings–carpet and rugs - Karastan-Bigelow Inc.
JOINT VENTURE - Wallets - Day-Timers, Inc.
JOINTCARE - Vitamins and nutritional supplements - Ayurvedic Concepts Ltd.
JOINTED A - Fishing lures - Bomber Bait Co.
JOINTED TADPOLLY - Sporting goods - James Heddon's Sons
JOINTED THUNDERSTICK - Fishing lures - Storm Manufacturing Co.
JOINTMASTER - Tools–hand-operated ☆ - Marshalltown Trowel Co.
JOINTMENT - Vitamins and nutritional supplements - Universal Protein
    Supplements, Inc.
JOJO - Drums–musical instruments - J.D. Calato Manufacturing Inc.
JOJOBA - Shampoos - Nature's Bounty, Inc.
JOJOBA FARMS - Hair care products - Carme Inc.
JOJOBA GOLD - Hair care products ☆ - Palm Beach Beauty Products
JOJOBA TREATMENT - Hair-care products - Tri-Institute of Trichology
JOJOBACARE - Hair-care products - Cabot Laboratories Inc.
JOKARI - Paper - Jokari/US, Inc.
JOKE-A-DAY - Publisher's imprints - Lame Duck, Inc.
JOKE IN A BOX - Pet products - Tawn Chi & Associates Inc.

☆ = Now out of production

JOKE RECORDS - Recording label - No Joke Records
JOKER - Apparel and accessories - Louis Freese
JOKER - Food products - Connell Co.
JOKER - Ophthalmic goods - Styl-Rite Optical Manufacturing Co., Inc.
JOKER - Paper–cigarette - Robert Burton Associates Ltd.
JOKER - Recording label - Lifetime Recordings
JOKER - Sporting goods - HO Sports Inc.
JOKER FRENZY - Games - Calverley Enterprises
JOKER, JOKER, JOKER - Games ☆ - Milton Bradley Co.
JOKERINO - Novelty items ☆ - United Mask & Novelty Co.
JOKER'S WILD - Wines ☆ - Warner Vineyards Inc.
JOKHA DESIGN - Jewelry - Jokha Gallery
JOKKO USA - Apparel and accessories - Patty Patterns Inc.
JOKWE - Floor coverings–carpet and rugs ☆ - Regal Rugs Inc.
JOLASTIC - Detergents - Jobst Institute Inc.
JOLEN - Skin care products - Jolen Inc.
JOLENE - Shoes - World Import Co. Inc.
JOLI - Floor coverings–carpet and rugs - J.L. Benson Co.
JOLI - Floor coverings–carpet and rugs ☆ - Patcraft Mills Inc.
JOLI - Slippers - Daniel Green Co.
JOLI - Stationery - Joli Greeting Card Co.
JOLI COLLECTION - Apparel and accessories - Warren Featherbone Co.
JOLI GLAZE - Finishing agents - Joli Plastics & Chemical Corp.
JOLI REVE - Women's sportswear - Joli Reve, Inc.
JOLI VAL - Wines - Clos du Val Wine Co. Ltd.
JOLIE - Floor coverings–carpet and rugs ☆ - Regal Rugs Inc.
JOLIE - Footwear - Stride Rite Corp.
JOLIE - Giftware - Gorham Inc.
JOLIE FEMME - Skin care products ☆ - T.N. Dickinson Co.
JOLIE FLEUR XMAS COLLECTION - Tableware–earthenware - Seymour Mann Inc.
JOLIE GIRL - Apparel stores–lingerie - H.F. Robbins
JOLIE MADAME - Colognes - Revlon Consumer Products Corp.
JOLIE OF LONDON - Crocheted and knitted items - Winston Manufacturing Corp.
JOLIE PAPIER - Wallpaper - Jolie Papier
JOLIE PAPIER DEUX - Wallpaper ☆ - Jolie Papier
JOLIE PAPIER TROIS - Wallpaper ☆ - Jolie Papier
JOLIEBOO - Medical apparatus - Bragel Inc.
JOLIESSE - Wines - Jean-Claude Boisset Wines, USA, Inc.
JOLIESSE J - Cosmetics - Joliesse, Inc.
JOLIET - Clocks ☆ - Ridgeway Clock Co.
JOLIETTE - Furniture ☆ - Stanley Furniture Co. Inc.
JOLITE - Glass–stained - Stanslaus
JOLITE - Hobby kits - Stanislaus Imports, Inc.
JOLLIE JUAN - Food products - United Citrus Products Corp.
JOLLIES - Candy ☆ - Leaf, Inc.
JOLLY - Amplifiers–musical instrument - Colombo & Sons Accordion Co.
JOLLY - Flowers, plants, and seeds - High View Church Farm, Inc.
JOLLY - Toys–stuffed ☆ - Gund, Inc.
JOLLY BEAR - Food products - Leavenworth Fruit Co.
JOLLY BOY - Food products ☆ - Hoody Corp.
JOLLY CLOWN - Toys–stuffed ☆ - Dakin Inc.
JOLLY CUBES - Puzzles ☆ - Fun World Inc.
JOLLY DOLLY - Toys ☆ - BRIO Corp.
JOLLY DUTCHMAN - Recording label - American Music Co.
JOLLY FARMER - Flowers, plants, and seeds - High View Church Farm, Inc.
JOLLY GENTLEMEN - Chocolate candy - Superior Fruit & Confections
JOLLY GOOD - Beverages - Krier Foods Inc.
JOLLY GOURMET CHEF - Housewares - Doranne
JOLLY JELLY BEANS - Candy - Leaf, Inc.
JOLLY JET - Toys - Shelcore Inc.
JOLLY JIM - Fruits and vegetables - Old Fashioned Food Processors Inc.
JOLLY JIM - Fruits and vegetables - Wenatchee-Beebe Orchard Co.
JOLLY JOAN - Food products - Ener-G Foods Inc.
JOLLY JOES - Candy - Just Born Inc.
JOLLY JOGGER - Video games - Taito America Corp.
JOLLY JOGGERS - Toys–stuffed - Fun World Inc.
JOLLY JUMBO - Candles - Columbia Wax Products Inc.
JOLLY KING - Clay–modeling - Sculpture House Inc.
JOLLY OLD SANTA CLAUS - Giftware - Roman, Inc.
JOLLY OLLIE - Toys ☆ - Playskool, Inc.
JOLLY-OPTICALS - Cables–fiber optic ☆ - Poly-Optical Products, Inc.
JOLLY PICKLE BARREL - Pickles - Green Bay Foods Co.
JOLLY POPS - Chocolate candy - Superior Fruit & Confections
JOLLY RANCHER - Candy - Leaf, Inc.

JOLLY RANCHER TROPICAL BLENDS - Candy - Leaf, Inc.
JOLLY RIDER - Strollers–baby - Jolly Jumper Inc.
JOLLY RIDER STRETCH - Strollers–baby - Jolly Jumper Inc.
JOLLY ROGER - Boats - Glen-L Marine Designs
JOLLY ROGER - Oysters–canned or cured - Wiegardt Brothers Inc.
JOLLY SANTA - Toys–stuffed - Fun World Inc.
JOLLY SANTAS - Chocolate candy - Superior Fruit & Confections
JOLLY SANTAS - Ice cream - Steve's Homemade Ice Cream Inc.
JOLLY SNACK - Rice ☆ - Better Foods
JOLLY TIME - Popcorn - American Pop Corn Co.
JOLLY TOYS - Toys - Jolly U.S.A., Inc.
JOLLY WALLY - Sporting goods - James Heddon's Sons
JOLLYBEAN - Infant product ☆ - Ming Ta Supply
JOLLYSPORT GLOVES - Gloves - Cosmopolitan Motors Inc.
JOLLYTIME - Puzzles ☆ - Milton Bradley Co.
JOLO - Curtains–shower - Paul Marshall Products L.P.
JOLT - Batteries - Jolt Corp.
JOLT - Beverages–carbonated - Global Beverage Co.
JOLT - Beverages–carbonated - Golden Brands Marketing
JOLT - Suntan lotions - Creative Laboratories Inc.
JOLT 25 - Beverages–carbonated ☆ - Global Beverage Co.
JOLT NO MORE - Sporting goods - Trident Corp.
JOLTIN' JUMP - Games ☆ - CBS Toys
JOLTZ - Office supplies - Bic Corp.
JOLYN - Ophthalmic goods - Swank Optical
JOMACO - Dryers–household - Johnke Manufacturing Co.
JOMAX - Cleaning preparations–household - Zehrung Corp.
JOMCO - Clippers–barber - Sunbeam-Oster Household Products
JOMITEK SYSTEMS - Electronic equipment - Basler Electric Co.
JOMOCO - Hammocks - Jomoco Products Co.
JOMON - Floor coverings–carpet and rugs - Masland Corp.
JON - Boats–motor - Alumacraft Boat Co.
JON-A-CHAIR - Health care products - Activeaid Inc.
JON ALLEN COLLECTION - Cosmetics ☆ - Rubigo Cosmetics Inc.
JON CANOE - Rum - Rums International, Inc.
JON CHI - Rice - La Cena Fine Foods Inc.
JON DONAIRE - Desserts - Presto Food Products, Inc.
JON E. - Cooking equipment–household ☆ - Nordic Ware
JON-E - Mittens–leather - Orbex Inc.
JON-E-BAKE - Cooking equipment–household ☆ - Nordic Ware
+JON +HART DESIGN - Handbags - Jon Hart Design Co., Inc.
JON LIEGE - Apparel and accessories - Barrow Manufacturing Co., Inc.
JON MARC - Apparel–men's - Cluett, Peabody & Co.
JON PAUL - Jewelry - Perm Inc.
JON PERRY - Apparel–women's - Perry Manufacturing Co.
+JON +SECADA - Recording label - Secada Productions, Inc.
JON SECADA - Recording label - Secada Productions, Inc.
JONAH DREW COLLECTION, THE - Apparel and accessories - H & H Trading Corp.
JONAS - Ophthalmic goods ☆ - Luxottica
JONATHAN - Eyeglasses - Art-Craft Optical Co.
JONATHAN BAY - Musical instrument accessories - Bay Woodwind Mouthpieces
JONATHAN BEAR - Toys–stuffed - Dakin Inc.
JONATHAN BRADLEY - Office supplies - Jonathan Bradley Pens Inc.
+JONATHAN +CHASE - Apparel–men's - Pamida, Inc.
+JONATHAN +CHASE II - Apparel–children's - Pamida, Inc.
JONATHAN EDWARDS - Jewelry ☆ - Ben Bridge Jeweler Inc.
JONATHAN HALE - Apparel and accessories - Jessica Hale Inc.
JONATHAN LOGAN - Apparel–women's - Jonathan Logan Inc.
JONATHAN LOGAN - Umbrellas - United Merchants and Manufacturers Inc.
JONATHAN LOUIS INTERNATIONAL - Furniture - Jonathan Louis International Ltd.
JONATHAN MARTIN - Apparel and accessories - Harkham Industries, Inc.
JONATHAN MARTIN KIDS - Apparel–women's - Harkham Industries, Inc.
JONATHAN MICHAEL - Apparel–children's - J.C. Penney Co., Inc.
JONATHAN QUALE - Apparel–men's - Big & Tall Associates
JONATHAN RICHARDS - Footwear–men's - Jonathan Richards Inc.
JONATHAN RICHARDS - Sweaters - Jonathan Richards Knitting Mills
JONATHAN SCOTT - Apparel and accessories - Swell Fashion, Inc.
JONATHAN STRONG - Apparel and accessories - Fishman and Tobin Inc.
JONATHAN TEMPLE - Thread - Advance Thread Corp.
JONATHAN VICTOR - Footwear–men's - Shonac Corp.
JONATHON BYRON - Figurines - Arnart Imports Inc.
JONATHON BYRON AMERICANA - Figurines - Arnart Imports Inc.
JONBIL - Apparel–women's - Jonbil Inc.

☆ = Now out of production

JONDEN - Apparel–women's - Jonden Manufacturing Co., Inc.
JONDICE - Toys - Tonka Corp.
JONEL - Manicure preparations - Barristo Ltd.
JONELL OIL - Oils–lubricating - Jonell Oil Corp.
JONES - Bacon - Bob Ostrow Co.
JONES - Enameled ware ☆ - Jones-Zylon Co.
JONES - Footwear - Vans, Inc.
JONES - Frames–eyeglass - Zylo Ware Corp.
JONES - Musical instrument accessories - Jones Double Reed Products
JONES - Sausages - Jones Dairy Farm
JONES - Sporting goods - J/B Sporting Goods Distributors, Inc.
JONES - Sporting goods - Michael J. Jones
JONES & CO - Apparel and accessories - Jones Investment Co., Inc.
JONES & MITCHELL - Apparel–athletic - Jones & Mitchell Sportswear
JONES DAIRY FARM - Sausages - Jones Dairy Farm
JONES DIGITAL CENTURY - Publisher's imprints - Jones International, Ltd.
JONES NEW YORK - Apparel–women's - Jones Apparel Group Inc.
JONES NEW YORK - Footwear ☆ - Brown Shoe Co.
JONES NEW YORK - Umbrellas - Jones Investment Co., Inc.
JONES NEW YORK DRESS - Apparel–women's ☆ - Jones Apparel Group Inc.
JONES NEW YORK PARFUM - Perfumes - Paul Sebastian, Inc.
JONES NEW YORK SPORT - Apparel–women's - Jones Apparel Group Inc.
JONES' ROOFCOAT - Paints - Jones Paint Co.
JONES WEAR - Apparel–women's - Jones Investment Co., Inc.
JONES-ZYLON - Medical apparatus - Jones-Zylon Co.
JONESBOROUGH - Floor coverings - Harris-Tarkett, Inc.
JONESPORT - Seafood products–canned or cured - R.B. & C.G. Stevens Co.
JONFISHER - Boats - Sears, Roebuck and Co.
JONI BLAIR OF CALIFORNIA - Apparel–women's - Joni Blair of California Inc.
JONINA - Lenses–optical - National Optical Co.
JONI'S COFFEE ROASTER CAFE - Coffee - Caesar's Coffee Inc.
JONKER FRIS - Food products - Sara Lee Corp.
JONKERS - Jewelry–precious - Harry Winston, Inc.
JONNI FRAME - Clocks - Jonni Fram Manufacturing Co.
JONNIE GEM - Septic cleaner ☆ - Jancyn Manufacturing Corp.
JONNY - Cigarettes - G.A. Georgopulo & Co. Inc.
JONNY - Cleaning preparations - Kiwi Brands, Inc.
JONNY - Skin care products - Eurostar Perfumes, Inc.
JONNY BLOK - Cleaning preparations - AmeriPlus Inc.
JONNY BLUE - Cleaning preparations–household - Sara Lee Corp.
JONNY BRITE - Cleaning preparations–household ☆ - Blue Cross Laboratories, Inc.
JONNY CAT - Pet products - A & M Products Inc.
JONNY CAT - Pet products - Excel-Mineral Co. Inc.
JONNY CAT PREMIUM - Pet products - Excel-Mineral Co. Inc.
JONNY COMFORT - Health care products - Commander-Omni Co. Inc.
JONNY FRESH - Cleaning preparations - AmeriPlus Inc.
JONNY GREEN - Cleaning preparations–household - Sara Lee Corp.
JONNY MOP - Cleaning preparations - Empire Brushes, Inc.
JONNY QUEST - Apparel and accessories - Hanna-Barbera Productions, Inc.
JONNY QUEST - Footwear - S. Goldberg and Co. Inc.
JONNYS JALOPYS BROOKLYN, USA - Clothing - Jonny's Jalopys USA, Inc.
JONQUIL - Apparel and accessories - Judy Bond Inc.
JONQUIL - Clocks ☆ - General Time Corp. (Westclox/Seth Thomas Div.)
JONQUIL - Dinnerware–glass ☆ - Nikko Ceramics Inc.
JONQUIL - Jewelry - James Breski & Co., Inc.
JON'S - Food products ☆ - Christopher Brookes Distinctive Foods
JONSIL - Rings–jewelry - Jonsil Inc.
JONTUE - Cosmetics - Revlon Consumer Products Corp.
JONTUE - Floor coverings–carpet and rugs ☆ - Columbus Mills, Inc.
JONVALDI - Apparel–children's - Jonvaldi
JOPA - Drums–musical instruments - Paul A. Real Sales
JORAINE - Apparel–women's - Val Mode Lingerie Inc.
JORAN - Drill bits - Danish Import Inc.
JORAT - Frames–eyeglass ☆ - Universal/Univis Inc.
JORDACHE - Apparel trimmings - Jordache Enterprises Inc.
JORDACHE - Briefcases - IMA Fashions Inc.
JORDACHE - Cosmetics - JC & F Inc.
JORDACHE - Footwear - R.G. Barry Corp.
JORDACHE - Footwear - Mercury International Trading Corp.
JORDACHE - Footwear - Pagoda Trading Co.
JORDACHE - Handbags - A.D. Sutton & Sons Inc.
JORDACHE - Leather goods - RGA Accessories Inc.
JORDACHE - Luggage - Gateway Travelware

JORDACHE - Luggage - York Luggage Co.
JORDACHE - Neckties - M. Aron Corp.
JORDACHE - Shoes - Sidney Rich Associates Inc.
JORDACHE - Sunglasses - Sungold Enterprises Ltd.
JORDACHE - Umbrellas ☆ - Essex Manufacturing Inc.
JORDACHE BY FERRADINI - Footwear ☆ - Diesse Shoes Inc.
JORDACHE SLIKERS - Waterproof outerwear ☆ - Essex Manufacturing Inc.
JORDACHE TIME - Watches - Alva Watch/Jordache Time
JORDAN - Amplifiers - CTC Music Inc.
JORDAN - Artists' materials - Jordan Specialty Co.
JORDAN - Clay–modeling - Sculpture House Inc.
JORDAN - Food products - Sherman Canning Co.
JORDAN - Ophthalmic goods - Styl-Rite Optical Manufacturing Co., Inc.
JORDAN - Wines - Jordan Vineyard & Winery
JORDAN ALMONDS - Candy - Sweet Candy Co.
JORDAN CHRISTOPHER - Apparel–men's - National Service Industries, Inc.
JORDAN GOURMET COFFEE - Coffee - Specialty Foods
JORDAN MAGIC - Toothbrushes - Dep Corp.
JORDAN MAID - Snack foods - Ferrara Pan Candy Co., Inc.
JORDAN PEDALS - Musical instrument accessories - CTC Music Inc.
JORDAN VS. BIRD: ONE ON ONE - Games - Milton Bradley Co.
JORDAN WATER - Skin care products ☆ - Freeman Industries LLC
JORDAN WINDOWS & DOORS - Doors - West Union Corp.
JORDANA - Ophthalmic goods ☆ - Luxottica
JORDAN'S - Breads - American Bakeries Co.
JORDIN - Apparel–men's - Jihad B. Akleh
JORDON - Watches - Bulova Corp.
JORDY - Ophthalmic goods ☆ - Luxottica
JORDYN ASHLEY - Food products - Todd M. Levin
JOREL - Cosmetics ☆ - Divina Products Co.
JORGE CANAVES - Saddles - Thornhill Enterprises, Inc.
JORGENSEN - Tools - Adjustable Clamp Co. Inc.
JORGENSEN CONVEYORS, INC. - Conveyors - Jorgensen Conveyors, Inc.
JORI - Looms ☆ - Northfield Loom
JORINA - Ophthalmic goods ☆ - Luxottica
JORY - Ophthalmic goods ☆ - Luxottica
JOS. - See also **JOSEPH**
JOS PALLA - Wines - St. Croix Winery
JOS. POELL - Bakery products - Jaret Specialties Inc.
JOSAIR - Glassware–household - H. Wittur & Co.
JOSCAR - Fabrics–silk - Joscar Industries Inc.
JOSE COTEL - Apparel and accessories - Ames International Group
JOSE CUERVO - Liquors - Heublein, Inc.
JOSE CUERVO MARGARITA - Beverages–alcohol - Heublein, Inc.
JOSE CUERVO MARGARITA SALT - Salt - Franco's Cocktail Products Inc.
JOSE EBER - Hair care products - Faberge Co.
JOSE JALAPENO - Olives–pickled or brined - Bri-AL, Inc.
JOSE LUCENA SPANISH GUITARS - Guitars - Music Imports Ltd.
JOSE LUIS DE CASASOLA - Figurines - Anna-Perenna Inc.
JOSE MARIA - Guitars - Juan Orozco Corp.
JOSEF - Dolls - Applause, Inc.
JOSEF - Luggage - Universal Trav-ler Inc.
JOSEF II - Luggage - Universal Trav-ler Inc.
JOSEF BRIGL - Wines ☆ - Pellegrini Bros. Wines Inc.
JOSEF BRIQL, ALTO ADIGE - Wines - William Grant & Sons, Inc.
JOSEF DRATHEN - Liquors - European Beverage Co., Inc.
JOSEF-JONATHAN - Handbags - Josef-Rose Originals Inc.
JOSEF LORENZ - Violins - Ideal Musical Merchandise Co.
JOSEF NIEDERMAYR - Wines - Pellegrini Bros. Wines Inc.
JOSEF OF ROME - Wigs - Eva Gabor International, Ltd.
JOSEF SEIBEL - Footwear - Swenson Imports
JOSEF WEHR - Wines - Arthur G. Lombardi & Son
JOSELLE - Dolls - Barval Toys Inc.
JOSEP BOFILL - Figurines - Anna-Perenna Inc.
JOSEPH - See also **JOS.**
JOSEPH - Beverages–alcohol - World Shippers & Importers
JOSEPH - Ophthalmic goods ☆ - Luxottica
JOSEPH - Rings–jewelry - Joseph Ring Co. Inc.
JOSEPH A. BANK - Apparel and accessories - Joseph A. Banks Clothiers
JOSEPH ABBOUD - Apparel and accessories - Joseph Abboud Co.
JOSEPH ABBOUD - Apparel and accessories - Morgan Shirt Corp.
JOSEPH ABBOUND - Watches - E. Gluck Corp.
JOSEPH & FEISS - Apparel–children's - Joseph and Feiss Co.
JOSEPH B. EXCLUSIVE - Handbags - D.J. Benlolo
JOSEPH BERNARD - Leather goods - M.Z. Berger & Co. Inc.
JOSEPH CERNIGLIA WINERY - Wines - Joseph Cerniglia Winery Inc.

☆ = Now out of production

JOSEPH ENTERPRISES - Fertilizers - Joseph Enterprises Inc.
JOSEPH FILIPPI - Wines - J. Filippi Vintage Co.
JOSEPH FLEISCHER - Wigs - Joseph Fleischer Natural Coiffures, Inc.
JOSEPH GEE - Apparel—women's - Thomas E. Greene
JOSEPH HAMMIS - Musical instrument accessories - J.M. Sahlein Music Co. Inc.
JOSEPH M - Apparel—men's - Joseph Mack
JOSEPH MARTINI - Olive oil - California Olive Oil Corp.
JOSEPH PELKEY - Greeting cards ☆ - Editions Ltd.
JOSEPH PHELPS VINEYARDS - Wines - Joseph Phelps Vineyards
JOSEPH PICONE - Apparel—women's - Palm Beach Co., Inc.
JOSEPH SCHUSTER - Musical instrument accessories - M & M Distributing Co.
JOSEPH SWAN VINEYARDS - Wines - Joseph Swan Vineyards
JOSEPH VICTORI - Wines - Joseph Victori Wines Inc.
JOSEPH WALKER - Breads ☆ - Europa Foods Ltd.
JOSEPH ZAKAN WINERY - Wines - Joseph Zakon Winery Ltd.
JOSEPH ZAKON WINERY - Wines - Crown Regal Wine Cellars
JOSEPH ZUKER SELECTIONS - Wines ☆ - Royal Wine Corp.
JOSEPHINE - Fabrics - Gretchen Bellinger Inc.
JOSEPHINE - Glassware—household - Villeroy and Boch Tableware Ltd.
JOSEPHINE DE FRANCE - Luggage - Josephine Inc.
JOSEPHINE VP - Apparel—women's - Hooper Associates Ltd.
JOSEPHINEN HUTTE - Glassware—household - Villeroy and Boch Tableware Ltd.
JOSEPH'S - Cheese - MBC Foods
JOSEPH'S - Cookies - Lite Cookies Ltd.
JOSEPHS - Musical instruments - Smith & Smith Electric Co., Inc.
JOSEPHSON - Bags—duffel - Josephson Bag and Canvas Co., Inc.
JOSE'S - Coffee - F. Gavina and Sons Inc.
JOSE'S TERRA COTTA POTTERY - Terra cotta - Joseph C. Wax
JOSET - Hair care products ☆ - Sheila Brit Ltd.
JOSH - Frames—eyeglass - U.S. Optical Frame Co.
JOSH - Ophthalmic goods ☆ - Luxottica
JOSHUA - Child Matters
JOSHUA CLOTH - Fabrics - Dan River Inc.
JOSHUA HILL - Wines - Delicato Vineyards
JOSHUA MORRIS - Publisher's imprints - Reader's Digest Association, Inc.
JOSHUA ODELL EDITIONS - Publisher's imprints ☆ - Capra Press Inc.
JOSHUA SCOTT - Apparel—women's - Harvey Celler California Inc.
JOSHUA TREE - Apparel and accessories - Factorie Direct Services, Inc.
JOSHUA TUCKER'S - Teas - H.P. Hood & Sons Inc.
JOSHUAS - Food products - Blue Ridge Farms, Inc.
JOSI BALL - Cookies - Josi Ball Bakery
JOSIE - Apparel—women's - Natori Co. Inc.
JOSIE - Boots - Coast Shoes Inc.
JOSIE BY NATORI - Apparel—women's - Natori Co. Inc.
JOSIEJO - Food products - Josiejo & Co.
JOSLIN & MOONEY - Footwear—men's - Atsco Footwear Inc.
JOSLIN' CODE - Embossing machines - A.D. Joslin Manufacturing Co.
JOSSELYN - Toys - Tonka Corp.
JOSSEY-BASS - Publisher's imprints - Publishers Jossey-Bass Inc.
JOST - Jewelry - Jost Bros. Jewelry Manufacturing Corp.
JOSTA - Beverages—carbonated - Pepsi-Cola Co.
JOSTA - Beverages—carbonated - Pepsico, Inc.
JOSTENS - Jewelry - Jostens Inc.
JOSTENS LEARNING CORP. - Computer software - Jostens Inc.
JOSTENS LEARNING LITENET - Computer software - Jostens Inc.
JOSTENS SPORTSWEAR J - Apparel—women's - Jostens Inc.
JOT A NOTE - Business forms - Moore Business Forms, Inc.
JOT-A-WEEK - Calculators ☆ - Rediform
JOT-IT - Notebooks and notepads - Risto Inc.
JOT-THAT-THOUGHT - Notebooks and notepads - Jot-That-Thought, Inc.
JOTTA-CALL - Publisher's imprints - Kleer-Fax Inc.
JOTTER - Pens - Parker Pen USA
JOTTO! - Computer software - Recreational Mathemagical Software
JOTUAL - Cooking equipment—household - B. Westergaard & Co. Inc.
JOTUL - Kitchen appliances ☆ - SCI Scandicrafts Inc.
JOTUL - Stoves - Jotul North America
JOTUN - Figurines ☆ - Charles Zahn-Import Merchant
JOTZ THE SELFCLING COMMUNICATOR - Paper—writing - Cullman Ventures Inc.
JOU YU - Bicycles - Pikula Associates
JOUBERT - Beverages—alcohol - Consolidated Distilled Products Inc.
JOUBES - Soups—canned - Pacific Epicure Distributing Co.
JOUE A JOUE - Cosmetics - Lancome

JOUES CONTRASTE - Cosmetics - Chanel Inc.
JOUES LUMIERE - Cosmetics - Chanel Inc.
JOUJOU - Bags - Joujou Designs Inc.
JOULE - Computer hardware - La Cie. Ltd.
JOULE - Floor coverings—carpet and rugs ☆ - Evans-Black Carpet Mills
JOULE - Juices - Joule Beverages Inc.
JOULE BOX - Climate-control product - Intertechnology/Solar Corp.
JOURDAN - Attache cases - TJC, Inc.
JOURNAL - Footwear—athletic ☆ - Nike, Inc.
JOURNAL 24 - Photographic equipment - Leedal Inc.
JOURNAL MINDER, THE - Bookmarks - Waverly, Inc.
JOURNAL OF CLINICAL RHEUMATOLOGY - Publisher's imprints - Waverly, Inc.
JOURNAL OF FINANCIAL STATEMENT ANALYSIS, THE - Accounting services - Institutional Investor, Inc.
JOURNALIST - Computer software - Ped Software Corp.
JOURNALIST - Frames—eyeglass - Zylo Ware Corp.
JOURNEY - Floor coverings—carpet and rugs - Coronet Carpets Inc.
JOURNEY - Luggage - Shalam Imports Inc.
JOURNEY - Motor vehicles—motor homes - Journey Custom Motor Homes Inc.
JOURNEY - Printers—computer - Datasouth Computer Corp.
JOURNEY - Razors—electric - Parks Products Inc.
JOURNEY - Skates—roller - Rollerblade, Inc.
JOURNEY - Wines - Matanzas Creek Winery
JOURNEY INTO DARKNESS, A - Computer software ☆ - Earthware Computer Services
JOURNEY INTO SLEEP - Mattresses - Sleepwell Mattress Co. Inc.
JOURNEY INTO SPACE - Electronic equipment ☆ - Texas Instruments Inc.
JOURNEY JOURNAL - Paper products - Lyght Enterprises
JOURNEY TO BIRDS AND REPTILES - Electronic equipment - Texas Instruments Inc.
JOURNEY TO SEVEN - Publisher's imprints - McMillin Foley Publishing Co.
JOURNEY TO THE MUTHULAND - Games - Michael P. Smith
JOURNEYER - Firearms, accessories, and parts - Welsh Sporting Goods Corp. (Boyt Div.)
JOURNEYMAN - Brushes—paint - Wooster Brush Co.
JOURNEYMAN - Cases—musical instrument - Distex Corp.
JOURNEYMAN - Knives - Precise International/Wenger
JOURNEYMAN - Lighting fixtures - Heath Co.
JOURNEYMAN PROJECT 3-LEGACY OF TIME, THE - Video games - Presto Studios, Inc.
JOURNEYMAN PROJECT, THE - Computer software - Presto Studios, Inc.
JOURNEYMAN WIREMAN - Belts—apparel - Hard Hat Inc.
JOURNEY'S END - Blinds—venetian ☆ - Hunter Douglas, Inc.
JOURNEY'S END - Clothing - American Trouser Inc.
JOURNEY'S END BURIAL CASE - Pet products - Zerick Co.
JOURNEYS OF FAITH - Recording label - Lord Design and Merchandising Co.
JOURNEYS THROUGH THE BIBLE - Publisher's imprints - Sweet Publishing
JOURNEYS TO THE NEW AGE - Confections - Special Preparations Co.
JOURNEYWARE MEDIA - Computer storage devices—optical - Journeyware Media, Inc.
JOUSTERS - Shoes - Step Master Shoes
JOVAN - Perfumes - Coty Inc.
JOVAN - Shaving preparations - Quintessence Inc.
JOVAN ACTIVES - Deodorants—personal ☆ - RCN Products Inc.
JOVAN MUSK 2 - Perfumes - Quintessence Inc.
JOVAN MUSK2 - Colognes - Quintessence Inc.
JOVE - Publisher's imprints - Berkley Publishing Corp.
JOWAT GLUES HIGH POINT - Adhesives and sealants - Jowat Corp.
JOX - Footwear - Melville Corp.
JOX - Shoes—athletic - Thom McAn Shoe Co.
JOX PULSATOR - Footwear - Melville Corp.
JOY - Aerobic footwear ☆ - Autry Industries Inc.
JOY - Apparel—women's - Bi-Flex International
JOY - Bedding—linen - Dan River Inc.
JOY - Detergents - Procter & Gamble Co.
JOY - Electrical equipment ☆ - Cooper Industries, Inc.
JOY - Eyeglasses - Joy Enterprises
JOY - Giftware ☆ - Gorham Inc.
JOY - Glassware—household - ACC
JOY - Greeting cards - Royal Stationery Co.
JOY - Machinery - United Coatings, Inc.
JOY - Meat products—pork - Vincent Giordano Corp.
JOY - Perfumes - Jean Patou, Inc.
JOY - Pet products - Best Feeds and Farm Supplies Inc.
JOY - Yarn ☆ - Lion Brand Yarn Co.

☆ = Now out of production

JOY ATHLETIC - Apparel and accessories - Joy Athletic, Inc.
JOY BEAR - Toys–stuffed ☆ - Dakin Inc.
JOY BEARS - Figurines - Fort USA
JOY BEE'S - Candy ☆ - Just Born Inc.
JOY BROADCAST - Recording label - Stark Records & Tape Co.
JOY BUZZER - Novelty items - S.S. Adams Co.
JOY BY THE FORERS - Greeting cards ☆ - Brett-Forer Greetings Inc.
JOY CARDS - Greeting cards - Brett-Forer Greetings Inc.
JOY JUICE - Vitamins and nutritional supplements - Natural Organics, Inc.
JOY LIOTTA FOR T.J. - Footwear - T.J. Trading Co. Inc.
JOY-O-SOY - See **TOFU SHOP**
JOY OF CHICKEN - Salad dressings–bottled - R.T. French Co.
JOY OF COOKIES, THE - Cookies - Joy of Cookies
JOY OF EATING - Calendars ☆ - American Greetings Corp.
JOY OF GARLIC - Bagels - Spot Bagel Bakery, Inc.
JOY OF MUSIC, THE - Video production - Joy of Music, Inc.
JOY OF PAINTING - Artists' materials ☆ - Hunt Manufacturing Co.
JOY OF QUILTING - Publisher's imprints - Martingale & Co.
JOY OF SILK - Apparel–women's - Lotus Fashion Co.
JOY OF SOX, THE - Calendars - Gibson Greetings, Inc.
JOY OF SPEX, THE - Eyeglasses - Joy of Spex, Inc.
JOY RIDE - Infant product - Evenflo Co.
JOY RIDE - Infant product - Lisco, Inc.
JOY RIDE - Sport tubes - Intex Recreation Corp.
JOY RIDE TRAVEL SYSTEM - Infant product - Lisco, Inc.
JOY STEPS - Footwear - Kipling Shoe Co. Inc.
JOY STICK - Nautical instruments ☆ - C. Sherman Johnson Co. Inc.
JOY STIKS - Confections - Confectionately Yours, Ltd.
JOY STIX - Pens - Pen Werks, LLC.
JOY SWEEP - Brooms - Lighthouse Industries
JOY TABS - Vitamins and nutritional supplements - Natural Organics, Inc.
JOYA DE LA MANCHA - Spices and extracts - Clover Specialties
JOYART - Jewelry - Joyart Jewelry Co.
JOYAS DE GOYA - Fruit drinks–bottled or canned - Goya Foods, Inc.
JOYBUG - Publisher's imprints - Joybug Teaching Aids Inc.
JOYCE - Footwear–women's - Joyce Shoes
JOYCE - Office supplies ☆ - Rotary Files Inc.
JOYCE CHEN - Food products - Joyce Chen
JOYCE HOWELL - Wallpaper - Style-Tex Wallcoverings
JOYCE MORRIS CREATIONS - Towels - General Sales Co.
JOYCE ONARHEIM BOE - Apparel–women's - Legacy Collection, Inc.
JOYEANNA'S - Paper products - Joyeanna Chaudiere
JOYETT - Ice cream ☆ - Safeway Stores Inc.
JOYFUL - Food products - Tom Boy Inc.
JOYFUL - Rings–jewelry - Artcarved Inc.
JOYFUL EXPRESSIONS - Wallpaper ☆ - Imperial Wallcoverings, Inc.
JOYFUL HARVEST - Fruits–dried - Natural Foods Inc.
JOYFUL HEARTS - Greeting cards - Joyful Hearts Creations
JOYFUL JOURNEY - Recording label - New Life Treatment Centers, Inc.
JOYFUL NOISE - Calendars - Creative Studios, I, Inc.
JOYFUL NOISE - Chimes - Joyful Noise
JOYFUL YEARS - Dolls ☆ - Gorham Inc.
JOYFULLY YOURS - Greeting cards - Outreach Publications Inc.
JOYLASTIQUE - Girdles - Bonwit Teller & Co.
JOYOUS CRYSTAL - Meters–frequency - Ecliptek, Inc.
JOYOUS OCCASIONS - Dolls - Effanbee Doll Corp.
JOY'S FAVORITE - Candy - Norwalk Candies, Inc.
JOY'S FAVORITE REAL OLD FASHIONED FUDGE - Candy - Norwalk Candies, Inc.
JOYS OF CHRISTMAS - Giftware - Lenox, Inc.
JOY'S SIGNATURE SERIES - Jewelry - Ingenious Designs, Inc.
JOYSPRAY - Skin care products ☆ - J.I.C.
JOYSPRAY 888 - Skin care products - J.I.C.
JOYSTICK - Golfing equipment - Plop Golf Co.
JOYSTICK - Pet products - Ferret World Inc.
JOYSTICK SWITCHBOX - Computer peripheral equipment - Joystick Technologies (CH Products Division)
JOYVA - Candy - Joyva Corp.
JOYVA - Food products - Dairy Fresh Products Co.
JOYVA TAHINI - Food products - Joyva Corp.
JOYWALKERS - Shoes–athletic - Titleist & Foot-Joy Worldwide
JP - Food products - Jamaica Producers Marketing
JP - Handbags - Jean Patou, Inc.
JP - Jewelry - Jayposon Charm & Jewelry Manufacturing
J.P. - Snack foods - Tri-Sum Potato Chip Co. Inc.
JP - Sporting goods - Amblin' Entertainment, Inc.

J.P. ANGELA - Apparel–women's - R. & A. Collections Inc.
J.P. #BURLESON, INC. - Pet products - J.P. Burleson Inc.
J.P. CLUB - Apparel and accessories ☆ - Edison Brothers Stores, Inc.
JP CONNECTION - Computers - JP Foodservice, Inc.
JP DIRECTADVANTAGE - Computer software - JP Foodservice, Inc.
J.P. FALLS OLD PHILADELPHIA STYLE - Root beer - Choice USA Beverages
JP POWER - Cleaning preparations - JP Foodservice, Inc.
JP POWER BY JP FOODSERVICE, INC. - Cleaning preparations - JP Foodservice, Inc.
J.P. STEVENS - Draperies - West Point-Pepperell Inc.
JP STRAWBOTTOMS - Food products - JP Strawbottoms
JP SYSTEM 5 - Computer software - University of Utah
JPB ARTIST - Guitars - MBT International, Inc.
JPB-FG HI CAL - Vitamins and nutritional supplements - George Braun Oyster Co. Inc.
J.P.C. - Mallets - Mike Balter Mallets
JPG - Apparel–men's - Abdurrauf Ben Alamin
JPI - Audio equipment - Justin Products, Inc.
JPM - Jewelry–precious - J.P. Morton Co. Inc.
JPRINTER - Computer software - Bristol Technology, Inc.
JPS - Cigarettes - James B. Russell Inc.
J.P.'S ORIGINAL - Popcorn ☆ - Sonne Laboratories
JPW - Loudspeakers ☆ - Audiophile Systems Ltd.
JQ - T-shirts–men's - Joy of the Game, Inc.
J.Q.A. - Jewelry - J.Q. Adams Co.
JR. - See **JUNIOR**
JR - Candy - American Licorice Co.
JR - Handbags - Mutterperl Group Inc.
JR - Packaging film, paper products, etc. - James River Corp.
JR - Recording label ☆ - Joey Boy Records Corp.
JR ALTERNATIVE - Cigars - J.R. Tobacco of America, Inc.
J.R. GIBBS - Meats–luncheon - Trio Foods, Inc.
JR JEMINI - Hair curlers - Jheri Redding Products Inc.
J.R. LIGGETT'S OLD-FASHIONED BAR SHAMPOO - Toiletries - J.R. Liggett Ltd.
JR LTD. - Jewelry - James Reid Ltd.
J.R. MAD'S - Seasonings - Reidco, Inc.
J.R. OVERSEAS SEA-THRU - Measuring and dispensing pumps - J.R. Overseas Co.
JR PRO - Dryers–hair - Jheri Redding Products Inc.
J.R. PUBLICATIONS - Publisher's imprints - J.R. Publications
J.R. RIPPER - Sporting goods - O'Brien International
JRA FURNITURE - Furniture - James R. Arthur
JRAT - Apparel and accessories - FNF Inc.
JRB - Jewelry - John R. Benson & Co. Inc. Manufacturing Jewelers
JRC - Curling irons–electric ☆ - Cassidy Inc.
JRP INTERNATIONAL, INC. - Fertilizers - JRP International, Inc.
JRS. - See also **JUNIORS**
JR'S - Food products - JR's Hot Dogs Inc.
J.R.'S - Pizzas–frozen - Nation Pizza Products L.P.
JRS. BY BARAD - Apparel and accessories ☆ - Barad & Co.
J.S. - Musical instrument accessories ☆ - Micro Musical Products Corp.
JS - Plumbing fixtures - Zurn Industries, Inc.
J.S. - Skin care products - Andy Hung-Ying Shih
JS - Sports apparel ☆ - Jansport Inc.
JS COLLECTIONS - Apparel and accessories - JS Group USA Ltd.
JSE - Plant-care products - R & M Products
JSEP - Computer software - Florida State University
JSL - Lamps - J.S.L. Trading, Inc.
JSL - Office furniture–metal - Joyce International Inc.
J.S.M. - Garden equipment - S.P. Lummus Supply Co. Inc.
JST - Jewelry - Sumit Diamond Corp.
JST-300 - Pigments - Radiant Color Div.
JT - Computer software - Jackson and Tull
JT - Microphones ☆ - C.T.I. Audio Inc.
J.T. BLUES - Apparel–men's - Jeremy Dold Co.
J.T. PEASHOOTERS - Candy - American Chewing Gum Inc.
J.T. RACING - Goggles - Rothco Inc.
JT RECORDS - Recording label - Janice G. Spagnolia
JT SPORT - Apparel–men's - Jeremy Dold Co.
JTB - Bicycles - Just Two Bikes, Inc.
JTECH - Pagers - Jtech Inc.
JTG - Guitars ☆ - JTG of Nashville
JTG SERIES - Health care products - Activeaid Inc.

☆ = Now out of production

JTI JOHNSTECH INTERNATIONAL - Electrical testing instruments - Johnstech International Corp.

JTK - Tools–hand-operated - Stanley Works

JTL - Jewelry - Andin International Inc.

JTL BAT COMPANY - Aluminum bats - JTL Bat Co.

J.T.M. - Apparel and accessories - J.T.M. Provisions Co.

JTM - Popcorn - JTM

J.T.M. CINCY STYLE CHILI - Food products - J.T.M. Provisions Co.

J.T.M. OLD FASHION LONG-NECKER BEEF JERKY - Meat products–dried ☆ - J.T.M. Provisions Co.

JTT - Jewelry - Joseph E. Nikitczuk

JU-87D STUKA - Toys–models ☆ - Cox Products Inc.

JU-C - Fruit drinks–bottled or canned - Pennsylvania Dutch Birch Beer Inc.

JU-C-CHU - Candy ☆ - Glenn Confections Inc.

JUAN - Glassware–household - Durand International

JUAN HERNANDEZ - Wines - Wine Imports Ltd.

JUAN JIBER - Toys - Tonka Corp.

JUAN OROZCO - Guitars - Juan Orozco Corp.

JUAN O'SULLIVAN'S GOURMET SALSA - Sauces - Sean T. Sullivan

JUANITA - Frames–eyeglass - Pathway Optical Prods.

JUANITA'S - Food products - Juanita's Candy Kitchen

JUANITA'S - Soups–mixes - Juanita's Foods

JUAREZ - Beverages–alcohol - David Sherman Corp.

JUAREZ - Floor coverings - Mannington Resilient Floors

JUBA - Beverages–carbonated - Juba Beverages Corp.

JUBA NEW, FRESH BEVERAGES - Beverages - Juba Beverages Corp.

JUBE JELS - Candy - Brach and Brock Confections Inc.

JUBILANT - Floor coverings–carpet and rugs ☆ - World Carpets, Inc.

JUBILAR - Skin care products ☆ - Dynex International

JUBILATE - Dolls - Estee Productions, Inc.

JUBILATION - Floor coverings–carpet and rugs - Cabin Crafts Carpets

JUBILATION - Furniture ☆ - Arbek Furniture Manufacturing Inc.

JUBILATION - Furniture ☆ - Mersman Furniture Co.

JUBILATION - Hair care products - John Amico Expressive Hair Care Products

JUBILATION - Wallpaper - Mirage Wallcovering Co.

JUBILEE - Bakery goods - Flowers Family Bakeries, Inc.

JUBILEE - Boats - Glen-L Marine Designs

JUBILEE - Boats–motor - Mariah Boats, Inc.

JUBILEE - Bowls ☆ - Lenox Crystal, Inc.

JUBILEE - Cameras - Eastman Kodak Co.

JUBILEE - Candles - McCormick & Co., Inc.

JUBILEE - Cleaning preparations–household - S.C. Johnson & Son, Inc.

JUBILEE - Dairy products - Challenge Dairy Co.

JUBILEE - Dishes–china - Pickard Inc.

JUBILEE - Fabrics ☆ - Superior Shade & Blind Co. Inc.

JUBILEE - Floor coverings–carpet and rugs - Daltonian Carpet & Cushion Inc.

JUBILEE - Floor coverings–carpet and rugs - Eagle Carpets Inc.

JUBILEE - Floor coverings–carpet and rugs - J and J Industries Inc.

JUBILEE - Floor coverings–carpet and rugs - Quaker Inc.

JUBILEE - Floor coverings–carpet and rugs ☆ - Len Dal Carpets

JUBILEE - Floor coverings–carpet and rugs ☆ - Regal Rugs Inc.

JUBILEE - Floor coverings–carpet and rugs ☆ - Southern Carpet Mills

JUBILEE - Footwear - D. Myers and Sons Inc.

JUBILEE - Frames–eyeglass - Liberty Optical Manufacturing Co.

JUBILEE - Fruits–candied - Food Producers International Inc.

JUBILEE - Furniture ☆ - Bassett Furniture Industries, Inc.

JUBILEE - Glassware–household - Owens-Illinois Inc. (Libbey Div.)

JUBILEE - Guitars ☆ - International Music Corp.

JUBILEE - Hams - Oscar Mayer Foods Corp.

JUBILEE - Hearing aids - Beltone Electronics Corp.

JUBILEE - Housewares ☆ - Baum Bros. Imports Inc.

JUBILEE - Mattresses and box springs - Ohio Mattress Co.

JUBILEE - Organs–musical instrument ☆ - Strydel Inc.

JUBILEE - Paints - Lee Paint & Varnish Co.

JUBILEE - Paper ☆ - Fox River Paper Co.

JUBILEE - Recording label ☆ - London Records Inc.

JUBILEE - Ribbons ☆ - American Greetings Corp.

JUBILEE - Rice - Lundberg Family Farms

JUBILEE - Rice - Wehah Farm, Inc.

JUBILEE - Rings–jewelry ☆ - Artcarved Inc.

JUBILEE - Rope ☆ - Samson Cordage Works

JUBILEE - Tires - Bridgestone/Firestone, Inc.

JUBILEE - Vases - Crisa Corp.

JUBILEE - Vinegar - Erlander's Natural Products

JUBILEE - Wainscoting - Georgia-Pacific Corp.

JUBILEE - Wallpaper - Capital Carousel Inc.

JUBILEE - Wallpaper - Morton Jonap Co. Inc.

JUBILEE - Watches ☆ - Longines-Wittnauer Watch Co.

JUBILEE COLLECTION - Greeting cards - American Artists Group Inc.

JUBILEE GIRAFFE - Puppets - Dakin Inc.

JUBILEE KNIT - Apparel–children's - Jubilee Knitwear Co.

JUBILEE LIGHTS - Cigarettes ☆ - Nat Sherman, Inc.

JUBILEE MIX - Candy - Sweet Candy Co.

JUBILEE SUNFLOWER - Ships–sailing vessels ☆ - Snark Boats

JUBILLES - Watches - Bali Watch (L.A.) Inc.

JUCU - Recording label ☆ - Ray Lawrence Ltd.

JUCY-ADE - Beverages–carbonated - Universal Flavor USA

JU'CY ORANGE - Juices–frozen - Pennsylvania Dutch Birch Beer Inc.

JUDAIC COLLECTION - Giftware - Lenox, Inc.

JUDAICA GREETINGS - Greeting cards - Alef Judaica

JUDD LIGHT - Snuff - American Maize-Products Co.

JUDD'S HILL - Wines - Finkelstein Vineyards

JUDGE - Frames–eyeglass ☆ - Universal/Univis Inc.

JUDGE & JURY - Recording label - Matthew Gerard Mueller

JUDGE LITE - Golfing equipment - Founders Club Golf Co.

JUDGE MANSFIELD GROUP, THE - Furniture - Bean Station Furniture Factory Inc.

JUDGE 'N JURY - Games - Winning Moves Inc.

JUDGES CAVE - Tobacco products - F.D. Grave & Son, Inc.

JUDI - Frames–eyeglass - Zylo Ware Corp.

JUDI WITH AN EYE - Hobby kits - Judith G. Kauffman

JUDICATA - Computer peripheral equipment - Trion Technologies, Inc.

JUDICIAL SUEDE - Floor coverings–carpet and rugs ☆ - Mohawk Carpet Corp.

JUDICIAL TELESCHEDULER - Computer software - Stenograph Corp.

JUDI'S ORIJINALS - Infant product - Judi's Orijinals

JUDITH - Ophthalmic goods - Luxottica

JUDITH ANN - Pajamas–women's ☆ - Periphery Loungewear Inc.

JUDITH ANN - Skin care products - Judith Ann Inc.

JUDITH CONWAY - Jewelry–precious - JCM Designs, Inc.

JUDITH DEWITT APPLETON - Notebooks and notepads ☆ - Lake Mills Studios

JUDITH ETSTIEN - Jewelry - Silver for Less Inc.

JUDITH LEIBER - Leather goods - Judith Leiber Inc.

JUDITH LEIBER INTRINSICS - Health care products - Judith Leiber Inc.

JUDITH RIPKA - Jewelry–precious - Judith Ripka Creations Inc.

JUDITH RIPKA JEWELLERY - Jewelry–precious - Judith Ripka Creations Inc.

JUDITH ROSE - Scarves - Textillery Weavers

JUDO - Insecticide - Olympic Chemical Co.

JUDO-NO - Apparel and accessories - Tony R. Martinez

JUDSON - Candy - Judson-Atkinson Candies

JUDY - Garden equipment ☆ - Rubens Originals

JUDY-ANN - Food products - Wine & Schulz Inc.

JUDY BOND - Apparel and accessories - Judy Bond Inc.

JUDY HOOPER'S FRUIT & BLOOM - Fertilizers - Pima Research Co.

JUDY JAX - Bicycle parts and accessories - Rockshox, Inc.

JUDY JP PREEFER - Apparel–women's - Judy Preefer

JUDY LINDA - Apparel and accessories - Andmore Sportswear Corp.

JUDY MILLER, MOM - Bags–duffel - Proteus Design Group, Inc.

JUDY RANKIN - Golfing equipment - Pro Select Sports USA

JUDY RANKIN - Golfing equipment ☆ - Ram Golf Corp.

JUDY SEVERSON - Notebooks and notepads - Lake Mills Studios

JUDYANNA LTD. - Apparel–women's - Judyanna Ltd.

JUDY'S - Bakery products - Well-Bred Loaf

JUDY'S - Candy - ACB/Richard Watson

JUDY'S BAKERY - Pastries - Judy's Specialty Foods, Inc.

JUDY'S THINGS - Giftware - Vincent Lippe Co.

JUDYTH'S MOUNTAIN - Jams and jellies - Judyth's Mountain Inc.

JUEGO DE PISTA - Computer software ☆ - Gessler Publishing Co., Inc.

JUEL - Hair coloring preparations - Juel Co.

JUELENE - Hair care products - Juel Co.

JUERGENS - Cosmetics - C. K. Products Inc.

JUG - Wines ☆ - Wine Group Inc.

JUG IT - Bottles–glass - Amersave Products Corp.

JUG, THE - Food products - A. Camacho Inc.

JUG WINE - Silver products - Estus Export-Import

JUGALO - Games - Jax Ltd.

JUGALOBE - Games - Jax Ltd.

JUGGERNAUT - Banjos - OME Co. Inc.

JUGGERNAUT - Footwear–athletic - L.A. Gear, Inc.

JUGGERNAUT - T-shirts, swimwear, warm-up suits, etc. - Juggernaut Inc.

JUGGLE JAR - Exercising equipment - Jugglebug

JUGGLEBEANBALLS - Exercising equipment - Jugglebug
JUGGLEBUG - Exercising equipment - Jugglebug
JUGGLEMANIA - Exercising equipment - Jugglebug
JUGGLER - Computer software - Purespeech, Inc.
JUGGLERS - Candy - Uniconfis Corp.
JUGGLES BEAR - Toys–stuffed - Dakin Inc.
JUGGLES CLOWN - Toys–stuffed - Dakin Inc.
JUGGLESPORT - Exercising equipment ☆ - Jugglebug
JUGGLETIME - Exercising equipment - Jugglebug
JUGGLING JOKER - Games - Smethport Specialty Co.
JUGGO-LETTE - Games ☆ - Pacific Game Co.
JUGGS - Musical instrument accessories - Juggs Percussion
JUGHEAD MAKE-A-MARKER - Sporting goods - Lindy Little Joe Inc.
JUGLER - Ice chests–plastic ☆ - Thermos Co.
JUGLONE - Pharmaceutical preparations ☆ - City Chemical Corp.
JUGRAN - Watches - Great Time International Corp.
JUGS - Sporting goods - Jugs, Inc.
JUGS MVP - Sporting goods - Jugs, Inc.
JUGTOWN MOUNTAIN SMOKEHOUSE - Meat products–poultry - Steophen McDonnell
JUGULAR - Sunglasses - Michael S. Lajtay
JUHAVA - Candles - Hackman Tabletop Inc.
JUICE - Ophthalmic goods - Embassy Creations Inc.
JUICE AMERICA INC. - Juice extracting devices - Juice America, Inc.
JUICE & MORE EXTRA FIBER - Juices - Gerber Products Co.
JUICE BITES - Candy - Sunkist Growers Inc.
JUICE BOMB, JR. - Frozen confection - Wells' Dairy, Inc.
JUICE BOOST - Beverages - Mega Health
JUICE BOOST - Juices - Chiquita Brands, Inc.
JUICE BOWL - Fruit drinks–bottled or canned - Juice Bowl Products Inc.
JUICE BROTHERS - Juices ☆ - Apple and Eve Inc.
JUICE BURST - Juices - H & H Products Co.
JUICE BUSTER - Cleaning preparations - Shipp Chemical Co., Inc.
JUICE CADDY - Juices - Sysco Food Services
JUICE CREATIONS - Beverages–carbonated - Pepsico, Inc.
JUICE FIZZ - Beverages–carbonated - Tree Top, Inc.
JUICE IN A BOX - Juices ☆ - Real Fresh, Inc.
JUICE-IT SYSTEM 30 - Housewares - Goodnature Products Inc.
JUICE LADY - Machinery - Salton/Maxim Housewares, Inc.
JUICE MASTER - Kitchen appliances - LSJ Imports, Ltd.
JUICE-MATE - Beverages - Pro-Form Laboratories
JUICE MATE - Housewares - New Chicago Systems Inc.
JUICE-MATE - Vitamins and nutritional supplements - Fairhill Foods
JUICE-O-MATIC - Kitchen appliances - Rival Manufacturing Co.
JUICE ON A STICK - Frozen foods - J & J Snack Foods Corp.
JUICE-ON-TAP - Beverages ☆ - Tree Top, Inc.
JUICE PAC - Containers - Igloo Products Corp.
JUICE PLUS - Baby foods - Beech-Nut Nutrition Corp.
JUICE PLUS - Juices - L and A Juice Co. Inc.
JUICE PLUS + - Vitamins and nutritional supplements - NSA International, Inc.
JUICE PLUS+ LITE - Vitamins and nutritional supplements - NSA International, Inc.
JUICE RIVERS - Fruit drinks–bottled or canned - Tree Top, Inc.
JUICE SERVICES - Beverages - Juice Services Inc.
JUICE SPARKLERS - Beverages - Corr's Natural Beverages Inc.
JUICE SQUEEZE - Juices - Crystal Geyser Water Co.
JUICE STICKS - Fruit drinks–bottled or canned - Ferraro's Fine Juices
JUICE STIX - Juices–frozen - Borden, Inc.
JUICE TEN - Beverages - The Sqwincher Corp.
JUICE TIGER - Juice extracting devices - Media Arts International
JUICE TREE - Fruit drinks–bottled or canned - Paul Deutsch
JUICE UP - Lemonade ☆ - Dr. Pepper/Seven Up, Inc.
JUICE-UPS - Beverages - Veryfine Products, Inc.
JUICE WITH THE FLAVOR, THE - Beverages - Ollie Jackson
JUICE WORKS - Juices - TCBY Systems Inc.
JUICEFULS - Candy - Prince of Peace Enterprises Inc.
JUICEFULS - Candy - Ragold Inc.
JUICELETS - Snack foods ☆ - F & F Laboratories, Inc.
JUICEMAKERS - Beverages - Welch Foods Inc.
JUICEMAN - Publisher's imprints - James C. Littlejohn
JUICEMAX - Vitamins and nutritional supplements - Alex Duarte
JUICER, THE - Juice extracting devices ☆ - General Housewares Corp.
JUICERS - Automotive parts and accessories ☆ - Wells Manufacturing Corp.
JUICERS - Vitamins and nutritional supplements - Synergy Plus
JUICES TO GO - Fruit drinks–bottled or canned - Coca-Cola Co.
JUICESICLE - Confections ☆ - Good Humor Corp.

JUICEWORKS - Juices - Campbell Soup Co.
JUICIT - Juice extracting devices - Hamilton Beach/Proctor-Silex Inc.
JUICY - Beverages–carbonated - Pennsylvania Dutch Birch Beer Inc.
JUICY 2 - Candy ☆ - Storck USA L.P.
JUICY BEANS - Candy - Brock Candy Co. Inc.
JUICY FRUIT - Chewing gum - Wm. Wrigley Jr. Co.
JUICY JOE - Food products - Janson's Foods Inc.
JUICY JUICE - Fruit drinks–bottled or canned - Nestle Beverage Co.
JUICY LIPS - Cosmetics - Pentech International Inc.
JUICY LUCY - Candy ☆ - Sunline Brands
JUICY MOO - Fruit drinks–bottled or canned ☆ - American Fruit Processors
JUICY ORANGE - Chewing gum ☆ - Leaf, Inc.
JUICY PEACH - Wines - Diamond Island Cellars Inc.
JUICY RIPE THE HAPPY TOMATOES - Shirts - J.R. Produce, Inc.
JUICY STIX - Candy ☆ - Sunline Brands
JUICYBIRD - Turkeys ☆ - Super Valu Inc.
JUJUBES - Candy - Henry Heide, Inc.
JUJYFRUITS - Candy - Henry Heide, Inc.
JUKE - Recording label - Vandor Motion Pictures, Phonorecords & Music Publishing Group
JUKE BOX - Candy ☆ - Haviland Candy Inc.
JUKE BOX - Cosmetics - Maybelline Co.
JUKE BOX - Ophthalmic goods - Embassy Creations Inc.
JUKE BOX - Recording label - Starbound Publishing
JUKEBOX - Computer software - Spinnaker Software Corp.
JUKEBOX - Musical instrument accessories - Marketing Insights, Inc.-Frank Luppino Jr., and Associates
JUKEBOX - Pizzas–mixes - International Food & Beverage Inc.
JUKEBOX JEWELRY - Jewelry - Marketing Insights, Inc.-Frank Luppino Jr., and Associates
JUKEBOX MUSIC SHOP - Toys–musical - Mattel, Inc.
JUKEMEISTER - Computer software ☆ - OTG Software
JULABO - Electronic equipment - Julabo USA, Inc.
JULBO - Eyeglasses - Climb High Inc.
JULE KAKA - Breads - Norsland Kitchens
JULELAL'S - Bedding–linen - Ramodi's
JULEP - Beverages - Julep Co.
JULES - Apparel and accessories - MJW Designs, Inc.
JULES REVAN - Musical instruments - J.M. Sahlein Music Co. Inc.
JULES VERNE - Watches - Gruen Marketing Corp.
JULI - Underwear and nightwear ☆ - Carole Hochman Designs Inc.
JULI DUROCHE FOR AFTER FIVE - Apparel and accessories - Party Formals Inc.
JULI JR., A - Underwear and nightwear ☆ - Slumbertogs Inc.
JULI OF SLUMBERTOGS - Underwear and nightwear - Slumbertogs Inc.
JULIA - Apparel and accessories - Julia, Inc.
JULIA - Beverages–alcohol - Distillerie Stock USA Ltd.
JULIA - Flowers, plants, and seeds - Jacklin Seed
JULIA - Food products - Wally Sea Products Corp.
JULIA - Glass–leaded ☆ - Orrefors Inc.
JULIA WHITE - Kitchenware–china - H. Wittur & Co.
JULIAN BASHIR - Computer software - Paramount Pictures Corp.
JULIAN MESSNER - Publisher's imprints - Simon & Schuster, Inc.
JULIANA - Cosmetics ☆ - Bonne Bell, Inc.
JULIANA - Floor coverings–carpet and rugs ☆ - Eurotex Inc.
JULIANA - Watches - Bulova Corp.
JULIANA - Wines - Pope Valley Winery
JULIANA - Yarn ☆ - JCA, Inc.
JULIANE - Floor coverings–carpet and rugs ☆ - Regal Rugs Inc.
JULIANN - Greeting cards - Juli A. Nardini
JULIANNA - Footwear–women's ☆ - U.S. Water
JULIANO'S - Pizzas–frozen - Nation Pizza Products L.P.
JULIARA - Underwear and nightwear - Juliara, Ltd.
JULIA'S - Food products - Protein Foods Inc.
JULIA'S PEPPERONI ROLL - Bakery products - Chico Dairy Co. Inc.
JULIE - Floor coverings–carpet and rugs ☆ - Regal Rugs Inc.
JULIE - Frames–eyeglass - U.S. Optical Frame Co.
JULIE - Rings–jewelry - Artcarved Inc.
JULIE - Shrimp–fresh or frozen - Darik Enterprises Inc.
JULIE - Wigs - Jean Paree Weegs Inc.
JULIE AND LEONARD - Apparel–women's - Second Shot, Inc.
JULIE BEE - Cookies - Julie Benton Rogers
JULIE COLLECTION - Wallpaper ☆ - Surface Industries Inc.
JULIE/DON RAMON - Shrimp–fresh or frozen - Darik Enterprises Inc.
JULIE GIRL - Apparel and accessories - I. Amsterdam Co. Inc.
JULIE HOWARD - Cosmetics - SunQuest Products

☆ = Now out of production

JULIE HUTTON - Apparel - Factory Ltd.

JULIE JOFFRIN - Apparel and accessories - Wongas International Textiles, Ltd.

JULIE MANGO - Apparel and accessories - Shyan, Inc.

JULIE UELAND - Housewares - Julie Ueland

JULIEN - Boats–canoes - Durham Boat Co. Inc.

JULIEN - Food containers ☆ - Dubuque Foods, Inc.

JULIEN - Glassware–household ☆ - Dansk International Designs, Ltd.

JULIEN TANN - Beverages–alcohol - Wine Imports Ltd.

JULIENNE - Sinks–metal - Kohler Co.

JULIE'S JOURNEY - Figurines - American Design Co.

JULIE'S KITCHEN - Fabrics–tapestry ☆ - Columbus Coated Fabrics Co.

JULIET - Brassieres (Bras) - Vanity Fair Mills Inc.

JULIET - Clocks ☆ - Robertshaw Controls Co.

JULIET - Dishes–china - Pickard Inc.

JULIET - Flatware - Insilco Corp.

JULIET - Floor coverings–carpet and rugs ☆ - Regal Rugs Inc.

JULIET - Frames–eyeglass - Pathway Optical Prods.

JULIET - Furniture - Bean Station Furniture Factory Inc.

JULIET - Glass–leaded - Seneca Glass Co.

JULIET - Jewelry - Treasures of Paradise

JULIET - Rings–jewelry - Artcarved Inc.

JULIET - Vases ☆ - Lenox Crystal, Inc.

JULIET - Veils - Chicago Bead Works Ltd.

JULIET - Watches - Bulova Corp.

JULIET TIGER - Toys–stuffed - Russ Berrie and Co., Inc.

JULIETTE - Belts - Waist Wear Ltd.

JULIETTE - Christmas tree ornaments - Cracker Box Inc.

JULIETTE - Glassware–household - ACC

JULIETTE - Glassware–household - Crisa Corp.

JULIETTE - Glassware–household - Lancaster Colony Corp.

JULIETTE - Handbags - Melbourne Manufacturing Co. Inc.

JULIETTE - Wallpaper - Storeys Wallcoverings

JULIETTE MANICURE - Cosmetics - Beauty Aids Inc.

JULIO LOPEZ - Toys - Tonka Corp.

JULIUS - Giftware - Sasaki

JULIUS AMBER - Giftware - Sasaki

JULIUS ANDERSEN - Horseradish - Silver Spring Gardens Inc.

JULIUS COHEN - Jewelry - Julius Cohen

JULIUS ECHTER DUNKEL WEISSBIER - Beverages–malt - St. Killian Importing Co.

JULIUS ECHTER HEFE WEISS - Beverages–malt ☆ - St. Killian Importing Co.

JULIUS ECHTER HEFE-WEISSBIER - Beverages–malt - St. Killian Importing Co.

JULIUS JUICERS - Fruit drinks–bottled or canned - Orange Julius of America

JULIUS KAYSER - Wines - Seagram's Chateau & Estate Wines Co.

JULIUS MARLOW - Men's shoes - Interco Inc.

JULIUS RESNICK - Handbags - Mutterperl Group Inc.

JULIUS SEYMOUR - Fireplace equipment - Seymour Manufacturing Co.,Inc.

JULIUS SUPREME - Beverages - Orange Julius of America

JULLIAN - Furniture - Fairyland Corp.

JUMA - Jewelry - Juma, Inc.

JUMANJI - Games - Hasbro, Inc.

JUMBALASSY - Recording label - Jumbalassy Inc.

JUMBEAU - Medical apparatus ☆ - Lois Noyes California Unusuals

JUMBLE JET - Computer software - Unicorn Software

JUMBLEZZZ - Computer software - Mind Play

JUMBO - Animal feeds ☆ - Foster Canning Inc.

JUMBO - Beverages - Double Cola Co.-USA

JUMBO - Bicycles - Columbia Manufacturing Inc.

JUMBO - Boats - O.M.C. Aluminum Boat Group

JUMBO - Brooms - F.M. Thorpe Manufacturing Co.

JUMBO - Brushes - Wright-Bernet

JUMBO - Cigarettes - R.J. Reynolds Tobacco Co.

JUMBO - Cooking equipment–household - Birmingham Stove & Range Co.

JUMBO - Electronics equipment - Peerless Sales Co.

JUMBO - Food products - R.A. Fayard Seafood Co. Inc.

JUMBO - Food products - Shopper's Food Warehouse

JUMBO - Games - Dollsandreams

JUMBO - Golfing equipment - Northwestern Golf Co.

JUMBO - Metals - Wilian Holding Co.

JUMBO - Musical instruments - Fender Musical Instruments

JUMBO - Office supplies - Alvin and Co. Inc.

JUMBO - Peanut butter - Frank Foods Co.

JUMBO - Pet products - Old Mother Hubbard Dog Food Co., Inc.

JUMBO - Rice - Newfield Partners, Ltd.

JUMBO - Steel wool - International Steel Wool Corp.

JUMBO - Thread - Threads USA Div.

JUMBO - Tools–plumbing - Covers Co. Inc.

JUMBO - Toys–automobiles - Nylint Toy Corp.

JUMBO-CAN - Fruits and vegetables - Seneca Foods Corp.

JUMBO CLUB - Paper–toweling - Potlatch Corp.

JUMBO CUDDLE DOLL - Toys - Samet & Wells Inc.

JUMBO CUDDLES - Toys–stuffed - Dakin Inc.

JUMBO DOUBLE SIDED DOMINOES - Games - Guidecraft Inc.

JUMBO EXPO II - Markers–felt-tip - Sanford Corp.

JUMBO FASCIA BRACKET - Aluminum guttering - Seamless Gutter Corp.

JUMBO FIT-A-LETTER - Puzzles - Lauri Inc.

JUMBO FLAG GREETINGS - Flags - Securitag Corp.

JUMBO GLITES - Toys - North Pacific Products Inc.

JUMBO GLT - Tires–automobile - General Tire, Inc.

JUMBO GREETINGS - Greeting cards - American Greetings Corp.

JUMBO GRILLERS - Frankfurters - Hatfield, Inc.

JUMBO HI-BULK - Soap - Sanitary Soap Co. Inc.

JUMBO JET - Bicycles - Columbia Manufacturing Inc.

JUMBO JET - Luggage - Airline Textile Manufacturing Co.

JUMBO JOE - Barbecue and grill accessories - Weber-Stephen Products Co.

JUMBO JUG - Ice chests–plastic ☆ - Thermos Co.

JUMBO JUTE - Yarn ☆ - Lily Craft Products

JUMBO LIPSTIC - Lipsticks - Cici Cosmetic Co.

JUMBO OLD MAID - Games - Milton Bradley Co.

JUMBO PAK - Food products - Fleming Companies, Inc.

JUMBO PAK - Rubber bands - Alliance Rubber Co.

JUMBO PEANUTS - Food products - Uncle Dave's Kitchen

JUMBO PENGUIN - Deodorizers ☆ - Car-Freshner Corp.

JUMBO POLYHEDRAL - Novelty items - Koplow Games

JUMBO ROCKET - Candy ☆ - Ce De Candy Inc.

JUMBO ROLLER - Tools - Ekco Housewares, Inc.

JUMBO SEALANT TRAY - Tools - Ekco Housewares, Inc.

JUMBO SHADOW - Cosmetics - Cici Cosmetic Co.

JUMBO SLATE - Toys ☆ - Henry Gordy International Inc.

JUMBO SPORT TOTE - Sporting goods ☆ - Frabill Inc.

JUMBO STICK - Candy - Glenn Confections Inc.

JUMBO STICK-UPS - Wallpaper - Priss Prints Inc.

JUMBO SWEEP - Brooms - Kellogg Brush Manufacturing Co.

JUMBO TEX - Paper - Fortifiber Corp.

JUMBO TRAC - Tires - Denman Tire Corp.

JUMBOBO - Apparel and accessories - Bruce Donald Brazier

JUMBOLINA - Shrimp - Continental Seafoods Inc.

JUMBOLITES - Reflectors–optical - Acme-Lite Manufacturing Co.

JUMBOMIN - Pet products - Tetra Sales USA

JUMBOS - Garden equipment ☆ - Oil-Dri Corp. of America

JUMBUK - Apparel and accessories - ETP International

JUMBY BAY - Wines - Banfi Vintners

JUMBY BAY PROPRIETOR'S RUM - Beverages–alcohol - Banfi Vintners

JUMER - Beverages–malt - Jumer's Castle Lodge, Inc.

JUMP - Greeting cards - Renaissance Greeting Cards Inc.

JUMP-A-HOOP - Exercising equipment - Rushmore Medical

JUMP AHEAD - Apparel and accessories - Regent International Corp.

JUMP AVE. - Apparel and accessories - Todd Number 1

JUMP-BACK JACKS - Pickles - Jardine's Texas Foods

JUMP BALL CLUB - Apparel and accessories - Haddad Apparel Group Ltd.

JUMP BANDS - Exercising equipment - Kathryn Short Productions

JUMP FOR JOY - Toys - Tonka Corp.

JUMP-IT - Sporting goods - Excel Sports Products

JUMP-MASTER - Battery chargers - K & K Jump Start/Chargers, Inc.

JUMP MY BONES - Toys–stuffed - Dakin Inc.

JUMP-N-CARRY - Battery chargers - K & K Jump Start/Chargers, Inc.

JUMP-N-CRUISE - Automotive parts and accessories - K & K Jump Start/Chargers, Inc.

JUMP N SQUEAK - Toys ☆ - Knickerbocker Toy Co. Inc.

JUMP 'N' STACK SPLASH - Toys - Discovery Toys, Inc.

JUMP-O-LENE - Toys - Intex Recreation Corp.

JUMP RAVEN - Games - Cyberflix, Inc.

JUMP-RING MASTER - Tools - Anthony Mesquida

JUMP SHOT - Sporting goods - Porter Athletic Equipment Co.

JUMP SHOT - Trading cards and stamps - ANCO Collector Supplies, Inc.

JUMP SOLES - Exercising equipment - Kytec Innovative Sports Equipment

JUMP STAR - Exercising equipment - Gerstung/Gym-Thing Inc.

JUMP START - Coffee - Coffee Works, Inc.

JUMP START - Golfing equipment - Golfsmith International Inc.

☆ = Now out of production

JUMP START - Health care products - Pdk Labs, Inc.
JUMP START - Soap - Origins Natural Resources Inc.
JUMP START - Tents - Jumpstart, Inc.
JUMP-START - Vitamins and nutritional supplements - Sage Group
JUMP START KINDERGARTEN - Computer software - Knowledge Adventure, Inc.
JUMP-UPS - Toys–stuffed - Fun World Inc.
JUMPBUSTER - Toys–automobiles - Mattel, Inc.
JUMPEES - Candy - Pangburn Candy Co.
JUMPER JOE - Toys - Tonka Corp.
JUMPERS BY DINGO - Footwear - Acme Boot Co., Inc.
JUMPERS FOOT PRINTS - Shoes–orthopedic - Jumpers Shoe Service
JUMPHORSE - Games - Equiplay, Inc.
JUMPIN' BLACK BEANS - Soups–mixes - Fantastic Foods Inc.
JUMPIN B.U.M. - Apparel–men's - Chauvin International Ltd.
JUMPIN' JACK FLASH - Toys - Brittoys
JUMPIN JAX - Apparel–children's ☆ - Brill Bros. Inc.
JUMPIN' JEEBIES - Toys–stuffed - Russ Berrie and Co., Inc.
JUMPIN' JIMINY - Sporting goods - Natural Science Industries, Ltd.
JUMPIN' JO PLUS - Games - Universal Manufacturing Co., Inc.
JUMPIN JOKERS - Game machines - Bally Gaming International, Inc.
JUMPIN' MONKEYS - Games - Pressman Toy Corp.
JUMPIN' PUMPKINS - Toys–stuffed - Fun World Inc.
JUMPING CURLS - Hair care products - Image Laboratories, Inc.
JUMPING JACK - Electronic equipment ☆ - Fleetwood Furniture Co.
JUMPING JACKS - Apparel–children's - Jumping-Jacks Shoes Inc.
JUMPING-JACKS - Footwear–children's - Jumping-Jacks Shoes Inc.
JUMPING JACKS - Shoes - Osage Footwear, Inc.
JUMPING JOY - Apparel and accessories - Krystal K. International Inc.
JUMPMAN - Computer software - Epyx Inc.
JUMPMAN JUNIOR - Computer software - Epyx Inc.
JUMPMASTER - Uniforms–tailored - Topps Manufacturing Co.
JUMPMAX - Batteries - James P. Wright
JUMPO - Electronic equipment - Ronlad A. Darby
JUMPOLEEN - Hobby kits - Rapco
JUMPSIE - Dolls - Toy Biz, Inc.
JUMPSOLES - Sporting goods - Metapro, Inc.
JUMPSTART - Computer software - Knowledge Adventure
JUMPSTART - Mats - JCH International Inc.
JUMPSTART - Pharmaceutical preparations - Pro Cap
JUMPSTART PRESCHOOL - Games - Knowledge Adventure, Inc.
JUMPSTART SERIES - Computer software - Knowledge Adventure
JUMPSTART TODDLERS - Electronic equipment - Knowledge Adventure, Inc.
JUMPSTART YOUR JOB SKILLS - Computer software - UP Software, Inc.
JUNCKERS - Floor coverings–carpet and rugs - Junckers Hardwood Inc.
JUNCKERS STANDARD - Flooring–hardwood - Junckers Hardwood Inc.
JUNCTION - Fungicides - Griffin Corp.
JUNCTURES - Floor coverings–carpet and rugs ☆ - J and J Industries Inc.
JUNE - Wigs - Helene Curtis Industries Inc.
JUNE AMOS GRAMMER - Dolls ☆ - Schmid Inc.
JUNE APPAL - Recording label - Appalshop Inc.
JUNE BARBARA - Candy - Federal Candy Co.
JUNE BOY - Pickles - W.B. Roddenbery Co., Inc.
JUNE GARLAND - Dinnerware–glass ☆ - Royal China & Porcelain Companies Inc.
JUNE IN JANUARY - Food products - Escalon Frozen Foods
JUNE IS TURKEY LOVERS' MONTH - Turkeys - National Turkey Federation
JUNE ROSE - Dinnerware–glass ☆ - Charles Zahn-Import Merchant
JUNE SHOCHY - Beverages–alcohol - Mutual Trading Co. Inc.
JUNE TAILOR - Sewing machine cabinets–wood - June Tailor Inc.
JUNEAU - Toilets–enameled - Kohler Co.
JUNEAU - Toys–stuffed - Dakin Inc.
JUNEX - Apparel–men's ☆ - Sampson Inc.
JUNEX INTERNATIONAL - Apparel–men's ☆ - Sampson Inc.
JUNG - Flowers, plants, and seeds - J. W. Jung Seed Co.
JUNG - Flowers, plants, and seeds - J.W. Jung Seed Co. Inc.
JUNGAL - Apparel and accessories - World Jungle, Inc.
JUNGAMALS - Lip balms - Nu Skin International, Inc.
JUNGEL GYM - Pet products - American Cat Emporium
JUNGFRAU - Food products - Jungfrau
JUNGHANS - Clocks - La Crosse-McCormick
JUNGHANS - Clocks ☆ - Holzerwatch Co. Inc.
JUNGHANS - Watches ☆ - Aristo Import Co. Inc.
JUNGHANS ASTRO-CHRON - Clocks ☆ - Holzerwatch Co. Inc.
JUNGLE - Aquariums–household - Jungle Laboratories Corp.
JUNGLE - Juices ☆ - Dairymen Inc. (Farm Best Div.)

JUNGLE BABIES - Toys–stuffed - Dakin Inc.
JUNGLE BAG - Bags–duffel - Christian Strehlau
JUNGLE BALL - Balls–basketball ☆ - Mikasa Sports
JUNGLE BALL - Pet products - Boomer Ball
JUNGLE BARS - Confections - Famous Pacific Dessert Co.
JUNGLE BOOK, THE - Games - Virgin Interactive Entertainment, Inc.
JUNGLE CRITTERS - Stuffed animals with cologne ☆ - Cosrich Inc.
JUNGLE FEVER - Fabrics - Interials Inc.
JUNGLE FIGHTERS - Toys - Mattel, Inc.
JUNGLE FORMULA - Pharmaceutical preparations ☆ - Ole Time Woodsman
JUNGLE FRIEND - Toys ☆ - Gerber Products Co.
JUNGLE FUN - Glassware–household - Fun Factory, Inc.
JUNGLE GARDENIA - Perfumes - Coty Inc.
JUNGLE GUM - Chewing gum - Wild Things, Inc.
JUNGLE HABITAT - Apparel–athletic - Snake Creek Manufacturing Co., Inc.
JUNGLE HOOKS - Hooks - Frantz Industries, Inc.
JUNGLE HUNT - Video games ☆ - Taito America Corp.
JUNGLE JACK - Toys–stuffed - Jack Hanna Productions Inc.
JUNGLE JACK'S - Flowers, plants, and seeds - Jungle Jack's Palms
JUNGLE JADE - Toys - Tonka Corp.
JUNGLE JAKE - Degreasing solvents - Stearns Packaging Corp.
JUNGLE JAMMERS - Cookies - Moran Foods, Inc.
JUNGLE JAVA BLEND - Coffee - Coffee Masters, Inc.
JUNGLE JAWS - Toys–automobiles - Mattel, Inc.
JUNGLE JEMS - Nuts–salted, roasted, cooked, or canned - From the Rain Forest, Inc.
JUNGLE JOCKS - Posters - Terry D. Naughton
JUNGLE JOKE NOTES - Greeting cards ☆ - Kersten Bros. Studios
JUNGLE JON'S - Sandwiches–prepackaged - Discovery Foods
JUNGLE JUICE - Chemical preparations - Jungle Juice Inc.
JUNGLE JUICE - Fertilizers - Security Products Co.
JUNGLE JUICE - Fruit drinks–bottled or canned - Universal Flavor USA
JUNGLE JUICE - Insect repellents - NutriBiotic
JUNGLE JUICE TK7 GASOLINE ENGINE RACING FORMULA UPPER LUBRICATION POWER BOOSTER - Fuel additives - Jungle Juice Inc.
JUNGLE KING - Toys - Mannix Co., Ltd.
JUNGLE KING - Watches - Hampden Corp.
JUNGLE KINGDOM - Toys - Processed Plastic Co.
JUNGLE KINGS - Vitamins and nutritional supplements - Millennium Marketplace, Inc.
JUNGLE KITTENS - Puzzles ☆ - Warren Industries Inc.
JUNGLE LOVE - Toys–stuffed - Russ Berrie and Co., Inc.
JUNGLE MARKETING - Recording label - Executive Staff Corp.
JUNGLE MASTER - Watches - Hampden Corp.
JUNGLE MORNINGS - Coffee - Jungle Mornings Coffee Co.
JUNGLE MUNCH - Snack foods - The Rainforest Co.
JUNGLE NATION - Apparel and accessories - America's Best, Inc.
JUNGLE NIGHTS - Fireworks - Ingram Enterprises, Inc.
JUNGLE PAL - Toys ☆ - Gerber Products Co.
JUNGLE PATROL - Apparel and accessories - Lifeforms International, Inc.
JUNGLE PETS - Toys–stuffed - Fun World Inc.
JUNGLE PLAYGROUND - Toys - Mattel, Inc.
JUNGLE PLUS - Pharmaceutical preparations ☆ - Ole Time Woodsman
JUNGLE POND - Water treating compounds - Jungle Laboratories Corp.
JUNGLE PREDATORS - Toys–stuffed - Trendmasters, Inc.
JUNGLE PRINTS - Pillows - Centsable Toys Inc.
JUNGLE RAGS - Apparel - Darrell Ratliff
JUNGLE RAIN - Soap - Christopher J. Klein
JUNGLE ROCKERS - Rocking horses - Rothkopf Enterprises, Inc.
JUNGLE ROOTS - Aquarium accessories - Blue Ribbon Pet Products, Inc.
JUNGLE ROOTS COLLECTION - Aquarium accessories - Blue Ribbon Pet Products, Inc.
JUNGLE ROSES - Flowers, plants, and seeds - Joan Child Prothero Jungle Roses
JUNGLE SAFARI - Art supplies - E.K. Success Ltd.
JUNGLE SAFARI - Computer software - Orange Cherry Software
JUNGLE STICKS - Pens - Arnold Pen Co. Inc.
JUNGLE TAILS - Greeting cards - Joli Greeting Card Co.
JUNGLE TOWER - Playground equipment - Child Life Inc.
JUNGLE TRAIN - Computer software ☆ - Knowledge Adventure
JUNGLE TUFF CAT - Pet products - Booda Products, Inc.
JUNGLE VINES - Pet products - Dura Pro Products
JUNGLE WORLD - Toys–stuffed ☆ - Gund, Inc.
JUNGLE WORLD - Writing product ☆ - Binney & Smith Inc.
JUNGLEE - Knives–hunting - Grizzly Knife & Tackle, Inc.
JUNGLETALK - Pet products - American Manufacturing Group, Inc.

☆ = Now out of production

JUNGOL - Games - Seastar Trading Co.
JUNI DESIGNS - Clothing patterns - U-Mei Art Studio, Inc.
JUNIE MOON OF LA JOLLA MINI-BISCOTTI - Gingerbread–mixes - California Style Gourmet
JUNIOR - Ammunition - B-West Imports, Inc.
JUNIOR - Apparel–women's - Wacoal America Inc.
JUNIOR - Boats ☆ - Zodiac of North America
JUNIOR - Drums–musical instruments - LP Music Group
JUNIOR - Electronic equipment - Micro-Gen Equipment Corp.
JUNIOR - Floor coverings - Dexter Corp. (Mercer Plastics Div.)
JUNIOR - Frames–picture - Framemica Co.
JUNIOR - Health care products ☆ - Halsey Drug Co. Inc.
JUNIOR - Motors–outboard - Outboard Marine Corp.
JUNIOR - Office supplies - R.A. Stewart Superior
JUNIOR - Pet products - Willinger Bros., Inc.
JUNIOR - Pipes - National Briar Pipe Co.
JUNIOR - Projection screens ☆ - Da-Lite Screen Co. Inc.
JUNIOR - Puzzles - Milton Bradley Co.
JUNIOR - Scooters–motorized - Leisure Lift, Inc.
JUNIOR - Tiles–asphalt - Garden Way Inc.
JUNIOR - Tools–hand-operated - Stanley Works
JUNIOR - Toys ☆ - Lawn-Boy
JUNIOR - Toys–automobiles ☆ - Roadmaster Corp.
JUNIOR - Tripods–photographic ☆ - QuickSet International Inc.
JUNIOR - Wet-mop handles - American Textile Products Co.
JR. - Wheelchairs - X-L Manufacturing Co. Inc.
JUNIOR - Wigs ☆ - Jean Paree Weegs Inc.
JR. 1 - Helmets–athletic ☆ - Bell Sports Corp.
JR. 2 - Helmets–athletic - Bell Sports Corp.
JUNIOR-2-12 - Cough medicines - Vita-Fore Products Co.
JUNIOR 5 - Pet products - Rolf C. Hagen (USA) Corp.
JUNIOR 1000 - Balls ☆ - Mikasa Sports
JR. AIRBRUSH - Toys - SLM Inc.
JR. AIRLINE - Luggage - Airline Textile Manufacturing Co.
JUNIOR ARCADE - Computer software - Humongous Entertainment, Inc.
JR. ATTORNEY - Ophthalmic goods - Foremost Optical Products
JUNIOR BAZAAR - Apparel–children's - Sears, Roebuck and Co.
JR. CAMPING - Sporting goods - Tara Toy Corp.
JR. CHAMPION - Children's watchbands and straps - Jacoby-Bender Inc.
JUNIOR CHEX - Cereal - Ralston Purina Co.
JUNIOR CLUB - Women's apparel - India Garments Inc.
JUNIOR COMP - Sporting goods - Outboard Marine Corp.
JR. COMPETITOR - Weightlifting equipment ☆ - EFI Total Gym
JR. CONCEPT - Coats–children's - S. Rothschild & Co., Inc.
JR. CRAFT SAW - Toys - Steven Manufacturing Co.
JR. D-ZZASTER - Board games and cards - Qual-T-Med, Inc.
JUNIOR EFFICIENCY - Duplicating machines ☆ - Heyer Inc.
JR. ELF BOOKS - Publisher's imprints ☆ - Rand McNally & Co.
JUNIOR EXECUTIVE - Computer software - Mind Play
JR. EXECUTIVE - Frames–eyeglass - Hudson Optical Corp.
JUNIOR EXECUTIVE PONY - Toys ☆ - Hartco Inc.
JUNIOR FIT-A-SPACE - Toys - Lauri Inc.
JR. FLASH - Sporting goods - Midwest Sporting Goods Manufacturing Co.
JR. FLIP UP - Feather dusters - Texas Feathers Inc.
JR. FLIPS - Potato chips - R & R Productions, Inc.
JR. FLYER - Frames–eyeglass ☆ - Universal/Univis Inc.
JUNIOR FLYER - Luggage - American Flyer Travelware, Inc.
JR. G.I. - Apparel–children's - Rothco Inc.
JR. GRAND SLAM - Food products - Denny's Inc.
JUNIOR HEATER - Aquariums–household - GM Aquatics
JR. HI - Handbags ☆ - J.C. Penney Co., Inc.
JUNIOR HIGH - Publisher's imprints - Scholastic Inc.
JUNIOR HIT - Rackets–tennis - Head Sports USA
JR. HOP - Frames–eyeglass - Zylo Ware Corp.
JUNIOR IMAGE - Apparel–women's - Wal-Mart Stores Inc.
JUNIOR INTIMATES - Apparel and accessories ☆ - Warnaco Inc.
JUNIOR JAM - Balls–basketball - Hutch Sports USA Inc.
JUNIOR JAZZ - Paints - Van Aken International
JUNIOR JELS - Gelatin - Original Herkimer County Cheese Co. Inc.
JUNIOR JETSTAR - Auto-body shell for racing - All American Soap Box Derby Inc.
JUNIOR JOHN - Apparel and accessories ☆ - Imperial Knitting Co. Inc.
JR. JOJO'S - Vegetables–frozen ☆ - Lamb-Weston, Inc.
JUNIOR JUICE - Fruit drinks–bottled or canned - McCain Citrus, Inc.
JUNIOR JUICE - Juices - McCain Foods Inc.
JUNIOR/KIDDIE SPORT - Sunglasses - Jack Martin Co.

JR. KNOCKABOUT, THE - Jackets - Howe K. Sipes Co.
JUNIOR LANE - Apparel–women's - Brand & Puritz
JUNIOR LIBRARY - Juvenile history books - American Heritage
JR. MARKSMAN - Toys - Brumberger Co. Inc.
JR. MINI PUZZLES - Puzzles ☆ - Warren Industries Inc.
JUNIOR MINTS - Candy - Tootsie Roll Industries, Inc.
JUNIOR MISS - Brooms ☆ - Deshler Broom Factory Inc.
JUNIOR MISS - Hair care products - Willat Co.
JR. MISS - Leather goods - St. Thomas Inc.
JUNIOR MISS - Watches - Zell Bros.
JR. MONARCH - Towels - Monarch Towel Co.
JR. MRS. - Apparel–women's - Bali Co. Inc.
JUNIOR OLYMPIC - Toys ☆ - Rollin Wilson Co. Inc.
JUNIOR PARADE - Footwear–children's ☆ - Edison Brothers Stores, Inc.
JUNIOR PARLIAMENT - Fabrics - Greenwood Mills Inc.
JR. PARTNER - Computer storage devices - Millennium Integrated Software, Ltd.
JUNIOR PETITE - Apparel–women's - Wacoal America Inc.
JR. PILOT - Ophthalmic goods - Rozin Optical Export Corp.
JUNIOR PLACE - Crocheted and knitted items ☆ - Isaac Hazan & Co.
JR. PLENTY - Dresses–women's - Lane Bryant, Inc.
JUNIOR PONY - Toys ☆ - Hartco Inc.
JUNIOR PRO - Footwear–athletic - Head Sports USA
JR.PRO - Skis - Wellington Leisure Products, Inc.
JR. PRO - Sporting goods - Schutt Manufacturing Co.
JUNIOR RADIAL - Footwear–athletic - Head Sports USA
JUNIOR RAT CAFETERIA - Rodenticides - Solvit Inc.
JR. REFLECTIONS - Apparel and accessories - Montgomery Ward & Co. Inc.
JUNIOR REX - Fishing lures - Weezel Bait Co.
JUNIOR ROADMASTER - Toys–automobiles ☆ - Roadmaster Corp.
JR. SENATOR - Golf clubs - Austad Co.
JR. SHORT STACK - Food products - Denny's Inc.
JUNIOR SNAPS - Toys - Learning Products Inc.
JUNIOR SPECIAL - Guns ☆ - Remington Arms Co., Inc.
JUNIOR SPORT - Toys - Southern States Marketing, Inc.
JUNIOR SPORTS - Menus - All Kitchens of America
JUNIOR STANDARD - Steel easels ☆ - James-Howard Co.
JUNIOR STEP - Furniture - Cosco, Inc.
JR. STREET HOCKEY - Toys ☆ - Steven Manufacturing Co.
JR. STRIKING BAG - Punching bags ☆ - Logan Electric Specialty Manufacturing Co.
JUNIOR SWINGER - Bicycles ☆ - J.C. Penney Co., Inc.
JR. SWIVELER - Garment hangers - Selfix, Inc.
JR. THUNDERSTICK - Fishing lures - Storm Manufacturing Co.
JUNIOR TITAN - Jogging suits ☆ - Felco Athletic Wear Co.
JR. TOTEM POLE - Candy ☆ - Gilliam Candy Co. Inc. (Gilliam Candy Brands)
JUNIOR TUNNEL - Toys - E-Z Sales & Manufacturing, Inc.
JUNIOR ULTRA STAKE - Plastics - John Henry Co.
JR. VARSITY - Children's apparel - Perrier Inc.
JR. VARSITY - Floor coverings–carpet and rugs - Porter Carpet Mills Inc.
JUNIOR VIEW - Underwear and nightwear ☆ - Lovable Co.
JUNIOR WHIRL - Playground equipment - Miracle Recreation Equipment Co.
JR. WOODWORKERS TOY FACTORY - Wood products - Natural Science Industries, Ltd.
JR. WORDPERFECT - Computer software - Wordperfect Corp.
JUNIORFLEX - Apparel stores–lingerie - S. Sunkin & Son Inc.
JUNIORMATES - Underwear and nightwear - Youthcraft-Charmfit
JUNIORS - See also **JRS.**
JUNIORS - Cakes - Tasty Baking Co.
JUNIORS - Candy ☆ - Leaf, Inc.
JUNIORS - Figurines - Sandicast
JUNIORS - Greeting cards - American Artists Group Inc.
JUNIPER - Apparel stores–lingerie ☆ - Formfit Rogers
JUNIPER - Apparel–children's - S. Schwab Co., Inc.
JUNIPER - Banjos - OME Co. Inc.
JUNIPER - Publisher's imprints - Ballantine Books Inc.
JUNIPER - Tableware–earthenware - Pfaltzgraff Investment Co.
JUNIPEROSAN - Skin care products - Bioforce of America Ltd.
JUNIUS - Horseradish - Junius Food Products Corp.
JUNK DRAWER - Housewares - Steven Epstein
JUNK YARD - Games ☆ - CBS Toys
JUNKBOTS - Games - Tyco Toys
JUNKET - Ice cream–powdered - Redco Foods Inc.
JUNKET DANISH DESSERT - Pies–frozen - Redco Foods Inc.
JUNKET RENNET - Custard–frozen - Redco Foods Inc.
JUNKHEAD - Toys - Tyco Toys

☆ = Now out of production

JUNKIES - Apparel and accessories - Junkies
JUNKMAN'S DAUGHTER - Apparel and accessories - Junkman's Daughter, Inc.
JUNKYARD - Toys - Troma, Inc.
JUNKYARD DOGS - Footwear–women's ☆ - U.S. Water
JUNO - Cleaning preparations–carpet and rug - Flo-Pac Corp.
JUNO - Lawn mowers - Lambert Manufacturing Corp.
JUNO - Ophthalmic goods ☆ - Luxottica
JUNO - Recording label - GP Records & Tapes
JUNO - Watches - Bulova Corp.
JUNO BRA - Brassieres (Bras) ☆ - Q-T Foundations Co. Inc.
JUNO HUSKY - Toys–stuffed - Russ Berrie and Co., Inc.
JUNON - Glassware–household - Durand International
JUPINA - Beverages–carbonated - Cawy Bottling Co., Inc.
JUPITER - Adhesives and sealants - Binford Products, Inc.
JUPITER - Apparel and accessories - Kmart Corp.
JUPITER - Bathtubs–enameled ☆ - Lasco Products Group
JUPITER - Binoculars ☆ - Pentax Corp.
JUPITER - Boats–motor ☆ - Seajay Boats Inc.
JUPITER - Fireplaces ☆ - Majestic Co.
JUPITER - Floor coverings - American Floor Products Co. Inc.
JUPITER - Floor coverings–carpet and rugs - Lees Carpets
JUPITER - Floor coverings–carpet and rugs - Mica Inc.
JUPITER - Floor coverings–carpet and rugs ☆ - Galaxy Carpet Mills Inc.
JUPITER - Glassware–household ☆ - Fenton Art Glass Co.
JUPITER - Housewares - Prince Castle Inc.
JUPITER - Kitchen appliances - Miracle Exclusives Inc.
JUPITER - Lawn product - Bruner Ivory Handle Co.
JUPITER - Musical instruments - Deg Music Products Inc.
JUPITER - Musical instruments - Jupiter Band Inst. Inc.
JUPITER - Pacemakers - Berco Tableworks
JUPITER - Pencils ☆ - Faber-Castell Corp.
JUPITER - Photographic equipment - QuickSet International Inc.
JUPITER - Skin care products - Takara Belmont USA, Inc.
JUPITER - Sporting goods - Daiwa Corp.
JUPITER - Staplers - ACCO USA, Inc.
JUPITER - Tires - ITOCHU International Inc.
JUPITER - Watches - Temlex/Jupiter Watch Corp.
JUPITER C - Toys–models ☆ - Estes Industries
JUPITER MISSION 1999 - Games ☆ - Avalon Hill Game Co.
JUPITER STUFF KIT - Novelty items - Dynamic Development
JUPITERLITE - Lamps ☆ - Anes Electronics Burglar Alarm Systems
JUPITER'S - Candy ☆ - Leaf, Inc.
JUPPA - Food products - Royal Source, Inc.
JURASSIC CRITTERS - Novelty items - Dynamic Development
JURASSIC PARK - Candy - Creative Confection Concepts, Inc.
JURASSIC PARK - Candy - Ferrara Pan Candy Co., Inc.
JURASSIC PARK - Footwear - S. Goldberg and Co. Inc.
JURASSIC PARK - Novelty items - Amblin' Entertainment, Inc.
JURGENS - Barbecues and grills - Thermal Systems Inc.
JURISMONITOR - Electronic equipment - Bodyguard Technologies, Inc.
JURIST BOND - Paper–bond - Engravers Paper Corp.
JURIVIEW - Computer software - Integrated Concepts, Inc.
JURLIQUE - Skin care products - D'Namis Ltd.
JUS' LIKE ME - Dolls - Jus' Like Me
JUS LIKE U - Film–motion picture - Sam & Venu. a Partnership, Inc.
JUS NATURALE - Apparel and accessories - Monnvey & Monnvey, Ltd.
JUS-NUF - Cleaning preparations ☆ - Stoner Inc.
JUS' RITE ROPE, THE - Ropes - Rieken Ropes
JUS SQUEEZD - Fruit drinks–bottled or canned - Lykes Services Co.
JUSSARA - Apparel–women's - Jussara Lee
JUST - Lighting equipment - Sam Flax
JUST 2 COLD - Beverages–malt - Anheuser-Busch Companies Inc.
JUST 4 BOYS - Apparel and accessories - Victor B. Handal & Bros. Inc.
JUST 4 GIRLS - Apparel and accessories - Victor B. Handal & Bros. Inc.
JUST 4 KIDS - Apparel and accessories - Victor B. Handal & Bros. Inc.
JUST 4 ME - Garment storage bags - H. J. Rashti & Co., Inc.
JUST 4 TRAVEL - Knapsacks - Victor B. Handal & Bros. Inc.
JUST 5 - Hair coloring preparations - Combe Inc.
JUST-A - Hair care products - Waverly Beauty Products
JUST A BREEZE - Housewares - Minka Lighting, Inc.
JUST-A-DROP - Guitar polish ☆ - Jan-Mar Industries
JUST-A-JESTER - Dolls ☆ - Bradley Import Co.
JUST A KISS - Greeting cards - AGC, Inc.
JUST A MINIT - Food products - King's Command Foods Inc.
JUST A MINUTE - Games - Tah Dah Inc.

JUST A MOUTHFUL - Publisher's imprints - Betty Ramsey Publisher
JUST-A-NOTE - Stationery - Current, Inc.
JUST-A-RISER - Sprinklers–lawn - William R. Marshall
JUST A SECRET - Floor coverings–carpet and rugs - Tuftex Carpet Mills, Inc.
JUST A SHADE SMALLER - Sunglasses - Cliff Weil, Inc.
JUST-A-TOUCH - Fabrics–felt - National Nonwovens
JUST A WAVE - Hair care products - Waverly Beauty Products
JUST-ABIT-MORE - Posters - Carol T. Armendinger
JUST ABOUT ME - Publisher's imprints - Sunny Skyes
JUST ADD CEDAR PET BED - Pet products - L/M Animal Farms, Inc.
JUST ADD LETTUCE - Salad dressings–mixes - A. Angonoa Inc.
JUST A'JUST - Apparel–women's - Exquisite Form Industries
JUST APPLES - Fruits–dried - Just Tomatoes Co.
JUST APPLES - Stoneware dinnerware - Iron Mountain Stoneware Inc.
JUST AROUND THE CORNER - Figurines - Ganz
JUST BABY & ME - Toys–stuffed - Rita Silvestri
JUST BANNERS - Vinyl banners - Dareo E. Fontaine
JUST BE CUZ - Hobby kits - Darrow Production Co., Inc.
JUST BEAD IT! - Hobby kits - Papermates, Inc.
JUST BECAUSE - Apparel and accessories - Michael John Kent
JUST BECAUSE - Apparel–women's ☆ - Kellwood Co.
JUST BEGUND BRIDE - Toys–stuffed ☆ - Gund, Inc.
JUST BEGUND GROOM - Toys–stuffed ☆ - Gund, Inc.
JUST BELL PEPPERS - Vegetables–dried - Just Tomatoes Co.
JUST BEPAWS PET ACCESSORIES - Pet products - Laid Back Enterprises, Inc.
JUST BETWEEN US - Lubricants - Key West Fragrance & Cosmetics Inc.
JUST BIG - Apparel and accessories - Think Big Sportswear, Inc.
JUST BISCOTTI - Cookies ☆ - Just Desserts Inc.
JUST BLUSH! - Cosmetics - Estee Lauder Inc.
JUST BOARDS - Apparel and accessories - Bon-Ton Trade Corp.
JUST-BODA - Giftware ☆ - Alpine Crafts Co. Inc.
JUST BODY - Cosmetics - Revlon-Realistic Professional Products Inc.
JUST BONES - Dog food - Pet Center, Inc.
JUST BORN - Candy - Just Born Inc.
JUST BORN - Pet products - Farnam Cos. Inc.
JUST BORN - Toys - Eugene Doll & Novelty Co. Inc.
JUST BRASS - Music–sheet - MMB Music Inc.
JUST BRASS LOLLIPOPS - Music–sheet - MMB Music Inc.
JUST BRILLIANT - Shampoos - Demert & Dougherty, Inc.
JUST BROWSING - Cosmetics - Origins Natural Resources Inc.
JUST BUTTONS - Computer software ☆ - Chrisalan Designs, Inc.
JUST CHARMING - Bedding–linen - Dan River Inc.
JUST CHILI CALIFORNIA HOT SAUCE - Chili sauce - Just Chili, Inc.
JUST CLASS - Women's apparel - India Garments Inc.
JUST CLEAR - Shampoos ☆ - Carme Inc.
JUST CLOSETS - Closet organizers - Eberli-Kirk Properties, Inc.
JUST CLOTHES - Apparel–women's - Susan Burrowes, Ltd.
JUST CLOWNS - Dolls - Uneeda Doll Co., Inc.
JUST COOL CLOTHES - Apparel and accessories - Victor Des Prez
JUST COTTON - Apparel and accessories - Elliott J. Saunders
JUST CRISPS - Snack food - Just Off Melrose
JUST CROUTONS - Croutons - Just Off Melrose
JUST CURLS - Hair care products - Paula Payne Products Co. Inc.
JUST DESSERTS - Food products - Just Desserts Inc.
JUST DIPPED CHOCOLATE - Lipstick ☆ - Cosrich Inc.
JUST DO IT. - Apparel and accessories - Nike, Inc.
JUST DO IT - Binders - BRS, Inc.
JUST DUCKS - Decoys - Craft-Tex Inc.
JUST DUCKY - Air purification systems ☆ - Medo Industries, Inc.
JUST DUCKY - Frames–picture - Terragrafics Inc.
JUST DUCKY - Housewares ☆ - Treasure Craft Co.
JUST EAT IT. - Seafood products–fresh or frozen - Noel A. Turner
JUST ELEGANCE - Wallcoverings - John T. Raisin Corp.
JUST ELEMENTS - Apparel–women's - Viva Sportswear Inc.
JUST ENJOY THE GAME - Golf carts - Paradigm Sports, Inc.
JUST ENOUGH - Bagel chips - Sweet & Savory Bagel Chips
JUST ENOUGH - Colognes ☆ - Avon Products, Inc.
JUST ENOUGH - Dinners–frozen - Mayacamas Fine Foods, Inc.
JUST ENOUGH - Paint sets–hobby - Carnival Arts, Inc.
JUST ENOUGH - Skin care products - Almay Inc.
JUST ENOUGH - Snack foods - Pet Inc.
JUST ENOUGH CUPS - Food products - Blackmores
JUST ENOUGH PASCAL - Computer software - Symantec Corp.
JUST FINE - Food products - Boykin & Southern Wholesale Grocers Inc.
JUST FLICK IT - Games - Tabletop Enterprises

☆ = Now out of production

JUST FLORA - Apparel–women's - Flora Nikrooz Inc.
JUST FOR BABY - Bleach ✩ - Clorox Co.
JUST FOR BABY SET - Toys - Playskool, Inc.
JUST FOR CHILI - Tomato pastes and sauces - Curtice-Burns Foods, Inc.
JUST FOR COPIES - Correction fluid - Liquid Paper Corp.
JUST-FOR-DOGS - Insecticides - Mallinckrodt Veterinary, Inc.
JUST FOR EWE - Apparel and accessories - Ann Fairchild
JUST FOR FUN - Cologne, mirror and comb tote, etc ✩ - Cosrich Inc.
JUST FOR FUN - Shoes - Osage Footwear, Inc.
JUST FOR FUN - Toys - Jak-Pak Inc.
JUST FOR GIRLS - Toys - Jak-Pak Inc.
JUST FOR GOLFERS - Golfing equipment - Winn, Inc.
JUST FOR HIM ORIGINALS - Greeting cards - Reta England Partnership
JUST FOR HOLIDAYS - Footwear - Melville Corp.
JUST FOR JILDOR - Shoes - Jildor Shoes, Inc.
JUST FOR KICKS - Shoes - Valley Lane Industries Co.
JUST FOR KICKS - Toys–musical - Mattel, Inc.
JUST FOR KIDS - Comforters - Franco Manufacturing Co., Inc.
JUST FOR KIDS - Jams and jellies - J.M. Smucker Co.
JUST FOR KIDS - Recording label - Integrity Music, Inc.
JUST FOR KIDS - Skin care products - Tanning Research Laboratories Inc.
JUST FOR LEATHER - Oils–lubricating - North American Oil Co.
JUST FOR ME - Frozen foods ✩ - Wilton Foods Inc.
JUST FOR ME! - Hair care products - Pro-Line Corp.
JUST FOR ME - Toys - Libby Lee Toys Inc.
JUST FOR MEN - Hair coloring preparations - Combe Inc.
JUST FOR NAILS - Nail care products - Spilo/Mehaz Worldwide
JUST FOR PUTTERS - Golfing equipment - Winn, Inc.
JUST FOR THE PUN OF IT - Games - David Hatch
JUST FOR US - Hams - Wilson Foods Corp.
JUST FOR US - Wallpaper - Galaxie Handprints
JUST FOR WRAPS - Apparel - Just for Wraps, Inc.
JUST FOR WRAPS - Hair care products - Esirg's Manufacturing Co. Inc.
JUST FOR YOU - Cosmetics - Dicon, Inc.
JUST FOR YOU - Greeting cards - P.S. Greetings
JUST FOR YOU - Hosiery - Mayer/Berkshire Corp.
JUST FOR YOU - Skin care products - Perry Products
JUST FOR YOU - Window coverings - Bamboo Abbott Florida Corp.
JUST FOR YOU-CLAYLIA - Health care products - Claylia's Own
JUST FRIENDS - Dolls ✩ - Effanbee Doll Corp.
JUST FRUIT - Fruit butters - Jake & Amos Co.
JUST FRUIT SNACKS - Fruits–dried - Just Tomatoes Co.
JUST FUN - Wallcoverings - Authentic Reproductions
JUST FUN - Wallpaper - Patterson Piazza
JUST GAMES - Games - Just Games
JUST GIRLS - Jewelry–costume - Lewis Galoob Toys, Inc.
JUST GRANDMA AND ME - Computer software - Broderbund Software, Inc.
JUST GREAT - Deodorizers - E. Davis Inc.
JUST GREAT - Floor coverings–carpet and rugs - Cabin Crafts Carpets
JUST GREAT - Sandwiches–prepackaged - E.A. Sween Co.
JUST HOLD - Hair care products - Gold Medal Hair Products Inc.
JUST HOLLY - Dinnerware–glass ✩ - Cuthbertson Imports Inc.
JUST HOOK IT UP - Audio equipment - Monster Cable Products, Inc.
JUST HOOPS - Jewelry - Studex Corp.
JUST HOWARD - Umbrellas ✩ - American Umbrella Co. Inc.
JUST IMAGINE - Puzzles ✩ - Milton Bradley Co.
JUST-IN-CASE - First aid kits - Sentinel Consumer Products, Inc.
JUST-IN-TEAM - Computer software - Joseph Valentine
JUST IN TIME - Apparel and accessories - Sir Richard Hyun
JUST IN TIME - Cleaning preparations - Servaas Laboratories Inc.
JUST IN TIME - Hair care products - John Amico Expressive Hair Care Products
JUST-IN-TIME - Shampoos ✩ - Ampro Industries, Inc.
JUST IN TIME - Skin care products - Ilona, Inc.
JUST IN TIME ENTERPRISE SYSTEM - Computer software ✩ - Fourth Shift Corp.
JUST JOCKEY - Apparel and accessories - Jockey International, Inc.
JUST JODIE - Underwear and nightwear - Heckler Manufacturing & Investment Group Inc.
JUST JUICE - Candy ✩ - Willy Wonka Brands
JUST JUICE - Health care products - Acorn Natural Foods Co.
JUST LEMON - Teas - Eastern Shore Tea Co.
JUST LIBBY - Footwear - Sam & Libby, Inc.
JUST LIGHT - Charcoal - Arrow Industries, Inc.
JUST LIKE A PRO - Brushes–paint - Bestt-Liebco
JUST LONG HAIR - Hair care products - Roberts Research Laboratories, Inc.

JUST LOTION - Skin care products - Care-Tech Laboratories Inc.
JUST MARRIED - Paper–gummed - Wry Idea Co.
JUST ME - Apparel–women's - Catherines of California, Inc.
JUST ME - Health care products - Colgate-Palmolive Co.
JUST ME AND SNUFFLES - Toys–stuffed ✩ - Gund, Inc.
JUST ME KINGERGUND BEAR - Toys–stuffed ✩ - Gund, Inc.
JUST MY SIZE - Apparel–athletic - Saramar Corp.
JUST MY SIZE - Hosiery - Sara Lee Corp.
JUST MY STYLE - Greeting cards - American Greetings Corp.
JUST MY STYLE - Toys - Fisher-Price, Inc.
JUST MY STYLE - Wallpaper ✩ - Sanitas Wallcoverings
JUST 'N CASE - Holsters - Gusty Winds Corp.
JUST NAMES - Plaques - Nightshift International Inc.
JUST NUTS - Candy - Elmer Candy Corp.
JUST ONE - Coffee - Eagle Affiliates, Inc.
JUST ONE - Fruits and vegetables - Sunkist Growers, Inc.
JUST ONE - Housewares - Silver Bells Music
JUST ONE BITE - Pesticides–household - Security Products Co.
JUST ONE BITE - Rodenticides - Farnam Cos. Inc.
JUST ONE EARTH - Apparel and accessories - J.A. Apparel Corp.
JUST ONE HAND - Tiles–asphalt - Garden Way Inc.
JUST ONE PER DAY - Pharmaceutical preparations - Reese Chemical Co.
JUST PANTS - Apparel–men's - Just Pants
JUST PEACHY - Apparel–children's - May Apparel Group, Inc.
JUST PEACHY - Wallpaper ✩ - Ginger Tree Designs
JUST PERFECT - Floor coverings–carpet and rugs ✩ - Patcraft Mills Inc.
JUST PERFECT - Meat products–poultry - Carolina Turkeys
JUST PERFECT - Pet products - Eagle Beauty Laboratories Inc.
JUST PERSIMMONS - Fruits–dried - Just Tomatoes Co.
JUST PICKED - Lipstick ✩ - Cosrich Inc.
JUST PICTURE THIS. - Photo albums - New Vision, Inc.
JUST PIK'T - Juices–frozen - Fresh Juice Co. Inc.
JUST PIK'T JR. - Juices–frozen - Fresh Juice Co. Inc.
JUST PLAIN SUE - Dolls - Nancy Sue Spurlock
JUST PLAY IT! - Games - Play Sports Games, Inc.
JUST POLES/JUST NETS - Sporting goods - Douglas Industries Inc.
JUST POP'T - Candy - Brach Van Houten Holding Inc.
JUST POUR - Coffee - Eagle Affiliates, Inc.
JUST PREMIUM - Beverages–malt ✩ - Eastern Brewing Corp.
JUST PRETTY - Bedding–linen - Dan River Inc.
JUST RACING - Chairs–metal - Just Racing, Ltd.
JUST RICHARD - Umbrellas - American Umbrella Co. Inc.
JUST RIGHT - Cereal - Kellogg Co.
JUST RIGHT - Floor coverings–carpet and rugs - Calladium & Marglen
JUST RIGHT - Floor coverings–carpet and rugs - Trend Carpet
JUST RIGHT - Floor coverings–carpet and rugs ✩ - Galaxy Carpet Mills Inc.
JUST RIGHT - Thermostats - Hunter Fan Co.
JUST RIGHT - Yogurt ✩ - Old Home Foods Inc.
JUST RIGHT BOOKS - Publisher's imprints - Random House, Inc.
JUST RIM - Racks - Robert D. Brooks
JUST RIPE - Olives–canned - Musco Olive Products Inc.
JUST-RITE - Musical instrument accessories ✩ - Carpenter Co.
JUST ROSES - Flowers, plants, and seeds - Just Roses, Inc.
JUST SARAH FOR CATO KIDS - Apparel and accessories - Cato Corp.
JUST SAY HEMP - Coats - Thomas J. Holland
JUST SAY NUTS - Food products - Dberger & Associates, Inc.
JUST SAY YO - Frozen yogurt - International Yogurt Co.
JUST SCOOP 'N ADD - Cat litter - A & M Pet Products Inc.
JUST SHEER - Hosiery - Sara Lee Corp.
JUST SITTIN' DOWN - Toys - J & G Toys
JUST SMALL - Apparel and accessories - Think Big Sportswear, Inc.
JUST SO - Hair care products - J. Strickland & Co.
JUST SOCCER, LTD. - Shirts - Just Soccer, Ltd.
JUST SOUTH - Footwear–women's ✩ - Jarman Shoe Co.
JUST SPORTS - Sporting goods - Just Toys, Inc.
JUST STUFF - Lockers–metal - Suncast Corp.
JUST TAP IT - Sporting goods - Just Tap It , Inc.
JUST TEARS - Health care products - Blairex Laboratories, Inc.
JUST THE EARS - Candy - Monogramme Confections Co.
JUST THE FAX - Correction fluid ✩ - With International Inc.
JUST THE RIGHT CHEMISTRY - Chemical preparations - EM Industries, Inc.
JUST THE THING - Giftware ✩ - Treasure Masters
JUST THE TWO OF US - Greeting cards ✩ - American Greetings Corp.
JUST THINKING OF YOU - Greeting cards - American Greetings Corp.
JUST TIPS - Cosmetics - Classic Laboratories Inc.
JUST-TO-LOVE BABIES - Toys–stuffed ✩ - CBS Toys

✩ = Now out of production

JUST TO SAY - Candy - Securitag Corp.
JUST TOMATOES - Fruits–dried - Just Tomatoes Co.
JUST TONEY - Apparel–women's - Swirl II Ltd.
JUST TOUCH - Computer peripheral equipment - Spiritus, Inc.
JUST TRY ME - Canned corn - F.O. Mitchell & Bro. Inc.
JUST TWO BIKES - Bicycles - Just Two Bikes, Inc.
JUST US BEARS - Toys–stuffed ☆ - Fun World Inc.
JUST US KIDS - Bread - Interstate Brands Corp.
JUST US KIDS - Educational materials - Just Us Books, Inc.
JUST VEGGIES - Vegetables–dried - Just Tomatoes Co.
JUST WATER - Water purification systems - Ecowater Systems, Inc.
JUST WESTERN - Apparel–men's - Scholian International Inc.
JUST WHAT THE DOCTOR ORDERED - Laxatives ☆ - Biopractic Group II Inc.
JUST WHISTLE - Shaving preparations - Gillette Co.
JUST WHITE - Glass products ☆ - Corning Inc.
JUST WILD - Wallpaper - Somerville Designs
JUST WONDERFUL - Hair care products - Faberge Co.
JUST WONDERFUL - Slippers ☆ - Sheffield Industries Inc.
JUST WONDERFUL LEGS - Hosiery ☆ - Sheffield Industries Inc.
JUST-WRAP - Tools - OK Industries Inc.
JUST WRITE - Computer software ☆ - Borland International, Inc.
JUST WRITE - Novelty items - Securitag Corp.
JUST YOUNG - Apparel–women's - Anne Klein & Co.
JUST YOUR FIT - Brassieres (Bras) - Warnaco Inc.
JUST YOUR STYLE - Paper - Fort Howard Corp.
JUST YOUR STYLE - Wallpaper - Bayview Wallcoverings
JUST YOUR TYPE - Computer software ☆ - Right on Programs
JUSTA BEAR POPS - Candy - Pennsylvania Dutch Candies
JUSTA BITE - Citrus fruits - Florida Global Citrus Ltd.
JUSTA CRUST - Breads - Piemonte Foods Inc.
JUSTE DUO - Lotions - LVMH Moet Hennesy Louis Vuitton Inc.
JUSTER - Recording label - Tee Vee Toons, Inc.
JUSTERS - Apparel–women's - Phillips-Van Heusen Corp.
JUSTICE - Food containers - Farmhouse Foods
JUSTICE - Recording label - Justice Record Co.
JUSTICE - Self-defense spray - Guardian Personal Security Products, Inc.
JUSTICE AMERICA - Apparel and accessories - Clayton D. Blehm
JUSTICE LEAGUE - Games ☆ - Mayfair Games, Inc.
JUSTICE SOUNDBOARD - Compact discs–prerecorded - Randall H. Jamail
JUSTIFIED - Apparel and accessories - Critter Productions, Inc.
JUSTIFIER, THE - Computer software ☆ - Konami (America) Inc.
JUSTIN - Boots - Justin Cos.
JUSTIN - Cabinets - Imperial Cabinet Co. Inc.
JUSTIN - Leather tanning and finishing - Boot Royalty Co., LP
JUSTIN ALLEN'S ISLANDERS - Apparel–women's - Parsytec Inc.
JUSTIN B. JONES - Apparel–women's - Thomas E. Greene
JUSTIN BEAR - Toys–stuffed - Dakin Inc.
JUSTINA - Guitars - JTG of Nashville
JUSTINE - Toys - Tonka Corp.
JUSTINE HENRIQUES FILHOS - Wines - W.J. Deutsch & Sons Ltd.
JUSTINE'S LOLLYPOP - Cosmetics - Justine Custom Cosmetics
JUSTINE'S PUTTY - Cosmetics - Justine Custom Cosmetics
JUSTINO MADERA - Wines - Monsieur Henri Wines Ltd.
JUSTINSANE - Apparel and accessories - Epic Designs Inc.
JUSTMAN - Apparel–men's ☆ - Sampson Inc.
JUSTOYS - Toys - Just Toys, Inc.
JUSTRITE - Bathroom fixtures - Justrite Ceramics

JUSTRITE - Garden equipment - The Fountainhead Group, Inc.
JUSTRITE - Lanterns–electric - Justrite Manufacturing Co.
JUSTRITE - Office supplies - Louis Melind Co.
JUSTRITE - Pens ☆ - Faber-Castell Corp.
JUSTRITE - Safety cans - General Scientific Equipment Co.
JUSTRITE - Scissors–hand-operated - K.A. Vogel Sons Inc.
JUSTRITE - Spices and extracts - Oscar Mayer Foods Corp.
JUSTVOICE - Computer software - Interactive Products, Inc.
JUSTWHITES - Eggs - Ballas Food Products Corp.
JUSTWIN - Apparel and accessories - Georges Marciano
JUSTY - Motor vehicles–automobiles - Subaru of America, Inc.
JUTE BOX - Pet products - American Cat Emporium
JUTE-TONE - Thread - Belding Heminway Co. Inc.
JUTESTOK - Envelopes - National Fiberstok Corp.
JUTLAND - Computer software - Writing Wizardry, Inc.
JUTLAND - Floor coverings–carpet and rugs - Eurotex Inc.
JUTLAND - Games ☆ - Avalon Hill Game Co.
JUVE - Beverages - Great North Coast Beverage Co.
JUVENIA - Health care products - Bio-Research Laboratories
JUVENILE - Fabrics–broadcloth - Desire Mills Co. Inc.
JUVENILE DELINQUENTS - Greeting cards - Vivian Greene Inc.
JUVENILE JUNCTION - Furniture ☆ - Simon Corp.
JUVENILE SCULPTURE - Artists' materials - Artisan House Inc.
JUVENILES III - Fabrics–tapestry ☆ - Coloroll Inc.
JUWEL - Garden equipment - Kinsman Co. Inc.
JUWEL - Pet products - Vitakraft Pet Products Co., Inc.
JUXTAFELT - Fabrics - Bacon Felt Co. Inc.
JUZO - Health care products - JUZO
JUZO LITE LINE - Health care products - JUZO
JVC - Electronic equipment - JVC Co. of America
JVK OMNI-LOCK - Medical apparatus - Smithers Medical Products, Inc.
JV'S - Footwear - Morse Shoe, Inc.
JV'S BY STUART FRAZIER - Footwear–men's - Morse Shoe, Inc.
JW - Apparel and accessories - Edison Brothers Stores, Inc.
JW - Cigarettes - House of Vegas, Inc.
JW - Jewelry - Gold Creations, Inc.
JW - Jewelry - Joseph Weinreich Co. Inc.
J.W. - Tuna–canned - US Foodservice
JW - Vegetables–canned - Clifton Canning Co.
JW CANNED FOODS - Food products - House of Vegas, Inc.
JW DUNDEE'S HONEY BROWN LAGER - Beverages–malt - Genesee
Brewing Co., Inc.
JW EDIBLE OILS - Oils–edible - House of Vegas, Inc.
JW JEANS WEST - Apparel and accessories - Edison Brothers Stores, Inc.
JW JENNISON-WRIGHT - Asphalt - Stelwood Industries, Inc.
J.W. PROVISIONS - Slacks–men's - Glen Oaks Industries Inc.
JW STANARD - Musical instruments ☆ - J.W. Stannard Co.
JWO - Apparel–women's - Japanese Weekend, Inc.
JX - Combines–agricultural - Rigaflex, Inc.
JX-7 - Doors–glass - Jeld-Wen, Inc.
JY - Jewelry - Janet Yaseen
JYM BAGGY - Bags–duffel - Patricia A. Rizzo
JYO - Hair-cutting shears - B.W. Boyd Shears Inc.
JYOTI CUISINE INDIA - Food products - Gourmand Inc.
JZ - Fruit drinks–bottled or canned - Everfresh Beverages, Inc.
JZ - Signal flares - Koch Engineering Co., Inc.
JZ RICHARDS - Apparel and accessories - RJZ Limited
J'ZAM - Apparel–children's - J'Zam Inc.

☆ = Now out of production

K

Addresses and phone numbers for the companies cited in the brands below
are available in the Company Listings section immediately following the brands listings.

K - Housewares - K.K. Merchandise, Inc.
K - Insulating materials - Thermal Ceramics Inc.
K+ - Jewelry–precious - Karlan & Associates, Inc.
K - Pens - Sheaffer Inc.
K - Recording label - K-Tel International, Inc.
K - Recording label - Kathy Kolbe
K - Whiskey - W.A. Gaines and the Old Crow Distillery Co.
K-1 - Ice making machinery - Anderson-Barrows Metals Corp.
K-1 - Shoes - KangaROOS USA Inc.
K-1 ENTERPRISES - Glassware–household - Pamela Konecny
K-II - Film - Eastman Kodak Co.
K-2 - Sporting goods - K-2 Corp.
K 2 - Sprinklers–lawn - K-Rain Manufacturing Corp.
K-3 - Motors–hydraulic - General Electric Co.
K-5 INDUSTRIES, INC. - Luggage - K-5 Industries Inc.
K-7 - Machine parts - K-7 Co., Inc.
K-9 - Household appliance stores - Emerson Electric Co.
K-9 - Pens - K-9 Pen Co.
K-9 - Pet collars - JFK Enterprises
K-9 - Pet products - K-9 Pet Products
K-9 - Pet products - Mr. Mutt Pet Products Inc.
K-9 BOOTIES - Pet products - R.A.F. Trading Inc.
K-9 CALM - Veterinary nutritional supplements - Oralx Corp.
K-9 CAR ALARM - Automotive parts and accessories - Kenneth E. Flick
K-9 CLASSICS - Pet products - ID Store
K-9 COMMAND - Pet products - Kindly Products Co.
K-9 CORRAL - Pet products - International Development Corp.
K-9 FREEDOM - Pet products - Foodscience Laboratories Inc.
K-9 I - Pet products - Electric Cleaner Co.
K-9 II - Pet products - Electric Cleaner Co.
K-9 KABLE - Pet products - Mr. Mutt Pet Products Inc.
K-9 KENNEL MIX - Dog food - K-9 Kustom Mix Inc.
K-9 KNACKS - Dog food - C & G Baking Co.
K-9 KUMALONG - Pet products - Mustang Products, Inc.
K-9 KUSTOM MIX - Dog food - K-9 Kustom Mix Inc.
K-9 NITE WALKER - Pet products ☆ - James Thompson and Co. Inc.
K-9 SCOOPEE - Pet products - Diversified Innovations
K-9 SOLAR HOMES - Pet products - Innovative Pet Homes
K-9 UNITS - Motor vehicles–buses - Turtle Top Specialty Products
K-9'S DOG TYE - Pet products - Village Products
K-28 - Sporting goods - Wilson Sporting Goods Co.
K-35 - Projectors–photographic - Kopykake
K-37 - Cleaning preparations - Roebic Laboratories Inc.
K-47 - Cleaning preparations - Roebic Laboratories Inc.
K-57 - Cleaning preparations - Roebic Laboratories Inc.
K-60 - Roofing materials–slate - L.D. Sterns Corp.
K-67 - Cleaning preparations - Roebic Laboratories Inc.
K-77 - Cleaning preparations - Roebic Laboratories Inc.
K-80 - Guns - Krieghoff International
K-87 - Cleaning preparations - Roebic Laboratories Inc.
K 100'S KINGSPORT - Cigarettes - Eve Holdings Inc.
K-225 - Footwear–athletic - Kaepa Inc.
K-600 - Pigments - Radiant Color Div.
K-800 - Pigments - Radiant Color Div.
K-911 - Recording label - K-911 Inc.
K-7000 - Pigments - Radiant Color Div.

K-A KIDS TO ADULTS AGES 6+ - Computer software - Interactive Digital Software Association
K-A-V-S - Veterinary medical equipment ☆ - Durham's Products Co.
K-AMP - Hearing aids - Etymotic Research Inc.
K & B - Toys–trains - K and B Manufacturing Inc.
K & B CLASSICS - Wallpaper ☆ - Brewster Wallcovering Co.
K & B COUNTRY OPEN HOUSE - Fabrics–tapestry ☆ - Columbus Coated Fabrics Co.
K & B SUPER POXY - Epoxy coatings - K and B Manufacturing Inc.
K & E - Artists' materials - Keuffel & Esser Co.
K & F - Coffee - Kittridge & Frederickson
K & G - Musical instrument accessories - Kagan & Gaines Co. Inc.
K & H - Electronic equipment ☆ - G Prime Limited
K & K - Jewelry - K & K Jewelry, Inc.
K & K - Meat products–beef - K & K Gourmet Meats Inc.
K & K - Musical instruments - K & K Musical Instrument Co. Inc.
K & K - Water purification systems - K & K Enterprises, Inc.
K. & L. - Beverages–alcohol - Standard Distillers Products Inc.
K. & M. - Silver products - Kirk & Matz Ltd.
K M INTERNATIONAL - Toys–stuffed - K & M International, Inc.
K & Q - Watches - Hing Yip Watches USA Inc.
K & S - Fertilizers ☆ - Aircap Industries Corp.
K & S - Jewelry - Kopelman & Shatz Inc.
K AND S - Pickles - Kruger and Sons Inc.
K & T - Calendars - Dennison National Co.
K & W - Adhesives and sealants - K & W Products
K & W - Cleaning preparations - K & W Products
K-ASHARE - Computer software - Xinet, Inc.
K-ASSAY - Medical laboratories - Kohji Kamiya
K B GOLF - Golfing equipment - K.B. Golf Manufacturing, Inc.
K-B-L - Diuretics - D.L. Hunter & Co.
K. B. TWISTER - Bread - The Kroger Co.
K-BEAM - Electronic equipment - Kistler Instrument Corp.
K BITS - Saddles - Smith-Worthington Saddlery Co. Inc.
K-BLAZER - Food products - Kraft Food Ingredients Corp.
K-BOBS - Food products - K-Bob's USA, Inc.
K-BOB'S FAMOUS KABOB - Food products - K-Bob's USA, Inc.
K-BOB'S KABOB - Food products - K-Bob's USA, Inc.
K-BOND - Adhesives and sealants - Key Laboratories Inc.
K BOOM - Lamps - Inventure
K-BOS - Shirts ☆ - Crown Prince Inc.
K-C - Jewelry - Jaymark Jewelry
K-C - Musical instruments - Ed Myers Co.
K-C - Pharmaceutical preparations - Century Pharmaceuticals Inc.
K-CAP - Filters–air - Air Kontrol Inc.
K-CEL - Footwear - K-Cel International Corp.
K-CEY - Calendars - Keith Clark Inc.
K-CHROME - Film - Eastman Kodak Co.
K-CILLIN-250 - Pharmaceutical preparations ☆ - Merz Inc.
K-CLOR-REX - Pharmaceutical preparations - C.S. Ruckstuhl Co. Inc.
K-COLOR - Film - Eastman Kodak Co.
K-CORDS - Toys–stuffed - Kamar International Inc.
K CUSTOM - Cymbals - Avedis Zildjian Co.
K-CUTTER - Hair care products - Capitol Novelty Co.
K-D - Pet product - Insul-House
K-DAIRY - Bakery products–frozen ☆ - Bubbles Baking Co.

☆ = Now out of production

1151

K-DEC - Vitamins and nutritional supplements - Schein Pharmaceutical Inc.

K-DEE-DEE - Recording label - Sharon Productions Inc.

K-DERM CREAM - Skin care products - S.F. Group, Inc.

K-DET - Cleaning preparations - Washington Chemical Sales of California Inc.

K-DRIVE - Engines–marine ☆ - Mercury Hi-Performance Group

K-DUR - Potassium compounds - Key Pharmaceuticals Inc.

K F - Valves - Watts Investment Co.

K FACTORS, THE - Vitamins and nutritional supplements - Alacer Co.

K-FERON - Health care products - Kay Pharmacal Co. Inc.

K-FLEX - Health care products - Kay Pharmacal Co. Inc.

K-FORMER - Machinery - Knudson Manufacturing Inc.

K-FORTE - Pharmaceutical preparations ☆ - Columbia Laboratories Inc.

K-FS - Computer software - Xinet, Inc.

K-G - Pharmaceutical preparations - Geneva Generics Inc.

K-GLUCON - Pharmaceutical preparations - Wesley Pharmacal Co. Inc.

K-GUARD - Electronic equipment - Kistler Instrument Corp.

K-GUM - Dental compounds - Parthenon Co. Inc.

K HAWK - Machinery ☆ - Knudson Manufacturing Inc.

K-HOOK - Hearing aids - Etymotic Research Inc.

K-J VINEYARDS AND WINERY - Wines - Kendall Jackson Winery, Ltd.

K-KARE - Skin care products ☆ - K-Zyme Laboratories Inc.

K KELLER - Doors–metal - Keller Industries Inc.

K KELMAC - Luggage - Kelmac International Corp.

K KIRKWOOD REGISTER - Non-metal building materials - Kirkwood Stair Co. Inc.

K KNAACK - Tool boxes - Knaack Manufacturing Co.

K KOSTIS KOSMOS INC. - Recording label - Kostis Kosmos Inc.

K-KOTE - Adhesives and sealants - Kenyon Consumer Products Inc.

K-KOTE - Firearms, accessories, and parts - Sigarms Inc.

K KRESICS TOTAL BODY WORKOUT - Bags–duffel - Kresics

K-KUBES - Chemical preparations - United Salt Corp.

K-KURL - Hair care products - Marianna Imports, Inc.

K-LAX - Pharmaceutical preparations - Econo Med Pharmaceuticals Inc.

K-LINE - Tools - K-Line Industries

K-LINE - Toys–trains - K-Line

K-LINE - Yarn ☆ - Knitting Fever Inc.

K LINE, THE - Novelty items - Kuepper Favor Co., Inc.

K-LINEVILLE - Toys - K-Line

K-LITE - Laser systems–medical - Kentek Corp.

K-LITE - Lighting equipment - ICI Acrylics Inc.

K-LITH VISIONEASE - Music–sheet - Trophy Music Co.

K LOK - Medical apparatus - K-Lok, Inc.

K-LOR - Health care products - Abbott Laboratories

K-LUX - Tiles–ceiling ☆ - ICI Acrylics Inc.

K-LYTE - Potassium compounds - Bristol-Myers Squibb Co.

K-M - Paper–thermoplastics coated - K & M Co.

K M BROWN BEAR - Firearms, accessories, and parts - Markesbery Muzzle Loaders, Inc.

K-MACHINE - Sporting goods - K Lin Specialties

K-MAG - Electronic equipment - Fischer & Porter Co.

K-MAG ASPARTATE - Vitamins and nutritional supplements - Source Naturals

K-MAG C - Vitamins and nutritional supplements - Source Naturals

K-MAG K-G - Vitamins and nutritional supplements - Source Naturals

K-MAN - Trading cards and stamps - Score Group, Inc.

K MART - Apparel and accessories - Kmart Corp.

K-MASK - Electronics equipment - Grass Valley Group Inc.

K-MASTER - Balls - Worth Inc.

K-MATTING - Mats–grass, reed, and jute - Koffler Sales Co.

K-MECH - Wire products - Kaspar Wire Works, Inc.

K-MEDIC - Medical apparatus - K-Medic, Inc.

K-MG - Nutritional supplements - International Nutrition

K-MIN - Health care products - Holistic Laboratories Inc.

K-MON - Apparel and accessories - Mark Boldi Productions

K. MUELLER - Musical instrument accessories - St. Louis Music Supply Co.

K-MYCIN - Veterinary pharmaceutical preparations - Dyna Pet Inc.

K-NIFE - Valves - Keystone International Holdings Corp.

K. O. KRUISER - Toys - Mattel, Inc.

K-O-TATES - Vitamins and nutritional supplements - Alacer Co.

K-O'D - Sweaters - Edan Products, Inc.

K-P - Pharmaceutical preparations ☆ - Century Pharmaceuticals Inc.

K-P-SOL - Veterinary pharmaceutical preparations - Evsco Pharmaceuticals

K-PACK - Beef - Kenosha Beef International Ltd.

K-PAK - Hair care products - Joico Laboratories, Inc.

K-PASA - Shoes ☆ - Tessler Shoe Corp.

K-PAVA - Health care products ☆ - Kay Pharmacal Co. Inc.

K-PEK - Pharmaceutical preparations - Rugby Laboratories Inc.

K-PETS - Toys–stuffed - Kamar International Inc.

K-PHEN - Antihistamine preparations - Kay Pharmacal Co. Inc.

K-PHOS M.F. - Pharmaceutical preparations - Beach Pharmaceuticals, Inc.

K-PHOS NEUTRAL - Pharmaceutical preparations - Beach Pharmaceuticals, Inc.

K-PHOS NO. 2 - Pharmaceutical preparations - Beach Pharmaceuticals, Inc.

K-PHOS ORIGINAL - Pharmaceutical preparations - Beach Pharmaceuticals, Inc.

K-PLANES - Boats - Mercury Hi-Performance Group

K-PLUSH - Toys–stuffed - Kamar International Inc.

K-POP - Toys–guns - Tyco Toys

K-POWER - Publisher's imprints - Scholastic Inc.

K-R - Abrasive products ☆ - Park Metallurgical Corp.

K RACE LIGHT - Bicycles - Kona-USA

K-REX - Pharmaceutical preparations - C.S. Ruckstuhl Co. Inc.

K-ROD - Toys - Tonka Corp.

K-SALT - Salt ☆ - Century Pharmaceuticals Inc.

K. SCHILLER - Musical instruments - American Music Group Ltd.

K-SERIES - Engines - Kohler Co.

K-SERIES - Musical instrument accessories - G. Leblanc Corp.

K-SERIES CIRCUIT - Hearing aids - Electone Inc.

K-SHEEN PETS - Toys–stuffed - Kamar International Inc.

K-SINE - Microcircuitry tools - Pacifico Ultrasonics, Inc.

K-SIX-PLUS - Rivets–metal - Pharmex Inc.

K SNAP - Gutters–plastic - Plastmo Inc.

K-SORB HYDROPHOBIC - Chemical preparations - Ecosorb International Inc.

K-SPOOL - Computer software - Xinet, Inc.

K-STAR - Boats–fishing ☆ - Klamath Boat Co. Inc.

K STEEL - Saddles - Smith-Worthington Saddlery Co. Inc.

K-STONE - Wallcovering - Marbled Elegance, Inc.

K-STUDIO - Sweatshirts - Ritepoint Inc.

K-SUL - Fertilizers - Hickson Kerley, Inc.

K-SUN LABEL SHOP - Labeling machinery - K-Sun Corp.

K-SUN LETTER QUICK - Ribbons–inked - K-Sun Corp.

K-SWISS - Footwear–athletic - K-Swiss Inc.

K-T - Dog food - Kennel-Town Pet Supply

K-TAB - Pharmaceutical preparations - Abbott Laboratories

K TAILS - Fishing lures - Kalin Co.

K-TALK - Computer software - Xinet, Inc.

K-TALK - Textbooks - Communication Skill Builders, Inc.

K-TAPE - Tape–adhesive - Kenyon Consumer Products Inc.

K-TEL - Labels–paper - K-Tel International, Inc.

K. TONE - Amplifiers - Il Young Park

K-TOO - Jewelry - Katrina Inc.

K-TOTS - Toys–stuffed - Kamar International Inc.

K-TRACTOR - Rulers–metal - Lenore E. Perry

K-TUBE - Medical apparatus ☆ - Biosearch Medical Products Inc.

K-USA - Jewelry–precious - Kaleidoscope USA, Inc.

K-V - Hardware - Knape and Vogt Manufacturing Co.

K-VENIENCE - Hardware - Knape and Vogt Manufacturing Co.

K-WAY - Brushes–hair ☆ - Harry D. Koenig & Co.

K WOOD - Cabinets–wood - Kitchen Kompact Inc.

K-Y - Fruits–canned ☆ - Purcell International

K-Y - Lubricants - Johnson & Johnson

K-Y PLUS - Pharmaceutical preparations - Johnson & Johnson

K. ZILDJIAN - Cymbals - Avedis Zildjian Co.

K-ZYME - Pet products - BioZyme Inc.

K2 - Amplifiers - Crown International, Inc.

K2 - Catheters - Medtronic, Inc.

K2 - Computer software - K2 Interactive LLC

K2 - Sporting goods - K2 Inc.

K2+ KLIP - Antennas–satellite - Antenna Co.

K2 SYSTEMS - Computer peripheral equipment - MB's Computer Warehouse of Orlando, Inc.

K2R - Cleaning preparations - Spontex, Inc.

K3 - Golfing equipment - Arcal Golf Inc.

K3 - Particle board - MacMillan Bloedel Building Materials

K3 - Sprinklers–lawn - K-Rain Manufacturing Corp.

K3 ROYAL - Shelving units–wood - MacMillan Bloedel Building Materials

K3 WASCANA - Shelving units–wood - MacMillan Bloedel Building Materials

K4 - Golfing equipment - Arcal Golf Inc.

K4N - Apparel–children's ☆ - Nature Co.

K4SL - Golfing equipment - Arcal Golf Inc.

K7 - Hair care products - Keystone Laboratories Inc.

K9 - Pet products ☆ - Precious Paws

K27 - Ducts–metal - United McGill Corp.

☆ = Now out of production

K40 - Computers–personal - American Antenna Corp.

K40 - Radar systems and equipment - Gabriel, Inc.

K200 - Sporting goods - Keiser Sports Health Equipment

K300 - Sporting goods - Keiser Sports Health Equipment

K5000 - Projectors–photographic - Kopykake

KA-BAR - Knives–pocket ☆ - Cole Consumer Products Inc.

KA-BEL-WAER - Jewelry–costume - Ka-Bel-Waer, Inc.

KA-BLUEY - Candy - Zeebs Enterprises, Inc.

KA-BOING - Balls - Cap Toys, Inc.

KA-KUM-ON - Massage cream - American Hygienic Laboratories Inc.

KA-LOK - Knives–pocket ☆ - Cole Consumer Products Inc.

KA ME - Food products - Liberty Richter Inc.

KA-ME - Food products - Shaffer, Clark & Co. Inc.

KA MOCHA - Liquors ☆ - White Rock Distilleries Inc.

KA-O-PEKTIN - Veterinary pharmaceutical preparations ☆ - Evsco Pharmaceuticals

KA-PEK - Diarrhea medication - American Pharmaceutical Co.

KA-SPLASH - Toys–guns - Diversified Specialists, Inc.

KAANAPALI - Balls–football - AMFAC/JMB Hawaii, Inc.

KAARINA - Bedding–linen - Dan River Inc.

KAAT II PLUS - Pumps - Arrow International Investment Corp.

KAB-KING - Tractors - Burch Manufacturing Co. Inc.

KABA - Lock cylinders - Kaba High Security Locks Corp.

KABA NOVA - Electronic locks - Kaba High Security Locks Corp.

KABABAYAN - Food products - H & N Fish Co.

KABALA - Games ☆ - Thomas Lowe Ventures, Inc.

KABANA - Jewelry - Kabana Inc.

KABEL - Floor coverings–carpet and rugs - Milliken & Co. Inc.

KABELL - Recording label - Jazz Composer's Orchestra Association Inc.

KABIKINASE - Pharmaceutical preparations - Kabi Pharmacia Inc.

KABIL - Watches - M.P.H. Inc.

KABINITE - Paints, etc. - American Paints

KABIR - Floor coverings–carpet and rugs - Masland Corp.

KABLE - Pens - Major Metalfab Co.

KABLE - Pens - MMF Industries

KABLE-KIT - Automotive parts and accessories - Manlee Industries Inc.

KABLE LITE - Electrical equipment - Tech Lighting Inc.

KABOB-N GRILL - West Bend Co.

KABOLIN - Pharmaceutical preparations - Legere Pharmaceuticals Inc.

KABONKERS - Clothing - Nuvo Accessories, Ltd.

KABOODLES - Hobby kits ☆ - Hazel Pearson Handicrafts

KABOODLES - Noodles - Foulds Inc.

KABOOM - Cereal - General Mills, Inc.

KABOOM! - Children's clothing - Buster Brown Apparel Inc.

KABOOM - Fireworks - North Central Industries, Inc.

KABOOMERS - Games - CBS Toys

KABOS - Jeans–men's - Meijer, Inc.

KABRONZE - Signboards - Photo-Cut Graphics, Inc.

KABUKI - Apparel and accessories - Harwood Companies Inc.

KABUKI - Canned foods - C. Itoh & Co. America Inc.

KABUKI - Handwork supplies - Bernat Yarn & Craft Corp.

KABUKI - Novelty items - Rockeffects (Canada) Inc.

KABUKI - Wines - Guadalajara Imports, Ltd.

KABUTO - Bicycles ☆ - Kent International Inc.

KABUTO - Wallpaper - Textile Wallcoverings International Ltd.

KACE - Luggage - DLCO and Associates

KACES - Bags - Ace Product

KACHINA - Wines - Gallup Sales Co. Inc.

KACHOOS - Facial tissues - Scott Paper Co.

KACO SEALS - Automotive parts and accessories - CRP Industries, Inc.

KACY - Apparel–women's ☆ - Mayer/Berkshire Corp.

KACY - Toys–stuffed ☆ - Gund, Inc.

KAD-A-LAC FINISHES - Lacquers - Gemini Coatings, Inc.

KADDI-TEK U.S.A. - Carrying cases - Jameslee Corp.

KADDIE STAND - Golf-bag stands - Kaddie Stand Inc.

KADEE - Toys–trains - Kadee Quality Products

KADENZA - Electronics equipment - Grass Valley Group Inc.

KADET - Fire extinguishers ☆ - Kidde Safety

KADET - Luggage - I.J.K. Sales Corp.

KADET - Toys–models - Estes Industries

KADET TRAINERIFLE - Toys–guns - Parris Manufacturing Co.

KADIMA - Games - Drybranch Inc./Sport Design

KADO - Bath salts ☆ - Chase Collection, Inc.

KADO - Recording label - Nesak International

KADONO - Musical instruments ☆ - Dauphin Co.

KADOODLE - Puzzles - S.J. Miller Co.

KAE - Beverages–malt - Kalsec, Inc.

KAEFE - Candy ☆ - Andre Prost Inc.

KAEMARK - Cosmetics - Kaemark Inc.

KAENE POINT - Floor coverings–carpet and rugs - Hartford Carpet Mills

KAEPA - Footwear–athletic - Kaepa Inc.

KAEPOX - Paints - Kansas Paint & Color Co.

KAF-TAN - Cleaning preparations–household - Tops Manufacturing Co. Inc.

KAFCO - Musical instrument accessories - David Wexler & Co.

KAFFREE - Teas - Worthington Foods Inc.

KAFFREE ROMA - Beverages - Worthington Foods Inc.

KAFIRIMAR - Floor coverings–carpet and rugs - Couristan Inc.

KAFKO - Cleaning preparations ☆ - Kafko International Ltd.

KAFOCIN - Pharmaceutical preparations ☆ - Eli Lilly and Co.

KAGE KARDZ - Pet products - Aaronco Grooming Products

KAHALA - Floor coverings–carpet and rugs - Customweave Carpets Inc.

KAHALA COLLECTION, THE - Jewelry - Sultan Co.

KAHALA PLUS - Floor coverings–carpet and rugs ☆ - Customweave Carpets Inc.

KAHANA - Furniture - Tropitone Furniture Co. Inc.

KAHER FORGED IRONS - Golfing equipment - Kahler International

KAHL HAT STIFFENER - Chemical preparations - Bickmore Inc.

KAHLE - Fishing tackle - Wright & McGill Co.

KAHLENBERG - Health care products - Glenwood LLC

KAHLER - Musical instrument accessories - Kahler International

KAHLUA - Beverages–alcohol - Hiram Walker & Sons, Inc.

KAHLUA - Candy - Harry Gelman Co.

KAHLUA - Liqueurs - Kahlua Co.

KAHLUA - Seasonings ☆ - Silver Foods Corp.

KAHLUA BLACK RUSSIAN - Beverages–alcohol - Hiram Walker & Sons, Inc.

KAHLUA DELIGHT - Floor coverings–carpet and rugs - Burlington House Carpets

KAHLUA KOALA - Toys–stuffed ☆ - Dakin Inc.

KAHLUA PECANS - Food products - Mrs. Powell's Gourmet Pecans

KAHLUA ROYALE - Beverages–alcohol - Hiram Walker & Sons, Inc.

KAHLUA STINGER - Beverages–alcohol - Hiram Walker & Sons, Inc.

KAHLUA UNTOASTED ALMOND - Beverages–alcohol - Hiram Walker & Sons, Inc.

KAHN - Hams - Sara Lee Corp.

KAHN - Pencils ☆ - Dixon Ticonderoga Co.

KAHN'S - Food products - Hillshire Farm Co.

KAHO MAI - Rice - Busch Agricultural Resources Inc.

KAHUKU - Fruits and vegetables - Halekulani Corp.

KAHUNA - Golfing equipment - Gear Fit Golf Inc.

KAHUNA'S SHADESAVERS - Ophthalmic goods - Robert Frank Fremont

KAI - Computer software - HSC Software

KAI - Hair care products ☆ - Designer's Edge International

KAIBAB - Gasoline - Kaibab Industries

KAIK - Boats–dinghies - Sea Eagle

KAILA KOALA - Toys–stuffed - Dakin Inc.

KAIMANA COOLER - Beverages–carbonated - Asean Pacific Beverages

KAIMILOA - Sporting goods - Applied Engineering Products Co.

KAIOWA - Meat products–canned - Sampco Inc.

KAIRE INTERNATIONAL - Vitamins and nutritional supplements - Kaire International, Inc.

KAI'S POWER TOOLS - Computer software - Harvard Systems Corp.

KAISEKI SELECT - Food products - Granum Inc.

KAISER - Adhesives and sealants - Laticrete International Inc.

KAISER - Beverages–malt - Renfroe Co. Inc.

KAISER - Confections - C. & J. Willenborg Inc.

KAISER - Cooking equipment–household ☆ - Haram-Christensen Corp.

KAISER - Foil–aluminum ☆ - Kaiser Aluminum & Chemical Corp.

KAISER - Photographic equipment - H.P. Marketing Corp.

KAISER - Playpens–metal - Kaiser Manufacturing Co.

KAISER - Ships–sailing vessels - John Kaiser Associates Inc.

KAISER - Wines - Joseph E. Seagram & Sons, Inc.

KAISER FARMS - Vitamins and nutritional supplements - Kaiser Farms, Inc.

KAISER FOTOTECHNIK - Electronic equipment - H.P. Marketing Corp.

KAISER PLATES - Giftware - Viking Import House Inc.

KAISER T-FORM - Aluminum products - Kaiser Aluminum & Chemical Corp.

KAISERDOM RAUCHBIER - Beverages–malt - Merchant du Vin Corp.

KAISERHOF - Window frames - Kaiserhof Windows, Inc.

KAITA - Bedding–linen - Dan River Inc.

KAITLIN ASHLEY - Apparel and accessories - Pow Kids Inc.

KAITLIN CONNER - Apparel–women's - Oxford Industries, Inc.

KAITLIN STAR - Toys - Saban Entertainment, Inc.

KAIZEN - Toners - Midwest Typewriter and Computer Co. Inc.

KAJAC - Recording label ☆ - Ozark Opry Records
KAJAL - Cosmetics - Isla Cosmetique
KAJI - Artists' materials - Andrews/Nelson/Whitehead
KAJON - Garden equipment - Lindig Manufacturing Corp.
KAJUN - Recording label - Master-Trak Sound Recorders
KAJUN GOURMET - Seafood - Boja's Foods Inc.
KAKADU TRADERS AUSTRALIA - Apparel and accessories - Kakadu Traders Australia
KAKE-KING - Shortening - Patrick Cudahy Inc.
KAKE MATE - Bakery products - Mallet and Co.
KAKTUSRACK - Mats - Cactus Mat Manufacturing Co.
KAKUSHO - Dishes–earthenware - Mikasa Co.
KAL - Vitamins and nutritional supplements - Makers of Kal, Inc.
KAL-CEIL - Paints - Talon Paint Inc.
KAL-CLEAR - Cups–plastic - Fabri-Kal Corp.
KAL-EQUIP - Automotive parts and accessories - Mitech
KAL-FOIL - Foil–aluminum - Kalamazoo Label Co.
KAL-GLAS - Automotive parts and accessories - Ellay Inc.
KAL-GUM - Labels–gummed - Kalamazoo Label Co.
KAL KAN - Pet products ☆ - Kal Kan Foods, Inc.
KAL KOTE - Gypsum products - National Gypsum Co.
KAL MAG ZINC - Vitamins and nutritional supplements - Garcoa Labs/Vitamin Classics
KAL-N-ZYME - Pharmaceutical preparations - Makers of Kal, Inc.
KAL-NAMEL - Labels–gummed - Kalamazoo Label Co.
KAL-Q-LATOR - Photographic equipment ☆ - Kalart Victor Corp.
KAL-STIK - Labels–gummed - Kalamazoo Label Co.
KALA - Apparel–women's - Amit Kashanian
KALA - Vitamins and nutritional supplements - Freeda Vitamins Inc.
KALA-WOOD - Wood products - Cutlers Owens
KALAGA - Frames–picture - La Casa De Carlo
KALAH - Games - Games & Graphics, Inc.
KALAHARI - Floor coverings–carpet and rugs - Couristan Inc.
KALAMAR - Cabinets–wood ☆ - Kemper
KALAMAZOO - Cigarette lighters - Bowers Lighter Co.
KALAMAZOO - Musical instruments - Gibson Strings & Accessories
KALAMAZOO - Toys–trains - Victor's Railroad
KALANI - Coffee - Kalani Organica
KALAR - Rubber–extruded - Hardman
KALART - Photographic equipment - Kalart Victor Corp.
KALASH - Health care products ☆ - Fibertone Co.
KALATEL - Video equipment - Kalatel, Inc.
KALAVOX - Electronic equipment - Kalart Victor Corp.
KALAYA EMU OIL SHAMPOO - Pet products - Glo-Marr Products Inc.
KALAYA OIL - Skin care products - New World Technology, Inc.
KALBRITE - Paints - Cloverleaf Paint & Varnish
KALCINATE - Health care products - Kay Pharmacal Co. Inc.
KALCO - Labels–gummed - Kalamazoo Label Co.
KALDI - Liqueurs ☆ - Shaw-Ross International Importers
KALEEB - Sunglasses - Kaleeb, Inc.
KALEID-O-LITE - Novelty items ☆ - Lava-Simplex Internationale
KALEIDACOLOR - Stamps–hand - Tsukineko, Inc.
KALEIDAGRAPH - Computer software - Synergy Software
KALEIDASCOPE - Recording label - Metropolitan Recording Corp.
KALEIDESCOPE - Toilets–enameled - Kohler Co.
KALEIDISKETTES - Computer storage devices–magnetic - Allenbach Industries Inc.
KALEIDOCARD - Paper - Nimco Quality Photography Inc.
KALEIDOS - Tiles–ceramic - American Marazzi Tile, Inc.
KALEIDOSAURS - Kaleidoscopes - Gemini Kaleidoscopes
KALEIDOSCOPE - Bedroom furniture - Impact Furniture
KALEIDOSCOPE - Blinds–vertical - Kaleidoscope Industries Inc.
KALEIDOSCOPE - Christmas tree ornaments - Cracker Box Inc.
KALEIDOSCOPE - Deodorizers - PRH Products Co.
KALEIDOSCOPE - Electronics equipment - Grass Valley Group Inc.
KALEIDOSCOPE - Fabrics - Kaleidoscope International Ltd.
KALEIDOSCOPE - Floor coverings–carpet and rugs - Galaxy Carpet Mills Inc.
KALEIDOSCOPE - Floor coverings–carpet and rugs - Philadelphia Carpets
KALEIDOSCOPE - Floor coverings–carpet and rugs - Trans-Ocean Import Co. Inc.
KALEIDOSCOPE - Floor coverings–carpet and rugs ☆ - Burtco Enterprises Inc.
KALEIDOSCOPE - Floor coverings–carpet and rugs ☆ - Colonial Mills Inc.
KALEIDOSCOPE - Floor coverings–carpet and rugs ☆ - Karastan-Bigelow Inc.
KALEIDOSCOPE - Footwear–athletic - E.S. Originals, Inc.
KALEIDOSCOPE - Greeting cards - American Greetings Corp.

KALEIDOSCOPE - Housewares ☆ - Doranne
KALEIDOSCOPE - Identification tags - Precision Dynamics Corp.
KALEIDOSCOPE - Nail care products - Entrecap Corp.
KALEIDOSCOPE - Paper - Riverside Paper Corp.
KALEIDOSCOPE - Pens - Sheaffer Inc.
KALEIDOSCOPE - Tableware–china ☆ - Villeroy and Boch Tableware Ltd.
KALEIDOSCOPE - Tiles–facing - Edward Lowe Glass Designs, Inc.
KALEIDOSCOPE - Wallpaper - Illuminations Wallcoverings & Fabrics Inc.
KALEIDOSCOPE - Wallpaper ☆ - Wall-Pride Inc.
KALEIDOSCOPE ART - Kaleidoscopes - Gemini Kaleidoscopes
KALEIDOSCOPE BOOKS - Publisher's imprints ☆ - New Readers Press
KALEIDOSCOPE II - Floor coverings–carpet and rugs - Kelly Group Inc.
KALEIDOSOFT - Computer software - Kaleidoscope Software
KALEIDOSTRIPS - Tiles–ceramic ☆ - American Olean Tile Co.
KALEIDOWAVE - Giftware - Art Zone Studio
KALENE - Rubber–extruded - Hardman
KALENE - Skin care products ☆ - Lee Products Co.
KALEX - Rubber–urethane - Hardman
KALFSKIN - Cases–eyeglass - California Optical Leather Inc.
KALGLO - Heating equipment - Kalglo Electronics Co. Inc.
KALI OREXI! - Salad dressings–mixes - T.J.'s Food Factory & Carry Out, Inc.
KALI PRESS - Publisher's imprint - Kali Press
KALIBER - Beverages–malt - Guinness Import Co.
KALIBRE - Jewelry–costume - Kalibre
KALIBU - Snack foods ☆ - Oakmont Investments Co.
KALICHROME - Lenses - Bausch & Lomb Inc.
KALIDOR - Computer peripheral equipment - Alps Electric (USA), Inc.
KALIFORNIA KOLORS - Paints - Krylon/Dupli-Color
KALIFORNIA KROSSING - Apparel–children's - Swat Fame, Inc.
KALIKO - Games - Kadon Enterprises Inc.
KALIMAR - Cameras - Kalimar, Inc.
KALIMARA - Floor coverings–carpet and rugs - Masland Corp.
KALIMAT PRESS - Publisher's imprints - Kalimat Press
KALIN CELLARS - Wines - Kalin Cellars
KALIN CELLARS - Wines ☆ - Diamond Wine Merchants
KALINKA NO. 12 - Cosmetics - Perfumer's Workshop Ltd.
KALIROY - Fruits and vegetables - G.A.C. Produce Co. Inc.
KALIUM - Deicing fluid - Pasvalco
KALLI - Handbags - Payless Shoesource Worldwide, Inc.
KALLI-GUARD - Valves–intake - Kallista Inc.
KALLIGAMOS - Bathtubs–enameled - Kallista Inc.
KALLIGRAPHOS - Bathtubs–enameled - Kallista Inc.
KALLIKRENOS - Bathtubs–enameled - Kallista Inc.
KALLIMERA - Bathtubs–enameled - Kallista Inc.
KALLIMIKRI - Bathtubs–enameled - Kallista Inc.
KALLINIKOS - Bathtubs–enameled - Kallista Inc.
KALLINOPOS - Bathtubs–enameled - Kallista Inc.
KALLISPERIA - Bathtubs–enameled - Kallista Inc.
KALLISTA - Faucets - Kallista Inc.
KALLITHEA - Bathtubs–enameled - Kallista Inc.
KALLOFLEX - Cameras - Kowa American Corp.
KALM PACKS - Vitamins and nutritional supplements - Natural Organics, Inc.
KALM PLEX - Vitamins and nutritional supplements - Natural Organics, Inc.
KALM VITE - Vitamins and nutritional supplements - Natural Organics, Inc.
KALMAR - Serving carts - Kalmar Designs Inc.
KALMBACH - Publisher's imprints - Kalmbach Publishing Co.
KALMM - Tranquilizers ☆ - Scrip-Physician Supply Co.
KALO - Seats–automobile - Krueger International, Inc.
KALO - Veterinary medical equipment - Kalo Co.
KALO K.O. - Veterinary pharmaceutical preparations - Kalo Co.
KALON - Housewares - Dura-Ware of America Inc.
KALOSCA - Giftware - Schildkraut Giftware Corp.
KALOVITA - Vitamins and nutritional supplements - American Sales Corp.
KALOZYME - Veterinary pharmaceutical preparations - Kalo Co.
KALPANA - Computer peripheral equipment - Kalpana Inc.
KALPEC - Pharmaceutical preparations ☆ - Wyeth-Ayerst Laboratories
KALSEC - Food products - Kalsec, Inc.
KALSHIELD - Siding–metal ☆ - Kaiser Aluminum & Chemical Corp.
KALUGA - Figurines - Mattel, Inc.
KALULA KIDS - Apparel–children's - Kahn Lucas Lancaster Inc.
KALVA - Syrup - Kalva Corp.
KALVELAX - Laxatives ☆ - Makers of Kal, Inc.
KALWITE - Brushes - Wright-Bernet
KALYN - Computer software - Kalyn Corp.
KALYX - Recording label - Vandor Motion Pictures, Phonorecords & Music Publishing Group

☆ = Now out of production

KAM - Engines–marine ☆ - Mercury Hi-Performance Group

KAM - Pet products - Strongheart Products, Inc.

KAM-LOK - Hardware - Brink's Locking Systems Inc.

KAMA BY ST. JOHN - Clothing - St. John Knits, Inc.

KAMA SUTRA - Recording label - Essex Entertainment, Inc.

KAMADROX - Pharmaceutical preparations ☆ - ICN Pharmaceuticals Inc.

KAMALA - Skin care products - Kamala Perfumes

KAMAN - Musical instruments - Ovation Instruments

KAMAN STRINGS - Guitars ☆ - Kaman Music Corp.

KAMAR - Toys–stuffed - Kamar International Inc.

KAMAR COLLECTIBLES - Toys–stuffed - Kamar International Inc.

KAMAR KLASSIKS - Toys–stuffed - Kamar International Inc.

KAMAR REALISTICS - Toys–stuffed - Kamar International Inc.

KAMASUTRA - Incense - Excelsior Incense Works

KAMAYAN - Shrimp–canned or cured - Town Fiesta Trading, Inc.

KAMBA - Cooking utensils–aluminum - Athi-Mara Magadi

KAMBLY OF SWITZERLAND - Cookies ☆ - FCW Imports

KAMCHATKA - Caviar - Caviarteria Inc.

KAMCHATKA - Vodka - Jim Beam Brands Co.

KAMERON - Dolls - Mattel, Inc.

KAMET - Marine rigging - Henssgen Hardware Corp.

KAMEYAMA - Candles - Kameyama USA Ltd.

KAMIKAZE - Desserts - Gilbert-Robinson Inc.

KAMIKAZE MID - Athletic footwear - Reebok International Ltd.

KAMIL'S GOURMET PIES - Pies–fresh - Kamil's Gourmet Pies, Inc.

KAMINOMOTO - Cosmetics - Osuttag Oriental Cosmetic Products Inc.

KAMINSKY - Slacks–men's - H.R. Kaminsky & Sons Inc.

KAMLOOPER - Sporting goods - Acme Tackle Co.

KAMMBACK - Motor vehicles ☆ - DaimlerChrysler

KAMMER - Valves–industrial - Valtek Inc.

KAMO KOMBATTER - Toys–guns - Parris Manufacturing Co.

KAMORA - Beverages–alcohol - Jim Beam Brands Co.

KAMOTION - Recording label - Candy Records

KAMOTSURU SAKE - Sake - Mutual Trading Co. Inc.

KAMP DAKOTA - Campgrounds - Kamp Dakota Inc.

KAMP KID - Sporting goods ☆ - Kellwood Co.

KAMP KING - Sporting goods - Imperial Schrade Corp.

KAMP KING OF TEXAS - Trailers–travel - P & S Camper Manufacturing Co.

KAMP PACK - Food products - Bernard Fine Foods Inc.

KAMPAI - Beverages–alcohol - Consolidated Distilled Products Inc.

KAMPAROO - Trailers–boat - Handy Bikes Corp.

KAMPERS - Pharmaceutical preparations ☆ - Ole Time Woodsman

KAMPERS KIT - Pharmaceutical preparations - Packaging Concepts Assoc. Inc.

KAMPGROUNDS OF AMERICA - Campgrounds - Kampgrounds of America Inc.

KAMPIT - Apparel and accessories - Duxbak Inc.

KAMPKID - Sleeping bags ☆ - Kellwood Co.

KAMS - Bicycles ☆ - Kent International Inc.

KAMSLY - Jewelry - Samuel Kamsly Inc.

KAMUCO - Guitars - Kansas Music Co. Inc.

KAMURO - Bicycles ☆ - Kent International Inc.

KAMUT - Spaghetti - San Francisco Herb & Natural Food Co.

KAMUTIOS - Cereal - New Morning

KAMUT'N HONEY - Cereal - Breadshop's Natural Foods

KAN-DO - Fishing tackle - R.E.H.N. Enterprises Inc.

KAN-DU - Cleaning preparations - Uncle Sam Chemical Co., Inc.

KAN HANDLER - Insulating materials - Life-Like Products Inc.

KAN II - Recording label - Kansa Records Corp.

KAN KADDIE - Novelty items - Kan Kaddie, Inc.

KAN KOOLER - Insulating materials ☆ - Life-Like Products Inc.

KAN-KOR - Pharmaceutical preparations - Pharmex Inc.

KAN TONG - Food products - Uncle Ben's, Inc.

KAN-TONG - Rice - Mars, Inc.

KAN-TOTE - Housewares ☆ - Arctic Products Inc.

KAN-TUNG - Rice - Uncle Ben's, Inc.

KANACYN - Pet products ☆ - Aquatronics-Filtronics

KANADIAN KWALITY - Flour–blended ☆ - ConAgra Grain Co.

KANAGAWA - Thread - YLI Corp.

KANALKA - Pharmaceutical preparations - Lannett Inc.

KANALOA - Apparel–athletic - McSquid Ltd.

KANARA - Floor coverings–carpet and rugs - Milliken & Co. Inc.

KANATA - Floor coverings–carpet and rugs ☆ - Kelly Group Inc.

KANATA VALLEY - Floor coverings–carpet and rugs ☆ - Kelly Group Inc.

KANDAHAR - Boots ☆ - Miura Sports Inc.

K&B - Paints - Benjamin Moore & Co.

KANDEL - Apparel and accessories - Columbia Knit Inc.

KANDEL - Scarves - Kandel Knitting Mills

KANDEL INSTANT SIGHTING TARGET - Toys–guns - Kandel Instant Sighting Targets

KANDESN - Cosmetics - Sunrider Corp.

KANDI - Dolls - Goldberger Doll Manufacture Co.

KANDI-ROOS - Popcorn ☆ - Nalley's Fine Foods

KANDIDAPLEX - Vitamins and nutritional supplements - Vitamin Research Products Inc.

KANDISHEEN - Yarn - Melrose Yarn Co. Inc.

KANDIYOHI - Water–mineral - Kandiyohi Bottled Water

KANDLESTIX - Candles - North Georgia Candle Works, Inc.

K&R CIMS - Computer software - Ralph J. Hochendoner

KANDU - Detergents ☆ - The Kroger Co.

KANDULOT - Toys - Eicart Inc.

KANDURA - Fabrics - M. Lowenstein Corp.

KANDY - Frames–eyeglass - Hudson Optical Corp.

KANDY KAKES - Cakes - Tasty Baking Co.

KANDY KART - Candy ☆ - E. Rosen Co.

KANDY KEG - Candy ☆ - Brock Candy Co. Inc.

KANDY KRITTERS - Candy ☆ - Securitag Corp.

KANE - Pet products - Kane Manufacturing Co.

KANE - Placemats - Kane Industry Corp.

KANE CUTLERY CO. - Pocket knives - Tennessee River Valley Knife Association Inc.

KANE KUTLERY - Scissors–hand-operated ☆ - Kane Industry Corp.

KANEDAI SEITOSHO - Dinnerware ☆ - Sakura Inc.

KANELINE - Housewares - Sullivan Sales Marketing

KANENAKA - Dishes–china - Mikasa Co.

KANE'S - Food products ☆ - Nature's Pride Inc.

KANESON - Health care products - Omron Healthcare, Inc.

KANEY'S - Food products - AMK for Service

K'ANG HSI COLLECTION - Furniture - Tomlinson of High Point Inc.

KANGA - Footwear–athletic - KangaROOS USA Inc.

KANGA - Manicure preparations - Creative Nail Design, Inc.

KANGA BACK - Padding–foam - Textile Rubber and Chemical Co. Inc.

KANGA HYDE - Padding–foam - Textile Rubber and Chemical Co. Inc.

KANGA-ROCKA-ROO - Infant product - Century Products Co.

KANGA ROOFPOUCH - Automotive parts and accessories - Kanga Co. Inc.

KANGA RUTH - Dolls - Mattel, Inc.

KANGA TRAC - Padding–foam - Textile Rubber and Chemical Co. Inc.

KANGAROO - Bicycles - Ross Bicycles USA, Ltd.

KANGAROO - Computer software - Seven Hills Software

KANGAROO - Envelopes - National Fiberstok Corp.

KANGAROO - Food products - Kangaroo Brand Inc.

KANGAROO - Game machines - IGT - North America

KANGAROO - Handbags ☆ - Sarne Co. Inc.

KANGAROO - Health care products - Sherwood Medical Co.

KANGAROO - Key rings - Norstar Enterprises

KANGAROO - Liquors - European Beverage Co., Inc.

KANGAROO - Telescopes - Northern Telecom, Inc.

KANGAROO BAGGS - Sporting goods - Alpenlite Inc.

KANGAROO CASE - File folders - Risto Inc.

KANGAROO COURT - Footwear–athletic - KangaROOS USA Inc.

KANGAROO KARRY ALL - Vehicle spare tire cover - Majestak Creations, Inc.

KANGAROO KUE - Balls–billiard - Gene V. Albrecht

KANGAROO MOTOR CADDIE - Golfing equipment - Kangaroo Golf Ltd.

KANGAROO PLAYMATES - Toys–stuffed ☆ - Century Products Co.

KANGAROOCAP - Hats - KangaROOS USA Inc.

KANGAROOS - Apparel–children's ☆ - Elder Manufacturing Co., Inc.

KANGAROOS - Footwear–athletic - KangaROOS USA Inc.

KANGAROOS - Pretzels ☆ - Toad-Ally Snax Inc.

KANGAROOS COIL R1 - Footwear–athletic - KangaROOS USA Inc.

KANGAROOSPORTS - Footwear–athletic - KangaROOS USA Inc.

KANGAWRAP - Diaper covers - Von International Trading Co., Inc.

KANGO - Dropcloths - Sunshine Industries Inc.

KANGO - Hammers–electric ☆ - New England Carbide

KANGOL HEADWEAR INC. - Hats - Kangol Inc.

KANGORA - Leather goods - Korchmar Case Co.

KANGOUROU - Infant product ☆ - Century Products Co.

KANGS - Footwear–athletic - KangaROOS USA Inc.

KANGY - Air purification systems ☆ - Medo Industries, Inc.

KANI - Clothing - Jones & Williams Corp.

KANI - Footwear - Karl Kani

KANI - Footwear - Carl Williams

KANIMAGE - Photographic equipment - Cosmos Communications Corp.

KANIMI - Seafood products–canned or cured - Shining Ocean Inc.
KANIMI-HEALTHY 1 - Seafood products–fresh or frozen - Shining Ocean Inc.
KANINE KABINS - Pet products - Handy Home Products
KANINE KAVIAR - Dog food - KFC Agri-Service
KANINE KENNEL KOT - Pet shops - Dunwishin Enterprises
KANINE KOOKIE KUTTERS - Pet products - Barkleigh Productions, Inc.
KANJI KAPS - Apparel and accessories - Kanji Koncepts
KANJIWORD - Computer software - Pacific Software Publishing, Inc.
KANK-A - Health care products - Blistex Inc.
KANNER'S KETTLE - Cooking equipment–household ☆ - General Housewares Corp.
KANOLD - Candy ☆ - Bahlsen Inc.
KANON - Colognes - Frances Denney
KANON KONSERVERA - Skin care products ☆ - Frances Denney
KANSAI - Water colors - Boko-Undo USA Inc.
KANSAS - Guitars - Westheimer Corp.
KANSAS - Meat products–beef - Midtown Provision Co. Inc.
KANSAS BRAND - Beef - Frank Foods Co.
KANSAS CITY - Beverages–carbonated - Green River Corp.
KANSAS CITY - Tools ☆ - Regent Sheffield, Ltd.
KANSAS CITY B-BQ - Food products ☆ - Lightlife Foods, Inc.
KANSAS DIAMOND - Flour–blended - Acme-Evans/A.D.M. Milling Co.
KANSAS PACIFIC STEAMSHIPS - Shirts - Sheridan G. Tucker
KANSAS STATE UNIVERSITY - Hats - Kansas State University
KANSAS SUN - Flour–blended - The Wall-Rogalsky Milling Co.
KANSU - Floor coverings–carpet and rugs - Trans-Ocean Import Co. Inc.
KANT KINK - Sporting goods - Weber Industries Inc.
KANT-LEAK - Heating equipment - Radiator Specialty Co.
KANT-MISS - Food products ☆ - Marshfield Foods
KANT-ROLL - Clothespins - Penley Corp.
KANT-SAG - Hardware ☆ - United Steel Products Co.
KANT SLAM - Hardware - Bloomfield Manufacturing Co.
KANT-SLIP - Hair care products - Goody Products, Inc.
KANT-SLIP - Labels–gummed - Standard Register Co.
KANT-SPLASH - Ammunition ☆ - Olin Corp. (Winchester Div.)
KANT-STIK - Carbon and graphite products - Codo Manufacturing Corp.
KANT TAMP - Fuses–electric - Gem Electric Manufacturing Co. Inc.
KANT-TWIST - Clamps - Clamp Manufacturing Co., Inc.
KANT-TWIST - Tools - Plus Manufacturing Co.
KANTANA - Flour–blended - Ross Industries Inc.
KANTITA - Vitamins and nutritional supplements - Kroeger Herb Products Co. Inc.
KANTLEAK - Heating equipment - Anderson Brass Co.
KANTLEAK - Tarpaulins - Foster Corp.
KANTREX - Antibiotics - Bristol-Myers Squibb Co.
KANTRIM - Veterinary pharmaceutical preparations - Bristol-Myers Squibb Co.
KANTROLL - Crayons - Dixon Ticonderoga Co.
KANTSTRAND - Thread - Blue Mountain Industries, Inc.
KANTWET - Mattresses ☆ - Evenflo Juvenile Furniture Co.
KANU CUSTOMIZED - Hair care products - Kanu, Inc.
KANULASE - Health care products - Dorsey Laboratories
KANUMODIC - Health care products - Dorsey Laboratories
KANVET - Pennants - Chicago Show Printing Co.
KANYON KIDS - Apparel–children's ☆ - Nitches, Inc.
KANYON ROAD - Apparel–men's ☆ - MU Industries Inc.
KAO LIANG - Alcoholic beverages - American International Trading Co.
KAO-LOK - Hardware ☆ - Thermal Ceramics Inc.
KAO-NOR - Pharmaceutical preparations ☆ - Vortech Pharmaceuticals
KAO-PAVERIN - Pharmaceutical preparations - Reese Chemical Co.
KAO-PAVERIN CAPS - Pharmaceutical preparations - Reese Chemical Co.
KAO-PAVERINE - Pharmaceutical preparations ☆ - Reese Chemical Co.
KAO-PG - Pharmaceutical preparations ☆ - Roberts/Hauck Pharmaceuticals Inc.
KAO-SPAS - Pharmaceutical preparations ☆ - Wendt-Bristol Co.
KAOBEL - Health care products ☆ - Halsey Drug Co. Inc.
KAODENE - Pharmaceutical preparations - Pfeiffer Pharmaceuticals Inc.
KAOGORIC - Pharmaceutical preparations ☆ - Wesley Pharmacal Co. Inc.
KAOLINPEC - Pharmaceutical preparations - C.O. Truxton Inc.
KAOMAGMA - Pharmaceutical preparations ☆ - Wyeth-Ayerst Laboratories
KAOPAR - Health care products ☆ - Halsey Drug Co. Inc.
KAOPECTATE - Pharmaceutical preparations - Upjohn Co.
KAOPECTATE I-D - Pharmaceutical preparations - Upjohn Co.
KAOPECTOLIN - Pharmaceutical preparations - Parmed Pharmaceuticals, Inc.
KAOSET - Insulating materials - Thermal Ceramics Inc.
KAOTIC - Apparel and accessories - Biscayne Apparel International, Inc.
KAOWOOL - Insulating materials - Thermal Ceramics Inc.

KAP - Trailers–travel - Winnebago Industries, Inc.
KAP KING - Hats - MU Industries Inc.
KAP-UTS - Glass products - Bellco Glass Inc.
KAPALA - Liquors - White Rock Distilleries Inc.
KAPALUA - Furniture ☆ - Tropitone Furniture Co. Inc.
KAPALUA - Musical instrument accessories - E. & O. Mari Inc.
KAPCO - Adhesive laminated sheet - Kent Adhesive Products Co.
KAPECTOLIN - Pharmaceutical preparations - Barre-National, Inc.
KAPER RECORDS - Recording label - New Sound Records, Inc.
KAPERS - Shoes - Kinney Shoe Corp.
KAPIGAM - Pharmaceutical preparations ☆ - Solvay Pharmaceuticals Inc.
KAPITALIZATION - Computer software - SourceView Software International
KAPKITZ - Buttons - High Intencity Corp.
KAPLAN - Musical instrument accessories ☆ - J. D'Addario & Co. Inc.
KAPLAN - Postcards - Fotofolio Inc.
KAPLAN KOLORS - Artists' materials - Kaplan's School Supply Inc.
KAPOW - Novelty items - Roger Gordon Phillips
KAPPA ALPHA THETA - Hobby kits - Kappa Alpha Theta Fraternity Inc.
KAPPADIONE - Pharmaceutical preparations ☆ - Eli Lilly and Co.
KAPS - Apparel and accessories - Richton International Corp.
KAPSULKOTE - Paints ☆ - Hampton Paint Manufacturing Co.
KAPTAIN KIWI'S - Juices - Wagner Excello Foods Inc.
KAPTCLEAN - Bottles–glass - All-Pak, Inc.
KAPTOGGLE - Hardware - ESC Industries
KAPU - Coffee - Endo Endo and II da Partnership
KAPU GLOBAL SURF GEAR - Luggage - Thomas A. Deem
KAPUT! - Pet products - Novalek, Inc.
KAR - Photographic equipment - Eastman Kodak Co.
KAR-BO AEROBIC KICKBOXING - Athletic associations - JKD Development, Inc.
KAR GRABBER - Automotive parts and accessories - Grabber Manufacturing Co.
KAR KADDY - Cigarette holders - Molor Products Co.
KAR KAPS - Automotive parts and accessories - Sterling Products Co. Inc.
KAR-KOTE - Motor vehicle parts and accessories ☆ - Coastal Industries Inc.
KAR KWIPS - Dentifrices - Surco Products Inc.
KAR 'N HOME - Coffee makers–electric - Metal Ware Corp.
KAR-OBICS - Apparel and accessories - Kar-Obics Fitness Partners
KAR-RITE - Automotive parts and accessories - Manlee Industries Inc.
KAR RITE - Car-top carriers - American Sports Inc.
KAR SAFE - Automotive parts and accessories - Molor Products Co.
KAR-SCENT - Deodorizers - Sterling Co.
KAR-VIC - Watch movement - Leon Blechman
KARA - Bathtubs–enameled - Briggs Plumbing Products, Inc.
KARA - Toys–stuffed - Russ Berrie and Co., Inc.
KARA DYNASTY - Floor coverings–carpet and rugs - Karastan-Bigelow Inc.
KARA KORAM - Footwear - Eddie Bauer Inc.
KARA KUM - Floor coverings–carpet and rugs - Masland Corp.
KARA MAR - Floor coverings–carpet and rugs - Karastan-Bigelow Inc.
KARA SHAH - Floor coverings–carpet and rugs - Karastan-Bigelow Inc.
KARA-SOFTSPUN - Apparel–women's ☆ - Jubilee Knitwear Co.
KARA-SQUARES - Floor coverings–carpet and rugs ☆ - Karastan-Bigelow Inc.
KARAAT - Floor coverings–carpet and rugs - V & B Carpet
KARABLUE - Plywood ☆ - Harbor Sales Co.
KARADSHEH'S SPICE BAZAAR - Spices and extracts - Karadsheh's Spice Bazaar, Inc.
KARAKAL - Rackets–badminton ☆ - Rackets International (Racket Sports Div.)
KARAMALZ - Beverages–malt - Kreiner Imports
KARAMAN - Floor coverings–carpet and rugs - Couristan Inc.
KARAMEIKOS - Games - Tsr, Inc.
KARAOKE CLASSIC - Audio equipment - Kent Television Marketing Inc.
KARAPOINT - Floor coverings–carpet and rugs ☆ - Karastan-Bigelow Inc.
KARA'S KLOSET - Underwear and nightwear - J.C. Penney Co., Inc.
KARASTAN - Floor coverings–carpet and rugs - Karastan-Bigelow Inc.
KARAT - Crayons - Staedtler, Inc.
KARAT - Drill bits ☆ - Hawera Inc.
KARAT CROWN - Lighters - Colibri Inc.
KARAT PATCH, THE - Novelty items - S.J. Miller Co.
KARATBOND - Jewelry - Sun Fashion Designs Inc.
KARATCHROME - Automotive parts and accessories - Quest Industries, Inc.
KARATCLAD - Jewelry - Enthone-OMI
KARATE ANGELS - Paper products - Alexander Delgado Productions
KARATE BEAR - Toys–stuffed - Dakin Inc.
KARATE DEFENDERS, THE - Toys ☆ - Imperial Toy Corp.

☆ = Now out of production

KARATE FIGHTERS - Games - Hasbro, Inc.
KARATE POPS - Candy ☆ - ATGT, Inc.
KARATE POPS - Confections - Andrew Marcos
KARATEKA - Computer software ☆ - Broderbund Software, Inc.
KARATEN - Medical apparatus - Uni-Patch
KARATGOLD - Automotive parts and accessories - Quest Industries, Inc.
KARATHANE - Fungicides - Rohm and Haas Co.
KARATTI - Toys - Mattel, Inc.
KARAYA - Skin care products ☆ - Sween Corp.
KARAYA GUM - Health care products - Geritrex Corp.
KARBA - Electronic equipment - Leica USA Inc.
KARBAR - Automotive parts and accessories - Automatic Equipment Manufacturing Co.
KARBO-SILEKON - Health care products ☆ - Blistex Inc.
KARBONITE - Fertilizers - Howard Fertilizer Co., Inc.
KARBOUT - Cleaning preparations - Shaler Co.
KARCHECK - Automotive parts and accessories - Mitech
KARCHECK XR - Automotive parts and accessories - Mitech
KARD KARRIER - Envelopes - Tension Envelope Corp.
KARD KARRIER - Pet products - Aaronco Grooming Products
KARD KEEPER - Billing machines - Angler's Roslyn Group Ltd.
KARD KITS - Greeting cards - Peabody's-Toys that Teach Inc.
KARD-VEYER - File folders - Kardex Systems, Inc.
KARDEX - File folders - Kardex Systems, Inc.
KARDEX - Wallets - Kleer-Vu Plastics Inc.
KARDIA - Statuary - Kardia
KARDS FOR KIDS - Learning activity cards - Creative Learning Products Inc.
KARDVELOPE - Envelopes - Tension Envelope Corp.
KARE - Health care products - National Tea Co.
KARE - Recording label - Summit Enterprises
KARE-FUL-PAK - Fruits and vegetables ☆ - Prentice Packing & Storage Co.
KARE KIT - Ophthalmic goods ☆ - Alcon Laboratories, Inc.
KAREEM - Apparel and accessories - Ain Jeem, Inc.
KAREEM ABDUL-JABBAR - Socks - Moretz Hosiery Mills Inc.
KAREEM'S CHOICE - Socks - Ain Jeem, Inc.
KAREEM'S SPORT - Shirts - Ain Jeem, Inc.
KAREL I - Cigars - Gesty Trading & Manufacturing Corp.
KARELIA - Cigarettes - G.A. Georgopulo & Co. Inc.
KARELIA FILTRO - Cigarettes - G.A. Georgopulo & Co. Inc.
KAREN - Slippers - Daniel Green Co.
KAREN - Trays ☆ - Eagle Glass Products
KAREN - Watches - Bulova Corp.
KAREN ALEXANDER - Apparel–women's - Shady Grove Inc.
KAREN ALEXANDER CALIFORNIA - Apparel–women's - Shady Grove Inc.
KAREN & CO. - Apparel–women's - Catherines of California, Inc.
KAREN GREEN - Apparel–women's - Karen Green, Ltd.
KAREN KANE COLLECTION - Apparel and accessories - Karen Kane, Inc.
KAREN LUCAS COLLECTION - Apparel - Positive Attitude, Inc.
KAREN SAWYER - Handbags - Kadin Brothers Inc.
KAREN SCOTT - Apparel–women's - May Department Stores Co.
KAREN'S - Food products - Sauces & Salsas, Ltd.
KAREN'S CLIP KIDS - Computer software - Karen's Kids
KAREN'S FABULOUS - Cookies - Biscotti & Co., Inc.
KAREN'S KRINGLE - Bakery products - Scandinavian Descent Inc.
KARESSA - Brushes–hair - The Montclair Co.
KARESSAH - Underwear and nightwear - Henson-Kickernick Inc.
KARESSE - Toys - Tonka Corp.
KARG - Cakes ☆ - National Tea Co.
KARGES - Furniture - Karges Furniture Co. Inc.
KARGES BY HAND - Apparel–women's - Karges Furniture Co. Inc.
KARI-ALL BAG - Bags - Lefkowitz and Santangelo Co.
KARI-CHAIR - High chairs - Holst Inc.
KARI-OUT - Wines - Perk-Up, Inc.
KARI-RINSE - Pharmaceutical preparations ☆ - Lorvic Corp.
KARIBO - Apparel and accessories - Wal-Mart Stores Inc.
KARIDIUM - Vitamins and nutritional supplements - Lorvic Corp.
KARIGEL - Dental compounds - Lorvic Corp.
KARIGEL-N - Dental compounds - Lorvic Corp.
KARIM - Skin care products ☆ - T.N. Dickinson Co.
KARIN - Glassware–household - Dansk International Designs, Ltd.
KARIN MODELS - Advertising agencies - Models Management Group, Inc.
KARINA - Typewriters - Unlimited Export Services Corp.
KARINA HAIR ACCESSORIES - Hair care products - Karina Inc.
KARINA MIRRORS - Mirrors - Karina Inc.
KARINA SOLINGEN - Hair care products - Karina Inc.
KARIN'S IN THE KITCHEN - Bakery products - BKB Bakings, Inc.

KARISE - Glassware–household - Dansk International Designs, Ltd.
KARISMA - Flowers–artificial - Magicsilk
KARISMA - Yarn - National Spinning Co., Inc.
KARITE - Hair care products - Rene Furterer
KARITE SHEA - Soap - Orjene Natural Cosmetics
KARITH - Cleaning preparations - Rukin Industries Inc.
KARKAP - Automotive parts and accessories - Kashino Enterprises, Inc.
KARKOV - Liquors - United States Distilled Products Co.
KARKOV ROYAL - Vodka - United States Distilled Products Co.
KARL BANG - Attache cases - Chantelle Publishing Co.
KARL BANG - Novelty items–paper - University Products, Inc. (Chantelle Publishing Co.)
KARL BECK - Violins - Pacific Music Supply Co.
KARL BERNARD - Violins - Deltex Music Corp.
KARL FUHRMANN - Figurines - Estus Export-Import
KARL HAUSER - Guitars - Ideal Musical Merchandise Co.
KARL HOFNER - Musical instruments - Entertainment Music Marketing Corp.
KARL-JOSEPH SCHNEIDER - Musical instruments - Shar Products, Inc.
KARL KNILLING - Musical instruments - St. Louis Music Supply Co.
KARL LAGERFELD - Footwear–women's - Charles Jourdan
KARL LAGERFELD - Scarves - Jerry Kohn Inc.
KARL MANHEIM - Wines ☆ - Safeway Stores Inc.
KARL SHUMAN BAND, THE - Recording label - Karl Shuman
KARL STRAUSS - Beverages–malt - Associated Microbreweries, Ltd.
KARL VON STETTON - Whiskey - M.S. Walker Inc./Seacoast
KARL WUNDERLICH - Musical instruments - Hershman Musical Instrument
KARL ZIESS - Musical instruments - Dekalb Musicians Supply Co. Inc.
KARLA COLLETTO - Apparel–women's - Karla Colletto Swimwear, Inc.
KARLA REID - Apparel–men's - Rafael R. Pichardo Cruz
KARLI - Tubes–copper ☆ - Helenor Industries
KARLINA - Glassware–household - Arrow International, Inc.
KARLINK, INC. - Computer software - Karlink, Inc.
KARLO - Office furniture–plastic - Karl Manufacturing Co.
KARLOF - Beverages–alcohol - Consolidated Distilled Products Inc.
KARLOVY VARYBATH - Health care products - Norimoor Co.
KARLSBAD KAFFEE MACHINE - Coffee makers–electric - Westerlo House Inc. of Albany
KARLSBRAU - Water–mineral ☆ - HDT Importers Inc.
KARLSKRONA - China cabinets–wood - Swedish Products Inc. (Sojo Inc.)
KARLY - Wines - Karly Wines
KARLY KOALA - Puppets - Dakin Inc.
KARMA - Beverages - Juba Beverages Corp.
KARMA - Cosmetics and hair-care productss - Karma Cosmetics
KARMA - Floor coverings–carpet and rugs - Roxbury Carpet Co.
KARMA - Furniture - Corry Hiebert
KARMA - Rings–jewelry - Artcarved Inc.
KARMA KUBES - Novelty items - Karmatorium, Inc.
KARMA SUTRA - Vitamins and nutritional supplements - Natural Energy, Inc.
KARMANN GHIA - Motor vehicles–automobiles ☆ - Volkswagen of America Inc.
KARMEX - Herbicides - E.I. Dupont de Nemours and Co.
KARMIC STUFF - Calendars - Patricia T. Windom
KARM'L DAPPLE - Confections - California Snack Foods, Inc.
KAR'N - Jewelry–precious - Karen Heilman
KARNOVITA - Health care products - D'Franssia Corp.
KARNTNERLAND - Accordions - Castiglione Accordion
KARNUVAL - Footwear ☆ - Conjac Inc.
KARO - Syrup - CPC International Inc.
KAROBICS - Video production - Karobics Fitness Partners
KAROLTON - Envelopes ☆ - Kimberly-Clark Corp. (Karolton Envelope Div.)
KARONA - Building materials - Karona Inc.
KAROOS - Boots - Karoos Inc.
KAROUN DAIRIES - Dairy products - Karoun Dairies Inc.
KAROUSEL - Stereos - Kopykake
KARP - Publisher's imprints - Willis Music Co.
KARPEN - Furniture - Schnadig Corp.
KARPETFLEX - Paper–coated - Permalin Products Co.
KARPETREET II - Cleaning preparations–carpet and rug ☆ - Hako Minuteman Inc.
KARPEX - Cleaning preparations–carpet and rug - Harley Chemicals
KARPOWER - Computer software - Kelley Blue Book
KARRAN - Sinks–metal - VMR Inc.
KARRIE - Trays ☆ - Eagle Glass Products
KARRIO - Toys ☆ - Mego Financial Corp.
KARRITE - Motor vehicle parts and accessories - Kar-Rite LP
KARRITIUM - Metals - Boston Headjoint Co.

☆ = Now out of production

KARRO - Audio tapes–blank - Caribbean Export Appliances, Inc.
KARRY KOOL - Furniture - Wellington Home Products (Plastic Woven Products Div.)
KARRY PACK - Paperboard - Salwen Paper Co. Inc.
KAR'S - Food products - Kar Nut Products Co.
KART - Engines ☆ - McCulloch Corp.
KART-A-BAG - Carts - Remin Laboratories, Inc. (Kart-a-Bag Div.)
KART WHEELS - Motor vehicles - Carter Brothers Manufacturing Co., Inc.
KARTA SEAT - Infant product ☆ - Welsh Co.
KARTKADDY - Ice chests–plastic - Barkart Corp.
KARTKADDY MINIBAR SYSTEM - Ice chests - Barkart Corp.
KARTMASTER - Carts - Remin Laboratories, Inc. (Kart-a-Bag Div.)
KARTOTE - Dollies–industrial - Automatic Equipment Manufacturing Co.
KARTU - Carrying bags - Gayle Martz, Inc.
KARY-KART - Carts - American Locker Security Systems
KARYOMAX - Chemical preparations - Life Technologies, Inc.
KAS - Potato chips - Borden, Inc.
KAS-ETTE - Electronic equipment - SRW Computer Components, Inc.
KAS-KEL - Wiring devices - Kas-Kel Electric Co. Inc.
KAS-KORD - Wiring devices - Kas-Kel Electric Co. Inc.
KASBAH - Floor coverings–carpet and rugs ☆ - Mohawk Industries Inc.
KASCO - Pet food - Pet Products Plus
KASE:SET - Computer software - Kase Systems, Inc.
KASE:VIP - Computer software - Kase Systems, Inc.
KASEN - Dinnerware–glass ☆ - Peter Pan Industries
KASEREI CHAMPIGNON DELLA MONTE - Cheese - Champignon N.A.
KASET - Recording label - Kaset, Inc. (Times Mirror Division)
KASEWORKS - Computer software - Kaseworks, Inc.
KASH KLIP - Giftware - H.C. Meyers Co.
KASHI - Floor coverings–carpet and rugs ☆ - Trans-Ocean Import Co. Inc.
KASHI - Food products - Kashi Co.
KASHI - Wallpaper - Koroseal Wallcoverings
KASHI BRITTLES - Food products ☆ - Kashi Co.
KASHI GOOD FRIENDS - Cereal - Kashi Co.
KASHI MEDLEY - Cereal - Kashi Co.
KASHIAN - Cymbals - Atlas Accordions Inc.
KASHIMAR - Floor coverings–carpet and rugs - Couristan Inc.
KASHIR - Floor coverings–carpet and rugs ☆ - Hollytex Carpet Mills Inc.
KASHKAVAL - Cheese - Tatra Sheep Cheese Co.
KASHMAR - Floor coverings–carpet and rugs - Milliken & Co. Inc.
KASHMIR - Floor coverings–carpet and rugs ☆ - Capel, Inc.
KASHMIR - Food products - Commissariat Imports, Inc.
KASHMIR - Furniture ☆ - Lane Co. Inc.
KASHMIR - Paper–coated - Simpson Plainwell Paper Co.
KASHMIR - Wallpaper - Capital Carousel Inc.
KASHMIR - Yarn ☆ - Tahki Imports Ltd.
KASHMIR COLLECTION - Wallpaper - Dekortex Inc.
KASHMIRI MARINADE - Sauces - Cinnabar Specialty Foods, Inc./Neera's Products
KASHO - Hair care products ☆ - Designer's Edge International
KASIA CRE-A-TURES - Giftware - Faroy Sales
KASILOF FISH CO. - Seafood - Kasilof Fish Co.
KASIMIR - Dolls - Mattel, Inc.
KASKEY'S - Soups–canned - Moran Group Inc.
KASKIA - Cabinets - White Consolidated Industries, Inc.
KASMIR - Draperies - Kasmir Fabrics
KASOCO - Food products - Hillshire Farm Co.
KASOF - Laxatives - McNeil Pharmaceuticals
KASPELO - Health care products ☆ - D'Franssia Corp.
KASPER - Apparel–women's - Leslie Fay Companies Inc.
KASPER A.S.L. - Suits–women's - Leslie Fay Companies Inc.
KASPER COAT - Apparel–women's - New England Mackintosh Co. Inc.
KASPIA SYSTEMS - Computer software - Kaspia Systems, Inc.
KASPIAN - Floor coverings–carpet and rugs ☆ - Trans-Ocean Import Co. Inc.
KASPIANA - Caviar - Gourmand Inc.
KASS & CO. - Apparel–women's - Pants 'R Us
KASS U.S.A. - Giftware - Kass China Co.
KASSER 51 - Beverages–alcohol - Kasser Laird Distilling Co.
KASSIE - Computer peripheral equipment - Farmstead Telephone Group, Inc.
KASSON & KELLER - Construction equipment - Federal Aluminum Products
KAST-A-WAY - Fishing lures - South Bend Sporting Goods Inc.
KASTAR - Tools–hand-operated - Kastar Inc.
KASTELET - Wines - Stanley Stawski Distributing Co.
KASTERKAT - Wheels - Standex International Corp.
KASTIN - Candy - Leader Candies Inc.
KASTINGER - Boots ☆ - Climb High Inc.

KASTMASTER - Sporting goods - Acme Tackle Co.
KASTO - Coats–women's - Christine W. Kolisch
KASUAL - Tablecloths - Cascade Fibers Co.
KASUAL KIXS - Shoes - Garfield & Rosen Inc.
KASUALAIRE - Stools–metal - Ever-Ready Appliance Manufacturing Co.
KASUGA - Dinnerware–glass ☆ - Sango Co. Ltd. (Sango USA Div.)
KASUGAI - Mushrooms - Excel Mass Merchandiser, Inc.
KASUGAI JAPANESE - Candy - JFC International, Inc.
KASUGAMI - Artists' materials - Andrews/Nelson/Whitehead
KASUMI - Bedding–linen - Dan River Inc.
KASUMI - Hair care products - Fromm Industries
KASWELL'S - Flooring–hardwood - Kaswell & Co., Inc.
KASWELL'S WOOD BLOCK - Floor coverings - Norman Kaswell
KASZELEX - Cough drops - Polam Wholesale Inc.
KAT - Lumber - Continental Wood Preservers Inc.
KAT A ROOS - Pet products - Jennifer B. Johnson
KAT-BOX KING - Pet products - Kat-Box King, Inc.
KAT BOX STEP ONE - Pet products - Alfa-Pet Inc.
KAT KARE - Cat food - Blue Seal Feeds Inc.
KAT KNOT - Pet products - Dura Pro Products
KAT KOLLEGE - Apparel–children's ☆ - Kellwood Co.
KAT KOT - Pet products ☆ - Booda Products, Inc.
KAT KRAWLER - Pet products - Dura Pro Products
KAT KRUNCHIES - Cat food - Blue Seal Feeds Inc.
KAT PAK - Pet products - Petmaster, Inc.
KAT TALES - Greeting cards ☆ - Amberley Greeting Card Co.
KAT TRACKS - Pet products - Educational Insights, Inc.
KATA - Video production ☆ - Nalpak Video Sales, Inc.
KATAHDIN - Beverages–malt - Casco Bay Brewing Co.
KATAHDIN - Boats–canoes - Old Town Canoe Co.
KATAHDIN - Cheese - State of Maine Cheese
KATAHDIN - Tires–bicycles - Schwinn Cycling & Fitness Inc.
KATAHDIN HEAT'N HONEY - Mustard - C.V. Finer Foods Inc.
KATAHDIN TRAIL - Shoes - Thomas M. Kennedy Co.
KATALOR - Finishing agents - Wampler Chemical Corp.
KATAMA - Powerboat ☆ - Boston Whaler, Inc.
KATANI BORA SISAL - Floor coverings - Merida Meridian, Inc.
KATAREX - Cold remedies - Polam Wholesale Inc.
KATARINA WITT BY DANSKIN - Apparel and accessories - Danskin, Inc.
KATCHKEY - Tools - Diamond Machining Technology Inc.
KATE ALLEN - Apparel–women's - Leslie Fay Companies Inc.
KATE COVINGTON - Apparel–women's - Evan-Picone Inc.
KATE GLEESON'S LITTLE BEASTIES - Publisher's imprints - Kate Gleeson
KATE GREENAWAY - Dolls - Bradley Import Co.
KATE GREENAWAY - Dresses–girls' - Micronaut Industries Inc.
KATE GREENAWAY - Posters - One-of-a-Kind Workshop
KATE GREENAWAY - Tiles ☆ - Bernard W. Bernthal Inc.
KATE MCNAUGHTON - Suits–women's - Norton Mcnaughton of Squire, Inc.
KATEK - Computer diskettes–blank - Triple-K Technology, Inc.
KATELIN - Fabrics - Atlantic Mills, Inc.
KATERINA ANASTASIA - Toys - Tonka Corp.
KATES - Easels - Sam Flax
KATE'S SOUTHERN CUISINE - Relishes - Kate's Southern Cuisine Co.
KATFISH PICKINS - Cat food - Ralston Purina Co.
KATGO - Pet products - National Display Materials
KATHARINE BEECHER - Candy - Pennsylvania Dutch Candies
KATHE KRUSE - Toys–stuffed - Fagan International
KATHERINE - Dolls ☆ - Effanbee Doll Corp.
KATHERINE K. - Jewelry - Rams Fashions, Ltd.
KATHERINE K - Underwear and nightwear ☆ - Kellogg Industries Inc.
KATHERINE MARIE - Apparel–women's - Norton Mcnaughton of Squire, Inc.
KATHERINE'S - Candy - Great Expectations Confections
KATHERINE'S NATURAL SPRING WATER - Water–bottled or canned - CP (USA), Inc.
KATHIE LEE - Apparel and accessories - Kellwood Co.
KATHIE LEE - Apparel–women's - Kathie Lee Gifford
KATHLEEN - Earthenware ☆ - Waterford Wedgewood USA, Inc.
KATHLEEN - Floor coverings–carpet and rugs ☆ - Regal Rugs Inc.
KATHLEEN - Watches - Bulova Corp.
KATHLEEN CANTIN - Posters - Kathleen Cantin Etchings
KATHLEEN FOR SWEET HERB - Shawls - Sweet Herb
KATHMANDU - Pet jewelry - Michelle International Ltd.
KATHMANDU - Wallpaper - Fairwinds Studio
KATHRYN CONOVER - Apparel–women's - Kathryn Conover
KATHRYN KENNEDY - Wines - Kathryn Kennedy Winery
KATHRYN KLEINMAN - Notebooks and notepads ☆ - Lake Mills Studios

☆ = Now out of production

KATHY - Chocolate candy ☆ - Dae Julie, Inc.
KATHY - Footwear - Kisco International Corp.
KATHY ANN - Key rings - C.M. Paula Co.
KATHY DALLAS - Skin care products - Kathy Dallas Cosmetic Corp.
KATHY IRELAND - Apparel—women's - Kathy Ireland Inc.
KATHY IRELAND - Watches - Fada Industries Inc.
KATHY IRELAND ACTIVE - Apparel—women's - Kmart Corp.
KATHY SMITH - Audio tapes—blank - Kathy Smith Enterprises, Inc.
KATHY SMITH - Footwear - S. Goldberg and Co. Inc.
KATHY SMITH'S WALK FITT - Recording label - Kathy Smith Enterprises, Inc.
KATHY'S - Food products - Kathy's Cakes
KATHY'S K-9'S - Figurines - Brennan Studio Inc.
KATIA - Furniture - Haworth, Inc.
KATIA'S CATS - Dishes—china ☆ - WMF/USA
KATIE - Floor coverings—carpet and rugs ☆ - Regal Rugs Inc.
KATIE CATERPILLAR - Dolls - Mattel, Inc.
KATIE'S - Food products ☆ - Mrs. Powell's Gourmet Pecans
KATIE'S GARDEN - Salads—prepackaged - Missa Bay Citrus Co., Inc.
KATIE'S KOOKIES - Cookies - Katie's Kookies Inc.
KATIJA - Housewares - Royal Cathay Trading Co.
KATIMEX - Hand tools - Katimex, USA
KATIN - Bathing suits - K2 Inc.
KATITI - Children's apparel - La Petite Fleur Inc.
KATJES - Candy - Holland-American Importing Co. Inc.
KATKIT - Pet products - Oil-Dri Corp. of America
KATLAN - Electronic equipment - Amcor Group Ltd.
KATLAN 11 - Electronic equipment ☆ - Amcor Group Ltd.
KATMANDU - Floor coverings—carpet and rugs ☆ - Regal Rugs Inc.
KATNIP KANDY - Pet products - R.A.F. Trading Inc.
KATOUFS - Greeting cards - Kreative Kharacter Kreations Inc.
KATRICINI - Thread - TexCom Inc.
KATRINA - Furniture ☆ - Telescope Casual Furniture Inc.
KATRINA - Toys - Eugene Doll & Novelty Co. Inc.
KATRINA BALLERINA - Toys—stuffed ☆ - Dakin Inc.
KATRINA'S WORLD - Wallpaper ☆ - Tattersalls
KATS - Slippers - Okawa Trading
KATS DELIGHT - Pet products - Kmart Properties, Inc.
KATSU - Vitamins and nutritional supplements - Kenshin Trading
KATSURA - Floor coverings—carpet and rugs ☆ - Karastan-Bigelow Inc.
KATT - Electrical testing instruments - Mod-Tap W Corp.
KATTIE - Bedding—linen - Dan River Inc.
KATTS - Computer software - Telemedia Inc.
KATUN - Photocopy machines - Katun Corp.
KATY - Toys—stuffed ☆ - Gund, Inc.
KATY-BAR-THE-DOOR - Locks—door - Fulton Corp.
KATY DID'S - Dolls - Overly-Raker
KATY KITCHEN - Food products - Bruce Foods Corp.
KATY KITTEN - Toys—stuffed - Dakin Inc.
KATY LINENS - Bedding—linen - Mouchet Corp.
KATY-TEXAS EXCESSORIES USA - Luggage - John Paul Pearson
KATYBETH - Greeting cards - Hallmark Cards Inc.
KATYDID - Toys—models - Cox Products Inc.
KATYDID DESIGNS FANCY FLORALS - Frames—picture - Marie C. Bouman
KATZ - Underwear and nightwear - Dallco Industries Inc. (Katz Div.)
KATZ-N-FLOCKEN - Cat food - Solid Gold Holistic Animal/Equine Nutrition Center
KATZENBACH & WARREN KIDS III - Wallpaper - Imperial Wallcoverings, Inc.
KATZENBACH CLASSICS/REBOOK - Wallpaper ☆ - Imperial Wallcoverings, Inc.
KATZENBACH KIDS - Wallpaper ☆ - Imperial Wallcoverings, Inc.
KAUAI - Hammocks - E-Z Sales & Manufacturing, Inc.
KAUAI - Water—bottled or canned - Aqua Vie Beverage Corp.
KAUAI GARDEN - Soap - Softsoap Enterprises, Inc.
KAUFMAN - Boats - Marine Metals Inc.
KAUFMAN - Boots - Kaufman Footwear
KAUFMAN'S - Uniforms—academic ☆ - Superior Surgical Manufacturing Co. Inc.
KAUGHT LOOKING - Apparel and accessories - Hit Man Baseball, LLC
KAUKAUNA - Cheese - Kaukauna Cheese
KAUMA - Skin care products ☆ - Stiefel Laboratories, Inc.
KAUNIS - Bedding—linen - Dan River Inc.
KAUPP - Recording label - Kaupp Records
KAUTZ IRONSTONE VINEYARDS KAUTZ LIBRARYCOLLECTION - Wines - Kautz Vineyards, Inc.
KAV - Electronic equipment - Ken-A-Vision Manufacturing Co. Inc.
KAVA - Coffee - Borden, Inc.

KAVA KAVA - Health care products - East Earth Herb Inc.
KAVA KAVA EXTRACT - Vitamins and nutritional supplements - Vitamin Research Products Inc.
KAVA QUIL - Vitamins and nutritional supplements - Great Earth International, Inc.
KAVA-SOLV - Vitamins and nutritional supplements - Tishcon Corp.
KAVALARIAN - Chemical preparations - American Ingredients, Inc.
KAVATROL - Herbal products - Natrol, Inc.
KAVION'S - Leather and sheep-lined clothing - Susan G. Armstrong
KAVLI - Food products - Dairy Fresh Products Co.
KAVLOK - Veterinary medical equipment - Jenrik Marketing Group Inc.
KAVRIN - Pharmaceutical preparations ☆ - Hyrex Pharmaceuticals
KAWAI - Musical instruments - Kawai America Corp.
KAWARE - Computer software - Knowledge Access International, Inc.
KAWASAKI - Motor vehicles - Kawasaki Motors Corp. USA
KAWNEER - Hardware - Blaine Window Hardware Inc.
KAX - Chemical preparations - Environmental Technologies Alternatives, Inc.
KAY - Cleaning preparations - Ecolab Inc.
KAY - Musical instruments - Kay Guitar Co.
KAY - Musical instruments - Santa Rosa Folk Guitar Co.
KAY - Photographic equipment ☆ - Edixa Camera Co.
KAY - Recording label - Stark Records & Tape Co.
KAY - Splints - Sammons Preston
KAY-B-PLEX - Health care products - Kay Pharmacal Co. Inc.
KAY-BEE - Seafood products—canned or cured - Florida Chip Steak Co. Inc.
KAY CIEL - Pharmaceutical preparations - Forest Pharmaceuticals Inc.
KAY DEE KAY - Underwear and nightwear ☆ - Kaydette Manufacturing
KAY DEE OF HOLLYWOOD - Cosmetic applicators - Victoria Vogue, Inc.
KAY-KOB - Pet products - Kaytee Products Inc.
KAY LAYNE - Apparel—women's - Specialty Department Stores, Inc.
KAY NYNE CLOTHES COLLECTION - Pet products - Bobcat Sportswear Manufacturing Inc.
KAY NYNE THREADS - Pet products - Bobcat Sportswear Manufacturing Inc.
KAY PARK - Grills, tables - Austin Athletic Equipment Corp.
KAY-POTE - Potassium compounds ☆ - Vitarine Pharmaceuticals Inc.
KAY-TITE - Waterproofing compounds - Kay-Tite Co.
KAY-TOWNES - Antennas ☆ - Kay-Townes Inc.
KAY-VAC - Filters—water - Kaydon Corp.
KAY-VI-C - Pharmaceutical preparations ☆ - Kay Pharmacal Co. Inc.
KAY WHITNEY - Dresses—women's ☆ - Huntington Industries Inc.
KAY WINDSOR - Apparel—women's - Kay Windsor Inc.
KAYA-MITE - Boats—motor ☆ - Dolphin Boats Ltd.
KAYA NATURE'S CREATIVE ENERGY - Skin care products - Dial Corp.
KAYAK - Apparel and accessories - Kayak International Softwear, Ltd.
KAYAK - Boats - Glen-L Marine Designs
KAYAK POOLS - Pool chlorine - James S. Metz
KAYAN - Floor coverings—carpet and rugs - Milliken & Co. Inc.
KAYBIOTIC - Wesley Pharmacal Co. Inc.
KAYBOVITE - Health care products - Kay Pharmacal Co. Inc.
KAYCART - Cosmetics - Burmax Co. Inc.
KAYCEL - Washboards - Kimberly-Clark Corp.
KAYCLIPS - Hairpins - Kayline Enterprises Inc.
KAYCO - Giftware - Kilb & Co.
KAYCO THE KAY COMPANY INC. - Display cases—metal - Kay Co., Inc.
KAYCORT H.C. - Pharmaceutical preparations - Wesley Pharmacal Co. Inc.
KAYCREST - Paper—gift wrap ☆ - Papercraft Corp.
KAYDEE KAY - Apparel—women's ☆ - Lady Ester Lingerie Corp.
KAYDOE - Gloves—leather - Liz Claiborne Inc.
KAYDRY - Paper—toweling - Kimberly-Clark Corp.
KAYE - Computer software ☆ - Kaye Instruments Inc.
KAYEM - Food products - Kayem Foods, Inc.
KAYEM OLD TYME - Frankfurters - Kayem Foods, Inc.
KAYEXALATE - Pharmaceutical preparations - Sterling Winthrop Inc.
KAYFLO - Filters—water - Kaydon Corp.
KAYGO - Games - Learning Things Inc.
KAYLA - Dolls - Mattel, Inc.
KAYLA - Frames—eyeglass - U.S. Optical Frame Co.
KAYLA - Toys - Tonka Corp.
KAYLA - Whirlpools - Lasco Products Group
KAYLA'S KITTY TEES - Apparel and accessories - Kayla's Kitty Cards & Tees
KAYLINE - Cabinets - Kayline Enterprises Inc.
KAYLINE - Filters—water - Kaydon Corp.
KAYLINE - Hair care products - Spilo/Mehaz Worldwide
KAYLINE - Skin care products - Hess Hair Milk Laboratories Inc.
KAYLIXIR - Pharmaceutical preparations - Lannett Co. Inc.
KAYMAR - Wallpaper ☆ - Tannery Lane Co. Inc.

☆ = Now out of production

KAYMAX - Filters–water - Kaydon Corp.
KAYMET OF ENGLAND - Trays - Hemisphere Corp.
KAYNEE - Apparel–men's - Kaynee Co.
KAYO - Apparel and accessories - Breton Industries
KAYO - Beverages - Sara Lee Corp.
KAYO - Chocolate flavorings - Saramar Corp.
KAYO - Toys - Mattel, Inc.
KAYOT - Boats–pontoons - Harris-Kayot Inc.
KAYPECTOL - Health care products - Kay Pharmacal Co. Inc.
KAYPRO - Computers–personal - Kaypro Corp.
KAYPRO 2 - Computers–personal ☆ - Kaypro Corp.
KAYPRO 2X - Computers–personal ☆ - Kaypro Corp.
KAYPRO 10 - Computers–personal ☆ - Kaypro Corp.
KAYPRO 2020 - Computers–personal - Kaypro Corp.
KAYPRO MICRO 1 - Computers–personal - Kaypro Corp.
KAYPRO NEW 2 - Computers–personal ☆ - Kaypro Corp.
KAYPRO PC - Computers–personal - Kaypro Corp.
KAYS - Ice cream - Kay's Ice Cream
KAY'S - Mushrooms - P. Mastrippolito & Sons Inc.
KAY'S - Pharmaceutical preparations ☆ - Hays Pharmaceutical Co.
KAY'S - Salads–prepackaged - Kay's Distributing Co. Inc.
KAYSER - Beauty aids - Henry Kayser & Fils Inc.
KAYSER - Girdles - Kayser-Roth Corp.
KAYSER - Violins - Gemeinhardt Co., Inc.
KAYSINE - Health care products - Kay Pharmacal Co. Inc.
KAYSONS - Candy ☆ - Leader Candies Inc.
KAYTAR - Pharmaceutical preparations - Wesley Pharmacal Co. Inc.
KAYTRATE - Health care products ☆ - Kay Pharmacal Co. Inc.
KAYWOOD - Window coverings - Joanna Western Mills Co.
KAYWOODIE - Pipes–tobacco - S.M. Frank & Co. Inc. (Kaywoodie-Yello-Bole-Medico)
KAZ - Medical apparatus - Kaz, Inc.
KAZ - Skin care products - Spilo/Mehaz Worldwide
KAZ - Vaporizers - Kaz Business Systems Inc.
KAZ GOURMET - Hotplates - Kaz Business Systems Inc.
KAZAAM - Apparel and accessories - Interscope Communications, Inc.
KAZAMA - Sporting goods - O-U Sports Inc.
KAZAN BOOKS - Publisher's imprints ☆ - Volcano Press, Inc.
KAZARI - Thread ☆ - Cronar Ltd.
KAZBEK PAPIROSY - Cigarettes - G.A. Georgopulo & Co. Inc.
KAZI - Publisher's imprints - Kazi Publications, Inc.
KAZMAR - Fabrics - Dan River Inc.
KAZMEL - Apparel–women's - Kenar Enterprises, Ltd.
KAZOO - Fabrics - Dan River Inc.
KAZOO - Plastics - Lapin Products Inc.
KAZOO - Toys - Tonka Corp.
KAZOO - Toys–musical - David Wexler & Co.
KAZOOCO - Musical instruments - Brimms Inc.
KAZOOM - Jewelry - J.C. Penney Co., Inc.
KAZUKI - Apparel–men's - Nasett International Corp.
KAZUKO - Hair clippers–veterinary - Major International Inc.
KAZZAN - Artists' materials - Stangren Co.
K.B. - Adhesives and sealants - Laticrete International Inc.
KB - Amplifiers–musical instrument - Peavey Electronics Corp.
KB - Beverages–malt - Mission Imports Inc.
K.B. - Fishing lures ☆ - Fred Arbogast Co. Inc.
KB - Food products - Fleming Companies, Inc.
KB - Paper–writing - Kurtz Bros. Inc.
KB - Vegetables–dried - Kelley Bean Co., Inc.
KB - Vitamins and nutritional supplements - Nature's Way Products, Inc.
KB-30 - Housewares - Tel-O-Post Co.
KB-AEROTECH - Electronics equipment ☆ - Krautkramer-Branson Inc.
KB BRAND - Dried beans - KBL Trading and Processing Co.
KB CO2 DIVISION KENNETH BARNARD LTD. - Clothing - Kenneth Barnard Ltd.
K.B IDEAS 6 - Wallcovering - Fashon Wallcoverings
KB SERVER - Computer storage devices - Knowledge Based Systems, Inc.
KB-SQL - Computer software - Knowledge Based Systems, Inc.
KBC - Cleaning preparations - Roebic Laboratories Inc.
KBI - Cordage and twine - Koring Brothers Inc.
KBI - Food products - Excel Corp.
KBI-SCOTTSDALE - Golfing equipment - Bobby Grace Classic Clubs
KBJ - Jewelry - Kakesako Bros. Jewelers Inc.
KBL - Cleaning preparations - Kleen Brite Laboratories Inc.
K'BOODLES - Jewelry - Tuffet Creates
KBP FORMULA HERBAL - Vitamins and nutritional supplements - Vital Energy

KBP/O - Pharmaceutical preparations ☆ - Forest Pharmaceuticals Inc.
KB'S AMERICAN RIB COMPANY - Meat products–pork - K.B. Foods, Inc.
KC - Baking powder - KC Foods
KC - Hardware - KC Metal Products, Inc.
K.C. - Pet products - K.C. Pharmacal Inc.
KC - Trading cards and stamps - Kansas City Chiefs Football Club, Inc.
K.C. 16-1 - Shampoos - K.C. Pharmacal Inc.
KC 1000 - Cleaning preparations–household - KC Products, Inc. (Sharon D. Spence)
K.C. CAL - Vitamins and nutritional supplements - K.C. Pharmacal Inc.
KC LUNGA - Floor coverings–carpet and rugs ☆ - Regal Rugs Inc.
KC MASTERPIECE - Barbecue sauce - Clorox Co.
KC MASTERPIECE - Food products - HVR Co.
KC MASTERPIECE - Potato chips - HV Food Products Co.
K.C. MUNCHKIN - Toys–electronic ☆ - Philips Consumer Electronics Co.
K.C. PARKER - Apparel and accessories - Hartstrings, Inc.
KC R ROYALS - Apparel and accessories - Kansas City Royals Baseball Corp.
+KC +WHITNEY - Apparel and accessories - Mercantile Stores Co., Inc.
KCA - Apparel–women's ☆ - R. & M. Kaufmann
KCB-10 - Lenses–optical - X-Cel Optical Co.
KCB-12 - Lenses–optical - X-Cel Optical Co.
KCC - Galvanizeed steel - Kobe Coating Co.
KCD - Glassware–household - French Collection
KCH - Tiles–ceramic ☆ - Amsterdam Corp.
KCI - Jewelry - Kelman Casting Co., Inc.
KCI - Sporting goods - C. Itoh & Co. America Inc.
KCL - Electronic equipment - Moor Electronics Inc.
KCL-TF - Vitamins and nutritional supplements - KV Pharmaceutical Co.
KCP - Dental equipment - American Dental Laser Inc.
KCP - Recording label - Eagle Mountain International Church
KCP - Twine ☆ - King Cotton Cordage Co.
KCS - Weather stripping - Kessler Products Ltd.
KCS 3.5 - Computer software - Dr. T's Music Software Inc.
KC'S CITRUS - Degreasing solvents - KC Products, Inc. (Sharon D. Spence)
K.C.'S KRAZY CHASE - Toys–electronic ☆ - Philips Consumer Electronics Co.
KC'S SLAVE - Degreasing solvents - KC Products, Inc. (Sharon D. Spence)
KC'S SUPER FUN ADVENTURES - Frozen foods - Conagra, Inc.
KD - Apparel–athletic - Russian International Baseball
KD - Housewares - White Mountain Freezer Inc.
KD - Jewelry - Kattan Diamonds & Jewelry Inc.
K.D. - Tools–hand-operated - Danaher Tool Group
KD-4845 - Containers - Menasha Corp.
KD ORIGINALS - Greeting cards - Kimberly Dawn Winnubst
K.D. PET COLOGNE & DEODORANT - Veterinary pharmaceutical preparations - K.C. Pharmacal Inc.
KD PRODUCTS - Swimming pools - KD Products Inc.
KD200 - Projectors–photographic - Kopykake
KDA - Tires - Kelly-Springfield Tire Co.
KDD - Cosmetics ☆ - London International U.S. Holdings
K.D.S. - Health care products - Sherwood Medical Co.
KDS - Jewelry - K.D.S. Jewelry Co., Inc.
KDT - Labels–paper - Kaumagraph Co. Inc.
KE-BOR - Musical instrument accessories - G. Leblanc Corp.
KE-BRITE - Musical instrument accessories ☆ - G. Leblanc Corp.
KE-GLAZE - Musical instrument accessories ☆ - G. Leblanc Corp.
KE-LUBE - Oils–lubricating - G. Leblanc Corp.
KE-MIN - Chemical preparations - Georgia-Pacific Corp.
KE NUI - Apparel and accessories - Peter Johnson
KE:NX - Computer software - Don Johnston Inc.
KE:NX ON:BOARD - Computer software - Don Johnston Inc.
KE-SET - Locks–padlocks - Valhi Inc. National Cabinet Lock
KE-VATES - Vitamins and nutritional supplements - Alacer Co.
KE2 - Hair care products - KE2 Laboratories
KEA - Computer software - Attachmate Corp.
KEANY PRODUCE CO. - Fruit and vegetable markets - P.J.K. Food Service Corp.
KEARSARGE - Photographic equipment - American Photographic Appliance Corp.
KEATING FORMALS - Stationery - Keating Line Inc.
KEATON CHASE - Apparel and accessories - Asher Co.
KEATS PUBLISHING - Publisher's imprints - NTC Contemporary Publishing Group
KEBR - Photographic equipment - Eastman Kodak Co.
KED - Cleaning preparations - Gibson-Homans Co.
KEDDIE - Apparel–athletic - Century Sports Inc.

☆ = Now out of production

KEDDIE CREATIONS - Sporting goods ☆ - L & M Distribution Inc.
KEDEM - Wines - Kedem Royal Wine Corp.
KEDEM - Wines - Royal Wine Corp.
KEDEM MAL-OZ - Crackers - Kedem Royal Wine Corp.
KEDEM MITZ DE MUSCATO - Fruit drinks–bottled or canned - Kedem Royal Wine Corp.
KEDEM MITZBARIE - Fruit drinks–bottled or canned - Kedem Royal Wine Corp.
KEDETTES - Footwear ☆ - Stride Rite Corp.
KEDRAL - Pharmaceutical preparations ☆ - Kenyon Drug Co. Inc.
KEDS - Apparel and accessories - Signal Knitwear Co.
KEDS - Apparel–athletic - Fuqua Industries Inc.
KEDS - Footwear - Stride Rite Corp.
KEDS - Handbags - SR Holdings Inc.
KEDS - Watches - SR Holdings Inc.
KEDS & CO - Footwear - SR Holdings Inc.
KEDS COMFORT ARCH - Footwear - SR Holdings Inc.
KEDS OUTDOOR - Shoes - SR Holdings Inc.
KEE - Combs ☆ - Fromm Industries
KEE - Pipes - Kee Industrial Products Inc.
KEE-BLOK - Locks - Bolen Industries Inc.
KEE KLAMP - Pipes - Kee Industrial Products Inc.
KEE-NOA - Food products - Lewis Laboratories International Ltd.
KEE PAL - Key rings - Hill Security Products
KEE-TYPE - Electronic equipment - Kee Inc.
KEEBIES - Crackers ☆ - Keebler Co.
KEEBLER - Crackers - Keebler Co.
KEECO - Lamps - L. Kee & Co., Inc.
KEEFE KITCHENS - Food products - Crawford Group, Inc.
KEEFSAFE - Housewares - Seymour Housewares Corp.
KEEL - Golfing equipment - Joe Hernberg Industries, Inc.
KEEL - Kites ☆ - Hi-Flier Manufacturing Co.
KEEL, THE - Golfing equipment - Joe Hernberg Industries, Inc.
KEEL TRACK - Boats–canoes - Coleman Co., Inc.
KEELER - Flowers–artificial - Deli, Inc.
KEELER BAY - Apparel and accessories - Stein Mart, Inc.
KEELERS - Wines ☆ - Heublein, Inc.
KEELEY USA - Apparel and accessories - Keeley USA, Inc.
KEELEY'S - Candy ☆ - Melster Candies Inc.
KEEN - Scouring pads - Purex Industries Inc. (Kurly Kate Div.)
KEEN-ARC - Tools ☆ - Becker Bros. Carbon Corp.
KEEN-CUT - Tools ☆ - Becker Bros. Carbon Corp.
KEEN-EDGE - Paper - Rediform
KEEN KLEEN - Cleaning preparations - Repeat-O-Type Manufacturing Corp.
KEEN KUTTER - Tools - Val-Test Distributors Inc.
KEEN-POINT - Pencils - Dur-O-Lite Inc.
KEEN-RITE - Ribbons–inked ☆ - Codo Manufacturing Corp.
KEENALOY - See OLIVER BLADES
KEENE - Bedding–linen - Dan River Inc.
KEENE - Office supplies ☆ - Newell Office Products
KEENE - Windows–screen - Keene Corp. (Penn Metal Div.)
KEENE LINE - Stationery ☆ - Diagraph Corp.
KEENEDGE - Housewares - Serr-Edge Machine Co.
KEENER PACKING - Salmon–smoked, salted, dried, or pickled - Keener Packing Co. Inc.
KEENSERTS - Threaded insert - Auto Vehicle Parts Co.
KEENY/YORK - Recording label - TMA Records
KEEP - Toothpaste - Action Laboratories Inc.
KEEP-A-CLIP - Hats - Sue Ellen Deutsch Herzberg
KEEP-A-COUNT - Health care products ☆ - Trimline Medical Products Corp.
KEEP-A-FLOAT - Children's swim vests ☆ - Atlantic-Pacific
KEEP A FLOAT - Sporting goods - Kellwood Co.
KEEP-A-KOPY - Office supplies - Adams Business Forms Inc.
KEEP ALERT - Pharmaceutical preparations - Reese Chemical Co.
KEEP ALIVE - Electronic equipment - Schlumberger Technologies, Inc.
KEEP AMERICA BEAUTIFUL - Furniture ☆ - Lexington Furniture Industries, Inc.
KEEP AMERICA CLEAN - Brooms - O-Cedar/Vining Household Products Co.
KEEP AMERICA CLEAN - Cleaning preparations–household ☆ - Abkit, Inc.
KEEP AMERICA CLEAN - Vacuum cleaners and accessories - Royal Appliance Manufacturing Co.
KEEP BLUSHING - Cosmetics - Revlon Consumer Products Corp.
KEEP CLAM - Novelty items - Ivar's Inc.
KEEP CLEAR - Health care products ☆ - Avon Products, Inc.
KEEP CUPS - Cups–plastic - Akay Corp.
KEEP-DRI - Bedding–linen - Gotham Industries II

KEEP 'EM HAPPY - Apparel–children's - Kohl's Department Stores, Inc.
KEEP FIT - Apparel–women's ☆ - OTC Professional Appliances
KEEP FOREVER - Dinnerware–glass - Noritake Co. Inc.
KEEP GOING - Pharmaceuticals - Block Drug Co., Inc.
KEEP-IN-SHAPE - Underwear and nightwear ☆ - Lovable Co.
KEEP IN VIEW - Computer software - Portable Computer Support Group, Inc.
KEEP-IT - Office supplies - Esselte Corp.
KEEP-IT-CLIP - Infant product - American Baby Concepts
KEEP IT COOL - Containers - East Hampton Industries Inc.
KEEP IT COOL - Ice boxes–household - Elmar Manufacturing Co.
KEEP IT IN YOUR SNEAKER - Health care products - Gold Bond Pharmaceutical Corp.
KEEP IT SIMPLE STIRFRY - Frozen food products - Turtle Island Foods
KEEP IT UNDER WRAPZ - Bandages - Sport Wrapz, Inc.
KEEP IT UP - Apparel and accessories - Marcus K. Layton
KEEP KASES - Frames–picture - Cider Mill Art & Frame
KEEP KLEEN - Fuel additives - K & W Products
KEEP ME IN COLOR 'N CURLS - Hair coloring preparations - Helene Curtis Industries Inc.
KEEP ME POSTED - Posters - Posted Communications L.P.
KEEP MOVING GOODIES - Cigars - Swisher International, Inc.
KEEP NEAT - Hardware - Aluminum Hardgoods Inc.
KEEP OFF - Pet products - Four Paws Products Ltd.
KEEP ON MARCHING! - Novelty items–paper - Proud Enterprises
KEEP ON TRUCKING - Toys ☆ - Strombecker Corp.
KEEP PACE - Publisher's imprints - Taglines Inc.
KEEP QUIET - Games - Kopptronix Co.
KEEP/SAFE - Safes - Sentry Group
KEEP SAKE - Infant product - Chase Holding Co. Inc.
KEEP-SET - Apparel and accessories - Action Laboratories Inc.
KEEP SHINING - Lipsticks - Revlon Consumer Products Corp.
KEEP SNUG - Metals - Alway, Inc.
KEEP-STAKE - Household appliance stores - Emerson Electric Co.
KEEP THE CHANGE! - Apparel and accessories - GTI Telecom, Inc.
KEEP UP THE GOOD WORK - Notebooks and notepads - Anric Corp.
KEEP YOUR COOL - Candy - That's My Favorite Inc.
KEEP YOUR MILK FROM GETTING LONELY - Cookies - Nabisco Foods Group
KEEP YOUR OCEAN BLUE - Paper - Dive N' Surf, Inc.
KEEP YOUR PANTS ON - Games - Mattel, Inc.
KEEP YOUR PLACE - Bookmarks - Norstar Enterprises
KEEPAROOS - Computer storage devices - Alpha Enterprises, Inc.
KEEPER - Apparel and accessories - Academic Church and Choir Gowns Co., Inc.
KEEPER - Containers - World Container Corp.
KEEPER - Figurines - Shenandoah Designs International Inc.
KEEPER - Rubber–molded - Keeper Corp.
KEEPER II - Batteries - Eagle-Picher Industries Inc.
KEEPER BOTTLE - Pet products - Ginger, Inc.
KEEPER BOTTLE - Water dispensers - Princess Pet Products
KEEPER CAP - Sealing devices - Nalco Chemical Co.
KEEPER-OF-THE-GREEN - Tools–hand-operated - Golf Design USA
KEEPER PACK - Paper–gift wrap - That's A Wrap Inc.
KEEPERS - Containers - Rubbermaid Inc.
KEEPERS - Hosiery - Keepers International
KEEPERS - Magnets - Brown Sugar Designs, Inc.
KEEPER'S KIDSTUFF - Paper - Lavoie Concepts, Inc.
KEEPERS TWO - Furniture ☆ - Thomasville Furniture Industries Inc.
KEEPFUL SERVICE - Chemical preparations - Environmental Biotech, Inc.
KEEPIN' TABS - Publisher's imprints - Mead Corp.
KEEPING IT S-I-M-P-L-E - Kitchen appliances - Indian River Kitchens Inc.
KEEPING LOVE ALIVE - Compact discs–prerecorded - Michele Weiner-Davis Training Corp.
KEEPING YOU IN COLOR - Artists' materials - Dec-Art Co.
KEEPING YOU ORGANIZED - Office supplies - Smead Manufacturing Co.
KEEPS - Cleaning preparations - Willert Home Products, Inc.
KEEPS-IT-CLEAN - Mats - Akro Corp.
KEEPS IT KOOL - Containers–insulated - Bill Bauer
KEEPS YOUR WORLD CLEAN - Cleaning preparations - Sunshine Makers, Inc.
KEEPSAFE - Apparel and accessories - Tennessee Valley Authority
KEEPSAFE - Bags–storage - Manco, Inc.
KEEPSAFE DIAMOND - Fencing–wood - Keystone Steel & Wire Co.
KEEPSAKE - Bakery products - Community Bakeries
KEEPSAKE - Brushes–paint - M. Grumbacher Inc.
KEEPSAKE - Calendars - Keith Clark Inc.

KEEPSAKE - Candles - Keepsake Candles
KEEPSAKE - Candles - Lillian Rose Collection
KEEPSAKE - Clocks ☆ - General Time Corp. (Westclox/Seth Thomas Div.)
KEEPSAKE - Dinnerware–glass - Nikko Ceramics Inc.
KEEPSAKE - Dolls ☆ - Effanbee Doll Corp.
KEEPSAKE - Floor coverings–carpet and rugs - Calladium & Marglen
KEEPSAKE - Floor coverings–carpet and rugs - Galaxy Carpet Mills Inc.
KEEPSAKE - Floor coverings–carpet and rugs ☆ - Regal Rugs Inc.
KEEPSAKE - Garden furniture–rattan - Lloyd/Flanders Industries
KEEPSAKE - Greeting cards - Gibson Greetings, Inc.
KEEPSAKE - Jewelry - CJC Holdings, Inc.
KEEPSAKE - Posters - C.M. Paula Co.
KEEPSAKE - Recording label - Sound Inc.
KEEPSAKE - Rings–jewelry - Artcarved Inc.
KEEPSAKE - Shoes - Endicott Johnson Corp.
KEEPSAKE - Tablecloths - K. Katen & Co. Inc.
KEEPSAKE - Yarn - Lion Brand Yarn Co.
KEEPSAKE V - Wallpaper ☆ - Eisenhart Wallcoverings Co.
KEEPSAKE VI - Wallpaper ☆ - Eisenhart Wallcoverings Co.
KEEPSAKE A LA CARD - Greeting cards - Joyeanna Chaudiere
KEEPSAKE ASSORTMENT - Candy - Russell Stover Candies, Inc.
KEEPSAKE BEAR - Toys–stuffed ☆ - Dakin Inc.
KEEPSAKE BEAR - Toys–stuffed ☆ - Gund, Inc.
KEEPSAKE BOX, THE - Music boxes - Sentimental Journeys Inc.
KEEPSAKE CASES - Cases–plastic ☆ - Jesse Jones Box Corp.
KEEPSAKE COLLECTION - Faucets - Sterling Plumbing Group Inc.
KEEPSAKE COLLECTION - Giftware - Lenox, Inc.
KEEPSAKE COLLECTION - Giftware - Russ Berrie and Co., Inc.
KEEPSAKE COLLECTION - Toys - Mattel, Inc.
KEEPSAKE COLLECTION, THE - Boxes - Glynda Turley Prints Inc.
KEEPSAKE CRAFTS - Craft supplies - VIP/VIP Crafts
KEEPSAKE CREATIONS - Giftware ☆ - Treasure Masters
KEEPSAKE DIAMOND REPLICA - Jewelry - CJC Holdings, Inc.
KEEPSAKE DISPLAY - Window frames - North American Enclosures Inc.
KEEPSAKE KEEPER - Craft supplies - Plaid Enterprises, Inc.
KEEPSAKE LOCKET BEAR - Toys–stuffed - AGC, Inc.
KEEPSAKE LOCKET BEARS - Toys–stuffed - American Greetings Corp.
KEEPSAKE ORNAMENT - Christmas tree ornaments - Hallmark Cards Inc.
KEEPSAKE PERSONALIZED MARRIAGE RING - Jewelry - CJC Holdings, Inc.
KEEPSAKES - Furniture - Pulaski Furniture Corp.
KEEPTABS - Anchors - Securtech Co.
KEEP.TRAC - Computer software - ShopTrac Data Collection Systems Inc.
KEES - Lawn mowers ☆ - F.D. Kees Power Equipment LLC
KEES KASTER - Lawn mowers ☆ - F.D. Kees Power Equipment LLC
KEES KRAWLER - Sprinklers–lawn ☆ - F.D. Kees Power Equipment LLC
KEET:BELL - Pet products - Hill Top Enterprises
KEET KIDS - Ice pops - Kool Kokito, Inc.
KEET LIFE - Pet products - Longlife Pet Products
KEET SEED - Pet products ☆ - Silco Pet Products
KEET WAFER - Pet products - Hill Top Enterprises
KEETO - Luggage - Keeto Imports Inc.
KEF - Audio equipment - KEF Electronics of America
KEFF - Pharmaceutical preparations ☆ - Lemmon Co.
KEFIR - Yogurt culture - International Yogurt Co.
KEFKITS - Audio equipment - KEF Electronics of America
KEFLEX - Pharmaceutical preparations - Dista Products Co.
KEFLIN - Antibiotics - Eli Lilly and Co.
KEFZOL - Pharmaceutical preparations - Eli Lilly and Co.
KEG - Yarn ☆ - Caron International Inc.
KEG-A-QUE - Barbecue and grill accessories - John D. McGourthy, Jr.
KEG O' KETCHUP - Seasonings - H.J. Heinz Co.
KEG TOTAL QUALITY MANAGEMENT - Electronic equipment - Kent Electronics Corp.
KEG WRAP - Cooling systems–cryogenic - ILC Dover, Inc.
KEGEKI - Video games - Taito America Corp.
KEGETTE - Barrels–wood - Greif Bros. Corp.
KEGLE BRAU - Beverages–malt ☆ - Cold Spring Brewing Co.
KEGLER - Pencils ☆ - Dixon Ticonderoga Co.
KEGLEVICH - Beverages–alcohol - Distillerie Stock USA Ltd.
KEGS - Computer software - Michael F. Lesser
KEGS OF CURLING RIBBON - Ribbons - Berwick Industries, Inc.
K'EHLEYR - Toys - Paramount Pictures Corp.
KEI - Sporting goods - Kent Sports, Inc.
KEIJE - Cabinets - Clairson International Corp.
KEIKI - Slippers - Okawa Trading

KEIKO - Hair clippers–veterinary - Major International Inc.
KEIKO RABBIT - Puppets - Dakin Inc.
KEIL - Locks–padlocks - ILCO Unican Corp.
KEILLER'S OF SCOTLAND - Candy - Dae Julie, Inc.
KEIL'S - Food products - Keil's Food Stores
KEILWORTH - Saxophones - Orpheus Music Inc.
KEISER - Exercising equipment - Keiser Corp.
KEISHA DOLL - Dolls - Helen Johnson Steward
KEITH - Musical instrument accessories - Beacon Banjo Co. Inc.
KEITH - Recording label ☆ - Soul-Po-Tion Records
KEITH ANDERSON - Bicycles - Keith Anderson Cycles Inc.
KEITH ANTHONY COLLECTION, THE - Apparel–women's - FineField Group, Inc.
KEITH MILL - Paper ☆ - Strathmore Paper Co.
KEITH ROSCOE - Guitars - Roscoe Guitars
KEITH'S - Food products machinery - Ben E. Keith Co.
KEKAB - Cabinets–metal - H.P.C. Inc.
KEL - Waterproofing compounds - Kellogg's Professional Products Inc.
KEL-102 - Silicon products - Kellogg's Professional Products Inc.
KEL-105 - Silicon products - Kellogg's Professional Products Inc.
KEL-108 - Oils–lubricating - Kellogg's Professional Products Inc.
KEL-109 - Lubricants - Kellogg's Professional Products Inc.
KEL-110 - Silicon products - Kellogg's Professional Products Inc.
KEL-115 - Cleaning preparations - Kellogg's Professional Products Inc.
KEL-116 - Waterproofing compounds - Kellogg's Professional Products Inc.
KEL-135 - Cleaning preparations - Kellogg's Professional Products Inc.
KEL-140 - Cleaning preparations - Kellogg's Professional Products Inc.
KEL-BAN - Bandages ☆ - Kellogg's Professional Products Inc.
KEL-EEZ - Weather stripping - KEL-EEZ
KEL-EEZ - Weather stripping ☆ - Die-Gem Co., Inc.
KEL-H2O-D - Rust removers - Kellogg's Professional Products Inc.
KEL-LUB OIL - Oils–lubricating - Kellogg's Professional Products Inc.
KELA - Vitamin supplements - Lifezone
KELADON - Inks - Keladon Corp.
KELAMINS - Vitamins and nutritional supplements - Better Health Products
KELAR - Sporting goods ☆ - Gladding Braided Products Inc.
KELATION PLUS + - Vitamins and nutritional supplements - Life Plus International Inc.
KELCHNER'S - Horseradish - Wye Chemicals Inc.
KELCO - Aluminum jalousie windows ☆ - Continental Aluminum Products Co. Inc.
KELCO - Oils–lubricating - Elf Lubricants North America, Inc.
KELCO - Water purification systems - Kelco Water Engineering, Inc.
KELDAX - Padding–foam ☆ - Kaswell & Co., Inc.
KELEX - Pharmaceutical preparations - Nutrition Control Products
KELIGEN - Food products - Dowelanco
KELLER - Floor coverings–carpet and rugs - Keller Industries Inc.
KELLER - Noodles - MBC Foods
KELLER - Rocking horses - T.C. Timber/Habermaass Corp.
KELLER-GEISTER - Wines - Canandaigua Wine Co. Inc.
KELLER'S - Vinegar - Keller Food Products Co.
KELLEY - Dolls - Mattel, Inc.
KELLEY - Soups–canned - H.E. Kelley & Co. Inc.
KELLI KAYE - Dresses–women's - R. & M. Kaufmann
KELLING KERNEL FRESH - Nuts–salted, roasted, cooked, or canned - Fairmont Snacks Group Inc.
KELLIS' HOLIDAY BUNNIES - Wood products - Susan A. Stiefel
KELLNER - Food products - M.J. Kellner Co.
KELLOGG - Bird feeds - Kellogg Inc.
KELLOGG - Brushes–paint - Kellogg Brush Manufacturing Co.
KELLOGG - Girdles ☆ - Kellogg Industries Inc.
KELLOGG - Watches - Bulova Corp.
KELLOGG'S - Envelopes ☆ - Westvaco Corp.
KELLOGG'S - Pharmaceutical preparations - Smithkline Beecham Corp.
KELLOGG'S ALL-BRAN - Cereal ☆ - Kellogg Co.
KELLOGG'S APPLE CINNAMON RICE KRISPIES - Cereal ☆ - Kellogg Co.
KELLOGG'S APPLE CINNAMON SQUARES - Cereal - Kellogg Co.
KELLOGG'S APPLE JACKS - Cereal - Kellogg Co.
KELLOGG'S APPLE RAISIN CRISP - Cereal ☆ - Kellogg Co.
KELLOGG'S BLUEBERRY SQUARES - Cereal - Kellogg Co.
KELLOGG'S BRAN BUDS - Cereal - Kellogg Co.
KELLOGG'S CINNAMON MINI BUNS - Cereal ☆ - Kellogg Co.
KELLOGG'S COCOA KRISPIES - Cereal - Kellogg Co.
KELLOGG'S COLLECTION - Buttons - JHB International Inc.
KELLOGG'S COMPLETE BRAN FLAKES - Cereal - Kellogg Co.
KELLOGG'S CORN FLAKE CRUMBS - Cereal - Kellogg Co.

☆ = Now out of production

KELLOGG'S CORN FLAKES - Cereal - Kellogg Co.
KELLOGG'S FIBER PACK - Cereal ☆ - Kellogg Co.
KELLOGG'S FROSTED BRAN - Cereal ☆ - Kellogg Co.
KELLOGG'S FROSTED FLAKES - Cereal - Kellogg Co.
KELLOGG'S FROSTED KRISPIES - Cereal - Kellogg Co.
KELLOGG'S LOW FAT - Granola bars ☆ - Kellogg Co.
KELLOGG'S RAISIN BRAN - Cereal - Kellogg Co.
KELLOGG'S TEMPTATIONS - Cereal ☆ - Kellogg Co.
KELLS INNOVATIONS, INC. - Computer programming services - Kells Innovations, Inc.
KELLS KOMM - Computer software - Kells Innovations, Inc.
KELLWOOD FASHIONS - Apparel and accessories - Kellwood Co.
KELLWOOD KASUALS - Apparel and accessories ☆ - Kellwood Co.
KELLY - Bicycle parts and accessories - Kelly Bike Co.
KELLY - Dinnerware—glass - Lenox, Inc.
KELLY - Dolls - Mattel, Inc.
KELLY - Flatware - Kirk Stieff Co.
KELLY - Flowers, plants, and seeds - Jacklin Seed
KELLY - Meat products—canned - Kelly Foods Inc.
KELLY - Medical apparatus - Ortho-Kinetics, Inc.
KELLY - Potato chips - Kelly Food Products Inc.
KELLY - Shoe polish - Fiebing Co. Inc.
KELLY - Tires—automobile - Kelly-Springfield Tire Co.
KELLY - Tools - Paratech Inc.
KELLY & ELLY - Dolls - Goldberger Doll Manufacture Co.
KELLY-CRESWELL - Paint sprayers - Kelly-Creswell Co., Inc.
KELLY FARMS - Food products - Copperhead Brands, Inc.
KELLY GOLD - Flatware - Kirk Stieff Co.
KELLY-GOODWIN - Floor coverings - Pankratz Forest Industries
KELLY HAYES - Apparel—women's - Frederick Atkins, Inc.
KELLY KLOSURE - Hardware - Kelly Industries, Inc.
KELLY KRUNCH - Candy ☆ - Chris Candies Inc.
KELLY PERFECT - Tools ☆ - True Temper Hardware Co.
KELLY PLUS - Medical apparatus - Ortho-Kinetics, Inc.
KELLY RENEE - Apparel—women's - Ms. Tops of California
KELLY STEVENS - Dishes—china - Reco International Corp.
KELLY STRYKER - Apparel and accessories - Central Falls Inc.
KELLY'S - Hobby kits - Kelly's Crafts
KELLY'S COIN - Tobacco—chewing or smoking - Amar Blends Co.
KELLY'S HOME ENTERTAINMENT & APPLIANCES - Audio equipment - Ed Kelly, Inc.
KELLY'S KIDS - Staple foods ☆ - Kelly Foods Inc.
KELLYTOY - Toys—stuffed - Kellytoy (USA), Inc.
KELMAR - Paints - Master Builders Inc.
KELNEED - Pharmaceutical preparations - Hanlon Drug Products
KELO - Bedding—linen - Dan River Inc.
KELOKATR - Plastic tags - John F. Robison
KELON - Musical instruments ☆ - Selmer Co. Inc.
KELPMATE - Vitamins and nutritional supplements - Petfood Warehouse
KELSEY - Audio equipment - Dallas Music Industries Ltd.
KELSEY - Floor coverings—carpet and rugs - Tuftex Carpet Mills, Inc.
KELSEY CREEK - Wines - Konocti Winery
KELSEY LAKE - Jewelry - Diamond Co. N.L.
KELSO - Brushes—hair - Wright-Bernet
KELSTAR - Inks—lithographic - Kelstar Enterprises, Inc.
KELTGEN - Flowers, plants, and seeds - United Agriseeds Inc.
KELTHANE - Pesticides—household - Bonide Products, Inc.
KELTIE - Tableware—china - Pfaltzgraff Investment Co.
KELTY - Sporting goods - Kellwood Co.
KELVIN - Computer software - Orchid Technology
KELVIN - Pharmaceutical ☆ - IDE-Interstate Inc.
KELVINATOR - Washing machines—household - White Consolidated Industries, Inc.
KELYA - Floor coverings—carpet and rugs - Kelaty International, Inc.
KEM - Deodorizers - Coughlan Products Corp.
KEM - Paints - Sherwin-Williams Automotive Finishes Corp.
KEM - Playing cards - KEM Plastic Playing Cards Inc.
KEM OUTSIDE BARB HOOKS - Fishing lures - Kem Co.
KEM-REALITY - Computer software - Kemtec Educational Corp.
KEM SAVE-LITES - Paints ☆ - Sherwin-Williams Automotive Finishes Corp.
KEM-TEK - Chemical preparations - Chem Lab Products, Inc.
KEM-TONE - Paints - Sherwin-Williams Automotive Finishes Corp.
KEM-WOOD - Wood products - Jibco Industries Inc.
KEMACH - Food products - Greenfield Noodle & Specialty
KEMADRIN - Pharmaceutical preparations - Burroughs Wellcome Co.
KEMAL - Floor coverings—carpet and rugs ☆ - Capel, Inc.

KEMBALI - Giftware - Hillside House of Originals
KEMBLEFIELD ESTATE WINERY - Wines - Southern Cross Imports, Inc.
KEMERIE - Nuts—salted, roasted, cooked, or canned - Holland-American Importing Co. Inc.
KEMEX - Chlorine - Chem Lab Products, Inc.
KEMFIELD - Cleaning preparations - American Specialty Products Corp.
KEMI-KLEEN - Dust cloths ☆ - Veratec
KEMI OYL - Hair care products - Kemi Laboratories, Inc.
KEMI PRO-GEL-PLUS - Skin care products - Kemi Laboratories, Inc.
KEMIKO - Adhesives and sealants - Epmar Corp.
KEMIKO COL-R-TONE - Hardware stores - Epmar Corp.
KEMIN - Veterinary pharmaceutical preparations - Kemin Industries, Inc.
KEMKO - Caulking compounds - Chemco Systems, Inc.
KEMLITE - Cameras - Amglo-Kemlite
KEMLITE - Construction equipment - Kemlite Co., Inc.
KEMLITE ENVISION - Wallpaper - Kemlite Co., Inc.
KEMLITE GLASBORD - Wallpaper - Kemlite Co., Inc.
KEMLITE SANIGRID - Tiles—ceiling - Kemlite Co., Inc.
KEMLUX - Lighting fixtures - Hubbell Lighting, Inc. (Lighting Div.)
KEMP - Furniture ☆ - Masco Corp.
KEMP - Furniture ☆ - Universal Flooring
KEMP - Nuts—salted, roasted, cooked, or canned ☆ - Germack Pistachio Co.
KEMPCO - Ships—patrol boats - T.F. Twardzik
KEMPER - Apparel stores—sports - Sun Ice USA
KEMPER - Artists' materials - Creek-Turn Inc. (Ceramic Supply Div.)
KEMPER - Cabinets - White Consolidated Industries, Inc.
KEMPER MAPLE RIDGE - Cabinets—wood ☆ - Kemper
KEMPER TOOLS - Tools - Kemper Enterprises, Inc.
KEMPF - Computers - Kempf
KEMPF'S DONUT BANK BAKERY & COFFEE SHOP - Doughnuts - Donut Bank Inc.
KEMPLY - Plywood - Kemlite Co., Inc.
KEMPS - Ice cream - Marigold Foods Inc.
KEMP'S - Seafood products—canned or cured - A. Kemp Fisheries Inc.
KEMP'S ALL AMERICAN - Ice cream - Marigold Foods Inc.
KEMPS COFFEE RIGHT - Cream - Marigold Foods Inc.
KEMPS GIRL SCOUT COOKIE ICE CREAM - Ice cream - Marigold Foods Inc.
KEMPS JR. - Yogurt - Marigold Foods Inc.
KEMPS LITE - Yogurt - Marigold Foods Inc.
KEMPS PREMIUM - Ice cream - Marigold Foods Inc.
KEMPS YO-J - Yogurt - Marigold Foods Inc.
KEMPWRIGHT - Cookies - Gilbey's International
KEMRESIN - Furniture—laboratory - Kewaunee Scientific Corp.
KEMSHIELD - Furniture—laboratory - Kewaunee Scientific Corp.
KEMTRACE - Animal feed supplements - Kemin Industries, Inc.
KEMZIN - Animal feed supplements - Kemin Industries, Inc.
KEN - Dolls - Mattel, Inc.
KEN - Jewelry - Rona K. Corp.
KEN-A-VISION - Microscopes - Ken-A-Vision Manufacturing Co. Inc.
KEN & ROBERT'S VEGGIE BURGERS - Food products - Imagine Foods Inc.
KEN & ROBERT'S VEGGIE POCKETS - Food products - Imagine Foods Inc.
KEN BROWN - Artists' materials - Ken Brown Studio of Calligraphic Art Inc.
KEN-CARE - Pet products - Bramton Co.
KEN CORNET - Wallpaper - A. Musticorn & Co.
KEN DAVIS - Barbecue sauce - Ken Davis Products Inc.
KEN-DO - Conveyors - Arrowhead Industries Inc.
KEN DONE - Apparel and accessories - Oxford Industries, Inc.
KEN DONE - Greeting cards - Recycled Paper Products, Inc.
KEN DONE - Luggage - Oroton USA Inc.
KEN-GUARD - Lighting equipment ☆ - Kenergy Skylights (Kennedy Sky-Lites Div.)
KEN-KAGE - Pet products - Suburban Surgical Co. Inc.
KEN-L RATION - Dog food - Heinz Pet Products Co.
KEN-LAB COMMANDER - Cameras - Ken-Lab Inc.
KEN-LAB UNIVERSAL - Binoculars - Ken-Lab Inc.
KEN MAR - Food products ☆ - Rex Pacific
+KEN +MICHAELS - Furniture - Milwaukee Mattress & Furniture, Inc.
KEN-PATCH - Floor coverings - Kentile Floors Inc.
KEN-RAD - Electronics equipment - Vantage Lighting , Inc.
KEN-REISHI - Mushrooms ☆ - Naturade Inc.
KEN-SEAL - Adhesives and sealants - Kenergy Skylights (Kennedy Sky-Lites Div.)
KEN SMITH - Guitars - Ken Smith Basses Ltd.
KEN-TEX - Thread - Signal Thread Co. Inc.
KEN-TOOL - Tools—hand-operated - Summit Tool Co.
KEN USTON'S BLACKJACK - Computer software - Brown Bag Software Inc.

☆ = Now out of production

KENACORT - Pharmaceutical preparations - Bristol-Myers Squibb Co.

KENAI - Gloves - Swan Enterprises, Inc.

KENALOG - Pharmaceutical preparations - Bristol-Myers Squibb Co.

KENALONE - Health care products - Kay Pharmacal Co. Inc.

KENAR - Bags–duffel - Kenar Enterprises, Ltd.

KENAR ETC. - Apparel–women's - Kenar Enterprises, Ltd.

KENAR NECKWEAR - Neckties - Gordon & Ferguson of Delaware, Inc.

KENAZIDE H - Pharmaceutical preparations ☆ - Kenyon Drug Co. Inc.

KENBERRY - Housewares - Kenberry Specialties

KENBLUE - Flowers, plants, and seeds - Jacklin Seed

KENBRIDGE - Furniture - LADD Furniture Inc.

KENCILLIN - Pharmaceutical preparations ☆ - Kenyon Drug Co. Inc.

KENCO - Automotive parts and accessories - Kenco Corp.

KENCOVE - Vinyl - Kentile Floors Inc.

KENCRAFT - Candy - Kencraft, Inc.

KENCRAFT - Firearms, accessories, and parts - Kennedy Manufacturing Co.

KENDA - Tires - Kenda Rubber Industrial Co. Ltd.

KENDALE - Floor coverings–carpet and rugs - Barrett Carpet Mills Inc.

KENDALL - Lamps ☆ - Italia Collections

KENDALL - Lighting fixtures ☆ - Liteway

KENDALL - Oils–lubricating - Witco Corp.

KENDALL - Pencils - J.L. Hammett Co.

KENDALL - Transmission equipment–industrial - Fairchild Industrial Products Co.

KENDALL - Veterinary pharmaceutical preparations - Dr. B.J. Kendall

KENDALL COUNTER-IRRITANT - Skin care products - Dr. B.J. Kendall

KENDALL-JACKSON - Wines - Kendall Jackson Winery, Ltd.

KENDALL LIME JUICE - Juices - Parman-Kendall Corp.

KENDALL MOULDING & FRAMES - Frames–picture - Art Mart Inc.

KENDER GEAR - Luggage - American Hemp Mercantile, Inc.

KENDO PRODUCTS - Mops - New Knight Inc.

KENDON - Candy - Kendon Candies Co.

KENDURA - Cosmetics - Kendura Sandelos USA

KENERGY - Hardware - SNE Enterprises Inc.

KENEVILLE - Apparel–women's - United Fashion Industries Inc.

KENFAIR - Blinds–venetian - Kenfair Manufacturing Co.

KENFAST - Adhesives and sealants - Kentile Floors Inc.

KENGRADE - Floor coverings - Kentile Floors Inc.

KENGRIP - Floor waxes - Kentile Floors Inc.

KENGRIP - Machinery - Kennametal Inc.

KENHAR D KENHAR DYSON INC. - Motor vehicle parts and accessories - Kenhar Dyson Inc.

KENIC - Pet products - Glo-Marr Products Inc.

KENIC NATURAL VITAMIN - Veterinary nutritional supplements - Glo-Marr Products Inc.

KENIFED - Pharmaceutical preparations ☆ - Kenyon Drug Co. Inc.

KENILWORTH - Clocks ☆ - General Time Corp. (Westclox/Seth Thomas Div.)

KENILWORTH - Crocheted and knitted items - Garland Knitting Mills

KENILWORTH - Stainless steel - Pfaltzgraff Investment Co.

KENILWORTH - Weather tracking equipment ☆ - Airguide Instrument Co.

KENILWORTH COLLECTION - Furniture–upholstered - Southwood Furniture Corp.

KENIVERT - Pharmaceutical preparations ☆ - Kenyon Drug Co. Inc.

KENJI - Apparel–women's - TJX Companies, Inc.

KENKO FARMS - Rice cakes ☆ - Empress Foods, Inc.

KENKOH - Footwear - Kenkoh American Co.

KENKRETE CONSTRUCTION COMPANY - Toys - Tonka Corp.

KENLAM - Golfing equipment - Kenneth Smith Inc.

KENLASTIC - Surgical instruments - James R. Kendrick Co. Inc.

KENLEIGH - Food products ☆ - Europa Foods Ltd.

KENLON - Paints - Alpha Coating Industries Inc.

KENLUBE - Oils–lubricating - Witco Corp.

KENMAR - Caulking guns - Kenmar Manufacturing Co.

KENMAR - Furniture - Ethan Allen, Inc.

KENMARE - Earthenware ☆ - Waterford Wedgewood USA, Inc.

KENMEI - Cereal ☆ - Kellogg Co.

KENMORE - Door frames - Kenmore Industries Inc.

KENMORE - Food products - Janney-Marshall Co.

KENMORE - Housewares - Sears, Roebuck and Co.

KENMORE - Paper–toweling - Kenmore Association Inc.

KENMORE - Watches - Bulova Corp.

KENN-L-KARDS - Pet products - Barkleigh Productions, Inc.

KENNAFRAME - Hardware - J.G.R. Enterprises Inc.

KENNEBEC - Boats–canoes ☆ - Old Town Canoe Co.

KENNEBUNK RIVER - Recording label - Aztec Corp.

KENNEBUNKPORT - Bells - North Country Wind Bells Inc.

KENNEDALE STRIP - Floor coverings - Bruce Hardwood Floors

KENNEDY - Boats–pontoons - Kennedy Inc.

KENNEDY - Mattresses - Simmons USA

KENNEDY - Salad dressings–bottled ☆ - Lehmann Farms, Inc.

KENNEDY - Sausages - Potok Packing Co.

KENNEDY - Shoes ☆ - Allen-Edmonds Shoe Corp.

KENNEDY - Tool boxes - Kennedy Manufacturing Co.

KENNEDY - Window frames - Hallett Building Materials Inc.

KENNEDY GROUP, THE - Labels–paper - Kennedy Group Inc.

KENNEDY'S - Whiskey - M.S. Walker Inc./Seacoast

KENNEDY'S DIRECTORY OF VENTURE CAPITAL FIRMS - Dishwashers–household - Kennedy Information

KENNEDY'S INTERNATIONAL DIRECTORY OF EXECUTIVE RECRUITERS - Dishwashers–household - Kennedy Information

KENNEDY'S POCKET GUIDE TO WORKING WITH EXECUTIVE RECRUITERS - Publisher's imprints - Kennedy Information

KENNEL - Pet products - Gerard-Pellham Co.

KENNEL AID - Pet products ☆ - Trophy Animal Health Care

KENNEL-AIRE - Pet products - Kennel-Aire Inc.

KENNEL-AIRE - Pet products - R.C. Steele Co.

KENNEL-BLOCKS - Iodine - West Agro, Inc.

KENNEL CAB - Pet products - Doskocil Manufacturing Co., Inc.

KENNEL CAB II - Pet products - Doskocil Manufacturing Co., Inc.

KENNEL CAB II - Pet products - R.C. Steele Co.

KENNEL CARE - Pet products - Straight Arrow Products, Inc.

KENNEL CLUB - Giftware ☆ - Arnart Imports Inc.

KENNEL COLLECTION - Bronze figurines - Aus-Ben Studios

KENNEL CONTROLLER - Pet products - Kennelsoft

KENNEL CUBES - Pet food - American Nutrition, Inc.

KENNEL CUBES - Pet products - Rocky Mountain Milling Co.

KENNEL FAVORITES - Wall plaques - Aus-Ben Studios

KENNEL GARD - Dog food - American Pharmacal Inc.

KENNEL-KLEEN - Disinfectants - Dexol Industries

KENNEL KRUNCHERS - Dog food - AGP Petfoods

KENNEL MASTER - Dog food - Bartlett and Co.

KENNEL MASTER - Pet products - Toogood Laboratories

KENNEL MATE - Dog food - Sauder's Farm Inc.

KENNEL MATS - Pet products - Zerick Co.

KENNEL #5 - Pet products ☆ - Gerard-Pellham Co.

KENNEL PAL - Pet products - Dandy Products Inc.

KENNEL PRO - Hair clippers–veterinary - Wahl Clipper Corp.

KENNEL SILENCER - Pet products - Texmark Enterprises Inc.

KENNEL SPRING - Pet products - Kennel Spring

KENNELGUARD - Deodorizers - Ole Time Woodsman

KENNELKOF - Pet products - Gerard-Pellham Co.

KENNELSOL - Pet products - Alpha Tech Pet Inc.

KENNELWORTH - Occasional tables - JDI Group, Inc.

KENNER - Boats–canoes - Kenner Manufacturing Co. Inc.

KENNER - Toys - Kenner Products

KENNERFLEX ANIMALS - Toys–stuffed ☆ - Kenner Products

KENNESAW - Furniture - Homecrest Industries Inc.

KENNETH - Housewares ☆ - United Merchants and Manufacturers Inc.

KENNETH COLE - Apparel and accessories - G-III Apparel Group, Ltd.

KENNETH COLE - Shoes - Kenneth Cole Productions Inc.

KENNETH COLE COLLECTION - Coats–leather - K.C.P.L., Inc.

KENNETH COLE NEW YORK - Leather goods - Kenneth Cole Productions Inc.

KENNETH J. LANE - Barrettes ☆ - Riviera Trading, Inc.

KENNETH J. LANE - Jewelry - Costume Jewelry Co.

KENNETH J. LANE - Watches - Margrove Industries Inc.

KENNETH JAY LANE - Eyeglasses - Windsor Optical Inc.

KENNETH JAY LANE - Giftware ☆ - Schertz Umbrellas Inc.

KENNETH JAY LANE PERFECT PANSY - Jewelry - Avon Products, Inc.

KENNETH MCDONALD DESIGNER SERIES - Wallpaper - Kenneth McDonald Designs

KENNETH MICHAEL - Headwear - Northern Cap Manufacturing Co.

KENNETH SMITH - Golfing equipment - Kenneth Smith Inc.

KENNETH STEVENS - Men's apparel - Frederick Atkins, Inc.

KENNETT - Bedding–linen - Dan River Inc.

KENNETT - Floor coverings–carpet and rugs - Karastan-Bigelow Inc.

KENNETT SQUARE - Floor coverings ☆ - Tarkett, Inc.

KENNEY - Drapery hardware - Kenney Manufacturing Co.

KENNI-RINSE - Pet shops - Dermo Inc.

KENNINGTON - Shirts - Kennington Limited Inc.

KENNINGTON LTD CLASSICS - Apparel and accessories - Kennington Limited Inc.

KENNIT - Surgical instruments - James R. Kendrick Co. Inc.

☆ = Now out of production

KENNY - Dolls - Mattel, Inc.

KENNY G - Apparel and accessories - Turner Management Group

KENNY MONDAY - Apparel–athletic - Logan Knitting Mills, Inc.

KENNY ROGERS - Belts–apparel ☆ - Lyntone Belts Inc.

KENNY ROGERS - Boots - United States Shoe Corp.

KENNY VAN CAGO - Apparel and accessories - Kenneth Stephen Wienchus

KENNYCONNECTS - Computer software - McGraw-Hill Companies, Inc.

KENNY'S KIDDEES - Apparel–children's ☆ - Bend 'n Stretch Inc.

KENO - Clocks - General Time Corp. (Westclox/Seth Thomas Div.)

KENOCO - Naphthalene chips ☆ - Willert Home Products, Inc.

KENOLAX - Pharmaceutical preparations - Kenyon Drug Co. Inc.

KENORA - Floor coverings–carpet and rugs - Eagle Carpets Inc.

KENPASTE - Floor coverings - Kentile Floors Inc.

KENRA - Hair care products - Kenra Laboratories, Inc.

KENRA NATURALS - Hair care products - Kenra Laboratories, Inc.

KENRAX - Pharmaceutical preparations ☆ - Kenyon Drug Co. Inc.

KENRICH - Broadcasting equipment - Kenrich Electronics Inc.

KENRO - Dinnerware–glass ☆ - Kenro Inc.

KEN'S - Pizzas–mixes - Mazzio's Corp.

KEN'S - Salad dressings–bottled - Ken's Foods Inc.

KEN'S STEAK HOUSE - Salad dressings–bottled - Ken's Foods Inc.

KENSBRIDGE - Furniture ☆ - Lane Co. Inc.

KENSERT - Floor coverings ☆ - Kentile Floors Inc.

KENSHIN - Toys - Mirage Studios

KENSINGTON - See **FAHRENHEAT**

KENSINGTON - Cabinets ☆ - Aristokraft, Inc.

KENSINGTON - Cabinets ☆ - Decora

KENSINGTON - Cabinets ☆ - Medallion Kitchens of Minnesota Inc.

KENSINGTON - Cigarettes - Brown & Williamson Tobacco Corp.

KENSINGTON - Computer peripheral equipment - Kensington Microware Ltd.

KENSINGTON - Dinnerware–glass ☆ - Royal China & Porcelain Companies Inc.

KENSINGTON - Dishes–china - Mikasa Co.

KENSINGTON - Dishes–china ☆ - Gorham Inc.

KENSINGTON - Fishing rods - Maurice Sporting Goods, Inc.

KENSINGTON - Floor coverings - Congoleum Corp.

KENSINGTON - Floor coverings–carpet and rugs ☆ - Atlas Carpet Mills Inc.

KENSINGTON - Furniture - Homecrest Industries Inc.

KENSINGTON - Furniture ☆ - Hickory Chair Co.

KENSINGTON - Furniture–upholstered - Maharam Vertical Surfaces

KENSINGTON - Gin - M.S. Walker Inc./Seacoast

KENSINGTON - Locks–door - Baldwin Hardware Corp.

KENSINGTON - Mattresses - Stearns & Foster Bedding Co.

KENSINGTON - Motor vehicle parts and accessories - Lancaster Colony Automotive Group

KENSINGTON - Pipes–tobacco - S.M. Frank & Co. Inc. (Kaywoodie-Yello-Bole-Medico)

KENSINGTON - Publisher's imprints - Kensington Publishing Corp.

KENSINGTON - Stationery - Samuel Ward Manufacturing Inc.

KENSINGTON - Wines - Fortino Winery

KENSINGTON & WORTH LTD. - Pet products - Kensington & Worth Ltd.

KENSINGTON BEAR - Toys–stuffed - Russ Berrie and Co., Inc.

KENSINGTON BOX - Artists' materials - Winsor & Newton

KENSINGTON COLLECTION - Trays - Knobler International Ltd.

KENSINGTON COURT - Furniture - Lane Co. Inc.

KENSINGTON COURT - Furniture ☆ - Bassett Furniture Industries, Inc.

KENSINGTON ESTATES - Lamps - Wal-Mart Stores Inc.

KENSINGTON HOUSE - Publisher's imprints - Kensington House Publishing Ltd.

KENSINGTON KNIT - Knit sweaters - Z.H.G. Industries, Inc.

KENSINGTON PARK - Fabrics–tapestry - Coloroll Inc.

KENSINGTON PARK 2 - Fabrics–tapestry - Coloroll Inc.

KENSINGTON ROAD - Apparel and accessories - Chadwick's of Boston, Ltd.

KENSINGTON ROSE - Luggage - Airway Industries, Inc.

KENSINGTON SQUARE - Wallpaper - Warner of London

KENSINGTON, THE - Fencing–plastic - Nebraska Plastics, Inc.

KENSITAS - Cigarettes - American Tobacco Co.

KENSTRUCT - Toys - Tonka Corp.

KENT - Animal feeds - Grain Processing Corp.

KENT - Apparel–children's - Gerber Products Co.

KENT - Bicycles - Kent International Inc.

KENT - Cheese - Avonmore-Kent Inc.

KENT - Cigarettes - Lorillard Tobacco Co.

KENT - Erasers - B. Carter Lykins-Importer

KENT - Flashlights ☆ - Bright Star Industries Inc.

KENT - Floor cleaning equipment - Kent Co.

KENT - Frames—eyeglass - Rozin Optical Export Corp.

KENT - Glassware—household ☆ - Crystal Clear Importing Co. Inc.

KENT - Guitars ☆ - On-Site Music Group

KENT - Office furniture—metal - Joyce International Inc.

KENT - Paper—kraft ☆ - Canson-Talens Inc.

KENT - Pesticides—household - Kent Feeds, Inc.

KENT - Photographic equipment - Kalimar, Inc.

KENT - Playing cards - Hoyle Products

KENT - Publisher's imprints - PWS Publishing

KENT - Recording label - Cadet Records Inc.

KENT - Sausages - Kent Provision Co.

KENT - Wallpaper ☆ - Wolf-Gordon Inc.

KENT & HOWARD - Shoes ☆ - Jack Schwartz Shoes, Inc.

KENT CONNECTION - Apparel and accessories - Kent Street Group, Inc.

KENT GARDEN - Tableware—china ☆ - Lenox, Inc.

KENT GOLDEN LIGHTS - Cigarettes - Lorillard Tobacco Co.

KENT III - Cigarettes - Lorillard Tobacco Co.

KENT K SERIES - Pet products - Kent Fixture Corp.

KENT MARINE - Water purification systems - Kent Marine

KENT OF LONDON - Brushes—hair - Karina Inc.

KENT STAFFORDSHIRE DOGS AND FIGURINES - Dishes—china - Heirloom Editions Ltd.

KENTE - Floor coverings—carpet and rugs - Foreign Accents

KENTEA - Teas - Kentea Ltd.

KENTECH - Footwear - Deerstags Inc.

KENTECH - Shutters—plastic - Kentech Plastics, Inc.

KENTFIELD - Dinnerware - Sky 1, Inc.

KENTFIELD - Fishing reels - American Import Co.

KENTH - Apparel and accessories - Kenth Andersson N.Y. Ltd.

KENTIA PALM COMPANY, THE - Trees - Bradley Miller

KENTILE - Floor coverings - Kentile Floors Inc.

KENTILE BRITE'N SHINY - Wood products - Kentile Floors Inc.

KENTILE TOUCH-DOWN - Floor coverings—tile - Kentile Floors Inc.

KENTMERE COLLECTION, THE - Candy - Casanova Chocolate Co.

KENTOCS - Clocks - Ohio Ceramic Supply Inc.

KENTON - Canvas—artists' ☆ - Winsor & Newton

KENTON - Dolls - Mattel, Inc.

KENTON MANOR - Floor coverings—carpet and rugs ☆ - Lees Carpets

KENTROX WANCARD - Communications equipment - Kentrox Industries, Inc.

KENT'S PRIDE - Vegetables—canned - Kent Canning Co.

KENTUCK - Food products - Standard Foods Inc.

KENTUCKIAN - Clocks ☆ - General Time Corp. (Westclox/Seth Thomas Div.)

KENTUCKIAN - Toys—guns - Parris Manufacturing Co.

KENTUCKY - Floor coverings - Kentucky Wood Floors Inc.

KENTUCKY - Tobacco - Conwood Co. L.P.

KENTUCKY - Whiskey - Four Roses Distillers Co.

KENTUCKY AROMATIC - Pet products - Northeastern Products Corp.

KENTUCKY AROMATIC RED - Sawdust ☆ - Northeastern Products Corp.

KENTUCKY BUBBLING - Water—bottled or canned - Kentucky Bubbling Springs

KENTUCKY CHEROOT - Cigars - Avanti Cigar Co.

KENTUCKY CLASSICS - House furnishings ☆ - Lea Industries Inc.

KENTUCKY CLUB - Tobacco products - John Middleton Inc.

KENTUCKY COLONEL MUSIC - Publisher's imprints - Sierra Records, Books & Home Video

KENTUCKY DALE - Beverages—alcohol - Sazerac Co. Inc.

KENTUCKY EQUINE RESEARCH - Animal feeds - Kentucky Equine Research, Inc.

KENTUCKY FARM - Sausages - Kentucky Sausage Co. Inc.

KENTUCKY FRIED CHICKEN - Restaurants—fast food - KFC Corp.

KENTUCKY GENTLEMAN - Liquors - Canandaigua Wine Co. Inc.

KENTUCKY GENTLEMAN - Whiskey - Barton Brands, Ltd.

KENTUCKY GOLD - Meats—luncheon - Field Packing Co.

KENTUCKY KERNEL SEASONED FLOUR - Flour—blended - Hodgson Mill

KENTUCKY KING TWIST - Tobacco products - Scott Tobacco Co.

KENTUCKY KINGS - Cigarettes - Brown & Williamson Tobacco Corp.

KENTUCKY KOMFORT - Fireplace logs—electric - Stamping Ground Tool & Die Inc.

KENTUCKY LIFE - Whiskey - Standard Distillers Products Inc.

KENTUCKY MAID - Combs - F. Wolkow & Sons

KENTUCKY MAID - Seasonings - Silver Foods Corp.

KENTUCKY MANOR - Floor coverings - Congoleum Corp.

KENTUCKY MINTS - Candy - Brach and Brock Confections Inc.

KENTUCKY SENATOR - Liquors - Hughes Markets Inc.

KENTUCKY SILK - Beverages—alcohol ☆ - Jim Beam Brands Co.

KENTUCKY SPIRIT - Whiskey - Austin, Nichols & Co., Inc.

KENTUCKY SPRING - Tongs - Kyle Ellison
KENTUCKY TAVERN - Liquors - Canandaigua Wine Co. Inc.
KENTUCKY TWIST - Tobacco products - Scott Tobacco Co.
KENTUCKY VINTAGE - Bourbon whiskey - Pure Kentucky Distilling Co.
KENTUCKY WILDCATS - Paper–writing - University of Kentucky
KENTUCKY WONDER STYLE - Vegetables–canned - Allen Canning Co.
KENTUCKY YARNS - Yarn - January and Wood Co. Inc.
KENTUCKY'S BEST - Food products - Blue Grass Provisions Co., Inc.
KENTUCKY'S BEST - Tobacco products ☆ - Scott Tobacco Co.
KENTWOOD - Stereos - American Hi-Fi International 26, Inc.
KENTWOOD - Water–distilled - Suntory Water Group. Inc.
KENTWOOD - Water–mineral - Kentwood Spring Water
KENURIL - Pharmaceutical preparations ☆ - Kenyon Drug Co. Inc.
KENVET NUTRITIONAL CARE - Dog food ☆ - Hess & Clark, Inc.
KENWAY - Floor coverings–carpet and rugs - Milliken & Co. Inc.
KENWOOD - Golfing equipment - Kenneth Smith Inc.
KENWOOD - Stereos - Kenwood Electronics Inc.
KENWOOD - Vitamins and nutritional supplements - Kenwood Laboratories Inc.
KENWOOD - Wallpaper ☆ - Advent Industries Inc.
KENWOOD VINEYARDS - Wines - Kenwood Vineyards
KENWORTH - Motor vehicles - Kenworth Truck Co.
KENWORTH - Motor vehicles–trucks - Paccar Inc.
KENWORTH - Stereos - American Hi-Fi International 26, Inc.
KENWORTH - Toys–automobiles - ERTL Co., Inc.
KENWORTH AERODYNE - Motor vehicles–trucks - Kenworth Truck Co.
KENWORTH COURT - Furniture ☆ - Bassett Furniture Industries, Inc.
KENWORTHY - Instructional materials - Bemiss-Jason Corp.
KENWORTHY VINEYARDS - Wines ☆ - Sunny Grace Vineyard
KENY - Fruits and vegetables - Makenger Import & Export, Inc.
KENYA - Dolls - Tyco Toys
KENYA - Floor coverings–carpet and rugs ☆ - Regal Rugs Inc.
KENYA - Hair care products - Belt Distributors Inc.
KENYA - Teas - Eastern Shore Tea Co.
KENYA - Yarn ☆ - William Unger & Co. Inc.
KENYA CLUB - Women's apparel - India Garments Inc.
KENYA GEM - Jewelry–costume - Kenya Gem Co.
KENYAN - Handbags - Maryesta Carr International
KENYA'S COUSINS LITTLE AFRICAN PRINCESSES - Dolls - Tyco Industries, Inc.
KENYAS, THE - Handbags - Tandem Imports Corp.
KENYATTA SKI WEAR EXPERT ONLY - Apparel and accessories - Kenyatta Ski Wear
KENYETTA MUSIC - Recording label - Spelman College
KENYON - Cameras - Ken-Lab Inc.
KENYON - Clocks ☆ - General Time Corp. (Westclox/Seth Thomas Div.)
KENYON - Dishes–china - Waterford Wedgwood USA, Inc.
KENYON - Spars, masts, and hardware - International Marine Industries
KENYON - Stoves - Outdoor Sports Industries
KENYON - Underwear and nightwear - Kenyon Consumer Products Inc.
KENYON - Wines - Delicato Vineyards
KENYON EXPLORER - Cameras - Ken-Lab Inc.
KENYON TOASTYS - Underwear and nightwear ☆ - Kenyon Consumer Products Inc.
KEO - Beer, wine, liquor - Attiki Imports & Distributors
KEOKE - Boats–motor ☆ - Hobie Cat Co.
KEONDA - Apparel and accessories - Crystal Gomez
KEORA - Perfumes - Classic Fragrances Ltd.
KEOUGH - Fishing lures - Keough Hackles
KEP-O-LOK - Valves - Kepner Products Co.
KEPEX - Electronics equipment - Valley Audio Products, Inc.
KEPEX II - Musical instrument accessories - Valley Audio Products, Inc.
KEPPEL KIDS - Candy - Keppel's Inc.
KEPPEL'S - Candy - Keppel's Inc.
KEPSEL - Valves - Kepner Products Co.
KEPWEL SPRING - Water–bottled or canned - Kepwel Spring Water Co.
KER-4-HAIR - Hair care products - I. Sekine Co. Inc.
KER CADELAC - Cookies - Jaret Specialties Inc.
KERA 10 - Hair care products - Rossan Laboratories Inc.
KERA-BAN - Depilatories - Kera-Ban Products Inc.
KERA-BAN MELTING POT - Depilatories - Kera-Ban Products Inc.
KERA-BAN PLASTA WAX - Depilatories - Kera-Ban Products Inc.
KERA CLENZ - Hair care products - Image Laboratories, Inc.
KERABRADE - Pharmaceutical preparations ☆ - Freeman Industries LLC
KERACILS - Cosmetics - Lancome
KERACOVER - Skin care products ☆ - Freeman Industries LLC
KERADUR - Tiles–ceramic ☆ - Amsterdam Corp.

KERAFIRM - Hair care products ☆ - Cosmair Inc.
KERAFLAKE - Animal feeds - Novalek, Inc.
KERAFLAKE - Aquarium accessories - Aquaculture Aquavet
KERAFUSE - Hair care products - Amethyst Investment Group, Inc.
KERAGEL - Veterinary product ☆ - NNQ Inc.
KERAGENICS - American International Industries
KERAION - Tiles–ceramic - Buchtal USA
KERAION-QUADRO - Tiles–ceramic - Buchtal USA
KERAIOTHERM - Tiles–ceramic - Buchtal USA
KERAKLEN - Pharmaceutical preparations ☆ - Freeman Industries LLC
KERALOGIE - Cosmetics - Cosmair Inc.
KERALYT - Pharmaceutical preparations - Westwood-Squibb Pharmaceuticals, Inc.
KERAMATIC - Cosmetics - Dr. Babor Natural Cosmetics
KERAMIC - Tools ☆ - Raybestos/Brake Parts Inc.
KERAMOIST - Hair care products - New Image Laboratories, Inc.
KERANIS AROMA - Cigarettes - G.A. Georgopulo & Co. Inc.
KERANIS DELPHI - Cigarettes - G.A. Georgopulo & Co. Inc.
KERANIS ETHNOS - Cigarettes - G.A. Georgopulo & Co. Inc.
KERANIS OSCAR - Cigarettes - G.A. Georgopulo & Co. Inc.
KERANIS PALLAS - Cigarettes - G.A. Georgopulo & Co. Inc.
KERAPHIX - Hair care products - Nexxus Products Co.
KERAPIBBS - Hair care products - P.S. Pibbs
KERAPLACENTA - Hair care products - P.S. Pibbs Inc.
KERAPRO - Hair care products - Joico Laboratories, Inc.
KERARIV - Tiles–ceramic ☆ - Federal Tile Imports Inc.
KERASHIELD - Ophthalmic goods - Allergan Medical Optics
KERASOFT - Hair care products - Redken Laboratories, Inc.
KERASOL - Skin care products ☆ - Upsher-Smith Laboratories, Inc.
KERASOLV - Veterinary pharmaceutical preparations - DVM Pharmaceuticals, Inc.
KERASTACE - Hair care products ☆ - Cosmair Inc.
KERATAN - Cosmetics - Estee Lauder Inc.
KERATEX - Hair care products - Amethyst Investment Group, Inc.
KERATEX - Skin care products - Syosset Laboratories Inc.
KERATIN MAGIC - Hair care products ☆ - Palm Beach Beauty Products
KERATREAT - Hair care products - Jheri Redding Products Inc.
KERAVISION - Ophthalmic goods - Keravision, Inc.
KERBA - Shortening - Kraft Food Ingredients Corp.
KERBER KIDS - Greeting cards - American Greetings Corp.
KERBOOM - Fishing lines - Cortland Line Co., Inc.
KERBY'S - Salad dressings–bottled - Melco Inc.
KERENE - Hair care products - Helene Curtis Industries Inc.
KEREX - Garden equipment - Lawn & Garden Supply Co.
KERI - Electrical equipment - Keri Systems, Inc.
KERI - Glassware–household ☆ - Dansk International Designs, Ltd.
KERI - Skin care products - Westwood-Squibb Pharmaceuticals, Inc.
KERI JUG - Containers - Igloo Products Corp.
KERI SILKY SMOOTH - Skin care products - Bristol-Myers Squibb Co.
KERI SYSTEMS, INC. - Electronic equipment - Keri Systems, Inc.
KERICHO - Wallpaper - Koroseal Wallcoverings
KERICOURT - Skin care products - Westwood-Squibb Pharmaceuticals, Inc.
KERID - Health care products - Blair Laboratories Inc.
KERITE - Insulated wire and cable - Hubbell Lighting, Inc. (Lighting Div.)
KERJOBA - Hair care products ☆ - Demert & Dougherty, Inc.
KERKER - Motor vehicle parts and accessories - Supertrapp Industries
KERMA - Sporting goods - Skis Dynastar, Inc.
KERMAN - Area rugs - Arthur J. Beacom & Co.
KERMIT - Toys - Jim Henson Productions, Inc.
KERMIT THE FROG - Watches - Jim Henson Productions, Inc.
KERN - Binoculars ☆ - Heitz Service Corp.
KERN SEAL - Paints ☆ - Ponderosa Paint Manufacturing Co. Inc.
KERN SWISS - Binoculars ☆ - Heitz Service Corp.
KERN TEX - Paints ☆ - Ponderosa Paint Manufacturing Co. Inc.
KERN TONE - Paints ☆ - Ponderosa Paint Manufacturing Co. Inc.
KERNAL-FRESH - Nuts–salted, roasted, cooked, or canned ☆ - Germack Pistachio Co.
KERNALS KORN - Popcorn - Our House Inc.
KERNEL-FRESH - Nuts–salted, roasted, cooked, or canned - Fairmont Snacks Group Inc.
KERNEL POPS - Popcorn - Royale International
KERNEL, THE - Toiletries - French & Pacific Trading Corp.
KERN'L KORN - Food products - House-Autry Mills, Inc.
KERNLAND - Nuts–candied - Riverside Date International Inc.
KERNMANTLE - Rope - New England Ropes Inc.
KERN'S - Fruit drinks–bottled or canned - Nestle Beverage Co.

☆ = Now out of production

KERN'S - Sausages - Kern's Sausages
KERN'S COLOR MAGIC - Paints ☆ - Ponderosa Paint Manufacturing Co. Inc.
KERN'S HOME STYLE - Breads - Kern's Bakeries, Inc.
KERO-FAN - Heaters–kerosene - Albano & Hamilton Manufacturing Corp.
KERO-SUN - Heaters–kerosene - Kero-Sun Inc.
KERODEX - Pharmaceutical preparations - Whitehall Laboratories
KEROMATE - Heaters–kerosene - Keromate Products Inc.
KEROSENE -
KERPLUNK - Fishing tackle - Cortland Line Co., Inc.
KERPLUNK - Games - CBS Toys
KERR - Concrete products - KBW Holding, Inc.
KERR - Food containers - Alltrista Corp.
KERR - Jars–glass - Kerr Group, Inc.
KERR - Juices - Kerr Concentrates Inc.
KERR - Pens - Kerr-Changepoint
KERR-MCGEE - Petroleum - Kerr-McGee Chemical Corp.
KERRA - Housewares ☆ - Zrike Co. Inc.
KERRAGENICS - Hair care products - Ardell International Inc.
KERRI - Dolls - Totsy Manufacturing Co., Inc.
KERRI KLEAN - Cleaning preparations - Atlantic Mills, Inc.
KERRI KLEAN WIPERS - Cleaning preparations - Atlantic Mills, Inc.
KERRI N KELSEY - Sweaters - Fu Kong Inc.
KERRICH - Flowers, plants, and seeds - Limrick Inc.
KERRIKORD - Cordage and twine - Harco Co.
KERR'S - Thread ☆ - Susan Bates Inc.
KERRVILLE FOLK FESTIVAL - Recording label - Kerrville Music Foundation Inc.
KERRY - Fans–electric - Nutone Inc.
KERRY - Pet shops - Dermo Inc.
KERRY INGREDIENTS - Chemical preparations - Beatreme Foods, Inc.
KERRYBITS - Spices and extracts - Kerry Ingredients, Inc.
KERRYDALE - Dinnerware–glass ☆ - Johnson Brothers, USA, Inc.
KERRY'S ETCETERA - Glassware–household - Kerry's Etcetera
KERRYXTRA - Seasonings - Beatreme Foods, Inc.
KER'S WINE HOUSE - Apparel and accessories - Winghouse, Inc.
KERSPLASH - Amusement rides - Frederick S. Miler
KERSTEN CHRISTMAS - Greeting cards - Kersten Bros. Studios
KERSTIN FLORIAN THE SPA PROGRAMME - Cosmetics - Kerstin Florian, Inc.
KERTINS - Curtains - Arley Corp.
KERUINGPLANK - Floor coverings - Overseas Hardwoods Co.
KERYGMA - Recording label ☆ - Sparrow Corp.
KES - Scientific apparatus - Kes Irrigation Systems, Inc.
KES - Toys - Paramount Pictures Corp.
KESHIN - Apparel and accessories - Keshin Chang
KESITOS - Snack foods - Matthews, Von Sydow, Rand & Associates Inc.
KESSAMIN - Pharmaceutical preparations - McKesson Home Health Care
KESSER - Wines - Crown Regal Wine Cellars
KESSER - Wines - Joseph Zakon Winery Ltd.
KESSLER - Whiskey - House of Seagram
KESSLER - Whiskey - Jim Beam Brands Co.
KESSLING - Thermometers - E. Kessling Thermometer Co.
KESTELL - Chairs–folding - Kestell Furniture Co. Inc.
KESTER - Solder - Kester Solder Co.
KESTREL - Aircraft - Kestrel Aircraft Co.
KESTREL - Binoculars - Swift Instruments, Inc.
KESTREL - Measuring instruments - Nielsen-Kellerman Co.
KESTRIN - Pharmaceutical preparations - Hyrex Pharmaceuticals
KESTRONE - Pharmaceutical preparations - Hyrex Pharmaceuticals
KESU - Hair care products ☆ - Holistic Laboratories
KESWICK - Fabrics - Dan River Inc.
KESWICK - Floor coverings - Mannington Resilient Floors
KESWICK CLUB - Apparel and accessories - Ashley House, Inc.
KET-CHIPS - Potato chips ☆ - Charles Chip Corp.
KETA - Seafood products–canned or cured - Health Sea, Inc.
KETA MUSIC - Recording label - Jazz Composer's Orchestra Association Inc.
KETAJECT - Pharmaceutical preparations - Phoenix Pharmaceutical, Inc.
KETAJECT - Pharmaceutical preparations ☆ - Bristol-Myers Squibb Co.
KETALAR - Pharmaceutical preparations - Parke-Davis
KETASET - Veterinary pharmaceutical preparations - Bristol-Myers Squibb Co.
KETCHAM & MCDOUGALL - Desks - Park Sherman
KETCHIPS - Potato chips - Bon Ton Foods Inc.
KETCHIPS - Snack foods - Borden, Inc.
KETCHUCK - Toys - Mattel, Inc.
KETCHUM RELEASE - Fishing lures - C1 Design Group LLC
KETER - Sewing machines–household - Fleur De Paris

KETER KOSHER - Cleaning preparations - Durawool Inc.
KETO - Bedding–linen - Dan River Inc.
KETO-DIASTIX - Chemical preparations - Miles Inc.
KETOCHOL - Pharmaceutical preparations - G. D. Searle & Co.
KETOSIN - Veterinary pharmaceutical preparations ☆ - C.J. Martin Co.
KETOSTIX - Chemical preparations - Miles Inc.
KETOTIFEN - Pharmaceutical preparations - Sandoz Pharmaceuticals Corp.
K.E.T.S. - Golfing equipment - Kin Taka Golf Works, Inc.
KETT - Saws–power - Kett Tool Co.
KETTCARS - Toy cars - International Products Trading Inc.
KETTINGS - Food products - Top Taste Bakery Inc.
KETTLE CHIPS - Potato chips - Kettle Foods
KETTLE CLASSICS - Soups–mixes - Delta Pride Catfish Inc.
KETTLE CREATIONS - Soups–mixes - Lipton Investments, Inc.
KETTLE FRESH - Candy - Eddyleon Chocolate Co. Inc.
KETTLE JIAS - Tortillas ☆ - Kettle Foods
KETTLE KORN KRUNCH - Confections - Nut Kettle East Inc.
KETTLE KORN KRUNCH - Popcorn - Hardie's Korn Kettle, Inc.
KETTLE KRISP - Snack foods - UTZ Quality Foods Inc.
KETTLE PAC - Popcorn - Widman Popcorn Co.
KETTLE POPPINS - Popcorn - Kettle Foods
KETTLE RICH - Food products - John Sexton and Co.
KETTLE ROASTER FRESH - Margarine - Kettle Foods
KETTLE SCENTS - Sachets - Natural Products Corp.
KETTLE TIAS - Tortillas ☆ - Kettle Foods
KETTLE TORTILLA CHIPS - Potato chips - Kettle Foods
KETTLEMASTER - Barbecues and grills - Sunbeam Corp.
KETTLER - Children's furniture, toy cars - International Products Trading Inc.
KETTMEIR - Wines - Paterno Imports, Ltd.
KEUKA HIGHLANDS - Wines - McGregor Vineyard Winery
KEV KORD - Rope - New England Ropes Inc.
KEVEK - Amplifiers - Kevek Speaker Technology
KEVI - Furniture - Walker and Zanger Inc.
KEVIN - Dolls - Mattel, Inc.
KEVIN MCANDREW - Hats ☆ - Resistol Hats
KEVIN TODD - Slacks–men's - Kalikow Bros. Inc.
KEVIS - Skin care products - Genki USA
KEVLAR - Gloves - Jomac Products Inc.
KEVLAR - Rope - New England Ropes Inc.
KEVLAR - Sporting goods - E.I. Dupont de Nemours and Co.
KEVLAR BLEND - Sports rackets and accessories - Gexco Enterprises
KEVLAR KM2 - Fiber - E.I. Dupont de Nemours and Co.
KEW - Washing machine parts - Alto U.S. Inc.
KEW KIDS - Wallpaper ☆ - Imperial Wallcoverings, Inc.
KEWAUNEE - Playpens–metal ☆ - Kewaunee Equipment Co.
KEWPIE - Dolls - Roseart Inc.
KEWPIE - Dolls ☆ - Strombecker Corp.
KEWPIE TWINS - Shoes - Clinic Shoe Co.
KEWT SEA - Food products - Wally Sea Products Corp.
KEWTIE-DOLL - Now out of production ☆ - Intex Recreation Corp.
KEX - Adhesives and sealants - Rutland Products
KEX - Computer software - Knowledge Exchange LLC
KEY - Coveralls - Key Industries, Inc.
KEY - Golfing equipment - STX, Inc.
KEY - Health care products - Ambu Inc.
KEY - Paints - Eaglo Paint & Varnish Corp.
KEY - Stationery ☆ - Springfield Tablet Co.
KEY - Thermometer - Hanna Instruments, Inc.
KEY - Thread ☆ - Perfect Thread Co. Inc.
KEY - Vegetables–canned ☆ - Johnston Farms
KEY - Vitamins and nutritional supplements ☆ - J.R. Carlson Laboratories Inc.
KEY - Wines ☆ - Wine Group Inc.
KEY-ADE - Vitamins and nutritional supplements ☆ - J.R. Carlson Laboratories Inc.
KEY ADVANTAGE PROGRAM - American Lock Co.
KEY ALERT - Alarms–personal - DAC Technologies of America, Inc.
KEY AMERICA - Key rings - Specialty House of Creation International, Inc.
KEY AND TUF-NUT - Apparel–men's - Tuf-Nut Co. Inc.
KEY-BAK - Key rings - West Coast Chain Manufacturing Co.
KEY BISCAYNE - Mobile homes - Golden West Homes
KEY BISCAYNE - Wallpaper - Frankford Wallcoverings Inc.
KEY-BLOCK - Blocks–concrete - Key Block Corp.
KEY CADDY - Key rings - L.S. Starrett Co. Inc. (Consumer Products Div.)
KEY CALF MILK REPLACER - Animal feed supplements ☆ - Agri-King Inc.
KEY CASSETTE - Communications equipment–marine - Sycon Corp.
KEY CONTROL - Keypunch cards - Key Control Systems Inc.

☆ = Now out of production

KEY COURIER - Key rings - Paige E. Evans
KEY CUTIE - Leather goods - Oppenheim Products Co.
KEY-DECK - Building materials—concrete - Cardinal Manufacturing Co.
KEY DEFENDER - Aluminum products - Armament Systems and Procedures, Inc.
KEY-E - Vitamins and nutritional supplements - J.R. Carlson Laboratories Inc.
KEY-E-KAPS - Vitamins and nutritional supplements - J.R. Carlson Laboratories Inc.
KEY ELECTRONICS - Electronics stores - Key Communications Service, Inc.
KEY FINDER - Educational materials - Desk Top Publishing Studios
KEY FLAMINGO - Cosmetics - Revlon Consumer Products Corp.
KEY FOOD - Pizza - Continental Food Products Inc.
KEY FRIEND - Identification tags - Business Services, Inc.
KEY GARD - Key rings - Prince Gardner Inc.
KEY GARDE - Computer peripheral equipment - Daubert Industries - ECP
KEY GAS COMPONENTS - Gas machinery - Roy Kuhn Enterprises, Inc.
KEY-GLOVE - Keys - Pliant Plastics Corp.
KEY-HIDE - Key rings - Art Craft Wallets Inc.
KEY INGREDIENTS - Cheese - Key Ingredients Inc.
KEY KADDY - Leather goods - AR Accessories Group Inc.
KEY-KEEPER - American Lock Co.
KEY KEEPER - Key rings ☆ - Park Sherman
KEY KIT - Leather goods - St. Thomas Inc.
KEY KNIFE - Knives - T.M. Shea Products Inc.
KEY LARGO - Beverages—alcohol - Jim Beam Brands Co.
KEY LARGO - Bicycles ☆ - Huffy Corp.
KEY LARGO - Computer hardware - Don Johnston Inc.
KEY LARGO - Eyewear - Competitive Edge, Inc.
KEY LARGO - Floor coverings—carpet and rugs - Whitecrest Carpet Mills
KEY LARGO - Furniture - Homecrest Industries Inc.
KEY LARGO - Furniture ☆ - Bassett Furniture Industries, Inc.
KEY LARGO - Furniture ☆ - Riverside Furniture Corp.
KEY LARGO - Motor vehicles—motor homes - Baron Motor Homes Inc.
KEY LARGO - Wallpaper - Advance Wallcoverings
KEY LARGO PIE COMPANY - Pies - Kokomo Investments Inc.
KEY LIMA COLADA - Teas - Eastern Shore Tea Co.
KEY LIME - Colognes - Brandy Harvest
KEY LIME - Cookies - Nikki's Cookies, Inc.
KEY LIME MIST - Sachets - Andre Richard
KEY LIME PIE - Christmas tree ornaments - Cracker Box Inc.
KEY-LINE - Rubber cement ☆ - Loctite Corp.
KEY LINK - Hardware - U.S. Home Security Systems
KEY-LITE - Cases—plastic ☆ - Mautner Co. Inc.
KEY LITE - Flashlights - Garrity Industries
KEY/LOC - Fasteners—snap - Nupla Corp.
KEY LOCK - Pet products - R.A.F. Trading Inc.
KEY-MAN - Apparel—men's - Hortex Inc.
KEY-MAN - Pipes—tobacco - Bradberry Briar Pipe Corp.
KEY MAST - Computer software - Great American Insurance Co.
KEY-MATE - Flashlights ☆ - Streamlight, Inc.
KEY MATES - Key rings - Curtis Industries Inc.
KEY-MEM - Electronics equipment - Grass Valley Group Inc.
KEY-MIN - Vitamins and nutritional supplements - J.R. Carlson Laboratories Inc.
KEY-NOTER - Dictating machines ☆ - Lanier Voice Products
KEY NOTER - Key rings ☆ - Park Sherman
KEY NOTES - Notebooks and notepads - Key Institute for Learning Strategies Inc.
KEY OF G - Apparel and accessories - Sally Gee Inc.
KEY PALS SCENTED - Key chains - Plasticolor Molded Products, Inc.
KEY-PER - Key rings - West Coast Chain Manufacturing Co.
KEY-PLEX - Pharmaceutical preparations - Hyrex Pharmaceuticals
KEY POWER - Toys - Elmar Products Co.
KEY-PRED - Pharmaceutical preparations - Hyrex Pharmaceuticals
KEY-RECT - Labels—paper - RGR & CL Products
KEY-RON - Vitamins and nutritional supplements - J.R. Carlson Laboratories Inc.
KEY-SAFE - Hooks - Woodcraft Manufacturing Co.
KEY SAFE - Key rings - Hill Security Products
KEY SAFE - Pet products - R.A.F. Trading Inc.
KEY-SERPINE - Pharmaceutical preparations ☆ - Hyrex Pharmaceuticals
KEY-SPIDER - Key rings - West Coast Chain Manufacturing Co.
KEY STONE MEDALLION - Aircraft—helicopters - Keystone Helicopter Corp.
KEY-TAINER - Wallets - Buxton Inc.
KEY-TEX - Paints ☆ - Valspar Corp.
KEY THOUGHTS - Notebooks and notepads - Inventrepreneur

KEY TO GREENER LAWNS - Fertilizers - Amcorn Hybrids Inc.
KEY TOPPERS - Novelty items - Happiness Express Inc.
KEY-TRAK - Electronic equipment - Key-Trak, Inc.
KEY-TRAK INC. - Electronic equipment - Key-Trak, Inc.
KEY TREASURES - Leather goods - St. Thomas Inc.
KEY-TROL - Keypunch cards - Key Control Systems Inc.
KEY VALET - Leather goods - St. Thomas Inc.
KEY VALUE - Brake pads - Nissan Motor Corp. USA
KEY WEST - Boats - Glen-L Marine Designs
KEY WEST - Floor coverings—carpet and rugs ☆ - Catalina Carpet Mills Inc.
KEY WEST - Floor coverings—carpet and rugs ☆ - Playfield International Inc.
KEY WEST - Floor coverings—carpet and rugs ☆ - Walter Carpet Mills
KEY WEST - Frames—eyeglass - U.S. Optical Frame Co.
KEY WEST - Furniture - A. Brandt Co. Inc.
KEY WEST - Garden furniture—rattan ☆ - Lloyd/Flanders Industries
KEY WEST - Mobile homes - Golden West Homes
KEY WEST - Seafood products—fresh or frozen ☆ - Singleton Seafood Co.
KEY WEST - Siding—insulating - Champion International Corp.
KEY WEST - Skin care products - Key West Aloe Inc.
KEY WEST - Trailers—travel - Fleetwood Enterprises, Inc.
KEY WEST ALOE - Beauty shops - Key West Aloe Inc.
KEY WEST ALOEGENETIC SOLUTION - Skin care products - Key West Fragrance & Cosmetics Inc.
KEY WEST COCONUT COMPANY - Posters - Key West Coconut Co.
KEY WEST COOLER - Beverages—alcohol - Florida Brewing Co.
KEY WEST GOLD - Colognes - Key West Aloe Inc.
KEY WEST LIME AND PIE - Juices - Parman-Kendall Corp.
KEY WEST SMOOTH SHAVE - Colognes - Key West Aloe Inc.
KEY WEST SMOOTH SHAVE - Skin care products - Key West Fragrance & Cosmetics Inc.
KEY WEST SODA LIFE PRESERVER - Dishes—plastic - John Seney, Inc.
KEY WEST TAN - Suntan lotions - Key West Aloe Inc.
KEY-WORD BOOKS - Publisher's imprints - Word, Inc.
KEY-WRITE - Paper—carbon ☆ - Eaton Allen Ko-Rec-Type Corp.
KEYAKI - Floor coverings - Nittoh Tile Corp.
KEYBAK - Fabrics—broadcloth - Chicopee
KEYBOARD - Apparel and accessories - HPS Corp.
KEYBOARD - Recording label - Band Box Record Co.
KEYBOARD - Toys - Tonka Corp.
KEYBOARD ARPEGGIOS - Computer software - Electronic Courseware Systems Inc.
KEYBOARD BLUES - Computer software - Electronic Courseware Systems Inc.
KEYBOARD BUDDY - Musical instrument accessories - Tamarkin Co.
KEYBOARD CADET - Computer software - Mindscape Software Inc.
KEYBOARD CHORDS - Computer software - Electronic Courseware Systems Inc.
KEYBOARD COMMAND - Computer software - Compu-Tations Inc.
KEYBOARD COMMANDER - Electronics equipment - AMX Corp.
KEYBOARD CREATIONS - Toys—electronic ☆ - Philips Consumer Electronics Co.
KEYBOARD EXTENDED JAZZ HARMONIES - Computer software - Electronic Courseware Systems Inc.
KEYBOARD FINGERINGS - Computer software - Electronic Courseware Systems Inc.
KEYBOARD FLIP - Computer peripheral equipment - Basic Needs Inc.
KEYBOARD INSTRUCTOR, THE - Computer software - Educational Methods, Inc.
KEYBOARD INTERVALS - Computer software - Electronic Courseware Systems Inc.
KEYBOARD JAZZ HARMONIES - Computer software - Electronic Courseware Systems Inc.
KEYBOARD KAPERS - Computer software - Electronic Courseware Systems Inc.
KEYBOARD KOMFORT - Computers - Aldrich's Innovative Inc.
KEYBOARD MAGIC - Synthesizers—musical instrument - JTG of Nashville
KEYBOARD NAMEGAME - Computer software - Electronic Courseware Systems Inc.
KEYBOARD NOTE DRILL - Computer software - Electronic Courseware Systems Inc.
KEYBOARD SLIDEAWAY - Computer peripheral equipment ☆ - Kensington
KEYBOARD SPECIALTIES - Pianos - Keyboard Specialties
KEYBOARD SPEED READING - Computer software - Electronic Courseware Systems Inc.
KEYBOARD TUTOR - Computer software - Electronic Courseware Systems Inc.

☆ = Now out of production

KEYCAPPERS - Computer-keyboard labels - Powerbyte Inc.
KEYCELL - Wiring devices - World Communication Group Inc.
KEYCHAIN CRITTERS - Key rings - Tops Pen Co.
KEYCHAIN KASH - Novelty items - Knox Concepts
KEYCORDER - Semiconductors - Sharper Image Corp.
KEYCOTE - Rust removers - Elf Lubricants North America, Inc.
KEYCOUNTER - Duplicating machines - Hecon Corp.
KEYCURE - Epoxy - Key Laboratories Inc.
KEYCUT - Oils–lubricating - Elf Lubricants North America, Inc.
KEYD-IT - Drums–musical instruments - Silver St. Inc.
KEYDATA - Computers - Datapro International, Inc.
KEYDECK - Wire - Keystone Steel & Wire Co.
KEYFORCE - Toys–automobiles - Mattel, Inc.
KEYGEAR - Lubricants - Elf Lubricants North America, Inc.
KEYHOLE - Fasteners–snap - Penn Engineering and Manufacturing Corp.
KEYING STATION - Locks–door - Emhart Inc.
KEYKLEEN - Cleaning preparations - Elf Lubricants North America, Inc.
KEYKO - Margarine - Van Den Bergh Foods Co.
KEYKODE - Film - Eastman Kodak Co.
KEYLATED - Feed supplements for animals - Chelated Minerals, Inc.
KEYLESS - Binders - Fred Procter Co.
KEYLEX - Vitamins and nutritional supplements - Ingersoll & Associates
KEYLINE - Cabinets ☆ - Crystal Cabinet Works Inc.
KEYLINE - Electronics equipment - Grass Valley Group Inc.
KEYLINE - Hardware - Keystone Steel & Wire Co.
KEYLINK - Electronics equipment - Grass Valley Group Inc.
KEYLINKS - Publisher's imprints - Psychological Corp.
KEYLITE - Flashlights - Wonder Corp. of America
KEYLOC - Building materials–concrete - Surebond, Inc.
KEYMAN - Musical instrument accessories - Suzuki Corp.
KEYMAN - Musical instruments - Suzuki Musical Instruments Corp.
KEYMAPPER - Computer software - Data-Cal Corp.
KEYMARK - Locks–padlocks - Medeco Security Locks, Inc.
KEYMESH - Netting - Keystone Steel & Wire Co.
KEYMMANDERS - Toys–automobiles - Mattel, Inc.
KEYMONICA - Toys–musical - Proll Toy Co.
KEYNOTE - Computers - Datapro International, Inc.
KEYNOTE - Floor coverings - Congoleum Corp.
KEYNOTE - Floor coverings–carpet and rugs - Dan River Inc.
KEYNOTE - Pagers - Motorola, Inc. (Land Mobile Products Sector)
KEYNOTE - Paper–carbon ☆ - Curtis-Young Corp.
KEYNOTES - Notebooks and notepads - Kristin Elliott Inc.
KEYPAK - Computer software - FTP Software, Inc.
KEYPARK - Office supplies - Rubbermaid Office Products Inc.
KEYPARTNERS - Paper–gummed - Michele M. Hilland and Jeffrey E. Hilland Partnership
KEYPER - Cabinets–metal - Marcon International, Inc.
KEYPERS - Footwear - Chadwick Industries
KEYPERS - Toys - Tonka Corp.
KEYPLEX - Fertilizers - Morse Enterprises Ltd.
KEYPLUS 20 - Telephones - At&T Corp.
KEYPORT - Computer peripheral equipment - Lintek Inc.
KEYPORT - Floor coverings ☆ - Congoleum Corp.
KEYREST - Computer peripheral equipment ☆ - Hunt Manufacturing Co.
KEYREZ - Epoxy - Key Laboratories Inc.
KEYS - Computer software ☆ - Dr. T's Music Software Inc.
KEYS - Glassware–household ☆ - Crisa Corp.
KEYS & CASH - Toys ☆ - Henry Gordy International Inc.
KEYS & STANDART - Apparel and accessories - Crowley, Milner and Co.
KEYS ANGLER - Ships–sailing vessels - Glander Boats Inc.
KEYS GRANITE - Floor coverings–tile - Keys Granite, Inc.
KEYS OF LEARNING - Games - CBS Toys
KEYS-ON-A-RING - Toys - Gerber Products Co.
KEYS TO RESPONSIBLE DRIVING - Computer software - CBS Software
KEYSCAPE - Locks–padlocks ☆ - Weiser Lock Corp.
KEYSCO - Tools - S & H Industries, Inc.
KEYSEALERS - Office supplies ☆ - Amherst International Enterprises Co.
KEYSONIC - Computer peripheral equipment - Powercom America Inc.
KEYSPIN - Lubricants - Elf Lubricants North America, Inc.
KEYSTONE - Automotive parts and accessories - Keystone Automotive Industries Inc.
KEYSTONE - Beverages–malt - Adolph Coors Co.
KEYSTONE - Bicycles - Columbia Manufacturing Inc.
KEYSTONE - Blocks–concrete - Keystone Retaining Wall Systems, Inc.
KEYSTONE - Cabinets - Beatrice Cos. Inc.
KEYSTONE - Cameras - Concord Camera Corp.

KEYSTONE - Cases–plastic ☆ - Mautner Co. Inc.
KEYSTONE - Chimney globes ☆ - Corning Inc.
KEYSTONE - Clamps - Murray Corp.
KEYSTONE - Cosmetics ☆ - Marianna Imports, Inc.
KEYSTONE - Electronic equipment - Silicon Valley Bus Co., Inc.
KEYSTONE - Expansion shields - MKT Fastening, LLC
KEYSTONE - Fencing–steel - Keystone Steel & Wire Co.
KEYSTONE - Floor coverings - Tarkett, Inc.
KEYSTONE - Fruits and vegetables - Nuchief Sales Inc.
KEYSTONE - Lubricants - Elf Lubricants North America, Inc.
KEYSTONE - Mushrooms - Manfredini Enterprises
KEYSTONE - Occasional tables ☆ - JDI Group, Inc.
KEYSTONE - Office furniture–metal ☆ - Joyce International Inc.
KEYSTONE - Paper–writing - Champion International Corp.
KEYSTONE - Pretzels - Keystone Pretzel Bakery
KEYSTONE - Sewing machines–household - VWS Inc.
KEYSTONE - Shovels - Rugg Manufacturing Co. Inc.
KEYSTONE - Snack foods - Keystone Food Products
KEYSTONE - Stationery ☆ - Mead Corp.
KEYSTONE CASUALS - Apparel and accessories - Key Industries, Inc.
KEYSTONE COWBOY - Games - Universal Manufacturing Co., Inc.
KEYSTONE DRY - Beverages–malt - Adolph Coors Co.
KEYSTONE FARMS - Juices - Keystone Food Products
KEYSTONE FASTENERS - Hardware - Keystone Consolidated Industries, Inc.
KEYSTONE FRANKLIN - Metals - Waxman Industries Inc.
KEYSTONE KOPS - Books–comic - Keystone Kops
KEYSTONE KOPS - Toys - Carol Leveque Pransky
KEYSTONE KWENCH - Juices ☆ - Keystone Food Products
KEYSTONE LIGHT - Beverages–malt - Adolph Coors Co.
KEYSTONE MEDALLION - Aircraft–helicopters - Keystone Helicopter Corp.
KEYSTONE MORIN - Actuators–hydraulic - Keystone International Holdings Corp.
KEYSTONE PORTABLE LIGHTING - Lamps - RLT Enterprises, Inc.
KEYSTONE POWERFUEL - Gasoline - United Refining Co.
KEYSTONE RIDGEWAY - Giftware - Wilson Brothers
KEYSTONES - Floor coverings - Tarkett, Inc.
KEYSTOPPER - Lenses–projection - Buhl Optical Co.
KEYSTORE - Computer software - Keystar Systems, Inc.
KEYSTROKE - Tables–metal ☆ - Cramer Inc.
KEYTAP - Lubricants - Elf Lubricants North America, Inc.
KEYTEC - Computer peripheral equipment - Keytec, Inc.
KEYTEX - Computer software - Keytex Corp.
KEYTWIST - Nails–horseshoe - Keystone Consolidated Industries, Inc.
KEYVIEWPOINT - Computer software - Inworld VR, Inc.
KEYVUE - Packaging–foam - Murrah Packing Inc.
KEYWARE - Computer software - Racotek, Inc.
KEYWAY - Lubricants - Elf Lubricants North America, Inc.
KEYWORKS - Computer software - Alpha Software Corp.
KF - Cookware - Regal Ware, Inc.
KF LTD - Hosiery - Kinney Shoe Corp.
KF3 - Golfing equipment - Advanced Retrofit Components Associated
K.F.B. - Liquors - United States Distilled Products Co.
KFC - Restaurants–fast food - KFC Corp.
KFEEDERS - Bird feeders - K-Feeders Enterprises, Inc.
KFM - Lenses–magnifying - Luxo Corp.
KFR - Office machines ☆ - Eaton Allen Ko-Rec-Type Corp.
KG - Jewelry–precious - Kurt Gaum, Inc.
KG - Luggage - American Hemp Mercantile, Inc.
KG INDUSTRIES - Motor vehicles - Kwik Goal, Ltd.
KGA - Valves - Clarkson Co.
KGB - T-shirts–men's - Timothy M. Arman
KGB I - Games - Franklin Merchandising Co.
KGB II - Games - Franklin Merchandising Co.
KGD - Valves - Clarkson Co.
KGD PLUS - Electrical equipment - Micron Semiconductor Inc.
KGP - Teas–herbal - Korean Ginseng Products Co., Ltd.
KGRO - Fertilizers - Kmart Corp.
KGRO - Lawn mowers - Kmart Properties, Inc.
KH - Tiles–mosaic - Capitol Tile Import Co.
KH-6 - Vitamins and nutritional supplements - De Lalut Marketing Corp.
KH-C VANONI - Vitamins and nutritional supplements - Vanoni Marketing Corp.
KHAAM - Floor coverings–carpet and rugs ☆ - Mohawk Industries Inc.
KHADDAR - Floor coverings–carpet and rugs - Masland Corp.
KHADELY - Scarves - Khadely Fabrics
KHAFRA - Jewelry - Khafra Engineering Consultants, Inc.
KHAKI - Watches ☆ - SMH (US) Inc.

KHAKI MATE - Watches ☆ - SMH (US) Inc.
KHAKI TOPS - Socks - Marmon Holdings, Inc.
KHAMPHOUK - Vegetables–canned - H.C. Foods Co., Ltd.
KHAO-SOI - Food products - Tucuru
KHAYYAM - Dinnerware–glass ☆ - Johnson Brothers, USA, Inc.
KHELLIN - Pharmaceutical preparations - City Chemical Corp.
KHEPRI - Pharmaceutical preparations - Khepri Pharmaceuticals, Inc.
K.H.G. 7 - Vitamins and nutritional supplements - Health Products Corp.
KHI - Apparel and accessories - Kin Hing International, Inc.
KHOLUI - Papier-mache articles - Siamese Imports Co.
KHOMBU - Footwear - Khombu
KHOTAR - Dinnerware–glass - Franciscan by Johnson Brothers, USA, Inc.
KHOURY - Furniture - Khoury, Inc.
KHQ - Apparel and accessories - Wear Me Apparel Corp.
KHROME WERKS - Motorcycle parts and accessories - DS Manufacturing, Inc.
KHS - Bicycles - KHS Inc.
KHS CLASSIC - Bicycles - Kung Hsue She, Inc.
KHS GRAN SPORT - Bicycles - Kung Hsue She, Inc.
KHS MONTANA - Bicycles - Kung Hsue She, Inc.
KHS MONTANA COMP - Bicycles - Kung Hsue She, Inc.
KHS MONTANA CREST - Bicycles - Kung Hsue She, Inc.
KHS MONTANA DESCENT - Bicycles - Kung Hsue She, Inc.
KHS MONTANA JUNIOR - Bicycles - Kung Hsue She, Inc.
KHS MONTANA PRO - Bicycles - Kung Hsue She, Inc.
KHS MONTANA SPORT - Bicycles - Kung Hsue She, Inc.
KHS MONTANA SUMMIT - Bicycles ☆ - Kung Hsue She, Inc.
KHS MONTANA SUPER - Bicycles - Kung Hsue She, Inc.
KHS MONTANA TEAM - Bicycles - Kung Hsue She, Inc.
KHS MONTANA TRAIL - Bicycles - Kung Hsue She, Inc.
KHS MONTANA XT - Bicycles ☆ - Kung Hsue She, Inc.
KHS PROFESSIONAL - Bicycles - Kung Hsue She, Inc.
KHS TEAMPRO - Bicycles ☆ - Kung Hsue She, Inc.
KHS TRIATHLETE - Bicycles - Kung Hsue She, Inc.
KHS TRIATHLETE PLUS - Bicycles ☆ - Kung Hsue She, Inc.
KHS TRIATHLETE PRO - Bicycles - Kung Hsue She, Inc.
KHS WINNER - Bicycles ☆ - Kung Hsue She, Inc.
KHYBER - Floor coverings–carpet and rugs ☆ - Gulistan Carpet Inc.
KHYBER - Floor coverings–carpet and rugs ☆ - Trans-Ocean Import Co. Inc.
KHYBER - Knives–pocket ☆ - Cole Consumer Products Inc.
KI - Furniture - Krueger International, Inc.
KI INC - Jewelry - Kishek International, Inc.
KI-KO-MO - Apparel and accessories - Kikomo, Ltd.
KI-WI - Floor coverings–tile ☆ - Pawling Corp. (Standard Products Div.)
KIAMA-CAPE - Crocheted and knitted items - Towne & King Inc.
KIAMA KID - Crocheted and knitted items - Towne & King Inc.
KIANA - Paper - Georgia-Pacific Corp.
KIANA, KENYA'S LITTLE SISTER - Dolls - Tyco Industries, Inc.
KIARA - Fabrics–broadcloth - Chicopee
KIARA - Wallpaper ☆ - Gilford Corp.
KIAWAH - Furniture - Romweber Co.
KIB-LETS - Dog food - Stevens Industries Inc.
KIBBLE KORNER HIDEAWAY - Toys–stuffed - Lewis Galoob Toys, Inc.
KIBBLE SELECT - Dog food - Dad's Products Co. Inc.
KIBBLE SELECTABLES - Pet products - Dad's Products Co. Inc.
KIBBLES AND CHEEZY CHEWS - Dog food - Ralston Purina Co.
KIBBLES AND CHUNKS - Dog food - Ralston Purina Co.
KIBBLES 'N BITS - Dog food - Heinz Pet Products Co.
KIBBLES 'N BITS 'N BITS 'N BITS - Dog food - Ralston Purina Co.
KIBCOH - Pageholder/bookmark - Hammerstein Music & Theater Co. Inc.
KIBIBI - Dolls - Kibibi in the Moon
KIBUN - Seafood products–fresh or frozen - Kibun Products International Inc.
KIBUN GOLD - Seafood products–fresh or frozen - Kibun Products International Inc.
KIC FUEL - Vitamins and nutritional supplements - Twinlab
KICAB - Enamels - Sherwin-Williams Automotive Finishes Corp.
KICH'N KOMPOSTER - Housewares - Carbco Industries Inc.
KICK - Beverages–carbonated - Royal Crown Cola Co.
KICK - Cleaning preparations - Absorb, Inc.
KICK-A-SCENT - Hunting equipment - Southern Hunters Sports Products
KICK-A-SCORE - Games - Smethport Specialty Co.
KICK-A-SHAY - Games - Yetken International
KICK-A-WAY - Underwear and nightwear - Wundies Inc.
KICK AND RUN - Video games ☆ - Taito America Corp.
KICK ASS KRUTONS - Croutons - Krutons
KICK ASS LIMITED - Apparel–athletic - John Kontopuls
KICK ASS RECORDS - Recording label - U.M.M. Recording, Inc.

KICK AXION - Apparel–athletic - Steadman-Gibson Corporate Design, Inc.
KICK BACKS - Hosiery - Sara Lee Corp.
KICK BUTT - Golfing equipment - Callaway Golf Co.
KICK HOOP - Sporting goods - Rimball Marketing and Development, Inc.
KICK IT UP - T-shirts–men's - Nova Promotion Group, Inc.
KICK M-UP - Food products - Jardine's Texas Foods
KICK 'N WINGS - Meat products–poultry - Perdue Farms Inc.
KICK-OFF - Crocheted and knitted items ☆ - Schuessler Knitting Mills Inc.
KICK START - Clothing - Alperin, Inc.
KICK START - Veterinary pharmaceutical preparations - Imu-Tek Animal Health, Inc.
KICK START - Video games - Taito America Corp.
KICK-START PRESS - Publisher's imprints - Harold David Barber
KICKAPOO JOY JUICE - Beverages–carbonated - Monarch Co., Inc.
KICKER - Adhesives and sealants - Pacer Technology
KICKER - Audio equipment - Speakerkits Inc.
KICKER - Audio equipment - Stillwater Designs & Audio Inc.
KICKER - Barbecue sauce - Jardine's Texas Foods
KICKER - Bicycles ☆ - Huffy Corp.
KICKER PAD - Motors–outboard - C. Sherman Johnson Co. Inc.
KICKER-PANTS - Underwear and nightwear - Henson-Kickernick Inc.
KICKER, THE - Heating equipment - Slant/Fin Corp.
KICKERINOS - Shoes - MSF Corp.
KICKERNICK - Underwear and nightwear - Henson-Kickernick Inc.
KICKERS - Ophthalmic goods - Foremost Optical Products
KICKERS - Vitamins and nutritional supplements - Armand Kramedjian
KICKI PHUT - Apparel and accessories - James D. Thorpe
KICKIE - Dolls - Mattel, Inc.
KICKIN FRESH CARROT HORSERADISH - Horseradish - Uncle Dave's Kitchen
KICKIN GRILL - Barbecue sauce - Uncle Dave's Kitchen
KICKIN KETCHUP - Catsup - Uncle Dave's Kitchen
KICKIN' KOUNTRY - Video production - Kickin' Kountry, Inc.
KICKIN MUSTARD W/HORSERADISH - Mustard - Uncle Dave's Kitchen
KICKING MULE - Recording label - Kicking Mule Records Inc.
KICKLES - Candy - Joveta Rose Glidewell
KICK'M-UP - Mustard ☆ - Texxstar Resources (USA), Inc.
KICK'N BUTT - Seasonings - Melba Food Specialties Inc.
KICKOFF - Soccer equipment - Mikasa Sports
KICKOFF CLASSIC - Balls - Mikasa Sports
KICKOFF KING - Balls ☆ - Mikasa Sports
KICKOFF ULTRA LITE - Balls ☆ - Mikasa Sports
KICKPAD - Musical instrument accessories - Aquarian Accessories Corp.
KICKRIDER - Toys - Aqua-Leisure Industries, Inc.
KICKS - Apparel and accessories - Stahl-Urban Co.
KICKS - Hosiery - Mayer/Berkshire Corp.
KICKS - Luggage - Samsonite Corp.
KICKS - Toys - Jak-Pak Inc.
KICKS - Toys–stuffed - Kamar International Inc.
KICKS - Trading cards and stamps - Kicks Inc.
KICKS EXPLOSIVE SPORTSWEAR - T-shirts–men's - Kicks Explosive Sportswear
KICKSTAND - Woodworking machinery - Delta International Machinery Corp.
KICKSTART - Insecticides - Helena Chemical Co.
KICKUM - Cigarettes - R & A Adventures
KICKY DICKEY - Apparel and accessories - Gelmart Industries Inc.
KICKY NICKY - Dolls - Mattel, Inc.
KID - Identification tags - Michel & Washer Enterprises, Inc.
KID AMERICA BY DOBIE - Apparel–children's - Dobie Industries Inc.
KID ARMOR - Sporting goods - Nicholas B. Paffett
KID ASHWORTH - Apparel–children's - Charter Golf, Inc.
KID ATHLETE - Apparel–children's - Hey Kids, Inc.
KID BIZ - Apparel and accessories ☆ - Edison Brothers Stores, Inc.
KID CAD - Computer software ☆ - Knowledge Adventure
KID CALC - Computer software - E. David & Associates
KID CARE - Bandages - Tsumura International Inc.
KID CLASSICS - Toys - Learning Curve Toys, LLC
KID CLEANER - Bathroom fixtures - Alsons Corp.
KID COMFORT - Juvenile product - Par Industries, Inc.
KID CONNECTION - Apparel–children's - Wal-Mart Stores Inc.
KID CONTROL - Remote control devices - Tele-Communications Inc.
KID CORRUPTION KIT - Candy - Harry London's Candies Inc.
KID COVER - Skin care products - Robert F. Berlucchi
KID CRAFT - Craft supplies ☆ - VIP/VIP Crafts
KID CUISINE - Dinners–frozen - Conagra, Inc.
KID CUSHIONED - Floor coverings - Congoleum Corp.

☆ = Now out of production

KID CUTS - Computer programs ☆ - Broderbund Software, Inc.
KID DESIGNS - Tape players - Kid Designs Inc.
KID DESK - Computer software - Edmark Corp.
KID DIMENSION - Toys - Kid Dimension, Inc.
KID-DING - Bedding–linen - Continental Quilting Co. Inc.
KID DRACULA - Toys–electronic ☆ - Konami (America) Inc.
KID DUDS - Apparel–children's - Kid Duds
KID-E-CALC - Health care products - Christopher Enterprises Inc.
KID-E-COL - Health care products - Christopher Enterprises Inc.
KID-E-DRY - Health care products - Christopher Enterprises Inc.
KID-E-KABIN - Toys ☆ - Handy Home Products
KID-E-MUNE - Health care products - Christopher Enterprises Inc.
KID FINISH - Stationery - Crane & Co. Inc.
KID I - Frames–eyeglass - Rozin Optical Export Corp.
KID-I-TREET - Candy ☆ - Super Valu Inc.
KID ICARUS - Video games - Nintendo of America Inc.
KID II - Frames–eyeglass - Rozin Optical Export Corp.
KID JAZZ - Apparel - Derrick Douglas Price
KID KAPSULE - Playground equipment - BCI Burke Co., Inc.
KID-KART - Cushions - Jay Medical Ltd.
KID KASE - Cases–plastic ☆ - Newell Office Products
KID KLOK - Clocks - Franklin Instrument Co. Inc.
KID KOMFORT - Shoe insoles ☆ - Spenco Medical Corp.
KID KORE - Toys - Kid Kore International Ltd.
KID-KUFF - Furniture - Kid-Kuff Inc.
KID KUSION - Pillowcases - Walter Lee and Cynthia L. Bowen Partnership
KID-LEIDOSCOPE - Computer software - Mind Play
KID MCGEE - Computer software ☆ - Knowledge Adventure
KID MID PLUS - Sporting goods ☆ - Gold Eagle/Arnold Palmer
KID MIX - Bedding–linen - Beacon Looms Inc.
KID MOHAIR 2000 - Yarn - Henry's Attic
KID N KABOTTLE - Infant product - Daniel Mulhern
KID NATURAL - Vitamins and nutritional supplements - Healthy 'N Fit Nutritionals
KID NEPTUNE - Apparel and accessories - Jeffrey Clay Sholk
KID-OPHILUS - Vitamins and nutritional supplements - International Health Products, Inc.
KID PHONICS - Computer software ☆ - Knowledge Adventure
KID PHONICS 2 - Computer software ☆ - Knowledge Adventure
KID PICS - Cereal - General Mills, Inc.
KID PIX - Computer software - Broderbund Software, Inc.
KID PIX 2 - Computer software - Broderbund Software, Inc.
KID PIX COMPANION - Computer software ☆ - Broderbund Software, Inc.
KID PIX FUN PACK - Computer software - Broderbund Software, Inc.
KID PLEAS'N EAT'N - Food products - Oscar Mayer Foods Corp.
KID POWER - Breads ☆ - Flowers Industries Inc.
KID POWER - Shoes - Kid Power USA Inc.
KID POWER - Wheelchairs - Everest and Jennings International Ltd.
KID PRO QUO - Computer software ☆ - Softsync Inc.
KID-PROOF - Floor coverings–carpet and rugs - Diamond Rug & Carpet Mills
KID PROOF - Flowers, plants, and seeds - Seed Corp. of America
KID PRUF - Infant product ☆ - Playing Mantis
KID RIDERS - Plaything - Iron Mountain Forge Corp.
KID-ROW - Boats - Glen-L Marine Designs
KID SISTER - Toys - Playskool, Inc.
KID SIZE - Fruits–canned - Pacific Coast Producers
KID SPORT - Apparel–children's ☆ - Health-Tex Inc.
KID STARTER - Food products - Denny's Inc.
KID STUFF - Video games ☆ - I.J.E. Inc.
KID STUFF - Vitamins and nutritional supplements - Hillestad International, Inc.
KID TALK - Computer software ☆ - First Byte Inc.
KID-TEL - Phonographs - K-Tel International, Inc.
KID TILES - Playground equipment matting - Iron Mountain Forge Corp.
KID TO KID - Furniture - Kid to Kid Franchise System, Inc.
KID TOUGH - Bicycles ☆ - Roadmaster Corp.
KID TOUGH - Footwear ☆ - E.S. Originals, Inc.
KID TUFF - Floor coverings–carpet and rugs - Diamond Rug & Carpet Mills
KID-U-NOT - Apparel and accessories - Kid-U-Not Inc.
KID VID - Video games ☆ - I.J.E. Inc.
KID WARMERS - Apparel–children's - Meijer, Inc.
KID WORKS - Computer software ☆ - Knowledge Adventure
KID WORKS DELUXE - Computer software - Knowledge Adventure
KID ZONE - Greeting cards - American Greetings Corp.
KIDABBLERS - Hobby kits - Fleiner's, Inc.
KIDABLES - Hair care products - Beauticontrol Cosmetics Inc.

KIDABLES - Vitamins and nutritional supplements - BC International Cosmetics & Image Services, Inc.
KIDACO - Footwear - Steve Crisafi
KIDBASIX - Underwear and nightwear - Impact Imports International, Inc.
KIDBOARD - Computer peripheral equipment - Kidboard Inc.
KIDCARE - Identification tags - Polaroid Corp.
KIDCATCHER - Sporting goods - Robert W. Huebner
KIDD - Marshmallows - Kidd & Co.
KIDD BOXERS - Apparel–children's - Superior Togs of California, Inc.
KIDD-E - Toys ☆ - South Bend Toy Manufacturing Co.
KIDDE - Fire extinguishers - Kidde Safety
KIDDE KARE - Furniture–children's - Service Merchandise Co., Inc.
KIDDE NIGHTHAWK - Alarm systems - Kidde Safety
KIDDER USA - Bags–canvas - Kidder International Inc.
KIDDI POP - Candy - Yost Candy Co.
KIDDICRAFT - Toys - Fisher-Price, Inc.
KIDDIE - Publisher's imprints - Samuel Lowe Co.
KIDDIE - Shoes - Footwear International Corp.
KIDDIE ART - Toys - Samuel Lowe Co.
KIDDIE BATHTIME - Skin care products - Paris Presents Ltd.
KIDDIE BOUNCER - Toys ☆ - Hedstrom Corp.
KIDDIE CAMERA - Toys - Mattel, Inc.
KIDDIE CAMPER - Playpens–wood - Lisco, Inc.
KIDDIE COMPUTER - Toys - Mattel, Inc.
KIDDIE CORRAL - Furniture ☆ - Gerry Wood Products
KIDDIE CRUISER - Toys ☆ - Gerber Products Co.
KIDDIE CYCLES - Toys–automobiles ☆ - Hedstrom Corp.
KIDDIE FONDUE - Toys–models ☆ - Kenner Products
KIDDIE KAB - Strollers - Central Specialties Ltd.
KIDDIE KANDIES - Candy ☆ - Phoenix Confections Inc.
KIDDIE KANTEENS - Toys - A.R.C. Toys Inc.
KIDDIE KAP - Helmets–athletic - All American Products Inc.
KIDDIE KAP BUDDIES - Vitamins and nutritional supplements - Republic Drug Co. Inc.
KIDDIE KAR - Toys ☆ - Gerber Products Co.
KIDDIE KAR - Toys–automobiles ☆ - Hedstrom Corp.
KIDDIE KART - Bicycles - Kiddie Kart International Inc.
KIDDIE KARTS - Infant product ☆ - Graco Children's Products
KIDDIE KASSETTE STORYBOARD VIEWER - Toys - Samuel Lowe Co.
KIDDIE KATCH - Locks–door - Shur-Lok Corp.
KIDDIE KLASSICS - Infant product ☆ - Judi's Orijinals
KIDDIE KLUTCH - Toys ☆ - Gerber Products Co.
KIDDIE KOBRA - Bicycles - Ross Bicycles USA, Ltd.
KIDDIE KOFF - Cold remedies - Republic Drug Co. Inc.
KIDDIE KOOKIES - Cookies ☆ - Dairy State Foods Inc.
KIDDIE KOOLS - Candy ☆ - Leonhardt Inc.
KIDDIE KOPTER - Toys–airplanes - Marlin Toy Products Inc.
KIDDIE KORNER - Fans–electric - Duracraft Corp.
KIDDIE-KRAFT - Jewelry - Marathon Co. Inc.
KIDDIE KURL - Hair care products ☆ - Pro-Line Corp.
KIDDIE LINKS - Toys - Playskool, Inc.
KIDDIE PACK - Infant product - Gerry Baby Products Co.
KIDDIE POPS - Candy ☆ - Crystal Pure Candy Co.
KIDDIE POWDER - Pharmaceutical preparations - Gordon Laboratories
KIDDIE PURSE - Plastics - Lapin Products Inc.
KIDDIE RYDER - Sporting goods - All American Products Inc.
KIDDIE-SAFE - Sporting goods - Hedstrom Corp.
KIDDIE SPRAY - Paints ☆ - Sheffield Bronze Paint Corp.
KIDDIE SWING - Infant product ☆ - Gerry Wood Products
KIDDIE TREATS - Candy - Sweet Candy Co.
KIDDIE UPS - Diapers–disposable - G. Hirsch and Co., Inc.
KIDDIE WALKER - Toys ☆ - Hedstrom Corp.
KIDDIE YARD - Infant product ☆ - Gerry Wood Products
KIDDIELAND - Toys ☆ - Henry Gordy International Inc.
KIDDIES - Cough medicines ☆ - Vitarine Pharmaceuticals Inc.
KIDDIES KORNER - Wallpaper ☆ - Andover Wallcovering
KIDDIGEM - Jewelry - Uncas Manufacturing Co.
KIDDING AROUND - Publisher's imprints - John Muir Publications
KIDDING AROUND - Wallpaper - Sellers & Josephson
KIDDIPAKS - Candy - Yost Candy Co.
KIDDLE - Barbecues and grills - Toastmaster Inc.
KIDDO - Paints - Standard Brands Paint Co.
KIDD'S - Confections - Kidd & Co.
KIDDY CABBY - Tricycles ☆ - Hedstrom Corp.
KIDDY CHEWS - Vitamins and nutritional supplements - Schein Pharmaceutical Inc.

KIDDY COP - Housewares - Leviton Manufacturing Co., Inc.
KIDDY KADDY - Infant product ☆ - Healthometer
KIDDY KARRELL - Electronics equipment - Educational Electronics Corp.
KIDDY KATS - Apparel–children's - Valtex, Inc.
KIDDY KOOK - Toys ☆ - Chilton-Globe, Inc.
KIDDY-MATIC - Toys - Chilton-Globe, Inc.
KIDDY MO AIRPORT - Games ☆ - CBS Toys
KIDDY MO BRIDGE & FERRY SET - Games ☆ - CBS Toys
KIDDY MO CITY & AIRPORT - Games ☆ - CBS Toys
KIDDY POOL-KORRAL - Swimming pools - Meyco Products Inc.
KIDDYTEA - Teas - Natureworks Inc.
KIDERIFFICS - Apparel–children's - Baby Bliss Inc.
KIDFETTI - Apparel–children's - Kidfetti, Inc.
KIDFRESH - Paper - Scott Paper Co.
KIDGUARD - Vitamins and nutritional supplements - Shaperite Concepts, Ltd.
KIDLETTES - Stationery - Tamera Lei Pelikan
KIDLOOKS - Apparel–children's - Beall's, Inc.
KIDMARK - Recording label - Trimark Holdings, Inc.
KIDMATCH - Electrical equipment - Talon Medical Ltd.
KIDNAPS - Napkins–paper - Idea Group
KIDNEY-BLADDER SUPPORT - Health care products - Healthwatchers System
KIDNEY-FLUSH - Health care products - Ion Laboratories Inc.
KIDNEY GLANDULAR PLUS - Vitamins and nutritional supplements - Ethical Nutrients
KIDNEY QI - Health care products - East Earth Herb Inc.
KIDNEY YANG QI - Health care products - East Earth Herb Inc.
KIDNEY YIN QI - Health care products - East Earth Herb Inc.
KIDNIC - Tables–wood - Heritage Woodworks
KIDNICINE - Veterinary pharmaceutical preparations ☆ - Zirin Laboratories International
KIDOODLES - Jewelry - Hannan-Copanezos, Joy
KIDOPHILUS - Vitamins and nutritional supplements - International Health Products, Inc.
KIDPAD - Computer peripheral equipment - Penmanship, Inc.
KIDPOINT - Computer peripheral equipment - Kidboard Inc.
KIDPRO - Clothing - Leslie G. Bromberg
KIDPROOF - Apparel–children's - Health-Tex Inc.
KIDPROOF - Paints - Yenkin Majestic Paint Corp.
KIDPUTER - Computers–personal - George A. Davey
KIDREAD - Computer software - Wright Group Publishing, Inc.
KIDREAD - Publisher's imprints - The Wright Group
KIDS - Broadcasting stations–television - United Paramount Network
KIDS - Calendars - Swim Publishing Corp.
KIDS - Cameras - Eastman Kodak Co.
KIDS - Carriages–baby - Ben's Trading International Inc.
K*I*D*S - Computer software - Electronic Courseware Systems Inc.
KIDS - Cups–paper - Kids Cups & Canteens
KIDS - Jewelry - 1928 Jewelry Co.
KID'S - Pharmaceutical preparations - Mentholatum Co.
KIDS - Toys - Jak-Pak Inc.
KIDS' - Toys - Today's Kids Inc.
KIDS II - Lighting fixtures - Kids II, Inc.
KIDS 14K GOLD CORNER - Jewelry - Baby Gold Jewelry, Inc.
KIDS, A - Recording label - Peter W. Hickey
KIDS & MORE - Apparel–children's - Sears, Roebuck and Co.
KIDS' ARMY - Publisher's imprints - Estelle Webre Elledge
KIDS' ART - Floor coverings–carpet and rugs - Bentley Mills, Inc.
KID'S ART - Novelty items - Papel Freelance, Inc.
KIDS' ART FOR THE FLOOR - Floor coverings–carpet and rugs - Bentley Mills, Inc.
KIDS AT PLAY - Computer peripheral equipment - Program Systems, Inc.
KIDS AT PLAY - Pillows - Kohl's Department Stores, Inc.
KIDS BY LA BELLE FASHIONS, INC. - Apparel–children's - La Belle Fashions, Inc.
KIDS CAN! - Publisher's imprints - Williamson Publishing, Co.
KIDS CAN CRAFT - Patterns–clothing - Kids Can Sew & Craft
KIDS CAN DRAW & PAINT TOO! - Paint sets–hobby ☆ - Martin F. Weber Co.
KIDS CAN SEW - Patterns–clothing - Kids Can Sew & Craft
KIDS CAN SEW - Patterns–clothing ☆ - Simplicity Pattern Co., Inc.
KIDS' CANDY COMPANY, THE - Candy - Catco, Inc.
KIDS CARAVAN - Wallpaper - Stroheim & Romann, Inc.
KID'S CARE - Furniture ☆ - Lexington Furniture Industries, Inc.
KIDS CARE - Wallcovering - Colortree Designs
KIDS CARE - Wallpaper - Eisenhart Wallcoverings Co.

KIDS' CHOICE - Breads - Purity Baking Co.
KIDS CHOICE - Candy - R.L. Albert & Son, Inc.
KID'S CHOICE - Playground equipment - Miracle Recreation Equipment Co.
KIDS CHOICE - Wallpaper - Bayview Wallcoverings
KIDS' CHOICE COUGH POP - Cough medicines - Golden Apples Candy Co., Inc.
KIDS CLASSICS - Candy - Grist Mill Co.
KIDS CLUB - Bicycles ☆ - Huffy Corp.
KID'S CLUB - Chairs–plastic - Syroco
KID'S CLUB - Toys ☆ - Jak-Pak Inc.
KIDS CLUB - Wallpaper - Mokena Mills Inc.
KID'S COLLECTIBLES - Jewelry–costume - Howard Eldon Ltd.
KIDS COLLECTION - Computer software - Capstone Software
KID'S COLORS - Pens - Liqui-Mark
KID'S COMMUTER - Medical apparatus - Fortress Inc.
KIDS COMPANION, A - Vitamins and nutritional supplements - Natrol, Inc.
KIDS CONNECTIONS - Bedding–linen - Montgomery Ward & Co. Inc.
KIDS COOKIE MIX - Cookies - Kids Food and Cookie Co.
KIDS COOKIN - Cooking utensils–aluminum ☆ - Anchor Hocking Glass, Inc.
KIDS CORN DOGS - Frankfurters - NBCS, Inc.
KID'S CORNER - Health care products - Barcolene Inc.
KIDS' CORNER - Hobby kits - Greene Plastics Corp.
KIDS COUNTRY - Dinnerware–glass ☆ - Amole Inc.
KID'S COURT - Sporting goods - Lifetime Products, Inc.
KID'S COVER UP - Toys - M.&S. Shillman Inc.
KID'S CUSTOM - Medical apparatus - Fortress Inc.
KIDS CUTS - Recording label - BJS Communication, Inc.
KID'S DAY - Flowers - Nurserymen's Exchange, Inc.
KID'S ECOLOGY - Puzzles - M.W. Kasch Co.
KID'S EDGE - Medical apparatus - Fortress Inc.
KID'S ESSENTIALS - Vitamins and nutritional supplements - Vitamin Research Products Inc.
KIDS EXPRESS - Educational products - Treehouse Publications Ltd.
KIDS' FACTORY - Furniture ☆ - Something Special
KID'S FAVORITE RAZZMATAZZ - Fruit drinks–bottled or canned - H.P. Hood & Sons Inc.
KIDS FOOTLOCKER - Shoe stores - Kinney Shoe Corp.
KIDS FOR A NEW TOMORROW - Infant product ☆ - European Toy Collection/ Crocodile Creek
KIDS FOR NATURE - Apparel–children's ☆ - Nature Co.
KIDS GENERATION - Socks - Shogren Industries, Inc.
KIDS GIFTS - Dolls - Eden LLC
KIDS IN A JIFFY - Yarn ☆ - Lion Brand Yarn Co.
KIDS IN THE NEIGHBORHOOD - Apparel–children's - Federated Department Stores, Inc.
KIDS IN TOUCH - Games - Nynex Corp.
KIDS INNOVATIONS - Apparel–children's - Silk Screen Inc.
KIDS KARDS BY BETTY - Greeting cards - Kids Kards by Betty
KIDS, KIDS, KIDS: ALL STAR EDITION - Wallpaper - Imperial Wallcoverings, Inc.
KID'S KITCHEN - Food products - Hormel Foods Corp.
KID'S KITCHEN KITS - Toys - A.R.C. Toys Inc.
KIDS KLASSICS - Video production - Goodtimes Home Video Corp.
KIDS KLOSET - Apparel - Colberts, Inc.
KIDS KLOSET - Closet organizers - Clairson International Corp.
KIDS KLUB - Jewelry - Claire's Boutiques, Inc.
K.I.D.S. K.L.U.B. - Toys ☆ - Himark Enterprises Inc.
KIDS KOLORS - Apparel–children's - Union Underwear Co., Inc.
KID'S KRUNCH - Cereal - Aldi Inc.
KID'S KUTS - Cosmetics - Kaemark Inc.
KID'S LIBERTY - Medical apparatus - Fortress Inc.
KIDS LIDS - Apparel–children's - Samii Clothes
KID'S LINKS - Apparel and accessories - Kid's Links, Inc.
KIDS LOVE COLLECTION - Video production - Atlas Video, Inc.
KID'S LOVE NOTE - Paper products - Kid's Love Notes Inc.
KIDS MANHATTAN - Underwear and nightwear - Salant/Manhattan Industries
KID'S MEAL - Sandwiches–prepackaged - A and W Restaurants, Inc.
KIDS 'N' KOLOR - Furniture–children's - Ameriwood Industries International Corp.
KIDS N' KURLS - Hair care products ☆ - Summit Laboratories
KIDS 'N LA - Apparel and accessories - Baross Inc.
KIDS NUTRITION BAR - Candy - Increda-Meal Corp.
KIDS OF AMERICA - Toys - Kids of America Corp.
KIDS OF COLOR - Toys - Playskool, Inc.
KIDS OF COLOR DRESS-ME-UP PALS - Dolls - Playskool, Inc.
KIDS ON BOARD - Luggage - Shalam Imports Inc.

☆ = Now out of production

KIDS ON KEYS - Computer software - Queue Inc.
KIDS ONLY - Breads - American Bakeries Co.
KIDS ONLY! - Toys - Continental Industries, Inc.
KID'S PANTRY - Bakery products - Primary Colors, Inc.
KIDS' PASSPORT TO THE ARTS - Publisher's imprints - Steven R. Schechter
KIDS PERCH - Playground equipment - Miracle Recreation Equipment Co.
KIDS PLEX JR. - Vitamins and nutritional supplements - Performance Nutrition, Inc.
KIDS PLUGS - Plugs–ear - Karlen Manufacturing, Inc.
KIDS PLUS - Paints - Perry & Derrick Co.
KIDS PORT USA - Apparel and accessories - Health-Tex Inc.
KIDS' PRINTS - Paper–toilet - Georgia-Pacific Corp.
KIDS R SMART ENRICHMENT PROGRAMS - Educational materials - Janet Browning
KIDS R US - Apparel–children's - Kids R Us Co.
KIDS RESEARCH UNLIMITED - Consulting services - Teenage Research Unlimited
KID'S RETREAT - Furniture - Lexington Furniture Industries, Inc.
KID'S ROOM - Pigments–paint - Swimc, Inc.
KIDS: RUBBER DUCKIE - Wallpaper ☆ - Imperial Wallcoverings, Inc.
KIDS: RUBBER DUCKIE II - Wallpaper ☆ - Imperial Wallcoverings, Inc.
KID'S SAFE SEAL - Plugs–ear - Aearo Co.
KIDS SAVE THE DARNDEST THINGS - Apparel–children's - Pacific Enterprise Development Inc.
KIDS SCOOPS - Ice cream - Alpenrose Dairy, Inc.
KIDS SILICONE EAR PLUGS - Plugs–ear - Karlen Manufacturing, Inc.
KIDS SMART - Containers–plastic - SRW Computer Components, Inc.
KIDS SNACK PACK - Bakery products - Flowers Family Bakeries, Inc.
KID'S START - Health care products ☆ - Fresh Start Vitamin Co. (Pacific Packaging Concepts Inc.)
KIDS STEPS BY MESSINA - Shoes - Messer Import Corp.
KIDS STORE - Apparel–children's - Montgomery Ward & Co. Inc.
KID'S STUFF - Furniture - Alexvale Furniture, Inc.
KIDS STUFF - Hair care products - HHits Inc.
KID'S STUFF - Wallpaper - Pickhardt & Siebert USA Inc.
KIDS STYLE - Yogurt - Dannon Co., Inc.
KIDS SUPPLY CO. U.S.A. - Apparel and accessories - Vintage Industries USA, Inc.
KIDS TEAM - Apparel and accessories - Kevin Schmidt
KIDS THINGS - Pillowcases - JAE Holdings Inc.
KIDS TOGS HEDGEHOG - Apparel–children's - Lynette Hershler
KIDS' TOWN - Furniture–children's - O'Sullivan Industries, Inc.
KID'S TOY BOX - Wallpaper ☆ - Pickhardt & Siebert USA Inc.
KIDS UNIVERSITY - Computer software - Camelot Business Inv.
KIDS UNIVERSITY - Computer software - Camelot Corp.
KIDS VIEW - Wallcovering - Colortree Designs
KIDS WORKS - Shirts - Matchbox Toys USA
KIDS WORLD - Household cleaners - Gentle Earth International, Inc.
KID'S WORLD OF MUSIC - Recording label - A and M Records, Inc.
KIDS WRITE - Stationery - Mara-Mi, Inc.
KIDS YOGURT - Yogurt - Penn Maid Foods Inc.
KIDS ZONE PAINT - Paints - Valspar Corp.
KIDSAFE - Eyeglasses - Pearle, Inc.
KIDSBEARS - Jewelry - Baby Gold Jewelry, Inc.
KIDSCAPE - Toys–stuffed - Kidscape Children's Products, Inc.
KIDSCOOK - Aprons - Now Designs
KID'SCRAFT - Hobby kits - Manco, Inc.
KIDSEEDS - Flowers, plants, and seeds - NK Lawn & Garden Co.
KIDSENSE - Furniture - Sally L. Boutin
KIDSKIN - Cleaning preparations - Aarita Limelight, Inc.
KIDSLING - Infant product - Over the Shoulder Baby Holder
KIDSOFT - Computer software - Kidsoft, Inc.
KIDSONGS - Toys - Tyco Toys
KIDSOX - Apparel and accessories - Ridgeview Inc.
KIDSPACE - Toys - M.L. Cartwright Co.
KIDSPACE M. L. CARTWRIGHT CO - Toys - M.L. Cartwright Co.
KIDSPEACE - Recording label - Kidspeace Corp.
KIDSPECS - Frames–eyeglass - Shawnee Optical, Inc.
KIDSPLAY - Musical instruments - International Music Corp.
KIDSPORT - Strollers–baby - Combi International Corp.
KIDSPORT - Sunblocks - Solar Gear Inc.
KIDSPRINTS - Wallpaper - Norwall Wallcoverings
KIDSSCAPE - Wallpaper - Rubbermaid Inc.
KIDSTAR - Toys ☆ - Revell-Monogram, Inc.
KIDSTER - Health care products - Gunnell Inc.
KIDSTIME - Skin care products - Blue Cross Laboratories Inc.

KIDSTONE - Inks - Rubber Stampede
KIDSTONE - Inks - Sam's Group, Inc.
KIDSTOR - Containers–plastic - Eagle Affiliates, Inc.
KIDSTRUCTION - Play equipment - Kidstruction
KIDSTUFF - Bedding–linen - Dan River Inc.
KIDSTUFF - Children's carrying case - Mirant Industries, Inc.
KIDSVIEW - Bedding–linen - Dan River Inc.
KIDSVIEW - Dolls - Direct Connect International Inc.
KIDSWARE - Housewares - Eagle Affiliates, Inc.
KIDSWHEEL - Publisher's imprints - Environmental Hazards Management Institute Inc.
KIDSWITCH - Electric lighting equipment - Greg O'Sullivan
KIDSWOOD - Apparel and accessories - Goldenwood International, Inc.
KIDSYSTEMS - Backpacks - Tough Traveler Inc.
KIDTECH INC. - Computer software - Kidtech Inc.
KIDTIME VIDEO - Video production - Victorian Video Productions, Inc.
KIDTRONIC - Computer peripheral equipment - Key Tronic Corp.
KIDTRONICS - Toys–electronic - Safety 1st, Inc.
KIDTUFF - Bedding–linen - Beacon Manufacturing Co.
KIDUCATION - Toys–models - Creative Teaching Press
KIDURRIES - Floor coverings–carpet and rugs - Century Rug Corp.
KIDVANTAGE - Apparel–children's - Sears, Roebuck and Co.
KIDWARE - Educational materials - Mobius Corp.
KIDWIZ - Sliding puzzles ☆ - American Publishing Corp.
KIDWRITER - Computer software - Queue Inc.
KIDYAK - Boats - Glen-L Marine Designs
KIDZ - Bath salts - Benjamin Ansehl Co.
KIDZ - Breads ☆ - Natural Ovens of Manitowoc Inc.
KIDZ - Dairy products - Crowley Foods, Inc.
KIDZ BEDZZZ - Furniture - Big Sur Waterbeds, Inc.
KIDZ BTIZ - Toy storage bins - KB Concepts Inc.
KIDZ CORNER - Computer software - GT Interactive Software Corp.
KIDZ GALLERY - Clothing - Kids Gallery Inc.
KIDZ GALLERY - Socks - Kis Gallery Inc.
KIDZ KALENDAR - Calendars - Kidz Kalendar
KIDZ 'N JOY - Snack foods - Prepco
KIDZ 'NJOY - Pretzels - Prepared Products Co., Inc.
KIDZ ON LOCATION - Video production - Avrotec, Inc.
KIDZ-RAPZ - Ophthalmic goods - Karlen Manufacturing, Inc.
KIDZ WIZDOM - Notebooks and notepads - Wallace Computer Services, Inc.
KIDZELS - Apparel–athletic - Bachman Co.
KIDZMO - Tape player - Teleconcepts Inc.
KIDZOO - Blankets - Biederlack of America
KIDZOOKS - Apparel–children's - Gadzooks, Inc.
KIDZTIME - Apparel–children's - Sherry Manufacturing Co. Inc.
KIDZTIME TV - Broadcasting stations–cable television - Kidztime T.V., Inc.
KIE - Pharmaceutical preparations - Laser Inc.
KIEFER BUILT - Trailers–truck - Kiefer Built, Inc.
KIEHL'S - Perfumes - Kiehl's Since 1851, Inc.
KIEKHAEFER - Boats - Mercury Hi-Performance Group
KIEL - Cigars - Gesty Trading & Manufacturing Corp.
KIELBASA POLKA - Recording label - Michele Audio Corp.
KIELER - Seafood products–fresh or frozen ☆ - C. & J. Willenborg Inc.
KIENE - Gauging instruments - Kiene Diesel Accessories, Inc.
KIENZLER - Weather vanes - German Products Distributing Inc.
KIESELSTEIN-CORD - Apparel and accessories - Barry Kieselstein-Cord
KIFFE - Apparel and accessories - Len Scheer, Inc.
KIHO - Pet products - Nishiki Koi USA Inc.
KII - Automotive parts and accessories - Kaper II, Inc.
KIIKA - Computer terminals - Gordon Simms
KIK - Beverages–carbonated - Procter & Gamble Co.
KIK AZZ - Recording label - Ichiban Records, Inc.
KIKA - Crackers - Star Bakery, Inc.
KIKA - Ophthalmic goods ☆ - Luxottica
KIKI - Lenses–optical - National Optical Co.
KIKI DELUXE - Underwear and nightwear - Kiki International
KIKI INTERNATIONAL - Underwear and nightwear - Kiki International
KIKI KIDS - Underwear and nightwear - Kiki International
KIKIT - Footwear ☆ - E.S. Originals, Inc.
KIKIT - Games - Carrom Co.
KIK'KER - Bags - Tivoli Corp.
KIKKOMAN - Soy sauce - Kikkoman International Inc.
KIKKOMAN - Soy sauce - Ozeki San Benito Inc.
KIKO - Toys–stuffed - Bantam Collections Inc.
KIKO - Wallcoverings - Penthouse Wallcoverings Ltd.
KIKO - Wallpaper - Riverside Silkscreen

KIK'R - Manicure preparations - Backscratchers, Inc.

KIKR - Recording label - Paid Records

KIKSTEP - Stools–metal - Cramer Inc.

KIKU - Sake ☆ - Palace Brands Co.

KIKU MASAMUNE - Wines - Heublein, Inc.

KIKUI - Hair care products - Shear World International

KIKX - Leather goods - Leather Shop Inc.

KIKYO - Bedding–linen - Dan River Inc.

KIL-N-KLEAN - Cleaning equipment - Contec, Inc.

KIL-O-WATTS - Candy - Uniconfis Corp.

KIL-ROT - Paints - Schulte Paint & Lacquer Manufacturing Co., Inc.

KIL-RUST - Paints - Harrison Paint Co.

KIL-SECT - Coatings - Consolidated Protective Coatings Corp.

KILAMANJARO - Backpacks - Schwartzman Export-Import, Inc.

KILBEAD - Sporting goods ☆ - Trueflight Manufacturing Co. Inc.

KILBRUSH - Pesticides–household - Bonide Products, Inc.

KILBURN - Thread - New Bedford Thread Co. Inc.

KILBURN PORTFOLIO, THE - Wallpaper ☆ - Eisenhart Wallcoverings Co.

KILCASH - Earthenware ☆ - Waterford Wedgewood USA, Inc.

KILDARE - Earthenware ☆ - Waterford Wedgewood USA, Inc.

KILEAK THE DNA IMPERATIVE - Computer software - Sony Interactive Entertainment Inc.

KILEMS - Floor coverings–carpet and rugs - Capel, Inc.

KILEY - Ophthalmic goods - Styl-Rite Optical Manufacturing Co., Inc.

KILFROST - Lubricants - Elf Lubricants North America, Inc.

KILGORE - Posters - Aegis Entertainment, Inc.

KILGORE - Recording label - Kilgore Records Co.

KILGORE - Signal flares - Kilgore Corp.

KILGOUR, FRENCH AND STANBURY - Apparel–men's - Greif Cos.

KILHIM - Yarn - Joseph Galler Inc.

KILIM - Floor coverings–carpet and rugs - Kilim Rug Co.

KILIMANJARO - Fabrics - Dan River Inc.

KILIMANJARO - Floor coverings–carpet and rugs ☆ - Robertex Associates Inc.

KILIMANJARO - Sunglasses ☆ - Corning Inc.

KILIMINJERO - Shoes - L.B. Evans' Son Co.

KILIMS DE CAHIERS - Wallpaper - Capital Carousel Inc.

KILINDO - Cables - MacWhyte Co.

KILKENNY - Apparel–men's - Alps Sportswear Manufacturing Co.

KILL COURT - Sporting goods - Centerline Sports, Inc.

KILL-KO - Insecticides - Rigo Co.

KILL MIST-ER - Insecticides - Hub States Corp.

KILLARNEY - Bedding–linen - Dan River Inc.

KILLARNEY - Candy, nut and confectionery stores ☆ - Bewley Irish Imports

KILLARNEY - Handwork supplies - Bernat Yarn & Craft Corp.

KILLARNEY - Lenses–optical - Kelley & Hueber

KILLASK - Wiring devices - Hubbell Electrical Products

KILLBROOD - Toys - Karl Art Publishing

KILLEBREW - Beverages–carbonated - Killebrew Beverages

KILLEEN - Frames–eyeglass ☆ - Universal/Univis Inc.

KILLER - Audio equipment - Magnadyne Corp.

KILLER - Bait ☆ - Siberian Salmon Egg Co.

KILLER - Barbecue sauce - Jardine's Texas Foods

KILLER - Bicycles - Python USA, Inc.

KILLER - Recording label - Little Giant Records

KILLER APPLE, THE - Chocolate-dipped apple - Attivo

KILLER B - Sporting goods - Dana Design Ltd.

KILLER BEE - Golfing equipment - Golfsmith International Inc.

KILLER BEE - Golfing equipment - Koala Ventures, LLC

KILLER BEE II - Golfing equipment - Golfsmith International Inc.

KILLER BEE XLD-3 - Golfing equipment - Golfsmith International Inc.

KILLER BEES - Ball bearings - Rollerblade, Inc.

KILLER BEES - Toys–electronic ☆ - Philips Consumer Electronics Co.

KILLER BEES WAX - Apparel and accessories - Joel Mojica Co.

KILLER COBRA - Darts and dart games - Dart Mart Inc.

KILLER COPTER - Toys–automobiles - Mattel, Inc.

KILLER GAP - Binders - Executive Edge, Inc.

KILLER HASH - Ice cream - Emack & Bolio's

KILLER INSTINCT - Video games - Nintendo of America Inc.

KILLER KANE - Herbicides - Security Products Co.

KILLER KITS - Fishing lures - Sheldons', Inc.

KILLER KRAWDAD - Fishing lures - Creme Lure Co.

KILLER LOOPS - Toys - Majorette Toys (U.S.) Inc.

KILLER ON BOARD - Puzzles - Hasbro, Inc.

KILLER PYTHONS - Candy ☆ - Bohemian Biscuit Co.

KILLER SALSA - Food products - Panchita's, Inc.

KILLER STRAWS - Vegetables–frozen - Promark International, Inc.

KILLER T-REX - Games - Smart Industries Corp.

KILLER TORNADO - Fireworks - American Promotional Events, Inc.

KILLER WHALE - Golfing equipment - Wilson Sporting Goods Co.

KILLIAN'S IRISH BROWN - Beverages–malt - Adolph Coors Co.

KILLIAN'S IRISH RED - Beverages–malt - Adolph Coors Co.

KILLING CLOUD - Computer software ☆ - Konami (America) Inc.

KILLING TIME - Computer software - 3do Co.

KILLINGTON - Floor coverings - Tarkett, Inc.

KILLZONE - Books–comic - Brian Pulido

KILMARNOCK - Recording label - Jazz Composer's Orchestra Association Inc.

KILMORLIE - Floor coverings–carpet and rugs - Masland Corp.

KILMORY - Paper–writing - Simpson Paper Co.

KILN JACK - Chemical preparations - Colonial Refining and Chemical Co.

KILN ROYAL - Floor coverings - Congoleum Corp.

KILO - Bicycles - Columbia Manufacturing Inc.

KILO PAK - Marine generator - Reagan Equipment Co., Inc.

KILO TWISTS - Leather–rawhide - Migatz & Migatz, Inc.

KILOBASS - Amplifiers–musical instrument - Peavey Electronics Corp.

KILOBOTTLE - Jewelry - Metalor USA Refining Corp.

KILOMETER - Jeans–men's - Englishtown Sportswear Ltd.

KILOMETRICO - Pens - Gillette Co.

KILON JEANS - Jeans–men's - Blue Pilot, Inc.

KILOVAC - Electrical switches - Kilovac Corp.

KILOWATT - Toys–stuffed ☆ - Gund, Inc.

KILOWATT KANE - Toys - Those Characters from Cleveland, Inc.

KILPATRICK'S - Bakery products - Campbell Taggart Inc.

KILSBY ROBERTS - Sporting goods - D.L.C. Fabricating Co. Inc.

KILSTAIN - Paints - Devoe & Raynolds Co.

KILSTAIN - Stains - Zynolyte Products Co.

KILT KORD - Fabrics - Dan River Inc.

KILT LIFTER SCOTCH ALE - Beverages–malt - The Pike Brewing Co.

KILTEE - Apparel and accessories - Kiltee Ladies Golf Apparel

KILTIE - Food products - Tartan Sysco Food Services Inc.

KILWIN'S - Candy - Kilwin's Candy Kitchens Inc.

KILZ - Adhesives and sealants - Masterchem Industries, Inc.

KILZ 2 - Primers - Masterchem Industries, Inc.

KIM - Apparel–children's - Seibel & Stern Corp.

KIM - Cigarettes - Brown & Williamson Tobacco Corp.

KIM - Dolls ☆ - Effanbee Doll Corp.

KIM - Health care products - L.T. York Co.

KIM - Jewelry–costume - Kim Craftsmen Ltd.

KIM - Wallpaper - Kim Originals Inc.

KIM & KELLY - Apparel and accessories - Onde Design Inc.

KIM CRAFTSMEN - Jewelry–costume - Kim Craftsmen Ltd.

KIM JACOB'S - Calendars ☆ - Amcal Inc.

KIM LAUBE & COMPANY - Hair clippers–veterinary - Kim Laube & Co. Inc.

KIM ORIGINALS - Christmas tree ornaments - Kim Originals Inc.

KIM-RAK - Glass products - Owens-Illinois Inc. (Libbey Div.)

KIM SAN - Fruits and vegetables - Johnston Farms

KIM TU DIEN - Electronic equipment - Goldic Electrical Inc.

KIMAC - Photographic equipment - Kimac Co. Ltd.

KIMAL KLEAN KUT - Lumber - Kimal Lumber Co.

KIMARA - Floor coverings–tile - Allstate Rubber Corp.

KIMARRA'S POPCORN COMPANY - Popcorn - Corn and More, Inc.

KIMAX - Glass products - Owens-Illinois Inc. (Libbey Div.)

KIMBALL - Labels–paper - Litton Industrial Automation Systems

KIMBALL - Pianos - Kimball International, Inc.

KIMBALL HALL - Furniture - Singer Furniture Co.

KIMBER KABLE - Cables–coaxial - RKB Industrial, Inc.

KIMBERKIDZ - Mattresses - Namaco Industries, Inc.

+KIMBERLEE +PRICE - Cosmetics - Kimberlee Price Cosmetics, Inc.

KIMBERLY - Dishes–china ☆ - Martin's Herend Imports Inc.

KIMBERLY - Dishes–china ☆ - Pickard Inc.

KIMBERLY - Dishes–earthenware ☆ - Denby USA Limited

KIMBERLY - Floor coverings - Mannington Resilient Floors

KIMBERLY - Glass–leaded - Seneca Glass Co.

KIMBERLY - Paper–bond - Kimberly-Clark Corp.

KIMBERLY - Pencils - General Pencil Co.

KIMBERLY - Toys–stuffed - Jolly U.S.A., Inc.

KIMBERLY - Vinegar - De Medici Imports Ltd.

KIMBERLY - Vinegar - Kimberly Wine Vinegar Works

KIMBERLY - Watches ☆ - SMH (US) Inc.

KIMBERLY - Wigs - Jean Paree Weegs Inc.

KIMBERLY CLARK - Cosmetics ☆ - Marianna Imports, Inc.

KIMBERLY-CLARK - Skin care products - Kimberly-Clark Corp.

☆ = Now out of production

KIMBERLY HALL - Cabinets - Belwood Inc.

KIMBERLY HOPE - Women's apparel - D.B. Royalty Inc.

KIMBERLY HUNTER - Apparel—women's - Mishaan International Corp.

KIMBERLY KREEK RECORDINGS - Recording label - Kimberly Kreek Recordings

KIMBERLY LANE - Apparel—women's - Nap, Inc.

KIMBERTON - Floor coverings—carpet and rugs - Lees Carpets

KIMBIES - Diapers—disposable - Kimberly-Clark Corp.

KIMBLE - Glassware—household - Owens-Illinois Inc. (Kimble Div.)

KIMBO - Recording label - Folkraft/Dance Record

KIMBO EDUCATIONAL - Recording label - United Sound Arts

KIMBOLON - Recording label - Stardust/Wizard/Doss Records

KIMBRIDGE - Seafood products—canned or cured ☆ - Hansen Caviar Co.

KIMBROUGH - Whiskey ☆ - SPAR Inc.

KIMCO - Giftware - Kimco International Inc.

KIMCO - Labeling machinery ☆ - Litton Industrial Automation Systems

KIMCOPY - Film - Kimberly-Clark Corp.

KIME'S - Food products - Kime's Cider Mill

KIMGUARD - First aid kits - Kimberly-Clark Corp.

KIMKLOTH - Washboards - Kimberly-Clark Corp.

KIMLARK - Paper—toilet - Kimberly-Clark Corp.

KIMLON - Bedding—linen - Kimberly-Clark Corp.

KIMLOR MILLS - Bed linens - Kimlor Mills Inc.

KIMMARK - Paper—toilet - Kimberly-Clark Corp.

KIMMI K - Apparel—children's - Traci Lynn of California, Inc.

KIMMY - Frames—eyeglass - May Optical Co. Inc.

KIMMY CAT - Toys—stuffed - Russ Berrie and Co., Inc.

KIMNOFF - Vodka - M.S. Walker Inc./Seacoast

KIMONO - Frames—eyeglass - May Optical Co. Inc.

KIMONO - Prophylactics - Mayer Laboratories, Inc.

KIMONO - Wallpaper ☆ - Wallquest, Inc.

KIMONO MICROTHIN - Prophylactics - Mayer Laboratories, Inc.

KIMONO SENSATION - Prophylactics - Mayer Laboratories, Inc.

KIMONO SILKS COLLECTION - Nail care products ☆ - Noxell Corp.

KIMO'S - Nail care products - Kimo's Nail Charms

KIMPAK - Cushions - Kimberly-Clark Corp.

KIMPPU - Bedding—linen - Dan River Inc.

KIMPRESS - Labeling machinery ☆ - Litton Industrial Automation Systems

KIM'S - Food products - John Labatt Foods

KIMSILK - Flowers, plants, and seeds - Kim Originals Inc.

KIMTEX - Washboards - Kimberly-Clark Corp.

KIMTOWELS - Paper—toweling - Kimberly-Clark Corp.

KIMWEAR - Gloves - Kimberly-Clark Corp.

KIMWIPES - Paper—toweling - Kimberly-Clark Corp.

KIMWRAP - Hair care products - Kimberly-Clark Corp.

KIN-AM-EL - Enamels - Lilly Perfection Paint

KIN-DER-LINK - Stools—wood - Skools, Inc.

KINAMATIC - Electrical equipment - General Electric Co.

KINATECHNICS - Work benches - Marshall Industries

KINCADE - Cigarettes - Brown & Williamson Tobacco Corp.

KINCADE'S - Veterinary pharmaceutical preparations - Traileze Veterinary Products Inc.

KINCAID - Cabinets - Aristokraft, Inc.

KINCAID - Floor coverings—carpet and rugs - Dundee Mills, Inc.

KINCAID - Furniture - Kincaid Furniture Co. Inc.

KINCAID - Furniture - La-Z-Boy Chair Co.

KINCAID ROMAN ARCH - Cabinets - Aristokraft, Inc.

KINCAID'S - Potato chips - Pepsico, Inc.

KINCO - Gloves—work - Kinco International Inc.

KIND - Cleaning preparations ☆ - Noxell Corp.

KIND COMB, THE - Hair care products - Helene Curtis Industries Inc.

KIND EARTH ORGANICS - Fruits and vegetables - Griffin Produce Co., Inc.

KIND NESS - Toys - Abrams/Gentile Entertainment, Inc.

KIND, SOFT & CERTAIN - Cleaning preparations - W.L. Young Inc.

KIND TO COLOR - Hair care products ☆ - Clairol Inc.

KIND TOUCH - Skin care products - Sween Corp.

KIND WIND - Apparel and accessories - Island Designs Outlet Inc.

KINDALIKE BUGS - T-shirts—women's - Susan A. Kunzelman

KINDEL - Furniture - Kindel Furniture Co.

KINDER - Frames—eyeglass - Zylo Ware Corp.

KINDER - Furniture—children's - Kinderworks Corp.

KINDER - Toys—banks - Ferrero U.S.A Inc.

KINDER ART - Hobby kits - Binney & Smith Inc.

KINDER BEAR - Toys—stuffed ☆ - Gund, Inc.

KINDER BY KAUFMAN - Towels - Ben Kaufman Sales Co., Inc.

KINDER CASE - Ophthalmic goods ☆ - Fidelity Case Corp.

KINDER-CHINDER - Musical instrument accessories - M & M Distributing Co.

KINDER COLOR EXPRESS - Furniture - Kinderworks Corp.

KINDER COLORS - Paints - Valspar Corp.

KINDER COUNTRY - Granola bars - Ferrero U.S.A Inc.

KINDER FRIENDS - Toys—stuffed - Ferrero U.S.A Inc.

KINDER GENTLER BUSH - Food products - Hagen House

KINDER-GRIP - Bottles—plastic - Playtex Beauty Care, Inc.

KINDER-GRIP - Infant product - Kinder-Grip International Inc.

KINDER GUARD - Paints - Valspar Corp.

KINDER HEATHER - Toys—stuffed ☆ - Gund, Inc.

KINDER KART - Strollers—baby - Western Advanced Engineering Co.

KINDER LINER, A - Cosmetics - Dolly Parton Inc.

KINDER RATTLE - Toys—stuffed ☆ - Gund, Inc.

KINDER RATTLE BEAR - Toys—stuffed ☆ - Gund, Inc.

KINDER RATTLE GIRAFFE - Toys—stuffed ☆ - Gund, Inc.

KINDER SET - Furniture - Kinderworks Corp.

KINDER SHAKES - Vitamins and nutritional supplements - Tishcon Corp.

KINDER SNUFF - Toys—stuffed ☆ - Gund, Inc.

KINDER VISION - Video production - Maxwell Enterprises, Inc.

KINDER-VITES - Vitamins and nutritional supplements - Tishcon Corp.

KINDER ZOO - Toys—stuffed ☆ - Gund, Inc.

KINDERACTIVE - Computer software - Harber Brothers Productions, Inc.

KINDERAMA - Computer software - Unicorn Software

KINDERBLOCK N' BALL - Toys—stuffed - Gund, Inc.

KINDERCAL - Pharmaceutical preparations - Mead Johnson & Co.

KINDERCARE - Recording label - Kindercare Learning Centers, Inc.

KINDERCARE - Wooden toys - TCA Ground Inc.

KINDERCARE WOODEN TOYS - Toys - Kindercare Learning Centers, Inc.

KINDERCOLLECTION - Furniture - Paris Co. Inc.

KINDERCOMP - Computer software - Queue Inc.

KINDERDANCE - Dance-studio franchise - Kinder Dance International

KINDERFRIENDS - Toys - Importoys

KINDERGAARD - Life preservers ☆ - Stearns Manufacturing Co.

KINDERGARD - Identification tags - Kindergard Corp.

KINDERGARTEN - Frames—eyeglass - Zylo Ware Corp.

KINDERGARTEN PLACE - Educational materials - Silver Burdett Ginn Inc.

KINDERGESIC - Vitamins and nutritional supplements - Tishcon Corp.

KINDERGRAPHICS - Greeting cards ☆ - American Artists Group Inc.

KINDERGYM - Toys - Globe United Inc.

KINDERKRAFT - Furniture—children's - KinderKraft Inc.

KINDERLOGS - Toys - Tootsietoy

KINDERMANN - Photographic equipment - Argraph Corp. (Samigon Div.)

KINDEROO - Toys—stuffed ☆ - Gund, Inc.

KINDERPANTS - Diapers—disposable - Paragon Trade Brands, Inc.

KINDERPHONE - Telephone apparatus - Educational Methods, Inc.

KINDERPRINT - Fingerprinting equipment - Pioneer Balloon Co.

KINDERSIZE - Toys - Learning Products Inc.

KINDERSLED - Sleds - Paris Co. Inc.

KINDERTOOLS - Toothbrushes - FGT Enterprises, Inc.

KINDERVENTURES - Recording label - Optical Data Corp.

KINDERVITES - Vitamins and nutritional supplements - Tishcon Corp.

KINDERWOOD - Wines - San Antonio Winery Inc.

KINDEST CUT, THE - Bathing suits - Lands' End Inc.

KINDEX - Office supplies ☆ - Majestic Penn State Inc.

KINDLE BITS - Animal feeds - Bluebonnet Milling Co.

KINDLES - Toys—stuffed - CBS Toys

KINDLESTIX - Wood products - F.M. Industries, Inc.

KINDLING KONES - Fireplace logs—treated - Kindling Kones Oasis Ventures Inc.

KINDNESS - Dryers—hair - Remington Products Co.

KINDOGRAPH - Crayons - Dixon Ticonderoga Co.

KINDRED - Posters - Aegis Entertainment, Inc.

KINDRED KONNECTIONS - Computer software - Fficiency Software, Inc.

KINDRED SPIRITS - Papier-mache articles - Silver Deer Ltd.

KINDRED SPIRITS - Posters - Laurel Burch Inc.

KINDRED: THE EMBRACED - Dolls - Spelling Television, Inc.

KINE B - Food products - Great West Foods

KINEFILM - Plastic laminating film - General Binding Corp.

KINEGON - Photographic equipment ☆ - Edixa Camera Co.

KINEO COLLECTION - Furniture - Moosehead Manufacturing Co.

KINERET - Food products - Kineret Foods Corp.

KINERGETICS - Compact disc players ☆ - GNP Audio Video Inc.

KINESE - Bathing suits - Kinese, Inc.

KINESED - Pharmaceutical preparations ☆ - Zeneca Inc.

KINESIS - Apparel—men's - Mercantile Stores Co., Inc.

KINESIS - Computers - Kinesis Corp.

KINESTAT - Cleaning equipment - Kinetronics Corp.
KINESTIM - Health care products - Promatek Medical Systems Inc.
KINETEC - Health care products - Smith & Nephew Richards, Inc.
KINETIC - Mopeds ☆ - Cosmopolitan Motors Inc.
KINETIC - Recording label - Marz Records
KINETIC - Remote control devices - Kinetic Marketing Inc.
KINETIC - Shoes - Edge Quest, Inc.
KINETIC EXPANSION SYSTEM - Apparel and accessories - I. Spiewak and Sons Inc.
KINETIC II - Golfing equipment - Ralph Maltby Enterprises Inc.
KINETIC MOPEDS - Cosmopolitan Motors Inc.
KINETIC WEDGE - Footwear - Wolverine World Wide, Inc.
KINETICARE - Furniture - Haworth, Inc.
KINETICO - Water purification systems - Kinetico Inc.
KINETICS - Apparel–children's - Osaga Footwear, Inc.
KINETICS - Blinds–vertical - Tontine/VyTech Industries Inc.
KINETICS - Floor coverings–carpet and rugs - Karastan-Bigelow Inc.
KINETICS - Floor coverings–carpet and rugs ☆ - Heuga USA
KINETICS - Floor coverings–carpet and rugs ☆ - J and J Industries Inc.
KINETICS - Furniture - Haworth, Inc.
KINETICS - Wallpaper ☆ - Old Deerfield Fabrics Inc.
KINETIDEX - Computer software - Micromedex, Inc.
KINETIX - Eyeglasses - Solar-Mates Sunglasses
KINETIX INSTRUMENTS - Surgical equipment - Kinetix Instruments, Inc.
KINEVAC - Pharmaceutical preparations - Bristol-Myers Squibb Co.
KINEWIND - Electronics equipment - RTI Research Technology International
KINEXUS - Computer software - Kinetic Concepts, Inc.
KINFO - Notebooks and notepads - Jewn Co.
KINFOLKS - Food products - Athens Foods
KING - Brooms - Lighthouse Industries
KING - Candy - H. Hamstra & Co.
KING - Cigarettes - R.J. Reynolds Tobacco Co.
KING - Clay–modeling - Sculpture House Inc.
KING - Dog food - Dry Fork Milling Co. Inc.
KING - Food products - American Whipped Products
KING - Heaters–gas - Martin Industries, Inc.
KING - Inks - UNI International Ink, Inc.
KING - Leather goods - St. Thomas Inc.
KING - Meat products–beef ☆ - Cargill Corp.
KING - Musical instruments - King Musical Instruments
KING - Musical instruments - United Musical Instruments USA Inc.
KING - Paints - Graham Paint and Varnish Co.
KING - Paints - Sterling-Clark-Lurton Corp.
KING - Plumbing fixtures–metal ☆ - Jameco Industries, Inc.
KING - Polishing rouge ☆ - Fair Haven Industries Inc.
KING - Recording label - Gusto Records Inc.
KING - Recording label - Highland Music Inc.
KING - Refrigerators - King Refrigerator Corp.
KING - Rubber product ☆ - Ace Hose and Rubber Co.
KING - Rulers–metal ☆ - Argee Corp.
KING - Sporting goods ☆ - Gold Eagle/Arnold Palmer
KING - Toys–musical ☆ - Kazoo Co. Inc.
KING - Varnishes ☆ - Klean-Strip
KING AIR - Aircraft–airplanes - Beech Aircraft Corp.
KING ALBERT - Eyeglasses - Art-Craft Optical Co.
KING & PRINCE - Seafood products–fresh or frozen - King & Prince Seafood Corp.
KING APPLE - Fruit and vegetable markets - Fruit Acres Inc.
KING ARCTIC - Shovels - Hardware & Industrial Tool Co., Inc.
KING ARENABOARD - Plastics - King Plastic Corp.
KING ARTHUR - Brooms ☆ - W.E. Kautenberg Co.
KING ARTHUR - Candy ☆ - Foreign Candy Co. Inc.
KING ARTHUR - Clocks ☆ - King Arthur Clock Co. Inc.
KING ARTHUR - Fertilizer - Farmers Elevator Co. of Arthur
KING ARTHUR - Floor coverings–carpet and rugs ☆ - Masland Corp.
KING ARTHUR - Flowers, plants, and seeds - New Plants
KING ARTHUR - Giftware ☆ - Gorham Inc.
KING ARTHUR - Waterproof outerwear - Distributors Service Corp.
KING ARTHUR & THE KNIGHTS OF JUSTICE - Video games - Enix America Corp.
KING ARTHUR MULTI-PURPOSE - Flour–blended - King Arthur Flour
KING ARTHUR PENDRAGON - Games - Chaosium Inc.
KING B - Fruits and vegetables - BTV Crown Equities, Inc.
KING BABY EST. 1960 JEANS - Slacks - Silvercord, Inc.
KING BEAR - Automotive repair shops - King Bear Enterprises
KING BEE - Cabinets - Bee Cabinet Corp.

KING BEE - Tobacco products - Alfred & Christian Petersen U.S. Ltd.
KING BIO NATURAL MEDICINE - Vitamins and nutritional supplements - King Bio Pharmaceuticals, Inc.
KING BISCUIT - Flour - Interstate Grocer Co. Inc.
KING BRITISH - Pet products - Southwest Tropical
KING CAB - Motor vehicles–trucks - Nissan Motor Corp. USA
KING CAL - Meat products–poultry - Squab Producers of California
KING CARB SU - Carburetors - Rivera Engineering, Inc.
KING CARE - Herbal products - East Health
KING CARTER - Food products - Virginia Seafoods Inc.
KING CHARLES - Giftware ☆ - Gorham Inc.
KING CHARLES - Snack foods - Pride of the Farm
KING CHARLES - Tobacco–chewing or smoking - G.A. Georgopulo & Co. Inc.
KING-CHECK - Pencils - Listo Pencil Corp.
KING CHELAN - Fruits–canned - Skookum Packers Association Inc.
KING-CHEM - Paints - Graham Paint and Varnish Co.
KING CHOLESTEROL FREE - Food products - American Whipped Products
KING CHROME - Toys - Mattel, Inc.
KING COBRA - Beverages–malt - Anheuser-Busch Companies Inc.
KING COBRA - Darts and dart games - Dart Mart Inc.
KING COBRA - Golfing equipment - Cobra Golf Inc.
KING COBRA - Revolvers - Colt's Manufacturing Co. Inc.
KING COBRA - Saw blades - Sandvik Saws & Tools
KING COBRA - Toys - Tonka Corp.
KING COBRA TI - Golfing equipment - Cobra Golf Inc.
KING COBRA TITANIUM - Golfing equipment - Cobra Golf Inc.
KING COLE - Food products - Draper-King Cole Inc.
KING COLE - Snack foods ☆ - Bachman Co.
KING COLE - Socks - Sockyard Co. Inc.
KING COLONIAL - Furniture - Interco Inc.
KING CONCEPT - Photographic equipment - Omega/Arkay
KING CONE - Ice cream cones - Good Humor Corp.
KING-CONGO - Floor coverings ☆ - Congoleum Corp.
KING CONNECTORS - Wiring devices - King Safety Products
KING CORONET - Paper–tissue - Georgia-Pacific Corp.
KING-COTE - Floor waxes ☆ - C.B. Dolge Co.
KING COTTON - Cigars - A.J. Golden Inc.
KING COTTON - Handkerchiefs ☆ - Carolina Manufacturing Inc.
KING COTTON - Meats–luncheon - King Cotton Foods
KING COTTON - Socks - WorkAbles for Women
KING COTTON - Twine - King Cotton Cordage Co.
KING COTTON - Wines - Monarch Wine Co. of Georgia
KING COTTON LITES - Meats–luncheon - King Cotton Foods
KING CRUZ - Bicycles - Emory Manufacturing Co.
KING CUSTOM - Trailers - Mobile Structures, Inc.
KING CUTTERS - Tools - LRH Enterprises Inc.
KING CUTTING BOARD XL - Cutting boards - King Plastic Corp.
KING CUTTINGBOARD - Paper products - King Plastic Corp.
KING DADDY - Golfing equipment - Kliker Golf Co.
KING DAVID - Brandy - Kedem Royal Wine Corp.
KING DAVID - Food products ☆ - Baldanza Bakery Inc.
KING DAVID - Musical instrument accessories - David Wexler & Co.
KING DAVID'S ALL NATURAL FOODS - Food products - King David's All Natural Foods
KING DELITE - Food products - Natural Food World
KING DEVILED CRABCAKES - Crab meat–canned or cured - R.J. McCoy, Inc.
KING EDWARD - Cigars - Swisher International, Inc.
KING EDWARD - Eyeglasses - Art-Craft Optical Co.
KING EDWARD - Giftware - Gorham Inc.
KING EDWARD DIAMONDS - Cigars - Swisher International, Inc.
KING ELEPHANT - Rice - Great Year Import Co., Inc.
KING ERIC - Pipes - National Briar Pipe Co.
KING ESTATE - Wines - King Estate Vineyards, Inc.
KING FASTENER - Staples - Stanley-Parker Inc.
KING FILING - Index cards - File-A-Dex Inc.
KING FIRE - Sporting goods ☆ - Gold Eagle/Arnold Palmer
KING FOR ALL TIME - Games ☆ - Mayfair Games, Inc.
KING FRANCIS - Flatware - Reed and Barton Corp.
KING GASPARILLA - Food products - Surf Side Seafoods Inc.
KING GEL - Gelatin - American Whipped Products
KING GHIDORAH - Toys - Toho Co., Ltd.
KING GOLD - Juices - Osceola Fruit Distributors
KING HUBBARD - Flour–blended - Hubbard Milling Co.
KING JAMES - Firearms, accessories, and parts - Texas Longhorn Arms, Inc.
KING JAMES SILHOUETTE - Paper - Crown Vantage Inc.

☆ = Now out of production

KING JAMMER - Toys - Tonka Corp.

KING KAT - Bicycles - Murray, Inc.

KING KITE - Kites - Kingstone International Corp.

KING KLAVE - Drums–musical instruments - LP Music Group

KING KLIPS - Paper clips - Baumgarten's

KING KOIL - Bedding–linen ☆ - Kinder Manufacturing Corp.

KING KOIL - Mattresses - King Koil Licensing Co., Inc.

KING KOIL KIDS - Mattresses - King Koil Licensing Co., Inc.

KING KOIN - Toys–banks - A.J. Renzi Plastic Corp.

KING KOIN JR. - Toys–banks - A.J. Renzi Plastic Corp.

KING KOLD - Food products - King Kold Frozen Foods Inc.

KING KONG - Pet products - Kong Co.

KING KONG - Shoes - Carolina Shoe Co.

KING KONG CASTLE - Playground equipment - Rainbow Play Systems, Inc.

KING KONG SERIES - Playground equipment - Rainbow Play Systems, Inc.

KING KONG SKID STEER - Tires–automobile - Galaxy Tire & Wheel, Inc.

KING KOOKER - Spices and extracts - Metal Fusion Inc.

KING KOOL - Thread ☆ - Perfect Thread Co. Inc.

KING KORN - Vegetables–canned - Dean Foods Co.

KING KOTE - Paints - Reliance Paint Co. Inc.

KING KRAB - Imitation crab - Multi Food

KING KULLEN - Food products - King Kullen Grocery Co. Inc.

KING KUTTER - Kitchen appliances - Kitchen-Quip Inc.

KING LEAR - Cutlery ☆ - Lifetime Hoan Corp.

KING LEO - Candy - Standard Candy Co. Inc.

KING LEO - Toys - MGM Records Inc.

KING LOCK - Sewing machines–household - Knitking Corp.

KING LOUIE - Sporting goods - King Louie International Inc.

KING LYONS - Brushes–paint - Linzer Products Corp.

KING MACKEREL - Van Loi Trading

KING MAG WART - Fishing lures - Storm Manufacturing Co.

KING MARIGAUX - Oboes ☆ - King Musical Instruments

KING MIDAS - Flour–blended - Conagra, Inc.

KING MIDAS - Watches - Rolex Watch USA, Inc.

KING MIDAZ THE TOUCH OF GOLD - Video production - Midaz Touch Productions

KING O FISH - Seafood products–fresh or frozen ☆ - Chinook Packing Co.

KING-O-LAWN - Lawn mowers - California Flexrake Corp.

KING O' NORTH - Crocheted and knitted items - Wrights Knitwear Corp.

KING O PEDIC - Mattresses - Kingsdown, Inc.

KING OF ALL KLEENER - Cleaning preparations - King of All Manufacturing, Inc.

KING OF BEERS - Beverages–malt - Anheuser-Busch Companies Inc.

KING OF BUCKS - Museums - Bass Pro Trademarks, LP

KING OF CABLES - Crocheted and knitted items - Towne & King Inc.

KING OF CHESS - Chessboards - Cambor Enterprises Inc.

KING OF CRIME - Games ☆ - Mayfair Games, Inc.

KING OF CROOKS - Cigars - A.J. Golden Inc.

KING OF DIAMONDS - Wallpaper ☆ - Gilford Corp.

KING-OF-EASE - Furniture - Kittinger Co.

KING OF FANS - Fans–electric - King of Fans Inc.

KING OF HAWAII - Juices - Maui Pineapple Co.

KING OF KINGS - Recording label - King of Kings International Records

KING OF NORWAY - Food products - B. Westergaard & Co. Inc.

KING OF ROCK & ROLL - Popcorn - Elvis Presley Enterprises Inc.

KING OF ROCK 'N' ROLL MUSIC - Recording label - King of Rock 'n' Roll Music, Inc.

KING OF SIAM - Dinners–frozen - King of Siam, Inc.

KING OF SLAM - Apparel and accessories - Big Ball Sports, Inc.

KING OF SPORTS - Dog food - King of Sports Mill

KING OF THE BEACH - Balls - Sideout Sport, Inc.

KING OF THE BEACH - Sporting goods ☆ - Mikasa Sports

KING OF THE BEASTS - Toys–stuffed - Trendmasters, Inc.

KING OF THE HILL - Publisher's imprints - Douglas Press, Inc.

KING OF THE ISLANDS - Pies–fresh - Nabisco Foods Group

KING OF THE JUNGLE - Puppets - Dakin Inc.

KING OF THE MOUNTAIN - Publisher's imprints - Douglas Press, Inc.

KING OF THE PAINT - Toy action figures - Tonka Corp.

KING OF THE ROAD - Automotive parts and accessories - King of the Road Mirrors Inc.

KING OF THE ROAD - Bicycles - Columbia Manufacturing Inc.

KING OF THE ROAD - Motor vehicles–motor homes - Chief Industries, Inc.

KING OF THE ROAD - Trailers–travel - King of the Road

KING OF THE ROOF - Roofing materials–concrete - Mobile Paint Manufacturing Co.

KING OF THE SEA - Games ☆ - CBS Toys

KING OF THE WEST - Food products - Betters International Food Corp.

KING OIL - Games ☆ - Milton Bradley Co.

KING ORANGE - Fruits and vegetables - Kings River Packing, Inc.

KING ORANGE JAMBOREE PARADE - Publisher's imprints - Orange Bowl Committee, Inc.

KING ORCHARD - Cider - King Orchard

KING OSCAR - Fish–canned or cured - King Oscar Inc.

KING PHARR - Food products ☆ - Cherokee Products Co.

KING PIN - Adhesives and sealants - Testworth Laboratories Inc.

KING PIN - Cookware - Foredom Electric Co.

KING-PIN LOK - Locks–padlocks ☆ - Kwikset Powdered Metal Products

KING PINE - Disinfectants - Johnson Chemical Co., Inc.

KING PINS - Crocheted and knitted items ☆ - Reliable of Milwaukee

KING PIPEGRADE - Plastics - King Plastic Corp.

KING PLASTIBAL - Plastics - King Plastic Corp.

KING PLASTISHIELD - Polyethylene film sheets - King Plastic Corp.

KING POPS - Candy - Helms Candy Manufacturing Co. Inc.

KING PUTT - Sporting goods ☆ - Chesal Golf

KING REGGAE - Dolls - Susan Sona

KING RICHARD - Candy ☆ - American Candy Co.

KING RICHARD - Eyeglasses - Art-Craft Optical Co.

KING RICHARD - Glassware–household - Towle Manufacturing Co.

KING ROLAND - Seafood - American Roland Food Corp.

KING ROYAL - Motor vehicles–motor homes ☆ - Honey Recreational Vehicles Inc.

KING RULER - Rulers–metal ☆ - Argee Corp.

KING RUNNER - Boats–motor ☆ - Hewes Marine Co.

KING SCOT - Apparel–athletic ☆ - Midstates Sportswear

KING SIZE - Markers–felt-tip - Sanford Corp.

KING-SIZE - Office supplies - Alvin and Co. Inc.

KING SIZE CAPSULES - Novelty items - Doc's Apothecary

KING SIZE KRITTERS - Toys - Toymax Inc.

KING SMOOTHEE - Food products - Dairy Fresh Products Co.

KING SOBIESKI - Pickles - Pikle-Rite Co. Inc.

KING SOLOMON - Fruits and vegetables - Craig Consaul

KING SOLOMON - Wines - Laird and Co.

KING SPHINX - Toys - Saban Entertainment, Inc.

KING SPORT - Archery equipment - Precision Shooting Equipment Inc.

KING SPORTRIM - Frames–eyeglass - Hudson Optical Corp.

KING STAR - Bicycles - Gulf Cycle Corp.

KING STARBOARD - Cutting boards - King Plastic Corp.

KING STARBOARD AS - Cutting boards - King Plastic Corp.

KING STARBOARD XL - Cutting boards - King Plastic Corp.

KING STARBOND - Adhesives and sealants - King Plastic Corp.

KING STARLITE XL - Plastics film - King Plastic Corp.

KING STREET BLUES - Barbecue sauce - Ashman Distributing Co.

KING STREET BLUES - Sauces - Ralph Capobianco

KING SUN - Juices - Osceola Fruit Distributors

KING TALC - Talcum powders - King Research, Inc.

KING-TAPER - Frames–eyeglass - Liberty Optical Manufacturing Co.

KING THREADS - Gloves - Kombi Ltd.

KING TONE - Amplifiers–musical instrument - Seymour Duncan Pickups

KING TOPPER - Food products - Philip Olender & Co.

KING TUFF-TEX - Identification tags - Fearing Manufacturing Co. Inc.

KING TURLOCK LAVASH - Breads - Ara-Z Inc.

KING TUT - Colognes - Schnapp Enterprises Inc.

KING TUT - Jewelry ☆ - J. & C. Ferrara Co. Inc.

KING TUT'S - Toys - George Lamoureaux

KING TYPE - Computer software - Frontier Software Inc.

KING VITAMAN - Cereal - Quaker Oats Co.

KING-VOX - Musical instruments ☆ - King Musical Instruments

KING WALK - Labels–paper - King Walk Inc.

KING WILLIAM - Meat products–beef - Mosinee Paper Corp.

KING WILLIAM IV - Whiskey - Schenley Industries Inc.

KING WORLD - Video production - King World Productions, Inc.

KINGAN - Food products - Hygrade Food Products Corp.

KINGCALK - Putties - Sterling-Clark-Lurton Corp.

KINGCOCK WORM-ALL TRIPLE ACTION - Veterinary pharmaceutical preparations - Harrison Wholesale Products Inc.

KINGCOM - Computer software - OTC Corp.

KINGCOTE - Paints - Sterling-Clark-Lurton Corp.

KINGCOTE - Paper - Milliken & Co.

KINGCYCLE - Bicycles - Cosimex, Inc.

KINGDOM - Blinds–vertical - Kingdom Vertical Blinds Manufacturing Inc.

KINGDOM - Floor coverings–carpet and rugs - Patcraft Mills Inc.

KINGDOM CARD - Coupons - Colorado Mountain Lodging, Inc.

☆ = Now out of production

KINGDOM CRITTERS - Toys - Rainfall Inc.

KINGDOM CRUSADE - Computer software - Electro Brain Corp.

KINGDOM OF BATH - Soap - Carlton Marketing Group

KINGDOM OF DENMARK - Food products ☆ - Eddyleon Chocolate Co. Inc.

KINGERY - Popcorn poppers - Gold Medal Products Co.

KINGFIELD - Floor coverings - Mannington Resilient Floors

KINGFIELD - Furniture - Moosehead Manufacturing Co.

KINGFILE - Artists' materials - H. Schreiber Co.

KINGFISH - Bicycles - Ross Bicycles USA, Ltd.

KINGFISH - Boats–fishing - Glassmaster Co.

KINGFISH - Electronic equipment - Moor Electronics Inc.

KINGFISHER - Beverages–alcohol - American United Breweries

KINGFISHER - Boats - Glen-L Marine Designs

KINGFISHER - Boats–canoes - Old Town Canoe Co.

KINGFISHER - Boats–fishing ☆ - C-G Industries Inc.

KINGFISHER - Boats–motor - Master Molders Inc.

KINGFISHER - Furniture ☆ - Halcyon Inc.

KINGFISHER - Rope - Wellington Leisure Products, Inc.

KINGFISHER - Wallpaper - Forbo Wallcoverings Inc.

KINGKUTTER INCORPORATED - Farm machinery - King Kutter, Inc.

KINGLAZE - Putties - Sterling-Clark-Lurton Corp.

KINGLET CARDS INC. - Greeting cards - JoAnn Allen

KINGLETS - Food products ☆ - Stokely USA, Inc.

KINGLINE DINNERWARE - Dinnerware - Carlisle Foodservice Products, Inc.

KINGLY - Apparel–women's - Kingley Manufacturing Corp.

KINGMAKER - Games - Avalon Hill Game Co.

KINGMAN - Frames–eyeglass - U.S. Optical Frame Co.

KINGMAN COLLECTION - Jewelry - Carlisle Jewelry Co., Inc.

KINGMATIC - Watches - Movado Time Corp.

KINGMAX - Vitamins and nutritional supplements - Hops Sports and Veterinary Supplies Inc.

KINGPACK - Bags - Point Sport, Inc.

KINGPIN - Bats–baseball - Markwort Sporting Goods Co.

KINGPIN - Boats - Glen-L Marine Designs

KINGPIN - Eyeglasses - Goat Eyewear

KINGPIN - Frames–eyeglass - Liberty Optical Manufacturing Co.

KINGPIN - Kilns ☆ - Paragon Industries Inc.

KINGPIN - Sporting goods - Kingpin Enterprises, Inc.

KINGPINS - Trading cards and stamps - Collect-a-Card Corp.

KINGPLASTIK - Paints - Graham Paint and Varnish Co.

KINGRED - Spices and extracts - Schoenfeld and Sons Inc.

KINGS - Apparel–athletic - Sacramento Kings L.P.

KINGS - Cigar boxes–wood - Consolidated Cigar Corp.

KINGS - Coleslaw - Kings Super Markets, Inc.

KINGS - Flatware - Wallace International Silversmiths, Inc.

KING'S - Food products - King's Food Products Inc.

KING'S - Food products - Southern Foods

KING'S - Paints - Reliance Paint Co. Inc.

KINGS - Wines - Laird and Co.

KINGS BREAD - Crackers - A.V. Olsson Trading Co., Inc.

KINGS CANYON - Floor coverings–carpet and rugs - Karastan-Bigelow Inc.

KINGS CANYON CRANBERRY - Flooring–hardwood - Harris-Tarkett, Inc.

KING'S CHOICE - Bags–plastic - Essex Plastics, Inc.

KINGS CHOICE - Cheese - Swissrose International Inc.

KING'S CHOICE - Floor coverings–carpet and rugs - Eagle Carpets Inc.

KING'S CHOICE - Pickles - Food City Pickle Co. Inc.

KING'S CHOICE - Seafood products–fresh or frozen - K & C Food Sales

KING'S COLLECTION - Toys–stuffed - Kamar International Inc.

KING'S COMMAND - Food products - King's Command Foods Inc.

KING'S CORKSCREW - Corkscrews - Franmara Co. Inc.

KINGS COTTAGE - Floor coverings–carpet and rugs - Gulistan Carpet Inc.

KING'S COURT - Beverages–carbonated ☆ - Universal Flavor USA

KINGS COURT - Floor coverings ☆ - Congoleum Corp.

KINGS COURT - Floor coverings–carpet and rugs - Hartford Carpet Mills

KINGS CRAFT - Boats–canoes - Kings Craft Inc.

KINGS CREST - Liquors - Paramount Distillers Inc.

KINGS CROSSING - Floor coverings–carpet and rugs - Gulistan Carpet Inc.

KING'S CROWN - Fruits and vegetables - BTV Crown Equities, Inc.

KINGS CROWN - Whiskey - Montebello Brands, Inc.

KING'S CROWN PRESS - Publisher's imprints - Columbia University Press

KING'S DELIGHT - Fruits and vegetables - Symms Fruit Ranch, Inc.

KING'S DELITE - Food products - Spice King Corp.

KINGS GAP - Floor coverings–carpet and rugs ☆ - Masland Corp.

KING'S GOLD - Barbeque sauce - King's Gold, Inc.

KINGS GRANT - Furniture - Pilliod Co.

KINGS HARBOUR - Floor coverings–carpet and rugs - Gulistan Carpet Inc.

KINGS HOUSE - Meat products–poultry - Sleepy Eye Foods

KINGS IN THE CORNER - Games - Jax Ltd.

KINGS INN - Cutlery ☆ - Lifetime Hoan Corp.

KINGS INN - Floor coverings–carpet and rugs ☆ - Barrett Carpet Mills Inc.

KING'S LYNN - Pens - Empire Berol USA

KING'S MARK - Beverages–alcohol ☆ - SPAR Inc.

KING'S MEN - Hosiery–men's - Harriss and Covington Hosiery Mills

KINGS MILL - Furniture - Pilliod Co.

KINGS MOUNTAIN - Furniture ☆ - Kincaid Furniture Co. Inc.

KING'S PALACE - Floor coverings–carpet and rugs - Galaxy Carpet Mills Inc.

KINGS PANTRY - Fruit and vegetable markets - Strohmeyer and Arpe Co.

KING'S PATTERN - Flatware - Kirk & Matz Ltd.

KINGS POINT - Computer software - Sorrells Enterprises, Inc.

KINGS POINT - Dinnerware–glass ☆ - Lenox, Inc.

KINGS POINT - Steel springs–railroad - Needlecraft Industries

KINGS POINT 28 - Floor coverings–carpet and rugs ☆ - Cumberland Mills Inc.

KINGS POINTE - Wallpaper ☆ - Wolf-Gordon Inc.

KING'S PRIDE - Beef - Formico Food Co.

KINGS QUALITY - Vegetables–canned - Kings Creek Canning Co. Inc.

KINGS QUEENS & PAUPERS - Games - Deborah A. Coon

KING'S QUEST - Computer software - Sierra On-Line, Inc.

KING'S RANSOM - Christmas tree ornaments - Cracker Box Inc.

KINGS RANSOM - Floor coverings–carpet and rugs ☆ - Porter Carpet Mills Inc.

KINGS RANSOM - Frames–eyeglass - Hudson Optical Corp.

KINGS RANSOM - Teas - Blue Ridge Tea & Herb Co.

KINGS RANSOM - Wallcoverings - WallCapers Ltd.

KINGS RANSOM - Wallpaper - Sunnyside Prints

KING'S RAN$UM - Games - Charitable Equipment, Inc.

KINGS REWARD - Beverages–alcohol - Canandaigua Wine Co. Inc.

KING'S ROAD - Beverages–alcohol - King's Road Vineyard, Inc.

KINGS ROAD - Floor coverings–carpet and rugs - Mattel Carpet & Rug Inc.

KING'S ROAD - Furniture ☆ - Broyhill Furniture Industries, Inc.

KING'S ROYAL CHOICE - Seafood products–fresh or frozen - Impex Shrimp & Fish Co.

KING'S RUBY - Fruits and vegetables - Corrin

KING'S RULE, THE - Computer software - Sunburst Communications, Inc.

KING'S TASTE - Barbecue sauce - King's Taste B.B.Q. Sauce Inc.

KINGS-WALL - Blocks–concrete - King's Material Inc.

KING'S WILD AMERICAN GINSENG TEA - Teas - Asia Co.

KINGSBAY FINE LINE - Fabrics - Burlington House Fabrics Group

KINGSBERRY - Cabinets - Dewils Industries Inc.

KINGSBRIDGE - Dishes–china - Waterford Wedgwood USA, Inc.

KINGSBRIDGE - Eyeglasses - Art-Craft Optical Co.

KINGSBRIDGE - Tools - Kingsbridge Cycle Supply Inc.

KINGSBROOK - Mobile homes - Western Homes Corp.

KINGSBURY - Beverages–malt - The Stroh Brewery Co.

KINGSBURY - Cabinets - American Woodmark Corp.

KINGSBURY - Clocks ☆ - General Time Corp. (Westclox/Seth Thomas Div.)

KINGSBURY - Floor coverings - Mannington Resilient Floors

KINGSBURY - Floor coverings–carpet and rugs - Galaxy Carpet Mills Inc.

KINGSBURY - Frames–eyeglass - May Optical Co. Inc.

KINGSBURY - Furniture ☆ - Bassett Furniture Industries, Inc.

KINGSBURY - Machine tools - Kingsbury Corp.

KINGSBURY COLLECTION - Furniture - Moosehead Manufacturing Co.

KINGSBURY NEAR BEER - Beverages–malt - The Stroh Brewery Co.

KINGSBURY RED NA - Beverages–malt - The Stroh Brewery Co.

KINGSCREST - Flowers, plants, and seeds ☆ - NK Lawn & Garden Co.

KINGSDALE - Floor coverings–carpet and rugs - Evans-Black Carpet Mills

KINGSDOWN - Mattresses - Kingsdown, Inc.

KINGSDOWN POSTURE - Mattresses - Kingsdown, Inc.

KINGSDOWN TUFF GRIP - Mattresses ☆ - Kingsdown, Inc.

KINGSFORD - Barbecues and grills - Kingsford Products Co.

KINGSFORD - Charcoal - Kingsford Co.

KINGSFORD - Corn starch - CPC International Inc.

KINGSFORD - Fabrics - Dan River Inc.

KINGSFORD - Food products - Kingsford Packing Co.

KINGSFORD - Shutters–wood ☆ - Kingsford Building Products

KINGSFORD STRIP - Floor coverings - Hartco Flooring Co.

KINGSFORD STRIP - Floor coverings - Hartco Wood Flooring

KINGSHEAD KIDS, THE - Scissors–hand-operated - Grace Shafir, Inc.

KINGSIZE - Rope - Samson Cordage Works

KINGSLEY - Cabinets–wood - Merillat Industries, Inc.

KINGSLEY - Enameled ware - British American Imports

KINGSLEY - Floor coverings–carpet and rugs - Milliken & Co. Inc.

KINGSLEY - Frames–eyeglass - Hudson Optical Corp.

☆ = Now out of production

KINGSLEY - Mirrors - Harry D. Koenig & Co.

KINGSLEY - Musical instruments - Macie Publishing Co.

KINGSLEY - Playing cards - Kingsley Machine Co.

KINGSLEY - Wallpaper - Kingfisher Wallcoverings

KINGSLEY & CROWNE - Coffee - Enterprise Coffee & Supply Co.

KINGSLEY ARCH - Furniture - Merillat Industries, Inc.

KINGSLEY-BATE - Furniture - Kingsley-Bate, Ltd.

KINGSLEY CAVENDISH - Food products - Turner Gourmet & International Foods

KINGSLEY COLLECTION - Floor coverings—carpet and rugs ☆ - Callaway Carpets

KINGSLEY NO-FAULT - Identification tags - Kingsley Machine Co.

KINGSLEY PALACE - Floor coverings—carpet and rugs - Gulistan Carpet Inc.

KINGSLEY TOOLS - Tools—hand-operated - Kingsley Tools Corp.

KINGSMAN - Colognes - Wibco Enterprises

KINGSMAN - Eyeglasses - Art-Craft Optical Co.

KINGSMAN - Trailers—travel ☆ - Coachmen Industries, Inc.

KINGSMARK - Apparel and accessories ☆ - Winer Industries Inc.

KINGSMEN - Cutlery - Maryland Plastics Inc.

KINGSMEN, THE - Recording label - Kingsmen

KINGSMERE - Floor coverings—carpet and rugs ☆ - World Carpets, Inc.

KINGSMILL - Cabinets - Riviera Cabinets Inc.

KINGSMONT - Furniture ☆ - Bassett Furniture Industries, Inc.

KINGSPIN - Pottery products - Gilmour Campbell

KINGSPOINT - Stereos ☆ - Kingspoint Corp.

KINGSPORT - Blinds—vertical - Tontine/VyTech Industries Inc.

KINGSPORT - Fabrics - Burlington House Fabrics Group

KINGSPORT - Floor coverings - Harris-Tarkett, Inc.

KINGSPORT - Floor coverings—carpet and rugs - Mattel Carpet & Rug Inc.

KINGSPORT - Floor coverings—carpet and rugs ☆ - Fieldturf & Carpet Inc.

KINGSPORT - Rum ☆ - Marie Brizard Wines & Spirits, USA

KINGSPORT COLLECTION - Furniture - O'Sullivan Industries, Inc.

KINGSPORT SHADOWS - Blinds—vertical - Tontine/VyTech Industries Inc.

KINGSRIDGE - Apparel—men's - J. Schoeneman Inc.

KINGSRIDGE - Floor coverings—carpet and rugs ☆ - Criterion Mills Inc.

KINGSTAKE - Tents - Hypark Specialty Co., Inc.

KINGSTATE - Dolls - Kingstate Corp.

KINGSTON - Belts—apparel - S. Kopel Inc.

KINGSTON - Bicycles - Murray, Inc.

KINGSTON - Boats ☆ - Lanness K. McKee & Co.

KINGSTON - Boats—motor ☆ - Holiday Distributing Co.

KINGSTON - Brushes—paint - Corona Brushes Inc.

KINGSTON - Cabinets - American Woodmark Corp.

KINGSTON - Cabinets - Grandview Products Co.

KINGSTON - Cabinets - Marsh Furniture Co.

KINGSTON - Cabinets—wood - Kemper

KINGSTON - Clocks - General Time Corp. (Westclox/Seth Thomas Div.)

KINGSTON - Clocks ☆ - Ridgeway Clock Co.

KINGSTON - Doors—glass - ODL, Inc.

KINGSTON - Fireplace equipment - Design Specialties Inc.

KINGSTON - Floor coverings ☆ - Azrock Commercial Flooring

KINGSTON - Floor coverings—carpet and rugs - Trans-Ocean Import Co. Inc.

KINGSTON - Floor coverings—carpet and rugs ☆ - Blue Ridge Carpet Mills

KINGSTON - Floor coverings—carpet and rugs ☆ - Cumberland Mills Inc.

KINGSTON - Floor coverings—carpet and rugs ☆ - Quaker Inc.

KINGSTON - Food products - Kingston Marketing Co.

KINGSTON - Guitars - Westheimer Corp.

KINGSTON - Luggage - American Tourister, Inc.

KINGSTON - Mirrors - Leigh

KINGSTON - Mobile homes - Golden West Homes

KINGSTON - Motor vehicles—motor homes ☆ - Coachmen Industries, Inc.

KINGSTON - Pens - Kingston Corp.

KINGSTON - Tableware—china - Lenox, Inc.

KINGSTON - Toilets—enameled - Kohler Co.

KINGSTON - Vacuum cleaners and accessories ☆ - Douglas/Quikut

KINGSTON-ALDER - Cabinets ☆ - Quality Cabinets

KINGSTON CLASSIC - Bicycles - Murray, Inc.

KINGSTON COUNTRY - Furniture - Athens Furniture Industries Inc.

KINGSTON COURT - Floor coverings—carpet and rugs - Evans-Black Carpet Mills

KINGSTON ESTATE - Wines - Ashwood Grove, Inc.

KINGSTON HOME FURNISHINGS - Furniture - Test-Rite Products Corp.

KINGSTONE - Dinnerware—glass ☆ - Nikko Ceramics Inc.

KINGSTONE - Games - Kingstone International Corp.

KINGSTOWN - Frames—eyeglass - Universal/Univis Inc.

KINGSTOWN II - Frames—eyeglass - Universal/Univis Inc.

KINGSTOWNE - Silverware - Imperial Schrade Corp.

KINGSTREE - Primers - Mule-Hide Products Co., Inc.

KINGSWAY - Floor coverings - Mannington Resilient Floors

KINGSWAY - Floor coverings—carpet and rugs - Kelly Group Inc.

KINGSWAY - Frames—eyeglass - Zylo Ware Corp.

KINGSWAY - Jewelry ☆ - Hirsch Speidel Inc.

KINGSWAY - Recording label - Maranatha Music Inc.

KINGSWAY - Shoes - Interco Inc.

KINGSWELL - Apparel and accessories - Kellwood Co.

KINGSWELL KASUALS - Apparel and accessories ☆ - Kellwood Co.

KINGSWOOD - Cabinets ☆ - H.J. Scheirich Co.

KINGSWOOD - Cabinets—wood - Kingswood Kitchens Co., Inc.

KINGSWOOD - Furniture - Dinaire Corp.

KINGSWOOD - Manufactured homes - Redman Industries, Inc.

KINGSWOOD - Motor vehicles ☆ - General Motors Corp. (Chevrolet Motor Div.)

KINGSWOOD - Optical scanners—computer - Titmus Optical, Inc.

KINGSWOOD - Prefabricated buildings—wood - Champion Enterprises Inc.

KINGSWOOD - Siding—insulating ☆ - Certainteed Corp. (Roofing Products Group)

KINGSWOOD - Wallpaper - Laminating Services Inc.

KINGSWOOD BOOKS - Publisher's imprints - Abingdon Press

KINGSWOOD PRESS, THE - Publisher's imprints ☆ - Columbia Publishing Co., Inc.

KINGTREADS - Boots - Kaufman Footwear

KINGTRIM - Wood products - MacMillan Bloedel Building Materials

KINGWIPE - Sporting goods ☆ - Chesal Golf

KINGWOOD - Bathroom fixtures ☆ - Artesian Industries

KINGWOOD - Floor coverings - Congoleum Corp.

KINGWOOD - Food products - Oregon Fruit Products Co., Inc.

KINGWOOD - Glassware—household - Kingwood Ceramics

KINGWOOD - Pet products - Kingwood Co.

KINGWOOD - Sporting goods - Total Sports Source

KINGWOOD BLINDS - Blinds—vertical - Woodland Blinds, Inc.

KINGZIP - Plastic bags - Lock-On Plastic

KINGZITE - Paints - Reliance Paint Co. Inc.

KINGZONE - Paints - Reliance Paint Co. Inc.

KINIGIN - Wallpaper ☆ - Maya Romanoff Corp.

KINK - Hair care products - R.M. Walker Healthcare Products Inc.

KINK AGGRESSIVE - Shirts - Schwartz Communications Inc.

KINKA - Giftware ☆ - Enesco Corp.

KINKA - Valves - Kinka Valve Co., Inc.

KINKEAD - Bathroom accessories - Kinkead/Tub/Shower Doors

KINKEAD - Hardware - Dap Products Inc.

KINKEAD'S - Kitchenware—earthenware - Restaurant 2000 Corp.

KINKID - Gloves ☆ - Fownes Brothers & Co., Inc.

KINKLAITH - Beverages—malt - European Beverage Co., Inc.

KINKO'S - Paper products - Kinko's Graphics Corp.

KINKY BLINDFOLD - Novelty items - Edibles, Etc., Inc.

KINKY KUFFS - Novelty items - Edibles, Etc., Inc.

KINLOCH - Floor coverings—carpet and rugs - Milliken & Co. Inc.

KINLOCH - Floor coverings—carpet and rugs ☆ - Bellbridge Carpets

KINLOCK - Faucets - Kohler Co.

KINNETT DAIRIES - Dairy products - Kinnett Dairies, Inc.

KINNEY - Jewelry - Kinney Concepts Inc.

KINNEY'S - Shoes - Kinney Shoe Corp.

KINO - Beverages - Kalil Bottling Co.

KINOETIC ADVENTURE - Computer software - Cinematrix, Inc.

KINOPTIK - Lenses—photographic - Heitz Service Corp.

KINOPTIK APOCHROMATS - Lenses - Heitz Service Corp.

KINOR - Cheese - LMSM Holding Corp.

KINOR - Cheese - Miller's Cheese Corp.

KINOX - Containers - Hormel Corp.

KINS - Rings—jewelry - L & M Castings Inc.

KINSALE - Earthenware ☆ - Waterford Wedgewood USA, Inc.

KINSEN - Wines - Takara Sake USA

KINSER - Food products - Mrs. Giles Country Kitchens Inc.

KINSEY - Paints - Impervious Paint Industries Ltd.

KINSEY - Shoes ☆ - Allen-Edmonds Shoe Corp.

KINSLOW'S - Nuts—salted, roasted, cooked, or canned - Cal-Leaf Health Products Inc.

KINSMAN - Garden equipment ☆ - Kinsman Co. Inc.

KINSMAN - Rings—jewelry - L & M Castings Inc.

KINSMAN'S - Cigarettes ☆ - J.H. Guild Co. Inc.

KINSTON - Floor coverings—carpet and rugs - Eagle Carpets Inc.

KINSTONES - Jewelry - Kinstones Inc.

☆ = Now out of production

KINSUI - Sound equipment - Teevee Toons, Inc.
KINTARO - Dinners–frozen - Kraft Foods, Inc.
KINTRIM - Bathroom accessories ☆ - Kinkead/Tub/Shower Doors
KINTRIM - Faucets - Sterling Plumbing Group Inc.
KINTRONIC - Watches - Movado Time Corp.
KINTYRE - Floor coverings–carpet and rugs - Milliken & Co. Inc.
KINWASHI - Artists' materials - Andrews/Nelson/Whitehead
KINZUA VALLEY - Sausage and cheese - Kinzua Valley, Inc.
K.I.O. - Insecticides - J.T. Eaton and Co.
KION - Furniture - Harter
KIONA VINEYARD, THE - Wines - Kiona Vineyards Winery
KIOPHYLLIN - Pharmaceutical preparations ☆ - G. D. Searle & Co.
KIORITZ - Garden equipment - Echo, Inc.
KIOSK INFORMATION SYSTEMS - Computer software - Kiosk Information Systems, Inc.
KIOWA - Archery equipment - Rollin Wilson Co. Inc.
KIOWA - Knives–pocket ☆ - W.R. Case & Sons Cutlery Co.
KIPLING - Floor coverings–carpet and rugs - Marcella Corp.
KIPLING - Luggage - Tumi Luggage, Inc.
KIPLING - Perfumes ☆ - Classic Fragrances Ltd.
KIPLING - Toys–stuffed ☆ - Gund, Inc.
KIPP - Computer programs - Kofax Image Products, Inc.
KIPPER - Neckties ☆ - Salant/Manhattan Industries
KIPPER KOALA - Puppets - Dakin Inc.
KIPPER SNACKS - Food products - Zaloom Brothers Co. of New Jersey
KIPPY KNITS - Apparel and accessories - Gotham Apparel Corp.
KIPS BAY - Bicycles - Ross Bicycles USA, Ltd.
KIPTAR - Electrical equipment - Schneider Optics, Inc.
KIPTARON - Electrical equipment - Schneider Optics, Inc.
KIRA - Dolls - Mattel, Inc.
KIRA - Floor coverings–carpet and rugs - Milliken & Co. Inc.
KIRA - Toys - Tonka Corp.
KIRBY - Vacuum cleaners and accessories ☆ - Douglas/Quikut
KIRBY MORGAN - Sporting goods - Diving Systems International
KIRBY PUCKETT - Pancakes–mixes ☆ - Homestead Mills
KIRBY VACUETTE - Vacuum cleaners and accessories ☆ - Douglas/Quikut
KIRBYLOK2000 - Metals - Kirby Building Systems, Inc.
KIRBY'S DREAM LAND - Video games - Nintendo of America Inc.
KIRCO - Drapery hardware - Kirsch Co.
KIRI - Jewelry - Kirie Corp.
KIRIGIN CELLARS - Wines - Kirigin Cellars
KIRIN - Beverages–malt ☆ - Kirin USA, Inc.
KIRIN - Health care products - East Earth Herb Inc.
KIRIN DRAFT - Beverages–malt - Kirin USA, Inc.
KIRIN DRY - Beverages–malt ☆ - Kirin USA, Inc.
KIRIN ICHIBAN SHIBORI - Beverages–malt - Kirin USA, Inc.
KIRIN LAGER - Beverages–malt - Kirin USA, Inc.
KIRIN LIGHT - Beverages–malt - Kirin USA, Inc.
KIRK - Frames–eyeglass - Rozin Optical Export Corp.
KIRK - Health care products - Procter & Gamble Co.
KIRK - Leather goods - David Kirk (London)
KIRK - Silver products - Kirk Stieff Co.
KIRK - Visors ☆ - Kirk Plastic Co. Inc.
KIRK - Watches - Bulova Corp.
KIRK & MATZ - Knives–carving - Kirk & Matz Ltd.
KIRK DIAL - Jewelry - Kirk Dial of Pennsylvania
KIRK KING - Flatware - Kirk Stieff Co.
KIRK ROSE - Flatware ☆ - Kirk Stieff Co.
KIRK-SIL - Silicon products - Kirkhill Rubber Co.
KIRK STIEFF - Giftware - Kirk Stieff Co.
KIRK VERMEIL - Jewelry ☆ - Kirk Stieff Co.
KIRKHILL - Gaskets - Kirkhill Rubber Co.
KIRKLAND - Toiletries - Costco Wholesale Corp.
KIRKLAND CUSTOM SEAFOODS - Seafood products–fresh or frozen - Kirkland Custom Seafood
KIRKLAND SIGNATURE - Apparel and accessories - Costco Wholesale Corp.
KIRKMAN - Borax - Colgate-Palmolive Co.
KIRKPATRICK - Gun holsters and slings - American Sales & Manufacturing Co.
KIRKPATRICK'S - Food products - Mark 7 Seafood & Industries
KIRK'S TRUCK ALARM - Clocks - Kirkland Enterprises Inc.
KIRKSEAL - Bathroom accessories - Kirkhill Rubber Co.
KIRKSHIELD - Firefighting apparatus - Kirkhill Rubber Co.
KIRKWOOD - Apparel and accessories ☆ - Sara Lee Knit Products Inc.
KIRKWOOD - Floor coverings–carpet and rugs - Karastan-Bigelow Inc.
KIRKWOOD - Horseradish - Kirkwood Farms Inc.

KIRKWOOD - Manufactured homes - Redman Industries, Inc.
KIRKWOOD - Watches - Bulova Corp.
KIRKWOOD LIMITED - Manufactured homes - Redman Industries, Inc.
KIRKWOOD STAIR - Staircases–wood - Kirkwood Stair Co. Inc.
KIRLANGIC - Olive oil - Kirlangic Imports
KIRLON - Drapery hardware - Kirsch Co.
KIRRA - Apparel and accessories - Pacific Sunwear of California Inc.
KIRSBERRY - Beverages–alcohol - Blair Importers Ltd.
KIRSCH - Blinds–vertical - Vertical Blind Factory
KIRSCH - Curtains - Cooper Industries, Inc.
KIRSCH - Drapery hardware - Kirsch Co.
KIRSHNER - Tape players–cassette - Sony Music Entertainment Inc.
KIRSTEN - Cigarette holders - Kirsten Pipe Co. Inc.
KIRSTEN - Dolls - Pleasant Co.
KIRSTEN - Flatware - Utica Cutlery Co.
KIRSTEN - Glassware–household ☆ - Anchor Hocking Glass, Inc.
KIRSTEN - Glassware–household ☆ - Dansk International Designs, Ltd.
KIRSTEN - Watches - Bulova Corp.
KIRTLAND - Bicycles - HS Industries, Inc.
KIRTZ - Shutters–wood - Shutter Mill, Inc.
KIS - Laboratory apparatus - BLH Electronics
KISA - Ophthalmic goods - Swank Optical
KISCA - Frames–eyeglass - Pathway Optical Prods.
KISCO - See **WESTWOOD**
KISCO - Water treating compounds - Kisco Water Treatment Co.
KISEI-DO - Vitamins and nutritional supplements - Hanil Management Co., Ltd.
KISEKI - Phonographs ☆ - Sumiko Inc.
KISHAN - Oils–edible - Sachu Importers & Wholesalers
KISII - Hair conditioner - Roux Laboratories, Inc.
KISKA - Adhesives and sealants - Metacrylics
KISKEYA - Cigars ☆ - Tropical Tobacco, Inc.
KISMET - Dishes–earthenware ☆ - Denby USA Limited
KISMET - Eyeglasses - Art-Craft Optical Co.
KISMET - Floor coverings–carpet and rugs - Robertex Associates Inc.
KISMET - Games - Lakeside Games
KISMET - House furnishings - Dan River Inc.
KISMET - Yarn - Joseph Galler Inc.
KISOL - Cold remedies ☆ - Laser Inc.
KISS - Game ☆ - American Publishing Corp.
KISS - Nail care products - Kiss Products, Inc.
KISS - Printers–computer - QMS, Inc.
KISS - Recording label - Kiss Catalog Ltd.
KISS - Skin care products - Kimo's Nail Charms
KISS & CUDDLE - Dolls - Mattel, Inc.
KISS AND GO! - Hair care products - Kiss My Face
KISS KIDS - Skin care products - Kiss My Face
KISS ME - Frames–eyeglass - Hudson Optical Corp.
KISS ME - Novelty items ☆ - Papel Freelance, Inc.
KISS ME IN THE GARDEN - Oils–essential - Jonathan Mandell
KISS-ME LITTLE BABY - Toys - Eugene Doll & Novelty Co. Inc.
KISS ME QUICK - Jewelry–costume - Yes Group, Inc.
KISS-ME-SWEET - Food products - Osceola Fruit Distributors
KISS MY FACE - Cosmetics - Deer Valley Farm
KISS MY FACE - Soap - Kiss My Face
KISS MY FACE ALL DAY - Skin care products - Kiss My Face
KISS MY FACE ALL NIGHT - Skin care products - Kiss My Face
KISS 'N COLORS - Bandages - Crackle Creations, Inc.
KISS N TELL BEAR - Toys–stuffed - Great American Fun Corp.
KISS-O-FLAVOR - Fruits and vegetables - A. Camacho Inc.
KISS OF MINT - Prophylactics - Ansell Inc. (Personal Products Div.)
KISS OF PEACE - Oils–essential - Beso De Luna, Inc.
KISS OFF - Stain removers - General Pencil Co.
KISS OFF - Suntan lotions ☆ - Kiss My Face
KISS PLUS - Printers–computer - QMS, Inc.
KISS PRO - Nail care products - Kiss Products, Inc.
KISS-X - Archery equipment - Saunders Archery Co.
KISS-XL - Archery equipment - Saunders Archery Co.
KISSCARE - Pharmaceutical preparations - Kent Integrated Scientific Systems, Inc.
KISSED WITH HONEY - Yogurt–frozen - Elgin-Honey Hill Corp.
KISSES - Greeting cards - Vivian Greene Inc.
KISSES - Jewelry - J. & C. Ferrara Co. Inc.
KISSES - Musical instrument accessories - Dimarzio, Inc.
KISSES BY CLIMAX - Shoes - R. Josephs Sportswear, Inc.
KISSI - Lenses–optical - National Optical Co.
KISSIMMEE - Water–mineral - Kissimmee Spring Water Co.

☆ = Now out of production

KISSIN' COUSIN - Toys–stuffed ☆ - Fun World Inc.
KISSIN INSURANCE - Luggage ☆ - Alger Creations Inc.
KISSIN KARROTS - Dolls - Mattel, Inc.
KISSING FRESH - Cosmetics - Maybelline Co.
KISSING KOOLERS - Lipsticks - Maybelline Co.
KISSING POTION - Lipsticks - Maybelline Co.
KISSING READY - Vitamins and nutritional supplements - Tishcon Corp.
KISSING SANTAS - Christmas tree ornaments - Rauch Industries, Inc.
KISSING SLICKS - Lipsticks - Maybelline Co.
KISSING STICK - Lipsticks - Maybelline Co.
KISSING SWEET - Lipsticks - Pavion Ltd.
KISSLE - Yogurt ☆ - Whitney Foods, Inc.
KISSLE CLASSICS - Yogurt - Whitney Foods, Inc.
KISSLINGS - Sauerkraut - A.C. Kissling Co.
KISSNET - Computer software - Versalan Inc.
KISSPROOF - Cosmetics - Lord & Berry, Ltd.
KISSROFF - Computer software - QMS, Inc.
KISSTORY - Publisher's imprints - Kiss Catalog Ltd.
KISSUMS - Dolls - Uneeda Doll Co., Inc.
KISSY - Ophthalmic goods ☆ - Luxottica
KISSY PUPS - Dolls - Mattel, Inc.
KISSYFUR - Publisher's imprints - Scholastic Inc.
KISSYFUR - Toys ☆ - Jak-Pak Inc.
KIST - Beverages - Monarch Co., Inc.
KISTLER VINEYARDS - Wines - Kistler Vineyards
KISTY - Frames–eyeglass - Hudson Optical Corp.
KIT - Automotive parts and accessories - Northern Labs, Inc.
KIT - Trailers–travel ☆ - Kit Manufacturing Co.
KIT BAG - Pet products - Aero/Byne Co.
KIT CARSON - Toy guns - Daisy Manufacturing Co.
KIT CARSON - Toys - Geronimo Productions Inc.
KIT CAT KLOCK - Clocks - California Clock Co.
KIT COMPANION - Motor vehicles–motor homes - Kit Manufacturing Co.
KIT FILM - Plastics film - Rexam Flexible Packaging
KIT GRAPHICS - Plastics - Paul J. Golasz
KIT GUN - Revolvers - Smith & Wesson Corp.
KIT KAT - Candy - Hershey Chocolate USA
KIT KAT - Pet products ☆ - Strongheart Products, Inc.
KIT 'N KABOODLE - Cat food - Ralston Purina Co.
KIT PREMIUM - Animal feeds - Kit Farms Inc.
KIT-TEA - Tea kettles–nonelectric - Lincoware International, Inc.
KIT TEES - Pet products ☆ - Precious Paws
KITA WARE - Dinnerware–glass ☆ - Block China Co.
KITAKATA - Artists' materials - Andrews/Nelson/Whitehead
KITANIHON - Crackers - Commerce Foods Inc.
KITCH-N-KRAFT - Vegetables–canned - Allen Canning Co.
KITCHEN ACCENTS - Towels - Arden Corp.
KITCHEN ADDITIONS - Glassware–household - Crisa Corp.
KITCHEN-AID - Mats - Matworks
KITCHEN AND BATH - Paints - Hirshfield's Paint Manufacturing
KITCHEN & BATH - Wallpaper - Mayfair Wallcoverings
KITCHEN & BATH CATALOG VOL. 4 - Wallcovering - Fashon Wallcoverings
KITCHEN & BATH CHOICES - Wallcovering - Gencorp Inc.
KITCHEN & BATH DELIGHTS - Wallpaper - Sanitas Wallcoverings
KITCHEN & BATH DELIGHTS II - Wallpaper - Sanitas Wallcoverings
KITCHEN & BATH FAIR - Wallpaper - Essex Wallcoverings
KITCHEN & BATH FAVORITES - Fabrics–tapestry ☆ - Columbus Coated Fabrics Co.
KITCHEN & BATH FOCUS III - Wallpaper - Parkview Designs
KITCHEN & BATH MAGIC - Wallpaper - Warner Co.
KITCHEN & BATH MAGIC II - Wallpaper - Warner Co.
KITCHEN & BATH NATURALS - Wallcovering - Gencorp Inc.
KITCHEN & BATH POTPOURRI - Wallpaper ☆ - Sanitas Wallcoverings
KITCHEN & BATH SETTINGS III - Wallpaper - Essex Wallcoveringss
KITCHEN & BATH SHOWCASE IV - Wallpaper - Essex Wallcoveringss
KITCHEN & BATH STYLE - Wallpaper - Sanitas Wallcoverings
KITCHEN ANGEL - Figurines - Anchor Sales & Marketing, Inc.
KITCHEN ART - Aprons - Whang Sports, Inc.
KITCHEN ART - Cooking equipment–household ☆ - Old Dutch International Ltd.
KITCHEN BATH & BORDERS - Wallpaper ☆ - Brewster Wallcovering Co.
KITCHEN BILLBOARDS - Sponges - National Sponge Corp.
KITCHEN BOUQUET - Snack foods - Clorox Co.
KITCHEN CAFE - Kitchen appliances - Sun Television and Appliances, Inc.
KITCHEN CAPERS - Toys - Tonka Corp.
KITCHEN CARE - Cleaning preparations - Colgate-Palmolive Co.

KITCHEN CENTER - Food processors - Sunbeam-Oster Household Products
KITCHEN CHANGER - Kitchen appliances ☆ - Nutone Inc.
KITCHEN CHEMISTRY - Glassware–household ☆ - Pilgrim Glass Corp.
KITCHEN CLASSICS - Cooking utensils–earthenware - Anchor Hocking Glass, Inc.
KITCHEN CLASSICS - Floor coverings–carpet and rugs ☆ - Callaway Carpets
KITCHEN CLIP - Housewares - Guardsman Products, Inc.
KITCHEN CLIP JR. - Housewares - Guardsman Products, Inc.
KITCHEN CLUB - Knives - Ymt International, Inc.
KITCHEN COACH - Educational materials - Coach Master International Corp.
KITCHEN COMPANIONS - Cooking equipment–household - Imperial Schrade Corp.
KITCHEN COMPANY - Greeting cards - Heartprint Inc.
KITCHEN CONCEPTS - Housewares - Himark Enterprises Inc.
KITCHEN COTTON - Yarn - Lion Brand Yarn Co.
KITCHEN COUNTER COOKBOOKS - Catalogs - Sally Miller Loeb
KITCHEN CREATIONS - Kitchen appliances - High Performance Appliances, Inc.
KITCHEN CUPBOARD - Bakery products - Perfection Bakeries, Inc.
KITCHEN DE-LITE - Candles ☆ - Candle-Lite Co.
KITCHEN DE SOL - Food products - W.J. Clark & Co.
KITCHEN DIMENSIONS - Appliance parts - Toastmaster Inc.
KITCHEN DIVAS - Broadcasting stations–cable television - Angela Shelf Medearis
KITCHEN ESSENTIALS - Housewares - Anchor Hocking Glass, Inc.
KITCHEN EXPRESS - Kitchen utensils–aluminum - Kitchen Express
KITCHEN FAIR - Cookware - Regal Ware, Inc.
KITCHEN FARMS - Food products - Kitchen Farms Inc.
KITCHEN FOR THE MIND, A - Recording label - Intellectual Equities, Inc.
KITCHEN FRESH - Candy ☆ - Sathers Inc.
KITCHEN FUN - Dolls - Mattel, Inc.
KITCHEN GEAR - Towels - Gear Holdings, Inc.
KITCHEN GEM - Food products - US Foodservice
KITCHEN GOURMET - Kitchen appliances - Walgreen Co.
KITCHEN GRAND - Food products - Loyal Canning Corp.
KITCHEN GUARD - Ashtrays–glass ☆ - Frank J. Curran-Esquire Chemical Co.
KITCHEN HEARTH - Cookies - Pepperidge Farm Inc.
KITCHEN HELPER - Tools–hand-operated - Sales Magic, Inc.
KITCHEN HELPERS - Bakery machines ☆ - National Housewares
KITCHEN HOLIDAY - Food products - Conagra, Inc.
KITCHEN IMPS - Magnets - Dynacast
KITCHEN KARE - Serving carts - Acrylic Plastic Products, Inc.
KITCHEN KEEPERS - Rubber bands - Alliance Rubber Co.
KITCHEN KETTLE - Cooking equipment–commercial - National Presto Industries, Inc.
KITCHEN KEWTIES - Posters ☆ - One-of-a-Kind Workshop
KITCHEN KING - Fruits and vegetables - Magic Valley Foods Inc.
KITCHEN KING - Peanut butter ☆ - J.M. Smucker Co.
KITCHEN KLENZER - Cleaning preparations - Fitzpatrick Bros. Inc.
KITCHEN KLENZER - Cleaning preparations - Tri-Par Corp.
KITCHEN KORNER - Food products ☆ - Longs Drug Stores Corp.
KITCHEN KRAFT - Flour–blended ☆ - Safeway Stores Inc.
KITCHEN KUT - Vegetables–dried - Sun Garden Packing Co., Inc.
KITCHEN MAID - Clocks ☆ - General Time Corp. (Westclox/Seth Thomas Div.)
KITCHEN MILL - Kitchen appliances - R & R Mill Co. Inc.
KITCHEN NUTRITION - Publisher's imprints - Regal Ware, Inc.
KITCHEN PAL - Housewares - Alwin Products
KITCHEN PANTRY - Housewares - Boston Warehouse Trading Corp.
KITCHEN PLAY - Toys - Tonka Corp.
KITCHEN POLICE - Cleaning preparations - Pioneer Manufacturing Co.
KITCHEN POWER - Cleaning preparation - Blue Coral, Inc.
KITCHEN PRIDE - Bakery products - Campbell Taggart Inc.
KITCHEN PRIDE - Clocks ☆ - General Time Corp. (Westclox/Seth Thomas Div.)
KITCHEN PRIDE - Cooking equipment–household ☆ - Mirro Corp.
KITCHEN PRIDE - Juices–frozen - Quality Kitchen Corp.
KITCHEN PRO - Kitchen appliances - Regal Ware, Inc.
KITCHEN QUEEN - Food products - Aunt Nellie's Farm Kitchens Inc.
KITCHEN SAFE - Cleaning preparations–household - Miles Inc.
KITCHEN SCENTS - Candle-making kits ☆ - Corning Inc.
KITCHEN SCRUB - Brushes - Suburbanite Industries
KITCHEN SECRETS - Containers ☆ - Beaverite Products Inc.
KITCHEN SINK PRESS - Postcards - Fotofolio Inc.
KITCHEN SOFTSOAP - Soap - Colgate-Palmolive Co.

KITCHEN SOLUTIONS - Kitchen utensils–enameled ☆ - Robbins Industries, Inc.
KITCHEN-SORB - Chemical preparations - Rainforest Moose, Ltd.
KITCHEN SWEET - Tomato pastes and sauces - Lake Packing Co. Inc.
KITCHEN-TESTED - Flour–blended - General Mills, Inc.
KITCHEN THRIFT - Food products - Cascade Food Sales Inc.
KITCHEN TOSSED SALADS - Salads–prepackaged - Old Fashioned Enterprises Inc.
KITCHEN TREAT - Food products - Conagra, Inc.
KITCHEN UTILITY CONTAINER - Bags–trash - Ironclad LP
KITCHEN WARE - Toys - Little Tikes Co.
KITCHEN WINDOW - Breads - Kitchen Products Inc.
KITCHEN WORKS - Housewares - Barth-Dreyfuss of California
KITCHENAID - Kitchen appliances - Kitchenaid
KITCHENAID WHISPER QUIET - Dishwashers–household - Whirlpool Properties, Inc.
KITCHENART - Kitchenware–plastic - Robbins Industries, Inc.
KITCHENEER - Kitchen appliances - Rival Manufacturing Co.
KITCHENEER - Mats - Matworks
KITCHENER - Sporting goods ☆ - Allsop, Inc.
KITCHENETICS - Kitchen appliances - K-Tec, Inc.
KITCHENETTE - Housewares - Division Sales, Inc.
KITCHENLINK - Kitchen utensils–aluminum - Modern Housewares, Inc.
KITCHENMATE - Kitchen appliances - R. Foster Enterprises
KITCHENRY - Housewares - Ironees Co.
KITCHENS & BATHS IV - Wallpaper - Pantasote Inc. (Wallcovering Div.)
KITCHENS, BATHS & BORDERS II - Wallpaper - Brewster Wallcovering Co.
KITCHEN'S BEST - Kitchen appliances - Windmere Corp.
KITCHEN'S BEST - Wines - Gibson Wine Co.
KITCHENS OF THE OCEANS - Seafood products–fresh or frozen - Kitchens of the Oceans Inc.
KITCHENS OF THE SEA - Food products - Viking Seafoods Inc.
KITCHENSILL - Seeds–salted, roasted, cooked, or canned - Kingfisher Inc.
KITCHENVISION - Televisions - J. Keith Green
KITCHINDEX - Publisher's imprints - Direct Impact
KITCHMASTER - Food processors - Sunbeam-Oster Household Products
KITCH'N FIX'N - Meat products–beef - Park 100 Foods Inc.
KITCH'N-HANDY - Racks - Washington Products Inc.
KITE - Strollers–baby - Graco Children's Products
KITE - Tobacco–chewing or smoking - Brown & Williamson Tobacco Corp.
KITE-A-MARAN - Kites - Spectra Star Kites
KITE BIRD - Kites ☆ - Gayla Industries Inc.
KITE DECOYS - Kites - Sports Innovations Inc.
KITE FACTORY, THE - Kites - Kite Factory
KITE HILL VINYARDS - Wines ☆ - Diamond Wine Merchants
KITE-MOSAIK - Puzzles - Kadon Enterprises Inc.
KITE SHUTTLE SYSTEM - Kites ☆ - Gayla Industries Inc.
KITE TRAIN - Kites - Hi-Flier Manufacturing Co.
KITFOX - Aircraft–airplanes - SkyStar Aircraft Corp.
KITFOX LITE - Aircraft–airplanes - SkyStar Aircraft Corp.
KITH & KIN - Toys - Kith & Kin
KIT'N KABOODLE - Cat food - Ralston Purina Co.
KITNIPS - Pet food - Kal Kan Foods, Inc.
KITO KIDS - Stationery - Tenten Inc.
KITS - Candy - Gilliam Candy Brands
KITS - Candy - Gilliam Candy Co. Inc. (Gilliam Candy Brands)
KITS FOR KIDS - Bird cages - Vitos Products
KITS FOR KIDS - Craft supplies ☆ - Western Trimming Corp.
KITS FOR THE BIRDS - Bird cages - Vitos Products
KITSCH'N COUTURE - Linen - Mitchell B. Manasse
KITSHEEN - Paints - Graham Paint and Varnish Co.
KITT & KABOODLE - Toys–stuffed ☆ - CBS Toys
KITTATINNY - Food products - Mountain Brook Orchards Inc.
KITTEN - Dolls - Alexander Doll Co. Inc.
KITTEN - Ophthalmic goods - Embassy Creations Inc.
KITTEN - Synthesizers–musical instrument ☆ - Syn-Cordion Musical Instruments Corp.
KITTEN - Yarn ☆ - JCA, Inc.
KITTEN CALICO - Yarn ☆ - JCA, Inc.
KITTEN CHOW - Cat food - Ralston Purina Co.
KITTEN CONNECTION - Greeting cards - Originals by Maris (O.B.M. Publishing)
KITTEN KNITS - Giftware ☆ - Enesco Corp.
KITTEN-KNITS - Greeting cards - Morehead, Inc.
KITTEN SOFT - Crocheted and knitted items ☆ - Roosevelt Mills Inc.
KITTEN WAX - Polishing rouge ☆ - Park Metallurgical Corp.

KITTENS - Underwear and nightwear - Dallco Industries Inc. (Katz Div.)
KITTENS, KIDS, AND A FROG - Computer software - Hartley Courseware Inc.
KITTENS TO CATS - Pet products - Media West Home Video Inc.
KITTERY SKIFF - Boats–skiffs - Alden Ocean Shells Inc.
KITTI KITCHEN - Pet products - Haugen Pet Products Inc.
KITTI POTTI - Pet products - Haugen Pet Products Inc.
KITTI ROOST - Pet products - Haugen Pet Products Inc.
KITTINGER - Furniture - Kittinger Co.
KITTIWAKE - Ships–sailing vessels - Ray Greene Industries
KITTRICH - Blinds–vertical - Kittrich Corp.
KITTRICH - Blinds–vertical - Vertical Blind Factory
KITTY - Barrettes - Accessories International
KITTY - Brooms - Lighthouse Industries
KITTY - Cat food ☆ - Kitty Food Corp.
KITTY - Jars–glass - Metro/Thebe, Inc.
KITTY - Ophthalmic goods ☆ - Luxottica
KITTY AND HER KIDDIE KAR - Dolls ☆ - Uneeda Doll Co., Inc.
KITTY BLOOM - Veterinary nutritional supplements - J.E. Ronicker Labs Inc.
KITTY BOX - Pet products - Waverly Mineral Products Co.
KITTY CAT - Tripods–photographic - Phoenix Corp. of America
KITTY CAT BEANS - Dolls - Mattel, Inc.
KITTY CAT GRASS - Cat food - Cosmic Cat Corp.
KITTY CAVE - Pet products ☆ - Flexi-Mat Corp.
KITTY CHALET - Pet products ☆ - Mapes Industries Inc.
KITTY CHECK-UP - Toys–stuffed - Tonka Corp.
KITTY CITY - Pet shops - Petco Animal Supplies, Inc.
KITTY CLUB - Pet products - Golden Cat Corp.
KITTY COED - Dolls ☆ - Fun World Inc.
KITTY COMB - Dolls - Susan Sona
KITTY CONDO - Pet products - Kitty Condo
KITTY COTTAGE - Pet products - Easy Living Pet Products Inc.
KITTY CREAMCHEESE - Toys–stuffed ☆ - Dakin Inc.
KITTY CRYSTALS - Pet products - Zeotech Corp.
KITTY CUCUMBER - Figurines - Schmid Inc.
KITTY CUCUMBER - Paper products - B. Shackman & Co.
KITTY CUCUMBER AND FRIENDS - Toys ☆ - Toy Works, Inc.
KITTY CUISINE - Cat food - Winn-Dixie Stores, Inc.
KITTY DAZZLER - Pet products - Peak Pet Products
KITTY DISH - Pet products - V.K. Industries Inc.
KITTY DITTY - Pet products - LYC, Inc.
KITTY DOUGHNUT - Pet products - Peak Pet Products
KITTY-DRI - Pet products - Oil-Dri Corp. of America
KITTY DRI - Pet products - Paxon Manufacturing Co.
KITTY EASY DRAW - Pet products - K.O.S. Industries Inc.
KITTY FISHIN' - Pet products - Wannabe
KITTY FLUSH - Pet products - Absorption Corp.
KITTY GLOW - Lamps ☆ - Lamplight Farms, Inc.
KITTY GREENS - Pet products - Superior Brands Inc.
KITTY GUNDS - Toys–stuffed ☆ - Gund, Inc.
KITTY HAIR - Automotive parts and accessories - Fibre Glass-Evercoat Co. Inc.
KITTY HAWK - Kites ☆ - Airplane Kite Co.
KITTY HERBS - Cat food - Cosmic Cat Corp.
KITTY HIDE-A-BED - Pet products - Peak Pet Products
KITTY HIDEAWAY - Pet products ☆ - Flexi-Mat Corp.
KITTY HUTCH - Pet products - Flexi-Mat Corp.
KITTY-JOHN - Scoops ☆ - Perky-Pet Products Co.
KITTY JON - Pet products - Excel-Mineral Co. Inc.
KITTY KADDY - Pet products - Home Tech Products, Inc.
KITTY KALLER - Pet products - Richard J. Margenot
KITTY KAP - Crocheted and knitted items ☆ - Schuessler Knitting Mills Inc.
KITTY KARE - Pet products - Excel-Mineral Co. Inc.
KITTY KASTLE - Pet products ☆ - Black Sheep Inc.
KITTY KAT - Candy - Superior Fruit & Confections
KITTY KAT - Pet products - Vo-Toys Inc.
KITTY KAT - Toys–banks - A.J. Renzi Plastic Corp.
KITTY KAT ALPHABET BINGO - Pet products - Educational Insights, Inc.
KITTY KAT KOMB - Pet products - Tangler-Wrangler Inc.
KITTY KAVIAR - Cat food - International Trade & Imports Ltd.
KITTY KIST - Cat food - Gold Kist Inc.
KITTY KIT - Pet products - Excel-Mineral Co. Inc.
KITTY, KITTY, KITTY - Bedding–linen - Dan River Inc.
KITTY KOEHLER'S - Cakes - Kitty Koehler's Kitchens
KITTY KOMFORTER - Pet products - Posh Pet Products Inc.
KITTY KONDO - Pet products - O'Donnell Industries Inc.
KITTY KONG - Pet products - Kong Co.

☆ = Now out of production

KITTY KOOLERS - Pet products - Petco Inc.
KITTY KORNER - Pet products - Golden Cat Corp.
KITTY KORNER - Pet products - Rolf C. Hagen (USA) Corp.
KITTY KORNER KLAWER - Pet products - St. Jon Pet Care Products Inc.
KITTY KORNER KOMBER - Pet products - St. Jon Pet Care Products Inc.
KITTY KRAWLER - Pet products - Dura Pro Products
KITTY KRAZE - Pet products - Vo-Toys Inc.
KITTY KREAM - Cat food - AGP Petfoods
KITTY KREEK - Containers–plastic - Kay G. Kemp
KITTY KRITTERS - Pet products - Blue Ribbon Pet Products, Inc.
KITTY KRUMPETS - Cat food ☆ - John Morrell & Co.
KITTY KUP - Pet products - Flexi-Mat Corp.
KITTY KUPS - Pet products - R.C. Steele Co.
KITTY KURLS - Pet products - Keeter Kreations, Inc.
KITTY LATRINE - Pet products - Mark J. Zemoyski
KITTY LETTERS - Toys - Tonka Corp.
KITTY LITTER - Patterns–clothing - Ann's Cottage
KITTY LITTER MAXX - Pet products - Golden Cat Corp.
KITTY LOUNGE - Pet products - Argee Corp.
KITTY MAGIC - Pet products - Gold Kist Inc.
KITTY MALT - Pet products - St. Aubrey
KITTY NAPPER - Pet products ☆ - Flexi-Mat Corp.
KITTY ONE STEP - Pet products - K.O.S. Industries Inc.
KITTY O'S - Pet products - ALPO Petfoods Inc.
KITTY PLAY GROUND - Pet products - Abeta Products Inc.
KITTY PLEASERS - Pet products - American Cat Emporium
KITTY PRIVY - Pet products - Cattus Ltd.
KITTY Q'S - Pet food - Sergeant's Pet Products, Inc.
KITTY QUEEN - Cat food - Kitty Queen Pet Foods
KITTY QUEEN - Cat food ☆ - Kitty Food Corp.
KITTY QUICK DRAW - Pet products ☆ - K.O.S. Industries Inc.
KITTY ROYAL PARTY PAK - Pet products - JW Products Co.
KITTY SAMPLER - Pet products - Gimborn U.S., Inc.
KITTY SKOOP - Pet products - Dandy Products Inc.
KITTY SNICKER - Cat food - Foster Canning Inc.
KITTY SUSHI - Pet products - Maggie Mae's Gourmet Pet Products Inc.
KITTY TASSLE - Pet products - Peak Pet Products
KITTY TEASE - Toys–stuffed - Galkie Co.
KITTY TUNA CAN - Pet products - Southern California Foam, Inc.
KITTY TWIRL - Pet products - Peak Pet Products
KITTY VIDEO - Pet products - Lazy Cat Ranch
KITTY VITE - Pet products - St. Aubrey
KITTY WHITE - Pet products - Mid-Florida Mining Co.
KITTY WHITE SCOOP - Pet products - Mid-Florida Mining Co.
KITTY WISHES - Pet products - Multipet International Inc.
KITTYBITS - Pet products - 8 in 1 Pet Products Inc.
KITTYBITS - Pet products - St. Aubrey
KITTYCAT - Snowmobiles - Arctco, Inc.
KITTYLAC - Veterinary nutritional supplements - Landco
KITTYMEW - Toys–stuffed ☆ - Dakin Inc.
KITTYPAWS - Cat food - DOCA USA, Inc.
KITTY'S KAROUSEL - Pet products - Lucky Yuppy Puppy Co.
KITTY'S KIDS - Apparel–children's - Kitty's Kids, Inc.
KITTY'S KITTY LITTER - Pet products - Zorbite Corp.
KITTY'S SALAD BOWL - Pet products - Aero/Byne Co.
KITTYSTARS - Pet products - Mardel Laboratories, Inc.
KITTYSTARS - Pet products - USA-Petrx
KITZBUHEL - Apparel–men's - Alps Sportswear Manufacturing Co.
KITZYME - Pet products ☆ - Pet Supply Imports Inc.
KIVA - Apparel–women's - E. Benjamin, Inc.
KIVA - Furniture ☆ - Hammary Furniture Co. Inc.
KIVAR PERFORMA - Paper products - REXAM DSI
KIVAR ULTRA - Paper - REXAM DSI
KIVINEN - Bedding–linen - Dan River Inc.
KIWANO - Fruit and vegetable markets - Frieda's, Inc.
KIWI - Bicycles - XLM Corp.
KIWI - Cases–camera - Kiwi
KIWI - Cases–camera ☆ - Innovative Manufacturing Corp.
KIWI - Comforters - Kiwi Products International
KIWI - Computer hardware - Kiwi Computer, Inc.
KIWI - Frames–eyeglass - May Optical Co. Inc.
KIWI - Office supplies - Kiwi Marketing, Inc.
KIWI - Seafood products–fresh or frozen - Empress International Ltd.
KIWI - Shampoos - Cheveux Inc.
KIWI - Shoe accessories - Kiwi Brands, Inc.
KIWI - Toys–stuffed - Russ Berrie and Co., Inc.

KIWI - Toys–stuffed ☆ - Gund, Inc.
KIWI - Waterproofing compounds - Sara Lee Corp.
KIWI CAMP DRY - Waterproofing compounds - Sara Lee Corp.
KIWI CLEAN AND GLEAM - Cleaning preparations - Kiwi Brands, Inc.
KIWI KARTOONS - Toys - Chiquita Brands, Inc.
KIWI LIME MIST - Cookies - Savannah Cookie Co.
KIWI MATRIX - Machinery - Kiwi Coders Corp.
KIWI SHINE WIPES - Towels - Kiwi Brands, Inc.
KIWI SLUSH BUSTER - Cleaning preparations - Kiwi Brands, Inc.
KIWI SPORT - Footwear - Kiwi Brands, Inc.
KIWI SUEDE & NUBUCK - Cleaning preparations - Kiwi Brands, Inc.
KIWI, THE - Regulators–voltage - Electronic Protection Devices
KIWI WET PRUF - Waterproofing compounds - Kiwi Brands, Inc.
KIWIENVELOPES! - Computer software - Kiwi Software, Inc.
KIWILD - Beverages–carbonated - I.C. Refreshment Co., Inc.
KIWK EDGE - Adhesives and sealants - Woodtape Co.
KIWOCOL QUANTUM - Chemical preparations - Kiwo Inc.
KIX - Cereal - General Mills, Inc.
KIXX PROFESSIONAL ATHLETICS - Sporting goods - Kixx Athletics, Inc.
KIYAK - Skin care products - Connie Stevens Forever Spring the Beauty System Inc.
KIZUKISHI - Artists' materials - Andrews/Nelson/Whitehead
KJ - Jewelry - King's of New Castle Inc.
KJ KILON JEANS - Jeans–men's - Blue Pilot, Inc.
KJELLANDER - China cabinets–wood - Swedish Products Inc. (Sojo Inc.)
KJIRST - Beverages–malt ☆ - Lipton Investments, Inc.
KJOS WEST - Publisher's imprints - Neil A. Kjos Music Co.
KK - Electrical equipment - RKB Industrial, Inc.
KK - Jewelry–precious - K & K Jewelry, Inc.
KK 2000 - Cabinets–wood - Kitchen Kompact Inc.
KK EXPRESS - Toys–automobiles - Tyco Toys
KK FIRE ENGINE - Toys–automobiles - Tyco Toys
KK KLENK - Tools–hand-operated - Klenk Industries, Inc.
KK2 - Fire extinguishers - Kidde Safety
KKI - Motor vehicles–automobiles - Krystal Koach, Inc.
KKNNIITTSS - Apparel and accessories ☆ - Gallron
KKS - Sporting goods ☆ - Continental Sports Supply Inc.
KL - Colognes - Elizabeth Arden Inc.
KL - Tools–power-driven - K-Line Industries
K.L. 7 - Pet products ☆ - Glo-Marr Products Inc.
KL-990 - Paints ☆ - Rule Industries, Inc.
KL B-6 - Headsets–telephone - Nature's Bounty, Inc.
KL SELECT - Leather goods - Kensington KL Select
KLAATU - Toys - Lucasfilm Ltd.
KLADDERS - Pet products - Pet-Ag, Inc.
KLAE - Hair care products - Redmond Products, Inc.
KLAFASUNA - Sauna products - Klafs Sauna Corp.
KLAFSUN - Spas–home - M.S. Halpern & Associates, Inc.
KLAFSUN - Sunblocks - Klafs Sauna Corp.
KLAM - Brakes–motor vehicle - Diesel Service & Sales Co., Inc.
KLAMATH - Boats–fishing - Klamath Boat Co. Inc.
KLAMATH - Doors - Jeld-Wen, Inc.
KLAMATH BLUE GREEN ALGAE - Pharmaceutical preparations - Klamath Blue Green, Inc.
KLAMATH CARGO - Boats - Klamath Boat Co. Inc.
KLAMATH DELUXE - Boats–fishing - Klamath Boat Co. Inc.
KLAMATH EXPLORER - Boats–motor - Klamath Boat Co. Inc.
KLAMATH FALLS - Milk - Klamath Dairy Products
KLAMATH JAC - Boats–fishing - Klamath Boat Co. Inc.
KLAMATH LAKE ALGAE - Food products - Rossha Enterprises, Inc.
KLAMATH OPEN - Boats–fishing - Klamath Boat Co. Inc.
KLAMATH SHORES - Vitamins and nutritional supplements - American Health, Inc.
KLAMATH UDO - Boats–fishing ☆ - Klamath Boat Co. Inc.
KLAMP-IT - Clamps - RMD Industries, Inc.
KLANNERITE - Silica - Heatshield Technologies, Inc.
KLAR - Broth ☆ - General Mills, Inc.
KLAR EIS - Beverages–alcohol - Hiram Walker & Sons, Inc.
KLARBRUNN - Beverages - Klarbrunn Inc.
KLARION-BUELL - Horns–motor vehicle - Buell Manufacturing Co.
KLARK-TEKNIK - Audio equipment - EVI Pro Audio Group
KLARON - Antibiotics ☆ - Dermik Laboratories Inc.
KLASIK KARDS LONDON - Postcards ☆ - Fotofolio Inc.
KLASS - Fibers–synthetic - Conneaut Industries, Inc.
KLASSIC KARDS - Greeting cards ☆ - American Greetings Corp.
KLASSIC KNISHES - Pastries - R.F. Bakery

☆ = Now out of production

KLASSIC-LITE - Wheelchairs - Kareco International Inc.

KLASSIC-PLUS - Wheelchairs - Kareco International Inc.

KLASSIC-STANDARD - Wheelchairs - Kareco International Inc.

KLASSICS BY KURTIS - Christmas tree ornaments - Curtis J. Posuniak

KLASSY KATS - Apparel–children's - Valtex, Inc.

KLATTER BALLS - Infant product ☆ - Binky-Griptight Co.

KLAUER - Gutters–metal - Klauer Manufacturing Co.

KLAUS BECKER - Musical instrument accessories - M & M Distributing Co.

KLAUSS-ITALIA - Furniture - Klaussner Corporate Services, Inc.

KLAUSSNER - Furniture - Klaussner Corporate Services, Inc.

KLAUSSNER - Furniture - Klaussner Furniture Industries, Inc.

KLAVIKORDAL - Pharmaceutical preparations ☆ - U.S. Ethicals Inc.

KLAWS - Toys - Tonka Corp.

KLAX - Video games - Atari Games Corp.

KLAXON - Horns–motor vehicle - General Motors Corp. (AC Delco Div.)

KLAY BIRD - Ammunition ☆ - Remington Arms Co., Inc.

K.L.A.Z.Z. - Shirts ☆ - Pacific Oasis Enterprise, Inc.

KLC - Lubricants - Elf Lubricants North America, Inc.

KLE-NU-POL - Cleaning preparations–household - H. Behlen & Bro. Inc.

KLEAN-CLEAN - Paint removers ☆ - Klean-Strip

KLEAN-EZR - Degreasing solvents - Arrowak Manufacturing and Distributors,Inc.

KLEAN-FAX - Paper ☆ - Ner Data Products, Inc.

KLEAN-GREEN - Paints ☆ - Klean-Strip

KLEAN KLAY - Clay–modeling - Art Chemical Products Inc.

KLEAN-KOTE - Paints - Masterchem Industries, Inc.

KLEAN KOTE - Paints - Standard T Chemical Co. Inc.

KLEAN-KUTTER - Paint removers - Klean-Strip

KLEAN LAM - Plaster–wallboard - BAV Inc.

KLEAN-LITE - Gasoline ☆ - Klean-Strip

KLEAN 'N PRIME - Cleaning preparations - Loctite Corp.

KLEAN 'N SHINE - Furniture polish and wax - S.C. Johnson & Son, Inc.

KLEAN SHOT - Machine tools - Self-Cleaning Environments USA, Inc.

KLEAN STAT - Paper ☆ - Ner Data Products, Inc.

KLEAN-STRIP - Paint removers - Klean-Strip

KLEAN STRIP AFTER WASH - Paint removers - Klean-Strip

KLEAN STRIP EASY OFF - Paint removers - Klean-Strip

KLEAN-STRIP GREEN - Cleaning preparations ☆ - Klean-Strip

KLEAN STRIP XYLENE - Paint removers - Klean-Strip

KLEAN-WRITE - Office supplies - Ner Data Products, Inc.

KLEANBORE - Ammunition - Remington Arms Co., Inc.

KLEANHANDS - Inks - Graphic Utilities, Inc.

KLEANLINE - Filters–fuel - American Meter Co.

KLEANSTRIP - Paint removers - Klean-Strip

KLEANSTROKE - Cleaning preparations - National Interchem Corp.

KLEANTIES - Twine ☆ - Geo. B. Carpenter Co.

KLEANTRINE - Chemical preparations - Applied Biochemists, Inc.

KLEAR - Floor waxes - S.C. Johnson & Son, Inc.

KLEAR - Medical apparatus - Cas Medical Systems Inc.

KLEAR COAT - Food products - Sysco Corp.

KLEAR-CONNECT - Medical apparatus - Cas Medical Systems Inc.

KLEAR FINISH - Hair care products - P.S. Pibbs Inc.

KLEAR KNIT - Apparel and accessories - Klear Knit Inc.

KLEAR-O-LINE - Chemical preparations - Stewart-Hall Chemical Corp.

KLEAR-PAK - Food products ☆ - Wally Sea Products Corp.

KLEAR POR - Containers - Plastics, Inc. (Anchor Hocking Plastics)

KLEAR STOR - Containers - Plastics, Inc. (Anchor Hocking Plastics)

KLEAR-STREAM - Nozzles - H.B. Sherman Manufacturing Co.

KLEAR-TEMP - Thermometers - Cas Medical Systems Inc.

KLEARBACK - Checkbooks - Romo Corp.

KLEARFOLD - Containers - Klearfold Inc.

KLEARLITE - Hobby kits ☆ - R.B. Howell Co.

KLEARSTROTE - Automotive parts and accessories - National Interchem Corp.

KLEARTEX - Gloves–rubber - Intermed Laboratories

KLEARTONE - Musical instrument accessories ☆ - Grossman Music Corp.

KLEARTONE - Paints - Cowman-Campbell Paint Co.

KLEARTONE - Paints - Valspar Corp.

KLEARVIEW - Plastic film - American Mirrex Corp.

KLEARVISION - Thread - Witten Sales Corp.

KLEBPHEN - Pharmaceutical preparations ☆ - Smithkline Beecham Corp.

KLEE-PRUF - Adhesives and sealants - Klee Chemical Coatings

KLEE WONDER SEAL - Adhesives and sealants - Klee Chemical Coatings

KLEECO - Anchors - Erie Industries Inc.

KLEEN - Cleaning preparations - Surco Products Inc.

KLEEN - Mops - Bouras Mop Manufacturing Co.

KLEEN - Pet products ☆ - Nala Barry Laboratories

KLEEN-A-BRUSH - Paint removers - Sheffield Bronze Paint Corp.

KLEEN AID - Septic tank enzyme - Arthur Mourad

KLEEN & KIND - Shampoos - Rossan Laboratories Inc.

KLEEN-B-TWEEN - Health care products ☆ - Woltra Corp.

KLEEN-BALL - Coatings - Cramer Products Inc.

KLEEN-D - Denture cleaners - Kleen Chemical Manufacturing Co.

KLEEN EARTH - Scissors–hand-operated - Acme United Corp.

KLEEN EM ALL - Cleaning preparations ☆ - Iron Out, Inc.

KLEEN-ETCH - Cleaning preparations - Waterlox Coatings Corp.

KLEEN EZY - Disinfectants - Federated Department Stores, Inc.

KLEEN EZY - Mats - Longwood Elastomers, Inc.

KLEEN FLOOR - Cleaning preparations–carpet and rug ☆ - S.C. Johnson & Son, Inc.

KLEEN-GARD - Filters–air - Research Products Corp.

KLEEN GLASS - Cleaning preparations–window - Uncle Sam Chemical Co., Inc.

KLEEN GREEN - Cleaning preparations - Serv-All Co.

KLEEN GUARD - Furniture polish and wax - Alberto-Culver Co.

KLEEN-IT - Cleaning preparations - Unival Corp.

KLEEN KAN - Bags–trash - Carlisle Plastics, Inc.

KLEEN KING - Housewares - Britt Manufacturing

KLEEN KING - Plumbing fixtures–metal ☆ - Moen Inc.

KLEEN KING - Stain removers - Faultless Starch/Bon Ami Co.

KLEEN KITTY - Pet products - Superior Brands Inc.

KLEEN KITTY PLUS - Pet products - Superior Brands Inc.

KLEEN-KLOTH - Musical instrument accessories - G. Leblanc Corp.

KLEEN KOMFORT - Pet products - Superior Brands Inc.

KLEEN KUT - Lawn mowers - Orgill Brothers and Co.

KLEEN-LIFE - Cleaning preparations - Kleen Chemical Manufacturing Co.

KLEEN LINE - Regulators–voltage - Electronic Specialists, Inc.

KLEEN-N-WAX - Furniture polish and wax ☆ - W.J. Hagerty & Sons Ltd. Inc.

KLEEN-OFF - Erasers ☆ - Faber-Castell Corp.

KLEEN PAK - Automotive parts and accessories ☆ - Champion Laboratories, Inc.

KLEEN PET SHAMPOO - Pet products - Nala Barry Laboratories

KLEEN-POWER - Rotors - Gillette Manufacturing, Inc.

KLEEN-QUAT - Disinfectants - Unit Chemical Corp.

KLEEN QUIK - Varnish removers ☆ - Golden Star Inc.

KLEEN-RITE - Cleaning preparations–window - M.B. Walton, Inc.

KLEEN SEAL - Adhesives and sealants ☆ - Pratt & Lambert United, Inc.

KLEEN SEAL - Lighting fixtures - JJI Lighting Group, Inc.

KLEEN-SITE - Cleaning preparations - Kleen Chemical Manufacturing Co.

KLEEN-STIK - Artists' materials - Vogart Crafts Corp.

KLEEN-STIK - Tape–adhesive - Compac Corp. (Pressure Sensitives Div.)

KLEEN STREAM - Water purification systems ☆ - Moen Inc.

KLEEN SWEEP - Aquariums–household - Marineland Aquarium Products

KLEEN SWEEP - Cleaning preparations - Akona Chemical Corp.

KLEEN-SWEEP - Rakes - Rugg Manufacturing Co. Inc.

KLEEN SWEEP - Rubber matting - Ace Rubber Products Inc.

KLEEN SWEEP - Snowblowers - Colonial Refining and Chemical Co.

KLEEN SWEEP - Vacuum cleaners and accessories - Minuteman International, Inc.

KLEEN-TEK - Cleaning preparations - Repair Technology, Inc.

KLEEN-TEST - Automotive lubricants and filters - Cotter & Co.

KLEEN-TINT - Paints ☆ - Valspar Corp.

KLEEN TONG - Cleaning preparations–household - Quality Rubber Co.

KLEEN-UP SOLVENT - Paint removers - Hillyard Enterprises, Inc.

KLEEN-VUE - Cleaning preparations ☆ - Apothecary Products, Inc.

KLEEN WHEELS - Automotive parts and accessories - Kleen Wheels Corp.

KLEENAIRE - Electron tubes - Tecumseh Products Co. Engine and Transmission Group

KLEENCO - Cleaning preparations–carpet and rug - Kleenco Products, Inc.

KLEENCUT - Scissors–hand-operated - Acme United Corp.

KLEENCUT KIDS - Scissors–hand-operated - Acme United Corp.

KLEENCUT-ULTRA - Scissors–hand-operated - Acme United Corp.

KLEENEDGE - Tape–masking - Daubert Coated Products, Inc.

KLEENER - Hair care products ☆ - Nutrine Ltd.

KLEENER-SHINER MAINTAINER - Floor waxes ☆ - Uncle Sam Chemical Co., Inc.

KLEENERASE - Paper - Stuart Hall Co., Inc.

KLEENEST - Pipes - National Briar Pipe Co.

KLEENEX - Paper–toweling - Kimberly-Clark Corp.

KLEENEX BOUTIQUE - Paper–toilet - Kimberly-Clark Corp.

KLEENEX CASUALS - Paper–toilet - Kimberly-Clark Corp.

KLEENEX FOR KIDS - Facial tissues - Kimberly-Clark Corp.

KLEENEX SOFTIQUE - Paper–toilet - Kimberly-Clark Corp.

☆ = Now out of production

KLEENEX ULTRA - Paper–toilet - Kimberly-Clark Corp.
KLEENFAST - Sponges - Glit, Inc.
KLEENGUARD - Apparel and accessories - Kimberly-Clark Corp.
KLEENITE - Denture cleaners - Regent Labs, Inc.
KLEENITE - Denture cleaners - Richardson-Vicks USA
KLEENKOTE - Paints ☆ - Adelphi Coatings Co.
KLEENKOTE - Tubes–steel - Welded Tube Co. of America
KLEENMASTER - Deicing fluid - Chemical Products Co.
KLEENOL - Stain removers - Ronson Consumer Products Corp.
KLEENRAW - Sugar–granulated, refined, or powdered - California and Hawaiian Sugar Co.
KLEENS - Cleaning preparations ☆ - Frank J. Curran-Esquire Chemical Co.
KLEENS ALL - Cleaning preparations - Hillestad International, Inc.
KLEENSCREEN - Telephone accessories - David Horowitz
KLEENSCREEN - Telephone accessories - David C. Horowitz
KLEENSEAL - Lighting fixtures - Guth Lighting
KLEENSHIELD - Roofing materials–clay - L.D. Sterns Corp.
KLEENTRED - Floor coverings - U.S. Rubber Recycling Inc.
KLEENUP - Herbicides - Chevron Chemical Co.
KLEENUPS - Paper–toweling - Kimberly-Clark Corp.
KLEENWAVE - Electrical testing instruments - Accent Marketing Inc.
KLEENWAY - Cleaning preparations - American Natural Products Inc.
KLEENZ-EM - Brush cleaners - Cotter & Co.
KLEER - Cleaning preparations - Scentex Inc.
KLEER - Pharmaceutical preparations ☆ - Scrip-Physician Supply Co.
KLEER - Thread - American & Efird, Inc.
KLEER BLU - Bleach ☆ - Dowbrands L.P.
KLEER-BRITE - Floor waxes ☆ - Uncle Sam Chemical Co., Inc.
KLEER-FILE - File folders - Angler's Roslyn Group Ltd.
KLEER FLAME - Fuel additives - K & W Products
KLEER FOAM - Shampoos - Ampro Industries, Inc.
KLEER FRAME - Frames–picture ☆ - North American Enclosures Inc.
KLEER KOLOR - File folders - Angler's Roslyn Group Ltd.
KLEER KOLOR - Paints - Fry Plastics International Inc. (O)
KLEER LOOP - Industrial machinery - Kleer-Loop Co.
KLEER-LOZ - Pharmaceutical preparations ☆ - Scrip-Physician Supply Co.
KLEER 'N KOOL - Reflectors–optical ☆ - Optical Coating Laboratory Inc.– Santa Rosa Div.
KLEER 'N KOZY - Reflectors–optical ☆ - Optical Coating Laboratory Inc.– Santa Rosa Div.
KLEER-OUT - Degreaser for septic tanks - Comstar International Inc. (IPC Div.)
KLEER-POLY - File folders - Angler's Roslyn Group Ltd.
KLEER-POOL - Cleaning preparations ☆ - Roccorp, Inc.
KLEER-SITE - Cleaning preparations ☆ - Cathay International
KLEER-TUSS - Pharmaceutical preparations ☆ - Scrip-Physician Supply Co.
KLEER-VU - Stationery - Kleer-Vu Plastics Inc.
KLEER-VUE - Labels–gummed - Malow Corp.
KLEER-VUE - Windows–storm - APC Corp.
KLEERAWAY - Agricultural products - Monsanto Co.
KLEERCLEAN - Cleaning preparations - American Writing Ink Co. Inc.
KLEERFLEX - Tape–adhesive - Central Products Co.
KLEERITE - Floor coverings ☆ - Congoleum Corp.
KLEERITE - Office supplies - American Writing Ink Co. Inc.
KLEERKUT - Abrasive products ☆ - Park Metallurgical Corp.
KLEERLON - Film - Kleerpak Manufacturing Co./Western Summit Packaging
KLEERMAT - Housewares - Commercial Plastics Co.
KLEEROIL - Oils–lubricating - American Writing Ink Co. Inc.
KLEEROUT - Office supplies - American Writing Ink Co. Inc.
KLEERSHIELD - Cleaning preparations–window - Gold Eagle Co.
KLEERSHOT - Sporting goods ☆ - Gexco Enterprises
KLEERSPAR - Varnishes ☆ - KCI Coatings, Inc.
KLEERSTIK - Adhesives and sealants - American Writing Ink Co. Inc.
KLEERSTRIP - Weather stripping - E.S. Robbins Corp.
KLEERTEMP - Thermometers - Electro-Optix Inc.
KLEERTITE - Screws - Research Engineering & Manufacturing Inc.
KLEIN - Bicycles - Klein Bicycle Corp.
KLEIN - Candy - Klein Chocolate Co.
KLEIN - Jewelry - Klein Jewelers
KLEIN & HUMMEL - Amplifiers - G Prime Limited
KLEIN-BENFIELD - Tools - Klein Tools Inc.
KLEIN DEATHGRIP - Tires–bicycles - Klein Bicycle Corp.
KLEIN-FLEX - Tools - Klein Tools Inc.
KLEIN-KORD - Tools - Klein Tools Inc.
KLEIN-LITE - Tools - Klein Tools Inc.
KLEIN LOK - Fasteners–snap - Klein Tools Inc.
KLEIN TLG - Apparel–women's - Jacqueline P. Klein

KLEINBERG SHERRILL - Handbags - Kleinberg Sherrill Inc.
KLEINE KINDER - Infant product - Kleine Kinder, Inc.
KLEINERT'S - Apparel–children's - Kleinert's Inc.
KLEINGUENTHER - Guns - Robert A. Kleinguenther
KLEINOMETER - Electrical testing instruments - M & A Klein
KLEINPETER DAIRY - Milk - Kleinpeter Farms Dairy Inc.
KLEMENT - Food products - Klement Sausage Co. Inc.
KLENAL - Cleaning preparations–household - Quality Rubber Co.
KLENE - Licorice - Holland-American Importing Co. Inc.
KLENK - Knives - Klenk Industries, Inc.
KLENSA - Paint removers - Standard T Chemical Co. Inc.
KLENSIA - Skin care products - Ambrosia Cosmetics Inc.
KLENSTRINGENT - Skin care products - Ambrosia Cosmetics Inc.
KLENZ KLOTH - Cleaning preparations - Geritrex Corp.
KLENZADE - Cleaning preparations - Ecolab Inc.
KLENZALL - Cleaning preparation - Ecolab Inc.
KLENZER - Cosmetics - Research Council of Make-Up Artists Inc.
KLENZO - Erasers - Empire Berol USA
KLENZPRO - Cleaning preparations - Ecolab Inc.
KLENZTONE - Cleaning preparations - K & E Chemical Co. Inc.
KLERFLO - Lacquers - Wampler Chemical Corp.
KLERIST-D - Pharmaceutical preparations - Glenwood LLC
KLERZYME - Spices and extracts - Gist-Brocades Food Ingredients Inc.
KLEVER-KLEEN - Toiletries - Gene R. Olson
KLEX - Cleaning preparations–household - H. Behlen & Bro. Inc.
KLF 20 - Radiofrequency measuring equipment - Klipsch, Inc.
KLF 30 - Radiofrequency measuring equipment - Klipsch, Inc.
KLH - Audio equipment - KLH
KLI - Screw machine products and socket headed products - Kerr Lakeside Inc.
KLI MAX - See **FIRST STEP**
KLIBAN CAT - Pet products ☆ - St. Jon Pet Care Products Inc.
KLIBAN KAT - Jewelry - Gift Creations, Inc.
KLICK - Health care products - Dean Rubber Co.
KLICKETTES - Footwear - Tobin-Hamilton Co. Inc.
KLIENT KARDS - Pet products - Barkleigh Productions, Inc.
KLIGNE - Skin care products - Odette de Paris
KLIK - Rivets–metal - Marson Creative Fastener Group
KLIK-ER - Rivets–metal - Marson Creative Fastener Group
KLIK-FAST - Rivets–metal - Marson Creative Fastener Group
KLIK! SHOWCASE PHOTOGRAPHY - Publisher's imprints - American Showcase, Inc.
KLIKA - Toys - Classic Items of Chicago Inc.
KLIKER - Rivets–metal - Marson Creative Fastener Group
KLIKER II - Rivets–metal - Marson Creative Fastener Group
KLIKIT - Bicycle parts and accessories - Girvin Inc.
KLIKIT - Cameras - E.T. Trading Ltd.
KLIKIT - Fasteners–hook and eye - Rau Fastener Inc.
KLIM - Milk - Borden, Inc.
KLIMER - Infant product - NK Medical Products Inc.
KLINE - Water–bottled or canned - Kline's Quality Water Inc.
KLINETTES - disposable diapers ☆ - Principle Business Enterprises Inc.
KLING - Bandages - Johnson & Johnson
KLING - Easels - MagnaPlan Corp.
KLING - Furniture - Ethan Allen, Inc.
KLING - Office supplies - Louis Melind Co.
KLING - Toothpaste - Sterling Winthrop Inc.
KLING-EEZ - Girdles - Milady Brassiere & Corset Co., Inc.
KLING-FELT - Hardware ☆ - Courtaulds Aerospace Inc.
KLING KLIPS - Paper clips - Labelon Corp.
KLINGBEIL - Footwear - Klingbeil Shoe Laboratories Inc.
KLINGBERG WING - Toys–models - Future Flight
KLINGENBERG - Tiles–ceramic ☆ - Amsterdam Corp.
KLINGERS - Window coverings - Klingers
KLINGON - Toys–models - Paramount Pictures Corp.
KLINGONS - Hats - Paramount Pictures Corp.
KLINGSHIRN - Wines - Klingshirn Winery
KLINKY - Apparel and accessories - Lynn Nielsen Eeg
KLIO - Slacks - Himm Inc.
KLIOT - Tools - Lacis
KLIP-2000 - Sporting goods - Court & Slope Inc.
KLIP-BILT II - Shelving units–metal - Frick-Gallagher Manufacturing Co.
KLIP-DURA - Sporting goods - Court & Slope Inc.
KLIP HANGERS - Paper clips - Baumgarten's
KLIP-IT - Hardware - Handi-Wares Corp.
KLIP-IT - Pet products - Bass Equipment Co.
KLIP KARDS - Pet products - Barkleigh Productions, Inc.

☆ = Now out of production

KLIP-LOK - Shingles--asphalt or tar - Globe Building Materials Inc.

KLIP-LON - Sporting goods - Court & Slope Inc.

KLIP-'N-GO - Wigs - Rene of Paris Inc.

KLIP N' SAND - Sanders and grinders - Glit, Inc.

KLIP-O-MATIC - Pens ☆ - Universal Fountain Pen & Pencil Co.

KLIP-POLY - Sporting goods - Court & Slope Inc.

KLIP-STIK - Ophthalmic goods - Hilsinger Corp.

KLIPETTE - Scissors--hand-operated - Hollis Co.

KLIPEZE - Clippers--nail - Cutting Edge Products

KLIPIT - Cutlery - Gesty Trading & Manufacturing Corp.

KLIPLES - Fasteners - Baumgarten's

KLIPP - Pens ☆ - Sheaffer Inc.

KLIPP-EE - Key rings - Johnston & Schmitt

KLIPPER WIZARD - Pet products - Tomlyn Products

KLIPPERMATE - Sporting goods - Court & Slope Inc.

KLIPPONS - Barrettes - Accessories International

KLIPPY KIT - Hobby kits - Craft Supplies Service

KLIPSCH - Amplifiers - Klipsch and Associates Inc.

KLIRA - Guitars ☆ - Castiglione Accordion

KLISTO DESIGNS - Frames--picture ☆ - Intercraft Industries

KLITTER KORDE - Craft supplies - Textile Enterprises Inc.

KLIX - Disinfectants - Klix Corp.

KLIX - Footwear - Goodwear Shoe Co. Inc.

KLIX - Thread - Cincinnati Thread Co.

KLIXX - Toys - ADL Partners

KLJCI - Jewelry - Klein Jewelry Co. Inc.

KLOAX - Skates--roller - Moneyline International

KLODT COLLECTION - Desk sets ☆ - Newell Office Products

KLOINZ - Games - Richard Mellor

KLOK - Artists' materials - Utley Co. Inc.

KLOMPEN KOGGEN - Tobacco products - 1776 Tobacco Co.

KLONDIKE - Boats - Glen-L Marine Designs

KLONDIKE - Cables - General Cable Corp.

KLONDIKE - Cheese ☆ - Dan Carter Inc.

KLONDIKE - Heating equipment - Yukon Energy Corp.

KLONDIKE - Ice-cream bars - Islay Klondike

KLONDIKE - Laces--boot and shoe ☆ - St. Louis Braid Co.

KLONDIKE BEARSKIN - Toys--stuffed ☆ - Dakin Inc.

KLONDIKE COLLECTION - Firearms, accessories, and parts - Fair Haven Industries Inc.

KLONDIKE GOLD - Paper--gift wrap - Heller & Usdan Inc.

KLONDIKE IKE - Toys--stuffed - Oz Enterprises, Inc.

KLONDIKE LITE - Ice-cream bars - Islay Klondike

KLONDIKE SENSATION - Frozen novelty ☆ - Islay Klondike

KLONDIKER - Hobby kits - Bemiss-Jason Corp.

KLONDYKE - Gloves - Boss Manufacturing Co.

KLONE - Drums--musical instruments ☆ - Paul A. Real Sales

KLONKS - Shoes ☆ - Deckers Outdoor Corp.

KLONOPIN - Pharmaceutical preparations - Roche Laboratories

KLOPMAN - Fabrics--cotton - Klopman Mills

KLOR-CON - Pharmaceutical preparations - Upsher-Smith Laboratories, Inc.

KLORAMIN - Health care products - Halsey Drug Co. Inc.

KLORAMINE - Pharmaceutical preparations - Wesley Pharmacal Co. Inc.

KLORANE - Hair care products - Bristol-Myers Squibb Co.

KLORASPAN - Pharmaceutical preparations - Wesley Pharmacal Co. Inc.

KLORAZINE - Pharmaceutical preparations ☆ - Hyrex Pharmaceuticals

KLORFEN - Pharmaceutical preparations ☆ - Columbia Drug Co. Inc.

KLORO-TIME - Vitamins and nutritional supplements - Nutrition Headquarters, Inc.

KLOROCOL - Cough medicines ☆ - Chase Laboratories Inc.

KLORVESS - Pharmaceutical preparations - Sandoz Pharmaceuticals Corp.

KLOS KLIP - Clothespins - National Clothespin Co. Inc.

KLOSTER ELERBACH - Wines - H. Schmitt Soehne, Inc.

KLOSTERGARTEN WEINKELLEREI - Wines - Winesellers Ltd.

KLOTEN - Frames--eyeglass ☆ - Universal/Univis Inc.

KLOTRIX - Potassium compounds - Bristol-Myers Squibb Co.

KLOVERGOLD - Dairy products - Kalamazoo Creamery Co.

KLOZ - Apparel and accessories - Mevisions International Inc.

KLOZ - Dresses--girls' - Kloz for Girls Corp.

KLOZLYNE - Apparel and accessories - Mevisions International Inc.

KLOZURE - Apparel and accessories - Eagle Button Co.

KLP SHAMPOO PLUS - Shampoos - Lan-O-Sheen, Inc.

KLR-BAK - Decals and transfers - Versa-Tags Inc.

KLS CORP. - Video production - Keystone Learning Systems Corp.

KLU-KO - Denture cleaners ☆ - I. Putnam Inc.

KLUB - Recording label - Mark Five Sandcastle

KLUBB - Cigarettes - G.A. Georgopulo & Co. Inc.

KLUCKERS - Cat food - Ralston Purina Co.

KLUGE - Luggage - Kingport International Corp.

KLUMPER SIFTAWAY - Pet products - Alfa-Pet Inc.

KLUNK - Toys--stuffed - Toy Works, Inc.

KLUNKY OAK - Trays ☆ - Vermillion Inc.

KLUSSERAGHER MOSEL - Wines - Old Europe Inc.

KLUTCH - Denture materials - I. Putnam Inc.

KLUTCH BALL - Balls - Gerber Products Co.

KLUXEN - Wines - Herman A. Kluxen Wines

KLV SLAX - Slacks--men's ☆ - Kalikow Bros. Inc.

KLYMAX - Machine parts - Klymax, Inc.

KLYNE AUDIO ARTS - Amplifiers - GNP Audio Video Inc.

KM - Gasoline - Kerr-McGee Chemical Corp.

KM III - Rope - New England Ropes Inc.

KM-LOC - Machine parts - Kennametal Inc.

KM2000 - Computer peripheral equipment - Krikorian Miller Associates, Inc.

KMA - Recording label - Jam-Power, Inc.

KMC - Food products - Nobel-Sysco Food Services Co.

KMD - Amplifiers--musical instrument ☆ - Kaman Music Corp.

KMDIGITAL - Controls--air conditioning systems - Kreuter Manufacturing Co., Inc.

KMER - Photographic equipment - Eastman Kodak Co.

KMETT - Salt - Gunther Salt Co.

KMF - Cosmetics - Kiss My Face

KMG CATALYTIC - Stoves--wood-burning - BKI, Inc.

KML - Wallpaper - K.M.L. Industries

KML SUEDES - Wallpaper - K.M.L. Industries

KMM - Waterproofing compounds ☆ - Kop-Coat, Inc.

KMP - Jewelry - Kemp Metal Products, Inc.

KMQ - Stationery - Yes Group, Inc.

KMR - Cat food - Pet-Ag, Inc.

KMR DESIGNS - Apparel and accessories - Kimberly Renner

KMS - Hair care products - KMS Research Inc.

KMS CONTROL - Hair care products ☆ - KMS Research Inc.

KMS HAIRCARE - Hair care products - KMS Research Inc.

KMX-CLIMBER - Bicycles ☆ - Kent International Inc.

KMXR - Photographic equipment - Eastman Kodak Co.

KNAACK - Tool boxes - Knaack Manufacturing Co.

KNABE - Pianos ☆ - Sohmer Corp.

KNACK - Herbicides - Valent USA Corp.

KNACK, THE - Shaving preparations - Gillette Co.

KNACKPACK - Stationery items - Lisa Frank, Inc.

KNACKY - Frames--eyeglass - May Optical Co. Inc.

KNAPP - Shoe stores - Knapp Shoes Inc.

KNAPP - Sporting goods ☆ - Signature Brands, LLC

KNAPP - Wines - Knapp Farms, Inc.

KNAPP ANGUS PERFORMANCE ANGUS BREEDERS - Agricultural products - Regena Knapp

KNAPP ATVS - Boots - Knapp Shoes Inc.

KNAPP ATVS U.S.A. 2000 SERIES - Boots - Knapp Shoes Inc.

KNAPP MONARCH - Heaters--gas - Frigid Products Inc.

KNAPP STUDIO KIDS - Apparel and accessories - Joel & Judy Knapp Corp.

KNAPPEHUSET - Buttons - Norsk Engros USA Inc.

KNAPSACK - Food products - Marin Food Specialties

KNAPSTRUP - Dinnerware--glass ☆ - Svend Jensen of Denmark Inc.

KNAUB'S CAKES - Bakery products - Original Knaub's Delicious Cakes, Inc.

KNAUF - Insulating materials - Knauf Fiber Glass

KNAUST - Mushrooms - H.K. Canning Inc.

K.NE - Apparel and accessories - Kenneth C. Keel

KNEAD-O - Clay--modeling - Got Inc.

KNEADABLE - Erasers - Faber-Castell Corp.

KNEADATITE - Epoxy - Polymeric Systems, Inc.

KNEADED RELIEF - Cosmetics - Kneaded Relief, Ltd.

KNECK - Food products - Sadler's Bar-B-Que Sales Inc.

KNEE-ACTION - Food processors ☆ - Sunbeam-Oster Household Products

KNEE-CAP - Apparel and accessories ☆ - Eagle Knitting Mills Inc.

KNEE COMFORT - Hardware - McGuire-Nicholas Co., Inc.

KNEE CPM - Health care products ☆ - Invacare Corp.

KNEE GARD - Ships--patrol boats - Fem Gard Inc.

KNEE-GUARD - Sporting goods - Trace Athletic Corp.

KNEE HUGGERS - Hosiery - Sara Lee Corp.

KNEE KEEPER - Safety products - Portable Products, Inc.

KNEE-MUFFS - Crocheted and knitted items ☆ - Reliable of Milwaukee

KNEE NURSER - Socks - Sanda Hosiery Mills Inc.

KNEE-PAK - Ice - Active Marketing

☆ = Now out of production

KNEE SHOCKS - Socks - Gerber Products Co.
KNEE-TOW - Sport tubes ☆ - Intex Recreation Corp.
KNEELAND - Floor coverings - Congoleum Corp.
KNEELING SANTA - Figurines - Roman, Inc.
KNEELONS - Apparel and accessories - Greenbest Inc.
KNEERANGER - Braces–orthopedic - Professional Care Products Inc.
KNEES EASE - Sporting goods - Fabrionics Inc.
KNEESKI XT - Skis - Wellington Leisure Products, Inc.
KNEESPORT - Health care products - Camp, Inc.
KNEIDELS & KRUMBS - Bakery products - Orthodox Baking Co. Inc.
KNEIP - Food products - E.W. Kneip Inc.
K'NEX - Hats - Connector Set L.P.
KNG RECORDS - Recording label - Anthony A. Smith
KNICEST - Food products - Whipple Co.
KNICK-KNACK - Frames–eyeglass - Hudson Optical Corp.
KNICKERBOCKER - Communications equipment - Time Warner Entertainment Co., L.P.
KNICKERBOCKER - Food products - Knickerbocker Meats Inc.
KNICKERBOCKER - Frames–eyeglass ☆ - Universal/Univis Inc.
KNICKERBOCKER - Hardware - Blaine Window Hardware Inc.
KNICKERBOCKER - Toys - Knickerbocker Toy Co. Inc.
KNICKERBOCKER/TOP HAT - Meat - Plymouth Beef Co.
KNICKERS - Wallpaper - York Wall Coverings Inc.
KNICKERS II - Wallpaper - York Wall Coverings Inc.
KNIFE AND STEEL - Uniforms–tailored - Chef Revival USA Inc.
KNIFE EDGE - Footwear - L.L. Bean Inc.
KNIFE-GUARD - Safety products - Brandis Accessories
KNIFE MAKERS CHOICE - Knives–pocket ☆ - G-96 Products Co. Inc.
KNIFE STATION - Containers ☆ - Hunt Manufacturing Co.
KNIFE, THE - Rods–motor vehicle - Falicon Performance Engineering, Inc.
KNIGHT - Bedspreads - Spartan Mills
KNIGHT - Boats - MCP Inc.
KNIGHT - Brushes - Corona Brushes Inc.
KNIGHT - Dental equipment - Knight Manufacturing, Inc.
KNIGHT - Firearms, accessories, and parts - Modern Muzzle Loading, Inc.
KNIGHT - Golfing equipment - King Par Corp.
KNIGHT - Hair-cutting shears - B.W. Boyd Shears Inc.
KNIGHT - Heating equipment ☆ - Birmingham Stove & Range Co.
KNIGHT - Leather goods - Knight Leather Co.
KNIGHT - Motor vehicle parts and accessories - Leer Inc.
KNIGHT - Thread - Threads USA Div.
KNIGHT - Trailers–travel ☆ - Coachmen Industries, Inc.
KNIGHT - Watches - Precise International/Wenger
KNIGHT 2000 - Toys–stuffed - Kenner Products
KNIGHT-GUARD - Alarm systems - Super Products Inc.
KNIGHT KITS - Toiletries - DKC Marketers, Inc.
KNIGHT LIGHT - Prophylactics - Puria Group Inc.
KNIGHT MAYOR - Toys–stuffed - CBS Toys
KNIGHT N ARMOR - Jewelry - Jacoby-Bender Inc.
KNIGHT-O-REST - Mattresses - Montgomery Ward & Co. Inc.
KNIGHT OF DIAMONDS - Computer software - Sir-Tech Software, Inc.
KNIGHT OF SALES - Computer software - 1st Desk Systems, Inc.
KNIGHT RIDDER - Office supplies - MCA Universal Studios
KNIGHT RIDER - Caps, hats ☆ - Arlington Hat Co. Inc.
KNIGHT RIDER - Games ☆ - Parker Brothers
KNIGHT RIDER - Toys ☆ - Tyco Toys
KNIGHT RIDER - Toys–automobiles - Kenner Products
KNIGHT RIDER - Toys–models - ERTL Co., Inc.
KNIGHT RIDER - Toys–stuffed - CBS Toys
KNIGHT SLAYER - Toys–automobiles - Mattel, Inc.
KNIGHT STAR - Inks–letterpress - J.M. Huber Corp.
KNIGHT STICK - Herbal products - 21st Century Manna
KNIGHT TO PLANET 3 - Games ☆ - Mayfair Games, Inc.
KNIGHTS - Cigars ☆ - House of Windsor Inc.
KNIGHT'S - Colognes - Old 97 Co.
KNIGHTS - Oscillators - CTS Corp. (Frequency Control Div.)
KNIGHTS ARMOR - Floor coverings–carpet and rugs ☆ - Cumberland Mills Inc.
KNIGHTS BRIDGE - Floor coverings–tile - Porcelanite, Inc.
KNIGHTS MARK - Floor coverings–carpet and rugs ☆ - Lees Carpets
KNIGHTS OF LEGEND - Video games - Origin Systems, Inc.
KNIGHTS OF THE AIR - Games - Avalon Hill Game Co.
KNIGHTS OF THE ROUND TABLE - Games ☆ - Gamescience
KNIGHT'S SPRAY NINE - Disinfectants - Knight Marketing Corp.
KNIGHT'S TOMB, THE - Toys - Hasbro, Inc.
KNIGHT'S TOP MOP - Detergents ☆ - Knight Marketing Corp.

KNIGHTS VALLEY - Wines ☆ - Sullivan Vineyards Winery
KNIGHTS VALLEY RANCH - Wines ☆ - Sullivan Vineyards Winery
KNIGHTSBRIDGE - Cabinets ☆ - Riverside Furniture Corp.
KNIGHTSBRIDGE - Cigarettes ☆ - West Park Tobacco Inc.
KNIGHTSBRIDGE - Dinnerware–glass - Royal China & Porcelain Companies Inc.
KNIGHTSBRIDGE - Floor coverings–carpet and rugs ☆ - Cabin Crafts Carpets
KNIGHTSBRIDGE - Jackets–men's - Kmart Corp.
KNIGHTSBRIDGE - Mattresses - Stearns & Foster Bedding Co.
KNIGHTSBRIDGE - Wallpaper - Blumenthal
KNIGHTSTRIKE - Posters - Rob Liefeld, Inc.
KNILLING-BUCHAREST - Musical instruments - St. Louis Music Supply Co.
KNILLING-NAGOYA SUZUKI - Musical instruments - St. Louis Music Supply Co.
KNILLING-SUMMIT - Musical instruments - St. Louis Music Supply Co.
KNIPEX - Pliers - Anglo American Enterprises Corp.
KNIRPS - Umbrellas - Mespo Umbrella Co. Inc.
KNISH-ETTES - Food products - Gabila & Sons Manufacturing Inc.
KNISHETTES - Food products - Gabila & Sons Manufacturing Inc.
KNIT 2 - Apparel stores–lingerie - Formfit Rogers
KNIT/BAC - Fabrics - Custom Laminations Inc.
KNIT CHEK - Needles–sewing ☆ - Coats and Clark Inc.
KNIT CHEK - Needlework supplies ☆ - Susan Bates Inc.
KNIT COUNTRY - Fabrics - Dan River Inc.
KNIT-CRO-SHEEN - Thread - Coats and Clark Inc.
KNIT-I-KINS - Crocheted and knitted items - La Femme Knitting Mills Inc.
KNIT KIT - Hats - Gitano Licensing, Ltd.
KNIT KNACK - Apparel and accessories - Edison Brothers Stores, Inc.
KNIT KNOT - Slippers - Totes, Inc.
KNIT LAND - Fabrics - Dan River Inc.
KNIT LUSTER - Yarn - SCT Yarns Inc.
KNIT MAGIC - Toys - Mattel, Inc.
KNIT-NIX - Apparel–women's - Newton Manufacturing Corp.
KNIT ONE - Fabrics - Guilford Mills, Inc.
KNIT SET - Fabrics - Pico Manufacturing Sales Corp.
KNIT TO FIT - Patterns–clothing - Scandinavian House Imports Inc.
KNIT TOWN - Fabrics - Dan River Inc.
KNIT VILLE - Fabrics - Dan River Inc.
KNITCOTE - Wire - Maryland Specialty Wire Inc.
KNITDOWNS - Sweaters - Geneco Inc.
KNITIMOTTO - Apparel and accessories - Texollini, Inc.
KNITITE - Apparel and accessories - Worcester Knitting Co.
KNITIVO - Apparel–women's - Leslie Fay Companies Inc.
KNITLOK - Thread - Threads USA Div.
KNITMAKERS - Crocheted and knitted items - Beldoch Industries Corp.
KNITMATES - Fasteners–hook and eye - Boye Needle
KNITMATES - Mittens - Gerber Products Co.
KNITMEISTER - Apparel–men's - Alps Sportswear Manufacturing Co.
KNITOWN - Apparel–children's - Doe Spun Inc.
KNITRON - Crocheted and knitted items - Royal Knitting Mills Inc.
KNITT MIXX - Apparel–women's - L. P. Brylane
KNITTEN - Cushions - Mark One Healthcare Products Inc.
KNITTER'S SPECIAL - Thread - Quality Thread Co.
KNITTING ARCHITECT, THE - Patterns–clothing - Knitting Fever Inc.
KNITTING FEVER - Yarn - Knitting Fever Inc.
KNITTING JENNY - Craft supplies - Milton Bradley Co.
KNITTINGPAL - Craft supplies - Walter Palange Inc.
KNITWAVES - Apparel–children's - Knitwaves Inc.
KNITWITS - Bags–canvas - Puiforcat
KNITWITTY COLLECTION - Cosmetics - Cosmair Inc.
KNIZE TEN - Colognes - Caswell-Massey Co. Ltd.
KNK - Handbags - KNK Inc.
KNO-GLOSS - Paints ☆ - Watson-Standard Co.
KNO-SAND - Paint removers - Hillyard Enterprises, Inc.
KNO-SKAR - Varnishes - C.M. Athey Paint Co.
KNOALT - Waterproofing compounds - Triple L Manufacturing, Inc.
KNOB CREEK - Whiskey - Jim Beam Brands Co.
KNOB-LOC - Locks–door ☆ - Fulton Corp.
KNOB-LOCK - Hardware - Predator Industries, Inc.
KNOB-TOP RUNNER - Floor coverings - Superior Manufacturing Group/Notrax Floor Matting
KNOBBLE - Health care products - Knobble Associates
KNOBBY - Musical instrument accessories - Fender Musical Instruments
KNOBHILL - Cabinets ☆ - Medallion Kitchens of Minnesota Inc.
KNOBLE ESQUIRE - Trailers–travel - Peterson Industries Inc.
KNOBLER IMPORTS - Housewares - Knobler International Ltd.

☆ = Now out of production

KNOBLER'S CANAPE SPREADER COLLECTION - Trays - Knobler International Ltd.
KNOBLER'S FUN IN THE SUN - Toys - Knobler International Ltd.
KNOBLER'S PLAYTIME - Toys - Knobler International Ltd.
KNOBLER'S SPONGEWARE - Trays - Knobler International Ltd.
KNOBSAVER - Appliance parts - Edgerton Enterprises, Inc.
KNOCABOUT - Luggage ☆ - Hartmann Luggage Co.
KNOCK-ABOUT - Shotguns - Abercrombie & Fitch
KNOCK-ABOUTS - Underwear and nightwear ☆ - L.V. Myles
KNOCK 'ER LOOSE - Oils–lubricating - K & W Products
KNOCK KNOCK - Computer software - Tekworks, Inc.
KNOCK ON WOOD - Novelty items - Scott S. Waxenberg
KNOCK-OUT - Cleaning preparations - AmeriPlus Inc.
KNOCK OUT - Cleaning preparations - State Chemical Manufacturing Co.
KNOCK OUT - Detergents - Dar-Lin Products Inc.
KNOCK-OUT - Games ☆ - Milton Bradley Co.
KNOCK OUT BY DR. DENTON - Apparel–men's - Obion Denton
KNOCK-OUT FLEAS - Pet products - Knock-Out
KNOCK OUT YOUR OPPONENT WITH TKO - Toys - Play Co. Toys
KNOCK WOOD - Jewelry - Jessie L. Frees
KNOCKABOUT, THE - Wigs ☆ - Penthouse for Men
KNOCKABOUT, THE - Jackets - Howe K. Sipes Co.
KNOCKABOUTS - Apparel–women's - Pendleton
KNOCKANDO - Beverages–alcohol - Paddington Corp.
KNOCKER - Apparel and accessories - Uni Hosiery Co., Inc.
KNOCKER STOCKER - Toys–automobiles - Mattel, Inc.
KNOCKOFF - Drafting supplies - Martin Universal Design Inc.
KNOCKOUT - Apparel–children's - Camptown Togs Inc.
KNOCKOUT - Candy ☆ - Leaf, Inc.
KNOCKOUT - Floor coverings–carpet and rugs - Kelly Group Inc.
KNOCKOUT - Floor coverings–carpet and rugs - Quaker Inc.
KNOCKOUT - Floor coverings–carpet and rugs ☆ - Calladium & Marglen
KNOCKOUT! - Games - Milton Bradley Co.
KNOCKOUT - Games ☆ - Avalon Hill Game Co.
KNOCKOUT - Herbicides - Pennington Seed, Inc.
KNOCKOUT - Pet products - Red Bell Inc.
KNOCKOUT HITS - Recording label - Entertainment Resources USA, Inc.
KNOCKOUTS - Window coverings - Blind Design Inc.
KNOK - Playing cards - United States Playing Card Co.
KNOK & NURTZ - Playing cards - United States Playing Card Co.
KNOLL - Office furniture–wood - Westinghouse Electric Corp.
KNOLL EXTRA - Lamps - Westinghouse Electric Corp.
KNOLL GROUP, THE - Office furniture–wood - Westinghouse Electric Corp.
KNOLL STUDIO - Furniture - Westinghouse Electric Corp.
KNOLLACCENTS - Desk sets - Knoll International
KNOLLEXTRA - Desks - Knoll International
KNOLLOFFICE - Furniture - Knoll International
KNOLLS - Floor coverings–carpet and rugs - Karastan-Bigelow Inc.
KNOLLSTUDIO - Furniture - Knoll International
KNOLLTEXTURES - Wallpaper - Knoll International
KNOLLWOOD - Floor coverings–tile - Kentile Floors Inc.
KNOLLWOOD PARK - Furniture–upholstered ☆ - Webb Furniture Enterprises Inc.
KNORM - Vitamins and nutritional supplements - Fisons Corp.
KNORR - Beekeeping supplies - Knorr Beeswax Products Inc.
KNORR - Soups–mixes - CPC International Inc.
KNOT ABOVE, THE - Neckties - Knot Above, Inc.
KNOT CRAFT - Hobby kits - Wellington Leisure Products, Inc.
KNOT FREE - Hair care products - Origins Natural Resources Inc.
KNOT JUST PRETZELS - Pretzels - Knot Just Pretzels Corp.
KNOT PERFECT - Blankets - Kentucky Woodcrafts Co. Inc.
KNOT PIZZA - Pretzels - Pretzelmaker, Inc.
KNOT SHOPPE - Hobby kits - Wellington Leisure Products, Inc.
KNOT-TO-BE - Ophthalmic goods - Foremost Optical Products
KNOTHE - Pajamas–men's - Knothe Corp.
KNOTHEAD - Hats - George M. Borkovic
KNOTS - Ophthalmic goods - Foremost Optical Products
KNOTS 'N' SQUARES - Floor coverings–carpet and rugs - J and J Industries Inc.
KNOTS OF LUCK - Luggage - Hunting World, Inc.
KNOTT'S BERRY FARM - Food products - Knott's Berry Farm
KNOTTS BERRY FARM - Jams and jellies - Hunt-Wesson, Inc.
KNOTT'S SUNDAY BEST - Jams and jellies - Knott's Berry Farm
KNOTTY BUOY - Apparel and accessories - Lance Peacock and Connie Vidmar Partnership
KNOTTY CORD - Craft supplies - Synthetic Textiles Inc.

KNOTTY PROBLEMS - Pet products - Carter-Wallace, Inc.
KNOW AIDS - Apparel and accessories - Willard H. Dow, II
KNOW & GROW TALKING COMPUTER - Toys–electronic - Vtech Industries, Inc.
KNOW-BODIES - Apparel and accessories ☆ - Vanity Fair Mills Inc.
KNOW-IT-ALL - Computer software ☆ - iCat
KNOW IT ALLS - Publisher's imprints - McClanahan Book Co., Inc.
KNOW IT. LIVE IT. WEAR IT. - Apparel and accessories - Tut Enterprises, Inc.
KNOW NO BOUNDS - Housewares - Success Ware, Inc.
KNOW NOISE - Recording label - Minnesota Society for the Prevention Of Blindness and Preservation of Hearing
KNOW-PED - Scooters–motorized - Patmont Motor Werks
KNOW PHONE - Telephone answering machines - PhoneMate Inc.
KNOW PROBLEM - Computer software - Showgrammer Productions, Inc.
KNOW-TO-GO - Publisher's imprints - Calcar Advertising, Inc.
KNOW-WEAR - Apparel and accessories - Danny T. Pun
KNOW YOUR AMERICA - Games - Cadaco Div.
KNOW YOUR AMERICA - Games - Rapid Mounting and Finishing Co.
KNOW YOUR ENEMY - Apparel and accessories - Know Your Enemy
KNOW ZONE, THE - Games - Ingenius
KNOWHERE - Furniture - MG Taylor Corp.
KNOWING - Perfumes - Estee Lauder Inc.
KNOWING K - Computers–personal - Jetson Trading Ltd.
KNOWLEDGE ADVENTURE - Games - Knowledge Adventure, Inc.
KNOWLEDGE-BASED CONFIGURATOR - Computer software - Trimin Systems, Inc.
KNOWLEDGE COMMUNICATION - Educational materials - Knowledge Communication
KNOWLEDGE COMPANY, THE - Video production ☆ - Steven A. Devore
KNOWLEDGE CONNECTION, THE - Education materials - Effective Learning Systems, Inc.
KNOWLEDGE EXPLORER - Computer software ☆ - Grolier Electronic Publishing, Inc.
KNOWLEDGE INDUSTRIES - Computer software - Knowledge Industries, Inc.
KNOWLEDGE IS POWER - Shirts - Second Season, Inc.
KNOWLEDGE KEYS - Toys–electronic - Vtech Industries, Inc.
KNOWLEDGE MASTER - Computer software - Academic Hallmarks, Inc.
KNOWLEDGE NAVIGATOR - Computer software - Apple Computer Inc.
KNOWLEDGE NOW - Computer software - Cogito Learning Media, Inc.
KNOWLEDGE-PAKS - Computer software - Serviceware, Inc.
KNOWLEDGE QUEST - Computer software - Pacifica Data Services, Inc.
KNOWLEDGE WORKER - Office machines - A.B. Dick Co.
KNOWLEDGE WORKS - Computer software - Milliken Publishing Co.
KNOWLEDGELAND - Computer software - Knowledge Adventure, Inc.
KNOWLEDGEMAPPER - Computer software - Guideware, Inc.
KNOWLEDGENET - Computer software - KnowledgeNet Inc.
KNOWLEDGEVIEW - Computer software - Price Waterhouse Llp
KNOWLEDGEWAVE - Computer software - Ginesys Corp.
KNOWLEX - Computer storage devices - Knowlex, Inc.
KNOWLTON - Dairy products - Southland Corp.
KNOWS ALL TALKING CRYSTAL BALL - Toy stores - Excite Inc.
KNOWWARE - Computer software - Lowell Jay Arthur
KNOWWARE - Computer software - Knowware
KNOX - Gelatin - Lipton Investments, Inc.
KNOX - Hats - Resistol Hats
KNOX - Safe deposit boxes - Knox Co.
KNOX BROTHERS' KNOCK KNOCK JOKE GAME, THE - Games ☆ - Decipher Inc.
KNOX ELECTRONIC - Safes - Knox Electronic, Ltd.
KNOX FIT - Gloves - Knoxville Glove Co.
KNOXAGE - Water–bottled or canned - Knoxage Cuyamaca Water
KNOXFORD - Faucets - Kohler Co.
KNOXVILLE RACING ACADEMY - Apparel and accessories - Knoxville Racing Academy, Inc.
KNR - Apparel and accessories - Kenar Enterprises, Ltd.
KNS - Wallpaper - K.M.L. Industries
KNU-FANGLE - Knives - Remark Technologies, Inc.
KNU-VISE - Clamps - Lapeer Manufacturing Co.
KNUBBY WOOL - Crocheted and knitted items - Garland Knitting Mills
KNUCKLE DOWN - Games - Lori Reiter
KNUCKLE HEAD - Amplifiers–musical instrument - Rivera Research & Development Corp.
KNUCKLE HEAD - Toys ☆ - Those Characters from Cleveland, Inc.
KNUCKLE SANDWICH - Pet products - Old West Pet Treats
KNUCKLE SANDWICH - Sandwiches–prepackaged - Sam C. Meiner

☆ = Now out of production

KNUCKLEHEAD RECORDS, INC. - Recording label - Knucklehead Records Inc.

KNUCKLES - Furniture - Haworth, Inc.

KNUCKLES - Skin care products ☆ - Knight Marketing Corp.

KNUCKLES UP - Cleaning preparations ☆ - W.E. Kautenberg Co.

KNUDSEN - Dairy products - Knudsen Dairy Products

KNUDSEN - Fruit butters - J.M. Smucker Co.

KNUDSEN - Juices - Knudsen & Sons Inc.

KNUDSEN-ERATH - Wines ☆ - Erath Vineyards Winery

KNUDSEN FAMILY - Food products - Knudsen & Sons Inc.

KNUDSEN FREE - Yogurt - Kraft Foods, Inc.

KNUFE - Knives - Remark Technologies, Inc.

KNUTH SONGBIRD - Posters - Stanton & Lee

KNUTS - Candy - Beacon Sweets, Inc.

KNUTSHUKAR - Manual nut cracker - Cecil R. Jones

KNUTZ - Toasted corn ☆ - Cornnuts Inc.

K.O. - Deodorizers - Pioneer Manufacturing Co.

KO - Lubricants - Pyroil Co. Inc.

KO - Truck bodies - Gem Top Manufacturing Inc.

KO CORRAL - Beef - Tengu Co., Inc.

K.O. DIRT BLASTER - Cleaning preparations - Stewart-Hall Chemical Corp.

KO PRO - Vitamins and nutritional supplements ☆ - Freeda Vitamins Inc.

KO-REC-AERO - Ribbons ☆ - Eaton Allen Ko-Rec-Type Corp.

KO-REC-AIDE - Office machines - Eaton Allen Ko-Rec-Type Corp.

KO-REC-ALL - Correction fluid - Eaton Allen Ko-Rec-Type Corp.

KO-REC-COPY - Ribbons - Eaton Allen Ko-Rec-Type Corp.

KO REC HY LITE - Pens - Barouh Eaton Allen Corp.

KO-REC-KIT - Ribbons ☆ - Eaton Allen Ko-Rec-Type Corp.

KO-REC-KOTE - Paper–carbon - Eaton Allen Ko-Rec-Type Corp.

KO-REC-LON - Ribbons ☆ - Eaton Allen Ko-Rec-Type Corp.

KO-REC-OUT - Ribbons ☆ - Eaton Allen Ko-Rec-Type Corp.

KO-REC-T'BLE - Ribbons - Eaton Allen Ko-Rec-Type Corp.

KO-REC-TYPE - Ribbons - Eaton Allen Ko-Rec-Type Corp.

KO-SEAL - Adhesives and sealants - House of Kolor, Inc.

KO SERIES - Lighting fixtures - Elliptipar, Inc.

KOA SURF CLASSICS - Skateboards - Tomlinson Corp.

KOAL-BLAK - Pencils ☆ - Faber-Castell Corp.

KOALA - Chairs–folding ☆ - Cramer Inc.

KOALA - Fruit pops–frozen - Koala Springs International Inc.

KOALA - Health care products - Liberty Natural Products

KOALA - Labels–paper - Koala Records Inc.

KOALA - Nail care products - Odette de Paris

KOALA - Seafood products–fresh or frozen ☆ - Central Seaway Co.

KOALA BEAR KARE - Infant product - JBJ Industries, Inc.

KOALA BEAR KARE - Infant product - Koala Corp.

KOALA BLOOMS - Flowers, plants, and seeds - Koala Blooms USA Ltd.

KOALA BLUE - Apparel and accessories - Oxford Industries, Inc.

KOALA BLUE - Apparel–women's - Koala Blue Inc.

KOALA BUFFER - Emery products - Creative Nail Design, Inc.

KOALA GOLD - Hair care products - ETS, Inc.

KOALA KIDS - Health care products - Arizona Natural Products

KOALA KLUB - Toys–stuffed - Dakin Inc.

KOALA KOLOGNE - Animal figurine with cologne ☆ - Cosrich Inc.

KOALA LEAF - Shampoos - Kim Laube & Co. Inc.

KOALA SLING COLLECTION - Furniture - Telescope Casual Furniture Inc.

KOALA SPRINGS ESSENCES - Bottled water - Koala Springs International Inc.

KOALA-T - Apparel and accessories - Eagle Button Inc.

KOALA-T - Apparel and accessories - Bob M. Sheron

KOALA TEA TREE - Skin care products - Liberty Natural Products

KOALA-TEE - Furniture - Fleetwood Furniture Co.

KOALA WOOD SLAT COLLECTION - Furniture - Telescope Casual Furniture Inc.

KOALA YUMMIES - Cookies - Lotte USA Inc.

KOALAGRAMS - Computer software - Koala Technologies Corp.

KOALAPAD - Computer software - Koala Technologies Corp.

KOALAPAINTER - Computer software - Koala Technologies Corp.

KOALAS - Shoes - KangaROOS USA Inc.

KOALATY BEARS - Toys–stuffed ☆ - Gund, Inc.

KOAT-ALL - Paints - Fuller-O'Brien Paints Inc.

KOATED KITCHEN WIRE - Housewares - Artwire Creations Inc.

KOAX - Exchangers–heat - Koax Corp.

K.O.B. - Key rings - Anheuser-Busch Companies Inc.

KOB-KNOBS - Cooking equipment–household ☆ - C.J. Schneider Manufacturing Co. Inc.

KOBAKO - Perfume - Bourjois Ltd.

KOBALD - Photographic equipment ☆ - Heitz Service Corp.

KOBAN - Radio communications equipment - Ohra Corp.

KOBBLE TILE - Tiles–ceramic ☆ - Stonelight Tile Inc.

KOBE - Cutlery - J.C. Penney Co., Inc.

KOBE - Food products ☆ - Liberty Richter Inc.

KOBE-GRIP - Sporting goods - Total Sports Source

KOBE HOUSE BAKERY - Bakery products - Kobe House, Inc.

KOBE KITCHEN - Cooking utensils–cast iron - J.C. Penney Co., Inc.

KOBE PROFESSIONAL - Cooking utensils–cast iron - J.C. Penney Co., Inc.

KOBEE - Vitamins and nutritional supplements - Freeda Vitamins Inc.

KOBEEF - Meat ☆ - Ezcorp, Inc.

KOBENHAGN - Ice cream - Jewel Food Stores, Inc.

KOBENHAVN - Flatware - Dansk International Designs, Ltd.

KOBENSTYLE - Housewares - Dansk International Designs, Ltd.

KOBOLD HALL - Games ☆ - Mayfair Games, Inc.

KOBOR & WHITE - Beverages–malt - Kobor & White Brewing, Inc.

KOBOR&WHITE - Beverages–malt - Kobor & White Brewing, Inc.

KOBRA - Projectors–photographic - Kopykake

KOBRA KHAN - Toys - Mattel, Inc.

KOBRAKOIL - Pet products - Loos and Co. Inc.

KOBRICKS - Coffee - Kobrick's Coffee Co. Inc.

KOBRON - Luggage - Kobron International USA Inc.

KOBUK - Apparel and accessories - Kobuk Inc.

KOCH - Recording label - Koch International

KOCH & LOWY - Lighting fixtures - Koch & Lowy Inc.

KOCH CHROMATIC - Harmonicas - Hohner Inc.

KOCH INTERNATIONAL - Recording label - Koch International

KOCH POULTRY - Food products - Aspen Foods, a division of Koch Poultry

KOCH SCHWANN - Recording label - Koch International

KOCHI - Artists' materials - Andrews/Nelson/Whitehead

KOCHLEN - Recording label - Northeastern Records

KOCH'S - Beverages–malt - Fred Koch Brewery Inc.

KOCH'S GOLDEN ANNIVERSARY - Beverages–malt - Fred Koch Brewery Inc.

KOCH'S HOLIDAY - Beverages–malt - Fred Koch Brewery Inc.

KOCO BLANCO - Beverages - Yoo-Hoo Chocolate Beverage Corp.

KOCOONA - Infant product ☆ - Summer Infant Products Inc.

KOD - Electronic equipment - Scientific Technology, Inc.

KODABLITZ - Flashlights - Eastman Kodak Co.

KODABROME - Paper–photographic - Eastman Kodak Co.

KODABROMIDE - Paper–photographic - Eastman Kodak Co.

KODACEL - Film - Eastman Kodak Co. (Eastman Chemicals Div.)

KODACHROME - Film - Eastman Kodak Co.

KODACHROME-X - Film - Eastman Kodak Co.

KODACOLOR - Film - Eastman Kodak Co.

KODACOLOR GOLD - Film - Eastman Kodak Co.

KODACOLOR GOLD 100 - Film - Eastman Kodak Co.

KODACOLOR-X - Film - Eastman Kodak Co.

KODACRAFT - Photographic equipment - Eastman Kodak Co.

KODAFIX - Photographic equipment - Eastman Kodak Co.

KODAFLAT - Adhesives and sealants - Eastman Kodak Co.

KODAFLECTOR - Lighting equipment ☆ - Eastman Kodak Co.

KODAGRAPH - Photographic equipment - Eastman Kodak Co.

KODAIRE - Horns–motor vehicle - Faraday Inc.

KODAIRE - Photographic equipment - Eastman Kodak Co.

KODAK - Crayons - Rose Art Industries, Inc.

KODAK - Leather goods ☆ - Westport Corp.

KODAK - Lenses–optical - Signet Armorlite, Inc.

KODAK - Photographic equipment - Eastman Kodak Co.

KODAK - Photographic equipment - Tiffen Manufacturing Corp.

KODAK BEACON - Photographic equipment - Eastman Kodak Co.

KODAK BISNET - Computer software - Eastman Kodak Co.

KODAK BOOKS - Publisher's imprints - The Tiffen Co.

KODAK BROWSER - Computer software - Eastman Kodak Co.

KODAK DC40 - Cameras - Eastman Kodak Co.

KODAK DIGITAL SCIENCE - Cameras - Atlantic International Products & Services Co.

KODAK GOLD - Film - Eastman Kodak Co.

KODAK GOLD PLUS - Film - Eastman Kodak Co.

KODAK LENS - Lenses–optical - Eastman Kodak Co.

KODAK PICTURE EXCHANGE - Computer software - Eastman Kodak Co.

KODALINE - Film - Eastman Kodak Co.

KODALITE - Lighting equipment - Eastman Kodak Co.

KODALITH - Photographic equipment - Eastman Kodak Co.

KODALK - Flashlights - Eastman Kodak Co.

KODALUX - Flashlights - Eastman Kodak Co.

☆ = Now out of production

KODALY - Music–sheet - MMB Music Inc.

KODAMA - Tools - Ryobi North America, Inc.

KODAMA - Wallpaper - Quality House Inc.

KODAMATIC - Photographic equipment - Eastman Kodak Co.

KODAPAK - Paper–thermoplastics coated - Eastman Kodak Co. (Eastman Chemicals Div.)

KODAR - Photographic equipment - Eastman Kodak Co.

KODASCAN - Photographic equipment - Eastman Kodak Co.

KODASCOPE - Photographic equipment ☆ - Eastman Kodak Co.

KODASLIDE - Photographic equipment - Eastman Kodak Co.

KODASTAR - Photographic equipment - Eastman Kodak Co.

KODATAPE - Adhesives and sealants ☆ - Eastman Kodak Co.

KODATRON - Flashlights ☆ - Eastman Kodak Co.

KODAVISION - Electronic equipment - Eastman Kodak Co.

KODE - Labeling machinery - Litton Industrial Automation Systems

KODEL - Polyester film sheets - Eastman Kodak Co. (Eastman Chemicals Div.)

KODELON - Photographic equipment ☆ - Eastman Kodak Co.

KODET - Photographic equipment - Eastman Kodak Co.

KODEWORD - Electronic equipment - Eastman Kodak Co.

KODIAC - Boats–motor ☆ - Larson Boat Div.

KODIAC - Trailers - Kodiak Components, Inc.

KODIAK - Alarm systems - U-Con Corp.

KODIAK - Bicycles - Columbia Manufacturing Inc.

KODIAK - Boats - Glen-L Marine Designs

KODIAK - Exercising equipment - National Barbell Supply, Inc.

KODIAK - Firearms, accessories, and parts - Beeman Precision Airguns

KODIAK - Food products ☆ - Ocean Beauty Seafood, Inc.

KODIAK - Fungicides - Gustafson Inc.

KODIAK - Snuff - Conwood Co. L.P.

KODIAK - Sporting goods - Bear Archery Inc.

KODIAK - Tools - Black & Decker Corp.

KODIAK - Wood products - ISK Biosciences Corp.

KODIAK HUNTER - Knives–pocket - W.R. Case & Sons Cutlery Co.

KODIKOOK - Codfish–smoked, salted, dried, or pickled - Los Angeles Smoking & Curing Co.

KODOFILL - Polyester film sheets - Eastman Kodak Co. (Eastman Chemicals Div.)

KODOFILL PLUS - Polyester film sheets - Eastman Kodak Co. (Eastman Chemicals Div.)

KODONYL - Health care products ☆ - Halsey Drug Co. Inc.

KODOSOFF - Polyester film sheets - Eastman Kodak Co. (Eastman Chemicals Div.)

KODY KARTS - Motor vehicles–motor homes - Munroe Machine Works Inc.

KOE - Deodorizers - Thornell Corp.

KOEGEL - Food products - Koegel Meats Inc.

KOEHLER - Bakery products - Koehler Bakery Co.

KOEHLER WHEAT LITE - Lighting equipment - Mr. Mutt Pet Products Inc.

KOEHRING - Heaters–space ☆ - Desa International, Inc.

KOELLING - Machinery parts - Morgan Construction Co.

KOENIG - Artists' materials ☆ - The Creative Store

KOENIG - Knives–carving - Harry D. Koenig & Co.

KOENIG ART EMPORIUM - Artists' supply stores ☆ - The Creative Store

KOEPPENS - Food products ☆ - American Home Food Products Inc.

KOEPPLINGER'S - Bakery products - Koepplingers Bakery Inc.

KOEPPLINGER'S LITE - Breads - Koepplingers Bakery Inc.

KOETSU - Electronic equipment - Koetsu USA Inc.

KOEX - Tiles–mosaic - Capitol Tile Import Co.

KOEZE'S - Peanut butter ☆ - Koeze Co.

KOF-EZE - Cough medicines - Roberts/Hauck Pharmaceuticals Inc.

KOFEL - Soups–mixes - Kedem Food Products Co.

KOFF - Music–sheet - Koff Music Co.

KOFF-BALLS - Pharmaceutical preparations ☆ - Church and Dwight Co. Inc.

KOFF-FIVEISKY - Music–sheet ☆ - Koff Music Co.

KOFF-MANNIE KLEIN - Music–sheet - Koff Music Co.

KOFFEE KING - Coffee makers–electric - Bloomfield Industries Inc.

KOFFEE KUP BAKERY - Bakery products - Koffee Kup Bakery, Inc.

KOFFEE SNACKERS - Crackers - Vista Bakery, Inc.

KOGEE - Apparel–women's - Sally Gee Inc.

KOGY - Portable kerosene heaters ☆ - Consort Products Corp.

KOH HAK - Recording label - Creav Inc. USA

KOH-I-FINE - Markers–felt-tip ☆ - Koh-I-Noor, Inc.

KOH-I-LAR - Lead products - Koh-I-Noor, Inc.

KOH-I-NOOR - Pens - Koh-I-Noor, Inc.

KOH-I-NOOR EDUCATOR - Pens ☆ - Koh-I-Noor, Inc.

KOH-I-NOOR RAPIDOGRAPH - Artists' materials - Koh-I-Noor, Inc.

KOH-I-RAISE - Pencils ☆ - Koh-I-Noor, Inc.

KOH-I-SOFT - Pencils ☆ - Koh-I-Noor, Inc.

KOHALA - Floor coverings–carpet and rugs ☆ - J.L. Benson Co.

KOHI - Cookies - FCW Imports

KOHINOOR - Jewelry - Kohinoor Diamond Corp.

KOHL - Office supplies - Sam Flax

KOHL FORMULA - Cosmetics - Almay Inc.

KOHLER - Health care products ☆ - J.H. Guild Co. Inc.

KOHLER - Plumbing fixtures–enameled - Kohler Co.

KOHLER - Tiles–ceramic - Dal-Tile Corp.

KOHLER & CAMPBELL - Pianos - Kohler & Campbell Inc.

KOHLER BATHROOM KITCHEN CAULK - Caulking compounds - OSI Sealants, Inc.

KOHLER COLORS HIGH GLOSS CAULK - Caulking compounds - OSI Sealants, Inc.

KOHLER COORDINATES - Bathroom accessories - Kohler Co.

KOHLER FOCUS - Bathroom accessories - Kohler Co.

KOHLER POWERPLAY - Generators–electric - Kohler Co.

KOHLER POWERPRO - Generators–electric - Kohler Co.

KOHLERT - Bassoons - Multivox/Sorkin Music Co. Inc.

KOHLERT - Musical instruments - Entertainment Music Marketing Corp.

KOHL'S - Cleaning preparations - Kohl's Department Stores, Inc.

KOHMAN'S - Yeast - Roland Industries Inc.

KOHNO - Guitars - Dauphin Co.

KOHO DEVLE - Fishing lures - Eppinger Manufacturing Co.

KOHPLASTIC - Erasers ☆ - Koh-I-Noor, Inc.

KOHR - Stringed-instrument accessories - Howard Core & Co. Inc.

KOHR BROS FROZEN CUSTARD - Custard–frozen - Kohr Bros., Inc.

KOHRS - Food products - Oscar Mayer Foods Corp.

KOI - Hair care products - J.A. Fleuridas Co.

KOI - Water colors - Sakura of America

KOI FISH FOOD - Water treating compounds - Mardel Laboratories, Inc.

KOI-KOI BIOFILTER - Pet products - Blalock Wholesale Distributors

KOI-PREMIUM GREEN - Pet products - Aquatrol, Inc.

KOI VITAL - Pet products - Tetra Sales USA

KOILIT - Electrical equipment - Koil-it Inc.

KOILIT II - Telephone apparatus - Softalk Inc.

KOILIT III - Telephone apparatus - Softalk Inc.

KOINU - Stainless steel - Darwell Import Co. Inc.

KOITE - Bedding–linen - Dan River Inc.

KOJAK - Alarm systems ☆ - Universal Security Instruments Inc.

KOJAK POPS - Candy ☆ - Beacon Sweets, Inc.

KOKANEE - Beverages–malt - Labatt Importers Inc.

KOKEN - Cleaning preparations - Koken Manufacturing Co. Inc.

KOKO - Mats - U.S. Mat & Rubber Co. Inc.

KOKO BITS - Chocolate candy - Grace Cocoa Associates, L.P.

KOKO CLOWN - Dolls - Russ Berrie and Co., Inc.

KOKO GOLD - Oils–edible - Mallet and Co.

KOKO GORILLA - Toys–stuffed - Dakin Inc.

KOKO KANU - Beverages–alcohol - Carriage House Imports Ltd.

KOKO KANU - Liqueurs - Rums International, Inc.

KOKO KNOT - Apparel and accessories - In Gear Fashions, Inc.

KOKOLO BREEZE - Seafood products–canned or cured - Kokolo Breeze

KOKOMO - Apparel–women's - Swat Fame, Inc.

KOKOMO - Ice cream - Samana, Inc.

KOKOMO - Photographic equipment - Eastman Kodak Co.

KOKOMO GLASS ORIGINALS - Glass–flat - Kokomo Opalescent Glass Co. Inc.

KOKOMO GRANITE CATSPAW - Glass–flat - Kokomo Opalescent Glass Co. Inc.

KOKOMO JOE'S MALANGA CHIPS - Snack foods - Handcraft Foods, Inc.

KOKOMO RIPPLE - Glass–flat - Kokomo Opalescent Glass Co. Inc.

KOKOMO RONDALITE - Glass–flat - Kokomo Opalescent Glass Co. Inc.

KOKOMO SMOOTH CATSPAW - Glass–flat - Kokomo Opalescent Glass Co. Inc.

KOKOMO SUN - Suntan lotions - Kokomo Sun Care Products, Inc.

KOKOMO WAVOLITE - Glass–flat - Kokomo Opalescent Glass Co. Inc.

KOKONE - Apparel and accessories - Ethos Inc.

KOKOPELI DIGITAL STUDIOS - Computer software - THQ Inc.

KOKOPELLI'S PIZZA - Pizzas–frozen - Kokopelli's Pizza, LLC

KOKORO SHEARS - Clippers–barber - Designer's Edge International

KOKUPA - Scissors–hand-operated - Aaronco Grooming Products

KOKUPA - Scissors–hand-operated - Aaronco Pet Products, Inc.

KOKUPA ULTRA - Scissors–hand-operated - Aaronco Grooming Products

KOKURA - Dinnerware–glass - Noritake Co. Inc.

KOKUSAI - Rice - Rice Growers of California

☆ = Now out of production

KOKUSAI ROSE - Rice - Rice Growers of California
KOL - Jewelry - Koltun Jewelry Co.
KOL-CAP - Pharmaceutical preparations ☆ - Parmed Pharmaceuticals, Inc.
KOL-GARD - Finishing agents ☆ - Eastern Safety Equipment Co. Inc.
KOL KUP - Insulated drink holders ☆ - Divajex
KOL-SPANS - Pharmaceutical preparations ☆ - Reese Chemical Co.
KOL-SPANS/SINA-SPANS - Cold remedies ☆ - Reese Chemical Co.
KOLA CHAMPAGNE - Beverages - Canada Dry Corp.
KOLA LACAYE - Beverages–carbonated - Brooklyn Bottling Corp.
KOLA LOKA - Adhesives and sealants - Krazy Glue Inc.
KOLA SHANPAN - Soft drinks - La Cascada Bottling Co.
KOLACHE FACTORY - Bakery products - Kolache Factory, Inc.
KOLAGE - Underwear and nightwear - Henson-Kickernick Inc.
KOLANTYL - Antacids - Marion Merrell Dow
KOLAPS-A-TANK - Tanks–storage - Burch Manufacturing Co. Inc.
KOLATIN BRAND KOSHER GELATIN - Chemical preparations - Koltech Industries, Inc.
KOLBY - Giftware ☆ - Brushcreek Creative Co.
KOLBY - Glassware–household - Dansk International Designs, Ltd.
KOLCRAFT - Seats–automobile - Kolcraft Enterprises, Inc.
KOLD-FLO - Adhesives and sealants - Hy-Grade Corp.
KOLD HOLD - Plates–plastic - Tranter Manufacturing Inc. (Edgefield Div.)
KOLD KIST - Meat products–beef - Kold Kist Brands Inc.
KOLD KOMPRESS - Pharmaceutical preparations - Apex Medical Corp.
KOLD KUTTER - Motor vehicle parts and accessories - Inter-State Oil Co.
KOLDETS - Cough drops - Pfeiffer Pharmaceuticals Inc.
KOLDGALV - Paints - Triangle Coatings Inc.
KOLDWAVE - Air conditioning equipment - Heat Exchangers Inc.
KOLE-BINS - Bins - Kole Industries Inc.
KOLE TOTERS - Boxes - Kole Industries Inc.
KOLECT-A-MATIC - File folders ☆ - Kardex Systems, Inc.
KOLEPHRIN - Pharmaceutical preparations - Pfeiffer Pharmaceuticals Inc.
KOLEPHRIN DM - Cough medicines - Pfeiffer Pharmaceuticals Inc.
KOLEPHRIN GG/DM - Cough medicines - Pfeiffer Pharmaceuticals Inc.
KOLESTON 2000 - Hair care products - Wella Corp. (Consumer Products Div.)
KOLESTRAL - Hair care products - Wella Corp. (Consumer Products Div.)
KOLIBRI - Boats–motor - Havencraft of New England
KOLINSKI GOLDEN - Nail care products - Opi Products, Inc.
KOLINSKI PETITE - Nail care products - Opi Products, Inc.
KOLINSKY-PLUS - Artists' materials - Binney & Smith Inc.
KOLINSKY SPEED WAXER - Cleaning equipment - Malm Chemical Corp.
KOLLARKEEPER - Jewelry - Richard H. Sprick
KOLLECTAINER - Gloves–rubber - Delyle Inc.
KOLLECTION - Dresses–women's - Jonathan Logan Inc.
KOLLECTION, THE - Apparel–women's - Jonathan Logan Inc.
KOLLER - Springs–mechanical - Jason Inc.
KOLLIE FLOWER - Toys–banks - A.J. Renzi Plastic Corp.
KOLLMORGEN SILVERLINE - Motors - Kollmorgen Corp.
KOLLN - Cereal - Liberty Richter Inc.
KOLLN - Food products ☆ - Edward & Sons Trading Co., Inc.
KOLLN VINEYARDS - Wines ☆ - Kolln Vineyards (O)
KOLNEX - Cameras ☆ - Edixa Camera Co.
KOLOB - Recording label - Polygram Records, Inc.
KOLONIAL KETTLES - Decorative aluminum pots - Grandview Aluminum Products Inc.
KOLOR BAK - Hair-care products ☆ - Benjamin Ansehl Co.
KOLOR KEEPER - Artists' materials - M. Grumbacher Inc.
KOLOR KEY - Cleaning preparations - Bardahl Manufacturing Corp.
KOLOR KLAY - Clay–modeling - Crown Delta Corp.
KOLOR KOLLAR KK - Clamps - Kolor Kollar, Inc.
KOLOR KOTER - Brushes–paint - Kolor Koter Corp.
KOLOR KREATIONS - Hair care products - Roux Laboratories, Inc.
KOLOR-ROO - Baked cookies ☆ - Grocers Baking Co.
KOLOR STOR - Portable household containers - Jareen Co.
KOLOR-TREET - Cosmetics ☆ - Duart Industries Ltd.
KOLORAMA - Projection screens - Kolorama Distributing Co. Inc.
KOLORFAST - Paper–tissue - Bemiss-Jason Corp.
KOLORFUL KLOTHING - Apparel - Sunkisses Hawaii
KOLORITE - Shingles–wood - Weyerhaeuser Co.
KOLORMATIC - Paints ☆ - Kyanize Paint Co.
KOLORMATIC II - Paints ☆ - Kyanize Paint Co.
KOLORPINS - Hardware - Independent Nail Inc.
KOLORZIT - Skin care products - Pro-Capa Products Inc.
KOLOSSAL PYRAMID - Puzzles - Kadon Enterprises Inc.
KOLPIN - Sporting goods - Kolpin Manufacturing, Inc.
KOLPIN KING KOBRA - Sporting goods - Kolpin Manufacturing, Inc.

KOLPIN TWISTER - Sporting goods - Kolpin Manufacturing, Inc.
KOLSTEIN'S - Musical instruments - Kolstein Music Inc.
KOLT - Bicycles - Ross Bicycles USA, Ltd.
KOLVAC - Pharmaceutical preparations - Alva-Amco Pharmacal Co.
KOLVET - Cameras ☆ - Edixa Camera Co.
KOLYNOS - Toothpaste - Whitehall Laboratories
KOLYUM - Health care products - Fisons Corp.
KOM-A-DAY - Recording label - Flat Town Music Co.
KOM-FORT LATCH - Seat belts - Indiana Mills & Manufacturing, Inc.
KOMAR - Underwear and nightwear - Charles Komar and Sons Inc.
KOMAR PHOTOMURALS - Wallpaper ☆ - Parkview Designs
KOMAR PHOTOMURALS II - Wallpaper - Parkview Designs
KOMATEX - Artists' materials - Harbor Sales Co.
KOMAZINE - Pharmaceutical preparations ☆ - Hyrex Pharmaceuticals
KOMBI - Motor vehicles–automobiles ☆ - Volkswagen of America Inc.
KOMBI - Sporting goods - Kombi Ltd.
KOMBI BEAM - Machine parts ☆ - Roper Whitney of Rockford, Inc.
KOMBI KOOL - Apparel stores–sports ☆ - Kombi Ltd.
KOMBI TRI-ACTION - Pens - Staedtler, Inc.
KOMBO - Sporting goods ☆ - Rod Caddy Industries
KOMBO BRUSH - Pet products - Marineland Aquarium Products
KOMBO KLEEN - Pet products - Marineland Aquarium Products
KOMBUCHION - Vitamins and nutritional supplements - Greenfield Home Care Ltd.
KOMCRAFT - Winches - Quik-Fab Aluminum Manufacturing Co. Inc.
KOMED - Ophthalmic goods - Barnes-Hind Inc.
KOMET - Pharmaceutical preparations - Tri Hawk Corp.
KOMEX - Skin care products - Barnes-Hind Inc.
KOMFIT - Watchbands - Jacoby-Bender Inc.
KOMFORT EAZE - Mattresses - Kingsdown, Inc.
KOMFORT-KUSHIONS - Sporting goods - Arnold Health Equipment Co.
KOMFORT KUT - Scissors–hand-operated - Kane Industry Corp.
KOMFORT MONITOR - Health-care products - Principle Business Enterprises Inc.
KOMFORT-ZONE DOME - Portable enclosure - Komfort-Zone Dome
KOMIC KARDS - Stationery ☆ - Joli Greeting Card Co.
KOMM MIT! - Publisher's imprints - Harcourt Brace & Co.
KOMMERLING - Hardware - Aluplast Roll Shutter Systems Inc.
KOMMISH, THE - Computer software - Fantasy Sports, Inc.
KOMODO - Computer hardware - Sceptre Technologies Inc.
KOMODO - Key rings - Kuaii & Co., Inc.
KOMOR - Jewelry–costume - Komor Manufacturing
KOMPAKT - Filing cabinets–metal - Kardex Systems, Inc.
KOMPERDELL - Sporting goods ☆ - Ballco Products Inc.
KOMPLEMENT - Health care products - Thermo Trim USA Inc.
KOMPLY CATALYST - Paints - House of Kolor, Inc.
KOMPLY KLEAR - Paints - House of Kolor, Inc.
KOMPRESS - Office supplies - Ames Safety Envelope Co.
KOMPSPIN - Centrifuges–industrial - Composite Rotor, Inc.
KOMPUTER KINDERGARTEN - Video production - Positive Response Marketing, Inc.
KOMSTAR - Photographic equipment - Eastman Kodak Co.
KON KOR - Cushions - Commander-Omni Co. Inc.
KON-KRETE - Finishing agents - Windsor Wax Co. Inc.
KON TIKI - Food products ☆ - Darik Enterprises Inc.
KONA - Bicycles - Kona-USA
KONA - Chocolate candy - Paradise Farms Co.
KONA - Fabrics - Robert Kaufman Co., Inc.
KONA - Yarn - Joseph Galler Inc.
KONA BLEND - Coffee - Nature's Finest Products Inc.
KONA BREWING CO. - Beverages–malt - Kona Brewing Co.
KONA CLASSIC - Coffee - S & D Coffee, Inc.
KONA COAST - Food products - Kona Coast Products Inc.
KONA COAST - Sauces ☆ - G.L. Mezzetta Inc.
KONA COAST - Seasonings - Dairy Fresh Products Co.
KONA-CRETE - Paints - La Habra Products, Inc.
KONA GOODNESS IN EVERY CUP - Coffee - C Brewer Co. Limited
KONA KAI - Boats - Glen-L Marine Designs
KONA KAVA - Coffee - Jonathan P. O'Bergin
KONA KRUNCH - Candy - Ternus & Co., Inc.
KONA LEI PLANTATIONS - Coffee - Fairwinds Gourmet Coffee Co. Inc.
KONA SUPER WASH - Yarn - Henry's Attic
KONAKION - Pharmaceutical preparations - Roche Laboratories
KONAMI SPORTS SERIES - Computer storage devices–optical - Konami (America) Inc.
KONARK - Publisher's imprints - Advent Books Inc.

☆ = Now out of production

KONATENE - Vitamins and nutritional supplements - Cyanotech Corp.
KONDIMENT KADDY - Barbecue and grill accessories - Porcelain Metals Corp.
KONDREMAL - Laxatives - Fisons Corp.
KONECKIES - Fasteners–snap - David L. Lisenby
KONFETTI - Fabrics - Dan River Inc.
KONFORM - Sealing compounds - Chemtronics Inc.
KONG - Pet products - Kong Co.
KONG KEE - Chinese food products - Kong Kee Food Corp.
KONGAROO - Pet products ☆ - Kong Co.
KONGE - Flatware ☆ - Henriksen Imports Inc.
KONGO - Flatware ☆ - Dansk International Designs, Ltd.
KONICA - Cameras - Konica USA Inc.
KONICA CENTURY - Photographic equipment ☆ - Konica USA Inc.
KONICA COLOR 7 - Photographic equipment ☆ - Konica USA Inc.
KONICA HEXAR - Cameras - Konica USA Inc.
KONICA NICE PRINT SYSTEM - Photographic equipment - Konica USA Inc.
KONICA VX - Film - Konica USA Inc.
KONICA Z-UP 110 - Cameras - Konica USA Inc.
KONICA Z-UP 140 - Cameras - Konica USA Inc.
KONICAMETER - Photographic equipment ☆ - Konica USA Inc.
KONICOLOR - Film ☆ - Konica USA Inc.
KONIFILTER - Photographic equipment ☆ - Konica USA Inc.
KONIFLEX - Cameras ☆ - Konica USA Inc.
KONIG - Beverages–malt - Acme Food Specialties Inc.
KONIG FUSSBALL - Publisher's imprints - Beyne Development, Inc.
KONIHOOD - Photographic equipment ☆ - Konica USA Inc.
KONILETTE 35 - Cameras ☆ - Konica USA Inc.
KONKOTE - Paints - Universal Protective Coatings
KONKRETE KOAT - Enamels - Bridges Smith & Co.
KONNECTO - Toys–blocks ☆ - Learning Products Inc.
KONNIE O - Apparel and accessories - Breton Industries
KONOCTI BOOKS - Publisher's imprints - Konocti Books/Cannonade Press
KONOCTI WINERY - Wines - Konocti Winery
KONOSTATIC - Filters–air - Air Kontrol Inc.
KONRIKO - Food products - Conrad Rice Mill Inc.
KONTAIN! - Liquid odor control - Arn Industries, Inc.
KONTAK - Audio equipment - Sumiko Inc.
KONTAKT - Coffee makers–electric - Starbucks Corp.
KONTOS - Food products - Kontos Foods
KONTROL - Denture cleaners - Mark Allen Co.
KONTROL-FLO - Filters–air - Air Kontrol Inc.
KONTROL-FLO - Racks ☆ - Jarke Corp.
KONTROL KOLOR-BRITE - Shampoos ☆ - Mark Allen Co.
KONTROL-PAK - Filters–air - Air Kontrol Inc.
KONTROL-SEAL - Filters–air - Air Kontrol Inc.
KONTRON ELEKTRONIK GMBH - Cameras - Atlantic International Products & Services Co.
KONTURA - Machinery - Townsend Engineering Co.
KONZYME - Vitamins and nutritional supplements - Brunswick Laboratories Inc.
KOO-KOO - Candy ☆ - Leaf, Inc.
KOO-KOO KITTY - Toys - Trendmasters, Inc.
KOO-KOO KITY - Toys–stuffed - Trendmasters, Inc.
KOO KOO ROO ORIGINAL - Chickens - Lean Chick Inc.
KOO ZOO - Toys - Tyco Toys
KOOBIE - Candy - Mars, Inc.
KOOCHEES - Disposable diapers - Braha Industries Inc.
KOOK-A-ROO - Greeting cards - David Stillman
KOOKA - Bicycles - Single Track, Inc.
KOOKABURRAS - Cookies - Sunshine/Salerno Inc.
KOOKIE JARS - Containers - Heritage Mint, Ltd.
KOOKIE-KAKES - Cookies - Linda Nemes
KOOKIE KOSTUMES - Pet products - Debonair Pets of California
KOOKIE SPOOKIES - Novelty items - International Silver Co.
KOOKS SURF GEAR - Apparel and accessories - Wade O. Morse
KOOKY COOKS - Toys - Empire of Carolina Inc.
KOOKY KARS - Toys - Tyco Toys
KOOKY KATCHERS - Toys - Alchemy II Inc.
KOOKY KLOWN - Toys - Spearhead Industries Inc.
KOOKY KOPTER - Toys - Tyco Toys
KOOKY KREATIONS - Shirts - GRK Manufacturing
KOOKY SPOOKIES - Stationery - Giordano Art, Ltd.
KOOKY SPOOKS - Toys - Spearhead Industries Inc.
KOOL - Candy ☆ - Chex Co.
KOOL - Cigarettes - Brown & Williamson Tobacco Corp.
KOOL-A-RAMIC - Thread ☆ - Perfect Thread Co. Inc.
KOOL ALL - Chemical preparations - Doall Co.

KOOL ARC - Gloves - Knoxville Glove Co.
KOOL BLUE - Hair care products - Redken Laboratories, Inc.
KOOL-BRITE - Paints - Mobile Paint Manufacturing Co.
KOOL CARE - Cleaning preparations - Kool Seal
KOOL CONDITIONED - Thread ☆ - Perfect Thread Co. Inc.
KOOL COVER - Awnings - Alumi-Cover Awning Co., Inc.
KOOL CRUISER - Food warming equipment - Igloo Products Corp.
KOOL-EZE - Skin care products ☆ - Concord Chemists
KOOL F/X - Apparel and accessories - Raging Angel Productions, Inc.
KOOL-FOOT - Health care products ☆ - Blistex Inc.
KOOL GHOUL - Cosmetics - Paper Magic Group Inc.
KOOL GHOUL - Novelty items - Paper Magic Group, Inc.
KOOL GRIP - Lamp shades–fabric - Spartus Corp.
KOOL HOME - Awnings - NSC Corp. (Johnson Tent Div.)
KOOL-IT - Automotive parts and accessories ☆ - Unival Corp.
KOOL JAZZ - Floor coverings–carpet and rugs - Lotus Carpets
KOOL KAN - Beverages - Texas Recreation Corp.
KOOL KAN - Sporting goods - Wellington Leisure Products, Inc.
KOOL KAP - Apparel and accessories - Texace Corp.
KOOL-KAP - Paints - Synkoloid Co.
KOOL KATS - Toys - Strombecker Corp.
KOOL KATZ - Apparel–athletic - Kool Katz, Inc.
KOOL KEEPER - Fishing tackle - Frabill Inc.
KOOL KEEPER - Ice chests - Mathews Witte International Inc.
KOOL KIDZ - Socks - Softouch Co. Inc.
KOOL KIT - Health care products ☆ - Swede-O, Inc.
KOOL KLUTE - Gloves - Knoxville Glove Co.
KOOL KNIT - Thread - Belding Heminway Co. Inc.
KOOL KOOSHION - Automotive parts and accessories - Arthur Fulmer Co.
KOOL KOOSHION - Cushions ☆ - Perfect Rubber Seat Cushion Co.
KOOL KORNERS - Posters - Grafeeties Co. Internt'l Inc.
KOOL KUFFS - Cuff and sleeve protectors - American Guard-It Manufacturing Co. Inc.
KOOL KUFFS - Jewelry - Grafika Commercial Printing, Inc.
KOOL LIGHTS - Cigarettes - Brown & Williamson Tobacco Corp.
KOOL-LITE - Electronic equipment - Harper-Wyman Co.
KOOL-LITE - Plastics film - Klerk's Plastic Products Manufacturing, Inc.
KOOL-LITE - Window coverings - Clear-View Shade Inc.
KOOL LOOKS - Toothbrushes - Colgate-Palmolive Co.
KOOL-LUBE - Lubricants - Sunbeam Corp.
KOOL MADE - Refrigerators - Hy Ten Die and Development Corp.
KOOL MATE - Ice chests–plastic - Igloo Products Corp.
KOOL MILDS - Cigarettes - Brown & Williamson Tobacco Corp.
KOOL-MOR - Motor vehicle parts and accessories ☆ - Dunham Bush, Inc.
KOOL-N-CASUAL - Apparel - Beverly D. Wilson
KOOL N'JUICY - Chewing gum ☆ - Amurol Confections Co.
KOOL-O-MATIC - Ventilation equipment - Kool-O-Matic Corp.
KOOL OFF - Neckties - Premier Equity Inc.
KOOL PAC - Coolers–electric ☆ - Flambeau Products Corp.
KOOL PAK - Carrying cases - Kool Pak
KOOL-PAK - Electronics equipment - Melmat Inc.
KOOL-PAK - Resistors - Caddock Electronics Inc.
KOOL PAL - Medical apparatus - SLD Pad, Inc.
KOOL PATCH - Cement - Kool Seal
KOOL PLY - Roofing material - Robert Hageman
KOOL REST - Ice chests–plastic - Igloo Products Corp.
KOOL RIDER - Ice chests–plastic - Igloo Products Corp.
KOOL-SCREEN - Window shades - View-Guard Shade Co.
KOOL SEAL - Adhesives and sealants - Kool Seal
KOOL SEAL - Roofing materials - Kool Seal, Inc.
KOOL SHADES - Electronic equipment - Alaron Inc.
KOOL SHADES - Toys - Imperial Toy Corp.
KOOL SHOT - Fans–electric ☆ - Jobar International Inc./Bibi Products
KOOL-STOP - Bicycle parts and accessories - Kool Stop Originals, Inc.
KOOL-STOP ORIGINALS - Trailers - Kool Stop Originals, Inc.
KOOL STRIDE - Strollers–baby - Kool Stop Originals, Inc.
KOOL SUIT - Apparel and accessories - Spray Sok Co. Inc.
KOOL SUPER LIGHTS - Cigarettes - Brown & Williamson Tobacco Corp.
KOOL-TAB - Resistors - Caddock Electronics Inc.
KOOL-TEK - Insulating materials - Katchall Industries International, Inc.
KOOL ULTRA - Cigarettes - Brown & Williamson Tobacco Corp.
KOOL VENT - Floor coverings ☆ - Texas Aluminum Industries Inc.
KOOL ZONE - Heating equipment - Slant/Fin Corp.
KOOLAROO - Ice chests–plastic ☆ - Thermos Co.
KOOLCRETE - Concrete products - Stepstone, Inc.
KOOLEE - Beverages - Quiktrip Corp.

☆ = Now out of production

KOOLER KOASTERS - Housewares ☆ - Life-Like Products Inc.
KOOLETTES - Ice making machinery ☆ - Flambeau Products Corp.
KOOLGLO - Automotive accessories - Kool Glo Industries, Inc.
KOOLIE - Pet products - Texas Recreation Corp.
KOOLIE - Scarves - Glad Rags
KOOLIT - Ice chests–foam - FDC Packaging Inc.
KOOLITE - Insulating materials - Thermal Ceramics Inc.
KOOLITE - Projectors–photographic ☆ - Buhl Optical Co.
KOOLKART - Air conditioning equipment - Scientific Systems Corp.
KOOLKAT - Cleaning preparations - Tenneco Minerals Co.
KOOLSHADE - Window shades - Delaware Valley Solar Screens
KOOLSOL - Oils–lubricating - Pennzoil Products Co.
KOOLTOG - Apparel–men's ☆ - Kaynee Co.
KOOLVENT - Electronic equipment - Acme-Lite Manufacturing Co.
KOOLVENT - Gloves - Knoxville Glove Co.
KOOLVENT - Window frames - Koolvent Aluminum Products
KOOLVUE - Glass–flat ☆ - AFG Industries Inc. (Glass Group Div.)
KOOLWARE - Cooking equipment–household ☆ - Mirro Corp.
KOOLWAYS - Lubricants - Pennzoil Products Co.
KOOLY - Eyeglasses ☆ - Cable Car Eyeware
KOOOOOO KARS - Toys ☆ - Henry Gordy International Inc.
KOOPMANS - Food products - Holland-American Importing Co. Inc.
KOOPS - Mustard - Holland Mills Inc.
KOOS - Fertilizers - Vigoro Industries, Inc.
KOOSH - Bags - Sirco International Corp.
KOOSH - Toys - Oddzon Products, Inc.
KOOSH BASKETBALL - Toys - Oddzon Products, Inc.
KOOSH BAT AND BALL - Toys - Oddzon Products, Inc.
KOOSH BOOKMARKS - Toys - Oddzon Products, Inc.
KOOSH CHARACTERS - Novelty items - Oddzon Products, Inc.
KOOSH CREATIVE - Artists' materials - Oddzon Products, Inc.
KOOSH CREATIVE PAINT - Toys - Oddzon Products, Inc.
KOOSH CRITTERS - Toys - Oddzon Products, Inc.
KOOSH FLINGSHOTS - Toys - Oddzon Products, Inc.
KOOSH FLINGSHOTS GAME - Toys - Oddzon Products, Inc.
KOOSH GLOVE AND BALL - Toys - Oddzon Products, Inc.
KOOSH JUMBO BINGO - Balls ☆ - Oddzon Products, Inc.
KOOSH KEY RING - Novelty items ☆ - Oddzon Products, Inc.
KOOSH KITES - Toys - Oddzon Products, Inc.
KOOSH LAWN DARTS - Games ☆ - Oddzon Products, Inc.
KOOSH PADDLE'S BIRDIE SET - Toys ☆ - Oddzon Products, Inc.
KOOSH PENCIL TOPPERS - Novelty items - Oddzon Products, Inc.
KOOSH POGO JUMPER - Toys ☆ - Oddzon Products, Inc.
KOOSH POUECDBALL - Toys ☆ - Oddzon Products, Inc.
KOOSH SKOOPS - Toys - Oddzon Products, Inc.
KOOSH SKYBLASTER TURBO CATCH - Toys - Oddzon Products, Inc.
KOOSH SKYBLSTER - Toys - Oddzon Products, Inc.
KOOSH SLYBLASTER HOWLER - Toys - Oddzon Products, Inc.
KOOSH SOCCER BINGO - Balls ☆ - Oddzon Products, Inc.
KOOSH SPORT BOINGO - Balls - Oddzon Products, Inc.
KOOSH STATIONERY - Stationery - Oddzon Products, Inc.
KOOSH STICK BALL - Games ☆ - Oddzon Products, Inc.
KOOSH SURE GRIP FOOTBALL - Toys ☆ - Oddzon Products, Inc.
KOOSH VORTEX FOOTBALL - Toys - Oddzon Products, Inc.
KOOSH VORTEX HOWLER - Toys - Oddzon Products, Inc.
KOOSH VORTEX JR. - Toys - Oddzon Products, Inc.
KOOSH YO-YO - Toys - Oddzon Products, Inc.
KOOSH ZIPPER PULLS - Novelty items - Oddzon Products, Inc.
KOOSIES - Diapers–disposable - Kooshies Diapers International Inc.
KOOTENAY - Beverages–malt ☆ - Labatt Importers Inc.
KOP-WRITE - Accounting machines ☆ - Master-Craft Corp.
KOPALD - Shortening - Humko Products
KOPALD RICHMIX - Shortening - Humko Products
KOPAUI - Jewelry - Deborah West Accessory Art Collection
KOPEL - Window coverings - Curtron Curtain Inc.
KOPHANE - Cough medicines - Pfeiffer Pharmaceuticals Inc.
KOPI-GIDE - Typewriters ☆ - Master Products Manufacturing Inc.
KOPI KATS - Footwear - Her-Man Imports Inc.
KOPI-SNAP - Business forms ☆ - Master-Craft Corp.
KOPI-SPOT - Computer software - Ameriforms Inc.
KOPIKAT - Tools–hand-operated - Glen B. Hart
KOPOUT - Publisher's imprints - Graphic Arts Technical Foundation
KOPPER CUTTER - Saw blades - Q.E.P. Co. Inc.
KOPPER KATE - Scouring pads - Purex Industries Inc. (Kurly Kate Div.)
KOPPER'S - Candy - Koppers Chocolate Specialty Co. Inc.
KOPPERS - Tar - Koppers Industries, Inc.

KOPPERS - Waterproofing compounds ☆ - Kop-Coat, Inc.
KOPY-AID - Frames–picture - Fellowes Manufacturing Co.
KOPY KAT - Apparel–women's - NCC Industries, Inc.
KOPY KAT - Fishing nets - Four Rivers Tackle Co.
KOPY KLEENER - Electronic equipment - Apollo Audiovisual Div.
KOPYKAKE - Projectors–photographic - Kopykake
KOPYKAT - Computer software - Hilgraeve Inc.
KOPYRITE - Projectors–photographic - Kopykake
KOR - Photographic equipment - Eastman Kodak Co.
KOR-JELS - Candy - Thos. D. Richardson Co.
KOR STONE - Counter tops–laminated - Oakland Solid Surfacing & Countertop, Inc.
KOR-X - Hair care products - Gold Medal Hair Products Inc.
KORA KANGAROO - Toys–stuffed - Dakin Inc.
KORADO/PUCH - Mopeds - American Jawa Ltd.
KORAI - Mats–grass, reed, and jute - Hokkaido-Karate Equipment Manufacturing Co.
KORAL - Watches - Koral International
KORALEX - Flags - Valley Forge Flag
KORALITE - Vinyl mats - Ace Hose and Rubber Co.
KORAN - Mattresses - Sino-In Trading Inc.
KORATRON - Fabric binding - Koratron Co. Inc.
KORBACH - Tools - Columbine International
KORBARA - Floor coverings–carpet and rugs - Masland Corp.
KORBEL - Wines - F. Korbel and Bros. Inc.
KORD KONTROL - Audio equipment - Se-Kure Controls Inc.
KORD-O-ROI - Wallpaper - Koroseal Wallcoverings
KORD-O-TEX - Leather goods - Lefkowitz and Santangelo Co.
KORD-O-VAN - Leather goods - Lefkowitz and Santangelo Co.
KORDE - Laces–boot and shoe ☆ - Samuel Ehrman Co. Inc.
KORDEN - Filing cabinets–metal - Korden Inc.
KORDITE - Bags–plastic - Mobil Chemical Co. Plastics Div.
KORDON - Aquarium accessories - Kordon
KORDON - Aquarium accessories - Novalek, Inc.
KORE - Apparel and accessories - T.Y. Brown
KORE - Detergents - King Research, Inc.
KORE - Sporting goods - Kore Products, Inc.
KORE M - Communications equipment - Motorola, Inc.
KOREAN GINSENG - Health care products - Prince of Peace Enterprises Inc.
KOREAN PARTNER - Computer software - Twinbridge Software Corp.
KOREAN WAR, THE - Games - Avalon Hill Game Co.
KOREANA BLANKET - Blankets - Chung Soo Suh
KOREGIN - Vitamins and nutritional supplements - Jil Moramarco
KORELOCK - Paneling - Marlite
KORES - Correction fluid - Kores Nordic USA Corp.
KORET - Apparel–women's - Koret North America
KORET - Handbags - Koret Inc.
KORET OF CALIFORNIA - Apparel–women's - Koret North America
KORET OF CANADA - Apparel–women's - Koret North America
KORET SMALL - Handbags - Koret Inc.
KOREX - Sporting goods - Korex Corp.
KORFIL - Blocks–concrete - Concrete Block Insulating Systems, Inc.
KORFIL - Insulating materials - Grace Construction Products
KORG - Synthesizers–musical instrument - Korg USA
KORI - Musical instruments - Custom Music Co.
KORINA - Wood products - Georgia-Pacific Corp.
KORINEK - Pastries - Frank Korinek & Co.
KORK-EZE - Musical instrument accessories - G. Leblanc Corp.
KORK FARM - Novelty items ☆ - Michael G. Puckett
KORKEASE - Footwear - Cherokee Group
KORKER - Beverages–carbonated - Virginia Dare Extract Co., Inc.
KORKERS - Corn chips - Nabisco Foods Group
KORKIES - Coasters, hot pads, placemats - Cork Specialty Co.
KORKTEX - Fibers–synthetic - Georgia-Bonded Fibers, Inc.
KORKY - Apparel–athletic - Ron Jon Surf Shop
KORKY - Plumbing fixtures - Lavelle Industries Inc.
KORN - Apparel and accessories - Korn Partnership
KORN HEADS - Candy - Fleer Corp.
KORNER KEEPERS - Glassware–household - Owens-Illinois Inc. (Libbey Div.)
KORNER KLEEN - Pet products - Marineland Aquarium Products
KORNERS FOR KIDS - Furniture–children's - ABC School Supply, Inc.
KORNI-AID - Lotions - Korni-Aid, Inc.
KORNKOBS - Food products ☆ - Good Food Inc.
KORNLAND - Meat extracts - Famous Brands
KORNLAND - Meat extracts - John Morrell & Co.
KORNO - Pharmaceutical preparations ☆ - Old 97 Co.

KORN'S - Lithographic plates - William Korn Inc.
KORO-BOUSHKA - Educational materials - Twinson Co.
KORO-FLEX - Pharmaceutical preparations - Schmid Laboratories
KORO-FLEX ARCING SPRING DIAPHRAGM - Diaphragms - London International U.S. Holdings
KORODE KURE - Chemical preparations - Acton Technologies Inc.
KOROGARD - Guardrails - RJF International Corp.
KOROKLEAR - Adhesives and sealants - RJF International Corp.
KOROLITE - Floor coverings - B.F. Goodrich Co.
KOROMEX - Health care products - LRC North America, Inc.
KOROMEX - Pharmaceutical preparations - Schmid Laboratories
KOROMEX COIL SPRING DIAPHRAGM - Diaphragms - London International U.S. Holdings
KOROMEX CONTRACEPTIVE CREAM - Pharmaceutical preparations - London International U.S. Holdings
KOROMEX CONTRACEPTIVE FOAM - Pharmaceutical preparations - London International U.S. Holdings
KOROMEX CONTRACEPTIVE INSERTS - Pharmaceutical preparations - London International U.S. Holdings
KOROMEX CONTRACEPTIVE JELLY - Pharmaceutical preparations - London International U.S. Holdings
KOROMEX CRYSTAL CLEAR GEL - Pharmaceutical preparations - London International U.S. Holdings
KOROMEX GEL/JELLY/CREAM APPLICATOR - Pharmaceutical preparations - London International U.S. Holdings
KOROSEAL - Wallpaper - Koroseal Wallcoverings
KOROSEAL - Wallpaper - RJF International Corp.
KOROTRENDS - Paints ☆ - B.F. Goodrich Co.
KORPINE - Wood products - Willamette Industries, Inc.
KORPREME - Thread ☆ - Premier Thread Co.
KORRECT BAR - Metals - KB Alloys, Inc.
KORRECT-WAY - Wood and metal furniture - Lozier Corp.
KORRVU - Packaging–paper - Sealed Air Corp.
KORSAIR III - Wallpaper - Koroseal Wallcoverings
KORSCH - Calendars - Sormani Inc.
KORSKI - Vodka - Paramount Distillers Inc.
KORT - Pharmaceutical preparations ☆ - Scrip-Physician Supply Co.
KORTA FRIO - Health care products ☆ - D'Franssia Corp.
KORTEAM - Computer software - Korteam International, Inc.
KORTH - Firearms, accessories, and parts ☆ - Beeman Precision Airguns
KORTRON - Wood products - Willamette Industries, Inc.
KORUM - Pharmaceutical preparations - Armenpharm Ltd.
KORUS - Hosiery - Sung Kon Park
KORVAN - Agricultural machinery - Korvan Industries, Inc.
KORVET - Vacuum cleaners and accessories - Yard Vac Products, Inc.
KORY - Recording label - Countrywide Tape & Record Distributors Inc.
KORYO - Wallpaper - Capital Carousel Inc.
KORZILIUS - Tiles–ceramic - United Ceramic Tile Corp.
K.O.S. - Pet products - K.O.S. Industries Inc.
KOS KIDS - Apparel–children's - KOS USA
KOSART - Skin care products - Weckerle Sales Corp.
KOSCHI - Handbags - Magnum Fashions Inc.
KOSCIUSKO - Mustard - Plochman, Inc.
KOSCIUSZKOWY - Pickles - Green Bay Foods Co.
KOSELANO - Health care products - Halsey Drug Co. Inc.
KOSHER FOR PASSOVER BEEF STEW - Meat products–poultry - My Own Meals Inc.
KOSHER FOR PASSOVER CHICKEN STEW - Meat products–beef - My Own Meals Inc.
KOSHER KIDS - Greeting cards - A + A
KOSHER KING - Meat products–beef ☆ - Hebrew Foods Inc.
KOSHERIFIC - Food products - Kineret Foods Corp.
KOSHI HIKARI USA IMPERIAL QUALITY RICE - Rice - Chris Isbell
KOSHU - Wines - Takara Sake USA
KOSHU MASAMUNE - Wines - Takara Sake USA
KOSLOWSKI FARMS - Jams and jellies - Koslowski Farms Inc.
KOSMIC - Paints - House of Kolor, Inc.
KOSMIC GLO - Paints - House of Kolor, Inc.
KOSMIC KANDLES - Candles - Michael R. Widmer
KOSMIC KOLOR - Paints - House of Kolor, Inc.
KOSMOS - Yarn ☆ - National Spinning Co., Inc.
KOSS - Artists' materials - JBC Imports & Marketing
KOSS - Electronic equipment - Koss Corp.
KOSS CLASSICS - Recording label - Koss Corp.
KOSS KORDLESS - Headphones ☆ - Koss Corp.
KOSSACK - Jewelry - Alan K. Ebert

KOSSUTH - Office supplies - R.A. Stewart Superior
KOST KUT - Envelopes - Westvaco Corp.
KOSTER - Bakery products ☆ - Allied Bakers Co.
KOSTO - Puddings–canned - Kosto Food Products Co.
KOSTOMA-VAN KOOTEN - Cookies - Holland-American Importing Co. Inc.
KOTA-POOL - Paints - Blue Ribbon Paint Co.
KOTA-WALL - Paints - Blue Ribbon Paint Co.
KOTABARB - Pharmaceutical preparations - Wesley Pharmacal Co. Inc.
KOTAFLOOR - Enamels - Blue Ribbon Paint Co.
KOTAK - Cigarettes - G.A. Georgopulo & Co. Inc.
KOTALL - Enamels - California Products Corp.
KOTE A DECK - Adhesives and sealants - Oregon Research & Development Corp.
KOTE-GLO - Veterinary pharmaceutical preparations ☆ - N-R Laboratories Inc.
KOTE-GLO CONCENTRATED - Pet products - N-R Laboratories Inc.
KOTE-GLO FINIS - Pet products - N-R Laboratories Inc.
KOTE-GLO LUSTRE - Pet products - N-R Laboratories Inc.
KOTENOL - Coatings - American Nickeloid Co.
KOTEX - Sanitary napkins - Kimberly-Clark Corp.
KOTEX NATURAL CURVED - Tampons - Kimberly-Clark Corp.
KOTEX PERSONALS - Sanitary napkins - Kimberly-Clark Corp.
KOTEX SECUREHOLD PADS - Sanitary napkins - Kimberly-Clark Corp.
KOTO - Frames–eyeglass - Creative Imaging Corp.
KOTO - Hardware ☆ - Travaco Laboratories Inc.
KOTTON KLOSE - Apparel–women's - Gul Tex Inc.
KOULD BE BEAR - Beverages - Atlas Bottling Co.
KOULD BE BEAVER - Beverages - Atlas Bottling Co.
KOULD BE MOOSE - Beverages - Atlas Bottling Co.
KOUNTRY AIRE - Trailers–travel - Newmar Corp.
KOUNTRY COMFORT - Trailers–travel - Travel Line Enterprises Inc.
KOUNTRY KERNEL - Animal feeds - Kountry Kernel
KOUNTRY KITCHEN - Cooking utensils–cast iron ☆ - National Housewares
KOUNTRY KLANGERS - Novelty items - Schaffert Manufacturing Co., Inc.
KOUNTRY KLASSIC - Meat products–beef - Ranch Hand Foods Inc.
KOUNTRY KWIK - Fruits and vegetables - Dawn Food Products Inc.
KOUNTRY LITE - Trailers–travel ☆ - Newmar Corp.
KOUNTRY STAR - Trailers–travel - Newmar Corp.
KOUNTY KIST - Vegetables–canned - Green Giant Co.
KOUNTY KIST - Vegetables–canned - Pillsbury Co.
KOUROS - Perfumes - Yves St. Laurent Parfum Corp.
KOUROS FRAICHEUR - Perfumes - Yves St. Laurent Parfum Corp.
KOURT KIDS - Shoes - Endicott Johnson Corp.
KOUTBACK - Sporting goods - Kombi Ltd.
KOUVALIAS - Toys ☆ - Reeves International, Inc.
KOUZINA - Faucets - Kallista Inc.
KOVACS - Clocks ☆ - George Kovacs Lighting Inc.
KOVAR'S - Video production - Kovar's Karate Center, Inc.
KOVE AND BASEBOARD CLEANER - Cleaning preparations - Uncle Sam Chemical Co., Inc.
KOVER KADDY - Sporting goods - Golf Products
KOVER KRACK - Adhesives and sealants - VIP/Lighthouse Products
KOVER-UP - Ribbons - Eaton Allen Ko-Rec-Type Corp.
KOVERALL - Craft supplies - Sig Manufacturing Inc.
KOVERALL - Jeans - Levi Strauss & Co.
KOVERCOTE - Paints ☆ - Steelcote Manufacturing Corp.
KOVERLUM - Insulating materials ☆ - Norandex, Inc.
KOVITE - See **QUINTABS**
KOVITE-M - See **MONOCAPS**
KOVITONIC - Vitamins and nutritional supplements - Freeda Vitamins Inc.
KOW-BALL MARKER - Markers–felt-tip - Western Sales Inc.
KOW-KARE - Veterinary pharmaceutical preparations ☆ - Dairy Association Co. Inc.
KOWA - Cameras - Kowa American Corp.
KOWALSKI - Meat products–pork - Kowalski Sausage Co. Inc.
KOWALSKI KOWALITY - Meat products–pork - Kowalski Sausage Co. Inc.
KOWBOY KORN - Popcorn - Merrie Heath
KOWL - Toys - Mattel, Inc.
KOYLON - Foam rubber ☆ - Uniroyal Engineered Products
KOYO STONE - Dinnerware–glass ☆ - Sango Co. Ltd. (Sango USA Div.)
KOYOTO GARDEN - Wallpaper - Quality House Inc.
KOYUKI - Wines ☆ - Wine Imports Ltd.
KOZAK - Motor vehicle parts and accessories - KozaK Auto Drywash Inc.
KOZI KNIT - Hats - Becker Glove International, Inc.
KOZIOL - Housewares ☆ - Chase Collection, Inc.
KOZLOWSKI FARMS - Salad dressings–bottled - Kozlowski Farms Inc.
KOZMIC - Toys - Merchandising Service of America Inc.

☆ = Now out of production

KOZMO - Toys–stuffed - Russ Berrie and Co., Inc.
KOZY - Apparel and accessories ☆ - Kozy Shack, Inc.
KOZY - Heating pads–electric - Electrozot Corp.
KOZY HEAT - Fireplaces - Hussong Manufacturing Co., Inc.
KOZY KIDS - Dolls ☆ - Uneeda Doll Co., Inc.
KOZY KITTEN - Cat food - Heinz Pet Products Co.
KOZY KITTY - Pet products - Lee-Mar Pet Supplies
KOZY KRITTER - Dog food - Heinz Pet Products Co.
KOZY KUP - Pet products - Flexi-Mat Corp.
KOZY LOGS - Controls–air conditioning systems - Root Equipment Corp.
KOZY SHACK - Desserts - Kozy Shack, Inc.
KOZY SHACK - Puddings–canned - Kozy Shack Inc.
KP - Loudspeakers - WWR Technology, Inc.
KP - Oils–lubricating - Epicor Industries, Inc.
K.P. KIDS & CO BY KARI PEARSON - Fabrics - Kari Pearson
KPI - Publisher's imprints - Routledge
KPL - Photographic equipment - Eastman Kodak Co.
KPM - Tiles–ceramic ☆ - Federal Tile Imports Inc.
KPM USA - Automotive parts and accessories - Kinetic Parts Manufacturing, Inc.
KPN - Vitamins and nutritional supplements - Freeda Vitamins Inc.
KPOD - Paneling - Progressive System Technologies, Inc.
KPR - Photographic equipment - Eastman Kodak Co.
KPS - Rings–jewelry - Artcarved Inc.
KPS DAKOTA NATURAL BEEF - Beef - Dakota Natural Beef Corp.
KPS DAKOTA ORGANIC BEEF - Beef - Dakota Natural Beef Corp.
KPT - Tiles–ceramic - KPT Inc.
KPT - Tiles–ceramic - United Ceramic Tile Corp.
KPT COOL TOOLS - Computer software - HSC Software
KR - Jewelry - Kirchner Corp.
KR - Jewelry - Kent Raible
KR - Publisher's imprints ☆ - Krieger Publishing Co.
KRAAL II - Floor coverings - Bellbridge Carpets
KRAAL I - Floor coverings - Bellbridge Carpets
KRABBYCAKES - Food products - Fish King Processors Inc.
KRAC-KALK - Hardware - American Stone-Mix Inc.
KRACK-KOTE - Paints - Tuff-Kote Co. Inc.
KRACK-UPS - Trading cards and stamps - Comstock Cards Inc.
KRACKAJACK - Crackers - Global Marketing (US) Inc.
KRACKEL - Candy - Hershey Chocolate USA
KRACKER JOK - Bedding–linen - Dan River Inc.
KRACKIN' EGG - Puzzles - Bleyer Industries (Peoria Plastics Div.)
KRACKLIN - Dog food - Sunshine Mills Inc.
KRACKS AWAY - Plaster–wallboard - Midco Products Co. Inc.
KRACO - Radios–citizens' band - Kraco Enterprises Inc.
KRAFSTOK - File folders - National Fiberstok Corp.
KRAFT - Computer software - Kraft Systems Inc.
KRAFT - Food products - Kraft Foods, Inc.
KRAFT - Seasonings - Kraft Foods, Inc.
KRAFT-FLEX - Insulating materials ☆ - Foil-Ray Inc.
KRAFT FREE - Salad dressings–bottled - Kraft Foods, Inc.
KRAFT FREE TO GO - Salad dressings–bottled - Kraft Food Ingredients Corp.
KRAFT LIGHT - Mayonnaise - Kraft Foods, Inc.
KRAFT SALSA RANCH - Salad dressings–bottled - Kraft Foods, Inc.
KRAFT SAUCEWORKS - Food products - Kraft Food Ingredients Corp.
KRAFT-SYSTEM - Tires ☆ - General Tire, Inc.
KRAFT TEDDY BEAR - Marshmallows - Kraft Food Ingredients Corp.
KRAFTALL - File folders ☆ - ACCO USA, Inc.
KRAFTBATH - Cabinets - KraftMaid Cabinetry Inc.
KRAFTBILT - Office supplies - Kraftbilt Products
KRAFTEC - Health care products - Silcraft Corp.
KRAFTEE - Hobby kits - Textile Enterprises Inc.
KRAFTEX - Lighting fixtures - Acme-Lite Manufacturing Co.
KRAFTILE - Tiles–clay - Kraftile Co.
KRAFTLINE - Cabinets - KraftMaid Cabinetry Inc.
KRAFTMAID - Cabinets - KraftMaid Cabinetry Inc.
KRAFTMAID - Cabinets - Masco Corp.
KRAFTOBESE - Pharmaceutical preparations - Kraft Pharmaceutical Co.
KRAFTOLAMINE - Pharmaceutical preparations - Kraft Pharmaceutical Co.
KRAFTRITE - Paper–kraft - Permalin Products Co.
KRAFTSMAN - Garden equipment ☆ - American Building Components Co.
KRAFTWARE - Ice buckets - Kraftware Corp. (Morgan Div.)
KRAFTY - Brushes - Wright-Bernet
KRAFTY DEVIL TOOLS - Tools–hand-operated - S & J Products, Ltd.
KRAFTY KATCHER - Fishing tackle - Krafty Katcher, Inc.
KRAFTY KRITTERS - Moldings–plaster ∑ of paris ☆ - DecoArt, Inc.

KRAG - Recording label - Gark Records (O)
KRAGEN - Dog collars ☆ - B & B Leather Co.
KRAIT - Cables–steel - Kryptonite Corp.
KRAK-A-JACK - Gloves - Knoxville Glove Co.
KRAK STIK - Caulking compounds - La-Co Industries, Inc.
KRAKAPOZ! - Apparel - Krakapoz
KRAKATOA - Computer software - Cadis, Inc.
KRAKATOA - Food products - Stache Foods
KRAKAUS - Food products - Atalanta Corp.
KRAKOW - Food products - Chas. F. Cates & Sons Inc.
KRAKS WAFER ROLLS - Candy ☆ - Spangler Candy Co.
KRAKUS - Beverages–malt - Laureate Imports Co.
KRAKUS - Beverages–malt - Stanley Stawski Distributing Co.
KRAKUS - Hams - Cameco Inc.
KRAM - Video games - Taito America Corp.
KRAMARH - Greeting cards - Burgoyne Inc./Curtis Swann
KRAMARK - Greeting cards - Burgoyne Inc./Curtis Swann
KRAMER - Guitars - Kramer
KRAMES COMMUNICATIONS - Publisher's imprints - Krames Communications Inc.
KRAML - Milk - Swiss Valley Farms Co.
KRAMM 7 - Skin care products - Jan Stuart Co.
KRANK 20 - Beverages–carbonated - Global Beverage Co.
KRANK'S - Shaving product - Benjamin Ansehl Co.
KRANKY KUMQUAT INC., THE - Bakery products - Kranky Kumquat, Inc.
KRANSCO - Sporting goods - Kransco Manufacturing Inc.
KRAPPER-FLAPPER, THE - Toilet seats - Melvin York
KRAPPY DICE - Games - Macdavid Co.
KRASDALE - Food products - Krasdale Foods Inc.
KRASKIN - Toys - Kraskin Baton Co.
KRASNEY PREMIUM RED STAR VODKA - Beverages–alcohol - Archer Daniels Midland Co.
KRATT - Harmonicas - William Kratt Co.
KRAUS - Footwear–women's - Argyris Inc.
KRAUSE - Corn–flour or meal - Semple Co.
KRAUSE - Tillers–rotary - Krause Plow Corp.
KRAUSE STABILO - Ladders–metal - Dumarco Corp.
KRAUSES - Sofas - Krause's Sofa Factory Inc.
KRAUSE'S SOFA FACTORY - Furniture - Krause's Sofa Factory Inc.
KRAUSZER'S - Food products - Krauszer's Food Stores
KRAUT OLE - Food products ☆ - J.G. Van Holten & Son Inc.
KRAUTLI-ZURICH - Leather goods - David Kirk (London)
KRAZ - Artists' materials - Kraz
KRAZE - Recording label - Maze Records
KRAZEE-WHEELS - Toys ☆ - Intex Recreation Corp.
KRAZY - Perfumes ☆ - Key West Aloe Inc.
KRAZY BEACH - Skin care products - Cosmyl, Inc.
KRAZY BOWL - Video games - American Sammy Corp.
KRAZY CLAYTON'S CHOCOLATE MADNESS - Chewing gum ☆ - Zeebs Enterprises, Inc.
KRAZY CLEAN - Cleaning preparations–household - Marine Development & Research Corp.
KRAZY CLUSTERS - Pet products - Pet-Ag, Inc.
KRAZY CUTTER - Office supplies - A & W Products Co., Inc.
KRAZY FORK - Novelty items - Sansom, Inc.
KRAZY GEL - Nail care products - Kristy Wells Inc.
KRAZY GLUE - Adhesives and sealants - Krazy Glue Inc.
KRAZY GLUE - Glue–household or industrial - Borden, Inc.
KRAZY JUNGLE - Skin care products - Cosmyl, Inc.
KRAZY KADOODLE BAND - Toys - Proll Molding Co., Inc.
KRAZY KAJUN FORTUNE COOKIE - Cookies - Krazy Kajun Enterprises, Inc.
KRAZY KAPS - Games - C.S.A. Worldwide
KRAZY KARD KO - Greeting cards and wrapping paper - Garnett C. Brown, Jr.
KRAZY KENO - Computer software - Silicon Gaming, Inc.
KRAZY KIDS - Apparel–children's ☆ - Happy Kids Ltd.
KRAZY KIDZ - Floor coverings - Beaulieu of America, Inc.
KRAZY KLACKERS - Publisher's imprints - Paul L. Chamberlain
KRAZY KLOTH - Polishing cloths - Cadie Products Corp.
KRAZY KNIFE - Novelty items - Sansom, Inc.
KRAZY KNUTS - Food products - Chips Inc.
KRAZY KOOLERS - Novelty items - Fun-Time International, Inc.
KRAZY KRITTERS - Apparel–children's - Land 'n Sea, Inc.
KRAZY LOCK - Adhesives and sealants - Krazy Glue Inc.
KRAZY NAILS - Nail care products - Kristy Wells Inc.
KRAZY SPOON - Novelty items - Sansom, Inc.
KRAZY STRAWS - Novelty items - Fun-Time International, Inc.

☆ = Now out of production

KRAZY UTENSILS - Novelty items - Fun-Time International, Inc.

K.R.C. - Recording label - Ozark Opry Records

KRC-7 - Cleaning preparations - Chemique Inc.

KREAM KRUST - Breads - Dairy Mart Convenience Stores, Inc.

KREATIONS - Moldings and trim - Gossen Corp.

KREATIVE KANVAS - Artists' materials - Foss Manufacturing Co., Inc.

KREBS CYCLONES - Machinery - Krebs Engineers

KREDIT KARDS - Novelty items–paper - Antioch Publishing Co.

KREDIT KARDZ - Chewing gum - Zeebs Enterprises, Inc.

KREEGER FARMS - Ice cream - Cloverdale Farms Dairy Inc.

KREEMIT - Cream - Borden, Inc.

KREEMY - Cream ☆ - Kellogg Co.

KREEMY TOP - Whipped topping–powdered - Presto Food Products, Inc.

KREEN - Cleaning preparations - Kano Laboratories Inc.

KREEPY KADET - Cleaning equipment - Kreepy Krauly USA, Inc.

KREEPY KLEAR - Water purification systems - Kreepy Krauly USA, Inc.

KREEPY KRAULY - Cleaning equipment - Kreepy Krauly USA, Inc.

KREGEL PUBLICATIONS - Publisher's imprints - Kregel Publications & Bookstores

KREINIK - Leather goods - Kreinik Manufacturing Co. Inc.

KREINIK BALGER - Thread - Kreinik Manufacturing Co. Inc.

KREINIK FACETS - Trimmings–fabric - Kreinik Manufacturing Co. Inc.

KREINIK SILK SERICA - Thread - Kreinik Manufacturing Co. Inc.

KREISLER - Lighters - Colibri Inc.

KREISLER - Watches - Regal Industries, Inc.

KRELL - Audio equipment - Krell Industries

KRELL - Computer software - Krell Software Corp.

KRELL DIGITAL INC. - Audio equipment - Krell Industries

KREM - Food products ☆ - Staff Supermarket Associates, Inc.

KREMAY - Food products - Beatrice Cheese Co.

KREME KRIMPIES - Bakery products - Tasty Baking Co.

KREMENTZ - Jewelry - Krementz & Co.

KREMENTZ CLASSIC - Jewelry - Krementz & Co.

KREMENTZ CONTEMPO - Jewelry - Krementz & Co.

KREMINI - Cookies - Commerce Foods Inc.

KREML - Hair care products - Smithkline Beecham Corp.

KREMLYOVSKAYA - Vodka - Montebello Brands, Inc.

KREMOL - Disinfectants - Claflin Co.

KRENTLUM - Draperies - O'Krent Fabrics Inc.

KREO-BENZ - Health care products - Halsey Drug Co. Inc.

KREONITE - Photographic equipment - Kreonite Inc.

KRESGE - Apparel and accessories - Kmart Corp.

KRESICS - Video tapes - Kresics

KRESO - Cleaning preparations - Kreso Manufacturing Inc.

KRESO DIP NO. 1 - Cleaning preparations - Kreso Manufacturing Inc.

KRESPI AND WHITE - Jewelry - Krespi & White Jewelry Inc.

KREST - Combs - Krest Products Corp.

KREST KING - Apparel and accessories - San Saba Cap, Inc.

KRESTEX - Aprons ☆ - Cassidy Inc.

KRETSCHMAR - Meat products–beef - John Morrell & Co.

KRETSCHMER - Wheat germ - Quaker Oats Co.

KREUTZER - Violins - Grossman Music Corp.

KREUTZKAMM - Bakery products ☆ - C. & J. Willenborg Inc.

KREW - Depilatories - Master Chemical Co.

KREW - Towels ☆ - Marson Creative Fastener Group

KREY - Food products - Chiquita Brands, Inc.

KRIB KIDS - Footwear - Shoeware Ltd.

KRIBKINS - Furniture ☆ - Evenflo Juvenile Furniture Co.

KRICKET KRAP - Fertilizers - Bricko Farms, Inc.

KRICKETS - Apparel–children's - Cantex Apparel Inc.

KRIEGER - Publisher's imprints - Krieger Publishing Co.

KRIEGER - Watches - Ira S. Krieger

KRIEGHOFF - Guns - Krieghoff International

KRIEGSPIEL - Games ☆ - Avalon Hill Game Co.

KRIEK - Beverages–malt - Merchant du Vin Corp.

KRIKIT - Automotive parts and accessories - Gates Rubber Co. (Automotive Aftermarket/Hardware Sales Div.)

KRIL FINISH - Paints - Miller Paint Co., Inc.

KRILI-KOTE - Paints - Devoe Paint Co.

KRILIUM - Chemical preparations ☆ - Monsanto Co.

KRILL - Games - Ampersand Press

KRILL-E - Pet products - Tetra Sales USA

KRIMPETS - Cakes - Tasty Baking Co.

KRIMPETTES - Hair care products - Morris-Flamingo Inc.

KRIMPTITE - Electrical equipment - Molex-Etc Inc.

KRIMSKAYA - Vodka - Distilled Trading International

KRINCH KRUNCH - Nuts–salted, roasted, cooked, or canned - Funda's Kitchen

KRINGELS - Apparel and accessories - Joan Renate Jones

KRINGLE - Toys–stuffed ☆ - Russ Berrie and Co., Inc.

KRINGLE KAKES - Cakes - Tasty Baking Co.

KRINGLE TOWN COLLECTIBLES - Novelty items ☆ - Noma International, Inc.

KRINGLEKINS - Toys - Debra Lynn Lietzman

KRINGLES - Candy - R.M. Palmer Co.

KRINKL - Metals - S. Ronald Barnette

KRINKLE TRIM - Christmas tree ornaments - J. Kinderman and Sons Brite Star Manufacturing Co.

KRINKLESPUN - Yarn - Glen Raven Mills Inc.

KRINKLGLAS - Plastics - Dimensional Plastics Corp.

KRINKLIE GRAINS - Cereal ☆ - Breadshop's Natural Foods

KRINKS - Toys ☆ - Oddzon Products, Inc.

KRINOS - Food products - Krinos Foods, Inc.

KRIPTIN - Pharmaceutical preparations ☆ - Whitehall Laboratories

KRIS BINGLE - Toys–stuffed ☆ - Gund, Inc.

KRIS BY AHTD/PTDA - Computer software - Automated Catalogue Services LP

KRIS CREATIONS - Stationery - Northman Co.

KRIS DEE - Apparel–women's - L.A. Willco, Inc.

KRIS-KROS - Housewares - San Francisco Bay Co., Inc.

KRISK - Food products machinery - SCI Scandicrafts Inc.

KRISKA - Apparel and accessories - Kriska Painting on Silk

KRISLIN - Pet products - Wolverton Krislin, Inc.

KRISMARK - Hair care products - Sundiata International

KRISMOOSE - Soaps & Toiletries - Country Lane Enterprises Inc.

KRISNKEV'S - Wallpaper - Area Rugs Manufacturing Inc.

KRISP BAR - Candy bars - Peter Paul

KRISP-IT - Food products - Krisp-It, Ltd.

KRISP 'N FLAKY - Pizzas–mixes - Luigino's

KRISPEE-KORN - Popcorn - R.L. Stiles Inc.

KRISPEN - Breads - Wachtel Biscuit

KRISPIE - Nuts–salted, roasted, cooked, or canned - Fleming Companies, Inc.

KRISPIE CORN FLAKES - Cereal - Breadshop's Natural Foods

KRISPIE TREATS - Candy - Ternus & Co., Inc.

KRISPOP - Popcorn - National Oats Co. Inc.

KRISPPE - Breads–mixes - Casa Visco Finer Foods

KRISPROLLS - Breads - Pogens Family Bakery

KRISPS - Candy - M-B Candies Inc.

KRISPUDS - Potato chips - Red Seal Quality Foods Inc.

KRISPY - Bags–paper ☆ - Great Western Products Inc.

KRISPY - Crackers - Sunshine Biscuits, Inc.

KRISPY - Pet products - Gimborn U.S., Inc.

KRISPY CRULLERS - Doughnuts - Hdn Corp.

KRISPY JUNIORS - Doughnuts - Krispy Kreme Doughnut

KRISPY KAN - Food containers - Luce Corp.

KRISPY KITCHENS - Food products - Krispy Kitchens Inc.

KRISPY KNIBBLERS - Snack foods - Krispy Kreme Doughnut

KRISPY KRAUT - Sauerkraut ☆ - Curtice-Burns Foods, Inc.

KRISPY KREME - Coffee - HDN Development Corp.

KRISPY KREME - Cooking equipment–commercial - Hdn Corp.

KRISSY - Wigs - Jean Paree Weegs Inc.

KRIST STREET STYLE - Skates–roller - Seneca Sports, Inc.

KRISTA - Bedding–linen - Dan River Inc.

KRISTA - Mattresses - Namaco Industries, Inc.

KRISTAAL - Cooking equipment–household - Chantal Cookware Corp.

KRISTAL - Skin care products - Lisane Aesthetics, Inc.

KRISTAL COLLECTION - Dishes–earthenware - In-Mar Trading, Inc.

KRISTAL CZARSKAYA - Wines - Pacific Sales and Imports

KRISTAL INTERNATIONAL - Recording label - Stargem Records Inc.

KRISTALINE - Tiles–ceramic - Monarch Tile Inc.

KRISTALINO - Glassware–household ☆ - Crisa Corp.

KRISTALL KRISLA - Glass–leaded ☆ - Charles Norman Inc.

KRISTALLI - Bedding–linen - Dan River Inc.

KRISTALUXUS COLLECTION - Glassware–household ☆ - Crisa Corp.

KRISTEN CARDS - Greeting cards - Burgoyne Inc./Curtis Swann

KRISTEN'S FLORAL - Giftware ☆ - Fenton Art Glass Co.

KRISTI - Furniture - Millco Inc.

KRISTI STREET BEAT - Skates–roller - Seneca Sports, Inc.

KRISTIAN KANE - Apparel and accessories - Leather Coats, Inc.

KRISTIAN REGALE - Cider ☆ - August Schell Brewing Co.

KRISTIE CAT - Toys–stuffed - Russ Berrie and Co., Inc.

KRISTIE'S KREATIONS - Stationery - Gibson Holders, Inc.

KRISTIINA - Wallpaper - Motif Designs, Inc.

☆ = Now out of production

KRISTIN ELLIOTT - Greeting cards - Kristin Elliott Inc.
KRISTIN INTERNATIONAL - Sports apparel ☆ - Dionysian Inc. (Jacobs Div.)
KRISTIN PAIGE - Apparel–women's - Wal-Mart Stores Inc.
KRISTINA - Apparel and accessories - Chester County Sportswear Co. Inc.
KRISTINA - Blinds–vertical - Kingdom Vertical Blinds Manufacturing Inc.
KRISTI'S ANSWER - Bags - PFP Inc.
KRISTONE - Wines - Kendall Jackson Winery, Ltd.
KRISTOPH COLLECTION, THE - Skin care products - Signature Financial/ Marketing, Inc.
KRISTY - Tableware–china - Lenox, Inc.
KRISTY - Trays ☆ - Eagle Glass Products
KRISTY WELLS - Nail care products - Vigor Co.
KRISWILL - Tobacco pouches - Sutliff Tobacco Co.
KRITER - Wines - Patriarche Pere & Fils
KRITTER - Pet products - United Pacific Mills
KRITTER KASTLE - Pet products ☆ - Pets International, Ltd.
KRITTER KATCHER - Pet products - Reflex Corp.
KRITTER KLIPS - Containers - Cascade Toy, Ltd.
KRITTER MITTS - Toys - All American Toy Co.
KRITTER PUPS - Toys - All American Toy Co.
KRIZIA - Eyeglasses ☆ - Private Eyes Sunglass Corp.
KRIZIA UOMO - Skin care products - Sanofi Beaute Inc.
KRK - Audio equipment - KRK Monitoring Systems
KRO FLIES - Toys ☆ - Kro Flies Kites
KRO-FLITE - Sporting goods - Spalding Sports Worldwide
KRO-KLING - Paints ☆ - Allentown Paint Manufacturing Co. Inc.
KROCK KURED - Food products - Chas. F. Cates & Sons Inc.
KROEGER - Pianos - Kohler & Campbell Inc.
KROFIL - Paints ☆ - Thomas Waterproof Coatings Co.
KROGEDAL - Craft supplies - Norsk Engros USA Inc.
KROGER - Food products - The Kroger Co.
KROIL - Oils–lubricating - Kano Laboratories Inc.
KROILER - Tools - Kano Laboratories Inc.
KROKUS-VARIMEX - Photographic equipment ☆ - Exakta Camera Co. Inc.
KROM - Audio equipment ☆ - TDK Electronics Corp.
KROMA - Chalk ☆ - Dixon Ticonderoga Co.
KROMA - Sporting goods - Awards Etc.
KROMA JET - Cooking equipment–commercial - Kopykake
KROMA KOLORS - Cooking equipment–commercial - Kopykake
KROMA-SEAL - Varnishes ☆ - KCI Coatings, Inc.
KROMA-X - Bleach ☆ - Hilex Co.
KROMAGNUS - Tools - Kromhard Twist Drill Co.
KROMAKOTE - Protective coatings - Abatron, Inc.
KROMALLOY - Tools - Kromhard Twist Drill Co.
KROMALUX - Paints - Triangle Coatings Inc.
KROMALUX - Tools - Kromhard Twist Drill Co.
KROMAX - Paints ☆ - Thomas Waterproof Coatings Co.
KROME - Paper products - Signs & Glassworks, Inc.
KROME-COTE - Floor waxes ☆ - C.B. Dolge Co.
KROME-KING - Saw blades - Vermont American Corp.
KROMEKOTE - Paper–writing - Champion International Corp.
KROMEL - Recording label - Jazz Composer's Orchestra Association Inc.
KROMER - Gloves - Kromer Cap Co. Inc.
KROMER KLEAN KLOTH - Hats - Kromer Cap Co. Inc.
KROMHARD - Tools - Kromhard Twist Drill Co.
KROMIK - Paints - Sherwin-Williams Automotive Finishes Corp.
KROMKUT - Tools - Kromhard Twist Drill Co.
KROMMNIE - Floor coverings–linoleum - Area Rugs Manufacturing Inc.
KROMOTEX - Enamels - Standard T Chemical Co. Inc.
KROMOX - Paints - Sampson Coatings Inc.
KROMULTRA - Tools - Kromhard Twist Drill Co.
KROMVAR - Tools - Kromhard Twist Drill Co.
KRON - Chocolate candy - St. Moritz Chocolatier
KRON-LUME - Fireplace logs–treated - Kron Enterprises, Inc.
KRONA - Margarine - Van Den Bergh Foods Co.
KRONE - Shoes ☆ - Saga House Inc.
KRONEHOF - Lenses–optical - Bausch & Lomb Inc.
KRONEN - Breads ☆ - Liberty Richter Inc.
KRONEN CASEWORK - Computer stores - Salisbury Millwork Inc.
KRONENBRAU - Beverages–malt - The Stroh Brewery Co.
KRONENOST - Cheese - Roth Kase USA, Ltd.
KRONENWEIN - Wines - Wine Imports Ltd.
KRONER - Musical instruments - Custom Music Co.
KRONER-COOPER - Musical instruments - Custom Music Co.
KRONNER CANNULA SITE STITCHER - Medical apparatus - Kronner Medical
KRONNER FOOT CASTING STAND - Medical apparatus - Kronner Medical

KRONNER MANIPUJECTOR - Medical apparatus - Kronner Medical
KRONOHIST - Health care products ☆ - Ferndale Laboratories, Inc.
KRONOS - Computer software - Kronos Digital Entertainment, Inc.
KRONRING - Hair clippers–veterinary - Major International Inc.
KRONUS - Computer hardware - Hendra Sutandinata
KROOPS - Boots - A.M. Kroop & Sons Inc.
KROPPS & BOBBERS - Hair care products - Body Torq, Inc.
KROSFIRE - Games ☆ - Sipa Sipa Games
KROSHETTA - Sweaters - Papillon Eastern Imports, Inc.
KROSS A KROSS - Exercising equipment - Kross a Kross, Inc.
KROTCH TOP - Apparel - Krotch Top, Inc.
KROUNOS - Faucets - Kallista Inc.
KROUPANA - Leather - Wolverine World Wide, Inc.
KROUPA'S - Fruits–canned - Kroupa's Inc.
KROVAR - Herbicides - E.I. Dupont de Nemours and Co.
KROWN TTD - Health care products - Compu TTY
KROWN TTD - Health care products - Krown Manufacturing
KROY - Electronic equipment - Kroy, Inc.
KROY KRAFTER - Office accessories - Kroy, Inc.
KROYDON - Exercising equipment - Aqua-Leisure Industries, Inc.
KRRRISP KRAUT - Sauerkraut - Flanagan Bros. Inc.
KRRRISP KRAUT - Sauerkraut - Great Lakes Kraut Co. LLC
KRUEGER - Beverages–alcohol ☆ - Falstaff Brewing Corp.
KRUEGER - Casters - Young's
KRUEGER - Musical instruments - Maas-Rowe Carillons Inc.
KRUG - Wallpaper - Koroseal Wallcoverings
KRUG - Wines - Remy Martin Amerique Inc.
KRUGER - Boats–canoes - Kruger Paddle Co.
KRUGER - Pickles - Kruger and Sons Inc.
KRUISER - Trailers–travel - USA Venturcraft Corp.
KRUISER, THE - Sandwiches–prepackaged - Cold Cut Kruise, Inc.
KRUMBITS - Toys - Cinnamuffs, Inc.
KRUMBLE BALL - Ammunition ☆ - Remington Arms Co., Inc.
KRUMBLE KRUNCH - Confections - Sycamore Creek Co. (INARI, Ltd.)
KRUMFIN - Muffins - D-D's Country Bakery
KRUMFINS - Bakery products–frozen - Van Den Bergh Foods Co.
KRUNCH - Candy - Clasen Quality Coating Inc.
KRUNCH - Glassware–household - Bartlett-Collins Co.
KRUNCH BAR - Candy ☆ - Leaf, Inc.
KRUNCHEES - Snack foods ☆ - Sunshine Biscuits, Inc.
KRUNCHERS! - Potato chips - Borden, Inc.
KRUNCHIE WEDGES - Vegetables–frozen - J.R. Simplot Co.
KRUNCHIES - Candy - Nestle USA
KRUNCHIES - Dog food - Blue Seal Feeds Inc.
KRUNCHKIES - Candy - Intersweet Candy Inc.
KRUNCHY STIXS - Food products - Dalmatian Bay Wine Co. Inc.
KRUNCHY STIXS - Snack foods - Tina, Son & Co.
KRUPNIK - Liquors - Adamba Imports International Inc.
KRUPTOCABLE - Cables–steel - Kryptonite Corp.
KRUSE CONTINUUM - Computer software - Kruse, Inc.
KRUSE CONTINUUM LITE - Computer software - Kruse, Inc.
KRUSE CONTINUUM PRO - Computer software - Kruse, Inc.
KRUSE CONTROL - Computer software - Kruse, Inc.
KRUSE PROVUE - Computer software - Kruse, Inc.
KRUSE SIG - Floor coverings–carpet and rugs - Artistic Rugs Inc.
KRUSTEAZ - Food products - Continental Mills, Inc.
KRUSTY KORN KOB - Pans ☆ - General Housewares Corp.
KRUT - Cymbals ☆ - Deltex Music Corp.
KRUTCH KRIDDER - Novelty items - K/C-B Inc.
KRUX - Apparel–athletic - NHS, Inc.
KRYABSORBER - Exchangers–heat - Contaminant Separations, Inc.
KRYLON - Paints - Krylon/Dupli-Color
KRYOCLEAN - Filters–industrial - BOC Group Inc.
KRYOLAN - Cosmetics - Victoria's Dance-Theatrical Supply
KRYOS - Watches - Jaeger-Le Coultre SA
KRYPTKEEPER - Cables–steel - Kryptonite Corp.
KRYPTO - Apparel and accessories - Joseph R. Lennon
KRYPTO - Games - Mph Games Co.
KRYPTO CABLE - Locks–padlocks - Kryptonite Corp.
KRYPTO LOK - Locks–padlocks - Kryptonite Corp.
KRYPTODISC - Cables–steel - Kryptonite Corp.
KRYPTODISC DFS - Cables–steel - Kryptonite Corp.
KRYPTODISCO - Cables–steel - Kryptonite Corp.
KRYPTOFLEX - Cables–steel - Kryptonite Corp.
KRYPTOLITE - Lamp bulbs–incandescent - Angelo Brothers Co.
KRYPTOLOK - Cables–steel - Kryptonite Corp.

KRYPTON - Lighting equipment ☆ - Duro-Lite Lamps Inc.
KRYPTON - Sporting goods ☆ - O'Brien International
KRYPTON D-CELLS - Flashlights ☆ - Streamlight, Inc.
KRYPTONITE - Locks–padlocks - Kryptonite Corp.
KRYPTONITE - T-shirts–children's - DC Comics
KRYS-KROSS - Potato flakes - Krystal Co.
KRYSTA - Handwork supplies - Bernat Yarn & Craft Corp.
KRYSTAD - Tableware–china - Sara Lee Corp.
KRYSTAL - Beverages–carbonated - Krystal Co.
KRYSTAL - Mats–grass, reed, and jute ☆ - Charleswater
KRYSTAL - Wigs ☆ - Jean Paree Weegs Inc.
KRYSTAL BEVEL - Glass products - Glass Unlimited of High Point, Inc.
KRYSTAL FLUTES - Glass products - AFG Industries Inc. (Glass Group Div.)
KRYSTAL FLUTOS - Glass products - AFG Industries Inc. (Glass Group Div.)
KRYSTAL KEYS - Tiles–ceramic - Monarch Tile Inc.
KRYSTAL KITTY - Toys–stuffed - Dakin Inc.
KRYSTAL KLEAR - Envelopes - Westvaco Corp.
KRYSTAL KLEER - Cleaning preparations–window - Burnishine Products
KRYSTAL KLEER - Glass products - AFG Industries Inc. (Glass Group Div.)
KRYSTAL SUNRISER - Food products - Krystal Co.
KRYSTAL VIEW - Desk sets - Artistic Office Products
KRYSTALCAST - Furniture - Tables International Corp.
KRYSTILE - Varnishes ☆ - Sampson Coatings Inc.
KRYSTINEL - Magnets - MMG North America Inc.
KRYSTLAC - Enamels - C.M. Athey Paint Co.
KRYSTLE - Perfumes - Yves St. Laurent Parfum Corp.
KRYTON - Thread - Advance Thread Corp.
KRYWELD - Office supplies - American Envelope Co.
KRYZEN - Pharmaceutical preparations - Wesley Pharmacal Co. Inc.
KS - Flatware - Kirk Stieff Co.
KS - Hair-texturizing shears - B.W. Boyd Shears Inc.
KS - Health care products - Kwok Shing Import-Export Inc.
KS - Pencil sharpeners ☆ - Hunt Manufacturing Co.
KS - Recording label - Carmel Records
KS-3 - Paint removers - Klean-Strip
KS HEAVY BODIED - Paint removers - Klean-Strip
KS JAPAN DRIER - Paint dryers - Klean-Strip
KS KLEAN-CRETE - Cleaning preparations - Klean-Strip
KS KLEAN-HAND - Cleaning preparations - Klean-Strip
KS SOURCE - Motor vehicle parts and accessories - K Source, Inc.
KSA - Neckties ☆ - Kelly-Springfield Tire Co.
KSA COLLECTIBLES - Giftware - Kurt S. Adler Inc.
KSB 1.1 - Radiofrequency measuring equipment - Klipsch, Inc.
KSBP - Coatings - Kent Integrated Scientific Systems, Inc.
KSD - Hardware - D & K Technologies, Inc.
KSI-PRODUCTS - Bicycle parts and accessories - Kool Stop Originals, Inc.
KSL - Apparel - Karin Stevens, Inc.
KSL - Computer hardware - Progen Technology Inc.
KSL - Lubricants - Elf Lubricants North America, Inc.
KSR - Computer peripheral equipment - Kendall Square Research Corp.
KSR FORTRAN - Computer software - Kendall Square Research Corp.
KSS MUSIC CO. - Publisher's imprints - The Keene Music Group
K*STAR TOOLS - Tools–hand-operated - Winmark Co.
KSW 50 - Radiofrequency measuring equipment - Klipsch, Inc.
KSW 100 - Radiofrequency measuring equipment - Klipsch, Inc.
KSW 150 - Radiofrequency measuring equipment - Klipsch, Inc.
KSW 200 - Radio communications equipment - Klipsch, Inc.
KT - Hair-cutting shears - B.W. Boyd Shears Inc.
K.T. - Thread ☆ - Signal Thread Co. Inc.
KT - Work benches - Marshall Industries
KT-26 - Footwear–athletic - Osaga Footwear, Inc.
K.T. KEMPLE'S - Apparel and accessories - Kmart Properties, Inc.
KTD - Tools - Kromhard Twist Drill Co.
KTF - Vitamins and nutritional supplements ☆ - Freeda Vitamins Inc.
KTFR - Photographic equipment - Eastman Kodak Co.
KTG-1 - Musical instrument accessories - Seymour Duncan Pickups
KTG-2075 - Amplifiers - Seymour Duncan Pickups
KTG-2100 - Amplifiers - Seymour Duncan Pickups
KTO-LITE - Candles ☆ - Arizona Natural Resources
KTOOLS - Computer software - Chase W. Ashley
KTOURR - Apparel and accessories - HMJ Clothing Co. Ltd.
KTRON - Electronic equipment - K-Tron Technologies, Inc.
K.T.'S KITCHENS K - Pizzas–mixes - KT Kitchens
KTX - Thermometers - Dickson/Unigage, Inc.
KU-DOES - Shoes - Interco Inc.
KU-PON - Enamels - Diamond/Kuhn Paint Co.

KU-SEAL - Adhesives and sealants - Diamond/Kuhn Paint Co.
KU-STRIP - Paint removers - Diamond/Kuhn Paint Co.
KU-ZYME - Pharmaceutical preparations - Schwarz Pharma
KUAN - Furniture ☆ - Fancher Furniture Co. Inc.
KUBANEY - Recording label - Kubaney Publishing Corp.
KUBE KEEPER - Ice chests–plastic ☆ - Life-Like Products Inc.
KUBE-KEG - Barrels–wood - Greif Bros. Corp.
KUBERRAND - Office furniture–plastic - BTS Solid Brass Specialties
KUBLA KHAN - Food products - Kubla Khan Food Co.
KUCHARIK - Apparel and accessories - Kucharik Bicycle Clothing Inc.
KUCHENMEISTER - Cakes - Haram-Christensen Corp.
KUCKUCK - Recording label - Celestial Harmonies
KUDDLE ME TOYS - Toys–stuffed - Kellytoy (USA), Inc.
KUDDLE SHUTTLE - Pet products - Kuddle Shuttle, Inc.
KUDDLES - Toys–stuffed - Gund, Inc.
KUDDLEY KEWTIE - Dolls ☆ - Intex Recreation Corp.
KUDELATE - Pharmaceutical preparations ☆ - Ulmer Pharmacal Co.
KUDL-PAK - Electronics equipment - Melmat Inc.
KUDOS - Granola bars - Mars, Inc.
KUDROX - Antacids - Schwarz Pharma
KUDZU - Apparel and accessories - Kudzu LLC
KUDZU EXTRACT - Vitamins and nutritional supplements - Vitamin Research
   Products Inc.
KUECHLE - Biscuits - Kreiner Imports
KUEHN - Wines ☆ - Connolly & Co. Inc.
KUEHNE - Food products - John Sommer Inc.
KUFCO - Fencing–chain link - Davidson Plastics Corp.
KUFIKIRI - Games - Games & Graphics, Inc.
KUFLINKS - Fencing–chain link - Davidson Plastics Corp.
KUHN-LAC - Lacquers - Diamond/Kuhn Paint Co.
KUHNE - Food products - Acme Food Specialties Inc.
KUHNE - Food products - Haddon House Food Products Inc.
KUKIE KARDS - Greeting cards ☆ - Fran Mar Greeting cards Ltd.
KUKKA - Bedding–linen - Dan River Inc.
KUKKASARI - Bedding–linen - Dan River Inc.
KUKKUU KIMPPU - Bedding–linen - Dan River Inc.
KUKUI - Fruits–canned - Hawaiian Fruit Specialties Ltd.
KULIEN - Shoes - Kulien Shoes
KULKA - Lighting equipment - Voltarc Technologies, Inc.
KULM-KEASE - Dairy products - Swissrose International Inc.
KULO - Sportswear - Hollywood Games
KULTURE KARDS - Greeting cards - Recycled Paper Products, Inc.
KULTURE KIDS - Dolls - Golden Ribbon Playthings Inc.
KULTURE MAGZ - Magnets - Infinite Conceptions, Inc.
KUMA SPORT - Apparel and accessories - Kuma Sport, Inc.
KUMALONG - Concrete products - Goldblatt Tool Co.
KUMAR - Fabrics - Dan River Inc.
KUMBERKU - Skin care products - Cococare Products Inc.
KUMEU RIVER - Wines - Wilson Daniels Ltd.
KUMHO - Tires - Kumho USA Inc.
KUMSI-KUMSA - Fabrics - Burlington Industries, Inc.
KUMUTIOS - Cereal - New Morn, Inc.
KUN - Musical instrument accessories - International Violin Co. Ltd.
KUN-ALL - Ovens–industrial - A-10 Equipment Corp.
KUNAM - Enamels - Diamond/Kuhn Paint Co.
KUNDE - Wines - Kunde Estate Winery
KUNER'S - Vegetables–canned - Faribault Foods Inc.
KUNG FOOD - Video games - Atari Games Corp.
KUNG FU DRAGONS - Games - Gamescience
KUNG FU YUM - Pet food - Judee K. Creations, Inc. (Crazy Corn Division)
KUNG FU YUM - Pet products - Crazy Corn
KUNGENS - Biscuits ☆ - A.V. Olsson Trading Co., Inc.
KUNGSBORSTEN - Brushes - SCI Scandicrafts Inc.
KUNGSHOLM - Flatware - Utica Cutlery Co.
KUNGTONE - Musical instrument accessories - Fredrico Percussion
KUNIKO - Hair clippers–veterinary - Major International Inc.
KUNZLER - Meat products–beef - Kunzler and Co. Inc.
KUP-A-LONG - Housewares - Dale L. Beetler
KUP HANDLER - Insulating materials ☆ - Life-Like Products Inc.
KUP-L-TAP - Electrical equipment - KSCO Corp.
KUPELWEISER - Beverages–alcohol ☆ - Connolly & Co. Inc.
KUPFERBERG - Wines ☆ - Buena Vista Winery, Inc.
KUPKINS - Dolls - Cinnamuffs, Inc.
KUPPENHEIMER - Apparel–men's - Hartmarx Retail Group
KUPREX - Paints ☆ - Valspar Corp.
KUPUR - Table lamps - Frederick Cooper Inc.

☆ = Now out of production

KUR-SEAL - Varnishes ☆ - KCI Coatings, Inc.
KURAMIC - Epoxy coatings - KCI Coatings, Inc.
KURBRO - Paper–writing - Kurtz Bros. Inc.
KURFEES - Paints - KCI Coatings, Inc.
KURGLO - Paints ☆ - KCI Coatings, Inc.
KURIOS - Watches - Michael G. Mullendore
KURL - Floor coverings–carpet and rugs ☆ - Monterey, Inc.
KURL-KATCHER - Combs - Diane Products Inc.
KURL-OFF - Paint removers - Hillyard Enterprises, Inc.
KURLASH - Cosmetics - London International U.S. Holdings
KURLAWSH/DIAMOND DEB - Cosmetics - Marianna Imports, Inc.
KURLENE - Cosmetics ☆ - London International U.S. Holdings
KURLEX - Hair care products - Waverly Beauty Products
KURLEY KUT - Hair care products ☆ - Aquamint Laboratories Inc.
KURLEY-QUE - Hair care products - Nexxus Products Co.
KURLIE - Yarn ☆ - William Unger & Co. Inc.
KURLY DOG - Cooking utensils - Ryan Research
KURLY KATE - Scouring pads - Purex Industries Inc. (Kurly Kate Div.)
KURLY KURL - Hair care products - Organifly Laboratories
KURLY SHIRLEY - Dolls - Hodge Manufacturing Co. Inc.
KURO - Bedding–linen - Dan River Inc.
KUROD - Hair-texturizing shears - B.W. Boyd Shears Inc.
KUROKAWA - Toilets–portable - American Standard Inc.
KURT - Dolls - Mattel, Inc.
KURT WITTELSBACH - Violins ☆ - Deltex Music Corp.
KURTAIN KRAFT - Curtains - S & L Products, Inc.
KURTONE - Paints ☆ - KCI Coatings, Inc.
KURVEBALL - Balls - Pick Point Sports
KURVELVET - Paints ☆ - KCI Coatings, Inc.
KURYAKYN USA - Motorcycle parts and accessories - KuryAkyn Holdings
KURZCO - Jewelry - H. Kurzon Co.
KURZWEIL 250 - Synthesizers–musical instrument - Kurzweil Applied Intelligence Inc.
KUSAK - Glassware–household - Kusak Cut Glass Works
KUSAN - Toys - Tyco Toys
KUSH N KOLLAR - Footwear - Chippewa Shoe Co.
KUSHION AIRE - Trailers–boat - Fulton Manufacturing Corp.
KUSHION KRADLE - Motor vehicle parts and accessories - Fulton Manufacturing Corp.
KUSHION KRAFT - Packaging–paper - Mason Box Co. Inc.
KUSHION KRAFT - Packaging–paper - Sealed Air Corp.
KUSHION LOK - Mats - U.S. Mat & Rubber Co. Inc.
KUSHION SUPREME - Foam rubber - Eastern Foam Products Inc.
KUSHIONFLEX - Orthopedic products - Smith & Nephew Inc. (Rehabilitation Div.)
KUSMI - Teas - De Medici Imports Ltd.
KUSS - Mattresses ☆ - DLM Plastics Corp.
KUSTOM DEZIGNED - Jewelry - Arly Diamond Co.
KUSTOM-FIT KAPS - Smokestacks - Jomoco Products Co.
KUSTOM KAST - Hardware - Grandview Aluminum Products Inc.
KUSTOM KAT - Cat food - K-9 Kustom Mix Inc.
KUSTOM KOLOR - Paints - House of Kolor, Inc.
KUSTOMSORB - Containers - Duncan Environmental Services, Inc.
KUT - Wigs - Jean Paree Weegs Inc.
KUT-A-KEY - Tools - Medalist Industries Inc.
KUT & DRI - Cosmetics ☆ - Hydro-Tex Corp.
KUT-KOTE - Varnish removers - James B. Day and Co.
KUT 'N' SERVE - Kitchen utensils–aluminum - Molor Products Co.
KUT 'N TWINE - Twine - Baumgarten's
KUT NO MOR - Hair care products - Major/Advance International
KUTA - Cigarettes - G.A. Georgopulo & Co. Inc.
KUTALL - Saw blades ☆ - Spartan Saw Works Inc.
KUTANI CRANE - Dishes–china - Waterford Wedgewood USA, Inc.
KUTAPRESSIN - Pharmaceutical preparations - Schwarz Pharma
KUTE KIDDIE - Coats–children's - S. Rothschild & Co., Inc.
KUTMASTER - Knives - Utica Cutlery Co.
KUTRASE - Pharmaceutical preparations - Schwarz Pharma
KUTRIMMER - Office supplies - Michael Business Machines
KUTSIT - Knives ☆ - Newell Office Products
KUTTER - Lawn mowers - F.D. Kees Power Equipment LLC
KUTTER - Paintbrushes, rollers ☆ - Corona Brushes Inc.
KUTTO - Knives - Modern Specialties Co.
KUTZ RUST - Cleaning preparations ☆ - Savogran Co.
KUTZIT - Varnish removers - Savogran Co.
KUVERITE - Enamels - Dean and Barry Co.
KUZARI WORKSHOP - Judaica - Israeli Accents

KV-1 - Amplifiers - Klipsch and Associates Inc.
KV-2 - Audio equipment - Klipsch and Associates Inc.
KV-3 - Audio equipment - Klipsch and Associates Inc.
KVAL - Machinery - KVAL Inc.
KVIK - Housewares - Warner Manufacturing Co.
KVIKA - Tents - Coleman Co., Inc.
KVL - Beverages–alcohol - Distillerie Stock USA Ltd.
KW - Electronic equipment - KW Control Systems Inc.
KW - Jewelry - Kelly Waters, Inc.
KW - Toys - Paccar Inc.
KW, INC. - Apparel and accessories - Kik Wear, Inc.
KWAK BELGIUM - Beverages–malt - EFCO Importers
KWAL - Paints - Kwal-Howells Inc.
KWAL-KOTE - Paints ☆ - Kwal-Howells Inc.
KWAL-KRETE - Paints - Kwal-Howells Inc.
KWAL-LUSTRE - Paints ☆ - Kwal-Howells Inc.
KWAL-MARK - Varnishes ☆ - Kwal-Howells Inc.
KWALU - Furniture - Kwalu Inc.
KWAN SING - Tea kettles–nonelectric ☆ - Robinson Knife & Fiddlers Plastics
KWANGCHOW ENAMELS - Statuary - Seymour Mann Inc.
KWANZAA - Coffee - Pan American Coffee Co., Inc.
KWANZAA - Dolls - Golden Ribbon Playthings Inc.
KWANZAA PRIDE - Stationery - Kwanzaa Pride Co., Inc.
KWARE - Computer software - Robbins Industries, Inc.
KWARTET - Packaging–paper - C.L. Downey Co.
KWASHENKA - Dairy products - Lifeway Foods, Inc.
KWAST - Bakery products - Kwast American Bakeries Inc.
KWEI-LIN - Furniture ☆ - Bassett Furniture Industries, Inc.
KWELCOF - Pharmaceutical preparations - B.F. Ascher & Co. Inc.
KWELL - Pharmaceutical preparations - Reed & Carnrick
KWENCHER - Beverages - Golden Brands Marketing
KWESI - Toys–stuffed - ABC International Co.
KWIC-BRITE - Paint removers - Perry & Derrick Co.
KWICK CHECK - Computer software - Kohler Co.
KWICK-CLAMP - Fireplace equipment ☆ - Hy-C Co. Inc.
KWICK-KHORD - Musical instrument accessories - Carl Seeger Henry and Steven Toce Partnership
KWICK KLEAN - Filters–air - Air Kontrol Inc.
KWICK-SCALE - Musical instrument accessories - Carl Seeger Henry and Steven Toce Partnership
KWICK-SEAL - Sealing compounds - Briner Paint Manufacturing Co. Inc.
KWICKOFF - Varnish removers - Remien & Kuhnert Co.
KWIK - Adhesives and sealants - Adhesive Products, Inc.
KWIK - Batteries - Eastman Kodak Co.
KWIK - Beverages–malt - Cardo Trade Co.
KWIK - Paint removers - Klean-Strip
KWIK - Paints - Chemical Products Co.
KWIK-AID - Manicure preparations - Del Pharmaceuticals, Inc.
KWIK-BILT - Steel products - Kwik-Bilt Inc.
KWIK-BITS - Tools–hand-operated - Greenlee Textron Inc.
KWIK-BOLT - Hardware - Hilti Inc.
KWIK-BOND - Adhesives and sealants - Sig Manufacturing Inc.
KWIK-BOND - Glue–household or industrial - Columbia Cement Co. Inc.
KWIK BURN - Vitamins and nutritional supplements - Labrada Nutritional Systems, Inc.
KWIK-CHANGE - Couplings - Milton Industries Inc.
KWIK CHANGE - Knives–pocket - Allway Tools Inc.
KWIK CHUK - Tools–hand-operated - Alvord-Polk Inc.
KWIK CLASSIC FILLET - Meat products - G & W Packing Co., Inc.
KWIK CLIP - Office supplies - Mead Corp.
KWIK COMFORT - Heating equipment - Slant/Fin Corp.
KWIK-CON - Hardware ☆ - Hilti Inc.
KWIK COVER - Tents - Colorado Mineral Strike, Inc.
KWIK CYCLE - Tools–hand-operated - Greenlee Textron Inc.
KWIK-DAM - Bowling balls - Master Industries Inc.
KWIK-DRAW - Cases–binocular - Bausch & Lomb Inc.
KWIK-DRAW - Solder - Kester Solder Co.
KWIK DRI - Clay products ☆ - Golden Cat Corp.
KWIK-DRILLERS - Drills–electric - Hilti Inc.
KWIK-DRIVER - Tools–power-driven - Hilti Inc.
KWIK DRY - Adhesives and sealants - Chemray Coatings Corp.
KWIK-FAX - Binders ☆ - Boorum & Pease Co.
KWIK-FILL - Publisher's imprints - Elkay Plastics Co., Inc.
KWIK FIT - Exercising equipment - California Gym Equipment
KWIK-FIT - Motor vehicles–trucks - Superior Industries International, Inc.
KWIK-FIX - Caulking compounds - Blue Ridge Talc Co. Inc.

☆ = Now out of production

KWIK FIXERS - Audio equipment - Pro-Co. Sound Co. Inc.
KWIK FOAM - Insulating materials–foam - Dap Products Inc.
KWIK-GLAZE - Sugar–granulated, refined, or powdered - Sweetener Products Co.
KWIK-GLYDE - Tools–hand-operated ☆ - Buchanan Construction Products, Inc.
KWIK GOAL - Sporting goods - Kwik Goal, Ltd.
KWIK GOAL LIMITED - Soccer equipment - Kwik Goal, Ltd.
KWIK GRID - Tiles–ceiling - ICI Acrylics Inc.
KWIK-HEAT - Pharmaceutical preparations - Kwik-Kold Inc.
KWIK-IN - Thermostats - Brass Craft Manufacturing Co.
KWIK-JEL - Jams and jellies - White Stokes Co.
KWIK-KAP - Vitamins and nutritional supplements - Leiner Health Products Inc.
KWIK-KAPP - Paper products - Kwik-Kover Manufacturing Co.
KWIK KEY - Keys - Armament Systems and Procedures, Inc.
KWIK KILL - Insecticides ☆ - Mackwin Co.
KWIK KIT - Furniture - Stone City Products Inc.
KWIK KITS - Cakes - Coast Novelty Manufacturing Co.
KWIK KK KAMP - Pop-up campers and trailers - USA Venturcraft Corp.
KWIK-KLASP - Envelopes - Tension Envelope Corp.
KWIK KLEEN - Bars–iron - Crestline
KWIK KLEEN - Pet products - Charles Bland, III
KWIK KLEEN - Vacuum cleaners and accessories ☆ - Bissell Inc.
KWIK KLIP - Display cases–plastic ☆ - Equality/Stribbons
KWIK KLIP - Pet products - Leather Brothers Inc.
KWIK KLIP - Pins–safety - Star Tech
KWIK-KNOB - Tools - Granberg International
KWIK-KOLD - Health care products - Cramer Products Inc.
KWIK-KOLD - Ice - Kwik-Kold Inc.
KWIK-KOOK - Meat products–beef - Harris-Teeter Inc.
KWIK-KOPY PRINTING - Paper - Kwik Kopy Corp.
KWIK-KOTE - Adhesives and sealants - Davis Paint Co.
KWIK KOVER - Housewares ☆ - United Merchants and Manufacturers Inc.
KWIK KREAM - Specialty foods–canned - Saco Foods, Inc.
KWIK KUT - Cutlery - Cadie Products Corp.
KWIK-LITE - Flashlights - Fulton Industries Inc.
KWIK LOCK - Fencing–gates and posts - Mapes Industries Inc.
KWIK LOK - Archery equipment - Saunders Archery Co.
KWIK-LOK - Buckles - Indiana Mills & Manufacturing, Inc.
KWIK-LOK - Hardware - Indiana Marine Co. (Indiana Mills & Manufacturing)
KWIK-LOK II - Machine parts - Esco Corp.
KWIK-MARK - Pens - General Pencil Co.
KWIK-MASK - Hardware - Tufco Technologies Inc.
KWIK-N-EZY - Paints ☆ - Vogel Paint and Wax Co., Inc.
KWIK NOCK - Archery equipment - Saunders Archery Co.
KWIK-OFF - Paint removers - Jones Blair Co.
KWIK-OP - Door openers–electronic - Chase Industries, Inc.
KWIK OP - Door openers–electronic - Door Dynamics Inc.
KWIK-PLANTER - Tools–garden - Lefkow Specialties, Inc.
KWIK-PLEAT - Housewares ☆ - Barnhart Industries Inc.
KWIK-PLUG - Bowling balls - Master Industries Inc.
KWIK POT - Electrical equipment ☆ - Toastmaster Inc.
KWIK POWER - Gasoline - Kwik Shop Inc.
KWIK PRIME - Paints - Buten Paint & Wallpaper
KWIK-RAZE - Searchlights - Havis-Shields Equipment Corp.
KWIK-RITE - Pens - General Pencil Co.
KWIK-SAND - Paints ☆ - McCloskey Corp.
KWIK SCENT - Deodorants–personal - Surco Products Inc.
KWIK-SEAL - Boxes - U.S. Box Crafts Inc.
KWIK SEAL - Caulking compounds - Dap Products Inc.
KWIK-SET - Adhesives and sealants - Sig Manufacturing Inc.
KWIK SET - Cosmetics - Kaemark Inc.
KWIK SEW - Patterns–clothing - Kwik Sew Pattern Co. Inc.
KWIK-SHADE - Automotive parts and accessories - Wright Group, Inc.
KWIK SHADE - Tents - Colorado Mineral Strike, Inc.
KWIK SHEEN - Cleaning preparations - C.W. Parker Co.
KWIK-SHOT SOOT STOPPER - Cleaning preparations–household - Rutland Products
KWIK SILE - Animal feed supplements - Ronald W. Jones
KWIK-SKAN - Thermometers - Trademark Corp.
KWIK-SLIDE - Hitches–trailer - Reese Products, Inc.
KWIK SLITTER - Tools–hand-operated - Greenlee Textron Inc.
KWIK-SNAP - Office supplies - Accurate Business Forms Co. Inc.
KWIK SOLDER - Solder and flux paste - Vibe Records Inc.
KWIK-START - Fertilizers - Actagro, Inc.
KWIK STEP BITS - Tools–hand-operated - Greenlee Textron Inc.

KWIK STICK - Fishing tackle - South Bend Sporting Goods Inc.
KWIK STIK - Automotive parts and accessories ☆ - Fibre Glass-Evercoat Co. Inc.
KWIK-STIX - Fishing tackle - South Bend Sporting Goods Inc.
KWIK STOP - Pet products - Rich Health
KWIK STRIP - Paint removers - Morris Paint & Varnish Co.
KWIK SUPER-FAST - Paint removers - Klean-Strip
KWIK-TAK - Envelopes - Western States Envelope Co.
KWIK-TAPPER - Tools–power-driven - Hilti Inc.
KWIK-TINT - Paints ☆ - Waterlox Coatings Corp.
KWIK-TIP - Machine parts - Esco Corp.
KWIK-TIP - Paint sprayers - Dunn Edwards Corp.
KWIK-TONG - Office supplies - The Union Group
KWIK-TRACE - Craft supplies - Ramco Arts
KWIK TURF - Floor coverings–carpet and rugs ☆ - Olympic Carpets Inc.
KWIK-TWIST - Drills–electric ☆ - Smead Manufacturing Co.
KWIK TWIST - Mops - Northwestern Converting Co.
KWIK-WAY - Lawn mowers ☆ - K-W Manufacturing Co. Inc.
KWIK-WEIGH - Dollies–industrial - Aatlas Kwik-Weigh, Inc.
KWIK-WET - Electronic equipment ☆ - Edwal Scientific Products Corp.
KWIKAUDIT PRO - Electronic scale and calculator - B. Forrest Taylor
KWIKBOND - Adhesives and sealants - Kwik-Affix Products
KWIKBXS - Computer software - Higdon Realty Corp.
KWIKCUTTER - Machmeters - Henke Machine, Inc.
KWIKDRY - Enamels - Standard T Chemical Co. Inc.
KWIKEE - Motor vehicles - Kwikee Products Co., Inc.
KWIKEE - Paper–writing - Multi-Ad Services Inc.
KWIKEE KWIVER - Archery equipment - Kwikee-Kwiver Co., Inc.
KWIKEEZE - Cleaning preparations - Savogran Co.
KWIKER - Paints - Blue Ribbon Paint Co.
KWIKIE - Office supplies - A & W Products Co., Inc.
KWIKKAKES - Bakery products - Flowers Family Bakeries, Inc.
KWIKLINK - Electronic equipment - Christopher J. O'Connor
KWIKMIXER - Machine parts - Henke Machine, Inc.
KWIKMOLD - Latex - Adhesive Products, Inc.
KWIK'N EZ - Sealing compounds - Pittsburgh Corning Corp.
KWIKSERV - Ice chests–plastic - Coleman Co., Inc.
KWIKSET - Locks–padlocks - Kwikset Powdered Metal Products
KWIKSET - Musical instrument accessories - Micro Musical Products Corp.
KWIKSHREDDER - Machinery - Henke Machine, Inc.
KWIKSTAND - Traps–animal - United Industries Corp.
KWIKSTIK - Adhesives and sealants - Columbia Cement Co. Inc.
KWIKSTIK - Photographic equipment - Acme-Lite Manufacturing Co.
KWIKWAY - Paints - Graham Paint and Varnish Co.
KWIKWAY - Washboards ☆ - Columbus Washboard Co.
KWIKWORK - Enamels - Standard T Chemical Co. Inc.
KWIK'ZORB - Cleaning preparations - Minuteman Trading, Inc.
KWILT KREATIONS - Pillows - Alliance Development Corp.
KWIP - Skin care products - Omni-Tech Group, Inc.
KWIT - Insecticides - Scotts Co. (Organics Business Group)
KWIXSET - Cement - Hartline Products Co. Inc.
KWIXTURES - Lamp bulbs - Prestigeline Inc.
KWM - Jewelry - Kuo W.M. Co.
KWO - Giftware - Old World Christmas
KWONG ON TONG - Teas–herbal - Kwong on Tong Chinese Herbal Variety Corp.
KWONG SANG - Tea - American Roland Food Corp.
K.W.V. - Beverages–alcohol - Baum Wine Imports
KX - Screws and bolts - Emhart Inc.
KX SERIES - Sound equipment - DCM Corp.
KY-PRO - Paints - Kyanize Paint Co.
KY-SIL - Paper–gift wrap - Harold-Lawrence Associates Inc.
KYANIZE - Paints - Kyanize Paint Co.
KYANOIL - Paints - Kyanize Paint Co.
KYBA-KRUNCH - Veterinary feed supplement ☆ - American Equine Products Inc.
KYBER PASS - Floor coverings–carpet and rugs - Gulistan Carpet Inc.
KYBRUN - Paints ☆ - Kyanize Paint Co.
KYDD - Musical instruments - Kydd Products
KYDEX - Wallpaper ☆ - Rohm and Haas Co.
KYENNE - Fragrance ☆ - Redken Laboratories, Inc.
KYGRON - Paints ☆ - Kyanize Paint Co.
KYGUARD - Paints - Kyanize Paint Co.
KYKNOS - Food products - Krinos Foods, Inc.
KYLA - Dolls - Mattel, Inc.
KYLABARB - Pharmaceutical preparations - Kyle Laboratories Inc.

☆ = Now out of production

KYLADON - Pharmaceutical preparations - Kyle Laboratories Inc.

KYLAHIST - Pharmaceutical preparations - Kyle Laboratories Inc.

KYLAR - Plant growth regulators ☆ - Uniroyal Chemical Co. Inc. (Crop Protection Div.)

KYLATINIC IMPROVED - Pharmaceutical preparations - Kyle Laboratories Inc.

KYLATRATE - Pharmaceutical preparations - Kyle Laboratories Inc.

KYLAX - Pharmaceutical preparations - Kyle Laboratories Inc.

KYLE - Skin care products - Kyle Health Care Products Inc.

KYLE CROCODILE - Health care products - Apothecary Products, Inc.

KYLE PETTY - Toys ☆ - ERTL Co., Inc.

KYLECILLIN 250 - Pharmaceutical preparations - Kyle Laboratories Inc.

KYLEEN - Mouthwashes ☆ - Kyle Health Care Products Inc.

KYLEMORE - Earthenware ☆ - Waterford Wedgewood USA, Inc.

KYLICIN - Lip balms ☆ - Campbell Laboratories Inc.

KYLIX - Giftware - Sasaki

KYLOBEE - Pharmaceutical preparations - Kyle Laboratories Inc.

KYLOMYCIN - Pharmaceutical preparations - Kyle Laboratories Inc.

KYLOVITE PLUS - Pharmaceutical preparations - Kyle Laboratories Inc.

KYMERA - Computer software - Advanced Medical Systems, Inc.

KYNAR 500VLD - Resins–synthetic - Elf Atochem North America, Inc.

KYNATAL - Pharmaceutical preparations - Kyle Laboratories Inc.

KYNE SPORT - Golfing equipment - Kyne Sport Inc.

KYO - Lamps - Kyo Trading Co. Ltd., Inc.

KYO-CHROME - Pharmaceutical preparations - Wakunaga of America Co., Ltd.

KYO-CUT - Beauty shop equipment - Diane Products Inc.

KYO-DOPHILUS - Vitamins and nutritional supplements - Wakunaga of America Co., Ltd.

KYO-FLAX - Vitamins and nutritional supplements - Wakunaga of America Co., Ltd.

KYO-GINSENG - Vitamins and nutritional supplements - Wakunaga of America Co., Ltd.

KYO-GREEN - Vitamins and nutritional supplements - Wakunaga of America Co., Ltd.

KYOCERA - Computer peripheral equipment - Kyocera America Inc.

KYOLIC - Vitamins and nutritional supplements - Wakunaga of America Co., Ltd.

KYOLIC AGED GARLIC EXTRACT - Vitamins and nutritional supplements - Kyolic/Wakunaga

KYOLIC-EPA - Vitamins and nutritional supplements - Wakunaga of America Co., Ltd.

KYOSHO - Toys–automobiles ☆ - Motor Bikes Import

KYOTE DESIGNS - Jewelry - Austin Collection

KYOTO - Floor coverings–carpet and rugs ☆ - Cabin Crafts Carpets

KYOTO - Glassware–household - Durand International

KYOTO - Jewelry - Uncas Manufacturing Co.

KYOTO DREAMS - Wallpaper - Maya Romanoff Corp.

KYOTO GARDEN - Wallpaper - Advance Wallcoverings

KYPERCIL - Pharmaceutical preparations - Kyle Laboratories Inc.

KYPRIME - Paints - Kyanize Paint Co.

KYRANDIA - Computer storage devices–optical - Westwood Studios, Inc.

KYRIAZI FINAS - Cigarettes - G.A. Georgopulo & Co. Inc.

KYROL HI GLUTEN - Flour–blended - ConAgra Grain Co.

KYROLUX - House furnishings - Madden Corp.

KYRON - Fabrics ☆ - West Point-Pepperell Inc.

KYROPLUS - House furnishings - Madden Corp.

KYROPVC - House furnishings - Madden Corp.

KYSIL - Paints ☆ - Kyanize Paint Co.

KYSKA - Jewelry–costume - H.S. Strygler & Co. Inc.

KYSOR//BANGOR - Refrigerators - Kysor Industrial Corp.

KYSTRIP - Paint removers ☆ - Kyanize Paint Co.

KYTRIL - Pharmaceutical preparations - Smithkline Beecham Corp.

KYUSHO JITSU TUITE JITSU - Computer peripheral equipment - Oyata Enterprises, Inc.

KZ 400 SPECIAL - Motor vehicles ☆ - Kawasaki Motors Corp. USA

KZ TUFF KOTE - Paints - Kysor Industrial Corp.

KZK - Apparel–women's ☆ - Nitches, Inc.

KZP - Jewelry–precious - KZP

☆ = Now out of production

L

Addresses and phone numbers for the companies cited in the brands below
are available in the Company Listings section immediately following the brands listings.

L - Apparel and accessories - Logo 7 Inc.

L - Automotive parts and accessories - Littelfuse, Inc.

L - Facsimile equipment - Smith Corona Corp.

L - Jewelry - Liso Jewelry Manufacturing Corp.

L - Locksmithing hand tools - Lockmasters, Inc.

L - Motor vehicles–automobiles - Lon G. Myers

L - Publisher's imprints - Gerald Loren Fishkin

L - Shoes - Wolfgang Enterprise Inc.

L - Textile machinery - Lummus Corp.

L - Tools–hand-operated ☆ - Allied Wholesale Inc.

L-7 - Clarinets ☆ - G. Leblanc Corp.

L-7 - Coatings - American Grease Stick Co.

L-10 - Chemical preparations - Monogram Sanitation Co.

L-13 MC - Apparel and accessories - Bobby Anthony Kloetzly

L-33 - Sporting goods - Brine Inc.

L-50 - Tobacco - Fred Stoker & Sons, Inc.

L-56 - Recording label - Jazz Composer's Orchestra Association Inc.

L-2000 - Nail care products - Opi Products, Inc.

L-A-ROXX - Apparel and accessories - L.A. Roxx, Inc.

L. A. TEES - T-shirts–men's - Midstates Sportswear

L & A - Juices - L and A Juice Co. Inc.

L & A - Razor blades - Barber Razor Blade Co.

L & A - Skin care products ☆ - Hess Hair Milk Laboratories Inc.

L & B - Giftware - Loretz & Benoit

L. & C. HARDTMUTH - Pencils ☆ - Koh-I-Noor, Inc.

L & H - Pet products - L & H Packing Co.

L & J - Gauging instruments - L & J Engineering Inc.

L & J - Jewelry - L and J Manufacturing Co.

L & J - Wines - Monarch Wine Co. of Georgia

L & J LITE - Cookies - Fancy Foods of Virginia Inc.

L & L - Beef - L & L Packing Co.

L & L - Blackboards–slate - Master Addresser Co.

L & M - Adhesives and sealants - Mapei East Corp.

L & M - Cigarettes - Liggett Group Inc.

L & M - Labels–gummed - L & M Products

L & M 30'S - Cigarettes ☆ - Liggett Group Inc.

L & M CREATIONS - Figurines ☆ - Lipper International Inc.

L & M LIGHTS - Cigarettes - Liggett Group Inc.

L & M SUPERIOR - Cigarettes ☆ - Liggett Group Inc.

L & R - Recording label - Optimism Inc.

L & S - Fastener devices - Lord and Sons

L & S - Fishing lures - L & S Bait Co. Inc.

L & T - Shelving units–metal - Tennsco Corp.

L-ARGININE - Vitamins and nutritional supplements - Great Life Laboratories Inc.

L. B. EVANS - Footwear–men's - L.B. Evans' Son Co.

L-BONES - Furniture - David R. Downing and Lorraine A. Downing Partnership

L-BOW - Artists' materials - Stangren Co.

L. C. PAGE & CO. - Publisher's imprints - Farrar, Straus and Giroux Inc.

L-CATH - Catheters - Sims Deltec, Inc.

L. CLEAN - Skin care products ☆ - Dubl Duck/Jet Set Inc.

L-COM - Computer accessories - L-Com Inc.

L. DE VALLOUIT - Wines ☆ - William Grant & Sons, Inc.

L DESCHAUX - Wines - Leonard Kreusch, Inc.

L E G T O P PODEUM - Computer peripheral equipment - Rach, Inc.

L. E. SMITH - Glassware–household - L.E. Smith Glass Co.

+L' EXFOLIANT - Skin care products - Mastey De Paris

L-FILM - Polyester film sheets ☆ - W.R. Grace & Co.- Conn. (Cryovac Division)

L. G. HAIG - Shoes ☆ - Edison Brothers Stores, Inc.

+L. G. +WRIGHT GLASS - Lamps - L.G. Wright Glass Co.

L 'GANTE - Apparel–women's - Nardis, Inc.

L GATO - Boats - Glen-L Marine Designs

L. GISSELBRECHT - Wines - Winesellers Ltd.

L-GLUTAVITE - Pharmaceutical preparations ☆ - Berlex Laboratories, Inc.

+L' HYDRATE - Skin care products - Mastey De Paris

L-ISOLEUCINE - Pharmaceutical preparations - Spectrum Chemical Manufacturing Corp.

L. J. MINOR - Soups–mixes - F.I.S. Inc.

L. J. SIMONE NEW YORK - Handbags - L.J. Simone Inc.

L. J. SIMONE N.Y. - Footwear - L.J.S. Accessory Collection Inc.

L. JOSEF - Cellos and basses - Howard Core & Co. Inc.

L-K - Hotels and motels - Lodge Keeper Group, Inc.

L LATERALPRO TECHNOLOGY - Computer software - Mark Chang

L LEGACY - Tape players–cassette - Sony Music Entertainment Inc.

L LESHNER - Linen - Leshner Corp.

L LETO RNEAU - Machinery - Letourneau, Inc.

L LEXJET - Plastics film - Lexjet Corp.

L LIFESTYLE ACADEMY - Publisher's imprints - Lifestyle Academy Inc.

L LINAS - Skin care products - Eastern Pacific Marketing, Inc.

L LOCUS COMPUTING CORP. - Computer software - Locus Computing Corp.

L LUXURY WHEELS O.E. PLATING - Wheels–motor vehicle - Luxury Wheels O.E. Plating, Inc.

L/M ANIMAL FARMS - Bird feeds - L/M Animal Farms, Inc.

L. M. DICKSON - Sporting goods and fishing tackle - American Import Co.

L MAQUILLEUSE - Cosmetics - L. Maquilleuse

L. MAWBY - Beverages–alcohol - L. Mawby Vineyards-Winery

L-N - Windshields–glass - Orient Glass Inc.

L. NICHOLE FOR MEN - Wallpaper ☆ - Imperial Wallcoverings, Inc.

L. PALAIS - Wines - Alimar & Cie. Inc.

L-PER - Electronics equipment - L-Tronics

L-PHENYLALANINE - Vitamins and nutritional supplements - Great Life Laboratories Inc.

L. PISONI - Musical instrument accessories - Enzo Pizzi

L. POWELL - Giftware - L. Powell Co.

L R - Toys - Learning Resources, Inc.

L/R CAST - Concrete–mixture - P-G Industries, Inc.

L/R RAM - Concrete–mixture - P-G Industries, Inc.

L REPORT - Publisher's imprints - Lambesis, Inc.

L. ROEDERER CRISTAL - Wines ☆ - European Beverage Co., Inc.

L/S - Pumps - Cole-Parmer Instrument Co.

L/S - Skin care products - Waverly Beauty Products

L-S-C - Lubricants ☆ - Radiator Specialty Co.

L-S-C - Thread - Cincinnati Thread Co.

L. S. TUCCI - Product description unknown - Leonard S. Tucci

L SERIES - Air conditioning equipment - Lennox Industries Inc.

L-STATION - Electronic equipment ☆ - Steck-Vaughn/EDL

L-TEC ELECTRONICS - Audio equipment - Barry Fishman

L-TORO - Pens ☆ - K-9 Pen Co.

L-TRA - Electronic components - Coilcraft Inc.

L-TRYPTOPHAN - Vitamins and nutritional supplements ☆ - Natrol, Inc.

L-ZYMO GENIC - Health care products - Pacific Genesis Inc.

L2 - Apparel and accessories - Levi Strauss & Co.

☆ = Now out of production

L2 - Computer software - National Science Center Foundation Inc.
L2 - Tool boxes - Artcadi Products
L100 - Electronic equipment - Olympus America Inc.
L200 - Electronic equipment - Olympus America Inc.
L250 - Electronic equipment - Olympus America Inc.
L400 - Electronic equipment - Olympus America Inc.
L737 - Frames—eyeglass - Rozin Optical Export Corp.
L747 - Frames—eyeglass - Rozin Optical Export Corp.
L757 - Frames—eyeglass - Rozin Optical Export Corp.
LA - Apparel and accessories - Los Angeles Dodgers, Inc.
LA - Bags—duffel - L.A. Gear, Inc.
L.A. - Beverages—malt ☆ - Anheuser-Busch Companies Inc.
LA - Guitars - MBT International, Inc.
LA-12 - Pharmaceutical preparations - Hyrex Pharmaceuticals
L.A. 37 - Apparel—athletic - Kass and Co.
LA ABRA - Wines - La Abra Farm & Winery Inc.
LA ADHESIVE - Glue—household or industrial ☆ - Bond Adhesives Co.
LA & R - Jewelry - Newstedt Loring Andrews
L.A. BAG - Handbags - Tandem Imports Corp.
LA BAG - Leather goods - Hugo Bosca Co., Inc.
LA BALANCE - Hair care products - Cosmair Inc.
LA BALEINE - Salt - Liberty Richter Inc.
LA BALLADE - Cosmetics - Cosmair Inc.
LA BANDERITA - Food products - Ole Mexican Foods, Inc.
LA BARGE - Furniture ☆ - Masco Corp.
LA BARONESS - Calendars - House of Doolittle
LA BASTILLE - Footwear - French Dressing Inc.
LA BELLA - Bread crumbs - Jason Dairy Products Co. Inc.
LA BELLA - Footwear - M & R Shoes Inc.
LA BELLA - Musical instrument accessories - E. & O. Mari Inc.
LA BELLA - Shampoos - Golden Sun Vitamins
LA BELLA DONNA NATURALE THERAPY - Cosmetics - La Bella Donna Naturale Therapy, Ltd.
LA BELLA ROSA - Pasta - American Beauty Macaroni
LA BELLA ROSA - Pasta - Homestead, Inc.
LA BELLA VILLA - Food products - Unifax, Inc.
LA BELLAROSA - Macaroni ☆ - Pastamania
LA BELLE - Bags—duffel - Holiday Fair, Inc.
LA BELLE - Hats ☆ - Bee Hat Co.
LA BELLE - Wines - Raymond Vineyard and Cellar Inc.
LA BELLE - Women's shoes - Thos. Cort Inc.
LA BELLE FRANCE - Cheese - Universal Foods Corp.
LA BELLE MAISON - Wallpaper - Stroheim & Romann, Inc.
LA BELLE SANDRINE - Cordials - Crown Capital USA Inc.
LA BERBERINE COTES DU RHONE - Wines - Bercut-Vandervoort & Co.
LA BIBLIA DE LAS AMERICAS - Publisher's imprints - Lockman Foundation
LA BIOSTETIQUE - Skin care products - Laboratoire Biosthetique Ltd.
LA BLANCA - Bathing suits - Apparel Ventures, Inc.
LA BLANCHE - Cosmetics - Peck Skin Insititute
LA BO DE - Soy sauce - Chan Phong Food Co.
LA BOITE MAGIQUE - Perfumes - Lancome
LA BONTE - Cheese - Swissrose International Inc.
L.A. BOP - Hair care products - Giovanni Cosmetics Inc.
LA BOU - Coffee - World of Good Taste Inc.
LA BOUCHERE - Housewares ☆ - Washington Forge Inc.
LA BOULI - Bakery products - World of Good Taste Inc.
LA BOUTIQUE - Apparel and accessories ☆ - Design Circle Ltd.
LA BRERA - Pasta - Teresa's II , Inc.
L.A. BRIEF - Attache cases - TJC, Inc.
L.A. BRITES - Cameras - Vivitar Corp.
LA BUENA VIDA VINEYARDS - Wines - La Buena Vida Vineyards
LA BUNRITA - Food products - Reser's Fine Foods Inc.
LA BUONA CUCINA - Aprons ☆ - Now Designs
LA BUSSIERE - Floor coverings - Parquet de France Inc.
LA CADE - Hair care products - Eden Beauty Products
LA CADE ULTRA - Hair care products - Eden Beauty Products
LA CAJA DE CUENTOS - Publisher's imprints - Wright Group Publishing, Inc.
LA CAJA DE CUENTOS - Publisher's imprints - Thomas C. Wright, Inc.
LA CALENITA - Cheese - S & F Diaz Inc.
LA CALZADA - Beverages—alcohol ☆ - Distributors & Condal Imports
LA CAMPANELLA - Ceramic tile ☆ - Integrity Tile Co.
LA CANASTA - Potato chips - La Canasta of Minnesota, Inc.
+LA CANASTA - Tortillas - Sparta Foods, Inc.
LA CANTINA - Salad dressings—bottled - D'Forte/La Cantina Brands
LA CARAVELLE - Glassware—household - ACC
LA CARIBENA - Apparel—women's - La Caribena Ltd.

LA CARRE - Underwear and nightwear ☆ - Korex Corp.
LA CARTE DE FRANCE - Computer software ☆ - Gessler Publishing Co., Inc.
LA CASA - Floor coverings—carpet and rugs - Foreign Accents
LA CASA - Motor vehicles—motor homes - Brougham Industries Inc.
LA CASA BROWN - Dinnerware—glass ☆ - Metlox Pottery Shoppe
LA CASA GRANDE - Food products - Bunker Hill Foods
LA CASITA - Tomato pastes and sauces - Sunset Food & Beverage Corp.
LA CASITA'S - Tortillas - La Casita's Homestyle Mexican Foods Inc.
LA-CE-EDGE - Lace ☆ - Narrow Fabric Industries Inc.
LA-CE-LASTIC - Fabrics ☆ - Narrow Fabric Industries Inc.
LA CENA - Wines - La Cena Fine Foods Inc.
LA CHANTEUSE - Dolls ☆ - Bradley Import Co.
LA CHASE - Floor coverings—carpet and rugs ☆ - Trans-Ocean Import Co. Inc.
LA CHATEAU - Furniture ☆ - Broyhill Furniture Industries, Inc.
LA CHATTE - Boats - Glen-L Marine Designs
LA CHEDDA - Cheese - Land O'Lakes Inc.
LA CHEESERIE - Cheese - Bongrain Cheese USA
LA CHEMISE BLANCHE - Apparel—women's - La Chemise Blanche
LA CHIARA - Wines ☆ - William Grant & Sons, Inc.
LA CHICA - Tortillas - Del Rey Tortilleria Inc.
LA CHIP - Frozen confectioneries - International Ice Cream Corp.
LA CHIRIPADA WINERY - Wines - La Chiripada Winery
LA CHOCOLATE - Yogurt ☆ - Johanna Foods, Inc.
LA CHOY - Chow mein - Hunt-Wesson, Inc.
LA CHOY - Food products - La Choy Food Products Co.
LA CIGALE - Bakery products - J.S.K. Trading Corp.
L.A. CINNAMON BREAD - Breads - Swatt Baking Co.
LA CLASSICS - Wallpaper ☆ - Bolta Wallcoverings
LA CLASSIQUE - Musical instrument accessories - GHS Strings
LA CLOISONNE - Lamps - Kaadan Ltd.
LA-CO - Solder - La-Co Industries, Inc.
LA-CO LOC - Adhesives and sealants - La-Co Industries, Inc.
LA COCINA - Snack foods - Fiesta Foods Inc.
LA COCINA DE MC MCCORMICK - Spices and extracts - McCormick & Co., Inc.
LA COCINA REAL - Seasonings ☆ - McCormick & Co., Inc.
LA COLLECTION FRANCAISE - Wallpaper - Tony Putnam Inc.
LA COLMENA - Food products - La Colmena, Inc.
LA COLOMBE TORREFACTION - Coffee - La Colombe Torrefaction, Inc.
LA COMEDIE FRANCAISE - Recording label - Everest Record Group
LA COMIDA - Flowers, plants, and seeds - White Swan, Ltd.
LA CONCHA - Food products - Gourmet America
LA-CONS - Containers - Loritz and Associates, Inc.
LA COPA QUE CRECE - Apparel—women's - Wacoal America Inc.
LA COPITA - Wines - Southwest Distributing Inc.
LA CORNEILLE - Artists' materials - Loew-Cornell Inc.
LA CORONA - Cigar boxes—wood - Consolidated Cigar Corp.
LA CORONA - Milk - La Corona Foods Inc.
LA CORRIDA DE TOROS - Computer software ☆ - Gessler Publishing Co., Inc.
LA CORTINA - Drapery hardware ☆ - Spring Window Fashions Division, Inc.
LA COSECHITA - Food products - Reynoso Bros. International
LA COSTA - Floor coverings—carpet and rugs - Western Carpet Mills
LA COSTA - Food products - Del Monte Corp.
LA COSTA - Occasional tables - JDI Group, Inc.
LA COSTA - Shoes ☆ - Daniel Green Co.
LA COSTA - Skin care products - Lever Brothers Co. Inc.
LA COSTA - Window shades ☆ - John Dixon Inc.
LA COUTELLERIE - Cutlery ☆ - Imperial Schrade Corp.
LA COVINA - Leather goods - Home Shopping Club, Inc.
LA CRASIA - Gloves - La Crasia Inc.
LA CREMA - Wines - Kendall Jackson Winery, Ltd.
LA CREMA VINERA - Wines - La Crema Vinera
LA CREME - Whipped topping—frozen - Pet Inc.
LA CREME RICHE - Cosmetics - Lancome
LA CREOLE - Fruits—frozen ☆ - Westar Foods Inc.
LA CRESCENTA - Floor coverings—carpet and rugs - Western Carpet Mills
LA CROIX - Cigarette papers - American Tobacco Co.
LA CROIX - Hardware ☆ - Amerock Corp.
LA CROIX - Water—bottled or canned - WinterBrook Beverage Group
LA CROIX - Water—mineral - The Stroh Brewery Co.
LA CROSSE - Bicycles - Murray, Inc.
LA CROSSE - Cosmetics - Redi Products Laboratories
LA CROSSE FOOTWEAR - Footwear - La Crosse Footwear, Inc.

☆ = Now out of production

LA CROSSE PREMIUM WATER - Water–bottled or canned - Western Wisconsin Water Conditioning, Inc.

LA CUBANA - Cigarettes - G.A. Georgopulo & Co. Inc.

LA CUESTA - Coffee - Ag Trading, Inc.

LA CUISINE - Cooking utensils–aluminum ☆ - Mirro Corp.

LA CUISINE - Cutlery ☆ - Imperial Schrade Corp.

LA CULINAIRE - Hardware ☆ - Vance Industries Inc.

LA CURVE - Razor Now out of production ☆ - American Safety Razor Co.

LA CUTICLE - Nail care products - La Cuticle Inc.

L.A. DAYS - Sunglasses - Face 2 Face Corp.

LA DECEMA - Cigars - A.J. Golden Inc.

LA DEE DA BABY COLLECTION - Infant product - Michel & Co.

LA DELICIA - Candy ☆ - Tower Candy Co.

LA DEMOISELLE - Wines - House of Burgundy Inc.

L.A. DESIGN - Pet products - Vo-Toys Inc.

L.A. DEZONE - Pharmaceutical preparations ☆ - Solvay Pharmaceuticals Inc.

L.A. DIAMANTE - Footwear - L.A. Diamante Inc.

LA DIFFERENCE - Floor coverings–carpet and rugs ☆ - Masland Corp.

LA DIFFERENCE - Hair care products - Waverly Beauty Products

LA DIFFERENCE - Perfumes - Palm Beach La Difference Inc.

LA DIFFERENCE - Wallpaper ☆ - Capital Carousel Inc.

LA DIFFERENCE - Wallpaper ☆ - Jolie Papier

LA DIP - Ice-cream sandwiches - International Ice Cream Corp.

LA DOLCE VITA - Salad dressings–bottled - Korbro Oil Corp.

LA DONITA - Shoes - Sunsand Shoe Corp.

LA DONNA - Floor coverings–carpet and rugs ☆ - Olympic Carpets Inc.

LA DONNA - Footwear - Baris Shoe Co. Inc.

LA DOOR - Doors–metal - Wing Industries, Inc.

LA DOOR - Giftware - Wing Industries Inc.

LA ESPECIAL - Food products - Vlasic Foods Inc.

LA ESTELLA - Soccer equipment - Mikasa Sports

L.A. EXPRESS - Jewelry - AAI

L.A. EXPRESS - Sunglasses - M.Z. Berger & Co. Inc.

LA FACTANO - Tiles–ceramic ☆ - Maxsam Sales, Inc.

LA FAMA - Candy - Palmer Candy Co.

LA FAMIGLIA DI ROBERT MONDAVI - Wines - Robert Mondavi Winery

LA FAMOSA - Fruit drinks–bottled or canned - Borden, Inc.

LA FAMOUS - Tortillas - Borden, Inc.

LA FAYETTE - Sprinklers–lawn - La Fayette Brass Co. Inc.

LA FAYETTE - Wines - La Fayette Vineyards & Winery

LA FE - Food products - Gonzalez & Tapanes Inc.

LA FEMME - Cosmetics - La Femme Cosmetics Inc.

LA FEMME - Frames–picture ☆ - Acme Frame Products, Inc.

LA FEMME BOUTIQUE - Skin care products ☆ - Van Guard Studios of North Carolina

LA FEMME DE VANITY FAIR - Apparel and accessories ☆ - Vanity Fair Mills Inc.

LA FENDRICH - Cigars - National Cigar Corp.

LA FERME GOURMANDE - Food products - Gourmand Inc.

LA FIEGE - Skin care products - Retha Ray Fiege

LA FIESTA - Cheese - Nelson-Ricks Creamery Co.

LA FIESTA - Dried beans - KBL Trading and Processing Co.

LA FIESTA - Onions - Seville Olive Co.

LA FIESTA - Tiles–ceramic ☆ - American Olean Tile Co.

LA FIESTA - Tortillas - Gruma Corp.

LA FIGURA - Underwear and nightwear - Rago Foundations Inc. LLC

LA FITE - Dishes–china - Sterling China Co. Inc.

LA FITTE - Ships–sailing vessels - La Fitte Yachts Inc.

L.A. FLAME - Apparel and accessories - L.A. Gear, Inc.

LA FLEUR - Housewares - Analab Inc.

LA FLEUR - Wines - Wines Ltd.

LA FLOR - Greeting cards - American Greetings Corp.

+LA FLORALIE - Wines ☆ - Parliament Import Co.

LA FOGATA - Sauces - La Fogata, Inc.

LA FONTAINE FOR MEN - Cologne - Jean Philippe Fragrances, Inc.

LA FONTANA - Cigars - Caribe Imported Cigars, Inc.

LA FORCE - Footwear–women's - Famolare Inc.

LA FOREST - Food products - Campbell Soup Co.

LA FOREST PERIGORD - Food products - Campbell Soup Co.

LA FORME - Hair care products - Helene Curtis Industries Inc.

LA FORMIDABLE - Cosmetics - Nino Originals

LA FORNARINA - Wines - House of Burgundy Inc.

LA FRANCESCA - Wines - W.J. Deutsch & Sons Ltd.

LA FRESQUITA - Beverages–alcohol - Sierra Wine Corp.

LA FRONTERA - Wines - Seven Lakes Vineyard

LA GADGETERIE - Housewares ☆ - Imperial Schrade Corp.

LA GARDE - Leather goods - AR Accessories Group Inc.

LA GARDE - Leather goods - Rolfs Leather Products

LA GARZA - Rice - Newfield Partners, Ltd.

LA GATE - Apparel and accessories - L.A. Gate Fashion Inc.

L.A. GEAR - Apparel and accessories - L.A. Gear, Inc.

L.A. GEAR - Socks - Moretz Hosiery Mills Inc.

LA GELATINA - Gelatin - Bela Corp.

LA GENTILE - Nuts–salted, roasted, cooked, or canned - De Choix Specialty Foods Co.

LA GERLA - Wines - House of Burgundy Inc.

LA GLORIETTE - Giftware - French & Pacific Trading Corp.

L.A. GRAB - Hair care products - Giovanni Cosmetics Inc.

LA GRANDE COUPE - Kitchen cutlery items - C.S.B. Commodities Inc.

LA GRANGE - Bathtubs–enameled - CR-PL L.P.

LA GRANGE - Furniture ☆ - Bassett Furniture Industries, Inc.

LA GUARDIA - Wines - C. Daniele & Co., Inc.

LA GUILLOTINE - Computer software - Gessler Publishing Co., Inc.

LA GUSTOSA - Food products - Pet Inc.

LA GYMMEES - Apparel and accessories - L.A. Gymmees

LA HABRA STUCCO - Adhesives and sealants - La Habra Products, Inc.

LA HABRA WALL - Coatings - La Habra Products, Inc.

LA HAYE - Pharmaceutical preparations - LaHaye Laboratories Inc.

+LA HEALTH SNAX - Cookies - Health Snax

LA HOJA SELECTA - Cigars - P. Cerlis Corp.

LA HONDA - Wood products - Simpson Timber Co.

L.A. HORNS - Musical instruments - L.A. Sax Co.

LA HUDA! - Apparel and accessories - Flavorit Product, Inc.

LA INA - Wines ☆ - Domecq Importers Inc.

LA INDIA - Food products - La India

L.A. INTIMATES - Apparel and accessories - Kellwood Co.

LA ITALIA - Coffee makers–electric - Salton/Maxim Housewares, Inc.

LA ITALIA - Meat products–beef - Gallo Salame Inc.

LA ITALIA - Sausages - Saramar Corp.

LA JEUNESSE - House furnishings ☆ - Lea Industries Inc.

LA JOLLA - Dishes–china - Brastoff Designs Inc.

LA JOLLA - Fabrics - Thompson of California Inc.

LA JOLLA - Floor coverings–carpet and rugs ☆ - Atlas Carpet Mills Inc.

LA JOLLA - Food products - Mexi-Frost Specialties Co.

LA JOLLA - House furnishings ☆ - Lexington Furniture Industries, Inc.

LA JOLLA - Pet products - La Jolla Group Inc.

LA JOLLA - Tiles–ceramic ☆ - Porcelanite, Inc.

LA JOLLA CLUB - Golfing equipment - La Jolla Club, Ltd.

LA JOLLA DESERT GOURMET - Wood products - La Jolla Group Inc.

LA JOLLA GOURMET - Pet products - La Jolla Group Inc.

LA JOLLA MUSIC - Publisher's imprints - Neil A. Kjos Music Co.

LA JOLLA TRADITIONS N E S W - Apparel and accessories - Westbury Knitwear Co. Inc.

LA KOSTA - Wallpaper - Koroseal Wallcoverings

LA-KRI-SAN - Tobacco products - James B. Russell Inc.

LA LACE - Brassieres (Bras) - Montgomery Ward & Co. Inc.

LA LADERA ESTATE - Wines - Chiavario Vineyards

L.A. LADY - Footwear–women's - Argyris Inc.

LA LANNE - Breads - American Bakeries Co.

LA LANZA - Drapery hardware ☆ - Spring Window Fashions Division, Inc.

L.A. LAW - Computer software - Capstone Software

LA-LED - Steel products - LaSalle Steel Co.

LA LEG - Hosiery - La Leg Ltd.

L.A. LIGHTING - Lighting fixtures - Beverly Hills Fan Co.

L.A. LIGHTS - Beverages–carbonated - Beverage Alternatives, Inc.

L.A. LIGHTS - Footwear - L.A. Gear, Inc.

LA LINDA - Snack foods - Mexican Food Manufacturing of Omaha Inc.

LA LLAVA - Coffee - F. Gavina and Sons Inc.

LA LOMA - Gravy - Worthington Foods Inc.

L.A. LOOKS - Hair care products - Dep Corp.

LA LOUISIANE - Recording label - La Louisiane Records & Studio

L.A. LUCKY FARMER BRAND - Meat products - L.A. Lucky Trading, Inc.

LA LUEUR - Skin care products - La Lueur International Inc.

LA MACHINE - Food products - Regal Ware, Inc.

LA MACRAME - Garden equipment ☆ - Rubens Originals

LA MAGNITA - Cigars - National Cigar Corp.

LA MAISON - Furniture ☆ - Bernhardt Industries

LA MAISON - Silverware - Ginkgo International Ltd.

LA MAISON - Wallpaper - Parkview Designs

LA MAISON LA CUISINE BELLE ET BONNE - Tea kettles–nonelectric - Roshco, Inc.

LA MANCHA - Cigar boxes–wood ☆ - Consolidated Cigar Corp.

LA MANCHA - Dinnerware–glass ☆ - Metlox Pottery Shoppe
LA MANCHA - Guitars - Multivox/Sorkin Music Co. Inc.
LA MANCHA - Guitars - Jerry Roberts Guitars
LA MAR - Suits–women's - Bowdon Manufacturing Co.
LA MARCA - Food products - Design Foods
LA MARCA - Wines - Tyfield Importers
LA MARCA DEL LOBO - Beverages–malt - Anheuser-Busch Companies Inc.
LA MARCHE - Converters–electric - Judaulf Trademark Partnership
LA MARCHE - Electronic equipment - La Marche Manufacturing Co.
LA MAREE - Clocks - Ridgeway Clock Co.
LA MARNE - Vinegar ☆ - Liberty Richter Inc.
LA MARNE CHAMPAGNE VINEGAR - Vinegar - Europa Foods Ltd.
LA MARNE CORNICHONS - Fruits and vegetables - Europa Foods Ltd.
LA MARQUE - Watches - La Marque Watch Co. Inc.
LA-MART - Apparel–men's ☆ - Lacy Corp.
LA MARTINIQUE - Salad dressings–bottled - Wm. B. Reily & Co. Inc.
LA MARZOCCO - Coffee makers–electric - La Marzocco International
LA MAS FRIA! - Beer - Miller Brewing Co.
LA MAXIMILIANA - Cigars - Cigars of Honduras, Inc.
+LA MELODIA - Musical instruments - Fender Musical Instruments
LA MELODIE - Apparel–children's ☆ - Eagle Knitting Mills Inc.
LA MENAGERIE - Apparel and accessories - Richton International Corp.
LA MER - Brushes–paint - M. Grumbacher Inc.
LA MER - Toilets–enameled - Gerber Plumbing Fixtures Corp.
LA MESA - Floor coverings ☆ - Congoleum Corp.
LA MESA - Food products - Del Monte Corp.
LA MESA - Furniture ☆ - Bassett Furniture Industries, Inc.
LA MESA - Wines ☆ - Safeway Stores Inc.
LA MEXICANITA - Food products - Intermex Products, Inc.
LA MICHOACANA - Tortillas - La Michoacana Tortilla Bakery
LA MINERVA - Housewares - Glen Mills Inc.
LA MIRADA - Luggage - Airway Industries, Inc.
LA MIRAGE - Floor coverings–carpet and rugs ☆ - World Carpets, Inc.
LA MODE - Buttons - Blumenthal/Lansing Co.
LA MODE - Dolls ☆ - Creative Playthings Ltd.
LA MODE - Thread - Belding Heminway Co. Inc.
LA MODENESE - Beverages–alcohol - Valley Cheese, Wine & Food Co.
LA MONDIALE - Boots ☆ - Miura Sports Inc.
LA MONEGASQUE - Food products - De Choix Specialty Foods Co.
LA MONICA - Wines - Chatham Imports, Inc.
LA MONNAIE DE PARIS - Jewelry - Puiforcat
LA MOUSSE - Bakery products - La Mousse
LA MOY - Cosmetics - Neo Derma Laboratories, LLC
L.A. NAIL CREATIONS - Nail-care products - International Beauty Design, Inc.
LA NAPOLETANA - Food products - Pastene Companies Ltd.
LA NAPOLETANA - Pasta - Pastene Companies Ltd.
LA NATURA - Skin care products - New Fragrance Continental, Inc.
LA NATURAL - Food products - Cheese Smokers Inc.
LA NEWBORN - Dolls - Barval Toys Inc.
L.A. NIGHTS - Apparel and accessories - Kellwood Co.
LA NINA OUR DARLING - Flour–blended - Stevens Industries Inc.
LA NUIT - Perfumes - Paco Rabanne Parfums
LA NUIT - Watches - Advance Watch Co. Ltd.
L.A. NUT BINS - Food products - Dairy Fresh Products Co.
L.A. OBSERVER, THE - Publisher's imprints - New York Observer Co., Inc.
LA PAGODA - Window shades ☆ - Colony Shade Co.
LA PAILLE D'OR - Cookies - Sunshine/Salerno Inc.
L.A. PAINTS - Apparel and accessories - Pandelco, Inc.
LA PALAPA - Apparel–women's - Humberto De Las Mercedes Gonzalez
LA PALINA - Cigar boxes–wood - Consolidated Cigar Corp.
LA PALMA DE ORO - Cigars - Cuban Cigar Factory, Inc.
LA PARADE - Floor coverings–carpet and rugs - Masland Corp.
LA PAREE - Musical instruments - David Wexler & Co.
LA PARFUMERIE - Perfumes - Preview Products
LA PARIS - Serving carts - Robert D. Murray & Associates
LA PARISIENNE - Wallpaper ☆ - Decor International Wallcovering Inc.
LA PAROT - Hair care products - Keystone Laboratories Inc.
LA PARRILLA AUTHENTIC CARNE SECA NORTHERN STYLE - Meat products–beef - New Lion International
LA PASTA MACHINE - Kitchen appliances ☆ - Regal Ware, Inc.
LA PAZ - Cigarettes - G.A. Georgopulo & Co. Inc.
LA PAZ - Floor coverings–carpet and rugs - Wunda Weve Carpet Co.
LA PAZ - Mexican food products - La Paz Products
LA PELLICIA - Yarn - William Unger & Co. Inc.
LA PERLA - Food products - Scally Imperial Importing Co.
LA PERLA - Meat products–cured - Continental Deli Foods, Inc.

LA PERLA CLASSIC - Perfumes - La Parfumerie Inc.
LA PERLE - Jewelry, watches - Universe International Inc.
LA PERRUCHE - Sugar–granulated, refined, or powdered - Gourmet America
LA PETITE - Brassieres (Bras) - Lady Marlene
LA PETITE - Buttons - Blumenthal/Lansing Co.
LA PETITE - Cream - Oberlin Farms Dairy Inc.
LA PETITE - Depilatories - Spilo/Mehaz Worldwide
LA PETITE - Floor coverings–carpet and rugs ☆ - Bellbridge Carpets
LA PETITE - Furniture ☆ - Bassett Furniture Industries, Inc.
LA PETITE - Jewelry - Jacoby-Bender Inc.
LA PETITE - Watches - Bulova Corp.
LA PETITE - Window coverings - Wrisco Industries Inc.
LA PETITE BOULANGERIE - Coffee - Java City
LA PETITE BY HOBE - Jewelry ☆ - Hobe Cie. Ltd.
LA PETITE FEMME - Eyeglasses - Windsor Optical Inc.
LA PETITE FLEUR - Apparel and accessories ☆ - Design Circle Ltd.
LA PETITE HIPPO - Publisher's imprints - La Petite Hippo, Inc.
LA PETITE ROMANCE DE PARIS - Apparel stores–lingerie - Gold Seal Garter Corp.
LA PHONE - Telephones - Cathay International
LA PICCOLINA - Food products - La Piccolina and Co. Inc.
LA PINA - Flour–blended - General Mills, Inc.
LA PIPETTE - Candy ☆ - Finnfoods Div.
LA PIRAMIDE - Tortillas - Ver-Mex Food Inc.
LA PIZZA LOCA - Pizzas–mixes - La Pizza Loca, Inc.
L.A. PIZZA REVUE - Restaurants–pizzerias - Robert J. Mandell
LA PIZZERIA - Pasta ☆ - Ore-Ida Foods, Inc.
LA PLACITA MEXICANA - Vegetables–canned - Goya Foods, Inc.
LA PLAIDE - Floor coverings–carpet and rugs ☆ - Blue Ridge Carpet Mills
LA PLATE - Disposable dishes and cups - James River Corp.
LA PLAYA - Fabrics - Dan River Inc.
LA PLAYA - Musical instruments - LPD Music International
LA PLUCK - Skin care products - Tweezerman Corp.
LA PLUME - Fabrics ☆ - Stylecrest Fabrics Ltd.
LA PLUME DE PORTHAULT - Bedding–linen - Dan River Inc.
LA POINT O'BRIEN - Sporting goods ☆ - O'Brien International
LA POMMERAIE - Liquors - William Grant & Sons, Inc.
LA PORTE - Furniture - Homecrest Industries Inc.
LA POSADA - Vinegar ☆ - Liberty Richter Inc.
LA POSADA SHERRY WINE VINEGAR - Vinegar - Europa Foods Ltd.
LA POUFFETTE - Apparel–women's - Wacoal America Inc.
LA PRAIRIE - Skin care products - La Prairie Inc.
LA PREFERIDA - Food products - La Preferida Inc.
LA PRIMA - Cosmetics ☆ - Marianna Imports, Inc.
LA PRIMA - Floor coverings–carpet and rugs - Tuftex Carpet Mills, Inc.
LA PRIMA - Footwear - M & R Shoes Inc.
LA PRIMA - Liquors - Paramount Distillers Inc.
LA PRIMADORA - Cigars - Swisher International, Inc.
LA PRIMAVERA - Food products - Pepper Source
LA PRINCESA - Shampoos ☆ - Golden Sun Vitamins
LA PROVENCE - Watches - North American Watch Corp.
LA PURA FRIA - Beverages–malt ☆ - Anheuser-Busch Companies Inc.
LA QUESTA - Wines - Woodside Vineyards
LA QUINTA - Hotels and motels - La Quinta Inns Inc.
L.A. RAYS - Sunglasses - Face 2 Face Corp.
L.A. RAYS ORIGINALS - Sunglasses - Face 2 Face Corp.
LA REGINA - Macaroni ☆ - Paramount Macaroni Co. Inc.
LA REGINA'S - Vinegar - Golden Whisk Pasta Partners
LA REINE - Flatware ☆ - Wallace International Silversmiths, Inc.
LA REINE - Glassware–household ☆ - Anchor Hocking Glass, Inc.
L.A. RESCUE - Bags–duffel - L.A. Rescue, Inc.
LA RESERVA DE LA FAMILIA DE JOSE CUERVO - Beverages–alcohol - Heublein, Inc.
LA RESTAURANTE - Tortillas - Curtice-Burns Foods, Inc.
LA RHAPSODIE - Cosmetics - Cosmair Inc.
LA RINASCENTE - Flour–blended ☆ - Liberty Richter Inc.
LA RINASCENTE SEMOLINA FLOUR - Bakery products - Europa Foods Ltd.
LA ROCCA - Wines - La Rocca Wine Co.
LA ROCHELLE - Floor coverings - Mannington Resilient Floors
LA ROCK - Electronic equipment - Diversified Specialists, Inc.
LA ROMAGNOLA - Pasta - Consolidated Food Management Corp.
LA ROMANA REDS - Food products - Golden Whisk Pasta Partners
LA ROND - Dishes–china ☆ - Pickard Inc.
LA RONDA - Cigars - Consolidated Cigar Corp.
LA RONDE - Wigs - Master Appliances Inc.
LA ROSA - Thermostats - Gooch Foods Inc.

☆ = Now out of production

LA ROSA BAKERY - Bakery products - La Rosa Cake, Inc.
LA ROSE JACQUEMINOT - Fragrance ☆ - Coty Inc.
LA ROSSA - Beverages—malt - Labatt Importers Inc.
LA ROYALE PETITE - Jewelry - Jacoby-Bender Inc.
LA ROYANETTE - Chocolate candy ☆ - Liberty Richter Inc.
LA RUE - Belts—apparel - La Rue International, Inc.
LA RUTA - Corned beef - Berns & Koppstein
LA SALLE - Bicycles - Murray, Inc.
LA SALLE - Clocks ☆ - Ridgeway Clock Co.
LA SALLE - Cordials - Paramount Distillers Inc.
LA SALLE - Fish—fresh or frozen - Clegg Shrimp Co. Inc.
LA SALLE - Food products - John Sexton and Co.
LA SALLE - Ice cream - La Salle Ice Cream Co., Inc.
LA SALLE - Motor vehicles—automobiles ☆ - General Motors Corp. (Cadillac Motor Car Div.)
LA SAUCE - Food products - Romanoff International Inc.
L.A. SAX - Musical instruments - L.A. Sax Co.
LA SCALA - Dishes—china - Pasmantier Co. Inc.
LA SCALA - Fabrics - Gretchen Bellinger Inc.
LA SCALA - Flatware - Gorham Inc.
LA SCALA - Floor coverings ☆ - Tarkett, Inc.
LA SCALA - Fretted instruments ☆ - International Music Corp.
LA SCALA - Musical instruments - C. Bruno & Son Inc.
LA SCALA DEBUT - Christmas tree ornaments - Cracker Box Inc.
LA SCENE - Floor coverings—carpet and rugs - Monticello Carpet Mills
LA SCULPTURETTE - Hair care products - HK Industries
LA SEINE - Colognes ☆ - Avon Products, Inc.
LA SEMANA - Jewelry - L & M Castings Inc.
LA SHAPEUR - Apparel and accessories ☆ - Strouse, Adler Co.
LA-SHEE - Cosmetics - CTS Laboratories Inc.
LA SHELF - Bookcases—wood ☆ - Park Sherman
LA SHUFFLE - Shirts - La Shuffle Merchandising, Inc.
LA SIERRA - Paper - Silver Leaf Paper Co.
LA SIESTA - Food products - La Siesta Foods Inc.
LA SIGUARAYA - Baked goods - La Borinquena Bakery Inc.
LA SILHOUETTE KNITS - Sweaters - La Silhouette Apparel USA, Inc.
LA SIOUX - Dolls - Stanislaus Imports, Inc.
LA SOLAIRE - Suntan lotions - Schering-Plough Healthcare Products
LA SONORA MELIYARA - Recording label - Luna Music Corp.
LA SOUFFLEE - Cooking equipment—household ☆ - Nordic Ware
LA SPAGNOLA - Vegetable oil - Catania-Spagna Corp.
L.A. SPECIAL - Musical instrument accessories - Pro-Mark Corp.
LA SPIRITE - Girdles ☆ - Strouse, Adler Co.
L.A. SPORT - Watches - Western Watches International
LA SQUADRA - Men's sportswear - Botany 500
L.A. STAR - Fans—electric - Beverly Hills Fan Co.
LA STELLA - Meat products—beef - Armour Swift-Eckrich
LA STRADA - Cases—musical instrument ☆ - PowerMark Case Corp.
LA STRADA - Floor coverings—carpet and rugs - Roxbury Carpet Co.
LA STRADA - Floor coverings—tile ☆ - Kentile Floors Inc.
LA STRADA - Trailers—travel - Chateau RV Inc.
L.A. STRIPES - Shoelace ties - L.A. Stripes Enterprises
L.A. STUDIO - Leather goods - Novo-Las Corp.
LA SUPREMA - Tortillas - La Suprema
LA SUPREME - Apparel—women's - Lily of France Inc.
LA SYMPHONIE - Cosmetics - Cosmair Inc.
L.A. TAN - Health care products - Creative Laboratories Inc.
LA TAPATIA - Tortillas - La Tapatia Tortilleria Inc.
LA TARANTELLE - Cosmetics - Cosmair Inc.
LA TASTE - Olives—canned ☆ - Dean & Deluca Inc.
LA TAUSCA - Jewelry - Imperial-Deltah Inc.
LA TAVERNA - Vegetables—canned - Stanislaus Food Products Co.
L.A. TECH - Socks - Moretz Hosiery Mills Inc.
LA TEMPESTA - Cookies - La Tempesta Bakery Confections, Inc.
LA TERRY - Apparel—women's - Terry Moss
LA TEXEINT - Apparel and accessories - Vanity Corset Co. Inc.
LA TIQUE - Bags—duffel - La Tique, Inc.
LA TOILETTE - Skin care products - HK Industries
LA TOLTECA TORTILLAS - Tortillas - La Tolteca Foods Inc.
LA TORTILLERIA - Tortillas - La Tortilleria, Inc.
LA TORTILLITA - Housewares - Life-Like Products Inc.
LA TOSCA - Musical instruments ☆ - Fred Gretsch Enterprises
LA TOUR D'ARGENT - Rice - Connell Co.
LA TOUR D'OR - Rice - Connell Co.
LA TOURAINE - Coffee - La Touraine Coffee Co.
LA TRAFFIC - Apparel stores—children's ☆ - D. Glasgow & Sons Inc.

+LA TRAVIATA - Musical instruments - Fender Musical Instruments
LA TREILLE DE RASHI - Wines ☆ - Royal Wine Corp.
LA TREND, A - Hair care products ☆ - Spilo/Mehaz Worldwide
LA TRESSE - Brushes—hair - American Greetings Corp.
LA TRIOMPHE - Jewelry - Astoria Jewelry Manufacturing Co., Inc.
LA TRIQUE - Brassieres (Bras) - Valmont Inc.
LA TROPICALISIMA - Recording label ☆ - Musical Productions, Inc.
LA TUCHE - Infant product ☆ - Pyramid Handbags Inc.
LA TULIPE - Glassware—household - Lancaster Colony Corp.
LA TULIPE - Nail care products - Cosmair Inc.
LA-TWEEZE EASY - Skin care products - Victoria Vogue, Inc.
L.A. TWILIGHT - Footwear - L.A. Gear, Inc.
LA UNICA - Cigars - J.C. Newman Cigar Co.
LA UNITED - Apparel and accessories - Forum Soccer, Inc.
LA VACA DULCE - Milk—canned or powdered - Santini Foods
LA VACA LINDA - Cheese - Swissrose International Inc.
LA VACARICA - Cheese - Specialty Cheese Co., Inc.
LA VACHE QUI RIT - Cheese - Fromageries Bel, Inc.
LA VALLE - Oils—essential - Euro International
LA VALLIERE - Skin care products - Specialty Products Co.
LA VANS - Coffee - La Vans Coffee Co.
LA VAZZA - Coffee - Thomas A. Campbell Co.
LA VENCEDORA - Spices and extracts - Ria Distributing
LA VENEZOLANA - Flour—blended - Lavenezolana Corp.
LA VICTORIA - Food products - La Victoria Foods Inc.
LA VIDA - T-shirts—men's - Yamo Designs
LA VIE EN ROSE - Dolls ☆ - Effanbee Doll Corp.
LA VIE EN ROSE - Watches - Bulova Corp.
LA VIE OF BEVERLY HILLS - Cosmetics - La Vie Cosmetics Inc.
LA VILLA - Tomato pastes and sauces - Byrd Foods Inc.
LA VILLA VENETA - Wines - Amalia Moretti, Inc.
L.A. VINTAGE - Apparel—women's - MCB, Inc.
LA VIOLA - Skin care products - High Country Cosmetics Inc.
LA VITA - Floor coverings—carpet and rugs - Helios Carpets
LA VITA - Footwear - M & R Shoes Inc.
LA VIVA - Floor coverings - Mannington Resilient Floors
LA VOSGIENNE - Candy - Holland-American Importing Co. Inc.
LA VOSH - Crackers - Made in France
LA VOZ - Musical instrument accessories - Rico International
LA VRAIE - Vitamins and nutritional supplements ☆ - Desert Health Products, Inc.
LA WEST - Motor vehicles—vans - La West, Inc.
LA YOGURT - Yogurt - Johanna Foods, Inc.
LA YOGURT SABOR - Yogurt - Johanna Foods, Inc.
LA YOGURT SABOR LATINO - Yogurt - Johanna Dairies Inc.
LA-Z-BOY - Chairs—upholstered - La-Z-Boy Chair Co.
LA-Z-BOY CLASSICS - Chairs—upholstered - La-Z-Boy Chair Co.
LA-Z-BOY COMPATABLES - Tables—wood ☆ - La-Z-Boy Chair Co.
LA-Z-COIL - Sofas - La-Z-Boy Chair Co.
LA-Z-LOUNGER - Chairs—upholstered - La-Z-Boy Chair Co.
LA-Z-LUX - Cushions - La-Z-Boy Chair Co.
LA-Z-REST - Chairs—upholstered - La-Z-Boy Chair Co.
LA-Z-ROCKER - Rocking chairs - La-Z-Boy Chair Co.
LA-Z-SLEEPER - Sofabeds - La-Z-Boy Chair Co.
LA-Z-SOFA - Sofas - La-Z-Boy Chair Co.
LA-Z-TIME - Sofas - La-Z-Boy Chair Co.
LA-Z-TIME MOTION-MODULARS - Furniture—upholstered - La-Z-Boy Chair Co.
LA-Z-TOUCH - Furniture - La-Z-Boy Chair Co.
LA50 - Printers—computer - Digital Equipment Corp.
LAB - Computer software - Mind Play
LAB - Concrete products - Tamms Industries Co.
LAB - Runners - Ace Hose and Rubber Co.
LAB ALERT - Audio equipment - A. Daigger & Co., Inc.
LAB ASSISTANT - Laboratory apparatus - Manostat Corp.
LAB CALC - Computer software - Galactic Industries Corp.
LAB DIET - Pet food - Purina Mills, Inc.
LAB-EZ - Pharmaceutical preparations - Synbiotics Corp.
LAB GUARD - Medical apparatus - Instruments for Research and Industry, I2R Inc.
LAB I - Footwear—athletic - Puma Inc.
LAB IN A BAG - Chemical preparations - Osprey Biotechnics, Inc.
LAB LITTER - Pet products - K.C. Pharmacal Inc.
LAB-LUBE - Lubricants - Alvin Products Inc.
LAB MENU - Pet products - Petland, Inc.
LAB-METAL - Coatings - Alvin Products Inc.

☆ = Now out of production

LAB QUALITY AT YOUR FINGERTIPS - Medical apparatus - Mallinckrodt Medical, Inc.

LAB SERIES - Skin care products - Aramis Inc.

LAB SERIES - Skin care products - Estee Lauder Inc.

LAB-SOLVENT - Coatings - Alvin Products Inc.

LAB TRAX - Computer peripheral equipment - Lab-Interlink, Inc.

LABABY - Dolls - Barval Toys Inc.

LABACCESS - Computer software - Sunquest Information Systems, Inc.

LABAIRE - Electronic equipment ☆ - Leedal Inc.

LABAIRE - Hearing aids - Worchester Hearing Aid Co.

LABATT'S - Beverages—malt ☆ - Labatt Importers Inc.

LABATT'S 50 - Beverages—malt - Labatt Importers Inc.

LABATT'S BLUE - Beverages—malt - Labatt Importers Inc.

LABATT'S BLUE LIGHT - Beverages—malt - Labatt Importers Inc.

LABATT'S CANADIAN DRY - Beverages—malt ☆ - Labatt Importers Inc.

LABATT'S COPPER - Beverages—malt - Labatt Importers Inc.

LABATT'S ICE - Beverages—malt - Labatt Importers Inc.

LABATT'S LIGHT - Beverages—malt ☆ - Labatt Importers Inc.

+L'ABBE - Fruits—pickled or brined ☆ - Europa Foods Ltd.

LABCONCO - Laboratory apparatus - Labconco Corp.

LABCOST - Med Data Systems, Inc.

LABDAQ - Computer software - Antek, Inc.

LABEL CENTER - Computer software - Identification Software, Inc.

LABEL CONNECTION, THE - Self-adhesive labels - United Ad Label Co., Inc.

LABEL EXPRESS - Computer software - Rolodex Corp.

LABEL-IT - Labels—paper - Ben Clements & Sons Inc.

LABEL KWIK - Label dispensers - Automatic Business Products, Inc.

LABEL LOGIC - Computer software - E-8 Publications, Inc.

LABEL PEN - Markers—felt-tip - Sanford Corp.

LABEL PRESS - Computer software - Synex

LABEL PRO - Adhesives and sealants - Glue-Fast Equipment Co. Inc.

LABEL RITE - Machinery - New Jersey Machine Inc.

LABEL SEARCH+ - Computer software - J.J. Keller & Associates

LABEL SHOOTER - Label dispensers - Automatic Business Products, Inc.

LABEL STATION, THE - Office supplies - Briggs Corp.

LABEL TRAXX - Computer software - Tailored Solutions, Inc.

LABEL WHORE - Apparel and accessories - Peter Kavehzadeh

LABEL WIZARD - Computer software - Sato America, Inc.

LABEL WORKS - Computer software ☆ - Zephyr Services

LABEL X - Recording label - Fifth Continent Music Corp.

LABELER - Pens - Empire Berol USA

LABELFLEX - Film - Plastic Suppliers, Inc.

LABELID-PROTEX - Boxes - Columbia Specialty Co. Inc.

LABELIFE - Labels—paper - Greenwood Graphics Inc.

LABELING ANSWER, THE - Computer software - T.L. Ashford & Associates, Inc.

LABELINK - Computer software - Moore Business Forms, Inc.

LABELIZER - Labeling machinery - Brady USA Inc.

LABELKWIK - Electronic equipment - Reeves Soundcraft

LABELLA - Footwear—women's ☆ - P.H. Volk Co.

LABELLA - Musical instrument accessories - International Violin Co. Ltd.

LABELLE CREAM - Cordials - White Rock Distilleries Inc.

LABELLE FRANCE - Cheese ☆ - Schratter Import

LABELLE ORANGE - Cordials - White Rock Distilleries Inc.

LABELMASTER - Label printers - Electronic Label Technology Inc.

LABELMASTER - Office supplies - Seal-O-Matic Corp.

LABELMAX - Computer software - Advanced Labeling Systems, Inc.

LABELOF - Wine label remover - Polytechnic Inc.

LABELON - Paper - Labelon Corp.

LABELON/GRAFFCO - Office supplies - Labelon Corp.

LABELON/NOESTING - Stationery - Labelon Corp.

LABELPRO - Computer software - Avery Dennison Corp.

LABELS EXPRESS - Computer software - Parsons Technology, Inc.

LABELS PLUS - Labels—paper - Labels Plus, Inc.

LABELS PLUS - Labels—paper - Phillips Industrial Supply Inc.

LABELSAVER - Paperboard - Sonoco Products Co.

LABELSMITHS - Labels—gummed - Uni-Label & Tag Corp.

LABELWORKS - Computer label program - American Microsystems

LABFARVE - Teas—herbal - Labfarve, Inc.

LABFORCE - Employment agencies—temporary help - Uniforce Services

LABGEM - Computer software - Diamond Computing Co.

LABGUARD - Computer software - Med Data Systems, Inc.

LABID - Pharmaceutical preparations - Norwich-Eaton Pharmaceuticals

LABINDUSTRIES - Laboratory apparatus - Barnstead Thermolyne Corp.

LABKLENZ - Detergents - E.R. Squibb & Sons, Inc.

LABMASTER - Photographic equipment - Houston Fearless 76 Inc.

LABOISSIERE - Perfumes - Anjac Inc.

LABOR-EASE - Health care products - Natural Laboratories Corp.

LABOR PRO - Computer software - Expertek Systems, Inc.

LABOR SAVER - Finishing agents - Rust-Oleum Corp.

LABOR-SAVER - Floor waxes - Uncle Sam Chemical Co., Inc.

LABOR SAVING DEVICES - Tool boxes - Labor Saving Devices, Inc.

LABOR TRAKER - Computer terminals ☆ - Accu-Time Systems, Inc.

LABORATORY SERIES - Recording label - Sonic Arts Corp.

LABORATORY SKIN CARE - Skin care products - Laboratory Skin Care, Inc.

LABORETT - Pet products - Tetra Sales USA

LABORSAVER - Computer software - Martin Consulting Enterprises

LABORSOURCE - Computer software - Cooperative Computing, Inc.

LABORWATCH - Computer software - MCIS, Inc.

LABPAC - Air conditioning units - Monsen Engineering Co.

LABPAK - Computer software - Fletcher-Flora Computer Products, Inc.

LABQUET - Health care products ☆ - Graham-Field Inc.

LABRADOR - Sporting goods - Panek Precision Products

LABRATOR - Health care products ☆ - Graham-Field Inc.

LABRE - Vitamins and nutritional supplements - Source Naturals

LABROMIX - Concrete products - Gibraltar National Corp.

LABSCAN II - Artists' materials - HunterLab

LABSITE - Medical apparatus - Migada Inc.

LABSPEC - Spectrometers - Analytical Spectral Devices Inc.

LABSTAR - Blood pressure apparatus ☆ - Graham-Field Inc.

LABSTAT - Computer software - Community Health Computing, Inc.

LABSUITE - Computer software - National Instruments Corp.

LABSYS - Electronic equipment - Califone International Inc.

LABTALK - Computer software - Information Access Technology, Inc.

LABTALK - Computer software - Microcal Software, Inc.

LABTALK - Computers - Medi-Comp Innovations Group

LABTEMP - Health care products - Biosynergy Inc.

LABTHERM - Thermostats ☆ - Graham-Field Inc.

LABTRON - Blood pressure apparatus - Graham-Field Inc.

LABTRONIX - Blood pressure apparatus ☆ - Graham-Field Inc.

LABWATCH - Laboratory apparatus - Kaye Instruments Inc.

LABWORKS - Computer software - General Signal Corp.

LABWORKS II - Computer hardware - Jones and Bartlett Publishers, Inc.

LABYRINTH - Motoman, Inc.

LABYRINTH - Candy ☆ - Topps Co., Inc.

LABYRINTH - Computer software - DS Ltd.

LABYRINTH - Games ☆ - Crestline Manufacturing Co.

LABYRINTH - Napkins—fabric - Fort Howard Corp.

LABYRINTH - Plotter pen - Dia-Nielsen USA Inc.

LABYRINTH - Wallpaper ☆ - Gilford Corp.

LABYRINTHINE MAZE - Games ☆ - Carrom Co.

LAC - Computers - Lloyd-Allan Corp.

LAC - Hair care products - Faberge Co.

LAC FRENCH - Padding—foam - Star Finishing Products Inc.

LAC-HYDRIN - Skin care products - Westwood-Squibb Pharmaceuticals, Inc.

LAC-KOTER - Lacquers - Dunn Edwards Corp.

LAC MICHIGAN - Greeting cards - Chicago Jan

LAC-O-NU - Cleaning preparations - Nusteel Co.

LAC PAPIER - Wallpaper ☆ - Maya Romanoff Corp.

LAC-STAIN - Finishing agents - Lenmar Inc.

LAC-TOL - Pharmaceutical preparations ☆ - Endovations Inc.

LACAYE - Beverages—carbonated ☆ - Brooklyn Bottling Corp.

LACCATO - Furniture ☆ - Broyhill Furniture Industries, Inc.

+L'ACCENT - Buckles—shoe - Design Circle Ltd.

LACCO - Lacquers - Red Spot Paint & Varnish Co., Inc.

LACE - Artists' materials - Andrews/Nelson/Whitehead

LACE - Dishes—china ☆ - Pickard Inc.

LACE - Electroacoustic sensors - Donald A. Lace

LACE - Floor coverings—carpet and rugs - Downs Carpet Co. Inc.

LACE - Floor coverings—carpet and rugs - Langhorne Carpet Co. Inc.

LACE - Frames—eyeglass - Diaco

LACE - Frames—eyeglass - U.S. Optical Frame Co.

LACE - Glassware—household ☆ - ACC

LACE-A-BUNNY - Puppets - Lauri Inc.

LACE A MAJIG - Shoe accessories - It's America Inc.

LACE-A-PERSON - Puppets - Lauri Inc.

LACE-A-PET - Puppets - Lauri Inc.

LACE-A-PUPPET - Puppets - Lauri Inc.

LACE-A-SAURUS - Puppets - Lauri Inc.

LACE-A-SHAPE - Toys - Montgomery Schoolhouse

LACE & ROSES - Wallpaper - Bassett & Vollum Wallpapers

LACE BOUQUET - Dinnerware - Corning Inc.

☆ = Now out of production

LACE BOUQUET - Dinnerware–glass - Salem China Co.
LACE CONFECTION - Underwear and nightwear - Maidenform Inc.
LACE ELEGANCE - Apparel–women's - Warnaco Inc.
LACE EMBRACE, THE - Apparel–women's - Lily of France Inc.
LACE ENCOUNTER - Underwear and nightwear - Henson-Kickernick Inc.
LACE ETTE - Girdles - Rago Foundations Inc. LLC
LACE-EVER-AFTER - Brassieres (Bras) ☆ - Lovable Co.
LACE FACE - Underwear and nightwear ☆ - Lovable Co.
LACE FLIP - Apparel–women's - Wacoal America Inc.
LACE-FORM - Girdles - Sears, Roebuck and Co.
LACE FROSTING - Apparel–women's - Exquisite Form Industries
LACE GLACEE - Apparel and accessories - Warnaco Inc.
LACE IT, LOCK IT, LEAVE IT. - Athletic shoe laces - NRG Inc.
LACE LASTIQUE - Fabrics - Liberty Fabrics, Inc.
LACE-LITES - Laces–boot and shoe - Lami Products, Inc.
LACE LUXURIES - Underwear and nightwear - Maidenform Inc.
LACE LUXURY - Apparel–women's - NCC Industries, Inc.
LACE MATES - Apparel–women's - Wacoal America Inc.
LACE ME AND LOVE ME - Brassieres (Bras) ☆ - Lovable Co.
LACE MICRO MATRIX COMB - Electro acoustic sensors - Actodyne General, Inc.
LACE MINIATURES - Wallpaper ☆ - Andover Wallcovering
LACE MINIATURES II - Wallpaper ☆ - Mirage Wallcovering Co.
LACE MYSTIQUE - Underwear and nightwear - Maidenform Inc.
LACE N' GLOW - Hobby kits ☆ - Colorforms
LACE 'N LOVELY - Underwear and nightwear ☆ - Lovable Co.
LACE 'N SMOOTH - Apparel–women's - Bali Co. Inc.
LACE OBSESSION - Underwear and nightwear - Henson-Kickernick Inc.
LACE PARFAIT - Underwear and nightwear - Lovable Co.
LACE PERFECTION - Hosiery - Sara Lee Corp.
LACE POINT - Floor coverings–carpet and rugs - World Carpets, Inc.
LACE POINT - Floor coverings–carpet and rugs ☆ - Zenith Carpets
LACE POINT - Glassware–household ☆ - Lenox Crystal, Inc.
LACE POINT - Tableware–china ☆ - Lenox, Inc.
LACE PRO - Skates–ice - Up in the Air, Inc.
LACE SENSOR - Sensors - Actodyne General, Inc.
LACE-SET - Fabrics - Borlan Industries Inc.
LACE TAPESTRY - Underwear and nightwear - Maidenform Inc.
LACE TREASURE - Apparel–women's - V.F. Corp.
LACE VALENTINE - Brassieres (Bras) ☆ - Lovable Co.
LACE WEIGHTS - Weightlifting equipment - Whitely Fitness Products
LACECRAFTER - Cutting tools - Start to Finish Hardwood Floors
LACELETTES - Garters - Suzanne Gardner
LACELLA - Yarn - Melrose Yarn Co. Inc.
LACER LATEX CERAMIC INSULATION - Insulating materials - Broomall Enterprises, Inc.
LACET - Yarn - Joseph Galler Inc.
LACEWING - Wallpaper - Koroseal Wallcoverings
LACEWOOD - Wallpaper ☆ - Gagne Wallcovering, Inc.
LACEY - Dolls - Mattel, Inc.
LACEY - Wigs - Lacey Costume Wigs
LACEY-DAISY - Apparel–women's - Wacoal America Inc.
LACEY GREETINGS - Art prints - Continental Art-Craft
LACEY LAMB - Toys–stuffed - Russ Berrie and Co., Inc.
LACEYS - Food products - Desserts On Us Baklava
LACHAN'S - Beverages–alcohol - Bel Air Imports Inc.
LACHAT INSTRUMENTS - Distilling apparatus–laboratory - Lachat Instruments, Inc.
LACHLE'S ORIGINALS - Health care products - Healthway Natural Foods
LACHNEL - Accordions - Castiglione Accordion
LACI LE BEAU - Teas - Nutrition Products Corp.
LACIES BY SIMONE - Apparel–women's - Leading Lady Companies Inc.
LACING AND TRACING CASTLE - Toys - Lauri Inc.
LACING AND TRACING PUPPETS - Toys - Lauri Inc.
LACING BEARS - Toys - Lauri Inc.
LACING FOR CHRISTMAS - Toys ☆ - Lauri Inc.
LACING PADS - Toys - Lauri Inc.
LACING SHAPES - Toys - Lauri Inc.
LACING STUFFERS - Toys ☆ - Lauri Inc.
LACINGS - Underwear and nightwear - Maidenform Inc.
LACKAWANNA - Shoes - B. Levy & Son
LACKRITZ - Jewelry - Marks Brothers Jewelers Inc.
LACLED ALLOY - Containers–plastic - Laclede Chain Manufacturing Co.
LACLEDE - Mouthwashes - Laclede Research Laboratories
LACLEDE BARK - Containers–plastic - Laclede Chain Manufacturing Co.

LACLEDE FLUORIDE FOAM - Skin care products - Laclede Professional Products, Inc.
LACMATE - Filters–water - Robert Lehrer Associates, Inc.
LACO - Brushes–paint ☆ - Laitner Brush Co.
LACO - Olive oil - Pompeian Inc.
LACO - Watches - Nicolet International Inc.
LACOMBE - Furniture - Homecrest Industries Inc.
LACONIA - Paper–bond ☆ - Parsons Paper Co.
LACOSTA - Floor coverings - Aladdin Mills, Inc.
LACOSTA - Floor coverings–carpet and rugs - Burtco Enterprises Inc.
LACOSTE - Apparel and accessories - Crystal Brands Inc.
LACOVERS - Wallpaper ☆ - Robert Crowder & Co.
LACQUERELLE - Wallpaper ☆ - Maya Romanoff Corp.
LACQUERS - Wallpaper - Robert Crowder & Co.
LACRATE - Wire products - Design Ideas Ltd.
LACRI-LUBE NP - Ophthalmic goods - Allergan, Inc.
LACRI-LUBE S.O.P. - Ophthalmic goods - Allergan, Inc.
LACRIL - Ophthalmic goods ☆ - Allergan, Inc.
LACRISERT - Pharmaceutical preparations - Merck & Co., Inc. (Merck Research Laboratories)
LACROSS - Floor coverings–carpet and rugs - Quaker Inc.
LACROSSE - Clocks - La Crosse-McCormick
LACROSSE - Footwear - La Crosse Footwear, Inc.
LACROSSE - Frames–eyeglass ☆ - Universal/Univis Inc.
LACROSSE - Occasional tables ☆ - JDI Group, Inc.
LACT-A-PET - Pet products - BenePet Pet Care Products
LACT B - Infant product - Ameda/Egnell Corp.
LACT E - Infant product - Ameda/Egnell Corp.
LACTA/CARE - Pharmaceutical preparations - Nutra/Balance Products
LACTAID - Cheese ☆ - Dan Carter Inc.
LACTAID - Milk ☆ - Ryan Foods Co.
LACTAID - Pharmaceutical preparations - Lactaid Inc.
LACTAID 100 - Health care products - McNeil Consumer Products Co.
LACTALINS - Vitamins and nutritional supplements - Health Products Corp.
LACTANA/B - Pharmaceutical preparations ☆ - Bio-Nutritional Products
LACTEST - Diagnostic substances - JWT, Inc.
LACTICARE - Skin care products - Stiefel Laboratories, Inc.
LACTICARE-HC - Skin care products - Stiefel Laboratories, Inc.
LACTINEX - Pharmaceutical preparations - Becton Dickinson Microbiology Systems
LACTINOL-E - Pharmaceutical preparations - Pedinol Pharmacal Inc.
LACTINOL LOTION - Pharmaceutical preparations - Pedinol Pharmacal Inc.
LACTISOL - Pharmaceutical preparations - Glenwood LLC
LACTO - Milk - Lacto Milk Products Corp.
LACTO - Skin care products - Lendan USA Co.
LACTO-CALCIUM - Vitamins and nutritional supplements - Cyvex Technologies, Inc.
LACTO-SACC - Veterinary nutritional supplements - Alltech, Inc.
LACTO-STIM - Infant product ☆ - Graham-Field Inc.
LACTO-WHEY - Agricultural products - Haas Chemical Co., Inc.
LACTOBREV - Vitamins and nutritional supplements - Source Naturals
LACTOCAL - Pharmaceutical preparations ☆ - Laser Inc.
LACTOCAL-F - Pharmaceutical preparations - Laser Inc.
LACTOEASE - Pharmaceutical preparations - Wesley Pharmacal Co. Inc.
LACTOENZYME - Vitamins and nutritional supplements - Weider Health and Fitness
LACTOFERRIN - Vitamins and nutritional supplements - Vitamin Research Products Inc.
LACTOFREE - Infant product - Bristol-Myers Squibb Co.
LACTOGEST - Vitamins and nutritional supplements ☆ - Thompson Medical Co., Inc.
LACTOL - Nail care products - Revlon Consumer Products Corp.
LACTONA - Toothbrushes - Lactona Corp.
LACTOPLEX - Vitamins and nutritional supplements - Great Life Laboratories Inc.
LACTOPRIV/B - Pharmaceutical preparations - Bio-Nutritional Products
LACTOSORB - Medical apparatus - Biomet, Inc.
LACTRASE - Pharmaceutical preparations - Schwarz Pharma
LACTREAT - Ice cream - Gelato Amare
LACTROL - Antibiotics - Pfizer Inc.
LACTZYME - Vitamins and nutritional supplements - Vitech America Corp.
LACY - Apparel and accessories ☆ - Lacy Corp.
LACY - Ophthalmic goods ☆ - Luxottica
LACY - Pet collars - Leatherite-Nylorite Manufacturing Inc.
LACY AFTERNOON - Footwear - Home Shopping Club, Inc.
LACY BOWS - Floor coverings–carpet and rugs - Regal Rugs Inc.

LACY CAPETTE - Hair care products - Andre Fantasies Inc.
LACY FRIES - Vegetables–frozen ☆ - Ore-Ida Foods, Inc.
LACY LADIES - Dolls - Bradley Import Co.
LACY LUXURIES - Underwear and nightwear - Warnaco Inc.
LACY POINT - Rings–jewelry - Artcarved Inc.
LACY SECRET - Hair care products - Andre Fantasies Inc.
LACY SKAMP - Apparel–women's - Bali Co. Inc.
LACY SKAMP - Underwear and nightwear - Henson-Kickernick Inc.
LAD - Fluid flow diffusers - Cheng Fluid Systems Inc.
LAD - Recording label - TH Records & Tapes Inc.
LAD - Syrup ☆ - Gem Inc.
LAD-SAF - Safety products - D B Industries, Inc.
LADARVISION - Ophthalmic apparatus - Autonomous Technologies Corp.
LADCO - Paints - Ladco Industries
LADD - Fastening system - ITW Ramset/Red Head
LADDAWN - Bags–plastic - Northeast Poly Bag Co., Inc.
LADDER-CINCH - Hardware - Werner Co.
LADDER JAX - Ladders–metal - Advanced Design Products Inc.
LADDER LASH - Safety products - Wy-Tech, Inc.
LADDER-LOC - Antennas - James D. Hagerty
LADDER MITTS - Ladders–metal - H.F. Staples & Co. Inc.
LADDERFRAK - Bedding–linen - Dan River Inc.
LADDERUP - Safety post for fixed ladders - Bilco Co.
LADDIE - Eyeglasses - Art-Craft Optical Co.
LADDIE - Pencils - Dixon Ticonderoga Co.
LADDIE BOY - Dog food - Laddie Boy Dog Foods Inc.
LADDIE LADDER - Ladder - Dalton C. Bergan, Jr.
LADENA - Toilets–enameled - Kohler Co.
LADERACH - Chocolate candy - Albert Uster Imports Inc.
LADE'S - Seafood products–fresh or frozen - Lade's Fish & Seafoods
LADIES CHOICE - Desk sets - Fort USA
LADIES CHOICE - Food products ☆ - R & S Pickle Co. Inc.
LADIES' CHOICE - Frames–eyeglass ☆ - Universal/Univis Inc.
LADIES CHOICE - Safety eyewear - H.L. Bouton Co. Inc.
LADIES FLOWER GARLAND - Dishes–china - Portmeirion USA
LADIES' GEMS - Golf clubs - Callaway Golf Co.
LADIES' HOME JOURNAL - Publisher's imprints - Meredith Corp.
LADIES LINE - Pens - A.T. Cross Co.
LADIES MAID - Gloves - Knoxville Glove Co.
LADIES MAN - Lenses–optical - Ditto Industries Inc.
LADIES PUMICE - Health care products ☆ - Requa Manufacturing Co. Inc.
LADIES SERIES - Pens - Quill Co. Inc.
LADIES SEWING CIRCLE AND TERRORIST SOCIETY - Apparel and accessories - V. Sena
LADIES' SLALOM - Sporting goods - Wellington Leisure Products, Inc.
LADINO - Food products - Oakdale Poultry Co.
LADO - Skin care products - Lado Co. of America
LADOGA - Food products - Ladoga Frozen Food & Locker Service
LADOLEMONO - Salad dressings–bottled - Peloponnese
LADOUCETTE - Wines - Heublein, Inc.
LADOVE - Hair care products - LaDove Inc.
LADUETTE - Cooking equipment–household ☆ - Imperial Schrade Corp.
LADY - Dolls - Tonka Corp.
LADY - Perfumes - Quintessence Inc.
LADY ALBA - Underwear and nightwear - Alba-Waldensian, Inc.
LADY ALPHA - Crocheted and knitted items ☆ - Alpha Mills Corp.
LADY ALSONS - Bathroom fixtures - Alsons Corp.
LADY ANATONE - Girdles - Magic Mold Inc.
LADY ANGORA - Yarn ☆ - Plymouth Yarn Co.
LADY-ANN - Food products - Bridgford Foods Corp.
LADY ANN - Optical scanners–computer - Tart Optical
LADY ANNA - Food products - Olfisco Inc.
LADY ANNE - Flatware - Gorham Inc.
LADY ANNE - Paper–gift wrap - Pen-Tab Industries
LADY ANNE GOLD - Glassware–household - Gorham Inc.
LADY ARIES - Golfing equipment - Ram Golf Corp.
LADY ARISTETTE - Dryers–hair ☆ - Metal Ware Corp.
LADY ARROW - Apparel and accessories - Cluett, Peabody & Co.
LADY ASCOT - Dolls ☆ - Effanbee Doll Corp.
LADY ASHLEY - Dolls ☆ - Effanbee Doll Corp.
LADY ASHLEY - Underwear and nightwear - Maidenform Inc.
LADY ASHTON - Apparel and accessories - Ashford Fashions, Inc.
LADY ASTER - Food products - Culinary Foods Inc.
LADY ASTOR - Wallpaper ☆ - Pantasote Inc. (Wallcovering Div.)
LADY AUSTIN - Soap - James Austin Co.
LADY B. GOODE - Furniture - Lady B. Goode, Inc.

LADY BALTIMORE - Dialing devices–telephone - Baltimore Luggage Co.
LADY BALTIMORE PERFECTION - Cakes ☆ - Bissinger's Inc.
LADY BANKHEAD - Optical scanners–computer - Tart Optical
LADY BARON - Golfing equipment - Golfco, Inc.
LADY BARTON'S - Skin care products - Pro-Capa Products Inc.
LADY BAYARD - Apparel and accessories - Salant/Manhattan Industries
LADY BE GOOD - Christmas tree ornaments - Cracker Box Inc.
LADY BEA - Recording label - Lady Bea Productions, Inc.
LADY BECKWITH - Fruits–canned - Oasis Foods Inc.
LADY BEN - Clocks - General Time Corp. (Westclox/Seth Thomas Div.)
LADY BENCHELEY - Coffee - Premium Coffee
LADY BERKSHIRE - Watches - Bulova Corp.
LADY BETTY - Girdles ☆ - Marcus & Wiesen Inc.
LADY BETTY - Juices - Algood Food Co.
LADY BETTY - Margarine - Van Den Bergh Foods Co.
LADY BETTY WHIPT CREME - Candy - Nestle USA
LADY BIKE - Sporting goods - Bike Athletic Co.
LADY BORDEN - Ice cream - BDH Two, Inc.
LADY BORDEN - Ice cream - Borden, Inc.
LADY BOSCA - Leather goods and gifts - Hugo Bosca Co., Inc.
LADY BOSTONIAN - Women's shoes ☆ - Bostonian Shoe Co.
LADY BOTANY - Socks - Rudin & Roth Inc.
LADY BOUNTIFUL - Bedding–linen - Dan River Inc.
LADY BRITON - Frames–eyeglass - Hudson Optical Corp.
LADY BRITTANY'S ENGLISH GARDEN SEEDS - Flowers, plants, and seeds - Micky's Mini-Flora Express, Ltd.
LADY BRONZINI - Frames–eyeglass - Universal/Univis Inc.
LADY BUG - Bicycles - Murray, Inc.
LADY BUG - Games - Hasbro, Inc.
LADY BUG - Massage products - Homedics Inc.
LADY BUG - Toys - Fisher-Price, Inc.
LADY BUG - Toys - South Bend Toy Manufacturing Co.
LADY BUG FARM - Toys ☆ - Natural Science Industries, Ltd.
LADY BULOVA - Watches - Bulova Corp.
LADY BURD EXCLUSIVE COSMETICS USA - Cosmetics - Lady Burd Exclusive Cosmetics, Inc.
LADY BUXTON - Wallets - Buxton Inc.
LADY B.V.D. - Underwear and nightwear ☆ - B.V.D. Co. Inc.
LADY CAMEO - Footwear–women's - St. Louis Shoe Co. Inc.
LADY CAMEO - Hair care products - Cameo Coutures
LADY CANTERBURY - Belts–apparel - Canterbury Belts Ltd.
LADY CANTERBURY - Rings–jewelry - Artcarved Inc.
LADY CARDINI - Frames–eyeglass ☆ - Vanity Optical Manufacturing Co. Inc.
LADY CAREL - Dryers–hair - Dazey Corp.
LADY CAROLINA - Hair care products - Carolina Absorbent Cotton
LADY CASINO - Frames–eyeglass - May Optical Co. Inc.
LADY CATA-POLE - Sporting goods - Sport Supply Group, Inc.
LADY CHARLENE - Candy - Zachary Confections Inc.
LADY CHIC - Apparel–women's ☆ - Chic Lingerie Co.
LADY CHRON - Watches - Elgin Watch Co.
LADY CLAIRE - Flatware - Kirk Stieff Co.
LADY CLAIROL - Hair coloring preparations - Clairol Inc.
LADY CLASSIC - Golfing equipment - Golfsmith International Inc.
LADY COBRA - Apparel and accessories - Cobra Golf Inc.
LADY CORA - Skin care products ☆ - Church and Dwight Co. Inc.
LADY COURT - Women's shoes - Thos. Cort Inc.
LADY COVENTRY - Jewelry - Sarah Coventry Fashion Jewelry
LADY CREAM DROPS - Chocolate candy ☆ - Maillard Corp.
LADY CUE - Apparel–women's ☆ - Bali Co. Inc.
LADY CURVEX - Watches - Gruen Marketing Corp.
LADY DANBURY - Belts–apparel ☆ - Gem-Dandy, Inc.
LADY DATEJUST - Watches - Rolex Watch USA, Inc.
LADY DEATH - Books–comic - Brian Pulido
LADY DEE - Jewelry - Jacoby-Bender Inc.
LADY DEE CEE - Apparel–women's - Washington Manufacturing Co.
LADY DELIGHT - Ice cream - Cass-Clay Creamery Inc.
LADY DEVON - Apparel–women's - Devon Apparel
LADY DI - Frames–eyeglass ☆ - Universal/Univis Inc.
LADY DIANA - Artists' materials ☆ - Artoptic International Corp.
LADY DIANA - Floor coverings–carpet and rugs ☆ - Calladium & Marglen
LADY DIANA - Footwear - Orly Shoe Corp.
LADY DIANE - Beauty shop equipment - Diane Products Inc.
LADY DOMANI - Apparel and accessories - Domani
LADY DUKE - Apparel–athletic ☆ - Royal Textile Mills Inc.
LADY DYMPNA - Waterproofing compounds - Dympna M. Smith
LADY EBONITE - Bowling balls - Ebonite International, Inc.

☆ = Now out of production

LADY ELECTRA - Watches - Croton Watch Co., Inc.
LADY ELEGANCE - Toys - Proll Toy Co.
LADY ELEGANCE - Toys–musical - Magnus Organ Co.
LADY ELEPHANT - Rice - James E. Barrett Corp.
LADY ELGIN - Watches - Elgin Watch Co.
LADY ELITE - Sports rackets and accessories ☆ - Victor Sports
LADY ELIZABETH - Sponges - Schroeder & Tremayne, Inc.
LADY ELLEN - Cosmetics - Capitol Novelty Co.
LADY ELLEN - Flour–blended - Cahokia Flour Co.
LADY ELLEN - Frames–eyeglass - Hudson Optical Corp.
LADY ELLEN - Hair curlers - Spilo/Mehaz Worldwide
LADY ELLEN - Health care products ☆ - Conair Corp.
LADY EMILY - Apparel and accessories ☆ - Glamorise Foundations Inc.
LADY ENDEN - Hair care products - Helene Curtis Industries Inc.
LADY ENGLANDER - Mattresses - United States Bedding Co.
LADY ERIN - Ophthalmic goods - Styl-Rite Optical Manufacturing Co., Inc.
LADY ESTER - Apparel–women's - Lady Ester Lingerie Corp.
LADY ESTHER - Shoes–athletic - American Asian Trading Co.
LADY ESTHER - Skin care products - Smithkline Beecham Corp.
LADY ETON - Watches - Dundee Watch Co.
LADY EVE - Hair care products - Eve Industries Inc.
LADY EXECUTIVES BY HY-TEST - Footwear–women's - Hy Test Inc.
LADY FAIR - Furniture - Astorloid Manufacturing Co.
LADY FASHION - Shoes - Interco Inc.
LADY FINGER - Skin care products - ManChild Inc.
LADY FINGERS - Hand moisturizer - Jafra Cosmetics Inc.
LADY FLEUR - Flowers–artificial - National Potteries
LADY FLEX - Frames–eyeglass - Liberty Optical Manufacturing Co.
LADY FOOT LOCKER CASUALS - Apparel–women's - Kinney Shoe Corp.
LADY FOREST - Food products machinery - Forest Packing Co.
LADY-FORM - Brassieres (Bras) - Milady Brassiere & Corset Co., Inc.
LADY FOX - Sporting goods - FTM Sports
LADY FREE - Medical apparatus - Camda Corp.
LADY G - Watches ☆ - Gubelin Inc.
LADY GALA - Fruits–frozen - GLG Agricultural Properties
LADY GARDENER - Tools–garden - Uniontools, Inc.
LADY GILLETTE - Shaving preparations - Gillette Co.
LADY GODIVA - Lenses–optical - Ditto Industries Inc.
LADY GOLF - Golfing equipment - Soburn Enterprises, Inc.
LADY GRACE - Glass–optical - Welling International
LADY GRACE - Pickles ☆ - Whitfield Foods, Inc.
LADY GRAJDON - Teas ☆ - Bewley Irish Imports
LADY GRECIAN - Hair coloring preparations - Combe Inc.
LADY GREY - Dolls ☆ - Effanbee Doll Corp.
LADY HAMILTON - Glass–flat ☆ - Hamilton Glass Products Inc.
LADY HAMILTON - Watches ☆ - SMH (US) Inc.
LADY HAMPTON - Skin care products ☆ - T.N. Dickinson Co.
LADY HARDKORE - Apparel and accessories - Hardkore, Inc.
LADY HARDWICK - Apparel–women's - Hardwick Clothes Inc.
LADY HARRISON - Fabrics - Stonebridge Co.
LADY HATHAWAY - Apparel and accessories - Warnaco Inc.
LADY HAWKE - Fishing tackle - Fenwick
LADY HAZAN - Apparel–athletic - Isaac Hazan & Co.
LADY HELEN - Candy ☆ - Square Shooter Candy Co.
LADY HILDA - Hair care products - Edward A. Sport Laboratory
LADY HILTON - Flatware - Westmorland Sterling, Inc.
LADY HUDSON - Frames–eyeglass - Hudson Optical Corp.
LADY HUNTRESS - Apparel - Phyllis Urbach
LADY-IN-RED - Perfumes - Lady in Red, Ltd.
LADY IN WHITE - Perfumes - Lady in Red, Ltd.
LADY JAC - Apparel–women's ☆ - Kellwood Co.
LADY JANE - Eyeglasses - Art-Craft Optical Co.
LADY JANE - Skin care products - Jane Murdoch Miller
LADY JANE - Wallpaper ☆ - Brewster Wallcovering Co.
LADY JANE LTD. - Stationery - Jaymor Designs, Inc.
LADY JIFFIES - Slip covers - Kayser-Roth Corp.
LADY JUSTICE - Apparel and accessories - Big Entertainment, Inc.
LADY K - Jeans–women's - Key Industries, Inc.
LADY KATHRYN - Panty hose - Albertson's Inc.
LADY KAY - Bakery products - Kern's Bakeries, Inc.
LADY KAY - Food products - United Stores
LADY KENMORE - Housewares - Sears, Roebuck and Co.
LADY KENNY - Apparel and accessories - Donnkenny Inc.
LADY KOZAK - Cleaning preparations–household ☆ - KozaK Auto Drywash Inc.
LADY L - Frames–eyeglass - Liberty Optical Manufacturing Co.

LADY LANCASTER - Watches ☆ - SMH (US) Inc.
LADY LANE - Watches - M.Z. Berger & Co. Inc.
LADY LASER - Pistols - Concept Development Corp.
LADY LAURA - Apparel–women's - Russ Togs Inc.
LADY LAVENDER - Paints ☆ - Krylon/Dupli-Color
LADY LEE - Food products - American Stores Inc.
LADY LEE - Jeans–women's ☆ - Lee Apparel Co. Inc.
LADY LENNOX - Hair coloring preparations - Keystone Laboratories Inc.
LADY LENORE - Shampoos ☆ - General Nutrition Inc.
LADY LIBERTY - Frames–eyeglass - Liberty Optical Manufacturing Co.
LADY LIEUTENANT - Watches - Hampden Corp.
LADY LIGHT - Beverages–malt - Killian Bayer
LADY LIGHT - Irons–electric ☆ - Hamilton Beach/Proctor-Silex Inc.
LADY LIGHT - Wigs ☆ - Jean Paree Weegs Inc.
LADY LINDA - Bedspreads - Lady Linda Covers Inc.
LADY LINGERIE - Underwear and nightwear - Kirkhill Inc.
LADY LITE - Flashlights ☆ - Garrity Industries
LADY LITE - Frames–eyeglass ☆ - Universal/Univis Inc.
LADY LITE - Hair care products - Perfector Products
LADY LITE - Medical apparatus - Medicore, Inc.
LADY LOGGERS - Trees - Curtis H. Bod
LADY LONG-LEGS - Apparel–women's ☆ - Olga Co.
LADY LORA - Hair care products - Scolding Locks Corp.
LADY LORAINE - Hair care products - Old 97 Co.
LADY LOU - Eyeglasses - Art-Craft Optical Co.
LADY LOVE - Frames–eyeglass ☆ - Universal/Univis Inc.
LADY LOVE - Rings–jewelry - Artcarved Inc.
LADY LOVELYLOCKS - Dolls ☆ - Mattel, Inc.
LADY LUCK - Floor coverings–carpet and rugs ☆ - Masland Corp.
LADY LUCK - Frames–eyeglass - Pathway Optical Prods.
LADY LUCK - Hair care products - Master Chemical Co.
LADY LUCY - Watches - Elgin Watch Co.
LADY LYNN - Bottles–glass - Duray Co.
LADY LYNNE - Apparel–women's - Lady Lynne Lingerie Inc.
LADY LYNT - Closet accessories - Novelette Industries Inc.
LADY M. - Blouses–women's - Salant/Manhattan Industries
LADY M - Footwear - Scottie Industries Inc.
LADY MAC - Apparel–women's ☆ - Lady Mac Corset Co. Inc.
LADY MAC - Cases–eyeglass ☆ - California Optical Leather Inc.
LADY MADISON - Apparel–women's ☆ - Gem-Dandy, Inc.
LADY MADISON - Giftware ☆ - Gorham Inc.
LADY MANHATTAN - Apparel–women's - Manhattan International
LADY MANHATTAN - Fireworks - South Carolina Distributors, Inc.
LADY MANHATTAN - Frames–eyeglass - May Optical Co. Inc.
LADY MANHATTAN - Frames–eyeglass - Salant Corp.
LADY MARGARET - Bedding–linen - Dan River Inc.
LADY MARGARET - Silver products ☆ - Towle Silversmiths
LADY MARLENE - Apparel–women's - Lady Marlene
LADY MARTIN - Hardware - Martin Paint Stores
LADY MAVERICK - Apparel–women's - Wrangler Apparel Co.
LADY MICHELLE - Skin care products - Major/Advance International
LADY MILFORD - Thread - Belding Heminway Co. Inc.
LADY MITCHUM - Health care products - Revlon Consumer Products Corp.
LADY MONTINI - Footwear–women's - Bergmann Imports Ltd.
LADY N PINK - Computers - Dynacraft Industries Inc.
LADY NELSON - Watches - M.Z. Berger & Co. Inc.
LADY NEWPORT - Jewelry ☆ - Komor Manufacturing
LADY NOR - Playing cards ☆ - United States Playing Card Co.
LADY NORELCO - Cosmetics ☆ - Philips Electronics North America Corp.
LADY NORTHERNER - Footwear ☆ - Servus Footwear Co.
LADY OF DREAMS - Furniture - King Koil Licensing Co., Inc.
LADY OF PARIS - Hosiery - Virginia Maid Hosiery Mills Inc.
LADY OF SPAIN - Jewelry - Jewelex Collection
LADY OF THE LAKE - Fruits and vegetables - Mount Konocti Growers Inc.
LADY PADMORE - Shoes ☆ - Clarks of England Inc.
LADY PENBROOKE - Apparel–children's - A and H Sportswear Co., Inc.
LADY PEP - Vitamins and nutritional supplements - Natural Balance, Inc.
LADY PEPPERELL - Bedding–linen - West Point-Pepperell Inc.
LADY PETITE - Golfing equipment - Square Two Golf
LADY PETITE - Housewares - Pro Hardware Inc.
LADY PINNACLE - Sweaters - Pine State Knitwear Co.
LADY PLAYER - Hosiery - Desoto Hosiery Mills, Inc.
LADY POWER - Deodorants–personal - Faberge Co.
LADY POWERSTICK - Deodorants–personal - Chesebrough-Pond's USA Co.
LADY PRINGLE - Apparel and accessories - Warnaco Inc.
LADY PRO - Apparel and accessories - Kenneth P. Neumann

☆ = Now out of production

LADY PROTEX - Prophylactics - Protex

LADY PURITAN - Crocheted and knitted items ☆ - Puritan Sportswear Corp.

LADY QUEEN - Apparel–women's - Queen Casuals Inc.

LADY RAMPANT - Golfing equipment - Slotline Golf

LADY RECEPTOR - Golfing equipment - Aldila, Inc.

LADY RED WINGS - Shoes ☆ - Red Wing Shoe Co. Inc.

LADY REMINGTON - Electrical equipment - Remington Products Co.

LADY ROEN - Watches - Elgin Watch Co.

LADY ROSE - Food products machinery - Food Specialties Co. Inc.

LADY ROYAL - Watches - Elgin Watch Co.

LADY RUSS - Apparel–women's ☆ - Russ Togs Inc.

LADY SABINO - Apparel and accessories ☆ - Kellwood Co.

LADY SANSABELT - Apparel–women's - Jaymar-Ruby Inc.

LADY SCOTT - Paper–toilet ☆ - Scott Paper Co.

LADY SEAFARER - Apparel–women's - Jays Industries Inc.

LADY SETH - Clocks ☆ - General Time Corp. (Westclox/Seth Thomas Div.)

LADY SEYMOUR - Ironing boards - Seymour Housewares Corp.

LADY SHADES - Visors - Russ Berrie and Co., Inc.

LADY SHAKLEE - Health care products ☆ - Shaklee Corp.

LADY SHAPELY - Apparel–women's ☆ - Leslie Fay Separates

LADY SHAVE - Razors - Philips Electronics North America Corp.

LADY SHAVER - Bic Corp.

LADY SHAVEX - Razors–electric ☆ - Electro Engineering Products Co. Inc.

LADY SHEAFFER - Pens - Sheaffer Inc.

LADY SHIELD - Bulletproof vests - A & B Industries Inc.

LADY SLIPPER - Wines - Minnesota Winegrowers Cooperative

LADY SNOW - Dolls ☆ - Effanbee Doll Corp.

LADY SOLO - Attache cases - United States Luggage Co. L.P.

LADY SPEED DRY - Deodorizers - Mennen Co.

LADY SPEED SPRAY - Deodorizers - Mennen Co.

LADY SPEED STICK - Deodorizers - Mennen Co.

LADY SPEEDSTICK - Deodorants–personal - Colgate-Palmolive Co.

LADY SPENCER - Giftware ☆ - Gorham Inc.

LADY SPRINGFIELD - Watches - Bulova Corp.

LADY SQUIRE - Hobby kits - Lady Squire Colors

LADY STARKER - Shoes–athletic - Sam Brilliant Sporto

LADY STELLA - Cookies - Stella D'Oro Biscuit Co. Inc.

LADY STERLING - Golfing equipment - Golfsmith International Inc.

LADY STETSON - Fragrance - Coty Inc.

LADY STETSON - Frames–eyeglass - Zylo Ware Corp.

LADY STETSON - Sweaters ☆ - Stetson Hat Co. Inc.

LADY STING - Golfing equipment ☆ - Square Two Golf

LADY SUB - Watches - Rolex Watch USA, Inc.

LADY SUNBEAM - Razors–electric - Sunbeam-Oster Household Products

LADY SUNDOWNERS - Footwear–women's ☆ - R.G. Barry Corp.

LADY SUPREME - Hosiery - Mayer/Berkshire Corp.

LADY SURF - Watches - Movado Time Corp.

LADY SUSAN - Furniture - S.S. Dweck & Sons Inc.

LADY SUSAN - Underwear and nightwear ☆ - Marcus & Wiesen Inc.

LADY SUZANNE - Foundation garments–women's ☆ - Spencer Supports Ltd.

LADY SYROCO - Bathroom accessories ☆ - Syroco

LADY T - Shirts - Sara Lee Knit Products Inc.

LADY TECH - Cigarette lighters ☆ - K. Ogawa & Co. Inc.

LADY TECHMATIC - Shaving preparations - Gillette Co.

LADY, THE - Pet products - Glo-Marr Products Inc.

LADY TITAN - Uniforms–athletic ☆ - Felco Athletic Wear Co.

LADY TORTOISE - Toys ☆ - A.R.C. Toys Inc.

LADY TOUR - Golfing equipment - Golfsmith International Inc.

LADY TRAC II - Shaving preparations - Gillette Co.

LADY VANITY - Toilets–enameled - Kohler Co.

LADY VOLPE - Footwear–women's - Volpe Shoe Co.

LADY WAHL - Razors - Wahl Clipper Corp.

LADY WALTHAM - Watches - Elgin Watch Co.

LADY WALTON'S - Coffee - Lady Walton's Cookies, Inc.

LADY WELLCO - Shorts–women's - Wellco Enterprises Inc.

LADY WEST - Jackets ☆ - Pacific Trail, Inc.

LADY WIMBLETON - Watchbands–base metal - Hirsch Speidel Inc.

LADY WINDSOR - Sweaters - Binghamton Knitting Co.

LADY WINSTED - Kitchen appliances - Capitol Products Co.

LADY XPC - Golfing equipment - Golfsmith International Inc.

LADY XPC PLUS - Golfing equipment - Golfsmith International Inc.

LADYBEADS - Jewelry - Denise M. Adamsany

LADYBIRD - Clothespins - Benhof Inc.

LADYBIRD - Food products ☆ - Acme Continental Foods Inc.

LADYBIRD - Publisher's imprints ☆ - Merry Thoughts Inc.

LADYBUG - Cosmetics ☆ - Philips Electronics North America Corp.

LADYBUG - Garden equipment - H.D. Hudson Manufacturing Co.

LADYBUG - Lamps ☆ - Tensor Corp.

LADYDATE - Watches - Rolex Watch USA, Inc.

LADYFINGER - Household and garden gloves - Boss Manufacturing Co.

LADYFINGER - Paints - Plaid Enterprises, Inc.

LADYFINGERS - Brushes ☆ - Brushtech Inc.

LADYFINGERS - Cosmetics - Ladyfingers

LADYFINGERS - Gloves ☆ - Aris Isotoner Inc.

LADYFINGERZ - Scissors–hand-operated - Aaronco Pet Products, Inc.

LADYLUX - Faucet - Grohe America Inc.

LADY'S AID - Housewares - United States Pumice Co.

LADY'S AIDE - Cleaning equipment - United States Pumice Co.

LADY'S BEST FRIEND - Containers - Jeannie P. Murphy

LADY'S CHOICE - Deodorants–personal - Carter-Wallace, Inc.

LADY'S CHOICE - Floor coverings–carpet and rugs - Lees Carpets

LADY'S CHOICE - Vinegar - American Foods Corp.

LADYS COBRA II - Golfing equipment - Cobra Golf Inc.

LADY'S COMFORT - Teas - Merz Apothecary Inc.

LADY'S DAY - Stationery - Michael Wilkerson Jones

LADY'S FIRST - Beverages - American Beverage Corp.

LADY'S FIRST - Beverages - Daily Juice Products Inc.

LADY'S MBC - Razors - American Safety Razor Co.

LADY'S PARADISE, A - Apparel–women's - Henri Bendel, Inc.

LADY'S PRIDE - Craft supplies - Ohio Bag Corp.

LADYSMITH - Firearms, accessories, and parts - Smith & Wesson Corp.

LADYWORKS - Shoes - Wal-Mart Stores Inc.

L.A.E. - Pharmaceutical preparations - Seatrace Co.

L.A.F. - Apparel and accessories - Clark Screen Printing Co.

LAFAYETTE - Bathroom accessories - Baldwin Hardware Corp.

LAFAYETTE - Fabrics–denim - Emil Katz & Co.

LAFAYETTE - Floor coverings–carpet and rugs - Atlas Carpet Mills Inc.

LAFAYETTE - Furniture ☆ - Hickory Chair Co.

LAFAYETTE - Glass–leaded - Seneca Glass Co.

LAFAYETTE - Musical instruments ☆ - Fred Gretsch Enterprises

LAFAYETTE COLLEGE - Apparel, ceramicware, giftware, etc. - Lafayette College

LAFAYETTE INTERIOR FASHIONS - Window shades - Lafayette Venetian Blind, Inc.

LAFAYETTE MANOR - Wallpaper ☆ - Cherry Hill Studio

LAFEBER'S - Animal feeds - Lafeber Co.

LAFEMME - Brushes–hair ☆ - Phillips Brush Corp.

LAFEMME - Glassware–household - Owens-Illinois Inc. (Libbey Div.)

LAFEMME - Medical apparatus - William H. Cicio

LAFERS - Thread - Belding Heminway Co. Inc.

LAFF LINES - Greeting cards - American Greetings Corp.

LAFFARGUE & CIE. - Beverages–alcohol - Nor-Glo Import Co.

LAFFRO - Wigs - Fun World Inc.

LAFFS - Greeting cards - Joli Greeting Card Co.

LAFFS BY MARCEL - Greeting cards - Schurman Fine Papers

LAFFUN HEADS - Novelty items - Jobar International Inc./Bibi Products

LAFITTE CORK & CAPSULE - Corks - Lafitte Cork & Capsule, Inc.

LAFITTE'S BLACKENED SHRIMP - Food products - My Favorite Year Inc.

LAFLEX - Novelty items ☆ - Dakin Inc.

LAFLIRT - Hair care products ☆ - Joico Laboratories, Inc.

LAFORET - Apparel and accessories ☆ - Edison Brothers Stores, Inc.

LAFORMZ - Cookware - Kaiser Bakeware, Inc.

LAFUERZA - Deodorizers - Botanica Lamilagrosa, Inc.

LAFUMA - Apparel and accessories ☆ - Alpine Crafts Co. Inc.

LAG ENTERTAINMENT, INC. - Compact discs–prerecorded - Lago Entertainment, Inc.

LAG SHIELD - Anchors - Rawlplug Co., Inc.

LAGA-MICA - Moldings–plaster of paris - Reflective Creations Ltd.

LAGALERIE - Furniture - Stanley Furniture Co. Inc.

+L'AGANTE - Cosmetics - L'Agante Ltd.

LAGAZZI - Luggage - Global Fashion Accessories, Inc.

LAGERFELD - Colognes - Elizabeth Arden Inc.

LAGERFELD - Perfumes - Parfums International Ltd.

LAGERFELD PHOTO - Colognes - Parfums International Ltd.

LAGERMAN - Candy ☆ - Jaret Specialties Inc.

LAGNIAPPE - Crackers - Vista Bakery, Inc.

LAGNIAPPE - Food products - Christopher Layne Foods

LAGNIAPPE - Rice ☆ - Estherwood Rice Sales

LAGO - Handbags - Sears, Roebuck and Co.

LAGOL - Anesthetics - Alvin Last Inc.

LAGONDA - Motor vehicles ☆ - Aston Martin Lagonda of North America Inc.

LAGOON - Bowls - Svend Jensen of Denmark Inc.

☆ = Now out of production

LAGOON - Dinnerware–glass ☆ - Royal China & Porcelain Companies Inc.
LAGOON - Floor coverings–carpet and rugs ☆ - Dorsett Carpet Mills Inc.
LAGOON - Floor coverings–carpet and rugs ☆ - Masland Corp.
LAGOON - Fruit - Florida Fresh
LAGOON - Kitchenware–earthenware - Arita Sales Co. Inc.
LAGUITOS - Cigars - Cigars by Santa Clara N.A. Inc.
LAGUNA - Boats–motor - Thompson Boat Co.
LAGUNA - Brushes–paint - Corona Brushes Inc.
LAGUNA - Building materials - Cavco Industries, Inc.
LAGUNA - Cabinets ☆ - Decora
LAGUNA - Cosmetics - Laguna Brush Co.
LAGUNA - Dinnerware–glass ☆ - Nikko Ceramics Inc.
LAGUNA - Floor coverings - American Floor Products Co. Inc.
LAGUNA - Floor coverings–carpet and rugs - Mandate-Dawn Carpet Mills
LAGUNA - Floor coverings–carpet and rugs ☆ - Royalweve Carpet Mills
LAGUNA - Fruit drinks–bottled or canned - Laguna Beverage Co., Inc.
LAGUNA - Fruits and vegetables - West Indies Tropical Sales Co.
LAGUNA - Furniture ☆ - Riverside Furniture Corp.
LAGUNA - Handbags - Shane Handbags
LAGUNA - Hats - Arlington Hat Co. Inc.
LAGUNA - Jewelry - Laguna
LAGUNA - Lamps - Harris Industries
LAGUNA - Motor vehicles–motor homes - Forest River, Inc.
LAGUNA - Pet products - Rolf C. Hagen (USA) Corp.
LAGUNA - Pottery products - Laguna Clay Co.
LAGUNA - Shoes - Daniel Green Co.
LAGUNA - Shoes - R. Josephs Sportswear, Inc.
LAGUNA - Soap ☆ - Clearly Natural Products
LAGUNA - Swimming pools - KDI American Products, Inc.
LAGUNA - Tiles–ceramic - Dal-Tile Corp.
LAGUNA - Ukuleles - European Crafts/USA
LAGUNA - Window shades - Castec Window Shading Inc.
LAGUNA - Yarn ☆ - Tahki Imports Ltd.
LAGUNA ART - Greeting cards - Regency Thermographers Inc.
LAGUNA BAY - Bicycles ☆ - Huffy Corp.
LAGUNA BEACH - Floor coverings–carpet and rugs - Lees Carpets
LAGUNA BEACH - Floor coverings–carpet and rugs - Prestige Mills Inc.
LAGUNA BLUE - Dinnerware–glass ☆ - Metlox Pottery Shoppe
LAGUNA COLOR - Hair care products - American International Industries
LAGUNA EAST - Wallpaper ☆ - Capital Carousel Inc.
LAGUNA LIGHTING - Lamps - Rembrandt Lamps
LAGUNA LIGHTNING - Toys–automobiles - Mattel, Inc.
LAGUNA SUNSET - Hair care products - American International Industries
LAGURA - Food products - Lagura Foods Inc.
LAGX - Bedsprings - HARD Manufacturing Co. Inc.
LAHAINA - Beverages - Stars Beverage Co.
LAHAINA SAILOR - Apparel and accessories - Reyn Spooner, Inc.
LAHANA - Perfumes - Avon Products, Inc.
LAHOLM - Tiles–ceramic - Swedish Products Inc. (Sojo Inc.)
LAHTEX - Glass products - Seaply International
LAHTI - Sporting goods - Jarvinen USA
LAHTITE - Cosmetics - Ardell International Inc.
LAHVOSH - Bread - Tony Ingoglia Salami and Cheese Co. Inc.
LAI GROUP - Locks–door - Lock America, Inc.
LAICA - Candy - Murray-Allen International Inc.
LAID BACK GOLFERS - Giftware - Laid Back Enterprises, Inc.
LAIDBACK LEMONADE - Fruit-flavored cordial - Brown-Forman Corp.
+L'AIMANT - Perfume, hand and body lotion, etc. - Coty Inc.
LAINE ABSOLUTE - Floor coverings–carpet and rugs - LaVelle Textile
  Marketing Inc.
LAINE COLBERT - Fabrics–wool - DMC Corp.
LAINE SOUVERAINE - Floor coverings–carpet and rugs - LaVelle Textile
  Marketing Inc.
LAINERAL - Floor coverings–carpet and rugs ☆ - Eurotex Inc.
'LAINE'S BEST O'PESTO - Tomato pastes and sauces - Laine Products, Inc.
+L'AIR D'OR - Perfumes - Peterson Group, Inc.
+L'AIR DU TEMPS - Skin care products - Parfums Nina Ricci
LAIRD RAIN HOOD - Cases–camera - A. Laird Photo Accessories
LAIRD'S - Beverages–alcohol - Laird and Co.
LAIRDS - Jams and jellies ☆ - Bewley Irish Imports
LAIRD'S PREMIUM CANADIAN - Whiskey - Laird and Co.
LAIT A DEMAQUILLER - Skin care products - Ella Bache Inc.
LAIT BRONZANT - Cosmetics ☆ - Sothys USA Inc.
LAIT ENRICHI REQUIN - Skin care products - Ella Bache Inc.
LAIT EXOTIQUE - Skin care products - Ella Bache Inc.
LAITRAM - Food processors - Laitram Corp.

LAJ - Jewelry - Los Angeles Jewelry Production Inc.
LAJEN - Apparel - Clubhouse Marketing, Inc.
LAJE'S - Cookies - Baders Dutch Biscuit Co., Inc.
LAJO - Sausages - Lajo's, Inc.
LAJOIE - Nail care products - Cosmar Corp.
LAKCO - Sporting goods - Lake Country Products
LAKE - Brushes–paint - Corona Brushes Inc.
LAKE - Cleaning preparations - Lake Products Co. Inc.
LAKE - Food products - Stokes Fish Co.
LAKE 97 - Cleaning preparations - Lake Products Co. Inc.
LAKE AUSTIN - Golfing equipment - Golfsmith International Inc.
LAKE CHAMPLAIN - Fruits–canned - Champlain Valley Apple Storage Inc.
LAKE CHARLEVOIX - Food products - Sherman Canning Co.
LAKE COUNTRY - Wines - Taylor Wine Co. Inc.
LAKE COUNTY - Recording label ☆ - Domino Ltd.
LAKE COUNTY FAIR - Clothing - Lake County Agricultural Society, Inc.
LAKE COVE - Fruits and vegetables - Mount Konocti Growers Inc.
LAKE CRYSTAL - Salt - North American Salt Co.
LAKE DYE - Dyes and pigments - C.B. Dolge Co.
LAKE ERIE - Food products - Empire Butter & Egg Co.
LAKE ERIE ISLANDS - Wines - Heineman Winery
LAKE FERNS, INC. - Flowers, plants, and seeds - Lake Ferns, Inc.
LAKE-FLITE - Boats–motor - Lake-Flite Searay Boats
LAKE FOREST - Furniture - Athens Furniture Industries Inc.
LAKE FOREST - Furniture ☆ - Bassett Furniture Industries, Inc.
LAKE FOREST - Occasional tables ☆ - JDI Group, Inc.
LAKE FOREST - Siding - Aluminum Co. of America
LAKE HARMONY - Apparel and accessories - Berwick Knitwear, Inc.
LAKE HARMONY ROWING CLUB - Apparel and accessories - Charles Komar
  and Sons Inc.
LAKE ISLAND - Thread ☆ - Susan Bates Inc.
LAKE JON - Boats - O.M.C. Aluminum Boat Group
LAKE MASTER - Boats–motor ☆ - Alumacraft Boat Co.
LAKE MEMPHREMAGOG SUNRISE - Teas - Vermont Tea & Maple
LAKE MILLS - Milk - Lake Mills Coop. Creamery
LAKE NIAGARA - Wines - Widmer's Wine Cellars Inc.
LAKE OF THE WOODS - Footwear - Lake of the Woods
LAKE ONTARIO - Food products - United Apple Sales Inc.
LAKE PLACID - Apparel–men's - Sandess Manufacturing Co. Inc.
LAKE PLACID - Footwear–athletic - Roller Derby Skate Corp.
LAKE PLACID - Window coverings ☆ - Vertilux-Louverlux Inc.
LAKE POINTE - Floor coverings–carpet and rugs - Alexander Smith Carpets
LAKE POINTE - Trailers–travel - Fleetwood Enterprises, Inc.
LAKE REGION - Vegetables–canned - Dean Foods Co.
LAKE ROSELLE - Wines - Widmer's Wine Cellars Inc.
LAKE SHACKLEFORD - Food products - Antique Mall & Crown
LAKE SHORE - Charcoal - Milazzo Industries Inc.
LAKE SHORE - Dinnerware–glass ☆ - Lenox, Inc.
LAKE SHORE - Honey - W.F. Straub & Co.
LAKE SHORE DRIVE - Housewares - Impressions Handprinters Inc.
LAKE SHORE DRIVE - Wallpaper ☆ - Capital Carousel Inc.
LAKE SONOMA - Wines - Lake Sonoma Winery
LAKE SONOMA WINERY - Wines - House of Burgundy Inc.
LAKE SPRINGS - Trailers–travel - Fleetwood Enterprises, Inc.
LAKE SUPERIOR - Food products - Bodin Fisheries
LAKE TAHOE - Wines - Madrona Vineyards
LAKE TAHOE BREWING COMPANY - Beverages–malt - Lake Tahoe
  Brewing Co., Inc.
LAKE TO LAKE - Cheese - Lake to Lake Dairy
LAKE VALLEY - Flowers, plants, and seeds - Lake Valley Seed Inc.
LAKE VALLEY - Pickles - Harrison Packing Co. Inc.
LAKE VIEW - Floor coverings–carpet and rugs - Galaxy Carpet Mills Inc.
LAKE WALES - Fruit drinks–bottled or canned - Citrus World Inc.
LAKE WENATCHEE - Food products - Leavenworth Fruit Co.
LAKEFIELD - Sinks–metal - Kohler Co.
LAKEFRESH - Food products - Bay Port Fish Co.
LAKELAND - Garden equipment ☆ - L.J. Rench & Co.
LAKELAND - Paper - Silver Leaf Paper Co.
LAKELAND - Sinks–porcelain - American Standard Inc.
LAKEMASTER - Boats–motor ☆ - Ebbtide Corp.
LAKEMASTER - Pumps–water - Underhill International Corp.
LAKEMASTER - Watches - Zell Bros.
LAKEMONT - Clocks - Ridgeway Clock Co.
LAKER - Seafood products–fresh or frozen - Aquamarine, Inc.
LAKEROL - Candy - Skandia Foods Inc.
LAKE'S - Pet products - Lake's Unlimited, Inc.

LAKESCRAFT - Boats–pontoons - Lakes Manufacturing Inc.

LAKESHIRE - Apparel and accessories ☆ - California Manufacturing Co. Inc.

LAKESHIRE - Occasional furniture ☆ - JDI Group, Inc.

LAKESHORE - Games - Lakeshore Learning Materials

LAKESHORE - Mushrooms ☆ - Manfredini Enterprises

LAKESHORE - Mustard - Bewley Irish Imports

LAKESIDE - Carts - Young's

LAKESIDE - Colognes - Avon Products, Inc.

LAKESIDE - Floor coverings–carpet and rugs ☆ - Colonial Mills Inc.

LAKESIDE - Games - Lakeside Games

LAKESIDE - Manufactured homes - Redman Industries, Inc.

LAKESIDE - Vegetables–frozen - Lakeside Packing Co.

LAKESIDE - Wines - Lukens Vineyard Inc.

LAKESIDE DAIRY - Milk - Lakeside Dairy

LAKESIDE LEDGER, THE - Publisher's imprints - Lakeside Publishing Co., Inc.

LAKESPRING WINERY - Wines - Lakespring Winery

LAKEVIEW - Food products - Pies Inc.

LAKEVIEW, THE - Construction equipment - Sentry Building

LAKEWOOD - Automotive parts and accessories - Echlin Inc.

LAKEWOOD - Cabinets - Aristokraft, Inc.

LAKEWOOD - Clocks - Ridgeway Clock Co.

LAKEWOOD - Fans–electric - Lakewood Engineering and Manufacturing Co.

LAKEWOOD - Floor coverings–carpet and rugs - Queen Carpet Corp.

LAKEWOOD - Food products - Country Life Natural Foods

LAKEWOOD - Furniture - Pilliod Co.

LAKEWOOD - Furniture ☆ - Bassett Furniture Industries, Inc.

LAKEWOOD - Juices - Florida Bottling Inc.

LAKEWOOD - Motor vehicles–motor homes - Baron Motor Homes Inc.

LAKEWOOD - Occasional tables - JDI Group, Inc.

LAKEWOOD - Sporting goods ☆ - Maurice Sporting Goods, Inc.

LAKORUS - Luggage - Korus Co., Inc.

LAKOTA - Bicycles - Huffy Corp.

LAKOTA - Moccasins - Oglala Sioux Products Inc.

LAKRITS - Candy ☆ - Andre Prost Inc.

LALANI - Fruit drinks–bottled or canned ☆ - Safeway Stores Inc.

LALAPALOZA - Pans ☆ - General Housewares Corp.

LALA'S BAR & GRILL - Food products - Golden Whisk Pasta Partners

LALIQUE - Fabrics–taffetas - Burlington House Fabrics Group

LALIQUE - Glassware–household - Lalique North America

LALLIE BABIES - Notebooks and notepads - Lallie Inc.

LALO'S - Tortillas - Lalo Restaurants, Inc.

LAM-BAC - Fabrics - Custom Laminations Inc.

LAM FAB - Paints - E-Z Paintr Corp.

LAM-I-GRAPHS - Quilts - Extra Special Products Corp.

LAM-O-TEX - Maps ☆ - American Map Corp.

LAM PAC INT'L - Medical apparatus - Lampac International Ltd.

LAM RESEARCH - Semiconductor manufacturing machinery - Lam Research Corp.

LAMA THE LLAMA - Dolls - Donald Eric Black

LAMACADO - Dog food - American Superior Feeds, Inc.

LAMALOON - Window shades - Distinctive Window Fashions

LAMAR - Pet products - Quiktrip Corp.

LAMAR - Recording label - Lamar Music Co.

LAMARLE - Food containers - Frye International Corp.

LAMARTINIQUE SALAD DRESSINGS - Food products - Reily Foods

LAMAZE - Cribs–wood - American Society for Psychoprophylaxis in Obstetrics, Inc.

LAMAZE INFANT DEVELOPMENT SYSTEM - Toys - Learning Curve Toys, LLC

LAMB & LION - Labels–paper - Koala Records Inc.

LAMB & RICE DOG TREATS - Dog food - Mardel Laboratories, Inc.

LAMB CHOP - Steering mechanisms–motor vehicle - Benjamin & Medwin Inc.

LAMB-KNIT - Apparel–men's - Obion Denton

LAMB LOLETTE - Food products - Veal Connection Corp.

LAMB PLUSH - Seat covers - Saddleman, Inc.

LAMB PRO - Dog food - Merrick Petfoods Inc.

LAMB, THE - Figurines - Liberty Ridge

LAMB TOUCH COW - Coats–leather - Pelle Leather, Ltd.

LAMB-WESTON - Vegetables–frozen ☆ - Lamb-Weston, Inc.

LAMBA-FI - Apparel–men's - Alps Sportswear Manufacturing Co.

LAMBADA - Yarn - Tahki Imports Ltd.

LAMBCHOP - Novelty items–paper - Unique Industries, Inc.

LAMBDA - Industrial machinery - U.S. Tsubaki, Inc.

LAMBDA FAZE - Laboratory apparatus - Biotecx Laboratories, Inc.

LAMBERHURST FRENCH AOC VARIETALS - Wines ☆ - Maison Jomere Ltd.

LAMBERHURST GIN - Wines ☆ - Maison Jomere Ltd.

LAMBEROLA - Recording label - Acoustographic Records

LAMBERT & BUTLER - Cigarettes - G.A. Georgopulo & Co. Inc.

LAMBERT & BUTLER 100'S - Cigarettes - G.A. Georgopulo & Co. Inc.

LAMBERT BRIDGE - Wines - Lambert Bridge

LAMBERTH'S FORLAG - Greeting cards - Foge Jensen Imports

LAMBERTI - Wines - Prestige Wine Imports Corp.

LAMBERTON - Dishes–china - Sterling China Co. Inc.

LAMBERTS - Pasta - Anco Foods Corp.

LAMBETH WALK - Floor coverings ☆ - Tarkett, Inc.

LAMBI KINS - Toys–stuffed - Fun World Inc.

LAMBIE PIE - Toys–stuffed - Russ Berrie and Co., Inc.

LAMBLEND - Sweaters - Puritan Sportswear Corp.

LAMBO - Apparel and accessories - James R. Lambright

LAMBORN FAMILY VINYARDS - Wines ☆ - Diamond Wine Merchants

LAMBRECHT - Weather tracking equipment - Watrous & Co. Inc.

LAMBRIA - Wallpaper ☆ - Wall-Pride Inc.

LAMBRIDGE - Floor coverings ☆ - Teak International

LAMBROS MILONA - Apparel and accessories - Lambros Milona Fashions Ltd.

LAMB'S - Vegetables–frozen ☆ - Lamb-Weston, Inc.

LAMBS & IVY - Bedding–linen - Lambs & Ivy

LAMBS CLUB - Cigars - Finck Cigar Co.

LAMBS FARM - Preserved foods–prepackaged - Lambs, Inc.

LAMB'S NATURAL - Vegetables–frozen ☆ - Lamb-Weston, Inc.

LAMB'S NAVY - Beverages–alcohol - Hiram Walker & Sons, Inc.

LAMB'S SELECT - Vegetables–frozen ☆ - Lamb-Weston, Inc.

LAMB'S SUPREME - Vegetables–frozen ☆ - Lamb-Weston, Inc.

LAMBSALOT - Toys–stuffed ☆ - Gund, Inc.

LAMBSDOWN - Paper–tissue - Romar International Corp.

LAMBSEY DIVEY - Toys–stuffed - Dakin Inc.

LAMBSKYN - Paint rollers - Rol-Brush Manufacturing, Div. (Michigan Brush Mfg. Co., Inc.)

LAMBSWOOL 100 - Paint rollers - Wooster Brush Co.

LAMBSWORLD - Sweaters - Puritan Sportswear Corp.

LAMBTEX - Paint rollers - Adams Brush Manufacturing Co., Inc.

LAMBY - Comforters - J.K. Properties, Inc.

LAMBY NURSERY COLLECTION FROM THE LAMB DOWN UNDER - Infant product - J.K. Properties, Inc.

LAMCHORD - Wood products - Weyerhaeuser Co.

LAMCLAD - Office supplies - International Paper (Decorative Products Division)

LAMCO - Audio equipment - AVES Audio Visual Systems Inc.

LAME - Yarn - Lion Brand Yarn Co.

LAME DUCK - Calendars - Lame Duck, Inc.

LAMENDOLA - Footwear - Rossini Industries

LAMESA - Furniture ☆ - Bassett Furniture Industries, Inc.

LAMFORD - Cooking equipment–household - Southeast Fixtures, Inc.

LAMI-BOARD - Wood products - Georgia-Pacific Corp.

LAMI-FLOOR - Floor coverings–linoleum - Georgia-Pacific Corp.

LAMI-GUIDE - Tools ☆ - Ralph Wilson Plastics Co.

LAMI-LABELS - Labels–paper - Ever-Ready Label Corp.

LAMI-LOK - Labels–paper ☆ - Litton Industrial Automation Systems

LAMI-MESSAGE - Novelty items ☆ - Norstar Enterprises

LAMIBAG - Rubber–extruded - Mabex Universal Corp.

LAMICAN - Elevators - Columbia Elevator Products Co., Inc.

LAMICLAD - Fiberboard - NVF Co. (Molded Products Div.)

LAMICLEAR - Liners and covers–Swimming pool - Swimline International Corp.

LAMICOR - Fiberboard - NVF Co. (Molded Products Div.)

LAMIFILM BAG - Rubber–extruded - Mabex Universal Corp.

LAMIFOAM - Rubber–extruded - Mabex Universal Corp.

LAMIGLAS - Sporting goods - Lamiglas Inc.

LAMIGRAM - Artists' materials - Web Communications Group, Inc.

LAMILACE - Fabrics - Plever Industries Inc.

LAMILUX - Cartons–paperboard - Georgia-Pacific Corp.

LAMIN-ALL - Adhesives and sealants - Sureguard, Inc.

LAMINA - Pharmaceutical preparations ☆ - Merrick Medicine Co. Inc.

LAMINA - Tubes–plastic - Cobe Laboratories, Inc.

LAMINA XXV - Metals ☆ - Kawneer Co., Inc.

LAMINAR - Cosmetics ☆ - Stanley Fay Co.

LAMINAR - Work benches - Troemner Inc.

LAMINART - Plastics–laminated - Lamin-Art, Inc.

LAMINEER - Wood products - Weyerhaeuser Co.

LAMINENE - Artists' materials - Keuffel & Esser Co.

LAMINET - Reinforced fabric - Conwed Plastics

LAMINEX - Wood products - Cavert Wire Co. Inc.

LAMKIN - Gloves - Leisure Leather Ltd.

LAMM AUDIO LABORATORY - Audio equipment - Vladimir V. Shushurin

☆ = Now out of production

LAMMATES - Counter tops–laminated - International Paper (Decorative Products Division)

LAMMERMOOR - Tableware–china - Lenox, Inc.

LAMMY - Toys–stuffed ☆ - Russ Berrie and Co., Inc.

LAMMY-WHAMMIES - Pet food ☆ - Petsations Pet Products

LAMNECK - Fittings–cast iron ☆ - Clayton & Lambert Manufacturing Co.

LAMODE - Musical instrument accessories - Prestini Reed Corp.

LAMON - Recording label - Lamon Records

LAMONT - Housewares - Lamont Ltd.

LAMONTAGE - Floor coverings–carpet and rugs - MGK Group Inc.

LAMONT'S AUTHENTIC SOUTHERN MARINADES - Sauces - Lamont N. Burns

+L'AMOR BY GREKA - Apparel and accessories - Euramco International

LAMORA - Bathing suits - Catalina

LAMORETTE - Underwear and nightwear - Lamorette, Inc.

LAMOSA - Tiles–ceramic ☆ - Huntington/Pacific Ceramics Inc.

LAMOTT - Musical instruments - Jack Spratt Woodwind Shop

LAMOTTE - Chemical preparations - LaMotte Chemical Co.

+L'AMOUR - Bedding–linen - Dan River Inc.

+L'AMOUR - Infant product - Im-Link Corp.

+L'AMOUR - Jewelry - Page Jewelers

LAMOUS - Wallcoverings - American Silk Mills

LAMP A LITES - Giftware ☆ - Bar & Barbeque Products Inc.

LAMP DRY - Skin care products - Spilo/Mehaz Worldwide

LAMP LITE - Lighting equipment ☆ - Home Equipment Manufacturing Co.

LAMP-LOCK - Miniature electric lights - Minami International Corp.

LAMP LUSTRE - Nail care products - Light Logic, Inc.

LAMP MANAGER - Lighting equipment - BHK Inc.

LAMP-O-MATIC - Lamps - House of Rand

LAMP PALS - Infant product ☆ - Reliance Products Corp.

LAMP SCENT RING - Deodorizers - Quality of Life Associates

LAMPA - Lamp bulbs–incandescent ☆ - Angelo Brothers Co.

LAMPANG - Bedding–linen - Dan River Inc.

LAMPARIUM - Lamps ☆ - Kaadan Ltd.

LAMPART - Furniture - U.S. Furniture Industries Inc.

LAMPARTS - Hardware ☆ - Angelo Brothers Co.

LAMPCRAFTERS - Lamps - Lampcrafters, Inc.

LAMPGARD - Circuit boards - Energy Savings, Inc.

LAMPHOLDER - Lighting fixtures - Swivelier Co. Inc.

LAMPHUGGER - Lighting fixtures - Swivelier Co. Inc.

LAMPHUGGERS - Lighting equipment - Bernard Cappelli Inc.

LAMPIN' - Footwear - Vans, Inc.

LAMPLIGHT - Christmas tree ornaments - Cracker Box Inc.

LAMPLIGHT - Furniture - Thomasville Furniture Industries Inc.

LAMPLIGHTER - Apparel stores–children's - Tom and Jerry Boyswear Inc.

LAMPLIGHTER - Fabrics ☆ - Uniroyal Engineered Products

LAMPLIGHTER - Mail boxes - Leigh

LAMPLIGHTER - Trailers–travel ☆ - Coachmen Industries, Inc.

LAMPLIGHTER BOOKS - Publisher's imprints ☆ - Zondervan Publishing House

LAMPMASTER - Projectors–photographic - General Audio-Visual Inc.

LAMPOST MEATS - Meat products–pork - Waking S Farms, Ltd.

LAMPRENE - Antibiotics - Ciba-Geigy Corp.

LAMPREP - Balsa wood for boat-building - Baltek Corp.

LAMPS OF BEAUTY - Lamps–table - Mario Sales Inc.

LAMPUS - Wallpaper - Doshi Wallcoveringss Inc.

LAMSON - Cutlery - Lamson and Goodnow Manufacturing Co.

LAMSON - Fishing tackle - Sage Manufacturing Corp.

LAMSON SHARP - Cutlery - Lamson and Goodnow Manufacturing Co.

LAMSPUN - Crocheted and knitted items - Garland Knitting Mills

LAMUTHANE - Fabrics–coated - Custom Laminations Inc.

LAMY - Pens - Hampton-Haddon Marketing

LAN - Computer hardware - Cimetrics, Inc.

LAN 75 - Cables - Cable Design Technologies, Inc.

LAN-ACES - Computer peripheral equipment - LAN-ACES Inc.

LAN COMMANDER - Computer software - Power on Software, Inc.

LAN/CORE - Computer software - Teknekron Communications Systems Inc.

LAN DISTANCE - Computer software - International Business Machines Corp.

LAN ELEC - Food processors - Am-Mac Inc.

LAN ESCORT - Computer software ☆ - Pearson Technical Software Inc.

LAN EXPANDER - Computer software - Gateway Communications Inc.

LAN-GARD - Novelty items - Seron Manufacturing Co.

LAN GUARD - Electrical equipment - MCG Electronics, Inc.

LAN-HOPPER - Computer peripheral equipment - J.C. Baugh Consulting

LAN-LAY - Cosmetic oil - Sunny More International Inc.

LAN-LAY - Hair care products ☆ - La Lueur International Inc.

LAN-LIN - Cleaning preparations - Radiator Specialty Co.

LAN MAN - Computer peripheral equipment - Engineered Data Products Inc.

L.A.N. MARK - Computer software - Trimark Technologies Inc.

LAN-O-GLO - Veterinary pharmaceutical preparations - Happy Jack, Inc.

LAN-O-SHEEN - Cleaning preparations - Lan-O-Sheen, Inc.

LAN-O-SIL - Skin care products - Greever's

LAN-O-SOFT - Cosmetics - Lan-O-Sheen, Inc.

LAN-O-WIPE - Cleaning preparations - Lan-O-Sheen, Inc.

LAN-TABS - Pharmaceutical preparations - Columbia Drug Co. Inc.

LAN WAY - Electronic equipment ☆ - Jupiter Technology, Inc.

LAN WORKPLACE - Computer software - Novell, Inc.

LAN-X - Cables - Cable Design Technologies, Inc.

LANA - Artists' materials - Andrews/Nelson/Whitehead

LANA - Computer hardware - Lan Access Corp.

LANA - Crocheted and knitted items - Lana Inc.

LANA - Frames–eyeglass - Rozin Optical Export Corp.

LANA - Yarn ☆ - Tahki Imports Ltd.

LANA KALA - Eyeglasses ☆ - Cable Car Eyeware

LANABAC - Pharmaceutical preparations - Lannett Co. Inc.

LANABARB - Pharmaceutical preparations - Lannett Co. Inc.

LANABEE-C - Vitamins and nutritional supplements - Lannett Co. Inc.

LANABIOTIC - Antibiotics - Combe Inc.

LANABURN - Pharmaceutical preparations - Lannett Co. Inc.

LANABUTAZON COMPOUND - Pharmaceutical preparations - Lannett Co. Inc.

LANACANE - Skin care products - Combe Inc.

LANACANE MAXIMUM STRENGTH - Skin care products - Combe Inc.

LANACILLIN - Antibiotics - Lannett Co. Inc.

LANACILLIN VK - Pharmaceutical preparations - Lannett Co. Inc.

LANACLIENT - Computer software - Lan Access Corp.

LANACORT 10 - Skin care products - Combe Inc.

LANACOTTA - Fabrics ☆ - Stylecrest Fabrics Ltd.

LANAGER - Computer software - Micro Technology Inc.

LANAHEX - Skin care products - Lannett Co. Inc.

LANAI - Fabrics - Vertilux-Louverlux Inc.

LANAI - Lumber - Georgia-Pacific Corp.

LANA'I BREEZE - Juices ☆ - Dole Food Co., Inc.

LANAI CUSHION - Furniture - Tropitone Furniture Co. Inc.

LANAI SLING - Furniture - Tropitone Furniture Co. Inc.

LANAKILA - Dolls - Lanakila Crafts

LANAMINS - Vitamins and nutritional supplements - Lannett Co. Inc.

LANAPHILIC - Pharmaceutical preparations - Medco Lab Inc.

LANARK - Wallpaper - Wall Fashion Inc.

LANAS KATIA - Yarn - Knitting Fever Inc.

LANASED - Pharmaceutical preparations - Lannett Co. Inc.

LANATOSIDE C - Pharmaceutical preparations ☆ - City Chemical Corp.

LANATRATE - Pharmaceutical preparations - Lannett Co. Inc.

LANATUSS - Cold remedies - Lannett Co. Inc.

LANAURINE - Pharmaceutical preparations - Lannett Co. Inc.

LANAVITE - Pharmaceutical preparations - Lannett Co. Inc.

LANAZETS - Vitamins and nutritional supplements - Lannett Co. Inc.

LANCASHIRE - Bond paper - Copco Papers Inc.

LANCASHIRE - Furniture ☆ - Drexel Heritage Furnishings, Inc.

LANCASTER - Batteries - East Penn Manufacturing Co., Inc.

LANCASTER - Cabinets ☆ - Aristokraft, Inc.

LANCASTER - Cabinets–metal - American Woodmark Corp.

LANCASTER - Ceiling panels ☆ - Conwed Plastics

LANCASTER - Chewing tobacco - American Maize-Products Co.

LANCASTER - Clocks - Ridgeway Clock Co.

LANCASTER - Clocks ☆ - General Time Corp. (Westclox/Seth Thomas Div.)

LANCASTER - Dinnerware–glass - Royal China & Porcelain Companies Inc.

LANCASTER - Dishes–china - Waterford Wedgewood USA, Inc.

LANCASTER - Floor coverings–carpet and rugs - Trans-Ocean Import Co. Inc.

LANCASTER - Furniture ☆ - Bassett Furniture Industries, Inc.

LANCASTER - Glassware–household ☆ - Anchor Hocking Glass, Inc.

LANCASTER - Luggage - American Flyer

LANCASTER - Luggage - Naluco, Inc.

LANCASTER - Meats - American Stores Co.

LANCASTER - Nuts–salted, roasted, cooked, or canned - Lancaster Nut Co. Inc.

LANCASTER - Paper–writing - Gilbert Paper Co.

LANCASTER - Skates–roller ☆ - Lancaster Toy Co.

LANCASTER - Skin care products - Smithkline Beecham Corp.

LANCASTER - Tobacco–chewing or smoking - Swisher International, Inc.

LANCASTER COLONY - Candles - Candle-Lite Co.

LANCASTER COUNTRY STENCILS - Wallpaper ☆ - Eisenhart Wallcoverings Co.

LANCASTER COUNTY - Clocks ☆ - SMH (US) Inc.
LANCASTER COUNTY ORIGINAL - Candy - Keppel's Inc.
LANCASTER COUNTY PENNSYLVANIA DUTCH - Candy - Keppel's Inc.
LANCASTER COUNTY WINERY - Wines - Lancaster County Winery Ltd.
LANCASTER FARMS WHOLESALE NURSERY - Nurseries and garden stores - Lancaster Farms, Inc.
LANCASTER GLASS - Glassware–household - Lancaster Glass Corp.
LANCASTER JET HAWKS - Trading cards and stamps - Clutch Play Baseball, LLC
LANCASTER LIBRARY COLLECTION - Furniture ☆ - Bassett Furniture Industries, Inc.
LANCASTER SQUARE - Furniture ☆ - Lane Co. Inc.
LANCAT - Electronic equipment - Datacom Tech., Inc.
LANCATCH - Computer software - FTP Software, Inc.
LANCE - Automotive parts and accessories - Lancaster Colony Automotive Group
LANCE - Candy - Lance, Inc.
LANCE - Craft supplies - A. Meyers & Sons Corp.
LANCE - Drain cleaner ☆ - Jancyn Manufacturing Corp.
LANCE - Giftware - Lance Corp.
LANCE - Jewelry - Jacoby-Bender Inc.
LANCE - Motor vehicles–motor homes - Lance Camper Manufacturing Corp.
LANCE-A-LITTLE - Toys–stuffed - CBS Toys
LANCE ALPHA - Boats–canoes ☆ - Black River Canoes
LANCE BETA - Toys–models - Estes Industries
LANCE MINI - Tortillas - Lance, Inc.
LANCE RING-O-LING - Games - Toyvision, Inc.
LANCELOT - Bedding–linen - Pillowtex Corp.
LANCELOT - Cabinets ☆ - Triangle Pacific Corp. (Cabinet Division)
LANCELOT - Floor coverings - Aladdin Mills, Inc.
LANCELOT - Pens - Pentel of America, Ltd.
LANCELOT - Sinks–metal - Moen Inc.
LANCELOT - Sodium compounds - Mallet and Co.
LANCELOT - Waterproof outerwear - Distributors Service Corp.
LANCELOT LION - Toys–stuffed - Russ Berrie and Co., Inc.
LANCER - Artists' materials - Robert Simmons Inc.
LANCER - Cabinets - Grandview Products Co.
LANCER - Duplicating machines - Dietzgen Corp.
LANCER - Electronic equipment - GAF Corp.
LANCER - Envelopes–paper ☆ - Saxon Paper Co.
LANCER - Fireplaces - Malm Fireplaces Inc.
LANCER - Glassware–household - Durand International
LANCER - Golf clubs - King Par Corp.
LANCER - Motor vehicles ☆ - Chrysler Corp. (Dodge Car Div.)
LANCER - Pipes–tobacco - S.M. Frank & Co. Inc. (Kaywoodie-Yello-Bole-Medico)
LANCER - Thread - Threads USA Div.
LANCER - Tools–machine - Cincinnati Machine
LANCER - Toys–models ☆ - Estes Industries
LANCER - Trailers–travel ☆ - Hop-Cap Inc.
LANCER - Wheelchairs - Everest and Jennings International Ltd.
LANCER II - Floor coverings–carpet and rugs - Trend Carpet
LANCERS - Cigars ☆ - House of Windsor Inc.
LANCERS - Leather goods - Miller Harness Co., Inc.
LANCERS - Shoes - Sylvania Shoe Manufacturing Corp.
LANCERS - Wines - Heublein, Inc.
LANCETTI - Apparel–men's ☆ - Cavaliero Cravats
LANCETTI - Skin care products - European Esthetic Inc.
LANCETTI HANDBAGS - Handbags ☆ - Jerry Kohn Inc.
LANCIA - Motor vehicles–automobiles - Fiat USA, Inc.
LANCIA - Pizzas–mixes ☆ - General Mills, Inc.
LANCO - Paints - Growco Aerosol
LANCO - School bags, back packs, diaper bags - Bag Bazaar Ltd.
LANCO - Wood products - Langdale Forest Products Co.
LANCOME - Cosmetics - Lancome
LANCOME NIOSOME - Skin care products - Lancome
LANCOMIA - Cosmetics - Lancome
LANCOURT - Wines - European Beverage Co., Inc.
LAND-A-RANGER THOMPSON - Garden equipment - Thompson Custom Machine Works Ltd.
LAND-AND-SEA - Globes - Replogle Globes Inc.
LAND AND SKY THE QUALITY OF SLEEP - Mattresses - Land and Sky Manufacturing Inc.
LAND BEFORE TIME - Wallpaper ☆ - Priss Prints Inc.
LAND BY THE INCH - Novelty items - Irving Mishel
LAND-BY-THE-INCH - Soil–potting - Andyland Concepts Inc.

LAND CROSS - Shoes - Sports World, Inc.
LAND CRUISER - Apparel and accessories - K-Swiss Inc.
LAND FILL - Tires - Bridgestone/Firestone, Inc.
LAND GRABBERS - Agricultural products - Land Grabbers, Inc.
LAND HO - Food products ☆ - Pacmarine Products Inc.
LAND LEVELER - Garden equipment - Garden Pals, Inc.
LAND MAMMAL - Recording label - Jazz Composer's Orchestra Association Inc.
LAND-N-LAKES - Waterproof outerwear - Gordon & Ferguson of Delaware, Inc.
LAND O' JAZZ - Recording label - Land O' Jazz Records
LAND O' LACE - Trimmings–fabric - Novtex Corp.
LAND O' LAKES - Baked goods - Meyer's Bakeries
LAND O' LAKES - Caviar ☆ - Smith Brothers Food Service Inc.
LAND O PINES - Milk ☆ - Land O Pines Dairy Products
LAND O'DIXIE - Nuts–salted, roasted, cooked, or canned - Fisher Nut Co.
LAND OF LEGEND - Figurines ☆ - Gilbert Stone Enterprises Inc.
LAND OF NINJA - Games - Avalon Hill Game Co.
LAND OF NOD - Apparel - Donna Poulson
LAND OF OZ MEATS - Meat products - Donald W. Whitson
LAND OF THE FREE - Food products - Tofutti Brands Inc.
LAND OF THE TROLLS - Toys - Trendmasters, Inc.
LAND OF THE UNICORN - Computer software - Unicorn Software
LAND O'FROST - Meat products–beef - Land O Frost Inc.
LAND O'LAKES - Dairy products - Land O'Lakes Inc.
LAND O'LAKES - Honey - W.F. Straub & Co.
LAND O'LAKES - Milk - Land O' Lakes, Inc. (Fluid Dairy Division)
LAND O'SUN - Food products - Betters International Food Corp.
LAND RACE - Card game - International Games
LAND ROVER - Bicycles ☆ - Montgomery Ward & Co. Inc.
LAND ROVER - Motor vehicles–all-terrain - Land Rover North America Inc.
LAND ROVER - Shoes - Thom McAn Shoe Co.
LAND RUN - Apparel and accessories - Bricktown Brewery
LAND RUN LAGER - Shirts - Bricktown Brewery
LAND SEA AIR SQUAD - Video games ☆ - Taito America Corp.
LAND SHARK - Carpet sweepers - DBA Products Co.
LAND SHARK - Saws–power - DBNA Trademarks Holding Inc.
LAND SHARK - Toys–automobiles - Mattel, Inc.
LAND SPAN - Radio communications equipment - JFL Communications, Inc.
LAND SPEED RACER - Toys - Fisher-Price, Inc.
LAND-TRAC - Tires - Uniroyal Goodrich Tire Co.
LAND YACHT - Motor vehicles–motor homes - Airstream Inc.
LANDA - Recording label - Universal Record
LANDAU - Apparel and accessories - Landau Uniforms, Inc.
LANDAU - Automotive parts and accessories ☆ - Lancaster Colony Automotive Group
LANDAU - Boats–fishing - Landau Manufacturing Co.
LANDAU - Skin care products - Landau Skincare Products
LANDAU - Violins - Multivox/Sorkin Music Co. Inc.
LANDAU'S RESERVE - Skin care products - Landau Skincare Products
LANDCOMMANDER - Agricultural machinery - Brillion Iron Works Inc.
LANDCRUISER - Motor vehicles–sport-utility - Toyota Motor Sales USA Inc.
LANDCRUISER - Trailers–travel - Trotwood Corp.
LANDDESIGNER - Computer software - Green Thumb Software, Inc.
LANDDESIGNERPRO - Computer software - Green Thumb Software, Inc.
LANDECKER & BOZ - Wines - Columbia Winery
LANDEN WOOD - Floor coverings ☆ - Tarkett, Inc.
LANDER - Hair care products - Lander Co., Inc.
LANDER GRAPEFRUIT ESSENCE - Toiletries - Lander Co., Inc.
LANDER PEACH ESSENCE - Skin care products - Lander Co., Inc.
LANDER RADIANCE - Shampoos - Lander Co., Inc.
LANDER STRAWBERRY ESSENCE - Skin care products - Lander Co., Inc.
LANDER'S - Cookies ☆ - FCW Imports
LANDERWOOD - Shirts - Joe Claar
LANDES - Dishes–earthenware - Landes Marketing Corp.
LANDESK - Computer software - Intel Corp.
LANDEV - Computer software - Devplan, Inc.
LANDGRAF VON HESSEN - Wines - Seagram's Chateau & Estate Wines Co.
LANDHAUS - Cheese - Roth Kase USA, Ltd.
LANDIA - Lighting fixtures - Test-Rite Products Corp.
LANDINFO - Maps - Geocode, Inc.
LANDING GEAR - Braces–orthopedic - Kirschner Medical Corp.
LANDING GEAR - Luggage - York Partners, L.P.
LANDJET - Vans–conversion - Land Jet, Inc.
LANDKAAS - Cheese - Swissrose International Inc.
LANDKING - Tillers–rotary - Krause Plow Corp.

☆ = Now out of production

LANDLIGHT AQUA SUBMERSIBLE - Lighting fixtures - Rojey Corp.

LANDLORD & BROADMOOR - Garden tractors ✩ - Simplicity Manufacturing Inc.

LANDLORDING - Computer software - Leigh Robinson

LANDLUBBER - Jeans–men's - Williamson-Dickie Manufacturing Co.

LANDMARK - Audio equipment - Electro-Voice, Inc.

LANDMARK - Calendars - Landmark General Corp.

LANDMARK - Cheese - Rumiano Cheese Co.

LANDMARK - Clocks - Harris & Mallow Products

LANDMARK - Floor coverings - Gencorp Inc.

LANDMARK - Frames–eyeglass ✩ - Universal/Univis Inc.

LANDMARK - Furniture ✩ - Riverside Furniture Corp.

LANDMARK - Greeting cards ✩ - Nu-Art Inc.

LANDMARK - Health care products - Sav-a-Stop Inc.

LANDMARK - Heat pumps ✩ - Lennox Industries Inc.

LANDMARK - Ice making machinery - Nicola, Gudbranson, and Cooper

LANDMARK - Nautical instruments - Signet Marine

LANDMARK - Office supplies - Esselte Corp.

LANDMARK - Paper–bond ✩ - Fox River Paper Co.

LANDMARK - Recording label - Landmark Communications Group

LANDMARK - Shingles–asphalt or tar - Certainteed Corp. (Roofing Products Group)

LANDMARK - Telephone apparatus - Southwestern Bell Telecommunications, Inc.

LANDMARK - Wallpaper ✩ - Wall Fashion Inc.

LANDMARK - Whirlpools - Watkins Manufacturing Corp.

LANDMARK - Wines - Landmark Vineyards

LANDMARK BOOKS - Publisher's imprints - Random House, Inc.

LANDMARK EDITIONS - Publisher's imprints ✩ - University of Nebraska Press

LANDMARK III - Condensers ✩ - Lennox Industries Inc.

LANDMARK IV - Condensers ✩ - Lennox Industries Inc.

LANDMARK OPAQUE - Stationery - Georgia-Pacific Corp.

LANDMARK PRESERVES - Jams and jellies - Landmark Society of Western New York Inc.

LANDMARK STUDIES - Publisher's imprints ✩ - Rowman & Littlefield Publishers Inc.

LANDMARKS OF FREEDOM - Calendars - Brown and Bigelow Inc.

LANDMASTER - Herbicides - Monsanto Co.

LANDMASTER - Tillers–rotary ✩ - Krause Plow Corp.

LANDNET - Publisher's imprints - American Society of Landscape Architects

LANDOLFI'S - Food products - Landolfi Food Products Inc.

LANDON JONATHAN - Apparel–women's - Eber International

LANDOT NOIR - Wines - Ziem Vineyards

LANDRETH - Flowers, plants, and seeds - D. Landreth Seed Co.

LANDRY'S - Apparel and accessories - Landry's Trademark, Inc.

LANDS' END - Apparel–athletic ✩ - Lands' End Inc.

LANDS OF LORE - Video games - Westwood Studios, Inc.

LANDS-SWEEP - Cleaning preparations - Sunclipse, Inc.

LANDSAT - Communications equipment–satellite - Maritime Cellular Tele-Network, Inc.

LANDSAVER - Tillers–rotary - Krause Plow Corp.

LANDSBERG - Vegetables–canned - Haram-Christensen Corp.

LANDSCAN - Computer software - Stewart Title Co.

LANDSCAPE - Apparel and accessories - Charles Komar and Sons Inc.

LANDSCAPE - Floor coverings–carpet and rugs - Regal Rugs Inc.

LANDSCAPE - Floor coverings–carpet and rugs - Value Carpets Inc.

LANDSCAPE - Floor coverings–tile - Interface, Inc.

LANDSCAPE - Paper - Champion International Corp.

LANDSCAPE - Trailers–truck - U.S. Cargo, Inc.

LANDSCAPE DESIGN 3D - Computer software - Expert Software Inc.

LANDSCAPE EDGING - Blocks–concrete - Crown, Cork & Seal

LANDSCAPE ICE MELTER - Calcium compounds - Dow Chemical Co.

LANDSCAPE NATURALS - Cosmetics - Chesebrough-Pond's USA Co.

LANDSCAPE OF DREAMS - Dolls - Kish & Co.

LANDSCAPE PAVERS - Steps - Crown Hill Stone Inc.

LANDSCAPE RAKE - Machine parts - Glenmac Inc.

LANDSCAPE STEPPING STONES - Stone products - Crown Hill Stone Inc.

LANDSCAPER - Fencing–steel - Semmerling Fence and Supply Inc.

LANDSCAPER TOUGH - Yard tools - O. Ames Co.

LANDSCAPER'S PINE BARK - Flowers, plants, and seeds ✩ - Mulch Manufacturing, Inc.

LANDSCAPER'S SHREDDED CYPRESS - Agricultural products ✩ - Mulch Manufacturing, Inc.

LANDSCAPES - Floor coverings–carpet and rugs - Eagle Carpets Inc.

LANDSHARK - Bicycles - Landshark Bicycles Inc.

LANDSHIRE - Food products - Southland Corp.

LANDSLIDE - Bicycles - Roadmaster Corp.

LANDSLIDE - Recording label - Landslide Records Inc.

LANDSLIDE - Toys - Tonka Corp.

LANDSMAN - Tillers–rotary - Krause Plow Corp.

LANDSPORT - Apparel and accessories - J-M Business Enterprises, Inc.

LANDSTROM'S - Jewelry–precious - Landstrom's Original Black Hills Gold Creations

LANDTEC - Computer software - Landfill Control Technologies

LANE - Cookies - Lulabelle's Gourmet Cookies

LANE - Furniture - Lane Co. Inc.

LANE - Recording label - West Records

LANE BRYANT - Apparel–women's - Lane Bryant, Inc.

LANE BRYANT - Recording label - Lanco, Inc.

LANE COUNTRY - Food products - Laneco Inc.

LANE LEATHER - Wallets - Craft Billfold Corp.

LANE LINE STORAGE BENCHES - Swimming pools - Recreonics, Inc.

LANE TANNER - Wines - Lane Tanner

LANE'S - Honey - E.F. Lane & Son

LANES DAIRY - Food products - Lanes Dairy Inc.

LANESTRIN - Pharmaceutical preparations - Lannett Co. Inc.

LANEVIEW - Computer software - Tecom, Inc.

LANEX - Pencils–mechanical - Mokiem & Julian Ind Corp.

LANEX - Pharmaceutical preparations - Carma Laboratories Inc.

LANEX - Photographic equipment - Eastman Kodak Co.

LANEXPERT! - Computer software ✩ - Horizons Technology, Inc.

LANEXPRESS - Computer software - Microcom Systems, Inc.

LANFRANCO - Food products - De Choix Specialty Foods Co.

LANG - Jewelry - Irving Lang Inc.

LANG - Jewelry - Lang Jewelry Co.

LANG - Wines - Granite Springs Winery

LANGDON GATE - Tableware–china - Lenox, Inc.

LANGE - Boots - Skis Dynastar, Inc.

LANGE - Fertilizers - Lange-Stegmann Co.

LANGE' - Nail care products - Lange Laboratories, Inc.

LANGE - Skin care products ✩ - Lange Laboratories, Inc.

LANGE ELASTIN - Skin care products - Lange Laboratories, Inc.

LANGE GLYCOLIC - Skin care products - Lange Laboratories, Inc.

LANGE PANTHENOL - Skin care products - Lange Laboratories, Inc.

LANGENSTEIN FARM - Coffee - John J. Langenstein

LANGENTHAL - Dinnerware–glass - Block China Co.

LANGERS - Juices - L and A Juice Co. Inc.

LANGE'S - Gelatin - Nu-Vita Foods

LANGES - Hair coloring preparations - William Marvy Co., Inc.

LANGHORNE - Furniture ✩ - Bassett Furniture Industries, Inc.

LANGKA - Paint removers - Lawrence W. Johnson

LANGLEY - Dishes–earthenware - Denby USA Limited

LANGLEY - Wallcoverings - Laura Ashley

LANGLEY FARM - Bacon - Agar Food Products Co.

LANGLEY PARK - Floor coverings - Tarkett, Inc.

LANGLOIS - Food products - Langlois Frozen Foods

LANGLOIS-CHATEAU - Wines - Dreyfus Ashby Inc.

LANGNESE - Honey - Haram-Christensen Corp.

LANG'S - Pet products - Lang Feed Co. Inc.

LANG'S TANGY - Health care products - Lang Naturals

LANGSTON'S FAMOUS BARBECUE SAUCE - Sauces - Lang's Tangy Co.

LANGTREE - Floor coverings - Mannington Resilient Floors

LANGTRY - Wines - Guenoc & Langtry Estate Vineyards and Winery

LANGTRY LTD. - Apparel and accessories ✩ - Vanderbilt Shirt Co.

LANGUA - Seafood products–fresh or frozen ✩ - J.F. Clarke Corp.

LANGUA - Shrimp–fresh or frozen ✩ - Southeast Foods Inc.

LANGUAGE ANALYST - Computer software - Caere Corp.

LANGUAGE ASSISTANT - Computer software ✩ - Gessler Publishing Co., Inc.

LANGUAGE CARNIVAL - Computer software - SRA/McGraw-Hill (Div. of The McGraw-Hill Companies)

LANGUAGE COLLECTION - Computer software - SourceView Software International

LANGUAGE-CRAFT - Electronic equipment - Hamilton Electronics Corp.

LANGUAGE DYNAMICS TAKE THE FOREIGN OUT OF LANGUAGE - Recording label - Language Dynamics Inc.

LANGUAGE ENVIRONMENT - Computer software - International Business Machines Corp.

LANGUAGE EXPLORER - Computer software - Iliad

LANGUAGE MASTER - Electronic equipment ✩ - Franklin Computer Corp.

LANGUAGE OF CHOICE, THE - Video tapes–blank - Lumpkin Sankey & Associates Inc.

LANGUAGE OF LOVE - Colognes ✩ - Avon Products, Inc.

LANGUAGE OF LOVE, THE - Glassware–household - Fenton Art Glass Co.

LANGUAGE PLUS - Video production - Language Plus, Inc.

LANGUAGE WISE - Computer software - Tiger Electronics, Inc.

LANGUAGE WORKS SPELLING PROGRAM - Publisher's imprints - Mary Riggs

LANGUARDIAN - Computer hardware - Uunet Technologies, Inc.

LANGWOOD - Wood products - Langdale Forest Products Co.

LANI - Toys - Tonka Corp.

LANI KAI - Floor coverings–carpet and rugs ☆ - Customweave Carpets Inc.

LANI LAMB - Toys–stuffed - Russ Berrie and Co., Inc.

LANIAZID - Antiseptics - Lannett Co. Inc.

LANIEGE - Perfumes - Laniege Cosmetics, Inc.

LANIER - Apparel–men's - Oxford Industries, Inc.

LANIER - Clocks ☆ - Ridgeway Clock Co.

LANIER - Dictating machines ☆ - Lanier Voice Products

LANIER - Furniture ☆ - Bassett Furniture Industries, Inc.

LANIER/EDISETTE 1977 - Dictating machines ☆ - Lanier Voice Products

LANIROIF - Pharmaceutical preparations - C.O. Truxton Inc.

LANKY LION - Toys–stuffed ☆ - Dakin Inc.

LANLE - Cosmetics ☆ - La Lueur International Inc.

LANLINK MONITOR - Computer software - Wandel & Goltermann Technologies, Inc.

LANLORD - Computer software - Microcom Systems, Inc.

LANMARK-350 - Cables - Berk-Tek, Inc.

LANMETER - Electrical testing instruments - Fluke Corp.

LANNA - Toys–stuffed ☆ - Russ Berrie and Co., Inc.

LANNATE - Insecticides - E.I. Dupont de Nemours and Co.

LANNETT - Analgesics - Lannett Co. Inc.

LANNY LEOPARD - Toys–stuffed - Russ Berrie and Co., Inc.

LANO - Skin care products - Robert Delaney Associates

LANO-LO - Pharmaceutical preparations - Whorton Pharmaceuticals Inc.

LANO-LUBE - Liners and covers–pond, pit, and landfill - Flexbar Machine Corp.

LANOCARE - See LANSINOH

LANOFRESH - Antiseptics ☆ - Abco Dealers Inc.

LANOLGROOM - Hair care products ☆ - T.N. Dickinson Co.

LANOLIN -

LANOLIN PERFECTION - Hair care products - Bonat Inc.

LANOLINE - Skin care products - Burroughs Wellcome Co.

LANOLITE - Lipsticks - Revlon Consumer Products Corp.

LANOLOR - Skin care products - Numark Laboratories Inc.

LANOPHYLLIN - Pharmaceutical preparations - Lannett Co. Inc.

LANOPLEX - Vitamins and nutritional supplements - Lannett Co. Inc.

LANOR - Recording label - Lanor Records

LANORINAL - Pharmaceutical preparations - Lannett Co. Inc.

LANOTHAL - Laxatives - Lannett Co. Inc.

LANOTRESS - Hair care products - Gold Medal Hair Products Inc.

LANOXICAPS - Pharmaceutical preparations - Burroughs Wellcome Co.

LANOXIN - Pharmaceutical preparations - Burroughs Wellcome Co.

LANPHARAOH - Electrical equipment - Azure Technologies, Inc.

LANPOINT - Computer - Burr-Brown Corp.

LANPOINT SYSTEMS - Computers - Burr-Brown Corp.

LANRECORD - Computer software ☆ - Horizons Technology, Inc.

LANROD - Recording label - Carrie Records

LAN'S BEST FRIEND - Power switching equipment - American Power Conversion Corp.

LANSAS - Cleaning equipment - Vanderlans & Sons, Inc.

LANSCRIPT - Computer software - Lanquest Group

LANSDALE - Clocks ☆ - General Time Corp. (Westclox/Seth Thomas Div.)

LANSDOWNE - Weather tracking equipment - Swift Instruments, Inc.

LANSENTRY - Computer hardware - Chipcom Corp.

LANSFORD - Clocks - Ridgeway Clock Co.

LANSING - Loudspeakers - Altec

LANSINOH - Skin care products - Lansinoh Laboratories Inc.

LANSINOH TREATMENT FOR FEET - Skin care products - Lansinoh Laboratories Inc.

LANSKY - Knives - Rothco Inc.

LANSLEUTH - Computer software - Systems and Synchronous, Inc.

LANSON - Electronics equipment - Lanson Industries, Inc.

LANSON - Wines - Hiram Walker & Sons, Inc.

LANSON CHAMPAGNE - Wines - Admiral Wine Merchants

LANSTOR RAIDMASTER - Computer software - Storage Dimensions

LANSTOR RED ALERT - Computer software - Storage Dimensions

LANTALKER - Computer hardware - Multi-Tech Systems, Inc.

LANTANA - Dinnerware–glass ☆ - Lenox, Inc.

LANTANA - Spices and extracts - Lantana

LANTASTIC ON BOARD - Computer hardware and software - Artisoft, Inc.

LANTEC - Computer software - Lantec Inc.

LANTECH - Electronic equipment - Wavetek Corp.

LANTEEN - Pharmaceutical preparations ☆ - Oakhurst Co.

LANTEGRITY - Computer software - Network Integrity, Inc.

LANTERN GUARD - Gaskets - American Lantern Co.

LANTERN LIGHT - Floor coverings–carpet and rugs - Trend Carpet

LANTERN OF D'GAMMA - Computer software ☆ - Milliken Publishing Co. (Computer Software Div.)

LANTERNS - Flashlights - Garrity Industries

LANTERNSHIELD - Lighting fixtures - American Lantern Co.

LANTERNSTIR - Bar fixtures–plastic - Spir-it Inc.

LANTEX - Lawn product - Adjusta-Post Manufacturing Co.

LANTEX - Pharmaceutical preparations - Bolan Pharmaceutical Inc.

LANTIME ENTRY - Computer software - CMS/DATA Corp.

LANTISEPTIC - Health care products - Creomulsion Lantiseptic

LANTRAIL - Computer software ☆ - Horizons Technology, Inc.

LANTRISUL - Pharmaceutical preparations - Lannett Co. Inc.

LANTRONIX - Electronic equipment - Lantronix

LANTUSS-DM - Cough medicines - Columbia Drug Co. Inc.

LANTUSS-FORTE - Antihistamine preparations - Columbia Drug Co. Inc.

LANTUSS L.A. - Pharmaceutical preparations - Columbia Drug Co. Inc.

LANTUSS S.H. - Antihistamine preparations - Columbia Drug Co. Inc.

LANTUSS-XP - Pharmaceutical preparations - Columbia Drug Co. Inc.

LANUS - Computer software - Lanus Inc.

LANVIN - Apparel and accessories - Salant/Manhattan Industries

LANVIN - Apparel–men's - Greif Cos.

LANVIN - Jewelry - Universe International Inc.

LANVIN ARPEGE - Colognes - Frances Denney

LANVIN FOR MEN - Colognes - Mennen Co.

LANVIN MY SIN - Colognes - Frances Denney

LANVISONE - Pharmaceutical preparations - Lannett Co. Inc.

LANWORDS - Computer program - Saber Software Corp.

LANYA - Apparel and accessories - Samii Clothes

LANYARD - Flatware - Pfaltzgraff Investment Co.

LANZ - Apparel and accessories - LANZ, Inc.

LANZ FOR GIRLS - Apparel–children's - LANZ, Inc.

LANZ II - Apparel–women's - LANZ, Inc.

LANZ OF SALZBURG - Dolls - Eden LLC

LANZ OF SALZBURG - Underwear and nightwear - LANZ, Inc.

LANZ OF SALZBURG II - Underwear and nightwear - LANZ, Inc.

LANZ ORIGINALS - Dresses–women's - LANZ, Inc.

LANZ R.S.V.P. - Dresses–women's - LANZ, Inc.

LANZAR PLUS - Amplifiers - Lanzar Sound Corp.

LANZERA - Apparel and accessories - Intersport Ltd.

LANZERA MONDIALE - Apparel–athletic - Intersport Ltd.

LANZI - Granola bars ☆ - Barbara's Bakery, Inc.

LAO-SHEEN - Floor coverings–carpet and rugs ☆ - Trans-Ocean Import Co. Inc.

LAOS - Computer software - Robert A. Baron

LAOVERS - Candles - Merrill-West Publishing

LAP - Radar systems and equipment - Radian Corp.

LAP-EZE CADDIE - Pillows ☆ - Blue Ridge International Products Co., Inc.

LAP FRAMES - Frames–picture - Gibbs Manufacturing Co.

LAP LOCK - Construction equipment ☆ - Alcan Aluminum Corp. Alcan Building Products Div.

LAP-LOK - Building materials - Simonton Building Products, Inc.

LAP-LOOM - Looms - Decorator and Craft Corp.

LAP-O-VALVE - Machinery - United States Products Co.

LAP SERVICE - Trays - Ginatti Enterprises Inc.

LAP TRAP - Sporting goods - Fishing for Ideas, Inc.

LAP TRAP - Trays - V-Mar Inc.

LAP TRAVELER - Computer peripheral equipment - Interactive Products Corp.

LAP-WRAP - Medical equipment - Medical Dynamics, Inc.

LAPALISSE - Dishes–china - Viletta China Co.

LAPAROFAN - Medical apparatus - Origin Medsystems, Inc.

LAPAROLIFT - Medical apparatus - Origin Medsystems, Inc.

LAPAROSCOPE - Electromedical apparatus - AGA Corp.

LAPAZ - Floor coverings ☆ - Congoleum Corp.

LAPBUDDY - Cushions–foam - Professional Specialties Co.

LAPCONTROL - Computer software - Technology Development Systems, Inc.

LAPEL PIN PLUS - Jewelry - Janice L. Brach

LAPEL SCULPTURES - Jewelry - Creative Treasures, Inc.

LAPELS BY LANIER - Apparel–men's - Oxford Industries, Inc.

LAPEYRE - Ladders–metal - Laitram Corp.

LAPHAPPY - Animal feeds - Pet-Ag, Inc.

LAPHROAIG - Wines - Hiram Walker & Sons, Inc.
LAPIC - Wines - Lapic Winery Ltd.
LAPID - Glass products - Primex International Corp.
LAPIDES - Medical apparatus - LDB Medical, Inc.
LAPIN DU GOURMET - Meat products–cured ☆ - Pel-Freez Rabbit Meat, Inc.
LAPINAL - Perfumes - Redken Laboratories, Inc.
LAPIZ - Beverages–alcohol - Shaw-Ross International Importers
LAPKIN - Napkins–paper - Procorp, Inc.
LAPLINK REMOTE ACCESS - Computer software - Traveling Software, Inc.
LAPLS - Beverages–alcohol - Shaw-Ross International Importers
LAPLUCK - Cosmetics - S.R. Droescher Inc.
LAPO-CLAMP - Medical apparatus - Minnesota Scientific, Inc.
LAPODO - Pharmaceutical preparations - Sargeant Acnoid Pharmaceutical Co.
LAPOINT RADIUS - Sporting goods ☆ - O'Brien International
LAPOUFF - Cosmetics ☆ - Spilo/Mehaz Worldwide
LAPOUFF - Hair care products ☆ - Modern Research Laboratories
LAPPER - Tables–wood - Table Toys, Inc.
LAPPERT'S HAWAII - Bakery products - Walter A. Lappert
+L'APPLIQUE - Cosmetics ☆ - Spilo/Mehaz Worldwide
LAPRA-TY - Surgical supplies - Johnson & Johnson
LAPRO-LOOP - Surgical supplies - American Cyanamid Co.
LAPROVUE - Health care products - Biosynergy Inc.
LAPSANG - Cosmetics - Fiske Industries Inc.
LAPSANG SOUCHONG SMOKY NO. 1 - Teas - Grace Tea Co. Ltd.
LAPSAVER - Computer peripheral equipment - IQI Accessories
LAPSTRAP - Computer accessories - Rolf O. Anderson
LAPTOTE - Luggage - Laptote Luggage Systems, Inc.
LAPTREK - Electronic equipment - Connection Technology International
LAPURE WATER - Plumbing fixtures–enameled - Labure Water Products Inc.
LAPWASH SYSTEM - Medical apparatus - Devmed Group Inc.
LAQUA - Pharmaceutical preparations - C.S. Ruckstuhl Co. Inc.
LAQUE - Pens - Sheaffer Inc.
+L'AQUILONE - Figurines - Italianissimo Inc.
LARA - Parachutes - Vertigo, Inc.
LARA - Rings–jewelry - Artcarved Inc.
LARA LAMB - Toys–stuffed - Russ Berrie and Co., Inc.
LARA LOUIS - Apparel–women's - Lara Louis Hosiery Inc.
LARAINE - Wines - Gerber Vineyards
LARAMI - Toys - Larami Limited, Inc.
LARAMIE - Apparel and accessories - Wrangler Apparel Co.
LARAMIE - Floor coverings–carpet and rugs ☆ - Walter Carpet Mills
LARAMIE - Tableware–china - Susquehanna Glass Co.
LARAMIE - Tires - Laramie Tire Distributors, Inc.
LARAMIE - Trailers–travel - Fleetwood Enterprises, Inc.
LARAMIE - Window coverings ☆ - Joanna Western Mills Co.
LARAN - Computer peripheral equipment - Latelco Inc.
LARC - Glassware ☆ - Corning Inc.
+L'ARC DE TRIOMPHE - Food products - Crystal Food Import Corp.
LARCHMONT - Underwear and nightwear ☆ - Kellwood Co.
LARCOLOID - Enamels - California Products Corp.
LARDY - Toys ☆ - International Playthings Inc.
LAREAUX - Decorations - Ramco Trading Corp.
LAREDO - Apparel and accessories - Gentry Inc.
LAREDO - Barbecues and grills ☆ - Shepherd Products U.S. Inc.
LAREDO - Belts–apparel - Genesco Inc.
LAREDO - Belts–apparel - Lyntone Belts Inc.
LAREDO - Cigarettes - Brown & Williamson Tobacco Corp.
LAREDO - Cookware - Mesa International
LAREDO - House furnishings ☆ - Lea Industries Inc.
LAREDO - Motor vehicle parts and accessories - Seats Inc.
LAREDO - Paper–coated - Simpson Paper Co.
LAREDO - Racks - Royal Sound Co. Inc.
LAREDO - Rice - Southwest Rice Mill Co. Inc.
LAREDO - Seat covers - Saddleman, Inc.
LAREDO - Strollers–baby ☆ - Welsh Co.
LAREDO - Tires - Uniroyal Goodrich Tire Co.
LAREDO - Trailers–travel - Fleetwood Enterprises, Inc.
LAREGENTA - Cigars ☆ - United States Tobacco Co.
LARENSTAN - Floor coverings–carpet and rugs - Couristan Inc.
LAREX - Chemical preparations - Larex International, Inc.
LARGAS - Cigar boxes–wood - Consolidated Cigar Corp.
LARGE JASMIN - Tiles–mosaic - Capitol Tile Import Co.
LARGE KITCHEN UTILITY CONTAINER - Bags–trash - Ironclad LP
LARGE MARGE - Golf clubs - Wayne Products, Inc.
LARGELY LITERARY - Cups–plastic - Largely Literary Designs, Inc.
LARGESSE - Hosiery - Triumph Hosiery Corp.

LARGO - Brushes–paint - Corona Brushes Inc.
LARGO - Floor coverings–carpet and rugs ☆ - World Carpets, Inc.
LARGO - Floor coverings–tile - Collins & Aikman Corp.
LARGO - Furniture - Universal Flooring
LARGO - Furniture–wood - Ficks Reed Co. Inc.
LARGO - Glassware–household - Owens-Illinois Inc. (Libbey Div.)
LARGO - Glassware–household ☆ - National Housewares
LARGO - Rings–jewelry - Artcarved Inc.
LARGO - Statuary - Viking Import House Inc.
LARGO CALOT - Skin care products - Hanah Beauty & Health Inc.
LARGO COLOR KEEP - Hair care products - Hanah Beauty & Health Inc.
LARGO SANDS - Furniture - Universal Flooring
LARGO VISTA - Floor coverings - Mannington Resilient Floors
LARGON - Pharmaceutical preparations - Wyeth-Ayerst Laboratories
LARIANELLA - Cheese ☆ - Swissrose International Inc.
LARIAT - Beverages–carbonated - Wolmex Beverage Co.
LARIAT - Office supplies - Rack Service Co. Inc.
LARIAT - Orthodontic equipment - Jeffrey J. Staples
LARIAT - Wallpaper - Koroseal Wallcoverings
LARIAT LEATHERS - Leather and sheep-lined clothing - Green Valley Manufacturing Co.
+L'ARICI - Perfumes ☆ - Parfum de Coeur Ltd.
LARILEE - Oboes - Larilee Woodwind Corp.
LARIMER SQUARE - Posters - Ernest W. Hahn Inc.
LARISSA - Flatware - Washington Forge Inc.
LARISSA - Floor coverings - Mannington Resilient Floors
LARISSA SCOTT - Jewelry boxes - Larissa Scott
LARJEX - Paper–photographic - Rollei of America Inc.
LARK - Automotive parts and accessories - Hop-Cap Inc.
LARK - Brassieres (Bras) - Bi-Flex International
LARK - Chimes ☆ - J.W. Stannard Co.
LARK - Cigarettes - Liggett Group Inc.
LARK - Denture cleaners - Roosa & Ratliff Drug Co.
LARK - Dryers–hair - Helene Curtis Industries Inc.
LARK - Field glasses - Swift Instruments, Inc.
LARK - Flowers–artificial - European Imports of California Inc.
LARK - Glassware–household - Crisa Corp.
LARK - Guitars ☆ - Philadelphia Music Co. Inc.
LARK - Hair care products ☆ - Flamingo Products Inc.
LARK - Knives–surgical - Innovative Surgical Technology, Inc.
LARK - Luggage - Lark Luggage Co. Inc.
LARK - Motors–outboard ☆ - Outboard Marine Corp.
LARK - Orthopedic products - Ortho-Kinetics, Inc.
LARK - Paints - Passonno Paints
LARK - Pharmaceutical preparations - U.S. Ethicals Inc.
LARK - Pipes–tobacco - Dr. Grabow Pre-Smoked Pipes Inc.
LARK - Plumbing fixtures–metal ☆ - Moen Inc.
LARK - Recording label - Major Recording Co.
LARK - Wallpaper - Advance Wallcoverings
LARK - Weather tracking equipment ☆ - Bausch & Lomb Inc.
LARK 4 - Orthopedic products - Ortho-Kinetics, Inc.
LARK 92 - Wheelchairs ☆ - Ortho-Kinetics, Inc.
LARK 4392 - Orthopedic products - Ortho-Kinetics, Inc.
LARK 4635 - Orthopedic products - Ortho-Kinetics, Inc.
LARK LIFT - Orthopedic products ☆ - Ortho-Kinetics, Inc.
LARK LIGHTS - Cigarettes - Liggett Group Inc.
LARK-PAK - Luggage - Lark Luggage Co. Inc.
LARK RISE - Magnets ☆ - Chase Collection, Inc.
LARK-SUPERLIFT - Orthopedic products ☆ - Ortho-Kinetics, Inc.
LARKIN & MORRILL - Snuff ☆ - Byfield Snuff Co.
LARKIN'S - Seafood products–fresh or frozen - Larkin's Seafood
LARKMEAD - Wines - Larkmead Vineyards
LARKOTEX - Health care products - Larkotex Surgical Manufacturing Co.
LARKS - Footwear–women's - Wohl Shoe Co.
LARKSPUR - Bathroom fixtures - Kohler Co.
LARKSPUR - Bedding–linen - Dan River Inc.
LARKSPUR - Fabrics - Rosebar Textile Co.
LARKSPUR - Wood products - Weyerhaeuser Co.
LARNAUDIE - Food products ☆ - Europa Foods Ltd.
LAROBEC - Vitamins and nutritional supplements - Roche Laboratories
LARODOPA - Pharmaceutical preparations - Roche Laboratories
+L'AROMATICA AQUILANA - Nuts–salted, roasted, cooked, or canned - Schroeder Brothers
+L'AROMATICA AQUILANA AROMILLA - Teas - Schroeder Brothers
LARRABURU - Breads - Parisian Bakeries Inc.
LARRESSINGLE - Beverages–alcohol - Kobrand Corp.

☆ = Now out of production

LARRO - Animal feeds ☆ - General Mills, Inc.
LARROQUE - Artists' materials - Andrews/Nelson/Whitehead
LARROWE'S - Food products - Birkett Mills
LARRY - Dolls - Effanbee Doll Corp.
LARRY - Dolls - Mattel, Inc.
LARRY - Ophthalmic goods - Rozin Optical Export Corp.
LARRY ADLER - Hohner Inc.
LARRY CSONKA'S PRO FOOTBALL - Games ☆ - A.R.C. Toys Inc.
LARRY FORGIONE'S - Condiments and sauces - American Spoon Foods Inc.
LARRY FREEMAN - Cosmetics - Morris-Flamingo Inc.
LARRY LAND - Recording label - SK Productions
LARRY LASLO COLLECTION, THE - Dinnerware–glass - Sango Co. Ltd. (Sango USA Div.)
LARRY +LEVINE - Apparel and accessories - Larry Levine Inc.
LARRY MAHAN'S - Boots - Mahan Western Industries
LARRY MATHEWS - Health care products - Dynamic Classics Ltd.
LARRY MULKEY'S - Barbecue sauce - Old Chisholm Trail
LARRY MULKEY'S CHEESE STRAWS - Snack foods - Old Chisholm Trail
LARRY RAST'S - Music–sheet - Educational Productions
LARRY STUART - Shoes - Larry Stuart, Ltd.
LARRY STUART COLLECTION - Footwear - Brown Shoe Co.
LARRY STUART COLLECTION - Shoes - Larry Stuart, Ltd.
LARRY, THE POCKET TROUT - Flashlights - Eveready Battery Co., Inc.
LARRY VINCENT - Plastics film - Larry Vincent Speciality Advertising Inc.
LARRY'S - Food products - Design Foods
LARRYS - Food products - Eagle Crest Foods Inc.
LARRY'S - Ice cream - Larry's Ice Cream & Yogurt
LARRY'S - Veterinary pharmaceutical preparations - Larry E. Mitchener
LARRY'S - Video production - Nalpak Video Sales, Inc.
LARRY'S LITE - Ice cream - Larry's Ice Cream & Yogurt
LARS OF SWEDEN - Toys - Reeves International, Inc.
LARSBORG - Cheese - Webeco Foods Inc.
LARSCOM - Computer hardware - Larscom Inc.
LARSEN - Fabrics–broadcloth - Jack Lenor Larsen, Inc.
LARSEN - Musical instrument accessories - Ideal Musical Merchandise Co.
LARSEN - Pet products - Larsen Dog Self Feeder
LARSEN - Puzzles - Importoys
LARSEN - Vegetables–canned ☆ - Dean Foods Vegetable Co.
LARSEN'S - Fire extinguishing compositions - Larsen's Manufacturing Co.
LARSHIP ADMIRAL - Boats–motor - Albin Marine Inc.
LARSHIP EASTWIND - Boats–motor - Albin Marine Inc.
LARSON - Boats–motor - Larson Boat Div.
LARSON - Fruits–canned - Larson Fruit Co.
LARSON - Glass products - Arnold Larson Inc.
LARSON - Hardware - Charles O. Larson Co. Inc.
LARSON - Puzzles - Importoys
LARSON ARTIFACTS - Sculptures - Larson Co. Inc.
LARSON-JUHL - Frames–picture - Larson-Juhl Inc.
LARSONS II - Frames–picture ☆ - Larson II
+L'ART - Pickles - Green Bay Foods Co.
+L'ART DE CHINE - Ornamental products–glass - L'Art De Chine
+L'ARTISTE - Lipsticks - Cosmair Inc.
LARTONIC - Pharmaceutical preparations - Lardon Laboratories
LARVEX - Naphthalene chips - Coughlan Products Corp.
LARYDOL - Pharmaceutical preparations - Dolisos America, Inc.
LARYLGAN - Pharmaceutical preparations - Whitehall Laboratories
LARYNEX - Pharmaceutical preparations - Dover Pharmaceutical Inc.
LARYNGOFOAM - Medical apparatus - Luminaud Inc.
LAS BRIAS - Wallpaper - Advance Wallcoverings
LAS BRISAS - Floor coverings–carpet and rugs ☆ - Customweave Carpets Inc.
LAS BRISAS - Manufactured homes ☆ - Redman Industries, Inc.
LAS CALIFORNIAS - Sauces - Avoco
LAS CAMPANAS - Food products - Camino Real Foods
LAS FLORISTAS - Cooking utensils–cast iron ☆ - National Housewares
LAS LLAVES DEL EXITO - Recording label - Applied International Research Inc.
LAS LOMAS - Frozen foods - Mountain High Foods, Inc.
LAS MONTANAS - Apparel and accessories - LME Investors
LAS PALMAS - Chili sauce - Pet Inc.
LAS PALMAS - Soap - Heritage Store Inc.
LAS PALMAS - Sunglasses - Mirage Products, Inc.
LAS PALMAS - Vegetable sauces - Ramirez & Feraud Chili Co., Inc.
LAS POSAS VALLEY RANCHES - Salads–prepackaged - Agricultural Innovation & Trade Inc.
LAS-STIK - Dust cloths - Las-Stik Manufacturing Co.

LAS-TEX LIQUID - Concrete products - Tamms Industries Co.
LAS VEGAS - Bicycles - Ross Bicycles USA, Ltd.
LAS VEGAS - Floor coverings ☆ - Congoleum Corp.
LAS VEGAS - Games - Dynamic Classics Ltd.
LAS VEGAS - Seafood products–fresh or frozen - Southern Belle Frozen Foods Inc.
LAS VEGAS - Underwear and nightwear - Bestform Foundations, Inc.
LAS VEGAS CASINO CORNER - Games - ABC International Traders Inc.
LAS VEGAS DISCOUNT GOLF & TENNIS - Athletic associations - Las Vegas Discount Golf & Tennis, Inc.
LAS VEGAS HOLD'EM - Computer software - Manhattan Software
LAS VEGAS INTERNATIONAL MARATHON - Apparel and accessories - Las Vegas Marathon, Inc.
LAS VEGAS SENIOR CLASSIC - Apparel - Stars' Desert Inn and Country Club, Inc.
LAS VEGAS: THE GAME - Games - S. Alden Inc.
LASALLE - Drums–musical instruments ☆ - Castiglione Accordion
LASALLE - Floor coverings - American Floor Products Co. Inc.
LASALLE - Floor coverings–carpet and rugs - Concord/Aldon Industries Inc.
LASALLE - Lighting fixtures - LaSalle-Deitch Co. Inc.
LASALLE - Motor vehicles–motor homes - Champion Enterprises Inc.
LASALLE 10 - Skin care products - Allercare Inc.
LASALLE COUNTRY FRENCH - Furniture ☆ - Universal Flooring
LASALLE UNIVERSITY - Paper–newsprint - La Salle University
LASAN - Pharmaceutical preparations ☆ - Stiefel Laboratories, Inc.
LASAR - Electronic equipment - Unison Industries L.P.
LASAR - Motors–air - Magnetek Inc.
LASAREV - Sporting goods ☆ - Babolat
LASARPAC - Packaging–paper - McBee Loose Leaf Binders
LASC-O-TITE - Air conditioning equipment - Lasco Products Group
LASCALA - Watches - United Orient
LASCCO - Seafood products–canned or cured - Los Angeles Smoking & Curing Co.
LASCO - Food products - Allen Foods Inc.
LASCO - Golfing equipment - Slotline Golf
LASCO - Rubber footwear - International Seaway Trading Corp.
LASCO - Sporting goods - L.A. Steelcraft Products Inc.
LASCO - Whirlpools - Lasco Products Group
LASCO DOOR - Bathroom fixtures - Lasco Products Group
LASCO ESTATE - Bathroom fixtures ☆ - Lasco Products Group
LASCOAT - Glass products - Lasco Products Group
LASCOBOARD - Glass products - Lasco Products Group
LASCOLITE - Glass products - Lasco Products Group
LASE-ARRAY - Laser systems–medical - Photonics Research Inc.
LASER - Bathing suits - Ocean Pool Co.
LASER - Bathtubs–enameled - Lyons Industries Inc.
LASER - Bedding–linen - Dan River Inc.
LASER - Beverages–malt - Pabst Brewing Co.
LASER - Bicycles ☆ - Roadmaster Corp.
LASER - Chemical weapons - Defense Corp. of America
LASER - Cutlery - Regent Sheffield, Ltd.
LASER - Firearms, accessories, and parts - Beeman Precision Airguns
LASER - Fireplace equipment - Thermo-Rite Manufacturing Co.
LASER - Floor coverings–carpet and rugs - Cumberland Mills Inc.
LASER - Golfing equipment - Ram Golf Corp.
LASER - Laser detectors ☆ - Cobra Electronics Corp.
LASER - Lighting fixtures - Big Beam Emergency Systems Inc.
LASER - Motor vehicles–automobiles ☆ - Chrysler Corp. (Chrysler-Plymouth Div.)
LASER - Motor vehicles–motor homes ☆ - Kit Manufacturing Co.
LASER - Nail care products - HK Industries
LASER - Ophthalmic goods - Rozin Optical Export Corp.
LASER - Paper–bond - Georgia-Pacific Corp.
LASER - Patches, insignia, and emblems - Joy Insignia Inc.
LASER - Recording label - Statiras Records
LASER - Ships–sailing vessels - Sunfish Laser Inc.
LASER - Shoes - Converse Inc.
LASER - Skis - Stockli/Prestige USA
LASER - Stain removers - AmeriPlus Inc.
LASER - Thread ☆ - Perfect Thread Co. Inc.
LASER - Toys–models ☆ - Estes Industries
LASER - Video tapes–blank - Swire Magnetics Co.
LASER 5 - Tools - A. Meyers & Sons Corp.
LASER 286/2 - Computer peripheral equipment - Laser Computer Inc.
LASER 300 - Steering mechanisms–motor vehicle - Superior Industries International, Inc.

☆ = Now out of production

LASER 486 - Computer peripheral equipment - VTech Computers Inc.
LASER ACE - Lasers - Lasertrace, Inc.
LASER AIM - Electronics equipment - Emerging Technologies Inc.
LASER ART PLUS - Lasers - Borden & Riley Paper Co.
LASER ATTACK - Games ☆ - Milton Bradley Co.
LASER BEACON - Lasers - Laser Alignment, Inc.
LASER BEAMS - Apparel–women's - Kellwood Co.
LASER BLAST - Computer software - Activision, Inc.
LASER BLAZER - Fireworks - China Pyrotechnics, Inc.
LASER BOLT - Toys–automobiles - Mattel, Inc.
LASER BRIGHT - Paper - Rel Graphic Systems & Marketing Co.
LASER BRISTOL - Paper - Parsons Paper Co.
LASER BROWSER PAKS - Fixtures - Chicago One Stop/Browser Display
LASER-CAINE - Pharmaceutical preparations - Linda H. Dixon
LASER CASINO - Laser disc video game - Paws & Play Games, Inc.
LASER COMMAND - Toys - Tyco Toys
LASER CONCEPTS - Electronics equipment - Omega Organization International (Laser Concepts Div.)
LASER CUT - Clippers–barber - Marianna Imports, Inc.
LASER CUT - Jewelry - Christopher Designs, Inc.
LASER D - Computer storage devices - Disclosure Inc.
LASER DOCUMENT SOLUTIONS - Computer software - PBF Corp.
LASER-ENGINEERED - Envelopes ☆ - Kimberly-Clark Corp. (Karolton Envelope Div.)
LASER ENGINEERED - Paper - Georgia-Pacific Corp.
LASER FANG - Darts and dart games - Hasbro, Inc.
LASER-FASER - Toys–guns - Imperial Toy Corp.
LASER FIGHTERS - Toys - Mattel, Inc.
LASER FLASH - Computer software - Greatland Inc.
LASER FLASH - Toys–guns - Matchbox Toys USA
LASER FUSION - Tools - Regent Sheffield, Ltd.
LASER GLOW LIGHT - Markers–felt-tip - Topstone Industries Inc.
LASER GRAND PRIX - Video games - Taito America Corp.
LASER GS 300 - Skis - Wellington Leisure Products, Inc.
LASER GUARD - Automotive parts and accessories - Taylor-Bell Technologies, Inc.
LASER GUIDE - Computer software - General Research Corp.
LASER HOT - Batteries - Shumaker Battery Warehouse, Inc.
LASER II - Craft supplies - A. Meyers & Sons Corp.
LASER II - Wallpaper ☆ - Marburg Wallcoverings Inc.
LASER II - Whirlpool spa ☆ - Jacuzzi Inc.
LASER III - Wheelchairs - Medline, Industries, Inc.
LASER KOOLKIT - Stationery - Fantasma Inc.
LASER LIBRARIAN - Computer software - CP Systems, Inc.
LASER LIGHT - Toys–electronic - Just Toys, Inc.
LASER LINE - Greeting cards - Sunrise Publications, Inc.
LASER LINK - Transmitting apparatus - Antec Corp.
LASER-LITE - Electrical industrial apparatus - Blount, Inc.
LASER LITE - Plugs–ear - Howard S. Leight and Associates, Inc.
LASER LOOP - Toys–automobiles - Mattel, Inc.
LASER LORDS - Games ☆ - Today's Kids Inc.
LASER MAGIC - Computer software - Lasersoft, Inc.
LASER MAIL - Office supplies ☆ - Transkrit
LASER MASTER - Toys - Jak-Pak Inc.
LASER MED - Goggles - Glendale Protective Technologies Inc.
LASER-OPTIC - Stationery ☆ - Tab Products Co.
LASER PENCIL - Pens - National Pen & Pencil Co.
LASER PERFECT - Inks - Laser Perfect, Inc.
LASER PLATE - Electronic equipment - Laser Stealth Technology LLC
LASER PLUS - Cutlery - Regent Sheffield, Ltd.
LASER POINTER - Projectors–photographic - Apollo Audiovisual Div.
LASER POINTER - Projectors–photographic - Creatron Inc.
LASER PRO LENDING SUITE - Computer software - CFI Pro Services, Inc.
LASER QUEST - Computer software - General Research Corp.
LASER RADIAL - Ships–sailing vessels - Sunfish Laser Inc.
LASER RECORDS - Recording label - David M. Ehrlich
LASER RESONATOR STRUCTURE - Laser systems–medical - Kentek Corp.
LASER ROD - Antennas - Valor Enterprises, Inc.
LASER-SAFE - Lenses–optical - Fosta-Tek Optics, Inc.
LASER SAVE - Inks–duplicating - Central Technology, Inc.
LASER SCREED - Construction machinery - Somero Enterprises Inc.
LASER SDP - Computer system - Roadware Corp.
LASER SHEEN - Pet products - Farnam Cos. Inc.
LASER SINGLES - Labels–paper - May Tag and Label Co.
LASER SPEED - Office supplies - Georgia-Pacific Corp.
LASER STAX - Lasers - Curtis Manufacturing Co., Inc.

LASER SWORDS - Chewing gum - Philadelphia Chewing Gum Corp.
LASER TAG - Games ☆ - Worlds of Wonder
LASER TECH - Key rings - Laser Tech
LASER TRAC - Microscopes - Teletrac Inc.
LASER TRACER - Electronic equipment - Spectra-Physics Laserplane, Inc.
LASER-TUNE - Capacitors - Murata Erie North America, Inc.
LASER TWIST - Pens - Union Pen Co.
LASER V - Trailers–travel - Trotwood Corp.
LASER WAR - Fireworks - American Promotional Events, Inc.
LASER WRAP - Giftware ☆ - Flexo Craft Prints Inc.
LASER X - Buffing machines - Pioneer/Eclipse Corp.
LASER X2 - Saw blades - Vermont American Corp.
LASERACCESS CORP. - Computer hardware and software - Laseraccess Corp.
LASERACT - Computer software - Destiny Technology Corp.
LASERALIGN - Electromedical apparatus - Cyberoptics Corp.
LASERARC - Computer software - Imnet Systems, Inc.
LASERBACK - Computer software - Rexon/Tecmar Inc.
LASERBACK - Labels–gummed - Release International Inc.
LASERBAR - Computer software - Levin & Associates Inc.
LASERBENGALI - Computer storage devices–magnetic - Payne Loving Trust
LASERBLADES - Windshield wiper blades - Blu Blocker Corp.
LASERBRASS - Awards, plaques and medals - R.S. Owens and Co.
LASERBRITE - Awards, plaques and medals - Planter, Inc.
LASERCAT - Computer software - Triad Systems Corp.
LASERCHARGE - Computer franchise - LaserCharge Inc.
LASERCHECK - Computer storage devices - Bottomline Technologies, Inc.
LASERCOMP - Measuring instruments - Lasercomp
LASERCOPTIC - Computer storage devices–magnetic - Payne Loving Trust
LASERCRAFT - Book ends - Lasercraft, Inc.
LASERCUT PATCHES - Patches, insignia, and emblems - Pacific Sportswear and Emblem Co.
LASERDATA - Computer hardware - Laserdata, Inc.
LASERDESIGN! - Computer software - Computing!
LASERDEX - Pharmaceutical preparations ☆ - Laser Inc.
LASERDEX - Postcards - Continental Dataforms
LASERDISC - Video tapes–blank - Pioneer LDCA Inc.
LASERDOPP - Blood pressure apparatus - Vasamedics, Inc.
LASEREYE - Lasers - Cobra Electronics Corp.
LASERFIBRE - Sports rackets and accessories - Timothy P. Sullivan
LASERFIX - Electronic equipment - Tile EZ USA, Inc.
LASERFLEX - Flashlights - Pelican Products, Inc.
LASERFORCE - Computer peripheral equipment - Compton's NewMedia
LASERGARD - Goggles - Glendale Protective Technologies Inc.
LASERGLOSS - Paper - Paper Direct, Inc.
LASERHAWK - Guns - S/R Industries, Inc. (Marksman Products)
LASERHEARTBEAT - Audio and video equipment - S.N.S.T., Inc.
LASERIMAGE - Printers–computer - Personal Computer Products, Inc.
LASERIMPACT - Printing trades machinery - Comprotek Services, Inc.
LASERITE - Medical apparatus - Del Mar Avionics
LASERJET - Printers–computer - Hewlett-Packard Co.
LASERJET COMPANION - Computer software - Hewlett-Packard Co.
LASERKANNADA - Computer software - Payne Loving Trust
LASERKIT - Model buildings - American Model Builders, Inc.
LASERKRIB - Containers - Laserkrib, Inc.
LASERKRIB - Containers - Lawn-Boy
LASERLIFTER - Elevating columns - Spectra-Physics Laserplane, Inc.
LASERLIGHT DIGITAL - Recording label - Delta Entertainment Corp.
LASERLINE - Paperboard ☆ - Miller Cardboard Corp.
LASERLITE - Optical scanners–computer - Videx, Inc.
LASERMAINTENANCE - Computer franchise - LaserCharge Inc.
LASERMATE - Computer software - Micro Logic Corp.
LASERMATRIX - Printers–computer - Output Technology Corp.
LASERMAX - Sights–gun - Laser Max, Inc.
LASERMAX 40/50 - Printers–computer - Wallace Computer Services, Inc.
LASERMERGE - Computer software ☆ - Mindgate Technologies Inc.
LASERNET - Computers - Western Telematic Inc.
LASERPIX - Computer software - Xerographics Laser Images Corp.
LASERPOINT SOFTWARE SYSTEMS - Computer software - Laserpoint Software Systems Inc.
LASERPORT - Apparel and accessories - Eclipse Technologies
LASERPREMIUMS - Labels–paper - Paper Direct, Inc.
LASERPRESS 1200 - Printers–computer ☆ - Xante Corp.
LASERPRO - Flashlights - Pelican Products, Inc.
LASERPULSE - Tools–hand-operated - Chicago Pneumatic Tool Co. Inc.
LASERPUNJABI - Computer software - Payne Loving Trust

☆ = Now out of production

LASERQUIPT - Computer peripheral equipment - Laserquipt USA, Inc.
LASERRAK - Office furniture–wood - Hunt Holdings, Inc.
LASERSCOPE - Sights–gun - Laser Devices, Inc.
LASERSCREEN - Artists' materials - Philadelphia Ceramics Inc.
LASERSCRIPT - Computers - Everex Systems, Inc.
LASERSET - Business forms - Moore Business Forms, Inc.
LASERSHARE - Computer software - Apple Computer Inc.
LASERSIGN - Computer storage devices - Paper Direct, Inc.
LASERSMOOTH 1000 - Office supplies - Georgia-Pacific Corp.
LASERSOFT - Games - Lasersoft, Inc.
LASERSPIN - Toys - Pascal C. Wisznia
LASERSTAR - Electronic equipment - O'Ryan Industries
LASERSTAR BLACK MAGIC - Juke boxes ☆ - Rowe International, Inc.
LASERSTAR DIAMANTE - Juke boxes - Rowe International, Inc.
LASERSTAR LADY IN RED - Juke boxes ☆ - Rowe International, Inc.
LASERSYRIAC - Computer storage devices–magnetic - Payne Loving Trust
LASERTELUGU - Computer storage devices–magnetic - Payne Loving Trust
LASERTIME - Clocks ☆ - General Time Corp. (Westclox/Seth Thomas Div.)
LASERTRAC - Audio equipment - Northwest Audio Design Inc.
LASERTRAK - Electronic equipment - Honeywell Inc.
LASERTRAX - Compact discs–prerecorded - Hottrax Records
LASERTRIM - Capacitors - Johanson Dielectrics, Inc.
LASERULTRA - Paper - International Paper Co.
LASERVISION - Measuring instruments - Zircon Corp.
LASERWARE - Computer software - National Computer Systems, Inc.
LASERWASH - Machinery - PDQ Manufacturing, Inc.
LASERWAVE - Thermometers - Textron Systems Corp.
LASERWELL - Paper - Formstore Inc.
LASERWORLD - Welding machinery - Motoman, Inc.
LASERWRITER - Printers–computer - Apple Computer Inc.
LASERWRITER PLUS - Printers–computer - Apple Computer Inc.
LASERWRITER SELECT - Printers–computer - Apple Computer Inc.
LASERX - Film - Anacomp Inc.
LASERXCEL - Office supplies - Georgia-Pacific Corp.
LASERXL - Computer hardware - Laserdata, Inc.
LASF LILLI ANN - Apparel–women's - Lilli Ann Corp.
LASH - Television equipment - Television Equipment Associates
LASH & BROW - Cosmetics - Roux Laboratories, Inc.
LASH BUILDER - Cosmetics - Excelcis
LASH BY LASH - Cosmetics - Maybelline Intermediate Co.
LASH FLIP - Cosmetics - Noxell Corp.
LASH LIFE - Cosmetics - Tricho-Genous Inc.
LASH LOCK - Cosmetics - Olay Co., Inc.
LASH LURE - American International Industries
LASH MAKER - Cosmetics - Max Factor & Co.
LASH MASTER - Cordage - Ancra International Corp.
LASH-O-MATIC - Mascara applicator ☆ - Cosrich Inc.
LASH OUT - Cosmetics - Cosmair Inc.
LASH REPAIR - Cosmetics - Revlon Consumer Products Corp.
LASH TABS - Knapsacks - Coleman Co., Inc.
LASHBRUSH - Cosmetics - Ardell International Inc.
LASHCARE - Cosmetics - Ardell International Inc.
LASHERHOSE - Hoses ☆ - Seneca Knitting Mills Corp.
LASHFREE - Cosmetics - Ardell International Inc.
LASHFULL - Cosmetics - Revlon Consumer Products Corp.
LASHFULL CURVACEOUS - Cosmetics - Revlon Consumer Products Corp.
LASHGRIP - Artificial eyelash adhesive - Ardell International Inc.
LASHGRIP - Cosmetics - American International Industries
LASHGRIP STRIP - Cosmetics - Ardell International Inc.
LASHIRE - Knit goods - Coronet Casuals Inc.
LASHLEY LE GRANDE - Guitars - Emmons Guitar Co. Inc.
LASHLITES - Cosmetics - Ardell International Inc.
LASH'S BY FING'RS - Cosmetics - Entrecap Corp.
LASHTITE - American International Industries
LASICO - Measuring instruments - Los Angeles Scientific Instruments
LASIX - Pharmaceutical preparations - Hoechst-Roussel Pharmaceuticals Inc.
LASKO - Fans–electric ☆ - Lasko Metal Products Inc.
LASONIC - Tape players - Lasonic Electronics Corp.
L.A.S.P. - Health care products - Labeltape Meditect Inc.
LASR MARK - Labeling machinery - New Options, Inc.
LASSALE - Watches - Seiko Corp. of America
LASSE N HAWAII - Apparel and accessories - Trinity Products, Inc.
LASSEN - Granola bars - Lassen Foods
LASSEN HAWAII - Apparel and accessories - Lassen Art Publications, Inc.
LASSES KRISP - Popcorn - R.L. Stiles Inc.
LASSIE - Brushes–paint - Corona Brushes Inc.

LASSIE - Cereal - M.L. de Lange
LASSIE - Insecticides - Carter-Wallace, Inc.
LASSIE - Pet products - Lassie Pet Products
LASSIE - Toys ☆ - Knickerbocker Toy Co. Inc.
LASSIE - Veterinary pharmaceutical preparations - Palladium L.P.
LASSIE JANE - Pickles - W.B. Roddenbery Co., Inc.
LASSITERS' - Corn–flour or meal - House-Autry Mills, Inc.
LASSO - Dental equipment - Belport Co., Inc.
LASSO - Herbicides - Monsanto Co.
LASSO - Wire products - Trefilarbed Inc.
LASSO II - Fabrics ☆ - Charter Fabrics Inc.
LASSO LOCK - Locks–padlocks - Calibro Corp.
LASSO LURE - Fishing lures - Alvin L. Winburn
LASSOS - Ophthalmic goods - Tres Gatos Trading Co.
LASSY - Dog food - Hubbard Milling Co.
LAST - Audio equipment - LAST Factory
LAST - Recording label - Jazz Composer's Orchestra Association Inc.
LAST BAKEWARE YOU EVER NEED TO BUY, THE - Cooking utensils–aluminum - Wilton Industries, Inc.
LAST BOAT DOCK YOU WILL EVER NEED, THE - Docks - Ez Dock, Inc.
LAST BOUNTY HUNTER, THE - Video games - American Laser Games, Inc.
LAST CHANCE DETECTIVES - Recording label - Focus On The Family
LAST DAYS - Apparel and accessories - Angelo Zaragovia
LAST DROP - Nail care products - Nails 2000 International
LAST ELEGANT BEAR, THE - Toys–stuffed ☆ - Gund, Inc.
LAST EVENT - Floor coverings–carpet and rugs ☆ - Olympic Carpets Inc.
LAST FLIGHT OUT - Apparel and accessories - Last Flight Out International, Inc.
LAST HOP!, THE - Pet products - Petcraft, Inc.
LAST HOUR - Apparel and accessories - Last Hour
LAST LAFFS - Greeting cards - Michael Pratt & Bruce Pratt Partnership
LAST LAP, THE - Games - Stump Publishing Co.
LAST LAUGHS BEFORE TURNPIKE - Shirts - Last Laughs Before Turnpike, Inc.
LAST LOTION - Skin care products - G.S.R. Enterprises, Inc.
LAST N LAST - Finishing agents - Absolute Coatings Inc.
LAST-O-COAT - Waterproofing compounds ☆ - Flood Co.
LAST OUT - Toys–electronic - Tiger Electronics, Inc.
LAST SHOT, THE - Games - Victor Turner
LAST STAND, THE - Furniture - Dobi Specialties
LAST STEP (RATS & MICE) - Insecticides - Bacon Products Corp.
LAST STEP (ROACH) - Insecticides - Bacon Products Corp.
LAST STOP - Pet products - Barney Grey Enterprises
LAST STOP - Rodent and cockroach traps, safety goggles, dust mask - Abepco Manufacturing Co.
LAST STOP FLEA COMB CLEANER KIT - Pet products - Lazy Pet Products
LAST STRAW - Games - Tyco Toys
LAST TANGO - Floor coverings–carpet and rugs - Carpet Crafts Inc.
LAST THING, THE - Hair care products - Warner-Lambert Co.
LAST TRAIN FROM PARIS, THE - Games - Decipher Inc.
LAST WORD - Crocheted and knitted items - Winston Manufacturing Corp.
LAST WORD - Floor coverings–carpet and rugs ☆ - Alexander Smith Carpets
LAST WORD - Games ☆ - Milton Bradley Co.
LAST WORD - Hair care products - Helene Curtis Industries Inc.
LAST WORD - Tools - L.S. Starrett Co. Inc. (Consumer Products Div.)
LAST WORD IN MEMORY, THE - Computer memory - Camintonn Corp.
LAST WORD, THE - Games - Scramb-L-Gram, Inc.
LAST WORD, THE - Food products - United Citrus Products Corp.
LAST WRITES - Computer software - Space Coast Computer Solutions, Inc.
LASTEK - Adhesives and sealants - Maintenance Inc.
LASTI-TI - Wallets - Quality Park Products Co.
LASTIC LOVE - Brassieres (Bras) ☆ - Lovable Co.
LASTICAULK - Caulking compounds - United Gilsonite Laboratories
LASTING - Paints - Lasting Paints Inc.
LASTING BEAUTY - Cosmetics ☆ - Warner-Lambert Co.
LASTING BEAUTY - Floor coverings–carpet and rugs - Walter Carpet Mills
LASTING BEAUTY - Jewelry - Sandberg & Sikorski Diamond Corp.
LASTING CHARM - Floor coverings–carpet and rugs - Johnson's Carpets Inc.
LASTING COLOR - Lipsticks - Max Factor & Co.
LASTING COLOR BY LOVING CARE - Hair care products - Clairol Inc.
LASTING COMFORT - Apparel–women's - Lane Bryant, Inc.
LASTING DIMENSIONS - Vinyl - Aluminum Co. of America
LASTING ENDEARMENTS - Music boxes ☆ - Schmid Inc.
LASTING EXPRESSIONS - Giftware - Fort USA
LASTING GLOW - Cosmetics - Almay Inc.
LASTING IMAGE - Cosmetics - Cheveux Inc.

☆ = Now out of production

LASTING IMPRESSION - Skin care products - Mennen Co.

LASTING IMPRESSIONS - Flowers, plants, and seeds - Mikkelsens Inc.

LASTING IMPRESSIONS - Furniture - Lane Co. Inc.

LASTING IMPRESSIONS - Jewelry - Lasting Impressions Inc.

LASTING IMPRESSIONS - Soap - Lasting Impressions Picture Soap, Inc.

LASTING IMPRESSIONS - Toys - Heritage Mint, Ltd.

LASTING KEEPSAKES - Craft supplies - Mangelsen's

LASTING KEEPSAKES - Giftware - Mangelsen's (VDI)

LASTING LANDSCAPE - Horticultural product - J.T. Inman Co. Inc.

LASTING LASH - Cosmetics - Redken Laboratories, Inc.

LASTING LINEN WRAP - Cosmetics - American International Industries

LASTING LOFT - Pillows - E.I. Dupont de Nemours and Co.

LASTING LOOK - Cosmetics - Mana Products, Inc.

LASTING LOOK OF DUTCH BOY, THE - Coatings - Sherwin-Williams Automotive Finishes Corp.

LASTING LOVE - Rings–jewelry - Artcarved Inc.

LASTING LUSTER - Lipsticks - Del Pharmaceuticals, Inc.

LASTING LUXURIES - Hosiery–women's - Victoria's Secret Stores, Inc.

LASTING LUXURY - Cosmetics - Alexandra De Markoff, Ltd.

LASTING MEMORIES - Floor coverings–carpet and rugs ☆ - Hollytex Carpet Mills Inc.

LASTING MEMORIES - Giftware ☆ - American Greetings Corp.

LASTING MIST - Housewares - S.C. Johnson & Son, Inc.

LASTING MOMENTS - Cardboard - Lasting Moments

LASTING PERFORMANCE - Cosmetics ☆ - Noxell Corp.

LASTING PRIDE - Pet products - Oil-Dri Corp. of America

LASTING PRIDE PLUS - Pet products - Oil-Dri Corp. of America

LASTING SPLENDOUR - Floor coverings–carpet and rugs ☆ - Zenith Carpets

LASTING THOUGHTS LIBRARY - Greeting cards - American Greetings Corp.

LASTINGCOTE - Floor waxes ☆ - Uncle Sam Chemical Co., Inc.

LASTIX - Paints - Sampson Coatings Inc.

LASTO-FLEX - Apparel and accessories ☆ - Glamorise Foundations Inc.

LASTOLON - Apparel–women's ☆ - Bali Co. Inc.

LASTRADA - Floor coverings - Architectural Floor Systems, Inc.

LASTS SO LONG - Hair care products - Helene Curtis Industries Inc.

LASUPREMA - Snack foods - Curtice-Burns Foods, Inc.

LASZLES - Puzzles - High Tech Images

LAT-TEA - Teas ☆ - Canterbury Cuisine Inc.

LATA - Jewelry - Lata Export & Import, Inc.

LATAH CREEK - Wines - HDT Importers Inc.

LATAH CREEK - Wines - Latah Creek Wine Cellars

LATAMA - Knives–pocket ☆ - Latama Inc.

LATAMASTIC - Adhesives and sealants ☆ - Laticrete International Inc.

LATAPOXY - Adhesives and sealants - Laticrete International Inc.

LATCH - Brushes - Wright-Bernet

LATCH-A-MATIC - Hardware - Distlefink Designs, Inc.

LATCH-EZE - Lubricants ☆ - Stoner Inc.

LATCH-GARD - Hardware - Latch-Gard Inc.

LATCH LOC - Hardware - Sash Controls Inc.

LATCH-MATIC - Electronic equipment - Reading Body Works, Inc.

LATCHAM - Wines - Granite Springs Winery

LATCHLOK - Hooks - Columbus Mckinnon Corp.

LATCHMATIC - Doors–glass - Slideline, Inc.

LATCO - Tiles–ceramic ☆ - Latco Products

LATE HARVEST - Wines - Bully Hill Vineyards, Inc.

LATE HARVEST - Wines - Cilurzo Vineyard & Winery

LATE HARVEST ESTATE RIESLING & GERWURZTRAMINER - Wines ☆ - Kobrand Corp.

LATE NIGHT BLEND - Coffee - Barrie House Coffee Co., Inc.

LATE SHOW - Shirts - Worldwide Pants Inc.

LATE SHOW, THE - Apparel–women's - Richard Leeds International, Inc.

+L'ATELIER - Apparel–men's - Superba, Inc.

LATELLA - Cheese - Lactoprot USA, Inc.

LATER ALLIGATOR - Beverages - Homestead, Inc.

LATERAL - Wines - Kathryn Kennedy Winery

LATERITE - Water treating compounds ☆ - Aquarium Products Inc.

LATEX BOTTOM BRUSH - Brushes–paint - Corona Brushes Inc.

LATEX-CALK - Sealing compounds - Biddle Co.

LATEX CONCRETE REPAIR - Latex - Camp Co. Inc.

LATEX-ITE - Tar - Dalton Enterprises, Inc.

LATEX LIQUID FLOOR - Floor coverings - Camp Co. Inc.

LATEXTRA - Paints - Martin Paint Stores

LATH-ART - Sculpture reproductions ☆ - Austin Sculpture Inc.

LATHEGUARD - Safety products - Flexbar Machine Corp.

LATHER-A-PUP - Pet products - Davis Manufacturing

LATHER MAN - Containers ☆ - Sunbeam-Oster Household Products

LATHER-PACK - Insect repellents - Zema Corp.

LATHERINE - Rug shampoo - Continental Chemical Corp.

LATHERKING - Cosmetics - Morris-Flamingo Inc.

LATI-SEAL - Paints - Ponderosa Paint Manufacturing Co. Inc.

LATICE BASICS - Wood products - Universal Forest Products, Inc.

LATICRETE - Adhesives and sealants - Laticrete International Inc.

LATIGO - Floor coverings–carpet and rugs - Sweetwater Carpet Corp.

LATIGO SLING - Firearms, accessories, and parts - Brownells, Inc.

LATIN AMERICAN CURLS - Hair care products - Revlon Consumer Products Corp.

LATIN FIESTA - Colognes - Old 97 Co.

LATIN HANGMAN - Computer software - Dynacomp Inc.

LATIN IDENTITY - Apparel and accessories - Moises Villegas

LATIN INTERNATIONAL - Recording label - Sony Disco Inc.

LATIN JAZZ - Recording label - Sony Music Entertainment Inc.

LATIN LEGENDS - Herbal products - United American Industries, Inc.

LATIN MEN - Publisher's imprints - Mavety Media Group Ltd.

LATIN NOW! - Computer software - Transparent Language, Inc.

LATIN PERCUSSION - Drums–musical instruments - LP Music Group

LATIN PERCUSSION VENTURES - Recording label - LP Music Group

LATINA - Dinnerware–glass ☆ - Block China Co.

LATINA - Floor coverings ☆ - Congoleum Corp.

LATINA TRAVERTINE - Floor coverings - Congoleum Corp.

LATINAS - Shoes - Footwear Unlimited, Inc.

LATINI - Pasta - De Medici Imports Ltd.

LATIS - Imaging materials - Graphic Technology Inc.

LATITUDE - Computer software - Northwest Geografx

LATITUDE - Computers - Dell Computer Corp.

LATITUDE - Golfing equipment - Renaissance Golf Products, Inc.

LATITUDES - Broyhill Furniture Industries, Inc.

LATITUDES - Dinnerware–glass ☆ - Franciscan by Johnson Brothers, USA, Inc.

LATITUDES - Wallpaper - Textile Wallcoverings International Ltd.

LATMASTER - Exercising equipment - John A. Larkin

LATO - Health care products - Larkotex Surgical Manufacturing Co.

LATONIA - Fruits–canned - Pillsbury Co.

LATOSS 'N' CATCH - Toys - Southern States Marketing, Inc.

LATOUR - Floor coverings–carpet and rugs - Evans-Black Carpet Mills

LATOURAINE - Coffee - Chock Full O'Nuts Corp.

LATROBE AMERICAN PALE ALE - Beverages–alcohol - Latrobe Brewing Co.

LATSHAW - Tools - Wescon Products Co.

LATTA - Margarine - Lever Brothers Co. Inc.

LATTE - Apparel and accessories - Judy Ann of California

LATTE LUGGER - Paper products - Clfactor, Inc.

LATTECCINO - Coffee - Saramar Corp.

LATTELAND - Coffee - Latteland, Inc.

LATTICE - Chimes ☆ - Nutone Inc.

LATTICE - Floor coverings–carpet and rugs - Criterion Mills Inc.

LATTICE - Floor coverings–carpet and rugs - Langhorne Carpet Co. Inc.

LATTICE - Floor coverings–carpet and rugs - V & B Carpet

LATTICE - Floor coverings–carpet and rugs ☆ - Design Materials, Inc.

LATTICE - Floor coverings–carpet and rugs ☆ - Quaker Inc.

LATTICE - Floor coverings–carpet and rugs ☆ - Regal Rugs Inc.

LATTICE - Floor coverings–carpet and rugs ☆ - Stanton Carpet Corp.

+L'ATTICE - Girdles - H.F. Robbins

LATTICE - Jewelry - Frederick Goldman, Inc.

LATTICE - Tiles–ceramic - Monarch Tile Inc.

LATTICE COLLECTION, THE - Furniture - Shelby Williams Industries, Inc.

LATTICE GARDEN - Floor coverings–carpet and rugs - Playfield International Inc.

LATTICE SEMICONDUCTOR CORPORATION - Computer software - Lattice Semiconductor Corp.

LATTICECRAFT - Fencing–wood - K-D Wood Products Inc.

LATTISNET - Computer software - Synoptics Communications, Inc.

+L'ATTITUDES - Jewelry - Pakula & Co.

LAU & CONNAIRE - Blowers and fans - Tomkins Industries Inc.

LAU LURE - Fishing lures - Paul Warner Industries

LAUBE - Barber shop equipment - Kim Laube & Co. Inc.

LAUDER FOR MEN - Perfumes - Estee Lauder Inc.

LAUDERDALE - Shoes - Allen-Edmonds Shoe Corp.

LAUDER'S - Beverages–alcohol - Hiram Walker & Sons, Inc.

LAUDER'S - Liquors - Canandaigua Wine Co. Inc.

LAUDISIO - Breads - Laudisio Food Products, Inc.

LAUER LEATHERS - Apparel–men's - Milwaukee Glove Co.

LAUFEN - Tiles–ceramic ☆ - Laufen Ceramic Tile

LAUFERINI - Bags - Boschini Manufacturing
LAUGEL - Wines - Victoire Imports Co.
LAUGH & LEARN - Publisher's imprints - Price Stern Sloan Inc.
LAUGH TRACKS - Greeting cards - Oatmeal Studios, Inc.
LAUGH TRAKS - Toys—musical - Mattel, Inc.
LAUGHABLES - Figurines - Jody Bergsma Galleries, Inc.
LAUGHABLES - Figurines - Reco International Corp.
LAUGHIN' LEMON - Candy - Nabisco Foods Group
LAUGHIN' SPLASHIN' LAGOON - Toys - Marchon, Inc.
LAUGHING BEAR - Cookies - Parco Foods, Inc.
LAUGHING C.A.T., THE - Coffee - Laughing C.A.T.
LAUGHING COW, THE - Cheese - Fromageries Bel, Inc.
LAUGHING ELEPHANT - Stationery - Blue Lantern Publishing Inc.
LAUGHTER - Perfumes - Quintessence Inc.
LAUGHTER LIBRARY - Publisher's imprints - Price Stern Sloan Inc.
LAUNCELOT - Watches - Bulova Corp.
LAUNCH! - Computer software - Pagepath Technologies, Inc.
LAUNCH PAD - Boating equipment and accessories - Isotech Inc.
LAUNCH PAD - Computer peripheral equipment - Gregory H. Rice
LAUNCH PAD - Computer software - Berkeley Systems, Inc.
LAUNCH PAD - Radio communications equipment - Multipoint Networks, Inc.
LAUNCHBOARD - Computer peripheral equipment - Darwin Keyboards, Ltd.
LAUNCHIN' LOBSTERS - Games - Mattel, Inc.
LAUNCHPAD - Conveyors - Rocky Mountain Conveyer and Equipment, Inc.
LAUND-R-VENT - Laundry-venting products - Cole Sewell Corp.
LAUNDER MAID - Food products - Jewel Food Stores Inc.
LAUNDRIT - Detergents ☆ - Elcal Enterprises Ltd.
LAUNDROMAT - Apparel—men's - Santana Ltd.
LAUNDROMAT - Washing machines—commercial - White Consolidated Industries, Inc.
LAUNDRY BRAIN - Washing machine parts - Ecolab Inc.
LAUNDRY CADDY - Closet organizers - Hirsh Co.
LAUNDRY FRESH - Deodorants—personal - Surco Products Inc.
LAUNDRY MATE - Bags—laundry - Spencer Supports Ltd.
LAUNDRY STICK - Stain removers - Cadie Products Corp.
LAUNDRYLINE - Housewares - Seymour Housewares Corp.
LAUNDRYLINK - Computer software - Persyst, Inc.
LAUNDRYMATE - Clothespins - Tansy
LAUNDRYWARE - Housewares - Ironees Co.
LAUNDURA - Pillows - E.I. Dupont de Nemours and Co.
LAUNETTE SPECIAL - Detergents - Procter & Gamble Co.
LAUNIS - Food products - De Choix Specialty Foods Co.
LAURA - Bedding—linen - Dan River Inc.
LAURA - Dinnerware—glass - Metlox Pottery Shoppe
LAURA - Fabrics - Guilford Mills, Inc.
LAURA - Furniture - Haworth, Inc.
LAURA - Glassware—household - ACC
LAURA - Tableware—china ☆ - Lenox, Inc.
LAURA AND JOY - Kitchen utensils—aluminum ☆ - Reston Lloyd Ltd.
LAURA ASHLEY HOME - Wallpaper - Imperial Wallcoverings, Inc.
LAURA ASHLEY-NO. 1 - Perfumes - Alfin Fragrances Inc.
LAURA ASHLEY'S RUFFLES & FLOURISHES - Wallpaper ☆ - Raintree Designs Inc.
LAURA ASHLEY'S UPSTAIRS/DOWNSTAIRS - Wallpaper ☆ - Raintree Designs Inc.
LAURA BAUGH - Golfing equipment - Wilson Sporting Goods Co.
LAURA BETTINI - Footwear - Lily Bettini Inc.
LAURA BIAGIOTTI - Perfumes - Procter & Gamble Co.
LAURA CLAYTON - Apparel and accessories - Angelica Corp.
LAURA DARE - Apparel stores—children's - Tom and Jerry Boyswear Inc.
LAURA DARE - Apparel—children's - ICM
LAURA ELIZABETH - Publisher's imprints - Martingale & Co.
LAURA JEFFRIES - Apparel and accessories - G-III Apparel Group Ltd.
+LAURA +KIEFFER - Apparel—women's - Susan Burrowes, Ltd.
LAURA MAE - Apparel and accessories - M. Serman & Co. Inc.
LAURA SCUDDER'S - Snack foods - Laura Scudder's
LAURA SEDDON COLLECTION - Greeting cards - American Greetings Corp.
LAURA TYLER - Jewelry—costume - Caldor Corp.
LAURA'S - Sausages - Laura's Scottish Bakery
LAURA'S ATTIC - Figurines - Enesco Corp.
LAURA'S WAY - Floor coverings ☆ - Tarkett, Inc.
LAURE - Water—bottled or canned - Laure Beverage Co.
LAUREAT - Frames—eyeglass - Hudson Optical Corp.
LAUREATE - Paper—bond ☆ - Fox River Paper Co.
LAUREATE - Silverware - Towle Manufacturing Co.
LAUREATE - Toilets—enameled - Kohler Co.

LAUREATE RESERVE - Wines ☆ - Golden State Vintners
LAUREATE, THE - Pens ☆ - Bic Corp.
LAUREL - Artists' materials - Laurel St. Art Club, Inc.
LAUREL - Cellos - William Lewis & Son
LAUREL - Dishes—china ☆ - Gorham Inc.
LAUREL - Dishes—china ☆ - Pickard Inc.
LAUREL - Dolls - Goldberger Doll Manufacture Co.
LAUREL - Dolls ☆ - Effanbee Doll Corp.
LAUREL - Flatware ☆ - W.M.F. of America Inc.
LAUREL - Floor coverings - Bruce Hardwood Floors
LAUREL - Floor coverings—carpet and rugs - Bloomsburg Carpet Industries
LAUREL - Glass—leaded - Seneca Glass Co.
LAUREL - Greeting cards ☆ - American Greetings Corp.
LAUREL - Heating pads—electric - Walgreen Co.
LAUREL - Jewelry ☆ - Fantasy Diamond Corp.
LAUREL - Lamps - Instrument Systems Corp.
LAUREL - Motor vehicles—automobiles ☆ - Nissan Motor Corp. USA
LAUREL - Office furniture—wood ☆ - Haskell of Pittsburgh, Inc.
LAUREL - Plastics - Baumgarten's
LAUREL - Rings—jewelry - Artcarved Inc.
LAUREL - Vases ☆ - Crisa Corp.
LAUREL - Watches - Bulova Corp.
LAUREL & HARDY - Erasers ☆ - Diener Industries Inc.
LAUREL BAY - Bicycles ☆ - Huffy Corp.
LAUREL BURCH PAPER CO. - Greeting cards - Laurel Burch Inc.
LAUREL CANYON - Furniture - Henredon Furniture Industries Inc.
LAUREL CANYON - Housewares - Barth-Dreyfuss of California
LAUREL CREEK - Furniture - Bean Station Furniture Factory Inc.
LAUREL GLEN - Floor coverings—carpet and rugs - Evans-Black Carpet Mills
LAUREL GLEN VINEYARD - Wines - Laurel Glen Vineyard
LAUREL HILL - Clocks - Kirch Industrial Co. (USA) Ltd.
LAUREL HILL SOFTWARE - Computer software - Laurel Hill Software Co.
LAUREL LATTICE - Floor coverings—carpet and rugs ☆ - Regal Rugs Inc.
LAUREL LEAF - Publisher's imprints - Bantam Doubleday Dell Publishing Group, Inc.
LAUREL OAKS - Manufactured homes - Redman Industries, Inc.
LAUREL ORCHARDS - Food products ☆ - Paradigm Foodworks
LAUREL PAPERBACKS - Publisher's imprints - Bantam Doubleday Dell Publishing Group, Inc.
LAUREL PARK - Clocks - General Time Corp. (Westclox/Seth Thomas Div.)
LAUREL PARK - Floor coverings—carpet and rugs - Monticello Carpet Mills
LAUREL PRINTS - Wallpaper ☆ - Imperial Wallcoverings, Inc.
LAUREL PURE - Water—distilled - Holyoke Distilled Water Co. Inc.
LAUREL RIDGE - Floor coverings—carpet and rugs - Gulistan Carpet Inc.
LAUREL RIDGE - Food products - Musselman Fruit Products
LAUREL WAY - Floor coverings—carpet and rugs ☆ - Hollytex Carpet Mills Inc.
LAUREL WREATH - Glass—leaded - Seneca Glass Co.
LAURELCREST - Floor coverings—carpet and rugs - Fieldcrest Cannon, Inc.
LAURELEAF - Spices and extracts - John Lecroy & Son Inc.
LAURELLE BY VALERIE BARARD - Handbags ☆ - Mutterperl Group Inc.
LAURELSPUN - Crocheted and knitted items - Garland Knitting Mills
LAURELTON - Floor coverings ☆ - Tarkett, Inc.
LAURELTON HALL COLLECTION - Lamps - Antique Reproductions, Inc.
LAURELWOOD - Decals and transfers - Rubbermaid Inc.
LAURELWOOD - Glassware—household ☆ - WMF/USA
LAURELWOOD MANOR - Wallpaper - Seabrook Wallcoverings, Inc.
LAUREN - Floor coverings—carpet and rugs ☆ - Columbus Mills, Inc.
LAUREN - Glassware—household ☆ - Anchor Hocking Glass, Inc.
LAUREN - Guitars - MBT International, Inc.
LAUREN - Perfumes - Cosmair Inc.
LAUREN - Toys - Tonka Corp.
LAUREN - Wallpaper ☆ - Wolf-Gordon Inc.
LAUREN ALEXANDRA - Handbags - Federated Department Stores, Inc.
LAUREN HUTTON NEW YORK - Ophthalmic goods - Lauren Hutton
+LAUREN +LEE - Apparel—women's - Rhoda Lee, Inc.
LAUREN LEE - Apparel—women's - Rhoda Lee, Inc.
LAUREN LEE - Jewelry - Faturnace Corp.
LAUREN NICOLE - Apparel—women's - Duckwall-Alco Stores, Inc.
LAUREN SARA M - Apparel and accessories - Lauren Sara, Ltd.
LAUREN SCOTT - Apparel and accessories - Knight Textile Corp.
+LAUREN +WOODS - Apparel—women's - Barry Hazan Sportswear, Inc.
LAURENCIA - Wallpaper - Capital Carousel Inc.
LAURENE'S LOVE - Magnets - Self-Help Enterprises of Dayton
LAURENS - Cigarettes - G.A. Georgopulo & Co. Inc.
LAURENS LONGLIFE BOTTLES - Giftware - Ball-Incon

☆ = Now out of production

LAURENS ORIENT - Cigarettes - G.A. Georgopulo & Co. Inc.
LAURENT - Frames—eyeglass - May Optical Co. Inc.
LAURENT - Glassware—household ☆ - Lenox Crystal, Inc.
LAURENT - Tableware—china ☆ - Lenox, Inc.
LAURENTHIAN - Floor coverings - Tarkett, Inc.
LAURENTIAN - Floor coverings - Mannington Resilient Floors
LAURENTIS - Beverages - Sara Lee Corp.
LAURENWOOD PLACE - Tableware—china ☆ - Lenox, Inc.
LAURETAN - Wines - Seagram's Chateau & Estate Wines Co.
LAURETANA - Mineral water - Euromark Ltd.
LAURETO WHITE - Tableware—china ☆ - Villeroy and Boch Tableware Ltd.
LAURI - Eyeglasses - Art-Craft Optical Co.
LAURI EXPRESS - Toys ☆ - Lauri Inc.
LAURIE - Floor coverings—carpet and rugs ☆ - Regal Rugs Inc.
LAURIE - Recording label - Continental Communications Corp.
LAURIER - Jewelry—costume - Import Ltd.
LAURIER VINEYARDS - Wines - Bronco Wine Co.
LAURILAND NEIGHBORHOOD - Toys—erector sets ☆ - Lauri Inc.
LAURIN - Giftware - Gorham Inc.
LAURIN GOLD - Glassware—household - Gorham Inc.
LAURIN PLATINUM - Glassware—household - Gorham Inc.
LAURI'S PLAYMILL - Toys ☆ - Lauri Inc.
LAURO - Pharmaceutical preparations - Otis Clapp & Son Inc.
LAURO BIANDA - Apparel—men's - Lauro Bianda LLC
LAURO RIGHI - Footwear - Footlinks/CEJ Corp.
LAURON SCHRUBBE DESIGNS - Dolls - Bradley Import Co.
LAUSANNE - Dinnerware—glass - Nikko Ceramics Inc.
LAUSANNE - Dinnerware—glass ☆ - Johnson Brothers, USA, Inc.
LAUSANNE - Floor coverings - Mannington Resilient Floors
LAUSANNE - Frames—eyeglass ☆ - Universal/Univis Inc.
+L'AUTOMME - Cosmetics ☆ - Elysee Scientific Cosmetic Co.
LAUTREC - Beverages—alcohol - Consolidated Distilled Products Inc.
LAUVENT - Ventilation equipment - Lau Industrial and Commercial Fans Div.
LAV GUARD - Insulating materials - Truebro, Inc.
LAV-O-DERM - Skin care products - Professional Aids Corp.
LAV SHIELD - Meteorological instruments - Truebro, Inc.
LAVA - Health care products - Vesture Corp.
LAVA - Lighting fixtures - Haggerty Enterprises, Inc.
LAVA - Soap - Procter & Gamble Co.
LAVA - Sporting goods ☆ - O'Brien International
LAVA - Sunglasses - Uvex Sports, Inc.
LAVA - Trading cards and stamps - Malibu Comics Entertainment, Inc.
LAVA BOOTIES - Slippers - Vesture Corp.
LAVA CRETE - Adhesives and sealants - Lavastone Industries
LAVA FIRE LITES - Candles ☆ - Aloha Candle Manufacturing Co. Inc.
LAVA FLAME - Barbecues and grills - Char-Broil
LAVA JAVA - Dinnerware - Niche Marketing, Inc.
LAVA LARRY - Watches - Haggerty Enterprises, Inc.
LAVA LEAF - Jewelry - Michael Anthony Jewelers, Inc.
LAVA LITE - Lighting fixtures - Lava-Simplex Internationale
LAVA-PACK - Health care products - Regency Products
LAVA-SHOT - Toys - Tonka Corp.
LAVA TIME - Clocks ☆ - Lava-Simplex Internationale
LAVA TUBES - Games - Steven R. Loritz
LAVACOL - Home health care products - Warner-Lambert Co.
LAVACOL - Pharmaceutical preparations - Warner-Wellcome
LAVAL - Recording label - LaVal Record Co.
LAVALIER - Glass—leaded - Seneca Glass Co.
LAVAMIND - Computer software - Lavamind
LAVAN-SAN'S XT-1 - Detergents - Rovir, Inc.
LAVANA - Clothing - C & Y Sportswear, Inc.
LAVANDA - Oils—essential - Aromatherapy Institute
LAVANDE - Lenses—optical - Ditto Industries Inc.
LAVANDOU - Cosmetics - Lancome
LAVASTONE - Veneer - Lavastone Industries
LAVATAR - Pharmaceutical preparations ☆ - Doak Dermatologics
LAVAZZA - Coffee ☆ - Gillies Coffee Co.
LAVEI - Hair care products - Joico Laboratories, Inc.
LAVELLE - Moldings and trim - Lavelle Industries Inc.
LAVELLO - Musical instruments ☆ - Grossman Music Corp.
LAVENDA - Skin care products - L'anza Research International
LAVENDER - Dolls - Tonka Corp.
LAVENDER AIR - Perfumes - Karen Carson Creations
LAVENDER & LACE - Needles—sewing - Marilyn Leavitt-Imblum
LAVENDER & OLD LACE - Soap - Procter & Gamble Co.
LAVENDER & ROSES - Skin care products - Heritage Store Inc.

LAVENDER CREAM MOISTURIZER - Skin care products - Gold Medal Hair Products Inc.
LAVENDER DUET - Dolls - Mattel, Inc.
LAVENDER FIELDS - Colognes ☆ - Avon Products, Inc.
LAVENDER HALL - Christmas tree ornaments - Cracker Box Inc.
LAVENDER LADY - Apparel and accessories - Fact Facts Consultants, Inc.
LAVENDER LADY - Toys - Tonka Corp.
LAVENDER LANE - Oils—essential - Lavender Lane, Inc.
LAVENDER LAW - Publisher's imprints - National Lesbian and Gay Law Assn.
LAVENDER LOOKS - Dolls - Mattel, Inc.
LAVENDER MIST - Sachets - Andre Richard
LAVENDER OF PROVENCE - Skin care products - Jason Natural Products, Inc.
LAVENDER-OPAL PATTERN - Glassware—household - Nourot Glass Studio
LAVENDER ROBOT - Toys - Mike's Train House, Inc.
LAVENDER SACHET - Cleaning preparations - Reckitt & Colman Inc.
LAVENDER SACHET - Fabric softeners - Airwick Industries
LAVENDER SURPRISE - Dolls - Mattel, Inc.
LAVERDA - Motor vehicles - Slater Brothers
LAVERIN - Pharmaceutical preparations ☆ - Lemmon Co.
LAVERNE FLAMINGO - Toys—stuffed - Russ Berrie and Co., Inc.
LAVET - Veterinary medical equipment - Linda S. Levengood
LAVEX FLARE LOCK - Pipe joint kit - Lavex Corp.
LAVIA - Floor coverings—carpet and rugs ☆ - Newport Carpet Mills Inc.
LAVIE - Giftware - Lavie International
LAVILIN - Deodorants—personal - Micro Balanced Products Inc.
LAVINA-VILLERT - Watches ☆ - Henri Stern Watch Agency Inc.
LAVINIA - Dinnerware—glass - Royal China & Porcelain Companies Inc.
LAVINIA - Ophthalmic goods - Swank Optical
+L'AVION - Apparel and accessories ☆ - Edison Brothers Stores, Inc.
LAVISH - Ophthalmic goods - Foremost Optical Products
LAVISH LASH - Cosmetics - Elizabeth Arden Inc.
LAVIVA - Pet products - UG Enterprises, Inc.
LAVIVE - Leather goods - Lavive Leather, Inc.
LAVOPTIK - Cosmetics - Lavoptik Co. Inc.
LAVORIS - Mouthwashes - Dep Corp.
LAVORIS - Mouthwashes - Lavoris-Dep Corp.
LAVOSH - Breads - Lavosh Hawaii
LAVOSH FLATBREAD - Breads - Valley Lahvosh Baking Co.
LAVOSH HAWAII - Breads - Lavosh Hawaii
LAW - Business forms - Reynolds and Reynolds Co.
LAW - Computer software - Lawchek, Ltd.
LAW BOND - Office supplies - BlumbergExcelsior, Inc.
LAW ENFORCEMENT COMMAND POSTS - Motor vehicles—buses - Turtle Top Specialty Products
LAW FIVE - Apparel—athletic - MBF Enterprises Inc.
LAW IN A FLASH - Publisher's imprints - Emanuel Law Outlines, Inc.
LAW MADE EASY PRESS - Computer software - Martin M. Shenkman
LAW OF DARKNESS, THE - Games ☆ - Mayfair Games, Inc.
LAW PREP - Publisher's imprints - LawPrep Inc.
LAW PRINTING AUTOMOTIVE PRODUCTS - Business forms - Reynolds and Reynolds Co.
LAWCAST - Recording label - Vox Juris, Inc.
LAWCHEK - Computer software - Lawchek, Ltd.
LAWGIC - Computer software - Expert Systems Publishing Co.
LAWLET - Leather goods - David A. Eakin
LAWMAKER - Eyeglasses - Art-Craft Optical Co.
LAWMAN - Toys - Jak-Pak Inc.
LAWMAN GROUP INTERNATIONAL - Apparel and accessories - Texman Sportswear Inc.
LAWN & GARDEN - Brooms - Perfex Corp.
LAWN AND GARDEN - Lime products - Western Lime Corp.
LAWN BABY - Sprinklers—lawn - Lawn Baby Inc.
LAWN BOY - Garden equipment - Lawn-Boy
LAWN CHAMP - Lawn mowers - Aircap Industries Corp.
LAWN CHIEF - Power lawn mowers - Cotter & Co.
LAWN CLAW - Tools—garden - Faultless Starch/Bon Ami Co.
LAWN COMFORT - Furniture - Bemis Manufacturing Co.
LAWN CRAFTER - Garden equipment - Quaker Industries Ltd.
LAWN CYCLER - Lawn mowers - White Outdoor Products Inc.
LAWN CYCLER 2-IN-1 - Lawn mowers - White Outdoor Products Inc.
LAWN CYCLER 3-IN-1 - Lawn mowers - White Outdoor Products Inc.
LAWN DOCTOR - Lawn mowers - Marathon Projects
LAWN FLITE - Lawn mowers - MTD Products Inc.
LAWN FOOD - Fertilizers - Scotts Co. (Organics Business Group)
LAWN GENIE - Sprinklers—lawn - Hardie-Toro Irrigation

☆ = Now out of production

LAWN GROOM - Garden equipment - Precision Products Inc.
LAWN GUARD - Fencing–gates and posts - Northwestern Steel and Wire Co.
LAWN LITE - Candles - American Candle Co. Inc.
LAWN LITES - Lighting equipment - Kaadan Ltd.
LAWN MARVEL - Fertilizers - Plant Marvel Laboratories
LAWN MATE - Lawn mowers - Telsco Industries. Weather-Matic
LAWN PATCH - Flowers, plants, and seeds - Amturf
LAWN PRESCRIPTION - Fertilizers - B.C.A. Products
LAWN QUEEN - Hoses - Colorite Plastic Co.
LAWN REVIVER - Fertilizers - Scotts Co. (Organics Business Group)
LAWN SHARK - Tools–garden - Lawn Shark Inc.
LAWN TENDER - Lawn-care product - Brinly-Hardy Co.
LAWN TRACKER - Fertilizers - Custom Plastics Inc.
LAWN WITCH - Rakes - Rieadco Corp.
LAWNAIRE - Aerator - Ransomes-Cushman-Ryan
LAWNDALE - Hair curlers - Lawndale Products Inc.
LAWNDALE - Twine - Blue Mountain Industries, Inc.
LAWNFLITE - Lawn mowers - MTD Products Inc.
LAWNFORCE - Lawn mowers - Black & Decker Corp.
LAWNMASTER - Garden tools - Atlas Group
LAWNPLAY - Croquet sets - South Bend Toy Manufacturing Co.
LAWNSCAPE I - Floor coverings–carpet and rugs - Playfield International Inc.
LAWNWARE - Bird feeds - Lawn & Garden Supply Co.
LAWRENCE - Cordials - White Rock Distilleries Inc.
LAWRENCE - Food products - Lawrence Foods Inc.
LAWRENCE - Food products ☆ - Burnette Foods Inc.
LAWRENCE - Hardware - Lawrence Brothers Inc.
LAWRENCE - Lead products - Metalico Granite, Inc.
LAWRENCE - Paper–writing ☆ - Kurtz Bros. Inc.
LAWRENCE - Pet products - Pet Supply Imports Inc.
LAWRENCE - Rope - Endisco Supply Co.
LAWRENCE - Wallpaper - Koroseal Wallcoverings
LAWRENCE - Wallpaper ☆ - Lawrence Wallcoverings
LAWRENCE - Wines ☆ - Foreign Vintages Inc.
LAWRENCE AUSTIN - Apparel–men's ☆ - Michaels/Stern & Co. Inc.
LAWRENCE BENTLEY DESIGNS - Jewelry - Lawrence Jewelry Co.
LAWRENCE BRUCE - Apparel and accessories - Winer Industries Inc.
LAWRENCE GROUP - Furniture - Bean Station Furniture Factory Inc.
LAWRENCE HERBST - Recording label - Holy Bible Gospel Ministry of The Body of Christ, Yeshua, of the Holy Land,
LAWRENCE LIMITED - Slacks–men's - H.R. Kaminsky & Sons Inc.
LAWRENCE METAL PRODUCTS - Metals - Nelson Beck of Washington
LAWRENCE READY-TO-SERVE - Beverages–alcohol - White Rock Distilleries Inc.
LAWRENCE SCOTT - Apparel–women's - Lawrence Scott Kumpf
LAWRENCE SUEDE - Wallpaper - Lawrence Wallcoverings
LAWRENCE WINERY - Wines ☆ - Corbett Canyon Vineyards
LAWRENCEVILLE - Floor coverings - Congoleum Corp.
LAWRY'S - Salad dressings–bottled - Lawry's Foods Inc.
LAWSON - Cigarettes - Brown & Williamson Tobacco Corp.
LAWSON - Convenience stores - Dairy Mart Convenience Stores, Inc.
LAWSON - Heaters–gas ☆ - United States Stove Co. Inc.
LAWSON - Heating equipment ☆ - Bradford-White Corp.
LAWSON - Wastebaskets - F.H. Lawson Co.
LAWSON 10 - Food products - Associated Grocers Mutual of Carolinas Inc.
LAWSON MARDON POSTCARDS - Postcards ☆ - Fotofolio Inc.
LAWSON RANCH - Wines - Lockwood Partners, L.P.
LAWSTAR - Computer software - SourceView Software International
LAWTON - Dishes–china - Waterford Wedgewood USA, Inc.
LAWTON HARBOR - Shirts - Dillard Department Stores Inc.
LAWWILL LEADER - Bicycle components - Mert Lawwill
LAWYER PRO - Computer storage devices - CFI Proservices, Inc.
LAWYER'S DESKTOP, THE - Computer software - Datapro Enterprises, Inc.
LAX - Beverages–malt ☆ - Anheuser-Busch Companies Inc.
LAX - Floor coverings–carpet and rugs - Lock Weave Carpet Mills Inc.
LAX - Hair care products - Paula Payne Products Co. Inc.
LAX-ACTIN - Vitamins and nutritional supplements - Natural Organics, Inc.
LAX-HERB - Pharmaceutical preparations ☆ - Fibertone Co.
LAX-O-CAT - Veterinary pharmaceutical preparations ☆ - Vortech Pharmaceuticals
LAX WORLD - Apparel and accessories - Lax World, Inc.
LAXA STAT - Pet products - Tomlyn Products
LAXACARE - Vitamins and nutritional supplements - Ayurvedic Concepts Ltd.
LAXAGEL - Laxatives - Banner-Pharmacaps Inc. (Advanced Nutritional Technology Division)

LAXAHERB - Vitamins and nutritional supplements ☆ - J.R. Carlson Laboratories Inc.
LAXAID - Laxatives ☆ - Purdue Frederick Co.
LAXATONE - Laxative - Carol Bond Health Foods, Inc.
LAXATONE - Veterinary pharmaceutical preparations - Evsco Pharmaceuticals
LAXATROL - Pet products ☆ - Trophy Animal Health Care
LAXCAPS - Laxatives - Sterling Winthrop Inc.
LAXINATE 100 - Pharmaceutical preparations ☆ - Roberts/Hauck Pharmaceuticals Inc.
LAXISAN - Pharmaceutical preparations - Dolisos America, Inc.
LAXMAR - Pharmaceutical preparations - Marlop Pharmaceuticals Inc.
LAXOGEN IMPROVED - Pharmaceutical preparations ☆ - Vortech Pharmaceuticals
LAXOSE BELL - Pharmaceutical preparations - Hollings-Smith Co. Inc.
LAXOVEMMS - Pharmaceutical preparations ☆ - C.O. Truxton Inc.
LAXPILLS - Laxatives - G and W Laboratories Inc.
LAXTO - Plugs–nose - Bomark Group Inc.
LAXULES - Health care products ☆ - Halsey Drug Co. Inc.
LAY - Food products - Lay Packing Co.
LAY-FLAT - Laminating film - General Binding Corp.
LAY-FLEX - Binders - Norfin, Inc.
LAY OF THE LANS, THE - Computer software - Network Intelligence, Inc.
LAY-RITE - Glue–household or industrial ☆ - Standard Paste & Glue Co.
LAY-ROW-CATCH-A-MELLOW - Barbecue sauce - Rite Kind Products
LAY-SET - Preformed wire rope - Babcock Industries Inc. (Babcock Control Group)
LAY TITE - Paints ☆ - Steelcote Manufacturing Corp.
LAYBACK ARCH - Sporting goods - Patterson-Williams Manufacturing Co. Inc.
LAYBARB - Pharmaceutical preparations ☆ - C.O. Truxton Inc.
LAYER STACK, THE - Computer software - John L. Moore
LAYERED LONGIES - Sporting goods - Ski Country Imports, Inc.
LAYERS OF LEARNING - Puzzles - GFS Creations
LAYETTE/TRAYETTE - Dolls - Goldberger Doll Manufacture Co.
LAYLA - Ophthalmic goods - Swank Optical
LAYMON'S - Candy - Laymon Candy Co. Inc.
LAYOUT - Bacon - Hormel Foods Corp.
LAY'S - Potato chips - Frito-Lay, Inc.
LAYTITE - Wood floor covering - Continental Hardwood Floor Distributors Inc.
LAYTON - Air conditioning equipment - Layton Manufacturing Corp.
LAYTON - Bedspreads - Layton Home Fashions
LAYTON - Leather goods ☆ - Smith-Worthington Saddlery Co. Inc.
LAYTON - Motor vehicles - Skyline Corp.
LAYTON'S - Soups–mixes - Campbell Soup Co.
LAYTON'S - Soups–mixes - Douglas Food Co., Inc.
LAZ-ART - Paper - Steiner Paper Corp.
LAZ E-FORMS - Business forms - Custom Business Systems, Inc.
LAZARE - Jewelry - Elleard B. Heffern, Inc.
LAZARE - Jewelry - Lazare Kaplan International Inc.
LAZARO - Wedding gowns - Jim Hjelm a Private Collection, Inc.
LAZAR'S - Candy - Lazar's Chocolate Inc.
LAZART COLOR LASER REPRODUCTIONS - Apparel and accessories - Lazart
LAZARUS - Window coverings - Covoc Corp.
LAZER - Boats–motor ☆ - Larson Boat Div.
LAZER - Brass musical instruments - Dennis Bamber Inc.
LAZER - Footwear ☆ - Swenson Imports
LAZER - Helmets–metal - Lazer Helmets Inc.
LAZER - Motors–outboard - Zebco Corp.
LAZER - Paper–sand - Spirakut Products
LAZER - Pens - Sheaffer Inc.
LAZER - Pharmaceutical preparations - Pedinol Pharmacal Inc.
LAZER - Strollers–baby ☆ - Welsh Co.
LAZER BLAZERS - Toy vehicles - Innoland, Inc.
LAZER CHEWS - Candy - Bee International
LAZER FLAIR - Plastics - EM Industries, Inc.
LAZER HOOP - Sporting goods - LI Best & Co. Sports
LAZER MIRRORS - Sunglasses - Jack Martin Co.
LAZER POPS - Candy - Cap Toys, Inc.
LAZER SHARP - Fishing tackle - Wright & McGill Co.
LAZER-SIGNS - Signs - Russell & Miller, Inc.
LAZER SITE - Toys–automobiles - Mattel, Inc.
LAZER TAG - Footwear ☆ - Mercury International Trading Corp.
LAZER-TEK DESIGNS LTD - Artists' materials - Scanova, Ltd.
LAZER WEAR - Jewelry - Lazer Wear, Inc.
LAZERBALL - Sporting goods - Wassco Corp.
LAZERBLADE - Artists' materials - Alvin and Co. Inc.

☆ = Now out of production

LAZERBLADE - Knives - Spectrum Razor Tools

LAZERFORMALYDE - Health care products - Pedinol Pharmacal Inc.

LAZERLINE - Wood products - Paneling Instructions (Paneling Div.)

LAZERMARK - Guns - Weatherby Inc.

LAZERQUICK - Computer storage devices - Graphic Information Systems, Inc.

LAZERQUICK IMAGES - Computer storage devices–optical - Graphic Information Systems, Inc.

LAZERSPORIN-C - Health care products - Pedinol Pharmacal Inc.

LAZERTEX - Wood products - Paneling Instructions (Paneling Div.)

LAZI-TROL - Motors–outboard ☆ - Byrd Industries Inc.

LAZIO'S - Seafood products–canned or cured - Pacific Choice Seafoods

LAZO - Shirts and ties - Laurentian Group

LAZO SPORT - Men's sweaters - Laurentian Group

LAZO UOMO - Men's apparel - Laurentian Group

LAZOR - Barber shop equipment - Kim Laube & Co. Inc.

LAZOR BLADES - Clippers–barber ☆ - Kim Laube & Co. Inc.

LAZOR RODS - Hair curlers - Spilo/Mehaz Worldwide

LAZY ACE - Toys–airplanes - Paul K. Guillow Inc.

LAZY ACRES - Eggs - Almark Inc.

LAZY BABY - Dolls - Uneeda Doll Co., Inc.

LAZY BEE - Toys–models - Cox Products Inc.

LAZY BONES - Fabrics - Greenwood Mills Inc.

LAZY-BONES - Frames–eyeglass - Liberty Optical Manufacturing Co.

LAZY BONES - Greeting cards - Gibson Greetings, Inc.

LAZY BONES - Shoes - Clinic Shoe Co.

LAZY BOY - Machinery - Parmi Tool Co. Inc.

LAZY CAT LODGE - Cardboard - Tarel Seven Design Inc.

...THE LAZY COOK - Publisher's imprints - Armus Enterprises, Inc.

...THE LAZY COOK - Publisher's imprints - Armus Enterprises, Inc.

LAZY CREEK - Wines - Lazy Creek Vineyard

LAZY CRUZ - Ships - Gibson Fiberglass Products Inc.

LAZY DASIE - Beverages–alcohol - Daiquiri Shoppe, Inc.

LAZY DAY - Fishing tackle - South Bend Sporting Goods Inc.

LAZY DAYS - Boats–houseboats - Lazy Days Manufacturing Co.

LAZY DAZE - Boats - Glen-L Marine Designs

LAZY DAZE - Motor vehicles - Lazy Daze Inc.

LAZY DOG - T-shirts–men's - Lazy Dog Inactive Wear

LAZY JACKS - Marine rigging - Harken Yacht Fittings

LAZY JOE - Men's shoes - Interco Inc.

LAZY L - Belts–apparel - Lyntone Belts Inc.

LAZY LADY - Frames–eyeglass ☆ - Universal/Univis Inc.

LAZY LAWYER - Furniture - La-Z-Boy Chair Co.

LAZY LINE - Nautical instruments - C. Sherman Johnson Co. Inc.

LAZY-MAN - Barbecues and grills - LazyMan, Inc.

LAZY MAPLE - Meat products–pork - Armour Swift-Eckrich

LAZY N - Trailers–horse - Lazy N Inc.

LAZY PANTS BY JOHN WEITZ - Slacks–men's - Glen Oaks Industries Inc.

LAZY PET - Pet products - Southern California Foam, Inc.

LAZY RIVER - Breads–mixes - Bon Melange Inc.

LAZY-SPINS - Fishing lures - Paul Warner Industries

LAZY SUSAN - Candy ☆ - Brock Candy Co. Inc.

LAZY SUSAN - Clocks ☆ - Sunbeam Precision Measurement

LAZY SUSAN - Furs–artificial - Cross at the Green...Not in Between Enterprises

LAZY SUSAN - Lighting fixtures - Swivelier Co. Inc.

LAZY-W - Food products - Waldman's Meats Inc.

LAZY W - Rings–jewelry - Artcarved Inc.

LAZYBOL - Games - Creatnetics

LAZZARI - Pet products - Active Pet Supplies

LAZZARONI - Food products - Campbell Soup Co.

LAZZY LEGS - Skating equipment - Lazzy Legs In-Line Skating Sporting Goods & Promotions, Inc.

LB - Ammunition ☆ - Olin Corp. (Winchester Div.)

LB - Apparel–women's - Lanco, Inc.

LB - Pumps–water - Larson-Becker Co., Inc.

LB 1-800-LOONEY BINS - Containers–trash - Myan Spaccarelli

L.B. JAMISON'S - Soups–mixes - Harvest States Cooperatives

LB SPORT - Apparel–women's - Lane Bryant, Inc.

L.B. WHITE - Torches - L.B. White Co., Inc.

LBC - Coatings - Fiberlock Technologies, Inc.

LBF 1000 COMPLEX - Vitamins and nutritional supplements - Great Life Laboratories Inc.

L.B.G. - Brassieres (Bras) - Custom Maid Brassiere Co.

LBG - Computer peripheral equipment - Langer Biomechanics Group, Inc.

LBGP - Apparel and accessories - Grand Prix Association of Long Beach, Inc.

LBI - Recording label - LBI

LBIC - Tools - Frederick Reid Lynch

LBMS PROCESS ENGINEER - Computer software - Learmonth & Burchette Management Systems, Inc.

LBS-36 - Vitamins and nutritional supplements - Great Life Laboratories Inc.

LBS LEAN BODY SYSTEMS - Apparel and accessories - Town Sports International

LBXVME - Computer hardware - Applied Data Sciences Inc.

LC - Anvils - L.C. Licensing, Inc.

LC - Artists' materials - Loew-Cornell Inc.

LC - Desks - Krueger International, Inc.

L.C. - Housewares - Better Living Products Inc.

LC - Stationery - Lasercraft, Inc.

LC-65 - Ophthalmic goods - Allergan, Inc.

LC BASICS COLLECTION - Eyeglasses - United States Shoe Corp.

L.C. GERMAIN - Cutlery ☆ - Lifetime Hoan Corp.

LC LAMSON SMARTMETER - Electrical components - Lamson Corp.

LCAN SYNDICATOR - Computer software - Precision Software Corp.

LCD - Cleaning preparations - Roebic Laboratories Inc.

LCD-600 - Nautical instruments ☆ - Ray Jefferson

LCD 3001 - Watches - Elgin Watch Co.

LCD MOUNT - Video equipment - Draper Shade and Screen Co. Inc.

LCH - Vitamins and nutritional supplements - American Cyanamid Co.

L'CHAYIM TO LIFE - Greeting cards - American Greetings Corp.

LCI - Jewelry - Louis Creations Inc.

LCM - Tractors - LMC Corp.

LCM - Vans–conversion - LCM, Inc.

LCN - Door openers–electronic - LCN Closers

LCR 400 ID - Marine-depth sounders - Techsonic Industries, Inc.

LCS - Apparel and accessories - LSC America, Inc.

LCS - Dry erase boards - Claridge Products and Equipment Inc.

LCS - Loudspeakers - Labtec Enterprises, Inc.

LCS SONGS - Music–sheet - Lorenz Creative Services Corp.

LCT - Jewelry - Lee Chong Tai Enterprises Ltd.

LCX - Chemical preparations - Abbott Laboratories

+L'CYSTEINE - Skin care products - Bonat Inc.

LD - Jewelry - Frederick Goldman, Inc.

LD - Silverware - Leonore Doskow Inc.

LD - Wines - Iron Horse Vineyards

LD 400 - Optical machinery - Dicon

LD-LAN - Computer hardware - Extension Technology Corp.

L.D. TRADING DIRECT FLORAL IMPORTERS - Florists - Lawrence Developments, Inc.

LD2 - Electrical equipment - University Corp. for Atmospheric Research

LDC - Electronic equipment - Moor Electronics Inc.

L.D.I. - Jeans–women's - Lewis Distribution Inc.

LDI - Jewelry - Gordon Brothers Corp.

LDI GREASE GOBBLER - Fans–exhaust - LDI MFG Co., Inc.

LDM/XP - Computer software - Legent Corp.

LDO - Oils–lubricating ☆ - Amoco Oil Co.

LDPI - Lighting equipment - L.P.I., Inc.

LDR - Plumbing supplies - Waterby Products

LDT - Cleaning preparations - Roebic Laboratories Inc.

LE - Audio and video tapes - Limited Edition Recording, Inc.

LE - Jewelry - Epstein & Son Jewelry Inc.

LE - Paper products - Quantum Entertainment, Inc.

LE - Screws - Lake Erie Screw Corp.

LE BAGNATURE - Perfumes - Revlon Consumer Products Corp.

LE BAIN - Health care products - Tambrands Inc.

LE BAIN NATURAL - Skin care products - Frances Denney

LE BAR - Fruits–frozen - Kozy Shack Inc.

LE BARON - Apparel–men's - Steven Kurtzman Inc.

LE BARON - Bicycles - Columbia Manufacturing Inc.

LE BARON - Calendars - House of Doolittle

LE BARON - Clocks ☆ - Ridgeway Clock Co.

LE BARON - Floor coverings–carpet and rugs - Queen Carpet Corp.

LE BARON - Motor vehicles–automobiles - Chrysler Corp. (Chrysler-Plymouth Div.)

LE BARON - Ophthalmic goods - Embassy Creations Inc.

LE BARON - Wallets - Le Baron Manufacturing Corp.

LE BARON - Watches - I.D. Enterprises

LE BARON GTS - Motor vehicles–automobiles ☆ - Chrysler Corp. (Chrysler-Plymouth Div.)

LE BARON ROULE - Cheese - Frenex Distributors

LE BAY CELLARS - Wines - Diamond Oaks Vineyard

LE BEAU - Containers - Prolon Dinnerware

LE BEST - Shoes ☆ - Spanish Creation Shoe Imports, Inc.

☆ = Now out of production

LE BIARRITZ - Floor coverings–carpet and rugs - Prestige Mills Inc.
LE BIENVENU - Wines ✩ - Palm Bay Imports, Inc.
LE BISQUIT - Crackers - I. Rokeach and Sons Inc.
LE BLANC - Wines - Golden State Vintners
LE BLEACH FROSTING & HIGHLIGHTING - Hair-care products - Matrix Essentials, Inc.
LE-BO - Audio equipment - Le-Bo Peerless
LE BOCCE - Beverages–alcohol - Trebon Wine & Spirit Corp.
LE BODY - Cosmetics - Lancome
LE BOIS - Cosmetics - Pace Manufacturing Inc.
LE BOULANGER THE BAKER - Bakery products - Le Boulanger Inc.
LE BOURGET - Hosiery–women's ✩ - Globus Mercantile Corp.
LE BOUTON - Buttons - Blumenthal/Lansing Co.
LE BRELLA - Umbrellas - George R. Chaby, Inc.
LE BRUSH - Finishing agents ✩ - Flecto Co. Inc.
LE BUFF - Cosmetics ✩ - Worldwide Cosmetics
+LE +BUNNY - Chocolate candy - Superior Fruit & Confections
+LE CAFE - Coffee ✩ - Pokka, Inc.
LE CAM - Recording label - Le Cam Records
LE CAN-CAN - Wines - Wine Caves, Inc.
LE CAP - Caps–leather ✩ - Smith-Worthington Saddlery Co. Inc.
LE CAR - Motor vehicles - Renault Inc.
LE CHAMPAGNE - Cookies - Sunshine/Salerno Inc.
LE CHAT - Housewares ✩ - Vermillion Inc.
LE CHATEAU - Floor coverings - Mannington Resilient Floors
LE CHATEAU - Floor coverings–carpet and rugs ✩ - Customweave Carpets Inc.
LE CHATEAU - Glass–leaded - Seneca Glass Co.
LE CHATEAU - Wallpaper - Norwall Wallcoverings
LE CHATEAU - Wines - White Rock Distilleries Inc.
LE CHEESE TOAST - Food products - My Favorite Year Inc.
LE CHIC - Buttons - Blumenthal/Lansing Co.
LE CHIC - Leather goods - N.S. Gustin Co.
LE CHIC - Thread - Belding Heminway Co. Inc.
LE CIRQUE - Frames–eyeglass - May Optical Co. Inc.
LE CIRQUE - Tableware–china ✩ - Villeroy and Boch Tableware Ltd.
LE CLAIR - Cookware, servingware, storage containers ✩ - Corning Inc.
LE CLIC - Cameras - Keystone Camera Corp.
LE CLIP - Nail care products - Noymer Leather and Gifts Ltd.
LE CLUB - Games - Alex Cramer Co.
LE CLUB - Luggage - Shalam Imports Inc.
LE CLUB ACTIVE - Apparel–women's ✩ - J.C. Penney Co., Inc.
LE CLUB COTTON - Fabrics - Dan River Inc.
LE COIN - Clocks and timepieces - North American Foreign Trading Corp.
LE COLLECTION - Apparel and accessories - Le Collection Inc.
LE COLONNE - Wines - House of Burgundy Inc.
LE CONCENTRE - Skin care products - Universal Health Products Inc.
LE CONCERTO - Cosmetics - Cosmair Inc.
LE CONE - Belts, hair accessories - Trenz Inc.
LE CONTINENTAL - Food products - VMI Corp.
LE COQ ROUGE - Baskets–wood - Coe & Dru Inc.
LE CORD - Fabrics - Greenwood Mills Inc.
LE CORPS ACTIF - Cosmetics - Chanel Inc.
LE CORRIGE-TOUT - Correction fluid - Barouh Eaton Allen Corp.
LE CRAYON - Cosmetics - Lancome
LE CREME FORMAGG - Cakes ✩ - Galaxy Foods Co.
LE CRESCENDO - Cosmetics - Cosmair Inc.
LE CREUSET - Barbecues and grills ✩ - Estus Export-Import
LE CREUSET - Cookware - Le Creuset of America, Inc.
LE CROMIE - Tiles–ceramic - American Marazzi Tile, Inc.
LE CRYSTAL NATUREL - Dentifrices - French Transit Ltd.
LE CRYSTAL NATUREL - Deodorants–personal ✩ - Nature de France
LE DE - Perfumes - Parfums Givenchy, Inc.
LE DELIZIE - Cookies ✩ - Liberty Richter Inc.
LE DERNIER CRI - Lamps and fixtures - Le Dernier Cri, Inc.
LE DESKTOP - Paper - Four Corners Paper Co., Inc.
LE DESSINATEUR - Floor coverings–carpet and rugs - J.L. Benson Co.
LE DEVELOPER - Hair coloring preparations - Mastey De Paris
LE DISC - Earring backings - Fashion Solutions USA Inc.
LE DOMAINE - Beverages–alcohol - Canandaigua Wine Co. Inc.
LE DOMAINE - Wines - Heublein, Inc.
LE DOME - Fans–electric - Beverly Hills Fan Co.
+LE DOON - Ice cream - Bonnie Doon Ice Cream
LE FAUCET - Kitchen faucet - Interbath, Inc.
LE FERME GOURMANDE - Food products - Gourmand Inc.
LE FILE - Beauty aids - International Beauty Design, Inc.

LE FIN DU FIN - Cosmetics - Lancome
LE FISH - Pet products - Maggie Mae's Gourmet Pet Products Inc.
LE FLEUR - Glassware–household ✩ - National Housewares
LE FLEUR - Tiles–ceramic - Kowa Texas Inc.
LE FLING - Apparel and accessories - Jan Stras Inc.
LE FONT - Window coverings ✩ - Vertical Blind Factory
LE FOUNTAIN PEN - Pens - Uchida of America Corp.
LE FRAME - Frames–eyeglass - Zylo Ware Corp.
LE FRANCAIS - Breads - Holsum Bakery Inc.
LE FRANTE - Olive oil - Giova Food International Inc.
LE FRENCH FRYER - Cooking equipment–household ✩ - General Housewares Corp.
LE FROIS - Food products - Le Frois Foods Corp.
LE FRONT - Luggage - LeFront Industrial Corp.
LE FUTUR - Cosmetics - Cosmair Inc.
LE GALLIENE - Ophthalmic goods - Styl-Rite Optical Manufacturing Co., Inc.
LE GARLIC - Cheese - Swissrose International Inc.
LE GARZA - Apparel and accessories - Ted S. Chang
LE GEAR - Pet products - Le Gear Animal Health
LE GEL - Hair care products - Mastey De Paris
LE-GI-CODE - Computer peripheral equipment - Legicode, Inc.
LE GLASS - Cups–plastic - Majestic Gifts
LE GLOVE - Footwear–men's - Harbor Footwear Group Ltd.
LE GLUE - Glue–household or industrial - Itoya of America, Ltd.
LE GOAT - Wines - Bully Hill Vineyards, Inc.
LE GOURMAND - Kitchen utensils–aluminum - Universal International, Inc.
LE GOURMAND - Knives - Taylor Woodcraft Inc.
LE GOURMET - Pet products - Breeder's Choice Pet Foods, Inc.
LE GOURMET - Rice - Producers Rice Mill, Inc.
LE GOUT - Food containers - CPC Food Service
LE GRACIEUX - Baskets–steel - Golden French Imports
LE GRAND - Cosmetics - Cosmair Inc.
LE GRAND - Floor coverings–carpet and rugs ✩ - Walter Carpet Mills
LE GRAND - Hair care products ✩ - Dep Corp.
+LE GRAND CAFE - Coffee - Melitta North America Inc.
LE GRAND CHENEAU - Wines - Sunbelt Beverage Corp.
LE GRAND CONFECTIONARY - Chocolate candy - Le Grand Confectionary, Inc.
LE GRAND LUXE - Cheese - Swissrose International Inc.
LE GRAND NORD - Apparel and accessories - Brambilla USA, Inc.
LE GRANDE - Food products - CPC Best Foods
LE GRANDE - Guitars - Emmons Guitar Co. Inc.
LE GRANGE - Apparel–women's - Protrend Ltd.
LE GRANT - Apparel and accessories ✩ - Warnaco Inc.
LE GUN - Cosmetics ✩ - Divina Products Co.
LE GYM - Footwear–men's - Harbor Footwear Group Ltd.
LE HAVEN - Floor coverings–carpet and rugs - Monticello Carpet Mills
LE HAVRE - Floor coverings–carpet and rugs ✩ - Customweave Carpets Inc.
LE HAVRE - Furniture ✩ - Bassett Furniture Industries, Inc.
LE HOL$TER - Wallets ✩ - Apothecary Products, Inc.
LE HUNT - Frames–eyeglass - May Optical Co. Inc.
LE JACQUARD FRANCAIS - Fine french linens - Palais Royal Inc.
LE JACQUE - Luggage - Universal Trav-ler Inc.
LE JARDIN - Colognes - Max Factor & Co.
LE JARDIN - Garden equipment - Original Designs/Famor Inc.
LE JARDIN - Glassware–household ✩ - National Housewares
LE JARDIN D'AMOUR - Colognes - Max Factor & Co.
LE JARDIN DE MAX FACTOR - Colognes - Max Factor & Co.
LE JARDINET - Wines - Alimar & Cie. Inc.
LE JAUNE ROYALE - Pepper - Sun World International
LE JON - Pet products ✩ - Vigoro Consumer & Professional Products Group
LE JOUR - Brushes–paint - Linzer Products Corp.
LE JOY - Hair care products - Le Joy Products Inc.
LE JUICE - Fruit drinks–bottled or canned - Cliffstar Corp.
LE KAIR - Hair care products - Le Kair Scientific Research Products Inc.
LE KIT - First aid kits - Boiron Inc.
LE-KO - Nuts–salted, roasted, cooked, or canned ✩ - McMullen Food Bank Inc.
LE LAC - Wines ✩ - Alimar & Cie. Inc.
LE LAVANDOU - Dishes–china - Viletta China Co.
LE LITE - Mirrors - Nailtex Inc.
LE LOCK - Locks–padlocks - Hampton International
LE LOOK - Cosmetics - Cosmair Inc.
LE LOOP - Belts, hair accessories - Trenz Inc.
LE LYS - Bedding–linen - Dan River Inc.
LE MAJ - Women's apparel - Hickory Hills Industries Inc.

✩ = Now out of production

LE MANS - Bicycles - Murray, Inc.

LE MANS - Cases–camera - Lefkowitz and Santangelo Co.

LE MANS - Floor coverings–carpet and rugs - Regal Rugs Inc.

LE MANS - Floor coverings–carpet and rugs ☆ - Mohawk Industries Inc.

LE MANS - Infant product ☆ - Welsh Co.

LE MANS - Luggage ☆ - American Tourister, Inc.

LE MANS - Motor vehicles–automobiles - General Motors Corp. (Pontiac/GMC Div.)

LE MANS - Motorcycles ☆ - Suzuki of America Automotive Corp.

LE MANS - Pens - Park Lane Associates, Inc.

LE MASK-CS - Skin care products - Fallien, Ltd.

LE MEMOIRE - Hair care products - Vancar Research Inc.

LE MENU - Dinners–frozen - Campbell Soup Co.

LE MENU HEALTHY - Dinners–frozen - Campbell Soup Co.

LE MENU LIGHTSTYLE - See **LE MENU HEALTHY**

LE MENU NEW AMERICAN CUISINE - Dinners–frozen - Campbell Soup Co.

LE MESURIER - Paints–artists' ☆ - Masury Paint Co.

LE MEURSAULT DE ROPITEAU - Wines ☆ - Palm Bay Imports, Inc.

LE MINI - Cameras - Keystone Camera Corp.

LE MISTRAL - Wines - World Wide Wine and Spirits Inc.

LE MODA II - Sweaters - Gillman Knitwear Co.

LE MOM - Toys - Simmons Juvenile Products Co., Inc.

LE MOMENT - Watches - Heather Classics Inc.

LE MONDE DE PARIS - Cosmetics - Arthur Matney Co., Inc.

LE MONT - Frames–eyeglass ☆ - Universal/Univis Inc.

LE MONTRE - Watches - Wakmann Watch Co. Inc.

LE MOOD - Floor coverings–carpet and rugs ☆ - Columbus Mills, Inc.

+LE MOULIN - Bread - Le Moulin

LE MOULIN - Oils–edible - Gourmet America

LE MYSTERE - Apparel–women's - M.A. Rabinowitz Corp.

LE NEWS - Cosmetics - Dri Mark Products, Inc.

LE NOTRE - Dishes–china - Viletta China Co.

LE OTTA - Apparel and accessories - Le Otta, Inc.

LE PACTOLE - Musical instrument accessories - Micro Musical Products Corp.

LE PAGE'S - Tape–adhesive - Le Pages Inc.

LE PAK - Food products - Tone Brothers, Inc.

LE PAN - Cooking equipment–household - Bo-Nash, Inc.

LE PARFAIT - Brandy - Alimar & Cie. Inc.

LE PARFAIT - Hair care products ☆ - Chase Products Co.

LE PARFAIT - Jars–glass - VMC French Glassware

LE PATRON - Snack foods - Consolidated Food Management Corp.

LE PAYS INTERNATIONAL - Sportswear - Le Pays International

LE PEACH PANACHE - Skin care products - Express Dental Products Inc.

LE PEN - Pens - Uchida of America Corp.

LE PERLE - Flatware - Couzon USA

LE PET BAG - Pet products - Doggiduds, Inc.

LE PETIT-BEURRE - Crackers - Sunshine/Salerno Inc.

LE PETIT CHATEAU - Floor coverings–carpet and rugs ☆ - Karastan-Bigelow Inc.

LE PETIT ECOLIER - Cookies - Sunshine/Salerno Inc.

LE PETIT GLAZIK - Biscuits ☆ - Liberty Richter Inc.

+LE PETIT GOURMET - Pate - Fabrique Delices

LE PETIT MARSEILLAIS - Soap - L'Essentiel de Provence

LE PIENO'S BEST - Cheese - Protein Palace Inc.

LE PLAID - Floor coverings–carpet and rugs ☆ - Mohawk Industries Inc.

LE PLAISIRS MAGIQUES - Perfumes - Lancome

LE PLAN - Diaries - Overseas Marketing Systems

LE PLI - Window shades - Window Quilt

LE PLUG - Corks ☆ - Vintage Concepts

LE PONT - Cosmetics ☆ - Doak Dermatologics

LE POUCH - Cases–eyeglass ☆ - California Optical Leather Inc.

LE POUDRE MAGIQUE - Cosmetics - Lancome

LE POUF - Apparel and accessories ☆ - Design Circle Ltd.

LE POUF - Hobby kits - Nuage Flowers, Inc.

LE POUT - Lipsticks - Cosmair Inc.

LE PREMIER CRU - Wines - Monarch Wine Co.

LE PRINCE - Cutlery - Ginkgo International Ltd.

LE PRINO - Cheese ☆ - Leprino Foods

LE PRIX - Silverware - Ginkgo International Ltd.

LE-PRO - Cheese ☆ - Leprino Foods

LE PUMP - Bottles–plastic - Belle De St. Claire

LE PUMP - Health care products ☆ - Graham-Field Inc.

LE PUPILLE - Wines ☆ - Dreyfus Ashby Inc.

LE RAFFINE - Dairy products ☆ - Besnier USA, Inc.

LE RAT - Pet products - Maggie Mae's Gourmet Pet Products Inc.

LE RED - Lipsticks - Lancome

LE REGALE - Handbags - La Regale Ltd.

LE REMOUVER - Shampoos - Mastey De Paris

LE REVE - Eyeglasses - La Salle Imports, Inc.

LE RICHE - Liquors - Heaven Hill Distilleries, Inc.

LE RITUEL DU BAIN - Skin care products - Frances Denney

LE ROI - Apparel–children's - Le Roi/Princeton

LE ROUGE ROYALE - Pepper ☆ - Sun World International

LE ROUX DELUXE - Brandy - Joseph E. Seagram & Sons, Inc.

LE ROY - Crocheted and knitted items - Le Roy Knitted Sportswear Inc.

LE ROY CALIF. - Crocheted and knitted items - Le Roy Knitted Sportswear Inc.

LE SABLE - Wines - Wines of the World Inc.

LE SABRE - Motor vehicles–automobiles - General Motors Corp. (Buick Motor Div.)

LE SABRE CUSTOM - Motor vehicles–automobiles - General Motors Corp. (Buick Motor Div.)

LE SABRE ESTATE WAGON - Motor vehicles–automobiles - General Motors Corp. (Buick Motor Div.)

LE SABRE LIMITED - Motor vehicles–automobiles - General Motors Corp. (Buick Motor Div.)

LE SAC - Apparel and accessories - Richton International Corp.

LE SAC BIJOU - Perfumes - Lancome

LE SAH PETITE - Crocheted and knitted items - Le Roy Knitted Sportswear Inc.

LE SALON - Pet products - Rolf C. Hagen (USA) Corp.

LE SAN-WICH - Croissants - Sara Lee Corp.

LE SEIGE - Chairs–upholstered - United Chair Co., Inc.

LE SEMEUR - Vegetables–canned ☆ - Liberty Richter Inc.

LE SERBET - Wines - Prestige Wine Corp.

LE SHARO - Motor vehicles–motor homes - Winnebago Industries, Inc.

LE SHEE - Skin care products - AMRA International, Ltd.

LE SHEEN - Hair care products - Gold Medal Hair Products Inc.

LE SHOCK - Cosmetics - Cosmair Inc.

LE SILK - Fabrics - Interials Inc.

LE SKIZI - Athletic product - Intromark Inc.

LE SOAP - Soap - Go-Jo Industries Inc.

LE SOFT - Shirts - Salant/Manhattan Industries

LE SOLEIL - Apparel - Le Soleil, Inc.

LE SPORT - Footwear–men's - Harbor Footwear Group Ltd.

LE SPORT - Frames–eyeglass - Zylo Ware Corp.

LE SPORT - Sporting goods ☆ - USA Sport Eyewear

LE SPORTSAC - Luggage - Le Sportsac

LE SPORTSAC - Slippers - Two Step by Air Baby Slippers

LE SPORTSAC - Umbrellas - Storm Hero Umbrella Co. Inc.

LE SPRAY - Finishing agents ☆ - Flecto Co. Inc.

LE STAGE - Jewelry - Le Stage Manufacturing Co.

LE STAMP - Stamps–hand - Personal Impressions Inc.

LE STICK - Deodorants–personal - Nature de France

LE STICK FLORAL - Deodorants–personal - Nature de France

LE STICK GARDENIA - Deodorants–personal - Nature de France

LE STICK HERBAL - Deodorants–personal - Nature de France

LE STICK POWDER FRESH - Deodorants–personal - Nature de France

LE STICK UNSCENTED - Deodorants–personal - Nature de France

LE STIMULE - Hair care products - Mastey De Paris

LE STUDIO CLASSIC - Clothing - Specialty Department Stores, Inc.

LE STYLO - Lipsticks - Lancome

LE SUEDE - Floor coverings–carpet and rugs - Philadelphia Carpets

LE SUEDE - Floor coverings–carpet and rugs - Trend Carpet

LE SUEUR - Food products - Green Giant Co.

LE SUN - Health care products ☆ - Hoffmann-La Roche Inc.

LE TAMBOURIN - Cosmetics - Cosmair Inc.

LE TAN - Seat covers - Saddleman, Inc.

LE TAN - Vitamins and nutritional supplements - Le Tan

LE THIN COW - Margarine/butter blend - Sodiaal North America Corp.

LE TIGRE - Men's apparel - Interco Inc.

LE TIGRE - Watches - M.Z. Berger & Co. Inc.

LE TIPS - Nail care products ☆ - Orly International Inc.

LE TOP BABY - Apparel–children's - Chung Kai Industries, Inc.

LE TOP KIDS - Apparel–children's - Chung Kai Industries, Inc.

LE TOPPER AQUAFOODS - Fish–fresh or frozen - Blue Mountain Brands, Inc.

LE TOR' - Apparel–women's - Custom Maid Brassiere Co.

LE TOUQUET - Furniture - Pilliod Co.

LE TOUR - Apparel and accessories - Team Pro Enterprises, USA, Inc.

LE TOUR III - Bicycles - Schwinn Cycling & Fitness Inc.

LE TOUR IV - Bicycles - Schwinn Cycling & Fitness Inc.

LE TRAC - Traction apparatus–medical - Lossing Orthopedic Co.

☆ = Now out of production

LE TRAVELER - Health care products ☆ - Helmac Products Corp.
LE TRE GRAZIE - Wheat–flour or meal ☆ - Dean & Deluca Inc.
LE TRESORS MAGIQUES - Perfumes - Lancome
LE TUBE - Sporting goods - O'Brien International
LE TWILL - Fabrics–twill ☆ - Greenwood Mills Inc.
LE-TWIST - Hair accessories - Moni International, Inc.
LE VELVET FILM - Cosmetics - Physicians Formula Cosmetics Inc.
LE' VERIA - Jewelry - Replicas, Inc.
LE VINAIGRE - Vinegar - Continental Food Corp.
LE VODKA - Vodka ☆ - Beauvignot International Inc.
LE VODKA PECHE - Vodka ☆ - Beauvignot International Inc.
LE VOYAGER - Infant product - Evenflo Co.
LE VOYAGEUR - Handbags - SOS Rescue Inc.
LE Y BRA - Brassieres (Bras) - Juliana Glasner
LE YOUGHURT - Yogurt ☆ - Alta-Dena Certified Dairy, Inc.
LEA - Furniture - Lea Industries Inc.
LEA - Skin care products - Lea Haller International, Inc.
LEA - Tiles–terrazzo - Imperial Tile and Marble Corp.
LEA & PERRINS - Vegetable sauces - Lea and Perrins Inc.
LEA COSMETICS INTERNATIONAL PERSONAL CARE SYSTEMS - Skin care products - Lea Haller International, Inc.
LEA FARMS - Meat products–beef ☆ - Schweigert Foods
LEA HALLER - Skin care products - Lea Haller International, Inc.
LEA THE BEDROOM PEOPLE - Furniture - LADD Furniture Inc.
LEACH - Vegetables - Leach Farms, Inc.
LEACH & GARNER GOLD - Jewelry - Leach & Garner Co.
LEACOCK - Wines - World Shippers & Importers
LEAD BARRIER - Coatings - Coronado Paint Co.
LEAD BLOCK - Coatings - Premier Coatings, Inc.
LEAD CHECK - Lead-detection kits - Hybrivet Systems, Inc.
LEAD CORE - Fishing lures - Mason Tackle Co.
LEAD HEADS - Sporting goods - Gapen Co.
LEAD-IN SOFTWARE - Computer software - Direct Communications International, Inc.
LEAD 'N COLLA - Pet products ☆ - Rex-E Products (O)
LEAD-O-MATIC - Writing product ☆ - Itoya of America, Ltd.
LEAD OFF MAN - Ophthalmic goods - Embassy Creations Inc.
LEAD PREP - Cleaning preparations - Fiberlock Technologies, Inc.
LEAD ROUND NOSE - Bullets - Olin Corp. (Winchester Div.)
LEAD SAFE - Bullets - Rainier Ballistics Corp.
LEAD-SEAL - Lead products - Deniston Co.
LEAD SEMI-WAD CUTTER - Bullets - Olin Corp. (Winchester Div.)
LEAD STOP - Coating for lead based paints - Lead Stop/Lead Block, Inc.
LEAD STOP - Paints - Certified Technologies Corp.
LEAD ZONE - Paper goods - Enzone Inc.
LEADCHECK - Paints - Homax, Inc.
LEADER - Ammunition ☆ - Olin Corp. (Winchester Div.)
LEADER - Candy - Leader Candies Inc.
LEADER - Caulking guns - Great American Marketing, Inc.
LEADER - Desks - Wood Design Inc.
LEADER - Envelopes - Butler Paper Co.
LEADER - Floor coverings–tile - Interface, Inc.
LEADER - Floor finishing machines–commercial ☆ - Clarke Industries, Inc.
LEADER - Garden equipment - H.D. Hudson Manufacturing Co.
LEADER - Guitars ☆ - International Music Corp.
LEADER - Hair-cutting shears ☆ - B.W. Boyd Shears Inc.
LEADER - Hammers - Ames Lawn & Garden Tool Co.
LEADER - Musical instrument accessories - Grover/Trophy Musical Products Inc.
LEADER - Musical instrument accessories - Louis A. Varisco Co.
LEADER - Musical instrument accessories - Whirlwind Music Distributors, Inc.
LEADER - Office supplies - Elco Manufacturing Co. Inc.
LEADER - Office supplies - Ever-Ready Co.
LEADER - Ophthalmic goods - Foremost Optical Products
LEADER - Padding–foam - Crain Industries Inc.
LEADER - Rice - Beaumont Rice Mills Inc.
LEADER - Sporting goods - Century Sports Inc.
LEADER - Sporting goods ☆ - L & M Distribution Inc.
LEADER - Tables–wood ☆ - Anco Wood Specialties Inc.
LEADER - Tools - O.P. Link Handle Co. Inc.
LEADER - Wheels - Hamilton Caster & Manufacturing Co.
LEADER 1 - Toys - Tonka Corp.
LEADER BOARD - Computer software ☆ - Access Software Inc.
LEADER ENTERPRISES, INC. - Advertising agencies - Leader Enterprises, Inc.
LEADER IN LIGHTING SOLUTIONS - Lighting fixtures - Holophane Corp.

LEADER IN PRIVATE BRAND, THE - Apparel and accessories - Tropical Sportswear International Corp.
LEADER IN RELAXATION, THE - Furniture - JB Research, Inc.
LEADER IN SPORTS NUTRITION, THE - Vitamins and nutritional supplements - Twinlab
LEADER IN THE FIELD - Firearms, accessories, and parts - Schoellkopf Sports Inc.
LEADER LINKS - Sporting goods - Wright & McGill Co.
LEADER OF BAND - Toys–musical ☆ - Proll Toy Co.
LEADER OF THE PACK - Vitamins and nutritional supplements - Old Fashioned Natural Products, Inc.
LEADER OF THE PACKS - Luggage - Eastpak
LEADER OF THE STACK, THE - Apparel and accessories - Trov USA, Inc.
LEADER, THE - Notebooks and notepads - Gralan Distributors Inc.
LEADER, THE - Paints–artists' ☆ - Peerless Color Laboratories
LEADERBOARD - Apparel and accessories - Team Effort, Inc.
LEADERLASTIC - Thread - Leader Thread Corp.
LEADERLEACRA - Thread - Leader Thread Corp.
LEADERS - Thread - Leader Thread Corp.
LEADER'S BEST - Thread - Leader Thread Corp.
LEADERS IN LEVELING - Construction equipment - Somero Enterprises Inc.
LEADERS OF THE PACK, THE - Pet products - Eagle Products, Inc.
LEADER'S TRANSLUCENT - Thread - Leader Thread Corp.
LEADERSHIP ARCHITECT - Computer software - Lominger Limited, Inc.
LEADERSHIP FOR ENVIRONMENT AND DEVELOPMENT - Computers - Lead International Inc.
LEADGEN - Computers and parts - Ultima Electronics Corp.
LEADING CAREER INDICATORS - Publisher's imprints - Farren Associates, Inc.
LEADING EDGE - Animal feeds - Manna Pro Corp.
LEADING EDGE - Computers–personal - Leading Edge Hardware Products
LEADING EDGE - Fans–electric - Leading Edge, Inc.
LEADING EDGE - Frames–eyeglass ☆ - Universal/Univis Inc.
LEADING EDGE - Motor vehicle parts and accessories - National Cycle Inc.
LEADING EDGE - Vitamins and nutritional supplements - Nutrilite, Div. of Amway Corp.
LEADING EDGE - Wallpaper - Capital Carousel Inc.
LEADING EDGE - Window coverings ☆ - Vertical Blind Factory
LEADING EDGE LV - Motor vehicle parts and accessories - National Cycle Inc.
LEADING EDGE SAFETY SYSTEMS - Safety products - Leading Edge Safety Systems, Inc.
LEADING FROM WITHIN - Educational materials - Taking Charge, Inc.
LEADING LADY - Apparel–women's - Leading Lady Companies Inc.
LEADING LADY - Christmas tree ornaments - Cracker Box Inc.
LEADING LADY - Eyeglasses - Art-Craft Optical Co.
LEADING LADY - Floor coverings–carpet and rugs ☆ - Zenith Carpets
LEADING LADY - Paper–toilet - Georgia-Pacific Corp.
LEADING LADY - Watches - Bulova Corp.
LEADING LIGHT - Rings–jewelry - Artcarved Inc.
LEADING LIZ - Optical scanners–computer - Tart Optical
LEADISK - Computer software - Berkshire Computer Processing Center, Inc.
LEADMAKER - Computer software - R.L. Polk & Co.
LEADMAN - Electronic equipment - Leadman Electronics
LEADMASTER - Coatings - Fiberlock Technologies, Inc.
LEADS - Computer software - Landstar System, Inc.
LEADS WMR - Recording label - Jazz Composer's Orchestra Association Inc.
LEADSORB - Chemicals - John R. Grawe
LEADWORKS - Housewares ☆ - Xonex International, Inc.
LEAF - Dinnerware - Corning Inc.
LEAF - Floor coverings–carpet and rugs - Regal Rugs Inc.
LEAF - Glass products ☆ - AFG Industries Inc. (Glass Group Div.)
LEAF - Trading cards and stamps - Leaf, Inc.
LEAF-ACT 80 - Pesticides–agricultural - Crop Production Services Inc.
LEAF CATCHER - Cleaning equipment - Baracuda International Corp.
LEAF CLEAN - Skin care products - Nu Skin International, Inc.
LEAF-EATER - Mulchers - Flowtron Outdoor Products
LEAF GARLAND - Floor coverings–carpet and rugs ☆ - Regal Rugs Inc.
LEAF LIFE - Fertilizers - Crop Production Services Inc.
LEAF MASTER - Hardware ☆ - Bemis Manufacturing Co.
LEAF NET - Garden equipment - Dalen Products Inc.
LEAF O GOLD - Dishes–china - Taylor, Smith & Taylor Co.
LEAF PATTERN - Bowls - Grainware Co.
LEAF RIVER 90 - Wood products - Georgia-Pacific Corp.
LEAF TRAPPER - Chemical preparations - Caretaker Systems Inc.
LEAFGO - Gutters–plastic ☆ - Genova Products Inc.
LEAFGUARD - Flowers, plants, and seeds - Hybritech Seed International, Inc.

☆ = Now out of production

LEAFLETS - Candy - Leaf, Inc.

LEAFMINTS - Candy - Leaf, Inc.

LEAFSOMES - Candy - Leaf, Inc.

LEAFY-WEAR - Jackets - Carter Canvas Co., Inc.

LEAGUE - Ammunition ☆ - Federal Cartridge Co.

LEAGUE LEADER - Trading cards and stamps - Fleer Corp.

LEAGUE MACHINE - Computer software - Valley Recreation Products Inc.

LEAGUE MASTER - Sporting goods - Biotech Corp.

LEAH - Flowers, plants, and seeds - George W. Park Seed Co., Inc.

LEAH - Lenses–optical - National Optical Co.

LEAK - Amplifiers - British Industries Co.

LEAK DATA ACQUISITION ORR LEAKDAS - Computer peripheral equipment - Environmental Compliance Systems Corp.

LEAK MASTER - Ultrasonic testing equipment - SDT-USA

LEAK-NOT - Roofing materials–slate - National Metal Roof Services, Inc.

LEAK SEEK - Adhesives and sealants - Comstar International Inc. (IPC Div.)

LEAK SEEKER - Filters–air - Midwesco Filter Resources, Inc.

LEAK-SEEKER - Measuring instruments - CPS Products, Inc.

LEAK SENTRY - Plumbing fixtures - Fluidmaster, Inc.

LEAK STOP - Cement - Bil-Dry Corp.

LEAK-TROL - Chemical preparations - Betz Laboratories, Inc.

LEAKATOR - Measuring instruments - Bacharach, Inc.

LEAKLOCK - Sealing compounds - Highside Chemicals Inc.

LEAKSTOPPER - Adhesives and sealants - Klee Chemical Coatings

LEAKSTOPPER - Metal-repair compound - Devcon Consumer Products (ITW Devcon)

LEAKTITE - Brushes–paint - Leaktite Corp.

LEAKTRACKER - Measuring instruments - Fugitive Emission Control, Inc.

LEAKY ROOF SEALER - Adhesives and sealants - Somay Products Inc.

LEAN - Vitamins and nutritional supplements - Unipro Inc.

LEAN-ACTION - Vitamins and nutritional supplements - Action Labs, Inc.

LEAN AND FIRM - Vitamins and nutritional supplements - Liferich Limited Co.

LEAN & LITE - Meat products–beef - Mrs. Paul's Kitchen

LEAN & LOW - Food products - Holten Meat, Inc.

LEAN BEAN - Candy - World's Smallest, Inc.

LEAN CHOICE - Meat products - Jones Dairy Farm

LEAN CREAM - Sour cream - Land O'Lakes Inc.

LEAN CUISINE - Frozen foods - Stouffer Foods Corp.

LEAN CUISINE CAFE CLASSICS - Food products - Nestle USA

LEAN DREAM - Dips–sour cream based - Land O'Lakes Inc.

LEAN ERA - Animal feeds - Hubbard Milling Co.

LEAN FIGURE - Vitamins and nutritional supplements - Beso Biological Research Center, Inc.

LEAN GAINER - Vitamins and nutritional supplements - Champion Nutrition

LEAN GENERATION - Animal feed - Purina Mills, Inc.

LEAN LEG MACHINE - Exercising equipment - Brenda Dykgraaf

LEAN LEGS THE AMINOPHYLLINE CELLULITE GEL - Skin care products - Image Cosmetics, Ltd.

LEAN LINKS - Food products - Lightlife Foods, Inc.

LEAN LIVING - Dinners–frozen - Health Valley Food

LEAN MAGIC - Food products - Pierre Frozen Foods Inc.

LEAN MAGIC - Meat products - Hudson Foods, Inc.

LEAN MIX - Animal feed supplements - Golden Sun Feeds, Inc.

LEAN MUSCLE TECHNOLOGY - Vitamins and nutritional supplements - Nutrasutical Corp.

LEAN N' HARD VICTORY MASS 1000 - Vitamins and nutritional supplements - Weider Health and Fitness

LEAN N' TENDER - Food products - Peck Foods Corp.

LEAN 'N TENDER - Meat products–beef - Emmber Foods, Inc.

LEAN 'N TRIM - Meat products - Tav Brands Inc.

LEAN ON ME - Canes - Pharmaceutical Innovations

LEAN ON ME - Tools - Richard Jacobsen

LEAN ON ME BOLSTER - Infant product - Summer Infant Products Inc.

LEAN POCKETS - Frozen foods - Chef America, Inc.

LEAN REALITY PAK - Animal feed supplements - Triple F, Inc.

LEAN SOLUTION - Vitamins and nutritional supplements - Weider Health and Fitness

LEAN START - Pet food - Hubbard Milling Co.

LEAN SUPREME - Meat products–beef - Armour Swift-Eckrich

LEANCARE - Vitamins and nutritional supplements - Ayurvedic Concepts Ltd.

LEANDRA - Whirlpools - Lasco Products Group

LEANER THAN BACON - Meat products–beef - Armour Swift-Eckrich

LEANER WIENERS - Frankfurters - Kunzler and Co. Inc.

LEANER WIENERS - Frankfurters - Northern Soy

LEANERS - Playing cards - Fun World

LEANEST NAME IN DELI MEATS, THE - Meat products - Hatfield, Inc.

LEANGROW - Animal feeds - Land O'Lakes Inc.

LEANI - Ophthalmic goods ☆ - Luxottica

LEANIES - Meat extracts - Miles Inc.

LEANIN' TREE - Artists' materials - Leanin' Tree Inc.

LEANLIFE - Dietary food supplements - Nutrition for Life International, Inc.

LEAN'N POST - Boating equipment and accessories - Zebco Corp.

LEANNE'S NO FAT DELIGHTS - Bakery products - Leanne McVicker

LEANORE - Glassware–household - ACC

LEAP - Computers - Leap, Inc.

LEAP - Games - Kadon Enterprises Inc.

LEAP FROG - Game machines - IGT - North America

LEAP FROG - Games - Kling Magnetics Inc.

LEAP FROGS - Games - Tyco Toys

LEAP OF FAITH - Computer software - Thinktank, Ltd.

LEAPER - Weightlifting equipment - FTG Manufacturing

LEAPFROG - Toys–electronic - Leapfrog RBT LLC

LEAPIN' DEMONS - Toys–automobiles - Mattel, Inc.

LEAPIN' LENTILS OVER COUSCOUS - Soups–mixes - Fantastic Foods Inc.

LEAPIN' LILY PADS - Games - Hasbro, Inc.

LEAPIN' LIZARDS - Sauces - Promark International, Inc.

LEAPIN' LIZARDS - Toys–stuffed - Dakin Inc.

LEAPIN' WIZARD PRODUCTIONS - Infant product - European Toy Collection/ Crocodile Creek

LEAPRO - Sporting goods - Leapro Sports Co., Inc.

LEAPS & BOUNDS - Computer software - Muse Software

LEAPS & BOUNDS - Toys - Leaps & Bounds, Inc.

LEAR SIEGLER - Computer peripheral equipment ☆ - Borroughs Corp.

LEARN-A-CRAFT - Needles–sewing - Dimensions, Inc.

LEARN ABOUT ASTRONOMY - Computer software ☆ - Optimum Resource, Inc.

LEARN ABOUT COMPUTER PROGRAMMING - Computer software ☆ - Optimum Resource, Inc.

LEARN ABOUT COMPUTERS - Computer software ☆ - Optimum Resource, Inc.

LEARN ABOUT FRACTIONS - Computer software ☆ - Optimum Resource, Inc.

LEARN ABOUT THE HUMAN BODY - Computer software ☆ - Optimum Resource, Inc.

LEARN ALONG SONGS - Recording label - Moonlight Rose Publications

LEARN & PLAY - Publisher's imprints - McGraw-Hill Companies, Inc.

LEARN AND PLAY WITH WILBUR AND FRIENDS - Video tapes–blank - EKA Productions

LEARN AS YOU GROW - Publisher's imprints - Marlon Creations

LEARN BY DOING - Electronic equipment - Elenco Electronic, Inc.

LEARN-EASE - Notebooks and notepads - Dennison National Co.

LEARN PC - Computer software - Learn PC, Inc.

LEARN THE ALPHABET - Computer software ☆ - Optimum Resource, Inc.

LEARN THE ART OF MAGIC - Computer software - Broderbund Software, Inc.

LEARN TO - Publisher's imprints - Pen Notes Inc.

LEARN TO ADD AND SUBTRACT - Computer software ☆ - Optimum Resource, Inc.

LEARN-TO-CARE - Dolls - Mattel, Inc.

LEARN TO COUNT - Computer software ☆ - Optimum Resource, Inc.

LEARN TO DO - Computer software - Allegro New Media, Inc.

LEARN TO DRAW NOW - Artists' materials - General Pencil Co.

LEARN-TO-DRESS - Dolls - Mattel, Inc.

LEARN TO EARN! - Educational materials - TBSC Learning Systems, Inc.

LEARN-TO-FLY - Toys - Mattel, Inc.

LEARN TO MULTIPLY AND DIVIDE - Computer software ☆ - Optimum Resource, Inc.

LEARN TO READ IN WONDERLAND - Computer software ☆ - Optimum Resource, Inc.

LEARN TO SEW FOR FUN - Patterns–clothing ☆ - Mccall Pattern Co.

LEARN-TO-SPACE - Paper - Bemiss-Jason Corp.

LEARN-TO-WRITE - Paper - Bemiss-Jason Corp.

LEARNADA - Computer software - Aetech Inc.

LEARN&PLAY - Computer software - UBI Soft Inc.

LEARNER - Pencils - General Pencil Co.

LEARNERFIRST - Computer software - Learner First, Inc.

LEARNER'S WORLD/U.S.A. - Publisher's imprints - Price Stern Sloan Inc.

LEARNING 100 - Computer software - Steck-Vaughn Publishing Corp.

LEARNING ABOUT MY WORLD - Toys - Mattel, Inc.

LEARNING ADVANTAGE, THE - Educational materials - Learning Advantage

LEARNING BANK, THE - Educational materials - Dennis M. Kelly

LEARNING CENTERS CLUB - Educational materials - Education Center, Inc.

LEARNING CHANNEL, THE - Computer software - Discovery Channel

LEARNING CIRCUS - Computer software - Big Top Productions Inc.
LEARNING CLOCK - Toys - Learning Resources, Inc.
LEARNING CURVE INTERNATIONAL - Toys - Learning Curve Toys, LLC
LEARNING DOS - Computer software - Microsoft Corp.
LEARNING-EDGE - Electronic equipment - Learning-Edge, Inc.
LEARNING ENGINE - Computer software - Ricorso
LEARNING FUN FACTORY - Computer software - Hartley Courseware Inc.
LEARNING FUN FOR KIDS - Computer software ☆ - Optimum Resource, Inc.
LEARNING IN MOTION - Computer software - Learning in Motion, Inc.
LEARNING INSTRUMENTS - Computer software - B & W, Inc.
LEARNING LADDERS - Publisher's imprints - Random House, Inc.
LEARNING LIBRARY - Toys - Fisher-Price, Inc.
LEARNING LION - Computer software ☆ - Don Johnston Inc.
LEARNING LOGIC - Computer software - National Science Center Foundation Inc.
LEARNING LUNCH BAG - Bags - Alexis Johnson
LEARNING MACHINE, THE - Electronic equipment - Zygon International, Inc.
LEARNING MAGNETS - Educational materials - Claire C. Huking
LEARNING ODYSSEY, THE - Educational materials - Agency for Instructional Technology
LEARNING-ON-DEMAND - Computer software - Icon Associates, Inc.
LEARNING POINT - Computer software - Moore Business Forms, Inc.
LEARNING POTPOURRI - Computer software ☆ - Ventura Educational Systems
LEARNING RESEARCH INC. - Video production - Learning Research, Inc.
LEARNING ROAD - Toys - Playthings International, Ltd.
LEARNING ROUNDS - Toys–blocks - Gerber Products Co.
LEARNING SEEDS - Publisher's imprints - Home Team Press
LEARNING SHEET, THE - Bedding–linen - Dan River Inc.
LEARNING STEPS - Toys - Hasbro, Inc.
LEARNING SYSTEMS LS - Publisher's imprints - Learning Systems Inc.
LEARNING TEE, THE - Apparel and accessories - America's Best, Inc.
LEARNING TO BE WATER WISE AND ENERGY EFFICIENT - Publisher's imprints - Fan-Fi International Inc.
LEARNING TO SAIL - Computer software - SourceView Software International
LEARNING TO SEW - Educational materials - Vacuum Dealers Trade Association Ltd
LEARNING TREE INTERNATIONAL - Computer hardware - Learning Tree International, Inc.
LEARNING TYPE MEASURE - Educational materials - Excel International Group Inc.
LEARNING UNLIMITED - Musical instrument accessories - Hal Leonard Corp.
LEARNING WALL, THE - Partitions–wood - USG Interiors, Inc.
LEARNING-WINDOW - Toys–electronic - Video Technology U.S. Inc.
LEARNING WITH LEATHER - Leather goods - Tandy Leather Co.
LEARNING WORKS, THE - Publisher's imprints - Learning Works Inc.
LEARNING YEARS - Toys - F.J. Strauss Co. Inc.
LEARNINGAMES - Games - Educational Materials Associates, Inc.
LEARNIT! - Games - Human Resource Development Press, Inc.
LEARNITURE - Furniture–children's - Mark St. Gaudens
LEARNIX - Publisher's imprints - Learnix Inc.
LEARNNET - Computer software - Multimedia Learning, Inc.
LEARSI COLLECTION - Hosiery–women's - Learsi Collection
LEASA - Milk–canned or powdered - Leasa Industries Co., Inc.
LEASE LINK - Computer software - Lease Marketing Ltd.
LEASE4U - Motor vehicle dealers - Automotive Assistance Group, Inc.
LEASEMAP - Computer software - Geographix, Inc.
LEASETRACKER - Office accessories - Krapf Business Systems, Inc.
LEASEWRITER - Computer software - Nolo Press/Folklaw Inc.
LEASH - Eyeglasses - Martin-Copeland Eyewear Corp.
LEASING CAREER INDICATORS - Paper–book - Career Systems, Inc.
LEASINGHAM - Wines - House of Burgundy Inc.
LEAST BRA, THE - Apparel stores–lingerie - Goddess Bra
LEASTRAC 2000 - Computer software - Stockholder Systems, Inc.
LEATHER - Apparel and accessories ☆ - Fidelity Sportswear Co.
LEATHER - Tiles–ceramic - KPT Inc.
LEATHER AMORE - Cleaning preparations - Bee Natural Leathercare Inc.
LEATHER AND CHROME - Leather goods ☆ - AR Accessories Group Inc.
LEATHER AND LOVE - Pet products - Leather and Love, Inc.
LEATHER & TWEEDS - Upholstered furniture - American Furniture Co. Inc.
LEATHER BY THE YARD - Leather - Collins & Aikman Corp.
LEATHER DENIMS - Fabrics - Dan River Inc.
LEATHER FEATHERED FRIENDS - Toys–stuffed - Joy Zee Enterprises
LEATHER-FINESSE - Chairs–upholstered - La-Z-Boy Chair Co.
LEATHER FORCE - Handbags ☆ - Sarne Co. Inc.
LEATHER GODDESSES OF PHOBOS - Computer software - Activision, Inc.

LEATHER-GRAIN DO-ALL - Floor coverings - American Floor Products Co. Inc.
LEATHER INNOVATIONS - Leather goods - Leather Innovations Inc.
LEATHER LEGACY - Leather goods ☆ - Samsill Corp.
LEATHER LIFE - Leather tanning and finishing ☆ - Greentree Laboratories, Inc.
LEATHER LOCK - Jewelry ☆ - Hirsch Speidel Inc.
LEATHER LOFT SHAFMASTER LEATHER CO. - Photo albums - Leather Loft Stores, Inc.
LEATHER LOTION - Cleaning preparations ☆ - Edison Brothers Stores, Inc.
LEATHER LOVE - Leather tanning and finishing ☆ - Original Mink Oil Inc.
LEATHER LUSTER - Cleaning preparations - Leather Luster Inc.
LEATHER MARK - Leather goods - Art Craft Wallets Inc.
LEATHER MASTER - Leather goods - S and S Leather Goods
LEATHER-NEW - Saddles - Farnam Cos. Inc.
LEATHER ON - Shoe lasts - McNett Corp.
LEATHER ONE - Footwear - D'Bello Shoe Corp.
LEATHER-ORR - Leather goods - IMA Fashions Inc.
LEATHER RAINCOAT - Adhesives and sealants ☆ - Edison Brothers Stores, Inc.
LEATHER ROSE - Hair care products - Leather Rose, Inc.
LEATHER SHOP, THE - Belts–apparel - Leather Shop Inc.
LEATHER SOF - Leather goods - Triple X Packaging Co.
LEATHER SOPHISTICATES - Leather goods - Leather Sophisticates
LEATHER STOCKING BOOKS - Publisher's imprints - Westport Publishers Inc. (Media Div.)
LEATHER THERAPY - Leather tanning and finishing - Unicorn Editions, Limited
LEATHER THERAPY - Oils–lubricating - Unicorn Editions Ltd.
LEATHER TREASURES - Leather goods - St. Thomas Inc.
LEATHER TYME, THE - Recliners - Stratford Co.
LEATHER ULTRA - Gloves - Saramar Corp.
LEATHER UP - Apparel and accessories - Leather Up, Inc.
LEATHER USA - Furniture - Leather USA
LEATHER-VITA - Cleaning preparations - Shore Chemical Co. Inc.
LEATHER WORKS BY FIDELITY - Apparel and accessories ☆ - Fidelity Sportswear Co.
LEATHER WORLD MANUFACTURING - Leather goods - Bugatti Inc.
LEATHER-X - Sporting goods - Unique Sports Products Inc.
LEATHERAMA - Publisher's imprints - Bentley Gifts Inc.
LEATHERCOLORS - Paints ☆ - Leather Factory Inc.
LEATHERCRAFT - Toys ☆ - Coloron Industries
LEATHERCRAFT CUSTOM - Aprons–leather - Custom Leathercraft Manufacturing
LEATHERCRAFT WORKSHOP - Leather goods - Tandy Leather Co.
LEATHERENE - Leather tanning and finishing ☆ - Traileze Veterinary Products Inc.
LEATHERHEAD - Toys - Playmates World Wide Inc.
LEATHERITE - Pet products - Leatherite-Nylorite Manufacturing Inc.
LEATHERLIFE - Wallets - ACCO USA, Inc.
LEATHERLINES - Desk sets - A and M Leatherlines Inc.
LEATHERLINK - Watchbands–base metal ☆ - Roma Industries
LEATHERMAN - Tools - Leatherman Tool Group, Inc.
LEATHERNECK - Games - Avalon Hill Game Co.
LEATHERNECK - Office supplies - Georgia-Pacific Corp.
LEATHEROCK - Apparel and accessories - Leatherock International Inc.
LEATHEROID - Leather goods - Quality Park Products Co.
LEATHERS - Wallpaper ☆ - Robert Crowder & Co.
LEATHERS BY CACCIOLA - Handbags - Mario Cacciola Leathers Inc.
LEATHERS BY EARHART - Dialing devices–telephone - Baltimore Luggage Co.
LEATHERSKIN - Steering mechanisms–motor vehicle - Superior Industries International, Inc.
LEATHERSMITH OF LONDON - Office supplies - Blue Star Leather Inc.
LEATHERTONE - Tobacco products ☆ - Doranne
LEATHERTREND - Furniture - Robinson & Robinson Inc.
LEATHERWAYS - Attache cases - Elizabeth Leather Bags
LEATHERWOOD - Furniture ☆ - Lane Co. Inc.
LEATHERWORK - Footwear - Leatherwork Manufacturing Co. Inc.
LEAVE-IN - Hair care products - Alberto-Culver Co.
LEAVE IN - Hair care products ☆ - Advanced Research Laboratories
LEAVENWORTH - Food products ☆ - Leavenworth Fruit Co.
LEAVES - Chocolate candy - H. Hamstra & Co.
LEAVES - Decorations - Mesa International
LEAVES - Dinnerware–glass ☆ - Cyclamen Studio
LEAVES - Glassware–household - ACC

☆ = Now out of production

LEAVES & WEAVES - Wallcoverings - Cork Products Co. Inc.

LEAVES-AWAY - Gutters–metal - Kinsman Co. Inc.

LEAVEX - Jewelry ☆ - Charles Zahn-Import Merchant

LEAWOOD - Bicycles - Western Auto Supply Co.

LEBANITE - Wood products - Georgia-Pacific Corp.

LEBANON - Balls - Lebanon Ball Co.

LEBARON SALON - Motor vehicles–automobiles ☆ - DaimlerChrysler

LEBLANC - Musical instruments - G. Leblanc Corp.

LEBLANC FRANCE - Musical instruments - G. Leblanc Corp.

LEBOURGET - Hosiery ☆ - M.A. Rabinowitz Corp.

LEBRA - Motor vehicle parts and accessories - Saddleman, Inc.

LEC-CAPS - Pharmaceutical preparations ☆ - Fibertone Co.

LEC E TIME - Vitamins and nutritional supplements - Nutrition Headquarters, Inc.

LEC-TRO-SPRAY - Enamels - Pratt & Lambert United, Inc.

LECCO - Vitamins and nutritional supplements - CS Animal Feeds, Inc.

LECH BEER - Beverages–malt - Stanley Stawski Distributing Co.

+L'ECHASSIER - Cordials - Crown Capital USA Inc.

LECHE FRESCA - Milk - Goya Foods, Inc.

LECHEF - Kitchen appliances - Sunbeam-Oster Household Products

LECHERE - Wines ☆ - Diamond Wine Merchants

LECHIC - Wallpaper ☆ - Cherry Hill Studio

LECI-KEY - Vitamins and nutritional supplements ☆ - J.R. Carlson Laboratories Inc.

LECI-PS - Vitamins and nutritional supplements - Lucas Meyer, Inc.

LECI SLIM - Vitamins and nutritional supplements - Natural Organics, Inc.

LECIGEN - Vitamins and nutritional supplements - Nutrition Enterprises

LECITREME - Shortening - Beatrice Cos. Inc.

LECIZYME - Pet products - Natural Animal Nutrition Inc.

LECLAIRE - Floor coverings - Bruce Hardwood Floors

LE'CLOCK - Clocks - Electro-Optix Inc.

LECLUSE LOIRE - Beverages–alcohol - Nor-Glo Import Co.

LECOGLASS - Wallcovering - The Creative Edge, Inc.

+L'ECOLE - Footwear - N Shasta Shoe

LECOME - Nail care products - Merchandising Concepts Inc.

LECOMTE - Apparel–women's - Lucia, Inc.

+L'ECONOME - Housewares ☆ - Selfix, Inc.

LECONTE - Furniture - Bean Station Furniture Factory Inc.

LECOR - Auto accessories - Nice One International Development Corp.

LECREME FIXX - Hair care products ☆ - Mahdeen Laboratory

LECROY - Spices and extracts - John Lecroy & Son Inc.

LECROY SCOPESTATION - Electrical equipment - LeCroy Corp.

LECTEL - Jewelry - Sterling Inc.

LECTERN LAB - Electronic equipment - Hamilton Electronics Corp.

LECTERN ONE - Electronic equipment - Sound-Craft Systems Inc.

LECTERN, THE - Electronic equipment - Screen Works

LECTERNETTE - Electronic equipment - Sound-Craft Systems Inc.

LECTRA - Toys–models - Cox Products Inc.

LECTRA - GLOVES - Gloves - Nordic Gear Inc.

LECTRA JACK - Hitches–trailer ☆ - Reese Products, Inc.

LECTRA-LIFT - Chairs–dentists' ☆ - La-Z-Boy Chair Co.

LECTRA-LINK - Chain hoist - Ingersoll-Rand Co.

LECTRA-LOUNGER - Recliners ☆ - La-Z-Boy Chair Co.

LECTRA-MITS - Apparel and accessories - Timely Products

LECTRA-MOTIVE - Cleaning preparations - CRC Chemicals USA/Siloo

LECTRA SAN EC - Toilets–porcelain - Raritan Engineering Co. Inc.

LECTRA-SOX - Apparel and accessories - Timely Products

LECTRA STREAM - Food warming equipment - Mayfair Molded Products

LECTRA-WEAR - Apparel and accessories - Timely Products

LECTRAJUST - Lectern motor - Van San Corp.

LECTRIC - Housewares - Warner Manufacturing Co.

LECTRIC POP - Popcorn - National Oats Co. Inc.

'LECTRIC SHAVE - Shaving preparations - J.B. Williams Co. Inc.

LECTRIC SNAKES - Drain pipe cleaners - Eagle Industries Inc.

LECTRICICEMAN DC1 009110 - Frigibar Industries Inc.

LECTRILITA - Lighters ☆ - Latama Inc.

LECTRO - Office supplies ☆ - Bates Manufacturing Co.

LECTRO - Pet products - Pet Heating Products Inc.

LECTRO-COVER - Pet products - Pet Heating Products Inc.

LECTRO KENNEL - Pet products - R.C. Steele Co.

LECTRO-LIFT - Elevators - Sedgwick Lifts Inc.

LECTRO PATCH - Medical apparatus - General Medical Co.

LECTRO-PLAQUE - Lighting fixtures ☆ - Simco

LECTRO SHAVE - Skin care products - William Stevens Perfumers

LECTRO-SPIRAL - Health care products - Vygon Corp.

LECTRO-STIK - Tools - Lectro-Stik Corp.

LECTROLITE - Fabrics–coated - Herculite Products, Inc.

LECTROLITE COMFORT - Fabrics–coated - Herculite Products, Inc.

LECTRON - Automotive parts and accessories - Lectron Fuel Systems, Inc.

LECTRON - Watches - Gruen Marketing Corp.

LECTRON II - Health care products - Pharmaceutical Innovations

LECTRONIC LECTERN - Electronic equipment - Thomson Consumer Electronics, Inc.

LECTROSTILL - Beverages - American Eagle Water Co.

LECTURA - Ophthalmic goods ☆ - Luxottica

LECTUREACTIVE - Computer programs - Archipelago Productions, Inc.

LECTURERS - Markers–felt-tip - MagnaPlan Corp.

LED-FLO - Pencils ☆ - Faber-Castell Corp.

LEDA - House furnishings - Dan River Inc.

LEDBETTER SUPREME - Meat products–beef - Empire Packing Co., LP

LEDDY'S - Boots - M.L. Leddy

LEDERLE - Pharmaceutical preparations - Lederle Laboratories

LEDERLE PARTNERS IN PATIENT CARE - Pharmaceutical preparations - American Cyanamid Co.

LEDERLE STANDARD PRODUCTS - Pharmaceutical preparations - American Cyanamid Co.

LEDERPLEX - Vitamins and nutritional supplements - Lederle Laboratories

LEDFORD - Musical instrument accessories - Ledfords Musical Instruments

LEDGE - Dinnerware–plastic ☆ - Plastics Manufacturing Co.

LEDGER - Office supplies - R.A. Stewart Superior

LEDGER, THE - Squeegees - Companion Tools, Ltd.

LEDGERMASTER - Computer software - Relational Data Systems, Inc.

LEDGEWOOD - Wood products - Grosfillex Inc.

LEDIMAR - Skin care products - Ledimar Inc.

LEDIZOLV - Cleaning preparations - Hin-Cor Industries, Inc.

LEDS - Computer software - Logicon, Inc.

LEDU - Lamps–desk - Ledu Corp.

LEDWI - Medical apparatus - Scientific Technology, Inc.

LEDZINOL - Paints - Chilton Paint Co.

LEE - Automotive parts and accessories - Champion Laboratories, Inc.

LEE - Bathing suits - Great American Industries Inc. (Robby Len Fashions Divison.)

LEE - Brushes–paint - Corona Brushes Inc.

LEE - Cleaning preparations - Lee Products Co.

LEE - Fishing lures - Taitex Enterprise Co.

LEE - Furniture - Boling Co.

LEE - Furniture–upholstered - Lee Industries Inc.

LEE - Hats ☆ - Stetson Hat Co. Inc.

LEE - Hobby kits - Lee Co.

LEE - Jeans–women's - Lee Apparel Co. Inc.

LEE - Skin care products - Lee Pharmaceuticals

LEE - Socks - Renfro Corp.

LEE - Sweatshirts - Midstates Sportswear

LEE - Tires - Kelly-Springfield Tire Co.

LEE - Tires - Lee Tire & Rubber Co.

LEE ANDERSON - Apparel–children's - Leah Palmer-Anderson Design Inc.

LEE ANDERSON'S - Food products - Covaldo Inc.

LEE BEACHWEST - Bathing suits - Great American Industries Inc. (Robby Len Fashions Divison.)

LEE DATA - Computer peripheral equipment - IIS Inc.

LEE FREDRICS - Jewelry ☆ - Weingeroff Enterprises, Inc.

LEE GALLERY - Greeting cards - Enthusiastic Enterprises

LEE JACKSON - Amplifiers - Lee Jackson

LEE JOFA - Wallpaper - Sterling Prints

LEE JOFA - Window coverings - Award Fabrics Inc.

LEE JUNIORS - Jeans–children's - Lee Apparel Co. Inc.

LEE KLEIN U S A - Apparel and accessories - Lee Klein II, Inc.

LEE KLEIN USA - Apparel and accessories - Lee Klein II, Inc.

LEE KUM KEE - Sauces - Gourmet America

LEE L. WOODARD - Furniture - Court Leisure

LEE LEENS - Jeans–women's ☆ - Lee Apparel Co. Inc.

LEE LEESURES - Jeans–men's ☆ - Lee Apparel Co. Inc.

LEE LEGENDS - Jeans–women's - Lee Apparel Co. Inc.

LEE LINER - Trailers–travel ☆ - Shasta Industries Inc.

LEE MAR - Women's blouses and tops - Athlone Industries Inc.

LEE MAXI - Automotive parts and accessories - Champion Laboratories, Inc.

LEE NAILS - Manicure preparations - Lee Pharmaceuticals

LEE OPTICAL - Lenses–optical - New West Eyeworks, Inc.

LEE PRESS ON NAILS - Manicure preparations - Lee Pharmaceuticals

LEE-RICK - Food products - Brown Derby, Inc.

LEE RIDERS - Jeans–women's - Lee Apparel Co. Inc.

LEE-ROWAN - Shelving units–metal - Lee-Rowan Co.

☆ = Now out of production

LEE SPORT - Apparel and accessories - H.D. Lee Co., Inc.
LEE SPORT GENUINE CASUALWEAR - Apparel and accessories - H.D. Lee Co., Inc.
LEE STEMER - Handbags - Ronay Inc.
LEE-TEX - Toys - United Industries Inc.
LEE TOYS - Toys - Lee Aluminum Foundry & Manufacturing Co.
LEE TREVINO - Garages - Penna Golf Co.
LEE TREVINO - Shoes–athletic ☆ - Brookfield Athletic Co. Inc.
LEE VS. GRANT - Games - Avalon Hill Game Co.
LEE WRIGHT - Apparel and accessories - Oxford Industries, Inc.
LEE WRIGHT'S GEOCENTRICS - Wallpaper - Kirk-Brummel
LEE WULFF - Fishing tackle - Royal Wulff Products
LEEBER - Silver products - Robert D. Murray & Associates
LEECE-NEVILLE - Motor vehicle parts and accessories - Prestolite Electric Inc.
LEECH - Adhesives and sealants - Leech Products Inc.
LEECH - Toys - Mattel, Inc.
LEECH-BOND - Glue–household or industrial - Leech Products Inc.
LEECH-BOND II - Glue–household or industrial ☆ - Leech Products Inc.
LEECH LOCKER - Sporting goods - Magic Products, Inc.
LEECH LODGE - Sporting goods - Magic Products, Inc.
LEECH-WELD - Adhesives and sealants ☆ - Leech Products Inc.
LEECRAFT - Lighting equipment - Lighting Components and Design, Inc.
LEEDAL - Photographic equipment - Leedal Inc.
LEEDALL - Paper–carbon - Leedall Products Manufacturing Co.
LEEDER - Musical instrument accessories - Mechanical Music Corp.
LEEDS - Ophthalmic goods - Embassy Creations Inc.
LEEDS - Shoe stores - Edison Brothers Stores, Inc.
LEEDS - Shoes - Allen-Edmonds Shoe Corp.
LEEDS HALL - Apparel stores–sports - Farnham Hall Sportswear
LEEDY - Drums–musical instruments ☆ - Fred Gretsch Enterprises
LEEHAVEN - Doors–storm - Weather Shield Manufacturing, Inc.
LEEK-PRUF - Bags - Walker Co.
LEEKA - Skin care products - Leeka Products
LEEKPROOF - Caulking compounds - Midland Chicago Corp.
LEELANAU - Fruits–candied - Leelanau Fruit Co.
LEELANAU CELLARS - Wines - Leelanau Wine Cellars, Ltd.
LEELANAU LIMITED - Wines - Leelanau Wine Cellars, Ltd.
LEEN - Health care products - Ray Drug Co.
LEENA STUDIO - Apparel–women's - Wings Manufacturing Corp.
LEEP SYSTEM 6000 - Surgical supplies - Coopersurgical, Inc.
LEEP VAC - Smoke evacuator equipment - Cooper Companies Inc.
LEERDAM - Statuary ☆ - Eastern Shore Trading Co.
LEE'S - Aquariums–household - L. Schultz, Inc.
LEES - Floor coverings–carpet and rugs - Lees Carpets
LEE'S - Ice cream - M & L Gourmet Ice Cream Co.
LEE'S - Pet products - Lee's Aquarium Products
LEE'S - Veterinary pharmaceutical preparations - Traileze Veterinary Products Inc.
LEE'S BIG BUTT - Barbecue sauce - Lee Hiram Sidney
LEE'S FAMOUS RECIPE CHICKEN - Restaurant franchise - Shoney's, Inc.
LEES FOR LIFE - Floor coverings–carpet and rugs - Burlington Industries, Inc.
LEE'S ICE CREAM - Fast-food franchise - Lee's Ice Cream
LEE'S MIAMI - Sporting goods - Lee's Tackle Inc.
LEE'S PRIDE - Fruits and vegetables - Merchants Distributors, Inc.
LEE'S SUPERPREMIUM - Ice cream - Lee's Ice Cream
LEESA WHITTEN - Greeting cards ☆ - Amcal Inc.
LEESFILTER - Filters–water - Koch Membrane Systems, Inc.
LEESON - Motors - Leeson Electric Corp.
LEETECH - Computer software - LeeTech Software Inc.
LEETONIA - Tools - Leetonia Tool Co.
LEETOV - Spices and extracts - Diamond Foods
LEEVERALL - Handles–metal - Alexander's/Leeverall Inc.
LEEVERLOC - Machine parts - Spaulding & Rogers Manufacturing Inc.
LEEWARD - Furniture–wood ☆ - Ficks Reed Co. Inc.
LEEWARD - Trailers–travel - Gladding Del-Rey
LEEWARD - Wines - Leeward Winery
LEEWARDS - Hobby kits - Leewards Creative Crafts, Inc.
LEEWAY - Pet products - Farm & Country Marketing
LEFEVER - Shotguns ☆ - Ithaca Gun Co. Inc.
LEFFE - Beverages–malt - Labatt Importers Inc.
+L'EFFLEUR - Fragrance, potpourri, candles - Coty Inc.
LEFRANC & BOURGEOIS - Artists' materials ☆ - Koh-I-Noor, Inc.
LEFSE - Potato chips - Norsland Kitchens
LEFT BANK - Coffee - First Colony Coffee and Tea Co. Inc.
LEFT BANK - Frames–eyeglass - Hudson Optical Corp.
LEFT LANE LORRAINE - Broadcasting stations–television - CBS Inc.

LEFT OUT - Games - Tyco Toys
LEFTHANDER - Notebooks and notepads - Norcom Inc.
LEFTON'S - Giftware - George Zolton Lefton Co.
LEFTON'S LIGHTHOUSE COLLECTION - Figurines - George Zolton Lefton Co.
LEFTON'S RAILROAD DEPOTS - Giftware - George Zolton Lefton Co.
LEFTON'S ROADSIDE DELITES - Figurines - George Zolton Lefton Co.
LEFTOVER LIFEGUARD - Housewares - Dianna L. Namisniak
LEFTY - Hair care products - Dubl Duck/Jet Set Inc.
LEFUNSKIN - Bathing suits - Christina USA Inc.
LEG-A-SEA - Seafood products–fresh or frozen - Nichirei Foods America
LEG APPEAL - Hosiery - Noe-Equal Hosiery Corp.
LEG CONCEALER - Hosiery–women's - Saks Fifth Avenue
LEG DESIGNS - Panty hose - Jockey International, Inc.
LEG EEZE - Furniture - Jereva Inc.
LEG FASHIONS - Panty hose - Jockey International, Inc.
LEG INVIGORATOR - Skin care products - Sara Lee Corp.
LEG LINES - Hosiery–women's - Leg Lines Ltd.
LEG LOOKS - Hosiery–women's - Kayser-Roth Corp.
LEG MAGIC - Cosmetics - Covermark Cosmetics
LEG MATE - Medical apparatus - Encore Products Inc.
LEG MATES - Apparel–women's - Wacoal America Inc.
LEG MENDER - Dermatological preparations - Norstar Consumer Products Co., Inc.
LEG PERFECTION - Hosiery–women's - Saks & Co.
LEG SAVER - Horseshoes - Thoro'bred Racing Plate Co., Inc.
LEG SNUGGLER - Socks - Leininger Mills Inc.
LEG UP - Foot rest - Ahhh!, Inc.
LEG UP - Medical apparatus - Kathvon Enterprises
LEG UP - Saddles - Manufacturer's Group
LEG WORKS, THE - Socks - Edison Brothers Stores, Inc.
LEGACE - Shampoos - S.C. Johnson & Son, Inc.
LEGACIES - Furniture - Hammary Furniture Co. Inc.
LEGACIES, THE - Apparel and accessories - Weyerhaeuser Co.
LEGACY - Alarm systems - Cardkey Systems, Inc.
LEGACY - Awnings - Carefree/Scott Fetzer Co.
LEGACY - Batteries - Douglas Battery Manufacturing Co.
LEGACY - Binoculars - Bausch & Lomb Inc.
LEGACY - Blinds–vertical - Royal Shutters Inc.
LEGACY - Cabinets - Aristokraft, Inc.
LEGACY - Cabinets - Yorktowne Inc.
LEGACY - Clocks - General Time Corp. (Westclox/Seth Thomas Div.)
LEGACY - Computer software - Epic Systems Corp.
LEGACY - Cooking equipment–household ☆ - Mirro Corp.
LEGACY - Cosmetics - Spornette International, Inc.
LEGACY - Dinnerware - Plastics, Inc. (Anchor Hocking Plastics)
LEGACY - Dinnerware–glass - Noritake Co. Inc.
LEGACY - Doors–wood ☆ - Masonite Corp.
LEGACY - Fireplace equipment - Design Specialties Inc.
LEGACY - Fishing rods - Powell Rod Co., Inc.
LEGACY - Fishing tackle - Fenwick
LEGACY - Floor coverings - Congoleum Corp.
LEGACY - Floor coverings–carpet and rugs - Karastan-Bigelow Inc.
LEGACY - Floor coverings–carpet and rugs ☆ - Bloomsburg Carpet Industries
LEGACY - Floor coverings–carpet and rugs ☆ - Galaxy Carpet Mills Inc.
LEGACY - Floor coverings–carpet and rugs ☆ - Regal Rugs Inc.
LEGACY - Flooring–hardwood - DeSoto Hardwood Flooring Co.
LEGACY - Frames–eyeglass - Hudson Optical Corp.
LEGACY - Fruits and vegetables - OSR Enterprises, Inc.
LEGACY - Furnaces–electric - Rheem Manufacturing Co.
LEGACY - Furniture - Bretford Manufacturing, Inc.
LEGACY - Furniture - Pilliod Co.
LEGACY - Furniture ☆ - Bassett Furniture Industries, Inc.
LEGACY - Games - Lisco, Inc.
LEGACY - Guns - Daisy Manufacturing Co.
LEGACY - Hardware - Sash Controls Inc.
LEGACY - Hardware ☆ - Amerock Corp.
LEGACY - Heating equipment ☆ - United States Stove Co. Inc.
LEGACY - Hobby kits ☆ - Craft World International Inc.
LEGACY - House furnishings ☆ - Lexington Furniture Industries, Inc.
LEGACY - Luggage - Samsonite Corp.
LEGACY - Manufactured homes - Redman Industries, Inc.
LEGACY - Markers–felt-tip ☆ - Sanford Corp.
LEGACY - Medical apparatus - Alcon Laboratories, Inc.
LEGACY - Motor vehicles–automobiles - Subaru of America, Inc.
LEGACY - Motor vehicles–motor homes - Airstream Inc.

☆ = Now out of production

LEGACY - Musical instrument accessories - Wenger Corp.
LEGACY - Rackets–tennis ☆ - Wilson Sporting Goods Co.
LEGACY - Remote control devices - Overhead Door Corp.
LEGACY - Sewing machines–household - Tacony Corp.
LEGACY - Sporting goods ☆ - James Heddon's Sons
LEGACY - Strollers–baby - Combi International Corp.
LEGACY - Tiles–ceramic - United States Ceramic Tile Co.
LEGACY - Tools–hand-operated - Handy Andy Home Improvement Centers, Inc.
LEGACY - Trailers–travel - Peterson Industries Inc.
LEGACY - Vacuum cleaners and accessories - The Hoover Co.
LEGACY - Wallpaper - Payne Fabrics
LEGACY - Whirlpools - Fort Wayne Plastics, Inc.
LEGACY - Whiskey - Sazerac Co. Inc.
LEGACY BASSIC - Guitars - Zon Guitars
LEGACY BORDER - Floor coverings–carpet and rugs - Capel, Inc.
LEGACY BOUQUET - Floor coverings–carpet and rugs - Regal Rugs Inc.
LEGACY COLLECTION - Clocks - Sligh Furniture Co.
LEGACY COLLECTION - Doors - Saroyan Lumber Co.
LEGACY COLLECTION - Faucets - Chicago Faucet Co.
LEGACY COLLECTION - Furniture - Lane Co. Inc.
LEGACY ELITE - Guitars - Zon Guitars
LEGACY FLAGS - Flags - Mildred Scott McConnell
LEGACY/INTEGRATOR - Computer software - Netwise, Inc.
LEGACY LAGER - Beer - Chicago Brewing Co.
LEGACY LEGWEAR - Hosiery–women's - Kayser-Roth Corp.
LEGACY LIGHT - Fishing equipment - Powell Rod Co., Inc.
LEGACY LS WAGON - Motor vehicles–automobiles - Subaru of America, Inc.
LEGACY OF GLORY - Games - Glory Games Inc.
LEGACY OF LLYLGAMYN - Computer software - Sir-Tech Software, Inc.
LEGACY PIECES GROUP - Furniture - Davis Cabinet Co.
LEGACY PLUS - Fishing tackle - Fenwick
LEGACY PRESS - Book stores - Jeppson Galleries Inc.
LEGACY RAGE - Trailers–travel - Peterson Industries Inc.
LEGACY RED ALE - Beer - Chicago Brewing Co.
LEGACY SOFTWARE - Computer software - Legacy Software
LEGACY SPORT - Luggage - Samsonite Corp.
LEGACY STANDARD - Guitars - Zon Guitars
LEGACY STRIPE - Floor coverings–carpet and rugs ☆ - Regal Rugs Inc.
LEGACY WREATH - Floor coverings–carpet and rugs ☆ - Regal Rugs Inc.
LEGACY'S ROCK EXPERIENCE - Recording label - Sony Music Entertainment Inc.
LEGAL 4 RACING - Chemical preparations - CRC Chemicals USA/Siloo
LEGAL ACTION - Bicycles - Seattle Bike Supply, Inc.
LEGAL AFFAIRS - Paper products - Legal-Ease Forms, Inc.
LEGAL ANYWHERE - Computer peripheral equipment - Legal Anywhere, LLC
LEGAL CASE, THE - Briefcases - S and S Leather Goods
LEGAL COPY - Pens - K-9 Pen Co.
LEGAL DOCUMENT PROFESSIONALS - Legal services - Legal Eagle, Inc.
LEGAL DON'T MAKE IT RIGHT - Apparel and accessories - Englishtown Sportswear Ltd.
LEGAL ESSENTIALS - Computer software - Legal Essentials Co.
LEGAL FORCE! - Computer software - David P. Solomon
LEGAL INSIGHT - Recording label - Legal Insight, Inc.
LEGAL MEDIA - Educational materials - Alfred E. Piombino
LEGAL STEROL COMPLEX - Vitamins and nutritional supplements - S & K Labs, Inc.
LEGAL VIEWS - Printers–computer - Carla Kaull McGrath
LEGALCHECK - Computer software - Avantos Performance Systems Inc.
LEGALE - Hosiery - DML Marketing Group, Ltd.
LEGALIZER - Automotive parts and accessories - Answer Products Inc.
LEGAL+PLUS - Computer software - Legal +Plus Software Group, Inc.
LEGALPOINT - Computer software - Teneron Corp.
LEGALSOFT - Computer software - David Sands Gilberts
LEGALSTAR - Computer software - Simpson Software, Inc.
LEGASUS SPORT CPM - Exercising equipment - Sutter Corp.
LEGATION SUEDE - Floor coverings–carpet and rugs ☆ - Mohawk Carpet Corp.
LEGATO - Medical apparatus - Freeman Manufacturing Co.
LEGATO - Ophthalmic goods - Rozin Optical Export Corp.
LEGATO CLASSICS - Recording label - Lyric Distribution Inc.
LEGATRIN - Pharmaceutical preparations - Columbia Laboratories Inc.
LEGCLEAN - Cleaning preparations - Walter G. Legge Co., Inc.
LEGEAR - Veterinary pharmaceutical preparations - Goodwinol Products Corp.
LEGEEZ - Health care products - Tishcon Corp.
LEGEND - Bicycles ☆ - Roadmaster Corp.

LEGEND - Boats–canoes ☆ - Sawyer Composite Products
LEGEND - Books–comic - John Byrne, Inc.
LEGEND - Colognes - Brandy Harvest
LEGEND - Cosmetics - Trend Media Inc.
LEGEND - Diaries - Legend Publications, Inc.
LEGEND - Door frames - Canyon Creek Cabinet Co.
LEGEND - Doors–metal - General Products Co. Inc.
LEGEND - Drums–musical instruments ☆ - Kaman Music Corp.
LEGEND - Faucets - Moen Inc.
LEGEND - Fencing–chain link - Master Halco Inc.
LEGEND - Fire and burglar alarms - Fire Burglary Instruments Inc.
LEGEND - Flashlights - Brinkmann Lighting Products
LEGEND - Floor coverings - Congoleum Corp.
LEGEND - Floor coverings–carpet and rugs - Regal Rugs Inc.
LEGEND - Frames–eyeglass - Liberty Optical Manufacturing Co.
LEGEND - Furniture - Bassett Furniture Industries, Inc.
LEGEND - Glassware–household - ACC
LEGEND - Goggles–safety - Parmelee Industries, Inc.
LEGEND - Goggles–safety - U.S. Safety Corp.
LEGEND - Guitars - Ovation Instruments
LEGEND - Harps - Folkcraft Instruments
LEGEND - Ice chests–plastic - Igloo Products Corp.
LEGEND - Motor vehicles - Pride Health Care, Inc.
LEGEND - Motor vehicles–automobiles - American Honda Motor Co. Inc. (Acura Div.)
LEGEND - Musical instrument accessories - G. Leblanc Corp.
LEGEND - Pens - Inventure Development Corp.
LEGEND - Pet products - Rexotic Products Co.
LEGEND - Powerboat - American Skier Boat Co.
LEGEND - Printing paper - James River Corp.
LEGEND - Printing trades machinery - Antec, Inc.
LEGEND - Projectors–photographic - Apollo Audiovisual Div.
LEGEND - Sauces - Seasons Harvest, Inc.
LEGEND - Ships–sailing vessels - Hunter Marine Corp.
LEGEND - Sunglasses - Tamarindo Trading Co. Inc.
LEGEND - Tape–adhesive - Tape Inc.
LEGEND - Toys ☆ - Combi International Corp.
LEGEND - Toys–guns - Daisy Manufacturing Co.
LEGEND - Trailers–travel - Viking Recreational Vehicles Inc.
LEGEND - Umbrellas - Haas-Jordan Co.
LEGEND - Wallcoverings ☆ - Koroseal Wallcoverings
LEGEND - Wallpaper - Forbo Wallcoverings Inc.
LEGEND - Wallpaper - Morton Jonap Co. Inc.
LEGEND - Wallpaper ☆ - Pickhardt & Siebert USA Inc.
LEGEND ARCH - Door frames - Canyon Creek Cabinet Co.
LEGEND GALLERY - Wallpaper ☆ - Legend Wallcoverings
LEGEND GAME CALLS - Hunting equipment - William B. Minor
LEGEND II - Heat pumps ☆ - Lennox Industries Inc.
LEGEND IN A NUTSHELL, A - Nuts–salted, roasted, cooked, or canned - Virginia Diner, Inc.
LEGEND IN SOUND, A - Amplifiers–public address - Klipsch and Associates Inc.
LEGEND KEEPER - Hobby kits - All American Plastics
LEGEND LINE - Boxes–corrugated paperboard - Mason Box Co. Inc.
LEGEND OF CAMELOT - Games - Brown and Bigelow Inc.
LEGEND OF KAGE - Video games ☆ - Taito America Corp.
LEGEND OF SANTA CLAUS, THE - Figurines - United Design Corp.
LEGEND PLUS - Medical apparatus - Medtronic, Inc.
LEGEND SQUARES - Wallpaper ☆ - Koroseal Wallcoverings
LEGENDARY - Chili sauce - Stubb's Legendary Kitchen
LEGENDARY - Coffee - Gillies Coffee Co.
LEGENDARY - Floor coverings–carpet and rugs ☆ - Downs Carpet Co. Inc.
LEGENDARY - Floor coverings–carpet and rugs ☆ - Royalweve Carpet Mills
LEGENDARY AMERICA - Recording label - Mythicmedia
LEGENDARY ARTIST - Lipsticks ☆ - Honey & Spice Toiletries
LEGENDARY BEAUTY - Floor coverings–carpet and rugs - World Carpets, Inc.
LEGENDARY BERRY - Food products - Jel Sert Co.
LEGENDARY BLADES - Cutlery - Gerber Legendary Blades
LEGENDARY CHINESE ART - Giftware - Arnart Imports Inc.
LEGENDARY CHOW CHOW - Relishes - Stubb's Legendary Kitchen
LEGENDARY EAST - Wallcoverings - Louis W. Bowen
LEGENDARY GOLF - Hats - T.S.S.C., Inc.
LEGENDARY LASH - Cosmetics - Max Factor & Co.
LEGENDARY MAKARA - Spices and extracts - Cinnabon, Inc.
LEGENDARY MOTORCARS - Toys–automobiles - Suzanne Dickson

☆ = Now out of production

LEGENDARY PIGNOSE - Amplifiers - Pignose Industries
LEGENDARY SPACE ENCOUNTERS - Toys–models - ERTL Co., Inc.
LEGENDRE - Liqueurs - Sazerac Co. Inc.
LEGENDRY - Office supplies - Georgia-Pacific Corp.
LEGENDS - Coffee - Melitta North America Inc.
LEGENDS - Computer software - Century Casinos Management, Inc.
LEGENDS - Frames–eyeglass - Zylo Ware Corp.
LEGENDS - Games - Wizards of the Coast, Inc.
LEGENDS - Hair care products - Ampro Industries, Inc.
LEGENDS - Recording label - Random House, Inc.
LEGENDS - Shoes–athletic - Wolfgang Enterprise Inc.
LEGENDS - Toys–automobiles - Majorette Toys (U.S.) Inc.
LEGENDS - Wallpaper - Beachwood Wallcoverings
LEGENDS - Wines - Delicato Vineyards
LEGENDS AND SUPERSTARS - Posters - Kelly Russell Studios, Inc.
LEGENDS AUTOGRAPH COLLECTION - Trading cards and stamps - International Sports Marketing, Inc.
LEGENDS BY LANE MASTERS - Cleaning preparations - Lane Masters, Inc.
LEGENDS IN GRAY - Pottery products - Henriksen Imports Inc.
LEGENDS LIFE - Shoes–athletic - Wolfgang Enterprise Inc.
LEGENDS N/S - Darts and dart games - Dart Mart Inc.
LEGENDS OF BASKETBALL - Hats - EDS West, Inc.
LEGENDS OF HOCKEY - Trading cards and stamps - Diamond Connection, Inc.
LEGENDS OF JAZZ - Broadcasting stations–radio - Broadcast Architecture, Inc.
LEGENDS OF ROBIN HOOD - Games - Avalon Hill Game Co.
LEGENDS OF THE DEAD SEA - Cosmetics - Topiclear Products of Florida, Inc.
LEGENDS OF THE DIAMOND - Toys–electronic - Bandai America Inc.
LEGENDS OF THE LOST REALM - Games - Avalon Hill Game Co.
LEGENDS OF THE OLD WEST - Beverages–alcohol - Olde St. Nick Distillery Inc.
LEGENDS OF THE WEST - Housewares - Geronimo Productions Inc.
LEGENDS OF THE WILD WEST - Toys–guns - Imperial Toy Corp.
LEGENDS OF YESTERYEAR SERIES - Dolls ☆ - Totsy Manufacturing Co., Inc.
LEGENDS SPORTS JERKY - Food products - K.T. Cuyler
LEGENT - Computer software - Legent Corp.
LEGERE LIGHT - Beverages–malt ☆ - Labatt Importers Inc.
LEGGALE - Hosiery, socks, and slippers - DML Marketing Group, Inc.
LEGGE-ACY - Floor waxes - Walter G. Legge Co., Inc.
LEGGERO - Wines ☆ - Distillerie Stock USA Ltd.
LEGGOONS - Apparel–athletic - Apparel Royalties Inc.
+L'EGGS - Hosiery - Sara Lee Corp.
+L'EGGS CLASSICS - Hosiery - Sara Lee Corp.
+L'EGGSWEAR - Hosiery - Sara Lee Corp.
LEGHORN - Paper - Silver Leaf Paper Co.
LEGHORN'S - Food products - ARA Services
LEGION - Drums–musical instruments ☆ - Grossman Music Corp.
LEGION - Floor coverings - Aladdin Mills, Inc.
LEGION - Food products - Chas. G. Summers, Jr. Inc.
LEGION - Frames–eyeglass - Hudson Optical Corp.
LEGION - Hardware - Harloc, Inc.
LEGION - Insecticides ☆ - Valent USA Corp.
LEGION OF SUPERHEROES - Games ☆ - Mayfair Games, Inc.
LEGIONAIRE - Waterproof outerwear - Distributors Service Corp.
LEGIONNAIRE - Games ☆ - Avalon Hill Game Co.
LEGIONS OF POWER - Footwear - Chadwick Industries
LEGIONS OF POWER - Toys - Tonka Corp.
LEGISLATOR - Floor coverings–carpet and rugs ☆ - Alexander Smith Carpets
LEGISLINK - Computer software - X-Link Corp.
LEGISLINK - Paper–newsprint - Pharmaceutical Care Management Association
LEGMATE - Razors - American Safety Razor Co.
LEGO - See **LAVIE**
LEGO - Toys–blocks - Lego Systems Inc.
LEGO DACTA - Toys–blocks - Lego Systems Inc.
LEGO DACTA CONNEXION, THE - Toys–blocks - Lego Systems Inc.
LEGO MANIAC - Toys–blocks - Lego Systems Inc.
LEGO SYSTEM - Toys–blocks - Lego Systems Inc.
LEGO TECHNIC - Toys–blocks - Lego Systems Inc.
LEGOLAND - Toys–blocks - Lego Systems Inc.
LEGRAN - Toilets–enameled - Kohler Co.
LEGRAND - Guitars - Gibson Guitar Corp.
LEGRAND - Recording label - Rockmasters International

LEGRAND GOURMET - Housewares - Cecil Saydah Co.
LEGRANDE - Bicycles ☆ - Huffy Corp.
LEGRANDE - Floor coverings–carpet and rugs - Whitecrest Carpet Mills
LEGS - Hardware - Rawlplug Co., Inc.
LEGS - Recording label - Legs Label Records
LEGS ALIVE - Health care products - Fiske Industries Inc.
LEGS OF STEEL - Publisher's imprints - Maier Group Inc.
LEGSEAL U - Sealing compounds - Walter G. Legge Co., Inc.
LEGSOLVE - Degreasing solvents - Walter G. Legge Co., Inc.
LEGSTAT - Electrical equipment - Walter G. Legge Co., Inc.
LEGSTRIP - Cleaning preparations - Walter G. Legge Co., Inc.
LEGSURE - Cleaning preparations - Walter G. Legge Co., Inc.
LEGUMASE - Vitamins and nutritional supplements - Body Mechanics, Inc.
LEGUMINANTE - Fertilizers - Alquimia Laboratories, Inc.
LEGUMOR - Food products - Newmarket
LEGUMORE DRIED GREEN BEANS - Food products ☆ - Europa Foods Ltd.
LEHIGH - Artists' materials ☆ - Hunt Manufacturing Co.
LEHIGH - Floor coverings–carpet and rugs - Karastan-Bigelow Inc.
LEHIGH - Footwear - Lehigh Safety Shoe Co.
LEHIGH - Gasoline - Lehigh Oil Co.
LEHIGH - Gasoline ☆ - Lehigh Portland Cement Co.
LEHIGH - Office furniture–wood - Joyce International Inc.
LEHIGH - Ophthalmic goods - Foremost Optical Products
LEHIGH - Twine - Lehigh Cordage
LEHIGH 100 - Footwear - Lehigh Safety Shoe Co.
LEHIGH-LEOPOLD - Office furniture–wood - Joyce International Inc.
LEHIGH LOO - Footwear - Lehigh Safety Shoe Co.
LEHIGH PORTLAND - Cement - Lehigh Portland Cement Co.
LEHIGH VALLEY - Food products - Lehigh Valley Dairies Inc.
LEHIGH VALLEY FARMS - Milk - Rosenbergers Dairies Inc.
LEHITEX - Thread - Perfect Thread Co. Inc.
LEHMAN - Food products - Castle Food Products
LEHMANN - Lathes - Lehmann Lathe Parts, Inc.
LEHMANN FARMS - Fruits–pickled or brined - Lehmann Farms, Inc.
LEHNARTZ - Giftware - Q.E.D. Industries
LEHNING - Health care products - Enzymatic Therapy, Inc.
LEHR - Beverages ☆ - C. & J. Willenborg Inc.
LEHTI - Bedding–linen - Dan River Inc.
LEI MAN, THE - Flowers, plants, and seeds - Steven F. Latour
LEIBERMAN - Ceramic tile ☆ - Integrity Tile Co.
LEIBNIZ - Cookies - Bahlsen Inc.
LEICA - Electronic equipment - Leica USA Inc.
LEICA - Salmon–smoked, salted, dried, or pickled ☆ - De Choix Specialty Foods Co.
LEICESTER - Scotch whiskey ☆ - Charles Jacquin et Compagnie Inc.
LEICHTE WAHL - Cigars - Gesty Trading & Manufacturing Corp.
LEIDEN LANE - Floor coverings–carpet and rugs - Masland Corp.
LEIDENHEIMER BAKING CO. - Bakeries - Leidenheimer Baking Co.
LEIF - Ophthalmic goods ☆ - Luxottica
LEIFHEIT - Housewares - SCI Scandicrafts Inc.
LEIGH - Ventilation equipment - Leigh
LEIGH BATH PAK - Bathroom fixtures - Leigh
LEIGH MORGAN - Candy - Tomeyko Corp.
LEIGH STEVENS - Xylophones - Marimba Productions Inc.
LEIGHT - Plugs–ear - Howard Leight Industries
LEIGHTON - Hair care products ☆ - Framesi USA/Roffler Industries Inc.
LEIGHTON - Ophthalmic goods - Styl-Rite Optical Manufacturing Co., Inc.
LEIGHTON - Umbrellas - Futai, Inc. (USA)
LEIGHTON - Wallpaper - Seabrook Wallcoverings, Inc.
LEIGHTON'S - Honey - Leighton's Honey Inc.
LEIKA - Iced tea–bottled or canned ☆ - Chase Collection, Inc.
LEIKRA - Flowers, plants, and seeds - Jacklin Seed
LEILANI - Apparel and accessories - Raisin Co., Inc.
LEILANI - Food products - Aloha Produce Corp.
LEILANI - Furniture ☆ - Tropitone Furniture Co. Inc.
LEILANI - Rum - House of Seagram
LEILANI JONES - Bathing suits - Raisin Co., Inc.
LEILA'S VEGI-PIES - Food products - Leila's All Natural Foods
LEILEI - Apparel and accessories - Bright Range Inc.
LEINENKUGEL - Beverages–malt - Jacob Leinenkugel Brewing Co., Inc.
LEINENKUGEL AUTUMN GOLD - Beverages–malt - Jacob Leinenkugel Brewing Co., Inc.
LEINENKUGEL BOCK - Beverages–malt - Jacob Leinenkugel Brewing Co., Inc.
LEINENKUGEL LIGHT - Beverages–malt - Jacob Leinenkugel Brewing Co., Inc.

☆ = Now out of production

LEINENKUGEL LIMITED - Beverages—malt - Jacob Leinenkugel Brewing Co., Inc.

LEINENKUGEL PREMIUM - Beverages—malt - Jacob Leinenkugel Brewing Co., Inc.

LEINENKUGEL'S AUBURN ALE - Beverages—malt - Jacob Leinenkugel Brewing Co., Inc.

LEINENKUGEL'S BIG BUTT DOPPLEBOCK - Beverages—malt - Jacob Leinenkugel Brewing Co., Inc.

LEINENKUGEL'S HONEY WEISS - Beverages—malt - Jacob Leinenkugel Brewing Co., Inc.

LEINENKUGEL'S NORTHWOODS LAGER - Beverages—malt - Jacob Leinenkugel Brewing Co., Inc.

LEINENKUGEL'S RED - Beer - Miller Brewing Co.

LEINENKUGEL'S RED LAGER - Beverages—malt - Jacob Leinenkugel Brewing Co., Inc.

LEINENKUGEL'S WINTER LAGER - Beverages—malt - Jacob Leinenkugel Brewing Co., Inc.

LEINEWEBER - Motor vehicle parts and accessories - Rivera Engineering, Inc.

LEINIE'S RED LAGER - Beverages—malt - Jacob Leinenkugel Brewing Co., Inc.

LEISUALS - Shoes - Genesco Inc.

LEISURAMA - Eyeglasses - Art-Craft Optical Co.

LEISURAMICS - Figurines - Gare Inc.

LEISURE - Boats—pontoons ☆ - Forester Boats Inc.

LEISURE - Chairs—upholstered - Franklin Corp.

LEISURE - Cutlery - Carvel Hall Inc.

LEISURE - Floor coverings—carpet and rugs - Southern Carpet Mills

LEISURE - Furniture ☆ - Birmingham Stove & Range Co.

LEISURE - Lanterns—kerosene - Coleman Co., Inc.

LEISURE - Publisher's imprints - Dorchester Publishing Co., Inc.

LEISURE ARTS - Hobby kits - Leisure Arts, Inc.

LEISURE ARTS PUBLICATIONS - Publisher's imprints - Leisure Arts, Inc.

LEISURE BED REST - Cushions - Better Sleep, Inc.

LEISURE CANTEEN - Containers - Five Star Plastics Inc.

LEISURE CART - Golfing equipment - Apple Sports, Inc.

LEISURE CAT - Footwear—athletic - Puma Inc.

LEISURE CRAFT - Boats—houseboats ☆ - Cron Houseboats

LEISURE GUARD - Footwear - Ambassador Shoe Corp.

LEISURE ISLAND - Boats—pontoons ☆ - Forester Boats Inc.

LEISURE LADY - Cosmetics - D-Orum Corp.

LEISURE LIFE - Paints - Devoe Paint Co.

LEISURE LIFT - Medical apparatus - Leisure Lift, Inc.

LEISURE LIVING - Enamels - North Jersey Paint Co. Inc.

LEISURE LOUNGE - Furniture - Bean Station Furniture Factory Inc.

LEISURE LOUNGERS - Footwear - Middletown Footwear Inc.

LEISURE LOVINS - Apparel and accessories - Deena Inc.

LEISURE MATE - Motor vehicle parts and accessories ☆ - Peterson Manufacturing Co.

LEISURE MATES - Fabrics - Guilford Mills, Inc.

LEISURE MATES - Footwear - Mike Mennies & Son Inc.

LEISURE MATT - Mattresses - Span-America Medical Systems, Inc.

LEISURE MOMENTS - Cleaning preparations—household ☆ - Franklin International, Inc.

LEISURE-O - Seafood products—fresh or frozen - Stein Food Co.

LEISURE-PEDIC - Beds—hospital - Sci-O-Tech Inc.

LEISURE POWER - Batteries - Power Battery Co.

LEISURE STEP - Shoes - Genesco Inc.

LEISURE SUIT LARRY - Computer software - Sierra On-Line, Inc.

LEISURE TIME - Floor coverings—carpet and rugs ☆ - World Carpets, Inc.

LEISURE TIME - Games - Avalon Hill Game Co.

LEISURE TIME - Optical scanners—computer - Titmus Optical, Inc.

LEISURE TIME - Paints - Royal Lustre Brands

LEISURE TIME - Tablecloths - Ullman Co. Inc.

LEISURE TIME - Water—bottled or canned - Leisure Time Spring Water

LEISURE TIME - Water—mineral - Mountain Valley Spring Co.

LEISURE TOUR - Bicycles - Murray, Inc.

LEISURE VAC - Vacuum cleaners and accessories ☆ - The Eureka Co.

LEISURE WARE - Luggage - Airway Industries, Inc.

LEISURECLAY - Artists' materials - Leisurecrafts

LEISURECRAFTS - Artists' materials - Leisurecrafts

LEISUREFORM - Prosthetic apparatus - Coloplast Corp.

LEISURELY - Floor coverings—carpet and rugs - Cabin Crafts Carpets

LEISUREPASTE - Glue—household or industrial - Leisurecrafts

LEISUREST - Furniture—upholstered - Imperial Leather Furniture Co.

LEISURETONE - Paints—artists' - Leisurecrafts

LEISURETYME - Hobby kits - Yaley Enterprises

LEISUREWARE - Flatware ☆ - Towle Silversmiths

LEIT-LINK - Irrigation equipment - Solatrol, Inc.

LEITER LITES - Lighting fixtures - Elias J. Leiter Co.

LEITZ - Surveying machinery ☆ - Sokkia Corp.

LEJABY - Underwear and nightwear ☆ - M.A. Rabinowitz Corp.

LEJAY-LAGOUTE - Wines - Paterno Imports, Ltd.

LEJON - Boots ☆ - Regina Imports

LEJON - Wines ☆ - The Beverage Source Inc.

LEJOS - Sandals ☆ - Playazul International Inc.

LEK RECIRCULATOR - Boats—fishing - Lek Manufacturing Co.

LEKI - Sporting goods - Omni International Distributors Inc.

LEKO - Lighting equipment - Strand Lighting Inc.

LEKOTEK - Video tapes - National Lekotek Center

LEKTRA - Photographic equipment - Lektra Service Corp.

LEKTRA-FILM-KARD - Carding and combing machines ☆ - Kardex Systems, Inc.

LEKTRA-LOK - Alarm systems—burglar - Amid A. Yousef

LEKTRA SUS-TENSION - Photographic equipment - Lektra Service Corp.

LEKTRAPRO - Paint sprayers ☆ - Speeflo Manufacturing Corp.

LEKTRIEVER - Carding and combing machines - Kardex Systems, Inc.

LEKTRO - Shaving preparations - Remington Products Co.

LEKTRO-COAT - Epoxy ☆ - William Hodges & Co.

LEKTRO SET - Hair care products - Gillette Co.

LEKTRO-TUNER - Musical instrument accessories ☆ - United Musical Instruments USA Inc.

LEKTRO-VEND - Vending machines - Polyvend Inc.

LEKTROCOTE - Lighting fixtures - Hubbell Lighting, Inc. (Lighting Div.)

LEKTROMESH - Wire products ☆ - Jelliff Corp.

LEKTRON - Electronic equipment - Paso Sound Products Inc.

LEKTRUGLAS - Glassware—household - Chattanooga Glass Co.

LELAND FARADAY - Machine part - Brownell Electro Inc.

LELE - Brassieres (Bras) - Bra-Tique Fashions Inc.

+L'ELYSEE - Skin care products - Cold Wax Co.

LEM - Electronics equipment - Synsor Corp.

LEM - Finishing agents - Daly's Inc.

LEM - Food products - Serv-Agen Corp.

LEM - Lighting fixtures - Swivelier Co. Inc.

LEM - Postcards - Fotofolio Inc.

LEM AND MEL - Candy - Just Born Inc.

LEM-ME - Dishwashing compounds ☆ - Swiss-Tex Inc.

LEM-O-OIL - Furniture polish and wax - James B. Day and Co.

LEM/S - Vitamins and nutritional supplements - Bioherb Inc.

LEMAIRE - Musical instruments ☆ - King Musical Instruments

LEMALL - Food products - H.C. Brill Co., Inc.

LEMANN R - Watches - Ridco Inc.

LEMANS - Bathtubs—enameled ☆ - Lyons Industries Inc.

LEMAN'S - Candy - Wm. Leman Inc.

LEMANS - Food products ☆ - VIP Sales Co. Inc.

LEMANS - Furniture - CTH/Sherrill Occasional

LEMANS - Furniture ☆ - Lane Co. Inc.

LEMANS - Tires - Bridgestone/Firestone, Inc.

LEMANS - Toy cars - Intex Recreation Corp.

LEMANS II - Floor coverings—carpet and rugs ☆ - Prestige Mills Inc.

LE'MAN'S, THE - Apparel—men's - Wide Pacific Development, Inc.

LEMBEY - Wines ☆ - Domecq Importers Inc.

LEMBO VINEYARDS - Wines - Lembo Vineyards

LEMBRUSCHINI - Wines - Lembo Vineyards

LEMCO - Glass—window - Croft Metals Inc.

LEME FRERES - Wines - Wine Imports Ltd.

LE'MEMO - Photo albums - Pioneer Photo Albums, Inc.

LEMI - Golfing equipment - Lemi Golf Inc.

LEMIEUX - Apparel and accessories - Shekar Agrawal

LEMISERP - Tranquilizers ☆ - Lemmon Co.

LEMIT - Furniture polish and wax - National Chemsearch Corp.

LEMIVITE M - Pharmaceutical preparations ☆ - Lemmon Co.

LEMIX - Syrup - HCH Corp.

LEMMA - Games - Kadon Enterprises Inc.

LEMMINGS - Computer software - Sirius Software Development Inc.

LEMMON - Candy ☆ - Van Melle Inc.

LEMMY - Food products ☆ - A.J. Lehman Co.

LEM'N-LIME LIGHT - Beverages—carbonated ☆ - American 76 Co.

LEM'N SAVORY - Food products - Cherchies Ltd.

LEMO-MINT - Hair coloring preparations - Stylors Inc.

LEMODA - Sweaters - Gillman Knitwear Co.

LEMON - Floor coverings—carpet and rugs ☆ - Regal Rugs Inc.

LEMON-AID - Cosmetics - Benefit Cosmetics

☆ = Now out of production

LEMON AID - Scouring pads - Arden Corp.
LEMON ALIVE - Beverages–carbonated ☆ - Snapple Beverage Corp.
LEMON & LIME - Christmas tree ornaments - Cracker Box Inc.
LEMON APPEAL - Teas - General Nutrition Inc.
LEMON BERRY INTUITION - Juices - Coca-Cola Co.
LEMON BLOSSOM - Dishes–china - Taylor, Smith & Taylor Co.
LEMON BUDS - Candy - Wilson Candy Co.
LEMON BURST - Deodorizers - Analab Inc.
LEMON CHILL - Beverages - Moore Enterprises, Inc.
LEMON CLEAN - Cleaning preparations - White Cap Inc.
LEMON COOLERS - Cookies - Sunshine Biscuits, Inc.
LEMON DEW - Tea - Boston Tea Co.
LEMON DILL GOURMET - Spices and extracts - Finest Kind Spices
LEMON DROP - Deodorizers - Mcauley's, Inc.
LEMON DROP - Dolls - Russ Berrie and Co., Inc.
LEMON DROP KIDS - Stationery ☆ - Lemon Tree Stationery Corp.
LEMON DROPS - Candy - Brach and Brock Confections Inc.
LEMON FLAKE - Candy - Pecan Deluxe Candy Co.
LEMON FREEZ'R - Frozen foods - American Dairy Queen Corp.
LEMON FROST - Frozen foods - Gary L. Jones
LEMON GRAHAM MINI-BITES - Cereal - New Morn, Inc.
LEMON GRILL - Food products - Lightlife Foods, Inc.
LEMON HART - Beverages–alcohol - Hiram Walker & Sons, Inc.
LEMON HEAD - Candy - Ferrara Pan Candy Co., Inc.
LEMON ICE - Christmas tree ornaments - Cracker Box Inc.
LEMON JAZZ - Spices and extracts - Stache Foods
LEMON JUNIORS - Cakes - Tastykake Inc.
LEMON KIST - Cleaning preparations - Cello Chemical Co.
LEMON KLEEN 32 - Disinfectants - Harley Chemicals
LEMON LIFT - Teas - R.C. Bigelow, Inc.
LEMON LIME BLITZER - Beverages–carbonated - Jel Sert Co.
LEMON LIME SPLASH - Herb tea - Celestial Seasonings, Inc.
LEMON LOGS - Candy ☆ - American Candy Co.
LEMON-MAID - Deodorizers - Orange-Mate, Inc.
LEMON-MATE - Deodorizers - Orange-Mate, Inc.
LEMON MINT - Teas–herbal - San Francisco Herb & Natural Food Co.
LEMON MIST - Teas–herbal - Celestial Seasonings, Inc.
LEMON 'N HERB - Seasonings - McCormick & Co., Inc.
LEMON OHS! - Cookies - Austin Quality Foods, Inc.
LEMON OIL - Furniture polish and wax - Holloway House, Inc.
LEMON OIL POLISH - Polishing rouge - Analab Inc.
LEMON OIL SPRAY - Furniture polish and wax - Holloway House, Inc.
LEMON PEAR - Fruit butters - Sarabeth's Kitchen
LEMON PEEL - Paint removers - Fiberlock Technologies, Inc.
LEMON PEELER - Bicycles - Schwinn Cycling & Fitness Inc.
LEMON PEPPER DEE-LICIOUS SEASONING - Spices and extracts - Modern Products, Inc.
LEMON POWER - Cleaning preparations–household - Blue Cross Laboratories Inc.
LEMON PREP - Juices - Crystals International Inc.
LEMON-QUAT - Disinfectants - Uncle Sam Chemical Co., Inc.
LEMON QUENCH - Beverages–carbonated - Monarch Co., Inc.
LEMON RIND - Christmas tree ornaments - Cracker Box Inc.
LEMON RINGS - Cookies ☆ - Sunshine Biscuits, Inc.
LEMON SAVORY GOURMET - Spices and extracts - Finest Kind Spices
LEMON-SOL - Cleaning preparations–household ☆ - Clorox Co.
LEMON SOOTHE LOVE MITT - Health care products - Elizabeth Van Buren Aromatherapy
LEMON SOOTHER - Teas - Lipton Investments, Inc.
LEMON SOUR - Candy - Nabisco Foods Group
LEMON SOURS - Candy - Judson-Atkinson Candies
LEMON SQUASH - Cookies - Sunshine/Salerno Inc.
LEMON STIX - Candy - Leaf, Inc.
LEMON TEASE - Spices and extracts - Stache Foods
LEMON TREE - Lemonade - Lipton Investments, Inc.
LEMON TWIST - Apparel and accessories - D. Stone Industries, Inc.
LEMON TWIST - Beverages - Smoothie King Franchises, Inc.
LEMON TYME - Skin care products - Rex Research Laboratories
LEMON UP - Shampoos - Gillette Co.
LEMON UPS - Cookies ☆ - Nanak's Gourmet Cookies
LEMON VERBENA - Sachets - Andre Richard
LEMON VIRGINIA - Tobacco–chewing or smoking - G.A. Georgopulo & Co. Inc.
LEMON WHIP - Candy ☆ - Brock Candy Co. Inc.
LEMON-X - Beverages–alcohol - Lemon-X Corp.
LEMON ZINGER - Teas–herbal - Celestial Seasonings, Inc.

LEMONADA - Deodorants–personal - Surco Products Inc.
LEMONADE - Christmas tree ornaments - Cracker Box Inc.
LEMONADE CHILLERS - Beverages - McSteven's
LEMONADE CRUISIN' COOL - Ice cream - Royale International
LEMONADE LOVE & HOPE - Water–bottled or canned - Coca-Cola Co.
LEMONAISE - Mayonnaise - Ojai Cook
LEMONATED, A - Liqueurs - Mango Bottling, Inc.
LEMONCARE - Soap - Cococare Products Inc.
LEMONDROP - Dinnerware–glass ☆ - Nikko Ceramics Inc.
LEMONEE 8 - Disinfectants - Harley Chemicals
LEMONETTE - Beverages–carbonated - Grapette International
LEMONEX - Cosmetics - La Femme Cosmetics Inc.
LEMONHEAD - Fruit drinks–bottled or canned - Ferrara Pan Candy Co., Inc.
LEMONIADA - Beverages–carbonated - United World Imports, Inc.
LEMONICCI - Frozen foods - Flichia Wholesale Distributing
LEMONSTONE - Recording label ☆ - Music for Little People
LEMONY - Apparel and accessories - Munico International Corp.
LEMONYU - Lemonade - Green Foods
LEMPIRA - Cigars - Tropical Tobacco, Inc.
LEMURIAN - Bicycles - Skyway Recreation Products
LEN-AQUA - Finishing agents - Lenmar Inc.
LEN-FAST III - Wallpaper - Norwall Wallcoverings
LEN-TEX III - Wallpaper - Norwall Wallcoverings
LEN-VAR - Finishing agents - Lenmar Inc.
LENA LIU - Figurines - Lena Liu
LENAPE - Bathroom accessories - Lenape Products Co., Inc.
LENAPE - Bathroom fixtures - New Jersey Porcelain Co.
LENA'S - Pizzas–frozen - Imo's Franchising, Inc.
LENATE - Pharmaceutical preparations - Maurry Biological Co. Inc.
LENATE CHIEF - Boats–canoes - Wm. Kaier Fiberglass Products Inc.
LENBRO - Cookies - Sunshine/Salerno Inc.
LENCH MOB - Apparel and accessories - Lench Mob Productions, Inc.
LENCH MOB RECORDS - Recording label - Lench Mob Productions, Inc.
LENCIA - Giftware - Thoma Imports
LENDER'S - Bagels - Lender's Bagel Bakery
LENDER'S BAGELETTES - Bagels - Lender's Bagel Bakery
LENDER'S NEW YORK STYLE - Bagels - Kraft Food Ingredients Corp.
LENDYS - Skin care products - Lendan USA Co.
LENEE - Bathing suits - Apparel America, Inc.
LENEX - Doors–metal - Dunbarton Corp.
LENITE - Floor waxes - L.D. Sterns Corp.
LENK - Tools - Wall Lenk Corp.
LENKERBROOK - Milk - Wengerts Dairy Inc.
LENKO-FLEK - Finishing agents - Lenmar Inc.
LENMAR - Photographic equipment - Lenmar Enterprises, Inc.
LENNON - Wallpaper - Norwall Wallcoverings
LENNOX - Floor coverings–carpet and rugs - Cumberland Mills Inc.
LENNOX - Furniture - Bean Station Furniture Factory Inc.
LENNOX - Heat pumps - Lennox Industries Inc.
LENNOX - Lighting fixtures ☆ - Liteway
LENNOX HILL - Floor coverings–carpet and rugs ☆ - Atlas Carpet Mills Inc.
LENNY - Ophthalmic goods - Rozin Optical Export Corp.
LENNY - Toys–stuffed ☆ - Russ Berrie and Co., Inc.
LENNY & LARRY'S - Bakery products - Lenny & Larry's
LENNY LIZZARD - Candy - Robert W. Lackey Corp.
LENNY LIZZARD LOLLIPOPS - Candy - R.L. Products Corp.
LENO - Musical instruments - Breezy Ridge Instruments
LENO-WEB - Fabrics - Veratec
LENOIR - Paints ☆ - Valspar Corp.
LENOIR - Wines - Val Verde Winery
LENOIR LOIRE - Wines - Leonard Kreusch Inc.
LENOLEX - Health care products ☆ - Halsey Drug Co. Inc.
LENORA'S - Jewelry–costume - Lenora's
LENOX - Apparel–athletic - Leonx, Inc.
LENOX - Artists' materials - Andrews/Nelson/Whitehead
LENOX - Artists' materials - Solo-Horton Brush Co.
LENOX - Bicycles - Columbia Manufacturing Inc.
LENOX - Candles ☆ - Carolina Designs Ltd.
LENOX - Enamels - Finnaren & Haley Inc.
LENOX - Globes - Replogle Globes Inc.
LENOX - Health care products - Melard Manufacturing Corp.
LENOX - Paints ☆ - Budeke's Paint
LENOX - Paper–lithograph - ANW-Crestwood Paper Co.
LENOX - Saw blades - American Saw & Manufacturing Co.
LENOX - Tableware–china - Lenox, Inc.
LENOX - Wallpaper - Koroseal Wallcoverings

☆ = Now out of production

LENOX - Watchbands–precious metal - Admiral Watchband Co. Inc.

LENOX - Watches - Bulova Corp.

LENOX CLASSIC MODERN - Tableware–china ☆ - Lenox, Inc.

LENOX CLOCK COLLECTION - Giftware - Lenox, Inc.

LENOX COURT - Floor coverings–carpet and rugs ☆ - Whitecrest Carpet Mills

LENOX CUISINE - Tableware–china ☆ - Lenox, Inc.

LENOX DIY MASTER - Saw blades - American Saw & Manufacturing Co.

LENOX DIY MASTER II - Saw blades - American Saw & Manufacturing Co.

LENOX DIY MASTER III - Saw blades - American Saw & Manufacturing Co.

LENOX FARMS - Bacon - Food Giant Inc.

LENOX FURN-MASTER - Saw blades - American Saw & Manufacturing Co.

LENOX GRADE - Office supplies - Esselte Corp.

LENOX HERITAGE - Tableware–china ☆ - Lenox, Inc.

LENOX HILL - Braces–orthopedic - Dobi-Simplex, Inc.

LENOX LEADER - Drill bits - American Saw & Manufacturing Co.

LENOX LEGEND - Tableware–china ☆ - Lenox, Inc.

LENOX LX - Hand tools and blades ☆ - American Saw & Manufacturing Co.

LENOX MASTERPIECE - Tableware–china ☆ - Lenox, Inc.

LENOX PLACE - Floor coverings–carpet and rugs - Gulistan Carpet Inc.

LENOX PORTRAIT GALLERY - Frames–picture - Lenox, Inc.

LENOX ROSE - Tableware–china ☆ - Lenox, Inc.

LENOX RX - Saw blades - American Saw & Manufacturing Co.

LENOX SQUARE - Cabinets - Wellborn Forest Products Inc.

LENOX SQUARE - Floor coverings ☆ - Tarkett, Inc.

LENOX SQUARE - Floor coverings–carpet and rugs - Mohawk Industries Inc.

LENOX SQUARE - Floor coverings–carpet and rugs - Monticello Carpet Mills

LENOX SQUARE II - Furniture ☆ - Singer Furniture Co.

LENOX TRADITION - Tableware–china ☆ - Lenox, Inc.

LENOXYL - Pharmaceutical preparations ☆ - Jones Medical Industries, Inc. (Medical Div.)

LENOY - Glassware ☆ - Israeli Accents

LENS - Beauty shop equipment - Lensco Products

LEN'S - Fruit drinks–bottled or canned - Len's Brokerage Inc.

LENS CATCHER - Drain screen - Amcon Laboratories, Inc.

LENS CLEANING CLOTHS - Ophthalmic goods - Karlen Manufacturing, Inc.

LENS-CLEAR - Chemicals–photographic - Merix Chemical Co.

LENS CLEAR - Lenses - G-96 Products Co. Inc.

LENS CLEAR - Ophthalmic goods ☆ - Allergan, Inc.

LENS END - Video production - Nalpak Video Sales, Inc.

LENS EZE - Contact lenses - Amcon Laboratories, Inc.

LENS FRESH - Ophthalmic goods ☆ - Allergan, Inc.

LENS FRIENDS - Lenses - Neville's Inc.

LENS LUBRICANT - Ophthalmic goods - Blairex Laboratories, Inc.

LENS MATE - Ophthalmic goods ☆ - Alcon Laboratories, Inc.

LENS PLUS - Ophthalmic goods - Allergan, Inc.

LENS RINS - Pharmaceutical preparations - Smithkline Beecham Corp.

LENS SERT - Ophthalmic goods - Apex Medical Corp.

LENS SERT - Ophthalmic goods - Karlen Manufacturing, Inc.

LENS-WET - Ophthalmic goods ☆ - Allergan, Inc.

LEN'S WIPES - Ophthalmic goods - Karlen Manufacturing, Inc.

LENSCOPE - Lenses–photographic - SP Systems/Saratons

LENSCOPE - Magnifiers - Bausch & Lomb Inc.

LENSCRAFTERS - Optical services - United States Shoe Corp.

LENSCREEN - Projection screens ☆ - Da-Lite Screen Co. Inc.

LENSEN - Pharmaceutical preparations - Armenpharm Ltd.

LENSET - Lenses–photographic - Sima Products Corp.

LENSFLEX - Cameras ☆ - Philips Communication & Security Systems Inc.

LENSGEN - Machinery - Aerotech, Inc.

LENSGUARD - Cases–eyeglass - Bausch & Lomb Inc.

LENSI - Pasta - Gourmet America

LENSINE 5 - Contact-lens solution - CooperVision Inc.

LENSKEEPER - Ophthalmic goods ☆ - Allergan, Inc.

LENSKLEEN - Cleaning preparations ☆ - Da-Lite Screen Co. Inc.

LENSLUX - Lighting fixtures - Edison Price Lighting

LENSMASTER - Computer software - Lighting Sciences Inc.

LENSON - Coffee - Maple Leaf Foods Inc.

LENSRINS - Ophthalmic goods ☆ - Allergan, Inc.

LENSTAG ACTIVE ID - Identification tags - Ecomark Inc.

LENSTAR - Apparel and accessories - Linstar Entertainment Enterprises, Inc.

LENSXTENDER - Lenses–photographic - SP Systems/Saratons

LENTE - Pharmaceutical preparations - Bristol-Myers Squibb Co.

LENTINA - Window coverings - Glare-Con Inc.

LENTINUS - Vitamins and nutritional supplements - Bioherb Inc.

LENTO STRIPE - Bedding–linen - Dan River Inc.

+L'ENVIE - Shampoos - S.C. Johnson & Son, Inc.

+L'ENVOI - Paper–bond - Parsons Paper Co.

LENWELLS - Insecticides ☆ - Cenol Co. Inc.

LENZ - Giftware - Sasaki

LENZ-CLENZ - Cleaning preparations - Lami Products, Inc.

LENZ VINEYARDS - Wines - Lenz Wineries

LENZFX - Computer software - Digimation, Inc.

LENZO - Eyeglasses ☆ - Lensco Products

LEO - Floor coverings–carpet and rugs - Hartford Carpet Mills

LEO - Glassware–household ☆ - Lotus Glass Co.

LEO - Lighting fixtures - Benjamin Electric Manufacturing Co.

LEO - Perfumes - Advertising to Women, Inc.

LEO - Recording label - American Academy of Ophthalmology, Inc.

LEO - Recording label - Jazz Composer's Orchestra Association Inc.

LEO - Teas–herbal - Calvin Thornton

LEO III - Electronic letter/parcel weighing system ☆ - Better Packages

LEO JR. - Toys ☆ - Princess Soft Toys

LEO LISKER - Jewelry–precious - Leo Lisker

LEO THE LION - Toys - MGM Records Inc.

LEO THE LION, KING OF THE JUNGLE - Video production - Front Row Entertainment, Inc.

LEO9 - Shampoos - John Odam

LEOCREME - Skin care products - Leo Products Co.

LEODA DE MAR - Wallpaper - Capital Carousel Inc.

LEOETTES - Footwear–athletic ☆ - Leo's Dancewear, Inc.

LEOINA - Sporting goods ☆ - Babolat

LEON AUBERT - Musical instruments - Entertainment Music Marketing Corp.

LEON BUCHHEIT - Cosmetics - Leon J.A. Buchheit Inc.

LEON CIGARS - Cigars - Black Rose Tobacco Co.

LEON ISRAEL DESIGNS - Religious jewelry - Israeli Accents

LEON LEVIN - Apparel and accessories - Leon Levin Sons, Inc.

LEON MILLOT - Wines - Ziem Vineyards

LEON NEON - Toys - Mattel, Inc.

LEONARD - Beverages–carbonated - Leonard Fountain Specialty

LEONARD - Dinnerware–glass ☆ - WMF/USA

LEONARD - Flatware ☆ - Towle Silversmiths

LEONARD - Kitchen appliances - Leonard International

LEONARD - Stoves - White Consolidated Industries, Inc.

LEONARD - Sunglasses - L'Amy Inc.

LEONARD - Toys–stuffed - Dakin Inc.

LEONARD +BERNSTEIN - Housewares - Jalni Publications Inc.

LEONARD DE SAINT-ALBAN - Wines - Parliament Import Co.

LEONARD DE ST. AUBIN - Wines - Parliament Import Co.

LEONARD FISHER FOR SIGNATURE GROUP - Wallpaper - Signature Wallcoverings

LEONARD KREUSCH - Wines - Leonard Kreusch, Inc.

LEONARD KREUSCH - Wines - Leonard Kreusch Inc.

LEONARD LOGSDAIL - Apparel and accessories - Burstow & Logsdail Ltd.

LEONARD MACY - Men's apparel - Interco Inc.

LEONARD OF PARIS - Fabrics - Leimtex Corp.

LEONARD PARDON'S FAUX FINISH - Paints - Oakart USA, Inc.

LEONARD PARIS - Scarves - Jerry Kohn Inc.

LEONARD STEVEN - Apparel–women's - Eber International

LEONARDA - Recording label ☆ - Leonarda Productions Inc.

LEONARDINI - Wines - Leonard Kreusch, Inc.

LEONARDINI - Wines - Leonard Kreusch Inc.

LEONARDO - Ceramic tile ☆ - Interceramic Inc.

LEONARDO! - Furniture - Hal Sandy

LEONARDO - Neckties - Spiegel, Inc.

LEONARDO - Paints–artists' - Da Vinci Paint Co. Inc.

LEONARDO - Tiles–ceramic - Maxsam Sales, Inc.

LEONARDO - Toys - Playmates World Wide Inc.

LEONARDO - Wigs - Chicago Hair Good Inc.

LEONARDO CLAY - Plastalene ☆ - Unnatural Resources Inc.

LEONARDO DA DOODLE - Paper - Riverside Paper Corp.

LEONARDO DA VINCI - Wines - House of Burgundy Inc.

LEONARDO DAVINCI - Artists' materials ☆ - M. Grumbacher Inc.

LEONARDO DA'VINCI FLYING MACHINES - Paper - Carlisle Corp.

LEONARDO LION - Toys–stuffed - Dakin Inc.

LEONARD'S - Fruits–dried ☆ - John Leonard

LEONE PRIDE - Food products - N. Leone and Sons Inc.

LEONETTI CELLAR - Wines - Leonetti Cellar

LEONG LEONG DESIGN - Frames–picture - Terence Leong

LEONHARDT'S - Candy - Leonhardt Inc.

LEONIA - Floor coverings - Mannington Resilient Floors

LEONIDA - Musical instrument accessories - Impecco, Ltd.

LEONIDAS - Watches - Tag-Heuer Time & Electronics Corp.

LEONORE DOSKOW PORTRAITS - Jewelry ☆ - Leonore Doskow Inc.

☆ = Now out of production

LEON'S - Food products - Leon's Fine Foods Inc.
LEOPALACE - Sportswear - MDI Guam Corp.
LEOPARD - Computer hardware - Alaris, Inc.
LEOPARD - Floor coverings—carpet and rugs - Langhorne Carpet Co. Inc.
LEOPARD - Rice - Connell Co.
LEOPARD - Thread - Threads USA Div.
LEOPARD - Washing machine parts - M.A. Bruder & Sons Inc.
LEOPARD SPOTS - Dragees ☆ - Chipurnoi Inc.
LEOPILLS - Pharmaceutical preparations - Leo Products Co.
LEOPOLD - Office furniture—wood - Joyce International Inc.
LEOPOLD - Toys—stuffed ☆ - Edumundo Productions, Inc.
LEOPOLD LEOPARD - Toys—stuffed - Russ Berrie and Co., Inc.
LEORA - Watches ☆ - Helbros International
LEO'S - Footwear—athletic - Leo's Dancewear, Inc.
LEO'S CELLAR - Wines - Rutherford Vintners Inc.
LEO'S FAMOUS GREEK SALAD DRESSING - Salad dressings—bottled - P & L Food Wholesalers, Inc.
LEO'S +'LECTRIC PAINTBRUSH - Computer software - Dunamis Inc.
LEO'S LINKS - Computer software - Dunamis Inc.
LEOSCAN - Computer peripheral equipment - Ficus Systems, Inc.
LEOTARD MATE - Cleaning preparations - Kleen Chemical Manufacturing Co.
LEPAGE - Tape—adhesive - Lepage's, Inc.
LEPAGE NEW YORK - Furniture, mirrors, and picture frames - Le Page New York, Inc.
LEPANIER - Furniture - Intelligent Playtime Corp.
LEPATCH - Pharmaceutical preparations - Transdermal Products, Inc.
+L'EPAYRIE - Wines - Bercut-Vandervoort & Co.
LEPEL - Electrical equipment - Lepel Corp.
LEPELA - Bags—canvas - Janet K. Ledford
LEPER'S CARMELED - Popcorn - Noble Distributors, Inc.
LEPIETRE - Tiles—ceramic - American Marazzi Tile, Inc.
LEPINOX G - Insecticides - Ecogen Inc.
LEPINOX WDG - Insecticides - Ecogen Inc.
LEPOPKORN - Confections ☆ - Nut Kettle East Inc.
LEPRECHAUN - Motor vehicles—motor homes - Coachmen Industries, Inc.
LEPRECHAUN - Recording label - MSK Productions Inc.
LEPRECHAUN - Skin care products - Nuco Inc.
LEPRECHAUN - Toys—models ☆ - Estes Industries
LEPRECON - Electronic equipment - CAE Inc.
LEPRINTEMPS - Cosmetics ☆ - Elysee Scientific Cosmetic Co.
LEPTOFERM - Veterinary pharmaceutical preparations - SmithKline Beecham Animal Health Products
LEPTYNE - Paints - PPG Industries, Inc.
LERACCE - Tiles—ceramic - American Marazzi Tile, Inc.
LERBAXIN - Pharmaceutical preparations ☆ - Legere Pharmaceuticals Inc.
LERC - Cables - Sine Companies, Inc.
LERD - Cables - Sine Companies, Inc.
LERIDA - Olive oil - Smith, Davidovac, Fierberg and Associates, Inc.
+L'ERMITAGE - Hair care products - Ashkenazy Property Management Corp.
LERNA - Dolls - Mattel, Inc.
LERNER PUBLICATIONS CO. - Publisher's imprints - Lerner Publishing Group
LEROI - Compressors—gas - Leroi International, Inc.
LEROUX - Liquors - House of Seagram
LEROUX ANISETTE - Whiskey - Jim Beam Brands Co.
LEROUX CREEK - Vegetables—dried - Leroux Creek Food Corp.
LEROUX POLISH POPPER - T-shirts—men's - Jim Beam Brands Co.
LEROY - Juices - Ira I. Fisher Inc.
LEROY - Letterpress plates - Keuffel & Esser Co.
LEROY - Thread - Threads USA Div.
LEROY LION - Dolls - Mattel, Inc.
LEROY NEIMAN - Postcards ☆ - Classico San Francisco Inc.
LERTON - Pharmaceutical preparations - Vita Elixir Co. Inc.
LES AMANDES - Candy - Albert Uster Imports Inc.
LES AQUATIQUES - Cosmetics - Cosmair Inc.
LES BELLES JAMBES - Apparel—women's - Transfer Products
LES BIJOUX - Jewelry - Universe International Inc.
LES BIOLOGICS - Skin care products - Biotherm
LES BLONDISSIMES - Hair coloring preparations - Cosmair Inc.
LES BRILLANTS - Cosmetics - Chanel Inc.
LES BRITE - Pens - Sheaffer Inc.
LES CACHEMIRES - Cosmetics - Cosmair Inc.
LES COIFFANTS - Hair care products - Rene Furterer
LES COMMUNIQUES - Stationery - Langhorne Press
LES DOUELLES - Wines - Monsieur Henri Wines Ltd.
LES DRAPE - Wallpaper - Carlton-Metro Wallcoverings
LES DRAPES - Wallpaper ☆ - Wallquest, Inc.

LES EDITIONS DOMINIQUE - Greeting cards - H. George Caspari Inc.
LES ENFANTS - Dolls ☆ - Effanbee Doll Corp.
LES ENFANTS - Footwear - N Shasta Shoe
LES EPICES DE LOUISIANE - Spices and extracts - Betty Ramsey Publisher
LES FANTASTIQUES - Cosmetics - Chanel Inc.
LES FAUVES - Jewelry - DS Imports Inc.
LES FEMMES - Giftware - Arnart Imports Inc.
LES FLEURS DES CHAMPS - Wines - William Grant & Sons, Inc.
LES FLEURS DU MONDE - Wallpaper - Academy Handprints Ltd.
LES FLEURS PORCELAIN - Flowers—artificial - Mangelsen's (VDI)
LES FLORALIES - Cosmetics - H.M. Coby Associates Inc.
LES FLORALIES - Wallpaper - Charles Barone Inc.
LES FORTS DE LATOUR - Wines - Seagram's Chateau & Estate Wines Co.
LES GARDENS - Wallpaper ☆ - Wallquest, Inc.
LES GIRLS - Dolls - Effanbee Doll Corp.
LES GRANDES FLEURS - Wallpaper - Roger Nicholson Designs Ltd.
LES GRANGES WINES - Wines - Marie Brizard Wines & Spirits, USA
LES HERBS DU CHATEAU - Herbal products - Euro International
LES JAMELLES - Wines - Masterwines Inc.
LES JEUNE PIEL RENUE - Cosmetics - Les Jeune Piel
LES MERRINES - Food products ☆ - Tour Eiffel
LES METROS - Pens - Sheaffer Inc.
LES MIRAGES - Skin care products - Rudolph International, Inc.
LES MODELES - Wallcoverings - R.K. Style Inc.
LES MUSES - Fragrance ☆ - Coty Inc.
LES NAILS HOT - Nail care products - Pavion Ltd.
LES NATURALS DE CHANEL - Cosmetics - Chanel Inc.
LES NATURELLES - Cosmetics - Guerlain Inc.
LES NOUVELLES - Skin care products - Jeannette Renta
LES NUTONS - Pates - International Marketing Services Inc.
LES OIGNONS DE PARIS - Earthenware - Seymour Mann Inc.
LES ORMES DE PEZ - Wines - Seagram's Chateau & Estate Wines Co.
LES PARASOLS DE PRINTEMPS - Cosmetics - Cosmair Inc.
LES PASTELS - Cosmetics - Chanel Inc.
LES PASTELS - Pens - Sheaffer Inc.
LES PAUL - Musical instrument accessories - Gibson Strings & Accessories
LES PAVOTS - Wines - Sugarloaf Farming Corp.
LES PEAUX ROUGE - Wallpaper - Bassett & Vollum Wallpapers
LES PETITES FLEURS - Kaleidoscopes - Gemini Kaleidoscopes
LES PLAISIRS DU CORP - Skin care products - Chanel Inc.
LES PLISSES - Wallpaper - Carlton-Metro Wallcoverings
LES ROUGES - Cosmetics - Chanel Inc.
LES SOINS SOLAIRES A LA MELANINE - Skin care products - Lancome
LES SPORT - Pens - Sheaffer Inc.
LES TRESORS DE BAIN - Cosmetics - Lancome
LES TROIS PETITS COCHONS - Food products ☆ - Les Trois Petits Cochons, Inc.
LES TROPIQUES - Cosmetics - Cosmair Inc.
LES TWILLS - Cosmetics - Cosmair Inc.
LES UTENSILES - Cooking equipment—household ☆ - Imperial Schrade Corp.
LES VERRIERES DE SAINT-GOBAIN - Glassware—household - St. Gobain International Glassware
LES VIGN DE RASTEAU - Beverages—alcohol - Wine Imports Ltd.
LES VINS GLORIEUX - Beverages—alcohol - Nor-Glo Import Co.
LES VINS LOUIS TETE - Wines - Maison Jomere Ltd.
LES VOGT'S PRO EQUINE - Saddles - Equine Professional Supplies, Inc.
LESABRE - Bicycles - Ross Bicycles USA, Ltd.
LESAL - Pottery - Lesal, Inc.
LESCAF - Teas - New England Dairies Inc.
LESCARE CUSTOM - Cabinets - Les-Care Kitchens Inc.
+L'ESCARGO - Apparel—men's - Drummond Knitwear Ltd.
LESCHEN RED STRAND - Rope - Wire Rope Corp. of America Inc.
LESCO - Counter tops—laminated - L.E. Smith Co.
LESCO - Paints - Lesco, Inc.
LESHER - Musical instruments ☆ - Selmer Co. Inc.
LESION - Toys - Tonka Corp.
LESLEY - Dolls - Effanbee Doll Corp.
LESLEY - Shampoos ☆ - Cassidy Inc.
LESLIE - Dolls - Horsman
LESLIE - Frames—eyeglass - U.S. Optical Frame Co.
LESLIE - Rings—jewelry - Artcarved Inc.
LESLIE - Salt - Leslie Salt Co.
LESLIE - Salt - Stevens Industries Inc.
LESLIE - Wigs - Jean Paree Weegs Inc.
LESLIE ANNE - Dolls - Horsman
LESLIE ANNE IVORY - Calendars ☆ - Amcal Inc.

☆ = Now out of production

LESLIE FAY - Dresses–women's - Leslie Fay Companies Inc.
LESLIE FAY - Footwear - Leslie Fay Separates
LESLIE FAY - Footwear - United States Shoe Corp.
LESLIE FAY GIRLS - Girls' apparel ☆ - Atlanta Apparel Group Ltd.
LESLIE FAY II - Apparel–women's - Leslie Fay Companies Inc.
LESLIE FAY PETITE - Apparel–women's - Leslie Fay Companies Inc.
LESLIE GIFFORD - Apparel–women's - Molto Fino, Inc.
LESLIE I - See **LESLIE FAY II**
LESLIE-LOCKE - Rails–iron - Leslie-Locke, Inc.
LESLIE POMER - Dresses–women's ☆ - Leslie Fay Companies Inc.
LESLIE'S OXIDIZER - Water treating compounds - Leslie's Poolmart
LESLINE - Cabinets - Les-Care Kitchens Inc.
LESMANN - Organs–musical instrument - Fender Musical Instruments
+L'ESPRESSO - Coffee makers–electric ☆ - Robert Krups North America
+L'ESPRESSO PLUS - Coffee makers–electric ☆ - Robert Krups North America
+L'ESPRIT - Motor vehicles–motor homes - Travco
+L'ESPRIT DE CHAMPAGNE - Fruits–dried ☆ - Gourmet America
+L'ESPRIT MAGIQUE - Perfumes - Lancome
LESS - Breads ☆ - Schmidt Baking Co., Inc.
LESS ACTIVE - Pet food - Iams Co.
LESS IS MORE II - Furniture - Thayer Coggin Inc.
LESS MESS - Hunting equipment - Jay A. Brewer
LESS STRESS - Health care products - East Earth Herb Inc.
LESS THAN A DAY - Furniture ☆ - Cosco, Inc.
LESSALT - Meat products–canned - Hansel 'n Gretel Brand, Inc.
LESSON OF SORTS, A - Computer software ☆ - Earthware Computer Services
LESSON ONE - Electronic equipment - Video Technology U.S. Inc.
LESSON PLANNER, THE - Computer software - Compu-Tations Inc.
LESSONWORKS - Educational materials - Wenger Corp.
LESSPACE - Office supplies - Esselte Corp.
+L'ESTANDON - Wines - Seagram's Chateau & Estate Wines Co.
+L'ESTATE CALAMATA - Olives–canned ☆ - Marin Food Specialties
LESTEAM - Exercising equipment - Cedarbrook Sauna Inc.
LESTER - Battery chargers - Storage Battery Systems
LESTER - Dolls - Goldberger Doll Manufacture Co.
LESTER LAMPERT - Jewelry - Lester Lampert, Inc.
LESTER LOBSTER - Swimming pools ☆ - Utikem Products
LESTER LOONEY BIRD - Toys–stuffed - Russ Berrie and Co., Inc.
LESTER THE KID - Toys–stuffed - Russ Berrie and Co., Inc.
LESTER THE LOONEY BIRD - Toys–stuffed - Russ Berrie and Co., Inc.
LESTER THE PRO - Toys–stuffed - Russ Berrie and Co., Inc.
LESTER THE UNLIKELY - Video games - DTMC, Inc.
LESTERINA BALLERINA - Toys–stuffed - Russ Berrie and Co., Inc.
LESTOIL - Cleaning preparations–household - Procter & Gamble Co.
LESUEUR - Vegetables–canned - Pillsbury Co.
LET-GO - Paints - Krylon/Dupli-Color
LET IT BEES - Apparel–athletic - Idea 101, Inc.
LET IT OUT - Beverages–carbonated - Coca-Cola Co.
LET IT RIP - Apparel and accessories - Lifeforms International, Inc.
LET IT SNOW - Electrical equipment - Noma International, Inc.
LET ME READ - Publisher's imprints - Harpercollins Publishers Inc.
LET OUR VIOLENCE END - Apparel and accessories - Robert H. Holt
LET-R-STIK - Letterpress plates ☆ - Heritage Springfield Inc.
LET THE EARTH BE GLAD - Greeting cards - Warner Press, Inc.
LET US COOK FOR YOU - Food products - Grace Culinary Systems Inc.
LET US COOK FOR YOU - Food products - Xanatech Inc.
LET US PLAY SPORTS CAMP - Athletic associations - Let Us Play Sports Camp, Inc.
+L'ETE - Cosmetics ☆ - Elysee Scientific Cosmetic Co.
LETERON - Signs - Leteron
LETERTAPE - Hardware - Leteron
LETERTITLE - Electronic equipment - Leteron
LETERTYPE - Office supplies - Leteron
LETH-R-WOOD - Calendars - Ad-a-Day Co. Inc.
LETHA-TONE - Office supplies - Globe-Weis
LETHAL - Apparel and accessories - JFP International, Inc.
LETHAL ENFORCERS - Video games - Konami (America) Inc.
LETHAL ENFORCERS II GUN FIGHTERS - Computer software - Konami (America) Inc.
LETHAL INTENTION - Darts and dart games - Dart Mart Inc.
LETHAL LIMIT - Bicycles - Roadmaster Corp.
LETHAL RECORDS - Compact discs–prerecorded - Prophet Motive Entertainment, Inc.
LETHERSCOPE - Cleaning preparations - Cramer Products Inc.

LETHOPHEROL - Vitamins and nutritional supplements ☆ - Nutrition Control Products
LETITIA - Corsets - John Wanamaker Inc.
LETIZIA - Handbags - Bags by Letizia
+L'ETOILE - Dinnerware–glass - Nikko Ceramics Inc.
+L'ETOILE - Rings–jewelry - Artcarved Inc.
LETOUR - Vases ☆ - Lenox, Inc.
LETRA SET - Electronic equipment - Letraset USA Inc.
LETRAFILM - Office supplies - Letraset USA Inc.
LETRAGRAPHICA - Decals and transfers - Letraset USA Inc.
LETRAJET - Office supplies ☆ - Esselte Corp.
LETRALETTERS - Office supplies - Esselte Corp.
LETRALINE - Office supplies - Letraset USA Inc.
LETRAMASK - Film - Letraset USA Inc.
LETRAMAX - Office supplies - Esselte Corp.
LETRAPAQUE - Office supplies - Letraset USA Inc.
LETRASET - Decals and transfers - Letraset USA Inc.
LETRASET - Office supplies - Esselte Corp.
LETRASIGN - Signs - Letraset USA Inc.
LETRATAPE - Decals and transfers ☆ - Letraset USA Inc.
LETRATONE - Film - Letraset USA Inc.
LET'S BE SAFE! - Games ☆ - Milton Bradley Co.
LET'S BEGIN - Health care products - RBR Productions, Inc.
LET'S BUY HOLLYWOOD - Games - Cardinal Industries, Inc.
LET'S CLIMB HIGHER! - Video production - Orchard Hill Productions
LET'S COLOR... - Computer software - Toto Computer Graphics, Inc.
LET'S COLOR. - Computer software - Toto Computer Graphics, Inc.
LET'S DO - Snack foods ☆ - Edward & Sons Trading Co., Inc.
LET'S DO IT! - Apparel and accessories - Christy Lane
LET'S DO LUNCH - Kites - Hi-Flier Manufacturing Co.
LETS EDGE IT! - Garden equipment - Argee Corp.
LETS EDGE IT! - Garden equipment - Argee Manufacturing Co. of San Diego, Inc.
LET'S EXPLORE SCIENCE - Calendars - Dorling Kindersley Publishing, Inc.
LET'S FACE IT - Clocks ☆ - Uniquity
LET'S FACE IT - Games - Centsable Toys Inc.
LET'S FACE IT - Skin care products - American Hygienic Laboratories Inc.
LET'S FIX IT! - Board games - Limardee Enterprises
LET'S GET F.I.T. - Video production - Rothhammer International Inc.
LET'S GET FRESH - Cosmetics ☆ - Cosrich Inc.
LET'S GET SOMETHING STRAIGHT - Hair care products - Cosmedic Concepts, Inc.
LET'S GO - Computer software - Gessler Publishing Co., Inc.
LET'S GO - Nail care products - Isabel Cristina Nail Care Products
LET'S GO! - Pet products - HTZ Investment Corp.
LET'S GO CAMINANDO - Computer software - Gessler Publishing Co., Inc.
LET'S GO FISHIN' - Games - Pressman Toy Corp.
LET'S GO SHOPPING - Board game - Trend Enterprises, Inc.
LET'S GO TO THE CIRCUS - Computer software ☆ - Laureate Learning Systems Inc.
LET'S GO TO THE RACES - Toys - Tonka Corp.
LET'S GROW - Cosmetics - RBR Productions, Inc.
LET'S GROW IT - Tools–garden - United States Marketing Corp.
LET'S HAVE A PARTY - Novelty items - Jak-Pak Inc.
LET'S HAVE A PARTY - Teas ☆ - Fun World Inc.
LET'S HAVE AN AFFAIR BEAR - Publisher's imprints - Vivian Greene Inc.
LET'S HAVE FUN - Recording label - Highlander Entertainment Group, Inc.
LET'S HOLD - Nail care products - RBR Productions, Inc.
LET'S JAM - Hair care products - Attitudes Unltd.
LETS LIGHT IT! - Garden equipment - Argee Corp.
LET'S MAKE A DEAL - Apparel and accessories - Let's Make a Deal
LET'S MAKE A WHEEL - Computer software - Gary Olander
LET'S-MAKE-BABY-HAPPY - Toys ☆ - Creative Playthings Ltd.
LET'S MAKE UP - Cosmetics - Sandy Silberman
LET'S MOVE, LET'S PLAY - Video production - Kindercare Learning Centers, Inc.
LET'S PAINT - Paints - DecoArt, Inc.
LET'S-PAINT-SOMETHING - Toys ☆ - Creative Playthings Ltd.
LET'S PARTY - Candles - Origins Natural Resources Inc.
LET'S PARTY - Halloween makeup - Cosrich Inc.
LET'S PLAY GAMES ARCADE - Children's card games - International Games
LET'S-PLAY-HOUSE - Toys ☆ - Creative Playthings Ltd.
LET'S-PLAY-MUSIC - Toys ☆ - Creative Playthings Ltd.
LET'S-PLAY-ROUGH - Toys ☆ - Creative Playthings Ltd.
LET'S POTTY - Toilets–portable - Sassy, Inc.
LET'S PRACTICE RUSSIAN - Computer software ☆ - EMC Publishing Corp.

☆ = Now out of production

LET'S PRETEND - Toys - Creative Art Activities Inc.
LET'S PRETEND - Toys - Jak-Pak Inc.
LET'S PRETEND - Wallcovering ☆ - Colortree Designs
LET'S ROCK U.S.A. - Shirts - George K. Setka
LET'S ROK IT - Tools–hand-operated - United States Marketing Corp.
LET'S SEE - Video production - RBR Productions, Inc.
LETS TALK ABOUT - now out of production - Peter Pan Industries
LET'S TALK ABOUT IT - Recording label - Family Communications, Inc.
LET'S TALK ABOUT ME. - Computer software - Simon & Schuster, Inc.
LET'S TALK CELLULAR - Telephones–cellular - Let's Talk Cellular of America, Inc.
LET'S TALK TEXTURES - Wallpaper ☆ - Laminating Services Inc.
LET'S TOUCH - Nail care products - Isabel Cristina Nail Care Products
LETSGO - Lubricants - Stewart-Hall Chemical Corp.
LETT-US HIDE - Product for hiding valuables, now out of production - Iwasaki Images of America
LETTEGRAM - Stationery - Leo Pevsner & Co.
LETTER CLERK - Computer software - Beyond, Inc.
LETTER-ETTES - Stationery - Gibson Greetings, Inc.
LETTER FROM HOME COOKIE COMPANY, A - Bakery products - A Letter from Home Cookie Co.
LETTER GETTER - Toys - Mattel, Inc.
LETTER-IT - Stencils - P-T Templet Co. Inc.
LETTER LADDER - Card game - International Games
LETTER-LIKKER - Office supplies ☆ - Dry-Tab Package Sealer Co.
LETTER LOCKER - Mail boxes - John Timpson Jeffs
LETTER LOOPS - Games ☆ - Milton Bradley Co.
LETTER 'N LABEL - Paper products - Avery Dennison Corp.
LETTER PERFECT - Decals and transfers - Rubbermaid Inc.
LETTER PERFECT - Key rings - Russ Berrie and Co., Inc.
LETTER PERFECT - Stationery ☆ - Berkshire Stationery Inc.
LETTER PERFECT - Underwear and nightwear - Maidenform Inc.
LETTER PERFECT - Uniforms–tailored - Horace Small Apparel Co.
LETTER PETS - Decals and transfers - Kamar International Inc.
LETTER RIP LIMITED - Stationery - Abraham, Reily & McNamara
LETTER SCENTERS - Sachets - Natural Products Corp.
LETTER SWEATER, THE - T-shirts - Bruce E. Hoar Inc.
LETTERA - Typewriters - Olivetti North America Inc. (Consumer Products Div.)
LETTERBOXES - Greeting cards - Recycled Paper Products, Inc.
LETTERGRAPH - Duplicating machines - Heyer Inc.
LETTERGUIDE - Office supplies - Letterguide Inc.
LETTERHEAD NOW - Computer software - Topitzes & Associates, Inc.
LETTERHEADS - Stationery - Jones Paper
LETTERIZER - Computer software - W.H. Brady Co.
LETTERJET - Computer software - Jetson Industries, Inc.
LETTERKRAFTS - Stationery - Graphic Center
LETTERMATES - Signs - Scott Sign Systems, Inc.
LETTERPERFECT - Computer software - Wordperfect Corp.
LETTERPRINTER - Printers–computer - Digital Equipment Corp.
LETTERPRO - Printers–computer - Data Technology Corp.
LETTERS - Apparel and accessories - Dayton Hudson Corp.
LETTERS - Cases–eyeglass - California Optical Leather Inc.
LETTERS BY THE YARD - Paper–writing ☆ - Jesse Jones Box Corp.
LETTERS FROM BARNEY - Computer software ☆ - SRA/McGraw-Hill (Div. of The McGraw-Hill Companies)
LETTERS FROM SANTA - Greeting cards ☆ - Stevenson Industries Inc.
LETTERS 'N NUMBERS - Toys ☆ - Coloron Industries
LETTERSCAN - File folders - Kardex Systems, Inc.
LETTERSHOP, THE - Hobby kits - Hunt Holdings, Inc.
LETTERTIME - Stationery ☆ - Case Stationery Co. Inc.
LETTERWRITER - Printers–computer - Digital Equipment Corp.
LETTS - Books–blank ☆ - Webway, Inc.
LETTUCE LOVE - Crackers, etc ☆ - Bowlby Candy Co. Inc.
LETTUCELINER - Paperboard–corrugated ☆ - International Paper Co.
LETWEED - Yarn - William Unger & Co. Inc.
LETZ - Paints - Perfection Letz Paint Co.
LEUKERAN - Pharmaceutical preparations - Burroughs Wellcome Co.
LEUKOBAC - Veterinary pharmaceutical preparations - American Animal Health, Inc.
LEUKOFIX - Bandages–surgical - Beiersdorf Inc.
LEUKOFLEX - Bandages–surgical - Beiersdorf Inc.
LEUKOGUARD-6 - Medical apparatus - Pall Corp.
LEUKOPOR - Bandages–surgical - Beiersdorf Inc.
LEUKOSCAN - Diagnostic apparatus - Immunomedics, Inc.
LEUKOSILK - Bandages–surgical - Beiersdorf Inc.
LEUPOLD - Sights–gun - Leupold and Stevens Inc.

LEUSTATIN - Pharmaceuticals - Johnson & Johnson
LEUTROL - Pharmaceutical preparations - Abbott Laboratories
LEV CHEK - Soldering equipment - Hexacon Electric Co.
LEV-L-ASTIC - Hardware - Allied Compositions
LEV-L-EASE - Floor coverings ☆ - L & F Products Inc.
LEV-O-LET - Switches–electric - Leviton Manufacturing Co., Inc.
LEV-U-DEX - Corn syrup - Nabisco Foods Group
LEVANT - Wallpaper - Norman/Baer Associates
LEVANTER - Wheels–motor vehicle - Sun Metal Products, Inc.
LEVANTO - Wallpaper - Winfield Design Associates, Inc.
LEVART ORIGINALS - Jewelry ☆ - Eastern Jewelry Manufacturing Co. Inc.
LEVASOLE - Veterinary pharmaceutical preparations - Schering-Plough Animal Health
LEVATOL - Pharmaceutical preparations - Reed & Carnrick
LEVEL 4 CORE - Bowling balls - Ebonite International, Inc.
LEVEL-6 - Tape–adhesive - Seam Master Industry
LEVEL-AIR - Musical instrument accessories ☆ - Selmer Co. Inc.
LEVEL BEST - Wood fillers - Savogran Co.
LEVEL CUT - Excavating equipment - Cable Arm Clamshell
LEVEL-EASY - Picture hangers ☆ - American Tack & Hardware Co., Inc.
LEVEL-ETT - Hardware - Baker Co.
LEVEL-EZE - Cement ☆ - Custom Building Products
LEVEL-EZE - Ladders–metal - Jershon Inc.
LEVEL-FLO - Floor coverings - Mapei East Corp.
LEVEL FOUR - Golfing equipment ☆ - Louisville Golf Club Co. Inc.
LEVEL GRIP - Horseshoes - Thoro'bred Racing Plate Co., Inc.
LEVEL-JAK - Jacks–hydraulic - Woodmack Products Inc.
LEVEL LINK - Sporting goods - Link Automation, Inc.
LEVEL-LOC - Electronic equipment ☆ - Shure Brothers, Inc.
LEVEL-MASTER - Ladders–metal - Werner Co.
LEVEL NINETY NINE - Apparel and accessories - Team Tactics, Inc.
LEVEL-OH! - Fasteners–snap - Gladys Sunshine
LEVEL-QUIK - Cement - Custom Building Products
LEVEL REMINDER - Computer software - Hunter Engineering Co.
LEVEL-RIGHT - Floor slabs–concrete - Maxxon Corp.
LEVEL-RIGHT FS10 - Floor slabs–concrete - Maxxon Corp.
LEVEL-RIGHT PLUS - Floor slabs–concrete - Maxxon Corp.
LEVEL-RITE HANGER - Mounting hangers - Gary Kloock
LEVEL TOP 1 - Floor topping - Construction Adhesives Co.
LEVEL-X52 - Floor coverings - Edison Coatings, Inc.
LEVEL5 AGENT - Computer software - Information Builders, Inc.
LEVELAWN - Tools - Ransomes-Cushman-Ryan
LEVELAYER - Floor slabs–concrete - Dayton Superior Corp.
LEVELBEST - Carbon paper - American Ribbon & Carbon Co.
LEVELFLOOR - Cement - C-Cure Corp.
LEVELITE - Electronic equipment - Technical Designs
LEVELITE - Tools - Levelite Technology, Inc.
LEVELIZER, THE - Cushions - Protecto, Inc.
LEVELLER - Musical instrument accessories - Valley Audio Products, Inc.
LEVELMATIC - Fishing tackle - Penn Fishing Tackle Manufacturing Co.
LEVELMATIC - Furniture levelers - Blake Industries
LEVELOAD - Motor vehicles–all-terrain - Leon L. Hansen
LEVELOK - Steel products ☆ - Laclede Steel Co.
LEVELON - Hardware - Allied Compositions
LEVELS - Hair care products - Dudley Products Inc.
LEVENGER TOOLS FOR SERIOUS READERS - Furniture - Levenger Co.
LEVER - Barber shop equipment - Kim Laube & Co. Inc.
LEVER - Cleaning preparations - Lever Investments Corp.
LEVER 2000 - Soap - Lever Brothers Co. Inc.
LEVER 2000 BODY WASH - Soap - Lever Brothers Co. Inc.
LEVER ACTION - Pumps–vacuum - Edson Corp.
LEVER-AIDE - Garden tools - Lever-Aide Products, Inc.
LEVER BAC - Soap - Conopco, Inc.
LEVER FRESH - Housewares and cleaning preparations - Lever Industrial Co.
LEVER-LOCK - Binders - K & M Co.
LEVER MILD - Soap - Lever Industrial Co.
LEVER PRINCIPLE - Electronics equipment - Telescript Inc.
LEVER SPRING - Mattresses - Restonic Corp.
LEVERAGE - Computer software - InterConnections Inc.
LEVERAGE EIS - Computer software - Leverage Systems, Inc.
LEVERAGED PERFORMANCE - Orthopedic products - Northwest Podiatric Laboratory, Inc.
LEVERCLAMP - Clamps - Mapletek Engineering, Inc.
LEVEREX - Locks–door - Securitech Group, Inc.
LEVERMATIC - Guns ☆ - Marlin Firearms Co.
LEVERMATIC - Tools–hand-operated - Plasplugs Inc.

☆ = Now out of production

LEVER'S - Toothbrushes - Chesebrough-Pond's USA Co.
LEVETI - Apparel and accessories - Lebas Fashion Imports of USA, Inc.
LEVI GARRETT - Chewing tobacco, snuff - Conwood Co. L.P.
LEVI STRAUSS - Apparel—men's - Aberdeen Sportswear Co.
LEVI STRAUSS & CO. - Eyeglasses - Martin-Copeland Eyewear Corp.
LEVIATHAN - Beverages—malt - Fish Brewing Co.
LEVIATHAN AQUAVERSE - Magazines - Future Fun Inc.
LEVIATHAN GEAR - Apparel and accessories - Bradford William Hutchinson
LEVILLE - Automotive parts and accessories ☆ - Lancaster Colony Automotive Group
LEVI'S - Belts—apparel - Humphrey's Inc.
LEVI'S - Footwear ☆ - Brown Shoe Co.
LEVI'S - Jeans and sportswear - Levi Strauss & Co.
LEVI'S - Watches - Genender International, Inc.
LEVI'S FOR FEET - Shoes - Levi Strauss & Co.
LEVI'S FOR MEN - Men's apparel - Levi Strauss & Co.
LEVIS FOR WOMEN - Jeans—women's - Levi Strauss & Co.
LEVI'S PANATELA - Men's sportswear ☆ - Levi Strauss & Co.
LEVI'S SILVER TAB - Blue jeans - Levi Strauss & Co.
LEVI'S WOMENS WEAR - Women's apparel - Levi Strauss & Co.
LEVI'S YOUTHWEAR - Apparel - Levi Strauss & Co.
LEVISON OF COPENHAGEN - Paper—gift wrap - H. George Caspari Inc.
LEVITEA - Teas—herbal - Unitea Herbs
LEVITEC - Communications equipment—satellite - MJ International, Inc.
LEVITON - Electrical equipment - Leviton Manufacturing Co., Inc.
LEVITRON - Novelty items - Creative Gifts, Inc.
LEVITY - Beverages—malt - Odell Brewing Co., Inc.
LEVO-DROMORAN - Pharmaceutical preparations - Roche Laboratories
LEVO SOMMELIER - Corkscrews - Franmara Co. Inc.
LEVOID - Pharmaceutical preparations - Nutrition Control Products
LEVOLON - Blinds—venetian - California Textiles Inc.
LEVOLOR - Blinds—vertical - Amsterdam Fabricators
LEVOLOR - Window coverings - Levolor Inc.
LEVOLOR EXPRESS - Blinds—venetian - Newell Operating Co.
LEVOLOR MICRO - Window coverings - Levolor Inc.
LEVOLOR READY MADE - Window coverings - Levolor Inc.
LEVOLOR RIVIERA - Window coverings - All Cedar Venetian Blind Manufacturing Co.
LEVON - Cigarettes - Levon Products Inc.
LEVOPHED BITARTRATE - Pharmaceutical preparations - Sterling Winthrop Inc.
LEVOTHROID - Pharmaceutical preparations - Forest Pharmaceuticals Inc.
LEVOXYL - Pharmaceutical preparations - Daniels Pharmaceuticals, Inc.
LEVOXYL - Pharmaceutical preparations - Jones Medical Industries, Inc. (Medical Div.)
LEVOXYL - Vitamins and nutritional supplements - Jones Pharma Inc.
LEVSIN - Pharmaceutical preparations - Schwarz Pharma
LEVSIN/SL - Pharmaceutical preparations - Schwarz Pharma
LEVSINEX - Pharmaceutical preparations - Schwarz Pharma
LEVSOUND - Wallpaper - Levwall Inc.
LEVTEX - Wallpaper - Levwall Inc.
LEVUCAL - Health care products ☆ - Kay Pharmacal Co. Inc.
LEVWALL - Wallpaper - Levwall Inc.
LEVY - Brushes—paint - Corona Brushes Inc.
LEVYS - Breads - Best Foods Baking Group
LEW CHASE - Musical instrument accessories - Scanlan Music Sales Inc.
LEWCORE - Thread - Lewis Threads Inc.
LEWES DAIRY - Milk - Lewes Dairy Inc.
LEWIS - Cleaning preparations - Boyle-Midway
LEWIS - Computer software - Strategic Weather Services
LEWIS - Floor coverings—carpet and rugs ☆ - Bellbridge Carpets
LEWIS - Health care products - First Aids Inc.
LEWIS - Knives - Seal-O-Matic Corp.
LEWIS - Musical instrument accessories - William Lewis & Son
LEWIS - Thread - Lewis Threads Inc.
LEWIS & CLARK - Beverages - Lewis & Clark Snake River Beverage Co.
LEWIS & CLARK - Beverages—alcohol - Alpha Industries, Inc.
LEWIS & CLARK - Publisher's imprints - Amereon Ltd.
LEWIS & CLARK SNAKE RIVER - Beverages - Lewis & Clark Snake River Beverage Co.
LEWIS & HYDE - Luggage - Skyway Luggage Co.
LEWIS & LEWIS - Terra cotta ☆ - Chase Collection, Inc.
LEWIS & ROBERTS - Costume jewelry ☆ - Lewis & Roberts (O)
LEWIS CARROLL'S CHESS WORD GAME - Games - Kadon Enterprises Inc.
LEWIS FRIMEL - Apparel and accessories - Donnkenny Inc.
LEWIS MACHINE - Machinery - Fastener Engineers Group Inc.

LEWIS N. CLARK - Electronic equipment - L.C. Industries, Inc.
LEWIS N. CLARK TRAVEL ACCESSORIES - Luggage - L.C. Industries, Inc.
LEWIS STUDIOS - Glass products - Light Opera Studios Inc.
LEWMAR - Ships—sailing vessels - Lewmar Marine Inc.
LEWSEW - Thread - Lewis Threads Inc.
LEWTEX - Building materials - Lewtex Technological Manufacturing, Inc.
LEX - Vitamins and nutritional supplements - Lex Pharmaceutical Inc.
LEX-CRETE - Adhesives and sealants - Rutland Products
LEX-I-CA - Computer software - WordStar International Inc.
LEXACAST - Lighting fixtures - Inter-Global, Inc.
LEXAIRE - Helmets—athletic - Lexington Safety Products Inc.
LEXAN - Plastics - General Electric Co.
LEXAN THERMOCLEAR - Plastics - General Electric Co.
LEXAN XL-1 - Plastics - General Electric Co.
LEXAR - Computer software - Fairchild Communications Services Co.
LEXAVITE - Pharmaceutical preparations ☆ - Eli Lilly and Co.
+L'EXCEL - Cheese - Anco Foods Corp.
LEXEL - Caulking compounds - Sashco Inc.
LEXEL - Sporting goods - Sports West USA Inc.
LEXFLEX - Hardware - Lexco Cable Manufacturing & Distributing
LEXI - Luggage - Lexi International Inc.
LEXIA - Beverages - N & N International Ltd.
LEXIBRIDGE - Computer software - Lexibridge Corp.
LEXICHECK - Computer software - Quark, Inc.
LEXICON 82 - Typewriters ☆ - Olivetti North America Inc. (Consumer Products Div.)
LEXIDE - Paper products - REXAM DSI
LEXIFIER - Computer software - Xerox Corp.
LEXINGTON - Artists' materials ☆ - Arthur Brown and Bros. Inc.
LEXINGTON - Attache cases - Lexington Leather Goods Co.
LEXINGTON - Automotive parts and accessories - Lancaster Colony Automotive Group
LEXINGTON - Bathroom fixtures ☆ - Artesian Industries
LEXINGTON - Bicycles - Columbia Manufacturing Inc.
LEXINGTON - Brushes—paint - Winsor & Newton
LEXINGTON - Cabinets - Marsh Furniture Co.
LEXINGTON - Cabinets - Yorktowne Inc.
LEXINGTON - Cabinets ☆ - Medallion Kitchens of Minnesota Inc.
LEXINGTON - Door frames - Canyon Creek Cabinet Co.
LEXINGTON - Fans—electric - Lamps Plus Inc.
LEXINGTON - Fixtures and fittings - American Standard Inc.
LEXINGTON - Flag poles - Annin and Co.
LEXINGTON - Floor coverings—carpet and rugs - Atlas Carpet Mills Inc.
LEXINGTON - Floor coverings—carpet and rugs - Patcraft Mills Inc.
LEXINGTON - Floor coverings—carpet and rugs ☆ - Cumberland Mills Inc.
LEXINGTON - Furniture ☆ - Masco Corp.
LEXINGTON - Glass—leaded - Seneca Glass Co.
LEXINGTON - Glassware—household - Owens-Illinois Inc. (Libbey Div.)
LEXINGTON - Glass—window - Taylor Building Products Co.
LEXINGTON - Helmets—athletic - St. Lawrence Sales Inc.
LEXINGTON - Motor vehicles—motor homes - Mallard Coach
LEXINGTON - Office supplies - Da-Lite Screen Co. Inc.
LEXINGTON - Pens ☆ - Alexander Manufacturing Co.
LEXINGTON - Prefabricated buildings—metal - Arrow Group Industries
LEXINGTON - Prefabricated buildings—wood - Skyline Corp.
LEXINGTON - Radios - Robert Bosch Corp.
LEXINGTON - Shoes ☆ - Allen-Edmonds Shoe Corp.
LEXINGTON - Tableware—china ☆ - Lenox, Inc.
LEXINGTON - Toys ☆ - Combi International Corp.
LEXINGTON - Watches - Bulova Corp.
LEXINGTON - Weather vanes - Swift Instruments, Inc.
LEXINGTON ARMS - Furniture ☆ - Bassett Furniture Industries, Inc.
LEXINGTON AVENUE - Furniture ☆ - Bassett Furniture Industries, Inc.
LEXINGTON BOOKS - Publisher's imprints - MacMillan Publishing Co. Inc.
LEXINGTON CHERRY - Furniture - Lexington Furniture Industries, Inc.
LEXINGTON COURT - Furniture - Universal Flooring
LEXINGTON FORGE - Cooking utensils—cast iron ☆ - National Housewares
LEXINGTON HALL - Dolls - Lexington Hall
LEXINGTON HALL - House furnishings - Lea Industries Inc.
LEXINGTON HEIGHTS - Furniture—wood - Johnston-Tombigbee
LEXINGTON II - Brushes—paint - Winsor & Newton
LEXINGTON LACE - Needles—sewing - Heritage Designs Inc.
LEXINGTON LEATHER - House furnishings - Lexington Furniture Industries, Inc.
LEXINGTON PARK - Floor coverings—carpet and rugs ☆ - Hollytex Carpet Mills Inc.

☆ = Now out of production

LEXINGTON PLANK - Floor coverings - Mannington Resilient Floors
LEXINGTON ROUNDOVER - Cabinets - Kent Moore Cabinets Inc.
LEXINGTON SQUARE - Floor coverings–carpet and rugs - Artistic Rugs Inc.
LEXINGTON SQUARE - Floor coverings–carpet and rugs - Patcraft Mills Inc.
LEXINGTON UPHOLSTERY - Furniture - Lexington Furniture Industries, Inc.
LEXINGTON XL MAPLE - Floor coverings - Robbins Inc.
LEXIS - Rackets–racquetball - Ektelon
LEXITE - Epoxy coatings - Metalcrete Industries Inc.
LEXIUM - Cleaning equipment - Geneva Group of Cos. Inc.
LEXMARK - Computers - Lexmark International, Inc.
LEXOCORT - Pharmaceutical preparations ☆ - Shannon Chemical Co. Inc.
LEXOCORT FORTE - Pharmaceutical preparations ☆ - Shannon Chemical Co. Inc.
LEXODERM - Pharmaceutical preparations ☆ - Shannon Chemical Co. Inc.
LEXOL - Leather tanning and finishing - Summit Industries, Inc.
LEXOL NF - Leather tanning and finishing - Summit Industries, Inc.
LEXOL PH - Leather tanning and finishing - Summit Industries, Inc.
LEXOLITE L.P. - Window coverings - Apex Mills Corp.
LEXON - Giftware - Zona Alta Projects, Inc.
LEXONE - Herbicides - E.I. Dupont de Nemours and Co.
LEXOR - Cleaning equipment - Restortek, Inc.
LEXOR - Games ☆ - Milton Bradley Co.
LEXOR - Pharmaceutical preparations ☆ - Lemmon Co.
LEXOR - Windshield frames–motor vehicle - Pylon Manufacturing Corp.
LEXOR - Wrenches ☆ - Allied Wholesale Inc.
LEXOTONE - Paper products - REXAM DSI
LEXOTONE 17 - Paper products - REXAM DSI
+L'EXPRESS - Lipsticks - Lancome
LEXSEARCH - Computer software - Mead Corp.
LEXSTAR - Computers and peripherals - CBM Inc.
LEXSTAR - Siding - Crane Plastics Co. L.P.
LEXSUCO - Lumber - B.F. Goodrich Co.
LEXTEL - Office machines - Lextel, Inc.
+L'EXTRA - Spices and extracts - Larex, Inc.
LEXTRON - Pharmaceutical preparations ☆ - Eli Lilly and Co.
LEXUM - Balls–basketball - Baden Sports, Inc.
LEXUS - Floor coverings–carpet and rugs - Cumberland Mills Inc.
LEXUS - Furniture - Singer Furniture Co.
LEXUS - Motor vehicles - Toyota Motor Sales USA Inc.
LEXUS - Paint rollers - Great American Marketing, Inc.
LEXUS ES300 - Motor vehicles–automobiles - Toyota Motor Sales USA Inc.
LEXUS GS300 - Motor vehicles–automobiles - Toyota Motor Sales USA Inc.
LEXUS LS 400 - Motor vehicles–automobiles - Toyota Motor Sales USA Inc.
LEXUS SC300 - Motor vehicles–automobiles - Toyota Motor Sales USA Inc.
LEXUS SC400 - Motor vehicles–automobiles - Toyota Motor Sales USA Inc.
LEXXEL - Pharmaceutical preparations - Astra Merck Inc.
LEXZINC - Pharmaceutical preparations ☆ - Shannon Chemical Co. Inc.
LEY/DOO - Shrimp–fresh or frozen - Ocean Pride Seafood, Inc.
LEYDEN - Cooking equipment–household ☆ - Old Dutch International Ltd.
LEYLAND - Golfing equipment - C.S.G. Inc.
LEYMAN - Motor vehicle parts and accessories - Leyman Manufacturing Corp.
LEYSE - Cooking utensils–aluminum - General Housewares Corp.
LEYSE PROFESSIONAL II - Cooking utensils–aluminum - General Housewares Corp.
LEYSON - Cooking utensils–aluminum ☆ - General Housewares Corp.
LEZARD - Cosmetics - Lancome
LEZIDOR BEGEDOR ITALIA - Leather - Lezidor Ltd.
LF - Electric motors - Brownell Electro Inc.
LF - Exercising equipment - Life Fitness
LF - Tiles–ceramic ☆ - Federal Tile Imports Inc.
LF-12 - Pharmaceutical preparations ☆ - Hyrex Pharmaceuticals
L.F.B. 12 - Pharmaceutical preparations ☆ - Ulmer Pharmacal Co.
LFC - Computer software - Studebaker Computing Technology, Inc.
LFE - Wood products ☆ - Champion International Corp.
LFIC - Prosthetic apparatus - Joseph F. Fetto
+L'FLEUR - Flatware - Yamazaki Tableware Inc.
+L'FLEUR GOLD ACCENT - Flatware - Yamazaki Tableware Inc.
LFS - Tiles–ceramic ☆ - Federal Tile Imports Inc.
LG - Computer software - Looking Glass Technologies, Inc.
LG - Containers–glass - Liberty Glass Co.
LG A LOOKING GLASS TECHNOLOGIES PRODUCTION - Computer software - Looking Glass Technologies, Inc.
LGB - Giftware - L.G. Balfour Co.
LGFS - Computer software - American Management Systems, Inc.
LGI - Jewelry - Lahav and Grunberg, Inc.
LGIN - Leather goods - L. G. International

LGP - Jewelry - LGP Gem Ltd.
LGS - Pharmaceutical preparations - L.G.S. Health Products
LGT - Safety goggles ☆ - Uvex Sports, Inc.
LH EXTRA I - Recording label ☆ - BASF Corp.
LH KIDS - Wrapping paper - Liberty House, Inc.
LH MAXIMA I - Audio cassettes ☆ - BASF Corp.
LH RESEARCH - Electronic equipment - L-H Research, Inc.
LHERITIER - Confections - R.L. Albert & Son, Inc.
+L'HERITIER GUYOT - Beverages–alcohol - Kobrand Corp.
+L'HERMITAGE - Cutlery ☆ - Towle Silversmiths
+L'HEURE BLEUE - Perfumes - Guerlain Inc.
LHI - Frames–eyeglass - Hoya Corp. USA
+L'HIVER - Cosmetics ☆ - Elysee Scientific Cosmetic Co.
+L'HOMME - Vitamins and nutritional supplements - Armenpharm Ltd.
LHP - Photographic equipment ☆ - Heitz Service Corp.
LHS - Motor vehicles - DaimlerChrysler
LI - Jewelry - Litton Systems, Inc. (Airtron Division)
LI-BAN - Pediculicide ☆ - Pfizer Inc.
LI KITES - Toys ☆ - Importoys
LI-POLIN - Pharmaceutical preparations ☆ - Pacific Mineral Industries
LIA - Jewelry - Lianna Inc.
LIA JENE - Skin care products ☆ - Sheila Brit Ltd.
LIA SCHORR - Cosmetics - Lia Schorr Skin Care Inc.
LIAISON - Computer peripheral equipment - APT Technology, Inc.
LIAISON - Furniture - Tomlinson of High Point Inc.
LIAISON - Office furniture–metal - Herman Miller, Inc.
LIAISON - Telescopes - Northern Telecom, Inc.
LIAISON - Trailers–travel - Royals International
LIAISONS - Underwear and nightwear - Maidenform Inc.
LIAM FINDS A STORY - Computer software ☆ - Knowledge Adventure
LIAN HWA FOODS - Crackers - Lian Hwa Foods (USA) Inc.
LIANA - Frames–eyeglass - U.S. Optical Frame Co.
LIAR - Apparel and accessories - Liar U.S. Products
LIARS MAZE - Game - International Games
LIARS SUSPENDERS - Apparel and accessories - Portable Products, Inc.
L.I.B. - Apparel and accessories - Talbot Street Pier, Inc.
LIB - Recording label - Koba Associates, Inc.
LIB-BERTY - Vinyl - Universal Molding Co.
LIB TECHNOLOGIES - Snowboards - Csoc Holdings, Inc.
LIBAIRE CALIFORNIA - Shoes - Libaire
LIBBEY - Glassware–household - Owens-Illinois Inc. (Libbey Div.)
LIBBEY SHEER RIM D.T.E. - Glassware–household - Owens-Illinois Inc. (Libbey Div.)
LIBBY - Food products - Nestle USA
LIBBY - Food products - Seneca Foods Corp.
LIBBY - Footwear ☆ - ASL Distribution Co. Inc.
LIBBY - Ophthalmic goods - Rozin Optical Export Corp.
LIBBY - Toys - Jennifer Stewart
LIBBY HILL - Food products - Sea Harvest Packing Co.
LIBBY LEE - Toys - Libby Lee Toys Inc.
LIBBY'S - Beverages - Nestle Beverage Co.
LIBBY'S ASIAN FAVORITES - Preserved foods–prepackaged - Nestle USA
LIBBY'S DINER - Food products - Nestle USA
LIBBY'S GOURMET DESSERTS - Bakery products - Jansen Confections, Inc.
LIBBY'S NECTAR - Fruit drinks–bottled or canned - Nestle Beverage Co.
LIBEADO - Jewelry - Jodi Baron
LIBENMUSIC - Recording label - Jazz Composer's Orchestra Association Inc.
LIBENN AROMA - Deodorizers - Libenn Aroma, Inc.
LIBER TEE'S - Apparel and accessories - Walls Industries, Inc.
LIBERAL CALCULATOR - Novelty items - Liberal Calculator Co.
LIBERATION - Computer software - Teledirect International, Inc.
LIBERATION - Juices ☆ - H.P. Hood & Sons Inc.
LIBERATION - Synthesizers–musical instrument ☆ - EJE Research Corp.
LIBERATOR - Batteries - Exide Corp.
LIBERATOR - Bicycles - Ross Bicycles USA, Ltd.
LIBERATOR - Boats–motor - Four Winns Inc.
LIBERATOR - Boats–pontoons - Harris-Kayot Inc.
LIBERATOR - Cleaning preparations–carpet and rug - Host/Racine Industries Inc.
LIBERATOR - Computer software - ASCI
LIBERATOR - Paints - Allpro Corp.
LIBERATOR - Thread - Threads USA Div.
LIBERATOR 20/30 - Beverages - Caire
LIBERATOR 45 - Beverages - Caire
LIBERATOR/STROLLER - Oxygen - Cryogenic Associates Inc.
LIBERESSE - Shampoos - Alberto-Culver Co.

☆ = Now out of production

LIBERMAN'S - Food products - Liberman Meat Products
LIBERTA MILANO - Sweaters - Gillman Knitwear Co.
LIBERTE - Brassieres (Bras) - Lady Marlene
LIBERTE - Floor coverings—carpet and rugs ☆ - Karastan-Bigelow Inc.
LIBERTE - Furniture - Bassett Furniture Industries, Inc.
LIBERTECH - Computer software - Libertech
LIBERTY - Apparel and accessories - Walls Industries, Inc.
LIBERTY - Apparel—children's - Liberty Childrenswear Co., LLC
LIBERTY - Artists' materials ☆ - A.I. Friedman Inc.
LIBERTY - Athletic footwear ☆ - Autry Industries Inc.
LIBERTY - Bathroom accessories - Franklin Brass Manufacturing Co.
LIBERTY - Batteries - C & D Charter Power Systems, Inc.
LIBERTY - Boats—motor - Liberty Yachts Inc.
LIBERTY - Boats—motor ☆ - Bayliner Marine Corp.
LIBERTY - Boats—motor ☆ - Yar-Craft, Inc.
LIBERTY - Boxes - Fellowes Manufacturing Co.
LIBERTY - Cabinets - Kent Moore Cabinets Inc.
LIBERTY - Cabinets - Quality Cabinets
LIBERTY - Cheese - Swissrose International Inc.
LIBERTY - Cleaning preparations - Delta Industries International, Inc.
LIBERTY - Clocks - Ridgeway Clock Co.
LIBERTY - Computer hardware - Evans & Sutherland Computer Corp.
LIBERTY - Computer hardware - Gateway 2000, Inc.
LIBERTY - Computer software - Aurora Systems
LIBERTY - Doors—garage - General American Door Co.
LIBERTY - Doughnuts—mixes - Dawn Food Products Inc.
LIBERTY - Fabrics—denim - Dan River Inc.
LIBERTY - Faucets - Woodmark International, Inc.
LIBERTY - Fireplace equipment ☆ - Hearth Craft
LIBERTY - Floor coverings—carpet and rugs - Sheridan Carpet Mills
LIBERTY - Floor coverings—carpet and rugs - Alexander Smith Carpets
LIBERTY - Floor coverings—carpet and rugs ☆ - Kelly Group Inc.
LIBERTY - Flowers, plants, and seeds - Jacklin Seed
LIBERTY - Flowers, plants, and seeds - Santa Rosa Tropicals
LIBERTY - Furniture - Dinaire Corp.
LIBERTY - Furniture - Universal Flooring
LIBERTY - Furniture—upholstered ☆ - Mersman Furniture Co.
LIBERTY - Gasoline - Liberty Petroleum Co.
LIBERTY - Glassware—household - Lenox Crystal, Inc.
LIBERTY - Glassware—household ☆ - Crisa Corp.
LIBERTY - Golfing equipment - Golfsmith International Inc.
LIBERTY - Golfing equipment - Lynx Golf, Inc.
LIBERTY - Hardware - Turner Industries Ltd.
LIBERTY - Heating equipment - Slant/Fin Corp.
LIBERTY - House furnishings - Liberty Vinyl Corp.
LIBERTY - Ladders—wood - John S. Tilley Ladders Co. Inc.
LIBERTY - Luggage ☆ - Ventura Travelware Inc.
LIBERTY - Maraschino cherries, glace fruits, mincemeat mix, olives - Aunt Nellie's Farm Kitchens Inc.
LIBERTY - Medical apparatus - Utah Medical Products, Inc.
LIBERTY - Motor oil - Specialty Oil Co. Inc.
LIBERTY - Motorcycle-speed radar detectors - Whistler Acquistion Corp.
LIBERTY - Musical instrument accessories - Ultimate Support Systems Inc.
LIBERTY - Occasional tables ☆ - JDI Group, Inc.
LIBERTY - Pencils ☆ - Faber-Castell Corp.
LIBERTY - Pens - Micropoint Inc.
LIBERTY - Pet products - Marineland Aquarium Products
LIBERTY - Recording label - Capitol Records, Inc.
LIBERTY - Seafood products—fresh or frozen - Liberty Fish & Oyster Co.
LIBERTY - Snowmobiles - Liberty Products, Inc.
LIBERTY - Tableware—china - Lenox, Inc.
LIBERTY - Teas - Eastern Shore Tea Co.
LIBERTY - Toys—models ☆ - Estes Industries
LIBERTY - Toys—stuffed ☆ - Gund, Inc.
LIBERTY - Vitamins and nutritional supplements - Royal Source, Inc.
LIBERTY - Wallpaper - Newmarket Designs Ltd.
LIBERTY - Water—bottled or canned - Sparkling American
LIBERTY - Wheelchairs - Fortress Inc.
LIBERTY - Window coverings - All Cedar Venetian Blind Manufacturing Co.
LIBERTY ADAMS - Apparel—women's - Strawbridge & Clothier
LIBERTY ALE - Beverages—malt - Anchor Brewing Co.
LIBERTY BELL - Food products - Liberty Bell Wholesale Grocery Co.
LIBERTY BELL - Games - S. Alden Inc.
LIBERTY BELL - Skin care products - Waverly Beauty Products
LIBERTY BELL - Sports apparel ☆ - Inside Edge

LIBERTY BELL CHRISTMAS - Christmas tree lights - Liberty Bell Christmas Inc.
LIBERTY BLUE - Fabrics—denim - Dan River Inc.
LIBERTY CLASSICS - Toys—banks - Liberty Classics Inc.
LIBERTY COIN CRACKER CO. - Tools—hand-operated - Gerald M. Costello
LIBERTY ELITE - Siding - Aluminum Co. of America
LIBERTY EMPIRE - Fruits and vegetables - Stanley Orchards Sales Inc.
LIBERTY FALLS - Figurines - International Resourcing Services, Inc.
LIBERTY FIREWORKS - Greeting cards ☆ - Gallant Greetings Corp.
LIBERTY GARDEN - Furniture - Homecrest Industries Inc.
LIBERTY HALL - Cabinets ☆ - Aristokraft, Inc.
LIBERTY HALL - Dinnerware—glass ☆ - Block China Co.
LIBERTY HILL - Furniture - Hammary Furniture Co. Inc.
LIBERTY HOUSE - Publisher's imprints - Tab Books
LIBERTY INN - House furnishings - Lexington Furniture Industries, Inc.
LIBERTY JONES - Apparel—women's - Oak Hill Sportswear Corp.
LIBERTY KIDS - Toys ☆ - Jak-Pak Inc.
LIBERTY LIFT - Health care products - Cheney Co. Inc.
LIBERTY LINK - Floor coverings ☆ - American Floor Products Co. Inc.
LIBERTY MASTERS SERIES - Recording label - Capitol Records, Inc.
LIBERTY MINT - Jewelry - Liberty Mint Inc.
LIBERTY OF LONDON - Neckties - Salant/Manhattan Industries
LIBERTY OR DEATH - Computer games ☆ - Koei Corp.
LIBERTY POCKET - Tobacco - American Tobacco Co.
LIBERTY RIDGE - Toys—stuffed - Liberty Ridge
LIBERTY RIDGE LUSTER - Yarn - Liberty Ridge
LIBERTY ROASTERS - Coffee - Richard Saunders International, Inc.
LIBERTY SAFES - Vaults - Liberty Safe and Security Products, Inc.
LIBERTY SCHOOL - Wines ☆ - Caymus Vineyards
LIBERTY SCHOOL GEAR - Apparel—children's - Liberty Childrenswear Co., LLC
LIBERTY SLIP - Lubricants - Delta Industries International, Inc.
LIBERTY SPECIAL - Flour—blended - Acme-Evans/A.D.M. Milling Co.
LIBERTY SPECIAL - Health care products - Cheney Co. Inc.
LIBERTY SPELL II - Computer software ☆ - DataPak Software Inc.
LIBERTY SPRINGS - Water—bottled or canned - North American Beverage Enterprises, Inc.
LIBERTY SQUARE - Floor coverings - Congoleum Corp.
LIBERTY SQUARE - Floor coverings—carpet and rugs ☆ - Cumberland Mills Inc.
LIBERTY SQUARE - Hobby kits - Craft World International Inc.
LIBERTY STENO - Frames—picture ☆ - Fellowes Manufacturing Co.
LIBERTY VELLE - Fabrics - Guilford Mills, Inc.
LIBERTYTREE - Recording label - Independent Institute
LIBFORM - Fabrics - Liberty Fabrics, Inc.
LIBFT - Computer software - At&T Corp.
LIBI-ORANGE - Vitamins and nutritional supplements - Winning Laboratories Corp.
LIBIDO - Vitamins and nutritional supplements - Lifesource International Inc.
LIBRA - Apparel and accessories - Libra Trading Co.
LIBRA - Cabinets - Triangle Pacific Corp. (Cabinet Division)
LIBRA - Cosmetics - Cabot Laboratories Inc.
LIBRA - Floor covering ☆ - Congoleum Corp.
LIBRA - Floor coverings—carpet and rugs ☆ - Galaxy Carpet Mills Inc.
LIBRA - Floor coverings—tile - Interface, Inc.
LIBRA - Furniture - Weiman Co.
LIBRA - Furniture ☆ - Bassett Furniture Industries, Inc.
LIBRA - Health care products - Wheel Ring Inc.
LIBRA - Lawn mowers - Lambert Manufacturing Corp.
LIBRA - Rings—jewelry - Artcarved Inc.
LIBRA - Teas—herbal - Calvin Thornton
LIBRA - Vitamins and nutritional supplements - Giovanni D. Luciano
LIBRA - Wine - Unique Wines, Inc.
LIBRA HOME ENTERTAINMENT - Video production - Saban Entertainment, Inc.
LIBRA INDUSTRIES - Electronic equipment - Libra Industries Inc.
LIBRA PICTURES INTERNATIONAL - Computer storage devices—optical - Saban Entertainment, Inc.
LIBRARIAN - Furniture ☆ - Bassett Furniture Industries, Inc.
LIBRARIAN, THE - Ophthalmic goods - Chums Ltd.
LIBRARY - Wood products - States Industries Inc.
LIBRARY - Wood products - Welsh Forest Products Inc.
LIBRARY ADVENTURE - Computer software - Learning Well
LIBRARY ADVENTURE SERIES - Recording label - Meritage, Inc.
LIBRARY COLLECTION, THE - Paper—lithograph - Dimensionalized Marketing, Inc.

☆ = Now out of production

LIBRARY-CRAFT - Electronic equipment - Hamilton Electronics Corp.

LIBRARY GREETINGS - Publisher's imprints ☆ - Blue Mountain Arts Inc.

LIBRARY LOONIES, THE - Greeting cards - A + A

LIBRARY MASTER - Computer software - Comprehensive Video Supply Corp.

LIBRARY OF COMPUTER & INFORMATION SCIENCES, THE - Publisher's imprints - MacMillan Publishing Co. Inc.

LIBRARY OF CONTEMPORARY LITERATURE - Publisher's imprints - Howard University Press

LIBRARY OF FAMOUS WOMEN - Publisher's imprints ☆ - Rosen Publishing Group & Pelion Press

LIBRARY OF FREEDOM - Publisher's imprints - Random House, Inc.

LIBRARY OF LITERARY CRITICISM, A - Publisher's imprints ☆ - Crossroad

LIBRARY OF SCIENCE - Toys - Natural Science Industries, Ltd.

LIBRARY OF SCIENCE, THE - Publisher's imprints - MacMillan Publishing Co. Inc.

LIBRARY OF SPECIAL EDUCATION, THE - Publisher's imprints - MacMillan Publishing Co. Inc.

LIBRARY OF SPEECH PATHOLOGY, THE - Publisher's imprints - MacMillan Publishing Co. Inc.

LIBRARY OF THE AMERICAN WEST - Publisher's imprints - Crown Publishers Inc.

LIBRARY OF URBAN AFFAIRS, THE - Publisher's imprints - MacMillan Publishing Co. Inc.

LIBRARY OF VICTORIAN CULTURE - Publisher's imprint - American Life Foundation & Study Institute

LIBRARY PRESS - Publisher's imprints - Open Court Publishing Co.

LIBRARY SELECTION - Wines - Trefethen Vineyards Winery Inc.

LIBRARY SELECTION CABERNET SAUVIGNON - Wines - Trefethen Vineyards Winery Inc.

LIBRARY SELECTION CHARDONNAY - Wines - Trefethen Vineyards Winery Inc.

LIBRARYXPRESS - Tape players - Overland Data, Inc.

LIBRASOFT - Computer software - Robert Cowart

LIBRAX - Pharmaceutical preparations - Roche Laboratories

LIBRETTO - Furniture - Stanley Furniture Co. Inc.

LIBREX - Computers - Librex Computer Systems Inc.

LIBRITABS - Tranquilizers - Roche Laboratories

LIBRIUM - Tranquilizers - Roche Laboratories

LIBROMOUNT - Photo albums - C.R. Gibson Co.

LIBROS VIAJERO - Publisher's imprints - Harcourt Brace & Co.

LIBSTE. - Computer software - Plum Hall Inc.

LIC-RIS-ETS - Candy - American Licorice Co.

LICA - Capacitors - AVX Corp.

LICE-A-WAY - Pharmaceutical preparations - Roberts/Hauck Pharmaceuticals Inc.

LICENSE PLATE BINGO - Games - Richard L. Galbraith

LICENSED LIFESTYLES - Motor vehicle parts and accessories - Tac Holdings, Inc.

LICENSED TO JAM - Trading cards and stamps - Treat Entertainment, Inc.

LICETROL 400 - Pharmaceutical preparations - Republic Drug Co. Inc.

LICH LORDS - Games ☆ - Mayfair Games, Inc.

LICHEN - Stoneware dinnerware ☆ - Iron Mountain Stoneware Inc.

LICHT & KAPLAN - Handbags - Regal Bag Corp.

LICIDE - Health care products - Reese Chemical Co.

LICIDE BLUE GEL - Pharmaceutical preparations ☆ - Reese Chemical Co.

LICIDE SPRAY - Pharmaceutical preparations - Reese Chemical Co.

LICIDE TREATMENT KIT - Pharmaceutical preparations ☆ - Reese Chemical Co.

LICIDE TREATMENT SHAMPOO - Pharmaceutical preparations - Reese Chemical Co.

LICK A COLOR - Confections - Good Humor Corp.

LICK-A-MINT - Candy ☆ - Tootsie Roll Industries, Inc.

LICK'EMS - Candy - Nabisco Foods Group

LICKETY MIX - Pet products ☆ - ALPO Petfoods Inc.

LICKETY QUICK - Toys - Mattel, Inc.

LICKETY SLICKS - Toys - Mattel, Inc.

LICKETY SPLIT - Candy - Sunshine/Salerno Inc.

LICKETY SPLIT - Kitchen appliances ☆ - Philips Electronics North America Corp.

LICKETY SPLITS - Footwear - Sr Holdings, Inc.

LICKHER - Massage products - Nebco, Inc.

LICKIT & LUVITT - Chocolate syrup - The Soft Wear Corp.

LICKITY LOG SPLITTER - Saws–chain - Piqua Engineering Inc.

LICKITY-SPLIT - Agricultural machinery - Kondex Corp.

LICKITY-SPLIT - Ice cream - Kosto Food Products Co.

LICKITY SPLITZ - Apparel and accessories - Lickity Splitz

LICKLERS - Candy - Yost Candy Co.

LICKS 'N KISSES - Plush toys - Tonka Corp.

LICKTISOUS NUMSUCKEL POPS - Candy - Spangler Candy Co.

LICON - Pharmaceutical preparations ☆ - U.S. Ethicals Inc.

LICOPLEX - Pharmaceutical preparations ☆ - Keene Pharmaceuticals Inc.

LICOR 43 - Beverages–alcohol - Sogrape USA Inc.

LICORICE - Candy - Goetze's Candy Co., Inc.

LICORICE - Toys–stuffed ☆ - Gund, Inc.

LICORICE CLIX - Candy - Banner Candy Manufacturing Corp.

LICORICE (DGL) - Vitamins and nutritional supplements - Vitamin Research Products Inc.

LICORICE KITTY - Toys–stuffed ☆ - Dakin Inc.

LICORICE LACES - Candy - American Licorice Co.

LICORICE LOGS - Candy - American Licorice Co.

LICORICE LONG FELLERS - Candy ☆ - Ferrara Pan Candy Co., Inc.

LICORICE NIPS - Candy - Nabisco Foods Group

LICORICE-POWER - Vitamins and nutritional supplements - Natur-Pharma, Inc.

LICORICE ROPES - Candy - American Licorice Co.

LICORICE SNAPS - Candy - American Licorice Co.

LICORICE STICKS - Candy - Sahagian & Associates, Inc.

LICORICE STIX - Candy - Leaf, Inc.

LICORICE STORE - Candy ☆ - Y & S Candies Inc.

LICORICE STRIP - Pet products - Coastal Pet Products, Inc.

LID-CLAW - Housewares - Lid-Claw Inc.

LID LEASH - Apparel and accessories - Carol Jean Mitchell

LID-LOK - Infant product - Mericon Corp.

LID MAID - Kitchenware–plastic - G.S. Design, Inc.

LID-OFF - Housewares - Madsen Products Inc. (MEPCO)

LID POPPER - Tools–hand-operated - McClarin Manufacturing

LID WIPES-SPF - Ophthalmic goods - Akorn Inc.

LIDA-MANTLE - Pharmaceutical preparations - Miles Inc.

LIDA-MANTLE-HC - Pharmaceutical preparations - Miles Inc.

LIDAFORM-HC - Pharmaceutical preparations - Miles Inc.

LIDATEK - Measuring instruments - Lidatek LLC

LIDCO - Christmas tree lights - Lidco Co.

LIDDELL HOMEOPATHIC FORMULAE - Apparel and accessories - Integra Health International

LIDDLE GRIDDLE - Griddles–electric - National Presto Industries, Inc.

LIDDLE KIDDLES - Dolls - Link Group International

LIDE A BOW - Gift wrap and ribbon - Bowmaster Inc.

LIDET - Candy ☆ - R.L. Albert & Son, Inc.

LIDEX - Pharmaceutical preparations - Syntex USA, Inc.

LIDIARTE - Postcards - Fotofolio Inc.

LIDL - Musical instruments - Geneva International Corp.

LIDL - Musical instruments - Ideal Musical Merchandise Co.

LIDLOCKER - Helmets - PDH Corp.

LIDO - Blankets–electric ☆ - Sunbeam-Oster Household Products

LIDO - Cookies - Pepperidge Farm Inc.

LIDO - Desk sets ☆ - Park Sherman

LIDO - Dinnerware–glass ☆ - WMF/USA

LIDO - Floor coverings–carpet and rugs - Coronet Carpets Inc.

LIDO - Floor coverings–carpet and rugs - Western Carpet Mills

LIDO - Floor coverings–tile - Federal Tile Imports Inc.

LIDO - Food products - Pitsweet Inc.

LIDO - Frames–eyeglass - Zylo Ware Corp.

LIDO - Furniture - Lane Co. Inc.

LIDO - Glassware–household ☆ - Anchor Hocking Glass, Inc.

LIDO - Glassware–household ☆ - Avitra Corp.

LIDO - Hosiery - Kayser-Roth Corp.

LIDO - Lighting fixtures - Swivelier Co. Inc.

LIDO - Locks–padlocks - Kwikset Powdered Metal Products

LIDO - Medical apparatus - Orthomerica Products, Inc.

LIDO - Ships–sailing vessels - Lido 14 Association

LIDO - Shoes ☆ - World Import Co. Inc.

LIDO - Tiles–ceramic ☆ - Maxsam Sales, Inc.

LIDO - Tobacco products - Philip Morris Companies Inc.

LIDO - Wallpaper ☆ - Capital Carousel Inc.

LIDO - Watches - Bulova Corp.

LIDO CAFE ITALIA - Spaghetti sauces ☆ - Lido Cafe Italia

LIDO ISLE - Floor coverings–carpet and rugs ☆ - Catalina Carpet Mills Inc.

LIDO ITALIAN RESTORANTE - See **LIDO CAFE ITALIA**

LIDO PLATINUM - Dishes–china - Pasmantier Co. Inc.

LIDOCAINE - Pharmaceutical preparations - Legere Pharmaceuticals Inc.

LIDOCAINE HCL - Pharmaceutical preparations - Forest Pharmaceuticals Inc.

LIDOJECT - Pharmaceutical preparations - Merz Inc.

LIDOMAR - Cold remedies - Marlop Pharmaceuticals Inc.

LIDONE - Pharmaceutical preparations ☆ - Abbott Laboratories

LIDOPAIN - Pharmaceutical preparations - APL, American Pharmed Dr. Liedtke Inc.

LIDOSPORIN - Pharmaceutical preparations ☆ - Burroughs Wellcome Co.

LIDOXIDE - Prescription drug - IDE-Interstate Inc.

LIDPAK - Medical apparatus - Artromick International, Inc.

LIDS - Apparel and accessories - Lids, Inc.

LIDS & LASHES - Cosmetics ☆ - Allergan, Inc.

LIE - Games - Fun Games Inc.

LIE-CHECK - Golfing equipment - Better Golf Products, Inc.

LIE-DETECTOR - Games - Mattel, Inc.

LIE DETECTOR - Games ☆ - Pressman Toy Corp.

LIEA - Blinds—vertical - Tontine/VyTech Industries Inc.

LIEBA - Jewelry ☆ - Latham Studios

LIEBCHEN - Wines ☆ - Bell Mountain Vineyards Inc.

LIEBERFOAM - Padding—foam - B & G Lieberman Co., Inc.

LIEBERMAN'S - Tobacco - Conwood Co. L.P.

LIEBERSEW - Padding—foam - B & G Lieberman Co., Inc.

LIEBERSIL - Padding—foam - B & G Lieberman Co., Inc.

LIEBESTRAUBEN - Wines - Warner Vineyards Inc.

LIEBLINGS - Giftware ☆ - Enesco Corp.

LIEBOTSCHANER CREAM ALE - Beverages—malt - Lion Brewery, Inc.

LIEFMANS FRAMBOZENBIER - Beverages—malt ☆ - Phoenix Imports Ltd.

LIEFMANS GOUDENBAND - Beverages—malt - Phoenix Imports Ltd.

LIEFMANS KRIEKBIER - Beverages—malt ☆ - Phoenix Imports Ltd.

LIEKEN - Food products ☆ - Norganic Foods USA Inc.

LIERRE - Floor coverings—carpet and rugs ☆ - Customweave Carpets Inc.

LIETTE - Infant product ☆ - Gerry Sportswear Corp.

LIETTE INTERNATIONAL - Bathroom accessories - Liette International Ltd.

LIEUTENANT - Ophthalmic goods - Foremost Optical Products

LIEUTENANT - Sunglasses - Command Marketing Corp.

LIEUTENANT COMMANDER TUVOK - Toys - Paramount Pictures Corp.

LIEUTENANT LEGG - Toys - Mattel, Inc.

LIEUTENANT TOM PARIS - Toys - Paramount Pictures Corp.

L.I.F. - Belts—apparel - Leon Fleischer, International Marketing

LIF-1Z - Pharmaceutical preparations ☆ - Boots Pharmaceuticals Inc.

LIF-LIK LURES - Fishing lures - McDonald Manufacturers and Lif-Lik Lures

LIF-O-GEN - Oxygen tents - Allied Healthcare Products Inc.

LIFA - Film—motion picture ☆ - Edixa Camera Co.

LIFA - Underwear and nightwear - Helly-Hansen Inc.

LIFAIR - Health care products - Respiratory Systems Inc.

LIFE - Apparel stores—lingerie - Formfit Rogers

LIFE - Cereal - Quaker Oats Co.

LIFE - Cigarettes - Brown & Williamson Tobacco Corp.

LIFE - Food products ☆ - Liberty Richter Inc.

LIFE - Hair care products - Del Pharmaceuticals, Inc.

LIFE - Hardware - Boatlife Inc.

LIFE - Medical apparatus - Life Corp.

LIFE - Paints—artists' ☆ - Canson-Talens Inc.

LIFE - Pharmaceuticals ☆ - Iodent Co.

LIFE - Underwear and nightwear - Jockey International, Inc.

LIFE - Water purification systems - Terragroup Corp.

LIFE-02 - Oxygen - Life Corp.

LIFE & DEATH - Computer software - Software Toolworks, Inc.

LIFE & TIMES - Photo albums - Grece Ellen Helmin

LIFE BASICS - Apparel and accessories - Jacob Rose Inc.

LIFE-BEARER - Veterinary pharmaceutical preparations - Aquarium Products Inc.

LIFE-CAFFE - Vitamins and nutritional supplements - Beverly Hills International, Inc.

LIFE-CALK - Caulking compounds - Boatlife Inc.

LIFE CHAMBER - Machine parts - Flowserve Corp. (Fluid Sealing Division)

LIFE CHANGES. WE'LL BE THERE. - Banks—commercial - Ohio National Life Insurance Co.

LIFE CHOICE - Vitamins and nutritional supplements - U.S. Pharmaceuticals, Inc.

LIFE COLOR-IN POSTERS - Posters - Sports Illustrated

LIFE-CORE - Doors—storm - Larson Manufacturing Co.

LIFE CRYSTALS - Vitamin and supplement drink - Life Crystals, Inc.

LIFE CYCLE - Exercising equipment - Life Fitness

LIFE CYCLE OF SEA LAMPREY - Computer software - Ventura Educational Systems

LIFE DATA - Vitamins and nutritional supplements - Life Data Labs, Inc.

LIFE DECK - Paints - Life Paint Corp.

LIFE DEFENSE - Vitamins and nutritional supplements - Source Naturals

LIFE ENERGY KIT, THE - Health care products ☆ - Oakmont Investments Co.

LIFE EXTENSION INTERNATIONAL - Vitamins and nutritional supplements - James M. Fobair

LIFE FITNESS - Exercising equipment - Life Fitness

LIFE-FLEX - Furniture ☆ - Sico Inc.

LIFE FLORA - Vitamins and nutritional supplements - Source Naturals

LIFE FORCE - Vitamins and nutritional supplements - Source Naturals

LIFE FORMS - Computer software - Kinetic Effects Inc.

LIFE FORMULA - Vitamins and nutritional supplements - King Bio Pharmaceuticals, Inc.

LIFE FREE - Bathroom fixtures - Showerlux USA

LIFE FROM THE SEA - Vitamins and nutritional supplements - Seaborne, Inc.

LIFE-GLAS - Hardware ☆ - Boatlife Inc.

LIFE GUARD - See **VITA GUARD**

LIFE GUARD - Chemical preparations - Defense Products, Inc.

LIFE GUARD - Giftware - Wyler Sales Corp.

LIFE GUARD - Gloves - Southern Pacific Coast Corp.

LIFE GUARD - Pet collars ☆ - Precious Paws

LIFE GUARD - Vitamins and nutritional supplements ☆ - Morton Pharmaceuticals Inc.

LIFE GUARDS - Labels—paper - Wetterau Inc.

LIFE IN THE COUNTRY - Dolls ☆ - Effanbee Doll Corp.

LIFE IN THE FAST LANE - Greeting cards ☆ - Brett-Forer Greetings Inc.

LIFE IN THE OCEANS - Computer software - Right on Programs

LIFE IS A SPORT DRINK IT UP. - Beverages - Stokely-Van Camp, Inc.

LIFE IS ART - Apparel and accessories - Carlskin Manufacturing Co., Inc.

LIFE IS BETTER WITH SEXX - Cosmetics - Hyman Levy

LIFE IS FUN - Posters - McCool Unlimited, Inc.

LIFE IS PRECIOUS - Book marks - Liberty Enterprises

LIFE IS SHORT. STAY AWAKE FOR IT. - Shirts - Caribou Coffee Co., Inc.

LIFE-JACKETS - Electronic equipment - General Binding Corp.

LIFE JOURNEY - Publisher's imprint - David C. Cook Publishing Co.

LIFE KEEPER - Diaries - Randall H. Bloem

LIFE LADDER - Fire-escape ladders - American La France

LIFE LIKE - Novelty items - Imagineering Inc.

LIFE-LIKE - Toys—trains - Life-Like Products Inc.

LIFE LIKE - Wigs - C.B. Manufacturing Co. Inc.

LIFE LIKE BABY - Dolls - Horsman

LIFE LINE - Food products - Universal Foods Corp.

LIFE LINE - Medical apparatus - Bristoline Inc.

LIFE LINE - Toothbrushes - Lever Brothers Co. Inc.

LIFE-LINE - Vitamins and nutritional supplements - Life-Line Inc.

LIFE LINES - Office supplies - Life Lines Manufacturing

LIFE LINK - Communications equipment - Operation Assistance, Inc.

LIFE-LINK - Sporting goods - Life-Link International, Inc.

LIFE-LITE - Flashlights - Garrity Industries

LIFE-LITE - Lighting fixtures - Garon Products Inc.

LIFE LITERS - Vitamins and nutritional supplements - Zontania Inc.

L.I.F.E. LIVING IN A FREE ENVIRONMENT - Apparel and accessories - Pourquoi? M.P.S. Inc.

LIFE LOCK - Flowers, plants, and seeds - W. Atlee Burpee and Co.

LIFE LOCK - Locks—padlocks - Life Lock Inc.

LIFE MAGAZINE REMEMBERS - Games ☆ - Milton Bradley Co.

LIFE MINERALS - Vitamins and nutritional supplements - Source Naturals

LIFE-MIST - Health care products - Roman Labs Inc.

LIFE-MIST II - Health care products - Roman Labs Inc.

LIFE MIX - Vitamins and nutritional supplements - Nutra-Source Corp.

LIFE O' THE PARTY - Napkins—paper - Beach Products

LIFE OF THE PARTY - Housewares ☆ - Ullman Co. Inc.

LIFE OFF - Cleaning preparations - Brothers Three Inc.

LIFE OXYGENPAC - Oxygen - Life Corp.

LIFE PAGER - Personal defense products - Westar Industries, Inc.

LIFE PLANT, THE - Flowers, plants, and seeds - Bizarre Products

LIFE PRECAUTIONS - Vitamins and nutritional supplements - Bioenergy Nutrient's Inc.

LIFE PRIORITY - Vitamins and nutritional supplements - Life Priority

LIFE PULSE - Vitamins and nutritional supplements - Planetary Formulas

LIFE-RENEWAL - Pharmaceutical preparations - Life-Renewal Inc.

LIFE SAFETY IS SERIOUS WORK - Safety products - United Fire Equipment Co.

LIFE SAVER - Dishes—plastic - Deka Plastics Inc.

LIFE SAVER - Toys - Azrak-Hamway International, Inc.

LIFE SAVERS - Bedding—linen - Dan River Inc.

LIFE SAVERS - Decorations - Nabisco Holdings Corp.

LIFE SAVERS - Infant product - Nabisco Brands Inc.

LIFE SAVERS - Puzzles ☆ - Ben Cooper Inc.

LIFE SAVERS SO FULL OF LIFE - Beverages - Nabisco Brands Co.

☆ = Now out of production

LIFE-SEAL - Caulking compounds - Boatlife Inc.

LIFE SHARK - Vitamins and nutritional supplements - MCL Enterprise, Inc.

LIFE SHIELD - Nutritional food supplement - New Moon Extracts, Inc.

LIFE SHIELD - Vitamins and nutritional supplements ☆ - Vitamin Research Products Inc.

LIFE SIGNS - Greeting cards ☆ - Thought Factory

LIFE SIZE SOFTEE - Dolls - Horsman

LIFE SLED - Sleds - Terry Allen Jesse

LIFE SOLUBLES - Vitamins and nutritional supplements - Integris Corp.

LIFE SOURCE - Pet products ☆ - Wysong Corp.

LIFE SPAN - Pet food - Petguard, Inc.

LIFE SPAN - Recording label - Institute of Preventive Medicine, Inc.

LIFE SPAN - Vitamins and nutritional supplements - Shaklee Corp.

LIFE-SPANNER - Vitamins and nutritional supplements - G.O. Spanner Inc.

LIFE SPARK - Vitamins and nutritional supplements - Source Naturals

LIFE SPIRIT - Greeting cards - Life Spirit

LIFE SPORTS - Apparel and accessories - Mr. Tees Imprinted Sportswear, Inc.

LIFE STAR - See **DEEP SPACE: OPERATION COPERNICUS**

LIFE START - Health care products - Natren Inc.

LIFE STRIDE - Footwear - Brown Shoe Co.

LIFE STYLE - Dishes–china - Mikasa Co.

LIFE-STYLE - Gloves - Fownes Brothers & Co., Inc.

LIFE STYLE - Vitamin and mineral supplements - Lifestyle Nutrition, Inc.

LIFE STYLER - Exercising equipment ☆ - American Athletic Inc.

LIFE STYLES - Glassware–household - Owens-Illinois Inc. (Libbey Div.)

LIFE-STYLES - Wallpaper - Madison Wallcoverings

LIFE SUPPORT - Medical apparatus - Carolon Co.

LIFE SUPPORT FOR ARTIFICIAL EYES - Ophthalmic goods - Integrated Orbital Implants

LIFE-TEX - Hair care products ☆ - Wella Corp. (Consumer Products Div.)

LIFE TIME - Faucet handles ☆ - Life Time Faucets Inc.

LIFE-TIME - Health care products - Nutritional Specialties Inc.

LIFE TIME - Pet products ☆ - Farnam Cos. Inc.

LIFE TIME FITNESS - Physical fitness centers - FCA, Ltd.

LIFE TIME PUBLISHERS, INC. - Publisher's imprints - Life Time Publishers, Inc.

LIFE, TIMES, AND MUSIC SERIES - Prerecorded compact discs - Michael Friedman Publishing Group

LIFE TONE - Audio equipment - Hiraoka New York Corp.

LIFE TOOLS - Vitamins and nutritional supplements - APIC USA, Inc.

LIFE TRACE - Medical apparatus - Graphic Controls Corp.

LIFE TREATS - Veterinary pharmaceutical preparations - Deprenyl Animal Health Inc.

LIFE-TRED - Floor coverings ☆ - Pantasote Inc. (Wallcovering Div.)

LIFE-VAC - Health care products - Roman Labs Inc.

LIFE VIVIT - Water–bottled or canned - John H. Brake

LIFE WITHOUT LIMITS - Recording label - Midwest Center for Stress and Anxiety, Inc.

LIFE WOOD - Wood products - Weyerhaeuser Co.

LIFE WORKS - Vitamins and nutritional supplements - Ontrend Enterprises, Inc.

LIFEAIR - Health care products - Respiratory Systems Inc.

LIFEANSWERS - Recording label - Sunday School Board of the Southern Baptist Convention

LIFEBOLT - Locks–door ☆ - Dexter Lock

LIFEBOUY - Soap - Lever Brothers Co. Inc.

LIFEBUOY - Containers - Lever Investments Corp.

LIFECAPSULE - Containers–plastic - Michael J. Davidson

LIFECARE - Health care products - Respironics, Inc.

LIFECHANGERS - Recording label - Life Changers, Inc.

LIFECHOICE - Food products - Conagra, Inc.

LIFECIRCUIT - Exercising equipment - Life Fitness

LIFECOTE - Chemical preparations - Lifecote, Inc.

LIFECOTE 2000 - Copper compounds ☆ - Regal Ware, Inc.

LIFECYCLE - Dental supplies - Midwest Dental Products Corp.

LIFECYCLE - Exercising equipment - Life Fitness

LIFECYCLE - Plastics - Advanced Environmental Recycling Technologies, Inc.

LIFECYCLES - Furniture ☆ - Lane Co. Inc.

LIFEESSENTIALS - Machinery - Round Grove Machine Corp.

LIFEEVENTS - Computer software - A.D.A.M. Software, Inc.

LIFEFACTS - Educational materials - James Stanfield and Co., Inc.

LIFEFORCE - Pharmaceutical preparations ☆ - Bewley Irish Imports

LIFEFORMS - Costumes - Lifeforms International, Inc.

LIFEFORMS INTERNATIONAL - Apparel and accessories - Lifeforms International, Inc.

LIFEGARD - Aquarium accessories - Rainbow Lifegard Aquarium Products

LIFEGARD - Safety products - Plastic Safety Systems, Inc.

LIFEGARD - Telephone apparatus - Allen Telecom Group, Inc.

LIFEGARD-CN - Safety products - Plastic Safety Systems, Inc.

LIFEGEAR GET YOUR LIFE IN GEAR! - Exercising equipment - Lifegear Inc.

LIFEGOALS - Computer software - Successful Money Management Seminars, Inc.

LIFEGUARD - Colognes - Brandy Harvest

LIFEGUARD - Computer software - Graphic Media, Inc.

LIFEGUARD - Fencing–steel - Sonco Wholesale Fence Corp.

LIFEGUARD - First aid kits - Pollenex Corp.

LIFEGUARD - Fruits–dried - Silver Springs Citrus

LIFEGUARD - Lamps - Philips Lighting Co.

LIFEGUARD SUIT, THE - Bathing suits - Gulbenkian Swim Inc.

LIFEGYM - Exercising equipment ☆ - Life Fitness

LIFEHOLD - Hair care products - European Tanning Systems Inc.

LIFEHOOD - Air purification systems - Knight International Holdings, Inc.

LIFEJACKET - Building materials - Alltrista Corp.

LIFEKEEPER - Computer software - NCR Corp.

LIFEKIT - Medical apparatus - Physio-Control Corp.

LIFELAST - Paints - Lifelast, Inc.

LIFELIFT - Health care products - Giant Lift Equipment

LIFELIGHTS - Backpacks - Travers Bay Manufacturing Inc.

LIFELIKE - Artists' materials - European Imports of California Inc.

LIFELINC - Health care products - Tronomed Inc.

LIFELINE - Amplifiers–public address - Lifeline Amplification Systems, Inc.

LIFELINE - Animal feed supplements - American Protein Corp.

LIFELINE - Curling irons–electric - Andis Co.

LIFELINE - Fertilizers - Pace National Corp.

LIFELINE - Fishing tackle - Ashaway Line & Twine Manufacturing Co.

LIFELINE - Health care products - Lifeline International

LIFELINE - Sporting goods - Mueller Sports Medicine Inc.

LIFELINE - Stains - Perma-Chink Systems, Inc.

LIFELINE/BENSON - Recording label ☆ - Benson Music Group

LIFELINE BOOKS - Publisher's imprints ☆ - Woodbridge Press Publishing Co.

LIFELINER PREMIUM - Tires ☆ - Cooper Tire & Rubber Co.

LIFELINES - Audio equipment - Pro-Co. Sound Co. Inc.

LIFELINES - Cables - PRO Manufacturing

LIFELINES - Floor coverings–carpet and rugs - Gencorp Inc.

LIFELITE - Lighting fixtures - Lights of America Inc.

LIFELONG - Filters–air - Philip A. Office

LIFELONG - Filters–air - Philo Marketing Group

LIFELONG - Skin care products - Goldline Laboratories, Inc.

LIFEMAPPING - Publisher's imprints - John Trent

LIFEMASTER 2000 - Paints - Glidden Co.

LIFEMASTER PRO - Paints - Glidden Co.

LIFEMATE - Computer software - Taylor Cos. Inc.

LIFEMATE - Vitamins and nutritional supplements - Nat-Rul Health Products, Inc.

LIFEMAX - Books–blank - Guilt-Free Time Management

LIFEMONITOR - Exercising equipment - Roadmaster Corp.

LIFEPAK - Vitamins and nutritional supplements - Nu Skin International, Inc.

LIFEPHASE - Vitamins and nutritional supplements - Lifephase Inc.

LIFEPOINTS - Computer software - Frank Russell Co.

LIFER-B - Pharmaceutical preparations - Physician Sales & Service

LIFER JUICE - Cups–paper - Liffer Juice

LIFERACER - Exercising equipment - Life Fitness

LIFERAVITE - Pharmaceutical preparations - Wesley Pharmacal Co. Inc.

LIFEROWER - Exercising equipment - Life Fitness

LIFE'S A BEACH BEAR - Toys–stuffed - Russ Berrie and Co., Inc.

LIFE'S A PITCH Q QUICKSILVER PROPELLERS - Apparel and accessories - Brunswick Corp.

LIFE'S A QUEST - Apparel and accessories - Quest Apparel and Novelties

LIFE'S A WAVE - Apparel and accessories - William Urbany

LIFE'S ENDEARMENTS - Figurines - Papel Freelance, Inc.

LIFE'S FINEST - Vitamins - Nutrition Headquarters, Inc.

LIFE'S GIFTS - Frames–picture - Terragrafics Inc.

LIFE'S LITTLE DETOURS - Novelty items - Agent Andy Inc.

LIFE'S LITTLE MERIT BADGES - Jewelry - Randall Parkin

LIFE'S MOTIVATIONS - Paper punches - AGC, Inc.

LIFE'S MUCH TOO SHORT TO BE SMALL - Apparel and accessories - Bashlin Industries Inc.

LIFE'S RUFF - Calendars - AGC, Inc.

LIFE'S RUFF - Calendars - American Greetings Corp.

LIFE'S TOO SHORT TO BE TIRED - Vitamins and nutritional supplements - Richardson Labs, Inc.

LIFESAKE - Flowers, plants, and seeds - Faster-Form Corp.

☆ = Now out of production

LIFESAKE - Flowers, plants, and seeds - Lifesake Faster-Form Co.
LIFESAVER - Alarm systems–fire - Fyrnetics Inc.
LIFESAVER - Health care products - Hudson Respiratory Care Inc.
LIFESAVER - Knives - Buck Knives, Inc.
LIFESAVER - Lighting fixtures - Big Beam Emergency Systems Inc.
LIFESAVER - Smoke detectors - Kidde Safety
LIFESAVER - Thread ☆ - Perfect Thread Co. Inc.
LIFESAVER HOT BUTTON - Alarm systems ☆ - Fyrnetics Inc.
LIFESAVER SOFTWARE - Computer software - Lifesaver Software, Inc.
LIFESAVERS - Candy - Nabisco Foods Group
LIFESAVERS - Candy - Planters LifeSavers Co.
LIFESAVERS HOLES - Candy - Planters LifeSavers Co.
LIFESAVERS POPS - Candy - Planters LifeSavers Co.
LIFESAVERS SUPER HOLES - Candy - Planters LifeSavers Co.
LIFESCAN ONE TOUCH - Medical apparatus - Johnson & Johnson
LIFESCAPES - Educational materials - Lifescapes Corp.
LIFESCAPES - Posters - Successories, Inc.
LIFESCAPES - Tape players–cassette - Arundel-Doerr-Harrison Co.
LIFESCAPES LITHOGRAPHS - Greeting cards - Celex Group, Inc.
LIFESCOPE - Computer software - Lee Lukehart
LIFESEQ - Computer software - Incyte Pharmaceuticals, Inc.
LIFESHIELD - Machine parts - Flowserve Corp. (Fluid Sealing Division)
LIFESIGHT - Lenses–optical - Gentex Corp.
LIFESIGN - Health care products - Health Innovations
LIFESIGN MI - Pharmaceutical preparations - Princeton Biomeditech Corp.
LIFESIZER - Lenses–photographic - SP Systems/Saratons
LIFESLIDER - Safety products - McGoff Enterprises, Inc.
LIFESONG - Recording label - Lifesong Records Inc.
LIFESONG/GOLDDIGGERS - Recording label - Lifesong Records Inc.
LIFESOUNDS - Electronic equipment - Marpac Corp.
LIFESPAN - Adhesives and sealants - XL Corp.
LIFESPAN - Furniture ☆ - Bassett Furniture Industries, Inc.
LIFESPAN - Hinges - Stanley Hardware Div.
LIFESPAN - Vitamins - Country Life
LIFESPINE - Mattresses - Fit For Life Sleep Inc.
LIFESTAGE - Vitamins and nutritional supplements - American Vitamin Products, Inc.
LIFESTAGE - Vitamins and nutritional supplements - Thompson and Formby
LIFESTAR - Vitamins and nutritional supplements - The Lifestar Millennium, Inc.
LIFESTEEL - Siding–metal - Alcan Aluminum Corp. Alcan Building Products Div.
LIFESTEP - Exercising equipment - Life Fitness
LIFESTORIES GAME - Games - Talicor Inc.
LIFESTREAM - Vitamins and nutritional supplements - Sunrider Corp.
LIFESTREAM - Vitamins and nutritional supplements - Sunrider International
LIFESTYLE - Brooms - DQB Industries
LIFESTYLE - Filters–air - Permatron Corp.
LIFESTYLE - Floor coverings–carpet and rugs - Philadelphia Carpets
LIFESTYLE - Floor coverings–carpet and rugs - Prestige Mills Inc.
LIFESTYLE - Furniture ☆ - Lexington Furniture Industries, Inc.
LIFESTYLE - Furniture ☆ - Virginia House Furniture Corp.
LIFESTYLE - Gloves - Fownes Brothers & Co., Inc.
LIFESTYLE - Mobile homes - Aluminum Co. of America
LIFESTYLE - Ovens–microwave ☆ - Quasar Co.
LIFESTYLE - Patterns–clothing ☆ - Simplicity Pattern Co., Inc.
LIFESTYLE - Plates–paper - Fonda Group, Inc.
LIFESTYLE - Shelving units–metal - Dorfile Manufacturing Co.
LIFESTYLE - Sound equipment - Bose Corp.
LIFESTYLE - Swimming pools - Home & Roam Leisure Products, Inc.
LIFESTYLE - Wallpaper - Surface Industries Inc.
LIFESTYLE - Wallpaper ☆ - Imperial Wallcoverings, Inc.
LIFESTYLE - Wigs - Revlon General Wig Manufacturers, Inc.
LIFESTYLE 2000 - Tables–wood - Quaker Industries Ltd.
LIFESTYLE ACADEMY - Publisher's imprints - Lifestyle Academy Inc.
LIFESTYLE COLLECTION - Watches ☆ - SMH (US) Inc.
LIFESTYLE ELEMENTS BY SONIA G. - Apparel and accessories ☆ - Kellwood Co.
LIFESTYLE II - Ovens–microwave ☆ - Quasar Co.
LIFESTYLE NUTRITION - Vitamins and nutritional supplements - North West Marketing Co.
LIFESTYLE ORGANIZER - Office supplies ☆ - Two's Co. Inc.
LIFESTYLER - Exercising equipment - Sears, Roebuck and Co.
LIFESTYLES - Bags - Duray Co.
LIFESTYLES - Blinds–venetian ☆ - Hunter Douglas, Inc.
LIFESTYLES - Floor coverings–carpet and rugs - Mohawk Carpet Corp.

LIFESTYLES - Giftware - Vargas Manufacturing Co.
LIFESTYLES - Glassware–household - Libbey Glass Inc.
LIFESTYLES - Greeting cards ☆ - American Greetings Corp.
LIFESTYLES - Pharmaceutical preparations ☆ - Warner-Lambert Co.
LIFESTYLES - Prophylactics - Ansell Inc. (Personal Products Div.)
LIFESTYLES - Recording label - Lso Ltd.
LIFESTYLES - Wallpaper - Bayview Wallcoverings
LIFESTYLES NON-STICK STAINLESS COOKWARE - Cooking equipment–household - Nordic Ware
LIFESTYLES OF THE 90'S - Wallpaper - Southland Wallcoverings
LIFESTYLES OF THE HOT WET & WILD - Post cards - Philip Mattes
LIFESTYLES OF THE NOT-SO-RICH - Giftware - Russ Berrie and Co., Inc.
LIFESUSTAINER - Medical apparatus - Bio-Preserve Medical Corp.
LIFETECH - Chemical preparations - FMC Corp.
LIFETECH - Vitamins and nutritional supplements - Lifetech Industries Ltd.
LIFETIME - Spilo/Mehaz Worldwide
LIFETIME - Bicycles - Columbia Manufacturing Inc.
LIFETIME - Brackets - S-B Manufacturing Co. Ltd.
LIFETIME - Calculators ☆ - Rediform
LIFETIME - Caulking compounds - Red Devil Inc.
LIFETIME - Cheese - Dairy Fresh Products Co.
LIFETIME - Cheese - Lifeline International
LIFETIME - Cutlery - Lifetime Hoan Corp.
LIFETIME - Doors–storm - Remington Building Products
LIFETIME - Easels ☆ - The Tiffen Co.
LIFETIME - Electronic equipment - Tandy Corp.
LIFETIME - Faucets - Life Time Faucets Inc.
LIFETIME - Flatware - Kimco International Inc.
LIFETIME - Floor coverings - Tarkett, Inc.
LIFETIME - Hair care products ☆ - Dubl Duck/Jet Set Inc.
LIFETIME - Knives–putty - Hyde Manufacturing Co.
LIFETIME - Mattress pads - Chatham Manufacturing Co.
LIFETIME - Motor vehicles–motor homes ☆ - Commodore Corp.
LIFETIME - Pens ☆ - Sheaffer Inc.
LIFETIME - Pet products - Pet-Master Products Co.
LIFETIME - Recording label - Lifetime Recordings
LIFETIME - Shelving units–wood ☆ - Home Equipment Manufacturing Co.
LIFETIME - Sporting goods ☆ - Mill Run Products Co.
LIFETIME - Thermometers - Republic Drug Co. Inc.
LIFETIME - Tools–hand-operated - Nupla Corp.
LIFETIME - Window coverings ☆ - Selfix, Inc.
LIFETIME - Wiring devices - Pass & Seymour, Inc.
LIFETIME AUTOMOTIVE PRODUCTS - Cleaning preparations - Lifetime Automotive Products Inc.
LIFETIME BRITE - Floor coverings - Tarkett, Inc.
LIFETIME DEL-RAIN - Heating equipment - Del-Rain Corp.
LIFETIME ELEGANCE - Floor coverings - Tarkett, Inc.
LIFETIME FAUCETS - Faucets - Life Time Faucets Inc.
LIFETIME FILTER - Filters–air - LifeTime Filter Inc.
LIFETIME FINISH FROM BALDWIN, THE - Coatings - Baldwin Hardware Corp.
LIFETIME GOLDEN - Cutlery ☆ - Lifetime Hoan Corp.
LIFETIME-ID - Medical apparatus - Bio-Pak Associates
LIFETIME LATTICE - Building materials - Fort Wayne Plastics, Inc.
LIFETIME LEISURE - Furniture - Lifetime Products, Inc.
LIFETIME LEISURE NO ASSEMBLY REQUIRED. - Tables–wood - Lifetime Products, Inc.
LIFETIME LIBRARY - Computer software - Liafail, Inc.
LIFETIME MATCH - Lighters - Spraz Co.
LIFETIME PLUS - Extension cords - General Cable Corp.
LIFETIME-QPF - Caulking compounds - Red Devil Inc.
LIFETIME RED - Glass products - Corning Inc.
LIFETIME SCHOLAR - Video production - Logos Productions Inc.
LIFETIME SHEFFIELD - Cutlery ☆ - Lifetime Hoan Corp.
LIFETIME SYSTEM, THE - Paper–book ☆ - Rediform
LIFETIME WHIRL - Playground equipment - Miracle Recreation Equipment Co.
LIFETIMER - Brushes–paint - American Brush Co. Inc.
LIFETIMERS - Jewelry - American Foreign Trade Inc.
LIFETONE - Cookies ☆ - Lifetone International Inc.
LIFETONE - Cosmetics ☆ - Elysee Scientific Cosmetic Co.
LIFETONE THINS - Crackers ☆ - Lifetone International Inc.
LIFEWALL - Wallpaper ☆ - Pantasote Inc. (Wallcovering Div.)
LIFEWATCH - Smoke detectors - Lifewatch
LIFEWAY - Yogurt - Lifeway Foods, Inc.
LIFEWAY LITE - Cakes ☆ - Lifeway Foods, Inc.
LIFEWEAR - Shoes - Messer Import Corp.

☆ = Now out of production

LIFEWISE - Vitamins and nutritional supplements - Lifewise Naturals, Inc.

LIFEWISE NATURALS - Vitamin supplements - Lifewise Naturals, Inc.

LIFEWISE NATURALS - Vitamins and nutritional supplements - Lifewise Naturals, Inc.

LIFEX - Batteries - Rayovac Corp.

LIFEX - Water purification systems - Life Ozone Corp.

LIFEZYME - Vitamins and nutritional supplements - Teamup International, Inc.

LIFF BELT - Medical equipment - Ida M. Butterfield

LIFO - Computer software - Ashford Software

LIFOAM - Ice chests–foam - Life-Like Products Inc.

LIFOCORT - Pharmaceutical preparations ☆ - Roberts/Hauck Pharmaceuticals Inc.

LIFOJECT - Pharmaceutical preparations ☆ - Merz Inc.

LIFOLBEX - Pharmaceutical preparations ☆ - Central Pharmaceutical Inc.

LIFOLEX - Pharmaceutical preparations - Pasadena Research Laboratories, Inc.

LIFOMIN - Health care products - Kay Pharmacal Co. Inc.

LIFT - Machinery - Lift Products

LIFT - Nuts–salted, roasted, cooked, or canned ☆ - Leavitt Corp.

LIFT-A-WAY - Health care products - Braun Corp.

LIFT-AID - Medical apparatus - Guardian Products Inc.

LIFT-AIDE - Automotive parts and accessories - Outboard Marine Corp.

LIFT ALL - Medical apparatus - Amigo Mobility International Inc.

LIFT AND CUT - Razors–electric - Phillips Electronics North America Corp.

LIFT & LOAD BUILDERS - Toys - Fisher-Price, Inc.

LIFT & LOAD LUMBER YARD - Toys - Fisher-Price, Inc.

LIFT & LOOK WOODEN PUZZLES - Puzzles - Guidecraft Inc.

LIFT AND SEAL - Doors–glass - Sterling Plumbing Group Inc.

LIFT AND TURN - Hardware - Southco, Inc.

LIFT CUSHION - Pillows - Better Sleep, Inc.

LIFT EASE - Electronic equipment - Hamilton Electronics Corp.

LIFT-ETTE - Elevators - Inclinator Co. of America

LIFT EXTREME - Skin care products - Monteil Paris

LIFT IT - Motor vehicle parts and accessories - AVM, Inc.

LIFT LINE - Racks - Brian Barry

LIFT-LOK - Stools–metal ☆ - Counterpoint

LIFT MASTER - Bowling balls ☆ - Master Industries Inc.

LIFT MATES - Shock absorbers–motor vehicle - Questor Corp.

LIFT N GO - Hoists - Capitol Tool and Die Co.

LIFT 'N LOOK - Puzzles - Playskool, Inc.

LIFT N PIK - Cosmetics - Capitol Novelty Co.

LIFT-N-SEAL - Envelopes - Mail-Well Envelope

LIFT N' SIFT - Pet products - Purrco Products Inc.

LIFT 'N STOW - Brackets - Reightley Co., Inc.

LIFT NO MORE - Manicure preparations - Flying Emery Board Inc.

LIFT-O-FLEX - Machinery - R on I, LLC

LIFT O' MATIC - Health care products - Craftmatic/Contour Industries Inc.

LIFT O MATIC - Health care products - Marc-Us Industries Inc.

LIFT-O-MATIC - Machinery - Worth Equipment Parts and Service Co., Inc.

LIFT OFF - Cleaning preparations - Twi-Laq Industries Inc.

LIFT OFF - Emulsifiers - Bond Adhesives Co.

LIFT OFF - Nail care products - No Lift Nails, Inc.

LIFT OFF - Paints - Midco Products Co. Inc.

LIFT-OFF - Ribbons ☆ - Eaton Allen Ko-Rec-Type Corp.

LIFT-OFF - Shampoos - Bissell Inc.

LIFT OFF! - Skin care products - Aramis Inc.

LIFT-OFF - Skin care products - Ardell International Inc.

LIFT-OFF - Vinyl - Richards Distributing, Inc.

LIFT RACK HANDLE PAN, THE - Pans - Handi-Foil Corp.

LIFT-RITE - Ribbons–inked - Smith Corona Corp.

LIFT SERUM - Skin care products - Chanel Inc.

LIFT THE DOT - Fasteners–snap - American Engineer Components

LIFT TICKET - Waterproof outerwear - Gordon & Ferguson of Delaware, Inc.

LIFT TICKET, THE - Computer software - Eugene F. Dente

LIFT-TRU - Sporting goods ☆ - King Louie International Inc.

LIFT-U - Adhesives and sealants - Hogan Manufacturing Inc.

LIFT-UP - Boxes–corrugated paperboard - Compulist, Inc.

LIFT-UP - Underwear and nightwear ☆ - Lovable Co.

LIFT/WALKER - Railroad equipment - Brookville Mining Equipment Corp.

LIFTA DECK - Automotive accessories - Ancra International Corp.

LIFTABLES - Decals and transfers ☆ - Sangray Corp.

LIFTAMI - Health care products - Uplift Enterprises Inc.

LIFTED GEAR - Apparel and accessories - Lifted Gear, LLC

LIFTED SPIRITS - Paper products - Colorbok Paper Products, Inc.

LIFTER - Soap - La-Co Industries, Inc.

LIFTER - Toys - Tonka Corp.

LIFTER, THE - Automotive parts and accessories - AP Parts

LIFTLIMIT - Computer software - U.E.S. Inc.

LIFTMASTER - Electrical equipment - Chamberlain Group Inc.

LIFTMASTER - Machinery - JLG Industries Inc.

LIFTMASTER FORKLIFT - Tires - Galaxy Tire & Wheel, Inc.

LIFTMATE - Medical apparatus - McKenney Group

LIFT'N LOCK - Stoves - White Consolidated Industries, Inc.

LIFTOFF - Publisher's imprints - McGraw-Hill Companies, Inc.

LIFTPAK - Motors–automotive - Reliance Electric Co.

LIFTSTATION - Sporting goods - Isotechnologies Inc.

LIFTX - Vitamins and nutritional supplements - Medicis Pharmaceutical Corp.

LIFTZ - Skin care products - Sequel Products Inc.

LIGA-TEND - Vitamins - Country Life

LIGANO - Floor coverings–carpet and rugs - Tek Stil Concepts Inc.

LIGHT - Breads - Natural Ovens of Manitowoc Inc.

LIGHT - Recording label - Light Records, Inc.

LIGHT 80 CAL - Low-calorie yogurt - Continental Culture Specialists Inc.

LIGHT AIR - Switches–electric - DPI Labs, Inc.

LIGHT ALERT - Floodlights - RAB Electric

LIGHT AM - Meat products–canned - Hansel 'n Gretel Brand, Inc.

LIGHT & DARK - Computer software - Thought I Could

LIGHT AND DARK - Novelty items - Cal Themes Inc.

LIGHT & DRY - Nail care products - International Beauty Design, Inc.

LIGHT & EASY - Golfing equipment - Square Two Golf

LIGHT & ELEGANT - Food products - Conagra, Inc.

LIGHT & FIT - Health care products - Earthnet

LIGHT & FLUFFY - Beverages - Smoothie King Franchises, Inc.

LIGHT & FREE - Shampoos - Revlon Consumer Products Corp.

LIGHT & LEAN - Meat products–pork - Hormel Foods Corp.

LIGHT & LEAN 97 - Food products - Hormel Foods Corp.

LIGHT & LIVELY - Dishes–china - Mikasa Co.

LIGHT & NATURAL - Breads - Holsum Bakers

LIGHT & NATURAL - Cosmetics - Max Factor & Co.

LIGHT & NATURAL - Fish–fresh or frozen - Mrs. Paul's Kitchen

LIGHT & SHADOW - Incense - Gauntlet, Inc.

LIGHT & SHINE - Hair care products - Helene Curtis Industries Inc.

LIGHT & TENDER - Fish–fresh or frozen - Sara Lee Corp.

LIGHT & THIRSTY - Mops - Drackett Co.

LIGHT APPETITE - Health care products - Earthnet

LIGHT ART - Toys - Rose Art Industries, Inc.

LIGHT AS A FEATHER - Cosmetics - Dolly Parton Inc.

LIGHT AS A SNOWFLAKE - Jewelry - Snowflake Manufacturing Ltd.

LIGHT AWAKENINGS - Meat products - Saramar Corp.

LIGHT BALANCE - Food products - Dial Corp.

LIGHT BEAM - Clocks ☆ - By Design Corp.

LIGHT BENDERS - Eyeglasses - Wal-Mart Stores Inc.

LIGHT BLASTER - Lighting fixtures - Alltrade Inc.

LIGHT BLEND - Salad dressings–bottled - Cains Foods, Inc.

LIGHT BLOCKS - Lighting equipment ☆ - Creative Concepts

LIGHT BRIGADE - Bicycles - Columbia Manufacturing Inc.

LIGHT BRIGADE - Cigars ☆ - General Cigar Co., Inc.

LIGHT-CALL - Electronic equipment - United Communication Technology, Inc.

LIGHT CHARMS - Lighting fixtures - Edison Price Lighting

LIGHT CHOICE - Cottage cheese - Kraft Food Ingredients Corp.

LIGHT CHOICE - Meat products–cured ☆ - Pel-Freez Rabbit Meat, Inc.

LIGHT CHORE DAY, THE - Eggs - Michael L. Whalen

LIGHT CLASSIC - Confections - Sara Lee Corp.

LIGHT CONCEPTS - Lighting fixtures - Lithonia Lighting

LIGHT COOLERS - Beverages–alcohol - Joseph E. Seagram & Sons, Inc.

LIGHT CRUST - Flour–blended - Stevens Industries Inc.

LIGHT CRYSTALS - Toys - Tedco Inc.

LIGHT CUISINE - Mats - Matworks

LIGHT DELIGHTS - Apparel and accessories - Strouse, Adler Co.

LIGHT DESIGNS - Hobby kits - Craft House Corp.

LIGHT-DOME - Tents - Creative Energies Inc.

LIGHT DUTY - Detergents - Procter & Gamble Co.

LIGHT EFFECTS - Hair coloring preparations - Clairol Inc.

LIGHT EXPRESS - Switches–power - Fiber Optic Network Solutions Corp.

LIGHT EYES - Frames–eyeglass - Viva Optique, Inc.

LIGHT F/X - Posters - Upper Deck Co.

LIGHT FANTASTIC - Apparel–men's - J. Schoeneman Inc.

LIGHT FANTASTIC - Bags - N.A. Taylor Co. Inc.

LIGHT FANTASTIC - Wallpaper ☆ - Bob Mitchell Designs

LIGHT FIGHT - Games ☆ - Milton Bradley Co.

LIGHT FORCE - Floodlights - RAB Electric

LIGHT-FORMS - Lamps - Lumax Industries Inc.

☆ = Now out of production

LIGHT FRESH - Deodorizers - Church & Dwight Co.
LIGHT FRY - Oils—edible - California Olive Oil Corp.
LIGHT GARDE - Window coverings - Newell Operating Co.
LIGHT GLIDERS - Toys—models - Estes Industries
LIGHT GRIP SILICONE EYELASH EURLER - Cosmetics - Victoria Vogue, Inc.
LIGHT HEARTED - Salad dressings—bottled - John E. Cain Co.
LIGHT HEARTY - Breads - Stroehmann Bakeries Inc.
LIGHT HOUSE - Apparel - Light House Fashion, Inc.
LIGHT HOUSE POINT - Furniture - Bean Station Furniture Factory Inc.
LIGHT-HUMOR - Flashlights ☆ - Garrity Industries
LIGHT KILL - Electronic equipment - Dunbar-Nunn Corp.
LIGHT LEMON MOIST - Skin-care products - I Natural Cosmetics
LIGHT LIFT - Hair coloring preparations - Helene Curtis Industries Inc.
LIGHT-LIFT - Windows - Interstate Aluminum Distributors, Inc.
LIGHT LINES - Greeting cards - Wilmer Graphics Inc.
LIGHT LINES - Wallpaper - Sanitas Wallcoverings
LIGHT LINES TWO - Wallpaper - Sanitas Wallcoverings
LIGHT LOCK - Lenses—photographic - Polaroid Corp.
LIGHT LUNCH IN A CUP - Yogurt—frozen - Penguin Frozen Foods, Inc.
LIGHT LUXURY - Brassieres (Bras) ☆ - Montgomery Ward & Co. Inc.
LIGHT MAGIC - Syrup - Whitfield Foods, Inc.
LIGHT MAKER - Lighting equipment ☆ - Stylmark Inc.
LIGHT-MATE - Lighting equipment - Plasticoid Manufacturing Inc.
LIGHT MECHANIC - Ladders—metal - Rich Ladder Co.
LIGHT MOODS - Glassware—household - Durand International
LIGHT MOTIONIZER - Solar cells - Solar World
LIGHT MOUNTAIN - Health care products - Lotus Brands Inc.
LIGHT MOUNTAIN - Soap - Ayurherbal Corp.
LIGHT MOVES - Safety lights - Sara Abatiell Baer
LIGHT N' BLOCK - Skin care products - Physician's Choice of Arizona, Inc.
LIGHT-N-DESK SET - Lamps ☆ - Roxter Lighting
LIGHT N' EASY - Caulking compounds - Dap Products Inc.
LIGHT 'N EASY - Irons—electric - Black & Decker Corp.
LIGHT 'N EASY ROMEO - Footwear - West Coast Shoe Co.
LIGHT 'N FANCY - Candy ☆ - Pet Inc. (Whitman's Chocolates Div.)
LIGHT 'N FLUFFY - Noodles ☆ - Pastamania
LIGHT N' FLUFFY - Pasta - Hershey Pasta Group
LIGHT-N-FREE - Hair care products - Kizure Products Co., Inc.
LIGHT 'N LACY - Underwear and nightwear ☆ - Lovable Co.
LIGHT 'N LIVELY - Dairy products - Kraft Foods, Inc.
LIGHT 'N LIVELY - Floor coverings ☆ - Congoleum Corp.
LIGHT N LIVELY - Pipes—tobacco - Buescher's Industries Inc.
LIGHT 'N LIVELY FREE - Yogurt - Kraft Foods, Inc.
LIGHT 'N LIVELY KID PACK - Yogurt - Kraft Foods, Inc.
LIGHT-N-PLAY - Music boxes - National Artcraft Co.
LIGHT 'N SHINY - Cosmetics ☆ - Bonne Bell, Inc.
LIGHT 'N SOUND - Toy kitchen - Meritus Industries, Inc.
LIGHT-N-SPICY - Food products - Tyson Foods Inc.
LIGHT NATURALS - Cheese - Kraft Foods, Inc.
LIGHT NEUFCHATEL - Cheese - Kraft Foods, Inc.
LIGHT OF PEACE - Jewelry - Zale Corp.
LIGHT-ON-LIGHT - Underwear and nightwear - Exquisite Form Industries
LIGHT PAINTS - Nail care products - International Beauty Design, Inc.
LIGHT PLATE - Electrical equipment - Huey Co.
LIGHT POINT - Computer hardware - NMB Technologies Inc. (Hi-Tek Div.)
LIGHT POINTER - Electronic equipment - Leica USA Inc.
LIGHT POWDER - Deodorants—personal - Carter-Wallace, Inc.
LIGHT PREMIUM - Ice milk - Kinnett Dairies, Inc.
LIGHT-PRO - Prosthetic apparatus - Rothschild's Orthopedics, Inc.
LIGHT-PROJECT - Lighting fixtures - Light-Project International, Inc.
LIGHT PUMP - Lighting equipment - Remote Source Lighting International, Inc.
LIGHT RACERS - Toys—automobiles - Mattel, Inc.
LIGHT RECIPE - Seafood products—fresh or frozen - General Mills, Inc.
LIGHT REFLECTIONS A FREDERIC JOY GALLERY - Photograph prints, books, note cards, and posters - Light Reflections
LIGHT ROM - Computer storage devices—optical - Graphic Detail
LIGHT SELTZER - See **MOUNTAIN SPRING SPARKLER**
LIGHT SHAPERS - Shutters—wood - Pinecrest, Inc.
LIGHT SHIELD - Ophthalmic goods - Flents Products Co. Inc.
LIGHT SHOW - Fabrics - Interface, Inc.
LIGHT SIZE CLUBS - Fruits and vegetables - Harry and David Inc.
LIGHT SKIN PEEL - Skin care products - Reviva Laboratories
LIGHT SLICE - Breads ☆ - Norganic Foods USA Inc.
LIGHT, SOUND, ACTION - Toys—airplanes - Imperial Toy Corp.
LIGHT SOURCE - Nail care products - International Beauty Design, Inc.
LIGHT SOURCES - Suntan lotions - American Sunlight Inc.

LIGHT SPEED - Archery equipment - Saunders Archery Co.
LIGHT-SPEED - Machine parts - Double E Co., Inc.
LIGHT SPEED - Propellers - Brunswick Corp.
LIGHT SPEED FIGHTER - Toys - Fisher-Price, Inc.
LIGHT SPEEDERS - Toys—automobiles - Mattel, Inc.
LIGHT STRIP - Lighting fixtures - Lucifer Lighting Co.
LIGHT STYLE - Breads - Pepperidge Farm Inc.
LIGHT SUPPLY - Flashlights - Custom Accessories, Inc.
LIGHT TASTY SPREAD - Margarine - Nabisco Foods Group
LIGHT TEST - Smoke detectors - BRK Electronics Inc.
LIGHT, THE - Golf clubs - Wynn B. Tredway, Sr.
LIGHT TONIGHT - Seafood products—canned or cured ☆ - National Sea Products U.S. Corp.
LIGHT TOUCH - Blankets—electric ☆ - Sunbeam-Oster Household Products
LIGHT TOUCH - Hair care products - Posner Laboratories Inc.
LIGHT-TOUCH - Screws - Emhart Inc.
LIGHT TOUCH - Skin care products - Lotus Brands Inc.
LIGHT TOUCH - Skin care products - Schering-Plough Healthcare Products
LIGHT TOUCH 1 - Brushes—hair - Phillips Brush Corp.
LIGHT TOUCH 2 - Brushes—hair - Phillips Brush Corp.
LIGHT TOUCH 3 - Brushes—hair - Phillips Brush Corp.
LIGHT TOUCH, THE - Lamps—floor - Butler Specialty Co.
LIGHT UP THE NIGHT - Lighting equipment - Marketing Insights, Inc.-Frank Luppino Jr., and Associates
LIGHT-UPS - Toys—trains - Life-Like Products Inc.
LIGHT WATCHMAN - Lighting equipment - Ripley Photocontrols
LIGHT WEIGHTS - Manicure preparations - Nail Gems by Cara
LIGHT WELD - Adhesives and sealants - Dymax Corp.
LIGHT-WELDER - Adhesives and sealants - Dymax Corp.
LIGHT WHEAT AND CREME - Cookies - Intersweet Candy Inc.
LIGHT WIND - Cutlery ☆ - Lifetime Hoan Corp.
LIGHT YEARS AHEAD - Cigarette lighters - Park Lane Associates, Inc.
LIGHT YEARS AHEAD - Cosmetics - Madeleine Mono Ltd.
LIGHTABLES - Novelty items - Eisenbraun Reiss Sales Inc.
LIGHTARGET - Archery equipment - Bear Archery Inc.
LIGHTBEAM - Electronic equipment - Squibb-Taylor Inc.
LIGHTBLOC - Window shades - Draper Shade and Screen Co. Inc.
LIGHTBRA - Motor vehicle parts and accessories - Target Motorsports
LIGHTBREAD - Crackers ☆ - Barbara's Bakery, Inc.
LIGHTCRIMP - Capacitors - Whitaker Corp.
LIGHTDAYS - Sanitary napkins - Kimberly-Clark Corp.
LIGHTED BLAZERS - Toys—stuffed ☆ - CBS Toys
LIGHTED ICE - Lamps ☆ - General Electric Co.
LIGHTED ICICLES - Skis - Miller Ski and Camp
LIGHTED MUSICAL LANTERNS - Christmas tree ornaments - Mr. Christmas, Inc.
LIGHTEN IT - Cosmetics - Circle of Beauty, Inc.
LIGHTEN UP - Fabrics ☆ - Bibb Co.
LIGHTEN UP - Sunglasses - Nassau Lens Co. Inc.
LIGHTEN-UP - Vitamins and nutritional supplements - Grifkin, Inc.
LIGHTENING - Boats—canoes - Sawyer Composite Products
LIGHTENING SCAN - Antennas - Wintenna Inc.
LIGHTER BAKE - Shortening - Sunsweet Growers Inc.
LIGHTER CHOICE - Popcorn - Boston Popcorn Co.
LIGHTER CHOICE - Popcorn - Boston Popcorn Co., Inc.
LIGHTER 'N JACK - Cheese - Swissrose International Inc.
LIGHTFALL - Nightlights - Aegis Holdings, Ltd.
LIGHTFOLIO - Handbags - Harold M. Jarrett, Jr.
LIGHTFORM - Photographic equipment - Bogen Photo Corp.
LIGHTHAWK - Lanterns—electric - Lectro Science, Inc.
LIGHTHEARTED GREETINGS - Greeting cards - Renaissance Greeting Cards Inc.
LIGHTHOUSE - Caulking compounds - VIP/Lighthouse Products
LIGHTHOUSE - Computer software - Neodata Services, Inc.
LIGHTHOUSE - Computer software - Sierra On-Line, Inc.
LIGHTHOUSE - Office supplies - Eaton Allen Ko-Rec-Type Corp.
LIGHTHOUSE - Wines - Bully Hill Vineyards, Inc.
LIGHTHOUSE CRABCAKE - Seafood products—fresh or frozen - Martin Foods
LIGHTHOUSE PRODUCTS - Caulking compounds - Coronado Laboratories, Inc.
LIGHTHOUSE PROJECT, THE - Educational materials - Lighthouse Foundation, Inc.
LIGHTHOUSE, THE - Aquarium thermometers ☆ - American Thermometer Co.
LIGHTING - Lamp bulbs - Phillips Electronics North America Corp.
LIGHTING AMERICA - Lighting fixtures - Lights of America Inc.
LIGHTING BOLT - Apparel and accessories - Sigallo Ltd.

LIGHTING BY CHOICE - Lamps - Lite Source Inc.
LIGHTING GRAPHICS - Computer software - Stahls' Inc.
LIGHTING RING - Electrical equipment - Christmas Tree Lighting Ring, Inc.
LIGHTJET - Computer hardware - Cymbolic Sciences International
LIGHTLIFE - Food products - Lightlife Foods, Inc.
LIGHTLINE - Christmas tree ornaments - Mr. Christmas, Inc.
LIGHTLINE - Wood products - States Industries Inc.
LIGHTLINES - Blinds–venetian - Hunter Douglas Intermountain Fabrication Co.
LIGHTLINES - Blinds–vertical - Hunter Douglas, Inc.
LIGHTLINES - Window shades - Spring Window Fashions Division, Inc.
LIGHTLINK - Lighting equipment - Cogent Light Technologies, Inc.
LIGHTLY - Toys ✩ - Playskool, Inc.
LIGHTLY EXPRESSED LTD. - Lighting fixtures - Lightly Expressed Ltd.
LIGHTMAKER - Door openers–electronic - Stanley Home Automation Inc.
LIGHTMAN - Lighting fixtures–street - Visibility Systems Connecticut Ltd.
LIGHTMATE - Lighting fixtures - Kenall Manufacturing Co.
LIGHTMATIC - Electric lighting equipment - Optex, Inc.
LIGHTMISER - Lighting fixtures - Hubbell Lighting, Inc. (Lighting Div.)
LIGHTMOVES - Sports apparel - Medalist Apparel Inc.
LIGHT'N JUICY - Fruit drinks–bottled or canned ✩ - Coca-Cola Co.
LIGHTNET - Computer software - Bell & Howell Publication Systems Co.
LIGHTNIN - Fishing lures - Sheldons', Inc.
LIGHTNIN' - Staples - Automation Fastening Co. Inc.
LIGHTNIN FAST - Paints - Masury Paint Co.
LIGHTNIN' RODS - Seymour Duncan Pickups
LIGHTNIN' SHAD - Fishing lures - Storm Manufacturing Co.
LIGHTNIN' STRIKE - Cleaning preparations - Partnership of Adam J. Holman, Virgil B. Holman and Billy F. Holman
LIGHTNING - Abrasive products - Norton Co.
LIGHTNING - Adhesives and sealants - Seal-O-Matic Corp.
LIGHTNING - Ammunition - Federal Cartridge Co.
LIGHTNING - Bicycles - Columbia Manufacturing Inc.
LIGHTNING - Bicycles - Lightning Cycle Dynamics
LIGHTNING - Bicycles ✩ - Huffy Corp.
LIGHTNING - Boats - Allen Boat Co.
LIGHTNING - Brushes–paint - Corona Brushes Inc.
LIGHTNING - Brushes–paint ✩ - PPG Industries, Inc.
LIGHTNING - Catheters - Cordis Corp.
LIGHTNING - Caulking compounds - White Lightning Products Corp.
LIGHTNING - Computer hardware - Gammagraphx, Inc.
LIGHTNING - Electronic equipment - Idexx Laboratories, Inc.
LIGHTNING - Floor coverings–carpet and rugs ✩ - Galaxy Carpet Mills Inc.
LIGHTNING - Flour–blended - Cargill, Inc.
LIGHTNING - Food products - GME, Inc.
LIGHTNING - Guitars - Nady Systems Inc.
LIGHTNING - Kites - Spectra Star Kites
LIGHTNING - Office machines - Bircher Co. Inc.
LIGHTNING - Paper–bond - Union Camp Corp. (Fine Paper Division)
LIGHTNING - Pet products - Lightning Products
LIGHTNING - Pet products - Sporodyne Co.
LIGHTNING - Scissors–hand-operated - F.W. Engels Inc.
LIGHTNING - Skates–roller - National Sporting Goods Corp.
LIGHTNING - Skates–roller - Rollerblade, Inc.
LIGHTNING - Sporting goods ✩ - Bear Archery Inc.
LIGHTNING - Tires–bicycles ✩ - Carlisle Tire & Rubber Co.
LIGHTNING - Tools–hand-operated - Southern Swings, Inc.
LIGHTNING - Tools–hand-operated - Vermont American Corp.
LIGHTNING - Wheelchairs - Everest and Jennings International Ltd.
LIGHTNING ALERT - Lightning detector - McCallie Manufacturing Corp.
LIGHTNING AUDIO - Electronic equipment - Lightning Audio Corp.
LIGHTNING BELT - Belts–apparel - Optiglo, Inc.
LIGHTNING BINGO - Game cards - Universal Manufacturing Co., Inc.
LIGHTNING BLEND SYSTEM - Cleaning preparations - IVAX Industries, Inc.
LIGHTNING BOLT - Apparel and accessories ✩ - Deckers Outdoor Corp.
LIGHTNING-BOLT - Firearms, accessories, and parts - Jagersport, Ltd.
LIGHTNING BOLT - Gloves - Swany America Corp.
LIGHTNING BOLT - Golfing equipment - Suarez Corp.
LIGHTNING BOLT - Kites ✩ - Hi-Flier Manufacturing Co.
LIGHTNING BOLT - Photographic equipment - International Licensing Corp.
LIGHTNING BOLT - Ships–patrol boats ✩ - Foam Design Consumer Products Inc.
LIGHTNING BOLT - Shoes ✩ - S. Goldberg and Co. Inc.
LIGHTNING BOLT - Watches - M.Z. Berger & Co. Inc.
LIGHTNING BOLTS - Musical instrument accessories - Pro-Mark Corp.
LIGHTNING BOMB - Fireworks - American Promotional Events, Inc.

LIGHTNING BUG - Lighting fixtures - Lightning Bug Ltd.
LIGHTNING CHARGER - Electrical equipment - Active Technologies, Inc.
LIGHTNING CREEK - Wines - Wine Group Inc.
LIGHTNING DART - Tires–bicycles ✩ - Carlisle Tire & Rubber Co.
LIGHTNING E.T. - Propellers - Brunswick Corp.
LIGHTNING-FIRE - Ammunition - Jagersport, Ltd.
LIGHTNING FRIES - Vegetables–frozen ✩ - Lamb-Weston, Inc.
LIGHTNING FURY - Lighting fixtures - Tandy Corp.
LIGHTNING GOLD - Toys–automobiles - Mattel, Inc.
LIGHTNING HOT - Pharmaceutical preparations - Sporodyne Co.
LIGHTNING JR. - Skates–roller ✩ - Rollerblade, Inc.
LIGHTNING LEAGUE - Toys - Mattel, Inc.
LIGHTNING LOK - Braces–orthopedic - Swede-O, Inc.
LIGHTNING POOL - Toys - ERTL Co., Inc.
LIGHTNING ROD - Sporting goods - Outdoor Technologies Group
LIGHTNING RODS - Antennas - Wintenna Inc.
LIGHTNING RODS - Automotive parts and accessories - Hurst Performance Inc.
LIGHTNING RODS - Musical instrument accessories - Pro-Mark Corp.
LIGHTNING ROSE - Games - K-2 Corp.
LIGHTNING SEVENS - Game machines - Bally Gaming International, Inc.
LIGHTNING SHINE - Polishes - Karseal Corp.
LIGHTNING SKETCH - Toys - Mattel, Inc.
LIGHTNING SPAR - Varnishes ✩ - Pettit Paint Co. Inc.
LIGHTNING SPEEDSTER - Sleds - Standard Novelty Works
LIGHTNING STARTER - Generators–electric - Active Technologies, Inc.
LIGHTNING STORM - Toys–automobiles - Mattel, Inc.
LIGHTNING STREAK - Toys–automobiles - Mattel, Inc.
LIGHTNING STRIKE - Archery equipment - Horton Manufacturing Co. Inc.
LIGHTNING STRIP - Chemical preparations - Real Products Manufacturing, Ltd.
LIGHTNING TRS - Skates–roller - Rollerblade, Inc.
LIGHTNING VAC - Pumps–water ✩ - Odyssey Systems
LIGHTNING WORD WIZARD - Computer software - Borland International, Inc.
LIGHTNINGS - Boats–canoes - Howmar Boat Corp.
LIGHTOLIER - Lighting fixtures - Lightolier Inc.
LIGHTPAD - Computer program - Electric Power Research Institute Inc.
LIGHTPATH - Lenses–optical - Lightpath Technologies, Inc.
LIGHTRENDER - Computer software - Systems Engineering Associates Corp.
LIGHTRONICS - Lighting fixtures ✩ - Guth Lighting
LIGHTS - Ophthalmic goods - Foremost Optical Products
LIGHTS & BRIGHTS - Cosmetics - Ardell International Inc.
LIGHTS & LACE - Dolls - Mattel, Inc.
LIGHTS, CAMERA, ACTION! - Board game - Spectrographics
LIGHTS! CAMERA! ACTION! - Broadcasting stations–cable television - GTE Service Corp.
LIGHTS CAMERA...ACTION...! - Paper - Image Group Inc.
LIGHTS, CAMERA.KOBRA! - Games ✩ - Mayfair Games, Inc.
LIGHTS FANTASTIC - Cosmetics - Alexandra De Markoff, Ltd.
LIGHTS FANTASTIC, THE - Lighting equipment - Creative Concepts
LIGHTS FANTASTIQUE - Cosmetics - Cosmair Inc.
LIGHTS 'N SOUNDS - Toys–musical - Fisher-Price, Inc.
LIGHTS 'N SURPRISE LAPTOP - Toys - Hasbro, Inc.
LIGHTS OF AMERICA - Floodlights - Lights of America Inc.
LIGHTS ON - Skin care products - Kenra Laboratories, Inc.
LIGHTS OUT - Apparel–women's ✩ - Lady Ester Lingerie Corp.
LIGHTS OUT - Games - Tiger Electronics, Inc.
LIGHTS OUT - Pharmaceutical preparations - Twinlab
LIGHTS OUT - Skin care products - Sogo Inc.
LIGHTSCAPER - Lighting fixtures - Hubbell Lighting, Inc. (Lighting Div.)
LIGHTSCAPING - Lighting fixtures - Hubbell Lighting, Inc. (Lighting Div.)
LIGHTSCREEN INDIRECT - Lighting fixtures - Peerless Lighting Corp.
LIGHTSHAPE - Buttons - American Cyanamid Co.
LIGHTSHIP LENS - Computer software ✩ - Pilot Software, Inc.
LIGHTSHIP SOFTWARE - Computer software - Lightship Software Inc.
LIGHTSIDE PRODUCTIONS - Games - Lightside Productions
LIGHTSMART - Syrup - I.C. Refreshment Co., Inc.
LIGHTSPEED - Dental equipment - Lightspeed Technology Inc.
LIGHTSPEED - Exercising equipment - Marcy Fitness Products
LIGHTSTAR - Audio equipment - Carver Corp.
LIGHTSTONE - Floor coverings - Toli International
LIGHTSTREAM - Audio equipment - Brook Electronics Corp.
LIGHTSTREAM - Communications equipment–satellite - Bolt Beranek and Newman, Inc.
LIGHTSTYLE - Window shades - Kirsch Co.
LIGHTSWORD - Lighting equipment - Aaron Jones Studios, Inc.

✩ = Now out of production

LIGHTSYSTEMS TECHNOLOGIES CORP. - Electric lighting equipment - Lightsystems Technologies Corp.

LIGHTTABLE - Computer peripheral equipment - Milsoft Integrated Solutions, Inc.

LIGHTTECH - Lighting fixtures - Lighttech Group, Inc.

LIGHTTOOLS - Computer software - Optical Research Associates

LIGHTTRAC - Medical apparatus - Schneider (USA) Inc.

LIGHTVAULT - Lighting fixtures - Kim Lighting Inc.

LIGHTWADES - Boots ☆ - Endicott Johnson Corp.

LIGHTWALKER - Cases–camera - Lightware, Inc.

LIGHTWARE - Cases–camera - Lightware, Inc.

LIGHTWARE - Lighting equipment - Cogent Light Technologies, Inc.

LIGHTWARE - Lighting fixtures - Artemide, Inc.

LIGHTWATCH II - Switches–electric - Linear Corp.

LIGHTWAVE - Pet products - SPI

LIGHTWATT - Lighting fixtures - Hubbell Lighting, Inc. (Lighting Div.)

LIGHTWATT II - Lighting fixtures ☆ - Hubbell Lighting, Inc. (Lighting Div.)

LIGHTWAVE - Computer software - Newtek, Inc.

LIGHTWAVE PICKUPS - Transducers - Audio Optics

LIGHTWAVE RESEARCH - Chemical preparations - High End Systems, Inc.

LIGHTWAVES - Hair care products - Gillette Co.

LIGHTWAY TO TRAVEL, THE - Luggage - Airway Industries, Inc.

LIGHTWEAR - Lighting equipment - Cogent Light Technologies, Inc.

LIGHTWEIGHT - Boats–canoes ☆ - Old Town Canoe Co.

LIGHTWEIGHT - Hair care products - Rene Furterer

LIGHTWEIGHT TRAVELER - Whirlpools - Jim Beam Brands Co.

LIGHTWIN - Motors–outboard - Outboard Marine Corp.

LIGHTWING - Toys–automobiles - Hasbro, Inc.

LIGHTWOOD - Drapery hardware ☆ - Endisco Supply Co.

LIGHTWOOD - Floor coverings - Toli International

LIGHTWOODS - Housewares ☆ - Dansk International Designs, Ltd.

LIGHTWORKS - Computer software - Euphonics

LIGHTWRIGHT 3 - Computer software - City Theatrical Inc.

LIGHTWRITE - Artists' materials - Alvin and Co. Inc.

LIGHTWRITER - Printers–computer - Zygo Industries Inc.

LIGHTZONES - Hair care products - Revlon Consumer Products Corp.

LIGIA - Furniture - Ligia Jamieson

LIGNE 7 - Sporting goods ☆ - Continental Sports Supply Inc.

LIGNE DE VIE - Cosmetics - Latech, Inc.

LIGNE DES LEVRES - Lip balms - Sothys USA Inc.

LIGNE DES YEUX - Cosmetics - Sothys USA Inc.

LIGNE DU CORPS - Skin care products - Sothys USA Inc.

LIGNE FONDAMENTALE - Skin care products ☆ - Sothys USA Inc.

LIGNE GRAND AIR - Skin care products ☆ - Sothys USA Inc.

LIGNE PEAU GRASSES - Skin care products ☆ - Sothys USA Inc.

LIGNE PEAU NORMALE - Skin care products ☆ - Sothys USA Inc.

LIGNE PEAU ROUGEUR DIFFUSES - Skin care products - Sothys USA Inc.

LIGNE PEAU SECHE - Skin care products - Sothys USA Inc.

LIGNE PEAU SENSIBLE - Skin care products ☆ - Sothys USA Inc.

LIGNE SOLAIRE - Tanning agents - Sothys USA Inc.

LIGNE VERTE - Pharmaceutical preparations ☆ - Boiron Inc.

LIGNOCELL - Fertilizers - Sorb-Tech, Inc.

LIGNOFLEX - Food products - Beatrice Cos. Inc.

LIGNOSITE - Chemical preparations - Georgia-Pacific Corp.

LIGONITE - Paneling - Georgia-Pacific Corp.

LIGORIO - Wines - Francis A. Bonanno, Inc.

LIGOSA - Recording label - Warlock Records

LIGURIA - Frankfurters ☆ - John Morrell & Co.

LIHIT - Office supplies - Yasutomo

LIHLI - Luggage - Lihli, Inc.

LIHN - Jams and jellies ☆ - Lifetone International Inc.

LIHN-JAM - Jams and jellies - Haram-Christensen Corp.

LIK - Insecticides ☆ - J. & L. Adikes Inc.

LIK-A-STIX YUMMY MUMMIES - Candy - Sunline Brands

LIK BIT - Candy ☆ - Pennsylvania Dutch Candies

LIK-M-AID - Candy - Sunline Brands

LIK STIK POPS - Candy - Gladstone Candies

LIK-WID - Shortening ☆ - Kraft Food Ingredients Corp.

LIKABLE LAC - Skin care products - Waverly Beauty Products

LIKE - Beverages–carbonated ☆ - Dr. Pepper/Seven Up, Inc.

LIKE - Candy - Bell'amore Imports Inc.

LIKE - Perfumes - Saxony Products Inc.

LIKE-A-GLOE - Skin care products - Ardell International Inc.

LIKE-A-PERM - Hair care products - Roberts Research Laboratories, Inc.

LIKE A SQUEEZE OF FRESH JUICE - Beverages - Brooklyn Bottling Corp.

LIKE AIR - Tractors - Detroit Steel Products, Inc.

LIKE EGGS - Egg substitutes - Pureggs Brands, Inc.

LIKE FRESH - Food products - General Grocer Co.

LIKE MAGIC - Cleaning preparations - Cello Chemical Co.

LIKE MOM'S - Food products ☆ - Pierre Frozen Foods Inc.

LIKE NATURAL - Hair care products - Zotos International Inc.

LIKE-NU - Automotive parts and accessories - Echlin Inc.

LIKE-RAGS - Paper–toweling - IFC Disposables, Inc.

LIKE WATER! - Lubricating oils - Red Line Synthetic Oil Corp.

LIKE YOUNG - Crocheted and knitted items - Winston Manufacturing Corp.

LIKEABLE - Floor coverings–carpet and rugs ☆ - Alexander Smith Carpets

LIKEFELT - Fabrics–felt - National Nonwovens

LIKEN - Deodorants–personal - Earth Science Inc.

LIKES N' GRIPES - Games ☆ - Pressman Toy Corp.

LIKIMBA - Harps ☆ - Sabine Musical Manufacturing Co. Inc.

LIKKI LIKKI - Juices–frozen - Paula Newman and Melinda Cohen Partnership

LIKOGEN - Pharmaceutical preparations - Wesley Pharmacal Co. Inc.

LIKWID - Tape–masking - Fibre Glass-Evercoat Co. Inc.

LIKWID TAPE - Adhesives and sealants - Projectapix-II

LIL' - Cribs–wood ☆ - Welsh Co.

LI'L ABNER - Toys - Co. Store

LI'L ABNER - Watches ☆ - Delta Impex Watch Corp.

LIL AGATHA - Dolls - Uneeda Doll Co., Inc.

LIL' ALPHA-BETTS - Decals and transfers ☆ - C-Thru Ruler Co.

LI'L AMOS - Pretzels ☆ - Quinlan Pretzel Co.

LIL' ANGEL - Bicycles - Columbia Manufacturing Inc.

LIL ANGEL - Bicycles ☆ - Raleigh USA Bicycle Co.

LI'L ANGELS - Cupcakes - Interstate Brands Corp.

LI'L ANNIE FRANNIE, A - Dolls - S & P Industries

LIL' ANNIE'S - Pizzas–mixes - Pooch Salon

LIL' AUTO STORE - Automotive parts and accessories - Lil' Auto Store, Inc.

LIL' AUTO STORE - Automotive parts and accessories - Lil' Drug Store Products, Inc.

LI'L BABY - Machinery - S. Morantz Inc.

LIL BABY IN BASKET - Dolls - Goldberger Doll Manufacture Co.

LI'L BABY THREE-IN-ONE - Cleaning equipment - S. Morantz Inc.

LI'L BABY TWO-IN-ONE - Cleaning equipment - S. Morantz Inc.

LI'L BEAR - Hair-care products, bubble bath - Benjamin Ansehl Co.

LIL' BEAR WALKER - Toys ☆ - Steven Manufacturing Co.

LI'L BEARER - Toys - Russ Berrie and Co., Inc.

LIL' BEGINNER - Toys - Mattel, Inc.

+L'IL BELL SHELL - Helmets–athletic - Bell Sports Corp.

LIL' BIGFOOT - Toys ☆ - Playskool, Inc.

LIL BIN - Pet products - Kane Manufacturing Co.

LI'L BINK - Infant product ☆ - Binky-Griptight Co.

LI'L BIT OF BUTTER - Margarine - Nabisco Foods Group

LIL' BIT O'SCRIPT - Decals and transfers ☆ - Dalco Athletic Lettering Inc.

LI'L BITS - Computer software - Bitstream Inc.

LIL' BITS - Figurines ☆ - E.M.I. Inc.

LIL BITSY - Bakery products - Metz Baking Co.

LI'L BITTY BITS - Giftware - Russ Berrie and Co., Inc.

LI'L BLANKIES - Toys - Playskool, Inc.

LIL' BLESSIN'S - Moldings–plaster of paris ☆ - DecoArt, Inc.

LIL' BLIZZARD BOMBER - Hats - Mad Bomber Co.

LI'L BLOSSOM - Dolls - Mattel, Inc.

LIL' BOOGLE - Publisher's imprints - Timothy John Cohorst

LI'L BRAT 4X4 - Toys ☆ - Combi International Corp.

LIL BRAVE - Meat products–canned - Zartic, Inc.

LIL' BROTHER - Dolls ☆ - Uneeda Doll Co., Inc.

LI'L BROTHER SAM - Cleaning preparations - State Chemical Manufacturing Co.

LIL BRUTES - Toys–automobiles - Buddy L Inc.

LIL' BUBBA - Colognes - Charleston Catalog Co.

LI'L BUBBLE BUG - Toys ☆ - Combi International Corp.

LI'L BUDDY - Barbecues and grills - Sunbeam Outdoor Products Inc.

LI'L BUDDY - Candy bars ☆ - Nellson Candies Inc.

LIL BUDDY - Pet products - Emerald Bird Caddy

LIL BUDDYS - Toys–automobiles - Buddy L Inc.

LI'L B.U.M. - Apparel–children's - Chauvin International Ltd.

LI'L BUNNY PALS - Toys–stuffed - Russ Berrie and Co., Inc.

LI'L BUNNY PLAYMATES - Toys–stuffed - Russ Berrie and Co., Inc.

LI'L BUSY BOX - Infant product - Playskool Baby Inc.

LI'L BUTTONS - Dolls ☆ - Fun World Inc.

LIL CAROL - Dolls - Goldberger Doll Manufacture Co.

LI'L CAROLER - Toys - Russ Berrie and Co., Inc.

LI'L CHAMP - See **CHAMPION MARBLES**

LIL CHARLES RECORDS - Recording label - Lil Charles Records Inc.

LIL CHARMS - Jewelry ☆ - American Traditional Stencils
LIL' CHICKEN FEATHERS - Toys–stuffed - Dakin Inc.
LIL CHIEF - Popcorn - Stock Popcorn Co. Inc.
LIL' CHIK - Bicycles - Schwinn Cycling & Fitness Inc.
LIL' CHILL - Soft drinks - Pantry Inc.
LIL CINDERELLA - Footwear–children's - A & S Imports Inc.
LI'L CLANG-ALONG - Toys ☆ - Combi International Corp.
LIL' CLUTCH - Toys - Gerber Products Co.
LI'L COOK - Cookware - Dazey Corp.
+L'IL COOLDATE - Ice chests–plastic - Thermos Co.
LIL' CORKY - Fishing lures - Yakima Bait Co.
LIL CRITTER - Toys ☆ - Gerber Products Co.
LI'L CRITTERS - Costumes - Paper Magic Group Inc.
LI'L CRITTERS - Costumes - Spearhead Industries Inc.
LIL DARLIN - Bicycles - Kent International Inc.
+L'IL DARLIN' - Dolls - Effanbee Doll Corp.
LIL DAWG POUND - Apparel and accessories - Hawaii-Pacific Apparel Group, Inc.
LI'L DAWGS - Pet food - Marcy, Inc.
LIL DAZZLE DINOSAUR - Toys ☆ - Steven Manufacturing Co.
LIL' DEVILS - Charcoal - West Oregon Wood Products, Inc.
LIL DEVLE - Fishing lures - Eppinger Manufacturing Co.
LIL' DINOS - Toys - Meritus Industries, Inc.
LI'L DIP - Dolls - Mattel, Inc.
LIL' DIVOT - Golfing equipment - Doyle W. Weatherby
LIL' DREAM BABY - Dolls - Doll Factory, Inc.
LI'L DRINK - Bottled water - Kissimmee Spring Water Co.
LI'L DRIP - Coffee makers–electric ☆ - Hamilton Beach/Proctor-Silex Inc.
LIL' DRUG STORE - Health care products - Lil' Drug Store Products, Inc.
+L'IL DUDES - Sausages - Sparrer Sausage Co., Inc.
LIL DUFFER - Golf clubs - Austad Co.
LIL DUSTER - Dusters–feather - Easy Day Manufacturing Co.
LIL' DUTCH MAID - Cookies - Fehr Foods, Inc.
+L'IL EASE - Apparel–women's - Lily of France Inc.
LI'L FEATHER - Dolls - Mattel, Inc.
LIL' FEET - Toys–stuffed - Kamar International Inc.
LIL' FELLER - Convenience stores - Schaeffer Oil Inc.
LI'L FIESTA - Dolls - Mattel, Inc.
LI'L FISHER - Machinery - Greenlee Textron Inc.
LIL FISHERMAN - Boats–pontoons ☆ - Weeres Industries Corp.
LIL' FISHERMAN - Fishing tackle - Frabill Inc.
LIL' FISHERMAN - Seafood products–fresh or frozen - Seafood Dimensions International Inc.
LIL' FLOSSERS - Disposable floss tools - Lil' Drug Store Products, Inc.
LIL FLOWERKINS - Dolls - Goldberger Doll Manufacture Co.
LIL FOLKS - Vitamins and nutritional supplements - Vita-Fore Products Co.
LI'L FRITTER - Kitchen appliances ☆ - Sunbeam-Oster Household Products
LIL' FRY - Pans ☆ - General Housewares Corp.
LIL' FURRARRI - Pet products - Dogloo Inc.
LIL' GARDENER - Toys - Processed Plastic Co.
LIL GATOR - Suntan lotions - Aloe Gator Suncare Co.
LI'L GENIUS - Toys–electronic - Hasbro, Inc.
LIL GINA - Confections - Cento Fine Foods Inc.
LIL GRILL - Pressure cookers ☆ - Farberware Inc.
LIL' GS - Bicycles - Schwinn Cycling & Fitness Inc.
LIL HELPER - Child-size outdoor furniture - Jack-Post Corp.
LI'L HOE - Tillers–rotary - Hoffco Inc.
LIL' HOMER - Alarm systems - Golden West Communications, Inc.
LIL HONEY - Toys - Eugene Doll & Novelty Co. Inc.
LI'L HOOKS - Dolls - Mattel, Inc.
'LIL HOOT - Kites - Gayla Industries Inc.
LI'L HOPPY - Toys–stuffed ☆ - Fun World Inc.
LIL' HOWIE'S FUN HOUSE - Computer software - 7th Level, Inc.
LIL HUG - Fruit drinks–bottled or canned - Ohio Pure Foods Inc.
LIL' HUG - Pillows - American Fiber Industries Corp.
LI'L HUGGERS - Paper - C.M. Paula Co.
LI'L HUMMER - Fishing lures - Lindy Little Joe Inc.
LI'L HUSKY - Rope ☆ - Crow Rope Industries LLC
LIL' HUSTLER - Motor vehicles–trucks - Nissan Motor Corp. USA
LI'L INNOCENTS - Dolls - Effanbee Doll Corp.
LIL' INNOCENTS INTERNATIONAL - Dolls - Effanbee Doll Corp.
LIL' INNOVATOR - Pet products - Dogloo Inc.
LI'L JOE - Boats–motor ☆ - Seajay Boats Inc.
LI'L JOE FISH N SKI - Boats–motor ☆ - Seajay Boats Inc.
LIL' JOGGER - Toys ☆ - Hedstrom Corp.
LIL' JON - Air purification systems - Lil' Jon Corp.

LIL-JUG-O-CLEAN - Cleaning preparations - Enersys3 Inc.
LIL KIDDIES - Candy - Yost Candy Co.
LI'L KIKI - Dolls - Russ Berrie and Co., Inc.
LIL' LADY BUG - Toys - South Bend Toy Manufacturing Co.
LIL' LAMBEE - Crocheted and knitted items - Le Roy Knitted Sportswear Inc.
LIL' LEARNERS - Easels - Anco Wood Specialties Inc.
LIL LIFEGUARD - Chairs–folding - Processed Plastic Co.
LIL' LIGHTS - Lamps - Kaadan Ltd.
LIL' LIMO - Strollers–baby - Kolcraft Enterprises, Inc.
LI'L LION RIDER - Toys ☆ - Combi International Corp.
LIL LITE - Lighters - Scripto-Tokai Corp.
LI'L LOGGERS - Toys - Tonka Corp.
LIL' LONGHORN STICK - Sausages - Fred Usinger, Inc.
LIL' LOVE LETTERS - Toys–stuffed - Fun World Inc.
LI'L LOVING CLOWNS - Dolls - Russ Berrie and Co., Inc.
LI'L LUV BUNTING - Greeting cards - Morehead, Inc.
LIL MAD BOMBER - Hats - Mad Bomber Co.
LI'L MASON - Toys ☆ - All-Foam Products Co.
LI'L MATT - Toys - Mattel, Inc.
LI'L ME - Frosting ☆ - Tyco Toys
LIL ME OF CALIFORNIA - Infant product - Tailored Baby Inc.
LIL' MECHANICS - Toys - Imperial Toy Corp.
LIL' MERMAID WATERFUL - Games - Milton Bradley Co.
LIL' MISS - Bicycles - Schwinn Cycling & Fitness Inc.
+L'IL MISS - Swimming pools - SLM Inc.
LI'L MISS - Toys - Mattel, Inc.
LI'L MISS CANDI STRIPES - Dolls - Mattel, Inc.
LI'L MISS DRESS UP - Dolls - Mattel, Inc.
LI'L MISS FASHIONS - Dolls - Mattel, Inc.
LIL' MISS FLYER - Ride-on toy - Radio Flyer Inc.
LI'L MISS MAGIC HAIR - Dolls - Mattel, Inc.
LI'L MISS MAGIC JEWELS - Dolls - Mattel, Inc.
LI'L MISS MAKEUP - Dolls - Mattel, Inc.
LIL MISS MOOTSIES - Footwear–children's - Mootsies Tootsies
LI'L MISS MOUSE - Dolls - Russ Berrie and Co., Inc.
LI'L MISS 'N ME - Dolls - Mattel, Inc.
LI'L MISS SINGING MERMAID - Dolls - Mattel, Inc.
LIL' MISS SUNSHINE - Bicycles ☆ - Hedstrom Corp.
LIL' MIXER SET - Toys - Tyco Toys
LI'L MOBILE PHONE - Toys - Mattel, Inc.
LIL MUFFIT - Toys–banks - A.J. Renzi Plastic Corp.
LIL' NAPPER - High chairs - Century Products Co.
LIL' NECESSITIES - Candles - Lil' Necessities, L.C.
LIL NIPPERS - Cosmetics - Kaemark Inc.
+L'IL NOTHINGS - Apparel–women's - Lily of France Inc.
LI'L ONES - Toys–automobiles - Nylint Toy Corp.
LIL' OSCAR - Ice chests–plastic - Coleman Co., Inc.
LIL PADUKE - Candy - Gilliam Candy Co. Inc. (Gilliam Candy Brands)
LIL' PAL - Bicycles - Columbia Manufacturing Inc.
LI'L PAL - Tools–garden - Uniontools, Inc.
LIL' PEACE OF HEAVEN CLOUD CUTIES, A - Playing cards - Bethann Shannon
LI'L PEACH - Beverages–carbonated - Li'l Peach of Massachusetts, Inc.
+L'IL PEACH - Food containers - Purity Supreme Supermarkets
LIL PEOPLE - Apparel–children's - Star Baby Inc.
LIL' PETUNIA - Deodorants–personal - Surco Products Inc.
LI'L PIERROT - Dolls - Morehead, Inc.
LIL PINK FLOWERS - Glassware–household - Durand International
LIL PLAYMATES - Toys - Playmates World Wide Inc.
LI'L POSIE - Dolls - J.C. Toys Group, Inc.
LIL' POSSUM - Recording label - Candy Records
LIL' POUTERS - Dolls - Bonnie Wrixton
LI'L PRO - Chairs–wood - Greenwich Industries, L.P.
LI'L PROFESSOR - Toys–stuffed - Russ Berrie and Co., Inc.
LI'L PUFF PUFF - Toys–stuffed ☆ - Russ Berrie and Co., Inc.
LIL PUNKIN - Toys–stuffed - Jolly U.S.A., Inc.
LIL' PUP - Toys - Tyco Toys
LIL RAINBOW - Bicycles - Kent International Inc.
LIL RASCAL - Toys–airplanes ☆ - Victor Stanzel and Co.
LI'L RED - Cat food - Agway Country Foods Inc.
LIL RED PUMPER - Motor vehicle parts and accessories ☆ - Purolator Products Co. (Motor Components Div.)
LIL' REMEDY STORE - Oils–mineral - Lil' Drug Store Products, Inc.
LIL' RIDDELL - Toys - Ridmark Corp.
LI'L RIDE - Toys ☆ - Combi International Corp.
LIL' RINGER - Toys ☆ - Hedstrom Corp.

☆ = Now out of production

LIL' ROCKER - Infant product - Century Products Co.
LI'L ROUGHNECK - Furniture - Rubbermaid Inc.
LIL RUFFIANS - Footwear–children's - A & S Imports Inc.
LIL SAFARI - Toys - Kransco Manufacturing Inc.
LI'L SAFE DRIVER - Toys - Mattel, Inc.
LIL' SAILOR - Surfboards - General Foam Plastics Corp.
LI'L SALT - Meat products–beef ☆ - Russer Foods
LIL' SAUCES - Seasonings ☆ - McCormick & Co., Inc.
LIL' SCAREE PETS - Toys–stuffed ☆ - Gund, Inc.
LI'L SCHOLAR - Furniture - Greenwich Industries, L.P.
LI'L SCREAMIN' DEMON FOR STRAT - Musical instrument accessories -
    Seymour Duncan Pickups
LI'L SCRUBMASTER - Brushes - Gemco Ware, Inc.
LI'L SECRETS - Dolls - Mattel, Inc.
LI'L SEWING MACHINE - Toys - Mattel, Inc.
LIL' SHAVER - Knives - Worth Co.
LI'L SHINIES - Toys - Mattel, Inc.
LIL' SIPPER - Containers - Igloo Products Corp.
LIL SISTERS - Dolls - Meritus Industries, Inc.
LI'L SIZZLER - Dolls - Russ Berrie and Co., Inc.
LI'L SKATEBOARD RIDER - Toys ☆ - Combi International Corp.
LIL' SKIPPER - Toys–electronic - General Foam Plastics Corp.
LIL' SLEEPYHEAD - Dolls - Doll Factory, Inc.
LI'L SLUGGER - Candy - Finnfoods Div.
LIL SLUGGER - Toys–banks - A.J. Renzi Plastic Corp.
LI'L SMOKIES - Food products - Conagra, Inc.
LIL' SNOOZERS - Figurines - Sandicast
LIL' SNUGGLE BUNNY - Dolls - Doll Factory, Inc.
LIL SOFSKIN - Dolls - Horsman
LIL SOFTEE - Dolls - Horsman
LI'L SOFTIES - Toys–stuffed - Russ Berrie and Co., Inc.
LIL' SPORT - Boats–motor ☆ - Sport-Craft Inc.
LIL' SPORTS JERSEY - Coin purses - J.F. Sports Co.
LIL' SPRINGER - Toys ☆ - Hedstrom Corp.
LI'L SPROUT - Dolls ☆ - Uneeda Doll Co., Inc.
+L'IL SQUIRT - Brooms - American Water Broom Co.
LIL SQUIRT - Games - Smethport Specialty Co.
LIL ' SQUIRTS - Toys - Tyco Toys
LIL' STAINER - Brushes–paint - Corona Brushes Inc.
LIL STARLET - Toys ☆ - A.R.C. Toys Inc.
LIL' STEELER - Toys ☆ - Hedstrom Corp.
LI'L STINKER - Toys - Tyco Toys
LI'L STRAWBERRY - Toys ☆ - Combi International Corp.
LIL STUFF - Infant product - Railnet Corp.
LI'L STUFFIES - Giftware ☆ - Russ Berrie and Co., Inc.
LIL' SUCKER - Veterinary pharmaceutical preparations ☆ - Tec Laboratories,
    Inc.
+L'IL SUNPACKER - Ice chests–plastic ☆ - Thermos Co.
+L'IL SUZIE SUNSHINE - Dolls ☆ - Effanbee Doll Corp.
LI'L SWEDE - Wrenches - Collins Industries International, Inc.
LIL' SWINGER - Infant product - Kolcraft Enterprises, Inc.
LIL' TALKER - Dolls - Goldberger Doll Manufacture Co.
LI'L-TEAMWEAR - Apparel and accessories - John R. Ericks
LI'L TEX - Fishing lures - Storm Manufacturing Co.
LI'L TODDLER CAR - Toys ☆ - Combi International Corp.
LIL TOT - Toys ☆ - Processed Plastic Co.
LIL TOTS - Dolls - Meritus Industries, Inc.
LIL' TRACTOR - Toys–automobiles - Empire Industries
LIL' TRAVELER - Infant product - Ming Ta Supply
LI'L TREATS - Dolls - Russ Berrie and Co., Inc.
LI'L TREETOPS - Toys - Russ Berrie and Co., Inc.
LI'L TRICKS - Giftware - Russ Berrie and Co., Inc.
LI'L TRIKE - Bicycles - Clover Toys, Inc.
LIL' TROUBLE - Toys–stuffed ☆ - Gund, Inc.
LI'L TUBBY - Fishing lures - Storm Manufacturing Co.
LI'L TUPPERS - Housewares - Tupperware Co.
LI'L TUTU'S - Toys–stuffed - Russ Berrie and Co., Inc.
LIL' TYKE - Bicycles - Columbia Manufacturing Inc.
LI'L VAGABOND - Giftware ☆ - Enesco Corp.
LI'L WETTING CHEETAH - Dolls - Mattel, Inc.
LI'L WHEELER - Boats - DMM Industries, Inc.
LI'L WILD RIDE - Toys - Clover Toys, Inc.
LIL' WILDCAT - Bicycles - Murray, Inc.
LI'L WORLD OF SPORTS - Giftware - Russ Berrie and Co., Inc.
LI'L ZAPPER - Telephone apparatus - SNC Manufacturing Co., Inc.
LIL' ZESTY - Sausages - Oh Boy! Oberto

LI'L ZOO PALS - Toys - Mattel, Inc.
LI'L ZOOKA - Toy gun - Trendmasters, Inc.
LILA - Beverages–alcohol - Deinhard & Partners
LILA - Dolls - Mattel, Inc.
LILA STYLA - Dolls - Mattel, Inc.
LILAC - Glassware–household ☆ - Fenton Art Glass Co.
LILAC - Recording label - Musica Femina Flute-Guitar Duo
LILAC & LOVELY - Dolls - Mattel, Inc.
LILAC FROST - Lipsticks ☆ - Elysee Scientific Cosmetic Co.
LILAC LACE - Nail care products - Cosmair Inc.
LILAC MIST - Sachets - Andre Richard
LILAC TIME - Christmas tree ornaments - Cracker Box Inc.
LILACAE - Hair care products - Redmond Products, Inc.
LILAGE - Nail care products - Orly International Inc.
LILAS - Lipsticks - Cosmair Inc.
LIL'BLOSSOM - Bicycles ☆ - Huffy Corp.
LIL'BOOGLE - Dolls - Timothy John Cohorst
LILEES - Apparel–women's - Lily of France Inc.
LILETTE - Looms ☆ - Lily Craft Products
LIL'HELPERS - Garment hangers - Tamor Corp. (HPI Company)
LILI - Dolls ☆ - Effanbee Doll Corp.
LILIAS - Thread - WesekPalley Tile Inc.
LILICALE - Bedding–linen ☆ - Sufolla Industries Inc.
LILICREPE - Bedding–linen ☆ - Sufolla Industries Inc.
LILING - Dishes–china - Tienshan, Inc.
LILIQUE - Furniture ☆ - Bassett Furniture Industries, Inc.
LILISATIN - Bedding–linen ☆ - Sufolla Industries Inc.
LILIUM - Glassware–household - Spiegelau Inc.
LILJEHOLMEN - Candles - Odin Ltd.-Scan Am Imports Inc.
LILJEHOLMENS - Candles - Arnold Larson Inc.
LILLEBONNE COEUR TENDRE - Dairy products ☆ - Besnier USA, Inc.
LILLENAS - Publisher's imprints - Nazarene Publishing House
LILLET - Beverages–alcohol ☆ - Shaw-Ross International Importers
LILLI ANN - Apparel–women's - Lilli Ann Corp.
LILLIAN - Tiles–ceramic - Kowa Texas Inc.
LILLIAN AUGUST - Bedspreads - Lillian August Designs, Inc.
LILLIAN AUGUST - Wallpaper - Milbrook Wallcoverings
LILLIAN AUGUST COLLECTION, THE - Photo albums - C.R. Gibson Co.
LILLIAN JAMES - Apparel stores–lingerie - Sharon M. Goetting
LILLIAN RUSSELL - Dolls ☆ - Effanbee Doll Corp.
LILLIAN RUSSELL - Furniture - Davis Cabinet Co.
LILLIAN STRAIGHT BACK - Corsets - John Wanamaker Inc.
LILLIAN VERNON - Housewares - Lillian Vernon Corp.
LILLIAN VERNON'S KITCHEN - Housewares - Lillian Vernon Corp.
LILLIBRIDGE - Hub caps ☆ - Neilson Wheel Co. Inc.
LILLIE - Bakery products - A.H. Walter Co. Inc.
LILLIE LANGTRY - Furniture - Pulaski Furniture Corp.
LILLIE PADS - Notebooks and notepads - Pen-Tab Industries
LILLIE RUBIN - Skin care products - Lillie Rubin Affiliates, Inc.
LILLIES - Floor coverings–carpet and rugs - Customweave Carpets Inc.
LILLIKENS - Christmas tree ornaments - Lillian Vernon Corp.
LILLIPUT - Cigars - Gesty Trading & Manufacturing Corp.
LILLIPUT - Toys - Walmer Dollhouses
LILLIPUT LANE - Figurines - Enesco Corp.
LILLIPUT LANE - Novelty items - Gift Link Inc.
LILLIPUTANO - Cigars - Gesty Trading & Manufacturing Corp.
LILLO - Infant product - Hiborn Inc.
LILLY - Health care products - Eli Lilly and Co.
LILLY - Ice cream - Southland Corp.
LILLY BIRD - Cookware - Bond Products
LILLY DACHE - Apparel–men's - Castle Neckwear Inc.
LILLY/MILLER - Garden equipment - Chas H. Lilly Co.
LILLY PULITZER - Apparel and accessories - Lilly Pulitzer, Inc.
LILLYBECKS - Antiseptics - Durr Drug of Mobile Inc.
LILLYS - Garden equipment - Chas H. Lilly Co.
LILLY'S BABIES - Infant product - Lillian Vernon Corp.
LILLY'S GARDEN - Garden equipment - Lillian Vernon Corp.
LILLY'S KIDS - Infant product - Lillian Vernon Corp.
LIL'ONE, THE - Candy - Jolly Good Industries Inc.
LILRES - Glassware–household - Crest Studios
LIL'S SCOPES - Kaleidoscopes - Gemini Kaleidoscopes
LILSPRING - Farm machinery - Ahrens Agricultural Industries, Inc.
LIL'STINKER - Deodorizers ☆ - Car-Freshner Corp.
LILT - Clocks ☆ - General Time Corp. (Westclox/Seth Thomas Div.)
LILT - Hair care products - Dep Corp.
LILT WAVY BY NATURE - Hair care products - Dep Corp.

☆ = Now out of production

LIL'THINGS - Toys - Lil'things, Inc.
LILTIMATE - Vitamins and nutritional supplements - North West Marketing Co.
LILY - Brooms - Zephyr Manufacturing Co.
LILY - Cases–eyeglass - Fidelity Case Corp.
LILY - Enamels ☆ - Sigma Coatings USA BV.
LILY - Flatware - Wallace International Silversmiths, Inc.
LILY - Frames–eyeglass ☆ - Universal/Univis Inc.
LILY - Giftware - Gorham Inc.
LILY - Glassware–household - Spiegelau Inc.
LILY - Meat products–beef ☆ - Emmber Foods, Inc.
LILY - Olives–canned - Tee Pee Olives Inc.
LILY - Rings–jewelry - Artcarved Inc.
LILY - Salmon–smoked, salted, dried, or pickled - Trident Seafoods Corp.
LILY - Yarn - Lily Craft Products
LILY B. - Apparel and accessories - Toufic Betesh
LILY BALI - Apparel and accessories - Shankar T. Jethani
LILY BETTINI - Footwear - Lily Bettini Inc.
LILY-CRAFT - Buttons ☆ - Blumenthal/Lansing Co.
LILY FROST-TONE - Yarn - Blumenthal/Lansing Co.
LILY LAKE - Cheese - Beatrice Cheese Co.
LILY LEMON - Dolls - Mattel, Inc.
LILY LITES - Sporting goods - Ziffco
LILY MAID - Apparel–women's - Lily of France Inc.
LILY O'BRIEN - Chocolate candy - Bewley Irish Imports
LILY OF FRANCE - Apparel–women's - Lily of France Inc.
LILY OF THE DESERT - Cosmetics - Vera Products Inc.
LILY OF THE VALLEY - Floor coverings–carpet and rugs ☆ - Capel, Inc.
LILY OF THE VALLEY - Giftware - Sasaki
LILY PAD - Medical apparatus - Lossing Orthopedic Co.
LILY PADS - Apparel–women's - Lily of France Inc.
LILY VANILLY - Toys - Mattel, Inc.
LILY WHITE - Codfish–smoked, salted, dried, or pickled - Slade Gorton and Co. Inc.
LILY WHITE - Underwear and nightwear - NCC Industries, Inc.
LILYBLOOM - Pet products - Tetra Sales USA
LILYETTE - Underwear and nightwear - NCC Industries, Inc.
LILYETTE SOFTON - Underwear and nightwear - NCC Industries, Inc.
LILYGRO - Pet products - Tetra Sales USA
LILYKINS - Apparel–children's - Lilykins, Inc.
LILYPAD - Computer software - Streams Online Media Development Corp.
LILYPAD - Toys–musical - Dakin Inc.
LIM - Jewelry–precious - Limor Diamonds, Inc.
LIM - Rubber–silicone - General Electric Co.
LIMA - Floor coverings–carpet and rugs - Gloria of America Inc.
LIMA - Food products - Eden Foods, Inc.
LIMA - Giftware - Sasaki
LIMA - Glassware–household - ACC
LIMA II - Glassware–household ☆ - ACC
+L'IMAGE - Binoculars ☆ - Bausch & Lomb Inc.
+L'IMAGE REALE - Jewelry - Krementz & Co.
+LIMAGES - Tableware–china - Rochard
+L'IMAGINE - Jewelry - Aurafin Corp.
LIMA'S - Food products ☆ - Bon Melange Inc.
LIMB FIVE DAY COLLECTION - Window coverings - Limb Corp.
LIMB-INATOR - Knives - Simonds Industries Inc.
LIMB LOCK - Marine rigging - Kay Jeanna King
LIMBER - Vitamins and nutritional supplements ☆ - Kroeger Herb Products Co. Inc.
LIMBER-JACKS - Apparel–athletic ☆ - Bassett-Walker Inc.
LIMBER LOUIE - Toys–stuffed - Great American Fun Corp.
LIMBER UP - Fabrics–spandex - Dan River Inc.
LIMBITROL - Pharmaceutical preparations - Roche Laboratories
LIMBO - Coffee - Caribbean Creations
LIMBO - Splints - Heelbo Inc.
LIMBO - Yarn - Tahki Imports Ltd.
LIMBO COLOR - Yarn - Tahki Imports Ltd.
LIMBO TWEED - Yarn ☆ - Tahki Imports Ltd.
LIMB'RTONE - Veterinary pharmaceutical preparations ☆ - Y-Tex Corp.
LIMBURG PRODUCTIONS - Apparel–children's - Mother Maid Co.
LIMCO - Canned hams - J & M Universal Sales Co.
LIMCO - Motor vehicle parts and accessories - BASF Corp.
LIMCO 1-2-3 - Motor vehicles - BASF Corp.
LIME - Computer software - Electronic Courseware Systems Inc.
LIME - Floor coverings–carpet and rugs ☆ - Regal Rugs Inc.
LIME-A-WAY - Chemical preparations - Ecolab Inc.
LIME-A-WAY - Cleaning preparations - Benckiser Consumer Products Inc.

LIME-A-WAY EXTRA - Cleaning preparations - Benckiser Consumer Products Inc.
LIME-A-WAY IMPACT - Cleaning preparations–household - Benckiser Consumer Products Inc.
LIME-AIR - Pet products ☆ - Aquatronics-Filtronics
LIME-ALL - Cleaning preparations - Analab Inc.
LIME BOWL - Food products ☆ - Parman-Kendall Corp.
LIME-BREST/LS - Meat products–poultry - Pierce Foods Corp.
LIME BRITE - Cleaning preparations - Calgon Vestal Laboratories
LIME BUSTER - Cleaning preparations - Whink Products Co.
LIME CHILL - Frozen foods - Moore Enterprises, Inc.
LIME CREST - Marble products - Medusa Minerals Co.
LIME DISSOLVE - Solvents - Comstar International Inc. (IPC Div.)
LIME DISSOLVER - Cleaning preparations - Comstar International Inc. (IPC Div.)
LIME DROPS - Skin care products ☆ - House of Lowell Inc.
LIME-IT - Water treating compounds ☆ - Aquatronics-Filtronics
LIME-MATE - Deodorizers - Orange-Mate Inc.
LIME N GREEN - Fertilizers - Seacoast Laboratories Inc.
LIME OFF - Aquariums–household - Jungle Laboratories Corp.
LIME OUT - Cleaning preparations ☆ - RPS Products Inc.
LIME-OUT - Deodorizers ☆ - Elcal Enterprises Ltd.
LIME PHZZZ - Health care products ☆ - Barristo Ltd.
LIME RICKEY - Beverages–carbonated - Snapple Beverage Corp.
LIME RITE - Lime products - Georgia Marble Co.
LIME SHERBET - Christmas tree ornaments - Cracker Box Inc.
LIME-SHINE - Cleaning preparations - Sterling Winthrop Inc.
LIME SULPHUR SOLUTION - Fungicides - Security Products Co.
LIME SUPREME - Shampoos - House of Lowell Inc.
LIMEA - Lubricating oils - Shell Oil Co.
LIMEBACKER - Beverages–malt - Barton Beers, Ltd.
LIMEKILN WINERY - Wines - ENZ Vineyards
LIMELIGHT - Cosmetics - Flori Roberts Inc.
LIMELIGHT - Floor coverings–carpet and rugs ☆ - Gulistan Carpet Inc.
LIMELIGHT - Furniture ☆ - Bassett Furniture Industries, Inc.
LIMELIGHT - Glassware–household - Federal Glass
LIMELIGHT - Knives - Russell Harrington Cutlery, Inc.
LIMELIGHT - Photographic equipment ☆ - Yankee Photo Products Inc.
LIMELIGHT - Rackets–tennis - Head Sports USA
LIMELIGHT - Wallcoverings - Ben Rose Ltd.
LIMELIGHT - Wallpaper - Carlton-Metro Wallcoverings
LIMELITE - Lighting equipment - Austin Innovations, Inc.
LIMELITE ELECTRIC ARTS - Limelite Electric Arts, Inc.
LIMERIC - Yarn - Brunswick Yarns
LIMERICK - Furniture - Herman Miller, Inc.
LIMERICK - Men's apparel - Schoeneman Enterprises, Inc.
LIMESTONE - Wines - ENZ Vineyards
LIMFJORD LUMPFISH CAVIAR - Caviar - Europa Foods Ltd.
LIMFJORD MUSSELS - Seafood products–fresh or frozen - Europa Foods Ltd.
LIMI-STAT - Mats ☆ - United Technical Products Inc.
LIMICOL - Health care products ☆ - CTS Laboratories Inc.
LIMINATOR - Pet products - Crowne Royale, Ltd.
LIMIT - Herbicides - Monsanto Co.
LIMIT - Milk - Tuscan
LIMIT - Pharmaceutical preparations ☆ - Bock Pharmacal Co.
LIMITAMP - Electrical equipment - General Electric Co.
LIMITED - Apparel and accessories - Donnkenny Inc.
LTD. - Apparel–women's ☆ - Leslie Fay Companies Inc.
LIMITED - Barbecues and grills - Thermos Co.
LIMITED - Boats–motor - Chris Craft Boats
LIMITED - Boats–motor ☆ - Harris-Kayot Inc.
LIMITED - Boats–pontoons - Forester Boats Inc.
LIMITED - Manufactured homes - Redman Industries, Inc.
LIMITED-IT - Mobile homes - Kit Manufacturing Co.
LIMITED - Motor vehicles - Airstream Inc.
LIMITED - Motor vehicles–motor homes ☆ - Fleetwood Enterprises, Inc.
LIMITED CATCH - Tuna–canned ☆ - Dole Food Co., Inc.
LIMITED COLLECTION BY CENTURY, THE - Furniture–wood ☆ - Century Furniture Co.
LIMITED COLLECTION, THE - Women's apparel - Limco Investments, Inc.
LIMITED EDITION - Apparel and accessories - Kellwood Co.
LIMITED EDITION - Apparel–men's ☆ - Haggar Corp.
LIMITED EDITION - Bicycles ☆ - Roadmaster Corp.
LIMITED EDITION - Coffee - Wechsler Coffee Corp.
LIMITED EDITION - Cooking utensils ☆ - Revere Ware Corp.

☆ = Now out of production

LIMITED EDITION - Dryers–hair - Helene Curtis Industries Inc.
LIMITED EDITION - Floor coverings–carpet and rugs - Trend Carpet
LIMITED EDITION - Fruits and vegetables - Andrew & Williamson Sales Co., Inc.
LIMITED EDITION - Hair care products - Waverly Beauty Products
LIMITED EDITION - Health care products - Biotics Research Corp.
LTD. EDITION - Luggage - Universal Trav-ler Inc.
LIMITED EDITION - Motor vehicle parts and accessories - Saddleman, Inc.
LIMITED EDITION - Motor vehicles–motor homes ☆ - Avco Aerostructures Inc.
LIMITED EDITION - Motor vehicles–motor homes ☆ - Georgie Boy Manufacturing, Inc.
LIMITED EDITION - Shirts - Pennshire Shirt Corp.
LIMITED EDITION - Shutters–wood - Ohline Corp.
LIMITED EDITION - Tires - Reinalt-Thomas Corp.
LIMITED EDITION - Tobacco products - Philip Morris Companies Inc.
LIMITED EDITION BY WEAR-EVER - Cookware - Anchor Hocking Glass, Inc.
LIMITED EDITION BY WEAREVER - Cookware - Anchor Hocking Glass, Inc.
LIMITED EDITION DOLLS - Dolls - Effanbee Doll Corp.
LIMITED EDITION STAR WARS B-WING FIGHTER - Toys–models - ERTL Co., Inc.
LIMITED EDITION STAR WARS TIE INTERCEPTOR - Toys–models - ERTL Co., Inc.
LIMITED EDITION STAR WARS X-WING FIGHTER - Toys–models - ERTL Co., Inc.
LIMITED EDITIONS - Craft supplies ☆ - VIP/VIP Crafts
LIMITED EDITIONS - Dresses–girls' - Mailo Designs, Inc.
LIMITED EDITIONS - Ice cream - Dreyer's Grand Ice Cream, Inc.
LIMITED EDITIONS PRINTS - Paper - Thomas Frederick Voight
LIMITED FLITE - Balls–golf - Lisco, Inc.
LIMITED HARVEST - Fruits–canned - Oregon Fruit Products Co., Inc.
LIMITED HARVEST - Rice - Select Origins Inc.
LIMITED JEANS - Apparel and accessories - Limco Investments, Inc.
LIMITED JEANS ESTABLISHED '63 - Apparel and accessories - Limco Investments, Inc.
LIMITED POINTER FLUTTER (LPF) - Gauging instruments - Uniweld Products, Inc.
LIMITED SPORT USA - Apparel–athletic - Limco Investments, Inc.
LIMITED TOO - Apparel and accessories - Limited Inc.
LIMITIMER - Electronic equipment - D'San Corp.
LIMITLESS POSSIBILITIES - Hair care products - Helene Curtis Industries Inc.
LIMITRON - Electrical supplies - Cooper Industries, Inc.
LIMMER - Shoes - Peter Limmer & Sons Inc.
LIM'NATE - Deodorizers - Ryter Corp.
LIMO COACH - Motor vehicles–buses - Turtle Top Specialty Products
LIMO-GARD - Window shades - Metallized Products Inc.
LIMO-GUARD - Plastics film - ITO Industries Inc.
LIMODINE - Pharmaceutical preparations - Wesley Pharmacal Co. Inc.
LIMOGE - Paper ☆ - Shiva Inc.
LIMOGES - Labels–gummed ☆ - Estus Export-Import
LIMOGES FRENCH PORCELAINE - Giftware - Alice Sturzinger Ltd.
LIMONATA - Beverages - San Pellegrino USA
LIMONNAYA - Vodka - Monsieur Henri Wines Ltd.
LIMONTA - Wallcoverings ☆ - Wallstars
LIMOSINE CLOTH - Fabrics - Gretchen Bellinger Inc.
LIMOUSINE - Flowers, plants, and seeds - Jacklin Seed
LIMOZEEN - Toys–automobiles - Mattel, Inc.
LIMP - Sporting goods - Weber Industries Inc.
LIMPERT - Food products - Limpert Bros. Inc.
LIMPERT - Wines - Limpert Fruit Farm
LIMPIADENT - Toothbrushes - Sara Lee Corp.
LIMPITO AL SUCIO LE PEGA DURO! - Cleaning preparations - Felipe A. Valls
LIMPY - Fishing lures - Sunset Line and Twine Co.
LIMRICK - Flowers, plants, and seeds - Limrick Inc.
LIMS+WARE - Computer software - Laboratory Information Management Systems, Inc.
LIN - Insecticides ☆ - Noble Pine Products Co.
LIN-A-CLOTH - Fabrics - Wolsey Co.
LIN-ART - Paints ☆ - Fry Plastics International Inc. (O)
LIN CHI TUDCHA TEA - Teas - Prestige Chinese Teas Co.
LIN FRESH - Trays - LinPac, Inc.
LIN GONE - Degradable plastic bags - LinPac, Inc.
LIN LEE - Dolls - Mattel, Inc.
LIN-SEAL - Concrete–mixture - W.R. Meadows Inc.
LIN-SOAP - Linseed-oil soap - Wood Kote Products, Inc.
LIN-TEX - Pharmaceutical preparations - Syosset Laboratories Inc.
LIN ZIP - Bags–plastic - LinPac, Inc.

LINA - Footwear - Aztec Imports Inc.
LINA - Ophthalmic goods - Rozin Optical Export Corp.
LINA-COUSTIC - Insulating materials - Manville/Schuller
LINA GALE - Cosmetics - Lina Gale, Inc.
LINABOND - Coatings - Allied Coatings Co., Inc.
LINAGRAPH - Photographic equipment - Eastman Kodak Co.
LINAHIST - Cough medicines ☆ - American Hygienic Laboratories Inc.
LINAS - Flowers, plants, and seeds ☆ - Coe & Dru Inc.
LINATONE - Pet products - Lambert-Kay
LINATONE PLUS - Pet products - Lambert-Kay
LINC - Computer software - Carlton International Corp.
LINC LUTHIER - Musical instruments - Clare L. Hoke Jr.
LINC-NET - Computer software ☆ - Proprietary Controls Systems Corp.
LINC-O-LIN - Shampoos ☆ - Delagar
LINCLASER - Computer software - Linc Corp.
LINCO - Cleaning preparations - Erbrich Products Co. Inc.
LINCO-SPECTIN - Veterinary pharmaceutical preparations - Upjohn Co.
LINCOCIN - Pharmaceutical preparations - Upjohn Co.
LINCODYNE - Pharmaceutical preparations - Lincoln Pharmacy Inc.
LINCOLN - Beverages - Sundor Brands Inc.
LINCOLN - Beverages–alcohol - House of Vegas, Inc.
LINCOLN - Floor coverings–carpet and rugs - Colonial Mills Inc.
LINCOLN - Food products - Speaco Foods Inc.
LINCOLN - Guitars - Music Distributors Inc.
LINCOLN - Machine parts - Production Tool Supply International
LINCOLN - Mattresses - Simmons USA
LINCOLN - Motor vehicles–automobiles - Ford Motor Co. (Lincoln-Mercury Div.)
LINCOLN - Shoe polish - Rothco Inc.
LINCOLN - Thread - Cincinnati Thread Co.
LINCOLN - Tiles–ceramic - KPT Inc.
LINCOLN CENTER - Floor coverings–carpet and rugs - Cumberland Mills Inc.
LINCOLN HEAD - Stationery ☆ - Mead Corp.
LINCOLN LOGS - Toys - Playskool, Inc.
LINCOLN LOGS FORT - Toys - Playskool, Inc.
LINCOLN LOGS HOUSE - Toys - Playskool, Inc.
LINCOLN LOGS LTD. - Log cabins–prefabricated - Original Lincoln Logs Ltd.
LINCOLN LOGS PLAYGROUND - Toys - Playskool, Inc.
LINCOLN LOGS VILLAGE - Toys - Playskool, Inc.
LINCOLN PARK - Bicycles - Ross Bicycles USA, Ltd.
LINCOLN ROAD MUSIC CO. - Publisher's imprints - The Keene Music Group
LINCOLN SERIES - Floor coverings - Anderson Hardwood Floors Inc.
LINCOLN TOWNHOUSE - Trailers–travel ☆ - Travel Line Enterprises Inc.
LINCOLNTON - Bedroom furniture - Lea Industries Inc.
LINCOMIX - Veterinary pharmaceutical preparations - Upjohn Co.
LINCORUB - Health care products - Lincoln Pharmacy Inc.
LINCOTUSS - Pharmaceutical preparations - Lincoln Pharmacy Inc.
LINCOURT VINEYARDS - Wines - Santa Ynez Valley Winery
LINCOWARE - Cookware - Lincoware International, Inc.
LINCRUSTA - Wallpaper - Bentley Brothers
LINCS - Computer software - Gerald Shapiro
LINCS - Lighting fixtures - Jji Lighting Group, Inc.
LINDA - Dolls - Goldberger Doll Manufacture Co.
LINDA - Dyes and pigments ☆ - Norma Dharma Trading Co.
LINDA - Floor coverings–carpet and rugs ☆ - Regal Rugs Inc.
LINDA - Flowers, plants, and seeds - Twyford International, Inc.
LINDA - Frames–eyeglass - Rozin Optical Export Corp.
LINDA - Jewelry - Jacoby-Bender Inc.
LINDA - Lingerie - DLC Lingerie, Inc.
LINDA FRATIANNE - Apparel–athletic ☆ - Elite Sportswear L.P.
LINDA HUTTON - Apparel–women's - A.P.S. USA Corp.
LINDA KAREN - Apparel and accessories - PsPlus Sizes, Plus Savings
LINDA LAVELLE - Cosmetics - Linda Lavelle Cosmetique, Inc.
LINDA LEAL - Apparel–women's - Jonden Manufacturing Co., Inc.
LINDA LEE - Toys–stuffed ☆ - Mary Meyer Corp.
LINDA LEWIS - Apparel and accessories - Ranidae International, Inc.
LINDA MCCARTNEY'S HOME STYLE COOKING - Food products - Fairmont Foods of Minnesota, Inc.
LINDA MCCARTNEY'S HOME STYLE COOKING - Food products - Go Veggie, Inc.
LINDA RICHARDS - Women's clothing - Linrich Designs
LINDA THORPE - Apparel–women's - Linda Thorpe Inc.
LINDA WADE - Giftware - N.S. Gustin Co.
LINDAL - Prefabricated buildings–wood - Lindal Cedar Homes Inc.
LINDANE - Veterinary pharmaceutical preparations - C.J. Martin Co.
LINDAR - Camera ☆ - Saul Bower Inc.

☆ = Now out of production

LINDA'S - Cakes - Linda's Desserts
LINDBECK - Brushes–paint - Wooster Brush Co.
LINDBERG - Recording label - Lindberg Records
LINDBERG - Toys–models - Craft House Corp.
LINDEAN MILL - Glass products ☆ - Westminster Trading Corp.
LINDELL - Garden equipment - Mid-States Metal Casters & Manufacturing Co.
LINDELL - Musical instruments ☆ - St. Louis Music Supply Co.
LINDEMANS LAMBIC - Beverages–malt - Merchant du Vin Corp.
LINDEN - Brushes–paint - Corona Brushes Inc.
LINDEN - Clocks - Cuckoo Clock Manufacturing Co. Inc.
LINDEN - Flatware - Kirk Stieff Co.
LINDEN - Floor coverings–carpet and rugs - Karastan-Bigelow Inc.
LINDEN - Food products ☆ - Curtice-Burns Foods, Inc.
LINDEN - Jewelry - Park Lane Associates, Inc.
LINDEN - Tripods–photographic ☆ - Velbon International Corp.
LINDEN - Wallpaper - Koroseal Wallcoverings
LINDEN BLACK FOREST - Clocks - Cuckoo Clock Manufacturing Co. Inc.
LINDEN COURT - Floor coverings - Tarkett, Inc.
LINDEN HALL - Floor coverings–carpet and rugs - Patcraft Mills Inc.
LINDEN HOUSE - Food products - Twin County Grocers Inc.
LINDEN MUSIC - Recording label ☆ - Cuneiform Records
LINDEN PARK - Footwear - Morse Shoe, Inc.
LINDEN PRESS - Publisher's imprints - Simon & Schuster, Inc.
LINDEN TEDLAR - Wallpaper - Koroseal Wallcoverings
LINDENMEYR MUNROE - Paper products - Central National-Gottesman Inc.
LINDEN'S - Cookies - Linden Cookies, Inc.
LINDENWOOD - Cribs–wood ☆ - Welsh Co.
LINDERO - Floor coverings - Congoleum Corp.
LINDEX - Skis - Erik Sports Inc.
LINDHAUS HEALTHCARE PRO - Vacuum cleaner - Lindhaus USA, Inc.
LINDIA - Photographic equipment - Heitz Service Corp.
LINDIG - Garden equipment - Lindig Manufacturing Corp.
LINDLEY - Medical apparatus - InterVentional Technologies Inc.
LINDLEY - Paper–gift wrap - Lindley Packaging Corp.
LINDOR - Jewelry - R.F. Simmons Co.
LINDORA - Pharmaceutical preparations - Westwood-Squibb Pharmaceuticals, Inc.
LINDQUIST - Candles - Swedish Products Inc. (Sojo Inc.)
LINDS - Shoes–athletic - Lind Shoe Co.
LINDSAY - Bags - Interstate Packaging Corp.
LINDSAY - Beverages–alcohol ☆ - Carradale Import Co.
LINDSAY - Dishes–china ☆ - Gorham Inc.
LINDSAY - Floor coverings ☆ - Congoleum Corp.
LINDSAY - Food products - Lindsay Olive Growers
LINDSAY - Grass seed - International Seeds, Inc.
LINDSAY - Jewelry - Lindsay-Hoenig Ltd.
LINDSAY - Mattresses and box springs - Ohio Mattress Co.
LINDSAY - Ships–sailing vessels - Mark Lindsay Boatbuilders
LINDSAY - Water purification systems - Ecowater Systems, Inc.
LINDSAY GOURMET - Giftware ☆ - Gorham Inc.
LINDSAY SARAH - Apparel and accessories - Granada Sales Corp.
LINDSAY STEVENS - Apparel–women's - Meijer, Inc.
LINDSAY'S TEAS - Teas - Mountanos Brothers Coffee Co., Inc.
LINDSEY - Dolls - M.&S. Shillman Inc.
LINDSEY DUNCAN'S HOME NUTRITION - Vitamins and nutritional supplements - Irwin Naturals/4 Health
LINDSEY SCOTT - Apparel–women's - Jerell, Inc.
LINDSHAMMAR - Dinnerware–glass - Arnold Larson Inc.
LINDT - Chocolate candy - Naron Candy Co. Inc.
LINDT - Chocolate candy ☆ - Perrier Group of America Inc.
LINDT BLANCOR - Chocolate bars - Grand Specialties Co.
LINDVIG - Signs - Odin Ltd.-Scan Am Imports Inc.
LINDY - Motor vehicles - Skyline Corp.
LINDY - Pens - K-9 Pen Co.
LINDY LEGS - Fishing lures ☆ - Lindy Little Joe Inc.
LINDY LION - Toys–stuffed - Russ Berrie and Co., Inc.
LINDY RIG - Fishing lures - Lindy Little Joe Inc.
LINDY STINGER - Fishing lures - Lindy Little Joe Inc.
LINDY WALKING SLIP SINKER - Fishing lures - Lindy Little Joe Inc.
LINDY'S - Cakes - Lindy's Food Products
LINDY'S - Sauces - Sona and Hollen Foods Inc.
LINDY'S SALSAS - Food products - Sona and Hollen Foods Inc.
LINDY'S TACO SAUCES - Food products - Sona and Hollen Foods Inc.
LINE - Flatware ☆ - W.M.F. of America Inc.
LINE - Skis - Line Skiboards Manufacturing Inc.
LINE, A - Apparel–women's - Anne Klein & Co.

LINE, A - Hosiery - Pennaco Hosiery Inc.
LINE-A-BED - Truck beds - Travelier Industries Inc.
LINE A DAY, A - Diaries - Samuel Ward Manufacturing Inc.
LINE A POT - Paints - Melrose Paint
LINE-A-TIME - File folders ☆ - Kardex Systems, Inc.
LINE-A-TIMERS - Pens - Eagle Marketing
LINE-BACK'R - Artists' materials ☆ - Charles Leonard Inc.
LINE BUSTER - Fishing lures - Texas Angler, Inc.
LINE CADDY - Nautical instruments - C. Sherman Johnson Co. Inc.
LINE CHANGE HOCKEY - Apparel–athletic - Jeffrey Scott Helfand
LINE DRIVE - Audio equipment - McCormack Audio Corp.
LINE DRIVE - Trading cards and stamps - Impel Marketing Inc.
LINE FREE - Eyeglasses - Optical Radiation Corp.
LINE FREE - Skin care products - Fiske Industries Inc.
LINE KING - Tools–garden - Polyarn Corp.
LINE-LEVEL - Surveying machinery - Spectra-Physics Laserplane, Inc.
LINE-LIFT - Skin care products - La Parfumerie Inc.
LINE LOCK - Containers - Inline Plastics Corp.
LINE MARKERS - Sporting goods - Dacon Manufacturing
LINE MARQUE - Paper - Fox River Paper Co.
LINE-MASTER - Boats - Falcon Safety Products, Inc.
LINE MASTER - Drafting supplies ☆ - Plan Hold Corp.
LINE-MATE - Sporting goods - Beacon Ballfields
LINE-O-HEAT - Heating equipment ☆ - Easy Heat Inc.
LINE-O-LIGHT - Lighting fixtures - Angelo Brothers Co.
LINE-O-LITE - Steel products - St. Louis Steel Products Co.
LINE-O-SCRIBE - Machinery - Morgan Sign Machine Co.
LINE-O-TAPE - Artists' materials - Artype Inc.
LINE-OUT - Chemical preparations - CCT Corp.
LINE POWERED SR2 - Computer software - Multi-Link, Inc.
LINE PRINTER PLUS - Computer software - Printronix, Inc.
LINE PRO - Electrical equipment - West Associates
LINE PUZZLE - Puzzles - Binary Arts Corp.
LINE RACERS - Toys–automobiles - Mattel, Inc.
LINE RADIATOR - Amplifiers ☆ - Electro-Voice, Inc.
LINE REFINE - Lip balms - Charles of the Ritz Group Ltd.
LINE-SAVER - Electronic equipment ☆ - Kalglo Electronics Co. Inc.
LINE SHOOTER - Electrical equipment - GB Electrical Inc.
LINE-STOP - Skin care products - Monteil Paris
LINE TAMER - Electrical equipment - Shape Electronics Inc.
LINE TAMER - Skin care products - Kristine M. Schoenauer
LINE TAMERS - Fishing tackle - Kathrin A. Dillashaw
LINE, THE - Tiles–ceramic ☆ - American Olean Tile Co.
LINE, THE - Wallpaper - Bock Designs Inc.
LINE UP. POWER UP. - Prepared meat entrees - Saramar Corp.
LINE WINDER - Sporting goods - Wellington Leisure Products, Inc.
LINEA - Tableware–china ☆ - Villeroy and Boch Tableware Ltd.
LINEA - Typewriters - Olivetti North America Inc. (Consumer Products Div.)
LINEA 70 - Fabrics–coated - Herculite Products, Inc.
LINEA DONATELLA - Underwear and nightwear - MGT Industries, Inc.
LINEA FIORENTO BY CAMBRIDGE MEMBERS - Apparel and accessories - Cambridge, U.S., Ltd.
LINEA FLEX - Frames–eyeglass - Eyetel Optics, Inc.
LINEA JET - Clocks ☆ - Robert Krups North America
LINEA NOTTE - Linen - I.J. Piccolo, Inc.
LINEA PERFETTA - Cosmetics - Revlon Consumer Products Corp.
LINEA UOMO - Apparel and accessories - Mondo, Inc.
LINEAGE - Dinnerware ☆ - Corning Inc.
LINEAGE - Furniture - Lineage Home Furnishings, Inc.
LINEAGE - Furniture ☆ - Masco Corp.
LINEAGE - Rings–jewelry - Dunn & Ewbank Inc.
LINEAGE - Wallpaper - Jolie Papier
LINEAGES - Computer software - Quinsept Inc.
LINEAIRE - Floor coverings–carpet and rugs - J.L. Benson Co.
LINEAL - Tables–wood - Krueger International, Inc.
LINEAR - Bicycles ☆ - Raleigh USA Bicycle Co.
LINEAR - Exercising equipment - Stairmaster Sports/Medical Products, Inc.
LINEAR - Furniture ☆ - Lane Co. Inc.
LINEAR - Glassware–household - Durand International
LINEAR - Lasers - Draper Shade and Screen Co. Inc.
LINEAR - Lighting fixtures - Swivelier Co. Inc.
LINEAR - Nail care products - Opi Products, Inc.
LINEAR - Telephones - AG Communication Systems Inc.
LINEAR - Wallcoverings - Coral of Chicago
LINEAR CONCEPTS - Floor coverings–carpet and rugs ☆ - Karastan-Bigelow Inc.

☆ = Now out of production

LINEAR DESIGNS - Decals and transfers - Lenda Products, Inc.
LINEAR DYNAMICS - Audio equipment - KLH
LINEAR POWER - Amplifiers–radio - Linear Power Inc.
LINEAR SELECTOR - Computer software - Thomson Industries, Inc.
LINEAR SERIES - Engines - Magnadyne Corp.
LINEAR SERIES - Mufflers–motor vehicle - Marine Exhaust Systems, Inc.
LINEAR SUPER ZZIPPER - Apparel and accessories - Zzip Designs
LINEASETA - Fabrics–silk - Joscar Industries Inc.
LINEBACK - Sporting goods - Marty Gilman Inc.
LINEBACKER - Floor coverings–carpet and rugs - Barrett Carpet Mills Inc.
LINEBERRY - Tools - Multt Metals
LINEDEX - Cameras–microfilm - Kardex Systems, Inc.
LINEDEX - Office supplies - Victor Systems & Equipment Co.
LINEERASER - Ribbons–inked - Smith Corona Corp.
LINEGARD - Electric lighting equipment - SL Waber Inc.
LINEGUARD DOC-SYS-II - Computer software - Henkel Corp. (Functional Products Div.)
LINELAZER - Paint sprayers - Graco Inc.
LINELITER - Inks - National Ink Inc.
LINELITES - Glassware–household - Anchor Glass Container Corp.
LINEMAN - Recording label ☆ - Nationwide Sound Distributors
LINEMAN'S LOTION - Lotions - Lineman's Lotion, Inc.
LINEMASTER - Chemical preparations - Chemcraft
LINEMASTER - Rulers–wood - Rol-Ruler Co.
LINEMATE - Tools–power-driven - Loctite Corp.
LINEMINDER - Fishing rods - Cuba Specialty Manufacturing Co.
LINEN 6 - Window shades - C-Mor Co.
LINEN-AIRE - Deodorants–personal - Surco Products Inc.
LINEN & COTTON - Yarn - Henry's Attic
LINEN BOUCLE - Blinds–venetian ☆ - Hunter Douglas, Inc.
LINEN HALL - Wallpaper - Hamilton Adams Imports Ltd.
LINEN LITES - Apparel and accessories - Target Licensing Corp.
LINEN LOOK - Tablecloths - Erving Paper Products Inc.
LINEN PROTECTORS - Health care products - Geri-Care Products, LLC
LINEN SAVER - Health care products - Geri-Care Products, LLC
LINEN SUITE COLLECTION - Mattresses - Restonic Inc.
LINEN WASH - Cleaning preparations - Le Blanc Linen Wash, Inc.
LINEN WORKS - Wallpaper ☆ - Wallquest, Inc.
LINENEZE - Apparel and accessories - Tex Venture Holding Ltd.
LINENS & WEAVES - Wallpaper - Textile Wallcoverings International Ltd.
LINENS BY ULSTER - Towels - Ulster Weaving Co. Limited
LINENSERVE - Napkins–paper - Georgia-Pacific Corp.
LINENSOFT - Paper napkins - James River Corp.
LINENWALL - Wallpaper - PCI Industries Inc.
LINENWALL II - Wallpaper - PCI Industries Inc.
LINENWALL III - Wallpaper - PCI Industries Inc.
LINENWORKS - Wallpaper - Koroseal Wallcoverings
LINEON - Fabrics, yarns, threads, etc. - R.K. Carbon Fibers Inc.
LINEPOLE - Marine rigging - Windline Marine
LINER ALERT - Firefighting suits - Globe Firefighters Suits, Inc.
LINER FREE - Labels–paper - Media Solutions, Inc.
LINER-LESS - Labels–paper - Chicago Tag & Label, Inc.
LINER LOCK - Beds–wood ☆ - Waterworth
LINER NOTES - Computer software - Systems Design Associates, Inc.
LINERASER - Industrial machinery - Surface Preparation Systems, Inc.
LINERTIA - Golfing equipment - Frank Kinoshita
LINES OF DEATH - Games ☆ - Mayfair Games, Inc.
LINESCAPES - Wallpaper ☆ - Capital Carousel Inc.
LINESIDE STRUCTURES BY AMERICAN MODEL BUILDERS, INC. - Toys–trains - American Model Builders, Inc.
LINESIM - Computer software - Hyperlynx, Inc.
LINESMAN - Ophthalmic goods - Styl-Rite Optical Manufacturing Co., Inc.
LINESMEN - Tents - Foster Corp.
LINESSA - Fabrics - Guilford Mills, Inc.
LINETEC INC. - Marking tape, hand warmers - Linetec Inc.
LINETTE - Candy - James P. Linette Inc.
LINETTE - Handwork supplies - Bernat Yarn & Craft Corp.
LINEUR INTENSE - Cosmetics - Cosmair Inc.
LINEWORKER - Computer software - In Software
LINEX - Dinnerware–glass ☆ - Himark Enterprises Inc.
LINFIELD - Cigarettes - Brown & Williamson Tobacco Corp.
LING-EEZ - Meat products–pork - Columbia Products Inc.
LING INTERNATIONAL - Hair care products ☆ - Charlene Hair Products Inc.
LING LING - Toys–stuffed - Russ Berrie and Co., Inc.
LING LING - Toys–stuffed ☆ - Gund, Inc.
LINGANORE - Wines - Berrywine Plantations Winery

LINGAS - Petroleum - Linweld, Inc.
LINGERIE BEAUCOUP - Apparel–women's - J.A.C. Manufacturing, Inc.
LINGERIE CACIQUE - Apparel and accessories - Limited Inc.
LINGERIE CACIQUE - Paper products - Caciqueco, Inc.
LINGERIE FOR LEGS - Hosiery - Victoria's Secret Stores, Inc.
LINGERIE LOOKS - Hosiery - Sara Lee Corp.
LINGERIE MATE - Cleaning preparations - Kleen Chemical Manufacturing Co.
LINGERIE TEDDIES - Toys–stuffed - Russ Berrie and Co., Inc.
LINGERIE WORN OUT - Lingerie - Intapp Group, Inc.
LINGERING PLEASURES COLLECTION - Cosmetics - Revlon Consumer Products Corp.
LINGHAMS - Chili sauce ☆ - Liberty Richter Inc.
LINGLE BROTHERS - Coffee - Lingle Brothers Coffee Inc.
LINGO - Apparel and accessories - Lingo, Inc.
LINGO - Electronic equipment - Atwater International, Ltd.
LING'S CHINESE DELI - Preserved foods–prepackaged - Ling Ling Foods, Inc.
LINGUA-CENTER - Electronic equipment ☆ - Fleetwood Furniture Co.
LINGUAFUN! - Games - Penton Overseas, Inc.
LINGUALINKS - Computer software - Summer Institute of Linguistics, Inc.
LINGUINE - Yarn ☆ - Tahki Imports Ltd.
LINGUIST, THE - Computer software ☆ - Gessler Publishing Co., Inc.
LINGUISTIC ADVANTAGE - Computer software - Linguistic Advantage
LINHOF - Photographic equipment - H.P. Marketing Corp.
LINI-MIST - Analgesics - Mead-Raymond Corp.
LINIA - Toilets–enameled - Kohler Co.
LINIA DECOR - Housewares ☆ - Himark Enterprises Inc.
LINICAL - Chemical preparations - International Enzymes, Inc.
LINIMENTO #1 - Health care products - D'Franssia Corp.
LINIT - Starch–laundry - First Place Inc.
LINK - Adhesives and sealants - Sta-Dri Co.
LINK - Computer software - 1 Source Corp.
LINK - Musical instrument accessories - Otto Link Inc.
LINK - Navigational instruments - Datamarine International Inc.
LINK - Telescopes - Northern Telecom, Inc.
LINK - Wrenches - Roberts Tool International (USA), Inc.
LINK 200, THE - Cables–coaxial - Transparent Audio Marketing, Inc.
LINK-A-LADDER - Pet products - Penn-Plax, Inc.
LINK-A-LOT - Toys - Tupperware Co.
LINK-ARC - Electrical equipment - Link-Arc
LINK BALANCER - Amplifiers - Advanced Milliwave Laboratories, Inc.
LINK-BELT - Bearings–motor vehicle - Rexnord Corp.
LINK-BY-LINK - Jewelry - Migerobe, Inc.
LINK CENTRAL - Computer software - Motorola, Inc. (Paging Products Group)
LINK/DBS - Computer software - Specific Designs, Inc.
LINK-KING - Computer software - J. Kings Food Service Professionals, Inc.
LINK-LABELS - Labels–gummed - Hexco Inc.
LINK LAUGHS - Calendars ☆ - American Greetings Corp.
LINK LINEAR F - Measuring instruments - EG&G Flow Technology, Inc.
LINK LOK - Chains - Eaton Brothers Corp.
LINK 'N' COUNT - Magnets - Learning Resources, Inc.
LINK-N-DOG - Sandwiches–prepackaged ☆ - Hudson Foods, Inc.
LINK 'N LEATHER - Watchbands–leather - Vogue Watch Strap Creations
LINK-N-LOCK - Wood products - Strata Products (USA), Inc.
LINK 'N' SPELL - Magnets - Learning Resources, Inc.
LINK-NET W-NT - Computer software - Proprietary Controls Systems Corp.
LINK RECORDS - Recording label - Link Records, Inc.
LINK STAR - Tools - O.P. Link Handle Co. Inc.
LINK SYSTEMS - Computer software - Link Systems
LINK-TAYLOR - Furniture ☆ - Masco Corp.
LINK-TECH - Clocks - Link-Tech International Corp.
LINK, THE - Hardware - Hickory Springs Manufacturing Co.
LINK, THE - Electrical equipment - Nady Systems Inc.
LINK-UPS - Garden equipment - Luster Leaf Products Inc.
LINK WOOD - Furniture - Link Corp.
LINK WOOD FURNITURE MFG. - Furniture–wood - Link Corp.
LINK21 - Computer software - Peerless Systems, Inc.
LINKABIT - Electronic equipment - Titan Corp.
LINKALERT - Computer software - Lanart Corp.
LINKBOTS - Toys - Lewis Galoob Toys, Inc.
LINKERS - Sporting goods - Real Manufacturing Co. Inc.
LINKING YOUR WORLDS - Computer peripheral equipment - Megahertz Corp.
LINKJOINT - Bags - Bradley Industrial Textiles, Inc.
LINKMATE - Communications equipment - Link Plus Corp.
LINKOVER - Computer software - CONDUIT
LINKPLUS - Computer software - SDM International Inc.

☆ = Now out of production

LINKPOINT - Computers–micro - Cardservice International Inc.
LINKS - Computer software ☆ - Access Software Inc.
LINKS - Furniture - LUI Corp.
LINK'S - Pharmaceutical preparations - Link Chemical Co.
LINKS - Tires - Carlisle Tire & Rubber Co.
LINKS 386 CD - Computer software - Access Software Inc.
LINKS 386 PRO - Computer software - Access Software Inc.
LINKS AROUND THE WORLD - Sausages - Leon's Sausage Co.
LINKS EDITION - Shirts - Aureus Ltd.
LINKS FOR LAW - Computer software - Infinity Resources, Inc.
LINKS LS - Computer software - Access Software Inc.
LINKS PRO MACINTOSH - Computer software - Access Software Inc.
LINKS TOUR COMPUTER SPORTS NETWORK, THE - Computer software -
   Telescan, Inc.
LINKSENTRY - Computer hardware - Milan Technology
LINKSKEEPER, THE - Golfing equipment - Craig A. Fazekas
LINKSMAN - Shirts, pants, golf equipment - Edwin Watts Golf Shops Inc.
LINKSWITCH - Computer peripheral equipment - 3Com Corp.
LINKUP - Computer software - Peregrine Group, Inc.
LINKWELL - Thread - Blue Mountain Industries, Inc.
LINKWOOD - Whiskey ☆ - Frank Sutton & Co.
LINKWORKS - Audio equipment - Metra Electronics Corp.
LINKY DINK GEOMETRICS - Toys–stuffed - Gund, Inc.
LINKY DINK HEARTS - Toys–stuffed - Gund, Inc.
LINKY DINK PANDA - Toys–stuffed - Gund, Inc.
LINKY DINK ZOO - Toys–stuffed ☆ - Gund, Inc.
LINN - Audio equipment - Audiophile Systems Ltd.
LINN PERENNIAL RYEGRASS - Flowers, plants, and seeds - Jacklin Seed
LINNEA - Floor coverings–carpet and rugs - Masland Corp.
LINNEA - Hosiery–women's - Fischer Hosiery Co.
LINNEA FRANCO - Apparel and accessories - Edison Brothers Stores, Inc.
LINNEMANN - Calendars - Sormani Inc.
LINNET BOOKS - Publisher's imprints - Shoe String Press Inc.
LINNEVAVERIET - Fabrics–linen - Odin Ltd.-Scan Am Imports Inc.
LINO - Floor coverings - Dexter Corp. (Mercer Plastics Div.)
LINO-GRAPH - Pencils–mechanical - Alvin and Co. Inc.
LINO-KLEENER - Cleaning preparations - Wiemer's Inc.
LINO-LOK - Binders ☆ - Spiral Binding Co. Inc.
LINO WALL - Wallcoverings ☆ - Wallstars
LINOFELT - Floor coverings - Congoleum Corp.
LINOFLEX - Floor coverings–linoleum ☆ - Forbo Industries, Inc.
LINOL-F - Pharmaceutical preparations ☆ - Fibertone Co.
LINOLESTROL - Pharmaceutical preparations ☆ - Vortech Pharmaceuticals
LINOPLEX - Veterinary pharmaceutical preparations ☆ - Evsco
   Pharmaceuticals
LINOTEX - Wallpaper - Walldesigns
LINOTUSS - Cough medicines ☆ - American Hygienic Laboratories Inc.
LINOTYPE - Printing trades machinery ☆ - Linotype-Hell Co. Inc.
LINOZIPS - Hardware ☆ - Hunt Manufacturing Co.
LINS - Fabrics–linen - Lionvale
LINSEY - Frames–eyeglass ☆ - Universal/Univis Inc.
LINSLEY - Paper ☆ - Hunt Manufacturing Co.
+L'INSOLENT - Colognes - Frances Denney
+L'INSTANT - Hobby kits - Silver Visions Publishing Co.
LINT-CHASER - Brushes ☆ - National Brush Co.
LINT-EX - Housewares - American Cord & Webbing Co., Inc.
LINT FREE - Cleaning preparations - Helmac Products Corp.
LINT GRABBERS - Brushes - Suburbanite Industries
LINT-LIFTER - Pharmaceutical preparations - Cadie Products Corp.
LINT-MIT - Apparel and accessories ☆ - Mactac Inc. (Packaging Closures
   Systems Div.)
LINT MITT - Housewares - Merrick Industries Inc.
LINT PIC-UP - Health care products - Helmac Products Corp.
LINT-SNARE - Tools - Edward O'Malley Valve Co.
+L'INTERDIT - Perfumes - Parfums Givenchy, Inc.
LINTEX - Fabrics–tapestry ☆ - Columbus Coated Fabrics Co.
LINTEX - Placemats - Lintex Linens, Inc.
+L'INTIMA - Fabrics - Guilford Mills, Inc.
LINTON - Musical instrument accessories ☆ - Armstrong Woodwinds
LINTONE - Musical instruments - J.M. Linton Co.
LINUS PAULING - Vitamins and nutritional supplements - L C Progeny
+LINUS +PAULING - Vitamins and nutritional supplements - LC Progeny
LINVATEC - Surgical equipment - Linvatec Corp.
LINVILLE COLLECTION, THE - Furniture ☆ - Bassett Furniture Industries, Inc.
LINWEAVE - Paper ☆ - Fox River Paper Co.
LINWOOD - Brushes–paint ☆ - PPG Industries, Inc.

LINWOOD - Clocks ☆ - General Time Corp. (Westclox/Seth Thomas Div.)
LINX - Cabinets - Wright Line Inc.
LINX - Science kits - Science Source
LINX DUO - Telephones–cellular - Snet Mobility, Inc.
LINXX-2010 - Computer software - Datamaxx Applied Technologies, Inc.
LINXX-2020 - Computer software - Datamaxx Applied Technologies, Inc.
LINYTRON - Electronic equipment - Sharp Electronics Corp.
LINYTRON/PLUS - Electronic equipment - Sharp Electronics Corp.
LINZER - Brushes–paint - Linzer Products Corp.
LINZER TARTS - Cookies - Joey's Fine Foods
LINZER TORTE - Confections - Famous Pacific Dessert Co.
LIOMEL - Pharmaceutical preparations - Western Research Laboratories
LION - Artists' materials ☆ - Riebe's Artist Materials Inc.
LION - Batteries - Saft America Inc.
LION - Brushes–paint ☆ - PPG Industries, Inc.
LION - Cheese ☆ - Chesman Inc.
LION - Food products - California-Omega Foods Inc.
LION - Hardware - Pootatuck Corp.
LION - Lubricating oils - Tosco Corp.
LION - Raisins - Lion Packing Co.
LION - Yarn - Lion Brand Yarn Co.
LION BREWERY ROOT BEER - Root beer–bottled or canned - Lion Brewery,
   Inc.
LION BUTTON - Buttons - L.S. Lion & Co. Inc.
LION CROSS - Teas–herbal - Tree of Life, Inc.
LION ENTERTAINMENT, INC. - Computer software - Lion Entertainment, Inc.
LION HUNTER - Recording label - Lion Hunter Music
LION IN THE SUN - Eyeglasses - Martin-Copeland Eyewear Corp.
LION KING, THE - Figurines - Sandicast
LION KING, THE - Novelty items - Walt Disney Co.
LION LEA - Leather goods - I.J.K. Sales Corp.
LION OF TROY - Shirts - Harwood Companies Inc.
LION RIDE 'EM - Toys - Steven Manufacturing Co.
LION THE PRINTER - Greeting cards ☆ - Shulsinger Sales Inc.
LION THUNDERZORD - Toys - Saban Entertainment, Inc.
LIONEL - Toys–trains - Lionel Trains Inc.
LIONEL GALLULA - Wines - Blair Importers Ltd.
LIONEL GREAT RAILWAY ADVENTURES - Toys - Learning Curve Toys, LLC
LIONEL PRESCHOOL - Toys–trains - Lionel Trains Inc.
LIONESS - Apparel–men's - Lioness International, Inc.
LIONESS - Eyeglasses - Art-Craft Optical Co.
LIONHEAD GOLDFISH FOOD - Pet products - Hikari Sales USA Inc.
LIONHEART SCOTTISH ALE - Beverages–malt - Tomcat Brewing Co., Inc.
LIONHEARTED - Apparel and accessories - Wemco, Inc.
LIONI BUFALA - Cheese - Lioni Bufala Corp.
LIONITE - Wood products - Lionite Hardboard Co.
LIONPAK - Display cases–plastic ☆ - General Loose Leaf Bindery Co.
LIONS - Beds–wood - Teh Tai Bed Co., Inc.
LION'S PRIDE - Playground equipment - Playgrounds, Inc.
LIONS PRIDE - Toys–stuffed - Dakin Inc.
LIONSHEAD - Beverages–malt ☆ - Lion Brewery, Inc.
LIONSHEAD DELUXE - Beverages–malt ☆ - Lion Brewery, Inc.
LIONSPERSE - Blend chemicals - Lion Industries Inc.
LIONSURF - Chemicals - Lion Industries Inc.
LIORNA - Leather goods - Korchmar Case Co.
LIP ADVANCE - Lipsticks - Noxell Corp.
LIP AID - Health care products - Republic Drug Co. Inc.
LIP BRIGHTS - Lipsticks ☆ - Lander Co., Inc.
LIP CADDY - Cosmetics - Capitol Novelty Co.
LIP-CLEAR - Lip balms - Thursday Plantation Ltd.
LIP CLIC - Lipsticks - Revlon Consumer Products Corp.
LIP COLOR FITNESS - Cosmetics - Elizabeth Arden Inc.
LIP DOCTOR - Cosmetics - Coty Inc.
LIP DUOS - Lipsticks - Reviva Laboratories
LIP-EZE - Lip balms - Frances Denney
LIP FITNESS - Cosmetics - Elizabeth Arden Inc.
LIP FLAVORS - Lip balms - Health-Tech, Inc.
LIP FLIPS - Lipsticks - Pavcom, Inc.
LIP-GARD - Pharmaceutical preparations ☆ - Whitehall Laboratories
LIP GLOSS - Apparel–women's - U.O.D., Inc.
LIP GRIP - Bottle caps ☆ - Moeller Products Co. Inc.
LIP-GUARD - Hardware - Trim-Lok Inc.
LIP HEALER - Cosmetics - CVC Specialties
LIP HUGGERS - Lipsticks - Sassaby Inc.
LIP INDULGENCE - Cosmetics - Maybelline Intermediate Co.
LIP IVO ALOE VERA - Lip balms - Lip IVO Lip Balms of California

☆ = Now out of production

LIP IVO ALOE VERA W/SPF 15 LIP BALM - Lip balms - Ivo of California
LIP IVO NATURAL - Lip balms - Lip IVO Lip Balms of California
LIP IVO NATURAL LIP BALM - Lip balms - Ivo of California
LIP IVO SINCE 1903 - Lip balms - Ivo of California
LIP IVO U.S.A. - Lip balms - Lip IVO Lip Balms of California
LIP IVO USA LIP BALM - Lip balms - Ivo of California
LIP IVO VITAMIN E - Skin care products - Lip IVO Lip Balms of California
LIP KIT - Cosmetics - Cici Cosmetic Co.
LIP LAST - Cosmetics - English Ideas
LIP-LATCH - Fishing tackle - Area Rule Engineering Inc.
LIP LICKERS - Lipsticks - FMG/Tsumara Medical
LIP LIFE - Lipsticks - Neutrogena Corp.
LIP LIFT - Lipsticks - La Parfumerie Inc.
LIP LINER PENCIL - Cosmetics - Viviane Woodard Industries, Ltd.
LIP LITES - Cosmetics - Bonne Bell, Inc.
LIP LOCK - Wastebaskets - E.S. Robbins Corp.
LIP MAGIC - Lipsticks - Transamerica Mailings, Inc.
LIP MENDER - Lip balms - Ilona, Inc.
LIP 'N CHEEK DUO - Skin care products - Viva Vera Aloe Vera
LIP PERFECTION - Skin care products - Pharmagel Corp.
LIP PLUMP - Cosmetics - Benefit Cosmetics
LIP PRIME - Lipsticks - Nat Robbins Ltd.
LIP PRIMER - Lipsticks - Sebastian International, Inc.
LIP-PRO - Skin care products - Sun-Pro of California Inc.
LIP PROOFER - Cosmetics ☆ - Bonne Bell, Inc.
LIP QUENCHER - Cosmetics - Sally Hansen
LIP QUENCHER - Lipsticks - Del Pharmaceuticals, Inc.
LIP RENEW - Lip balms - Max Factor & Co.
LIP RENEWAL - Cosmetics - Yves St. Laurent Parfum Corp.
LIP RESTORE - Cosmetics ☆ - Bonne Bell, Inc.
LIP REVITALIZER - Pharmaceutical preparations - Blistex Inc.
LIP-ROLLER - Cosmetics - Cosmo Cosmetics, Inc.
LIP RX - Lip balms - Frances Denney
LIP SAVER - Lip balms - Carter-Wallace, Inc.
LIP SAVERS - Lip balms - G. Leblanc Corp.
LIP SAVVY - Skin care products - Strong Skin Savvy Inc.
LIP SENSE - Lip balm - Autumn-Harp, Inc.
LIP SET - Cosmetics - Signature Beauty Care, Inc.
LIP SET - Lipsticks - Reviva Laboratories
LIP SHINER - Cosmetics - Bonne Bell, Inc.
LIP SLICKS - Lipsticks - Noxell Corp.
LIP SLIDE - Toys - Mattel, Inc.
LIP SMACKER - Cosmetics - Bonne Bell, Inc.
LIP SMACKERS - Pet products - Lip Smackers Inc.
LIP SMOOTH - Lipsticks - Neutrogena Corp.
LIP SMOOTHIES - Lip balms - Golden Temple Natural Products
LIP SOOTHER - Lip balms - A.H. Robins Co. Inc.
LIP SPICE - Lip balms - Autumn-Harp, Inc.
LIP SWEETS - Cosmetics - Theta Products Corp.
LIP THERAPY - Lip balms - Chesebrough-Pond's USA Co.
LIP TONE - Pharmaceutical preparations - Blistex Inc.
LIP TREATS - Cosmetics - Del Pharmaceuticals, Inc.
LIP TRICKS - Lipsticks - Pavion Ltd.
LIP TRIP - Lipsticks - Everybody Ltd.
LIP UM & CLIP UM - Fishing lures - Blue Fox Tackle Co.
LIP VISOR - Lip protector - Cabot Laboratories Inc.
LIP-VUE - Lipsticks - Schildkraut Giftware Corp.
LIP WHITES - Lipsticks - Wilson Marketing Enterprises, Inc.
LIPAN - Pharmaceutical preparations ☆ - Spirt & Co.
LIPARI - Stones–synthetic - Charles B. Chrystal Co. Inc.
LIPARIN - Pharmaceutical preparations ☆ - Solvay Pharmaceuticals Inc.
LIPASE - Pharmaceutical preparations - City Chemical Corp.
LIPATRIM - Vitamins and nutritional supplements - Source Naturals
LIPAVENA - Oats–rolled or meal - Beacon CMP Corp.
LIPCAINE - Lip balms - Key West Aloe Inc.
LIPCLEAR - Pharmaceutical preparations - Quantum, Inc.
LIPCREME - Cosmetics - Elizabeth Arden Inc.
LIPE - Automotive parts and accessories - Echlin Inc.
LIPIC - Pens - Jos. Lipic Pen Co.
LIPIDERM - Pet products - Bioglan Animal Products Inc.
LIPIDEX - Computer software - Lipidex Systems, Inc.
LIPIDTRACK - Computer software - Lipidex Systems, Inc.
LIPIGUARD - Medical apparatus - Pall Corp.
LIPKOTE - Lip balms - Schering-Plough Healthcare Products
LIPKRAYON - Lipsticks - Shannon Cosmetics, Inc.
LIPLOCK - Electronics equipment - Convergence Corp.

LIPMAGIK - Pharmaceutical preparations - Reese Chemical Co.
LIPMAN - Food products - Lipman Bros. Inc.
LIPMESA - Echlin Inc.
LIPO-ADRENAL CORTEX - Pharmaceutical preparations ☆ - Upjohn Co.
LIPO BC - Vitamins and nutritional supplements - Legere Pharmaceuticals Inc.
LIPO-CHO-TROL - Pharmaceutical preparations - Fibertone Co.
LIPO-EFX - Pharmaceutical preparations - Natural Efx, Inc.
LIPO FLAVONOID - Vitamins and nutritional supplements - Numark Laboratories Inc.
LIPO GANTRISIN - Pharmaceutical preparations - Roche Laboratories
LIPO-LO - Soap - Whorton Pharmaceuticals Inc.
LIPO-NICIN - Vitamins and nutritional supplements - ICN Pharmaceuticals Inc.
LIPO PLEX - Vitamins and nutritional supplements - Natural Organics, Inc.
LIPO-PLUS - Vitamins and nutritional supplements - J.R. Carlson Laboratories Inc.
LIPO-SOLV - Health care products - Tishcon Corp.
LIPO TAB - Pharmaceutical preparations - Physician Sales & Service
LIPO-TEARS - Eye lubricant - Cooper Companies Inc.
LIPO-THREE - Pharmaceutical preparations - Schein Pharmaceutical Inc.
LIPO-TRIM - Vitamins and nutritional supplements - First Security of Destin, Inc.
LIPO-V-PLEX - Veterinary pharmaceutical preparations ☆ - Goodwinol Products Corp.
LIPO-VITE COMPLEX - Skin care products - Vitamin Shoppe Industries Inc.
LIPOBEX - Pharmaceutical preparations - Dunhall Pharmaceuticals Inc.
LIPOCELL - Chemical additives - Intergen Co. L.P.
LIPODASE - Vitamins and nutritional supplements - Freeda Vitamins Inc.
LIPODERM - Pharmaceutical preparations ☆ - Spirt & Co.
LIPOEC - Vitamins and nutritional supplements - Henkel Corp. (Functional Products Div.)
LIPOGEN - Vitamins and nutritional supplements - Tishcon Corp.
LIPOGENOSOME - Medical apparatus - Anticancer, Inc.
LIPOGY SOFTGEL - Vitamins and nutritional supplements - Winning Laboratories Corp.
LIPOIC ACID CAPS - Vitamins and nutritional supplements - Vitamin Research Products Inc.
LIPOLEAN - Vitamins and nutritional supplements - Longevity Network, Ltd.
LIPOLEIT - Pharmaceutical preparations ☆ - Blaine Co. Inc.
LIPOLO - Vitamins and nutritional supplements ☆ - Great Life Laboratories Inc.
LIPOMECHOL - Pharmaceutical preparations ☆ - U.S. Ethicals Inc.
LIPOMUL - Pharmaceutical preparations ☆ - Upjohn Co.
LIPONOID - Pharmaceutical preparations - Schein Pharmaceutical Inc.
LIPONOL - Pharmaceutical preparations - Rugby Laboratories Inc.
LIPONORM - Vitamins and nutritional supplements - Tishcon Corp.
LIPORAL - Cosmetics - Hon Ly
LIPOSOME CREME - Hair coloring preparations - Chenice Beverly Hills
LIPOSOME CURE SYSTEM - Hair care products - Chenice Beverly Hills
LIPOSOME HAND & BODY CREME - Skin care products - Chenice Beverly Hills
LIPOSOMES HYDROGEL - Skin care products - Sothys USA Inc.
LIPOSYN - Pharmaceutical preparations - Abbott Laboratories
LIPOTRIAD - Vitamins and nutritional supplements - Numark Laboratories Inc.
LIPOTRIM - Vitamins and nutritional supplements ☆ - Tishcon Corp.
LIPOTROL - Pharmaceutical preparations - ACHC, LLC
LIPOTRON FORTE - Pharmaceutical preparations ☆ - U.S. Ethicals Inc.
LIPOTROPIC 1000 PLUS - Vitamins and nutritional supplements - Solaray
LIPOTROPIC FUEL - Vitamins and nutritional supplements - Twinlab
LIPOTROPIC PLUS - Vitamins and nutritional supplements - Ethical Nutrients
LIPOVITE - Pharmaceutical preparations - Rugby Laboratories Inc.
LIPOX - Pharmaceutical preparations - Abbott Laboratories
LIPPER - Wood products - Lipper International Inc.
LIPPINCOTT JUNIOR BOOKS - Publisher's imprints - Harper Junior Books Group
LIPPINCOTT PAGE-TURNERS - Publisher's imprints - Harper Junior Books Group
LIPS - Golfing equipment - Frankie Avalon Products, Inc.
LIPS - Lip balms - Solaray
LIPS GLYCYRRHETINIC HERB EXTRACT TEA TREE OIL - Lip balms - Solaray
LIPS LIKE HERS - Lipsticks - Alexandra De Markoff, Ltd.
LIPS PLUS - Skin care products - Donna Lee Cosmetics Inc.
LIPSERVICE - Skin care products - Les Femmes Inc.
LIPSEXXXY - Lipsticks - Revlon Consumer Products Corp.
LIPSEXXXY - Lipsticks - Charles Revson Inc.
LIPSILK - Lipsticks - California Cosmetics

LIPSNER-SMITH - Electronics equipment - RTI Research Technology International
LIPSTICK - Lipsticks - Kiss My Face
LIPSTICK - Recording label - Nova Records Inc.
LIPSTICK SAVER - Bags–cosmetic - Deanne D. Liburdi
LIPSTICK SHOPPE - Cosmetics - Cosmania, Inc.
LIPSTICK STALL - Bathroom accessories - Plastic Fabricators Inc.
LIPSTICK SURPRISE - Dolls - Tonka Corp.
LIPSTICKS - Candy - Ce De Candy Inc.
LIPSTIK - Furniture ☆ - Altec Lansing Consumer Products
LIPSTIQUE - Cosmetics - Lord & Berry, Ltd.
LIPSTIQUE SOLAIRE - Lipsticks - Cosmair Inc.
LIPSTIX - Lipsticks - Finger Mates Inc.
LIPTENSIVE - Cosmetics - Guthy-Renker Corp.
LIPTON - Frames–eyeglass ☆ - Universal/Univis Inc.
LIPTON - Teas - Lipton Investments, Inc.
LIPTON BRISK - Iced tea–bottled or canned - Lipton Investments, Inc.
LIPTON FLOW-THRU - Teas - Lipton Investments, Inc.
LIPTON NOODLES & SAUCE - Noodles - Lipton Investments, Inc.
LIPTON RICE & SAUCE - Rice - Lipton Investments, Inc.
LIPWRITER - Lipsticks - Coty Inc.
LIPZ - Pharmaceutical preparations - Basic Organics, Inc.
LIQ-U-WORM - Pet products - Thomas Veterinary Drug
LIQUA 4 - Soap - Dial Corp.
LIQUA AMBER ROYAL - Vitamins and nutritional supplements - Royal Kingdom Enterprises Inc.
LIQUA-FORM - Fertilizers - Plant Food Co., Inc.
LIQUA-GEL - Cleaning preparations–upholstery - Chemspec, Inc.
LIQUA HEALTH - Vitamins and nutritional supplements - Re-Vita Manufacturing Co., Inc.
LIQUA-LITE - Lighting fixtures ☆ - Lava-Simplex Internationale
LIQUA PAC - Centrifuges–industrial - Waterlink, Inc.
LIQUA-SHIELD - Uniforms–academic ☆ - Superior Surgical Manufacturing Co. Inc.
LIQUA SPIRULINA - Vitamins and nutritional supplements - Re-Vita Manufacturing Co., Inc.
LIQUA-TAPE - Insulating materials - Repair-It Industries Inc.
LIQUA-TEC - Footwear - E.S. Originals, Inc.
LIQUACAST - Jewelry - F.E. Knight, Inc.
LIQUACID - Cleaning preparations–carpet and rug - Certified International
LIQUADENT TOOTHWASH - Dentifrice - Hubert Inc.
LIQUAEMIN SODIUM - Pharmaceutical preparations - Organon Inc.
LIQUALGINE - Pharmaceutical preparations - Whorton Pharmaceuticals Inc.
LIQUALOR - Hair care products ☆ - Thomas & Thompson Co. Inc.
LIQUAMAR - Pharmaceutical preparations ☆ - Organon Inc.
LIQUAMIX - Veterinary nutritional supplements - Cargill, Inc.
LIQUAMYCIN LA-200 - Veterinary pharmaceutical preparations - Pfizer Inc.
LIQUATINE - Hair care products - Image Laboratories, Inc.
LIQUEURILLO - Cigars ☆ - National Cigar Corp.
LIQUI-BAN - Veterinary pharmaceutical preparations ☆ - Evsco Pharmaceuticals
LIQUI-BREAD-MIX - Shortening - Humko Products
LIQUI-CADDY - Toiletries - Brass Craft Manufacturing Co.
LIQUI-CAL - Vitamins and nutritional supplements - Banner-Pharmacaps Inc. (Advanced Nutritional Technology Division)
LIQUI-CAL/MAG - Vitamins and nutritional supplements - Banner-Pharmacaps Inc. (Advanced Nutritional Technology Division)
LIQUI-CHAR - Pharmaceutical preparations - JMI-Canton Pharmaceuticals
LIQUI-CHAR - Pharmaceutical preparations - Jones Medical Industries, Inc. (Medical Div.)
LIQUI CREAME - Cosmetics - Yves St. Laurent Parfum Corp.
LIQUI-CULT - Chemical preparations - Metalworking Chemicals & Equipment Co. Inc.
LIQUI-DET - Detergents - Oakite Products, Inc.
LIQUI-DOSS - Health care products - Ferndale Laboratories, Inc.
LIQUI-DRY - Bowling balls - Master Industries Inc.
LIQUI-FIVE - Herbal products - Sunrider Corp.
LIQUI-FLOW COATING EXTENDER - Paints - Enviro-Chem Inc.
LIQUI-FRY - Shortening - Kraft Food Ingredients Corp.
LIQUI-GLAZE - Wallpaper ☆ - Consolidated Coatings Corp.
LIQUI-K - Vitamins and nutritional supplements - Twinlab
LIQUI-LEA - Vitamins and nutritional supplements - Shaklee Corp.
LIQUI-MARK - Pens - Liqui-Mark
LIQUI-MAX - Irrigation equipment - Lor-AL Products, Inc.
LIQUI-NOX - Detergents - Alconox Inc.
LIQUI-PAK - Beverages - Premium Brands, Inc.

LIQUI-PLASTIC - Adhesives and sealants - Garon Products Inc.
LIQUI-PLY - Adhesives and sealants - MCI Quality Coatings
LIQUI-POUR - Dispensers - American Belt Co.
LIQUI-POUR JR. - Dispensers - American Belt Co.
LIQUI-SENSE - Monitors–electronic - Cole-Parmer Instrument Co.
LIQUI SORB - Chemical preparations - Amcol International Corp.
LIQUI-STEEL - Epoxy ☆ - Fosroc Inc.
LIQUI-THAW - Uncle Sam Chemical Co., Inc.
LIQUI-TOOL - Motor vehicle parts and accessories - Triangle Corp.
LIQUI-TRAC - Exercising equipment ☆ - Maxxim Medical Inc.
LIQUI-VITE - Vitamins and nutritional supplements - World Organics Products
LIQUI-ZIP - Bags–plastic - Com-Pac International Inc.
LIQUI-ZORB - Absorbent ☆ - Vaportek, Inc.
LIQUIBAND - Vitamins and nutritional supplements - Medlogic Global Corp.
LIQUIBARINE - Pharmaceutical preparations ☆ - Norgine Laboratories Inc.
LIQUICAPS - Pharmaceutical preparations - Richardson-Vicks USA
LIQUICHLOR - Veterinary pharmaceutical preparations - Evsco Pharmaceuticals
LIQUICOOL - Sporting goods - Unique Sports Products Inc.
LIQUID - Snowboards - Ride Snowboard Co.
LIQUID 8 - Pet products - Gerard-Pellham Co.
LIQUID 747 - Veterinary nutritional supplements - Y-Tex Corp.
LIQUID-ARMOR - Paints - Missouri Paint & Varnish Co.
LIQUID ASSETS - Apparel–women's - Diane Von Furstenberg Studio
LIQUID ASSETS - Shampoos - KMS Research Inc.
LIQUID BEADS - Arts and crafts kit - Plaid Enterprises, Inc.
LIQUID BLEND - Correction fluid - Eaton Allen Ko-Rec-Type Corp.
LIQUID BOOKS - Games - Lightspan Partnership, Inc.
LIQUID BREAD - Machine parts - Liquid Bread, Inc.
LIQUID BREAD - Valves - Thomas S. Moench
LIQUID BRUSH - Housewares - Britt Manufacturing
LIQUID CAL-600 - Vitamins and nutritional supplements - J.R. Carlson Laboratories Inc.
LIQUID CAULK - Caulking compounds - Gloucester Co., Inc.
LIQUID CHALK - Markers–felt-tip - MagnaPlan Corp.
LIQUID CLAY - Skin care products - Origins Natural Resources Inc.
LIQUID CONDOM - Prophylactics - Trimensa Corp.
LIQUID CORK - Sporting goods - Northwest Angler
LIQUID CRAK SEAL - Adhesives and sealants - Camp Co. Inc.
LIQUID CRAYON - Crayons ☆ - Duncan Enterprises
LIQUID CRYSTAL - Automotive parts and accessories - Turtle Wax, Inc.
LIQUID CRYSTAL - Skin care products - Origins Natural Resources Inc.
LIQUID CRYSTALS - Hobby kits ☆ - Blumenthal/Lansing Co.
LIQUID CULTURE - Apparel and accessories - Liquid Culture, Inc.
LIQUID DIAMOND - Cleaning preparations ☆ - Ziebart International Corp.
LIQUID DIAMONDS - Hair care products - Hayashi for Hair Inc.
LIQUID EMBROIDERY - Pens - Tri-Chem Inc.
LIQUID ENVELOPE - Paints - Essex Specialty Products, Inc.
LIQUID ERASER - Correction fluid - Itoya of America, Ltd.
LIQUID EXTRAC - Cleaning preparations–carpet and rug ☆ - Knight Marketing Corp.
LIQUID EYES & WORMS - Candy - Tyco Industries, Inc.
LIQUID FIRE - Housewares - Amazing Products Inc.
LIQUID FOIL - Inks - Fabco Products Inc.
LIQUID FORCE - Surfboards - Earth & Ocean Sports, Inc.
LIQUID FRENZY - Fishing lures - Precision Bait Co.
LIQUID FRUITSOURCE - Seasonings ☆ - Advanced Ingredients, Inc.
LIQUID GEL - Rust removers - Radiator Specialty Co.
LIQUID GLASS - Cleaning preparations–window - Liquid Glass Enterprises Inc.
LIQUID GLASS - Skin care products - Top Ten Cosmetics, Inc.
LIQUID GLAZE - Cleaning preparations - Liquid Glaze Inc.
LIQUID GLAZE - Skin care products - Sacha International
LIQUID GLO - Paints - O'Brien Corp.
LIQUID GLOVE - Cleaning preparations - Hudco Industrial Products, Inc.
LIQUID GLOVE - Skin care products ☆ - Enviro-Chem Inc.
LIQUID GOLD - Paints - T.J. Ronan Paint Corp.
LIQUID GOLD - Waxes–mineral - Hertel & Co. Inc.
LIQUID GROOVE - Recording label - Liquid Music Inc.
LIQUID GROUNDS - Liquid coffee - Grounds for Coffee Corp.
LIQUID HIDE - Paints - Franklin International, Inc.
LIQUID HILLS - Apparel and accessories - Alan Hills, II
LIQUID ICE - Cosmetics ☆ - St. Ives Laboratories, Inc.
LIQUID ICE SCRAPER - Automotive parts and accessories - National Interchem Corp.
LIQUID IRON & ZINC - Fertilizers - Security Products Co.

☆ = Now out of production

LIQUID JET-SOL - Cleaning preparations–carpet and rug - Certified International

LIQUID KELP FERTILIZER - Fertilizers - Sprout House

LIQUID KRT - Correction fluid - Eaton Allen Ko-Rec-Type Corp.

LIQUID-L - Housewares - Shaklee Corp.

LIQUID LAMINATE - Adhesives and sealants - Beacon Chemical Co. Inc.

LIQUID LANDSCAPE - Bath oil - Origins Natural Resources Inc.

LIQUID LATHER - Shampoos - Ulmer Pharmacal Co.

LIQUID LEAF - Paints - Plaid Enterprises, Inc.

LIQUID LEATHER - Paints ☆ - Tulip Productions

LIQUID LECTRIC TAPE - Tape–adhesive - Marine Development & Research Corp.

LIQUID LIFE - Herbal products - Liquid Life, Inc.

LIQUID LIGHT - Lamps - Lamplight Farms, Inc.

LIQUID LIGHTNING - Health care products - Natural Organics, Inc.

LIQUID LIP PEARLS - Lipsticks - Maybelline Co.

LIQUID LIPS - Skin care products ☆ - B & B Distributors

LIQUID-LITE - Enamels - Fuller-O'Brien Paints Inc.

LIQUID LIVER - Health care products - Enzymatic Therapy, Inc.

LIQUID LUSTER - Polishing rouge ☆ - Gold Eagle Co.

LIQUID LUSTRE - Enamels - Fuller-O'Brien Paints Inc.

LIQUID LUSTRE - Paints - O'Brien Corp.

LIQUID LUSTRE - Paints - Ponderosa Paint Manufacturing Co. Inc.

LIQUID MAGIC - Soap ☆ - Paxon Manufacturing Co.

LIQUID MAGNET - Cleaning preparations–carpet and rug - Jamie Industries, Inc.

LIQUID MUSCLE - Vitamins and food supplements - L & S Research Corp.

LIQUID MUSIC - Recording label - Instinct Records Corp.

LIQUID NAIL - Nail care products - Claire Topper Enterprises

LIQUID NAILS - Adhesives and sealants - Macco Adhesives

LIQUID NAILS - Nail care products - Nailtex Inc.

LIQUID NO-WASH REMOVER - Hardware - Allpro Corp.

LIQUID OPAL - Jewelry - Lawrence J. Rosen

LIQUID PAC - Hair care products - Mastey De Paris

LIQUID PAPER - Correction fluid - Liquid Paper Corp.

LIQUID PATCH, THE - Rubber–molded - North Shore Laboratories Corp.

LIQUID PEARL - Paints - Plaid Enterprises, Inc.

LIQUID PEARL - Paints - Vanguard Paints & Finishes Inc.

LIQUID PEARLS - Glue–household or industrial - Ranger Industries

LIQUID PEARLS - Lipsticks - Schering-Plough Healthcare Products

LIQUID PEARLS - Pottery products - Duncan Enterprises

LIQUID PLUG - Boiler sealer - Comstar International Inc. (IPC Div.)

LIQUID-PLUMBR BUILD-UP REMOVER - Drain pipe cleaners - Clorox Co.

LIQUID PLUMR - Drain pipe cleaners - Clorox Co.

LIQUID POWER - Automotive parts and accessories - Edelbrock Corp.

LIQUID POWER - Cleaning preparations–household - L & F Consumer Products

LIQUID POWER - Health care products - Basic Organics, Inc.

LIQUID PROTEIN - Hair care products - St. Ives Laboratories, Inc.

LIQUID PUZZLE SAVER - Adhesives and sealants - Milton Bradley Co.

LIQUID RAW-HIDE - Varnishes - Behr Process Corp.

LIQUID RE-TYPE - Correction fluid - Wirth International Inc.

LIQUID RESULTS - Cleaning preparations–carpet and rug - Promaster

LIQUID ROC - Adhesives and sealants - MKT Fastening, LLC

LIQUID ROCK - Vitamins and nutritional supplements - Ronald G. Ameral

LIQUID ROOTER - Drain pipe cleaners - A Corp.

LIQUID RUBBER - Coatings - Garon Products Inc.

LIQUID SATIN - Paints - O'Brien Corp.

LIQUID SEAL - Adhesives and sealants ☆ - Macco Adhesives

LIQUID SEQUINS - Paints ☆ - DecoArt, Inc.

LIQUID SHEEN - Cleaning preparations - Remwood Products Co. Inc.

LIQUID SHINE - Hair care products ☆ - Freeman Cosmetics Corp.

LIQUID SHINE - Nail care products - Salon Concepts

LIQUID-SILK - Finishing agents - Byrne Ceramic Supply Co. Inc.

LIQUID SKIN - Hair care products - Men's Hair Now, Ltd.

LIQUID SKY RECORDS - Recording label - Liquid Sky Records, Ltd.

LIQUID SLICKER - Pet products - Nature's Choice

LIQUID SOLUTIONS - Vitamins and nutritional supplements - Pharmaceutical Laboratories

LIQUID SPARKLE - Glass, tile, and floor cleaner - Aubrey Organics, Inc.

LIQUID SPONGE - Skin care products - Fanie International

LIQUID SPOTTER - Stain removers ☆ - Golden Star Inc.

LIQUID SPRAY MAGIC - Finishing agents ☆ - Calgon Vestal Laboratories

LIQUID STEEL - Adhesives and sealants - Loctite Corp.

LIQUID STITCH - Craft supplies - Prym Dritz Corp.

LIQUID STYPTIC - First aid kits - Flents Products Co. Inc.

LIQUID SUEDE - See **FASHION SUEDE**

LIQUID SUNSHINE - Beverages–malt - Technically Leading Consultants Co.

LIQUID SUNSHINE - Fruit drinks–bottled or canned ☆ - Maui Pineapple Co.

LIQUID SUNSHINE - Insecticides ☆ - New Plant Life

LIQUID SUPERSET - Hair care products - All Clubman

LIQUID SWABBY II - Cleaning preparations - Hillyard Enterprises, Inc.

LIQUID TAN - Tanning preparations - Rotheudt Enterprises, Inc.

LIQUID TECHNOLOGY - Beverages - Stokely-Van Camp, Inc.

LIQUID TELEVISION - Key rings - Viacom International Inc.

LIQUID-TEMP - Paints–artists' - Palmer Paint Products, Inc.

LIQUID TEX - Hair care products - Revlon Consumer Products Corp.

LIQUID TEX - Hair care products - Roux Laboratories, Inc.

LIQUID THREAD - Adhesives and sealants - Beacon Chemical Co. Inc.

LIQUID THREAD - Craft supplies - Milton Bradley Co.

LIQUID THREAD MINIATURES - Craft supplies - Milton Bradley Co.

LIQUID TILE - Paints - Sophir Morris Paint

LIQUID TILING - Paints ☆ - Devoe & Raynolds Co.

LIQUID-TO-POWDER - Cosmetics - Almay Inc.

LIQUID VELVET - Cosmetics - Monaco Import/Export Inc.

LIQUID VELVET - Paints - Fuller-O'Brien Paints Inc.

LIQUID VELVET - Paints - O'Brien Corp.

LIQUID VELVET - Pencils ☆ - Faber-Castell Corp.

LIQUID VINYL - Paints - Kwal-Howells Inc.

LIQUID WAVE - Apparel and accessories - M Hidary & Co., Inc.

LIQUID WINTREE - Detergents - Huish Detergents, Inc.

LIQUID WRENCH - Lubricants - Radiator Specialty Co.

LIQUIDARMOR - Tire inflators - A-Loop Offroads

LIQUIDATOR - Chemical preparations ☆ - Bio Huma Netics, Inc.

LIQUIDATOR - Housewares ☆ - Advance Machine Co.

LIQUIDATOR - Toy sporting equipment - Tonka Corp.

LIQUIDINE - Pharmaceutical - Jamol Laboratories Inc.

LIQUIDO - Skin care products - Victoria Vogue, Inc.

LIQUIDOSE - Food products - California-Omega Foods Inc.

LIQUIDSTRIP - Paint removers - Parks Corp.

LIQUIDTILE - Enamels - Impervious Paint Industries Ltd.

LIQUIDTRON - Watches - Elgin Watch Co.

LIQUIDWOOD - Finishing agents - Abatron, Inc.

LIQUIFILM - Ophthalmic goods - Allergan, Inc.

LIQUIFILM FORTE - Ophthalmic goods - Allergan, Inc.

LIQUIFILM TEARS - Ophthalmic goods - Allergan, Inc.

LIQUIFINE - Filters–industrial - Liquid Handling Specialists, Inc.

LIQUIFIX - Hair care products - BLF, Inc.

LIQUIFLO - Pharmaceutical preparations - Fresenius USA, Inc.

LIQUIFORGED - Pistons - AE Clevite Inc.

LIQUIFRY - Fish food - Aquarium Products Inc.

LIQUIFRY EGGLAYER - Pet products - Aquarium Products Inc.

LIQUIFRY LIVEBEARER - Pet products - Aquarium Products Inc.

LIQUIFRY MARINE - Pet products - Aquarium Products Inc.

LIQUIGEL - Cold remedies - R.P. Scherer Corp.

LIQUIMAT - Pharmaceutical preparations - Owen/Galderma Laboratories Inc.

LIQUIMATE - Chemicals–photographic - Gerald C. Parker Sr.

LIQUIMERIK - Machinery - Merrick Industries Inc.

LIQUIN - Artists' materials - Winsor & Newton

LIQUINET - Hair spray ☆ - Benjamin Ansehl Co.

LIQUINOL - Pharmaceutical - Iodent Co.

LIQUIPAK - Hardware - Revelation Sports Marketing

LIQUIPEX - Tubes–plastic - Embassy Industries Inc.

LIQUIPHARM - Health care products - Liquipharm Inc.

LIQUIPRIME - Vitamins and nutritional supplements - Enrich Corp.

LIQUIPRIN - Cough medicines - Smithkline Beecham Corp.

LIQUISEAL - Roofing materials–clay - Carlisle Corp.

LIQUISLIM - Food products ☆ - Warner-Lambert Co.

LIQUISOLE - Adhesives and sealants ☆ - McNett Corp.

LIQUISTRACT - Cleaning preparations–carpet and rug - Bronner Enterprises, Inc.

LIQUISTRIP - Paint removers - Sterling-Clark-Lurton Corp.

LIQUITEX - Paints - Binney & Smith Inc.

LIQUITILE - Paints - Hancock Paint & Varnish Co.

LIQUITRIM - Vitamins and nutritional supplements - Enrich Corp.

LIQUITRON - Mattresses - Spring Air Bedding Inc.

LIQUIVENT - Pharmaceutical preparations - Alliance Pharmaceutical Corp.

LIQUIX - Pharmaceutical preparations ☆ - ICN Pharmaceuticals Inc.

LIQUOR PAK - Bags–storage - Accurate Flannel Bag Co.

LIQUORE DI NOCE - Beverages–alcohol - Consolidated Distilled Products Inc.

LIQUORE ROIANO - Liquors - Disusa Imports Co.

LIQUORE STREGA - Cordials - Shaw-Ross International Importers

☆ = Now out of production

LIQWID CENTER - Cough drops ☆ - Iodent Co.
LIRA - Frames—eyeglass ☆ - Universal/Univis Inc.
LIRICO - Wines - Winesellers Ltd.
LIROVITE-12 - Pharmaceutical preparations - Blair Pharmacal
LIRS CLASSICS - Recording label - LIRS Classics
LIRUGEN - Vaccines - Marion Merrell Dow
LIS - Medical equipment - Linvatec Corp.
LIS LOGISTICS INFORMATION SYSTEMS - Computer software - Logistics Information Systems, Inc.
LIS NERIS PECORARI - Beverages—alcohol - Trebon Wine & Spirit Corp.
LIS PETERSEN - Belts, handbags, etc. - Limar Designs
LISA - Computer software - Associated Estates Realty Corp.
LISA - Computer software - iXL-San Diego
LISA - Computers—personal ☆ - Apple Computer Inc.
LISA - Doll - Olmec Toys, Inc.
LISA - Dolls - Mattel, Inc.
LISA - Floor coverings—carpet and rugs ☆ - Regal Rugs Inc.
LISA - Frames—eyeglass - U.S. Optical Frame Co.
LISA - Musical instrument accessories - Dimarzio, Inc.
LISA - Recording label ☆ - Arcade Record Co./Arzee Record Co.
LISA - Scissors—hand-operated - F.W. Engels Inc.
LISA - Shoes—athletic - Coast Shoes Inc.
LISA - Soap - Stahl Soap Corp.
LISA - Vegetables—canned - EFCO Importers
LISA ANNE - Novelty items - Lisa Anne
LISA D. CARPENTER - Posters - Old Port Artisans
+LISA +DEANE - Apparel—women's - Jean St. Germain, Inc.
LISA FRANK - Paper - Stuart Hall Co., Inc.
LISA FRANK - Toys—stuffed - Mighty Star Inc. (Special Effects Div.)
LISA FRANK MASTERPIECES - Erasers - Lisa Frank, Inc.
LISA GROWS UP - Dolls ☆ - Effanbee Doll Corp.
LISA II - Computers—personal ☆ - Apple Computer Inc.
LISA JARDINE'S - Salad dressings—bottled - Jardine's Texas Foods
LISA LANE - Toiletries - Benjamin Ansehl Co.
LISA LAYETTE - Toys - Eugene Doll & Novelty Co. Inc.
LISA LEE - Jewelry - Lisa Lee Creations, Inc.
LISA LITE - Fishing lures - EC Electronics Inc.
LISA LOREN - Leather goods - Leather Loft Stores, Inc.
LISA MARIE - Apparel—women's - Frederick Atkins, Inc.
LISA MARIE - Wallpaper - I. Gottlieb & Associates
LISA MARIE - Wallpaper - Marburg Wallcoverings Inc.
LISA MARIE - Wines - Renwood Winery, Inc.
LISA MARIE, THE - Paper products - Elvis Presley Enterprises Inc.
LISA MAXX - Hair accessories, jewelry - Hair Things
LISA NOLTA - Jewelry - Gabrielle Ferrar
LISA TODD - Apparel and accessories - Lisa Todd, Inc.
LISA-TONE - Frames—eyeglass ☆ - Universal/Univis Inc.
LISA-VICTORIA - Beds—metal - Lisa-Victoria
LISADRAW - Computer software - Apple Computer Inc.
LISA'S CHOICE - Candy - New York's Finest Chocolate Co., Inc.
LISA'S TEA TREASURES - Teas - Lisa's Tea Treasures
LISBOA - Dinnerware—glass - Block China Co.
LISBOA - Recording label ☆ - Penco Industries Inc.
LISBOA WHITE - Dishes—china - Block China Co.
LISBON - Brushes—paint ☆ - PPG Industries, Inc.
LISBON - Plumbing fixtures - Barclay Products Ltd.
LISBON - Wallpaper - Capital Carousel Inc.
LISBON - Wallpaper - Dekortex Inc.
LISBON - Wigs ☆ - Paula Young
LISBON - Wood products ☆ - Homasote Co.
LISE J - Apparel—women's - Dress Barn Inc.
LISEBERG - Dishes—china - Viletta China Co.
LISETTE - Frames—eyeglass - Pathway Optical Prods.
LISETTE - Handbags - Lisette Handbags Ltd.
LISIANTHUS, THE BLUE ROSE - Flowers, plants, and seeds - W. Atlee Burpee and Co.
LISMORE - Earthenware ☆ - Waterford Wedgwood USA, Inc.
LISNER - Jewelry - D. Lisner & Co.
LISPA STEERING DAMPENERS - Cosmopolitan Motors Inc.
LISRO - Jewelry - Lisitzky-Rosner Jewelry Inc.
LISSA ALEXANDER - Bathing suits - Raj Manufacturing, Inc.
LISSA B - Apparel—women's - Kaulkin International, Inc.
LISSA STUART - Apparel—women's - Kaulkin International, Inc.
LISSEN - Computer software - Skills Management International Ltd.
LIST - Posters - Pace Posters
LIST FINDERS - Office supplies - Bates Manufacturing Co.

LIST MAKERII - Computer software - MCI Communications Corp.
LIST XPRESS - Radiofrequency measuring equipment - Prairie Systems, Inc.
LISTADO - Fabrics ☆ - N. Erlanger, Blumgart & Co. Inc.
LISTEN - Collar buttons - H. Alpert and Co.
LISTEN - Computer software - Electronic Courseware Systems Inc.
LISTEN - Speech recognition software - Verbex Voice Systems Inc.
LISTEN & LEARN - Electronic equipment - Texas Instruments Inc.
LISTEN AND LEARN A LANGUAGE - Recording label - Twin Sisters Productions
LISTEN-CRAFT - Headsets—telephone - Hamilton Electronics Corp.
LISTEN, IMAGINE ADVENTURES - Publisher's imprints - Price Stern Sloan Inc.
LISTENING LIBRARY - Recording label - Listening Library Inc.
LISTENING STICK, THE - Novelty items - Listening Stick
LISTENING TO THE WIND - Chimes - Shenandoah Designs International Inc.
LISTENPRO - Computer software - English As A Second Language Institute Inc.
LISTER - Computer software - SourceView Software International
LISTEREX - Pharmaceutical preparations ☆ - Warner-Lambert Co.
LISTERINE - Antiseptics - Warner-Wellcome
LISTERMINT - Mouthwashes - Warner-Wellcome
LISTING ADVANTAGE - Computer software - Real Advantage, Inc.
LISTMAGIC - Computer software - Procd, Inc.
LISTO - Pencils - Listo Pencil Corp.
LISTOMATIC - Photographic equipment - Eastman Kodak Co.
LISTSERV - Computer software - Eric Thomas
LISTSTAR - Computer software - Starnine Technologies, Inc.
LISTWIN'S IMPORTED KODIAK - Beverages—malt - Kodiak Beverage International Inc.
LIT CASEWORKS - Computer software - Legal Information Technology, Inc.
LIT-NING - Office supplies ☆ - Hunt Manufacturing Co.
LITA - Apparel stores—lingerie ☆ - Formfit Rogers
+L'ITALIAN - Footwear ☆ - Lvichiny Destroy Imports Inc.
LITCHFIELD - Brushes—paint ☆ - PPG Industries, Inc.
LITCHFIELD - Floor coverings—carpet and rugs - Gulistan Carpet Inc.
LITCHFIELD - Furniture ☆ - Davis Cabinet Co.
LITCHFIELD - Pet products - Smith-Worthington Saddlery Co. Inc.
LITCHFIELD GARDEN - Tableware—china ☆ - Lenox, Inc.
LITE - Adhesives and sealants - National Gypsum Co.
LITE - Chemical preparations - Bio-Lab, Inc.
LITE - Computer storage devices—optical - Dwight's Energydata, Inc.
LITE - Eyeglasses - Art-Craft Optical Co.
LITE - Food products - Knouse Foods Cooperative, Inc.
LITE - Food products ☆ - Kraft Food Ingredients Corp.
LITE - Greeting cards - Hallmark Cards Inc.
LITE - Hair care products - Joico Laboratories, Inc.
LITE - Hair care products - Playtex Beauty Care, Inc.
LITE - Hair care products ☆ - Pro-Line Corp.
LITE - Hearing aids - G.N. Danavox Inc.
LITE - Pickles - Paramount Foods Inc.
LITE - Salad dressings—bottled - Ken's Foods Inc.
LITE - Salt - Morton International Inc. (Morton Salt Div.)
LITE - Spices and extracts - McCormick & Co., Inc.
LITE - Toilets—enameled - Kohler Co.
LITE 3 - Computer software - Tiger Electronics, Inc.
LITE 50 - Food products - Kaukauna Cheese
LITE-A-BAG - Charcoal - Hickory Ridge Charcoal Inc.
LITE-A-LOG - Fireplace logs—treated - Morgro Chemical Co.
LITE-A-MATIC - Electrical equipment - Eagle Electric Manufacturing Co., Inc.
LITE-A-WAY - Corner guard lights - Tri-Guards, Inc.
LITE-AID - Health care products ☆ - Activeaid Inc.
LITE & CREAMY - Food products ☆ - Rose International
LITE & EASY - Meat products—beef - North Star Foods Inc.
LITE AND EASY - Pet products - Glo-Marr Products Inc.
LITE & LACEY - Cheese - Harold Gottesman
LITE & TASTY - Meat products - American Foods Group
LITE AND ZESTY - Salad dressings—mixes ☆ - Ryan Foods Co.
LITE BAKERY - Bakery products - Galaxy Foods Co.
LITE BEAM - Reflectors and lenses for auto headlamps - Corning Inc.
LITE BEAMS - Lamps - Clover Lamp Co.
LITE BEND - Bent glass - American Tempering Inc. (Laminating Div.)
LITE BITES - Vitamins and nutritional supplements - Optimum Lifestyles, Inc.
LITE-BLOX - Power switching equipment ☆ - Lomar Industries Inc.
LITE BODY SLEEKER - Foundation garments, lingerie - Saramar Corp.
LITE BOX - Lanterns—kerosene - Streamlight, Inc.
LITE-BRITE - Games - Milton Bradley Co.

☆ = Now out of production

LITE BURST - Health care products - Futurebiotics
LITE-CATCHERS - Paint sets–hobby - Brite-Tone Co.
LITE-CATCHERS - Toys - Coloron Industries
LITE CHAIRS - Cribs–wood ☆ - Welsh Co.
LITE CHEF - Pasta ☆ - Barbara's Bakery, Inc.
LITE COMFORT - Footwear ☆ - Shakti Corp.
LITE CONTROL - Hair care products ☆ - Lustrasilk Corp. of America Inc.
LITE COTE - Ophthalmic goods - Benson Optical Co., Inc.
LITE COTE - Paints ☆ - Fuller-O'Brien Paints Inc.
LITE DIET - Food products - Bakers Franchise Corp.
LITE DIET SKINNY WAIST - Apparel and accessories - Strouse, Adler Co.
LITE-E-NUFF - Key rings - West Coast Chain Manufacturing Co.
LITE FANTASTIC - Novelty items ☆ - Debry-Pexton Inc.
LITE FANTASTICS - Frames–eyeglass ☆ - Universal/Univis Inc.
LITE-FIGHTER - Frames–eyeglass - May Optical Co. Inc.
LITE-FLEX - Lighting fixtures - Swivelier Co. Inc.
LITE-FLITE - Electronic equipment - A & S Case Co. Inc.
LITE FLITE - Frames–eyeglass - May Optical Co. Inc.
LITE-FLITE - Toys–airplanes - Paul K. Guillow Inc.
LITE-FOOT - Orthopedic products - St. John Companies, Inc.
LITE FOOT - Semiconductors - Siliconix Inc.
LITE-FORM - Concrete products - Lite-Form, Inc.
LITE GAIT - Medical apparatus - Mobility Research LLC
LITE GENUINE - Beer - Miller Brewing Co.
LITE GRAVY - Seasonings ☆ - McCormick & Co., Inc.
LITE GRIP - Lighting equipment - General Manufacturing Inc.
LITE-GRO - Fertilizers ☆ - Earthway Products Inc.
LITE-GUARD - Lighting equipment - S.G.P.
LITE-GUARD - Sporting goods - Lite-Guard Products Inc.
LITE-HEARTED - Frames–eyeglass ☆ - Universal/Univis Inc.
LITE HOOPS - Jewelry - Rainbow Sales, Inc.
LITE HOUSE - Salad dressings–bottled ☆ - Rowena's Gourmet Foods Inc.
LITE KNIFE - Knives–pocket - Colonial Knife Co. Inc.
LITE-LIFT - Pass doors - Pomeroy Inc.
LITE-LINE - Food products - Borden, Inc.
LITE LINE - Tights–stockings - Julius Zorn, Inc.
LITE LITE TOFUTTI - Food products - Tofutti Brands Inc.
LITE LOCK - Automotive parts and accessories - NI Industries Inc.
LITE-LOCK - Window shades - Draper Shade and Screen Co. Inc.
LITE LUNCH - Food products - Lipton Investments, Inc.
LITE LUNCH - Housewares - Igloo Products Corp.
LITE MATE - Infant product - American Baby Concepts
LITE-MATE - Office supplies - Alvin and Co. Inc.
LITE MEAL - Food products ☆ - Naturade Inc.
LITE MIKE - Dictating machines - Dictaphone Corp.
LITE-MIX - Chemical preparations - Georgia-Pacific Corp.
LITE MORN - Egg substitutes - Papetti's Hygrade Egg Products, Inc.
LITE 'N EASY - Beverages–alcohol - M.S. Walker Inc./Seacoast
LITE 'N EASY - Footwear–athletic - Mercury International Trading Corp.
LITE N' EASY - Manicure preparations - American Salon Products
LITE 'N HEALTHY - Cheese - Northfield Foods Inc.
LITE 'N HEARTY - Egg substitutes - Papetti's Hygrade Egg Products, Inc.
LITE 'N HEARTY - Food products - The Heart Institute of Spokane
LITE 'N KRISPY - Snack foods - SnackCracks
LITE 'N LACEY - Brassieres (Bras) - Sears, Roebuck and Co.
LITE 'N LESS - Cheese ☆ - Galaxy Foods Co.
LITE N' LOW - Food products - Conagra, Inc.
LITE 'N LOW - Food products - Kraft Food Ingredients Corp.
LITE 'N LUSCIOUS LUNCH - Seafood products–canned or cured - Golden Beach, Inc.
LITE 'N' NATURAL - Cleaning preparations - Bruce Hardwood Floors
LITE 'N NATURAL - Dairy products - Roundy's Inc.
LITE 'N' NATURAL - Spaghetti sauces - Ronzoni Foods Inc.
LITE 'N NATURAL OLD TIME - Ice milk - Roundy's Inc.
LITE-N-PLATE - Signs - I.D. Lite, Inc.
LITE 'N POWER - Underwear and nightwear ☆ - Lovable Co.
LITE 'N' RITE - Milk - Richfood, Inc.
LITE-N-TITE - Brushes - Perfex Corp.
LITE-N-TUFF - Carts - Hamilton Caster & Manufacturing Co.
LITE-N-UP - Bleach - Wood Kote Products, Inc.
LITE N' UP - Lighting fixtures - Gary Products Group, Inc.
LITE N' UP - Meats–luncheon ☆ - John Morrell & Co.
LITE NEST - Portable seating - Orthopedic Products Corp.
LITE-OF-THE-PARTY - Lighting fixtures ☆ - Brinkmann Lighting Products
LITE-PAC - Ledgers - Master-Craft Corp.
LITE-PARR - Frames–eyeglass - Liberty Optical Manufacturing Co.

LITE PATCH - Brushes–paint - Allpro Corp.
LITE-PLY - Plywood - Sig Manufacturing Inc.
LITE POWER - Generators–electric - Burrell Enterprises, Inc.
LITE-R-COBS - Chemical preparations - Andersons Management Corp.
LITE RED - Beverages–carbonated - Shasta Beverages, Inc.
LITE ROPE - Lamp bulbs–flashlight - American Cyanamid Co.
LITE-SAVER - Lighting fixtures - Swivelier Co. Inc.
LITE SAVERS - Lamp bulbs–fluorescent - Marvin Feig
LITE SCENTS - Lighting fixtures - GTE Products Corp.
LITE SEAT - Cribs–wood ☆ - Welsh Co.
LITE SENSATIONS - Meats–luncheon - Hillshire Farm Co.
LITE SET - Dictating machines - Dictaphone Corp.
LITE-SHEARS - Scissors–hand-operated - Alvin and Co. Inc.
LITE SHIELD - Alarms–personal - Pro-Gard Industries, LP
LITE SILKEN - Tofu - Morinaga Nutritional Foods, Inc.
LITE-SITE - Firearms, accessories, and parts - Bausch & Lomb Inc.
LITE SLICE - Sliced ham - Iowa Ham Processors, Inc.
LITE-SOFT BANGLE - Jewelry - Aurafin Corp.
LITE SOURCE - Lamps - Lite Source Inc.
LITE SPEED - Apparel and accessories - Lite Speed of Oregon
LITE-SPIKE - Shoes–athletic - Titleist & Foot-Joy Worldwide
LITE SPRAY - Adhesives and sealants - Imperial Adhesives Inc.
LITE-SPREE - Frames–eyeglass ☆ - Universal/Univis Inc.
LITE STAR - Sporting goods - Star Line Baton Co. Inc.
LITE STEP - Standing mats - Ace Hose and Rubber Co.
LITE STIK - Novelty items - Paper Magic Group Inc.
LITE-STIK - Toys - Spearhead Holdings, Inc.
LITE-STIK - Toys - Spearhead Industries Inc.
LITE STRAW - Hats - Bollman Hat Co.
LITE SWEPE - Brooms - Hamburg Broom Works Inc.
LITE-TAK 370 - Adhesives and sealants - Loctite Corp.
LITE-TAK 375 - Adhesives and sealants - Loctite Corp.
LITE-TAK 376 - Adhesives and sealants - Loctite Corp.
LITE-TECH - Luggage - Samsonite Corp.
LITE-TEX - Enamels ☆ - Wescon Products Co.
LITE THAT TASTES RIGHT, THE - Cheese - Churny Co., Inc.
LITE, THE - Lighting equipment - General Manufacturing Inc.
LITE, THE - Cables–fiber optic - Robert Serwatka
LITE TIME - Dairy products - Smith's Dairy Products Co.
LITE TIME - Ice cream - Hiland Dairy Co.
LITE TIME QUALITY CHEKD - Dairy products - Quality Chekd Dairy Products Association
LITE-TITE - Photographic equipment - SP Systems/Saratons
LITE TOUCH - Cameras ☆ - Nikon Inc.
LITE TOUCH - Cleaning preparations - S.C. Johnson & Son, Inc.
LITE TOUCH - Cots–metal - Leggett & Platt/Hartex
LITE TOUCH - Electronics equipment - L & M Auto Supply
LITE TOUCH - Frames–eyeglass - Pathway Optical Prods.
LITE TOUCH - Medical apparatus ☆ - Spenco Medical Corp.
LITE-TOUCH - Pens - Astro Pen Co.
LITE-TOUCH - Pens - Eversharp Pen Co.
LITE TOUCH - Razors–electric - Philips Electronics North America Corp.
LITE TOUCH - Wigs - Paula Young
LITE TRAC - Rug cleaning machines–commercial - Castex Industries Inc.
LITE TRACKER - Safety products - Grace Industries, Inc.
LITE TRAFFIC - Novelty items - Agent Andy Inc.
LITE-TRON - Lamp bulbs–fluorescent - Fleco Industries Inc.
LITE-TUFF - Boxes - RPM Industries Inc. (Dewitt Plastics Div.)
LITE ULTRA - Low-calorie beer - Miller Brewing Co.
LITE-UP LIGHTSTICKS - Toys - Tyco Toys
LITE-UPS - Candles - Russ Berrie and Co., Inc.
LITE-WAND - Lamps–floor ☆ - Prestigeline Inc.
LITE WATE - Pet products - K.A. Vogel Sons Inc.
LITE-WATE - Shovels - Rugg Manufacturing Co. Inc.
LITE WAY - Breads ☆ - Best Foods Baking Group
LITE-WEIGHT - Frames–eyeglass - Hudson Optical Corp.
LITE WEIGHT II - Automotive parts and accessories - Fibre Glass-Evercoat Co. Inc.
LITE WEIGHT SYSTEM - Golfing equipment - Nassau Precision Casting Co., Inc.
LITE WHIP - Food products ☆ - TKI Foods, Inc.
LITE-WRITER - Dry erase boards ☆ - Claridge Products and Equipment Inc.
LITE YEARS - Bearings–motor vehicle - Focus 21 International Inc.
LITE YEARS - Flashlights - Black & Decker Corp.
LITEAMP - Television equipment–cable - American Lightwave Systems, Inc.
LITEBAGS - Cases–camera - Lowel-Light Manufacturing Inc.

☆ = Now out of production

LITEBREEDS - Luggage ☆ - Ventura Travelware Inc.

LITECHECK - Telephone accessories - Fiber Plus International

LITECRETE - Bricks - North American Refractories Co.

LITEFELT HEADWEAR - Hats - Bollman Hat Co.

LITEFUSION - Computers - Mercury Computer Systems Inc.

LITEGLOW - Automotive parts and accessories - Liteglow Industries, Inc.

LITEHOUSE - Salad dressings–bottled - Litehouse Corp.

LITELINE - Adhesives and sealants - Mactac Inc. (Packaging Closures Systems Div.)

LITELINE 360 - Lighting equipment - Flexlite Inc.

LITELITE - Sporting goods - Weber Industries Inc.

LITEMASTER - Lamps–desk - Art Specialty Co. Inc.

LITEMASTER - Window coverings - Levolor Inc.

LITEMATE - Photographic equipment - Photo Research, Inc.

LITEMATE - Projectors–photographic - Apollo Audiovisual Div.

LITEMUX - Cables–fiber optic - Lans, Integrated Technologies & Engineering, Inc.

LITE'N FREE - Meat products–beef - Maverick Ranch Association

LITE'N UP - Games - Lite'n Up Enterprises Inc.

LITE'N UP 50 - Cigarette filters - Category One, Inc.

LITE'N UP 90 - Cigarette filters - Category One, Inc.

LITENIN RODS - Candy ☆ - American Candy Co.

LITENING - Shovels - Rugg Manufacturing Co. Inc.

LITENING BOLT PERFORMANCE PRODUCTS - Motor vehicle parts and accessories - Crites Industries

LITEPAK - Lighting equipment - Acme-Lite Manufacturing Co.

LITEPAR - Lamps - RCS Industries Inc.

LITEPHONE - Speaker phones ☆ - Whistler Acquistion Corp.

LITEPUFF - Lighting fixtures - National Service Industries, Inc.

LITE'R 35 - Breads - Metz Baking Co.

LITERAL - Moldings and trim - Literal Corp.

LITERARY BOOK-WRAP - Gift-wrapping products - Battledore, Ltd.

LITERARY CALLIGRAPHY - House furnishings - Calligraphy by Susan Loy, Inc.

LITERARY FRONTIERS - Publisher's imprints - University of Missouri Press

LITERATI - Greeting cards - American Artists Group Inc.

LITERATURE AND LIFE - Publisher's imprints ☆ - Crossroad

LITERATURE WORKS - Recording label - Silver Burdett Ginn Inc.

LITERIDER - Lighting fixtures - Tron Industries Inc.

LITERITE - Pens - Zebra Pen Corp.

LITERMETER - Medical apparatus - Erie Medical (Div. of Ocenco Incorporated)

LITES - Apparel and accessories ☆ - Hickory Industries, Inc.

LITES - Apparel–athletic - Grid, Inc.

LITES - Computer software - Thomas & Betts Holdings, Inc.

LITES - Drums–musical instruments - Aquarian Music

LITES - Illuminated display platforms for collectibles - Italia Collections

LITES - Snack foods - Health Valley Food

LITES - Tampons - Tambrands Inc.

LITES-A-LIVE - Handbags - SOS Rescue Inc.

LITESHOW - Computer peripheral equipment - In Focus Systems, Inc.

LITESHOW - Computer software ☆ - Onset Computer Corp.

LITESHOW - Electronic equipment - In Focus Systems, Inc.

LITESITE - Eyeglasses - Martin-Copeland Eyewear Corp.

LITESTAK - Lighting equipment - Federal Signal Corp.

LITESTAR - Motor vehicle parts and accessories ☆ - Leer Inc.

LITESTEP - Shoes ☆ - Hyde Athletic Industries Inc.

LITESTRIDE - Walkers - Orthopedic Systems Inc.

LITESTRIP - Lighting fixtures - Swivelier Co. Inc.

LITESTYLE - Eyeglasses - Optical Radiation Corp.

LITETONES - Floor coverings–tile - United States Ceramic Tile Co.

LITETONES MARQUISE - Tiles–ceramic - United States Ceramic Tile Co.

LITETRAK - Electrical equipment - Sarama Lighting

LITEVIEW - Windows–vinyl - Weather Shield Manufacturing, Inc.

LITEVUE - Lens coatings - Innotech, Inc.

LITEWALL - Cement - Elite Cement Products, Inc.

LITEWATE - Bicycles - Ross Bicycles USA, Ltd.

LITEWATE CHAMPION - Lighting fixtures - Acme-Lite Manufacturing Co.

LITEWAY - Lighting equipment - Columbia Lighting - LCA. Inc.

LITEWEIGHT - Floor coverings - Apache Mills Inc.

LITEWRITER - Pens - Accutec Inc.

LITEWSKI HONEY WINE - Wines - Stanley Stawski Distributing Co.

LITEX - Mops ☆ - Lighthouse Industries

LITH-EASE - Lubricants - American Grease Stick Co.

LITH-O-CRYLIC - Paintings and prints - Ronald Van Sweringen

LITH-O-GRAF PRINT - Educational materials - Dynacolor Graphics, Inc.

LITH-O-ZINC - Paints ☆ - Blue Ridge Talc Co. Inc.

LITH-X - Fire extinguishers - Ansul, Inc.

LITHANE - Pharmaceutical preparations - Miles Inc.

LITHE - Fabrics - Dan River Inc.

LITHE LINE - Apparel–women's - Lily of France Inc.

LITHIA SPRINGS - Water–mineral - Lithia Springs Water Co., Inc.

LITHIA SPRINGS NATURAL MINERAL WATER FAMOUS MARBLE PAVILLION - Water–mineral - Lithia Springs Water Co., Inc.

LITHIUM BALATA - Golfing equipment - Ram Golf Corp.

LITHIUM PLUS - Golfing equipment - Ram Golf Corp.

LITHO F - Photographic equipment - Edwal Scientific Products Corp.

LITHO FUSION - Labels–paper - Kaumagraph Co. Inc.

LITHO KING - Printing presses - King Press Corp.

LITHO-RITE - Pencils ☆ - Faber-Castell Corp.

LITHO-RUB - Erasers ☆ - Faber-Castell Corp.

LITHO SKETCH - Artists' materials - American Art Clay Co. Inc.

LITHO WOVE - Envelopes - Union Envelope Co.

LITHOBID/CIBALITH-S - Pharmaceutical preparations - Ciba-Geigy Corp.

LITHOCAL - Labels–paper - Kaumagraph Co. Inc.

LITHOCRAFT - Paper–writing - Butler Paper Co.

LITHOFILM - Electronic equipment - GAF Corp.

LITHOFORM - Paints ☆ - Parker & Amchem

LITHOGRAM - Trading cards and stamps - Upper Deck Co.

LITHOLINE - Film - Rollei of America Inc.

LITHOLINE - Oils–lubricating - Lyondell Petrochemical Co.

LITHOLINE COMPLEX EP - Lubricants - Lyondell Petrochemical Co.

LITHOLOPES - Envelopes - Murray Envelope Corp.

LITHOLUBE - Lubricants - Parr Products

LITHOMASTER - Paper–lithograph - Rapid Tec, Inc.

LITHONATE - Pharmaceutical preparations - Solvay Pharmaceuticals Inc.

LITHOPURE - Filters–water - Pall Corp.

LITHOTABS - Pharmaceutical preparations - Solvay Pharmaceuticals Inc.

LITHOTEX - Pedestals–wood ☆ - Blue Ridge Talc Co. Inc.

LITHOVERITE - Posters - Park South Communications

LITHOWIPES - Washboards - Kimberly-Clark Corp.

LITHOZIN - Paints ☆ - Impervious Paint Industries Ltd.

LITHPLEX - Lubricants - Texas Refinery Corp. (Lubricants Div.)

LITIGATION STREAMS - Office supplies - Paul Bergquist

LITKIT - File folders - Corpex Banknote Co., Inc.

LIT'L - Sausages - Sara Lee Corp.

LIT'L CHEDDY HOTS - Sausages - Saramar Corp.

LIT'L CRITTER - Fishing lures - Creme Lure Co.

LIT'L FISHIE - Fishing lures - Creme Lure Co.

LIT'L HAM - Hams - Hillshire Farm Co.

LIT'L HONEY HAM - Hams - Sara Lee Corp.

LIT'L TREASURES - Infant product ☆ - Judi's Orijinals

LITMUSTIK - Electrical testing instruments - Omega Engineering, Inc.

LIT'R KADDY - Wastebaskets ☆ - F.H. Lawson Co.

LITTCO - Hardware - Littlestown Hardware & Foundry Co. Inc.

LITTE-R-AID - Veterinary pharmaceutical preparations ☆ - Gerry Wood Products

LITTER-ALERT - Cat litter ☆ - Earth Animal

LITTER-BE-GONE - Pet product - ISE Inc.

LITTER BEST - Pet products - Aldi Inc.

LITTER BOX KLEEN - Deodorizers - G.G. Bean Inc.

LITTER CATCHER, THE - Pet products - Hyde & Associates

LITTER COMPANION - Pet products - Pets Natural Products, Inc.

LITTER CRITTER - Vacuum cleaners and accessories ☆ - Shop Vac Corp.

LITTER FRESH - Pet products - S.C. Johnson & Son, Inc.

LITTER GARD - Pet products - Flexi-Mat Corp.

LITTER GITTER - Vacuum cleaners and accessories - Yard Vac Products, Inc.

LITTER GOLD - Pet products ☆ - Mid-Florida Mining Co.

LITTER GREEN - Pet products ☆ - Clorox Co.

LITTER GUARD - Pet products - Mid-Florida Mining Co.

LITTER KING - Containers–trash - Victor Stanley, Inc.

LITTER-LINER - Pet products - Penn-Plax, Inc.

LITTER MAID - Pet products - Windmere-Durable Holdings, Inc. (Windmere Pet Div.)

LITTER MATE - Pet products - Theodore M. Kiebke

LITTER MATE - Pet products - Productive Alternatives Inc.

LITTER PUNCH - Vitamins and nutritional supplements - Yoder, Inc.

LITTER RENEW - Pet products - Novalek, Inc.

LITTER RIDDER - Housewares - Woodstream Corp.

LITTER-SCOOP - Pet products - Penn-Plax, Inc.

LITTER SNUG - Bags ☆ - Alger Creations Inc.

LITTER TECH - Pet products - Nutrisource Pet Products of Stewart, Inc.

LITTER-VAC - Vacuum cleaners and accessories - Clarke Industries, Inc.

LITTERACE - Veterinary nutritional supplements - Prince Agri Products, Inc.

LITTERARY PET - Pet product ☆ - Informative Amenities Inc.

LITTERLESS - Lunch boxes - Rubbermaid Inc.

LITTERLITE - Pet products - Wysong Corp.

LITTLE '59 FOR STRAT - Musical instrument accessories - Seymour Duncan Pickups

LITTLE '59 FOR TELE - Musical instrument accessories - Seymour Duncan Pickups

LITTLE ALBERT THE HIPPO - Furniture—children's - Maze Inc.

LITTLE AMANA - Wines - Little Amana Winery Inc.

LITTLE AMBASSADORS - Candy - Russell Stover Candies, Inc.

LITTLE ANGEL - Cradles ☆ - Colgate Mattress Co.

LITTLE ANGEL - Infant product - Ming Ta Supply

LITTLE ANGEL - Pet products - Barkleigh Productions, Inc.

LITTLE ANGEL CREATION, A - Crocheted and knitted items - Baby Togs, Inc.

LITTLE ANGELS - Deodorizers - Collections by Tomoyo Inc.

LITTLE ANGIE'S CANTINA - Housewares - Angie's Cantina, Inc.

LITTLE ANIMAL - Recording label - Jazz Composer's Orchestra Association Inc.

LITTLE APPLE - Publisher's imprints - Scholastic Inc.

LITTLE ARK - Kitchen appliances - R & R Mill Co. Inc.

LITTLE ARTIST - Toys - Coloron Industries

LITTLE ARTIST, THE - Toys—stuffed ☆ - Fun World Inc.

LITTLE ATOM - Fishing lures - Den Manufacturing Co.

LITTLE BABY BOOK - Child care books - ADVO, Inc.

LITTLE BABY WATER BABIES - Dolls - Lauer Toys Inc.

LITTLE BACKYARD PARKS - Playground equipment - Miracle Recreation Equipment Co.

LITTLE BALLOONEY FACES - Decals and transfers - C.M. Estes Enterprises, Inc.

LITTLE BANDIT - Games ☆ - Milton Bradley Co.

LITTLE BARE - Brassieres (Bras) ☆ - Lovable Co.

LITTLE BEACON - Electric lighting equipment ☆ - Bass Products

LITTLE BEAR - Food products - Little Bear Trading

LITTLE BEAR - Sporting goods - Bear Archery Inc.

LITTLE BEAR - Vegetables—dried - J & D Produce, Inc.

LITTLE BEAR CRUNCHITOS - Snack foods - Little Bear Organic Foods, Inc.

LITTLE BEAR FEET - Footwear - Bear Feet

LITTLE BEASTIES - Greeting cards - Pawprints Greeting Cards

LITTLE BEAUTY - Brooms - Hanset Brothers Inc.

LITTLE BEAVER - Brooms - Perfex Corp.

LITTLE BEGGARS - Giftware - Brushcreek Creative Co.

LITTLE BELL - Clocks ☆ - General Time Corp. (Westclox/Seth Thomas Div.)

LITTLE BENJAMIN - Toys—stuffed - Dakin Inc.

LITTLE BETSY - Toys - Empire of Carolina Inc.

LITTLE BIG BEN - Puzzles - Milton Bradley Co.

LITTLE BIG FOOT - Toys - Emsco Inc.

LITTLE BIG GIRL - Brassieres (Bras) - Custom Maid Brassiere Co.

LITTLE BIG HORN - Guitars ☆ - Emmons Guitar Co. Inc.

LITTLE BIG HORN - Slabs—concrete - Tropical Sportswear International Corp.

LITTLE BIG MEAL - Dog food - Ralston Purina Co.

LITTLE BIG MOUTHS - Toys—stuffed - Dakin Inc.

LITTLE BIG SHAPEZ - Packaging—paper - Z-Barten Productions

LITTLE BIG SHOT - Tape recorders ☆ - Sony Corp. of America

LITTLE BIG TOP - Giftware ☆ - Enesco Corp.

LITTLE BIG TOP - Greeting cards - Morehead, Inc.

LITTLE BIT - Apparel stores—lingerie - Fancee Free Manufacturing Co.

LITTLE BIT - Dolls ☆ - Fun World Inc.

LITTLE BIT-OF-BUNNY - Toys—stuffed - Fun World Inc.

LITTLE BIT OF HEAVEN - Dolls - Georgetown Collection, Inc.

LITTLE BIT OF HEAVEN - Greeting cards ☆ - American Greetings Corp.

LITTLE BIT OF LUCK, A - Giftware - Russ Berrie and Co., Inc.

LITTLE BITS - Chocolate candy - Nestle USA

LITTLE BLACK BOOK - Computer software - William S. Oliver

LITTLE BLACK BOOK, THE - Computer software ☆ - Everex Systems, Inc.

LITTLE BLESSINGS - Figurines - Susan M. Skoglund

LITTLE BLESSINGS - Publisher's imprints - Tyndale House Publishers, Inc.

LITTLE BO PEEP - Eyeglasses - Art-Craft Optical Co.

LITTLE BOJANGLES - Frames—eyeglass - Hudson Optical Corp.

LITTLE BOOKS - Publisher's imprints - The Berry Patch

LITTLE BOSTON TRADERS - Infant's and children's wear - Boston Trading Ltd. Inc.

LITTLE BOTTOMS - Skin care products - Vetco, Inc.

LITTLE BOW KEEP - Apparel and accessories - Beachhead Manufacturing

LITTLE BOW KEEPS - Infant product - Welcome to the World Inc.

LITTLE BOY BLUE - Beverages—alcohol - Daiquiri Shoppe, Inc.

LITTLE BOY BLUE - Blueing - Dial Corp.

LITTLE BREAD COMPANY - Breads - Little Bread Co., Inc.

LITTLE BROOK - Food products - Littlebrook Foods Inc.

LITTLE BROOK FOODS - Food products - Pioneer Food Sales Inc.

LITTLE BROTHER - Pencils - National Pen & Pencil Co.

LITTLE BROTHER - Synthesizers—musical instrument - Fender Musical Instruments

LITTLE BROWN & CO. - Publisher's imprints - Little, Brown and Co., Inc.

LITTLE BUCKET - Pastries - KFC Corp.

LITTLE BUDDY - Greeting cards - Modern Thought Combine

LITTLE B.U.M. - Children's apparel - Chauvin International Ltd.

LITTLE BUSTER - Brushes—paint - E-Z Paintr Corp.

LITTLE BUTCH BLASTER - Tools ☆ - Fimco Inc.

LITTLE BUTLER, THE - Garbage disposal units—household - Franke, Inc. (Kitchen Systems Division)

LITTLE BUTTERCUP - Footwear—children's - Yachett Shoe Manufacturing Corp.

LITTLE BY LITTLE - Wallpaper - Warner Co.

LITTLE CAESARS - Restaurants—pizzerias - Little Caesar Enterprises, Inc.

LITTLE CAESARS ITALIAN CHEESE BREAD - Breads - Little Caesar Enterprises, Inc.

LITTLE CAESARS ITALIAN KITCHEN - Restaurants—pizzerias - Little Caesar Enterprises, Inc.

LITTLE CAESARS PERSONAL PIZZA - Pizzas—mixes - Little Caesar Enterprises, Inc.

LITTLE CAESARS PIZZA SHOP - Restaurants—pizzerias - Little Caesar Enterprises, Inc.

LITTLE CAESARS SPECIALTY PLEASERS - Food products - Little Caesar Enterprises, Inc.

LITTLE CAMPER - Toys - Little Tikes Co.

LITTLE CAPEZIO - Footwear—children's - Jumping-Jacks Shoes Inc.

LITTLE CAPEZIO - Shoes - Osage Footwear, Inc.

LITTLE CARPENTER - Toys ☆ - Steven Manufacturing Co.

LITTLE CAT - Footwear—athletic - Puma Inc.

LITTLE CAT - Tableware—china ☆ - Villeroy and Boch Tableware Ltd.

LITTLE CATCHER - Hobby kits - Bear Creek Toys, Inc.

LITTLE CHAMP - Perfumes - Winsome Fragrance Co.

LITTLE CHAMP - Pliers - Channellock, Inc.

LITTLE CHARACTERS - Apparel—children's - Shady Character Ltd.

LITTLE CHARLIES - Food products - Little Charlies Entrees

LITTLE CHARLIES CONVENIENCE FOODS - Potato flakes - Schwan's Sales Enterprises, Inc.

LITTLE CHARMER - Bracelet and perfume ☆ - Cosrich Inc.

LITTLE CHARMER - Key rings - Russ Berrie and Co., Inc.

LITTLE CHARMERS - Dolls ☆ - Bradley Import Co.

LITTLE CHARMERS - Toys ☆ - Coloron Industries

LITTLE CHEESERS - Music boxes - Dawson Alliants Corp.

LITTLE CHEF - Food products - Morgan Foods Inc.

LITTLE CHICAGO - Recording label - Claiming Race Records

LITTLE CHIEF - Brooms - Perfex Corp.

LITTLE CHIEF - Food products - Southern Shell Fish Co.

LITTLE CHIEF - Footwear—children's ☆ - Livonia Catalog

LITTLE CHIEF - Harmonicas - William Kratt Co.

LITTLE CHRISTMAS VILLAGE AT LA VILLITA, A - Broadcasting stations— television - Waterman Broadcasting Corp. of Texas, Inc.

LITTLE CHUMS - Ophthalmic goods - Chums Ltd.

LITTLE CINNERS - Candy ☆ - Price Candy Co. Inc.

LITTLE CLIPPER - Toys ☆ - Creative Playthings Ltd.

LITTLE CREATURES - Apparel—children's - Little Creatures, Inc.

LITTLE CREATURES - Electronic equipment - Texas Instruments Inc.

LITTLE CREATURES - Notebooks and notepads - Norcom Inc.

LITTLE CRITTER - Computer software - Mercer Mayer, Ltd.

LITTLE CRITTER - Pet shops - Sergeant's Pet Products, Inc.

LITTLE CRITTER EASY READERS - Publisher's imprints - Western Publishing Co., Inc.

LITTLE CROW - Oils—edible ☆ - Little Crow Foods

LITTLE CRYSTAL - Jewelry - C. Bennett Scopes Inc.

LITTLE CUDDLERS - Toys—stuffed - Douglas Co. Inc.

LITTLE CURIOSITY, A - Hobby kits - Curiosity Development, Inc.

LITTLE CUTIES - Toys—stuffed - Russ Berrie and Co., Inc.

LITTLE DANDY - Sporting goods - Blount International, Inc. (Sporting Equipment Group)

LITTLE DARLIN - Eyeglasses - Art-Craft Optical Co.

LITTLE DAVID - Recording label - Atlantic Records

LITTLE DEBBIE - Cookies - McKee Foods Corp.

LITTLE DEBBIE SNACK CAKES - Snack foods - McKee Foods Corp.

LITTLE DECKER - Boats–fishing ☆ - Anchor Industries Inc.
LITTLE DEVIL - Abrasive products - American Hone Co.
LITTLE DIAMONDS - Perfumes - Dependable Gift & Novelty, Inc.
LITTLE DIGGERS - Toys - Emsco Inc.
LITTLE DIPPER - Apparel–women's - Jezebel-Renee of Hollywood
LITTLE DIPPER - Bathing suits - Little Dipper
LITTLE DIPPER - Bicycles - Columbia Manufacturing Inc.
LITTLE DIPPER - Cookies - San Anselmo's Cookies
LITTLE DIPPER - Lighting fixtures - Westinghouse Electric Corp.
LITTLE DIPPER - Tubes–plastic - Adhesive Technologies Inc.
LITTLE DOBY - Toys–stuffed - Dakin Inc.
LITTLE DOC - Skin care products - Schaffner Manufacturing Co. Inc.
LITTLE DOG RECORDS - Recording label - Little Dog Records
LITTLE DOLL - Bicycles - Western Auto Supply Co.
LITTLE DOLL - Lenses–optical - Ditto Industries Inc.
LITTLE DOT'S LOTTO - Games ☆ - Warren Industries Inc.
LITTLE DREAMERS - Statuary–marble - Henri Studio, Inc.
LITTLE DREAMS - Wallpaper ☆ - Marburg Wallcoverings
LITTLE DUCK HEAD - Apparel–children's - Alchem Capital Corp.
LITTLE DUCKIES - Toys - Kids II, Inc.
LITTLE DUTCHESS - Eyeglasses - Martin-Copeland Eyewear Corp.
LITTLE EAGLE - Sporting goods ☆ - Wright & McGill Co.
LITTLE EAGLE - Water purification systems - Eagle Spring Filtration, Inc.
LITTLE EASY - Remote controls - Universal Electronics Inc.
LITTLE EDDIES - Apparel–children's - Wormser Co.
LITTLE EGO - Apparel–children's - Names, Inc.
LITTLE ELVES - Snack foods - Millner Trading Co. Inc.
LITTLE ENCOUNTERS - Wallpaper - Thomas Strahan Wallcoverings
LITTLE ENGINE THAT COULD - Toy stores ☆ - Gund, Inc.
LITTLE E.N.U.F. - Apparel–children's - E.N.U.F. Internationale, Inc.
LITTLE ERIC - Footwear–children's - Little Eric Shoes, Ltd.
LITTLE ESSENTIALS - Apparel–children's - Lees Manufacturing Co.
LITTLE EVE EDITIONS - Greeting cards ☆ - Fran Mar Greeting cards Ltd.
LITTLE EXPRESS - Toys - Barval Toys Inc.
LITTLE EXTRA - Underwear and nightwear ☆ - Lovable Co.
LITTLE EXTRAS - Dolls - Mattel, Inc.
LITTLE EYES - Lighting fixtures - Point Electric
LITTLE FALLS - Footwear - Little Falls Footwear Inc.
LITTLE FARMERS - Posters - Reiman Publications, LP
LITTLE FIBBER - Apparel and accessories ☆ - Warnaco Inc.
LITTLE FILUP - Fishing tackle ☆ - Frabill Inc.
LITTLE FINGERS - Paper–writing - K-Tel International, Inc.
LITTLE FLIGHT - Helmets–athletic - Schwinn Cycling & Fitness Inc.
LITTLE FLOATER - Toys ☆ - Gerber Products Co.
LITTLE FLOWER - Floor coverings–carpet and rugs ☆ - Regal Rugs Inc.
LITTLE FLOWERS - Novelty items - Easter Unltd. Inc.
LITTLE FOLK ART - Furniture–children's - Little Folk Art, Inc.
LITTLE FOLKS - Toys - Simmons Juvenile Products Co., Inc.
LITTLE FOOLER - Fishing lures ☆ - Hildebrandt Corp.
LITTLE FOOT - Machine parts - Little Foot, Ltd.
LITTLE FOOT - Nail care products - Simplicity Nail Products
LITTLE FREDDY'S - Food products - Little Freddy's
LITTLE FRIENDS - Candles ☆ - Empire Manufacturing Co.
LITTLE FRIENDS - Jewelry - Kirk Stieff Co.
LITTLE FRIENDS - Toys ☆ - Gerber Products Co.
LITTLE FRIENDS THAT SMELL GOOD - Figurines - Gilbertie's Herb Gardens, Inc.
LITTLE FRIERS - Sausages - Oscar Mayer Foods Corp.
LITTLE FRISKIES - Casks–wood - Nestle USA
LITTLE FRY FORMULA - Pet products ☆ - Jungle Laboratories Corp.
LITTLE FUDGIES - Cookies - Nabisco Foods Group
LITTLE FUN-FRIENDS - Toys–stuffed - Dakin Inc.
LITTLE FUN STATION - Playground equipment and toys - A.C. Global Investments, Inc.
LITTLE GALLERY - Frames–picture ☆ - Howell Mouldings Inc.
LITTLE GALLERY - Giftware - Hallmark Cards Inc.
LITTLE GASSER - Trailers–travel ☆ - Viking Recreational Vehicles Inc.
LITTLE GEM - Brooms - F.M. Thorpe Manufacturing Co.
LITTLE GEM - Flowers, plants, and seeds - New Tomorrow Inc.
LITTLE GEM - Golfing equipment - Rick Hamilton Golf Co., Inc.
LITTLE GEM - Paint sets–hobby ☆ - Canson-Talens Inc.
LITTLE GEM - Shelving units–wood - Equipto
LITTLE GEM TEDDY BEAR - Toys–stuffed - Akira Trading Co., Inc.
LITTLE GETAWAYS - Wines ☆ - Weibel Vineyards
LITTLE GIANT - Bathroom fixtures ☆ - All American Manufacturing Co.
LITTLE GIANT - Brushes–paint ☆ - Linzer Products Corp.

LITTLE GIANT - Erasers - Quartet Manufacturing Co.
LITTLE GIANT - Fountains - Little Giant Pump Co.
LITTLE GIANT - Ladders–metal - Wing Enterprises, Inc.
LITTLE GIANT - Locks–padlocks ☆ - Master Lock Co.
LITTLE GIANT - Pet products - Miller Manufacturing Co. Inc.
LITTLE GIANT - Projectors–photographic - Apollo Audiovisual Div.
LITTLE GIANT - Recording label - Little Giant Records
LITTLE GIANT - Sporting goods ☆ - Mill Run Products Co.
LITTLE GIANT - Spotlights ☆ - Photogenic Machine Co.
LITTLE GIANT - Tools - Delta Industries International, Inc.
LITTLE GIANT - Tools - True Temper Hardware Co.
LITTLE GIRL - Ophthalmic goods - Styl-Rite Optical Manufacturing Co., Inc.
LITTLE GIRL WITH A CURL - See **THANK HEAVEN FOR LITTLE GIRLS**
LITTLE GIRLS - Dolls - Effanbee Doll Corp.
LITTLE GOBLINS - Dolls - Russ Berrie and Co., Inc.
LITTLE GODIVA - Apparel and accessories ☆ - Warnaco Inc.
LITTLE GOLDEN BOOK - Footwear ☆ - Pagoda Trading Co.
LITTLE GOLDEN BOOK LAND TOOTLE - Greeting cards - Western Publishing Co., Inc.
LITTLE GOLDEN BOOKS - Publisher's imprints - Western Publishing Co., Inc.
LITTLE GOLFER - Toys - Today's Kids Inc.
LITTLE GOLIATH - Staplers - ACCO USA, Inc.
LITTLE GORDO GORILLA - Toys–stuffed - Dakin Inc.
LITTLE GOURMET - Toys ☆ - Strombecker Corp.
LITTLE GREEN - Cleaning equipment - Bissell Inc.
LITTLE GREEN CLEAN MACHINE - Cleaning equipment - Bissell Inc.
LITTLE GREEN MACHINE - Vacuum cleaners and accessories - Bissell Inc.
LITTLE GREENE APPLES - Apparel–women's - Little Greene Apples, Inc.
LITTLE GUPPY - Fishing lures - Lindy Little Joe Inc.
LITTLE GUPPY JIG - Fishing lures - Lindy Little Joe Inc.
LITTLE GUY - Screws - Rawlplug Co., Inc.
LITTLE GUY, THE - Aquariums–household - Advanced Aquatic Technologies Inc.
LITTLE GUYS - Notebooks and notepads - Recycled Paper Products, Inc.
LITTLE GUYS - Novelty items - Koplow Games
LITTLE HAND FULLS - Toys - Tonka Corp.
LITTLE HANDS - Publisher's imprints - Williamson Publishing, Co.
LITTLE HARBOR - Ships–sailing vessels - Hood Enterprises, Inc.
LITTLE HARBOR - Ships–sailing vessels - Little Harbor Yachts
LITTLE HAUNTS - Giftware - Russ Berrie and Co., Inc.
LITTLE HEAD - Novelty items - Russi W. Arden
LITTLE HEART WARMER - Dolls - Lloyderson Dolls & Toys
LITTLE HELPER - Toys - Fisher-Price, Inc.
LITTLE HELPER, THE - Aprons - Jural Manufacturing Co.
LITTLE HERBIE - Biscuits - Herbruck Poultry Ranch
LITTLE HERCULES - Safes ☆ - Meilink Safe Co.
LITTLE HERO - Pumps - John C. Anderson
LITTLE HERON - Wines ☆ - Heron Hill Vineyards Inc.
LITTLE HIKER - Backpacks - Log House Designs Inc.
LITTLE HOG - Shovels - Uniontools, Inc.
LITTLE HOOKERS - Plastics - Effron Sales
LITTLE HUGGUMS - Dolls - Alexander Doll Co. Inc.
LITTLE HUMANIST CLASSICS - Publisher's imprints ☆ - Bandanna Books
LITTLE HUMANIST LIBRARY - Publisher's imprints ☆ - Bandanna Books
LITTLE HUMMER - Sporting goods ☆ - Wright & McGill Co.
LITTLE HUNK - Boats - Glen-L Marine Designs
LITTLE IMAGES - Apparel–children's - Ben Elias Industries Corp.
LITTLE IMP - Footwear–children's - Littonian Shoe Co.
LITTLE IMP BOOKS - Publisher's imprints - Impact Publishers, Inc.
LITTLE INCH - Tape dispensers ☆ - Better Packages
LITTLE INDIAN - Tobacco–chewing or smoking - Brown & Williamson Tobacco Corp.
LITTLE INSPIRATIONS - Greeting cards ☆ - Kalan Inc.
LITTLE ITALIAN KITCHEN - Food products - M & K Foods Inc.
LITTLE ITALY - Olives–canned - Little Italy Food Inc.
LITTLE JACK - Eyeglasses - Art-Craft Optical Co.
LITTLE JAZZ, A - Hair coloring preparations ☆ - Clairol Inc.
LITTLE JEWEL - Games ☆ - Carrom Co.
LITTLE JEWEL - Lighting fixtures - Hubbell Lighting, Inc. (Lighting Div.)
LITTLE JILL - Eyeglasses - Art-Craft Optical Co.
LITTLE JOB - Paints - Dap Products Inc.
LITTLE JOE - Easels ☆ - Teledyne Post
LITTLE JOE - Food products - Janson's Foods Inc.
LITTLE JOE - Leather-palm gloves ☆ - Boss Manufacturing Co.
LITTLE JOE - Paint rollers - Bestt-Liebco
LITTLE JOE - Toys–trains - Life-Like Products Inc.

☆ = Now out of production

LITTLE JOE II - Toys–models ☆ - Estes Industries
LITTLE JOE SPINNER - Fishing lures - Lindy Little Joe Inc.
LITTLE JOHN - Archery equipment ☆ - Martin Archery Inc.
LITTLE JOHN - Paint rollers - Bestt-Liebco
LITTLE JOHN - Toys–models ☆ - Estes Industries
LITTLE JON - Boats - O.M.C. Aluminum Boat Group
LITTLE JON - Trailers–travel ☆ - Mitchell & Sons Inc.
LITTLE-JONES - Lamps - Little-Jones Co. Inc.
LITTLE JOYS - Greeting cards - Carole Joy Creations, Inc.
LITTLE JUAN - Food products - Multifoods Inc.
LITTLE JUMBO - Ladders–wood - Wing Enterprises, Inc.
LITTLE KENNY - Games - Little Kenny Publications Inc.
LITTLE KENNY'S KARDS - Games ☆ - Little Kenny Publications Inc.
LITTLE KIDS - Candles ☆ - American Candle Co. Inc.
LITTLE KIDS - Toys - Little Kids, Inc.
LITTLE KIDS. BIG IDEAS. - Games - Viacom International Inc.
LITTLE KIDS BIG SHOES - Dolls - Davis Brothers & Madison Ltd.
LITTLE KINGS - Beverages–malt - Hudepohl-Schoenling Brewing Co.
LITTLE KINGS CREAM - Beverages–malt - Hudepohl-Schoenling Brewing Co.
LITTLE KINGS LIGHT! - Beverages–malt ☆ - Hudepohl-Schoenling Brewing Co.
LITTLE KITTY KAT - Toys–banks - A.J. Renzi Plastic Corp.
LITTLE KNOTTIES - Toys ☆ - Learning Curve Toys, LLC
LITTLE KOOL REST - Ice chests - Igloo Products Corp.
LITTLE KRIS: SANTA CLAUS' SON - Dolls - Adam Starchild
LITTLE LACE-UPS - Toys - Fisher-Price, Inc.
LITTLE LACY LOP EAR BUNNY - Toys–stuffed - Paper Magic Group Inc.
LITTLE LAD - Ophthalmic goods - Styl-Rite Optical Manufacturing Co., Inc.
LITTLE LADY - Brooms - Fluffo Mop & Broom Co. Inc.
LITTLE LADY - Crocheted and knitted items - A Trifle Bit Inc.
LITTLE LADY - Food products - Little Lady Foods Inc.
LITTLE LADY - Gowns ☆ - Forever Yours International Corp.
LITTLE LADY - Harmonicas - Hohner Inc.
LITTLE LADY BY FOREVER YOURS - Wedding gowns - Forever Yours International Corp.
LITTLE LAMBS - Infant product - Pansy Ellen Products, Inc.
LITTLE LEAGUE - Toys - Tonka Corp.
LITTLE LEAGUER YO YO'S - Toys ☆ - Steven Manufacturing Co.
LITTLE LEARNERS - Toys - Lauri Inc.
LITTLE L'EGGS - Hosiery–children's - Sara Lee Corp.
LITTLE LESLIE - Wigs - Jean Paree Weegs Inc.
LITTLE LESSONS - Infant product - Eden LLC
LITTLE LEVI'S - Jeans - Levi Strauss & Co.
LITTLE LIGHTHOUSE - Toys - Tupperware Co.
LITTLE LITES - Candles - Empire Manufacturing Co.
LITTLE LITES - Lamps - General Electric Co.
LITTLE LIVE ONES - Toys - Imperial Toy Corp.
LITTLE LOG PEGS - Toys - Lauri Inc.
LITTLE LONGEARS - Toys–stuffed - Fun World Inc.
LITTLE LOP - Figurines ☆ - Our Secret, Ltd.
LITTLE LOTTIE - Polishes - Kwick Kleen Industrial Solvents, Inc.
LITTLE LOU - Food products - Lewis W. Ver Sluis Celery Co.
LITTLE LOUIE - Hardware - Louisville Ladder Group LLC
LITTLE LOVABLES - Greeting cards ☆ - American Greetings Corp.
LITTLE LOVERS - Toys–stuffed ☆ - Fun World Inc.
LITTLE LOVES - Apparel–women's - Lily of France Inc.
LITTLE LOVUMS - Dolls ☆ - Effanbee Doll Corp.
LITTLE LULLABYES - Toys–musical - Playskool, Inc.
LITTLE LUV - Dolls - Uneeda Doll Co., Inc.
LITTLE LUVS - Dolls - Russ Berrie and Co., Inc.
LITTLE LUX - Vacuum cleaners - Sle, Inc.
LITTLE LUX II - Vacuum cleaners and accessories - Sle, Inc.
LITTLE LUXURIES - Underwear and nightwear - Maidenform Inc.
LITTLE MAC - Fishing lures - Storm Manufacturing Co.
LITTLE MAC - Kitchen appliances ☆ - Hamilton Beach/Proctor-Silex Inc.
LITTLE MADELYN - Footwear - D'Bello Shoe Corp.
LITTLE MAESTRO - Electronic equipment ☆ - Texas Instruments Inc.
LITTLE MAIDS - Footwear - Circle Shoe Co.
LITTLE MAJOR - Sporting goods - Major Racquet Strings International
LITTLE MAJOR - Toys–stuffed - Dakin Inc.
LITTLE MAMMOTH MEDIA - Video production - Vanderkloot Film and Television, Inc.
LITTLE MAN - Apparel and accessories - Warren K. Smith
LITTLE MANNERS - Greeting cards - Fleming and Co. Inc.
LITTLE MAX - Machinery - Belleterre Environmental Corp.
LITTLE MAX - Multiple vitamins - Basic Organics, Inc.

LITTLE ME - Toys - S. Schwab Co., Inc.
LITTLE ME SOFTSOCKS - Apparel–children's - LMH, Inc.
LITTLE ME SPORT - Apparel–children's - S. Schwab Co., Inc.
LITTLE MERMAID - Furniture - American Toy & Furniture Co.
LITTLE MERMAID, THE - Toys - Coloron Industries
LITTLE MERMAID, THE - Dolls ☆ - Effanbee Doll Corp.
LITTLE MERMAID, THE - Games - Milton Bradley Co.
LITTLE MERMAID, THE - Footwear - Pagoda Trading Co.
LITTLE MERMAID, THE - Wallpaper - Priss Prints Inc.
LITTLE MERMAID, THE - Cosmetics - Walt Disney Co.
LITTLE MERMAID UNDER-THE-SEA COUPE - Toys–automobiles - Buddy L Inc.
LITTLE MERMAID WATERFULS, THE - Games - Milton Bradley Co.
LITTLE MESSAGE OF LOVE, A - Giftware - Russ Berrie and Co., Inc.
LITTLE MIKE - Computer programming services - Berta-Max Inc.
LITTLE MILKMAID - Dolls ☆ - Effanbee Doll Corp.
LITTLE MISS - Apparel–children's ☆ - Donley Manufacturing Co. Inc.
LITTLE MISS - Dolls ☆ - Totsy Manufacturing Co., Inc.
LITTLE MISS BOTANY - Socks - Rudin & Roth Inc.
LITTLE MISS DUNE DECK - Apparel–children's ☆ - Backflips
LITTLE MISS HONEY & SPICE - Hair care products - Honey & Spice Toiletries
LITTLE MISS JORDACHE - Dresses–girls' - Micronaut Industries Inc.
LITTLE MISS KISS - Dolls - Mattel, Inc.
LITTLE MISS LOVABLE - Underwear and nightwear ☆ - Lovable Co.
LITTLE MISS MUFFET - Dolls ☆ - Effanbee Doll Corp.
LITTLE MISS MUFFIN - Bakery products - Staci Munic
LITTLE MISS PEA-BODY - Dolls ☆ - Fun World Inc.
LITTLE MISS ROGERS - Apparel stores–lingerie ☆ - Formfit Rogers
LITTLE MISS TEENFORM - Apparel–children's - Wacoal America Inc.
LITTLE MISS WALK-MATE - Dolls ☆ - Fun World Inc.
LITTLE MISTER - Boys' toiletries - Cosrich Inc.
LITTLE MOMENTS - Figurines - Precious Moments, Inc.
LITTLE MOMMIE - Food products - L.P. Shanks Co.
LITTLE MOMMY - Toys - M.&S. Shillman Inc.
LITTLE MONSTER - Computer software ☆ - Broderbund Software, Inc.
LITTLE MONSTER - Cookies ☆ - Masterson Co. Inc.
LITTLE MONSTER - Video production - Mercer Mayer, Ltd.
LITTLE MONSTERS - Cookies - Einstein Bros. Bagels, Inc.
LITTLE MOONLIGHTER - Tables–metal ☆ - Teledyne Post
LITTLE MOUSE - Computer peripheral equipment - Mouse Systems Corp.
LITTLE MS. - Toys - Processed Plastic Co.
LITTLE N - Fishing lures - Howe Now Inc.
LITTLE NANOOK - Toys–stuffed - Dakin Inc.
LITTLE NAPPER - Mattress pads - Span-America Medical Systems, Inc.
LITTLE NEW WORLD - Publisher's imprint, no longer in print - International Publishers Co. Inc.
LITTLE NIC - Saws - Cooper Industries, Inc.
LITTLE NICKY - Flowers, plants, and seeds - Hines Nurseries, Inc.
LITTLE NIFTY - Tool boxes - Merriam Manufacturing Co. Inc.
LITTLE NIP - Apparel–women's - Cupid Foundations Inc.
LITTLE NIPPER - Fishing lures - Lindy Little Joe Inc.
LITTLE NOSES - Pharmaceutical preparations - Vetco, Inc.
LITTLE NOTHING - Apparel–women's - Cupid Foundations Inc.
LITTLE NOTHING - Underwear and nightwear ☆ - Alba-Waldensian, Inc.
LITTLE NOTION - Underwear and nightwear - Maidenform Inc.
LITTLE NUDEY, A - Apparel and accessories ☆ - Warnaco Inc.
LITTLE OFF THE TOP, A - Hair care products - Salon Development Corp.
LITTLE OLD NEW YORK - Dolls - Effanbee Doll Corp.
LITTLE OLLIE - Flowers, plants, and seeds - Monrovia Nursery Co.
LITTLE ONES - Medical device - E.R. Squibb & Sons, Inc.
LITTLE ONES - Pretzels - Tom Sturgis Pretzels, Inc.
LITTLE ONES - Toys - Kid Kore International Ltd.
LITTLE ORPHAN ORANGE - Confections - Jel Sert Co.
LITTLE PAL - Barbecues and grills - McNiel Enterprises Inc.
LITTLE PAL - Dog food - Harvest Industries, Inc.
LITTLE PAL - Harmonicas - William Kratt Co.
LITTLE PAL - Pumps - ITT Jabsco
LITTLE PALS - Ophthalmic goods - Fidelity Case Corp.
LITTLE PANCHO - Food products ☆ - Queen International Foods
LITTLE PARKER WALL-IT - Bicycle parts and accessories - Bike Track, Inc.
LITTLE PEE-VEE - Tools - Proctor Products Co. Inc.
LITTLE PENGUIN, THE - Refrigerators - Penguin Refrigeration, Inc.
LITTLE PEOPLE - Footwear–children's ☆ - World Import Co. Inc.
LITTLE PEOPLE - Frames–eyeglass - U.S. Optical Frame Co.
LITTLE PEOPLE - Health care products - Natural Laboratories Corp.
LITTLE PEOPLE - Stationery ☆ - Joli Greeting Card Co.

☆ = Now out of production

LITTLE PEOPLE - Toys - Fisher-Price, Inc.
LITTLE PEOPLE - Toys ☆ - Henry Gordy International Inc.
LITTLE PEOPLE - Wallpaper ☆ - Motif Designs, Inc.
LITTLE PEOPLES CLAY PACK - Clay–modeling - Duncan Enterprises
LITTLE PEOPLES PAINTING PACK - Artists' materials ☆ - Duncan Enterprises
LITTLE PERFECTION GOES A LONG WAY, A - Bakery products - Anthony Bonviso
LITTLE PETE - Tools–plumbing - Moen Inc.
LITTLE PHOOL - Apparel–women's - Phool Fashion, Ltd.
LITTLE PIECE OF ART, A - Greeting cards - Constance Kay
LITTLE PIG - Barbecue sauce - Clements Food Co. Inc.
LITTLE PIG NOSE - Brooms - Fluffo Mop & Broom Co. Inc.
LITTLE PIZAZZ - Sporting goods - Little Pizazz, Inc.
LITTLE PLANET PUBLISHING - Recording label - Applied Learning Technologies, Inc.
LITTLE PLANNER - Games - Leisure Learning Products
LITTLE PLAYMATE - Ice chests–plastic - Igloo Products Corp.
LITTLE PLAYMATES - Toys–stuffed - Russ Berrie and Co., Inc.
LITTLE PLEASURE - Stationery ☆ - Mead Corp.
LITTLE POLAR BEAR - Toys–stuffed ☆ - Gund, Inc.
LITTLE PORT-A-SAT - Automotive parts and accessories - Norman Johns
LITTLE PRETTY - Dolls - Mattel, Inc.
LITTLE PRINCE - Sporting goods - Prince Manufacturing Inc.
LITTLE PRINCESS - Footwear–children's - Wiesner Products Inc.
LITTLE PRINCESS - Toys - South Bend Toy Manufacturing Co.
LITTLE PRINCESS SWEEPER - Toys - South Bend Toy Manufacturing Co.
LITTLE PRINTS - Wallpaper - Greeff Fabrics Inc.
LITTLE PRINTS CHARMING II - Wallpaper - Warner Co.
LITTLE PRINTS II - Wallpaper - Warner Co.
LITTLE PRO - Socks - Adams-Millis Corp.
LITTLE PRO - Tools - Vaughan & Bushnell Manufacturing Co.
LITTLE PROFESSOR - Book stores - Little Professor Book Center
LITTLE PROFESSOR - Electronic equipment - Texas Instruments Inc.
LITTLE PROTECTOR - Lighting fixtures - Voigt Lighting Industries Inc.
LITTLE PUCKERS - Chewing gum ☆ - Fleer Corp.
LITTLE PURR - Toys–stuffed ☆ - Gund, Inc.
LITTLE PUSHY, A - Apparel and accessories ☆ - Warnaco Inc.
LITTLE Q - Publisher's imprints - Price Stern Sloan Inc.
LITTLE QUEEN - Apparel–men's ☆ - Donley Manufacturing Co. Inc.
LITTLE QUINCY KOALA - Toys–stuffed - Dakin Inc.
LITTLE RAGGEDYS - Infant product ☆ - Dolly, Inc.
LITTLE RAGGEDYS - Wallpaper ☆ - Priss Prints Inc.
LITTLE RAINBOW - Apparel and accessories - Twin Togs Creations Inc.
LITTLE RANGER - Revolvers - Fie Corp.
LITTLE RASCALS - Dolls - Effanbee Doll Corp.
LITTLE RATTLE BABIES - Toys–stuffed - Russ Berrie and Co., Inc.
LITTLE REACH - Infant product ☆ - Gerber Products Co.
LITTLE RECIRC - Cleaning preperation - Little Chemical Co., Inc.
LITTLE RED - Brooms ☆ - Royal Paper Products Inc.
LITTLE RED HEN - Bags–duffel - H. J. Rashti & Co., Inc.
LITTLE RED SCHOOL HOUSE - Bottles–plastic - Admar International, Inc.
LITTLE RED WAGON - Wagons–children's ☆ - Steven Manufacturing Co.
LITTLE REMEDIES - Pharmaceutical preparations - Vetco, Inc.
LITTLE REMEMBRANCE GIFT EDITIONS - Books–blank - Makepeace Colony Press Inc.
LITTLE RICHIE - Labels–paper - LRJ Records
LITTLE RIDDLES - Computer software - Hartley Courseware Inc.
LITTLE RIDERS - Toys - Fisher-Price, Inc.
LITTLE RINGLET - Brassieres (Bras) ☆ - Lovable Co.
LITTLE ROCK - Butter - Little Rock Coop. Creamery
LITTLE ROCKET - Footwear–athletic - American Athletic Shoe Co.
LITTLE ROMANCE, A - Greeting cards - American Greetings Corp.
LITTLE ROMANCE.TO REMIND YOU OF ME, A - Greeting cards - AGC, Inc.
LITTLE ROOSTER - Publisher's imprints - Bantam Doubleday Dell Publishing Group, Inc.
LITTLE ROTISSERIE - Turkeys - Armour Swift-Eckrich
LITTLE ROUND TOP - Games ☆ - Avalon Hill Game Co.
LITTLE SAMMY - Pizzas–frozen - Sam's Sorrento Pizza, Inc.
LITTLE SAMURAI, THE - Computer software - Knowledge Adventure
LITTLE SARAH - Toys–stuffed - Dakin Inc.
LITTLE SAX - Toys ☆ - Playskool, Inc.
LITTLE SCOOPER - Fishing lures - Howe Now Inc.
LITTLE SCOTT - Ambulatory aid - American Wheelchair
LITTLE SCULPTOR - Toys - Coloron Industries
LITTLE SHAPE - Publisher's imprints ☆ - Antioch Publishing Co.

LITTLE SHARPIE - Pencil sharpeners - Wescosa Inc.
LITTLE SHAVER - Fishing lures - Hildebrandt Corp.
LITTLE SHAVERS - Footwear–children's - W.L. Kreider's Sons Manufacturing Co. Inc.
LITTLE SHIRT ANCHORS - Infant product ☆ - American Baby Concepts
LITTLE SHOP OF BAGELS - Bagels - Francesca Geralyn Fericano
LITTLE SHOT - Fire extinguishers - Hawk International, Inc.
LITTLE SIMON - Publisher's imprints - Simon & Schuster, Inc.
LITTLE SIOUX - Trailers–travel ☆ - Mitchell & Sons Inc.
LITTLE SISTER - Pet products ☆ - Tetra Sales USA
LITTLE SISTER - Wallpaper ☆ - Three Sisters Studio
LITTLE SIZZLER - Microwave browner ☆ - Corning Inc.
LITTLE SIZZLERS - Meat products–pork - Hormel Foods Corp.
LITTLE SKI - Sporting goods - Sweco
LITTLE SLEEPER - Infant product ☆ - Welsh Co.
LITTLE SLEEPY EYES - Recording label - Someday Baby, Inc.
LITTLE SLEEPYTIME BOOK, A - Publisher's imprints - Kidsbooks, Inc.
LITTLE SMART - Toys–electronic - Vtech Industries, Inc.
LITTLE SMART ALPHABET WRITING DESK - Toys - Vtech Industries, Inc.
LITTLE SMART ANSWERING MACHINE - Toys–electronic - Vtech Industries, Inc.
LITTLE SMART BABY BEAR PHONE - Games - Vtech Industries, Inc.
LITTLE SMART BABY CHOO CHOO - Toys–electronic - Vtech Industries, Inc.
LITTLE SMART BABY DRIVER - Toys–electronic - Vtech Industries, Inc.
LITTLE SMART BABY SHAPES 'N THINGS - Toys - Vtech Industries, Inc.
LITTLE SMART BABY TUNES - Game machines - Vtech Industries, Inc.
LITTLE SMART DIAL A SMILE - Toys - Vtech Industries, Inc.
LITTLE SMART DRIVER - Toys–electronic - Video Technology U.S. Inc.
LITTLE SMART DRIVING SCHOOL - Games - Vtech Industries, Inc.
LITTLE SMART FIRST STEPS - Infant product - Vtech Industries, Inc.
LITTLE SMART FLYER - Toys–electronic - Video Technology U.S. Inc.
LITTLE SMART FUN TO TALK PHONE - Toys - Vtech Industries, Inc.
LITTLE SMART MAGIC KEYS - Game machines - Vtech Industries, Inc.
LITTLE SMART NUMBER DESK - Toys–electronic - Vtech Industries, Inc.
LITTLE SMART SCHOOL WORDS - Toys–electronic - Vtech Industries, Inc.
LITTLE SMART SINGING GUITAR - Toys–musical - Vtech Industries, Inc.
LITTLE SMART SPELLING BOOK - Toys–electronic - Vtech Industries, Inc.
LITTLE SMART SPIN 'N SPEAK - Game machines - Vtech Industries, Inc.
LITTLE SMART SUPER SORTER - Toys - Vtech Industries, Inc.
LITTLE SMART TALK 'N SMILE - Toys–electronic - Vtech Industries, Inc.
LITTLE SMART TALK 'N STROLL - Toys - Vtech Industries, Inc.
LITTLE SMART TALK 'N TUMBLE - Toys - Vtech Industries, Inc.
LITTLE SMART TALKING PAL - Toys–electronic - Vtech Industries, Inc.
LITTLE SMART TINY TOUCH - Toys - Vtech Industries, Inc.
LITTLE SMART TOUCH 'N LEARN - Toys - Vtech Industries, Inc.
LITTLE SMART TOUCH 'N LIGHT - Toys - Vtech Industries, Inc.
LITTLE SMART TOUCH 'N TURN - Toys - Vtech Industries, Inc.
LITTLE SMOKIES - Sausages - Oscar Mayer Foods Corp.
LITTLE SNIFF-ITS - Puzzles ☆ - Western Publishing Co., Inc.
LITTLE SNOOPY - Toys - Fisher-Price, Inc.
LITTLE SOMETHING, A - Giftware ☆ - Brushcreek Creative Co.
LITTLE SOMETHING, A - Jewelry - Monmouth Capital Corp.
LITTLE SOMETHING FOR EVERYONE, A - Candy - Homestead, Inc.
LITTLE SOPHISTICATES - Dolls - Uneeda Doll Co., Inc.
LITTLE SPIRIT - Footwear - United States Shoe Corp.
LITTLE SPORT - Preserved foods–canned - Grocers Supply Co.
LITTLE SQUEEZERS - Toys ☆ - Xonex International, Inc.
LITTLE SQUIRT - Toys–guns - Imperial Toy Corp.
LITTLE SQUIRTS - Toys - Russ Berrie and Co., Inc.
LITTLE SQUIRTS - Vitamins and nutritional supplements - American Vitamin Products, Inc.
LITTLE STAR - Apparel–children's - Seibel & Stern Corp.
LITTLE STAR - Health care products - Wheel Ring Inc.
LITTLE STEPPERS - Footwear–children's - Norwich Shoe Co. Inc.
LITTLE STEPS - Publisher's imprints - Blue Cross & Blue Shield of Rhode Island
LITTLE STEPS TELEPHONE WALKER - Toys - Steven Manufacturing Co.
LITTLE STINKER - Fishing lures - Uncle Josh Bait Co.
LITTLE STINKERS, THE - Apparel and accessories - Joseph Stuart Group, Inc.
LITTLE STUFF - Cookies - Bud's Best Cookies Inc.
LITTLE SUB - Pet products ☆ - Tetra Sales USA
LITTLE SUNDAY DRESSES - Patterns–clothing - McCarn Enterprises Inc.
LITTLE SUPER VIT-A-BOOST - Vitamins and nutritional supplements - Naturally Vitamin Supplements Inc.

☆ = Now out of production

LITTLE SWEDE - Food products - Western Farmers Association
LITTLE SWEDE - Sporting goods ☆ - Normark Corp.
LITTLE SWEETIES - Cookies - Parco Foods, Inc.
LITTLE SWEETS - Dolls - Mattel Inc.
LITTLE SWIMMERS - Apparel–children's - Kimberly-Clark Corp.
LITTLE SWINGERS - Toys ☆ - A.R.C. Toys Inc.
LITTLE SWISS - Calendars - Sormani Inc.
LITTLE SWISS MAID - Cheese - Zimmerman Cheese
LITTLE TALKER - Walkie talkies - Kid Designs Inc.
LITTLE TALKING SCHOLAR - Toys–electronic - Video Technology U.S. Inc.
LITTLE TEETHERS - Pharmaceutical preparations - Vetco, Inc.
LITTLE THINGS - Wallpaper ☆ - W.H.S. Lloyd
LITTLE THINGS MEAN A LOT - Apparel–children's - Little Things Mean a Lot
LITTLE THINKER - Games - Little Thinker
LITTLE TIGER - Dolls ☆ - Effanbee Doll Corp.
LITTLE TIKES - Toys - Little Tikes Co.
LITTLE TIKES - Toys–electronic - Play-Tech, Inc.
LITTLE TIKES PLACE - Toys - Little Tikes Co.
LITTLE TIPPERS - Cigars ☆ - House of Windsor Inc.
LITTLE TOOL BOX - Tools–hand-operated - Little Tool Box Co., Inc.
LITTLE TORCH - Tools - Smith Equipment
LITTLE TOUCH-IT-UP - Paint rollers - Panda Brush Co.
LITTLE TOWN OF BETHLEHEM - Figurines - F.W. Woolworth Co.
LITTLE TRAVELER - Candy ☆ - R.M. Palmer Co.
LITTLE TRAVELER - Cosmetic case with cologne, toothbrush, soap, etc. - Cosrich Inc.
LITTLE TRAVELER - Games ☆ - Carrom Co.
LITTLE TRAVELERS - Paper–toilet - Kimberly-Clark Corp.
LITTLE TRAV'LER - Infant product - Graco Children's Products
LITTLE TREASURE - Mattresses - Evenflo Juvenile Furniture Co.
LITTLE TREASURE - Mattresses - Lisco, Inc.
LITTLE TREASURES - Pencil sharpeners - Lisa Frank, Inc.
LITTLE TREASURES - Publisher's imprints - Antioch Publishing Co.
LITTLE TREE - Deodorizers - Car-Freshner Corp.
LITTLE TREE - Publisher's imprints - Resource Publishers Inc.
LITTLE TRIPPER - Luggage - Lands' End Inc.
LITTLE TROUBLES - Greeting cards - Morehead, Inc.
LITTLE TRUCK RIGS - Toys - Fisher-Price, Inc.
LITTLE TRUCKS - Toys - Fisher-Price, Inc.
LITTLE TUB - Pet products ☆ - Tetra Sales USA
LITTLE TUG - Toys - Little Tikes Co.
LITTLE TUMMY'S - Pharmaceutical preparations - Vetco, Inc.
LITTLE TUNES - Toys–musical - Proll Molding Co., Inc.
LITTLE TWIRL - Curling irons–electric - Remington Products Co.
LITTLE TYKES - Puzzles ☆ - Warren Industries Inc.
LITTLE TYRONE - Remote-control device for home-entertainment equipment - Orion/Alpha Corp.
LITTLE WAFFLES—BIG TIME FUN! - Waffles–frozen ☆ - Kellogg Co.
LITTLE WHISPER - Toys–stuffed ☆ - Gund, Inc.
LITTLE WINNERS - Dolls ☆ - Fun World Inc.
LITTLE WIZARD - Lanterns–kerosene - R.E. Dietz Co.
LITTLE WOLF - Furniture - Little Wolf Cabinet Shop Inc.
LITTLE WOMAN - Apparel and accessories - Warren K. Smith
LITTLE WOMAN - Brassieres (Bras) - Wacoal America Inc.
LITTLE WOMEN - Dolls - Alexander Doll Co. Inc.
LITTLE WOMEN - Dolls - Seymour Mann Inc.
LITTLE WONDER - Brushes–hair - Spornette International, Inc.
LITTLE WONDER - Drain pipe cleaners - Durst Industries Inc.
LITTLE WONDER - Garden equipment - Little Wonder (Schiller-Pfeiffer, Inc.)
LITTLE WONDER - Measuring instruments ☆ - Fairgate Rule Co. Inc.
LITTLE WONDER - Screws ☆ - Creative Products Inc.
LITTLE WONDERS - Housewares - Tupperware Co.
LITTLE WORLD OF SPORTS - Giftware - Russ Berrie and Co., Inc.
LITTLE WORLDS OF LOVE - Giftware - Russ Berrie and Co., Inc.
LITTLE YAZOO - Boats–fishing ☆ - C-G Industries Inc.
LITTLE YO - Yogurt - Oberlin Farms Dairy Inc.
LITTLE ZIPPER - Toys ☆ - Creative Playthings Ltd.
LITTLE'S - Horseradish - Hammon Food Co. Inc.
LITTLES, THE - Publisher's imprints - Scholastic Inc.
LITTLEST ANGEL - Brassieres (Bras) - Wacoal America Inc.
LITTLEST ANGEL - Dolls - Vogue Dolls Inc.
LITTLEST ANGEL - Toys - Playmates World Wide Inc.
LITTLEST CHRISTMAS TREE, THE - Recording label - Little Tree Productions, Inc.
LITTLEST FIRST BORN - Dolls - Uneeda Doll Co., Inc.
LITTLEST PET SHOP - Lunch boxes - Thermos Co.

LITTLEST PET SHOP - Toys–stuffed - Tonka Corp.
LITTLEWAY - Thread - Blue Mountain Industries, Inc.
LITTLITE - Lamps - CAE Inc.
LITTRE - Pens ☆ - Zebra Pen Corp.
LITTY BITTYS - Greeting cards ☆ - Amberley Greeting Card Co.
LIV - Hair care products - Summit Laboratories
LIV-A-TOX - Health care products - Enzymatic Therapy, Inc.
LIV-FLUSH - Health care products - Ion Laboratories Inc.
LIV-IN LIMO - Toys–automobiles - Mattel, Inc.
LIV-KID BOOSTER - Health care products - Natural Laboratories Corp.
LIVAGEN - Skin care products - P.S. Pibbs Inc.
LIVAGYSTIC - Vitamins and nutritional supplements - Great Life Laboratories Inc.
LIVAH - Vitamins and nutritional supplements - Kroeger Herb Products Co. Inc.
LIVASYN - Vitamins and nutritional supplements - Great Life Laboratories Inc.
LIVE - Apparel and accessories - Action Front Unlimited, Inc.
LIVE - Banks–commercial - Flagstar Bank FSB
LIVE - Perfumes - Wilshire Fragrance Corp.
LIVE - Toys - WPC Holdings, Inc.
LIVE ACTION - Footwear ☆ - N Shasta Shoe
LIVE ACTION - Sporting goods - Mearthane Products Corp.
LIVE ACTION LIFT - Toys - Tonka Corp.
LIVE ACTION SPORTS - Footwear ☆ - N Shasta Shoe
LIVE ACTION VIDEO FOR KIDS - Video production - Power to Create, Inc.
LIVE AND LET DIE - Games - Avalon Hill Game Co.
LIVE APPLE - Juices ☆ - Odwalla, Inc.
LIVE. BREATHE. GOLF. - Real estate agencies - Mohawk Valley Ranch, Inc.
LIVE-CELL - Paper–carbon ☆ - Curtis-Young Corp.
LIVE CONCERT - Dolls - Mattel, Inc.
LIVE DRIVE - Computers - NetFRAME Systems Inc.
LIVE-EDGE - Automotive parts and accessories ☆ - Stant Corp.
LIVE FAST - Apparel and accessories - C.S.F. Corp.
LIVE FAST AND DYE YOUR HAIR - Cosmetics - Tish & Snooky's N.Y.C. Inc.
LIVE FIRE TRAINING SYSTEM - Simulation device - Symtron Systems Inc.
LIVE FROM AMERICA - Apparel and accessories - Ben Elias Industries Corp.
LIVE FROM THE PAST - Video production - New York Times Co.
LIVE FROM THE VAULTS - Recording label - Sony Music Entertainment Inc.
LIVE GREETINGS - Flowers, plants, and seeds - World Flower Center, Inc.
LIVE HARD - Novelty items–paper - Area Code Where? Ltd.
LIVE IMAGE - Jewelry - Jerry Wayne Beaty
LIVE IN COLOR - Wallpaper - Galaxie Handprints
LIVE IN COMFORT - Apparel and accessories - Nap, Inc.
LIVE INS - Jeans–women's ☆ - Gabriel Manufacturing Co.
LIVE LOAD - Knapsacks - Coleman Co., Inc.
LIVE LONG & LOVE IT! - Computer software - Seminar Software, Inc.
LIVE OAK - Furniture - Universal Flooring
LIVE OAK - Leather goods - Tandy Leather Co.
LIVE OAKS - Wines - Live Oaks Winery
LIVE ON - Pharmaceutical preparations - C.O. Truxton Inc.
LIVE ON TAPE - Broadcasting stations–television - Sen Entertainment, Inc.
LIVE PICTURE - Computer software - Fits Imaging
LIVE-SCAN FINGERPRINTING SYSTEM - Computer peripheral equipment - Digital Biometrics, Inc.
LIVE-TAIL - Fishing lures - Live-Tail Lure Manufacturing Co.
LIVE THE DREAM - Trading cards and stamps - Treat Entertainment, Inc.
LIVE THE GAME - Shorts–men's - Umbro USA
LIVE VIDEO BLACKJACK - Game machines - Innovative Gaming Corp. of America
LIVE VIDEO CRAPS - Video games - Innovative Gaming Corp. of America
LIVE WIRE - Apparel and accessories ☆ - Warnaco Inc.
LIVE WIRE - Footwear–children's - K-P Shoe Co. Inc.
LIVE WIRE - Toys - Mattel, Inc.
LIVE WIRES - Footwear ☆ - Brown Shoe Co.
LIVE WIRES - Musical instrument accessories - Seymour Duncan Pickups
LIVE WIRES - Notebooks and notepads ☆ - Union Camp Corp. (Fine Paper Division)
LIVE WIRES - Sunglasses - Face 2 Face Corp.
LIVE WIREZ - Ribbons - Z-Barten Productions
LIVE YOUR DREAM WITH... - Video production - Freemont Productions, Inc.
LIVEC - Pharmaceutical preparations - Enzyme Process Co. Inc.
LIVELINK - Fittings–cast iron - Hose Master, Inc.
LIVELY BABY - Dolls - Horsman
LIVELY DAYTIME - Food products - Health Valley Food
LIVELY EXPRESSIONS - Flowers, plants, and seeds - Milestone 2000, Inc.
LIVELY EYES - Dolls - Mattel, Inc.
LIVELY IMPRESSIONS - Coffee - Starbucks Corp.

☆ = Now out of production

LIVELY LEGS - Medical apparatus - Becton, Dickinson and Co.
LIVELY LIDS - Toilet seats ☆ - Bemis Manufacturing Co.
LIVELY LIGHTS - Ornamental products–glass - Colossal Jewelry and Accessories, Inc.
LIVELY LOVE - Dolls - Horsman
LIVELY ONES - Underwear and nightwear - Exquisite Form Industries
LIVELY SET - Cosmetics - Revlon Consumer Products Corp.
LIVELY SOFSKIN - Dolls - Horsman
LIVELY STEPPER - Footwear - Gotham Shoe Manufacturing Co.
LIVEN-UP - Vitamins and nutritional supplements - N.I.S.M. Inc.
LIVEPIX - Computer software - Live Picture, Inc.
LIVER BITS - Pet products ☆ - Vital Nutrition Products
LIVER CRUDE - Pharmaceutical preparations ☆ - Vortech Pharmaceuticals
LIVER DETOX - Health care products - East Earth Herb Inc.
LIVER EASE NEW VITA SINCE 1983 - Herbal products - Irena L. Cua
LIVER FORMULA - Vitamins and nutritional supplements - Source Naturals
LIVER GLANDULAR PLUS - Vitamins and nutritional supplements - Ethical Nutrients
LIVER GUARD - Vitamins and nutritional supplements - Source Naturals
LIVER KITTY STARS - Cat food - Mardel Laboratories, Inc.
LIVER-P - Pharmaceutical preparations ☆ - Vortech Pharmaceuticals
LIVER QI - Health care products - East Earth Herb Inc.
LIVER SUPPORT - Health care products - Healthwatchers System
LIVERBEX - Pharmaceutical preparations - G.O. Spanner Inc.
LIVERCAPS - Pharmaceutical preparations - Pro Cap
LIVERCARE - Health care products ☆ - Futurebiotics
LIVERCARE - Vitamins and nutritional supplements - Ayurvedic Concepts Ltd.
LIVERLICIOUS - Pet food - Charlee Bear Farms, Inc.
LIVERMORE - Footwear–men's - Livermore-Farmington Shoe Co.
LIVERMORE VALLEY CELLARS - Wines - Livermore Valley Cellars
LIVESAVERS PUNCH SODA - Beverages–carbonated - Planters LifeSavers Co.
LIVETOUCH - Computer software - Aristacom International, Inc.
LIVEWIRE - Amusement rides - Black Diamond Equipment, Ltd.
LIVEWIRE - Computer software - Metro Publishing Inc.
LIVEWIRES - Figurines - Livewires
LIVFIT - Vitamins and nutritional supplements - Tishcon Corp.
LIVID - Record stores - Ralph Christopher Henry
LIVIN DOLLS - Dolls - Kamar International Inc.
LIVIN' IN THE USA - Games - International Gamco, Inc.
LIVIN' LARGE! - Hosiery - Handcraft Manufacturing Corp.
LIVIN PETS - Toys–stuffed - Kamar International Inc.
LIVIN' SOUTHERN - Frozen foods - Marion Ashley Caldwell
LIVING - Gloves–rubber - Johnson & Johnson
LIVING - Gloves–rubber - Playtex Beauty Care, Inc.
LIVING - Hardware - Living Windows Corp.
LIVING - Mushrooms - Elite Mushroom Co., Inc.
LIVING AIR - Air purification systems - Environmental Health Services
LIVING & LEARNING - Toys - Brittoys
LIVING BASIL FLAVOR - Spices and extracts - International Flavors & Fragrances Inc.
LIVING BOOK - Computer software - Broderbund Software, Inc.
LIVING BOOKS - Electronic equipment - Living Books
LIVING BOSC PEAR - Chemical preparations - International Flavors & Fragrances Inc.
LIVING BOUQUET - Flowers, plants, and seeds - NTS Co.
LIVING CANTELOUPE - Chemical preparations - International Flavors & Fragrances Inc.
LIVING CARNATION - Chemical preparations - International Flavors & Fragrances Inc.
LIVING CELERY STALK - Chemical preparations - International Flavors & Fragrances Inc.
LIVING CENTER BY HAMMARY - Tables–wood - La-Z-Boy Chair Co.
LIVING COLLECTIBLES - Dolls - Waco Products Corp.
LIVING COLOR - Film - Genovese Drug Stores, Inc.
LIVING COLORS - Artists' materials - J.L. Hammett Co.
LIVING COLORS - Hair coloring preparations - Wella Corp. (Consumer Products Div.)
LIVING CURL - Hair care products - Revlon Consumer Products Corp.
LIVING DAIRYFREE HEALTHY - Food products - Tofutti Brands Inc.
LIVING DIGITAL - Computer software - Prodigy Services Co.
LIVING DOLL - Cosmetics - Faberge Co.
LIVING DOLLS - Dolls - Mangelsen's (VDI)
LIVING EASY - Floor coverings–carpet and rugs - Gulistan Carpet Inc.
LIVING EASY - Wallpaper ☆ - Greeff Fabrics Inc.
LIVING END - Furniture - Barcalounger Co.

LIVING END, THE - Hair care products - Helene Curtis Industries Inc.
LIVING ENDS - Book ends - Talus Corp.
LIVING ENERGY - Health care products - Futurebiotics
LIVING ENVIRONMENTS - Wallpaper - Essex Wallcoveringss
LIVING FIT - Apparel–athletic - Weider Health and Fitness
LIVING FLAVORS - Oils–essential - International Flavors & Fragrances Inc.
LIVING FLOWER - Oils–essential - International Flavors & Fragrances Inc.
LIVING FLOWER BOUQUET - Perfumes - International Flavors & Fragrances Inc.
LIVING FLOWER TECHNOLOGY - Chemical preparations - International Flavors & Fragrances Inc.
LIVING FOOD - Vitamins and nutritional supplements - Raw Materials Food Co.
LIVING FOOD CONCENTRATE - Vitamins and nutritional supplements - The Lifestar Millennium, Inc.
LIVING FRAGRANCE - Oils–edible - International Flavors & Fragrances Inc.
LIVING FRUIT - Oils–essential - International Flavors & Fragrances Inc.
LIVING GIFTS - Horticultural product - J.T. Inman Co. Inc.
LIVING GREEN - Lawn and garden franchise - Living Green Inc.
LIVING HISTORY LIBRARY - Publisher's imprints - Random House, Inc.
LIVING ICE - Toys - Mattel, Inc.
LIVING IN STYLE - Wallpaper - James Seeman Studios
LIVING IN STYLE II - Wallpaper - James Seeman Studios
LIVING KEY LIME FRESHNESS - Colognes - International Flavors & Fragrances Inc.
LIVING KITCHENS - Cabinets - Brammer Manufacturing Co.
LIVING LANGUAGE - Publisher's imprints - Crown Publishers Inc.
LIVING LANGUAGE ALL THE WAY - Recording label - Random House, Inc.
LIVING LANGUAGE IN-TENSE - Video production - Crown Publishers Inc.
LIVING LAWN - Fertilizers - Gold Kist Inc.
LIVING LEGEND - Motorcycle parts and accessories - Chrome Specialties, Inc.
LIVING LEGENDS - Giftware ☆ - Enesco Corp.
LIVING LEGENDS - Wallpaper ☆ - Legend Wallcoverings
LIVING LEGENDS - Wallpaper ☆ - Mayfair Wallcoverings
LIVING LIGHT - Food products - Thornton Foods Co.
LIVING LIGHT DAIRY BLEND - Dairy products - Thornton Foods Co.
LIVING LIGHTLY - Non-dairy frozen dessert - Turtle Mountain, Inc.
LIVING LIGHTLY - Oils–edible ☆ - Spectrum Naturals, Inc.
LIVING LILY OF THE VALLEY - Oils–essential - International Flavors & Fragrances Inc.
LIVING MAGNOLIA BLOSSOM - Chemical preparations - International Flavors & Fragrances Inc.
LIVING MANDARIN - Perfumes - International Flavors & Fragrances Inc.
LIVING MEDIA - Computer software - IMSI
LIVING MEDIA - Computer storage devices–optical - International Microcomputer Software, Inc.
LIVING MEMORIAL - Burial caskets - Batesville Casket Co., Inc.
LIVING MUSHROOM FLAVOR - Spices and extracts - International Flavors & Fragrances Inc.
LIVING MUSIC - Recording label - American Gramaphone Records
LIVING MUSK - Chemical preparations - International Flavors & Fragrances Inc.
LIVING NATURAL FRUIT FLAVORS - Oils–essential - International Flavors & Fragrances Inc.
LIVING NIGHTMARE - Toys–stuffed ☆ - Fun World Inc.
LIVING PEACH - Chemical preparations - International Flavors & Fragrances Inc.
LIVING PEONY - Perfumes - International Flavors & Fragrances Inc.
LIVING PINK LILY OF THE VALLEY - Chemical preparations - International Flavors & Fragrances Inc.
LIVING PLEASURES - Skin care products - Sears, Roebuck and Co.
LIVING PRETTY - Toys - Mattel, Inc.
LIVING PRINTS - Video production - Richie's Video
LIVING RAMP - Ramps - JH Industries Inc. (Copperloy Div.)
LIVING RASPBERRY - Colognes - International Flavors & Fragrances Inc.
LIVING REEF - Toys - Great American Fun Corp.
LIVING RIGHTLY - Frozen foods - Turtle Mountain, Inc.
LIVING ROOM - Motor vehicles–motor homes ☆ - Avco Aerostructures Inc.
LIVING SANDALWOOD - Perfumes - International Flavors & Fragrances Inc.
LIVING SEA - Aquariums–household - Rolf C. Hagen (USA) Corp.
LIVING SEED - Greeting cards ☆ - Evergreen Press
LIVING SOLE - Footwear ☆ - Kenkoh American Co.
LIVING STEREO - Recording label - BMG Entertainment North America
LIVING SYSTEMS - Furniture - Harry Allen & Associates
LIVING TEXTURES - Floor coverings–carpet and rugs - Columbus Mills, Inc.
LIVING, THE - Wallpaper - Scalamandre Silks Inc.
LIVING THINGS - Computer software - Right on Programs

☆ = Now out of production

LIVING TOMATO FLAVOR - Spices and extracts - International Flavors & Fragrances Inc.

LIVING TRUST - Computer software ☆ - Nolo Press/Folklaw Inc.

LIVING TRUST MAKER - Computer software - Nolo Press/Folklaw Inc.

LIVING WATER - Beverages–carbonated ☆ - Ginseng Up Corp.

LIVING WEDGE - Tools - Vaughan & Bushnell Manufacturing Co.

LIVING WITH FRAGRANCE - Deodorizers - Aphrodisia Products

LIVING WITH GERD - Pharmaceutical preparations - Eli Lilly and Co.

LIVING WITH TRADITIONS - Furniture ☆ - White Furniture Co.

LIVING WORLD - Animal food - Rolf C. Hagen (USA) Corp.

LIVING ZODIACS - Figurines ☆ - Cal Themes Inc.

LIVINGSKIN - Prosthetic apparatus - Aesthetic Concerns Prosthetics, Inc.

LIVINGSONG - Recording label - Epoch Universal Publications Inc.

LIVINGSTON - Boats - Mirage Manufacturing LLC

LIVINGSTON - Truck bodies - Livingston Corp.

LIVINGSTON MANOR - Floor coverings–carpet and rugs ☆ - American Carpet Mills

LIVINGWARE - Glassware - Corning Inc.

LIVINGWELL - Apparel and accessories - Livingwell Lady Fitness Centers

LIVIO FELLUGA - Wines - Palace Brands Co.

LIVIRON - Pharmaceutical preparations - Consolidated Midland Corp.

LIVITAMIN - Pharmaceutical preparations - Smithkline Beecham Corp.

LIVITOL - Pharmaceutical preparations - Consolidated Midland Corp.

LIVITRINSIC-F - Pharmaceutical preparations - Goldline Laboratories, Inc.

LIV'N EGG - Artists' materials - Visual Design Manufacturing Co. Inc.

LIVNLUBE - Lubricants - Washington Trading Co., Inc.

LIVOFIT - Vitamins and nutritional supplements ☆ - Tishcon Corp.

LIVOGEN - Vitamins and nutritional supplements - Tishcon Corp.

LIVOLEX - Pharmaceutical preparations - Legere Pharmaceuticals Inc.

LIVONAMINE - Health care products ☆ - Ferndale Laboratories, Inc.

LIVORNO - Floor coverings - Mannington Resilient Floors

LIVORNO II - Furniture ☆ - Hammary Furniture Co. Inc.

LIVOS - Floor coverings - Design Materials, Inc.

LIVOSTIN - Antihistamine preparations - Johnson & Johnson

LIVOSTIN - Prescription ophthalmic drug - Iolab Pharmaceuticals

LIVOWS SISAL - Floor coverings–carpet and rugs - Design Materials, Inc.

LIV'R'CRUNCH - Pet food - Old Mother Hubbard Dog Food Co., Inc.

LIVROBEN - Pharmaceutical preparations ☆ - Forest Pharmaceuticals Inc.

LIWAY - Food additives - Liway International, Inc.

LIX - Cough medicines - Lix Co.

LIXAGESIC - Pharmaceutical preparations ☆ - JMI-Canton Pharmaceuticals

LIXAMINOL - Health care products ☆ - Ferndale Laboratories, Inc.

LIXIT - Hardware - Lixit Corp.

LIXIT - Pet products - Morton Jones Co.

LIXIT - Pet products - Lixit Animal Care Products

LIXTIC - Medical apparatus - Cytech Bio-Medical, Inc.

LIZ - Frames–eyeglass - Rozin Optical Export Corp.

LIZ & CO. - Apparel–women's - Liz Claiborne Inc.

LIZ-ART - Jewelry - Liz-Art Inc.

LIZ AT HOME - Bedding–linen - Liz Claiborne Inc.

LIZ BAKER - Apparel–women's - J.C. Penney Co., Inc.

LIZ BARTON - Cosmetics ☆ - Beauty Aids Inc.

LIZ CARLO DI FERRARA - Pins–straight - J. & C. Ferrara Co. Inc.

LIZ CLAIBORNE - Apparel–women's - Liz Claiborne Inc.

LIZ CLAIBORNE - Colognes ☆ - Avon Products, Inc.

LIZ CLAIBORNE - Handbags - L.C. Licensing, Inc.

LIZ CLAIBORNE - Hosiery–women's - Kayser-Roth Corp.

LIZ CLAIBORNE - Shoes - Marx & Newman Co. Inc.

LIZ CLAIBORNE - Sunglasses - International Tropic-Cal Inc. (I SKI Div.)

LIZ CLAIBORNE COLLECTION - Eyeglasses - L.C. Licensing, Inc.

+LIZ #CLAIBORNE NIGHT - Dresses–women's - L.C. Licensing, Inc.

LIZ DECO - Wallets - Enger-Kress Co.

LIZ K - Scarves - Elizabeth Kurtzman

LIZ SANDERS DESIGNS - Bathroom accessories ☆ - Ransburg Accessories Inc.

LIZ SINCLAIR - Apparel and accessories - Durlacher & Co., Inc.

LIZ SPORT - Apparel–women's - Liz Claiborne Inc.

LIZ THOMAS - Handbags - Ames Department Stores, Inc.

LIZ WEAR - Apparel–women's - Liz Claiborne Inc.

LIZA - Bedding–linen - Dan River Inc.

LIZA - Fabrics - Vertilux-Louverlux Inc.

LIZA - Jewelry - Habif Jewelry Co. Inc.

LIZARD - Tools–hand-operated - Spellbound Development Group, Inc.

LIZARD KING - Bicycles ☆ - Huffy Corp.

LIZARD LADDER - Pet products - Zoo Med Laboratories, Inc.

LIZARD SKIN - Toys - Spearhead Industries Inc.

LIZARD WISP - Jewelry - Jacoby-Bender Inc.

LIZARDLIMB - Pet products - Tetra Sales USA

LIZARDMEN - Games ☆ - Mayfair Games, Inc.

LIZARD'S LAIR - Pet products - Northeastern Products Corp.

LIZIO'S SPAGHETTI VENDORS - Pasta - Spaghetti Vendors Franchise Systems, Inc.

LIZ'S CUFFIN THE COOKIE - Bakery products - Elizabeth Geringer

LIZSPORT - Cosmetics ☆ - Labelon Corp.

LIZZABELLE - Toys - Mattel, Inc.

LIZZY - Toys–stuffed - Ty, Inc.

LJ - Jewelry - Leenet Jewelry Corp.

LJ - Jewelry–precious - Lotus Jewelry Ltd.

L.J. BRUCK - Beverages–alcohol - James Moroney, Inc.

LJ-NTSU - Recording label ☆ - Ray Lawrence Ltd.

L.J. SMITH STAIR SYSTEMS - Wood products - L.J. Smith Co., Inc.

LJL - Jewelry - Landmark Jewelers Ltd.

LJP - Pharmaceutical preparations - La Jolla Pharmaceutical Co.

L.J.S. COLLECTION - Handbags - L.J.S. Accessory Collection Inc.

LJUNGDAHLS - Stationery ☆ - Merry Thoughts Inc.

LK-1 - Knives–pocket - Hot Tools Inc.

LK-93 KNIGHT LEGEND - Firearms, accessories, and parts ☆ - Modern Muzzle Loading, Inc.

L.K. BOWMAN - Frozen mushrooms - L.K. Bowman & Co. Inc.

LK LAMBERT KAY - Pet collars - Carter-Wallace, Inc.

LKB - Frozen mushrooms - L.K. Bowman & Co. Inc.

LKD - Electronic equipment - Moor Electronics Inc.

LKP - Games - Little Kenny Publications Inc.

LKP FLAIR - Games - Little Kenny Publications Inc.

LKP PROJECT II - Games - Little Kenny Publications Inc.

LKV DROPS - Vitamins and nutritional supplements - Freeda Vitamins Inc.

LKW - Apparel and accessories - Lee K. Wynn

LL - Clarinets - G. Leblanc Corp.

LL - Jewelry - L'Imagine Jewelry Concepts, Inc.

LL-2000 - Electrical equipment - LCC Inc.

L.L. BEAN - Bags–duffel ☆ - Eclipse Inc.

L.L. BEAN - Sporting goods - L.L. Bean Inc.

L.L. BEAR - Toys–stuffed - L.L. Bean Inc.

L.L. KIDS - Apparel–children's - L.L. Bean Inc.

LL SPORT - Apparel and accessories - Leon Levin Sons, Inc.

LLADRO - Figurines - Lladro USA, Inc.

LLAMA LOCOMOTOR ORIGINAL - Travel bags - Locomotor USA, Inc.

LLAMA SUPREME NIBBLETS - Animal feeds - Bluebonnet Milling Co.

LLANO ESTACADO - Wines - Llano Estacado Winery Inc.

LLEWELLYN PUBLICATIONS - Publisher's imprints - Llewellyn Publications

LLL LEANER-LIGHTER-LIVELIER - Health care products - High Life Formulas Inc.

LLM-WIN - Computer software - Loftware, Inc.

LLM-WINLAN - Computer software - Loftware, Inc.

LLMO - Water treating compounds - General Environmental Science Corp.

LLORD'S - Beverages–alcohol - Black Prince Distillery, Inc.

LLOYD - Automotive parts and accessories - Pep Boys Manny, Moe & Jack

LLOYD - Garden furniture–rattan ☆ - Lloyd/Flanders Industries

LLOYD - Photographic equipment - Lloyd Film Loader Co.

LLOYD & THOMAS - Footwear - Bob Le Vine Shoe Sales

LLOYD J. HARRISS - Pies–frozen - Chef Pierre Inc.

LLOYD MATHESON - Locks–door - Lloyd Matheson Inc.

LLOYD WILLIAMS - Apparel and accessories - Clothing Label Co. Inc.

LLOYD'S - Cleaning preparations - Lloyds, Inc.

LLOYD'S - Electronic equipment ☆ - Lloyd's Electronics Inc.

LLOYD'S - Food products - Lloyd's Food Products, Inc.

LLOYD'S - Meat products–beef ☆ - Normark & Associates

LLOYD'S BARBEQUE COMPANY - Meat products - Lloyd's Barbeque Co.

LLS - Chemical preparations - Georgia-Pacific Corp.

LLUMAR - Window coverings - Martin Energy Products

LLUMAR - Yarn - Smart Machine Technologies Inc.

LLUMAVISION - Lighting equipment - Sirchie Fingerprint Laboratories, Inc.

LM - Computers - Lasermaster Corp.

LM - Electronic equipment - Ludlum Measurements Inc.

LM-1 - Tools - Hot Tools Inc.

LM 002 - Motor vehicles–automobiles ☆ - DaimlerChrysler

LM-1200 - Computer hardware - Logic Modeling Corp.

LM EDITION - Apparel–children's - S. Schwab Co., Inc.

LM LIKE MAGIC - Disinfectants - Cello Chemical Co.

LM5 - Markers–felt-tip - Ideal Stencil Machine and Tape Co.

LM500 LABELING - Office supplies - Varitronic Systems, Inc.

L.M.A. - Brushes–paint - Venice Brushes & Rollers Inc.

☆ = Now out of production

+L'MAGE - Colognes - George Jaquith
LMAVG - Wines - L.M.A.V.G. Vineyard & Winery Inc.
LMC - Radios - RELM Communications Inc.
LMD LIMARDEE - Trays - Limardee Enterprises
+L'MER - Apparel and accessories ☆ - Edison Brothers Stores, Inc.
LMI - Integrated circuits - Linfinity Microelectronics Inc.
LMI - Lighting equipment - Lighting Methods Inc.
LMI/CCT - Lighting equipment - Lighting Methods Inc.
L.M.P. SYSTEMS - Compact discs–prerecorded - L.M.P. Systems
LMR - Cables–fiber optic - Smiths Industries Aerospace & Defense Systems Inc.
LMR - Tiles–ceramic ☆ - Maxsam Sales, Inc.
LMS - Furniture - Wright Line Inc.
L.M.S. TURSKI - Skis ☆ - Liberty Mountain Sports
LMT-AC - Elevator controls - Delaware Capital Formation Inc.
LMX - Lubricants - Witco Corp.
LMX LOW MOISTURE SOIL EXTRACTION SYSTEM - Cleaning preparations–carpet and rug - Von Schrader Co.
LN - Computer peripheral equipment - Wellfleet Communications, Inc.
LN7 - Motor vehicles–automobiles ☆ - Ford Motor Co. (Lincoln-Mercury Div.)
LNBY - Integrated antenna/downconverter - California Amplifier
LNCB - Burners - Babcock & Wilcox Co.
LNDA - Amplifiers - Pico Products, Inc.
LNG - Natural gas - Amoco Oil Co.
LNG - Vitamins and nutritional supplements - Vital Energy
LNI - Apparel and accessories - D. Lubell, Inc.
LNR - Apparel–women's - La Nouvelle Renaissance
LO - Hobby kits - Lee Co.
LO-AN - Food products - Lo-An/Florida Inc.
LO-AN - Food products - Sargento Inc.
LO-AQUA - Pharmaceutical preparations ☆ - Roberts/Hauck Pharmaceuticals Inc.
LO-BACK - Underwear and nightwear - Bestform Foundations, Inc.
LO-BLAST - Heating equipment ☆ - Midco International Inc.
LO-BLO - Air brooms - Lesco, Inc.
LO-BODY - Motorized vehicles - Evans Body Works Inc.
LO BOP'S - Traction apparatus–medical ☆ - Lossing Orthopedic Co.
LO BOY - Pumps - Hilo Industries
LO-BOY - Tripods–photographic ☆ - QuickSet International Inc.
LO BRITE - Lighting fixtures ☆ - Hubbell Lighting, Inc. (Lighting Div.)
LO CAB - Footwear - Vans, Inc.
LO-CAP - Cables - General Cable Corp.
LO-CHOL - Cheese - Swissrose International Inc.
LO CHOL - Vitamins and nutritional supplements - Pharmakon USA, Inc.
LO DECKER - Boats–fishing - Anchor Industries Inc.
LO-DISC - Floor coverings - R.C. Musson Rubber Co.
L.O. DOLLY - Dollies–industrial - Acme-Lite Manufacturing Co.
LO-DOSE - Surgical supplies - Becton, Dickinson and Co.
LO-DOWN LIMO - Toys–automobiles - Mattel, Inc.
LO DUCA - Musical instruments - Lo Duca Bros. Musical Instruments Inc.
LO-FATS - Cooking equipment–household - Chicago Metallic Products Inc.
LO FORE - Sporting goods - Chesal Golf
LO-GLO - Enamels - Frazee Paint
LO-GLO - Flashlights - RDM Sales
LO-GLO - Paints - Harrison Paint Corp.
LO-HEET - Cooking equipment–household - New Era Co.
LO-HENRY - Electrical equipment - Electronic Concepts, Inc.
LO-LAC - Milk - Johanna Foods, Inc.
LO MAS SELECTO - Thread - Quality Thread Co.
LO-MASS - Musical instrument accessories ☆ - Dimarzio, Inc.
LO MAXIMO - Snacks - Lo Maximo
LO MEJOR EN SU COCINA - Tomato pastes and sauces - Freiria & Co., Inc.
LO-NOVA - Pharmaceutical preparations - Berlex Laboratories, Inc.
LO-NOX - Stoves - S.T. Johnson Co.
LO/OVRAL - Pharmaceutical preparations - Wyeth-Ayerst Laboratories
LO-PRO - Drapery track system - Coral of Chicago
LO-PRO - Floor coverings - R.C.A. Rubber Co.
LO-PRO - Medical apparatus - Survivair, Inc.
LO-PROFILE - Medical apparatus - Douglas Medical Products, Inc.
LO RAN - Hobby kits - Dal-Craft Inc.
LO-RANGE - Detergents - Procter & Gamble Co.
LO-REX - Pharmaceutical preparations - C.S. Ruckstuhl Co. Inc.
LO-ROLL - Games ☆ - Crestline Manufacturing Co.
LO-RONDAL - Oral contraceptives - American Home Products Corp.
LO-SAL - Antacids - Sterling Winthrop Inc.
LO-SALT - Salt - Akzo America Inc.

LO-SHEEN - Enamels - Harrison Paint Corp.
LO-SHEEN - Pottery products - Duncan Enterprises
LO SHI - Skin care products ☆ - Lois Yee Cosmetics Inc.
LO/SO - Beverages - Dairy House Inc.
LO SODIUM SAUERKRAUT - Sauerkraut - New Morning
LO-SOUND - Paints - Sinclair Paint Co.
LO SUDZ - Detergents ☆ - Reen'o Corp.
LO-SWING - Sporting goods - Pachmayr Ltd.
LO-TABS - Pharmaceutical preparations - Parmed Pharmaceuticals, Inc.
LO-TACK - Adhesives and sealants - Pres-On Merchandising Corp.
LO TANK - Tanks–gas ☆ - Bettcher Manufacturing Corp.
LO-TEMP - Fabrics–nylon - Fibrex Corp.
LO-TEMP - Pans ☆ - General Housewares Corp.
LO-TOP - Gloves - Midwest Glove Co.
LO-TROL - Pharmaceutical preparations - Vangard Labs Inc.
LO-V-BACK - Apparel–women's - Jezebel-Renee of Hollywood
LO-VIS - Containers–plastic - Ropak Corp.
LO430 - Braces–orthopedic - Dewall Enterprises, Inc.
LOACKER - Cookies - FCW Imports
LOAD BEAR SERIES - Motor vehicle parts and accessories - W.F. Mickey Body Co., Inc.
LOAD EXPRESS - Computer software - Prophesy Transportation Software, Inc.
LOAD HANDLER - Toys - Tonka Corp.
LOAD HOG - Garden equipment - Precision Products Inc.
LOAD INDICATING WASHER - Hardware - TurnaSure LLC
LOAD-IT - Computer software - Setpoint Inc.
LOAD LAMA - Bicycle parts and accessories - Nett Designs, Inc.
LOAD LEVELER - Shock absorbers–motor vehicle - Monroe Auto Equipment Co.
LOAD-LEVELLER - Machine parts - Lawson Screen Products, Inc.
LOAD LIFTER - Gloves - Knoxville Glove Co.
LOAD LLAMA - Bicycle parts and accessories - Nett Designs, Inc.
LOAD LOCKER - Lockers–metal - Zamzow Manufacturing Co. Inc.
LOAD MASTER - Shock absorbers–motor vehicle - Bridgestone/Firestone, Inc.
LOAD MASTER - Tires - Oliver Rubber Co.
LOAD-MATIC - Health care products - Palco Laboratories
LOAD 'N' GO - Motor vehicle parts and accessories - Rick Albertini
LOAD-N-GO - Toys - Pinehouse Toys Inc.
LOAD-N-GO II - Health care products - Maddak Inc.
LOAD-O-MATIC - Staplers - Spotnails
LOAD SENTRY - Computer software - RTS Electronics Inc.
LOAD-UP - Pharmaceutical preparations - Bricker Laboratories
LOADED - Computer software - Interplay Productions
LOADEXPERT - Computer software - Niagara Mohawk Power Corp.
LOADHANDLER - Conveyors - Loadhandler Industries, Inc.
LOADHANDLER - Motor vehicle parts and accessories - Prestolite Electric Inc.
LOADING-COAL - Games - Ronald Dean Holmes
LOADLAB - Computer hardware - Ultrafast, Inc.
LOADLEVELER - Computer software - International Business Machines Corp.
LOADLOGIC - Computer software - Prophesy Transportation Software, Inc.
LOADMASTER - Engines - Springfield Remanufacturing Corp.
LOADMASTER - Photographic equipment ☆ - Omega/Arkay
LOADMASTER - Plastics film - AEP Industries, Inc.
LOADMASTER - Utility trailers - Econo-Recut
LOADMAX - Machinery - Lift-Tech International, Inc.
LOAD'N GO - Popcorn poppers - Gold Medal Products Co.
LOADOMAT - Photographic equipment ☆ - Yankee Photo Products Inc.
LOADRUNNER - Computer software - Mercury Interactive Corp.
LOADSTAR - Bags–plastic - Ultratech Plastics, Inc.
LOADSTAR - Toys–models - Estes Industries
LOADSTONE - Recording label - Loadstone, Lock & Open Record Co.
LOAFER - Guitars - Emmons Guitar Co. Inc.
LOAFER - Recliners - Flexsteel Industries Inc.
LOAFERS - Slacks–men's - Haggar Corp.
LOAFSAVER - Containers - Kraft Food Ingredients Corp.
LOAN ACCOUNTANT, THE - Computer software - Contour Software Inc.
LOAN HANDLER, THE - Computer software - Contour Software Inc.
LOAN REPORTER, THE - Computer software - Contour Software Inc.
LOAN SERVER 2000 - Computer software - Precision Software Corp.
LOAN SERVICING GATEWAY - Computer peripheral equipment - Interlinq Software Corp.
LOANDA - Soap - Carme Inc.
LOANKEY - Publisher's imprints - William M. Mercer, Inc.
LOANLINK - Computer software - Intech Systems, Inc.
LOANSCRIPT - Computer software - Vysion, Inc.
LOB-STER - Sporting goods - Century Sports Inc.

☆ = Now out of production

LOB-STER - Sporting goods - Lob-Ster Inc.
LOB, THE - Glassware–household - Ceraglass Inc.
LOBA CORPORATION - Housewares - Loba Corp.
LOBAC - Pharmaceutical preparations - Seatrace Co.
LOBAKE 275 - Paints - Triangle Coatings Inc.
LOBALM - Skin care products ☆ - Ulmer Pharmacal Co.
LOBANA - Skin care products - Ulmer Pharmacal Co.
LOBANA DERM-ADE - Skin care products - Ulmer Pharmacal Co.
LOBANA PERI-GARD - Pharmaceutical preparations - Ulmer Pharmacal Co.
LOBAY V - Lighting fixtures - Holophane Corp.
LOBBY - Brooms - Lighthouse Industries
LOBE LOVERS - Tools - L. Lawrence Products Inc.
LOBE STROBES - Jewelry - United States Fashion Corp.
LOBECANDY RECORDS - Compact discs–prerecorded - Digigami, Inc.
LOBEL - Plastics - Gladys E. Loeb Foundation, Inc.
LOBELIA - Flatware - Utica Cutlery Co.
LOBO - Apparel–men's ☆ - Pendleton
LOBO - Containers - Lobo Containers, Inc.
LOBO - Paint rollers - Hansteck Corp.
LOBO - Woodworking machinery - Lobo Power Tools Inc.
LOBOB - Pharmaceutical preparations - Lobob Laboratories Inc.
LOBOFLOR - See FLOTEX
LOBOSPORT - Floor coverings–carpet and rugs - Bonar & Flotex Inc.
LOBOY - Floor finishing machines–commercial - Mercury Floor Machines Inc.
LOBSTA' COOKIES FOR DOGS - Pet food - Old Mother Hubbard Dog Food Co., Inc.
LOBSTER - Sporting goods - Georgia's Tennis
LOBSTER - Tableware–china - Villeroy and Boch Tableware Ltd.
LOBSTER BISQUETTES - Food products - Tampa Maid Seafoods, Inc.
LOBSTER CLAUS - Christmas tree ornaments - Gayle's of Laughter, Inc.
LOBSTER DICE - Novelty items - Koplow Games
LOBSTER FLUFF - Combs - Kim Laube & Co. Inc.
LOBSTER LAB - Aquariums–household - Aquatic Farms Junior L.P.
LOBSTERETTES - Seafood products–fresh or frozen - Eat-All Frozen Food Co.
LOBSTERS TO GO! - Seafood products–fresh or frozen - Clambake Celebrations, Inc.
LOBSTERTINO - Food products - Diamond E Packers
LOBSTINO D'LUXE - Imitation lobster - Multi Food
LOBSTIR - Bar fixtures–plastic - Spir-it Inc.
LOBSTIRRER - Bar fixtures–plastic - Spir-it Inc.
LOBZZ - Apparel and accessories - Matthew Q. Raulerson
L.O.C. - Cleaning preparations - Amway Corp.
LOC BLOCS - Toys–blocks ☆ - Placo Products Co.
LOC-JAW - Pet products - Walfall Hardware
LOC JAW SNAP - Pet products - Walfall Hardware
LOC-KING - Boxes - U.S. Box Crafts Inc.
LOC-KOTE - Paints ☆ - Dunn Edwards Corp.
LOC-SEAL - Hardware - Nyltite Corp. of America
LOC-SET - Hair care products - Taylormade Hair Replacement
LOC-TIES - Garden equipment - Listo Pencil Corp.
LOC-TRAC - Electronic equipment - Arion Corp.
LOCAFLEX - Electrical equipment - Claymount North-America Corp.
LOCAL 101 RECORDS - Recording label - Northcott Productions Ltd.
LOCAL, A - Apparel and accessories - Dehylton Studio
LOCAL BOY'Z - Watches - Invasion Time Corp.
LOCAL COLOR - Wallpaper - Prelude Designs
LOCAL ELEMENTS - Apparel and accessories - Neiman Marcus Co.
LOCAL EXPERT - Compasses–magnetic - Pioneer Marketing & Research, Inc.
LOCAL JOE - Apparel and accessories - Arthur J. Cohen
LOCAL LINGO - Publisher's imprints - Mediterranean Classics Inc.
LOCAL MOTION - Leather goods - Local Motion, Inc.
LOCAL POSTALS - Greeting cards - Amberley Greeting Card Co.
LOCAL RAILROAD COMPANY - Vending machines - Local Railroad Co.
LOCALITE - Lighting equipment - Fostoria Industries Inc.
LOCALIX - Computer software - Ile Corp.
LOCALLY GROWN CANOPY GARDENS VINE RIPENED HYDROPONIC - Fruits and vegetables - Wisconsin Hydroponic Growers, LLC
LOCALS ONLY - Apparel and accessories - Super Shirts Inc.
LOCALS ONLY - Skateboards - Nash Manufacturing Inc.
LOCALTALK - Computer peripheral equipment - Apple Computer Inc.
LOCALTOUCH - Directories - U.S. West Marketing Resources Group, Inc.
LOCALTOUCH - Telephone directories - Localtouch Co., LP
LOCALVIEW - Modems - Motorola, Inc. (Land Mobile Products Sector)
LOCARNO - Floor coverings - Mannington Resilient Floors

LOCATE - Computer hardware - Scientific-Atlanta, Inc.
LOCATELLI PECORINO - Cheese - Ambriola Co. Inc.
LOCATION! LOCATION! LOCATION! - Apparel and accessories - Peter Matthew Productions, Inc.
LOCATOR - Golfing equipment - Golfsmith International Inc.
LOCATOR - Hearing aids - Widex Hearing Aid Co., Inc.
+L'OCCITANE - Bath salts ☆ - European Soaps Ltd.
LOCCOM - Computer software - Paragon Electric Co., Inc.
LOCH LOMOND GOLF CLUB - Apparel and accessories - Loch Lomond Golf Club
LOCH NERF MONSTER - Toys ☆ - Tonka Corp.
LOCH TAY - Floor coverings–carpet and rugs - Milliken & Co. Inc.
LOCHAN ORA - Liquors - House of Seagram
LOCHMOOR - Floor coverings–carpet and rugs ☆ - Masland Corp.
LOCHWOOD - Floor coverings - Tarkett, Inc.
LOCK - Recording label - Loadstone, Lock & Open Record Co.
LOCK 1776 - Furniture - Oak Land Furn. Manufacturing, Inc.
LOCK 2000 - Furniture - Oak Land Furn. Manufacturing, Inc.
LOCK-A-LETTER - Toys - Lauri Inc.
LOCK AND KEY - Computer software - SourceView Software International
LOCK & SHINE - Hair care products - KMS Research Inc.
LOCK & WALK - Locks–padlocks - Best Tool Inc.
LOCK-BAK - Tiles–ceramic ☆ - American Olean Tile Co.
LOCK BOND - Adhesives and sealants ☆ - Macklanburg-Duncan Co.
LOCK BOOSTER - Binders - Dennison National Co.
LOCK-EASE - Lubricants - American Grease Stick Co.
LOCK-GRIP - Tape–adhesive - Butler Paper Co.
LOCK-GRIP - Tools - Vermont American Corp.
LOCK IN - Golfing equipment ☆ - Progear, Inc.
LOCK-IT - Adhesives and sealants ☆ - Loctite Corp.
LOCK-IT - Hair care products - Tressa, Inc.
LOCK JAW - Alarm systems - International Business Development Corp.
LOCK JAW - Chewing gum - Zeebs Enterprises, Inc.
LOCK-JOINT - Hardware - Richards-Wilcox Manufacturing Co.
LOCK LINK - Hardware - Babcock Industries Inc. (Babcock Control Group)
LOCK LIPS - Toys ☆ - Those Characters from Cleveland, Inc.
LOCK-N-GO - Computer storage devices - Microplas Inc.
LOCK N KEY - Floor finish and reconditioner ☆ - Intex Chemical Inc.
LOCK 'N LIFT - Housewares - Trepte Wire and Metal Works
LOCK 'N LIGHT - Measuring tapes - U.S. Tape Co.
LOCK 'N ROLL - Hair curlers - Clairol Inc.
LOCK 'N SEAL - Containers - Nordic Ware
LOCK 'N SEAL - Electronic equipment - J & J Electronics, Inc.
LOCK-N-SEAL - Vials–glass - Capitol Vial, Inc.
LOCK 'N SPRAY - Tools–hand-operated - Monsanto Co.
LOCK 'N' STACK - Toys–blocks - Learning Products Inc.
LOCK-N-STITCH - Sewing machines–household - Lock-N-Stitch International
LOCK NOTCH - Electrical equipment ☆ - Monster Cable Products, Inc.
LOCK-O-MATIC - Binders - Dennison National Co.
LOCK-O-MATIC - Tents ☆ - Coleman Co., Inc.
LOCK-ON - Bathroom accessories ☆ - Frohock-Stewart Inc.
LOCK-ON - Electrical equipment - Eagle Electric Manufacturing Co., Inc.
LOCK-ON - Insecticides - Dowelanco
LOCK POCKET - Toys ☆ - Life-Link International, Inc.
LOCK-SEAL - Tape–adhesive - Beachler's, Inc.
LOCK SHOP - Display unit - Hampton Products International
LOCK-SOCKET - Shovels - Ames Lawn & Garden Tool Co.
LOCK-SPIKE - Shoes–athletic ☆ - Titleist & Foot-Joy Worldwide
LOCK-STEP - Ladders–metal - Garon Products Inc.
LOCK THAW - Antifreeze - Gold Eagle Co.
LOCK-TIGHT - Bags–plastic - Carlisle Plastics, Inc.
LOCK TILE - Floor coverings–tile - JCH International Inc.
LOCK-TITE - Fencing–steel - Nelson Industries
LOCK-TITE - Fishing nets - Blue Mountain Industries, Inc.
LOCK-TITE - Floor coverings ☆ - Robbins Inc.
LOCK TO - Locks–door - Master Lock Co.
LOCK TOP - Auto accessories - Keerin Systems
LOCK-TOP - Laboratory apparatus - USA/Scientific Plastics, Inc.
LOCK-TWIST - Fencing–steel - CF and I Steel L.P.
LOCK-UP - Fishing nets ☆ - G-96 Products Co. Inc.
LOCK UP - Jewelry - Deena Stein
LOCK-UP GARAGE - Toys ☆ - Little Tikes Co.
LOCK/XPRESS - Computer programs - Relational Data Services Inc.
LOCKBLOCKS - Clamps - Twofish Unlimited
LOCKBOX - Containers - Delta Consolidated Industries, Inc.
LOCKBOX - Fasteners–hook and eye - Thomas P. Bates

LOCKDEC - Wood products - Potlatch Corp.
LOCKDOWN - Tiles–ceiling - Environmental Interiors, Inc.
LOCKE - Shoes - Drew Shoe Corp.
LOCKED-IN-FLAVOR - Metals - Stuart & Paige Fine Coffees, Inc.
LOCKED-IN-LOVE - Rings–jewelry - Artcarved Inc.
LOCKER - Notebooks and notepads - J.B. Goodhouse Inc.
LOCKER BINN - Shelving units–plastic - Minnesota American, Inc.
LOCKER BOXES - Containers - Roll Right Industries
LOCKER KIT - Shelving units–plastic - Minnesota American, Inc.
LOCKER LINE - Apparel stores–sports - Top Line Inc.
LOCKER MAGNETS - Disk drives–computer - Minnesota American, Inc.
LOCKER POCKETS - Vinyl - Minnesota American, Inc.
LOCKER ROOM - House furnishings - Lexington Furniture Industries, Inc.
LOCKER ROOM, THE - Bags - SGI Inc.
LOCKER STOCKER - Bags–cosmetic - Viator Products Corp.
LOCKER STUFF - Cosmetics - Paris Presents Ltd.
LOCKER TALK - Trading cards and stamps - Upper Deck Co.
LOCKER ZONE - Lockers–plastic ☆ - Newell Office Products
LOCKERCENTER - Calendars - Cullman Ventures Inc.
LOCKERETTE - Garment racks - Vogel Peterson Furniture Co.
LOCKERIZER - Containers - Amorah Industries Inc.
LOCKERMAN - Lockers–metal - Steiner Co., Inc.
LOCKERMATE - Shelving units–plastic - Minnesota American, Inc.
LOCKET - Fish–fresh or frozen - Darik Enterprises Inc.
LOCKET SURPRISE - Dolls - Mattel, Inc.
LOCKETS - Cough drops - Mars, Inc.
LOCKETTE - Barrettes - American Greetings Corp.
LOCKGUARD - Film-forming chemicals - Lockhart Chemical Co.
LOCKHART BOND - Paper - William E. Lockhart
LOCKHEAD - Expansive bits - Irwin Co.
LOCKING GASKETS - Hardware - Trim-Lok Inc.
LOCKING TROCAR - Surgical supplies - Dexide, Inc.
LOCKIT - Pianos - Ford Piano Supply Co.
LOCKITS - Locks–padlocks ☆ - U.S. Fiberglass Inc.
LOCKJAW - Motor vehicle parts and accessories - Hull Industries, Inc.
LOCKJAW - Plugs–electric - Woods Industries, Inc.
LOCKMASTER - Binders - Dennison National Co.
LOCKMATIC - Easels ☆ - M. Grumbacher Inc.
LOCK'N SEAL - Adhesives and sealants ☆ - Loctite Corp.
LOCKOUT - Puzzles - Tri-Tec Industries Ltd.
LOCKPRINT - Tape–adhesive - American Tape Co.
LOCKRIM - Footwear - Lehigh Safety Shoe Co.
LOCKS BOX - Connectors–electrical - Dennis Marshall
LOCKS OF MEMORIES - Frames–picture - Professional Research
  Organization, Inc.
LOCKS-ON - Varnishes - Perry & Derrick Co.
LOCKSALL - Sealant ☆ - Vigor Co.
LOCKSIDE - Siding - ABT Co., Inc.
LOCKSMITH'S LOCK, THE - Metal padlocks - American Lock Co.
LOCKSOL - Lubricant additives - Lockhart Chemical Co.
LOCKSTEP - Finishing agents - Davis Paint Co.
LOCKSTROKE STRUT - Health care products - Paratech Inc.
LOCKTAGONS - Toys - Lauri Inc.
LOCKTITE - Office supplies - Faber-Castell Corp.
LOCKTOP - Mail boxes - Leigh
LOCKWELL - Tools–hand-operated - Lockwell Corp.
LOCKWOOD - Aluminum products ☆ - Remington Building Products
LOCKWOOD - House furnishings - Burruss Co.
LOCKWOOD - Locks–door - Lloyd Matheson Inc.
LOCKWOOD - Wines - Monterey Winery
LOCKWOOD'S - Dyes and pigments - Aljo Manufacturing Co.
LOCKWORKS - Locks–door - General Automotive Specialty Co., Inc.
LOCKZ - Skin care products - Sequel Products Inc.
LOCLO - Vitamins and nutritional supplements - Lifetrends International
LOCLOOP - Fabrics - Guilford Mills, Inc.
LOCO - Beverages - Ginger Spirits, Inc.
LOCO - Toys - Tonka Corp.
LOCO-ANIMALS - Toys–stuffed - Kay Mathews Designs
LOCO-BEAR - Toys–stuffed - Kay Mathews Designs
LOCO-BOZO - Toys–stuffed - Kay Mathews Designs
LOCO-BUN-ANNA - Toys–stuffed - Kay Mathews Designs
LOCO-BUNNY - Toys–stuffed - Kay Mathews Designs
LOCO-HOBO - Toys–stuffed - Kay Mathews Designs
LOCO-JUMBO - Toys–stuffed - Kay Mathews Designs
LOCO-KITTY - Toys–stuffed - Kay Mathews Designs
LOCO-KOLA - Toys–stuffed - Kay Mathews Designs

LOCO-LAMB - Toys–stuffed - Kay Mathews Designs
LOCO LIFE - Apparel - Noreek Davitian
LOCO-LING - Toys–stuffed - Kay Mathews Designs
LOCO-MOTIFS - Toys–stuffed - Kay Mathews Designs
LOCO-MOUSE - Toys–stuffed - Kay Mathews Designs
LOCO-PUP - Toys–stuffed - Kay Mathews Designs
LOCO SOMBRERO - Food products - Cantisano Foods, Inc.
LOCOID - Pharmaceutical preparations - Ferndale Laboratories, Inc.
LOCOID - Pharmaceutical preparations ☆ - Owen/Galderma Laboratories Inc.
LOCOMEX - Seafood products–canned or cured - American Heng-Seng
  Enterprises, Inc.
LOCOMOTION - Tricycles ☆ - The Coleman Co.
LOCOMOTIVE BREATH - Fireworks - B.J. Alan Co. Inc.
LOCONET - Toys–trains - Digitrax, Inc.
LOCORR - Deicing fluid - Akzo Nobel Salt Inc.
LOCOS - Ice cream - M & S Imports Inc.
LOCQUIC ACTIVATOR 707 - Adhesives and sealants - Loctite Corp.
LOCQUIC ACTIVATOR 792 - Adhesives and sealants - Loctite Corp.
LOCQUIC PRIMER N 764 - Adhesives and sealants - Loctite Corp.
LOCQUIC PRIMER NF 736 - Adhesives and sealants - Loctite Corp.
LOCQUIC PRIMER T 747 - Adhesives and sealants - Loctite Corp.
LOCSYS - Computer software - Locsys Inc.
LOCTITE - Adhesives and sealants - Loctite Corp.
LOCTITE 599 - Gaskets - Loctite Corp.
LOCTITE 640 - Adhesives and sealants - Loctite Corp.
LOCTITE 755 - Cleaning preparations - Loctite Corp.
LOCTITE 819 - Adhesives and sealants - Loctite Corp.
LOCTITE PST - Adhesives and sealants - Loctite Corp.
LOCTITE-WELD - Adhesives and sealants - Loctite Corp.
LOCTITE WORLDTECH 222 - Adhesives and sealants - Loctite Corp.
LOCTITE WORLDTECH 242 - Adhesives and sealants - Loctite Corp.
LOCTITE WORLDTECH 243 - Adhesives and sealants - Loctite Corp.
LOCTITE WORLDTECH 271 - Adhesives and sealants - Loctite Corp.
LOCTITE WORLDTECH 272 - Adhesives and sealants - Loctite Corp.
LOCTITE WORLDTECH 290 - Adhesives and sealants - Loctite Corp.
LOCTITE WORLDTECH 518 - Adhesives and sealants - Loctite Corp.
LOCTITE WORLDTECH 565 - Adhesives and sealants - Loctite Corp.
LOCUS POCUS - Novagen, Inc.
LOCUST - Floor coverings ☆ - Tarkett, Inc.
LOCUTUS - Toys - Paramount Pictures Corp.
LODE - Lamps ☆ - Luxo Corp.
LODE RUNNER - Computer software ☆ - Broderbund Software, Inc.
LODEL - Computer software - Tcsi Corp.
LODESTAR - Boats - Glen-L Marine Designs
LODESTAR - Compasses–gyroscopic ☆ - Rule Industries, Inc.
LODESTAR - Cosmetics - Bruce English
LODESTAR - Electronic equipment - Eastman Kodak Co.
LODESTAR - Floor coverings - Lodestar Group
LODESTAR - Hoists - Columbus Mckinnon Corp.
LODESTAR BOOKS - Publisher's imprints - E.P. Dutton Inc.
LODESTONE - Floor coverings - Mannington Resilient Floors
LODESTONE - Office supplies - Staver Westport Inc.
LODGE - Cabinets - Legeis Corp.
LODGE - Furniture ☆ - Bassett Furniture Industries, Inc.
LODGE - Pans - R & R Mill Co. Inc.
LODGE-ICAL - Computer software - Williamson Enterprises, Inc.
LODGE KEEPER - Hotels and motels - Lodge Keeper Group, Inc.
LODGE MAKES IT - Cooking utensils–cast iron - Lodge Manufacturing Co.
LODGECRAFT - Furniture–wood - Montana Wood Designs
LODGING - Floor coverings–carpet and rugs - Whitecrest Carpet Mills
LODI - Beverages–malt ☆ - Pabst Brewing Co.
LODI - Cabinets - Triangle Pacific Corp. (Cabinet Division)
LODIGIANI - Cheese - Bel Canto Fancy Foods Ltd.
LODIS - Briefcases - Lodis Corp.
LODI'S IDOL - Food products - Lodi Canning Inc.
LODRANE - Antihistamine preparations - ECR Pharmaceuticals
LODRANE LD - Pharmaceutical preparations - ECR Pharmaceuticals
LODRANE LIQUID - Pharmaceutical preparations - ECR Pharmaceuticals
LODTRAK - Electronic equipment - General Electric Co.
LODTRAK1 - Electronic equipment - General Electric Co.
LOEANDA - Wallpaper - Blumenthal
LOEB - Apparel and accessories - Oxford Industries, Inc.
LOEBLEIN CREATIONS - Furniture–upholstered - Loeblein Brothers Inc.
LOEBS - Food products - McLane Southern Grocery Distribution
LOEFFLER'S - Meat products–beef - Loeffler's Provisions Inc.
LOESTRIN - Pharmaceutical preparations - Parke-Davis

☆ = Now out of production

LOEW-CORNELL - Brushes–paint - Creek-Turn Inc. (Ceramic Supply Div.)

LOEWE SELECT ENGLISH - Pipes–tobacco - Mastercraft Pipes Inc.

LOF INACTIVE WEAR - Apparel and accessories - Don't Ask, Inc.

LOFENALAC - Pharmaceutical preparations - Bristol-Myers Squibb Co.

LOFENE - Pharmaceutical preparations - Lannett Co. Inc.

LOFERS - Apparel and accessories - Barrow Manufacturing Co., Inc.

LOFRANS - Marine rigging - Imtra Corp.

LOFREEZE - Inks–drawing ☆ - Martin F. Weber Co.

LOFSTRAND - Canes - Harvy Surgical Supply Corp.

LOFT - Audio equipment - Gold Line Connectors Inc.

LOFT - Health care products - Sanford Chemical Co. Inc.

LOFT - Wood products - Weyerhaeuser Co.

LOFT & BROWNSTONE - Apparel and accessories - R.H. Macy & Co.

LOFTEEZ - Shirts - Fruit of the Loom Inc.

LOFTELL - Fabrics–polyester - E.I. Dupont de Nemours and Co.

LOFTEX - Audio equipment - Gold Line Connectors Inc.

LOFTS - Flowers, plants, and seeds - AgriBioTech, Inc.

LOFTS - Food products - Barricini Foods Inc.

LOFTSPUN - Fabrics - Dan River Inc.

LOFTY - Golf clubs - Prostar L.P.

LOFTY LIVING - Furniture - Hammary Furniture Co. Inc.

LOG-A-RHYTHM - Electronic equipment - Nian-Crae, Inc.

LOG BUILDER SEALANT - Adhesives and sealants - Sashco Inc.

LOG CABIN - Food products - Temple Milling Co.

LOG CABIN - Glassware–household ☆ - Fenton Art Glass Co.

LOG CABIN - Margarine - Kraft Food Ingredients Corp.

LOG CABIN - Pet products ☆ - Zoo Med Laboratories, Inc.

LOG CABIN - Prefabricated buildings–wood ☆ - Log Cabin Homes Ltd.

LOG CABIN - Quilts ☆ - Martingale & Co.

LOG CABIN - Recording label - Jewel Records

LOG CABIN - Vinegar and worcestershire sauce - Inter-State Cider & Vinegar Co.

LOG CABIN COLLECTION - Linen - Notra Trading, Inc.

LOG CABIN FUN - Playground equipment - Cedar Brook Rustic Co.

LOG HOG - Wood products - Forest Time Products Inc.

LOG HOUSE - Bakery products - Log House Foods Inc.

LOG IT - Computer software - Comprehensive Video Supply Corp.

LOG IT! - Photo albums - Log Designs, Inc.

LOG JAM - Toys - T.J.K. Sales Inc.

LOG JAM CHINKING - Adhesives and sealants - Sashco Inc.

LOG LIGHTER - Lighters ☆ - Bernzomatic

LOG-MASTER - Waterproof boots and shoes - International Seaway Trading Corp.

LOG O' LIFE - Publisher's imprints - McMillin Foley Publishing Co.

LOG-O-NUTS - Candy bars ☆ - Standard Candy Co. Inc.

LOG PORT R - Fireplace equipment ☆ - Reichman Inc.

LOGAL - Computer software - Logal Software, Inc.

LOGAN - Artists' materials - Logan Graphic Products Inc.

LOGAN - Bags–duffel - Logan Inc.

LOGAN - Brushes - Perfex Corp.

LOGAN - Pipes - Pomona Pipe Products Co.

LOGAN - Staircases–metal - SpaceGuard Products

LOGAN CLUTCH CORPORATION - Machine clutches and brakes - Logan Clutch Corp.

LOGAN DELUXE - Liquors - House of Seagram

LOGAN LITE - Lamps–desk ☆ - Logan Electric Specialty Manufacturing Co.

LOGAN VOLLEY - Eggs - Milton G. Waldbaum Co.

LOGBOOK - Computer software - Microscope Corp.

LOGBOOK - Computer software - Onset Computer Corp.

LOGDB - Computer software - Schlumberger Technology Corp.

LOGE/KENRO - Cameras - LogEtronics Corp.

LOGE/ROBERTSON - Cameras - LogEtronics Corp.

LOGELINE - Photographic equipment - LogEtronics Corp.

LOGEN - Pharmaceutical preparations - Goldline Laboratories, Inc.

LOGENBERRY - Apparel and accessories - KSK International Inc.

LOGETEK - Photographic equipment - LogEtronics Corp.

LOGETHERM - Artists' materials - LogEtronics Corp.

LOGEXPRESS - Computer peripheral equipment - Alba Editorial, Inc.

LOGGER - Breads - Fluhrer Bakeries, Inc.

LOGGER SPIKES - Trees - Curtis H. Bod

LOGGER STICKS - Trees - Curtis H. Bod

LOGGINS LEGENDS - Seasonings - Loggins Meat Co., Inc.

LOGGINS MEAT COMPANY, INC. - Meat products - Loggins Meat Co., Inc.

LOGIC - Bicycles - Ritchey Design Inc.

LOGIC - Computer peripheral equipment - Logic Associates, Inc.

LOGIC - Computer peripheral equipment - Valentine Research, Inc.

LOGIC - Insecticides ☆ - D-Con Co. Inc.

LOGIC - Nutritional supplements - International Nutrition

LOGIC - Sweaters - Wenlee Enterprises Ltd.

LOGIC - Telescopes - Northern Telecom, Inc.

LOGIC - Water conditioning units - Water Conditioning, Inc.

LOGIC 1 - Electronics equipment - AMS Industries Inc.

LOGIC ANIMATOR - Computer software - Quickturn Design Systems Inc.

LOGIC ASSOCIATES - Computer software - Logic Associates, Inc.

LOGIC CONCEPTS - Computer software - Logic Concepts Inc.

LOGIC FACTORY, THE - Games - Logic Factory, Inc.

LOGIC MASTER, THE - Computer software - Unicorn Software

LOGIC SHOP - Computer software - Thomas J. Barrella

LOGIC SOUND LAB - Stereos - Ikon Audio International Inc.

LOGIC SYSTEM MIDI'S - Sound equipment - Castiglione Accordion

LOGIC-TOUCH - Exercising equipment - Tunturi, Inc.

LOGIC WISE - Games - Tiger Electronics, Inc.

LOGIC WORKBENCH - Computer software - Cadence Design Systems, Inc.

LOGICAL - Luggage - Kohl's Department Stores, Inc.

LOGICAL CHOICE - Vitamins - Caroline Owens

LOGICAL JOURNEY OF THE ZOOMBINIS - Computer software - Broderbund Software, Inc.

LOGICAL LYNX - Computer software ☆ - Krell Software Corp.

LOGICAL SPORT - Luggage - Kohl's Department Stores, Inc.

LOGICASE - Computer software - Aaron-Stone, Inc.

LOGICIAN - Computer software - Medicalogic, Inc.

LOGICMASTER 5-6 - Computer software - General Electric Co.

LOGICOOL - Air conditioning equipment - Liebert Corp.

LOGICS - Hair coloring preparations - Clairol Inc.

LOGICS IMPRINTS - Hair care products - Matrix Essentials, Inc.

LOGICVISION - Computer storage devices - LV Software, Inc.

LOGICWARE - Computer software - Logicware, Inc.

LOGISTIC CONCEPTS - Computer software - TLC Information Services, Inc.

LOGISTICS MANAGER 2-D - Computer software - Consolidated Freightways, Inc.

LOGISTICS PRO - Computer software - Summit Group, Inc.

LOGISTOP - Circuit boards - Automatic Devices Co.

LOGITECH - Computer peripheral equipment - Logitech, Inc.

LOGITEK - Electronic equipment - Logitek, Inc.

LOGITORQUE - Computer software - Limitorque Corp.

LOGITRAK - Computer software - American Technologies, Inc.

LOGITROL - Electronics equipment - Steiner-Atlantic Corp.

LOGIX - Communications equipment - ADC Telecommunications, Inc.

LOGIX - Floor coverings–carpet and rugs - Whitecrest Carpet Mills

LOGIX - Medical apparatus - Empi Inc.

LOGIX - Seats–automobile - Krueger International, Inc.

LOGIX - Toys–electronic ☆ - Philips Consumer Electronics Co.

LOGO - Brushes–hair - West Coast Beauty Supply Co.

LOGO - Pencils–mechanical - Sanford Corp.

LOGO II - Pens ☆ - Alexander Manufacturing Co.

LOGO ATHLETIC - Apparel and accessories - Logo 7 Inc.

LOGO CORDS - Ophthalmic goods - Karlen Manufacturing, Inc.

LOGO GRAM - Greeting cards ☆ - Lawson Marden Post Card

LOGO II - Pencils–mechanical - Sanford Corp.

LOGO III - Pencils–mechanical - Sanford Corp.

LOGO KID - Dolls - Annalee Mobilitee Dolls Inc.

LOGO KNITS - Crocheted and knitted items ☆ - Logo Knits Inc.

LOGO LITES - Lighting equipment–automotive - Creative Connections, Inc.

LOGO LOCK - Sporting goods - Franklin Sports, Inc.

LOGO M - Office supplies - Artistic Office Products

LOGO MAT - Floor coverings - Devon Corp.

LOGO MATE - Pens ☆ - Alexander Manufacturing Co.

LOGO PAD - Desk sets - Artistic Office Products

LOGO PARIS - Eyeglasses - Logo Paris, Inc.

LOGO ROBOT - Computer software - Scholastic Software Inc.

LOGO-SCRIPTS - Motor vehicle parts and accessories ☆ - Deflecta-Shield

LOGO SEATING - Chairs–upholstered - Krueger International, Inc.

LOGO SPHERE - Signs - Mirror Image, Inc.

LOGO TAGS - Boxes–corrugated paperboard - Logo-Tags, Inc.

LOGO TOUCHTOOLS - Computer software - Dunamis Inc.

LOGOCAM - Cameras - Epic USA

LOGOEXPRESSION - Electronic equipment - Steven D. Cole

LOGOGRASS - Floor coverings - Devon Corp.

LOGOMARK - Anvils - Logomark, Inc.

LOGOMATE - Display cases–plastic - Carroll Erdman

LOGOMATS - Automotive parts and accessories ☆ - Lancaster Colony Automotive Group

---

☆ = Now out of production

LOGOPADS - Computer peripheral equipment - Panel Graphics USA Inc.
LOGOS - Calculators - Olivetti North America Inc. (Consumer Products Div.)
LOGOS - Computer software - New World Systems Corp.
LOGOS - Greeting cards - Super Products, Inc.
LOGOS - Skin care products - Silver Spur Corp.
LOGOS & STRIPES - Toilets–porcelain - Friendship Designs
LOGOSCLIENT - Computer software - Logos Corp.
LOGOSZ - Surfboards - Logoszworks, Inc.
LOGPRO - Computer software - Resources Engineering Systems, Inc.
LOGSCAN - Computer software - Scanware, Inc.
LOHENGRIN - Apparel–men's - Siegfried & Parzifal, Inc.
LOHENGRIN - Tableware–china ☆ - Lenox, Inc.
LOHIGH VALLEY FARMS - Milk - Johanna Foods, Inc.
LOHMANN - Cabbage and pickled beets - Aunt Nellie's Farm Kitchens Inc.
LOHMEYER - Furniture stores - Consolidated Burris International
LOIE - Pillows - N.S. Gustin Co.
LOIS - Jewelry - Jacoby-Bender Inc.
LOIS BY UNCAS - Jewelry - Uncas Manufacturing Co.
LOIS PROFESSIONAL LIBRARY - Computer software - Law Office Information Systems, Inc.
LOIS RAE - Food products - Green Bay Foods Co.
LOIS YEE - Cosmetics - Lois Yee Cosmetics Inc.
+L'OISEAU-LYRE - Recording label - London Records Inc.
LOJACK - Alarm systems - LoJack Co.
LOK - Tires–automobile - Hayes Wheels International, Inc.
LOK-A-BOX - Tape–adhesive ☆ - Cavert Wire Co. Inc.
LOK-ALLOY - Wheels–motor vehicle - Hayes Wheels International, Inc.
LOK & FROST - Hair care products - Frost Enterprises Inc.
LOK BAND - Identification tags - Karlen Manufacturing, Inc.
LOK/BOLT - Anchors - Rawlplug Co., Inc.
LOK-COR - Pipes - WCI Steel Inc.
LOK-FAST - Hardware - Gates & Sons Inc.
LOK-GARD - Finishing agents - Hillyard Enterprises, Inc.
LOK-GARD - Hardware - U.S. Home Security Systems
LOK-IN-EL - Health care products - Maddak Inc.
LOK-LINE - Fencing–steel - CF and I Steel L.P.
LOK-MATIC - Automotive parts and accessories - Ward Products Corp.
LOK-O-MATIC - Pens - Ad-a-Day Co. Inc.
LOK-PAK - Containers - Source Three, Inc.
LOK-ROCK - Pet products - Penn-Plax, Inc.
LOK-TITE - Easels - Teledyne Post
LOK-TITE - Hearing aids - Mid-States Laboratories Inc.
LOK-TITE - Paints - M.A. Bruder & Sons Inc.
LOK-TITE - Valves–intake - Penn-Plax, Inc.
LOK-TO-CLOCK - Spectra-Physics Lasers, Inc.
LOK TUFF - Floor coverings ☆ - American Floor Products Co. Inc.
LOKADEX - Research–educational - Centaur Records
LOKARSO - Fudge - L. Karp & Sons, Inc.
LOKBAND - Electrical equipment - Advantek, Inc.
LOKIT - Anchors - Barrett Manufacturing Co.
LOKON - Hardware ☆ - Holo-Krome Co.
LOKOYA - Wines - Kendall Jackson Winery, Ltd.
LOKSWIV - Hardware ☆ - Shepherd Products U.S. Inc.
LOKTITE - Nuts and bolts ☆ - MKT Fastening, LLC
LOKTITE - Office supplies - The Union Group
LOKTITE - Rope - Tubbs Cordage Co.
LOKUT - Hosiery - Wigwam Mills Inc.
LOKVILLE - Playground equipment - Miracle Recreation Equipment Co.
LOKWELD - Adhesives and sealants - Ralph Wilson Plastics Co.
LOL - Glassware–household - Deanna Warren
L.O.L. - Skin care products - Covermark Cosmetics
LOLA - Chairs–wood ☆ - Krueger International, Inc.
LOLA - Food products - Cerami Sales Co. Inc.
LOLA - Food products ☆ - Oh Boy Corp.
LOLA JUPITER - Costumes - McCain Ellio's Foods, Inc.
LOLA PONS - Figurines ☆ - Anna-Perenna Inc.
LOLAC - Dairy products - Foremost Farms USA
LOLANA - Skin care products ☆ - Ulmer Pharmacal Co.
LOLI - Computer software - Chemadvisor, Inc.
LOLI - T-shirts–men's - Loli of Vermont, Inc.
LOLI POLI - Apparel–children's - Loli of Vermont, Inc.
LOLI PRO - Computer software - Chemadvisor, Inc.
LOLITA - Food products - Garcia Canning Co., Inc.
LOLITA - Perfumes ☆ - Tristar Corp.
LOLITA PINK - Lipsticks ☆ - Elysee Scientific Cosmetic Co.
LOLITOP - Candy - S.L. Kaye Co., Inc.

LOLLAPALOOZA - Apparel–men's - Westbury Knitwear Co. Inc.
LOLLI BOUQUETS - Candy - Russ Berrie and Co., Inc.
LOLLI-CLOCK - Clocks ☆ - General Time Corp. (Westclox/Seth Thomas Div.)
LOLLI-FOAM - Brushes–paint - Scratch-Art Co., Inc.
LOLLI POP - Bicycles - Murray, Inc.
LOLLI-PUPS - Dog food - Pet Life Foods Inc.
LOLLICOUGH - Cough suppressant - John F. Hinze
LOLLIDAY POPS - Candy - Impact Confections, Inc.
LOLLIE HOP - Dolls - Mattel, Inc.
LOLLIKEEP - Wood storage and display stands - Sparrow Ridge Corp.
LOLLIPACK - Medical apparatus - Centrix, Inc.
LOLLIPIGS - Candy - Robert A. Vaccarella
LOLLIPOP - Apparel and accessories - Bassett-Walker Inc.
LOLLIPOP - Christmas tree ornaments - Cracker Box Inc.
LOLLIPOP - Prophylactics - Lookinglass Inc.
LOLLIPOP - Toys - Uniquity
LOLLIPOP BEAR - Toys–stuffed ☆ - Dakin Inc.
LOLLIPOP CHICKEN - Frozen foods - Herb's Seafood, Inc.
LOLLIPOP DRUM - Musical instruments - Remo, Inc.
LOLLIPOP LAND - Candy - International Products Distributing Inc.
LOLLIPOPS - Beverage dispensing equipment ☆ - Kraftware Corp. (Morgan Div.)
LOLLIPOPS - Greeting cards - Charnel Development Corp.
LOLLIPOPS - Greeting cards - House of Oz
LOLLIPOPS & GUMDROPS - Bedding–linen - Rieta Santee
LOLLISTICKS - Candy - Squire Boone Caverns, Inc.
LOLLITOP - Candy - Rita Byrd
LOLLY DOLL - Dolls - Fisher-Price, Inc.
LOLLY FIZZ - Candy ☆ - Swizzels Matlow (USA) Ltd.
LOLLY-LOVES - Chocolate candy - Superior Fruit & Confections
LOLLY POPS - Shoes ☆ - Endicott Johnson Corp.
LOLLY WRAP - Plastics–laminated - Lolly LLC
LOLLYPOPS - Scissors–hand-operated - Armada Art Inc.
LOLLYPUP PUP - Toys–stuffed - Dakin Inc.
LOLO - Apparel and accessories - City Sites Sportswear Inc.
LOLO SCARVES - Scarves - Lois Bender Design
LOLON - Cables - Loos and Co. Inc.
LOMA - Housewares - Loma/Rubberqueen
LOMA LINDA - Food products - Worthington Foods Inc.
LOMAN COOL 2000 - Fans–attic - Lomanco Inc.
LOMANATE - Pharmaceutical preparations - Barre-National, Inc.
LOMANCO - Ventilation equipment - Lomanco Inc.
LOMANCO 700 - Ventilation equipment - Lomanco Inc.
LOMAR - Aluminum products - Alcan Aluminum Corp. Alcan Building Products Div.
LOMAS - Floor coverings ☆ - Tarkett, Inc.
LOMBARD - Thread ☆ - Perfect Thread Co. Inc.
LOMBARD STREET - Floor coverings–carpet and rugs ☆ - Hollytex Carpet Mills Inc.
LOMBARDI - Food products - Lombardi Foodservice
LOMBARDI - Seafood products–canned or cured - Lombardi's Seafood Inc.
LOMBARDIC - Tiles–ceramic ☆ - Summitville Tiles, Inc.
LOMBARDO - Beverages–alcohol - Arthur G. Lombardi & Son
LOMBARDO MARSALAS - Wines - Tyfield Importers
LOMBARDY - Floor coverings - Mannington Resilient Floors
LOMBARDY - Floor coverings–carpet and rugs ☆ - World Carpets, Inc.
LOMBARDY - Furniture ☆ - Lane Co. Inc.
LOMMA - Golf courses–miniature - Lomma Miniature Golf
LOMOD - Resins–synthetic - General Electric Co.
LOMODIX - Pharmaceutical preparations - Dixon-Shane Inc.
LOMOND - Floor coverings–carpet and rugs ☆ - Masland Corp.
LOMONOSOV - Dinnerware–glass - Andrew D. Darvas Inc.
LOMOTIL - Pharmaceutical preparations - G. D. Searle & Co.
LOMS - Computer software - Legal Software Publishing Co., Inc.
LONAID - Chemical preparations - Vanson Inc.
LONALAC - Food products - Bristol-Myers Squibb Co.
LONAS - Gasoline - Lonas Oil Co.
LONBRICK - Floor coverings ☆ - Lonseal Inc.
LONCOIN - Floor coverings - Lonseal Inc.
LONCORE - Solder - Union Carbide Corp. (Industrial Chemicals Div.)
LONCOURT - Floor coverings - Lonseal Inc.
LONDAX - Herbicides - E.I. Dupont de Nemours and Co.
LONDECK - Floor coverings - Lonseal Inc.
+L'ONDINE - Bathing suits - Finals
LONDON - Artists' materials ☆ - Winsor & Newton
LONDON - Brushes–paint ☆ - PPG Industries, Inc.

☆ = Now out of production

LONDON - Cases–musical instrument - M & M Distributing Co.
LONDON - Clocks - Alaron Inc.
LONDON - Floor coverings–carpet and rugs - Barrett Carpet Mills Inc.
LONDON - Fruits and vegetables - London Fruit Inc.
LONDON - Publisher's imprints - Theosophical Publishing House
LONDON - Recording label - London Records Inc.
LONDON - Tiles–ceramic - London Tile Co.
LONDON - Wigs - Paula Young
LONDON AIRE - Motor vehicles–motor homes - Newmar Corp.
LONDON & LONDON - Apparel and accessories - London London Sportswear, Inc.
LONDON ARMOURY CO. ENFIELD - Rifles–pellet - Euroarms of America
LONDON BLITZ - Games ✩ - Avalon Hill Game Co.
LONDON BRIDGE - Games - Tyco Toys
LONDON CHARACTER - Men's footwear ✩ - Bostonian Shoe Co.
LONDON CLASSIC - Floor coverings–carpet and rugs - Atlas Carpet Mills Inc.
LONDON CLASSIC BANGER - Sausage - Abbyland Processing
LONDON CLASSIC SUPREME - Floor coverings–carpet and rugs - Atlas Carpet Mills Inc.
LONDON CLUB - Tobacco–chewing or smoking - G.A. Georgopulo & Co. Inc.
LONDON DOCK - Tobacco products - John Middleton Inc.
LONDON EXPRESS - Apparel and accessories ✩ - Bruxton Shirt Co.
LONDON FLATS - Sandwiches–prepackaged - TBT Specialty Restaurants, Inc.
LONDON FLYER - Bicycles - Western Auto Supply Co.
LONDON FOG - Apparel and accessories - Londontown Corp.
LONDON FOG - Apparel–men's - Tandy Brands Accessories Inc.
LONDON FOG - Apparel–men's - TMG Corp.
LONDON FOG - Hats - Kraft Hat Manufacturers Inc.
LONDON FOG - Hats - Miller Bros. Industries Inc.
LONDON FOG - Shoes - Atsco Footwear Inc.
LONDON FOG - Umbrellas - D. Klein & Son
LONDON FOG - Umbrellas ✩ - Schertz Umbrellas Inc.
LONDON GRAIN - Luggage - Hunting World, Inc.
LONDON HERB - Teas–herbal - Liberty Richter Inc.
LONDON HERB AND SPICE - Teas ✩ - Chase Collection, Inc.
LONDON HOUSE - Health care products - Bernard Fine Foods Inc.
LONDON KNIGHTS - Publisher's imprints - Hard Hat Records
LONDON LIGHTS - Wallpaper ✩ - Brewster Wallcovering Co.
LONDON LIGHTS II - Wallpaper - Brewster Wallcovering Co.
LONDON LINEN LOOK - Luggage - Pantos Canvas Corp.
LONDON LOAF - Breads - American Bakeries Co.
LONDON LODGE - Pickles - Green Bay Foods Inc.
LONDON MAID CRUMPETS - Bakery products - London Maid Crumpets Inc.
LONDON MINT, THE - Candy - Harry London's Candies Inc.
LONDON MIXTURE - Tobacco–chewing or smoking - Alfred Dunhill of London Inc.
LONDON PANTRY - Food products - London Pantry Foods Inc.
LONDON PRIDE - Costume jewelry - S.P. Franklin Ltd.
LONDON PUB - Food products - World Finer Foods, Inc.
LONDON PUB - Mirrors ✩ - Compac Industries Inc.
LONDON QUICK LEAD - POLY - Pet products - Hamilton Products Inc.
LONDON RECORDS - Recording label - Faith No More
LONDON RIDERS - Jeans–women's - Lee Apparel Co. Inc.
LONDON SHELL - Flatware ✩ - Towle Silversmiths
LONDON/SQUARE - Apparel and accessories - Klear Knit Inc.
LONDON SQUARE - Apparel–men's - Nulook Fashions Menswear Inc.
LONDON SQUARE - Wallpaper ✩ - Glidden Co.
LONDON SQUIRE - Cigars ✩ - General Cigar Co., Inc.
LONDON SQUIRE - Tobacco–chewing or smoking - Amar Blends Co.
LONDON TOWER - Gin - Charles Jacquin et Compagnie Inc.
LONDONDERRY - Clocks - Londonderry Clockworks
LONDONDERRY - Floor coverings - Tarkett, Inc.
LONDONER - Apparel–men's - Cavaliero Cravats
LONDONER - Bicycles ✩ - Kent International Inc.
LONDON'S - Cosmetics - Worldwide Cosmetics
LONDON'S - Dairy products - London's Farm Dairy, Inc.
LONDON'S BUNING - Games - Avalon Hill Game Co.
LONDONTOWNE - Apparel and accessories ✩ - Londontown Corp.
LONDOT - Floor coverings - Lonseal Inc.
LONDURA - Floor coverings ✩ - Lonseal Inc.
LONE BIRCH - Fruit - Jackel Farms & Cold Storage
LONE EAGLE - Rackets–tennis - Dayton Racquet Co. Inc.
LONE FIR - Food products - Nuchief Sales Inc.
LONE PEAK - Backpacks - Lone Peak Designs Ltd.
LONE PINE - Food products machinery ✩ - Fort Lupton Canning Co.

LONE PINE - Rice - Cormier Rice Milling Co. Inc.
LONE RANGER - Apparel and accessories - Golden Books Publishing Co., Inc.
LONE ROO - Apparel and accessories - David P. Appleton
LONE STAR - Bakery products - Lone Star Consolidated Foods, Inc.
LONE STAR - Beverages–malt - Lone Star Brewing Co.
LONE STAR - Beverages–malt - The Stroh Brewery Co.
LONE STAR - Cigar boxes–wood - Consolidated Cigar Corp.
LONE STAR - Cutlery ✩ - Robinson Knife & Fiddlers Plastics
LONE STAR - Dog food - Lone Star Pet Foods
LONE STAR - Garden equipment ✩ - Seymour Manufacturing Co.,Inc.
LONE STAR - Music stands - Krauth & Benninghofen Inc.
LONE STAR - Recording label - Polygram Records, Inc.
LONE STAR - Tiles–ceramic - Lone Star Ceramics Co.
LONE STAR - Veterinary medical equipment - Y-Tex Corp.
LONE STAR BOCK - Beverages–malt - The Stroh Brewery Co.
LONE STAR BOOKS - Publisher's imprints - Gulf Publishing Co. (Book & Div.)
LONE STAR DRY - Beverages–malt - The Stroh Brewery Co.
LONE STAR GROWERS - Flowers, plants, and seeds - Lone Star Growers
LONE STAR ICE - Beverages–malt - The Stroh Brewery Co.
LONE STAR L.A. - Beverages–malt - The Stroh Brewery Co.
LONE STAR LIGHT - Beverages–malt - Lone Star Brewing Co.
LONE STAR LIGHT - Beverages–malt - The Stroh Brewery Co.
LONE STAR LIGHT ICE - Beverages–malt - The Stroh Brewery Co.
LONE STAR PARK AT GRAND PRAIRIE - Umbrellas - Grand Prairie Sports Facilities Development Corp., Inc.
LONE STAR PLYWOOD & DOOR CORP. - Wood products - Lone Star Plywood & Door Corp.
LONE STAR SHEARLING - Footwear - Lone Star Shearling
LONE STAR STICK - Sausages - Fred Usinger, Inc.
LONE TOY TREE - Bakery products ✩ - Lone Toy Tree Inc.
LONE TREE FARM - Dairy products - Den-Mar Products, Inc.
LONE WOLF - Golfing equipment - McCalla Co.
LONE WOLF & CUB - Games - Mayfair Games, Inc.
LONEL - Paints - E-Z Paintr Corp.
LONELIEST GUY IN TOWN, THE - Appliance parts - Maytag Corp.
LONESOME GEORGE CHIP - Cookies ✩ - Michael D's Cookies
LONESOME RED - Beverages–malt - Brazos Country Foods
LONESTAR - Alarm systems - Mother's Window Tint, Inc.
LONESTAR - Oils–lubricating - United Oil
LONESTAR - Trailers–travel ✩ - Starcraft Corp.
LONESTAR GRILLS - Barbecues and grills - Lone Star Grill Inc.
LONFLOOR - Floor coverings - Lonseal Inc.
LONFOAM - Floor coverings - Lonseal Inc.
LONG - Automotive parts and accessories - Echlin Inc.
LONG A - Fishing lures - Bomber Bait Co.
LONG AGO BOOKS - Paper–book - Chandler Press
LONG AID - Hair care products - Keystone Laboratories Inc.
LONG AID DYNASET - Hair care products - Keystone Laboratories Inc.
LONG & SILKY - Cosmetics - Beaute, Inc.
LONG & SILKY - Hair care products ✩ - Clairol Inc.
LONG BALL LEADERS - Trading cards - Leaf, Inc.
LONG BEACH - Doughs–frozen - S & J Importing Co. Inc.
LONG BEACH - Fishing tackle - Penn Fishing Tackle Manufacturing Co.
LONG BEACH GRAND PRIX - Apparel and accessories - Grand Prix Association of Long Beach, Inc.
LONG BEACH LEATHER COAT WORKS - Apparel and accessories - Derby Enterprises Corp.
LONG BEACH SEAFOODS CO. - Seafood products–canned or cured - Long Beach Seafoods Co.
LONG BOMB - Balls–football - Little Kids, Inc.
LONG BOY - Handles–wood - Wooster Brush Co.
LONG BOY STICKS - Candy - Bobs Candies Inc.
LONG-BRANCH FRIES - Food products - Universal Frozen Foods Co.
LONG CLIPS - Cosmetics - Nino Originals
L-O-N-G CRUISE - Marinas - Tempo Products Co.
LONG DADDY - Bathing suits - Gulbenkian Swim Inc.
LONG DEMI - Wigs - Jean Paree Weegs Inc.
LONG DISTANCE - Cosmetics - Revlon Consumer Products Corp.
LONG-DISTANCE GREETINGS - Greeting cards - Hallmark Cards Inc.
LONG FERRUL - Files–tools - O.P. Link Handle Co. Inc.
LONG GLO - Hair care products - Valmor Products Co.
LONG GONE - Sportswear - Long Gone
LONG GREIGE LINE, THE - Fabrics - Dan River Inc.
LONG GRIP - Hardware - H.B. Sherman Manufacturing Co.
LONG HAUL - Jeans–men's - Jonbil Inc.
LONG ISLAND - Ducks - Maple Leaf Farms Inc.

✩ = Now out of production

LONG ISLAND - Food products - Amende and Schultz

LONG ISLAND EEB EAST END BEVERAGE CORP. - Iced tea–bottled or canned - East End Beverage Corp.

LONG ISLAND ICED TEA - Teas - Gillies Coffee Co.

LONG ISLAND SALT WATER TAFFY - Confections - Long Island Salt Water Taffy Co.

LONG ISLAND SUN - Suntan lotions - Long Island Sun Products Inc.

LONG JACKS - Apparel–children's - Rahmey International Inc.

LONG JANES - Apparel stores–lingerie - Goddess Bra

LONG JAYNES - Underwear and nightwear - WorkAbles for Women

LONG JEANS - Apparel and accessories ☆ - Glamorise Foundations Inc.

LONG JOHN - Bicycles - Ross Bicycles USA, Ltd.

LONG JOHN - Candy ☆ - Leaf, Inc.

LONG JOHN - Fishing lures - Den Manufacturing Co.

LONG JOHN - Food products - Twin City Foods Inc.

LONG JOHN - Golfing equipment - Inventive Golf Technology, LLC

LONG JOHN - Musical instrument accessories ☆ - St. Louis Music Supply Co.

LONG JOHN - Paint rollers - Bestt-Liebco

LONG JOHN - Wet suits–rubber - Cut 'n Jump Ski Corp.

LONG JOHN SILVER SPICED RUM - Liquors - Jenkins Spirits Corp., Ltd.

LONG JON - Golfing equipment - Golfsmith International Inc.

LONG LAST LIPSTICKS - Cosmetics - Clinique Laboratories, Inc.

LONG LASTING DROP-IN - Cleaning preparations–household - Super Brands, Inc.

LONG LETTER, THE - Stationery - Thomas/Hoe Inc.

LONG LIFE - Antifreeze - Warren Distribution, Inc.

LONG LIFE - Brushes–paint - Sears, Roebuck and Co.

LONG-LIFE - Coffee makers–electric ☆ - Black & Decker Corp.

LONG LIFE - Curtains–shower - Showeray Corp.

LONG LIFE - Electrical equipment - Matsushita Consumer Electronics Co.

LONG-LIFE - Electronic equipment - Galileo Corp.

LONG LIFE - Enamels - Paris Paint & Varnish Co.

LONG LIFE - Floor coverings–carpet and rugs - No-Muv Corp., Inc.

LONG LIFE - Health care products - Futurebiotics

LONG LIFE - Hearing aids - Rexton Inc.

LONG LIFE - Heating equipment - Corning Inc.

LONG LIFE - Marine rigging - Outboard Marine Corp.

LONG-LIFE - Office supplies - Stempel Manufacturing Co.

LONG-LIFE - Oils–lubricating - Pennzoil Products Co.

LONG LIFE - Teas - Lotus Brands Inc.

LONG LIFE - Teas - Satori Fine Herbals

LONG LIFE - Teas–herbal - Korean Ginseng Products Co., Ltd.

LONG LIFE HOLDBACK - Clutches–industrial - Dana Corp.

LONG LIFE LL WATER FILTERS - Filters–water - Liberty Manufacturing, Inc.

LONG LIFE LTX - Paints - Mac-O-Lac Paints Inc.

LONG LIFE NOODLE - Noodles - Diamond Team International, Inc.

LONG LIFE P&D - Paints - Mac-O-Lac Paints Inc.

LONG LITES - Windows–storm - APC Corp.

LONG-MASK - Tape–adhesive - Minnesota Mining & Manufacturing Co.

LONG MATES - Underwear and nightwear - Gerber Products Co.

LONG 'N' HEALTHY - Cosmetics - Pfizer Inc.

LONG 'N LUSH - Cosmetics - Noxell Corp.

LONG N SHORT MEMO PADS - Novelty items - BRC Corp.

LONG NECK - Gauge, purge, and needle valves - Hansen Technologies Corp.

LONG-NOSE - Hardware - Gaunt Industries

LONG PLAY LETTER - Stationery - Graphic Center

LONG POINT - Seafood - Clouston Foods USA

LONG RANGER - Microphones - Lectrosonics Inc.

LONG RANGER - Oils–lubricating - MacMillan Ring-Free Oil Co. Inc.

LONG REACH - Cleaning preparations - National Sponge Corp.

LONG REACH - Lighters - Zelco Industries, Inc.

LONG REACH - Pet products - R.A.F. Trading Inc.

LONG RIDE - Batteries - Mattel, Inc.

LONG RIDER - Lubricating oils - Royal Purple Inc.

LONG RIDER - Meat products–beef - Curtice-Burns Meat Snacks Inc.

LONG RIDGE - Lumber - Georgia-Pacific Corp.

LONG SCRAWNIES - Cosmetics - Revlon Consumer Products Corp.

LONG SHINE - Cleaning preparations–household - J. Goddard & Sons

LONG SHOT - Golfing equipment - Golfsmith International Inc.

LONG SHOT - Toys–models ☆ - Estes Industries

LONG SMOKE - Cigars - Gesty Trading & Manufacturing Corp.

LONG SOFT FILE - Nail care products - Opi Products, Inc.

LONG STROKE - Fishing tackle - Zebco Corp.

LONG TAIL RECORDS - Recording label - Long Tail Records

LONG TALL SALLYS - Sausages ☆ - King B Jerky

LONG TOM DOOMBOAT - Toys–automobiles - Mattel, Inc.

LONG TRAIL HARVEST ALE BREWED IN VERMONT - Beverages–malt - Long Trail Brewing Co.

LONG VALLEY VINEYARDS - Wines - Mount Palomar Winery Inc.

LONG VINEYARDS - Wines - Long Vineyards

LONG WEARING - Cosmetics - Max Factor & Co.

LONG-WRITER - Pens ☆ - Faber-Castell Corp.

LONGABERGER CO. - Housewares - Longaberger Co.

LONGABERGER FOUNDRY COLLECTION - Iron products - Longaberger Co.

LONGABERGER HOMETOWN CHRISTMAS, A - Christmas tree ornaments - Longaberger Co.

LONGABERGER WOODCRAFTS - Wood products - Longaberger Co.

LONGACRE - Food processors ☆ - Wampler Foods Inc.

LONGACRE FAMILY - Food processors ☆ - Wampler Foods Inc.

LONGACRES - Dairy products - Longacres Modern Dairy

LONGBEACH - Cigarettes - Philip Morris Companies Inc.

LONGBEACH - Floor coverings - Bruce Hardwood Floors

LONGBOY - Bicycles - Columbia Manufacturing Inc.

LONGCHAMP - Glassware–household - Durand International

LONGCHAMP - Neckties - Italian Classics Inc.

LONGCHAMP - Watches - Bulova Corp.

LONGEES - Underwear and nightwear ☆ - Alba-Waldensian, Inc.

LONGER LIFE - Lamp bulbs - Philips Lighting Co.

LONGEST DAY, THE - Games - Avalon Hill Game Co.

LONGEST DRIVING SHAFTS, THE - Golfing equipment - Harrison Sports, Inc.

LONGETICS - Vitamins and nutritional supplements - Herbalife International, Inc.

LONGEVITE - Costumes - Karen E. Burke

LONGEVITEA - Teas–herbal - Unitea Herbs

LONGEVITY - Food products - U.S. Enterprise Corp.

LONGEVITY - Gloves - Mizuno Corp. of America

LONGEVITY - Orthopedic products - Zimmer, Inc.

LONGEVITY - Pharmaceutical preparations - Longevity Pure Medicine

LONGEVITY FORMULAS - Mouthwashes - LFI Ltd.

LONGEVITY PACK - Health care products - Bios

LONGEVITY RICH - Cosmetics - Soaring Eagle Ventures, Inc.

LONGEVITY SCIENCE - Health care products - Klabin Computer and Marketing Consultants Ltd., Inc.

LONGFELLOW - Grass seed - International Seeds, Inc.

LONGFELLOW BARS - Food products ☆ - Paradigm Foodworks

LONGFELLOW'S GREENHOUSES - Flowers, plants, and seeds - Longfellow's Greenhouses

LONGHORN - Brushes–paint ☆ - Linzer Products Corp.

LONGHORN - Bumpers–motor vehicle - Wedgestone Automotive Corp.

LONGHORN - Dog food - Three M Pet Foods

LONGHORN - Fabrics - Greenwood Mills Inc.

LONGHORN - Firearms, accessories, and parts - High Standard Manufacturing Corp.

LONGHORN - Fishing lures - Hildebrandt Corp.

LONGHORN - Food products ☆ - Hunt-Wesson, Inc.

LONGHORN - Giftware ☆ - Bar & Barbeque Products Inc.

LONGHORN - Guns - Chace Leather Products

LONGHORN - Leather goods - David Kirk (London)

LONGHORN - Motor vehicle parts and accessories ☆ - Saddleman, Inc.

LONGHORN - Musical instrument accessories - Pro-Mark Corp.

LONGHORN - Wines - Monarch Wine Co.

LONGHORN RANCH - Toys - ERTL Co., Inc.

LONGHORN STICK - Sausages - Fred Usinger, Inc.

LONGIFF - Spices and extracts - International Flavors & Fragrances Inc.

LONGINES - Watches - Longines-Wittnauer Watch Co.

LONGINES-WITTNAUER - Watches - Longines-Wittnauer Watch Co.

LONGING - Colognes - Coty Inc.

LONGITUDE - Bathing suits - Apparel America, Inc.

LONGITUDE - Bathing suits - Great American Industries Inc. (Robby Len Fashions Divison.)

LONGJONS - Decals and transfers - Happiness Inc.

LONGLAST - Brushes–paint ☆ - PPG Industries, Inc.

LONGLEAF HEART PINE - Flooring–hardwood - Mountain Lumber Co., Inc.

LONGLIFE - Controls–heating systems - Inter-City Products Corp. (USA)

LONGLIFE - Garden equipment - Plantation House & Garden Products Inc.

LONGLIFE - Lamp bulbs - Philips Lighting Co.

LONGLIFE - Machinery - Hypertherm Inc.

LONGLIFE - Pet products - Longlife Pet Products

LONGLIFE 90 DAY - Pet collars - Longlife Pet Products

LONGLIFE BLOCKADE - Pet products - Longlife Pet Products

LONGLIFE EXCEPTIONAL QUALITY & VALUE - Floormats for vehicles - Sagaz Industries Inc.

☆ = Now out of production

LONGLIFE LUBE - Oils–lubricating ☆ - Koch Marketing Co.
LONGLINER - Seafood products–fresh or frozen - Seafood Producers Cooperative
LONGMANS - Paints - Lee Paint & Varnish Co.
LONGMEADOW - Wallpaper - Longmeadow Studio
LONGMONT - Meat products–poultry ☆ - Longmont Foods
LONGMONT LITE SUPREME - Meat products–poultry - Longmont Foods
LONGNECK - Brushes - Wooster Brush Co.
LONGO DISCOVERY 2 IN 1 - Golfing equipment - Paul F. Longo
LONGOS - Coffee - Longo Coffee & Tea Inc.
LONGPOINT - Artists' materials - Robert Simmons Inc.
LONGROD - Bicycles - Columbia Manufacturing Inc.
LONGS - Fruits–dried - Longs Drug Stores California, Inc.
LONG'S - Jewelry - RJC Corp.
LONG'S DIXIE - Pens ☆ - Long's Dixie Pens
LONGSHADOW - Statuary - Charlotte Peters Gardens, Inc.
LONGSHOT - Trading cards and stamps - Upper Deck Co.
LONGSHOT GOLF - Golfing equipment - Longshot Golf Inc.
LONGSHOTS - Sausages - Oberto Sausage Co.
LONGSTREET - Apparel and accessories - Stretch-O-Rama, Inc.
LONGSTREET - Medical apparatus ☆ - Longstreet Pharmacal Corp.
LONGSTREET - Sandwiches–prepackaged - Golden Valley Farms Commodity Group, Inc.
LONGSTRIP - Floor coverings - Harris-Tarkett, Inc.
LONGSTROKE - Brushes–paint ☆ - PPG Industries, Inc.
LONGTON LC CROWN - Glassware–household - Longton Crown Collections, Ltd.
LONGTREE - Lumber - Woodex Lumber Corp.
LONGVIEW - Lenses–magnifying ☆ - Edroy Products Co.
LONGWEAR - Laces–boot and shoe ☆ - General Shoelace Co. Inc.
LONGWOOD - Easels - Anco Wood Specialties Inc.
LONGWOOD - Flatware - Reed and Barton Corp.
LONGWOOD - Furniture - Pavilion/Sunburst Furniture
LONGWOOD ESTATE - Furniture - National/Mt. Airy Furniture
LONGWOOD ESTATES - Wallpaper ☆ - Brewster Wallcovering Co.
LONGWOOD GARDEN - Wallpaper - Longwood Wallcovering
LONGWOOD GARDENS - Floor coverings ☆ - Tarkett, Inc.
LONGWOOD GARDENS - Wallpaper ☆ - Brewster Wallcovering Co.
LONGWOOD KIDS - Wallpaper ☆ - Longwood Wallcovering
LONGWOOD MANOR - Furniture - Bassett Furniture Industries, Inc.
LONGWOOD MANOR - Wallcovering - Brewster Wallcovering Co.
LONGWOOD MANOR - Wallpaper - Longwood Wallcovering
LONGWOOD MINIATURES - Wallpaper ☆ - Brewster Wallcovering Co.
LONGWOOD PARK - Wallpaper ☆ - Longwood Wallcovering
LONGWOOD VINEYARDS - Wines ☆ - Chaddsford Winery
LONI - Skin care products - Loni Anderson
LONI - Wigs - Jean Paree Weegs Inc.
LONICIN - Health care products - Bios
LONITEN - Pharmaceutical preparations - Upjohn Co.
LONOX - Pharmaceutical preparations - Geneva Generics Inc.
LONPLATE - Floor coverings - Lonseal Inc.
LONQFRUT - Fruits and vegetables - Marglo Products Corp.
LONQUAD - Floor coverings - Lonseal Inc.
LONRIB - Floor coverings ☆ - Lonseal Inc.
LONSDALE - Floor coverings - Mannington Resilient Floors
LONSTAGE - Floor coverings - Lonseal Inc.
LONSTONE - Floor coverings ☆ - Lonseal Inc.
LONSWIRL - Floor coverings - Lonseal Inc.
LONTECH - Floor coverings - Lonseal Inc.
LONWALL - Wallcovering - Lonseal Inc.
LONWAVE - Floor coverings - Lonseal Inc.
LONZ - Wines - Meier's Wine Cellars Inc.
LONZ - Wines - Paramount Distillers Inc.
LOO-KEE - Toys - Mattel, Inc.
LOOFA BAR - Soap - Karlen Manufacturing, Inc.
LOOFA BRITE - Sponges - Loofa Brite
LOOFOAM - Sponges - Multy Sponge, Inc.
LOOK - Antifreeze ☆ - Demert & Dougherty, Inc.
LOOK - Candy - Annabelle Candy Co. Inc.
LOOK - Cigarettes - Brown & Williamson Tobacco Corp.
LOOK - Cleaning preparations - National Purity Inc.
LOOK - Cleaning preparations–window - Butcher Co.
LOOK - Flatware ☆ - Utica Cutlery Co.
LOOK - Pet products - Aspen Pet Products
LOOK - Sporting goods - Skis Dynastar, Inc.
LOOK-A-LIKES - Toys - Judith H. Blau

LOOK-A-LITE - Mirrors ☆ - Schildkraut Giftware Corp.
LOOK-A-LIVE - Trees ☆ - Sullivan Manufacturing & Sales Corp.
LOOK-ALIVE! - Sporting goods - Rice Lake Products, Inc.
LOOK & FEEL - Skin care products - Nutra-Source Corp.
LOOK & FEEL - Vitamins and nutritional supplements ☆ - Vitamin Research Products Inc.
LOOK & LEARN - Infant product ☆ - Playtex Beauty Care, Inc.
LOOK & LEARN - Video production - V.I.E.W. Video Inc.
LOOK & LEARN ALPHABET BALL - Balls - Oliver Sporting Goods, Inc.
LOOK & LINK - Computer software - PERSONICS Corp.
LOOK & SEA - Apparel and accessories - Sirena Apparel Group Inc.
LOOK AT ME - Dresser-top mirror - Cosrich Inc.
LOOK AT ME - Mirrors - Mattel, Inc.
LOOK-AT-ME ELEPHANT - Toys - Fisher-Price, Inc.
LOOK AT THE SCHMUCK ON THAT CAMEL - Playing cards - Monarch Avalon, Inc.
LOOK BETTER - FEEL BETTER - HAVE MORE ENERGY - Vitamins and nutritional supplements - Alliance USA Inc.
LOOK DOWN THE VALLEY - Floor coverings–carpet and rugs ☆ - Regal Rugs Inc.
LOOK FOR THE ORANGE TURKEY - Turkeys - Hansel 'n Gretel Brand, Inc.
LOOK IS YOU, THE - Mirrors - Jack Gasnick, The Virtuous Locksmith
LOOK LOVELY - Ponytail holders with cologne and lipstick - Cosrich Inc.
LOOK MOM - Food products - William Bolthouse Farms Inc.
LOOK 'N DO - Games - Trend Enterprises, Inc.
LOOK' N FINE - Hair care products - Blue Cross Laboratories Inc.
LOOK 'N GOOD - Bicycles - Dynacraft Industries Inc.
LOOK 'N LISTEN - Electrical equipment - Gerry Baby Products Co.
LOOK 'N LISTEN - Toys - Rose Art Industries, Inc.
LOOK 'N LOVE - Dolls - Catalina Toys Inc.
LOOK OF A LEGEND, THE - Apparel and accessories - Westark Garment Manufacturing, Inc.
LOOK OF BETTER PERFORMANCE, THE - Machinery - White Consolidated Industries, Inc.
LOOK OF DIAMONDS - Jewelry - Erwin Pearl Inc.
LOOK OF GOLD - Jewelry - Erwin Pearl Inc.
LOOK OF LOVE - Wigs - Look of Love International
LOOK OF NATURE - Hair care products - Gillette Co.
LOOK OF SILK - Panty hose - Arrowood Mills Inc.
LOOK OF SILK, THE - Wallpaper ☆ - Bolta Wallcoverings
LOOK OF SILVER - Jewelry - Erwin Pearl Inc.
LOOK-OUT - Television equipment - CCTV Corp./GBC
LOOK-OUT - Toys–stuffed - Giftco, Inc.
LOOK RACING - Shoe accessories - SMT Walker Ltd.
LOOK-RUSCO - Hardware - Blaine Window Hardware Inc.
LOOK-SEE-DO - Toys - Mattel, Inc.
LOOK, THE - Hair care products - Demert & Dougherty, Inc.
LOOK, THE - Sporting goods - Ski Country Imports, Inc.
LOOK! THERE'S SANTA - Figurines - Noma International, Inc.
LOOK TO LEARN - Video production - Trustee of Parents' Choice Foundation, Massachusetts Charitable Trust
LOOK TOURING - Shoe accessories - SMT Walker Ltd.
LOOK TRIMMER IN SECONDS - Apparel stores–lingerie - A & H Sportswear Co., Inc.
LOOK UP - Apparel–men's - Sportailor Inc.
LOOK WHAT I MADE - Video production - Intervideo, Inc.
LOOK YOUR BEST - Printers–computer ☆ - Epson America, Inc.
LOOKART - Computer software - RT Computer Graphics, Inc.
LOOKCHANGERS - Video production - Conselle L.C.
LOOKER - Floor coverings–carpet and rugs ☆ - World Carpets, Inc.
LOOKERS - Binoculars - Kalimar, Inc.
LOOKIN GOOD - Cleaning preparations - Hill Manufacturing Co. Inc.
LOOKIN' GOOD - Hair care products - Major International Inc.
LOOKIN GOOD - Toys ☆ - A.R.C. Toys Inc.
LOOKIN' LEAN - Meat products–pork - Agar Food Products Co.
LOOKIN' LIVELY - Dolls - Mattel, Inc.
LOOKING AT YOU - Flower pots–earthenware ☆ - Rubens Originals
LOOKING GLASS ANIMALS - Novelty mirrors ☆ - Cosrich Inc.
LOOKING GLASS COLLECTION, THE - Mirrors ☆ - Hammary Furniture Co. Inc.
LOOKING GLASS DESIGN - Eyeglasses - Hart Specialties Inc.
LOOKING GLASS DOLLS - Dolls and doll clothing - Timeless Treasures
LOOKING GLASS LEGENDS - Figurines ☆ - Enesco Corp.
LOOKING GLASS, THE - Newsletters - Specialty Products, Inc.
LOOKING GLOSS - Lipsticks - Revlon Consumer Products Corp.
LOOKING GOOD - Floor coverings–carpet and rugs ☆ - Masland Corp.

LOOKING GOOD - Mirrors ☆ - Sunbeam-Oster Household Products
LOOKING GOOD - Teas–herbal ☆ - R.C. Bigelow, Inc.
LOOKING OUT FOR FLORIDA - Doors–glass ☆ - Nu-Air Manufacturing Co.
LOOKINGGLASS - Computer software - Looking Glass Technologies, Inc.
LOOKINGLAS - Polishing rouge ☆ - Lilly Perfection Paint
LOOKINGLASS - Sunglasses - Lookinglass Inc.
LOOKOUT - Apparel–children's - Pacific Trail, Inc.
LOOKOUT - Playground equipment - Newco, Inc.
LOOKOUT - Radar systems and equipment ☆ - Ray Jefferson
LOOKOUT CAR SEAT - Pet products - O'Donnell Industries Inc.
LOOKOUT GANG, THE - Coloring books - Peddler Publishing, Inc.
LOOKOUT MOUNTAIN - Stoneware dinnerware - Iron Mountain Stoneware Inc.
LOOKOUT, THE - Publisher's imprints - Standex International Corp.
LOOKOUT TOWER - Pet products - Penn-Plax, Inc.
LOOKOUT TOWER - Swing sets - Island Wood Products Inc.
LOOKOUTS - Paper - Engel Stadium Corp.
LOOKOUTS - Window coverings - Elkhart Door Inc.
LOOK'S - Food products - H.G. Norton
LOOKS ALIVE - Dolls - Mattel, Inc.
LOOKS BY JORDACHE - Skin care products - Jordache Enterprises Inc.
LOOKS LIKE A MATTRESS WORKS LIKE A BED - Mattresses - Mellen Air Manufacturing, Inc.
LOOKSEE - Ophthalmic goods - Foremost Optical Products
LOOKY - Skin care products ☆ - Ella Bache Inc.
LOOM-LOK - Fabrics - Polylok Corp.
LOOM LOOPERS - Toys - Coloron Industries
LOOM LUSTER - Yarn ☆ - SCT Yarns Inc.
LOOMCRAFT - Floor coverings–carpet and rugs - Karastan-Bigelow Inc.
LOOMCRAFT - Slips - Triangle Lingerie Corp.
LOOMKNITS - Crocheted and knitted items - Loomtogs Inc.
LOOMTEX - Floor coverings–carpet and rugs - P.S. Floorcoverings Inc.
LOOMTOGS - Crocheted and knitted items - Loomtogs Inc.
LOOMWEVE - Floor coverings - Congoleum Corp.
LOOMWOOD - Electronic equipment - Aeroshade Inc.
LOON - Beverages–malt - N.H. Custom Brewers, Inc.
LOON - Boats–canoes - Sawyer Composite Products
LOON - Boats–kayaks - Old Town Canoe Co.
LOON - Toilets–enameled - Kohler Co.
LOON DICE - Novelty items - Koplow Games
LOON-EYE - Apparel and accessories - Loon-Eye
LOON FLUTE - Sporting goods - Lake Ridge Enterprises, Inc.
LOON HAND CRAFTED PALE ALE LIVE FREE - Beverages–malt - N.H. Custom Brewers, Inc.
LOON LAKE - Wallpaper ☆ - Warner Co.
LOONETTE SAN FRANCISCO - Apparel–children's - Loo Na Inc.
LOONEY BALL - Balls - Trendmasters, Inc.
LOONEY BINS - Containers ☆ - Sanford Corp.
LOONEY LIME - Candy - Nabisco Foods Group
LOONEY LURES - Fishing lures - Brad Sorensen
LOONEY PHONE - Toys - Trendmasters, Inc.
LOONEY TUNE - Socks ☆ - High Point Knitting Inc.
LOONEY TUNES - Air purification systems - Medo Industries, Inc.
LOONEY TUNES - Bathroom accessories ☆ - Tsumura International Inc.
LOONEY TUNES - Candy - Warner Bros. Inc.
LOONEY TUNES - Food products ☆ - Tyson Foods Inc.
LOONEY TUNES - Frames–eyeglass - Marine Optical, Inc.
LOONEY TUNES - Jewelry - Gift Creations, Inc.
LOONEY TUNES - Leather goods - RGA Accessories Inc.
LOONEY TUNES - Lunch boxes - Thermos Co.
LOONEY TUNES - Novelty items–glass - Rawcliffe Corp.
LOONEY TUNES - Ornamental products–glass ☆ - Dave Grossman Creations Inc.
LOONEY TUNES - Puzzles - Playskool, Inc.
LOONEY TUNES - Shoes - S. Goldberg and Co. Inc.
LOONEY TUNES - Soap - Rovar Soap
LOONEY TUNES - Toothpaste - Schmid Laboratories
LOONEY TUNES - Toys–stuffed - Applause, Inc.
LOONEY TUNES - Toys–stuffed - Mighty Star Inc. (Special Effects Div.)
LOONEY TUNES - Umbrellas - Essex Manufacturing Inc.
LOONEY TUNES - Wallpaper - Priss Prints Inc.
LOONEY TUNES - Watches - E. Gluck Corp.
LOONEY TUNES - Watches ☆ - Genender International, Inc.
LOONEY TUNES LOVABLES - Apparel and accessories ☆ - S. Goldberg and Co. Inc.
LOONEY TUNES LOVABLES - Infant product - Time Warner Entertainment Co., L.P.
LOONY - Novelty items - CTI Industries Corp.
LOONY-TUNES - Apparel–athletic - Fuqua Industries Inc.
LOONY TUNES - Ice cream - Wells' Dairy, Inc.
LOOP - Locks–padlocks - Loop Lock Inc.
LOOP-A-LOOM - Hobby kits - Rose Art Industries, Inc.
LOOP & SPLASH - Toys - Mattel, Inc.
LOOP D LOOP - Fabrics–broadcloth - Desire Mills Co. Inc.
LOOP D' LOOP - Nail care products - Kimo's Nail Charms
LOOP LOCK - Locks–door - B.A.Y.
LOOP-LUBE - Electron tubes - Tecumseh Products Co. Engine and Transmission Group
LOOP MONITOR - Electronic equipment - Eberle Design Inc.
LOOP MUSIC CO. - Publisher's imprints - Neil A. Kjos Music Co.
LOOP-N-LACE - Crochet patterns - Annie's Attic, Inc.
LOOP-N-LOK - Medical apparatus - Lumex, Inc.
LOOP, THE - Golf bag strap - Bag-Pakkers, Inc.
LOOP, THE - Floor coverings–tile - Interface, Inc.
LOOP, THE - Cosmetics - Major International Inc.
LOOP THE LOOP - Games - Tyco Toys
LOOPER - Apparel and accessories - Donald Marshall Motsenbocker
LOOPER - Lighting fixtures - Swivelier Co. Inc.
LOOPER - Projectors–photographic - Rangertone Research Inc.
LOOPER, THE - Floor coverings - Apache Mills Inc.
LOOPERS - Engines - Outboard Marine Corp.
LOOPIN' LOUIE - Toys - Hasbro, Inc.
LOOPING - Toys - Hasbro, Inc.
LOOPING - Watches ☆ - Tag-Heuer Time & Electronics Corp.
LOOPY - Computers - Password Group
LOOPY LIZZIE CAR - Toys–automobiles - CBS Toys
LOOPY MOOSE COMPANY, THE - Apparel and accessories - Loopy Moose Co.
LOOSE BUT FIT - Apparel and accessories - Weekend Exercise Co., Inc.
LOOSE CHANGE - Apparel - Rutchick, Rutchick & Associates, Inc.
LOOSE DEUCE DEUCES WILD - Video games - IGT - North America
LOOSE PACK - Electrical equipment - Bicc Cables Corp.
LOOSEGROOVE - Recording label - Loosegroove Records
LOOSELEAF STREETWISE - Maps - Streetwise Maps Inc.
LOOSEN - Pharmaceutical preparations ☆ - Hyrex Pharmaceuticals
LOOT BAG - Candy ☆ - Topps Co., Inc.
LOOVER-LITE - Lamps–desk ☆ - Cannon Products Inc.
LOOZA - Juices - ABA Management & Development Inc.
LOOZWAYT - Diet product - American Hygienic Laboratories Inc.
LOPER, THE - Exercising equipment - Nick S. Karanges
+L'OPERA - Cosmetics - Cosmair Inc.
LOPERAMIDE - Health care products - L. Perrigo Co.
LOPERM - Automotive parts and accessories - ITT Corp.
LOPEZ - Apparel and accessories ☆ - Columbia Sportswear Co.
LOPI - Fireplaces - Travis Industries
LOPI - Yarn ☆ - JCA, Inc.
LOPID - Pharmaceutical preparations - Parke-Davis
LOPRO - Antennas - Northpoint Communication Products, Inc.
LO*PRO - Food products - Med-Diet Laboratories Inc.
LOPROX - Pharmaceutical preparations - Hoechst-Roussel Pharmaceuticals Inc.
LOPURIN - Pharmaceutical preparations - Boots Pharmaceuticals Inc.
LOR - Apparel and accessories - Edward T. Riley
LORA - Housewares - SCI Scandicrafts Inc.
LORA - Veterinary pharmaceutical preparations - Lora Laboratories Inc.
LORA FOR KARATS - Jewelry - Karats Fashion Jewelry
LORA GARETTI - Footwear–women's - Shoe Inn Inc.
LORABID - Antibiotics - Eli Lilly and Co.
LORAC - Cosmetics - Carol Shaw
LORAD - Glass products ☆ - Corning Inc.
LORAINE'S FORTUNE - Apparel and accessories - Loraine Bassett, Inc.
LORALYN FASHIONS - Apparel–athletic - I. Appel Corp.
LORAMET - Sedative - American Home Products Corp.
LORAN - Audio tapes–blank - Loran Cassettes & Audio Products
LORAN - Boats–motor - Loran Boat Corp.
LORAN - Jewelry - Queen of Hearts
LORAN-COMM - Electronic equipment - Megapulse, Inc.
LORANE VALLEY - Wines - King Estate Vineyards, Inc.
+L'ORANGE ROYALE - Pepper - Sun World International
+L'ORANGERIE - Wines ☆ - Canandaigua Wine Co. Inc.
LORANN - Oils–edible - Lorann Oils, Inc.

☆ = Now out of production

LORANN GOURMET - Oils—edible - Lorann Oils, Inc.

LORANN INTERNATIONAL GOURMET - Spices and extracts - Lorann Oils, Inc.

LORAY - Floor coverings—carpet and rugs ☆ - Evans-Black Carpet Mills

+L'ORBETTE - Depilatories - L'orbette Co. Inc.

LORCA - Trading cards and stamps - Enlightened Entertainment Partners, L.P.

LORCET-HD - Pharmaceutical preparations - Forest Pharmaceuticals Inc.

LORCH - Apparel—women's - Lorch Co.

LORCH DIAMOND CENTERS - Jewelry—precious - Wedlo, Inc.

LORD - Brushes—paint - Corona Brushes Inc.

LORD - Brushes—paint - Karmichael Industries Inc.

LORD - Frames—eyeglass - Rozin Optical Export Corp.

LORD - Shaving products - Universal Razor Industries

LORD & HODGE - Fasteners—snap - Lord & Hodge, Inc.

LORD & MASTER - Astringents - Master Chemical Co.

LORD & MAYFAIR - Mouthwashes - Marietta Corp.

LORD AND MAYFAIR BOTANICALS - Cosmetics - Marietta Corp.

LORD & TAYLOR - Apparel and accessories - Lord & Taylor

LORD ASTER - Food products - J. Manaster Co.

LORD BALTIMORE - Beverages—alcohol - Majestic Distilling Co.

LORD BALTIMORE - Cigars - A.J. Golden Inc.

LORD BALTIMORE - Cigars - F.X. Smiths Sons Co.

LORD BALTIMORE - Dialing devices—telephone - Baltimore Luggage Co.

LORD BALTIMORE - Teas - Eastern Shore Tea Co.

LORD BARTON'S - Skin care products - Pro-Capa Products Inc.

LORD BEACONSFIELD - Cigars - Villazon and Co.

LORD BENCHLEY - Breads—mixes - Dawn Food Products Inc.

LORD BENCHLY - Desserts - Regency Creative Foods

LORD BENTLY - Tobacco—chewing or smoking - Amar Blends Co.

LORD BUXTON - Wallets - Buxton Inc.

LORD BYRON - Apparel—men's - Byron Clothing Manufacturing Co. Inc.

LORD BYRON'S SMOKER'S - Candles - Arizona Natural Resources

LORD CALVERT - Dishes—earthenware ☆ - Royal China & Porcelain Companies Inc.

LORD CALVERT - Whiskey - Jim Beam Brands Co.

LORD CALVERT - Whiskey - Joseph E. Seagram & Sons, Inc.

LORD CHESELINE - Hair care products - Chesebrough-Pond's USA Inc.

LORD CHESTERFIELD - Vegetables—canned - McCall Farms Inc.

LORD CHESTERFIELD ALE - Beverages—malt - D.G. Yuengling & Son Inc.

LORD CLARIDGE - Cigars - General Cigar Co., Inc.

LORD CLINTON - Cigars - National Cigar Corp.

LORD DUGAN - Toys - Lord Dugan Co. Inc.

LORD ELGIN - Watches - Elgin Watch Co.

LORD ESSEX - Apparel—men's - Central-Samuels Inc.

LORD ETON - Watches - Dundee Watch Co.

LORD GEORGE - Decorations - BARD International, Inc.

LORD HAMILTON - Watches ☆ - SMH (US) Inc.

LORD HAMPTON - Skin care products ☆ - T.N. Dickinson Co.

LORD HERITAGE - Footwear - H. Gordon Shoe Corp.

LORD ISAACS - Beverages—alcohol - Hy-Vee Food Stores Inc.

LORD ISAACS - Slacks - I.C. Isaacs & Co.

LORD LANCASTER - Watches ☆ - SMH (US) Inc.

LORD LANE - Watches - M.Z. Berger & Co. Inc.

LORD MILFORD - Thread ☆ - Belding Heminway Co. Inc.

LORD-MOTT - Fruits—frozen ☆ - Mott's Inc.

LORD NELSON - Boats - Glen-L Marine Designs

LORD NELSON - Watches - M.Z. Berger & Co. Inc.

LORD NEWPORT - Jewelry ☆ - Komor Manufacturing

LORD NOR - Playing cards ☆ - United States Playing Card Co.

LORD ROBERT - Cigars - A.J. Golden Inc.

LORD ROCHESTER - Apparel—men's ☆ - Michaels/Stern & Co. Inc.

LORD SHEF - Paints - Sheffield Bronze Paint Corp.

LORD SPRINGFIELD - Watches - Bulova Corp.

LORD TARLETON - Pipes—tobacco - Bradberry Briar Pipe Corp.

LORD TUDDLEBURY'S JOLLY GOOD LOLLYS - Candy ☆ - R.L. Products Corp.

LORD WALTHAM - Watches - Elgin Watch Co.

LORD WEST - Tuxedos - Lord West Formals

LORDS - Footwear - H. Gordon Shoe Corp.

LORDS OF CONQUEST - Computer software - Electronic Arts Inc.

LORDS OF CREATION - Games ☆ - Avalon Hill Game Co.

LORDS OF KARMA - Games ☆ - Avalon Hill Game Co.

LORDS OF THE RISING SUN - Game discs - Philips Interactive Media of America

LORE - Toys - Paramount Pictures Corp.

LORE BLUMENKINDER - Figurines ☆ - Goebel of North America

LORE-TIE - Binding—fabric - Loretex Corp.

+L'OREAL - Nail care products - Cosmair Inc.

LOREDANA - Handbags - Mister Ernest Handbags Inc.

LOREDANO - Footwear - Aztec Imports Inc.

LOREDANO - Footwear - Loredano, Inc.

LOREDO - Wallpaper - Pickhardt & Siebert USA Inc.

LOREE - Musical instruments - Ardsley Musical Instrument Co.

LOREE - Musical instruments - Ideal Musical Merchandise Co.

LOREE RODKIN GOTHIC - Jewelry - Loree Rodkin

LORELCO - Pharmaceutical preparations - Marion Merrell Dow

LORELEE - Underwear and nightwear - Bestform Foundations, Inc.

LORELEI - Clocks ☆ - Ridgeway Clock Co.

LORELEI - Dishes—china ☆ - WMF/USA

LORELEI - Glassware—household - ACC

LORELEI - Rings—jewelry - Artcarved Inc.

LORELEI - Toys - Mattel, Inc.

LORELEI - Vases ☆ - Lenox Crystal, Inc.

LORELER - Costume jewelry ☆ - Robert Rose

LORELLE - Floor coverings—carpet and rugs - Evans-Black Carpet Mills

LORENTO - Floor coverings—carpet and rugs ☆ - Evans-Black Carpet Mills

LORENZ - Food products - Lorenz International

LORENZA DE MEDICI - Vinegar - De Medici Imports Ltd.

LORENZEN - Trailers—travel ☆ - Giles Industries

LORENZI OF ITALY - Apparel and accessories - Lorenzi of Italy Inc.

LORENZO - Dinnerware—glass - Denby USA Limited

LORENZO - Furniture - Tropitone Furniture Co. Inc.

LORENZO - Furniture ☆ - Bassett Furniture Industries, Inc.

LORENZO - Handbags - Larry Friedman Inc.

LORENZO DE'MEDICI - Dishes—china ☆ - Gorham Inc.

LORENZO LEOPARD - Toys—stuffed - Russ Berrie and Co., Inc.

LORENZO ORSINI - Apparel—men's - Intrep Imports, Inc.

LORENZO UOMO - Apparel and accessories - Echo Lake Industries, Ltd.

LORENZO'S - Confections - Lorenzo's Ice Creams, Inc.

LORESAL - Pharmaceutical preparations - Ciba-Geigy Corp.

LORETT - Jewelry - T & L Jewelry

LORETTE - Furniture ☆ - Bassett Furniture Industries, Inc.

LORFAN - Pharmaceutical preparations ☆ - Roche Laboratories

+L'ORGANOLA - Accordions - Hohner Inc.

LORI - Frames—eyeglass - U.S. Optical Frame Co.

LORI - Locks—door - Lori Lock

LORI - Pet products - Nekton USA Inc.

LORI - Vitamins and nutritional supplements ☆ - Freeda Vitamins Inc.

LORI DAVIS - Hair care products - American Telecast Corp.

LORI J - Cleaning preparations—household - Ramco Chemical Inc.

LORI JO - Cosmetics - Scott/Franklin International

LORI LIZ DESIGNS - Stationery - Renner-Davis Co.

LORI VERRIER - Darts and dart games - Dart Mart Inc.

LORIBOLT - Locks—door ☆ - Lori Lock

LORIDINE - Pharmaceutical preparations ☆ - Eli Lilly and Co.

LORIE - Yarn - Melrose Yarn Co. Inc.

LORIEN - Floor coverings—carpet and rugs ☆ - Robertex Associates Inc.

LORIEN - Furniture ☆ - Bassett Furniture Industries, Inc.

+L'ORIENT - Dinners—frozen ☆ - Campbell Soup Co.

+L'ORIENT - Housewares - Shafford Co. Inc.

+L'ORIGAN - Perfume, dusting powder, talc, etc. - Coty Inc.

LORIK - Nail care products - RJM International

LORILLARD - Cigarettes - Loews Corp.

LORILLARD MACCOBOY - Snuff - American Maize-Products Co.

LORILLARD SALT - Snuff - American Maize-Products Co.

LORILLARD SWEET - Snuff - American Maize-Products Co.

LORIMAR - Video tapes—blank - Lorimar

LORING & PAIGE - Belts, handbags, etc. - Milor Accessories Ltd.

LORIPLEX - Locks—door - Lori Lock

LORIS - Recording label - Jazz Composer's Orchestra Association Inc.

LORI'S KITCHEN - Bakery products - Schwan's Sales Enterprises, Inc.

LORI'S MEMORY HOLD - Hair-care productss - American Telecast Corp.

LORI'S PERFECTION - Hair care products - American Telecast Corp.

LORISA - Cosmetics - Summit Sales Co.

LORITE - Window coverings - Levolor Inc.

LORIVA - Oils—edible - De Choix Specialty Foods Co.

LORIVA - Salad dressings—bottled - Loriva Supreme Foods Inc.

LORIVA SUPREME - Oils—edible - Loriva Supreme Foods Inc.

LORIZONI - Dresses—women's - Lorizoni, Inc.

LORNA - Frames—eyeglass - Rozin Optical Export Corp.

LORNA DOONE - Cookies - Nabisco Foods Group

+L'OROCAL - Calculators - Orocal

☆ = Now out of production

LOROL - Pharmaceutical preparations - Econo Med Pharmaceuticals Inc.
LOROMAN - Housewares - Loroman Co.
LORONIX - Computer software - Loronix Information Systems
LOROX - Herbicides - E.I. Dupont de Nemours and Co.
LOROXIDE - Pharmaceutical preparations ☆ - Dermik Laboratories Inc.
LORPHEN - Pharmaceutical preparations - Armenpharm Ltd.
LORRAINE - Apparel–women's - Duck Head Apparel Co., Inc.
LORRAINE - Cheese - Stella Foods, Inc.
LORRAINE - Cheese - Universal Foods Corp.
LORRAINE - Dinnerware ☆ - Corning Inc.
LORRAINE - Dinnerware–glass ☆ - Denby USA Limited
LORRAINE - Dishes–earthenware - Advantage Marketing Group, Inc.
LORRAINE - Dolls ☆ - Effanbee Doll Corp.
LORRAINE - Electronic equipment - Xerox Corp.
LORRAINE - Floor coverings ☆ - National Floor Products Co., Inc.
LORRAINE - Furniture ☆ - Riverside Furniture Corp.
LORRAINE - Glassware–household - Owens-Illinois Inc. (Libbey Div.)
LORRAINE - Leather - A & A Sales
LORRAINE - Mattresses - Simmons USA
LORRAINE - Musical instruments - Ardsley Musical Instrument Co.
LORRAINE I - Furniture ☆ - White Furniture Co.
LORRAINE II - Furniture ☆ - White Furniture Co.
LORRAINE III - Furniture ☆ - White Furniture Co.
LORRAINE IV - Furniture ☆ - White Furniture Co.
LORRAINE V - Furniture ☆ - White Furniture Co.
LORRAINE VALLEY - Furniture ☆ - Bassett Furniture Industries, Inc.
LORRAINE VI - Furniture - White Furniture Co.
LORRAINE WARDY - Apparel–women's - Lorraine Wardy Enterprises
LORRE - Shampoos ☆ - Mid-America Chemical Inc.
LORRIE - Toys - Eugene Doll & Novelty Co. Inc.
LORRIE WALKER - Toys - Eugene Doll & Novelty Co. Inc.
LORRY LEOPARD - Toys–automobiles - Russ Berrie and Co., Inc.
LORRYMAGE - Sports clubs - Lorrymage, Inc.
LORSBAN - Insecticides - Dowelanco
LORTAB - Analgesics - Whitby Pharmaceuticals, Inc.
LORTAB 5 - Analgesics - Whitby Pharmaceuticals, Inc.
LORTAB 7 - Analgesics - Whitby Pharmaceuticals, Inc.
LORTEL - Candy ☆ - Brock Candy Co. Inc.
LORUS - Watches - Lorus
LORVAL - Wines - Cordier Estates Inc.
LORY LIFE - Pet products - Cuttlebone Plus
LORYL - Pharmaceutical preparations ☆ - Schwarz Pharma
LOS AGUIRRE - Compact discs–prerecorded - Luna Music Corp.
LOS ALTOS - Food products - Los Altos Food Products, Inc.
LOS ALTOS - Wines - Rapazzini Winery
LOS AMIGOS - Food products - A & A Food Products Corp.
LOS ANGELES - Robe hooks - Baldwin Hardware Corp.
LOS ANGELES . CA HARVEST ALE - Beverages–malt - Wolfgang D. Morandell
LOS ANGELES COUNTY DEPARTMENT OF CORONER - Dishes–china - Department of Coroner
LOS ANGELES NUT HOUSE - Health care products - Glico Harmony Foods Corp.
LOS ANGELES OBSERVER - Publisher's imprints - New York Observer Co., Inc.
LOS ANGELES PAJAMA DEPT. - Underwear and nightwear - Bentley Lingerie, Inc.
LOS ANGELES POTTERIES - Dishes–earthenware - N.S. Gustin Co.
LOS ANGELES ROSE - Medical uniforms - Allen Rosenblum
LOS ANGELES SEATTLE MOTOR EXPRESS - Toys–automobiles - Toy Truck Lines, Inc.
LOS ANGELES STARS - Apparel and accessories - John A. Busch
LOS ANGELES TOWN - Apparel and accessories - Hard Hat Records
LOS ARCOS - Cabinets - Superior Woodwork Inc.
LOS BOLDOS - Wines - Dreyfus Ashby Inc.
LOS CALDITOS - Bouillon - Borden Brands Foodservice Co.
LOS CARLOS - Recording label - Luna Music Corp.
LOS DOS - Bicycles - Cannondale Corp.
LOS DUKES - Recording label - Disco Fiesta Inc.
LOS FRESCOS - Snack foods - Great Western Tortilla Co.
LOS GAMMA - Recording label - Luna Music Corp.
LOS GATOS - Coffee - Los Gatos Coffee Roasting Co.
LOS HERMANOS - Wines - Wine World Inc.
LOS IRACUNDOS - Compact discs–prerecorded - Jesus Maria Febrero Galan
LOS LOBOS - Recording label - Los Lobos
LOS MORA - Recording label - Luna Music Corp.

LOS OLIVOS - Olives–pickled or brined - Seville Olive Co.
LOS OLIVOS VINTNERS - Wines - Los Olivos Vintners
LOS PADRES - Wines - Mosby Winery
LOS PADRES EN LA EDUCACION - Educational materials - U S West Education Foundation
LOS PATIOS - Floor coverings ☆ - Azrock Commercial Flooring
LOS REYES - Tortillas - Marcelo Reyes
LOS SABROSOS - Meat products–beef - Maid-Rite Steak Co. Inc.
LOS SABROSOS DEL MERENGUE - Recording label ☆ - Musical Productions, Inc.
LOS VINEROS - Wines - Los Vineros Winery Inc.
LOSE IT! - Apparel–women's - Exquisite Form Industries
LOSE-IT CAPS - Pharmaceutical preparations ☆ - Geneva Generics Inc.
LOSE THAT YELLOW - Shampoos - Giovanni Cosmetics Inc.
LOSE YOUR BLUES - Clothing - Perry Ellis Sportswear Inc.
LOSER WEAR - Apparel and accessories - Lovelace Designs
LOSHED - Pet products - Intermark Products, Inc.
LOSSING - Medical apparatus - Lossing Orthopedic Co.
LOST ACRES - Food products - Lost Acres
LOST ADMIRAL, THE - Video games - Quantum Quality Productions, Inc.
LOST & FOUND - Games ☆ - Milton Bradley Co.
LOST ARK, THE - Figurines - Edward P. Masessa Jr.
LOST BIRDS - Video production - Vision Entertainment, Inc.
LOST CAVERNS - Computer software - Activision, Inc.
LOST CIVILIZATIONS - Video production - Time Warner Entertainment Co., L.P.
LOST COAST PALE ALE - Beverages–malt - Table Bluff Brewing, Inc.
LOST CREEK FARMS - Cheese - Swissrose International Inc.
LOST EDEN - Computer software - Virgin Interactive Entertainment, Inc.
LOST FORESTS, THE - Toys–stuffed - The Lost Forests, Inc.
LOST HARVEST - Apparel and accessories - Eric Pearce
LOST HILLS VINEYARDS - Wines - Lost Hills Winery
LOST ISLE - Apparel and accessories - Lost Isle Partners
LOST KINGDOM - Socks - Wemco, Inc.
LOST LUGGAGE - Luggage - Insider Trading Co., Inc.
LOST MOUNTAIN - Jewelry - Lost Mountain Trading Co.
LOST MOUNTAIN - Wines - Lost Mountain Winery Inc.
LOST N' FOUNDS - Toys–stuffed - Lewis Galoob Toys, Inc.
LOST RECORDS - Recording label - Jazz Composer's Orchestra Association Inc.
LOST RIVER - Coats - Kellwood Co.
LOST SEA - Shrimp–fresh or frozen - Triton Aquaculture, Inc.
LOST SOUL - Apparel and accessories - Pat J. Burns
LOST SQUADRON - Novelty items - Roger Tonry Inc.
LOST TRAIL - Beverages–carbonated - Louisburg Cider Mill
LOST TRIBE, THE - Computer software - Knowledge Adventure
LOST UNIVERSE - Apparel and accessories - Big Entertainment, Inc.
LOST VIKINGS - Computer programs - Interplay Productions
LOST WORLD ADVENTURES - Apparel–athletic - Lost World Adventures, Inc.
LOSURDO - Food products - Losurdo Foods, Inc.
LOSVET - Pet products - Prime Pet Products
LOT-A-COLOR - House furnishings - Dan River Inc.
LOT$-A-DEAL$ - Apparel and accessories - Penn-Daniels, Inc.
LOT-A-SLOT - Toasters - Hamilton Beach/Proctor-Silex Inc.
LOT-A-WATA - Pet products - Blitz USA Inc.
LOT-A-WATA JR. - Pet products - Blitz USA Inc.
LOT LINK - Computer peripheral equipment - Hosmer Computing, LLC
LOTCA - Health care products - Maddak Inc.
LOTCA-G - Health care products - Maddak Inc.
LOTEMP - Paints - Dunn Edwards Corp.
LOTENSE - Pharmaceutical preparations ☆ - ICN Pharmaceuticals Inc.
LOTENSIN - Pharmaceutical preparations - Ciba-Geigy Corp.
LOTENSIN HCT - Pharmaceutical preparations - Ciba-Geigy Corp.
LOTEX - Pharmaceutical preparations - Roberts/Hauck Pharmaceuticals Inc.
LOTHAR SEMMLINGER - Cellos - Ideal Musical Merchandise Co.
LOTHAR WALTHER - Barrels–gun - Daisy Manufacturing Co.
LOTHLORIEN - Recording label - Jazz Composer's Orchestra Association Inc.
LOTHROP, LEE & SHEPARD CO. - Publisher's imprints - William Morrow and Co. Inc.
LOTHROP UNLIMITEDS - Publisher's imprints - William Morrow and Co. Inc.
LOTHSON - Guitars - Lothson Guitars
LOTIL - Cosmetics - Caswell-Massey Co. Ltd.
LOTIO ALSULFA - Skin care products ☆ - Doak Dermatologics
LOTIO-DERM - Skin care products ☆ - JMI-Canton Pharmaceuticals
LOTION-JEL - Pharmaceutical preparations ☆ - Grandpa Brands Co.

LOTION MILD - Dish detergent - James Austin Co.
LOTION NO. 1 - Skin care products - Chanel Inc.
LOTION PEAU GRASSE - Skin care products - Ella Bache Inc.
LOTION PUFF - Cosmetics - Lotion Puff Corp.
LOTION ROSEE DU MATIN - Skin care products - Ella Bache Inc.
LOTION SOFT - Skin care products - Calgon Vestal, Inc.
LOTIONSHAVE - Shaving preparations - Jean Alexander Cosmetics Inc.
LOTL SOCIETY - Apparel - Lotl Society, Inc.
LOTOCREME - Pharmaceutical preparations ☆ - Grandpa Brands Co.
LOT$OFF - Department stores - 50-Off Operating Co., Inc.
LOTREL - Pharmaceutical preparations - Ciba-Geigy Corp.
LOTRIMIN - Pharmaceutical preparations - Schering-Plough Healthcare Products
LOTRIMIN AF - Pharmaceutical preparations - Schering-Plough Healthcare Products
LOTRISONE - Pharmaceutical preparations - Schering-Plough Healthcare Products
LOTS-A-GUM - Chewing gum - National Chewing Gum Inc.
LOTS-A-GUM - Chewing gum ☆ - Pennsylvania Dutch Candies
LOTS A LOOKS - Cosmetics - Spearhead Industries Inc.
LOTS-A-LOTS-A-LEGGGGGGS - Toys–stuffed - Commonwealth Toy and Novelty Co. Inc.
LOTS-A-NOODLES - Soups–mixes - Lipton Investments, Inc.
LOTS BY DOTS - Computer software - Padco, Inc.
LOT'S O' GEARS - Toys - Childcraft Education Corp.
LOTS-O-LOT - Computer software - Capstone Software
LOTS O'BERRIES - Juices - Wagner Excello Foods Inc.
LOTS OF DOTS - Novelty items ☆ - Easter Unltd. Inc.
LOTS OF FEAR - Apparel and accessories - Environmental Artwear, Inc.
LOTS OF HUGS - Dolls - Diece-Lisa Industries, Inc.
LOTS OF LOVE - Frames–picture - Russ Berrie and Co., Inc.
LOTS OF LUXURY - Underwear and nightwear - Saramar Corp.
LOTSA' - Beverages–carbonated - Metro Beverage Co. Inc.
LOTSA BUBBLE MAKERS - Toys ☆ - Imperial Toy Corp.
LOTSA FUN - Toys - Strombecker Corp.
LOTSA HOT - Heaters–space - Lakewood Engineering and Manufacturing Co.
LOTSA LOOT - Candy ☆ - Topps Co., Inc.
LOTSA LOTTO - Games - Milton Bradley Co.
LOTSA MOZZARELLA - Pasta - Vermont Pasta
LOTSA SUDS - Cleaning preparations ☆ - Quality Products International Corp.
LOTSA WAYS - Toys - Strombecker Corp.
LOTSAPASTA - Food products - Park 100 Foods Inc.
LOTSHAW - Insecticides ☆ - Lotshaw Co.
LOTT - Photographic equipment - Arel Inc.
LOTTA CHILADAS, A - Sauces - David W. Kienzle
LOTTA CHOCOLATE - Dolls - Mattel, Inc.
LOTTA COLA - Beverages–carbonated - Regent Bottling
LOTTA ROCK DAIRY - Milk - Lotta Rock Inc.
LOTTABODY - Hair care products - Roux Laboratories, Inc.
LOTTABODY STRAIGHT STUFF - Hair care products - Roux Laboratories, Inc.
LOTTE - Chewing gum - Lotte USA Inc.
LOTTE HERBAL MINTS - Confections - Lotte USA Inc.
LOTTERY - Floor coverings–carpet and rugs - Ashley Commercial Carpets
LOTTERY GREETINGS - Greeting cards - Wilmer Graphics Inc.
LOTTERY GUIDE - Novelty items–paper - Arthur Charles Scott
LOTTERY LAUGHS - Greeting cards - Creative Marketing International Corp.
LOTTERY TREND ANALYSIS - Computer software - Computer Easy International, Inc.
LOTTI - Ophthalmic goods ☆ - Luxottica
LOTTIE D ENTERPRISES, INC. - Greeting cards - Lottie D Enterprises, Inc.
LOTTO - Beverages–malt - General Brewing Co.
LOTTO - Footwear - Lotto Sport USA
LOTTO FUN - Board game - Lotto-Fun, Inc.
LOTTO GOLD 2.1 - Computer software - Capstone Software
LOTTO LIGHTNING - Computer peripheral equipment - Massco Software, Inc.
LOTTO MANIA - Games - Smethport Specialty Co.
LOTTOCCASIONS - Greeting cards - Lottoccasions, Inc.
LOTTOGREETINGS - Paper products - Porcupine Productions, Inc.
LOTTOR - Leather ☆ - Formosa Crown
LOTTOUIJA - Toys - Tonka Corp.
LOTUS - Bicycles - Alpha Cycle & Supply Corp.
LOTUS - Cabinets - HomeCrest Corp.
LOTUS - Chimes ☆ - J.W. Stannard Co.
LOTUS - Computer software - Lotus Development Corp.
LOTUS - Cooking utensils–enameled - Jacksonville Manufacturing
LOTUS - Dinnerware–glass - Metlox Pottery Shoppe

LOTUS - Dinnerware–glass ☆ - Johnson Brothers, USA, Inc.
LOTUS - Figurines - Vincent Lippe Co.
LOTUS - Flatware - Wallace International Silversmiths, Inc.
LOTUS - Flowers–artificial - Hamilton-Hall Imports
LOTUS - Food products - Wei-Chuan U.S.A., Inc.
LOTUS - Frames–eyeglass - May Optical Co. Inc.
LOTUS - Giftware ☆ - Gorham Inc.
LOTUS - Glass products - Westmoreland Glass Co.
LOTUS - Glassware–household - Ralph E. Hall
LOTUS - Glassware–household ☆ - Rosenthal USA Ltd.
LOTUS - Guitars - Midco International
LOTUS - Medical apparatus - Lotus Health Care Products/Connecticut Art Craft
LOTUS - Motor vehicles–automobiles - Lotus/Cars USA Inc.
LOTUS - Nail care products - Cosmair Inc.
LOTUS - Recording label - Jazz Composer's Orchestra Association Inc.
LOTUS - Shrimp–fresh or frozen ☆ - Transpac Food
LOTUS - Slippers - Daniel Green Co.
LOTUS - Wallets ☆ - Enger-Kress Co.
LOTUS - Wallpaper - Koroseal Wallcoverings
LOTUS 1-2-3 - Computer software - Lotus Development Corp.
LOTUS 1757 - Flowers, plants, and seeds - Jacklin Seed
LOTUS ANNOTATOR, THE - Computer software - Lotus Development Corp.
LOTUS BLOSSOM - Dolls ☆ - Effanbee Doll Corp.
LOTUS BLOSSOMS - Milk–canned or powdered - Santini Foods
LOTUS COLLECTION - Computer software ☆ - SourceView Software International
LOTUS DE NUIT - Perfumes - Revlon Consumer Products Corp.
LOTUS DESKTOP MARKETING - Computer software - Lotus Development Corp.
LOTUS ESPRIT TURBO - Motor vehicles–automobiles - Lotus/Cars USA Inc.
LOTUS GARDEN - Tableware–china ☆ - Lenox, Inc.
LOTUS GLOSS - Paper - Japan Pulp & Paper (USA) Corp.
LOTUS II - Furniture ☆ - Hammary Furniture Co. Inc.
LOTUS LIGHT NATURAL TOUCH - Hair care products - Lotus Brands Inc.
LOTUS NOTES READY - Computer software - Lotus Development Corp.
LOTUS NOTES VIP - Computer software - Lotus Development Corp.
LOTUS ORGANIZER - Computer software - Lotus Development Corp.
LOTUS POND - Pottery ☆ - Rubens Originals
LOTUS REALTIME - Computer software - Lotus Development Corp.
LOTUS SMARTSUITE - Computer software - Lotus Development Corp.
LOTUS SUPREME - Bakery products - Lotus Manufacturing Co.
LOTUS WEI-CHUAN - Frozen foods - Wei-Chuan U.S.A., Inc.
LOTUSATE - Tranquilizers - Winthrop Pharmaceuticals
LOTY - Seafood products–fresh or frozen - International Wholesalers Corp.
LOU - Frames–eyeglass - Rozin Optical Export Corp.
LOU - Ophthalmic goods ☆ - Luxottica
LOU ANA - Vegetable oil - Ventura Foods LLC (Lou Ana Division)
LOU G. SIEGEL - Meats and processed foods - Lou G. Siegel, Inc.
LOU GEHRIG - Sporting goods - CMG Worldwide
LOU LOU - Bedding–linen - Dan River Inc.
LOU LOU'S - Cookies - Silverado Foods, Inc.
LOU +MITCHELL'S RESTAURANT & BAKERY - Bakery products - Lou Mitchell's, Inc.
LOU NARDI - Apparel and accessories - Explosive Clothing, Inc.
LOU PALOU - Cheese ☆ - Bongrain Cheese USA
LOU-RETTA'S BUFFALO GOLD - Pretzels - Lou-Retta's Custom Chocolates
LOU-RETTA'S CHOCOLATE LACES POPCORN - Popcorn - Lou-Retta's Custom Chocolates
LOU-ROD - Candy ☆ - Lou-Rod Candy Inc.
LOU TAYLOR - Handbags - B.H. Smith, Inc.
LOU TAYLOR - Luggage - Mitzi International Handbags & Accessories Ltd.
LOU-Z-ANA - Seafood products–fresh or frozen - Demerico Corp.
LOUANGEL - Hair care products - Schnapp Enterprises Inc.
LOUBABA - Olive oil - La Squisita Food Corp.
LOUBERE - Whiskey - Joseph E. Seagram & Sons, Inc.
LOUBINOX - Cutlery, knives, etc. - Cook Things
LOUBSOL - Sporting goods - Ski Country Imports, Inc.
LOUD & CLEAR - Antennas - R.A. Miller, Industries, Inc.
LOUD-KEY - Electronic equipment - Loud-Stik Corp.
LOUD-MATE - Alarm systems - Loud-Stik Corp.
LOUD MOUTH - Alarm systems - Universal Security Instruments Inc.
LOUD 'N CLEAR - Batteries ☆ - Rayovac Corp.
LOUDMOUTH - Electronic equipment - Earmark Inc.
LOUDMOUTH - Electronic equipment - Thomson Consumer Electronics, Inc.
LOUDMOUTH - Fishing lures - Mann's Bait Co.
LOUDMOUTHS - Candy - Glico Harmony Foods Corp.

☆ = Now out of production

LOUDON - Moldings–plaster of paris ☆ - Pacific Industries Inc.
LOUDY - Candy ☆ - Helms Candy Manufacturing Co. Inc.
LOUELLA - Evaporated milk, butter - American Stores Co.
LOUIE - Glass products - Louie Glass Co. Inc.
LOUIE BELLSON - Mallets - Mike Balter Mallets
LOUIE-BLOC RASPBERRY - Towels - National Pax Corp.
LOUIE-BLOO RASPBERRY - Confections - Jel Sert Co.
LOUIE LOBSTER - Toys–stuffed - Russ Berrie and Co., Inc.
LOUIE-LOOP - Nuts and bolts - Rawlplug Co., Inc.
LOUIE LOUIE - Fireworks - Ingram Enterprises, Inc.
LOUIE'S PLACE - Pet products - HTZ Investment Corp.
LOUIS - Ophthalmic goods - Rozin Optical Export Corp.
LOUIS - Watches - Hampden Corp.
LOUIS 5TH - Wines ☆ - California Wine Co.
LOUIS XVII - Tablecloths - Louis Nichole, Inc.
LOUIS ALLIS - Motors–hydraulic - Magnetek Inc.
LOUIS ARMSTRONG - Dolls ☆ - Effanbee Doll Corp.
LOUIS BIEN - Cheese - Raskas Foods, Inc.
LOUIS CARMINI - Shoes - Volpe Shoe Co.
LOUIS CYFER'S NIGHTMARE - Pepper - Habanero's Revenge Pepper Co.
LOUIS DUPRE - Wines ☆ - Alimar & Cie. Inc.
LOUIS FACELLI WINERY - Wines ☆ - Facelli Winery
LOUIS FEROUD - Frames–eyeglass - Euro-Frames Inc.
LOUIS FERRE - Wigs - Louis Ferre, Inc.
LOUIS GLUNZ - Wines - Louis Glunz Inc.
LOUIS GOLDSMITH INC. - Apparel–men's - Kayser-Roth Corp.
LOUIS-GRAVATTI - Apparel–men's - Intrep Imports, Inc.
LOUIS H. SULLIVAN - Iron - Historical Arts & Casting, Inc.
LOUIS H. SULLIVAN DECORATIVE DESIGN COLLECTION - Steel products - Historical Arts & Casting, Inc.
LOUIS HONIG - Wines ☆ - Honig Vineyard & Winery
LOUIS ICART - Giftware ☆ - Enesco Corp.
LOUIS ICART - Posters - One-of-a-Kind Workshop
LOUIS J. FOPPIANO - Wines ☆ - L. Foppiano Wine Co.
LOUIS JADOT - Wines - Kobrand Corp.
LOUIS JINDRA - Wines - Louis Jindra Winery
LOUIS K. MIHALY - Wines - Silverado Vineyards
LOUIS KEMP - Seafood products–fresh or frozen - Oscar Mayer Foods Corp.
LOUIS KEMP SEAFOOD CO. - Seafood products–canned or cured - Tyson Holding Co.
LOUIS KEMP SEAFOOD CO. - Seafood products–fresh or frozen - Louis Kemp Seafood Co.
LOUIS LANFRANCO - Shoes - Syd Levethan Shoes Inc.
LOUIS LOURIOUX - Cooking utensils–china ☆ - Lalique North America
LOUIS M. MARTINI - Wines - Louis M. Martini Corp.
LOUIS MAX - Wines ☆ - Shaw-Ross International Importers
LOUIS MEL - Wine - Wente Bros.
LOUIS NICHOLE - Wallpaper - Milbrook Wallcoverings
LOUIS NICHOLE FOR MEN - Wallpaper - Imperial Wallcoverings, Inc.
LOUIS PHILIPPE - Cosmetics - Chesebrough-Pond's USA Co.
LOUIS PHILIPPE - Furniture - National/Mt. Airy Furniture
LOUIS PHILIPPE - Luggage - Kingport International Corp.
LOUIS REGIS - Olive oil ☆ - Europa Foods Ltd.
LOUIS RICH - Meat products–poultry - Louis Rich Co.
LOUIS RICH - Meat products–poultry - Oscar Mayer Foods Corp.
LOUIS RICH CARVING BOARD - Meat extracts - Louis Rich Co.
LOUIS ROEDERER - Wines - Roederer U.S. Marketing Inc.
LOUIS ROTH - Apparel–men's - Steven Kurtzman Inc.
LOUIS ROYER - Beverages–alcohol - Blair Importers Ltd.
LOUIS SHERRY - Candy - Louis Sherry Candy Co.
LOUIS SHERRY - Ice cream - Borden, Inc.
LOUIS VUITTON - Luggage - Crouch & Fitzgerald Corp.
LOUIS W. BOWEN - Fabric ☆ - Louis W. Bowen
LOUIS XV - Furniture reproductions ☆ - Victorian Classics
LOUISA - Food products - Louisa Food Products Inc.
LOUISA - Ravioli–canned - V's Pasta Parlor
LOUISA BROOKS - Bathing suits - Apparel America, Inc.
LOUISA BROOKS - Bathing suits - Great American Industries Inc. (Robby Len Fashions Divison.)
LOUISE - Bedding–linen - Dan River Inc.
LOUISE - Glassware–household - Villeroy and Boch Tableware Ltd.
LOUISE - Kitchenware–china - H. Wittur & Co.
LOUISE WAUGH - Frames–picture ☆ - Chase Collection, Inc.
LOUISENBURG - Tableware–china ☆ - Villeroy and Boch Tableware Ltd.
LOUISE'S - Food products - Ore-Ida Foods, Inc.
LOUISE'S - Pasta - John Labatt Foods

LOUISE'S - Pasta - Promark International, Inc.
LOUISE'S - Potato chips - ATGTBT Inc.
LOUISE'S FAT-FREE - Potato chips - ATGTBT Inc.
LOUISIANA - Coffee - Wm. B. Reily & Co. Inc.
LOUISIANA - Cooking equipment–household ☆ - General Housewares Corp.
LOUISIANA - Food products - Bruce Foods Corp.
LOUISIANA - Shrimp–canned or cured - Robinson Canning Co. Inc.
LOUISIANA - Shrimp–fresh or frozen - Price Seafood Inc.
LOUISIANA - Wallcoverings - Stretchwall Fabrics Co.
LOUISIANA BILLIARD CLOTH - Wallcoverings - Stretchwall Fabrics Co.
LOUISIANA CAJUN - Spices and extracts - Finest Kind Spices
LOUISIANA CHOCOLATE FACTORY - Chocolate candy - Betty Ramsey Publisher
LOUISIANA CRAWFISH - Seafood products–fresh or frozen - Louisiana Premium Seafoods Inc.
LOUISIANA DIRTY - Rice - Mam Papaul's
LOUISIANA FISH FRY - Food products - Louisiana Fish Fry Products Ltd.
LOUISIANA GOLD - Food products - Bruce Foods Corp.
LOUISIANA GOLD - Seafood products–fresh or frozen - Paul Piazza & Son Inc.
LOUISIANA LIGHTNIN' - Snack foods - Mister Snacks Inc.
LOUISIANA NICKELS - Game machines - IGT - North America
LOUISIANA PREMIUM SEAFOODS - Seafood products–fresh or frozen - Louisiana Premium Seafoods Inc.
LOUISIANA RED - Food products - Arden International Kitchens Inc.
LOUISIANA SPICY HOT BARBECUE - Potato chips ☆ - Anheuser-Busch Companies Inc.
LOUISIANAS - Cookies - Sunshine/Salerno Inc.
LOUISIANA'S BEST - Seafood products–fresh or frozen - Ecrevisse Acadienne USA
LOUISVILLE - Apparel–athletic - Louisville Manufacturing
LOUISVILLE - Dishes–earthenware - Louisville Stoneware Co.
LOUISVILLE - Motor vehicles–trucks - Ford Motor Co.
LOUISVILLE CARDINALS - Apparel and accessories - University of Louisville
LOUISVILLE SLUGGER - Apparel–athletic ☆ - Cooper Sportswear Manufacturing Co., Inc.
LOUISVILLE SLUGGER - Bats–baseball - Hillerich & Bradsby Co.
LOUISVILLE SLUGGER MUSEUM - Apparel and accessories - Hillerich & Bradsby Co.
LOUKAS - Wines - Loukas Wines
+L'OULIBO - Food products - De Choix Specialty Foods Co.
LOULOU - Perfumes - Cosmair Inc.
LOULOU - Toys–stuffed ☆ - Gund, Inc.
LOULOU'S HOMEMADE! - Cookies - Lulabelle's Gourmet Cookies
LO.UN.GE! - Apparel and accessories - American Marketing Enterprises
LOUNGE - Floor coverings–carpet and rugs - Superior Manufacturing Group/ Notrax Floor Matting
LOUNGE - Hammocks - Algoma Net Co.
LOUNGE - Mats - Interstate Mat & Rubber
LOUNGE BENCH - Toys–stuffed ☆ - Dakin Inc.
LOUNGE HOUND - Toys–stuffed - Elaine T. Tinsley
LO.UN.GE! LONG UNDERWEAR GEAR - Apparel and accessories - American Marketing Enterprises
LOUNGEABOUTS - Shoes - Sam Brilliant Sporto
LOUNGELOKR - Garden furniture - MacPatrick Products, Inc.
LOUNGER - Apparel–men's - J. Schoeneman Inc.
LOUNGER - Pet products - Flexi-Mat Corp.
LOUNGER II - Chairs–upholstered - Franklin Corp.
LOUNGER'S - Slippers - International Seaway Trading Corp.
LOUNGING LILY - Pet products - Tetra Sales USA
LOUPER - Games - Gamescience
LOURDES - Pharmaceutical preparations - Vartex Pharmaceuticals Inc.
LOURIOUX - Cooking utensils–china ☆ - Lalique North America
LOURNAY - Skin care products ☆ - Colgate-Palmolive Co.
LOU'S EGGS DELITE - Eggs ☆ - Egg Low Farms Inc.
LOUSAN - Fabrics - SMS Textile Mills Inc.
LOUTRAKI - Water–mineral - John's Import Foods, Inc.
LOUVEAU - Floor coverings–carpet and rugs ☆ - Karastan-Bigelow Inc.
LOUVER - Cabinets ☆ - H.J. Scheirich Co.
LOUVER DRAPE - Blinds–vertical - Amsterdam Fabricators
LOUVER GROOVER - Blinds–vertical - Louverdrape Inc.
LOUVER MAGIC - Blinds–venetian - Royal Crest Inc.
LOUVERBORD - Wood products - Georgia-Pacific Corp.
LOUVERDRAPE - Window coverings - ESI
LOUVERDRAPE - Window coverings - Louverdrape Inc.
LOUVERLUX - Lighting equipment - Diffusa-Lite Co.

☆ = Now out of production

LOUVERLUX-MINIS - Fabrics - Vertilux-Louverlux Inc.
LOUVERMATE - Ventilation equipment - Triangle Metal and Manufacturing Inc.
LOUVERMATIC - Ventilation equipment - Triangle Metal and Manufacturing Inc.
LOUVERWOOD - Fabrics - Vertilux-Louverlux Inc.
LOUVIER - Handbags - Magnum Fashions Inc.
LOUVOIS - Glassware–household - Durand International
LOUVRE - Floor coverings–carpet and rugs - Couristan Inc.
LOUVRE KING - Jalousie windows, strip hardware - International Aluminum Corp.
LOUXOR - Flatware - Couzon USA
LOV-A-LIFT - Brassieres (Bras) ☆ - Lovable Co.
LOV-BO-GI-BOTS - Toys–electronic ☆ - Bandai America Inc.
LOV-EASE - Underwear and nightwear ☆ - Lovable Co.
LOV-ERE - Skin care products ☆ - Cenol Co. Inc.
LOV-IMALS - Toys ☆ - Steven Manufacturing Co.
LOV-N-MOIST - Cakes–mixes - J.W. Allen & Co.
LOV-UM - Food products - Victory Spud Service
LOVABLE - Apparel–women's - Lovable Co.
LOVABLE - Clocks ☆ - General Time Corp. (Westclox/Seth Thomas Div.)
LOVABLE - Ophthalmic goods - Foremost Optical Products
LOVABLE - Underwear and nightwear ☆ - Nantucket Industries Inc.
LOVABLE ADD-VANTAGE - Underwear and nightwear - Lovable Co.
LOVABLE BABIES - Dolls - Mattel, Inc.
LOVABLE BEGINNINGS - Underwear and nightwear - Lovable Co.
LOVABLE CATS - Housewares - Jibco Industries Inc.
LOVABLE LAMBS - Toys–stuffed - Fun World Inc.
LOVABLE LOOKING SHEER - Underwear and nightwear ☆ - Lovable Co.
LOVABLE LORRIE - Toys - Eugene Doll & Novelty Co. Inc.
LOVABLE LYNN - Dolls - Uneeda Doll Co., Inc.
LOVABLES - Greeting cards - Happiness Inc.
LOVABLES - Pet products - HTZ Investment Corp.
LOVABLES - Statuary–marble - Austin Productions, Inc.
LOVABLE'S BABY BARES - Underwear and nightwear ☆ - Lovable Co.
LOVAN - Shelving units–metal - Lovan Audio, Inc.
LOVAR - Tools ☆ - Keuffel & Esser Co.
LOVE - Apparel–women's ☆ - Berlei USA
LOVE - Coffee - Claud Rudolph Young
LOVE - Colognes - Jordache Enterprises Inc.
LOVE - Combs - Ajax Comb Co. (Div. of Antonio's Manufacturing, Inc.)
LOVE - Dishwashing compounds - Reen'o Corp.
LOVE - Giftware - Swiss Harmony Inc.
LOVE - Ophthalmic goods - Foremost Optical Products
LOVE - Recording label - Apon Record Co., Inc.
LOVE - Recording label - Random Enterprises Inc.
LOVE - Spices and extracts ☆ - Love Natural Foods
LOVE - Teas - San Francisco Herb & Natural Food Co.
LOVE-ABLES - Dolls ☆ - Effanbee Doll Corp.
LOVE AFFAIR - Lipsticks - Pavcom, Inc.
LOVE ALWAYS - Candy - R.M. Palmer Co.
LOVE ALWAYS/AMOUR TOUJOURS - Apparel–children's - Celebrity International, Inc.
LOVE & CHERISH - Frames–picture - Terragrafics Inc.
LOVE & KISSES - Candy - Madelaine Chocolate Novelties, Inc.
LOVE AND KISSES - Jewelry - Service Merchandise Co. Inc.
LOVE & KISSES - Skin care products - King Research, Inc.
LOVE AND LEARN - Toys - Tot Inc.
LOVE & LIFE - Publisher's imprints ☆ - Ballantine Books Inc.
LOVE & LOVE - Apparel–athletic - Emogene Hutman
LOVE AND MONEY - Apparel and accessories - Sandeep Gupta
LOVE & QUICHES - Food products - Love & Quiches Ltd.
LOVE & WAR - Video production - See Holdings Co.
LOVE AT FIRST BITE - Cheese - Love at First Bite
LOVE AT FIRST SIGHT - Floor coverings–carpet and rugs - Lock Weave Carpet Mills Inc.
LOVE BAXTER - Toys–stuffed - Russ Berrie and Co., Inc.
LOVE BEAD JEWELRY - Toys - Milton Bradley Co.
LOVE BEAR - Candy - Frankford Candy & Chocolate Co. Inc.
LOVE BEAR - Toys–stuffed ☆ - Dakin Inc.
LOVE BEAR JR. - Toys–stuffed - Russ Berrie and Co., Inc.
LOVE BED - Pet products - Flexi-Mat Corp.
LOVE BERRIES - Candy ☆ - Henry Heide, Inc.
LOVE-BERRIES - Vitamins and nutritional supplements - Natural Organics, Inc.
LOVE BIRD - Underwear and nightwear ☆ - Lovable Co.
LOVE BIRDS - Tableware–china - Pfaltzgraff Investment Co.
LOVE BITES - Ice cream ☆ - Chipwich Inc. (Chipwich Div.)

LOVE BITES - Pet food - Marcy, Inc.
LOVE BITES - Vitamins and nutritional supplements - Nature's Plus
LOVE BONES - Greeting cards - Mark R. Jones Citizens
LOVE BUFFS - Vitamins and nutritional supplements - Natural Organics, Inc.
LOVE BUG - Eyeglasses - Art-Craft Optical Co.
LOVE BUG - Golfing equipment - Love It Golf Co.
LOVE BUG - Hardware - Benhof Inc.
LOVE BUG - Insect repellents - Prince Lionheart, Inc.
LOVE BUG - Pet products - Precious Paws
LOVE BUG - Recreational vehicle dealers - Fabricated Products Co.
LOVE BUG II - Recreational vehicle dealers - Fabricated Products Co.
LOVE BUGS - Candy - Superior Fruit & Confections
LOVE BUTTER - Cocoa butter lotion - Aura Cacia Inc.
LOVE CHUMS - Toys - Advanced Design Concepts Inc.
LOVE COUPON - Novelty items - Four Score Inc.
LOVE CRITTERS - Toys–stuffed - Navajo Manufacturing Co.
LOVE DICE - Novelty items - Universal Marion Corp. (Parksmith Div.)
LOVE DOME - Apparel and accessories - Ronald P. Eldridge
LOVE DROPS - Veterinary nutritional supplements - Brewers Yeast Specialist
LOVE DROPS - Vitamins and nutritional supplements - Allan Rotberg
LOVE-E-LEE - Ice cream - Nestle USA
LOVE EARTH - Puzzles - Kling Magnetics Inc.
LOVE FLINGS - Toys–stuffed - Dakin Inc.
LOVE FOREVER - Jewelry - Something Old, Something New, Inc.
LOVE/FORTY - Apparel–athletic - Love/40 Tennis Collection Inc.
LOVE-FUEL - Health care products - Herbs of China Ltd.
LOVE GAME - Frames–eyeglass - May Optical Co. Inc.
LOVE GAMES - Computer software - SourceView Software International
LOVE GASKET - Prophylactics - Mayer Laboratories, Inc.
LOVE GLO - Underwear and nightwear ☆ - Lovable Co.
LOVE GLOVE - Pet products - Aaronco Grooming Products
LOVE GLOVE - Pet products - Four Paws Products Ltd.
LOVE GUM - Chewing gum - Gum Tech International
LOVE HANDLES - Infant product ☆ - American Baby Concepts
LOVE HANDLES - Office furniture–wood - LHS Technology
LOVE HATE PLAYMATE - Novelty items - Lynn Drexler
LOVE HEARTS - Candy - Ce De Candy Inc.
LOVE, HUGS N' KISSES - Apparel and accessories - Swat Fame, Inc.
LOVE-IN-MOTION - Toys–stuffed - Fun World Inc.
LOVE IS FASTER THAN LIGHT - Posters - John Mackesy
LOVE IS MAGIC - Dolls - Mattel, Inc.
LOVE-IT - Apparel, novelties - J & J Enterprises
LOVE IT - Health care products ☆ - Avon Products, Inc.
LOVE IT OR HATE IT - Games - Hilary Shepard
LOVE IT OR HATE IT - Games - Tyco Industries, Inc.
LOVE-ITS - Candy ☆ - Donruss Co.
LOVE JESUS - Pillows - Steven M. Keuter
LOVE KNOTS - Games - Scott C. Blanke
LOVE, KRISTIN - Figurines - Cast Art Industries, Inc.
LOVE KUBES - Novelty items - Karmatorium, Inc.
LOVE LACE - Rings–jewelry - Feature Enterprises
LOVE LACE - Underwear and nightwear ☆ - Lovable Co.
LOVE-LAMS - Greeting cards ☆ - Classic Plaques Inc.
LOVE LAND - Pet products - Normera Resources Corp.
LOVE LEE - Hair care products ☆ - Nutrine Ltd.
LOVE LETTER - Christmas tree ornaments - Cracker Box Inc.
LOVE LETTER - Eyeglasses - Art-Craft Optical Co.
LOVE LETTERS - Candy - Brach and Brock Confections Inc.
LOVE LETTERS - Novelty items - Agent Andy Inc.
LOVE LETTERS - Toys–stuffed - Fun World Inc.
LOVE LIFE - Apparel and accessories - Felice Pappas
LOVE LIFE FEMALE - Vitamins and nutritional supplements - Nutra-Source Corp.
LOVE LIFE MALE - Vitamins and nutritional supplements - Nutra-Source Corp.
LOVE LIGHT - Rings–jewelry - Artcarved Inc.
LOVE-LIKS - Candy - Lovelace Candy Manufacturing Co. Inc.
LOVE LINE - Wallets - Strand Enterprises
LOVE LINE - Women's sportswear - Van Buren, Inc.
LOVE LINK - Rings–jewelry - Feature Enterprises
LOVE LINKS - Craft supplies - Milton Bradley Co.
LOVE LITES - Candles - Russ Berrie and Co., Inc.
LOVE LITES - Dolls - Mattel, Inc.
LOVE LOCK LL WRAPS - Jewelry - Ostbye & Anderson, Inc.
LOVE LORE - Rings–jewelry ☆ - Artcarved Inc.
LOVE MAGIC - Colognes - Frances Denney
LOVE MATCH - Frames–eyeglass ☆ - Universal/Univis Inc.

☆ = Now out of production

LOVE MATE - Ophthalmic goods ☆ - Fidelity Case Corp.
LOVE MATE HIPPOS - Toys–stuffed ☆ - Russ Berrie and Co., Inc.
LOVE ME - Frames–eyeglass - U.S. Optical Frame Co.
LOVE ME ALWAYS PET UMS - Pet products - G.G. Bean Inc.
LOVE ME BABY - Dolls - Horsman
LOVE ME DUES - Greeting cards - DeLuCo
LOVE ME SOFSKIN - Dolls - Horsman
LOVE ME TENDER - Dolls - Tonka Corp.
LOVE ME TENDER - Flowers, plants, and seeds - W. Atlee Burpee and Co.
LOVE ME TENDER - Meat products–poultry - Whistlin' Dixie Fried Chicken Inc.
LOVE MESSENGER - Toys–stuffed ☆ - Dakin Inc.
LOVE MIST - Underwear and nightwear ☆ - Lovable Co.
LOVE MOBILE - Strollers–baby ☆ - Century Products Co.
LOVE, MOM - Giftware - Furginson, P. A.
LOVE MUGS - Glassware–household - Four Score Inc.
LOVE MY CARPET - Deodorizers - L & F Consumer Products
LOVE MY CARPET ULTRA PET - Deodorizers - L & F Consumer Products
LOVE MY DOLLY - Toys - Processed Plastic Co.
LOVE MY GOAT - Wines - Bully Hill Vineyards, Inc.
LOVE-MY-LOOFAH - Soap - Grandpa Brands Co.
LOVE 'N GO - Dolls - Mattel, Inc.
LOVE N' HERBS - Salad dressings–bottled - Da Silva-Klanko Ltd.
LOVE IN NUMBERS - Jewelry - Gold N Innovations Inc.
LOVE 'N SQUEEZE ME - Toys ☆ - Gerber Products Co.
LOVE N' STITCHE'S - Craft supplies - Yarn Kits Inc.
LOVE N' STUFF - Giftware ☆ - Enesco Corp.
LOVE 'N TOUCH - Dolls - Mattel, Inc.
LOVE N' TOUCH - Ostomy product - Convatec
LOVE-N-WAR - Recording label - Love-N-War
LOVE NOTES - Candy - Superior Fruit & Confections
LOVE NOTES - Dolls - Mattel, Inc.
LOVE NOTES - Glassware–household ☆ - Anchor Hocking Glass, Inc.
LOVE NOTES - Recording label - At Work Entertainment, Inc.
LOVE-NOTES - Telephone answering machines - Solana Technology Development Corp.
LOVE OF CHRISTMAS - Christmas tree ornaments - Cracker Box Inc.
LOVE OUR EARTH - Bags - North American Imports, Inc.
LOVE OUR EARTH - Giftware - Securitag Corp.
LOVE PANS - Foil–aluminum - E-Z-Por Corp.
LOVE PAT - Cosmetics - Revlon Consumer Products Corp.
LOVE-PATS - Greeting cards ☆ - Amberley Greeting Card Co.
LOVE PETS - Toys–stuffed - Fun World Inc.
LOVE PILL - Vitamins and nutritional supplements - Magni Co.
LOVE POTION - Perfumes - Times Suare Productions
LOVE POTION NO. 9 - Adult games - The Game Works, Inc.
LOVE POTION NUMBER 9 - Vitamins and nutritional supplements - Abundant Life Custom-Made Food Supplements
LOVE POTION NO. 69 - Beverages - J & H Food and Beverage, Inc.
LOVE PRESCRIPTION - Notebooks and notepads - Four Score Inc.
LOVE PUFFS - Toys–stuffed - Fun World Inc.
LOVE PUZZLE NOTES - Greeting cards - Four Score Inc.
LOVE QUEST, THE - Computer software ☆ - Capstone Software
LOVE RASCALS - Toys–stuffed ☆ - Fun World Inc.
LOVE RIOT - Recording label - Love Riot
LOVE ROCKS - Stone products - Bruce Edwin Stuckey
LOVE SCROLL - Rings–jewelry - Artcarved Inc.
LOVE SEAT - Underwear and nightwear ☆ - Lovable Co.
LOVE SET - Frames–eyeglass - May Optical Co. Inc.
LOVE SHOOTERS - Candy - Square Shooter Candy Co.
LOVE SHOW - YOUR WEDDING SHOWCASE, THE - Publisher's imprints - NRC Media Creations, Inc.
LOVE SNACKS - Fruits–dried - Hershey Import Co. Inc.
LOVE SOMEBODY LOVE YOURSELF - T-shirts–men's - Continnuus
LOVE SONG - Christmas tree ornaments - Cracker Box Inc.
LOVE SONG - Floor coverings–carpet and rugs - Lees Carpets
LOVE SONG - Rings–jewelry - Artcarved Inc.
LOVE SONG - Wallpaper ☆ - Imperial Wallcoverings, Inc.
LOVE SONNET - Rings–jewelry - Artcarved Inc.
LOVE SPELL - Publisher's imprints - Dorchester Publishing Co., Inc.
LOVE STARS - Rings–jewelry - Artcarved Inc.
LOVE STORIES - Wallpaper ☆ - Jack Denst Designs
LOVE STORY - Frames–eyeglass ☆ - Universal/Univis Inc.
LOVE STORY - Rings–jewelry - Artcarved Inc.
LOVE STRUCK - Games - International Gamco, Inc.
LOVE TABLE - Medical apparatus - Educare

LOVE TALES - Candy - Buy the Weigh Inc.
LOVE TALK - Glassware–household ☆ - Papel Freelance, Inc.
LOVE TALK ACCORDING TO HIM...ACCORDING TO HER - Greeting cards - American Greetings Corp.
LOVE-THAT-STRETCH - Underwear and nightwear ☆ - Lovable Co.
LOVE THINGS - Toys–stuffed - Kamar International Inc.
LOVE THIS MUCH BEAR - Toys–stuffed - Russ Berrie and Co., Inc.
LOVE TO LEARN - Recording label - Love to Learn, Inc.
LOVE TOKENS - Greeting cards - C.M. Paula Co.
LOVE TOUCH - Brassieres (Bras) ☆ - Warnaco Inc.
LOVE TRAP MICE - Animal figurines with cologne ☆ - Cosrich Inc.
LOVE UM'S - Novelty and standard writing instruments and rubber stampers - Impact International Inc.
LOVE WEAVE - Rings–jewelry ☆ - Artcarved Inc.
LOVE-WIPES - Skin care products - Stephen C. Lytle
LOVE YA PUP - Pet products - O.D. Funk Co.
LOVE YOUR BABY - Clippers–nail - F.D.C. Wholesale Corp.
LOVE YOUR BODY - Apparel and accessories - Sentra Sporting Goods USA Co.
LOVE YOUR BUNS CHEF - Toys–stuffed - Russ Berrie and Co., Inc.
LOVE YOUR DOG - Pet products - Hartz Mountain Corp.
LOVE YOUR DOG - Pet products - HTZ Investment Corp.
LOVE YOUR HOME - Fabrics–tapestry - Comark Wallcoverings
LOVE YOUR HUGS BEAR - Toys–stuffed - Russ Berrie and Co., Inc.
LOVE YOUR PLANET - Apparel and accessories - U.S. International Space Year Association
LOVE YOUR SKIN - Skin care products - Southco Sales Corp.
LOVE YOUR TOUCH - Skin care products ☆ - Winning Solutions Inc./Miracle of Aloe
LOVEALOT BEAR - Toys - Those Characters from Cleveland, Inc.
LOVEBEADS - Craft supplies - Walbead Inc.
LOVEBIRD - Dinnerware–glass - Franciscan by Johnson Brothers, USA, Inc.
LOVEBIRDS - Glassware–household - Crystal Clear Importing Co. Inc.
LOVEBIRDS - Meat products–poultry - Pierce Foods Corp.
LOVEBIRDS - Toys–stuffed ☆ - Fun World Inc.
LOVEBOAT - Toys - Multi Toys Corp.
LOVEBUCKETS - Cases–compacts - Royce Associates L.P.
LOVEBUG BY INFANTA - Knit goods - Infanta Knitting Mills
LOVEBUG JRS. - Knit goods - Infanta Knitting Mills
LOVEBURGER - Spices and extracts - Love Natural Foods
LOVEBYTES - Greeting cards - Advanced Research Corp.
LOVECAM - Greeting cards - Salvatore Gurrieri
LOVECHILD - Apparel and accessories - Rains, Rosalie
LOVEE - Toys - Lovee Doll and Toy Co. Inc.
LOVEJOY'S COLLEGE COUNSELOR - Computer software ☆ - Knowledge Adventure
LOVEKIN - Heating equipment ☆ - Bradford-White Corp.
LOVELABELS - Labels–fabric - Blumenthal/Lansing Co.
LOVELACE - Candy - Lovelace Candy Manufacturing Co. Inc.
LOVELACE FAMILY LTD., THE - Greeting cards - Lovelace Family Ltd.
LOVELADIES' COSTUMES - Catalogs - Djb Enterprises, Inc.
LOVELAND - Chimes ☆ - Nutone Inc.
LOVELAND - Giftware - Joseph Berland
LOVELEE - House furnishings ☆ - Foley & Robinson Inc.
LOVELIA ENTERPRISES - Floor coverings–carpet and rugs ☆ - Foley & Robinson Inc.
LOVELIGHTS - Candlesticks - Lancaster Colony Corp.
LOVELL DESIGNS - Jewelry - Lovell Designs Inc.
LOVELON - Underwear and nightwear ☆ - Lovable Co.
LOVELOOK - Frames–eyeglass - Pathway Optical Prods.
LOVELURE - Frames–eyeglass - Zylo Ware Corp.
LOVELY - Floor coverings–carpet and rugs - Shaheen Carpet Mills
LOVELY - Frames–eyeglass - Zylo Ware Corp.
LOVELY ANN - Yarn ☆ - Lion Brand Yarn Co.
LOVELY BREATH - Pet products - Tomlyn Products
LOVELY GIRL 105 - Slacks - Porto Chico Stores, Inc.
LOVELY LACE SECRETS - Underwear and nightwear - Maidenform Inc.
LOVELY LADY - Barrettes - Sta-Rite Ginnie Lou Inc.
LOVELY LADY - Cosmetics - Worldwide Cosmetics
LOVELY LADY - Eyeglasses - Art-Craft Optical Co.
LOVELY LADY - Food products ☆ - Rex Pacific
LOVELY LADY - Fruits–frozen - Buskirk Processing Inc.
LOVELY LADY - Toys - Jak-Pak Inc.
LOVELY LADY LOCKS - Bathroom accessories ☆ - Tsumura International Inc.
LOVELY LAVENDER - Toys - Tonka Corp.
LOVELY LIFT - Apparel–women's - Vesta Intimate Apparel

☆ = Now out of production

LOVELY LILIES - Bedding–linen - Dan River Inc.
LOVELY LISA - Toys–stuffed - Jolly U.S.A., Inc.
LOVELY LOCKET - Toys - Link Group International
LOVELY LOOKS - Toys - Toymax Inc.
LOVELY MUSIC - Recording label - Jazz Composer's Orchestra Association Inc.
LOVELY NESS - Toys - Abrams/Gentile Entertainment, Inc.
LOVELY SOFSKIN - Dolls - Horsman
LOVELY STUFF - Frames–eyeglass - Liberty Optical Manufacturing Co.
LOVELY TO LOOK AT - Cologne and necklace ☆ - Cosrich Inc.
LOVELY WAY - Hair care products - Helene Curtis Industries Inc.
LOVELYAIRE - Knitting machines - Collins & Aikman Corp.
+L'OVENBEST - Food products - Grand Union Co.
LOVEPAK - Underwear and nightwear - Wundies Inc.
LOVEPATS - Apparel and accessories - Wundies Enterprises, Inc.
LOVEPATS FOR GIRLS - Footwear - Americal Corp.
LOVEQUEST - Games - Jamie Turndorf
LOVEQUEST THE GAME OF FINDING MR. RIGHT - Games - Jamie Turndorf
LOVERA - Cigar boxes–wood - Consolidated Cigar Corp.
LOVERDRAPE - Blinds–venetian - Vertical Blind Factory
LOVERLY - Frames–eyeglass ☆ - Universal/Univis Inc.
LOVERLY - Rings–jewelry - Artcarved Inc.
LOVER'S COVERS - Medical apparatus - Lover's Covers Corp.
LOVER'S KNOT - Brassieres (Bras) ☆ - Lovable Co.
LOVER'S MOON - Perfumes - Allanco
LOVE'S - Bakery products - Love's Bakery-Daiichiya Inc.
LOVE'S - Barbecue sauce - Love's Enterprises Inc.
LOVE'S - Colognes - Mem Co., Inc.
LOVE'S BABY SOFT - Colognes - Mem Co., Inc.
LOVE'S CLEAN & NATURAL - Colognes - Mem Co., Inc.
LOVE'S DELIGHT - Apparel–women's - Randi Foundations Inc.
LOVE'S GARDEN BY BETTY CHAISSON - Giftware - Roman, Inc.
LOVE'S GENTLE MUSK - Cosmetics - Mem Co., Inc.
LOVES ME-LOVES ME NOT - Candy ☆ - R.M. Palmer Co.
LOVES ME TEDDY - Toys–stuffed ☆ - Dakin Inc.
LOVE'S SOFT JASMIN - Cosmetics - Mem Co., Inc.
LOVES THE JOBS YOU HATE - Cleaning preparations - S.C. Johnson & Son, Inc.
LOVE'S WHITE VANILLA - Colognes - Mem Co., Inc.
LOVESAVER - Jewelry - Jose Hess, Inc.
LOVESON - Boots - St. Lawrence Sales Inc.
LOVESONG - Frames–eyeglass - Pathway Optical Prods.
LOVESTICKS - Breads - Judy's Breadsticks of Mendocino
LOVESTONE - Novelty items - Curiosity Press
LOVESWEATS - Apparel–athletic - Shear Intensity
LOVESWEPT - Publisher's imprints - Bantam Doubleday Dell Publishing Group, Inc.
LOVEWEAR - Underwear and nightwear ☆ - Lovable Co.
LOVEWISE - Recording label - Romanceworks for Those Seeking Love and Marriage
LOVEY - Ophthalmic goods ☆ - Luxottica
LOVEY - Toys–stuffed - Russ Berrie and Co., Inc.
LOVEY BEAR - Wallpaper ☆ - Priss Prints Inc.
LOVEY BUNNIES - Toys–stuffed - Russ Berrie and Co., Inc.
LOVEY-DOVE - Underwear and nightwear ☆ - Lovable Co.
LOVEY DOVEYS - Toys - Mattel, Inc.
LOVEY DUCKEY - Toys - Gerber Products Co.
LOVEY KITTEN - Toys–stuffed - Russ Berrie and Co., Inc.
LOVEY'S - Food products - Lovey's Inc.
LOVFETTI - Fabrics–broadcloth - Foss Manufacturing Co., Inc.
LOVIA - Beverages–alcohol ☆ - Palm Bay Imports, Inc.
LOVIN - Food products ☆ - Countrymark Cooperative, Inc.
LOVIN' - Towels - Hoon Lee No. 1 Accessories
LOVIN' BEARS - Toys–stuffed - Fun World Inc.
LOVIN LITES - Cakes–mixes - Pillsbury Co.
LOVIN' LOAF - Cakes–mixes ☆ - Pillsbury Co.
LOVIN' SOUNDS NURSERY - Toys - Playskool, Inc.
LOVIN' SPOONFULS - Cat food - Ralston Purina Co.
LOVIN' TOUCH - Toys–stuffed - Fun World Inc.
LOVING - Frames–eyeglass - Zylo Ware Corp.
LOVING BADGES - Games - Fun World Inc.
LOVING BUNNY - Candy - Philadelphia Candies Inc.
LOVING CARE - Frames–eyeglass - Zylo Ware Corp.
LOVING CARE - Hair coloring preparations - Clairol Inc.
LOVING CHOICE - Baby blankets - Transamerica Mailings, Inc.
LOVING FAMILY COLLECTION - Jewelry - Carlisle Jewelry Co., Inc.

LOVING HANGUPS - Posters - Abbey Press Inc.
LOVING HEART - Vitamins and nutritional supplements - Ultravit Enterprises, Inc.
LOVING HEARTS - Cosmetics - Strom Sales, Inc.
LOVING HEARTS - Infant product - Ganz
LOVING LATHER - Soap - Care-Tech Laboratories Inc.
LOVING LATHER II - Skin care products - Care-Tech Laboratories Inc.
LOVING LIFT - Brassieres (Bras) - Moore Products
LOVING LOTION - Skin care products - Care-Tech Laboratories Inc.
LOVING MOMENTS - Jewelry - Avon Products, Inc.
LOVING PHRASES GENTLY SPOKEN OVER CALMING MUSIC - Recording label - Explorers
LOVING REFLECTIONS - Giftware - Russ Berrie and Co., Inc.
LOVING TEARS BABY - Dolls - Toy Biz, Inc.
LOVING THOUGHTS - Jewelry - Joyce A. Roark
LOVING TOUCH - Diapers–disposable - Weyerhaeuser Co.
LOVING TOUCH - Floor coverings–carpet and rugs - Ashley Commercial Carpets
LOVING TOUCH - Floor coverings–carpet and rugs ☆ - Empire Carpet Mills Inc.
LOVING TOUCH - Thread - Belding Heminway Co. Inc.
LOVING WONDER - Toys - Eugene Doll & Novelty Co. Inc.
LOVING YOU - Dolls - Mattel, Inc.
LOVINGGAME, THE - Games - RJE Games Inc.
LOVINGWEAR - Apparel–women's - Comme-Ci Comme-Ca Ltd.
LOVION - Skin care products - Lovion International, Inc.
LOVITES - Vitamins and nutritional supplements - Natural Organics, Inc.
LOVITT - Food products - Lovitt Mining Co. Inc.
LOVITT - Meat product - Jac Pac Foods
LOVLAST - Cleaning preparations - Foremost Chemicals Inc.
LOVOC - Adhesives and sealants - Crawford Laboratories
LOVOC - Concrete products - Sealwall Products Inc.
LOVUE - Cosmetics ☆ - Shaklee Corp.
LOVUMS - Dolls ☆ - Effanbee Doll Corp.
LOVY - Apparel and accessories - Adgar Inc.
LOW & BEHOLD - Cleaning preparations–carpet and rug - Ecolab Inc.
LOW & SASSY - Toys–automobiles - Mattel, Inc.
LOW BOY - Ice chests–plastic ☆ - Coleman Co., Inc.
LOW BOY - Trailers–travel ☆ - Mitchell & Sons Inc.
LOW CHOLESTEROL GOURMET - Computer software - Lynn Fischer
LOW COUNTRY - Furniture - Bassett Furniture Industries, Inc.
LOW CUT - Amplifiers–musical instrument - Seymour Duncan Pickups
LOW DOWN - Bicycles - Huffy Corp.
LOW-DOWN - Frames–eyeglass - May Optical Co. Inc.
LOW DOWN, THE - Apparel and accessories - Brazabra Corp.
LOW E - Doors–glass - Weather Shield Manufacturing, Inc.
LOW FAT GRANOLA BARS - Granola bars ☆ - Kellogg Co.
LOW FAT POP-TARTS - Pastries - Kellogg Co.
LOW FAT SWEET DO - Bakery products - Dawn Food Products Inc.
LOW FAT TRIOS - Pasta - Original Italian Pasta Products Co. Inc.
LOW KEY - Frames–eyeglass - Pathway Optical Prods.
LOW-LOFT - Fabrics - Fairfield Processing Corp.
LOW-LUSTRE - Paints - Adelphi Coatings Co.
LOW NUFF - Brassieres (Bras) - Lady Marlene
LOW-PEAK - Electrical supplies - Cooper Industries, Inc.
LOW PROFILE - Apparel–women's - Bali Co. Inc.
LOW PROFILE - Fans–electric - Hunter Fan Co.
LOW PROFILE - Health care products - Roho, Inc.
LOW PROFILE - Rifles - Redfield Co.
LOW-QUEL - Health care products - Halsey Drug Co. Inc.
LOW RESIDUE FORMULA - Animal feeds - Iams Co.
LOW RIDER - Sandwiches–prepackaged - H-D Michigan, Inc.
LOW-SEG - Optical machinery - Coburn Optical Industries Inc.
LOW SPIRIT USA - Recording label ☆ - Instinct Records Corp.
LOW T GRAY - Glass products ☆ - AFG Industries Inc. (Glass Group Div.)
LOW-TACK POLYCUSHION - Orthopedic products - Smith & Nephew Inc. (Rehabilitation Div.)
LOW TORQUE - Golfing equipment - Aldila, Inc.
LOW TOX - Oils–lubricating - Lubrication Engineers, Inc.
LOW VIEW - Lenses–optical - Ditto Industries Inc.
LOW VOC COVER-STAIN - Paints ☆ - William Zinsser & Co. Inc.
LOW VOC PENETROL - Paints - Flood Co.
LOWA - Boots ☆ - Climb High Inc.
LOWA - Footwear–athletic - Omni International Distributors Inc.
LOWBOY - Housewares ☆ - Advance Machine Co.
LOWDEN - Guitars - Cobble Hill International

LOWDIA - Containers ☆ - Elden Enterprises, Inc.
LOWE - Boats–motor - O.M.C. Aluminum Boat Group
LOWE - Excavators - Lowe Manufacturing Co., Inc.
LOWE - Games - Milton Bradley Co.
LOWE ALPINE - Sporting goods - Lowe Alpine Systems, Inc.
LOWEL TOTA-LIGHT - Lighting fixtures ☆ - Lowel-Light Manufacturing Inc.
LOWELL - Brushes–paint ☆ - PPG Industries, Inc.
LOWELL - Cabinets - American Woodmark Corp.
LOWELL - Sausages - Lowell Packing Co.
LOWELL - Tableware–china - Lenox, Inc.
LOWELL - Thread - Lowell G. Hays & Sons
LOWELL DAVIS - Figurines - Schmid Inc.
LOWELL HOUSE - Publisher's imprints - NTC Contemporary Publishing Group
LOWENBRAU - Beer - Miller Brewing Co.
LOWENBRAU DARK SPECIAL - Beer - Miller Brewing Co.
LOWENBRAU LIGHT - Low-calorie beer - Miller Brewing Co.
LOWENBRAU SPECIAL - Beer - Miller Brewing Co.
LOWENBRAU ZURICH - Beer - Inter-Floridana Import & Export
LOWENSENF - Mustards - Carl Brandt
LOWENSTEIN - Fabrics - M. Lowenstein Corp.
LOWER AWAY - Brassieres (Bras) ☆ - Lovable Co.
LOWER BURNER - Health care products - East Earth Herb Inc.
LOWER LAKE WINERY - Wines ☆ - Wildhurst Winery
LOWERS - Ophthalmic goods - Foremost Optical Products
LOWE'S - Cleaning preparations - Lowe's Companies Inc.
LOWE'S - Pet products ☆ - Golden Cat Corp.
LOWES FOODS - Dairy products - Lowes Foods
LOWE'S HOME SAFETY COUNCIL - Recording label - LF Corp.
LOWESTOFT FLOWERS - Dishes–china ☆ - Royal China & Porcelain Companies Inc.
LOWFLOW - Valves - Richards Industries, Inc.
LOWILA CAKE - Skin care products - Westwood-Squibb Pharmaceuticals, Inc.
LOWLAND - Scarves, neckwear - Calzeat & Co. Ltd.
LOWLOADER - Automotive parts and accessories - Detroit Wrecker Sales
LOWMOUNT - Lighting equipment - General Electric Co.
LOWNDS PATEMAN - Skin care products - Freund-Mayer & Co. Inc.
LOWOHM - Reflectors–optical - Optical Coating Laboratory Inc.–Santa Rosa Div.
LOWRANCE - Fishing tackle - Lowrance Electronics, Inc.
LOWRANCE AVIONICS - Electronic equipment - Lowrance Electronics, Inc.
LOWREY - Organs–musical instrument - Lowrey Organ Co.
LOWREY'S - Meat products–beef - Curtice-Burns Meat Snacks Inc.
LOWREY'S BIG BEEF - Meat products–beef - Curtice-Burns Meat Snacks Inc.
LOWREY'S COWBOY JO - Meat products–beef - Curtice-Burns Meat Snacks Inc.
LOWREY'S OLD FASHIONED - Meat products–beef - Curtice-Burns Meat Snacks Inc.
LOWRIDER - Electronic equipment - Mine Safety Appliances Co.
LOWRIDER - Fishing rods - Beckwith Sales, Inc.
LOWRIDER CAFE - Apparel and accessories - Park Avenue Publishing, Inc.
LOWTECH INNOVATIONS INC. - Hardware - Low Tech Innovations Inc.
LOWTEMP - Paints ☆ - Everseal International Sales Co. Inc.
LOWTHERM I ANTI-ICER - Deicing fluid - Chemmark Corp.
LOWTHERM INHIBITOR - Chemical preparations - Chemmark Corp.
LOWTIME - Frames–eyeglass - Liberty Optical Manufacturing Co.
LOWY - Frames–picture - Julius Lowy Frame & Restoring Co., Inc.
LOX - Adhesives and sealants - Bridgestone/Firestone, Inc.
LOX - Varnishes - Lox Systems Inc.
LOX-8 - Lubricants - Fluoramics Inc.
LOX FAST - Varnishes - Lox Systems Inc.
LOX-ON - Housewares - Aladdin Industries, Inc.
LOX + PLUS - Health care products - Essex Medical Products
LOX-RITE - Thread - Blue Mountain Industries, Inc.
LOX-RUST - Paints ☆ - Steelcote Manufacturing Corp.
LOX-SEAL - Paints - Sherwin-Williams Automotive Finishes Corp.
LOX SUPREME - Varnishes - Lox Systems Inc.
LOX-TITE - Toys–trains - Kadee Quality Products
LOXARMOR - Cables - Okonite Co. Inc.
LOXCREEN - Windows–screen - Loxcreen Co. Inc.
LOXIN - Nuts and bolts - Star Anchors & Fasteners
LOXITE - Adhesives and sealants - Bridgestone/Firestone, Inc.
LOXOL - Foil–aluminum - KVP Group
LOXSPRING - Fasteners–snap ☆ - North and Judd Inc.
LOXTITE - Paints - Standard Paint Co.
LOY - Resins–polymer - Ferro Corp.

LOYAL - Brushes–paint - Rubberset Co.
LOYALE - Motor vehicles–automobiles - Subaru of America, Inc.
LOYALTY - Floor coverings–carpet and rugs - Karastan-Bigelow Inc.
LOYALTY - Floor coverings–carpet and rugs ☆ - Mohawk Carpet Corp.
LOYALTY - Food products - Tip Top Canning Co.
LOYALTY - Furniture ☆ - A.A. Laun Furniture Co.
LOYALTY - Office supplies ☆ - Eaton Allen Ko-Rec-Type Corp.
LOYALTY - Sprayers - RL Flo-Master
LOYALTY - Vegetables–canned - Loyal Canning Corp.
LOYD ANTHONY - Apparel and accessories - Lloyd P. Brown and Anthony S. Whitaker
LOYD-B - Nipples–rubber - Lopuco Ltd.
LOYOLA COLLEGE - Stationery - Associated Professors of Loyola College
LOYOLA COLLEGE 1852 BALTIMORE MARYLAND - Stationery - Associated Professors of Loyola College
LOYOLA COLLEGE IN MARYLAND - Paper - Associated Professors of Loyola College
LOZEN - Fruits and vegetables - Diamond a
LOZIER - Hardware - Lozier Store Fixtures
LOZINCGES - Cough drops - Makers of Kal, Inc.
LP - Drums–musical instruments - LP Music Group
LP - Golfing equipment - Ram Golf Corp.
LP - Office furniture–metal - Davson Inc.
LP - Screws - Leland-Powell Fasteners Inc.
LP - Winches - Lindgren-Pitman, Inc.
LP-70 - Medical apparatus - Physical Research Corp.
LP-1000 - Fuel additives - Hydrotex, Inc.
LP/D - Dictating machines ☆ - Lanier Voice Products
LP FINISH 15, A - Animal feeds - Carl S. Akey Inc.
LP FINISH 60, A - Animal feeds - Carl S. Akey Inc.
LP FINISH BOOSTER - Animal feeds - Carl S. Akey Inc.
LP/NG - Oils–lubricating - Maxus Energy Corp.
LP TEEJET - Nozzles - Spraying Systems Co.
LP3 - Printers–computer - Comtec Information Systems, Inc.
LP6 - Medical apparatus - Aequitron Medical, Inc.
LPAC - Computer peripheral equipment - Personal Computer Products, Inc.
LPAUDIT - Computer software - Dan'l Systems
LPC - Cylinders - American Cylinder Co., Inc.
LPC - Jewelry–precious - Momme Tomo Inc.
LPC - Lighting fixtures - R.J. Howell Co., Inc.
LPCLAB - Computer software - Data Translation, Inc.
LPEFI - Motor vehicle parts and accessories - BDE, Ltd.
LPF ETC - Children's apparel - La Petite Fleur Inc.
LPGA - Golfing equipment - Square Two Golf
LPH - Detergents - Calgon Vestal Laboratories
LPH AG - Detergents - E.R. Squibb & Sons, Inc.
LPI - Clocks - License Products, Inc.
LPI - Elevators - L.P.I., Inc.
LPI - Joists–open web - Louisiana-Pacific Corp.
LPNET - Surveillance equipment - Dan'l Systems
LPP - Vitamins and nutritional supplements - Twinlab
LPR - Brakes–motorcycle - Linsco Private Ledger
LPS 2000 - Computer software - American Management Systems, Inc.
LPT - Hair care products - Waverly Beauty Products
LPTRENDS - Computer software - Dan'l Systems
LPX - Golf shoes - Acushnet Co.
LPX - Golfing equipment ☆ - Titleist & Foot-Joy Worldwide
LQ 1500 - Computers–personal ☆ - Epson America, Inc.
LR - Jewelry - Lee Read Jewelers Inc.
LR-OPTIMIZED - Chemical preparations - Genomyx, Inc.
LRF - Bicycles - Kent International Inc.
LRG - Drill bits - Rockbit International, Inc.
LRHP FORTE - Health care products - Life-Renewal Inc.
LRJ - Labels–paper - LRJ Records
LS - Adhesives and sealants - General Liquids Corp.
LS - Boats–motor - Thunderbird Products
LS - Boats–motor ☆ - Harris-Kayot Inc.
LS - Cigarettes - R.J. Reynolds Tobacco Co.
LS - Recording label - LS Records
LS-4 - Audio equipment - Recoton Corp.
LS-10 COOLSCAN - film scanner - Nikon Inc.
LS-2100R - Photographic equipment - LogEtronics Corp.
LS-2600 - Photographic equipment - LogEtronics Corp.
LS-2600R - Photographic equipment - LogEtronics Corp.
LS-3510AF - Photographic equipment - Nikon Inc.
LS STUDIO - Footwear - Brown Shoe Co.

☆ = Now out of production

L.S. WHEATS - Snack foods - New Generation Foods Inc.

LSAT FOR IBM & APPLE - Computer software - Krell Software Corp.

LSC - Compressors - Dunham Bush, Inc.

LSC - Cylinders - American Cylinder Co., Inc.

LSC - Electronics equipment - RTI Research Technology International

LSC - Heaters–gas - Martin Industries, Inc.

LSC - Measuring instruments - Compucyte Corp.

LSCO - Jewelry - L. Sparrow & Co. Inc.

LSD - Optical machinery - Physical Optics Corp.

LSI - Chemical preparations - Vysis, Inc.

LSI - Computer software - Liberty Systems International, Inc.

LSI - Spotlights - Rothco Inc.

LSLI - Computer software - Livermore Software Laboratories, Inc.

LSN LIFELINE - Computer software - Biological Abstracts Inc.

L.S.T. - Cutlery - Gerber Legendary Blades

LST - Rope - Wall Industries Inc.

LT - Garden equipment - Homelite, Inc.

LT - Helmets–athletic - LT Helmets Inc.

LT - Integrated circuits - Linear Technology Corp.

LT - Sinks–plastic - Laboratory Tops Inc.

L.T. - Tanning agents - Le Tan

LT. BIMO BRAGG - Toys - Mattel, Inc.

LT DESIGNS BY CENTURY - Furniture–wood ☆ - Century Furniture Co.

LT4X - Computer software - Infotec Development, Inc.

LTC ADVISOR - Computer software - Stratecision, Inc.

LTC AMERICAS - Machinery - Ltc Americas Inc.

LTC PAINT ME COLORS - Shirts - Walls Industries, Inc.

LTC QUOTE - Computer software - Stratecision, Inc.

LTCS - Computer software - Horizon Graphics Systems, Inc.

LTCS ACCESS - Computer peripheral equipment - Horizon Graphics Systems, Inc.

LTD - Flatware - Oneida Ltd.

LTD - Motor vehicles–automobiles ☆ - Ford Motor Co.

LTD - Radios–citizens' band - Cobra Electronics Corp.

LTD - Tires - Laramie Tire Distributors, Inc.

LTD - Watches - Advance Watch Co. Ltd.

LTD CROWN VICTORIA - Motor vehicles–automobiles ☆ - Ford Motor Co.

LTD GOLD CUP - Hoses - Radiator Specialty Co.

LTD II - Motor vehicles–automobiles ☆ - Ford Motor Co.

LTL - Construction equipment rental services - Integrated Silicon Systems Inc.

LTM - Mattresses - Big Sur Waterbeds, Inc.

LTM - Medical apparatus - Proclosure, Inc.

LTP - Jewelry - M. Fabrikant & Sons

LTP - Meat products–poultry ☆ - Longmont Foods

LTS - Bicycle parts and accessories - Foes Fabrications Inc.

LTS - Humidifiers - Dri-Steem Humidifier Co.

LTS - Wheels–motor vehicle - Aluminum Co. of America

LTV SCOUT - Toys–models ☆ - Estes Industries

LTX - Bags - Tamrac, Inc.

LTX - Tires - Michelin Tire Corp.

LU - Cookies - Sunshine/Salerno Inc.

LU-GEE - Toys - Park Plastics Co.

LU LU LOOPER - Paddle ball game - Sharon Industries

LU SEE - Medical apparatus - Cordis Corp.

LU VAN - Furniture–wood ☆ - Charlotte Co. Inc.

LUAU - Food products - Hawaiian Sun Products Inc.

LUAU - Recording label - Boddie Record Manufacturing & Recording Inc.

LUAU KIT - Housewares - Paul Marshall Products L.P.

LUAU LITE - Candles - Empire Manufacturing Co.

LUAU LITES - Candles ☆ - Aloha Candle Manufacturing Co. Inc.

LUAU MIX - Crackers - Umeya Rice Cake Co.

LUB-A-CABLE - Lubricants - Panef Corp.

LUB-A-GRAPH - Lubricants - Panef Corp.

LUB-A-KIT - Lubricants ☆ - Panef Corp.

LUB-A-LITE - Lubricants - Panef Corp.

LUB-A-LOCK - Lubricants - Panef Corp.

LUB-A-SPRAY - Powdered graphite - Panef Corp.

LUB-A-STICK - Lubricants - Panef Corp.

LUB-IT - Oils–lubricating - J.A. Fleuridas Co.

LUBA - Floor coverings–carpet and rugs ☆ - Regal Rugs Inc.

LUBALLOY - Oils–lubricating ☆ - K & W Products

LUBALOY - Bullets - Olin Corp. (Winchester Div.)

LUBASPORIN - Pharmaceutical preparations ☆ - Burroughs Wellcome Co.

LUBATH - Skin care products - Warner-Lambert Co.

LUBBABLE PUP - Toys–stuffed - Russ Berrie and Co., Inc.

LUBBERS DAIRY - Milk - Lubbers Dairy Products

LUBE - Automotive parts and accessories - General Motors Corp. (Harrison Radiator Div.)

LUBE-COAT - Automotive parts and accessories ☆ - K & W Products

LUBE CUBE - Containers–metal - Hoover Containment Systems, Inc.

LUBE-IT ALL - Adhesives and sealants - Federal Process Co.

LUBE-R-COAT - Rust removers - Rectorseal Corp.

LUBE-SHOT - Firearms, accessories, and parts - Bud Newell & Associates, Inc.

LUBE TUBE - Lubricating - Comstar International Inc. (IPC Div.)

LUBE-TUBE - Tubes–plastic - Carl Spatazza

LUBECRAFT - Lubricants - LubeCon Systems, Inc.

LUBEFAX - Lubricants - Gaines Industries, Inc.

LUBEGARD - Lubricants - Enterprise Oil Co.

LUBESOFT - Computer software - Integrated Services, Inc.

LUBESTER - Lubricants - LubeCon Systems, Inc.

LUBEZOL - Lubricants - Lubrizol Corp.

LUBIN - Fabrics–silk - Charles Lubin Co. Inc.

LUBIN - Skin care products - Frances Denney

LUBINOL - Oils–mineral - Purepac Pharmaceutical Co.

LUBISEPTOL - Veterinary products - Walco International, Inc.

LUBIT-8 - Lubricants - Fluoramics Inc.

LUBIUM - Chemical preparations - Southwestern Petroleum Corp.

LUBOIL - Lubricants - Conklin Co., Inc.

LUBRARICH - Razors - Gillette Co.

LUBRASOL - Skin care products ☆ - Pharmaceutical Specialties, Inc.

LUBREX - Bath salts - T/I Pharmaceuticals, Inc.

LUBRI-JOINT - Gaskets - La-Co Industries, Inc.

LUBRI-PEN - Oils–lubricating - Mehaz International, Inc.

LUBRI SCENT - Lubricants - S & S Innovations, Inc.

LUBRI-SHINE - Cleaning preparations - Auto Wax Co., Inc.

LUBRI-SOFT LOTION - Skin care products - Geritrex Corp.

LUBRI-TASGON - Lubricants ☆ - Samuel Cabot Inc.

LUBRIBOR - Fuel additives - Hammonds Fuel Additives, Inc.

LUBRICARE - Cosmetics - Leiner Health Products Inc.

LUBRICATH - Health care products - C.R. Bard, Inc.

LUBRICATION DYNAMICS - Oils–lubricating - Slick 50 Corp.

LUBRICITY PLUS - Fuel additives - Hydrotex, Inc.

LUBRICOAT - Pharmaceutical preparations - Johnson & Johnson

LUBRICONE - Lubricants - Kano Laboratories Inc.

LUBRICORT - Skin care products ☆ - Warner-Lambert Co.

LUBRIDERM - Skin care products - Warner-Wellcome

LUBRIDERM MOISTURE RECOVERY ALPHA HYDROXY - Skin care products ☆ - Warner-Wellcome

LUBRIDERM ONE STEP - Skin care products ☆ - Warner-Wellcome

LUBRIDERM SERIOUSLY SENSITIVE - Skin care products - Warner-Wellcome

LUBRIGLIDE - Inks - Gillette Co.

LUBRIKO - Oils–lubricating - Master Lubricants Co.

LUBRIKUHL - Lubricants - Lubrizol Corp.

LUBRIL - Chemical preparations - Rhone-Poulenc Surfactants and Specialties, L.P.

LUBRIMAR - Skin care products ☆ - Marlop Pharmaceuticals Inc.

LUBRIMATIC - Lubricants - Witco Corp.

LUBRIMIST - Lubricants - Witco Corp.

LUBRIN - Health care products - Kenwood Laboratories Inc.

LUBRIPLATE - Lubricants - Fiske Brothers Refining Co. (Lubriplate Div.)

LUBRISCAN - Ultrasonic testing equipment - Cosmaceutical Marketing, Inc.

LUBRISYN - Chemical preparations - Lubrizol Corp.

LUBRITEARS - Pharmaceutical preparations - Bausch & Lomb Inc.

LUBRITECH 2000 - Lubricants - Amtech USA, Inc.

LUBRITHANE - Automotive parts and accessories - Pleiger Plastics Co.

LUBRITITE - Tape–adhesive - Mystik Corp.

LUBRITRAK - Musical instrument accessories - Hamer Guitars

LUBROL - Oils–lubricating - Boehme Filatex, Inc.

LUC - Connectors–electrical - Lucent Technologies Inc.

LUC-E-CON - Projectors–photographic ☆ - Star Parts Inc.

LUCA + MARCO - Apparel and accessories - Too Italian Designers, Inc.

LUCALOX - Glassware–household - General Electric Co.

LUCAS - Automotive parts and accessories - Lucas Service

LUCAS - Luggage - I.J.K. Sales Corp.

LUCAS - Paints - Dutch Boy Group

LUCAS - Suntan lotions - American Sunlight Inc.

LUCAS ARTS - Computer software - Lucasfilm Ltd.

LUCAS CAV - Fuel systems–motor vehicle - Lucas Service

LUCAS FAMILY VINEYARDS - Wines - Lucas Winery

LUCAS FILM LTD. - Postcards ☆ - Classico San Francisco Inc.

LUCAS FX - Toys - Mattel, Inc.
LUCAS WINERY, THE - Wines - Lucas Winery
LUCASOL - Cleaning preparations - Lucas Products Corp.
LUCAYAN - Boats–motor - Lyn-Craft Boat Co.
LUCCA - Dishes–china - Pasmantier Co. Inc.
LUCCA - Food products - Lucca Packing Co. of California Inc.
LUCCHESE - Boots - Lucchese Boot Co.
LUCCHESE - Footwear - Acme Boot Co., Inc.
LUCCHI DELANO - Shoes - Mosinger-Cohn Inc.
LUCCIANO - Footwear - Wolverine World Wide, Inc.
LUCENT - Glass products - Gillinder Brothers Inc.
LUCENT - Wallpaper - Winfield Design Associates, Inc.
LUCENT/BOND - Paper–bond - American Coating Enterprise
LUCENT TECHNOLOGIES - Pens - Lucent Technologies Inc.
LUCENTVIEW - Photographic equipment ☆ - Buckingham
LUCERA - Office furniture ☆ - Inwood Office Furniture
LUCERA - Shoes ☆ - Allen-Edmonds Shoe Corp.
LUCERN - Fabrics - Dan River Inc.
LUCERNE - Cheese - Glencourt Products
LUCERNE - Floor coverings - Mannington Resilient Floors
LUCERNE - Ice cream - Safeway Stores Inc.
LUCERNE - Musical instruments - Custom Music Co.
LUCERNE - Watches - Lucerne Time
LUCHI - Shoes ☆ - Tessler Shoe Corp.
LUCHO - Skin care products - Lucho Inc.
LUCIA - Apparel–women's - Lucia, Inc.
LUCIA - Fabrics - J.B. Martin Co. Inc.
LUCIA - Harmonicas - Hohner Inc.
LUCIA - Tableware–china - Lenox, Inc.
LUCIANNO PAVAROTTI DONNA - Perfumes - Classic Fragrances Ltd.
LUCIANO - Fabrics - Dan River Inc.
LUCIANO FRANZONI - Men's suits and sportcoats - Intercontinental Branded Apparel
LUCIANO GATTI - Neckties - Allaudin's Designs, Inc.
LUCIANO PAVAROTTI HOMME - Perfumes - Classic Fragrances Ltd.
LUCIANO SOPRANI - Handbags, belts - Spettacolo Inc.
LUCID 3-D - Computer software - Lucid Corp.
LUCID AGONY - Perfumes - Proverbial Inc.
LUCID CLARITY - Health care products - East Earth Herb Inc.
LUCID LIGHT - Greeting cards - Carl Coffman
LUCIDA - Epoxy - Hartline Products Co. Inc.
LUCIDA - Jewelry, watches - Bloomfield International Inc.
LUCIDEX - Fabrics - Scan Lines Inc.
LUCIDITY - Caps and gowns–academic and clerical - Estee Lauder Inc.
LUCIDTY - Clocks ☆ - General Time Corp. (Westclox/Seth Thomas Div.)
LUCIE - Women's apparel - Jamie Shuken
LUCIE ANN - Underwear and nightwear - Lucie Ann Inc.
LUCIE ANN II - Apparel–women's - Lady Ester Lingerie Corp.
LUCIE ANNE II - Underwear and nightwear - Lucie Ann Inc.
LUCIE ARNAZ'S GUIDE TO DOING YOUR FAMILY HISTORY - Computer storage devices–optical - Konami (America) Inc.
LUCIEN - Toys–stuffed ☆ - Russ Berrie and Co., Inc.
LUCIEN DESCHAUX - Wines - Leonard Kreusch Inc.
LUCIEN PICCARD - Watches - Lucien Piccard/Arnex
LUCIENNE - Bedding–linen - Dan River Inc.
LUCILE'S - Seasonings - Creole Cafe Food Products
LUCILLE - Guitars - Kingsid Ventures, Ltd.
LUCILLE BALL - Dolls ☆ - Effanbee Doll Corp.
LUCILLE FARMS - Cheese - Lucille Farms, Inc.
LUCINA - Lubricants ☆ - Shell Oil Co.
LUCINDA - Frames–eyeglass - U.S. Optical Frame Co.
LUCINDA RHODES - Apparel–women's ☆ - Vera Sportswear
LUCIOUS ONE - Fabrics - Guilford Mills, Inc.
LUCITE - Brushes–paint - E.I. Dupont de Nemours and Co.
LUCITE GOURMET - Housewares ☆ - Knobler International Ltd.
LUCITE HOSTESS, THE - Cooking equipment–household ☆ - Kraftware Corp. (Morgan Div.)
LUCITE SAR - Scratch-resistant acrylic panels - Auburn Plastic Engineering
LUCITE-TUF - Building materials - ICI Acrylics Inc.
LUCK OR LOGIC - Games - Avalon Hill Game Co.
LUCK PLUS - Card game - International Games
LUCK TESTER - Novelty items - Adams Apple Distributing L.P.
LUCKERS - Footwear - Morning Bird, Inc.
LUCKIDAY, THE - Vacuum cleaners and accessories ☆ - Sunbeam-Oster Household Products
LUCKS - Bakery products - Lucks Co.

LUCK'S - Vegetables–canned - Lucks Inc.
LUCK'S COUNTRY STYLE - Bean sprouts - Lucks Inc.
LUCKSRONG - Floor coverings–linoleum - Lucky America Inc.
LUCKSRONG-SANDY - Floor coverings–linoleum - Lucky America Inc.
LUCKY - Animal feeds - Foster Canning Inc.
LUCKY - Beverages–alcohol ☆ - Falstaff Brewing Corp.
LUCKY - Beverages–malt - General Brewing Co.
LUCKY - Candy - Wellons Candy Co. Inc.
LUCKY - Tape–adhesive - American Stores Co.
LUCKY - Tiles–enamel - Lucky America Inc.
LUCKY - Toys ☆ - Playskool, Inc.
LUCKY - Vitamins and nutritional supplements - Lucky Stores, Inc.
LUCKY 2 FER'S - Games - World Wide Press, Inc.
LUCKY 4 - Game machines - Fitzgeralds Las Vegas, Inc. (Frank)
LUCKY 7 BALLS - Candy ☆ - American Candy Co.
LUCKY 13 - Games ☆ - A.R.C. Toys Inc.
LUCKY 13 - Sporting goods ☆ - James Heddon's Sons
LUCKY 21 BLACK JACK - Game machines - Kevin Sharp Enterprises, Inc.
LUCKY 100S - Cigarettes - American Tobacco Co.
LUCKY BALLS - Novelty items - Ronald A. Leibin
LUCKY BOY - Apparel–children's - Charles Greenberg & Sons Inc.
LUCKY BOY AMBASSADOR - Coffee - Emco Foodservice Systems, Inc.
LUCKY BOY DELEGATE - Coffee - Emco Foodservice Systems, Inc.
LUCKY BOY DIPLOMAT - Coffee - Emco Foodservice Systems, Inc.
LUCKY BOY ROYALE - Preserved foods–canned - Emco Foodservice Systems, Inc.
LUCKY BOY STATESMAN - Coffee - Emco Foodservice Systems, Inc.
LUCKY BUBBLE - Novelty items - Visionary Products, Inc.
LUCKY BUBBLES - Ornamental products–glass - Visionary Products, Inc.
LUCKY CARD - Cookies - Pure's Food Specialities Inc.
LUCKY CHARM - Bicycles - Murray, Inc.
LUCKY CHARM - Floor coverings–carpet and rugs - Queen Carpet Corp.
LUCKY CHARM STRING - Musical instrument accessories - Max Roisman
LUCKY CHARMS - Cereal - General Mills, Inc.
LUCKY CHEW - Candy ☆ - Glenn Confections Inc.
LUCKY CLOVER - Pet products - Hill Top Enterprises
LUCKY CLUCKER - Sporting goods - Penn's Woods Products Inc.
LUCKY DAY - Fishing lures - Mr. Bob's
LUCKY DIAMOND - Apparel–women's - Wacoal America Inc.
LUCKY DICE - Air purification systems - Medo Industries, Inc.
LUCKY DICE - Games ☆ - Milton Bradley Co.
LUCKY DOG - Dog food - Ralston Purina Co.
LUCKY DOG - Hair clippers–veterinary - Sunbeam Corp.
LUCKY DOG - Pet products - Lucky Dog Equipment Inc.
LUCKY DOG - Pet products - Mr. Mutt Pet Products Inc.
LUCKY DOG - Pet products - Sunbeam-Oster Household Products
LUCKY DOG - Recording label - Sony Music Entertainment Inc.
LUCKY DOG - Toys–marbles - Charlie's Woodshop
LUCKY DUCK - Giftware - Duck Press
LUCKY DUCKS - Games - Hasbro, Inc.
LUCKY DUCKY - Toys ☆ - Gerber Products Co.
LUCKY EAGLE POPS - Candy ☆ - American Candy Co.
LUCKY EDDIE - Toys - Mattel, Inc.
LUCKY EIGHTS - Tires–bicycles - Buck Enterprises
LUCKY ELEVEN - Games - Betty J. Herald
LUCKY FARMS - Fruits and vegetables - Lucky Farms, Inc.
LUCKY FILTERS - Cigarettes - American Tobacco Co.
LUCKY FIND - Vegetables–frozen - National Frozen Foods Corp.
LUCKY FISHERMEN - Food products - U.S. Freezer Co.
LUCKY GIRL - Apparel–children's - Charles Greenberg & Sons Inc.
LUCKY GOLD - Citrus fruits - Florida Global Citrus Ltd.
LUCKY GOLF SOCKS HOLE IN ONE - Apparel–athletic - Flagpin Productions
LUCKY HEARTS - Toys–stuffed ☆ - Fun World Inc.
LUCKY HORSESHOE - Novelty items - S.J. Miller Co.
LUCKY JACKPOT WASH - Games - American Primus Equipment Co.
LUCKY JACKS - Apparel and accessories - Petro PSC, L.P.
LUCKY JOE - Gloves - Midwest Glove Co.
LUCKY KENTUCKY - Hair care products - Miriam Collins - Palm Beach Laboratories Co.
LUCKY KENTUCKY - Hair care products - Palm Beach Beauty Products
LUCKY KENTUCKY - Shampoos - Lynwood Laboratories
LUCKY KNITS - Toys–stuffed - Kamar International Inc.
LUCKY LABRADOR BREWING COMPANY PORTLAND, OREGON - Beverages - Lucky Labrador Brewing Co.
LUCKY LADY - Cosmetics - L.T. York Co.
LUCKY LADY - Gloves–work - Kinco International Inc.

☆ = Now out of production

LUCKY LADY - Vegetables–frozen - J.R. Simplot Co.
LUCKY LAUNCHER - Pet products - Lucky Dog Equipment Inc.
LUCKY LEAF - Food products - Knouse Foods Cooperative, Inc.
LUCKY LIENER - Games - Universal Manufacturing Co., Inc.
LUCKY LIGHT - Beverages–malt - General Brewing Co.
LUCKY LOLLY - Ice cream ☆ - H.P. Hood & Sons Inc.
LUCKY LOTTERY - Candles - Mercado Latino, Inc.
LUCKY LOTTO PEN, THE - Writing product - Island Pen Manufacturing Corp.
LUCKY LOTTO PIC - Tools - L.L.S. & P. Production, LLC
LUCKY LOTTO STICK - Tools - L.L.S. & P. Production, LLC
LUCKY LUGGAGE TAG, THE - Labels–paper - Name Maker Corp.
LUCKY MUG LEGEND - Coffee - Coffee Beanery Inc.
LUCKY-PENNY - Hair coloring preparations - Cosmair Inc.
LUCKY PENNY - Pet products ☆ - Maggie Mae's Gourmet Pet Products Inc.
LUCKY PENNY SEEDS - Novelty items - Betty L. Boyce
LUCKY PET - Pet products - Vo-Toys Inc.
LUCKY PETS - Pet products - Safeguard Chemical
LUCKY PIERRE - Boats - Glen-L Marine Designs
LUCKY PUTT - Golfing equipment - Plawood Mormac Corp.
LUCKY RAINBOW - Games - International Gamco, Inc.
LUCKY ROASTERS - Meat products–poultry - American Stores Co.
LUCKY ROLLERS - Tires–bicycles - Buck Enterprises
LUCKY ROSE - Food products - Nishimoto Trading Co. Ltd.
LUCKY SCRATCH OFF SCRATCHER - Scrapers - Ronald J. Sedita
LUCKY SELLER - Food products - A. Levy & J. Zentner Co.
LUCKY SEVEN - Games - Twinson Co.
LUCKY SLOT GLOVES 777 - Gloves - Lanka Products Inc.
LUCKY SPOT - Games - Trade Products, Inc.
LUCKY STAR - Floor coverings–carpet and rugs - Burlington House Carpets
LUCKY STAR - Floor coverings–carpet and rugs - Galaxy Carpet Mills Inc.
LUCKY STAR - Publisher's imprints - Scholastic Inc.
LUCKY STAR - Rice - North American Food Distributing Co., Inc.
LUCKY STAR - Toys - Gerber Products Co.
LUCKY STARS - Glow-in-the-dark toy - Giggles Toy Co. Inc.
LUCKY START - Apparel–women's - Wacoal America Inc.
LUCKY STEER - Gloves - Brookville Glove Manufacturing Co.
LUCKY STIFF - Recording label - Smash Palace
LUCKY STONES - Garden equipment ☆ - Set Consumer Products Inc.
LUCKY STRIKE - Cigarettes - American Tobacco Co.
LUCKY STRIKE - Floor coverings–carpet and rugs ☆ - Calladium & Marglen
LUCKY STRIKE - Seafood products–fresh or frozen - Tri-Union International, LLC
LUCKY STRIKE - Thread - Threads USA Div.
LUCKY STRIKE 100S - Cigarettes - American Tobacco Co.
LUCKY STRIKE LIGHTS - Cigarettes - American Tobacco Co.
LUCKY STRIPE - Apparel–women's - Wacoal America Inc.
LUCKY TAB - Paper products - Ronald C. Clapper, Jr.
LUCKY TEN - Cigarettes - American Tobacco Co.
LUCKY THE DRAGON - Toys - Tyco Toys
LUCKY THINGS - Figurines ☆ - Cal Themes Inc.
LUCKY TIGER - Hair care products - L.T. York Co.
LUCKY TOUCH - Video games - Arachnid, Inc.
LUCKY TROLL - Toys–stuffed - Great American Fun Corp.
LUCKYPHANTS - Figurines - Banberry Designs
LUCKY'S AMERICAN APPAREL BUILDERS - Apparel - Mahan-Davis Sales & Manufacturing Inc.
LUCKY'S MAGIC HAT - Computer software - Advanced Ideas
LUCKYSPORTS - Apparel and accessories - Luckysports
LUCO - Artists' materials - Lucy's Foods
LUCOZADE - Beverages ☆ - Gilway Co. Ltd.
LUCRETIA VANDERBILT - Cosmetics - McKesson Home Health Care
LUCREZIA - Flatware - Buccellati Silver Ltd.
LUCREZIA DEL MARE - Food products - OTL Foods
LUCUL - Soups–mixes ☆ - H.J. Gasser Specialty Foods
LUCY - Watches - Bulova Corp.
LUCY & DESI: THE SCRAPBOOKS, VOL. 1 - Computer storage devices–optical - Konami (America) Inc.
LUCY & ME - Giftware ☆ - Enesco Corp.
LUCY BEARS - Giftware - C.R. Gibson Co.
LUCY JR. - Dresses–women's - Huntington Industries Inc.
LUCY LAMB - Candy - Keppel's Inc.
LUCY LAMB - Toys–stuffed - Russ Berrie and Co., Inc.
LUCY LEMON - Dolls - Mattel, Inc.
LUCY LIP COLOR - Cosmetic - Joe Blasco Enterprises, Inc.
LUCY MAXYM COLLECTIONS, THE - Giftware - Siamese Imports Co.
LUCY WATUSSI - Dolls - Mattel, Inc.

LUDA - Soups–mixes - Empire Dehydrated Products Inc.
LUDE - Glassware–household - Durand International
LUDELL - Hardware, tools - Atlas Group
LUDEN'S - Cough drops - Hershey Chocolate USA
LUDEN'S - Cough drops - Luden's Inc.
LUDEN'S CITRUS ASSORTMENT - Cough medicines - Hershey Foods Corp.
LUDEN'S HIGHLITES - Candy - Luden's Inc.
LUDEN'S RX - Cough drops - Luden's Inc.
LUDEN'S SUPER STRENGTH - Cough drops - Luden's Inc.
LUDICROUS GEAR - T-shirts–men's - Kevin Painchaud
LUDICROUS LION - Toys–stuffed ☆ - Dakin Inc.
LUDIGOL - Chemical preparations - Rhone-Poulenc Surfactants & Specialties, LP
LUDIOMIL - Pharmaceutical preparations - Ciba-Geigy Corp.
LUDLOW - Floor coverings–carpet and rugs ☆ - Ludlow Corp.
LUDMAN - Hardware - Blaine Window Hardware Inc.
LUDO - Toys–stuffed ☆ - Dakin Inc.
LUDOWICI-CELADON - Roofing materials - Ludowici-Celadon Inc.
LUDOX - Chemical preparations - E.I. Dupont de Nemours and Co.
LUDVIG SVENSSON - Tablecloths - Odin Ltd.-Scan Am Imports Inc.
LUDWICK'S - Doughnuts - Ludwick's Frozen Donuts
LUDWIG - Doors–storm - Ludwig Manufacturing Co. Inc.
LUDWIG - Food products - Ludwig Shrimp Co.
LUDWIG - Musical instruments ☆ - Selmer Co. Inc.
LUDWIG - Pianos ☆ - Cunningham Piano Co.
LUDWIG - Sausages - Haram-Christensen Corp.
LUDWIG HUDEPOHL OKTOBERFEST - Beverages–malt - Hudepohl-Schoenling Brewing Co.
LUDWIG HUDEPOHL SPECIAL BOCK - Beverages–malt - Hudepohl-Schoenling Brewing Co.
LUDWIG HUDEPOHL'S ORIGINAL BOCK - Beverages–malt ☆ - Hudepohl-Schoenling Brewing Co.
LUDWIG NEUHAUS - Wines - Victoire Imports Co.
LUFA - Vitamins and nutritional supplements - Rhone-Poulenc Rorer Pharmaceuticals Inc.
LUFA-LUX - Cleaning preparations - Swiss-Tex Inc.
LUFF SLOT - Marine rigging - Stearns Sailmakers
LUFFE - Ships–sailing vessels - Scandinavian Yachts
LUFFT - Weather tracking equipment - Abbeon Cal. Inc.
LUFFT - Weather tracking equipment - Watrous & Co. Inc.
LUFKIN - Measuring instruments - Lufkin Rule Co.
LUFKIN - Water purification systems - Lufkin Industries Inc.
LUFT DIFFUSER - Pet products - Tetra Sales USA
LUFT PUMP - Pet products - Tetra Sales USA
LUFTODIL - Pharmaceutical preparations ☆ - Wallace Laboratories
LUFTWAFFE - Games - Avalon Hill Game Co.
LUFUS - Apparel - Sam E. Tsouloufas
LUFYLLIN - Pharmaceutical preparations - Wallace Laboratories
LUFYLLIN-EPG - Pharmaceutical preparations - Wallace Laboratories
LUFYLLIN-GG - Pharmaceutical preparations - Wallace Laboratories
LUG-A-BIKE - Sporting goods - All American Products Inc.
LUG A TUG - Pet products - Code 26 Group Inc.
LUG-CENTRIC - Wheel mounting nut assembly - Consolidated International Automobile Inc.
LUG LUBE - Musical instrument accessories - LP Music Group
LUG NUT - Apparel and accessories - Charlotte Motor Speedway, Inc.
LUGANO - Dinnerware–glass - Johnson Brothers, USA, Inc.
LUGANO - Glassware–household - Villeroy and Boch Tableware Ltd.
LUGANO - Motor vehicles–automobiles ☆ - Ford Motor Co.
LUGANO - Shoes - Allen-Edmonds Shoe Corp.
LUGARO - Electronic equipment - Lugaro Inc.
LUGE - Medical apparatus - Cobe Laboratories, Inc.
LUGER - Firearms, accessories, and parts - Stoeger Industries
LUGER STANDARD - Toys - Park Plastics Co.
LUGGAGE BY U.S. - Luggage - United States Luggage Corp.
LUGGAGE CADDY - Luggage - L.C. Industries, Inc.
LUGGAGE GALLERY, THE - Luggage ☆ - Seward Luggage Co.
LUGGAGE-LOKS - Locks–padlocks - Luggage Loks Inc.
LUGGAGE RAP - Luggage - Net/Werk/USA, Inc.
LUGGAGE THAT COOPERATES - Luggage ☆ - American Tourister, Inc.
LUGI - Brushes–paint - Rubberset Co.
LUGNY - Glassware–household - Durand International
LUGVELOPE - Leather goods - Travel Technologies, Inc.
LUGZ - Footwear - Jack Schwartz Shoes, Inc.
LUHRS - Boats–motor - Luhrs Co.
LUI LUI EVERYWEAR - Apparel and accessories - Luis J. Hernandez

☆ = Now out of production

LUICHINY - Footwear–children's - Lvichiny Destroy Imports Inc.
LUICHINY - Shoes - Moreno Habif
LUIGI - Pizzas–frozen ☆ - Macomb Sandwich Inc.
LUIGI BEE - Toys–stuffed ☆ - Edumundo Productions, Inc.
LUIGI CECCHI - Wines - Banfi Vintners
LUIGI VITELLI - Tomato pastes and sauces - A. Sargenti Co. Inc.
LUIGIANA - Restaurants–pizzerias - Holland St. John Ltd.
LUIGI'S - Pizzas–frozen - Armato's Pizza Co.
LUIGI'S - Snack food - J & J Snack Foods Corp.
LUIGI'S - Tomato pastes and sauces - Luigi's Brand Food Products
LUIJCKX - Food products - De Choix Specialty Foods Co.
LUIS ALVEAR OUTERWEAR - Apparel–athletic - Novo-Las Corp.
LUIS MERA - Toys - Tonka Corp.
LUIS VITELLI - Eyeglasses - Optics International Inc.
LUKAS - Paints–artists' - Lukas USA/TVF Inc.
LUKE - Recording label - Luke Records Inc.
LUKE RAILSTON'S - Food products - Jardine's Texas Foods
LUKE SKYWALKER - Publisher's imprints - Lucasfilm Ltd.
LUKE SKYWALKER - Toys - Kenner Products
LUKE SKYWALKER VINYL FIGURE - Toys - ERTL Co., Inc.
LUKSUSOWA - Vodka - Adamba Imports International Inc.
LULABELLE - Cookies - Lulabelle's Gourmet Cookies
LULI - Slacks–women's - Luli, Inc.
LULL - Construction equipment - Lull International
LULL-A-BABY - Bedding–linen - Fine Art Pillow & Specialties Corp.
LULL-A-BABY - Music boxes - Coehler-Coptex Co.
LULL-A-BYE - Toys - Fine Art Pillow & Specialties Corp.
LULLABABIES - Figurines ☆ - Schmid Inc.
LULLABY - Craft supplies ☆ - VIP/VIP Crafts
LULLABY - Giftware ☆ - Gorham Inc.
LULLABY - Jewelry - Jacoby-Bender Inc.
LULLABY - Shoes - Conaway-Winter Inc.
LULLABY & GOOD NIGHT BY LOUIS NICHOLE DESIGN STUDIO - Linen - Louis Nichole, Inc.
LULLABY-BEAR - Toys–stuffed ☆ - Gund, Inc.
LULLABY CLUB - Linen - Dayton Hudson Corp.
LULLABY LAND - Apparel–children's - H.H. Cutler Co.
LULLABY LUVS - Dolls ☆ - Fun World Inc.
LULLABYE - Furniture - Evenflo Juvenile Furniture Co.
LULLABYE BABY - Dolls - Horsman
LULLABYE BIG BIRD - Toys–stuffed - Playskool, Inc.
LULLABYE BIRD - Toys–musical - Playskool, Inc.
LULLABYE COOKIE MONSTER - Toys–musical - Playskool, Inc.
LULLABYE LUV - Toys ☆ - Revell-Monogram, Inc.
LULU - Fishing tackle ☆ - Schumann's Fly Fish Kit Co.
LULU'S DESSERT FACTORY - Food products - Dairy Fresh Products Co.
LUMA - Artists' materials - Steig Products
LUMA - Projection screens - Draper Shade and Screen Co. Inc.
LUMA 2 - Flashlights ☆ - Rayovac Corp.
LUMA 2 - Lighting equipment - Exhibitgroup Inc.
LUMA 2 - Projection screens - Draper Shade and Screen Co. Inc.
LUMA-BENT - Automotive-exhaust parts - International Parts Corp.
LUMA-BENT - Mufflers–motor vehicle - Midas International Corp.
LUMA ELITE - Projection screens - Draper Shade and Screen Co. Inc.
LUMA GLO - Office supplies - W.W. Holes Manufacturing
LUMA GLO - Skin care products - Goubaud
LUMA-LEASH - Pet products ☆ - Protect-A-Pet Inc.
LUMA-LITE - Signs - Pelco Products, Inc.
LUMA MESH - Handbags - Lumured Corp.
LUMA-NET - Computer software - NSI Corp.
LUMA-SITE - Lighting fixtures - Coleman Cable Systems, Inc.
LUMA-STICK - Lamps - Philips Lighting Co.
LUMA WAX GRIP - Artists' materials - Steig Products
LUMABAND - Ribbons - Allsorts Premium Packaging
LUMACLAD - Flashlights - Eastman Kodak Co.
LUMADIAL - Watches - Hirsch Speidel Inc.
LUMADIAL EL - Watches - Hirsch Speidel Inc.
LUMAFRAME - Frames–picture - Bob Manrubia
LUMALAST - Chemical preparations ☆ - Woolsey Marine Industries
LUMALECTRIC - Projection screens - Draper Shade and Screen Co. Inc.
LUMALIGHT - Projection screens ☆ - Draper Shade and Screen Co. Inc.
LUMALINE - Novelty items - Abbas Ghandehari
LUMALITE-PHONE - Telephones - Columbia Tel-Com
LUMALITE-PHONE - Telephones - Columbia Telecommunications Group Inc.
LUMALOGIC - Lighting fixtures - Lumatech Corp.
LUMALUX - Electrical equipment - GTE Corp.

LUMAMESH - Handbags - Lumured Corp.
LUMAR MUSICA - Recording label - Cutting Records
LUMARIS PILLOW - Footwear–athletic - New Balance Athletic Shoe, Inc.
LUMARK - Lighting fixtures - Cooper Industries, Inc.
LUMASHIELD - Finishing agents - Kemlite Co., Inc.
LUMASHIELD - Paints - Tresco Paint Co. Inc.
LUMASPEC - Switches–electric - Pass & Seymour, Inc.
LUMASQUARE - Lighting fixtures - Hubbell Lighting, Inc. (Lighting Div.)
LUMASTER - Electric lighting equipment - Lutron Electronics Co., Inc.
LUMASTROBE - Lighting equipment - Precision Multiple Controls, Inc.
LUMATEC - Lighting fixtures - Lumatec Industries, Inc.
LUMATHREAD - Handles–wood - Flo-Pac Corp.
LUMATROL - Lighting equipment - Precision Multiple Controls, Inc.
LUMBAR EZE - Medical apparatus - Encore Products Inc.
LUMBAR LIGN - Mattresses - Namaco Industries, Inc.
LUMBAR LOUNGERS - Furniture–wood - Heritage Woodworks, Inc.
LUMBER JACK - Braces–orthopedic - Nada-Chair
LUMBER JACK - Syrup - Curtice-Burns Foods, Inc.
LUMBER JACK - Wood products - Grant County Mulch, Inc.
LUMBER LIFE - Paints - McCloskey Corp.
LUMBER LOCK - Adhesives and sealants - Miracle Adhesives
LUMBER LOCK - Adhesives and sealants - Pratt & Lambert, Inc. (Specialty Products Div.)
LUMBER MILL - Furniture ☆ - Universal Flooring
LUMBERCRAFT - Wood products - K-D Wood Products Inc.
LUMBERGARD - Adhesives and sealants - Gibson-Homans Co.
LUMBERJACK - Bakery products - Oven Fresh Bakery
LUMBERJACK - Cookies - Grocers Baking Co.
LUMBERJACK - Furniture - Brill Manufacturing Co.
LUMBERJACK - Furniture ☆ - Bassett Furniture Industries, Inc.
LUMBERJACK - Playground equipment - Hedstrom Corp.
LUMBERJACK BEAVER - Toys–stuffed - Dakin Inc.
LUMBERJACKET - Paints - Muralo Co. Inc.
LUMBERJACKS - Toys ☆ - Lauri Inc.
LUMBERLAST - Lumber - Syntal, Inc.
LUMBERLINE - Gloves–work - Red Steer Glove Co.
LUMBERLOCK - Orthopedic products - Chase Ergonomics Inc.
LUMBERMATE - Hardware - Alpine Engineered Products, Inc.
LUMBERMATER - Machinery - Alpine Engineered Products, Inc.
LUMBO 90 - Traction apparatus–medical - Shamrock Medical Inc.
LUME-A-LITE - Decals and transfers - Midwest Plastics Inc.
LUMEA - Electric lighting equipment - Lutron Electronics Co., Inc.
LUMEL - Lamps - Menasha Corp.
LUMEN - Computer software - Lumen Production Co.
LUMEN MASTER - Projectors–photographic - Apollo Audiovisual Div.
LUMENA - Computer software - Time Arts Inc.
LUMENARC - Electric lighting equipment - Light 33, Inc.
LUMENESSE - Lighting fixtures - Architectural Lighting Systems, Inc.
LUMENHANCE - Pharmaceutical - E.R. Squibb & Sons, Inc.
LUMENITE - Electronic equipment - Lumentie Electronic Co.
LUMENIZED - Photographic equipment - Eastman Kodak Co.
LUM'ESSENCE - Lamps - Aurora Art Inc.
LUMETAR - Lenses–photographic - Rollei of America Inc.
LUMEX - Medical apparatus - Lumex, Inc.
LUMEX FOR THE QUALITY OF LIFE - Showers and toilet seats - Lumex, Inc.
LUMI - Paper - Illuminations Inc.
LUMI-BRITE - Luggage - Universal Trav-ler Inc.
LUMI-CRAFT - Candles - Lumi-Lite Candle Co. Inc.
LUMI-FLO - Lighting fixtures - Benjamin Electric Manufacturing Co.
LUMI-FRAME, THE - Frames–picture ☆ - Lava-Simplex Internationale
LUMI-LITE - Candles - Lumi-Lite Candle Co. Inc.
LUMI NOX - Watches - Richard Barry Marketing Group
LUMI-SPERSE - Candles - Lumi-Lite Candle Co. Inc.
LUMI STAR - Lighting fixtures - Hygeia Industries Corp.
LUMIA I - Lamps - Lightolier Inc.
LUMICHROME - Pet products - M. Pencar Associates
LUMICHRON - Watches - Elgin Watch Co.
LUMICLAD - Adhesives and sealants - Miller Purcell Co.
LUMICOUNT - Measuring instruments - Packard Instrument Co., Inc.
LUMIDECK - Awnings - Mapes Industries Inc.
LUMIERE - Film - Eastman Kodak Co.
LUMI'ERE - Floor coverings–carpet and rugs - Regal Rugs Inc.
LUMIERE - Paints - Ivy Imports Inc.
LUMIERE - Wallpaper - Winfield Design Associates, Inc.
LUMIERE - Whirlpool bath ☆ - Jacuzzi Inc.
LUMIERE DU CORPS - Cosmetics - Chanel Inc.

☆ = Now out of production

LUMIFAST - Paper–photographic - Luminos Photo Corp.
LUMIFIER - Lighting fixtures ☆ - Zelco Industries, Inc.
LUMIFRAME - Lighting fixtures - Lightolier Inc.
LUMIGLO - Medical products - Kirkegaard and Perry Laboratories Inc.
LUMILEEN - Cables–fiber optic - Poly-Optical Products, Inc.
LUMILITE - Medical apparatus - PSI Medical Products, Inc.
LUMILON - Lamps - Lightolier Inc.
LUMILON II - Lamps–desk - Lightolier Inc.
LUMIMAX - Lighting fixtures - Daewoo International (America) Corp.
LUMIN - Jewelry - Lumin Jewelry Co.
LUMIN - Lighting fixtures - M G Products, Inc.
LUMIN - Medical apparatus - Utah Medical Products, Inc.
LUMIN-EZE - Lighting fixtures - Ac-cetera Inc.
LUMINA - Binoculars - Tasco Sales, Inc.
LUMINA - Furniture - Hammary Furniture Co. Inc.
LUMINA - Jewelry - Krementz & Co.
LUMINA - Lighting fixtures - Liteway
LUMINA - Motor vehicles - General Motors Corp. (Chevrolet Motor Div.)
LUMINA - Recording label - Jazz Composer's Orchestra Association Inc.
LUMINA - Skin care products - Revlon Consumer Products Corp.
LUMINA - Toys–models ☆ - Estes Industries
LUMINA - Trailers–travel - Forest River, Inc.
LUMINA - Yarn ☆ - DMC Corp.
LUMINA II - Lighting fixtures - Liteway
LUMINA 3000 - Bathroom fixtures ☆ - Aqua Glass Corp.
LUMINA APV - Motor vehicles - General Motors Corp. (Chevrolet Motor Div.)
LUMINAIR - Cosmetics - Cosmair Inc.
LUMINAIRE - Cosmetics - Elizabeth Arden Inc.
LUMINAIRE - Signs - Clearr Corp.
LUMINAIRE ULTRA II - Signs - Clearr Corp.
LUMINAL - Tranquilizers - Winthrop Pharmaceuticals
LUMINARC - Glassware–household - Durand International
LUMINARC - Lighting equipment–automotive - Osram Sylvania Inc.
LUMINARE - Computer software - Luminare Multimedia, Inc.
LUMINARY - Sinks–metal - Sterling Plumbing Group Inc.
LUMINATIONS - Candles - Luminations, Inc.
LUMINATIONS - Cases–plastic ☆ - Newell Office Products
LUMINATOR - Floodlights - RAB Electric
LUMINATOR - Lanterns–electric - Dorcy International, Inc.
LUMINATOR - Measuring instruments - Charm Bioengineering, Inc.
LUMINATORS - Toys - Revell-Monogram, Inc.
LUMINEB - Medical apparatus - Lumiscope Co. Inc.
LUMINESCENCE - Floor coverings–carpet and rugs - Karastan-Bigelow Inc.
LUMINESCENCE - Wallpaper - Robert Crowder & Co.
LUMINESCENTS - Candles - Main Street Candlery, Inc.
LUMINESQUE - Lipsticks - Revlon Consumer Products Corp.
LUMINESS - Jewelry - Princess House, Inc.
LUMINESSE - Cosmetics - Noxell Corp.
LUMINESSE SATIN - Nail care products ☆ - Noxell Corp.
LUMINETTE PRIVACY - Window coverings - Hunter Douglas, Inc.
LUMINEUX - Hair care products - Mastey De Paris
LUMINEX - Cosmetics - Revlon Consumer Products Corp.
LUMINEX - Foil–copper - Uniphot Corp.
LUMINEX - Lamps ☆ - Electrix Inc.
LUMINIERE - Lighting fixtures - Luminiere Corp.
LUMININAIREULTRA - Signs - Clearr Corp.
LUMINIQUE - Floor coverings–carpet and rugs - Philadelphia Carpets
LUMINIZE - Hair coloring preparations - Clairol Inc.
LUMINIZE RICH - Hair care products - Clairol Inc.
LUMINO - Black-light mobiles - Pacifico
LUMINOS - Paper–photographic - Luminos Photo Corp.
LUMINOS FLEXICON - Paper–photographic - Luminos Photo Corp.
LUMINOSA - Jewelry - Harry Winston, Inc.
LUMINOUS - Floor coverings–carpet and rugs - Eligere Carpets
LUMINOUS - Greeting cards - Gibson Greetings, Inc.
LUMIO - Yarn - William Unger & Co. Inc.
LUMIPAK - Film ☆ - Luminos Photo Corp.
LUMIPAN - Film ☆ - Luminos Photo Corp.
LUMIPLATE - Concrete products - Master Builders Inc.
LUMISCENTS - Candles - AmeriPlus Inc.
LUMISCOPE - Blood pressure apparatus - Lumiscope Co. Inc.
LUMISHADE - Awnings–metal - Mapes Industries Inc.
LUMISOFT - Lighting fixtures - RHC/Spacemaster Corp.
LUMISTAT - Paper–photographic - Luminos Photo Corp.
LUMITENE - Vitamins and nutritional supplements - Tishcon Corp.
LUMITEX - Wood products - Georgia-Pacific Corp.

LUMITONE - Lamps - Voltarc Technologies, Inc.
LUMITRED - Lighting fixtures - Tivoli Industries, Inc.
LUMITRON - Lighting fixtures - Luminiere Corp.
LUMITRONIC - Medical apparatus - Lumiscope Co. Inc.
LUMMI STICKS - Games - Twinson Co.
LUMMINETTES - Window coverings - Hunter Douglas Intermountain Fabrication Co.
LUMNITE - Gasoline ☆ - Lehigh Portland Cement Co.
LUMNITE - Paints - Bondex International Inc.
LUMOCOLOR AV - Pencils - Staedtler, Inc.
LUMOGRAPH - Pencils - Staedtler, Inc.
LUMOLABELS - Office supplies - Staedtler, Inc.
LUMOPLAST - Erasers - Staedtler, Inc.
LUMP O' COAL FOR THE NAUGHTY OR NICE! - Novelty items - Potter Management Co.
LUMPS & BUMPS - Candy ☆ - Price Candy Co. Inc.
LUMPY LOGS - Confections - Confectionately Yours, Ltd.
LUMPY'S GANG - Toys–stuffed - Stuffins Inc.
LUMURED - Handbags - Lumured Corp.
LUNA - Baskets–wood ☆ - Royal Cathay Trading Co.
LUNA - Brushes - Wright-Bernet
LUNA - Cymbals - European Crafts/USA
LUNA - Dinnerware–glass - Arita Sales Co. Inc.
LUNA - Erasers ☆ - Staedtler, Inc.
LUNA - Fabrics - Superior Shade & Blind Co. Inc.
LUNA - Floor coverings ☆ - Tarkett, Inc.
LUNA - Fruits–canned - Ancona Brothers Co.
LUNA - Giftware - Sasaki
LUNA - Oils–edible - Rosa Food Products Co.
LUNA - Whirlpools ☆ - Jacuzzi Inc.
LUNA BAY - Shrimp–fresh or frozen - Penguin Frozen Foods, Inc.
LUNA BLANCA - Recording label - Lauren Rickey Greene
LUNA GLO - Fluorescent paint and paper product - IMS Corp.
LUNA GLOW - Lamps ☆ - Anes Electronics Burglar Alarm Systems
LUNA LITE - Decorative and environmental lights - IMS Corp.
LUNA MYSTIQUE - Colognes - Chesebrough-Pond's USA Co.
LUNA PARK - Floor coverings - Mannington Resilient Floors
LUNA ROSA - Floor coverings - Mannington Resilient Floors
LUNACHIX - Apparel–women's - Cherie M. Duge
LUNACY - Apparel - William C. Braun
LUNADA BAY - Floor coverings–carpet and rugs ☆ - Royalweve Carpet Mills
LUNAIRE - Apparel–women's - Lumiere Intimates, Inc.
LUNAIRE MARINE - Air conditioning equipment - Marine Air Systems Inc.
LUNALITE - Apparel and accessories - Fada Industries Inc.
LUNAR - Floor coverings - American Floor Products Co. Inc.
LUNAR - Ophthalmic goods - Rozin Optical Export Corp.
LUNAR - Sporting goods - Fairfield Line, Inc.
LUNAR - Tiles–ceramic - Monarch Tile Inc.
LUNAR - Tiles–ceramic ☆ - Laufen Ceramic Tile
LUNAR ECLIPSE - Underwear and nightwear - Silvil Corp.
LUNAR ESSENCES - Incense - Matchless Gifts Inc.
LUNAR EXPLORER - Computer software ☆ - Spectrum Holobyte, Inc.
LUNAR FLOWER - Bedding–linen - Dan River Inc.
LUNAR FOX - Computer software - Corel USA
LUNAR IMAGES - Floor coverings–carpet and rugs ☆ - Galaxy Carpet Mills Inc.
LUNAR LAID - Paper–bond - Parsons Paper Co.
LUNAR LEMON - Tea - The Stroh Brewery Co.
LUNAR LITE - Lighting equipment ☆ - Bridgeport Metal Goods Manufacturing Co.
LUNAR LOONIES - Candy - Glenn Confections Inc.
LUNAR PHASE - Candles - Pacific Spirit Corp.
LUNAR PROBE - Toys - Park Plastics Co.
LUNAR RESCUE - Video games - Taito America Corp.
LUNAR SCHOONER - Glass products - Bartlett-Collins Co.
LUNAR-THE SILVER STAR - Video games - Working Designs
LUNAR TULIPS - Bedding–linen - Dan River Inc.
LUNAR VISION - Cameras - Gamla Enterprises NA Inc.
LUNASEA - T-shirts–men's - O.C. Seacrets, Inc.
LUNASTONE - Dinnerware–glass - Sango Co. Ltd. (Sango USA Div.)
LUNATIC'S REVENGE - Games - Smethport Specialty Co.
LUNATIME - Clocks - Schelling Manufacturing Corp.
LUNATIQUE - Draperies - Maya Romanoff Corp.
LUNCH BAG - Bags–paper - Kangaroo Brand Inc.
LUNCH BAR - Candy - Klein Chocolate Co.
LUNCH BOX BLOCKS - Toys–blocks - Tyco Industries, Inc.

☆ = Now out of production

LUNCH BOX PALS - Dental floss - Wentworth G. Eaton
LUNCH BREAKS - Food products - Louis Rich Co.
LUNCH BUCKET - Food products - Dial Corp.
LUNCH BUCKET LIGHT 'N HEALTHY - Food products - Dial Corp.
LUNCH BUNCH - Housewares - SGI Inc.
LUNCH BUNCH, THE - Fruits and vegetables - Corrin
LUNCH CASE - Lunch boxes ☆ - Thermos Co.
LUNCH ETUI - Candy ☆ - Brocks Candy Co.
LUNCH EXPRESS - Dinners–frozen - Stouffer Foods Corp.
LUNCH EXPRESS - Food products ☆ - Barbizon Lingerie
LUNCH FOR ONE - Food products - Dole Fresh Vegetables Inc.
LUNCH-IN - Placemats - Agent Andy Inc.
LUNCH LINE, THE - Food products ☆ - Ore-Ida Foods, Inc.
LUNCH LOCKS - Containers–plastic - Trillium Products, Inc.
LUNCH LUGGER - Lunch boxes - Thermos Co.
LUNCH MAKERS - Food products - Armour Swift-Eckrich
LUNCH 'N MUNCH - Food products - Bryan Foods, Inc.
LUNCH 'N MUNCH - Food products - Hillshire Farm Co.
LUNCH 'N MUNCH DIPPER'S - Meat snacks - Saramar Corp.
LUNCH PAK - Ice chests–plastic - Coleman Co., Inc.
LUNCH PAL - Lunch boxes - Marilyn M. Keil
LUNCH POCKETS - Food products - General American Foods Manufacturing Corp.
LUNCH RECORDS - Electronic equipment - Jeffrey L. Robbins
LUNCH-TIME - Food products - King's Command Foods Inc.
LUNCH TIME - Salads–prepackaged - Herman Miller, Inc.
LUNCH TOTE - Food containers - Rubbermaid Inc.
LUNCHABLES - Food products - Oscar Mayer Foods Corp.
LUNCHEON DELIGHT - Meat products–beef - So Good Bar-B-Q
LUNCHEON TREAT - Pork - So Good Bar-B-Q
LUNCHKINS - Bags ☆ - Aladdin Industries, Inc.
LUNCHMATE - Ice chests–plastic - Igloo Products Corp.
LUNCHMATE PLUS - Containers - Igloo Products Corp.
LUNCH'N MORE - Bags–plastic - First Brands Properties Inc.
LUNCH'N MUNCH - Food packages - Saramar Corp.
LUNCHPAK - Portable cooler - Coleman Co., Inc.
LUNCHSHAKE - Frozen foods - Ice Cold Novelty Products, Inc.
LUNCHTIME - Snack foods ☆ - Nestle USA
LUND - Boats–motor - Lund Boat Co.
LUNDBERG - Rice - Wehah Farm, Inc.
LUNDBERG COUNTRY WILD - Rice - Wehah Farm, Inc.
LUNDBERG'S - Food products - Lundberg Family Farms
LUNDBY - Toys ☆ - BRIO Corp.
LUNDENBURGH MARBLE - Floor coverings ☆ - Tarkett, Inc.
LUNDIA FULLSPACE - Shelving units–wood - Lundia
LUNDQUIST - Dog food - Lundquist Foods
LUNDQUISTS, THE - Greeting cards - Hallmark Licensing, Inc.
LUND'S - Food products - Lunds, Inc.
LUNDS - Pancakes–mixes - Swedish Food Products
LUNDS - Seafood products–canned or cured - Lunds Fisheries
LUNE BEST - Dairy products ☆ - Country Fresh Dairy
LUNE BLEUE - Cosmetics - Lancome
LUNETTA BADA - Eyeglasses - Bada USA, Inc.
LUNETTE - Floor coverings–carpet and rugs ☆ - World Carpets, Inc.
LUNG CARE - Vitamins and nutritional supplements ☆ - Ethical Nutrients
LUNG DISPERSING WATER - Health care products - East Earth Herb Inc.
LUNG QI - Health care products - East Earth Herb Inc.
LUNGAROTTI - Wines - Heublein, Inc.
LUNGEN - Bells and chimes - Edwards Co. Inc.
LUNGFUNG - Vermicelli - Anhing Corp.
LUNI BALL - Balls - Ronald E. Redondo
LUNI TICK APPAREL COMPANY - Apparel and accessories - Kenlin, Inc.
+L'UNIQUE - Kaleidoscopes - Gemini Kaleidoscopes
LUNKER - Boats - O.M.C. Aluminum Boat Group
LUNKER - Boats–motor - Alumacraft Boat Co.
LUNKER - Boats–motor ☆ - Duracraft Boats Inc.
LUNKER LIFT - Sporting goods - Ohio Electronics Machinery, Inc.
LUNKERMOBILE - Docks - Gary Covel
LUNKERSTIK - Fishing tackle - Fenwick
LUNNAR - Tripods–photographic ☆ - Edixa Camera Co.
LUNSTEAD - Furniture - Haworth, Inc.
LUNSTEAD - Furniture - Lunstead Inc.
LUNSTEAD METALS - Metals ☆ - Haworth, Inc.
LUNT - Tableware–earthenware - Lunt Silversmiths
LUNT SILVERSMITHS - Tableware–earthenware - Lunt Silversmiths
+L'UOMO - Eyeglass frames - Atlantic Optical Co., Inc.

LUP - Leather goods - Leather Up, Inc.
LUPERLA - Cosmetics - Lucoral Co. Inc.
LUPEX - Paper–photographic - Ansco Photo-Optical Products Corp.
LUPIN III - Video games - Taito America Corp.
LUPINE - Nail care products - Cosmair Inc.
LUPINE - Pet products - Lupine, Inc.
LUPINUS - Binoculars - Kowa American Corp.
LUPO - Cigars ☆ - Avanti Cigar Co.
LUPTON - Hardware - Blaine Window Hardware Inc.
LURA - Hair care products ☆ - Majestic Drug Co., Inc.
LURAVEL - Fabrics - Guilford Mills, Inc.
LURE - Fruits and vegetables - Trout, Inc.
LURE-FLY - Fly swatters - Farnam Cos. Inc.
LURE FLY - Flypaper - Security Products Co.
LURE GARD - Coatings - Amsoil, Inc.
LURE LOCK - Fishing equipment - Ronald Irving Simpler
LURE N KILL - Insecticides - Hercon Environmental Corp.
LUREMASTER - Paints - Crescent Bronze Powder
LURETAPE - Insecticides - Hercon Environmental Corp.
LUREX - Metals - Metal Film Co. Inc.
LURIDE - Pharmaceutical preparations - Colgate Oral Pharmaceuticals Inc.
LURIDE-SF - Pharmaceutical preparations - Colgate Oral Pharmaceuticals Inc.
LURKER - Shirts - Annette Maxwell
LURLINE - Pharmaceutical preparations - Fielding Pharmaceutical Co.
LURLYN LL - Apparel - Lurlyn, Inc.
LURON PINK - Soap - Dial Corp.
LUROPHASE - Skin care products - Ella Bache Inc.
LURUANA - Footwear - Eliot Co. Inc.
LUS - Pens - Importoys
LUSA - Lighting fixtures - Lusa Lighting Intl., Inc.
LUSAC - Automotive parts and accessories - Echlin Inc.
LUSAN - Hair care products - Lusan Inc.
LUSCHER PROFILE - Computer software - Mindscape Software Inc.
LUSCIOUS - Floor coverings–carpet and rugs - Lock Weave Carpet Mills Inc.
LUSCIOUS LAVENDER - Christmas tree ornaments - Cracker Box Inc.
LUSCIOUS LEAVES - Lettuce - Desert Gourmet Foods Inc.
LUSCIOUS LIME - Chewing gum - Planters LifeSavers Co.
LUSCIOUS LIPS - Cosmetics ☆ - Cosmetic Firsts Ltd.
LUSCIOUS LOAVES - Breads–mixes - Wildwood Creations
LUSCOMBE - Aircraft parts - Don Luscombe Aviation History Foundation
LUSCOMBE - Airplane parts - Dennis M. Collins
LUSEAUX - Detergents - Luseaux Laboratories Inc.
LUSH - Recording label ☆ - Ray Lawrence Ltd.
LUSH & LUSTRIOUS - Skin care products - Isla Cosmetique
LUSH DOG TAGS - Novelty items - Doc's Apothecary
LUSH KNIT - Fabrics - Guilford Mills, Inc.
LUSH LASH - Cosmetics - Del Pharmaceuticals, Inc.
LUSH LASH PLUS - Cosmetics - Del Pharmaceuticals, Inc.
LUSH LAWN - Fertilizers - Maxus Energy Corp.
LUSH LIFE - Fabrics - Guilford Mills, Inc.
LUSH LIFE - Wallpaper - Jack Denst Designs
LUSH LIFE II - Wallpaper - Jack Denst Designs
LUSH 'N HEALTHY - Cosmetics - Almay Inc.
LUSH PLUSH VELOUR - Fabrics–broadcloth - Desire Mills Co. Inc.
LUSHA - Leather goods - Accessories to the Fact
LUSOX - Fishing lures - Sheldons', Inc.
LUSSO - Portable bath ☆ - Jacuzzi Inc.
LUSSO AUTO BATHE - Cleaning preparations - Lusso Car Care Products, Inc.
LUSSO ITALIANO - Tiles–ceramic - Longust Distributing, Inc.
LUSSO ORO - Waxes–mineral - Lusso Car Care Products, Inc.
LUSSO REVITALIZING CREME - Cleaning preparations - Lusso Car Care Products, Inc.
LUSSTOR - Boxes ☆ - W.W. Holes Manufacturing
LUST BUSTER - Pet products - G.G. Bean Inc.
LUST-R-LO - Paints ☆ - Dunn Edwards Corp.
LUSTA FOAM - Cleaning preparations–carpet and rug - Analab Inc.
LUSTA-KLEER - Skin care products - Barrows Pharmacal Inc.
LUSTALL - Wines - Prestige Wine Corp.
LUSTAQUIK - Paints - Kyanize Paint Co.
LUSTAR - Pet products - Lustar Products Co.
LUSTARITE - Paints - Mobile Paint Manufacturing Co.
LUSTER - Hair care products - Andre Fantasies Inc.
LUSTER - Tiles–ceramic ☆ - Florida Tile Industries, Inc.
LUSTER BLUE - Pottery ☆ - Blue Delft Co. Inc.
LUSTER BRITES - Blinds–venetian - Hunter Douglas, Inc.
LUSTER BUFF - Cleaning preparations - Knight Marketing Corp.

☆ = Now out of production

LUSTER FOAM - Pet products ☆ - Zema Corp.
LUSTER LEAF - Garden equipment - Luster Leaf Products Inc.
LUSTER-LOC - Fabrics - Liberty Fabrics, Inc.
LUSTER LUX - Mattresses - Angel Echevarria Co. Inc.
LUSTER LUX - Mattresses - Somma Mattress Co.
LUSTER PLUS - Paints - Nowstar
LUSTER SEAL - Waterproofing compounds - Tamms Industries Co.
LUSTER SHEEN - Cleaning preparations - W.W. Grainger, Inc.
LUSTER SHIELD - Vehicle polish - Advanced Polishing Products
LUSTER-SKIN - Underwear and nightwear ☆ - Alba-Waldensian, Inc.
LUSTER-TONE - Posters ☆ - Milton Bradley Co.
LUSTERAY - Thread - Threads USA Div.
LUSTERCALE - Fabrics–broadcloth - Springs Industries, Inc.
LUSTERINE - Hair care products - Ampro Industries, Inc.
LUSTERITE - Thread - Threads USA Div.
LUSTERIZE - Cleaning preparations - R.M. Hollingshead Corp.
LUSTERIZER - Hair care products - Revlon Consumer Products Corp.
LUSTERLITE - Cleaning preparations - Protective Coatings Unlimited, Inc.
LUSTEROL - Cleaning preparations - International Products Co.
LUSTERON - Finishing agents - PLC
LUSTERPIC - Computer software - DataPak Software Inc.
LUSTERPLUS - Paints - Magicolor Co.
LUSTERPLUS - Pet products ☆ - Pet-Eze
LUSTERPRINT - Publisher's imprints - S.D. Warren Co.
LUSTER'S - Hair care products - Luster Products, Inc.
LUSTER'S AUTHENTIC SEAL OF QUALITY - Hair care products - Luster Products, Inc.
LUSTERSET - Cosmetics ☆ - Majestic Drug Co., Inc.
LUSTERSHEEN - Yarn - Coats and Clark Inc.
LUSTERSOFT - Bedding–linen - West Point-Pepperell Inc.
LUSTERTONE - Sinks–metal - Elkay Manufacturing Co.
LUSTEX - Fabrics - Wallerstein Textiles Inc.
LUSTEX - Thread ☆ - American & Efird, Inc.
LUSTIQUE - Fabrics ☆ - Vanity Fair Mills Inc.
LUSTOL - Pharmaceutical preparations ☆ - Lustol Co.
LUSTRA - Brooms ☆ - Flo-Pac Corp.
LUSTRA - Paints - Frazee Paint
LUSTRA - Paper–gift wrap ☆ - Mobil Chemical Co. Plastics Div.
LUSTRA - Toilet seats - Kohler Co.
LUSTRA-BUFF - Cleaning preparations ☆ - Flo-Pac Corp.
LUSTRA COTES - Paints - Harmar Associates
LUSTRA FOAM - Paints - Cleaning Systems, Inc.
LUSTRA-FONE - Cleaning preparations ☆ - Boyer Corp.
LUSTRA LOC - Finishing agents ☆ - Flo-Pac Corp.
LUSTRA SWEEP - Brooms ☆ - Flo-Pac Corp.
LUSTRADERM - Soap ☆ - Freeman Industries LLC
LUSTRAH - Bedding–linen - Dakotah, Inc.
LUSTRALUM - Pens ☆ - Autopoint Inc.
LUSTRASEW - Thread - Threads USA Div.
LUSTRASILK - Hair care products - Lustrasilk Corp. of America Inc.
LUSTRAWEAVE - Fabrics - E.R. Moore Co.
LUSTRE - Cleaning preparations ☆ - Malco Products, Inc.
LUSTRE - Clocks ☆ - General Time Corp. (Westclox/Seth Thomas Div.)
LUSTRE - Depilatories - Edith Imre Hair Fashions Inc.
LUSTRE - Hair care products ☆ - Nutrine Ltd.
LUSTRE - Health care products - Colgate-Palmolive Co.
LUSTRE - Housewares ☆ - LaSalle Marketing Corp.
LUSTRE - Jewelry - Earl Butler & Associates Inc.
LUSTRE - Phonographs ☆ - Sumiko Inc.
LUSTRE - Vitamins and nutritional supplements - Source Naturals
LUSTRE BRASS - Furniture–metal - Leggett and Platt, Inc.
LUSTRE BUFF - Nail care products - E.O.H. Industries, Inc.
LUSTRE CAR - Cleaning preparations - Viking Manufacturing Co. Inc.
LUSTRE-CEN - Furniture polish and wax - Central Solutions, Inc.
LUSTRE CLEAN - Cleaning preparations - Blue Lustre, LLC
LUSTRE-COAT - Adhesives and sealants - Polymer Plastic Corp.
LUSTRE COAT - Pet products - Glo-Marr Products Inc.
LUSTRE-CONN - Musical instruments ☆ - United Musical Instruments USA Inc.
LUSTRE-CORD - Ribbons - Norcross Inc.
LUSTRE-CREME - Hair care products - Colgate-Palmolive Co.
LUSTRE-CURL - Ribbons - Norcross Inc.
LUSTRE FINISH - Hair care products - Zotos International Inc.
LUSTRE-GLAZE - Paints - Floquil-Polly S Color Corp.
LUSTRE-GLO - Detergents - Lustre-Glo Chemical
LUSTRE-GLO - Paints - Gilman Co. Inc.
LUSTRE-GLO - Pet products - Glo-Marr Products Inc.

LUSTRE GLO - Polishes - Plant Marvel Laboratories
LUSTRE-GLOSS - Cleaning preparations - Hillyard Enterprises, Inc.
LUSTRE-LAC - Furniture polish and wax - Oil Specialties & Refining Co. Inc.
LUSTRE-LINK - Chains - Merchants Metals Inc.
LUSTRE LITE - Candles - Empire Manufacturing Co.
LUSTRE-LOFT - Floor coverings ☆ - Apache Mills Inc.
LUSTRE-LUXE - Photographic-paper surface - Eastman Kodak Co.
LUSTRE-MIST - Cleaning preparations - Hillyard Enterprises, Inc.
LUSTRE PUFF BOW - Ribbons - Norcross Inc.
LUSTRE SHEEN - Fabrics - Greenwood Mills Inc.
LUSTRE SHELL - Cooking utensils–earthenware ☆ - Anchor Hocking Glass, Inc.
LUSTRE-SILK - Apparel–women's - J.C. Penney Co., Inc.
LUSTRE-STONE - Blocks–concrete - Krichner Industries Inc.
LUSTRE-TIE - Ribbons - Norcross Inc.
LUSTRE TONE - Floor coverings - Mannington Resilient Floors
LUSTRE-TUFF - Mats ☆ - U.S. Mat & Rubber Co. Inc.
LUSTRE TWIST - Floor coverings - Apache Mills Inc.
LUSTRE-WIRE - Underwear and nightwear - Maidenform Inc.
LUSTRECLOTH - Polishing cloths - Cleveland Cotton Products Co.
LUSTRECON - Floor coverings - Mannington Resilient Floors
LUSTRECUPS - Medical equipment - Lustrecorp, Inc.
LUSTREGLAZE - Polishing rouge ☆ - Park Metallurgical Corp.
LUSTREKOTE - Paints - Hobbico Inc.
LUSTREKUT - Abrasive products ☆ - Park Metallurgical Corp.
LUSTRELETTERS - Hardware - Scott Sign Systems, Inc.
LUSTRELLE - Fabrics - Guilford Mills, Inc.
LUSTRE'S - Candy - Square Shooter Candy Co.
LUSTREVEL - Fabrics - J.B. Martin Co. Inc.
LUSTREX - Fabrics - Bacon Felt Co. Inc.
LUSTRLON - Sweaters - Hampshire Group, Ltd.
LUSTRO - Cleaning preparations ☆ - Adhesive Products, Inc.
LUSTRO - Flags - Dettra Flag Co. Inc.
LUSTRO - Floor coverings - Mannington Resilient Floors
LUSTRO - Paints - Farrell-Calhoun Inc.
LUSTRO - Pencils ☆ - Faber-Castell Corp.
LUSTRO - Wallpaper - Blumenthal
LUSTRO - Yarn - Nomis Yarn Co.
LUSTRO-FINISH - Paints - Harrison Paint Corp.
LUSTRO-WARE - Housewares - Lustro-Ware Housewares Inc.
LUSTROUS - Lipsticks - Revlon Consumer Products Corp.
LUSTROUS LIFE - Apparel–men's - Phillips-Van Heusen Corp.
LUSTROUS SPONGE-ON SATIN BLUSH - Cosmetics - Noxell Corp.
LUTALYSE - Veterinary pharmaceutical preparations - Upjohn Co.
LUTCHE - Vitamins and nutritional supplements - Nancy Park
LUTE-IT - Adhesives and sealants - Jeneric/Pentron Inc.
LUTECE - Glassware–household - Durand International
LUTECE - Mushrooms - Arbee Fine Foods Imports
LUTECE - Perfumes - Houbigant, Inc.
LUTEIN-BEADS - Spices and extracts - Pharmachem Laboratories, Inc.
LUTEIN CAPS - Vitamins and nutritional supplements - Vitamin Research Products Inc.
LUTEINPURE - Vitamins and nutritional supplements - Soft Gel Technologies, Inc.
LUTHIER'S CHOICE - Cleaning preparations - Gibson Strings & Accessories
LUTHIER'S TOOLS - Musical instrument accessories - Metropolitan Music Co.
LUTIZOL HP - Vitamins and nutritional supplements - International Health Products, Inc.
LUTOLIN-F - Pharmaceutical preparations - G.O. Spanner Inc.
LUTON - Floor coverings–carpet and rugs - Daltonian Carpet & Cushion Inc.
LUTRA - Recording label - Jazz Composer's Orchestra Association Inc.
LUTZ - Drafting supplies - Lutz Superdyne Inc.
LUTZ - Tiles–ceramic - Los Angeles Tile Co., Inc.
LUV - Infant product - Delta Enterprise Corp.
LUV - Motor vehicles ☆ - General Motors Corp. (Chevrolet Motor Div.)
LUV-A-BOW - Archery equipment - Louis Rangel
LUV-A-HUG TROLL - Dolls - Toymax Inc.
LUV-A-PUP - Toys–stuffed ☆ - Fun World Inc.
LUV BABY - Infant product - Delta Enterprise Corp.
LUV BIRD - Pottery ☆ - Rubens Originals
LUV-BITES - Pet products - Classic Products
LUV BONES - Pet products - Blue Ribbon Pet Products, Inc.
LUV BUF - Nail care products - E.O.H. Industries, Inc.
LUV-BUG - Garden equipment ☆ - H.D. Hudson Manufacturing Co.
LUV BUGGY - Strollers–baby - Delta Enterprise Corp.
LUV CRIB - Cribs–wood - Delta Enterprise Corp.

LUV DEVILS - Toys–stuffed ☆ - Fun World Inc.
LUV DOGS - Apparel and accessories - Jack Hanna Enterprises, Inc.
LUV DOLLS - Dolls - Russ Berrie and Co., Inc.
LUV-EWE - Slippers - Ardney Corp.
LUV IN EVERY BITE - Bakery products - Joseph Aihini
LUV MATCH - Brassieres (Bras) - Wacoal America Inc.
LUV-ME TOO - Toys–stuffed ☆ - Gund, Inc.
LUV N' CARE - Apparel and accessories - Admar International, Inc.
LUV N' CARE - Infant product - Tidy International Corp.
LUV N' KISSES - Dolls - Uneeda Doll Co., Inc.
LUV 'N STUFF - Dolls - Horsman
LUV NOTES - Stationery - Berkshire Stationery Inc.
LUV-NOTES - Toys–stuffed ☆ - Fun World Inc.
LUV PETS - Toys–stuffed - Russ Berrie and Co., Inc.
LUV-UMS - Greeting cards ☆ - Warner Press, Inc.
LUVABLE BURPEES - Apparel–children's - Vi M. Finch
LUVABLE HUGGABLES - Toys–stuffed - SKR International, Inc.
LUVABLES - Statuary - Seymour Mann Inc.
LUVABY - Infant product - Crystal Clear Importing Co. Inc.
LUVEL - Ice cream - Luvel Dairy Products Inc.
LUV'EM - Panty hose - Davis Sales
LUV'EM - Pet care products - Marketing Aspects, Inc.
LUVIA - Glassware–household - Mikasa Co.
LUVIT - Paper–toilet - Southland Corp.
LUVIT - Prefabricated buildings–wood - Luvit Products Corp.
LUVLEGS - Hosiery - Sheffield Industries Inc.
LUV'N STUFF - Hobby kits - Karen Lively and Barbara Bullen
LUVNUTS - Nuts–salted, roasted, cooked, or canned - Aster Nut Products Co. Inc.
LUVR-GRID - Construction equipment - Alcan Aluminum Corp. Alcan Building Products Div.
LUVS - Diapers–disposable - Procter & Gamble Co.
LUVS BABY GUARDS - Diapers–disposable - Procter & Gamble Co.
LUVS BABY PANTS - Diapers–disposable - Procter & Gamble Co.
LUVS LEAKGUARDS - Diapers–disposable - Procter & Gamble Co.
LUVS PHASES - Diapers–disposable - Procter & Gamble Co.
LUVS TRAINING PANTS - Diapers–disposable - Procter & Gamble Co.
LUVS YA BACK - Medical apparatus - Roloke Co.
LUVSPELL - Children's cologne ☆ - Cosrich Inc.
LUVTOUCH - Fabrics - Guilford Mills, Inc.
LUVY BEAR - Pet products - Hill Top Enterprises
LUVY BEAR - Toys–stuffed ☆ - Dakin Inc.
LUX - Clock radios - Fromm Industries
LUX - Floor coverings–carpet and rugs ☆ - Eurotex Inc.
LUX - Food products - George C. Brown's Biscuits & Confections
LUX - Motor vehicle parts and accessories ☆ - Lux Co. Inc.
LUX - Photographic equipment ☆ - Heitz Service Corp.
LUX - Soap - Lever Brothers Co. Inc.
LUX - Timers–appliance - Robertshaw Controls Co.
LUX FLAKES - Soap - Lever Brothers Co. Inc.
LUX HEALTH CARE - Health care products - Lux Co. Inc.
LUX LEISURE - Sporting goods - Lux Co. Inc.
LUX-LOCK - Ophthalmic goods ☆ - Luxottica
LUX-REE - Paints - C.M. Athey Paint Co.
LUX-RIGHT - Steel - St. Paul Corrugating Co.
LUX STEEL - Office accessories - Lux Co. Inc.
LUX-THERM - Heating equipment ☆ - Eraser Co. Inc.
LUXABLE - Apparel and accessories ☆ - Glamorise Foundations Inc.
LUXAIR - Yarn - Cascade Fibers Co.
LUXAIRE - Heating equipment - York International Corp.
LUXANA - Paper–writing - PNB Papers Inc.
LUXANE - Paints ☆ - Tenax Finishing Product
LUXATOR - Dental equipment - Js Dental Manufacturing, Inc.
LUXAWOOL - Apparel and accessories - Tricots St. Raphael, Inc.
LUXCEL - Telephones–cellular - Drive Phone Inc.
LUXCRAFT - Sinks–metal - Unarco Industries UNR
LUXDOR - Shelving units–plastic - Plastic Products Inc.
LUXE - Dinnerware–glass - Arita Sales Co. Inc.
LUXE - Posters - Brocato International
LUXE - Wallpaper ☆ - Capital Carousel Inc.
LUXE - Wallpaper ☆ - Wallpaper Imports Inc.
LUXE' BY ROMAN - Jewelry - Roman Co.
LUXE CARDS - Greeting cards - Swe-Den Inc.
LUXELON - Crocheted and knitted items ☆ - Hampshire Hosiery, Inc.
LUXFER - Health care products - S.L.O. Repair
LUXITE - Needles–sewing ☆ - Coats and Clark Inc.

LUXITE - Needlework supplies ☆ - Susan Bates Inc.
LUXITE - Trophies–metal ☆ - Classic Plaques Inc.
LUXITRON - Watches - Luxury International Inc.
LUXIVA - Skin care products - Merle Norman Cosmetics
LUXLIGHT - Thermostats - Lux Products Corp.
LUXLITE - Paints - Kelly-Moore/Preservative Paints
LUXMATIC - Electronic equipment - Dwa, LLC
LUXO - Doors, paneling, tile, etc. - BP & N Inc.
LUXO - Lamps - Luxo Corp.
LUXO BANHO - Soap - Kala Corp.
LUXO LIL - Lamps ☆ - Luxo Corp.
LUXO LOVO - Lighting fixtures - Luxo Corp.
LUXOID - Enamels - Wilson Paint Co.
LUXON - Shampoos - Analab Inc.
LUXON - Sporting goods ☆ - Gladding Braided Products Inc.
LUXOR - Bedding–linen - West Point-Pepperell Inc.
LUXOR - Dinnerware - Denby USA Limited
LUXOR - Drums–musical instruments ☆ - Grossman Music Corp.
LUXOR - Envelopes ☆ - Kimberly-Clark Corp. (Karolton Envelope Div.)
LUXOR - Floor coverings ☆ - Tarkett, Inc.
LUXOR - Floor coverings–carpet and rugs - Foreign Accents
LUXOR - Furniture - Pavilion/Sunburst Furniture
LUXOR - Housewares - Ramparts Inc.
LUXOR - Motor vehicles–motor homes - Winnebago Industries, Inc.
LUXOR - Paints - Triangle Coatings Inc.
LUXOR - Strollers–baby ☆ - Peg Perego USA Inc.
LUXOR - Thread - Soltex International Inc.
LUXOR - Wallpaper - Advance Wallcoverings
LUXOR - Wallpaper - Marburg Wallcoverings Inc.
LUXOR - Windows - Extech/Exterior Technologies, Inc.
LUXOR ENDURA - Tables–wood - Luxor
LUXOTTICA - Ophthalmic goods - Luxottica
LUXOUT - Draperies - Plastic Products Inc.
LUXOWITE - Enamels - North Jersey Paint Co. Inc.
LUXRI 13 - Napkins–paper - Wisconsin Tissue Mills Inc.
LUXRIFOLD - Napkins–paper - Wisconsin Tissue Mills Inc.
LUXRITE - Apparel and accessories - N. Seligman Co.
LUXSEAL - Fabrics - Rubie's Costume Co., Inc.
LUXSTAR - Watches - Luxury International Inc.
LUXTAR - Electronic equipment - Apollo Audiovisual Div.
LUXTHERM - Heating equipment - Eraser Co. Inc.
LUXTONE - Draperies ☆ - Plastic Products Inc.
LUXTRA - Doors - LTL Wholesale, Inc.
LUXTRA-PLY - Uniforms–tailored - Angelica Uniform Group
LUXTRA-PREST - Uniforms–tailored - Angelica Uniform Group
LUXTROL - Lighting equipment - Warner Electric/Superior Electric
LUXTUBE - Tubes–plastic - Agrenetics
LUXUR - Audio equipment - Sound-Tech Imports, Corp.
LUXURA - Paper–tissue - Romar International Corp.
LUXURA - Whirlpools - Jacuzzi Inc.
LUXURA NIGHT VISION - Electric lighting equipment ☆ - Bass Products
LUXURA STYLOUR - Plastics–laminated ☆ - Gilman Brothers Co.
LUXURAY - Flashlights - Accutec Inc.
LUXURCARE - Skin care products - Recreations
LUXUREST - Pillows - Vitafoam, Inc.
LUXURIA - Floor coverings–carpet and rugs ☆ - Patcraft Mills Inc.
LUXURIA - Floor coverings–carpet and rugs ☆ - Regal Rugs Inc.
LUXURIA - Furniture - Tomlinson of High Point Inc.
LUXURIANA - Floor coverings–carpet and rugs - Durkan Patterned Carpets
LUXURIANCE - Floor coverings–carpet and rugs - Karastan-Bigelow Inc.
LUXURIANCE - Hair care products - Helene Curtis Industries Inc.
LUXURIES - Wallpaper - Capital Carousel Inc.
LUXURIES - Wallpaper - Wall Fabrics Inc.
LUXURY - Bathtubs–enameled - Pearl Baths Inc.
LUXURY - Chessboards - Carrom Co.
LUXURY - Cooking equipment–household - New Era Co.
LUXURY - Cosmetics - Avon Products, Inc.
LUXURY - Fabrics - Greenwood Mills Inc.
LUXURY - Flatware - Reed and Barton Corp.
LUXURY - Floor coverings ☆ - Congoleum Corp.
LUXURY - Floor coverings–carpet and rugs ☆ - Regal Rugs Inc.
LUXURY - Padding–foam - National Foam Cushion Manufacturing Inc.
LUXURY - Pasta - Borden, Inc.
LUXURY - Pasta - National Food Products
LUXURY - Seafood - Clouston Foods USA
LUXURY - Skin care products - Paula Payne Products Co. Inc.

☆ = Now out of production

LUXURY - Watches - Luxury International Inc.

LUXURY/A STEP ABOVE - Floor coverings–carpet and rugs - Johnson's Carpets Inc.

LUXURY BATH LINERS - Bathroom accessories - Luxury Bath Liners, Inc.

LUXURY BATH SYSTEMS - Bathroom accessories - Luxury Bath Liners, Inc.

LUXURY BUBBLES - Skin care products ☆ - House of Lowell Inc.

LUXURY CARE - Hair care products - Alleghany Pharmacal Corp.

LUXURY COMFORT - Mattresses - Spring Air Bedding Inc.

LUXURY COMMERCIAL - Boats–pontoons - Boatel Marine, Inc.

LUXURY FOAM - Mattresses - Lisco, Inc.

LUXURY FOAM SUPREME - Mattresses - Lisco, Inc.

LUXURY-GRID - Floor covering, now out of production - American Floor Products Co. Inc.

LUXURY KNIT - Footwear - Brown Wooten Mills Inc.

LUXURY LANE - Floor coverings–carpet and rugs - Gulistan Carpet Inc.

LUXURY-LIFT - Chairs–dentists' - La-Z-Boy Chair Co.

LUXURY LIFT - Health care products - Pride Health Care, Inc.

LUXURY LIGHTING - Lighting fixtures - Luxury Lighting, Inc.

LUXURY LINER - Motor vehicles–motor homes ☆ - Georgie Boy Manufacturing, Inc.

LUXURY LINER - Trailers–travel ☆ - Shasta Industries Inc.

LUXURY LINERS - Cosmetics - Fran Wilson Creative Cosmetics

LUXURY LIVING - Floor coverings–carpet and rugs - Barrett Carpet Mills Inc.

LUXURY LIVING - Paints - Perry & Derrick Co.

LUXURY LIVING PLUS - Paints - Perry & Derrick Co.

LUXURY LOFT - Floor coverings–carpet and rugs ☆ - Regal Rugs Inc.

LUXURY LOOK - Apparel stores–lingerie - Formflex Foundations Inc.

LUXURY LOUNGE - Furniture–wood - Flexsteel Industries Inc.

LUXURY STRIPES - Brassieres (Bras) - Montgomery Ward & Co. Inc.

LUXURY-TRAC - Floor coverings - American Floor Products Co. Inc.

LUXURY VINYL TILE - Floor coverings - Congoleum Corp.

LUXURY WATER - Water treating compounds - RainSoft Water Conditioning Co.

LUXUS - Automotive parts and accessories - Lancaster Colony Automotive Group

LUXUS - Bicycles - Murray, Inc.

LUXUS - Floor coverings–carpet and rugs ☆ - Robertex Associates Inc.

LUXUS - Shower stalls–plastic - Mr. Shower Door, Inc.

LUXUS - Sinks–porcelain - UNR Industries, Inc.

LUXUS 9000 - Luggage ☆ - Ventura Travelware Inc.

LUXUS EST - Lighting equipment - Marketing Insights, Inc.-Frank Luppino Jr., and Associates

LUXWALL - Paints - Frazee Paint

LUYO - Skin care products - ABAR Beauty Supply Inc.

LUYTIES - Laxatives - Luyties Pharmacal Co.

LUZERNE OPTICAL LABORATORIES, LTD. - Lenses - Luzerne Optical Laboratories

LUZIANNE - Coffee - Reily Foods

LUZIANNE CAJUN CREOLE DINNERS - Food products - Wm. B. Reily & Co. Inc.

LUZIANNE CAJUN RICE DINNERS - Food products - Reily Foods

LUZIER - Cosmetics - Luzier Personalized Cosmetics, Inc.

LUZIER BATH & BODY ESSENTIALS - Lotions - Luzier Personalized Cosmetics, Inc.

LUZZATTI - Spaghetti sauces - Kraft Foodservice Holding Corp.

L.V. GOLDEN SMOKE - Seafood products–canned or cured - Los Angeles Smoking & Curing Co.

LVB-LITE - Window shades - Lafayette Venetian Blind, Inc.

LVE - Firearms, accessories, and parts - B-West Imports, Inc.

LVT - Photographic equipment - Eastman Kodak Co.

LW & CO. - Apparel and accessories ☆ - Warnaco Inc.

LW LABEL WHORE - Apparel–men's - Peter Kavehzadeh

L.W. PACKARD - Fabrics - L.W. Packard & Co., Inc.

LWB - Thread - Belding Heminway Co. Inc.

LWP - Footwear ☆ - Nike, Inc.

LX - Apparel–athletic - Sportmart, Inc.

LX - Golfing equipment - Ram Golf Corp.

LX - Vinyl - Innovations in Wallcoverings, Inc.

LX-LEBLANC - Clarinets - G. Leblanc Corp.

LX2000 - Clarinets - G. Leblanc Corp.

LXI - Computer software - LXI Corp.

LXM MASTER - Golfing equipment - Lynx Golf, Inc.

LXR BIOTECHNOLOGY - Pharmaceutical preparations - LXR Biotechnology Inc.

LXS - Seat covers - Saddleman, Inc.

LXX - Tires - Bridgestone/Firestone, Inc.

LXX MACH I - Tires - Bridgestone/Firestone, Inc.

LYC LABS - Cosmetics - Lois Yee Cosmetics Inc.

LYC-O-MIX - Spices and extracts - Pharmachem Laboratories, Inc.

LYCALL - Pharmaceutical preparations - Caleb Laboratories Inc.

LYCANTHROPES - Games ☆ - Mayfair Games, Inc.

LYCENTA LOVSJO SWEDEN - Chandeliers - Nordic Trading Inc.

LYCEUM - Electronic equipment - Thomson Consumer Electronics, Inc.

LYCEUM - Watches - North American Watch Corp.

LYCO - Food processors - Lyco Manufacturing, Inc.

LYCO/MEN - Vitamins and nutritional supplements - Desert Health Products, Inc.

LYCOFAST - Gas machinery - R.W. Lyall & Co., Inc.

LYCOFIBERS - Spices and extracts - Pharmachem Laboratories, Inc.

LYCOFOODS - Vitamins and nutritional supplements - Pharmachem Laboratories, Inc.

LYCOLAN - Pharmaceutical preparations - Lannett Co. Inc.

LYCOPENE CAPS - Vitamins and nutritional supplements - Vitamin Research Products Inc.

LYCRA - Fibers–synthetic - E.I. Dupont de Nemours and Co.

LYCRA LOVE - Fabrics–broadcloth - Desire Mills Co. Inc.

LYDIA - Frames–eyeglass - Rozin Optical Export Corp.

LYDIA GREY - Household paper products - Statler Industries, Inc.

LYDIA JANE - Linens - TJX Companies, Inc.

LYDIA JANE LTD. - Apparel–women's - TJX Companies, Inc.

LYDIA-K - Candy - Jacob Kern & Sons

LYDIA O'LEARY - Cosmetics - Covermark Cosmetics

LYDIA PINKHAM - Vitamins and nutritional supplements - Numark Laboratories Inc.

LYDIAN - Novelty items - J.W. Stannard Co.

LYDIARD EQUINOX - Athletic footwear - Converse Inc.

LYDIARD THUNDERBOLT - Athletic footwear - Converse Inc.

LYDICO BY LYDIARD - Running shoes - International Seaway Trading Corp.

LYDIE - Stencils - Elizabeth K. Wallace

LYDNEYPLY - Plywood - Harbor Sales Co.

LYELL'S - Nuts–salted, roasted, cooked, or canned ☆ - Liberty Richter Inc.

LYENA - Computer software - Lyena Development

LYETH - Wines ☆ - Silver Oak Wine Cellars

LYFE LYNE - Pet products - Theon Labs

LYFORCIN - Pharmaceutical preparations ☆ - U.S. Ethicals Inc.

LYGIENES - Skin care products - Sterling Winthrop Inc.

LYGIN - Dental equipment - Dentamerica

LYKA BEAR - Apparel–children's - Lyka Wear Inc.

LYKADREME - Brassieres (Bras) - Finebrand Inc.

LYKE-IT-LEAN - Meat products–beef - Lykes Bros. Inc. (Meat Packing Div.)

LYKE-SKYN - Apparel–women's - Cupid Foundations Inc.

LYKES - Meat products–beef - Lykes Services Co.

LYKES FAMILY CHOICE - Coffee - Lykes Services Co.

LYKES PREFERRED - Food products - Lykes Bros. Inc. (Meat Packing Div.)

LYKEWOOD - Hardware - Marley Mouldings Inc.

LYLE & SCOTT - Sweaters - Lyle & Scott Inc.

LYLE, LYLE, CROCODILE - Games - Bernard Weber

LYLE, LYLE, CROCODILE - Toys–stuffed ☆ - Gund, Inc.

LYMAN - Ships–sailing vessels - Lyman-Morse Boatbuilding Co. Inc.

LYMAN - Sights–gun - Lyman Products Corp.

LYMAN ALPHA I A - Photographic equipment - Nye Optical Co.

LYMAN ALPHA I LENS - Photographic equipment - Nye Optical Co.

LYME - Cigarettes - Brown & Williamson Tobacco Corp.

LYME - Skin care products - William Stevens Perfumers

LYME GREEN - Computer storage devices - Lyme Software Sales, Inc.

LYME ISLAND TWILIGHT - Teas - Vermont Tea & Maple

LYMPHA PRESS - Medical apparatus ☆ - Camp, Inc.

LYMPHAGEN - Vitamins and nutritional supplements - Great Life Laboratories Inc.

LYMPHODERM - Skin care products - Spa Technologies International, Inc.

LYN HOLLYN GARDEN - Wallpaper - Prelude Designs

LYN-LAD - Automotive parts and accessories - Lynn Ladder and Scaffolding Co. Inc.

LYNAE - Vitamins and nutritional supplements - Stason Industrial Corp.

LYNC - Computer software - Norton-Lambert Corp.

LYNCHBURG - Clocks ☆ - General Time Corp. (Westclox/Seth Thomas Div.)

LYNCHBURG - Furniture - Taylor-Ramsey Corp.

LYNCHBURG LEMONADE - Liquors - Jack Daniel's Distillery

LYNCO - Orthopedic products - Apex Foot Health Industries, Inc.

LYNDCOAT - Chemical preparations - Rhone-Poulenc Inc.

LYNDEE - Perfumes - Cameo Coutures

LYNDELL - Recording label - Lifetime Recordings

☆ = Now out of production

LYNDEN - Fruits and vegetables - Western Farmers Association
LYNDEN FARMS - Frozen foods - Pacific Valley Foods
LYNDEN FARMS - Potato flakes - Nestle USA
LYNDER'S - Soup mixes - Lynder Foods
LYNDER'S GOLD - Seasoning - Lynder Foods
LYNDHURST - Finishing agents ☆ - Flintkote Co.
LYNDHURST - Paints ☆ - GS Roofing Products Co.
LYNDON - Apparel and accessories - Hamrick's, Inc.
LYNDONVILLE - Food products ☆ - RHM Holdings (USA) Inc.
LYNELLE-FOURTH CUVEE - Wines - Diamond Wine Merchants
LYNETTE - Dolls - Horsman
LYNFRED - Wines - Lynfred Winery
LYNLITE - Wallpaper - J.M. Lynne Co. Inc.
LYNN - Ladders–metal - Lynn Ladder and Scaffolding Co. Inc.
LYNN - Shoe polish - George J. Kelly Div.
LYNN BROOK - Candy ☆ - Pet Inc. (Whitman's Chocolates Div.)
LYNN GERTENBACH - Calendars ☆ - Amcal Inc.
LYNN HAVEN - Manufactured homes ☆ - Redman Industries, Inc.
LYNN HOLBYN AT HOME - Wallpaper ☆ - Pelican Prints
LYNN HOLLYN AT HOME COLLECTION - Furniture - Lexington Furniture Industries, Inc.
LYNN LACAVA - Apparel–women's - Lynn Lacava Inc.
LYNN SUZANNE - Jewelry ☆ - Weingeroff Enterprises, Inc.
LYNN WILSON'S - Food products - Wilson Products Co. Inc.
LYNNCRAFT - Hobby kits - Janlynn Corp.
LYNNE - Wallpaper ☆ - J.M. Lynne Co. Inc.
LYNNE GREENE - Apparel stores–lingerie - Little Greene Apples, Inc.
LYNNE WELSING - Greeting cards - Recycled Paper Products, Inc.
LYNNESCAPE - Wallpaper - J.M. Lynne Co. Inc.
LYNNESCAPE II - Wallpaper - J.M. Lynne Co. Inc.
LYNNFIELD - Furniture ☆ - Bassett Furniture Industries, Inc.
LYNNGYDE - Computer software - SourceView Software International
LYNNS - Cooking equipment–household - Regent Alliance, Inc.
LYNN'S - Veterinary pharmaceutical preparations - Pfeiffer Pharmaceuticals Inc.
LYNORAL - Pharmaceutical preparations ☆ - Organon Inc.
LYNSOL - Epoxy coatings - Sterling-Clark-Lurton Corp.
LYNTON - Clocks ☆ - General Time Corp. (Westclox/Seth Thomas Div.)
LYNTONE - Belts–apparel - Gem-Dandy, Inc.
LYNTONE - Belts–apparel - Lyntone Belts Inc.
LYNWOOD - Clocks - Ridgeway Clock Co.
LYNWOOD - Floor coverings - Congoleum Corp.
LYNWOOD - Floor coverings–carpet and rugs - Evans-Black Carpet Mills
LYNWOOD FARMS - Spices and extracts - Bolner's Fiesta Products, Inc.
LYNX - Archery equipment ☆ - Martin Archery Inc.
LYNX - Batteries - East Penn Manufacturing Co., Inc.
LYNX - Bicycles - Ross Bicycles USA, Ltd.
LYNX - Cameras ☆ - Yashica Inc.
LYNX - Catheters - Cardiovascular Dynamics, Inc.
LYNX - Computer software - CH2M Hill, Inc.
LYNX - Computer software - International Imaging Networks Corp.
LYNX - Computer software - Lynx Networking, Inc.
LYNX - Computer software - Robbins-Gioia, Inc.
LYNX - Filters–water ☆ - Sta-Rite Industries Inc.
LYNX - Golfing equipment - Golfsmith International Inc.
LYNX - Golfing equipment - Lynx Golf, Inc.
LYNX - Lenses–magnifying ☆ - Swift Instruments, Inc.
LYNX - Luggage - Daewoo International (America) Corp.
LYNX - Motor vehicles–automobiles ☆ - Ford Motor Co. (Lincoln-Mercury Div.)
LYNX - Tripods–photographic - Phoenix Corp. of America
LYNX - Video equipment - BH Electronics, Inc.
LYNX 10 - Golfing equipment ☆ - Lynx Golf, Inc.
LYNX GOLF - Golfing equipment - Golfsmith International Inc.
LYNX LEVELERS - Automotive parts and accessories - Tri Lynx Corp.
LYNX MV - Golfing equipment - Lynx Golf, Inc.
LYNX OPAQUE - Paper–bond - Weyerhaeuser Co.
LYNX RADIUS - Golfing equipment - Lynx Golf, Inc.
LYNXWARE - Computer software - Cyberlynx
LYNXX - Radio communications equipment - Viasat Technology Corp.
LYON - Breads - Lyon Food Products Inc.
LYON - Coffee - Salina Coffee House Inc.
LYON - Furniture - Lane Co. Inc.
LYON - Hardware - Blaine Window Hardware Inc.
LYON - Rings–jewelry - Artcarved Inc.
LYON - Shelving units–metal - Young's
LYON & HEALY - Harps - Lyon & Healy Harps Inc.

LYON DESIGN - Clothing - Lyon Design
LYON SUPREME - Teas ☆ - Try Coffee Group Ltd.
LYONDELL - Oils–lubricating - Lyondell Petrochemical Co.
LYONS - Artists' materials - Duro Art Industries Inc.
LYONS - Artists' materials ☆ - M. Grumbacher Inc.
LYONS - Automotive parts and accessories - Peco Manufacturing Co. Inc.
LYONS - Bathroom accessories - Lyons Industries Inc.
LYON'S - Cookies - Wachtel Biscuit
LYONS - Food products - Lyons-Magnus Inc.
LYONS - Food products ☆ - Masterpeace Food Imports
LYONS - Hampers - R.H. Lyons Co. Inc.
LYONS - Musical instrument accessories ☆ - Selmer Co. Inc.
LYONS-MAGNUS - Syrup ☆ - Royal Cup, Inc.
LYONS NO-SMEAR - Cleaning preparations - Durasol Drug & Chemical Co.
LYON'S #1 - Coffee ☆ - Try Coffee Group Ltd.
LYON'S OWN - Tobacco–chewing or smoking - Philip Morris Companies Inc.
LYON'S PRIME - Food products - Olfisco Inc.
LYOPHILIZED CYTOXAN - Pharmaceutical preparations - Bristol-Myers Squibb Co.
LYOPHRIN - Ophthalmic goods ☆ - Alcon Laboratories, Inc.
LYOPINE VARI-DOSE - Pharmaceutical preparations ☆ - Hyrex Pharmaceuticals
LYRA - Fabrics - Superior Shade & Blind Co. Inc.
LYRA - Floor coverings–carpet and rugs ☆ - Galaxy Carpet Mills Inc.
LYRA - Floor coverings–carpet and rugs ☆ - Mohawk Carpet Corp.
LYRA - Musical instruments - C. Bruno & Son Inc.
LYRA LITE - Lamps - Cannon Products Inc.
LYRACHORD - Guitars - Ovation Instruments
LYRAL - Oils–essential - International Flavors & Fragrances Inc.
LYRE - Audio equipment ☆ - Shahinian Acoustics Ltd.
LYRE - Watches ☆ - Jaeger-Le Coultre SA
LYREC - Electronic equipment ☆ - G Prime Limited
LYRIC - Amplifiers–musical instrument ☆ - Pacific Music Supply Co.
LYRIC - Bird feeds - Lebanon Seaboard Corp.
LYRIC - Bird feeds - Stanford Seed Co.
LYRIC - Cabinets - HomeCrest Corp.
LYRIC - Candles - Candle Corp. of America
LYRIC - Candlesticks ☆ - Lenox Crystal, Inc.
LYRIC - Dinnerware–glass - Block China Co.
LYRIC - Giftware ☆ - Gorham Inc.
LYRIC - Glassware–household - Owens-Illinois Inc. (Libbey Div.)
LYRIC - Hearing aids - Beltone Electronics Corp.
LYRIC - Lamps–desk - Lightolier Inc.
LYRIC - Paper - Mactac Inc. (Packaging Closures Systems Div.)
LYRIC - Rings–jewelry - Artcarved Inc.
LYRIC - Sinks–metal - Kohler Co.
LYRIC - Thread - Threads USA Div.
LYRIC - Underwear and nightwear - Bestform Foundations, Inc.
LYRIC A - Rings–jewelry - Artcarved Inc.
LYRIC COLLECTION - Hair care products - Premiere Products, Inc.
LYRICATURES - Posters - Renaissance Publications Inc.
LYRICHORD - Recording label - Lyrichord Discs Inc.
LYRIQ - Computer integrated systems design services - Lyriq International Corp.
LYRIQ CROSSWORDS - Computer software - Lyriq International Corp.
LYRIQUE - Flatware - Couzon USA
LYRIS - Skin care products - Lendan USA Co.
LYRIX - Greeting cards - Malrite Communications Group, Inc.
LYRYC - Dinnerware–glass - Block China Co.
LYSE SPENARD - Apparel–women's - Leslie Fay Companies Inc.
LYSETTE - Health care products - L & F Consumer Products
LYSINE ASCORBS - Vitamins and nutritional supplements - Alacer Corp.
LYSINE HERBAL - Nutritional supplements - McZand Herbal, Inc.
LYSINE PLUS SUPER COMBO - Skin care products ☆ - Quantum, Inc.
LYSINE-POWER - Vitamins and nutritional supplements - Natur-Pharma, Inc.
LYSINYL - Vitamins and nutritional supplements - Tyson & Associates, Inc.
LYSODASE - Pharmaceutical preparations - Enzon Inc.
LYSODREN - Pharmaceutical preparations - Bristol-Myers Squibb Co.
LYSOFORM - Disinfectants - Chesebrough-Pond's USA Co.
LYSOL - Disinfectants - L & F Consumer Products
LYSOL - Toys–automobiles - Linden Corp.
LYSOL ANTIBACTERIAL KITCHEN CLEANER - Cleaning preparations–carpet and rug - Linden Corp.
LYSOL COUNTRY SCENT - Cleaning preparations–household - L & F Consumer Products
LYSTRALON - Paints - Conco Paint Co.

☆ = Now out of production

LYT-ALL - Paints - Pratt & Lambert, Inc.

LYTAR - Veterinary pharmaceutical preparations - DVM Pharmaceuticals, Inc.

LYTE-BYTE - Computers–personal - Micro Express Inc.

LYTE FIT - Orthopedic products - Langer Biomechanics Group, Inc.

LYTE MOVES - Hosiery - Viking Technology Inc.

LYTEBEAM - Lamps–desk - Lightolier Inc.

LYTECASTER - Lighting fixtures - Lightolier Inc.

LYTEERS - Ophthalmic goods - Barnes-Hind Inc.

LYTEFLOOD - Lighting fixtures - Genlyte Group Inc.

LYTEGEM - Lamps–desk - Lightolier Inc.

LYTEJACKS - Transformers–electric - Genlyte Group Inc.

LYTEPLUS - Lighting fixtures - Lamps Plus Inc.

LYTEQUEST - Lighting fixtures–stage - Gemini Sound Products Corp.

LYTESPAN - Lamps–floor - Lightolier Inc.

LYTLER & LYTLER - Toys–models - GHQ

LYTLEWARE - Apparel and accessories - Lytleware Enterprises

LYTOR - Chemical preparations - Georgia-Pacific Corp.

LYTREN - Pharmaceutical preparations - Bristol-Myers Squibb Co.

LYTTON SPRINGS - Wines - Ridge Vineyards Inc.

LYTTON SPRINGS - Wines ☆ - Lytton Springs Winery

LYVERINE - Vitamins and nutritional supplements - Lyverine Corp.

M

Addresses and phone numbers for the companies cited in the brands below
are available in the Company Listings section immediately following the brands listings.

M - Amplifiers - Maxtech, Inc.
M - Brushes–hair - Mebco Industries, Inc.
M - Chemical preparations - Columbian Chemicals Co.
M - Computer peripheral equipment - Lone Wolf, Inc.
M - Computer software - International Business Machines Corp.
M - Computer software - MFactory, Inc.
M - Computer software - Schneider Automation
M - Computers - Microland Electronics Corp.
M - Cutlery - Atlanta Cutlery Corp.
M - Desserts - Vermont Mountain Mousse Co.
M - Electronic equipment - Motorola, Inc. (Land Mobile Products Sector)
M - Floor coverings–carpet and rugs - Masland Corp.
M - Flowers, plants, and seeds - Mangelsdorf Seed Co.
M - Footwear - Mason Shoe Manufacturing Co.
M - Fruits and vegetables - Matson Fruit Co.
M - Furniture–public buildings ☆ - Novikoff, Inc.
M - Furniture–wood - Masterpiece Accessories, Inc.
M - Hats - Orlando Magic, Ltd.
M - Jewelry - M. Anson Inc.
M - Jewelry - Millerick's Design Studio Inc.
M - Jewelry - Marla K. Mishoulam
M - Jewelry - Paul Morelli Design, Inc.
M - Jewelry - Morning Sun Inc.
M - Photocopy machines - Xerox Corp.
M - Ribbons - Midori, Inc.
M - Screws - MNP Corp.
M - Siding–insulating ☆ - Aluminum Co. of America
M - Surfboards - Kransco Manufacturing Inc.
M - Tablecloths - Marko Intl.
M - Tools–hand-operated - Marion Tool Corp.
M - Wigs - Pacific Co. Inc.
M-1 - Paints - Jomaps Co.
M-1 HOUSE WASH - Cleaning preparations–household - Jomaps Co.
M-3X - Novelty items - PC Manufacturing Corp.
M-4 - Amusement rides - Triple Quest, Inc.
M/11+ - Computer software - InterSystems Corp.
M-14 - Tape recorders - Eastman Kodak Co.
M-15 - Frames–eyeglass - Rozin Optical Export Corp.
M-46 - Detergents - Imperial Manufacturing Co. Inc.
M 50-50 - Veterinary pharmaceutical preparations ☆ - Lemmon Co.
M-65 COMPOUND - Pharmaceutical preparations ☆ - R.A. McNeil Co.
M-87-190 - Pharmaceutical preparations - Alva-Amco Pharmacal Co.
M-99 - Pharmaceutical preparations ☆ - Lemmon Co.
M 100 MCNALLY - Wheelchairs - McNally Industries, Inc.
M-180 - Office supplies ☆ - McBee Loose Leaf Binders
M-255 - Frames–eyeglass ☆ - Universal/Univis Inc.
M-402 - Pencils–mechanical - Zebra Pen Corp.
M-1000 - Bicycles ☆ - Montague Corp.
M-1000 - Telephones - TIE Communications Inc.
M-1050 - Musical instrument accessories - Music Accessories Manufacturing Co. Inc.
M-1050G - Musical instrument accessories - Music Accessories Manufacturing Co. Inc.
M-1050RB - Musical instrument accessories - Music Accessories Manufacturing Co. Inc.

M-1050RBG - Musical instrument accessories - Music Accessories Manufacturing Co. Inc.
M-1080G - Musical instrument accessories - Music Accessories Manufacturing Co. Inc.
M-1080R - Musical instrument accessories - Music Accessories Manufacturing Co. Inc.
M-1081G - Musical instrument accessories - Music Accessories Manufacturing Co. Inc.
M-1081R - Musical instrument accessories - Music Accessories Manufacturing Co. Inc.
M-A - Solder - La-Co Industries, Inc.
M. A. BRUDER - Paints - M.A. Bruder & Sons Inc.
M. A. DOPPELT - Cases–vanity - Risto Inc.
M. A. GREEN - Jewelry - Luxbond & Green Inc.
M/A PRESS - Embossing plates - Dilithium Press
M-A-S 90 AUTOGRAPH - Computer software - State of the Art, Inc.
M-AMP - Pharmaceutical preparations ☆ - R.A. McNeil Co.
M & A - Candy ☆ - Jaret Specialties Inc.
M & B - Window coverings - M.A. Baskind Co.
M & D - Food products - M & D Foods Inc.
M & D KETCHIAN - Giftware - Ketchian Photographers
M & G VINS - Wines - Kedem Royal Wine Corp.
M & H - Gasoline - Miller and Holmes Inc.
M & H - Varnishes - Mantrose-Haeuser Co. Inc.
M & J - Recording label - Sharon Productions Inc.
M & K - Food products - M & K Foods Inc.
M & K SOUND - Audio equipment - Miller & Kreisel Sound Corp.
M & L - Hair care products - Nutrine Ltd.
M & L - Toiletries - Lanman & Kemp-Barclay & Co. Inc.
M & M - Amplifiers–radio - M & M Electronics
M & M - Coffee - Squire Foods
M & M - Gauging instruments - M & M Precision Systems Corp.
M & M - Luggage ☆ - Verdi Travelware
M & M - Wines - Dieter Steinmann Inc.
M & M'S - Candy - Mars, Inc.
M & M'S MINIS - Chocolate candy - Mars, Inc.
M & P - Hair care products - John Amico Expressive Hair Care Products
M. AND P. - Wines - Martini and Prati Wines Inc.
M & R - Toys - M & R Manufacturing Inc.
M & S PLUS - Tires - Uniroyal Goodrich Tire Co.
M & W SUPERGROOM - Hair care products - Eden Beauty Products
M ANDREW MCCLINTOCK COLLECTION, A - Apparel and accessories - Scott Andrew McClintock
M-APAP - Pharmaceutical preparations ☆ - R.A. McNeil Co.
M-B - Candy - M-B Candies Inc.
M B RANCH - Breads - My Bread Baking Co.
M-BAC - Binders - The Union Group
M-BAMATE - Pharmaceutical preparations - Michigan Pharmaceutical
M-BLADE - Actuators–hydraulic - Schwab-Koplin Associates, Inc.
M BOLT GRIP - Cement - Merlex Stucco, Inc.
M-BOND - Tubes–plastic - Markel Corp.
M BRACE - Braces–orthopedic - 4D Ventures
M-BRACE - Rubber bands - National Artcraft Co.
M-BRO BLOK - Toys - William J. Embro
M-CAL M - Pharmaceutical preparations - Misemer Pharmaceuticals Inc.
M-CAP - Chemical preparations - M-Cap Technologies International

☆ = Now out of production

M-CAPP - Computer software - Med Cap Resources, Inc.
M-CAPS - Pharmaceutical preparations - Pal-Pak Inc.
M. CHAPOUTIER - Wines - Paterno Imports, Ltd.
M. CHEVALLIER - Wines - Codorniu USA Inc.
M-CILLIN - Pharmaceutical preparations - Misemer Pharmaceuticals Inc.
M-CILLIN VK - Pharmaceutical preparations ☆ - R.A. McNeil Co.
M CLASSIC - Paint - Kimberton Enterprises, Inc.
M-CLEAR - Pharmaceutical preparations - R.A. McNeil Co.
M-COLIBLUE24 - Pharmaceutical preparations - Hach Co.
M DATA - Computer software - M Data Inc.
M-DEX - Pharmaceutical preparations - Misemer Pharmaceuticals Inc.
M-DONNA - Pharmaceutical preparations ☆ - R.A. McNeil Co.
M-E - Cleaning preparations–household ☆ - ICI Americas Inc.
M-END - Pharmaceutical preparations - R.A. McNeil Co.
M-ESTRO - Pharmaceutical preparations - Michigan Pharmaceutical
M. EVANS & CO. - Publisher's imprints - Henry Holt and Co.
M-EX BOARD - Computer peripheral equipment ☆ - Steinberg/Jones Corp.
M-EXPECTORANT - Pharmaceutical preparations ☆ - R.A. McNeil Co.
M-F - Fishing lures - M-F Manufacturing Co. Inc.
M-FORCE - Audio equipment - Pro-Co. Sound Co. Inc.
M FORCE - Toys - Imperial Toy Corp.
M FRAMES - Eyeglasses - Oakley, Inc.
M-FRIN - Ophthalmic goods - Misemer Pharmaceuticals Inc.
M-G - Sporting goods - Brimms Inc.
M. G. GRUNDMAN - Shoes - M.G. Grundman & Sons Inc.
M. G. VALLEJO - Wines - Glen Ellen Winery
M. GATES - Jewelry - Michael Gates Inc.
M GEMINI MASTERPIECE - Photographic finishes - Gemini Coatings, Inc.
M-GESIC - Pharmaceutical preparations ☆ - R.A. McNeil Co.
M. GIRAULT - Figurines ☆ - Estus Export-Import
M-GLUC - Pharmaceutical preparations - Michigan Pharmaceutical
M H - Wines - Sazerac Co. Inc.
M. H. M. - Dresses–women's - Halmode Apparel Inc.
M/H MANAGE - Computer software - M/H Group, Inc.
M-HIST - Pharmaceutical preparations ☆ - R.A. McNeil Co.
M-HIST T.D. - Pharmaceutical preparations ☆ - R.A. McNeil Co.
M. I. HUMMEL - Figurines - Goebel of North America
M INC. - Concrete products - Massarelli's Lawn Ornaments, Inc.
M-J - Chickens ☆ - Mar-Jac Processing Inc.
M. J. KUPPER - Cutlery - Smith Restaurant Supply Co., Inc.
M. J. LINN - Window coverings - Vertical Blind Factory
M/J MAR-JAC - Chickens - Mar-Jac Processing Inc.
M-JIVE - Bicycles - Neal Enterprises
M. K CHAM - Apparel–men's - Kazah Fashion Inc.
M-K RANCH MASTER KING - Food products - Master King Food Inc.
M-KYA - Pharmaceutical preparations - Nature's Bounty, Inc.
M. LACROIX - Musical instruments - Fred Gretsch Enterprises
M' LADY - Eyeglasses - Art-Craft Optical Co.
M-LASTIC - Sporting goods - Mueller Sports Medicine Inc.
M-LINE - Office furniture–metal - Invincible Metal Furniture Co.
M' LORD'S - Spices and extracts ☆ - Brandes Co.
M/M - Electronics equipment - Bencher Inc.
M M & K RECORDINGS - Compact discs–prerecorded - Johnny Mars Productions, International
M M-E-D-I-A MAGICIAN - Computer software - User Interface Technologies Corp.
M-M-M-M FRESCO - Desserts - Fresco Ice Desserts Corp.
M-M SUPREME - Electronics equipment - RTI Research Technology International
M MAGICELL - Batteries - Texas Tech Mart, Inc.
M MAGNA - Bicycles - Dynacraft Industries, Inc.
M MALDEN - Frames–picture - Malden Frames
M MALIBU - Computer software - Malibu Comics Entertainment, Inc.
M MANNINGTON CERAMIC TILE - Tiles–ceramic - Mannington Mills, Inc.
M. MARCHERE - Wines - M.S. Walker Inc./Seacoast
M MASSIMO MASSIMO - Bicycles - Huntington USA Inc.
M MASTER SHARP - Video tapes–blank - Rank Video Services America, Inc.
M MATURE AGES 17+ - Computer software - Interactive Digital Software Association
M MAYWOOD FURNITURE CORP. - Tables–wood - DeSaussure Equipment Co.
M MCDONALDLAND RACING TEAM - Toys–automobiles - Mcdonald's Corp.
M MCDONALD'S RACING TEAM - Key rings - Mcdonald's Corp.
M MEARL - Pigments - Mearl Corp.
M MEDALLA DE BARRIL - Beverages–malt - Cerveceria India, Inc.
M MEGABYTE MALL - Advertising agencies - Neusnet Advertising Group, Inc.

M MERCHANTS METALS THE FIRST NAME IN FENCE - Fencing–gates and posts - MMI Products, Inc.
M METAMORPHYSIQUE - Physical fitness centers - Metamorphysique
M MEYER - Machinery - Wm W. Meyer & Sons, Inc.
M MICHELOTTI - Watches - Abrim Enterprises, Inc.
M MICKEY - Motor vehicle parts and accessories - W.F. Mickey Body Co., Inc.
M MICROM - Computers - PC Plus Inc.
M MONOLITH CORPORATION - Computer hardware - Monolith Corp.
M MONZA - Bicycles - Liyang USA, Inc.
M MUSICMASTERS - Compact discs–prerecorded - Musicmasters
M-MYCIN - Pharmaceutical preparations ☆ - R.A. McNeil Co.
M MYRO - Housewares - Myro, Inc.
M-NALTABS - Pharmaceutical preparations - Michigan Pharmaceutical
M/NET - Computer software - InterSystems Corp.
M NETWORK - Games - Mattel, Inc.
M O E MADE ON EARTH - Apparel and accessories - Made on Earth, Inc.
M-O-M - Pharmaceutical preparations ☆ - JMI-Canton Pharmaceuticals
M-OATS - Cereal - Quaker Oats Co.
M-ONE - Circuit boards - Monolithic System Technology, Inc.
M-P-O - Meat product - Country Lane Foods Inc.
M-P SEALANT - Automotive parts and accessories - Radiator Specialty Co.
M-PAC - Veterinary nutritional supplements - Schering Corp.
M-PACT - Sporting goods - Diversified Products Corp.
M PAK - Containers–plastic - Packaging Concepts Assoc. Inc.
M-PAV - Pharmaceutical preparations - Michigan Pharmaceutical
M-PENTRATE - Pharmaceutical preparations - Michigan Pharmaceutical
M-PHEN - Pharmaceutical preparations - R.A. McNeil Co.
M-PLI'D-PAPER - Film - Plicon Corp.
M PLUS - Cleaning equipment - Microtron Abrasives, Inc.
M POINT - Drill bits - SDI Operating Partners
M-POXIDE - Pharmaceutical preparations - Michigan Pharmaceutical
M-PREDNISOL - Pharmaceutical preparations - Pasadena Research Laboratories, Inc.
M PROFESSIONAL - Cosmetics - Professional Makeup Co.
M-QUIN - Pharmaceutical preparations - Michigan Pharmaceutical
M-R WEATHERFOOT - Socks - Simmons Hosiery Mill Inc.
M/RINSE - Pharmaceutical preparations - Whitby Pharmaceuticals, Inc.
M ROC DONALD'S - Potato sticks - Mcdonald's Corp.
M-ROS SWITCHER - Computer software - Steinberg/Jones Corp.
M-S - Recording label - MSK Productions Inc.
M. S. WALKER PREMIUM - Whiskey - M.S. Walker Inc./Seacoast
M-SEL - Pharmaceutical preparations - Michigan Pharmaceutical
M SERIES - Audio equipment - Monster Cable Products, Inc.
M-SERIES - Couplings - ATR Sales, Inc.
M-SERP - Pharmaceutical preparations - Michigan Pharmaceutical
M-SPRAY 2000 - Health care products - Pharmaceutical Innovations
M-SPRAYTRODE - Health care products ☆ - Pharmaceutical Innovations
M STREAMLINE - Tubes–copper - Mueller Industries, Inc.
M-STRIPS - Sporting goods - Mueller Sports Medicine Inc.
M. SUZUKI - Musical instruments ☆ - Kaman Music Corp.
M/T - Tires - Max-Trac Tire Co.
M-TAPE - Sporting goods - Mueller Sports Medicine Inc.
M-TEL - Pharmaceutical preparations - Michigan Pharmaceutical
M-TETRA 250 - Pharmaceutical preparations - Misemer Pharmaceuticals Inc.
M-THIAZIDE - Pharmaceutical preparations - Michigan Pharmaceutical
M-TRACK - Computer software - Management Science Associates, Inc.
M-TRAN - Pharmaceutical preparations ☆ - R.A. McNeil Co.
M. TRIBAUT - Wines - European Beverage Co., Inc.
M. TRINCHERO - Wines - Sutter Home Winery, Inc.
M-TRON - Toys–blocks - Lego Systems Inc.
M-TUSS - Pharmaceutical preparations ☆ - R.A. McNeil Co.
M-V-P - Floor waxes - Brulin & Co., Inc.
M/VISION - Computer software - PDA Engineering
M/VM - Computer software - InterSystems Corp.
M. W. WHIDBEY - Beverages–alcohol - Stimson Lane Vineyards & Estates
M. WALKER - Puddings–canned - Cowan & Fransman
M WAVE - Computer peripheral equipment - International Business Machines Corp.
M-WIPE - Cleaning preparations - Texwipe Co. LLC
M-WLINK - Computer software - Merriam-Webster
M-WRAP - Sporting goods - Mueller Sports Medicine Inc.
M-ZIDE - Pharmaceutical preparations ☆ - R.A. McNeil Co.
M-ZYME - Water treating compounds - Aquarium Pharmaceuticals, Inc.
M1 - Electronic equipment - MacKenzie Laboratories Inc.
M1 - Hearing aids - Widex Hearing Aid Co., Inc.
M1 ABRAMS - Fireworks - China Pyrotechnics, Inc.

☆ = Now out of production

M1 BY MEZLAN - Shoes - Pacific Shoe Corp.

M1 SC - Sporting goods - Marker International Co.

M1 TANK PLATOON - Computer software ☆ - Microprose Software, Inc.

M1-X - Golf clubs - Ray Cook Co.

M2 - Computer software - M2 Software, Inc.

M2 - LAN servers - Network Connection, Inc.

M2 - Vitamins and nutritional supplements - M2 Corp.

M3 - Motor vehicles–automobiles ☆ - BMW of North America Inc.

M3 CHARGER - Rackets–tennis - Estusa Corp.

M3 CLUTCH - Motor vehicle parts and accessories - Moto Mirror, Inc.

M3 MULTI MEDIA MONITOR - Televisions - Covid, Inc.

M3 PRODUCTIONS/V-PAT RECORDS - Recording label - M-3 Productions/V-Pat Records

M3 PROFESSIONAL - Rackets–tennis - Estusa Corp.

M3 SUPRA - Rackets–tennis - Estusa Corp.

M4 - Computer software - Mapcom Systems, Inc.

M5 - Computer software - Promax Conceptual Strategies

M5 - Motor vehicles–automobiles ☆ - BMW of North America Inc.

M5 VELOCE - Computer equipment - Genoa Systems Corp.

M6 - Motor vehicles–automobiles ☆ - BMW of North America Inc.

M47 - Hardware - Black & Decker Corp.

M77 - Rifles - Sturm, Ruger & Co., Inc.

M95 - Hats - Snell Memorial Foundation, Inc.

M301 - Pencils–mechanical - Zebra Pen Corp.

M500 - Computer terminals - Nec Technologies, Inc.

M605 - Pencils–mechanical - Zebra Pen Corp.

M700 - Computer peripheral equipment - Nec Technologies, Inc.

M1300 - Projection screens - Draper Shade and Screen Co. Inc.

M2500 - Projection screens - Draper Shade and Screen Co. Inc.

M6100 - Telephones–cellular - Hughes Aircraft Co.

MA - Jewelry - Man-Am Creations, Ltd.

MA/AH PUBLISHING - Publisher's imprints - Sunflower University Press

MA BAENSCH - Food products - Baensch Food Products Co.

MA BELL'S - Potato chips ☆ - Sunshine Biscuits, Inc.

MA BROWN - Pickles - Green Bay Foods Co.

MA CHERIE - Dolls ☆ - Effanbee Doll Corp.

MA-CREPE - Dropcloths - D.C. May Corp.

MA-GEL - Antacids - Vita-Fore Products Co.

M.A. HADLEY - Dishes–earthenware - Hadley Pottery Co. Inc.

MA JOHNSON - Vegetables–frozen - Ma Johnson Frozen Foods Inc.

MA JOLIE - Hair accessories, jewelry - Sherwood Hamilton Co.

MA MURPHY'S - Seafood products–canned or cured - Mom's Ltd.

MA NATURZLE - Cosmetics - Research Council of Make-Up Artists Inc.

MA PEARL - Vitamins and nutritional supplements - Joenaz Co. Inc.

MA ROLLER - Massage products - Great Earth Nutrients, Inc.

M.A. SIMMS & CO. - Apparel and accessories - Molly Nelson

MAAC FOOTBALL LEAGUE - Apparel and accessories - Metro Atlantic Athletic Conference

MAAC-LEAN - Vitamins and nutritional supplements - Albion Laboratories, Inc.

MAACO - Automotive repair shops - Maaco Enterprises Inc.

MAALOX - Antacids - Rhone-Poulenc Rorer Pharmaceuticals Inc.

MAALOX ANTI-DIARRHEAL - Pharmaceutical preparations - Rhone-Poulenc Rorer Pharmaceuticals Inc.

MAALOX DAILY FIBER THERAPY - Laxatives - Rhone-Poulenc Rorer Pharmaceuticals Inc.

MAALOX HRF - Antacids - Rhone-Poulenc Rorer Pharmaceuticals Inc.

MAANATAC - Adhesives and sealants - Beacon Chemical Co. Inc.

MAAPS - Computer software - ETSI Inc.

MAARIANHAMINA - Bedding–linen - Dan River Inc.

MAAZA - Fruit drinks–bottled or canned - Parle America Inc.

M.A.B. - Paints - M.A. Bruder & Sons Inc.

M.A.B. PLUS 4 - Paints ☆ - M.A. Bruder & Sons Inc.

MABI - Computer software - Xcelerated Systems, Inc.

MABOND - Frames–eyeglass - May Optical Co. Inc.

MABRY - Brushes–paint - Corona Brushes Inc.

MABUCHI - Toys–electronic - Polk's Model Craft Hobbies, Inc.

MAC - Air purification systems - Mac Equipment, Inc.

M.A.C. - Apparel–women's - M.A.C. Sport Inc.

MAC - Batteries - Atlantic Battery Co., Inc.

MAC - Brushes–paint - Corona Brushes Inc.

MAC - Cigars ☆ - H.L. Neff & Co. Inc.

MAC - Computers - Apple Computer Inc.

MAC - Electrical testing instruments - MAC Panel Co.

MAC - Eyeglasses - Martin-Copeland Eyewear Corp.

MAC - Fencing–wood ☆ - MacGillis and Gibbs Co.

MAC - Food products - ICD Group Inc.

MAC - Garden equipment - McCulloch Corp.

MAC - Paints ☆ - Mac-O-Lac Paints Inc.

M.A.C. - Tobacco–chewing or smoking - Majestic Affiliated Companies, Inc.

MAC - Toys ☆ - Placo Products Co.

M.A.C. - Veterinary pharmaceutical preparations - Equest, Inc. (Saratoga Veterinary Products, Co.)

M.A.C. - Wheelchairs - Gunnell Inc.

MAC ACCESS - Computer software - Hypro Systems

MAC AND MOE - Apparel–children's - P and B Apparel, Inc.

MAC & MORE - Dinners–frozen - Campbell Soup Co.

MAC ARTHUR - Frames–eyeglass - Hudson Optical Corp.

MAC ARTHUR - Pipes–tobacco - Buescher's Industries Inc.

MAC ARTHUR PARK - Bicycles - Ross Bicycles USA, Ltd.

MAC ARTHUR PARK - Floor coverings–carpet and rugs ☆ - Hollytex Carpet Mills Inc.

MAC BAREN - Pipes–tobacco - Swisher International, Inc.

MAC BEAR - Apparel–children's - Kid Duds

MAC BEAR - Toys–stuffed ☆ - Dakin Inc.

MAC BETH - Cutlery ☆ - Lifetime Hoan Corp.

MAC BETH - Glassware - Corning Inc.

MAC BIRDIE - Apparel and accessories - Sports Kiosks, Inc.

MAC BOND - Adhesives and sealants - Mactac Inc. (Packaging Closures Systems Div.)

MAC CAFERRI - Musical instrument accessories - French American Reeds Manufacturing

MAC CHECKERS/REVERSI - Computer software ☆ - Videx, Inc.

MAC CLIP - Cases–eyeglass - California Optical Leather Inc.

MAC-COACH - Varnishes ☆ - Mac-O-Lac Paints Inc.

MAC COACH TRAINING - Computer software - ATI

MAC-CRAFTER - Craft supplies - Mac-Crafter Co.

MAC CUISINE - Computer software - Thomas Norman Macaulay

MAC D - Recording label - Ichiban Records, Inc.

MAC DEE - Underwear and nightwear - Stanwood Corp.

MAC-DET - Detergents ☆ - Elcal Enterprises Ltd.

MAC DONALD'S - Tobacco–chewing or smoking - G.A. Georgopulo & Co. Inc.

MAC DONALD'S BRITISH CONSOLS - Tobacco–chewing or smoking - G.A. Georgopulo & Co. Inc.

MAC DONALD'S EXTRA LITE - Cigarettes - G.A. Georgopulo & Co. Inc.

MAC DONALD'S LITE - Cigarettes - G.A. Georgopulo & Co. Inc.

MAC DONALD'S MEDIUM - Cigarettes - G.A. Georgopulo & Co. Inc.

MAC DONALD'S MILD - Cigarettes - G.A. Georgopulo & Co. Inc.

MAC DRIVE - Tools - Stanley Works

MAC DUFF SCOTTIE - Toys–stuffed ☆ - Dakin Inc.

MAC ENVIRONMENTAL - Air purification systems - Mac Equipment, Inc.

MAC FARLANE'S - Candy - Pangburn Candy Co.

MAC FARMS OF HAWAII - Nuts–salted, roasted, cooked, or canned - MacFarms of Hawaii

MAC-FLOOR - Varnishes ☆ - Mac-O-Lac Paints Inc.

MAC FORTH - Computer software - Creative Solutions

MAC GAMMON/CRIBBAGE - Computer software ☆ - Videx, Inc.

MAC GREGOR - Craft supplies ☆ - Brushcreek Creative Co.

MAC GREGOR - Footwear - Mercury International Trading Corp.

MAC HAMMER - Novelty items–glass - Sunrise Multimedia, Inc.

MAC-INTERIOR - Varnishes ☆ - Mac-O-Lac Paints Inc.

MAC JAC - Containers - Mac-Jac Manufacturing Co. Inc.

MAC-JACK - Computer software ☆ - DataPak Software Inc.

MAC JELLY TARTS - Pastries - Joey's Fine Foods

MAC JET - Computer software ☆ - QMS, Inc.

MAC JR. - Food products - Mcdonald's Corp.

MAC-LITE - Paper ☆ - Silver Leaf Paper Co.

MAC LITE - Reflectors–optical ☆ - Mactac Inc. (Packaging Closures Systems Div.)

MAC-LOCK - Nuts and bolts - MacLean-Fogg Co.

MAC MATCH - Computer software ☆ - Axlon Inc.

MAC-MEASURE - Craft supplies - Mac-Crafter Co.

MAC MILLAN - Petroleum - MacMillan Ring-Free Oil Co. Inc.

MAC MILLAN - Spices and extracts - Oscar Mayer Foods Corp.

MAC MOVER - Computer storage devices ☆ - Amherst International Enterprises Co.

MAC MUSIC - Computer software ☆ - Hal Leonard Corp.

MAC NEIL - Ophthalmic goods - Embassy Creations Inc.

MAC NUTRIPLAN - Computer software - Micromedx Computer Software Corp.

MAC-O-LAC - Paints - Mac-O-Lac Paints Inc.

MAC-O-LAC CLEAR - Lacquers ☆ - Mac-O-Lac Paints Inc.

MAC-O-LAC REALWHITE - Paints ☆ - Mac-O-Lac Paints Inc.

☆ = Now out of production

MAC-O-LAC SATIN-TONE - Paints ☆ - Mac-O-Lac Paints Inc.
MAC-O-LAC WEATHERTESTED - Paints ☆ - Mac-O-Lac Paints Inc.
MAC-O-LYTE - Insecticides - Mackwin Co.
MAC ONE WRITE - Computer software - Sierra On-Line, Inc.
MAC OS - Computer software - Apple Computer Inc.
MAC PAC - Hobby kits ☆ - Kool Pak
MAC-PAK - Fertilizers–nitrogenous ☆ - Vaughan products
MAC P&L - Computer software - State of the Art, Inc.
MAC PAPERS - Envelopes - Mac Papers, Inc.
MAC-POKER - Computer software ☆ - DataPak Software Inc.
MAC POLY - Computer software ☆ - Sabaki Corp.
MAC POWER PRO - Generators ☆ - McCulloch Corp.
MAC-RA-MAE-A-RUG - Hobby kits - A + A
MAC RACK - Computer peripheral equipment ☆ - Omni International Inc.
MAC ROBOTS - Computer software - Unicorn Software
MAC-SPAR - Varnishes - Mac-O-Lac Paints Inc.
MAC STRETCH - Computer hardware - Computer Care Inc.
MAC-SUN - Window shades - Mid-America Custom Inc.
MAC TAPE - Magnetic tape–blank - MAC Panel Co.
MAC-TRAK - Computer software - Pc Communications, Inc.
MAC TYPE - Computer software - Palsoft
MAC VEGAS - Computer software ☆ - Videx, Inc.
MAC/VSOP - Recording label - Michele Audio Corp.
MAC ZONE, THE - Catalogs - Multiple Zones International, Inc.
MAC2WIN - Computer software - Altura Software Inc.
MACA CHOCO - Candy - Tropicana Hawaii Candy, Inc.
MACABEE - Beverages–carbonated - Codman Trading Co.
MACABEE - Pizzas–frozen - Macabee Foods Inc.
MACABI - Apparel and accessories - Macabi
MACABI SHIRT, THE - Apparel and accessories - Macabi
MACADAM - Paper–bond ☆ - Saxon Paper Co.
MACADAMIA DIDDLE BRITTLE - Confections - Nut Kettle East Inc.
MACADAMIA NUTS SAMPLER - Nuts–salted, roasted, cooked, or canned - Mauna Loa Macadamia Nut Corp.
MACADAMIA SALUTES - Candy - Ethel M. Chocolates, Inc.
MACAL - Vinyl - Mactac Inc. (Packaging Closures Systems Div.)
MACALLAN - Beverages–alcohol - Remy Martin Amerique Inc.
MACALLAN - Beverages–malt - European Beverage Co., Inc.
MACALOA - Chocolate milk - Nestle USA
MACAN - Partitions - Sherrill Furniture Co.
MACANDO - Seafood products–fresh or frozen ☆ - J.F. Clarke Corp.
MACANDREWS DRY SCOT - Beverages–malt - Merchant du Vin Corp.
MACANUDO - Cigars - General Cigar Co., Inc.
MACANUDO VINTAGE - Cigars - General Cigar Co., Inc.
MACAO - Frames–eyeglass - May Optical Co. Inc.
MACAO - Occasional tables ☆ - JDI Group, Inc.
MACAPA - Apparel and accessories - Georges Marciano
MACAPP - Computer software - Apple Computer Inc.
MACAPPLY - Computer software - Apply Software Systems, Inc.
MACARIZ - Rice - Raj Sukul
MACARONI - Dolls - Alaska Momma
MACARONI & CHEESE CAKE - Macaroni - Taste Buds, Inc.
MACARONI GRILL - Wines ☆ - Delicato Vineyards
MACARONI KIDS - Books–comic - Frank M. Lamark, Sr.
MACARONI RIBBONS - Pasta - Creamette Co.
MACAROO - Cakes - McKee Foods Corp.
MACAROON MUNCH - Candy bars - Cloud Nine
MACAROON RACCOON - Toys–stuffed - Russ Berrie and Co., Inc.
MACAUTHORIZE - Computer software - Tellan Software Inc.
MACAW - Printers–computer - Zygo Industries Inc.
MACAW MASHER - Pet products - Polly's Pleasures
MACAYO - Food products - Fiesta Canning Co. Inc.
MACBEAN - Apparel stores–sports ☆ - Terramar Sports Worldwide, Ltd.
MACBETH - Circuit boards - Waveaccess Ltd.
MACBETH - Steel springs–railroad ☆ - Needlecraft Industries
MACBIBLE - Computer software - Zondervan Publishing House
MACC - Computer software - Region 18 Education Service Ctr.
MACCABLE - Electronic equipment - Monster Cable Products, Inc.
MACCAT - Saws–power - McCulloch Corp.
MACCHECK - Computer software - Apple Computer Inc.
MACCIM - Computer software - Compuserve Inc.
MACCLASS - Computer peripheral equipment - Hayes Microcomputer Products Inc.
MACCO - Adhesives and sealants - Macco Adhesives
MACCO-SPACKO - Adhesives and sealants ☆ - Macco Adhesives

MACCOPY - Paper - Mactac Inc. (Packaging Closures Systems Div.)
MACCOUNTING - Computer software - Woodard & Associates, Inc.
MACCOUSTIC** - Amplifiers–radio - McArty Enterprises Inc.
MACDNS - Computer software - Apple Computer Inc.
MACDONALD SELECT - Cigarettes - R.J. Reynolds Tobacco Co.
MACDONALD'S - Cigarettes - R.J. Reynolds Tobacco Co.
MACDONALD'S - Pressure cookers - MacDonald's Home Products
MACDONALD'S - Syrup - Borden, Inc.
MACDOUGAL - Liquors - Hughes Markets Inc.
MACDSS - Computer software - Apple Computer Inc.
MACE - Food products - Supreme Foods Inc.
MACE - Safety products - Mace Security International, Inc.
MACE FORMAT - Computer software - Fifth Generation Systems Inc.
MACE PERFORMANCE - Computer software - Fifth Generation Systems Inc.
MACE PREVENTION - Computer software - Fifth Generation Systems Inc.
MACE RECOVERY - Computer software - Fifth Generation Systems Inc.
MACE UTILITIES - Computer software - Fifth Generation Systems Inc.
MACEDONIA - Soap - Caswell-Massey Co. Ltd.
MACE...JUST IN CASE - Guns - Defense Technology Corp. of America
MACENVELOPE - Computer software - Synex
MACEY - Office supplies ☆ - Grand Filing Supply Co.
MACFEET - Computer peripheral equipment ☆ - Curtis Manufacturing Co., Inc.
MACFI - Electronic equipment - MacKenzie Laboratories Inc.
MACFREUD - Computer software - Ashley Bush
MACGREGOR - Ships–sailing vessels - MacGregor Yacht Corp.
MACGREGOR - Shoes–athletic - MacGregor Golf Co.
MACGREGOR - Sporting goods - MacGregor Sport Products Inc.
MACGREGOR REVERSE DRAFT RD - Golfing equipment - MacGregor Golf Co.
MACGREGOR'S - See **FRONTIER FOODS**
MACGREGOR'S - Fruits and vegetables - Calgene Fresh Inc.
MACGUIDE - Computer software - Elan Associates (GreenLight Software Division)
MACH - Bicycles - Columbia Manufacturing Inc.
MACH - Computer software ☆ - Data Translation, Inc.
MACH - Electrical equipment - American Rescue Technology Inc.
MACH - Electrical equipment - DATA RACE Inc.
MACH - Flatware - Trend Pacific Inc.
MACH 1 - Guitars - On-Site Music Group
MACH 1 - Saw blades - Vermont American Corp.
MACH-2 - Toys–models ☆ - Estes Industries
MACH 3 - Machinery - Food Machinery Sales, Inc.
MACH-3 - Toys - Tonka Corp.
MACH 4 - Lubricants - Mach 4, Inc.
MACH 5 - Bicycle parts and accessories - Answer Products Inc.
MACH 5 - Computer software ☆ - Access Software Inc.
MACH 5 - Paper products - Speed Racer Enterprises, Inc.
MACH 5 - Skates–roller - Seneca Sports, Inc.
MACH 7 - Toys–automobiles - Mattel, Inc.
MACH-10 - Antennas - Firestik Antenna Co.
MACH 128 - Computer software ☆ - Access Software Inc.
MACH 460 SOUND SYSTEM - Radiofrequency measuring equipment - Ford Motor Co.
MACH-I - Artists' materials ☆ - Artoptic International Corp.
MACH I - Automotive parts and accessories - Wolo Manufacturing Corp.
MACH I - Cleaning preparations - Scentex Inc.
MACH I - Exercising equipment - Marcy Fitness Products
MACH I - Footwear - United States Shoe Corp.
MACH I - Jewelry ☆ - Hirsch Speidel Inc.
MACH I - Watches - Ford Motor Co.
MACH II - Cleaning preparations - Scentex Inc.
MACH II - Fireworks - American Promotional Events, Inc.
MACH II - Luggage - Welsh Sporting Goods Corp. (Boyt Div.)
MACH TWO - Lighting fixtures - Tandy Corp.
MACHE - Handbags - Jenuine Performance International, Inc.
MACHETE - Herbicides - Monsanto Co.
MACHETE - Lawn mowers - Alamo Industrial
MACHETE - Propellers - Brunswick Corp.
MACHETE - Saw blades - Homelite, Inc.
MACHIAVELLI - Games - Monarch Avalon, Inc.
MACHIAVELLI - Games ☆ - Avalon Hill Game Co.
MACHIDA - Automotive parts and accessories - Machida, Inc.
MACHIDE - Paints - Triangle Coatings Inc.
MACHINE - Musical instrument accessories - Mirror Records Inc.
MACHINE AGE - Calendars and posters - Machine Age, Inc.
MACHINE BERM - Vinyl - New Pendulum Corp.

☆ = Now out of production

MACHINE GUARD - Electronic equipment - Computational Systems Inc.

MACHINE GUN - Apparel–men's - Hing Lung International Inc.

MACHINE HEAD - Recording label - Machine Head

MACHINE, THE - Tape recorders–cassette ☆ - Califone International Inc.

MACHO - Colognes - Faberge Co.

MACHO - Eyeglasses - Martin-Copeland Eyewear Corp.

MACHO - Hammers–electric - Black & Decker Corp.

MACHO - Knives–pocket - Precise International/Wenger

MACHO - Motor vehicle parts and accessories ☆ - Leer Inc.

MACHO - Wigs - Jean Paree Weegs Inc.

MACHO MAN - Fabrics - Guilford Mills, Inc.

MACHO MAN - Frames–eyeglass - U.S. Optical Frame Co.

MACHO MARACAS - Musical instruments - LP Music Group

MACHO-MINAS - Vitamins and nutritional supplements - Vartex Pharmaceuticals Inc.

MACHO NACHO - Cheese ☆ - Lactoprot USA, Inc.

MACHSPEED - Computers and peripherals - Sound Data Micro Technology, Inc.

MACIEIRA ROYAL - Brandy - Joseph E. Seagram & Sons, Inc.

MACIMDAD - Computer software - Molecular Applications Group

MACINTALK - Computer software - Apple Computer Inc.

MACINTOSH - Computers–personal - Apple Computer Inc.

MACINTOSH DUO - Computer peripheral equipment - Apple Computer Inc.

MACINTOSH PLUS - Computers–personal - Apple Computer Inc.

MACINTOSH QUADRA - Computers–mainframe - Apple Computer Inc.

MACINTOSH SYSTEM 7 - Computer software - Apple Computer Inc.

MACINVOICE - Computer software - Synex

MACIPX - Computer storage devices - Novell, Inc.

MACJET - Labels–paper - Mactac Inc. (Packaging Closures Systems Div.)

MACJUKE - Computer software - Workstation, Inc.

MACK - Apparel–women's ☆ - Leslie Fay Separates

MACK - Brushes–paint - Andrew Mack & Son Brush Co.

MACK - Footwear - E.S. Originals, Inc.

MACK - Motor vehicles - Mack Trucks Inc.

MACK - Toys–models - ERTL Co., Inc.

MACK & MOORE - Apparel–children's - Mack & Moore, Inc.

MACK BROS. - Food products - Mack Bros. Ltd.

MACK FRUIT FARMS - Wines - Frank & Hale Burch Farms Inc.

MACK MOLOUDJI - Clothing - Hub Distributing Inc.

MACK-VACK - Sporting goods - Pro-Mack Mining Supplies Inc.

MACKAY'S - Jams and jellies - Europa Foods Ltd.

MACKENZIE Z-MAC - Remote control devices ☆ - MacKenzie Laboratories Inc.

MACKEREL - Seafood products–fresh or frozen ☆ - Tri-Union International, LLC

MACKESON - Beverages–malt - All Brand Importers

MACKIE - Sausages - Mack Packing Co. Inc.

MACKIE - Toys–stuffed ☆ - Russ Berrie and Co., Inc.

MACKINAC - Boats–motor ☆ - Cruisers

MACKINAC - Paper - Fletcher Paper Co.

MACKINAC - Paper ☆ - Silver Leaf Paper Co.

MACKINAW - Fencing–wood - Machalk Enterprises Inc.

MACKINAW MILLING - Bakery products - Oven Fresh Bakery

MACKINAW MILLING - Cookies - Grocers Baking Co.

MACKINTOSH - Beverages–alcohol - Sunbelt Beverage Corp.

MACKINTOSH - Tables–wood - GRK Manufacturing

MACKINTOSH OF NEW ENGLAND - Apparel–women's - New England Mackintosh Co. Inc.

MACKISS - Computer peripheral equipment ☆ - QMS, Inc.

MACKISSIC - Garden equipment - Mackissic Inc.

MACK'S - Health care products - McKeon Products Co.

MACK'S - Salad dressings–bottled - Kosto Food Products Co.

MACK'S CAB COMPANY - Apparel stores–women's - Sonya Owens

MACKWIN - Insecticides - Mackwin Co.

MACKWIN MALATHION - Insecticides ☆ - Mackwin Co.

MACLANG - Computer software - Gessler Publishing Co., Inc.

MACLAREN - Infant product ☆ - Sassy Inc.

MACLAREN - Strollers–baby ☆ - Omron Healthcare, Inc.

MACLEANS - Toothpaste - Smithkline Beecham Corp.

MACLEO - Luggage - Locomotor USA, Inc.

MACLEOD - Veterinary products - Macleod Pharmaceuticals Inc.

MACMALL - T-shirts–men's - Creative Computers, Inc.

MACMASTER - Computer software - Samsung Electronics America, Inc.

MACMILLAN EDUCATIONAL CO. - Publisher's imprints - MacMillan Publishing Co. Inc.

MACMILLAN PUBLISHING CO. INC. - Publisher's imprints - MacMillan Publishing Co. Inc.

MACMILLAN RING-FREE M - Lubricating oils - Scot Lubricants of Pennsylvania, Inc.

MACNAUGHTON - Whiskey - Schenley Industries Inc.

MACNAV - Computer software - Compuserve Inc.

MACNEIL - Shoes - Allen-Edmonds Shoe Corp.

MACNEXUS - Electronic equipment ☆ - J.L. Cooper Electronics

MACNFS - Computer peripheral equipment - Thursby Software Systems, Inc.

MACO - Labels–gummed - Maco Tag and Label Inc.

MACO - Paints - Kwal-Howells Inc.

MACO MARINESPAR - Varnishes ☆ - Mac-O-Lac Paints Inc.

MACOLA - Computer software - Macola, Inc.

MACOLA - Recording label - Lamar Music Co.

MACOLA - Recording label - Macola Record Group Inc.

MACOLITE - Paints ☆ - Mac-O-Lac Paints Inc.

MACOMA - Lubricating oils ☆ - Shell Oil Co.

MACOMATIC - Labels–gummed - Maco Tag and Label Inc.

MACOMB SANDWICH - Sandwiches–prepackaged - Macomb Sandwich Inc.

MACON - Electrical equipment - Macon Electric Cooperative Inc.

MACON - Furniture - Boling Co.

MACON-LUGNY LES CHARMES - Wines - Seagram's Chateau & Estate Wines Co.

MACON PRISSE - Beverages–alcohol - World Shippers & Importers

MACON VILLAGES-PIERRES BLANCHES - Wines - Seagram's Chateau & Estate Wines Co.

MACON WHOOPEE - Apparel and accessories - Macon Whoopee Hockey Club, LLC

MACOPENER - Computer software - Dataviz, Inc.

MACOR - Glass–laboratory - Corning Inc.

MACOR - Manicure preparations - Dubl Duck/Jet Set Inc.

MACPATH - Computer hardware and software - System Analysis Corp.

MACPHERSON MEISTERGRAM - Yarn - Macpherson Meistergram, Inc.

MACPHONEBOOK - Computer software - Synex

MACPLAY - Computer software - Interplay Productions

MACPOISE - Computer software - Campus America Inc.

MACPROJECT - Computer software - Apple Computer Inc.

MACRA-BRAID - Rope - Gulf Rope & Cordage Inc.

MACRA-CORD - Hobby kits ☆ - Mangelsen's (VDI)

MACRA GROOVE - Blinds–venetian - Hunter Douglas, Inc.

MACRA KNIT - Blinds–venetian - Hunter Douglas, Inc.

MACRA-LITE COLLECTION - Fabrics ☆ - Decorative Aides Co. Inc.

MACRA-LOK - Fabrics - Polylok Corp.

MACRA-TWIST - Rope - Gulf Rope & Cordage Inc.

MACRAME - Pet products - Pet Manufacturing Concepts

MACRANAUT - Hobby kits - Stanislaus Imports, Inc.

MACREADER - Computer software - Gessler Publishing Co., Inc.

MACRENDERMAN - Computer software - Pixar

MACRINA - Wines ☆ - Kobrand Corp.

MACRO - Thermostats ☆ - Great Eastern Sun Trading Co. Inc.

MACRO BAG - Wallets - AR Accessories Group Inc.

MACRO-BLIND - Blinds–venetian - Bamboo Abbott Florida Corp.

MACRO-CON - Medical apparatus - Meridian Diagnostics, Inc.

MACRO-ELMAR - Photographic equipment - Leica USA Inc.

MACRO MATE - Computer software - Roger Wagner Publishing Inc.

MACRO MEDICAL - Medical apparatus - Macro Medical, Inc.

MACRO PASTA - Noodles - Great Eastern Sun Trading Co. Inc.

MACRO-PATCH48 - Cement - Edison Coatings, Inc.

MACRO SENSORS - Transducers - Howard A. Schaevitz Technologies, Inc.

MACRO-SIRONAR-N - Photographic equipment - H.P. Marketing Corp.

MACRO-SORB - Fertilizers - Nutramax Laboratories, Inc.

MACRO-SWITAR APOCHROMATS - Lenses–photographic - Heitz Service Corp.

MACRO-SYMMAR - Lenses–photographic - Schneider Optics, Inc.

MACRO-TECH - Amplifiers - Crown International, Inc.

MACRO TWIN - Clippers–barber ☆ - Sunbeam-Oster Household Products

MACROALGAE GROW - Pet shops - Florida Aqua Farms Inc.

MACROBEADS - Skin care products - Cataphote, Inc.

MACROBEL - Photographic equipment - SP Systems/Saratons

MACROBLADE - Skates–roller - Rollerblade, Inc.

MACROCHET KORDE - Craft supplies - Textile Enterprises Inc.

MACRODANTIN - Pharmaceutical preparations - Norwich-Eaton Pharmaceuticals

MACRODAPTER - Photographic equipment - SP Systems/Saratons

MACRODUCT - Diagnostic apparatus - Wescor, Inc.

MACROFLO - Medical apparatus - Mcgaw, Inc.

☆ = Now out of production

MACROJET - Printers–computer - Domino Amjet Inc.
MACROMAIL - Computer hardware - Macrovoice Corp.
MACROMAP - Computer software - Wide World of Maps, Inc.
MACROMASS - Computer software - Analytica of Branford, Inc.
MACROMAT - Photographic equipment - SP Systems/Saratons
MACROMEDIA - Computer software - Macromedia, Inc.
MACROMEDIA ACTION! - Computer software - Macromedia, Inc.
MACROMODEL - Computer software - Macromedia, Inc.
MACROMODEL - Computer software - Trustees of Columbia University in the City of New York
MACRON - Lubricating oils ☆ - Shell Oil Co.
MACRONIZER - Computer peripheral equipment - Superior Enterprises, Inc.
MACROPHONE - Audio equipment ☆ - DCM Corp.
MACROPORT - Medical apparatus - Strato Medical Corp.
MACRORING - Gaskets - Apple Rubber Products Inc.
MACROSCINT - Health care products - Johnson & Johnson
MACROSPECTAR - Lenses–photographic - Photo Research, Inc.
MACROSTAT - Photographic equipment ☆ - Heitz Service Corp.
MACROSTIGMAT - Photographic equipment - SP Systems/Saratons
MACROTACH - Photographic equipment - SP Systems/Saratons
MACROTAR - Photographic equipment - SP Systems/Saratons
MACROTEL - Photographic equipment - SP Systems/Saratons
MACROVAR - Photographic equipment - SP Systems/Saratons
MACROVISION - Electronic equipment - Macrovision Corp.
MAC'S - Automotive parts and accessories - Mac's Inc.
MACS - Machinery - Monex Resources Inc.
MAC'S CHOICE - Publisher's imprints - Rocky River Publishers
MAC'S GRILL - Speciality sandwiches - Mcdonald's Corp.
MAC'S-IT - Waxes–paraffin - Mac's Inc.
MAC'S SPARKLE - Cleaning preparations–window - Mac's Inc.
MAC'S SUPER GLOSS - Cleaning preparations - Mac's Inc.
MACSCAN - Labels–gummed - Mactac Inc. (Packaging Closures Systems Div.)
MACSIMIZER - Tool boxes - Stanley Works
MACSOFT - Computer software - WizardWorks Group Inc.
MACSPEAKER - Audio equipment - Monster Cable Products, Inc.
MACSTACKS - Computer software - Apple Computer Inc.
MACSTIM - Medical product - Genetics Institute Inc.
MACTAC - Adhesives and sealants - Mactac Inc. (Packaging Closures Systems Div.)
MACTAC METRO - Labels–gummed - Morgan Adhesives Co.
MACTARNAHAN'S - Beverages–malt - Portland Brewing Co.
MACTAVISH - Furniture - Aaron Investment Co.
MACTERMINAL - Computer software - Apple Computer Inc.
MACTIVITY - Hobby kits ☆ - Unicraft Products
MACTV - Video production - David Hall
MACULEN - Vitamins and nutritional supplements - La Haye Laboratories Inc.
MACVECTOR - Computer peripheral equipment - Oxford Molecular Group
MACVIEW - Computer software - Moore Business Forms, Inc.
MACVIEW - Electrical equipment - Sony Electronics Inc.
MACWAREHOUSE - Computer software - Micro Warehouse, Inc.
MACWORKS - Computer software - Apple Computer Inc.
MACWORKSTATION - Computer software - Apple Computer Inc.
MACWRITE - Computer software - Apple Computer Inc.
MACX - Computer software - Apple Computer Inc.
MACY KIDS - Backpacks - R.H. Macy & Co.
MACYS - Apparel–children's - R.H. Macy & Co.
MACYS CALIFORNIA - Apparel and accessories - R.H. Macy & Co.
MAD - Candy - E.C. Publications Inc.
MAD ABOUT PLAID - Bathing suits ☆ - Jantzen Inc.
MAD ALFRED E. NEUMAN LOOK-A-LIKE - Novelty items - Imagineering Inc.
MAD BATTER MUFFINS - Bakery products - C.D. Robin, Inc.
MAD BOMBER - Novelty items - Robert P. Sowash
MAD BULL - Chewing gum - Philadelphia Chewing Gum Corp.
MAD CARD - Toys ☆ - Parker Brothers
MAD CHEF - Spices and extracts - Mad Chef Enterprises
MAD CHEF GOURMET ADVENTURE - Sauces - Mad Chef Enterprises
MAD COMBO - Apparel–women's - Wacoal America Inc.
MAD DAWG - Candy - Sherman's Confections, Inc.
MAD DAWG SUPER SPEW - Chewing gum - How Can It Be So Sour Co.
MAD DOG - Barbecue sauce - Ashley Foods
MAD-DOG - Books–comic - Paramount Pictures Corp.
MAD DOG - Footwear–athletic - KangaROOS USA Inc.
MAD DOG - Sporting goods - Stearns Manufacturing Co.
MAD DOG - Wines - Mad Dog Wine Co.
MAD DOG - Writing instruments - Pentech International Inc.

MAD DOG MCCREE - Computer software - American Laser Games, Inc.
MAD FISH - Apparel - M.A. Graphics Inc.
MAD GRABBER - Toys ☆ - Jak-Pak Inc.
MAD HATTER - Fabrics - Dan River Inc.
MAD HATTER IN THIS STYLE, THE - Games - Mad Hatter Publishing, Inc.
MAD HATTER'S TEA PARTY - Flowers, plants, and seeds - White Swan, Ltd.
MAD HORNET - Toys–guns - Tonka Corp.
MAD HORSE CRAB CO. - Seafood products–fresh or frozen - Lower Creek Associates
MAD HOUSE - Apparel and accessories - Melissa McElrath Wyatt
MAD IDIOTIC FRUITY - Candy - Kraft Food Ingredients Corp.
MAD JACK - Liqueurs - Heublein, Inc.
MAD KITE - Kites - English Co.
MAD KNITS - Apparel and accessories - KNL, Inc.
MAD LIBS - Computer software ☆ - First Byte Inc.
MAD MAGAZINE - Games ☆ - Parker Brothers
MAD MAGAZINE SPY VS. SPY - Games ☆ - Milton Bradley Co.
MAD MARBLES - Toys - Lakeside Games
MAD MAX - Fireworks - Neptune Wholesale, Inc.
MAD MAX - Skates–roller - Sierra Bridge, Inc.
MAD MIKE'S - Food products - G. M. Mike McCoy
MAD MOD BUTTONS - Chewing gum - Philadelphia Chewing Gum Corp.
MAD MOON - Apparel and accessories - Sutton Creations, Inc.
MAD MORPHER - Candy - World Candies Inc.
MAD MURPHY - Recording label - Jazz Composer's Orchestra Association Inc.
MAD MYSTERIES - Publisher's imprints - Price Stern Sloan Inc.
MAD PAD - Stationery - Just Your Pal, Inc.
MAD PLANET - Bags–cosmetic - Mad Planet Products
MAD — POPPER, THE - Microwave popcorn dish - William Berkoff
MAD RAQ - Sports rackets and accessories - Mad Raq Sports, Ltd.
MAD RIVER - Food products - Mad River Traders, Inc.
MAD RIVER - Vodka - Vermont Distillers
MAD RIVER FARM - Jams and jellies - Mad River Farm
MAD RIVER MOUNTAIN - Teas - Mad River Traders, Inc.
MAD RIVER VALLEY - Snack foods - Rothschild Berry Farm, Inc.
MAD ROCKS - Candy - American Chewing Gum Inc.
MAD ROLLERCYCLE - Toys ☆ - Those Characters from Cleveland, Inc.
MAD ROOK'S GAMBIT - Games ☆ - Mayfair Games, Inc.
MAD RUNNER - Fishing lures - Paul Warner Industries
MAD SAD GLAD GAME, THE - Games - Peak Potential Inc.
MAD SCIENTIST - Toys - Mattel, Inc.
MAD SOUNDS - Audio equipment - Motown Record Co. L.P.
MAD STICKERS - Chewing gum ☆ - Fleer Corp.
MAD STOCKING STUFFER - Candy - Kraft Food Ingredients Corp.
MAD TROOPER - Hats - Mad Bomber Co.
MADACIDE - Disinfectants - Mada Medical Products Inc.
MADACYLINDER - Medical apparatus - Mada Medical Products Inc.
MADAFA - Stain removers - Eplo Products Corp.
MADAGASCAR ARTS - Paper products - Forests of the World, LLC
MADAGASCAR CHIP - Cookies ☆ - Michael D's Cookies
MADAJET - Medical apparatus - Mada Medical Products Inc.
MADALINE - Chocolate candy - Naron Candy Co. Inc.
MADAM - Food products - Nozaki America Inc.
MADAME - See also **MME.**
MADAME - Dolls - Alexander Doll Co. Inc.
MADAME ALEXANDER - Dolls - Alexander Doll Co. Inc.
MADAME BUTTERFLY - Christmas tree ornaments - Cracker Box Inc.
MADAME BUTTERFLY - Dolls ☆ - Effanbee Doll Corp.
MADAME C. J. WALKER - Hair care products ☆ - Madame C.J. Walker Inc.
MADAME DU BARRY - Dolls ☆ - Effanbee Doll Corp.
MADAME GOUGOUSSE - Rice - Madame Gougousse Food Corp.
MADAME MINT BEAR - Toys–stuffed - Frivals n Friends
MADAME PELE - Candles - Aloha Candle Manufacturing Co. Inc.
MADAME SABIA - Games - Sharon Discher
MADAME SUSHI - Clocks ☆ - Ridgeway Clock Co.
MADAME TARTINE - Jams and jellies - Liberty Richter Inc.
MADAME TARTINE PRESERVES - Europa Foods Ltd.
MADAME X - Flowers, plants, and seeds - Superior Florals, Inc.
MADAMIST - Medical apparatus - Mada Medical Products Inc.
MADA'N - Food products - Mada'n Corp.
MADAVAC - Medical apparatus - Mada Medical Products Inc.
MADBALLS - Games ☆ - Ben Cooper Inc.
MADBALLS - Toys - Those Characters from Cleveland, Inc.
MADBALLS MADMOBILE - Toys ☆ - Those Characters from Cleveland, Inc.
MADBRIDGE - Computer hardware - Xedia Corp.
MADCAP - Computer software - Madcap Software, Inc.

☆ = Now out of production

MADCAPS - Hats - Madcaps Co. Inc.
MADDACOMFORT - Health care products - Maddak Inc.
MADDACRAWLER - Health care products - Maddak Inc.
MADDACYCLE - Health care products - Maddak Inc.
MADDADAPT - Health care products - Maddak Inc.
MADDAGRIP - Health care products - Maddak Inc.
MADDAHOLD - Health care products - Maddak Inc.
MADDAHOOK - Health care products - Maddak Inc.
MADDAK - Health care products - Maddak Inc.
MADDALENA - Floor coverings ☆ - Tarkett, Inc.
MADDAN - Bathroom accessories ☆ - Grayline Housewares
MADDAPLAS - Health care products - Maddak Inc.
MADDAPULT - Health care products - Maddak Inc.
MADDAREST - Health care products - Maddak Inc.
MADDATHERM - Health care products - Maddak Inc.
MADDAVAN - Health care products - Maddak Inc.
MADDAWALKER - Health care products - Maddak Inc.
MADDAWASH - Health care products - Maddak Inc.
MADDAWEIGHTS - Health care products - Maddak Inc.
MADDAWG RECORDS - Recording label - BMG Music
MADDAWIPE - Health care products - Maddak Inc.
MADDEACARE - Health care products - Maddak Inc.
MADDELENA VINEYARD - Wines - San Antonio Winery Inc.
MADDEN - Backpacks - Madden/USA
MADDIE GLAD - Hobby kits - Carousel Crafts Co.
MADDIE MOD - Toys ☆ - Mego Financial Corp.
MADDOX ELECTROSTATIC SEASONING SYSTEM - Electronic equipment - Maddox Metal Works, Inc.
MADDY - Ophthalmic goods ☆ - Luxottica
MADDY K. BEAR - Apparel and accessories - Nantucket Cobblestones, Ltd.
MADE AT THE BEACH - Apparel and accessories - Trinity Products, Inc.
MADE BY HAND FOR THE HEART - Lamps - L.D. Kichler Co.
MADE 'EM MYSELF - Cookies - Nabisco Foods Group
MADE ESPECIALLY FOR YOU BY DELTA BURKE D; ESIGN - Apparel—women's ☆ - Delta Blues, Inc.
MADE ESPECIALLY FOR YOU BY DELTA BURKE DESIGN - Apparel—women's - Delta Blues, Inc.
MADE FOR A LIFETIME - Vitamins and nutritional supplements - Pharmavite Corp.
MADE FOR MEN - Vitamins - Just Natural
MADE FOR MN - Paints - Hirshfield's Paint Manufacturing
MADE FOR WOMEN - Vitamins - Just Natural
MADE-FOR-YOU - Patterns—clothing - Mccall Pattern Co.
MADE FROM SCRATCH - Apparel and accessories - Kore Sourcing, Inc.
MADE IN AMERICA BRAND - Pet food - Hereford Bi-Products, Inc.
MADE IN CHINA - Housewares - World Wide Ex-Im, Inc.
MADE IN FRANCE - Skin care products - Henry Beauty Imports Inc.
MADE IN ITALY - Skin care products - Henry Beauty Imports Inc.
MADE IN NEW YORK - Belts—apparel - Amplaco Group Inc.
MADE IN OCCUPIED AMERICA - Apparel and accessories - Robert Nicholas Marzolino
MADE IN THE KITCHEN, NOT IN THE SCIENCELAB - Cereal - Geebees, Inc.
MADE IN THE SHADE - Apparel and accessories - Made in the Shade by Prime Time
MADE IN THE SHADE - Automotive parts and accessories - Rosenblume Co. Inc.
MADE IN THE SHADE - Juices - Apple and Eve Inc.
MADE IN THE SHADE - Umbrellas - Galtech Computer Corp.
MADE IN THE USA DESTINATION DESIGNS - Apparel and accessories - Jewel & Co., Inc.
MADE IN USA - Infant product - Lisco, Inc.
MADE IN USA CARVER - Amplifiers - Carver Corp.
MADE IN USA PURE STROKE - Golfing equipment - Pure Stroke Golf, Inc.
MADE IN USA WORKIN'WOOLY WOOL BLENDED WASH MITT - Cleaning equipment - Workin' Wooly Manufacturing
MADE 'N WOOD - Furniture - Waffer International Corp.
MADE ON MARS - Apparel and accessories - Made on Mars Inc.
MADE RIGHT - OVERJOHNS - Cabinets—wood - Coastal Wood Products, Inc.
MADE RIGHT PRODUCTS - Cabinets—wood - Coastal Wood Products, Inc.
MADE RIGHT - VANITIES - Cabinets—wood - Coastal Wood Products, Inc.
MADE RITE - Potato chips - Made Rite Potato Chip Co. Inc.
MADE-RITE - Shaving preparations - Made Rite Brush Manufacturing Co. Inc.
MADE SIMPLE - Publisher's imprints - Bantam Doubleday Dell Publishing Group, Inc.
MADE STRONG TO LAST LONG - Gloves—rubber - Playtex Beauty Care, Inc.
MADE THICK TO STICK - Cleaning preparations - Sterling Winthrop Inc.

MADE WITH CARE - Floor coverings—carpet and rugs - Cooperative for American Relief Everywhere, Inc.
MADE WITH CARE BY KID KORE - Games - Kid Kore International Ltd.
MADE WITH HORSE SENSE - Polo equipment - Rachael Theora Sapyta
MADEIRA - Cabinets ☆ - Aristokraft, Inc.
MADEIRA - Chimes - Nutone Inc.
MADEIRA - Christmas tree ornaments - Cracker Box Inc.
MADEIRA - Cosmetics - Spornette International, Inc.
MADEIRA - Dinnerware—glass - Franciscan by Johnson Brothers, USA, Inc.
MADEIRA - Floor coverings—carpet and rugs - Atlas Carpet Mills Inc.
MADEIRA - Floor coverings—carpet and rugs - Alexander Smith Carpets
MADEIRA - Guitars ☆ - Guild Music Corp.
MADEIRA - Hardware ☆ - Amerock Corp.
MADEIRA - Stationery ☆ - Mead Corp.
MADEIRA - Tobacco products ☆ - R.J. Reynolds Tobacco Co.
MADEIRA - Vases ☆ - Lenox Crystal, Inc.
MADEIRA - Wallpaper - Pickhardt & Siebert USA Inc.
MADEIRA GOLD - Cigarettes - R.J. Reynolds Tobacco Co.
MADEIRS - Floor coverings ☆ - Bellbridge Carpets
MADELAINE - Chocolate candy - Madelaine Chocolate Novelties, Inc.
MADELAINE - Tableware—china - Pfaltzgraff Investment Co.
MADELAINE SMITH CRAFTS - Lacquers - Madelaine Smith Crafts Inc.
MADELAINE SWEET ADDITION - Chocolate candy - Madelaine Chocolate Novelties, Inc.
MADELEINE - Dinnerware—glass - Block China Co.
MADELEINE - Dolls ☆ - Effanbee Doll Corp.
MADELEINE DE MADELEINE - Perfumes - Madeleine Mono Ltd.
MADELINE - Floor coverings—carpet and rugs - Alexander Smith Carpets
MADELINE - Handbags - Pyramid Handbags Inc.
MADELINE - Hosiery—women's - Perfect Plus, Inc.
MADELINE - Toys—stuffed - Eden LLC
MADELYN - Footwear - D'Bello Shoe Corp.
MADEMOISELLE - See also MLLE.
MADEMOISELLE - Eyeglasses - Art-Craft Optical Co.
MADEMOISELLE - Luggage ☆ - Hartmann Luggage Co.
MADEMOISELLE - Pelts ☆ - Mademoiselle
MADEMOISELLE - Watches - Bulova Corp.
MADEMOISELLE BOUTIQUE - Cases—vanity ☆ - Acme Frame Products, Inc.
MADEMOISELLE CHANEL 31 RUE CAMBON - Perfumes - Chanel Inc.
MADEMOISELLE COCO - Perfumes ☆ - Chanel Inc.
MADERA - Floor coverings ☆ - Congoleum Corp.
MADERA - Paints - Frazee Paint
MADERA - Stools—metal ☆ - Samsonite Furniture Co. (Consumer Products Div.)
MADERA - Tools—woodworking - Anglo American Enterprises Corp.
MADERA - Window coverings - Joanna Western Mills Co.
MADERIA - Spices and extracts - Ottens Flavors
MADERITE - Paper—bond ☆ - Mead Corp.
MADERNO - Floor coverings—carpet and rugs ☆ - Karastan-Bigelow Inc.
MADESKO - Food products - Mitchell Madesko
MADEWELL - Brushes - Wright-Bernet
MADHUB - Computers - Xedia Corp.
MADICO - Insulating materials - Madico, Inc.
MADIERA - Clocks - General Time Corp. (Westclox/Seth Thomas Div.)
MADINI ORIENT - Perfumes - Talisman
MADISON - Apparel and accessories - Cherokee Group
MADISON - Bicycles - Schwinn Cycling & Fitness Inc.
MADISON - Canvas—artists' ☆ - Winsor & Newton
MADISON - Cigars - Havatampa Inc.
MADISON - Desks - Joyce International Inc.
MADISON - Fireplace equipment - Design Specialties Inc.
MADISON - Floor coverings - Bruce Hardwood Floors
MADISON - Floor coverings ☆ - Tarkett, Inc.
MADISON - Floor coverings—carpet and rugs - Colonial Mills Inc.
MADISON - Food products ☆ - Worthington Foods Inc.
MADISON - Frames—eyeglass - Hudson Optical Corp.
MADISON - Furniture - American Blueprint Co. Inc.
MADISON - Furniture - Boling Co.
MADISON - Furniture - Madison Furniture Industries
MADISON - Furniture ☆ - Donghia Furniture Co. Ltd.
MADISON - Furniture—children's - Child Craft Industries Inc.
MADISON - Glassware—household - Lenox Crystal, Inc.
MADISON - Locks—door - Baldwin Hardware Corp.
MADISON - Pianos - Music Industries Inc.
MADISON - Pickles - Green Bay Foods Co.
MADISON - Recording label - Madison Station Productions

☆ = Now out of production

MADISON - Rings–jewelry - Artcarved Inc.
MADISON - Sporting goods - Brunswick Corp.
MADISON - Switches–electric - Madison Co.
MADISON - Trailers–travel ☆ - Marathon Homes Corp.
MADISON 100'S - Cigarettes - G.A. Georgopulo & Co. Inc.
MADISON & RHODES - Apparel–men's - Bradlees Stores, Inc.
MADISON AVE. - Floor coverings–carpet and rugs ☆ - Walter Carpet Mills
MADISON AVENUE - Dolls - Mattel, Inc.
MADISON AVENUE - Eyeglasses - Art-Craft Optical Co.
MADISON AVENUE - Fruits and vegetables - Belmont Produce Sales, Inc.
MADISON AVENUE - Furniture–upholstered ☆ - Romweber Co.
MADISON AVENUE - Wallpaper ☆ - Fidelity Industries, Inc.
MADISON AVENUE FUND FOR CHILDREN - Computer stores - Madison Avenue Fund for Children, Inc.
MADISON AVENUE, THE - File folders - Angler's Roslyn Group Ltd.
MADISON AVENUE, THE - Briefcases ☆ - Samsill Corp.
MADISON BRANDS, INC. - Teas - Madison Brands, Inc.
MADISON BRICK - Finishing agents ☆ - Flintkote Co.
MADISON BRICK - Paints ☆ - GS Roofing Products Co.
MADISON CABLE - Electrical equipment - Whitaker Corp.
MADISON COLLECTION - Frames–picture - Holson Burnes Group
MADISON HOUSE - Frozen fried chicken products - Winn-Dixie Stores, Inc.
MADISON KIDS - Apparel and accessories - NSK Industries Inc.
MADISON MANOR - Furniture ☆ - Bassett Furniture Industries, Inc.
MADISON PARK - Dolls ☆ - Effanbee Doll Corp.
MADISON PARK - Greeting cards - Me Two Corp.
MADISON SPECIALTIES - Cases–eyeglass - Madison Specialties Inc.
MADISON SQUARE - Bedding–linen - Dan River Inc.
MADISON STATION - Recording label - Madison Station Productions
MADISON TRADER - Apparel–men's - Sero Co., Inc.
MADISON WELLS - Apparel–women's - Rosemead Boulevard Corp.
MADIX - Display cases–metal - Madix Store Fixtures Inc.
MADLINK - Computer peripheral equipment - Xedia Corp.
MADLY - Colognes - Charles Revson Inc.
MADMATE - Circuit boards - Xedia Corp.
MADNESS - Apparel–men's - Alan Brisbane
MADNESS - Petunia seeds - Geo. J. Ball, Inc.
MADOKA - Pet products - Pets Pacifica Inc.
MADOLENE - Food products - Vlasic Foods Inc.
MADON - Frames–eyeglass - May Optical Co. Inc.
MADONNA - Greeting cards - Reproducta Co., Inc.
MADONNA - Jewelry - Hobe Cie. Ltd.
MADONNA HADDAD BROTHERS, INC. SINCE 1947 - Apparel–children's - Haddad Brothers Inc.
MADORA QUEEN OF LONG HAIR BEAUTY SALON EXCLUSIVE - Hair care products - George Michael of Madison Ave.
MADORA SALON APPROVED - Hair care products - Madora, Inc.
MADRAS - Eyeglasses - Martin-Copeland Eyewear Corp.
MADRAS - Paper–tissue - Crystal Tissue Co. Inc.
MADRAS U.S.A. - Fabrics - Dan River Inc.
MADRE - Occasional tables ☆ - JDI Group, Inc.
MADRE PERLA - Skin care products - DLC Enterprises, Inc.
MADREAU - Floor coverings–carpet and rugs ☆ - Karastan-Bigelow Inc.
MADRIA MADRIA - Wines - Ernest and Julio Gallo Winery
MADRIBON - Antibiotics ☆ - Roche Laboratories
MADRID - Blinds–vertical - Kittrich Corp.
MADRID - Dinnerware ☆ - Corning Inc.
MADRID - Eyeglasses - Art-Craft Optical Co.
MADRID - Floor coverings ☆ - Tarkett, Inc.
MADRID - Floor coverings–carpet and rugs - Barrett Carpet Mills Inc.
MADRID - Floor coverings–carpet and rugs ☆ - Capel, Inc.
MADRID - Glassware–household - Crisa Corp.
MADRID - Plumbing fixtures–metal - Barclay Products Ltd.
MADRID - Tobacco products - Sterling Tobacco Co.
MADRID - Wallpaper ☆ - Marburg Wallcoverings Inc.
MADRID - Wood products ☆ - Lami Wood Products Inc.
MADRID COLLECTION - Luggage - Universal Trav-ler Inc.
MADRID II - Wallpaper ☆ - Marburg Wallcoverings Inc.
MADRIGAL - Cheese - Besnier USA, Inc.
MADRIGAL - Dishes–china - Waterford Wedgewood USA, Inc.
MADRIGAL - Fabrics - Piedmont Collections
MADRIGAL - Floor coverings - Mannington Resilient Floors
MADRIGAL - Footwear - Sonic Shoe Corp.
MADRIGAL - Rings–jewelry - Artcarved Inc.
MADRIGAL - Sinks–metal - Kohler Co.
MADRIGAL - Wallpaper - Seabrook Wallcoverings, Inc.

MADRIGALE - Furniture ☆ - Bernhardt Industries
MADRIGALS - Three-dimensional Christmas ornaments ☆ - Alltrista Corp.
MADRONA - Wines - Madrona Vineyards
MADRUGADA - Skin care products - Faberge Co.
MADURA - Motorcycles - Suzuki of America Automotive Corp.
MADWARE - Computer software - Xedia Corp.
MADYES - Footwear - R.G. Barry Corp.
MAE BLOOM - Dishes–china ☆ - Gorham Inc.
MAE WEST - Dolls ☆ - Effanbee Doll Corp.
MAEDA-EN - Teas - G. T. Japan, Inc.
MAELEE - Ophthalmic goods ☆ - Luxottica
MAELY - Motorcycles - Maely Industries
MAERI - Pianos - North American Music Inc.
MAES - Beverages–alcohol - Anthony Distributors Inc.
MAES PILS - Beverages–malt - Thames America Trading Co. Ltd.
MAESTRI MAJOLICARI - Ceramic tile - Integrity Tile Co.
MAESTRO - Bathtubs–enameled - Kohler Co.
MAESTRO - Brushes–hair - Nino Originals
MAESTRO - Cigars ☆ - General Cigar Co., Inc.
MAESTRO - Computers–personal - Beuchat-USA Inc.
MAESTRO - Condiments - House of Herbs Inc.
MAESTRO - Electric lighting equipment - Lutron Electronics Co., Inc.
MAESTRO - Floor coverings–carpet and rugs - National Foam Cushion Manufacturing Inc.
MAESTRO - Floor coverings–carpet and rugs ☆ - Masland Corp.
MAESTRO - Furniture ☆ - Romweber Co.
MAESTRO - Golfing equipment - Backswing Management, Inc.
MAESTRO - Jewelry ☆ - Hirsch Speidel Inc.
MAESTRO - Medical apparatus - Respironics, Inc.
MAESTRO - Musical instrument accessories - Grossman Music Corp.
MAESTRO - Musical instrument accessories - Trophy Music Co.
MAESTRO - Ophthalmic goods ☆ - Styl-Rite Optical Manufacturing Co., Inc.
MAESTRO - Printers–computer - Comtec Information Systems, Inc.
MAESTRO - Recording label ☆ - Essex Entertainment Inc.
MAESTRO - Shoes–athletic - Etonic Inc.
MAESTRO - Wallcoverings - Ronald Redding Designs
MAESTRO - Windows - International Window Corp.
MAESTRO II - Lamps - Cannon Products Inc.
MAESTRO II - Weather tracking equipment - Maximum Inc.
MAESTRO-MA-2000 - Musical instrument accessories - Gibson Strings & Accessories
MAESTRO SCOPIC - Computer software - Maestro Music Inc.
MAESTRO, THE - Remote control devices - Gerrold General Instrument Corp.
MAEVE - Glassware–household - Waterford Wedgewood USA, Inc.
MAFCO - Giftware - Meier & Frank Merchandise Co. Inc.
MAFCOTE INDUSTRIES - Paper products - Mafcote Industries, Inc.
MAFIOSO - Board game ☆ - Intromark Inc.
MAFIROL - Refrigerators - G.O. Aeurofiamma, Inc.
MAFRA - Back support belts - Mafra Corp.
MAFS - Packaging machines - TL Systems Corp.
MAFU - Recording label - Foundation for God Realization
MAG - Alarm systems–burglar - Protom Inc.
MAG - Archery equipment ☆ - High Country American
MAG - Bicycles - Schwinn Cycling & Fitness Inc.
MAG - Motors–automotive - Johnson Fishing Inc.
MAG - Musical instrument accessories - Seymour Duncan Pickups
MAG-1 - Glass–optical - Criss Optical Manufacturing Co.
MAG 1 - Lubricating oils - Warren Distribution, Inc.
MAG 5 - Pharmaceutical preparations ☆ - Legere Pharmaceuticals Inc.
MAG 10 - Shotguns - Ithaca Gun Co. Inc.
MAG-12 - Fishing lures ☆ - Frabill Inc.
MAG ASCORBS - Vitamins and nutritional supplements - Alacer Co.
MAG B-6 - Vitamins and nutritional supplements - Great Life Laboratories Inc.
MAG BAG - Sports bags - Hit 'N' Stik of America Inc.
MAG BAT - Bats–baseball ☆ - Hillerich & Bradsby Co.
MAG-BREAK - Circuit breakers - General Electric Co.
MAG-C - Vitamins and nutritional supplements - Vitamin Research Products Inc.
MAG C GEL - Vitamins and nutritional supplements - Desert Health Products, Inc.
MAG-CAL - Vitamins and nutritional supplements - Fibertone Co.
MAG-CAL MEGA - Vitamins and nutritional supplements - Freeda Vitamins Inc.
MAG CHARGER - Flashlights - Mag Instrument Inc.
MAG CLIMBER - Bicycles ☆ - Kent International Inc.
MAG-DRIVES - Pet products - Beckett Corp.
MAG F/S - Bicycles ☆ - Raleigh USA Bicycle Co.

☆ = Now out of production

MAG FORCE - Bicycles ☆ - Roadmaster Corp.
MAG GRIP - Flashlights - Team Products
MAG INNOVISION - Computer peripheral equipment - Mag Innovision, Inc.
MAG-IRON - Fertilizers - Plant Marvel Laboratories
MAG-LITE - Flashlights - Mag Instrument Inc.
MAG-LITE RECHARGEABLE - Flashlights - Mag Instrument Inc.
MAG NAIL - Measuring instruments - Robert C. Zaenkert
MAG-NEAT-OS - Picture frames - Robert M. Kirchner
MAG-NIF - Games - Mag-Nif Inc.
MAG-NO-GLARE - Computer peripheral equipment ☆ - Fred Silver and Co. Inc.
MAG NOTES - Magnetic notepad - Coronet General Corp.
MAG-NUM STAR - Lamp bulbs–flashlight - Mag Instrument Inc.
MAG-O-TAB - Cough drops - Alacer Co.
MAG O.E.M. - Cleaning preparations - Ardex Laboratories, Inc.
MAG-OX - Pharmaceutical preparations - Blaine Co. Inc.
MAG-OXIDE - Pharmaceutical preparations - Parmed Pharmaceuticals, Inc.
MAG POWER - Fishing tackle ☆ - Penn Fishing Tackle Manufacturing Co.
MAG RAG - Housewares - General Ribbon Corp.
MAG-ROC - Gypsum products - F.H. Leinweber Co. Inc.
MAG SCRAMBLER - Bicycles - Schwinn Cycling & Fitness Inc.
MAG SCRAMBLER SX100 - Bicycles - Schwinn Cycling & Fitness Inc.
MAG-SHIELD - Pesticides–agricultural - Chemmart Associates, Inc.
MAG-SS - Glass–optical - Criss Optical Manufacturing Co.
MAG SS - Wire - General Cable Corp.
MAG STIK - Boats - Electro-Mechanical Products Inc.
MAG STOP - Clutches–industrial - Dana Corp.
MAG SWEEP - Brooms - Kellogg Brush Manufacturing Co.
MAG-TRAP - Fishing lures - Sports Design and Development, Inc.
MAG TUNED - Fishing tackle - Penn Fishing Tackle Manufacturing Co.
MAG WART - Fishing lures - Storm Manufacturing Co.
MAG ZINC, A - Vitamins and nutritional supplements - Garcoa Labs/Vitamin Classics
MAGA DESIGN - Sunglasses - B. Robinson Sunglasses
MAGABLASTERS - Toys–guns - Jak-Pak Inc.
MAGAFILE - Boxes - Magafile Co.
MAGALDRATE - Antacids ☆ - Wyeth-Ayerst Laboratories
MAGAZINE 8 - Cameras ☆ - Eastman Kodak Co.
MAGAZINE ARTICLE FILER - Computer software - Right on Programs
MAGBALL - Video production - Greystone Technology, Inc.
MAGCYL - Laxatives ☆ - ICN Pharmaceuticals Inc.
MAGDA - Footwear - Diesse Shoes Inc.
MAGDA - Ophthalmic goods - Swank Optical
MAGDA - Recording label ☆ - Marsal Productions Inc.
MAGDALENA'S - Nuts–salted, roasted, cooked, or canned - Classic Roasters
MAGDESIAN - Footwear–women's - Magdesian Bros.
MAGDUCT - Pipes–plastic - Dura-Line Corp.
MAGEFESA CASTILLE - Cooking equipment–household - Intersolving, Inc.
MAGEIA - Tables–wood ☆ - Koch & Lowy Inc.
MAGELLAN - Computer software - Systems Science Inc.
MAGELLAN - Electronic equipment - Galileo Corp.
MAGELLAN - Fabrics - Dan River Inc.
MAGELLAN - Furniture - Magellan International Inc.
MAGELLAN - Optical scanners–computer - Spectra-Physics Scanning Systems, Inc.
MAGELLAN - Underwater exploration vehicles - Oceaneering Technologies, Inc.
MAGELLAN - Watches - Bulova Corp.
MAGEMS - Magnets - Mug Shanty
MAGENTA - Dinnerware–glass - Nikko Ceramics Inc.
MAGENTA - Fruit juice drinks - Bakerview Farms
MAGENTA SKY - Hair care products - Redmond Products, Inc.
MAGEYE'S - Lenses–magnifying - MFD Enterprises, Inc.
MAGFLASH - Marine rigging - Outboard Marine Corp.
MAGGI - Food products - Haram-Christensen Corp.
MAGGI JAMAICAN - Soups–mixes - Nestle USA
MAGGI STOVER - Apparel - Karin Stevens, Inc.
MAGGIE - Amplifiers ☆ - Magnepan Inc.
MAGGIE - Bicycles - Ross Bicycles USA, Ltd.
MAGGIE - Housewares ☆ - White Metal Rolling & Stamping Corp.
MAGGIE - Ophthalmic goods - Rozin Optical Export Corp.
MAGGIE - Ophthalmic goods ☆ - Luxottica
MAGGIE & MAX - Apparel–women's - H.S.R. Apparel Group, Inc.
MAGGIE & ZOE - Apparel–children's - Baylis Brothers Inc.
MAGGIE DOODLE - Toys - Pilot Pen Corp. of America
MAGGIE JOHNSON MODERN WOMAN - Greeting cards - Hallmark Cards Inc.

MAGGIE LAWRENCE - Shoes - C.S.F. Corp.
MAGGIE MACKALL - Apparel–children's - Grace Co.
MAGGIE MAE'S GOURMET - Pet products - Maggie Mae's Gourmet Pet Products Inc.
MAGGIE'S MUSIC - Recording label - Maggie's Music Inc.
MAGGIE'S ORGANIC COTTON - Apparel and accessories - Clean Clothes, Inc.
MAGGIES SEW FREE BUTTONS - Buttons - Margaret A. Rentos
MAGGOT - Toys - Tonka Corp.
MAGGOT TIPPER - Fishing tackle - Schumann's Fly Fish Kit Co.
MAGI - Computer software - Manufacturing Action Group, Inc.
MAGI - Electronic equipment - Telex Communications, Inc.
MAGI - Fruits and vegetables - Magi Inc.
MAGI - Rust removers - Warren Distribution, Inc.
MAGI II - Electronic equipment ☆ - J.L. Cooper Electronics
MAGI-CAL - Vinyl - Joseph Struhl Co., Inc.
MAGI-CARPET - Vacuum cleaners and accessories ☆ - Kent Co.
MAGI CLEAR - Aquariums–household - Jungle Laboratories Corp.
MAGI-KILL - Irons–electric - Roxide International, Inc.
MAGI-KLIP - Housewares - Morse-Starrett Products Co. (Pell Cable Cutter Div.)
MAGI-MOIST - Sponges ☆ - Newell Office Products
MAGI-NAIL - Nail care products - Maji Nail Inc.
MAGI-PAINT - Paint sets–hobby ☆ - Milton Bradley Co.
MAGI-TUNE - Electronics equipment - Clarion Corp. of America
MAGIA - Apparel and accessories - Campus Casuals of California
MAGIA ORIENTAL - Soap ☆ - Hair Specialty Co.
MAGIBALL - Massage products - Freeland Products, Inc.
MAGIC - Bakery products - Sumptious Selection
MAGIC - Baskets–steel - Golden French Imports
MAGIC - Bicycles - Murray, Inc.
MAGIC - Binders - Fellowes Manufacturing Co.
MAGIC - Catalogs - Robert S. Prokopowicz
MAGIC - Cooking equipment–household ☆ - Hamilton Glass Products Inc.
MAGIC - Cosmetics - Maybelline Co.
MAGIC - Depilatories - Carson Products Co.
MAGIC - Detergents - Dial Corp.
MAGIC - Electrical equipment - Victor Specialties Inc.
MAGIC - Floor coverings–carpet and rugs - Orian Rugs Inc.
MAGIC - Flowers–artificial - New Tomorrow Inc.
MAGIC - Frames–eyeglass - Zylo Ware Corp.
MAGIC - Garden equipment ☆ - H.D. Campbell Co.
MAGIC - Giftware - Magic Garden Products (New Tomorrow, Inc.)
MAGIC - Glue–household or industrial ☆ - Magic American Corp.
MAGIC - Hair curlers - Burmax Co. Inc.
MAGIC - Moldings–plaster of paris - Biltrite Corp.
MAGIC - Office supplies - Wescosa Inc.
MAGIC - Organs–musical instrument ☆ - Kimball International, Inc.
MAGIC - Paint rollers ☆ - Wooster Brush Co.
MAGIC - Paint sets–hobby ☆ - Canson-Talens Inc.
MAGIC - Plumbing fixtures–metal ☆ - Moen Inc.
MAGIC - Ships–sailing vessels - Hobie Cat Co.
MAGIC - Skin care products - Colonial Refining and Chemical Co.
MAGIC - Skin care products ☆ - Victoria Vogue, Inc.
MAGIC - Sporting goods - Magic Products, Inc.
MAGIC - Sporting goods ☆ - Gladding Braided Products Inc.
MAGIC - Stationery ☆ - Majestic Penn State Inc.
MAGIC - Thread - American & Efird, Inc.
MAGIC - Toys - Kransco Manufacturing Inc.
MAGIC - Trading cards and stamps - Wizards of the Coast, Inc.
MAGIC - Umbrellas - Mespo Umbrella Co. Inc.
MAGIC - Wallpaper - Bayview Wallcoverings
MAGIC - Window coverings - A-Pro Tinting Co.
MAGIC ACCESS - Door openers–electronic - Stanley Works
MAGIC AIR - Pet products - Oscar Enterprises Inc.
MAGIC-AIRE - Dryers–hair - Helene Curtis Industries Inc.
MAGIC AISLE - Filing cabinets–metal - ACME Design Technology
MAGIC ALPHABET - Hobby kits - Extra Special Products Corp.
MAGIC ARROW - Thermometers - Crossbow Inc.
MAGIC ATTIC CLUB, THE - Video production - Georgetown Collection, Inc.
MAGIC BAG - Food containers - Wrapco International NV
MAGIC BAKE - Flour–blended - Fleming Companies, Inc.
MAGIC BAND - Apparel stores–lingerie - Goddess Bra
MAGIC BAND - Shorts–women's ☆ - Wellco Enterprises Inc.
MAGIC BARS - Games - Sigma Game Inc.
MAGIC BEAN - Publisher's imprint - McDougal, Littell & Co.

MAGIC BEAR, THE - Stuffed toys - Oz Enterprises, Inc.
MAGIC BEAT - Colognes - Max Factor & Co.
MAGIC BED - Motor vehicles–motor homes - Flexsteel Industries Inc.
MAGIC BIRD MIST - Pet products - 8 in 1 Pet Products Inc.
MAGIC BLEND - Salad dressings–bottled ☆ - Nalley's Fine Foods
MAGIC BLUSH - Skin care products ☆ - Palm Beach Beauty Products
MAGIC BOARD - Bulletin boards–cork ☆ - Webway, Inc.
MAGIC BOTTLE - Toys - South Bend Toy Manufacturing Co.
MAGIC BOTTLE BABY - Dolls - Tyco Toys
MAGIC BOTTLE TWINS - Toys - South Bend Toy Manufacturing Co.
MAGIC BOX - Publisher's imprints - Cromwell Brooks Inc.
MAGIC BREAKFAST PARTY - Toys - Playskool, Inc.
MAGIC BRUSH - Brushes ☆ - Mautner Co. Inc.
MAGIC BRUSH - Sanders and grinders - Val-A Co.
MAGIC BRUSHES - Hair care products - Raymac Corp. Hair & Skin Technology
MAGIC BUBBLES - Chewing gum - Philadelphia Chewing Gum Corp.
MAGIC CAP - Computer software - General Magic, Inc.
MAGIC CARPET - Boats–pontoons - Lakes Manufacturing Inc.
MAGIC-CARPET - Floor coverings - American Floor Products Co. Inc.
MAGIC CARPET - Pet shops - Dunwishin Enterprises
MAGIC CARPET - Shoes - L.B. Evans' Son Co.
MAGIC CARPET RIDE - Boats–pontoons - Lakes Manufacturing Inc.
MAGIC CARPET RIDE - Recording label - Pond Tune Productions
MAGIC-CARS - Toys–automobiles - Majorette Toys (U.S.) Inc.
MAGIC CAST - Clay–modeling - Dakota Chemaclay Corp.
MAGIC CHANGE - Dolls - Mattel, Inc.
MAGIC CHARM - Apparel–women's - Latex Foundations Co. Inc.
MAGIC CHARM - Floor coverings–carpet and rugs - Tuftex Carpet Mills, Inc.
MAGIC CHEF - Cutlery ☆ - Lifetime Hoan Corp.
MAGIC CHEF - Food products - Goodmark Foods, Inc.
MAGIC CHEF - Kitchen appliances - Magic Chef Inc.
MAGIC CHEF - Spices and extracts ☆ - Arrow Industries, Inc.
MAGIC CHERRY - Chewing gum - Philadelphia Chewing Gum Corp.
MAGIC CHERRY BLOSSOM TREE - Trees–artificial - New Tomorrow Inc.
MAGIC CHILES - Seasonings - Magic Seasoning Blends
MAGIC CHRISTMAS TREE - Trees–artificial - New Tomorrow Inc.
MAGIC CIRCLE - Bathroom accessories ☆ - Selfix, Inc.
MAGIC CIRCLE - Insecticides - J.C. Ehrlich Chemical Co.
MAGIC CIRCLE - Olives–canned - Haase Foods Inc.
MAGIC CLING - Photo albums ☆ - Esselte Corp.
MAGIC CLING - Toys - Internatural Designs, Inc.
MAGIC CLING - Vinyl - Joseph Struhl Co., Inc.
MAGIC CLIP - Office supplies - Wescosa Inc.
MAGIC COAT - Pet products - Four Paws Products Ltd.
MAGIC CODE - Toys - Fisher-Price, Inc.
MAGIC COLOR - Glassware–household - Houze Glass Corp.
MAGIC COLOR - Paint - Insilco Corp.
MAGIC COLORS - Chewing gum - Philadelphia Chewing Gum Corp.
MAGIC COLORS - Dyes–food - Spearhead Industries Inc.
MAGIC COMBO - Bags–plastic - Audit Security Bags, Inc.
MAGIC CONNECTION - Computer software - Compsoft Services, Inc.
MAGIC CONNECTION - Vibrators - Uniquity
MAGIC CONNECTION TWO - Vibrators - Uniquity
MAGIC COOKING SHEETS - Ovens–microwave - Thomas Paper, Inc.
MAGIC COPIER - Toys - Tyco Toys
MAGIC CORNER - Building materials - Trim-Tex, Inc.
MAGIC CORNER - Publisher's imprints - Western Publishing Co., Inc.
MAGIC-COTE - Paints - Morwear Paint Co.
MAGIC-COVER - Paper - Kittrich Corp.
MAGIC CRADLE MEGAN - Dolls - Tyco Industries, Inc.
MAGIC CRAYONS - Computer software - Sega of America, Inc.
MAGIC-CREME - Polishing rouge ☆ - Golden Star Inc.
MAGIC CROSS - Brassieres (Bras) - Montgomery Ward & Co. Inc.
MAGIC CRUST - Food products - Dadco Food Products Inc.
MAGIC CRUST THIN RISE - Pizzas–frozen - Dadco Food Products Inc.
MAGIC CRYSTAL - Glassware–household ☆ - Miller Import Corp.
MAGIC CRYSTALS - Chemical preparations - Embassy Imports, Inc.
MAGIC CUFF - Bowling balls - Master Industries Inc.
MAGIC CUP - Confections - North American Laboratory Co.
MAGIC DANCE - Audio and video tapes - Magic Dance, Inc.
MAGIC DIP - Craft supplies - Queen Ann Macaroni Manufacturing Co.
MAGIC DIP - Paints - Latham Studios
MAGIC DISK - Cleaning preparations - Vapor Products
MAGIC DISK MAN, THE - Vending machines - Magic Gumball International Corp.

MAGIC DOOR STOP & HOLDER - Hardware - Anne's Machine Product
MAGIC DRAGON - Food products - Magic Dragon, Inc.
MAGIC DRAWING SET - Toys ☆ - Tracies Co.
MAGIC DRI - Paints - Martin Paint Stores
MAGIC DUST - Floor coverings–carpet and rugs ☆ - Olympic Carpets Inc.
MAGIC-EAR - Hearing aids ☆ - Dahlberg, Inc.
MAGIC EDGE - Apparel and accessories - Magic Edge, Inc.
MAGIC ELASTIC - Apparel and accessories - Glamorise Foundations Inc.
MAGIC ELECTRICAL PRODUCTS - Telephone accessories - Magic Electrical Products, LLC
MAGIC EYE - Greeting cards - N.E. Thing Enterprises Inc.
MAGIC EYE - Mirrors - Paris Presents Ltd.
MAGIC EYE SEALER - Cosmetics - Victoria Vogue, Inc.
MAGIC EYES - Eyeglasses - Art-Craft Optical Co.
MAGIC FACTORY - Giftware - N.S. Gustin Co.
MAGIC FARM - Flowers, plants, and seeds - NTS Co.
MAGIC FAX - Toys - Falmon Falls Pet Products
MAGIC FENCE - Pet products ☆ - Amtek
MAGIC FINGER CLUTCH - Music stands - Manhasset Specialty Co.
MAGIC FIRE - Lighter fluid - R.M. Hollingshead Corp.
MAGIC FIREPLACE HEATER - Heating equipment ☆ - Magic Heat Corp.
MAGIC FIRM-LIFT - Skin care products ☆ - Palm Beach Beauty Products
MAGIC FIT - Apparel–women's - Pyke Manufacturing Co.
MAGIC FIT - Lenses–optical - Ditto Industries Inc.
MAGIC FIX - Archery equipment - Magic Fix, Inc.
MAGIC FLAKE - Snack foods - Fleming Companies, Inc.
MAGIC FLAVORS - Chewing gum - Philadelphia Chewing Gum Corp.
MAGIC FLO - Toys - M.&S. Shillman Inc.
MAGIC FLOCKED - Apparel–women's - Bi-Flex International
MAGIC FLOOR - Patching compound - Pioneer Manufacturing Co.
MAGIC FLOWERS - Chewing gum - Philadelphia Chewing Gum Corp.
MAGIC FLOWERS - Flowers–artificial - New Tomorrow Inc.
MAGIC FLUTE - Glassware–household ☆ - Rosenthal USA Ltd.
MAGIC FONE CORD - Telephone accessories - Magic Electrical Products, LLC
MAGIC FRUIT - Chewing gum - Philadelphia Chewing Gum Corp.
MAGIC FUNNEL - Containers–paper - Magic Funnel, Inc.
MAGIC GARDEN - Dinnerware–glass ☆ - Lenox, Inc.
MAGIC GARDEN - Flower pots–earthenware - New Tomorrow Inc.
MAGIC GARDEN - Flowers–artificial ☆ - First American Artificial Flowers Inc.
MAGIC GARDEN - Food products - International Frozen Foods Inc.
MAGIC GARDEN - Spices and extracts - Bruce Foods Corp.
MAGIC GAS CAN - Toys ☆ - Henry Gordy International Inc.
MAGIC GENIE - Computer software - Compsoft Services, Inc.
MAGIC GIFT TINTZL - Packaging–paper - Z-Barten Productions
MAGIC GLAMOUR PARTY - Toys - Playskool, Inc.
MAGIC GLOVE - Gloves–work - Magid Manufacturing Co. Inc.
MAGIC GLOW - Floor coverings–carpet and rugs - Alexander Smith Carpets
MAGIC GLOW - Wallcovering - Wildfire, Inc.
MAGIC GLUES - Glue–household or industrial ☆ - Magic American Corp.
MAGIC GRAPE - Chewing gum - Philadelphia Chewing Gum Corp.
MAGIC GREASE MOP - Degreasing solvents - SCI Scandicrafts Inc.
MAGIC GREEN - Fertilizers - Wommack's Hardwood Farms
MAGIC GRIP - Flashlights - Hipwell Manufacturing Co.
MAGIC GRIP - Office supplies - Wescosa Inc.
MAGIC GRO-CUP - Brassieres (Bras) - Wacoal America Inc.
MAGIC GROOM - Pet products - Blue Magic Products Inc.
MAGIC-HAND EATING PLAN - Publisher's imprints - Varnes
MAGIC HANDS - Recording label - Michael I. Gold
MAGIC HAT BREWING COMPANY - Beverages–malt - Magic Hat Brewing Co. & Performing Arts Center, Inc.
MAGIC HEART - Pet products - Hill Top Enterprises
MAGIC HEART HELPLINGS - Toys–stuffed - Those Characters from Cleveland, Inc.
MAGIC HEAT - Heating equipment - Magic Heat Corp.
MAGIC ICE CREAM MAKER - Toys ☆ - A.R.C. Toys Inc.
MAGIC ICE CREAM PARTY - Toys - Playskool, Inc.
MAGIC IMAGES - Apparel and accessories - Magic Images Inc.
MAGIC INKWELL - Computer software - ISTR Inc.
MAGIC INTERLUDE - Wallpaper - Advance Wallcoverings
MAGIC ISLE - Floor coverings–carpet and rugs - Queen Carpet Corp.
MAGIC JACKPOTS - Game machines - Universal Distributing of Nevada, Inc.
MAGIC JAR, THE - Exercising equipment ☆ - Jugglebug
MAGIC JOHNSON - T-shirts–women's - June Bug Enterprises, Inc.
MAGIC KEY - Alarm systems - Interactive Technologies, Inc.
MAGIC-KEY - Hardware ☆ - Slip Seal Co.
MAGIC KINGDOM - Toys–blocks - Mattel, Inc.

☆ = Now out of production

MAGIC KLENZ - Cleaning equipment - Apollo Environmental Corp.
MAGIC KNITTER - Knitting machines - White Consolidated Industries, Inc.
MAGIC LABEL - Hair care products - Menley & James Laboratories, Inc.
MAGIC LABEL - Labels–paper - Magiclabel Corp.
MAGIC LADY - Eyeglasses - Art-Craft Optical Co.
MAGIC LADY - Underwear and nightwear - Exquisite Form Industries
MAGIC LAMP - Housewares ☆ - Gerett Products Div.
MAGIC LAMP - Video games - WMS Gaming Inc.
MAGIC LANTERN - Electrical equipment ☆ - Toastmaster Inc.
MAGIC LANTERN GUIDES - Publisher's imprints - The Tiffen Co.
MAGIC LANTERNS - Glassware–household - Ottoman's, Inc.
MAGIC LEAF - Novelty items - Magic Leaf Inc.
MAGIC LEAF - Polishing cloths ☆ - Fair Haven Industries Inc.
MAGIC LEMONADE PARTY - Toys - Playskool, Inc.
MAGIC LIGHTNING BUG - Toys ☆ - Steven Manufacturing Co.
MAGIC LINE - Frames–eyeglass - Pathway Optical Prods.
MAGIC LINE - Pans - Parrish's Cake Decorating Supplies Inc.
MAGIC LINE - Wallpaper - Bayview Wallcoverings
MAGIC LINE II - Wallpaper - Bayview Wallcoverings
MAGIC LINK - Electronic equipment - Sony Corp. of America
MAGIC LIPS - Skin care products - Donna Lee Cosmetics Inc.
MAGIC-LITE - Doors–garage - Clopay Millwork
MAGIC-LOC - Locks–padlocks - Harris-Johnson Industries, Inc.
MAGIC LOCKET - Toys ☆ - Coloron Industries
MAGIC LOOP - Brassieres (Bras) - Q-T Foundations Co. Inc.
MAGIC LOTION - Skin care products - Triumph Associates
MAGIC LOTTO BALL - Novelty items - Richard Kuhns
MAGIC LUX - Paints - Royal Lustre Brands
MAGIC MAGNET - Pet products - Rolf C. Hagen (USA) Corp.
MAGIC MAGNETS - Magnets - Magic Magnets
MAGIC MAID - Brushes–paint ☆ - Wooster Brush Co.
MAGIC MAID - Housewares - Son-Chief Electrics Inc.
MAGIC MAILER - Envelopes - Desco Manufacturing Co. Inc.
MAGIC MAKER - Toys - Toymax Inc.
MAGIC MAN MCCURDY - Toys - Those Characters from Cleveland, Inc.
MAGIC MAP OF FEELINGS GAME, THE - Games - Peak Potential Inc.
MAGIC MAPLE - Topping - Pelican Bay Ltd. Inc.
MAGIC MARBLE - Kaleidoscopes - Gemini Kaleidoscopes
MAGIC MARY - Games ☆ - Milton Bradley Co.
MAGIC MASK - Paper–transfer - Stahls' Inc.
MAGIC MASKER - Paints - Hobsco Inc.
MAGIC MASKER - Paints - Wm. K. Walthers Inc.
MAGIC MAT - Fabrics–broadcloth ☆ - Fairfield Processing Corp.
MAGIC MAT - Mats - Novalek, Inc.
MAGIC MATCH - Polishes - Turtle Wax, Inc.
MAGIC MATCH PATCH - Adhesives and sealants - Magic Match Patch Co.
MAGIC MATE - Vacuum cleaners and accessories - Figgie Licensing Corp.
MAGIC MATES - Children's shoes ☆ - Consolidated Shoe Co., Inc.
MAGIC MATH PLUS - Computer software - Recreational Mathemagical Software
MAGIC MAZES - Printed materials - Stry-Lenkoff Co.
MAGIC MCGEE - Candy ☆ - R.M. Palmer Co.
MAGIC MEAL - Meat products–beef - Penthouse Meat Co.
MAGIC MEG - Dolls - Uneeda Doll Co., Inc.
MAGIC MEMORIES - Apparel and accessories - Oxford Industries, Inc.
MAGIC MENDER - Waxes–sealing ☆ - Magic American Corp.
MAGIC MICRO - Publisher's imprints - Scholastic Inc.
MAGIC MIDDLES - Cookies ☆ - Keebler Co.
MAGIC MILK PITCHER - Novelty items - S.S. Adams Co.
MAGIC MILL III - Home-grain-milling machines - Constellation Inc.
MAGIC MIND FINDER - Novelty items - Hypnocrafts Inc.
MAGIC MIND FINDER - Novelty items - Richard Kuhns
MAGIC MIRRORS - Mirrors - Vis-U-Wall Co.
MAGIC MIST - Food products - Parrish's Cake Decorating Supplies Inc.
MAGIC MIST - Pet products ☆ - 8 in 1 Pet Products Inc.
MAGIC MITTS - Games - General Sportcraft Co. Ltd.
MAGIC MOLD - Apparel and accessories - Magic Mold Inc.
MAGIC MOLD - Pans - Parrish's Cake Decorating Supplies Inc.
MAGIC MOMENT - Floor coverings–carpet and rugs ☆ - Karastan-Bigelow Inc.
MAGIC MOMENT - Mattresses - King Koil Licensing Co., Inc.
MAGIC MOMENT - Puzzles ☆ - Milton Bradley Co.
MAGIC MOMENT - Skin care products - Gillette Co.
MAGIC MOMENT - Underwear and nightwear - Maidenform Inc.
MAGIC MOMENTS - Apparel–children's - Good Lad Co.
MAGIC MOMENTS - Christmas tree ornaments - Cracker Box Inc.

MAGIC MOMENTS - Deodorizers - Willert Home Products, Inc.
MAGIC MOMENTS - Wallpaper ☆ - Glidden Co.
MAGIC MOMENTS III - Fabrics–tapestry - Comark Wallcoverings
MAGIC MOOD - Candles - Will & Baumer, Inc.
MAGIC MOODS - Wallpaper ☆ - Gagne Wallcovering, Inc.
MAGIC MOP - Degreasing solvents ☆ - Gourmet Center
MAGIC MOTION - Underwear and nightwear - Bestform Foundations, Inc.
MAGIC MOTOR HOME - Toys–automobiles - Mattel, Inc.
MAGIC MOUNTAIN - Deodorants–personal - Surco Products Inc.
MAGIC MOUNTAIN - Pencils - Collector's Gallery
MAGIC MOUNTAIN - Salad dressings–bottled - Romanoff International Inc.
MAGIC MOUNTAIN MEMORY - Computer software - Electronic Courseware Systems Inc.
MAGIC MOUNTS - Hardware - Miller Studio
MAGIC MOUSE CREATIONS - Patterns–clothing - Virgina G. Watson
MAGIC MOVES - Dolls - Mattel, Inc.
MAGIC MR X - Games - American Sammy Corp.
MAGIC MUNCHIES - Snack foods - Simple Foods Inc.
MAGIC MUSHROOM - Deodorizers - Airwick Industries
MAGIC MUSHROOM - Flower pots–earthenware - New Tomorrow Inc.
MAGIC MUSHROOM - Salt and pepper mills - William Bounds, Ltd.
MAGIC MUSIC - Floor coverings–carpet and rugs - Mohawk Carpet Corp.
MAGIC NIGHT - Floor coverings–carpet and rugs ☆ - Zenith Carpets
MAGIC NUMBER GAME - Games ☆ - Molor Products Co.
MAGIC NURSERY - Dolls - Mattel, Inc.
MAGIC OF GOALS - File boxes - JCD & Associates
MAGIC OF MAIN ST., THE - Food products - Trendmasters, Inc.
MAGIC OF MASLAND - Floor coverings–carpet and rugs ☆ - Masland Corp.
MAGIC OF SOY, THE - Vitamins and nutritional supplements - MLO Products, Inc.
MAGIC OF THOUGHTFULNESS - Greeting cards - Gibson Greetings, Inc.
MAGIC OF WATER GARDENING, THE - Fountains - Rena Corp.
MAGIC ON MYLAR - Wallpaper - James Seeman Studios
MAGIC OOZE - Toys - Larami Limited, Inc.
MAGIC-PAD - Erasers ☆ - Faber-Castell Corp.
MAGIC PADDLES - Games - General Sportcraft Co. Ltd.
MAGIC PAINT BRUSH - Toys ☆ - Coloron Industries
MAGIC PAPER - Computer software - International Business Machines Corp.
MAGIC PATCH - Agricultural products - Agrotec Corp.
MAGIC PATCH - Paints - Synkoloid Co.
MAGIC PENCIL BOOKS - Publisher's imprints ☆ - Gallant Greetings Corp.
MAGIC PENCILGRIP - Office supplies - Wescosa Inc.
MAGIC PIANO - Computer software ☆ - Edusoft
MAGIC-PINK - Erasers ☆ - Faber-Castell Corp.
MAGIC PITCHER 'N PUNCH SET - Toys ☆ - South Bend Toy Manufacturing Co.
MAGIC PLANTS - Flowers–artificial - New Tomorrow Inc.
MAGIC PLASTICS - Model kit compounds - Adica Pongo Inc.
MAGIC PLATEN - Printing trades machinery - Lawson Screen Products, Inc.
MAGIC POLYWEB - Fusible web ☆ - Coats and Clark Inc.
MAGIC POP - Fireworks - American Promotional Events, Inc.
MAGIC POP - Fireworks - China Pyrotechnics, Inc.
MAGIC POP - Popcorn - Wagner Farms Magic Pop Popcorn
MAGIC POPPERS - Pet food - L/M Animal Farms, Inc.
MAGIC POPS - Food products - North American Laboratory Co.
MAGIC POTION - Skin care products - Alacer Co.
MAGIC POTTY BABY - Dolls - Tyco Toys
MAGIC POWER - Apparel and accessories ☆ - Warnaco Inc.
MAGIC PUFFS - Cereal - Wal-Mart Stores Inc.
MAGIC PUFFS - Cereal ☆ - General Mills, Inc.
MAGIC PULL - Paper–gift wrap - That's A Wrap Inc.
MAGIC QUIK-EPOXY - Adhesives and sealants ☆ - Magic American Corp.
MAGIC RAIN - Hair care products - Willat Co.
MAGIC RAINBOW - Markers–felt-tip - K-9 Pen Co.
MAGIC REALM - Floor coverings–carpet and rugs ☆ - World Carpets, Inc.
MAGIC REALM - Games - Avalon Hill Game Co.
MAGIC RIBS - Underwear and nightwear - Jockey International, Inc.
MAGIC RING BY LOVABLE - Underwear and nightwear - Lovable Co.
MAGIC ROCKS - Hobby kits - Craft House Corp.
MAGIC ROLL - Bowling balls - Master Industries Inc.
MAGIC ROLLER - Dusters - Helmac Products Corp.
MAGIC-ROLLERS - Hair care products - Nino Originals
MAGIC-RUB - Erasers - Faber-Castell Corp.
MAGIC RUST CONVERTER - Coatings ☆ - Atlas Chemical Co.
MAGIC RUST 'N ALUMINUM JELLY - Automotive parts and accessories ☆ - Magic American Corp.

☆ = Now out of production

MAGIC S - Dust mops ☆ - American Textile Products Co.
MAGIC S SWIVEL - Dust mops ☆ - American Textile Products Co.
MAGIC SAND - Toys ☆ - Wham-O Manufacturing Co.
MAGIC SANDER - Sanders and grinders - Val-A Co.
MAGIC-SANDY - Nail care products - GG's Nail Systems
MAGIC SCARF - Scarves - Bonnie J. Ehrlich
MAGIC SCENT - Crayons - Binney & Smith Inc.
MAGIC SCENT - Deodorizers - Modern Concepts, Inc.
MAGIC SCHOOL BUS - Publisher's imprints - Scholastic Inc.
MAGIC SCHOOL BUS, THE - Video production - Scholastic Inc.
MAGIC SCRAPER - Bowling balls ☆ - DBA Products Co.
MAGIC SCRUB - Boating equipment and accessories - Hawie Manufacturing Co.
MAGIC SEAL - Caulking compounds - Magic Seal Corp.
MAGIC SEALER - Varnishes ☆ - McCloskey Corp.
MAGIC SEASONING BLENDS - Spices and extracts ☆ - Magic Seasoning Blends
MAGIC SEAT - Equestrian equipment - Mary Sue Tate
MAGIC SHADOWS - Floor coverings—carpet and rugs - Ebsco Carpet Mills
MAGIC SHAPES - Cereal - Federated Group, Inc.
MAGIC SHEET - Health care products - Patient Care Corp.
MAGIC SHELL - Confections - J.M. Smucker Co.
MAGIC SHINE - Automobile cleaning supplies - Positive Response Marketing, Inc.
MAGIC SHOULDERS - Shoulder pads - Stay Put Shoulder Pads
MAGIC SHOW - Floor coverings—carpet and rugs - Trend Carpet
MAGIC SHOW - Toys - Fisher-Price, Inc.
MAGIC SILK - Underwear and nightwear - Magic Moments International, Inc.
MAGIC SILVER DIP - Cleaning preparations - Magic American Corp.
MAGIC SIZING - Starch—laundry - Faultless Starch/Bon Ami Co.
MAGIC SKIN - Apparel and accessories - Glamorise Foundations Inc.
MAGIC SKIN - Toys—stuffed - CBS Toys
MAGIC SKIRT - Skirts—women's - Norm Thompson Outfitters, Inc.
MAGIC SLATE - Computer software ☆ - Sunburst Communications, Inc.
MAGIC SLATE - Toys - Western Publishing Co., Inc.
MAGIC SLICE - Meat products—beef - Armour Swift-Eckrich
MAGIC SLIPPER - Slippers - Magic Slipper Co.
MAGIC SMOKING GRILL - Toys - Playskool, Inc.
MAGIC SMOKING GRILL HAMBURGER/SHISH-KE-BOB - Toys - Playskool, Inc.
MAGIC SMOKING GRILL PICNIC BASKET - Toys - Playskool, Inc.
MAGIC SNAKE - Games - Hirsch Co.
MAGIC SOFT - Paper—toweling - American Tissue Corp.
MAGIC SOFT SKIN BABY - Toys - Eugene Doll & Novelty Co. Inc.
MAGIC SOUNDS - Dolls - Mattel, Inc.
MAGIC SPELL - Embossing tool - International Rotex Inc.
MAGIC SPELLS - Computer software ☆ - The Learning Co., Inc.
MAGIC SPICE MIX - Spices and extracts - Ind-Us Enterprises, Inc.
MAGIC SPLASH - Dolls - Mattel, Inc.
MAGIC SPLENDOR - Floor coverings—carpet and rugs - Evans-Black Carpet Mills
MAGIC SPRAY - Frames—eyeglass - Hudson Optical Corp.
MAGIC SPRINKLER - Paint removers - Atlas Chemical Co.
MAGIC SQUARE, THE - Hobby kits ☆ - Latham Studios
MAGIC STARCH - Starch—laundry - Faultless Starch/Bon Ami Co.
MAGIC STARFIRE GEM - Toys - Saban Entertainment, Inc.
MAGIC STARS - Diapers—disposable - Universal Converter, Inc.
MAGIC START - Flowers, plants, and seeds - Ringer Corp.
MAGIC-STAT - Thermostats - Quad Six Inc.
MAGIC STEEL - Steel ☆ - Magic American Corp.
MAGIC STEPS - Shoes - Montgomery Ward & Co. Inc.
MAGIC STICK - Boating equipment and accessories - Hawie Manufacturing Co.
MAGIC STICK - Scrapbooks ☆ - Webway, Inc.
MAGIC STONES - Novelty items—glass - Arcadian Design
MAGIC STRETCH BY HAGGAR - Fabrics—spandex ☆ - Haggar Corp.
MAGIC STRETCH LITE - Fabrics—spandex - Haggar Corp.
MAGIC STRETCH NATURALL - See **NOVA**
MAGIC STUFF - Clay—modeling - Rose Art Industries, Inc.
MAGIC STYL'O - Cosmetics - MCN International Inc.
MAGIC SUPER GLUE - Adhesives and sealants ☆ - Magic American Corp.
MAGIC SURPRISE - Dolls - Mattel, Inc.
MAGIC TAILS - Imitation lobster - Jana Brands
MAGIC TALK - Toys - Mattel, Inc.
MAGIC TEA PARTY - Toys - Playskool, Inc.
MAGIC TEX - Paints - Royal Lustre Brands

MAGIC THE GATHERING - Games - Wizards of the Coast, Inc.
MAGIC THEATRE - Computer software - Instinct Corp.
MAGIC THIMBLE - Sewing machines—household - White Consolidated Industries, Inc.
MAGIC-TIP - Dental equipment - Js Dental Manufacturing, Inc.
MAGIC-TIP - Food products - Parrish's Cake Decorating Supplies Inc.
MAGIC TIP - Tools ☆ - Danaher Tool Group
MAGIC TONES - Floor coverings—carpet and rugs ☆ - Galaxy Carpet Mills Inc.
MAGIC TOP - Latex - Royal Lustre Brands
MAGIC TOP - Toys ☆ - Steven Manufacturing Co.
MAGIC TOUCH - Bottles—glass - Johnson & Johnson
MAGIC TOUCH - Cosmetics - Apothecary Products, Inc.
MAGIC TOUCH - Detergents - Promaster
MAGIC TOUCH - Dolls - Tonka Corp.
MAGIC TOUCH - Drapery hardware - Kenney Manufacturing Co.
MAGIC TOUCH - Electronic equipment - Keytec, Inc.
MAGIC TOUCH - Floor coverings—carpet and rugs - Monticello Carpet Mills
MAGIC TOUCH - Food products - Beatrice Cos. Inc.
MAGIC TOUCH - Frames—eyeglass - Pathway Optical Prods.
MAGIC TOUCH - Furniture ☆ - Brooks Furniture Manufacturing Inc.
MAGIC TOUCH - Hobby kits ☆ - Hunt Manufacturing Co.
MAGIC TOUCH - Insect-bite treatment - Infa-Lab Inc.
MAGIC TOUCH - Lighting equipment - Lights of America Inc.
MAGIC TOUCH - Nail care products - Magic Touch/Pacific Airbrush
MAGIC TOUCH - Novelty items - Michael I. Gold
MAGIC TOUCH - Office supplies - Wescosa Inc.
MAGIC TOUCH - Paint rollers - Great American Marketing, Inc.
MAGIC TOUCH - Skin care products - Waverly Beauty Products
MAGIC TOUCH - Toys - Brite-Tone Co.
MAGIC TOUCH - Whirlpool-bath switch - Jacuzzi Inc.
MAGIC TOUCH - Wigs - Baek, in Taek
MAGIC TOUCH GROOMING SPRAY - Pet products - Crowne Royale, Ltd.
MAGIC TOUCH, THE - Decals and transfers - TMT North America Inc.
MAGIC TRAIL - Trailers—boat - Magic Tilt Trailers, Inc.
MAGIC TRAIN - Toys—trains - Mattel, Inc.
MAGIC TREE - Deodorizers - Car-Freshner Corp.
MAGIC TREE - Trees—artificial - New Tomorrow Inc.
MAGIC TRIK KARDS - Novelty items ☆ - D. Robbins & Co. Inc.
MAGIC TROLLS - Kites - Hi-Flier Manufacturing Co.
MAGIC TROLLS BABY - Dolls ☆ - Applause, Inc.
MAGIC TURTLES - Toys ☆ - Steven Manufacturing Co.
MAGIC TYPE - Office supplies - Wescosa Inc.
MAGIC VAC - Toys - Fisher-Price, Inc.
MAGIC VALLEY - Floor coverings—carpet and rugs - Queen Carpet Corp.
MAGIC VALLEY - Potato flakes - Magic Valley Foods Inc.
MAGIC VANITY - Toys - Mattel, Inc.
MAGIC VIEW - Dolls - Mattel, Inc.
MAGIC VISALIZER - Paper—bond - Bee Paper Co. Inc.
MAGIC WALL - Cabinets - Amco Corp.
MAGIC WALL - Posters - Kling Magnetics Inc.
MAGIC WAND - Detergents - Edwards Creative Products, Inc.
MAGIC WAND - Electronic equipment ☆ - Texas Instruments Inc.
MAGIC WAND - Orthopedic products - Smith & Nephew Inc. (Rehabilitation Div.)
MAGIC WAND TILTER - Window coverings - Levolor Inc.
MAGIC WAX BOARD 60-SECOND NAIL MIRACLE - Nail treatment - Pri-Form Inc.
MAGIC WEAVE - Foundation garments—women's - Merit Foundations Inc.
MAGIC WINDOW - Computer software - ARTSCI Inc.
MAGIC WINKER - Electrical equipment - Eagle Electric Manufacturing Co., Inc.
MAGIC WIPERS - Motor vehicle parts and accessories ☆ - Delfino Products Inc.
MAGIC WOOD - Wood fillers ☆ - Magic American Corp.
MAGIC WOODBLEND - Putties ☆ - Magic American Corp.
MAGIC WORKS - Toys - Hasbro, Inc.
MAGIC XCHANGE - Computer software - Intellilink Corp.
MAGIC YARN - Yarn ☆ - William Unger & Co. Inc.
MAGICA - Rust removers - Magica, Inc.
MAGICA - Scooters—children's ☆ - Peg Perego USA Inc.
MAGICAIRE II - Food dehydrator - Constellation Inc.
MAGICAL BALLROOM - Dolls - Mattel, Inc.
MAGICAL BLEND OF MUSIC AND THE SOUNDSOF NATURE, A - Recording label - Metacom Inc.
MAGICAL BORDERS - Wallpaper - Warner Co.
MAGICAL BOTANICALS - Health care products - Magick Mud
MAGICAL LIPS - Lipsticks - New Cal Development, Inc.

☆ = Now out of production

MAGICAL MACARONI AND CHEESE - Preserved foods–prepackaged - Conagra, Inc.
MAGICAL MANE - Hair care products - Conair Corp.
MAGICAL MANSION - Dolls - Mattel, Inc.
MAGICAL MESSAGE BOARD - Games - Monte Farber
MAGICAL MINIATURES - Candy - R.M. Palmer Co.
MAGICAL MOMENTS - Calendars - Marci Stamm
MAGICAL MOMENTS - Kaleidoscopes ☆ - Gemini Kaleidoscopes
MAGICAL MONSTER GUARDZ - Toys - Layon Enterprises
MAGICAL MOTOR HOME - Dolls - Mattel, Inc.
MAGICAL MOVIN' PICTURES - Toys - SLM Inc.
MAGICAL MUSICAL STICK - Toys - Richard C. Levy
MAGICAL MUSK - Colognes - Max Factor & Co.
MAGICAL MYTHS - Computer software - Unicorn Software
MAGICAL ODDS - Video games - Micro Manufacturing, Inc.
MAGICAL SEASON - Perfumes - Countryside Fragrances Inc.
MAGICAL TONIC - Game machines - Micro Manufacturing, Inc.
MAGICALLY MEXICAN - Spices and extracts - Jodie's Kitchen Inc.
MAGICAP - Caps–baseball - Pacific Sportswear and Emblem Co.
MAGICAP - Dyes–cosmetic ☆ - Bobby Co.
MAGICAP DISPOSABLE - Hair care products - Bobby Co.
MAGICAP-ELITE - Hair care products - Bobby Co.
MAGICAP X - Hair care products - Bobby Co.
MAGICARE - Furniture polish and wax - Apple Polishes Inc.
MAGICATER - Barbecues and grills - Magikitch'n Inc.
MAGICBIND - Computer software - Computer Editype
MAGICBODY - Apparel–athletic - A & H Sportswear Co., Inc.
MAGICDISC - Computer software - Toshiba America Information Systems, Inc.
MAGICFIT - Window shades - Newell Window Furnishing Co.
MAGICFOLD - Toys - S. Pal Asija
MAGICFORM - Apparel–women's - Latex Foundations Co. Inc.
MAGICIAN - Candles - Merrill-West Publishing
MAGICIAN - Frames–eyeglass - Zylo Ware Corp.
MAGICIAN - Thread - Witten Sales Corp.
MAGICIAN - Toys–models ☆ - Estes Industries
MAGICIAN, THE - Vending machines - Magic Gumball International Corp.
MAGICK MUD - Skin care products - Magick Mud
MAGICKALLY-MADE - Incense - Lady Desiree's Bewitchery
MAGICLEEN - Cleaning preparations - Klein & Co.
MAGICLINK - Amplifiers - JBL Inc.
MAGICLIP - Giftware - Lorac Co.
MAGICLOUD - Underwear and nightwear - Youthcraft-Charmfit
MAGICMAIL - Office machines - General Magic, Inc.
MAGICMEDIA - Toys–electronic - Magicmedia, Inc.
MAGICODE - Computer software - Magicode, Inc.
MAGICOIL - Sofas ☆ - La-Z-Boy Chair Co.
MAGICOLOR - Printers–computer - QMS, Inc.
MAGICOLOR - Toys - Samuel Lowe Co.
MAGICOOKA - Cookware - Nutri-Stahl, Inc.
MAGICPRINT - Decals and transfers ☆ - Sangray Corp.
MAGICRAFT - Metals ☆ - Magic American Chemical Corp. (Magicraft Div.)
MAGIC'S 32 - Apparel and accessories ☆ - Magic Johnson Enterprises Inc.
MAGICSEPS - Computer software - Candela, Ltd.
MAGICSHRED - Office machines - Martin Yale Industries, Inc.
MAGICSILK - Flowers–artificial - Magicsilk
MAGICSTAT - Thermostats - Honeywell Inc.
MAGICSTITCH - Computer software - Softart Associates
MAGICSUIT - Bathing suits - A and H Sportswear Co., Inc.
MAGICTOUCH - Fabrics - Pioneer-Leimel Fabrics, Inc.
MAGICUBE - Photographic equipment - General Electric Co.
MAGICUPS - Brassieres (Bras) - Brazabra Corp.
MAGICUS - Pencils - Faber-Castell Corp.
MAGICUT - Files, saws - Cooper Industries, Inc.
MAGICVISION - Novelty items - S.S. Adams Co.
MAGICWAND - Jewelers' findings - L & R Manufacturing Co.
MAGICWOOD - Frames–picture - Eric Schuster Corp.
MAGIE - Perfumes - Lancome
MAGIE NOIRE - Perfumes - Lancome
MAGIFIT - Shoe soles - Orthofeet, Inc.
MAGIGLOW - Barbecues and grills - Magikitch'n Inc.
MAGIK - Soap - Polyproducts Corp.
MAGIK BRUSH - Health care products - Helmac Products Corp.
MAGIK BY AMALFI - Footwear - United States Shoe Corp.
MAGIK FUZZ BUSTER - Shaving preparations - Helmac Products Corp.
MAGIK MATES - Health care products - Helmac Products Corp.
MAGIK MODULES - Furniture–wood - Intro Europe

MAGIK SEAL BEFORE YOU GO FLAT - Automotive parts and accessories - A&J International, Inc.
MAGIKAGE - Paint rollers - Wooster Brush Co.
MAGIKEY - Computer peripheral equipment - Micro Processor Systems, Inc.
MAGIKEY - Computer software - WPI Micro Processor Systems, Inc.
MAGIKITCH'N - Barbecues and grills - Magikitch'n Inc.
MAGIKOTER - Paint rollers - Wooster Brush Co.
MAGINARY'S - Infant product ☆ - Gerry Baby Products Co.
MAGINOT - Fishing reels - American Import Co.
MAGIQUE - Beverages–alcohol - Levecke Corp.
MAGIQUE - Croissants - LDA Inc.
MAGIQUE - Hairpins - Mars Custom Plastics Inc.
MAGIQUE - Lipsticks - Cosmair Inc.
MAGIQUE - Watches - Helbros International
MAGISPARK - Barbecues and grills - Meteor Inc.
MAGISTRATE - Fishing tackle ☆ - Gladding Braided Products Inc.
MAGISTRATE COLLECTION - Floor coverings–carpet and rugs - Milliken & Co. Inc.
MAGITILT - Office furniture–wood ☆ - Royal Seating Corp.
MAGIX - Musical instrument accessories - Keyes-Davis Co.
MAGLA - Ironing board pads - Magla Products Inc.
MAGLA KNOB HILL - Towels ☆ - Magla Products Inc.
MAGLI - Apparel and accessories ☆ - Skea Ltd.
MAGLI - Wines - House of Burgundy Inc.
MAGLINER - Video production - Nalpak Video Sales, Inc.
MAGLINK - Vitamins and nutritional supplements - M.M.R.C., Ltd. Co.
MAGLITE - Flashlights - Rothco Inc.
MAGLOR - Pharmaceutical preparations - Wesley Pharmacal Co. Inc.
MAGLYS - Magnets - Mug Shanty
MAGMA - Barbecues and grills - Magma Products, Inc.
MAGMA - Bicycles - Columbia Manufacturing Inc.
MAGMA - Health care products - Above All Health Inc.
MAGMA - Sporting goods - Moody & Co. Inc.
MAGMA - Sporting goods ☆ - O'Brien International
MAGMA BEPPU - Bath salts - Green Foods
MAGMAG - Infant product - Omron Healthcare, Inc.
MAGMALIN - Pharmaceutical preparations ☆ - Pal-Pak Inc.
MAGMAONSEN - Bath salts - Green Foods
MAGMAR - Toys - Tonka Corp.
MAGMATHERAPY - Skin care products - Lisane Aesthetics, Inc.
MAGN-O-MATIC 10 - Vestments–academic and clerical - Ponsness-Warren
MAGNA - Amplifiers–public address - Fender Musical Instruments
MAGNA - Cigarettes - R.J. Reynolds Tobacco Co.
MAGNA - Floor coverings - Mannington Resilient Floors
MAGNA - Floor coverings–carpet and rugs - Collins & Aikman Corp.
MAGNA - Floor coverings–carpet and rugs ☆ - Burtco Enterprises Inc.
MAGNA - Footwear - Kisco International Corp.
MAGNA - Handbags - Lumured Corp.
MAGNA - Paints - Bocour Artist Colors Inc.
MAGNA - Paints ☆ - Homax, Inc.
MAGNA - Printers–computer ☆ - A.B. Dick Co.
MAGNA - Signs - Bizarre Products
MAGNA - Tools - Multt Metals
MAGNA - Whirlpool bath ☆ - Jacuzzi Inc.
MAGNA-BAR - Displays racks and bins - Cannon Equipment Co.
MAGNA-BAR - Lenses–magnifying - Bausch & Lomb Inc.
MAGNA-BEAM - Flashlights ☆ - Plano Molding Co.
MAGNA-BRITE - Toothpaste - Dental Concepts Inc.
MAGNA BRUTE - Sporting goods - James Heddon's Sons
MAGNA-BURN - Hardware - Ament Enterprises Inc.
MAGNA BY COUNTRY COACH - Motor vehicles–buses - Country Coach, Inc.
MAGNA CAL PLUS - Pharmaceutical preparations - Nutritional Research Associates Inc.
MAGNA CARTA - Pens - Douglas C. Schwarzwaelder
MAGNA CARTA - Recording label ☆ - Roadrunner Records, Inc.
MAGNA-CASE - Lenses–optical - Kelley & Hueber
MAGNA CHART - Cameras–video - Magna Visual, Inc.
MAGNA-CLIP - Paper clips ☆ - Newell Office Products
MAGNA-CORE - Doors–storm - Larson Manufacturing Co.
MAGNA DESIGN - Office furniture–metal - Magna Design, Inc.
MAGNA DOODLE - Toys - Fisher-Price, Inc.
MAGNA-DOODLE - Toys–electronic - CBS Toys
MAGNA DOODLE DAN - Toys - Pilot Pen Corp. of America
MAGNA FIRE - Spark plugs - Ultra Performance International, Inc.
MAGNA-FLEX - Magnets - Norstar Enterprises
MAGNA-FLIP - Games - Williams Electronics Games, Inc.

MAGNA-FOLD - Folding doors and partitions ☆ - American Door Co. Inc.
MAGNA FORCE - Automotive parts and accessories - Zoor Inc.
MAGNA FORCE - Compressors–air - Sanborn Manufacturing Co.
MAGNA FORCE - Flashlights - Fulton Industries Inc.
MAGNA FORCE - Vitamins and nutritional supplements - Natural Organics, Inc.
MAGNA-FRAME - Electronic equipment - Telex Communications, Inc.
MAGNA-FRAME - Windows–plastic ☆ - Aluminum Co. of America
MAGNA GALLERY - Frames–picture - Collector's Gallery
MAGNA GEAR - Bicycle parts and accessories - Dynacraft Industries Inc.
MAGNA-GEL - Pharmaceutical preparations ☆ - Vortech Pharmaceuticals
MAGNA-GRAIN - Doors–wood ☆ - Wells Aluminum
MAGNA-GUARD - Ovens–microwave - Amana Refrigeration Inc.
MAGNA HDR - Toys ☆ - Wham-O Manufacturing Co.
MAGNA-HOLD - Paperboard ☆ - Magna Visual, Inc.
MAGNA I - Typewriters ☆ - A.B. Dick Co.
MAGNA KARMA - Novelty items - Karmatorium, Inc.
MAGNA-LIFT - Electronic equipment - Chief Manufacturing Co.
MAGNA-LOK - Frames–picture - Engineered Products Co.
MAGNA MAGNETS - Magnets ☆ - Homax, Inc.
MAGNA MELT - Deicing fluid - Cargill Salt
MAGNA MINS - Vitamins and nutritional supplements - Natural Organics, Inc.
MAGNA-MOUNT - Hardware - Rice Lake Weighing Systems, Inc.
MAGNA PAC - Novelty items - Magna Pac
MAGNA-PAGE - Magnifiers - Bausch & Lomb Inc.
MAGNA PAINT - Paints ☆ - Homax, Inc.
MAGNA PAK - Meat product - American Stores Co.
MAGNA PAK - Vitamins and nutritional supplements - Nature's Concept Inc.
MAGNA POINT - Floor coverings–carpet and rugs - Whitecrest Carpet Mills
MAGNA POWER - Batteries - East Penn Manufacturing Co., Inc.
MAGNA POWER - Hearing aids ☆ - United Hearing Systems Inc.
MAGNA-PROJECT - Electronic equipment - Chief Manufacturing Co.
MAGNA ROD - Sporting goods - James Heddon's Sons
MAGNA-RULE - Lenses–magnifying - Bausch & Lomb Inc.
MAGNA SCENTS - Sachets - Natural Products Corp.
MAGNA-SCRAPER - Disinfectants - Penn-Plax, Inc.
MAGNA-SEAL - Adhesives and sealants - Commercial Chemical Co. Inc.
MAGNA-SEE - Electronic equipment - Reeves Soundcraft
MAGNA-SET - Tools–hand-operated - Woodstock International, Inc.
MAGNA SHARP - Cutlery - General Housewares Corp.
MAGNA-SHELF - Electronic equipment - Chief Manufacturing Co.
MAGNA SOUND 2000 - Headphones - Telebrands Corp.
MAGNA-STAMP - Ink-stamping systems - Clearsnap, Inc.
MAGNA-SWEEP - Pet products - Penn-Plax, Inc.
MAGNA-TABS - Pet products - Nutra-Vet Research Corp.
MAGNA TECH PROFESSIONAL - Cutlery - General Housewares Corp.
MAGNA-TEX - Paints - Commercial Chemical Co. Inc.
MAGNA-TITE - Fasteners–hook and eye - Huck International, Inc.
MAGNA-TITE - Hardware - Engineered Products Co.
MAGNA-TITE - Lighting fixtures - Vimco Inc.
MAGNA TORQ - Hardware - Aluminum Co. of America
MAGNA-TORQ 2000 - Machine parts - Aluminum Co. of America
MAGNA TOUCH - Measuring instruments - Baker Hughes Inc.
MAGNA-TRACTIVE MOTOR - Toys–trains - Life-Like Products Inc.
MAGNA-TRAK - Electronic equipment - Chicago Steel Tape Co.
MAGNA TRENDS - Floor coverings–carpet and rugs - Innovative Flooring Systems Inc.
MAGNA-TWIN - Hearing aids - Telex Communications, Inc.
MAGNA TWIN - Rug cleaning machines–commercial - Castex Industries Inc.
MAGNA-VIEW - Electronic equipment - Chief Manufacturing Co.
MAGNA-VIEW - Electronic equipment - Telex Communications, Inc.
MAGNA-VIEW - Office supplies - Wescosa Inc.
MAGNA-VIEW - Photographic equipment ☆ - Logan Electric Specialty Manufacturing Co.
MAGNA VIEW - Scales–industrial - Chronos Richardson Inc.
MAGNA VISION - Eyeglasses ☆ - Nelkin/Piper Health Products
MAGNA VOGUE SERIES - Bicycles - Dynacraft Industries, Inc.
MAGNA-VUE - Photographic equipment ☆ - Charles Beseler Co.
MAGNA WEIGH - Scales–industrial - Chronos Richardson Inc.
MAGNA-WOOD - Folding doors and partitions - American Door Co. Inc.
MAGNA X - Buffing machines - Pioneer/Eclipse Corp.
MAGNABAND - Construction equipment - Alcan Aluminum Corp. Alcan Building Products Div.
MAGNABAR - Housewares - Phelon Magnagrip Co. Inc.
MAGNABRITE - Cooking equipment–household ☆ - General Housewares Corp.
MAGNABRITE - Lenses–magnifying - Visual Aid Lab, Inc.

MAGNABRITE - Photographic equipment - Tiffen Manufacturing Corp.
MAGNACAL - Health care products - Sherwood Medical Co.
MAGNACAL - Soil testing kits - Troy Mallett
MAGNACARE - Water purification systems - Ultra Modern Pools, Inc.
MAGNACLAD - Paneling - International Paper (Decorative Products Division)
MAGNACOLOR - Metals - International Pipe & Steel Corp.
MAGNACORE - Pans - All-Clad Metalcrafters Inc.
MAGNADOR - Pet products - Plaza Enterprises Inc. (Magnador Div.)
MAGNADOR - Pet products - R.C. Steele Co.
MAGNADRUM - Filters–water - Hyde Products Inc.
MAGNADUSTR - Cleaning equipment - Contec, Inc.
MAGNADYNE - Audio equipment - Magnadyne Corp.
MAGNAFLEX - Electronics equipment - Marty Bahn & Co.
MAGNAFLEX - Rubber–molded - Mid-American Rubber Co., Inc.
MAGNAFLOAT HG - Electrical equipment - R.F. Gridley
MAGNAFOLD - Magnetic billfold - Hugo Bosca Co., Inc.
MAGNAFORM - Office supplies - Magnaform Corp.
MAGNAFORUM - Computer software - Forum Systems, Inc.
MAGNAGEL - Pharmaceutical preparations - Roberts/Hauck Pharmaceuticals Inc.
MAGNAGRAPH - Sporting goods - James Heddon's Sons
MAGNAGRID - Construction equipment - Alcan Aluminum Corp. Alcan Building Products Div.
MAGNAGRIP - Bathroom accessories - Jeffrey D. Hempel
MAGNAGRIP - Housewares - Phelon Magnagrip Co. Inc.
MAGNAGROW - Fertilizers - PQ Corp.
MAGNAHOLD - Electronic equipment - Magna Visual, Inc.
MAGNAHOME - Prefabricated buildings–wood ☆ - Magnahome Inc.
MAGNAKIT - Toys - Smethport Specialty Co.
MAGNALAWN 2000 - Garden equipment - YBM Magnetics, Inc.
MAGNALITE - Cooking utensils–aluminum - General Housewares Corp.
MAGNALITE - Fabrics–polyester - Topvalue Fabrics, Inc.
MAGNALITE - Frames–eyeglass - Pathway Optical Prods.
MAGNALITE - Lawn mowers - Lawn-Boy
MAGNALITE - Signs - Thomas A. Schutz Co.
MAGNALITE CLASSIC - Cooking utensils–aluminum - General Housewares Corp.
MAGNALITE MASTERY - Cooking utensils–aluminum ☆ - General Housewares Corp.
MAGNALITE PLUS - Cooking utensils–aluminum ☆ - General Housewares Corp.
MAGNALITE PROFESSIONAL - Cooking utensils–aluminum - General Housewares Corp.
MAGNALOCK - Locks–door - Sargent Manufacturing Co.
MAGNALOCK - Locks–door - Securitron-Magnalock
MAGNALON - Crocheted and knitted items ☆ - Roosevelt Mills Inc.
MAGNALOX - Pharmaceutical preparations - Schein Pharmaceutical Inc.
MAGNALOY - Pumps–water ☆ - Flint & Walling Industries, Inc.
MAGNALUG - Electrical equipment - Quick Cable Corp.
MAGNALUME - Ophthalmic goods - Styl-Rite Optical Manufacturing Co., Inc.
MAGNALUX - Lighting equipment - Badger USA
MAGNAMAX DVR - Generators–electric - Marathon Electric Manufacturing Corp.
MAGNAMUSIC-BATON - Music–sheet ☆ - MMB Music Inc.
MAGNAN - Audio equipment - Sumiko Inc.
MAGNAN - Jewelry - Gallotta-Houghton Industries Inc.
MAGNAPEARL - Pearlescent pigments - Mearl Corp.
MAGNAPLAN - Office supplies - MagnaPlan Corp.
MAGNAPRIN - Pharmaceutical preparations - Rugby Laboratories Inc.
MAGNAPROX - Lenses–magnifying ☆ - Buhl Optical Co.
MAGNAROK - Cement - Metalcrete Industries Inc.
MAGNARUN - Machinery - Hermes Machine Tool Co., Inc.
MAGNASCOPE - Electronic equipment ☆ - H. Wilson Co.
MAGNASEAL - Paints - Triangle Coatings Inc.
MAGNASHEET - Magnets - Mangelsen's (VDI)
MAGNASIGHT - Photographic equipment - Bestwell Optical Instrument Co.
MAGNASNAPPER - Clamp - Krapf Business Systems, Inc.
MAGNASPARK - Motor vehicle parts and accessories - Claude's Buggies, Inc.
MAGNASTAR - Projectors–photographic - Apollo Audiovisual Div.
MAGNASTAR - Radios - Mesc Electronic Systems, Inc.
MAGNASTIKS - Toys - Childcraft Education Corp.
MAGNASTIX - Pet products - Best Products Co.
MAGNASTONE - Computer peripheral equipment - Stone Age Technologies, Inc.
MAGNASTRIP - Magnets - Mangelsen's (VDI)
MAGNATE - Floor coverings–carpet and rugs ☆ - Walter Carpet Mills

☆ = Now out of production

MAGNATE - Ophthalmic goods - Styl-Rite Optical Manufacturing Co., Inc.

MAGNATECH - Cutlery - General Housewares Corp.

MAGNATEK - Machine parts - Interlake Companies, Inc.

MAGNATEX - Pumps–oil well - Magnatex Pumps, Inc.

MAGNATITE DORGARDS - Motor vehicle parts and accessories - Target Motorsports

MAGNATONE - Hearing aids - Magnatone Hearing Aid Corp.

MAGNATONE - Publisher's imprints - Magnatone Entertainment Group, Ltd.

MAGNATONES - Siding - GAF Corp.

MAGNATRIL - Antacids - Lannett Co. Inc.

MAGNATRON - Distributors–automotive - United States Auto Parts Inc.

MAGNATRON - Kites - Gayla Industries Inc.

MAGNATUBE - Tubes–plastic - Quick Cable Corp.

MAGNATUFF PLUS - Fabrics–polyester - Topvalue Fabrics, Inc.

MAGNAVET - Medical apparatus - Integra Health International

MAGNAVIEW - Electronic equipment ☆ - Daktronics Inc.

MAGNAVISION - Electronic equipment - Philips Consumer Electronics Co.

MAGNAVOX - Apparel and accessories - Philips Electronics North America Corp.

MAGNAVOX - Radios - Philips Consumer Electronics Co.

MAGNAWASH - Brushes - Wright-Bernet

MAGNAWAVE PERFECTION - Cooking utensils–glass - General Housewares Corp.

MAGNE-AID-MAGNETIC - Orthopedic products - Gustave Rick Rinz

MAGNE CHARGE - Electrical equipment - Delco Electronics Corp.

MAGNE-KLEEN - Cleaning preparations - Aquarium Products Inc.

MAGNE-MATIC - Toys–trains - Kadee Quality Products

MAGNE MUSIC - Electronic equipment - Telex Communications, Inc.

MAGNE-PATCH - Sealing compounds - Stewart-Hall Chemical Corp.

MAGNEAT MOMENTS - Magnets - D.C.T. Enterprises Inc.

MAGNEATOES - Toys - Mary Meyer Corp.

MAGNEBELL - Bells and chimes - Schulmerich Carillons Inc.

MAGNEBLOCKS - Electronics equipment - Rappaport Exhibits Inc.

MAGNECATCH - Hardware - National Manufacturing Co.

MAGNECHLOR - Health care products - Allergy Resources/Ecologic

MAGNECORD - Electronic equipment - Telex Communications, Inc.

MAGNECORDETTE - Electronic equipment - Telex Communications, Inc.

MAGNEFLECTOR - Mirrors ☆ - California Glass Bending Co.

MAGNEFLEX - Lighting equipment - Cable Electric Products

MAGNEFLEX - Wire–insulated - Southwire Co.

MAGNEFLEX MAGNETICALLY OPERATED BETWEEN-GLASS - Blinds–venetian - Hunter Douglas, Inc.

MAGNEHELIC - Pressure gauges - Dwyer Instruments, Inc.

MAGNEONS - Magnets - Ashley D. Clemens

MAGNEPLANAR - Audio equipment - Magnepan Inc.

MAGNEPLATE - Doors–metal - Rainbow Doors Inc.

MAG_NESIUM - Hair coloring preparations - Mastey De Paris

MAGNESTATIC - Mops - Royal Maid Association for the Blind Inc.

MAGNET - Lubricants ☆ - Ashland Oil, Inc.

MAGNET - Paints - Magnet Paint & Shellac Co. Inc.

MAGNET - Pet products - Berolina Imports

MAGNET - Recording label - MGM Inc.

MAGNET BABIES - Magnets - Kling Magnetics Inc.

MAGNET BACKEASE BELT - Medical apparatus - Alvin A. Bakst

MAGNET BONDER - Adhesives and sealants - Dymax Corp.

MAGNET BROOM - Brooms - Kaminstein Imports

MAGNET HIGH EFFICIENCY ALLERGEN PARTICLE FILTER - Filters–air - Columbus Industries, Inc.

MAGNET MARBLES - Toys–marbles - Imperial Toy Corp.

MAGNET-STOP - Hardware - Portaseal Inc.

MAGNET, THE - Sporting goods - Chesal Golf

MAGNET, THE - Vitamins and nutritional supplements ☆ - Ethical Nutrients

MAGNET VUE - Photo albums - Holson Co.

MAGNETAC - Artists' materials ☆ - Sakura of America

MAGNETAPE - Magnets - Craft World International Inc.

MAGNETEK - Television equipment ☆ - Television Equipment Associates

MAGNETIC - Floor coverings–carpet and rugs - Patcraft Mills Inc.

MAGNETIC - Perfumes - Frances Denney

MAGNETIC - Skin care products ☆ - Hess Hair Milk Laboratories Inc.

MAGNETIC ART - Toys - Educational Insights, Inc.

MAGNETIC ATTRACTIONS - Greeting cards ☆ - Miller Studio

MAGNETIC BOOK FRIDGE FRIEND, THE - Publisher's imprints - Laurie Moulton Flower

MAGNETIC CONSTRUCTION SITE - Toys - Smethport Specialty Co.

MAGNETIC DINOSAURS - Toys - Smethport Specialty Co.

MAGNETIC DOLL HOUSE - Toys - Smethport Specialty Co.

MAGNETIC DOZER - Toys - Smethport Specialty Co.

MAGNETIC FARM - Toys - Smethport Specialty Co.

MAGNETIC-FOAM - Brooms ☆ - Master Manufacturing Co., Inc.

MAGNETIC FRIDGE FIGURES - Magnets - Four Score Inc.

MAGNETIC GOODIES - Magnets - Magnetic Goodies

MAGNETIC HOMES - Picture frames - Gerrard Brothers Construction Co.

MAGNETIC KNIGHTS & DRAGONS - Toys - Smethport Specialty Co.

MAGNETIC MAGIC - Magnets - Mother Moose Enterprises

MAGNETIC MAILMAN - Toys - Tyco Toys

MAGNETIC MAP COLLECTION - Magnets - Magnetic Goodies

MAGNETIC MARVEL - Locks–padlocks - Weil Service Products Corp.

MAGNETIC MOSAIC - Toys - Smethport Specialty Co.

MAGNETIC PERSONALITIES - Notebooks and notepads - Recycled Paper Products, Inc.

MAGNETIC PLAYSET - Toys - Smethport Specialty Co.

MAGNETIC POETRY KIT - Games - Dave Kapell

MAGNETIC POUCH - Giftware ☆ - Great Graphic Originals

MAGNETIC RECUMBIKE - Exercising equipment - CSA, Inc.

MAGNETIC SHIELD V - Windows–storm ☆ - Nichols-Homeshield Inc.

MAGNETIC SLATES - Toys - Smethport Specialty Co.

MAGNETIC SPACE ADVENTURE - Toys - Smethport Specialty Co.

MAGNETIC SPELLWRITER - Learning aid - American Visual Aids

MAGNETIC SPIN-EMS - Games - Geospace Products Co. Inc.

MAGNETIC SPRINGS - Water–distilled - Magnetic Springs Water Co.

MAGNETIC TOWN - Toys - Smethport Specialty Co.

MAGNETIC TRAVEL BINGO - Games - Smethport Specialty Co.

MAGNETIC WONDER CLEAN - Aquariums–household - Midwest Tropical Inc.

MAGNETIC ZOO - Toys - Smethport Specialty Co.

MAGNETICALLY ALIGNED - Office supplies - MagnaPlan Corp.

MAGNETICS USA - Electronic equipment - Magnetics USA Inc.

MAGNETIGHT - Chemical preparations - Novagen, Inc.

MAGNETIP - Medical apparatus - Cabot Technology Corp.

MAGNETIQUE - Ophthalmic goods - Styl-Rite Optical Manufacturing Co., Inc.

MAGNETIQUE - Skin care products ☆ - Frances Denney

MAGNETITE - Windows–storm - Magnetite Corp.

MAGNETIX - Activity sets, puzzles - American Publishing Corp.

MAGNETIZER - Water purification systems - Meyer Furnace Co.

MAGNETO - Books–comic - Marvel Entertainment Group, Inc.

MAGNETO - Paints - A.I. Technology Inc.

MAGNETOOL I - Childrens' magnetic play sets - Anatex Enterprises Inc.

MAGNETRACKER - Weather tracking equipment - Gerald B. Mendes

MAGNETRACT - Letter-box plates - H.B. Ives

MAGNETRIP - Circuit breakers - General Electric Co.

MAGNETRIX - Games ☆ - Pacific Game Co.

MAGNETWORKS - Hobby kits - Educational Insights, Inc.

MAGNEVIEW - Electronic equipment - Daktronics Inc.

MAGNEX - Metals - Hal Sandy

MAGNEX SCIENTIFIC - Electrical equipment - NMR Magnex Scientific, Inc.

MAGNI - Beverages–alcohol - Valley Cheese, Wine & Food Co.

MAGNI - Electronics equipment - Magni Systems Inc.

MAGNI - Motorcycles - Commerce Overseas Corp.

MAGNI-FIQUE - Mirrors ☆ - Nino Originals

MAGNI-FOCUSER - Ophthalmic apparatus - Edroy Products Co.

MAGNI-SINO - Floor coverings–carpet and rugs - Couristan Inc.

MAGNI-TONE - Musical instrument accessories ☆ - Selmer Co. Inc.

MAGNI-VIEW 2000 - Electronic equipment - Dukane Corp.

MAGNI VIEWER - Lenses–magnifying - Bausch & Lomb Inc.

MAGNI-VUE - Binoculars - Century Labs Inc.

MAGNIBAR - Lenses–magnifying - Al Nyman and Son

MAGNIBOX - Optical machinery - H & A Optics

MAGNICARD - Lenses–magnifying - Al Nyman and Son

MAGNICATOR - Magnets - Red Devil Inc.

MAGNIF-EYES - Eyeglasses - Magnif-Eyes, Inc.

MAGNIFICATION IN DENTISTRY - Publisher's imprints - Dennis A. Shanelec

MAGNIFICENT - Floor coverings–carpet and rugs ☆ - World Carpets, Inc.

MAGNIFICENT - Hair care products - J. Strickland & Co.

MAGNIFICENT - Mattresses - King Koil Licensing Co., Inc.

MAGNIFICENT - Mirrors–optical - Zelco Industries, Inc.

MAGNIFICENT - Watches - Hampden Corp.

MAGNIFICENT 7 - Game machines - Universal Distributing of Nevada, Inc.

MAGNIFICENT 30'S - Floor coverings–carpet and rugs - Trend Carpet

MAGNIFICENT EXPRESSION - Floor coverings–carpet and rugs ☆ - Callaway Carpets

MAGNIFICENT MODIFIERS - Electronic equipment ☆ - Texas Instruments Inc.

MAGNIFICENT MOMENT - Floor coverings–carpet and rugs - Evans-Black Carpet Mills

☆ = Now out of production

MAGNIFICENT MOOD - Floor coverings–carpet and rugs - Lees Carpets
MAGNIFICENT OBSESSION - Christmas tree ornaments - Cracker Box Inc.
MAGNIFICENT SEVEN - Golfing equipment - Goldwin Golf USA, Inc.
MAGNIFICENT TOUCH - Floor coverings–carpet and rugs ☆ - Prestige Mills Inc.
MAGNIFICO - Cleaning preparations–household - Sunshine Quality Products, Inc.
MAGNIFICO - Wallpaper - Capital Carousel Inc.
MAGNIFICUS - Toys–stuffed - Dakin Inc.
MAGNIFIERS - Lenses–magnifying - Karlen Manufacturing, Inc.
MAGNIFILE - Office supplies - Methods Research Corp.
MAGNIFIQUE - Fabrics–broadcloth - Collins & Aikman Corp.
MAGNIFIQUE - Floor coverings–carpet and rugs ☆ - J.L. Benson Co.
MAGNIFIQUE - Lenses–magnifying - S.J. Miller Co.
MAGNIFIQUE - Luggage - United States Luggage Corp.
MAGNIFIQUE - Mirrors - Irving W. Rice & Co. Inc.
MAGNIFIQUE - Rings–jewelry - Artcarved Inc.
MAGNIFIQUE - Wallpaper - K.M.L. Industries
MAGNIFIQUE - Wallpaper ☆ - Capital Carousel Inc.
MAGNIFIQUE - Wallpaper ☆ - Jolie Papier
MAGNIFISCENTS - Incense - Shoyeido Corp.
MAGNIFOODS - Meat products - Burke Marketing Corp.
MAGNIFRY - Oils–edible - JP Foodservice, Inc.
MAGNIFYING - Eyeglasses - Vangurd Sunglasses Inc.
MAGNINIQUE - Women's hosiery - R.H. Macy & Co.
MAGNISCOPE - Toys - Educational Insights, Inc.
MAGNISET - Jewelry - Goodman & Co.
MAGNISLIDE - Drafting supplies - Vemco Corp.
MAGNITIME - Watches - Scott Resources
MAGNITUDE - Floor coverings–carpet and rugs - Cabin Crafts Carpets
MAGNITUDE - Office furniture–metal - Vogel Peterson Furniture Co.
MAGNITUDE - Video equipment - Compression Labs, Inc.
MAGNIVIEW - Projectors–photographic - Dukane Corp.
MAGNIVISION - Lenses–magnifying - Al Nyman and Son
MAGNO - Glass–leaded - Norwegian Silver Corp.
MAGNOLIA - Beverages - San Miguel USA Inc.
MAGNOLIA - Dinnerware–glass ☆ - Dansk International Designs, Ltd.
MAGNOLIA - Dolls ☆ - Effanbee Doll Corp.
MAGNOLIA - Floor coverings–carpet and rugs ☆ - Regal Rugs Inc.
MAGNOLIA - Flour, corn meal, pet food, etc. - Attala Co.
MAGNOLIA - Food products - Antique Mall & Crown
MAGNOLIA - Hair care products - Para Laboratories Inc.
MAGNOLIA - Jewelry - Magnolia Diamonds Inc.
MAGNOLIA - Meats–luncheon - Ramar International Corp.
MAGNOLIA - Milk–canned or powdered - Borden, Inc.
MAGNOLIA - Pencils - Reliance Pen & Pencil Corp.
MAGNOLIA - Perfumes - Tennessee Gold Inc.
MAGNOLIA - Rope - Wellington Leisure Products, Inc.
MAGNOLIA - Shutters–metal - Rushman Magnolia Shutters
MAGNOLIA - Toilet seats - Magnolia Products
MAGNOLIA - Vases - Crisa Corp.
MAGNOLIA - Window coverings - ESI
MAGNOLIA - Wines - Duplin Wine Cellars
MAGNOLIA CORDIALS - Candy ☆ - Maillard Corp.
MAGNOLIA COURT - Floor coverings–carpet and rugs ☆ - Hollytex Carpet Mills Inc.
MAGNOLIA HALL COLLECTION - Tables–metal - Service Merchandise Co., Inc.
MAGNOLIA LANE - Wallcovering - BDH Two, Inc.
MAGNOLIA PLACE - Furniture ☆ - Hammary Furniture Co. Inc.
MAGNOLIA RIDGE - Wines - Charles F. Shaw Vineyard & Winery
MAGNOLIA SOUND - Recording label - MCA Universal Studios
MAGNOLIAWOOD - Toilet seats ☆ - Magnolia Products
MAGNOLIAWOOD RUSTICS - Toilet seats ☆ - Magnolia Products
MAGNOPTX - Medical apparatus - OPTX 20/20
MAGNOR - Glass–leaded - Norwegian Silver Corp.
MAGNOTES - Paper–writing ☆ - Homax, Inc.
MAGNOX - Pharmaceutical preparations ☆ - JMI-Canton Pharmaceuticals
MAGNU-GLO - Lighting fixtures ☆ - Hubbell Lighting, Inc. (Lighting Div.)
MAGNU-GRO - Lighting fixtures ☆ - Hubbell Lighting, Inc. (Lighting Div.)
MAGNU V - Lighting fixtures - Hubbell Lighting, Inc. (Lighting Div.)
MAGNUCUBE - Lighting fixtures ☆ - Hubbell Lighting, Inc. (Lighting Div.)
MAGNUDISC - Lighting fixtures - Hubbell Lighting, Inc. (Lighting Div.)
MAGNUFORM - Lighting fixtures - Hubbell Lighting, Inc. (Lighting Div.)
MAGNULITER - Lighting fixtures - Hubbell Lighting, Inc. (Lighting Div.)
MAGNUM - Archery equipment ☆ - Bear Archery Inc.

MAGNUM - Audio equipment - MTX
MAGNUM - Automotive parts and accessories - Monroe Auto Equipment Co.
MAGNUM - Bags–trash - Rollpak Corp.
MAGNUM - Boats–motor - Magnum Marine Corp.
MAGNUM - Cigar boxes–wood - Consolidated Cigar Corp.
MAGNUM - Darts and dart games ☆ - Dart World Inc.
MAGNUM - Drills–electric - Milwaukee Electric Tool Corp.
MAGNUM - Drums–musical instruments ☆ - Fred Gretsch Enterprises
MAGNUM - Electrical equipment - Dexsil Corp.
MAGNUM - Engines - Kohler Co.
MAGNUM - Engines–marine - Brunswick Corp.
MAGNUM - Engines–motor vehicle - DaimlerChrysler
MAGNUM - Fire extinguishers - Ansul, Inc.
MAGNUM - Fishing lures - Normark Corp.
MAGNUM - Fishing tackle - Plano Molding Co.
MAGNUM - Flags - Plastics Research and Development Co.
MAGNUM - Floor coverings - John T. Beynon
MAGNUM - Floor coverings–tile - Porcelanite, Inc.
MAGNUM - Fly swatters - Farnam Cos. Inc.
MAGNUM - Footwear - Hi-Tec Sports USA Inc.
MAGNUM - Footwear–athletic - Head Sports USA
MAGNUM - Furniture - Cramer Inc.
MAGNUM - Glassware–household ☆ - National Housewares
MAGNUM - Goggles–safety - Outdoor Optics, Inc.
MAGNUM - Guns - Crosman Corp.
MAGNUM - Guns ☆ - Euroarms of America
MAGNUM - Health care products - Mueller Sports Medicine Inc.
MAGNUM - Health care products ☆ - Ingersoll & Associates
MAGNUM - Lighters - Park Lane Associates, Inc.
MAGNUM - Malt liquor - Miller Brewing Co.
MAGNUM - Motor vehicle parts and accessories - Federal Parts Corp.
MAGNUM - Motor vehicle parts and accessories - Seats Inc.
MAGNUM - Motor vehicles ☆ - Chrysler Corp. (Dodge Car Div.)
MAGNUM - Musical instrument accessories - Dean Markley Strings, Inc.
MAGNUM - Office supplies - McBee Loose Leaf Binders
MAGNUM - Pens ☆ - Alexander Manufacturing Co.
MAGNUM - Pens ☆ - Sanford Corp.
MAGNUM - Pet products - Marineland Aquarium Products
MAGNUM - Pharmaceutical preparations ☆ - Whitby Pharmaceuticals, Inc.
MAGNUM - Photo albums - Holson Co.
MAGNUM - Pipes–plastic - Bunzl Plastics, Inc.
MAGNUM - Printers–computer - QMS, Inc.
MAGNUM - Prophylactics - Carter-Wallace, Inc.
MAGNUM - Pumps - Jacuzzi Brothers
MAGNUM - Puzzles - Milton Bradley Co.
MAGNUM - Recreational vehicle dealers - Commonwealth Inc.
MAGNUM - Revolvers - Smith & Wesson Corp.
MAGNUM - Rug cleaning machines–commercial - Castex Industries Inc.
MAGNUM - Safes ☆ - Meilink Safe Co.
MAGNUM - Sealing compounds - Laporte Construction Chemicals North America, Inc.
MAGNUM - Skates–roller - Variflex, Inc.
MAGNUM - Soldering equipment - Hexacon Electric Co.
MAGNUM - Sporting goods - Ektelon
MAGNUM - Sporting goods - Figgie International Inc.
MAGNUM - Sporting goods - Wellington Leisure Products, Inc.
MAGNUM - Staplers ☆ - ITW Paslode
MAGNUM - Steel springs–railroad - Needlecraft Industries
MAGNUM - Tires - Magnum Tire Corp.
MAGNUM - Tools–machine - Cincinnati Machine
MAGNUM - Toys–airplanes - Hobby Shack Inc.
MAGNUM - Toys–models ☆ - Estes Industries
MAGNUM - Ventilation equipment - Magnum Products Corp.
MAGNUM - Veterinary pharmaceutical preparations - Nutra-Vet Research Corp.
MAGNUM - Water purification systems - Atlantic Ultraviolet Corp.
MAGNUM - Wheelchairs ☆ - Everest and Jennings International Ltd.
MAGNUM - Windows–storm - Marvin Windows and Doors
MAGNUM 7'S - Game machines - Sigma Game Inc.
MAGNUM 44 - Markers–felt-tip - Sanford Corp.
MAGNUM 440 X-2 - Toys - Tyco Toys
MAGNUM 1300 - Food containers - Calmar Inc.
MAGNUM 3000 - Computer hardware - MIPS Computer Systems Inc.
MAGNUM AY - Sporting goods - Wellington Leisure Products, Inc.
MAGNUM BOOGIE - Flags - Plastics Research and Development Co.
MAGNUM BUCK - Animal feeds - John A. Van Den Bosch Co.
MAGNUM BY DELTA - Containers - Delta Consolidated Industries, Inc.

☆ = Now out of production

MAGNUM CARTRIDGE - Office supplies - Magnum Laser Systems Inc.
MAGNUM CROSS - Bar fixtures—metal - Kallista Inc.
MAGNUM CUISINE - Housewares - May Department Stores Co.
MAGNUM DESERT EAGLE DESDE MCMLXIX - Coats - Magnum Research, Inc.
MAGNUM DYNALAB - Audio equipment - GNP Audio Video Inc.
MAGNUM ELITE - Goggles—safety - Outdoor Optics, Inc.
MAGNUM ENFORCER - Toys - Imperial Toy Corp.
MAGNUM FORCE - Air purification systems - Simco
MAGNUM FORCE - Fireworks - American Promotional Events, Inc.
MAGNUM FOURCE - Agricultural products - Amadas Industries, Inc.
MAGNUM FRIEZE - Floor coverings - Aladdin Mills, Inc.
MAGNUM GAMEFISH - Fishing tackle - Mason Tackle Co.
MAGNUM HOT 'N TOT - Fishing lures - Storm Manufacturing Co.
MAGNUM II - Exercising equipment - Badger Fitness Equipment
MAGNUM JET - Firearms, accessories, and parts - Beeman Precision Airguns
MAGNUM MAGNETICS - Magnets - Magnum Magnetics Corp.
MAGNUM MAILBOX - Mail boxes - Power Aisle Inc.
MAGNUM MILLS - Bedding—linen - Custom Designs
MAGNUM MOVER - Toys - Tonka Corp.
MAGNUM MYSTERIUM - Rings—jewelry - Cana-Nuptial
MAGNUM OF CALIFORNIA - Handbags - Magnum Fashions Inc.
MAGNUM ONE - Health care products - Pierson Co.
MAGNUM OPUS - Furniture ☆ - Bassick Casters
MAGNUM PLUS - Ice - Strike Master Inc.
MAGNUM PLUSH - Seat covers - Saddleman, Inc.
MAGNUM POLYPROPYLENE BALER TWINE - Twine - Bridon Cordage LLC
MAGNUM PREDATOR - Boats—pontoons - Lakes Manufacturing Inc.
MAGNUM PRO - Dryers—hair - Windmere Corp.
MAGNUM SERIES - Stereos - Recoton Corp.
MAGNUM SPRAYDOME - Shower stalls—metal - Kallista Inc.
MAGNUM SYSTEMS - Roofing materials and waterproof coatings - Magnum Waterproofing Systems Inc.
MAGNUM TADPOLLY - Sporting goods - James Heddon's Sons
MAGNUM TILT TURN - Windows—storm - Marvin Windows and Doors
MAGNUM TOUR - Golfing equipment - Rawlings Golf
MAGNUMZOO - Tool boxes - Waterloo Industries Inc.
MAGNUPAR - Lighting fixtures ☆ - Hubbell Lighting, Inc. (Lighting Div.)
MAGNUS - Frames—picture - Magnus Molding Inc.
MAGNUS - Lubricants - Phillips 66 Propane Co.
MAGNUS - Office furniture - Inwood Office Furniture
MAGNUS - Toys—musical - Magnus Organ Co.
MAGNUS - Wines ☆ - Ventana Vineyards Winery Inc.
MAGNUS ROBOT FIGHTER - Books—comic ☆ - Western Publishing Co., Inc.
MAGNUSHIELD - Lighting fixtures - Hubbell Lighting, Inc. (Lighting Div.)
MAGNUSOFTWARE - Computer software - Magnus Software Corp.
MAGNUSOL - Cleaning preparations - Man-Gill Chemical Co.
MAGNUSON - Toys—models - Magnuson Models Inc.
MAGNUSON - Toys—models - Wm. K. Walthers Inc.
MAGNUSON VEHICLES - Motor vehicles ☆ - Wm. K. Walthers Inc.
MAGNUSQUARE - Lighting fixtures - Hubbell Lighting, Inc. (Lighting Div.)
MAGNUSSON DOWNTOWN - Furniture - Westinghouse Electric Corp.
MAGNUSSON MIDTOWN - Furniture - Westinghouse Electric Corp.
MAGNUSSON UPTOWN - Furniture - Westinghouse Electric Corp.
MAGNUTS - Greeting cards - C.T. Baylock
MAGOLO - Antacids - Dr. Peter Fahrney & Sons Co.
MAGONATE - Pharmaceutical preparations - Fleming & Co.
MAGPHEMMS - Pharmaceutical preparations ☆ - C.O. Truxton Inc.
MAGPIES GOURMET PIZZA - Restaurants—pizzerias - Mark D. Grossman
MAGPIE'S HANGUP - Jewelry boxes - Kathleen R. Mattox
MAGRITE - Puzzles - Importoys
MAGRITE - Wallcovering - Walltalkers, Inc.
MAGRO - Furniture - Magro, Inc.
MAGSAL - Pharmaceutical preparations - U.S. Pharmaceutical Corp.
MAGSHIELD - Chemical preparations - Martin Marietta Magnesia Specialties, Inc.
MAGSTAR - Magnets - Magstar Technologies Corp.
MAGTONE - Audio and video components - Lynns Corp. of America
MAGTRAC - Bathroom fixtures - Showerlux USA
MAGTRONIC - Compasses—gyroscopic - E.S. Ritchie & Sons Inc.
MAGUIRE - Jewelry - John Maguire & Sons
MAGUS - Spices and extracts - Magus Co.
MAGVIEW - Magnetic recording equipment - Geneva Group of Cos. Inc.
M.A.H. - Pharmaceutical - IDE-Interstate Inc.
MAH CHENA - Food products - Mah Chena Corp.
MAH-DI - Skin care products - Goubaud

MAH-LOWE - Games ☆ - Milton Bradley Co.
MAH-ZELL ALUMINAID - Medical apparatus - Mah-Zell Aluminaid Co.
MAHA - Skis - Maharajah Water Ski Inc.
MAHANI - Beverages—alcohol - Western International Imports Inc.
MAHARAJA - Floor coverings - American Floor Products Co. Inc.
MAHARAJA - Games - Avalon Hill Game Co.
MAHARAJAH - Cigars ☆ - General Cigar Co., Inc.
MAHARAM - House furnishings - Anthony House Inc.
MAHARANEE MOOD - Apparel and accessories - Mondi of America
MAHARANI - Food products - Connell Co.
MAHARISHI AYURVEDA - Health care products - Maharishi Ayurveda Products International Inc.
MAHATMA - Rice - Riviana Foods Inc.
MAHATMA - Sandals - Vans, Inc.
MAHATMA BROWN RICE - Rice - Riviana Foods Inc.
MAHATMA INSTANT RICE - Rice - Riviana Foods Inc.
MAHATMA RICE MIXES - Rice - Riviana Foods Inc.
MAHDEEN - Hair care products - Mahdeen Laboratory
MAHDI - Recording label - York's Productions
MAHINDRA - Farm machinery - Mahindra USA, Inc.
MAHITAS - Food products - Zuzu, Inc.
MAHOGANY - Recording label - Dagene/Cabletown Corp.
MAHOGANY - Wallpaper ☆ - Linden Street Gallery
MAHOGANY BARBECUE - Barbecue sauce - Ashman Distributing Co.
MAHOGANY COAST - Agricultural products - G.W. Kent, Inc.
MAHOGANY COLLECTION, THE - Furniture - Thomasville Furniture Industries Inc.
MAHOGANY ENTERTAINMENT - Recording label - State of Fresh American Entertainment
MAHOGANY HALL - Apparel and accessories - GCI Inc. (Great Chefs Television/Publishing Div.)
MAHOGANY KING - Fishing tackle - U.S. Line Co.
MAHON-MADE - Dolls - Mahon Made
MAHOOT - Fabrics - Dan River Inc.
MAH'S - Food products - Mah Chena Corp.
MAHVA-F - Vitamins and nutritional supplements ☆ - Freeman Industries LLC
MAI - Jewelry - Maico Industries Inc.
MAI - Recording label - Word, Inc.
MAI BOCK - Beverages—malt - Sprecher Brewing Co. Inc.
MAI KANAN - Apparel—women's - Mai Kanan Fashions
MAI LING - Dolls - Russ Berrie and Co., Inc.
MAI TAI - Boats - Glen-L Marine Designs
MAI TAI - Furniture ☆ - Stanley Furniture Co. Inc.
MAI TAI - Sporting goods - Karlen Manufacturing, Inc.
MAI WAI - Mushrooms - Tree of Life, Inc.
MAIBOCK - Beverages—malt - Merchant du Vin Corp.
MAICO - Hearing aids - Maico Hearing Instruments Inc.
MAID-BRITE - Cleaning preparations ☆ - Dacar Chemical Co.
MAID-EASY - Cleaning preparations—household ☆ - ICI Americas Inc.
MAID-IN-A-BUCKET - Cleaning preparations - Trenton Janitorial Supply Co., Inc.
MAID MARIAN - Dolls ☆ - Effanbee Doll Corp.
MAID-O'-METAL - Hobby kits - St. Louis Crafts Inc.
MAID-O'-MIST - Ventilation equipment - Maid-o-Mist
MAID OF HONOR - Cleaning preparations - National Interchem Corp.
MAID-RITE - Housewares - Meijer, Inc.
MAID-RITE - Meat products—beef - Maid-Rite Steak Co. Inc.
MAID-RITE - Washboards - Columbus Washboard Co.
MAIDEN AMERICA - Curtains—shower - Maiden America, Inc.
MAIDEN AMERICA - Footwear - Wolverine World Wide, Inc.
MAIDEN CURLYCROWN - Dolls ☆ - Mattel, Inc.
MAIDEN FAIRHAIR - Dolls ☆ - Mattel, Inc.
MAIDEN LANE - Chocolate candy - Hoffman Candy Co.
MAIDEN LANE - Hair care products - Willat Co.
MAIDEN ROCK - Wallpaper - Bock Designs Inc.
MAIDENETTE - Brassieres (Bras) - Maidenform Inc.
MAIDENFORM - Underwear and nightwear - Maidenform Inc.
MAIDEN'S JOURNEY - Dolls - Wyse Womyn Creations, Inc.
MAIDSTONE - Beverages—alcohol - Margolis Wines & Spirits
MAIDTUFF - Containers - Maidware Products, Inc.
MAIDWELL - Apparel and accessories - Glamorise Foundations Inc.
MAIER-HANCOCK - Tape recorders - Compco Photographic/Goldberg Bros.
MAIERS - Breads - Maier's Sunbeam Bakery
MAIL - Stationery ☆ - Mead Corp.
MAIL-A-MEADOW - Paper products - Wildseed Farms

☆ = Now out of production

MAIL-A-TAPE - Electronic equipment - Benjamin Electroproducts Inc. (Robins Div.)
MAIL-A-TOY - Greeting cards ☆ - Smethport Specialty Co.
MAIL BOX - Clocks - General Time Corp. (Westclox/Seth Thomas Div.)
MAIL CALL - Novelty items ☆ - Sell-O Manufacturing Inc.
MAIL CALL - Stationery ☆ - T.V. Allen Co.
MAIL CENTER - Computer software ☆ - Videx, Inc.
MAIL CENTER 2000 - Mailing machines - Pitney Bowes Inc.
MAIL-LITE - Packaging–blisterwrap - Avery Dennison Corp.
MAIL MASTER - Mail boxes - Cutler Manufacturing Corp.
MAIL-N-SAVE - Photofinishing laboratories - Alves Photofinishing Store
MAIL-O-GRAMS - Envelopes - Whitehall Inc.
MAIL-O-PAKE - Envelopes - Quality Park Products Co.
MAIL ON THE RUN! - Computer software - River Run Software Group Inc.
MAIL ORDER GOURMET - Office supplies - Metro Files Inc. (Rolodex Corp.)
MAIL ORDER MONSTERS - Computer software ☆ - Electronic Arts Inc.
MAIL POUCH - Chewing tobacco - American Maize-Products Co.
MAIL POUCH - Envelopes - Western States Envelope Co.
MAIL POUCH - Tobacco–chewing or smoking - Swisher International, Inc.
MAIL POUCH, THE - Apparel and accessories - Variegated Productions Inc.
MAIL RIGHT - Computer software - Hunter Systems
MAIL ROOM - Work benches - Metal Components Inc. (Flexible Furniture Div.)
MAIL SAFE II - Mailboxes - Babco
MAIL SAFETY - Bicycles - Rideable Bicycle Replicas Inc.
MAIL TIME! - Signals–traffic - J.H. Wonderworks
MAIL-VANE - Novelty items - Ansan Industries Ltd.
MAIL WATCH - Mail box attachment - Robilco, Inc.
MAIL-WELL - Envelopes - Mail-Well Envelope
MAILABLE MAGNETS - Postcards - Sangray Corp.
MAILAIRE - Packaging–paper - Century Products, Inc.
MAILBOX - Candy - Fleer Corp.
MAILBOX COVERALLS - Hobby kits - H.P. & H.F. Hunt Co.
MAILBOX HUGGIE - Flower boxes - H & D Designs, Inc.
MAILBOX JAVA - Coffee - Direct Marketing Development Corp.
MAILBOX, THE - Educational materials - Education Center, Inc.
MAILBUS - Computer software - Digital Equipment Corp.
MAILCOMMITTEEMAND - Computer software - Command Software Systems, Inc.
MAILFLOW SYSTEMS - Cabinets–metal - Kwik-File Inc.
MAILGATE - Computer software - Graphnet, Inc.
MAILGUARD - Mail boxes - Leigh
MAILING TUBES - Tubes–plastic - VisiPak
MAILITE - Siding–insulating ☆ - Aluminum Co. of America
MAILLARDS - Candy - Maillard Corp.
MAIL*LINK - Electronic mail software - Starnine Technologies, Inc.
MAILMAN 32, THE - T-shirts–children's - Malone Enterprises Inc.
MAILMARK - Business cards - Mailmark Enterprises, LLC
MAILMASTER - Boxes - Mason Box Co. Inc.
MAILMASTER - Gloves - Dakota Corp.
MAILMATIC - Labeling machinery ☆ - Standard Duplicating Machines Corp.
MAILNOTIFY! - Computer software - EX Machina, Inc.
MAILPAQ - Envelopes - Innotech Flexpad Inc.
MAILROOM - Computer software - Oblique Filing Systems
MAILSOUTH - Advertising agencies - Mailsouth, Inc.
MAIMERI - Paints ☆ - Charvoz
MAIN ATTRACTION - Cleaner, deodorizer - Contact Industries Inc.
MAIN ATTRACTION - Floor coverings–carpet and rugs ☆ - Zenith Carpets
MAIN BATTLE TANK - Games - Avalon Hill Game Co.
MAIN CHANCE - Floor coverings–carpet and rugs ☆ - Masland Corp.
MAIN COURSE - Wallpaper ☆ - Gencorp Inc.
MAIN COURSE, THE - Wallcovering - Fashon Wallcoverings
MAIN EVENT - Floor coverings–carpet and rugs - Fieldturf & Carpet Inc.
MAIN EVENT - Floor coverings–carpet and rugs - Kelly Group Inc.
MAIN EVENT - Floor coverings–carpet and rugs ☆ - Calladium & Marglen
MAIN EVENT - Floor coverings–carpet and rugs ☆ - Regal Rugs Inc.
MAIN GATE - Attache cases - Liberty Leather Products Co., Inc.
MAIN IDEA GOLD RUSH - Computer software - Gamco Industries Inc.
MAIN IDEA MAZE - Computer software - Southwest Edpsych Services Inc.
MAIN LINE - Paints ☆ - Decorative Coverings Inc.
MAIN LINE - Toys–trains - Life-Like Products Inc.
MAIN MEALS - Entrees - American Home Food Products Inc.
MAIN PLATE - Cookware, servingware - Corning Inc.
MAIN ST. - File folders - Angler's Roslyn Group Ltd.
MAIN ST. - Luggage - Tumi Luggage, Inc.
MAIN STREET - Bicycles - Huffy Corp.
MAIN STREET - Cigarettes - Star Tobacco Corp.

MAIN STREET - Cooking equipment–household ☆ - Albert E. Price, Inc.
MAIN STREET - Food products - Conagra, Inc.
MAIN STREET - Games ☆ - Milton Bradley Co.
MAIN STREET - Lubricants - Lubricating Specialties Co.
MAIN STREET - Toys - Fisher-Price, Inc.
MAIN STREET MUFFINS - Bakery products - Main Street Muffins Inc.
MAIN STREET USA - Garden equipment - Garden Pals, Inc.
MAIN STREET U.S.A. - Jewelry - Darlene Jewelry Manufacturing Co., Inc.
MAIN3D - Computer peripheral equipment - Schlumberger Technology Corp.
MAINCARE SUPER LARGE - Health care products - Inbrand Corp.
MAINCOATS - Men's apparel - Interco Inc.
MAINCOR - Computer software - Client/Server Technologies, Inc.
MAINE - Slippers ☆ - Acorn
MAINE AIRES - Footwear - MSF Corp.
MAINE AIRES - Shoes ☆ - Penobscot Shoe Co.
MAINE ATTRACTION - Sandwiches–prepackaged - Southland Corp.
MAINE BAY - Apparel and accessories - Stanley Blacker Inc.
MAINE BEAUTY - Food products ☆ - Agway Country Foods Inc.
MAINE CLASSICS - Footwear - MacDonald Manufacturing Co.
MAINE COAST - Potato chips - State Line Potato Chip Co.
MAINE COAST - Seafood products–canned or cured - Coastal Fisheries Inc.
MAINE COURSE - Seafood - R & R Seafood Processing
MAINE GOLD - Syrup - Bald Mountain Maple
MAINE GUIDE - Apparel and accessories - Congress Sportswear Co. Inc.
MAINE GUIDE - Catheters - Medtronic, Inc.
MAINE GUIDE - Sporting goods - L.L. Bean Inc.
MAINE HOOTY OWL - Bells - North Country Wind Bells Inc.
MAINE IAC - Apparel–athletic - Mitchell Danielson
MAINE KITCHEN - Potato chips - Associated Grocers of Maine Inc.
MAINE LIFESTYLES - Furniture ☆ - Moosehead Manufacturing Co.
MAINE LINE - Handsewn footwear - J.L. Coombs & Co. Inc.
MAINE LOUNGER, THE - Chairs–folding - Byer of Maine
MAINE MADE - Footwear - Wolverine World Wide, Inc.
MAINE MAID - Food products ☆ - One Pie Canning Co.
MAINE MAID - Shrimp–fresh or frozen - Stinson Seafood Co.
MAINE MAYO - Mayonnaise - Hagen House
MAINE POINT - Blankets - Marco Polo, Inc.
MAINE SCARE CAT - Bells - North Country Wind Bells Inc.
MAINE SOURCE, THE - Water–bottled or canned - Poland Spring Bottling Co.
MAINE STREET - Furniture - Moosehead Manufacturing Co.
MAINE STREET - Slippers ☆ - Acorn
MAINE TERRAIN - Slippers - Acorn
MAINE WOODS - Footwear - Maine Woods Inc.
MAINEBRITE - Paper–writing - Champion International Corp.
MAINFRAME - Display cases–plastic - Synectics Corp.
MAINFRAME - Music stands - Evets Corp.
MAINFRAMES - Electric lighting equipment - City Theatrical Inc.
MAINFURL - Sporting goods - Blue Water Marine Inc.
MAINGAB - Fabrics - Greenwood Mills Inc.
MAINGLAZE - Fabrics - Greenwood Mills Inc.
MAINLAND CHINA ARTGOODS - Glassware–household ☆ - Queen Lace Co.
MAINLAND EXPRESS - Food products - Lehmann Farms, Inc.
MAINLANDER - Luggage ☆ - Hartmann Luggage Co.
MAINLIGHTER - Lamps - General Electric Co.
MAINLINE - Cables - Distex Corp.
MAINLINE - Floor coverings–carpet and rugs - Patcraft Mills Inc.
MAINLINE - Sporting goods ☆ - Outdoor Technologies Group
MAINLINE EXPRESS - Toys–trains ☆ - Life-Like Products Inc.
MAINLINER - Apparel and accessories ☆ - Campus Sportswear Co.
MAINLINER - Desks - Art Metal-U.S. Corp.
MAINLINER - Hoses - HBD Industries, Inc.
MAINLY MULTIPLES - Paper - Mainly Multiples Inc.
MAINSAIL - Apparel–men's - Alps Sportswear Manufacturing Co.
MAINSAIL - Bathing suits - Catalina
MAINSAIL - Bathtubs–enameled - Kohler Co.
MAINSAIL - Fabrics - Greenwood Mills Inc.
MAINSAIL II - Fabrics–poplin - Greenwood Mills Inc.
MAINSHIP - Boats–motor - Silverton Marine Corp.
MAINSOFT - Computer software - Mainsoft Corp.
MAINSQUEEZE - Soap - Highside Chemicals Inc.
MAINSTAY - Beverages–alcohol - Carradale Import Co.
MAINSTAY - Dog food - Ralston Purina Co.
MAINSTAYS - Shoe trees - Wal-Mart Stores Inc.
MAINSTONE PUBLICATIONS - Posters - Graphic Arts Unltd. Inc.
MAINSTREAM - Adhesives and sealants - Buckeye International, Inc.
MAINSTREAM - Bathing suits - A and H Sportswear Co., Inc.

☆ = Now out of production

MAINSTREAM - Boots - Weinbrenner Shoe Co. Inc.
MAINSTREAM - Fabrics - Charter Fabrics Inc.
MAINSTREAM - Fish–fresh or frozen - Stavis Seafoods Inc.
MAINSTREAM - Housewares - Exclusive Products Co.
MAINSTREAM - Recording label - Mainstream Records Inc.
MAINSTREAM - Wallpaper - Chapters Wallcoverings
MAINSTREET - Cheese - Jack Greenberg Inc.
MAINSTREET - Floor coverings–carpet and rugs ☆ - J and J Industries Inc.
MAINSTREET - Siding–insulating - Certainteed Corp. (Roofing Products Group)
MAINSTREET COLLECTION - Figurines - Seasonal Specialties Electrics, Inc.
MAINSTREETERS - Shoes ☆ - Penobscot Shoe Co.
MAINTAIN - Garden equipment ☆ - Pace International Corp.
MAINTAIN - Pharmaceutical preparations - London International U.S. Holdings
MAINTAIN - Pharmaceutical preparations - Schmid Laboratories
MAINTAIN CHUNKS - Pet food - American Nutrition, Inc.
MAINTAIN HERBAL HOLDING SPRAY - Hair spray - NVO Corp.
MAINTAIN NIBBLES - Pet food - American Nutrition, Inc.
MAINTAINER - Containers–insulated - Par Aide Products Co.
MAINTAINER, THE - Battery chargers - Solar Electric Engineering Inc.
MAINTAINIT - Computer software - Datastream Systems Inc.
MAINTAL - Jams and jellies ☆ - Liberty Richter Inc.
MAINTEK - Computer peripheral equipment - Harry L. Garrett
MAINTENANCE MANUAL FOR YOUR BODY, THE - Publisher's imprints - Health Journal Associates
MAINTENANCE NOTEBOOK, THE - Computer software - Westland Corp.
MAINTENANCE PRO - Banks–commercial - Sherwin-Williams Automotive Finishes Corp.
MAINTENANCE SAVER - Batteries - East Penn Manufacturing Co., Inc.
MAINTENANCE SYSTEM BY TMW, THE - Computer software - TMW Systems Solutions, Inc.
MAINTENON - Floor coverings - Parquet de France Inc.
MAINTENON - Glassware–household - Durand International
MAINTRACER - Computer software - J B Systems, Inc.
MAINTZ - Paints - WCC Industries Inc.
MAINWIN - Computer software - Mainsoft Corp.
MAINZ OIL - Lubricants - R.H. Foster, Inc.
MAISEL - Beverages–malt - Wolfgang Morandell Import
MAISEL WEISSE - Beverages–malt - Maisel Weisse
MAISLIN - Toys–automobiles - Toy Truck Lines, Inc.
MAISON - Floor coverings ☆ - Azrock Commercial Flooring
MAISON - Furniture - Homecrest Industries Inc.
MAISON - Furniture - Tropitone Furniture Co. Inc.
MAISON - Furniture ☆ - Bassett Furniture Industries, Inc.
MAISON - Glassware–household ☆ - National Housewares
MAISON - Lamps - Herman Kashins
MAISON BLANC - Wines - Safeway Stores Inc.
MAISON BLUE - Kitchenware–china - H. Wittur & Co.
MAISON D'ALIOTTA - Cosmetics - Maison D'aliotta, Inc.
MAISON DE SOUL - Recording label - Flat Town Music Co.
MAISON DE VIE - Toiletries - Maison de Vie, Inc.
MAISON DES GRANDS CRUS - Wines - House of Burgundy Inc.
MAISON DEUTZ - Wines - Wine World Inc.
MAISON D'ORLEANS - Floor coverings - Mannington Resilient Floors
MAISON FAIRE - Glassware–household ☆ - Anchor Hocking Glass, Inc.
MAISON FERME - Furniture ☆ - Bassett Furniture Industries, Inc.
MAISON FLEECE - Fabrics - Dyersburg Fabrics Inc.
MAISON JOMERE - Wines - Maison Jomere Ltd.
MAISON JOSEPH DROUHIN - Wines - Dreyfus Ashby Inc.
MAISON LA FITTE - Floor coverings - Mannington Resilient Floors
MAISON L'AIGLON - Wines - L'aiglon Wine and Spirits Import Co., Inc.
MAISON LOUIS JADOT - Wines - Kobrand Corp.
MAISON MAGIQUE - Women's apparel - Creative Imports
MAISON PROSPER MAUFOUX - Wines - House of Burgundy Inc.
MAISON PROVENCAL - Wallpaper - Greeff Fabrics Inc.
MAISON ROCHER - Clocks - Roxhall Time Corp.
MAISON-ROYAL - Pepper - Food Trading Corp. of America
MAISON THOMAS-BASSOT - Wines - Parliament Import Co.
MAISON THORIN - Wines ☆ - Buena Vista Winery, Inc.
MAISONAIX - Scarves, neckwear ☆ - Jewel Case Inc.
MAISONETTE II - Furniture - Hammary Furniture Co. Inc.
MAISTO - Toys–models - Small World Toys
MAISY & DAISY - Dolls - Georgia-Pacific Corp.
MAITAKE D-FRACTION - Pharmaceutical preparations - Maitake Products, Inc.
MAITLAND - Computer software - Maitland
MAITLAND SMITH - House furnishings ☆ - Masco Corp.

MAITRE CHEF - Cookware - Master Cookware Corp.
MAITRE CONFISEUR - Chocolate candy - Perugina Chocolate & Confections Inc.
MAITRE D' - Candy - Thos. D. Richardson Co.
MAITRE D' - Cheese - Advantage International Food Corp.
MAITRE D II - Floor coverings–carpet and rugs ☆ - Playfield International Inc.
MAITRE D'ESTOURNEL - Wines - Kobrand Corp.
MAITRE JACQUES - Vinegars, olive oil, herbs, etc. - International Marketing Services Inc.
MAITRE PROVI - Food products - Bel Canto Fancy Foods Ltd.
MAITRE PROVI - Onions - Gourmet America
MAITRE PROVI - Pickles - Bri-AL, Inc.
MAITRE'D - Food products - Tree of Life, Inc.
MAIZE - Christmas tree ornaments - Cracker Box Inc.
MAIZE TO POP - Popcorn - Possum Trot Vineyards
MAIZE-WARE - Giftware - Terrace Ceramics Inc.
MAIZIE'S FRESH & NATURAL - Popcorn - Maizie's Gourmet Popcorn
MAJAY - Trimmings–fabric ☆ - Novtex Corp.
MAJCO - Fireplaces - Majestic Co.
MAJER - Suits–men's - Majer Co./Diversified
MAJESCO - Cutlery - Majestic Silver Co.
MAJESTAN - Floor coverings–carpet and rugs - Couristan Inc.
MAJESTIC - Apparel–athletic - Majestic Athletic Wear, Ltd.
MAJESTIC - Artists' materials - Glenview Products Inc.
MAJESTIC - Artists' materials ☆ - Robert Simmons Inc.
MAJESTIC - Automotive parts and accessories - Lancaster Colony Automotive Group
MAJESTIC - Bedding–linen - Dan River Inc.
MAJESTIC - Blinds–venetian ☆ - Hunter Douglas, Inc.
MAJESTIC - Boats–motor ☆ - Regal Marine Industries Inc.
MAJESTIC - Cabinets - Aristokraft, Inc.
MAJESTIC - Canned fruit - Independent Food Processors Corp.
MAJESTIC - Coffee - Robert G. Gard
MAJESTIC - Cutlery - Majestic Silver Co.
MAJESTIC - Doughnuts–mixes - Dawn Food Products Inc.
MAJESTIC - Dust cloths - Majestic Industries Inc.
MAJESTIC - Fireplaces - Majestic Co.
MAJESTIC - Floor coverings - Congoleum Corp.
MAJESTIC - Floor coverings–carpet and rugs - Cabin Crafts Carpets
MAJESTIC - Floor coverings–carpet and rugs ☆ - Len Dal Carpets
MAJESTIC - Floor coverings–carpet and rugs ☆ - Robertex Associates Inc.
MAJESTIC - Floor coverings–carpet and rugs ☆ - Royalweve Carpet Mills
MAJESTIC - Games - Carrom Co.
MAJESTIC - Garden equipment - Cobraco Manufacturing, Inc.
MAJESTIC - Giftware - World of Porcelain & Glassware
MAJESTIC - Glassware–household - Crystal Clear Importing Co. Inc.
MAJESTIC - Greeting cards - Masterpiece Studios Inc.
MAJESTIC - Hair care products ☆ - Astra International Corp.
MAJESTIC - Hams - Bob Ostrow Co.
MAJESTIC - Hardware and tools - Atlas Group
MAJESTIC - Leather tanning and finishing - Snowshoe Laboratories
MAJESTIC - Lighting fixtures ☆ - Thomas Industries Inc.
MAJESTIC - Musical instruments - C. Bruno & Son Inc.
MAJESTIC - Paints - Frazee Paint
MAJESTIC - Paper clips - Majestic Staple Corp.
MAJESTIC - Paper–construction - Sax Arts & Crafts
MAJESTIC - Pet products - Rolf C. Hagen (USA) Corp.
MAJESTIC - Photo albums - Camille Co. Inc.
MAJESTIC - Puzzles ☆ - Warren Industries Inc.
MAJESTIC - Sewing machines–household - VWS Inc.
MAJESTIC - Shingles - U.S. Intec, Inc.
MAJESTIC - Skin care products - Majestic Drug Co., Inc.
MAJESTIC - Telephones - Haim Dweck
MAJESTIC - Thread - Imperial Threads Inc.
MAJESTIC - Toys - Tonka Corp.
MAJESTIC - Vacuum cleaners and accessories - Health-Mor Inc.
MAJESTIC - Wallpaper - Exeter Wallcoverings
MAJESTIC - Watches ☆ - Longines-Wittnauer Watch Co.
MAJESTIC - Wigs ☆ - Paula Young
MAJESTIC - Yarn ☆ - Joseph Galler Inc.
MAJESTIC BUTTERFLY - Pet products - Hill Top Enterprises
MAJESTIC CHARM - Floor coverings–carpet and rugs ☆ - Callaway Carpets
MAJESTIC CONTROL - Recording label - DNA International Inc.
MAJESTIC GEYSER - Fireworks - B.J. Alan Co. Inc.
MAJESTIC LIONS - Games - Bally Gaming International, Inc.
MAJESTIC MAGENTA - Kites ☆ - Hi-Flier Manufacturing Co.

☆ = Now out of production

MAJESTIC MESSAGE - Mats - Majestic Mat Co.

MAJESTIC ONYX - Bathtubs–enameled ☆ - Pearl Baths Inc.

MAJESTIC PENN STATE - Office supplies - Majestic Penn State Inc.

MAJESTIC ROYALE - Rum - Majestic Distilling Co.

MAJESTIC SANDS - Christmas tree ornaments - Majestic Sands Co.

MAJESTIC SHOWER - Shower stalls–plastic - Kallista Inc.

MAJESTIC SILK - Wallpaper ☆ - Gilford Corp.

MAJESTIC SLATE - Floor coverings - National Floor Products Co., Inc.

MAJESTIC TOUCH - Floor coverings–carpet and rugs - Evans-Black Carpet Mills

MAJESTIC VALLEY - Brandy - Majestic Distilling Co.

MAJESTIC VELVET - Floor coverings–carpet and rugs - Alexander Smith Carpets

MAJESTIC VIEW - Doors - ODL, Inc.

MAJESTIGRID - Mats - U.S. Mat & Rubber Co. Inc.

MAJESTIK COLOR SERIES - Photocopy machines - Xerox Corp.

MAJESTIQUE - Candy - World's Finest Chocolate, Inc.

MAJESTITHERM - Fireplaces ☆ - Majestic Co.

MAJESTRON-MAJESTIME - Watches - Majesti Watch Co. Inc.

MAJESTY - Balls - Lisco, Inc.

MAJESTY - Brushes - Corona Brushes Inc.

MAJESTY - Floor coverings ☆ - Congoleum Corp.

MAJESTY - Floor coverings–carpet and rugs - Galaxy Carpet Mills Inc.

MAJESTY - Floor coverings–carpet and rugs - Johnson's Carpets Inc.

MAJESTY - Floor coverings–carpet and rugs - Trans-Ocean Import Co. Inc.

MAJESTY - Floor coverings–carpet and rugs ☆ - Regal Rugs Inc.

MAJESTY - Furniture - National/Mt. Airy Furniture

MAJESTY - Glassware–household - Libbey Glass Inc.

MAJESTY - Glassware–household ☆ - WMF/USA

MAJESTY - Meat products–pork - Majesty Inc.

MAJESTY - Trees - Roger L. Ashton & Associates

MAJESTY COLLECTION - Dinnerware–glass - Sango Co. Ltd. (Sango USA Div.)

MAJESTY SPORTS - Apparel and accessories - Majestic Athletic Wear, Ltd.

MAJI - Nail care products - Maji Nail Inc.

MAJI-GLOW - Automobile burglar-alarm accessory ☆ - Auto Alarm Supply Corp.

MAJI-NAIL - Nail care products - Maji Nail Inc.

MAJIAJUN - Vitamins and nutritional supplements - S & R Tech-Trade Corp.

MAJIBLOND - Hair coloring preparations - Cosmair Inc.

MAJIC CARPETY - Boats–pontoons ☆ - Lakes Manufacturing Inc.

MAJIC CIRCLES - Cooking equipment–household - Jacksonville Manufacturing

MAJIC DIAMOND HARD - Epoxy - Mac-O-Lac Paints Inc.

MAJIC DRAIN - Plumbing fixtures–plastic - J-Trap Inc.

MAJIC ENAMELS - Enamels - Mac-O-Lac Paints Inc.

MAJIC HEAT CIRCULATOR - Fireplaces ☆ - Majestic Co.

MAJIC LTX EPOXYS - Epoxy - Mac-O-Lac Paints Inc.

MAJIC POLYURATHANES - Adhesives and sealants - Mac-O-Lac Paints Inc.

MAJIC PRIMERS - Paints - Mac-O-Lac Paints Inc.

MAJIC STAINS - Varnishes - Mac-O-Lac Paints Inc.

MAJICSOFT - Computer software - Majicsoft, Inc.

MAJIGLOSS - Hair care products - Cosmair Inc.

MAJII - Recording label - Cheetah Records Inc.

MAJIK - Toy - Chilton-Globe, Inc.

MAJIK MARKETS - Food products - Munford Inc.

MAJIREL - Hair coloring preparations - Cosmair Inc.

MAJOLICA - Dinnerware–glass ☆ - Sango Co. Ltd. (Sango USA Div.)

MAJOLICA - Earthenware - Shafford Co. Inc.

MAJOR - Bakery products ☆ - Lawrence Foods Inc.

MAJOR - Cigarettes - G.A. Georgopulo & Co. Inc.

MAJOR - Floor coverings - American Floor Products Co. Inc.

MAJOR - Herbicides - Nomix, Inc.

MAJOR - Nail care products - Major International Inc.

MAJOR - Puppets - Dakin Inc.

MAJOR - Recording label - Thomas J. Valentino Inc.

MAJOR - Toys ☆ - Hedstrom Corp.

MAJOR - Toys ☆ - Roadmaster Corp.

MAJOR, A - Recording label ☆ - Parr-X Corp.

MAJOR ACCENT - Markers–felt-tip - Sanford Corp.

MAJOR BUCK$ - T-shirts–men's - Major Buck$

MAJOR COMFORT - Skin care products - Major Pharmaceutical Corp.

MAJOR DAMAGE - Bicycles - Dynacraft Industries Inc.

MAJOR DELUXE - Sporting goods - Major Racquet Strings International

MAJOR DISASTER - Toys - Troma, Inc.

MAJOR GIL JONES - Dolls - Totsy Manufacturing Co., Inc.

MAJOR IMPACT - Markers–felt-tip - Sanford Corp.

MAJOR IMPACT - Sporting goods - Easton Aluminum Inc.

MAJOR IMPACT - Trading cards and stamps - Impel Marketing Inc.

MAJOR KIRA NERYS - Toys - Paramount Pictures Corp.

MAJOR LEAGUE - Colognes - Brandy Harvest

MAJOR LEAGUE - Flowers, plants, and seeds - Major League Baseball Properties, Inc.

MAJOR LEAGUE - Games ☆ - Tudor Inc.

MAJOR LEAGUE BASEBALL - Apparel and accessories - Garan, Inc.

MAJOR LEAGUE BASEBALL - Apparel–athletic - Fuqua Industries Inc.

MAJOR LEAGUE BASEBALL - Chewing gum ☆ - Amurol Confections Co.

MAJOR LEAGUE BASEBALL - Novelty items - Papel Freelance, Inc.

MAJOR LEAGUE MUSTARD - Mustard - Major League Baseball Properties, Inc.

MAJOR LEAGUE POCKET BASEBALL - Toys - Hirsch Co.

MAJOR METALFAB - Pens - Major Metalfab Co.

MAJOR MINTY - Candy - Chocolate House, Inc.

MAJOR MO - Toys - Tonka Corp.

MAJOR MOTION DANCEWEAR - Apparel–women's - Major Motion Inc.

MAJOR MUFFINS - Food products - Forest Park Hotel Management Group

MAJOR MUNCH - Toys - Mattel, Inc.

MAJOR ONE - Pens - Major One Pen Co.

MAJOR PETERS' - Beverages - Red Wing Co., Inc.

MAJOR PETERS - Beverages–alcohol - RHM Industrial Specialty Foods Inc.

MAJOR POKER - Games - Micro Manufacturing, Inc.

MAJOR QUALITY - Pharmaceuticals - Major Pharmaceuticals

MAJOR TOM - Apparel and accessories - Douglas C. Siegel

MAJORA - Whirlpools - Jacuzzi Inc.

MAJORCA - Dishes–china - Mikasa Co.

MAJORCA - Floor coverings–carpet and rugs - Couristan Inc.

MAJORCA - Furniture - Homecrest Industries Inc.

MAJORCA - Tiles–ceramic - United Ceramic Tile Corp.

MAJORCA - Tiles–mosaic - TJ Imports

MAJORCA AND MAKER - Floor coverings–tile - Federal Tile Imports Inc.

MAJORELLE - Bedding–linen - Dan River Inc.

MAJORETTE - Automotive parts and accessories ☆ - Ward Products Corp.

MAJORETTE - Fabrics–broadcloth - Desire Mills Co. Inc.

MAJORETTE - Nail care products - Major International Inc.

MAJORETTE - Toys - Majorette Toys (U.S.) Inc.

MAJORETTES - Hosiery - Virginia Maid Hosiery Mills Inc.

MAJOREX - Aquatic pharmacuetical preparations ☆ - Aquatronics-Filtronics

MAJORNAS - Food products - B. Westergaard & Co. Inc.

MAJORSEAL - Adhesives and sealants - Major Adhesives

MAJORSKA - Gin - Black Prince Distillery, Inc.

MAJORSKA - Gin - Star Industries, Inc.

MAJORSKA VODKA ROYALE - Vodka - Black Prince Distillery, Inc.

MAJUVY - Giftware - Belmont International Inc.

MAK-A-KEY - Tools - Medalist Industries Inc.

MAK-A-PIN - Tools - Medalist Industries Inc.

MAK ART - Toys–marbles ☆ - Marble King Inc.

MAKAHA - Skateboards ☆ - Gold Medal Recreational Products

MAKAHA - Slippers - Okawa Trading

MAKARA - Spices and extracts - Cinnabon, Inc.

MAKASYRUP - Syrup ☆ - Jel Sert Co.

MAKBLADE - Saw blades - Makita USA, Inc.

MAKE 7 - Games - Pressman Toy Corp.

MAKE-A-BED - Sofabeds - A. Brandt Co. Inc.

MAKE A BIG SPLASH - Wallpaper - Imperial Wallcoverings, Inc.

MAKE-A-BOOK - Educational materials - Abrams and Co. Publishers Inc.

MAKE-A-CHRISTMAS STOCKING - Toys - Lauri Inc.

MAKE-A-CLAMP - Clamps - Breeze Industrial Products

MAKE-A-DOCK - Docks ☆ - Daka Corp.

MAKE-A-FACE - Cosmetics - Ben Cooper Inc.

MAKE-A-FACE - Toys - Advanced Design Concepts Inc.

MAKE-A-LAMP - Hardware - Angelo Brothers Co.

MAKE-A-MAP - Computer software - Fern Greene

MAKE-A-MASK - Hobby kits - Educational Insights, Inc.

MAKE-A-MAT - Toys ☆ - Makit Products

MAKE-A-MEAL - Clay–modeling - Tonka Corp.

MAKE-A-MEAL - Containers - E-Z-Por Corp.

MAKE A MEAL - Meat sauces ☆ - Hunt-Wesson, Inc.

MAKE-A-MESS MAT - Infant product - Rock-A-Bye Baby Inc.

MAKE A MILLION - Toys - Tonka Corp.

MAKE-A-MOBILE - Ornamental products–glass - Down Island, Inc.

MAKE A MOVE - Apparel–athletic - Pandelco, Inc.

MAKE-A-MUG - Hobby kits - Makit Products

☆ = Now out of production

MAKE-A-NAME PUZZLE - Games - Centro Manufacturing Co. Inc.

MAKE-A-PLATE - Hobby kits - Makit Products

MAKE-A-RAINBOW - Candles ☆ - Muench-Kreuzer Candle Co.

MAKE-A-SIGN - Bulletin boards–cork - Nu-Dell Plastics Corp.

MAKE-A-STRAP - Hardware - Indiana Marine Co. (Indiana Mills & Manufacturing)

MAKE-A-TREE - Hobby kits - Makit Products

MAKE A WATCH - Jewelry - Watch Us, Inc.

MAKE & MELT - Hobby kits ☆ - Greene Plastics Corp.

MAKE & PLAY - Publisher's imprints - Creatnetics

MAKE & SHAKE - Ice making machinery - East Hampton Industries Inc.

MAKE BELIEVE - Wallpaper ☆ - Capital Carousel Inc.

MAKE BELIEVE IT'S YOU - Publisher's imprints - Scholastic Inc.

MAKE-BELIEVE PILLS - Novelty items - Doc's Apothecary

MAKE BELIEVES - Toys - Mattel, Inc.

MAKE DUSTING A DELIGHT - Cleaning equipment - Carstens, Inc.

MAKE EVERY DAY SPECIAL - Confections - Signature Brands, LLC

MAKE EVERY MINUTE COUNT - Jewelry - Bulova Corp.

MAKE EVERY STROKE COUNT - Apparel–athletic - Stroke Play

MAKE HEALTH A HABIT - Recording label - American Kid Fitness, Inc.

MAKE IT A RULE TO PLAN - Rulers–metal - Premier Agendas, Inc.

MAKE IT CLICK - Computer software ☆ - Sunburst Communications, Inc.

MAKE-IT-EASY - Rice - Riviana Foods Inc.

MAKE-IT-EASY PAKS - Coffee - Donovan Coffee Co., Inc.

MAKE-IT MOLD - Housewares - Make-It Mold, Inc.

MAKE-IT MOSAICS - Craft supplies - Plaid Enterprises, Inc.

MAKE IT PEARL! - Coatings - Sherwin-Williams Automotive Finishes Corp.

MAKE IT SNAPPY - Hair care products - Giovanni Cosmetics Inc.

MAKE IT STONE! - Paints - Sherwin-Williams Automotive Finishes Corp.

MAKE IT TASTY SPICE CO. - Spices and extracts - Continnuus

MAKE IT TONIGHT - Patterns–clothing ☆ - Mccall Pattern Co.

MAKE LOVE, NOT HASTE! - Massage products - Solothurnli Corp.

MAKE MILLIONS - Computer software - Voyager Software Corp.

MAKE MY OWN FUN - Hobby kits - Xoxo International, Inc.

MAKE 'N MEND - Adhesives and sealants ☆ - Tec Inc.

MAKE N MOVE - Toys ☆ - Barval Toys Inc.

MAKE N MOVE SLIDE & LOCK - Toys ☆ - Barval Toys Inc.

MAKE 'N STRETCH - Toys–models - Toymax Inc.

MAKE-OFF - Skin care products ☆ - Mark Allen Co.

MAKE-OVERS - Cosmetics - Karlen Manufacturing, Inc.

MAKE SOMEONE A STAR - Novelty items - Securitag Corp.

MAKE THE CONNECTION - Tools–hand-operated - Robert D. Newman

MAKE THE CUT - Apparel and accessories - MTC Sports, LLC

MAKE THE EARTH BEARABLE - Toys–stuffed - Commonwealth Toy and Novelty Co. Inc.

MAKE THE RIGHT CALL - Publisher's imprints - Triumph Books, Inc.

MAKE THE RIGHT CALL - Video production - Anheuser-Busch Companies Inc.

MAKE THE RIGHT CHOICE - Games - D. Bass and Associates

MAKE-TYTE - Putties - J.C. Whitlam Manufacturing Co.

MAKE-UP EXCHANGE - Lipsticks - Atlanta Center for Aesthetics, Inc.

MAKE-UP PRETTY - Dolls - Mattel, Inc.

MAKE WAVES - Cosmetics ☆ - Avon Products, Inc.

MAKE YOUR MARK! - Computer software - American Companies, Inc.

MAKE YOUR MOVE - Boardgame - Yellow Corp.

MAKE YOUR OWN - Toys–erector sets - Charles O. Larson Co. Inc.

MAKE-YOUR-OWN KEEPSAKES - Toys - Coloron Industries

MAKE YOUR OWN MURDER PARTY - Computer software ☆ - Electronic Arts Inc.

MAKE YOUR POINT - Computer software ☆ - Asymetrix Corp.

MAKE YOUR POINT - Textbooks - Erwin Gold

MAKE YOURSELF COMFORTABLE - Apparel and accessories - Cherokee Group

MAKEDISC - Computer software - Young Minds, Inc.

MAKEPEACE COLONY - Wood products - Makepeace Colony Press Inc.

MAKEPEACE COLONY PRESS - Books–blank - Makepeace Colony Press Inc.

MAKERCLEAN - Cleaning preparations - Maurer-Shumaker Inc.

MAKEREADY - Glue–household or industrial ☆ - Evans Adhesive Corp.

MAKERS' - Paper–writing - Potlatch Corp.

MAKER'S MARK - Beverages–alcohol - Maker's Mark Distillery Inc.

MAKERS MARK - Seasonings ☆ - Silver Foods Corp.

MAKER'S MARK - Whiskey - Hiram Walker & Sons, Inc.

MAKER'S MARK SIV - Chocolate candy - Maker's Mark Distillery, Inc.

MAKERS PRIDE - Golfing equipment - Golf Supply America, Inc.

MAKERY BAKERY - Toys - Toymax Inc.

MAKES MOUTHS HAPPY! - Candy - Homestead, Inc.

MAKES SCENTS - Air purification systems - Medo Industries, Inc.

MAKES SENSE - Computer software - Create-A-Check, Inc.

MAKES THE BEST OIL BETTER - Lubricating oils - Unelko Corp.

MAKES THE PARTY - Popcorn - National Oats Co. Inc.

MAKET FUN COMPANY - Novelty gift packages - Maket Fun Co.

MAKEUP + - Cosmetics - Estee Lauder Inc.

MAKEUP MADE EASY - Lipsticks - Barbara Salomone and Associates, Inc.

MAKI - Rodenticides ☆ - LiphaTech Inc.

MAKI SUSHI KI - Kitchen utensils–aluminum - Imperial Imports

MAKI-TUSS - Pharmaceutical preparations - Pharma Serve

MAKIMIDORI RED CLOVER - Flowers, plants, and seeds - Jacklin Seed

MAKIN BACON - Cookware - A De F Ltd.

MAKIN' BREAKFAST - Dolls - Mattel, Inc.

MAKIN' TRACKS - Shirts - J.B.'s Caribbean Soul Inc.

MAKIN' WAVES - Key rings - Russ Berrie and Co., Inc.

MAKINA-VIEW - Cameras - Harrison Camera Corp.

MAKING COMMITMENTS AND STICKING TO THEM - Labels–gummed - Superior Label Systems, Inc.

MAKING EYES - Cosmetics ☆ - Avon Products, Inc.

MAKING IT - Colognes ☆ - Avon Products, Inc.

MAKING MUSIC ON MICROS - Computer software - Random House, Inc.

MAKING OF A CHAMPION - Recording label - Success Motivation, Inc.

MAKING OF AMERICA - Magazines - Farrar, Straus and Giroux Inc.

MAKING TECHNOLOGY WORK FOR YOU - Computer peripheral equipment - Openlink Software Inc.

MAKING THE GRADE - Computer software - Cambridge Educational

MAKING TRACKS - Syrup - Making Tracks

MAKING TRAVEL LESS PRIMITIVE - Luggage - American Tourister, Inc.

MAKING WAVES - Bathing suits - Water Colors of Florida Inc.

MAKING WORKSPACES WORK - Furniture–metal - Lista International Corp.

MAKING YOU FEEL RIGHT AT HOME - Radios - Pollenex Corp.

MAKING YOUR DREAMS COME TRUE - Recording label - Wieder Enterprises

MAKINIS - Skin care products - Vicki B. Alsup

MAKIT-GLO - Toys - Tonka Corp.

MAKIT HANG - Toys - Tonka Corp.

MAKITA - Drapery hardware - Endisco Supply Co.

MAKITA - Tools–power-driven - Makita USA, Inc.

MAK'N FACES - Toys - Smethport Specialty Co.

MAKO - Boats–motor - Mako Marine Inc.

MAKO - Guitars ☆ - Kaman Music Corp.

MAKO - Knives–pocket - W.R. Case & Sons Cutlery Co.

MAKO - Orthopedic products - Medassist-Op, Inc.

MAKO BAY - Apparel and accessories - Darrell Ratliff

MAKOCHE - Recording label - Makoche Recording Co.

MAKOTO - Giftware - Makoto Inc.

MAKPAK ORANGE BATTERY SERIES - Tools–power-driven - Makita USA, Inc.

MAKRO-KILAR - Lenses–photographic - Heitz Service Corp.

MAKRO-SIRONAR - Photographic equipment - Berkey Marketing Cos.

M.A.L. - Apparel and accessories - Majestic Athletic Wear, Ltd.

MAL-X - Deodorizers - Enviro-Green Specialty Products Inc.

MALABAR - Bathroom fixtures ☆ - Artesian Industries

MALACHITE - Floor coverings–carpet and rugs - Customweave Carpets Inc.

MALACHITE & MARBLE - Wallpaper - Patterson Piazza

MALACHITE PLUS - Pet products - Marine Enterprises International, Inc.

MALACO - Recording label - Malaco Records Inc.

MALACO JAZZ - Recording label - Malaco Records Inc.

MALACO'S - Candy ☆ - Jaret Specialties Inc.

MALAGA - Floor coverings - Mannington Resilient Floors

MALAGA - Floor coverings–carpet and rugs - Couristan Inc.

MALAGA - Giftware - Sasaki

MALAGA COVE - Floor coverings–carpet and rugs ☆ - Royalweve Carpet Mills

MALAGA LITE - Chimes ☆ - Nutone Inc.

MALAGUTI - Mopeds - Marina Mobili Inc.

MALAHINI - Boats - Glen-L Marine Designs

MALAKA - Cheese - VMC Corp.

MALAKA - Kitchen appliances ☆ - Nature's Own Inc.

MALAKA BRAND - Food products - Nature's Own Inc.

MALAMAR - Floor coverings - Congoleum Corp.

MALANGE - Floor coverings–carpet and rugs - Bloomsburg Carpet Industries

MALAR SHELL - Prosthetic apparatus - Implantech Associates, Inc.

MALARKEY - Apparel–women's - Shenanigans Knits Ltd.

MALATAL - Pharmaceutical preparations - Roberts/Hauck Pharmaceuticals Inc.

MALATCHIE FARMS - Nuts—salted, roasted, cooked, or canned ☆ - Signal Thread Co. Inc.
MALATE COMPLEX - Vitamins and nutritional supplements - Vitamin Research Products Inc.
MALAWI/VICTORIA BUFFER - Pet products - Seachem Laboratories
MALAY - Furniture ☆ - Hammary Furniture Co. Inc.
MALAY - Infant product ☆ - Welsh Co.
MALAYA - Fabrics - Dan River Inc.
MALAYSIA - Tableware—china ☆ - Lenox, Inc.
MALAYSIA CLUB - Shrimp - Continental Seafoods Inc.
MALBA - Bathroom accessories - Zenith Products Corp.
MALCI - Seasonings - North American Laboratory Co.
MALCO - Chemical preparations - Malco Products, Inc.
MALCO MAID - Housewares - Malco Industries
MALCOGEL - Pharmaceutical preparations ☆ - Upjohn Co.
MALCOLM - Shirts - Malcolm Brooks
MALCOLM & CO. - Apparel—women's - San Simeon, Inc.
MALCOLM HEREFORD'S COWS - Liquors ☆ - Heublein, Inc.
MALCOLM MORAN STUDIOS - Statuary ☆ - Couroc of Monterey Inc.
MALCOLM X - Clothing - Betty Shabazz
MALDEC - Pharmaceutical preparations - H.R. Cenci Laboratories Inc.
MALDEN FRAME - Frames—picture - Malden Frames
MALDEN KNITTING MILLS - Apparel—men's - Fred Roth Associates
MALDEN MILLS - Fabrics - Malden Mills Industries, Inc.
MALE ADVANTAGE - Vitamins and nutritional supplements - Body Wise International, Inc.
MALE AND FEMALE SEX CHROMOSOME GENDER DICE - Educational materials - Origins Products
MALE BAG - Health care products - Park Surgical Co. Inc.
MALE BOOSTER - Health care products - Natural Laboratories Corp.
MALE CALL - Bags - A.J. Siris Products Corp.
MALE CHAUVINIST - Men's cosmetics ☆ - London International U.S. Holdings
MALE CONCEPTS - Apparel—men's - Male Concepts Ltd.
MALE DRI - Health care products ☆ - Nelkin/Piper Health Products
MALE DUDS - Apparel—men's ☆ - Warnaco Inc.
MALE EDITION - Hair care products - Focus 21 International Inc.
MALE ESSENTIAL - Pharmaceutical preparations - Longevity Pure Medicine
MALE EXPRESS - Footwear - United States Shoe Corp.
MALE FACT - Vitamins - Country Life
MALE INSTINCT - Colognes ☆ - Avon Products, Inc.
MALE MATTERS - Apparel and accessories - Easton Sportswear Inc.
MALE PERFORMANCE - Vitamins and nutritional supplements - Home Health Products, Inc.
MALE POTENTIAL - Vitamins and nutritional supplements - Planetary Formulas
MALE POWER - Apparel—men's - Comme-Ci Comme-Ca Ltd.
MALE POWER - Vitamins and nutritional supplements - Pdk Labs, Inc.
MALE PRIDE - Prophylactics - Wetoo, Inc.
MALE TONER - Teas ☆ - Traditional Medicinals, Inc.
MALE VITALITY PLUS - Vitamins and nutritional supplements - Bio Genetic Health Group, Inc.
MALEE'S - Cookies ☆ - Bon Melange Inc.
MALENA - Ointment ☆ - Benjamin Ansehl Co.
MALENIUM - Sunglasses - Blublocker Corp.
MALERAS GLASSWORKS - Giftware - Scan-Agent
MALETTO - Elastic - Erich M. Reich Inc.
MALFA - Paints—artists' ☆ - Martin F. Weber Co.
MALI - Blinds—venetian ☆ - Hunter Douglas, Inc.
MALIA - Apparel and accessories - Uniforms by Malia Inc.
MALIA MILLS SWIM WEAR - Apparel and accessories - Malia Mills, Inc.
MALIBOO - Giftware ☆ - WMF/USA
MALIBU - Aircraft - New Piper Aircraft, Inc.
MALIBU - Barbecues and grills ☆ - M.E. Heuck Co. Inc.
MALIBU - Bathing suits - Catalina
MALIBU - Blinds—vertical ☆ - C-Mor Co.
MALIBU - Boats—pontoons - O.M.C. Aluminum Boat Group
MALIBU - Books—comic - Malibu Comics Entertainment, Inc.
MALIBU - Cabinets ☆ - Aristokraft, Inc.
MALIBU - Cabinets ☆ - Decora
MALIBU - Cigarettes - American Tobacco Co.
MALIBU - Cigarettes - Commonwealth Brands, Inc.
MALIBU - Dining room furniture ☆ - John Boos and Co. Inc.
MALIBU - Dolls - Mattel, Inc.
MALIBU - Fencing—plastic - Nebraska Plastics, Inc.
MALIBU - Fireplaces - Dyna Corp.
MALIBU - Floor coverings - American Floor Products Co. Inc.

MALIBU - Floor coverings - Mannington Resilient Floors
MALIBU - Floor coverings—carpet and rugs - Regal Rugs Inc.
MALIBU - Floor coverings—carpet and rugs ☆ - Mandate-Dawn Carpet Mills
MALIBU - Furniture - Link-Taylor Corp.
MALIBU - Furniture ☆ - Bassett Furniture Industries, Inc.
MALIBU - Glassware—household - Owens-Illinois Inc. (Libbey Div.)
MALIBU - Goggles—safety - Aearo Co.
MALIBU - Lighting systems - Intermatic Inc.
MALIBU - Motor vehicles ☆ - General Motors Corp. (Chevrolet Motor Div.)
MALIBU - Motor vehicles—motor homes - Forest River, Inc.
MALIBU - Paints - Sinclair Paint Co.
MALIBU - Pens - Paper Mate Co.
MALIBU - Rum - Paddington Corp.
MALIBU - Shoes - Cole-Haan
MALIBU - Underwear and nightwear - Youthcraft-Charmfit
MALIBU - Vegetables—canned ☆ - Case-Swayne Co. Inc.
MALIBU - Watches - Malibu Jewelry Corp.
MALIBU - Watches - David G. Steven Inc.
MALIBU - Window coverings - Lenyo Corp./Paul Heinley Shutters
MALIBU II PLANK - Floor coverings - Robbins Inc.
MALIBU 2000 - Hair care products - Action Environmental Products
MALIBU BEACH - Childrens' sunglasses - Nasta Industries Inc.
MALIBU BEACH CLUB - Apparel and accessories - Oxford Industries, Inc.
MALIBU BEACH VOLLEYBALL - Video games - ABC International Traders Inc.
MALIBU CANYON - Furniture - Lane Co. Inc.
MALIBU CLASSIC - Motor vehicles ☆ - General Motors Corp. (Chevrolet Motor Div.)
MALIBU COUNTRY CLUB - Apparel and accessories - California Fuji International, Inc.
MALIBU EAST - Wallpaper ☆ - Capital Carousel Inc.
MALIBU EXPRESS - Bicycles ☆ - Huffy Corp.
MALIBU EYES - Skin care products - Action Environmental Products
MALIBU FACES - Skin care products - Action Environmental Products
MALIBU FARMS - Seasonings - Malibu Farms Co.
MALIBU FOR WOMEN - Apparel stores—sports - Sub-4 Inc.
MALIBU FUN STUFFED! - Toys—stuffed - Malibu Fun Stuffed, Inc.
MALIBU GIRL - Cosmetics - New Cal Development, Inc.
MALIBU GOLD - Cosmetics - New Cal Development, Inc.
MALIBU GRAND PRIX - Communications equipment - Time Warner Entertainment Co., L.P.
MALIBU GYM - Apparel and accessories - Armand M. Grant
MALIBU LIGHTS - Electrical supplies - Intermatic Inc.
MALIBU MIST - Hair care products - Rescue Marketing Group
MALIBU MIX - Vegetables—frozen - Patterson Frozen Foods, Inc.
MALIBU MUDD - Skin care products - Action Environmental Products
MALIBU MUSK - Perfumes - Parfum de Coeur Ltd.
MALIBU PET PRODUCTS - Pet products - Southern California Foam, Inc.
MALIBU SCRUB - Skin care products - Action Environmental Products
MALIBU SUMMER - Skin care products - Louise Bianco Skin Care, Inc.
MALIBU SUN - Books—comic - Malibu Comics Entertainment, Inc.
MALIBU SUNSET - Christmas tree ornaments - Cracker Box Inc.
MALIBU SUNSET - Floor coverings—carpet and rugs - Lees Carpets
MALIBU TAN - Skin care products - Creative Laboratories Inc.
MALIBU, THE - Recliners - Lane Co. Inc.
MALIBU TWO - Boats—kayaks - Ocean Kayak, Inc.
MALIC ACID PLUS - Vitamins and nutritional supplements - M.M.R.C., Ltd. Co.
MALIC MAG - Vitamins and nutritional supplements - Ethical Nutrients
MALICE - Musical instrument accessories - Adder Plus Corp.
MALICE IN WONDERLAND - Record stores - No Man's Land
MALICIOUS VINYL - Recording label - Delicious Vinyl, Inc.
MALIKA MALIKA AFRICAN TREASURE - Jewelry—precious - Lucoral Co. Inc.
MALINA - Yarn ☆ - Caron International Inc.
MALINDI - Yarn ☆ - William Unger & Co. Inc.
MALIQUE - Jewelry ☆ - Hobe Cie. Ltd.
MALKA - Jewelry - Roslyn Goldstein
MALKINS PURE - Health care products - Nieland Marketing, Inc.
MALL - Sporting goods ☆ - Ballco Products Inc.
MALL CAT - Apparel and accessories - Emily Jean Westling
MALL DAWN - Doors—metal - Alpine Overhead Doors Inc.
MALL MADNESS - Games ☆ - Milton Bradley Co.
MALL OF AMERICA - Jewelry - Mall of America Co.
MALL RAT - Apparel and accessories - Gym Rat, Inc.
MALL RIDER - Strollers—baby ☆ - Evenflo Co.
MALL TROLL - Clothing - Be Rad Ltd., Inc.

☆ = Now out of production

MALL VIDEO - Billboards - SMG, Inc.

MALL WALKERS - Shoes - KangaROOS USA Inc.

MALLAMINT - Pharmaceutical preparations - Roberts/Hauck Pharmaceuticals Inc.

MALLARD - Boats—pontoons ☆ - Customflex Inc.

MALLARD - Glassware—household - Rezler & Howell Co.

MALLARD - Luggage - Heritage Industries

MALLARD - Motor vehicles—all-terrain - Mallard Coach

MALLARD - Pencils ☆ - Sanford Corp.

MALLARD - Pens - Mallard Pen & Pencil Co. Inc.

MALLARD - Peroxides—inorganic - Roberts/Hauck Pharmaceuticals Inc.

MALLARD - Tableware—china - Susquehanna Glass Co.

MALLARD - Trailers—travel - Fleetwood Enterprises, Inc.

MALLARD - Watch - Jules Borel & Co.

MALLARD - Wheelchairs - AM Scooters

MALLARD MASTER - Games - Mallard Master

MALLARD POND FARMS - Popcorn - Mallard Pond Farms Inc.

MALLARD PRESS - Publisher's imprints - Bantam Doubleday Dell Publishing Group, Inc.

MALLARDS - Gift wrap - Highland Supply Corp.

MALLARD'S - Salad dressings - Mallard's Restaurants, Inc.

MALLARDS ROOTS - Hair care products - Thomas H. Jung

MALLARDS ROOTS - Hair care products - United Beauty Products

MALLAZINE - Ophthalmic goods - Roberts/Hauck Pharmaceuticals Inc.

MALLERGAN-VC - Pharmaceutical preparations ☆ - Roberts/Hauck Pharmaceuticals Inc.

MALLET ARTS - Recording label - Jazz Composer's Orchestra Association Inc.

MALLETECH - Xylophones - Marimba Productions Inc.

MALLEY'S SUPREME - Ice cream ☆ - Dairymens

MALLINCKRODT METHADONE MANAGEMENT - Computer software - Mallinckrodt Tmh

MALLIN'S BEST - Food products ☆ - L. Mallin & Sons

MALLISOL - Antiseptics - Roberts/Hauck Pharmaceuticals Inc.

MALLMAR - Meat products - Shofar Kosher Foods, Inc.

MALLO CUP - Candy - Boyer Candy Co., Inc.

MALLO MM - Jams and jellies - White Stokes Co.

MALLOMARS - Cookies - Nabisco Foods Group

MALLOPRESS - Pharmaceutical preparations ☆ - Roberts/Hauck Pharmaceuticals Inc.

MALLOREDDUS - Pasta - Dean & Deluca Inc.

MALLORIES DAIRY - Milk - Mallories Dairy Inc.

MALLORY - Batteries ☆ - Duracell Co. USA

MALLORY - Toys - Mattel, Inc.

MALLORY & CHURCH - Neckties - Mallory and Church Corp.

MALLORY & KRAFT - Apparel—women's - Mallory and Kraft Ltd.

MALLORY'S FINEST - Snack foods - A.L. Schutzman Co., Inc.

MALLORY'S MARVELOUS MUFFINS - Dolls - Leslie A. Zieger

MALLOWS - Fishing lures - Brown Bear Bait Co.

MALM - Fireplaces - Malm Fireplaces Inc.

MALMAISON - Fabrics - Gretchen Bellinger Inc.

MALMO GREEN - Fertilizers - Ernst Home Center Inc.

MALM'S - Polishing rouge - Malm Chemical Corp.

MALMSTROM - Chemical preparations - Brooks Industries, Inc.

MALOLEYS - Dairy products - Maloley Bros. Inc.

MALOLO - Bathing suits - Catalina

MALONE - See BASSETT BEDDING

MALONE - Clay products - Sculpture House Inc.

MALONE - Slippers ☆ - Tru-Stitch Footwear (Div. of Wolverine World Wide)

MALONEY'S PUB - Adult game ☆ - American Publishing Corp.

MALOTRONE - Pharmaceutical preparations ☆ - Bluco Inc.

MALOTUSS - Cough medicines ☆ - Roberts/Hauck Pharmaceuticals Inc.

MALPASO - Apparel and accessories - Clint Eastwood

MALPASO RECORDS - Recording label - Clint Eastwood

MALPOTANE - Vitamins and nutritional supplements - Health Products Corp.

MALROV - Hats - MU Industries Inc.

MALT BARLEY CHOCOLATE CLUSTERS - Candy - Charity's Food

MALT CUP - Food products ☆ - Knudsen Dairy Products

MALT DUCK - Beverages—malt - The Stroh Brewery Co.

MALT-O-MEAL - Cereal - Malt-O-Meal Co.

MALT RIVER - Beverages—alcohol - Malt River Brewing Co. LLC

MALT SHOPPE - Dolls - Mattel, Inc.

MALT STAR - Beverages - Kedem Food Products Co.

MALTA - Doors—wood - Tomkins Industries Inc.

MALTA - Flatware ☆ - Sterling China Co. Inc.

MALTA - Floor coverings ☆ - Tarkett, Inc.

MALTA - Floor coverings—carpet and rugs - Couristan Inc.

MALTA CANDY - Beverages—carbonated - Cawy Bottling Co., Inc.

MALTA CORONA - Beverages—malt - Joseph Victori Wines Inc.

MALTA DUKESA - Beverages—malt - Eastern Brewing Corp.

MALTA EL SOL - Beverages—malt - Eastern Brewing Corp.

MALTA LOS ISLAS - Beverages—carbonated - Canada Dry Corp.

MALTA REINA - Juices - Connell Co.

MALTA THERMACLAD - Windows—storm ☆ - Malta Co.

MALTAGLIATI - Pasta - Parmalat USA Corp.

MALTED MEMORIES - Beverages—malt - Malted Memories, Inc.

MALTED MILK EGGS - Candy - Leaf, Inc.

MALTED SHREDDED WHEAT - Cereal - Quaker Oats Co.

MALTEENS - Chocolate milk ☆ - Nestle USA

MALTESE - Glassware—household - Precision Bache Glass

MALTESE - Tiles—ceramic ☆ - Wenczel Tile Co.

MALTESE CROSS - Fruits and vegetables - Reter Fruit Co.

MALTESE MAGNUM - Boats—motor - Magnum Marine Corp.

MALTESER - Candy - Leaf, Inc.

MALTETTS - Candy - Leaf, Inc.

MALTEX - Food products - American Home Food Products Inc.

MALTGLIATI - Pasta ☆ - Fred Montesi Super Markets

MALTHAUS BOUQUET - Beverages—malt - John A. Hemingway

MALTIC ACID - Vitamins and nutritional supplements - M.M.R.C., Ltd. Co.

MALTIES - Candy ☆ - Nestle USA

MALTO-BELLA - Candy - JLM Specialty Foods

MALTOROME - Coffee - Arancia Flavors & Ingredients, Inc.

MALTOSE - Pharmaceutical preparations - Pfanstiehl Laboratories Inc.

MALTSUPEX - Laxatives - Wallace Laboratories

MALTY CRUNCH - Candy bars ☆ - Nellson Candies Inc.

MALULANI ESTATE - Coffee - Coffees of Hawaii Inc.

MALUMEL - Pharmaceutical preparations ☆ - Solvay Pharmaceuticals Inc.

MALUNA - Giftware - Aloha Candle Manufacturing Co. Inc.

MALUNA SALES - Giftware - Aloha Candle Manufacturing Co. Inc.

MALVA - Glassware—household - Spiegelau Inc.

MALVA - Skin care products ☆ - Nature's Answer (Bio Botanica)

MALVA LEAF - Hair care products - Holistic Laboratories

MALVERNE - Floor coverings—carpet and rugs ☆ - Rugby Rugs Inc.

MAM - Infant product - Sassy Inc.

MAM PAPAUL MARDI GRAS KING - Cakes—mixes - Louisiana Gourmet

MAMA - Crackers - Sunshine/Salerno Inc.

MAMA & BABY - Toys—stuffed - Dakin Inc.

MAMA & PIGLET - Toys—stuffed - Dakin Inc.

MAMA AURELIO'S SPINACH CALABRESE - Pizzas—frozen - Aurelio's Pizza Inc.

MAMA BEAR'S COLD CARE - Teas—herbal - Celestial Seasonings, Inc.

MAMA CAMPIZZI'S - Sauces - Red Wing Co., Inc.

MAMA CELLA'S - Spaghetti sauces - Sea House Ltd.

MAMA CRECCO'S FAMOUS ITALIAN DOG BISCOTTO - Dog food - Michael Crecco

MAMA C'S - Pizzas—mixes - Coborn's Inc.

MAMA GWORK - Toys—stuffed - Russ Berrie and Co., Inc.

MAMA IRENE'S - Candy - Mama Irene's Specialty Candies, Inc.

MAMA JO'S - Fruits—candied - Mama Jo's Garden

MAMA K - Food products - M & K Foods Inc.

MAMA KIN - Key rings - Svengali Merchandising Inc.

MAMA LEONE - Pasta - American Home Food Products Inc.

MAMA LUCIA - Meat products—beef - Quaker Maid Meats Inc.

MAMA MARY'S - Pizzas—mixes - Spartan Foods Inc.

MAMA MENDIETA'S - Tortillas - Mama Mendieta, Inc.

MAMA METAFORA COMPANY, THE - Cookies - Jeanette A. Melnick

MAMA MIA - Yarn - Tahki Imports Ltd.

MAMA MIA COLOR - Yarn - Tahki Imports Ltd.

MAMA MIA CRISSCUT FRIES - Vegetables—frozen ☆ - Lamb-Weston, Inc.

MAMA RAP'S - Food products - Rapazzini Winery

MAMA ROSA - Food products - A.M. Gilardi and Sons, Inc.

MAMA ROSA'S - Pizzas—frozen - A.M. Gilardi and Sons, Inc.

MAMA ROSA'S CLASSICS - Pizzas—frozen - A.M. Gilardi and Sons, Inc.

MAMA ROSIE'S - Ravioli—canned - Mama Rosie's Ravioli

MAMA RUBINO'S - Vegetables—canned - Valley View Packing Co., Inc.

MAMA RUSSO'S - Spaghetti sauces - Russo Bros. Inc.

MAMA SADIE - Fruits and vegetables ☆ - Stanley Orchards Sales Inc.

MAMA SHAW - Seafood products—fresh or frozen - Southern Belle Frozen Foods Inc.

MAMA TISH'S - Confections - Mama Tish's Italian Specialties, Inc.

MAMA TISH'S ORIGINAL - Ice cream - Mama Tish's Italian Specialties, Inc.

MAMA Z'S - Pizzas—frozen ☆ - Mr. Z's Fund Raising Corp.

MAMACITA SOFRITO - Seasonings - Goya Foods, Inc.

MAMACITA'S - Food products - Conagra, Inc.
MAMACOCA - Beverages–carbonated - Douglas A. Willinger
MAMAMIM - Food products - H & H International Co. USA
MAMARCO - Stencils ☆ - Mason Marking Systems Corp.
MAMA'S - Bakery products - Mama's Strudel Co.
MAMA'S - Cookies - Delicious Brands, Inc.
MAMA'S - Cookies - Sunshine/Salerno Inc.
MAMA'S - Herring–smoked, salted, dried, or pickled - Florida Smoked Fish Co.
MAMA'S BABIES - Toys - KVK Inc.
MAMA'S BABY - Dolls ☆ - Effanbee Doll Corp.
MAMA'S HOMEMADE - Sauces - Falcoma, Inc.
MAMA'S KITCHEN - Jams and jellies - Ina Christine Horowitz
MAMA'S LI'L DARLIN' - Dolls ☆ - Effanbee Doll Corp.
MAMATERRA - Apparel and accessories - HMC Sports, Inc.
MAMATOTO - Skin care products - The Body Shop
MAMAW'S - Pickles - Linda H. Russell
MAMBA - Archery equipment - Martin Archery Inc.
MAMBA - Beverages–malt - Highland Distributing Co.
MAMBA - Bicycles - Python USA, Inc.
MAMBA - Candy - Storck USA L.P.
MAMBO - Cigarettes - ITI Interamericana Trade, Inc.
MAMBO MONKEY - Toys–stuffed - Bijou Enterprises Inc.
MAMBRO - Apparel and accessories ☆ - Mamiye Brothers, Inc.
MAMIE - Jams and jellies ☆ - Bongrain Cheese USA
MAMIYA - Photographic equipment - Berkey Marketing Cos.
MAMIYA 7 II - Cameras - Mamiya America Corp.
MAMLENE - Pharmaceutical preparations ☆ - Ulmer Pharmacal Co.
MAMMA BELLA - Breads - Ausmac Inc.
MAMMA LINA - Food products - Mamma Lina's Ravioli Co.
MAMMA MIA - Meat products–beef - Thorn Apple Valley Inc.
MAMMA RO - Dinnerware - Palmer-Watson Inc.
MAMMA ROMANO - Food products - Mamma Romano & Six Sons Foods Inc.
MAMMA ROSA - Food products - Panfredi Inc.
MAMMARY PMG - Vitamins and nutritional supplements - Standard Process Inc.
MAMMOL - Health care products - Abbott Laboratories
MAMMORX - Bathtubs–enameled - Diacor Inc.
MAMMOTH - Compact discs–prerecorded ☆ - Pinnacle Micro, Inc.
MAMMOTH - Mats - Azo
MAMMOTH BONE - Pet products - Classic Products
MAMMOTH CAVE TWIST - Tobacco products - Scott Tobacco Co.
MAMMOTH DINOZORD - Toys - Saban Entertainment, Inc.
MAMMOTH MELTDOWN - Computer software - Gamco Industries Inc.
MAMMOTH MOUNTAIN - Postcards - Mammoth Mountain Ski Area, Inc.
MAMMOTH RECORDS - Recording label - Mammoth Records Inc.
MAMMOVISION - Medical apparatus - Fischer Imaging Corp.
MAMMUT - Rope ☆ - Climb High Inc.
MAMONDE - Cosmetics - Pacific Corp. of America
MAMSELLE - Apparel–women's - Chauvin International Ltd.
MAM'SELLE - Dolls ☆ - Effanbee Doll Corp.
MAMSELLE - Floor coverings–carpet and rugs ☆ - Hollytex Carpet Mills Inc.
MAMSELLE - Jewelry–costume - B.B. Greenberg Co.
MAMZELLE - Apparel and accessories - Beverly Vogue Co.
MAN - Shaving preparations - Quintessence Inc.
MAN ACT, THE - Shaving preparations ☆ - Quintessence Inc.
MAN ALIVE - Skin care products - Colgate-Palmolive Co.
MAN-ALOE - Vitamins and nutritional supplements - Emprise International, Inc.
MAN AND HIS IMAGE - Apparel and accessories - Gentry Inc.
MAN AND MACHINE - Toys - Tonka Corp.
MAN-AT-ARMS - Toys - Mattel, Inc.
M.A.N. DESIGN BY.LOU NARDI - Apparel and accessories - Explosive Clothing, Inc.
MAN-E-FACES - Toys - Mattel, Inc.
MAN-FISHER - Food products - Reede International Seafood Corp.
MAN FOR ALL SEASONS - Apparel–men's ☆ - Genesco Inc.
MAN IN MOTION - Underwear and nightwear - Jockey International, Inc.
MAN-KNITS - Apparel–men's ☆ - Manhattan International
MAN LAND GEAR - Apparel and accessories - Marketing by Design, Inc.
MAN-MADE - Diamond powder - General Electric Co.
MAN MADE - Vitamins and nutritional supplements - BC International Cosmetics & Image Services, Inc.
MAN-MADE CHAMOIS - Cleaning equipment - Bloch/New England, Inc.
MAN-MATE - Machinery - Western Space and Marine Inc.
MAN-O - Skin care products - Man-O Products
MAN O SERVICE - Watches - Hampden Corp.

MAN-O-TILE - Floor coverings - Mannington Resilient Floors
MAN-O-TOP - Floor coverings - Mannington Resilient Floors
MAN O WAR - Seafood products–fresh or frozen - Chinook Packing Co.
MAN O WAR - Sporting goods - Man O War
MAN-O-WAR - Toys - Tonka Corp.
MAN-O-WAR - Varnishes ☆ - McCloskey Corp.
MAN OF DISTINCTION - Jewelry ☆ - Hirsch Speidel Inc.
MAN OF THE WORLD - Apparel and accessories - Gentry Inc.
MAN OF THE YEAR - Colognes - Brandy Harvest
MAN-ON-THE-GO - Luggage - United States Luggage Corp.
MAN OVER BOARD - Apparel and accessories - Freestyle of Duluth, Inc.
MAN OVERBOARD - Life preservers - Stearns Manufacturing Co.
MAN O'WAR - Shampoos - Farnam Cos. Inc.
MAN SIZE - Paper–toilet - Kimberly-Clark Corp.
MAN TRANS - Chemical preparations - Petrolon Management, Inc.
MAN TRAPS - Novelty items - Doc's Apothecary
MAN-VITES - Vitamins and nutritional supplements - Nature's Bounty, Inc.
MAN WARMERS - Lined leather gloves - Boss Manufacturing Co.
MAN WITH NO EYES, THE - Toys - Bandai America Inc.
MAN WITH THE GOLDEN GUN - Games - Avalon Hill Game Co.
MANA - Cosmetics ☆ - Chem Spray Aerosols Inc.
MANACID - Pharmaceutical preparations ☆ - Hyrex Pharmaceuticals
MANAGE - Computer software - United Software Associates, Inc.
MANAGE! - Computer software - United Software Associates, Inc.
MANAGE BEFORE THE FACT - Computer hardware - Before the Fact Management Systems, Inc.
MANAGEABLES - Calendars - Cullman Ventures Inc.
MANAGED CARE FORECASTER - Computer software - Inforum, Inc.
MANAGED CARE PERFORMANCE PROJECT, THE - Publisher's imprints - Managed Care Performance Project
MANAGEL - Hair care products - BLF, Inc.
MANAGEMENT CONTROL SERIES, THE - Computer software - PPG Industries, Inc.
MANAGEMENT PERFORMANCE SYSTEM - Computer software - Management Systems International, Inc.
MANAGEMENT R&D - Computer software - Management R&D, Inc.
MANAGEMENT SOFTWARE - Computer software - Sum/It Systems
MANAGEPRO - Computer programs - Avantos Performance Systems Inc.
MANAGER - Clocks - General Time Corp. (Westclox/Seth Thomas Div.)
MANAGER - Knives–pocket - Swiss Army Brands, Ltd.
MANAGER II - Computer peripheral equipment - Polytel Computer Products Corp.
MANAGER, THE - Computer software - Commodore Business Machines Inc.
MANAGER, THE - Computer software - Seven Hills Software
MANAGERIAL - Files–tools - Northwest Metal Products Co.
MANAGER'S ASSISTANT BASEBALL SOFTBALL - Computer software - Logical Solutions, Inc.
MANAGER'S PARTNER - Computer software - Donaldson, Lufkin and Jenrette Securities Corp.
MANAGEWARE - Computer software ☆ - High Technology Software Corp., Inc.
MANAGING SOLUTION - Cosmetics - Origins Natural Resources Inc.
MANAGING UUCP AND USENET - Publisher's imprints - O'Reilly & Associates, Inc.
MANAGING YOUR MONEY - Computer software - Meca Software, Inc.
MANALE - Apparel–women's - Beyond the Moment, Inc.
MANAM - Floor coverings - Manhattan American Terrazzo Strip Co.
MANANTIAL - Water–mineral - A.C.M.
MANAS - Computer software - MediaPlan, Inc.
MANATEE - Prefabricated buildings–wood - Champion Enterprises Inc.
MANAXX - Food products - Leon Javier
MANBONE - Pet product - Items Inc.
MANCALA - Games - Little Harbor Corp.
MANCER - Tableware–earthenware ☆ - Villeroy and Boch Tableware Ltd.
MANCHANIL - Skin care products - D'Franssia Corp.
MANCHA'S - Sauces - Mancha's
MANCHESTER - Apparel and accessories - Oxford Industries, Inc.
MANCHESTER - Cabinets - Dewils Industries Inc.
MANCHESTER - Cabinets - Imperial Cabinet Co. Inc.
MANCHESTER - Cabinets ☆ - Medallion Kitchens of Minnesota Inc.
MANCHESTER - Cabinets–wood - Parcraft Distinctive Cabinetry
MANCHESTER - Clocks ☆ - General Time Corp. (Westclox/Seth Thomas Div.)
MANCHESTER - Doors–wood - Jeld-Wen, Inc.
MANCHESTER - Floor coverings - Bruce Hardwood Floors
MANCHESTER - Floor coverings ☆ - Tarkett, Inc.
MANCHESTER - Floor coverings–carpet and rugs ☆ - Blue Ridge Carpet Mills

☆ = Now out of production

MANCHESTER - Floor coverings–carpet and rugs ☆ - Calladium & Marglen
MANCHESTER - Food products ☆ - Curtice-Burns Foods, Inc.
MANCHESTER - Furniture ☆ - Athens Furniture Industries Inc.
MANCHESTER - Furniture ☆ - Hammary Furniture Co. Inc.
MANCHESTER - Giftware ☆ - Boardman Silversmiths Inc.
MANCHESTER - Hardware - Baldwin Hardware Corp.
MANCHESTER - Occasional tables - JDI Group, Inc.
MANCHESTER - Shoes - Allen-Edmonds Shoe Corp.
MANCHESTER - Stoves ☆ - Quaker Stove Co. Inc.
MANCHESTER - Tires - Dunlap and Kyle Co. Inc.
MANCHESTER - Wallpaper - Koroseal Wallcoverings
MANCHESTER FARMS - Eggs - Manchester Farms
MANCHESTER INN - House furnishings ☆ - Lexington Furniture Industries, Inc.
MANCHESTER-PIERCE - Fireplaces ☆ - Majestic Co.
MANCHESTER SQUARE - Cabinets–wood - Kemper
MANCHU - Furniture - American Furniture Co. Inc.
MANCHU - Pasta - Quaker Oats Co.
MANCILLAS - Apparel and accessories - Mancillas International Ltd.
MANCINI - Vegetables–canned - Mancini Packing Co.
MANCINI A. MANCINI - Sauces - Mancini Packing Co.
MANCO - Cooking utensils–enameled ☆ - Seymour Mann Inc.
MANCO - Gocarts - Manco Products, Inc.
MANCO - Gocarts - Motor Bikes Import
MANCO - Office supplies - Manco, Inc.
MANDA II - Apparel and accessories ☆ - Salant/Manhattan Industries
MANDABERRY - Beverages–carbonated - Vitamin Beverage Corp.
M&ADESK - Computer software - Commscan, Inc.
MANDALA - Glass products - Mandala Productions
MANDALAY - Cooking utensils–enameled ☆ - National Housewares
MANDALAY - Dishes–china ☆ - WMF/USA
MANDALAY - Fabrics–cotton - Dan River Inc.
MANDALAY - Floor coverings–carpet and rugs - Philadelphia Carpets
MANDALAY - Food products - Mandalay Food Products Corp.
MANDALAY - Furniture - Mersman Furniture Co.
MANDALAY - Pharmaceutical preparations - Beutlich L.P. Pharmaceuticals
MANDALAY - Rice - Producers Rice Mill, Inc.
MANDALAY - Rings–jewelry - Artcarved Inc.
MANDALAY - Toilets–enameled - Kohler Co.
MANDAN - Inks ☆ - Winsor & Newton
MANDARIN - Apparel stores–uniforms - Royal China & Porcelain Companies Inc.
MANDARIN - Boats–pontoons - Godfrey Marine Co.
MANDARIN - Caviar - Tsar Nicoulai Caviar
MANDARIN - Computer software - Social Issues Resources Series, Inc.
MANDARIN - Faucets - Kallista Inc.
MANDARIN - Floor coverings–carpet and rugs - Trans-Ocean Import Co. Inc.
MANDARIN - Food products ☆ - Seasia
MANDARIN - Frozen foods - Vip Foods, Inc.
MANDARIN - Pottery ☆ - Rubens Originals
MANDARIN CLASSICS - Floor coverings–carpet and rugs - Trans-Ocean Import Co. Inc.
MANDARIN COLLECTION - Furniture - National/Mt. Airy Furniture
MANDARIN MAGIC - Degreasing solvents ☆ - Harley Chemicals
MANDARIN MAGIC - Health-care products - Aubrey Organics, Inc.
MANDARIN MELON - Lipsticks - Estee Lauder Inc.
MANDARIN MIST - Coffee ☆ - Boyd Coffee Co.
MANDARIN ORANGE - Christmas tree ornaments - Cracker Box Inc.
MANDARIN ORANGE SPICE - Teas–herbal - Celestial Seasonings, Inc.
MANDARINA DUCK - Luggage - Delsey Luggage Inc.
MANDARINE - Perfume, cosmetics - Bourjois Ltd.
MANDARINE NAPOLEON - Liquors ☆ - SPAR Inc.
MANDARINE NAPOLEON LIQUER - Liqueurs - Canandaigua Wine Co. Inc.
MANDARINS - Shoes - Somersworth Shoe Co. Inc.
MANDASTAT - Pharmaceutical preparations ☆ - American Urologicals Inc.
MANDATE - Computer software - Computer Aided Systems, Inc.
MANDATE - Furniture - Mandate Sales Co.
MANDATE - Furniture - Thomasville Furniture Industries Inc.
MANDATE PRESS - Publisher's imprints - William Carey Library
M&C SPORT - Apparel–children's - USANM Corp.
MANDELAMINE - Pharmaceutical preparations - Parke-Davis
MANDELAY - Pharmaceutical preparations - Majestic Drug Co., Inc.
MANDELLA - Boats–motor - Brummett Marine
MANDEL'S - Pharmaceutical preparations ☆ - Humco
MANDEX - Pharmaceutical preparations ☆ - Pal-Pak Inc.
M&GN - Jewelry - M & G National Jewelry, Inc.
MANDI - Computer hardware - Mandi Corp.

MANDI PUPPY - Dolls - Mattel, Inc.
MANDINGO - Prophylactics - Stanley Oliver
M&M - Splints - MMAR Medical Group, Inc.
M&M FUN FRIENDS CHARACTERS - Toys–stuffed - Mary Meyer Corp.
M&M PRO - Computer software - Omnicomp Graphics Corp.
M&M'S - Toys - Mars, Inc.
MANDOGUITAR - Musical instruments - Jack Charles Meussdorfer
MANDOL - Pharmaceutical preparations - Eli Lilly and Co.
MANDOLIN - Flatware - Reed and Barton Corp.
MANDRAKE - Cleaning preparations–household - Puritan-Churchill Chemical Co.
MANDRIELLE - Wines - Banfi Vintners
MANDRILL - Floor coverings–carpet and rugs - Ashley Commercial Carpets
M&W - Farm machinery - M & W
MANDY - Apparel and accessories ☆ - Toll-Gate Garment Co.
MANDY - Floor coverings–carpet and rugs ☆ - Regal Rugs Inc.
MANDY - Office supplies ☆ - Brushcreek Creative Co.
MANDY - Shoes–athletic ☆ - Coast Shoes Inc.
MANDY OLD FASHIONED PEANUT BRITTLE - Candy - Atkinson Candy Co.
MANE - Wigs - Jean Paree Weegs Inc.
MANE ATTRACTION - Dolls - Susan Sona
MANE CLIPS - Hair care products - Mane Inc.
MANE DRAIN - Sink hair trap - West Coast Beauty Supply Co.
MANE EVENT - Toys - Tonka Corp.
MANE EVENT, THE - Nail care products - Cut-Heal Animal Care Products, Inc.
MANE MAGIC - Pet products - Revere Manufacturing
MANE MAULER - Toys - Mattel, Inc.
MANE MIRACLE - Hair care products - E.O.H. Industries, Inc.
MANE SECRET, THE - Hair care products - E.O.H. Industries, Inc.
MANE STREET - Hair care products - Mane Street Products USA
MANE TAMER - Barrettes - Kathleen Mahfood
MANE TAMER - Hair care products - Mebco Industries, Inc.
MANEATER - Apparel and accessories - Dan Barry
MANEATER III - Toys ☆ - Imperial Toy Corp.
MANEHANDLER - Brushes–hair - The Montclair Co.
MANEL - Sporting goods ☆ - George D. Donovan & Sons Inc.
MANETO - Floor coverings - Mannington Resilient Floors
MANETTA HOME FASHIONS - Blankets - Pillowtex Corp.
MANEX - Herbicides - Griffin Corp.
MANFIELD - Shoes - C. & J. Clark America, Inc.
MANFLANNEL - Apparel–men's ☆ - Jantzen Inc.
MANFRED HORTH - Beverages–alcohol - Joseph Gies Import
MANFRED VIERTHALER - Wines - Manfred Vierthaler Winery Inc.
MANFREDO - Apparel–men's - Mcgregor Corp.
MANFROTTO - Photographic equipment - Bogen Photo Corp.
MANG - Garden equipment - Mang Tiller Inc.
MANG-BRONZE - Propellers - Columbian Bronze Corp.
MANGA - Vitamins and nutritional supplements - Alacer Co.
MANGAMANIA - Recording label - Mangamania, Inc.
MANGE MEDIC - Pet products - Gerard-Pellham Co.
MANGIA - Computer software - Upstill Software
MANGIA! - Silverware - Zelco Industries, Inc.
MANGIA BENE - Vegetables–canned - Stanislaus Food Products Co.
MANGIAMELI - Belts, handbags, etc. - La Ceeho International
MANGILAO GOLF CLUB - Apparel and accessories - TH Corp.
MANGLOR MOUNTAIN - Toys–electronic ☆ - CBS Toys
MANGLORS - Toys–electronic ☆ - CBS Toys
MANGO - Recording label - Island Records Inc.
MANGO - Teas - Eastern Shore Tea Co.
MANGO CHUTNEY - Seasonings - Cinnabar Specialty Foods, Inc./Neera's Products
MANGO MADNESS - Beverages–carbonated - Snapple Beverage Corp.
MANGO MAGIC - Fruit drinks–bottled or canned - Hansen Beverage Co.
MANGO MAN - Fruits and vegetables - London Fruit Inc.
MANGO MANIA - Beverages - Best Flavors, Inc.
MANGO MONTAGE - Fruit drinks–bottled or canned - J.M. Smucker Co.
MANGO PASSION - Beverages–alcohol - Marie Brizard Et Roger, Inc.
MANGO PASSION - Liquors ☆ - Marie Brizard Wines & Spirits, USA
MANGO TANGO - Juices ☆ - Odwalla, Inc.
MANGO TREE - Apparel and accessories - Floridian Card Products
MANGOLD - Food products - Chiquita Brands, Inc.
MANGONEO - Beverages–carbonated - City Club Beverage Corp.
MANGORITA - Beverages–alcohol - Islands Restaurants, Inc.
MANHANDLERS - Soups–canned ☆ - Campbell Soup Co.
MANHASSET - Lamps - Manhasset Specialty Co.
MANHASSET - Musical instrument accessories - King Musical Instruments

MANHASSET BAY TRADING - Nuts–salted, roasted, cooked, or canned - Fiesta Nut Corp.

MANHATTAN - Apparel and accessories - Manhattan International

MANHATTAN - Apparel and accessories - Salant/Manhattan Industries

MANHATTAN - Apparel and accessories ☆ - California Manufacturing Co. Inc.

MANHATTAN - Apparel–men's - American Trouser Inc.

MANHATTAN - Baskets–wood ☆ - Burlington Basket Co. Inc.

MANHATTAN - Clocks ☆ - Ridgeway Clock Co.

MANHATTAN - Coffee - Manhattan Coffee Co.

MANHATTAN - Computer software - Intracom USA, Inc.

MANHATTAN - Cooking utensils–aluminum ☆ - Mirro Corp.

MANHATTAN - Dishes–china ☆ - Gorham Inc.

MANHATTAN - Floor coverings–carpet and rugs - Richmond Carpet Mills

MANHATTAN - Frames–eyeglass - Marine Optical, Inc.

MANHATTAN - Furniture - Bassett Furniture Industries, Inc.

MANHATTAN - Furniture - Taylor-Ramsey Corp.

MANHATTAN - Glass–window - Taylor Building Products Co.

MANHATTAN - Greeting cards - Paper Magic Group Inc.

MANHATTAN - Hearing aids - Argosy Electronics, Inc.

MANHATTAN - Mattresses ☆ - California Concepts

MANHATTAN - Meat products–beef - Marathon Enterprises, Inc.

MANHATTAN - Neckties ☆ - Randa Corp.

MANHATTAN - Occasional furniture ☆ - JDI Group, Inc.

MANHATTAN - Pickles - Green Bay Foods Co.

MANHATTAN - Recording label - MGM Inc.

MANHATTAN - Snack foods - That's Entertainment

MANHATTAN - Stationery - Manhattan Greeting

MANHATTAN - Trailers–travel - Transportation Equipment Sales Corp.

MANHATTAN - Watches - Croton Watch Co., Inc.

MANHATTAN - Watches - General Time Corp. (Westclox/Seth Thomas Div.)

MANHATTAN - Window shades - Hunter Douglas Intermountain Fabrication Co.

MANHATTAN BREWING COMPANY, THE - Beverages–alcohol - Soho Suds Inc.

MANHATTAN CHOCOLATES - Candy - Shufra Chocolates Food Corp.

MANHATTAN DIAMONDS - Jewelry - Andin International Inc.

MANHATTAN EXCHANGE - Food products - Crystal Farms Inc.

MANHATTAN EXPRESS - Bread - SB Royalty Co. Inc.

MANHATTAN FRUITIER - Food products - Manhattan Fruitier, Inc.

MANHATTAN II-E - Flowers, plants, and seeds - Jacklin Seed

MANHATTAN INTERNATIONAL - Apparel and accessories - Salant/Manhattan Industries

MANHATTAN LEVERS - Locks–padlocks - Weiser Lock Corp.

MANHATTAN MISSIONS - Computer software ☆ - Konami (America) Inc.

MANHATTAN MOVING CO. - Blouses–women's ☆ - Salant/Manhattan Industries

MANHATTAN PALETAS - Desserts - Manhattan Frozen Products

MANHATTAN SKYLINE - Fabrics–tapestry - Coloroll Inc.

MANHATTAN SPECIAL - Beverages–carbonated - Manhattan Special Bottling Corp.

MANHATTEN - Faucets - Kallista Inc.

MANHATTEN CIRCUIT - Hearing aids - Argosy Electronics, Inc.

MANHATTWAN LINE - Pet products - Classic Products

MANHELP - Brushes–paint - Elder & Jenks, Inc.

MANHOOD COLLECTIONS - Paper products - Manhood Collections, Inc.

MANHUNT - Games ☆ - Milton Bradley Co.

MANI - Manicure preparations - Brand Nails

MANI - Sauces - Mary Rose, Inc.

MANI-G 'RAPS - Wrapping paper - Mani-G 'Raps & Co.

MANI MAGIC - Nail care products ☆ - Pfizer Inc.

MANIA CHALLENGE - Vials–glass - Taito America Corp.

MANIAC - Games ☆ - CBS Toys

MANIAC - Perfumes - Colgate-Palmolive Co.

MANIAC - Toys–models - Estes Industries

MANIAC SPORTS - Video games - Amazing Media, Inc.

MANIACS - Toys - Tonka Corp.

MANIAX - Toys - Mattel, Inc.

MANIBELLE - Recording label ☆ - Telemark Dance Records

MANIC PANIC - Cosmetics - Tish & Snooky's N.Y.C. Inc.

MANICARDI - Vinegar - Bel Canto Fancy Foods Ltd.

MANICARE 10 - Clippers–nail - Chesebrough-Pond's USA Co.

MANICARE 5000 - Manicure appliances ☆ - London International U.S. Holdings

MANICARE USA - Cosmetics - Stratton of London Inc.

MANICURE - Nail care products ☆ - Maybelline Co.

MANICURE CENTER, THE - Nail care products - Windmere Corp.

MANICURE IN A BOTTLE - Nail care products - Colour Grow Cosmetics Intl.

MANICURE MACHINE - Manicure preparations - ABAR Beauty Supply Inc.

MANICURE MINIATURES - Manicure kits - Orly International Inc.

MANICURE PLUS - Cosmetics - Ladyfingers

MANIFEST - Herbicides - BASF Corp.

MANIFESTATIONS - Greeting cards - Manifestations Inc.

MANIFOLD SAVER - Automotive parts and accessories - Tomco, Inc.

MANIFOLD TECHNOLOGY - Audio equipment - Electro-Voice, Inc.

MANIKIN - Footwear–women's ☆ - Avanti Shoe

MANIKIT - Manicure preparations - Capitol Novelty Co.

MANILA - Baskets–wood ☆ - Burlington Basket Co. Inc.

MANILA - Floor coverings–carpet and rugs ☆ - Stanton Carpet Corp.

MANILA - Thread - Threads USA Div.

MANILA GOLD - Beverages - Nobelt Co.

MANILA GOLD - Beverages - Ramar International Corp.

MANILAC - Rope - Wellington Leisure Products, Inc.

MANIPULITE - Educational materials - A. Daigger & Co., Inc.

MANIQUETTE - Mannequins ☆ - Canson-Talens Inc.

MANIQUICK - Manicure preparations - Arius-Eickert Co. Inc.

MANIRON - Pharmaceutical preparations ☆ - JMI-Canton Pharmaceuticals

MANISCHEWITZ - Food products - Bakers Franchise Corp.

MANISCHEWITZ - Food products - B. Manischewitz Co.

MANISCHEWITZ KOSHER WINE - Beverages–alcohol - Canandaigua Wine Co. Inc.

MANISHA PRESS - Publisher's imprints - Sita R. Kaura

MANISTEE - Footwear - B-W Footwear Co. Inc.

MANISYL - Pharmaceutical preparations - Sylka Managing Co., Inc.

MANITA - Seafood products–fresh or frozen ☆ - King Oscar Inc.

MANITERA - Pharmaceutical preparations ☆ - Vitarine Pharmaceuticals Inc.

MANITEX - Cranes–truck - Manitowoc Co. Inc.

MANITEX - Floor coverings - Mannington Resilient Floors

MANITOBA - Bicycles - Raleigh USA Bicycle Co.

MANITOBA - Bicycles ☆ - Huffy Corp.

MANITOCK - Water–bottled or canned - Manitock Spring Water Co.

MANITOU - Floor coverings ☆ - Tarkett, Inc.

MANITOU AND COG WHEEL ROUTE PIKE'S PEAK RAILWAY - Apparel - Manitou and Pikes Peak Railway Co.

MANITOU SPARKLERS - Water–bottled or canned - Manitou Springs Sparklers Inc.

MANIVIM - Pharmaceutical preparations ☆ - Vitarine Pharmaceuticals Inc.

MANJOO - Floor coverings–carpet and rugs ☆ - Trans-Ocean Import Co. Inc.

MANKALA - Games - Games & Graphics, Inc.

MANKIND - Apparel and accessories - Mankind Apparel

MANKIND - Apparel and accessories ☆ - Barrow Manufacturing Co., Inc.

MANKIND - Shaving preparations ☆ - Johnson & Johnson

MANKOCIDE - Pesticides–agricultural - Griffin Corp.

MANLEY - Automotive-service equipment - Babcock Industries Inc. (Babcock Control Group)

MANLEY - Motor vehicle parts and accessories - Rivera Engineering, Inc.

MANLEY - Valves–engine - Manley Performance Products, Inc.

MANN - Apparel and accessories - Mcgregor Corp.

MANN - Health care products - Mann Chemical Corp.

MANN MADE - Music boxes - Seymour Mann Inc.

MANN-MADE-MUGS - Tableware–earthenware - Seymour Mann Inc.

MANNA - Crackers ☆ - B. Manischewitz Co.

MANNA - Nutritional supplements - Intracell Nutrition Inc.

MANNA PRO - Animal feeds - St. Lawrence Sales Inc.

MANNA SENIOR - Animal feeds - Manna Pro Corp.

MANNAN-DEX - Vitamins and nutritional supplements - Nutrition Enterprises

MANNATEC - Computer software - Mannatec, Inc.

MANNEQUIN - Shoes - Genesco Inc.

MANNER - Cookies - Holland-American Importing Co. Inc.

MANNER - Cookies - Pez Candy Inc.

MANNER - Crackers - Sunshine/Salerno Inc.

MANNERS IN A FLASH - Educational materials - At Ease Inc.

MANNESMANN TALLY - Printers–computer - Mannesmann Tally Corp.

MANNESMANN TALLY 160L - Printers–computer ☆ - Mannesmann Tally Corp.

MANNEST - Pharmaceutical preparations ☆ - Kenneth A. Manne Co.

MANNEX - Apparel and accessories - Unnex Industrial Corp.

MANNIE - Ophthalmic goods - Rozin Optical Export Corp.

MANNING STREET - Crocheted and knitted items - Heritage Sportswear

MANNING SYSTEMS, INC. - Alarm systems - Manning Systems, Inc.

MANNING'S - Food products - Mrs. M. Manning Inc.

MANNINGTON - Flooring–hardwood - Mannington Wood Floors

☆ = Now out of production

MANNINGTON AWARD SERIES - Cleaning preparations - Mannington Mills, Inc.

MANNINGTON CARPETS - Floor coverings–carpet and rugs - Mannington Mills, Inc.

MANNINGTON CLASSIC - Floor coverings - Mannington Mills, Inc.

MANNINGTON COMMERCIAL - Floor coverings–tile - Mannington Mills, Inc.

MANNINGTON GOLD - Floor coverings - Mannington Resilient Floors

MANNINGTON STERLING - Floor coverings - Mannington Resilient Floors

MANNISH - Recording label - Grind Stone Records

MANNITE CONOSCENTI - Natural sweetener - Royal Source, Inc.

MANNIX - Floor coverings–carpet and rugs ☆ - Burtco Enterprises Inc.

MANNONI - Cheese - Cerami Sales Co. Inc.

MANNONS SPICE COMPANY - Soups–mixes - Mannons Chocolates, Inc.

MANN'S - Dinners–frozen ☆ - Mann's International Meat Specialties Inc.

MANN'S - Fruits and vegetables - Elwin R. Mann

MANN'S - Music boxes - Seymour Mann Inc.

MANN'S CANNERY - Giftware - Seymour Mann Inc.

MANN'S INTERNATIONAL - Food products ☆ - Mann's International Meat Specialties Inc.

MANN'S INTERNATIONAL GOURMET APPETIT' - Frozen foods - Mann's International Meat Specialties Inc.

MANN'S INTERNATIONAL GOURMET EXPRESS - Frozen foods - Mann's International Meat Specialties Inc.

MANN'S INTERNATIONAL PREPARED ENTREES - Frozen foods - Mann's International Meat Specialties Inc.

MANN'S INTERNATIONAL PREPARED MEXICAN FOODS - Frozen foods - Mann's International Meat Specialties Inc.

MANN'S INTERNATIONAL PREPARED SOUPS - Frozen foods - Mann's International Meat Specialties Inc.

MANN'S SUNNY SHORES - Fruits and vegetables - Mann Packing Co., Inc.

MANN'S WORLD - Giftware - Seymour Mann Inc.

MANNY T. - Toys–stuffed - Gund, Inc.

MANNY'S - Tortillas - Mexican Accent, Inc.

MANO - Drums–musical instruments - Remo, Inc.

MANO-WATCH - Vacuum and pressure controllers - Instruments for Research and Industry, I2R Inc.

MANOIR - Rings–jewelry - Artcarved Inc.

MANOIR - Tableware–china - Villeroy and Boch Tableware Ltd.

MANOLA - Pharmaceutical preparations - Luyties Pharmacal Co.

MANOLEUM - Floor coverings - Mannington Resilient Floors

MANOLUX - Floor coverings - Mannington Resilient Floors

MANOMOY - Boats–skiffs - European Custom Yachts Ltd.

MANOR - Bakery products - Campbell Taggart Inc.

MANOR - Clocks - General Time Corp. (Westclox/Seth Thomas Div.)

MANOR - Floor coverings - Mannington Resilient Floors

MANOR - Floor coverings–carpet and rugs - Columbus Mills, Inc.

MANOR - Floor coverings–carpet and rugs - Langhorne Carpet Co. Inc.

MANOR - Floor coverings–carpet and rugs - Patrick Carpet Mills

MANOR - Furniture - American Furniture Co. Inc.

MANOR - Manufactured homes - Redman Industries, Inc.

MANOR - Pet products - American Cat Emporium

MANOR CONFECTIONS - Candy - Oregon Manor

MANOR COURT - Floor coverings–tile ☆ - Kentile Floors Inc.

MANOR GALLERY - Glassware–household - W.C. Bunting Co.

MANOR HALL - Paints - PPG Industries, Inc.

MANOR HALL - Wallpaper ☆ - Wallquest, Inc.

MANOR HOUSE - Cabinets - Imperial Cabinet Co. Inc.

MANOR HOUSE - Cabinets - Wellborn Cabinet, Inc.

MANOR HOUSE - Doors–metal ☆ - Johnson Metal Products

MANOR HOUSE - Faucets ☆ - Moen Inc.

MANOR HOUSE - Floor coverings - Mannington Resilient Floors

MANOR HOUSE - Floor coverings–carpet and rugs - Mohawk Carpet Corp.

MANOR HOUSE - Floor coverings–carpet and rugs - Whitecrest Carpet Mills

MANOR HOUSE - Floor coverings–carpet and rugs ☆ - Calladium & Marglen

MANOR HOUSE - Mobile homes - Wick Building Systems Inc. (Manufactured Home Div./North)

MANOR HOUSE - Turkeys - Safeway Stores Inc.

MANOR HOUSE - Wallpaper - Hunting Valley Prints

MANOR HOUSE CHERRY SQUARE - Cabinets - Wellborn Cabinet, Inc.

MANOR OAK - Siding - Aluminum Co. of America

MANOR RIDGE - Floor coverings–carpet and rugs ☆ - World Carpets, Inc.

MANOR TURF - Floor coverings–carpet and rugs - Proffitt Manufacturing Co.

MANOR VIEW - Seat covers - Saddleman, Inc.

MANOR WALK - Tiles–ceramic - Porcelanite, Inc.

MANORA - Hot tubs–fiberglass - Watkins Manufacturing Corp.

MANORSTONE - Blocks–concrete - Mutual Materials Co.

MANORWOOD - Cabinets - H.J. Scheirich Co.

MANORWOOD - Floor coverings - Congoleum Corp.

MANORWOOD - Furniture–upholstered ☆ - Woodmark Originals

MANORWOOD - Giftware - Service Merchandise Co. Inc.

MANOTENSIN - Pharmaceutical preparations - Dunhall Pharmaceuticals Inc.

MANPOWER - Employment agencies–temporary help - Manpower Inc.

MANRICO - Perfumes - Maglificio Di Marsciano USA, Inc.

MAN'S BEST FRIEND - Calendars ☆ - American Greetings Corp.

MAN'S BEST FRIEND - Figurines ☆ - Dave Grossman Creations Inc.

MAN'S CHOICE - Colognes - United Enterprises Inc. (Nyla Laboratories)

MAN'S FRIEND - Pet products ☆ - Staff Supermarket Associates, Inc.

MAN'S LAV - Toilets–enameled - Kohler Co.

MAN'S WORLD - Colognes - Parfum de Coeur Ltd.

MAN'S WORLD - Wigs - New Image

MANSCO - Apparel–men's - Manhattan International

MANSFIELD - Boats–canoes - Stowe Canoe and Snowshoe Co. Inc.

MANSFIELD - Clocks - Ridgeway Clock Co.

MANSFIELD - Drums–musical instruments ☆ - Grossman Music Corp.

MANSFIELD - Floor coverings - Mannington Resilient Floors

MANSFIELD - Frames–eyeglass ☆ - Universal/Univis Inc.

MANSFIELD - Glass–leaded - Seneca Glass Co.

MANSFIELD - Glassware–household ☆ - Lenox Crystal, Inc.

MANSFIELD - Plumbing fixtures–metal - Mansfield Plumbing Products, Inc.

MANSFIELD - Rings–jewelry - Artcarved

MANSFIELD - Scales–industrial - Sterling Manufacturing

MANSFIELD - Tableware–china - Lenox, Inc.

MANSFIELD - Toys–stuffed - Mary Meyer Corp.

MANSFIELD PARK - Wallpaper - Parkview Designs

MANSFIELD PROFESSIONAL ACRYLIC SERIES - Sinks–porcelain - Mansfield Plumbing Products, Inc.

MANSION - Handles–metal - A.J.P. Weslock Industries Co.

MANSION - Staircases–wood - Mansion Industries Inc.

MANSION FANCY - Candy - Home of the Hebert Candies, Inc.

MANSION HOUSE - Paints ☆ - Pratt & Lambert United, Inc.

MANSION SAMPLER - Candy - Home of the Hebert Candies, Inc.

MANSIONS IN MINIATURE - Dolls - Dura-Craft Inc.

MANSMITH'S - Spices and extracts - Mansmith Enterprises

MANSON - Tape–adhesive - Okonite Co. Inc.

MANSOUR - Stethoscopes - R.J. Mansour, Inc.

MANSPORT - Apparel–men's - Manhattan International

MANTA - Audio equipment ☆ - Telequest Inc.

MANTA - Boats–motor - Manta Marine Corp.

MANTA - Boats–motor ☆ - Larson Boat Div.

MANTA - Computer hardware - Digital Ocean, Inc.

MANTA - Fishing tackle - Braid Products Ltd., Inc.

MANTA - Motor vehicles–automobiles ☆ - General Motors Corp. (Buick Motor Div.)

MANTA - Toys–models - Estes Industries

MANTA BOMBER - Toys–models ☆ - Estes Industries

MANTA CLIPPER - Boats–motor - Tillotson-Pearson Inc.

MANTA LUXUS - Motor vehicles–automobiles ☆ - General Motors Corp. (Buick Motor Div.)

MANTA RALLYE - Motor vehicles–automobiles ☆ - General Motors Corp. (Buick Motor Div.)

MANTA RAY - Anchors - Foresight Products Inc.

MANTA RAY - Bicycles - Schwinn Cycling & Fitness Inc.

MANTA RAY - Exercising equipment - Advanced Fitness, Inc.

MANTADIL - Pharmaceutical preparations - Burroughs Wellcome Co.

MANTASTIC - Girdles - Preferred Foundations

MANTECH - Manifolds–motor vehicle - PHD, Inc.

MANTECH - Toys - Azrak-Hamway International, Inc.

MANTECOL - Candy - Tomeyko Corp.

MANTEKOL - Candy - Tomeyko Corp.

MANTELETTE - Clocks ☆ - General Time Corp. (Westclox/Seth Thomas Div.)

MANTENNA - Toys - Mattel, Inc.

MANTEO GROUP - Furniture - Conover Chair Co. Inc.

MANTERROR - Toys - Hasbro, Inc.

MANTEY - Wines - Firelands Winery

MANTEY - Wines - Meier's Wine Cellars Inc.

MANTIS - Forceps–medical - Linvatec Corp.

MANTIS - Guitars ☆ - Peavey Electronics Corp.

MANTIS LT - Guitars ☆ - Peavey Electronics Corp.

MANTISAUR - Toys - Mattel, Inc.

MANTLE VASE - Glassware–household - Nourot Glass Studio

MANTOPS - Shirts ☆ - Manhattan International

MANTRA - Bicycles - Klein Bicycle Corp.

☆ = Now out of production

MANTRA - Skin care products - Vijay Maya Rampersaud
MANTROSE-HAEUSER - Varnishes - Mantrose-Haeuser Co. Inc.
MANTUA - Furniture - Mantua Manufacturing Co.
MANTUA - Toys–trains - Mantua/Cosom Sporting Goods
MANU VITTA - Vitamins and nutritional supplements - Nutra Vitta Natural Products, Inc.
MANUAL MATE - Electronic equipment - Dukane Corp.
MANUAL MATIC - Electronic equipment - Dukane Corp.
MANUAL-PAK - Magazine racks - Custom-Pak Inc.
MANUDO - Toys - Multi Toys Corp.
MANUEL - Cigars ☆ - G.W. Van Slyke & Horton
MANUEL CANOVAS - Wallpaper - Manuel Canovas Inc.
MANUEL DANTE - Apparel and accessories - MGRR, Inc.
MANUFACTORY - Computer software - Setpoint Inc.
MANUFACTURING MANAGER FROM DATA TECHNICAL RESEARCH, THE - Computer software - Data Technical Research, Inc.
MANUFACTURING STREAM - Computer software - Dun and Bradstreet Software Services, Inc.
MANUKAI PINEAPPLE ISLE - Wines - Fruit Wines of Florida Inc.
MANUMATIC - Projectors–photographic - Rollei of America Inc.
MANURE MOVERS OF AMERICA - Pet products - Noble Beasts Graphics
MANUSCRIPT - Floor coverings–carpet and rugs ☆ - Karastan-Bigelow Inc.
MANUSCRIPT - Wallcoverings - Ronald Redding Designs
MANVILLE - Greeting cards - Fravessi Greetings, Inc.
MANVITOL - Pharmaceutical preparations ☆ - Vitarine Pharmaceuticals Inc.
MANWICH - Meat sauces - Hunt-Wesson, Inc.
MANX - Seafood - Brooklyn Bagel Boys
MANY-BRAN - Breads - Buckeye Beans & Herbs, Inc.
MANY FACES COLOR-FULL - Skin care products - Unique Specialty Products Ltd.
MANY MAC - Chowders–canned - Buckeye Beans & Herbs, Inc.
MANY MINI'S! - Wallcovering - Gencorp Inc.
MANY VICKERS - Figurines ☆ - Schmid Inc.
MANY VOICES - Recording label - Scholastic Inc.
MANY WORLDS OF JEAN B., THE - Wallpaper ☆ - James Seeman Studios
MANZAN - Skin care products - Church and Dwight Co. Inc.
MANZANIS - Herbal products - Jose M. Gonzalez-Blanco
MANZANITA RANCH - Juices - Manzanita Ranch
MANZATE - Fungicides - E.I. Dupont de Nemours and Co.
MANZAVINO - Wines ☆ - S & J Importing Co. Inc.
MANZETTI - Apparel–men's - Cliftex Corp.
MAOLA DAIRY - Dairy products - Maola Milk and Ice Cream Co.
MAOLATE - Pharmaceutical preparations - Upjohn Co.
MAORI - Floor coverings–carpet and rugs ☆ - Evans-Black Carpet Mills
MAOX - Antacids - Kenneth A. Manne Co.
MAP - Apparel and accessories - Georges Marciano
MAP-FRESH - Machinery - Jescorp, Inc.
MAP IMAGE METAFILE - Compact discs–prerecorded - U.S. Bureau of the Census
MAP IN THE BOX - Containers–metal - Information Please, Inc.
MAP JACKET - Apparel and accessories - MST Corp.
MAP-O-GRAPH - Projectors–photographic ☆ - Artograph Inc.
MAP SEAL - Sealing compounds - Trondak, Inc.
MAP SKILLS - Computer software - Optimum Resource, Inc.
MAP STOP - Display cases–plastic - Informing Design, Inc.
MAPAC - Packaging–blisterwrap - AEP Industries, Inc.
MAPBASIC - Computer software - Mapping Information Systems Corp.
MAPBLASTER - Computer software - Software Projects, Inc.
MAPCAT - Electronic equipment - Datacom Tech., Inc.
MAPCO - Paints - Farrell-Calhoun Inc.
MAPCY - Drums–musical instruments - Washburn International
MAPEASY - Maps - MapEasy Inc.
MAPEASY - Maps - MapEasy Inc.
MAPEI - Adhesives and sealants ☆ - Maxsam Sales, Inc.
MAPEL - Adhesives and sealants - Lowy Group Inc.
MAPES - Dolls - Mapes Industries Inc.
MAPES - Musical instrument accessories - Mapes Piano String Co.
MAPES - Paneling - Mapes Industries Inc.
MAPESCRIB - Cribs–wood - Mapes Industries Inc.
MAPESMAID - Dryers–household - Mapes Industries Inc.
MAPESPET - Pet products - Mapes Industries Inc.
MAPESTOY - Toys - Mapes Industries Inc.
MAPGEN - Computer software - Information & Graphics Systems Inc.
MAPGUIDE - Maps - Rand McNally & Co.
MAPICS - Computer software - International Business Machines Corp.
MAPIX - Computer software - Delta Data Systems, Inc.

MAPLE - Bicycles - Ross Bicycles USA, Ltd.
MAPLE - Computer software - Electronic Courseware Systems Inc.
MAPLE - Dinnerware–glass ☆ - Nikko Ceramics Inc.
MAPLE - Drums–musical instruments ☆ - Pearl Corp.
MAPLE - Flooring–hardwood - Biwood Flooring
MAPLE ACRES - Syrup - Maple Acres Inc.
MAPLE BRAND - Beverages - Zhi Ming Li
MAPLE BUTTERMILK - Skin care products - Longaberger Co.
MAPLE CHASE - Thermostats - Maple Chase Co.
MAPLE CHIPMUNK - Toys–stuffed - Dakin Inc.
MAPLE CORNS - Cereal - Arrowhead Mills, Inc.
MAPLE FARMS - Candy ☆ - American Maple Products Corp.
MAPLE FAWN - Toys–stuffed - Russ Berrie and Co., Inc.
MAPLE FOREST - Furniture ☆ - Athens Furniture Industries Inc.
MAPLE GARLIC - Seasonings - Lillieville Farm Foods Inc.
MAPLE GARLIC BARBEQUE HOT & SPICY - Barbecue sauce - Lillieville Farm Foods Inc.
MAPLE GARLIC BARBEQUE ORIGINAL - Barbecue sauce - Lillieville Farm Foods Inc.
MAPLE GARLIC HORSERADISH SAUCE - Horseradish - Lillieville Farm Foods Inc.
MAPLE GARLIC MUSTARD - Mustard - Lillieville Farm Foods Inc.
MAPLE GARLIC STEAK SAUCE - Seasonings - Lillieville Farm Foods Inc.
MAPLE GARLIC STIR-FRY - Seasonings - Lillieville Farm Foods Inc.
MAPLE GARLIC STIR-FRY HOT & SPICY - Seasonings - Lillieville Farm Foods Inc.
MAPLE GARLIC VINAIGRETTE - Salad dressings–bottled - Lillieville Farm Foods Inc.
MAPLE GROVE FARMS - Salad dressings–bottled - Maple Grove Farms of Vermont, Inc.
MAPLE GROVE FARMS OF VERMONT - Syrup - Maple Grove Farms of Vermont, Inc.
MAPLE HILL - Milk - Maple Hill Farms Inc.
MAPLE HONEY - Candy ☆ - Homestead Products (Homestead Sugar Division)
MAPLE ISLAND - Milk–canned or powdered - Maple Island Inc.
MAPLE KNOLLS - Floor coverings ☆ - Congoleum Corp.
MAPLE LANE - Bedroom furniture - Jamestown Sterling
MAPLE LEAF - Apparel–athletic - Sportco Corp.
MAPLE LEAF - Glass products - Westmoreland Glass Co.
MAPLE LEAF - Paper–coated - Datacom Inc.
MAPLE LEAF - Pencils ☆ - Faber-Castell Corp.
MAPLE LEAF FARMS - Ducks - Maple Leaf Farms Inc.
MAPLE LEAF FOODS - Food products - Maple Leaf Foods Inc.
MAPLE MAID - Meats–luncheon - John Liber & Co. Inc.
MAPLE MAID FARMS - Syrup - Bellegem Waffle Corp.
MAPLE MANOR - Furniture ☆ - Kincaid Furniture Co. Inc.
MAPLE MOUNTAIN - Syrup - Naturally Fresh
MAPLE MOUNTAIN FOODS - Food products - Coombs Maple Products Inc.
MAPLE-NUT - Tobacco–chewing or smoking - Amar Blends Co.
MAPLE NUT GOODIES - Candy - Brach and Brock Confections Inc.
MAPLE NUT GRANOLA - Cereal ☆ - Arrowhead Mills, Inc.
MAPLE ORCHARDS - Syrup - Borden, Inc.
MAPLE PEPPER - Seasonings - Vermont Highland Products Co.
MAPLE RICH - Maple syrup - Torbitt & Castleman Co.
MAPLE RIDGE - Furniture ☆ - Kincaid Furniture Co. Inc.
MAPLE RIDGE - Syrup - Moran Foods, Inc.
MAPLE RIVER - Sausages - Farmland Foods, Inc.
MAPLE SKATEBOARDS - Skateboards - Watson Laminates, Inc.
MAPLE SPARKLING WATER - Water–bottled or canned - Lillieville Farm Foods Inc.
MAPLE SPRINKLES - Candy - Vermont Country Maple Inc.
MAPLE SUGAR - Christmas tree ornaments - Cracker Box Inc.
MAPLE TOWN - Toys - Tonka Corp.
MAPLE VALLEY COLLECTION - Furniture ☆ - Southern Furniture Co. of Conover
MAPLE VALLEY FARMS - Food products - Den-Bere International Ltd.
MAPLEAN - Hams - Patrick Cudahy Inc.
MAPLEBROOK - Bedding–linen - Dan River Inc.
MAPLEHURST - Dairy products - Maplehurst Farms Inc.
MAPLEINE - Spices and extracts - Pacific Foods Inc.
MAPLEJAK - Syrup - Maplejak Products Co., Inc.
MAPLELEAF - Dishes–china ☆ - WMF/USA
MAPLENUT FARM II - Wallpaper ☆ - Imperial Wallcoverings, Inc.
MAPLETON - Clocks ☆ - General Time Corp. (Westclox/Seth Thomas Div.)
MAPLETON - Tobacco products - House of Windsor Inc.
MAPLEVIEW - Cabinets - Grandview Products Co.

☆ = Now out of production

MAPLEWOOD - Clocks ☆ - General Time Corp. (Westclox/Seth Thomas Div.)
MAPLINX - Computer software - Maplinx Corp.
MAPMARKER - Computer software - Mapinfo Corp.
MAPMETRICS - Computer software - Penmetrics, Inc.
MAP'N'GO - Computer software - Delorme Publishing Co., Inc.
MAPO - Skin care products - Allergan Skin Care
MAPOLE - Golf club covers - Arizona Manufacturing & Embroidery Inc.
MAPP - Beds–hospital - Humanetics Inc.
MAPP GAS - Gasoline - Mapp Products/Airco Distributor Gases
MAPPING - Educational materials - Aroostook Mental Health Services, Inc.
MAPPLE OATMEAL IRISH STYLE - Cereal - Lillieville Farm Foods Inc.
MAPPLE PANCAKE MIX - Pancakes–mixes - Lillieville Farm Foods Inc.
MAPPLICATION - Computer software - Caliper Corp.
MAPPRO - Computer storage devices–optical - Mappro, Inc.
MAPS - Electronic equipment - Entech Design, Inc.
MAPS 'N' FACTS - Computer software - Broderbund Software, Inc.
MAPS ON FILE - Publisher's imprints - Facts on File Inc.
MAPS THAT MOVE - Computer software - Now What Software
MAPSTAR - Computer software - Satloc, Inc.
MAPVIEW - Computer software - Procd, Inc.
MAPVIEWER - Computer software - Golden Software, Inc.
MAPWIZARD - Computer software - Caliper Corp.
MAPXPRESS - Recording label - Mapinfo Corp.
MAQUAT - Ammonium phosphates - Mason Chemical Co.
MAQUETTE - Toys–models - David Perceval
MAQUICILS - Cosmetics - Lancome
MAQUICONTROLE - Cosmetics - Lancome
MAQUIFINISH - Cosmetics - Lancome
MAQUIGLACE - Lipsticks - Lancome
MAQUILLAJE SOTHYS - Cosmetics - Sothys USA Inc.
MAQUIMAT - Cosmetics - Lancome
MAQUIRICHE - Cosmetics - Lancome
MAQUISATIN - Cosmetics - Lancome
MAR - Jewelry - M.A.R. Creations
MAR-A-LAGO COLLECTION - Furniture - John Widdicomb Co.
MAR-BELLS - Hobby kits - Accento Plastic Manufacturing Inc.
MAR BRAVO - Seafood products–fresh or frozen ☆ - Pocasset Seafoods Inc.
MAR CHLOR - Water treating compounds - Mardel Laboratories, Inc.
MAR-CLAY MANOR - Furniture–factory - Clayton Marcus Co. Inc.
MAR COR - Water purification systems - Mar Cor Medical Services, Inc.
MAR-GLO - Polishing rouge ☆ - Golden Star Inc.
MAR-GON - Hardware - United Gilsonite Laboratories
MAR-HYDE - Paints - Mar-Hyde Corp.
MAR-HYDE ONE-STEP - Paints - Mar-Hyde Corp.
MAR-HYDE TILTIP - Paints - Mar-Hyde Corp.
MAR-K - Apparel–women's ☆ - Gem-Dandy, Inc.
MAR-KLEEN - Erasers - Marsh Chalkboard Co.
MAR LINDO - Shrimp–fresh or frozen - Deep Sea Shrimp Importing Co. Inc.
MAR MINNOW - Fishing tackle - Best Tackle Manufacturing Co.
MAR-NOT - Varnishes - Sherwin-Williams Automotive Finishes Corp.
MAR-O-OIL - Shampoo ☆ - Benjamin Ansehl Co.
MAR-PARV - Margarine - Harvest States Cooperatives
MAR-PARV - Margarine - Miami Margarine Co. Inc.
MAR-PIPER - Veterinary pharmaceutical preparations - C.J. Martin Co.
MAR-PRED 40 - Pharmaceutical preparations ☆ - Vortech Pharmaceuticals
MAR-PRED 80 - Pharmaceutical preparations ☆ - Vortech Pharmaceuticals
MAR-RAY - Paints - Impervious Paint Industries Ltd.
MAR-RAY - Vitamins and nutritional supplements - Margie Joiner
MAR-SALLE - Beverages–alcohol - Western International Imports Inc.
MAR-TECH - Cleaning preparations–household - Park Corp.
MAR-TEE - Golf clubs - Marty Irving Custom Club Co.
MAR-V-CIDE - Disinfectants - William Marvy Co., Inc.
MAR-V-LUS - Shoes - Edison Brothers Stores, Inc.
MAR-V-LUS - Apparel stores–sports - Jem Sportswear Inc.
MAR VISTA - Furniture - Hammary Furniture Co. Inc.
MAR Y SOL - Bathing suits - Glowear Inc.
MARA - Beverages - Triple L Distributing Co., Inc.
MARA - Frames–eyeglass - Rozin Optical Export Corp.
MARA - Neckties - Countess Mara Inc.
MARA - Whirlpools - Lasco Products Group
MARA COLLECTION - Neckties - Countess Mara Inc.
MARA LYNNE - Hair care products ☆ - Pennex Products
MARA-MI - Stationery - Mara-Mi, Inc.
MARABELLA - Beads - Accento Plastic Manufacturing Inc.
MARABELLA - Floor coverings - Mannington Resilient Floors
MARABOU - Candy - Hershey Chocolate USA

MARABOU - Christmas tree ornaments - Santa's Best
MARABU - Furniture ☆ - Koh-I-Noor, Inc.
MARACAS - Giftware ☆ - WMF/USA
MARACID - Pharmaceutical preparations - Marin Pharmaceuticals
MARACIDE - Veterinary pharmaceutical preparations - Mardel Laboratories, Inc.
MARACYN - Veterinary pharmaceutical preparations - Mardel Laboratories, Inc.
MARACYN-TWO - Veterinary pharmaceutical preparations - Mardel Laboratories, Inc.
MARADA - Boats - Armada Manufacturing Co.
MARAE - Cosmetics - Seahawk Research Group, Inc.
MARAFINO - Floor coverings - Mannington Resilient Floors
MARAFLUID - Lubricating oils - Marathon Oil Co.
MARAFUEL - Gasoline - Marathon Oil Co.
MARAGOR BOLD - Coffee - Nestle USA
MARAHAM - Draperies - Brooks Window Coverings Inc.
MARAIS - Footwear - K-Swiss Inc.
MARAKESH - Floor coverings–carpet and rugs - Harbinger Co.
MARAKESH EXPRESS - Fabrics - Interface, Inc.
MARALUBE MOLY - Oils–lubricating - Marathon Oil Co.
MARAMA - Apparel and accessories - Fiji Wear Inc.
MARAMOR - Candy - Maramor Candy Co.
MARAMOR KITCHENS - Candy - Maramor Candy Co.
MARANATHA - Butter - Maranatha! Natural Foods
MARANATHA! - Recording label - Maranatha Music Inc.
MARANATHA PRAISE - Recording label - Corinthian Group
MARANTE - Tape recorders - Saul Mineroff Electronics Inc.
MARANTI - Frames–picture - Frame Factory
MARANTZ - Audio equipment - Marantz Co.
MARAPLEX - Oils–lubricating - Marathon Oil Co.
MARASCA - Maraschino cherries - Gray & Co.
MARASCHINO - Apparel and accessories - Cherry Stix Ltd.
MARASCHINO - Liquors - Disusa Imports Co.
MARATECH INTERNATIONAL - Paper products - Maratech International, Ltd.
MARATHERM - Paper–transfer - Marathon Label Co., Inc.
MARATHON - Adhesives and sealants - W.F. Taylor Co.
MARATHON - Air purification systems - Willson/Dalloz Safety
MARATHON - Apparel stores–sports - Jefferies Socks
MARATHON - Automotive parts and accessories - Optibelt Corp.
MARATHON - Batteries - Marathon Battery Co.
MARATHON - Beverages ☆ - Florida Bottling Inc.
MARATHON - Beverages–malt - Athenee Importers and Distributors, Ltd.
MARATHON - Boats–canoes - Marathon Boat Group, Inc.
MARATHON - Boats–motor ☆ - Commander Marine
MARATHON - Candy bars - Mars, Inc.
MARATHON - Cosmetics - Noxell Corp.
MARATHON - Darts and dart games ☆ - Dart World Inc.
MARATHON - Desks - Haskell of Pittsburgh, Inc.
MARATHON - Fabrics–poplin ☆ - Greenwood Mills Inc.
MARATHON - Filters–oil ☆ - Marathon Oil Co.
MARATHON - Floor coverings - Congoleum Corp.
MARATHON - Floor coverings ☆ - Harris-Tarkett, Inc.
MARATHON - Floor coverings–carpet and rugs - Dan River Inc.
MARATHON - Floor coverings–carpet and rugs - Quaker Inc.
MARATHON - Furniture ☆ - Halcyon Inc.
MARATHON - Health care products ☆ - Bonne Bell, Inc.
MARATHON - Knives - Spectrum Razor Tools
MARATHON - Leather–chamois - Acme Sponge & Chamois Co., Inc.
MARATHON - Luggage ☆ - American Tourister, Inc.
MARATHON - Motor vehicles–motor homes - Marathon Coach, Inc.
MARATHON - Office furniture–metal ☆ - Marvel Group Inc.
MARATHON - Office paper products - Waban Inc.
MARATHON - Office supplies - Deforms
MARATHON - Paints - Hancock Paint & Varnish Co.
MARATHON - Paints - PPG Industries, Inc.
MARATHON - Paper–toweling - Genesco Inc.
MARATHON - Pesticides–household - Olympic Chemical Co.
MARATHON - Rackets–racquetball - Ektelon
MARATHON - Recording label - Polygram Records, Inc.
MARATHON - Shoes–athletic ☆ - Sidney Rich Associates Inc.
MARATHON - Skates–roller - National Sporting Goods Corp.
MARATHON - Socks - WorkAbles for Women
MARATHON - Tiles–ceramic - Buchtal USA
MARATHON - Tires - Goodyear Tire & Rubber Co.
MARATHON - Tools - American Tool Companies Inc.
MARATHON - Towels - Deroyal Textiles, Inc.

☆ = Now out of production

MARATHON - Trailers–travel - Marathon Homes Corp.

MARATHON - Vegetables–canned - Produce Magic

MARATHON - Video equipment - Concept Design, Inc.

MARATHON - Watches - Timex Corp.

MARATHON - Water heaters–household - Marathon Water Heater Co.

MARATHON - Water purification systems - Mountain Safety Research, Inc.

MARATHON - Water purification systems - Penn-Plax, Inc.

MARATHON - Waterproof outerwear - Marathon Rubber Products Co.

MARATHON 25 - Finishing agents - C.B. Dolge Co.

MARATHON 25K INSERT - Veterinary medical equipment - Engler Engineering Corp.

MARATHON BOOKS - Publisher's imprints - Icarus Press Inc.

MARATHON BRA - Apparel–women's - Darling Body Fashions, Inc.

MARATHON B.U.M. - Apparel–men's - Chauvin International Ltd.

MARATHON GOLD - Home health care products - Baxter International Inc.

MARATHON II - Floor coverings–carpet and rugs ☆ - Hollytex Carpet Mills Inc.

MARATHON IIE - Grass seed and sod - Southland Sod Farms

MARATHON RELAY - Medical apparatus - Baxter International Inc.

MARATHON SERIES - Computers - Total Control Products, Inc.

MARATHON SIDE-BY-SIDE - Washing machines–household - Speed Queen Co.

MARATHONER - Health care products - Equi-Tron Inc.

MARATHONER - Medical apparatus - Erie Medical (Div. of Ocenco Incorporated)

MARATHONER - Ovens–convection - Marshall Middleby, Inc.

MARATHONER GOLD - Ovens–convection - Marshall Middleby, Inc.

MARATHRON 25 - Finishing agents - C.B. Dolge Co.

MARATONA - Apparel–athletic - Enzo Racing Co.

MARAUDER - Bicycles - Murray, Inc.

MARAUDER - Boats - Glen-L Marine Designs

MARAUDER - Boats ☆ - Correct Craft Inc.

MARAUDER - Brushes–paint - Allpro Corp.

MARAUDER - Firearms, accessories, and parts ☆ - Marlin Firearms Co.

MARAUDER - Fishing lures - Braid Products Ltd., Inc.

MARAUDER - Golfing equipment - Harv Morgan Co. Inc., The

MARAUDER - Motor vehicles–automobiles ☆ - Ford Motor Co. (Lincoln-Mercury Div.)

MARAUDER - Paints - Paint Equipment People

MARAUDER - Rodenticides - Kent Feeds, Inc.

MARAUDER - Skates–roller - Seneca Sports, Inc.

MARAUDER - Toys–models ☆ - Estes Industries

MARAVILLA - Pharmaceutical preparations - Humphreys Pharmacal Inc.

MARAX - Pharmaceutical preparations - J.B. Roerig & Co.

MARAZIDE - Pharmaceutical preparations ☆ - Vortech Pharmaceuticals

MARAZIDE II - Pharmaceutical preparations ☆ - Vortech Pharmaceuticals

MARAZZI - Tiles–ceramic - American Marazzi Tile, Inc.

MARAZZI - Tiles–ceramic - Maxsam Sales, Inc.

MARAZZI ENDURO - Tiles–ceramic ☆ - American Marazzi Tile, Inc.

MARAZZI ENDURO OCEAN - Tiles–ceramic ☆ - American Marazzi Tile, Inc.

MARB-L-CHIP - Floor coverings ☆ - National Floor Products Co., Inc.

MARBADAN - Cleaning preparations - Stone Care International

MARBALEX - Cleaning preparations - Stone Care International Inc.

MARBAMIST - Cleaning preparations - Stone Care International Inc.

MARBAXIN-750 - Pharmaceutical preparations ☆ - Vortech Pharmaceuticals

MARBEC - Vitamins and nutritional supplements ☆ - Marlyn Co. Inc.

MARBELITE - Toilet seats ☆ - Bemis Manufacturing Co.

MARBELIZERS - Hair care products - Conair Corp.

MARBELLA - Footwear–women's - Avanti Shoe

MARBELLA - Furniture ☆ - Loroman Co.

MARBELLA - Handbags - Shoe Show, Inc.

MARBELLA - Pasta - Nobelt Co.

MARBELLA - Yarn ☆ - William Unger & Co. Inc.

MARBELLE II - Garden furniture–metal ☆ - Samsonite Furniture Co. (Consumer Products Div.)

MARBELLENE - Marble products - Jibco Industries Inc.

MARBELON - Paints - Continental Coatings Co., Inc.

MARBELOUS - Cleaning preparations - Twi-Laq Industries Inc.

MARBERT - Jewelry - Hadley Roma Corp.

MARBETT - Conveyors - Rexnord Corp.

MARBLCAST - Bathroom accessories ☆ - White Consolidated Industries, Inc.

MARBLCAST - Bathroom fixtures - Richwood

MARBLE - Floor coverings - Congoleum Corp.

MARBLE - Floor coverings–carpet and rugs ☆ - Regal Rugs Inc.

MARBLE - Giftware - Crafts International Inc.

MARBLE 200 - Tiles–ceramic ☆ - American Olean Tile Co.

MARBLE AND GRANITE - Cement - Custom Building Products

MARBLE ARCH - Dinnerware–glass ☆ - Royal China & Porcelain Companies Inc.

MARBLE ARCH - Housewares - Marble Arch Designs Ltd.

MARBLE ARCH - Linen - Armand Diradourian and Douglas Weiss Partnership

MARBLE BAY - Floor coverings–carpet and rugs - Downs Carpet Co. Inc.

MARBLE BORDERS - Tiles–ceramic - Monarch Tile Inc.

MARBLE CLASSICS - Ice cream - Kraft Foods, Inc.

MARBLE COLUMNS - Apparel–women's - H. Pacifica, Inc.

MARBLE COMPOSITION - Notebooks and notepads - American Scholar Inc.

MARBLE COVE - Floor coverings - Mannington Resilient Floors

MARBLE CRAFT - Paints - Krylon/Dupli-Color

MARBLE CREST - Wines - European Beverage Co., Inc.

MARBLE DROP - Computer software - Maxis, Inc.

MARBLE FARMS - Ice cream - Marble Farms Dairy Inc.

MARBLE GARDEN - Tableware–china - Pfaltzgraff Investment Co.

MARBLE HALL - Floor coverings - Mannington Resilient Floors

MARBLE HEAD - Games ☆ - CBS Toys

MARBLE ISLAND - Furniture - Pilliod Co.

MARBLE KING - Toys–marbles - Marble King Inc.

MARBLE KRAFT - Cardboard - Simpson Tacoma Kraft Co.

MARBLE-LITE - Candles ☆ - Candle-Lite Co.

MARBLE MADNESS - Computer software - Electronic Arts Inc.

MARBLE MADNESS - Games ☆ - Milton Bradley Co.

MARBLE MAGIC - Housewares - Magic American Corp.

MARBLE MAID - Cleaning preparations - Klein & Co.

MARBLE MOLD - Bathroom accessories ☆ - Kinkead/Tub/Shower Doors

MARBLE REDINGTON - Pens - Sanford Corp.

MARBLE RUN - Floor coverings - Mannington Resilient Floors

MARBLE SET - Adhesives and sealants - Southern Grouts & Mortars Inc.

MARBLE-SHINE - Adhesives and sealants ☆ - Custom Building Products

MARBLE SOF-TYLE - Mats - Superior Manufacturing Group/Notrax Floor Matting

MARBLE TECHNICS - Marble, granite, and limestone tile ☆ - Integrity Tile Co.

MARBLE TONE - Chimes - Nutone Inc.

MARBLE TRACKER - Computer peripheral equipment - Logitech, Inc.

MARBLE WHACKER - Games - Michael D. Spikes

MARBLECOAT - Calcium compounds - ECC International

MARBLECRETE - Stucco - Premix-Marbletite Manufacturing Co.

MARBLEHEAD - Floor coverings–carpet and rugs - Capel, Inc.

MARBLEHEAD - Floor coverings–carpet and rugs - Collins & Aikman Corp.

MARBLEHEAD ACOUSTIC DESIGN - Audio equipment - Marblehead Acoustic Design

MARBLEHEAD BY BOSTON - Clocks ☆ - Chelsea Clock Co. Inc.

MARBLEHEAD TRAINER - Ships–sailing vessels ☆ - E.R. Butler & Sons

MARBLEINE - Marble products - Visador Co.

MARBLEIZED - Floor coverings - Tarkett, Inc.

MARBLEMAX - Calcium compounds - ECC International Inc.

MARBLEMITE - Calcium compounds - ECC International

MARBLEMOLD - Floor slabs–concrete - Sterling Plumbing Group Inc.

MARBLEN - Antacids - Fleming & Co.

MARBLERAMA - Wallpaper - Carlton-Metro Wallcoverings

MARBLES - Fabrics–tapestry ☆ - Coloroll Inc.

MARBLE'S - Guns - Marble Arms Corp.

MARBLES - Sporting knives - Tennessee River Valley Knife Association Inc.

MARBLES - Toys - Tonka Corp.

MARBLESQUE - Floor coverings - Congoleum Corp.

MARBLESQUE - Pedestals–plaster of paris - Summitville Tiles, Inc.

MARBLESQUE - Tiles–ceramic - Monarch Tile Inc.

MARBLESTONE - Fabrics - Uniroyal Engineered Products

MARBLETITE - Stucco - Premix-Marbletite Manufacturing Co.

MARBLETONE - Floor coverings - Congoleum Corp.

MARBLETONE - Wood products ☆ - Masonite Corp.

MARBLETONES - Floor coverings–carpet and rugs ☆ - Quaker Inc.

MARBLEX - Clay–modeling - American Art Clay Co. Inc.

MARBLIKE - Vases - Rubens Originals

MARBLING - Inks - Boko-Undo USA Inc.

MARBLITE - Flatware - Trend Pacific Inc.

MARBLOC - Floor coverings - Mannington Resilient Floors

MARBO - Thread - Chicago Sole Leather Distributors Inc.

MARBORO - Publisher's imprints - Marboro Books Inc.

MARBRE - Furniture ☆ - Singer Furniture Co.

MARBRE-WOOL - Yarn ☆ - Joseph Galler Inc.

MARBRISA - Floor coverings–carpet and rugs - Western Carpet Mills

MARBRO - Lamps ☆ - Masco Corp.

MARBU DORADA - Biscuits - Nabisco Holdings Corp.

MARBURG - Wallpaper - Marburg Wallcoverings Inc.
MARBURY - Dishes–china ☆ - Gorham Inc.
MARBURY - Floor coverings–carpet and rugs - Gulistan Carpet Inc.
MARBURY ART - Greeting cards ☆ - Paper Magic Group Inc.
MARC - Lamps - General Electric Co.
MARC - Recording label - Titan Records
MARC ANDREW - Shoes - Speen & Co. Inc.
MARC BUCHANAN - Luggage - Pelle Pelle, Inc.
MARC/DESIGNER - Computer software - Marc Analysis Research Corp.
MARC DUVALL - Watches - Nicolet International Inc.
MARC I - Paint and wallpaper stores - Jay Bee Paint Co.
MARC JACOBS - Apparel and accessories - Jacobs-Duffy Designs, Inc.
MARC-MATE - Computer software - Personal Bibliographic Software Inc.
MARC MATTIS - Apparel and accessories - Comint Leather Goods, Inc.
MARC NICOLET - Watches - Nicolet International Inc.
MARC PERRY - Apparel–women's - Perry Manufacturing Co.
MARC PIERCE - Apparel–men's - H.I.S. Sportswear
MARC ROGER - Liquors - Crestfield Importers Ltd.
MARC SORENT - Apparel–men's - Michael Shlafer
MARCA CORONA - Floor coverings–tile - Federal Tile Imports Inc.
MARCAD - Microphones - Shure Brothers, Inc.
MARCAL - Paper - Marcal Paper Mills, Inc.
MARCALA - Coffee - Coffee Co. of the Americas
MARCALCULATE - Paper - Marcal Paper Mills, Inc.
MARCALINE - Thread - Elmore-Pisgah, Inc.
MARCAM - Hair care products - Alvin Last Inc.
MARCAMAR - Food products - C-Corp.
MARCAMAR ROYAL RED - Food products - C-Corp.
MARCANTILE - Floor coverings–carpet and rugs - Heuga USA
MARCAST - Floor coverings–tile - Walker and Zanger Inc.
MARCEA BY LEOS - Footwear - Leo's Dancewear, Inc.
MARCEL - Cosmetics - F. Wolkow & Sons
MARCEL - Girdles - Abraham & Straus/Jordan Marsh Co.
MARCEL - Watches - Marcel Watch Corp.
MARCEL AMANCE - Wines - House of Burgundy Inc.
MARCEL BOUCHER - Watches - Marcel Boucher
MARCEL ET HENRI - Food products - Marcel & Henri Charcuterie Francaise
MARCEL GEM - Paper clips - Noesting Inc.
MARCEL LAPIERRE - Newsstands - Berry Best Farm
MARCEL MARTIN - Beverages–alcohol - Nor-Glo Import Co.
MARCEL RAGNAUD - Liquors - Seagram's Chateau & Estate Wines Co.
MARCEL RECORBET - Newsstands - Berry Best Farm
MARCEL SCHURMAN - Giftware - Schurman Fine Papers
MARCELLA - Floor coverings–carpet and rugs - Marcella Corp.
MARCELLA BORGHESE - Cosmetics - Revlon Consumer Products Corp.
MARCELLE - Cosmetics - Lachine Inc.
MARCELLE - Watches - Bulova Corp.
MARCELLO - Apparel–men's - MX2, Inc.
MARCELLO GOLD - Jewelry - Stan-Lee Corp.
MARCELLO'S ITALIAN STYLE - Pizzas–frozen - Marshall & Marshall Inc.
MARCH TO THE CHAMPIONSHIP - Beverages–malt - Anheuser-Busch Companies Inc.
MARCHAM AMERICAN NUTRITIONALS - Vitamins and nutritional supplements - Marcham Laboratories, Inc.
MARCHAND - Floor coverings–carpet and rugs ☆ - Evans-Black Carpet Mills
MARCHELLONI'S PRIMO - Pizzas–frozen - Italian Express Franchise Corp.
MARCHESA - Harmonicas - Hohner Inc.
MARCHESA - Wallpaper - Gagne Wallcovering, Inc.
MARCHESI DE FRESCOBALDI - Wines - Paterno Imports, Ltd.
MARCHESI DI BAROLO WINES OF PIEMONTE - Wines - Palm Bay Imports, Inc.
MARCHESI DI GRESY - Wines ☆ - Pellegrini Bros. Wines Inc.
MARCHETTA - Apparel–women's - Frank Marchetta
MARCHING BAND - Toys - Fisher-Price, Inc.
MARCHIONE - Guitars - Stephen Marchione
MARCHIONESS - Girdles - R.H. Macy & Co.
MARCHISI DE BAROLO - Beverages–alcohol - Musa Inc.
MARCHLOR - Water treating compounds - Mardel Laboratories, Inc.
MARCHON - Eyeglasses - Marchon and Marcolin Eyewear Inc.
MARCHON - Toys - Marchon, Inc.
MARCIA - Frames–eyeglass - Rozin Optical Export Corp.
MARCIA - Glassware–household - ACC
MARCIA LYNN - Knitting supplies ☆ - Susan Bates Inc.
MARCIA LYNN - Needles–sewing ☆ - Coats and Clark Inc.
MARCIANO - Apparel and accessories - Guess?, Inc.
BRANCIANO COLLECTION - Apparel and accessories - Guess?, Inc.

MARCIA'S PRIDE - Produce - Jackel Farms & Cold Storage
MARCIE - Frames–eyeglass - U.S. Optical Frame Co.
MARCIE - Wigs - Jean Paree Weegs Inc.
MARCIL - Clothing - CPC (Aztec)
MARCINKIEWICZ - Musical instrument accessories - Marcinkiewicz Music Products
MARCK KREYDENWEISS - Wines - Wilson Daniels Ltd.
MARCO - Communications equipment - Motorola, Inc. (Land Mobile Products Sector)
MARCO - Cutting boards ☆ - Woodfold-Marco Manufacturing Inc.
MARCO - Electronic equipment - General Magic, Inc.
MARCO - Epoxy coatings - Marco Products Inc.
MARCO - Food products - Marco Food Products Inc.
MARCO - Glassware–household ☆ - Mark Ross and Co. International
MARCO - Lighting fixtures - Marco/Hubbell Lighting Inc.
MARCO AMBARELLI - Footwear–women's - Mariando International Inc.
MARCO AVANE - Handbags - Great American Leatherworks Inc.
MARCO BAY - Floor coverings–carpet and rugs - Karastan-Bigelow Inc.
MARCO CORONA - Tiles–terrazzo - Imperial Tile and Marble Corp.
MARCO DELLI - Apparel and accessories - Marco Delli
MARCO DI SARRANO - Wallets - Art Craft Wallets Inc.
MARCO ISLAND - Funnels - Kmart Corp.
MARCO MOUSE - Toys–stuffed - Russ Berrie and Co., Inc.
MARCO POLO - Food products - Adria Imports Inc.
MARCO POLO - Food products - Mah Chena Corp.
MARCO POLO - Luggage - Airway Industries, Inc.
MARCO POLO - Pasta - Cumberland Pasta Co., Inc.
MARCO POLO TRADERS BY PRINCE GARDNER - Leather goods ☆ - Prince Gardner Inc.
MARCO RICCI - Leather accessories - International Accessories Corp.
MARCO TRONO - Apparel–men's - Ital Clothing, Inc.
MARCO VICCI - Shoes - Kotoni Trading Inc.
MARCOLIN - Eyeglasses - Marchon and Marcolin Eyewear Inc.
MARCOLIN - Glassware–household - Riedel Crystal of America Inc.
MARCOLIN 883 - Sunglasses ☆ - Marchon and Marcolin Eyewear Inc.
MARCOM - Rubber bands - B.F. Goodrich Co.
MARCON - Hearing aids - Marcon Hearing Instruments Inc.
MARCONI - Oils–edible - Vincent Formusa Co.
MARCONI - Wines - Barcamerica International Corp. USA
MARCOR - Computer software - Marcor, Inc.
MARCO'S - Meat products–beef - Marco Food Products Inc.
MARCOS ERGAS - Apparel and accessories - Cebal Corp.
MARCOUX 45 - Looms - J.L. Hammett Co.
MARCOVITCH - Cigarettes - G.A. Georgopulo & Co. Inc.
MARCOZZI - Pizzas–frozen - Primo's Italian Foods
MARCRAFT - Rackets–tennis ☆ - Century Sports Inc.
MARCREST - Crocheted and knitted items - Marcrest Knitting Mills
MARCREST - Floor coverings ☆ - Congoleum Corp.
MARCREST - Lamps - J.F. Marr Co. Inc.
MARCREST - Paper–kraft ☆ - Marvin Envelope & Paper Co.
MARC'S COFFEE MILL - Coffee - Marcus Restaurants, Inc.
MARCSMEN - Lamps - David Wexler & Co.
MARCUS - Apparel–men's - Neiman Marcus Co.
MARCUS - Computer software - Mueller and Smith
MARCUS DAIRY - Milk - Marcus Dairy Inc.
MARCUS JAMES - Wines - Canandaigua Wine Co. Inc.
MARCY - Exercising equipment - Impex Inc.
MARCY - Exercising equipment - Marcy Fitness Products
MARCY - Mops ☆ - Helen Keller Services for the Blind
MARCY - Thread ☆ - Perfect Thread Co. Inc.
MARCY & ROBIN - Jewelry - Hilary Lynn Designs
MARCY G - Adhesives and sealants - Super Glue Corp.
MARCY'S - Uniforms–tailored - Marcy's Groom-a-Pet
MARDA - Bowls - Svend Jensen of Denmark Inc.
MARDALE - Relishes - Mardale Inc.
MARDELI - Seafood products–fresh or frozen ☆ - J.F. Clarke Corp.
MARDI BRA - Brassieres (Bras) - Custom Maid Brassiere Co.
MARDI-GRAS - Bags–duffel - SGI Inc.
MARDI GRAS - Balls - Voit Corp.
MARDI GRAS - Bathing caps ☆ - Alger Creations Inc.
MARDI GRAS - Christmas tree ornaments - Cracker Box Inc.
MARDI GRAS - Cigarettes ☆ - Nat Sherman, Inc.
MARDI GRAS - Copper compounds ☆ - Regal Ware, Inc.
MARDI GRAS - Dinnerware–glass - Nikko Ceramics Inc.
MARDI GRAS - Eyeglasses - Willson/Dalloz Safety
MARDI-GRAS - Fireworks - American Promotional Events, Inc.

☆ = Now out of production

MARDI GRAS - Flatware - Washington Forge Inc.
MARDI-GRAS - Floor coverings–carpet and rugs - Couristan Inc.
MARDI GRAS - Floor coverings–carpet and rugs - Marco Products Inc.
MARDI GRAS - Floor coverings–carpet and rugs - West Point-Pepperell Mill Store
MARDI GRAS - Hair care products - Helene Curtis Industries Inc.
MARDI GRAS - Housewares - Himark Enterprises Inc.
MARDI GRAS - Paper - Fort Howard Corp.
MARDI GRAS - Paper ☆ - Fox River Paper Co.
MARDI GRAS - Seasonings - Carnival Seasonings
MARDI GRAS - Stationery - Mardi Gras Enterprises
MARDI GRAS - Tiles–ceramic - Wenczel Tile Co.
MARDI GRAS - Tools ☆ - Regent Sheffield, Ltd.
MARDI GRAS - Window shades ☆ - Spring Window Fashions Division, Inc.
MARDI GRAS - Yarn ☆ - Tahki Imports Ltd.
MARDI GRAS GIFT BAGS - Rice - Estherwood Rice Sales
MARDI PARTI - Cups–plastic - C.V. Gambina Inc.
MARDOL - Pharmaceutical preparations - Marlop Pharmaceuticals Inc.
MARDON - Pharmaceutical preparations - Armenpharm Ltd.
MARDO'S - Food products - Mexican Foods
MARDROPS - Cold remedies - Marlop Pharmaceuticals Inc.
MARDUK - Yarn - Smart Machine Technologies Inc.
MARDURE - Crocheted and knitted items - Marcrest Knitting Mills
MARE NOSTRUM - Buckles - Azor Trader Inc.
MARE PLUS - Animal feeds - Farnam Cos. Inc.
MAREBE - Artists' materials - Riebe's Artist Materials Inc.
MARECHAL FOCH - Wines - Meredyth Vineyard
MARECYCLE - Oils–lubricating ☆ - Marathon Oil Co.
MAREDRET - Cheese ☆ - Swissrose International Inc.
MAREDSOUS - Cheese ☆ - Swissrose International Inc.
MAREE - Sports apparel - Reebok International Ltd.
MARELLE - Floor coverings - Parquet de France Inc.
MAREMMANA - Rice - De Choix Specialty Foods Co.
MAREMONT - Exhaust systems–motor vehicle - Maremont Exhaust Products Inc.
MAREN - Apparel–women's - Synari, Ltd.
MAREN SPORT - Apparel–women's - Synari, Ltd.
MARENA - Apparel and accessories - Kellwood Co.
MARENA - Bandages–surgical - Marena Group, Inc.
MARENGO - Floor coverings–carpet and rugs - Capel, Inc.
MARENGO - Lighters - Colibri Inc.
MARENGO 2 - Housewares - Bammental Wallcoverings Inc.
MARES - Scuba diving equipment - Head Sports USA
MARE'S MILK PLUS - Animal feeds - Buckeye Feed Mills, Inc.
MARETSA - Drawing table - Martin Universal Design Inc.
MAREX - Aquatic pharmacuetical preparations ☆ - Aquatronics-Filtronics
MAREZINE - Pharmaceutical preparations - Burroughs Wellcome Co.
MAREZINE - Pharmaceutical preparations - Martin Himmel Inc.
MARFAK - Envelopes–glassine - Texaco Lubricants Co.
MARFLEX - Pharmaceutical preparations ☆ - Vortech Pharmaceuticals
MARFONYL - Pharmaceutical preparations - Wesley Pharmacal Co. Inc.
MARFORD - Seafood products–fresh or frozen - Hang Tat Foods USA Inc.
MARFORT - Tiles–ceramic ☆ - Dal-Tile Corp.
MARGANNI - Wines - Richard Adlai Corp.
MARGARD - Plastics - General Electric Co.
MARGAREET COLLECTION - Pet jewelry - Michelle International Ltd.
MARGARET - Eyeglasses - Art-Craft Optical Co.
MARGARET - Glassware–household - Crystal Clear Importing Co. Inc.
MARGARET - Glassware–household ☆ - Herman Dodge & Son Inc.
MARGARET - Tableware–china - Lenox, Inc.
MARGARET BAKER'S - Food products - Margaret Baker's Foods Inc.
MARGARET GERALD - Footwear - Margaret Gerald
MARGARET HOLMES - Vegetables–canned - McCall Farms Inc.
MARGARET K. MCELDERRY BOOKS - Publisher's imprints - Maxwell/McMellan Inc.
MARGARET KEANE - Figurines ☆ - Dave Grossman Creations Inc.
MARGARET OLEARY - Apparel and accessories - Margaret O'Leary, Inc.
MARGARET STUDIOS - House furnishings - Margaret Studios Inc.
MARGARET WOODBURY STRONG - Games - J. Hermes
MARGARETWARE - Dishes–wood ☆ - Richmond Cedar Works Manufacturing Corp.
MARGARITA - Cleaning preparations - Ruby's Beauty Supply, Inc.
MARGARITA - Fabrics - Dan River Inc.
MARGARITA - Juices - Real Fresh, Inc.
MARGARITA BAY - Syrup - Lehmann Farms, Inc.
MARGARITA MADNESS - Blenders - Dynamics Corp. of America

MARGARITA PECANS - Food products - Mrs. Powell's Gourmet Pecans
MARGARITA UNIVERSITY - Napkins–paper ☆ - Pepe's Inc.
MARGARITA'S MARGARITA - Liqueur - Cointreau Corp.
MARGARITAVILLE - Apparel and accessories - Margaritaville Store Inc.
MARGARITAVILLE - Beverages–alcohol - Jimmy Buffett
MARGATE - Eyeglasses - Martin-Copeland Eyewear Corp.
MARGATE - Flatware - Pfaltzgraff Investment Co.
MARGATE - Floor coverings–carpet and rugs - Glen Eden Wool Carpets
MARGATE - Floor coverings–carpet and rugs ☆ - Karastan-Bigelow Inc.
MARGATE - Shoes ☆ - Allen-Edmonds Shoe Corp.
MARGAUX - Flatware - Towle Manufacturing Co.
MARGAUX - Floor coverings–carpet and rugs ☆ - Hollytex Carpet Mills Inc.
MARGAUX - House furnishings - Link-Taylor Corp.
MARGAUX - Music–sheet - GSP
MARGAUX CAT - Toys–stuffed - Russ Berrie and Co., Inc.
MARGE CARSON - Furniture ☆ - Masco Corp.
MARGEN - Blinds–venetian - Margen Blinds Manufacturing Co.
MARGERY WIND FOR BEACON - Shoes ☆ - Beacon Shoe Co.
MARGESIC - Pharmaceutical preparations ☆ - Vortech Pharmaceuticals
MARGESIC COMPOUND - Pharmaceutical preparations ☆ - Vortech Pharmaceuticals
MARGHERITA - Meats–luncheon ☆ - Hunt-Wesson, Inc.
MARGHESTONE - Marble products - Verona Marble Co.
MARGIE - Frames–eyeglass - Pathway Optical Prods.
MARGIE - Window frames - Quaker Window Products Co.
MARGIE DARNELL LTD. - Apparel–women's - Margie Darnell Ltd.
MARGIN BUILDER - Computer software - Prosolutions, Inc.
MARGIN BUILDERS - Bathing suits ☆ - Jantzen Inc.
MARGIN MAKER - Computer software - Rosen's Inc.
MARGIN MASTER - Office supplies - McBee Loose Leaf Binders
MARGINAL VALUE ENGINE - Computer software - Decision Focus Inc.
MARGLASS - Automotive parts and accessories ☆ - Marson Creative Fastener Group
MARGO - Eyeglasses - Martin-Copeland Eyewear Corp.
MARGO - Food products - Pet Inc.
MARGO GERARD - Footwear–women's ☆ - Combine Group Division Inc.
MARGOT - Eyeglasses - Art-Craft Optical Co.
MARGOT PARIS - Hobby kits - Gilt Import Co. Inc.
MARGRACE - Eyeglasses - Martin-Copeland Eyewear Corp.
MARGRAVE - Eyeglasses - Martin-Copeland Eyewear Corp.
MARGROVE - Watches - Margrove Industries Inc.
MARGUETRY - Tableware–china - Pfaltzgraff Investment Co.
MARGUS - Seafood products–fresh or frozen - Kitchens of the Oceans Inc.
MARHEAS - Seafood - Bayside Imports Inc.
MARHILL - Eyeglasses - Martin-Copeland Eyewear Corp.
MARHIST - Pharmaceutical preparations ☆ - Marlop Pharmaceuticals Inc.
MARI-DEAN - Fruits–frozen - Scenic Fruit Co.
MARI-MANN'S SIT-R-SIMMER - Giftware ☆ - Mari-Mann Herb Co., Inc.
MARI-NET - Bags - U.S. Netting, Inc.
MARI SUPER-TONE - Musical instrument accessories - E. & O. Mari Inc.
MARIA - Dolls - Russ Berrie and Co., Inc.
MARIA - Footwear ☆ - Swedish Clogs Inc.
MARIA - Frames–eyeglass - Rozin Optical Export Corp.
MARIA - Furniture - Haworth, Inc.
MARIA - Occasional tables - JDI Group, Inc.
MARIA - Recording label - Johnny Angel Music Entertainment
MARIA BOTERO - Jewelry - Rolo Manufacturing Co., Inc.
MARIA CASERO - Apparel and accessories - Casero's & Associates
MARIA ISABEL - Food products - C-Corp.
MARIA NO - Women's apparel - KWBL Clothing & Apparel Corp.
MARIA ROSA - Apparel–women's - Vida Enterprise Corp.
MARIA SANSANO - Footwear - D'Bello Shoe Corp.
MARIA TERESA - Food products - Maria Teresa Inc.
MARIACHI - Apparel–women's - Wacoal America Inc.
MARIACHI - Sauces - Victoria's Treasure Inc.
MARIACHI - Tortillas - Azteca Foods, Inc.
MARIACHI - Tortillas - Meadowlands Foods Inc.
MARIAH - Boats–motor - Mariah Boats, Inc.
MARIAH - Floor coverings–carpet and rugs - Helios Carpets
MARIAH - Kites ☆ - Hi-Flier Manufacturing Co.
MARIAH VIRTUS INTEGRITAS - Boats–motor - Mariah Boats, Inc.
MARIAH'S BLEND - Coffee - House of Coffee
MARIAK - Window coverings - Vertical Blind Factory
MARIAN - Bells and chimes ☆ - Schulmerich Carillons Inc.
MARIAN - Ophthalmic goods ☆ - Luxottica
MARIAN SEA - Shrimp–fresh or frozen - Darik Enterprises Inc.

☆ = Now out of production

MARIANA - Floor coverings - Mannington Resilient Floors
MARIANELLI - Electronic equipment - Tano Inc.
MARIANELLI - Wines - Wine Merchants Ltd.
MARIANI - Blouses–women's - Gailord Classics Inc.
MARIANI - Food products - Mariani Frozen Foods
MARIANNA - Footwear - G. O. Max International, Inc.
MARIANNA - Hair care products - Marianna Imports, Inc.
MARIANNA - Lenses–optical - Ditto Industries Inc.
MARIANNA'S - Meat products–beef - Sicilian Chef, Inc.
MARIANNE - Cigars - Gesty Trading & Manufacturing Corp.
MARIANNE - Dolls ☆ - Effanbee Doll Corp.
MARIANNE - Glassware–household ☆ - Svend Jensen of Denmark Inc.
MARIANNE - Leather–chamois ☆ - Schroeder & Tremayne, Inc.
MARIANNE - Tableware–china ☆ - Lenox, Inc.
MARIANNE - Underwear and nightwear - Spirite Industries Inc.
MARIANNE'S BEST - Decorations - Corradetti Enterprises, Inc.
MARIANO'S - Beverages - Mariano's Specialty Products
MARIARDEN - Floor coverings–carpet and rugs - Masland Corp.
MARIA'S - Food products - Queen International Foods
MARIA'S EASY 2 STEP STITCH - Yarn - Maria Pignone
MARIA'S ROBLEDO ORIGINAL - Vegetable sauces - Maria Robledo Original
MARICAO - Recording label - Hard Hat Records
MARICH - Confections ☆ - Holland-American Importing Co. Inc.
MARICHE HERBAL - Cosmetics ☆ - Levlab, Inc.
MARICHO - Flowers–artificial - Vincent Lippe Co.
MARICIDE - Pet products - Mardel Laboratories, Inc.
MARICOM - Nautical instruments - Maritime Communications Inc.
MARICOPA - Floor coverings–carpet and rugs - Masland Corp.
MARIDA - Furniture–public buildings - Vogel Peterson Furniture Co.
MARIDEE - Hosiery ☆ - Arrowood Mills Inc.
MARIDIA - Office furniture–wood - Vogel Peterson Furniture Co.
MARIE - Dishes–china - Waterford Wedgewood USA, Inc.
MARIE - Eyeglasses - Martin-Copeland Eyewear Corp.
MARIE ANTOINETTE - Christmas tree ornaments - Cracker Box Inc.
MARIE BRIZARD - Liquors - Schieffelin and Somerset Co.
MARIE BRIZARD LIQUEUR CHARLESTON FOLLIES - Beverages–alcohol - Marie Brizard Et Roger, Inc.
MARIE BRIZARD LIQUEURS - Beverages–alcohol - Marie Brizard Wines & Spirits, USA
MARIE CALLENDAR'S - Food products - Marie Callender Pie Shops Inc.
MARIE CALLENDER'S - Food products - MC Retail Foods Inc.
MARIE CLAIRE - Handbags ☆ - Jerry Kohn Inc.
MARIE CLAIRE - Publisher's imprints - Hearst Corp.
MARIE ELISABETH - Sardines–canned ☆ - Strohmeyer and Arpe Co.
MARIE FERRA - Jewelry - Felicity Associates Inc.
MARIE LOURDES - Watches - Timeplus Inc.
MARIE LU - Biscuits - Sunshine/Salerno Inc.
MARIE PRODUCTS - Crocheted and knitted items - Marie Products
MARIE ROUGE - Dinnerware–glass ☆ - WMF/USA
MARIE Y - Apparel and accessories - Mirp, Inc.
MARIEL WINERY - Wines - Geerlings & Wade, Inc.
MARIELLA - Glassware–household - Durand International
MARIELLA BURANI - Colognes - Gary Farn Ltd.
MARIELLE - Bedding–linen - Dan River Inc.
MARIELLO - Wines - Wine Imports Ltd.
MARIENBAD - Apparel and accessories - Marienbad, Ltd.
MARIENBAD - Beverages–carbonated - Great Lakes Beverages Corp.
MARIENBERGER - Wines - Winesellers Ltd.
MARIE'S - Salad dressings–bottled - Campbell Soup Co.
MARIE'S - Salad dressings–bottled - Specialty Brands Inc.
MARIE'S - Salads–prepackaged - CSC Brands, Inc.
MARIE'S LUSCIOUS LOW FAT - Salad dressings–bottled - C & D Flavor Co.
MARIETTA - Draperies - Marietta Hardware Co.
MARIETTA'S - Cookies - Lewis E. Misterly, Jr.
MARIGAUX - Oboes - Orpheus Music Inc.
MARIGO - Bathing suits - Andmore Sportswear Corp.
MARIGOLD - Apparel and accessories - Urban Vogue
MARIGOLD - Eyeglasses - Martin-Copeland Eyewear Corp.
MARIGOLD - Floor coverings ☆ - Tarkett, Inc.
MARIGOLD - Food products - ICD Group Inc.
MARIGOLD - Industrial detergents - Delex Chemicals, Inc.
MARIGOLD - Milk - Marigold Foods Inc.
MARIGOLD - Paper - Safeway Stores Inc.
MARIGOLD - Pencils ☆ - Faber-Castell Corp.
MARIGOLD - Seafood products–fresh or frozen ☆ - J.F. Clarke Corp.
MARIGOLD - Shampoos - S.C. Johnson & Son, Inc.

MARIGOLD - Vases - Crisa Corp.
MARIGOLD - Wigs - Paula Young
MARIGOLD SYSTEMS - Detergents - Delex Chemicals, Inc.
MARIKA - Exercise apparel - Weekend Exercise Co., Inc.
MARIKA 4 R MOMS 2 B - Maternity exercise wear - Weekend Exercise Co., Inc.
MARIKA CONTROL - Women's exercise wear - Weekend Exercise Co., Inc.
MARIKA KIDS - Children's exercise apparel - Weekend Exercise Co., Inc.
MARIKA S.P. SPORT/PERFORMANCE - Apparel–women's - Weekend Exercise Co., Inc.
MARIKO - Frames–eyeglass - Hoya Corp. USA
MARIKO - Perfumes - Cameo Coutures
MARILYN - Belts–apparel - Marilyn USA
MARILYN - Floor coverings–carpet and rugs ☆ - Regal Rugs Inc.
MARILYN B - Apparel–women's - Hot Stuff, Inc.
MARILYN BURNS BRAINY DAY BOOK, A - Publisher's imprints - Marilyn Burns Education Associates
MARILYN BURNS BRAINY DAY BOOKS - Publisher's imprints - Marilyn Burns Education Associates
MARILYN MANSON - Apparel and accessories - Brian Hugh Warner
MARILYN MANSON - Recording label - Brian Hugh Warner
MARILYN MIGLIN - Perfumes - Marilyn Miglin L.P.
MARILYN MONROE - Postcards ☆ - Classico San Francisco Inc.
MARILYN MONROE - Posters - Edward Weston Fine Arts
MARILYN MONROE - Sunglasses ☆ - Ambassador Eyewear Group
MARILYN SIMANDLE - Calendars ☆ - Amcal Inc.
MARILYN USA - Handbags - Marilyn USA
MARIMBA - Colognes ☆ - Andrew Jergens Co.
MARIMBA - Music–sheet - Marimba Productions Inc.
MARIMBA - Seafood products–fresh or frozen ☆ - J.F. Clarke Corp.
MARIMBA ONE - Musical instruments - Marimba One, Inc.
MARIMEKKO - Desk sets ☆ - A and M Leatherlines Inc.
MARIMEKKO - Glassware–household ☆ - Hackman Tabletop Inc.
MARIMEKKO - Wallpaper ☆ - Motif Designs, Inc.
MARIMEKKO PIKKU - Bedding–linen - Perfect Fit Industries, Inc.
MARIMEKKO PLUS - Wallpaper ☆ - Motif Designs, Inc.
MARIMIX - Asphalt - Felix A. Marino Co., Inc.
MARIMIX - Snack foods - Marimix Co.
MARIN - Cheese - Marin French Cheese Co.
MARIN - Food products - Marin Food Specialties
MARIN BAGEL - Bagels - Marin Bagel Co.
MARIN COUNTY - Furniture ☆ - Riverside Furniture Corp.
MARIN-OOMED - Pet products - Tetra Sales USA
MARINA - Apparel stores–sports - Jem Sportswear Inc.
MARINA - Bathroom tissue - James River Corp.
MARINA - Bicycles ☆ - Raleigh USA Bicycle Co.
MARINA - Hammocks - E-Z Sales & Manufacturing, Inc.
MARINA - House furnishings - Lexington Furniture Industries, Inc.
MARINA - Pet products - Rolf C. Hagen (USA) Corp.
MARINA - Playground equipment ☆ - Little Tikes Co.
MARINA - Seafood products–fresh or frozen ☆ - Robert W. Hayman Inc.
MARINA - Skin care products - Imperial Inc.
MARINA - Tiles–ceramic - American Marazzi Tile, Inc.
MARINA - Toys - Tonka Corp.
MARINA - Toys–models ☆ - Sterling Motor Cars
MARINA - Water purification systems ☆ - Flint & Walling Industries, Inc.
MARINA BAY - Floor coverings–carpet and rugs ☆ - Catalina Carpet Mills Inc.
MARINA BY NEWPORT HARBOR - Outerwear - Whaling Manufacturing Co. Inc.
MARINA CAY - Floor coverings–carpet and rugs - Eagle Carpets Inc.
MARINA CITY - Women's apparel - Carole Sherman Apparel Inc.
MARINA ISETTA ARTISTIC CERAMICS - Lamps - Marina Isetta
MARINA MARINOS DESIGNS - Apparel and accessories - Marinos California Inc.
MARINA OAK - Furniture - Lexington Furniture Industries, Inc.
MARINA PATE - Lithographic plates - Europa Foods Ltd.
MARINA PATE - Seafood products–canned or cured - Liberty Richter Inc.
MARINA SPA - Apparel and accessories - Betty Dain Creations Inc.
MARINA SPADAFORA - Apparel and accessories - Spadafora USA Inc.
MARINA VILLAS - Boats–houseboats - Marina Villas Inc.
MARINADE EXPRESS - Seasonings ☆ - McCormick & Co., Inc.
MARINADE IN MINUTES - Food products - Conopco, Inc.
MARINAPAC - Shrimp–fresh or frozen - Kirad Importing Corp.
MARINAPLY - Wood products - Harbor Sales Co.
MARINARA MIA - Food products - Golden Whisk Pasta Partners
MARINE - Boats–canoes - Coleman Co., Inc.

☆ = Now out of production

MARINE - Fuel additives - Index Industries Inc.
MARINE - Sandals ☆ - Kenkoh American Co.
MARINE AIR SYSTEMS - Air conditioning equipment - Marine Air Systems Inc.
MARINE BAND - Harmonicas - Hohner Inc.
MARINE BUFFER - Pet products - Seachem Laboratories
MARINE CATCH - Food products - Cuisine Crafts
MARINE CLEAN - Cleaning preparations ☆ - Pompanette Inc.
MARINE CORE - Paint rollers - Arsco International Inc.
MARINE CRYSTAL - Toys–marbles - Al Sandberg
MARINE CUISINE - Barbecue and grill accessories - Magma Products, Inc.
MARINE CURE R - Pharmaceutical preparations - Marine World
MARINE DECK 2000 - Boating equipment and accessories - Marquipt
MARINE ENTERPRISES, INC. - Chemical preparations - Marine Enterprises
    International, Inc.
MARINE ENVIRONMENT - Pet products - Marine Environment/Aqua Craft
MARINE EPA - Pharmaceutical preparations - Hogan Regional Center
MARINE FIX - Epoxy - Titan Corp.
MARINE-FLEX - Cables - Falmat, Inc.
MARINE FORMULA 6-56 - Lubricants - CRC Chemicals USA/Siloo
MARINE-GLOW - Novelty items–paper - Romar Enterprises Ltd.
MARINE GOOP - Adhesives and sealants - Eclectic Products Inc.
MARINE GREEN - Pet products - Marine Environment/Aqua Craft
MARINE-GUARD - Lubricants - Fiske Brothers Refining Co. (Lubriplate Div.)
MARINE INVERTEBRATE DIET - Pet products - Hawaiian Marine Imports Inc.
MARINE INVERTEBRATES - Computer software - Ventura Educational
    Systems
MARINE JET - Sporting goods - San Diego Cycle Supply Distributing
MARINE KETTLE - Barbecue and grill accessories - Magma Products, Inc.
MARINE KIT - Paint rollers - Corona Brushes Inc.
MARINE LIFE - Aquariums–household - Wilmar Products, Inc.
MARINE LIFE - Cosmetics ☆ - Cosmair Inc.
MARINE LIFE SERIES BUNDLE - Computer software - Ventura Educational
    Systems
MARINE LINK - Jewelry - Metal Marketplace International
MARINE-LUBE - Lubricants - Fiske Brothers Refining Co. (Lubriplate Div.)
MARINE MASTER - Radio communications equipment - Genave-NRC
MARINE MATE - Radio communications equipment - Genave-NRC
MARINE MATES - Medical apparatus - Bio-Pak Associates
MARINE MOLY - Automotive parts and accessories - Pacific Lubricants
MARINE MOTIONS - Electronics equipment - Marine Motions, Inc.
MARINE MUFFLER VERSA PORT - Mufflers–motor vehicle ☆ - Marine
    Muffler Corp.
MARINE NITE FIGHTER - Spotlights ☆ - Micro Optics Co.
MARINE PAINT REMOVER - Paints - Allpro Corp.
MARINE PENETROL - Paints - Flood Co.
MARINE PROLONG - Pet products - Marine Environment/Aqua Craft
MARINE-RITE - Pumps - Hynautic Inc.
MARINE-SAT - Communications equipment - Frank Carlson
MARINE SCAPERS - Pet products - Rolf C. Hagen (USA) Corp.
MARINE SKIPPER - Fans–exhaust - Delwyn
MARINE STAR - Watches - Bulova Corp.
MARINE STRIP - Varnish removers - James B. Day and Co.
MARINE TECH - Pet products - RT 4 Marine Technology Inc.
MARINE-TEX - Hardware - Travaco Laboratories Inc.
MARINE THERAPIE ACTIVE-SEA - Skin care products ☆ - Monteil Paris
MARINE TRADER - Ships - Marine Trading International Inc.
MARINE-TUFF - Doors - Daytona Plastix, Inc.
MARINE VITA-PEP - Pet products - Marine Environment/Aqua Craft
MARINECARE - Chemical preparations - Guardsman Products, Inc.
MARINEFIX - Adhesives and sealants - Titan Corp.
MARINEGARD - Lubricants - Gard Corp.
MARINELAND MAGNUM - Aquariums–household - Marineland Aquarium
    Products
MARINELANDER - Apparel and accessories - Californians Inc.
MARINELITE - Lamps - Angelo Brothers Co.
MARINELLA - Food products - D. Coluccio & Sons, Inc.
MARINELLA MARSALAS - Wines - Bercut-Vandervoort & Co.
MARINEMASTER - Hoses - Willcox Engineered Products, Inc.
MARINER - Bathroom fixtures ☆ - Crane Plumbing/Fiat Products
MARINER - Binoculars - Minolta Corp.
MARINER - Boats - Clark Craft Boat Co.
MARINER - Boats - Mariner Co.
MARINER - Boats - Stuart Marine
MARINER - Boats–houseboats ☆ - Cron Houseboats
MARINER - Boats–liferafts - W. Waller & Son Inc.
MARINER - Boats–motor - Carver Boat Corp.

MARINER - Boats–motor ☆ - Seajay Boats Inc.
MARINER - Brushes–paint - Elder & Jenks, Inc.
MARINER - Brushes–paint - Wooster Brush Co.
MARINER - Cabinets ☆ - Gragg Cabinet Industries
MARINER - Candlesticks ☆ - Carolina Designs Ltd.
MARINER - Compasses–gyroscopic - Rule Industries, Inc.
MARINER - Fabrics ☆ - Gretchen Bellinger Inc.
MARINER - Fire extinguishers - Kidde Safety
MARINER - Fishing tackle - Penn Fishing Tackle Manufacturing Co.
MARINER - Floor coverings–carpet and rugs - Barrett Carpet Mills Inc.
MARINER - Floor coverings–carpet and rugs - Newport Carpet Mills Inc.
MARINER - Floor coverings–carpet and rugs ☆ - Olympic Carpets Inc.
MARINER - Food products - Nestle USA
MARINER - Food products ☆ - Darik Enterprises Inc.
MARINER - Footwear–athletic - Mark's Athletic Soles Inc.
MARINR - Glassware–household ☆ - Lenox Crystal, Inc.
MARINER - Lawn mowers - Lambert Manufacturing Corp.
MARINER - Lighting fixtures - Swivelier Co. Inc.
MARINER - Motors–outboard - Mercury Marine
MARINER - Radiotelephones - Intech Inc.
MARINER - Rope - Nylon Net Co.
MARINER - Rope - Wellington Leisure Products, Inc.
MARINER - Shoes - Genesco Inc.
MARINER - Swimming accessories - North American Marketing Corp.
MARINER CLOTH BY HARTMANN - Luggage ☆ - Hartmann Luggage Co.
MARINER ELITE - Brushes–paint - Pettit Paint Co. Inc.
MARINER FISH N SKI - Boats–motor ☆ - Seajay Boats Inc.
MARINER I - Furniture - Tropitone Furniture Co. Inc.
MARINER II - Furniture - Tropitone Furniture Co. Inc.
MARINER III - Furniture - Tropitone Furniture Co. Inc.
MARINER JACK - Seafood products–fresh or frozen - Sahlman Seafoods, Inc.
MARINER OUTBOARDS - Apparel - Brunswick Corp.
MARINER RACING - Apparel - Brunswick Corp.
MARINER SKI TEAM - Apparel–athletic - Brunswick Corp.
MARINER TRANSOM-MOUNT - Mufflers–motor vehicle ☆ - Marine Muffler
    Corp.
MARINER'S - Food products ☆ - Rowena's Gourmet Foods Inc.
MARINERS - Seafood products–fresh or frozen - O'Donnell-Usen Fisheries
    Corp.
MARINER'S - Skin care products - Gillette Co.
MARINERS COVE - Soups–canned - Curtice-Burns Foods, Inc.
MARINERS COVE - Soups–canned - H.J. Heinz Co.
MARINER'S EYE - Computer software - JJM Systems, Inc.
MARINER'S POINT - Floor coverings–carpet and rugs ☆ - Catalina Carpet
    Mills Inc.
MARINERS WAY - Coffee - First Colony Coffee and Tea Co. Inc.
MARINES AT WORK - Calendars - Mach 1, Inc.
MARINETEK - Engines–marine - Holman Enterprises
MARINETRAC - Drapery hardware - Kirsch Co.
MARINETTE - Boats–houseboats ☆ - Boating Corp. of America
MARINEX - Glassware–household ☆ - St. Gobain International Glassware
MARINGOUIN SPORT - Apparel and accessories - Arthur L. Schmitt Jr.
MARINI - Wines - DeRosa Imports
MARINITE - Insulating materials–asbestos - BNZ Materials, Inc.
MARINIUM - Hardware - Wilcox-Crittenden
MARINO BOUTIQUE - Shoes - New York Transit, Inc.
MARINONI - Bicycles - Marinoni USA
MARINO'S - Ice cream - Olympic Ice Cream Co. Inc.
MARINO'S - Seafood products–fresh or frozen - Product Possibilities, Inc.
MARINO'S - Soups - Atlantic Foods
MARINOS CALIFORNIA - Apparel and accessories - Marinos California Inc.
MARINOS ECLECTIC - Apparel and accessories - Marinos California Inc.
MARINOS SPORT - Apparel and accessories - Marinos California Inc.
MARINR - Catheters - Medtronic CardioRhythm
MARINUS - Seafood products–fresh or frozen - Stavis Seafoods Inc.
MARINVIT - Pet products ☆ - Sera Aquaristik USA Inc.
MARIO - Glassware–household - Crisa Corp.
MARIO - Olives–canned - Westin Inc.
MARIO ANDRETTI - Candy - Morley Candy Makers Co. Inc.
MARIO AROSIO - Bird cages - Active Pet Supplies
MARIO BENZI - Audio equipment - Caltex Manufacturing Distributing Inc.
MARIO BROS. - Video games - Nintendo of America Inc.
MARIO BUATTA - Wallpaper - Sterling Prints
MARIO BUATTA II - Wallpaper - Sterling Prints
MARIO CELLINNI - Crocheted and knitted items - Gillman Knitwear Co.
MARIO DE GERARD - Footwear–men's - Thom McAn Shoe Co.

☆ = Now out of production

MARIO DE PINTO - Apparel and accessories - M.D.P. Designs, Ltd.
MARIO IS MISSING - Software - Nintendo of America Inc.
MARIO LANZA - Wines - Wooden Valley Winery
MARIO LEONE - Shoes ☆ - Edison Brothers Stores, Inc.
MARIO PINNINI FOR ENNESI - Shoes ☆ - Ennesi Shoe Co. Inc.
MARIO STIVAL - Wines - House of Burgundy Inc.
MARIO VALENTINO - Apparel–men's - Superba, Inc.
MARION - Computer software - Marion Software Corp.
MARION - Food products ☆ - Seneca Foods Corp.
MARION - Glassware–household - Federal Glass
MARION - Tools–hand-operated - Marion Tool Corp.
MARION BOYARS - Publisher's imprints - Rizzoli International Publications Inc.
MARION-KAY - Spices and extracts - Marion-Kay-Reidco Inc.
MARION MODEL - Furniture ☆ - Foley & Robinson Inc.
MARIONETTE - Frames–eyeglass - Pathway Optical Prods.
MARIO'S CEMENT FACTORY - Video games - Nintendo of America Inc.
MARIO'S GREENE COUNTY - Food products - Greene County Importing Corp.
MARIOTTI - Footwear–men's ☆ - Avanti Shoe
MARIPAC - Seafood products–fresh or frozen ☆ - Fishery Products International USA
MARIPAI - Seafood products–fresh or frozen - Century Seafoods Inc.
MARIPE - Shoes - Lerner Shoes Inc.
MARIPOSA - Cosmetics - Mariposa Products Corp.
MARIPOSA - Floor coverings ☆ - Congoleum Corp.
MARIPOSA - Floor coverings–carpet and rugs - Helios Carpets
MARIPOSA - Frames–eyeglass - May Optical Co. Inc.
MARIPOSA - Furniture ☆ - Tropitone Furniture Co. Inc.
MARIPOSA - Paints - Pioneer Paint of Arizona
MARIPOSA - Solar energy collectors - Solardyne Corp.
MARIPOSA - Tableware–china - Villeroy and Boch Tableware Ltd.
MARIPOSA - Wines - Kendall Jackson Winery, Ltd.
MARIPOSA DANBY - Marble products - Carl Schilling Stoneworks
MARIQUITA - Wines ☆ - Caymus Vineyards
MARIS - Optical scanners–computer - Tart Optical
MARISA CHRISTINA - Apparel–women's - Marisa Christina Inc.
MARISSA - Apparel–women's - Goodman Knitting Co. Inc.
MARISSA - Frames–eyeglass - May Optical Co. Inc.
MARISSA - Tableware–china ☆ - Lenox, Inc.
MARISTAR - Boats - Master Craft Boat Co.
MARISYSTEMS - Electronics equipment - Marisystems, Inc.
MARIT - Games - Jax Ltd.
MARITENNA - Nautical instruments - Maritime Communications Inc.
MARITEX - Marine vinyl ☆ - Athol Corp.
MARITHANE - Marine rigging - Windline Marine
MARITIME - Antennas - Submarine Research Laboratories Inc.
MARITIME - Floor coverings–carpet and rugs - Robertex Associates Inc.
MARITIME - Watches - Abko Inc.
MARITIME - Watches - Louis M. Schukar and Associates
MARITIME ROSE - Dishes–china ☆ - Royal China & Porcelain Companies Inc.
MARITIME SERIES - Clocks - Chelsea Clock Co. Inc.
MARITIMER - Seafood products–fresh or frozen - Fishery Products International USA
MARIXX - Computers - Aries Research, Inc.
MARJA - Negligees ☆ - Marja Foundations
MARJORIE - Beads - Elliot, Greene & Co. Inc.
MARJORIE - Underwear and nightwear - Heavenly Intimate Inc.
MARK - Accordions - Newark Musical Merchandise Co.
MARK - Apparel–children's - Mark Trouser Inc.
MARK - Bicycles - Columbia Manufacturing Inc.
MARK - Boats - McDaniel Boats Inc.
MARK - Clocks - Burmax Co. Inc.
MARK - Containers - Mark Industries Inc.
MARK - Floor coverings–carpet and rugs - Columbus Mills, Inc.
MARK - Frames–eyeglass - Liberty Optical Manufacturing Co.
MARK - Furniture–wood - CM International, Inc.
MARK - Guns ☆ - Crosman Corp.
MARK - Knives - Mark Specialty Co.
MARK - Pet products - Lee-Mar Pet Supplies
MARK - Ships - Bay Manufacturing
MARK - Ships–sailing vessels - Sumner Boat Co., Inc.
MARK - Sporting goods - Marshall Manufacturing Inc.
MARK - Trailers–travel - Beaver Camper Co.
MARK I - Boats - Zodiac of North America
MARK I - Face shield ☆ - General Scientific Equipment Co.
MARK I - Footwear - Seaway Importing Co.

MARK 1 - Guitars ☆ - Guild Music Corp.
MARK I - Helmets–athletic ☆ - Bell Sports Corp.
MARK I - Machine tools - T.J. Gundlach Machine Co.
MARK I - Paper–tissue - Paper Service Ltd.
MARK 1 - Tools - Van Mark Products Corp.
MARK I STEP UP - Nuclear core structures - Perry Manufacturing Co. Inc.
MARK II - Binoculars ☆ - Swift Instruments, Inc.
MARK II - Boats - Zodiac of North America
MARK II - Boats–fishing - McDaniel Boats Inc.
MARK II - Combs - Comare Corp.
MARK II - Copper compounds ☆ - Regal Ware, Inc.
MARK II - Doors–glass - Noranda Building Products Co.
MARK II - Footwear - Seaway Importing Co.
MARK 2 - Guitars ☆ - Guild Music Corp.
MARK 2 - Housewares - Vantage Tool Inc.
MARK II - Infant product - Nurserytyme Products/Doppelt Industries
MARK II - Inks - Specialty Ink Co. Inc.
MARK II - Motor vehicles–automobiles ☆ - Toyota Motor Sales USA Inc.
MARK II - Paper–tissue - Paper Service Ltd.
MARK II - Printing trades machinery - Vidac
MARK II - Structural clay ☆ - Rollex Corp.
MARK II - Toys–models ☆ - Estes Industries
MARK II - Trunks - PowerMark Case Corp.
MARK II MAGNI-FOCUSER - Lenses–magnifying - Edroy Products Co.
MARK III - Boats - Zodiac of North America
MARK III - Computers - General Electric Co.
MARK III - Cosmetics - Ladyfingers
MARK III - Epoxy coatings - Consolidated Coatings Corp.
MARK 3 - Guitars ☆ - Guild Music Corp.
MARK III - Health care products - Arjo Manufacturing Co.
MARK III - Markers–felt-tip - Avery Dennison Corp.
MARK III - Motor vehicles–automobiles ☆ - Ford Motor Co. (Lincoln-Mercury Div.)
MARK III - Truck conversions - Mark III Industries Inc.
MARK III EPOXY FLOORING - Epoxy coatings - Consolidated Coatings Corp.
MARK IV - Artists' materials ☆ - LogEtronics Corp.
MARK IV - Beverages–carbonated ☆ - Nash-Finch Co.
MARK 4 - Bicycles ☆ - GT Bicycles Inc.
MARK IV - Cigars - House of Windsor Inc.
MARK IV - Copper compounds ☆ - Regal Ware, Inc.
MARK IV - Engines–internal combustion - Tecumseh Products Co.
MARK IV - Footwear - Seaway Importing Co.
MARK IV - Furniture–upholstered - Woodland Furniture Manufacturing Co.
MARK 4 - Guitars ☆ - Guild Music Corp.
MARK IV - Hair care products - Marianna Imports, Inc.
MARK 4 - Health care products - Puritan-Bennett Corp.
MARK IV - Health care products - Temco Health Care
MARK IV - Lamps - Sperti Sunlamp
MARK IV - Motor vehicles–automobiles ☆ - Ford Motor Co. (Lincoln-Mercury Div.)
MARK IV - Ophthalmic goods - Foremost Optical Products
MARK IV - Pens - Paper Mate Co.
MARK IV - Projectors–photographic - Buhl Industries, Inc.
MARK IV - Tools - Van Mark Products Corp.
MARK IV - Vinyl runner ☆ - American Floor Products Co. Inc.
MARK IV AUDIO CONTROL TECHNOLOGY - Computer hardware - Altech Lansing Corp.
MARK IV BASS - Amplifiers–musical instrument - Peavey Electronics Corp.
MARK IV MAGNATES - Cigars - House of Windsor Inc.
MARK IV R5A - Artists' materials ☆ - LogEtronics Corp.
MARK IV R5A/DS - Artists' materials ☆ - LogEtronics Corp.
MARK V - Ammunition - Olin Corp. (Winchester Div.)
MARK V - Automotive repair shops–glass ☆ - Lamps Ltd.
MARK V - Combs - Comare Corp.
MARK V - Engines–internal combustion - Tecumseh Products Co.
MARK V - Fishing tackle - South Bend Sporting Goods Inc.
MARK V - Floor coverings - Congoleum Corp.
MARK 5 - Guitars ☆ - Guild Music Corp.
MARK V - Guns - Weatherby Inc.
MARK V - Health care products - Temco Health Care
MARK V - Lighting equipment - Phillips Electronics North America Corp.
MARK V - Motor vehicles–automobiles ☆ - Ford Motor Co. (Lincoln-Mercury Div.)
MARK V - Projectors–photographic - Alan Gordon Enterprises Inc.
MARK V - Publisher's imprints - Davis & Box Manufacturing Co.
MARK 5 - Siding–insulating ☆ - Aluminum Co. of America

☆ = Now out of production

MARK V - Trailers–travel - Chateau RV Inc.
MARK 6 - Guitars ☆ - Guild Music Corp.
MARK-6 - Heating equipment - Aqua Queen
MARK VI - Machinery - Lamps Ltd.
MARK VI - Motor vehicles–automobiles ☆ - Ford Motor Co. (Lincoln-Mercury Div.)
MARK VI - Saxophones ☆ - Selmer Co. Inc.
MARK VI - Socks - Adams-Millis Corp.
MARK VII - Doors–glass - Noranda Building Products Co.
MARK-7 - Heating equipment ☆ - Aqua Queen
MARK VII - Lighting equipment - Phillips Electronics North America Corp.
MARK VII - Motor vehicles–automobiles - Ford Motor Co. (Lincoln-Mercury Div.)
MARK VII - Saxophones ☆ - Selmer Co. Inc.
MARK 7 - Seafood products–fresh or frozen - Mark 7 Seafood & Industries
MARK VII - Shirts - Shelburne Shirt Co. Inc.
MARK VII - Sofabeds - Flexsteel Industries Inc.
MARK VIII - Motor vehicles–automobiles - Ford Motor Co. (Lincoln-Mercury Div.)
MARK 10 - Cigarettes - G.A. Georgopulo & Co. Inc.
MARK X - Doors–glass - Norandex, Inc.
MARK X - Firearms, accessories, and parts - International Armament Corp.
MARK 10 - Floor coverings - Harris-Tarkett, Inc.
MARK X - Footwear ☆ - Seaway Importing Co.
MARK 10C - Floor coverings - Harris-Tarkett, Inc.
MARK 12 - Adding machines ☆ - Adler-Royal Business Machines Inc.
MARK XII - Shoes - Craddock-Terry Inc.
MARK 21 - Dart game equipment - Valley Recreation Products Inc.
MARK XXII - Guns ☆ - Weatherby Inc.
MARK 30 - Projection screens ☆ - Da-Lite Screen Co. Inc.
MARK 50 - Pencils - SLH Products, Inc.
MARK 60 - Lighting equipment - Yardney Technical Products Inc.
MARK 75 - Games - Bonus Games Inc.
MARK 80 - Motor vehicle parts and accessories - Purolator Products Co.
MARK 80 - Shingles–asphalt or tar - Bird Inc.
MARK 95 - Lighting equipment ☆ - Yardney Technical Products Inc.
MARK 280 - Lighting equipment ☆ - Yardney Technical Products Inc.
MARK 500 CERTIFIED - Rope ☆ - Columbian Rope Co.
MARK 3000 SERVICE - Computer programming services - General Electric Co.
MARK-A-BULL - Game machines - Custom Manufacturing, Inc.
MARK A KEY - Labels–paper - Stranco Products Inc.
MARK ALAN - Sporting goods ☆ - National Sporting Goods Corp.
MARK & CODE - Pens - Dykem Co.
MARK ANGELI - Wines - Chartrand Imports
MARK ARTABLES - Harmonicas - Adamany Art and Design
MARK ATA - Trunks - PowerMark Case Corp.
MARK-AWAY - Erasers - Sanford Corp.
MARK-B-GONE - Craft supplies - Prym Dritz Corp.
MARK CROSS - Apparel and accessories ☆ - A.T. Cross Co.
MARK CROSS - Leather goods - Mark Cross Inc.
MARK FIVE - Fishing tackle ☆ - Gladding Braided Products Inc.
MARK FIVE - Recording label - Mark Five Sandcastle
MARK FORE - Golfing equipment - Brandell Products, Inc.
MARK-FORE - Health care products - Nepsco, Inc.
MARK, FORE & STRIKE - Apparel and accessories - Mark Group, Inc.
MARK-FOUR GAME - Games ☆ - Molor Products Inc.
MARK HAMPTON COLLECTION - Furniture - Hickory Chair Co.
MARK-HAVEN - Doors–screen - Weather Shield Manufacturing, Inc.
MARK I - Binoculars ☆ - Swift Instruments, Inc.
MARK I - Home health care products - Arjo Manufacturing Co.
MARK I - Printers–computer - Unimark Inc.
MARK I FLITE - Trunks - PowerMark Case Corp.
MARK II QUALITY MUSIC ACCESSORIES - Microphones - Universal Music, Inc.
MARK INN - Hotels and motels - Mark Inns of America
MARK IT - Bookmarks - Keith B Whitney
MARK-IT - Fertilizers - Turf Industries, Inc.
MARK-IT - Golfing equipment - Mark-It of Colorado Ltd.
MARK-IT - Office supplies - C.H. Hanson Co.
MARK JEFFREY - Footwear - J. Baker Inc.
MARK LEES - Skin care products - Mark Lees Skin Care Inc.
MARK-LESS BEAUTY COLLECTION - Floor coverings–carpet and rugs - Galaxy Carpet Mills Inc.
MARK LEVENSON - Audio equipment - Madrigal Ltd.
MARK-LITE - Lamps - Tektite Industries, Inc. (Tektite Manufacturing Division)
MARK MASTER - Markers–felt-tip - Mark Master Inc.

MARK MATHIEU - Shirts - Shelburne Shirt Co. Inc.
MARK-N-DRAW - Markers–felt-tip ☆ - Marsh Co.
MARK-N-WIPE - Bulletin boards–wood - Quartet Manufacturing Co.
MARK OF A MAN - Colognes ☆ - Pfizer Inc.
MARK OF FIFTH AVENUE - Apparel–children's - Mark Trouser Inc.
MARK OF GOLD - Frames–eyeglass - Hudson Optical Corp.
MARK OF SAVINGS, THE - Frames–picture - Shalom International Corp.
MARK ONE - Health care products - Mark One Healthcare Products Inc.
MARK-OUT - Paints - Mason Marking Systems Corp.
MARK PERRYMAN FOR OSCEOLA - Footwear - Osceola Shoe Co. Inc.
MARK-PL-M - Jewel mountings–precious metal - Arly Diamond Co.
MARK-RITE - Inks - Marking Devices
MARK-RITE - Tools–hand-operated - Mark-Rite Distributing Corp.
MARK RUBIN - Recording label - Alcazar Productions
MARK SCOT - Golfing equipment - Tommy Armour Golf Co.
MARK SERIES - Lighting equipment - Tri Lite
MARK SIXTY - Faucets - Moen Inc.
MARK SMARTIE - Pens - Lanir Trading Co., Inc.
MARK SOSIN'S SALTWATER JOURNAL - Apparel and accessories - Mark Sosin Communications, Inc.
MARK T - Hand tool - E-Z Red Co.
MARK TEN - Tobacco products - Philip Morris Companies Inc.
MARK TEN B - Motor vehicle parts and accessories - Delta Products Corp.
MARK-TEX - Markers–felt-tip - Mark-Tex Corp.
MARK, THE - Sporting goods - Eagle Golf Co.
MARK, THE - Automotive parts and accessories - Lancaster Colony Automotive Group
MARK THE MINNOW CARDS - Greeting cards - Mark T. Myer
MARK TIME - Cosmetics - Marianna Imports, Inc.
MARK TRAYNOR - Cosmetics - Mark Traynor Inc.
MARK-TROL - Pencils ☆ - Faber-Castell Corp.
MARK TWAIN - Boats - Glen-L Marine Designs
MARK TWAIN - Dolls ☆ - Effanbee Doll Corp.
MARK TWAIN SHOWBOATS - Cigars ☆ - House of Windsor Inc.
MARK VII - Apparel and accessories - Sunrise Apparel, Inc.
MARK WEST VINEYARDS - Wines - Mark West Vineyards
MARK X - Lighting equipment - Philips Electronics North America Corp.
MARK-X - Stationery - Diagraph Corp.
MARK YOUR LINE EVERYTIME - Bookmarks - Michael Miroyan
MARK YOUR WORDS - Computer software - Patent Videos Inc.
MARKAL - Markers–felt-tip - Markal Co.
MARKANT - Floor coverings ☆ - Azrock Commercial Flooring
MARKAWAY - Erasers - Sanford Corp.
MARKAZUL - Rope - Sunshine Cordage Corp.
MARKEN FOODS - Sauces - Esco Foods Inc.
MARKER - Cigarettes - R.J. Reynolds Tobacco Co.
MARKER - Luggage - Marker International Co.
MARKER - Toys - Tonka Corp.
MARKER BUOY RACK PAC - Sporting goods - Lindy Little Joe Inc.
MARKER FIX - Artists' materials ☆ - Loctite Corp.
MARKER MATES - Toys–stuffed - Play by Play Toys and Novelties, Inc.
MARKERS - Display cases–plastic - Charles Bredwell
MARKERWIPE - Washcloths - Texwipe Co. LLC
MARKET ACTION TIMER - Computer software - Tempo Investment Products, Inc.
MARKET BASKET - Food products - Bush Brothers and Co.
MARKET BASKET - Food products - Ritchie Grocer Co.
MARKET CAFE - Coffee - Boyd Coffee Co.
MARKET CHOICE - Cheese - Western Family Foods, Inc.
MARKET DAYS - Giftware - Enesco Corp.
MARKET EXCHANGE - Apparel–women's ☆ - Bobbie Brooks Inc.
MARKET EXPRESS - Computer software - Federal National Mortgage Association
MARKET FLOWERS - Bedding–linen - Dan River Inc.
MARKET FORCES - Games ☆ - Avalon Hill Game Co.
MARKET HOUSE - Wallpaper ☆ - Three Sisters Studio
MARKET MACHINE, THE - Computer software - Chicago Corp.
MARKET MAID - Fruits and vegetables - Salem Fruit Growers Coop. Association
MARKET MANAGEMENT REPORT: RESEARCH FOR INVESTORS - Paper - Market Management International Inc.
MARKET MARKER - Paints - Kent Feeds, Inc.
MARKET-MASTER - Refrigerators - White Consolidated Industries, Inc.
MARKET MAX - Computer software - Tri-Star Market Data Inc.
MARKET MONITOR - Computer software - Castle Consulting
MARKET MOVER - Banks–commercial - Knutson Mortgage Corp.

☆ = Now out of production

MARKET NET - Computer software - Information Clearinghouse, Inc.

MARKET PLACE - Fabrics–tapestry - Comark Wallcoverings

MARKET PLACE - Floor coverings - Mannington Resilient Floors

MARKET PLACE - Floor coverings–carpet and rugs ☆ - American Carpet Mills

MARKET PLACE - Wallpaper - Style-Tex Wallcoverings

MARKET PLACE SALE - Cups–plastic - Tel Phil Enterprises Inc.

MARKET RUN! - Computer software - TH Associates

MARKET SPICE - Teas - Market Spice Inc.

MARKET SQUARE - Flatware - J.C. Penney Co., Inc.

MARKET SQUARE - Floor coverings - Mannington Resilient Floors

MARKET SQUARE - Furniture ☆ - Bassett Furniture Industries, Inc.

MARKET SQUARE - Wallpaper - Gencorp Polymer Products

MARKET STREET - Floor coverings–carpet and rugs ☆ - Hollytex Carpet Mills Inc.

MARKET STREET - Water–distilled - Market Street

MARKET STREET COBBLE - Floor coverings ☆ - Tarkett, Inc.

MARKET STREET SWEETS - Candy - NMS, Inc.

MARKET STYLE - Beef - Excel Corp.

MARKET WATCHER - Computer peripheral equipment - Micro Trading Software, Inc.

MARKETALKERS - Labels–paper - Wessel Co., Inc.

MARKETFAX - Computers - Alternative Technology Corp.

MARKETING RESOURCES PLUS - Computer software - U.S. West Marketing Resources Group, Inc.

MARKETING WORKBENCH - Computer software - National Demographics and Lifestyles Inc.

MARKETLENS - Construction equipment rental services - Market Decisions, Inc.

MARKETMEXICO - CD-Roms and floppy disks - Demosphere International, Inc.

MARKETMINER - Computer software - Abtech Corp.

MARKETPLACE - Greeting cards - American Greetings Corp.

MARKETPRO - Computer software - Datamap, Inc.

MARKETRATE - Computer software - MCIS, Inc.

MARKET'S BEST - Food products - Tropical Preserving Co.

MARKETSOURCE - Fruits and vegetables - International Market Brands, Inc.

MARKETSPICE - Teas - Samuel & Co., Inc.

MARKET*STAR - Computer software - Electronic Data Systems Corp.

MARKETTE - Markers–felt-tip - Faber-Castell Corp.

MARKHAM - Cigarettes - Brown & Williamson Tobacco Corp.

MARKHAM - Wines - Markham Vineyards

MARKHIDE - Skin care products - Gold Medal Hair Products Inc.

MARKIE - Toys–stuffed - Lisa Frank, Inc.

MARKIN MAXI - Toys–trains - Marklin Trains

MARKINGS - Floor coverings–carpet and rugs ☆ - Lees Carpets

MARKINGS - Paper–writing - Thomas Nelson, Inc.

MARKIT - Food products ☆ - Curtice-Burns Foods, Inc.

MARKIT - Office supplies - Russell Industries Inc.

MARKKO - Beds–wood - Markko International, Inc.

MARKKO - Wines - Markko Vineyard

MARKLEYS - Pharmaceutical preparations ☆ - C&M Pharmacal, Inc.

MARKLIN - Toys–trains - Marklin Trains

MARKLIN DIGITAL - Toys–trains - Marklin Trains

MARKLIN HO - Toys–trains - Marklin Trains

MARKLIN I - Toys–trains - Marklin Trains

MARKLIN METALL - Toys–erector sets - Marklin Trains

MARKLIN MINI-CLUB - Toys–trains - Marklin Trains

MARKLIN Z - Toys–trains - Marklin Trains

MARKLINE CB - Trailers - Mobile Structures, Inc.

MARKLITER - Pens - Pilot Pen Corp. of America

MARKMASTER - Paints - Floquil-Polly S Color Corp.

MARKOFF - Stain removers ☆ - Auto Cellular Systems

MARKPARK - Electrical equipment - Pabetaber Ltd.

MARKRITE - Fabrics - Stearns Technical Textiles Co.

MARKRITE - Stamps–hand ☆ - Mayhew Steel Products

MARKROSS - Food products ☆ - Ocean Beauty Seafood, Inc.

MARKS - Locks–door - Marks Hardware Inc.

MARK'S - Shoe soles - Mark's Athletic Soles Inc.

MARKS-A-LOT - Markers–felt-tip - Avery Dennison Corp.

MARK'S FEED STORE - Vegetable sauces - Mark's Feed Store, Inc.

MARKS OF INSPIRATION - Greeting cards - Russ Berrie and Co., Inc.

MARKS OF PRIDE - Stationery - Benjamin R. Darnell

MARKSMAN - Adhesives and sealants - Gibson-Homans Co. (Sealant Technology)

MARKSMAN - Alarm systems - Magnadyne Corp.

MARKSMAN - Ammunition ☆ - Olin Corp. (Winchester Div.)

MARKSMAN - Boats - Clark Craft Boat Co.

MARKSMAN - Bottle openers - Crossbow Inc.

MARKSMAN - Camping products - Marksman Products Inc.

MARKSMAN - Darts and dart games - Dart World Inc.

MARKSMAN - Electronic equipment - ArtMold Products Corp.

MARKSMAN - Firearms, accessories, and parts - Welsh Sporting Goods Corp. (Boyt Div.)

MARKSMAN - Floor coverings–carpet and rugs ☆ - Porter Carpet Mills Inc.

MARKSMAN - Oils–lubricating - Farmland Industries Inc.

MARKSMAN - Pens - Union Pen Co.

MARKSMAN - Printers–computer - Imaging Technologies LLC

MARKSMAN - Sporting goods - Rothco Inc.

MARKSMAN - Surveying machinery - Topcon America Corp.

MARKSMAN - Video games - Hasbro, Inc.

MARKSMAN, THE - Gloves - Dakota Corp.

MARKSTEIN AMBER - Beverages–malt - Markstein Beverage Co.

MARKUSE - Mail boxes - Markuse Corp.

MARKVISION - Computer software - Lexmark International, Inc.

MARKWELL - Brushes–paint ☆ - M. Grumbacher Inc.

MARKWELL - Staplers - Markwell Manufacturing Co. Inc.

MARKWORT - Sporting goods - Markwort Sporting Goods Co.

MARKY - Cosmetics - Comare Corp.

MARKY MARK AND THE FUNKY BUNCH - Posters - Donnie D. Productions Inc.

MARLA - Cheese - Detroit City Dairy Inc.

MARLA - Ophthalmic goods - Foremost Optical Products

MARLAND - Eyeglasses - Martin-Copeland Eyewear Corp.

MARLATT'S - Fruits and vegetables - Marlatt's Fruit Farm

MARLBORO - Cigarettes - Philip Morris Companies Inc.

MARLBORO - Eyeglasses - Martin-Copeland Eyewear Corp.

MARLBORO - Floor coverings ☆ - Congoleum Corp.

MARLBORO - Paints - Cloverleaf Paint & Varnish

MARLBORO - Watches - Bulova Corp.

MARLBORO 100S - Cigarettes - Philip Morris Companies Inc.

MARLBORO EXPRESS - Cigarettes - Philip Morris Companies Inc.

MARLBORO LIGHTS - Cigarettes - Philip Morris Companies Inc.

MARLBORO MEDIUM - Cigarettes - Philip Morris Companies Inc.

MARLBORO MENTHOL - Cigarettes - Philip Morris Companies Inc.

MARLBORO REDS - Cigarettes - Philip Morris Companies Inc.

MARLBOROUGH - Floor coverings–carpet and rugs ☆ - Porter Carpet Mills Inc.

MARLBOROUGH - Frames–eyeglass ☆ - Universal/Univis Inc.

MARLBOROUGH - Lamps - Kaadan Ltd.

MARLBOROUGH MANOR COLLECTION - Furniture ☆ - Harden Furniture Co. Inc.

MARLBOROUGH SPRAYS - Dishes–earthenware - Royal China & Porcelain Companies Inc.

MARLEEN - Glassware–household ☆ - ACC

MARLEN - Guitars - Stadler Music Co.

MARLEN - Surgical instruments - Marlen Manufacturing & Developing Co.

MARLENE - Eyeglasses - Martin-Copeland Eyewear Corp.

MARLENE'S - Shampoos - Fleetwood Co.

MARLETTE - Dog food - Armada Grain Co.

MARLETTE - Eyeglasses - Martin-Copeland Eyewear Corp.

MARLEX - Sporting goods ☆ - FNT Industries Inc.

MARLEY - Eyeglasses - Martin-Copeland Eyewear Corp.

MARLEY - Fruit and vegetable markets - Jack Frost Fruit Co.

MARLEY - Fruits and vegetables - Marley Orchards Corp.

MARLEY HODGSON COLLECTION, THE - Leather goods ☆ - TGL Corp.

MARLIBAR A - Pharmaceutical preparations ☆ - Shannon Chemical Co. Inc.

MARLIE - Handbags - Mid-Continent Ltd./MCL

MARLIN - Batteries - G.M.B. Battery Inc.

MARLIN - Bicycles - Ross Bicycles USA, Ltd.

MARLIN - Boats - McKenzie Boat Manufacturing Co.

MARLIN - Boats–canoes - Fishin' Ski Barge

MARLIN - Boats–motor - Grady-White Boats, Inc.

MARLIN - Boats–motor ☆ - Trojan Yacht

MARLIN - Floor coverings - American Floor Products Co. Inc.

MARLIN - Frames–eyeglass ☆ - Universal/Univis Inc.

MARLIN - Guns - Marlin Firearms Co.

MARLIN - Insulating materials - Marlin Fiberglass Co.

MARLIN - Measuring instruments - MTI Corp.

MARLIN - Motors–outboard - Jetco Inc.

MARLIN - Sporting goods - Pompanette Inc.

MARLIN-RITA - Beverages–alcohol - Blue Marlin Restaurants, Inc.

☆ = Now out of production

MARLIN TEASE - Apparel and accessories - Ralph Marlin & Co., Inc.
MARLINS - Bags–duffel - Florida Panthers Hockey, Ltd.
MARLIN'S FINEST - Mustard - Marlin's Finest Gourmet Foods
MARLIPIDS III - Oils–edible ☆ - Fibertone Co.
MARLITE - Building materials - Marlite
MARLITE - Eyeglasses - Martin-Copeland Eyewear Corp.
MARLO - Apparel and accessories - Bi-Rite Corp.
MARLO - Furniture stores - Marlo Furniture Co., Inc.
MARLO BAGS - Apparel and accessories - Bi-Rite Corp.
MARLO SPORT - Apparel and accessories - Bi-Rite Corp.
MARLOK - Electronic equipment - ILCO Unican Corp.
MARLON - Toys - Marlon Creations
MARLON CHERRIES - Candy ☆ - Just Born Inc.
MARLOP - Pharmaceutical preparations ☆ - Marlop Pharmaceuticals Inc.
MARLO'S CHILDREN'S CORNER - Fabrics ☆ - Princess Fabrics Inc.
MARLOW - Flatware ☆ - W.M.F. of America Inc.
MARLOW - Marine rigging - Imtra Corp.
MARLOW - Sporting goods - Avon Marine
MARLOWE - Cabinets - Formitex Inc.
MARLOWE - Furniture - Haworth, Inc.
MARLOY - Plastics - Nova Group, Inc.
MARLSTONE - Wines - Clos du Bois Wines
MARLY SKIN GUARD - Pharmaceutical preparations - Varn Aegis Inc.
MARLYN OMEGA-3 - Vitamins and nutritional supplements - Marlyn Co. Inc.
MARMAC - Publisher's imprints - Pelican Publishing Co. Inc.
MARMADUKE - Labels–paper - United Feature Syndicate, Inc.
MARMADUKE - Toys–stuffed - Mighty Star Inc. (Special Effects Div.)
MARMALADE - Cutlery ☆ - Lifetime Hoan Corp.
MARMALADE - Dinnerware, wallcoverings, appliances - International China Corp.
MARMALADE - Teas - Eastern Shore Tea Co.
MARMARA - Cigars - G.A. Georgopulo & Co. Inc.
MARMET - Window frames - Marmet Corp.
MARMI - Tiles–ceramic ☆ - American Marazzi Tile, Inc.
MARMINE - Pharmaceutical preparations ☆ - Vortech Pharmaceuticals
MARMITE - Bouillon - Cornwall Group Inc.
MARMOL - Ceramic tile - Interceramic Inc.
MARMOLEUM DUAL - Floor coverings–linoleum - Forbo Industries, Inc.
MARMOLEUM FRESCO - Floor coverings–linoleum - Forbo Industries, Inc.
MARMOLEUM REAL - Floor coverings–linoleum - Forbo Industries, Inc.
MARMON - Motor vehicles–automobiles ☆ - Marmon Motor Co.
MARMON-HERRINGTON - Motor vehicles–automobiles ☆ - Marmon-Herrington Co.
MARMONT - Pipes–tobacco ☆ - S.M. Frank & Co. Inc. (Kaywoodie-Yello-Bole-Medico)
MARMOOSKA - Fishing tackle - HT Enterprises, Inc.
MARMOR - Wallpaper - Advance Wallcoverings
MARMORA - Floor coverings - Mannington Resilient Floors
MARMOT - Figurines ☆ - Reco International Corp.
MARNAL - Pharmaceutical preparations ☆ - Vortech Pharmaceuticals
MARNAY - Brandy ☆ - Winesellers Ltd.
MARNAY - Office furniture–metal - Marnay Sales & Manufacturing Co. Inc.
MARNAY-COMMODORE - Desk sets ☆ - Marnay Sales & Manufacturing Co. Inc.
MARNE - Mustard - Holland-American Importing Co. Inc.
MARO - Cleaning equipment - Maro International Corp.
MAROC - Bedding–linen - Dan River Inc.
MAROC - Floor coverings–carpet and rugs - Couristan Inc.
MAROC - Perfumes - Revlon Consumer Products Corp.
MAROCCINI - Shotguns - Fie Corp.
MARON WAY - Floor coverings–carpet and rugs ☆ - Hollytex Carpet Mills Inc.
MARONA - Girdles - Dayton Hudson Corp.
MARONN - Candy - Chocolate House, Inc.
MAROONED - Hair care products - Cosmair Inc.
MAROVELLI - Jewelry - Designer Lines Inc.
MAROXY - Aquariums–household - Mardel Laboratories, Inc.
MARPE - Vitamins and nutritional supplements - Vital Food Sources, Inc.
MARPLAN - Pharmaceutical preparations - Roche Laboratories
MARPLEX - Water treating compounds - Mardel Laboratories, Inc.
MARPRO - Candy - Marshmallow Products
MARPROOF - Finishing agents - Cloverleaf Paint & Varnish
MARQ PLUS - Computer peripheral equipment ☆ - Mouse Systems Corp.
MARQUAND - Liqueur ☆ - Charles Jacquin et Compagnie Inc.
MARQUEE - Christmas tree lights - Noma International, Inc.
MARQUEE - Manufactured homes - Redman Industries, Inc.
MARQUEE - Novelty items - Cal Themes Inc.

MARQUEE - Tiles–ceramic - American Olean Tile Co.
MARQUES - Tableware–china ☆ - Anna-Perenna Inc.
MARQUES DE ARIENZO - Brandy ☆ - Domecq Importers Inc.
MARQUES DE DOMECQ - Brandy ☆ - Domecq Importers Inc.
MARQUES DE MURRIETA - Wines - William Grant & Sons, Inc.
MARQUES DE RISCAL - Wines - Schieffelin and Somerset Co.
MARQUES DE RISCAL - Wines - Shaw-Ross International Importers
MARQUES DE SAN CRISTOBAL - Cigars - P. Cerlis Corp.
MARQUESA - Fabric stores ☆ - Amoco Fabrics and Fibers Co.
MARQUESA - Floor coverings–carpet and rugs ☆ - American Carpet Mills
MARQUESA - Tableware–china ☆ - Lenox, Inc.
MARQUESA LANA - Yarn - Amoco Fabrics and Fibers Co.
MARQUESS - Rings–jewelry - Artcarved Inc.
MARQUESSA - Candy - Kraft Foods, Inc.
MARQUESSA - Floor coverings - Mannington Resilient Floors
MARQUETRY - Floor coverings–carpet and rugs - Bellbridge Carpets
MARQUETRY BEAR - Furniture - Evenflo Juvenile Furniture Co.
MARQUETTE - Battery chargers, welding equipment and accessories - Lincoln Automotive
MARQUETTE - Furniture ☆ - Hammary Furniture Co. Inc.
MARQUETTE - Lighting equipment–aircraft ☆ - Dove Foods
MARQUETTE - Medical apparatus - Marquette Electronics, Inc.
MARQUETTE - Thread ☆ - Kreinik Manufacturing Co. Inc.
MARQUETTE DECLINE'S RECESSION OWE DE COLOGNE POOR HOMBRE - Perfumes - Topical Products Inc.
MARQUETTE PARK 22 - Floor coverings–carpet and rugs ☆ - Hollytex Carpet Mills Inc.
MARQUETTE PARK 24 - Floor coverings–carpet and rugs ☆ - Hollytex Carpet Mills Inc.
MARQUETTE PARK 26 - Floor coverings–carpet and rugs ☆ - Hollytex Carpet Mills Inc.
MARQUEZ - Food products - Multifoods Inc.
MARQUEZ PRIMERA & LITTLE ONES SUPREME - Food products - Multifoods Inc.
MARQUIS - Amplifiers ☆ - Electro-Voice, Inc.
MARQUIS - Aquariums–household - O'Dell Industries
MARQUIS - Attache cases - Airway Industries, Inc.
MARQUIS - Bathroom fixtures ☆ - Price Pfister Co.
MARQUIS - Blinds–venetian ☆ - C-Mor Co.
MARQUIS - Boats–motor ☆ - Ebko Industries Inc.
MARQUIS - Brushes - Corona Brushes Inc.
MARQUIS - Cosmetics - Lancome
MARQUIS - Curtain rods - Newell Window Furnishing Co.
MARQUIS - Dinnerware–glass ☆ - WMF/USA
MARQUIS - Dishes–china - Pickard Inc.
MARQUIS - Doors - Morgan Products Ltd.
MARQUIS - Doors–wood ☆ - Maywood Inc.
MARQUIS - Dryers–hair - Roux Laboratories, Inc.
MARQUIS - Flashlights ☆ - Mag Instrument Inc.
MARQUIS - Floor coverings - E.R. Carpenter Co.
MARQUIS - Floor coverings - Mannington Resilient Floors
MARQUIS - Floor coverings–carpet and rugs - Atlas Carpet Mills Inc.
MARQUIS - Floor coverings–carpet and rugs - Couristan Inc.
MARQUIS - Floor coverings–carpet and rugs - Philadelphia Carpets
MARQUIS - Glassware–household - Crisa Corp.
MARQUIS - Glassware–household - Crystal Clear Importing Co. Inc.
MARQUIS - Glassware–household - Oneida Ltd.
MARQUIS - Headphones ☆ - GC Thorsen, Inc.
MARQUIS - Health care products - Sunrise Medical
MARQUIS - Linen - Bibb Co.
MARQUIS - Motor vehicles–automobiles - Ford Motor Co. (Lincoln-Mercury Div.)
MARQUIS - Motor vehicles–motor homes - Beaver Coaches Inc.
MARQUIS - Musical instrument accessories - C.F. Martin & Co., Inc.
MARQUIS - Neckties - Mallory and Church Corp.
MARQUIS - Paints - Bel-Mar Paint Corp.
MARQUIS - Pool tables - Goods Manufacturers International
MARQUIS - Rings–jewelry - Artcarved Inc.
MARQUIS - Tiles–ceiling ☆ - Certainteed Corp. (Roofing Products Group)
MARQUIS - Tiles–ceramic - Monarch Tile Inc.
MARQUIS - Wallpaper ☆ - Rigo Wallcoverings Inc.
MARQUIS - Window shades - Verosol
MARQUIS COLLECTION - Fabrics - Vertilux-Louverlux Inc.
MARQUIS COLLECTION OF BEVERLY HILLS - Furniture - Marquis Collection of Beverly Hills
MARQUIS DE BORDEAUX - Food products - Europa Foods Ltd.

☆ = Now out of production

MARQUIS DE CAUSSADE ARMAGNAC - Beverages–alcohol - Blair Importers Ltd.

MARQUIS DE GOULAINE - Wines ☆ - IDV Wines (Beaulieu Vineyard)

MARQUIS DE LAFAYETTE - Cheese - Besnier USA, Inc.

MARQUIS DE MONTESQUIOU - Armagnac - Austin, Nichols & Co., Inc.

MARQUIS HOME COLLECTION - Bedding–linen - Bibb Co.

MARQUIS MEDLEY - Rings–jewelry - Sandberg & Sikorski Diamond Corp.

MARQUIS MILL CONES - Yarn - Henry's Attic

MARQUISAT - Wines - European Beverage Co., Inc.

MARQUISE - Bakery products - Awrey Bakeries, Inc.

MARQUISE - Boats–motor ☆ - Four Winns Inc.

MARQUISE - Christmas tree ornaments - Cracker Box Inc.

MARQUISE - Cleaning preparations–carpet and rug - Ecolab Inc.

MARQUISE - Doors–glass - Therma-Tru Corp.

MARQUISE - Footwear–women's - Wohl Shoe Co.

MARQUISE - Fretted instruments ☆ - International Music Corp.

MARQUISE - Girdles - Abraham & Straus/Jordan Marsh Co.

MARQUISE - Glassware–household - H. Wittur & Co.

MARQUISE - Tiles–ceramic - United States Ceramic Tile Co.

MARQUISE - Watches - Bulova Corp.

MARQUISE DE POMPADOUR - Fruits–candied ☆ - Liberty Richter Inc.

MARQUISE DE SEVIGNE - Chocolate candy ☆ - Liberty Richter Inc.

MARQUITA - Skin care products - Fromm Industries

MARRAKECH - Floor coverings ☆ - Bellbridge Carpets

MARRAKECH - Floor coverings–carpet and rugs ☆ - Hollytex Carpet Mills Inc.

MARRAKESH - Dinnerware - Denby USA Limited

MARRAKESH - Floor coverings–carpet and rugs - Couristan Inc.

MARRAKESH - Floor coverings–carpet and rugs - Cameron Pande and Co. of New York, Inc.

MARRAKESH - Floor coverings–carpet and rugs ☆ - Eurotex Inc.

MARRAKESH - Floor coverings–carpet and rugs ☆ - Interloom Ltd.

MARRAKESH - Floor coverings–tile - Interface, Inc.

MARRAKESH - Furniture - Tropitone Furniture Co. Inc.

MARRAKESH EXPRESS - Food products - Sheffield Foods Inc.

MARRAZZI - Ceramic tile ☆ - Integrity Tile Co.

MARREKESH - Flowers, plants, and seeds - Monrovia

MARRESI - Bicycling shoes - Corso Bicycle Distributor Inc.

MARRIAGE - Colognes ☆ - Avon Products, Inc.

MARRIAGE HEART - Jewelry - Sandberg & Sikorski Diamond Corp.

MARRIAGE SAVER - Novelty items - Lyon Design, Inc.

MARRIAGE SAVER - Transmitting apparatus - DAK Industries Inc.

MARRIAGE WISH - Novelty items ☆ - Wry Idea Co.

MARRIED WITH CHILDREN - Greeting cards - Elp Communications

MARRIED WITH CHILDREN - Watches ☆ - Delta Impex Watch Corp.

MARRIOTT - Food products - Fairfield Farm Kitchens

MARRIOTT - Hotels and motels - Marriott International Inc.

MARROBONE - Pet products ☆ - USA-Petrx

MARROW PLUS - Vitamins and nutritional supplements - ADG Concerns, Inc.

MARRYAT - Fishing lures - Fritz Von Schlegell

MARS - Bathroom accessories - KLR Products, Inc.

MARS - Brushes–paint - Corona Brushes Inc.

MARS - Candy bars - Mars, Inc.

MARS - Golfing equipment - Mars Golf Supply

MARS - Pencils - Staedtler, Inc.

MARS - Pet products - Berolina Imports

MARS - Pies–frozen - Mars Fudge & Fruit Co. Inc.

M.A.R.S. - Roofing materials–clay - Carlisle Corp.

MARS - Tape recorders - Eastman Kodak Co.

MARS 2000 - Paints - Mobile Automobile Reconditioning Systems

MARS ATTACKS - Trading cards and stamps - Topps Co., Inc.

MARS-CHROMA - Pencils - Staedtler, Inc.

MARS DRAFT - Pencils–mechanical - Staedtler, Inc.

MARS-DURAGLIDE - Pens - Staedtler, Inc.

MARS-DURAGRAPH - Pencils - Staedtler, Inc.

MARS-DURALAR - Pencils - Staedtler, Inc.

MARS-DYNAGRAPH - Pencils - Staedtler, Inc.

MARS EARTH TECHNOLOGIES - Computer software - James E. Tillman

MARS LANDER - Toys–models ☆ - Estes Industries

MARS LIFE KIT - Novelty items - Dynamic Development

MARS-LUMOCHROM - Pencils - Staedtler, Inc.

MARS-MASTERBOW - Drafting supplies - Staedtler, Inc.

MARS-NON-PRINT - Pencils - Staedtler, Inc.

MARS-OMNICHROM - Pencils - Staedtler, Inc.

MARS-PLASTIC - Erasers - Staedtler, Inc.

MARS PLOT - Pens - Staedtler, Inc.

MARS-POLYCOLOR - Markers–felt-tip - Staedtler, Inc.

MARS-RASOR - Erasers - Staedtler, Inc.

MARS SNOOPER - Toys–models ☆ - Estes Industries

MARS-SUPERBOW - Pencils - Staedtler, Inc.

MARS-TECHNICO - Pencil holders - Staedtler, Inc.

MARS TECHNO - Pens - Staedtler, Inc.

MARSALA - Floor coverings–carpet and rugs - Milliken & Co. Inc.

MARSALA - Olive oil - Nick Sciabica & Sons

MARSALA - Sinks–metal - Kohler Co.

MARSALLA - Floor coverings ☆ - Congoleum Corp.

MARSEILLE - Frames–picture - Terragrafics Inc.

MARSEILLE - Furniture ☆ - Bassett Furniture Industries, Inc.

MARSEILLE - Ophthalmic goods - Foremost Optical Products

MARSEILLE LITE - Chimes ☆ - Nutone Inc.

MARSEILLES - Clocks ☆ - General Time Corp. (Westclox/Seth Thomas Div.)

MARSEILLES - Dinnerware–glass - Nikko Ceramics Inc.

MARSEILLES - Rings–jewelry - Artcarved Inc.

MARSEILLES - Thread - Threads USA Div.

MARSEILLES - Tiles–ceiling - Lifetime Rooftile Co.

MARSEL - Mirrors - Marsel Mirror and Glass Products Co. Inc.

MARSETTA LANE - Employment agencies–temporary help - Marsetta Lane Temp Service

MARSGRAPHIC - Markers–felt-tip - Staedtler, Inc.

MARSGRAPHIC 3000 - Markers–felt-tip - Staedtler, Inc.

MARSH - Bulletin boards–wood - Marsh Chalkboard Co.

MARSH - Cabinets ☆ - Marsh Furniture Co.

MARSH - Inks - Marsh Co.

MARSH - Milk - Maplehurst Farms Inc.

MARSH - Pottery - Marsh Industries Inc.

MARSH HARBOR - Floor coverings ☆ - Tarkett, Inc.

MARSH LANDING - Apparel–women's - May Department Stores Co.

MARSH-LITE - Bulletin boards–wood ☆ - Marsh Chalkboard Co.

MARSH MASTER - Games - Great Blue Productions, Inc.

MARSH MELLOW - Staircases–metal - Bridgestone/Firestone, Inc.

MARSH OF CALIFORNIA - Pottery - Marsh Industries Inc.

MARSH STENCIL - Inks - Marsh Co.

MARSH SUPREME - Cigars - M. Marsh & Son

MARSH TIPS - Cigars - M. Marsh & Son

MARSH WHEELING BLACK - Tobacco–chewing or smoking - M. Marsh & Son

MARSHA - Athletic footwear ☆ - Autry Industries Inc.

MARSHA BERGEN - Apparel and accessories - Colonial Textile Manufacturing Corp.

MARSHA WHITNEY - Cleaning preparations - Layton Marketing Group Inc.

MARSHAL - Tires - Kumho USA Inc.

MARSHAL - Toys–guns - Strombecker Corp.

MARSHAL BLAST - Toys - Mattel, Inc.

MARSHALL - Amplifiers - Korg USA

MARSHALL - Audio equipment - Marshall Electronics Inc.

MARSHALL - Automotive parts and accessories - G.M.B. Battery Inc.

MARSHALL - Blood pressure apparatus ☆ - Omron Healthcare, Inc.

MARSHALL - Boats - Marshall Marine

MARSHALL & SWIFT THE BUILDING COST PEOPLE - Publisher's imprints - Marshall & Swift

MARSHALL BRAVESTARR - Bathroom accessories ☆ - Tsumura International Inc.

MARSHALL CARDS - Canvas–artists' - Fabulous Forgeries Ltd.

MARSHALL DURBIN - Meat products–poultry - Marshall Durbin Food Corp.

MARSHALL JAMES - Furniture - Marshall/James, Inc.

MARSHALL MALLOW - Cocoa–powders or mixes - Nestle Beverage Co.

MARSHALL MASTERPIECES - Canvas–artists' - Fabulous Forgeries Ltd.

MARSHALL MOO MONTANA - Toys - Hasbro, Inc.

MARSHALL PAC - Braces–orthopedic - JUZO

MARSHALL STUDIOS - Earthenware - Marshall Studios Inc.

MARSHALLAN - Furniture - Marshallan Manufacturing Co.

MARSHALLCRAT - Metals - Precision Industries, Inc.

MARSHALLOY MQ - Metals - Precision Industries, Inc.

MARSHALLS - Apparel–men's - Melville Corp.

MARSHALL'S - Candy - Marshall's Mackinac Trail Inc.

MARSHALL'S - Cigarettes ☆ - J.H. Guild Co. Inc.

MARSHALL'S - Paints–artists' - John G. Marshall Manufacturing Co.

MARSHALL'S BEST - Fish–canned or cured - Marshall Smoked Fish Co. Inc.

MARSHALLTOWN - Tools–hand-operated - Marshalltown Trowel Co.

MARSHEEN - Enamels ☆ - Morton International Traffic Markings

MARSHFIELD - Doors–wood - Weyerhaeuser Co.

MARSHFIELD - Food products ☆ - Marshfield Foods

MARSHLANDER - Waterproof outerwear - Neese Industries, Inc.

☆ = Now out of production

MARSHMALLOW - Recliners - Stratford Co.
MARSHMALLOW CANDIES - Candy - Judson-Atkinson Candies
MARSHMALLOW CLOWN - Toys–stuffed - Russ Berrie and Co., Inc.
MARSHMALLOW FLUFF - Desserts - Durkee-Mower Inc.
MARSHMALLOW GLITTERS - Cereal - Jasper Foods, Inc.
MARSHMALLOW MARTIANS - Toys - Smart Alec Toys, Inc.
MARSHMALLOW MATEYS - Cereal - Malt-O-Meal Co.
MARSHMALLOW MUNCHIE - Snack foods - Heritage Brands Holdings, Inc.
MARSHMALLOW PEEPS - Candy - Just Born Inc.
MARSHMALLOW TREASURE - Cereal - Malt-O-Meal Co.
MARSHMALLOW TWIRLS - Cookies - Nabisco Foods Group
MARSHMALLOW TWISTS - Candy - Keppel's Inc.
MARSHMALLOWLOVERS - Cocoa–powders or mixes ☆ - Hunt-Wesson, Inc.
MARSHMALLOWS - Balls ☆ - Precise International/Wenger
MARSHMALLOWS - Women's shoes - Interco Inc.
MARSHMALLOWS TOO! - Shoes - Interco Inc.
MARSHMELLO - Wallpaper - Carlton-Metro Wallcoverings
MARSHMELLOW BEAR - Toys–stuffed - Dakin Inc.
MARSHMELLOW ELEPHANT - Toys–stuffed ☆ - Dakin Inc.
MARSILIO - Publisher's imprints - Rizzoli International Publications Inc.
MARSINT - Tiles–ceramic ☆ - Dal-Tile Corp.
MARSJET - Markers–felt-tip - Staedtler, Inc.
MARSKIN - Paper–kraft ☆ - Marvin Envelope & Paper Co.
MARSMAGNO - Pens - Staedtler, Inc.
MARSMATIC 700 - Pens - Staedtler, Inc.
MARSMICRO - Pencils–mechanical - Staedtler, Inc.
MARSOLVE - Rust removers - Robert Louis Associates of Newtown, Inc.
MARSON - Automotive parts and accessories ☆ - Marson Creative Fastener Group
MARSONA - Audio equipment - Marpac Corp.
MARSON'S - Cakes - New Life Bakery Inc.
MARSPAC - Floor coverings–tile - Walker and Zanger Inc.
MARSTON - Toilets–enameled - Kohler Co.
MARSTON HALL - Floor coverings - Mannington Resilient Floors
MARSTON'S MILL - Candles ☆ - General Housewares Corp.
MARSTRON - Sporting goods - Avon Marine
MARTA - Looms - Northfield Loom
MARTE MK 2 - Toys–models ☆ - Estes Industries
MARTEAU - Wines - Hammer Co.
MARTEC - Propellers - Martec Engineering Corp.
MARTECH - Health care products - Martech/Laurel Medical
MARTECTOR - Truck beds - Martec Products International
MARTEGANI - Shoes - Footgear
MARTEL - Fish–canned or cured - Atalanta Corp.
MARTEL - Musical instruments ☆ - Hershman Musical Instrument
MARTEL - Trays - Hemisphere Corp.
MARTELL - Beverages–alcohol - J. & F. Martell Inc.
MARTELLI - Pasta - Bel Canto Fancy Foods Ltd.
MARTELLI - Pasta - Dean & Deluca Inc.
MARTELLI - Wines ☆ - Pellegrini Bros. Wines Inc.
MARTENITZA - Wines - Icarus International Inc.
MARTENN - Food products - Sara Lee Corp.
MARTEST 21 - Furniture - Virco Manufacturing Corp.
MARTEX - Bedding–linen - West Point-Pepperell Inc.
MARTEX - Fabrics - Sero Sales
MARTEX WRINKLE FREE - Linen - W Point-Pepperell Enterprises, Inc.
MARTGUILD - Giftware - Martguild Inc.
MARTHA - Bedding–linen - Dan River Inc.
MARTHA - Tomato pastes and sauces - Delicato Foods, Inc.
MARTHA ANN - Confections - Grace A. Rush Inc.
MARTHA GOOCH - Pasta - Gooch Foods Inc.
MARTHA GRAHAM - Apparel and accessories - Ronald Protas
MARTHA LORRAINE - Cosmetics ☆ - Neutrogena Corp.
MARTHA SCOTT - Skin care products ☆ - Household Research Corp.
MARTHA TOWNSEND'S - Food products ☆ - Townsends Inc.
MARTHA WASHINGTON - Dolls ☆ - Effanbee Doll Corp.
MARTHA WASHINGTON - Glass–leaded - Seneca Glass Co.
MARTHA WASHINGTON - Watches - Bulova Corp.
MARTHA WHITE - Corn–flour or meal - Martha White Foods Inc.
MARTHAS - Beverages–malt - Marthasville Brewing Co.
MARTHA'S FLOWERS - Stoneware dinnerware - Iron Mountain Stoneware Inc.
MARTHASVILLE CREAMERY - Milk - Harry's Farmers Market, Inc.
MARTHINSEN - Silver products - Norwegian Silver Corp.
MARTHRITIC - Pharmaceutical preparations - R.A. McNeil Co.
MARTI - Apparel–women's - Zebulon Manufacturing Inc.

MARTIAL ARTS EXPLORER, THE - Computer software - Future Vision Holding, Inc.
MARTIAL ARTS NUTRITION - Vitamins and nutritional supplements - 4 Health, Inc.
MARTIAN DREAMS - Video games - Origin Systems, Inc.
MARTIAN PROBE - Toys - Park Plastics Co.
MARTILE - Floor coverings–tile - Walker and Zanger Inc.
MARTIN - Archery equipment - Martin Archery Inc.
MARTIN - Coffee - Martin Coffee Co.
MARTIN - Fishing tackle - Martin Reel Co.
MARTIN - Food products - Sea Greene Co.
MARTIN - Frames–eyeglass - U.S. Optical Frame Co.
MARTIN - Gasoline - Martin Oil Marketing Ltd.
MARTIN - Gasoline ☆ - J.D. Streett & Co. Inc.
MARTIN - Guitars - Castiglione Accordion
MARTIN - Guitars - C.F. Martin & Co., Inc.
MARTIN - Heaters–gas - Martin Industries, Inc.
MARTIN - Motor vehicle parts and accessories ☆ - Highland Group
MARTIN - Musical instruments - G. Leblanc Corp.
MARTIN - Pet products - C.J. Martin Co.
MARTIN - Vegetables–canned - Foster Canning Inc.
MARTIN - Wines - Martin's Wines Inc.
MARTIN AND MATTHEW - Shirts - Louie Bernard, Inc.
MARTIN AUDIO - Audio equipment - Bob White Associates
MARTIN BLUE LITES - Sunglasses - Jack Martin Co.
MARTIN BROTHERS - Wines - Martin Brothers Winery
MARTIN BROTHERS CAFE - Salad dressings–bottled - Jeff Martin and Karl Martin Partnership
MARTIN COLLET - Cheese - Besnier USA, Inc.
MARTIN GALAXY - Musical instruments ☆ - G. Leblanc Corp.
MARTIN HUGGETT - Harpsichords - Peter Redstone Harpsichords
MARTIN-KILPATRICK - Sports rackets and accessories - Martin-Kilpatrick Table Tennis Co.
MARTIN LAWRENCE GALLERIES - Publisher's imprints - Martin Lawrence Limited Editions, Inc.
MARTIN LITES - Sporting goods - Jack Martin Co.
MARTIN LOGAN - Amplifiers - GNP Audio Video Inc.
MARTIN MASTERALL - Motor vehicle parts and accessories ☆ - J.D. Streett & Co. Inc.
MARTIN POURET - Vinegar - De Medici Imports Ltd.
MARTIN SABER - Archery equipment - Martin Archery Inc.
MARTIN-SENOUR - Paints - Martin-Senour Co.
MARTIN SHENANDOAH - Guitars ☆ - C.F. Martin & Co., Inc.
MARTIN SHOOTERS - Eyeglasses - Jack Martin Co.
MARTIN SNOGLASS - Sunglasses - Jack Martin Co.
MARTIN TRADITIONAL - Windows - Martin Millwork, Inc.
MARTIN TRAINER - See ALDEN MARTIN
MARTIN VENTURI - Stoves - Martin Industries, Inc.
MARTIN V.T.C. - Amplifiers–musical instrument - C.F. Martin & Co., Inc.
MARTIN WONG - Apparel–men's - Ambiance Neckwear Inc.
MARTIN YALE - Desk sets - Premier
MARTINA - Rings–jewelry - Artcarved Inc.
MARTINDALE - Food products - Bruce Foods Corp.
MARTINDALE - Health care products ☆ - Martindale Electric Co.
MARTINELLI - Juices - S. Martinelli and Co.
MARTINELLI BY M & H - Footwear - M & H Shoes Inc.
MARTINELLI'S - Candy - Billy Burden
MARTINELLI'S - Nuts–salted, roasted, cooked, or canned - John Martinelli Inc.
MARTINER KONBIER - Beverages–malt - International Marketing Consortium, Inc.
MARTINERA - Housewares - Casa Karen
MARTINE'S CHOCOLATES - Candy - Martine's Chocolate Collection, Inc.
MARTINETT - Vacuum cleaners and accessories - Maatz Engineering Inc.
MARTINEZ & GASSIOT - Wines ☆ - Admiral Wine Merchants
MARTINI - Automotive parts and accessories - Thexton Manufacturing Inc.
MARTINI - Paints–artists' ☆ - Riebe's Artist Materials Inc.
MARTINI - Sunglasses - Lozza USA
MARTINI AND PRATI - Wines - Martini and Prati Wines Inc.
MARTINI & ROSSI - Wines - Bacardi Imports Inc.
MARTINI & ROSSI ASTI SPUMANTE - Wines - Bacardi Imports Inc.
MARTINI QUICKSET - Saddles - Weaver Leather Goods, Inc.
MARTINI SHERRI - Beverages–alcohol - Musa Inc.
MARTINIC - Vitamins and nutritional supplements - Marlop Pharmaceuticals Inc.
MARTINIQUE - Bathing suits - Ocean Pool Co.

☆ = Now out of production

MARTINIQUE - Blinds–venetian - Kenney Manufacturing Co.
MARTINIQUE - Boats ☆ - Correct Craft Inc.
MARTINIQUE - Colognes - Andrew Jergens Co.
MARTINIQUE - Dishes–china - Pickard Inc.
MARTINIQUE - Fabrics - Gretchen Bellinger Inc.
MARTINIQUE - Floor coverings ☆ - Congoleum Corp.
MARTINIQUE - Floor coverings–carpet and rugs ☆ - Trans-Ocean Import Co. Inc.
MARTINIQUE - Garden furniture - Winston Furniture Co. Inc.
MARTINIQUE - Glassware–household - Crisa Corp.
MARTINIQUE - Hairpins - Jack Martin Co.
MARTINIQUE - Wallpaper ☆ - Winfield Design Associates, Inc.
MARTINIQUE - Water - Islands International
MARTINIS - Olive oil - Euroamericana
MARTINO - Vegetables–canned - Foster Canning Inc.
MARTINOIL - Oils–lubricating - Martin Oil Marketing Ltd.
MARTIN'S - Beverages–alcohol - Blair Importers Ltd.
MARTIN'S - Food products - Martin Brothers Seafood Co. (food products)
MARTINS - Whiskey ☆ - Marie Brizard Wines & Spirits, USA
MARTINS LAMAR - Uniforms–academic - Superior Surgical Manufacturing Co. Inc.
MARTIN'S TAMPA - Uniforms–academic - Superior Surgical Manufacturing Co. Inc.
MARTIN'S VIRGINIA ROAST - Vitamins and nutritional supplements - Famarco Ltd. Inc.
MARTIN'S VVO - Scotch whiskey ☆ - Marie Brizard Wines & Spirits, USA
MARTIN'S VVO - Whiskey - David Sherman Corp.
MARTINSON - Coffee - Tetley Inc.
MARTMATE - Carts - Assembled Products Corp.
MARTON ESTATE - Wines ☆ - Prestige Wine Imports Corp.
MARTUSS - Cough medicines ☆ - Marlop Pharmaceuticals Inc.
MARTY - Computer software - Maxis, Inc.
MARTY GRIFFIN'S BIG RED - Wines - Hop Kiln Winery
MARTY HOGAN - Sporting goods ☆ - L & M Distribution Inc.
MARTY J - Lawn mowers - Deines Manufacturing Corp.
MARTY MOOSE - Toys–stuffed - Dakin Inc.
MARTY MOUSE - Toys–stuffed - Russ Berrie and Co., Inc.
MARTY SCULPTURE INC. - Statuary - Marty Sculpture
MARTY'S JUICE CREATIONS - Juices - Marty's Beverage Co.
MARTY'S MUNCHABLES - Dog food - Petcare Plus, Inc.
MARU-HI - Soybean oil - Hawaiian Miso & Soy Co. Ltd.
MARUATE SPANTAB - Pharmaceutical preparations ☆ - Vortech Pharmaceuticals
MARUBA THERAPY - Teas–herbal - Merickston L. Nicholson
MARUKAN - Vinegar - Marukan Vinegar USA Inc.
MARUMAN - Soy sauce - Oriental Trading Co., Inc.
MARUMASA - Soy sauce - Honolulu Sake Brewery Co. Ltd.
MARUSHKA - Decals and transfers - Michigan Rag Co.
MARV-L-MED - Pet products - Reptilia
MARVA-MAID - Milk - Marva Maid Dairy
MARVAC - Vacuum cleaners and accessories - Tammie P. Wu
MARVAL - Meat products–poultry - Rocco Investments, Inc.
MARVAL - Turkeys ☆ - Rocco Turkeys Inc.
MARVALKOTE - Paints - United States Refining Co.
MARVALON - Plastics–laminated ☆ - Mactac Inc. (Packaging Closures Systems Div.)
MARVEL - Amplifiers–musical instrument - Multivox/Sorkin Music Co. Inc.
MARVEL - Brushes–paint - Elder & Jenks, Inc.
MARVEL - Cabinets–metal ☆ - Marvel Group Inc.
MARVEL - Cooking utensils–aluminum - M.E. Heuck Co. Inc.
MARVEL - Detergents - Imperial Manufacturing Co. Inc.
MARVEL - Dryers–hair - P.S. Pibbs Inc.
MARVEL - Flowers, plants, and seeds - Panamerican Seed
MARVEL - Footwear - S. Goldberg and Co. Inc.
MARVEL - Furniture - Masco Corp.
MARVEL - Glassware–household ☆ - Wallace International Silversmiths, Inc.
MARVEL - Jewelry - Tru-Kay Manufacturing Co.
MARVEL - Lamp bulbs - Marvel Lighting Corp.
MARVEL - Paints ☆ - Hampton Paint Manufacturing Co.
MARVEL - Paper punches - Bates Manufacturing Co.
MARVEL - Pet products - Aquarium Products Inc.
MARVEL - Petroleum - Marvel Oil Co. Inc.
MARVEL - Saws–power - Armstrong Blum Manufacturing Co.
MARVEL - Skates–roller - Globe United Inc.
MARVEL - Sponges ☆ - Penn Champ Inc.
MARVEL - Sports rackets and accessories - Martin-Kilpatrick Table Tennis Co.

MARVEL - Tape–adhesive - Adhesive Tapes International, Inc.
MARVEL - Toys - Lancer Industries Inc.
MARVEL - Toys - Marvel Entertainment Group, Inc.
MARVEL - Wallpaper - Sherburne Ewing Wallcovering Co.
MARVEL - Yeast ☆ - Freeda Vitamins Inc.
MARVEL AID - Pet products - 8 in 1 Pet Products Inc.
MARVEL-AIR - Floor coverings - Mannington Resilient Floors
MARVEL AIRFLOW - Water purification systems - Aquarium Products Inc.
MARVEL COMICS - Books–comic - Marvel Entertainment Group, Inc.
MARVEL MANIA - Marvel Entertainment Group, Inc.
MARVEL MARKER - Markers–felt-tip ☆ - Craft World International Inc.
MARVEL MIDNIGHT SONS - Books–comic ☆ - Marvel Entertainment Group, Inc.
MARVEL MYSTERY OIL - Oils–lubricating - Marvel Oil Co. Inc.
MARVEL POWER PALS - Toys ☆ - Marvel Entertainment Group, Inc.
MARVEL SUPER HEROES - Umbrellas - Shaw Creations Inc.
MARVEL-TEK - Paints - Passonno Paints
MARVEL-TEX - Hearing aids - Mid-States Laboratories Inc.
MARVEL TWIST - Floor coverings–carpet and rugs - Barrett Carpet Mills Inc.
MARVELANE - Paints ☆ - Waterlac Industries Inc.
MARVELITE 5 YEAR - Lamps - Marvel Lighting Corp.
MARVELLA - Apparel and accessories - Crystal Brands Inc.
MARVELLA - Jewelry - Trifari
MARVELLE - Cooking equipment–household ☆ - Sunbeam-Oster Household Products
MARVELLISSIMA - Skin care products - Marvellissima International Ltd.
MARVELO - Varnishes - Muralo Co. Inc.
MARVELOAF - Cakes - Marveloaf Corp.
MARVELON - Floor finish ☆ - Cook and Dunn Paint Corp.
MARVELOUS - Floor coverings - Aladdin Mills, Inc.
MARVELOUS - Floor coverings–carpet and rugs ☆ - World Carpets, Inc.
MARVELOUS - Floor coverings–carpet and rugs ☆ - Zenith Carpets
MARVELOUS - Shrimp–canned or cured - Reuther's Seafood Co. Inc.
MARVELOUS CREATIONS - Desserts - Regency Creative Foods
MARVELUSTRE - Paint - Cotter & Co.
MARVETTI - Ivory engravings - Marv Art Designs Inc.
MARVIBE - Building materials - Martin Marietta Magnesia Specialties, Inc.
MARVIN - Fans–electric - W.B. Marvin Co.
MARVIN - Music–sheet ☆ - Centerstream Publications
MARVIN - Stationery ☆ - Webway, Inc.
MARVIN - Toys - F.J. Strauss Co. Inc.
MARVIN - Windows–storm - Marvin Windows and Doors
MARVIN MONKEY - Toys–stuffed - Russ Berrie and Co., Inc.
MARVIN THE MARTIAN - Apparel and accessories - Time Warner Entertainment Co., L.P.
MARVIN'S MAGIC - Toys - DGI/Buki
MARVITE - Vitamins and nutritional supplements ☆ - Marlop Pharmaceuticals Inc.
MARVITE PLUS - Vitamins and nutritional supplements ☆ - Marlop Pharmaceuticals Inc.
MARVY - Containers - Hess Hair Milk Laboratories Inc.
MARVY - Cosmetics - Marianna Imports, Inc.
MARVY - Pens - Uchida of America Corp.
MARVY - Shaving preparations - William Marvy Co., Inc.
MARVY - Stationery - Hero Arts Rubber Stamps Inc.
MARVY FOAM - Foam rubber ☆ - All-Foam Products Co.
MARWOOD SPARKLING WINES - Wines - Palm Bay Imports, Inc.
MARX - Toys - American Plastic Equipment Inc.
MARXMAN - Pipes–tobacco - Mastercraft Pipes Inc.
MARXMAN DELUXE - Pipes–tobacco ☆ - Mastercraft Pipes Inc.
MARY B. - Belts, handbags, hair accessories, jewelry, etc. - Mary B. Hetz
MARY BAKER - Cakes–mixes - Fleming Companies, Inc.
MARY BARR - Kites ☆ - Northeast Knitting Mills Inc.
MARY BETH ROZKEWICZ - Jewelry - Loom Co.
MARY CARTER - Paints - MCI Quality Coatings
MARY CHESS - Skin care products - M.C. Products Ltd.
MARY DAVINS - Skin care products - Mary Davins Inc.
MARY DUNBAR - Food products - Jewel Food Stores Inc.
MARY ELLEN - Jams and jellies - J.M. Smucker Co.
MARY ELLEN - Salad dressings–bottled - Spartan Stores Inc.
MARY ENGELBREIT - Frames–picture - Terragrafics Inc.
MARY ENGELBREIT - Greeting cards - Sunrise Publications, Inc.
MARY ENGELBREIT - Hobby kits - Distinctive Design
MARY ENGELBREIT - Paper - Stephen Lawrence Co.
MARY ENGELBREIT - Rubber stamps - All Night Media, Inc.
MARY ENGELBREIT COLLECTION - Toys - Toy Works, Inc.

☆ = Now out of production

MARY GILLIATT - Wallpaper ☆ - Sandpiper Studios
MARY GORDON - Negligees - A.H. Schreiber Co.
MARY GREEN - Apparel–women's - Mary Green Enterprises
MARY GREGORY - Glass products - Westmoreland Glass Co.
MARY HAD A LITTLE LAMB - Dolls - Effanbee Doll Corp.
MARY HAD A LITTLE LAMB - Kites ☆ - Hi-Flier Manufacturing Co.
MARY JANE - Apparel–women's - Middendorf Enterprises Inc.
MARY JANE - Candy - New England Confectionery Co.
MARY JANE - Candy - Stark Candy Co.
MARY JANE MARCASIANO - Apparel–women's - Marcasiano Inc.
MARY JANE SUPER WHITE - Breads - Kotarides Baking Co., Inc.
MARY-KATE & ASHLEY'S FUN CLUB - Apparel and accessories - Dualstar Entertainment Group, Inc.
MARY KAY - Containers - Mary Kay Inc.
MARY KAY - Skin care products - Mary Kay Cosmetics Inc.
MARY KAY INTOUCH - Computer software - Mary Kay Inc.
MARY KITCHEN - Food products - Hormel Foods Corp.
MARY LAKE-THOMPSON - Photo albums ☆ - Webway, Inc.
MARY LAMB - Hair- and skin-care products, fragrance, etc. - Benjamin Ansehl Co.
MARY LEE - Food products - Ellenbee Foods Inc.
MARY LEE - Food products - Gilster-Mary Lee Corp.
MARY LEE TAYLOR - Ice milk ☆ - Pet Dairy
MARY LOU - Dolls - Holiday Fair, Inc.
MARY LOU - Food products - Sar-A-Lee Inc.
MARY LOU - Frames–eyeglass - U.S. Optical Frame Co.
MARY-LOU - Pickles ☆ - Aunt Jane's Foods
MARY MAESTRI'S - Food products - Maestri Co.
MARY-MAGIC - Cleaning preparations - International Products Co.
MARY, MARY - Apparel–women's ☆ - Kellwood Co.
MARY MAXIM - Craft supplies - Mary Maxim Inc.
MARY MCFADDEN - Crocheted and knitted items ☆ - Heritage Sportswear
MARY MCFADDEN - Eyeglasses - Mary McFadden, Inc.
MARY MCFADDEN - Greeting cards ☆ - Brett-Forer Greetings Inc.
MARY MCFADDEN'S MOSAIC DREAMS - Wallpaper - Kirk-Brummel
MARY MELCHER - Greeting cards - Recycled Paper Products, Inc.
MARY MEYER - Toys–stuffed - Mary Meyer Corp.
MARY PANG'S - Food products - Mary Pang's Food Products Inc.
MARY POPPINS - Dolls ☆ - Effanbee Doll Corp.
MARY POPPINS - Games ☆ - Parker Brothers
MARY PROCTOR - Housewares - Gustin-Kramer Co.
MARY PROCTOR - Kitchen appliances ☆ - Hamilton Beach/Proctor-Silex Inc.
MARY QUANT - Greeting cards ☆ - Brett-Forer Greetings Inc.
MARY SHERMAN - Skin care products ☆ - Warner-Lambert Co.
MARYANN'S BOUTIQUE - Bags - Belk Stores Services, Inc.
MARYBETH - Health care products ☆ - Myra Hogan
MARYKATE - Cleaning preparations - Marikate Ship Shape, Inc.
MARYLAND - Bolts and nuts - Babcock Industries Inc. (Babcock Control Group)
MARYLAND - Food products ☆ - Mott's Inc.
MARYLAND CHIEF - Vegetables–frozen - Hanover Foods Corp.
MARYLAND CLUB - Coffee ☆ - Coca-Cola Co.
MARYLAND CRABCAKE-N-BUN - Sandwiches–prepackaged ☆ - Martin Foods
MARYLAND HOUSE - Seafood products–fresh or frozen - Nanticoke Seafood Corp.
MARYLAND ROSE - Flatware ☆ - Kirk Stieff Co.
MARYLAND-VIRGINIA - Flowers, plants, and seeds - Seed Corp. of America
MARYLIN - Recording label - Ron-Dom Productions Inc.
MARY'S - Gourmet popcorn - Norvex
MARY'S ARMY - Children's apparel and craft kits - Catco, Inc.
MARY'S BEARS - Greeting cards - Hallmark Licensing, Inc.
MARY'S HIDEAWAY - Furniture ☆ - Hammary Furniture Co. Inc.
MARY'S LAMB - Bedding–linen - Dan River Inc.
MARY'S MOO MOOS - Figurines - Enesco Corp.
MARY'S PATTERNS - Patterns–clothing - Mary Leigh Wolz
MARY'S THINS - Food products - Paradigm Foodworks
MARYSE BOXER DESIGNS - Dinnerware–plastic - Maryse Boxer Designs Inc.
MARZ - Recording label - Marz Records
MARZAN - Musical instruments ☆ - Deg Music Products Inc.
MARZANO - Tomato pastes and sauces - Ralph L. Mason Inc.
MARZANO - Tomato pastes and sauces - Williamsburg Canning Co.
MARZETTI - Relishes - T. Marzetti Co.
MARZIA - Jewelry - Dayton Hudson Corp.
MARZINETTES - Candy ☆ - Maillard Corp.

MARZO LOCO - Beverages–malt - Anheuser-Busch Companies Inc.
MARZOCCHI SUSPENSION - Motorcycle accessories - Cosmopolitan Motors Inc.
MAS-D-TEC - Dairy equipment - Wescor, Inc.
MA'S OLIVES - Olives–canned - Ma's Olives
MAS-Q-LIN MAN - Wigs - Crowning Creations Importers
MAS-TROL - Veterinary pharmaceutical preparations ☆ - Bingman Laboratories, Inc.
MAS VIGOR - Vitamins and nutritional supplements - Vita-Fore Products Co.
MASA - Artists' materials - Andrews/Nelson/Whitehead
MASA HARINA - Flour–blended - Quaker Oats Co.
MASA MAMI - Housewares ☆ - Treasure Craft Co.
MASA RICA - Food products - Goya Foods, Inc.
MASA TRIGO - Tortillas - Quaker Oats Co.
MASADA - Cosmetics - Masada Marketing
MASADA - Guitars - On-Site Music Group
MASADA BLEND - Coffee - Barrie House Coffee Co., Inc.
MASADA SECURITY - Alarm systems - Masada Security, Inc.
MASADA SPA - Skin care products - Masada Marketing
MASAI - Hair care preparations - Roux Laboratories, Inc.
MASALA CHAI SHANTIS - Teas - Health & Wealth International Inc.
MASALI CHAI - Beverages–alcohol - Masala Chai Co.
MASAMI - Jewelry - Lucoral Co. Inc.
MASCAGNI - Frames–picture - Sam Flax
MASCARA - Cosmetics - Kiss My Face
MASCARA - Cosmetics - Viviane Woodard Industries, Ltd.
MASCARELLO - Wines - William Grant & Sons, Inc.
MASCAROFF - Mascara remover - American Hygienic Laboratories Inc.
MASCARRA - Artists' materials - Stangren Co.
MASCOT - Apparel and accessories - John R. Hawk
MASCOT - Clocks - General Time Corp. (Westclox/Seth Thomas Div.)
MASCOT - Fishing lures - Paul Warner Industries
MASCOT - Food products - Gilbert Orchards Inc.
MASCOT - Gasoline - Sun Co. Inc.
MASCOT - Golfing equipment - Plawood Mormac Corp.
MASCOT - Medical apparatus - Mentor O & O Inc.
MASCOT - Nuts–salted, roasted, cooked, or canned - T & K Manufacturing Inc.
MASCOT - Tools - Mascot Precision Tools
MASCOT SHIELDS - Martial arts equipment - Ketanyd Corp.
MASCOTA - Perfumes ☆ - Frances Denney
MASCOTT - Footwear - Scottie Industries Inc.
MASCOTTE - Hair care products - P.S. Pibbs Inc.
MASCRU - Masonry fasteners - Ackerman Johnson Fastening Systems Inc.
MASCULIN - Fragrance - Bourjois Ltd.
MASCULINE BALANCE - Vitamins and nutritional supplements ☆ - Ethical Nutrients
MASCUS - Housewares - Market Place
MASE - Steel products - Nabors Industries, Inc.
MASECA - Corn flour - Azteca Milling
MASEDA - Skin care products ☆ - ICN Pharmaceuticals Inc.
MASELTOV - Food products ☆ - Strohmeyer and Arpe Co.
MASER - Apparel and accessories - Skane Ltd.
MASERATI - Footwear - Brown Shoe Co.
MASERATI - Motor vehicles–automobiles - Maserati Automobiles Inc.
MASETTI - Neckties - Resisto Tie Makers
MASEUR - Footwear - Saramar Corp.
MASEUR MASSAGE - Footwear - Maseur Products
MASGRES - Tiles–ceramic - Balgres Distributing Co.
MASH - Apparel and accessories - Twentieth Century Fox Film Corp.
MASHAR FASHION - Apparel–athletic - Maschock Associates
MASHER - Toys - Tonka Corp.
MASHUGA COOKIES - Cookies - Mashuga Nuts, Inc.
MASHUGA NUTS - Nuts–salted, roasted, cooked, or canned - Mashuga Nuts, Inc.
MASI - Wines ☆ - IDV Wines (Beaulieu Vineyard)
MASIA BACH - Beverages–alcohol - Codorniu USA Inc.
MASIC - Xlnt, Inc.
MASIO - Office supplies - W & P Co.
MASK - Games ☆ - Ben Cooper Inc.
M.A.S.K. - Games ☆ - Parker Brothers
MASK - Toys - Kenner Products
MASK-A-MILLION - Hobby kits - Banana Moon Products Inc.
MASK & PEEL - Paints ☆ - Klean-Strip
MASK-EASE - Artists' materials - Scratch-Art Co., Inc.
MASK FUN - Costumes - Z-Barten Productions

☆ = Now out of production

MASK-IT - Paints - Bear Archery Inc.

MASK 'N PEEL - Artists' materials - Duncan Enterprises

MASK-OFF - Abrasive products - Craftics Inc.

MASK-OR - Tape—masking - Plastic Suppliers, Inc.

MASK, THE - Lunch boxes - Thermos Co.

MASK-U-LIN - Cosmetics - Alvin Last Inc.

MASKE - Frames—eyeglass - Euro-Frames Inc.

MASKED RIDER - Footwear - S. Goldberg and Co. Inc.

MASKED RIDER - Toothbrushes - Saban Entertainment, Inc.

MASKED RIDER - Toys - Bandai America Inc.

MASKED RIDER SUPER BLUE - Toys - Saban Entertainment, Inc.

MASKED RIDER SUPER GOLD - Toys - Saban Entertainment, Inc.

MASKINS - Photographic equipment - Heindl Masks 'n' Mounts

MASKOID - Cosmetics - Andrew Jeri Co. Inc.

MASKUMM - Medical apparatus - Trademark Corp.

MASKUMM - Surgical supplies - Intellimed Bioresearch, Inc.

MASLACH - Giftware - N.S. Gustin Co.

MASLAN - Chairs—wood ☆ - Fixtures Furniture

MASLAND - Floor coverings—carpet and rugs ☆ - Masland Corp.

MASLAND CONTRACT - Floor coverings—carpet and rugs - Masland Carpets, Inc.

MASLAND DURAN - Fabrics - Uniroyal Engineered Products

MASON - Apparel—athletic ☆ - Mount Vernon Mills Inc.

MASON - Awnings - A & E Blind & Awning Co.

MASON - Candy - Tootsie Roll Industries, Inc.

MASON - Decoys - Mason's Decoy Factory Inc.

MASON - Handbags - Blaine Window Hardware Inc.

MASON - Lighting equipment - Standex International Corp.

MASON - Ships—sailing vessels - Pacific Asian Enterprises Inc.

MASON - Shoes - Mason Shoe Manufacturing Co.

MASON & HAMLIN - Pianos - Sohmer Corp.

MASON & RISCH - Pianos - Aeolian Pianos Inc.

MASON BED RENTER - Mattresses - Mason Medical Products

MASON BERRIES - Candy - Tootsie Roll Industries, Inc.

MASON CASH - Cooking utensils—stoneware - Elite Design

MASON-COTE - Paints - California Products Corp.

MASON CROWS - Candy - Tootsie Roll Industries, Inc.

MASON-DIXON - Food products - Hepburn Orchards Inc.

MASON DIXON - Milk - Mason Dixon Farms Inc.

MASON DOTS - Candy - Tootsie Roll Industries, Inc.

MASON-DRI - Paints - Proctor Paint & Varnish Co. Inc.

MASON HILL FARM - Jams and jellies - Mason Hill Farm, Inc.

MASON MINTS - Candy ☆ - Tootsie Roll Industries, Inc.

MASON NATURAL - Vitamins and nutritional supplements - Mason Distributors, Inc.

MASON PEARSON - Brushes—hair - Harry D. Koenig & Co.

MASON PREMIER - Toys - Co. Store

MASON WILD CHERRY DROPS - Candy - Tootsie Roll Industries, Inc.

MASONCRAFT - Desk sets - Mason Stationery Products Inc.

MASONETTE - Furniture ☆ - Hammary Furniture Co. Inc.

MASONITE - Wood products - Masonite Corp.

MASON'S - Beverages—carbonated - Monarch Co., Inc.

MASON'S - Earthenware ☆ - Waterford Wedgwood USA, Inc.

MASON'S - Gasoline - Racetrac Petroleum Inc.

MASON'S CHOICE - Bricks - Stanson Inc. (Dacor Brick Div.)

MASON'S CHOICE - Cement - Independent Cement Corp.

MASON'S CHOICE - Fertilizers - Mass Natural Fertilizer Inc.

MASON'S QUAIL - Dinnerware—glass - S.P. Skinner Co. Inc.

MASPERO - Cigarettes - G.A. Georgopulo & Co. Inc.

MASPERO SPECIALS - Cigarettes - G.A. Georgopulo & Co. Inc.

MASPETH - Music boxes ☆ - Coehler-Coptex Co.

MASQ - Computer software - KMSystems, Inc.

MASQKE MUUGOO - Novelty items - StoryTime

MASQUE - Apparel and accessories - Seirus Innovative Accessories, Inc.

MASQUE - Deodorants—personal - Caswell-Massey Co. Ltd.

MASQUE - Recording label - Azra International

MASQUE A LA MOUSSE - Skin care products - Revlon Consumer Products Corp.

MASQUE FRAPPE - Skin care products - Dorothy Gray Cosmetics Ltd.

MASQUE LUMIERE - Skin care products - Chanel Inc.

MASQUE ONE - Skin care products - Fanie International

MASQUE SOUND - Sound equipment - Masque Sound and Recording Corp.

MASQUE TWO - Skin care products - Fanie International

MASQUERADE - Apparel and accessories - Kimberlon Inc.

MASQUERADE - Brassieres (Bras) - Maidenform Inc.

MASQUERADE - Floor coverings—carpet and rugs - Tuftex Carpet Mills, Inc.

MASQUERADE - Floor coverings—carpet and rugs ☆ - World Carpets, Inc.

MASQUERADE - Perfumes ☆ - Prince Matchabelli

MASQUERADE - Sunglasses - Argus Optical, Inc.

MASQUERADE - Wallpaper - Vymura

MASQUERADE - Yarn ☆ - JCA, Inc.

MASQUERADE BALL - Dolls - Mattel, Inc.

MASQUERADE BALL - Dolls ☆ - Effanbee Doll Corp.

MASQUERADERS - Sofabeds - Flexsteel Industries Inc.

M.A.S.S. - Display cases—metal - M.A.S.S. Systems, Inc.

MASS BAY TRADING - Apparel and accessories - Fidelity Sportswear Co.

MASS CONFUSION! - Apparel—men's - Mass Confusion

MASS COSTAL - Seafood products—fresh or frozen - Missouri Fish Co.

MASS EXTINCTION - Apparel and accessories - Dinexco, Inc.

MASS FUEL - Vitamins and nutritional supplements - Twinlab

MASS FUEL ANABOLIC AMINO ACID COMPLEX - Vitamins and nutritional supplements - Twinlab

MASS FUEL HIGH PERFORMANCE CARBOHYDRATE COMPLEX - Vitamins and nutritional supplements - Twinlab

MASS MICROSYSTEMS - Computer peripheral equipment - MASS Microsystems Inc.

MASS PROBAR - Measuring instruments - Dieterich Standard, Inc.

MASS-TER MOVER - Conveyors - Hutchinson/Mayrath

MASS TRANSIT - Apparel and accessories - Mass Transit

MASS XCELERATOR - Vitamins and nutritional supplements - Juice Pak

MASSAG-A-MALS - Medical apparatus - Paris Presents Inc.

MASSAGABACK POWER MASSAGE TABLE - Medical apparatus - Backman Products, Inc.

MASSAGE-A-GRAM - Novelty items - Judith Via Cava

MASSAGE ACTION - Bathroom fixtures - Alsons Corp.

MASSAGE COMPANY, THE - Massage products - Everett Associates Inc.

MASSAGE INSOLES FOR HAPPY FEET - Shoe soles - Goosebumps Products, Inc.

MASSAGE MASTER - Medical apparatus - Wahl Clipper Corp.

MASSAGE MY FEET - Skin care products - Wilson Marketing Enterprises, Inc.

MASSAGE WAND - Health care products - Sunbeam-Oster Household Products

MASSAGEBOARD - Medical apparatus - Christopher Patrick Wincek

MASSAGETT - Health care products - Sunbeam-Oster Household Products

MASSAI - Flatware ☆ - Couzon USA

MASSE - Pharmaceutical preparations - Ortho Pharmaceutical Corp.

MASSENEZ - Brandy - Dreyfus Ashby Inc.

MASSENGILL - Pharmaceutical preparations - SmithKline Beecham Consumer Healthcare

MASSENGILL - Pharmaceutical preparations - Smithkline Beecham Corp.

MASSETO - Wines - Kobrand Corp.

MASSETTI - Food products - Spruce Foods Inc.

MASSEY-FERGUSON - Tractors—lawn - Agco Corp.

MASSIMA - Wheat flour - Italgrani USA, Inc.

MASSIMO - Food products - US Foodservice

MASSIMO - Oils—edible - Rykoff-Sexton, Inc.

MASSIMO - Yarn ☆ - Tahki Imports Ltd.

MASSIMO LIVIO - Apparel and accessories - International Fashion Trading

MASSIMO RICCI - Luggage - Luggage America Inc.

MASSIVE - Jackets - Charles H. Ross Jr.

MASSIVE INTERACTIVE - Computer software - Massive Interactive, Inc.

MASSIVE MAX - Toys—airplanes - Comet Montrose Ltd.

MASSIVE PRODUCTIONS - Stationery - Massive Productions

MASSLINN - Towels - Chicopee

MASSMEDIA - Recording label - Massmedia

MASSON LIGHT CHABLIS - Wines - Seagram's Chateau & Estate Wines Co.

MASSON VINEYARDS - Wines ☆ - Canandaigua Wine Co. Inc.

MASSPHORESIS - Spectrometers - Ciphergen Biosystems

MASSS-TER FLOW - Conveyors - Hutchinson/Mayrath

MAST - Electronic equipment - David Clark Co. Inc.

MASTA 5 STAR - Paints - Paris Paint & Varnish Co.

MASTACLASP - Jewelry - Frank Mastoloni & Sons, Inc.

MASTACUT - Apparel—men's ☆ - Sampson Inc.

MASTADON - Computer software - Jerome K. Swink

MASTAGEM - Jewelry - Frank Mastoloni & Sons, Inc.

MASTAN TUONO - Wines - Mastantuono Winery

MASTAR - Welding equipment - Uniweld Products, Inc.

MASTENDR - Ships—sailing vessels ☆ - Hutchins Co. Inc.

MASTER - Artists' materials ☆ - Hunt Manufacturing Co.

MASTER - Bowling balls - Master Industries Inc.

MASTER - Breads - Metz Baking Co.

MASTER - Brushes - MasterForce Inc.

MASTER - Brushes–paint - Corona Brushes Inc.
MASTER - Brushes–paint - Elder & Jenks, Inc.
MASTER - Cameras–video - Minolta Corp.
MASTER - Chalk - Tweeten Fibre Co.
MASTER - Drafting supplies ☆ - Mayline/Hamilton
MASTER - Drums–musical instruments - Eames Drum Co.
MASTER - Easels - Anco Wood Specialties Inc.
MASTER - Engines - Reliance Electric Co.
MASTER - Flooring–hardwood ☆ - Biwood Flooring
MASTER - Furniture - Haworth, Inc.
MASTER - Furniture–upholstered ☆ - Mersman Furniture Co.
MASTER - Golf carts - Bag Boy Inc.
MASTER - Guitars ☆ - International Music Corp.
MASTER - Hair care products - Andis Co.
MASTER - Hair care products - Fromm Industries
MASTER - Hair care products - Master Chemical Co.
MASTER - Hair curlers - Lawndale Products Inc.
MASTER - Heaters–space - Desa International, Inc.
MASTER - Heaters–space - Master Appliance Corp.
MASTER - Kitchen appliances - Vaughan Manufacturing Co. Inc.
MASTER - Knives - Precise International/Wenger
MASTER - Knives–pocket - Colonial Knife Co. Inc.
MASTER - Metals - Master Lock Co.
MASTER - Mufflers–motor vehicle - Goerlich's
MASTER - Office supplies - Master Caster Co.
MASTER - Paint removers - Embee Corp.
MASTER - Paint rollers - Bestt-Liebco
MASTER - Paper punches - Master Products Manufacturing Inc.
MASTER - Peanut butter - Stevens Industries Inc.
MASTER - Photographic equipment - Yankee Photo Products Inc.
MASTER - Photographic equipment ☆ - Kalart Victor Corp.
MASTER - Recording label - Skylite-Sing Inc.
MASTER - Saws–power - Allway Tools Inc.
MASTER - Skin care products - Major/Advance International
MASTER - Sporting goods - Head Sports USA
MASTER - Sporting goods - Sport Supply Group, Inc.
MASTER - Telephones - Master Telecom Inc.
MASTER - Thread - Lewis Threads Inc.
MASTER - Toys - Wham-O Manufacturing Co.
MASTER - Wet-mop handles - American Textile Products Co.
MASTER 5 - Recording label - A.V.I. Entertainment Group
MASTER-21 - Electronics equipment - Grass Valley Group Inc.
MASTER 2000 - Bullets - Detroit Armor Corp.
MASTER A MEAL - Pasta - Moran Foods, Inc.
MASTER-ART - Musical instruments - Metropolitan Music Co.
MASTER ART STUDIO - Paint sets–hobby - Martin F. Weber Co.
MASTER BAKERS BLEND - Flour–blended - Conagra, Inc.
MASTER BALL - Giftware - Baekgaard Ltd.
MASTER-BAND - Saw blades - American Saw & Manufacturing Co.
MASTER-BILT - Display cases–plastic - Standex International Corp.
MASTER BLASTER - Sporting goods - Wellington Leisure Products, Inc.
MASTER BLASTER - Toys - Tonka Corp.
MASTER-BLEND - Cement - Custom Building Products
MASTER BLEND G - Artists' materials ☆ - M. Grumbacher Inc.
MASTER BLEND PREMIUM - Dog food ☆ - Central Soya Co. Inc.
MASTER BLENDED - Animal feed supplements ☆ - Central Soya Co. Inc.
MASTER BOND - Adhesives and sealants - Master Bond Inc.
MASTER BRAND - Mushrooms - United Canning Corp.
MASTER BUCK - Sporting goods - SSR Inc.
MASTER CAMPER - Cooking equipment–household ☆ - Mirro Corp.
MASTER CANADA - Craft supplies - Scott Publishing Co. Inc.
MASTER CELL PROTECTOR - Vitamins and nutritional supplements - Great American Products, Inc.
MASTER CELLARS - Wines ☆ - Anheuser-Busch Companies Inc.
MASTER CHEF - Food containers ☆ - Purity Products Inc.
MASTER CHEF - Food products - IGA Inc.
MASTER CHEF - Griddles–electric - Rocky Mountain Cookware
MASTER CHEF - Kitchen appliances ☆ - Sunbeam-Oster Household Products
MASTER CHEF - Pans - All-Clad Metalcrafters Inc.
MASTER CHOICE - Food products - Great Atlantic & Pacific Tea Co., Inc.
MASTER CLEAN - Fabrics - Dan River Inc.
MASTER CLEAN - Housewares - Amana Refrigeration Inc.
MASTER COAT - Paints - Buten Paint & Wallpaper
MASTER COLLECTION - Cookies - Simmers Products
MASTER COLLECTION - Wallpaper - James Seeman Studios
MASTER CONTROL - Computer software - Ansan Industries Ltd.

MASTER CONTROL LINK - Electronic equipment - Bang & Olufsen of America Inc.
MASTER CRAFT - Boats - Master Craft Boat Co.
MASTER CRAFT - Cabinets - Whirlpool Kitchens Inc.
MASTER CRAFT - Windows–vinyl - Home Improvement Supply Co., Inc.
MASTER CUISINE - Cookware - Caldor Corp.
MASTER-CYLINDER - Lighting fixtures - Swivelier Co. Inc.
MASTER DECK - Computer peripheral equipment - Curtis Manufacturing Co., Inc.
MASTER DECORATOR, THE - Paints ☆ - Kwal-Howells Inc.
MASTER DELIVERY SERIES - Computer software - Group 1 Software, Inc.
MASTER DETECTIVE SET - Toys - Natural Science Industries, Ltd.
MASTER DICTATE - Computer storage devices–magnetic - Masterson International Marketing, Inc.
MASTER E-Z BLEED CYLINDER - Brake master cylinders - Standard Motor Products, Inc.
MASTER EDITION - Figurines - Fort USA
MASTER EL GRECO - Artists' materials ☆ - Binney & Smith Inc.
MASTER ELECTRICIAN - Computer software - Snapz Software, Inc.
MASTER ELECTRICIAN - Electrical product - Cotter & Co.
MASTER ETCH - Printing trades machinery - Dick Blick Co.
MASTER FASHION - Furniture - Master Design Furniture
MASTER FIND - Computer software - Kapak Design
MASTER FISHERMAN - Knives - Precise International/Wenger
MASTER FRESH - Air purification systems - Master-Fit Corp.
MASTER-G - Electrical equipment ☆ - Acu-Rite Inc.
MASTER GARDENER - Garden equipment - Cobraco Manufacturing, Inc.
MASTER GARDENERS - Garden equipment - Master Mark Plastic Products
MASTER GEL - Varnishes - H. Behlen & Bro. Inc.
MASTER GOLD - Paints - Cotter & Co.
MASTER GREEN - Food processors - White Consolidated Industries, Inc.
MASTER GRIPPER - Adhesives and sealants - Golden Grip Products Inc.
MASTER GRIPS - Cutlery - Lifetime Hoan Corp.
MASTER-GRIT - Band saw blades - American Saw & Manufacturing Co.
MASTER GROOM - Pet products - Toogood Laboratories
MASTER GUARD - Chemical preparations - VV3 Masterguard, Inc.
MASTER-GUARD - Paints - Devoe & Raynolds Co.
MASTER GUARD - Waterproofing compounds - Conklin Co., Inc.
MASTER HERBALIST - Herbal products - Chase Collection, Inc.
MASTER HIGH FREQUENCY - Hair care products - Fromm Industries
MASTER-HOLD - Pet products - Leatherite-Nylorite Manufacturing Inc.
MASTER-HUNG - Doors–wood - Master-Hung Door Equipment Co.
MASTER HUNTER - Knives–hunting - Cold Steel Inc.
MASTER HUNTER - Telephone apparatus - Tempo Research Corp.
MASTER IMPERIAL - Golfing equipment - Lynx Golf, Inc.
MASTER IN SOUND - Radios - Royal Sound Co. Inc.
MASTER INSTALLER - Vehicle parts - Garnat Brakes, Inc.
MASTER JAC - Apparel and accessories ☆ - Kellwood Co.
MASTER JUMBO - Egg cartons - Packaging Corp. of America
MASTER KEY - Harmonicas - William Kratt Co.
MASTER KEY PLUS - Dietary supplements - Nutrition for Life International, Inc.
MASTER-KOTE - Paints - Midwest Paint Manufacturing Co.
MASTER LAWN - Flowers, plants, and seeds - Agrono-Tec Seed Co.
MASTER LETTER BACKGROUND - Posters - Clement Communications Inc.
MASTER LINE - Cleaning preparations - Blue Coral Chemical, Inc.
MASTER LINGUIST - Recording label - R.D. Cortina Co.
MASTER LINK - Hardware - Crown Bolt, Inc.
MASTER LOAF - Flour–blended ☆ - Stevens Industries Inc.
MASTER LOCK - Locks–door - Master Lock Co.
MASTER-MADE - Coveralls - Walls Industries, Inc.
MASTER MAG - Firearms, accessories, and parts ☆ - Servistar Corp.
MASTER MARINE - Seafood - International Oceanic Enterprises Inc. of Alabama
MASTER MARK - Garden equipment - Master Mark Plastic Products
MASTER MASON - Concrete products - Akona Chemical Corp.
MASTER MATCH - Smethport Specialty Co.
MASTER MATCH - Computer software - Advanced Ideas
MASTER MATH - Computer software - PMI Inc.
MASTER MAX - Sporting goods ☆ - Soccer Sport Supply Co. Inc.
MASTER MECHANIC - Tools and accessories - Cotter & Co.
MASTER MEND - Adhesives and sealants - Loctite Corp.
MASTER MIDI - Accordions - Titano Accordion Co. International
MASTER MIDI - Sound equipment - Castiglione Accordion
MASTER MIDI KITS - Musical instrument accessories - Ernest Deffner Inc.
MASTER MIND - Sporting goods - Edgeroy Co. Inc.

☆ = Now out of production

MASTER MITE - Heaters–space - Master Appliance Corp.

MASTER MODEL - Projectors–photographic - Rollei of America Inc.

MASTER MOUSE COMPUTER - Computer software - Tiger Electronics, Inc.

MASTER MOVES - Games ☆ - Tsr, Inc.

MASTER-MP - Electrical equipment ☆ - Acu-Rite Inc.

MASTER MURALS - Wallpaper - James Seeman Studios

MASTER MUSICIANS - Publisher's imprints - Littlefield, Adams & Co.

MASTER NINJA - Computer software ☆ - Microprose Software, Inc.

MASTER NO-TOW - Trailers–travel ☆ - Master Lock Co.

MASTER NURSERY - Tools–hand-operated - Master Nurserymen's Association

MASTER NURSERYMEN - Chemical preparations - Master Nurserymen's Association

MASTER OF DISASTER - Toys - Tonka Corp.

MASTER OF DISGUISE - Games - Fun World Inc.

MASTER OF MIX - Beverages - Hamilton Foods Co. Inc.

MASTER OF ORION - Games - Microprose Software, Inc.

MASTER OF THE LAMPS - Computer software - Activision, Inc.

MASTER PAINTER - Paint sprayers - E-Z Paintr Corp.

MASTER PAINTER - Paints ☆ - Budeke's Paint

MASTER PAINTER - Varnishes - Barrett Varnish Co.

MASTER PAINTERS - Paints - Sampson Coatings Inc.

MASTER PIECE - Computer storage devices - Kensington

MASTER PIECE - Fireworks - American Promotional Events, Inc.

MASTER PIECE - Patterns–clothing - J & J Enterprises of Iowa, Inc.

MASTER PINK - Erasers ☆ - Bright Boy Abrasives

M.A.S.T.E.R. PLAN - Motor vehicle dealers - Half-A-Car-Co.

MASTER PLANNER - Floor coverings–carpet and rugs ☆ - Lees Carpets

MASTER PLAYING CARDS - Playing cards - Magic Masters, Inc.

MASTER PLUMBER - Plumbing fixtures–porcelain - Durst Industries Inc.

MASTER PLUMBER - Plumbing product - Cotter & Co.

MASTER PLUNGER - Plumbing fixtures–plastic - G.T. Water Products Inc.

MASTER PLUS - Mufflers–motor vehicle - Goerlich's

MASTER POGO - Toys - Master Juvenile Products Inc.

MASTER POND TEST KIT - Water treating compounds - Jungle Laboratories Corp.

MASTER POOLS - Tools - Sta-Rite Industries Inc.

MASTER POUR - Syrup - Coca-Cola Co.

MASTER PREST - Fabrics - Dan River Inc.

MASTER-PRO - Paints ☆ - Pratt & Lambert United, Inc.

MASTER PROTECTOR, THE - Paints ☆ - Kwal-Howells Inc.

MASTER REFERENCE - Electronic equipment - Matsushita Electric Corp. of America

MASTER RING INDICATOR - Telephone devices and light signals for the deaf - American Communications Corp.

MASTER SEAL - Burial vaults–concrete - Doric Products Inc.

MASTER SERIES - Cooking equipment–household - Dansk International Designs, Ltd.

MASTER SERIES - Pagers - Harris Corp.

MASTER SERIES - Trading cards and stamps - Megacards, Inc.

MASTER-SET - Tiles–ceramic ☆ - American Olean Tile Co.

MASTER SHIELD HORIZON - Siding - Master Shield Building Products Co., LP

MASTER SHUTTERS - Shutters–wood - Mid-America Building Products Corp.

MASTER SILVER - Paints - Cotter & Co.

MASTER SKYLITE - Artists' materials - Robert Simmons Inc.

MASTER SLAB - Shingles–asphalt or tar - Certainteed Corp. (Roofing Products Group)

MASTER SLACK, THE - Slacks–men's - Master Industries Corp.

MASTER SOLOS - Publisher's imprints - Hal Leonard Corp.

MASTER SOUND - Musical sound recordings - Sony Music Entertainment Inc.

MASTER SPORT - Bicycles ☆ - Raleigh USA Bicycle Co.

MASTER-STROKE - Paints ☆ - DecoArt, Inc.

MASTER-STROKER - Sporting goods - Hudson Manufacturing Co.

MASTER STUDIO - Clocks - Service Merchandise Co. Inc.

MASTER SUITE - Floor coverings–carpet and rugs ☆ - World Carpets, Inc.

MASTER SUITE COLLECTION - Fans–electric - Hunter Fan Co.

MASTER SUITES - Wallcovering ☆ - Fashon Wallcoverings

MASTER SUITES II - Wallcovering ☆ - Fashon Wallcoverings

MASTER SYSTEM - Electronics equipment - Grass Valley Group Inc.

MASTER SYSTEM - Ventilation equipment - Mid-America Building Products Corp.

MASTER TALE - Skin care products - Master Chemical Co.

MASTER TEA - Teas–herbal - BNG Enterprises, Inc.

MASTER-TENNA - Electronic equipment - Thomson Consumer Electronics, Inc.

MASTER, THE - Cutlery - Burrell Cutlery Co. Inc.

MASTER THE MARKET - Computer software - SourceView Software International

MASTER TOOLBOX - Computer software - Meta-Software, Inc.

MASTER-TOUCH - Barbecues and grills - Weber-Stephen Products Co.

MASTER TOUCH - Drums–musical instruments - Remo, Inc.

MASTER TOUCH - Electronic equipment - Thomson Consumer Electronics, Inc.

MASTER TOUCH - Toys ☆ - Wm. K. Walthers Inc.

MASTER-TP - Electrical equipment ☆ - Acu-Rite Inc.

MASTER TRACKS - Computer software - Passport Designs Inc.

MASTER TRACKS JR. - Computer software ☆ - Passport Designs Inc.

MASTER TRACKS PRO - Computer software - Passport Designs Inc.

MASTER-TRAK - Recording label - Master-Trak Sound Recorders

MASTER-TRIM - Tiles–ceramic ☆ - American Olean Tile Co.

MASTER TUFT - Floor coverings–carpet and rugs ☆ - World Carpets, Inc.

MASTER TURF - Mats - Proffitt Manufacturing Co.

MASTER UNIT - Pencils - General Pencil Co.

MASTER VAC - Vacuum cleaners and accessories - Fasco Industries Inc. (Consumer Products Div.)

MASTER VIDEO PAINTER - Toys–electronic - Vtech Industries, Inc.

MASTER VIT - Vitamins and nutritional supplements - Georgia Bariatrics Pc

MASTER-WALL - Shelving units–wood - Modular Systems Inc.

MASTER-WEAVE - Paper–toweling - Cleveland Cotton Products Co.

MASTER WHIZ-RING - Toys - North Pacific Products Inc.

MASTER WOODCRAFTERS - Cabinets - Bradford Manufacturing, Inc.

MASTER WORKS - Jewelry and watches - Shube's Manufacturing, Inc.

MASTER WORKSHOP - Toys - Natural Science Industries, Ltd.

MASTER-WRITER - Office supplies - Bell & Howell Co.

MASTERBANKING - Computer software - MasterCard International Inc.

MASTERBATH - Bathtubs–enameled - Kohler Co.

MASTERBILT - Musical instrument accessories ☆ - Micro Musical Products Corp.

MASTERBILT - Shingles–asphalt or tar - Bird Inc.

MASTERBLASTER - Shirts - Water Ride Concepts, Inc.

MASTERBLASTER - Toys - NBGS International, Inc.

MASTERBLEND - Computer software - Merrick Industries Inc.

MASTERBOTIX - Toys - Trendmasters, Inc.

MASTERBUILDER - Computer software - Masterchart, Inc.

MASTERBYTE - Computer software - Martin Green

MASTERCART - Lounge chair/cart - Invention Prototypes & Marketing Corp.

MASTERCAT - Computer software - Triad Systems Corp.

MASTERCHARGE - Battery chargers - Metabo Corp.

MASTERCHEF - Barbecues and grills - Sunbeam Outdoor Products Inc.

MASTERCHEM - Paints - Masterchem Industries, Inc.

MASTERCLAD - Electrical equipment - Square D Co.

MASTERCLASS PRODUCTIONS INC. - Computer software - Masterclass Productions, Inc.

MASTERCLIPS - Computer software - Masterclip Graphics, Inc.

MASTERCOAT PLUS - Adhesives and sealants ☆ - Induron Coatings Inc.

MASTERCOM - Electronic equipment - Bally Gaming International, Inc.

MASTERCOM - Telephone apparatus ☆ - Philips Business Systems Co.

MASTERCOOK - Ovens–microwave - Amana Refrigeration Inc.

MASTERCOOL - Electrical equipment - Adobe Air Inc.

MASTERCOOL 2-STAGE - Electrical equipment - Adobe Air Inc.

MASTERCOPY - Paper - Butler Paper Co.

MASTERCORD - Floor coverings–carpet and rugs ☆ - Karastan-Bigelow Inc.

MASTERCOVER - Awnings–plastic - Mark Alan Espinosa

MASTERCRAFT - Candy - Elmer Candy Corp.

MASTERCRAFT - Floor coverings–tile - Kentile Floors Inc.

MASTERCRAFT - Furniture - Baker, Knapp & Tubbs

MASTERCRAFT - Hardware - Servistar Corp.

MASTERCRAFT - Heating pads–electric - Walgreen Co.

MASTERCRAFT - Pens - Mastercraft Pen Co.

MASTERCRAFT - Pipes–tobacco - Mastercraft Pipes Inc.

MASTERCRAFT - Tires - Cooper Tire & Rubber Co.

MASTERCRAFT - Windows–storm - Duo-Temp

MASTERCRAFT MEMORIALS - Burial monuments - Mastercraft Memorial Services Inc.

MASTERCRAFT OF GRAND RAPIDS - Furniture - Baker, Knapp & Tubbs

MASTERCRAFT POWER - Engines–marine - Master Craft Boat Co.

MASTERCRAFTERS - Clocks - Mastercrafters Clock Corp.

MASTERCRON - Concrete products - Master Builders Inc.

MASTERCUT - Garden equipment - Aircap Industries Corp.

MASTERCUT - Jewelry–precious - United Star Corp.

MASTERCUT - Meat products–cured - Stevens Industries Inc.

MASTERCUT - Steel products - A.M. Castle & Co.

☆ = Now out of production

MASTERCUTS - Hair care products - Regis Corp.

MASTERCUTTER - Tools - Red Devil Inc.

MASTERDOCK - Audio equipment - Mark IV Audio, Inc.

MASTERDUO - Egg cartons - Tenneco Packaging Inc.

MASTERFAX - Duplicating machines - Bell & Howell Co.

MASTERFILE - Office supplies - Plan Hold Corp.

MASTERFIT - Metals - Senco Products, Inc.

MASTERFIT CONTACT LENS - Humphrey Systems

MASTERFLEX - Hoses - Hose Master, Inc.

MASTERFLEX - Laboratory apparatus - Cole-Parmer Instrument Co.

MASTERFLOW 928 - Building materials–concrete - Master Builders Inc.

MASTERFOLD - Napkins–paper - Wisconsin Tissue Mills Inc.

MASTERFONIC - Accordions ✰ - Grossman Music Corp.

MASTERFUL - Door frames - Dunbarton Corp.

MASTERGAIN - Feed supplement ✰ - Central Soya Co. Inc.

MASTERGEAR - Boats - Master Craft Boat Co.

MASTERGLIDE - Shelving units–wood - L & P Property Management Co.

MASTERGRAPHICS - Paints–artists' - Master Marking Co., Inc.

MASTERGRIP - Golf equipment - MasterGrip Inc.

MASTERGUILD - Cutting boards - Stanley Roberts, Inc.

MASTERING BUSINESS DEVELOPMENT - Publisher's imprints - Sales Management Systems, Inc.

MASTERING THE GRE - Computer software - CBS Software

MASTERING THE SAT - Computer software - CBS Software

MASTERING YOUR POTENTIAL - Recording label - Pacific Institute Inc.

MASTERKEY - Tools–hand-operated - Tri-Tech Inc.

MASTERKITS - Furniture - Fournier Furniture, Inc.

MASTERKRAFT - Tiles–ceramic - Kraftile Co.

MASTERKURE - Concrete repair products - Master Builders Inc.

MASTERLIFE - Floor coverings–carpet and rugs - E.I. Dupont de Nemours and Co.

MASTERLINE - Amplifiers - Blonder-Tongue Laboratories Inc.

MASTERLINE - Compressors–air - Curtis Toledo Inc.

MASTERLINE - Electronics equipment - York Controls

MASTERLINE - Paints ✰ - Pratt & Lambert United, Inc.

MASTERLINE - Seats–automobile - Charvoz

MASTERLINE - Stamps–hand - Mark Master Inc.

MASTERLINE PLUS - Amplifiers - Blonder-Tongue Laboratories Inc.

MASTERLINK - Computer terminals - Video Lottery Technologies, Inc.

MASTERLOADER - Trailers–boat - Magic Tilt Trailers, Inc.

MASTERMARINE & TEST KIT SET - Chemical preparations - Mydor Industries Inc.

MASTERMARK - Steps - Simpson Timber Co.

MASTERMAT - Mats - Master Woodcraft Inc.

MASTERMATIC - Watches - Bulova Corp.

MASTERMIDI - Accordions - Pancordion Inc.

MASTERMIKE - Cables - Pro-Co. Sound Co. Inc.

MASTERMIND - Computer software - CA Management Inc.

MASTERMIND - Games - Pressman Toy Corp.

MASTERMIND DREAMAKERS - Printed materials - Mary Lou Greek

MASTERMODEL - Computer hardware and software - Zeelan Technology, Inc.

MASTERMOLD - Chemical preparations - Abatron, Inc.

MASTERNET - Humphrey Systems

MASTERPAGE - Computer software ✰ - LXI Corp.

MASTERPATH - Recording label - Masterpath, Inc.

MASTERPEACE RAGZ - Apparel and accessories - Talkington, Ricky

MASTERPIECE - Adhesives and sealants - Golden Grip Products Inc.

MASTERPIECE - Brushes–hair - Spornette International, Inc.

MASTERPIECE - Brushes–paint - Sanlu Art Industries Inc.

MASTERPIECE - Chimes ✰ - Nutone Inc.

MASTERPIECE - Cleaning equipment - L & F Products Inc.

MASTERPIECE - Coffee - Saramar Corp.

MASTERPIECE - Dishes–china ✰ - Gorham Inc.

MASTERPIECE - Enamels ✰ - Kelly-Moore Paint Co. Inc.

MASTERPIECE - Epoxy - Polymerica, Inc.

MASTERPIECE - Fabrics - Lackawanna Leather Co. Inc.

MASTERPIECE - Floor coverings–carpet and rugs - Monticello Carpet Mills

MASTERPIECE - Floor coverings–carpet and rugs - Quaker Inc.

MASTERPIECE - Floor coverings–carpet and rugs - Alexander Smith Carpets

MASTERPIECE - Games ✰ - Parker Brothers

MASTERPIECE - Giftware - Lenox, Inc.

MASTERPIECE - Greeting cards - Royal Stationery Co.

MASTERPIECE - Hams - Wilson Foods Corp.

MASTERPIECE - Heaters–space - Martin Industries, Inc.

MASTERPIECE - Hobby kits ✰ - Craft House Corp.

MASTERPIECE - Hotplates ✰ - Donald Art Co.

MASTERPIECE - Jewelry - Fantasy Diamond Corp.

MASTERPIECE - Lenses–magnifying - Donegan Optical Co. Inc.

MASTERPIECE - Mats - Andersen Co.

MASTERPIECE - Musical instrument accessories - French American Reeds Manufacturing

MASTERPIECE - Neckties - Countess Mara Inc.

MASTERPIECE - Paints - Columbia Paint and Coatings, Inc.

MASTERPIECE - Paints - Perry & Derrick Co.

MASTERPIECE - Paints - Suntec Paint Inc.

MASTERPIECE - Paper - Paper Direct, Inc.

MASTERPIECE - Pens - Sheaffer Inc.

MASTERPIECE - Refrigerators - White Consolidated Industries, Inc.

MASTERPIECE - Revolvers - Smith & Wesson Corp.

MASTERPIECE - Siding - Master Shield Building Products Co., LP

MASTERPIECE - Sporting goods - Gold Medal Recreational Products

MASTERPIECE - Wallpaper - Finnaren & Haley Inc.

MASTERPIECE - Wallpaper ✰ - Bolta Wallcoverings

MASTERPIECE - Watches ✰ - SMH (US) Inc.

MASTERPIECE COLLECTION - Candles - Muench-Kreuzer Candle Co.

MASTERPIECE COLLECTION - Floor coverings ✰ - Congoleum Corp.

MASTERPIECE COLLECTION - Giftware - Lenox, Inc.

MASTERPIECE COLLECTION, THE - Wallcovering - Gilford Corp.

MASTERPIECE EDITION - Publisher's imprints - DML Associates, Inc.

MASTERPIECE ETCHED - Hobby kits - Craft House Corp.

MASTERPIECE GARDENS - Garden equipment - NK Lawn & Garden Co.

MASTERPIECE IN A MOMENT, A - Spices and extracts - To Market to Market

MASTERPIECE OPAQUES - Dental compounds - Jeneric/Pentron Inc.

MASTERPIECE SERIES - Cooking equipment–household - LazyMan, Inc.

MASTERPIECE STUDIOS - Greeting cards - Masterpiece Studios Inc.

MASTERPIECE, THE - Surgical supplies - Anago Inc.

MASTERPIECE THEATRE - Video production - WGBH Educational Foundation

MASTERPIECE TOBACS - Tobacco–chewing or smoking - Swedish Math North America Inc.

MASTERPIECES - Chocolate candy - New England Confectionery Co.

MASTERPIECES - Cooking utensils–earthenware ✰ - Anchor Hocking Glass, Inc.

MASTERPIECES IN CHOCOLATES - Chocolate candy - Maxfield Candy Co.

MASTERPIECES IN WAX - Candles ✰ - Colonial Candle of Cape Cod

MASTERPIECES-ON-TILE - Giftware ✰ - Sangray Corp.

MASTERPLATE - Concrete products - Master Builders Inc.

MASTERPLUG - Nuts and bolts - Aztec Washer Co., Inc.

MASTERPOINT - Floor coverings–carpet and rugs - J and J Industries Inc.

MASTERPOINT - Floor coverings–carpet and rugs - Karastan-Bigelow Inc.

MASTERPOOR - Novelty items - Greg Alsch & Tom Lindl

MASTERRIB - Roofing materials - Union Corrugating Co.

MASTERS - Beverages–malt ✰ - Adolph Coors Co.

MASTERS - Cleaning preparations - General Pencil Co.

MASTERS - Drums–musical instruments - Pearl Corp.

MASTERS - Footwear–athletic - Ken-Pin Inc.

MASTERS - Hosiery - Hole-in-None Hosiery

MASTER'S - Telephones - Cathay International

MASTERS BEST - Paint - James Porche

MASTERS CANDIES - Candy - Masters Candies Inc.

MASTER'S CHOICE - Beverages–malt - Florida Brewing Co.

MASTER'S CHOICE - Floor coverings–carpet and rugs - Barrett Carpet Mills Inc.

MASTER'S CHOICE SQUARES - Pet products - Superior Brands Inc.

MASTERS COLLECTION - Floor coverings–carpet and rugs - Karastan-Bigelow Inc.

MASTERS COLLECTION - Glassware–household - Crisa Corp.

MASTERS' FORMULA LIMESTONE - Agricultural products - National Lime & Stone Co.

MASTER'S HAND - Flowers–artificial - Adrienne L. Mercer

MASTER'S MARK - Paints - PPG Architectural Finishes, Inc.

MASTERS OF DESTRUCTION - Pet products - Picture Perfect Parrot

MASTERS OF STRATEGY SERIES - Computer software - Microprose Software, Inc.

MASTERS OF SUCCESS - Recording label - F.P. Publishing Co., Inc.

MASTERS OF THE GAME - Video games - Acclaim Entertainment Inc.

MASTERS OF THE IMAGINATION - Computer software - Future Visionary, Inc.

MASTERS OF THE IMPOSSIBLE - Recording label - Ringling Bros.-Barnum & Bailey Combined Shows, Inc.

MASTERS OF THE RIVER - Figurines - Enesco Corp.

MASTERS OF THE UNIVERSE - Bathroom accessories ✰ - Tsumura International Inc.

✰ = Now out of production

MASTERS OF THE UNIVERSE - Candy ☆ - Topps Co., Inc.
MASTERS OF THE UNIVERSE - Games ☆ - Ben Cooper Inc.
MASTERS OF THE UNIVERSE - Kites ☆ - Spectra Star Kites
MASTERS OF THE UNIVERSE - Toys - Chilton-Globe, Inc.
MASTERS OF THE UNIVERSE - Toys - Mattel, Inc.
MASTERS OF THE UNIVERSE - Toys–models ☆ - Grenadier Models
MASTERS OF THE UNIVERSE BATTLE FOR ETERNIA - Games - Mattel, Inc.
MASTERS OWN - Musical instrument accessories - Horn & Son String Instruments Inc.
MASTER'S PORTFOLIO, A - Wallpaper - Andover Wallcovering
MASTERS PREMIUM DIET - Pet food - Pet Food Warehouse, Inc.
MASTERS PRESS - Publisher's imprints - NTC Contemporary Publishing Group
MASTER'S PRIDE - Paints - Distribution America, Inc.
MASTER'S PRIDE - Paints - Valspar Corp.
MASTERS SERIES - Musical instruments - Pearl Corp.
MASTER'S TOUCH - Greeting cards - Challenge Card Co.
MASTER'S TOUCH - Sauces - Custom Food Products Inc.
MASTER'S TOUCH - Wallpaper - Statter Wallpaper Mills
MASTERSAFE - Computer software - Eliashim Microcomputers, Inc.
MASTERSCORE - Computer software - Steinberg/Jones Corp.
MASTERSCREEN - Fireplace equipment - Thomas Industries Inc. (Portland Willamette Div.)
MASTERSEAL - Chemical preparations - Gulfway Chemical Co., Inc.
MASTERSEAL - Concrete products - Master Builders Inc.
MASTERSEAL - Shelving units–metal - Metal Masters Foodservice Equipment Co., Inc.
MASTERSENSE - Computer peripheral equipment - Kensington Microware Ltd.
MASTERSET - Brushes–paint - E-Z Paintr Corp.
MASTERSET - Electrical equipment - Landis and Gyr Inc.
MASTERSET - Metal fasteners - Masterset Corp.
MASTERSHADE - Sporting goods - J.A. Cissel Manufacturing Co.
MASTERSHADE - Window coverings - Awnings by Sunair/Sunair Awnings
MASTERSHIELD - Epoxy coatings - Polymerica, Inc.
MASTERSHIFT - Automotive parts and accessories - Hurst Performance Inc.
MASTERSHOWER - Faucets - Kohler Co.
MASTERSON - Cigarettes - Brown & Williamson Tobacco Corp.
MASTERSON INTERNATIONAL MARKETING - Computer software - Masterson International Marketing, Inc.
MASTERSPEC - Epoxy - Polymerica, Inc.
MASTERSTAND - Computer peripheral equipment ☆ - Kensington
MASTERSTAT - Thermostats - Adobe Air Inc.
MASTERSTEP - Ladders–metal - Material Control Inc.
MASTERSTROKE - Artists' materials - Dick Blick Co.
MASTERSTROKE - Pens - Gruga USA
MASTERSTYLIST - Hair care products - Variety Imports
MASTERTAK - Hardware ☆ - Biwood Flooring
MASTERTAN - Leather–chamois - Schroeder & Tremayne, Inc.
MASTERTECH - Hand tools - General Tech International Corp.
MASTERTECH - Primers - Masterwork Paint, Inc.
MASTERTEX - Paints ☆ - Goldblatt Tool Co.
MASTERTONE - Drums–musical instruments - Eames Drum Co.
MASTERTONE - Musical instruments - Gibson Strings & Accessories
MASTERTONE - Paints - Graham Paint and Varnish Co.
MASTERTONE - Recording label - Mark Five Sandcastle
MASTERTONES - Floor coverings–carpet and rugs - Callaway Carpets
MASTERTOP - Adhesives and sealants - Master Builders Inc.
MASTERTOUCH - Fans–electric - Holmes Products, Corp.
MASTERTOUCH - Ovens–microwave - Amana Refrigeration Inc.
MASTERTRAPPER - Traps–animal - Jameg Industry Corp.
MASTERTURF - Floor coverings - R.W. Beattie Carpet Industries Inc.
MASTERTURF - Floor coverings–carpet and rugs - Value Carpets Inc.
MASTERTURF - Flowers, plants, and seeds - Weyerhaeuser Co.
MASTERTYPE - Computer software - Voyager Software Corp.
MASTERVENT - Ventilation equipment - Triangle Metal and Manufacturing Inc.
MASTERVIEW - Humphrey Systems
MASTERVISIONS - Trading cards and stamps - Topps Co., Inc.
MASTERVOX - Computer software - Mastermind Technologies, Inc.
MASTERVUE - Medical apparatus - Optical Radiation Corp.
MASTERWALL - Siding–insulating - Bird Inc.
MASTERWARE - Cookware - M.E. Heuck Co. Inc.
MASTERWEAR - Fabrics–broadcloth - Foss Manufacturing Co., Inc.
MASTERWEAR - Floor coverings–carpet and rugs - West Point-Pepperell Mill Store
MASTERWOOD - Cabinets - Superior Woodwork Inc.

MASTERWOOD - Golf clubs - MasterGrip Inc.
MASTERWORD - Computer software - Alki Software Corp.
MASTERWORK - Paints ☆ - Devoe & Raynolds Co.
MASTERWORK - Posters - Greenwich Workshop, Inc.
MASTERWORKS - Computer software - Lasermaster Corp.
MASTERWORKS - Floor coverings ☆ - Robbins Inc.
MASTERWORKS - Glass products ☆ - Fenton Art Glass Co.
MASTERWORKS - Jewelry and pewter figurines - Shube's Manufacturing, Inc.
MASTERWORKS - Tape players–cassette - Sony Music Entertainment Inc.
MASTERWORKS - Wallpaper ☆ - Winfield Design Associates, Inc.
MASTERWORKS LTD. - Giftware ☆ - Handcraft Designs Inc.
MASTERY - Floor coverings–carpet and rugs ☆ - Karastan-Bigelow Inc.
MASTERY-DL - Cleaning preparations - Hako Minuteman Inc.
MASTERY MODULE - Electronic equipment - Vermax Inc.
MASTERY UNIVERSITY - Apparel and accessories - Robbins Research International, Inc.
MASTEX - Roofing materials–clay - Savannah Paint Manufacturing Co.
MASTEY - Skin care products - Mastey De Paris
MASTHEAD - Fabrics - Greenwood Mills Inc.
MASTI - Liquors - Orion Imports Ltd.
MASTIC - Siding - Aluminum Co. of America
MASTIC OFF - Mastic remover - Construction Adhesives Co.
MASTICDENT MASTICDENT WITH NATURAL MASTIC OIL - Toothpaste - Leather Line Imports, Inc.
MASTIK - Apparel–women's - D.F.G. Inc.
MASTIK - Automotive parts and accessories ☆ - Allen Products Corp.
MASTISOL - Health care products - Ferndale Laboratories, Inc.
MASTODON - Clamps - Wade Manufacturing Co.
MASTOP - Pharmaceutical preparations ☆ - U.S. Ethicals Inc.
MASTRO - Drums–musical instruments ☆ - French American Reeds Manufacturing
MASTRO DE PAJA PER FUMATORI - Pipes–tobacco - Mastro de Paja (USA) Inc.
MASTROBERARDINO - Beverages–alcohol - Palace Brands Co.
MASTROBERARDINO - Wines - Heublein, Inc.
MASUMI - Fragrance ☆ - Coty Inc.
MASUR-OIL - Adhesives and sealants - Masury Paint Co.
MASUREEL - Wallpaper - Masureel International
MASUREEL INTERNATIONAL - Wallpaper - Masureel International
MASURY - Finishing agents - Masury Paint Co.
M.A.T. - Alarm systems - Kenneth E. Flick
MAT-A-DOOR - Mats - Ludlow Composites Corp.
MAT-A-DOR FINGERTIP - Mats - Ludlow Composites Corp.
MAT-KINS - Mats - Serendipity Designs Inc.
MAT-LOK - Mats - Interstate Mat & Rubber
MAT-LOK - Mats - Ludlow Composites Corp.
MAT MAGIC - Mat boards - Dahle USA
MAT MANIA - Video games - Taito America Corp.
MAT-MATE - Mats - Serendipity Designs Inc.
MAT MATES - Pillows - Russell & Latterman, Inc.
MAT N PRINT - Paint sets–hobby - Winbar Designs
MAT PLUS - Floor coverings–carpet and rugs - LaVelle Textile Marketing Inc.
MAT TEC - Computer hardware - Mattec Corp.
MATA HARI - Sunglasses - Argus Optical, Inc.
MATADOR - Alarm systems - Mother's Window Tint, Inc.
MATADOR - Cigars - General Cigar Co., Inc.
MATADOR - Drums–musical instruments - LP Music Group
MATADOR - Floor-cleaning machine - Advance Machine Co.
MATADOR - Floor coverings–carpet and rugs ☆ - Eurotex Inc.
MATADOR - Food products - RHSCO Enterprises Inc.
MATADOR - Food products ☆ - Vincent Food Industries Inc.
MATADOR - Liquors - Heublein, Inc.
MATADOR - Mats - Interstate Mat & Rubber
MATADOR - Motor vehicles ☆ - DaimlerChrysler
MATADOR - Office furniture–wood ☆ - McDowell and Craig Manufacturing Co.
MATADOR - Recording label - Matador Records, Inc.
MATADOR - Staplers - ACCO USA, Inc.
MATADOR - Tires ☆ - Greenball Corp.
MATADOR - Underwear and nightwear - Sara Lee Knit Products Inc.
MATAGIRI - Stationery - Matagiri
MATAGORDA - Fish–fresh or frozen - Clegg Shrimp Co. Inc.
MATAKE - Footwear - Kowa American Corp.
MATALWARE - Giftware - Olde Country Reproductions Inc.
MATANUSKA MAID - Dairy products - Matanuska Maid Dairy
MATANUSKA'S - Milk - Matanuska Maid Dairy
MATANZAS CREEK WINERY - Wines - Matanzas Creek Winery

☆ = Now out of production

MATASHA - Blinds–vertical - Kingdom Vertical Blinds Manufacturing Inc.
MATASORB - Chemical preparations - Matarah Industries Inc.
MATAWAY - Agricultural machinery - Ransomes-Cushman-Ryan
MATBREAKER - Pet products - Imaginetics
MATCH - Dryers–hair - Ross Sales Co.
MATCH - Rackets–racquetball - Head Sports USA
MATCH - Sporting goods ☆ - Daiwa Corp.
MATCH - Tiles–ceramic - Monoceram
MATCH-ABILITY - Games ☆ - Cadaco Div.
MATCH ADVICE - Computer software - Integrated Decision Support Corp.
MATCH & MATE - Greeting cards ☆ - Cleo Inc.
MATCH & MOVE MEMORY - Games - Milton Bradley Co.
MATCH & PATCH - Floor coverings–carpet and rugs - Custom Tapes, Inc.
MATCH BALANCE - Measuring instruments - FMC Corp.
MATCH BOX - Audio equipment - Barcus-Berry Inc.
MATCH BULLET—HANDGUN - Bullets - Olin Corp. (Winchester Div.)
MATCH CARD - Greeting cards - H & L Novelties Inc.
MATCH-ESPANOL - Computer software - Hartley Courseware Inc.
MATCH FACTORY - Apparel–children's - J.C. Penney Co., Inc.
MATCH-FIT - Apparel–athletic - Match-Fit Athletic Apparel Ltd.
MATCH-FRANCAIS - Computer software - Hartley Courseware Inc.
MATCH GAME, THE - Games ☆ - Milton Bradley Co.
MATCH-GRUV - Golfing equipment - Ben Hogan Co.
MATCH II - Boats–kayaks - Phoenix Products Inc.
MATCH II - Games - CBS Toys
MATCH IT - Computer programming services - Berta-Max Inc.
MATCH-IT - Puzzles ☆ - Ceaco, Inc.
MATCH LIGHT - Charcoal - Kingsford Co.
MATCH-MAKER - Puzzles - Hasbro, Inc.
MATCH MAKERS - Identification tags - Star Tech
MATCH MAKERS - Labels–fabric - John M. Joseph
MATCH MARKERS - Plastic indentification tags - John M. Joseph
MATCH MASTER - Housewares - Hiac/Royco Co.
MATCH MATE - Sporting goods - U.S. Sports Equipment Co.
MATCH-MATES - Bedding–linen - Dan River Inc.
MATCH MATES - Furniture ☆ - Athens Furniture Industries Inc.
MATCH MATES - Playthings - Meritus Industries, Inc.
MATCH ME - Games - Trend Enterprises, Inc.
MATCH MODELS - Scoreboards - Daktronics Inc.
MATCH 'N LEARN - Computer software - Simon & Schuster Computer Software
MATCH 'N MAIL - Greeting cards - International Stamp Art, Inc.
MATCH 'N MIX - Toys ☆ - Placo Products Co.
MATCH 'N PLAY - Toys - Tonka Corp.
MATCH 'N STACK - Games ☆ - Cadaco Div.
MATCH-O-MATIC - Electronic equipment - Airguide Instrument Co.
MATCH-ON-A-MAC - Computer software - Teach Yourself By Computer Software Inc.
MATCH PERFECT - Thread ☆ - Perfect Thread Co. Inc.
MATCH PLAY - Cleaning preparations–carpet and rug - W.W. Grainger, Inc.
MATCH-PLAY - Sporting goods ☆ - Semmerling Fence and Supply Inc.
MATCH POINT - Archery equipment - Pro Line Co.
MATCH POINT - Hosiery–women's - Dan River Inc.
MATCH POINT - Rackets–tennis ☆ - Wilson Sporting Goods Co.
MATCH STIX - Golfing equipment - Mammoth Industries, Inc.
MATCH STIX - Sporting goods ☆ - Ski Accessories Co.
MATCH TRACK - Drapery hardware - Baker Drapery Corp.
MATCH-UP - Apparel and accessories - Match Maker Inc.
MATCH-UP - Lipstick and nail polish ☆ - Cosrich Inc.
MATCH-UP - Pumps - Rebound Systems Inc.
MATCH-UPS - Games - Smethport Specialty Co.
MATCH-UPS - House furnishings ☆ - Miller Studio
MATCH UPS - Toilet seats ☆ - Magnolia Products
MATCH UPS - Toys - Playskool, Inc.
MATCH UPS - Window coverings - Corona Curtain Manufacturing Co., Inc.
MATCH WITS - Computer software - CBS Software
MATCHABELLI - Colognes - Chesebrough-Pond's USA Co.
MATCHABLES - Cosmetics ☆ - Nina International, Inc.
MATCHABLES - Fabrics–linen - Maytex Mills
MATCHABLES - Footwear–children's - L.A. Gear, Inc.
MATCHBOX - Toys–models - Matchbox Toys USA
MATCHBOX CAP CARS - Toys–automobiles ☆ - Matchbox Toys USA
MATCHBOX DREAM MACHINES - Toy vehicles - Matchbox Toys USA
MATCHBOX MINI FLEXIES - Erasers - Diener Industries Inc.
MATCHBOX MOTOR CITY - Toys–automobiles - Matchbox Toys USA
MATCHBOX MOTORS - Toys–automobiles - Matchbox Toys USA

MATCHBOX ORIGINALS - Toys - Matchbox Toys USA
MATCHBOX SKY-BUSTERS - Toys–airplanes - Matchbox Toys USA
MATCHBOX SUPERCHARGERS - Toys–automobiles - Matchbox Toys USA
MATCHBOX SUPERFAST - Toys–automobiles - Matchbox Toys USA
MATCHBOX TRAFFIC GAME - Games ☆ - Matchbox Toys USA
MATCHED CORALS - Lipstick and nail polish ☆ - Cosrich Inc.
MATCHED IN MOTION - Golf clubs - Prostar L.P.
MATCHED PAIR - Golfing equipment - Robert E. Schneebeli
MATCHES - Apparel and accessories - Munsingwear, Inc.
MATCHEZ - Coffee - Herold & Miller Inc.
MATCHFINDER - Computer software - Blackbaud, Inc.
MATCHIMALS - Games ☆ - Lauri Inc.
MATCHING HOUSES GAME - Games - Lauri Inc.
MATCHLESS - Electrical equipment - Advanced Energy Industries, Inc.
MATCHLESS - Electronic equipment - Matchless Ltd.
MATCHLESS - Floor coverings–carpet and rugs - Calladium & Marglen
MATCHLESS - Golfing equipment - Fabre Golf Products
MATCHLESS - Motor vehicles - Slater Brothers
MATCHLESS - Tomato pastes and sauces - Acme Preserve Co. Inc.
MATCHLESS - Wallpaper ☆ - Glidden Co.
MATCHLESS EXCELLENCE IN POTATOES - Agricultural machinery - Nonpareil Processing Corp.
MATCHLINE - Modular furniture ☆ - Inwood Office Furniture
MATCHMAKER - Bathroom accessories - Price Pfister Co.
MATCHMAKER - Belts–automotive - Goodyear Tire & Rubber Co.
MATCHMAKER - Computer software - American Companies, Inc.
MATCHMAKER - Electronic equipment - Winsted Corp.
MATCHMAKER - Inks–letterpress - Flexible Products Co.
MATCHMAKER - Paints ☆ - Foy-Johnston Inc.
MATCHMAKER - Paper–gift wrap - Gift Wrap Co.
MATCHMAKER - Sporting goods - Stebco Industries Inc.
MATCHMAKER - Thread ☆ - Perfect Thread Co. Inc.
MATCHMAKER - Toys–electronic ☆ - Philips Consumer Electronics Co.
MATCHMAKER - Veterinary nutritional supplements - Diamond V Mills Inc.
MATCHMAKER COLLECTION - Bathroom fixtures ☆ - Alsons Corp.
MATCHMAKER, THE - Musical instrument accessories - William N. Hockenberry Violins
MATCHMAKERS - Bathing suits - Patricia Byrnes Kane
MATCHMAKERS - Fabrics - Guilford Mills, Inc.
MATCHMAKERS - Fabrics–tapestry ☆ - Columbus Coated Fabrics Co.
MATCHMAKERS XV - Fabrics–tapestry ☆ - Columbus Coated Fabrics Co.
MATCHMAKERS XVI - Fabrics–tapestry ☆ - Columbus Coated Fabrics Co.
MATCHMAKERS XVII - Fabrics–tapestry ☆ - Columbus Coated Fabrics Co.
MATCHMAN - Electronics equipment - Allen Avionics, Inc.
MATCHMASTER - Guns ☆ - Remington Arms Co., Inc.
MATCHMATE - Fireplace equipment ☆ - Condar Co.
MATCHMATE - Musical instrument accessories ☆ - Whirlwind Music Distributors, Inc.
MATCHMATE - Toilet seats ☆ - Magnolia Products
MATCHMATE - Towels - Sears, Roebuck and Co.
MATCHMATE - Yarn - Melrose Yarn Co. Inc.
MATCHMATES - Apparel and accessories - Avon Products, Inc.
MATCHMATES - Floor coverings–carpet and rugs - Alexander Smith Carpets
MATCHMATES - Floor coverings–carpet and rugs ☆ - Monterey, Inc.
MATCHMATES - Matching keyholders, money clips, etc. - Jacoby-Bender Inc.
MATCHPACK PLAYFUL PETS - Games ☆ - Fun World Inc.
MATCHPAK - Golfing equipment - SPL International, Inc.
MATCHPAK BRASS - Golfing equipment - SPL International, Inc.
MATCHSAK - Golfing equipment - SPL International, Inc.
MATCHSTICK FRIES - Preserved foods–prepackaged - Brinker Restaurant Corp.
MATCHWARE - Computer software - Matchware Technologies, Inc.
MATCHWOOD - Wood fillers ☆ - Loctite Corp.
MATCRETE - Concrete-casting forms - Precision Stamped Concrete Tools
MATE - Boats–motor ☆ - Kennedy Inc.
MATE - Motors–outboard ☆ - Outboard Marine Corp.
MATE - Recording label - Kubaney Publishing Corp.
MATE - Teleprinters–computer ☆ - Metro-Tel Corp.
MATE - Wigs - Jean Paree Weegs Inc.
MATE GUARD - Pet products - Pet Biotics Inc.
MATE-TRAC - Electronic equipment - Arion Corp.
MATEFLEX - Floor coverings - Mateflex-Mele Corp.
MATERA - Shoes ☆ - Allen-Edmonds Shoe Corp.
MATERBAG - Bags–trash - Biocorp, Inc.
MATERDA - Beverages–carbonated - Cawy Bottling Co., Inc.
MATERIAL CULTURE - Antique stores - Material Culture, Inc.

☆ = Now out of production

MATERIAL WORLD - Games - Strange Magic Games, Inc.
MATERIALI - Jewelry - B. Tekel
MATERIALS HANDLING TECHNOLOGY USA - Conveyors - Materials Handling Technology Inc.
MATERIALS SYSTEM BUILDER - Computer software - PDA Engineering
MATERIALSPEC - Computer software - Autodesk Inc.
MATERNA - Vitamins and nutritional supplements - Lederle Laboratories
MATERNA-LINE - Apparel–women's ☆ - Bali Co. Inc.
MATERNAL JOURNAL, THE - Printed materials - Conceivable Concepts
MATERNAL KRADLE - Health care products - Bodyline Comfort Systems
MATERNITE - Apparel–women's - Cave Springs, Inc.
MATERNITEA - Teas–herbal - Unitea Herbs
MATERNITEE - Apparel–women's - Continnuus
MATERNITY BODY THERAPY REDEFINED - Skin care products - Pea in the Pod Inc.
MATERNITY FACTORY OUTLET, THE - Apparel stores–women's - David Lederman
MATERNITY MOODS BY MARLA - Apparel–women's - Marla Maples
MATERNITY SASH - Girdles ☆ - Kellogg Industries Inc.
MATERNITY WORKS - Apparel–women's - Cave Springs, Inc.
MATES - Gloves - Grandoe Corp.
MATES - Prophylactics - Ansell Inc. (Personal Products Div.)
MATESON - Crocheted and knitted items ☆ - Manchester Knitted Fashion Inc.
MATESON - Beverages–alcohol - Canandaigua Wine Co. Inc.
MATEUS - Beverages–alcohol - Sogrape USA Inc.
MATEUS - Floor coverings ☆ - National Floor Products Co., Inc.
MATEY - Desserts ☆ - Presto Food Products, Inc.
MATEY - Health care products - Maddak Inc.
MATEY'S - Crocheted and knitted items ☆ - Manchester Knitted Fashion Inc.
MATEY'S - Food products - Rich-Seapak Corp.
MATFER - Baking utensils and pans - Cook Things
MATFORM - Glass fiber sheets - C.A. Lawton Co.
MATH-A-MAGIC - Toys–electronic ☆ - Philips Consumer Electronics Co.
MATH ACE - Computer software - Earthquest Inc.
MATH ADVANTAGE - Computer software - Aces Research, Inc.
MATH ADVANTAGE PLUS - Computer software - Aces Research, Inc.
MATH ALIVE! - Textbooks - Math Learning Center
MATH AND ME - Computer software ☆ - Knowledge Adventure
MATH & THE MIND'S EYE - Textbooks - Math Learning Center
MATH ASSOCIATES INC. - Cables–fiber optic - Math Associates, Inc.
MATH BINGO - Computer software - SRA/McGraw-Hill (Div. of The McGraw-Hill Companies)
MATH BLASTER! - Computer software - Knowledge Adventure
MATH BLASTER, JR. - Computer software ☆ - Knowledge Adventure
MATH BLASTER MYSTERY - Computer software ☆ - Knowledge Adventure
MATH CAP MADNESS - Games - Trend Enterprises, Inc.
MATH CHASE - Educational materials - Scott Resources, Inc.
MATH DODGE - Computer software ☆ - Knowledge Adventure
MATH EXPRESS - Computer software - Aces Research, Inc.
MATH FACTORY - Educational materials - Educational Insights, Inc.
MATH FACTS LOTTERY - Computer software - Electronic Courseware Systems Inc.
MATH FOOTBALL - Computer software - Gamco Industries Inc.
MATH FOR SUCCESSFUL LIVING - Computer software - Gamco Industries Inc.
MATH FOR THE YOUNG CONSUMER - Computer software - Orange Cherry Software
MATH GRAN PRIX - Video games - Atari Games Corp.
MATH GRAPHER - Computer software - Electronic Courseware Systems Inc.
MATH IN A BAG - Publisher's imprints - Water Street Mathematics Co.
MATH IN BRIEF - Publisher's imprints - Scott Resources, Inc.
MATH IN MOTIONS - Textbooks - Math Learning Center
MATH INVADERS - Computer software - Dynacomp Inc.
MATH IS COOL! - Pencils - Gannett Co., Inc.
MATH KEYS - Computer software - Softkey International Inc.
MATH LEAP FROG - Computer software - Gamco Industries Inc.
MATH MACHINE BOOKS, THE - Publisher's imprints - Joybug Teaching Aids Inc.
MATH MACHINE, THE - Computer software - Southwest Edpsych Services Inc.
MATH MADE EASY - Video production - Video Tutorial Service, Inc.
MATH MAGIC - Computer software - Mind Play
MATH MAJORS, THE - Computer software - Nordic Software, Inc.
MATH MAN - Computer software - Scholastic Software Inc.
MATH MARVEL - Electronic equipment ☆ - Texas Instruments Inc.
MATH MARVELS - Computer software - Houghton Mifflin Co.
MATH MASTERS - Computer software - Houghton Mifflin Co.

MATH MASTERS - Computer software - SRA/McGraw-Hill (Div. of The McGraw-Hill Companies)
MATH MASTERY - Computer software - Random House, Inc.
MATH MAZE - Computer peripheral equipment - Compton's NewMedia
MATH MILEAGE - Computer software - CBS Software
MATH MOUNTAIN - Games - Nicole Burdick
MATH MUNCHERS DELUXE - Computer software - Softkey International Inc.
MATH MYSTERY - Recording label - EDCON Publishing
MATH PC - Software - Mathematica Policy Research, Inc.
MATH PLAY - Puzzles - Lauri Inc.
MATH POP QUIZ - Computer software - SourceView Software International
MATH POWER - Computer software - Instructional/Communications Technology Inc.
MATH POWER THROUGH MENTAL ART - Computer software - Orange Cherry Software
MATH RABBIT - Computer software - The Learning Co., Inc.
MATH SEQUENCES - Computer software - Milliken Publishing Co. (Computer Software Div.)
MATH SMART - Educational materials - Princeton Review Publishing, LLC
MATH SOLUTIONS - Educational materials - Marilyn Burns Education Associates
MATH STAR - Electronic equipment - Texas Instruments Inc.
MATH STARTER - Toys - Fisher-Price, Inc.
MATH STORY PROBLEMS - Computer software - Orange Cherry Software
MATH TEACHERS PRESS, INC. - Publisher's imprints - Math Teachers Press, Inc.
MATH TEST GENERATOR, THE - Computer software - Optimum Resource, Inc.
M-A-T-H: THE FUNDAMENTALS - Computer software - Krell Software Corp.
MATH TREE - Computer software - SourceView Software International
MATH WARS - Computer software - Southwest Edpsych Services Inc.
MATH WIZARD - Computer software - Unicorn Software
MATH WORD PROBLEM—TRAVEL - Computer software - Optimum Resource, Inc.
MATH WORD PROBLEMS - Computer software - Optimum Resource, Inc.
MATH WORD PROBLEMS—CAREERS - Computer software - Optimum Resource, Inc.
MATH WORD PROBLEMS FRACTIONS AND DECIMALS - Computer software - Optimum Resource, Inc.
MATH WORD PROBLEMS—MONEY - Computer software - Optimum Resource, Inc.
MATH WORD PROBLEMS—SPORTS - Computer software - Optimum Resource, Inc.
MATH WORKSHOP - Computer software - Broderbund Software, Inc.
MATHEMAGICAL FARRAGO - Computer software - Recreational Mathemagical Software
MATHEMATICAL LEARNING SYSTEMS - Computer software - Creative Education Institute, Inc.
MATHEMATICS IS ELEMENTARY - Educational materials - Agency for Instructional Technology
MATHEMATICS PLUS - Publisher's imprints - Harcourt Brace & Co.
MATHEMEDIA - Educational materials - Agency for Instructional Technology
MATHEW & MARCUS - Toys–stuffed ☆ - Gund, Inc.
MATHEWS READYMIX - Cement - Centex Corp.
MATHEY-TISSOT - Perfumes - Mathey Tissot International
MATHEY TISSOT - Watches - Mathey Tissot International
MATHFLASH - Computer software ☆ - Palsoft
MATHIAS - Shoes - Oberle Custom Shoes
MATHIAS THOMA - Musical instruments - Entertainment Music Marketing Corp.
MATHILDA & BABY KANGAROO - Toys–stuffed - Dakin Inc.
MATHIS DAIRY - Milk - Mathis Dairy
MATHIS MATICS - Board game - Ronald Wayne Mathis
MATHKIT - Computer software - University of North Carolina at Chapel Hill
MATHLAND - Publisher's imprints - Ideal School Supply Corp.
MATHMASTER - Calculators - Stokes Publishing Co., Inc.
MATHMATE - Counting devices - Gerald James Crowley
MATHMATES - Textbooks ☆ - Communication Skill Builders, Inc.
MATHOLOGY - Computer software - Lawrence Productions, Inc.
MATHOLOGY - Computer software ☆ - Knowledge Adventure
MATHPLAN 3.0 - See **PLANPERFECT**
MATHPROGRAM - Computer software ☆ - CONDUIT
MATHQUEST - Computer software - ITP Licensing Corp.
MATHSHEET - Computer software - Houghton Mifflin Co.
MATHTALK - Computer software ☆ - First Byte Inc.
MATHVISION - Computer program - Seven Seas Software, Inc.

☆ = Now out of production

MATHWORLD COMMANDER - Computer software - Orange Cherry Software
MATIC - Adhesives and sealants - Loctite Corp.
MATIE - Wallpaper - Capital Carousel Inc.
MATIERE - Dinnerware–glass - Arita Sales Co. Inc.
MATILDA BAY - Wine-based beverages - Miller Brewing Co.
MATILDE'S - Pastries ✫ - Chase Collection, Inc.
MATILIJA - Water–bottled or canned - Matilija Water Co.
MATILIJA WHITE POPPY - Dinnerware–glass ✫ - Metlox Pottery Shoppe
MATINEE - Cigarettes - G.A. Georgopulo & Co. Inc.
MATINEE - Computer screen saver - Access Softek
MATINEE - Fabrics - J.B. Martin Co. Inc.
MATINEE - Floor coverings–carpet and rugs ✫ - World Carpets, Inc.
MATINEE - Footwear - Olem Shoe Corp.
MATINEE - Furniture - Universal Flooring
MATINEE - Ophthalmic goods - Foremost Optical Products
MATINEE - Paper - Mactac Inc. (Packaging Closures Systems Div.)
MATINEE TODAY - Dolls - Mattel, Inc.
MATINESSE - Fabrics - BASF Corp.
MATISSA - Whirlpools - Jason International, Inc.
MATISSE - Artists' materials - Van Aken International
MATISSE - Floor coverings–carpet and rugs - Bellbridge Carpets
MATISSE - Floor coverings–carpet and rugs - Eagle Carpets Inc.
MATLAB - Computer software - Mathworks, Inc.
MATLAW'S - Food products - Matlaw's Food Products Inc.
MATLOW'S - Candy - Swizzels Matlow (USA) Ltd.
MATMAN - Sporting goods - Nichols Wrestling Products Inc.
MATMATE - Tools - Fletcher-Terry Co.
MATO-MIX - Food products - Pet Inc.
MATON - Guitars - Garden State Music Supply
MATOU - Occasional tables ✫ - JDI Group, Inc.
MATOUK'S - Staple foods - Highgate Investment Corp.
MATOWAC - Tools–hand-operated - Marion Tool Corp.
MATRA - Candy ✫ - Jaret Specialties Inc.
MATRA - Recording label - Jazz Composer's Orchestra Association Inc.
MATRAYS - Trays - Convergence Corp.
MATRECS - Audio equipment ✫ - MTX
MATRIKX - Water purification systems - KX Industries, L.P.
MATRIKX + CTO - Water purification systems ✫ - KX Industries, L.P.
MATRIQUE - Fabrics ✫ - Dan River Inc.
MATRIX - Cabinets ✫ - Aristokraft, Inc.
MATRIX - Chairs–wood - Krueger International, Inc.
MATRIX - Cleaning preparations–upholstery - Jon-Don Products, Inc.
MATRIX - Computer software - Matrix Real Estate Advisors, Inc.
MATRIX - Fabrics - Kimberly-Clark Corp.
MATRIX - Fabrics–tapestry ✫ - Coloroll Inc.
MATRIX - Floor coverings - Matrix Trading Co.
MATRIX - Floor coverings–carpet and rugs - Couristan Inc.
MATRIX - Floor coverings–carpet and rugs ✫ - Porter Carpet Mills Inc.
MATRIX - Floor coverings–tile - Collins & Aikman Corp.
MATRIX - Goggles–safety - Parmelee Industries, Inc.
MATRIX - Hair care products - Matrix Essentials, Inc.
MATRIX - Herbicides - E.I. Dupont de Nemours and Co.
MATRIX - Lighting equipment - Thomas Industries Inc.
MATRIX - Medical apparatus - Smith & Nephew Richards, Inc.
MATRIX - Musical instrument accessories - Kaman Music Corp.
MATRIX - Musical instrument accessories ✫ - Armstrong Woodwinds
MATRIX - Paper - Mead Corp.
MATRIX - Pet products - Seachem Laboratories
MATRIX - Photographic equipment - Leedal Inc.
MATRIX - Rackets–tennis ✫ - Wilson Sporting Goods Co.
MATRIX - Rubber cement - Econo Products Inc.
MATRIX - Safety products - U.S. Safety Corp.
MATRIX 2 - Band saw blades - American Saw & Manufacturing Co.
MATRIX 5+ - Hair care products - Matrix Essentials, Inc.
MATRIX 7 - Copper compounds ✫ - Regal Ware, Inc.
MATRIX 2000 - Bags - Matrix Group Limited
MATRIX BALANCING - Hair care products - Matrix Essentials, Inc.
MATRIX CARBON - Pet products - Seachem Laboratories
MATRIX ELECTRON WELD - Band-saw blade - American Saw & Manufacturing Co.
MATRIX ENGINE - Computer software ✫ - DataPak Software Inc.
MATRIX ESSENTIALS - Apparel and accessories - Matrix Essentials, Inc.
MATRIX II - Pet products ✫ - Seachem Laboratories
MATRIX MASTER - Machinery - Matrix Master, Inc.
MATRIX PLUS - Communications equipment - Clear-Com Intercom Systems
MATRIX PRINT - Floor coverings–tile - Collins & Aikman Corp.

MATRIX REFRACTORIES, INC. - Ceramic products - Matrix Refractories Inc.
MATROCOLOR - Office supplies - Transfertech Inc.
MATROSE - Wines - Pat Paulsen Vineyards
MATS - Computer software - Binghamton Simulator
MATS ETC. - Placemats - Mats Etc. Inc.
MATS JONASSON - Giftware - Scan-Agent
MATSATIONAL - Floor coverings–carpet and rugs ✫ - LaVelle Textile Marketing Inc.
MATSIDE - Scoreboards - Daktronics Inc.
MATSON - Finishing agents - Farwest Paint Manufacturing Co. Inc.
MATSON - Fruits and vegetables - Matson Fruit Co.
MATSONIC - Computer hardware - Eurone L. A., Inc.
MATSPLUS - Communications equipment - Wiltron Co.
MATSUE - Floor coverings–carpet and rugs - Milliken & Co. Inc.
MATSUHATO - Needles–sewing - Japanese Bunka Embroidery
MATSURI - Frames–eyeglass - United States Shoe Corp.
MATT - Cases–musical instrument ✫ - Protec International
MATT-AWAY - Pet products - Larry Products Co.
MATT HILLE - Hair care products - Matt Hille Inc.
MATT HOUSTON - Toys ✫ - Jak-Pak Inc.
MATT-KLEEN - Disinfectants - Cramer Products Inc.
MATT TRAKKER - Toys - Tonka Corp.
MATT WOOD - Boat dealers - Composite Engineering Inc.
MATTA DOOR - Car-door protector - NoBrainer Inc.
MATTADOR - Bicycles - Columbia Manufacturing Inc.
MATTASE BY NUSHA - Skin care products - Nusha, Ltd.
MATTAWANG GOLF CLUB, THE - Apparel and accessories - Mattawang Golf Club, LLC
MATTE - Ashtrays–glass ✫ - Van Guard Studios of North Carolina
MATTE - Tiles–ceramic - United States Ceramic Tile Co.
MATTE BOITE FRONT PROJECTION MATERIAL - Projection screens - Screen Works
MATTE DE LUXE - Cosmetics ✫ - Monteil Paris
MATTE EMBROIDERY COTTON - Thread - DMC Corp.
MATTE GLAZE - Tiles–ceramic - Monarch Tile Inc.
MATTE GRANDE - Crocheted and knitted items - Fab. Industries Inc.
MATTE-PLUS - Tiles–ceramic - Monarch Tile Inc.
MATTE-TEX - Finishing agents ✫ - Dunn Edwards Corp.
MATTEL - Toys - Mattel, Inc.
MATTEL & DESIGN - Toys - Mattel, Inc.
MATTEL ELECTRONICS - Games - Mattel, Inc.
MATTEL INC. M. TOYMAKERS - Games - Mattel, Inc.
MATTEL-O-PHONE - Toys - Mattel, Inc.
MATTELIUM - Toys - Mattel, Inc.
MATTEO INTERNATIONAL - Bags - Matteo International, Inc.
MATTER & ENERGY - Computer software - Right on Programs
MATTER OF DEGREES - Apparel - Spiegel, Inc.
MATTER OF TIME AFRICA AMERICA - T-shirts–men's - Lehman Riley
MATTERHORN - Apparel–men's ✫ - Superba, Inc.
MATTERHORN - Floor coverings–carpet and rugs - Collins & Aikman Corp.
MATTERHORN - Floor coverings–carpet and rugs ✫ - Hollytex Carpet Mills Inc.
MATTERHORN - Knives - Precise International/Wenger
MATTERHORN - Nurseries and garden stores - Dyna Corp.
MATTERHORN - Pens - Day-Timers, Inc.
MATTERHORN - Tiles–ceramic - Porcelanite, Inc.
MATTERHORN SUNDAE BAR - Ice cream cones - Matterhorn Ice Cream Co.
MATTES - Pens - Sheaffer Inc.
MATTHEW MALLARD - Toys–stuffed - Animal Fair Inc.
MATTHEW WALKER - Bakery products - Jaret Specialties Inc.
MATTHEWS - Cleaning preparations–household ✫ - J.H. Guild Co. Inc.
MATTHEY - Television equipment - Television Equipment Associates
MATTINGLY & MOORE - Liquors - Heaven Hill Distilleries, Inc.
MATTIQUE - Cosmetics - Cosmair Inc.
MATTISON GRINDING MACHINE - Grinders - Devlieg-Bullard Services Group
MATTISON WOODWORKING MACHINE - Woodworking machinery - Devlieg-Bullard Services Group
MATTONI - Water–mineral - Beauvignot International Inc.
MATTRACKS - Automotive parts and accessories - Track Division of National Transmission
MATTRESS MASSAGER - Massage products - Raffel Product Development Corp.
MATTRESS WORLD - Department stores - Milton H. Kober
MATTRIX - Medical apparatus - Medtronic, Inc.
MATT'S LIGHT - Beverages–malt - F.X. Matt Brewing Co.
MATT'S LIGHT BEERBALL - Beverages–malt ✫ - F.X. Matt Brewing Co.

✫ = Now out of production

MATT'S PREMIUM - Beverages–malt - F.X. Matt Brewing Co.
MATTUS - Ice cream - Mattus Group, Inc.
MATUA VALLEY - Wines ☆ - Prestige Wine Imports Corp.
MATULANE - Pharmaceutical preparations - Roche Laboratories
MATURE - Floor coverings - Toli International
MATURE BALANCE - Vitamins and nutritional supplements - Pharmavite Corp.
MATURE CHOICES - Vitamins and nutritional supplements - Rexall Sundown, Inc.
MATURITY CONTINUUM - Publisher's imprints - Covey Leadership Center, Inc.
MATURNA - Brassieres (Bras) - C I Medical, Inc.
MATVAR - Varnishes - Martin F. Weber Co.
MATVEYOR - Machine parts - Regina Emerson Co.
MATWORKS - Mats - Matworks
MATYO - Crocheted and knitted items ☆ - Charles Zahn-Import Merchant
MAUD HUMPHREY - Posters - One-of-a-Kind Workshop
MAUD HUMPHREY BOGART - Giftware ☆ - Enesco Corp.
MAUD PARFUM - Skin care products - Maud Boutique, Inc.
MAUDE CLAIRE - Knitting machines - Fortune Knits Inc.
MAUI - Beverages–alcohol - White Rock Distilleries Inc.
MAUI - Brushes–paint - Corona Brushes Inc.
MAUI - Cigarettes - Commonwealth Brands, Inc.
MAUI - Floor coverings–carpet and rugs - Regal Rugs Inc.
MAUI - Floor coverings–carpet and rugs ☆ - Kelly Group Inc.
MAUI - Giftware - Sasaki
MAUI - Hammocks - E-Z Sales & Manufacturing, Inc.
MAUI - Water–bottled or canned - Aqua Vie Beverage Corp.
MAUI ARTS & MUSIC ASSOCIATION - Recording label - Survivor Records/ Dream Makers Inc.
MAUI BLANC - Wines - Tedeschi Vineyards Ltd.
MAUI BLUSH - Wines - Tedeschi Vineyards Ltd.
MAUI BROWNIE MADNESS - Ice cream - Baskin-Robbins Inc.
MAUI BRUT - Wines ☆ - Tedeschi Vineyards Ltd.
MAUI CARAMACS - Candy - Hawaiian Host Inc.
MAUI COFFEE CO. - Coffee - Pacific Coffee, Inc.
MAUI COUNTRY - Recording label - Hit Records/USA Entertainment
MAUI GOLD - Jewelry - American Business Systems, Inc.
MAUI GROVE - Beverages - J.M. Smucker Co.
MAUI ISLAND - Snack foods - Acme Food Specialties Inc.
MAUI MAGIC - Hair care products - Garcoa Labs/Vitamin Classics
MAUI MAID - Candy - Maui Maid Inc.
MAUI MAUI - Beverages - Triple H Food Processors Inc.
MAUI MISS - Bicycles - Dynacraft Industries Inc.
MAUI MONKEY - Apparel and accessories - Maui Monkey
MAUI NOUNEAU - Wines - Tedeschi Vineyards Ltd.
MAUI ONION AND GARLIC - Nuts–salted, roasted, cooked, or canned - Mauna Loa Macadamia Nut Corp.
MAUI RAIN - Perfumes - Hawaiian Classic Perfumes
MAUI SPORTS - Games - Maui Toys
MAUI SURF CLUB - Sporting goods - Matrix Group Limited
MAUI TAN - Suntan lotions ☆ - Golden Sun Vitamins
MAUI VALLEY LINES - Apparel–men's - Sportailor Inc.
MAUI VISTA - Floor coverings–carpet and rugs - Newport Carpet Mills Inc.
MAUI WOWI - Beverages - Maui Wowi, Inc.
MAUICCINO - Candy - Michael D. Blair
MAUI'S FAVORITE - Potato chips - Yick Lung Co., Inc.
MAUI'S KAANAPALI COFFEE - Coffee - AMFAC/JMB Hawaii, Inc.
MAUL - Posters and comic magazines - Brandon Choi
MAUL - Toys - Aegis Entertainment, Inc.
MAUL-MASTER - Mauls - Star Quest, Inc.
MAULL'S - Barbecue sauce - Louis Maull Co.
MAUNA KEA - Syrup ☆ - Wilsey Foods, Inc.
MAUNA KEA CHAMPIONSHIP COURSE - Computer software - Access Software Inc.
MAUNA LAI - Fruit drinks–bottled or canned - Ocean Spray Cranberries Inc.
MAUNA LANI BAY - Floor coverings–carpet and rugs ☆ - J.L. Benson Co.
MAUNA LOA - Nuts–salted, roasted, cooked, or canned - Mauna Loa Macadamia Nut Corp.
MAUREA - Whirlpools - Jacuzzi Inc.
MAUREEN - Earthenware ☆ - Waterford Wedgewood USA, Inc.
MAUREEN - House furnishings - Dan River Inc.
MAUREEN BENUN - Apparel and accessories - Maureen Benun
MAURELL - Boats–pontoons - Maurell Products Inc.
MAURENTANIA - Floor coverings–carpet and rugs - Milliken & Co. Inc.
MAURER - Chemicals–photographic - Maurer Photo Products Co.
MAURER - Meat products–beef - Maurer Meat Processors Inc.

MAURI - Footwear - Mauri USA Inc.
MAURICE ASHLEY TEACHES CHESS - Computer software ☆ - Knowledge Adventure
MAURICE BADLER FINE JEWELRY - Jewelry - Maurice Badler Fine Jewelry
MAURICE BESSINGER'S - Barbecue sauce - Piggie Park Enterprises Inc.
MAURICE KATZ - Jewelry - Michael Anthony Jewelers Inc.
MAURICE SASSON - Apparel and accessories - Jays Industries Inc.
MAURICE'S - Barbecue sauce - Maurice's Gourmet Barbecue
MAURICE'S GOURMET BBQ - Marinas - Piggie Park Enterprises Inc.
MAURO BASSANI - Footwear - De La Rentis Imports Inc.
MAURO BRUNI - Apparel–men's - Ciro Esposito
MAURO M - Hair care products - Mauro Spina
MAURO PISANI - Footwear - Olem Shoe Corp.
MAURRY - Pharmaceutical preparations - Maurry Biological Co. Inc.
MAURY ISLAND FARM - Food products - Maury Island Farming Co. Inc.
MAUTHE - Clocks ☆ - Coehler-Coptex Co.
MAUVE GLACE - Lipsticks - Estee Lauder Inc.
MAUVE MIST - Baskets–wood ☆ - Royal Cathay Trading Co.
MAUVE MOIRE - Cosmetics - Lancome
MAUVE TAPESTRY - Nail care products - Cosmair Inc.
MAUXION - Chocolate candy - Morris National Inc.
MAUXION - Chocolate candy ☆ - Bell'amore Imports Inc.
MAVADE' - Shoes–athletic - MVP Products, Inc.
MAVERICK - Apparel and accessories - Wrangler Co.
MAVERICK - Archery equipment ☆ - Martin Archery Inc.
MAVERICK - Boats–motor - Alumacraft Boat Co.
MAVERICK - Boats–motor ☆ - Commander Marine
MAVERICK - Bumpers–motor vehicle - Wedgestone Automotive Corp.
MAVERICK - Catheters - Scimed Life Systems, Inc.
MAVERICK - Colognes - Brandy Harvest
MAVERICK - Dog food - Ralston Purina Co.
MAVERICK - Fishing lures - William C. Willard, Jr.
MAVERICK - Furniture - JSJ Seating Corp.
MAVERICK - Furniture–wood ☆ - Charvoz
MAVERICK - Gloves - Champion Glove Manufacturing Co.
MAVERICK - Helmets–metal - ERB Industries, Inc.
MAVERICK - Kitchen appliances - Maverick Industries, Inc.
MAVERICK - Motor vehicles–automobiles ☆ - Ford Motor Co.
MAVERICK - Motor vehicles–motor homes - Georgie Boy Manufacturing, Inc.
MAVERICK - Office supplies - Alvin and Co. Inc.
MAVERICK - Playing cards - Hoyle Products
MAVERICK - Pumps–water - Odyssey Systems
MAVERICK - Recording label - Maverick Recording Co.
MAVERICK - Tools–hand-operated - Phillips Electronics North America Corp.
MAVERICK - Toys - Master Juvenile Products Inc.
MAVERICK - Toys–models ☆ - Estes Industries
MAVERICK - Watches - Elgin Watch Co.
MAVERICK - Wheelbarrows - Ames Lawn & Garden Tool Co.
MAVERICK AIRWAYS - Benches–plastic - Maverick Airways Corp.
MAVERICK AUTOMATICS - Apparel and accessories ☆ - Wrangler Co.
MAVERICK CAREERS - Publisher's imprints - Ronin Publishing, Inc.
MAVERICK GRABBER - Motor vehicles–automobiles ☆ - Ford Motor Co.
MAVERICK GUIDE - Publisher's imprints - Pelican Publishing Co. Inc.
MAVERICK II - Drafting supplies - Alvin and Co. Inc.
MAVERICK M - Electrical equipment - Phillips Electronics North America Corp.
MAVERICK SUGARBUSH - Apparel and accessories - Maverick Sugarbush Inc.
MAVERICK TRADING COMPANY - Apparel and accessories - Wrangler Apparel Co.
MAVERICK VACUUM SYSTEM ACCESSORY - Pumps–vacuum - Odyssey Systems
MAVERIK - Convenience stores - Maverik Country Stores Inc.
MAVEST - Apparel–men's - Mavest Inc.
MAVICA - Cameras - Sony Corp. of America
MAVIN TUNES - Headbands - Reliable of Milwaukee
MAVINS & MACHERS - Game - Contemporary Designs
MAVIPAK - Electronics equipment - L & M Auto Supply
MAVIS - Colognes - All Clubman
MAVIS - Toys–stuffed ☆ - Russ Berrie and Co., Inc.
MAVIS BEACON TEACHES TYPING! - Computer software - Software Toolworks, Inc.
MAVRIC - Electrical equipment - Metric Systems Corp.
MAX - Agricultural products - L.E. Cooke Co.
MAX - Audio equipment - Mark IV Audio Magnetic, Inc.
MAX - Batteries - Scherer Batteries
MAX - Beverages–carbonated ☆ - Coca-Cola Co.

MAX - Calculators - Max Business Machines Corp.
MAX - Cigarettes - Lorillard Tobacco Co.
MAX - Computer software - Aspen Technology, Inc.
MAX - Computer software - Midwest Stock Exchange, Inc.
MAX - Computer software - Pittsburgh Tag Co.
MAX - Computer storage devices–optical - CMP Publications, Inc.
MAX - Computer terminals - Image Systems Corp.
MAX - Containers - Longview Fibre Co.
MAX - Dishes–earthenware ☆ - Max Burton Enterprises Inc.
MAX - Drafting supplies ☆ - Wolsey Co.
MAX - Electrical surge protectors - Panamax
MAX - Glassware–household - Heller Inc.
MAX - Hair care products - Kenra Laboratories, Inc.
MAX - Hair care products - Worlds of Curls Inc.
MAX - Hammers - Hawera Inc.
MAX - Medical apparatus ☆ - Ortho-Kinetics, Inc.
MAX - Motor vehicles - Recreatives Industries Inc.
MAX - Motor vehicles–buses - Country Coach, Inc.
MAX - Office furniture–wood - Joyce International Inc.
MAX - Plugs–ear ☆ - Karlen Manufacturing, Inc.
MAX - Screws - Mid-States Screw Corp.
MAX - Sporting goods - Sierra Bridge, Inc.
MAX 1 - Motor oils - Irving Oil Corp.
MAX II - Paper - Goodwin Graphics, Inc.
MAX-100 - Latex gloves - Justin International Inc.
MAX 200E - Golfing equipment ☆ - Dunlop Maxfli Sports Corp.
MAX 200G - Natural dyestuffs - Dunlop Maxfli Sports Corp.
MAX 357 - Golfing equipment - Dunlop Maxfli Sports Corp.
MAX A - Skin care products - Beauty Innovations Inc.
MAX-A-FORM - Metals - Symons Corp.
MAX-ABOL - Vitamins and nutritional supplements - JBN Enterprises, Inc.
MAX AIR - Fans–electric - Walker Radiator Works, Inc.
MAX AIR - Shock absorbers–motor vehicle - Monroe Auto Equipment Co.
MAX-AMINE - Chemical preparations - Betz Process Chemicals, Inc.
MAX-AMINO - Animal feeds - Farmland Industries Inc.
MAX & EDDIE - Apparel and accessories - Intimate Resources, Ltd.
MAX & MABEL - Apparel–women's - Max & Mabel, Inc.
MAX AWARD - Computer peripheral equipment - CMP Publications, Inc.
MAX AWARD 1993 COMM WEEK - Computer software - CMP Publications, Inc.
MAX BACKTALK - Games ☆ - Milton Bradley Co.
MAX-BARREL - Bats–baseball - Easton Aluminum Inc.
MAX BAUER - Food products - Max Bauer Meat Packer Inc.
MAX-BILT - Recording label - Private, Inc.
MAX BINDER - Office supplies - Esselte Corp.
MAX BLASTER - Toys–guns - Technical Publications Service, Inc.
MAX BOND - Adhesives and sealants - Tec Inc.
MAX BY COUNTRY COACH - Motor vehicles–buses - Country Coach, Inc.
MAX C - Barium diagnostic agents - Smith & Nephew Richards, Inc.
MAX C - Candy ☆ - Brock Candy Co. Inc.
MAX C PLEX - Vitamins and nutritional supplements - Naturally Vitamin Supplements Inc.
MAX CAT - Cat food - Nutro Products, Inc.
MAX CAT-KITTEN - Cat food - Nutro Products, Inc.
MAX CAT LITE - Cat food - Nutro Products, Inc.
MAX CHECKOUT - Surveillance equipment - Sensormatic Electronics Corp.
MAX CLEAN - Cleaning preparations - Cyclo Industries, LLC
MAX COMFORT - Sports rackets and accessories - Dunlop Maxfli Sports Corp.
MAX-CON - Insecticides - Y-Tex Corp.
MAX CRAW - Fishing lures - Michael J. Brackus
MAX CUVEE - Wines - Fife Vineyards LLC
MAX DRY - Paper products - Jomar Management Corp.
MAX DRY - Paper products - Shepherd Tissue, Inc.
MAX-E-LAC - Animal feed supplements - Hubbard Milling Co.
MAX-E2 - Motors–outboard - Teco American Inc.
MAX-ENERGY - Vitamins and nutritional supplements - Vitamin Classics, Inc.
MAX ESCHIG - Music–sheet - GSP
MAX FACTOR - Cosmetics - Max Factor & Co.
MAX FEED - Machine parts ☆ - Valenite Inc.
MAX FIFTY - Vitamins and nutritional supplements - Gold'n Nutrition
MAX FISH - Apparel and accessories - Sun Apparel, Inc.
MAX-FIT - Exhaust systems–motor vehicle - AP Parts
MAX-FLO - Pumps - Hayward Pool Products Inc.
MAX-FLOW - Water heaters–household - National Dynamics Corp.
MAX FORCE - Toys–guns - Tonka Corp.
MAX FREEBOARD - Sporting goods ☆ - O'Brien International

MAX-G - Wallets - Martin Carbone Inc.
MAX GERMAN - Meat products–beef - Max German Packing Co.
MAX GRIP - Adhesives and sealants - Roberts Consolidated Industries, Inc.
MAX GRUMBACHER - Artist paints - M. Grumbacher Inc.
MAX GRUMBACHER - Paints–artists' - Koh-I-Noor, Inc.
MAX HEADREST - Wheelchairs - Adaptive Engineering Lab Inc.
MAX HEADROOM - Candy ☆ - Topps Co., Inc.
MAX-HIDE - Paints - Mantrose-Haeuser Co. Inc.
MAX HOLD - Hardware - Von Duprin, Inc.
MAX I - Dinnerware–glass - Heller Inc.
MAX II - Business forms - Goodwin Graphics, Inc.
MAX-II - Sporting goods - AFC
MAX IMPACT - Sporting goods - Dunlop Maxfli Sports Corp.
MAX IT - Apparel–men's - Intimo, Inc.
MAX JONES - Toys - Tonka Corp.
MAX KITTEN - Cat food ☆ - Nutro Products, Inc.
MAX KLEIN - Containers - Sevko, Inc.
MAX KOHL MK - Apparel and accessories - CS Crable Sportswear, Inc.
MAX LITE - Plugs–ear ☆ - Karlen Manufacturing, Inc.
MAX LT - Sporting goods ☆ - Dunlop Maxfli Sports Corp.
MAX-LUBE - Motor vehicle parts and accessories - Max-Torque Ltd.
MAX MACHINE - Toys - Tyco Toys
MAX/MAP - Computer software - MAXM Systems Corp.
MAX-MASTER TABLE - Tables–metal - Norix Group, Inc.
MAX MAYER'S - Gloves - Thornton Glove & Accessories Inc.
MAX MINI - Dog food - Nutro Products, Inc.
MAX MOTION STEREO ENGINEERING MAX BOX - Electronic equipment - Max Motion Inc.
MAX NATURALLY PRESERVED - Dog food - Nutro Products, Inc.
MAX NICOLE - Apparel–women's - Sarcotex, Inc.
MAX NOTES - Publisher's imprints - Research and Education Assn.
MAX NUGUS - Apparel and accessories - Max Nugus Fashions Inc.
MAX OUT - Skin care products - High-Tech Sun Research, Inc.
MAX PAC - Containers - Core Technologies, Inc.
MAX-PAK - Exercising equipment - Hayward Pool Products Inc.
MAX PAK - Food products - Duso Food Distributors
MAX PLEAT - Fabrics–linen - Maytex Mills
MAX PLUS - Golfing equipment - Dunlop Maxfli Sports Corp.
MAX POLISHING SYSTEMS - Cleaning preparations - Max Polishing Systems
MAX POWER - Lawn mowers - Dorcy Power Products and Max Power Precision Parts
MAX POWR - Batteries - East Penn Manufacturing Co., Inc.
MAX PUPPY - Dog food - Nutro Products, Inc.
MAX RAD - Sunglasses - Jack Martin Co.
MAX RAY - Toys - Tonka Corp.
MAX RE-LACKS - Hair care products - Paul Brown Salon & Spa
MAX SCHNELL - Toys - Tonka Corp.
MAX-SEA - Seafood products–fresh or frozen - Eldorado Seafoods, Inc.
MAX SEAL - Adhesives and sealants ☆ - Tec Inc.
MAX/SNMP - Computer software - MAXM Systems Corp.
MAX SPECIAL - Dog food - Nutro Products, Inc.
MAX SPLASH - Paper products - Lisa Frank, Inc.
MAX-STAX - Musical instrument accessories ☆ - D & F Products Inc.
MAX-STIKS - Musical instrument accessories - D & F Products Inc.
MAX-STOR - Shelving units–metal - Richards-Wilcox Manufacturing Co.
MAX STRESS - Dog food ☆ - Nutro Products, Inc.
MAX-TAC - Apparel and accessories - Brigade Quartermasters Ltd.
MAX TECH - Sporting goods - Dunlop Maxfli Sports Corp.
MAX-TEX - Thread - Threads USA Div.
MAX, THE - Musical instruments ☆ - Charles Colin Music Publishers
MAX, THE - Health care products ☆ - Everest & Jennings
MAX THE MOOSE - Recording label - Joyful Heart Music
MAX THE MOUSE - Toys ☆ - Picture Book Studio
MAX TRAC - Rug cleaning machines–commercial - Castex Industries Inc.
MAX-TRACK - Shelving units–metal - Lee Rowan Co.
MAX TRACKER - Drafting supplies - Max Business Machines Corp.
MAX TRAN - Mobile railcar movers - Trackmobile Inc.
MAX TRAX - Recording label - Zapset, Inc.
MAX TRUMPET UNLIMITED - Musical instruments - Charles Colin Music Publishers
MAX WAX - Lubricants - McNett Corp.
MAX WEAR - Apparel and accessories - Forest City Auto Parts Co.
MAX WEISS - Food products - George C. Brown's Biscuits & Confections
MAX WHEEL - Pottery products - Max Concepts Inc.
MAX WHITE - Coatings - Michelman Inc.
MAX YOUR RAM - Computer hardware - Desktop Sales, Inc.

☆ = Now out of production

MAX ZELLER - Furs–artificial - Max Zeller Furs Inc.
MAXA - Amplifiers ☆ - Fender Musical Instruments
MAXA - Generators - Coleman Powermate, Inc.
MAXAIR - Automotive parts and accessories - Wynn's Climate Systems Inc.
MAXALARM - Security alarms - Timber Group, Inc.
MAXALON - Brushes–hair - Professional Beauty Distributors
MAXAM - Bath salts - Chinese Native Products
MAXAM - Locks–door - B and F System Inc.
MAXAMAG - Antacids ☆ - Vitarine Pharmaceuticals Inc.
MAXAROME - Yeast - Gist-Brocades Food Ingredients Inc.
MAXAROUSE - Vitamins and nutritional supplements - Institute of Professional Athletics, Inc.
MAXATIVA - Health care products - Futurebiotics
MAXAUTO - Computer software - Systems Design Associates, Inc.
MAXAVOR - Yeast - Gist-Brocades Food Ingredients Inc.
MAXBOLT - Nuts and bolts - Textron Aerospace Fasteners
MAXBRITE - Paper–writing - Officemax, Inc.
MAXC FLAMEGUARD - Gypsum products - Boral Gypsum Inc.
MAXCALL - Radio communications equipment - Maxcom Electronics Inc.
MAXCAP - Insulating materials - Carborundum Co.
MAXCESS - Computer software - Impact Technologies Group, Inc.
MAXCOLA - Health care products - Johnson Laboratories, Inc.
MAXCON II - Audio equipment ☆ - C.T.I. Audio Inc.
MAX'D OUT - Apparel - In Private Inc.
MAX'E' - Oils–edible - Food Extrusion, Inc.
MAXELL - Computer diskettes–blank - Maxell Corp. of America
MAXEPA - Vitamins and nutritional supplements - Makers of Kal, Inc.
MAXERCISER - Exercising equipment - Thomas Kusel
MAXFIELD - Gloves–safety - Sierra Bridge, Inc.
MAXFIELD PARRISH - Posters - Icart Vendor Graphics Inc.
MAXFIELD'S - Candy - Maxfield Candy Co.
MAXFIRE - Flashlights - Brinkmann Corp.
MAXFIRE - Flashlights - Brinkmann Lighting Products
MAXFIT - Safety products ☆ - U.S. Safety Corp.
MAXFLEX - Paints - Duron, Inc.
MAXFLI - Golfing equipment - Dunlop Maxfli Sports Corp.
MAXFLI CD - Balls–golf - Dunlop Maxfli Sports Corp.
MAXFLI MD - Balls–golf - Dunlop Maxfli Sports Corp.
MAXFLI RM - Balls–golf - Dunlop Maxfli Sports Corp.
MAXFLI SLX - Golfing equipment - Dunlop Maxfli Sports Corp.
MAXFLI TOUR LTD. - Sporting goods - Dunlop Maxfli Sports Corp.
MAXFLOW - Automotive parts and accessories - Vortech Engineering, Inc.
MAXFORCE - Insecticides - Clorox Co.
MAXFORCE - Insecticides - Kingsford Products Co.
MAXFORT - Locks–padlocks - Maxfort Corp.
MAXGAR - Vitamins and nutritional supplements - R.P. Scherer Corp.
MAXGAR - Vitamins and nutritional supplements - Solgar Vitamin and Herb Co., Inc.
MAXGARD - Chemical preparations - United Resource Recovery Corp.
MAXGON - Railroad equipment - Thrall Car Manufacturing Co.
MAXGRIP - Electrical equipment - Pass & Seymour, Inc.
MAXGUARD - Switches–electric - Command Communications, Inc.
MAXHESIVE - Adhesives and sealants ☆ - General Signal Corp.
MAXHESIVE - Concrete products - Master Builders Inc.
MAXI - Awnings - Awnings by Sunair/Sunair Awnings
MAXI - Brushes–hair - Beautee Sense Inc.
MAXI - Computer peripheral equipment - Chyron Corp.
MAXI - Confections - George C. Brown's Biscuits & Confections
MAXI - Cosmetics - Max Factor & Co.
MAXI - Filters–oil - Champion Laboratories, Inc.
MAXI - Fuses–electric - Littelfuse, Inc.
MAXI - Health care products - Medical Industries America, Inc.
MAXI - Locks–padlocks ☆ - Fort Lock Corp.
MAXI - Skin-care products - Country Life
MAXI - Vitamins and nutritional supplements ☆ - Ethical Nutrients
MAXI ALPHA 3 - Toys–models ☆ - Estes Industries
MAXI ATC - Automotive fuses ☆ - Cooper Industries, Inc.
MAXI AUTO - Motor vehicle parts and accessories - CK Motoring Accessories
MAXI-AWL - Awls ☆ - Alexander Manufacturing Co.
MAXI-B - Vitamins and nutritional supplements - Fanie International
MAXI BABY - Vitamins - Country Life
MAXI BABY-C - Vitamins and nutritional supplements - Country Life
MAXI BABY DOPHILUS - Vitamins - Country Life
MAXI-BALE - Chemical preparations - Purina Mills, Inc.
MAXI-BANK - Humidifiers - Dri-Steem Humidifier Co.
MAXI BEARS - Vitamins and nutritional supplements - Country Life

MAXI BIFIDUS DF - Vitamins and nutritional supplements - Ethical Nutrients
MAXI BLONDE - Hair care products - Clairol Inc.
MAXI BLUE - Shampoos ☆ - Demert & Dougherty, Inc.
MAXI-BOND - Floor coverings–carpet and rugs ☆ - Custom Tapes, Inc.
MAXI BRUTE - Amplifiers ☆ - Polytone Musical Instruments Inc.
MAXI-BTU - Fuel additives - Hamilton Farm Bureau
MAXI-BTU - Heating equipment - Hamilton Farm Bureau
MAXI CARE - Furniture - Avant Industries
MAXI-CARE - Prenatal vitamins - Country Life
MAXI CASTAWAY - Cosmetics - Max Factor & Co.
MAXI CHARGE 2000 - Vitamins and nutritional supplements - Muscle Dynamics Fitness Network, Inc.
MAXI-CLIPPER - Electronic equipment - Mueller Electric Co.
MAXI-CLOG-AWAY - Drain pipe cleaners - Eagle Industries Inc.
MAXI COLOR CLENZ - Heart monitors - ADH Health Products
MAXI COLOR-ON-COLOR - Cosmetics - Max Factor & Co.
MAXI COLORKOHL - Cosmetics - Max Factor & Co.
MAXI COLORS DIMENSIONAL GLITTER - Paints - Wellington Leisure Products, Inc.
MAXI COLORS-TO-GO - Cosmetics - Max Factor & Co.
MAXI-COMFORT - Automotive parts and accessories - Convo Corp.
MAXI-CURE - Glue–household or industrial - Bob Smith Industries
MAXI CURLY - Cosmetics - Max Factor & Co.
MAXI-CUT - Garden equipment - Echo, Inc.
MAXI-CUT II - Garden equipment - Echo, Inc.
MAXI-DEET - Insect repellents - Saffeta Inc.
MAXI DOPHILUS - Vitamins and nutritional supplements - Metagenics, Inc.
MAXI DOPHILUS DF - Vitamins and nutritional supplements - Ethical Nutrients
MAXI-DORM - Concrete products - Oldcastle Precast East, Inc.
MAXI-DUTY - Wheels - Hamilton Caster & Manufacturing Co.
MAXI ENDLESS SHINE - Manicure preparations - Max Factor & Co.
MAXI ENDLESS SUN - Cosmetics - Max Factor & Co.
MAXI-E.P.O. - Vitamins and nutritional supplements - Ethical Nutrients
MAXI EXTRA-LONG THICK - Cosmetics - Max Factor & Co.
MAXI-FELT - Hats - American Hat Co. Inc.
MAXI-FLEX - Electrical equipment - All Flex, Inc.
MAXI-FLO - Aquariums–household ☆ - Marineland Aquarium Products
MAXI-FLORAL POTPOURRI - Cleaning preparations - Gisele, Inc.
MAXI-FORCE - Toys–models - Estes Industries
MAXI-FRESH - Cosmetics - Max Factor & Co.
MAXI FRIES - Vegetables–frozen ☆ - Ore-Ida Foods, Inc.
MAXI-FRUITS - Candy - California Hi-Lites, Inc.
MAXI GET WICKED - Cosmetics - Max Factor & Co.
MAXI-GLOW - Cosmetics - Max Factor & Co.
MAXI-GRIP - Brushes–hair ☆ - Belson Products
MAXI-GRIP - Mops - Geerpres Wringer Co.
MAXI-GROW - Animal feeds - Southern States Cooperative Inc.
MAXI-GUARD - Alarm systems - Maxi-Guard
MAXI-HAIR - Vitamins and nutritional supplements - Country Life
MAXI HAIR DARE - Hair care products - Revlon Consumer Products Corp.
MAXI-HEAT - Curling irons–electric - Conair Corp.
MAXI ICARUS - Toys–models ☆ - Estes Industries
MAXI-JACK - Metals - C & R Pier Manufacturing Co.
MAXI JECT - Veterinary medical equipment - Addison Biological Laboratory
MAXI-JET - Pumps–water - Aquarium Systems, Inc.
MAXI K - Pharmaceutical preparations - Barth's Nutra Products
MAXI-LASH - Cosmetics - Max Factor & Co.
MAXI LIFT - Combs - Comare Corp.
MAXI LIFT - Toys - Tonka Corp.
MAXI-LITE - Projectors–photographic - Neumade Products Corp.
MAXI LITTER SCOOP - Pet products ☆ - Shippan Distributors Inc.
MAXI-LOK - Alarm systems - Maxi-Guard
MAXI-LUX - Electronic equipment - General Electric Co.
MAXI-MASK - Dust cloths - Flents Products Co. Inc.
MAXI-MELT - Deicing fluid - Howe Co.
MAXI-MINERALS - Vitamins and nutritional supplements - Freeda Vitamins Inc.
MAXI MINI - Motor homes - Diamond Coach Corp.
MAXI-MISER - Paint sprayers - Apollo Sprayers International, Inc.
MAXI-MITE - Infant product - Evenflo Co.
MAXI-MIX - Veterinary nutritional supplements - Y-Tex Corp.
MAXI MIZER - Computer software ☆ - Portage Newspaper Supply Co.
MAXI-MOD - Concrete products - Oldcastle Precast East, Inc.
MAXI-MOIST - Lipsticks - Max Factor & Co.
MAXI MOUSE - Microphones - Lectrosonics Inc.
MAXI-MYST - Housewares ☆ - Bristol-Myers Squibb Co.
MAXI-O - Audio equipment - Valley Audio Products, Inc.

MAXI ONE-COAT - Manicure preparations - Max Factor & Co.
MAXI-PAD - Transformers–electric - General Electric Co.
MAXI-PIER - Metals - C & R Pier Manufacturing Co.
MAXI POLE - Paint sprayers - ASM Co.
MAXI PROS PLUS - Vitamins and nutritional supplements - Ethical Nutrients
MAXI-Q - Electronic equipment - Valley Audio Products, Inc.
MAXI-QUOTABLES - Greeting cards - Stevenson Industries Inc.
MAXI-REM - Vitamins and nutritional supplements ☆ - Ethical Nutrients
MAXI-ROCKER - Infant product ☆ - Evenflo Co.
MAXI-ROOTER - Tools–power-driven - General Wire Spring Co.
MAXI RUB - Electromedical apparatus - Max Buchanan Co.
MAXI-SEAL - Electrical equipment - Peterson Manufacturing Co.
MAXI-SEAT - Infant product ☆ - Evenflo Co.
MAXI-SHARP - Tools–hand-operated - Simonds Industries Inc.
MAXI-SHOT - Toys–guns - Jak-Pak Inc.
MAXI-SHUK - Cooking utensils–aluminum - Bendal Enterprises, Inc.
MAXI SLC - Microwave capacitors - AVX Corp.
MAXI-SNACK MINI-MEAL - Snack foods - Tanimura & Antle, Inc.
MAXI SOFT LUSTRE - Lipsticks - Max Factor & Co.
MAXI SPORTABLES - Cosmetics - Max Factor & Co.
MAXI-SPRAY - Paint - Iowa Paint Manufacturing Co. Inc.
MAXI STAND - Photographic equipment - SP Systems/Saratons
MAXI-START - Animal feeds - Southern States Cooperative Inc.
MAXI-STOR - Furniture - Republic Storage Systems Co. Inc.
MAXI STREAK - Toys–models ☆ - Estes Industries
MAXI-SWEEP - Brooms - Allmand Bros. Inc.
MAXI SWEET THING - Cosmetics - Max Factor & Co.
MAXI SWIRLSTICK - Lipsticks - Max Factor & Co.
MAXI-T - Vitamins and nutritional supplements - Fanie International
MAXI-TAXI - Strollers–baby ☆ - Evenflo Co.
MAXI-THERM - Vitamins and nutritional supplements - Creative Nutritional Concepts, Inc.
MAXI-THICK - Cosmetics - Max Factor & Co.
MAXI TIPS - Paint sprayers - ASM Co.
MAXI-TOTE - Infant product ☆ - Evenflo Co.
MAXI TRAC - Tires - Armtec Industries Inc.
MAXI-TUBE - Thread - Belding Heminway Co. Inc.
MAXI TUFF LITE - Flashlights - Garrity Industries
MAXI TWIN - Fishing lures - Shannon Lure Co.
MAXI UNSHINE - Cosmetics - Max Factor & Co.
MAXI-VIEW - Television equipment - Krown Research
MAXI-VITE - Pharmaceutical preparations - Goldline Laboratories, Inc.
MAXI-VUE - Mirrors - Molor Products Co.
MAXI-WHEELER - Briefcases - Softech Cases Inc.
MAXI-ZINC - Vitamins and nutritional supplements - Country Life
MAXIAL - Computer peripheral equipment - General Automation Inc.
MAXIBIFIDUS - Vitamins and nutritional supplements - Ethical Nutrients
MAXIBOLIN - Pharmaceutical preparations ☆ - Organon Inc.
MAXIBRAID - Rope - Yale Cordage, Inc.
MAXIBRAKE - Automotive parts and accessories - Echlin Inc.
MAXICARE - Health care products - Inbrand Corp.
MAXICHEM MAXIFLOC - Cleaning preparations - Maxichem, Inc.
MAXICHEM MAXIKILL - Cleaning preparations - Maxichem, Inc.
MAXICHEM MAXITHERM - Cleaning preparations - Maxichem, Inc.
MAXICHEM MC - Cleaning preparations - Maxichem, Inc.
MAXICHOP - Glass products - PPG Industries, Inc.
MAXICLENS - Soap - Schein Pharmaceutical Inc.
MAXICON - Computer software - International Data Group, Inc.
MAXICORD - Audio equipment - Time Line Technologies, Inc.
MAXICUM - Chemical preparations - Georgia-Pacific Corp.
MAXICUT - Hair care products - Fromm Industries
MAXIDAY - Vitamins and nutritional supplements ☆ - American Hygienic Laboratories Inc.
MAXIDEX - Ophthalmic goods - Alcon Laboratories, Inc.
MAXIDOPHILUS - Vitamins and nutritional supplements - Ethical Nutrients
MAXIDRIVE - Electrical industrial apparatus - Maxwell Products
MAXIDRY - Skin care products - Texas Pharmacal Co.
MAXIDYNE - Iodine - West Agro, Inc.
MAXIE - Boats - Zodiac of North America
MAXIE - Dolls - Hasbro, Inc.
MAXIE - Footwear–women's - Maxwell Shoe Co. Inc.
MAXIE - Skin care products - Unipharm Inc.
MAXIE AND ME - Greeting cards - Susan Schwartz
MAXIE POODLE - Toys–banks - A.J. Renzi Plastic Corp.
MAXIEDGE - Garden equipment - Arnold Corp.

MAXIFAT BURNING SYSTEM - Vitamins and nutritional supplements - Action Labs, Inc.
MAXIFLO BULB - Blood pressure apparatus - Graham-Field Inc.
MAXIFLOR - Skin care products - Allergan, Inc.
MAXIFORCE - Tools - Paratech Inc.
MAXIGESIC - Analgesics ☆ - Bradley Pharmaceutical Co., Inc.
MAXIGEST - Vitamins and nutritional supplements - Ethical Nutrients
MAXIGLIDE - Lubricants - Maxiglide Products, Inc.
MAXIGLIDE - Waxes–sealing - Erik Sports Inc.
MAXIGLIDE XC - Lubricants - Maxiglide Products, Inc.
MAXIGRIP - Hardware - Liberty Hardware Manufacturing Corp.
MAXIGRO - Hair care products - Ecostyle, Inc.
MAXIGROW - Nutritional supplements for plants - Living Green Inc.
MAXIGUARD - Toothpaste - Addison Biological Laboratory
MAXIHEARTH - Fireplaces - Martin Industries, Inc.
MAXILACT - Food products - Gist-Brocades Food Ingredients Inc.
MAXILAN - Computers–personal - United Barcode Industries, Inc.
MAXILEANE - Vitamins and nutritional supplements - Achievers Unlimited, Inc.
MAXILIFE - Vitamins and nutritional supplements - Twinlab
MAXILIFE BRAIN PROTECTOR - Vitamins and nutritional supplements - Twin Laboratories, Inc.
MAXILIFE CARDIO PROTECTOR - Vitamins and nutritional supplements - Twin Laboratories, Inc.
MAXILIFE COLON PROTECTOR - Vitamins and nutritional supplements - Twin Laboratories, Inc.
MAXILIFE JOINT PROTECTOR - Vitamins and nutritional supplements - Twin Laboratories, Inc.
MAXILIFE PROSTATE PROTECTOR - Vitamins and nutritional supplements - Twin Laboratories, Inc.
MAXILIFT - Axles - Boler Co.
MAXILIFT - Home health care products - Arjo Manufacturing Co.
MAXILIFT CUSHIONS - Jacks–hand-operated - Paratech Inc.
MAXILOCK - Knives–hunting - Buck Knives, Inc.
MAXILOUPE - Photographic equipment - Bestwell Optical Instrument Co.
MAXILUBE - Lubricants - Mission Pharmacal Co.
MAXIM - Antennas - Andrew Corp.
MAXIM - Automotive parts and accessories - Maxim, Inc.
MAXIM - Beauty shop equipment - Monaco Import/Export Inc.
MAXIM - Bowling balls - Ebonite International, Inc.
MAXIM - Cabinets - Schrock
MAXIM - Cigars ☆ - Havatampa Inc.
MAXIM - Cleaning preparations - Midlab, Inc.
MAXIM - Coffee - Maxwell House
MAXIM - Domestic appliance - Salton/Maxim Housewares, Inc.
MAXIM - Electronic equipment - Maxim Technology Corp.
MAXIM - Floor coverings–carpet and rugs - Galaxy Carpet Mills Inc.
MAXIM - Floor coverings–carpet and rugs - Roxbury Carpet Co.
MAXIM - Food products - Maxim Co. Ltd.
MAXIM - Food products - John Sexton and Co.
MAXIM - Fungicides - Ciba-Geigy Corp.
MAXIM - Garden equipment - Maxim Manufacturing Co.
MAXIM - Insulating materials–foam - Eastern Foam Products Inc.
MAXIM - Photographic equipment - LogEtronics Corp.
MAXIM - Rope - New England Ropes Inc.
MAXIM - Signal surveillance equipment - Delfin Systems
MAXIM - Spark plugs - Federal Parts Corp.
MAXIM - Tools–machine - Cincinnati Machine
MAXIM - Wallpaper - Koroseal Wallcoverings
MAXIM - Wheelchairs - Theradyne Healthcare Product Div.
MAXIM 2000 - Toilets–portable - Satellite Industries, Inc.
MAXIM BALM - Health care products - Maxim Chemicals Ltd.
MAXIM IV - Bowling balls - Ebonite International, Inc.
MAXIM L - Vitamins and nutritional supplements - Omega Pharmaceutical, Inc.
MAXIM LTD. - Apparel–men's - Merrill-Sharpe Ltd.
MAXIM MARINE - Furniture - Maxim Marine Co. Inc.
MAXIM MAXIM - Floor coverings–carpet and rugs - Maxim Sorbents Inc.
MAXIM SIGNAL PRODUCTS - Transmitters, receivers, and scramblers - Delfin Systems
MAXIMA - Electrical equipment - White's Electronics, Inc.
MAXIMA - Fishing tackle - Jatra International
MAXIMA - Floor coverings–carpet and rugs - Eligere Carpets
MAXIMA - Furniture ☆ - Hooker Furniture Corp.
MAXIMA - Gate hardware - Ameristar Fence Products, Inc.
MAXIMA - Health care products - Staodyn, Inc.
MAXIMA - Juice extracting devices - Angel Life Corp.
MAXIMA - Lighting fixtures - Edison Price Lighting

☆ = Now out of production

MAXIMA - Metals - McElroy Metal Mill, Inc.

MAXIMA - Motor vehicles–automobiles - Nissan Motor Corp. USA

MAXIMA - Paper - M. Grumbacher Inc.

MAXIMA - Pet products - Rolf C. Hagen (USA) Corp.

MAXIMA - Recording label - Vandor Motion Pictures, Phonorecords & Music Publishing Group

MAXIMA - Wallpaper - Textile Wallcoverings International Ltd.

MAXIMA - Wallpaper ☆ - Wallpaper Imports Inc.

MAXIMA - Wallpaper ☆ - Wolf-Gordon Inc.

MAXIMA 8000 - Carports - Texas Aluminum Industries Inc.

MAXIMA FORTE' - Medical apparatus - Medtronic, Inc.

MAXIMA PLUS - Medical apparatus - Medtronic, Inc.

MAXIMA PLUS PRF - Medical apparatus - Medtronic, Inc.

MAXIMAL - Floor coverings–carpet and rugs - Whitecrest Carpet Mills

MAXIMAL ART - Clocks - Maximal Art, Inc.

MAXIMAN - Wigs - Jean Paree Weegs Inc.

MAXIMARKETER - Computer software - Okra Marketing Corp.

MAXIMATCH - Torches - Gardner Marketing Services, Inc.

MAXIMATTE - Cosmetics - Lord & Berry, Ltd.

MAXIME - Machinery - Redicon Corp.

MAXIMENT - Concrete products - Master Builders Inc.

MAXIMEYES - Sporting goods - Oceanic

MAXIMHEALTH - Pharmaceutical preparations - Associated Independent Marketers Inc. of America

MAXIMICER - Coolers–electric - Maximicer, LLC

MAXIMILLIAN - Briefcases ☆ - Maximillian Luggage Corp.

MAXIMISER - Shock absorbers–motor vehicle - Fluidrive Inc.

MAXIMIZE YOUR LIFE - Broadcasting stations–television - Bay to Bay Distribution, Inc.

MAXIMIZER - Bicycles - Schwinn Cycling & Fitness Inc.

MAXIMIZER - Brassieres (Bras) - Gelmart Industries Inc.

MAXIMIZER - Cardboard - Acco World Corp.

MAXIMIZER - Chemical preparations - Bio-Lab, Inc.

MAXIMIZER - Flowers, plants, and seeds - Ciba-Geigy Corp.

MAXIMIZER - Hair care products - Philip Kingsley

MAXIMIZER - Office supplies - ACCO USA, Inc.

MAXIMIZER - Shortening - Procter & Gamble Co.

MAXIMIZER - Water purification systems - Hague Quality Water International

MAXIMIZER FOOD BAR - Food products - Carlisle Foodservice Products, Inc.

MAXIMIZERS, THE - Office supplies ☆ - McDonald Products

MAXIMO - Computer software - PSDI

MAXIMO - Scuba diving equipment - Beuchat-USA Inc.

MAXIMORE - Flowers, plants, and seeds - Abbott & Cobb Inc.

MAXIM'S - Beverages–alcohol - Sogrape USA Inc.

MAXIM'S BLANCHE - Dinnerware–glass ☆ - WMF/USA

MAXIM'S DE PARIS - Colognes ☆ - Gary Farn Ltd.

MAXIM'S DE PARIS - Dinnerware–glass ☆ - WMF/USA

MAXIM'S DE PARIS - Scarves ☆ - Jewel Case Inc.

MAXIMUM - Batteries - Rayovac Corp.

MAXIMUM - Cereal - Grist Mill Co.

MAXIMUM - Doughnuts–mixes - L. Karp & Sons, Inc.

MAXIMUM - Fireplace equipment - Schaefer Co.

MAXIMUM - Medical apparatus - Daig Corp.

MAXIMUM - Paints ☆ - Shiva Inc.

MAXIMUM - Truck caps - Jackson Enterprises Inc.

MAXIMUM - Weather tracking equipment - Imtra Corp.

MAXIMUM ACCELERATION - Vitamins - Caroline Owens

MAXIMUM ALKALINE - Batteries - Rayovac Corp.

MAXIMUM CARNAGE - Toys ☆ - Marvel Entertainment Group, Inc.

MAXIMUM CHILL FACTOR - Beverages–malt - The Stroh Brewery Co.

MAXIMUM CLASSIC - Fireplace equipment ☆ - Schaefer Co.

MAXIMUM COLOR - Lipsticks - Avon Products, Inc.

MAXIMUM COMFORT - Footwear insoles - Schering-Plough Healthcare Products

MAXIMUM COOKIE - Bakery products - Quality Food Centers, Inc.

MAXIMUM COVER - Cosmetics - Estee Lauder Inc.

MAXIMUM EFFORT - Apparel and accessories - Maximum Effort Bodywear

MAXIMUM ENTROPY - Computer software - Maximum Entropy Partners

MAXIMUM EPA - Pharmaceutical preparations ☆ - Lunsco Inc.

MAXIMUM LASH MASCARA - Cosmetics - A-Veda Corp.

MAXIMUM LIVING ANGEL-C - Vitamins and nutritional supplements - Bay to Bay Distribution, Inc.

MAXIMUM LIVING HYSSOP CLEANSE - Vitamins and nutritional supplements - Bay to Bay Distribution, Inc.

MAXIMUM LIVING JOINGASSURE - Vitamins and nutritional supplements - Bay to Bay Distribution, Inc.

MAXIMUM LIVING LITTLE ANGELS - Vitamins and nutritional supplements - Bay to Bay Distribution, Inc.

MAXIMUM LIVING OPTIMAX - Vitamins and nutritional supplements - Bay to Bay Distribution, Inc.

MAXIMUM LIVING PROGESTIMAX - Vitamins and nutritional supplements - Bay to Bay Distribution, Inc.

MAXIMUM LIVING SOLU-C - Vitamins and nutritional supplements - Bay to Bay Distribution, Inc.

MAXIMUM LIVING VITA SPROUT - Vitamins and nutritional supplements - Bay to Bay Distribution, Inc.

MAXIMUM MALE - Vitamins and nutritional supplements - Highland Laboratories

MAXIMUM MAX - Apparel and accessories - Product Code 31 Inc.

MAXIMUM MIDAS TOUCH - Game machines - Universal Distributing of Nevada, Inc.

MAXIMUM MOBILITY - Vitamins and nutritional supplements - Amrion, Inc.

MAXIMUM NUTRITION - Animal feeds - Stoltenberg Supply, Inc.

MAXIMUM PERFORMANCE - Cosmetics - Chem Spray Aerosols Inc.

MAXIMUM POTENTIAL ENERGY - Golfing equipment - James I. Park

MAXIMUM POWER E.R.S. - Pharmaceutical preparations - Vita Plus Industries Inc.

MAXIMUM PROTECTION - Veterinary nutritional supplements - Dr. Goodpet

MAXIMUM SECURITY + - Locks–door - Adams Rite Manufacturing Co.

MAXIMUM SECURITY - Toiletries - Bob Barker Co., Inc.

MAXIMUM SHINE - Hair care products - Altobella Hair Products Inc.

MAXIMUM STRATEGY, INC. - Computer hardware - Maxstrat Corp.

MAXIMUM STRENGTH CORTICAINE - Pharmaceutical preparations - Whitby Pharmaceuticals, Inc.

MAXIMUM STRESS - Pharmaceutical preparations - Pro Cap

MAXIMUM SUPPORT - Vitamins and nutritional supplements - Futurebiotics

MAXIMUM SUPPORT ZONE - Cushions - Professional Product Research, Inc.

MAXIMUM TERRAIN - Bicycles - Kent International Inc.

MAXIMUMS - Sanitary napkins - Kimberly-Clark Corp.

MAXIMUNE - Veterinary pharmaceutical preparations - Biomune Co.

MAXIMUR - Wallpaper ☆ - Winfield Design Associates, Inc.

MAXIMUS - Beverages–malt ☆ - F.X. Matt Brewing Co.

MAXIMUS - Computer hardware - Maximus Computers, Inc.

MAXIMUS - Cushions ☆ - Jay Medical Ltd.

MAXIMUS - Exercising equipment ☆ - Maximus Fitness Products

MAXIMUS - Recording label - Jazz Composer's Orchestra Association Inc.

MAXIMUS - Wallpaper - Capital Carousel Inc.

MAXIMUS - Wallpaper - Gloria Merrill Enterprises

MAXIMUS - Watches - Elgin Watch Co.

MAXIMUS II - Floor coverings–carpet and rugs ☆ - Columbus Mills, Inc.

MAXIMUS SUPER - Beverages–malt ☆ - F.X. Matt Brewing Co.

MAXINE! - Computer peripheral equipment - Chyron Corp.

MAXINE ROBINSON - Footwear - Maxine Robinson Inc.

MAXINI COLLEZIONE - Apparel–men's - A.F.M.K. Inc.

MAXINVERT - Food products - Gist-Brocades Food Ingredients Inc.

MAXION - Antacids - Miles Inc.

MAXIPANEL - Siding - Maxitile, Inc.

MAXIPEDIC - Mattresses - Simmons USA

MAXIPEN - Antibiotics - J.B. Roerig & Co.

MAXIPLANK - Siding - Maxitile, Inc.

MAXIPLAY - Recording label - Counter Culture

MAXIPREME - Rubber - Briner Paint Manufacturing Co. Inc.

MAXIPRO - Blood pressure apparatus - Graham-Field Inc.

MAXIRAY - Electronic equipment - General Electric Co.

MAXIRON - Vitamins and nutritional supplements ☆ - Ethical Nutrients

MAXIS - Electronic games - Sim-Business

MAXIS - Floor coverings–carpet and rugs ☆ - Customweave Carpets Inc.

MAXISHIELD - Diapers–disposable - Whitestone Products Inc.

MAXISOFT - Computer software - Maxisoft Corp.

MAXISONIC - Iron - Pick Five Imports, Inc.

MAXISORT - Computer software - Postal Technologies, Inc.

MAXISPRAY - Disinfectants - Henry Schein, Inc.

MAXISTRIP - Electrical equipment ☆ - Panamax

MAXIT - Computer hardware - Link Technologies, Inc.

MAXITHINS - Health care products - Tambrands Inc.

MAXITHINS - Hygienic product - Hospital Specialty Co.

MAXITONE - Musical instruments - C. Bruno & Son Inc.

MAXITORQ - Automotive parts and accessories - Carlyle Johnson Machine Co.

MAXITOX - Chemical preparations ☆ - Woolsey Marine Industries

MAXITROL - Ophthalmic goods - Alcon Laboratories, Inc.

MAXITRON - Pet products ☆ - Aquatronics-Filtronics

MAXIVAC - Veterinary pharmaceutical preparations - Schering-Plough Animal Health

MAXIVENT - Medical apparatus - Roberts Laboratories Inc.

MAXIVISION - Vitamins and nutritional supplements - Medical Ophthalmics, Inc.

MAXIVISIONS - Wallpaper - Innervisions Corp.

MAXIWASH - Washing machines–commercial - D.J. Giancola Exports, Inc.

MAXLITE - Bats–baseball - Easton Aluminum Inc.

MAXLITE - Lamp bulbs–fluorescent - SK America, Inc.

MAXLOAD - Computer peripheral equipment - Tops Engineering Corp.

MAXLOGIC - Computer peripheral equipment - Everex Systems, Inc.

MAXLYB - Optical scanners–computer - Maxoptix Corp.

MAXM - Computer software - International TeleManagement Corp.

MAXM EXPRESS - Computer software - MAXM Systems Corp.

MAXMATE - Computer software - Visioneer Communications, Inc.

MAXMORE - Shirts–polo - Rugby & Soccer Supply

MAXO 2 - Oxygen ☆ - Caire

MAXOLON - Pharmaceutical preparations - Smithkline Beecham Corp.

MAXON - Communications equipment–mobile - Maxon Electronics Corp. of America, Inc.

MAXON - Radio communications equipment - Maxcom Electronics Inc.

MAXOPAQUE - Paper ☆ - Howard Paper Mills Inc.

MAXOUT - Vitamins and nutritional supplements - Tishcon Corp.

MAXOVITE - Pharmaceutical preparations - Tyson & Associates, Inc.

MAXOVITE - Vitamins and nutritional supplements - Integrated Health, Inc.

MAXPAK - Ophthalmic apparatus - Allergan, Inc.

MAXPEED - Computer peripheral equipment - Maxpeed Corp.

MAXPLUS - Games - Bingo Card Minder Corp.

MAXPLY FORT - Sporting goods ☆ - Dunlop Maxfli Sports Corp.

MAXPOWER - Sporting goods - Dunlop Maxfli Sports Corp.

MAXPRO - Sporting goods - Proacq Corp.

MAXQ - Computer software - Maxq Technologies, Inc.

MAXRAM - Corkscrews ☆ - Franmara Co. Inc.

MAXRIDER - Prefabricated buildings–metal - Matrex Furniture Components, Inc.

MAX'S - Dog food - Nutritreat, Ltd.

MAX'S - Pickles - M.A. Gedney Co.

MAX'S - Sauces - O'Garvey Sauces, Inc.

MAX'S PURR-FECT CAT - Pet products - Max & Co.

MAXSENSE - Chemical preparations - Enzo Biochem, Inc.

MAXSIX - Computer software - Secureware, Inc.

MAXSPAN - Siding–insulating - Certainteed Corp. (Roofing Products Group)

MAXSPERSE - Chemical preparations - Chemax, Inc.

MAXSTAR - Lanterns–electric - Brinkmann Lighting Products

MAXTALK - Electronic modules - Ungermann-Bass, Inc.

MAXTAN - Brassieres (Bras) ☆ - Q-T Foundations Co. Inc.

MAXTEC - Fishing tackle - Wholesale Buying Group Inc.

MAXTECH - Adhesives and sealants - Premier Coatings, Inc.

MAXTECH - Amplifiers - Maxtech, Inc.

MAXTECH - Automotive parts and accessories - Auto Accessories of America

MAXTEMA - Goggles ☆ - Glendale Protective Technologies Inc.

MAXTEX - Wallpaper - S.A. Maxwell Co.

MAXTIME - Computer software - Toshiba America Information Systems, Inc.

MAXTONE - Drums–musical instruments - On-Site Music Group

MAXTOUCH - Sports rackets and accessories - Dunlop Maxfli Sports Corp.

MAXTRA - Shampoos - Mahdeen Laboratory

MAXTRAC - Cabinets - Datel, Inc.

MAXUM - Finishing agents - Advance Cleaning Products Inc.

MAXUM - Locks–padlocks - Medeco Security Locks, Inc.

MAXUM - Luggage racks–automotive - Maxum Automotive, Inc.

MAXUM - Paints - Premier Coatings, Inc.

MAXUM - Rackets–racquetball - Ektelon

MAXUM BLOCKER - Primers - Premier Coatings, Inc.

MAXVAC - Ophthalmic apparatus - Alcon Laboratories, Inc.

MAXVAR - Paints - McWhorter Technologies

MAXVIDEO - Projectors–photographic - Ammart

MAXVIEW - Goggles–safety - Sellstrom Manufacturing Co.

MAXVIS - Sporting goods - Oceanic

MAXWELL - Marine rigging ☆ - Imtra Corp.

MAXWELL - Paper ☆ - Howard Paper Mills Inc.

MAXWELL GREY - Clothing - Hub Distributing Inc.

MAXWELL HOUSE - Beverages - Maxwell House

MAXWELL HOUSE CAPPUCCINO - Coffee - Kraft Food Ingredients Corp.

MAXWELL HOUSE LITE - Coffee - Maxwell House

MAXWELL MANOR - Games ☆ - Avalon Hill Game Co.

MAXWELL STREET DELI - Meats–luncheon - Vienna Sausage Manufacturing Co.

MAXWELL STREET KLEZMER BAND - Musical instruments - Lori Lippitz

MAXWIN - Drums–musical instruments - N.H.F. Musical Merchandise Corp.

MAXWIN BY PEARL - Musical instrument accessories ☆ - Westheimer Corp.

MAXWOOD - Finishing agents - Duron, Inc.

MAXX - Beverages–malt - Pabst Brewing Co.

MAXX - Brushes–hair - Phillips Brush Corp.

MAXX - Prophylactics - Mayer Laboratories, Inc.

MAXX - Trading cards and stamps - J.R. Maxx, Inc.

MAXX - Transmission equipment–motor vehicle - Morse Controls

MAXX 2 MAGNETICS - Frames–eyeglass - Carrera Eyewear Corp.

MAXX GRIP - Knives–putty - Hyde Manufacturing Co.

MAXX-MASS - Vitamins and nutritional supplements - JBN Enterprises, Inc.

MAXX-MOUNT - Electronic equipment - Panor Corp.

MAXX-PURE - Chemical preparations - Teledyne Laars

MAXX RACE CARDS 1988-1992 - Trading cards and stamps - J.R. Maxx, Inc.

MAXX, THE - Vitamins and nutritional supplements - Head Start Vitamin Products

MAXX, THE - Alarm systems - Maxi-Guard

MAXXA - Guitars ☆ - Washburn International

MAXXALUM - Screws - Parker-Kalon Inc.

MAXXCARD - Computer software - Datamaxx Applied Technologies, Inc.

MAXXI - Diapers–disposable - Topco Associates, Inc.

MAXXI - Floor coverings - Dexter Corp. (Mercer Plastics Div.)

MAXXI-TRIACTION - Floor coverings - Mercer Products Co., Inc.

MAXXIMUM - Hair care products - Nexxus Products Co.

MAXXIS CLASSIC - Tires - Cheng Shin Rubber USA, Inc.

MAXXIS TOURING - Tires - Cheng Shin Rubber USA, Inc.

MAXXISTYLER - Hair care products - Nexxus Products Co.

MAXXON - Fibers–synthetic - Georgia-Bonded Fibers, Inc.

MAXXPAK - Containers - Maxxair Vent Corp.

MAXXUM - Boats–motor ☆ - Checkmate Boats Inc.

MAXXUM - Motor vehicles–motor homes - Coachmen Recreational Vehicle Co.

MAXXUM - Tires - Dunlop Tire Corp.

MAXXUM 3000 - Cameras - Minolta Corp.

MAXXUM 7000 - Cameras - Minolta Corp.

MAXXUM 9000 - Cameras - Minolta Corp.

MAXXUS - Surgical supplies - Johnson & Johnson

MAY - Frames–eyeglass - Rozin Optical Export Corp.

MAY - Milking machines - Randall May International

MAY AIRE - Ventilation equipment - Snappy A.D.P.

MAY-BARRIER - Dropcloths - D.C. May Corp.

MAY BOK - Beverages–malt ☆ - St. Killian Importing Co.

MAY COVE - Cosmetics - May Cove Inc.

MAY FLOWERS - Perfumes - Crabtree & Evelyn, Ltd.

MAY FLOWERS - Tableware–china ☆ - Lenox, Inc.

MAY FRESH - Food products - Detroit City Dairy Inc.

MAY GLO - Fruits and vegetables ☆ - Sun World International

MAY I? - Games - Milton Bradley Co.

MAY-LEE COLLECTION, THE - Costume jewelry - Continental Crafts Co.

MAY-LO-NAISE - Food products - Pet Inc.

MAY MEADOW - Dishes–china ☆ - Gorham Inc.

MAY MORN - Tableware–china ☆ - Lenox, Inc.

MAY-O-MATIC - Drafting supplies ☆ - Mayline/Hamilton

MAY QUEEN - Frames–picture - Terragrafics Inc.

MAY QUEEN - Hosiery ☆ - Sara Lee Corp.

MAYA - Cigars - Tropical Tobacco, Inc.

MAYA - Computer peripheral equipment - Electronic Data Systems Corp.

MAYA - Cosmetics - Central Trading Agency

MAYA - Dinnerware–glass ☆ - Cyclamen Studio

MAYA - Floor coverings - American Floor Products Co. Inc.

MAYA - Giftware - Sasaki

MAYA - Pumpkin seeds - American Import & Export Co. Inc.

MAYA - Seafood products–canned or cured - Ludwig Shrimp Co.

MAYA - Shoes - Edge Quest, Inc.

MAYA - Sporting goods - Markwort Sporting Goods Co.

MAYA AND ME FOR WRAPPER - Apparel–children's - Just for Wraps, Inc.

MAYA RAINBOW - Apparel and accessories - Maya Rainbow

MAYA YOGURT - Yogurt - Alta-Dena Certified Dairy, Inc.

MAYACAMAS - Soups–mixes - Mayacamas Fine Foods, Inc.

MAYACAMAS - Wines - Mayacamas Vineyards Inc.

MAYAMAIZE - Seasonings - Nile Spice Foods Inc.

MAYAN - Floor coverings ☆ - Tarkett, Inc.

MAYAN - Tiles–ceramic - Dal-Tile Corp.

MAYAN MIND BENDER - Apparel and accessories - Six Flags Theme Parks Inc.

☆ = Now out of production

MAYAN NECKLACE - Dinnerware–glass ☆ - Metlox Pottery Shoppe
MAYAN PRIDE - Fruits and vegetables - Central American Produce, Inc.
MAYAN SISAL - Floor coverings–carpet and rugs - Richmond Carpet Mills
MAYAN SWEETS - Onions - Keystone Fruit Marketing Inc.
MAYANA - Snack foods ☆ - Indian Foods Co.
MAYARI - Cosmetics - Mayra C. Donnell & Ariadne E. Donnell Partnership
MAYATEX - Wallpaper - Design Materials, Inc.
MAYBELLINE - Cosmetics - Maybelline Co.
MAYBELLINE - Tweezers - Maybelline Intermediate Co.
MAYBERRY - Furniture - Vaughan Furniture Co. Inc.
MAYBERRY - Wallpaper ☆ - Linden Street Gallery
MAYBERRY COLLECTION, THE - Candy ☆ - R.L. Products Corp.
MAYBERRY SQUARE - Furniture ☆ - Bassett Furniture Industries, Inc.
MAYBERRYS - Confections - Richardson Brands
MAYBRIK - Bricks - Gloria Enterprises Inc.
MAYBUD - Cheese - Dairy Fresh Products Co.
MAYCHILD - Food products - Hearty-Virginia Inc.
MAYCO - Lubricants - Castrol Industrial Inc.
MAYCO - Office supplies - Mayer Manufacturing Corp.
MAYCOM - Communications equipment–mobile - Maycom Communication
MAYDAY - Guns ☆ - Fie Corp.
MAYDAY - Radios–citizens' band - Kraco Enterprises Inc.
MAYDAY - Stain removers - Carpet Products Co.
MAYER - Cosmetics - Mayer Laboratories, Inc.
MAYER - Hosiery - Mayer/Berkshire Corp.
MAYER BROS. - Cider - Mayer Bros. Apple Products, Inc.
MAYES MASTER - Tools - Mayes Brothers Tool Manufacturing
MAYFAIR - Apparel–women's - Lily of France Inc.
MAYFAIR - Bedding–linen - Dan River Inc.
MAYFAIR - Candles ☆ - Will & Baumer, Inc.
MAYFAIR - Candlesticks - H. Wittur & Co.
MAYFAIR - Cleaning preparations - Bloch/New England, Inc.
MAYFAIR - Cookies - Nabisco Foods Group
MAYFAIR - Dairy products - Mayfair Ice Cream Inc.
MAYFAIR - Dinnerware–plastic ☆ - Brookpark Plastics Inc.
MAYFAIR - Doors–garage ☆ - Raynor Manufacturing Co.
MAYFAIR - Drums–musical instruments ☆ - Grossman Music Corp.
MAYFAIR - Fans–electric - Hunter Fan Co.
MAYFAIR - Floor coverings ☆ - Azrock Commercial Flooring
MAYFAIR - Floor coverings–carpet and rugs - Atlas Carpet Mills Inc.
MAYFAIR - Floor coverings–carpet and rugs - Glen Eden Wool Carpets
MAYFAIR - Floor coverings–carpet and rugs ☆ - Dorsett Carpet Mills Inc.
MAYFAIR - Fruits–dried - Mayfair Packing Co.
MAYFAIR - Furniture ☆ - Athens Furniture Industries Inc.
MAYFAIR - Glassware–household ☆ - Knobler International Ltd.
MAYFAIR - Handbags - Sara Lee Corp.
MAYFAIR - Lamps ☆ - Lamplight Farms, Inc.
MAYFAIR - Luggage - Airway Industries, Inc.
MAYFAIR - Luggage ☆ - Hartmann Luggage Co.
MAYFAIR - Paper–gift wrap - Papercraft Inc.
MAYFAIR - Rings–jewelry - Artcarved Inc.
MAYFAIR - Stationery ☆ - Berkshire Stationery Inc.
MAYFAIR - Tableware–china ☆ - Lenox, Inc.
MAYFAIR - Toilet seats - Bemis Manufacturing Co.
MAYFAIR - Wallpaper - Forbo Wallcoverings Inc.
MAYFAIR - Wallpaper - Mayfair Wallcoverings
MAYFAIR - Watches - Accutime Watch Corp.
MAYFAIR 10 - Wallpaper ☆ - Mayfair Wallcoverings
MAYFAIR LTD. - Apparel and accessories - Piedmont Industries Inc.
MAYFAIR PLACE - Floor coverings–carpet and rugs - Atlas Carpet Mills Inc.
MAYFAIRE GOLD ACCENT - Flatware - Yamazaki Tableware Inc.
MAYFIELD - Dinnerware–glass - Royal China & Porcelain Companies Inc.
MAYFIELD - Furniture ☆ - Lane Co. Inc.
MAYFIELD - Sinks–metal - Kohler Co.
MAYFIELD - Wallpaper - Vymura
MAYFIELD PUBLISHING - Computer software - Mayfield Publishing Co.
MAYFLORA - Herbal products - Mayflora Products, Inc.
MAYFLOWER - Bathtubs–enameled - Kohler Co.
MAYFLOWER - Coffee - Kobrick's Coffee Co. Inc.
MAYFLOWER - Dishes–earthenware ☆ - Denby USA Limited
MAYFLOWER - Dishes–earthenware ☆ - Royal China & Porcelain Companies Inc.
MAYFLOWER - Flatware - Kirk Stieff Co.
MAYFLOWER - Floor coverings–carpet and rugs - Milliken & Co. Inc.
MAYFLOWER - Ships–sailing vessels ☆ - Snark Boats
MAYFLOWER - Tiles–ceramic - United States Ceramic Tile Co.

MAYFLOWER - Wines - Chicama Vineyards
MAYFLOWER BOOKS - Publisher's imprints ☆ - Smithmark Publishers
MAYFLOWER GLASS - Giftware - H.C. Meyers Co.
MAYFLOWERS - Dinnerware–glass - Nikko Ceramics Inc.
MAYFRESH - Chili–canned ☆ - Arden Group Inc.
MAYIM CHAIM - Beverages–carbonated - Great Lakes Beverages Corp.
MAYLE INSTINCT - Apparel–athletic - Monte Gillespie
MAYLINE - Drafting supplies - Mayline/Hamilton
MAYLING - Furniture - Union National Inc.
MAYLITE - Frames–eyeglass - May Optical Co. Inc.
MAYMONT - Clocks - Ridgeway Clock Co.
MAYMONT - Floor coverings–carpet and rugs - Customweave Carpets Inc.
MAYMONT - Floor coverings–carpet and rugs ☆ - World Carpets, Inc.
MAYNARD - Cosmetics - Maynard Inc.
MAYNARD - Firearms, accessories, and parts - Gaintwist Barrel Co.
MAYNARD - Sporting goods - Brunswick Corp.
MAYNOR - Vinegar - Specialty Brands Inc.
MAYO SPRUCE - Apparel and accessories ☆ - Tultex Corp.
MAYOACCESS - Software - Mayo Foundation
MAYOKNIFE - Kitchen utensils–aluminum - Compac Industries Inc.
MAYOLITH - Ophthalmic goods - Styl-Rite Optical Manufacturing Co., Inc.
MAYONADE - Salad dressings–bottled - Nalley's Fine Foods
MAYONESA - Measuring and dispensing pumps - Kraft Food Ingredients Corp.
MAYOQUEST - Chemical preparations - Mayo Chemical Co., Inc.
MAYOR - Frames–eyeglass - Liberty Optical Manufacturing Co.
MAYOR'S - Hair coloring preparations ☆ - Mayor Co.
MAYO'S CUT PLUG - Tobacco - American Tobacco Co.
MAYOTIC SUSPENSION - Pharmaceutical preparations ☆ - Merz Inc.
MAYPO - Cereal - American Home Food Products Inc.
MAYPOLE - Yarn ☆ - Oregon Worsted Co.
MAYPOLE DANCE - Educational materials - Twinson Co.
MAYRON - Frames–eyeglass - May Optical Co. Inc.
MAYROSE - Meat products–beef - Armour Swift-Eckrich
MAYSON'S - Beverages–carbonated - Mayson Food Products, Inc.
MAYSVILLE - Floor coverings–carpet and rugs - January and Wood Co. Inc.
MAYTAG - Appliance parts - Maytag Corp.
MAYTEX - Fabrics–linen - Maytex Mills
MAYTIME - Frames–eyeglass - May Optical Co. Inc.
MAYTIME BOUQUET - Bedding–linen - Dan River Inc.
MAYTOP - Frames–eyeglass - May Optical Co. Inc.
MAYTREX - Pharmaceutical preparations ☆ - Merz Inc.
MAYTRON - Refrigerants - Mondy Global, Inc.
MAYWINE - Beverages–alcohol - Old Europe Inc.
MAYWOLFIA - Pharmaceutical preparations ☆ - Merz Inc.
MAYWOOD - Doors–wood - Maywood Inc.
MAYWOOD - Dusters - Maywood Industries Inc.
MAYWOOD - Flatware - Kirk Stieff Co.
MAYWOOD - Furniture - Dinaire Corp.
MAYWOOD - Glassware–household ☆ - Lenox Crystal, Inc.
MAYWOOD - Tableware–china - Lenox, Inc.
MAYWOOD CLASSIC - Furniture - Dinaire Corp.
MAYWOOD SATIN - Flatware - Kirk Stieff Co.
MAZ - Rings–jewelry - W. & R. Mazza & Sons Inc.
MAZAGRAN - Beverages - North American Coffee Partnership
MAZAGRAN - Beverages–carbonated - Starbucks Corp.
MAZANOR - Pharmaceutical preparations - Wyeth-Ayerst Laboratories
MAZARIN - Flatware - Couzon USA
MAZARINE - Tableware–china - Pfaltzgraff Investment Co.
MAZATLAN FOODS - Seafood products–fresh or frozen - Marquez Brothers Mexican Imports, Inc.
MAZAY - Toys - Pleazure Concepts, Inc.
MAZDA - Motor vehicles–automobiles - Mazda Motor of America Inc.
MAZDA MIATA - Toys–electronic ☆ - Bird Bromiticous Inc.
MAZDAZNAN - Audio and video tapes - Mazdaznan Elector
MAZE - Apparel and accessories - Double B
MAZE - Floor coverings–carpet and rugs ☆ - Regal Rugs Inc.
MAZE - Hardware - Maze Nails
MAZE - Recording label - Maze Records
MAZE - Tiles–ceramic - United States Ceramic Tile Co.
MAZE CRAZE - Video games - Atari Games Corp.
MAZE FACTORY - Publisher's imprints - Steven Andrew Cecil
MAZE N' NEST - Pet products - Boomer Ball
MAZE RUNNER - Toys–electronic - Interactive Network, Inc.
MAZE 'TIL YA CRAZE - Games - Compoz-A-Puzzle Inc.
MAZEL - Recording label - Periscope Record Co.
MAZELAYGUE - Fruits–candied ☆ - Liberty Richter Inc.

☆ = Now out of production

MAZELCUBE - Novelty items - Always Changing, Inc.
MAZEMADE - Hardware - Maze Nails
MAZEMATICS - Games - Brown and Bigelow Inc.
MAZERONE - Games ☆ - Mego Financial Corp.
MAZES IN STAGES - Toys - Tedco Inc.
MAZETTI - Food products - B. Westergaard & Co. Inc.
MAZINE - Pharmaceutical preparations - C.S. Ruckstuhl Co. Inc.
MAZO LERCH - Fruits and vegetables - Mazo-Lerch Co. Inc.
MAZO LERCH GREEN STANDARD - Fruits and vegetables - Mazo-Lerch Co. Inc.
MAZO LERCH RED EXTRA STANDARD - Fruits and vegetables - Mazo-Lerch Co. Inc.
MAZO LERCH WHITE FANCY/CHOICE - Fruits and vegetables - Mazo-Lerch Co. Inc.
MAZOLA - Vegetable oil - CPC International Inc.
MAZOLA LIGHT - Margarine - CPC International Inc.
MAZOLA NO STICK - Margarine - CPC International Inc.
MAZOLA RIGHT BLEND - Vegetable oil - CPC International Inc.
MAZON - Pharmaceutical preparations - Smithkline Beecham Corp.
MAZURI - Exotic and zoological animal food - Purina Mills, Inc.
MAZURKA - Apparel and accessories ☆ - Kellwood Co.
MAZURKA - Fabrics ☆ - Gretchen Bellinger Inc.
MAZURKA - Pickles - San-Del Packing Co.
MAZZA VINEYARDS - Wines - Mazza Vineyards Inc.
MAZZEI - Water purification systems - Mazzei Injector Corp.
MAZZETTA CO. - Seafood products–fresh or frozen - Mazzetta Co.
MAZZETTI - Fruits–candied - Liberty Richter Inc.
MAZZIO'S - Pizzas–mixes - Mazzio's Corp.
MAZZO - Surfboards - Mazzo, Inc.
MAZZOLI - Coffee - Mazzoli Coffee Inc.
MAZZONE'S - Ice cream - Mazzone Enterprises Inc.
MB - Beer ☆ - Marie Brizard Wines & Spirits, USA
MB - Caps–baseball - Milwaukee Bucks, Inc.
MB - Jewelry - M'lou Brubaker
MB - Stoves–gas ☆ - Max Burton Enterprises Inc.
MB-5 - Plastics film - Viskase Corp.
MB AE 90 - Concrete–mixture - Master Builders Inc.
MB CAP - Roofing materials - Consolidated Fiber Glass Products Co.
MB CAP 100 - Roofing materials - Consolidated Fiber Glass Products Co.
M.B. EDUCATION - Artists' materials ☆ - Milton Bradley Co.
MB KIDS CLUB - Apparel–children's - Maison Blanche, Inc.
MB QUART - Audio equipment - MB Quart Electronics USA, Inc.
MB SHUTTLES - Automotive parts and accessories - Walter Odemer Co. Inc.
MB5 - Motorcycles ☆ - American Honda Motor Co. Inc. (Acura Div.)
MBA - Apparel and accessories - Men's Wearhouse
M.B.A. - Frames–eyeglass ☆ - Universal/Univis Inc.
MBA - Hardware - Michael Bondy Inc.
MBA FORUMS - Educational materials - Graduate Management Admission Council
MBC - Apparel and accessories - Oxford Industries, Inc.
MBC - Computers–personal ☆ - Sanyo Fisher (USA) Corp.
MBC - Electronics equipment - Marty Bahn & Co.
MBC - Hardware - Massoud & Bros, Co., Ltd.
MBC - Hearing aids ☆ - Magnatone Hearing Aid Corp.
MBC - Rivets–metal - Textron Aerospace Fasteners
MBC MOVING BLADE CARTRIDGES - Razors - American Safety Razor Co.
MBC RAZOR - Razors - American Safety Razor Co.
MBD - Musical instrument accessories - Tamarkin Co.
MBG - Diamond powder - General Electric Co.
MBI - Pharmaceutical preparations - Molecular Biosystems Inc.
M.B.I. - Photo albums - M.B.I. Merchandise Industries Inc.
MBL - Fuel additives - Bell Additives, Inc.
MBM - Office supplies - Michael Business Machines
MBM BEADS - Beads - Unnatural Resources Inc.
MBOSS - Computer hardware - Scitex Digital Video, Inc.
MBP - Apparel and accessories - M.B.P. Neckwear Corp.
MBS - Diamond powder - General Electric Co.
MBSREPO - Computer software - Horizon Real-Time Systems, Inc.
MBT - Broth - Borden, Inc.
MBVR - Concrete–mixture - Master Builders Inc.
MBX - Chemical preparations - Metabolix Inc.
MBX 2500 - Tools–power-driven - XI International, Ltd.
MC - Artists' materials ☆ - LogEtronics Corp.
MC - Cabinets - H. Wilson Co.
MC - Cameras ☆ - Canon USA, Inc.
MC - Jewelry - Master Craft Jewelry Co., Inc.

MC - Jewelry - QVC, Inc.
MC - Pigments - Radiant Color Div.
MC - Tiles–enamel - Federal Tile Imports Inc.
MC - Washers–metal - Wrought Washer Manufacturing, Inc.
MC-1 - Audio equipment - ADA Signal Processors Inc.
MC-1 - Motor vehicles - Municipal Industries
MC-500 - Chemical preparations - Monogram Sanitation Co.
MC-500 - Deodorizers - Mag Aerospace Industries, Inc.
MC 501 - Chemical preparations - Neozyme International, Inc.
MC 900 FT JESUS - Paper products - Mark Griffin
MC-1000 - Chemical preparations - Monogram Sanitation Co.
MC-2000 - Chemical preparations - Monogram Sanitation Co.
MC-2000 - Deodorizers - Mag Aerospace Industries, Inc.
MC CERA - Glassware–household - Ceraglass Inc.
MC DESIGN/ESTIMATING - Computer software - Management Computer Controls, Inc.
MC FAST - Boats–motor ☆ - Monark Boat Co.
M.C. FREE - Paints - Allpro Corp.
MC II - Apparel–women's ☆ - Malouf Co.
MC-IOL - Medical apparatus - Emmetropia, Inc.
MC JEANS - Jeans–men's - Klayman Pants Co.
MC-LEAD STRIP - Paint removers - International Protective Coatings Corp.
MC MASTER - Circuit boards - Aox Inc.
MC MATARI COOPER - Apparel and accessories - Matari Charles Cooper
MC MILLIN'S - Pies–fresh - Pet Inc.
MC/OF - Cables - WPFY, Inc.
MC/OS - Computers - Mercury Computer Systems Inc.
MC PET - Pet products ☆ - Pacific Industries Inc.
MC PIC - Computer software - Magnum Software Corp.
MC POLY-E - Twine - Malow Corp.
MC POWER - Footwear - Christian Michael & Power, Inc.
MC WALKER - Medical apparatus - Smith & Nephew Richards, Inc.
MC2 - Computerized entertainment devices - Dean Freiwald
MC2 - Electrical equipment - Crane Nuclear, Inc.
MC2 - Radio communications equipment - Motorola, Inc. (Land Mobile Products Sector)
MC² - Vitamins and nutritional supplements - Schiff Products, Inc.
MC2 - Washers–metal - Wrought Washer Manufacturing, Inc.
MC2M - Integrated microcircuits - Valtronic USA, Inc.
MC3 - Computer software - Medical Cost Containment Consultants, Inc.
MC860 - Computers - Mercury Computer Systems Inc.
MC2000 - Cooking utensils–aluminum - West Bend Co.
MCA - Music–sheet - Hal Leonard Corp.
MCA - Recording label - MCA Universal Studios
MCAA - Cables - General Cable Industries, Inc.
MCADAM - Cheese - Dairy Fresh Products Co.
MCADAMS - Baking chocolate - Grace Cocoa Associates, L.P.
MCADAMS - Locks–coin-operated - United States Distilled Products Co.
MCADAMS PREMIUM CANADIAN WHISKEY - Whiskey - United States Distilled Products Co.
MCAFEE - Computer programs - Mcafee Associates, Inc.
MCALLISTER - Ophthalmic goods - Embassy Creations Inc.
MCALLISTER - Shoes ☆ - Allen-Edmonds Shoe Corp.
MCARTHUR - Dairy products - Dean Foods Co.
MCARTHUR - Dairy products - McArthur Dairy Inc.
MCAULEY'S POTPOURRI - Deodorizers - Mcauley's, Inc.
MCB - Apparel and accessories - MCB Sportswear, Inc.
MCB - Jewelry - Mirjam Butz-Brown
MCBACK - Seat covers - McCarty's Sacro-Ease
MCBACON DELUXE - Sandwiches–prepackaged - Mcdonald's Corp.
MCBEE - Packaging–paper - McBee Loose Leaf Binders
MCBRIAR - Apparel–men's - Drummond Knitwear Ltd.
MCBRIDE - Leather goods - Smith-Worthington Saddlery Co. Inc.
MCBURNEY'S - Whiskey - SPAR Inc.
MCCADAM - Cheese - McCadam Cheese
MCCAIN - Vegetables–frozen - McCain Foods Inc.
MCCAIN ELLIO'S - Pizzas–frozen - McCain Ellio's Foods, Inc.
MCCAJUN - Food products - Mcdonald's Corp.
MCCALL - Gasoline - McCall Oil and Chemical Co.
MCCALL - Refrigerators - McCall Refrigeration
MCCALLS - Beverages–alcohol - Montebello Brands, Inc.
MCCALL'S - Patterns–clothing - Mccall Pattern Co.
MCCALLS/REBOUNDER - Sporting goods - Sorensen-Christian Industries Inc.
MCCANN'S - Cereal ☆ - Liberty Richter Inc.
MCCANNS - Oats–rolled or meal - Bewley Irish Imports
MCCARTHY FARMS - Fertilizers - Agro-Fibers, Inc.

☆ = Now out of production

MCCARTY - Meat products–poultry - McCarty Foods Inc.
MCCARTY - Musical instruments - Paul Reed Smith Guitars
MCCARTY FOODS - Food products - McCarty Farms Inc.
MCCASTLE STUDIO - Recording label - Toro'na International
MCCAULEY'S - Animal feed supplements - McCauley Brothers Inc.
MCCAULEY'S CANADIAN - Whiskey - Sazerac Co. Inc.
MCCAW - Telephones - McCaw Cellular Communications, Inc.
MCCHICKEN - Sandwiches–prepackaged - Mcdonald's Corp.
MCCLAREN - Tires - Bridgestone/Firestone, Inc.
MCCLASSIC - Tape recorders–cassette ☆ - Lanier Voice Products
MCCLEARY - Snack foods - McCleary Inc.
MCCLELANDS, THE - Figurines ☆ - Reco International Corp.
MCCLELLAN - Pet products - Berolina Imports
MCCLELLAND - Figurines ☆ - Reco International Corp.
MCCLOSKEY - Paints - McCloskey Corp.
MCCLOUD - Frames–eyeglass - U.S. Optical Frame Co.
MCCLURES - Cocoa–powders or mixes ☆ - K.H. McClure & Co. Inc.
MCCOL - Beverages–carbonated ☆ - Ginseng Up Corp.
MCCOLLS GOLD LABEL - Beverages–alcohol - Star Liquor Imports Inc.
MC.COM - Computers - Mercury Computer Systems Inc.
MCCONNELL - Luggage - McConnell Co.
MCCONNON - Health care products ☆ - Mackwin Co.
MCCORD - Gaskets - AE Clevite Inc.
MCCORD, THE - Golfing equipment - U.S. Grips, Inc.
MCCORMACK - Audio equipment - Mod Squad Inc.
MCCORMICK - Beverages–alcohol - Mccormick Distilling Co., Inc.
MCCORMICK - Biscuits - Haddon House Food Products Inc.
MCCORMICK - Crackers ☆ - Christie, Brown & Co.
MCCORMICK - Food products - Golden West Foods Inc.
MCCORMICK - Spices and extracts - McCormick & Co., Inc.
MCCORMICK BLEND - Beverages–alcohol - Mccormick Distilling Co., Inc.
MCCORMICK CANADIAN - Beverages–alcohol - Mccormick Distilling Co., Inc.
MCCORMICK COLLECTION - Farm machinery - McCormick & Co., Inc.
MCCORMICK GIRL - Beverages–alcohol - Mccormick Distilling Co., Inc.
MCCORMICK GOLD LABEL - Beverages–alcohol - Mccormick Distilling Co., Inc.
MCCORMICK GREEN LABEL - Beverages–alcohol - Mccormick Distilling Co., Inc.
MCCORMICK HOMESTYLE - Seasonings - McCormick & Co., Inc.
MCCORMICK/SCHILLING - Spices and extracts - McCormick & Co., Inc.
MCCORMICK/SCHILLING MAKES IT - Spices and extracts - McCormick & Co., Inc.
MCCORMICK SIGNATURE X - Beverages–alcohol - Mccormick Distilling Co., Inc.
MCCORMICKS - Seasonings ☆ - Tidelands Sales Co. Inc.
MCCOWANS - Confections - Morris National Inc.
MCCOY'S - Garden equipment - J.T. Eaton and Co.
MCCOY'S - Health care products - McCoy's Products Inc.
MCCOY'S CAKE & PIE SHOP - Cakes - McCoy's Cake & Pie Shop, Inc.
MCCRACKEN'S - Snack foods - Pepsico, Inc.
MCCRARY - Tools - Multt Metals
MCCRAW'S - Candy - McCraw Candies Inc.
MCCRYSTAL'S - Snuff - G.A. Georgopulo & Co. Inc.
MCCS - Computer software - Fannie Mae
MCCUBBIN - Hosiery - McCubbin Hosiery Inc.
MCCUBBIN CLASSICS - Hosiery–men's - McCubbin Hosiery Inc.
MCCUBBIN FOR KIDS - Hosiery–children's - McCubbin Hosiery Inc.
MCCULLOCH - Saws–chain - McCulloch Corp.
MCCULLOCH MAC CAT - Saws–chain - McCulloch Corp.
MCCULLOCH MAC VAC - Vacuum cleaners and accessories - McCulloch Corp.
MCCULLOCH MOTORS MCC - Saws–chain - McCulloch Corp.
MCCULLOCH'S CANADIAN - Water–bottled or canned - New Wave Beverage
MCCULLOH SPACE-DISTANCE ROPE - Educational materials - Karen McCulloh and Associates, Inc.
MCCULLOUGH'S - Pet products ☆ - Geo. W. Hill and Co., Inc.
MCCUTCHEON'S - Fruit drinks–bottled or canned - McCutcheon Apple Product
MCD - Bandages–surgical - Medical Concepts Development, Inc.
MCD - Cigarettes - Nat Sherman, Inc.
MCD - Computer software - FYI Inc.
MCD - Dehumidifiers - MCD, Inc.
MCD LIGHTS - Cigarettes - Nat Sherman, Inc.
MCDAN - Fabrics - Dan River Inc.
MCDANIEL'S - Coffee - Moran Foods, Inc.

MCDAVID - Orthopedic supports - McDavid Knee Guard Inc.
MCDONALD - Artists' materials - Sureguard, Inc.
MCDONALD - Dairy products - McDonald Dairy Co.
MCDONALD - Fruits and vegetables - Oceana Canning Co.
MCDONALD - Office supplies - McDonald Products
MCDONALD PORTABLE BUILDINGS - Storage buildings - James William McDonald
MCDONALDS - Candy - McDonalds Home Made Candy
MCDONALD'S RACE TEAM CHALLENGE - Toys–automobiles ☆ - Life-Like Products Inc.
MCDONNELL - Coffee - New England Coffee Co.
MCDOUGAL LITTELL - Computer software - Houghton Mifflin Co.
MCDOWELL - Recording label - McDowell Records
MCDOWELL CELLARS - Wines - McDowell Cellars Inc.
MCDOWELL VALLEY VINEYARDS - Wines - McDowell Cellars Inc.
MCDUFF - Appliance parts - Sav-a-Stop Inc.
MCDUFFS - Beverages–alcohol - White Rock Distilleries Inc.
MCDUGAL MCPRETZEL - Frozen soft pretzels ☆ - J & J Snack Foods Corp.
MCE - Computers - Motion Control Engineering, Inc.
MCE - Magnets - Magnetic Circuit Elements, Inc.
MCEASE - Chemical preparations - McGean-Broker, Inc.
MCELHANEY'S MASTER ADVOCATE SERIES - Educational materials - Professional Education Group, Inc.
MCEVERS - Food products - Gold Kist Inc.
MCEWAN'S EXPORT ALE - Beverages–malt - Scottish & Newcastle Importers Co.
MCEWAN'S SCOTCH ALE - Beverages–malt - Scottish & Newcastle Importers Co.
MCEXEC - Computers - Mercury Computer Systems Inc.
MCF - Chemical preparations - Metaullics Systems Co., L.P.
MCFADDEN - Eyeglasses - Art-Craft Optical Co.
MCFARLANE TOYS - Toys - TMP International, Inc.
MCGARVEY - Coffee - McGarvey Superior Coffee
MCGARVEY - Coffee - Saramar Corp.
MCGEE - Computer software - Lawrence Productions, Inc.
MCGEE - Fireplace equipment - McGee Brothers Co., Inc.
MCGEE SCHOOL DAYS - Computer software - Knowledge Adventure
MCGEE SERIES - Computer software ☆ - Knowledge Adventure
MCGILL - Sporting goods ☆ - Powell Skateboards
MCGILL'S - Horseradish ☆ - Silver Spring Gardens Inc.
MCGOWAN'S - Liqueurs - Shaw-Ross International Importers
MCGRAW-EDISON - Lighting fixtures - Cooper Industries, Inc.
MCGREGGOR - Hats - Miller Bros. Industries Inc.
MCGREGOR - Apparel and accessories - Mcgregor Corp.
MCGREGOR - Beverages–alcohol - White Rock Distilleries Inc.
MCGREGOR - Hats - Arlington Hat Co. Inc.
MCGREGOR - Underwear and nightwear - Nantucket Industries Inc.
MCGREGOR - Watches - M.Z. Berger & Co. Inc.
MCGREGOR FAMILY RECIPE - Hams - Cumberland Gap Provision Co.
MCGREGOR FOR BOYS - Shirts - Hampton Industries, Inc.
MCGREGOR STRAPLESS BOX, THE - Cartons–paperboard - McGregor Printing Corp.
MCGREGOR VINEYARD - Wines - McGregor Vineyard Winery
MCGREVOR - Paints - Magnet Paint & Shellac Co. Inc.
MCGRILLED CHICKEN - Chicken sandwich - Mcdonald's Corp.
MCGRUFF - Toys–stuffed - Commonwealth Toy and Novelty Co. Inc.
MCGUFFEY ANA - Dolls - Alexander Doll Co. Inc.
MCGUFFEY'S - Publisher's imprints - International Thomson Publishing Inc.
MCGUIGAN BROTHERS - Wines - Barden E. Stevenot
MCGUIRE-NICHOLAS - Apparel and accessories - McGuire-Nicholas Co., Inc.
MCGUIRE'S - Garden equipment - Geo. W. McGuire Co. Inc.
MCGUIRES ORIGINAL - Beverages–alcohol - Consolidated Distilled Products Inc.
MCH6 - Computers - Mercury Computer Systems Inc.
MCH9 - Computers - Mercury Computer Systems Inc.
MCHENRY VINEYARD - Wines - McHenry Vineyard
MCHOAGIE - Sandwiches–prepackaged - Mcdonald's Corp.
MCI - Handbags - Larry Friedman Inc.
M.C.I. - Jewelry–precious - Morton Cohen Inc.
MCI - Rustproofing compounds - Cortec Corp.
MCI IN A BOX - Computer software - MCI Communications Corp.
MCI MAIL EXPRESS - Computer software - MCI Communications Corp.
MCI PERSPECTIVE - Computer software - MCI International
MCI PERSPECTIVE CUSTOM QUERY - Computer software - MCI Communications Corp.
MCI VIDEOPHONE - Telephone - MCI Communications Corp.

☆ = Now out of production

MCILCHERE - Bakery products - H. Hamstra & Co.

MCILHENNY CO. TABASCO PEPPER SAUCE - Apparel and accessories ☆ - McIlhenny Co.

MCILHENNY FARMS - Food products ☆ - McIlhenny Co.

MCINERNEYS - Beverages - North American Beverage Co.

MCINTAKE - Valves–intake - Virgil M. McGuire, Jr.

MCINTOSH - Audio equipment - McIntosh Laboratory, Inc.

MCJ - Jewelry - Michael's Creative Jewelry Inc.

MCKAY - Pharmaceutical preparations - Bickmore Inc.

MCKAY - Welding equipment - Hobart Brothers Co.

MCKAY EMPIRE - Cultivators–agricultural - Empire Plow Co. Inc.

MCKAY'S - Seasonings - Dismat Corp.

MCKAY'S MAXLIN - Veterinary pharmaceutical preparations - Bickmore Inc.

MCKEE - Doors–metal - McKee Door, Inc.

MCKEE BRANDS - Food products - McKee Foods Corp.

MCKEE CRAFT SPECIAL - Boats ☆ - Lanness K. McKee & Co.

MCKEE DOOR - Doors–metal - McKee Door, Inc.

MCKEEVER - Publisher's imprints - Hayes Brothers Printing

MCKEEVER & DANLEE - Bakery products - Mckeever & Danlee Confectionery Co.

MCKEM - Crock pots ☆ - Wonderknit

MCKENNA'S BRITTLE - Candy - McKenna's Brittle

MCKENZIE - Boats ☆ - Valco Aluminum Boats

MCKENZIE - Food products - Gerawan Foods Inc.

MCKENZIE - Health care products - Orthopedic Physical Therapy Products

MCKENZIE - Prefabricated buildings–wood - Georgia-Pacific Corp.

MCKENZIE FARMS - Bakery products - United States Bakery

MCKENZIE GOLD KING - Food products - Curtice-Burns Foods, Inc.

MCKENZIES - Cigar boxes–wood - Consolidated Cigar Corp.

MCKENZIE'S - Food products - Curtice-Burns Foods, Inc.

MCKENZIE'S - Fruits and vegetables - Southern Frozen Foods Inc.

MCKENZIE'S NATURAL CHOICE - Food products ☆ - Curtice-Burns Foods, Inc.

MCKEON - Doors–metal - McKeon Rolling Steel Door Co., Inc.

MCKERNAN - Surgical instruments - Laparoscopic Laser Surgery, P.C.

MCKIDS - Apparel–children's - Sears, Roebuck and Co.

MCKIDS - Skin care products - Mennen Co.

MCKIE - Markers–felt-tip - Zebra Pen Corp.

MCKINLEY - Floor coverings–carpet and rugs ☆ - Karastan-Bigelow Inc.

MCKINLEY - Frames–eyeglass - May Optical Co. Inc.

MCKINLEY - Glassware–household ☆ - Lenox Crystal, Inc.

MCKINLEY - Tableware–china - Lenox, Inc.

MCKINLEY ACCENTS - Floor coverings–carpet and rugs ☆ - Karastan-Bigelow Inc.

MCKINNEY - Confections - Hygeia Dairy Co.

MCKINNEY - Hardware - McKinney Products Co.

MCKINSEY & CO. - Computer software - McKinsey Holdngs, Inc.

MCKNIGHT - Fishing lures - Triple Teazer Co.

MCKNIGHT - Fishing lures - Yakima Bait Co.

MCKNIT - Bags–plastic - McDowell Industries, Inc.

MCL - Apparel and accessories - My Crazy Life

MCL - Food products - Mescol Corp.

MCLAUGHLIN - Excavators - Mclaughlin Manufacturing Co.

MCLAUGHLIN BORING SYSTEMS - Tools–boring - Mclaughlin Manufacturing Co.

MCLEAN DELUXE - Food products - Mcdonald's Corp.

MCLUBE - Chemical preparations - Mcgee Industries Inc.

MCMAHON - Fasteners–snap - Outdoor Technologies Group

MCMASTER - Floor coverings–carpet and rugs ☆ - Karastan-Bigelow Inc.

MCMASTERS - Whiskey - Heublein, Inc.

MCMILLIN - Fruits and vegetables - Pet Inc.

MCMILLIN'S LUNCH BOX - Desserts - Pet Inc.

MCMULLEN BOOKS - Publisher's imprints - Farrar, Straus and Giroux Inc.

MCNALLY - Apparel–women's - Montgomery Ward & Co. Inc.

MCNALLY WELLMAN - Machinery - Svedala Industries, Inc.

MCNEIL - Frames–picture - D & L Stained Glass Supply, Inc.

MCNEILUS - Motor vehicles - McNeilus Truck and Manufacturing, Inc.

MCNESS - Farm machinery - Furst-McNess Co.

MCP - Apparel and accessories - MCP

MCP - Paper ☆ - Rediform

MCP - Tires–bicycles - Aero-Lastic MCP Tires, Inc.

MCPEARSON - Apparel and accessories - McPearson Sportswear of America, Inc.

MCPHAIL - Pianos - Kohler & Campbell Inc.

MCPHILBEN - Lighting fixtures - Thomas Industries Inc.

MCPRETZEL - Frozen pretzels ☆ - J & J Snack Foods Corp.

MCQUAY-NORRIS - Automotive parts and accessories - Krizman International Inc.

MCQUIK'S OIL LUBE - Motor vehicle parts and accessories - Quaker State Oil Refining Corp.

MCR - Recording label - Charta Records

MCRAY'S - Cosmetics - L.T. York Co.

MCRETYPE - Computer software - Micrologic Software Inc.

MCROBERTS - Seafood products–fresh or frozen - McRoberts Sales Co.

MCS - Audio equipment - J.C. Penney Co., Inc.

MCS - Drum-cleaning/polishing product - Box Maker

MCS - Electronic equipment - J.L. Cooper Electronics

MCS - Hair care products - Hanah Beauty & Health Inc.

MCS - Pagers - Monitor Crystal Service

MCS 2000 - Radio communications equipment - Motorola, Inc. (Land Mobile Products Sector)

MCS-III - Health care products - Meyer Equipment Co. Inc.

MCS MODULA-2 - Computer software - Interface Technologies Inc.

MCSORLEY'S ALE - Beverages–malt - The Stroh Brewery Co.

MCSORLEY'S BLACK & TAN - Beverages–malt - The Stroh Brewery Co.

MCSORT - Office supplies - McDonald Products

MCSTEVEN'S - Beverages - McSteven's

M.C.T. - Hearing aids - Innovative Technology Sciences, Inc.

MCT - Paints - Multicolor Specialties Inc.

MCT - Pharmaceutical preparations - Bristol-Myers Squibb Co.

MCT - Twine - Malow Corp.

M.C.T. - Vitamins and nutritional supplements - Allergy Resources/Ecologic

MCT MAINFRAME CLASS TAPE - Electrical equipment - Overland Data, Inc.

MCTOY COMPANY - Shirts - Mcdonald's Corp.

MCU - Telephone apparatus - Tollgrade Communications, Inc.

MCV - Filters–water - Umpqua Research Co.

MCV6 - Computers - Mercury Computer Systems Inc.

MCV9 - Computers - Mercury Computer Systems Inc.

MCWILLIAM'S BARWANG - Wines ☆ - Parliament Import Co.

MCWILLIAM'S ESTATE HANWOOD - Wines ☆ - Parliament Import Co.

MCWOODS - Window coverings - Shades of Color Inc.

MCX - Golfing equipment ☆ - MacGregor Golf Co.

MCX - Modular computer terminals - Network Computing Devices Inc.

MCZEE - Apparel and accessories - Microsoft Corp.

MD - Adhesives and sealants - Dymax Corp.

MD - Adhesives and sealants - Macklanburg-Duncan Co.

MD - Belts–apparel - Martin Dingman

MD - Brushes - Milwaukee Dustless Brush Co.

MD - Caulking compounds ☆ - Macklanburg-Duncan Co.

MD - Cosmetics - Alleghany Pharmacal Corp.

MD - Jewelry - Melanie Diedrich

MD - Medical apparatus - Relaxacizor Products Inc.

MD - Paper–toilet - Georgia-Pacific Corp.

MD 7 - Soap - Dial Corp.

MD-68 - Firearms, accessories, and parts - Attenuation Technology, Inc.

MD-90 - Aircraft - McDonnell Douglas Corp.

MD 500E - Aircraft–helicopters - McDonnell Douglas Helicopter Co.

MD ANDERSON CANCER CTR. CHILDREN'S ART PROJECT - Greeting cards - Board of Regents of the University of Texas

MD EXPLORER - Aircraft–helicopters - McDonnell Douglas Helicopter Co.

M.D. FORMULATIONS - Cosmetics and hair-care products - Allergan Skin Care

M.D. FORTE - Cosmetics - Allergan Elite, Inc.

MD FORTE - Skin care products - Allergan Skin Care

MD-II - Electronic equipment - Peavey Electronics Corp.

MD KIDS' PRINTS - Bathroom tissue - Georgia-Pacific Corp.

MD OVERLAY 1+1 - Plywood - Hardel Mutual Plywood Corp.

MD PLUS - Consulting services - Larry Weidel

MD SYSTEM - Building materials - Dryvit Systems, Inc.

MD*4 - Lighting fixtures - Genlyte Group Inc.

MDC - Organs–musical instrument - Allen Organ Co.

MDC-2010 - Computer software - Datamaxx Applied Technologies, Inc.

MDC-2020 - Computer peripheral equipment - Datamaxx Applied Technologies, Inc.

MDC BLANC MADRID NOI'R AMERICA - Apparel and accessories - Toni J. Prados

MDCC-2010 - Computer software - Datamaxx Applied Technologies, Inc.

MDCC-2020 - Computer software - Datamaxx Applied Technologies, Inc.

MDH - Skin care products - Dermac Laboratories, Inc.

MDI - Steel products - A. Finkl & Sons Co.

MDJ - Jewelry - Jackie Suberi, Inc.

MDL - Water–mineral - Aqua Pure Drinking Waters

☆ = Now out of production

MDM - Hair care products ✰ - Moro Beauty College
MDM CUSTOM - Audio equipment - Digital Audio Labs, Inc.
MDNET - Computer software - Medicus, Inc.
M.D.O. - Plywood - Harbor Sales Co.
MDP - Coats–women's - M.D.P. Designs, Ltd.
MDP - Computer software - Early, Cloud & Co.
MDP - Microfiche equipment - Dukane Corp.
MDR - Cleaning preparations - Titan Laboratories
MDR - Food products ✰ - H.P. Hood & Sons Inc.
MDR - Frames–eyeglass - Hoya Corp. USA
MDR - Pharmaceutical preparations - MDR Fitness Corp.
M.D.R. FORMULA - Vitamins and nutritional supplements ✰ - Nutritional Research Associates Inc.
MDRAM - Circuit boards - Monolithic System Technology, Inc.
MDS - Brass products ✰ - H.C. Meyers Co.
MDS - Optical services - Varilux Co.
MDSC - Calorimeters–laboratory - TA Instruments, Inc.
MDVS - Computers - Mercury Computer Systems Inc.
MDX 119 - Oxygen - Cryogenic Associates Inc.
MDX HEALTH DIGEST - Computer software - Medical Data Exchange
ME - Apparel–women's - Anne Klein & Co.
ME - Apparel–women's ✰ - Miss Elaine, Inc.
ME - Beads - ME Enterprises
ME - Floor coverings ✰ - Congoleum Corp.
ME - Grinders - Miracle Exclusives Inc.
ME - Navigational instruments - Raytheon Co.
ME 2 - Nightgowns ✰ - Miss Elaine, Inc.
ME-90 - Air purification systems ✰ - Master Appliance Corp.
ME-109 - Toys–models - Cox Products Inc.
ME & EWE - Toys - Lisco, Inc.
ME & MINE - Apparel–women's - Middendorf Enterprises Inc.
ME & MY CAT - Cat food - Maple Leaf Pet Foods
ME AND MY COLORS - Crayons - Papel Freelance, Inc.
ME AND MY PALS SLEEPERS - Apparel - May Department Stores Co.
ME AND MY TEDDY - Frames–picture - Atlan Pacific Industries Inc.
ME AND MY WORLD - Computer peripheral equipment - Future Vision Holding, Inc.
M.E. BY MISS ELAINE - Robes ✰ - Miss Elaine, Inc.
ME DESIGN - Electric lighting equipment - General Cable Corp.
ME-N-ED'S PIZZA PARLORS - Pizzas–mixes - D.F.&W. Restaurant Management Services, Inc.
ME O 'MY BREAD PUDDIN' PIE - Bakery products - Sweet Street Desserts, Inc.
ME ON A TEE - Shirts - Kelley Morgan-Ensley
M.E. SPORTS I IMPRINTS - Apparel–men's - Roytex, Inc.
ME SUA - Shampoos - Jorge Suarez Menendez
ME-TOO! - Jewelry ✰ - Pakula & Co.
ME TOO BY U-R-FREE - Jeans–children's - Kentogs Corp.
ME101 - Computer software - Bechtel Group, Inc.
MEA - Hair care products - Mea Corp.
MEA-DOW - Milk - Meadow Gold Dairy
MEAD - Paper - Mead Corp.
MEAD JOHNSON - Pharmaceutical preparations - Bristol-Myers Squibb Co.
MEADOBROOK - Dairy products - Pioneer Dairy Inc.
MEADOLAKE - Margarine - Kraft Food Ingredients Corp.
MEADOW - Bedding–linen - Dan River Inc.
MEADOW - Cabinets - Merillat Industries, Inc.
MEADOW - Cabinets - Prestige Inc.
MEADOW - Dinnerware ✰ - Corning Inc.
MEADOW - Toys - Tonka Corp.
MEADOW BANK - Dishes–china ✰ - Denby USA Limited
MEADOW BLEND - Cosmetics - Shaklee Corp.
MEADOW BLOOMS - Glassware–household ✰ - Fenton Art Glass Co.
MEADOW BLOSSOM - Glassware–household ✰ - Fenton Art Glass Co.
MEADOW BOUQUET - Toiletries - Crabtree & Evelyn, Ltd.
MEADOW BREEZE - Dinnerware–glass - Lenox, Inc.
MEADOW BROOK - Milk - Meadow Brook Dairy Co.
MEADOW BROOK - Watches and handbags - R. Josephs Sportswear, Inc.
MEADOW BROOK FARM - Candy ✰ - Williams & Randolph Inc.
MEADOW CLOVER - Health care products ✰ - Avon Products, Inc.
MEADOW CREEK - Infant product - BetLar, Inc.
MEADOW CREEK - Prefabricated buildings–wood - Champion Enterprises Inc.
MEADOW-CRETE - Concrete repair products - W.R. Meadows, Inc.
MEADOW FLOWER - Cooking utensils–aluminum ✰ - General Housewares Corp.

MEADOW FLOWERS - Deodorizers - Container Store, Inc.
MEADOW FLOWERS - Perfumes - Luzier Personalized Cosmetics, Inc.
MEADOW FRESH - Bird feeds - Petland, Inc.
MEADOW FRESH - Dairy products - Beatrice Cheese Co.
MEADOW FRESH - Flowers, plants, and seeds - CFX, Inc.
MEADOW GOLD - Cheese - BDH Two, Inc.
MEADOW GOLD - Dinnerware–plastic - Federal Glass
MEADOW GOLD - Juices - Borden, Inc.
MEADOW GOLD - Snack foods - Beatrice Cos. Inc.
MEADOW GREEN - Glassware–household ✰ - Lenox Crystal, Inc.
MEADOW GREENS - Floor coverings–carpet and rugs ✰ - Karastan-Bigelow Inc.
MEADOW HEARTH - Floor coverings–carpet and rugs - Capel, Inc.
MEADOW LARK - Tableware–china ✰ - Lenox, Inc.
MEADOW MADNESS - Perfumes - Colgate-Palmolive Co.
MEADOW MATE - Veterinary nutritional supplements - Agrestore, Inc.
MEADOW MILK - Candy - McDonald Candy Co. Inc.
MEADOW MOUSE - Sporting goods - James Heddon's Sons
MEADOW PINKS - Dinnerware–glass ✰ - Lenox, Inc.
MEADOW QUEEN - Dairy products - Valley Lea Dairies Inc.
MEADOW ROSE - Dinnerware–glass - Franciscan by Johnson Brothers, USA, Inc.
MEADOW ROSE - Flatware - Wallace International Silversmiths, Inc.
MEADOW SONG - Christmas tree ornaments - Cracker Box Inc.
MEADOW SONG - Flatware - Towle Manufacturing Co.
MEADOW SONG - Tableware–china ✰ - Lenox, Inc.
MEADOW SONG - Wallpaper - Warner Co.
MEADOW SONG II - Wallpaper - Warner Co.
MEADOW SPRINGS - Whiskey - Old Boone Distillery Co.
MEADOW, THE - Potpourri - Countryside Fragrances Inc.
MEADOW VIEW - Floor coverings ✰ - Congoleum Corp.
MEADOWBROOK - Bedding–linen - West Point-Pepperell Inc.
MEADOWBROOK - Cabinets - Karman Kitchens Inc.
MEADOWBROOK - Cooking utensils–enameled ✰ - National Housewares
MEADOWBROOK - Dishes–china ✰ - WMF/USA
MEADOWBROOK - Fabrics - Dan River Inc.
MEADOWBROOK - Fencing–wood ✰ - MacGillis and Gibbs Co.
MEADOWBROOK - Floor coverings–carpet and rugs ✰ - Downs Carpet Co. Inc.
MEADOWBROOK - Floor coverings–carpet and rugs ✰ - Royalweve Carpet Mills
MEADOWBROOK - Manufactured homes - Redman Industries, Inc.
MEADOWBROOK - Siding - Aluminum Co. of America
MEADOWDOWN - Crocheted and knitted items - Garland Knitting Mills
MEADOWFLOWERS - Wallpaper ✰ - Wallquest, Inc.
MEADOWLACE - Wallpaper - J. Chesterfield Studio
MEADOWLAKE - Floor coverings–carpet and rugs - Gulistan Carpet Inc.
MEADOWLAND - Bedding–linen - Dan River Inc.
MEADOWLANE - Tableware–china - Pfaltzgraff Investment Co.
MEADOWLARK - Frames–eyeglass ✰ - Universal/Univis Inc.
MEADOWLARK - Recording label - Sparrow Corp.
MEADOWOOD - Cabinets - Riviera Cabinets Inc.
MEADOWOOD - Furniture - Bernhardt Industries
MEADOWS - Wallpaper - Madison Wallcoverings
MEADOWSILK - Hair care products - Redmond Products, Inc.
MEADOWSONG - Pillows - Hoechst Celanese Corp.
MEADOWVIEW - Furniture - Vaughan Furniture Co. Inc.
MEADOWYCK - Floor coverings - Tarkett, Inc.
MEAD'S - Food products - Golden Pantry West Inc.
MEAGAN'S NEST - Wallpaper ✰ - Warner Co.
MEAL BOATS - Breads - Parco Foods, Inc.
MEAL JOY - Olives–pickled or brined - Robert Benestelli
MEAL MAKER - Dog food - Ralston Purina Co.
MEAL MAKER - Toasters ✰ - Hamilton Beach/Proctor-Silex Inc.
MEAL MAKERS - Seasonings - Conopco, Inc.
MEAL MANAGER - Vitamins and nutritional supplements - Healthway, Inc.
MEAL MART KOSHER FOODS - Food products - Schreiber Caterers
MEAL MATES - Breads - Nabisco Foods Group
MEAL 'N MINUTES - Pet products - Plaza Enterprises Inc. (Magnador Div.)
MEAL PACK - Food products - Inter Mountain Trading Co.
MEAL TIME SAVORS - Food products - Stop and Shop Companies Inc.
MEAL WITH A STOVE INSIDE, THE - Preserved foods–prepackaged - Zestotherm Inc.
MEALETTES - Food products ✰ - Natrol, Inc.
MEALMASTER - Pet products - Petmaster, Inc.
MEALS-TO-GO - Food products - Sara Lee Corp.

MEALTHYME - Computer software - Timothy J. Flick
MEALTIME BASICS - Infant product - Lisco, Inc.
MEALTIME PAL - Toys - All American Toy Co.
MEAN 18 - Computer software - Accolade Inc.
MEAN & CLEAN - Cleaning preparations - Yale Engineering Co.
MEAN AND GREENS - Candy - Stanico, Inc.
MEAN BEAN - Seasonings - Garden Valley Foods
MEAN BEAN, THE - Coffee - Mean Bean Ltd.
MEAN BEAVER - Apparel and accessories - Paul S. Wyatt
MEAN DREAM RACER - Toys–automobiles - Mattel, Inc.
MEAN GREEN - Towels - Magla Products Inc.
MEAN GREEN PASSION - Toys–automobiles - Mattel, Inc.
MEAN GREEN PUNCHER - Juices - General Mills, Inc.
MEAN MACHINE - Bicycles - Columbia Manufacturing Inc.
MEAN MACHINE - Degreasing solvents - Murrell's Wholesale and Manufacturing, Inc.
MEAN MACHINE - Toys - Mattel, Inc.
MEAN MACHINE - Toys–models - Estes Industries
MEAN MIKE - Cement - Rectorseal Corp.
MEAN MOUNTAIN MUSIC - Recording label - Mean Mountain Music
MEAN 'N TOUGH 4 X 4'S - Toys - Toymax Inc.
MEAN SCREAMER - Toys - Nylint Toy Corp.
MEAN STREAK - Apparel and accessories - Peter C. Tomassetti
MEAN STREAK - Markers–felt-tip - Sanford Corp.
MEAN STREAK - Rackets–racquetball - Spalding & Evenflo Companies, Inc.
MEAN STREETS - Computer software ☆ - Access Software Inc.
MEAN STRING - Hardware - Shakespeare Fishing Tackle
MEAN WEENER - Toys–automobiles - Mattel, Inc.
MEANER CLEANER - Cleaning preparations - Pettit Paint Co. Inc.
MEANIE - Toys–models ☆ - Estes Industries
MEANING OF LIFE - Coffee - 1 Uno Espresso, Inc.
MEANINGFUL - Floor coverings–carpet and rugs ☆ - Patcraft Mills Inc.
MEANINGS - Floor coverings–carpet and rugs - Lees Carpets
MEARLIN - Water treating compounds - Mearl E. Ellison
MEARLMAID - Pigments - Mearl Corp.
MEARLMICA - Cosmetics - Mearl Corp.
MEARLTALC - Talcum powders - Mearl Corp.
MEASON - Musical instrument accessories - Jones Double Reed Products
MEASURABLE DIFFERENCE, THE - Sanitary napkins - Arquest, Inc.
MEASURE - Computer software - National Instruments Corp.
MEASURE AID - Chemical preparations - Coastal Industries Inc.
MEASURE FRESH - Beverage dispensing equipment - Tops Manufacturing Co. Inc.
MEASURE MASTER - Measuring instruments - Rolatape Corp.
MEASURE METER - Measuring instruments - Rolatape Corp.
MEASURE RITE SYSTEM - Measuring instruments - Weight Watchers International, Inc.
MEASURE STIX - Tape measures - L.S. Starrett Co. Inc. (Consumer Products Div.)
MEASURE THE DIFFERENCE - Computer software - Omni Flow Computers, Inc.
MEASURE UP - Breads ☆ - Best Foods Baking Group
MEASURE-UPS - Apparel and accessories - Executive Apparel, Inc.
MEASUREMIND - Computer software - Optical Gaging Products, Inc.
MEASUREMINDER - Tape measures - Warren Mack Lindsey
MEASURESPY - Computer software - Productivity-Quality Systems Inc.
MEASURETTE - Girdles - Cupid Foundations Inc.
MEASURIN - Analgesics - Sterling Winthrop Inc.
MEASURLINK - Computer software - MTI Corp.
MEAT HEAD - Bats–baseball - Pacers Sports
MEAT LOAF CARVER - Food products - Boston Chicken, Inc.
MEAT MASTER - Meat products–beef - Schnuck Markets, Inc.
MEAT MATE - Barbecue sauce - Nalley's Fine Foods
MEAT-N-MARRO - Dog food - Horton Co., Inc.
MEAT N' POTATOES - Apparel–men's - Smart Style Industries Inc.
MEAT (NOT!) - Food products - Dixie, USA, Inc.
MEAT-O-MAT - Meat products–beef - Meat-O-Mat Corp.
MEAT OF WHEAT - Meat alternatives - Ivy Foods
MEAT PACKER - Fishing lures - Windsor Products, Inc.
MEAT RED MARKET - Wines - Bully Hill Vineyards, Inc.
MEAT SNACKERY, THE - Sausages - Goodmark Foods, Inc.
MEAT-TENDER - Refrigerators - White Consolidated Industries, Inc.
MEAT TRIO - Pet products - ALPO Petfoods Inc.
MEATBALL BAIT - Fishing lures - Meatball Bait Distributor Inc.
MEATBUSTER - Pizza - Mazzio's Corp.
MEATEX - Meat products–canned - Sampco Inc.

MEATHEAD - Fishing lures - Zoom Bait Co.
MEATHEAD - Toys–stuffed - Davis Brothers & Madison Ltd.
MEATLESS LIGHTBURGERS - Food products - Lightlife Foods, Inc.
MEATLESS SEATONE - Vitamins and nutritional supplements - Hillestad International, Inc.
MEATLOAF CIRCUS - Greeting cards ☆ - American Greetings Corp.
MEATMASTER - Fishing tackle - Gudebrod, Inc.
MEATSA!MEATSA! - Food products - Little Caesar Enterprises, Inc.
MEATY BONE - Dog food - Heinz Pet Products Co.
MEATY JUMBOS - Frankfurters - Lykes Bros. Inc. (Meat Packing Div.)
MEATY TREATS - Dog food - Purebred Pet Products, Inc.
MEBARAL - Pharmaceutical preparations - Sterling Winthrop Inc.
MEBCO - Hair care products - Mebco Industries, Inc.
MEBROIN - Pharmaceutical preparations ☆ - Winthrop Pharmaceuticals
MECA - Apparel and accessories - Meca Sportswear Inc.
MECA - Computer software - Meca Software, Inc.
MECANUS - Motor vehicle parts and accessories - NFC Industries, Inc.
MECAROBOT GOLF - Computer software - Toho Co., Ltd.
MECCA - Floor coverings–carpet and rugs ☆ - Porter Carpet Mills Inc.
MECCA - Medical apparatus ☆ - APT Technology, Inc.
MECCA - Thread - Threads USA Div.
MECCANO - Figurines, etc. - Ava International Inc.
MECH - Artists' materials ☆ - A.I. Friedman Inc.
MECH WARRIORS 2 - Computer software - Activision, Inc.
MECHADEUS - Computer software - Mechadeus
MECHANIC - Ladders–metal ☆ - Lynn Ladder and Scaffolding Co. Inc.
MECHANIC - Ladders–metal ☆ - Michigan Ladder Co. Inc.
MECHANIC - Recording label - MCA Universal Studios
MECHANIC - Stepladders - W.W. Babcock Co. Inc.
MECHANICAL COLLECTIBLES - Christmas tree ornaments - Mr. Christmas, Inc.
MECHANICAL DIODE - Machine parts - Epilogics Inc.
MECHANICAL FLEX-WING MOWERS - Lawn mowers - Alamo Industrial
MECHANICAL MIRROR WORKS - Mirrors - Mechanical Mirror Works Inc.
MECHANICHEM - Aquarium accessories - Aquarium Systems, Inc.
MECHANICS - Automotive parts and accessories - Blue Coral, Inc.
MECHANICS SUPREME - Tools - Our Own Hardware Co.
MECHANIX - Gloves - AXO Sport-America, Inc.
MECHANO - Paper ☆ - Parsons Paper Co.
MECHI-TECH - Games - Gamescience
MECHOL - Pharmaceutical preparations - Kenneth A. Manne Co.
MECHOLYL - Pharmaceutical preparations - Gordon Laboratories
MECHOSHADES - Window shades - Mecho Shade Corp.
MECI-I-TRON - Health care products - Meyer Equipment Co. Inc.
MECKLENBURG - Furniture - Sumter Cabinet Co., Inc.
MECKLER - Publisher's imprints - Meckler Corp.
MECKLEY'S FLAVOR FRUIT FARM - Cider - Flavor Fruit Farm
MECLAN - Pharmaceutical preparations - Ortho Pharmaceutical Corp.
MECLAREX - Pharmaceutical preparations - C.S. Ruckstuhl Co. Inc.
MECLAVERT - Pharmaceutical preparations ☆ - Hyrex Pharmaceuticals
MECLOMEN - Pharmaceutical preparations ☆ - Parke-Davis
MECO - Cups–plastic - Massachusetts Envelope Co.
MECO - Furniture - Meco Corp.
MECO - Machine parts - Woodex Bearing Co., Inc.
MECO-MARINE - Machine parts - Woodex Bearing Co., Inc.
MED - Pet products ☆ - Sera Aquaristik USA Inc.
MED-A-CALL - Health care products - Silent Call Corp.
MED ART GALLERY - Artists' materials ☆ - Dynamic Graphics Inc.
MED-DENT - Chemicals–photographic - White Mountain Imaging, Inc.
MED-DIET - Food products - Med-Diet Laboratories Inc.
MED FOR MIX - Computer software - Crowell Systems
MED GROUP, THE - Medical apparatus - Medical Equipment Distributors, Inc.
MED-I-SUN - Lamps - Phillips Electronics North America Corp.
MED ICE - Analgesics - Crowne Royale, Ltd.
MED-ICH - Water treating compounds - Silco Pet Products
MED-IDENT TAGS - Jewelry - Republic Drug Co. Inc.
MED LIT - Computer software - Sterling Technologies, Inc.
MED-LO - Pharmaceutical preparations - Whorton Pharmaceuticals Inc.
MED MASK - Health care products - Sellstrom Manufacturing Co.
MED MITE - Oxygen - Cryogenic Associates Inc.
MED PASS - Alarm systems - American Medical Alert Corp.
MED-POLL - Computer software - Laser Concepts, Inc.
MED PROFILE - Computer software - Care Med Corp.
MED-PSYCH PUBLICATIONS - Publisher's imprints - Westport Publishers Inc. (Media Div.)
MED SET - Office supplies - Bissell Inc.

☆ = Now out of production

MED-THREADS - Medical uniforms - Trademark Corp.

MED VIEW - Computer storage devices - Lanier Voice Products

MED-VUE - Goggles—safety - Trademark Corp.

MED YACHTS INTERNATIONAL - Ships - Marine Trading International Inc.

MEDA-CAP - Analgesics - Circle Pharmaceuticals Inc.

MEDA-FOAM - Health care products - Mark One Healthcare Products Inc.

MEDA-PEDIC - Bedding—linen - Nurserytyme Products/Doppelt Industries

MEDA-PLAST - Health care products - Mark One Healthcare Products Inc.

MEDA-TAB - Analgesics - Circle Pharmaceuticals Inc.

MEDABOOT - Medical apparatus - Medassist-Op, Inc.

MEDACHE - Analgesics ☆ - Organon Inc.

MEDACLEAR - Hair care products - John Amico Expressive Hair Care Products

MEDACTON - Antiseptics - Laclede Research Laboratories

MEDADYNE - Pharmaceutical preparations - Vetco, Inc.

MEDAGLIA D'ORO - Coffee - Tetley Inc.

MEDAILION AU BEURRE - Cookies - PF Brands, Inc.

MEDAILLION AU BEURRE - Cookies - Pepperidge Farm Inc.

MEDAILLON - Wallpaper ☆ - Marburg Wallcoverings Inc.

MEDAL MATES - Frames—picture - About Frames, Inc.

MEDAL OF HONOR - Cigars - Lane Ltd.

MEDAL TURF - Floor coverings—carpet and rugs ☆ - Olympic Carpets Inc.

MEDALIAS - Jewelry - Foree Hunsicker, Inc.

MEDALINE - Pharmaceutical preparations ☆ - U.S. Ethicals Inc.

MEDALIST - Apparel and accessories - Windsor Apparel Partners, L.P.

MEDALIST - Balls—golf - Acjshnet Co.

MEDALIST - Binders - Dennison National Co.

MEDALIST - Binoculars - Bausch & Lomb Inc.

MEDALIST - Cigars - E. Regensburg & Sons

MEDALIST - Computer peripheral equipment - Seagate Technology, Inc.

MEDALIST - Doors—glass - Peterson Window Corp.

MEDALIST - Floor coverings - Congoleum Corp.

MEDALIST - Floor coverings—carpet and rugs - Conquest Carpet Mills Inc.

MEDALIST - Floor coverings—carpet and rugs - Karastan-Bigelow Inc.

MEDALIST - Floor coverings—carpet and rugs ☆ - Heuga USA

MEDALIST - Garden equipment - NK Lawn & Garden Co.

MEDALIST - Golfing equipment - MacGregor Sport Products Inc.

MEDALIST - Guns - Crosman Corp.

MEDALIST - Hardware - Medalist Industries Inc.

MEDALIST - Hardware ☆ - Amerock Corp.

MEDALIST - Luggage - Samsonite Corp.

MEDALIST - Mattresses - Simmons USA

MEDALIST - Oils—lubricating - Paccar Inc.

MEDALIST - Paper—sand - Carborundum Abrasives North America

MEDALIST - Pencils ☆ - Faber-Castell Corp.

MEDALIST - Pens - A.T. Cross Co.

MEDALIST - Photographic equipment - Eastman Kodak Co.

MEDALIST - Pipes—tobacco - S.M. Frank & Co. Inc. (Kaywoodie-Yello-Bole-Medico)

MEDALIST - Printing trades machinery - Vidac

MEDALIST - Rifles ☆ - Harrington & Richardson Inc.

MEDALIST - Ships—sailing vessels ☆ - A. Le Comte Co. Inc.

MEDALIST - Skates—roller - Chicago Roller Skate Co.

MEDALIST - Skates—roller - National Sporting Goods Corp.

MEDALIST - Sporting goods - Jarvinen USA

MEDALIST - Sporting goods - Shakespeare Fishing Tackle

MEDALIST - Sporting goods - Wellington Leisure Products, Inc.

MEDALIST - Sports apparel - Medalist Apparel Inc.

MEDALIST - Switches—electric - Pass & Seymour, Inc.

MEDALIST - Tools - GC Thorsen, Inc.

MEDALIST - Vitamins and nutritional supplements - McKesson Home Health Care

MEDALIST - Watches ☆ - SMH (US) Inc.

MEDALIST - Welding equipment - Victor Equipment Co.

MEDALIST - Wood products ☆ - Stuhr Enterprises Inc.

MEDALIST 432 - Balls—golf ☆ - All American Golf Sales, Inc.

MEDALIST AMERICA - Flowers, plants, and seeds - Jacklin Seed

MEDALIST-BLACK AMERICANS - Computer software - Hartley Courseware Inc.

MEDALIST-CONTINENTS - Computer software - Hartley Courseware Inc.

MEDALIST-CREATE - Computer software - Hartley Courseware Inc.

MEDALIST GOLD - Agricultural products - Jacklin Seed

MEDALIST-PRESIDENTS - Computer software - Hartley Courseware Inc.

MEDALIST-STATES - Computer software - Hartley Courseware Inc.

MEDALIST-WOMEN IN HISTORY - Computer software - Hartley Courseware Inc.

MEDALLA BEER - Beverages—malt - Century Importers Inc.

MEDALLA DE BARRIL - Beverages—malt - Cerveceria India, Inc.

MEDALLION - Air conditioning equipment ☆ - Nordyne Inc.

MEDALLION - Aluminum products ☆ - Valley Aluminum Products Corp.

MEDALLION - Archery equipment - Pro Line Co.

MEDALLION - Bicycles ☆ - Roadmaster Corp.

MEDALLION - Blinds—venetian - Kirsch Co.

MEDALLION - Boats - Pro-Line Boats Inc.

MEDALLION - Boats—motor ☆ - Regal Marine Industries Inc.

MEDALLION - Bottle caps - Franmara Co. Inc.

MEDALLION - Cabinets - Medallion Kitchens of Minnesota Inc.

MEDALLION - Cameras ☆ - Eastman Kodak Co.

MEDALLION - Christmas tree ornaments - Cracker Box Inc.

MEDALLION - Cooking equipment—household ☆ - Mirro Corp.

MEDALLION - Cutting boards ☆ - Bemis Manufacturing Co.

MEDALLION - Dinnerware—glass ☆ - Metlox Pottery Shoppe

MEDALLION - Dishes—china - Sterling China Co. Inc.

MEDALLION - Doilies - Mafcote Industries, Inc.

MEDALLION - Drapery hardware - Cooper Industries, Inc.

MEDALLION - Enamels - Colony Paints Div.

MEDALLION - Exercising equipment - Schwinn Cycling & Fitness Inc.

MEDALLION - Fish—fresh or frozen - Meridian Products, Inc.

MEDALLION - Floor coverings - Mannington Resilient Floors

MEDALLION - Floor coverings - Sponge-Cushion Inc.

MEDALLION - Floor coverings—carpet and rugs - Columbus Mills, Inc.

MEDALLION - Floor coverings—carpet and rugs - Fieldturf & Carpet Inc.

MEDALLION - Floor coverings—carpet and rugs ☆ - Blue Ridge Carpet Mills

MEDALLION - Floor coverings—carpet and rugs ☆ - Regal Rugs Inc.

MEDALLION - Food products - Gold Kist Inc.

MEDALLION - Furniture - Vaughan Furniture Co. Inc.

MEDALLION - Furniture ☆ - Mersman Furniture Co.

MEDALLION - Greeting cards ☆ - Cleo Inc.

MEDALLION - Infant product - Lisco, Inc.

MEDALLION - Lockers—metal - Penco Products Div.

MEDALLION - Melamine product - Boonton Molding Co. Inc.

MEDALLION - Motor vehicles ☆ - DaimlerChrysler

MEDALLION - Musical instruments - LPD Music International

MEDALLION - Plastic tubing - American Granby Inc.

MEDALLION - Rackets—racquetball - Ektelon

MEDALLION - Seafood products—fresh or frozen - Meridian Products

MEDALLION - Siding - Amerimark Building Products, Inc.

MEDALLION - Silver compounds - Sterling Polish, Ltd.

MEDALLION - Sporting goods ☆ - Outdoor Technologies Group

MEDALLION - Toys—models - Cox Products Inc.

MEDALLION - Watches ☆ - SMH (US) Inc.

MEDALLION-60 - Floor finishing machines—commercial - United Floor Machine Co.

MEDALLION GROUP OF QUALITY PRODUCTS & DESIGN - Doors - Georgia-Pacific Corp.

MEDALLIONS - Seafood products—fresh or frozen - Northwest Natural

MEDALO - Hair care products - Gold Medal Hair Products Inc.

MEDALOX - Antacids - Medical Chemical Corp.

MEDANA - Watches - Medana Watch Corp.

MEDANA - Watches - Webster Watch Co. Associates

MEDAPRIN - Pharmaceutical preparations ☆ - Upjohn Co.

MEDAQUA - Aquarium accessories - Kordon

MEDAQUA - Water treating compounds - Novalek, Inc.

MEDAREX - Pharmaceutical preparations - Medarex, Inc.

MEDART - Hardware - Blaine Window Hardware Inc.

MEDAVANCE - Pharmaceuticals - PharmaThera

MEDAWAY - Fabrics ☆ - Veratec

MEDAXON - Recording label - American Society of Health-System Pharmacists, Inc.

MEDBASE - Computer software - Doctor Friendly, Ltd.

MEDBURY - Clocks ☆ - General Time Corp. (Westclox/Seth Thomas Div.)

MEDCAM - Computers - Mercury Computer Systems Inc.

MEDCHAIR - Medical apparatus - Techni-Floe Inc.

MEDCREST - Health care products - Aedline, Industries, Inc.

MEDDATA - Paper products - Priority Healthcare Benefits, Inc.

MEDDOLAND - Tomato pastes and sauces - Lico Brands, Inc.

MEDDOLAND - Tomato pastes and sauces - Stanislaus Food Products Co.

MEDEA - Ophthalmic goods ☆ - Luxottica

MEDEBRAL - Pharmaceutical preparations - Medical Products Panamericana Inc.

MEDECO - Locks—door - Medeco Security Locks, Inc.

MEDECOR - Health care products - Aedline, Industries, Inc.

MEDERA - Floor coverings–carpet and rugs - Mannington Carpets, Inc.
MEDEX - Fiberboard - Harbor Sales Co.
MEDFILE - Containers - Kerfoot Corp.
MEDFILMS - Video production - Medfilms Inc.
MEDFLEX - Elastic - Southern Webbing Mills, Inc.
MEDFLEX - Medical uniforms - First Medical Infection Control Associates, Inc.
MEDFO - Video production - Medfo, Inc.
MEDFORD - Cabinets - Del Mar Cabinets
MEDFORD - Cabinets - Sunny Wood Products Co. Inc.
MEDFORD - Clocks ☆ - General Time Corp. (Westclox/Seth Thomas Div.)
MEDFORD - Frames–eyeglass - U.S. Optical Frame Co.
MEDFORD - Fruits–canned - Rogue River Packing Corp.
MEDFORD - Lacquers ☆ - Talisman of Georgia
MEDFORD - Paper ☆ - Southworth Co.
MEDFORD - Shoes ☆ - Allen-Edmonds Shoe Corp.
MEDFORD - Tableware–china ☆ - Lenox, Inc.
MEDFORD - Trailers–travel - Fleetwood Enterprises, Inc.
MEDFORD FARMS - Salad dressings–bottled - Tidelands Sales Co. Inc.
MEDFORD FARMS - Snack foods - Haddon House Food Products Inc.
MEDFORD FARMS GRAND PRIZE - Barbecue sauce - Haddon House Food Products Inc.
MEDFORD-PLAYMORE - Apparel–women's - Warnaco Inc.
MEDFORD'S - Meat products–beef - Hatfield, Inc.
MEDI - Health care products - Medi Inc.
MEDI - Medical apparatus - Medi USA L.P.
MEDI-AID - Eyeglasses - Clinical Diagnostics Inc.
MEDI-AIR - Floor mat - RJ Medical, Inc.
MEDI-AIR - Oxygen tents - Penox Technologies Inc.
MEDI-BAND - Pharmaceutical preparations - Afassco
MEDI CARRY - Medical apparatus ☆ - Apex Medical Corp.
MEDI/CHEST - Medical apparatus - Apex Medical Corp.
MEDI-CHRON - Medical apparatus ☆ - General Time Corp. (Westclox/Seth Thomas Div.)
MEDI-CIL - Antacids - Medical Chemical Corp.
MEDI-CLEEN - Pet products - Lambert-Kay
MEDI-CORT - Pharmaceutical preparations ☆ - Mahdeen Laboratory
MEDI-CRUSH - Health care products - Maddak Inc.
MEDI-CURE - Adhesives and sealants - Dymax Corp.
MEDI-DAN - Shampoos - Mahdeen Laboratory
MEDI-DAN PLUS - Hair care products - Mahdeen Laboratory
MEDI-DESK - Desks - Budget Buddy Co.
MEDI-DINE - Pet products - Glo-Marr Products Inc.
MEDI-DOT - Medication-reminder labels - Medi-Dot Inc.
MEDI-DRY - Bath salts - Helene Curtis Industries Inc.
MEDI-EVIL MAULER - Toys - Mattel, Inc.
MEDI EZ-FLO - Health care products - Medi Inc.
MEDI-FECT - Pharmaceutical preparations - Medical Chemical Corp.
MEDI FIRST - First aid kits - Medique Products
MEDI-FLU - Cold remedies ☆ - Warner-Lambert Co.
MEDI-FOODS - Vitamins and nutritional supplements - Aerotech Fasteners, Inc.
MEDI-HAIR - Hair-replacement product and scalp-care product - International Hairgoods Inc.
MEDI-HAIR FORMULA PLUS - Hair-care products - International Hairgoods Inc.
MEDI-JECTOR - Medical apparatus - Mediject Corp.
MEDI-KAY - Pharmaceutical preparations - L.T. York Co.
MEDI-KOOL - Mouthwashes ☆ - Parmed Pharmaceuticals Inc.
MEDI-KOOL - Veterinary product ☆ - American Equine Products Inc.
MEDI-KOOL PAK - Pet products - Farnam Cos. Inc.
MEDI-KOOL TITENER - Pet products - Farnam Cos. Inc.
MEDI LIFT - Recliners - Penox Technologies Inc.
MEDI-LOFT - Health care products - Inbrand Corp.
MEDI-LYTE - Pharmaceutical preparations - Medique Products
MEDI-MASQUE - Cosmetics ☆ - Bonne Bell, Inc.
MEDI-MIST - Oxygen - Caire
MEDI-MIST - Vitamins and nutritional supplements ☆ - Mayor Pharmaceutical Laboratories
MEDI-MODULAR - Floor coverings–carpet and rugs - Olympic Carpets Inc.
MEDI-MOIST - Hair care products ☆ - Mahdeen Laboratory
MEDI-MONITOR - Medical apparatus - David A. Lang
MEDI-PACK - Holsters - Cramer Products Inc.
MEDI-PAK - Medical apparatus ☆ - Trademark Corp.
MEDI-PH - Skin care products - TDC Dermatologicals
MEDI-PHITE - Health care products - Medical Chemical Corp.
MEDI-PRO - Hair care products - Mahdeen Laboratory
MEDI-PRO - Vitamins and nutritional supplements - Medi-Foods, Inc.

MEDI-QUIK - Health care products - L & F Consumer Products
MEDI REST - Mattresses - Bemco Associates, Inc.
MEDI-SEPTIC - Pet products - Vo-Toys Inc.
MEDI-SIL - Medical apparatus - Microsonic Inc.
MEDI-SMOOTH - Skin care products - TDC Dermatologicals
MEDI-SOLV - Pharmaceutical preparations ☆ - Mahdeen Laboratory
MEDI-SPAS - Pharmaceutical preparations - Medical Chemical Corp.
MEDI-SPOON - Infant product ☆ - Binky-Griptight Co.
MEDI STAT - Blood derivatives - Mueller Sports Medicine Inc.
MEDI-STIK - Analgesics ☆ - Vitarine Pharmaceuticals Inc.
MEDI-STIX - Adhesives - Aetna Felt Corp.
MEDI STRUMPF - Health care products - Medi USA L.P.
MEDI-STUDS - Skin care products - J. Hewitt Inc.
MEDI-SUN SUNBURN RELIEF - Sunburn relief ointment - Blue Dolphin Manufacturing & Distributing Co., Inc.
MEDI-SYSTEM - Skin care products - J. Hewitt Inc.
MEDI-TAR - Shampoos - Ray Drug Co.
MEDI-TAR - Veterinary pharmaceutical preparations - Glo-Marr Products Inc.
MEDI-THIN - Skin care products ☆ - TKI Foods, Inc.
MEDI-TONIC - Pharmaceutical preparations - Medical Chemical Corp.
MEDI-TOUCH - Gloves–rubber - Ansell Inc. (Personal Products Div.)
MEDI-TRATING - Pharmaceutical preparations - Richardson-Vicks USA
MEDI-TYPE - Medical apparatus - West Co., Inc.
MEDI-VET - Veterinary pharmaceutical preparations - Equest, Inc. (Saratoga Veterinary Products, Co.)
MEDI-VISION - Frames–eyeglass - Pathway Optical Prods.
MEDI-WIPES - Health care products - Inbrand Corp.
MEDI-ZYME - Veterinary pharmaceutical preparations - Farnam Cos. Inc.
MEDIA - Audio equipment - General Kinetics Inc.
MEDIA - Health care products - Pall Biomedical Inc.
MEDIA - Pencils - Reliance Pen & Pencil Corp.
MEDIA - Thread - Threads USA Div.
MEDIA - Watches - Criterion Watch Co. Inc.
MEDIA 100 - Computer peripheral equipment - Data Translation, Inc.
MEDIA BOSS - Computer hardware - Arkay Technologies Inc.
MEDIA CITY - Video tapes–blank - Media City Inc.
MEDIA CLEANER - Computer software - Terran Interactive, Inc.
MEDIA COMPOSER - Computer terminals - Avid Technology, Inc.
MEDIA COOLER - Boxes–paperboard - Schwab Corp.
MEDIA DEPOT - Computers - Media Depot, Inc.
MEDIA DOCK - Furniture - Metropolitan Furniture Co.
MEDIA FAX - Paper–rolls - Autron Inc.
MEDIA-FLEX - Furniture ☆ - ACME Design Technology
MEDIA FORMS - Electronic equipment - A.L.S. Industries Inc.
MEDIA INTERSTELLAR MUSIC - Recording label - Clay Pigeon Records
MEDIA KING 2000 - Printing presses - King Press Corp.
MEDIA LINK - Cabinets - Wright Line Inc.
MEDIA MAGICIAN - Computer peripheral equipment - User Interface Technologies Corp.
MEDIA MASTER - Computer software - Advanced Remote Technologies Inc.
MEDIA MASTER - Electronic equipment - Columbia Scientific Industries Corp.
MEDIA MASTER SERIES - Filters–water - Doughboy Recreational Inc.
MEDIA MASTERS - Recording label - Rashid Sales Co.
MEDIA MOSAIC - Computer software - Media Mosaic, Inc.
MEDIA MOVER - Computer software - Sony Corp. of America
MEDIA NAVIGATOR - Computer software - R.M. Dudley Corp.
MEDIA PRINT - Paper ☆ - Silver Leaf Paper Co.
MEDIA RECORDER - Computer hardware - Avid Technology, Inc.
MEDIA-SAFE - Cabinets - Luxor
MEDIA SALES EXCELERATOR - Computer software - Softad Group, Inc.
MEDIA SOURCE - Computer software - CRS Inc.
MEDIA SOURCE - Electronic equipment - Trans World Entertainment Corp.
MEDIA SUITE - Computer peripheral equipment - Avid Technology, Inc.
MEDIA SUITE PRO - Computer software - Avid Technology, Inc.
MEDIA-TRON - Electronics equipment - RTI Research Technology International
MEDIA ZONE - Audio equipment - Creative Point Inc.
MEDIA4 - Computer hardware - Media4, Inc.
MEDIAACTIVE - Computer software - Harcourt Brace & Co.
MEDIABANK - Office supplies - Rubbermaid Office Products Inc.
MEDIABLITZ! - Computer software - Asymetrix Corp.
MEDIABOOK - Computers - Diamond Flower Electric Instruments Co. (USA), Inc.
MEDIACONNECT - Computer hardware - Intervoice LP
MEDIAFORGE - Computer software - Strata, Inc.
MEDIAGARDEN - Computer software - Mediagarden, Inc.
MEDIAHOUSE - Computer software - Ultima Electronics Corp.

☆ = Now out of production

MEDIALIVE - Computer storage devices–optical - CD Technology, Inc.

MEDIAMAKER - Computer software - Macromedia, Inc.

MEDIAMARK - Labels–paper - Unimark Inc.

MEDIAMARK REPORTER - Computer software - Mediamark Research Inc.

MEDIAMATCH - Computers–mainframe - Avid Technology, Inc.

MEDIAMATCH - Ribbons–inked - Acucote, Inc.

MEDIAMATE - Computer hardware - Hunt Holdings, Inc.

MEDIAMATE - Computer peripheral equipment ☆ - Hunt Manufacturing Co.

MEDIAMATRIX - Audio equipment - Peavey Electronics Corp.

MEDIAMAX - Surge suppressors ☆ - Panamax

MEDIAMIX - Computer hardware - Avid Technology, Inc.

MEDIAMOBILES - Educational materials - MediaMobiles, Inc.

MEDIANEXT - Computer peripheral equipment - Radio Data Group, Inc.

MEDIANIX - Computer peripheral equipment - Medianix Semiconductor, Inc.

MEDIARC - Computer software - DRG International Inc.

MEDIASHARE - Computer software - MediaShare Inc.

MEDIASHOW - Cameras–microfilm - Sayett Technology Inc.

MEDIASOFT - Computer software - Mediasoft Corp.

MEDIASTREAMER - Computer hardware - International Business Machines Corp.

MEDIASTUDIO - Computer software - U-Lead Systems, Inc.

MEDIASTUDIO PRO - Computer software - Unlead Systems, Inc.

MEDIATOR - Computer software - Lachman Technology, Inc.

MEDIATOR - Computer software - Medi Connectors, Inc.

MEDIATRIC - Pharmaceutical preparations - Wyeth-Ayerst Laboratories

MEDIATRONICS - Computer software - Charles H. Meyer

MEDIATWIST - Cables - Belden Wire & Cable Co.

MEDIAVAULT - Safes - Empire Safe Co. Inc.

MEDIAWEB - Paper–writing - Champion International Corp.

MEDIBACK-PLUS - Floor coverings–carpet and rugs - Prince Street Holding Co.

MEDIBAR MONITOR - Medical apparatus - Medibar Medical Industries Inc.

MEDIBASE - Diet aids - Dean Distributors, Inc.

MEDIBOTTLE - Medical apparatus - TMBC, Inc.

M.E.D.I.C. - Emergency information capsules - Protect-UR-Life

MEDIC - Health care products ☆ - Cumberland-Swan, Inc.

MEDIC - Medical apparatus - Medisystems Corp.

MEDIC - Ophthalmic goods - Foremost Optical Products

MEDIC - Skin care products - Key West Aloe Inc.

MEDIC-AIR - Health care products ☆ - Halsey Drug Co. Inc.

MEDIC-BATH - Health care products - Rehab Equipment Distributors

MEDIC EAR - Jewelry - Studex Corp.

MEDIC MOIST - Hair care products - Raymac Corp. Hair & Skin Technology

MEDICA 28 - Medical uniforms - First Medical Infection Control Associates, Inc.

MEDICA DC10 - Medical uniforms - First Medical Infection Control Associates, Inc.

MEDICA V - Plugs–ear - All American Mold Laboratories Inc.

MEDICAID - Ophthalmic goods - Foremost Optical Products

MEDICAID ADMINISTRATOR - Computer software - Systems Consulting Co., Inc.

MEDICAINE - Health care products ☆ - Halsey Drug Co. Inc.

MEDICAL - Recording label - Whirlwind Records

MEDICAL - Shampoos - Palm Beach Beauty Products

MEDICAL & DENTAL CABS - Motor vehicles–buses - Turtle Top Specialty Products

MEDICAL CENTER - Pharmaceutical preparations - Hunt Products Inc.

MEDICAL CENTER - Thermometers - Becton, Dickinson and Co.

MEDICAL DATA RESEARCH - Computer databases - Medicode, Inc.

MEDICAL DEVICE REGISTER ON DISK - Computer software - Me Licensing Corp.

MEDICAL DISPOSABLES - Health care products - Inbrand Corp.

MEDICAL DISPOSABLES - Medical apparatus - Medical Disposables Co.

MEDICAL DOCTORS' RESEARCH - Skin care products - MDR Fitness Corp.

MEDICAL DRUG REFERENCE - Computer software - Parsons Technology, Inc.

MEDICAL EDGE INTERNATIONAL - Medical apparatus - Medical Edge International, Inc.

MEDICAL ESCROW SOCIETY, THE - Banks–commercial - Medical Escrow Society, Inc.

MEDICAL LAND PAK - First aid kits - Medical Sea Pak. Co.

MEDICAL MANAGER, THE - Computer software - Systems Plus Inc.

MEDICAL OFFICE LIFE SUPPORT - Publisher's imprints - Emergency Medical Training Institute

MEDICAL PARTNER - Computer software - Medical Solutions, Inc.

A+ MEDICAL PRODUCTS - Medical apparatus - A+ Medical Products, Inc.

MEDICAL SERVICES - Medical apparatus - National Medical Care

MEDICAL UCR PAYMENT SYSTEM - Computer storage devices - Medicode, Inc.

MEDICALIA - Electronic equipment - Management Science Associates, Inc.

MEDICALOGIC - Computer software - Medicalogic, Inc.

MEDICAP - Fertilizers - Creative Sales Inc.

MEDICASE - Health care products ☆ - Sharon Specialty Products

MEDICATION ENHANCEMENT DEVICE - Containers–glass - Rupert W. Knierim

MEDICHAIR - Recliners - Stratford Co.

MEDICHAIR - Wheelchairs - Guardian Products Inc.

MEDICHEST - Containers–paper - William Stearns

MEDICI - Fans–electric - Davoil, Inc.

MEDICI - Faucets - Kallista Inc.

MEDICI - Flatware - Gorham Inc.

MEDICI - Jewelry - Armbrust Corp.

MEDICI - Rings–jewelry - Artcarved Inc.

MEDICI - Tableware–china - Villeroy and Boch Tableware Ltd.

MEDICI FRESCO - Wallpaper - Maya Romanoff Corp.

MEDICI GALLERY - Stationery - Parkwest Publications Inc.

MEDICI MOIRE - Wallpaper ☆ - Wallquest, Inc.

MEDICI SOCIETY - Posters - Graphic Arts Unltd. Inc.

MEDICINE CHEST BASICS - Containers - Abbott Laboratories

MEDICINE DANCE MUSIC - Compact discs–prerecorded - Medicine Dance Productions, Inc.

MEDICINE DROPPER - Medicine droppers - Karlen Manufacturing, Inc.

MEDICINE KIT IN A BOTTLE - Pharmaceutical preparations - Mitech Laboratories, Inc.

MEDICINE MAN - Fireplace equipment - Chippewa Traders Ltd.

MEDICINE SHOPPE - Health care products - Medicine Shoppe International Inc.

MEDICINE SHOPPE, THE - Pharmaceutical preparations - Medicine Shoppe International Inc.

MEDICINE SPRINGS - Water–mineral - Lithia Springs Water Co., Inc.

MEDICINE WHEEL - Health care products - Natural Laboratories Corp.

MEDICIS - Dermatological preparations - Medicis Pharmaceutical Corp.

MEDICIS - Yarn - DMC Corp.

MEDICLEAN - Chemical preparations - J.V. Manufacturing Co., Inc.

MEDICLEAR - Herbicides - Monsanto Co.

MEDICLEAR - Pet products - St. Jon Pet Care Products Inc.

MEDICO - Ophthalmic goods - Foremost Optical Products

MEDICO - Pipes–tobacco - S.M. Frank & Co. Inc. (Kaywoodie-Yello-Bole-Medico)

MEDICOLLARS - Veterinary medical equipment - Evsco Pharmaceuticals

MEDICOLOGY - Vitamins and nutritional supplements - Makers of Kal, Inc.

MEDICOLOR - Veterinary medical equipment - Syrvet, Inc.

MEDICONE - Pharmaceutical preparations - E.E. Dickinson Co.

MEDICONE DERMA - Pharmaceutical preparations ☆ - E.E. Dickinson Co.

MEDICONET - Pharmaceutical preparations ☆ - E.E. Dickinson Co.

MEDICOOL - Health care products - Medicool Inc.

MEDICOPASTE - Health care products - Graham-Field Inc.

MEDICORP - Vitamins and nutritional supplements - Medicorp

MEDIC'S CHOICE - Health care products - K.C. Pharmaceuticals, Inc.

MEDICUS FORMULAS, INC. - Skincare products - Medicus Formulas, Inc.

MEDIEVAL LADY - Dolls - Mattel, Inc.

MEDIEVAL MADNESS - Bicycles - Dynacraft Industries Inc.

MEDIEVAL OAK COLLECTION - Shelving units–wood - Naomi Gale Wall Systems

MEDIEVAL PUPPETS - Toys - Lauri Inc.

MEDIEVAL SPAWN - Toys - Todd McFarlane Productions, Inc.

MEDIFAST - Vitamins and nutritional supplements - Jason Pharmaceuticals Inc.

MEDIFAST MAINTAIN - Vitamins and nutritional supplements - Jason Pharmaceuticals Inc.

MEDIFIL - Bandages - Biocore Inc.

MEDIFIN - Pet products - Tetra Sales USA

MEDIFLECTOR - Lamp bulbs - Carley Lamps Inc.

MEDIFLEX - Surgical instruments - Flexbar Machine Corp.

MEDIFOR-X - Hardware - Connecticut Innovations, Inc.

MEDIFRESH - Cleaning preparations–carpet and rug - Castex Industries Inc.

MEDIGESIC - Pharmaceutical preparations ☆ - U.S. Pharmaceutical Corp.

MEDIGESIC PLUS - Pharmaceutical preparations - U.S. Pharmaceutical Corp.

MEDIGLOVE - Gloves ☆ - Ross Laboratories

MEDIGUARD - Gloves–rubber - Jason Marketing Co.

MEDIHALER - Pharmaceutical preparations - Minnesota Mining & Manufacturing Co.

MEDIHALER-EPI - Pharmaceutical preparations - Minnesota Mining & Manufacturing Co.

☆ = Now out of production

MEDIHALER ERGOTAMINE - Pharmaceutical preparations - Minnesota Mining & Manufacturing Co.
MEDIJEL - Pharmaceutical preparations - Republic Drug Co. Inc.
MEDIKETS - Health care products - Halsey Drug Co. Inc.
MEDIKIT - First aid kits - Queensgate Manufacturing Co.
MEDILAX - Laxatives ☆ - Mission Pharmacal Co.
MEDILINK - Motor vehicles–ambulances - Emergency One, Inc.
MEDILOG - Jewelry - Hirsch Speidel Inc.
MEDIMORPHOSIS - Catheters - Louisville Laboratories
MEDINFORM - Computer software - Medecision, Inc.
MEDINOX - Pharmaceutical preparations - Medinox, Inc.
MEDIOCRE MAN - Books–comic - Ransom N. Hundley
MEDIOEVO - Vinegar - Melanie Lane Farms, Inc.
MEDIPAD/GEL - Pharmaceutical preparations - Maxxim Medical Inc.
MEDIPADS - Health care products - Neuromedics
MEDIPEDIC - Mattresses - Mid South Mattress Co.
MEDI+PET - Pet products - Medi+Pet USA, Inc.
MEDIPLANNER - Medical apparatus - Apex Medical Corp.
MEDIPLAST - Bandages - Beiersdorf Inc.
MEDIPLASTER - Pharmaceutical preparations ☆ - Sato Pharmaceutical Inc.
MEDIPLEX - Pharmaceutical preparations - U.S. Pharmaceutical Corp.
MEDIPREN - Analgesics ☆ - McNeil Consumer Products Co.
MEDIQ - First aid kits - MEDIQ Inc.
MEDIQUELL - Cough medicines ☆ - Warner-Lambert Co.
MEDIQUICK - Health care products - Mentholatum Co.
MEDIROM 2000 - Computer software - Kelly/Waldron & Co.
MEDIS - Pharmaceutical preparations - Medis Corp.
MEDISAVE - Vitamins and nutritional supplements - Medisave Pharmacies, Inc.
MEDISCO - Hair care products ☆ - Graham-Field Inc.
MEDISEPT - Tools–hand-operated - Studex USA Inc.
MEDISET - Medical apparatus - Apothecary Products, Inc.
MEDISET - Medical apparatus - Applied Medical Technology, Inc.
MEDISIGN - First aid kits - Romanoff Products Inc.
MEDISPECTRA - Optical machinery - MediSpectra, Inc.
MEDISPHERE - Recording label - Medisphere Corp.
MEDISPRAY - Pharmaceutical preparations - Medical Products Panamericana Inc.
MEDISTYP - Veterinary pharmaceutical preparations - New England Serum Co.
MEDITATION CANDLE - Candles - Solarbonne
MEDITATION GAME - Games - Wff'n Proof Learning Games Associates
MEDITATION MASQUE - Homeopathic remedies - Jason Natural Products, Inc.
MEDITATIONS - Incense ☆ - Chase Collection, Inc.
MEDITE - Fiberboard - Medite Corp.
MEDITERRANEAN - Baskets–wood ☆ - Burlington Basket Co. Inc.
MEDITERRANEAN - Floor coverings ☆ - National Floor Products Co., Inc.
MEDITERRANEAN - Floor coverings–carpet and rugs ☆ - Hollytex Carpet Mills Inc.
MEDITERRANEAN - Furniture–wood - Design Line Cabinets
MEDITERRANEAN - Lanterns–electric - General Electric Co.
MEDITERRANEAN - Seasonings - Peloponnese
MEDITERRANEAN - Shelving units–wood ☆ - Hirsh Co.
MEDITERRANEAN - Tableware–earthenware - Maurice Ceramics of California
MEDITERRANEAN - Tiles–ceramic ☆ - Wenczel Tile Co.
MEDITERRANEAN CLASSIC - Floor coverings - Mannington Resilient Floors
MEDITERRANEAN COLLECTION, THE - Knobs–wood - Schlage Lock Co.
MEDITERRANEAN DELIGHT - Sandwiches–prepackaged - GDF, Inc.
MEDITERRANEAN GOURMET - Spices and extracts - Finest Kind Spices
MEDITERRANEAN GYROS - Lamb - Corfu Foods, Inc.
MEDITERRANEAN LATORTA - Food products - G & G Specialty Foods, Inc.
MEDITERRANEAN MARJORAM - Perfumes - Dana Perfumes Corp.
MEDITERRANEAN MYSTIQUE - Spices and extracts - Spicemill, Ltd.
MEDITERRANEAN RUSTICS - Tiles–ceramic - Capitol Tile Import Co.
MEDITERRANEAN SUN - Hair care products - Revlon Consumer Products Corp.
MEDITERRANEE - Food products - De Medici Imports Ltd.
MEDITERRANEE - Frames–eyeglass ☆ - Universal/Univis Inc.
MEDITERRANIA - Dishes–china - Mikasa Co.
MEDITORQUE AMERICA - Dental equipment - Medidenta International, Inc.
MEDITRAY - Medical apparatus - Case Medical, Inc.
MEDITUSSIN-X - Pharmaceutical preparations ☆ - Roberts/Hauck Pharmaceuticals Inc.
MEDIUM SALSA - Sauces - Guiltless Gourmet, Inc.
MEDIUM XPRESS - Paper - Fairfield Recycled Papers Inc.
MEDIVAC - Vacuum cleaners and accessories–commercial - Kent Co.
MEDIVATORS - Garbage disposal units–commercial - MediVators Inc.

MEDIVISION - Optical machinery - Medivision Scope Service Center, Inc.
MEDIVISIONS - Medical apparatus - Medivisions, Inc.
MEDI+VITE - Vitamins and nutritional supplements - Edward M. Andujar
MEDIZINC - Pharmaceutical preparations ☆ - U.S. Pharmaceutical Corp.
MEDLEY - Computer peripheral equipment - Lexmark International, Inc.
MEDLEY - Computer software ☆ - Milliken Publishing Co. (Computer Software Div.)
MEDLEY - Floor coverings–carpet and rugs - Colonial Mills Inc.
MEDLEY - Floor coverings–carpet and rugs ☆ - Richmond Carpet Mills
MEDLEY - Furniture - Key City Furniture Co.
MEDLEY - Hardware ☆ - Amerock Corp.
MEDLEY - Herbicides - Nomix, Inc.
MEDLEY - Lenses–optical - Kelley & Hueber
MEDLEY - Puzzles - Hasbro, Inc.
MEDLEY - Rings–jewelry - Artcarved Inc.
MEDLEY - Tableware–china ☆ - Lenox, Inc.
MEDLEY - Tiles–ceramic ☆ - American Olean Tile Co.
MEDLEY - Underwear and nightwear - Maidenform Inc.
MEDLEY - Wallpaper - Capital Carousel Inc.
MEDLEY COLLECTION BY PAUL LEVY - Wallpaper - Regency Mills Inc.
MEDLEY COLLECTION, THE - Tableware–china ☆ - Pfaltzgraff Investment Co.
MEDLEY OF CAROLS - Christmas ornaments ☆ - Alltrista Corp.
MEDLIN - Fungicides ☆ - Noble Pine Products Co.
MEDLINX - Computer software - Medical Technology Inc.
MEDLOG - Computer software - Information Analysis Corp.
MEDMARC RISKASSIST - Computer software - Medmarc Insurance Co., Inc.
MEDMODEL - Computer software - Promodel Corp.
MEDNET - Computer software ☆ - Cerner Corp.
MEDNEXT - Medical equipment - Mednext Inc.
MEDO - Deodorizers - Medo Industries, Inc.
MEDO MAID - Butter ☆ - Commercial Creamery Co.
MEDOPTICS - Lenses–optical - Younger Manufacturing Co.
MEDOS - Computer software - Nynex Corp.
MEDOSWEET FARMS - Dairy products - C & F Distributors, Inc.
MEDOTAR - Pharmaceutical preparations - Medco Lab Inc.
MEDPLUS - Computer peripheral equipment - Medplus, Inc.
MEDPLUS - Computer software - Solutions Plus Inc.
MEDPOPDISPLAY - Pet products - Seachem Laboratories
MEDQUERY - Computer software - Aetna Life Insurance Co.
MEDRALONE - Pharmaceutical preparations - Keene Pharmaceuticals Inc.
MEDREX - Pharmaceutical preparations - C.S. Ruckstuhl Co. Inc.
MEDROL - Pharmaceutical preparations - Upjohn Co.
MEDRONE - Health care products - Kay Pharmacal Co. Inc.
MEDSAVER - Hypodermic needles - Becton, Dickinson and Co.
MEDSCHED - Computer software - Principal Decision Systems International
MEDSCORE - Computer software - The MEDSTAT Group, Inc.
MEDSEARCH - Computer software - Global Learning Systems, Inc.
MEDSELECT SYSTEMS - Medical apparatus - Medselect Systems, Inc.
MEDSERIES4 - Computer software - Shared Medical Systems Corp.
MEDSOURCE PRN - Health care products ☆ - Medical Data Institute
MEDSTAFF - Computer software - Health Planning Consultants
MEDSTOR - Desk sets - Mailbox International, Inc.
MEDTEACH - Publisher's imprints - American Society of Health-System Pharmacists, Inc.
MEDTECH - Health care products - Medtech Laboratories Inc.
MEDTEXX - Gloves - Latex Partners, Inc.
MEDTOOLS CORPORATION - Computer software - Protech Medical Software, Inc.
MEDTRAK - Computers–personal - Medical Technology Systems, Inc.
MEDTRONIC - Pharmaceutical preparations - Medtronic, Inc.
MEDUCATOR - Computer software - Interactive Information, Inc.
MED$URE - Computer storage devices - Time Solutions Inc.
MEDURI FARMS - Fruits–dried - Meduri Farms, Inc.
MEDUSA - Bicycles - Python USA, Inc.
MEDUSA - Fish–canned or cured - Bel Canto Fancy Foods Ltd.
MEDUSA - Musical instrument accessories - Whirlwind Music Distributors, Inc.
MEDUSA - Recording label - Enigma Entertainment
MEDUSA/HIGH-EARLY - Cement ☆ - Medusa Corp.
MEDVIEW - Computer hardware - Fakespace, Inc.
MEDVISION - Computer software - Imnet Systems, Inc.
MEDVISION - Labels–paper - Timemed Labeling Systems, Inc.
MEDVITA - Health care products - Medical Information Systems
MEDWISE - Notebooks and notepads - Wiseman Medical Documents, Inc.
MEDWORD - Tape recorders - Lanier Voice Products
MEDXPERT - Computer software - Multiview Inc.

☆ = Now out of production

MEE CHUN - Sauces and dressings ☆ - American Roland Food Corp.
MEE TU - Noodles - Allied Old English, Inc.
MEEKER - Wallets - Meeker Co.
MEEKONG - Fabrics - Dan River Inc.
MEEKS FIREWOOD - Fireplace logs–treated - Meeks Firewood Co., Ltd.
MEERO - Cosmetics - Pacific Corp. of America
MEERSCHAUM - Pipes–tobacco - Dr. Grabow Pre-Smoked Pipes Inc.
MEESE FAMILY, THE - Toys–stuffed - Lois Hall Creations
MEESTERHAND - Cookies - Holland-American Importing Co. Inc.
MEET SHEET, THE - Paper - Nextech, Inc.
MEET THE COMPUTER - Computer software ☆ - Sunburst Communications, Inc.
MEET THE DINOSAURS - Craft supplies ☆ - VIP/VIP Crafts
MEETER - Food products - Stokely USA, Inc.
MEETIN' UP - Paper products - Jimmie Mae Franks
MEETING CONEXION - Computer peripheral equipment - Leadership 2000, Inc.
MEETING MAGIC - Computer software - Frank S. Bruffey, Jr.
MEETING MINDER - Timers–appliance - Stokes Publishing Co., Inc.
MEETING PLACE - Furniture ☆ - Hammary Furniture Co. Inc.
MEETING POINT SEAL - Weather stripping - KEL-EEZ
MEETING ROOM, THE - Computer software - Eden Systems Corp.
MEETING SPACE - Computer software - World Benders, Inc.
MEETINGHOUSE - Furniture - Vermont Tubbs Inc.
MEETINGPLACE - Communications equipment - Latitude Communications, Inc.
MEETINGRIGHT - Computer software - Xerox Corp.
MEEYOWL - Toys–stuffed ☆ - Gund, Inc.
MEFIX - Health care products - Scott Health Care
MEFOXIN - Antibiotics - Merck & Co., Inc. (Merck Research Laboratories)
MEG - Computer software - Procomp Software, Inc.
MEG - Frames–eyeglass - Zylo Ware Corp.
MEG - Slippers - Daniel Green Co.
MEG ADJUST - Playground equipment - Swings & Things
MEG GREEN'S FINANCIAL WORKOUT - Recording label - Meg Green's Financial Workouts Inc.
MEG-MUSIC - Musical instruments ☆ - Oscar Schmidt International Inc.
M.E.G. RECORDS - Recording label - M.E.G. Records Co.
MEGA - Amplifiers ☆ - Fender Musical Instruments
MEGA - Aquariums–household - Vacor USA
MEGA - Cleaning preparations - Topco Associates, Inc.
MEGA - Drilling anchors ☆ - ITW Ramset/Red Head
MEGA - Floor coverings–carpet and rugs - Lees Carpets
MEGA - Hair care products - Cosmair Inc.
MEGA - Hair care products ☆ - Charlene Hair Products Inc.
MEGA - Metals - Spectra Products Corp.
MEGA - Mops - Empire Brushes, Inc.
MEGA - Prophylactics - Ansell Inc. (Personal Products Div.)
MEGA 10 PAK BUBBLE YUM - Chewing gum - Nabisco Brands Inc.
MEGA 75 - Vitamins and nutritional supplements - Dixon-Shane Inc.
MEGA-2000 - Vitamins and nutritional supplements - Pharmavite Corp.
MEGA-ACTION-SHEET - Wallpaper ☆ - Environmental Graphics Inc.
MEGA AM-PRO - Pharmaceutical preparations ☆ - Saron Pharmacal Corp.
MEGA ANTI-OXIDANT COMPLEX - Vitamins and nutritional supplements - Natural Organics, Inc.
MEGA BALANCE - Vitamins and nutritional supplements - Slim for Life, Inc.
MEGA BASS - Amplifiers–musical instrument - Peavey Electronics Corp.
MEGA BEAM - Spotlights - United States Stove Co. Inc.
MEGA BITE - Golfing equipment - Besco USA
MEGA BLAST - Fireworks - L. W. Loyd Co., Inc.
MEGA BLASTER - Toys ☆ - Matchbox Toys USA
MEGA BLASTER - Toys–guns - Diversified Specialists, Inc.
MEGA BURNER 5000 - Vitamins and nutritional supplements - Basic Organics, Inc.
MEGA C-BIO - Vitamins and nutritional supplements - Naturally Vitamin Supplements Inc.
MEGA CAL - Pharmaceutical preparations ☆ - Holistic Products Corp.
MEGA CBR - Vitamins and nutritional supplements - Source Naturals
MEGA CD CHANGER - Audio equipment - Matsushita Electric Corp. of America
MEGA CEE COMPLETE - Vitamins and nutritional supplements - Natural Organics, Inc.
MEGA CELL - Batteries - Exide Corp.
MEGA-CELL - Vitamins and nutritional supplements - Farnam Cos. Inc.
MEGA CELLULITE - Health care products - Above All Health Inc.
MEGA CHAMBER SYSTEM - Audio equipment - Vincent E. Pernell

MEGA CHROMIUM PICOLINATE - Vitamins and nutritional supplements - Source Naturals
MEGA COTTONS - Dickeys - Signal Apparel Co. Inc.
MEGA CURLS - Hair care products - Cabot Laboratories Inc.
MEGA CYCLE - Batteries - Exide Corp.
MEGA-E - Computer software - Larscom Inc.
MEGA-EPA - Pharmaceutical preparations - Rugby Laboratories Inc.
MEGA EPA - Vitamins and nutritional supplements - Source Naturals
MEGA-FLEECE - Shirts - Signal Knitwear Co.
MEGA-FLEX - Cables - Horizon Music, Inc.
MEGA FLOOD - Floodlights - RAB Electric
MEGA FORCE - Toys - Tonka Corp.
MEGA FORCE - Vitamins and nutritional supplements - Natural Organics, Inc.
MEGA FORTUNE - Games - Fortunet, Inc.
MEGA FRUIT - Candy - Leaf, Inc.
MEGA-GARLIC - Pharmaceutical preparations - Michigan Pharmaceutical
MEGA-GENTIC - Batteries - Berison Industries Inc.
MEGA GLA-260 - Vitamins and nutritional supplements - Source Naturals
MEGA GLA-300 - Vitamins and nutritional supplements - Source Naturals
MEGA-GLO - Fishing lures - Den Manufacturing Co.
MEGA GRIP - Pens - Scripto-Tokai Corp.
MEGA-HOLD - Hair care products - Jingles International
MEGA INTERNATIONAL RECORDS - Recording label - Doc Holiday's Hit Factory's Inc.
MEGA IV - Tires–automobile ☆ - Hercules Tire & Rubber Co.
MEGA KID - Vitamins and nutritional supplements - Source Naturals
MEGA-LASER - Inks - Van Son Holland Ink Corp. of America
MEGA-LIFE - Vitamins and nutritional supplements - Michigan Pharmaceutical
MEGA-LIFT - Skin care products - Mana Products, Inc.
MEGA-LOC - Antislip rug treatment - American Non-Slip Products
MEGA-LOCK - Locks–padlocks ☆ - Kryptonite Corp.
MEGA LOSS 1000 - Pharmaceuticals - Taleigh, Inc.
MEGA MAGIC - Fireworks - Alamo Fireworks, Inc.
MEGA MASS - See **MR. MASS**
MEGA MASS - Vitamins and nutritional supplements - Sportstar Health & Fitness
MEGA MAX - Photo albums - May Department Stores Co.
MEGA MEAL - Food products - KFC Corp.
MEGA MEATS - Meat products - Mega Meats Inc.
MEGA MELTS - Sandwiches–prepackaged - Newport Creamery, Inc.
MEGA METAL - Drums–musical instruments ☆ - LP Music Group
MEGA METRIC - Automotive repair shops–tires - Summit Tire and Battery, Inc.
MEGA MIGHTY MALTS - Candy - New England Confectionery Co.
MEGA MILLET - Bird feeds - American Bird Products, Inc.
MEGA MIRACLE - Hair care products - Redmond Products, Inc.
MEGA MOLDS - Toys - Toymax Inc.
MEGA MORPH - Computer software - Advantageware, Inc.
MEGA MOTO-BOTS - Toy robot/trucks ☆ - Intex Recreation Corp.
MEGA MOVERS - Toys - Mega Toys
MEGA MUG - Housewares - Aladdin Industries, Inc.
MEGA MUGS - Containers–insulated - Aladdin Industries, Inc.
MEGA MULTI - Health care products - Above All Health Inc.
MEGA-MUNCH - Potato chips - Liberty Bell Management Co.
MEGA-PAK - Decals and transfers - Paper Magic Group Inc.
MEGA-PAK - Filters–air - Air Kontrol Inc.
MEGA PC - Vitamins and nutritional supplements - Ingersoll & Associates
MEGA PERM - Hair care products - Focus 21 International Inc.
MEGA PLEX - Vitamins and nutritional supplements - Natural Organics, Inc.
MEGA PLEX MINORS - Fertilizers - Howard Fertilizer Co., Inc.
MEGA POKER - Game machines - IGT - North America
MEGA POTS - Flower pots–plastic - Contico International Inc.
MEGA POWER - Electrical equipment - Magl Power & Electronics, Inc.
MEGA POWER MP - Fuel additives - Mega Power, Inc.
MEGA PRO - Printers–computer ☆ - Image Systems Corp.
MEGA PRO 110 - Rackets–tennis - Spalding Sports Worldwide
MEGA-RACK - Shelving units–metal - Hirsh Co.
MEGA RELLA - Food products ☆ - Rella Good Cheese Co.
MEGA RIPPED - Recording label - Weider Nutrition Group, Inc.
MEGA-ROM - Computer storage devices–optical - Quantum Leap Technologies, Inc.
MEGA-SAN - Cleaning preparations - West Agro, Inc.
MEGA-SANA - Vitamins and nutritional supplements - Bio San Laboratories Inc.
MEGA SCENT - Deodorizers - Westland Sales Inc.
MEGA-SEAL - Adhesives and sealants - International Mega Seal Corp.

MEGA-SEAL - Caulking compounds - Nu Puttie Corp.
MEGA-SHIELD - Surgical supplies - Superior Surgical Manufacturing Co. Inc.
MEGA-SHOCK - Electrical equipment - Fi-Shock Inc.
MEGA SIZZ - Toys–models ☆ - Estes Industries
MEGA-SOUND - Audio equipment - Royal Sound Co. Inc.
MEGA SPARK - Automotive parts and accessories - Northern Automotive Corp.
MEGA-SPARKEL - Fishing lures - Den Manufacturing Co.
MEGA SPEED READING - Recording label - Tru-Vantage International Inc.
MEGA SPORT - Sporting goods - Toshoku America Inc.
MEGA STAMP - Stamps–hand - California Rubber Stamp Co., Inc.
MEGA STAR - Archery equipment - Golden Key Futura, Inc.
MEGA TALKING - Toys - Mattel, Inc.
MEGA TAN - Suntan lotions - Richardson-Vicks USA
MEGA-TARSAL PLUS - Sporting goods - Wildlife Research Center, Inc.
MEGA-TEE - T-shirts–men's - Signal Knitwear Co.
MEGA-TIME - Vitamins and nutritional supplements - Nutrition Enterprises
MEGA TONE - Musical instrument accessories ☆ - Selmer Co. Inc.
MEGA-TOYS - Pet products - Pyramid Bird Toys
MEGA TR - Tires–automobile - Hercules Tire & Rubber Co.
MEGA TRANSPORT - Toys - Mega Toys
MEGA TREND - Furniture - Vaughan Furniture Co. Inc.
MEGA UNI CEE - Vitamins and nutritional supplements - Natural Organics, Inc.
MEGA VEG - Vitamins and nutritional supplements - Natural Organics, Inc.
MEGA-VITA - Pharmaceutical preparations - Saron Pharmacal Corp.
MEGA-VITAL - Vitamins and nutritional supplements - Great Life Laboratories Inc.
MEGA-VITE 85 - Vitamins and nutritional supplements - Source Naturals
MEGA WARHEADS - Candy - Foreign Candy Co. Inc.
MEGA WATERPROOF - Suntan lotions - Maui Skin Research, Inc.
MEGA WATT - Bicycles - Huffy Corp.
MEGA-WEAPONS - Toys–guns - Mattel, Inc.
MEGA WHITE - Mouthwashes ☆ - Dep Corp.
MEGA WRITER - Computer software - Megahaus, Inc.
MEGA ZINC - Vitamins and nutritional supplements - Natural Organics, Inc.
MEGABEE - Pharmaceutical preparations - Wesley Pharmacal Co. Inc.
MEGABERRY - Beverages–carbonated - Jel Sert Co.
MEGABIT - Gasoline - Solkatronic Chemicals, Inc.
MEGABLOCS - Toys–blocks - Learning Products Inc.
MEGABOND - Nail care products - Pavion Ltd.
MEGABOND - Nail glue - Pavcom, Inc.
MEGABOSS - Vacuum cleaners and accessories - The Eureka Co.
MEGABOX - Cabinets - Eagle Affiliates, Inc.
MEGABUBBLES - Toys - Pearl Toys Inc.
MEGABUFFER - Computer hardware buffer - D.E.W. International Corp.
MEGACACHE - Computer peripheral equipment - Imperial Technology, Inc.
MEGACARD - Medical emergency card - Microcard Systems
MEGACARD - Paper - Megacards, Inc.
MEGACARDS - Trading cards and stamps - Megacards, Inc.
MEGACE - Pharmaceutical preparations - Bristol-Myers Squibb Co.
MEGACLIP - Paper clips - Acco World Corp.
MEGACODE - Garage door openers - Linear Corp.
MEGACOLORS - Lipsticks - Pavion Ltd.
MEGACORP - Computer games - Emil D. Scheifler
MEGACORP INTERNATIONAL - Computer software - Emil D. Scheifler
MEGACRIMP - Hoses - Gates Rubber Co. (Automotive Aftermarket/Hardware Sales Div.)
MEGACRISP - Frozen vegetables - J.R. Simplot Co.
MEGACRUNCH - Vegetables–frozen - J.R. Simplot Co.
MEGADEUCY - Games - Mega Games, Inc.
MEGADITTO - Jewelry - Henry A. Bartholomay
MEGADITTOS - Games - Richard Madison
MEGADOPHILUS - Health care products - Natren Inc.
MEGADOSE - Pharmaceutical preparations - Nature's Bounty, Inc.
MEGADRAW - Electronic equipment - Incom, Inc.
MEGADRIVE - Guitars - Dimarzio, Inc.
MEGADYNE - Electrical equipment - MMI
MEGAEPA - Vitamins and nutritional supplements - Source Naturals
MEGAFASHION U.S.A. - Apparel and accessories - Sing Lin Wong
MEGAFEND - Boats - Yacht Ten, Inc.
MEGAFILE - Artists' materials ☆ - Dahle USA
MEGAFLEX - Computer software - First Financial Resources, Inc.
MEGAFLEX - Exercising equipment - Diversified Products Corp.
MEGAFLOW - Connectors–electrical - Coilhose Pneumatics Inc.
MEGAFLOW - Fluid pumps - Interpro, Inc.
MEGAFONTS - Computer software - Marshall Graphics Systems

MEGAFOOD - Vitamins and nutritional supplements - Bio San Laboratories Inc.
MEGAFORCE - Bicycles ☆ - Huffy Corp.
MEGAFORCE - Recording label - Atlantic Records
MEGAFORK - Forks - Universal Food Fork Corp.
MEGAGAMMON - Games - Mega Games, Inc.
MEGAGEARS - Gears - Power Engineering & Manufacturing, Ltd.
MEGAGOLD - Vitamins and nutritional supplements - Savior Int'l., Inc.
MEGAGUARD - Sealant - Kent Integrated Scientific Systems, Inc.
MEGAHELTH 75 - Vitamins and nutritional supplements - Health Products Corp.
MEGAHERT - Toys - Mattel, Inc.
MEGAHERTZ - Modems - Megahertz Corp.
MEGAHIT - Golfing equipment - Lawrence Y. Igarashi
MEGAKENO - Game machines - IGT - North America
MEGAKINETICS - Tape players–cassette - Megakinetics Inc.
MEGALASH - Cosmetics - Pavion Ltd.
MEGALASTINE - Housewares - Helga Van Dyke Skin Care
MEGALINK - Computer software - Insmark, Inc.
MEGALIT - Video game cartridges - Takara USA Corp.
MEGALOC - Clamps–metal - Game Time, Inc.
MEGALON - Automotive parts and accessories - Surface Science Corp.
MEGALUX - Lighting equipment - Badger USA
MEGAMAZE - Games ☆ - Polymedia Communications Corp.
MEGAMEDIA - Computer hardware - Megamedia Computer Corp
MEGAMILE - Tires - Oliver Rubber Co.
MEGAMIN - Vitamin - Pharma-Rex, Inc.
MEGAMIND - Vitamins and nutritional supplements - Source Naturals
MEGAMIX - Audio equipment ☆ - C.T.I. Audio Inc.
MEGAMIX - Concrete–ready-mix ☆ - Sakrete Inc.
MEGAMODULE - Cabinets - Eagle Affiliates, Inc.
MEGAMOTION - Circuit boards - Alpha Systems Lab, Inc.
MEGAN - Bedding–linen - Dan River Inc.
MEGAN - Dolls - Hasbro, Inc.
MEGAN - Frames–eyeglass - Hoya Corp. USA
MEGAN - Frames–eyeglass - U.S. Optical Frame Co.
MEGAN O'NEAL - Underwear and nightwear - Shamrock Outlet Stores, Inc.
MEGANOPOLY - Games - Mega Games, Inc.
MEGAOATS - Horse feed - Milo A. Martin
MEGAPAGE - Radio communications equipment - Marketronics Corp.
MEGAPAK - Computer software - Megamedia Computer Corp
MEGAPLEX - Vitamins and nutritional supplements - Legere Pharmaceuticals Inc.
MEGAPOTS - Flower pots–earthenware ☆ - Contico International Inc.
MEGAPOWER - Liquid crystal displays - USA Megapower Technologies, Inc.
MEGARACE - Computer storage devices–optical - Mindscape Software Inc.
MEGARAD - Plastics - Dow Chemical Co.
MEGARAMA - Hardware - Merchandising Inventives, Inc.
MEGAS - Cotton–sterilized - Marianna Imports, Inc.
MEGAS - Floor coverings–carpet and rugs - Cumberland Mills Inc.
MEGAS - Skin care products ☆ - B & B Distributors
MEGAS SUPER SOFT - Cosmetics - Megas Beauty Care, Inc.
MEGASAR - Film - Imnet Systems, Inc.
MEGASCOPE - Telescopes - Wild Planet Toys, Inc.
MEGASERVE - Printers–computer ☆ - Image Systems Corp.
MEGASERVER - Computer software - Baseline II Inc.
MEGASIL - Concrete–ready-mix ☆ - Sakrete Inc.
MEGASPIDER - Toys - Tonka Corp.
MEGASTAR - Soccer equipment - Mikasa Sports
MEGATECH - Audio equipment - International Music Corp.
MEGATECH - Computer software - Megatech & Design, Inc.
MEGATECH - Golfing equipment - Golfsmith International Inc.
MEGATEK X-CELLERATOR - Computer circuit board - Megatek Corp.
MEGATON - Pharmaceutical preparations - Hyrex Pharmaceuticals
MEGATONE - Recording label - Megatone Records Inc.
MEGATONE - Toners - Ner Data Products, Inc.
MEGATONE HOUSE - Recording label - Megatone Records Inc.
MEGATOR - Toys - Mattel, Inc.
MEGATRAX - Recording label - Megatrax Production Music, Inc.
MEGATREND - Eyeglasses - Martin-Copeland Eyewear Corp.
MEGATREND - Floor coverings–carpet and rugs ☆ - J and J Industries Inc.
MEGATRON - Carburetors - Lectron Fuel Systems, Inc.
MEGATRON - Water purification systems - Atlantic Ultraviolet Corp.
MEGATRON 75 - Vitamins - Jamco Inc.
MEGATUFF - Hoses - Gates Rubber Co. (Automotive Aftermarket/Hardware Sales Div.)

☆ = Now out of production

MEGAVIMS - Vitamins and nutritional supplements ☆ - Great Life Laboratories Inc.

MEGAVITAL FORTE - Health care products - Futurebiotics

MEGAVITAL HP FORTE - Vitamins and nutritional supplements - Futurebiotics

MEGAVITAL II - Vitamins and nutritional supplements ☆ - Futurebiotics

MEGAVOICE - Audio equipment - Paso Sound Products Inc.

MEGAWARE - Computer storage devices - Megaware, Inc.

MEGAWARE KEEL GUARD - Boating equipment and accessories - Megaware Boat Protection Products, Inc.

MEGAWATT - Vitamins and nutritional supplements - Shaperite Concepts, Ltd.

MEGAWORX - Furniture - Hunt Holdings, Inc.

MEGAZINE - Books—comic ☆ - Marvel Entertainment Group, Inc.

MEGAZOID - Bicycles - Dynacraft Industries Inc.

MEGAZONE - Shirts - Dev Imports Ltd.

MEGAZYMES - Vitamins and nutritional supplements - Bio San Laboratories Inc.

MEGGAHORN - Containers—plastic - Nickel Industries, Inc.

MEGGEZONES - Cough drops ☆ - The Montclair Co.

MEGGIE - Dolls - Dakin Inc.

MEGHA - Apparel—women's - Indigo Inc.

MEGHAM - Ophthalmic goods ☆ - Luxottica

MEGHAN ELISSE - Apparel—men's - B.I.Y.A.Y.C.D.A.

MEGO - Toys ☆ - Mego Financial Corp.

MEGOXY - Vitamins and nutritional supplements - Bio San Laboratories Inc.

MEGS - Automotive parts and accessories - Cone Engineering, Inc.

MEGUIAR'S - Automotive parts and accessories - Meguiar's, Inc.

MEHAZ COLLECTION - Manicure preparations - Mehaz International, Inc.

MEHAZ MEDCIDE MEDALLION DISINFECTANT - Disinfectants - Mehaz International, Inc.

MEHERRIN RIVER OUTFITTERS - Men's apparel and footwear - Peebles Inc.

MEHICA - Microscopes - Avriel Group, Inc.

MEHKI COLLECTIONS - Apparel—women's - Mehki Designs, Inc.

MEHRON - Cosmetics - Mehron Inc.

MEHU-MAIJA - Housewares - Mehu-Maija Products

M.E.I. - Backpacks - Mountain Equipment, Inc.

MEI - Belts—industrial - Mechanical Elastomerics, Inc.

MEI - Circuit boards—printed - Maddox Enterprises, Inc.

MEI - Luggage - Mountain Equipment, Inc.

MEI-BEE - Wallpaper - Heritage House Designs

MEI-CHA - Cosmetics - Mei-Chi-Na Hsinyen Co., Ltd.

MEI FA - Barrettes - Shaune Bazner Accessories, Inc.

MEI LU - Floor coverings—carpet and rugs ☆ - Rugby Rugs Inc.

MEI MEI - Cookies - Mei Mei Chocolate Dipped Fortune Cookies & Confections

MEI-MEI - Stationery - Smithsonian Institution

MEI TOO! - Barrettes ☆ - Shaune Bazner Accessories, Inc.

MEIER'S - Fruit drinks—bottled or canned - John C. Meier Grape Juice Co.

MEIER'S - Wines - Meier's Wine Cellars Inc.

MEIJI - Food products - L.J. Rench & Co.

MEIKAI - Cameras - Pierre Cardin Electronique

MEIKEI - Cameras - Archer Worldwide

MEIKI - Pens - Archer Worldwide

MEILINK - Safes - Meilink Safe Co.

MEILINK-SDP-1 - Safes ☆ - Meilink Safe Co.

MEILLEUR - Food products ☆ - Vincent Food Industries Inc.

MEIN STREET WOK - Paper products - Sysco Corp.

MEINEKE DISCOUNT MUFFLERS - Office accessories - Meineke Discount Muffler Shops, Inc.

MEINHART - Apparel and accessories - Meinhart & Associates, Inc.

MEINL WESTON - Musical instruments - Orpheus Music Inc.

MEISEL - Musical instruments - Meisel Music Inc.

MEISSONER - Artists' materials - M. Grumbacher Inc.

MEISTER - Sweaters - Hagemeister-Lert Inc.

MEISTER BRAU - Beer - Miller Brewing Co.

MEISTER BRAU LIGHT - Reduced-calorie beer - Miller Brewing Co.

MEISTER-TOPF - Soups—canned - Stockmeyer North America

MEISTERGRAM - Craft supplies - Meistergram Inc.

MEISTERKLASSE - Harmonicas - Hohner Inc.

MEISTERMATIC - Craft supplies ☆ - Meistergram Inc.

MEISTERSATZ REPAIR KITS - Automotive parts and accessories - CRP Industries, Inc.

MEISTERSTUCK - Pens ☆ - Koh-I-Noor, Inc.

MEJORAL - Analgesics - Sterling Winthrop Inc.

MEJORALITO - Analgesics - Sterling Winthrop Inc.

M.E.K. - Paint removers - Klean-Strip

MEK-LOCK - Nuts and bolts - Mek-Lock Fasteners USA

MEKAN-I-KLOTH - Paper—toweling - Georgia-Pacific Corp.

MEKANECK - Toys - Mattel, Inc.

MEKHONG - Beverages—alcohol - Tucuru

MEKKA - Tape players ☆ - Fortune Star Products Corp.

MEKONTROL - Switches—electric - Joslyn Clark Controls, Inc.

MEKOR - Electrical equipment - Drew Chemical Corp.

MEKTON - Games - R. Talsorian Games, Inc.

MEL - Ophthalmic goods - Rozin Optical Export Corp.

MEL BAY - Musical instrument accessories - Mel Bay Publications Inc.

MEL-DEK - Adhesives and sealants - W.R. Meadows Inc.

MEL-EZY - Disinfectants ☆ - ICI Americas Inc.

MEL-O-BAKE - Shortening - Humko Products

MEL-O-BRIAR - Pipes—tobacco ☆ - Mastercraft Pipes Inc.

MEL O CREAM - Food products - G.C. Bear & Co.

MEL-O-CREME - Honey - Melford Olson Honey Co.

MEL-O-DEE - Harmonicas - William Kratt Co.

MEL-O-DEES - Toys—stuffed ☆ - Fun World Inc.

MEL-O-DINE - Food products ☆ - Lawrence Foods Inc.

MEL-O-HONEY - Honey - Melford Olson Honey Co.

MEL-O-PURE - Shortening - Kraft Food Ingredients Corp.

MEL-O-TILE - Rubber—molded - Melflex Products Co.

MEL-O-TREDS - Steps - Melflex Products Co.

MEL-ROL - Adhesives and sealants - W.R. Meadows Inc.

MELA-CAL - Vitamins and nutritional supplements - Melaleuca, Inc.

MELA MIRACLE - Pet products - Melacorp of Australia

MELA MIRACLE - Pet shops - Melaleuca, Inc.

MELA OIL PLUS - Pet products - Hansen's Pet Products Co.

MELAFACE - Paneling - International Paper (Decorative Products Division)

MELAJUVEN - Vitamins and nutritional supplements - Barth-Spencer Corp.

MELAJUVEN - Vitamins and nutritional supplements - Barth's Nutra Products

MELALENS - Lenses—optical - DWH Inc.

MELALEUCA - Skin care products - Rene Furterer

MELALEUCA - Skin care products - Melaleuca, Inc.

MELAMAGIC - Cleaning preparations - Melaleuca, Inc.

MELAMINE - Chemical preparations - Melamine Chemicals, Inc.

MELAMINE - Paints - Kyanize Paint Co.

MELAMITE - Plastics—laminated ☆ - Manville/Schuller

MELANEX - Pharmaceutical preparations - Neutrogena Corp.

MELANGE - Fabrics - Greenwood Mills Inc.

MELANGE - Floor coverings—carpet and rugs - First Editions Wallcoverings & Fabrics Inc.

MELANGE - Floor coverings—carpet and rugs - Whitecrest Carpet Mills

MELANGE - Handbags - Design by Pristine Inc.

MELANGE - Lenses—optical - Kelley & Hueber

MELANGE - Perfumes - Kristine M. Schoenauer

MELANGE - Wallpaper - Tony Putnam Inc.

MELANGE - Yogurt ☆ - Dannon Co., Inc.

MELANGE A TROIS - Wines ☆ - Fife Vineyards LLC

MELANIE - Floor coverings—carpet and rugs - Queen Carpet Corp.

MELANIE - Ophthalmic goods - Swank Optical

MELANIE - Tableware—china ☆ - Lenox, Inc.

MELANIE - Toys - Eugene Doll & Novelty Co. Inc.

MELANIE MCQUADE MATERNITY - Apparel—women's - Kohl's Department Stores, Inc.

MELANIN PLUS - Skin care products - Frances Christian Gaskin Inc.

MELANOL - Pharmaceutical preparations - Syosset Laboratories Inc.

MELANZONA - Apparel and accessories - Item Ltd.

MELAPLAS - Adhesives and sealants - Woodtape Co.

MELAPOWER - Detergents - Melaleuca, Inc.

MELARD - Bathroom fixtures - Masco Corp.

MELASOL - Fungicides - Metabolic Products Corp.

MELATEX - Shelving units—wood - Modar Inc.

MELATILE - Plastics—laminated - Plywood & Panels Inc.

MELATONIC - Vitamins and nutritional supplements - Barth's Nutra Products

MELATONICIN - Vitamins and nutritional supplements - Health Products Corp.

MELATONIN - Pharmaceutical preparations - Global Pharmaceutical Corp.

MELATONIN - Vitamins and nutritional supplements - Vitamin Research Products Inc.

MELATONIN COMPLEX - Vitamins and nutritional supplements - Source Naturals

MELATONIN PLUS - Pharmaceutical preparations - Vita Plus Industries Inc.

MELATONIN SUBLINGUAL - Vitamins and nutritional supplements - Better Health Products

MELATONIN ULTRA - Vitamins and nutritional supplements - Freelife International LP

MELAWOOD - Furniture - Columbia Forest Products, Inc.

MELBA - Cigars ☆ - Phillies Cigar Co.

☆ = Now out of production

MELBA - Food products - Martin Brothers Seafood Co. (food products)
MELBA - Food products - Melba Food Specialties Inc.
MELBERN - Wallpaper ☆ - Wolf-Gordon Inc.
MELBOURNE - Boats–motor ☆ - Holiday Distributing Co.
MELBOURNE - Office supplies - Faber-Castell Corp.
MELBOURNE - Pillows - Pillowtex Corp.
MELBOURNE - Tables–wood - Riverside Furniture Corp.
MELBOURNE & PERTH - Giftware - Brushcreek Creative Co.
MELBOURNE GROUP, THE - Furniture - Bean Station Furniture Factory Inc.
MELBOURNE, THE - Fencing–chain link - Nebraska Plastics, Inc.
MELBRO - Food products - Conagra, Inc.
MELBROKE - Neckties - Spiegel, Inc.
MELCARD - Electronic equipment - Mitsubishi Electronics America Inc.
MELCH'S - Specialty salads - Melch's Food Corp.
MELCO - Cigars ☆ - Geo. Melhado & Co.
MELCO - Serving carts - Tomlinson Industries
MELCOR II - Plastics–laminated - Sterling Engineered Products Inc.
MELDAC - Recording label - Creav Inc. USA
MELE - Jewelry - Lisa Mele Thomson
MELE - Music boxes - Mele Manufacturing Co. Farrington Packaging Co.
MELEA - Floor coverings ☆ - Tarkett, Inc.
MELENE - Floor coverings - Mannington Resilient Floors
MELETTI - Wines - Paterno Imports, Ltd.
MELF THE DWELF - Toys ☆ - Brushcreek Creative Co.
MELFIAT-105 UNICELLES - Pharmaceutical preparations - Solvay Pharmaceuticals Inc.
MELFLEX - Steps - Melflex Products Co.
MELFORD - Wines ☆ - European Beverage Co., Inc.
MELGES - Boats - Melges Boat Works Inc.
MELIA - Fruits–dried - Joseph Caragol Inc.
MELIA - Lenses–optical - National Optical Co.
MELIKA - Ophthalmic goods - Swank Optical
MELILLO - Wines - Jack Poust & Co. Inc.
MELINA - Floor coverings–carpet and rugs ☆ - Galaxy Carpet Mills Inc.
MELINA - Lubricating oils - Shell Oil Co.
MELINA - Tableware–china - Villeroy and Boch Tableware Ltd.
MELIND - Office supplies - Louis Melind Co.
MELINDA - Dolls - Russ Berrie and Co., Inc.
MELINDA - Watches - Bulova Corp.
MELINDA - Wigs - Helene Curtis Industries Inc.
MELINDA ENG - Apparel–women's - Melinda Eng
MELINDA'S - Food products - Figueroa International Inc.
MELINI - Jewelry ☆ - Roman Co.
MELINI - Wines - Frederick Wildman and Sons Ltd.
MELIOR - Apparel and accessories - Melior, Inc.
MELIOR - Coffee makers–electric - Charles F. La Malle
MELISANDE - Tableware–china ☆ - Lenox, Inc.
MELISSA - Apparel–women's - Jerell, Inc.
MELISSA - Bath product - Jean Sorelle
MELISSA - Cosmetics - Verla International, Ltd.
MELISSA - Dolls - Uneeda Doll Co., Inc.
MELISSA - Floor coverings–carpet and rugs ☆ - Regal Rugs Inc.
MELISSA - Lighting fixtures - Melissa Lighting, Inc.
MELISSA - Pasta - Krinos Foods, Inc.
MELISSA - Perfumes ☆ - London International U.S. Holdings
MELISSA - Shampoos - IT&LY Hairfashion NA Inc.
MELISSA - Tableware–china ☆ - Lenox, Inc.
MELISSA - Wigs - Jean Paree Weegs Inc.
MELISSA DALE - Apparel–women's - Frederick Atkins, Inc.
MELISSA HARPER - Apparel and accessories - Kellwood Co.
MELISSA HARPER MISSY - Apparel and accessories - Kellwood Co.
MELISSA NAVY SWISS DOT DIAPER BAG - Infant product - Children on the Go, Inc.
MELISSA RICE & COMPANY - Apparel and accessories - Melissa Rice & Co.
MELISSA'S - Vegetables–dried - World Variety Produce Inc.
MELISSA'S KRAZY KREPE - Food products ☆ - World Variety Produce Inc.
MELITA INTERNATIONAL - Electronic equipment - Melita International Corp.
MELITTA - Coffee - Melitta North America Inc.
MELIVE-CHOL - Vitamins and nutritional supplements ☆ - Pharmed Group Corp.
MELJAN - Jewelry - Meljan Jewelers
MELK FABRIEK FRIESLAND - Pasta - Holland-American Importing Co. Inc.
MELLARIL - Pharmaceutical preparations - Sandoz Pharmaceuticals Corp.
MELLENNIUM - Spices and extracts - David Michael & Co.
MELLINI - Candy ☆ - Van Melle Inc.
MELLO CHROMATIC - Harmonicas - William Kratt Co.

MELLO-CUT - Food products - Waldman's Meats Inc.
MELLO-DENT - Pharmaceutical preparations - Barre-National, Inc.
MELLO GOLD - Flour–blended - Nu-Vita Foods
MELLO GOLD - Oils–edible - Mallet and Co.
MELLO-LITE - Paints - Sherwin-Williams Automotive Finishes Corp.
MELLO MINT - Candy - Luden's Inc.
MELLO-MIST - Hair care products - Faberge Co.
MELLO-MIX - Shortening - Humko Products
MELLO NUT - Tobacco–chewing or smoking - Amar Blends Co.
MELLO SMELLOS - Scented stickers - International Designs, Inc.
MELLO-TEX - Paints - Sherwin-Williams Automotive Finishes Corp.
MELLO YELLO - Beverages–carbonated - Coca-Cola Co.
MELLOBATH - Health care products ☆ - Beiersdorf Inc.
MELLOBLEND - Candy ☆ - Glade Taffy Town, Inc.
MELLOCREAM FUDGE - Fudge - J. Hungerford Smith Co.
MELLOCREMES - Candy - Herman Goelitz Candy Co., Inc.
MELLOS - Candy - Ferrara Pan Candy Co., Inc.
MELLOTONE - Enamels - Sherwin-Williams Automotive Finishes Corp.
MELLOTONE - Fabrics - Mellotone
MELLOTONE RECORDS - Recording label - April Barrows
MELLOTRON - Musical instruments - David Thomas Kean
MELLOW CUP - Coffee - Multifoods Inc.
MELLOW ICE - Eyeglasses - Art-Craft Optical Co.
MELLOW LUSTRE - Paints - Sophir Morris Paint
MELLOW MINT - Teas–herbal ☆ - Celestial Seasonings, Inc.
MELLOW MONK - Wines - E & K Wine Co.
MELLOW MOOD - Rings–jewelry - Artcarved Inc.
MELLOW MULBERRY - Lipsticks ☆ - Honey & Spice Toiletries
MELLOW OIL - Salad dressings–bottled - Mallet and Co.
MELLOW ORANGE & SPICE - Teas - Seelect, Inc.
MELLOW OUT - Hair care products ☆ - Attitudes Unltd.
MELLOW OUT - Health care products - East Earth Herb Inc.
MELLOW ROAST - Coffee - Maxwell House
MELLOW T - Vitamins and nutritional supplements - Natural Organics, Inc.
MELLOW-VITES - Vitamins and nutritional supplements - Natural Organics, Inc.
MELLOW WHISKEY - Tobacco products - John Middleton Inc.
MELLOW YELLOW - Cosmetics - Ben Nye Inc.
MELLOW YELLOW - Toys - Tonka Corp.
MELLOWEVE - Pajamas–men's - Knothe Corp.
MELLOWLUSTRE - Paints - Morris Paint & Varnish Co.
MELLOWOOD - Cabinets–wood ☆ - Kitchen Kompact Inc.
MELLOWOOD - Organs–musical instrument ☆ - Strydel Inc.
MELLOWTONES - Tiles–ceramic - American Olean Tile Co.
MELLWOOD - Bacon - Fischer Packing Co.
MELNAR - Adhesives and sealants - W.R. Meadows Inc.
MELNOR - Tools–garden - Melnor Inc.
MELO CROWN - Cigars - M. Marsh & Son
MELO-GLOW - Fruits and vegetables - Half Moon Fruit & Produce Co.
MELO-ORGAN - Accordions - Castiglione Accordion
MELO-RAY - Eyeglasses - Art-Craft Optical Co.
MELO-TRED - Shoes - Edison Brothers Stores, Inc.
MELODEE - Apparel–children's - Jo Lene Co., Inc.
MELODEON - Recording label - Biograph Records Inc.
MELODIA - Recording label - Polish Record & Video Center of America
MELODIC - Floor coverings–carpet and rugs ☆ - World Carpets, Inc.
MELODIC II - Tea kettles–nonelectric ☆ - Robinson Knife & Fiddlers Plastics
MELODICA - Musical instruments - Hohner Inc.
MELODIE - Cigars - Gesty Trading & Manufacturing Corp.
MELODIES OF SARNA - Giftware ☆ - S.S. Sarna Inc.
MELODIGRAND - Pianos - Aeolian Pianos Inc.
MELODIJA - Accordions - Castiglione Accordion
MELODIPRO - Pianos - Aeolian Pianos Inc.
MELODIST - Furniture ☆ - Altec Lansing Consumer Products
MELODIYA - Recording label - Koch International
MELODIYA - Recording label - Mobile Fidelity Sound Lab
MELODY - Bathtubs–enameled - Arjo-Century Inc.
MELODY - Bells ☆ - Lenox Crystal, Inc.
MELODY - Chimes - Nutone Inc.
MELODY - Chocolate candy ☆ - Candymax, Inc.
MELODY - Christmas tree ornaments - Cracker Box Inc.
MELODY - Clocks - General Time Corp. (Westclox/Seth Thomas Div.)
MELODY - Computer software - Acxiom Corp.
MELODY - Dinnerware ☆ - Corning Inc.
MELODY - Dolls - Mattel, Inc.
MELODY - Dolls - Russ Berrie and Co., Inc.
MELODY - Eyeglasses - Art-Craft Optical Co.

☆ = Now out of production

MELODY - Floor coverings ☆ - Congoleum Corp.
MELODY - Floor coverings–carpet and rugs - Trend Carpet
MELODY - Giftware - Sasaki
MELODY - Gloves - Melody Gloves Inc.
MELODY - Golfing equipment - S2 Golf, Inc.
MELODY - Hearing aids - Beltone Electronics Corp.
MELODY - Home health care products - Arjo Manufacturing Co.
MELODY - Housewares - Melody USA, Corp.
MELODY - Recording label - Gospel Publishing House
MELODY - Rings–jewelry - Artcarved
MELODY - Stones–synthetic - Pebble Creek Products Inc.
MELODY ANN - Gloves - Wells Lamont Corp.
MELODY BEAR - Toys–stuffed - Gund, Inc.
MELODY BROOKE - Apparel and accessories ☆ - Edison Brothers Stores, Inc.
MELODY BUNNY - Toys–stuffed - Dakin Inc.
MELODY CHARMY - Toys ☆ - Combi International Corp.
MELODY COACH - Motor vehicles–motor homes - Melody Coach Industries Inc.
MELODY DESIGNS - Jewelry - Melody Mayer
MELODY IN COLOR - Paints - St. Louis Paint Manufacturing Co.
MELODY IN FLIGHT - Jewelry - Avon Products, Inc.
MELODY IN MOTION - Figurines - Waco Products Corp.
MELODY KING - Harmonicas - Hohner Inc.
MELODY LANE - Floor coverings–carpet and rugs - Monticello Carpet Mills
MELODY LIGHTS GO-ROUND - Toys - Mattel, Inc.
MELODY MADNESS - Electronic equipment ☆ - GAF Corp.
MELODY MAKERS - Greeting cards - American Greetings Corp.
MELODY MAYER - Leather goods - Melody Mayer
MELODY MEXICO - Cameras–video - Good Times Home Video Corp.
MELODY POPS - Candy - Uniconfis Corp.
MELODY PUSH CHIME - Toys - Fisher-Price, Inc.
MELODY THOMAS SCOTT - Skin care products - Melody Thomas Scott
MELOIDS - Artists' materials - Cunningham Distributors
MELON - Floor coverings–carpet and rugs ☆ - Regal Rugs Inc.
MELON - Glassware–household ☆ - Dansk International Designs, Ltd.
MELON BALLS - Candy ☆ - Sunline Brands
MELON BUD - Giftware - Gorham Inc.
MELON-ON-BRIGHT - Cosmetics - Frances Denney
MELON RAGS - Hats - Melon Rags, Inc.
MELONBERRY COCKTAIL - Juices - Snapple Beverage Corp.
MELONE - Cordials - Marie Brizard Wines & Spirits, USA
MELONGE - Beverages–carbonated - McCain Citrus, Inc.
MELOR - Toys–stuffed - Anne Rooney
MELOS - Audio cabinets - Melos Audio Inc.
MELOSPUN - Crocheted and knitted items - Garland Knitting Mills
MELOSTRETCH - Crocheted and knitted items - Garland Knitting Mills
MELOSWEET - Bacon - Conagra, Inc.
MELOSWEET - Meat products–beef - Armour Swift-Eckrich
MELOTUK - Handwork supplies - Bernat Yarn & Craft Corp.
MELOVAX - Vaccine - Medvac Corp.
MELOVEL - Fabrics - A. Wimpfheimer & Brother Inc.
MELOZ - Paper products - Music Mentor Corp.
MELOZETS - Pharmaceutical preparations - Smithkline Beecham Corp.
MELROSE - Apparel and accessories - Kellwood Co.
MELROSE - Apparel–women's ☆ - En Chante
MELROSE - Floor coverings–carpet and rugs - Eligere Carpets
MELROSE - Floor coverings–carpet and rugs - Glen Eden Wool Carpets
MELROSE - Frames–eyeglass ☆ - Universal/Univis Inc.
MELROSE - Giftware - Gorham Inc.
MELROSE - Luggage - Ricardo Beverly Hills
MELROSE - Tables–wood - Riverside Furniture Corp.
MELROSE - Teas ☆ - Chase Collection, Inc.
MELROSE - Yarn - Melrose Yarn Co. Inc.
MELROSE OPTIONS - Apparel–women's - Kellwood Co.
MELROSE OPTIONS PETITIES - Apparel and accessories - Kellwood Co.
MELROSE PETITES - Apparel–women's - Kellwood Co.
MELROSE PLACE - Perfumes - Richard Barrie Fragrances, Inc.
MELROSE PLACE - Publisher's imprints - Spelling Television, Inc.
MELROSE STUDIO - Apparel and accessories - Kellwood Co.
MELROSE TERRACE - Floor coverings - Mannington Resilient Floors
MELROSE WOMAN - Apparel and accessories - Kellwood Co.
MELROSE'S - Teas - Jacques F. Weber Co.
MELSON MEAT COMPANY - Meat products–beef - Melson Meat Co. Inc.
MELSTER - Candy - Melster Candies Inc.
MELT - Crayons - Dixon Ticonderoga Co.
MELT-A-WAY - Cookies - Nabisco Foods Group

MELT-A-WAY - Cosmetics - European Touch Co.
MELT-A-WAY - Fertilizers - Jonathan Green, Inc.
MELT AWAY - Salt - United Salt Corp.
MELT-DOWN - Cleaning preparations - Promaster
MELT-IN-YOUR-MOUTH - Breads - Rowena's Gourmet Foods Inc.
MELT MAN PLUS - Deicing fluid - Lange-Stegmann Co.
MELT-TO-TENSILE - Rods–steel - GS Technologies Corp.
MELTARELLA - Cheese - Whitehall Specialties, Inc.
MELTDOWN - Bicycles ☆ - Huffy Corp.
MELTDOWN - Sauces - Graf Wolf Development Inc.
MELTERS - Cookies - Daniel G. Rothschild
MELTING POT - Publisher's imprints - Kevin B. Eastman
MELTON - Apparel and accessories - Melton Shirt Co., Inc.
MELTON SPORTSMASTER - Apparel and accessories - Melton Shirt Co., Inc.
MELTONIAN - Chemical preparations - Kiwi Brands, Inc.
MELTS - Candles - Hanna's Potpourri Specialties, Inc.
MELTZIT - Salt ☆ - Akzo America Inc.
MELTZZA - Food products - Sue Baker Heller
MELVERN - Recording label - Lamar Music Co.
MELVILLE - Candy - Nabisco Foods Group
MELVIN - Games - Milton Bradley Co.
MELVIN - Musical instrument accessories - Adder Plus Corp.
MELVIN MOOSE - Toys–stuffed ☆ - Dakin Inc.
MELVIN PAUL'S - Bagels - 21st Century Foods
MELWAY - Recording label ☆ - Music of Polynesia Inc.
MELWOOD - Cases–plastic - Lerner Manufacturing Inc.
MELWOOD SPRINGS - Water–bottled or canned - Georgia Crown Distributing
MEM - Soap - Mem Co., Inc.
MEM-CLEAR - Water purification systems - American Water Technologies, Inc.
MEM-FREE - Batteries - Tocad America, Inc. (Tocad Co. Ltd.)
MEM-O-BOARD - Bulletin boards–wood - Timewise
MEMA - Flatware - Swedish Products Inc. (Sojo Inc.)
MEMAR - Electronic equipment - GAF Corp.
MEMBACK - Fabrics - Veratec
MEMBER MAGIC - Computer software - Frank S. Bruffey, Jr.
MEMBER ONLY - Frames–eyeglass - Creative Optiks
MEMBERS ONLY - Colognes - Mem Co., Inc.
MEMBERS ONLY - Eyeglasses - Art-Craft Optical Co.
MEMBERS ONLY - Furniture - Europe Craft Imports Inc.
MEMBERS ONLY - Luggage - York Luggage Co.
MEMBERS ONLY - Motor vehicle parts and accessories - Allison Corp.
MEMBERS ONLY - Watches - Advance Watch Co. Ltd.
MEMBERSHIP BOUNCE - Apparel–athletic - Membership Bounce, Inc.
MEMBERSHIP MASTER - Computer software - SourceView Software International
MEMBERSHIP PLUS - Computer software - Parsons Technology, Inc.
MEMBRAIN - Audio equipment - Autosound 2000, Inc.
MEMBRANES - Vases–glass ☆ - Nourot Glass Studio
MEMBRS - Computer software - Usable Systems, Inc.
MEMCARD - Medical apparatus - Del Mar Avionics
MEMCO - Welding equipment - Miller Electric Manufacturing Co.
MEMCOR - Magnetic recording equipment - Corning Inc.
MEMENTO - Burial caskets - Batesville Casket Co., Inc.
MEMENTO - Clocks ☆ - General Time Corp. (Westclox/Seth Thomas Div.)
MEMENTO - Furniture ☆ - Bassett Furniture Industries, Inc.
MEMENTO - Giftware ☆ - Gorham Inc.
MEMENTO - Jewelry - Kallman Diamond Corp.
MEMO-A-MEMO - Paper - Cathay International
MEMO BOOK - Candy - Topps Co., Inc.
MEMO EXPRESS - Radio communications equipment - Motorola, Inc. (Land Mobile Products Sector)
MEMO EXPRESS - Radios - Motorola, Inc. (Paging Products Group)
MEMO FOLD - Leather goods - St. Thomas Inc.
MEMO-LITE - Paper–gummed ☆ - Park Sherman
MEMO-LITE - Pens - Accutec Inc.
MEMO MASTER - Paper–gummed ☆ - Park Sherman
MEMO-MASTER - Paper–writing - Akay Corp.
MEMO MATE - Audio equipment - DTR Associates, LP
MEMO MATE - Housewares - R & D Products Inc.
MEMO MATES - Notebooks and notepads - Wellspring
MEMO MATES - Office supplies ☆ - Faber-Castell Corp.
MEMO MINDER - Paper - Superior Industries International, Inc.
MEMO PALS - Dolls - Waco Products Corp.
MEMO-REES - Paper–writing ☆ - Alger Creations Inc.
MEMO-RI-MINDER - Office accessories - RKR, Inc.
MEMO RX - Plastics - Republic Drug Co. Inc.

MEMO-SCRIBER - Dictating machines - Sanyo Fisher (USA) Corp.
MEMO STACK - Notebooks and notepads - Paper Factory of Wisconsin, Inc.
MEMO VVE - Desk sets - Artistic Office Products
MEMO WIPE-OFF - Bulletin boards—cork ☆ - Webway, Inc.
MEMO WRITER - Computer software - Phase One Systems
MEMODEX - Office supplies - Rolodex Corp.
MEMOFILE - Index cards - Memindex Inc.
MEMOIR - Computer software - Lean Software Corp.
MEMOIR - Tableware—china ☆ - Lenox, Inc.
MEMOIRE - Jewelry - Memoire Corp.
MEMOIRE CHERIE - Colognes - Elizabeth Arden Inc.
MEMOIRS - Floor coverings—carpet and rugs ☆ - Cabin Crafts Carpets
MEMOIRS - Furniture - Stanley Furniture Co. Inc.
MEMOIRS - Furniture - Thomasville Furniture Industries Inc.
MEMOMASTER - Electronics equipment ☆ - Electrosonic Systems Inc.
MEMOMATIC - Office supplies - Park Sherman
MEMOR-ACTIN - Vitamins and nutritional supplements - Natural Organics, Inc.
MEMOR-AID - Pharmaceutical preparations - Vita-Fore Products Co.
MEMORABLE - Floor coverings - Aladdin Mills, Inc.
MEMORABLE - Frames—eyeglass - Pathway Optical Prods.
MEMORABLE MINISTURES 8 - Wallpaper - Pantasote Inc. (Wallcovering Div.)
MEMORABLE MOMENTS - Trading cards and stamps - Maxx Race Cards, Inc.
MEMORABLES - Giftware - Jibco Industries Inc.
MEMORASE - Erasers - UVP Inc.
MEMOREX - Audio equipment - Tandy Corp.
MEMOREX - Health care products - Healthwatchers System
MEMORIAL - Burial caskets - Marsellus Casket Co.
MEMORIAL TRACKER - Computer software - Spectar Solutions, Inc.
MEMORIC - Glass products - Nowstar
MEMORIE - Scales—bathroom - Sunbeam-Oster Household Products
MEMORIES - Christmas tree ornaments - Cracker Box Inc.
MEMORIES - Dinnerware—glass - Metlox Pottery Shoppe
MEMORIES - Dolls ☆ - Effanbee Doll Corp.
MEMORIES - Floor coverings—carpet and rugs - Heuga USA
MEMORIES - Floor coverings—carpet and rugs - Mohawk Industries Inc.
MEMORIES - Floor coverings—carpet and rugs ☆ - Downs Carpet Co. Inc.
MEMORIES - Floor coverings—carpet and rugs ☆ - Royalweve Carpet Mills
MEMORIES - Furniture - Keller Manufacturing Co.
MEMORIES - Greeting cards - Pawprints Greeting Cards
MEMORIES - Invitations - Classic Thermographers Ltd.
MEMORIES - Tableware—china ☆ - Lenox, Inc.
MEMORIES - Tableware—earthenware ☆ - Denby USA Limited
MEMORIES AND MELODIES - Dolls - Lawton Doll Co.
MEMORIES & REFLECTIONS - Publisher's imprints - Milli Brown Whitworth
MEMORIES FOREVER - Paper products - Western Trimming Corp.
MEMORIES FORLIFE - Scrapbooks - Westrim Crafts
MEMORIES IN MINUTES - Artists' materials - Ellison Educational Equipment, Inc.
MEMORIES IN THE MAKING - Calendars - Alzheimer's Disease and Related Disorders Association of Orange County
MEMORIES MOVIE STAR - Watches - Temlex/Jupiter Watch Corp.
MEMORIES OF ME - Publisher's imprints - Life Time Publishers, Inc.
MEMORIES OF PARIS - Perfumes ☆ - Andrew Jergens Co.
MEMORIES OF SANTA - Christmas ornaments - Christmas Reproductions Inc.
MEMORIES OF YESTERDAY - Figurines ☆ - Enesco Corp.
MEMORIES STEP BACK IN TIME - Furniture - Memories–Step Back in Time Inc.
MEMORIES THAT LAST FOREVER - Computer hardware - Centon Electronics, Inc.
MEMORIZER - Photographic equipment ☆ - Tiffen Manufacturing Corp.
MEMORY - Candy - Brock Candy Co. Inc.
MEMORY - Eyeglasses - Art-Craft Optical Co.
MEMORY - Rings—jewelry - Artcarved Inc.
MEMORY - Wallpaper - Lin-Gor Wallcoverings
MEMORY - Yarn - Melrose Yarn Co. Inc.
MEMORY 35 - Camera - Aimex Camera Inc.
MEMORY BANK - Floor coverings—carpet and rugs ☆ - Karastan-Bigelow Inc.
MEMORY BANK - Games - Kadon Enterprises Inc.
MEMORY BANK - Handbags - Eastman Kodak Co.
MEMORY BASKET - Medical apparatus - Wilson-Cook Medical Inc.
MEMORY BELL - Jewelry—precious - Sharon Bowden
MEMORY BOOST - Vitamins and nutritional supplements - Vitamin Research Products Inc.
MEMORY BOOSTER - Vitamins and nutritional supplements - Nature's Bounty, Inc.

MEMORY BOX, THE - Boxes - BBA Holdings
MEMORY BUILDING BLOCKS - Computer software - Sunburst Communications, Inc.
MEMORY CARDS - Publisher's imprints - Memory Cards, Inc.
MEMORY CASTLE - Computer software ☆ - Sunburst Communications, Inc.
MEMORY CHIP - Floor coverings—carpet and rugs ☆ - Karastan-Bigelow Inc.
MEMORY-FLEX - Mattresses - L & P Property Management Co.
MEMORY-FREE - Batteries - Tocad America, Inc. (Tocad Co. Ltd.)
MEMORY FUEL - Nutritional supplements - Life Services Supplements, Inc.
MEMORY GAMES - Computer software ☆ - Optimum Resource, Inc.
MEMORY II - Cushions - Mason Medical Products
MEMORY II - Wallpaper - Lin-Gor Wallcoverings
MEMORY KEEPERS - Frames—picture - Joan Rodgers
MEMORY LANE - Candy ☆ - Maxfield Candy Co.
MEMORY LANE - Eyeglasses - Art-Craft Optical Co.
MEMORY LANE - Furniture - Moosehead Manufacturing Co.
MEMORY LANE GOSPEL - Recording label - Memory Lane Gospel
MEMORY LENS - Medical apparatus - Mentor O & O Inc.
MEMORY MADNESS - Puzzles - Great American Puzzle Factory Inc.
MEMORY MAILER - Envelopes - Fuji Trucolor Photo, Inc.
MEMORY MANAGER - Computer software ☆ - DataPak Software Inc.
MEMORY MASTER - Computer hardware - P.N.Y. Electronics, Inc.
MEMORY MATCH - Computer software - Hartley Courseware Inc.
MEMORY-MATE - Books—blank - Beckson Marine Inc.
MEMORY MATE - Vitamins and nutritional supplements - Freelife International LP
MEMORY MATES - Frames—picture - Tupperware Co.
MEMORY MATIC - Calendars ☆ - Ampad Corp.
MEMORY MISER 386 - Computer software - Softlogic Solutions, Inc.
MEMORY PEOPLE, THE - Computer hardware - BSM Corp.
MEMORY PLUS - Vitamins and nutritional supplements - Rexall Sundown, Inc.
MEMORY PRINTER - Telephone apparatus - Krown Research
MEMORY REDUCTION TECHNOLOGY (MRT) - Computer software - Peerless Systems Corp.
MEMORY ROD - Umbrellas - Stanley Hochfeld
MEMORY SAFE - Burial caskets - Batesville Casket Co., Inc.
MEMORY SHOPPE, THE - Photo albums ☆ - Kleer-Vu Plastics Inc.
MEMORY WEAR - Decals and transfers - Tulip Productions
MEMORY WORKS, THE - Computer software - Compact Disc Inc.
MEMORY YARN - Yarn - Sara Lee Corp.
MEMORYGARD - Calculators - Sanyo Fisher (USA) Corp.
MEMORYMARKER - Markers—felt-tip - Crown Photo Systems Inc.
MEMORYMASTER - Computer software - Insoft Limited
MEMORYMATE - Computer software ☆ - Broderbund Software, Inc.
MEMORYMATS - Photographic equipment - Mulberry Graphics Corp.
MEMORYMAX - Vitamins and nutritional supplements - Natural Connections
MEMORYMOOG - Synthesizers—musical instrument ☆ - EJE Research Corp.
MEMORYPLEX - Hair care products - Nioxin Research Laboratories Inc.
MEMORYSAFE - Burial caskets - Batesville Casket Co., Inc.
MEMORYWRITER - Typewriters - Xerox Corp.
MEMOSAIL - Chronographs ☆ - Chronosport Inc.
MEMOTRAY - Notebooks and notepads ☆ - Success Business Industries, Inc.
MEMOVOX - Watches with alarms ☆ - Jaeger-Le Coultre SA
MEMOWORKX - Notebooks and notepads - Michael P. Patterson
MEMOZZI - Candy ☆ - Y & S Candies Inc.
MEMPHIS - Apparel and accessories - Knight Industries
MEMPHIS - Bathroom accessories - KLR Products, Inc.
MEMPHIS - Cigarettes - G.A. Georgopulo & Co. Inc.
MEMPHIS - Floor coverings—carpet and rugs ☆ - Regal Rugs Inc.
MEMPHIS - Flooring—hardwood - Memphis Hardwood Flooring Co.
MEMPHIS - Furniture - Landes Manufacturing Co.
MEMPHIS - Guitars ☆ - Kaman Music Corp.
MEMPHIS - Radio communications equipment - Robert Bosch Corp.
MEMPHIS - Wallpaper - Capital Carousel Inc.
MEMPHIS - Water—bottled or canned - Memphis Water Bottling Co.
MEMPHIS CHICKS - Trading cards and stamps ☆ - Professional Sports & Entertainment Associates of Tennessee, L.P.
MEMPHIS IMPORT CO. - Giftware - Harold-Lawrence Associates Inc.
MEMPHIS MATH - Computer software - Waterford Institute Inc.
MEMPHIS MODERN COLLECTION - Statuary ☆ - Artisan House Inc.
MEMPHIS MYSTERY - Recording label - Le Cam Records
MEMPHIS TAMS, THE - Apparel and accessories - NBA Properties, Inc.
MEMPLUS - Computer software - Answersoft, Inc.
MEMRI AUTOGRAPH - Computer software - Mediamark Research Inc.
MEMRIC - Pharmaceutical preparations - Smithkline Beecham Corp.
MEMROFLEX - Frames—eyeglass - Zylo Ware Corp.

☆ = Now out of production

MEMS VIEW - Computer software - Aprex Corp.
MEN AT WORK - Belts–apparel - Reborn Products Co., Inc.
MEN AT WORK - Garden equipment - Structron Corp.
MEN BEHIND THE LINE - Apparel and accessories - National Football League Properties, Inc.
MEN BY GEOFF THOMPSON - Hair care products - Men by Geoff Thompson Ltd.
MEN FROM EARTH - Toys - Future Fun Inc.
MEN, MEN, MEN - Wallpaper - Tattersalls
MEN OF AUTUMN - Trading cards and stamps - Score Group, Inc.
MEN OF STEEL - Video production - Atlantic Steel Vision Inc.
MEN-ONLY! - Frames–eyeglass - Liberty Optical Manufacturing Co.
MEN-ZO-LIN - Pharmaceutical preparations - Zidrep Laboratories
MENA - Ophthalmic goods ☆ - Luxotica
MENACE - Apparel and accessories - Menace, Inc.
MENACE - Skates–roller - Rollerblade, Inc.
MENACE - Toys–models ☆ - Estes Industries
MENACE TO THE GAME - Apparel and accessories - Rush Sportswear
MENADOL - Pharmaceutical preparations - Rugby Laboratories Inc.
MENAGE A TROPIQUE - Juices ☆ - Odwalla, Inc.
MENAGEN - Pharmaceutical preparations ☆ - Parke-Davis
MENAGERIE - Furniture - Lane Co. Inc.
MENAGERIE - Pet products - Michelle International Ltd.
MENAGERIE - Puzzles - Warren Industries Inc.
MENAGERIE - Toys–stuffed - First & Main, Inc.
MENAGERIE ALPHABETS - Toys - Extension Inc.
MENAGERIE COLLECTION - Giftware - N.S. Gustin Co.
MENAI - Computer software - Menai Corp.
MENAVAL-20 - Pharmaceutical preparations - Legere Pharmaceuticals Inc.
MEND - Hair care products - Summit Laboratories
MEND-A-NAIL - Cosmetics - Sally Hansen
MEND-A-NAIL - Manicure preparations - Del Pharmaceuticals, Inc.
MEND-A-RAIL - Rails–aluminum - Hollaender Manufacturing Co.
MEND-EZ-ZE - Denture materials - Pacific Sales Pharmacal Co.
MENDA - Fluid power pumps - Menda Scientific Products
MENDAM - Fireplace equipment - Majestic Co.
MENDEL PALACE - Video games - Hudson Soft USA Inc.
MENDELSON - Lamps - L. Mendelson Co. Inc.
MENDES FARMS - Meat products–pork - Squab Producers of California
MENDEX - Hair care products - Roux Laboratories, Inc.
MENDEZ-KOFF - Music–sheet - Koff Music Co.
MENDING SOLUTION - Cosmetics - Origins Natural Resources Inc.
MENDOCINO - Apparel and accessories - San Francisco Sales, Inc.
MENDOCINO - Water–bottled or canned - Mendocino Beverages International Inc.
MENDOCINO - Wines - Guild Wineries
MENDOCINO COOPERAGE - Barrels–wood - Fetzer Vineyards Inc.
MENDOCINO PASTA CO. - Pasta - Mendocino Pasta Co.
MENDOCINO VINEYARDS - Wines - Guild Wineries
MENDOSA ARGENTINA - Wines - Tosi Vintners International
MENDOTA - Bathtubs–enameled - Kohler Co.
MENDOTA SPRINGS - Water–mineral ☆ - Coca-Cola Co.
MENDOZA - Floor coverings - Mannington Resilient Floors
MENDOZA PEAKS - Wines - Vinos Argentinos Imports USA
MENDSWARE - Tiles–ceramic ☆ - DecoArt, Inc.
MENDTITE - Adhesives and sealants - Zecol Inc.
MENEHUNE - Water–bottled or canned - Menehune Water Co.
MENEHUNE MAC - Cookies - Hawaiian Candies and Nuts Ltd.
MENEHUNE MAGIC - Backpacks - Menehune Magic, Inc.
MENEMSHA BITES - Seafood products–fresh or frozen - Poole's Fish Inc.
MENENDEZ - Cigars - Antillian Cigar Corp.
MENEST - Pharmaceutical preparations - Smithkline Beecham Corp.
MENETREL - Specialty foods–canned - A. Sargenti Co. Inc.
MENGAGEMENT - Jewelry - Joan Oliphant Millton
MENGEN - Shoes - Mengen-Ulla
MENI-D - Pharmaceutical preparations - Seatrace Co.
MENINGOVAX - Vaccines ☆ - Merck & Co., Inc. (Merck Research Laboratories)
MENINNO - Salad dressings–bottled - Meninno Brothers
MENITONE - Paints–artists' ☆ - Woolsey Marine Industries
MENIXX - Health care products - Pharma Botanixx
MENKEMATIC - Propellers - Palmer Johnson Inc.
MENLO PARK - Chimes ☆ - Nutone Inc.
MENLO PARK - Floor coverings - Mannington Resilient Floors
MENLO PARK - Floor coverings–carpet and rugs ☆ - Walter Carpet Mills
MENNEN - Skin care products - Mennen Co.

MENNEN E - Deodorants–personal - Mennen Co.
MENNER'S - Rice ☆ - Curtice-Burns Foods, Inc.
MENNUCCI - Pasta ☆ - Liberty Richter Inc.
MENNUCCI QUINCENTENNIAL - Pasta - Rino Gnesi
MENO-FEM - Vitamins and nutritional supplements - Prevail Corp.
MENO-HERBS - Vitamins and nutritional supplements - Alvin Last Inc.
MENO-MOIST WILD YAM - Skin care products - Jason Natural Products, Inc.
MENO-SELECT - Vitamins and nutritional supplements - Matrix Health Products, Inc.
MENO-VITES - Vitamins and nutritional supplements - BRS Industries Group Inc.
MENOCARE - Pharmaceutical preparations - Boericke & Tafel
MENOCARE - Vitamins and nutritional supplements - Ayurvedic Concepts Ltd.
MENOCOM - Vitamins and nutritional supplements - Vitaquest International, Inc.
MENOJECT-L.A. - Pharmaceutical preparations ☆ - Merz Inc.
MENOMUNE - Pharmaceutical preparations - Elkins-Sinn Inc.
MENOPHASE - Health care products - Futurebiotics
MENOPHASE - Vitamins and nutritional supplements - Pdk Labs, Inc.
MENOPLEX - Health care products - Fiske Industries Inc.
MENOPOISE - Vitamins and nutritional supplements - Amrion, Inc.
MENORABLES - Giftware - Roman, Inc.
MENORAHS LTD. - Candles - Biedermann & Sons Inc.
MENORCA - Jewelry - Perfect Pearl Co. Inc.
MENOSAN - Pharmaceutical preparations ☆ - Bioforce of America Ltd.
MENRAD - Frames–eyeglass - Windsor Optical Inc.
MENRED - Frames–eyeglass - Tura Inc.
MENRIUM - Tranquilizers - Roche Laboratories
MEN'S CHOICE - Hair coloring preparations - Clairol Inc.
MEN'S CHOICE AFTER SHAVE - Shaving preparations - Blue Cross Laboratories Inc.
MEN'S CLASSIC - Colognes - Frances Denney
MEN'S CLASSIC - Wallpaper ☆ - Imperial Wallcoverings, Inc.
MEN'S CLUB - Wallpaper - Frankford Wallcoverings Inc.
MEN'S CLUB II - Wallpaper - Frankford Wallcoverings Inc.
MEN'S COMPANY, THE - Apparel - Maurices Inc.
MEN'S DIAMOND ENGAGEMENT RING BY STARCRAFT - Jewelry - Washington Jewelers, Inc.
MENS ET MANUS - Personal lubricant - Robb D. Carr
MEN'S FRAGRANCE FOR LIFE, THE - Colognes - Ventresca Ltd.
MEN'S LIFE - Video production - Christian Reformed Board of Home Missions
MEN'S PLACE - Wallpaper - Seabrook Wallcoverings, Inc.
MEN'S SPECIAL - Vitamins and nutritional supplements - Kroeger Herb Products Co. Inc.
MEN'S STOCK - Personal-care product - Aubrey Organics, Inc.
MEN'S TITANIUM - Sunblocks - California North
MENSCH, WEISSTE, WAS! - Computer software ☆ - Gessler Publishing Co., Inc.
MENSCHIES - Jewelry - Phyllis Woloshin
MENSTRA-VITES - Vitamins and nutritional supplements - BRS Industries Group Inc.
MENSTRESS - Pharmaceutical preparations - Pharmex Inc.
MENSTRICARE - Vitamins and nutritional supplements - Ayurvedic Concepts Ltd.
MENSTRUAL-EASE - Health care products ☆ - Nature's Herbs
MENSTRUSAN - Pharmaceutical preparations ☆ - Bioforce of America Ltd.
MENSTUFF - Colognes - Key West Aloe Inc.
MENSWEAR - Colognes - BC International Cosmetics & Image Services, Inc.
MENSWEAR COLLECTION II, THE - Wallpaper ☆ - Imperial Wallcoverings, Inc.
MENSWEAR II - Wallpaper - Imperial Wallcoverings, Inc.
MENTADENT - Mouthwashes - Conopco, Inc.
MENTADENT - Toothpaste - Chesebrough-Pond's USA Co.
MENTAL - Apparel and accessories - Do Rags, Inc.
MENTAL ADVANTAGE - Homeopathic remedies - Phyto Pharmica, Inc.
MENTAL AUTOMATION - Computers peripherals, and software - Mental Automation Inc.
MENTAL BLOK - Puzzles - Parris Manufacturing Co.
MENTAL CLARITEA - Teas–herbal - Unitea Herbs
MENTAL EDGE - Vitamins and nutritional supplements - Source Naturals
MENTAL EDGE, THE - Recording label - Jeffrey Wildfogel
MENTAL FOCUS - Herbal products - Boutique Alternare, Inc.
MENTAL HEADGEAR - Apparel and accessories - Do Rags, Inc.
MENTAL HIGH - Food products - Laci Le Beau Corp.
MENTAL REHEARSAL - Recording label - Reading Genius
MENTALERT - Pharmaceutical preparations ☆ - Keene Pharmaceuticals Inc.

MENTALLY TOUGH - Recording label - Loehr Groppel Saddlebrook Sport Science, Inc.

MENTANASE-12 - Pharmaceutical preparations - Schering Corp.

MENTANE - Pharmaceutical preparations - Hoechst-Roussel Pharmaceuticals Inc.

MENTANIUM - Medical apparatus - Mentor O & O Inc.

MENTANOL - Vitamins and nutritional supplements ☆ - Tishcon Corp.

MENTAT - Computer software - Marc Analysis Research Corp.

MENTH-O-DROPS - Pharmaceutical preparations - Rogers' Drug Co.

MENTHACIN - Analgesics - Mentholatum Co.

MENTHACOL - Pharmaceutical preparations - Cincinnati Pharmacal Co.

MENTHO-DENT - Pharmaceutical preparations - Barre-National, Inc.

MENTHO PLUS - Cough drops - Murray-Allen International Inc.

MENTHOLATUM DEEP HEATING RUB - Analgesics - Mentholatum Co.

MENTHORUB - Cold remedies - Schein Pharmaceutical Inc.

MENTIONABLES - Apparel stores–lingerie - Formflex Foundations Inc.

MENTOR - Artists' materials ☆ - M. Grumbacher Inc.

MENTOR - Floor coverings–carpet and rugs ☆ - Gulistan Carpet Inc.

MENTOR - Knives - Buck Knives, Inc.

MENTOR - Medical apparatus - Mentor Corp.

MENTOR - Medical apparatus - Mentor O & O Inc.

MENTOR - Office supplies ☆ - Faber-Castell Corp.

MENTOR - Publisher's imprints - Penguin USA

MENTOR - Rackets–racquetball - Ektelon

MENTOR DRIVER PROGRAM - Video production - Morse Bros., Inc.

MENTOR MUSIC - Recording label - Mentor Music Group Inc.

MENTOR VISION - Electronic equipment - Acuity Imaging, Inc.

MENTOS - Candy - Van Melle Inc.

MENTOS - Hair care products - Mentos Products Co.

MENTROLZ - Pharmaceutical preparations - Mayer Laboratories, Inc.

MENTWORKING - Paper–book - Career Systems, Inc.

MENTX - Pharmaceutical preparations - Penederm Inc.

MENU - Prepared salads - Atlas Horn Food Service

MENU COMPANION - Publisher's imprints - Weight Watchers International, Inc.

MENU-ETTE - Cookware, servingware ☆ - Corning Inc.

MENU MAGIC - Food products - North American Laboratory Co.

MENU MAGIC - Stoves - Montgomery Ward & Co. Inc.

MENU MAKER - Meat products–poultry - Rymer Chicken Inc.

MENU MAKER - Meat products–poultry - Simmons Foods

MENU MASTERPIECE - Food products ☆ - Presco Food Seasonings Inc.

MENU MATES - Crackers - Nabisco Foods Group

MENU OF FINE DINING - Furniture ☆ - Harden Furniture Co. Inc.

MENU-READY - Salads–prepackaged - Suter Co. Inc.

MENU SCAN - Computer software - Campbell Soup Co.

MENU SERVICE - Publisher's imprints - National Purchasing Corp.

MENUCO - Vitamins and nutritional supplements - Menuco Corp.

MENUDO GRANDE POT - Cooking utensils–aluminum ☆ - General Housewares Corp.

MENUETTE - Food products ☆ - John Labatt Foods

MENUFORMS - Computer storage devices - Robinson, Bradshaw & Hinson, P.A.

MENUKEY - Computer software - LCS/Telegraphics Inc.

MENUMASTER - Microwave ovens - Menumaster Inc.

MENUMASTER - Ovens–microwave - Amana Refrigeration Inc.

MENZOBERRANZAN - Video games - Tsr, Inc.

MEOW - Computer software - Robbins-Gioia, Inc.

MEOW - Jewelry - REO Co.

MEOW - Underwear and nightwear - Dallco Industries Inc. (Katz Div.)

MEOW MAT - Pet products - Southern California Foam, Inc.

MEOW MEOW KITTY - Toys–stuffed - Trendmasters, Inc.

MEOW MIX - Cat food - Ralston Purina Co.

MEOW MOMENTS - Pet food - American Leather Specialties

MEOWY CHRISTMAS - Recording label - Jingle Cats Music

MEOWZ KITTEN - Toys–stuffed - Dakin Inc.

MEPAL - Glassware–household - Genin Trudeau and Co. Ltd.

MEPCO - Labels–gummed - Mepco Labeling Systems

MEPERGAN - Pharmaceutical preparations - Wyeth-Ayerst Laboratories

MEPERGAN FORTIS - Pharmaceutical preparations - Wyeth-Ayerst Laboratories

MEPHE-GESIC - Pharmaceutical preparations - Dade Pharmaceuticals Inc.

MEPHISTO - Pencils ☆ - Koh-I-Noor, Inc.

MEPHISTO - Tools–hand-operated - Mephisto Tool Co. Inc.

MEPHOHAB - Pharmaceutical preparations ☆ - JMI-Canton Pharmaceuticals

MEPHYTON - Vitamins and nutritional supplements - Merck & Co., Inc. (Merck Research Laboratories)

MEPLA MATCH - Hardware - Mepla Inc.

MEPPEL - Computer software - Ari Network Services, Inc.

MEPPS - Fishing lures - Sheldons', Inc.

MEPPS MINO - Fishing lures - Sheldons', Inc.

MEPRIAM - Pharmaceutical preparations ☆ - Lemmon Co.

MEPRO - Tools - Solcoor Inc.

MEPROBAMATE - Pharmaceutical preparations ☆ - Roberts/Hauck Pharmaceuticals Inc.

MEPROCON - Pharmaceutical preparations - Consolidated Midland Corp.

MEPROGESE - Pharmaceutical preparations - Geneva Generics Inc.

MEPRON - Pharmaceutical preparations - Burroughs Wellcome Co.

MEPROSPAN - Tranquilizers ☆ - Wallace Laboratories

MEPROTABS - Tranquilizers ☆ - Wallace Laboratories

MEPROZINE - Pharmaceutical preparations - Vintage Pharmaceuticals, Inc.

MEQUIN - Pharmaceutical preparations ☆ - Lemmon Co.

MER/ART - Paperboard - Salwen Paper Co. Inc.

MER-ESTRONE - Pharmaceutical preparations ☆ - Keene Pharmaceuticals Inc.

MER-MAN - Toys - Mattel, Inc.

MER SOLEIL - Wines - Mer Soleil Winery

MERA - Cosmetics - Natural Products Corp.

MERA - Hair care products - Creative Laboratories Inc.

MERACQ - Candy bars - Cosmo Food USA

MERAK - Motor vehicles–automobiles ☆ - Maserati Automobiles Inc.

MERAN - Glassware–household - Oneida Ltd.

MERANO - Guitars - J.M. Sahlein Music Co. Inc.

MERANO - Liquors - Transamerica Wine Corp.

MERANO - Whirlpools - Jacuzzi Inc.

MERAPI - Food products - Merapi Foods

MERB - Dolls - Carole A. Lenz

MER.BON. PRODUCTS - Exercising equipment - Alpine Tooling, Inc.

MERC - Ships - Bay Manufacturing

MERC-LOC - Blood pressure apparatus - Trimline Medical Products Corp.

MERCANDESCENT - Lamps - Public Service Lamp Corp.

MERCANTILE - Pencils ☆ - Empire Berol USA

MERCAP - Floor coverings - Dexter Corp. (Mercer Plastics Div.)

MERCASONIC - Tape players - Mercury Radio & Battery Corp.

MERCATOR - Computer software - TSI International

MERCEDES - Apparel and accessories - Wilson Brothers

MERCEDES - Floor coverings–carpet and rugs - Barrett Carpet Mills Inc.

MERCEDES - Flowers, plants, and seeds - Patten Seed Co.

MERCEDES - Hair care products - Dubl Duck/Jet Set Inc.

MERCEDES - Microphones ☆ - Westheimer Corp.

MERCEDES - Musical instruments ☆ - Vincent Bach-Selmer Co.

MERCEDES - Wallpaper - Capital Carousel Inc.

MERCEDES 300 - Cosmetics - Dubl Duck/Jet Set Inc.

MERCEDES 500 - Cosmetics - Dubl Duck/Jet Set Inc.

MERCEDES-BENZ - Motor vehicles–automobiles - Mercedes-Benz of North America Inc.

MERCEDES GOURMET - Cookies - Party Systems by Mercedes, Inc.

MERCEDES II - Musical instruments ☆ - Vincent Bach-Selmer Co.

MERCEDES TURBO - Hair care products - Dubl Duck/Jet Set Inc.

MERCEDEZ BEANS - Candy ☆ - Chiodo Candy Co.

MERCENARIES, SPIES & PRIVATE EYES - Games - Flying Buffalo Inc.

MERCENARY - Recording label - Celluloid Records

MERCER - Floor coverings–carpet and rugs ☆ - Gulistan Carpet Inc.

MERCER - Ships–sailing vessels - Cape Cod Shipbuilding Co.

MERCER AND BRATT - Quilts - Michael G. Bratt

MERCER BRICK - Floor coverings - Congoleum Corp.

MERCER STREET EXPRESS - Apparel and accessories ☆ - Pacific Trail, Inc.

MERCHANT'S - Batteries - Merchants, Inc.

MERCHANTS - Food products - K-Bob's USA, Inc.

MERCHANTS - Pencils ☆ - Faber-Castell Corp.

MERCHANTS FAST RATE - Computer software - Merchants Fast Motor Lines, Inc.

MERCHANTS OF VENUS - Games - Avalon Hill Game Co.

MERCHANTWARE - Computer software - Paul Rony

MERCI - Apparel–women's - Classy Lady Corp.

MERCI - Water–bottled or canned - Vess Beverages Inc.

MERCIER - Jewelry - David G. Steven Inc.

MERCKENS - Chocolate candy - Merckens Chocolate Co.

MERCKENS - Food products - ADM Cocoa

MERCO - Olives–canned ☆ - Joseph Caragol Inc.

MERCO - Seafood products–fresh or frozen - Arrowac Fisheries Inc.

MERCO - Thread - Threads USA Div.

MERCO - Trays–warming - Welbilt Corp.

MERCODOL - Cough medicines ☆ - Marion Merrell Dow

MERCOLEDI - Apparel and accessories - Castle Apparel Group, Inc.

☆ = Now out of production

MERCOSIL - Metals - Brunswick Corp.
MERCOVE - Floor coverings - Dexter Corp. (Mercer Plastics Div.)
MERCROCHET - Yarn - Lily Craft Products
MERCRUISER - Boating equipment and accessories - American Marine Ltd.
MERCRUISER - Boats–pontoons - Weeres Industries Corp.
MERCRUISER - Motors–outboard - Mercury Marine
MERCS - Posters - Wildstorm Productions
MERCULITE - Health care products - Omron Healthcare, Inc.
MERCULYN - Pharmaceutical preparations - Wesley Pharmacal Co. Inc.
MERCUROCHROME - Pharmaceutical preparations ☆ - Becton Dickinson Microbiology Systems
MERCURONATE - Health care products ☆ - JMI-Canton Pharmaceuticals
MERCURY - Apparel and accessories - Worcester Knitting Co.
MERCURY - Artists' materials ☆ - Keuffel & Esser Co.
MERCURY - Band-saw blades - American Saw & Manufacturing Co.
MERCURY - Bathroom accessories - KLR Products, Inc.
MERCURY - Bathtubs–enameled - Lasco Products Group
MERCURY - Binoculars - Bausch & Lomb Inc.
MERCURY - Brooms - Laitner Brush Co.
MERCURY - Computers ☆ - SCI Systems, Inc.
MERCURY - Electronic equipment - Teledyne Post
MERCURY - Fabrics - Greenwood Mills Inc.
MERCURY - Fans–electric - Nutone Inc.
MERCURY - Fireplaces ☆ - Majestic Co.
MERCURY - Floor coverings - American Floor Products Co. Inc.
MERCURY - Forklifts - Pettibone Corp.
MERCURY - Kites ☆ - Hi-Flier Manufacturing Co.
MERCURY - Luggage - Mercury Luggage Manufacturing Co.
MERCURY - Motor vehicles–automobiles - Ford Motor Co. (Lincoln-Mercury Div.)
MERCURY - Motor vehicles–automobiles - Ford Motor Co.
MERCURY - Motors–outboard - Brunswick Corp.
MERCURY - Musical instrument accessories ☆ - Selmer Co. Inc.
MERCURY - Office supplies - Bentson Industries Inc.
MERCURY - Office supplies - Master Caster Co.
MERCURY - Outboard motors - American Marine Ltd.
MERCURY - Paints - Mercury Paint Co. Inc.
MERCURY - Pens - General Pencil Co.
MERCURY - Pens - Mercury Pen Co. Inc.
MERCURY - Printing machines - Heidelberg Harris Inc.
MERCURY - Recording label - Polygram Records, Inc.
MERCURY - Recording label ☆ - Philips Electronics North America Corp.
MERCURY - Rifles - Tradewinds Inc.
MERCURY - Skis ☆ - Nash Manufacturing Inc.
MERCURY - Slippers - Kayser-Roth Corp.
MERCURY - Sporting goods - D & R Industries, Inc.
MERCURY - Telephones - TIE Communications Inc.
MERCURY - Tripods–photographic ☆ - QuickSet International Inc.
MERCURY - Watches - Bulova Corp.
MERCURY ATLAS - Toys–models - Estes Industries
MERCURY BY MURRAY - Bicycles - Murray, Inc.
MERCURY CASUALS - Apparel–men's ☆ - Cross Country Clothes
MERCURY CLASS - Boats–dinghies - Moore Boats
MERCURY CONNECT - Computer software - Florists' Transworld Delivery Association, Inc.
MERCURY KLEAN UP KIT - Cleaning preparations - Geritrex Corp.
MERCURY MUSIC - Music–sheet - Theodore Presser Co.
MERCURY REDSTONE - Toys–models ☆ - Estes Industries
MERCURY'S PHILLIPS - Medical apparatus - Mercury Enterprises, Inc.
MERCUTHEOLIN - Pharmaceutical preparations ☆ - Roberts/Hauck Pharmaceuticals Inc.
MERE CIE - Giftware - Mere Cie.
MERE IMAGE - Apparel–women's - Mere Image Inc.
MEREDITH - Apparel–women's - Oxford Industries, Inc.
MEREDITH - Dishes–china ☆ - Royal China & Porcelain Companies Inc.
MEREDITH - Seafood products–fresh or frozen - Meredith Fish Co. of California
MEREDITH - Stoves–wood-burning - Ohio Steel Industries Inc.
MEREDITH - Toys - Tonka Corp.
MEREDITH'S - Seafood products–fresh or frozen - Meredith and Meredith Inc.
MEREDYTH VINEYARDS - Wines - Meredyth Vineyard
MERELY ME - Underwear and nightwear - Maidenform Inc.
MEREX - Fruits and vegetables - Merex Inc.
MEREZAN - Emulsifiers - Meer Corp.
MERFLUAN - Toothpowder, mouthwash - American Merfluan Inc.
MERGAL - Chemical preparations - Troy Corp.

MERGE LEFT - Apparel and accessories - Jonathan Y. Saferstein
MERGE/PURGE LIBRARY - Computer software - i.d. Centric
MERGE/PURGE LIBRARY - Computer software - Postalsoft, a Firstlogic Technology
MERGENT & GAUNTLET INTERRET FIREWALL - Computer software ☆ - Utimaco Mergent
MERGERS - Apparel–men's - Montgomery Ward & Co. Inc.
MERH - Pharmaceutical preparations - Summum
MERHOW - Trailers–horse ☆ - Merhow Industries
MERIBEAU - Wines - Seagram's Chateau & Estate Wines Co.
MERIBEL - Mattresses and box springs - Ohio Mattress Co.
MERIBIN - Pharmaceutical preparations - Mericon Industries Inc.
MERICO - Bakery products - Campbell Taggart Inc.
MERICO BUTTER-ME-NOTS - Biscuits - Campbell Taggart Inc.
MERIDA - Dinnerware–glass ☆ - WMF/USA
MERIDA - Floor coverings–carpet and rugs - Merida Meridian, Inc.
MERIDEA - Jewelry - Meridea Trading Co.
MERIDIA - Pharmaceutical preparations - Knoll Pharmaceutical Co.
MERIDIAN - Awnings - Alcan Aluminum Corp. Alcan Building Products Div.
MERIDIAN - Chemical preparations - Graver Chemical Co.
MERIDIAN - Cutlery ☆ - National Housewares
MERIDIAN - Dinnerware–glass - Nikko Ceramics Inc.
MERIDIAN - Doors–storm - Canyon Creek Cabinet Co.
MERIDIAN - Draperies - Maharam Vertical Surfaces
MERIDIAN - Floor coverings ☆ - Azrock Commercial Flooring
MERIDIAN - Floor coverings–carpet and rugs ☆ - Catalina Carpet Mills Inc.
MERIDIAN - Furniture - Meridian, Inc.
MERIDIAN - Furniture - Stanley Furniture Co. Inc.
MERIDIAN - Furniture ☆ - Mersman Furniture Co.
MERIDIAN - Giftware - Sasaki
MERIDIAN - Housewares - Meridian (USA) Ltd.
MERIDIAN - Luggage - American Tourister, Inc.
MERIDIAN - Paints - Graham Paint and Varnish Co.
MERIDIAN - Paper - M. Grumbacher Inc.
MERIDIAN - Pens - Accutec Inc.
MERIDIAN - Publisher's imprints - Penguin USA
MERIDIAN - Recording label - Meridian Records Inc.
MERIDIAN - Saddles - Libertyville Saddle Shop, Inc.
MERIDIAN - Seafood products–fresh or frozen - Meridian Products
MERIDIAN - Shelving units–wood ☆ - Republic Storage Systems Co. Inc.
MERIDIAN - Siding–insulating - Certainteed Corp. (Roofing Products Group)
MERIDIAN - Sporting goods - John D. Henderson
MERIDIAN - Tires–bicycles ☆ - Carlisle Tire & Rubber Co.
MERIDIAN - Wallpaper - B. Berger Co.
MERIDIAN - Watches - Medana Watch Corp.
MERIDIAN - Water treating compounds - Aquarium Products Inc.
MERIDIAN - Whirlpool spa ☆ - Jacuzzi Inc.
MERIDIAN 100'S - Cigarettes - Eve Holdings Inc.
MERIDIAN CIRCULATION - Health care products - East Earth Herb Inc.
MERIDIAN COLLECTION - Awards, plaques and medals - Associates Engraving Co., Inc.
MERIDIAN COLLECTION - Giftware - Lenox, Inc.
MERIDIAN PASSAGE - Health care products - East Earth Herb Inc.
MERIDIAN STONE - Floor coverings - Bruce Hardwood Floors
MERIDIAN STONE - Flooring–hardwood - Triangle Pacific Corp. (Cabinet Division)
MERIDIAN VINEYARDS - Wines - Wine World Estates Co.
MERIDIAN VINEYARDS - Wines - Wine World Inc.
MERIDIEN - Cabinets - Aristokraft, Inc.
MERIDIEN - Clocks - Ridgeway Clock Co.
MERIDIEN - Furniture ☆ - Tropitone Furniture Co. Inc.
MERIDIEN - Glassware–household - Durand International
MERIDIEN COLLECTION - Floor coverings–carpet and rugs ☆ - Cumberland Mills Inc.
MERIDIEN COLLECTION - Footwear ☆ - Allen-Edmonds Shoe Corp.
MERIDITH HAZE - Hair accessories, jewelry - Baby Doll Art
MERIDYNE - Radios - Shell Oil Co.
MERILAB - Tools–power-driven - MERILab Inc.
MERILAC - Food products - Novartis Nutrition Corp.
MERILEUM - Sashes–window - American Home Improvement
MERILLAT - Cabinets - Merillat Industries, Inc.
MERIMAC - Floor coverings–carpet and rugs - Gulistan Carpet Inc.
MERIMIX - Custard–frozen - Novartis Nutrition Corp.
MERINGUE - Christmas tree ornaments - Cracker Box Inc.
MERINO - Eyeglasses - Silton USA Corp.
MERINO - Skin care products - Pacific Rim International Inc.

☆ = Now out of production

MERION - Flowers, plants, and seeds - Jacklin Seed
MERION KING - Yarn - Joseph Galler Inc.
MERION MUSIC - Music–sheet - Theodore Presser Co.
MERION PAINTER - Paints - Finnaren & Haley Inc.
MERIRUUSU - Bedding–linen - Dan River Inc.
MERISTAR - Medical apparatus - Meridian Diagnostics, Inc.
MERIT - Abrasive products - Merit Abrasive Products, Inc.
MERIT - Cigarettes - Philip Morris Companies Inc.
MERIT - Crackers - Malone and Hyde Inc.
MERIT - Electronic equipment - Eastman Kodak Co.
MERIT - Exhaust systems–motor vehicle - Merit Automotive Exhaust Systems
MERIT - Flatware - Crate and Barrel
MERIT - Floor coverings–carpet and rugs - Patrick Carpet Mills
MERIT - Floor coverings–carpet and rugs - S and S Mills Inc.
MERIT - Floor coverings–carpet and rugs ☆ - J and J Industries Inc.
MERIT - Foundation garments–women's - Merit Foundations Inc.
MERIT - Gasoline - Merit Oil Corp.
MERIT - Hardware - Merit Metal Products Corp.
MERIT - Insecticides - Bayer Corp. (Agriculture Div.)
MERIT - Musical instrument accessories ☆ - McMillan Music Co.
MERIT - Orthopedic products - Smith & Nephew Inc. (Rehabilitation Div.)
MERIT - Paper–toweling - Procter & Gamble Co.
MERIT - Pencils ☆ - Faber-Castell Corp.
MERIT - Shoes ☆ - Endicott Johnson Corp.
MERIT - Siding–metal - Armor Bond Building Products, Inc.
MERIT - Soap - DL/Banite
MERIT - Tiles–ceramic ☆ - American Olean Tile Co.
MERIT - Tires–automobile - Hercules Tire & Rubber Co.
MERIT - Watches - Merit Watch Co. Inc.
MERIT 100S - Cigarettes - Philip Morris Companies Inc.
MERIT II - Mufflers–motor vehicle ☆ - Merit Automotive Exhaust Systems
MERIT-MADE - Housewares - Ironees Co.
MERIT MASTER PLUS - Mufflers–motor vehicle - Merit Automotive Exhaust Systems
MERIT ULTIMA - Cigarettes - Philip Morris Companies Inc.
MERIT ULTRA LIGHTS - Cigarettes - Philip Morris Companies Inc.
MERITA - Breads - American Bakeries Co.
MERITA LITE - Breads - American Bakeries Co.
MERITA OLD FASHIONED - Breads - American Bakeries Co.
MERITAGE - Video production - Meritage, Inc.
MERITAL - Cotton–balls - National Patent Medical
MERITE - Figurines ☆ - Polk's Model Craft Hobbies, Inc.
MERITE - Skis - Sports Specialists Limited
MERITENE - Vitamins and nutritional supplements - Novartis Nutrition Corp.
MERITEX - Polishing cloths - Rodel, Inc.
MERITEX - Uniforms–tailored - Angelica Uniform Group
MERITEX - Watches - Merit Watch Co. Inc.
MERITOR - Watches - Merit Watch Co. Inc.
MERITT - Floor coverings ☆ - Tarkett, Inc.
MERIWETHER'S - Tobacco - American Tobacco Co.
MERIWETHER'S PIGTAIL - Tobacco products - Scott Tobacco Co.
MERIX - Circuit boards–printed - Merix Corp.
MERIX - Static eliminator - Merix Chemical Co.
MERIX RINS - Static eliminator - Merix Chemical Co.
MERKT'S - Food products - Merkt Cheese Co., Inc.
MERKUR - Cigars - Gesty Trading & Manufacturing Corp.
MERKUR SCORPIO - Motor vehicles–automobiles - Ford Motor Co. (Lincoln-Mercury Div.)
MERKUR XR4TI - Motor vehicles–automobiles - Ford Motor Co. (Lincoln-Mercury Div.)
MERLE - Apparel–women's - Merle Limited, Inc.
MERLE NORMAN - Cosmetics - Merle Norman Cosmetics
MERLENATE - Pharmaceutical preparations ☆ - Vortech Pharmaceuticals
MERLESEAL - Adhesives and sealants - Merlex Stucco, Inc.
MERLIN - Automotive lubricants and solvents - One Shot Products Corp.
MERLIN - Beverages–alcohol - Consolidated Distilled Products Inc.
MERLIN - Computer software - Dahlberg, Inc.
MERLIN - Computer software - Roger Wagner Publishing Inc.
MERLIN - Construction equipment - Stirling Lloyd Products, Inc.
MERLIN - Display cases–plastic - Capo, Inc.
MERLIN - Floor coverings–carpet and rugs ☆ - Interloom Ltd.
MERLIN - Gloves–safety - Bettcher Industries Inc.
MERLIN - Golfing equipment - Merlin Industries, Inc.
MERLIN - Lenses–optical - Innotech, Inc.
MERLIN - Pet product - Interwood Corp.
MERLIN - Surgical instruments - Linvatec Corp.

MERLIN - Telephones - At&T Corp.
MERLIN - Timers–appliance - Prince Castle Inc.
MERLIN - Toys–electronic ☆ - Parker Brothers
MERLIN - Wallpaper ☆ - Wolf-Gordon Inc.
MERLIN - Work benches - Maximum Inc.
MERLIN EXPRESS - Electronic equipment - Varitronic Systems, Inc.
MERLIN EXPRESS ELECT - Labeling machinery - Varitronic Systems, Inc.
MERLIN FREELANCERS - Employment agencies–temporary help - Merlin Freelancers, Inc.
MERLIN PFC - Telephones - At&T Corp.
MERLIN PRO - Computer software - Roger Wagner Publishing Inc.
MERLIN THE MAGICIAN - Toys - Natural Science Industries, Ltd.
MERLINO - Pasta - Merlino & Sons
MERLINO'S - Pasta - Borden, Inc.
MERLIN'S - JTM Products Inc.
MERLIN'S - Candy - Crowley Candy Co., Inc.
MERLIN'S ALE - Beverages–malt - Phoenix Imports Ltd.
MERLINS CLOSET - Apparel–children's - Tom Togs of Carolina, Inc.
MERLIN'S MAGIC - Novelty items - Merlin Technologies, Inc.
MERLIN'S MAGIC HAT - Toys - Natural Science Industries, Ltd.
MERLIN'S WAND - Blinds–vertical - Newell Operating Co.
MERLOT - Flatware - Reed and Barton Corp.
MERLOT - Wines - Cilurzo Vineyard & Winery
MERLOT - Wines - Fife Vineyards LLC
MERLOT - Wines - Merryvale Vineyards
MERLTOR HK - Telephones - TIE Communications Inc.
MERMADE - Garden equipment - Hytrous/Flash Sales Inc.
MERMADE - Shampoos - Cosmair Inc.
MERMAID - Bathing suits - Ocean Pool Co.
MERMAID - Canned oysters - Liberty Gold Fruit Co.
MERMAID - Fabrics - Manart-Hirsch Co. Inc.
MERMAID - Faucets ☆ - Milwaukee Faucets Inc.
MERMAID - Food products - Atalanta Corp.
MERMAID - Kites - Hi-Flier Manufacturing Co.
MERMAID - Paints–artists' ☆ - Woolsey Marine Industries
MERMAID - Recording label - Rustron Music Productions
MERMAID - Vegetable oil - Ventura Foods LLC (Lou Ana Division)
MERMAID - Watches - Bulova Corp.
MERMAID - Water–bottled or canned - Water Services Corp.
MERMAID - Wet mops - Bouras Mop Manufacturing Co.
MERMAID DRAMABOOKS - Magazines - Farrar, Straus and Giroux Inc.
MERMAID PRINCESS - Shrimp–fresh or frozen - Neptune Sea Food Co.
MERMAID QUEEN - Boats–motor ☆ - Holiday Distributing Co.
MERMAID'S GOLD - Video games - WMS Gaming Inc.
MERMAID'S LUNCH - Food products - Van Camp Seafood Co. Inc.
MERMISTA - Toys - Mattel, Inc.
MERNO'S - Pickles ☆ - Safie Bros. Pickle Co.
MEROCEL - Medical apparatus - Merocel Corp.
MEROCEL 2000 - Pharmaceutical preparations - Merocel Corp.
MERONA - Apparel and accessories - Oxford Industries, Inc.
MERONA - Bedding–linen - Merona Industries Inc.
MERONA - Watches - Merona Industries Inc.
MERONA SPORT - Apparel–athletic ☆ - Renny
MEROPS - Computer software - IFF, Inc.
MERPHENE - Pharmaceutical preparations - Barry Laboratories Inc.
MERPLUS - Gloves - Mer, Inc.
MERRELL - Hiking and climbing boots - Karhu USA Inc.
MERRELL FRONT RANGE - Boots - Karhu USA Inc.
MERREMONT - Crocheted and knitted items - Grand Knitting Mills, Inc.
MERRI - Toys–stuffed ☆ - Russ Berrie and Co., Inc.
MERRI-GO-RHYMES - Infant product - Welcome to the World Inc.
MERRI-MATES - Infant product - Welcome to the World Inc.
MERRI-SHADES - Sunglasses - Welcome to the World Inc.
MERRI-SHOOZ - Apparel and accessories - Welcome to the World Inc.
MERRI-TOTS - Infant product - Welcome to the World Inc.
MERRIAM - Cash boxes - Merriam Manufacturing Co. Inc.
MERRIAM-WEBSTER - Publisher's imprints - Merriam-Webster
MERRICK - Dog food - Merrick Petfoods Inc.
MERRICKLEIN - Bicycles - Klein Bicycle Corp.
MERRICORR - Cardboard - Merrimac Paper Co., Inc.
MERRIE CHRISTMAS - Greeting cards - Regency Thermographers Inc.
MERRIE MELODIES - Apparel and accessories - Time Warner Entertainment Co., L.P.
MERRIGOLD - Artists' materials - Western Publishing Co., Inc.
MERRIGOLD PRESS - Publisher's imprints - Western Publishing Co., Inc.

☆ = Now out of production

MERRIGOLD PRESS TELL-A-TALE, A - Publisher's imprints - Western Publishing Co., Inc.
MERRILEE'S - Apparel—women's - Merrilee's Inc.
MERRILL - Lifting clamps, etc ☆ - Cooper Industries, Inc.
MERRILL - Water system products - Merrill Manufacturing Co., Inc.
MERRILL BLUEBERRY FARMS - Fruits—frozen - Merrill Blueberry Farms Inc.
MERRILL-SHARPE - Apparel—men's - Merrill-Sharpe Ltd.
MERRILL SINCE 1933 - Fruits and vegetables - Merrill Farms
MERRILY - Rings—jewelry - Artcarved Inc.
MERRIMAC - Apparel—men's - Alps Sportswear Manufacturing Co.
MERRIMACK MAGNETICS - Transformers—electric - Merrimack Magnetics Corp.
MERRIMAID OF VERMONT - Apparel and accessories ☆ - Vermont Sports Apparel Inc.
MERRIMENT - Dinnerware—glass ☆ - Lenox, Inc.
MERRIMINTS - Candy - Ultimate Nut Co., Inc.
MERRIMOUSE - Toys—stuffed ☆ - Gund, Inc.
MERRITONE - Inks - Phillips Process Co. Inc.
MERRITT - Wines - Merritt Estate Winery Inc.
MERRIVALE - Rings—jewelry - Artcarved Inc.
MERRIWEATHER - Glassware—household - Owens-Illinois Inc. (Libbey Div.)
MERRY - Brooms - Corcoran Manufacturing Co., Inc.
MERRY - Recording label - Bestway Group Inc.
MERRY AERATOR - Garden equipment ☆ - Mackissic Inc.
MERRY BEARY - Toys—stuffed ☆ - Gund, Inc.
MERRY BELLS - Candy - R.M. Palmer Co.
MERRY BERRY - Sachets - SLPCO Enterprises, Inc.
MERRY BUNNIES - Toys—stuffed - Dakin Inc.
MERRY CAPERS - Apparel and accessories ☆ - Umbro USA
MERRY CHRISMEWS - Dolls - Susan Sona
MERRY CHRISTMAS - Christmas tree ornaments - Cracker Box Inc.
MERRY CHRISTMAS - Dinnerware—glass ☆ - Johnson Brothers, USA, Inc.
MERRY CHRISTMAS - Glassware—household - Ceraglass Inc.
MERRY CHRISTMAS HAPPY NEW YORK - Greeting cards - Pablo Villarroel
MERRY CRISS-CROSS - Games - International Gamco, Inc.
MERRY EDGER - Garden equipment ☆ - Mackissic Inc.
MERRY ENGLAND TOFFEE - Candy - Murray-Allen International Inc.
MERRY GIFTS OF CHRISTMAS, THE - Apparel and accessories - Kmart Properties, Inc.
MERRY-GO-ROUND - Bakery products - SB Royalty Co. Inc.
MERRY-GO-ROUND - Office supplies - Roto Photo Co. Inc.
MERRY-GO-ROUND - Pet products - Petland, Inc.
MERRY-GO-ROUND - Recording label - Country International Records
MERRY-GRAMS - Toys—stuffed - Fun World Inc.
MERRY LITTLE MURDER, A - Puzzles - Hasbro, Inc.
MERRY MAC - Garden equipment - Mackissic Inc.
MERRY MAID - Food products - Rex Pacific
MERRY MAKE-KIT - Hobby kits - Evergreen International, Inc.
MERRY MAKERS - Figurines - Department 56 Inc.
MERRY MARY - Fabrics - MM Fab, Inc.
MERRY MATES - Shoes - Beacon Shoe Co.
MERRY MESSAGES - Gas masks - Stephen Lawrence Co.
MERRY MESSENGERS - Giftware - Russ Berrie and Co., Inc.
MERRY MIDGET - Lamps - General Electric Co.
MERRY MINIATURES - Figurines - Hallmark Cards Inc.
MERRY MIX - Candy - M-B Candies Inc.
MERRY MIX - Snack foods ☆ - Nalley's Fine Foods
MERRY MIX-UP - Fruits—dried - Harry and David Inc.
MERRY MIXINGS - Wallpaper ☆ - Pantasote Inc. (Wallcovering Div.)
MERRY MOOSE - Paper—gift wrap - World's Finest Chocolate, Inc.
MERRY MORSELS - Chocolate candy - Nestle USA
MERRY MOUSE - Toys—stuffed - Fun World Inc.
MERRY MUFFIN LAND - Toys - Mattel, Inc.
MERRY MULES - Footwear - Beacon Shoe Co.
MERRY MUSHROOM - Cooking utensils—cast iron ☆ - General Housewares Corp.
MERRY POPPINS - Popcorn ☆ - TV Time Foods Inc.
MERRY RIDER - Toys - Processed Plastic Co.
MERRY STRESSMAS - Greeting cards - Alden M. Howells
MERRY THOUGHTS - Publisher's imprints - Merry Thoughts Inc.
MERRY TILLER - Garden equipment - Mackissic Inc.
MERRY TREATS - Candy ☆ - R.M. Palmer Co.
MERRY WEDDING - Dolls - Mattel, Inc.
MERRY WHISK - Brooms ☆ - Lighthouse Industries
MERRY WIDOW - Apparel and accessories - Warnaco Inc.
MERRYBRITE - Hooks - Melville Corp.

MERRYCURL - Toys - Mattel, Inc.
MERRYGARDEN - Uniforms—academic - Katzenberg Bros. Inc.
MERRYLINE - Apparel—women's ☆ - Gem-Dandy, Inc.
MERRYMAKING - Wines - Chase Collection, Inc.
MERRYMATES - Hair care products - Shalom International Corp.
MERRYPOND - Liners and covers—Swimming pool - White Rose Nurseries Limited, Inc.
MERRYTHOUGHT - Toys - Tide-Rider Inc.
MERRYWEATHER - Floor coverings—carpet and rugs - West Point-Pepperell Mill Store
MERRYWOOD - Rings—jewelry - Artcarved Inc.
MERSALINE - Pharmaceutical preparations ☆ - Physician Sales & Service
MERSALO - Pharmaceutical preparations ☆ - C.O. Truxton Inc.
MERSALYL THEOPHYLLINE - Pharmaceutical preparations ☆ - Legere Pharmaceuticals Inc.
MERSALYN - Pharmaceutical preparations ☆ - Keene Pharmaceuticals Inc.
MERSE - Cleaning preparations - Sybron Chemical Holdings Inc.
MERSENE - Denture cleaners - Colgate-Palmolive Co.
MERSEY - Recording label - Country Star International
MERSEY - Seafood products—fresh or frozen - Pocasset Seafoods Inc.
MERSMAN - Furniture - Mersman Furniture Co.
MERSO - Thread - Cincinnati Thread Co.
MERSOL - Pharmaceutical preparations - Century Pharmaceuticals Inc.
MERSTICK - Wood products - Dexter Corp. (Mercer Plastics Div.)
MERTHIOLATE - Pharmaceutical preparations - Eli Lilly and Co.
MERTWINS - Dolls - Tyco Industries, Inc.
MERUMEC - Wines - Peaceful Bend Vineyard
MERUVAX II - Vaccines - Merck & Co., Inc. (Merck Research Laboratories)
MERVEILLE - Floor coverings—carpet and rugs - J.L. Benson Co.
MERVYN'S UNIVERSITY - Calculators - Mervyn's
MERYL WAITZ - Jewelry - Loom Co.
MERZON - Brassieres (Bras) ☆ - Q-T Foundations Co. Inc.
MES - Jewelry - Modern Design Inc.
MES JOURS - Cosmetics ☆ - Paloma Picasso for Lopez Cambil, Ltd.
MES NUITS - Cosmetics ☆ - Paloma Picasso for Lopez Cambil, Ltd.
MESA - Beer ☆ - Miller Brewing Co.
MESA - Brushes—paint - Corona Brushes Inc.
MESA - Cabinets - Marsh Furniture Co.
MESA - Cabinets ☆ - Medallion Kitchens of Minnesota Inc.
MESA - Computer software - Green Mountain Geophysics, Inc.
M.E.S.A. - Computer software ☆ - Rolandcorp US
MESA - Curtain rods - Kirsch Co.
MESA - Dinnerware—glass - Dansk International Designs, Ltd.
MESA - Floor coverings - Congoleum Corp.
MESA - Floor coverings—carpet and rugs ☆ - Blue Ridge Carpet Mills
MESA - Floor coverings—carpet and rugs ☆ - Regal Rugs Inc.
MESA - Flowers, plants, and seeds - Jonathan Green, Inc.
MESA - Flowers, plants, and seeds - Jacklin Seed
MESA - Frames—picture - Terragrafics Inc.
MESA - Hardware - Harloc, Inc.
MESA - Occasional tables - JDI Group, Inc.
MESA - Recording label ☆ - Nationwide Sound Distributors
MESA - Structural steel - Tensar Corp.
MESA - Tables—wood - Krueger International, Inc.
MESA - Trailers—travel ☆ - Marathon Homes Corp.
MESA - Wallpaper - Bob Mitchell Designs
MESA - Wines - Llano Estacado Winery Inc.
MESA 3800 - Floor coverings—tile - Dal-Tile Corp.
MESA CERVEZA - Beverages—malt - Four Corners Brewing Co., LLC
MESA COLLECTION, THE - Bedding—linen - Dan River Inc.
MESA ENVIRONMENTAL - Automotive parts and accessories - Mesa Operating Co.
MESA GRANDE - Tiles—ceramic - American Olean Tile Co.
MESA GRANDE - Tortillas - Great Western Tortilla Co.
MESA RUNNER - Bicycles - Schwinn Cycling & Fitness Inc.
MESA SAGUAROS - Novelty items - Arizona Fall League, Inc.
MESA VERDE - Campers - American Sterling Corp.
MESA VERDE - Clocks - Terragrafics Inc.
MESA VERDE - Floor coverings—carpet and rugs - Mannington Carpets, Inc.
MESA VINEYARD - Wines - Ross Keller Winery
MESABI - Paint - American Paints
MESALT - Health care products - Scott Health Care
MESANTOIN - Pharmaceutical preparations - Sandoz Pharmaceuticals Corp.
MESAVENTURES CULTURELLES - Computer software ☆ - Gessler Publishing Co., Inc.
MESCOLARE - Wines - Weisinger's of Ashland, Inc.

☆ = Now out of production

MESCOLOR - Antihistamine preparations - Horizon Pharmaceutical Corp.
MESH FINDER - Artists' materials - Davis International, Inc.
MESH GARD - Fishing nets - Frabill Inc.
MESH-MATES - Handbags - Whiting & Davis Co.
MESHED - Floor coverings—carpet and rugs - Trans-Ocean Import Co. Inc.
MESHUBACH - Food products - KFP International, Ltd.
MESINGER - Seats—bicycle - Persons-Majestic Manufacturing Co.
MESKER - Hardware - Blaine Window Hardware Inc.
MESMERA - Toys - Lancer Industries Inc.
MESMERIZE - Colognes - Avon Products, Inc.
MESOPIN - Health care products ☆ - Du Pont Pharmaceuticals
MESOPOTAMIA FOOD INC. - Food products - Mesopotamia Food Inc.
MESOZOIC UNIVERSITY - Leather goods - Creative Capers Entertainment
MESOZOIC UNIVERSITY EST. 1893 VERTEBRATE PALEONTOLOGY - Apparel and accessories - Creative Capers Entertainment
MESPO MAGIC - Umbrellas - Mespo Umbrella Co. Inc.
MESQHEAT - Barbecue charcoal - Mesquite Charcoal Co.
MESQUITE 50 - Charcoal - Hickory Specialties, Inc.
MESQUITE BROIL - Meat products—beef - Gorges Foodservice, Inc.
MESQUITE MIST - Cooking oil - Par-Way Group
MESS-ENDER - Tool boxes - Center Products Inc.
MESS-FREE WATERPROOF BURPING CLOTH - Infant product - TL Care Inc.
MESS-REE VINYL MATTRESS COVER - Infant product - TL Care Inc.
MESS, THE - Musical instrument stores - Todd Papaleo
MESSAGE - Recording label - Executive Suite Records
MESSAGE - Recording label ☆ - Shanachie Records Corp.
MESSAGE ALERT - Desk sets ☆ - Creative Concepts
MESSAGE CAMERA - Photographic equipment - Concord Camera Corp.
MESSAGE CENTER - Facsimile equipment - Brother International Corp.
MESSAGE CENTER - Toys - Fisher-Price, Inc.
MESSAGE CENTER, THE - Computer software ☆ - Capstone Software
MESSAGE CLIP - Stationery - Clix Products, Inc.
MESSAGE D'AMOUR - Skin care products - Michel Skin Care Enterprises Inc.
MESSAGE DESK - Computer software - VMX Inc.
MESSAGE EXPRESS - Software - Horizon Strategies Inc.
MESSAGE FOR A MOM MUG - Giftware - Avon Products, Inc.
MESSAGE-FOR-ME - Toys - Mattel, Inc.
MESSAGE FROM THE GRAVE - Puzzles - Hasbro, Inc.
MESSAGE FROM YOUR HEART - Recording label - Pacific Institute Inc.
MESSAGE HEARTS - Toys—stuffed - Fun World Inc.
MESSAGE MAKER COMPANION - Pagers - NEC America, Inc.
MESSAGE MAKER EXEC - Pagers - NEC America, Inc.
MESSAGE MAKER TRACKER - Pagers - NEC America, Inc.
MESSAGE MASTER - Telephone answering machines ☆ - Dictaphone Corp.
MESSAGE MATES - Memo pads ☆ - Riverside Solutions
MESSAGE MINDER - Desks ☆ - Softalk Inc.
MESSAGE-MINDER - Telephone answering machines - TT Systems Corp.
MESSAGE-MOUNT - Communications equipment—mobile - Gamber-Johnson Inc.
MESSAGE MOUSE - Toys—stuffed - Fun World Inc.
MESSAGE MUG, THE - Glassware—household - Thomas E. Ford
MESSAGE ONE - Facsimile equipment - AudioFax Inc.
MESSAGE STOPPER - Electronic equipment - Designtech International, Inc.
MESSAGE TO MOTHER - Glassware—household ☆ - Fenton Art Glass Co.
MESSAGECONNECT! - Communications equipment - Motorola, Inc.
MESSAGEFLASH - Computer software - McCaw Cellular Communications, Inc.
MESSAGEMAKER - Audio equipment - Applied American Technologies, Inc.
MESSAGEMAKER - Chemical preparations - Life Technologies, Inc.
MESSAGEPAD - Computers - Apple Computer Inc.
MESSAGE!PRODUCTS - Checkbooks - Message Product, Inc.
MESSAGES - Bedding—linen - Dan River Inc.
MESSAGESOFT - Computer software - Mobilemedia Communications, Inc.
MESSAGEWATCH - Electronic equipment - Seiko Communications of America Inc.
MESSENGER - Candy ☆ - Pet Inc. (Whitman's Chocolates Div.)
MESSENGER - Computer software - Puuoa Software Development of Hawaii, Inc.
MESSENGER - Electronic equipment - Telex Communications, Inc.
MESSENGER - Electronic equipment ☆ - E.F. Johnson Co.
MESSENGER - Hearing aids - Dahlberg, Inc.
MESSENGER - Tape recorders—cassette - Lanier Voice Products
MESSENGER OF LOVE PUPPY - Toys—stuffed - Russ Berrie and Co., Inc.
MESSENGER, THE - Tape recorders ☆ - Crestwood Co.
MESSINA - Floor coverings ☆ - Congoleum Corp.
MESSINA - Floor coverings—carpet and rugs ☆ - Karastan-Bigelow Inc.
MESSINA - Shoes - Messer Import Corp.

MESSINA BOUTIQUES - Shoes - Messer Import Corp.
MESSINA HOF - Food products - Messina Hof Wine Cellars
MESSING PRETTY - Toys - Playskool, Inc.
MESSINGER BOY - Apparel—men's ☆ - Michaels/Stern & Co. Inc.
MESSLER - Fishing tackle - Wright & McGill Co.
MESSY PLAY & HOBBY TRAY - Toys - Childcraft Education Corp.
MESTAMED - Computer software - MestaMed
MESTEMACHER PARTY ROUNDS - Baked goods - Carl Brandt
MESTER - Music—sheet ☆ - James Hendrix Enterprises
MESTINON - Pharmaceutical preparations - Roche Laboratories
MESUROL - Insecticides ☆ - Bayer Corp. (Agriculture Div.)
MET-ALL - Automotive parts and accessories - Dars Met-All Industries Inc.
MET BRAU - Beverages—malt - The Stroh Brewery Co.
MET-L-COTE - Cleaning preparations—household - J.N.T. Manufacturing Co. Inc.
MET-L-ETCH - Cleaning preparations - Sherwin-Williams Automotive Finishes Corp.
MET-L-FIL - Adhesives and sealants ☆ - W.J. Ruscoe Co.
MET-L-KYL - Fire extinguishers - Ansul, Inc.
MET-L-LINK - Window coverings - General Drapery Services Inc.
MET-L-MESH - Window coverings - General Drapery Services Inc.
MET-L-RAX - Floor waxes - Sanitek Products Inc.
MET-L-SPHERE - Window coverings - General Drapery Services Inc.
MET-L-VEIL - Window coverings - General Drapery Services Inc.
MET-L-X - Fire extinguishers - Ansul, Inc.
MET-MAX - Vitamins and nutritional supplements - Champion Nutrition
MET-RELIEF - Footcare products - Dr. Fabricant's Foot Health Products, Inc.
MET-RX - Vitamins and nutritional supplements - Met-Rx USA Inc.
MET-SEP - Machinery - Technology & Trade, Inc.
META - Computer software - Meta-Software, Inc.
META - Hair care products - Meta International Inc.
META - Sporting goods - Klein Bicycle Corp.
META - Uniforms—academic - Ottenheimer and Co. Inc.
META 1 STEP - Hair coloring preparations - Meta International Inc.
META-21 - Vitamins and nutritional supplements - Australian Bodycare Enterprises, Inc.
META-C - Vitamins and nutritional supplements - NutriBiotic
META-LEAN - Vitamins and nutritional supplements - Shaperite Concepts, Ltd.
META LUNDIA - Shelving units—wood - Lundia
META MACHINE, THE - Industrial machinery - Digital Tool, Inc.
META-SOFTWARE - Computer software - Meta-Software, Inc.
META-SPEED - Circuit boards - Video Post & Transfer
META-TYPE - Vitamins and nutritional supplements - Pierson Co.
META2 - Funnels - Funnel-Gage Co., Inc.
METAAL - Dinnerware—plastic - Grainware Co.
METAB HERBS - Pharmaceutical preparations - Merz Apothecary Inc.
METABA-TROL - Pharmaceuticals - Rexall Sundown, Inc.
METABAL - Vitamins and nutritional supplements - Mickey A. Hall
METABALANCE - Animal feeds - Consolidated Nutrition, L.C.
METABALM - Analgesics ☆ - P.J. Noyes Co., Inc.
METABASIS - Computer software - Daniel Martin Klein
METABLANACE 44 - Vitamins and nutritional supplements - Sunrider Corp.
METABLEND - Chemicals—photographic - AGFA-Gevaert Inc.
METABOL - Pharmaceutical preparations - Wesley Pharmacal Co. Inc.
METABOLIC 2000 - Vitamins and nutritional supplements - Metabolic & Nutritional Reserch Institute Inc.
METABOLIC TECHNOLOGIES - Vitamins and nutritional supplements - Metabolic Technologies, Inc.
METABOLIFE - Vitamin and mineral supplements - Diet Fitness Weight Loss Centers, Inc.
METABOLISM BOOSTER - Pharmaceutical preparations - Bricker Laboratories
METABOLIX - Chemical preparations - Metabolix Inc.
METABOLOL - Vitamins and nutritional supplements - Champion Nutrition
METABOLOL ENDURANCE FORMULA - Vitamins and nutritional supplements - Champion Nutrition
METABOLOSS - Vitamins and nutritional supplements - Nutrition & Fitness IMG, Inc.
METABOOST - Vitamins and nutritional supplements - NutriBiotic
METABOOSTER - Fertilizers - Green Releaf Consumer Products, Inc.
METABOOSTERS - Fertilizers - Green Releaf Consumer Products, Inc.
METABORIGHT - Vitamins and nutritional supplements - Great Life Laboratories Inc.
METABRIDGE - Computer software ☆ - Metabridge, Inc.
METABRITE - Cleaning preparations ☆ - Dynasurf Corp.
METABYTE - Computer software - Metabyte, Inc.

☆ = Now out of production

METACALM - Vitamins and nutritional supplements - Metabolic Technologies, Inc.

METACAP - Pharmaceutical preparations - Ramesh C. Khurana

METACAULK - Adhesives and sealants - Rectorseal Corp.

METACLAD - Paints - Grow Group, Inc.

METACOLOR - Dyes and pigments - Phillips Process Co. Inc.

METACOM - Computer software ☆ - SDM International Inc.

METACRYLICS - Adhesives and sealants - Metacrylics

METAFLO - Computer software - Valis Group

METAFLOC - Industrial chemicals - Morton International Inc. (Morton Salt Div.)

METAFORM - Awnings - KD Kanopy, Inc.

METAFRAME - Pet products - Rolf C. Hagen (USA) Corp.

METAFREIGHT - Computer software - Metasys Inc.

METAGENICS - Vitamins and nutritional supplements - Metagenics, Inc.

METAGRAPHICS - Wallpaper ☆ - J. Josephson, Inc.

METAHANCE - Vitamins and nutritional supplements - Southwest Health & Life Style, Inc.

METAHYDRIN - Pharmaceutical preparations - Marion Merrell Dow

METAINFO - Computer software - Metainfo, Inc.

METAIRIE - Cocktail tables ☆ - JDI Group, Inc.

METAL - Fishing lures - Charles E. Nuckols

METAL - Perfumes - Paco Rabanne Parfums

METAL 2 METAL - Firearms, accessories, and parts - Beeman Precision Airguns

METAL 3 - Nail care products - Cosmair Inc.

METAL & LACE — THE BATTLE OF THE ROBO BABES - Computer software - Liberty International Components, Inc.

METAL-ART - Figurines ☆ - Anna-Perenna Inc.

METAL ART - Giftware - Shafford Co. Inc.

METAL BLADE - Recording label - Enigma Entertainment

METAL BLEU - Cosmetics - Lancome

METAL CLAD SQUARED - Electrical equipment - Coleman Cable Systems, Inc.

METAL CLADDING - Adhesives and sealants - Master's Choice Inc.

METAL DECOR - Trophies–precious metal - Metal Decor

METAL DESIGNS - Furniture - CTH/Sherrill Occasional

METAL EDGE - Metals - Klein & Co.

METAL FACE - Toys - Tonka Corp.

METAL FINDINGS - Patches, insignia, and emblems - Sports Access/America

METAL FLEX - Frames–eyeglass - Hudson Optical Corp.

METAL-FLO III - Industrial machinery - H & H Tube & Manufacturing Co.

METAL GLOW - Candlesticks - Galow Metal Products Inc.

METAL GLOW - Polish - Continental Chemical Corp.

METAL GUARD - Motor vehicle parts and accessories - Quaker State Oil Refining Corp.

METAL-GUARD - Paints - Vanguard Paints & Finishes Inc.

METAL-HEAD - Toys - Hasbro, Inc.

METAL KLEAN - Cleaning preparations - Sunbeam-Oster Household Products

METAL-LITES - Fabrics–nylon - Emtex Inc.

METAL-LOK - Insulating materials ☆ - Manville/Schuller

METAL LUMBER - Shelving units–wood - Republic Storage Systems Co. Inc.

METAL MAGIC - Epoxy ☆ - Fel-Pro Inc.

METAL MAN, THE - Ornamental products–metal - Metal Man, Inc.

METAL MARK - Crayons - Dixon Ticonderoga Co.

METAL MASH - Toys - Tonka Corp.

METAL MASTER - Cleaning preparations - Robarb Inc.

METAL MATE - Paints - Jones Blair Co.

METAL-MATIC - Guns - Ponsness-Warren

METAL MENDER - Solder - Kester Solder Co.

METAL MITES - Toys–automobiles - Nylint Toy Corp.

METAL MUSCLE - Toys–automobiles - Nylint Toy Corp.

METAL REROOF - Roofing materials - Master's Choice Inc.

METAL SAVER - Finishing agents - Rust-Oleum Corp.

METAL SHIELD - Roofing materials - Consolidated Fiber Glass Products Co.

METAL-STAK - Office furniture–metal - Joyce International Inc.

METAL STORM - Recording label - Azra International

METAL TAP - Lubricants - Chem-Pak Inc.

METAL TAPPING - Toys - Natural Science Industries, Ltd.

METAL TREAT - Rust removers - Klean-Strip

METAL WEAVE - Containers - Baker Hughes Inc.

METAL-WIZZ - Tools - Wiss-Cooper Tools

METAL WORKS - Ophthalmic goods - Foremost Optical Products

METAL-X - Brake pads - S.B.C. Ltd., Inc.

METAL-X-VAPOR - Lamp bulbs - Damar Worldwide, Inc.

METALANGUAGE - Recording label - Jazz Composer's Orchestra Association Inc.

METALARC PRO-TECH - Lamps - Osram Sylvania Inc.

METALART - Novelty items - Crownmark Corp.

METALAST - Chemical preparations - Metalast International, Inc.

METALAST - Chemical preparations - Woolsey Marine Industries

METALAST-10 - Finishing agents - Building Protective Industries

METALASTIC - Waterproofing compounds ☆ - Andek Corp.

METALBESTOS - Hardware - Selkirk Metalbestos

METALCLAD - Enamels - Devoe & Raynolds Co.

METALCLENE - Cleaning preparations ☆ - Klean-Strip

METALCO - Metals - Metalco Industries Inc.

METALCRAFT - Frames–picture - Intercraft Industries

METALCRAFT - Furniture - Koch Originals Inc.

METALCRAFT - Hardware ☆ - Waxman Industries Inc.

METALCRAFT - Welding equipment - Victor Equipment Co.

METALEAF - Paints ☆ - PPG Industries, Inc.

METALECTRICS - Lenses–optical - Wilson Optical Laboratories, Inc.

METALESS - Cleaning preparations - Cello Chemical Co.

METALEX - Hair care products - Clairol Inc.

METALEX - Paper–carbon - Kores Nordic USA Corp.

METALFIX - Adhesives, patching compounds, metal-repair kits - Abatron, Inc.

METALFLEX - Hair care products - Goody Products, Inc.

METALFLEX - Machinery - Spiral Duct Equipment Co.

METALGLO - Candles ☆ - Will & Baumer, Inc.

METALHIDE - Paints - PPG Industries, Inc.

METALIKE - Floor waxes - Twi-Laq Industries Inc.

METALINE - Cash registers - Continental Industries Inc.

METALIQUE - Ribbons - Berwick Industries, Inc.

METALIQUE - Wallpaper - Sellers & Josephson

METALIST - Fencing–iron - Gilpin Inc.

METALIST - Floor waxes - L & F Consumer Products

METALITE - Abrasive products - Norton Co.

METALITE - Cosmetics - Lancome

METALITE - Golfing equipment - Titleist & Foot-Joy Worldwide

METALITE - Musical instrument accessories - Rico International

METALITE PLUS - Golfing equipment - Foot-Joy, Inc.

METALITH - Chemicals–photographic - AGFA-Gevaert Inc.

METALITHIC SYSTEMS - Computer software - Metalithic Systems, Inc.

METALL - Cooking equipment–household - Grainware Co.

METALLEX - Embossing machines - New Hermes Inc.

METALLIC - Prefabricated buildings–wood - NCI Building Systems, Inc.

METALLIC ELEGANCE - Paper–gift wrap - Papercraft Corp.

METALLIC ELEMENTS - Wallpaper ☆ - Archetonic

METALLIC IMPRESSIONS - Boxes - Cui, Inc.

METALLIC JEWELS - Floor coverings - Meadowbrook Inventions Inc.

METALLIC M II - Rifles - Ponsness-Warren

METALLIC PLASTER - Wallcovering - Galice, Inc.

METALLICS - Pens - Sheaffer Inc.

METALLICS - Scratch and smell stickers - Internatural Designs, Inc.

METALLICS - Silver products ☆ - Hambly Studios

METALLICS - Wallpaper - Seabrook Wallcoverings, Inc.

METALLICS AND MYLARS - Wallcoverings - Elm Grounds

METALLIFEROUS - Tools–hand-operated - Metalliferous, Inc.

METALLIQUE - Bathroom accessories ☆ - Ransburg Accessories Inc.

METALLISCANNER - Electronic equipment - Zircon Corp.

METALLITE - Paints - Glidden Co.

METALLO - Jewelry - Grando, Inc.

METALLO - Pencils ☆ - Faber-Castell Corp.

METALLURE - Housewares - Glass Unlimited of High Point, Inc.

METALMAST - Boats ☆ - Metalmast Marine

METALMASTER - Tools - Wiss-Cooper Tools

METALMASTERS - Furniture - LADD Furniture Inc.

METALMIST - Lubricants - Elf Lubricants North America, Inc.

METALOIL - Oils–lubricating - Wynn Oil Co.

METALOK - Shingles–asphalt or tar ☆ - Manville/Schuller

METALON - Fabrics - Guilford Mills, Inc.

METALOON - Aircraft–balloons - Tillotson Rubber Co.

METALOSATES - Vitamins and nutritional supplements - Albion Laboratories, Inc.

METALPREP - Cleaning preparations - Parker & Amchem

METALSEP - Battery separators - W.R. Grace & Co.

METALSHIELD - Electronic equipment - Corrosion Consultants, Inc.

METALSITE - Chalk ☆ - Quartet Manufacturing Co.

METALSMITH - Dining room furniture - Imperial Manufacturing Co.

METALSTAND - Furniture - A/S Custom Furniture

METALSTAR - Faucets ☆ - Moen Inc.

METALTAP - Screws - VSI Fasteners, Inc.

METALTECH - Computer software - Dynamix, Inc.
METALTEX - Housewares ☆ - SCI Scandicrafts Inc.
METALTIGHT - Paints - Moline Paint Manufacturing Co.
METALTONE - Novelty items - Lumi-Lite Candle Co. Inc.
METALTONE - Paints ☆ - Zynolyte Products Co.
METALUX - Fluorescent lighting - Cooper Industries, Inc.
METALWAVE - Emery products - Revlon Consumer Products Corp.
METALWORKS - Automotive parts and accessories - Fibre Glass-Evercoat Co. Inc.
METALWORKS - Sunglasses - Smith Sport Optics Inc.
METALWORKS - Wallpaper - Gencorp Inc.
METALYZER, THE - Measuring instruments - Environmental Technologies Group, Inc.
METAMAP - Computer software - Metamap, Inc.
METAMATRIX TOOLBOX - Computer peripheral equipment - Atlantic Aerospace Electronics Corp.
METAMEC - Clocks ☆ - Leland Limited Inc.
METAMIX - Chemicals–photographic - AGFA-Gevaert Inc.
METAMORPH - Computer peripheral equipment ☆ - Expansion Programs International Inc.
METAMORPHIC FORCE - Computer software ☆ - Konami (America) Inc.
METAMORPHOSIS - Dietary supplement - Tea Garden Products, Inc.
METAMORPHOSIS - Vitamins and nutritional supplements - Healthy 'N Fit Nutritionals
METAMORPHOSIS 21 - Wallpaper - Jack Denst Designs
METAMUCIL - Laxatives - Procter & Gamble Co.
METAMYOSYN - Vitamins and nutritional supplements - Met-Rx USA Inc.
METANDREN - Pharmaceutical preparations - Ciba-Geigy Corp.
METANETICS - Computer hardware - Metanetics Corp.
METANOL - Vitamins and nutritional supplements ☆ - Tishcon Corp.
METAPERF - Metals - A. Zahner Sheet Metal Co.
METAPHASE - Vitamins and nutritional supplements - Metaphaz Sports Nutrition Inc.
METAPHEN - Antiseptics - Abbott Laboratories
METAPHOR - Chemical preparations - FMC Corp.
METAPHOR MIXER - Computer software - Paul Marshall
METAPHORS - Shoes - Reebok International Ltd.
METAPHOTOS - Computer software - Metatools, Inc.
METAPHYSICAL NINJA MANIAC CHAINSAW VITAMIN JUNKIES - Games - Gamescience
METAPHYSIQUE - Apparel and accessories - Metaphysique
METAPLAN - Office furniture–wood - Novikoff, Inc.
METAPOST - Tables–metal ☆ - Teledyne Post
METAPOST II - Tables–metal ☆ - Teledyne Post
METAPREL - Pharmaceutical preparations - Dorsey Laboratories
METAPRO - Footwear - Iron Age Corp.
METAQUEUE - Computer software - Metasys Inc.
METAREST - Vitamins and nutritional supplements - Bio/Chem Research
METAREST - Vitamins and nutritional supplements - NutriBiotic
METASCAPE - Games - High Tower Games, Inc.
METASEP - Shampoos - Milance Laboratories Inc.
METASOLV - Computer software - Metasolv Software, Inc.
METASONICS - Tapes and compact discs - Metasonics
METASPHERICS - Rings–jewelry - Sharon Johnston
META*STAR - Computer software - Cincom Systems, Inc.
METASTOCK - Computer peripheral equipment - Equis International Inc.
METASYSTEM - Vitamins and nutritional supplements - Dean Guy Tornabene
METASYSTOX-R - Insecticides ☆ - Bayer Corp. (Agriculture Div.)
METATALK - Computer software - Metalogic, Inc.
METATENSIN - Pharmaceutical preparations - Marion Merrell Dow
METATONE - Cough medicines ☆ - Parke-Davis
METATRAK - Computer software - Mimetics Corp.
METATRON - Audio equipment - Spiritus, Inc.
METAULLICS - Pumping units - Metaullics Systems Co., L.P.
METAXCHANGE - Computer software - Metasys Inc.
METAYARD - Computer software - Metasys Inc.
METAZENE - Deodorants–personal - Surco Products Inc.
METCO - Cheese - Swissrose International Inc.
METCOM - Computer software - Interface Technologies Inc.
METED - Shampoos - Genderm Corp.
METEOR - Audio equipment ☆ - Meteor Light & Sound Co.
METEOR - Balls - Regent Sports Corp.
METEOR - Barbecues and grills - Meteor Inc.
METEOR - Bicycles - Raleigh USA Bicycle Co.
METEOR - Boats - Wellcraft Marine Corp.
METEOR - Cartridges–ammunition - Lazzeroni, Inc.

METEOR - Chemical preparations - Chemical and Pigment Co.
METEOR - Cups–paper - Sweetheart Cup Co. Inc.
METEOR - Fabrics ☆ - Greenwood Mills Inc.
METEOR - Footwear–athletic - Puma Inc.
METEOR - Golfing equipment - Golfsmith International Inc.
METEOR - Guitars ☆ - International Music Corp.
METEOR - Hardware ☆ - Shepherd Products U.S. Inc.
METEOR - Jewelry ☆ - Hirsch Speidel Inc.
METEOR - Musical instruments ☆ - N.H.F. Musical Merchandise Corp.
METEOR - Radios - Motorola, Inc. (Land Mobile Products Sector)
METEOR - Recording label - Meteor Records
METEOR - Swimming pools - KDI American Products, Inc.
METEOR - Thread - Threads USA Div.
METEOR - Toys - Tonka Corp.
METEOR - Toys–models ☆ - Estes Industries
METEOR - Watches - 1668 International Inc.
METEOR ABC - Audio equipment ☆ - Meteor Light & Sound Co.
METEOR CRATER - Dinnerware ☆ - Meteor Crater Enterprises, Inc.
METEOR II - Typewriters - Adler-Royal Business Machines Inc.
METEOR MISSION - Computer software - SRA/McGraw-Hill (Div. of The McGraw-Hill Companies)
METEOR MULTIPLICATION - Computer software - SRA/McGraw-Hill (Div. of The McGraw-Hill Companies)
METEOR STORM - Fireworks - L. W. Loyd Co., Inc.
METEOR WASH - Jeans–men's - Salant Corp.
METEORA - Floor coverings ☆ - Azrock Commercial Flooring
METEORBS - Toys - Mattel, Inc.
METEORITE - Fabrics ☆ - Greenwood Mills Inc.
METEORITE POWDER - Cosmetics - Guerlain Inc.
METER-EZE - Veterinary nutritional supplements - Conopco, Inc.
METER-MATE - Transmitting apparatus - Wein Products Inc.
METER READER - Signs - Electromark Co.
METER-TEK - Chemical preparations - Graphic Technologies, Inc.
METERCAP - Pharmaceutical preparations - Schering Corp.
METERED RELEASE - Pet products - Farnam Cos. Inc.
METERJET - Nozzles - Spraying Systems Co.
METERLINK - Computer software - Southern Co.
METERLUBE - Lubricants - Lamson Oil Co.
METERNET - Computer software - Meternet Corp.
METERREADER - Computer peripheral equipment - Energy Management Software Solutions, Inc.
METERWARE - Computer software - Technically Elite, Inc.
METESTONE - Pharmaceutical preparations - Vita Elixir Co. Inc.
METH-BLUE - Water treating compounds - Silco Pet Products
METH-CHOLINE - Pharmaceutical preparations - Schein Pharmaceutical Inc.
METH-EX - Fertilizers - Lebanon Seaboard Corp.
METH-EX 40 - Fertilizers - Lebanon Seaboard Corp.
METHA-BLUE - Pharmaceutical preparations ☆ - Scrip-Physician Supply Co.
METHABOLIC - Pharmaceutical preparations ☆ - Keene Pharmaceuticals Inc.
METHACHOLINE - Pharmaceutical preparations - Goldline Laboratories, Inc.
METHACROL - Lubricants - E.I. Dupont de Nemours and Co.
METHADONE HYDROCHLORIDE - Pharmaceutical preparations - Eli Lilly and Co.
METHADROL - Pharmaceutical preparations ☆ - Hyrex Pharmaceuticals
METHAFORT - Pharmaceutical preparations - Barre-National, Inc.
METHAGUAL - Pharmaceutical preparations - Gordon Laboratories
METHALATE - Pharmaceutical preparations ☆ - Vortech Pharmaceuticals
METHAMPEX - Pharmaceutical preparations ☆ - Lemmon Co.
METHANOX - Insecticides ☆ - Farnam Cos. Inc.
METHAZINE - Pharmaceutical preparations ☆ - Vangard Labs Inc.
METHAZOLATE - Pharmaceutical preparations - Lannett Co. Inc.
METHELON - Photographic equipment - Eastman Kodak Co.
METHENAREX - Pharmaceutical preparations ☆ - Rex Research Laboratories
METHENDELATE - Pharmaceutical preparations ☆ - Kenyon Drug Co. Inc.
METHERGINE - Pharmaceutical preparations - Sandoz Pharmaceuticals Corp.
METHIBON - Pharmaceutical preparations - Barrows Pharmacal Inc.
METHIGEL - Veterinary pharmaceutical preparations - Evsco Pharmaceuticals
METHIO-TABS - Veterinary pharmaceutical preparations - Vet-A-Mix, Inc.
METHIOKAP - Pharmaceutical preparations ☆ - Pal-Pak Inc.
METHIOPLEX - Pharmaceutical preparations - Lincoln Diagnostics
METHIOTEIN - Pharmaceutical preparations ☆ - Pharmex Inc.
METHISCHOL - Vitamins and nutritional supplements - Rhone-Poulenc Rorer Pharmaceuticals Inc.
METHLYPRED-40 - Pharmaceutical preparations - Seatrace Co.
METHOD - Pencils - Reliance Pen & Pencil Corp.
METHODE - Electrical equipment - Methode Electronics, Inc.

☆ = Now out of production

METHODE - Wines ☆ - Hermann J. Wiemer Vineyard

METHODMAKER - Computer software - Mark V Systems Inc.

METHODS - Fishing tackle - Fenwick

METHODS ARCHITECT - Computer software - Applied Business Technology Corp.

METHODS INTERNATIONAL DIAGNOSTIC SOURCES - Medical apparatus - Walid El-Andere

METHOGEN - Veterinary pharmaceutical preparations ☆ - Vineland Laboratories Inc.

METHORPHAN - Pharmaceutical preparations - Medical Chemical Corp.

METHOSARB - Pharmaceutical preparations ☆ - Upjohn Co.

METHYBLU - Aquatic pharmacuetical preparations ☆ - Aquatronics-Filtronics

METHYBLU - Pet products ☆ - Aquatrol, Inc.

METHYLDIOL - Pharmaceutical preparations ☆ - Vortech Pharmaceuticals

METHYLENE BLUE TAB - Pharmaceutical preparations - Kenneth A. Manne Co.

METHYLSEPTIC - Pharmaceutical preparations ☆ - Legere Pharmaceuticals Inc.

METI-DERM - Antibiotics - Schering-Plough Healthcare Products

METICORTELONE - Pharmaceutical preparations - Schering-Plough Healthcare Products

METICORTEN - Pharmaceutical preparations - Schering-Plough Healthcare Products

METIER - Floor coverings–carpet and rugs - Monticello Carpet Mills

METIER - Furniture–public buildings - Baker Manufacturing Co., Inc.

METIER SYSTEM - Office furniture–metal - Metier Furniture Corp.

METIMYD - Pharmaceutical preparations - Schering-Plough Healthcare Products

METIPRANOLOL - Laxatives - Raway Pharmacal Inc.

METISSE - Motor vehicle parts and accessories - Target Motorsports

METIZOL - Pharmaceutical preparations - Glenwood LLC

METL-KING - Brake parts - Raybestos/Brake Parts Inc.

METLINK - Computer software - Metropolitan Life Insurance Co.

METLON F - Yarn - Metlon Corp.

METLON LMP - Yarn - Metlon Corp.

METLUND - Water conservation equipment - Act Distribution, Inc.

METLVENT - Ventilation equipment - Hart and Cooley Inc.

METO - Office supplies - Esselte Corp.

METOFANE - Veterinary pharmaceutical preparations - Schering-Plough Animal Health

METOLIUS - Sporting goods - Metolius Mountains Products, Inc.

METOMPKIN - Seafood products–fresh or frozen - Metompkin Bay Oyster Co.

METONE - Musical instrument accessories - Metone Graphics

METOPIRONE - Pharmaceutical preparations - Ciba-Geigy Corp.

METOX - Pet products - Tomlyn Products

METPAK - Connectors–electrical - Robinson Nugent, Inc.

METPAR - Hardware - Blaine Window Hardware Inc.

METRA - Audio equipment - Metra Electronics Corp.

METRA - Pharmaceutical preparations ☆ - Forest Pharmaceuticals Inc.

METRA BIOSYSTEMS - Medical apparatus - Metra Biosystems, Inc.

METRAPHOT - Photographic equipment - Heitz Service Corp.

METRAXT - Chemicals - Integrated Chemistries Inc.

METRAZOL - Pharmaceutical preparations ☆ - Knoll Pharmaceutical Co.

METRECOM - Measurement equipment - Faro Medical Technologies, Inc.

METRETON - Pharmaceutical preparations - Schering-Plough Healthcare Products

METREX RESEARCH CORPORATION - Medical apparatus - Metrex Research Corp.

METRI-PACK - Automotive parts and accessories - Packard Electric Div.

METRIBASE - Floor coverings–carpet and rugs ☆ - Lees Carpets

METRIC - Cabinets - Legeis Corp.

METRIC 21 - Pharmaceutical preparations ☆ - Fielding Pharmaceutical Co.

METRIC BIAS SQUARE - Measuring instruments - Martingale & Co.

METRIC TR - Tires–automobile - Jetzon/Telstar Tire

METRICS SOFTWARE - Computer software - Alliance Technologies, Inc.

METRIKA - Medical apparatus - Metrika Laboratories, Inc.

METRIMIST - Deodorizers - Metrex Research Corp.

METRINA - Electronic equipment ☆ - JTG of Nashville

METRINA MULTI - Electronic equipment ☆ - JTG of Nashville

METRIS - Microscopes - Burleigh Instruments, Inc.

METRIX - Computers - Metrix Computers, Inc.

METRIX - Shoes - Clarks of England Inc.

METRIXWARE - Computer peripheral equipment - Metrix Group, Inc.

METRO - Apparel–men's - Melville Corp.

METRO - Artists' materials - A.I. Friedman Inc.

METRO - Bicycles - Columbia Manufacturing Inc.

METRO - Boats–motor ☆ - Skeeter Products Inc.

METRO - Cabinets - Gragg Cabinet Industries

METRO - Clocks - Metro Corp.

METRO - Cooking equipment–household - Metro/Thebe, Inc.

METRO - Cosmetics - Spornette International, Inc.

METRO - Detergents - Mid-Atlantic Materials Inc.

METRO - Fans–electric - Homestead Products

METRO - Floor coverings - Mannington Resilient Floors

METRO - Floor coverings–carpet and rugs ☆ - Karastan-Bigelow Inc.

METRO - Health care products ☆ - Combi International Corp.

METRO - Jackets ☆ - Horace Small Apparel Co.

METRO - Jams and jellies - Dawn Food Products Inc.

METRO - Maraschino cherries - Continental Components

METRO - Motor vehicles - General Motors Corp. (Chevrolet Motor Div.)

METRO - Office furniture–metal - Hon Co.

METRO - Paint rollers ☆ - Arsco International Inc.

METRO - Tiles–ceramic - Metropolitan Ceramics

METRO - Trailers–travel - Fireball Industry Inc.

METRO - Wheelchairs - Everest and Jennings International Ltd.

METRO - Window shades - Vertical Blind Factory

METRO 200 - Communications equipment–mobile - Motorola, Inc. (Land Mobile Products Sector)

METRO AIR FORCE - Garden equipment - Metropolitan Vacuum Cleaner Co. Inc.

METRO AIR FORCE COMMANDER - Pet products - Metropolitan Vacuum Cleaner Co. Inc.

METRO BOOKS INC. - Publisher's imprints - Harlan Davidson Inc.

METRO BRICK - Tiles–ceramic ☆ - Metropolitan Ceramics

METRO BY SUNNYMAY - Apparel–athletic - Sunnymay Enterprises, Inc.

METRO CLUB - Apparel–men's - Hartmarx Corp.

METRO DATA VAC - Vacuum cleaners and accessories - Metropolitan Vacuum Cleaner Co. Inc.

METRO DATA-VAC ELECTRICDUSTER - Vacuum cleaners and accessories - Metropolitan Vacuum Cleaner Co. Inc.

METRO DUO-VOLT - Vacuum cleaners and accessories ☆ - Metropolitan Vacuum Cleaner Co. Inc.

METRO E-Z-SWEEP - Vacuum cleaners and accessories ☆ - Metropolitan Vacuum Cleaner Co. Inc.

METRO FILE - Office supplies - Metro Files Inc. (Rolodex Corp.)

METRO FLOW - Cosmetics - Spornette International, Inc.

METRO GNOMES - Dolls - Barbara E. Soet

METRO GOLDWYN MAYER ARS GRATIA ARTIS - Film - Metro-Goldwyn-Mayer Inc.

METRO LIGHTS - Cigarettes - R.J. Reynolds Tobacco Co.

METRO-LITE - Projectors–photographic - George R. Snell Associates, Inc.

METRO MAGIC-AIR - Vacuum cleaners and accessories - Metropolitan Vacuum Cleaner Co. Inc.

METRO MANIA - Bags–duffel - Leslie S. Tucker

METRO MANIA! - Games - GMS Partners Inc.

METRO-MARK - Labels–gummed - Mininome Inc.

METRO MAX Q - Shelving units–metal - Metro Industries, Inc.

METRO MAXIMA - Burial caskets - Casket Shells Inc.

METRO METEOR - Vacuum cleaners and accessories ☆ - Metropolitan Vacuum Cleaner Co. Inc.

METRO MIX - Soil–potting - W.R. Grace & Co.

METRO ONE - Apparel–men's - Manufacturers Discount Furniture & Bedding, Inc.

METRO QUARRY - Tiles–ceramic ☆ - Metropolitan Ceramics

METRO STAR - Antennas - Winegard Co.

METRO VAC 'N' BLO - Vacuum cleaners and accessories - Metropolitan Vacuum Cleaner Co. Inc.

METROBLADE - Skates–roller ☆ - Rollerblade, Inc.

METROBOOK - Computers–personal - Metropolitan Technical Services, Inc.'FNM Pam

METROCORT - Pharmaceutical preparations ☆ - Lexis Laboratories Inc.

METRODIN - Pharmaceutical preparations - Serono Laboratories Inc.

METROFLEX - service carts and dollies - InterMetro Industries Corp.

METROGESIC - Pharmaceutical preparations ☆ - Lexis Laboratories Inc.

METROGLO - Fabrics - Dan River Inc.

METROGNOMES' MUSIC - Computer software ☆ - The Learning Co., Inc.

METROL - Pharmaceutical preparations ☆ - Rhone-Poulenc Rorer Pharmaceuticals Inc.

METROLINE INDUSTRIES, INC - Lubricating oils - Metroline Industries, Inc.

METROLINK - Measuring instruments - Metrometer 1993, Inc.

METROLITE - Shelving - InterMetro Industries Corp.

METROLOCK - Locks–padlocks - Medeco Security Locks, Inc.

METROLOGIC - Electronic equipment - Metrologic Instruments, Inc.

METROLOGY & MOTION PEOPLE, THE - Gauging instruments - M & M Precision Systems Corp.

METROLOK - Tiles–ceramic ☆ - Metropolitan Ceramics

METROMARK - Switches–power - Metro Mark, Inc.

METROMAX - Fuel additives - Metro Fuel Oil Corp.

METROMAX - Shelving and accessories - InterMetro Industries Corp.

METRON - Audio equipment ☆ - Cerwin-Vega Inc.

METRON - Chairs–wood - Metron Optics Inc.

METRON - Watches - Kruckemeyer & Cohn Inc.

METRONIC - Darts and dart games ☆ - Dart World Inc.

METRONID - Pharmaceutical preparations ☆ - B.F. Ascher & Co. Inc.

METRONIDAZOLE - Pharmaceutical preparations - Goldline Laboratories, Inc.

METROPAGE - Communications equipment–mobile - Motorola, Inc. (Land Mobile Products Sector)

METROPANE - Motor vehicle parts and accessories - Metropane, Inc.

METROPHONES - Drums–musical instruments - Big Bang Distribution/A.P.I.

METROPHONES - Headphones - Eastman Percussion Peripherals

METROPLEX - Floor coverings–carpet and rugs - Whitecrest Carpet Mills

METROPLOITAN - Fabrics - Interface, Inc.

METROPOL - Giftware ☆ - W.M.F. of America Inc.

METROPOL - Wallpaper - Capital Carousel Inc.

METROPOLE - Wallpaper ☆ - Wolf-Gordon Inc.

METROPOLIS - Dryers–hair - Helen of Troy Corp.

METROPOLIS - Furniture - Lane Co. Inc.

METROPOLIS - Jackets - Couloir USA, Inc.

METROPOLIS - Pens - A.T. Cross Co.

METROPOLIS - Perfumes - Estee Lauder Inc.

METROPOLIS - Wallpaper - Bayview Wallcoverings

METROPOLIS - Wallpaper - Pageant Wallpaper Corp.

METROPOLIS STYLE - Wallpaper - Pageant Wallpaper Corp.

METROPOLITAN - Bathroom accessories - Nutone Inc.

METROPOLITAN - Bicycles - Ross Bicycles USA, Ltd.

METROPOLITAN - Coffee - Sara Lee Corp.

METROPOLITAN - Coffee - Saramar Corp.

METROPOLITAN - Cutlery - General Housewares Corp.

METROPOLITAN - Draperies - Maharam Vertical Surfaces

METROPOLITAN - Floor coverings - Congoleum Corp.

METROPOLITAN - Furniture ☆ - Bassett Furniture Industries, Inc.

METROPOLITAN - Glassware–household ☆ - Spiegelau Inc.

METROPOLITAN - Motor vehicles ☆ - DaimlerChrysler

METROPOLITAN - Paints - Kelly-Moore/Preservative Paints

METROPOLITAN - Recording label - Metropolitan Recording Corp.

METROPOLITAN - Seafood products–fresh or frozen - Metropolitan Poultry and Seafood Co.

METROPOLITAN - Sunglasses - Lantis Corp.

METROPOLITAN - Tableware–china - Lenox, Inc.

METROPOLITAN - Toasters - Black & Decker Corp.

METROPOLITAN COLLECTION - Wallpaper - Coverwalls Inc.

METROPOLITAN COLLECTION - Wallpaper ☆ - Capital Carousel Inc.

METROPOLITAN II - Wallpaper - Coverwalls Inc.

METROPOLITAN INTRASCAPES - Window treatments - Intrascapes

METROPOLITAN MUSEUM OF ART - Wallpaper - Milbrook Wallcoverings

METROPOLITAN MUSEUM OF ART II - Wallpaper - Milbrook Wallcoverings

METROPOLITAN MUSEUM OF ART, THE - Giftware - Metropolitan Museum of Art

METROPOLITAN PRAIRIE - Children's apparel - Timothy Joseph Bernardy

METROPOLITAN STONE QUARRY - Wallpaper - Coverwalls Inc.

METROQUADRO - Ceramic tile ☆ - Integrity Tile Co.

METROSPAN - Telephone equipment - DSC Communications Corp.

METROSPORT - Tools - Bomark Group Inc.

METROSTAR - Recording label - Terry Cashman and Barbara Kurnit Partnership

METROSTAR - Recording label - Metrostar Records

METROTECH - Apparel and accessories - Mobile 8 Apparel Corp.

METROTECH - Electronic equipment - Metrotech Corp.

METROTILE - Floor coverings - American Floor Products Co. Inc.

METROTILE - Tiles–ceramic - Metropolitan Ceramics

METROTONE - Enamels ☆ - Crescent Bronze Powder

METROTREAD - Tiles–ceramic - Metropolitan Industries, Inc.

METROTRED - Floor coverings - American Floor Products Co. Inc.

METROTWIST - Floor coverings–carpet and rugs - J and J Industries Inc.

METROVITE H.P. - Vitamins and nutritional supplements ☆ - Lexis Laboratories Inc.

METRUM INFORMATION STORAGE - Duplicating machines - Alliant Techsystems Inc.

METRYL - Pharmaceutical preparations ☆ - Lemmon Co.

M.E.T.S. - Machinery - Ensotech, Inc.

METTLER OF SWITZERLAND - Fabrics ☆ - Leimtex Corp.

METTLER TOLEDO - Labeling machinery - Mettler-Toledo, Inc.

METUCO - Hardware ☆ - Metal Utilities Co. Inc.

METYLAN - Wallpaper - Conros Corp.

METZ - Photographic equipment - Bogen Photo Corp.

MEUKOW - Brandy - Nicholas Enterprises

MEV - Wines - Mt. Eden Vineyards

MEVA - Shortening - Kraft Food Ingredients Corp.

MEVACOR - Pharmaceutical preparations - Merck & Co., Inc. (Merck Research Laboratories)

MEVANIN-C - Pharmaceutical preparations - Beutlich L.P. Pharmaceuticals

MEVATINIC-C - Pharmaceutical preparations - Beutlich L.P. Pharmaceuticals

MEVISTO - Women's apparel - Prive Sportswear

MEW - Pet products - Nippon Pet Food

MEW-TATIONS HIPHOPRAPCATS - Toys and games - Walter J. McGivney

MEW YORK, MEW YORK - Pet products - Feline Enterprises Inc.

MEWSMENTS - Pet products - Petcare Plus, Inc.

MEX - Cleaning preparations - United Gilsonite Laboratories

MEX-IT - Sauces - Hearth Products, Inc.

MEX TERRACOTTA - Tiles–ceramic - United Ceramic Tile Corp.

MEX TO THE MAX - Seasonings - Nabisco Foods Group

MEXATE - Pharmaceutical preparations - Bristol-Myers Squibb Co.

MEXCRAFT - Giftware - Tradeways Inc.

MEXENE - Food products - Bruce Foods Corp.

MEXI CHEF - Sauces - Prepco

MEXI-CONE - Food products - Super Printer II of Hawaii Inc.

MEXI-KITS - Food products - Morrison Milling Co.

MEXI MAGIC - Snack foods - Pinnacle Food Products, Inc.

MEXI-MARY - Beverages - Judy Montgomery

MEXI MIX - Food products - Cheryl Stewart Slatton

MEXI-MUNCHIES - Snack foods - Creative Food 'N Fun Co.

MEXI-PEP - Vegetable sauces - Trappey's Fine Foods Inc.

MEXI ROLLS - Frozen foods - Taco John's International Inc.

MEXI-SNAX - Snack foods - Mexi-Snax Inc.

MEXICAL - Seafood products–fresh or frozen - Mexical Marine Products, Inc.

MEXICALI - Snack foods - Wyandot, Inc.

MEXICALI BURGER - Sandwiches–prepackaged - Denny's Inc.

MEXICALI DOG - Frankfurters ☆ - Hormel Foods Corp.

MEXICALI MUSK - Men's fragrance ☆ - Coty Inc.

MEXICALIDAD - Pickles - Green Bay Foods Co.

MEXICAN ACCENT - Tortillas - Mexican Accent, Inc.

MEXICAN AGATE - Floor coverings - Tarkett, Inc.

MEXICAN BEAR - Tortillas - La Tolteca Foods Inc.

MEXICAN BUNDLES - Cigars - Villco Imports Inc.

MEXICAN CLASSICS - Food products - General Host Corp.

MEXICAN FIESTA - Cooking equipment–household - Joyce Chen, Inc.

MEXICAN FIESTA - Vegetable sauces - Keilen Ltd.

MEXICAN HATS - Candy - Henry Heide, Inc.

MEXICAN HOLIDAY - Food products - General Host Corp.

MEXICAN MEDLEY - Vegetables–canned ☆ - John F. Cope Co., Inc.

MEXICAN MOCHA - Beverages - Colorado Spice Co.

MEXICAN ORIGINAL - Food products - Tyson Foods Inc.

MEXICAN POTTERY - Clay–modeling - American Art Clay Co. Inc.

MEXICANA - Food products - La Preferida Inc.

MEXICATESSAN - Specialty foods–canned ☆ - Ruiz Food Products Inc.

MEXICHEF - Food products - Prepco

MEXICO - Giftware - Royal Copenhagen Porcelain Inc.

MEXICO KING - Fruits and vegetables - Giumarra Vineyards

MEXICORN - Vegetables–canned - Green Giant Co.

MEXIFROST - Food products - Mexi-Frost Specialties Co.

MEXIMELT - Food products - Taco Bell Corp.

MEXIOS - Food products - GDF, Inc.

MEXITALIAN - Pasta - Vermont Pasta

MEXITOS - Tortillas - La Canasta of Minnesota, Inc.

MEXO SEAL 5000 - Housewares - Elon Inc.

MEXSANA - Pharmaceutical preparations - Schering-Plough Healthcare Products

MEY - Adhesives and sealants ☆ - Steelcote Manufacturing Corp.

MEYCO - Swimming pool covers - Meyco Products Inc.

MEYDA - Lighting fixtures - Meyda Tiffany Inc.

MEYENBERG - Milk - Jackson-Mitchell Inc.

MEYER - Clarinet and saxophone mouthpieces - J.J. Babbitt Co. Inc.

MEYER - Clarinets - Ideal Musical Merchandise Co.

MEYER - Heating pads–electric - Meyer Furnace Co.

☆ = Now out of production

MEYER - Lenses–photographic ☆ - Edixa Camera Co.
MEYER - Vacuum cleaners and accessories - William W. Meyer & Sons, Inc.
MEYER DAIRY - Milk - H. Meyer Dairy Co.
MEYER-GASTERS - Office supplies ☆ - Evergreen Press
MEYER GRAIN DRYERS - Electronic equipment - Beard Industries, Inc.
MEYER-HUB - Thread - New Bedford Thread Co. Inc.
MEYER PRODUCTS - Plows - Louis Berkman Co.
MEYERS - Boats - Meyers Boat Inc.
MEYERS - Fabrics–polyester - Clarence L. Meyers Inc.
MEYER'S - Food products - Chadalee Farms
MEYERS - Horseradish - Silver Spring Gardens Inc.
MEYERS - Seafood products–fresh or frozen - Tri-Novie Distributors Corp.
MEYLAN - Watches - Meylan Corp.
MEYLOCATOR - Medical apparatus - Seymour W. Meyer
MEYRA - Health care products - Five Star Mobility
MEZA - Vegetable sauces - G & G Foods, Inc.
MEZLAN - Footwear - Pacific Shoe Corp.
MEZLIN - Antibiotics - Miles Inc.
MEZZ-TREAD - Wood products - Sylvan Forest Products, Inc.
MEZZA LUNA - Apparel and accessories - Modi Rubber Ltd.
MEZZALUNA - Corkscrews - Franmara Co. Inc.
MEZZANINE - Computer software - Saros Corp.
MEZZETTA - Sauces - G.L. Mezzetta Inc.
MEZZMATONE RECORDS - Recording label - Robert G. Heft
MEZZO - Floor coverings–carpet and rugs - Concepts International
MEZZO - Hearing aids ☆ - Beltone Electronics Corp.
MEZZO-FORTE - Mallets - Slobeat Industries
MEZZO GREENS - Pharmaceutical preparations ☆ - Highland Laboratories
M.F. - Heels–boot and shoe - M-F Athletic Co. Inc.
MF - Recording label - Jazz Composer's Orchestra Association Inc.
MF - Vegetables–frozen - Watermill Foods, Inc.
MF ADMIRAL-HOLTON - Musical instruments - G. Leblanc Corp.
MF HORN-HOLTON - Musical instruments - G. Leblanc Corp.
MF MICROFRAME INC. - Electronic equipment - Microframe, Inc.
MF SUPERBONE-HOLTON - Musical instruments - G. Leblanc Corp.
MFA - Gasoline ☆ - M.F.A. Oil Co.
MFC - Cylinders - American Cylinder Co., Inc.
MFC - Skin care products - Mennen Co.
MFC II - Orthopedic products - Smith & Nephew Inc. (Rehabilitation Div.)
MFG - Automotive parts and accessories - Molded Fiber Glass Cos.
MFJ - Electrical equipment - MFJ Enterprises Inc.
MFL - Flooring–hardwood - Monticello Flooring & Lumber Co. Inc.
MFMA - Flooring–hardwood - Maple Flooring Manufacturers Association, Inc.
MFP - Chemical preparations - Woolsey Marine Industries
MFP - Cording - Samson Cordage Works
MFR - Jewelry - Gold-Fine Jewelry
MFS - Fishing tackle - Doskocil Manufacturing Co., Inc.
MFTP - Computer software - Starburst Communications Corp.
MFVIA - Computer peripheral equipment - Prolinx Labs Corp.
MG - Amplifiers - M & G Electronics
MG - Apparel and accessories - Constance M. Mckinley
MG - Artists' materials ☆ - M. Grumbacher Inc.
MG - Chairs–cane - Stylex Inc.
MG+ - Hair care products - KMS Research Inc.
MG - Health care products - Guy O'Neill Co.
MG - Motor vehicles–automobiles ☆ - Sterling Motor Cars
MG - Novelty items - M-G Novelty Co.
MG - Paints–artists' - Koh-I-Noor, Inc.
MG - Recording label - Jazz Composer's Orchestra Association Inc.
MG 400 - Shampoos - Guy O'Neill Co.
MG-BLUE - Pharmaceutical preparations ☆ - Saron Pharmacal Corp.
M.G. VALLEJO - Wines - Heublein, Inc.
M.G. VALLEJO - Wines - IDV Wines (Beaulieu Vineyard)
MG WHITE - Paints–artists' - M. Grumbacher Inc.
MG217 - Shampoos - Guy O'Neill Co.
MGA - Electronic equipment - Mitsubishi Electric America, Inc.
MGA - Mushrooms - Mushroom Cooperative Co.
MGA - Veterinary pharmaceutical preparations - Upjohn Co.
MGA SOFTWARE - Computer software - Mitchell & Gauthier Associates, Inc.
MGB - Toys–models ☆ - Sterling Motor Cars
M.G.C. - Cleaning preparations - Better Living Products Inc.
MGC - Computers - Max Group Corp.
MGD LIGHT - Beverages–malt - Miller Brewing Co.
MGF - Construction machinery - MGF Machine Works, Inc.
MGHR - Vitamins and nutritional supplements ☆ - Vitamin Research Products Inc.

MGI - Pharmaceuticals - MGI PHARMA Inc.
MGI PHARMA - Pharmaceutical preparations - MGI PHARMA Inc.
MGM - Food products - Cedar Lake MGM Foods
MGM - Pipes–tobacco - Mastercraft Pipes Inc.
MGM - Postcards ☆ - Classico San Francisco Inc.
MGM - Recording label - Polygram Records, Inc.
MGM - Recording label - Turner Entertainment Co.
MGM LION - Toys–stuffed - Dakin Inc.
MGM RECORDS - Recording label - Metro-Goldwyn-Mayer Inc.
MGM STUDIO 10 - Nail-care products - M.T.S. Associated
MGTS - Computer peripheral equipment - Tekelec Inc.
MGV - Circuit boards - MGV International, Inc.
MGW - Eggs - Milton G. Waldbaum Co.
MH - Musical instruments - Molinari Enterprises, Inc.
MH & H - See MILLER OFFICE SEATING
M.H.M. - Apparel and accessories - Kellwood Co.
MHR COMMUNICATIONS - Recording label - Milton H. Ranck
MHS CASTER & EQUIPMENT CO. - Wheels - W.T.F., Inc.
MHT - Hardware - Wagner Spray Tech Corp.
MHT - Industrial machinery - Materials Handling Technology Inc.
MI - Audio tapes–blank - Metro Magnetics USA, Inc.
MI - Computer software - Micro-Integration Corp.
MI - Computers–mainframe - Micro Industries Corp.
MI - Hardware ☆ - Merchandising Inventives, Inc.
MI - Machinery - Metal Improvement Co., Inc.
MI - Printing paper - MAX International Converters Inc.
MI - Water treating compounds - Aquamatch Inc.
MI ALAZAN - Shirts - Jose Luis Solorzano
MI BABY - Shoes - Conaway-Winter Inc.
MI BANDERA - Cheese - Mi Bandera Corp.
MI BEBE - Dolls - Doll Factory, Inc.
MI-C-B - Pharmaceutical preparations - Dixon-Shane Inc.
MI CASA - Salad dressings–bottled - R.T. French Co.
MI-CEBRIN - Vitamins and nutritional supplements - Dista Products Co.
MI CLASSIC - Beverages–carbonated - Orange Crush of Puerto Rico, Inc.
MI COCINA - Kitchen utensils–aluminum - Vilore Foods Co., Inc.
MI-DEL - Crackers - Tree of Life, Inc.
MI-DEL - Food products - Health Foods, Inc.
MI-HOUSEHOLD INVENTORY - Books–blank - Pfening & Snyder
MI KC - Apparel–women's - Mere Image Inc.
MI LADY - Handkerchiefs ☆ - Carolina Manufacturing Inc.
MI-LEM - Beverages - Romanoff International Inc.
MI-LIFE - Alarms–personal - Mi-Life Security Systems, Inc.
MI MASA ES SU MASA - Food products - Texas Tamale Co., Inc.
MI-MEMORY - Leather goods - AR Accessories Group Inc.
MI MIXED IMAGE - Apparel and accessories - Bentley Lingerie, Inc.
MI MUSIC INTERACTIVE - Computer software - Hal Leonard Corp.
MI-PET - Pet products - Middle West Pet Foods Inc.
MI-PILO - Ophthalmic goods ☆ - Barnes-Hind Inc.
MI RANCHITO - Tortillas - Great Western Tortilla Co.
MI-REFERENCE - Books–blank - Pfening & Snyder
MI SECRETO - Spices and extracts - Pet Inc.
MI-STOCKS & BONDS - Books–blank - Pfening & Snyder
MI-T-DARK - Fabrics - Munters Corp.
MI-T-FOG - Dehumidifiers - Munters Corp.
MI-T-HOT - Washers–metal - Mi-T-M Corp.
MI-T-VAC - Vacuum sweepers, truck mount loader ☆ - Lesco, Inc.
MI TIERRA - Apparel and accessories - M.T.C., Inc.
MI TIERRA - Greeting cards - AGC, Inc.
MI TIERRA - Greeting cards - American Greetings Corp.
MI-TOT - Infant product ☆ - Woltra Corp.
MI VIDA - Condoms - Sime Health Ltd. (Sime Darby Group)
MI-VITA - Vitamins and nutritional supplements - Vita-Fore Products Co.
MIA - Apparel and accessories - Aileen Inc.
MIA - Cosmetics - Faberge Co.
MIA - Costume jewelry - American Gift Corp.
MIA ARMAND OF BEVERLY HILLS - Bedding–linen - Mia Armand of Beverly Hills Inc.
MIA CLOGS - Shoes ☆ - Mia Clogs
MIA DESIGNS - Shoes - Mia Clogs
MIA NOLA - Sweaters - Knits-Cord Ltd.
MIA TIA - Food products ☆ - Breadshop's Natural Foods
MIAMI - Bicycles - Columbia Manufacturing Inc.
MIAMI - Brooms - Wright-Bernet
MIAMI - Food products - Bee International
MIAMI - Fragrance - Pat Booth's Miami, Inc.

☆ = Now out of production

MIAMI - Hardware - Blaine Window Hardware Inc.
MIAMI - Musical instrument accessories - Hershman Musical Instrument
MIAMI - Paper–tissue - Crystal Tissue Co. Inc.
MIAMI - Recording label - Miami Records & Distributing Corp.
MIAMI - Shortening - Miami Margarine Co. Inc.
MIAMI - Window coverings - Vertilux-Louverlux Inc.
MIAMI BEACH OCEAN CLUB - Apparel and accessories - James Place Development Corp.
MIAMI-CAREY - Hardware - Miami-Carey Co.
MIAMI CAREY - Switches–electric - Nutone Inc.
MIAMI COOLERS - Candy - Bee International
MIAMI FLORIDIANS ABA - Apparel and accessories - NBA Properties, Inc.
MIAMI INTIMATES - Apparel–women's - J.R. United Industries Inc.
MIAMI MAID - Pens ☆ - Long's Dixie Pens
MIAMI MISS - Bicycles ☆ - Hedstrom Corp.
MIAMI N'ICE - Iced tea–bottled or canned - Atlantic Marketing Systems, Inc.
MIAMI PREMIUM - Beverages–malt - Florida Brewing Co.
MIAMI RAYS - Apparel and accessories - Miami Rays, Inc.
MIAMI STONE - Bricks - Miami Brick & Stone Co.
MIAMI SUPER BILT - Toilets–portable - Stello Products Inc.
MIAMI'S ORIGINAL ICED COFFEE - Beverage dispensing equipment - Miami Ice Coffee, Inc.
MIASMACT - Filters–air - Mac Equipment, Inc.
MIATA - Motor vehicles–automobiles - Mazda Motor of America Inc.
MIATA MX5 - Motor vehicles–automobiles - Mazda Motor of America Inc.
MIBCO - Brushes–paint - Rol-Brush Manufacturing, Div. (Michigan Brush Mfg. Co., Inc.)
MIC-120 ABM - Metal finishing equipment - M.I.C. Industries, Inc.
MIC-240 ABM - Machine parts - M.I.C. Industries, Inc.
MIC ELIMINATOR - Audio equipment - Whirlwind Music Distributors, Inc.
MIC-EZE - Clamps - Ac-cetera Inc.
MIC MURDOCK - Toys - Tonka Corp.
MICA - Apparel–athletic - Mica Sportswear
MICA - Hair care products - U.K. Abba Products, Inc.
MICA - Nail care products - Cosmair Inc.
MICA - Wallpaper - Bayview Wallcoverings
MICA - Wallpaper - Capital Carousel Inc.
MICA - Woodworking tools - Seco Machine Tools, Inc.
MICA-LUSTRE - Cleaning preparations - Multi-Care Corp.
MICA TOO - Wallpaper - Bayview Wallcoverings
MICAFIL - Insulating materials ☆ - Vigoro Consumer & Professional Products Group
MICAFILM - Toys–airplanes - Coverite
MICAFLEC - Floor coverings - Mannington Resilient Floors
MICALETTERS - Hardware - Scott Sign Systems, Inc.
MICALS - Bicycles - Jeffrey M. Harrington
MICALUX - Wallpaper - Advance Wallcoverings
MICALUX - Wallpaper - Capital Carousel Inc.
MICALUX - Wallpaper - Quality House Inc.
MICAP - Pigments–lead oxide - Micap Technology Corp.
MICARD - Advertising agencies - Marketing Innovators International, Inc.
MICARTA - Plastics - Westinghouse Electric Corp. (Decorative Micarta Div.)
MICASTAT - Plastics–laminated - Desco Industries Inc.
MICATIN - Pharmaceutical preparations - Ortho Pharmaceutical Corp.
MICE-A-FOURS - Bakery goods - Divine Delights Inc.
MICE DOOM - Rodenticides ☆ - Fairfax Biological Laboratory
MICELI DAIRY - Dairy products - Miceli Dairy Products Co.
MICELLI - Floor coverings ☆ - Tarkett, Inc.
MICELUX II - Wallpaper - Quality House Inc.
MICETRO - Computer accessories - Western Commercial Services, Inc.
MICETRO, THE - Computer peripheral equipment - Western Commercial Services, Inc.
MICEVILLE - Giftware ☆ - Enesco Corp.
MICH GOLDEN DRAFT - Beverages–malt - Anheuser-Busch Companies Inc.
MICHAEL - Door frames - Quaker Window Products Co.
MICHAEL ALAN - Apparel–men's ☆ - Craftex Creations Inc.
MICHAEL & CORNELIA BESSIE BOOK, A - Publisher's imprints - Harper & Row Publishers Inc.
MICHAEL AND NORMAN - Watches ☆ - Crawford Watch Co. Inc.
MICHAEL ANGELO - Jewelry - Michael Angelo Design
MICHAEL B. - Jewelry - Michael B. Inc.
MICHAEL CHRISTOPHER - Cologne - Michael Christopher, Ltd.
MICHAEL CRAIG - Jewelry - Elka Jewel Industries Inc.
MICHAEL D - Belts–apparel - American Belt Co.
MICHAEL D'S - Cookies - Michael D's Cookies
MICHAEL F COX - Statuary - Michael F. Cox

MICHAEL FINELLI - Footwear - Allen Shoe Co. Inc.
MICHAEL GRAVES - Flatware - Reed and Barton Corp.
MICHAEL GROVES - Fruits and vegetables - Earring Point Groves Inc.
MICHAEL HAGUE - Calendars ☆ - Amcal Inc.
MICHAEL HARRIS - Apparel and accessories - Barrel-Marvin Apparel, Inc.
MICHAEL HARRIS - Apparel–men's - Oxford Industries, Inc.
MICHAEL HOBAN - Apparel and accessories - Michael Hoban, Inc.
MICHAEL JACKSON - Candy ☆ - Topps Co., Inc.
MICHAEL JACKSON - Colognes - Max Factor & Co.
MICHAEL JACKSON - Games - S. Alden Inc.
MICHAEL JACKSON - Recording label - Triumph International, Inc.
MICHAEL JAMES - Apparel–children's - J.C. Penney Co., Inc.
MICHAEL JAMES - Jewelry ☆ - Pakula & Co.
MICHAEL JOHN KENT - Apparel and accessories - Michael John Kent
MICHAEL JOSEPH - Apparel and accessories - Baguda Wear Inc.
MICHAEL LAWRENCE - Jackets–leather - A & K Inc.
MICHAEL LEVA - Women's sportswear - Michael Leva
MICHAEL LITE - Chemical preparations - David Michael & Co.
MICHAEL MALCOM - Skin care products - Michael Malcom & Co., Inc.
MICHAEL MERCURIO - Wallpaper - K.M.L. Industries
MICHAEL MORGAN - Apparel–men's - Fred Meyer, Inc.
MICHAEL RAYMOND COLLECTION, THE - Giftware - Wilson Marketing Concepts
MICHAEL SCOTT - Office supplies - Michael Scott Inc.
MICHAEL SEASON'S - Snack foods - Season's Enterprises Ltd.
MICHAEL SEROY - Apparel–women's - Michael Seroy
MICHAEL SHEA'S - Beverages–malt - Genesee Brewing Co., Inc.
MICHAEL SHEA'S BLACK & TAN - Beverages–malt - Genesee Brewing Co., Inc.
MICHAEL SHEA'S IRISH AMBER - Beverages–malt - Genesee Brewing Co., Inc.
MICHAEL SIMON - Apparel and accessories - Michael Petito
MICHAEL STANFIELD - Infant product - Playspaces
MICHAEL-THERMICS - Beverages - David Michael & Co.
MICHAEL TOSCHI - Apparel and accessories - Michael Toschi International, Inc.
MICHAEL WINSTON - Apparel and accessories ☆ - Weekendz-Off, Inc.
MICHAELANGELO - Toys - Playmates World Wide Inc.
MICHAELANGELO - Wedding gowns - Phillie Bridals, Inc.
MICHAELENE - Jewelry - Quinn Enterprises Inc.
MICHAELENE'S CAPPUCCINO CRUNCH - Granola bars - Michaelene's
MICHAELO - Novelty items–paper - Michaelo Espresso
MICHAELOK - Spices and extracts - David Michael & Co.
MICHAELS - Canvas–artists' - Michaels Stores Inc.
MICHAEL'S - Custard–frozen - Michael's Frozen Custard
MICHAEL'S - Vitamins and nutritional supplements - Inner Health Group, Inc.
MICHAEL'S BAGS - Travel accessories - American Guard-It Manufacturing Co. Inc.
MICHAEL'S GOLD N' GOOD - Potato chips - Michael Distributing Co., Inc.
MICHAEL'S ISLAND - Fruits and vegetables - Earring Point Groves Inc.
MICHAEL'S KIDS - Bedding–linen - Michael Friedman Corp.
MICHAEL'S ORCHID ISLAND - Fruits and vegetables - Earring Point Groves Inc.
MICHAELS/STERN - Apparel–men's - Michaels/Stern & Co. Inc.
MICHAEL'S SYNERGISTIC - Health care products - Michael's Health Products
MICHAELWAVE - Spices and extracts - David Michael & Co.
MICHAIL GORENOK - Violins ☆ - Ideal Musical Merchandise Co.
MICHALE'S NATUROPATHIC PROGRAMS - Vitamins and nutritional supplements - Michael's Naturopatic Products
MICHALLET - Paper–kraft ☆ - Canson-Talens Inc.
MICHEL - Apparel and accessories ☆ - St. Michel Sportswear Ltd.
MICHEL - Cosmetics - Michel Skin Care Enterprises Inc.
MICHEL - Cosmetics ☆ - Cassidy Inc.
MICHEL - Glassware–household ☆ - Dansk International Designs, Ltd.
MICHEL - Watches ☆ - Crawford Watch Co. Inc.
MICHEL & COMPANY - Stationery - Michel & Co.
MICHEL & PFEFFER - Hardware - Blaine Window Hardware Inc.
MICHEL BERNARD - Watches - E. Gluck Corp.
MICHEL GONET - Wines - Pellegrini Bros. Wines Inc.
MICHEL REDDE - Wines - Kobrand Corp.
MICHEL SCHNEIDER - Wines - Dieter Steinmann Inc.
MICHEL SPORT - Apparel and accessories ☆ - St. Michel Sportswear Ltd.
MICHEL STUDIO - Apparel–women's - St. Michel Sportswear Ltd.
MICHELANGELO - Artists' materials ☆ - M. Grumbacher Inc.
MICHELANGELO - Checkbooks - Checks in the Mail, Inc.
MICHELANGELO - Glassware–household - Spiegelau Inc.

☆ = Now out of production

MICHELANGELO COLLECTION - Lighting fixtures - Angelo Brothers Co.

MICHELE - Apparel–athletic - Isaac Hazan & Co.

MICHELE - Flatware ☆ - Wallace International Silversmiths, Inc.

MICHELE - Recording label - Michele Audio Corp.

MICHELE BRADEN'S - Vinegarette - Fast & Fabulous Products

MICHELE CHIARLO VARIETAL GRAPPAS - Wines - Kobrand Corp.

MICHELE GENNARO - Nail care products - Organifyl Laboratories

MICHELE LOISI - Footwear - Donna Shoes Inc.

MICHELE VINCENT - Apparel–women's - Michele Vincent Inc.

MICHELE'S CONTINENTAL - Food products - Michele's Restaurant

MICHELEX - Tape recorders–cassette - Michele Audio Corp.

MICHELIN - Tires - Michelin Tire Corp.

MICHELIN TRIALS - Motorcycle parts and accessories - Cosmopolitan Motors Inc.

MICHELINA'S - Food products - Luigino's

MICHELL - Handbags ☆ - Fashion Express

MICHELLE - Floor coverings–carpet and rugs - Burtco Enterprises Inc.

MICHELLE - Floor coverings–carpet and rugs ☆ - Regal Rugs Inc.

MICHELLE - Furniture - Hammary Furniture Co. Inc.

MICHELLE - Watches ☆ - Helbros International

MICHELLE LYNN - Apparel–children's - Roget Industries Ltd.

MICHELLE'S MINK X-TRA - Skin moisturizer - Continental Quest Research Corp.

MICHELOB - Beverages–malt - Anheuser-Busch Companies Inc.

MICHELOB AMBER BOCK - Beverages–malt - Anheuser-Busch Companies Inc.

MICHELOB CENTENNIAL - Beverages–malt - Anheuser-Busch Companies Inc.

MICHELOB CLASSIC DARK - Beverages–malt ☆ - Anheuser-Busch Companies Inc.

MICHELOB DRY - Beverages–malt - Anheuser-Busch Companies Inc.

MICHELOB GOLDEN DRAFT - Beverages–malt - Anheuser-Busch Companies Inc.

MICHELOB GOLDEN DRAFT LIGHT - Beverages–malt - Anheuser-Busch Companies Inc.

MICHELOB HEFEWEIZEN - Beverages–malt - Anheuser-Busch Companies Inc.

MICHELOB LIGHT - Beverages–malt - Anheuser-Busch Companies Inc.

MICHELOB MALT - Beverages–malt - Anheuser-Busch Companies Inc.

MICHELOB THE AMERICAN CLASSIC - Beverages–malt - Anheuser-Busch Companies Inc.

MICHELOFF - Liquors - Hughes Markets Inc.

MICHEL'S - Waffles–frozen ☆ - Allied Bakers Co.

MICHEL'S CHERUB COLLECTION - Paper–gift wrap - Michel & Co.

MICHEL'S MAGNIFIQUE - Meat products–canned - Michel's Magnifique Ltd.

MICHELSEN - Spoons - Viking Import House Inc.

MICHELSEN'S - Colognes - Caswell-Massey Co. Ltd.

MICHEM COAT - Coatings - Michelman Inc.

MICHESHELLS - Jewelers' findings - Ramodi's

MICHEV - Cheese ☆ - Bongrain Cheese USA

MICHI-CRAFT - Boats–canoes - Meyers Boat Inc.

MICHIGAN - Audio equipment ☆ - Electro-Voice, Inc.

MICHIGAN - Boats–motor ☆ - Yar-Craft, Inc.

MICHIGAN - Ladders–metal - Michigan Ladder Co. Inc.

MICHIGAN APPLE - Fruits and vegetables - Heeren Brothers Inc.

MICHIGAN AVENUE - Bicycles - Ross Bicycles USA, Ltd.

MICHIGAN AVENUE - Floor coverings–carpet and rugs ☆ - Hollytex Carpet Mills Inc.

MICHIGAN AVENUE - Lighting fixtures - New Chao Industrial Corp.

MICHIGAN BAY - Vegetables–canned - Honee Bear Canning Co.

MICHIGAN BEST - Food products - Jack Mall Potato Co. Inc.

MICHIGAN BULB - Flowers, plants, and seeds - Michigan Bulb Co.

MICHIGAN DRIED - Fruits–canned - Cherry Central Cooperative Inc.

MICHIGAN EXPRESS, INC. - Toys–models - Toy Truck Lines, Inc.

MICHIGAN FINEST - Fruits–canned - Honee Bear Canning Co.

MICHIGAN FINEST - Fruits–canned - Packers Canning Co., Inc.

MICHIGAN FLAVOR - Fruits and vegetables - Heeren Brothers Inc.

MICHIGAN FRIARS - Wines ☆ - St. Julian Wine Co.

MICHIGAN GOURMET - Broadcasting stations–television - G.W. Pepper Communications Inc.

MICHIGAN GREEN - Flowers, plants, and seeds - Michigan State Seed Co.

MICHIGAN HARVEST - Honey - Harvest Foods

MICHIGAN J. FROG - Apparel and accessories - Time Warner Entertainment Co., L.P.

MICHIGAN MADE - Fruits–canned - Honee Bear Canning Co.

MICHIGAN MADE - Fruits–canned - Packers Canning Co., Inc.

MICHIGAN MAID - Dairy products - Michigan Milk Producers Association

MICHIGAN PACKERS - Fruits–canned - Honee Bear Canning Co.

MICHIGAN PACKER'S - Fruits–canned - Packers Canning Co., Inc.

MICHIGAN QUEEN - Fruits–canned - Packers Canning Co., Inc.

MICHIGAN RAG CO. - Tote bags - Michigan Rag Co.

MICHIGAN RUMMY - Games ☆ - Milton Bradley Co.

MICHIGAN SPECIAL - Food products - Amendt Milling Co.

MICHIGAN STATIONERY CO. - Greeting cards - Michigan Stationery Co.

MICHIGAN STEAK CO. - Beef - Hoekstra Meat Co.

MICHIGAN TRAVEL - Games - Hillsdale Educational Publishers

MICHIKO - Dolls - Mattel, Inc.

MICHIKO - Puppets - Dakin Inc.

MICHIKO MONKEY - Toys–stuffed - Dakin Inc.

MICHLIN - Chemical preparations ☆ - Gibraltar National Corp.

MICHROMATIC - Musical instruments - Ernest Deffner Inc.

MICHTERS - Whiskey - Michter's Distillery Inc.

MICHTEX - Chemical preparations - David Michael & Co.

MICIO & COMPANY FIVE - Wallpaper - Micio & Co. Inc.

MICIO & CO. INC. - Wallpaper - Micio & Co. Inc.

MICIO & COMPANY SIX - Wallpaper - Micio & Co. Inc.

MICK - Medical apparatus - Mick Radio-Nuclear Instruments, Inc.

MICK MCQUAID - Tobacco–chewing or smoking - G.A. Georgopulo & Co. Inc.

MICKELBERRY - Meat products–canned ☆ - Mickelberry Corp.

MICKELBERRY'S - Meat products–beef - Willow Foods Inc.

MICKELBERRY'S OLD FARM - Meat products–canned ☆ - Mickelberry Corp.

MICKEY - Breads - American Bakeries Co.

MICKEY - Computer peripheral equipment ☆ - Videomedia, Inc.

MICKEY - Recording label - Mickey Records

MICKEY - Sunglasses - Riviera Trading, Inc.

MICKEY & CO. - Apparel and accessories - Pyramid Handbags Inc.

MICKEY & CO. - Underwear and nightwear - L.V. Myles

MICKEY & CO. BY NAPIER - Jewelry - Napier Co.

MICKEY & MINNIE - Children's toiletries - Cosrich Inc.

MICKEY & MINNIE - Shoes ☆ - Sidney Rich Associates Inc.

MICKEY & PALS - Bandages - National Patent Medical

MICKEY BOYS - Dolls ☆ - Effanbee Doll Corp.

MICKEY GILLETTE - Musical instrument accessories ☆ - Rico International

MICKEY MELON - Beverages–carbonated - A.J. Canfield Co.

MICKEY MOUSE - Apparel and accessories - Mighty-Mac

MICKEY MOUSE - Leather goods - RGA Accessories Inc.

MICKEY MOUSE - Playhouses, bop bags - Intex Recreation Corp.

MICKEY MOUSE - Publisher's imprints - Walt Disney Co.

MICKEY MOUSE - Sunblocks ☆ - Schering-Plough Healthcare Products

MICKEY MOUSE - Toothbrushes–electric ☆ - Kenner Products

MICKEY MOUSE - Toys - Sky-Way Products

MICKEY MOUSE - Toys–stuffed - CBS Toys

MICKEY MOUSE - Wallpaper ☆ - Priss Prints Inc.

MICKEY MOUSE MEMORY - Games - Milton Bradley Co.

MICKEY MOUSE MUNCHIES - Candy - Confections by Sandra

MICKEY MOUSE/SNOOPY - Games ☆ - Ben Cooper Inc.

MICKEY MOUSE SPIN A-ROUND - Games ☆ - Milton Bradley Co.

MICKEY MOUSE T-BOUNCER - Playground equipment - Miracle Recreation Equipment Co.

MICKEY SAYS - Games - Milton Bradley Co.

MICKEY STUFF FOR KIDS - Apparel and accessories - Pyramid Handbags Inc.

MICKEY TESSLER - Shoes ☆ - Tessler Shoe Corp.

MICKEY THE BALANCING BAKER - Games - Milton Bradley Co.

MICKEY THE CLOWN - Recording label - Real Folks Music

MICKEY TREATS - Candy - American Candy Co.

MICKEY UNLIMITED - Socks - High Point Knitting Inc.

MICKEY UNLIMITED - Underwear and nightwear - L.V. Myles

MICKEY'S - Beverages–malt - The Stroh Brewery Co.

MICKEY'S - Dental equipment ☆ - Ranir Corp.

MICKEY'S FINEST - Ice cream ☆ - Jack & Jill Ice Cream Co.

MICKEY'S ICE - Beverages–malt - The Stroh Brewery Co.

MICKEY'S LIGHT ICE - Beverages–malt - The Stroh Brewery Co.

MICKEY'S MALT LIQUOR - Beverages–malt - The Stroh Brewery Co.

MICKEY'S PARADE - Ice cream cones ☆ - Ace Baking Co. L.P.

MICKEY'S RED - Beverages–malt - The Stroh Brewery Co.

MICKEY'S ROOM MATES - Floor coverings–carpet and rugs - Couristan Inc.

MICKEY'S STUFF FOR KIDS - Lamps - Dolly, Inc.

MICKEY'S STUFF FOR KIDS - Puzzles - Playskool, Inc.

MICKEY'S STUFF FOR KIDS - Wallpaper - Priss Prints Inc.

MICKEY'S TOONTOWN - Novelty items - Walt Disney Co.

MICKEY'S WORKOUT WEAR - Apparel–women's ☆ - Jacques Moret, Inc.

☆ = Now out of production

MICKEYTOWN - Toys–trains - Mattel, Inc.
MICKSANTA - Manufactured homes - Redman Industries, Inc.
MICKY - Tobacco products ☆ - R.J. Reynolds Tobacco Co.
MICKY BASET - Nail care products - Claire Topper Enterprises
MICO - Gasoline - Mico Oil Co. Inc.
MICO - Gauging instruments - Mico, Inc.
MICO - Pharmaceutical preparations ☆ - Scrip-Physician Supply Co.
MICON - Cardboard boxes - Micon Packaging Products, Inc.
MICOR-FLEX - Floor coverings ☆ - Flintkote Co.
MICOR-FLEX - Floor coverings ☆ - GS Roofing Products Co.
MICORN - Pet products ☆ - Sera Aquaristik USA Inc.
MICOZALL - Antifungal cream - Major Pharmaceuticals
MICR WIPE - Stain removers ☆ - Auto Cellular Systems
MICRA - Skin diving equipment - U.S. Divers Co., Inc.
MICRA-DOCUMENT - Envelopes - Western States Envelope Co.
MICRACOR - Lasers - Micracor, Inc.
MICRAININ - Tranquilizers - Wallace Laboratories
MICRAN - Dinnerware–glass ☆ - Kenro Inc.
MICRARRAY - Lasers - Micracor, Inc.
MICREL - Circuit boards - Micrel Inc.
MICREL - Cooking equipment–household - Rubbermaid Inc.
MICREL MINI 8 - Circuit boards - Micrel Inc.
MICRIL - Thread - Advance Thread Corp.
MICRIN - Mouthwashes ☆ - Johnson & Johnson
MICRJET - Computer peripheral equipment - Addmaster Corp.
MICRO - Barber shop equipment - Kim Laube & Co. Inc.
MICRO - Cleaning preparations - International Products Co.
MICRO - Clocks - Village Time, Inc.
MICRO - Cooking equipment–household ☆ - Mirro Corp.
MICRO - Electronic equipment - Kyocera America Inc.
MICRO - Fuses–electric - Littelfuse, Inc.
MICRO - Knives–pocket - Allway Tools Inc.
MICRO - Musical instrument accessories - Micro Musical Products Corp.
MICRO - Paint rollers - Great American Marketing, Inc.
MICRO - Pens ☆ - Charvoz
MICRO - Rackets–tennis - Pro Kennex, Inc.
MICRO - Toys - Peg Perego USA Inc.
MICRO - Trading cards and stamps - Topps Co., Inc.
MICRO 1 - Electronic equipment - Phillips Electronics North America Corp.
MICRO-3 - Underwear and nightwear - Jockey International, Inc.
MICRO-6 - Medical apparatus - Circon Corp.
MICRO-90 - Cleaning preparations - International Products Co.
MICRO 850 - Health care products - Wholesale Medical Import
MICRO 2000 - Skin care products - Elizabeth Arden Inc.
MICRO-AAL - Audio equipment ☆ - American Acoustics
MICRO ADVENTURE - Publisher's imprints - Scholastic Inc.
MICRO AIR - Air purification systems - Metal-Fab Inc.
MICRO AIR - Concrete–mixture - Master Builders Inc.
MICRO-AIR - Filters–air - Home Care Industries, Inc.
MICRO AIR - Medical apparatus - Omron Healthcare, Inc.
MICRO-AIRE - Insulating materials - Schuller International, Inc.
MICRO-AIRE DUCT BOARD - Insulating materials - Manville/Schuller
MICRO ARC - Laboratory apparatus - Pilot Industries, Inc.
MICRO-ARMOUR - Toys–models - GHQ
MICRO ASSOCIATED STOCK CAR RACERS - Toys–automobiles - Keith E. Namanny
MICRO AVENGER - Toys–automobiles - Tyco Industries, Inc.
MICRO B-1 - Veterinary nutritional supplements - Oralx Corp.
MICRO B-12 - Veterinary nutritional supplements - Oralx Corp.
MICRO BAGS - Handbags - L.C. Licensing, Inc.
MICRO-BAKE - Stoves - White Consolidated Industries, Inc.
MICRO BAND - Computer software - Electronic Courseware Systems Inc.
MICRO-BARRIER - Pet products - Tanner Products
MICRO BI-LEVEL - Stoves ☆ - White Consolidated Industries, Inc.
MICRO BILLING SYSTEMS - Coffee makers–electric - Micro Billing Systems, Inc.
MICRO-BLAZE OUT - Fire extinguishers - Verde Environmental Inc.
MICRO BRAID - Fishing tackle - Cortland Line Co., Inc.
MICRO-BREEZE - Cleaning preparations - Flo-Pac Corp.
MICRO BREW HOME BREWING SYSTEMS - Beverages–malt - Micro Brew, Llc
MICRO BREW OF BARBECUE, THE - Salad dressings–mixes ☆ - Horsefeathers of North Windham, Inc.
MICRO-BUNABLES - Food products - Gorges Foodservice, Inc.
MICRO-CAM - Hardware - John Sterling Corp.
MICRO-CANNULA - Health care products - Salter Labs

MICRO-CAST - Sporting goods ☆ - Wright & McGill Co.
MICRO CERAMIC - Pens - Sunmex Imports Corp.
MICRO-CHANNEL - Lighting equipment - Legion Lighting Co., Inc.
MICRO CHILL - Refrigerators - Micro Chill International, Ltd.
MICRO CHOKE - Guns ☆ - Marlin Firearms Co.
MICRO CITE - Radio communications equipment - Motorola, Inc. (Land Mobile Products Sector)
MICRO CLASSIC - Sandwiches–prepackaged - Zartic, Inc.
MICRO CLAY - Clay–modeling - Van Aken International
MICRO-CLEAN - Vacuum cleaners and accessories - Home Care Industries, Inc.
MICRO-CLEAR - Inks ☆ - Formulabs, Inc.
MICRO-CLEAR - Swimming pools - Hayward Pool Products Inc.
MICRO-CLICK - Archery equipment - Martin Archery Inc.
MICRO CLIP - Barber shop equipment - Kim Laube & Co. Inc.
MICRO-CLIPPER - Electronic equipment - Mueller Electric Co.
MICRO COAT - Coatings ☆ - Microscale Industries Inc.
MICRO COLORS - Pigments - Lasting Impression I Inc.
MICRO-COM - Radios - RELM Communications Inc.
MICRO CON - Saws–power - DBNA Trademarks Holding Inc.
MICRO COOKBOOK - Computer software - Pinpoint Publishing
MICRO-CORR - Paper products - Calumet Carton Co.
MICRO-COUSTIC - Insulating materials ☆ - Manville/Schuller
MICRO CRAFT - Motor vehicle parts and accessories - Micro Craft, Inc.
MICRO-CRISP - Food containers - E-Z-Por Corp.
MICRO CRISPERS - Pregnancy test kits ☆ - Ore-Ida Foods, Inc.
MICRO-CROWN - Lighting fixtures - Swivelier Co. Inc.
MICRO CRYO-TRAP - Laboratory apparatus - Scientific Instrument Services, Inc.
MICRO CUP - Soups–canned - Hormel Foods Corp.
MICRO CUP MEALS - Food products - Hormel Foods Corp.
MICRO CURL - Hair care products - Helene Curtis Industries Inc.
MICRO-CUT - Craft supplies - Midwest Products Co. Inc.
MICRO CUT 2000 - Polishes - Blue Lustre, LLC
MICRO-DATER - Stamps–hand - Cosco Industries Inc.
MICRO-DEC - Computer software - Medical Equipment Distributors, Inc.
MICRO-DESIGNS SOFTWARE CORPORATION - Computer software - Micro-Designs Software Corp.
MICRO-DIAL - Expansive bits - Irwin Co.
MICRO DIAMOND - Audio-video product - Cornerstone/Clearlight
MICRO DIAMOND-POINT - Surgical instruments - Snowden Pencer, Inc.
MICRO DIGITAL ELITE - Communications equipment - Motorola, Inc. (Land Mobile Products Sector)
MICRO DIGITAL LITE - Radio communications equipment - Motorola, Inc. (Land Mobile Products Sector)
MICRO DISCOVERY - Computer software ☆ - SRA/McGraw-Hill (Div. of The McGraw-Hill Companies)
MICRO DISSOLVE 3 - Audio-video products - Cornerstone/Clearlight
MICRO-DOWNLITE - Lighting fixtures - Swivelier Co. Inc.
MICRO-DRAG - Sporting goods ☆ - Shakespeare Fishing Tackle
MICRO E - Medical equipment - Zimmer, Inc.
MICRO-EAR - Hearing aids - Micro Sound Products
MICRO-EASE - Containers - E-Z-Por Corp.
MICRO-EDGE - Hair care products - Buttercut Shear Co.
MICRO EXPLORER - Toys - Fisher-Price, Inc.
MICRO EYEGLASS REPAIR KIT - Ophthalmic goods - Karlen Manufacturing, Inc.
MICRO FENCE - Woodworking machinery - Richard L. Wedler
MICRO-FILE - Electronic equipment - Bell & Howell Co.
MICRO FINE - Containers - Central Fine Pack, Inc.
MICRO-FINE - Medical apparatus - Becton, Dickinson and Co.
MICRO FINELINES - Blinds–venetian - Spring Window Fashions Division, Inc.
MICRO-FLEET - Electronic equipment - Telex Communications, Inc.
MICRO-FLEX - Insulating materials ☆ - Manville/Schuller
MICRO FLOOD - Lighting fixtures - Kim Lighting Inc.
MICRO FLORIST, THE - Computer storage devices - Microcode Corp.
MICRO FLUID - Pens - Schneider Pens USA
MICRO-FOAM - Fishing lines ☆ - Cortland Line Co., Inc.
MICRO-FOIL - Insulating tape - Manville/Schuller
MICRO FORCE - Bicycles - Kent International Inc.
MICRO-FREEZE - Plastics film - Reynolds Consumer Products, Inc.
MICRO FRUIT - Fruits–dried ☆ - Sunsweet Growers Inc.
MICRO-FRYER - Cooking utensils–aluminum ☆ - Revere Ware Corp.
MICRO FUL IT - Automotive parts and accessories - Fibre Glass-Evercoat Co. Inc.
MICRO-GATOR - Battery testers - Mueller Electric Co.

☆ = Now out of production

MICRO GEMS - Cosmetics - Revlon Consumer Products Corp.
MICRO-GO-ROUND - Cooking equipment–household - Nordic Ware
MICRO-GO-ROUND PLUS - Cooking equipment–household ☆ - Nordic Ware
MICRO GRAPH - Floor coverings–carpet and rugs ☆ - Mohawk Carpet Corp.
MICRO GRIPPERS - Toy vehicles - Intex Recreation Corp.
MICRO GROOVE - Golfing equipment - Lisco, Inc.
MICRO-GROOVE - Rifles - Marlin Firearms Co.
MICRO GUARD - Health care products - Cable Call
MICRO-GUARD - Mordants - Sanitized Inc.
MICRO-GUARD - Skin care products - Sween Corp.
MICRO-GUARD - Telephones–cellular - International Specialty Products, Inc.
MICRO-HEAT - Heating pad - Cara, Inc.
MICRO HEATER - Medical apparatus - Grandoe Corp.
MICRO HOUSE - Computer software - Micro House International, Inc.
MICRO-HUB - Communications equipment - ADC Telecommunications, Inc.
MICRO HUSH - Audio equipment - Rocktron Corp.
MICRO ILLUMINATION - Lighting equipment - Cogent Light Technologies, Inc.
MICRO ILLUSTRATOR - Computer software - Dunamis Inc.
MICRO INDUSTRIES - Computers–mainframe - Micro Industries Corp.
MICRO INDUSTRIES AN ISO-9001 COMPANY - Circuit boards–printed - Micro Industries Corp.
MICRO INFINITY - Electronic equipment - Newport Electronic, Inc.
MICRO-INSTANT - Dinnerware–glass - Salem China Co.
MICRO-JET - Electronic equipment - The Fogmaster Corp.
MICRO-JET - Pumps–water - Aquarium Systems, Inc.
MICRO-JET-ARRAY - Industrial machinery - Q-JET DSI Inc.
MICRO-K - Fire extinguishing compositions - Ansul, Inc.
MICRO-KETTLE, THE - Glassware–household - Gemco Ware, Inc.
MICRO-KILL - Disinfectants - Promaster
MICRO KNIT - Fabrics - Guilford Mills, Inc.
MICRO-KONTROL - Filters–air - Air Kontrol Inc.
MICRO KRISTAL KLEAR - Adhesives and sealants - Microscale Industries Inc.
MICRO-LADS - Computer software - Laureate Learning Systems Inc.
MICRO LEAGUE BASEBALL 4 - Computer software - Micro League Sports Association
MICRO LEAGUE BASEBALL-FANTASY MANAGER - Computer software - Micro League Sports Association
MICRO LEAGUE BASKETBALL - Computer software - Micro League Sports Association
MICRO LEAGUE FOOTBALL 2 - Computer software - Micro League Sports Association
MICRO LEGEND - Sporting goods - Ashaway Line & Twine Manufacturing Co.
MICRO LIBRARY - Medical apparatus - Oxford Micro Devices, Inc.
MICRO LIBRARY SYSTEM - Electrical equipment - International Data Engineering, Inc.
MICRO-LIFE - Identification tags ☆ - Classic Plaques Inc.
MICRO-LINER - Vacuum cleaners and accessories - Home Care Industries, Inc.
MICRO LIQUID DECAL FILM - Coatings - Microscale Industries Inc.
MICRO LIQUITAPE - Adhesives and sealants - Microscale Industries Inc.
MICRO-LITE - Craft supplies - Midwest Products Co. Inc.
MICRO-LITE - Insulating materials - Manville/Schuller
MICRO-LITE - Medical apparatus - Air-Shields, Inc.
MICRO-LITE 400 - Golfing equipment - Northwestern Golf Co.
MICRO-LOK - Insulating materials - Manville/Schuller
MICRO-LOK - Insulating materials - Schuller International, Inc.
MICRO LOOSE TUBE - Cables–fiber optic - Mohawk Cable & Wire Corp.
MICRO LUX - Electronics equipment - Burgess Inc.
MICRO MACHINES - Toys–automobiles - Lewis Galoob Toys, Inc.
MICRO MAGIC - Food containers - American Direct Marketing, Inc.
MICRO MAGIC - Sandwiches–prepackaged - J.R. Simplot Co.
MICRO-MAN - Books–comic - Larry F. Houston
MICRO MANAGER, THE - Computer software - Microcode Corp.
MICRO MARKETING - Floor coverings–carpet and rugs - Milliken & Co. Inc.
MICRO-MASK - Adhesives and sealants - Microscale Industries Inc.
MICRO-MASTER - Microfiche equipment ☆ - Keuffel & Esser Co.
MICRO-MATE - Electrical equipment - Popper & Sons Inc.
MICRO-MATIC - Jewelry - Jacoby-Bender Inc.
MICRO-MATIC III - Tape recorders–cassette - Lanier Voice Products
MICRO-MATRIX - Computer peripheral equipment - Telenex Corp.
MICRO MAX - Barbecues and grills - Nordic Ware
MICRO MAX - Containers - Packaging Corp. of America
MICRO MAX - Flashlights - Brinkmann Lighting Products
MICRO-MAX - Vitamins and nutritional supplements - Source Inc.
MICRO MAXX - Alarm systems - Maxi-Guard

MICRO MEATS IN MINUTES - Meat products - Aussie Meats of North America, Inc.
MICRO-MED - Computer software - Micro-Med Enterprises, Inc.
MICRO-MESH - Appliance parts - Maytag Corp.
MICRO-MESH - Musical instrument accessories - International Violin Co. Ltd.
MICRO METAL FOIL ADHESIVE - Adhesives and sealants - Microscale Industries Inc.
MICRO METER - Measuring instruments - Clack Corp.
MICRO MEXICANA - Food products - Sonora Foods Systems Inc.
MICRO MEXICANA - Pork rinds - Micro Mexicana
MICRO-MIKE - Microscopes - Dumaurier Co.
MICRO-MIKE - Pagers ☆ - MLI Industries
MICRO MIL - Analgesics ☆ - Noxell Corp.
MICRO-MINI - Lighting fixtures - Swivelier Co. Inc.
MICRO-MINI - Motor homes - Diamond Coach Corp.
MICRO MINI - Pens - Micropoint Inc.
MICRO-MINI - Umbrellas - Totes, Inc.
MICRO MINI PRIMO - Hearing aids - Rexton Inc.
MICRO MIST - Medical apparatus - Hudson Respiratory Care Inc.
MICRO-MITE - Ovens–microwave - Welbilt Appliances Inc.
MICRO-MIZER - Electrical equipment - Conxall Inc.
MICRO MO - Electronic equipment - Micro Mo Electronics, Inc.
MICRO-MOBLE - Computer terminals - Mead-Hatcher, Inc.
MICRO MONSTER - Tools–machine - Desert Carbide Co.
MICRO MORPHIN PLAYSET - Toys - Saban Entertainment, Inc.
MICRO MOUSE - Toys–stuffed - Dakin Inc.
MICRO MUSTANG - Pool tables - Micro Manufacturing, Inc.
MICRO-NAUTS - Toys–models - GHQ
MICRO NEEDLES - Surgical instruments - Lasting Impression I Inc.
MICRO OVEN - Machinery - OK Industries Inc.
MICRO-OVEN BRIQUE - Cooking equipment–household ☆ - Nordic Ware
MICRO-PAC - Computer software - Microsystems Software, Ltd.
MICRO-PAC - Craft supplies - Midwest Products Co. Inc.
MICRO-PACK - Automotive parts and accessories - Packard Electric Div.
MICRO-PAD - Transformers–electric - General Electric Co.
MICRO PANS - Cooking equipment–household - Chicago Metallic Products Inc.
MICRO PARTICLE ARREST - Bags–plastic - Scott Fetzer Co.
MICRO PEARLS ADVANTAGE BENZOYL-PLUS - Veterinary pharmaceutical preparations - Evsco Pharmaceuticals
MICRO PEARLS ADVANTAGE DERMAL-SOOTHE - Veterinary pharmaceutical preparations - Evsco Pharmaceuticals
MICRO PEARLS ADVANTAGE EUSCO-DINE - Veterinary pharmaceutical preparations - Evsco Pharmaceuticals
MICRO PEARLS ADVANTAGE EUSCO-TAR - Veterinary pharmaceutical preparations - Evsco Pharmaceuticals
MICRO PEARLS ADVANTAGE HYDRA-PEARLS - Veterinary pharmaceutical preparations - Evsco Pharmaceuticals
MICRO PEARLS ADVANTAGE SEBA-MOIST - Veterinary pharmaceutical preparations - Evsco Pharmaceuticals
MICRO-PEEL - Containers - Fres-Co System USA Inc.
MICRO-PEN - Surgical instruments - Lasting Impression I Inc.
MICRO-PERFECT - Electronics equipment - RTI Research Technology International
MICRO-PERK, THE - Glassware–household - Gemco Ware, Inc.
MICRO PLACER - Machinery - OK Industries Inc.
MICRO/PLANE - Paperboard - Stacor Corp.
MICRO PLASTICS - Wire products - Micro Plastics Inc.
MICRO PLATE - Medical apparatus - Biolog, Inc.
MICRO-PLUS - Automotive parts and accessories - Edelbrock Corp.
MICRO PLUSH - Fabrics - Monterey, Inc.
MICRO-PLY - Craft supplies - Midwest Products Co. Inc.
MICRO POINT - Garden equipment - Altra Corp.
MICRO POP - Popcorn - Ryt-Way Industries, Inc.
MICRO PREMIUM MALT LIQUOR BRAEMOUNT SELECT - Beverages–malt - Dafoe International, Ltd.
MICRO PRO - Lighting fixtures - Genlyte Group Inc.
MICRO-PROP - Plant growth regulators - Loveland Industries, Inc.
MICRO PURGE - Pumps - QED Environmental Systems, Inc.
MICRO Q - Computer hardware - Towercom Inc.
MICRO-QUARTZ - Insulating materials - Manville/Schuller
MICRO QUICK - Vegetables–frozen ☆ - Dean Foods Vegetable Co.
MICRO-RANGE - Machine parts - Michigan Drill Corp.
MICRO-RANGE - Stoves ☆ - White Consolidated Industries, Inc.
MICRO-READY - Meat products–beef - Bridgford Foods Corp.

☆ = Now out of production

MICRO REALITY MOTOR SPORTS INTERNATIONAL - Toys–automobiles - Keith E. Namanny

MICRO RELIEF - Heating pads–electric - Best Buys Direct, Inc.

MICRO REMOTE - Audio-video products - Cornerstone/Clearlight

MICRO-RESPONDER - Electronics equipment - MPC Educational Systems Inc.

MICRO RULE - Measuring device - Graphics West Micro Systems, Inc.

MICRO RULE - Office supplies - Theodore Alteneder & Sons

MICRO-SCAN - Projectors–photographic - Montage Productions Inc.

MICRO SCAN ACCENT - Markers–felt-tip - Sanford Corp.

MICRO-SCOPE - Computer software - Cross Educational Software Inc.

MICRO SCRABBLE - Computer software ☆ - Gessler Publishing Co., Inc.

MICRO SCREEN - Electrical equipment - Remington Products Co.

MICRO SCREEN ELITE - Electrical equipment - Remington Products Co.

MICRO-SEAL - Cooking equipment–household - Dazey Corp.

MICRO SEAL 2000 - Adhesives and sealants - Blue Lustre, LLC

MICRO SERVICES GROUP - Software - Micro Services Group, Inc.

MICRO SET - Coatings - Microscale Industries Inc.

MICRO-SET - Easels - Chief Manufacturing Co.

MICRO-SET - Hardware - John Sterling Corp.

MICRO SHAKE - Spices and extracts ☆ - DCA Food Industries, Inc.

MICRO-SHEAR - Tools–hand-operated - Xuron Corp.

MICRO SHELF - Ovens–bakery - Whirlpool Properties, Inc.

MICRO SHIELD - Fabrics–coated - Maharam Fabric Corp.

MICRO SHIELD - Lubricants - Sage Corp.

MICRO SHOTS - Toys - Just Toys, Inc.

MICRO SLIDES - Linear motion tables - Anorad Corp.

MICRO SOFT - Window shades - Del Mar Window Coverings

MICRO SOL - Coatings - Microscale Industries Inc.

MICRO SONIC - Air conditioning equipment - Fedders North America Inc.

MICRO SORB - Tape–adhesive - Paper Conversions Inc.

MICRO-SPOT - Lighting fixtures - Swivelier Co. Inc.

MICRO STENCIL - Stencils - OK Industries Inc.

MICRO-STEP - Lighting fixtures - Swivelier Co. Inc.

MICRO-STRIP - Fasteners–snap - Klein Tools Inc.

MICRO-STRIP - Lighting equipment - Legion Lighting Co., Inc.

MICRO SURGE - Cleaning preparations - Comstar International Inc. (IPC Div.)

MICRO/SYS - Computer hardware - Micro/Sys, Inc.

MICRO TAC - Telephones - Motorola, Inc. (Land Mobile Products Sector)

MICRO TECH 1200 - Amplifiers - Crown International, Inc.

MICRO-TECH TRANSMITTER BUG - Transmitting apparatus - Edge Co.

MICRO-TEK - Toys - Maryland Toy Corp.

MICRO-TEMP - Health care products - Seabrook Medical Systems, Inc.

MICRO-TEXT - Computer programs - Thomas D. Jonovic

MICRO-THERMOMETER - Electrical equipment - General Electric Co.

MICRO THIN - Clippers–barber ☆ - Sunbeam-Oster Household Products

MICRO TINT - Containers - Fluid Management

MICRO-TITE - Clamps - Wittek Manufacturing

MICRO TOUCH - Fishing rods - Maurice Sporting Goods, Inc.

MICRO-TOUCH - Photographic equipment - Adams Retouching Machine Co.

MICRO-TRACK - Lighting fixtures - Lite Source Inc.

MICRO-TRAINS - Toys–trains - Micro-Trains Line Co.

MICRO-TUNED - Communications equipment–mobile - Mid-West Electronics Inc.

MICRO TUTOR - Computer software - Locus Systems

MICRO TWEEZE - Depilatories - Kenra Laboratories, Inc.

MICRO-TWIN - Housewares - Fort Howard Corp.

MICRO TWIN - Toys - Peg Perego USA Inc.

MICRO-V - Belts–automotive - Gates Rubber Co. (Automotive Aftermarket/ Hardware Sales Div.)

MICRO-VID - Cameras–video - Southland Instruments, Inc.

MICRO VISUALIZATION - Lighting equipment - Cogent Light Technologies, Inc.

MICRO-VTLS - Computer software - VTLS, Inc.

MICRO WAFER - Headphones - Stanton Magnetics Inc.

MICRO WELD - Adhesives and sealants - Microscale Industries Inc.

MICRO WHITES - Cooking utensils–glass ☆ - Himark Enterprises Inc.

MICRO-WICHES - Sandwiches–prepackaged - Pierre Frozen Foods Inc.

MICRO-X - Fishing lures - Sunset Line and Twine Co.

MICRO X - Kayaks - Wave Sports, Inc.

MICRO XPERTS - Computers–personal - Micro Experts, Inc.

MICRO XX - Animal feed supplements - Agri-King Inc.

MICRO Z - Toys - Lewis Galoob Toys, Inc.

MICRO ZOOMERS - Toys - Tyco Toys

MICRO21 - Microscopes - Intelligent Medical Imaging, Inc.

MICROAGE POWERDISC - Computer peripheral equipment - Microage Computer Centers, Inc.

MICROAIDES - Cooking equipment–commercial ☆ - Eagle Affiliates, Inc.

MICROAIR - Health care products - GSI Medical Systems

MICROALGAE GROW - Pet shops - Florida Aqua Farms Inc.

MICROALIGNMENT - Computer software - Applied Intelligent Systems Inc.

MICROAUTOMATION - Computer software - MicroAutomation, Inc.

MICROBALANCE - Snack foods - New Generation Foods Inc.

MICROBALL - Pens - Staedtler, Inc.

MICROBALLAST - Lighting fixtures - Micro-Technology, Inc.

MICROBAN - Cleaning preparations–carpet and rug - Von Schrader Co.

MICROBAN-X580 - Pet products - Microban Germicide Co.

MICROBANK - Tape recorders–cassette - Dictaphone Corp.

MICROBARRIER - Chemical preparations - Agrotec Corp.

MICROBASE - Computers - Microbase Corp.

MICROBASS - Amplifiers–musical instrument - Peavey Electronics Corp.

MICROBEST - Cleaning preparations - Microbest Products, Inc.

MICROBIOTONE - Vitamins and nutritional supplements - American Laboratories, Inc.

MICROBLADE - Skates–roller - Rollerblade, Inc.

MICROBLOCKER - Fabrics - Synthetic Industries, Inc.

MICROBLUSH - Cosmetics - Cosmair Inc.

MICROBOARD - Wood products - Weyerhaeuser Co.

MICROBOND - Nail care products - Opi Products, Inc.

MICROBOND - Welding equipment - Unitek Miyachi Corp.

MICROBOND UV - Nail care products - Opi Products, Inc.

MICROBOW - Office supplies ☆ - Charvoz

MICROBUDDY - Containers - Kent & Spiegel Direct, Inc.

MICROBURST - Cleaning preparations - Morris Morgan

MICROBURST - Popcorn ☆ - Wyandot, Inc.

MICROBYTES - Candy - Allan Chapman

MICROCABLE - Cables–fiber optic - Andrew Corp.

MICROCARE - Insecticides - Whitmire Research Laboratories, Inc.

MICROCASSETTE - Electronic equipment ☆ - Olympus America Inc.

MICROCAST - Fishing equipment - Shakespeare Fishing Tackle

MICROCAT - Boats - Micromarine, Ltd.

MICROCAT - Chemical preparations - National Starch and Chemical Co.

MICROCELL - Photographic equipment ☆ - Photo Research, Inc.

MICROCENTRE - Office furniture–wood - Continental Engineering Group, Inc.

MICROCEPTOR - Antennas–satellite - Conifer Corp.

MICROCERAM - Cooking utensils–earthenware ☆ - Anchor Hocking Glass, Inc.

MICROCHAMBER - Electrical testing instruments - Cascade Microtech, Inc.

MICROCHAMBER - Paper products - Conservation Resources International, Inc.

MICROCHEM - Medical apparatus - Ciba Corning Diagnostics Corp.

MICROCHEM - Toys - Natural Science Industries, Ltd.

MICROCLEEN - Filters–water - CWP Industries, Inc.

MICROCOG - Computer software - Risk Management Foundation of the Harvard Medical Institutions, Inc.

MICROCOLOR - Floor coverings–carpet and rugs ☆ - Heuga USA

MICROCOM CORPORATION - Computer peripheral equipment - Microcom Corp.

MICROCOMMANDER - Engines–marine - MMC Inc.

MICROCOMMUNICATOR - Circuit boards - Peregrine Semiconductor Corp.

MICROCON - Air purification systems - Bio-Logical Controls, Inc.

MICROCON - Filters–industrial - W.R. Grace & Co.

MICROCONTACT - Laser systems–medical - Endeavor Surgical Products, Inc.

MICROCONTROL - Spices and extracts - Baltimore Spice, Inc.

MICROCORE - Plastics film - Alliedsignal Inc.

MICROCORE - Slippers - R.G. Barry Corp.

MICROCORT - Pharmaceutical preparations - Alto Pharmaceuticals Inc.

MICROCOST - Computer programs - Kaden Arnone, Inc.

MICROCOST I - Computer programs - Kaden Arnone, Inc.

MICROCOTT - Fabrics - Coville Inc.

MICROCOUNT - Electronic equipment - Golden Gate Microsystems Inc.

MICROCOZM - Figurines - Norman Rockwell Gallery, Ltd.

MICROCRAFT - Toys–electronic - CBS Toys

MICROCRISP - Housewares - Microcrisp USA

MICROCROWNS - Denture materials - Sang-Jin Lee

MICROCURE - Electronic equipment - EIT, Inc.

MICRODEAL - Musical instruments - Michtron, Inc.

MICRODENT - Dental compounds - Whitehill Oral Technologies, Inc.

MICRODOL-X - Photographic equipment - Eastman Kodak Co.

MICRODOLLY - Tripods–photographic - Durant/Sherbourne Ent., Inc.

MICRODOT - Fabrics - Freudenberg Nonwovens Apparel Division

MICRODOWN - Pillows - Louisville Bedding Co.

MICRODOWSER - Measuring instruments - Saes Pure Gas, Inc.

☆ = Now out of production

MICRODRAFT - Drafting supplies - Micropoint Inc.
MICRODREEME - Fabrics - Guilford Mills, Inc.
MICRODUCT - Conduit - Furon Co.
MICRODYNAMICS - Computer peripheral equipment - Gerber Garment Technology, Inc.
MICRODYNE - Computer peripheral equipment - Microdyne Corp.
MICROEASE - Desserts - Regency Creative Foods
MICROEDGE - Photographic equipment - Eastman Kodak Co.
MICROENHANCER - Tatooing apparatus - Micropigmentation Devices Inc.
MICROFAX - Microfiche equipment ☆ - Dietzgen Corp.
MICROFEATURE - Fertilizers - Platte Chemical Co.
MICROFELT HEADWEAR - Hats - Bollman Hat Co.
MICROFET - Electronic equipment - Baylor Electric Products
MICROFET - Medical apparatus - Hoggan Health Industries Inc.
MICROFIBER CLUSTERS - Pillows - Pacific Coast Feather Co.
MICROFIL - Pillows - Pacific Coast Feather Co.
MICROFINE AMPINE - Fiberboard - Georgia-Pacific Corp.
MICROFINISH - Finishing agents - Champions Choice Inc.
MICROFIX - Pencils ☆ - Staedtler, Inc.
MICROFLAME - Blow torches - Microflame Inc.
MICROFLASH - Spectrometers - Applied Color Systems, Inc.
MICROFLEX - Health care products - Vygon Corp.
MICROFLEX - Microphones - Shure Brothers, Inc.
MICROFLEX INC. - Automotive parts and accessories - Microflex Inc.
MICROFLO - Grain products–corn - CoRoN Corp.
MICROFLUSH - Toilets–porcelain - Microphor Inc.
MICROFOAM - Padding–foam - Astro-Valcour, Inc.
MICROFOIL - Novelty items - Pioneer Balloon Co.
MICROFOLD - Computer peripheral equipment - MicroComputer Accessories Inc.
MICROFOREST - Chemical preparations - Microforest, Inc.
MICROFORM - Computer software - FormAtion Technologies Inc.
MICROFOX - Telephone apparatus - Telco Systems, Inc.
MICROFRAGRANCE - Chemical preparations - Minnesota Mining & Manufacturing Co.
MICROFRAME - Microcomputers - Union Friendly Systems, Inc.
MICROFRESH - Eggs - Milton G. Waldbaum Co.
MICROFRESH - Vegetables–frozen - Patterson Frozen Foods, Inc.
MICROFUNNEL - Laboratory apparatus - Pall Gelman Sciences
MICROGARD - Chemical preparations - Wesman Foods, Inc.
MICROGEL - Lubricants - Shell Oil Co.
MICROGEL - Medical apparatus - Microtek Medical, Inc.
MICROGLUE - Computer peripheral equipment - Golden Gate Microsystems Inc.
MICROGRAPH - Pencils - Staedtler, Inc.
MICROGRIP - Medical apparatus - Teleflex Inc.
MICROGUARD - Health care products - Omni Group Inc.
MICROGUARD - Industrial machinery - Triad Controls, Inc.
MICROGUARD - Industrial machinery - White Consolidated Industries, Inc.
MICROHARD - Computer hardware - Microhard Technologies, Inc.
MICROHART - Computer software - Kaden Arnone, Inc.
MICROHEDRA - Games - Gamescience
MICROHELP - Computer peripheral equipment - Microhelp, Inc.
MICROHUB - Computer hardware - Compex, Inc.
MICROHUB PLUS - Computer hardware - Compex, Inc.
MICROIL - Oils–lubricating - Kano Laboratories Inc.
MICROINCH - Surgical instruments - Flexbar Machine Corp.
MICROIRON II - Vitamins and nutritional supplements - Sanofi Winthrop, Inc.
MICROJECT - Intravenous apparatus - Microject Corp.
MICROLAB - Toys ☆ - Revell-Monogram, Inc.
MICRO–LAM - Lumber - Trus Joist MacMillan L.P.
MICROLAM - Veneer - Universal Forest Products Inc.
MICROLEAGUE - Computer software - Microleague Multimedia, Inc.
MICROLENGTH 196 - Electronic equipment - Electro-Sensors, Inc.
MICROLENS - Hearing aids - Widex Hearing Aid Co., Inc.
MICROLEVEL - Electronic equipment - Clark-Reliance Corp.
MICROLEX - Computers - Tandy Name Brand Retail Group
MICROLIGHT - Chemical preparations - Gougeon Brothers, Inc.
MICROLIGHT - Door sensors - Delaware Capital Formation Inc.
MICROLIGHT - Lighting equipment - Cogent Light Technologies, Inc.
MICROLIGHT - Lighting fixtures - Lusa Lighting Intl., Inc.
MICROLINE - Electronics equipment - York Controls
MICROLINE - Printers–computer - Okidata
MICROLINE MX - Water purification systems - Clack Corp.
MICROLINER - Pencils ☆ - Dixon Ticonderoga Co.
MICROLINK - Lighting equipment - Cogent Light Technologies, Inc.

MICROLIPID - Health care products - Sherwood Medical Co.
MICROLITE - Abrasive products - Norton Co.
MICROLITE - Building materials - Specrete-Ip Inc.
MICROLITE - Electrical equipment - Pittway Corp.
MICROLITE - Fabrics - Albany International Corp.
MICROLITE - Food products ☆ - Tony's Pizza Service
MICROLITE - Generators–automotive - Onan Corp.
MICROLITE - Insulating materials - Schuller International, Inc.
MICROLITE - Water purification systems - General Ecology, Inc.
MICROLITE - Wheelchairs - Morgan Technology, Inc.
MICROLITE TD - Golfing equipment - FM Precision Golf Corp.
MICROLITES - Eyeglasses - Style Eyes of California
MICROLITTER - Lighting fixtures - Hubbell Lighting, Inc. (Lighting Div.)
MICROLLOY - Pianos - Mapes Piano String Co.
MICROLOCK - Alarm systems - Sensormatic Electronics Corp.
MICROLOG - Medical apparatus - Biolog, Inc.
MICROLOK - Cleaning preparations - Birchwood Casey
MICROLON - Electronic equipment - Grayhill, Inc.
MICROLOY - Chains - Webb Forging Co.
MICROLPM - Computer hardware ☆ - Proprietary Controls Systems Corp.
MICROLUX - Floodlights - Hubbell Inc.
MICROLUX - Lighting fixtures - Hubbell Lighting, Inc. (Lighting Div.)
MICROLUX - Medical apparatus - Luxtec Corp.
MICROMAESTRO - Computer software - Dunamis Inc.
MICROMANAGER - Computer peripheral equipment - MicroComputer Accessories Inc.
MICROMAPS - Maps - Advertising Unlimited Inc.
MICROMARC - Printers–computer - Texas Instruments Inc.
MICROMARINADER - Containers ☆ - ISI North America, Inc.
MICROMASTER - Animal feed supplements - Loveland Industries, Inc.
MICROMATCHED - Golfing equipment ☆ - John Rouzee Green Co., Inc.
MICROMATE - Computers–personal - Personal Micro Computers Inc.
MICROMATE - Microwave browning vessels - Corning Inc.
MICROMATE - Video equipment - Navitar, Inc.
MICROMATES - Bakery products - PH Orth Co.
MICROMATH - Computer software ☆ - Spinnaker Software Corp.
MICROMATH 6-PAK - Computer software - J. Weston Walch, Publisher
MICROMATH SCIENTIST - Computer software - MicroMath Inc.
MICROMATIC - Electronic equipment - Dukane Corp.
MICROMATIC - Pencils - Staedtler, Inc.
MICROMATIC II - Audio equipment - Dukane Corp.
MICROMATION - Electronic product - AVG, Inc.
MICROMAX - Machinery - T.D. Williamson, Inc.
MICROMAX - Pens - Oriente De Oro Co., Inc.
MICROMAX - Television equipment - Zenith Electronics Corp.
MICROMAX - Tools–hand-operated - Genesis Materials International
MICROMAX DESIGNER - Containers - Packaging Corp. of America
MICROMAZE - Laboratory apparatus - Kurt J. Lesker Co.
MICROMBX - Computer software - Martin Green
MICROMEDIA - Computer software - Boston Acoustics Inc.
MICROMEDICINE - Pharmaceutical preparations - Allen M. Kratz
MICROMEGA - Electronic equipment - Omega Engineering, Inc.
MICROMET - Chemical preparations - Nu-Calgon Wholesaler, Inc.
MICROMETER MASTER - Sextants–navigational - Davis Instruments Corp.
MICROMEWI - Medical apparatus - Micro Therapeutics, Inc.
MICROMIND - Computer software - SourceView Software International
MICROMITE - Insecticides - Uniroyal Chemical Co. Inc. (Crop Protection Div.)
MICROMIX - Audio equipment - Yorkville Sound
MICROMIZER - Hearing aids - Widex Hearing Aid Co., Inc.
MICROMMAC - Computer peripheral equipment - Cabletron Systems, Inc.
MICROMODEM - Electronic equipment - Hayes Microcomputer Products Inc.
MICROMODULE SYSTEMS - Integrated circuits - Micromodule Systems, Inc.
MICRON - Bags–paper - The Eureka Co.
MICRON - Binoculars - Swift Instruments, Inc.
MICRON - Boat-bottom coating - Interlux Yacht Finishes
MICRON - Electronics equipment - Marty Bahn & Co.
MICRON - Fishing tackle - Cortland Line Co., Inc.
MICRON - Hearing aids - Audiotone, Inc.
MICRON - Medical apparatus - Smith & Nephew Richards, Inc.
MICRON - Toys–models ☆ - Estes Industries
MICRON 33 - Boat-bottom coating - Interlux Yacht Finishes
MICRON AIR JET SIEVE - Electronic equipment - Hosokawa Micron International Inc.
MICRON CLEAN - Apparel stores–uniforms - Micron-Clean Uniform Service, Inc.
MICRON CSC - Boat-bottom coating - Interlux Yacht Finishes

☆ = Now out of production

MICRON MEGA - Sporting goods - Canstar Sports USA
MICRONAIR - Fibers–synthetic - Freudenberg Nonwovens L.P.
MICRONAIRE - Cleaning preparations - Summit Hill Laboratories
MICRONASE - Pharmaceutical preparations - Upjohn Co.
MICRONAUT - Toys ☆ - Mego Financial Corp.
MICRONEB - Laboratory apparatus - Cetac Technologies Inc.
MICRONEFRIN - Medical apparatus - Bird Products Corp.
MICRONEX - Computer software - Micronex, Inc.
MICRONIL - Vitamins and nutritional supplements - Gary Null & Associates, Inc.
MICRONIMS - Computer storage devices ☆ - Framateme Technologies, Inc.
MICRONITE - Chemical preparations - Micro-Lite, Inc.
MICRONIZED IRON - Fertilizers - Luster Leaf Products Inc.
MICRONIZER - Computer software - Superior Enterprises, Inc.
MICRONN - Toys - Mattel, Inc.
MICRONOR - Pharmaceutical preparations - Ortho Pharmaceutical Corp.
MICRONORM - Pens ☆ - Charvoz
MICRONOVA - Pharmaceutical preparations - Berlex Laboratories, Inc.
MICRONOX - Cylinders–metal - Microflame Inc.
MICRONOX - Film - Caddock Electronics Inc.
MICRONTA - Radar systems and equipment - Tandy Corp.
MICRONUTRIENTS TBCC - Animal feed supplements - Heritage Environmental Services, Inc.
MICROPAGES - Electronic equipment - Selectronics, Inc.
MICROPAK - Electronic equipment - Chaparral Communications, Inc.
MICROPAK - Electronics equipment - L & M Auto Supply
MICROPAN - Electronic equipment - Nikon Inc.
MICROPATCH - Cement - Specrete-Ip Inc.
MICROPATH - Computer peripheral equipment - Compumachine, Inc.
MICROPATH - Computer software - Micropath Corp.
MICROPEAKER - Electronic equipment - Baylor Electric Products
MICROPEARLS - Pet products - Evsco Pharmaceuticals
MICROPEN - Pens ☆ - Staedtler, Inc.
MICROPERE - Microscopes - Cadillac Optical Corp.
MICROPERFORATOR - Hole punching machines - Weldotron Corp.
MICROPERM - Pens - Sakura Color Products of America, Inc.
MICROPERM - Pens - Sakura of America
MICROPHEN - Chemical preparations - ILFORD Photo Corp.
MICROPLAY - Computer software - Microprose Software, Inc.
MICROPLEX - Veterinary nutritional supplements - Zinpro Corp.
MICROPLOT - Computer software - Microplot Systems Co.
MICROPLUS - Soap - Kinpak, Inc.
MICROPOINT - Pens - Micropoint Inc.
MICROPOLYX - Tubes–plastic - Microlumen, Inc.
MICROPOR-SIL - Batteries - Microporous Products, Inc.
MICROPORE - Fabrics - Easy Gardener Inc.
MICROPORE - Health care products - Minnesota Mining & Manufacturing Co.
MICROPORE - Stamps–hand - Avery Dennison Corp.
MICROPORT - Catheters - Strato Medical Corp.
MICROPORT - Combines–agricultural - Forrest Keith Blair
MICROPORT SYSTEMS - Computers - Forrest Keith Blair
MICROPOWER OMNIBUS - Electronic equipment - Tideland Signal Corp.
MICROPOWER/PASCAL - Computer software - Digital Equipment Corp.
MICROPOWER/PASCAL-RSX - Computer software - Digital Equipment Corp.
MICROPRESS - Medical apparatus - Meyer R. Rosen
MICROPRINT - Office supplies - Georgia-Pacific Corp.
MICROPRINT ONE - Office supplies - Georgia-Pacific Corp.
MICROPRO - Computer software - WordStar International Inc.
MICROPROBE - In vitro reagents - MicroProbe Corp.
MICROPROOF - Housewares - Plastics, Inc. (Anchor Hocking Plastics)
MICROPULL - Welding equipment - Unitek Miyachi Corp.
MICROPULSE - Battery chargers - Gemini Industries, Inc.
MICROPULSE - Medical apparatus - Sierra Medical Systems, Inc.
MICROPURE - Cylinders - Solkatronic Chemicals, Inc.
MICROPURE - Filters–fuel - Micropure Filtration Inc.
MICROPURE - Floor coverings - Hartco Inc.
MICROPURE - Glass–laboratory - Chase Instruments Corp.
MICROQUARTZ - Watches - Croton Watch Co., Inc.
MICRORAVE - Food products - General Mills, Inc.
MICRORESTAURANT - Computer software - To Be Good, Inc.
MICRO'RIGINALS - Food products - Gorges Foodservice, Inc.
MICROROLLER - Conveyors - Sparks Belting Co.
MICROSAFE - Product description unknown - Doranne
MICROSAIC - Adhesives and sealants - Peace Flooring Co. Inc.
MICROSAURS - Toys - Trendmasters, Inc.
MICROSAURUS REX - Bicycles - Raleigh USA Bicycle Co.

MICROSAVER - Computer software - Kensington
MICROSCALE - Decals and transfers - Microscale Industries Inc.
MICROSCALE - Measuring instruments - Acu-Rite Inc.
MICROSCAN - Electronic equipment - Microscan Systems Inc.
MICROSCOPY - Computer storage devices–optical - Digital Imaging Associates Inc.
MICROSCOPY'S TRUE DIMENSIONS - Microscopes - Edge Scientific Instrument Corp.
MICROSCRIBE - Electronic equipment ☆ - Houston Instrument
MICROSCRIPT - Pens ☆ - Charvoz
MICROSEAL - Spices and extracts - Dragoco Inc.
MICROSEIVE - Pet products - Aquapro
MICROSHARP - Pencils–mechanical ☆ - C-Thru Ruler Co.
MICROSHIELD - Computer software - Framateme Technologies, Inc.
MICROSHOOTER - Nozzles - Wet Labs Inc.
MICROSHOT - Photographic equipment - Egripment USA, Inc.
MICROSIGHT - Archery equipment - Huey P. Savage
MICROSIGHT - Photographic equipment - Bestwell Optical Instrument Co.
MICROSIZE - Machinery - Micromatic Operations Inc.
MICROSKYSHINE - Computer software - Framateme Technologies, Inc.
MICROSLIP - Boats–kayaks - Phoenix Products Inc.
MICROSMOOTH - Underwear and nightwear - Vanity Fair, Inc.
MICROSOC THINKING GAMES - Computer software - American Guidance Service Inc.
MICROSOCIETY - Computer software - Micro Society, Inc.
MICROSOFT - Computer software - Microsoft Corp.
MICROSOFT AT WORK - Publisher's imprints - Microsoft Corp.
MICROSOFT BACKOFFICE - Computer software - Microsoft Corp.
MICROSOFT HOME - Computer software - Microsoft Corp.
MICROSOFT MOUSE 25 - Computer peripheral equipment - Microsoft Corp.
MICROSOFT OFFICE COMPATIBLE - Computer software - Microsoft Corp.
MICROSOFT POCKET AUTOMAP - Computer software - Microsoft Corp.
MICROSOFT POCKET WORD - Computer software - Microsoft Corp.
MICROSOFT PROJECT - Computer software - Microsoft Corp.
MICROSOFT QUICKBASIC - Computer software - Microsoft Corp.
MICROSOFT WINDOWS NT - Computer software - Microsoft Corp.
MICROSONIC - Pet products - Biological Engineering/High Tech Pet Products
MICROSPACER - Medical equipment - Respiratory Delivery Systems, Inc.
MICROSPAN - Microwave radio communications equipment - Alliance Telecommunications Corp.
MICROSPARC - Integrated circuits - Sparc International, Inc.
MICROSPEEDREAD - Computer software - CBS Software
MICROSPIN - Fishing rods - Shakespeare Fishing Tackle
MICROSPIN BY WAUKESHA - Filters–oil - Dresser Industries, Inc.
MICROSPLIT - Watches - Tag-Heuer Time & Electronics Corp.
MICROSS - Toners - Pierce Companies, Inc.
MICROSTACK - Electrical equipment - Whitaker Corp.
MICROSTAR - Computer software ☆ - Decision Dynamics, Inc.
MICROSTAT - Oxygen - Caire
MICROSTAT - Vacuum cleaners and accessories - Kent Co.
MICROSTAT 2 - Disinfectants - Septodont, Inc.
MICROSTATION - Computer software - Bentley Systems, Inc.
MICROSTATION DESCARTES - Computer software - Bentley Systems, Inc.
MICROSTATION FIELD - Computer software ☆ - Bentley Systems, Inc.
MICROSTATION GEOGRAPHICS - Computer software - Bentley Systems, Inc.
MICROSTATION MODELER - Computer software - Bentley Systems, Inc.
MICROSTATION POWERDRAFT - Computer software - Bentley Systems, Inc.
MICROSTATION POWERSCOPE - Computer software - Bentley Systems, Inc.
MICROSTATION REVIEW - Computer software ☆ - Bentley Systems, Inc.
MICROSTATION SYSTEM - Medical apparatus - Biolog, Inc.
MICROSTATION TRIFORMA - Computer software - Bentley Systems, Inc.
MICROSTIM - Computer software - MicroStim Inc.
MICROSTRATEGY - Computer software - Microstrategy, Inc.
MICROSUEDE - Fabrics–flock - Microfibres, Inc.
MICROSUL - Pharmaceutical preparations - Star Pharmaceuticals Inc.
MICROSULFON - Pharmaceutical preparations - Consolidated Midland Corp.
MICROSUPREME - Fibers–acrylic - American Cyanamid Co.
MICROSURE - Water treating compounds - Pall Gelman Sciences
MICROSWEEP - Vacuum cleaners and accessories - Oreck Corp.
MICROSYSTEMS - Computer software - Microsystems Software Inc.
MICROTAB II - Audio equipment - ADA Signal Processors Inc.
MICROTAC DIGITAL ELITE - Telephones–cellular - Motorola, Inc. (Land Mobile Products Sector)
MICROTAC ELITE - Radio communications equipment - Motorola, Inc. (Land Mobile Products Sector)

☆ = Now out of production

MICROTAC ULTRA LITE - Telephones–cellular - Motorola, Inc. (Land Mobile Products Sector)

MICROTAC VIB - Radio communications equipment - Motorola, Inc. (Land Mobile Products Sector)

MICROTALK - Radio communications equipment - Cobra Electronics Corp.

MICROTEC ZOOM - Cameras - Yashica Inc.

MICROTECH - Pet collars - Elexis Corp.

MICROTECH - Ventilation equipment - Snydergeneral Corp.

MICROTECH GEFELL - Microphones - G Prime Limited

MICROTEK - Stoves - Nautilus Industries

MICROTEX - Fabrics - Albany International Corp.

MICROTEX - Film - Uniflex, Inc.

MICROTHERM - Ophthalmic goods ☆ - Alcon Laboratories, Inc.

MICROTHIN - Lenses–optical - Pearle, Inc.

MICROTHIN PLUS - Lenses–optical - Pearle, Inc.

MICROTINT - Dispensers - Fluid Management

MICROTOME - Computer software - VayTek, Inc.

MICROTOMIC - Pencils ☆ - Faber-Castell Corp.

MICROTOTES - Cases–plastic - Microplas Inc.

MICROTOUCH - Electrical equipment - General Electric Co.

MICROTOX - Lab chemicals - Microbics Corp.

MICROTRAC - Computer software - Microtrac Systems, Inc.

MICROTRAC - Shaving preparations - Gillette Co.

MICROTRAK - Computer software - American Technologies, Inc.

MICROTRAK - Medical apparatus - Syva Co.

MICROTRAK CX - Cameras - Bell & Howell Co.

MICROTRAN - Electronics equipment - Microtran Co. Inc.

MICROTRAX - Computer software - CMX Systems, Inc.

MICROTREAT - Chemical preparations - Loveland Industries, Inc.

MICROTREND - Health care products - Australasia Ventures

MICROTRON - Fuses - Cooper Industries, Inc.

MICROTRON ABRASIVES, INC. - Abrasive products - Microtron Abrasives, Inc.

MICROTRUX - Computer storage devices - Jeff Simning

MICROTUBE - Audio equipment - ADA Signal Processors Inc.

MICROTURN - Computer software - CNC Controls, Inc.

MICROTUTOR - Computer software - Applied Learning

MICROTYPE - Computer software - Bayer Corp.

MICROVEL - Paper–bond - Dietzgen Corp.

MICROVENT - Containers - Prism Products, Inc.

MICROVER - Water transportation - Benthos Inc.

MICROVERSATRIP - Circuit breakers - General Electric Co.

MICROVISION - Endoscopic equipment - Galileo Corp.

MICROVISION - Optical microscope units - Stephen Goldsmith

MICROWALL/BE - Microphones - Shure Brothers, Inc.

MICROWARE - Cooking equipment–household - Plastics, Inc. (Anchor Hocking Plastics)

MICROWARE - Microwave components ☆ - Anchor Hocking Glass, Inc.

MICROWARE OS-9 - Veterinary pharmaceutical preparations - Microware Systems Corp.

MICROWAREHOUSE - Computers - Micro Warehouse, Inc.

MICROWATER MAKER - Water purification systems - Shigeru Otsuki

MICROWAVE - Communications equipment–microwave - Microwave Filter Co., Inc.

MICROWAVE - Synthesizers–musical instrument - Steinberg/Jones Corp.

MICROWAVE ASSOCIATES - Electronic equipment ☆ - Ma-Com Inc.

MICROWAVE DATA SYSTEMS - Radio equipment - Microwave Data Systems, Inc.

MICROWAVE HOT SANDWICHES - Sandwiches–prepackaged ☆ - J.T.M. Provisions Co.

MICROWAVE MAGIC - Popcorn - National Oats Co. Inc.

MICROWAVE MORNING - Food products ☆ - Golden Valley Microwave Foods, Inc.

MICROWAVE NETWORKS INCORPORATED - Antennas - Microwave Networks, Inc.

MICROWAVE OVEN MAGIC - Cleaning preparations - Magic American Corp.

MICROWAVE PLUS - Cookware - Corning Inc.

MICROWAVE READY - Cheese - Kraft Food Ingredients Corp.

MICROWAVE RECIPE - Rice ☆ - Uncle Ben's, Inc.

MICROWAVEABLE READY TO SERVE PROMPT PASTA - Pasta - Leone's Original Recipes

MICROWAY - Computers - Microway, Inc.

MICROWAY - Precision linear roller bearings - Anorad Corp.

MICROWEAR - Metals - Fox Sales, Inc.

MICROWHITE - Housewares - Doranne

MICROWIDE - Lenses ☆ - Buhl Optical Co.

MICROWIT - Glass products ☆ - Crystal International Corp.

MICROWOOD - Window coverings - A.J. Boyd Industries Inc.

MICROWORD - Audio tapes–blank - Dobbs-Stanford Corp.

MICROX - Diuretics - Fisons Corp.

MICROYAG - Laser systems–medical - Gish Biomedical, Inc.

MICROZIDE - Pharmaceutical preparations - Watson Laboratories, Inc.

MICROZINE - Computer software - Scholastic Software Inc.

MICROZINE JR. - Computer software - Scholastic Software Inc.

MICROZIP - Computer software - Microzip Corp.

MICROZOOM - Computer software - Estek Corp.

MICROZOOM - Microscopes - Bausch & Lomb Inc.

MICTOR - Electrical equipment - Whitaker Corp.

MICTRIN - Pharmaceutical preparations - Kabi Pharmacia Inc.

MICTROL - Pharmaceutical preparations - Misemer Pharmaceuticals Inc.

MID - Boots - Skis Dynastar, Inc.

MID AM TRADE SHOW - Trade Associations - Mid-America Horticultural Trade Show

MID-AMERICA - Paints - Farrell-Calhoun Inc.

MID-AMERICA FARMS - Milk - Mid-America Dairymen Inc. Southern Div.

MID-AMERICA MASTER SERIES - Ventilation equipment - Mid-America Building Products Corp.

MID ANCHOR-POINT - Golfing equipment - Dale Miller Inc.

MID-ARC, INC. - Welding equipment - Mid-Arc, Inc.

MID-ATLANTIC - Seafood products–fresh or frozen - Mid Atlantic Foods Inc.

MID-BAK - Sporting goods - Midwest Lettering Inc.

MID BEAM 4 - Spotlights - W.F. Harris Lighting, Inc.

MID CONTINENT - Cabinets - Norcraft Companies Inc.

MID-CURE - Epoxy - Bob Smith Industries

MID-EAST - Drums–metal - Mid-East Manufacturing Inc.

MID-GRADE EXTRA - Gasoline - Atlantic Richfield Co.

MID GRAPH - Floor coverings–carpet and rugs ☆ - Mohawk Carpet Corp.

MID-HI - Footwear - San Shoe Trading Corp.

MID-LIFT - Engines–internal combustion - Miller Engineering, Inc.

MID-MOUNT ESTATE - Lawn mowers - Alamo Group

MID-OVERSIZE - Golfing equipment - Pro Kennex, Inc.

MID PACIFIC - Seafood products–canned or cured - Bumble Bee Seafoods, Inc.

MID-SKI-TOW - Skis - Ve-Ve Inc.

MID STATES - Ceramic tile - Integrity Tile Co.

MID STATES - Furniture - Lowy Group Inc.

MID-STATES - Hearing aids - Mid-States Laboratories Inc.

MID-SUPPORT ZONE - Mattresses - Ohio Mattress Co.

MID-TOWN FORMALS - Footwear–women's - Middletown Footwear Inc.

MID-VALLEY - Fruits–frozen - Mid-Valley Products Corp.

MID VUE - Lenses–optical - Empire Vision Centers, Inc.

MID WEDGE - Golfing equipment - Lisco, Inc.

MID-WEST - Catsup - Mid-West Food Packers Inc.

MID WESTERN - Apparel and accessories - Berlin Glove Co. Inc.

MID-WESTERN - Apparel and accessories - Mid-Western Sport Togs

MID-WESTERN SPORT TOGS - Leather–glove - Berlin Glove Co. Inc.

MIDAHIST - Cough medicines ☆ - Vangard Labs Inc.

MIDAMOR - Diuretics - Merck & Co., Inc. (Merck Research Laboratories)

MIDANEED - Pharmaceutical preparations - Hanlon Drug Products

MIDANI ERBE - Bath salts - European Soaps Ltd.

MIDAPECTIN - Pharmaceutical preparations ☆ - Vangard Labs Inc.

MIDAS - Audio equipment - EVI Pro Audio Group

MIDAS - Consulting services - Midas Management Corp.

MIDAS - Fishing rods - Zebco Corp.

MIDAS - Floor coverings - R.W. Beattie Carpet Industries Inc.

MIDAS - Jewelry–precious - Midas-Sattler Inc.

MIDAS - Mufflers - Midas International Corp.

MIDAS - Water–bottled or canned - Midas Spring Water Inc.

MIDAS FUND - Consulting services - Midas Fund, Inc.

MIDAS GOLD - Computer software - M.S. Gerber & Associates Inc.

MIDAS GOLD - Varnishes - Reichhold Chemicals, Inc.

MIDAS MAGIC - Video games ☆ - WMS Gaming Inc.

MIDAS MINI - Motor vehicles–motor homes ☆ - Coachmen Industries, Inc.

MIDAS SYSTEM - Hearing aids - Firstaid for Hearing Aids

MIDAS TECHNOLOGY - Computer software - OverDrive Systems Inc.

MIDAS TOOLS - Tools–hand-operated - Leather Factory Inc.

MIDAS TOUCH - Fabrics ☆ - Princess Fabrics Inc.

MIDAS TOUCH - Hair care products ☆ - Dubl Duck/Jet Set Inc.

MIDASNET - Computer peripheral equipment - PPG Industries, Inc.

MIDATANE - Pharmaceutical preparations ☆ - Vangard Labs Inc.

MIDATAPP - Pharmaceutical preparations ☆ - Vangard Labs Inc.

MIDAX - Printers–computer - Moore Business Forms, Inc.

☆ = Now out of production

MIDCO - Musical instrument accessories - Midco International
MIDCO - Sporting goods - Midwest Sporting Goods Manufacturing Co.
MIDCON - Electrical equipment - Esterline Technologies Corp.
MIDCOR - Faucets ☆ - Moen Inc.
MIDCORE - Computer software - Midcore Software, Inc.
MIDDLE ATLANTIC - Shelving units–wood ☆ - ARS Electronics
MIDDLE ATLANTIC - Toys–models - Toy Truck Lines, Inc.
MIDDLE BURNER - Health care products - East Earth Herb Inc.
MIDDLE EARTH - Posters - Fairfax Prints Ltd.
MIDDLE EAST - Cigarettes - General Cigar Co., Inc.
MIDDLE EAST LITERATURE - Publisher's imprints - Syracuse University Press
MIDDLE WEIGHT '150' - Nail care products - Opi Products, Inc.
MIDDLEAF - Chocolate candy - Maxfield Candy Co.
MIDDLEBROOK - Floor coverings–carpet and rugs - Karastan-Bigelow Inc.
MIDDLEBURY - Clocks ☆ - General Time Corp. (Westclox/Seth Thomas Div.)
MIDDLEBURY COLLEGE PRESS - Publisher's imprints - University Press of New England
MIDDLEFIELD - Manufactured homes - Redman Industries, Inc.
MIDDLEFIELD MIX - Milk–canned or powdered - Middlefield Holding Co.
MIDDLELINE - Food products - Whipple Co.
MIDDLESEX - Artists' materials ☆ - Hunt Manufacturing Co.
MIDDLESEX - Food products ☆ - Whipple Co.
MIDDLETON - Clocks - General Time Corp. (Westclox/Seth Thomas Div.)
MIDDLETON - Tobacco products - John Middleton Inc.
MIDDLETON 5 - Tobacco products - John Middleton Inc.
MIDDLETON PLACE - Floor coverings - Mannington Resilient Floors
MIDDLETON PLACE - Wainscotting - Georgia-Pacific Corp.
MIDDLETON'S - Cigars - JMTM, Inc.
MIDDLETOWNER'S - Footwear–women's - Middletown Footwear Inc.
MIDEL - Crackers - American Natural Snacks
MIDELWATE - Lighting fixtures - Acme-Lite Manufacturing Co.
MIDERN - Computer peripheral equipment - Midern Computer Inc.
MIDEX - Computer peripheral equipment - Steinberg/Jones Corp.
MIDFLOC - Chemical preparations - Rochester Midland Corp.
MIDGARD PRESS - Publisher's imprints - Westport Publishers Inc. (Media Div.)
MIDGE - Dolls - Mattel, Inc.
MIDGEE - Flowers, plants, and seeds - Monrovia Nursery Co.
MIDGEES - Candy - Tootsie Roll Industries, Inc.
MIDGET - Bicycles - Schwinn Cycling & Fitness Inc.
MIDGET - Brooms - Hamburg Broom Works Inc.
MIDGET - Cash boxes - Merriam Manufacturing Co. Inc.
MIDGET - Labeling machinery ☆ - Litton Industrial Automation Systems
MIDGET - Paints - Zynolyte Products Co.
MIDGET - Pencil sharpeners ☆ - Empire Berol USA
MIDGET - Stoves–wood-burning - Fatsco
MIDGET - Toys–models ☆ - Sterling Motor Cars
MIDGET - Ventilation equipment - Midget Louver Co.
MIDGET - Washboards - National Washboard Co.
MIDGET MEMO - Stationery ☆ - Mead Corp.
MIDGET RAILWAY - Toys–trains - Montgomery Schoolhouse
MIDGET RIVER RUNT SPOOK - Sporting goods - James Heddon's Sons
MIDGET ROLLAWAY - Computer-printer stands - Atlantic Furniture Systems
MIDGET SHADE - Lighting fixtures - Swivelier Co. Inc.
MIDGETOY - Toys - Midgetoy
MIDGETS - Cigars ☆ - Phillies Cigar Co.
MIDGETS - Toys - Montgomery Schoolhouse
MIDGI - Combs - Comare Corp.
MIDGITROL - Valves - ITT Corp.
MIDI - Automotive parts and accessories - Littelfuse, Inc.
MIDI - Food products - Cinnamon Bakery
MIDI - Golfing equipment - Besco USA
MIDI - Lighting fixtures - Meyda Tiffany Inc.
MIDI BASS WORKS - Computer software - Electronic Courseware Systems Inc.
MIDI BEACON - Audio equipment ☆ - Russ Jones Marketing
MIDI COMMANDER - Musical instrument accessories - Meico Electronics
MIDI-CON - Audio equipment - Meico Electronics
MIDI D - Water purification systems - Pure Water Inc.
MIDI JAZZ IMPROVISATION - Computer software - Electronic Courseware Systems Inc.
MIDI KIT - Computer software - Midisoft Corp.
MIDI-LARM - Clocks ☆ - General Time Corp. (Westclox/Seth Thomas Div.)
MIDI MAGIC - Computer software ☆ - Q-R-S Music Rolls Inc.
MIDI MASTER - Computer peripheral equipment - Peavey Electronics Corp.
MIDI MATE - Computer peripheral equipment - Media Vision Technology Inc.

MIDI MINUS ONE - Recording label ☆ - MMO Music Group Inc.
MIDI MOTOR - Audio equipment - Midimotor, Inc.
MIDI PATCHER - Musical instrument accessories - 360 Systems
MIDI RECORDING STUDIO - Computer software - Dr. T's Music Software Inc.
MIDI SCREEN SAVER - Computer software - Electronic Courseware Systems Inc.
MIDI STEP - Audio equipment ☆ - Russ Jones Marketing
MIDI STILL - Water purification systems - Pure Water Inc.
MIDI TRANSPORT - Computer software ☆ - Passport Designs Inc.
MIDICEL - Pharmaceutical preparations ☆ - Parke-Davis
MIDIM - Electronic equipment - Dinsmore Instrument Co.
MIDIMAN - Electronics equipment - Midiman
MIDIRON - Golfing equipment - Besco USA
MIDITZER - Musical instruments - Teac America, Inc.
MIDJIT CRAWLER - Fishing lures - Creme Lure Co.
MIDKNIGHT BLUE - Flowers, plants, and seeds - Monrovia Nursery Co.
MIDLAND - Agricultural products - Midland Seeds, Inc.
MIDLAND - Automotive parts and accessories - Echlin Inc.
MIDLAND - Bicycles - Western Auto Supply Co.
MIDLAND - Communications equipment–mobile - Midland International Corp.
MIDLAND - Dishes–china - Midland Enterprises Inc.
MIDLAND - Liquid crystal displays - Midland Manufacturing Corp.
MIDLAND - Medical apparatus - Sammons Preston
MIDLAND - Pennants - Flags International Inc.
MIDLAND BOOKS - Publisher's imprint - Indiana University Press
MIDLAND FLYER - Bicycles - Western Auto Supply Co.
MIDLIFE CRISIS - Apparel and accessories - Papel Freelance, Inc.
MIDLINE - Rifles - Redfield Co.
MIDLINE PADS - Notebooks and notepads - Pen-Tab Industries
MIDNIGHT - Artists' materials - M. Grumbacher Inc.
MIDNIGHT - Audio equipment - Sanyo Fisher (USA) Corp.
MIDNIGHT - Eye shadow ☆ - Coty Inc.
MIDNIGHT - Floor coverings–carpet and rugs - Colonial Mills Inc.
MIDNIGHT - Mushrooms - Emil Lerch Inc.
MIDNIGHT - Prophylactics - Ansell Inc. (Personal Products Div.)
MIDNIGHT - Tableware–earthenware ☆ - Denby USA Limited
MIDNIGHT - Tobacco–chewing or smoking - Sterling Tobacco Co.
MIDNIGHT BLOSSOMS - Dinnerware–glass - Lenox, Inc.
MIDNIGHT BLUE - Cosmetics - Lancome
MIDNIGHT BLUES - Microphones - Audio-Technica U.S., Inc.
MIDNIGHT CAT - Toys–stuffed - Russ Berrie and Co., Inc.
MIDNIGHT CLIPPER - Watches - Bulova Corp.
MIDNIGHT CONTESSA - Dishes–china ☆ - Gorham Inc.
MIDNIGHT COOKIES & CREAM - Ice cream - Haagen-Dazs Brands, Inc.
MIDNIGHT EXPRESS - Travelware - Action Travelware
MIDNIGHT FLASHER - Games - Universal Manufacturing Co., Inc.
MIDNIGHT FLYER - Toys–trains ☆ - Lionel Trains Inc.
MIDNIGHT FRIGHT - Publisher's imprints - Troll Associates, Inc.
MIDNIGHT FROLIC - Skin care products - Sterling Winthrop Inc.
MIDNIGHT GALA - Dolls - Mattel, Inc.
MIDNIGHT GLITTER - Dolls - Mattel, Inc.
MIDNIGHT HORSEMAN - Shoes - Cypress Shoes
MIDNIGHT HOUR - Underwear and nightwear - Wal-Mart Stores Inc.
MIDNIGHT LACE - Hair care products ☆ - Nutrine Ltd.
MIDNIGHT MADNESS - Novelty items - Imagineering Inc.
MIDNIGHT MAGIC - Jewelry ☆ - Hirsch Speidel Inc.
MIDNIGHT MAGIC - Mulch - H. Hafner & Sons Inc.
MIDNIGHT MARBLE - Pens - Pentel of America, Ltd.
MIDNIGHT MOOD - Glassware–household ☆ - Lenox Crystal, Inc.
MIDNIGHT NETWORKS - Computer software - Midnight Networks Inc.
MIDNIGHT PEARL - Faucets ☆ - Chicago Faucet Co.
MIDNIGHT RED SPUR - Trees - Columbia Basin Nursery
MIDNIGHT RESCUE! - Computer software - The Learning Co., Inc.
MIDNIGHT ROSE - Dishes–china ☆ - Pickard Inc.
MIDNIGHT RUN - Apparel - Anjali Imports Inc.
MIDNIGHT RUN - Video production - Konami (America) Inc.
MIDNIGHT SHADOWS - Furniture - O'Sullivan Industries, Inc.
MIDNIGHT SHIMMER - Cosmetics - Lancome
MIDNIGHT SPECIAL - Fishing tackle - Strike King Lure Co.
MIDNIGHT SPECIAL - Toys - Duncan Toys Co.
MIDNIGHT SPECIALTIES - Teas–herbal - Josephine Inc.
MIDNIGHT STAR - Rings–jewelry - Artcarved Inc.
MIDNIGHT STAR - Watches - Bulova Corp.
MIDNIGHT STYLE DESIGNS - T-shirts–men's - Timothy Wayne McCullough
MIDNIGHT SUN - Bedding–linen - Dan River Inc.
MIDNIGHT SUN - Food products ☆ - Liberty Richter Inc.

☆ = Now out of production

MIDNIGHT SUN - Generators—gas - Lewis M. Fraas
MIDNIGHT SUN - Hair care products ☆ - Clairol Inc.
MIDNIGHT SUN - Juices - B. Westergaard & Co. Inc.
MIDNIGHT SUN - Recording label - Phillips Brothers Investments
MIDNIGHT SUN - Tableware—china - Pfaltzgraff Investment Co.
MIDNIGHT SURFER - Sporting goods - Coming Attractions
MIDNIGHT TAPESTRY - Dinnerware ☆ - Corning Inc.
MIDNIGHT TOUCH - Floor coverings—carpet and rugs - Lees Carpets
MIDNIGHT WHITE - Pet products - Double K Industries, Inc.
MIDNITE - Glassware—household ☆ - Lotus Glass Co.
MIDNITE-BLU - Jewelry—precious - David Dattner, Inc.
MIDNITE LACE - Hair care products - Andre Fantasies Inc.
MIDNITE SNACK - Apparel—women's - Knucklehead Inc.
MIDOCS - Communications equipment—microwave - McDonnell Douglas Corp.
MIDOL - Pharmaceutical preparations - Bayer Corp. (Consumer Care Div.)
MIDORI - Bedding—linen - Dan River Inc.
MIDORI - Liquors - Suntory International Corp.
MIDPA - Computer software - Frieda C. Sharon
MIDPOINT - Computer software - Midcore Software, Inc.
MIDRIFF - Girdles - Bonwit Teller & Co.
MIDRIN - Pharmaceutical preparations - Carnick Laboratories Inc.
MIDSHIP - Jackets ☆ - Fox Point Sportswear Inc.
MIDSHIPMAN - Clocks - Maximum Inc.
MIDSHIPMAN - Watches - Bulova Corp.
MIDSONG INTERNATIONAL - Recording label - MCA Universal Studios
MIDSTATES - Wire products - Mid-States Wire
MIDSUMMER - Giftware - Sasaki
MIDSUMMER - Tableware—china ☆ - Lenox, Inc.
MIDSUMMER - Wallpaper ☆ - Motif Designs, Inc.
MIDSUMMER DREAM - Bedding—linen - Dan River Inc.
MIDSUMMER DREAM - Floor coverings—carpet and rugs - Capel, Inc.
MIDSUMMER DREAM - Health care products ☆ - Avon Products, Inc.
MIDSUMMER NIGHT SWING - Apparel and accessories - Lincoln Center for the Performing Arts, Inc.
MIDSUMMER'S NIGHT DREAM - Figurines ☆ - Dave Grossman Creations Inc.
MIDTEE - T-shirts—women's - Bomark Group Inc.
MIDTOWN - Clocks - General Time Corp. (Westclox/Seth Thomas Div.)
MIDTOWN - Floor coverings—carpet and rugs - Coronet Carpets Inc.
MIDTOWN - Thread - Threads USA Div.
MIDULLA VINEYARDS - Wines - Fruit Wines of Florida Inc.
MIDUS - Diagnostic apparatus - Urometrics, Inc.
MIDWAY - Games - Avalon Hill Game Co.
MIDWAY - Lighting fixtures - Frank Lloyd Wright Foundation
MIDWAY - Playing cards - United States Playing Card Co.
MIDWAY - Publisher's imprints - University of Chicago Press
MIDWAY - Underwear and nightwear - Jockey International, Inc.
MIDWAY CAMPAIGN - Games ☆ - Avalon Hill Game Co.
MIDWAY COUTURE - Hair care products - Wella Corp. (Consumer Products Div.)
MIDWAY HOTELS - Hotels and motels - Hummert Management Group Inc.
MIDWAY MOTOR LODGE - See MIDWAY HOTELS
MIDWAY SPORTS EXCLUSIVE - Game machines - Midway Manufacturing Co.
MIDWEST - Apparel and accessories - Midwest Embroidery, Inc.
MIDWEST - Awnings—plastic - Fox Point Sportswear Inc.
MIDWEST - Beverages—alcohol - Midwest Grain Products Inc.
MIDWEST - Electrical equipment - General Electric Co.
MIDWEST - Fruits and vegetables - Midwest Blueberry Farms
MIDWEST FARMS - Dairy products - Schepps-Foremost, Inc.
MIDWEST LACQUER MULTIFLEX - Paints - Midwest Lacquer Manufacturing Co.
MIDWEST MARKETING, INC. - Advertising agencies - Midwest Marketing, Inc.
MIDWEST-MIGHTY BEAM - Automotive parts and accessories - Midwest Manufacturing Co.
MIDWEST OF CANNON FALLS - Giftware - Midwest of Cannon Falls Inc.
MIDWEST PRAIRIE CANDLES - Candles - Midwest Prairie, Ltd.
MIDWEST PRIDE - Meat products—beef - J & B Wholesalers Distributing
MIDWEST RECORDS - Recording label - Midwest
MIDWEST SUPREME - Grass seed - Kellogg Inc.
MIDWEST TRADERS - Watches - Venture Stores, Inc.
MIDWEST VOLLEYBALL WAREHOUSE - Apparel and accessories - Midwest Volleyball Warehouse, Inc.
MIDWESTERN - Thread ☆ - Perfect Thread Co. Inc.
MIDWINTER - Bedding—linen - Dan River Inc.
MIDWINTER - Dinnerware—glass ☆ - Waterford Wedgwood USA, Inc.
MIDWOOD - Golfing equipment - Besco USA
MIDWOOD - Wood products ☆ - Anco Wood Specialties Inc.

M.I.E. MAINER IN EXILE - Stationery - Maine Exile Products
MIELE CLASSIC - Ovens—convection - Miele Appliances, Inc.
MIENNE OF CALIFORNIA - Hair accessories - Elwin Manufacturing Co. Inc.
MIFA - Pens ☆ - Lyon
MIFER - Tools—woodworking ☆ - Anglo American Enterprises Corp.
MIFF - Recording label - Jazz Composer's Orchestra Association Inc.
MIFINE - Skin care products - Michel Skin Care Enterprises Inc.
MIFLEX - Pharmaceutical preparations - Misemer Pharmaceuticals Inc.
MIFLIN'S CHOICE CAMEROON - Cigars - M. Marsh & Son
MIG - Computer software - Laila J. Rubstein
MIG PILOT - Vodka - Clearly Vermont Products, Inc.
MIGDAL - Cheese - Peacock Foods Inc.
MIGERGOT - Health care products - G and W Laboratories Inc.
MIGHTI-RIB - Siding—metal - Alcan Aluminum Corp. Alcan Building Products Div.
MIGHTI-SCRUBB - Soap - Georgia-Pacific Corp.
MIGHTIEST MULTI - Health care products - Above All Health Inc.
MIGHTY - Guns - Unitron Industries, Inc.
MIGHTY - Tools—power-driven - Mighty Industrial, Inc.
MIGHTY ADVENTURE BUGGY - Toys - Tonka Corp.
MIGHTY ANT - Computer software - Miaco Corp.
MIGHTY ATLAS - Jacks—hydraulic - Cardinal American Corp.
MIGHTY BALL - Balls ☆ - Playing Mantis
MIGHTY BITE - Candy - Nabisco Holdings Corp.
MIGHTY BITE - Candy - Phoenix Confections Inc.
MIGHTY BOOST - Automotive parts and accessories - Coleman Cable Systems, Inc.
MIGHTY BOSS - Tool belts - Portable Products, Inc.
MIGHTY BOX - Boxes—corrugated paperboard - Whitmor Manufacturing Co. Inc.
MIGHTY BOX - Electrical equipment - Bowers Manufacturing Corp.
MIGHTY BOXER - Apparel—women's - May Department Stores Co.
MIGHTY BRA, THE - Bathing suits - Beach Patrol, Inc.
MIGHTY BRITE II - Rechargeable lights ☆ - Jameson Home Products Inc.
MIGHTY BUBBLE - Chewing gum - Philadelphia Chewing Gum Corp.
MIGHTY CART - Plastic cart - Spectrum International, Inc.
MIGHTY CARTOON HEROES - Books—comic - Barry Alan Kraus
MIGHTY CAT - Pet products - Mid-Florida Mining Co.
MIGHTY CHARACTERS - Apparel—children's - Haddad Apparel Group Ltd.
MIGHTY CLUB - Luggage - Travelers Club Luggage Inc.
MIGHTY DOG - Dog food - Nestle USA
MIGHTY DROP - Pharmaceutical preparations ☆ - Apex Medical Corp.
MIGHTY DUCKS - Apparel and accessories - Walt Disney Co.
MIGHTY FIGHTERS OF THE FUTURE - Toys - Those Characters from Cleveland, Inc.
MIGHTY GOOD PRODUCTS BAKED WITH PRIDE - Breads - H and S Bakery Inc.
MIGHTY GREEN - Food processors - White Consolidated Industries, Inc.
MIGHTY GREENS - Vitamins and nutritional supplements - Pines International, Inc.
MIGHTY GRIP - Floor coverings - Superior Manufacturing Group/Notrax Floor Matting
MIGHTY GRIP - Vises - Woodcraft Manufacturing Co.
MIGHTY GRIPPER - Jars—glass - Compac Industries Inc.
MIGHTY HERO - Toys - Ben Cooper Inc.
MIGHTY ICE - Medical apparatus - Dura*Kold Corp.
MIGHTY JOE - Garden equipment - Seymour Manufacturing Co.,Inc.
MIGHTY LASH - Cosmetics - Arthur Matney Co., Inc.
MIGHTY LIGHTS - Toys - Steven Manufacturing Co.
MIGHTY LITE - Fish—fresh or frozen - Frionor USA Inc.
MIGHTY LITE - Ladders—metal - Werner Co.
MIGHTY-LITE - Lamps—desk - Mobilite-Spartus
MIGHTY-LITE - Wrenches ☆ - Curtis Toledo Inc.
MIGHTY LOCK - Collars and leashes - Pets R Us
MIGHTY-MAC - Apparel and accessories - Mighty-Mac
MIGHTY-MAC - Apparel—children's - Haddad Apparel Group Ltd.
MIGHTY MAC - Exercising equipment - McCauley Metal Products Div.
MIGHTY MAC - Garden equipment - Mackissic Inc.
MIGHTY MAC - Lighting fixtures ☆ - Kenall Manufacturing Co.
MIGHTY MAC - Socks - Sockyard Co.
MIGHTY MAC - Toys—trains ☆ - Life-Like Products Inc.
MIGHTY MACK - Racks - Crawford Products Inc.
MIGHTY MAGNOR - Books—comic - Malibu Comics Entertainment, Inc.
MIGHTY MALTS - Candy - New England Confectionery Co.
MIGHTY MALTS - Candy ☆ - Haviland Candy Inc.
MIGHTY MALTS PUMPKIN PALS - Candy - Borden, Inc.

☆ = Now out of production

MIGHTY-MARK - Office supplies - Faber-Castell Corp.
MIGHTY MATCH - Lighters - Scripto-Tokai Corp.
MIGHTY MATE - Cleaning supplies ☆ - American Textile Products Co.
MIGHTY MATE - Pumps - Zoeller Co.
MIGHTY MATES - Blouses–women's - May Department Stores Co.
MIGHTY MAULERS - Toys - Mattel, Inc.
MIGHTY MAX - Heaters–swimming pool - Teledyne Industries Inc.
MIGHTY MAX - Motor vehicles–automobiles - Mitsubishi Motor Sales of America Inc.
MIGHTY-MAX PLUS - Aquariums–household - Aqua Plex Products Inc.
MIGHTY MEAL - Food products - Ogden Services Corp.
MIGHTY METAL - Furniture - Woodmate Corp.
MIGHTY MIDGET - Pumps–water - California Flexrake Corp.
MIGHTY MIKE - Electronic equipment - Hamilton Electronics Corp.
MIGHTY MIKEY - Chemical preparations - Oppenheimer Environmental Co., Inc.
MIGHTY MIND CHALLENGER - Games - Leisure Learning Products
MIGHTY MIND TELLS TIME - Games - Leisure Learning Products
MIGHTY MINERALS - Pet products - Polly's Pleasures
MIGHTY MINI - Hardware - Products Finishing Corp.
MIGHTY MINI - Oil machinery - Abanaki Corp.
MIGHTY-MINI - Vacuum cleaners and accessories - Shop Vac Corp.
MIGHTY MINS - Vitamins and nutritional supplements - Natural Organics, Inc.
MIGHTY MINT - Candy ☆ - Haviland Candy Inc.
MIGHTY MINTS - Candy - New England Confectionery Co.
MIGHTY-MITE - Air conditioning equipment - Welbilt Appliances Inc.
MIGHTY-MITE - Bicycles - Columbia Manufacturing Inc.
MIGHTY-MITE - Bicycles - Graber Products, Inc.
MIGHTY MITE - Dryers–hair ☆ - Philips Electronics North America Corp.
MIGHTY MITE - Guitars - Westheimer Corp.
MIGHTY MITE - Hockey equipment - Sun Hockey, Inc.
MIGHTY MITE - Lamps - Leen & Associates, Inc.
MIGHTY-MITE - Magnetic catches - H.B. Ives
MIGHTY MITE - Plumbing fixtures–metal - Moen Inc.
MIGHTY MITE - Saws–chain ☆ - Desa International, Inc.
MIGHTY MITE - Vacuum cleaners and accessories - The Eureka Co.
MIGHTY MITE II - Vacuum cleaners and accessories - The Eureka Co.
MIGHTY MIX - Concrete–ready-mix - Granite City Ready Mix Inc.
MIGHTY MIXER - Audio equipment - Marketing Insights, Inc.-Frank Luppino Jr., and Associates
MIGHTY MO - Staplers - Arrow Fastener Co. Inc.
MIGHTY MOD - Computer peripheral equipment - Passive Devices, Inc.
MIGHTY MOE - Toys–models ☆ - Estes Industries
MIGHTY MOLE - Tools–boring - Mclaughlin Manufacturing Co.
MIGHTY MOO - Yogurt - Stonyfield Farm, Inc.
MIGHTY MOP - Mops ☆ - Suburbanite Industries
MIGHTY MORPHIN POWER RANGERS - Footwear–children's - S. Goldberg and Co. Inc.
MIGHTY MORPHIN POWER RANGERS - Novelty items - Saban Entertainment, Inc.
MIGHTY MORPHIN POWER RANGERS - Toothbrushes - Colgate-Palmolive Co.
MIGHTY MORPHIN POWER RANGERS - Toys - Bandai America Inc.
MIGHTY MOS - Toys - Playskool, Inc.
MIGHTY MO'S - Toys–stuffed ☆ - CBS Toys
MIGHTY-MOUNT - Tape–adhesive - Mitten Designer Letters
MIGHTY MOUSE - Apparel and accessories - Viacom International Inc.
MIGHTY MOUSE - Cheese - Land O'Lakes Inc.
MIGHTY MOUSE - Juices–frozen - Vroman Foods Inc.
MIGHTY MOUSE - Vitamins and nutritional supplements ☆ - ICN Pharmaceuticals Inc.
MIGHTY MOVER - Motor vehicles - Louis Demongin
MIGHTY MOVER FURNITURE SLIDERS - Office supplies - Master Caster Co.
MIGHTY MOVERS - Toys - ERTL Co., Inc.
MIGHTY MUGS - Dinnerware–glass - Prolon Dinnerware
MIGHTY MULE - Toys - Tonka Corp.
MIGHTY OAK - Cutlery - Imperial Schrade Corp.
MIGHTY O.J. - Juice extracting devices - Metrokane
MIGHTY ONE - Vitamins and nutritional supplements - Trulife Inc.
MIGHTY PAC - Motor vehicle parts and accessories - Bob Bartlett & Associates Inc.
MIGHTY PINE - Cleaning preparations - Moran Holding Co., Inc.
MIGHTY PINE - Cleaning preparations–household - Blue Cross Laboratories Inc.
MIGHTY PITCHER - Cooking equipment–household ☆ - Nordic Ware
MIGHTY PRESS - Machine parts - Stahls' Inc.

MIGHTY PURE - Water purification systems - Atlantic Ultraviolet Corp.
MIGHTY RAMP - Ramps ☆ - Guardian Products Inc.
MIGHTY REST - Beds–metal - Raye's, Inc. (Wheelchairs of Kansas)
MIGHTY RIGS - Toys–automobiles - Mattel, Inc.
MIGHTY ROBOTS - Toys - Tonka Corp.
MIGHTY SIZZLER - Cooking equipment–household - Nordic Ware
MIGHTY SOFT - Photographic equipment - Eastman Kodak Co.
MIGHTY SONIC - Horns–motor vehicle - Falcon Safety Products, Inc.
MIGHTY SORTER - File folders - Newell Office Products
MIGHTY SOUL SONIC - Recording label - Mark Carvel Enterprises Inc.
MIGHTY SOY - Food products - Soy Power Co. Inc.
MIGHTY SWEATS - Apparel–women's - May Department Stores Co.
MIGHTY T - Apparel–women's - May Department Stores Co.
MIGHTY TACKY - Glue–household or industrial - Activa Products Inc.
MIGHTY TIDY - Garbage disposal units–household - Werlor, Inc.
MIGHTY TIGER - Recording label - Chase Music Group
MIGHTY-TITE - Tools–hand-operated - Compressor Tech, Inc.
MIGHTY TONKA - Toys - Tonka Corp.
MIGHTY TOUGH - Footwear - Iron Age Corp.
MIGHTY TOUGH RUGGED LEATHER BOOTS - Boots - Iron Age Corp.
MIGHTY TUFF - Boxes - Flambeau Products Corp.
MIGHTY VERBS - Electronic equipment ☆ - Texas Instruments Inc.
MIGHTY-VITE - Pharmaceutical preparations - Schein Pharmaceutical Inc.
MIGHTY WASH - Detergents - Edwards Creative Products, Inc.
MIGHTY WHITE - Paints - Colony Paints Div.
MIGHTY WINGS - Meat products–poultry - Mcdonald's Corp.
MIGHTY WIPE - Fabrics - Freudenberg Nonwovens Apparel Division
MIGHTYBEE - Pollen extracts ☆ - Glorybee Food Inc.
MIGHTYLITES - Knee pads - Portable Products, Inc.
MIGHTYMAK - Laboratory apparatus - U.S. Thin Film Products Inc.
MIGHTYMINI - Antennas - Antenna Co.
MIGHTYS - Toys - Tonka Corp.
MIGIS - Pharmaceutical preparations - Tanox Biosystems Inc.
MIGMASTER - Electric arc welders - Esab Welding & Cutting Products
MIGNON - Dinnerware–glass - Franciscan by Johnson Brothers, USA, Inc.
MIGNON CRAQUELLE - Audio equipment ☆ - Telequest Inc.
MIGNONETTE - Footwear - Mignonette Co.
MIGOTIN - Pharmaceutical preparations ☆ - U.S. Ethicals Inc.
MIGRACARE - Vitamins and nutritional supplements - Enzymatic Therapy, Inc.
MIGRACIN - Health care products ☆ - Nature's Herbs
MIGRAGARD - Vitamins and nutritional supplements - Solaray
MIGRAIDE - Pharmaceutical preparations - Boericke & Tafel
MIGRAINEX - Pharmaceutical preparations - Buffington
MIGRAINEX - Pharmaceutical preparations - Otis Clapp & Son Inc.
MIGRAINOSAN - Pharmaceutical preparations ☆ - Bioforce of America Ltd.
MIGRAL - Pharmaceutical preparations ☆ - Burroughs Wellcome Co.
MIGRANOL - See **MIGRAINEX**
MIGRATING CORROSION INHIBITORS - Rustproofing compounds - Cortec Corp.
MIGRATION - Wines - St. Helena Wine Co., Inc.
MIGRELIEF - Analgesics - Quantum, Inc.
MIGREXX - Health care products - Pharma Botanixx
MIGTOOL - Computer software - Delta Microsystems, Inc.
MIGUEL ANGEL - Footwear - Larry's Standard Brand Shoes, Inc.
MIGUEL TORRES - Wines - Seagram's Chateau & Estate Wines Co.
MIGUEL'S - Tortillas - Miguel's Stowe-Away
MIGUEL'S GREEN CHILE - Chili sauce - Miguel's Stowe-Away
MIGUEL'S STOWE-AWAY - Snack foods - Miguel's Stowe-Away
MIH - Jewelry - M.J. Harrington & Co., Inc.
MIHANG - Apparel–women's - Noah Enterprises, Ltd.
MIHELS - Food products - Chateau Food Products Inc.
MII - Jewelery - Mariloff International Inc.
MIJIT - Lighting fixtures - Acme-Lite Manufacturing Co.
MIKA - Apparel–women's - Carter Hawley Hale Stores Inc.
MIKADO - Chairs–wood ☆ - Krueger International, Inc.
MIKADO - Dinnerware–glass ☆ - Royal China & Porcelain Companies Inc.
MIKADO - Furniture ☆ - Bassett Furniture Industries, Inc.
MIKADO - Games ☆ - Milton Bradley Co.
MIKADO - Hardware ☆ - Amerock Corp.
MIKADO - Scuba diving equipment - Dacor Corp.
MIKADO - Yarn - Henry's Attic
MIKAFILM - Office supplies - Imagemaker Films Inc.
MIKAGE - Floor coverings - Nittoh Tile Corp.
MIKASA - Dishes–china - Mikasa Co.
MIKASA - Sporting goods - Mikasa Sports
MIKASA FAMILY - Balls - Mikasa Sports

☆ = Now out of production

MIKASA MAN - Balls - Mikasa Sports
MIKASA WOMAN - Balls - Mikasa Sports
MIKASOME - Pharmaceutical preparations - Vestar, Inc.
MIKAWAYA - Ice cream - Mikawaya, Inc.
MIKE - Frames–eyeglass - Rozin Optical Export Corp.
MIKE - Frames–eyeglass - U.S. Optical Frame Co.
MIKE - Medical apparatus - Gaumard Scientific Co., Inc.
MIKE - Twine - Blue Mountain Industries, Inc.
MIKE & IKE - Candy - Just Born Inc.
MIKE BENET FORMALS - Apparel–women's - Mike Benet Formals
MIKE CORBIN CARE - Cleaning preparations - Corbin Pacific, Inc.
MIKE DANGER - Apparel and accessories - Big Entertainment, Inc.
MIKE DITKA'S - Pork - L & L Packing Co.
MIKE DOUGLAS - Apparel–men's ☆ - Salant/Manhattan Industries
MIKE HUNT'S - Apparel and accessories - Rhododendron Corp.
MIKE 'N MATT'S - Department stores - Hidden Treasures, Inc.
MIKE ROSE - Food products - Mike Rose Foods Inc.
MIKE SCHMIDT - Sporting goods ☆ - Franklin Sports, Inc.
MIKE-SELL'S - Potato chips - Mike-Sell's Inc.
MIKE STERNBERG'S BIG CITY REDS - Meat products - Good Food Co.
MIKELMAN - Dolls - Michael Alexander
MIKES - Food products - Tops Meat Co. Inc.
MIKE'S MOJO - Aprons - Crawfish Connection
MIKE'S ORIGINAL - Ice cream cones - Melanie Lane Farms, Inc.
MIKEY - Apparel–children's - Sara's Prints, Inc.
MIKEY MOUSE - Toys–stuffed - Russ Berrie and Co., Inc.
MIKHA MELON LIQUER - Liquors - Sazerac Co. Inc.
MIKI WALKS - Dolls - Uneeda Doll Co., Inc.
MIKIMOTO - Jewelry - Mikimoto America Co. Ltd.
MIKKI - Pet products - Classic Products
MIKKI MONKEY - Toys–stuffed ☆ - Dakin Inc.
MIKKO IMAGE - Apparel and accessories - Mikko Image, Inc.
MIKKO MUSICAL BEAR - Toys–stuffed - Dakin Inc.
MIKO - Dolls - Mattel, Inc.
MIKO - Meats–luncheon - Miko Meat Corp.
MIKOHN - Electronics equipment - Mikohn, Inc.
MIKRO-ACM - Machinery - Hosokawa Micron International Inc.
MIKRO-BANTAM - Machinery - Hosokawa Micron International Inc.
MIKRO-PULSAIRE - Vacuum cleaners and accessories–commercial - Hosokawa Micron International Inc.
MIKRO TIP - Brushes–paint - Hobsco Inc.
MIKRO TIP - Brushes–paint - Wm. K. Walthers Inc.
MIKROKOSMIC - Recording label - Jazz Composer's Orchestra Association Inc.
MIKRON - Filters–fuel ☆ - Bechik Products Inc.
MIKROPAN - Pet products ☆ - Sera Aquaristik USA Inc.
MIL - Machinery - Svedala Industries, Inc.
MIL-CARB - Chemical preparations - Baker Hughes Inc.
MIL-CARB - Hardware - Wrought Washer Manufacturing, Inc.
MIL-COMM - Lubricants - Mil-Comm Products Co., Inc.
MIL-DEW'NT - Stain removers ☆ - Elcal Enterprises Ltd.
MIL-DU-GAS - Chemical preparations - Mil-Du-Gas Co.
MIL-E-QUAL - Cables - Conxall Inc.
MIL-KIL - Paint additive - Pro Power, Inc.
MIL-KLEAN - Stain removers ☆ - Klean-Strip
MIL-NYMO - Thread - Belding Heminway Co. Inc.
MIL-NYMO-TEE - Thread - Belding Heminway Co. Inc.
MIL-TEK - Stain remover - Pro Power, Inc.
MIL-X - Housewares ☆ - Zehrung Corp.
MILA - Electrical feeding devices for the handicapped ☆ - Mila Medical
MILA - Veterinary pharmaceutical preparations - Mila International, Inc.
MILA ONE-STEP - Medical apparatus - Mila Medical
MILA PAOLI - Footwear - Marshalls, Inc.
MILA SCHON BIJOUX - Belts, handbags, jewelry, scarves, etc. - Italtrade
MILACATH - Veterinary nutritional supplements - Mila International, Inc.
MILADY - Apparel–women's - Milady Brassiere & Corset Co., Inc.
MILADY - Golfing equipment - Ram Golf Corp.
MILADY - Watches - Bulova Corp.
MILADY TOFFEES - Candy ☆ - R.L. Albert & Son, Inc.
MILADY'S - Housewares ☆ - Schwarz Bros. Plastics
MILAGRO - Recording label ☆ - Ray Lawrence Ltd.
MILAMO - Yarn ☆ - Melrose Yarn Co. Inc.
MILAN - Cabinets - Marsh Furniture Co.
MILAN - Cabinets - H.J. Scheirich Co.
MILAN - Compact discs–prerecorded - Milan Entertainment, Inc.
MILAN - Cribs–wood ☆ - Welsh Co.

MILAN - Floor coverings–carpet and rugs ☆ - Kelly Group Inc.
MILAN - Floor coverings–carpet and rugs ☆ - Regal Rugs Inc.
MILAN - Recording label - Milan America Inc.
MILAN - Watches - M.Z. Berger & Co. Inc.
MILAN CLASSIC - Containers–plastic - Holiday Housewares, Inc.
MILAN COLLEZIONE - Skin care products - Robert Sindlinger
MILANESE - Fabrics ☆ - Mohawk Fabric Co. Inc.
MILANI - Cosmetics - Nina International, Inc.
MILANI - Food products - Alberto-Culver Co.
MILANI - Food products - Precision Foods, Inc.
MILANI 1890 - Vegetable sauces - Alberto-Culver Co.
MILANI MATCHABLES - Cosmetics ☆ - Nina International, Inc.
MILANO - Apparel and accessories - Crystal Brands Inc.
MILANO - Artists' materials ☆ - Artisan House Inc.
MILANO - Boats–motor ☆ - Larson Boat Div.
MILANO - Cabinets - Kabom Kitchen & Bath Manufacturing
MILANO - Cabinets - Legeis Corp.
MILANO - Cabinets - Major Line Products Co. Inc.
MILANO - Cabinets ☆ - Decora
MILANO - Cookies - Pepperidge Farm Inc.
MILANO - Darts and dart games ☆ - Dart Mart Inc.
MILANO - Dishes–china - Pasmantier Co. Inc.
MILANO - Dryers–hair - Nino Originals
MILANO - Flatware - W.M.F. of America Inc.
MILANO - Floor coverings - Mannington Resilient Floors
MILANO - Floor coverings–carpet and rugs - Alexander Smith Carpets
MILANO - Furniture ☆ - Hammary Furniture Co. Inc.
MILANO - Furniture ☆ - Singer Furniture Co.
MILANO - Furniture ☆ - Stanley Furniture Co. Inc.
MILANO - Furniture ☆ - Universal Flooring
MILANO - Giftware - Seymour Mann Inc.
MILANO - Glassware–household - Villeroy and Boch Tableware Ltd.
MILANO - Housewares - Eagle Affiliates, Inc.
MILANO - Jewelry ☆ - Donald Bruce & Co.
MILANO - Kitchenware–earthenware ☆ - Le Creuset of America, Inc.
MILANO - Motor vehicles–automobiles ☆ - Alfa Romeo Distributors of North America
MILANO - Shampoos - S.C. Johnson & Son, Inc.
MILANO - Tiles–ceramic ☆ - American Olean Tile Co.
MILANO - Toys - Peg Perego USA Inc.
MILANO - Wallpaper - Fidelity Industries, Inc.
MILANO - Whirlpools - Jacuzzi Inc.
MILANO - Wines - Milano Winery
MILANO ARGENTO - Motor vehicles–automobiles ☆ - Alfa Romeo Distributors of North America
MILANO DESIGNS - Lamps–table - Milano Designs, Inc.
MILANO GOLD - Motor vehicles–automobiles ☆ - Alfa Romeo Distributors of North America
MILANO NECKWEAR - Neckties - Gordon & Ferguson of Delaware, Inc.
MILANO PLATINUM - Motor vehicles–automobiles ☆ - Alfa Romeo Distributors of North America
MILANO SERIES - Frames–picture - Milano Series International Products, Ltd.
MILANO UOMO - Apparel and accessories - Phillips-Van Heusen Corp.
MILANOMEAL - Pizzas–frozen - Nation Pizza Products L.P.
MILANOS - Footwear - D. Myers and Sons Inc.
MILANOS BY MYERS - Shoes - D. Myers and Sons Inc.
MILANTI - Accordions ☆ - Bell Duovox Corp.
MILASTIC - Paints - Miller Paint Co., Inc.
MILBEN - Microscopes, telescopes, prepared slides and accessories - B-R Importing Co. Inc.
MILBER - Watches - Design Time USA Inc.
MILBOND-TX - Chemical preparations - Milwhite, Inc.
MILBRIDGE - Furniture–wood - Merillat Industries, Inc.
MILBROOK ELEGANCE - Wallpaper - Milbrook Wallcoverings
MILCAMPS - Pastries - Candymania Inc.
MILCO - Apparel–women's - Milco Industries, Inc.
MILD - Hair care products - Le Joy Products Inc.
MILD AND NATURAL - Soap ☆ - Carme Inc.
MILD & WILD - Bathroom fixtures ☆ - H.B. Sherman Manufacturing Co.
MILD BLACK BEAN DIP - Sauces - Guiltless Gourmet, Inc.
MILD-C - Vitamins and nutritional supplements - J.R. Carlson Laboratories Inc.
MILD ENGLISH - Tobacco–chewing or smoking - Amar Blends Co.
MILD KINGDOM, THE - Greeting cards - Originals by Maris (O.B.M. Publishing)
MILD-N-SOFT - Shoe accessories - PediFix Footcare Co.
MILD SALSA PICOSITO - Spices and extracts - Finest Kind Spices

MILD SEVEN - Cigarettes - Japan Tobacco Inc.
MILD SEVEN LIGHTS - Cigarettes - Japan Tobacco Inc.
MILD SEVEN SUPER LIGHTS - Cigarettes - Japan Tobacco Inc.
MILD TO WILD PEPPER & HERB CO. - Sauces - Mild to Wild Pepper & Herb Co.
MILDE SORTE - Cigarettes - G.A. Georgopulo & Co. Inc.
MILDEW-CHECK - Cleaning preparations–household - PPG Industries, Inc.
MILDEW CONTROL BAGS - Cleaning preparations - Star Brite
MILDEW RELIEF - Household disinfectant - Intex Chemical Inc.
MILDEWCIDE - Cleaning preparations - Vapor Products
MILDEWDISK - Cleaning preparations ✩ - Vapor Products
MILDEW'S GONE! - Stain removers ✩ - Benckiser Consumer Products Inc.
MILDEX - Fungicides ✩ - Nott Manufacturing Co. Inc.
MILDEX - HOME product - Atlanta Sundries Inc.
MILDOOM - Cleaning preparations - Jonski Home Products
MILDOOR - Windows–storm ✩ - Miller Industries Inc.
MILDRED SEELEY - Dolls - Commemorative Imports
MILDRIL - Tool boxes - Custanite Precision Inc.
MILDU-BAN - Health care products - Surco Products Inc.
MILE-A-THON - Office supplies ✩ - Empire Berol USA
MILE AFTER MILE COMFORT - Orthopedic products - Northwest Podiatric Laboratory, Inc.
MILE HI - Meat products–beef - Sigman Meat Co. Inc.
MILE HIGH - Footwear - Diesse Shoes Inc.
MILE HIGH LASAGNA - Food products ✩ - Morrison Restaurants Inc.
MILE HIGH PUBLISHING - Publisher's imprints - Natural Supplement Association, Inc.
MILE-MAKER - Gasoline - Marathon Oil Co.
MILE MASTER - Tires - Oliver Rubber Co.
MILE-RITE - Pens - Rolamech Inc.
MILE ROCK - Seafood products–canned or cured - Pacific Choice Seafoods
MILEAGE - Paper–bond ✩ - Fox River Paper Co.
MILEGUARD - Filters–oil - JLAF Purchasing Coop Inc.
MILEMAKER - Computer software - Rand McNally & Co.
MILEMAKER PC - Computer software - Rand McNally-TDM, Inc. (Rand McNally & Co.)
MILEMARKING - Publisher's imprints - Mile Publications
MILEMASTER - Computer software - Highwaymaster Communications, Inc.
MILENA'S SPICES INC. - Spices and extracts - Milena's Spices, Inc.
MILEQUIP - Electronics equipment - Miller Professional Equipment Inc.
MILER - Bicycles ✩ - Roadmaster Corp.
MILES - Chemical preparations - Miles Laboratories (Union Div.)
MILES - Chemicals - Miles Inc.
MILES - Gin - Sazerac Co. Inc.
MILES - Homes - Insilco Corp.
MILES - Toys–stuffed ✩ - Gund, Inc.
MILES AHEAD - Gasoline - Shell Oil Co.
MILES AHEAD BODY GEAR - Clothing - Miles Ahead, Inc.
MILES MAYHEM - Toys - Tonka Corp.
MILES NERVINE - Analgesics - Bayer Corp. (Consumer Care Div.)
MILES O'BRIEN - Toys - Paramount Pictures Corp.
MILES OF TILES MARBLE & CERAMIC TILE - Tiles–ceramic - Miles of Tiles Inc.
MILES TONNE - Recording label - John J. Meilinger, III
MILESTONE - Computer software - Digital Marketing Corp.
MILESTONE - Floor coverings–carpet and rugs ✩ - Blue Ridge Carpet Mills
MILESTONE - Phonographs - Fantasy Inc.
MILESTONE - Wallpaper - Essex Wallcoveringss
MILESTONE 12 - Guitars - Peavey Electronics Corp.
MILESTONE LH - Guitars - Peavey Electronics Corp.
MILESTONE PRODUCTIONS 1 MILE - Video production - John Arthur Milestone
MILESTONES OF THOUGHT - Publisher's imprints ✩ - Crossroad
MILEX - Pharmaceutical preparations - Milex Products Inc.
MILFIORE - Food products - US Foodservice
MILFIORE - Oils–edible - Rykoff-Sexton, Inc.
MILFORD - Cabinets - American Woodmark Corp.
MILFORD - Lighting fixtures - Liteway
MILFORD - Paints–artists' ✩ - Winsor & Newton
MILFORD - Pet products - Alver Bros. Co.
MILFORD - Saw blades - Sandvik Saws & Tools
MILFORD - Teas - Harris Tea Co.
MILFORD GUILD BY INDECOR - Glassware and decorative accessories - Indecor Inc.
MILFORD OYSTER FESTIVAL - Apparel and accessories - Annual Milford Oyster Festival, Inc.

MILFORD SPORTSWEAR - Apparel and accessories - Milford Sportswear Inc.
MILGARD WINDOWS - Windows - Milgard Windows
MILGARD WINDOWS MW - Windows - Milgard Windows
MILGAUSS - Watches - Rolex Watch USA, Inc.
MILGURT - Juices - Sales Mark Southern California
MILIBIS - Pharmaceutical preparations ✩ - Winthrop Pharmaceuticals
MILISSA - Wallpaper - Koroseal Wallcoverings
MILITARY FORCE - Toys - SLM Inc.
MILITARY ISSUE - Apparel and accessories ✩ - Edison Brothers Stores, Inc.
MILITARY/MARINE - Binoculars - Pioneer Marketing & Research, Inc.
MILITARY MUSCLE MEN - Toys - Original San Francisco Toymakers
MILIZ - Cosmetics - Focus 21 International Inc.
MILK - Tools - Pedro's USA, Inc.
MILK & COOKIES - Recording label - Edible Records
MILK & COOKIES - Toys–stuffed - Dan-Dee International Ltd.
MILK-BONE - Dog food - Nabisco Foods Group
MILK-BONE DOGGIE BAG TREATS - Dog food - Nabisco Foods Group
MILK-BONE TC - Dog food - Nabisco Foods Group
MILK BOX - Kitchenware–plastic - Metrokane
MILK BREAK - Snack foods ✩ - Pillsbury Co.
MILK CHERRY HUMPS - Candy ✩ - Brock Candy Co. Inc.
MILK CHOCOLATE GENEVA - Candy - Home of the Hebert Candies, Inc.
MILK CLENZ - Skin care products - Image Laboratories, Inc.
MILK COOLERS/STEAMERS - Seasonings - McSteven's
MILK COVERS MAINLAND - Games - Milk Covers Mainland Marketing Group, Inc.
MILK DUDS - Candy - Leaf, Inc.
MILK FORMULA F21C - Toiletries - Fresh Inc.
MILK-IT - Dairy products - Richard Thompson
MILK KRATE - Coolers–electric - Stevens-Lee Co.
MILK-MAID - Candy - Brach and Brock Confections Inc.
MILK MAN - Bottles–glass ✩ - Metrokane
MILK-MATE - Chocolate syrup - Del Monte Corp.
MILK MECKY - Candy bars ✩ - Brocks Candy Co.
MILK 'N COOKIES - Candy bar - Intersweet Candy Inc.
MILK 'N HONEE - Cosmetics - Jheri Redding Products Inc.
MILK-N HONEES - Candy - Andre Prost Inc.
MILK 'N' HONEY - Cheese - Harold Gottesman
MILK OF MAGNESIA - See **PHILLIPS' MILK OF MAGNESIA**
MILK PAINT - Paints - Tulip Productions
MILK PLUS 6 - Hair care products - Revlon Consumer Products Corp.
MILK PROTECTORS - Tableware–china - Susquehanna Glass Co.
MILK SAVER - Animal feed supplements - A.L. Gilbert & Co.
MILK THISTLE - Vitamins and nutritional supplements - Ethical Nutrients
MILK THISTLE PLUS - Vitamins and nutritional supplements - Action Labs, Inc.
MILK TRAC - Scales–industrial - Universal Dairy Equipment, Inc.
MILK TRAY - Candy - Peter Paul
MILK-WHITE - Glassware–household ✩ - Anchor Hocking Glass, Inc.
MILKA - Candy bars - Brocks Candy Co.
MILKADE - Veterinary pharmaceutical preparations - Happy Jack, Inc.
MILKINOL - Laxatives - Schwarz Pharma
MILKLINE - Animal feed supplements - Kent Feeds, Inc.
MILKMAID - Clocks ✩ - General Time Corp. (Westclox/Seth Thomas Div.)
MILKQUAKE - Beverages - Kahlua Co.
MILKSHAKE - Candy - Leaf, Inc.
MILKSHAKE - Cosmetics ✩ - Elysee Scientific Cosmetic Co.
MILKTRUCK DELIVERY - Computer software - Milktruck, LLC
MILKVIS - Food products - Marcel Trading Corp.
MILKY - Hair care products - Helene Curtis Industries Inc.
MILKY - Toys - Tonka Corp.
MILKY THE MARVELOUS MILKING COW - Toys–stuffed ✩ - Kenner Products
MILKY WAY - Candy bars - Mars, Inc.
MILKY WAY - Christmas tree ornaments - Cracker Box Inc.
MILKY WAY - Ice cream - Dove International
MILKY WAY - Yarn - Henry's Attic
MILKY WAY II - Candy bars - Mars, Inc.
MILKY WAY LITE - Chocolate bars - Mars, Inc.
MILKY WAY MERCHANT - Computer software - SourceView Software International
MILKY WAY MINIATURES - Chocolate candy - Mars, Inc.
MILKY'S - Cheese - Milk House Cheese Corp.
MILKYWAY - Wigs - Shake-N-Go Fashions, Inc.
MILL - Milk - Wendt's Dairy
MILL CITY - Beverages–malt - Lowell Brewing Co., Inc.
MILL CREEK - Cabinets–wood ✩ - Kemper

✩ = Now out of production

MILL CREEK - Dog food - Ani Biscuit Co.
MILL CREEK - Furniture - Vaughan Furniture Co. Inc.
MILL CREEK - Skin care products - Carme Inc.
MILL CREEK FARMS - Pet products - Renick Farms Inc.
MILL CREEK VINEYARDS - Wines - Mill Creek Vineyards
MILL DANCE - Cheese - Chesman Inc.
MILL-END - Fishing tackle - Mason Tackle Co.
MILL FALLS - Product description unknown - Harold-Lawrence Associates Inc.
MILL GATE - Wallpaper - Seabrook Wallcoverings, Inc.
MILL HAND - Gloves - Good Luck Glove Co.
MILL HOLLOW COLLECTION, THE - Framed pictures - Books of Love, Inc.
MILL HOUSE COLLECTION - Furniture - Sumter Cabinet Co., Inc.
MILL POND MINIATURES - Wallpaper ☆ - Westchester Prints
MILL POND PRESS - Artists' materials - Mill Pond Press Inc.
MILL-R - Envelopes–paper - Geo. W. Millar & Co. Inc.
MILL RIDGE - Furniture ☆ - Bassett Furniture Industries, Inc.
MILL-RITE - Kitchen appliances - R & R Mill Co. Inc.
MILL RIVER TIMBERLAND WORK BOOTS - Footwear - Timberland Co.
MILL RUN - Furniture ☆ - Athens Furniture Industries Inc.
MILL STREAM - Furniture ☆ - Bassett Furniture Industries, Inc.
MILL, THE - Treadmill - Lumex, Inc.
MILL VALLEY - Food products - Mill Valley
MILL VALLEY - Furniture ☆ - Hooker Furniture Corp.
MILL WHEEL - Stencils - Mill Wheel Stencil Arts
MILL WHISTLE - Fabrics - Dan River Inc.
MILL WHITE - Paints - Devoe & Raynolds Co.
MILL-WORKS - Tools - Vermont American Corp.
MILLANT - Musical instruments ☆ - Vitali Import Co. Inc.
MILLAVEL - Polishing cloths - Glasflex Div.
MILLBANK - Cigarettes - Brown & Williamson Tobacco Corp.
MILLBOURN - Artists' materials ☆ - Andrews/Nelson/Whitehead
MILLBRITE - Pigments - ISK Biosciences Corp.
MILLBRITE - Tiles–ceramic - Monarch Tile Inc.
MILLBROOK - Bread - Interstate Brands Corp.
MILLBROOK - Floor coverings–carpet and rugs - Gulistan Carpet Inc.
MILLBROOK - Manufactured homes - Redman Industries, Inc.
MILLBROOKE - Floor coverings - Tarkett, Inc.
MILLBROOKE ICE-FLOE - Food processors - Kohler Co.
MILLBURN - Soil–potting ☆ - Millburn Peat Co. Inc.
MILLBURNE - Wallpaper ☆ - Advent Industries Inc.
MILLCRAFT - Hobby kits - Distinctive Design
MILLCREST - Siding–insulating - Certainteed Corp. (Roofing Products Group)
MILLCREST - Spices and extracts - Pacific Choice Brands Inc.
MILLDUTY - Cranes - Whiting Corp.
MILLE BORNES - Games - Parker Brothers
MILLE FLEUR - Fabrics - Dan River Inc.
MILLE LACS - Food products - Mille Lacs Maple Products Corp.
MILLEFIORE - Dinnerware–glass ☆ - Cyclamen Studio
MILLEFIORE - Jewelry - Alice Sturzinger Ltd.
MILLEFLEURS - Bath gel - Crabtree & Evelyn, Ltd.
MILLEFLEURS - Rings–jewelry - Artcarved Inc.
MILLENIA - Hearing aids - Qualitone
MILLENIA - Motor vehicles–automobiles - Mazda Motor of America Inc.
MILLENIA - Watches - Bulova Corp.
MILLENIA - Window coverings - Hunter Douglas, Inc.
MILLENIA MUD - Hair care products - Excelsior Beauty Products
MILLENIUM - Darts and dart games - Dart World Inc.
MILLENIUM - Saw blades - DBNA Trademarks Holding Inc.
MILLENIUM - Skin care products - Elizabeth Arden Inc.
MILLENIUM - Watches ☆ - SMH (US) Inc.
MILLENIUM 2000 ESP - Toys - Play Visions
MILLENIUM COLLECTION, THE - Research–scientific - Franklin Mint
MILLENIUM DAY - Skin care products - Elizabeth Arden Inc.
MILLENIUM SERIES - Giftware - Roman, Inc.
MILLENIUM WARRIORS - Computer software - First Star Software Inc.
MILLENNIA - Cabinets - Canyon Creek Cabinet Co.
MILLENNIA - Chairs–upholstered - La-Z-Boy Chair Co.
MILLENNIA - Mattresses - Ther-A-Pedic Associates, Inc.
MILLENNIA - Medical apparatus - Invivo Research, Inc.
MILLENNIA - Pens - Sheaffer Inc.
MILLENNIA - Tiles–ceiling - USG Interiors, Inc.
MILLENNIUM - Air conditioning equipment - York International Corp.
MILLENNIUM - Aquarium accessories - Aquarium Systems, Inc.
MILLENNIUM - Batteries - Gates Energy Products Inc.
MILLENNIUM - Beverages - E. Excel International, Inc.
MILLENNIUM - Bicycles ☆ - Raleigh USA Bicycle Co.

MILLENNIUM - Boats–kayaks - Old Town Canoe Co.
MILLENNIUM - Cameras - Panavision International
MILLENNIUM - Ceramic tiles - Stark Ceramics Inc.
MILLENNIUM - Chemical preparations - Coyne Cylinder Co.
MILLENNIUM - Communications equipment - Hayes Microcomputer Products Inc.
MILLENNIUM - Computer software - Dun and Bradstreet Software Services, Inc.
MILLENNIUM - Computers - Mega Drive Systems Inc.
MILLENNIUM - Cookware - Farberware Inc.
MILLENNIUM - Electronic equipment - Laser Images, Inc.
MILLENNIUM - Fabrics - Milliken & Co.
MILLENNIUM - Floor coverings - Mannington Wood Floors
MILLENNIUM - Furniture - Harter
MILLENNIUM - Jewelry - Millennium International, Inc.
MILLENNIUM - Labels–paper - Moore Business Forms, Inc.
MILLENNIUM - Machinery - Santinelli International, Inc.
MILLENNIUM - Maps - Rand McNally & Co.
MILLENNIUM - Musical instruments - Peavey Electronics Corp.
MILLENNIUM - Telephone apparatus - Cortelco Systems Inc.
MILLENNIUM - Vacuum cleaners and accessories - White Consolidated Industries, Inc.
MILLENNIUM - Wallpaper - Morton Jonap Co. Inc.
MILLENNIUM - Water purification systems - West Bend Co.
MILLENNIUM - Water–bottled or canned - Southern Import Distributors
MILLENNIUM - Wheelchairs - Everest and Jennings International Ltd.
MILLENNIUM - Wheelchairs - Medical Composite Technology
MILLENNIUM - Wines - Columbia Winery
MILLENNIUM II - Musical instrument accessories - Pro-Mark Corp.
MILLENNIUM III - Books–comic - Mike W. Barr
MILLENNIUM 2000 - Pharmaceutical preparations - Millennium 2000
MILLENNIUM AUCTION - Computer software - Personal Media International, Inc.
MILLENNIUM BY SKIVERTEX - Paper products - REXAM DSI
MILLENNIUM CAGES - Pet products - Petporium Ltd.
MILLENNIUM CHAMPAGNE - Wines - Southern Import Distributors
MILLENNIUM CHRONICLES, THE - Publisher's imprints - Electronic Systems & Software Corp.
MILLENNIUM COLLECTION - Furniture ☆ - Bernhardt Industries
MILLENNIUM CYLINDERS - Machinery - Superior Air Parts, Inc.
MILLENNIUM FALCON - Toys–models - ERTL Co., Inc.
MILLENNIUM FALCON - Toys–models - Lucasfilm Ltd.
MILLENNIUM T'S 2000 A.D. - Apparel and accessories - John Schofill
MILLENNIUM WALL MAPS - Maps - Rand McNally & Co.
MILLER - Air conditioning equipment - Nordyne Inc.
MILLER - Apparel and accessories ☆ - Miller Stockman Western Wear
MILLER - Apparel–athletic - Miller Group Inc.
MILLER - Chickens - Markel-Johnson Poultry Co.
MILLER - Cookies - Banner Biscuit Co. Inc.
MILLER - Dairy products - Edgar Miller Co.
MILLER - Dispensers - Fluid Management
MILLER - Housewares ☆ - K.J. Miller Corp.
MILLER - Lighting fixtures - Hubbell Lighting, Inc. (Lighting Div.)
MILLER - Office furniture–metal - Miller Desk Inc.
MILLER - Paints - Miller Paint Co., Inc.
MILLER - Sporting goods - Miller Ski and Camp
MILLER - Tires - Uniroyal Goodrich Tire Co.
MILLER - Towels - Miller Manufacturing Co.
MILLER AMISH COUNTRY POULTRY - Chickens - Pine Manor, Inc.
MILLER & WOODWARD - Jewelry - Miller & Woodward Manufacturing Jewelers
MILLER BARBER LOUISVILLE - Golfing equipment ☆ - Hillerich & Bradsby Co.
MILLER-BRODY - Recording label - Random House, Inc.
MILLER BROS. - Apparel and accessories ☆ - Miller Bros. Industries Inc.
MILLER BROS. USA - Pocket knives - Tennessee River Valley Knife Association Inc.
MILLER CASCADE - Frankfurters ☆ - Olympic Foods Inc.
MILLER CITRO - Lime-flavored beer ☆ - Miller Brewing Co.
MILLER CROSS - Skis - Miller Ski and Camp
MILLER FARMS - Cakes–mixes - Powersource Inc.
MILLER GENUINE DRAFT - Beer - Miller Brewing Co.
MILLER GENUINE DRAFT DE ETIQUETA NEGRA - Beverages–malt - Miller Brewing Co.
MILLER HIGH LIFE - Beer - Miller Brewing Co.
MILLER HIGH LIFE ICE - Beer - Miller Brewing Co.

☆ = Now out of production

MILLER HOWARD - Clocks - Howard Miller Clock Co.
MILLER INTERNATIONAL - Recording label - Fifth Continent Music Corp.
MILLER LITE - Low-calorie beer - Miller Brewing Co.
MILLER LITE ICE - Beer - Miller Brewing Co.
MILLER OFFICE SEATING - Chairs–metal - MH & H Seating Co. Inc.
MILLER PAINTS TRADE MARK - Coatings - Miller Paint Co., Inc.
MILLER PYRAMID - Golf bags, clubs, etc. - Ron Miller Associates Inc.
MILLER RESERVE AMBER ALE - Beer - Miller Brewing Co.
MILLER RESERVE LIGHT - Low-calorie beer - Miller Brewing Co.
MILLER RESERVE VELVET - Stout beer - Miller Brewing Co.
MILLER ROGASKA - Glassware–household - Miller-Rogaska Inc.
MILLER SINCE 1855 - Beverages–malt - Miller Brewing Co.
MILLER SOFT - Skis - Miller Ski and Camp
MILLER SUPER INDY - Toys–electronic - Bird Bromiticous Inc.
MILLER Y ANGLE - Artists' materials - PMC Industries Inc. (Draftette Div.)
MILLERHAUS' - Health care products ☆ - CTS Laboratories Inc.
MILLER'S - Cheese - Miller's Cheese Corp.
MILLERS - Eggs - Miller Poultry & Feed Inc.
MILLER'S - Honey - Miller's Honey Co.
MILLER'S - Horseradish - Silver Spring Gardens Inc.
MILLER'S - Vitamins and nutritional supplements - Nature's Bounty, Inc.
MILLER'S - Water–bottled or canned - Miller's Spring Water Inc.
MILLERS CREEK - Bedroom furniture - American Drew
MILLERS CROSSING - Wallpaper - Borden, Inc.
MILLER'S EXPERT STANDARD INSURANCE POLICIES ANNOTATED - Computer software - Legal Research Systems, Inc.
MILLERS FALLS - Tools–hand-operated - Millers Falls Tool Co.
MILLERS FORGE - Scissors–hand-operated - Miller's Forge Inc.
MILLERS GOOD HEALTH - Cheese - Miller's Cheese Corp.
MILLER'S PRIDE - Pancake and gravy mixes - Pioneer Flour Mills
MILLER'S QUALITY - Meat products–canned - Miller Packing Co. Corp.
MILLER'S STANDARD INSURANCE POLICIES ANNOTATED - Paper–book - Legal Research Systems, Inc.
MILLET - Apparel and accessories - Suunto USA
MILLFORD - Furniture ☆ - Bassett Furniture Industries, Inc.
MILLHEATH - Fabrics - Burlington Industries, Inc.
MILLI WAVE - Amplifiers–radio - TRW MilliWave, Inc.
MILLIE AUGUST - Wallpaper - Plaid Enterprises, Inc.
MILLIE MATS - Craft supplies - Milton Bradley Co.
MILLIE, THE - Health care products - Viscot Industries Inc.
MILLIE'S - Soups–mixes - Westfield Foods
MILLIE'S BUCKTAILS - Fishing lures - Key Largo Trading Co., Inc.
MILLIKEN - Fabrics - Milliken & Co. Inc.
MILLIKEN WORD PROCESSOR - Computer software ☆ - Milliken Publishing Co. (Computer Software Div.)
MILLIMOIST - Cleaning equipment - Milliken & Co.
MILLINA'S FINEST - Seasonings - Organic Food Products
MILLING ROAD - Furniture - Baker, Knapp & Tubbs
MILLION AIR - Floor coverings - Mannington Resilient Floors
MILLION $$$ BABY - Apparel–children's - Valerie Lyn Thivierge
MILLION CYCLE PLUS - Electronic equipment - Shure Brothers, Inc.
MILLION DOLLAR BABY - Apparel and accessories ☆ - Warnaco Inc.
MILLION DOLLAR BABY - Furniture - Daryan International Inc.
MILLION DOLLAR BONNET - Hair care products - Color Design Systems
MILLION DOLLAR NITE CREME - Skin care products - Viviane Woodard Industries, Ltd.
MILLION DOLLAR ROULETTE - Games - Smethport Specialty Co.
MILLION DOLLAR SKINCARE - Skin care products - Viviane Woodard Industries, Ltd.
MILLIONAIRE - Colognes - Mennen Co.
MILLIONAIRE - Sporting goods - Daiwa Corp.
MILLIONAIRE BLEND - Tobacco–chewing or smoking - Sterling Tobacco Co.
MILLIONAIRES - Candy - Pangburn Candy Co.
MILLIONS DAILY - Paper clips - Noesting Inc.
MILLIONTH KNIGHT, THE - Electronic equipment - Texas Instruments Inc.
MILLIPEDE - Connectors–electrical - Augat Inc.
MILLIPEN - Markers–felt-tip - Zebra Pen Corp.
MILLIPORE - Water - Continental Water
MILLISEAL - Towels - Milliken & Co.
MILLISHIELD - Apparel and accessories - Milliken & Co.
MILLITE - Paints - Devoe & Raynolds Co.
MILLMASTER - Gloves - Boss Manufacturing Co.
MILLMATE - Computer peripheral equipment ☆ - Acu-Rite Inc.
MILLPLANK - Wainscotting - Georgia-Pacific Corp.
MILLPOINT - Apparel–athletic - Anywear USA Inc.
MILLPWR - Electronic equipment - Acu-Rite Inc.

MILLRACE - Template software - Old Mill Software Co.
MILLRACE - Vegetables–canned - Norpac Services, Inc.
MILLROCK - Display cases–wood - Millrock Inc.
MILLS - Coffee - Mills Coffee Roasting Co.
MILLS - Containers - Mills Specialty Products Inc.
MILLS - Hardware - Blaine Window Hardware Inc.
MILLS - Sails - Wm. J. Mills & Co.
MILLS - Wines - Calera Wine Co.
MILLS COLLEGE - Recording label - Jazz Composer's Orchestra Association Inc.
MILLS VALLEY - See **HOMESTYLE**
MILLSKIN - Fabrics - Milliken & Co. Inc.
MILLSTEAD - Cabinets - Schrock
MILLSTIK - Bags–plastic - Millhiser Inc.
MILLSTONE - Coffee - Millstone Coffee, Inc.
MILLSTONE - Meat extracts - Millstone Foods Inc.
MILLSTONE - Tiles–ceramic - Monarch Tile Inc.
MILLSTREAM - Beverages - Millstream Brewing Co.
MILLSTREAM - Floor coverings–carpet and rugs ☆ - Criterion Mills Inc.
MILLSTREAM - Furniture ☆ - Bassett Furniture Industries, Inc.
MILLSTREAM PINK - Dinnerware–glass ☆ - Johnson Brothers, USA, Inc.
MILLSTREAM WHEAT - Beverages–malt - Millstream Brewing Co.
MILLTIPLICITY - Figurines ☆ - Estus Export-Import
MILLTOWN LOGGETTES - Briquettes - Milltown Products
MILLTURN - Machinery - Barbara H. Ganem
MILLUGATOR - Paperboard–corrugated - Pratt Industries (USA), Inc.
MILLVILLE - Fabrics - Dan River Inc.
MILLWOOD - Cabinets - American Woodmark Corp.
MILLY COW - Puppets - Dakin Inc.
MILMEYER - Motor vehicle parts and accessories - Rivera Engineering, Inc.
MILMO - Pillows - Milmo, Inc.
MILNE TRUCK LINES, INC. - Toys - Toy Truck Lines, Inc.
MILNER - Hotels and motels - Milner Hotels Inc.
MILNOR - Glassware–household - Denby USA Limited
MILNOR HEMP - Placemats - Denby USA Limited
MILNOR TEAK - Dishes–wood - Denby USA Limited
MILNOT - Milk–canned or powdered - Milnot Co.
MILO - Thread - Threads USA Div.
MILO OF CALIFORNIA - Footwear–women's - Milo Inc.
MILO SHIMLEY COLLECTION, THE - Greeting cards - Hallmark Cards Inc.
MILOCIDE - Veterinary pharmaceutical preparations ☆ - Vineland Laboratories Inc.
MILON - Sporting goods - Matman Wrestling Co.
MILONTIN - Pharmaceutical preparations - Parke-Davis
MILORD MALLARD - Toys–stuffed - Dakin Inc.
MILPACK - Electrical equipment - Solid State Devices, Inc.
MILPATH - Pharmaceutical preparations ☆ - Wallace Laboratories
MILPREM - Pharmaceutical preparations ☆ - Wallace Laboratories
MILQUOTE - Computer peripheral equipment - Overseas Military Sales Corp.
MILRITE - Ladders–metal - Rich Ladder Co.
MILRON - Pharmaceutical preparations ☆ - Mill-Mark Pharmaceuticals Inc.
MILSAN - Shirts–polo - Milsan Mills Inc.
MILSHIRE - Gin - Heublein, Inc.
MILSOFT - Computer software - Milsoft Integrated Solutions, Inc.
MILSTAR - Floor coverings–carpet and rugs - Milliken & Co. Inc.
MILTEX - Medical supplies - Miltex Instrument Co., Inc.
MILTEX - Paper–tissue - Fort Howard Corp.
MILTON - Pianos - Kohler & Campbell Inc.
MILTON BRADLEY - Paper - Milton Bradley Co.
MILTON DUFF - Beverages–alcohol - Sunbelt Beverage Corp.
MILTOWN - Tranquilizers - Wallace Laboratories
MILTRATE - Pharmaceutical preparations ☆ - Wallace Laboratories
MILT'S MATH DRILLS - Computer software - Hartley Courseware Inc.
MILUMIL - Baby foods - Milupa Co.
MILUPA - Baby foods - Milupa Co.
MILWAUKEE - Cribs–metal - HARD Manufacturing Co. Inc.
MILWAUKEE - Dollies–industrial - Gleason Corp.
MILWAUKEE - Tools - MHT Products Inc.
MILWAUKEE 1851 - Beverages–malt - The Stroh Brewery Co.
MILWAUKEE 1851 DRAFT - Beverages–malt - The Stroh Brewery Co.
MILWAUKEE 1851 ICE - Beverages–malt - The Stroh Brewery Co.
MILWAUKEE 1851 LIGHT - Beverages–malt - The Stroh Brewery Co.
MILWAUKEE BREWERS - Frankfurters - Cher-Make Sausage Co.
MILWAUKEE BUCKS - Apparel and accessories - Milwaukee Bucks, Inc.
MILWAUKEE BUCKS - Frankfurters ☆ - Cher-Make Sausage Co.
MILWAUKEE FAUCETS - Faucets - Milwaukee Faucets Inc.

☆ = Now out of production

MILWAUKEE HEAT TOOL - Hardware - Wagner Spray Tech Corp.

MILWAUKEE HEAT TOOL - Tools - MHT Products Inc.

MILWAUKEE IRON - Electrical equipment - GB Electrical Inc.

MILWAUKEE KNIT - Apparel–athletic ✩ - Midstates Sportswear

MILWAUKEE PILS - Beverages–malt - Sprecher Brewing Co. Inc.

MILWAUKEE PREMIUM - Beverages–malt ✩ - Eastern Brewing Corp.

MILWAUKEE SCHOOL OF ENGINEERING - Paper–writing - Milwaukee School of Engineering

MILWAUKEE WEISS - Beverages–malt - Sprecher Brewing Co. Inc.

MILWAUKEE'S BEST - Beer - Miller Brewing Co.

MILWAUKEE'S BEST LIGHT - Beer - Miller Brewing Co.

MILWOOD - Wood products - Olde Towne Artisans Inc.

MIMAX S.L. - Footwear–women's ✩ - J.R. Carus Inc.

MIMBRENO - Dinnerware–glass - Pipestone

MIMBRENO TRADING CO. - Boxes - American Classics/Mimbreno Trading Co.

MIMBRES MAN - Apparel–athletic - Barin H. Beard

MIMBRES WARE - Dinnerware–plastic - Mallek Kay Studios

MIMEO-LITH - Stencils ✩ - Repeat-O-Type Manufacturing Corp.

MIMEOGRAPH - Duplicating machines - A.B. Dick Co.

MIMEOSCOPE - Office machines - A.B. Dick Co.

MIMEOTONE - Inks - A.B. Dick Co.

MIMEOTRONIC - Stencils - Mimeo Manufacturing Co. Inc.

MIMEOTYPE - Paper–stencil ✩ - A.B. Dick Co.

MIMI - Bags–plastic - Interstate Packaging Corp.

MIMI - Dolls - Mattel, Inc.

MIMI - Dolls ✩ - Effanbee Doll Corp.

MIMI & THE MITES - Computer software - Unobstructed Reason Corp.

MIMI BEAR - Vitamins and nutritional supplements - Winning Laboratories Corp.

MIMI LITE - Crutches - Winnie Walker Co.

MIMI NAIL - Nail care products ✩ - Palm Beach Beauty Products

MIMI SUR LA COTE - Apparel and accessories - Meyerson's Enterprises Inc.

MIMIC - Electronic equipment - Display Laboratories, Inc.

MIMIC - Medical apparatus - Nomos Corp.

MIMI'S MUFFINS - Bakery products - Jeffrey D. Hall

MIMIX - Computer software - Lakeview Technology Inc.

MIMIX - Computer software - Steinberg/Jones Corp.

MIMOSA - Cosmetics - Elysee Scientific Cosmetic Co.

MIMOSA - Floor coverings–carpet and rugs - Alexander Smith Carpets

MIMOSA - Furniture ✩ - Singer Furniture Co.

MIMOSA - Garden furniture - Winston Furniture Co. Inc.

MIMOSA - Ophthalmic goods - Swank Optical

MIMOSA - Wallcoverings - Ben Rose Ltd.

MIMS - Computer software - Medical Information Systems

MIMS - Gin - Sazerac Co. Inc.

MIMS & THOMAS - Doors–glass ✩ - MW Manufacturers, Inc.

MIMY - Pet products - Nippon Pet Food

MIN-BAR - Photographic equipment ✩ - Logan Electric Specialty Manufacturing Co.

MIN-FLEX - Springs–furniture - Hoover Group, Inc.

MIN/MAX - Computers ✩ - Grolier Inc.

MIN-O-LIFE - Fishing tackle - Frabill Inc.

MIN-O-MAG - Laxatives - Bristol-Myers Squibb Co.

MIN-O-MAX - Fishing tackle - Sportsmax Inc.

MIN PLEX - Vitamins and nutritional supplements - Nima Products Inc.

MIN SHAN - Coffee - Mayway Corp.

MIN. SPEC. PROD. - Giftware - H.C. Meyers Co.

MIN-SUB - Watches - Rolex Watch USA, Inc.

MIN TONG - Herbal tea extracts - Min Tong Herbs, Inc.

MIN-VITERAL - Pharmaceutical preparations ✩ - Kay Pharmacal Co. Inc.

MINA KOO - Apparel–women's - Mina Koo

MINA-TABS - Pet products - Nutra-Vet Research Corp.

MINAMAX - Lubricants ✩ - Ashland Oil, Inc.

MINAR - Soap - A & H Laboratories LLC

MINARD'S - Pharmaceutical preparations ✩ - Smithkline Beecham Corp.

MINARETTE - Hearing aids - Widex Hearing Aid Co., Inc.

MINATURES - Wallpaper ✩ - Motif Designs, Inc.

MIND ACTIVES - Vitamins and nutritional supplements - Marlyn Nutraceuticals, Inc.

MIND BENDER - Magnets - Six Flags Theme Parks Inc.

MIND BODY & ATTITUDE - Apparel and accessories - Robert McCleave

MIND, BODY & SOUL NETWORK, THE - Computer peripheral equipment - Alchemy Communications, Inc.

MIND/BODY EXERCISE SYSTEM - Electronic equipment - Cognitech Corp.

MIND BODY SOUL MBS - Apparel - MBS - Mind Body Soul

MIND CASTLE - Computer software ✩ - Knowledge Adventure

MIND CONCEPTS TIME CORPORATION - Recording label - Mind Concepts and Time Corp.

MIND EFFECTS - Apparel and accessories - Jeffrey Scott Busche

MIND/FITNESS - Recording label - Kelly Todd Burris,

MIND FLARE - Hats - Shahab Farzanegan

MIND FOREVER VOYAGING, A - Computer software - Activision, Inc.

MIND IN MOTION - Computer storage devices - Black Mountain Multimedia, Inc.

MIND MATTER - Recording label - Jazz Composer's Orchestra Association Inc.

MIND-MAX - Herbal products - Lifetrends International

MIND MIRROR - Computer software ✩ - Electronic Arts Inc.

MIND MUNCHIES - T-shirts–men's - Thunderbay Ltd.

MIND/MUSCLE - Signs - Zananda, Inc.

MIND OF CHRIST - Recording label - Sunday School Board of the Southern Baptist Convention

MIND OPENER - Recording label - Cohen/Gebler Associates, Inc.

MIND OVER GRAVITY - Exercising equipment - MLH Marketing, Inc.

MIND OVER MATTER - Computer software - Learning Well

MIND PATH - Computer software - Mind Path Technologies Inc.

MIND PEAK - Health care products - East Earth Herb Inc.

MIN'D PICK - Musical instrument accessories - Miller's Fossils

MIND PLAY WORKS - Computer software - Mind Play

MIND PLUS - Vitamins and nutritional supplements - Maharishi Ayurveda Products International Inc.

MIND POWER I - Computer software - SRA/McGraw-Hill (Div. of The McGraw-Hill Companies)

MIND QUEST - Computer storage devices–optical - Blue Mountain Software, Inc.

MIND SHAPES - Toys - Wimmer-Ferguson Inc.

MIND YOUR MANNERS - Games - At Ease Inc.

MIND YOUR MANNERS - Games - Smethport Specialty Co.

MIND YOUR MANNERS - Video production - James Stanfield and Co., Inc.

MINDAME - Pharmaceutical preparations - Edward's Pharmacy Inc.

MINDBOOSTERS - Video production - Mindworld

MINDBUSTER - Games ✩ - Milton Bradley Co.

MINDCARE - Vitamins and nutritional supplements - Ayurvedic Concepts Ltd.

MINDCHATTER - Recording label - Randy W. Brolsma

MINDEN - Cigarettes - G.A. Georgopulo & Co. Inc.

MINDJOGGER - Video production - McGraw-Hill Companies, Inc.

MINDMATTERS - Educational materials - Mindmatters, Inc.

MINDMUSCLE - Exercising equipment - Roxanne Bell

MINDNET - Computer software - Intelix Corp.

MINDORO BLUE - Cheese - Tri-State Milk Cooperative

MINDQ - Computer software - Mindq Publishing, Inc.

MINDREADER - Alarm systems - Specific Cruise Systems, Inc.

MINDREADERS - Novelty items - Agent Andy Inc.

MIND'S EYE, THE - Video production - Odyssey Visual Design

MINDS ON LINES - Apparel and accessories - Thomas R. Toliver

MINDS OVER NETWORKS SMARTS - Computer hardware - System Management Arts

MINDSCAPE - Video games - Mindscape Software Inc.

MINDSCAPE COMPLETE REFERENCE LIBRARY - Computer peripheral equipment - Mindscape Software Inc.

MINDSET - Computer peripheral equipment - Mindset Technologies, LLC

MINDSET - Computer software - Mindset Corp.

MINDSHADOW - Computer software - Activision, Inc.

MINDSIGHT - Computer software - Mindsight, Inc.

MINDSTREET - Computer software - Mindstreet, LLC

MINDWEAR - Apparel and accessories - Klier Brother Alliance

MINDWHEEL - Computer software ✩ - Broderbund Software, Inc.

MINDWIRE - Computer software - Durand Communications Network, Inc.

MINDY - Glassware–household - Owens-Illinois Inc. (Libbey Div.)

MINDY - Ophthalmic goods - Rozin Optical Export Corp.

MINDY - Ophthalmic goods ✩ - Luxottica

MINDY WALKER - Dolls ✩ - Uneeda Doll Co., Inc.

MINDZ - Shirts - Mary C. Cavanaugh

MINE - Boots ✩ - Distributors Service Corp.

MINE - Frames–eyeglass - May Optical Co. Inc.

MINE & MOMMY'S - Doughs–frozen - Mine & Mommy's

MINE MAULER - Tires - Uniroyal Goodrich Tire Co.

MINED - Jeans–men's - California Liberal Art Fashion, Inc.

MINEHAHA - Pharmaceutical preparations ✩ - Ulmer Pharmacal Co.

MINEIRO - Cheese - Reinaldo O. Barbosa

MINERAL BATH - Shampoos - Anasazi Salon System, Inc.

MINERAL CLEAR - Cleaning preparations - Locey Swim Pool Co.

MINERAL CLOCKS - Clocks - American Mineral Gift Co.

MINERAL COMPLEET - Vitamins and nutritional supplements ☆ - J.R. Carlson Laboratories Inc.

MINERAL COMPLEX AM/PM - Health care products - Alta Health Products

MINERAL CORE - Hardware - Weyerhaeuser Co.

MINERAL ESSENCE - Skin care products ☆ - Thompson Medical Co., Inc.

MINERAL ICE - Analgesics - Bristol-Myers Squibb Co.

MINERAL LIFE - Health care products - Lotus Brands Inc.

MINERAL MUD - Hair care products - Conair Corp.

MINERAL MUNCH - Snack foods - Soaring Eagle Ventures, Inc.

MINERAL NECTAR - Health care products - Healthwatchers System

MINERAL-RIGHT, INC. - Water treating compounds - Mineral-Right, Inc.

MINERAL RIVER - Recording label - Alcazar Productions

MINERAL SPA - Skin care products - Alessio International

MINERAL SPLASH - Hair care products - Anasazi Salon System, Inc.

MINERALIGHT - Lamps–ultraviolet - UVP Inc.

MINERALITE - Watches - Bulova Corp.

MINERALRICH - Vitamins and nutritional supplements - Ross B. Gordon

MINERALSYN - Vitamins and nutritional supplements - Great Life Laboratories Inc.

MINERON - Watch crystals - Longines-Wittnauer Watch Co.

MINER'S & PUDDLERS - Tobacco - American Tobacco Co.

MINER'S CHOICE, THE - Machinery - Dry-Tab Package Sealer Co.

MINER'S GOLD - Beef jerky - ITC Products

MINER'S REVENGE - Game machines - Lazer-Tron Corp.

MINERVA - Computer software - Minerva Systems, Inc.

MINERVA - Olive oil - Krinos Foods, Inc.

MINERVA - Ophthalmic goods ☆ - Luxottica

MINERVA - Watches - M. Ducommun Co.

MINERVA DAIRY - Milk - Minerva Dairy Inc.

MINERVA LACE - Cheese - Minerva Dairy Inc.

MINERVA PAVERS - Floor coverings–tile ☆ - Kepcor, Inc./SSI Tiles

MINERVA PUBLISHER - Computer software - Minerva Systems, Inc.

MINERVA STREET - Candy - Minerva Street Chocolates Inc.

MINERVA STUDIO - Computer software - Minerva Systems, Inc.

MINERVE - Nuts–salted, roasted, cooked, or canned - Liberty Richter Inc.

MINES - Computer software - Mid-America Manufacturing Technology Center, Inc.

MINES OF MORIA - Computer software - SourceView Software International

MINETS - Pharmaceutical preparations - Lunsco Inc.

MINETS 500 - Pharmaceutical preparations - Lunsco Inc.

MINETS SUPER - Pharmaceutical preparations - Lunsco Inc.

MINETTE - Frames–eyeglass ☆ - Universal/Univis Inc.

MING - Furniture - CTH/Sherrill Occasional

MING ART - Apparel and accessories - Eton Trading America, Inc.

MING BLOSSOM - Tableware–china ☆ - Lenox, Inc.

MING CHA - Tea - Boston Tea Co.

MING DYNASTY - Wallpaper - Koroseal Wallcoverings

MING DYNASTY BY CHEN - Dresses–women's - Worldscape Industries Inc.

MING II - Yarn - Roselon Industries, Inc.

MING JOY - Floor coverings–carpet and rugs - Masland Corp.

MING MAGIC - Scissors–hand-operated - Magic Distributing Ltd.

MING MICRO MASTER - Scissors–hand-operated - Magic Distributing Ltd.

MING ROSE - Dinnerware–glass - Franciscan by Johnson Brothers, USA, Inc.

MING TAI - Jewelry ☆ - Hirsch Speidel Inc.

MING TERRACE - Furniture ☆ - Singer Furniture Co.

MING TREASURES - Furniture ☆ - Drexel Heritage Furnishings, Inc.

MING TREE - Dinnerware–glass ☆ - Nikko Ceramics Inc.

MINGALICIOUS - Sauces - Minga's Mexican Food Restaurant

MINGA'S SPECIAL ULTRA-LITES - Food products - Minga's Mexican Food Restaurant

MINGEI - Calendars - Yasutomo

MINGLERS - Crocheted and knitted items ☆ - Puritan Sportswear Corp.

MINGMING - Compact discs–prerecorded - James J. Bohannon

MINGO RIVER - Nuts–candied - Young Pecans Sales Corp.

MINGOS - Footwear - Mingos Boot Co.

MINH - Snack foods - Minh Food Corp.

MINH EXPRESS - Food products - Minh Food Corp.

MINI - Bicycles - Columbia Manufacturing Inc.

MINI - Forms–preprinted - Dress Rite Forms

MINI - Fuses–electric - Littelfuse, Inc.

MINI - Manicure preparations ☆ - Cameo Inc.

MINI - Medical apparatus - Sebra

MINI - Sporting goods - Ranging Inc.

MINI-1 - Electromedical apparatus - TH Charters, Inc.

MINI-14 - Rifles - Sturm, Ruger & Co., Inc.

MINI-30 - Rifles - Sturm, Ruger & Co., Inc.

MINI 2000 - Compasses–magnetic - Pioneer Marketing & Research, Inc.

MINI A - Fishing lures - Bomber Bait Co.

MINI-ADS - Novelty items–paper - All American Emblem Corp.

MINI ALL ROUND - Brushes–hair ☆ - I. Sekine Co. Inc.

MINI ALL-STARS - Rubber stamps - All Night Media, Inc.

MINI-AUTO - Marine rigging - Presto-Tek

MINI AVALANCHE - Puzzles - Lauri Inc.

MINI BAGEL DOGS - Kosher hot dogs - Bessin Corp.

MINI-BAILER - Sporting goods ☆ - Wilcox-Crittenden

MINI-BAITER - Rodenticides - Solvit Inc.

MINI-BAK - Key rings - West Coast Chain Manufacturing Co.

MINI-BAK I.D. - Identification tags - West Coast Chain Manufacturing Co.

MINI-BAK/NIPPER - Fishing tackle - West Coast Chain Manufacturing Co.

MINI BAKERS - Vegetables–frozen ☆ - Lamb-Weston, Inc.

MINI-BALE - Hay - Novalek, Inc.

MINI-BALES - Pet products - Nutritional Research Associates Inc.

MINI-BANK - Humidifiers - Dri-Steem Humidifier Co.

MINI BANQUET - Pet products - Aquatrol, Inc.

MINI BAR - Tools - Vaughan & Bushnell Manufacturing Co.

MINI-BASEBALL - Candy ☆ - Leaf, Inc.

MINI-BASKET - Washing machines–commercial - General Electric Co.

MINI-BASKETBALL - Games ☆ - Logan Electric Specialty Manufacturing Co.

MINI-BATCH - Computer hardware - Moore Epitaxial, Inc.

MINI-BATTERY - Lamps - Roxter Lighting

MINI BEACON - Laser beam projector ☆ - Laser Alignment, Inc.

MINI BEEP - Scooters–motorized ☆ - C.F. Struck Corp.

MINI-BEEPER - Electrical testing instruments - Concept Industries, Inc.

MINI-BERRIES - Candy - California Hi-Lites, Inc.

MINI-BERTHA - Toys–models ☆ - Estes Industries

MINI BETTER LETTER - Decals and transfers - C-Thru Ruler Co.

MINI BIG WHEEL - Toys–automobiles - Empire of Carolina Inc.

MINI-BIKINIS - Apparel–women's - Nuvogue Creations

MINI-BIN - Containers - Rubbermaid Inc.

MINI BINGO - Games - Smethport Specialty Co.

MINI-BINKS - Candy ☆ - R.M. Palmer Co.

MINI BITES - Pasta - American Home Food Products Inc.

MINI BLADE CASE - Barber shop equipment - Kim Laube & Co. Inc.

MINI BLASTER - Blasting compounds - W.R. Brown Co.

MINI-BLEND - Containers - Sunbeam-Oster Household Products

MINI BLENDER - Scissors–hand-operated - F.W. Engels Inc.

MINI BLIND - Blinds–venetian - Clopay Building Products Co., Inc.

MINI-BLINDS N' MORE! - Blinds–vertical - Mini-Blinds N' More

MINI-BOARD - Housewares - Ever-Ready Appliance Manufacturing Co.

MINI BODY TONERS - Hosiery - Sara Lee Corp.

MINI-BOOM - Lighting equipment - Smith-Victor Corp.

MINI-BORE - Machine tools - Lenore E. Perry

MINI-BOUTIQUE - Crocheted and knitted items - Winston Manufacturing Corp.

MINI BRAIDS - Cosmetics - Nino Originals

MINI BREW - Coffee makers–electric ☆ - Black & Decker Corp.

MINI-BRICK - Bricks - Huntington/Pacific Ceramics Inc.

MINI BRIEF - Underwear and nightwear - Exquisite Form Industries

MINI BRITES - Laces–boot and shoe ☆ - Mitchellace Inc.

MINI BROWN MACHINE - Dryers–hair - Magic Distributing Ltd.

MINI BRUTE - Amplifiers - Polytone Musical Instruments Inc.

MINI-BRUTE - Bicycles - Ross Bicycles USA, Ltd.

MINI-BULBS - Lamp bulbs–incandescent - Ever-Ready Co.

MINI BUNDLE - Cables–fiber optic - Siecor Corp.

MINI-BUNDT - Pans ☆ - Nordic Ware

MINI BUS - Circuit boards–printed - Circuit Components Inc.

MINI-CABLE - Television equipment–cable - Channel One Communications Corp.

MINI-CAKES - Cakes - Dockside Cakes

MINI-CAR - Automotive parts and accessories ☆ - Hurst Performance Inc.

MINI-CARTRIDGE - Veterinary medical equipment - Genesis Industries Inc.

MINI-CEPTOR - Antennas–satellite ☆ - Winegard Co.

MINI-CHECK - Lockers–metal - American Locker Security Systems

MINI CHEW - Pet products - HMH Productions

MINI CHIMI ROLLS - Preserved foods–prepackaged - Minh Food Corp.

MINI CHIPS - Chocolate candy - Hershey Chocolate USA

MINI CHOL - Cheese - Swissrose International Inc.

MINI CHUNKS - Dog food - Iams Co.

MINI CINE - Projection screens - Draper Shade and Screen Co. Inc.

MINI-CIRC - Pet products - Electric Cleaner Co.

MINI-CLAMP - Clamps–hose - Murray Corp.

MINI CLASSICS - Food products - Sargento Cheese Co. Inc.

MINI CLASSICS - Wallpaper ☆ - Kingfisher Wallcoverings

☆ = Now out of production

MINI CLAW - Tools–garden - Faultless Starch/Bon Ami Co.
MINI-CLIK - Sprinklers–lawn - Glen-Hilton Products, Inc.
MINI-CLIK II - Irrigation equipment - Glen-Hilton Products, Inc.
MINI-CLIPPER - Electronic equipment - Mueller Electric Co.
MINI-COBRA - Toys–models - Estes Industries
MINI-COBS - Fruits and vegetables ☆ - Ore-Ida Foods, Inc.
MINI-COCKTAIL - Meat products–beef - Armour Swift-Eckrich
MINI-COLLINS - Pipes - Rothenberger USA, Inc.
MINI COLOR - Paints - Plaid Enterprises, Inc.
MINI-COM - Electronic equipment - Panduit Corp.
MINI-COM - Radios - RELM Communications Inc.
MINI-COMPACT - Hearing aids - Widex Hearing Aid Co., Inc.
MINI CONES - Thread - Signal Thread Co. Inc.
MINI CONTROL, THE - Beds–metal - Thermal Technology Inc.
MINI-COOL - Electronics equipment - Burgess Inc.
MINI-COPTER - Toys - Fisher-Price, Inc.
MINI CORD - Craft supplies - Synthetic Textiles Inc.
MINI CRAFT - Boats - Regatta Boats
MINI-CRIB - Infant product - Delta Enterprise Corp.
MINI CRITTERS - Giftware - Piccadilly
MINI-CUBE - Housewares - General Electric Co.
MINI CUBIC - Sporting goods ☆ - Powell Skateboards
MINI CUDDLES - Toys–stuffed - Dakin Inc.
MINI-CUP - Candles - Empire Manufacturing Co.
MINI CUPBAKES - Bakery products - Sunset Paper Products Inc.
MINI-CURE - Manicure preparations - Concord Shear Co.
MINI CURL FIX - Curling irons–electric - Helene Curtis Industries Inc.
MINI CUTIES - Toys–stuffed - Russ Berrie and Co., Inc.
MINI-DEX - Tools - Norton Co.
MINI DEX-A-PHONE - Telephone accessories - Rest-a-Phone Corp.
MINI DHURRIE - Floor coverings–carpet and rugs - Rugby Rugs Inc.
MINI-DIAMOND - Garden equipment ☆ - Valley View Specialties Co.
MINI DIMENSIONS - Apparel–children's - Kleinert's Inc.
MINI-DISER - Brushes–paint - Wooster Brush Co.
MINI-DONUTS - Bakery products - Tasty Baking Co.
MINI-DOT - Clocks ☆ - General Time Corp. (Westclox/Seth Thomas Div.)
MINI-DRAFTER - Office supplies - Alvin and Co. Inc.
MINI-EAR - Hearing aids - Vanco Industries Inc.
MINI-EASYDRIVER - Tools ☆ - Creative Products Inc.
MINI EEGOR - Electrical equipment - GB Electrical Inc.
MINI-ELITE - Hearing aids - Vanco Industries Inc.
MINI FISHERMAN - Fishing tackle - K-Tel International, Inc.
MINI-FLEX - Glass–optical - Welling International
MINI FLIP CLIP - Artists' materials - Wolsey Co.
MINI-FLIRT - Apparel–women's - Wacoal America Inc.
MINI-FLOATER - Candles ☆ - Fox Run Craftsmen
MINI-FLORA - Flowers, plants, and seeds - J. Benjamin Williams
MINI FLUSH - Toilet-tank float - Mini Flush Co. Inc.
MINI-FOLD - Electronic equipment ☆ - Da-Lite Screen Co. Inc.
MINI-FONATOR - Hearing aids - Siemens Hearing Instruments Inc.
MINI FOOD 'N' FOUNTAIN (CAT) - Pet products - Molor Products Co.
MINI-FORTRUSS - Hardware - Louisville Ladder Group LLC
MINI-FRAGRANCE - Candles ☆ - Will & Baumer, Inc.
MINI-FRAMES - Frames–picture - Arlan Art Products
MINI-FRUITS - Candy - California Hi-Lites, Inc.
MINI, FRUITS, FLORAL & SWAGS - Wallpaper - Mirage Wallcovering Co.
MINI FUN CHIPS - Confections - Richardson Brands
MINI FURNITURE - Toys - Ibssl, Inc.
MINI GALLERY - Posters - C.M. Paula Co.
MINI-GARDEN - Flower pots–plastic ☆ - A.H. Hoffman Inc.
MINI-GARDENS - Novelty items - West Coast Wood Specialties
MINI-GASSER - Trailers–travel ☆ - Viking Recreational Vehicles Inc.
MINI-GATOR - Battery testers - Mueller Electric Co.
MINI-GIFTS - Flowers–artificial - Contemporary Inc.
MINI-GIRL - Underwear and nightwear - Spirite Industries Inc.
MINI GO LIGHTLY - Strollers–baby - Aprica Kassai USA Inc.
MINI GOLF - Video game - Bally Sente Inc.
MINI GRAPE - Candy ☆ - Leaf, Inc.
MINI-GRATE - Fireplace equipment ☆ - Duraflame, Inc.
MINI GUNDY - Toys–stuffed ☆ - Gund, Inc.
MINI HEARTH - Heaters–space - Desa International, Inc.
MINI-HOG ROAST - Meat - Shoup Processing, Inc.
MINI HOLD - Adhesives and sealants - Handcraft Designs Inc.
MINI HOME - Motor vehicles–motor homes - Space Craft Manufacturing Inc.
MINI-HOOKS - Hooks - Miller Studio
MINI HOPPER - Toys–automobiles - Tyco Toys

MINI HOT SHOCKS - Toys - Tyco Toys
MINI-JAMA - Apparel–women's - Wacoal America Inc.
MINI-JET - Pumps–water - Aquarium Systems, Inc.
MINI-JET - Toys–airplanes ☆ - Victor Stanzel and Co.
MINI-JUMP - Cables - E.I. Dupont de Nemours and Co.
MINI K-9 - Pet products - Electric Cleaner Co.
MINI K-TOTS - Toys–stuffed - Kamar International Inc.
MINI KADDY - Containers–trash - F.H. Lawson Co.
MINI-KAT - Surveillance equipment - Combi International Corp.
MINI-KAT - Surveillance equipment - Philips Communication & Security Systems Inc.
MINI-KEG - Kegs–wood ☆ - Spaulding & Frost Co. Inc.
MINI KING - Bilge pumps ☆ - Attwood Corp.
MINI KINS - Candy - Murray-Allen International Inc.
MINI-KITCHENS - Refrigerators - King Refrigerator Corp.
MINI KOOSH - Toys - Oddzon Products, Inc.
MINI-KOTER - Paint rollers - Wooster Brush Co.
MINI-LABS - Science kits - Educational Design Inc.
MINI-LAMP - Lighting equipment - Ever-Ready Co.
MINI-LASE - Laser systems–medical - Kentek Corp.
MINI LASS - Watches - Hampden Corp.
MINI-LEAD - Pet products - Berolina Imports
MINI-LIGHT - Clocks ☆ - General Time Corp. (Westclox/Seth Thomas Div.)
MINI LIMITER - Audio equipment - MXR Innovations Inc.
MINI-LITE - Lenses–magnifying - Bausch & Lomb Inc.
MINI-LITE - Lighting fixtures - Swivelier Co. Inc.
MINI-LITE - Watches - Helbros International
MINI LITE 5000 PACKAGE - Clamps–metal - Sign-Up Corp.
MINI-LOK - Bicycle parts and accessories - Sunshine U-Lok Corp.
MINI-LOVE THOUGHTS - Novelty items - West Coast Wood Specialties
MINI LUV - Dolls - Russ Berrie and Co., Inc.
MINI-MA - Massage products - Great Earth Nutrients, Inc.
MINI MACKS - Toy construction trucks - Intex Recreation Corp.
MINI-MAG - Lenses–magnifying ☆ - Edroy Products Co.
MINI-MAG - Thermometers - Taylor Environmental Instruments
MINI-MAG LITE - Lamps - Roxter Lighting
MINI MAGLITE - Flashlights - Mag Instrument Inc.
MINI MAGNA-FX - Orthopedic screw - Zimmer, Inc.
MINI-MAGNUM - Archery equipment ☆ - Bear Archery Inc.
MINI MAGNUM - Goggles–safety - Outdoor Optics, Inc.
MINI-MARKERS - Electronic equipment - Dixon Ticonderoga Co.
MINI-MARKET - Toys - Mattel, Inc.
MINI MARS LANDER - Toys–models ☆ - Estes Industries
MINI-MARVEL - Water purification systems - Aquarium Products Inc.
MINI MASK - Automotive parts and accessories - Alco Manufacturing Co. Inc.
MINI MASTER - Hearing aids ☆ - Rexton Inc.
MINI-MATE PLUS - Kitchen appliances - Cuisinart Inc.
MINI MATES - Barrettes - Fantasia Accessories Ltd.
MINI MATES - Dining room furniture ☆ - Daystrom Furniture Inc.
MINI-MATES - Jewelry - Bates Creations Inc.
MINI MATES - Wallpaper - United Wallcoverings
MINI MATES 6TH EDITION - Wallpaper - United Wallcoverings
MINI-MATIC - Computer storage devices ☆ - Mead-Hatcher, Inc.
MINI-MATIC - Film - Dukane Corp.
MINI-MATT - Pet products - Larry Products Co.
MINI-MAX - Cases–eyeglass - California Optical Leather Inc.
MINI-MAX - Cleaning preparations - PDG Precision, Inc.
MINI MAX - Health care products - Medisonic USA Inc.
MINI-MAX - Health care products - Roho, Inc.
MINI MAX - Medical apparatus - United States Manufacturing Co.
MINI MAX - Umbrellas - International Rainwear, Inc.
MINI-MAX CLEANER - Cleaning equipment - Max Friedheim
MINI-MAX STEAMER - Generators - Max Friedheim
MINI-MEADOW - Flowers, plants, and seeds ☆ - Applewood Seed & Garden Group
MINI-MEAN MACHINE - Toys–models ☆ - Estes Industries
MINI-MED MYCIN JR. - Veterinary pharmaceutical preparations - Dyna Pet Inc.
MINI-MED PURAZONE JR. - Veterinary pharmaceutical preparations - Dyna Pet Inc.
MINI-MEDICAL - Dental equipment - AFP Imaging Corp.
MINI-MEGA - Pet products - Pyramid Bird Toys
MINI MESSAGES - Greeting cards - Current, Inc.
MINI-METER - Voltmeters - A.W. Sperry Instruments, Inc.
MINI-MICRO - Dishes–plastic - Projectapix-II
MINI MILK - Ice milk - Good Humor Corp.
MINI-MILL - Tools - Granberg International

☆ = Now out of production

MINI-MINI - Low-sodium salt - Frank J. Italiano Inc.
MINI MINS - Vitamins and nutritional supplements - Natural Organics, Inc.
MINI-MIRACLE - Brushes - Maywood Industries Inc.
MINI MISER - Kitchen appliances ☆ - Regal Ware, Inc.
MINI-MISER - Motor vehicles - Ransomes-Cushman-Ryan
MINI MISS - Bicycles - Columbia Manufacturing Inc.
MINI MISS FLYER - Ride-on toy - Radio Flyer Inc.
MINI MIST PORTABLE COOLING SYSTEM - Hoses - Arizona Mist
MINI MITE - Battery chargers - Electro-Mech Co.
MINI-MITE - Toys ☆ - Henry Gordy International Inc.
MINI MITE - Vacuum cleaners and accessories - The Eureka Co.
MINI-MIX - Microphones ☆ - Switchcraft Inc.
MINI-MIZER - Connectors–electrical - Conxall Inc.
MINI-MIZER - Water purification systems - King Technology, Inc.
MINI MOBILES - Beads - Greene Plastics Corp.
MINI-MOD - Toys - M.&S. Shillman Inc.
MINI MODULARS - Craft supplies ☆ - Western Trimming Corp.
MINI-MODULE - Racks - Jarke Corp.
MINI MONSTER - Fireworks - American Promotional Events, Inc.
MINI MONSTER - Garbage disposal units–household - JWC Environmental
MINI MONSTERS MUNCHERS - Candy - Brach and Brock Confections Inc.
MINI MOO'S - Dairy products - Land O'Lakes Inc.
MINI-MOOS - Dairy products ☆ - Land O' Lakes, Inc. (Fluid Dairy Division)
MINI MOOS - Puddings–canned ☆ - Dannon Co., Inc.
MINI MOPS - Greeting cards ☆ - Fran Mar Greeting cards Ltd.
MINI MOPS - Toys–stuffed - Russ Berrie and Co., Inc.
MINI MORES - Food products - Pritikin Systems, Inc.
MINI-MORNAP - Napkins–paper - Fort Howard Corp.
MINI-MORSELS - Food products - General Mills, Inc.
MINI MOTOR - Motors–outboard - Seaborne Systems Inc.
MINI MOTOR MACHINES - Toys–automobiles - Imperial Toy Corp.
MINI-MOTORS - Toys - Classic Coachworks Toys Inc.
MINI-MOTORS - Toys - Learning Resources, Inc.
MINI MOTT'S - Juices - Cadbury Beverages Inc.
MINI MOUNTAIN - Deodorizers - Surco Products Inc.
MINI-MOUNTIE - Bicycles ☆ - Raleigh USA Bicycle Co.
MINI MOUSE - Amplifiers–musical instrument ☆ - Lectrosonics Inc.
MINI MOVER - Pet products ☆ - Doskocil Manufacturing Co., Inc.
MINI-MOVIE - Video production - Taweel-Loos & Co.
MINI-MULE - Tools - Deuer Manufacturing Inc.
MINI MULTI-MIRROR - Electronic equipment - Thomson Consumer Electronics, Inc.
MINI MULTI-MIRROR - Lamps - General Electric Co.
MINI-MUM WALL-IT - Bicycle parts and accessories - Bike Track, Inc.
MINI-MUMS - Ophthalmic goods - Foremost Optical Products
MINI MUNCHERS - Bags ☆ - Gold Medal Inc.
MINI MUNCHIES - Snack foods - Hain Food Group, Inc.
MINI-MUSEUMS - Hobby kits - Educational Insights, Inc.
MINI MUSIC CENTER - Display rack - Close Marketing
MINI-NAILER - Tools–power-driven ☆ - ITW Paslode
MINI NEPTUNE - Pet products - Tetra Sales USA
MINI NOTE CUBE - Tape–adhesive - Paper Conversions Inc.
MINI NUGGETS - Stoves–wood-burning - Union Camp Corp. (Fine Paper Division)
MINI PACK - Meat products–beef - Colonial Beef Co.
MINI-PACK - Vacuum cleaners and accessories ☆ - Home Care Industries, Inc.
MINI-PAK - Cylinders - American Cylinder Co., Inc.
MINI PASS - Watches - Hampden Corp.
MINI-PATRIOT - Toys–models - Estes Industries
MINI PEARLS - Fruits and vegetables - Minnesota Foodservice, Inc.
MINI-PERISTACTIC - Medical apparatus - Mentor O & O Inc.
MINI-PETS - Toys–stuffed ☆ - Knickerbocker Toy Co. Inc.
MINI PIG PREMIUM - Animal feeds - Bluebonnet Milling Co.
MINI PLANER - Machinery - DBNA Trademarks Holding Inc.
MINI-PLUG - Electrical equipment - General Cable Corp.
MINI POLE - Paint sprayers - ASM Co.
MINI POLE - Skin care products - Hess Hair Milk Laboratories Inc.
MINI PONY - Toys ☆ - Hartco Inc.
MINI PORTRAIT - Cameras - Polaroid Corp.
MINI-POSTER - Novelty items–paper - Strand Enterprises
MINI POT - Pans ☆ - General Housewares Corp.
MINI POUCH - Cases–eyeglass - California Optical Leather Inc.
MINI-POUR - Dispensers - American Belt Co.
MINI POW-R-NOZZLE - Brushes–paint - Health-Mor Inc.
MINI-POWER BTE - Hearing aids - Widex Hearing Aid Co., Inc.

MINI POWER STRIP - Electrical equipment - Gem Electric Manufacturing Co. Inc.
MINI PRIMO - Hearing aids - Rexton Inc.
MINI PRIMO+ - Hearing aids ☆ - Rexton Inc.
MINI PRINTER - Stamps–hand - Artistic Greetings, Inc.
MINI-PRINTS - Paper–gift wrap - Current, Inc.
MINI-PRINTS - Posters ☆ - Stevenson Industries Inc.
MINI PRO - Boats–motor ☆ - Caddo Boat Manufacturing Co.
MINI PRO - Saws–chain - McCulloch Corp.
MINI-PROBE - Electrical testing instruments - A.W. Sperry Instruments, Inc.
MINI PROP CLASSICS - Toys–airplanes - Imperial Toy Corp.
MINI PRO'S - Toys–stuffed - Gund, Inc.
MINI-PROX - Electronic equipment - Electrocorp
MINI PUMP POWER - Air purification systems ☆ - Medo Industries, Inc.
MINI-PUTT - Computer software ☆ - Accolade Inc.
MINI PYTHON - Fireworks - American Promotional Events, Inc.
MINI QUARTZ - Clocks ☆ - General Time Corp. (Westclox/Seth Thomas Div.)
MINI-QUICK - Cases–camera - SP Systems/Saratons
MINI-QUICK - Connectors–electrical - Hubbell Inc.
MINI-QUICK - Vitamins and nutritional supplements - Twinlab
MINI-QUOTABLES - Posters - Stevenson Industries Inc.
MINI-QUOTES - Novelty items–paper - Strand Enterprises
MINI RAD FLYER - Ride-on toy - Radio Flyer Inc.
MINI RAM - Motor vehicles ☆ - Chrysler Corp. (Dodge Car Div.)
MINI-RANGER - Tools–power-driven - Utility Solutions, Inc.
MINI-RATCHET - Buckles - Ancra International Corp.
MINI-RIDER - Wheelchairs - Ricon Corp.
MINI-RIGS - Toys - Tonka Corp.
MINI-RING - Photographic equipment - SP Systems/Saratons
MINI RINOS - Toys–stuffed ☆ - Dakin Inc.
MINI-ROCKET - Toys–airplanes ☆ - Victor Stanzel and Co.
MINI-ROOTER - Tools–power-driven - General Wire Spring Co.
MINI-ROVER - Lighters ☆ - Ronson Consumer Products Corp.
MINI ROYAL - Game machines - Bally Gaming International, Inc.
MINI-SAFE KEY CHAIN - Key rings - Karlen Manufacturing, Inc.
MINI SATELLITE - Bathroom accessories - Surco Products Inc.
MINI SCALE COMBO - Toys–models ☆ - Estes Industries
MINI-SCALLY - Fishing lures - Creme Lure Co.
MINI SCRAMBLER - Bicycles - Schwinn Cycling & Fitness Inc.
MINI-SCRUB - Brooms - Lighthouse Industries
MINI-SEEDER - Fertilizers - Greenview Lawn & Garden Products
MINI SENTRY - Alarm systems - Astro-Guard Industries Inc.
MINI SERIES - Toxins - Mine Safety Appliances Co.
MINI-SHEETS - Labels–paper - Avery Dennison Corp.
MINI SHOE HOUSE - Games - J. Hermes
MINI-SHOP - Tools ☆ - Cooper Industries, Inc.
MINI SHOT - Photographic equipment - Egriment USA, Inc.
MINI SHUTTLE - Toys–models ☆ - Estes Industries
MINI-SINK - Housewares - Fesco Plastics Corp.
MINI-SOFTALK - Telephone apparatus - Softalk Inc.
MINI SONIC - Horns–motor vehicle ☆ - Falcon Safety Products, Inc.
MINI SORTER - File folders - Newell Office Products
MINI SOUND CATCHER - Microphones - Sima Products Corp.
MINI SOURS - Candy - Murray-Allen International Inc.
MINI-SPACE - Furniture - Ard Manufacturing Co. Inc.
MINI SPACEMAKERS - Leather goods - St. Thomas Inc.
MINI-SPAN - Metals - Kelly Klosure Systems
MINI-SPHERE - Clocks ☆ - General Time Corp. (Westclox/Seth Thomas Div.)
MINI-SPLASH - Bar fixtures–metal ☆ - Crossbow Inc.
MINI SPORT - Cameras ☆ - Pentax Corp.
MINI-SPORTEE - Cooking equipment–household - Birmingham Stove & Range Co.
MINI SPORTS - Pool tables, etc. - Indian Industries Inc.
MINI-SPORTS - Tires - Bridgestone/Firestone, Inc.
MINI-SPORTS KITS - Now out of production ☆ - Orange Products Inc.
MINI-SPOT - Spotlights - Roxter Lighting
MINI SPRAYMAID - Housewares ☆ - Compac Industries Inc.
MINI-SQUIRT - Garden equipment ☆ - H.D. Hudson Manufacturing Co.
MINI-STACKERS - Shelving units–wood - Hirsh Co.
MINI STAGE - Electronic equipment - Buhl Industries, Inc.
MINI-STAGGERED CHANNEL - Lighting equipment - Legion Lighting Co., Inc.
MINI STICKS - Candy - Cosmo Food USA
MINI STIMS - Pharmaceutical stimulant ☆ - Richard A. Deer
MINI-STOP - Musical instrument accessories - M & M Distributing Co.
MINI-STOPPER - Sporting goods ☆ - Nashmarine
MINI-STOVE - Stoves - Perfection Tip Co.

☆ = Now out of production

MINI-STRIP - Lighting equipment - Legion Lighting Co., Inc.
MINI STX - Sporting goods - STX, Inc.
MINI-STYLER - Curling irons–electric ☆ - Master Appliance Corp.
MINI SUPREME - Tools–garden - Gilmour Manufacturing Co.
MINI-SWADE - Paint - Sherwin-Williams Automotive Finishes Corp.
MINI SWEETS - Onions - Fort Boise Produce Co.
MINI SWINGER - Bicycles ☆ - J.C. Penney Co., Inc.
MINI-SWITCHMODE - Electronic equipment - Johanson Dielectrics, Inc.
MINI SYSTEMS - Audio equipment - Aiwa America Inc.
MINI-SZPALTIA - Sporting goods - Lindy Little Joe Inc.
MINI-TACOS - Snack foods - Pet Inc.
MINI TAILS - Infant product - Tails Aloft
MINI TANGOES - Games - Rex Games, Inc.
MINI TARTLETS - Pastries - Dufour Pastry Kitchens Inc.
MINI TATER TOTS - Food products - Promark International, Inc.
MINI-TAURUS - Orthodontic equipment - RMO, Inc.
MINI THEFT STOPPER - Alarm systems–fire - Safety Technology International, Inc.
MINI THIN - Contact lenses ☆ - Conforma Contact Lenses
MINI THUMBALL - Computer software - IMSI
MINI TIFFANY - Lamps - Meyda Tiffany Inc.
MINI TIME & FUN - Toys–electronic - Video Technology U.S. Inc.
MINI TINKLE CRINKLE - Toys–stuffed - Gund, Inc.
MINI TOGS - Infant product - Tidy International Corp.
MINI TORCHES AND ACCESSORIES - Torches - Bernzomatic
MINI-TRACH - Medical apparatus - Smiths Industries Medical Systems, Inc.
MINI-TRACK - Lighting fixtures - Roxter Lighting
MINI-TRAK KIT - Skin care products ☆ - Freeman Industries LLC
MINI-TRAMPOLINES - Sporting goods - M.T.I. Corp.
MINI-TREE - Racks - Jarke Corp.
MINI TRI PAK - Toys–models ☆ - Estes Industries
MINI-TRIARAMA - Hardware - Merchandising Inventives, Inc.
MINI-TRIEVER - Floor sweeper - Advance Machine Co.
MINI TRONICS - Die-cast toy vehicles - Matchbox Toys USA
MINI TUFF LITE - Flashlights - Garrity Industries
MINI TURBO 1250 - Dryers–hair ☆ - Sunbeam-Oster Household Products
MINI-TWIN - Paper–toilet - Fort Howard Corp.
MINI TWINN - Bicycles - Schwinn Cycling & Fitness Inc.
MINI-TWIST-ON - Hardware - Merchandising Inventives, Inc.
MINI-VAC - Pumps - Simer Pump Co.
MINI-VAC - Vacuum cleaners and accessories - Randal Marketing Corp.
MINI VAPOR SCREEN - Deodorizers - Surco Products Inc.
MINI-VENTS - Ventilation equipment - N.H. Rudeen Co.
MINI-VIEW - Electronic equipment ☆ - Da-Lite Screen Co. Inc.
MINI-VOX - Medical apparatus - Luminaud Inc.
MINI-VUE - Frames–eyeglass - May Optical Co. Inc.
MINI WAGON - Trailers–travel - Wells Cargo Inc.
MINI-WASH - Washing machines–commercial - General Electric Co.
MINI-WATER-MATIC - Pet waterer - Roto Dyne Plastics West
MINI-WAVE - Toys–electronic - Kenner Products
MINI-WAVE - Welding equipment - Pace, Inc.
MINI WEBPHONE - Computer software - Netspeak Corp.
MINI WHEEL FLYERS - Toys–automobiles - Imperial Toy Corp.
MINI-WHEELS - Motor vehicles - Bird Bromiticous Inc.
MINI-WHIZ-RING - Toys - North Pacific Products Inc.
MINI WIGLET - Wigs - Paula Young
MINI WIND UPS - Toys - Imperial Toy Corp.
MINI WING - Antennas - Wintenna Inc.
MINI-WIRE - Underwear and nightwear - Maidenform Inc.
MINI WISHES - Giftware - Russ Berrie and Co., Inc.
MINI WOOSH - Toys - Oddzon Products, Inc.
MINI WORK-FORCE - Saws–power - Rayco Manufacturing, Inc.
MINI WORKS M W - Apparel–children's - Beyond Basics Kids, Inc.
MINI-WORLD - Aquariums–household - Pets International, Ltd.
MINI-WRITE - Computer software - Minico Inc.
MINI Z'S - Toys - Lewis Galoob Toys, Inc.
MINIAC - Lighting fixtures - Xantech Inc.
MINIATURE - Brushes–hair ☆ - Phillips Brush Corp.
MINIATURE - Frames–eyeglass - May Optical Co. Inc.
MINIATURE BASEBALL - Games - Base-Hit, Inc.
MINIATURE COLLECTION - Lighting fixtures–underwater - Planet Earth Inc.
MINIATURE MONSTER KIT - Novelty items - Dynamic Development
MINIATURE TALKING EGGS - Candy - Stark Candy Co.
MINIATURE THIN - Candy ☆ - F.B. Washburn Candy Corp.
MINIATURE TREASURES - Giftware - Craft World International Inc.

MINIATURE WONDERS - Flowers, plants, and seeds - Micky's Mini-Flora Express, Ltd.
MINIATURE ZEN - Hobby kits - Sarut Inc.
MINIATURES - Leather goods - St. Thomas Inc.
MINIATURES - Wallpaper - Quality House Wallcoverings
MINIATURES - Wallpaper ☆ - Imperial Wallcoverings, Inc.
MINIATURES IN FASHION - Crocheted and knitted items - Baby Togs, Inc.
MINIAX - Laboratory apparatus - Kurt J. Lesker Co.
MINIBAR SYSTEMS - Refrigerators - Minibar North America, Inc.
MINIBAY - Lighting fixtures - Hubbell Lighting, Inc. (Lighting Div.)
MINIBEND - Cables–coaxial - Astrolab, Inc.
MINIBITS - Cookies - Ripon Foods, Inc.
MINIBLASTER ARROW - Archery equipment - Rocket Aerohead Corp.
MINIBOAT - Marine rigging - Nar Laboratories, Inc.
MINIBRA - Apparel and accessories - Beverly Vogue Co.
MINIBULK - Containers–trash - Advanced Delivery & Chemical Systems, Ltd.
MINIBUOY - Nautical instruments ☆ - Soderberg Manufacturing Co. Inc.
MINICAD - Computer software - Diehl Graphsoft Inc.
MINICAPS - Pharmaceutical preparations - Wesley Pharmacal Co. Inc.
MINICARD - Photographic equipment - Eastman Kodak Co.
MINICASE - Gears - Nord Gear Corp.
MINICHAMP - Knives–pocket ☆ - Swiss Army Brands, Ltd.
MINICLASIX - Blankets - Impact Imports International, Inc.
MINICLOCKS - Clocks - Miniclock Co.
MINICOM - Watches - Helbros International
MINICOM III - Telephones–text ☆ - Ultratec, Inc.
MINICOM IV - Telephones–text - Ultratec, Inc.
MINICON - Hearing aids - Oticon Corp.
MINICRAFT - Toys–models ☆ - Minicraft Models Inc.
MINICRAFTER - Welding equipment ☆ - Controls Corp. of America
MINICRATES - Wood products ☆ - Carousel Crafts Co.
MINICUBE - Clocks ☆ - General Time Corp. (Westclox/Seth Thomas Div.)
MINICUBE - Salt - North American Salt Co.
MINIDAPTER - Photographic equipment - SP Systems/Saratons
MINIDART - Toys ☆ - Placo Products Co.
MINIDOME - Hobby kits - Avionics Plastics Corp.
MINIEYE - Ophthalmic goods ☆ - Luxottica
MINIFAST - Food supplement - Essen Nutrition Corp.
MINIFISH - Ships–sailing vessels ☆ - Sunfish Laser Inc.
MINIFLECTOR - Antennas - Scala Electronic Corp.
MINIFLOOD - Lighting fixtures ☆ - Hubbell Lighting, Inc. (Lighting Div.)
MINIFLORA - Candles ☆ - Candle-Lite Co.
MINIFOGGER - Nozzles - Spraying Systems Co.
MINIFOIL - Kites - Kite Factory
MINIFOLD - Paper–toilet - Georgia-Pacific Corp.
MINIFOLD READER - Sporting goods - USA Sport Eyewear
MINIFORCE - Tools–hand-operated - Uniontools, Inc.
MINIFORM - Paper products - Georgia-Pacific Corp.
MINIGARD - Diapers–disposable - Whitestone Products Inc.
MINIGARDEN - Self-watering planters - Holtkamp Greenhouses Inc.
MINIGATE - Construction equipment rental services - Graphnet, Inc.
MINIGO - Strollers–baby - Aprica Kassai USA Inc.
MINIGRAPHICS - House furnishings ☆ - Foley & Robinson Inc.
MINIGRATED - Blast furnaces - Acme Steel Co.
MINIGROOVE - Sealing devices - Tetrafluor Inc.
MINIHEART - Medical apparatus - Vortran Medical Technology, Inc.
MINIHONI - Manicure preparations - Creative Nail Design, Inc.
MINIHOONIES - Toys - Robert Kachler
MINIKIN - Clocks - General Time Corp. (Westclox/Seth Thomas Div.)
MINIKINO - Electronics equipment - Marty Bahn & Co.
MINIKINS - Fabrics - Dan River Inc.
MINIKINS - Greeting cards - Fravessi Greetings, Inc.
MINILIFTER - Machine tools - D & L Inc.
MINILINE - Rope - Yale Cordage, Inc.
MINILINK - Transmitting apparatus - Microtek Electronics
MINILITE - Photographic equipment - SP Systems/Saratons
MINILITER - Lighting fixtures - Hubbell Lighting, Inc. (Lighting Div.)
MINILOG - Labels–gummed - Goda & Associates, Inc.
MINILOGS - Fireplace logs–treated - Buck Creek Mesquite
MINILOOK - Ophthalmic goods - Robin Optical
MINILOON - Novelty items - CTI Industries Corp.
MINILUX - Photographic equipment ☆ - Luminos Photo Corp.
MINILYNXX - Transmitting apparatus–radio - Mobile Satellite Products Corp.
MINIM - Pens ☆ - Parker Pen USA
MINIM EYES - Frames–eyeglass - May Optical Co. Inc.
MINIMA - Lighting fixtures - Edison Price Lighting

☆ = Now out of production

MINIMA - Window coverings - Joanna Western Mills Co.
MINIMAC - Electronic equipment ☆ - MacKenzie Laboratories Inc.
MINIMAG - Sporting goods - Airgun Designs, Inc.
MINIMAG - Tools ☆ - General Tools Manufacturing Co. Inc.
MINIMAL - Recording label - Quark, Inc.
MINIMALS - Toys–stuffed - Sandra Boynton
MINIMAN - Radios - Jonathan Blau
MINIMASTERS - Paints–artists' - Cottage Editions, Ltd.
MINIMAT - Floor coverings - Devon Corp.
MINIMAT - Mats - Master Woodcraft Inc.
MINIMATE - Containers - Igloo Products Corp.
MINIMATE - Mixers–concrete - Strong Manufacturing Co., Inc.
MINIMATIC - Watches - Movado Time Corp.
MINIMATS - Stamps–hand - Sixta Manufacturing
MINIMAX - Ammunition ☆ - Olin Corp. (Winchester Div.)
MINIMAX - Heaters–swimming pool - PacFab, Inc.
MINIMAX - Thermometers - Maximum Inc.
MINIMAX - Wire–insulated - Cable Design Technolgies, Inc.
MINIMESH - Metals - Keene Corp. (Penn Metal Div.)
MINIMICROSPHERES - Pharmaceutical preparations - Solvay Pharmaceuticals Inc.
MINIMILL - Housewares - Tom David Inc.
MINIMISER - Animal feed supplements - Moorman Manufacturing Co.
MINIMITE - Lighting equipment - General Electric Co.
MINIMITE - Tools - Emerson Electric Co.
MINIMIXER - Electronics equipment - AMS Industries Inc.
MINIMIZE - Apparel–women's - NCC Industries, Inc.
MINIMIZER - Brassieres (Bras) - Custom Maid Brassiere Co.
MINIMIZER - Heat pumps ☆ - York International Corp.
MINIMIZER - Underwear and nightwear - NCC Industries, Inc.
MINIMIZER - Window coverings - Blind Design Inc.
MINIMOD - Switches–electric - Power Solutions Inc.
MINIMOOG - Synthesizers–musical instrument ☆ - EJE Research Corp.
MINIMOTOR - Electronic equipment - Micro Mo Electronics, Inc.
MINIMOUNT - Lighting equipment - General Electric Co.
MINIMUG - Wood products ☆ - Spaulding & Frost Co. Inc.
MINIMURAL - Artists' materials - Glenview Products Inc.
MINIMUS - Electronic equipment - Tandy Corp.
MINIMUX - Circuit boards - Precision Digital Corp.
MININAC - Electronic equipment - Hypercom Inc.
MININOME - Musical instrument accessories - Mininome Inc.
MINIO 2 - Oxygen ☆ - Caire
MINIOX - Health care products - Mine Safety Appliances Co.
MINIPAK - Hammocks - E-Z Sales & Manufacturing, Inc.
MINIPLEX - Pharmaceutical preparations - Wesley Pharmacal Co. Inc.
MINIPLEX - Tools–power-driven ☆ - Dico Products Corp.
MINIPLIER - Staplers - ACCO USA, Inc.
MINIPLUS - Vitamins and nutritional supplements - Amicon, Inc.
MINIPORT - Computer hardware - Ministor Peripherals Corp.
MINIPRESS - Pharmaceutical preparations - Pfizer Inc.
MINIPRESS XL - Pharmaceutical preparations - Pfizer Inc.
MINIPRINT 225 - Telephones–text - Ultratec, Inc.
MINIPRINT 425 - Telephones–text - Ultratec, Inc.
MINIPRO - Computers - Duracom Computer Systems
MINIPRO - Kitchen appliances - Robert Krups North America
MINIPURE - Water purification systems - Atlantic Ultraviolet Corp.
MINIREEF - Pet products - International Seaboard Corp.
MINIREX II - Photographic exposure meter ☆ - Saul Bower Inc.
MINIROUTER - Computer software - Hypercom Inc.
MINIS - Chewing gum - Nabisco Foods Group
MINI'S - Jewelry - Berry
MINI'S - Toys–stuffed - Kamar International Inc.
MINISCOPE - Binoculars - Pioneer Marketing & Research, Inc.
MINISETTE - Electronic equipment - Tandy Corp.
MINISHOOTER - Nozzles - Wet Labs Inc.
MINISIGHT - Photographic equipment - Bestwell Optical Instrument Co.
MINISLALOM - Boats–kayaks ☆ - Old Town Canoe Co.
MINISLIP - Boats–kayaks - Phoenix Products Inc.
MINISPEC - Frames–eyeglass - Pathway Optical Prods.
MINISPOT - Spotlights - Photogenic Machine Co.
MINISQUARE - Lighting fixtures ☆ - Hubbell Lighting, Inc. (Lighting Div.)
MINISTAR - Nautical instruments ☆ - Soderberg Manufacturing Co. Inc.
MINISTAT - Cleaning equipment - Kinetronics Corp.
MINISTATION - Computer peripheral equipment - Compaq Computer Corp.
MINISTER - Ophthalmic goods ☆ - Luxottica
MINISTICKERS - Decals and transfers - Bucher Brothers Inc.

MINISTOR - Computer hardware - Ministor Peripherals Corp.
MINISTRY RESOURCES LIBRARY - Publisher's imprints - Zondervan Publishing House
MINISTUDIO - Audio equipment - Teac America, Inc.
MINISWITCHER - Computer hardware - Intelligent Resources Integrated Systems, Inc.
MINISYSTEMS - Sporting goods ☆ - Daiwa Corp.
MINIT BOW MAKER - Novelty items - Sell-O Manufacturing Inc.
MINIT-CHEF - Meat products–beef - Maid-Rite Steak Co. Inc.
MINIT-CURL - Hair care products - Fleetwood Co.
MINIT-DRI - Paints - M.A. Bruder & Sons Inc.
MINIT LITE - Charcoal - Royal Oak Enterprises, Inc.
MINIT-LUBE - Automotive repair shops - Minit-Lube
MINIT-MAN - Automotive parts and accessories - Fibre Glass-Evercoat Co. Inc.
MINIT/MAXIT/TARGIT - Computer software ☆ - Milliken Publishing Co. (Computer Software Div.)
MINIT-RUB - Analgesics - Bristol-Myers Squibb Co.
MINIT SET - Spackling compound - D.I.Y. Products
MINITAB - Machinery - Heidelberg Harris Inc.
MINITANK - Holding tank - ITT Jabsco
MINITAPE - Tape recorders - Stancil Corp.
MINITEL - Photographic equipment - SP Systems/Saratons
MINITHERM - Heaters–swimming pool ☆ - Teledyne Laars
MINITHERM - Water heaters–household - Bel-Aire Sales Corp.
MINITILL - Computer hardware - CAP Automation
MINITIME - Clocks ☆ - General Time Corp. (Westclox/Seth Thomas Div.)
MINITOF - Laboratory apparatus - Comstock, Inc.
MINITONES - Floor coverings–carpet and rugs ☆ - Quaker Inc.
MINITOR II - Pagers - Motorola, Inc. (Land Mobile Products Sector)
MINITORCH - Blow torches ☆ - Kidde Safety
MINITOTE - Containers - Fruitcrown Products Corp.
MINITRAN - Nitroglycerin - Minnesota Mining & Manufacturing Co.
MINITREE - Craft supplies - Western Trimming Corp.
MINITRIM - Wood products - Georgia-Pacific Corp.
MINITRIX - Toys–trains - Model Power
MINITRON - Dry-foam shampooer - Advance Machine Co.
MINITRON - Pet products ☆ - Aquatronics-Filtronics
MINITS - Candy ☆ - Leaf, Inc.
MINITSET - Spackle paste - American Steel Wool Manufacturing Co. Inc.
MINIVATOR - Residential elevator - Access Industries, Inc.
MINIVAULT - Holsters - T.L. Industries, Inc.
MINIVECTOR - Thermostats - Chatham Brass Co. Inc.
MINIVEIL CLIMATE CONTROLLER - Air curtain doors - Berner International Corp. (Miniveil Air Curtain Div.)
MINIVENUS LITE - Automotive parts and accessories ☆ - Optronics Inc.
MINIVEX - Ships–sailing vessels ☆ - Lewmar Marine Inc.
MINIVEYOR HOLMAN - Cooking equipment–commercial - Holman Cooking Equipment, Inc.
MINIVIKE - Sanders and grinders - Black & Decker Corp.
MINIVISIONS - Wallpaper - Innervisions Corp.
MINIVOLT - Luggage - Ronde
MINIVOX LITE - Cellular phone - Audiovox Corp.
MINIWAVES - Apparel–children's - Knitwaves Inc.
MINIWEAR - Apparel–children's - Geoffrey Inc.
MINIWEAR - Apparel–children's - Kids R Us Co.
MINIWHACKER - Fishing lures - Bomber Bait Co.
MINIWRITER - Computer peripheral equipment - Data Entry Systems, Inc.
MINIWRITER - Dictating machines ☆ - Dictaphone Corp.
MINIZZA - Crackers - Nabisco Foods Group
MINK - Hair care products - Paul Mazzotta Inc.
MINK - Thread - New Bedford Thread Co. Inc.
MINK & PEARLS - Perfumes ☆ - Quintessence Inc.
MINK COAT - Cosmetics - Prince Matchabelli
MINK CREEK - Manufactured homes - Redman Industries, Inc.
MINK DIFFERENCE - Hair care products - Gillette Co.
MINK FAST SET - Hair care products - Posner Laboratories Inc.
MINK GARD - Cages–wire - Gilbert and Bennett Manufacturing Co.
MINK LASH - Cosmetics - Pfizer Inc.
MINK MAGIC - Automotive parts and accessories - Original Mink Oil Inc.
MINK MAGIC - Personal care products - Beauty Network, Inc.
MINK OIL - Hair coloring preparations - Stylors Inc.
MINK PRO - Hair care products - Posner Laboratories Inc.
MINK PRO-TECT - Hair care products - Posner Laboratories Inc.
MINK SELECTION - Hair care products - Keystone Laboratories Inc.
MINKA-AIRE - Fans–electric - Minka Lighting, Inc.
MINK'S - Candy - L.C. Good Candy Co. Inc.

☆ = Now out of production

MINKSHEEN - Veterinary pharmaceutical preparations - Dermac Laboratories, Inc.

MINN KOTA - Motors - Johnson Worldwide Associates, Inc.

MINN KOTA - Motors–automotive - Johnson Fishing Inc.

MINNCLEAN - Disinfectants - Minntech Corp.

MINNEAPOLIS-MOLINE - Toys–models - Agco Corp.

MINNEAPOLIS QUALITY - Flour–blended - Pillsbury Co.

MINNEHAHA - Water–bottled or canned - Minnehaha Spring Water Co.

MINNEHAHA MOCCASINS - Footwear - Rodeo Leather Goods Co. Inc.

MINNESOTA - Paints - Valspar Corp.

MINNESOTA BLUES - Apparel and accessories - Red Wing Shoe Co. Inc.

MINNESOTA CLE - Video production - Minnesota State Bar Association

MINNESOTA COMPOSER'S FORUM - Recording label - Jazz Composer's Orchestra Association Inc.

MINNESOTA DAIRY - Milk - Minnesota Dairy Co. Inc.

MINNESOTA FATS - Darts and dart games - Dart Mart Inc.

MINNESOTA FATS - Game tables - Minnesota Fats Billiard Factory Inc.

MINNESOTA FATS - Pool tables - Goods Manufacturers International

MINNESOTA FATS POOL LEGEND - Computer software - Data East USA Inc.

MINNESOTA GAMBLER - Games - Universal Manufacturing Co., Inc.

MINNESOTA HATS - Hats - MU Industries Inc.

MINNESOTA HEARTLAND - Soups–canned - Frontier Soups

MINNESOTA HOT - Thompson's Fine Foods, Inc.

MINNESOTA RATS - Apparel and accessories - James J. Feuling

MINNESOTA SLIM - Food products - Minnesota Slim Inc.

MINNESOTA TECHNICAL RESEARCH - Electronic equipment - MTR, Inc.

MINNESOTA TIMBER TOYS - Toys–automobiles - K & A Products, Inc.

MINNESOTA TIMBERWOLVES - Apparel–athletic - Minnesota Timberwolves Basketball LP

MINNESOTA VIKINGS - Trading cards and stamps - Minnesota Vikings Football Club, Inc.

MINNESOTA'S - Beverages–malt - Minnesota Brewing Co.

MINNETONKA - Footwear - Minnetonka Moccasin Co. Inc.

MINNIE - Motor vehicles–motor homes - Winnebago Industries, Inc.

MINNIE 300 - MOTOR HOMES - Motor vehicles–motor homes - Winnebago Industries, Inc.

MINNIE & MAGGIE - Magnets - Fisher-Price, Inc.

MINNIE LUBE - Lubricating oils ☆ - Hodgdon Powder Co. Inc.

MINNIE MOUSE - Publisher's imprints - Walt Disney Co.

MINNIE 'N ME - Furniture - American Toy & Furniture Co.

MINNIE 'N ME - Games - Walt Disney Co.

MINNIE 'N ME - Wallpaper ☆ - Priss Prints Inc.

MINNIE WINNIE - Motor vehicles–motor homes - Winnebago Industries, Inc.

MINNIEMAX - Food processors ☆ - National Presto Industries, Inc.

MINNITANK - Industrial gases - Airosol Co. Inc.

MINNOW - Boats - Westgate Research Inc.

MINNOW - Boats–kayaks - Rotocast Plastic Products

MINNOW SPOON - Fishing lures - Normark Corp.

MINNOWS - Medical apparatus - Marquette Electronics, Inc.

MINNTECH - Disinfectants - Minntech Corp.

MINNY HOONEY - Giftware ☆ - Aloha Candle Manufacturing Co. Inc.

MINO-MIZER - Fishing lures - Hypark Specialty Co., Inc.

MINOBOSSI - Leather goods - Italian Classics Inc.

MINOCQUA - Vegetables–canned - Loyal Canning Corp.

MINOKA - Frames–eyeglass - Hoya Corp. USA

MINOLTA - Photographic equipment - Minolta Corp.

MINOLTA MASTER C-522 - Cameras–video - Minolta Corp.

MINOLTA MOVIE - Cameras–video ☆ - Minolta Corp.

MINOM - Flour–blended - Minom, Inc.

MINOR - Soups–canned - Freskeeto Frozen Foods Inc.

MINOR LEAGUE - Colognes - Brandy Harvest

MINOR SCALES - Musical instrument accessories - Minor Scales

MINORA - Razor blades - Gillette Co.

MINORAX - Surgical instruments - Minorax Corp.

MINOREX - Aquatic pharmacuetical preparations ☆ - Aquatronics-Filtronics

MINORI - Rice - Williams Rice Milling Co.

MINOS - Faucets - Kallista Inc.

MINOT - Fruits and vegetables - Minot Food Packers Inc.

MINOT - Powerboat ☆ - Boston Whaler, Inc.

MINOTAL - Pharmaceutical preparations - Bolan Pharmaceutical Inc.

MINOTAL - Pharmaceutical preparations ☆ - Carnick Laboratories Inc.

MINOTAUR - Mats–rattan ☆ - Golden Star Inc.

MINOTAURE - Frames–eyeglass - Rafael Lopez Cambil

MINOTAURE - Mens' fragrance - Paloma Picasso for Lopez Cambil, Ltd.

MINOTAURE - Shaving preparations - Cosmair Inc.

MINOVA - Health care products - ETAC USA Inc.

MINOWA - Food processors - Wapsie Produce Inc.

MINOX - Cameras ☆ - H.P. Marketing Corp.

MINQUILLA - Imitation fur ☆ - Ivy International Ltd.

MINRO-PLEX - Pharmaceutical preparations - Roberts/Hauck Pharmaceuticals Inc.

MINSA - Corn flour mix - T & D Prec-Tool's

MINSK 50 - Vodka - Ron Matusalem Co.

MINSKI - Wines - Fruit Wines of Florida Inc.

MINSTER - Catsup - Brooks Foods

MINSTREL - Chimes ☆ - J.W. Stannard Co.

MINSTREL - Dishes–earthenware - Denby USA Limited

MINSTREL - Floor coverings–carpet and rugs ☆ - Karastan-Bigelow Inc.

MINSTREL - Musical instrument accessories - Grover/Trophy Musical Products Inc.

MINSTREL - Publisher's imprints - Simon & Schuster, Inc.

MINSTREL - Recording label - Collegium Sound Inc.

MINT - Computers - Micro-International, Inc.

MINT - Dinnerware–glass ☆ - Nikko Ceramics Inc.

MINT 20 - Cleaning preparations - W.W. Grainger, Inc.

MINT *A* BURST - Candy - American Chicle Co.

MINT A BURST - Chewing gum - Warner-Lambert Co.

MINT & MENTHOL - Cigar boxes–wood ☆ - Consolidated Cigar Corp.

MINT BALLS - Candy - R.L. Albert & Son, Inc.

MINT-CARD - Metals - Bullion International, Inc.

MINT CHANGEMAKER - Candy ☆ - Brock Candy Co. Inc.

MINT CHOCOLATE SENSATIONS - Candy - S.L. Kaye Co., Inc.

MINT COLLECTION OF ENIGMA - Puzzles - Enigma

MINT CONDITION - Cleaning preparations - Amway Corp.

MINT CONDITION - Skin-care products - Origins Natural Resources Inc.

MINT COOKIE JOYS - Cookies - Crate and Barrel

MINT COOLERS - Candy - Brach and Brock Confections Inc.

MINT CRUNCH - Candy ☆ - Holland American Wafer Co.

MINT DELIGHTS - Candy ☆ - Pennsylvania Dutch Candies

MINT DELIGHTS - Cookies ☆ - Keebler Co.

MINT DEODORANT - Cleaning preparations - Analab Inc.

MINT DREAM BAR - Candy - Russell Stover Candies, Inc.

MINT EDITION - Slacks–men's - Jaymar-Ruby Inc.

MINT EDITION - Toys–automobiles - Racing Champions Inc.

MINT GREEN - Glassware–household ☆ - Lenox Crystal, Inc.

MINT HYDROX - Cookies ☆ - Sunshine Biscuits, Inc.

MINT JULEP - Deodorants–personal - Para Laboratories Inc.

MINT JULEP - Dolls ☆ - Effanbee Doll Corp.

MINT JULEP - Jewelry - A. Schein Co., Inc.

MINT JULEP - Teas - Eastern Shore Tea Co.

MINT JULEP MASQUE - Skin care products - Para Laboratories Inc.

MINT KRISPY - Candy - See's Candy Shops, Inc.

MINT LEAF - Glassware–household - Rezler & Howell Co.

MINT LEAVES - Candy - Frankford Candy & Chocolate Co. Inc.

MINT LUMPS - Candy - Helms Candy Manufacturing Co. Inc.

MINT MADNESS CHOCOLATE CHIP - Cookies - Vermont Country Foods Inc.

MINT MAGIC - Teas–herbal - Celestial Seasonings, Inc.

MINT MALLO - Candy ☆ - Boyer Candy Co., Inc.

MINT MALLOW PARFAIT - Candy ☆ - Brock Candy Co. Inc.

MINT MARVELS - Candy novelties - Bortz Chocolate Co.

MINT MEDLEY - Teas–herbal - R.C. Bigelow, Inc.

MINT MELTAWAYS - Candy - World's Finest Chocolate, Inc.

MINT MIRAGE - Coffee ☆ - Boyd Coffee Co.

MINT MOUNTAIN JELLY - Jams and jellies - Mountain Maid Gourmet Jelly

MINT 'OH'S - Chocolate bars - Saco Foods, Inc.

MINT PARFAIT - Candy - Nabisco Foods Group

MINT PEARLS - Candy - Brach and Brock Confections Inc.

MINT PRINT - Stamps–hand - Sanford Corp.

MINT PUFFS - Candy - Helms Candy Manufacturing Co. Inc.

MINT SENSATION - Mouthwashes - Pfizer Inc.

MINT SNUFF - Tobacco products - Oregon Mint Snuff Co.

MINT SOUFFLES - Candy ☆ - Pet Inc. (Whitman's Chocolates Div.)

MINT STARLIGHT - Candy ☆ - Helms Candy Manufacturing Co. Inc.

MINT STREET - Shoes - R.B. Alexander & Co. Ltd.

MINT-T-FRESH - Health care products - Equinox International Corp.

MINT TELLA - Candy ☆ - Van Melle Inc.

MINT TWIST STICK - Candy - Atkinson Candy Co.

MINTANE - Disinfectants ☆ - Dualle Products

MINTED CREAM - Glassware–household ☆ - Fenton Art Glass Co.

MINTEE-DISINFECTANT - Cleaning preparations - Analab Inc.

MINTEQ - Chemicals - Minteq International Inc.

MINTEX - Skin care products - Savogran Co.

MINTEZOL - Pharmaceutical preparations - Merck & Co., Inc. (Merck Research Laboratories)

MINTFERRONE - Iron oxide - Rogers' Drug Co.

MINTLETS - Candy - Brock Candy Co. Inc.

MINTOES ROLLS - Candy - Murray-Allen International Inc.

MINTON - Dinnerware–glass - Royal Doulton-Somerset UK Ltd.

MINTON - Glassware–household ☆ - Lotus Glass Co.

MINTON HOLLINS - Tiles–ceramic - Amsterdam Corp.

MINTONE - Iron oxide - Rogers' Drug Co.

MINTS JOTS - Candy - Brach and Brock Confections Inc.

MINTSENG - Candy ☆ - Bee Creek Botanicals

MINTY BELLS - Candy - R.M. Palmer Co.

MINTY HEARTS - Candy - R.M. Palmer Co.

MINTY MINDY - Toys - Tonka Corp.

MINTY MONSTERS - Candy ☆ - R.M. Palmer Co.

MINTY Q - Disinfectants - Harley Chemicals

MINUEL - Food products - Thriftway, Inc.

MINUET - Bathroom fixtures - Crane Plumbing/Fiat Products

MINUET - Boats - Glen-L Marine Designs

MINUET - Cabinets - Aristokraft, Inc.

MINUET - Chimes ☆ - J.W. Stannard Co.

MINUET - Christmas tree ornaments - Cracker Box Inc.

MINUET - Dishes–china ☆ - Pickard Inc.

MINUET - Food products - Staff Supermarket Associates, Inc.

MINUET - Hearing aids ☆ - Beltone Electronics Corp.

MINUET - Recording label - Holson Co.

MINUET - Tableware–china - Pfaltzgraff Investment Co.

MINUET - Trailers–travel - Airstream Inc.

MINUET - Underwear and nightwear - Bestform Foundations, Inc.

MINUET - Wallpaper ☆ - Capital Carousel Inc.

MINUET - Watches - Bulova Corp.

MINUETTA - Accordions - Fred Gretsch Enterprises

MINUETTE - Brushes–hair - Spornette International, Inc.

MINUETTE - Electronic equipment - Infinity Systems, Inc.

MINUIT - Cookies - Sunshine/Salerno Inc.

MINUM - Veterinary pharmaceutical preparations - Nutra-Vet Research Corp.

MINUS - Toys - Mattel, Inc.

MINUS-3 - Golf clubs ☆ - Raymon W. Cook

MINUS 40 - Footwear - Chippewa Shoe Co.

MINUS 50 - Apparel and accessories - RefrigiWear Inc.

MINUS MISSION - Computer software - SRA/McGraw-Hill (Div. of The McGraw-Hill Companies)

MINUS SINUS - Herbal products - Jaime Robertson

MINUSCYL - Optical scanners–computer - Titmus Optical, Inc.

MINUTE BARB - Wire–barbed ☆ - Dare Products Inc.

MINUTE BOW MAKER - Musical instruments - Fiddle Factory Inc.

MINUTE FLUSH - Chemical preparations - Zecol Inc.

MINUTE FRESH - Seafood products–fresh or frozen - Eat-All Frozen Food Co.

MINUTE GLON SERIES - Cooking equipment–household - LazyMan, Inc.

MINUTE GOURMET - Food products - Beatrice Cos. Inc.

MINUTE GRILL LIMITED, THE - Barbecues and grills - Thermos Co.

MINUTE GRILL, THE - Barbecues and grills - Thermos Co.

MINUTE MAID - Fruit drinks–bottled or canned - Coca-Cola Co.

MINUTE MAID FRUIT BARS - Ice cream ☆ - Eskimo Pie Corp.

MINUTE MAID NATURALS - Juices - Coca-Cola Co.

MINUTE MAID ORCHARD'S BEST - Juices - Coca-Cola Co.

MINUTE MAID ORIGINALS - Fruit drinks–bottled or canned - Coca-Cola Co.

MINUTE MAID PREMIUM CHOICE - Juices - Coca-Cola Co.

MINUTE MAKER - Cameras ☆ - Polaroid Corp.

MINUTE MAN - Cleaning preparations - New Method Manufacturing Co.

MINUTE-MAN - Fencing–gates and posts - Dare Products Inc.

MINUTE MAN - Fertilizers - Vigoro Industries, Inc.

MINUTE MAN - Fruit and vegetable markets - J.P. Sullivan & Co.

MINUTE MAN - Furniture ☆ - Athens Furniture Industries Inc.

MINUTE MAN - Hardware - Delta Products Corp.

MINUTE MAN - Meat products–beef - Colonial Beef Co.

MINUTE MAN - Publisher's imprints - Everyday Learning Corp.

MINUTE MAN - Restaurants–fast food - Minute Man of America

MINUTE MAN - Toys–models ☆ - Estes Industries

MINUTE MAN - Watches - Bulova Corp.

MINUTE MAN - Wet mops - American Textile Products Co.

MINUTE MARINATOR - Food processors - Minute Marinator Inc.

MINUTE MARKER - Laser transmitter - Spectra-Physics Laserplane, Inc.

MINUTE MEAL - Food products - H.J. Heinz Co.

MINUTE MENU - Sandwiches–prepackaged - Devault Packing Co.

MINUTE MENUS - Publisher's imprints - Hannaford Brothers Co.

MINUTE MINDER - Timers–appliance - Lux Time

MINUTE MINDERS - Timers–appliance - Robertshaw Controls Co.

MINUTE-MISER - Motor vehicles - Ransomes-Cushman-Ryan

MINUTE MOUNT - Motor vehicles–snowplows - Douglas Dynamics Inc.

MINUTE RAISE - Doughnuts–mixes - Roland Industries Inc.

MINUTE REPEATER - Watches - Blancpain (Time Products Inc.)

MINUTE SHINE - Cleaning preparations - Turtle Wax, Inc.

MINUTE SHINE - Shoe polish - Barcolene Inc.

MINUTE SOAP - Soap - Skat Co.

MINUTE-SOLV - Paints - Dap Products Inc.

MINUTE WAXER - Automotive parts and accessories - Turtle Wax, Inc.

MINUTEMAN - Adhesives and sealants - Monsey Products Co.

MINUTEMAN - Guns ☆ - Precise International/Wenger

MINUTEMAN - Hardware - Distribution America, Inc.

MINUTEMAN - Siding–insulating ☆ - Aluminum Co. of America

MINUTEMAN - Sporting goods ☆ - Bear Archery Inc.

MINUTEMAN - Wire–insulated - General Cable Industries, Inc.

MINUTEMAN - Work clothes - Minuteman, Inc.

MINUTEMAN ALLIANCE - Electronic equipment - Para Systems, Inc.

MINUTEMAN II - Boilers–gas - Burnham Corp.

MINUTEMAN LANMASTER - Computer software - Para Systems, Inc.

MINUTEMAN NOVO 2 - Inhalers - Stephenson Industries Inc.

MINUTEMAN SCOUT - Inhalers - Stephenson Industries Inc.

MINUTEMAN SENTRY - Inhalers - Stephenson Industries Inc.

MINUTEMAN STANDARD - Inhalers - Stephenson Industries Inc.

MINUTEMEN EXPRESS - Binders - McBee Loose Leaf Binders

MINVAR - Tools - Lufkin Rule Co.

MINVITEIN - Vitamins and nutritional supplements - Essen Nutrition Corp.

MINWAX - Floor waxes - Minwax Co., Inc.

MINWAX PASTELS - Varnishes - Minwax Co., Inc.

MINWAY - Vitamins and nutritional supplements - Kenneth S. Ross

MINX - Amplifiers–musical instrument - Peavey Electronics Corp.

MINX - Boats–motor ☆ - Donzi Marine Corp.

MINX - Electrical equipment - Datapoint Corp.

MINX - Frames–eyeglass - May Optical Co. Inc.

MINX - Hair care products - Windmere Corp.

MINX - Sleeping bags - Coleman Co., Inc.

MIO - Cosmetics - Michael Thomas, Inc.

MIO - Pet products - Nippon Pet Food

MIO-REL - Pharmaceutical - International Ethical Labs

MIOCHOL - Prescription ophthalmic - Iolab Pharmaceuticals

MIOLO - Margarine - Miami Margarine Co. Inc.

MION - Dental equipment - Mion International Corp.

MIONE - Soap - Mione Manufacturing Co.

MIOSTAT - Pharmaceutical preparations - Alcon Laboratories, Inc.

MIOTTO - Furniture - Miotto International Co.

MIP - Computer software - Micro Information Products, Inc.

MIP - Machine parts - Modern Industrial Plastics, Inc.

MIP FUND ACCOUNTING - Computer software - Micro Information Products, Inc.

MIP NONPROFIT SERIES - Computer software - Micro Information Products, Inc.

MIPOLAM - Floor coverings - Huls America Inc. (Trocellen Foam Div.)

MIPROM 21 VF - Electrical equipment - Montgomery Kone Inc.

MIPROM 21 VFM - Elevators - Montgomery Kone Inc.

MIPROM SL - Electrical equipment - Montgomery Kone Inc.

MIQUELON - Seafood products–fresh or frozen - F.W. Bryce Inc.

MIR-O-LEN - Cleaning preparations–household - P.A. Clausing, Inc.

MIRA - Juices - Mira International Foods Inc.

MIRA - Paper - Mere Cie.

MIRA - Projection screens - Claridge Products and Equipment Inc.

MIRA - Whirlpools - Jacuzzi Inc.

MIRA-9 - Hair care products - Redken Laboratories, Inc.

MIRA-CLEAN - Cleaning equipment - Clean ESD Products, Inc.

MIRA-CLEAR - Varnishes - Perry & Derrick Co.

MIRA CURLS - Hair care products - Redmond Products, Inc.

MIRA-DIP - Golfing equipment - Club Kit Inc.

MIRA-DOMES - Novelty items–glass - Bell Glass & Mirror Co.

MIRA FILLER - Golfing equipment - Club Kit Inc.

MIRA-FLO - Paints - Alden's Inc.

MIRA-FOAM - Plastic cups - James River Corp.

MIRA-GLAZE - Paper cups - James River Corp.

MIRA KLEEN - Cleaning cloth for eyeglasses - Amcon Laboratories, Inc.

MIRA KOTE - Golfing equipment - Club Kit Inc.

MIRA-LUG - Footwear - Lehigh Safety Shoe Co.

MIRA PARIS - Posters - Mira Paris, Inc.

☆ = Now out of production

MIRA-PLATE - Finishing agents - O'Brien Corp.
MIRA-PLATE - Paints - Fuller-O'Brien Paints Inc.
MIRA-SPRAY - Golfing equipment - Club Kit Inc.
MIRA STAIN - Golfing equipment - Club Kit Inc.
MIRA-TEX - Flour–blended ☆ - Central Soya Co. Inc.
MIRA VISTA - Boots - Larry's Standard Brand Shoes, Inc.
MIRABEAU - Wallcovering ☆ - Colortree Designs
MIRABEL - Ophthalmic goods - Swank Optical
MIRABEL - Seafood - Clouston Foods USA
MIRABELL - Dinnerware–glass - WMF/USA
MIRABELL MOZARTKUGELN - Confections - Haram-Christensen Corp.
MIRABELLA - Pasta - Signature Foods Inc.
MIRABELLE - Dolls - Tiger Electronics, Inc.
MIRABELLE - Watches - North American Watch Corp.
MIRABOUND - Binders ☆ - Stationers Loose Leaf Co.
MIRACALE - Bedding–linen - Springs Industries, Inc.
MIRACHEM - Cleaning preparations - Mirachem Corp.
MIRACHOL - Vitamins and nutritional supplements - Centennial Foods, Inc.
MIRACID - Plant growth regulators - Scotts Miracle-Gro Products, Inc.
MIRACL-EDGE - Knives–pocket ☆ - W.R. Case & Sons Cutlery Co.
MIRACLAIR - Wines - Montelle Winery
MIRACLAY - Building materials - Nicolon Corp.
MIRACLE - Cleaning preparations - R & S Industries Corp.
MIRACLE - Cleaning preparations–household - Kristee Products Co.
MIRACLE - Computer peripheral equipment - Miracle Business Inc.
MIRACLE - Cooking equipment–household - E-Z-Por Corp.
MIRACLE - Cooking utensils–aluminum - M.E. Heuck Co. Inc.
MIRACLE - Cosmetics - Miracle Products Co.
MIRACLE - Eyeglasses - Art-Craft Optical Co.
MIRACLE - Fishing tackle - Cortland Line Co., Inc.
MIRACLE - Fishing tackle - Miracle Tackle Co., Inc.
MIRACLE - Floor coverings - Pratt & Lambert, Inc.
MIRACLE - Garden equipment - Ames Lawn & Garden Tool Co.
MIRACLE - Goat milk ☆ - Jackson-Mitchell Inc.
MIRACLE - Hair care products - Winning Solutions Inc./Miracle of Aloe
MIRACLE - Juice extracting devices - Miracle Exclusives Inc.
MIRACLE - Lime products - Western Lime Corp.
MIRACLE - Musical instrument accessories - French American Reeds Manufacturing
MIRACLE - Paint sets–hobby ☆ - Canson-Talens Inc.
MIRACLE - Polishing cloths - Stainless Steelcraft Co.
MIRACLE - Putties - Sav-Cote Chemical Laboratories Inc.
MIRACLE - Ships–sailing vessels - Hobie Cat Co.
MIRACLE - Tape–adhesive - Lepage's, Inc.
MIRACLE - Tape–adhesive ☆ - Le Pages Inc.
MIRACLE - Thread ☆ - SCT Yarns Inc.
MIRACLE - Water treating compounds - Jungle Laboratories Inc.
MIRACLE - ADHESIVES - DRB - Adhesives and sealants - Miracle Adhesives
MIRACLE AGE - Paints ☆ - Bradley Paint Co.
MIRACLE ALERT - Hair care products - Alleghany Pharmacal Corp.
MIRACLE AUTO PAINTING & BODY REPAIR - Automotive repair shops - Miracle Auto Painting Inc.
MIRACLE BAG, THE - Medical apparatus - Mary Rose Johnson
MIRACLE BAIT FRESH - Sporting goods ☆ - Life-Like Products Inc.
MIRACLE BASE COAT - Nail care products - Cosmair Inc.
MIRACLE BLADE - Cutlery - Kent Television Marketing Inc.
MIRACLE BLEND - Spices and extracts - Gugi's Global Foods, Inc.
MIRACLE BOOST - Jeans–women's - Sun Apparel, Inc.
MIRACLE BOW - Barrettes - International Trade Network, Inc.
MIRACLE BRA, THE - Apparel–women's - Victoria's Secret Stores, Inc.
MIRACLE BRUSH - Brushes–paint - K-Tel International, Inc.
MIRACLE BUBBLE BLASTER - Toys - Imperial Toy Corp.
MIRACLE BUBBLE MAKER - Toys - Imperial Toy Corp.
MIRACLE BUBBLES - Toys - Imperial Toy Corp.
MIRACLE CARESS - Skin care products - Senoret Chemical Co.
MIRACLE CLEAT CLEANER, THE - Sporting goods - Golf Specialty Corp.
MIRACLE CLIP - Automotive parts and accessories - John McCarthy
MIRACLE COLLAR - Pet products - Leonard Lookingbill
MIRACLE COLLECTION, THE - Neckties - Jos. A. Bank Clothiers, Inc.
MIRACLE CREME - Hair care products - A.P. Products Ltd.
MIRACLE CURE - Optical machinery - Coburn Optical Industries Inc.
MIRACLE DIVING - Transpersonal Swimming Institute, LLC
MIRACLE E - Soap - Tropical Soap Co.
MIRACLE EAR - Hearing aids ☆ - Dahlberg, Inc.
MIRACLE EAR II - Hearing aids ☆ - Dahlberg, Inc.
MIRACLE-EAR CLARIFIER - Hearing aids ☆ - Dahlberg, Inc.

MIRACLE-EAR SPECTRUM - Hearing aids - Dahlberg, Inc.
MIRACLE ERASER - Paints - Goodwin Insulation Distributors Inc.
MIRACLE FINISH - Hair care products - Zotos International Inc.
MIRACLE FLAGGING TAPE - Agricultural products - L.E. Cooke Co.
MIRACLE FOOT REPAIR - Pharmaceutical preparations - Jess Clarke & Sons Inc.
MIRACLE FREEZE - Yogurt–frozen - Gary W. Wilcoxson
MIRACLE FUEL - Nutritional supplement ☆ - Jackson Enterprises Inc.
MIRACLE GARDEN TIE - Agricultural products - L.E. Cooke Co.
MIRACLE GRIP - Denture adhesive - Medical Polymers Technologies, Inc.
MIRACLE-GRO - Plant growth regulators - Scotts Miracle-Gro Products, Inc.
MIRACLE GROW - Fertilizers - Central Garden & Pet Supply Inc.
MIRACLE HEALTH - Health care products - Bertae Health Specialties Inc.
MIRACLE HEAT - Heating equipment - United States Stove Co. Inc.
MIRACLE HOLD - Padding–foam - Vantage Industries Inc.
MIRACLE KLEEN - Detergents - Columbia Chemical Co.
MIRACLE KNEE SUPPORT - Braces–orthopedic - Professional's Choice Sports Medicine Products, Inc.
MIRACLE-LITE - Eyeglasses - Art-Craft Optical Co.
MIRACLE LOTION - Skin care products - Century Systems Inc.
MIRACLE MAGIC - Toys - D. Robbins & Co. Inc.
MIRACLE MAIZE - Breads–mixes - Little Crow Foods
MIRACLE MALT - Pet products - Four Paws Products Ltd.
MIRACLE MAN - Epoxy - Club Kit Inc.
MIRACLE MAT, THE - Floor covering stores - Flo-Arrest Technologies, Inc.
MIRACLE MELT - Deicing fluid - Scotwood Industries, Inc.
MIRACLE MESH - Electrical equipment - Federal Products, Co.
MIRACLE MESH - Liners and covers–pond, pit, and landfill - Magnuson Industries Inc.
MIRACLE METHOD - Bathroom accessories - Vermax Inc.
MIRACLE MIDDLES - Frosting - Crompton and Knowles Corp.
MIRACLE MILD PHILLIES - See PHILLIES
MIRACLE MIST - Cleaning preparations - Miracle Mist
MIRACLE MONO - Fishing lines - Cortland Line Co., Inc.
MIRACLE MULCH - Garden equipment - Dalen Products Inc.
MIRACLE MYRRH - Manicure preparations - Nails Naturally, Inc.
MIRACLE NAIL - Nail care products ☆ - Worldwide Cosmetics
MIRACLE OF ALOE - Health care products - Winning Solutions Inc./Miracle of Aloe
MIRACLE OF ALOE - Pharmaceutical preparations - Jess Clarke & Sons Inc.
MIRACLE OIL - Health care products - Century Systems Inc.
MIRACLE PET - Cat food - Specialty Pet Products
MIRACLE PLASTIC - Aprons - Vivitar Corp.
MIRACLE PLASTIC - Paints ☆ - Mac-O-Lac Paints Inc.
MIRACLE RELIEF GEL - Analgesics - Sportstech International, Inc.
MIRACLE RUB - Pharmaceutical preparations - Winning Solutions Inc./Miracle of Aloe
MIRACLE-SAFE - Cleaning preparations–household - Miracle-Safe Products, Inc.
MIRACLE SCRUB - Cleaning preparations–household - American Industrial Chemicals, Inc.
MIRACLE SHEEN - Hair care products - Shark Products Inc.
MIRACLE SILK - Fabrics–silk - European Imports of California Inc.
MIRACLE SMILE - Toothpaste - Merica Inc.
MIRACLE SNORKELING - Transpersonal Swimming Institute, LLC
MIRACLE SPA - Bath salts - Halftime Boosters Inc.
MIRACLE STICK - Skin care products - Miracle Products Co.
MIRACLE STONE - Skin care products - Miracle Products Co.
MIRACLE STRETCH - Apparel and accessories - L & M Adjustable Dress Form Co.
MIRACLE STROKE - Sporting goods - Roger G. Summer
MIRACLE SWEEP - Cleaning preparations ☆ - Upright Inc.
MIRACLE TAN - Tanning agents - Kent & Spiegel Direct, Inc.
MIRACLE, THE - Computer software - Software Toolworks, Inc.
MIRACLE-THIGHS - Skin care products - Allan Palmer Laboratories, Inc.
MIRACLE THIN - Yarn - Delaine Worsted Mills
MIRACLE WATER - Water purification systems - Ecowater Systems, Inc.
MIRACLE WATER - Water–distilled - Alacer Co.
MIRACLE WEAR - Cosmetics - Cosmair Inc.
MIRACLE WEDGE - Doors–garage - Overhead Door Corp.
MIRACLE WHIP - Salad dressings–bottled - Kraft Foods, Inc.
MIRACLE WHIP LIGHT - Salad dressings–bottled - Kraft Foods, Inc.
MIRACLE WHITE - Fabric softeners - Kiwi Brands, Inc.
MIRACLE WOOD - Wood fillers - H.F. Staples & Co. Inc.
MIRACLE WORKER - Glassware–household ☆ - Regent Sheffield, Ltd.
MIRACLEAN - Cleaning preparations - Mirachem Corp.

☆ = Now out of production

MIRACLEFLITE - Balls–golf - Bost Enterprises, Inc.
MIRACLES HAPPEN - Christmas tree ornaments - Don't Panic Designs, Inc.
MIRACLES, MADNESS & MASTERY - Publisher's imprints - Brighter World Books
MIRACLES OF THE SEA - Jewelry - Frank Mastoloni & Sons, Inc.
MIRACLOTH - Towels - Chicopee
MIRACLY - Skin care products - Saybaritic Inc.
MIRACOL - Chemical preparations ☆ - Woolsey Marine Industries
MIRACOL - Skin care products - Merle Norman Cosmetics
MIRACON - Contact lenses - Bausch & Lomb Inc.
MIRACOOL - Hats - Occunomix International Inc.
MIRACRIL - Paints - Ponderosa Paint Manufacturing Co. Inc.
MIRACRYL - Ice boxes–household - Carlisle Foodservice Products, Inc.
MIRACULOUS - Jewelry - Kaspar & Esh Inc.
MIRACULOUS - Stain removers - Embassy Rug & Upholstery Cleaning Co. Inc.
MIRACULOUS MANDARIN - Wallpaper - Kirk-Brummel
MIRACULOUS ME - Shirts - Miraculous Me!!!
MIRACURE - Nail care products - Jess Clarke & Sons Inc.
MIRACURE - Pharmaceutical preparations - Winning Solutions Inc./Miracle of Aloe
MIRADA - Bicycles - Schwinn Cycling & Fitness Inc.
MIRADA - Boats–motor - Century Boat Co.
MIRADA - Floor coverings–carpet and rugs ☆ - Blue Ridge Carpet Mills
MIRADA - Footwear - E.S. Originals, Inc.
MIRADA - Goggles–safety - Parmelee Industries, Inc.
MIRADA - Goggles–safety - U.S. Safety Corp.
MIRADA - Motor vehicles–automobiles ☆ - DaimlerChrysler
MIRADA - Motor vehicles–motor homes - Eldorado Motor Corp.
MIRADA - Rackets–racquetball - Ektelon
MIRADA II - Floor coverings–carpet and rugs ☆ - Blue Ridge Carpet Mills
MIRADA XL - Boats–motor - Century Boat Co.
MIRADO - Boats–motor ☆ - Larson Boat Div.
MIRADO - Pencils - Empire Berol USA
MIRADO - Pencils - Sanford Corp.
MIRADON - Pharmaceutical preparations - Schering-Plough Healthcare Products
MIRADOR - Bicycles ☆ - Roadmaster Corp.
MIRADOR - Cabinets - Nutone Inc.
MIRADOR - Furniture - Haworth, Inc.
MIRAFINISH - Siding–metal - CM Exteriors Inc.
MIRAFIORE - Wines - Paterno Imports, Ltd.
MIRAFLEX - Insulating materials - Owens Corning
MIRAFLOW - Contact-lens cleaner - CooperVision Inc.
MIRAFONE - Musical instruments - Orpheus Music Inc.
MIRAFOUNT - Farm machinery - Ahrens Agricultural Industries, Inc.
MIRAGE - Amplifiers - GNP Audio Video Inc.
MIRAGE - Awnings - Carefree/Scott Fetzer Co.
MIRAGE - Bicycles ☆ - Roadmaster Corp.
MIRAGE - Boats - Glen-L Marine Designs
MIRAGE - Boxes–corrugated paperboard - Mason Box Co. Inc.
MIRAGE - Candlesticks ☆ - Carolina Designs Ltd.
MIRAGE - Catheters - Scimed Life Systems, Inc.
MIRAGE - Children's shoes ☆ - Consolidated Shoe Co., Inc.
MIRAGE - Christmas tree ornaments - Cracker Box Inc.
MIRAGE - Containers - Bianchi International
MIRAGE - Cutlery - Washington Forge Inc.
MIRAGE - Dishes–china - Pickard Inc.
MIRAGE - Engines–marine - Brunswick Corp.
MIRAGE - Exercising equipment - Pro-Tec Inc.
MIRAGE - Eyeglasses - Optical Radiation Corp.
MIRAGE - Fabrics - Teters Floral Products Inc.
MIRAGE - Fire protection systems - Viking Corp.
MIRAGE - Fishing lures - RM Engineered Products, Inc.
MIRAGE - Fishing tackle - South Bend Sporting Goods Inc.
MIRAGE - Floor coverings - Mannington Resilient Floors
MIRAGE - Floor coverings–carpet and rugs - Couristan Inc.
MIRAGE - Floor coverings–carpet and rugs - Criterion Mills Inc.
MIRAGE - Floor coverings–carpet and rugs - Fieldturf & Carpet Inc.
MIRAGE - Floor coverings–carpet and rugs - Lotus Carpets
MIRAGE - Floor coverings–carpet and rugs - World Carpets, Inc.
MIRAGE - Floor coverings–carpet and rugs ☆ - Alliance Industries Inc.
MIRAGE - Floor coverings–carpet and rugs ☆ - American Carpet Mills
MIRAGE - Floor coverings–carpet and rugs ☆ - Interloom Ltd.
MIRAGE - Floor coverings–carpet and rugs ☆ - Kelly Group Inc.
MIRAGE - Food products - Cream Products Co. Inc.

MIRAGE - Furniture ☆ - Hammary Furniture Co. Inc.
MIRAGE - Giftware - World of Porcelain & Glassware
MIRAGE - Glass products - Libbey-Owens-Ford Co.
MIRAGE - Glassware–household - Denby USA Limited
MIRAGE - Glassware–household ☆ - Lenox Crystal, Inc.
MIRAGE - Hair care products - Hairnet Corp. of America
MIRAGE - Hardware - Truth Hardware Corp.
MIRAGE - Hearing aids - Audiotone, Inc.
MIRAGE - Hearing aids ☆ - Dahlberg, Inc.
MIRAGE - Lenses–magnifying - C. Bennett Scopes Inc.
MIRAGE - Lenses–optical ☆ - Bausch & Lomb Inc.
MIRAGE - Machinery - Halliburton Co.
MIRAGE - Manufactured homes - Redman Industries, Inc.
MIRAGE - Motor vehicles–automobiles - Mitsubishi Motor Sales of America Inc.
MIRAGE - Musical instrument accessories - SLM Marketplace
MIRAGE - Musical instruments - Ensoniq
MIRAGE - Occasional tables ☆ - JDI Group, Inc.
MIRAGE - Office supplies - Nina Enterprises, Inc.
MIRAGE - Ophthalmic goods - Opti-Gone Associates Inc.
MIRAGE - Rings–jewelry - Artcarved Inc.
MIRAGE - Saunas - Trayco, Inc.
MIRAGE - Sporting goods - O'Brien International
MIRAGE - Sunglasses - Metro Fashions Ltd.
MIRAGE - Tables–wood - Koch & Lowy Inc.
MIRAGE - Tableware–plastic - Robinson Knife & Fiddlers Plastics
MIRAGE - Tiles–ceramic - KPT Inc.
MIRAGE - Toilets–porcelain - Gerber Plumbing Fixtures Corp.
MIRAGE - Toys - Hasbro, Inc.
MIRAGE - Toys–models - Estes Industries
MIRAGE - Wallpaper - Robert Crowder & Co.
MIRAGE - Wallpaper ☆ - Mirage Wallcovering Co.
MIRAGE - Watches - Longines-Wittnauer Watch Co.
MIRAGE - Wheelchairs ☆ - Everest and Jennings International Ltd.
MIRAGE - Window shades - Comfortex Corp.
MIRAGE - Windshield frames–motor vehicle ☆ - National Cycle Inc.
MIRAGE - Wines - Chateau Julien
MIRAGE 3D - Toys ☆ - Tedco Inc.
MIRAGE ANNIVERSARY - Wallpaper ☆ - Mirage Wallcovering Co.
MIRAGE ANNIVERSARY II - Wallpaper - Mirage Wallcovering Co.
MIRAGE COLLECTION - Giftware - Lenox, Inc.
MIRAGE CONTEMPORARY TEXTURES - Wallpaper - Mirage Wallcovering Co.
MIRAGE GEM - Jewelry - William Chalson & Co., Inc.
MIRAGE INNOVATIONS - Wallpaper ☆ - Mirage Wallcovering Co.
MIRAGE INNOVATIONS II - Wallpaper ☆ - Mirage Wallcovering Co.
MIRAGE IX - Wallpaper ☆ - Mirage Wallcovering Co.
MIRAGE KITCHEN & BATH - Wallpaper - Mirage Wallcovering Co.
MIRAGE RADAR SCRAMBLER - Radar systems and equipment - Edge Co.
MIRAGE SG - Electronic access control equipment - Checkpoint Systems Inc.
MIRAGE SIGNATURE - Wallpaper - Mirage Wallcovering Co.
MIRAGE, THE - Aquariums–household ☆ - Cole Enterprises
MIRAGE XI - Wallpaper - Mirage Wallcovering Co.
MIRAGLASS - Glass products - Midland Glass Co. Inc.
MIRAGUM - Footwear - Lehigh Safety Shoe Co.
MIRAKEL - Hair care products - Paula Payne Products Co. Inc.
MIRAL - Pharmaceutical preparations - Armenpharm Ltd.
MIRALECTRIC - Projection screens ☆ - Claridge Products and Equipment Inc.
MIRALINK - Computer hardware - Miralink Corp.
MIRALUG - Shoes - Endicott Johnson Corp.
MIRAMAR - Boats–motor - Century Boat Co.
MIRAMAR - Floor coverings–carpet and rugs - Barrett Carpet Mills Inc.
MIRAMAR - Floor coverings–carpet and rugs - Couristan Inc.
MIRAMAR - Floor coverings–carpet and rugs - Western Carpet Mills
MIRAMAR - Furniture - Homecrest Industries Inc.
MIRAMAR - Liquors - Transamerica Wine Corp.
MIRAMAR - Ophthalmic goods - Styl-Rite Optical Manufacturing Co., Inc.
MIRAMAR - Seafood products–fresh or frozen - Purcell International
MIRAMAR - Shrimp–canned or cured ☆ - Darik Enterprises Inc.
MIRAMAR PASTELS - Floor coverings–carpet and rugs - Western Carpet Mills
MIRAMAR XL - Boats–motor - Century Boat Co.
MIRAMARE - Dinnerware–glass ☆ - WMF/USA
MIRAMARE - Glassware–household ☆ - Oneida Ltd.
MIRAMAX - Apparel–women's - Miramax Apparel, Inc.
MIRAMAX - Motion picture distributors–prerecorded - Walt Disney Co.

☆ = Now out of production

MIRAMENT - Cement - Blackthorn, Inc.
MIRAMONTE - Shoes ☆ - Marx & Newman Co. Inc.
MIRAMONTE - Vegetables–canned - Langan Associates
MIRANA COCOA MULCH - Nurseries and garden stores - Abdi Mirashrafi
MIRANDA - Bedding–linen - Dan River Inc.
MIRANDA - Cameras ☆ - AIC International Inc.
MIRANDA - Dinnerware–glass ☆ - WMF/USA
MIRANDA - Dolls - Mattel, Inc.
MIRANDA - Perfumes - Kiehl's Since 1851, Inc.
MIRANDA - Rings–jewelry - Artcarved Inc.
MIRANDA PANDA - Toys–stuffed - Dakin Inc.
MIRANDETTE - Photographic equipment - AIC International Inc.
MIRANDO - Jewelry - Mirando Jewelry Inc.
MIRAPACA - Apparel and accessories - Smith & Weber Co.
MIRARI FOR LUXOTTICA - Ophthalmic goods ☆ - Luxottica
MIRASEPT - Ophthalmic goods - Alcon Laboratories, Inc.
MIRASHIELD - Cleaning preparations - Cleaning Systems, Inc.
MIRASOL - Contact-lens solution ☆ - CooperVision Inc.
MIRASOL - Frames–eyeglass - Hudson Optical Corp.
MIRASOL - Tiles–ceramic ☆ - SCI Scandicrafts Inc.
MIRASORB - Health care products - Johnson & Johnson
MIRASPEC - Industrial chemicals - Rhone-Poulenc Specialty Chemicals Co.
MIRASSOU - Wines - Mirassou Vineyards
MIRAT - Computer software - Tools for Timing
MIRATA - Bathing suits - Andmore Sportswear Corp.
MIRATEX - Fabrics - A and H Sportswear Co., Inc.
MIRATEX - Paints ☆ - Valspar Corp.
MIRATEX - Ribbons–inked - Buckeye Business Products Inc.
MIRATI - Furniture - Hon Co.
MIRAVEL - Paints ☆ - Valspar Corp.
MIRAVISTA - Shingles - Owens Corning
MIRAVON - Colognes ☆ - Avon Products, Inc.
MIRAZYME - Deodorizers - McNett Corp.
MIRCO JET - Tools - Unival Corp.
MIRCO ONE - Medical apparatus - Mentor O & O Inc.
MIRCO SURE - Laboratory apparatus ☆ - Pall Gelman Sciences
MIRE-A-FOLD - Musical instrument accessories - Humes & Berg Manufacturing Co. Inc.
MIREE - Cheese - Swissrose International Inc.
MIRELLA - Ophthalmic goods ☆ - Luxottica
MIRIAM - Belts–apparel ☆ - Leon Fleischer, International Marketing
MIRIAM - Ophthalmic goods - Swank Optical
MIRIAM - Tiles–ceramic ☆ - Maxsam Sales, Inc.
MIRIAM GATES - Prosthetic apparatus - Randi Foundations Inc.
MIRIAM HASKELL - Jewelry–costume - Haskell Jewels, Ltd.
MIRIAM MIRANI - Perfumes - Miriam Gilbert
MIRIDIEN XL - Boats–motor - Century Boat Co.
MIRIELLE - Rings–jewelry - Artcarved Inc.
MIRIMAR - Cigars ☆ - General Cigar Co., Inc.
MIRINDA - Beverages–carbonated - Pepsi-Cola Co.
MIRKO - Ophthalmic goods ☆ - Luxottica
MIRO - Figurines - Anna-Perenna Inc.
MIRO - Flatware - Reed and Barton Corp.
MIRO - Lenses–optical - Ditto Industries Inc.
MIRO - Pencils - MPG Import, Ltd.
MIRO CAVA - Wines - Wines of the World Inc.
MIRO-FLEX - Motor vehicle parts and accessories - Fulton Manufacturing Corp.
MIROLITE - Mirrors - John O.Butler Co.
MIRRA-COAT - Veterinary nutritional supplements - Pet-Ag, Inc.
MIRRACO - Hardware - J.W. Goss Co.
MIRRAFORM - Paper products - Georgia-Pacific Corp.
MIRRAGE - Brushes–hair - Nailtex Inc.
MIRREX - Mirrors - Apache Products Co.
MIRRO - Cooking equipment–household - Mirro Corp.
MIRRO-ARCHES - Mirrors - Hoyne Industries Inc.
MIRRO-FOIL - Cooking equipment–household ☆ - Mirro Corp.
MIRRO GLIDE - Enamels - Frazee Paint
MIRRO-KROME - Greeting cards - Lawson Marden Post Card
MIRRO-MATIC - Housewares ☆ - Mirro Corp.
MIRRO-SCENES - Mirrors - Hoyne Industries Inc.
MIRRO-STRIPS - Mirrors - Hoyne Industries Inc.
MIRRO-TILE - Mirrors - Hoyne Industries Inc.
MIRROFLEX - Fixtures–plastic - Advanced Technology Inc.
MIRROLAC - Enamels - Devoe & Raynolds Co.
MIRROLITE - Lighting equipment - Acme-Lite Manufacturing Co.
MIRROLURES - Fishing lures - L & S Bait Co. Inc.

MIRROMATIC - Eyeglasses - International Tropic-Cal Inc. (I SKI Div.)
MIRROR - Cosmetics - Cici Cosmetic Co.
MIRROR - Pencils ☆ - Empire Berol USA
MIRROR - Recording label - Mirror Records Inc.
MIRROR - Threads - International Thread Co.
MIRROR - Tiles–ceramic - Kowa Texas Inc.
MIRROR - Window coverings - Courtaulds Performance Plus
MIRROR-ACULOUS - Games - Ooz & Oz, Inc.
MIRROR ART - Toys - Tot Inc.
MIRROR-BACK - Mirrors ☆ - Penn-Plax, Inc.
MIRROR BALL - Recording label - Hollywood Records of California
MIRROR BRICK - Mirrors - California Acrylic Industries Inc.
MIRROR/COPY - Paper–writing - Von Drehle Corp.
MIRROR CORD - Hardware - Anchor Wire Corp.
MIRROR CUTIES - Giftware - Russ Berrie and Co., Inc.
MIRROR EDGE - Rulers–metal - Simonds Industries Inc.
MIRROR FACET - Polishing equipment–jewelry - Prospector's Pouch Inc.
MIRROR FILM - Window coverings - Courtaulds Performance Plus
MIRROR FINISH - Paints - Dexter Corp. (Mercer Plastics Div.)
MIRROR FINISH - Paper–sand - Carborundum Abrasives North America
MIRROR GLAZE - Cleaning preparations - Meguiar's, Inc.
MIRROR GLOSS - Coatings - Woodcraft Manufacturing Co.
MIRROR GO LIGHTLY - Mirrors - Windmere Corp.
MIRROR GOLD - Blinds–venetian ☆ - Hunter Douglas, Inc.
MIRROR IMAGE - Binders ☆ - Better Office Products, Inc.
MIRROR IMAGE - Dolls - Edmund A. Grasso
MIRROR IMAGE - Floor waxes - Mission Kleensweep Products, Inc.
MIRROR IMAGE - Golfing equipment - Donald Jeen Chang Sun
MIRROR IMAGES - Mirrors - Creative Accessories Ltd.
MIRROR LINK - Computer software - Summatec Computer Corp.
MIRROR-LITE - Hardware ☆ - Shower-Rite Corp.
MIRROR MAGIC - Cosmetic set ☆ - Cosrich Inc.
MIRROR MAGIX - Silver compounds ☆ - Deep Flex Plastic Molds Inc.
MIRROR MESSAGES - Deodorizers - Safesyte, L.C.
MIRROR MIRROR - Automotive parts and accessories - Seagull Enterprises Inc.
MIRROR MITTENS - Motor vehicle parts and accessories - ETC Enterprises, Inc.
MIRROR MONTAGE - Fireplace equipment - Contractors Wardrobe, Inc.
MIRROR MUFF - Cleaning preparations ☆ - Scentex Inc.
MIRROR NOTES - Blank notes ☆ - Coronet General Corp.
MIRROR PLUS - Cabinets - Robern, Inc.
MIRROR POND PALE ALE - Beverages–malt - Deschutes Brewery
MIRROR RECORDS - Recording label - Michael A. Wilson
MIRROR SILVER - Blinds–venetian ☆ - Hunter Douglas, Inc.
MIRROR SURPRISE - Toys - Welcome World Creations
MIRROR WIPE - Housewares - Molor Products Co.
MIRROR WRAP - Jewelry - Sandberg & Sikorski Diamond Corp.
MIRRORA COLLECTION - Mirrors - Floral Glass & Mirror Inc.
MIRRORBRA - Motor vehicle parts and accessories - Target Motorsports
MIRRORDOR - Doors–wood - Panelfold Inc.
MIRRORGLO - Frames–eyeglass - Pathway Optical Prods.
MIRRORGOLD - Bronze products - Obron Atlantic Corp.
MIRRORLETTERS - Hardware - Scott Sign Systems, Inc.
MIRRORLITE - Glassless mirrors - Hudson Photographic Industries Inc.
MIRRORLITE - Mirrors - Victoria's Dance-Theatrical Supply
MIRRORLYK - Musical instrument accessories - Trophy Music Co.
MIRROS - Analgesics - Nutra Mir
MIRROTACH - Photographic equipment - SP Systems/Saratons
MIRROTHANE - Trees - Devoe & Raynolds Co.
MIRTH - Dolls - Estee Productions, Inc.
MIRTHA'S - Skin care products - Mirtha De Perales, Inc.
MIRUS - Computer software - Specialty Plus, Inc.
MIS TEE V-US - Apparel and accessories - Mis-Tee-V-Us Inc.
MISCERAMIC - See **COLOR TILE**
MISCHA - Perfumes - Sanofi Beaute Inc.
MISCHIEF - Deodorants–personal - Carter-Wallace, Inc.
MISCHIEF - Frames–eyeglass - May Optical Co. Inc.
MISCHIEF MAKERS - Backpacks - Mischief Makers Inc.
MISCHIEF MOUSE - Toys - Gerber Products Co.
MISCHIEF MOUSE - Toys–stuffed - Russ Berrie and Co., Inc.
MISE AU GREEN - Apparel and accessories - Bentley Lingerie, Inc.
MISENER - Saws–power - Misener Manufacturing Co. Inc.
MISER - Lamp bulbs–incandescent - General Electric Co.
MISER BEAM - Spotlights - W.F. Harris Lighting, Inc.
MISER, THE - Flush valves ☆ - Mansfield Plumbing Products, Inc.

MISFITS - Recording label - Glenn Danzig
MISFITS SUPER STRONG JEANS TO LAST FOREVER CALIFORNIA USA -
 Apparel and accessories - Marble Sportswear, Inc.
MISH - Jewelry - Mish Tworkowski Jewelry, Inc.
MISHA - Colognes - Richard Barrie Fragrances, Inc.
MISHA - Laboratory apparatus - Shandon Inc.
MISHA - Ophthalmic goods - Rozin Optical Export Corp.
MISHA - Women's bodywear - Mikhail Baryshnikov
MISHU - Computer software - Xanatech Inc.
MISIA - Perfumes - Chanel Inc.
MISIONERO VEGETABLES - Fruits and vegetables - Griffin Produce Co., Inc.
MISKIT - Artists' materials - M. Grumbacher Inc.
MISO-CUP - Soups—mixes - Edward & Sons Trading Co., Inc.
MISO MASTER - Miso - Great Eastern Sun Trading Co. Inc.
MISO-PLUS - Dips—sour cream based ☆ - Edward & Sons Trading Co., Inc.
MISS '76 - Eyeglasses - Martin-Copeland Eyewear Corp.
MISS AMERICA - Bathing suits - Miss America Organization
MISS AMERICA - Brooms - Hamburg Broom Works Inc.
MISS AMERICA - Foam materials - American Foam Latex Corp.
MISS AMERICA - Frames—eyeglass ☆ - Universal/Univis Inc.
MISS AMERICA - Pompons - James Industries, Inc.
MISS AMERICA - Toys—airplanes ☆ - Cox Products Inc.
MISS AMERICA - Watches - Bulova Corp.
MISS AMERICA CHEERLEADER - Sporting goods - Valley Decorating Co.
MISS AMERICA PAGEANT GAME, THE - Games ☆ - Parker Brothers
MISS AMERICANA - Underwear and nightwear - Youthcraft-Charmfit
MISS AMY - Shoes - Shoe Masters Inc.
MISS AUSTIN - Apparel—women's - Palm Beach Co., Inc.
MISS BABA - Book series ☆ - Contemporary Books Inc.
MISS BALMAIN - Colognes - Frances Denney
MISS BESTIEN - Costumes ☆ - Robert Bestien
MISS BI-CENTENNIAL - Eyeglasses - Martin-Copeland Eyewear Corp.
MISS BIERNER - Bierner and Son Inc.
MISS BRECK - Hair care products - Dial Corp.
MISS BUDGIE - Skin care products - Major/Advance International
MISS BUXTON - Wallets - Buxton Inc.
MISS CAKETTE - Ornamental products—glass ☆ - Standard Doll Co.
MISS CALDERON - Handbags - Ann Klein for Oroton
MISS CALIFORNIA - Apparel and accessories - Beverly Vogue Co.
MISS CARLOS - Wines - Old South Winery
MISS CARLOS DRY - Wines - Old South Winery
MISS CELEBRITY - Frames—eyeglass - Liberty Optical Manufacturing Co.
MISS CHERRYDALE - Apparel—women's ☆ - Umbro USA
MISS CHIPS - Dolls ☆ - Effanbee Doll Corp.
MISS CLAIROL - Hair coloring preparations - Clairol Inc.
MISS CLAIROL ULTRA BLONDE - Hair care products - Clairol Inc.
MISS COLORIFFICS - Shoes - Speen & Co. Inc.
MISS COOL - Hair care products - Soft Sheen Products Co.
MISS COUNTRY FAIR - Meat products—poultry - Jerome Foods Inc.
MISS DEN - Cosmetics ☆ - Major International Inc.
MISS DIAMOND - Apparel and accessories - BCNY International Inc.
MISS DIOR - Perfumes - Parfums Christian Dior U.S. Corp.
MISS DIOR - Skin care products - Christian Dior Perfumes Corp.
MISS DIOR - Underwear and nightwear - Slumbertogs Inc.
MISS ELAINE - Nightgowns - Miss Elaine, Inc.
MISS ELAINE AT HOME - Apparel—women's - Miss Elaine, Inc.
MISS E'LANA - Hobby kits - Famous Knitwear Corp.
MISS ELLIE A TASTE OF LOVE - Chocolate candy - Expo El Inc.
MISS EVELINE - Apparel - Daled Children's Wear Corp.
MISS EXQUISITE - Footwear - Southern Shoe Importers Inc.
MISS FASHION - Frames—eyeglass - Hudson Optical Corp.
MISS FASHIONALITY - Apparel—women's - Miss Fashionality
MISS FEM - Eyeglasses - Martin-Copeland Eyewear Corp.
MISS FLAIR - Dolls ☆ - Totsy Manufacturing Co., Inc.
MISS FLEX - Glass—optical - Welling International
MISS FORTUNE - Games - International Gamco, Inc.
MISS FRANCE - Frames—eyeglass - Hudson Optical Corp.
MISS GAZE - Ophthalmic goods - Foremost Optical Products
MISS GERMANY - Frames—eyeglass - Hudson Optical Corp.
MISS GINNY - Dolls - Vogue Dolls Inc.
MISS GOLDY - Meat products—poultry - Sanderson Farms Inc.
MISS HATTIES - Food products ☆ - House-Autry Mills, Inc.
MISS HELENE - Hair care products - Helene Curtis Industries Inc.
MISS INFORMAL - Greeting cards - Norcross Inc.
MISS INGENUE - Knit goods ☆ - Three by Three
MISS IOWA - Food containers - Dubuque Foods, Inc.

MISS JANTZEN - Apparel—women's ☆ - Jantzen Inc.
MISS JEANNIE - Children's shoes - B & B Originals Inc.
MISS JILENE - Flowers, plants, and seeds - Hillis Nursery Co., Inc.
MISS JONI OF CALIFORNIA - Apparel—women's - Joni Blair of California Inc.
MISS KING PINS - Crocheted and knitted items ☆ - Reliable of Milwaukee
MISS KING'S - Bakery products - Miss Kings Kitchen Inc.
MISS KITTY - Underwear and nightwear - Scanti Lingerie Co. Inc.
MISS KRISTI - Footwear - Shonac Corp.
MISS LANCASTER - Watches ☆ - SMH (US) Inc.
MISS LEE - Skin care products - Lee Pharmaceuticals
MISS LEJABY - Foundation garments—women's - Warnaco Inc.
MISS LIBERTY - Apparel—women's - Wm. Rifkin & Sons
MISS LIBERTY - Colognes ☆ - Avon Products, Inc.
MISS LIBERTY - Floor coverings—carpet and rugs - Cabin Crafts Carpets
MISS LIBERTY - Floor coverings—carpet and rugs - Walter Carpet Mills
MISS LIBERTY - Watches - Bulova Corp.
MISS LIL'S - Food products - Garcia Canning Co., Inc.
MISS LONG-EZE - Apparel—women's - Cupid Foundations Inc.
MISS LOU - Shrimp—fresh or frozen - Southern Shell Fish Co.
MISS LOVABLE - Underwear and nightwear ☆ - Lovable Co.
MISS LOVE - Wines - Bully Hill Vineyards, Inc.
MISS LULA'S FOODS - Barbecue sauce - Miss Lula's Foods Inc.
MISS M - Bicycles - Columbia Manufacturing Co.
MISS MARION - Skin care products - Sandra Ness Co.
MISS MARTHA'S - Figurines ☆ - Enesco Corp.
MISS MARY'S SUPERPHONICS - Recording label - Achievement Dynamics
 Corp.
MISS MATCHBOX - Dolls ☆ - Matchbox Toys USA
MISS MEOW'S - Vitamins and nutritional supplements - Natural Organics, Inc.
MISS MERINGUE - Cookies - Champagne, Inc.
MISS MOOSE - Health care products - Jerome Russell Cosmetics, Inc.
MISS MUFFET - Food products - United Pacific Packers
MISS MUFFET - Hair care products - Gaylord Products Inc.
MISS NANCY'S - Snack foods - That's Entertainment
MISS NANNETTE - Apparel—children's - Nannette Manufacturing Co. Inc.
MISS NUTRINE - Hair care products - Nutrine Ltd.
MISS PEEP - Dolls ☆ - South Bend Toy Manufacturing Co.
MISS PENDLETON - Apparel—women's ☆ - Pendleton
MISS PIGGY - Toys - Jim Henson Productions, Inc.
MISS PLUM'S TOOTH OR CONSEQUENCES - Games - Lilith Lyle O'leary
MISS PRINCESS - Manicure preparations - Nailtex Inc.
MISS QUALICRAFT - Shoes ☆ - Edison Brothers Stores, Inc.
MISS QUEEN - Apparel—women's - Sportswave Inc.
MISS RAQUET - Hosiery ☆ - Wigwam Mills Inc.
MISS REXIE - Skin care products - Major/Advance International
MISS ROCKER - Bicycles ☆ - Huffy Corp.
MISS RODEO U.S.A. - Boots - Acme Boot Co., Inc.
MISS RONNIE - Apparel—children's ☆ - House of Ronnie, Inc.
MISS ROUX - Hair coloring preparations - Roux Laboratories, Inc.
MISS SAIGON - Bathing suits ☆ - Jantzen Inc.
MISS SALLY'S - Seafood products—fresh or frozen - Carrington Foods Co.
MISS SAYLOR'S CANDIES - Candy - Miss Saylor's Candies
MISS SBICCA - Footwear - Items International Airwalk Inc.
MISS SCARLETT - Condiments - Miss Scarlett
MISS SCARLETT - Wines - Old South Winery
MISS SECRETARY - Hosiery - Jack Constant Inc.
MISS SOPHISTICATES - Apparel—women's ☆ - Pendleton
MISS SPIDER - Toys - Callaway & Kirk Co. LLC
MISS SUNSHINE - Toys - Tonka Corp.
MISS TEEN - Bicycles - Schwinn Cycling & Fitness Inc.
MISS TIPSTER - Hair care products ☆ - Hydro-Tex Corp.
MISS TON-HI - Fruits and vegetables ☆ - Regal Fruit Cooperative
MISS TOURNAMENT - Crocheted and knitted items ☆ - Reliable of Milwaukee
MISS TWINKLE - Skin care products - Frances Denney
MISS UNITED STATES - Bathing suits - Catalina
MISS UNIVERSE - Bathing suits - Catalina
MISS UNIVERSE - Toys - Multi Toys Corp.
MISS UNIVERSE - Watches - Bulova Corp.
MISS VANITY - Apparel and accessories - Vanity Corset Co. Inc.
MISS WEBRIL - Fabrics - Veratec
MISS WEBRIL - Fabrics—cotton - Burston Inc.
MISS WISCONSIN - Vegetables—canned - Stokely USA, Inc.
MISS WISCONSIN LITE - Dairy products - Armour Swift-Eckrich
MISS WONDERFUL - Shoes - Interco Inc.
MISSILE - Boats - Glen-L Marine Designs
MISSILE CHIP - Novelty items - Universal Art Corp.

☆ = Now out of production

MISSILE COMMAND - Video games - Atari Games Corp.
MISSILE FUDGE - Confections - Wells' Dairy, Inc.
MISSILE-PAK - Wire - Aluminum Co. of America
MISSILE POPS - Confections - Wells' Dairy, Inc.
MISSING LINK - Plastics - Kufco Inc.
MISSING LINK - Puzzles ☆ - CBS Toys
MISSING LINK, THE - Vitamins and nutritional supplements - Designing Health, Inc.
MISSING LINK, THE - Veterinary pharmaceutical preparations - Petscriptions, Inc.
MISSING LINK, THE - Apparel and accessories - Wormtrap, Inc.
M-SS-NG L-NKS: A GAME OF LETTERS AND LANGUAGE - Computer software - Sunburst Communications, Inc.
M-SS-NG L-NKS: CLASSICS, OLD AND NEW - Computer software ☆ - Sunburst Communications, Inc.
M-SS-NG L-NKS: ENGLISH EDITOR - Computer software ☆ - Sunburst Communications, Inc.
M-SS-NG L-NKS: MICROENCYCLOPEDIA - Computer software ☆ - Sunburst Communications, Inc.
M-SS-NG L-NKS: YOUNG PEOPLE'S LITERATURE - Computer software ☆ - Sunburst Communications, Inc.
MISSING LINX - Fencing-chain link - Linx Systems Inc.
MISSING MASTERPIECE - Toys - Hasbro, Inc.
MISSION - Cabinets - Superior Woodwork Inc.
MISSION - Cabinets ☆ - American Woodmark Corp.
MISSION - Couplings - MCP Industries, Inc.
MISSION - Dinnerware-glass - Cyclamen Studio
MISSION - Flooring-hardwood - Memphis Hardwood Flooring Co.
MISSION - Food containers - Quaker Oats Co.
MISSION - Fruits and vegetables - Mission Produce, Inc.
MISSION - Greeting cards - Regency-Sonnell Greetings Inc.
MISSION - Incense - Excelsior Incense Works
MISSION - Lamps - Meyda Tiffany Inc.
MISSION - Paints ☆ - Frazee Paint
MISSION - Pasta - Mission Macaroni
MISSION - Tiles-ceramic - American Marazzi Tile, Inc.
MISSION - Tortillas - Mission Foods Corp.
MISSION 660 - Video games - Taito America Corp.
MISSION: ALGEBRA - Computer peripheral equipment - Compton's NewMedia
MISSION BAY - Floor coverings-carpet and rugs ☆ - Hollytex Carpet Mills Inc.
MISSION BAY - Furniture ☆ - Bassett Furniture Industries, Inc.
MISSION BAY CO. - Apparel and accessories ☆ - Nitches, Inc.
MISSION BELL - Wines ☆ - The Beverage Source Inc.
MISSION CANDLES - Candles - Reed Candle Co.
MISSION CONTROL - Magnets - Susan Andrews Kaiden
MISSION CONTROL - Sporting goods - Klein Bicycle Corp.
MISSION CONTROL SYSTEM - Automotive parts and accessories - Gamber-Johnson Inc.
MISSION CONTROL WORD GAMES - Computer software - Gamco Industries Inc.
MISSION COURT - Tiles-ceramic ☆ - Quarry Tile Co.
MISSION CRITICAL - Computer software - Legend Entertainment Co.
MISSION FATHERS - Beverages-alcohol - James A. Robertson Co.
MISSION HILLS - Floor coverings-carpet and rugs - Criterion Mills Inc.
MISSION HILLS - Furniture - Hammary Furniture Co. Inc.
MISSION HILLS - Furniture - Pilliod Co.
MISSION HOST - Brandy ☆ - Oak Ridge Vineyards
MISSION IMPOSSIBLE - Apparel and accessories - Paramount Pictures Corp.
MISSION LIGHT - Tortillas - Mission Foods Corp.
MISSION OAK - Floor coverings - Congoleum Corp.
MISSION OBISPO - Food products - AMK for Service
MISSION PRENATAL - Vitamins and nutritional supplements - Mission Pharmacal Co.
MISSION PRENATAL F.A. - Vitamins and nutritional supplements - Mission Pharmacal Co.
MISSION PRENATAL H.P. - Vitamins and nutritional supplements - Mission Pharmacal Co.
MISSION QUARRY - Floor coverings ☆ - Azrock Commercial Flooring
MISSION RIDGE - Fruits-canned - Skookum Packers Association Inc.
MISSION SAN JUAN - Juices - Pokka, Inc.
MISSION SIX - Slacks - Abraham Gilbreath
MISSION TERMINUS - Computer software ☆ - Gessler Publishing Co., Inc.
MISSION, THE - Burial caskets - Marsellus Casket Co.
MISSION TRAIL - Brandy - Gaetano Specialties Ltd.
MISSION TRAIL - Olive oil - Nick Sciabica & Sons
MISSION UNSTOPPABLE - Games - Kevin Albright

MISSION VALLEY - Furniture ☆ - American Drew
MISSION VIEW ESTATE - Wines - House of Burgundy Inc.
MISSION WEAR - Apparel and accessories - James Daids
MISSION X-24 - Floor coverings-carpet and rugs ☆ - Blue Ridge Carpet Mills
MISSION X-28 - Floor coverings-carpet and rugs ☆ - Blue Ridge Carpet Mills
MISSIONRIPE - Fruits and vegetables - Mission Produce, Inc.
MISSISSIPPI - Bacon - Dubuque Foods, Inc.
MISSISSIPPI - Dog food - Diamond Feeds
MISSISSIPPI - Glass products - HGP Industries Inc.
MISSISSIPPI - Rifles - Euroarms of America
MISSISSIPPI - Water-bottled or canned - Mississippi Bottled Water
MISSISSIPPI BLUESMAN - Sunglasses - Big Al, Inc.
MISSISSIPPI BLUESMAN - Sunglasses - Shady Deal Corp.
MISSISSIPPI BRITTLE - Candy - Mississippi Brittle, Ltd.
MISSISSIPPI DELTA - Food products - Antique Mall & Crown
MISSISSIPPI JIGS - Fishing lures - Armstrong's Cricket Farm
MISSISSIPPI MADNESS - Fruits and vegetables - Mississippi Madness, Inc.
MISSISSIPPI MUD - Fudge sauce - Minnesota Made Gourmet, Inc.
MISSISSIPPI MUD - Ice cream - Borden, Inc.
MISSISSIPPI NICKELS - Game machines - IGT - North America
MISSISSIPPI POTASH, INC. - Potash - Mississippi Chemical Corp.
MISSISSIPPI QUEEN - Jewelry - Delta Queen Steamboat Co.
MISSISSIPPI QUEEN - Seafood products-fresh or frozen - Alphin Bros. Inc.
MISSISSIPPI RIVER - Cigars - A.J. Golden Inc.
MISSISSIPPI SOUND - Cigars - A.J. Golden Inc.
MISSISSIPPI TRAILS OUTFITTERS - Wallets - Eric Scott Leathers, Ltd.
MISSISSIPPI VALLEY EQUIPMENT - Machinery - Mississippi Valley Equipment Co.
MISSLETOAD - Candy ☆ - Cherrydale Farms Inc.
MISSONI - Neckties ☆ - Salant/Manhattan Industries
MISSONI - Scarves, neckwear, and umbrellas - Sprague & Coultas
MISSONI BY MALERBA - Hosiery - Pull & Co.
MISSONI OCCHIALI - Sunglasses - Solargenics
MISSOULA - Floor coverings-carpet and rugs - Bloomsburg Carpet Industries
MISSOURI - Flooring-hardwood - Missouri Hardwood Flooring Co.
MISSOURI BROWN DARK ALE TRAILHEAD BREWING CO - Beverages-malt - Trailhead Brewing Co., LLC
MISSOURI DANDY - Nuts-salted, roasted, cooked, or canned - Hammons Products Co.
MISSOURI HARVEST - Bread mix - Baron Spices, Inc.
MISSOURI HICKORY - Spices and extracts - Pacific Choice Brands Inc.
MISSOURI MEERSCHAUM - Pipes - Missouri Meerschaum Co.
MISSOURI MEERSCHAUM BULLDOG - Pipes - Missouri Meerschaum Co.
MISSOURI MUD - Bakery products - Our Name is Mud, Inc.
MISSOURI PREMIUM - Juices - Bardenheier Wine Cellars
MISSOURI TRADITION - Wines ☆ - Bardenheier Wine Cellars
MISSOURI'S FINEST - Rice - Louis Dreyfus Holding Co. Inc.
MISSY - Bedding-linen - Dan River Inc.
MISSY - Detergents ☆ - The Kroger Co.
MISSY - Floor coverings-carpet and rugs - Alexander Smith Carpets
MISSY - Shoes - Daniel Green Co.
MISSY - Shoes-athletic - Coast Shoes Inc.
MISSY - Toys-stuffed - Tonka Corp.
MIST - Computer software - Farradyne Systems Inc.
MIST - Dishes-china ☆ - Pickard Inc.
MIST-AIR - Aquarium accessories - Kordon
MIST-AIR - Aquarium accessories - Novalek, Inc.
MIST-COAT II - Paints - Jones Blair Co.
MIST DE MER - Perfumes - Revlon Consumer Products Corp.
MIST DE NUIT - Cosmetics - Lancome
MIST E - Skin care products - Fanie International
MIST-EASE - Medical apparatus - General Physiotherapy, Inc.
MIST-ER - Colognes ☆ - Mem Co., Inc.
MIST-ER CHAIR - Combination lawn chair/water sprinkler - Mist-Er Tan Enterprises Inc.
MIST FINE BUBBLE DIFFUSER - Water purification systems - Aeromix Systems, Inc.
MIST-GLO - Floor waxes - Uncle Sam Chemical Co., Inc.
MIST KIST - Fruits-canned - Ocean Spray Cranberries Inc.
MIST MISER - Garden equipment - Splash Inc.
MIST MISS - Boats - Glen-L Marine Designs
MIST 'N CURL - Hair curlers - Pollenex Corp.
MIST 'N DRY - Hair curlers ☆ - Sunbeam-Oster Household Products
MIST N' SHINE - Finishing agents - C.B. Dolge Co.
MIST OF GIORGIO BEVERLY HILLS, THE - Colognes - Giorgio Beverly Hills, Inc.

MIST OF MUSK - Perfumes - Prince Matchabelli
MIST OF SPRING - Perfumes - Prince Matchabelli
MIST RAY - Hoses ☆ - Melnor Inc.
MIST SET - Hair curlers ☆ - Sunbeam-Oster Household Products
MIST-STICK - Hair curlers ☆ - Sunbeam-Oster Household Products
MIST-TONE - Thread - Belding Heminway Co. Inc.
MISTAIR - Weather tracking equipment ☆ - Maximum Inc.
MISTAKE OUT - Correction fluid - Liquid Paper Corp.
MISTE' - Dryers–hair - Sharon D. Tucker
MISTE - Tiles–ceramic ☆ - Florida Tile Industries, Inc.
MISTEE - Hair curlers ☆ - Sunbeam-Oster Household Products
MISTELLE - Yarn ☆ - Coats and Clark Inc.
MISTER - See also MR.
MISTER ALUMINUM - Housewares - Nasco Industries, Inc.
MISTER BOTTOMS - Apparel–men's - Perry Lewis Ltd.
MISTER COOKIE FACE - Food products - Thin's Inn Inc.
MISTER COOKIE FACE - Ice cream - Mister Cookie Face Inc.
MISTER DAY - Cookies - Parmalat USA Corp.
MISTER DEW DROP - Pet products - American Pet Products Inc.
MISTER DONUT - Restaurants–coffee shops - Mister Donut of America Inc.
MISTER DRAGON - Vaporizers - C and S Distributing Co.
MISTER EASE AEROSOL - Lubricants ☆ - Demert & Dougherty, Inc.
MISTER ERNEST - Handbags - Mister Ernest Handbags Inc.
MISTER FUDGE - Fudge - Calico Cottage, Inc.
MISTER HUSH - Footwear - Wolverine World Wide, Inc.
MISTER JINX - Cleaning preparations - Claire Manufacturing Co.
MISTER JR. - Apparel–children's ☆ - Gem-Dandy, Inc.
MISTER L - Shoes ☆ - Edison Brothers Stores, Inc.
MISTER LIFTER - Mechanical hoists - Louis Berkman Co.
MISTER LISTER - Computer software - Compu-Tations Inc.
MISTER-MASTER - Fertilizers ☆ - Luster Leaf Products Inc.
MISTER MEATLOAF - Dinners–frozen ☆ - Clorox Co.
MISTER MISER URINAL - Urinals–porcelain - Thomas E. Tushaus
MISTER MO VEHICLES - Toys–automobiles ☆ - CBS Toys
$ MISTER MONEY USA PAWN LOANS - Used merchandise stores - Mister
   Money - USA, Inc.
MISTER MOVIE - Motion picture distributors–prerecorded - Act III Theatres
MISTER MUSTARD - Mustard - House of Herbs Inc.
MISTER NOAH - Apparel–women's - Leonard A. Feinberg Inc.
MISTER PLUMBER - Cleaning preparations–household - Guardsman
   Products, Inc.
MISTER PRETZEL - Pretzels - Nabisco Foods Group
MISTER PROSTATE - Vitamins and nutritional supplements - Reyman Drug
   Co., Inc.
MISTER QUICK - Floor coverings–carpet and rugs - Carpet Products Co.
MISTER ROGERS' PLANET PURPLE - Electronic equipment ☆ - Texas
   Instruments Inc.
MISTER SALTY - Pretzels - Nabisco Foods Group
MISTER SHOES - Shoes - Markon Footwear Inc.
MISTER SHRED - Lawn mowers ☆ - Hoffco Inc.
MISTER SOFTEE MOBILE ICE CREAM TRUCKS - Motor vehicles–trucks -
   Mister Softee Inc.
MISTER SPEAR - Fruits and vegetables - Mister Spear Inc.
MISTER STRIPPER - Chemical preparations - Wilson Imperial Co.
MISTER THINK! - Games - Rich Manufacturing Co.
MISTER THIRSTY - Fruit drinks–bottled or canned - Readington Farms
MISTER TOUCH-UP - Clippers–barber ☆ - Sunbeam-Oster Household
   Products
MISTER TWISTER - Hardware - Melard Manufacturing Corp.
MISTER TWISTER - Novelty items ☆ - Jobar International Inc./Bibi Products
MISTER TWISTER - Pretzels - J & J Snack Foods Corp.
MISTER WHISKER - Toys - Smethport Specialty Co.
MISTI - Floor coverings–carpet and rugs ☆ - Zenith Carpets
MISTI - Yarn - William Unger & Co. Inc.
MISTIC BREEZE - Iced tea–bottled or canned - Mistic Brands, Inc.
MISTIC GRAPE STRAWBERRY - Fruit drinks–bottled or canned - Joseph
   Victori Wines Inc.
MISTIC-MIST - Lubrication equipment–industrial - Aetna Manufacturing Co.
MISTICKS - Deodorizers - Bernard Cappelli Inc.
MISTIFIER - Hair care products - Goody Products, Inc.
MISTINGUETTE - Apparel–women's - Mast Industries Inc.
MISTIQUE - Floor coverings–carpet and rugs ☆ - Karastan-Bigelow Inc.
MISTIQUE - Floor coverings–carpet and rugs ☆ - Stanton Carpet Corp.
MISTIQUE ACCENTS - Floor coverings–carpet and rugs ☆ - Karastan-Bigelow
   Inc.
MISTIQUE BY TREVIVE - Cosmetics - Han Beauty, Inc.

MISTLAND - Fruits and vegetables - Oregon Prune Exchange
MISTLETOE - Food products - Butler Wholesale Products
MISTLETOE - Toys–stuffed ☆ - Gund, Inc.
MISTLETOE BLEND - Coffee - Bucks County Nut and Coffee Co.
MISTLETOE BOOKS - Publisher's imprints ☆ - Garber Communications Inc.
MISTLETOE MOUSE - Toys–stuffed ☆ - Dakin Inc.
MISTLETOE MUSIC - Recording label - United American Video Corp.
MISTLON - Bottles–glass ☆ - Seventh Generation Wholesale Inc.
MISTMASTER - Fabrics - Graniteville Co.
MISTOL - Pharmaceutical preparations - Oakhurst Co.
MISTOP - Dehumidifiers - Mistop, Inc.
MIST'R CRISP'R - Housewares - Hydro-Crisper, Inc.
MISTRA - Filters–water - N.R.G. Enterprises, Inc./Mistra Inc.
MISTRAL - Bedding–linen - Dan River Inc.
MISTRAL - Dishes–china - Waterford Wedgewood USA, Inc.
MISTRAL - Floor coverings–carpet and rugs ☆ - Interloom Ltd.
MISTRAL - Glassware–household ☆ - National Housewares
MISTRAL - Pens and pencils - Greyhound Leisure Services, Inc.
MISTRAL - Ships–sailing vessels - Simonds Boats
MISTRAL - Wheels–motor vehicle - Sun Metal Products, Inc.
MISTRAL PALETTE - Wallpaper - Dekortex Inc.
MISTREE - Filters and humidifiers - Mistree Corp.
MISTRON VAPOR - Chemical preparations - Luzenac America Inc.
MISTVEL - Fabrics - A. Wimpfheimer & Brother Inc.
MISTY - Bicycles - Dynacraft Industries Inc.
MISTY - Bicycles ☆ - Roadmaster Corp.
MISTY - Carpet mats, now out of production - American Floor Products Co. Inc.
MISTY - Cigarettes - American Tobacco Co.
MISTY - Cleaning preparations - Roman Research, Inc.
MISTY - Dolls - Justin Products, Inc.
MISTY - Floor coverings–carpet and rugs - Coronet Carpets Inc.
MISTY - Garden equipment - H.D. Hudson Manufacturing Co.
MISTY - Lubricants - Amrep Inc.
MISTY - Skin care products - Fanie International
MISTY - Toys–stuffed ☆ - Gund, Inc.
MISTY - Wallpaper - Pageant Wallpaper Corp.
MISTY BLONDES, THE - Hair coloring preparations - Helene Curtis Industries
   Inc.
MISTY BLUE - Christmas tree ornaments - Cracker Box Inc.
MISTY BLUE DAYDREAM - Glassware–household - Owens-Illinois Inc.
   (Libbey Div.)
MISTY FAVORITE - Floor coverings–carpet and rugs ☆ - Alexander Smith
   Carpets
MISTY GARDEN - Dishes–china ☆ - Pickard Inc.
MISTY HARBOR - Apparel and accessories - United Merchants and
   Manufacturers Inc.
MISTY HARBOR - Floor coverings–carpet and rugs ☆ - Karastan-Bigelow Inc.
MISTY HARBOR - Luggage - Misty Harbor Properties
MISTY HARBOR - Umbrellas - Essex Manufacturing Inc.
MISTY KITTY - Puppets - Dakin Inc.
MISTY LACE - Perfumes - Prince Matchabelli
MISTY LADY - Cosmetics - Nutrine Ltd.
MISTY MAGIC - Bicycles ☆ - Huffy Corp.
MISTY MAUVE - Lipsticks ☆ - Honey & Spice Toiletries
MISTY MEADOW - Furniture ☆ - Bassett Furniture Industries, Inc.
MISTY MINT - Teas - Farmer Bros. Co.
MISTY MOMENTS - Fruit juices, soft drinks, and syrups - Arizona Extra
MISTY MOOD - Floor coverings–carpet and rugs ☆ - Walter Carpet Mills
MISTY MORN - Floor coverings–carpet and rugs - Galaxy Carpet Mills Inc.
MISTY MORN - Silverware ☆ - Imperial Schrade Corp.
MISTY MORN SAFE COMPANY - Safes - Misty Morn Safe Co., Inc.
MISTY MORNING - Bedding–linen - Dan River Inc.
MISTY MORNING - Dinnerware ☆ - Corning Inc.
MISTY MOUNTAIN - Water–bottled or canned - Misty Mountain Spring Water
   Co.
MISTY MOUNTAIN SPRING WATER - Beverage - Carolyn M. Greenwood
MISTY OX - Health care products - Medical Molding Corp. of America
MISTY RABBIT - Toys–stuffed - Dakin Inc.
MISTY RIDGE - Wine - Staton Hills Winery Co. Ltd.
MISTY RIVER - Furniture - Lane Upholstery (Venture Furniture Div.)
MISTY ROSE - Bicycles - Columbia Manufacturing Inc.
MISTY ROSE - Cosmetics - Sebastian International, Inc.
MISTY ROSE - Flagstones - Jarvis Stone Co.
MISTY ROSE DAYDREAM - Glassware–household - Owens-Illinois Inc.
   (Libbey Div.)
MISTY SHADOWS - Cosmetics - Elizabeth Arden Inc.

☆ = Now out of production

MISTY SKIES - Cosmetics ☆ - Bonne Bell, Inc.
MISTY SLIM - Cigarettes - American Tobacco Co.
MISTY TEA ROSE - Perfumes - Quintessence Inc.
MISTY THE MERMAID - Publisher's imprints ☆ - Antioch Publishing Co.
MISTY ULTRA LIGHTS - Cigarettes - American Tobacco Co.
MISTY VALE - Vegetables–frozen - National Frozen Foods Corp.
MISTY WEATHER - Coats–women's - Kmart Corp.
MISTY WHITE - Dinnerware - Corning Inc.
MISTY WOODS - Floor coverings–carpet and rugs ☆ - Evans-Black Carpet Mills
MISU - Artists' materials - Andrews/Nelson/Whitehead
MISUKI EAU DE PARFUM - Perfumes - Holzman and Stephanie Perfumes, Inc.
MISURA - Pasta ☆ - Liberty Richter Inc.
MIT - Audio equipment - GNP Audio Video Inc.
MIT - Computer software - Massachusetts Institute of Technology
M.I.T. - Lenses–optical - Ditto Industries Inc.
MIT KIT - Sporting goods - Matrix Group Limited, Inc.
MIT SLOAN - Housewares - Massachusetts Institute of Technology
MITA - Office machines - Mita Copystar America Inc.
MITA-CLEAR - Veterinary pharmaceutical preparations - SmithKline Beecham Animal Health Products
MITABAN - Veterinary pharmaceutical preparations - Upjohn Co.
MITADEX - Pet products ☆ - Tomlyn Products
MITAKI-JAPAN - Electronic equipment - B and F System Inc.
MITANI - Dinnerware–glass ☆ - Nikko Ceramics Inc.
MITAPET - Pet products - Leathercraft Co.
MITAPLEX-P - Pet products ☆ - Tomlyn Products
MITAPLEX R - Pet products - Tomlyn Products
MITAWOOD - Mitre boxes ☆ - Royal Merchandise Co.
MITCHBRAND - Agricultural products - Hershey Import Co. Inc.
MITCHEL CRAIG - Giftware ☆ - Golden State Box Factory
MITCHELA - Health care products - Zidrep Laboratories
MITCHELL - Disinfectants ☆ - ICI Americas Inc.
MITCHELL - Firearms ☆ - Ithaca Gun Co. Inc.
MITCHELL - Fishing rods - Johnson Worldwide Associates, Inc.
MITCHELL - Furniture - Boling Co.
MITCHELL - Motor vehicles–automobiles ☆ - Mitchell Motors Inc.
MITCHELL - Trailers–travel - Mitchell & Sons Inc.
MITCHELL ARMS - Firearms, accessories, and parts - Mitchell Arms, Inc.
MITCHELL DESIGNS - Wallpaper - Borden, Inc.
MITCHELL DESIGNS - Wallpaper - Bob Mitchell Designs
MITCHELL LANE KITCHENS - Food products - Mitchell Lane Kitchens
MITCHELL LURIE - Musical instrument accessories - Rico International
MITCHELLACE - Laces–boot and shoe - Mitchellace Inc.
MITCHELL'S - Food products - F.O. Mitchell & Bro. Inc.
MITCHELTON - Wines - Dreyfus Ashby Inc.
MITCH'S DELICIOUS - Bakery products - Lipkin & Sons Bakery Inc.
MITCHUM - Health care products - Revlon Consumer Products Corp.
MITE - Toilets–enameled - Kohler Co.
MITE-AWAY - Pet products - Aquatronics-Filtronics
MITE BEATER - Pesticides–household - Bonide Products, Inc.
MITE-E-LITE - Generators - Dukane Corp.
MITE-E-LITE - Generators ☆ - McCulloch Corp.
MITE-NO-MORE - Pet products - Rael Co.
MITE RX - Pet products - Tetra Sales USA
MITEE - Chemical preparations - Dap Products Inc.
MITEE - Hardware - Barrett Manufacturing Co.
MITEE-MITE - Girdles - Formflex Foundations Inc.
MITEE MUSCLE - Oils–lubricating - Dap Products Inc.
MITEGUARD - Chemical preparations ☆ - Mardel Laboratories, Inc.
MITEM - Computer software - Mitem Corp.
MITEMVIEW - Computer software - Mitem Corp.
MITEPRO - Computer peripheral equipment - Laurel Group
MITER MAKER - Saw blades ☆ - Hirsh Co.
MITEX - Veterinary pharmaceutical preparations - Happy Jack, Inc.
MITEY - Anchors - M-F Manufacturing Co. Inc.
MITEY GRIP - Mats–rattan - Golden Star Inc.
MITEY MATE - Chairs–folding - Garelick Manufacturing Co.
MITEY-MITE - Fishing lures - Hofmanns Lures
MITEY MONSTER - Fishing jigs - American Import Co.
MITHRACIN - Pharmaceutical preparations - Miles Inc.
MITI - Computer software - Management Information Technology, Inc.
MITI - Water purification systems - Miti Manufacturing Co., Inc.
MITIA - Food products - Wilson Products Co. Inc.
MITIGATOR - Safety products - Standard Safety Equipment Co.

MITIS - Computer software - City of Cleveland
MITO - Whirlpools - Jacuzzi Inc.
MITOKU MACRO - Pasta ☆ - Great Eastern Sun Trading Co. Inc.
MITOTRACKER - Chemical preparations - Molecular Probes, Inc.
MITOX - Veterinary pharmaceutical preparations - SmithKline Beecham Animal Health Products
MITRAFLEX - Pharmaceutical preparations ☆ - M. Polymedica Corp.
MITRAN - Pharmaceutical preparations ☆ - Roberts/Hauck Pharmaceuticals Inc.
MITRAZOL - Pharmaceutical preparations - Healthpoint Medical Ltd.
MITRE - Apparel–athletic - Mitre Sports
MITRELLE - Fibers–synthetic ☆ - ICI Americas Inc.
MITRENAIL - Hardware - Active Sales Co. Inc.
MITROLAN - Pharmaceutical preparations - A.H. Robins Co. Inc.
MITSOUKO - Perfumes - Guerlain Inc.
MITSUBA - Computer peripheral equipment - Mitsuba Corp.
MITSUBA - Photographic equipment - Hsueh-Chen Shih
MITSUBISHI - Cameras–video - Mitsubishi Electric America, Inc.
MITSUBISHI - Motor vehicles - Mitsubishi Motor Sales of America Inc.
MITSUBISHI - Printing trades machinery - Graphline, Inc.
MITSUBISHI - Toners - Pinestar Technology, Inc.
MITSURU - Bedding–linen - Dan River Inc.
MITSUSHIBA - Golfing equipment - Mitsushiba International, Inc.
MITT MANAGER - Sporting goods - Markwort Sporting Goods Co.
MITT MANAGER, THE - Sporting goods - Ronald Eugene Spradling
MITTBOARD - Toys - Wizard of Ahhs, Inc.
MITTEN - Office supplies - Mitten Designer Letters
MITTEN-STAY - Adhesives and sealants - Mitten Designer Letters
MITTENS - Toys - Russ Berrie and Co., Inc.
MITY-FILE - Dental equipment - Js Dental Manufacturing, Inc.
MITY-LITE - Furniture - Mity-Lite, Inc.
MITY LITE - Spotlights - Roxter Lighting
MITY-MITE - Battery chargers - Schumacher Electric Corp.
MITY-MITE - Key rings - West Coast Chain Manufacturing Co.
MITY MITER - Tools - Granberg International
MITY-MYCIN - Pharmaceutical preparations ☆ - Solvay Pharmaceuticals Inc.
MITY NICE - Juices–frozen - Mariani Frozen Foods
MITY QUIET - Archery equipment ☆ - Bear Archery Inc.
MITY-QUIN - Pharmaceutical preparations ☆ - Solvay Pharmaceuticals Inc.
MITY-SWEET - Fruits–dried - Valley View Packing Co., Inc.
MITY-THIN - Electronic equipment - Tandy Corp.
MITYFILL - Pumps - Neward Enterprises Inc.
MITYGUARD - Eyeglasses ☆ - Neward Enterprises Inc.
MITYLITE - Flashlights - Pelican Products, Inc.
MITYSWEET - Fruits and vegetables - Valley View Packing Co., Inc.
MITYTUFF - Furniture–metal - Mity-Lite, Inc.
MITYVAC - Automotive parts and accessories - Prism Enterprises, Inc.
MITYVAC - Pumps–vacuum - Neward Enterprises Inc.
MITZ DE ROUGE - Fruit drinks–bottled or canned - Kedem Royal Wine Corp.
MITZI - Briefcases - Mitzi International Handbags & Accessories Ltd.
MITZI - Wigs ☆ - Jean Paree Weegs Inc.
MITZI DITZI - Fishing tackle - Best Tackle Manufacturing Co.
MITZIE POODLE - Toys–stuffed ☆ - Dakin Inc.
MIURA - Boots - Miura Sports Inc.
MIURA - Motor vehicles–automobiles ☆ - DaimlerChrysler
MIURALASKA - Boots - Miura Sports Inc.
MIVERT - Pharmaceutical preparations - Misemer Pharmaceuticals Inc.
MIX - Glassware–household ☆ - European Imports of California Inc.
MIX-A-COLOR - Artists' materials - Art Enterprises
MIX-A-MOLD - Artists' materials - American Art Clay Co. Inc.
MIX A TUB - Garden equipment - Argee Corp.
MIX & MATCH - Adhesives and coatings - American Synthetics Co.
MIX & MATCH - Games - Smethport Specialty Co.
MIX & MATCH - House furnishings ☆ - Foley & Robinson Inc.
MIX & MATCH - Wallpaper - Mayfair Wallcoverings
MIX AND MATCH PACK, THE - Cakes - Tasty Baking Co.
MIX & MATCHABLES - Tiles–ceramic ☆ - American Olean Tile Co.
MIX & MATCHABLES GRANDE - Tiles–ceramic ☆ - American Olean Tile Co.
MIX AND SPELL - Games ☆ - Uncle Milton Industries Inc.
MIX 'EM UP MONSTERS - Toys - Current, Inc.
MIX-EZY - Shortening - Kraft Food Ingredients Corp.
MIX FINDER - Food processors - Sunbeam-Oster Household Products
MIX-I-GO - Fuel additives - Bell Additives, Inc.
MIX IT UP SEE WHAT HAPPENS - Beverages–alcohol - Joseph E. Seagram & Sons, Inc.
MIX MASTER - Mixers–concrete - DBNA Trademarks Holding Inc.

MIX MATCH - Apparel–women's - Wacoal America Inc.
MIX MATES - Pans - E-Z-Por Corp.
MIX-ME-NOT - Cakes - Campbell Taggart Inc.
MIX 'N' BAKE - Bakeware - Corning Inc.
MIX N DRINK - Milk–canned or powdered - Saco Foods, Inc.
MIX 'N EAT - Cereal - Nabisco Foods Group
MIX 'N' MATCH - Photographic equipment - Heindl Masks 'n' Mounts
MIX 'N' MEASURE - Bowls - Corning Inc.
MIX 'N SPIN - Toys - Mattel, Inc.
MIX-N-STOR - Housewares - Tupperware Co.
MIX 'N WASH - Toys - Mattel, Inc.
MIX NOUVEAU NEW YORK - Apparel–women's - Sanjiv K. Khandelwal
MIX-O-MATIC - Kitchen appliances - Rival Manufacturing Co.
MIX OR MATCH! - Restaurants–pizzerias - Little Caesar Enterprises, Inc.
MIX-RITE - Gasoline - Tecumseh Products Co. Engine and Transmission Group
MIX TRAK 100 - Audio equipment - Broadcast Electronics, Inc.
MIX-UPS - Candy ☆ - Willy Wonka Brands
MIX-UPS - Markers–felt-tip - Avery Dennison Corp.
MIXCOLOR - Hair care products - Framesi USA/Roffler Industries Inc.
MIXED BLUES - Apparel and accessories - J.C. Penney Co., Inc.
MIXED BOUQUET - Dinnerware–glass - Cyclamen Studio
MIXED COMPANY - Cakes–mixes - Mixed Co. Inc.
MIXED DRIED ASIAN - Chili peppers–powdered ☆ - Frieda's, Inc.
MIXED DRIED LATIN - Chili peppers–powdered ☆ - Frieda's, Inc.
MIXED DRIED NEW MEXICO - Chili peppers–powdered ☆ - Frieda's, Inc.
MIXED DRIED SOUTHWESTERN - Chili peppers–powdered ☆ - Frieda's, Inc.
MIXED EMOTION - Recording label - Little Major Record Distributors Inc.
MIXED IMAGE - Apparel and accessories - Bentley Lingerie, Inc.
MIXED MEDIA - Floor coverings–carpet and rugs ☆ - Regal Rugs Inc.
MIXED MEDIA - Wallpaper ☆ - Capital Carousel Inc.
MIXED MESSAGES - Bathing suits ☆ - Jantzen Inc.
MIXED NUT HEAVEN - Nuts–salted, roasted, cooked, or canned - Ross Nut Co.
MIXED NUTS - Puzzles ☆ - Ben Cooper Inc.
MIXED PECANS - Lipstick and nail polish ☆ - Cosrich Inc.
MIXED PIECES - Apparel–children's - Donna R. Bender
MIXED UP MOLLY - Dolls ☆ - Phace Toys, Inc.
MIXEDBLESSING - Greeting cards - Mixedblessing, Inc.
MIXER MIKE - Microphones - Sima Products Corp.
MIXER/MILL - Laboratory apparatus - Spex CertiPrep, Inc.
MIXER ON A STICK - Mixers–concrete - ITT Flygt Corp.
MIXER, THE - Kitchen utensils–aluminum ☆ - Bonny Products Inc.
MIXER WORKS - Kitchen appliances ☆ - Regal Ware, Inc.
MIXERATOR - Garden equipment ☆ - Schultz Co.
MIXERDOCK - Amplifiers - Mark IV Audio, Inc.
MIXERS - Linen - Eddie Bauer Inc.
MIXERS, THE - Apparel and accessories - Phillips-Van Heusen Corp.
MIXET - Bathroom fixtures - Alsons Corp.
MIXET MASTER - Hardware - Alsons Corp.
MIXETTE - Cooking equipment–household ☆ - Mirro Corp.
MIXING-JET-COOKER - Industrial machinery - Q-JET DSI Inc.
MIXIT - Computer software - Agricultural Software Consultants, Inc.
MIXIT - Handbags - J.C. Penney Co., Inc.
MIXM - Paint sprayers - Midwest Mixing
MIXMASTER - Electronic equipment - J.L. Cooper Electronics
MIXMASTER - Food processors - Sunbeam-Oster Household Products
MIXMIX - Apparel and accessories - Rutchick, Rutchick & Associates, Inc.
MIXO - Oils–edible ☆ - Super Valu Inc.
MIXON - Juices - Mixon Fruit Farms Inc.
MIXPAD - Audio equipment - Sam Ash Music Corp.
MIXPUR - Pet products ☆ - Sera Aquaristik USA Inc.
MIXSON - Firearms, accessories, and parts - Mixson Corp.
MIXTARD - Insulin - Novo Nordisk Pharmaceuticals Inc.
MIXTE-X - Bicycles - Burley Design Cooperative
MIXTIQUE - Artists' materials - Loew-Cornell Inc.
MIXTURE-79 - Cigar boxes–wood - Consolidated Cigar Corp.
MIXTURE NO. 79 - Tobacco pouches - Consolidated Cigar Corp.
MIXTURE NO. 79 - Tobacco pouches - Sutliff Tobacco Co.
MIXUS - Paint sprayers - Willamette Valley Co.
MIXXER - Computer software - Alaris Corp.
MIXXODERM - Hair care products - Kenlor Industries, Inc.
MIXXSTIXX - Golfing equipment - SPL International, Inc.
MIYACHI - Welding equipment - Unitek Miyachi Corp.
MIYAKO - Furniture–wood ☆ - Ficks Reed Co. Inc.
MIYAKO EDAMAME - Food products - Mutual Trading Co. Inc.

MIYAO - Dishes–earthenware - Mikasa Co.
MIYATA - Scissors and shears - Illinois Razor Strop
MIYAZAWA - Flutes - West Music Co., Inc.
MIZ - Golfing equipment - Mizuno Corp. of America
MIZ LIZ - Pancakes–mixes - Dolefam Corp.
MIZANI - Hair care products - Future Source Inc.
MIZANNE - Apparel–athletic - Mizanne
MIZER - Motor vehicles ☆ - Chrysler Corp. (Dodge Car Div.)
MIZUHIKI - Artists' materials - Yasutomo
MIZYME - Pharmaceutical preparations - Misemer Pharmaceuticals Inc.
MIZZY - Mouthwashes - Mizzy Inc.
MIZZY & ZIZZY - Publisher's imprints - Jack Brown Enterprises, Inc.
MJ - Apparel–women's - Jonathan Logan Inc.
MJ - Coffee - Darbe Group, Ltd.
MJ - Jewelry - Jacob Marshak & Sons Inc.
MJ ART - Jewelry - Majestic Art Jewelry
MJ DESIGNER LINE - Christmas tree ornaments - Dupey Management Corp.
MJ JAVA - Coffee - Darbe Group, Ltd.
M.J. KNOUD - Buckles - Piggaletta, Inc.
M.J. STEVENS - Apparel–women's - Allison Blair Inc.
MJB - Coffee - Nestle Beverage Co.
MJB LITE - Coffee - Nestle Beverage Co.
MJB MOCHA - Coffee - Nestle Beverage Co.
M.J.C. - Dolls - Harold-Lawrence Associates Inc.
MJF BOOKS - Publisher's imprints - Fine Creative Media Inc.
MJG - Jewelry - M. & J. Grosbard, Inc.
MK - Apparel and accessories - CS Crable Sportswear, Inc.
MK - Cleaning preparations - Klein & Co.
MK - Housewares - M. Kamenstein, Inc.
MK - Jewelry - Karr Jewelry Inc.
MK - Jewelry - Mason-Kay Inc.
MK III - Cosmetics - Ladyfingers
MK IV - Cosmetics - Ladyfingers
MK-20 - Musical instrument accessories ☆ - Ultimate Support Systems Inc.
MK-85 - Firearms, accessories, and parts - Modern Muzzle Loading, Inc.
MK CLUB - Jackets–leather ☆ - A & K Inc.
MK DINGHY - Ships–sailing vessels - Cape Cod Shipbuilding Co.
MK-IV - Electronic equipment - Buhl Industries, Inc.
MK TODAY - Apparel–athletic ☆ - Midstates Sportswear
MK ULTRA - Compact discs–prerecorded - Artichoke
MK V - Amplifiers–musical instrument - Peavey Electronics Corp.
MK3 - Computer software - Midway Manufacturing Co.
MK16 - Fabrics - Wangner Systems Corp.
MK35 - Computer peripheral equipment - Scangraphics, Inc.
MKA MOTION PICTURE EQUIPMENT - Cameras–motion picture - International Creative Business Management
MKCONNECTIONS - Advertising agencies - Mary Kay Inc.
MKD - Work benches - Sky Climber, Inc.
MKI - Shoes–orthopedic ☆ - Tru-Mold Shoes Inc.
MKIDS - Optical machinery - Psychological Corp.
MKII - Aircraft - Raytheon Aircraft Co.
MKM - Sporting goods ☆ - Pro Line Co.
MKP - Anchors - Simpson Strong-Tie Co., Inc.
MKT - Tools–power-driven - MKT Manufacturing, Inc.
MKX-600 HOME GYM - Exercising equipment - Maximus Fitness Products
ML - Jewelry and watches - Moonlight Jewelry Inc.
ML - Medical apparatus - Kaman Aerospace Corp.
ML - Rings–jewelry - Marshall Littman Manufacturing Jewelry Inc.
ML - Skin care products - Mark Lees Skin Care Inc.
ML - Thread - Belding Heminway Co. Inc.
ML-1 - Musical instruments - E.K. Blessing Co. Inc.
ML-200 - Tools - David White Inc.
ML CAMPBELL - Lacquers - M.L. Campbell Co.
MLA - Computer software - Medical Laboratory Automation, Inc.
MLA-1 - Electronic equipment - J.L. Cooper Electronics
MLA-10 - Electronic equipment - J.L. Cooper Electronics
MLAD/FRML - Computer software - Laureate Learning Systems Inc.
M'LADY - Napkins–paper - Kittrich Corp.
MLB - Handbags - Pyramid Handbags Inc.
MLB - Sporting goods - Hutch Sports USA Inc.
MLB-TEMP - Glass–flat - M.L. Burke Co.
MLBPA BOTTOM OF THE 9TH - Computer storage devices–optical - Konami (America) Inc.
MLC - Dry erase boards - Claridge Products and Equipment Inc.
M.L.D. MINIMUM LETHAL DOSE - Recording label - Steven E. Ford
M'LIS - Skin care products - Beneficial International

☆ = Now out of production

MLJ - Jewelry - Evan Lloyd
MLLE. - See also **MADEMOISELLE**
MLM - Insulating materials - Lantec Products, Inc.
MLS - Lighting fixtures ☆ - Ranging Inc.
MLS-12D - Switchboards–telephone - At&T Corp.
MLS-LINK - Computer software - PRC Inc.
MLS PICTOURS - Computer software - Pictours, Inc.
MLX-10 - Telephone system - At&T Corp.
MLX-10DP - Telephone apparatus - At&T Corp.
MLX-20L - Telephone system - At&T Corp.
MM - Eyeglasses - Paralax, Inc.
MM - Lubricants - Phillips 66 Propane Co.
MM - Publisher's imprints - Management and Marketing Corp. International
MM - Recording label - Musicmasters
MM - Seafood products–fresh or frozen ☆ - J.F. Clarke Corp.
MM - Vitamins and nutritional supplements - Nature Health
MM 7800 - Waterproofing compounds - American Hydrotech, Inc.
MM MAGIC MASTER - Signs - Joseph Struhl Co., Inc.
MM MPI MULTIMEDIA - Video production - Maljack Productions, Inc.
MM-SERIES - Electrical surge protectors - Sutton Designs, Inc.
MMARC - Drafting supplies - Safe-T Products, Inc.
MMATS - Circuit boards - MMATS, Inc.
MMB - Jewelry - J & MB Jewelry Ltd.
MMB MUSIC - Music–sheet - MMB Music Inc.
MMC - Hearing aids - Beltone Electronics Corp.
MMC - Recording label - Relativity/Combat/In-Effect
MMCC - Nuts and bolts - Metric & Multistandard Components Corp.
MMCF - Apparel–women's - Mary McFadden, Inc.
MMD - Pharmaceutical preparations - Marion Merrell Dow
MME. - See also **MADAME**
MME. GRACE - Apparel stores–lingerie - H.F. Robbins
MME. LAUTREC - Beverages–alcohol - Consolidated Distilled Products Inc.
MMG - Recording label - Moss Music Group Inc.
MMI PRO MIX - Building materials–concrete - MMI Products, Inc.
MML - Firearms, accessories, and parts - Modern Muzzle Loading, Inc.
MMM - Hair-cutting shears - B.W. Boyd Shears Inc.
MMM MUSIC - Recording label - Sugo Records Inc.
MMO - Computer software ☆ - MMO Music Group Inc.
MMOS MULTIMEDIA OPERATING SYSTEM - Computer software - Scala, Inc.
MMPA - Dairy products - Michigan Milk Producers Association
MMR - Electronic equipment - Dukane Corp.
MMR - Publisher's imprints - Market Management International Inc.
MMR II - Vaccines - Merck & Co., Inc. (Merck Research Laboratories)
MMS NO LAUGHING MATTER - Publisher's imprints - Block Sales and Distributing, Inc.
MM'S ON PAPER - Notebooks and notepads - MM's Designs
MMSPC - Computer software - Abbey Etna Machine Co.
MMT - Beverages - Hamilton Foods Co. Inc.
MN-7 - Cutting line - Shakespeare Fishing Tackle
MN-MACRA - Hobby kits - Stanislaus Imports, Inc.
MN MONTNEEL - Toys - Montnell Design, Inc.
MNA - Publisher's imprints - Clintec Nutrition Co.
MNEMO - Posters - Aegis Entertainment, Inc.
MNN MEDICAL NEWS NETWORK - Electrical equipment - Mosby-Year Book, Inc.
MNV - Fruits and vegetables - Magi Inc.
MNX - Pharmaceutical preparations - Enzyme Process Co. Inc.
MO - Apparel–women's - 17 North Inc.
MO-BAY TYE - Ophthalmic goods - Karlen Manufacturing, Inc.
MO' BETA - Juices ☆ - Odwalla, Inc.
MO EVER - T-shirts–men's - Continnuus
MO FAB - Paints - E-Z Paintr Corp.
MO HOTTA MO BETTA - Food products - Mo Hotta Mo Betta, Inc.
MO-JAC - Apparel and accessories ☆ - Modern Jacket Co. Inc.
MO-JO - Candy - Wilkinson-Spitz Ltd.
MO-JO MONKEY - Toys–stuffed ☆ - Dakin Inc.
MO-MAX - Tools - Cleveland Twist Drill Co.
MO' MONEY - Recording label - Ichiban Records, Inc.
MO' MUSCLE - Apparel and accessories - Amy N. Peterson
MO-PA-CO - Paints - Mobile Paint Manufacturing Co.
MO-SE - Dolls - Mo-Se Productions
MO-ST - Tools - Morse-Starrett Products Co. (Pell Cable Cutter Div.)
MO' TIV - Apparel and accessories - James Brian Mullin
MO-TOE MOTORCYCLE TOWING SYSTEM - Trailers–industrial - Invenex
MO-VI - Pet products - Strongheart Products, Inc.
MO-WOOD - Recording label - Didaczeck Records

MOAB - Bicycle parts and accessories - Schwinn Cycling & Fitness Inc.
MOAB - Protective eyewear - Smith Sport Optics Inc.
MOAG - Medical apparatus - Unisurge, Inc.
MOANA KAI - Floor coverings–carpet and rugs ☆ - Customweave Carpets Inc.
MOB - Jewelry - J.P. Morton Co. Inc.
M.O.B MEN OF BUSINESS - Apparel and accessories - Robert McCleave
MOB TIES - Apparel and accessories - Milton Lampe
MOB TIES - Apparel and accessories - The Lighted Lamp
MOBAN - Pharmaceutical preparations - Du Pont Pharmaceuticals
MOBAY CITRUM - Rum - Rums International, Inc.
M.O.B.B. RECORDS - Recording label - Mighty M.O.B.B. Records Inc.
MOBI - Juvenile furniture ☆ - Mobi Corp.
MOBIA'S TRIP - Musical instruments - Paul Hoffman
MOBIDEM - Modems - General Electric Co.
MOBIDESK - Auto accessories - Portable Network Solutions, Inc.
MOBIDIN - Pharmaceutical preparations - B.F. Ascher & Co. Inc.
MOBIFILE - Desk sets ☆ - Marnay Sales & Manufacturing Co. Inc.
MOBIGESIC - Pharmaceutical preparations - B.F. Ascher & Co. Inc.
MOBIL - Containers ☆ - Mobil Chemical Co. Plastics Div.
MOBIL - Petroleum - Mobil Oil Corp.
MOBIL 1 - Oils–lubricating - Mobil Oil Corp.
MOBIL DURAVIEW - Food containers - Mobil Oil Corp.
MOBIL-MATES - Dining room furniture ☆ - Daystrom Furniture Inc.
MOBIL SILHOUETTES - Firearms, accessories, and parts - David J. Reinart
MOBIL TRAVEL GUIDES - Publisher's imprints - Simon & Schuster, Inc.
MOBILAID - Health care products ☆ - Invacare Corp.
MOBILAIRE - Air conditioning equipment - White Consolidated Industries, Inc.
MOBILAIRE - Health care products ☆ - Invacare Corp.
MOBILE - Adhesives and sealants - Monsey Products Co.
MOBILE - Dolls ☆ - Effanbee Doll Corp.
MOBILE - Drafting supplies - Mayline/Hamilton
MOBILE - Health care products - ETAC USA Inc.
MOBILE ACCESS - Computer software - Notable Technologies, Inc.
MOBILE ARMORED STRIKE KOMMAND - Toys - Tonka Corp.
MOBILE ASSISTANT - Computers–personal - Xybernant Corp.
MOBILE BAT CARTS - Sporting goods - Dacon Manufacturing
MOBILE CEILING - Floor coverings - Congoleum Corp.
MOBILE CELLUTIONS - Telecommunication equipment - PLN Enterprises, Inc.
MOBILE CLASS ROOMS - Motor vehicles–buses - Turtle Top Specialty Products
MOBILE ELECTRONICS, INC. - Electronic equipment - Bob Bartlett & Associates Inc.
MOBILE EXPRESS - Computer software - Teknow, Inc.
MOBILE GLOBAL LEARNING LABORATORIES - Educational materials - Mobile Global Laboratories
MOBILE MAKER - Educational materials - Trend Enterprises, Inc.
MOBILE MANAGER - Computer peripheral equipment - MicroComputer Accessories Inc.
MOBILE MARK - Antennas - Mobile Mark, Inc.
MOBILE MATE - Boxes - Igloo Products Corp.
MOBILE-MATE - Medical apparatus - Lumex, Inc.
MOBILE MLS - Computer software - Advanced Resources Partners
MOBILE MUG - Containers - Alpha Products, Inc.
MOBILE MYSTICKS - Apparel and accessories - Mobile Professional Hockey, Inc.
MOBILE OFFICE - Briefcases - S J B Enterprises, Inc.
MOBILE OFFICE - Computer software - On Technology Corp.
MOBILE PC 5110 - Computers - Duracom Computer Systems
MOBILE PHONE - Toys - Small World Toys
MOBILE STORAGE COMPANY, THE - Computer hardware - Integral Peripherals Inc.
MOBILE TECHNOLOGY FURNITURE - Furniture - Wheelit Inc.
MOBILE-TEK - Alarm systems - Stereo King, Inc.
MOBILE TEK - Computer software - Smith Advanced Technology, Inc.
MOBILE THEATRE - Audio equipment - River Park, Inc.
MOBILECALC - Computer software - Mobilesoft Corp.
MOBILECELL - Telephones–cellular - Mobilecell Communications, Inc.
MOBILECRIMP - Fluid power pumps - Gates Corp.
MOBILEER - Musical instrument accessories - GRK Manufacturing
MOBILEFLOR - Floor coverings - Congoleum Corp.
MOBILEJET - Printers–computer - Mannesmann Tally Corp.
MOBILEMATE - Computers - Mobilemedia Communications, Inc.
MOBILEMATH - Computer software - Mobilesoft Corp.
MOBILEMAX - Computer storage devices - Maxtor Corp.
MOBILEMAX DESKRUNNER - Computer storage devices - Maxtor Corp.

MOBILEMEDIA - Medical apparatus - Del Mar Avionics
MOBILEMEDIA - Pagers - Mobilemedia Communications, Inc.
MOBILENOTES - Notebooks and notepads - Stanson Products, Inc.
MOBILEPC - Computers - Meridian Computer Corp., Inc.
MOBILERA - Computer software - Business Partner Solutions Inc.
MOBILESPEC - Audio equipment - D.A.S. Distributors, Inc.
MOBILEVANTAGE - Computer hardware - U.S. Computer Services
MOBILEVISION - Computer software - CE Software, Inc.
MOBILEWALL - Floor coverings - Congoleum Corp.
MOBILEWARE - Computer software - 21 Cennet, Inc.
MOBILEWEAR - Communications equipment - Pier Marketing, Inc.
MOBILEWORKS - Computer software - PI Systems Corp.
MOBILEX - Skin care products - Dome Cosmetics
MOBILI - Plumbing fixtures–metal ☆ - Barclay Products Ltd.
MOBILIA - Furniture - CM Furniture Inc.
MOBILIMB - Health care products - Toronto Medical Inc.
MOBILITE - Health care products ☆ - Invacare Corp.
MOBILITE - Lighting fixtures - Spartus Corp.
MOBILITY - Battery chargers - Japlar Acquisition Co. (Japlar/Schauer)
MOBILITY - Floor coverings–tile - Collins & Aikman Corp.
MOBILITY - Shoes–orthopedic - M.J. Markell Shoe Inc.
MOBILITY EQUIPPED VANS - Motor vehicles–buses - Turtle Top Specialty Products
MOBILITY PRODUCTS - Motor vehicles - Turtle Top Specialty Products
MOBILITY SPORT - Apparel–women's - Kohl's Department Stores, Inc.
MOBILOGIC - Computer software - Mobilogic, Inc.
MOBILSUDS - Detergents - Mobil Oil Corp.
MOBILWORKS - Roofing materials–clay ☆ - Master's Choice Inc.
MOBISYL - Pharmaceutical preparations - B.F. Ascher & Co. Inc.
MOBIUS - Computer peripheral equipment - Professional Dental Technologies, Inc.
MOBIUS - Games - Flying Buffalo Inc.
MOBIUS STRIP - Recording label - Jeffrey A. Ammeen
MOBJACK - Ships–sailing vessels - Moorman Manufacturing Co.
MOBY - Jojoba oil - J & J Jojoba
MOBY BOOKS - Publisher's imprints - Playmore Inc. Publishers
MOBY BRICK - Computers–personal ☆ - The Brick Computer Co.
MOBY DICK - Fish–fresh or frozen ☆ - Slade Gorton and Co. Inc.
MOBY DICK - Yarn ☆ - Henry's Attic
MOBY DINK - Boats–dinghies ☆ - Snark Boats
MOBY DISKS - Computer diskettes–blank - Allenbach Industries Inc.
MOBY DUCK - Fabrics ☆ - Avondale Mills
MOBY GRAPE - Recording label - Matthew Katz
MOBY LICK - Toys - Mattel, Inc.
MOBY WIZARD - Greeting cards - Remigraphics, State of the Heart
MOC - Resins–polymer - Georgia-Pacific Corp.
MOC-BARIL - Wines - Kobrand Corp.
MOCADAMIA - Food products - Gwetzli Foods
MOCAFINO - Coffee - Faust Annoni
MOCAFINO - Coffee - Europa Foods Ltd.
MOCALI & MOCALI - Buckles ☆ - Erich M. Reich Inc.
MOCASSIN - Yarn ☆ - SCT Yarns Inc.
MOCC-STOMPERS - Footwear - Dunham Boot Makers
MOCCAMIT - Mittens ☆ - Fairfield Line, Inc.
MOCCAPUMP - Footwear - San Antonio Shoe Co. Inc.
MOCCASIN - Leather goods - AR Accessories Group Inc.
MOCCASIN - Watchbands–base metal - Utopia Marketing Corp.
MOCEAN - Apparel–athletic - Kimberley L. Pierson
MOCHA - Dinnerware–glass ☆ - Nikko Ceramics Inc.
MOCHA - Skin care products - California SunCare, Inc.
MOCHA-FREEZE - Ice coffee - Del's Lemonade & Refreshments
MOCHA JOE'S - Coffee, tea, and cocoa - Mocha Joe's Inc.
MOCHA KISS - Beverages–alcohol - DNA, Inc.
MOCHA MADNESS LATTE CAPPUCCINO MOCH ESPRESSO - Coffee - Mocha Madness Express
MOCHA MAGIC - Candy - Fine Foods Northwest
MOCHA MANIA - Desserts - Turtle Mountain, Inc.
MOCHA MELTS - Candy - Crate and Barrel
MOCHA MELTS - Chocolate candy - Harry London's Candies Inc.
MOCHA MIX - Food products - Presto Food Products, Inc.
MOCHA MIX SIGNATURE - Cream - Presto Food Products Inc.
MOCHA PIE - Desserts - Natural Nectar Corp.
MOCHA ROUGE - Lipsticks - Lancome
MOCHA RUMBA - Food products - Dearborn
MOCHA SIDAMO - Coffee - White Coffee Corp.
MOCHACCINO - Cocoa–powders or mixes - Boyd Coffee Co.

MOCHADAMIA MYSTIQUE - Coffee ☆ - Boyd Coffee Co.
MOCHADOODLE - Coffee - Executive Coffee Service Co.
MOCHEDDA - Cheese - Land O'Lakes Inc.
MOCHI - Food products - Grainaissance
MOCHI - Ice cream - Mikawaya, Inc.
MOCHIZUKI - Window shades ☆ - Gulf Coast Window Covering
MOCK MY WORDS - Games - TW2 Ltd.
MOCKINGBIRD BOOKS - Publisher's imprints - Mockingbird Books Inc.
MOCKSFORD - Fabrics - Dan River Inc.
MOCKSPUN - Yarn - Glen Raven Mills Inc.
MOCO MOUNTAIN - Food products - Mampeza International Inc.
MOCO SPORT - Apparel and accessories - Moco Sportswear
MOCODAMIA - Snack foods - Gwetzli Foods
MOCOMBO - Apparel–women's - Jezebel-Renee of Hollywood
MOCOMILON - Fabrics–nylon - Moultrie Textiles
MOCON - Brake parts - Carlisle Corp.
MOD - Candy - Nestle USA
MOD - Computer software - Dow Chemical Co.
MOD - Deodorizers ☆ - Car-Freshner Corp.
MOD - Giftware ☆ - Rubens Originals
MOD - Tools–garden ☆ - J.I. Case Co.
MOD - Toys–banks - A.J. Renzi Plastic Corp.
MOD - Watches - Hampden Corp.
MOD - Window frames ☆ - Biltbest Windows
MOD 4 - Hardware ☆ - Black & Decker Corp.
MOD-250/275 - Cameras - CCTV Corp./GBC
MOD-835C - Cameras - CCTV Corp./GBC
MOD BOD - Exercising equipment - Modern Body Design
MOD CAB - Cabinets–metal - Par Metal Products Inc.
MOD CALS - Novelty items ☆ - S.S. Adams Co.
MOD COLOR - Pigments–paint ☆ - Carnival Arts, Inc.
MOD-EE - Apparel–women's - Wacoal America Inc.
MOD-EEZ - Hardware - Modular Systems Inc.
MOD-FOUR - Aquarium accessories - Kordon
MOD-FOUR - Filters–water - Novalek, Inc.
MOD FRAME - Frames–picture - Structural Industries
MOD II INNER-SEAL - Storm windows ☆ - Continental Aluminum Products Co. Inc.
MOD MUSIC - Cosmetics ☆ - Duart Industries Ltd.
MOD PODGE - Finishing agents - Plaid Enterprises, Inc.
MOD-RAC - Computer furniture - Mead-Hatcher, Inc.
MOD-ROD - Curtain rods - Kirsch Co.
MOD SET - Hair care products - Waverly Beauty Products
MOD SQUAD - Audio equipment ☆ - GNP Audio Video Inc.
MOD-STRIPE - Brushes - Novelette Industries Inc.
MOD-U-ELL - Desks ☆ - Yawman and Erbe of California Corp.
MOD-U-KRAF - Prefabricated buildings–wood - Mod-U-Kraf Homes Inc.
MOD-U-LEX - Cables–insulated - General Cable Corp.
MOD-U-LINE - Boxes ☆ - Plastic Reel Corp. of America
MOD-U-LINE - Housewares - United Technologies Automotive
MOD-U-LINE - Lamps - General Electric Co.
MOD-U-LINE II - Office supplies - United Technologies Automotive
MOD-U-PLAN - Furniture - Williams Office Furniture Co.
MOD-U-SHELF - Furniture - RTC Industries, Inc.
MOD-U-SIGN - Signs - RTC Industries, Inc.
MOD V - Furniture–public buildings - Filing Equipment Inc.
MOD-WORMS - Fishing lures - Paul Warner Industries
MOD YARN - Yarn ☆ - Mangelsen's (VDI)
MODA - See AMERICA
MODA - Communications equipment–mobile - Moda Systems
MODA - Fabrics–cotton - United Notions, Inc.
MODA - Wheel rims–motor vehicle - The Tire Rack Wholesale
MODA 88 - Wallpaper - Arlin USA Inc.
MODA BELLA - Bags - Chateau International, Inc.
MODA COLLEZIONE - Neckties - West Coast Collection, Inc.
MODA DEL MONDO - Footwear - Robson Sales, Inc.
MODA GIOTELLI ITALIA - Jewelry - Moda Italia Inc.
MODA MADE IN ITALY CENTRO INTERNAZIONALE DELLA MODA ITALIANA - Apparel and accessories - Italian Trade Commission (Ceramic Tile Department)
MODA MORESCA - Floor coverings ☆ - Kentile Floors Inc.
MODA PRIMA - Apparel and accessories - James Lee Torti
MODA PRIMA BAMBINI - Bags–duffel - James Lee Torti
MODABOND INSULATORS - Fabrics - Delaware Valley Corp.
MODAC - Sealing compounds - Monsey Products Co.
MODAFINI - Hair care products - Modafini Inc.

☆ = Now out of production

MODAFINITY - Computer software - Modacad, Inc.
MODAFORMA - Hair care products - Modafini Inc.
MODAGE - Skin care products - Retired Persons Services, Inc.
MODALLION - Jewelry - Sottile Manufacturing Co.
MODAR - Furniture–wood - Modar Inc.
MODART - Corsets ☆ - Kellogg Industries Inc.
MODAX PLUS - Communications equipment–mobile - Motorola, Inc. (Land Mobile Products Sector)
MODBOD - Dolls - Seeley's
MODDERMAN - Cakes - Holland-American Importing Co. Inc.
MODE - Bedding–linen - Dan River Inc.
MODE - Lasers - Microoptical Devices, Inc.
MODE - Recording label - Jazz Composer's Orchestra Association Inc.
MODE DANISH - Tools ☆ - Regent Sheffield, Ltd.
MODE II LOUNGE - Chairs–upholstered ☆ - Victor Stanley, Inc.
MODE SYNC - Golfing equipment - Outdoor Technologies Group
MODEL - Luggage - Henry A. Enrich & Co. Inc.
MODEL 5H - Machinery - Oil Skimmers, Inc.
MODEL 6V - Machinery - Oil Skimmers, Inc.
MODEL 007 - Fans–electric - Lakewood Engineering and Manufacturing Co.
MODEL 30 CLASSIC - Medical apparatus - Mentor O & O Inc.
MODEL '71 - Ice boxes–household - Richmond Cedar Works Manufacturing Corp.
MODEL A - Fishing lures - Bomber Bait Co.
MODEL A - Office supplies - Ford Motor Co.
MODEL A - Projectors–photographic - Star Parts Inc.
MODEL-A SERIES - Cooking equipment–household - LazyMan, Inc.
MODEL AFFIRMATIVE ACTION - Computer software - Cambridge Information Group, Inc.
MODEL B - Projection screens - Da-Lite Screen Co. Inc.
MODEL BRONZE - Artists' materials ☆ - Dick Blick Co.
MODEL C - Projection screens - Da-Lite Screen Co. Inc.
MODEL CITIZEN - Apparel and accessories - Mark Andrew Ibbotson
MODEL DAIRY - Milk - Model Dairy
MODEL DIET - Computer software ☆ - Softsync Inc.
MODEL ELEVEN - Audio equipment - Cambridge SoundWorks Inc.
MODEL H20 - Optical scanners–computer - BEI Sensors & Systems Co.
MODEL HOME - Closet organizers - Henry A. Enrich & Co. Inc.
MODEL HOME - Paints - Nowstar
MODEL HOME - Paints - Pro Hardware Inc.
MODEL MACHINE - Toys - Lancer Industries Inc.
MODEL MAGIC - Clay–modeling - Binney & Smith Inc.
MODEL MASTER - Hobby kits - Testor Corp.
MODEL METAL - Artists' materials ☆ - Dick Blick Co.
MODEL ONE - Guitars - Dimarzio, Inc.
MODEL PLANK - Plastics - Tool Chemical Co., Inc.
MODEL POWER - Toys–trains - Model Power
MODEL RAILROAD HANDBOOK - Publisher's imprints - Kalmbach Publishing Co.
MODEL RAILROADERS - Computer software - SourceView Software International
MODEL V - Apparel and accessories - Michael Karl Jones & Luann Jones
MODELA - Clay–modeling - Caran D'Ache of Switzerland Inc.
MODELER - Computer software - Bose Corp.
MODELER - Computer software - Queue Inc.
MODELFLEX - Paints - Badger Air-Brush Co.
MODELGEN - Computer software - Software Systems
MODELING SPRAY - Hair care products - John Frieda, Inc.
MODELLA - Handbags - Living Things Manufacturing Co.
MODELMART - Computer peripheral equipment - Logic Works, Inc.
MODELMAX - Computer software - Advanced Software Applications Corp.
MODELO ESPECIAL - Beverages–malt - Barton Brands, Ltd.
MODELO ESPECIAL - Beverages–malt - Canandaigua Wine Co. Inc.
MODELPACK - Toys–electronic - MRC
MODELQUEST - Computer software - Abtech Corp.
MODELS COAT - Apparel and accessories - Swirl II Ltd.
MODELS OF YESTERYEAR - Toys–models - Matchbox Toys USA
MODEL'S PREFER - Cosmetics - David Schieffelin
MODELSERVER PUBLISHER - Computer software - Bentley Systems, Inc.
MODELTOOLS - Computer software - Logic Modeling Corp.
MODELUBE - Lubricants - Klotz Special Formula Products, Inc.
MODEM ASSIST - Computer software - Fresh Technology Co. Inc.
MODEM MADNESS - Computer software - Power User Software, Inc.
MODEM MATE - Electrical surge protectors - Woods Industries, Inc.
MODEM SAVER - Electronic equipment - Rodney E. Hosilyk
MODEMFONE - Telephones - Tandy Corp.

MODEMMAX - Electrical surge protectors - Panamax
MODEMNET - Computer software - Orrtax Software, Inc.
MODEMSURFR - Modems - Motorola, Inc. (Land Mobile Products Sector)
MODENA - Floor coverings - Mannington Resilient Floors
MODENA - Furniture - Lane Co. Inc.
MODENA - Furniture–children's ☆ - Child Craft Industries Inc.
MODENACETI - Vinegar - Source Atlantique
MODENACETI - Vinegar ☆ - Liberty Richter Inc.
MODERA - Mobile homes ☆ - Wick Building Systems Inc. (Manufactured Home Div./North)
MODERANT - Hair care products ☆ - Old 97 Co.
MODERATIONS - Hair care products - Matrix Essentials, Inc.
MODERN - Brooms ☆ - Deshler Broom Factory Inc.
MODERN - Chimes ☆ - Nutone Inc.
MODERN - Cigars ☆ - Havatampa Inc.
MODERN - Doors–glass - Green Hammer Metal Products Co.
MODERN - Firearms, accessories, and parts - Modern Muzzle Loading, Inc.
MODERN - Food products - Sweetener Products Co.
MODERN - Hardware - Amerock Corp.
MODERN - Laces–boot and shoe ☆ - St. Louis Braid Co.
MODERN - Lighting equipment–aircraft - Dove Foods
MODERN - Paper - Kurtz Bros. Inc.
MODERN - Recording label - Cadet Records Inc.
MODERN - Wigs - Wilshire Wigs & Accessories Inc.
MODERN AGE - Cabinets - Scott Manufacturing, Inc.
MODERN AGE - Hair care products ☆ - Palm Beach Beauty Products
MODERN AGE - Paints - United States Refining Co.
MODERN AGE BOOKS - Computer software - Modern Age Books, Inc.
MODERN AGE STUDIO - Apparel–women's - Chan Hee Park
MODERN AIR - Pumps - Aquaculture Research/Environmental Associates Inc.
MODERN-AIRE - Window shades ☆ - Sun Controls Products Inc.
MODERN AMUSEMENT - Apparel and accessories – Jeff Yokoyama
MODERN ART - Computer software - Logitech, Inc.
MODERN ART - Dinnerware–glass ☆ - WMF/USA
MODERN ART - Jewelry - Modern Art Jewelry
MODERN ART - Wallpaper - Bayview Wallcoverings
MODERN BLUES - Caps–baseball - Modern Blues Outerwear, Inc.
MODERN CONCEPTS - Manufactured homes - Redman Industries, Inc.
MODERN CRAFTS - Hobby kits - Modern Crafts Co.
MODERN CRAZE - Bicycles - Dynacraft Industries Inc.
MODERN-CULTURE - Apparel and accessories - SS Gear International, Ltd.
MODERN DAILY REMINDER - Calendars - Kurtz Bros. Inc.
MODERN DIVIDED LIGHTS - Glass products - Eagle Window & Door Inc.
MODERN ESSENCES - Hair care products - New Image Laboratories, Inc.
MODERN ESSENTIALS - Apparel and accessories - Sears, Roebuck and Co.
MODERN FLAME - Fireplace equipment - Rasmussen Iron Works Inc.
MODERN FOODS - Beef - Modern Foods Inc.
MODERN FORGE - House furnishings - Modern Forge Manufacturing Co.
MODERN GEOMETRICS - Fabrics–tapestry ☆ - Coloroll Inc.
MODERN GIRL - Shoes - Mother Goose Co.
MODERN GLOBE - Apparel and accessories - Bassett-Walker Inc.
MODERN GOLD - Frames–picture - A.P.F. Master Framemaker
MODERN GREEK - Computer software - Philip B. Payne and Nancy C. Payne
MODERN HANGING STRIPS - House furnishings ☆ - Modern Household Savers Inc.
MODERN HEROES - Sportswear, outerwear ☆ - Winer Industries Inc.
MODERN IRIS - Giftware - Russ Berrie and Co., Inc.
MODERN JR. - Apparel–women's - Jonathan Logan Inc.
MODERN LIBRARY - Publisher's imprints - Random House, Inc.
MODERN LOVE - Jewelry - Avon Products, Inc.
MODERN MAGIC SNACKS - Snack foods - Amway Corp.
MODERN MAID - Flour–blended - DCA Food Industries, Inc.
MODERN MAID - Refrigerator - Raytheon Co.
MODERN MAID - Rope - Wellington Leisure Products, Inc.
MODERN MAID - Stoves - Amana Refrigeration Inc.
MODERN MARVELS - Video production - A & E Television Network
MODERN MATRIX - Dining room furniture ☆ - Daystrom Furniture Inc.
MODERN MECHANIC - Motor vehicle parts and accessories - Standard Motor Products, Inc.
MODERN MIX - Broadcasting stations–radio - Hot Mix Radio Network, Inc.
MODERN MOVES - Handbags - Holiday Fair, Inc.
MODERN OPTIONS - Paints - Modern Options, Inc.
MODERN REFLECTION - Artists' materials ☆ - Donald Art Co.
MODERN SPORT STRIPS - House furnishings ☆ - Modern Household Savers Inc.
MODERN TIE STRIPS - House furnishings ☆ - Modern Household Savers Inc.

☆ = Now out of production

MODERN TIMES - Clocks - Marble Masterpieces Inc.
MODERN TIMES - Floor coverings - Congoleum Corp.
MODERN TREND - Guitars ☆ - International Music Corp.
MODERN VINTAGE - Drums–musical instruments - Aquarian Accessories Corp.
MODERN WIG MUSIC - Recording label - Toddilin' Town Recording Studio
MODERNAIRE - Desks ☆ - Invincible Metal Furniture Co.
MODERNE - Draperies - Maya Romanoff Corp.
MODERNE - Greeting cards ☆ - Moderne Card Co. Inc.
MODERNE - Housewares ☆ - Bammental Wallcoverings Inc.
MODERNE SHAPE - Trays ☆ - Quaker Industries Ltd.
MODERNESQUE - Floor coverings–carpet and rugs ☆ - World Carpets, Inc.
MODERNETTE - Modular furniture ☆ - Invincible Metal Furniture Co.
MODERNFOLD - Partitions–metal - Modernfold, Inc.
MODERNFOLD - Window coverings - Rex Venetian Blind Co.
MODERNISTIC - Office supplies - Mays/Marshall & Meier Van Valkenburg Co.
MODERNISTIC STAR PATCHWORK HOUSE - Fabrics - Oakley Farm Crafts, Inc.
MODERNITES - Candles ☆ - Will & Baumer, Inc.
MODERNLINE - Paper–writing - Kurtz Bros. Inc.
MODERNO - Cabinets - Contempri Kitchens
MODERNO - Glassware–household - Crisa Corp.
MODERNSCREEN - Fireplace equipment - Thomas Industries Inc. (Portland Willamette Div.)
MODERNTIME - Clocks - Recyco
MODERSERVER DISCOVERY - Computer software - Bentley Systems, Inc.
MODESS - Sanitary napkins - Johnson & Johnson
MODESTO - Floor coverings - Mannington Resilient Floors
MODESTO - Tiles–ceiling ☆ - Certainteed Corp. (Roofing Products Group)
MODESTO - Toilets–porcelain - Sterling Plumbing Group Inc.
MODESTO CARPET MILLS - Floor coverings–carpet and rugs - Aladdin Mills, Inc.
MODESTY - Apparel–women's - Treasures of Paris-Monogram Manufacturing Co.
MODESTY - Sanitary napkins - Medline, Industries, Inc.
MODESTY - Skin care products - Troika International Inc.
MODGLIN MAID - Cleaning preparations ☆ - Royal Maid Association for the Blind Inc.
MODI - Apparel and accessories - Modi Rubber Ltd.
MODI DENIM - Apparel and accessories - Modi Rubber Ltd.
MODI-FILE - Filing cabinets–metal - Art Metal-U.S. Corp.
MODIANO - Apparel–women's - Norton Mcnaughton of Squire, Inc.
MODICON - Pharmaceutical preparations - Ortho Pharmaceutical Corp.
MODIFIED FORMULA - Pet food - Vet's Choice
MODIFIER - Girdles ☆ - Kellogg Industries Inc.
MODIFIER - Tires - Uniroyal Goodrich Licensing Services, Inc.
MODIFIER, THE - Underwear and nightwear - Rago Foundations Inc. LLC
MODIFIERS - Toys–automobiles ☆ - ERTL Co., Inc.
MODIFYRE - Furnaces–electric ☆ - Field Controls Co.
MODIPHY - Hair care products - Tressa, Inc.
MODIS 120 - Nautical instruments - VDO Instruments Inc.
MODISH - Pet collars - Modish Craftsman Co.
MODISSA - Shoes ☆ - Mengen-Ulla
MODISTICS - Rings–jewelry - Feature Enterprises
MODITAL - Jewelry - Modital Corp.
MODLOC - Electrical equipment - Dynametric, Inc.
MODMATE - Computers–personal - Modular Computer Systems Inc.
MODMINDER - Electronic equipment - Modulation Sciences Inc.
MODNETICS - Hair curlers - Kayline Enterprises Inc.
MODO - Board games - Modo Inc.
MODO MIO - Apparel and accessories - John G. Boccella
MODOC - Food products - Modoc Orchard Co.
MODOC - Garden equipment ☆ - H.D. Hudson Manufacturing Co.
MODONETIC - Hair curlers - Capitol Novelty Co.
MODPAK - Cameras–video - Dotronix Inc.
MODPORT - Computer software - SDI Environmental Services, Inc.
MODRA - Vases - Henry Collection, Inc.
MODRENAL - Vitamins and nutritional supplements - Amrion, Inc.
MODROCK - Computer software - Calmat Co.
MODSEW - Computer storage devices - Ies in Time, Inc.
MODTROTTER - Clocks ☆ - General Time Corp. (Westclox/Seth Thomas Div.)
MODU-CUBE - Leather goods ☆ - AR Accessories Group Inc.
MODU-PANEL - Air conditioning equipment - Carrier Corp.
MODU-RAIL - Railings–wood - Newman Brothers Inc.
MODU-RAY - Electronic equipment - Kalglo Electronics Co. Inc.
MODU-STAK - Clamps - Hydra-Zorb Co.

MODU-TEK - Machine parts - Tekno, Inc.
MODUCAL - Pharmaceutical preparations - Bristol-Myers Squibb Co.
MODUCLASSIX - Furniture - Moduform, Inc.
MODUESQUE - Furniture - Moduform, Inc.
MODUFLEX - Electronic equipment - Deltron Inc.
MODUFLEX - Partitions–metal - Panelfold Inc.
MODUFRAME - Furniture - Moduform, Inc.
MODUGUARD - Furniture - Moduform, Inc.
MODULA - Toys–blocks - Learning Things Inc.
MODULAIR - Skin care products - Niche Research Inc.
MODULAIRE - Telephones - Tandy Corp.
MODULAIRE GROUP - Furniture–upholstered - Monarch Furniture Corp.
MODULAR - Food trucks and wagons - Tomlinson Industries
MODULAR - Paints ☆ - Binney & Smith Inc.
MODULAR - Toys–models - Estes Industries
MODULAR ART - Floor coverings–carpet and rugs - Milliken & Co. Inc.
MODULAR DOMINOES - Games - Learning Things Inc.
MODULAR-FLEX - Circuit boards–printed - Advanced Circuit Technology Inc.
MODULAR II - Automotive parts and accessories - Hill Parking Systems, Inc.
MODULAR IX - Scuba diving equipment - Parkway Systems
MODULAR MAGICIAN - Health care products - Equi-Tron Inc.
MODULAR MATES - Housewares - Tupperware Co.
MODULAR MULTIPLES - Lighting fixtures - Modular International, Inc.
MODULAR ONE - Medical apparatus - Mentor O & O Inc.
MODULAR OPTIONS - Floor coverings–carpet and rugs - Olympic Carpets Inc.
MODULAR PROTECTION - Fire extinguishers - Glenn Fire Protection Inc.
MODULAR WORKSTATIONS - Office furniture–metal - Marvel Group Inc.
MODULARLINK - Printer interface device - Primax Electronics
MODULARMOR - Floor coverings - Parquet de France Inc.
MODULAT - Hair care products - Schwarzkopf Inc.
MODULATE OS - Golfing equipment - Dunlop Slazenger Corp.
MODULATING VALVES - Swimming pools - Recreonics, Inc.
MODULATOR - Shelving units–plastic - Eric A. Knight and Lance E. McCloud Partnership
MODULBOX - Display cases–plastic - Visual Design Manufacturing Co. Inc.
MODULE - Electronic equipment - Buhl Industries, Inc.
MODULE - Wallpaper ☆ - Pickhardt & Siebert USA Inc.
MODULE-99 - Computer peripheral equipment - Lexar Computers
MODULE 600 - Lighting fixtures - Holophane Corp.
MODULEMATE - Electrical industrial apparatus - Berg Technology, Inc.
MODULETTE - Stereos - Tandy Corp.
MODULINE - Bookcases–wood ☆ - Modular Systems Inc.
MODULINK - Electronic equipment - Shure Brothers, Inc.
MODULITE - Automotive parts and accessories - Draw-Tite, Inc.
MODULITE LSSP - Motor vehicle parts and accessories - Budge Industries, Inc.
MODULOK - Mops ☆ - Golden Star Inc.
MODULOK - Toys - Mattel, Inc.
MODULON - Storage containers, drawer organizers, etc. - Interdesign, Inc.
MODULUBE - Construction equipment rental services ☆ - Boegh Building Systems
MODULUS - Bicycles ☆ - Raleigh USA Bicycle Co.
MODULUS - Furniture - Taylor-Ramsey Corp.
MODULUS - Guitars - Modulus Graphite Products
MODULUS EV40 - Golfing equipment - Emhart Industries Inc.
MODULUX - Lighting equipment - Diffusa-Lite Co.
MODUPEDIC - Furniture - Moduform, Inc.
MODUPHONE - Stereos - Tandy Corp.
MODUPLEX - Engines–marine - Detroit Marine Engineering
MODUPOLITAN - Furniture - Moduform, Inc.
MODURETIC - Pharmaceutical preparations - Merck & Co., Inc. (Merck Research Laboratories)
MODUROCKER - Furniture - Moduform, Inc.
MODUTANK - Swimming pools - PCA Industries Inc.
MODUTHERM - Heaters–swimming pool ☆ - Teledyne Laars
MOE - Computer software - Mobius Group, Inc.
MOE LIGHT - Glass products ☆ - Thomas Industries Inc.
MOE MO'ROC' CA N CAFE - Apparel and accessories - Restaurant Development Inc.
MOEBIQUIN - See DIQUINOL
MOEBIUS - Apparel and accessories - Starwatcher Graphics, Inc.
MOEBIUS: THE ORB OF CELESTIAL HARMONY - Video games - Origin Systems, Inc.
MOEC - Chemical preparations - Molecular Optoelectronics Corp.
MOELLER - Thermometers - Moeller Instrument Co. Inc.

☆ = Now out of production

MOEN - Faucets - Moen Inc.

MOENFLO - Faucets - Moen Inc.

MOENIQUE - Shower stalls–metal ☆ - Moen Inc.

MOENSTONE - Sinks–porcelain - Moen Inc.

MOENTROL - Faucets - Moen Inc.

MOERLEIN - Beverages–malt - Hudepohl-Schoenling Brewing Co.

MOERLEIN'S CINCINNATI BOCK - Beer - Schoenling Brewing Co.

MOERLEIN'S CINCINNATI BOCK BEER - Beverages–malt - Schoenling Brewing Co.

MOERS - Recording label - Jazz Composer's Orchestra Association Inc.

MOE'S BROADWAY BAGEL - Bakery products - Moe's Broadway Bagel, Inc.

MOE'S ITALIAN SANDWICHES - Sandwiches–prepackaged - Moestogo Corp.

MOE'S MO' ROC' N - Apparel and accessories - Restaurant Development Inc.

MOESCHINO - Collar buttons - H. Alpert and Co.

MOESCHINO POUR HOMME - Collar buttons - H. Alpert and Co.

MOET - Wines - Schieffelin and Somerset Co.

MOET & CHANDON - Wines - Schieffelin and Somerset Co.

MOET & CHANDON NECTAR IMPERIAL - Beverages–alcohol - Schieffelin & Co.

MOET-CHANDON - Beverages–alcohol - Co. Store

MOFLOW - Apparel - Pro-Tec-Dallas Baker Products

MOFO - Computer software - Morrison and Foerster L.L.P.

MOFOAM - Chemical preparations - Midwest Industrial Supply, Inc.

MOG - Recording label - Carmel Records

MOGAMI - Audio equipment - Marshall Electronics Inc.

MOGDEN DAVID - Wines - Wine Group Inc.

MOGEN DAVID - Food products - Dairy Fresh Products Co.

MOGLE - Computer software - Intergraph Corp.

MOGOLD-TEX - Food products - Monark Egg Corp.

MOGUL - Banjos - OME Co. Inc.

MOGUL - Binders - Dennison National Co.

MOGUL - Floor coverings–carpet and rugs ☆ - Regal Rugs Inc.

MOGUL - Lighting fixtures - Acme-Lite Manufacturing Co.

MOGUL HARDCORE SKI STUFF - Sporting goods - Mogul Sport

MOGULL - Clocks - Heritage International

MOGULS SKIER PUP - Toys–stuffed - Russ Berrie and Co., Inc.

MOHA - Cakes - Bertolli USA, Inc.

MOHA - Kitchen cabinets–metal - Foge Jensen Imports

MOHAIR DELIGHT - Yarn ☆ - Plymouth Yarn Co.

MOHAIR PLUS - Handwork supplies - Bernat Yarn & Craft Corp.

MOHALA - Liquors ☆ - Suntory International Corp.

MOHARA - Fabrics - Burlington Industries, Inc.

MOHAVE - Fabrics - Greenwood Mills Inc.

MOHAVE MANGO - Fruit drinks–bottled or canned - Empire State Beverage Co.

MOHAVE R/S - Tires - Reinalt-Thomas Corp.

MOHAWK - Abrasive products ☆ - Norton Co.

MOHAWK - Apparel–men's ☆ - Duxbak Inc.

MOHAWK - Artists' materials - Andrews/Nelson/Whitehead

MOHAWK - Bicycles - Mohawk Cycle Co.

MOHAWK - Boats–canoes - Mohawk Manufacturing Co.

MOHAWK - Brushes - Wright-Bernet

MOHAWK - Cabinets - Serway Brothers Inc.

MOHAWK - Cordials - Marie Brizard Wines & Spirits, USA

MOHAWK - Covers–tire - Flying W Caps Inc.

MOHAWK - Cutlery - Lamson and Goodnow Manufacturing Co.

MOHAWK - Dolls ☆ - Mego Financial Corp.

MOHAWK - Fencing–wood - Machalk Enterprises Inc.

MOHAWK - Finishing agents - GRK Manufacturing

MOHAWK - Floor coverings–carpet and rugs - Mohawk Carpet Corp.

MOHAWK - Fruits and vegetables - Villa Park Orchards

MOHAWK - Guns ☆ - Remington Arms Co., Inc.

MOHAWK - Handles–wood - Sequatchie Handle Works Inc.

MOHAWK - Ladders–metal - John S. Tilley Ladders Co. Inc.

MOHAWK - Petroleum ☆ - Getty Petroleum Marketing, Inc.

MOHAWK - Photographic equipment - Coast Acquisition Corp.

MOHAWK - Playing cards - United States Playing Card Co.

MOHAWK - Pretzels - Mohawk Beverage Inc.

MOHAWK - Recording label - Dragon Records (Div. of Agon Productions)

MOHAWK - Salmon–smoked, salted, dried, or pickled - Wards Cove Packing Co.

MOHAWK - Stereo speakers ☆ - Stillwater Designs & Audio Inc.

MOHAWK SAFARI - Apparel and accessories - Safari Enterprises, Inc.

MOHEX - Bags–trash - Mohawk Plastics Inc.

MOHICAN - Archery equipment ☆ - Bear Archery Inc.

MOHICAN - Motor vehicles–motor homes ☆ - Hi-Lo Trailer Co. Inc.

MOHINDER - Sporting goods - Mohinder Sports Inc.

MOHLAN - Yarn ☆ - National Spinning Co., Inc.

MOHO - Window shades - Sol-R-Veil Inc.

MOHR DECOR - Housewares - Bammental Wallcoverings Inc.

MOI REE - Jewelry - Napier Co.

MOI-STIR - Medical apparatus - Kingswood Laboratories Inc.

MOILLARD - Wines - Victoire Imports Co.

MOIRA - Computer software - Massachusetts Institute of Technology

MOIRA - Dinnerware–glass ☆ - Crownford Giftware Co. Inc.

MOIRA - House furnishings - Dan River Inc.

MOIRE - Floor coverings–carpet and rugs - Galaxy Carpet Mills Inc.

MOIRE - Wallpaper - Robert Crowder & Co.

MOIRE - Wallpaper - Queens Decorative Wallcoverings Inc.

MOIRE AND MORE - Wallpaper - Carlton-Metro Wallcoverings

MOIRE ARRAY - Toys ☆ - Tedco Inc.

MOIRE MAGIQUE - Wallpaper - Carlton-Metro Wallcoverings

MOIRE MAGIQUE II - Wallpaper - Carlton-Metro Wallcoverings

MOIRE MIRAGE - Wallcoverings - Cork Products Co. Inc.

MOIRE PLUS III - Floor coverings–tile - Interface, Inc.

MOIRELLA - Fabrics - Stylecrest Fabrics Ltd.

MOIRISE - Wallpaper ☆ - Wallquest, Inc.

MOISETTE CREME LUXE - Lipsticks ☆ - Monteil Paris

MOIST-10 - Pharmaceutical preparations - Jess Clarke & Sons Inc.

MOIST AGAIN - Skin care products - Lake Consumer Products

MOIST & CHEWY - Snack foods - Glenn Foods Inc.

MOIST & CHUNKY - Dog food - Ralston Purina Co.

MOIST & EASY - Bakery products - Procter & Gamble Co.

MOIST & MEATY - Pet products - Ralston Purina Co.

MOIST & SHEEN - Hair care products ☆ - Vigorol Inc.

MOIST DELUXE - Bakery products - Procter & Gamble Co.

MOIST-ENDER - Pharmaceutical preparations - Worcester Brush Co.

MOIST ENVIRONMENT NIGHT TREATMENT - Skin care products - Charles of the Ritz Group Ltd.

MOIST HEAT UNIT - Health care products - Thermo-Electric Co.

MOIST-O-MATIC - Office supplies - Wescosa Inc.

MOIST PENETRATOR - Hair care products - Gelle-International Ltd.

MOIST-SHUR - Hardware - The Centro Co. Inc.

MOIST STIC - Lip balms - Real Natural Products

MOIST SUPREME - Cakes–mixes - Pillsbury Co.

MOIST TOUCH - Skin care products - Lever Brothers Co. Inc.

MOISTAIRE - Air purification systems - Forum Group Inc.

MOISTCURE - Hair care products - Revlon Consumer Products Corp.

MOISTE - Skin care products - Mastey De Paris

MOISTEASE - Pharmaceutical preparations - An-Kar Products, Inc.

MOISTEX - Hair care products - Palm Beach Beauty Products

MOISTIN FACTOR - Hair care products ☆ - Mahdeen Laboratory

MOISTIQUE - Skin care products - Twinlab

MOIST'N RICH - Skin care products - Freeman Cosmetics Corp.

MOISTOP - Vaporizers - Fortifiber Corp.

MOISTRIO NITE CREME - Skin care products - Viviane Woodard Industries, Ltd.

MOISTRIO SKINCARE - Skin care products - Viviane Woodard Industries, Ltd.

MOISTRITE - Paper - Mead Corp.

MOISTRITE XO-2 - Paper - Mead Corp.

MOISTSTIC - Lip balm - Stuart S. Kauder

MOISTURE - Hair care products - Revlon Consumer Products Corp.

MOISTURE 7 - Lip balms - J.A. Freedman, Inc.

MOISTURE 2000 - Skin care products - Bonne Bell, Inc.

MOISTURE BALANCE - Hair care products - Cheveux Inc.

MOISTURE BALANCE - Skin care products - Almay Inc.

MOISTURE BALANCER - Hair care products - Hayashi for Hair Inc.

MOISTURE BAR - Soap - Reviva Laboratories

MOISTURE BATH - Hair care products - Scruples Professional Salon Products, Inc.

MOISTURE BLOCK - Chemical preparations - Sherwin-Williams Automotive Finishes Corp.

MOISTURE BOND - Paints - Coronado Paint Co.

MOISTURE BUBBLE - Perfumes - Revlon Consumer Products Corp.

MOISTURE BURST - Skin care products - Revlon Consumer Products Corp.

MOISTURE CLEANSE - Cosmetics - Paje Products

MOISTURE CONTROL - Health care products - Helene Curtis Industries Inc.

MOISTURE CREME - Hair care products - Brocato International

MOISTURE CREME BLUSH - Cosmetics - Viviane Woodard Industries, Ltd.

MOISTURE-DERM - Skin care products - Schein Pharmaceutical Inc.

MOISTURE DROPS - Ophthalmic goods - Bausch & Lomb Inc.

MOISTURE FACTOR - Hair care products - L'anza Research International

MOISTURE FACTOR LITE - Hair care products - L'anza Research International

MOISTURE FORMULA - Cosmetics - Johnson Products Co., Inc.

MOISTURE GAIN - Hair care products - Helene Curtis Industries Inc.

MOISTURE GLAZE II - Hair care products - Peter Hantz Co.

MOISTURE GLOSS - Cosmetics ☆ - Hazel Bishop International

MOISTURE-GUARD - Gypsum products - Georgia-Pacific Corp.

MOISTURE GUARD - Hair care products - Helene Curtis Industries Inc.

MOISTURE-GUARD - Tubes–plastic - Alvin and Co. Inc.

MOISTURE GUARD PLUS - Shingles - Tamko Roofing Products, Inc.

MOISTURE-IN - Skin-care products - Benjamin Ansehl Co.

MOISTURE JAM - Hair care products - Image Laboratories, Inc.

MOISTURE JUBILEEEE - Skin care products - Backscratchers, Inc.

MOISTURE JUICE - Hair care products - Image Laboratories, Inc.

MOISTURE LIGHT - Skin care products ☆ - Bonne Bell, Inc.

MOISTURE LOCK - Chemical preparations - Hydromax Inc.

MOISTURE MAGIC - Hair care products - Alleghany Pharmacal Corp.

MOISTURE MAGNET - Pet products - JLS Products Inc.

MOISTURE MAKEOVER - Skin care products - Dolly Parton Inc.

MOISTURE MANAGEMENT - Apparel and accessories - Softouch Co. Inc.

MOISTURE MANAGEMENT - Shampoos - Consac Industries, Inc.

MOISTURE MASTER - Garden equipment - Aquapore Moisture Systems, Inc.

MOISTURE MASTER - Piano dehumidifiers - American Piano Supply Co.

MOISTURE MAX - Hair care products - Lustrasilk Corp. of America Inc.

MOISTURE MIST - Cosmetics - Shiseido Cosmetics (America) Ltd.

MOISTURE MIST - Pet products - Zoecon Corp.

MOISTURE MIST PLUS - Hair care products - Hair Research X Inc.

MOISTURE-MOVER - Dehumidifiers - CTSI Corp.

MOISTURE MUNCHER - Drying agent - Pioneer Marketing & Research, Inc.

MOISTURE ON-CALL - Skin care products - Clinique Laboratories, Inc.

MOISTURE ON-LINE - Skin care products - Clinique Laboratories, Inc.

MOISTURE PERFECT - Hair care products ☆ - Advanced Research Laboratories

MOISTURE PLUS - Skin care products - Excelcis

MOISTURE POTION - Shampoos - Dowbrands L.P.

MOISTURE QUOTIENT - Hair care products - Helene Curtis Industries Inc.

MOISTURE RECOVERY - Hair care products - Revlon Consumer Products Corp.

MOISTURE RELEASE - Cosmetics - Revlon Consumer Products Corp.

MOISTURE RENEW - Skin care products - Almay Inc.

MOISTURE RESERVE - Skin care products - Alexandra De Markoff, Ltd.

MOISTURE RICH - Lipsticks - Max Factor & Co.

MOISTURE SHIELD - Nail care products - E.O.H. Industries, Inc.

MOISTURE SHIELD - Skin care products ☆ - Avon Products, Inc.

MOISTURE-SILK - Cosmetics - Frances Denney

MOISTURE-SILK - Cosmetics - Stephan Co.

MOISTURE SILK - Skin care products - Excelcis

MOISTURE STABILIZING - Skin care products - Helene Curtis Industries Inc.

MOISTURE THERAPY - Humidifiers - Duracraft Corp.

MOISTURE THERAPY - Skin care products - Avon Products, Inc.

MOISTURE TINT - Cosmetics - Revlon Consumer Products Corp.

MOISTURE WAVE - Hair care products - Zotos International Inc.

MOISTURE WHIP - Cosmetics - Maybelline Co.

MOISTURE WRAP - Skin care products - Heritage Cosmetics Inc.

MOISTUREE - Hair care products - Mastey De Paris

MOISTUREFUL - Cosmetics - Charles of the Ritz Group Ltd.

MOISTUREGARD POUCH - Tobacco - National Tobacco Co., L.P.

MOISTUREGLOSS - Cosmetics - Almay Inc.

MOISTUREGUARD - Furniture - Lexington Furniture Industries, Inc.

MOISTUREL - Hair care products - Chesebrough-Pond's USA Co.

MOISTUREL - Skin care products - Westwood-Squibb Pharmaceuticals, Inc.

MOISTURELOCK - Hair care products - European Tanning Systems Inc.

MOISTURERICH - Razors - Gillette Co.

MOISTUREWEAR - Cosmetics - Noxell Corp.

MOISTUREX - Hair care products - Scruples Professional Salon Products, Inc.

MOISTUREYES - Health care products ☆ - Carme Inc.

MOISTUREZE - Hair care products - Tressa, Inc.

MOISTURIFIC - Cosmetics - Dolly Parton Inc.

MOISTURINE - Pharmaceutical preparations ☆ - Mericon Industries Inc.

MOISTURIZER - Hair care products - Joico Laboratories, Inc.

MOISTURIZING DIAL PLUS - Skin care products - Dial Corp.

MOJADO BROTHERS - Apparel and accessories - Dan A. Calderon

MOJAVE - Aircraft ☆ - New Piper Aircraft, Inc.

MOJAVE - Cooking utensils–stoneware ☆ - Western Stoneware

MOJAVE - Floor coverings–carpet and rugs ☆ - Catalina Carpet Mills Inc.

MOJAVE - Floor coverings–carpet and rugs ☆ - Regal Rugs Inc.

MOJAVE - Floor coverings–tile - ECC International

MOJAVE - Furniture ☆ - Landes Manufacturing Co.

MOJAVE - Hosiery - Wigwam Mills Inc.

MOJAVE - Seasonings - McCormick & Co., Inc.

MOJAVE - Solar energy collectors - Heliodyne Inc.

MOJAVE - Spices and extracts - Mojave Foods Corp.

MOJAVE CORKS - Wallcoverings - Cork Products Co. Inc.

MOJAVE EXPRESS - Bicycles ☆ - Ming Ta Supply

MOJAVE GULCH - Bicycles ☆ - Huffy Corp.

MOJAVE MOO - Ice cream - Smith's Dairy Products Co.

MOJAVE MOTIF COLLECTION - Floor coverings–carpet and rugs - Masland Corp.

MOJAVE TRAIL - Automotive parts and accessories ☆ - Lancaster Colony Automotive Group

MOJAVE II - Wallpaper - Koroseal Wallcoverings

MOJAZZ - Recording label - Motown Record Co. L.P.

MOJO - Apparel and accessories - Ector County Independent School District

MOJO - Computer software - Adobe Systems Inc.

MOJO - Food products - Shakey's Inc.

MOJO - Hair care products ☆ - Capitol Novelty Co.

MOJO CRIOLLO - Sauces - Catalina Finer Foods

MOJO TONE - Amplifiers–musical instrument - Mojo Musical Supply

MOJOE - Publisher's imprints - Jack Brown Enterprises, Inc.

MOJUD - Hosiery - Kayser-Roth Corp.

MOJUD NEXT TO YOU - Hosiery - Kayser-Roth Corp.

MOKA ESTATE COFFEE - Coffee - AMFAC/JMB Hawaii, Inc.

MOKENA - Wallpaper - Mokena Mills Inc.

MOKENA MILLS - Wallpaper - Mokena Mills Inc.

MOKEY - Toys - Jim Henson Productions, Inc.

MOKKA ARIBA - Cookies - Bahlsen Inc.

MOKSHA - Socks - Moksha Worldwide, Inc.

MOL-IRON - Pharmaceutical preparations - Schering-Plough Healthcare Products

MOL-MIX - Animal feeds - Stevens Industries Inc.

MOLAFIL - Pharmaceutical preparations ☆ - Church and Dwight Co. Inc.

MOLAINE - Yarn ☆ - Lion Brand Yarn Co.

MOLD-A-PLACK - Hobby kits ☆ - Activa Products Inc.

MOLD & COLOR - Hobby kits - Brite-Tone Co.

MOLD AWAY - Stain removers - Marine Development & Research Corp.

MOLD BUILDER - Molding compounds–plastics - Environmental Technology, Inc.

MOLD-EASE - Lubricants - Merix Chemical Co.

MOLD-IN GRAPHICS SPRAY-IN ADHESIVE SYSTEM - Adhesives and sealants - Mold-In Graphic Systems

MOLD-IN GRAPHICS SPRAY-IN COLOR SYSTEM - Paints - Mold-In Graphic Systems

MOLD-IN GRAPHICS SPRAY-IN SURFACE ENHANCER - Adhesives and sealants - Mold-In Graphic Systems

MOLD-IT - Rubber–molded - Joli Plastics & Chemical Corp.

MOLD-KOTE - Adhesives and sealants - Hastings Plastics Co.

MOLD MM MAN - Toys - O.A.R. Tool and Die, Inc.

MOLD-TECH - Tools - Standex International Corp.

MOLD-TITE - Ammunition ☆ - Remington Arms Co., Inc.

MOLD-ZAP - Agricultural products - Alltech, Inc.

MOLDAN - Filters–air - Hallmark Holdings, Inc.

MOLDED MAGIC - Underwear and nightwear - Wonder Maid Inc.

MOLDED MIST - Apparel–women's - Blue Bay Inc.

MOLDER-AT-WORK - Giftware ☆ - Wilton Co.

MOLDFLOW - Connectors–electrical - Coilhose Pneumatics Inc.

MOLDIKINS - Apparel–women's ☆ - Blue Swan Outline Corp.

MOLDING MUD - Hair care products - Sebastian International, Inc.

MOLDOW - Calendars - Rolf Wallach Inc.

MOLE AWAY - Repellent - Scrypton Systems, Inc.

MOLE HOLE - Recording label - Bug Records Inc.

MOLE-NOTS - Rodenticides - Nott Manufacturing Co. Inc.

MOLE POBLANO - Food products - Reynoso Bros. International

MOLECTRON - Electronic products - Molectron Detector Inc.

MOLECULAR - Adhesives and sealants - Molecular Repair Systems, Inc.

MOLECULAR - Hair curlers - Celeste Co. Inc.

MOLECULAR ACTIVATED - Cleaning preparations - Seneca Research Inc.

MOLECULAR ACTIVATION - Cleaning preparations - Seneca Research Inc.

MOLECULAR BIOSYSTEMS - Pharmaceutical preparations - Molecular Biosystems Inc.

MOLECULAR EXPRESSIONS - Apparel and accessories - Stonehenge Ltd.

MOLECULAR PROTECTOR - Vitamins and nutritional supplements - Earth's Resources, Inc.

☆ = Now out of production

MOLECULAR RESTRUCTURE - Hair care products - Monique Quality Products Co. Inc.

MOLECULAR VAPOR - Health care products - Celeste Co. Inc.

MOLECULAR ZIPPERING ACTION - Chemical preparations - Helena Chemical Co.

MOLECULE - Telephones - Astronet Corp.

MOLECULE MAKER - Games - Teaching Concepts Inc.

MOLECULEMAKER - Computer software - Analytica of Branford, Inc.

MOLECUSORB - Filters—air - AIFCO Co.

MOLEHILL MT. EQUIPMENT - Infant product - Molehill Mountain Equipment, Inc.

MOLENBERG - Bakery products - Quality Bakers of America Cooperative Inc.

MOLESTICK - Foam rubber - Alimed, Inc.

MOLETOX II - Pesticides—household - Bonide Products, Inc.

MOLI-CURE - Tires ☆ - Bridgestone/Firestone, Inc.

MOLI-Q'S - Construction toy - James Industries, Inc.

MOLI-STAX - Construction toy, now out of production - James Industries, Inc.

MOLINA - Hair care products - Molina International

MOLINARD DE MOLINARD - Colognes ☆ - Gary Farn Ltd.

MOLINARD DE MOLINARD - Perfumes ☆ - Classic Fragrances Ltd.

MOLINARI - Meat products—beef - Dairy Fresh Products Co.

MOLINAS - Wines - Joseph Victori Wines Inc.

MOLINE TOOL WORKS - Tools—hand-operated - Serv-A-Lite Products, Inc.

MOLINO NICOLA - Food products ☆ - Dean & Deluca Inc.

MOLIONEX - Pet products ☆ - Aquatrol, Inc.

MOLITOR - Boats—canoes - Old Town Canoe Co.

MOLITOR - Golfing equipment - Spalding & Evenflo Companies, Inc.

MOLKOSAN - Health care products - Bioforce of America Ltd.

MOLLA - Furniture—metal - New Tradewinds Corp.

MOLLE - Shaving preparations - Alvin Last Inc.

MOLLENHAUER - Musical instruments - Custom Music Co.

MOLLER - Oils—edible - Haram-Christensen Corp.

MOLLER - Organs—musical instrument - King of Instruments, Inc.

MOLLIE KATZEN'S COOKING SHOW - Broadcasting stations—radio - Enchanted Broccoli, Inc.

MOLLIE MCBRIDE - Sweaters - Gillman Knitwear Co.

MOLLIE PARNIS - Underwear and nightwear - Carole Hochman Designs Inc.

MOLLIFENE - Pharmaceutical preparations - Pfeiffer Pharmaceuticals Inc.

MOLLIMENTUM - Veterinary pharmaceutical preparations - Y-Tex Corp.

MOLLY - Hardware - Cobra Anchor Corp.

MOLLY - Snowboards - Molly Manufacturing, Inc.

MOLLY BLACK GOLD - Lubricant - Gene E. Arthur

MOLLY BRIGHT - Aquariums—household - Jungle Laboratories Corp.

MOLLY MALLOY - Apparel—women's - Chorus Line Corp.

MOLLY MCBUTTER - Seasonings - Alberto-Culver Co.

MOLLY MCINTIRE - Toys - Pleasant Co.

MOLLY MONKEY - Toys—stuffed ☆ - Dakin Inc.

MOLLY TITE GRIP - Hardware ☆ - Cobra Anchor Corp.

MOLLYGOGGLES - Apparel - Katherine H. Johnson

MOLOUDJI - Women's apparel - Hub Distributing Inc.

MOLSON CANADIAN - Beverages—malt - Martlet Importing Co.

MOLSON EXPORT - Beverages—malt - Martlet Importing Co.

MOLSON GOLDEN - Beverages—malt - Martlet Importing Co.

MOLSON ICE - Beverages—malt - Martlet Importing Co.

MOLSON LIGHT - Beverages—malt - Martlet Importing Co.

MOLSON RED JACK ALE - Beverages—malt - Martlet Importing Co.

MOLTO FINO - Apparel—women's - Molto Fino, Inc.

MOLTO SMALTO - Cosmetics - Parlux Inc.

MOLTOBODY - Hair care products - Giovanni Cosmetics Inc.

MOLTOFIXX - Hair care products - Giovanni Cosmetics Inc.

MOLTOFUSION - Hair care products - Giovanni Cosmetics Inc.

MOLUB-ALLOY - Lubricants - Tribol Inc.

MOLUCAD - Computer peripheral equipment - New River Kinematics

MOLY - Saw blades - Clemson Brothers Inc.

MOLY-8 - Vitamins and nutritional supplements ☆ - J.R. Carlson Laboratories Inc.

MOLY GREASE AMG-10 - Lubricants - Pacific Lubricants

MOLY-LUBE - Lubricants - Rectorseal Corp.

MOLY MAX - Pistons - Total Seal, Inc.

MOLY NRG - Lubricants - Kent Oil Co., Inc.

MOLY PENE-LUBE - Lubricants - Dow Corning Corp.

MOLY-RICH - Lubricants - Rectorseal Corp.

MOLY-SEAL - Lubricants - Pacific Lubricants

MOLYFILM - Lubricants - Kano Laboratories Inc.

MOLYKOTE - Lubricants - Dow Corning Corp.

MOLYLITH - Lubricants - Amoco Oil Co.

MOLYTUFT - Tufting machines - Clemson Brothers Inc.

MOLYWELD - Saw blades - Clemson Brothers Inc.

MOLZAHN - Bakery products - Walter Molzahn & Co. Inc.

MOM - Recording label - Surfdog

MOM & POPCORN - Popcorn - Saratoga Brands Inc.

MOM EQUIPMENT - Apparel—women's - Chauvin International Ltd.

MOM 'N' POP'S - Meat products—pork - WSMP Inc.

MOM 'N' POP'S COUNTRY KITCHEN - Restaurants—fast food - WSMP Inc.

MOM 'N' POP'S FISH CAMPS - Restaurants—fast food ☆ - WSMP Inc.

MOM 'N' POP'S HAM HOUSE - Restaurants—fast food ☆ - WSMP Inc.

MOM-O-GRAM - Rings—jewelry - Feature Enterprises

MOM OF THE YEAR - Dolls ☆ - Mighty Star Inc. (Special Effects Div.)

MOMBASA - Netting - Yungjohann Hillman Co.

MOMBASA - Skin care products - Ethnic Gold Corp.

MOMBO KIDS, THE - Apparel and accessories - Mombo Graphix Co.

MOMENT - Clocks ☆ - General Time Corp. (Westclox/Seth Thomas Div.)

MOMENT OF TRUTH - Deodorants—personal - Colgate-Palmolive Co.

MOMENT SUPREME - Perfumes - Jean Patou, Inc.

MOMENTA - Tires - Uniroyal Goodrich Licensing Services, Inc.

MOMENTARY MADNESS - Candy - Doug Johnson, Inc.

MOMENTEAU - Floor coverings—carpet and rugs - Karastan-Bigelow Inc.

MOMENTI D'AMORE - Stationery - Nu-Art Inc.

MOMENTO - Clocks - General Time Corp. (Westclox/Seth Thomas Div.)

MOMENTO - Floor coverings—carpet and rugs - Galaxy Carpet Mills Inc.

MOMENTO - Floor coverings—carpet and rugs ☆ - Columbus Mills, Inc.

MOMENTOS - Prophylactics - Jaime H. Jaramillo

MOMENTOUS - Floor coverings ☆ - Aladdin Mills, Inc.

MOMENTS - Colognes - Frances Denney

MOMENTS - Floor coverings—carpet and rugs ☆ - World Carpets, Inc.

MOMENTS - Glassware—household - Anchor Hocking Glass, Inc.

MOMENTS BEFORE DETONATION - Eyeglasses - Bausch & Lomb Inc.

MOMENTS BY THE SEA - Suntan lotions - Annabelle's Inc.

MOMENTS BY THE SEA TANNING LOTION - Suntan lotions - Annabelle's Inc.

MOMENT'S DELIGHT - Floor coverings—carpet and rugs ☆ - Gulistan Carpet Inc.

MOMENTS IN MINNESOTA - Stationery - Kolling Cards

MOMENTS IN TIME LIMITED EDITIONS - Posters - Network II

MOMENTS IN TYME - Toys—models - Howell Ceramics, Inc.

MOMENTS OF INSPIRATION - Greeting cards - American Greetings Corp.

MOMENTS OF LOVE - Stationery - Taylor Corp.

MOMENT'S PAUSE, A - Greeting cards - Kokohar Publications, Inc.

MOMENTS TO REMEMBER - Giftware ☆ - Treasure Masters

MOMENTS TREASURED - Porcelain dolls - Home Shopping Club, Inc.

MOMENTUM - Analgesic - American Home Products Corp.

MOMENTUM - Animal feeds ☆ - Central Soya Co. Inc.

MOMENTUM - Apparel—children's - J.C. Penney Co., Inc.

MOMENTUM - Floor coverings—carpet and rugs - Ashley Commercial Carpets

MOMENTUM - Floor coverings—carpet and rugs - Dorsett Carpet Mills Inc.

MOMENTUM - Garden furniture—metal - Lloyd/Flanders Industries

MOMENTUM - Luggage - American Tourister, Inc.

MOMENTUM - Paper - Boise Cascade Corp.

MOMENTUM - Wallpaper - Bolta Wallcoverings

MOMINTS - Candy - Beacon Sweets, Inc.

MOMMA BRIGHTLY - Toys ☆ - Playskool, Inc.

MOMMESSIN WINES - Wines - Marie Brizard Wines & Spirits, USA

MOMMY - Ceramic wares - Pots by Gail

MOMMY & BABY - Dolls - Mattel, Inc.

MOMMY AND ME - Wallpaper - Pickhardt & Siebert USA Inc.

MOMMY CARE - Cleaning preparations - Alliance Consumer Industries

MOMMY I CAN DO IT MYSELF - Greeting cards - Creative Learning Products Inc.

MOMMY SONGS - Video production - Stargate Pictures, Inc.

MOMMY-TO-BE DOLL, THE - Dolls, clothing, and accessories - Judith Corp.

MOMMY'S BABY - Toys - Eugene Doll & Novelty Co. Inc.

MOMMY'S HELPER - Hair care products - Luster Products, Inc.

MOMO DESIGN - Watches - Chronosport Inc.

MOMOKAWA - Beverages—alcohol - Momokawa Sake Ltd.

MOMOYAMA - Tobacco—chewing or smoking - G.A. Georgopulo & Co. Inc.

MOM'S - Bags - Dan Dee Belt and Bag Co. Inc.

MOM'S - Baked goods - Mom's Food Co.

MOMS - Computer software ☆ - Trans Union/Dateq

MOM'S - Pans ☆ - General Housewares Corp.

MOM'S - Restaurants—pizzerias - Mom's Pizza Inc.

MOM'S BEST - Desserts - Fancy Foods of Virginia Inc.

MOM'S BEST - Food products - Mom's Best Cookies Inc.

MOM'S HOT TUB - Chili–canned - Stockpot Soups Inc.
MOM'S NIGHT OUT - Apparel–women's - Mom's Night Out, Inc.
MOM'S OLD FASHIONED - Food products - Country Club Foods Inc.
MOMS PADS - Containers - Breastfeeding Support Network
MOM'S SEAFOOD AND BARBEQUE - Restaurants–fast food ☆ - WSMP Inc.
MOM'S SECRET RECIPE - Meat products–poultry - Tyson Holding Inc.
MOMUS - Furniture - Momus Inc.
MOMWARE - Calendars - Michelle R. Trachtman
MON - Patterns–clothing - Pauloa Hawaii Ltd.
MON AMI - Wines - Meier's Wine Cellars Inc.
MON AMI - Wines - Mon Ami Historic Winery
MON AMIE - Underwear and nightwear - Bestform Foundations, Inc.
MON AMOUR - Perfumes - Jean Philippe Fragrances, Inc.
MON BOUDOIR - Perfumes ☆ - Houbigant, Inc.
MON BOUQUET - Wines ☆ - Banfi Vintners
MON CHER - House furnishings ☆ - Lea Industries Inc.
MON CHER CHOUCHOU - Animal feeds - Mon Cher Chouchou, Inc.
MON CHERI - Candy - Ferrero U.S.A Inc.
MON CHERI - Furniture - Universal Flooring
MON CHOU CHOU - Jewelry boxes ☆ - Boca Corporate Promotions, Inc.
MON COEUR EST A VOUS - Jewelry - Something Old, Something New, Inc.
MON DESIR - Cheese - Anco Foods Corp.
MON DESIR - Cheese - Churny Co., Inc.
MON-E-GUARD - Apparel and accessories - Viator Products Corp.
MON FLEUR - Furniture ☆ - Bassett Furniture Industries, Inc.
MON IMAGE - Cosmetics - Paris Presents Ltd.
MON JARDIN A - Tiles–ceramic ☆ - Monarch Tile Inc.
MON JARDIN B - Tiles–ceramic ☆ - Monarch Tile Inc.
MON-O-MIX - Shortening - Humko Products
MON PARIS - Food products ☆ - Liberty Richter Inc.
MON PETITE JOLIE - Dolls - Uneeda Doll Co., Inc.
MONA - Cheese - Imperia Foods Inc.
MONA - Frames–eyeglass - Rozin Optical Export Corp.
MONA - Wigs - Jean Paree Weegs Inc.
MONA LISA - Artists' materials - Houston Art, Inc.
MONA LISA - Crayons ☆ - Koh-I-Noor, Inc.
MONA LISA - Skin care products - Ritornelle Inc.
MONA LISA - Wallpaper - K.M.L. Industries
MONA LISA - Wallpaper - Textile Wallcoverings International Ltd.
MONACO - Apparel–men's ☆ - Michaels/Stern & Co. Inc.
MONACO - Bathing suits - Ocean Pool Co.
MONACO - Bathroom fixtures ☆ - Crane Plumbing/Fiat Products
MONACO - Bathtubs–enameled - Lyons Industries Inc.
MONACO - Bicycles - Murray, Inc.
MONACO - Boats - Glen-L Marine Designs
MONACO - Boats - Wellcraft Marine Corp.
MONACO - Boats–pontoons - O.M.C. Aluminum Boat Group
MONACO - Cabinets - Major Line Products Co. Inc.
MONACO - Cabinets - Wellborn Cabinet, Inc.
MONACO - Cabinets ☆ - H.J. Scheirich Co.
MONACO - Cigarettes - R.J. Reynolds Tobacco Co.
MONACO - Cordage and twine ☆ - Gladding Braided Products Inc.
MONACO - Dinnerware ☆ - Corning Inc.
MONACO - Dinnerware–glass - Crate and Barrel
MONACO - Dishes–china ☆ - Pickard Inc.
MONACO - Dryers–hair - Helene Curtis Industries Inc.
MONACO - Fabrics - Dan River Inc.
MONACO - Floor coverings - Congoleum Corp.
MONACO - Floor coverings–carpet and rugs - Barrett Carpet Mills Inc.
MONACO - Floor coverings–carpet and rugs - Criterion Mills Inc.
MONACO - Floor coverings–carpet and rugs - Patcraft Mills Inc.
MONACO - Floor coverings–carpet and rugs - V & B Carpet
MONACO - Furniture - Henredon Furniture Industries Inc.
MONACO - Garment racks - Loroman Co.
MONACO - Luggage - Airway Industries, Inc.
MONACO - Mirrors - Monaco Import/Export Inc.
MONACO - Motor vehicles ☆ - Chrysler Corp. (Dodge Car Div.)
MONACO - Pet products - Aspen Pet Products
MONACO - Plumbing fixtures - National Fiber Glass Products
MONACO - Strollers–baby - Kolcraft Enterprises, Inc.
MONACO - Tea kettles–nonelectric ☆ - National Housewares
MONACO - Tiles–ceramic ☆ - Dal-Tile Corp.
MONACO - Tires - Magnum Tire Corp.
MONACO - Toy race cars ☆ - Intex Recreation Corp.
MONACO - Toys ☆ - Strombecker Corp.
MONACO - Watches - Hampden Corp.

MONACO - Window coverings - Levolor Inc.
MONACO - Yarn - Bernat Yarn & Craft Corp.
MONACO LITE - Chimes ☆ - Nutone Inc.
MONACO MINTS - Candy - Glade Taffy Town, Inc.
MONACO SUPER 20 - Hair care products - Monaco Import/Export Inc.
MONAD RECORDS - Recording label - Monad Records, Inc.
MONADNOCK - Food products - Upland Farms Corp.
MONADNOCK - Water–mineral - New England Spring Water Inc.
MONADNOCK MOUNTAIN - Water–bottled or canned - Blue Hill Spring Water Co.
MONAHAN - Recording label - Jazz Composer's Orchestra Association Inc.
MONALEE - Apparel–women's - Nuart Fashions, Inc.
MONALISA - Wigs - Wig America Co.
MONARCA - Canned tomatoes - Saramar Corp.
MONARCA MARBLE - Floor coverings–tile - Kentile Floors Inc.
MONARCH - Adhesives and sealants ☆ - Induron Coatings Inc.
MONARCH - Aluminum products - Remington Building Products
MONARCH - Banjos - OME Co. Inc.
MONARCH - Bathroom accessories - Monarch Metal Products Corp.
MONARCH - Bathroom fixtures - New Jersey Porcelain Co.
MONARCH - Battery chargers - Monarch Marking Systems, Inc.
MONARCH - Beverages–alcohol - Hood River Distillers Inc.
MONARCH - Binders - Dennison National Co.
MONARCH - Blankets - Spartan Mills
MONARCH - Braces–orthopedic - Smith & Nephew DonJoy Inc.
MONARCH - Brushes - Corona Brushes Inc.
MONARCH - Brushes - Wright-Bernet
MONARCH - Brushes–paint - Winsor & Newton
MONARCH - Cabinets - Master Woodworks Kitchen Studio
MONARCH - Cables - MacWhyte Co.
MONARCH - Candles - Candle Corp. of America
MONARCH - Chairs–metal - Alvin and Co. Inc.
MONARCH - Chalk ☆ - Quartet Manufacturing Co.
MONARCH - Cigarettes - R.J. Reynolds Tobacco Co.
MONARCH - Cigars - Faber, Coe & Gregg Inc.
MONARCH - Cigars ☆ - Avanti Cigar Co.
MONARCH - Cosmetics - Rich On, Inc.
MONARCH - Cranes - Seatrax, Inc.
MONARCH - Curtain rods - Newell Window Furnishing Co.
MONARCH - Dating/numbering stamps - Consolidated Stamp Manufacturing Co. Inc.
MONARCH - Dishes–china - WMF/USA
MONARCH - Dog food - AGP Petfoods
MONARCH - Fencing–steel - Keystone Steel & Wire Co.
MONARCH - Fertilizers - Ameriscape Inc.
MONARCH - Fishing lures - Eppinger Manufacturing Co.
MONARCH - Floor coverings - Cactus Mat Manufacturing Co.
MONARCH - Food containers - PYA/Monarch Inc.
MONARCH - Food products - Delicious Foods Co.
MONARCH - Fruits and vegetables - Richelieu Trading Co.
MONARCH - Furniture - Lowy Group Inc.
MONARCH - Furniture - Monarch Furniture Corp.
MONARCH - Games - Way to Play, Inc.
MONARCH - Garbage disposal units–household - Whiterock Corp.
MONARCH - Glassware–household - Owens-Illinois Inc. (Libbey Div.)
MONARCH - Glassware–household ☆ - Colony Glass
MONARCH - Hardware ☆ - Clayton & Lambert Manufacturing Co.
MONARCH - Heating equipment - Monarch Ranges & Heaters
MONARCH - Helmets–athletic - Ankel International, Inc.
MONARCH - Kites ☆ - Hi-Flier Manufacturing Co.
MONARCH - Knives - Precise International/Wenger
MONARCH - Knives–hunting ☆ - Cole Consumer Products Inc.
MONARCH - Labels–paper - National Sales Co.
MONARCH - Luggage - Monarch Luggage Co., Inc.
MONARCH - Mail boxes - Steel City Corp.
MONARCH - Mirrors - Stanley Hardware Div.
MONARCH - Mirrors - Stanley Mirror Products
MONARCH - Mops - Majestic Industries Inc.
MONARCH - Motor vehicles–automobiles ☆ - Ford Motor Co. (Lincoln-Mercury Div.)
MONARCH - Motor vehicles–motor homes ☆ - Honey Recreational Vehicles Inc.
MONARCH - Office supplies - Monarch Industries Inc.
MONARCH - Paper - Windsor Card Co.
MONARCH - Paper cutters ☆ - Milton Bradley Co.
MONARCH - Pet products - Consolidated Nutrition, L.C.

☆ = Now out of production

MONARCH - Postage meters - Pelouze Scale Co.
MONARCH - Rifles - Nikon Inc.
MONARCH - Scissors–hand-operated ☆ - Acme United Corp.
MONARCH - Seafood products–canned or cured - Monarch Seafood Co.
MONARCH - Skin care products - Fibre-Metal Products Co.
MONARCH - Skis - Rollin Wilson Co. Inc.
MONARCH - Slippers - Okawa Trading
MONARCH - Sporting goods ☆ - Brunswick Corp.
MONARCH - Thread - Gudebrod, Inc.
MONARCH - Tiles–ceramic ☆ - Monarch Tile Inc.
MONARCH - Tires - Kelly-Springfield Tire Co.
MONARCH - Tires - Lee Tire & Rubber Co.
MONARCH - Toys - Brumberger Co. Inc.
MONARCH - Trailers–travel ☆ - Mitchell & Sons Inc.
MONARCH - Valves - Crane Nuclear, Inc.
MONARCH - Watches - Rolex Watch USA, Inc.
MONARCH - Wire - Antec Corp.
MONARCH ALPINE - Sporting goods - Rollin Wilson Co. Inc.
MONARCH CANADIAN - Whiskey - Hood River Distillers Inc.
MONARCH HORIZONS - Hobby kits - Janlynn Corp.
MONARCH II - Blood pressure apparatus ☆ - Graham-Field Inc.
MONARCH INTERNATIONAL - Vegetables–canned - Redwood Food Packing Co.
MONARCH KNITS - Apparel–athletic - Monarch Knit and Sportswear Inc.
MONARCH PHARMACEUTICALS - Pharmaceutical preparations - King Pharmaceuticals, Inc.
MONARCH PREMIUM - Fresh vegetables - Saramar Corp.
MONARCH PRESS - Publisher's imprints - Simon & Schuster, Inc.
MONARCH RECORDS - Recording label - Nashville International Entertainment Group
MONARCH RESERVE - Whiskey - Hood River Distillers Inc.
MONARCH RIB - Building materials - Metal Building Components, Inc.
MONARCH RIB - Siding and roofing - American Building Components Co.
MONARCH VANITY FLAIR - Mirrors - Stanley Mirror Products
MONARI & FEDERZONI - Vinegar - Dean & Deluca Inc.
MONARK - Ammunition - Federal Cartridge Co.
MONARK - Artists' materials - Sooner Arts & Crafts Inc.
MONARK - Batteries - Exide Corp.
MONARK - Boats - Monark Boat Co.
MONARK - Boats–motor - Starcraft Marine LLC
MONARK - Eggs - Monark Egg Corp.
MONARK - Leather goods ☆ - Perfecto Products Co.
MONARK - Skateboards - James J. Kwiatkowski
MONARK BRAND - Eggs - Monark Egg Corp.
MONARQUE - Computer software - Treasury Management Systems, Inc.
MONA'S - Food products - Bernardi Italian Foods Co.
MONAS - Frozen foods - Windsor Quality Food Co. Ltd.
MONAS - Shrimp–fresh or frozen - Clover International, Inc.
MONAS PASTA CAFE - Frozen foods - Windsor Quality Food Co. Ltd.
MONASTERY - Beverages–alcohol - Consolidated Distilled Products Inc.
MONASTERY - Cheese - Crystal Food Import Corp.
MONAX - Glass products ☆ - Corning Inc.
MONBEL - Wines - Victoire Imports Co.
MONCEAUX - Glassware–household - Durand International
MONCHEL - Soap - Procter & Gamble Co.
MONCHELL - Floor coverings–carpet and rugs ☆ - Burtco Enterprises Inc.
MONCHO - Dolls - Mattel, Inc.
MONCRIEF - Heating equipment - York International Corp.
MONDAY CLASSICS - Apparel and accessories - Monday Classics Inc.
MONDAY MORNING SYNDROME - Housewares - Curtis Neal Steadley, Jr.
MONDAY'S CHILD - Apparel–children's - Monday's Child Inc.
MONDAY'S CHILD - Soap - Naked Earth Inc.
MONDEGAO - Olive oil ☆ - Corte & Co.
MONDEO - Motor vehicles–automobiles - Ford Motor Co.
MONDER - Pasta - Liberty Richter Inc.
MONDIAL - Computer software - M-Usa Business Systems, Inc.
MONDIAL - Dinnerware–glass - WMF/USA
MONDIAL - Glassware–household ☆ - Oneida Ltd.
MONDIAL - Motor vehicles–automobiles - Ferrari North America Inc.
MONDIAL - Sporting goods - Skis Dynastar, Inc.
MONDIAL - Wallpaper ☆ - Marburg Wallcoverings Inc.
MONDO - Bags - Sirco International Corp.
MONDO - Candy - Jel Sert Co.
MONDO - Hair care products - Ian Malcolm Gavet
MONDO - Mannequins - Econoco Corp.
MONDO - Travelware - Action Travelware

MONDO COOLER - Automotive parts and accessories - Vortech Engineering, Inc.
MONDO FRUIT SQUEEZERS - Beverages–carbonated - Jel Sert Co.
MONDO KOOSH - Toys - Oddzon Products, Inc.
MONDO MUSIC - Recording label - Select Records
MONDO RAD - Bicycles ☆ - Hedstrom Corp.
MONDO UOMO - Neckties - LDM Neckwear & Accessories
MONDOBLADE - Skates–roller ☆ - Rollerblade, Inc.
MONDONICO - Bicycles - Torelli Imports
MONDORO - Wines ☆ - Canandaigua Wine Co. Inc.
MONDORO ASTI SPUMANTE - Beverages–alcohol - Canandaigua Wine Co. Inc.
MONDRIAN - Dinnerware–glass ☆ - Royal China & Porcelain Companies Inc.
MONDRIAN - Lockers–metal - Republic Storage Systems Co. Inc.
MONEL - Musical instrument accessories - Gibson Strings & Accessories
MONET - Apparel and accessories - Crystal Brands Inc.
MONET - Artists' materials ☆ - M. Grumbacher Inc.
MONET - Bathtubs–enameled - Americh Corp.
MONET - Fabrics - Vertilux-Louverlux Inc.
MONET - Floor coverings ☆ - Robbins Inc.
MONET - Floor coverings–carpet and rugs ☆ - Atlas Carpet Mills Inc.
MONET - Floor coverings–carpet and rugs ☆ - Columbus Mills, Inc.
MONET - Frames–eyeglass - Marine Optical, Inc.
MONET - Furniture ☆ - Bernhardt Industries
MONET - Glassware–household ☆ - Colony Glass
MONET - Jewelry–costume - Monet Jewelers
MONET - Musical instruments - Ideal Musical Merchandise Co.
MONET - Tiles–ceramic - Monarch Tile Inc.
MONET COLLECTION, THE - Brushes - MNI Products Inc.
MONET IMPRESSIONS - Wallpaper - Manuscreens
MONET-PARIS - Musical instruments - Ideal Musical Merchandise Co.
MONET'S GARDEN AT GIVERNY - Wallpaper - Pelican Prints
MONETTE - Prisms–optical ☆ - Kollmorgen Corp.
MONEX - Paper–tissue - Mag Aerospace Industries, Inc.
MONEX - Paper–toilet - Monogram Sanitation Co.
MONEY BAGS - Handbags - SOS Rescue Inc.
MONEY BAGS - Toys–banks ☆ - Reflectory
MONEY BALL - Balls–golf - Pick Point Sports
MONEY BEAR - Toys–banks - A.J. Renzi Plastic Corp.
MONEY CARD GAME - Games - Tyco Toys
MONEY CHAMBER, THE - Games - TCB Enterprises Inc.
MONEY CHRONICLE, THE - Calendars - Lakeside Marketing Services Inc.
MONEY CLIP - Novelty items - Jerry L. Avey
MONEY COMPANY, THE - Apparel and accessories - Paul Bernier Vultaggio
MONEY FACTORY - Toys–banks - Mag-Nif Inc.
MONEY HOUSE - Air fresheners - E. Davis Inc.
MONEY HOUSE BLESSING - Incense - E. Davis Inc.
MONEY HOUSE BLESSING GOLD - Deodorizers - E. Davis Inc.
MONEY HOUSE BLESSING SILVER - Incense/air freshners - E. Davis Inc.
MONEY IS NO OBJECT M.I.N.O. - Apparel and accessories - Richard W. Engen
MONEY LINES - Publisher's imprints - Blockbuster Periodicals, Inc.
MONEY MAGNETS - Toys–banks ☆ - U.S. Fiberglass Inc.
MONEY MAKER - Novelty items - S.S. Adams Co.
MONEY MANAGER - Binders ☆ - 20th Century Plastics
MONEY MASTER - Computer software - Pacific Data Systems Inc.
MONEY! MONEY! - Computer software - Hartley Courseware Inc.
MONEY PERSONAL FINANCE LIBRARY - Publisher's imprints - Time Inc.
MONEY PINE - Deodorizers - E. Davis Inc.
MONEY PIT - Games - International Gamco, Inc.
MONEY SAVERS - Hobby kits - A + A
MONEY SAVERS - Underwear and nightwear - Lovable Co.
MONEY SQUARES - Computer software - Gamco Industries Inc.
MONEY STORM - Game machines - IGT North America
MONEY TESTER - Novelty items - Adams Apple Distributing L.P.
MONEY-TIME - Computer software - Syrja Management Systems
MONEY TOWN - Computer software ☆ - Knowledge Adventure
MONEY TRACK - Computer software ☆ - Pacific Data Systems Inc.
MONEY TREE - Key rings ☆ - Webway, Inc.
MONEY X CHANGER - Calculators - Zelco Industries, Inc.
MONEY$COUNT - Calculator - Educational Skills for Individuals Inc.
MONEYCOUNTS - Computer software - Parsons Technology, Inc.
MONEYFILES - Publisher's imprints - Hume Group, Inc.
MONEYFIND - Computer software - American Financial Directories, Inc.
MONEY.HOW MUCH? - Computer software - Orange Cherry Software
MONEYMAGIC - Computer hardware - Magic Solutions, Inc.

MONEYMAKER - Fabrics - Staflex Harotex
MONEYMAP - Computer program - Alta Analytics Inc.
MONEYNET - Computer software - Applied Communications, Inc.
MONEYSAVER - Brushes–paint - American Brush Co. Inc.
MONEY$TUFFER - Greeting cards - Nicholodeon Productions Inc.
MONEYTREE - Recording label - Pet Records
MONEYWISE KIDS - Games - Aristoplay, Ltd.
MONFORT - Food products - Conagra, Inc.
MONFORT GOURMET - Food products - Conagra, Inc.
MONFORT OF COLORADO - Beef - Monfort, Inc.
MONFRINO - Beverages–alcohol - Rolar Imports Ltd.
MONG DAIRY - Milk - Mong Dairy Co.
MONGER - Metals - Monger Mounts, Inc.
MONGO - Bats–baseball - Wade McNary
MONGO RILLA - Toys–stuffed - Toy Works, Inc.
MONGOL - Pencils - Faber-Castell Corp.
MONGOLIAN FIRE - Seasoning - Universal Trading Industries
MONGOLIAN SABLE - Brushes–paint - FM Brush Co., Inc.
MONGOOSE - Bicycles - Ross Bicycles USA, Inc.
MONGOOSE - Bicycles - Service Cycle Supply Co.
MONGOOSE - Catheters - Schneider (USA) Inc.
MONGOOSE - Radios - Arthur W. Strayton, Jr.
MONGOOSE - Rakes - Ames Lawn & Garden Tool Co.
MONGOOSE - Toys–models - Estes Industries
MONGOOSE RAKE - Rakes - O. Ames Co.
MONHEGAN - Boats–motor - Thurston Co.
MONHEGAN - Ships–sailing vessels - Lyman-Morse Boatbuilding Co. Inc.
MONHEGAN - Yarn - Brunswick Yarns
MONHEGAN GROUP - Furniture ☆ - Moosehead Manufacturing Co.
MONI - Handbags - Monique Accessories Inc.
MONI - Recording label ☆ - Joey Records International Inc.
MONI-COM - Electronic equipment - P/H Electronics
MONI PONI - Hair care products - Moni International, Inc.
MONIA - Apparel and accessories - Monia Enterprises Inc.
MONICA - House furnishings - Dan River Inc.
MONICA - Tiles–ceramic ☆ - Maxsam Sales, Inc.
MONICA - Wigs - Jean Paree Weegs Inc.
MONICA GRAY - Women's outerwear - Arbetman Brothers, Inc.
MONICA HEART - Apparel–women's - Francine Browner Inc.
MONICA SMITH - Shoes - Consolidated Shoe Co., Inc.
MONICO - Furniture - Singer Furniture Co.
MONIES US - Jewelry - Sasco Industries, Inc.
MONIKA TILLEY AT EASE - Apparel–women's ☆ - Miss Elaine, Inc.
MONIKER - Computer software - Moniker, Inc.
MONILINK - Computer software - Monital Signal Corp.
MONIN - Syrup - De Medici Imports Ltd.
MONIN - Syrup - Lund Distribution, Inc.
MONIN - Syrup - Made in France
MONIPHOR - Cat litter ☆ - Earth Animal
MONIQUE - Dishes–china ☆ - Royal China & Porcelain Companies Inc.
MONIQUE - Dolls - Goldberger Doll Manufacture Co.
MONIQUE - Dolls - Monique Trading Corp.
MONIQUE - Dolls ☆ - Effanbee Doll Corp.
MONIQUE - Hair care products - Monique Quality Products Co. Inc.
MONIQUE - House furnishings - Lea Industries Inc.
MONIQUE - Housewares - Syracuse China Corp.
MONIQUE - Rings–jewelry - Artcarved Inc.
MONIQUE - Sunglasses - Lantis Corp.
MONIQUE FASHIONS - Women's apparel - Monique Fashions
MONIQUE LUO - Wedding gowns - Millennia Creations, Inc.
MONIQUE MUSIC LIBRARY - Recording label - Peer-Southern Organization
MONIQUE OTTO - Handbags - Bowonka
MONISTAT - Pharmaceutical preparations - Ortho Pharmaceutical Corp.
MONISTAT 5 - Tampons - Johnson & Johnson
MONISTAT 7 - Health care products - Johnson & Johnson
MONISTAT-DERM - Pharmaceutical preparations - Ortho Pharmaceutical Corp.
MONISTE - Bedding–linen - Dan River Inc.
MONITENNA - Antennas ☆ - Avnet, Inc.
MONITOR - Bathroom accessories - Sellstrom Manufacturing Co.
MONITOR - Brushes–paint - Corona Brushes Inc.
MONITOR - Clocks - General Time Corp. (Westclox/Seth Thomas Div.)
MONITOR - Drums–musical instruments ☆ - Grossman Music Corp.
MONITOR - Electrical equipment - Gavin Electronics
MONITOR - Floor coverings–carpet and rugs - Karastan-Bigelow Inc.
MONITOR - Floor coverings–carpet and rugs ☆ - Porter Carpet Mills Inc.
MONITOR - Flower pots–plastic - Chipurnoi Inc.

MONITOR - Hardware - Baker Manufacturing Co.
MONITOR - Hardware - Masco Corp. (Plumbing Products Div.)
MONITOR - Heaters–space - Kero-Sun Inc.
MONITOR - Insecticides - Bayer Corp. (Agriculture Div.)
MONITOR - Irons–electric - Sunbeam-Oster Household Products
MONITOR - Jewelry - Jacoby-Bender Inc.
MONITOR - Motor vehicle parts and accessories ☆ - Peterson Manufacturing Co.
MONITOR - Paper–toweling - Smurfit Newsprint Corp. (Cladwood Div.)
MONITOR - Photographic equipment - Eastman Kodak Co.
MONITOR - Tape recorders ☆ - Soundscriber Co.
MONITOR - Tools - Osborn Manufacturing Corp.
MONITOR - Wainscotting - Georgia-Pacific Corp.
MONITOR COLLECTORS - Recording label - Monitor Recordings Inc.
MONITOR FOR MVS, THE - Computer software - Landmark Systems Corp.
MONITOR FOR VSE, THE - Computer software - Landmark Systems Corp.
MONITOR INSTRUMENTS - Laboratory apparatus - Health and Hygiene/ELB
MONITOR KEYBOARD HARD DISK RON RUB - Computer software - Synex
MONITOR MATE - Sound monitoring system - Pertek Engineering, Inc.
MONITOR MINDER - Computer peripheral equipment - Comp Decor
MONITOR MOVER - Computer peripheral equipment - Lintek Inc.
MONITOR MUSIC OF THE WORLD - Recording label - Monitor Recordings Inc.
MONITOR, THE - Alarms - Robert Barr Trust
MONITOR, THE - Computer software - Landmark Systems Corp.
MONITRON - Monitors–electronic - Midtronics Inc.
MONIZ LINGUICA - Food products - Bob Ostrow Co.
MONK - Sandals - Vans, Inc.
MONKEY - Toothpaste - Caswell-Massey Co. Ltd.
MONKEY AROUND - Toys–stuffed - Dakin Inc.
MONKEY BAR - Confections - Famous Pacific Dessert Co.
MONKEY BARS - Playground equipment - Wonderline
MONKEY BUNCH - Toys–stuffed - Dakin Inc.
MONKEY BUSINESS - Beverages–alcohol - Daiquiri Shoppe, Inc.
MONKEY BUSINESS - Computer software - Dynacomp Inc.
MONKEY BUSINESS - Games - International Gamco, Inc.
MONKEY BUSINESS - Toys–stuffed - Kamar International Inc.
MONKEY CEE - Pet vitamin supplement - Purina Mills, Inc.
MONKEY GOD'S CURSE - Toys - War House
MONKEY GRIP - Gloves–work - Edmont
MONKEY MANIA - Games - Parker Brothers
MONKEY MITT - Toys - Wizard of Ahhs, Inc.
MONKEY NUGGETS - Pet products - Cuttlebone Plus
MONKEY PARADISE - Toys–stuffed - Ganz
MONKEY PAW - Anchors - Simpson Strong-Tie Co., Inc.
MONKEY RIVER - Beverages - Juba Beverages Corp.
MONKEY SEAT - Toys–banks - A.J. Renzi Plastic Corp.
MONKEY SEE - Puppets - Dakin Inc.
MONKEY SHINES - Candles - W and F Products Inc.
MONKEY TALES - Toys - Wizard of Ahhs, Inc.
MONKEY-TIE - Sporting goods ☆ - AC International
MONKEY WRENCH - Penetrating oil - Comstar International Inc. (IPC Div.)
MONKEY YUMS - Pet food - Purina Mills, Inc.
MONKEYPUZZLE - Puzzles ☆ - MonkeyPuzzle Inc.
MONKEYSHINES - Toys–electronic ☆ - Philips Consumer Electronics Co.
MONKEYWRENCH - Apparel and accessories - Alyasa J. Owerka-Moore
MONK'S CLOTH - Foil–aluminum - Highland Supply Corp.
MONK'S FORMULA - Pharmaceutical preparations - Pharmex Inc.
MONKS' K-9 - Health care products - Cutlery Associates Inc.
MONLAM - Mirrors - Stanley Mirror Products
MONMESSIN - Beverages–alcohol ☆ - William Grant & Sons, Inc.
MONMOUSSEAU - Wines - Wine World Inc.
MONMOUTH - Clay–modeling - Sculpture House Inc.
MONMOUTH - Cooking utensils–stoneware - Western Stoneware
MONMOUTH - Flatware - Washington Forge Inc.
MONMOUTH/EVERGREEN - Recording label - Monmouth Records
MONO - Concrete products - Sosroc Inc.
MONO 100 - Office supplies - American Tombow Inc.
MONO-CHLOR - Pharmaceutical preparations - Gordon Laboratories
MONO-COAT - Paints ☆ - GAF Corp.
MONO COLORS - Office supplies - American Tombow Inc.
MONO CONTROLS - Pharmaceutical preparations - Wampole Laboratories Div.
MONO-COTE - Paints - Proctor Paint & Varnish Co. Inc.
MONO-CREST - Bathroom accessories - Dec-Art Co.
MONO-DIFF - Pharmaceutical preparations - Wampole Laboratories Div.

☆ = Now out of production

MONO-EDGE - Floor coverings - Dexter Corp. (Mercer Plastics Div.)

MONO-GESIC - Analgesics - Central Pharmaceutical Inc.

MONO-LATEX - Pharmaceutical preparations - Wampole Laboratories Div.

MONO-LINE - Health care products - Pfizer Inc.

MONO MATTE - Cosmetics - Madeleine Mono Ltd.

MONO-OUTLOOK - Envelopes ☆ - Westvaco Corp.

MONO-PLUS - Pharmaceutical preparations - Wampole Laboratories Div.

MONO-PLUS WHOLE BLOOD - Pharmaceutical preparations - Wampole Laboratories Div.

MONO-RAIL - Blinds–venetian - Kirsch Co.

MONO-SCORE - Tiles–ceramic ☆ - Monarch Tile Inc.

MONO-SO - Thread - Blue Mountain Industries, Inc.

MONO-STAND - Photographic equipment ☆ - Omega/Arkay

MONO-STRIP - Weather stripping - Dorbin Metal Strip Manufacturing Co.

MONO-TARP - Fabrics - Lucky America Inc.

MONO-TEST - Pharmaceutical preparations - Wampole Laboratories Div.

MONO-TRAY - Furniture–factory - Mono-Systems, Inc.

MONO-TYPE - Blood derivatives - Dade International Inc.

MONO-VACC - Vaccines - Lincoln Diagnostics

MONOBLOC - Compact discs–prerecorded - Materials Research Corp.

MONOBLOC - Electromedical apparatus - TH Charters, Inc.

MONOBLOCK - Laser systems–medical - Kentek Corp.

MONOBOLTS - Nuts and bolts - Auto Vehicle Parts Co.

MONOCAL - Pharmaceutical preparations - Mericon Industries Inc.

MONOCANON - Guns ☆ - Armsport Inc.

MONOCAPS - Vitamins and nutritional supplements - Freeda Vitamins Inc.

MONOCEIVER - Integrated circuits - Analog Devices, Inc.

MONOCELL - Skis ☆ - Raichle Molitor USA, Inc.

MONOCERAM - Ceramic tile - Integrity Tile Co.

MONOCERAM - Tiles–ceramic - Monoceram

MONOCHEM - Chemical preparations - Monogram Sanitation Co.

MONOCHROME - Laboratory apparatus - American Diagnostica Inc.

MONOCIBEC - Tiles–ceramic - United Ceramic Tile Corp.

MONOCLEAR - Thread - Threads USA Div.

MONOCORT - Pharmaceutical preparations ☆ - Nortech Laboratories

MONOCRYL - Medical equipment - Johnson & Johnson

MONOCYL - Skin care products - Dome Cosmetics

MONODECK - Metal building materials - Aluma Shield Industries Inc.

MONODOX - Antibiotics - Oclassen Pharmaceuticals, Inc.

MONODYNE - Golfing equipment - Daiwa Corp.

MONOFACE - Audio equipment - Pro-Co. Sound Co. Inc.

MONOFINS - Sporting goods - Finis Inc.

MONOFLEX - Hoses ☆ - Monogram Sanitation Co.

MONOGIDE - Fishing tackle - American Pacific Tackle Co.

MONOGLAZE - Epoxy coatings - L.D. Sterns Corp.

MONOGLIDE - Motorcycles - Surgical-Steeds, Classic American Motorcycles, Inc.

MONOGRAM - Bathtubs–enameled - Rimar Inc.

MONOGRAM - Doors–glass ☆ - ODL, Inc.

MONOGRAM - Electrical testing instruments - Omega Engineering, Inc.

MONOGRAM - Floor coverings - Congoleum Corp.

MONOGRAM - Floor coverings–carpet and rugs - Calladium & Marglen

MONOGRAM - Frames–picture ☆ - Acme Frame Products, Inc.

MONOGRAM - Furniture - CTH/Sherrill Occasional

MONOGRAM - Glassware–household ☆ - Lotus Glass Co.

MONOGRAM - Hobby kits - Revell-Monogram, Inc.

MONOGRAM - Kitchen appliances - General Electric Co.

MONOGRAM - Medical apparatus - Monogram Manufacturing Co.

MONOGRAM - Medical instruments - Howmedica Inc.

MONOGRAM - Paints - Universal Paint Corp.

MONOGRAM - Paperboard ☆ - Canson-Talens Inc.

MONOGRAM - Perfumes - Cosmair Inc.

MONOGRAM - Pipes ☆ - Missouri Meerschaum Co.

MONOGRAM - Recording label - Jimmy Joe Lee Productions

MONOGRAM - Scrapbooks ☆ - Garber Communications Inc.

MONOGRAM - Siding–insulating - Certainteed Corp. (Roofing Products Group)

MONOGRAM - Skin care products - Larry Vincent Speciality Advertising Inc.

MONOGRAM - Wallcoverings - Ronald Redding Designs

MONOGRAM - Wines - Monarch Wine Co. of Georgia

MONOGRAM BLEND - Beverages–alcohol - Kasser Laird Distilling Co.

MONOGRAM II - Wallpaper - Capital Carousel Inc.

MONOGRAM MFG CO. - Belts–apparel - Carmen Foundations Inc.

MONOGRAM SERIES - Radios - General Electric Co.

MONOGRAM XL - Floor coverings - Robbins Inc.

MONOGRAM XL MAPLE - Floor coverings - Robbins Inc.

MONOGRAMABLES - Jewelry - Jenny H. Meeks

MONOGRAMS - Footwear - G.H. Bass and Co.

MONOGRIP - Skin care products - Dome Cosmetics

MONOGUARD - Burial caskets - Batesville Casket Co., Inc.

MONOHULL - Boats–pontoons - Boatel Marine, Inc.

MONOI TIARE TAHITI - Health care products - Hawaiian Resources Co. Ltd.

MONOJECT - Detergents - Ecolab Inc.

MONOJECT - Health care products - Sherwood Medical Co.

MONOJEL - Pharmaceutical preparations - Sherwood Medical Co.

MONOKET - Pharmaceutical preparations - Schwarz Pharma

MONOKORE - Pet products - Loos and Co. Inc.

MONOKOTE - Fireproofing materials - W.R. Grace & Co.

MONOKOTE - Toys–models - Top Flite Models

MONOLAC - Varnishes ☆ - Klean-Strip

MONOLEA - Tiles–ceramic - Maxsam Sales, Inc.

MONOLETTOR - Medical apparatus - Sherwood Medical Co.

MONOLIAN - Floor coverings–linoleum - Lucky America Inc.

MONOLITE - Building materials - Alexander Kaufman Consultants

MONOLITH - Bicycles - Huffy Corp.

MONOLITH - Floor slabs–concrete - L.D. Sterns Corp.

MONOLITH 1 - Motor vehicle parts and accessories - Products for Power

MONOLOGUE - Computer software - First Byte Inc.

MONOLON - Fabrics–nylon - William Skinner & Sons

MONOLUX - Microscopes - Compass Industries, Inc.

MONOMAGIC - Cleaning preparations ☆ - Monogram Sanitation Co.

MONOMANO - Computer peripheral equipment - Elmentry Enterprises

MONOMATIC - Toilets–portable - Mag Aerospace Industries, Inc.

MONOMATIC II - Toilets–portable ☆ - Monogram Sanitation Co.

MONOMAX - Building materials - Premier Refractories and Chemicals Inc.

MONOMID - Paints - Steelcote Manufacturing Corp.

MONOMID - Surgical supplies - C.P. Medical

MONONINE - Pharmaceutical - Armour Pharmaceutical Co.

MONOPAK - Photographic equipment - SP Systems/Saratons

MONOPEARL - Jewelry - Monopearl Inc.

MONOPIVOT - Automotive parts and accessories - Ridewell Corp.

MONOPLANE - Paper–bond - P.H. Glatfelter Co.

MONOPLANK - Paneling ☆ - Marlite

MONOPLEX - Microphones ☆ - Shure Brothers, Inc.

MONOPOLAWA - Vodka - Fred Bofird Co.

MONOPOLE - Musical instruments ☆ - Fred Gretsch Enterprises

MONOPOLY - Candy - Confections by Sandra

MONOPOLY - Flowers, plants, and seeds - Jacklin Seed

MONOPOLY - Games - Parker Brothers

MONOPOLY 1935 - Games - Parker Brothers

MONOPOLY JUNIOR - Games - Parker Brothers

MONOPOLY PLAYMASTER - Toys - Tonka Corp.

MONOPOST - Steel products - Akron Products Co.

MONORAIL - Bicycles - Motiv Sports Inc.

MONOSEAL - Burial caskets - Batesville Casket Co., Inc.

MONOSEAL - Waterproofing compounds - L.D. Sterns Corp.

MONOSENSOR - Electronic equipment - Fluid Components Intl, LLC.

MONOSPEC - Goggles–safety ☆ - Willson/Dalloz Safety

MONOTEL - Photographic equipment - SP Systems/Saratons

MONOTEX - Aprons - Edmont

MONOTEX - Fabrics - Advance Group

MONOTEX - Thread - Belding Heminway Co. Inc.

MONOTHREAD - Thread - Monofilaments International Inc.

MONOTILE - Vinyl - Lucky America Inc.

MONOTONATOR - Hearing aids - Siemens Hearing Instruments Inc.

MONOTOP - Floor coverings - Rock-Tred Corp.

MONOTRACK - Motorcycles - Target Motorsports

MONOTROL - Health care products ☆ - Sunrise Medical

MONOTUBE - Medical apparatus - Howmedica Inc.

MONOTYPE GREETING CARD MAKER - Computer software - Monotype Typography Inc.

MONOTYPE T-SHIRT DESIGN MAKER - Computer software - Monotype Typography Inc.

MONOVIAL - Tools - Empire Level Manufacturing Corp.

MONOWALL - Movable partitions ☆ - Yates Furniture Systems Corp.

MONREALE - Furniture ☆ - Lane Co. Inc.

MONRO-MAGNUM 60 - Shock absorbers–motor vehicle - Monroe Auto Equipment Co.

MONRO-MATIC - Shock absorbers–motor vehicle - Monroe Auto Equipment Co.

MONRO-MATIC PLUS - Vehicle parts - Monroe Auto Equipment Co.

MONROE - Anchors - Kermco-Dehaai, Inc.

MONROE - Binders - The Union Group

MONROE - Dinnerware—glass - Lenox, Inc.
MONROE - Floor coverings—carpet and rugs - Colonial Mills Inc.
MONROE - Food products ☆ - Curtice-Burns Foods, Inc.
MONROE - Fruits—frozen - Niagra Co.
MONROE - Glassware—household - Lenox Crystal, Inc.
MONROE - Hardware - Emhart Inc.
MONROE - Mattresses - Simmons USA
MONROE - Motor vehicle parts and accessories - Monroe Auto Equipment Co.
MONROE - Office machines - Monroe Systems for Business Inc.
MONROE - Pet products - Monroe Specialty Co.
MONROE FORMULA - Automotive parts and accessories - Monroe Auto Equipment Co.
MONROE FORMULA GP - Shock absorbers—motor vehicle - Monroe Auto Equipment Co.
MONROE INDY - Toys—electronic - Bird Bromiticous Inc.
MONROE LITE - Chimes ☆ - Nutone Inc.
MONROE-MATIC PLUS - Shock absorbers—motor vehicle - Monroe Auto Equipment Co.
MONROE TOP - Beds—metal - HARD Manufacturing Co. Inc.
MONROEVILLE AREA CHAMBER OF COMMERCE - Monroeville Area Chamber of Commerce
MONSANTO - Fibers—nylon - Monsanto Polymer Products
MONSANTO - Herbicides - Monsanto Co.
MONSANTO - Wines - Palace Brands Co.
MONSEY PREMIER - Asphalt - Kimberton Enterprises, Inc.
MONSEY PRODUCTS CO. - Paints, varnishes, and stains - Monsey Products Co.
MONSIEUR BALMAIN - Colognes - Frances Denney
MONSIEUR BON HOMME - Apparel—men's - Bon Homme Shirtmakers
MONSIEUR CROISSANT - Bakery products—frozen ☆ - Vie De France Corp.
MONSIEUR DAUMONT - Perfumes - Anjac Inc.
MONSIEUR DE GIVENCHY - Colognes - Parfums Givenchy, Inc.
MONSIEUR HENRI - Wines - Monsieur Henri Wines Ltd.
MONSIEUR HENRI - Wines - Sazerac Co. Inc.
MONSIEUR JOVAN - Cosmetics - Quintessence Inc.
MONSIEUR LEONARD - Perfumes - Classic Fragrances Ltd.
MONSIEUR L'HERBIER - Skin care products - L'Herbier De Provence Ltd.
MONSIEUR LUBIN - Colognes - Frances Denney
MONSIEUR MUSK - Colognes - Houbigant, Inc.
MONSIFUN CANINE - Pet collars - American Leather Specialties
MONSOON - Bicycle parts and accessories - Troxel-West
MONSOON - Boats - Glen-L Marine Designs
MONSOON - Pumps - Sta-Rite Industries Inc.
MONSOON - Seafood products—fresh or frozen - Zaloom Brothers Co. of New Jersey
MONSOON FLUME - Playground equipment - Miracle Recreation Equipment Co.
MONSTER - Candy - Confex Inc.
MONSTER - Drums—musical instruments - Fred Gretsch Enterprises
MONSTER - Fireworks - American Promotional Events, Inc.
MONSTER - Floor coverings - Etc. of Henderson, Inc.
MONSTER - Vitamins and nutritional supplements - Bristol-Myers Squibb Co.
MONSTER BALZAC - Games - Milton Bradley Co.
MONSTER BASH - Snack foods - Pepsico, Inc.
MONSTER BED - Lamp bulbs - Suntan U. Limited
MONSTER BIG THINGS - Toys—stuffed - Those Characters from Cleveland, Inc.
MONSTER BLASTS - Fireworks - American Promotional Events, Inc.
MONSTER BUBBLES - Toys ☆ - Wham-O Manufacturing Co.
MONSTER BUG - Toys—electronic - Bird Bromiticous Inc.
MONSTER CABLE - Audio equipment - Monster Cable Products, Inc.
MONSTER CARDS - Office supplies - Monster Cards
MONSTER CASTLE SERIES, THE - Playground equipment - Rainbow Play Systems, Inc.
MONSTER CHEWS - Candy - Confex Inc.
MONSTER CHOMP - Cookies - President Baking Co., Inc.
MONSTER COLISEUM - Games - Avalon Hill Game Co.
MONSTER COMBO - Sandwiches—prepackaged - Rally's, Inc.
MONSTER DICE - Games - Flying Buffalo Inc.
MONSTER DYE - Dyes - Monster Products
MONSTER FLESH - Toys - Mattel, Inc.
MONSTER FORCE - Toys - Playmates World Wide Inc.
MONSTER HOME THEATRE - Electronic equipment - Monster Cable Products, Inc.
MONSTER IN MY POCKET SKY-FLIER - Kites - Hi-Flier Manufacturing Co.
MONSTER JAM - Sporting goods - Hutch Sports USA Inc.

MONSTER LAB - Toys - Mattel, Inc.
MONSTER LAB ESCAPE - Games - Mattel, Inc.
MONSTER MANIA - Cosmetics - Rubie's Costume Co., Inc.
MONSTER MARKS - Chewing gum ☆ - Fleer Corp.
MONSTER MASH - Games - Tonka Corp.
MONSTER MASS - Pharmaceutical preparations - Bricker Laboratories
MONSTER MATH - Publisher's imprints - Lowell House
MONSTER MAULERS - Computer software - Konami (America) Inc.
MONSTER MINDS - Toys - Mattel, Inc.
MONSTER MITTS - Infant product ☆ - Dragons Are Too Seldom Inc.
MONSTER MITTS - Mittens - Paris Accessories, Inc.
MONSTER MOVIE CLASSICS - Cosmetics - Paper Magic Group Inc.
MONSTER MOVIE CLASSICS - Toys - Spearhead Industries Inc.
MONSTER MUFFINS - Bakery products - Monster Muffins & Such
MONSTER MULCH - Garden equipment - Menasha Corp.
MONSTER MUNNY - Candy - R.M. Palmer Co.
MONSTER PARTS - Decorations - Schering-Plough Healthcare Products
MONSTER PARTY - Confections - Price Co.
MONSTER PARTY POPPERS - Fireworks - American Promotional Events, Inc.
MONSTER PEP - Sausages - Oh Boy! Oberto
MONSTER PICK - Hair combs - Comfee Products, Inc.
MONSTER PILLOW - Pillows - Pillowtex Corp.
MONSTER PLANT - Novelty items - Dynamic Development
MONSTER POWER - Computer software - Monster Cable Products, Inc.
MONSTER RECORDS - Recording label - Douglas Bennett
MONSTER RIG - Toys—automobiles - Mattel, Inc.
MONSTER SERIES - Shoes ☆ - Hyde Athletic Industries Inc.
MONSTER SKIN - Candy - Tyco Industries, Inc.
MONSTER SLAM - Toys - Sports Concepts, Inc.
MONSTER STANDARD - Audio equipment - Monster Cable Products, Inc.
MONSTER TEETH - Candy - Glenn Confections Inc.
MONSTER TRIO - Fireworks - American Promotional Events, Inc.
MONSTER TRUCK BLOOPERS - Recording label - United Sports of America
MONSTER TRUCK MADNESS - Computer software - Microsoft Corp.
MONSTER TRUCK MOLD 'N MASH - Clay—modeling - Tonka Corp.
MONSTER VETTE - Toys—automobiles - Mattel, Inc.
MONSTER WARS - Toys - 4 Kids Productions, Inc.
MONSTER WARTS - Food products - Tyco Industries, Inc.
MONSTER/ZILLION BUBBLES - Toys ☆ - Wham-O Manufacturing Co.
MONSTEROUS - Toys - Tonka Corp.
MONSTERS AWAY - Novelty items - Creative Elements, Inc.
MONSTERS IN MOTION - Hobby kits - Skylar Bros. Entertainment Inc.
MONSTERS! MONSTERS! - Games - Flying Buffalo Inc.
MONSTERS OF MYTH & LEGEND - Games ☆ - Mayfair Games, Inc.
MONSTERS OF THE GRIDIRON - Beverages—carbonated - Coca-Cola Co.
MONSTERTALES - Publisher's imprints - Random House, Inc.
MONSTERVATOR - Toys - Mattel, Inc.
MONSTICKERS - Toys ☆ - Henry Gordy International Inc.
MONSTROID - Toys - Mattel, Inc.
MONSTROUS COMPENDIUM - Games - Tsr, Inc.
MONSTROUS MOVIE MUSIC - Compact discs—prerecorded - Monstrous Movie Music
MONT AUSTRIA - Cheese - Austrian Food Center
MONT BLANC - Apparel—athletic ☆ - United Knitwear Co. Inc.
MONT BLANC - Cheese ☆ - Swissrose International Inc.
MONT BLANC - Furniture - Bean Station Furniture Factory Inc.
MONT BLANC - Tiles—ceramic - Porcelanite, Inc.
MONT CLAIR - Wines - L'aiglon Wine and Spirits Import Co., Inc.
MONT CLAIRE - Bicycles ☆ - Huffy Corp.
MONT D'AIRD SPRING WATER - Beverages—carbonated - Hampton Associates and Son, Inc.
MONT ELISE VINEYARDS - Wines - Mont Elise Vineyards
MONT LA SALLE - Wines ☆ - IDV Wines (Beaulieu Vineyard)
MONT ROUCOUS - Water—bottled or canned - Perlinger Naturals
MONT ST. JOHN CELLARS - Wines - Mont St. John Cellars Inc.
MONT ST. MICHEL - Cheese - Swissrose International Inc.
MONT SOURCE - Skin care products - Mont Source, Inc.
MONTAG - Stationery - Montag Inc.
MONTAGE - Apparel and accessories - Mosaic Designs Inc.
MONTAGE - Dinnerware—glass ☆ - Nikko Ceramics Inc.
MONTAGE - Floor coverings—carpet and rugs ☆ - Playfield International Inc.
MONTAGE - Furniture - Steelcase Inc.
MONTAGE - Furniture ☆ - Hammary Furniture Co. Inc.
MONTAGE - Gloves, hats, scarves, etc. - I. Shalom and Co. Inc.
MONTAGE - Harnesses - Michael Bianco Inc.
MONTAGE - Plastics - Alta Industries Inc.

☆ = Now out of production

MONTAGE - Sunglasses - Sungold Enterprises Ltd.
MONTAGE - Wallpaper ☆ - Pickhardt & Siebert USA Inc.
MONTAGE - Window shades - C & M Shade Corp.
MONTAGE - Wines ☆ - IDV Wines (Beaulieu Vineyard)
MONTAGE - Yarn ☆ - William Unger & Co. Inc.
MONTAGNA - Bicycles - Leeworld Co.
MONTAGUE - Bedding–linen - Dan River Inc.
MONTAGUE - Bicycles - Montague Corp.
MONTAGUE - Ophthalmic goods ☆ - Luxottica
MONTAGUE - Paper–bond - Esleeck Manufacturing Co., Inc.
MONTAGUE - Toys–stuffed ☆ - Gund, Inc.
MONTAGUE JET - Paper - Esleeck Manufacturing Co., Inc.
MONTAGUE WRITING - Paper–bond - Esleeck Manufacturing Co., Inc.
MONTAHO - Wood products - National Bark Sales
MONTAIGNE - Crocheted and knitted items ☆ - Puritan Sportswear Corp.
MONTALCINO - Pasta - American Italian Pasta Co.
MONTALDO - Frames–picture - International House Inc.
MONTALEMBERT - Floor coverings - Parquet de France Inc.
MONTALI - Wine ☆ - Audubon Cellars Inc.
MONTALVO - Fruits and vegetables - Saticoy Lemon Association
MONTANA - Bicycles - KHS Inc.
MONTANA - Ceramic tile - Interceramic Inc.
MONTANA - Cigarettes - Brown & Williamson Tobacco Corp.
MONTANA - Computers - Liberty Research Group, Inc.
MONTANA - Fishing lures - Thomas and Thomas Rodmakers Inc.
MONTANA - Floor coverings–carpet and rugs ☆ - Capel, Inc.
MONTANA - Guitars - Kaman Music Corp.
MONTANA - Handbags ☆ - Hazan Imports Corp.
MONTANA - Sunglasses - Alain Mikli
MONTANA - Yarn - Henry's Attic
MONTANA BIG SKY - Vitamins and nutritional supplements - Montana Naturals Int'l. Inc.
MONTANA BLAKE - Recording label - Rustron Music Productions
MONTANA BLEND - Coffee - Coffee Traders, Inc.
MONTANA COVER - Paper–coated - Fiber Mark, Inc.
MONTANA COWBOY - Barbecue sauce - Western Trails
MONTANA GOLD - Breads - Bakeries Marketing Resources, Inc.
MONTANA LABS - Vitamins and nutritional supplements - Montana Naturals Int'l. Inc.
MONTANA LARIATS - Jewelry - Janco, Inc.
MONTANA MAID BRAND COFFEE HELENA, MONTANA - Coffee - Montana Maid River Blend Coffee
MONTANA ON MY MIND - Posters - Falcon Press Publishing Co., Inc.
MONTANA POKER II - Game machines - Dynamo Corp.
MONTANA RUSTLER - Barbecue sauce - Western Trails
MONTANA'S CREAM OF THE WEST - Cereal - Cream of the West
MONTANO BAY - Floor coverings–carpet and rugs - Karastan-Bigelow Inc.
MONTANOU - Cheese ☆ - Swissrose International Inc.
MONTANT - Gloves ☆ - Dakota Corp.
MONTARA - Doors - Simpson Timber Co.
MONTARA - Floor coverings–carpet and rugs ☆ - Hollytex Carpet Mills Inc.
MONTAUK - Flowers, plants, and seeds - Jonathan Green, Inc.
MONTAUK - Powerboat - Boston Whaler, Inc.
MONTAUK - Siding–insulating - Champion International Corp.
MONTAUK - Thread - United Thread Mills Corp.
MONTAWK - Frames–eyeglass - Zylo Ware Corp.
MONTAYA - Guitars - CHK Trading Co. Inc.
MONTBELLO - Luggage ☆ - Samsonite Corp.
MONTBLANC - Pencils ☆ - Koh-I-Noor, Inc.
MONTBLANC MASTERPIECE - Pens ☆ - Koh-I-Noor, Inc.
MONTBRAY - Wines - Montbray Wine Cellars Ltd.
MONTCALM - Eyeglasses - Art-Craft Optical Co.
MONTCALM BOOKS - Publisher's imprints - Stanyan Record Co.
MONTCLAIR - Brushes–hair - The Montclair Co.
MONTCLAIR - Cabinets - American Woodmark Corp.
MONTCLAIR - Cabinets ☆ - Aristokraft, Inc.
MONTCLAIR - Ceiling fans - Casablanca Fan Co.
MONTCLAIR - Cigarettes - American Tobacco Co.
MONTCLAIR - Cigarettes - Commonwealth Brands, Inc.
MONTCLAIR - Floor coverings ☆ - Azrock Commercial Flooring
MONTCLAIR - Floor coverings–carpet and rugs - Gulistan Carpet Inc.
MONTCLAIR - Furniture ☆ - Bassett Furniture Industries, Inc.
MONTCLAIR - Furniture–children's - Child Craft Industries Inc.
MONTCLAIR - Glass–leaded - Seneca Glass Co.
MONTCLAIR - Glassware–household ☆ - Lenox Crystal, Inc.
MONTCLAIR - Guitars ☆ - International Music Corp.

MONTCLAIR - Ophthalmic goods - Styl-Rite Optical Manufacturing Co., Inc.
MONTCLAIR - Recording label - Jazz Composer's Orchestra Association Inc.
MONTCLAIR - Rings–jewelry - Artcarved Inc.
MONTCLAIR - Tableware–china - Lenox, Inc.
MONTCLAIR - Vans–conversion - Ger-Win Corp.
MONTCLAIR - Water–bottled or canned - R.H. Mannix
MONTCLAIR DANBY - Marble products - Carl Schilling Stoneworks
MONTDOMAINE CELLARS - Wines - Horton Vineyards Inc.
MONTDORE - Dinnerware–glass - Franciscan by Johnson Brothers, USA, Inc.
MONTE - Wines - Leonard Kreusch Inc.
MONTE ALBAN - Beverages–alcohol - Barton Brands, Ltd.
MONTE ALBAN - Liquors - Canandaigua Wine Co. Inc.
MONTE ANTICO - Wines - Empson (USA) Inc.
MONTE BESTLO - Wines - Ridge Vineyards Inc.
MONTE CARLO - Bathtubs–enameled - Kallista Inc.
MONTE CARLO - Bathtubs–enameled - Lyons Industries Inc.
MONTE CARLO - Beverages–malt - Logret Import & Export Co.
MONTE CARLO - Blinds–venetian - C-Mor Co.
MONTE CARLO - Boats - Ebko Industries Inc.
MONTE CARLO - Boats ☆ - Wellcraft Marine Corp.
MONTE CARLO - Boats–motor - Arctco, Inc.
MONTE CARLO - Boats–motor - Cobia Boat Co.
MONTE CARLO - Chemical preparations - Monte Carlo Hairpiece Co.
MONTE CARLO - Chocolate candy ☆ - Sweet Candy Co.
MONTE CARLO - Cigarettes - General Cigar Co., Inc.
MONTE CARLO - Coffee - La Colombe Torrefaction, Inc.
MONTE CARLO - Dinnerware–glass ☆ - Royal China & Porcelain Companies Inc.
MONTE CARLO - Floor coverings ☆ - Congoleum Corp.
MONTE CARLO - Floor coverings–carpet and rugs - Couristan Inc.
MONTE CARLO - Floor coverings–carpet and rugs ☆ - Galaxy Carpet Mills Inc.
MONTE CARLO - Floor coverings–carpet and rugs ☆ - LaVelle Textile Marketing Inc.
MONTE CARLO - Frames–eyeglass - Zylo Ware Corp.
MONTE CARLO - Furniture - Pavilion/Sunburst Furniture
MONTE CARLO - Giftware ☆ - Gorham Inc.
MONTE CARLO - Glassware–household - ACC
MONTE CARLO - Luggage ☆ - American Tourister, Inc.
MONTE CARLO - Motor vehicles - General Motors Corp. (Chevrolet Motor Div.)
MONTE CARLO - Motor vehicles–motor homes ☆ - Honey Recreational Vehicles Inc.
MONTE CARLO - Shirts - Supreme International Corp.
MONTE CARLO - Tea kettles–nonelectric ☆ - National Housewares
MONTE CARLO - Toys ☆ - Intex Recreation Corp.
MONTE CARLO - Underwear and nightwear - Bestform Foundations, Inc.
MONTE CARLO FASHIONS - Apparel and accessories - Uwana Wash Frocks Inc.
MONTE CARLO II - Bathtubs–enameled - Kallista Inc.
MONTE CARLO POLO AND JOCKEY CLUB - Watches - Creation Time Corp.
MONTE CARLOWE - Games ☆ - Milton Bradley Co.
MONTE CHRISTO - Luggage - United States Luggage Corp.
MONTE CLAIRE - Glassware–household - H. Wittur & Co.
MONTE CLOTH - Uniforms–tailored - Angelica Uniform Group
MONTE CRISTO - Antique stores - Robert A. Kerstein
MONTE CRISTO - Frames–eyeglass - Pathway Optical Prods.
MONTE CRISTO - Nuts–salted, roasted, cooked, or canned - Paramount Farms Inc.
MONTE CRISTO II - Yarn - Henry's Attic
MONTE CRUZ - Cigar boxes–wood - Consolidated Cigar Corp.
MONTE LEONE - Floor coverings - Mannington Resilient Floors
MONTE OLEVITO - Wines - Francis A. Bonanno, Inc.
MONTE-PREST - Uniforms–tailored - Angelica Uniform Group
MONTE REAL - Cigars - Felipe A. Valls
MONTE REGALE - Pasta - Gazzola USA
MONTE ROSA - Apparel–women's - Dah Chong Hong Trading Corp.
MONTE SALINE - Wines - Paterno Imports, Ltd.
MONTE VERTINE - Beverages–alcohol - Trebon Wine & Spirit Corp.
MONTE VERTINE - Wines - Wine Imports Ltd.
MONTE VISTA - Floor coverings–carpet and rugs - Galaxy Carpet Mills Inc.
MONTEBELLO - Bathroom fixtures - Crane Plumbing/Fiat Products
MONTEBELLO - Beverages - Montebello Brands, Inc.
MONTEBELLO - Floor coverings - Congoleum Corp.
MONTEBELLO - Food products - Spruce Foods Inc.
MONTEBELLO - Furniture ☆ - Lane Co. Inc.
MONTEBELLO - Olive oil - California Olive Oil Corp.

MONTEBELLO SANITARY DAIRY - Milk - Broguiere's Farm Fresh Dairy, Inc.

MONTEBLDO - Food products - Source Atlantique

MONTEBUENO - Meat products–dried - Towers Meat & Seafood, Inc.

MONTECARLO - Weather tracking equipment ☆ - Airguide Instrument Co.

MONTECCHI - Leather goods - Leon Fleischer, International Marketing

MONTECITO - Apparel and accessories - Pro Athletes Golf League, Inc.

MONTECITO - Floor coverings–carpet and rugs ☆ - Atlas Carpet Mills Inc.

MONTECITO - Food products - Smart and Final Stores Corp.

MONTECLAIRE - Apparel and accessories - Mariall Apparel Inc.

MONTECO - Hair care products - Monte Carlo Hairpiece Co.

MONTECRISTO - Tobacco–chewing or smoking ☆ - Alfred Dunhill of London Inc.

MONTECRUZ - Cigars - Lane Ltd.

MONTEGO - Apparel–men's - J. Schoeneman Inc.

MONTEGO - Baskets–wood - Royal Cathay Trading Co.

MONTEGO - Boats - McKenzie Boat Manufacturing Co.

MONTEGO - Boats ☆ - Lanness K. McKee & Co.

MONTEGO - Boats–motor - Ebbtide Corp.

MONTEGO - Boats–motor - Glastex Co.

MONTEGO - Boats–motor - Penn Yan Boats Inc.

MONTEGO - Boats–motor ☆ - Bayliner Marine Corp.

MONTEGO - Boats–motor ☆ - Carver Boat Corp.

MONTEGO - Boats–motor ☆ - Starcraft Corp.

MONTEGO - Brushes–paint - Corona Brushes Inc.

MONTEGO - Building materials–concrete - Walker & Zanger (West Coast), Ltd.

MONTEGO - Cigarettes - Eve Holdings Inc.

MONTEGO - Clocks ☆ - General Time Corp. (Westclox/Seth Thomas Div.)

MONTEGO - Frames–eyeglass - May Optical Co. Inc.

MONTEGO - Furniture - Bean Station Furniture Factory Inc.

MONTEGO - Furniture - Homecrest Industries Inc.

MONTEGO - Furniture - Stanley Furniture Co. Inc.

MONTEGO - Jet boat - Arctco, Inc.

MONTEGO - Luggage - Airway Industries, Inc.

MONTEGO - Motor vehicles–automobiles ☆ - Ford Motor Co. (Lincoln-Mercury Div.)

MONTEGO - Motor vehicles–motor homes - Baron Motor Homes Inc.

MONTEGO - Mustard ☆ - Silver Foods Corp.

MONTEGO - Wallpaper - Four Seasons

MONTEGO - Watches - Wittnauer International Inc.

MONTEGO 500 - Steering mechanisms–motor vehicle - Superior Industries International, Inc.

MONTEGO BAY - Beverages - Montego Bay Beverage Co., Inc.

MONTEGO BAY - Furniture ☆ - Bassett Furniture Industries, Inc.

MONTEGO BAY GOURMET - Spices and extracts - Finest Kind Spices

MONTEGO MX - Motor vehicles–automobiles ☆ - Ford Motor Co. (Lincoln-Mercury Div.)

MONTEGO VILLAGER - Motor vehicles–automobiles ☆ - Ford Motor Co. (Lincoln-Mercury Div.)

MONTEITH - Holloware and drinkware - Corbell & Co.

MONTEJO - Beverages–alcohol - Tucuru

MONTEL - Recording label - Universal Record

MONTEL MICHELLE - Recording label - Flat Town Music Co.

MONTELIMAR - Glassware–household - Durand International

MONTELL - Water–bottled or canned - Edward A. Martin

MONTELLA - Handbags - Monique Accessories Inc.

MONTELLE VINEYARDS - Wines - Montelle Winery

MONTELLO CLUB - Apparel–women's - United Fashion Industries Inc.

MONTELVINI - Wines - European Beverage Co., Inc.

MONTENE MORRIS - Vegetables–canned ☆ - McCall Farms Inc.

MONTERA - Tomato pastes and sauces - Van Den Bergh Foods Co.

MONTEREY - Amerock Corp.

MONTEREY - Bathroom fixtures - Crane Plumbing/Fiat Products

MONTEREY - Bicycles - Murray, Inc.

MONTEREY - Blinds–vertical - Kittrich Corp.

MONTEREY - Brushes–paint - Corona Brushes Inc.

MONTEREY - Cabinets - American Woodmark Corp.

MONTEREY - Clocks ☆ - Toastmaster Inc.

MONTEREY - Cribs–wood ☆ - Welsh Co.

MONTEREY - Cutlery ☆ - National Housewares

MONTEREY - Fireplace equipment - Majestic Co.

MONTEREY - Flatware - Wallace International Silversmiths, Inc.

MONTEREY - Floor coverings - American Floor Products Co. Inc.

MONTEREY - Floor coverings - Bruce Hardwood Floors

MONTEREY - Floor coverings–carpet and rugs - American Rug Craftsmen Inc.

MONTEREY - Floor coverings–carpet and rugs - Cabin Crafts Carpets

MONTEREY - Floor coverings–carpet and rugs ☆ - Karastan-Bigelow Inc.

MONTEREY - Floor coverings–carpet and rugs ☆ - S and S Mills Inc.

MONTEREY - Food products - Monterey Mushrooms Inc.

MONTEREY - Furniture - American Furniture Co. Inc.

MONTEREY - Furniture - Singer Furniture Co.

MONTEREY - Furniture ☆ - Bassett Furniture Industries, Inc.

MONTEREY - Furniture ☆ - Mersman Furniture Co.

MONTEREY - Glassware–household - Owens-Illinois Inc. (Libbey Div.)

MONTEREY - Greeting cards ☆ - Regency-Sonnell Greetings Inc.

MONTEREY - Guitars, etc ☆ - International Music Corp.

MONTEREY - House furnishings ☆ - Lexington Furniture Industries, Inc.

MONTEREY - Jewelry - Jacoby-Bender Inc.

MONTEREY - Luggage ☆ - American Tourister, Inc.

MONTEREY - Manufactured homes ☆ - Redman Industries, Inc.

MONTEREY - Mattresses - Sealy Inc.

MONTEREY - Motor vehicles–automobiles ☆ - Ford Motor Co. (Lincoln-Mercury Div.)

MONTEREY - Motor vehicles–motor homes - Forest River, Inc.

MONTEREY - Motor vehicles–motor homes ☆ - Beaver Coaches Inc.

MONTEREY - Motor vehicles–motor homes ☆ - Honey Recreational Vehicles Inc.

MONTEREY - Musical instrument accessories - Sottile Manufacturing Co.

MONTEREY - Office furniture–wood - Bush Industries, Inc.

MONTEREY - Paper ☆ - M. Grumbacher Inc.

MONTEREY - Pens - Micropoint Inc.

MONTEREY - Shoes - Allen-Edmonds Shoe Corp.

MONTEREY - Shrimp - Central Coast Seafood Inc.

MONTEREY - Snack foods - Smokestone Farms

MONTEREY - Stoves–gas ☆ - Malm Fireplaces Inc.

MONTEREY - Tableware–china ☆ - Lenox, Inc.

MONTEREY - Tobacco products - Philip Morris Companies Inc.

MONTEREY - Trailers–travel - Leader Enterprises

MONTEREY - Trailers–travel ☆ - Hop-Cap Inc.

MONTEREY - Window shades - Castec Window Shading Inc.

MONTEREY - Yarn - Brunswick Yarns

MONTEREY BAY - Furniture - Singer Furniture Co.

MONTEREY BAY - Neckties - Cornell of California Inc.

MONTEREY CANYON - Apparel and accessories - Monterey Canyon, Inc.

MONTEREY CELLARS - Wines - Monterey Peninsula Winery

MONTEREY COLLECTION - Bathroom fixtures - Alsons Corp.

MONTEREY FARMS - Cheese - Swissrose International Inc.

MONTEREY II - Luggage - American Tourister, Inc.

MONTEREY INN - Food products - Lindsay Olive Growers

MONTEREY INTIMATES - Women's apparel - Goldenleo Trading Inc.

MONTEREY OMELETTE - Food products - Denny's Inc.

MONTEREY PASTA COMPANY - Pasta - Monterey Pasta Co.

MONTEREY PENINSULA WINERY - Wines - Monterey Peninsula Winery

MONTEREY VINEYARD, THE - Wines - The Monterey Vineyard

MONTEREY VINEYARD, THE - Wines - Joseph E. Seagram & Sons, Inc.

MONTERO - Motor vehicles–automobiles - Mitsubishi Motor Sales of America Inc.

MONTERRA - Wallpaper - Gagne Wallcovering, Inc.

MONTERRA - Wines - Delicato Vineyards

MONTERRA - Wines - Winequest

MONTERREY - Faucets - American Standard Inc.

MONTERREY - Floor coverings ☆ - Congoleum Corp.

MONTERREY - Floor coverings–carpet and rugs - Regal Rugs Inc.

MONTERREY - Floor coverings–carpet and rugs ☆ - Hollytex Carpet Mills Inc.

MONTERREY - Floor coverings–carpet and rugs ☆ - Trans-Ocean Import Co. Inc.

MONTERREY - Fruits and vegetables - Marglo Products Corp.

MONTERREY - Glassware–household - Crisa Corp.

MONTERREY - Watches - Hampden Corp.

MONTERREY CERAMICS - Bathroom accessories - T.T.R.F., Inc.

MONTERREY STONEWARE - Tiles–ceramic - Dal-Tile Corp.

MONTERREY TAPESTRY - Handbags - Tandem Imports Corp.

MONTESINO - Cigars - Tampa Sweetheart Cigar Co.

MONTESSORI LEARNING SOFTWARE - Computer programming services - Software Holdings, Inc.

MONTEVIDEO - Recording label - Celestial Harmonies

MONTEVINA - Wines - Montevina Wines

MONTEVINA - Wines - Sutter Home Winery, Inc.

MONTEX - Eggs ☆ - Monark Egg Corp.

MONTEZUMA - Beverages–alcohol - Barton Brands, Ltd.

MONTEZUMA - Food products - Sauces & Salsas, Ltd.

MONTEZUMA - Games - Utopia Technologies, Inc.

☆ = Now out of production

MONTEZUMA - Liquors - Canandaigua Wine Co. Inc.
MONTEZUMA'S REVENGE - Games - Tonka Corp.
MONTGOLFIER - Dinnerware - Williams-Sonoma, Inc.
MONTGOMERY - Floor coverings–carpet and rugs - Regal Rugs Inc.
MONTGOMERY - Furniture - Homecrest Industries Inc.
MONTGOMERY - Ophthalmic goods - Styl-Rite Optical Manufacturing Co., Inc.
MONTGOMERY - Paper–bond - Weyerhaeuser Co.
MONTGOMERY - Ships–sailing vessels - Montgomery Marine Products
MONTGOMERY COLLECTION - Apparel and accessories - Montgomery Ward & Co. Inc.
MONTGOMERY EXPRESS - Toys–trains ☆ - Montgomery Schoolhouse
MONTGOMERY NEW YORK - Apparel and accessories - Montgomery New York, Inc.
MONTGOMERY SCHOOLHOUSE - Toys - Montgomery Schoolhouse
MONTGOMERY STRIP - Floor coverings - Bruce Hardwood Floors
MONTGOMERY WARD - Furniture - Montgomery Ward & Co. Inc.
MONTH - Eggs ☆ - Monark Egg Corp.
MONTH-AT-A-GLANCE - Calendars - Keith Clark Inc.
MONTH-IN-VUE - Calendars - Samuel Ward Manufacturing Inc.
MONTH OF SUNDAYS, A - Anvils - Psychographic Design Group, Inc.
MONTH TO MONTH - Greeting cards - Amberley Greeting Card Co.
MONTHAVEN - Wines - Golden State Vintners
MONTHLIES - Pharmaceutical preparations - Boericke & Tafel
MONTHLY COMFORT - Vitamins and nutritional supplements - Source Naturals
MONTHLY EXECUTIVE PLANNER - Office supplies - Baldwin Cooke
MONTHLY MEMORIES - Calendars - Silvestri & Ciambella Advertising, Inc.
MONTHLY MESSENGER - Envelopes - National Church Supply Co. Inc.
MONTHLY-MINDER - Calendars ☆ - Keith Clark Inc.
MONTHLY MONITOR - Office supplies - Baldwin Cooke
MONTI - Product description unknown - Prandis Inc.
MONTI-JACK-LO - Cheese - Alpine Lace Brands, Inc.
MONTICELLI - Shoes - Kotoni Trading Inc.
MONTICELLO - Bathroom fixtures - Melard Manufacturing Corp.
MONTICELLO - Bedding–linen - Fieldcrest Cannon, Inc.
MONTICELLO - Building materials–concrete - National Aluminum Products Co.
MONTICELLO - Cabinets - Yorktowne Inc.
MONTICELLO - Cabinets ☆ - Decora
MONTICELLO - Calendars - Franklin Quest Co.
MONTICELLO - Clocks - Koch & Lowy Inc.
MONTICELLO - Clocks ☆ - General Time Corp. (Westclox/Seth Thomas Div.)
MONTICELLO - Dishes–china - Pickard Inc.
MONTICELLO - Fireplaces ☆ - Majestic Co.
MONTICELLO - Flatware - Washington Forge Inc.
MONTICELLO - Floor coverings - Bruce Hardwood Floors
MONTICELLO - Floor coverings - Tarkett, Inc.
MONTICELLO - Floor coverings ☆ - Anderson Hardwood Floors Inc.
MONTICELLO - Floor coverings ☆ - Robbins Inc.
MONTICELLO - Floor coverings ☆ - Teak International
MONTICELLO - Floor coverings–carpet and rugs - Burlington Industries, Inc.
MONTICELLO - Flooring–parquet - Memphis Hardwood Flooring Co.
MONTICELLO - Furniture - Pilliod Co.
MONTICELLO - Furniture - Vaughan Furniture Co. Inc.
MONTICELLO - Furniture ☆ - Stanley Furniture Co. Inc.
MONTICELLO - Giftware - Virginia Metalcrafters Inc.
MONTICELLO - Glassware–household ☆ - Lenox Crystal, Inc.
MONTICELLO - Office furniture - Inwood Office Furniture
MONTICELLO - Optical scanners–computer - Titmus Optical, Inc.
MONTICELLO - Plumbing fixtures - Moen Inc.
MONTICELLO - Sporting goods ☆ - Brunswick Corp.
MONTICELLO - Tableware–china ☆ - Lenox, Inc.
MONTICELLO - Tiles–ceramic ☆ - Monarch Tile Inc.
MONTICELLO - Wallpaper ☆ - Old Deerfield Fabrics Inc.
MONTICELLO - Windows–storm - Duo-Temp
MONTICELLO BELLE - Hosiery - Virginia Maid Hosiery Mills Inc.
MONTICELLO/LEXINGTON - Mattresses - Liberty Vinyl Corp.
MONTICELLO, THE - Display cases–plastic - Expostar Displays, Inc.
MONTICELLO/THOMAS JEFFERSON MEMORIAL FOUNDATION - Giftware - Virginia Metalcrafters Inc.
MONTIE MOUNTAIN GOAT - Toys–stuffed - Dakin Inc.
MONTIEL BAY - Floor coverings–carpet and rugs ☆ - Walter Carpet Mills
MONTIFORNIA - Apparel–athletic - Sandra Lou Hillman
MONTINI - Footwear - Bergmann Imports Ltd.
MONTINI - Vegetables–canned - Pet Inc.
MONTIQUE - Watches - Sterling Jewelry & Distributing Co. Inc.

MONTMARTE - Furniture ☆ - Universal Flooring
MONTMARTRE - Lenses–optical - Ditto Industries Inc.
MONTMORENCY - Fruits–canned - Cherry Central Cooperative Inc.
MONTORO - Fabrics ☆ - N. Erlanger, Blumgart & Co. Inc.
MONTOYA - Apparel–women's - Dana Montoya
MONTOYA - Tools–stonecutting - Montoya Art Studio Inc.
MONTPARNASSE - Compact discs–prerecorded - TRF Production Music Libraries
MONTPELIER - Floor coverings - Mannington Resilient Floors
MONTPELIER - Glassware–household - H. Wittur & Co.
MONTPELLIER - Wines ☆ - House of Burgundy Inc.
MONTPELLIER VINEYARDS - Wines - Bronco Wine Co.
MONTRACHET - Burial caskets - Batesville Casket Co., Inc.
MONTRACHET - Cheese - Bongrain Cheese USA
MONTRACHET - Furniture ☆ - Stanley Furniture Co. Inc.
MONTRAU - Footwear - K-Swiss Inc.
MONTREAL - Furniture ☆ - Universal Flooring
MONTREAL - Ginger ale–bottled or canned - Snapple Beverage Corp.
MONTREAL - Glassware–household - ACC
MONTREAL - Hockey equipment - Montreal Hockey Co.
MONTREAL - Meat products–cured - Delstar USA
MONTREAL - Ophthalmic goods - Rochester Optical Manufacturing Co.
MONTREAL - Tiles–ceramic ☆ - Federal Tile Imports Inc.
MONTREAL - Wigs - Paula Young
MONTREAU - Floor coverings - Mannington Resilient Floors
MONTREAUX - Floor coverings–carpet and rugs ☆ - Walter Carpet Mills
MONTREAUX CORD - Floor coverings–carpet and rugs ☆ - Mohawk Carpet Corp.
MONTRESS - Clocks ☆ - General Time Corp. (Westclox/Seth Thomas Div.)
MONTREUX - Frames–eyeglass - May Optical Co. Inc.
MONTREUX - Furniture - Stanley Furniture Co. Inc.
MONTROSE - Craft supplies - Montrose Products Inc.
MONTROSE - Dinnerware–glass - Celebrity China Co.
MONTROSE - Flatware - R.P. Products, Inc.
MONTROSE - Garment hangers - Montrose Hanger Co.
MONTROSE - Office furniture–metal - Hon Co.
MONTROSE - Wallpaper - Koroseal Wallcoverings
MONTROSE - Whirlpools - Lasco Products Group
MONTSERRAT - Hardware - Sebring & Co.
MONTSERRAT - Olive oil - Spruce Foods Inc.
MONTSERRAT - Tableware–china - Villeroy and Boch Tableware Ltd.
MONTSERRATI - Olive oil ☆ - Spruce Foods Inc.
MONTU - Apparel and accessories - Busch Entertainment Corp.
MONTUNO - Recording label - Jazz Composer's Orchestra Association Inc.
MONTVAL WATERCOLOR - Paper - Canson-Talens Inc.
MONTVALE - Dinnerware–glass - Nikko Ceramics Inc.
MONTY 3/9'S - Yarn - Henry's Attic
MONTY MURDOCK - Toys–stuffed - Dakin Inc.
MONTY PLAYS SCRABBLE - Computer software - Ritam International Ltd.
MONTY TRIALS BICYCLES - Bicycles and accessories - Cosmopolitan Motors Inc.
MONUMENT FUND, THE - Real estate agencies - John Akridge Co.
MONUMENTAL - Sausages - Cibao Meat Products, Inc.
MONUMENTAL IRON WORKS - Fencing–gates and posts - Anchor Fence Co. Inc.
MONUMENTS OF AMERICA - Shirts - Monuments of America, Inc.
MONUMENTS OF THE WORLD - Jewelry - Wieck Family L.P.
MONUROL - Pharmaceutical preparations - Forest Pharmaceuticals Inc.
MONVELLE - Fibers–nylon - Monsanto Polymer Products
MONYO - Novelty items - Darwell Import Co. Inc.
MONZA - Bicycles - Liyang USA, Inc.
MONZA - Boats–motor - Monza Marine Inc.
MONZA - Floor coverings - Mannington Resilient Floors
MONZA - Toys ☆ - Strombecker Corp.
MONZA 2+2 - Motor vehicles ☆ - General Motors Corp. (Chevrolet Motor Div.)
MONZA SPYDER - Motor vehicles ☆ - General Motors Corp. (Chevrolet Motor Div.)
MONZA TOWNE COUPE - Motor vehicles ☆ - General Motors Corp. (Chevrolet Motor Div.)
MONZINI - Adhesives and sealants - Adhesive Products, Inc.
MONZINI - Shirts - Monticello Manufacturing Co.
MOO BAG - Bags–printed - Moo Country, Ltd.
MOO CHEWS - Chocolate bars - Linda Grishman Chocolates, Inc.
M.O.O. CORPORATION - Electronic equipment - M.O.O. Corp.
MOO COUNTRY - Backpacks - Moo Country, Ltd.
MOO COWS - Figurines - Diener Industries Inc.

☆ = Now out of production

MOO DIRT - Soil–potting - Foster Brothers Farm, Inc.
MOO EARS - Pet products - Oink, Oink, Inc.
MOO GROW - Soil–potting - Foster Brothers Farm, Inc.
MOO KOOLER CLASSICCOW - Milk - American Dairy Association & Dairy Council Mid East
MOO MALT - Yogurt–frozen ☆ - TCBY Systems Inc.
MOO-MANIA - Milk–flavored - Givaudan Rare Flavors
MOO MINTS - Candy - Vernell's Fine Candies
MOO-MIX - Flowers, plants, and seeds ☆ - Akin Seed Co.
MOO MIX - Soil–potting - Foster Brothers Farm, Inc.
MOO-NURE - Soil–potting - Foster Brothers Farm, Inc.
MOO PLUS - Soil–potting - Foster Brothers Farm, Inc.
MOO RECORDS - Recording label - Maki Music Productions, Inc.
MOO SHOES - Dog food - Migatz & Migatz, Inc.
MOO SHOES - Pet products - Classic Products
MOO START - Soil–potting - Foster Brothers Farm, Inc.
MOO TOO'S - Dog food ☆ - Petsations Pet Products
MOOCH - Toys–stuffed - Dakin Inc.
MOOCHEY THE MUTT - Toys–stuffed - Trendmasters, Inc.
MOOCHIE BUNNY - Toys–stuffed - Russ Berrie and Co., Inc.
MOOD - Eyeglasses - Martin-Copeland Eyewear Corp.
MOOD - Flatware - Reed and Barton Corp.
MOOD - Perfumes - Kiehl's Since 1851, Inc.
MOOD BOOST'R - Vitamins and nutritional supplements - Vitamin Classics, Inc.
MOOD BROWN - Lipsticks ☆ - Honey & Spice Toiletries
MOOD CUPS - Glassware–household - Rax Restaurants, Inc.
MOOD ESSENCE - Perfume - Wilson Marketing Enterprises, Inc.
MOOD FACTORS - Vitamins and nutritional supplements - Consac Industries, Inc.
MOOD INDIGO - Apparel–children's - Kellwood Co.
MOOD INDIGO - Christmas tree ornaments - Cracker Box Inc.
MOOD INDIGO - Fabrics - Graniteville Co.
MOOD JEWELS - Jewelry - Prisma Products
MOOD LITES - Candles - Will & Baumer, Inc.
MOOD MAGIC - Electrical equipment - Eagle Electric Manufacturing Co., Inc.
MOOD MAGIC - Skin care products - CCA Industries, Inc.
MOOD MAKER - Fireplace logs–treated - Porterville Sheltered Workshop
MOOD MAKERS - Candles - Candle-Lite Co.
MOOD MAKERS - Glassware–household - Owens-Illinois Inc. (Libbey Div.)
MOOD MAKERS - Nail care products - Fing'rs
MOOD MAKERS, THE - Sunglasses - Bonneau Co.
MOOD MAKERS, THE - Eyeglasses - Foster Grant Co. Inc.
MOOD MATCHER - Skin-care products - Wilson Marketing Enterprises, Inc.
MOOD MIST - Fragrances - Scent Shop, Inc.
MOOD SENSATIONS - Candles - Busy Bee Candles Ltd.
MOOD SETTER - Lighting fixtures - KDI American Products, Inc.
MOOD SWING - Novelty items - Peter McNair
MOOD SWINGS - Cosmetics - Cosmania, Inc.
MOOD SYNC - Vitamins and nutritional supplements - M.M.R.C., Ltd. Co.
MOOD WOOD - Deodorizers - Bruce Kiefer
MOODBACKER - Recording label - Spectrum Research, Inc.
MOODMASTER - Electric lighting equipment - Carlon
MOODMASTER PLUS - Lighting equipment ☆ - Carlon
MOODMATCHER - Lipsticks - Fran Wilson Creative Cosmetics
MOODS - Apparel and accessories - Limited Inc.
MOODS - Kites ☆ - Hi-Flier Manufacturing Co.
MOODS & FEELINGS - Colognes - Pfizer Inc.
MOODS TO GO CALIFORNIA - Shoe accessories - Jayne M. Ransbottom
MOODSCAPES - Spices and extracts - Scentex Inc.
MOODSETTER - Robes - N. Edelson Sons Corp.
MOODSTAR - Deodorizers - Bernard C. Cappelli, Jr.
MOODSVILLE - Phonographs - Fantasy Inc.
MOODY - Boats - Water Street Yachts Service
MOODY - Tools–hand-operated - Moody Tools Inc.
MOODY CUTIES - Toys ☆ - Imperial Toy Corp.
MOODY KIT - Tools - Moody Tools Inc.
MOODY MAXI TOOL KIT - Tool boxes - Moody Tools Inc.
MOODY MOUSE - Novelty items - L & L Enterprises
MOODY POCKIT SETS - Tools - Moody Tools Inc.
MOODY STREET - Apparel–women's - Anne Klein & Co.
MOODY'S - Seasonings ☆ - Silver Foods Corp.
MOODY'S GOOSE - Apparel–women's ☆ - Bobbie Brooks Inc.
MOOG - Skis ☆ - Collins Ski Products Inc.
MOOGIES - Novelty items ☆ - Cobbs Manufacturing Co.
MOOKIEE - Toys–stuffed - Lucasfilm Ltd.

MOOKY - Toys–stuffed - Gund, Inc.
MOOLIT - Computer software - Unix Systems Laboratories Inc.
MOON - Candles - Merrill-West Publishing
MOON - Fruits and vegetables - Lloyd Garretson Co. Inc.
MOON - Golfing equipment - Alexander Stewart MacDougall
MOON - Office supplies - J.R. Moon Pencil Co., Inc.
MOON - Plumbing fixtures–plastic - Dent Manufacturing Inc.
MOON - Recording label - Moon Records
MOON/ALLENCO - Valves–industrial - Dent Manufacturing Inc.
MOON & ITS PHASES - Computer software - Southwest Edpsych Services Inc.
MOON & STAR - Cookies - Granny-Made Sweaters, Inc.
MOON AND STARS - Lamps ☆ - Lamplight Farms, Inc.
MOON BEACH - Pet products - Novalek, Inc.
MOON BEAM - Bicycles - Murray, Inc.
MOON BEAM - Frames–eyeglass - Zylo Ware Corp.
MOON BEAM - Fruits and vegetables - Nelson and Co. Inc.
MOON BEAMS - Swimming pools - Muskin Leisure Products Inc.
MOON BEAMS - Yarn - Brunswick Yarns
MOON BIRD - Kites - North Pacific Products Inc.
MOON-BLOB - Novelty items - Dynamic Development
MOON BOOT - Footwear ☆ - Seaway Importing Co.
MOON BOOT SLIPPERS - Slippers - Lea-Wayne Knitting Mills Inc.
MOON BREAD - Pizza shells - Papa's Frozen Pizza
MOON COUPE - Infant product ☆ - Century Products Co.
MOON DANCE - Floor coverings–carpet and rugs - Lees Carpets
MOON DANCE - Lenses–optical - Ditto Industries Inc.
MOON DREAM - Floor coverings–carpet and rugs ☆ - Galaxy Carpet Mills Inc.
MOON DRIFTER - Eyeglasses - Martin-Copeland Eyewear Corp.
MOON DROP - Eyeglasses - Martin-Copeland Eyewear Corp.
MOON DROPS - Cosmetics - Revlon Consumer Products Corp.
MOON DUST - Candy - Shelly Bros. Inc.
MOON DUST - Floor coverings–carpet and rugs - Mohawk Carpet Corp.
MOON DYNASTY - Oils–essential - Vinay K. Aggarwal
MOON EQUIPPED - Printed materials - Moon Eyes USA, Inc.
MOON FLOWER - Melamine product - Boonton Molding Co. Inc.
MOON GLAZE - Lipsticks - Glowing Lady Cosmetics Corp.
MOON GLEAM - Rings–jewelry - Artcarved Inc.
MOON GLOW - Cosmetics - Paper Magic Group Inc.
MOON GLOW - Floor coverings–carpet and rugs - Mohawk Carpet Corp.
MOON GLOW - Glassware–household - Federal Glass
MOON GLOW - Toys - Spearhead Industries Inc.
MOON LIGHT IV - Wallpaper - Hunting Valley Prints
MOON LIGHT KITCHEN - Bakery products - Moonlight Kitchen, Ltd.
MOON MAGIC - Floor coverings–carpet and rugs - Galaxy Carpet Mills Inc.
MOON MASTER - Publisher's imprints - Daniel Schooler
MOON MIST - Beverages–carbonated - Faygo Beverages, Inc.
MOON MIST - Fabrics - Guilford Mills, Inc.
MOON MONEY B'GUM - Chewing gum ☆ - R.L. Albert & Son, Inc.
MOON PANTS - Slacks - Chek-Med Systems Inc.
MOON PATROL - Games ☆ - Avalon Hill Game Co.
MOON PAVER - Road construction machinery - Moon Paver, Inc.
MOON-PHASE - Watches - Blancpain (Time Products Inc.)
MOON PHASE - Watches ☆ - Jaeger-Le Coultre SA
MOON PIE - Bakery products - Chattanooga Bakery Inc.
MOON PORT - Games ☆ - Carrom Co.
MOON RECORDS PHASE II - Recording label - Moon Records
MOON RIVER - Eyeglasses - Art-Craft Optical Co.
MOON RIVER - Wallpaper ☆ - Cherry Hill Studio
MOON RIVER NATURALS - Skin care products - Moon River Naturals, Inc.
MOON ROCK - Magnets - Mark Bauer
MOON ROCKET - Candy ☆ - Brock Candy Co. Inc.
MOON ROCKET - Fruits and vegetables - Exeter Citrus Association
MOON ROCKET - Playground equipment - Learning Products Inc.
MOON SHADES - Eyeglasses - Blublocker Corp.
MOON SHADOW - Lenses–optical - Ditto Industries Inc.
MOON SHADOW - Wallpaper - Textile Wallcoverings International Ltd.
MOON SHADOWS - Floor coverings–carpet and rugs - Coronet Carpets Inc.
MOON-SHINE - Electronic equipment - Infinitronix, Ltd.
MOON SHINE - Vitamins and nutritional supplements - Moon Shine Trading Co.
MOON SHOES - Toys - Hart Enterprises, Inc.
MOON STAR - Bicycles - Columbia Manufacturing Inc.
MOON STICK - Knives–pocket ☆ - W.R. Case & Sons Cutlery Co.
MOON STONE - Cosmetics - Moon Stone, Inc.
MOON STONE - Knives–pocket ☆ - W.R. Case & Sons Cutlery Co.
MOON VENTURE - Eyeglasses - Art-Craft Optical Co.

☆ = Now out of production

MOON-WALK - Amusement rides - Moon-Walk Enterprises Co. Inc.
MOON-WALK - Frames–eyeglass - Hudson Optical Corp.
MOON WALKER - Orthopedic products - Ortho-Kinetics, Inc.
MOON WEAVER - Apparel and accessories - Brenda Bailey
MOONBAT - Paper products - Joan C. Holthaus
MOONBEAM - Clocks ☆ - General Time Corp. (Westclox/Seth Thomas Div.)
MOONBEAM - Toys ☆ - Henry Gordy International Inc.
MOONBEAM - Toys–stuffed ☆ - Gund, Inc.
MOONBEAM - Yarn ☆ - JCA, Inc.
MOONBEAM ENTERTAINMENT - Video production - Full Moon Entertainment
MOONBEAM UNICORN - Toys–stuffed ☆ - Dakin Inc.
MOONBEAMS - Apparel–children's - ICM
MOONBEAMS - Christmas tree ornaments - Cracker Box Inc.
MOONBEAMS - Novelty items - Amundson Group
MOONBEAMS - Pencils - J.R. Moon Pencil Co., Inc.
MOONBOWLS - Bowls ☆ - Meteor Inc.
MOONBRIAR - Rings–jewelry - Artcarved Inc.
MOONCAPS - Games - Testy Putts Corp.
MOONCASTER - Toys - Testy Putts Corp.
MOONDANCE - Bicycles ☆ - Fuji America, Inc.
MOONDANCE - Jewelry - EFS International Corp.
MOONDANCE - Wallpaper - Sunwall of America
MOONDANCE - Wines - Columbia Winery
MOONDIAL - Floor coverings–carpet and rugs ☆ - Robertex Associates Inc.
MOONDOG - Toys ☆ - Jak-Pak Inc.
MOONDREAMS - T-shirts–men's - Classic Co. Inc.
MOONDRIFT - Floor coverings–carpet and rugs - Hollytex Carpet Mills Inc.
MOONDUST - Computer software - Creative Software
MOONEY'S - Beverages–malt - Murphy's Limited
MOONEY'S IRISH STOUT - Beverages–malt - Murphy's Limited
MOONEY'S MODULES - Postcards ☆ - Fotofolio Inc.
MOONEYTRACK - Computer software - Hertzler Systems Inc.
MOONFIRE - Candy ☆ - Leaf, Inc.
MOONFLITE - Frames–eyeglass ☆ - Universal/Univis Inc.
MOONFLOWER - Eyeglasses - Art-Craft Optical Co.
MOONGATE - Furniture - American Furniture Co. Inc.
MOONGLO - Apparel–women's - Wacoal America Inc.
MOONGLO - Cables - Nordost Corp.
MOONGLOW - Apparel and accessories ☆ - Geltman Industries
MOONGLOW - Cabinets ☆ - H.J. Scheirich Co.
MOONGLOW - Floor coverings - R.W. Beattie Carpet Industries Inc.
MOONGLOW - Hair care products - Tu-K Industries Inc.
MOONGLOW - Hobby kits - Cascade Fibers Co.
MOONGLOW - Watches - Cooper & Co., Inc.
MOONHAWVEN - Skin care products - Moonhawven Corp.
MOONHEX - Eyeglasses - Martin-Copeland Eyewear Corp.
MOONKIST - Vegetables–canned - Desoto Canning Co.
MOONLESS NIGHT - Hair care products - Redmond Products, Inc.
MOONLIGHT - Apparel–women's - Moonlight Design Inc.
MOONLIGHT - Breads - Country Epicure
MOONLIGHT - Cigarettes - R.J. Reynolds Tobacco Co.
MOONLIGHT - Dinnerware–glass ☆ - Royal China & Porcelain Companies Inc.
MOONLIGHT - Fabrics - Greenwood Mills Inc.
MOONLIGHT - Floor coverings–carpet and rugs - Alexander Smith Carpets
MOONLIGHT - Food products - Moonlight Mushrooms Inc.
MOONLIGHT - Hair coloring preparations - Cosmair Inc.
MOONLIGHT - Housewares ☆ - J.W. Stannard Co.
MOONLIGHT - Manicure preparations - American Salon Products
MOONLIGHT - Mushrooms - Mushroom Growers Association Sales Co.
MOONLIGHT - Wainscotting - Georgia-Pacific Corp.
MOONLIGHT - Wallpaper - Hunting Valley Prints
MOONLIGHT & MIST - Skin care products - Schering-Plough Healthcare Products
MOONLIGHT CRUISE - Eyeglasses - Art-Craft Optical Co.
MOONLIGHT GARDEN - Perfumes - Her Garden Inc.
MOONLIGHT IN VERMONT - Chocolate bars - Linda Grishman Chocolates, Inc.
MOONLIGHT LILAC - Dolls - Tonka Corp.
MOONLIGHT MAGIC - Dolls - Mattel, Inc.
MOONLIGHT MAGIC - Floor coverings–carpet and rugs - Evans-Black Carpet Mills
MOONLIGHT MOOD - Tableware–china ☆ - Lenox, Inc.
MOONLIGHT MUSK - Colognes - Tsumura International Inc.
MOONLIGHT SENSATION - Dolls - Mattel, Inc.

MOONLIGHT SERENADE - Floor coverings–carpet and rugs ☆ - World Carpets, Inc.
MOONLIGHT SERENADE - Floor coverings–carpet and rugs ☆ - Zenith Carpets
MOONLIGHT STRIPE - Bedding–linen - Dan River Inc.
MOONLIGHTER - Drafting supplies ☆ - Teledyne Post
MOONLIGHTER - Ladders–wood - Cross Tread Industries, Inc.
MOONLIGHTER - Thermostats - Kero-Sun Inc.
MOONLIT MEADOWS OSTRICH RANCH - Surfboards - Dean Allen Brumbaugh
MOONLITE - Apparel and accessories - Atara International, Inc.
MOONLITE - Barbecue sauce - MoonLite Bar-B-Q Inn Inc.
MOONLITE - Cosmetics - Lancome
MOONLITE - Lamps ☆ - Anes Electronics Burglar Alarm Systems
MOONLITE CHEESECAKES - Cakes - Moonlite Foods, Inc.
MOONLITERS - Lighting fixtures ☆ - Meteor Inc.
MOONLOVE - Cosmetics - Pantina Cosmetics, Inc.
MOONLUSTER - Thread - Elmore-Pisgah, Inc.
MOONMAGIC - Frames–eyeglass - Hudson Optical Corp.
MOONMAN - Clothing - Michael Eamon Juergens
MOONMIST - Computer software - Activision, Inc.
MOONMIST - Hair coloring preparations - Cosmair Inc.
MOONRIDGE - Floor coverings–carpet and rugs - Cabin Crafts Carpets
MOONRIDGE - Floor coverings–carpet and rugs - Walter Carpet Mills
MOONRISE - Floor coverings–carpet and rugs - Lees Carpets
MOONRISE - Glassware–household - Denby USA Limited
MOON'S - Sauces - Moon's Foods, Inc.
MOONSHADOW - Tableware–china ☆ - Pfaltzgraff Investment Co.
MOONSHADOW - Tea - Fred G. Farago
MOONSHADOW - Wood products - Georgia-Pacific Corp.
MOONSHADOWS - Cosmetics - Maybelline Co.
MOONSHINE - Flowers, plants, and seeds ☆ - Security Products Co.
MOONSHINE - Frames–eyeglass - May Optical Co. Inc.
MOONSHINE - Soft drink - Bottlers International Ltd.
MOONSHINE CROOKS - Cigars - T.E. Brooks & Co.
MOONSHINE SLIDES - Musical instruments - Theresa Lambert
MOONSHINER - Fishing tackle - Schumann's Fly Fish Kit Co.
MOONSHOT - Games ☆ - Mayfair Games, Inc.
MOONSILK - Apparel–women's - Salant/Manhattan Industries
MOONSONG - Frames–eyeglass ☆ - Universal/Univis Inc.
MOONSPELL - Artists' materials ☆ - Artoptic International Corp.
MOONSPINNER - Eyeglasses - Art-Craft Optical Co.
MOONSPUN - Glassware–household ☆ - Lenox Crystal, Inc.
MOONSPUN - Rings–jewelry - Artcarved Inc.
MOONSPUN - Tableware–china ☆ - Lenox, Inc.
MOONSTAR - Cosmetics - Lancome
MOONSTAR - Food products - Amende and Schultz
MOONSTAR - Games ☆ - Avalon Hill Game Co.
MOONSTONE - Christmas tree ornaments - Cracker Box Inc.
MOONSTONE - Dinnerware–glass - Denby USA Limited
MOONSTONE - Dinnerware–glass ☆ - Nikko Ceramics Inc.
MOONSTONE - Floor coverings ☆ - Kentile Floors Inc.
MOONSTONE - Ophthalmic goods ☆ - Fidelity Case Corp.
MOONSTONE - Vases–glass ☆ - Waterford Wedgewood USA, Inc.
MOONSTRUCK - Wallpaper ☆ - Wallquest, Inc.
MOONSTRUCK CHOCOLATIER - Bakery products - Moonstruck Chocolatier
MOONTIDE - Cologne, bath product ☆ - Bourjois Ltd.
MOONTIDE - House furnishings - Dan River Inc.
MOONTRACKER - Computer software - Zephyr Services
MOONWIND - Colognes ☆ - Avon Products, Inc.
MOONWIND - Eyeglasses - Martin-Copeland Eyewear Corp.
MOONWIND - Rings–jewelry - Artcarved Inc.
MOOOORE - Cheese - Borden Brands Foodservice Co.
MOOOORE MILK - Cheese - Borden Brands Foodservice Co.
MOOOORE MILK SINGLES - Cheese - Borden, Inc.
MOOR - Electronic equipment - Moor Electronics Inc.
MOOR - Health care products - Norimoor Co.
MOOR-DENSE - Flowers, plants, and seeds - Monrovia Nursery Co.
MOOR MASTER - Mooring devices - Indiana Galvanizing & Manufacturing Co.
MOOR-O-MATIC - Paints - Benjamin Moore & Co.
MOOR-RINGS - Food products - Moore's Food Products
MOORCRAFT - Paints - Benjamin Moore & Co.
MOORE - Office supplies - Moore Push-Pin Co.
MOORE - Pharmaceutical preparations - Moore Medical Corp.
MOORE & DORSEY - Food products - Moore & Dorsey Inc.
MOORE BUSINESS FORMS - Business forms - Moore Business Forms, Inc.

☆ = Now out of production

MOORE COMPASS - Computer software - Moore Business Forms, Inc.
MOORE DEFENDER - Business forms - Moore Business Forms, Inc.
MOORE-O-MATIC - Garage door openers - Moore-O-Matic, Inc.
MOORE SC - Ships–sailing vessels - Moore Boats
MOORE-TUSS - Pharmaceutical preparations - Moore Medical Corp.
MOORECOAT - Paper–coated - Moore Business Forms, Inc.
MOORELINK - Computer software - Moore Business Forms, Inc.
MOORELON - Fabrics - E.R. Moore Co.
MOORES - Bakery products - Rich Products Corp.
MOORE'S - Food products - Moore's Food Products
MOORE'S - Food products - Ore-Ida Foods, Inc.
MOORE'S - Frozen foods - Food Service Products Co.
MOORE'S - Paints - Benjamin Moore & Co.
MOORE'S - Potato chips - Borden, Inc.
MOORE'S MODERN METHODS - Binders - John C. Moore Corp.
MOORE'S RED LEAF - Tobacco products - Scott Tobacco Co.
MOORESVILLE - Fabrics - Burlington Industries, Inc.
MOOREWEAR - Apparel–athletic ☆ - E.R. Moore Co.
MOOREWOOD - Paints - Benjamin Moore & Co.
MOORGARD - Paints - Benjamin Moore & Co.
MOORGLO - Paints - Benjamin Moore & Co.
MOORING MASTER - Anchors ☆ - Davis Instruments Corp.
MOORINGS - Apparel and accessories - Warnaco Inc.
MOORINGS, THE - Ships–sailing vessels - Moorings-USA
MOORLAND - Wallpaper - Koroseal Wallcoverings
MOORLAND LITE - Wallpaper - Koroseal Wallcoverings
MOORLAND POTTERY - Dishes–earthenware - Heirloom Editions Ltd.
MOORLASTIC - Sealing compounds - Benjamin Moore & Co.
MOORMATE - Marine rigging - Worth Co.
MOORTONE - Paints ☆ - Benjamin Moore & Co.
MOORWHITE - Paints - Benjamin Moore & Co.
MOORWOOD - Paints - Benjamin Moore & Co.
MOOSE - Amplifiers–musical instrument ☆ - Lectrosonics Inc.
MOOSE - Cases–plastic - Brauer Brothers Manufacturing Co.
MOOSE CREEK JUNO OF CALIFORNIA - Apparel and accessories - Juno of California, Inc.
MOOSE DICE - Novelty items - Koplow Games
MOOSE ENTERPRISES - Toys - Marlon Creations
MOOSE JOOSE - Food products ☆ - American Fruit Processors
MOOSE JUICE - Motor vehicle parts and accessories - A-Loop Offroads
MOOSE LABEL - Recording label - Moose Records
MOOSE MANSION - Frames–picture - International Silver Co.
MOOSE MUNCH - Candy - Harry and David Inc.
MOOSE RACK - Bicycle parts and accessories - Burley Design Cooperative
MOOSE USA - Figurines - Singing Tree Farms, Inc.
MOOSEABEC - Sardines–canned - Stinson Seafood Co.
MOOSEHEAD - Beverages–malt - All Brand Importers
MOOSEHEAD CANADIAN - Beverages–malt - All Brand Importers
MOOSEHEAD COLLECTION, THE - Furniture - Moosehead Manufacturing Co.
MOOSEHEAD EXPORT - Beverages–malt - All Brand Importers
MOOSEHEAD GOLDEN LIGHT - Beverages–malt - All Brand Importers
MOOSEHEAD LIGHT - Beverages–malt - All Brand Importers
MOOSEHEAD LONDON - Beverages–malt - All Brand Importers
MOOSEHORN - Dental equipment - Moosehorn, Inc.
MOOSETALES - Apparel and accessories - Judy Seabase
MOOSEWINKLE - Dolls - Floyd E. Saderlund
MOOSH MALLOWS - Cakes ☆ - Drake Bakeries, Inc.
MOOSHIE - Toys–stuffed - Dakin Inc.
MOOSMANN - Bassoons - G. Leblanc Corp.
MOOTOOS - Paper–transfer - Sargento Cheese Co. Inc.
MOOTOWN - Hobby kits - J. Hermes
MOOTOWN SNACKERS - Snack foods - Sargento Cheese Co. Inc.
MOOTSIES KIDS - Footwear–children's - Maxwell Shoe Co. Inc.
MOOTSIES TOOTSIES - Footwear–women's - Mootsies Tootsies
MOOTZ CANDIES - Candy - Mootz Candies, Inc.
MOOVER GROOVERS - Toys - Meritus Industries, Inc.
MOOVIT - Oils–lubricating - ITW Fluid Products
MOOZZI - Processed food - C & F Foods Inc.
MOP-AID - Cleaning preparations–household ☆ - Paxon Manufacturing Co.
MOP & GLO - Floor waxes - L & F Consumer Products
MOP & SHINE - Cleaning preparations–household - Windsor Wax Co. Inc.
MOP ART - Cleaning preparations - Quickie Manufacturing Corp.
MOP-IT - Mops ☆ - Royal Maid Association for the Blind Inc.
MOP-LOK - Mops - Zephyr Manufacturing Co.
MOP MAGIC - Cleaning preparations - Care-Tech Laboratories Inc.
MOP N' FRESH - Deodorizers - Surco Products Inc.

MOP-ON BUTYL STRIPPER - Cleaning preparations - Hillyard Enterprises, Inc.
MOP PAC - Cleaning preparations–household - PortionPac Chemical Corp.
MOP PAC LITE - Cleaning preparations–household - PortionPac Chemical Corp.
MOP-PETS - Toys–stuffed ☆ - Fun World Inc.
MOP RENEW - Dustmop treatment - Continental Chemical Corp.
MOP TOP HAIR SHOP - Toys - Tonka Corp.
MOP-UP - Mops - Zephyr Manufacturing Co.
MOPAC - Computer software - James P. Stewart
MOPAC - Food products - Modoc Orchard Co.
MOPACOTE - Paints - Mobile Paint Manufacturing Co.
MOPAD - Forearm supports - Ergonotech Inc.
MOPAR - Motor vehicles–automobiles - DaimlerChrysler
MOPAXOL - Paints - Mobile Paint Manufacturing Co.
MOPET - Mopeds - Handy Bikes Corp.
MOPICO - Compressors - Pipeline Compressor Systems, Inc.
MOPIER - Printers–computer - Hewlett-Packard Co.
MOPLUX - Health care products - Euroclean
MOPMASTER - Car-washing product ☆ - Clean-Rite Products Co.
MOPOXY BLIP TILE - See **MOPOXY EPOXY**
MOPOXY EPOXY - Paints - Mobile Paint Manufacturing Co.
MOPPET - Frames–eyeglass ☆ - Universal/Univis Inc.
MOPPETS - Apparel and accessories - Wolf Manufacturing Co.
MOPPETS - Figurines ☆ - Gorham Inc.
MOPPETS - Greeting cards ☆ - Fran Mar Greeting cards Ltd.
MOPPETS - Toys - Knickerbocker Toy Co. Inc.
MOPPIN' SAUCE - Salad dressings–bottled - Stubb's Legendary Kitchen
MOPPIT - Artists' materials - Stangren Co.
MOPPOLLS - Hobby kits - Dupey Management Corp.
MOPRO - Animal feeds - Cocanougher Feed Co., Inc.
MOPROD - Automotive parts and accessories - Echlin Inc.
MOPSEY AND COTTONTAIL - Apparel–children's - USANM Corp.
MOPSY - Electrical equipment - Del Mar Avionics
MOPTOWN PARADE - Computer software ☆ - Gessler Publishing Co., Inc.
MOPUPS - Electrical equipment - Oneac Corp.
MOR - Detergents - Mor Marketing Inc.
MOR - Recording label - MOR Records
MOR-A-SORB - Diapers–disposable - Research Laboratory Sales Co. Inc.
MOR-BACK - Cushions - Rinz-L-O Pillow Co.
MOR-FLO - Cushions - Rinz-L-O Pillow Co.
MOR-FLO - Water heaters–household - Mor-Flo Industries Inc.
MOR-FREE - Adhesives and sealants - Morton International Inc. (Morton Salt Div.)
MOR-FRIES - Vegetables–frozen ☆ - Lamb-Weston, Inc.
MOR-FRUIT - Fruits–canned - Mor-Fruit Products, Inc.
MOR-GOLD PLUS - Vegetable oil - Ventura Foods LLC (Lou Ana Division)
MOR-GREEN - Fertilizers - Plant Marvel Laboratories
MOR HAIR - Hair care products ☆ - Image Laboratories, Inc.
MOR JAZZ - Recording label - MOR Records
MOR-LEAN - Animal feeds - Hubbard Milling Co.
MOR-LOK - Latex - Morton International Inc. (Morton Salt Div.)
MOR-TRIM - Adhesives and sealants - Morton International Inc. (Morton Salt Div.)
MOR-TUSSIN - Cough medicines ☆ - Moore Medical Corp.
MOR-VALUE - Sporting goods - Basics Food Centers
MOR-WHIP - Food products - Land O'Lakes Inc.
MORA - Apparel and accessories ☆ - Cofish International Inc.
MORA - Blankets - MTC
MORA - Fishing tackle - Strikemaster Corp.
MORA - Glassware–household - Hillside House of Originals
MORA - Ice - Strike Master Inc.
MORADA - Floor coverings–carpet and rugs - Criterion Mills Inc.
MORAFFWARE - Computer software - Steve R. Moraff
MORAGZ - Apparel and accessories - 24.7 Christ and Moragz
MORAINE - Boots - Brenco Enterprises Inc.
MORAINE - Fabrics - Interface, Inc.
MORAN - Cigarettes - Brown & Williamson Tobacco Corp.
MORANTZ - Cleaning equipment - S. Morantz Inc.
MORAT - Gears - Franz Morat, Inc.
MORATRONIC - Fabrics–broadcloth - Desire Mills Co. Inc.
MORAVAN - Cutlery ☆ - Lifetime Hoan Corp.
MORAVIA - Beverages–malt - The Stroh Brewery Co.
MORAVIA - Glassware–household - Crystal Clear Importing Co. Inc.
MORAVIAN - Abrasive products - American Hone Co.
MORAVIAN - Fireplaces ☆ - Quaker Stove Co. Inc.
MORAY - Lenses–optical - Kelley & Hueber

☆ = Now out of production

MORAY - Thread - A. Lewis Thread Co. Inc.
MORAY CALIFORNIA - Apparel–women's - Moray California
MORBEL - Outerwear - Ronlee Apparel Co.
MORBELLI - Wines - Paterno Imports, Ltd.
MORBID SCENTS - Incense - Hot Topic Inc.
MORBID THREADS - Apparel and accessories - Hot Topic Inc.
MORBIUS - Publisher's imprints ☆ - Marvel Entertainment Group, Inc.
MORBLOOM - Fertilizers - Alaska Fish Fertilizer Co.
MORBOND - Thread - A. Lewis Thread Co. Inc.
MORCLEAN - Cleaning preparations - Oakite Products, Inc.
MORCO - Fruit drinks–bottled or canned ☆ - Morrison Restaurants Inc.
MORCORE C - Thread - A. Lewis Thread Co. Inc.
MORCORE P - Thread - A. Lewis Thread Co. Inc.
MORDOCK THE BENZITE - Toys - Paramount Pictures Corp.
MORE - Aquarium accessories - Technological Aquatic Associated Manufacturing
MORE - Candy ☆ - Leaf, Inc.
MORE - Cigarettes - R.J. Reynolds Tobacco Co.
MORE - Computer software ☆ - Symantec Corp.
MORE - Cookies - Best Maid Cookie Co.
MORE - Pet products ☆ - Kaytee Products Inc.
MORE ALIKE THAN DIFFERENT - Recording label - Pacific Institute Inc.
MORE ANSWERS, LESS READING - Publisher's imprints - International Data Group, Inc.
MORE BEEF THAN BUN - Meat products - Bessin Corp.
MORE BOOM - Apparel and accessories - Boom Club Inc.
MORE BREAD FROM TOAST - Toasters - Holman Cooking Equipment, Inc.
MORE-CARE COLLECTION - Fabrics - Morbern USA Inc.
MORE CHOICE. BETTER MANAGEMENT. - Veterinary pharmaceutical preparations - Colgate-Palmolive Co.
MORE CLOWNIN' AROUND - Figurines - Delfino Products Inc.
MORE EMPHASIS - Hair care products - Scruples Professional Salon Products, Inc.
MORE ENGINE - Computer software - Ocron Inc.
MORE HAIR - Hair care products - Hobe Labs Inc.
MORE HILARIOUS - Computer software - Optimum Resource, Inc.
MORE II - Computer software - Symantec Corp.
MORE INTIMATE - Robes - Kellwood Co.
MORE INTIMATES - Apparel and accessories - Kellwood Co.
MORE KATZENBACH KIDS - Wallpaper ☆ - Imperial Wallcoverings, Inc.
MORE LIGHTS - Cigarettes - R.J. Reynolds Tobacco Co.
MORE MATTRESS FOR YOUR MONEY - Beds, mattresses, and box springs - King Koil Licensing Co., Inc.
MORE MAXIMA - Wallpaper - Textile Wallcoverings International Ltd.
MORE MEAT MATTERS - Pet products - Iams Co.
MORE NASTY DEMONS - Computer software ☆ - Right on Programs
MORE OF GIORGIO - Wallpaper - Lawrence Wallcoverings
MORE OF NORWAY - Apparel and accessories - Cofish International Inc.
MORE OF YOU - Apparel–women's - Exquisite Form Industries
MORE PINETES II - Wallpaper ☆ - H & S Sales Inc.
MORE PINETEX - Wallpaper ☆ - H & S Sales Inc.
MORE PINETEX III - Wallpaper ☆ - H & S Sales Inc.
MORE PINETEX II - Wallpaper ☆ - Capital Carousel Inc.
MORE SCIENCE EXPERIMENTS ON FILE - Publisher's imprints - Facts on File Inc.
MORE SCULPTURES - Wallpaper ☆ - Marburg Wallcoverings Inc.
MORE STRINGS - Wallpaper - Bayview Wallcoverings
MORE THAN - Food products - More Than Foods
MORE THAN A FLUSH - Chemical preparations ☆ - Wynn Oil Co.
MORE THAN A GRATER - Food processors - Robinson Knife & Fiddlers Plastics
MORE THAN A MEMORY - Scrapbooks - Paula Abram
MORE THAN A MUFFIN - Bakery products ☆ - Sprout Delights Inc.
MORE THAN A PANTY - Underwear and nightwear - Mark Knitting Mills
MORE THAN A SLICER - Food processors - Robinson Knife & Fiddlers Plastics
MORE-THAN-BEFORE - Apparel and accessories ☆ - Strouse, Adler Co.
MORE THAN BOXES CORRUGATED SOLUTIONS - Paperboard–corrugated - Pratt Industries (USA), Inc.
MORE THAN FRIENDS - Wallpaper - Cavalier Handprints Ltd.
MORE THAN GOURMET - Sauces - More than Gourmet, Inc.
MORE THAN HELLO - Labels–paper - Ramsey & Associates Design
MORE THAN MASCARA - Cosmetics - Estee Lauder Inc.
MORE THAN MILLET - Food products - More Than Foods
MORE THAN OIL - Food products - More Than Mustard Inc.
MORE THAN POTATOES - Food products - More Than Foods

MORE THAN RICE - Food products - More Than Foods
MORE THAN SKIN DEEP - Vitamins and nutritional supplements - Amrion, Inc.
MORE THAN TERRY - Towels - Dawson Home Fashions, Inc.
MORE THAN TEXTURES - Fabrics–tapestry - Comark Wallcoverings
MORE THAN TEXTURES 6 - Wallpaper - Style-Tex Wallcoverings
MORE THAN TILES - Wallpaper - Bayview Wallcoverings
MORE THE BERRIER, THE - Teas - Celestial Seasonings, Inc.
MORE TO LOVE - Dresses - Charles Castro Manufacturing Co., Inc.
MORE WALLWORKS - Wallcoverings - Wallworks
MORE WEAR - Garters - Moore Co.
MORE WINDOW WAYS - Blinds–venetian - More Window Ways, Inc.
MORE X - Scissors–hand-operated - Sensei Shear Systems
MORE Z - Scissors–hand-operated - Sensei Shear Systems
MOREA - Yarn - William Unger & Co. Inc.
MOREAY - Tablecloths ☆ - Bibb Co.
MOREBA - Soap - Moreba Pharmaceutical Corp.
MORECHAMP - Beverages–malt - Fredimo Industries, Inc.
MOREDOPHILUS POWDER - Vitamins and nutritional supplements - Freeda Vitamins Inc.
MOREFRED - Shoes - Sam Dunoff & Son Inc.
MOREHEAD INC. - Postcards ☆ - Classico San Francisco Inc.
MOREHOUSE - Epworth Morehouse-Cowles
MOREL - Beverages–alcohol - Distillerie Stock USA Ltd.
MORELLI - Musical instrument accessories ☆ - Herco Products
MORENA - Pet products ☆ - Sera Aquaristik USA Inc.
MOREPOWER - Computers–mainframe - Electronic Assistance Corp.
MORESEAL - Weather stripping - Mortite Inc.
MORESQUE - Floor coverings–carpet and rugs - Artistic Rugs Inc.
MORESQUE - Floor coverings–carpet and rugs - Philadelphia Carpets
MORESQUE - Floor coverings–carpet and rugs - Whitecrest Carpet Mills
MORESQUE - Wallpaper - Bill Villetto Designs Inc.
MORESTAN - Insecticides - Bayer Corp. (Agriculture Div.)
MORET - Musical instruments - Custom Music Co.
MORETTI - Beverages–malt - Labatt Importers Inc.
MORETTI'S - Catsup - Patch Park Foods
MORETZ - Socks - Moretz Hosiery Mills Inc.
MORETZ SPORTS - Socks - Moretz Hosiery Mills Inc.
MOREX - Fabrics - Morex Enterprises, Inc.
MOREY - Metals - Summit Machine Tool Manufacturing Corp.
MOREY BOOGIE - Apparel and accessories - Bayly Corp.
MOREY BOOGIE - Toys - Kransco Manufacturing Inc.
MOREY'S CHEESEA SPREAD - Cheese - Morey Fish Co.
MOREY'S FISH HOUSE - Seafood products–fresh or frozen - Morey Fish Co.
MORFLEX - Insect repellents - Morflex, Inc.
MORFOGEN - Vitamins and nutritional supplements - Great Life Laboratories Inc.
MORGA - Vegetable seasonings - Liberty Richter Inc.
MORGAN - Apparel–athletic - Suplay Products-Wrestling World
MORGAN - Coffee - Jelks Inc.
MORGAN - Food products ☆ - Burnette Foods Inc.
MORGAN - Motor vehicles - Morgan Buildings and Spas
MORGAN - Pickles - Morgan Pickle Co.
MORGAN - Ships–sailing vessels - Morgan Yacht Corp.
MORGAN - Telephones - TIE Communications Inc.
MORGAN - Toys–stuffed - Bantam Collections Inc.
MORGAN CLAN - Apparel and accessories - Caledonia Knitwear Co.
MORGAN CLASSIC - Boats - Catalina Yachts Inc.
MORGAN COOPER - Apparel and accessories - Cooper Sportswear Manufacturing Co., Inc.
MORGAN CREEK - Computer software - Morgan Creek Productions, Inc.
MORGAN CREEK - Recording label - Morgan Creek Music Group
MORGAN DESIGNS - Giftware ☆ - Kraftware Corp. (Morgan Div.)
MORGAN FARMS YOUNG TURKEY - Meat products–poultry - Midwest Turkey Hatchery, Inc.
MORGAN-GREER - Novelty items–paper - Morgan & Morgan
MORGAN HART - Men's neckwear - Specialty Department Stores, Inc.
MORGAN HILL - Floor coverings–carpet and rugs ☆ - Hollytex Carpet Mills Inc.
MORGAN HILL - Furniture ☆ - Bassett Furniture Industries, Inc.
MORGAN HILL CELLARS - Wines - Pedrizzetti Winery
MORGAN JONES - Bedding–linen ☆ - Springs Industries, Inc.
MORGAN KAUFMANN - Publisher's imprints - Morgan Kaufmann Publishers Inc.
MORGAN MARINE - Boats - Catalina Yachts Inc.
MORGAN PORTFOLIO - Computer software - Morgan Management Services Ltd.

☆ = Now out of production

MORGAN PRESS COLLECTION - Greeting cards - Morgan & Morgan
MORGAN SPUR - Trees - Willow Dr. Nursery, Inc.
MORGAN TAYLOR - Apparel and accessories - R.H. Macy & Co.
MORGANE LE FAY - Apparel–women's - Morgane Le Fay
MORGANMATES - Tiles–ceramic - Summitville Tiles, Inc.
MORGAN'S - Colognes - Frank E. Morgan & Sons Inc.
MORGANS' - Food products - Morgan Foods Inc.
MORGAN'S - Salad dressings–bottled - Morgan Food Corp.
MORGAN'S - Skin care products ☆ - Alvin Last Inc.
MORGAN'S RIFLES - Games - Mayfair Games, Inc.
MORGEL - Pharmaceutical preparations - Moore Medical Corp.
MORGLASS - Window shades - C-Mor Co.
MORGON SPRINGS - Wines - European Beverage Co., Inc.
MORGRAN - Pharmaceutical preparations ☆ - Moore Medical Corp.
MORHAND - Hardware - Moore-Handley Inc.
MORI - Flatware ☆ - Excel Cutlery Inc.
MORI LEE - Apparel–women's - Mori Lee Associates
MORI-NU - Tofu - Morinaga Nutritional Foods, Inc.
MORI-NU MATES - Spices and extracts - Morinaga Nutritional Foods, Inc.
MORIA - Ophthalmic goods - Swank Optical
MORIAH - Bath salts - Colora Henna
MORIAH - Floor coverings–carpet and rugs ☆ - Mohawk Industries Inc.
MORIAH - Yarn - Henry's Attic
MORIARTY - Apparel and accessories - Moriarty Hat and Sweater Co.
MORIARTY - Apparel and accessories - Edward Worcester Morrison
MORICH - Food products - H.C. Brill Co., Inc.
MORIKI - Artists' materials - Andrews/Nelson/Whitehead
MORILLA - Finishing agents ☆ - Flintkote Co.
MORILLA - Notebooks and notepads ☆ - Canson-Talens Inc.
MORILLA - Paints ☆ - GS Roofing Products Co.
MORILLA BOARD - Paper–kraft ☆ - Canson-Talens Inc.
MORIMER - Fibers–vinyl - Georgia-Bonded Fibers, Inc.
MORINA - Yarn ☆ - JCA, Inc.
MORINI - Mopeds ☆ - Herdan Corp.
MORITA DESIGNS - Greeting cards - Colonia Art Publications
MORITZ ICE CUBES - Candy - R.L. Albert & Son, Inc.
MORK & MINDY - Shoes - Glen Shoe Co. Inc.
MORLAND - Fabrics - Maen Line Fabrics Inc.
MORLEY - Candy - Morley Candy Makers Co. Inc.
MORLEY'S - Jams and jellies - Bewley Irish Imports
MORLINE - Paints - Morton International Inc. (Morton Salt Div.)
MORLINE - Paints - Morton International Traffic Markings
MORN - Computer software - Paramount Pictures Corp.
MORNAP - Napkins–paper - Fort Howard Corp.
MORNAP JR. - Napkins–paper - Fort Howard Corp.
MORNAY - Floor coverings–carpet and rugs ☆ - Evans-Black Carpet Mills
MORNE DELICE - Jams and jellies - Jamaica Producers Marketing
MORNFLAKE - Oats–rolled or meal - Europa Foods Ltd.
MORNIN', NOON & NIGHT WAWA DOES HOAGIESRIGHT! - Food products - Wild Goose Holding Co., Inc.
MORNIN' PICKED - Food products - Convenient Products Sales Corp.
MORNING - Cigars - Gesty Trading & Manufacturing Corp.
MORNING - Frames–eyeglass ☆ - Universal/Univis Inc.
MORNING BIRDSONG - Wallpaper - Doshi Wallcoverings Inc.
MORNING BLEND - Fruit drinks–bottled or canned - Knudsen & Sons Inc.
MORNING BLOSSOM - Tableware–china ☆ - Lenox, Inc.
MORNING BLUE - Dinnerware - Corning Inc.
MORNING BREEZE - Perfumes - Colgate-Palmolive Co.
MORNING BREW - Teas - Traditional Medicinals, Inc.
MORNING CALM - Flatware - Washington Forge Inc.
MORNING CALM - Wallpaper - K.M.L. Industries
MORNING CALM - Wallpaper - Textile Wallcoverings International Ltd.
MORNING CHEER - Fruits and vegetables - Half Moon Fruit & Produce Co.
MORNING CRUNCH - Granola bars - Sarabeth's Kitchen
MORNING DELIGHT - Food products ☆ - Birkett Mills
MORNING DELIGHT - Frozen foods - Moran Foods, Inc.
MORNING DEW - Rings–jewelry - Artcarved Inc.
MORNING DEW - Skin care products - Renee A. Gabet
MORNING DREAM - Dinnerware ☆ - Corning Inc.
MORNING FLIGHT - Wallpaper - Taylor Wallcoverings Inc.
MORNING FRESH - Cakes ☆ - Tasty Baking Co.
MORNING FRESH - Cleaning preparations - Merchants Distributors, Inc.
MORNING FRESH FARMS - Food products - Merchants Distributors, Inc.
MORNING FUNNIES - Cereal - Ralston Purina Co.
MORNING GARDEN - Housewares ☆ - Treasure Craft Co.
MORNING GLORY - Bicycles - Western Auto Supply Co.

MORNING GLORY - Candy ☆ - Johnson Candy Co.
MORNING GLORY - Cheese - AMPI/Morning Glory Farms
MORNING GLORY - Colognes - Andrew Jergens Co.
MORNING GLORY - Dinnerware - Bennington Potters
MORNING GLORY - Dinnerware ☆ - Corning Inc.
MORNING GLORY - Fibers–polyester - Morning Glory Products
MORNING GLORY - Frames–eyeglass ☆ - Universal/Univis Inc.
MORNING GLORY - Giftware - Russ Berrie and Co., Inc.
MORNING GLORY - House furnishings ☆ - Dan River Inc.
MORNING GLORY - Jams and jellies - Sigma Quality Foods Corp.
MORNING GLORY - Milk–canned or powdered - Defiance Milk Products Co.
MORNING GLORY - Recording label - Victori Promotions & Marketing Inc.
MORNING GLORY - Tile - Southland Stone USA, Inc.
MORNING GLORY - Wigs - Paula Young
MORNING GLOW - Flatware ☆ - Kirk Stieff Co.
MORNING GOLD - Flatware ☆ - Kirk Stieff Co.
MORNING IN MAY - Wallpaper - Quality House Wallcoverings
MORNING JOY - Coffee ☆ - American Coffee Co. Inc.
MORNING LIGHT - Dinnerware ☆ - Corning Inc.
MORNING LIGHT - Eyeglasses - Martin-Copeland Eyewear Corp.
MORNING LIGHT - Floor coverings–carpet and rugs - Colonial Mills Inc.
MORNING LIGHT - Food products - Conagra, Inc.
MORNING LIGHT - Tableware–earthenware - Pfaltzgraff Investment Co.
MORNING LIGHT COFFEE ROASTERS - Coffee - Montana Roastery Group, Inc.
MORNING MAC - Sandwiches–prepackaged - Mcdonald's Corp.
MORNING MAID - Sausages - Maglio Bros., Inc.
MORNING MAKER - Coffee makers–electric - Hamilton Beach/Proctor-Silex Inc.
MORNING MIST - Bicycles ☆ - Roadmaster Corp.
MORNING MIST - Christmas tree ornaments - Cracker Box Inc.
MORNING MIST - Dishes–china - Pickard Inc.
MORNING MOO - Toys–stuffed - Direct Connect International Inc.
MORNING MULTI - Vitamins and nutritional supplements - 4 Health, Inc.
MORNING NEWS - Underwear and nightwear - Wal-Mart Stores Inc.
MORNING ORANGE - Fruit drinks–bottled or canned - Land-O-Sun Dairies, Inc.
MORNING ORCHARD - Deodorizers - W.W. Grainger, Inc.
MORNING PLAID - Bedding–linen - Dan River Inc.
MORNING POWER - Cereal - Nabisco Foods Group
MORNING RAIN - Deodorizers - Reckitt & Colman, Inc.
MORNING RUSH, THE - Broadcasting stations–radio - Jonathon Rush
MORNING SELECT - Dairy foods - Ahava Dairy Products Corp.
MORNING SHADOWS - Floor coverings–carpet and rugs - Cabin Crafts Carpets
MORNING SONG - Rings–jewelry - Artcarved Inc.
MORNING SONG WILD BIRD FOOD - Bird feeds - Gutwein & Co., L.P.
MORNING STAR - Floor coverings–carpet and rugs - Mohawk Carpet Corp.
MORNING STAR - Flowers, plants, and seeds - Pennington Seed, Inc.
MORNING STAR - Greeting cards - Dayspring/Outreach Publications
MORNING STAR - Incense - Darwell Import Co. Inc.
MORNING STAR - Perfumes - Bruce English
MORNING STAR - Wallcovering - Wall Trends, Inc.
MORNING STAR COFFEE - Coffee - Morning Star Coffee, Inc.
MORNING STAR CREATIONS - Jewelry–precious - Stamper Black Hills Gold Jewelry, Inc.
MORNING START - Vitamins and nutritional supplements - MXM Essential Formulas Inc.
MORNING SUN - Frames–eyeglass ☆ - Universal/Univis Inc.
MORNING SWEETE - Bakeries - Willingham Corp.
MORNING THUNDER - Teas–herbal - Celestial Seasonings, Inc.
MORNING TREAT - Beverages - Morning Treat Coffee Co. Inc.
MORNING TULIP - Floor coverings–carpet and rugs - Regal Rugs Inc.
MORNING TWIST - Bakery products - Ferrara Food and Confections Inc.
MORNINGAIDE - Health care products - Mayday, Inc.
MORNINGBROOK FARMS - Dairy products - Quiktrip Corp.
MORNINGKISS - Toothbrushes - Malaytex USA Inc.
MORNINGSIDE - Furniture ☆ - Athens Furniture Industries Inc.
MORNINGSIDE - Lumber - Georgia-Pacific Corp.
MORNINGSIDE - Toilets–enameled - Kohler Co.
MORNINGSIDE BOOKS - Publisher's imprints - Columbia University Press
MORNINGSTAR - Controls–heating systems - Comforter Stove Works
MORNINGSTAR - Eyeglasses - Art-Craft Optical Co.
MORNINGSTAR - Floor coverings - Congoleum Corp.
MORNINGSTAR - Recording label - Eddie Crook Co.
MORNINGSTAR - Sleeping bags - Coleman Co., Inc.

☆ = Now out of production

MORNINGSTAR - Wines - Hill & Thoma Wines
MORNINGSTAR FARMS - Food products - Specialty Foods Investment Co.
MORNINGSTAR FARMS - Food products - Worthington Foods Inc.
MORNITAL - Pharmaceutical preparations ☆ - Morton Pharmaceuticals Inc.
MORO - Pencils - Reliance Pen & Pencil Corp.
MOROCCAN - Floor coverings–carpet and rugs - Ebsco Carpet Mills
MOROCCAN MINT - Teas - Eastern Shore Tea Co.
MOROCCAN SAND - Pottery products - Laguna Clay Co.
MOROCCAN SANDS - Floor coverings–carpet and rugs - Downs Carpet Co. Inc.
MOROCCAN SILVER - Hardware - Alumax Aluminum Corp.
MOROCCAN SPICE - Housewares - Crabtree & Evelyn, Ltd.
MOROCCO - Bathroom fixtures ☆ - Crane Plumbing/Fiat Products
MOROCCO - Clocks ☆ - General Time Corp. (Westclox/Seth Thomas Div.)
MOROCCO - Floor coverings - Mannington Resilient Floors
MOROCCO - Floor coverings–carpet and rugs - Quaker Inc.
MOROCCO - Flowers, plants, and seeds - Monrovia
MOROCCO - Glassware–household ☆ - Anchor Hocking Glass, Inc.
MOROCCO - Luggage - American Flyer
MOROCCO - Tiles–ceramic - KPT Inc.
MOROCCO - Yarn ☆ - Tahki Imports Ltd.
MOROLINE - Hair care products - Schering-Plough Healthcare Products
MORONEY - Beverages–alcohol - James Moroney, Inc.
MOROSCO - Sporting goods - Morris Rosenbloom & Co. Inc.
MOROSO - Epoxy coatings - Moroso Performance Products, Inc.
MOROTHANE - Paints - Sophir Morris Paint
MOROTOCK - Bedding–linen ☆ - Dan River Inc.
MORPEL - Insect repellents - Morflex, Inc.
MORPH MANAGER - Computer software - Advantageware, Inc.
MORPH MODELER - Computer software - Advantageware, Inc.
MORPHATRONS - Toys–electronic - Tiger Electronics, Inc.
MORPHEUS - Synthesizers–musical instrument - E-Mu Systems, Inc.
MORPHINE - Apparel and accessories - Jonathan W. Reeves
MORPHS - Toys - Tonka Corp.
MORPHWIZARD - Computer software ☆ - Imageware Software, Inc.
MORPOLY - Thread - A. Lewis Thread Co. Inc.
MORREA - Apparel–athletic - Queenie, Ltd.
MORRELL - Meat products–beef - John Morrell & Co.
MORRHYTHM - Recording label - Outstanding Records
MORRIS - Beds–metal - Casual Lifestyles Distribution, Inc.
MORRIS - Desk sets - Bert M. Morris Co.
MORRIS - Motor vehicle parts and accessories - Rivera Engineering, Inc.
MORRIS - Ophthalmic goods ☆ - Luxottica
MORRIS - Ships–sailing vessels - Morris Yachts
MORRIS - Wallcoverings - Arthur Sanderson and Sons North America Ltd.
MORRIS BRICK - Floor coverings - Tarkett, Inc.
MORRIS-BUDGET - Hair care products - Morris-Flamingo Inc.
MORRIS FEEL - Shooting gloves - Boss Manufacturing Co.
MORRIS-FLAMINGO - Hair care products - Morris-Flamingo Inc.
MORRIS FOLIO - Wallcoverings ☆ - Arthur Sanderson and Sons North America Ltd.
MORRIS INDEPENDENT LIFT - Medical apparatus - Morris Machine & Mold, Inc.
MORRIS ZIP FLAP - Shooting mitts - Boss Manufacturing Co.
MORRISET - Desk sets - Bert M. Morris Co.
MORRISHARP - Pencil sharpeners - Bert M. Morris Co.
MORRISMEM - Office supplies - Bert M. Morris Co.
MORRISON - Candy ☆ - Morla Corp.
MORRISON & SCHIFF - Meat products–beef ☆ - Hebrew Foods Inc.
MORRISON FARMS - Popcorn - Morrison Farms Popcorn
MORRISON KNUDSEN - Locomotives - Morrison Knudsen Corp.
MORRISON'S - Adhesives and sealants - Lawn & Garden Supply Co.
MORRISON'S - Cake mixes - Morrison Milling Co.
MORRISON'S - Food containers - PYA/Monarch Inc.
MORRISON'S BEST - Flour–blended - Morrison Milling Co.
MORRISTAR - Desk sets - Bert M. Morris Co.
MORRISTOWN BRICK - Finishing agents ☆ - Flintkote Co.
MORRISTOWN BRICK - Paints ☆ - GS Roofing Products Co.
MORRISTRAY - Office supplies - Bert M. Morris Co.
MORRO - Brushes–paint - Corona Brushes Inc.
MORRO BAY - Apparel–men's - J.C. Penney Co., Inc.
MORRO BAY - Floor coverings–carpet and rugs - Catalina Carpet Mills Inc.
MORRO BAY - Floor coverings–carpet and rugs ☆ - Customweave Carpets Inc.
MORRO BAY VINEYARDS - Wines - Pasternak Wine Imports
MORRO SANGRIA - Fruits and vegetables - Blue Banner Co. Inc.

MORROW - Apparel and accessories - Morrow Snowboards, Inc.
MORROW JUNIOR - Publisher's imprints - William Morrow and Co. Inc.
MORROW'S - Yogurt - Roney-Oatman Inc.
MORSE - Footwear - Morse Shoe, Inc.
MORSE - Saw blades - M.K. Morse Co.
MORSE CONTROLS - Electronic equipment - Imo Industries Inc.
MORSETH - Knives–hunting - A.G. Russell Knives Inc.
MORSITE - Cleaning preparations - J.I. Morris Co.
MORSO - Mitre boxes - Paul Victorius Framing Shop
MORSPACE - Furniture - Visador Co.
MORSTAR - Floor coverings–carpet and rugs ☆ - World Carpets, Inc.
MORSTAR - Meat products–pork - C.F.M. Sales Co.
MORTA-POXY - Adhesive, grout - Construction Adhesives Co.
MORTAL KOMBAT - Books–comic - Midway Manufacturing Co.
MORTAL KOMBAT - Games - Acclaim Entertainment Inc.
MORTAL KOMBAT - Toys - Kenner Products
MORTAL KOMBAT II - Games - Acclaim Entertainment Inc.
MORTAR - Building materials–concrete - Geocel Corp.
MORTAR MASTER - Mixers–concrete - DBNA Trademarks Holding Inc.
MORTAR MONITOR - Audio equipment - Harry Frank Conover, Jr.
MORTAR NET, THE - Construction equipment - Tom Sourlis
MORTARFIX - Epoxy coatings - Stay-Tite Products Co. Inc.
MORTELL - Weather stripping ☆ - Mortite Inc.
MORTEN MINIATURES - Hobby kits - American Buco Corp.
MORTENSEN MORE THAN MATH - Computer software - V.J. Mortensen Co.
MORTEX - Weather stripping - Mortite Inc.
MORTEX - Window shades - C-Mor Co.
MORTGAGE JOURNAL, THE - Publisher's imprints - Essay, Inc.
MORTGAGE MATE COMPUTERS - Computer software - Real Solutions, Inc.
MORTGAGE PUBLISHER - Computer software - FormAtion Technologies Inc.
MORTGAGE SERVICER, THE - Computer software - Servantis Systems, Inc.
MORTGAGE TERMINATOR, THE - Computer storage devices–magnetic - Mortgage Terminator, Inc.
MORTGAGEBASE - Computer software - Interlinq Software Corp.
MORTGAGEEDI - Computer software - Title Office, Inc.
MORTGAGEEXCEL - Computer software - Alexander Hamilton Life Insurance Co. of America
MORTGAGEFLEX SYSTEMS, INC. - Computer software - Mortgageflex Systems, Inc.
MORTGAGEMASTER - Computer software - Richard L. Coppola
MORTGAGES, INSURANCE & MORE - Computer peripheral equipment - Meca Software, Inc.
MORTICIA - Costumes - Paramount Pictures Corp.
MORTIMER - Games - Lucasarts Entertainment Co.
MORTIMER ICHABOD MARKER - Toys - Tyco Toys
MORTIMER SNERD - Dolls - Goldberger Doll Manufacture Co.
MORTITE - Weather stripping - Mortite Inc.
MORTON - Dog food - Hubbard Milling Co.
MORTON - Food products - Conagra, Inc.
MORTON - Furnaces–industrial - Morton Metalcraft Co.
MORTON - Pharmaceutical preparations - Morton Pharmaceuticals Inc.
MORTON - Salt - Morton International Inc. (Morton Salt Div.)
MORTON - Thread - A. Lewis Thread Co. Inc.
MORTON - Tools - D & L Stained Glass Supply, Inc.
MORTON COLLECTION - Apparel–men's - Central-Samuels Inc.
MORTON HOUSE - Meat products–canned - Bunker Hill Foods
MORTON KNIGHT - Waterproof outerwear - J. Pace Golf
MORTON MUNCHWICH - Food products - Del Monte Corp.
MORTON'S OF OMAHA - Food products - Excel Corp.
MORVALU - Washboards ☆ - Columbus Washboard Co.
MO'S - Soups–canned - Mo's Enterprises Inc.
MOS BOSS - Semiconductors - Unitrode Integrated Circuits Corp.
M.O.S.A. - Apparel–men's - Edison Brothers Stores, Inc.
MOSABAH - Food products - Nicola International, Inc.
MOSAIC - Antennas - Allen Telecom Group, Inc.
MOSAIC - Dinnerware–glass - Dansk International Designs, Ltd.
MOSAIC - Dinnerware–glass ☆ - Nikko Ceramics Inc.
MOSAIC - Dishes–china ☆ - Pickard Inc.
MOSAIC - Floor coverings–carpet and rugs - Lotus Carpets
MOSAIC - Floor coverings–carpet and rugs - Mohawk Industries Inc.
MOSAIC - Floor coverings–carpet and rugs - Regal Rugs Inc.
MOSAIC - Labels–paper ☆ - Cleo Inc.
MOSAIC - Musical instrument accessories - Dimarzio, Inc.
MOSAIC - Puzzles - Milton Bradley Co.
MOSAIC - Recording label - Mosaic Records Inc.
MOSAIC - Rings–jewelry - Artcarved Inc.

☆ = Now out of production

MOSAIC:2000 - Computer peripheral equipment - EMC Corp.
MOSAIC COLLECTION - Wallpaper ☆ - Carlton-Metro Wallcoverings
MOSAIC CRAFT - Hobby kits - A + A
MOSAIC/DESIGNER - Floor coverings–carpet and rugs - Johnson's Carpets Inc.
MOSAIC DESIGNS - Apparel–women's - Mosaic Designs Inc.
MOSAIC DREAMS - Wallpaper - Kirk-Brummel
MOSAIC EDITIONS - Posters - Mosaic Records Inc.
MOSAIC FUSION - Apparel–men's - Oxford Industries, Inc.
MOSAIC MANOR - Floor coverings ☆ - Congoleum Corp.
MOSAIC, MARBLE, & GRANITE - Wallpaper - Eisenhart Wallcoverings Co.
MOSAIC PALAZZO - Floor coverings ☆ - National Floor Products Co., Inc.
MOSAIC PUBLICATIONS, INC. - Publisher's imprints - Mosaic Publications, Inc.
MOSAIC TILE - Floor coverings–carpet and rugs ☆ - Blue Ridge Carpet Mills
MOSAICFRONT - Mosaics - Conrad Pickel Studio, Inc.
MOSAICS - Hair care products - Image Laboratories Inc.
MOSAICS - Ophthalmic goods - Foremost Optical Products
MOSAICS - Wallpaper - Pickhardt & Siebert USA Inc.
MOSAIQUE - Floor coverings–carpet and rugs - Harbinger Co.
MOSAIX - Computer software - Digital Systems International, Inc.
MOSBY LIFELINE - Publisher's imprints - Mosby-Year Book, Inc.
MOSBY WINERY - Wines - Mosby Winery
MOSBY'S RAIDERS - Games - Avalon Hill Game Co.
MOSCA BIANCA - Coffee - Paddington Corp.
MOSCATO CURIOSO - Wines - Preston Vineyards
MOSCHINO - Gloves - Portolano Products Inc.
MOSCHINO - Handbags and belts - Spettacolo Inc.
MOSCHINO OCCHIALI - Ophthalmic goods - Luxottica
MOSCO - Health care products - Medtech Laboratories Inc.
MOSCOW - Liquors ☆ - United States Distilled Products Co.
MOSCOW! AUCTION! - Board game - Planet-3 Games
MOSELFEST - Wines ☆ - Louis Glunz Inc.
MOSELGOLD CELLARS - Wines - Chrissa Imports Ltd.
MOSELLAND - Wines - Leonard Kreusch Inc.
MOSELLE - Wines - Beer Import Co.
MOSER - Giftware - Superlux Ltd.
MOSER - Milk ☆ - Natural Country Farms Inc.
MOSERA - Floor coverings–tile ☆ - Vida Mosaic Co. Inc.
MOSEY'S - Meat products–canned - Mosey's Inc.
MOSKETTO - Insecticides - PBI/Gordon Corp.
MOSLER-HARBOR - Bookcases–wood ☆ - Mosler Inc.
MOSLER JR. - Toys - Brumberger Co. Inc.
MOSLOW - Pharmaceutical preparations ☆ - R.A. McNeil Co.
MOSNESS - Salad dressings–bottled - Schlotterbeck and Foss Co.
MOSONEX - Soil–potting ☆ - Hydroponic Chemical Co. Inc.
MOSQUITO - Boats–motor ☆ - Bayliner Marine Corp.
MOSQUITO - Health care products - Vygon Corp.
MOSQUITO - Toys–models - Estes Industries
MOSQUITO BEATER - Pesticides–household - Bonide Products, Inc.
MOSQUITO HAWK - Electronic equipment - Environmental Concepts, Inc.
MOSQUITO VILLAGE - Figurines - Treasures & Trinkets, Inc.
MOSQUITOR - Toys - Mattel, Inc.
MOSRITE - Guitars ☆ - Pacific Music Supply Co.
M.O.S.S. - Health care products - Otto Bock Orthopedic Industry Inc.
MOSS BOSS - Sporting goods - James Heddon's Sons
MOSS CREEK TRADERS - Apparel–men's - J.C. Penney Co., Inc.
MOSS HOLLOW - Pet products - Petland, Inc.
MOSS HOPPER - Fishing nets - Four Rivers Tackle Co.
MOSS MAN - Toys - Mattel, Inc.
MOSS MASTER - Fishing lures - Snag Proof Manufacturing, Inc.
MOSS MASTER - Herbicides - Security Products Co.
MOSS MUSIC - Recording label ☆ - Essex Entertainment Inc.
MOSS ROSE - Flour–blended - Mercer Milling Co.
MOSS-SIMCO - Cutlery - S.I. Moss Co. Inc.
MOSSANT OF PARIS - Apparel–athletic - Leo H. Loring Co. Inc.
MOSSBERG - Firearms, accessories, and parts - O.F. Mossberg & Sons, Inc.
MOSSBERG SAFE SYSTEMS, INC. - Safes - Mossberg Safe Systems, Inc.
MOSSCRAFT - Agricultural products - Martin Antony Products Co.
MOSSER LEE - Garden equipment - Deli, Inc.
MOSSIMO - Bathing suits - Lunada Bay Corp.
MOSSIMO - Eyeglasses - Mossimo Inc.
MOSSIMO M - Eyeglasses - Mossimo Inc.
MOSSY OAK - Archery equipment ☆ - Martin Archery Inc.
MOST - Animal feeds - Moorman Manufacturing Co.
MOST - Fertilizers - Lange-Stegmann Co.

MOST - Housewares ☆ - Walton March
MOST AMAZING THING, THE - Computer software ☆ - Queue Inc.
MOST BEAUTIFUL - Botanical extracts - Northwest Packaging Inc.
MOST GENTLE EYE DEFINER - Cosmetics - Janet Sartin, Inc.
MOST HIGH - Recording label - Mighty Horn Ministries, Inc.
MOST IMPORTANT - Floor coverings–carpet and rugs ☆ - Lees Carpets
MOST LIKE MOTHER - Infant product - Playtex Beauty Care, Inc.
MOST OF ALL - Floor coverings–carpet and rugs ☆ - Lees Carpets
MOST ORDINARY BEARS - Novelty items - At the Zoo
MOST PRECIOUS - Frames–eyeglass - Hudson Optical Corp.
MOST PRECIOUS - Perfumes - Evyan Perfumes Inc.
MOST PRECISE BALL IN GOLF, THE - Balls–golf - Lisco, Inc.
MOST PRECISE SHAFTS, THE - Golfing equipment ☆ - Harrison Sports, Inc.
MOST SIGNIFICANT BITS - Computer software - Most Significant Bits
MOST, THE - Hair care products ☆ - Demert & Dougherty, Inc.
MOST, THE - Frames–eyeglass - Hudson Optical Corp.
MOST WANTED MADE ON EARTH BY HUMANS - Apparel and accessories - Outrageous Inc.
MOSTAR - Radios - Motorola, Inc. (Land Mobile Products Sector)
MOSTIERO - Beverages–malt - V & P Import
MOSTLY MEN - Skin care products - The Body Shop
MOSTLY MONOGRAMS - Apparel trimmings - Mostly Monograms
MOSTY - Skin care products ☆ - WES Publishing
MOSYS - Circuit boards - Monolithic System Technology, Inc.
MOTE ANDINO - Food products - Goya Foods, Inc.
MOTE BOWL - Pet products ☆ - Doggie Products of America
MOTEL 6 - Hotels and motels - Motel 6 Corp.
MOTEL 6 - Hotels and motels ☆ - Allstar Inns Inc.
MOTERCYCLE MOLY - Lubricants - Pacific Lubricants
MOTETTE - Recording label - Organ Literature Foundation
MOTEY QITSUM - Rum - Carriage House Imports Ltd.
MOTH - Ships–sailing vessels ☆ - International Marine
MOTH-AWAY - Insecticides - Richards Homewares Inc.
MOTH-B-GON - Insecticides ☆ - Chevron Chemical Co.
MOTH-ICE - Naphthalene chips - Willert Home Products, Inc.
MOTH-PROOFER - Naphthalene chips ☆ - Olin Corp.
MOTH-TEK - Skin care products - Excell Products Corp.
MOTHER - Skin care products - Special Moment Inc.
MOTHER - Video games - Nintendo of America Inc.
MOTHER AND BABY - Toys–stuffed - Fun World Inc.
MOTHER BERTHA MUSIC, INC. - Recording label - Phil Spector International (Warner-Spector Records Inc.)
MOTHER BUTLER PIES - Pies–fresh - Denny's Inc.
MOTHER CLEO - Recording label - MCP Davisound
MOTHER EARTH - Cough medicines - Heritage Store Inc.
MOTHER EARTH - Mushrooms ☆ - Mushroom Cooperative Co.
MOTHER EARTH - Tortillas ☆ - Stretch Island Fruit Inc.
MOTHER EARTH PILLOWS - Pillows - Mother Earth Designs, Inc.
MOTHER EARTH VINEYARDS WILDLIFE WINES MANATEE - Wines - Coastal Vintners, Inc.
MOTHER FLETCHER'S SOOPER JOOCE - Beverages–carbonated - Canada Dry Corp.
MOTHER GOLDSTEIN - Wines - Monarch Wine Co. of Georgia
MOTHER GOOSE - Cookies - Market Square Food Co. Inc.
MOTHER GOOSE - Dolls - Effanbee Doll Corp.
MOTHER GOOSE - Frames–eyeglass - Hudson Optical Corp.
MOTHER GOOSE - Games - Cadaco Div.
MOTHER GOOSE - Hobby kits - Educational Products Co.
MOTHER GOOSE - Housewares ☆ - Shafford Co. Inc.
MOTHER GOOSE - Infant product - Kessler Marketing Group, Inc.
MOTHER GOOSE - Maternity clothing - Jennifer George Inc.
MOTHER GOOSE - Meat products - Tobin's First Prize Meat
MOTHER GOOSE - Recording label - Cadet Records Inc.
MOTHER GOOSE - Shoes - Mother Goose Co.
MOTHER GOOSE - Tableware - Pecoware Products, Inc.
MOTHER GOOSE - Toys - Toy Works, Inc.
MOTHER GOOSE & GRIMM - Greeting cards - Recycled Paper Products, Inc.
MOTHER GOOSE & GRIMM - Toys–stuffed ☆ - Mighty Star Inc. (Special Effects Div.)
MOTHER GOOSE MONSTERS - Publisher's imprints ☆ - McClanahan Book Co., Inc.
MOTHER GOOSE PIN-UPS - Infant product ☆ - Dolly, Inc.
MOTHER GOOSE SAYS - Toys–musical - Mattel, Inc.
MOTHER HUBBARD - Dolls ☆ - Effanbee Doll Corp.
MOTHER HUBBARD - Flour–blended - Hubbard Milling Co.
MOTHER HUBBARD - Frames–eyeglass - Hudson Optical Corp.

☆ = Now out of production

MOTHER HUBBARD - Meat products–beef ☆ - Hubbard Beef Supply

MOTHER IN THE MAKING - Calendars - The Super Market

MOTHER KNOWS BEST - Baby foods - Colleen S. Taggart

MOTHER LODE MUD - Bakery products - Our Name is Mud, Inc.

MOTHER MEOW - Toys–stuffed ☆ - Dakin Inc.

MOTHER NATURE - Water–bottled or canned - Mother Nature Spring Water Inc.

MOTHER NATURE SAYS - Toys–musical - Mattel, Inc.

MOTHER NATURE TALES OF DISCOVERY - Video production - Discovery Channel

MOTHER NATURE'S BRAND - Pesticides–household - Dexol Industries

MOTHER NATURE'S NUTRITION CENTERS - Vitamins and nutritional supplements - Mother Nature's Nutrition Centers Inc.

MOTHER NATURE'S ODOR REMOVER - Deodorizers - Advanced Research, Inc.

MOTHER OF ALL ANTIOXIDANTS, THE - Vitamins and nutritional supplements - Intracell Nutrition Inc.

MOTHER OF ALL JAWBREAKERS - Candy - Creative Confection Concepts, Inc.

MOTHER OF ALL JEWELRY, THE - Jewelry - Mike Lemonakis

MOTHER OF ALL SUCKERS - Candy - Creative Confection Concepts, Inc.

MOTHER ONE - Books–comic - Aegis Entertainment, Inc.

MOTHER REYMOND'S - Bakery products - SB Royalty Co. Inc.

MOTHER SHIP OVER PARIS - Wines - Bully Hill Vineyards, Inc.

MOTHER TO BE - Apparel stores–sports - CMO Inc.

MOTHER TONGUE - Recording label - Mother Tongue

MOTHER VINEYARD SCUPPERNONG - Wines - Canandaigua Wine Co. Inc.

MOTHERHOOD MATERNITY - Apparel–women's - Motherhood Maternity Shops, Inc.

MOTHERLODE VINEYARDS - Wines - Karly Wines

MOTHERLOVE - Skin care products - Motherlove Herbal Co.

MOTHERS - Alarm systems - Mother's Window Tint, Inc.

MOTHERS - Cleaning preparations - Mothers Polishes Waxes Cleaners

MOTHER'S - Cookies - Mother's Cake & Cookie Co.

MOTHER'S - Food products - Mother's Food Products Inc.

MOTHER'S - Food products - I. Rokeach and Sons Inc.

MOTHERS - Giftware - Gorham Inc.

MOTHERS AID - First aid kits - E.H. Kneen Co.

MOTHERS AND DAUGHTERS, A SPECIAL BOND - Greeting cards ☆ - American Greetings Corp.

MOTHER'S ANGEL - Jewelry - Krementz & Co.

MOTHER'S BEST - Food products - Beatrice Cos. Inc.

MOTHER'S BEST - Food products - Tower Chicken Farm Inc.

MOTHER'S CHOICE - Apparel–women's - Bradlees Stores, Inc.

MOTHERS CHOICE - Baby product - London International U.S. Holdings

MOTHER'S CHOICE - Breads - Gais Northwest Bakeries

MOTHER'S CHOICE - Food products - I. Rokeach and Sons Inc.

MOTHER'S DAY PEN - Pens - Avon Products, Inc.

MOTHER'S DEVOTION - Jewelry - Tru-Kay Manufacturing Co.

MOTHER'S FRAGRANCES, THE - Incense - Mere Cie.

MOTHER'S FREE RANGE EGG CO. - Eggs - Chino Valley Ranchers

MOTHER'S FRIEND - Pharmaceutical preparations - S.S.S. Co.

MOTHER'S HEART, A - Jewelry - Sandberg & Sikorski Diamond Corp.

MOTHER'S HELPER - Games ☆ - Milton Bradley Co.

MOTHER'S HELPER - Pet products - Carter-Wallace, Inc.

MOTHERS HELPER - Pillows - Hollander Home Fashions Inc.

MOTHER'S JOY - Jewelry - Donald Bruce & Co.

MOTHER'S LITTLE MIRACLE - Stain/odor remover - Mother's Little Miracle, Inc.

MOTHER'S LODE - Video production - Mother's Lode Entertainment, Inc.

MOTHER'S LOVE - Brassieres (Bras) - Gelmart Industries Inc.

MOTHERS LOVE - Jewelry - J. & C. Ferrara Co. Inc.

MOTHER'S LOVE - Toys–stuffed - Russ Berrie and Co., Inc.

MOTHER'S LOVE, A - Giftware - Avon Products, Inc.

MOTHER'S MAGIC - Skin care products - Mennen Co.

MOTHER'S MAID - Food products - Burnette Foods Inc.

MOTHER'S MAKE - Fruit pie mixes - Dawn Food Products Inc.

MOTHER'S MILK - Teas–herbal - Traditional Medicinals, Inc.

MOTHER'S MILK STORAGE BAGS - Containers - Breastfeeding Support Network

MOTHER'S MOUNTAIN - Condiments - Mother's Mountain

MOTHER'S NATURAL PRODUCTS - Fertilizers - New England Ecological Development, Inc.

MOTHERS OF INVENTION, THE - T-shirts–women's - Zappa Family Trust

MOTHERS OF MANY STYLES - Infant product - Penley & Associates Inc.

MOTHER'S OWN - Food products - Mother's Food Products Inc.

MOTHERS PRIDE - Food products ☆ - Shawnee Milling Co.

MOTHER'S PRIDE - Jewelry - Steve Ertle

MOTHER'S SLIDE - Jewelry - Plainville Stock Co.

MOTHER'S SPECIAL BLEND - Skin care products - Everybody Ltd.

MOTHER'S SPECIAL LOVE, A - Jewelry - Peter Brams Designs, Ltd.

MOTHERS TO BE LOVEPATS - Footwear - Americal Corp.

MOTHERS TOUCH - Cleaning preparations–household ☆ - Whitestone Products Inc.

MOTHER'S TOUCH - Infant product - Ameda/Egnell Corp.

MOTHLIGHT - Recording label - Jazz Composer's Orchestra Association Inc.

MOTHRA - Video production - Toho Co., Ltd.

MOTI-K PLUS - Laxatives - Caraco Pharmaceutical Laboratories Ltd.

MOTIF - Audio equipment - Conrad-Johnson

MOTIF - Clocks ☆ - General Time Corp. (Westclox/Seth Thomas Div.)

MOTIF - Decals and transfers ☆ - Webway, Inc.

MOTIF - Faucets - Sterling Plumbing Group Inc.

MOTIF - Frames–eyeglass ☆ - Universal/Univis Inc.

MOTIF - Puzzles ☆ - Milton Bradley Co.

MOTIFS OF MYTHOLOGY - Jewelry - Blue Star Design

MOTION - Apparel–women's - J.C. Penney Co., Inc.

MOTION - Belts - Waist Wear Ltd.

MOTION - Orthopedic products - Raymond P. Popp

MOTION - Screws - Motion Systems Corp.

MOTION BAND - Medical apparatus - D.L.H. Industries

MOTION COMMOTION - Jewelry - Karen Kreations, Inc.

MOTION CURE - Pharmaceutical preparations ☆ - Wisconsin Pharmacal Co. Inc.

MOTION DETECTOR, THE - Floodlights - Lights of America Inc.

MOTION DIALOGUE - Computer software - Pacific Scientific Co.

MOTION-ETTES - Novelty items - Telco Creations, Inc.

MOTION EXPRESS - Furniture - Cleveland Chair Co.

MOTION FLOW - Hardware - Niagara Conservation Corp.

MOTION LITES - Christmas tree lights ☆ - General Enterprises Inc.

MOTION MADNESS - Furniture - Klein International, Ltd.

MOTION MADNESS - Hair care products - Moore Beauty Inc.

MOTION MAKER - Photographic equipment - SP Systems/Saratons

MOTION MAKER - Toys - Bates, Inc.

MOTION MAX I - Computers - Baker Motion Control Systems Inc.

MOTION-MODULARS - Furniture - La-Z-Boy Chair Co.

MOTION NEON POWER DRIVE - Transformers–electric - Marshall Electric Corp.

MOTION ONLY - Furniture–upholstered - Woodmark Originals

MOTION PICTURE STUNT - Apparel - Motion Pictures Stunt Productions

MOTION SCOPE 500 - Cameras–video ☆ - Redlake Imaging Corp.

MOTION SILHOUETTES - Novelty items ☆ - Noma International, Inc.

MOTION SPIRIT - Apparel and accessories - Henry Doneger Associates Inc.

MOTION SPORTS - Trading cards and stamps - Motion Sports Inc.

MOTION-STOP - Health care products - Natural Laboratories Corp.

MOTION SWITCH - Electronic equipment - Diablo Technologies Inc.

MOTION TECHNOLOGY - Exercising equipment - Hammer Corp.

MOTION WORKS - Furniture–upholstered ☆ - Berkline Corp.

MOTIONCRAFT - Furniture - Sherrill Furniture Co.

MOTIONEX - Computers - Motionex, Inc.

MOTIONLINK - Computer software - Kollmorgen Corp.

MOTIONMATES - Furniture - Lane Co. Inc.

MOTIONPAK - Electronic equipment - Intertial Division of Systron Donner

MOTIONSCOPE - Video equipment - Redlake Imaging Corp.

MOTIONSCOPE PCI - Computer peripheral equipment - Redlake Imaging Corp.

MOTIONSCOPE S - Cameras–video - Redlake Imaging Corp.

MOTIONSTAR WIRELESS - Computer software - Ascension Technology Corp.

MOTIONVIEW - Computer software - Altair Computing Inc.

MOTIONVISION - Trading cards and stamps - Motionvision, Inc.

MOTIVATE! - Computer software - Benchmark Resources, Inc.

MOTIVATING UNMOTIVATED LEARNERS - Video production - Canter and Associates, Inc.

MOTIVATION - Apparel–women's ☆ - Russ Togs Inc.

MOTIVATION! - Catalogs - One Write Systems, Inc.

MOTIVATION - Floor coverings–carpet and rugs ☆ - Masland Corp.

MOTIVATION STATION - Display cases–metal - Successories, Inc.

MOTIVATOR - Footwear–athletic ☆ - Nike, Inc.

MOTIVATOR - Hardware - Verosol

MOTIVE GEAR - Motor vehicle parts and accessories - Midwest Truck and Auto Parts Inc.

MOTIVE GEAR PERFORMANCE - Automotive parts and accessories - Midwest Truck and Auto Parts Inc.

☆ = Now out of production

MOTIVE POWER - Computer software - Computer Assistance, Inc.
MOTIVE POWER, INC. - Railroad equipment - Motive Power, Inc.
MOTIVISION - Computer software - Motivision, Inc.
MOTO - Bicycles - Cannondale Corp.
MOTO-BOTS - Toy robot/vehicles - Intex Recreation Corp.
MOTO-CROSSED - Toys–automobiles - Mattel, Inc.
MOTO-FLEX - Tools–power-driven - Dremel
MOTO FOUR - Automotive parts and accessories - Moto Mirror, Inc.
MOTO GUZZI - Motorcycles - Benelli/Moto Guzzi North America
MOTO-HUT - Automotive parts and accessories - TMCI
MOTO JACKET - Motor vehicle parts and accessories - Ranco Industries, Inc.
MOTO MATE - Automotive parts and accessories - Creative Controls Inc.
MOTO MIRROR - Automotive parts and accessories - Moto Mirror, Inc.
MOTO-MONSTERS - Toys–electronic - Axlon Inc.
MOTO MORINI - Motorcycles - Herdan Corp.
MOTO PLUS - Automotive parts and accessories - Moto Mirror, Inc.
MOTO-SAFE - Motorcycle parts and accessories - Rally Racks (Division of GNI)
MOTO-SKI - Snowmobiles - Bombardier Corp.
MOTO TRIVIA - Games - Steve Fernandez
MOTOBECANE - Bicycles - Spratt Cycle Support, Inc.
MOTOBOARD - Skateboards - Motoboard International
MOTOBRELLA - Automotive parts and accessories - K-Tel International, Inc.
MOTOCROSS - Frames–eyeglass ☆ - Universal/Univis Inc.
MOTODRIVE - Engines - Reliance Electric Co.
MOTOFEN - Pharmaceutical preparations - Carnick Laboratories Inc.
MOTOGEAR - Drills–hand-operated - Warshawsky & Co.
MOTOMAN - Motoman, Inc.
MOTOMARINA - Trailers–travel - Marina Mobili Inc.
MOTOMASTER - Motorcycles - TSR Racing Products
MOTOMAX - Motoman, Inc.
MOTOMITT - Towels - Marilyn A. Englund
MOTOPOGO - Hobby kits - Rapco
MOTOQUAD - Motorcycles - Demetrios L. Christopoulos
MOTOR - Thread - Threads USA Div.
MOTOR BIKE BOY - Watches - Ankuo International, Corp.
MOTOR BOATING & SAILING - Publisher's imprints - Hearst Corp.
MOTOR CITY - Brushes–paint - Rol-Brush Manufacturing, Div. (Michigan Brush Mfg. Co., Inc.)
MOTOR CITY - Food products - Motor City Muffin
MOTOR CITY MELTDOWN - Toys - Tonka Corp.
MOTOR CROSS TRYKE - Toys - A.J. Renzi Plastic Corp.
MOTOR CUSHION - Automotive parts and accessories ☆ - Gabriel Ride Control Products Div.
MOTOR CYCLE TRAILERS - Trailers–truck - U.S. Cargo, Inc.
MOTOR FACTORY - Tools–hand-operated - Chrome Specialties, Inc.
MOTOR FLUSHER - Motors–outboard - Tempo Products Co.
MOTOR INN - Trailers–travel - Winnebago Industries, Inc.
MOTOR KING - Batteries - Bridgestone/Firestone, Inc.
MOTOR MAGNETS - Cleaning preparations - V.G. Industries
MOTOR MANIA - Toys–automobiles - Mattel, Inc.
MOTOR MASTER - Cleaning preparations - United Industries Corp.
MOTOR-MATION - Electronic equipment - Trebor Power Systems, Inc.
MOTOR-MEDIC - Automotive parts and accessories - Radiator Specialty Co.
MOTOR MOUTH - Fishing lures - Area Rule Engineering Inc.
MOTOR MOUTH - Games - Tiger Electronics, Inc.
MOTOR MUSCLE - Automotive parts and accessories - Loctite Corp.
MOTOR PLAY - Toys–automobiles - Mattel, Inc.
MOTOR SAILERS - Ships–sailing vessels - Lion Yachts
MOTOR SKILLS - Apparel and accessories - Bradley J. Ayres
MOTOR STANDS - Automotive parts and accessories - Video Manuals
MOTOR SYSTEMS - Generators–electric - United Technologies Motor Systems, Inc.
MOTOR TOON GRAND PRIX - Eyeglasses - Sony Interactive Entertainment Inc.
MOTOR VEHICLE REPORTS - Computer software - Trans Union/Dateq
MOTORASER - Erasers - Keuffel & Esser Co.
MOTORBAY - Tools–hand-operated - Motor Bay Co.
MOTORBOOKS INTERNATIONAL - Publisher's imprints - Motorbooks International
MOTORCADE - Advertising agencies - Rod Steele, Inc.
MOTORCALC - Calculators - Calculated Industries, Inc.
MOTORCEUTICALS - Motor vehicle parts and accessories - Pinnacle Resource Corp.
MOTORCLOTHES - Apparel and accessories - Harley-Davidson, Inc.
MOTORCRAFT - Motor vehicle parts and accessories - Ford Motor Co.

MOTORCYCLE TRYKE - Toys - A.J. Renzi Plastic Corp.
MOTORDYNE - Safety controllers - Condyne Technology Inc.
MOTOREZE - Oils–lubricating - Unocal Corp.
MOTORING MARTY - Toys - HTZ Investment Corp.
MOTORMAN MIKE - Toys - Mattel, Inc.
MOTORMANIA THE DRIVING FORCE - Toys–automobiles - Azrak-Hamway International, Inc.
MOTORMATIC - Cameras–microfilm - Eastman Kodak Co.
MOTOROCK - Video tapes–blank - Pace Motor Sports - SRO
MOTOROLA - Communications equipment–mobile - Motorola, Inc. (Land Mobile Products Sector)
MOTOROLA - Semiconductors - ARS Electronics
MOTORS - Cups–paper - Nyman Manufacturing Co.
MOTORSPORT SVO - Toilets–portable - Ford Motor Co.
MOTORSPORT TRADITIONS - Apparel and accessories - Motorsport Traditions L.P.
MOTORTRAC - Trailers–truck ☆ - Wells Cargo Inc.
MOTORTRON - Fuses ☆ - Cooper Industries, Inc.
MOTORVAC 3 - Fuel additives - Motorvac Corp.
MOTORVATION - Toys–stuffed - Gund, Inc.
MOTORVATOR - Cleaning preparations - Kmart Properties, Inc.
MOTORVATOR - Toys–automobiles - Mattel, Inc.
MOTORWERKS OF ART - Automotive wax, apparel - Motorwerks of Art Inc.
MOTORX - Bicycles ☆ - Hunt-Wilde Corp.
MOTORYACHT - Boats–motor - Bayliner Marine Corp.
MOTOTILT - Boats–motor ☆ - Spandeck
MOTOTUNER - Cleaning preparations ☆ - Dacar Chemical Co.
MOTOWN - Recording label - Motown Record Co. L.P.
MOTRIN - Pharmaceutical preparations - Upjohn Co.
MOTRIN IB - Pharmaceutical preparations - Upjohn Co.
MOTSENBOCKER'S LIFT OFF - Cleaning preparations - Loctite Corp.
MOTT - Lawn mowers - Alamo Industrial
MOTTAHEDEH DESIGNS - Ornamental products–glass - Mottahedeh and Co.
MOTTO - Fencing–steel - Bekaert Corp. (Wire & Wire Products Div.)
MOTTO - Greeting cards - Gibson Greetings, Inc.
MOTT'S - Food products - Conagra, Inc.
MOTT'S - Food products - Mott's Inc.
MOTT'S - Iced tea–bottled or canned - Cadbury Beverages Inc.
MOTT'S A.M. - Juices - Mott's Inc.
MOTT'S FIGURE CONTROL - Food products ☆ - Mott's Inc.
MOTT'S IN-A-MINUTE - Juices - Mott's Inc.
MOTT'S P.M. - Juices - Mott's Inc.
MOUJAN - Skin care products - Coronet International
MOUJAN 2000 - Depilatories - T.R. International
MOULDING PEOPLE, THE - Frames–picture - Robert F. De Castro, Inc.
MOULET - Cigarette paper - Gesty Trading & Manufacturing Corp.
MOULI - Meat grinders - Mouli Manufacturing Corp.
MOULIN - Cheese ☆ - Swissrose International Inc.
MOULIN - Watches - Nelson Industries
MOULIN-AIR - Kitchen appliances ☆ - Regal Ware, Inc.
MOULIN DE LA BIDIERE - Wines ☆ - Alimar & Cie. Inc.
MOULIN DES CARRUADES - Wines - Seagram's Chateau & Estate Wines Co.
MOULIN DU GUE - Paper - Canson-Talens Inc.
MOULIN DU PERIGOURD - Food products - Europa Foods Ltd.
MOULIN GREEN PEPPERCORNS - Fruits and vegetables - Europa Foods Ltd.
MOULIN ROUGE - Dishes–china - Taylor, Smith & Taylor Co.
MOULIN ROUGE - Food products - Connell Co.
MOULIN TOUCHAIS - Beverages–alcohol - Rolar Imports Ltd.
MOULINS DE LA BRAGUE - Oils–edible - De Medici Imports Ltd.
MOUNDS - Candy bars - Peter Paul
MOUNT - See also **MT.**
MT. - See also **MOUNT**
MOUNT - Recording label - Outlet Records
MOUNT AIRE - Building materials–concrete - Strevell-Paterson Co.
MOUNT-ALL - Music stands - LP Music Group
MOUNT-ALL - Musical instrument accessories - Latin Percussion Inc.
MT. ANGEL - Health care products - Comfrey International Co.
MT. BAKER - Fruits and vegetables - Western Farmers Association
MT. BAKER BOND - Paper–bond - Union Printing Co.
MOUNT BAKER VINEYARDS - Wines - Mt. Baker Vineyards
MT. BLANC - Floor coverings–carpet and rugs - Rugby Rugs Inc.
MT. BLAZE - Bicycles - Huffy Corp.
MT. BRANSON - Apparel and accessories - Westpac Products Co. Inc.
MT. CHOCOLATE - Candy - Tom's Foods Inc.
MT. CLEMENS - Dinnerware–glass - Mt. Clemens Pottery Co.
MT. DORA - Brushes - Corona Brushes Inc.

☆ = Now out of production

MT. DURA - Footwear - Iron Age Corp.
MOUNT EDEN VINEYARDS - Wines - Mt. Eden Vineyards
MT. EVEREST - Beverages—malt - Hudepohl-Schoenling Brewing Co.
MT. EVEREST MALT LIQUOR - Beer - Schoenling Brewing Co.
MT. EVERWHITE BRAND - Vitamins and nutritional supplements - Sun Ming Hong (USA) Inc.
MOUNT-EZE - Jewelry - Carrie Adell
MT. FUJI - Food products - Treasure Isle Inc.
MT. FUJI - Mustard - Westbrae Natural Foods, Inc.
MOUNT GAY - Beverages—alcohol - Sunbelt Beverage Corp.
MOUNT GAY ECLIPSE - Beverages—alcohol - Sunbelt Beverage Corp.
MOUNT GAY SPECIAL RESERVE - Beverages—alcohol - Sunbelt Beverage Corp.
MOUNT GREY - Honey ☆ - Castle Food Products
MOUNT HAGEN - Coffee - InterNatural Foods
MT. HARLAN - Wines - Calera Wine Co.
MT. HOOD - Beer - Portland Brewing Co.
MT. HOOD - Food products - Duckwall-Pooley Fruit Co.
MT. HOOD - Wood products - Georgia-Pacific Corp.
MT. HOOD MEADOWS - Apparel and accessories - Mt. Hood Meadows, Oreg., Ltd.
MOUNT HOPE - Wines - Mt. Hope Estate & Winery
MOUNT HOPE CLOTHING CO. - Apparel—athletic - Weekend Warrior, Inc.
MT. HOUSE - Food products ☆ - Futurity Products
MT. JACKSON - Apple product - Bowman Apple Products Co. Inc.
MT. JEFFERSON - Food products ☆ - Agripac, Inc.
MT. KILAMANJARO - Cereal - Glico Harmony Foods Corp.
MT. KONOCTI - Fruits and vegetables - Mount Konocti Growers Inc.
MT. LAUREL - Mushrooms - Mt. Laurel Canning Corp.
MT. MADONNA - Food products - Mt. Madonna Natural Juices
MT. MADONNA - Wines - Emilio Guglielmo Winery
MOUNT MADRONA - Wines - Blair Importers Ltd.
MOUNT MASTER - Fixtures - Mid-America Building Products Corp.
MT. MAURICE - Vegetables—canned ☆ - Dean Foods Co.
MOUNT MAYA - Coffee - Mount Maya, Inc.
MT. MESA - Food products - Whitehouse-Skyland Apple Products
MT. MIST - Vegetables—frozen ☆ - Grimmway Frozen Foods
MT. OLIVE - Pickles - Mount Olive Pickle Co., Inc.
MT. OLIVE COCKTAIL MIDGETS - Pickles ☆ - Mount Olive Pickle Co., Inc.
MT. OLYMPUS - Food products - Stache Foods
MOUNT OLYMPUS - Water—distilled - Mt. Olympus Waters Inc.
MT. PALOMAR - Toys - Brumberger Co. Inc.
MOUNT PALOMAR - Wines - Mount Palomar Winery Inc.
MT. PARK - Food products - Acme Poultry Co.
MT. PEARL - Canned mushrooms - L.K. Bowman & Co. Inc.
MT. PLEASANT - Coffee - Try Coffee Group Ltd.
MT. PLEASANT - Shirts ☆ - Horace Small Apparel Co.
MOUNT PLEASANT - Wines - Mt. Pleasant Vineyards
MOUNT PLEASANT WINERY - Wines ☆ - Parliament Import Co.
MT. ROCK - Apparel—men's ☆ - Michaels/Stern & Co. Inc.
MOUNT ROGERS - Furniture ☆ - Virginia House Furniture Corp.
MOUNT ROSE - Food products - King George Packing Co. Inc.
MOUNT ROSE - Pickels and peppers - Millner Trading Co. Inc.
MT. ROUGHCUT - Cigars - M. Marsh & Son
MOUNT ST. CLARE VINEYARDS - Wines - Channing Rudd Cellars
MT. ST. HELENS - Trees - J. Frank Schmidt & Son Co.
MOUNT SHASTA - Wood products - National Bark Sales
MT. SNOW - Bicycles - Ross Bicycles USA, Ltd.
MOUNT SNOW - Fabrics ☆ - Rosebar Textile Co.
MOUNT SORREL - Floor coverings ☆ - Congoleum Corp.
MOUNT STIRLING - Food products - Pocahontas Foods USA Inc.
MT. STIRLING - Food products - J.W. Wood
MT. TAM PALE ALE - Beverages—malt - Marin Brewing Co., Inc.
MOUNT TWISTER - Toys—automobiles - Mattel, Inc.
MT. VEEDER - Wines - Mount Veeder Winery
MOUNT VEEDER WINERY - Wines - Franciscan Vineyards, Inc.
MOUNT VERNON - Apparel stores—sports - Gillman Knitwear Co.
MT. VERNON - Cabinets - Riviera Cabinets Inc.
MT. VERNON - Cabinets - Wellborn Cabinet, Inc.
MT. VERNON - Cabinets - Yorktowne Inc.
MOUNT VERNON - Cabinets—wood - Parcraft Distinctive Cabinetry
MT. VERNON - Fencing—wood - Machalk Enterprises Inc.
MT. VERNON - Floor coverings ☆ - Bruce Hardwood Floors
MT. VERNON - Floor coverings ☆ - Teak International
MOUNT VERNON - Floor coverings—carpet and rugs - Colonial Mills Inc.
MOUNT VERNON - Furniture ☆ - Bassett Furniture Industries, Inc.

MOUNT VERNON - Paints ☆ - North Jersey Paint Co. Inc.
MOUNT VERNON - Paneling - Georgia-Pacific Corp.
MT. VERNON - Tableware—china - Lenox, Inc.
MOUNT VERNON - Towels - Stevens Linen Associates Inc.
MOUNT VERNON - Whiskey - Jim Beam Brands Co.
MT. VERNON - Windows—storm - Duo-Temp
MT. VERNON BRICK - Floor coverings ☆ - Azrock Commercial Flooring
MT. VERNON CHERRY SQUARE - Cabinets - Wellborn Cabinet, Inc.
MOUNT VERNON COLLECTION - Furniture - Tomlinson of High Point Inc.
MOUNT VERNON COLLECTION, THE - Furniture - Hickory Chair Co.
MOUNT VERNON LITE - Chimes ☆ - Nutone Inc.
MOUNT VIEW - Wines - Obester Winery
MOUNT WHITNEY - Food products - Lindsay International
MOUNTAIN - Breads - Cedar's Mediterranean Foods, Inc.
MOUNTAIN - Candles - Smoky Mountain Products
MOUNTAIN - Candy - Brown & Haley
MOUNTAIN - Computer software - Mountain Network Solutions Inc.
MOUNTAIN - Fabrics - Vertilux-Louverlux Inc.
MOUNTAIN - Guitars - Music Imports Ltd.
MOUNTAIN - Recording label - Heritage Records
MOUNTAIN - Shoes ☆ - Atsco Footwear Inc.
MOUNTAIN - Sporting goods ☆ - Powell Skateboards
MOUNTAIN - Tents ☆ - Coleman Co., Inc.
MOUNTAIN - Water—bottled or canned - Wissahickon Spring Water Inc.
MOUNTAIN AIR - Cleaning preparations - Linden Corp.
MOUNTAIN AIR - Deodorizers - Natural Products Corp.
MOUNTAIN AIR - Heating equipment - Best Dressed Homes
MOUNTAIN AIR - Perfumes - R.T. French Co.
MOUNTAIN AIRE - Trailers—travel - Newmar Corp.
MOUNTAIN APPLE, THE - Recording label - Music of Polynesia Inc.
MOUNTAIN BAGGING INC. - Lubricants - Mountain Bagging, Inc.
MOUNTAIN BAR - Candy - Brown & Haley
MOUNTAIN BEAUTY - Tomato pastes and sauces ☆ - Progresso Quality Foods
MOUNTAIN BERRY - Skin care products - Del Pharmaceuticals, Inc.
MOUNTAIN BETTY - Wines - Pliska Winery
MOUNTAIN BLAST - Bicycles ☆ - Huffy Corp.
MOUNTAIN BLEND - Coffee - Nestle Beverage Co.
MOUNTAIN BOUQUET - Air freshener - Dial Corp.
MOUNTAIN BREEZE - Mouthwashes - Dial Corp.
MOUNTAIN BROOK - Food products - Mountain Brook Orchards Inc.
MOUNTAIN BROWNIES - Bakery products - Our Name is Mud, Inc.
MOUNTAIN BUSTER - Bicycles ☆ - Montgomery Ward & Co. Inc.
MOUNTAIN CASTLE - Wines - Safeway Stores Inc.
MOUNTAIN CAT - Pet products - Mountain Cat Inc.
MOUNTAIN CEMENT COMPANY - Cement - Centex Corp.
MOUNTAIN CHEDDAR - Cheese - Northfield Foods Inc.
MOUNTAIN CHEW - Chewing gum - Philadelphia Chewing Gum Corp.
MOUNTAIN CHOICE - Coffee ☆ - Van Cortlandt Coffee Corp.
MOUNTAIN CITY - Apparel and accessories - Empire Manufacturing Co.
MOUNTAIN CLEAR - Water—bottled or canned - Mountain Clear Water Systems Inc.
MOUNTAIN COLLECTION - Coffee - Hawaiian Kona Coffee Co., Ltd.
MOUNTAIN COMPUTER MUSIC SYSTEM - Computer software - Mountain Network Solutions Inc.
MOUNTAIN COUNTRY - Coffee - Coffee Express Co.
MOUNTAIN COUNTRY - Footwear - Melville Corp.
MOUNTAIN COUNTRY CELLARS - Wines - East-West Distributing Co.
MOUNTAIN COVE - Fruits and vegetables - Mountain Cove Orchards Inc.
MOUNTAIN COVE VINEYARDS - Wines - La Abra Farm & Winery Inc.
MOUNTAIN CRAFTS - Floor coverings—carpet and rugs - Mountain Craft Carpets Inc.
MOUNTAIN CREST - Floor coverings—carpet and rugs - Galaxy Carpet Mills Inc.
MOUNTAIN CREST - Ships—patrol boats ☆ - Kinco International Inc.
MOUNTAIN DEW - Beverages—carbonated - Pepsi-Cola Co.
MOUNTAIN DEW - Cigars - Jacobs Cigar Co.
MOUNTAIN DEW - Recording label ☆ - Peter Pan Industries
MOUNTAIN DEW - Toys—electronic - Bird Bromiticous Inc.
MOUNTAIN DEW SPORT - Beverages—carbonated - Pepsi-Cola Co.
MOUNTAIN DOGS - Shirts - Sonja Pedersen
MOUNTAIN EAGLE RIFLE - Rifles - Magnum Research, Inc.
MOUNTAIN EDGE - Fruits and vegetables - Yakima Fruit & Cold Storage Co.
MOUNTAIN ELSIE - Wines - Pliska Winery
MOUNTAIN EXPRESS - Sweaters - Specialty Department Stores, Inc.
MOUNTAIN FARM - Pastries - Flowers Family Bakeries, Inc.

☆ = Now out of production

MOUNTAIN FEVER QUALITY GEAR CO. - Apparel and accessories - Mountain Fever Inc.
MOUNTAIN FORCE - Bicycles - Lawee Inc.
MOUNTAIN FRESH - Deodorizers - Surco Products Inc.
MOUNTAIN FRESH - Food products - Mountainfresh Foods Co.
MOUNTAIN FRESH - Fruits–frozen - Watermill Foods, Inc.
MOUNTAIN FRESH - Pet products - L/M Animal Farms, Inc.
MOUNTAIN FRESH - Soap - Dial Corp.
MOUNTAIN FRESH - Water–bottled or canned - Culligan International Co.
MOUNTAIN FRESH AIR - Deodorizers - Surco Products Inc.
MOUNTAIN FURY - Bicycles - Huffy Corp.
MOUNTAIN FUZZ - Sporting goods - Kellwood Co.
MOUNTAIN GOAT - Bicycles - Mountain Goat Cycles
MOUNTAIN GOAT - Sleeping bags - Authentic Fitness Corp.
MOUNTAIN GOAT EDGE-TECH - Apparel and accessories - Authentic Fitness Corp.
MOUNTAIN GOLD - Honey - E.F. Lane & Son
MOUNTAIN GRANNY - Wines - Pliska Winery
MOUNTAIN GREEN MUSIC (BMI) - Publisher's imprints - SCP Records
MOUNTAIN GROWN - Apparel and accessories ☆ - Kellwood Co.
MOUNTAIN GROWN - Coffee - Folger Coffee Co.
MOUNTAIN-GROWN FANCY CEYLON - Teas - Grace Tea Co. Ltd.
MOUNTAIN GUN - Firearms, accessories, and parts - Smith & Wesson Corp.
MOUNTAIN HARD WEAR - Sleeping bags - Mountain Hardwear, Inc.
MOUNTAIN HARVEST - Skin care products - L. Perrigo Co.
MOUNTAIN HAWKS - Sporting goods - Lehigh University
MOUNTAIN HERBERY - Hair care products ☆ - Carme Inc.
MOUNTAIN HERITAGE - Fruits and vegetables ☆ - Ranson Fruit Co. Inc.
MOUNTAIN HIGH - Yogurt - Borden, Inc.
MOUNTAIN HIGH - Yogurt - Mountain High Yoghurt
MOUNTAIN HIGH HOSIERY LTD. - Socks - Mountain High Hosiery Ltd.
MOUNTAIN HIGH KNITTING INC. - Apparel and accessories - Mountain High Knitting Inc.
MOUNTAIN HIGH MAPS - Computer software ☆ - Digital Wisdom, Inc.
MOUNTAIN HOLLER - Beverages–carbonated - Moran Foods, Inc.
MOUNTAIN HOME - Juices - Seneca Foods Corp.
MOUNTAIN HOUSE - Food products - Oregon Freeze Dry Inc.
MOUNTAIN HOUSE - Furniture - Mountain House
MOUNTAIN IMAGES - Blinds–vertical - Tontine/VyTech Industries Inc.
MOUNTAIN IMAGES - Computer software - MPC Computing, Inc.
MOUNTAIN IMPACT - Backpacks - C.O.R.P. Inc.
MOUNTAIN JEWELS - Pet products - Colorado Aggregate Co. of New Mexico
MOUNTAIN JUNIPER - Perfumes - Dana Perfumes Corp.
MOUNTAIN KING - Trees–artificial - Papercraft Corp.
MOUNTAIN KING EXPRESS - Toys–trains - Diversified Specialists, Inc.
MOUNTAIN KLEIN - Bicycles - Klein Bicycle Corp.
MOUNTAIN LAKE - Butter - Mountain Lake Creamery, Inc.
MOUNTAIN LAKE - Computer software - Mountain Lake Software, Inc.
MOUNTAIN LEAF - Tobacco products - Lane Ltd.
MOUNTAIN LEASH - Pet products - Aspen Pet Products
MOUNTAIN LION - Fruits and vegetables - United Fruit Growers
MOUNTAIN LODGE - Syrup - Gem Inc.
MOUNTAIN LODGE - Tents - Coleman Co., Inc.
MOUNTAIN MAGIC - Bicycles - Hunt-Wilde Corp.
MOUNTAIN MAID - Meat products–poultry ☆ - Wampler Foods Inc.
MOUNTAIN MAIL - Computer software - Westech Corp.
MOUNTAIN MAMA - Wines - Pliska Winery
MOUNTAIN MAMA'S - Food products - Pierce Foods Corp.
MOUNTAIN MAN - Biscuits - Campbell Taggart Inc.
MOUNTAIN MAN - Heaters–space - Chippewa Traders Ltd.
MOUNTAIN MAN BOWIE - Knives ☆ - Tru-Balance Knife Co.
MOUNTAIN MASTER - Toys - Tonka Corp.
MOUNTAIN MEADOW - Deodorizers - S.C. Johnson & Son, Inc.
MOUNTAIN MEADOW - Skin care products - J. Gaunt Woodman Co.
MOUNTAIN MEADOWS - Pet products - Mountain Meadows Pet Products, Inc.
MOUNTAIN MEADOWS - Vegetables–frozen - Smith Frozen Foods Inc.
MOUNTAIN MEADOWS COUNTRY SPRINGS - Beverages - Logret Import & Export Co.
MOUNTAIN MIST - Fibers–synthetic - Stearns Technical Textiles Co.
MOUNTAIN MIST - Food products - Symons Frozen Foods Inc.
MOUNTAIN MIST - Wines ☆ - Karly Wines
MOUNTAIN MIST GOLD - Fabrics - Stearns Technical Textiles Co.
MOUNTAIN MOISTURIZING - Skin care products ☆ - Aloe Laboratories, Inc.
MOUNTAIN MUD - Bakery products - Our Name is Mud, Inc.
MOUNTAIN MUFFINS - Bakery products - Our Name is Mud, Inc.
MOUNTAIN MUNCHIE - Cookies - Boulder Brownie Co.

MOUNTAIN NUGGETS - Meat products–beef - Curtice-Burns Meat Snacks Inc.
MOUNTAIN ORCHARD - Fruits and vegetables - Mountain Orchard Cooperative Inc.
MOUNTAIN PAINT - Paints - Mountain Industries, Inc.
MOUNTAIN PANCAKES - Pancakes–mixes - ICS Corp.
MOUNTAIN PARK - Water–bottled or canned - Water House
MOUNTAIN PASS - Food products ☆ - Pet Inc.
MOUNTAIN PEAK - Bicycles - Columbia Manufacturing Inc.
MOUNTAIN PEAKS - Tiles–ceramic ☆ - American Marazzi Tile, Inc.
MOUNTAIN PERFORMANCE - Bicycles - Raleigh USA Bicycle Co.
MOUNTAIN PINE - Deodorizers - Medo Industries, Inc.
MOUNTAIN PINE - Siding - Temple-Inland Forest Products Corp.
MOUNTAIN PRODUCTS - Apparel stores–sports - Mountain Products Corp.
MOUNTAIN PRODUCTS - Apparel–athletic ☆ - Sportcaster Co. Inc.
MOUNTAIN RAILROAD - Recording label - Chameleon Music Group Inc.
MOUNTAIN RAINFALL - Deodorizers - Church and Dwight Co. Inc.
MOUNTAIN RIDGE - Bags–duffel - Mitzi International Handbags & Accessories Ltd.
MOUNTAIN ROASTED LAKE TAHOE - Coffee - Alpen Sierra Coffee Co.
MOUNTAIN ROSE - Dinnerware–glass - Nikko Ceramics Inc.
MOUNTAIN SCOUT - Bicycles - Raleigh USA Bicycle Co.
MOUNTAIN SHADES - Sunglasses - Mountain Shades Distributing Co.
MOUNTAIN SHADES VAIL, CO. - Sunglasses - Mountain Shades Distributing Co.
MOUNTAIN SHADOWS - Floor coverings–carpet and rugs ☆ - Lowe's Carpet Corp.
MOUNTAIN SHINE INTERNATUIONAL - Coffee - Mountain Shine Intl. Corp.
MOUNTAIN SIPPER - Beverages–alcohol - Jack Daniel's Distillery
MOUNTAIN SPLASH SPRING WATER - Water–bottled or canned - Mountain Splash Spring Water Co., Inc.
MOUNTAIN SPORT - Bicycles - Raleigh USA Bicycle Co.
MOUNTAIN SPRING - Bedding–linen - Dan River Inc.
MOUNTAIN SPRING DAWN - Detergents - Procter & Gamble Co.
MOUNTAIN SPRING SPARKLER - Water–bottled or canned - Crystal Geyser Water Co.
MOUNTAIN SPRING ULTRA DOWNY - Fabric softeners - Procter & Gamble Co.
MOUNTAIN SPRINGS SPAS - Hot tubs–fiberglass - Omega II, Inc.
MOUNTAIN SPRUCE - Deodorizers - Scarborough and Co. Inc.
MOUNTAIN STATE GOLDEN ROAST - Coffee - Rhoads Holdings, Ltd.
MOUNTAIN STATES - Pickles - Morgan Pickle Co.
MOUNTAIN STRAWBERRY - Beverages–alcohol - Jim Beam Brands Co.
MOUNTAIN SUN - Juices - Mountain Sun Juices
MOUNTAIN SUN NATURAL - Juices - Apple Hill Orchards Juice Co.
MOUNTAIN SURF - Waterproof outerwear - Mountain Surf, Inc.
MOUNTAIN TECHNIUM - Bicycles ☆ - Raleigh USA Bicycle Co.
MOUNTAIN TIMBERS - Furniture - Stanley Furniture Co. Inc.
MOUNTAIN TIMES, THE - Publisher's imprints - Sundown Times, Inc.
MOUNTAIN TOP - Food products - Sam Investments, Inc.
MOUNTAIN TOP - Food products - United Apple Sales Inc.
MOUNTAIN TOP - Pies–frozen - Quality Bakery Co.
MOUNTAIN TOTS HIDEAWAY - Toys–models ☆ - Kenner Products
MOUNTAIN TOUR - Bicycles - Raleigh USA Bicycle Co.
MOUNTAIN TRAIL - Footwear - Washington Shoe Co.
MOUNTAIN TRAILS - Bicycles ☆ - Raleigh USA Bicycle Co.
MOUNTAIN TRAILS - Coats - Karman Western Apparel
MOUNTAIN TREAM - Water purification systems - Conklin Co., Inc.
MOUNTAIN TRIKE BIKE - Bicycles - Fisher-Price, Inc.
MOUNTAIN TROUT - Seafood products–fresh or frozen - Virginia Trout Co. Inc.
MOUNTAIN VALLEY - Cheese - Washington Farms Distribution Inc.
MOUNTAIN VALLEY - Water–bottled or canned - Mountain Valley Spring Co.
MOUNTAIN VALLEY FARMS - Food products - Quail International, Inc.
MOUNTAIN VIEW - Dinnerware–glass - Lenox, Inc.
MOUNTAIN VIEW - Floor coverings–carpet and rugs ☆ - American Excelsior Co.
MOUNTAIN VIEW - Fruits and vegetables - Valley Sweet
MOUNTAIN VIEW - Furniture ☆ - Bassett Furniture Industries, Inc.
MOUNTAIN VIEW - Trailers–travel - Skyline Corp.
MOUNTAIN VIEW - Water–bottled or canned - Columbian Coffee Service, Inc.
MOUNTAIN VIEW - Windows - Allied Building Products Corp.
MOUNTAIN VIEW - Wines - Kevin A. Shannon
MOUNTAIN VIEW DARJEELING - Teas–herbal - M.I.M.T. Corp. of USA
MOUNTAIN VIPER - Sporting goods - Rossignol Ski Co., Inc.
MOUNTAIN WARRIOR - Apparel–athletic - Rodeo Tee's, Inc.

☆ = Now out of production

MOUNTAIN WAY - Floor coverings–carpet and rugs ☆ - Hollytex Carpet Mills Inc.

MOUNTAIN WHEAT - Beverages–alcohol - Breckenridge Brewery, Inc.

MOUNTAIN WHEEL - Sporting goods - Joe A. Bott

MOUNTAIN WOOL - Apparel–children's - Goodman Knitting Co. Inc.

MOUNTAIN ZONE - Leather goods - Chateau International, Inc.

MOUNTAINEER - Archery equipment - Martin Archery Inc.

MOUNTAINEER - Bicycles - Columbia Manufacturing Inc.

MOUNTAINEER - Cigars - M. Marsh & Son

MOUNTAINEER - Cooking equipment–household ☆ - Mirro Corp.

MOUNTAINEER - Firearms, accessories, and parts - Welsh Sporting Goods Corp. (Boyt Div.)

MOUNTAINEER - Fruit - Consolidated Orchard Co.

MOUNTAINEER - Fruits and vegetables - Summit Point Raceway

MOUNTAINEER - Knives - Precise International/Wenger

MOUNTAINEER - Motor vehicles - Ford Motor Co.

MOUNTAINEER - Motor vehicles–automobiles - Ford Motor Co. (Lincoln-Mercury Div.)

MOUNTAINEER - Outdoor furniture - Iron Mountain Forge Corp.

MOUNTAINEER - Tents - Coleman Co., Inc.

MOUNTAINEER - Toys - Hedstrom Corp.

MOUNTAINEER - Trailers–travel - Clay Camper Co. Inc.

MOUNTAINEER - Watches - Bulova Corp.

MOUNTAINEER-RAK - Bicycles - Graber Products, Inc.

MOUNTAINEER RUSTIC - Wood products - Three Mountaineers Inc.

MOUNTAINS IN MINUTES - Toys–models - Isle Laboratories Inc.

MOUNTAINSIDE FARMS - Milk - Mountainside Farms Inc.

MOUNTAINSIDE VINEYARD - Wines - Peaceful Bend Vineyard

MOUNTAINSMITH - Apparel and accessories - Aspen Leaf Inc.

MOUNTAINVIEW - Computer software - Accugraph Corp.

MOUNTAINWARE - Dinnerware–glass - Mt. Clemens Pottery Co.

MOUNTAINWOOD - Water–bottled or canned - Mountainwood Spring Water

MOUNTAIRE - Bicycles - Columbia Manufacturing Inc.

MOUNTANOS BROS. - Coffee - Mountanos Brothers Coffee Co., Inc.

MOUNTBATTEN - Dinnerware–glass - Royal China & Porcelain Companies Inc.

MOUNTBATTEN - Tobacco products - Lane Ltd.

MOUNTCOR - Artists' materials - Gilman Brothers Co.

MOUNTIAN RHINE - Wines - Arizona Vineyards

MOUNTIE - Paper - Potlatch Corp.

MOUNTIE - Rifles - Marlin Firearms Co.

MOUNTING MEMORIES - Adhesives and sealants - Beacon Chemical Co. Inc.

MOUNTMATE - Hanging brackets - Timothy J. Harrington

MOUNTROSE - Food products - Mountrose Ravioli & Macaroni Co.

MOUNTY - Lighting fixtures - Big Beam Emergency Systems Inc.

MOUQUIN - Brandy - Austin, Nichols & Co., Inc.

MOURNE - Floor coverings–carpet and rugs ☆ - Navan Carpets Inc.

MOURNE - Glassware–household - Waterford Wedgwood USA, Inc.

MOUSE - Amplifiers–musical instrument - Lectrosonics Inc.

MOUSE! - Computer peripheral equipment - Mouse Systems Corp.

MOUSE & BEAR ORIGINALS - Apparel–children's - Patrice Dean Anibal

MOUSE ARMOR - Decals and transfers - Software Toolworks, Inc.

MOUSE-B-GON - Rodenticides ☆ - Chevron Chemical Co.

MOUSE CREATIONS - Hobby kits - Green Apple

MOUSE DEPOT - Figurines - Robert W. Fornal, Sr.

MOUSE DIE-NER - Pesticides–household - Security Products Co.

MOUSE GUARD - Household traps - Howard Berger Co., Inc.

MOUSE HOUSE - Computer mouse holders ☆ - Pelikan, Inc.

MOUSE II - Computer peripheral equipment - Apple Computer Inc.

MOUSE-L-TOE - Giftware ☆ - Enesco Corp.

MOUSE-L-TOV - Porcelain figurines - Marjorie Sarnat & Associates, Inc.

MOUSE MANAGER - Computer peripheral equipment - Interactive Products Corp.

MOUSE MANIA - Pet products - Mason Distributing

MOUSE MASTER - Computer peripheral equipment - ACCO USA, Inc.

MOUSE MASTER - Computer peripheral equipment - Acco World Corp.

MOUSE/MOUSE PAD, THE - Computer peripheral equipment - Pasadena Computergraphic Imaging

MOUSE MOVER - Computer peripheral equipment - Magnum Software Corp.

MOUSE-'N-A-HOUSE - Toys–stuffed ☆ - Bradley Import Co.

MOUSE-NIP - Rodenticides - Roccorp, Inc.

MOUSE-NO-MORE - Traps–animal - Control Pak Inc.

MOUSE NOTES-N-PAD - Paper–writing - G. Gary Holt Enterprises, Inc.

MOUSE-NOTS - Rodenticides - Nott Manufacturing Co. Inc.

MOUSE-O-LEUM - Floor coverings–carpet and rugs ☆ - Custom Tapes, Inc.

MOUSE ON A COIL - Pet products - P.M. Pet Products

MOUSE-OUT - Rodenticides ☆ - LiphaTech Inc.

MOUSE-RID - Rodenticides ☆ - Mackwin Co.

MOUSE SHADOW - Wrist support device - Shadowtech International, Inc.

MOUSE SKINS - Computer peripheral equipment - SiSoft Inc.

MOUSE STAMPEDE - Computer software - Mark of the Unicorn Inc.

MOUSE STATION - Computer peripheral equipment - CP Research

MOUSE SYSTEMS - Computer peripheral equipment - Mouse Systems Corp.

MOUSE TAMER - Computer peripheral equipment - American Business Concepts, Inc.

MOUSE, THE - Computer peripheral equipment - Pasadena Computergraphic Imaging

MOUSE TUNNEL - Traps–animal - Atlantic Paste & Glue Co., Inc.

MOUSE WASH - Cleaning preparations - Peter Bregman

MOUSEAL - Anchors - Securtech Co.

MOUSEBAR - Computer peripheral equipment - James Baranowski

MOUSEHOLE COLLECTION, THE - Figurines - Mousehole Collection, Inc.

MOUSEKETOYS - Toys–stuffed - Walt Disney Co.

MOUSELOK - Locks–padlocks - Securtech Co.

MOUSEMEM - Computer software - Mitsubishi Electronics America, Inc.

MOUSEMETER - Computer software - Technology Management Group, Inc.

MOUSEPAINT - Computer software - Apple Computer Inc.

MOUSER - Electronic equipment - Mouser Electronics

MOUSER VINTAGE - Cabinets - Mouser Kitchens Inc.

MOUSER WOODBRIDGE - Cabinets - Mouser Kitchens Inc.

MOUSERS - Cat food - Ralston Purina Co.

MOUSERS - Computer peripheral equipment - Portal Publications, Ltd.

MOUSETOP - Novelty items - Time's Up, Inc.

MOUSETOWN USA COLLECTION BY DOLLY TINGLE - Figurines ☆ - Reco International Corp.

MOUSETRAP - Games - Milton Bradley Co.

MOUSETRAP HOTEL - Games ☆ - Milton Bradley Co.

MOUSEWASH - Cleaning preparations - Peter Bregman

MOUSEWAY - Computer peripheral equipment ☆ - Kensington

MOUSEWRITE - Computer software - Roger Wagner Publishing Inc.

MOUSEY - Toys–stuffed ☆ - Dakin Inc.

MOUSIE - Sporting goods - Weber Industries Inc.

MOUSOLEUM - Housewares - Joseph N. Giglietti

MOUSQUETAIRE - Sporting goods ☆ - Babolat

MOUSSE A LA MASQUE - Skin care products - Revlon Consumer Products Corp.

MOUSSE A RASER EXTRAORDINAIRE - Shaving preparations - Lancome

MOUSSE AU CHOCOLAT IN THE ROUND - Food products ☆ - Just Desserts Inc.

MOUSSE CAFE - Lipsticks - Cosmair Inc.

MOUSSE COIFFANTE - Hair care products - Booth Hair-care products

MOUSSE DI SANTO - Hair care products - Waverly Beauty Products

MOUSSE IT&LY - Hair care products - IT&LY Hairfashion NA Inc.

MOUSSE KA-POP - Food products - Mother Mousse, Ltd.

MOUSSETTE - Hair care products - Matrix Essentials, Inc.

MOUSSIE - Cakes - Presto Food Products, Inc.

MOUSSY - Beverages–malt - Adolph Coors Co.

MOUSTACHE WASH - Apparel and accessories - Marble Sportswear, Inc.

MOUSTE - Hair care products - Paje Products

MOUSTRIMONY - Toys–stuffed ☆ - Dakin Inc.

MOUTH BOMBS - Candy - Uniconfis Corp.

MOUTH CARE - Mouthwashes - Pharmac Laboratories

MOUTH EXPLOSION - Candy - Squire Boone Caverns, Inc.

MOUTH FRIENDLY - Toothpaste - Squigle, Inc.

MOUTH FULL - Candy ☆ - Donruss Co.

MOUTH ROT REMEDY - Pet products - Aquatronics-Filtronics

MOUTH-TO-MASK - Health care products - Vital Signs, Inc.

MOUTH WASH - Chewing gum and candy - Philadelphia Chewing Gum Corp.

MOUTHKOTE - Health care products - Parnell Pharmaceuticals Inc.

MOUTHPIECE MOUSE - Cleaning preparations - Rico International

MOUTHWASH - Chewing gum - Philadelphia Chewing Gum Corp.

MOUTON-CADET - Wines - Heublein, Inc.

MOUX - Food products - Reede International Seafood Corp.

MOV-E-LITE - Lighting fixtures - Acme-Lite Manufacturing Co.

MOV-MASTER - Musical instrument accessories - GRK Manufacturing

MOV NPLEJ TSHIAB VILLAGE - Rice - James Kon

MOVABLE BEAST, THE - Pet products - Miriam Feibus

MOVABLE RACK - Shelving units–metal - Kardex Systems, Inc.

MOVADO - Watches - Movado Time Corp.

MOVAMATICS - Electronic equipment ☆ - H. Wilson Co.

MOVAR - Finishing agents - Benjamin Moore & Co.

MOVASONIC - Watches - Movado Time Corp.

MOVASTRONIC - Watches - Movado Time Corp.
MOVE - Pharmaceutical preparations - Silipos
MOVE - Recording label - Fifth Continent Music Corp.
MOVE-EASE - Apparel–women's - Movie Star Lingerie
MOVE OUT - Games - Avalon Hill Game Co.
MOVE OVER BUTTER - Margarine - Nabisco Foods Group
MOVE TO A DIFFERENT BEAT - Candy - Nabisco Foods Group
MOVEABLE DENIMS, THE - Apparel and accessories - Eccobay Sportswear Inc.
MOVEABLE FEAST OF TEXAS, A - Meat sauces - A Moveable Feast, Inc.
MOVEABLE GABARDINES, THE - Apparel and accessories - Eccobay Sportswear Inc.
MOVEMENT FOR LIFE - Recording label - Novamotion, Ltd.
MOVENOT - Padding–foam - Vantage Industries Inc.
MOVER, THE - Vitamins and nutritional supplements - Kroeger Herb Products Co. Inc.
MOVERS - Toys–automobiles - Majorette Toys (U.S.) Inc.
MOVERS - Trading cards and stamps - Pinnacle Brands, Inc.
MOVERS AND SHAKERS - Salt and pepper shakers - FFSC, Inc.
MOVESAFE - Cribs–metal - HARD Manufacturing Co. Inc.
MOVEX 52 - Cameras–motion picture ☆ - Miles Inc. (Agfa Div.)
MOVICOL - Laxatives ☆ - Norgine Laboratories Inc.
MOVIE EXPERIENCE, THE - Broadcasting stations–cable television - Sanborn Theatres, Inc.
MOVIE FAVORITES - Candy ☆ - Sathers Inc.
MOVIE MAGIC BUDGETING - Computer software - Screenplay Systems, Inc.
MOVIE MAGIC SCHEDULING - Computer software - Screenplay Systems, Inc.
MOVIE MAKER - Computer software - Electronic Arts Inc.
MOVIE MAKERS - Lipsticks - Del Pharmaceuticals, Inc.
MOVIE MASTER - Computer software - Comprehensive Video Supply Corp.
MOVIE MEMORIES - Books–blank - Informative Amenities Inc.
MOVIE MENU - Giftware - Tap Fabrication
MOVIE MINDER - Novelty items - RCP Enterprises, Inc.
MOVIE MOGULS - Games ☆ - A.R.C. Toys Inc.
MOVIE MONSTERS - Toys ☆ - Uncle Milton Industries Inc.
MOVIE-MOVER - Projectors–photographic - H. Wilson Co.
MOVIE MUNCHIE KIDS PACK - Containers - Promotional Management Group, Inc.
MOVIE MUNCHIES - Containers–paper - Promotional Management Group, Inc.
MOVIE MUSICAL MADNESS - Computer software - CBS Software
MOVIE STAR - Apparel–women's - Movie Star Lingerie
MOVIE STARLET - Apparel–women's ☆ - Movie Star Lingerie
MOVIE STARS - Candy - P.T. Distributors Inc.
MOVIE STARS - Games ☆ - A.R.C. Toys Inc.
MOVIE STARS - Sponges - Delby System
MOVIE WALKER - Video-cassette cases - Ingram Entertainment
MOVIE WAVE - Audio equipment - Multiwave Innovation, Inc.
MOVIECORDER - Cameras–video - Tandy Corp.
MOVIEDECK - Photographic equipment - Eastman Kodak Co.
MOVIEFLO - Computer software - Valis Group
MOVIEMATIC - Electronic equipment - Kalart Victor Corp.
MOVIEPLAY - Cameras–video - Good Times Home Video Corp.
MOVIESCREAMER - Computer software - Digigami, Inc.
MOVIESHOP - Computer software - Apple Computer Inc.
MOVIESTAR MAGIC - Toys - Tonka Corp.
MOVIETALK - Computer software - Apple Computer Inc.
MOVIETONE - Electronic equipment - Neumade Products Corp.
MOVIEWORKS - Computer software - Interactive Solutions Inc.
MOVILINES - Video games - Fenex Playto Corp.
MOVIN HANDS - Clocks - Orion Industries
MOVIN' ON - Computer software - Hartley Courseware Inc.
MOVING AT THE SPEED OF CANDY - Candy - Promotion in Motion, Inc.
MOVING BLEU - Apparel and accessories - Hampshire Group, Ltd.
MOVING BLEU SYSTEM - Apparel and accessories - Hampshire Group, Ltd.
MOVING CHAIR, THE - Office furniture–metal ☆ - Stow/Davis Furniture Co.
MOVING DOCTOR, THE - Boxes–paperboard - The Moving Doctor
MOVING HAIR - Hair care products - Helene Curtis Industries Inc.
MOVING ON - Toys–models ☆ - ERTL Co., Inc.
MOVING PICTURE SHOW, THE - Aquariums–household ☆ - Cole Enterprises
MOVING PIX - Signs - Clearr Corp.
MOVING SOLUTIONS - Consulting services - Extra Steps, Inc.
MOVING TARGET - Recording label - Celluloid Records
MOVING TO WINHELP '95 - Computer software - Blue Sky Software Corp.
MOVING-UP - Apparel–women's - Russ Togs Inc.
MOVIOLA - Film/tape equipment - J and R Film Co. Inc.

MOVIPRESS - Electronic equipment ☆ - H.P. Marketing Corp.
MOVISCOP - Electronic equipment ☆ - H.P. Marketing Corp.
MOVR - Office machines - Harnischfeger Engineers, Inc.
MOW & FEED - Lawn mowers - Toro Co.
MOW EZE - Lawn mowers - Abilene Research & Development Corp.
MOW-N-MULCH - Lawn mowers - Lawn-Boy
MOWER POWER - Fuel additives - Castoleum Corp.
MOWEST - Recording label - Motown Record Co. L.P.
MOWGLI'S JUNGLE ADVENTURE - Perfumes - Fairytale Fragrances, Inc.
MOWING - Lawn mowing equipment - Mowing
MOWLESS - Flowers, plants, and seeds - Turf-Seed, Inc.
MOWR-KLEEN - Cleaning equipment - Jamco Enterprises Inc.
MOWY WOWY - Snack foods - Midwest/Northern, Inc.
MOX - Cleaning preparations–household - Conklin Co., Inc.
MOXEES - Footwear–women's ☆ - Jumping-Jacks Shoes Inc.
MOXI - Computer software - Amocams/Modular, Inc.
MOXIE - Beverages–carbonated - Monarch Co., Inc.
MOXIE - Yarn - Glen Raven Mills Inc.
MOXY - Apparel–women's - Greenstein Apparel Group
MOYCODENT - Toothpicks - Moyco Industries, Inc.
MOYE-KORNER SYSTEM - Tools ☆ - Goldblatt Tool Co.
MOYER - Wines - Moyer Vineyards Inc.
MOYER & SON - Pet products - Scarlett Co.
MOYER BELL - Publisher's imprints - Rizzoli International Publications Inc.
MOYERKNIT - Underwear and nightwear - Gerber Products Co.
MOYERMAID - Hosiery–children's - Gerber Products Co.
MOYER'S - Pet products - Scarlett Co.
MOYGASHEL - Fabrics - Hamilton Adams Imports Ltd.
MOY'S RIB MOUNTAIN GINSENG - Herbal products - Conrad M. Moy
MOZ-ALL - Lawn mowers - Hull Industries
MOZ-ALL EAZY RIDER - Lawn mowers - Hull Industries
MOZAIC - Ironing board pads - Magla Products Inc.
MOZAIKA - Puzzles - J & R Destics Co., Inc.
MOZAMBIQUE - Floor coverings–carpet and rugs ☆ - Masland Corp.
MOZART - Floor coverings–carpet and rugs - Barrett Carpet Mills Inc.
MOZART - Floor coverings–carpet and rugs - Columbus Mills, Inc.
MOZART - Food products ☆ - W.J. Weaver & Son
MOZART - Hearing aids - Magnatone Hearing Aid Corp.
MOZART - Liquors - Guinness Import Co.
MOZART - Plumbing fixtures - National Fiber Glass Products
MOZART BLU - Water–bottled or canned - Sysco Corp.
MOZART CHOCOLATE LIQUEUR - Beverages–alcohol - Niche Marketing Corp.
MOZARTKUGELN - Food products - R.J. Hirt Co.
MOZO - Bicycle parts and accessories - Huntington Cycle USA Inc.
MOZO - Shoes - Edge Quest, Inc.
MOZZA MARY - Beverages–alcohol - Morrison Restaurants Inc.
MOZZA POPPERS - Fruits and vegetables - Anchor Food Products, Inc.
MOZZA RITA - Beverages–alcohol - Morrison Restaurants Inc.
MOZZASHRED - Cheese - Bar-S Foods Co.
MOZZI - Apparel–men's ☆ - Hall of Fame Enterprises
MOZZI-RITE - Cheese - Lucille Farms, Inc.
MP - Calendars - Spelling Television, Inc.
MP - Cigars - Medardo Padron
MP - Jewelry–precious - Imperial World, Inc.
MP - Medical apparatus - United States Surgical Corp.
MP - Pet products - Zema Corp.
MP - Pigments - Radiant Color Div.
MP - Publisher's imprints - Mountain Press Publishing Co.
MP - Recording label - Musical Productions, Inc.
MP - Scales–industrial - Metal Products Engineering Inc.
MP - Tires - Imex of Florida, Inc.
MP-1 - Audio equipment - ADA Signal Processors Inc.
MP-1 CLASSIC - Audio equipment - ADA Signal Processors Inc.
MP-2 - Audio equipment - ADA Signal Processors Inc.
MP-4 - Cameras - Polaroid Corp.
MP-5 - Firearms, accessories, and parts - Beeman Precision Airguns
MP-90 - Projectors–photographic - Alan Gordon Enterprises Inc.
MP 2000 - Compact discs–prerecorded - TRF Production Music Libraries
MP BRAND - Food products - MP Foods, Inc.
M.P. FALCON - Brushes–paint - Wooster Brush Co.
M.P. FAVORITE - Brushes–paint - Wooster Brush Co.
MP FORCE - Vitamins and nutritional supplements - Med Pro Industries
MP HUSKY - Doors–metal - MP Husky Corp.
MP HUSKY - Hardware - Mphusky Corp.
MP-SEEL IT - Epoxy coatings ☆ - Stainless Steel Coatings Inc.

☆ = Now out of production

MP SERIES - Clocks - Franklin Instrument Co. Inc.
MP VIDEO - Video tapes–blank - MP Video Inc.
MP1 - Floor coverings - L.D. Brinkman & Co. Inc.
MP286L - Computers–personal - Mitsubishi Electric America, Inc.
MP5022 - Printers–computer - Comtec Information Systems, Inc.
MPA - Medical apparatus - Del Mar Avionics
MPA CAPS - Vitamins and nutritional supplements - Vitamin Research
   Products Inc.
MPACT - Computer software - EDP Systems, Inc.
MPB - Hats - Melville Corp.
MPC - Adhesives and sealants - Miller Purcell Co.
MPC - Audio equipment - ADA Signal Processors Inc.
MPC - Cleaning equipment - Babcock & Wilcox Co.
MPC - Guitars ✰ - St. Louis Music Supply Co.
MPC - Metal detectors - Eriez Manufacturing Co.
M.P.C. - Musical instruments ✰ - Midco International
MPC - Paints - Midwest Paint Manufacturing Co.
MPC - Photocopy–machine monitors - Monitel Products Corp.
MPC ERTL - Toys–models - ERTL Co., Inc.
MPC HYDROPRO - Sprinklers–lawn - Materials Processing Corp.
MPC MILWAUKEE PUNCH CORPORATION - Machine tools - Milwaukee
   Punch Corp.
MPC MULTIMEDIA PC - Computer peripheral equipment - Software Publishers
   Association
MPC PLATFORM SYSTEMS - Pallets–wood - Mills Pacific Corp.
MPD - Electronic equipment - Bogen Communications, Inc.
MPD INC. - Microwave components ✰ - ARS Electronics
MPEG FORGE - Computer software - Optibase, Inc.
MPEG FUSION - Computer hardware - Optibase, Inc.
MPEG MASTER - Computer software - Visionetics International Corp.
MPEG SHOWSITE - Computer peripheral equipment - Optibase, Inc.
MPEG TOOLS - Computer software - Futuretel, Inc.
MPEG VIDEOPRO - Computer hardware - Optibase, Inc.
MPEGLAB - Computer software - Optibase, Inc.
MPEGSTAT - Computer software - Imake Software and Services, Inc.
MPEGSTUDIO - Computer hardware - Optivision, Inc.
MPEGTHERE - Computer software - Futuretel, Inc.
MPF - Cleaning preparations–household - Fidelity Funding of California, Inc.
MPF - Food products ✰ - Dietary Specialties
MPF MICRO-PARTICULATE-FRACTIONALIZATION - Cleaning preparations–
   household - Sunshine Makers, Inc.
MPG - Apparel and accessories - Raf Industries, Inc.
MPG - Gloves ✰ - Superba, Inc.
MPGS - Computer software - Cray Research, Inc.
M.P.H. - Ophthalmic goods - Foremost Optical Products
MPI - Audio equipment - Miami Parts Import
MPI - Conveyors - Magnetic Products, Inc.
MPI - Flowers, plants, and seeds - Material Processing, Inc.
MPI - Publisher's imprints - Maljack Productions, Inc.
M.P.I. - Roofing materials - Texas Aluminum Industries Inc.
MPI - Toothpicks - Mulco Products Inc.
MPI HOME VIDEO - Video production - Maljack Productions, Inc.
MPI MULTIMEDIA - Computer software - Maljack Productions, Inc.
MPI MUSIC GROUP - Recording label - Master Projects Inc.
MPII - Photographic equipment - Eastman Kodak Co.
MPK - Knives - Mission Knives Inc.
MPL - Bicycles - Columbia Manufacturing Inc.
MPL - Health care products - I*Tec
MPM - Educational materials - Mpm Educational Institute
MPM - Glass products - PPG Industries, Inc.
MPM - Musical instruments - Music Industries Inc.
MPM CABLE POWER - Musical instruments ✰ - Music Industries Inc.
MPO VIDEOTRONICS - Video production - MPO Videotronics Inc.
MPORT - Computers - Micronics Computers Inc.
MPOWER - Computer software - Eastman Kodak Co.
MPP APPRENTICE - Computer storage devices - Cray Research, Inc.
MPR - Broadcasting stations–radio - Minnesota Public Radio
MPS - Computer software - Mentat, Inc.
MPS - Hair care products ✰ - Mahdeen Laboratory
MPS - Machinery - Flowtronex International, Inc.
MPS-32 - Sugar–granulated, refined, or powdered - Imperial Sugar Co.
MPS CHUNKS - Dog food - Mars, Inc.
MPSI'S CAPS - Computer software - Mpsi Systems Inc.
MPSI'S OPS - Computer software - Mpsi Systems Inc.
MPV - Motor vehicles–automobiles - Mazda Motor of America Inc.
MPV - Vacuum cleaners and accessories - Minuteman International, Inc.

MPVA MIDWEST PROFESSIONAL VOLLEYBALL ASSOCIATION - T-shirts–
   men's - Midwest Professional Volleyball Association
MPVT - Pumps - Patterson Pump Co.
MPW - Computer software - Apple Computer Inc.
MPXNET - Communications equipment - Multipoint Networks, Inc.
MPZ - Oils–lubricating - Torco International Corp.
MQ - Jewelry - Marquesa, Inc.
MQ-1 - Audio equipment ✰ - ADA Signal Processors Inc.
MQMS - Computer software - Cantor and Co.
MQPRO - Computer peripheral equipment - BCAM International, Inc.
MQS - Audio equipment - ADA Signal Processors Inc.
MR. - See also MISTER
MR - Boats–motor - Starcraft Corp.
MR - Floor coverings–tile - Mondo America Inc.
MR - Gypsum products - National Gypsum Co.
MR - Jewelry - Discoveries
MR - Jewelry - QVC, Inc.
MR - Jewelry - M. Rabbani Jewelry Co. Inc.
MR - Saunas - Cedarbrook Sauna Inc.
MR. - Skin care products - Holder Images
MR. 2 PLY - Slacks–men's - Horace Small Apparel Co.
MR. 3 PLY DELUXE - Slacks–men's ✰ - Horace Small Apparel Co.
MR. ACE - Apparel and accessories - Texace Corp.
MR. ADAM - Mannequins ✰ - Canson-Talens Inc.
MR. ALEX - Apparel–women's - Alex Colman Inc.
MR. ALFRED'S OWN - Tobacco–chewing or smoking ✰ - Alfred Dunhill of
   London Inc.
MR. AMERICA - Sporting goods ✰ - Slim-Ez Suit Co. Inc.
MR. & MRS. BABY - Apparel–children's - Haddad Brothers Inc.
MR. & MRS. BABY HADDAD BROTHERS, INC. SINCE 1947 - Apparel and
   accessories - Haddad Brothers Inc.
MR & MRS T - Beverages - Cadbury Beverages Inc.
MR. & MRS. T - Beverages - Mott's Inc.
MR. APPLE - Fruits and vegetables ✰ - Prentice Packing & Storage Co.
MR. AUGI'S SPORTSWEAR - Apparel and accessories - Mr. Augi's
   Sportswear, Inc.
MR. AUTOGRAPHS - Postcards - M. Wesley Marans
MR. AUTOMATIC - Coffee - Tetley Inc.
MR. BACK RELIEF - Medical apparatus - Kevin O. Boland
MR. BAKER - Wallpaper - J. Hermes
MR. BAKERMAN - Cookies ✰ - Sunshine Biscuits, Inc.
MR. BALDY - Toys–stuffed - Fun World Inc.
MR. BARCO - Medical uniforms - Barco of California
MR. BARTENDER - Bar fixtures–wood ✰ - Mr. Cheftender Products Inc.
MR. BATHROOM - Cleaner - American Home Products Corp.
MR. BICK - Apparel and accessories - Wolverine World Wide, Inc.
MR. BIDET - Bathtubs–enameled - American Bidet Inc.
MR. BIG - Paper products - Georgia-Pacific Corp.
MR. BIG - Vitamins and nutritional supplements - Ultimate Strength Systems
   Labs, Inc.
MR. BIG TOW - Automotive parts and accessories - Koch Industries Inc.
MR. BILDER - Blocks–concrete ✰ - Kingsford Building Products
MR. BINGLE MAISON BLANCHE - Apparel and accessories - Maison
   Blanche, Inc.
M.R. BIRDS - Apparel and accessories - Talbot Street Pier, Inc.
MR. BITTS - Bakery products - Barry B. Hermanson
MR. BLACKWELL - Leather goods ✰ - Gary's Leather Creations
MR. BLISTER - Coatings, etc ✰ - B and L Tool and Machine Co.
MR. BLOBBY - Shoes ✰ - S. Goldberg and Co. Inc.
MR. BONES - Candy - Fleer Corp.
MR. BONES - Novelty items - Fun World Inc.
MR. BOSTON - Liquors - Canandaigua Wine Co. Inc.
MR. BRAND - Thread ✰ - Perfect Thread Co. Inc.
MR. BRITE - Cleaning equipment - Pacific Oasis Enterprise, Inc.
MR. B'S - Food products ✰ - Cap's Italian Foods Inc.
MR. BUBBLE - Bathing soap powder - Reckitt & Colman, Inc.
MR. BUBBLES - Toys - Strombecker Corp.
MR. BUBBLES - Toys ✰ - Revell-Monogram, Inc.
MR. BUBBLES BUBBLE SWORD - Toys - Strombecker Corp.
MR. BUCKET - Games - Hasbro, Inc.
MR. BULKY - Paper–toweling - Cleveland Cotton Products Co.
MR. BUTLER - Food products - Saramar Corp.
MR. CAMPER - Lanterns–kerosene ✰ - Enerco Technical Products
MR. CANDY DANDY - Candy ✰ - Brock Candy Co. Inc.
MR. CAT DUDE - Art prints - Norman A. Forsberg
MR. CATFISH - Pans - Innovators Network, LLC

✰ = Now out of production

MR. CB - Electronics stores ☆ - Jasco Products Co. Inc.
MR. CHAIN - Chains - M R Plastics, Inc.
MR. CHAIN'S - Lawn mowers - Mr. Chain
MR. CHAIRMAN - Furniture–upholstered - Sam Moore Furniture Industries Inc.
MR. CHALKY - Chalk - American Art Clay Co. Inc.
MR. CHALLENGER - Games ☆ - Texas Instruments Inc.
MR. CHAMP - Fishing lures - Weber Industries Inc.
MR. CHAMP - Lubricants ☆ - Pyroil Co. Inc.
MR. CHARLES - Hats - Bierner and Son Inc.
MR. CHARLES' SALON - Hair care products - Mr. Charles' Salon Formulas, Inc.
MR. CHEFTENDER - Barbecues and grills - Mr. Cheftender Products Inc.
MR. CHIME - Electronic equipment - Detec Security Systems, Inc.
MR. CHIN'S GOURMET PARADISE - Electronic games - Romstar Inc.
MR. CHIPPER - Candy ☆ - R.M. Palmer Co.
MR. CHIPS - Barbecues and grills - Mr. Chips Inc.
MR. CHIPS - Cookies - Sunshine/Salerno Inc.
MR. CHIPS - Food products - Saydeetime Productions, Inc.
MR. CHIPS - Golf-chipping nets ☆ - Dennco, Inc.
MR. CHIPS - Marble products - Georgia Marble Co.
MR. CHRISTMAS - Christmas tree ornaments - Mr. Christmas, Inc.
MR. CHUCKLES TOY BOX - Chests–wood ☆ - Little Tikes Co.
MR. CITRUS - Fruit drinks–bottled or canned - Everfresh Beverages, Inc.
MR. CLEAN - Cleaning preparations–household - Procter & Gamble Co.
MR. CLICK - Embossing machines ☆ - Esselte Corp.
MR. CLUSTER - Candy - Palmer Candy Co.
MR. COAST - Footwear - Coast Shoes Inc.
MR. COCO - Juices - Mon Chong Loong Trading Corp.
MR. COFFEE - Coffee makers–electric - Mr. Coffee, Inc.
MR. COFFEE - Hotplates - Health O Meter, Inc.
MR. COFFEE CONCEPTS - Spices and extracts - Healthometer
MR. COLA - Beverages–carbonated - Grapette International
MR. COLOMBIA - Coffee ☆ - Coffee Holding Co.
MR. COMFORT - Furniture - Mark W. Nye
MR. COMPOST - Composting kit - Bio Industries Inc.
MR. CONTINENTAL - Seafood - Continental Seafoods Inc.
MR. CONVERTIBLE - Jackets ☆ - Horace Small Apparel Co.
MR. COOL - Tableware–china - New Products Sales and Marketing, Inc.
MR. COOL WHIP - Whipped topping–frozen - Kraft Foods, Inc.
MR CREEPY - Novelty items - Pressman Toy Corp.
MR. CRULLER - Bakery products - Koffee Kup Bakery, Inc.
MR. C'S - Pizzas–frozen - Cap's Italian Foods Inc.
MR. C'S - Snack foods - Mr. Chips Snack Food, Inc.
MR. C'S SKIN LOTION - Skin care products - Carter Drug Store, Inc.
MR. CULVER'S SPARKLERS - Deodorizers - Alberto-Culver Co.
MR. CURRY JAMAICA SOF-DRINKS - Beverages–carbonated - Worldwide Beverage
M.R. DECOYS - Apparel–athletic - Talbot Street Pier, Inc.
M.R. DEE CEE - Apparel and accessories ☆ - Washington Manufacturing Co.
MR. DEL ORO - Mustache-grooming implements ☆ - London International U.S. Holdings
MR. DELL'S - Food products - Mr. Dell Foods
MR. DENSON'S - Cookies - Mrs. Denson's Cookies
MR. DESTROYER - Insecticides - Vitarroz
MR. DIXIE - Food products - Twin City Foods Inc.
MR. DO - Toys - Hasbro, Inc.
MR. DOODLER - Markers–felt-tip - Dri Mark Products, Inc.
MR. DRI - Chemical preparations - Frank Miller and Sons Inc.
M.R. DUCKS - Apparel–athletic - Talbot Street Pier, Inc.
MR. DUDLEY - Spices and extracts - Dudley Kebow Inc.
MR. DUDLEY INTERNATIONAL - Kitchen utensils–enameled ☆ - Dudley Kebow Inc.
MR. EEZ - Gloves - Good Luck Glove Co.
MR. EGG'S NEIGHBORHOOD - Hobby kits ☆ - Bleyer Industries (Peoria Plastics Div.)
MR. ELI - Footwear - Orly Shoe Corp.
MR. EMGE - Frankfurters - Emge Packing Co. Inc.
MR. E'S LIBRARY OF CRIME CLASSICS - Publisher's imprints - International Polygonics Ltd.
MR. EVERGREEN - Irrigation equipment - Mr. Evergreen, Inc.
MR. EXCITEMENT - Clothing - Spencer Motor Ventures, Inc.
MR. FAUCET FIXER - Hardware - Melard Manufacturing Corp.
MR. FIGGS - Cookies - Sunshine/Salerno Inc.
MR. FIX - Tools ☆ - Marson Creative Fastener Group
MR. FIX-IT - Toys ☆ - Imperial Toy Corp.

MR. FIZZ - Whipping machines - Leland Limited Inc.
MR. FLAIR - Apparel and accessories - Uniflair Inc.
MR. FLAVOR - Fresh vegetables - Vessey and Co., Inc.
MR. FOOD - Kitchenware–plastic - Ginsburg Enterprises Inc.
MR. FRANCO - Skin care products - Mr. Franco Hair Center Ltd.
MR. FRED - Shoes - Colonial Shoe Co.
MR. FREEZ - Food products - Michigan Beef Co.
MR. FRITTER - Food products - Kingsford Packing Co.
MR. FRY - Vegetables–frozen - Fry Foods Inc.
MR. FUZZY - Candy ☆ - R.M. Palmer Co.
MR. G. - Apparel–men's - Ditto Legwear
MR. G - Food products - Ore-Ida Foods, Inc.
MR. G - Footwear - Chesapeake Shoe Co. of California
MR. G - Spices and extracts - G's Seasoning Co.
MR. G - Watches - E. Gluck Corp.
MR. GARDENER'S SALADS - Salads–prepackaged - Old Fashioned Enterprises Inc.
MR. GASKET - Automotive parts and accessories - Echlin Inc.
M.R. GEESE - Sweatshirts - Talbot Street Pier, Inc.
MR. GHE - Colognes - Nettie Rosenstein Inc.
MR. GIO'S - Sausages - Giovanni Mucciacciaro
MR. GLOW N. BONES - Novelty items - Paper Magic Group Inc.
MR. GOLF - Men's apparel - Interco Inc.
MR. GOOBER P. NUT - Erasers - Diener Industries Inc.
MR. GOODBAR - Candy - Hershey Chocolate USA
MR. GOODBAR - Candy - Homestead, Inc.
MR. GOODPUMP - Automotive parts and accessories - Allied Plastics
MR. GOURMET - Meat products–beef - K & K Gourmet Meats Inc.
MR. GRANITE - Cement - Medusa Minerals Co.
MR. GRIP - Hardware - Woodmate Corp.
MR. GRIP - Soap ☆ - ITW Fluid Products
MR. GUS - Jewelry - Herbert Stehberg Inc.
MR. GUTTER KLEEN - Building materials–concrete ☆ - Stone City Products Inc.
MR. HEAT - Furnaces–laboratory - Washington Stove Works
MR. HEATER - Heaters–space - Enerco Technical Products
MR. HEATER - Heating equipment - Mr. Heater Corp.
MR. HELPER - Saws–hand-operated - Loomco International
MR. HENRY'S - Cakes - Henry S. Morgan
MR. HORACE SMALL HERITAGE COLLECTION - Slacks–men's - Horace Small Apparel Co.
MR. HOST - Hams - Armour Swift-Eckrich
MR. HUNGRY - Vitamins and nutritional supplements - Atlantic Licensing Corp.
MR. INDOOR - Brooms - Wright-Bernet
MR. INSIDE - Mats - Akro Corp.
MR J - Colognes - Fashion Fair Cosmetics
MR. JAC - Apparel–men's ☆ - Craftex Creations Inc.
MR. JEREMY FISHER - Puzzles - Frederick Warne & Co., Inc.
MR. JET - Fishing tackle - Mr. Bob's
MR. JOHN - Boats - Glen-L Marine Designs
MR. JOHN - Cleaning preparations–household ☆ - Blue Cross Laboratories Inc.
MR. JOHN - Crock pots ☆ - Wonderknit
MR. JOHN - Hats - Arlington Hat Co. Inc.
MR. JOHN CLASSIC - Hats - Aldo Hat Corp.
MR. JOHN CLASSIC - Hats - Mr. John Fashion Boutiques, Inc.
MR. JOHN FAMOUS JEWELS - Hair accessories, jewelry - Herbert Stehberg Inc.
MR. JOHN SIGNATURE SERIES - Hats - Mr. John Fashion Boutiques, Inc.
MR. JOHNS-ON - Thermal underwear - Indera Mills Co.
MR. JOLLY - Chocolate candy - Superior Fruit & Confections
MR. JUMBO - Paper–toweling - Orchids Paper Products, Inc.
MR. K BARS - Candy - Klein Chocolate Co.
MR. KITZEL - See CHIPICO
MR. KNITS - Apparel and accessories - Burton Manufacturing Co.
MR. KNITS - Crock pots ☆ - Wonderknit
MR. K'S - Pizzas–frozen - Mr. K's Foods Inc.
MR. LEGGS - Jeans–men's - Lee Apparel Co. Inc.
MR. LEO'S - Statuary - Jason Leopold Lamparty
MR. LIGHT - Lighting fixtures - U.S. Fittings Corp.
MR. LINKS - Jewelry - Wideband Jewelry Corp.
MR. LONG-ARM - Paint rollers - Mr. Longarm Inc.
MR. LONGARM - Tools–hand-operated - Robert D. Newman
MR. LUBE-N-COOL - Barber shop equipment - Kim Laube & Co. Inc.
MR. LUGNUT - Automotive parts and accessories - Consolidated International Automobile Inc.

☆ = Now out of production

MR. MAC TUFF STUFF - Cleaning preparations - Frontline Cars

MR. MAGNET - Cleaning preparations - V.G. Industries

MR. MAGOO SPARKLE PAINTS - Paint sets–hobby ☆ - Kenner Products

MR. MARINADE - Food products - Romanoff International Inc.

MR. MASS - Pharmaceutical preparations - Bricker Laboratories

MR. MCGREGOR - Candy ☆ - R.M. Palmer Co.

MR. MCGREGOR - Dolls - Frederick Warne & Co., Inc.

MR. MEARS - Cosmetics - Lan-O-Sheen, Inc.

MR. MEASURE - Tape measures - With Design in Mind

MR. MEAT SMOKER - Barbecues and grills - Brinkmann Corp.

MR. MELON - Candy - Ferrara Pan Candy Co., Inc.

MR. MELT - Chemical preparations - Frank Miller and Sons Inc.

MR. MEN - Toys - Knickerbocker Toy Co. Inc.

MR. MEN/LITTLE MISS - Giftware ☆ - Schmid Inc.

MR. MESH - Lighters - Colibri Inc.

MR. MIGHTY - Housewares - Willow Molded Plastics

MR. MIGHTYMIND - Games - Leisure Learning Products

MR. MINUS - Propellers - Dymex Inc.

MR. MISTER - Water dispensers - Speciality Fabrication

MR. MIZZOU - Pipes ☆ - Missouri Meerschaum Co.

MR. MOOSE - Health care products - Jerome Russell Cosmetics, Inc.

MR. MORT - Apparel–women's - Russ Togs Inc.

MR. MORT - Dresses–women's - R. & M. Kaufmann

MR. MOTO - Toys - Tonka Corp.

MR. MOUTH - Games - Milton Bradley Co.

MR. MUNCH - Popcorn - National Oats Co. Inc.

MR. MURRY'S - Food products - Murry's Inc.

MR. MUSCLE - Cleaning preparations - Drackett Co.

MR. MUSCLE - Cleaning preparations–household - S.C. Johnson & Son, Inc.

MR. MUSCLE - Rope - Wellington Leisure Products, Inc.

MR. MUSHROOM - Vegetable sauces ☆ - Clorox Co.

MR. MUSTACHE - Mustache-grooming implements - London International U.S. Holdings

MR. MUTT'S - Pet products ☆ - Mr. Mutt Pet Products Inc.

MR. NATURAL - Fertilizers - Itsaul Natural, LLC

MR. NATURAL - Water–mineral - Mr. Natural Bottled Water

MR. NEAT - Garbage disposal units–household - Strout Plastics Inc.

MR. NEATS - Apparel and accessories - Mr. Neats Formal Wear

MR. NIBBLER - Popcorn - National Oats Co. Inc.

MR. NIBBLER - Snack foods - Waymouth Farms Inc.

MR. NO MO' - Apparel and accessories - Vertical Expressions, Inc.

MR. NORTHERN - Food products - Bush Brothers and Co.

MR. NUCCIO - Sausages - Foodbrands America, Inc.

MR. NUT - Peanut butter - Sunray Products

MR. NUTTY CONE - Frozen confectioneries - International Ice Cream Corp.

MR. OAK - Furniture - Universal Flooring

MR. OAK II - Furniture - Universal Flooring

MR. OMELET - Pans ☆ - Nordic Ware

MR. OUTDOOR - Brooms - Wright-Bernet

MR. OUTDOORS - Cooking equipment–household - Metal Fusion Inc.

MR. OUTSIDE - Mats - Akro Corp.

MR. PADCO - Paints - Padco Companies, Inc.

MR. PANCO - Housewares - Metal Masters Foodservice Equipment Co., Inc.

MR. PANDORA - Apparel and accessories - Pandora Sportswear Industries

MR. PAUL'S - Popcorn - American Horizons, Inc.

MR. PEANUT - Christmas tree ornaments - Nabisco Brands Inc.

MR. PEANUT - Peanut butter - Nabisco Foods Group

MR. PEAR - Fruits and vegetables ☆ - Prentice Packing & Storage Co.

MR. PEEL INCORPORATED - Tools - Mr. Peel Inc.

MR. PEP - Health care products - Chex Co.

MR. PET - Pet products - General Cage Corp.

MR. PET - Pet products - Mr. Pet Inc.

MR. PET - Wood products ☆ - Ozark Cedar Inc.

MR. PHIPPS - Corn chips - Nabisco Holdings Corp.

MR. PHIPPS - Pretzels - Nabisco Foods Group

MR. PIBB - Beverages–carbonated - Coca-Cola Co.

MR. PICK-UPS - Cosmetics - Reina Claire

MR. PICKLE - Pickles - Mrs. Dalton's Best Maid Products

MR. PICKY - Real estate agencies - Peter S. Becker

MR. PIGGY'S - Animal feeds - Du-1 Enterprises, Inc.

MR. PIKE - Boats–motor - Lund Boat Co.

MR. PINCH - Seasonings - Health Best Distributors Inc.

MR. PINE - Furniture - Universal Flooring

MR. PINE II - Furniture - Universal Flooring

MR. PITA - Breads - International Baking Co.

MR. P.J. - Apparel and accessories ☆ - Barad & Co.

MR. P.J. JR. - Apparel and accessories ☆ - Barad & Co.

MR. PLUMBER - Drain pipe cleaners - AmeriPlus Inc.

MR. POP - Games - Lakeside Games

MR. POTATO HEAD - Footwear - S. Goldberg and Co. Inc.

MR. POTATO HEAD - Potato chips - Street Kids

MR. POTATO HEAD - Toys - Playskool, Inc.

MR. PRAWN - Seafood products–fresh or frozen - Prawn Seafoods Inc.

MR. PRO - Glassware–household - Owens-Illinois Inc. (Libbey Div.)

MR. PRO - Mats - Akro Corp.

MR. P'S - Pizzas–frozen - Jeno's Inc.

MR. PUMPERNICKEL - Pumpernickel bread - Iversen Baking Co.

MR. PUPPY - Greeting cards - Mister Puppy Productions

MR. PURE - Juices - American Citrus Products Corp.

MR. PURE - Juices - Home Juice Co.

MR. PUSHY - Pens - National Pen Co.

MR. PUTZ'S NUTS - Snack foods - Mr. Putz

MR. QUARTERBACK - Toys–electronic - Hasbro, Inc.

MR. QUICK - Floor coverings–carpet and rugs - Carpet Products Co.

MR. RAGS - Apparel and accessories - Lux Corp.

MR. RATCHET - Screw drivers - Wescon Products Co.

MR. RAY'S - Housewares - Sewing Organizer

MR. RAYS - Seafood products–fresh or frozen - Martin Foods

MR. RAY'S DESIGN CURVE - Housewares - Sewing Organizer

MR. REMEDY - Vitamins and nutritional supplements - NBSP, Inc.

MR. RESNICK - Recording label - Stewart Resnick

MR. RIB - Pork - Wolverine Packing Co.

MR. ROBOT JR. - Toys - Bandai America Inc.

MR. ROEBIC - Cleaning preparations - Roebic Laboratories Inc.

MR. ROOTER - Sewage treatment equipment - Mr. Rooter Corp.

MR. ROTISSERIE - Chickens - Holly Poultry, Inc.

MR. ROUGHCUT - Tobacco products - M. Marsh & Son

MR. SALAD - Food products - Redi-Spuds of America

MR. SALESMAN CARDS - Novelty items - BRC Corp.

MR. SANDBAR - Novelty items - Power-Sun of Florida, Inc.

MR. SANDMAN - Paint sets–hobby - Vitos Products

MR. SCRAPPY - Kitchen appliances - Joneca Corp.

MR. SCRUBBY - Housewares - Hutzler Manufacturing Co.

MR. SERVICE - Motor vehicle parts and accessories - Hercules Tire & Rubber Co.

MR. SHARP - Cheese - Swiss American Import Co.

MR. SHARPY - Pencil sharpeners ☆ - Sunbeam-Oster Household Products

MR. SILENCER - Automotive parts and accessories - Victor Automotive Products, Inc.

MR. SKETCH - Water colors - Sanford Corp.

MR. SLICK - Silicone lubricant and treatment - Coughlan Products Corp.

MR. SLIMS - Tobacco products - Philip Morris Companies Inc.

MR. SLUSH BARREL - Ice chests–plastic - Glacier Ware Inc.

MR. SNIFFER - Deodorizers - New Ideas International, Inc.

MR. SPATS' CAT-A-COMB - Pet products - Tarel Seven Design Inc.

MR. SPATS' CORNER DINER - Pet products - Tarel Seven Design Inc.

MR. SPATS' PURRSUIT - Pet products - Tarel Seven Design Inc.

MR. SPICE - Sauces - Lang Naturals

MR. SPOCK VINYL FIGURE - Toys - ERTL Co., Inc.

MR. SPRAY - Paints - Plasti-Kote Co. Inc.

MR. SPUD - Potato flakes - Magic Valley Foods Inc.

MR. SQUEEGEE - Cleaning preparations–window - Jobar International Inc./ Bibi Products

MR. STEAK - Restaurants–fast food - Mr. Steak Inc.

MR. STEAM - Plumbing fixtures–metal - Bel-Aire Sales Corp.

MR STEAM - Saunas - Cedarbrook Sauna Inc.

MR. STICK - Glue–household or industrial ☆ - Loctite Corp.

MR. STRIP-IT - Brushes–paint - Wright-Bernet

MR. SUPER NATURAL - Pharmaceutical ☆ - Richard A. Deer

MR. SUPERMIND - Games - Leisure Learning Products

MR. SURE START - Lighter fluid ☆ - Ashland Oil, Inc.

MR. SWEEP - Sweeping compounds - Frank Miller and Sons Inc.

MR. T - Automotive parts and accessories - Moran Industries, Inc.

MR. T - Erasers ☆ - Diener Industries Inc.

MR. T - Kites ☆ - Spectra Star Kites

MR. T - Toys - Tyco Toys

MR. T GOLD CHAIN - Chewing gum ☆ - Amurol Confections Co.

MR. TABLE TENNIS - Table-tennis equipment ☆ - Indian Industries Inc.

MR. TAMBOURINE - Musical instruments - MBT International, Inc.

MR. TEES - T-shirts–men's - Mr. Tees Imprinted Sportswear, Inc.

MR. TENNIS - Men's sportswear - Interco Inc.

MR. TEXAS - Chocolate candy - Pangburn Candy Co.

☆ = Now out of production

MR. THINZIT - Antifreeze ☆ - Gibraltar National Corp.
MR. TIE - Neckties - Garys Enterprises Inc.
MR. TIPPY - Toys - Viacom International Inc.
MR. TOD - Music boxes ☆ - Schmid Inc.
MR. TOOL - Hardware - Kenneth B. Homan
MR. TOPS - Sporting goods - Gerry Cosby & Co., Inc.
MR. TOURNAMENT - Crocheted and knitted items ☆ - Reliable of Milwaukee
MR. TOY - Toys - M & R Manufacturing Inc.
MR. TOY - Toys - Wellpoint Corp.
MR. TRANSISTOR-T - T-shirts—men's - Chums Ltd.
MR. TRANSMISSION - Automotive repair shops - Mr. Transmission Inc.
MR. T'S - Beef - Mr. T's Wholesale
MR. TUFF - Bags, cleaners - B & E Sales Co. Inc.
MR. TUFFY - Bicycle parts and accessories - Mr. Tuffy Co., Inc.
MR TUFFY - Bicycle parts and accessories - Mr. Tuffy Co., Inc.
MR. TUFFY - Tires–bicycles - AC International
MR. TURBINE - Automotive repair shops - Turbine Generator Maintenance Inc.
MR. TURF - Mats - Akro Corp.
MR. TURKEY - Chickens - Bil Mar Foods
MR. TURKEY - Meat products - Sara Lee Corp.
MR. TURTLE - Fireworks - American Promotional Events, Inc.
MR. TURTLE - Toys - SLM Inc.
MR. TWISTEE - Toys ☆ - Henry Gordy International Inc.
MR. TWISTERTAILS - Fishing tackle - Mister Twister, Inc.
MR. UNIVERSE - Watches - Bulova Corp.
MR. V - Food products ☆ - Oh Boy Corp.
MR-VAX II - Vaccines - Merck & Co., Inc. (Merck Research Laboratories)
MR. WALLEYE - Fishing tackle - Church Tackle Co.
MR. WAX - Cleaning preparations - Mr. Wax, Inc.
MR. WHISK - Razors–electric - Panasonic Co.
MR. WHISKERS - Toys - Smith Enterprises Inc.
MR. WINDOW - Hardware ☆ - Aluma Trim EZ Roll Manufacturing Co.
MR. WONDERFULL SURPRISE - Cereal ☆ - General Mills, Inc.
MR. WRINGER - Wringers–laundry - Haack Products
MR. X - Apparel and accessories - Gentry Inc.
MR. XYLO - Toys ☆ - Playskool, Inc.
MR. ZIP - Lubricants - American Grease Stick Co.
MR. Z'S - Pizzas–frozen - Mr. Z's Fund Raising Corp.
MR. Z'S SWEET & TANGY - Barbecue sauce - Masterfoods Specialities, Inc.
MRII - Computers - Micro-Computer Imports, Inc.
MR2 - Motor vehicles–automobiles - Toyota Motor Sales USA Inc.
MRC - Adhesives and sealants - General Electric Co.
MRC - Health care products - Mason Medical Products
MRC - Hearing aids ☆ - Magnatone Hearing Aid Corp.
M.R.C. - Recording label - Major Recording Co.
MRC - Seafood products–fresh or frozen - Harrison Pierce & Co. Inc.
MRC - Toys–electronic - MRC
MRC - Transmission equipment–motor vehicle - Morse Controls
MRC - Wheelchairs - Labac Systems, Inc.
MRC SOUND 'N' POWER - Toys–electronic - MRC
MRD-2 - Cleaning preparations - Hillyard Enterprises, Inc.
M*R*E - Motorcycles - Murdoch Racing Enterprises
MRES 2000 - Electronic equipment - MPD Technologies, Inc.
MRH-1500 - Magnetic resonance imaging devices - Hitachi Medical Systems America, Inc.
MRIS - Computer software - Metropolitan Regional Information Systems, Inc.
MRIS/VIEW - Computer software - V.F. Corp.
MRK - Pharmaceutical preparations - Merck & Co., Inc. (Merck Research Laboratories)
MRL DIAGNOSTICS - Diagnostic apparatus - Focus/Mrl, Inc.
MRM - Recording label - Jazz Composer's Orchestra Association Inc.
MRNET - Software - Cerner Corp.
MRO - Paints - Seymour of Sycamore Inc.
MRO EXPLORER - Computer software - Quality Software Solutions
M.R.P. - Paints ☆ - Everseal International Sales Co. Inc.
MRP-20 - Magnetic resonance imaging devices - Hitachi Medical Systems America, Inc.
MRP-5000 - Magnetic resonance imaging devices - Hitachi Medical Systems America, Inc.
MRP-5000XLS - Magnetic resonance imaging devices - Hitachi Medical Systems America, Inc.
MRP-7000 - Magnetic resonance imaging devices - Hitachi Medical Systems America, Inc.
MRPLINK - Computer software - Integrated Design, Inc.
MRPX - Computer software - J.D. Edwards & Co.
MRS. ADLER'S - Food products - Mrs. Adler's Foods Inc.

MRS. ALISON - Bakery products - Mrs. Alison's Cookie Co. Inc.
MRS. ALISON'S COOKIES - Cookies - Mrs. Alison's Cookie Co. Inc.
MRS. AMERICA - Ironing-board cover and pad sets ☆ - American Foam Latex Corp.
MRS. APPLEYARD'S - Maple syrup, pancake mixes - American Maple Products Corp.
MRS. A'S - Paper products - Mrs. A's Corp.
MRS. ASIEN - Food products - Greenfield Noodle & Specialty
MRS. AULD'S - Food products - Mrs. Auld's Gourmet Foods
MRS. BAIRD'S - Food products - Mrs. Baird's Bakeries Inc.
MRS. BAIRD'S - Tortillas - Mrs. Baird's Bakeries, Inc.
MRS. BATEMAN'S BAKING BUTTER - Food products - Mrs. Bateman's Bakery-Baking Butter
MRS. BETHUNE'S TEA CAKES - Cookies - National Council of Negro Women, Inc.
MRS. B'S - Cookies - Bradlees Stores, Inc.
MRS. BUMBY'S - Potato chips ☆ - General Mills, Inc.
MRS. BUTTERWORTH'S - Breads - Conopco, Inc.
MRS. BUTTERWORTH'S - Cookies - Van Den Bergh Foods Co.
MRS. BUTTERWORTH'S - Syrup - Lever Brothers Co. Inc.
MRS. CARLTON'S - Breads ☆ - General Host Corp.
MRS. CARROL'S - Candy - Gourmet Confections Inc.
MRS. CLARK'S - Food products - Mrs. Clark's Foods
MRS. CLAUS RUNS AMOK - Greeting cards - Charles A. Hardinger, Jr.
MRS. COLUMBUS SUPER PIES - Pies - Mrs. Columbus Super Pies, Inc.
MRS. CONDIES' - Fabric softeners - Condies Foods
MRS. CRUTCHFIELD'S - Bakery products - Spangler's Flour Mills, Inc. of Mt. Joy
MRS. C'S PARTY GAMES - Games - Carolyn M. Clark
MRS. CUBBISON'S - Stuffing - Interstate Brands Corp.
MRS. CUBBISON'S STUFFIN' SACK - Disposable cooking sack - Interstate Brands Corp.
MRS. DASH - Seasonings - Alberto-Culver Co.
MRS. DAVIS - Candy - H.R. Davis Candy Co.
MRS. DAY'S IDEAL - Footwear–children's - Mrs. Day's Ideal Baby Shoe Co.
MRS. DENSON'S - Cookies - Mrs. Denson's Cookies
MRS. DEWSON'S WILLIE BRIM - Hats - Ruth Dewson
MRS. DIFILLIPPO'S - Meat products–beef - Steakwich
MRS. DOE PEE'S SPECIAL BLEND - Hunting equipment - Collora's Critters
MRS. EVE - Mannequins ☆ - Canson-Talens Inc.
MRS. EWALD'S - Beverages - Aloe Laboratories, Inc.
MRS. FANNING'S - Pickles - GFA Brands Inc.
MRS. FEARNOW'S - Soups–canned - Fearnow Bros. Inc.
MRS. FIELDS - Cookies - Mrs. Fields Development Corp.
MRS. FIELD'S - Cookies - Mrs. Fields' Original Cookies, Inc.
MRS. FIELDS - Ice cream - Marigold Foods Inc.
MRS. FILBERT'S - Margarine - Van Den Bergh Foods Co.
MRS FILBERTS FAMILY SPREAD - Vegetable oil - Conopco, Inc.
MRS. FLAHERTY'S - Lollipops - Flaherty's Fine Confections Inc.
MRS. FRIDAY'S - Fish–fresh or frozen - Fish King Processors Inc.
MRS. FRIDAY'S GALLEY CLASSICS - Seafood products–fresh or frozen - Fish King Processors Inc.
MRS. GERRY'S - Salads–prepackaged - Mrs. Gerry's Kitchen Inc.
MRS. GILES - Food products - Mrs. Giles Country Kitchens Inc.
MRS. GOOCH'S - Food products - Mrs. Gooch's Natural Food Markets Inc.
MRS. GOODCOOKIE - Bakery products - Pride of the Farm
MRS. GOODCOOKIE - Food products ☆ - Ore-Ida Foods, Inc.
MRS. GOODCOOKIE - Snack foods - J & J Snack Foods Corp.
MRS. GOODMUFFIN - Snack foods ☆ - Pride of the Farm
MRS. GRASS - Bouillon cubes - Cracker Jack
MRS. GRASS - Pasta - Borden, Inc.
MRS. GRASS - Soups–mixes - Mrs. Grass
MRS. GRIMES - Vegetables–canned - Faribault Foods Inc.
MRS. HOBBS - Gravy - Durkee French Foods
MRS. HOWARD'S - Meat sauces - Earsie Howard's Old Time Foods Inc.
MRS. INSIDE - Mats - Akro Corp.
MRS. J. G. MCDONALD - Chocolate candy - McDonald Candy Co. Inc.
MRS. KARLS - Bread - Interstate Brands Corp.
MRS. KATZ - Horseradish - Sam Katz Brokerage
MRS. KLEEN - Vacuum cleaners and accessories ☆ - Home Care Industries, Inc.
MRS. K'S - Food products ☆ - Old Fashioned Kitchen Inc.
MRS. LANES - Food products - Wetterau Inc.
MRS. MAFFUCCI'S MORNING PIZZA - Pizzas–frozen - Vito's Pizzaria Inc.
MRS. MINIVER - Dolls ☆ - Effanbee Doll Corp.
MRS. MITCHELL'S COUNTRY KITCHEN - Wallpaper - Borden, Inc.

☆ = Now out of production

MRS. MOMMY - Toys - Mattel, Inc.

MRS. MOSKOWITZ'S MUNCHIES - Snack foods - Mrs. Moskowitz's Munchies, Inc.

MRS. MOUSE - Novelty items–paper - Demco Inc.

MRS. MULLIGAN - Golfing equipment - Preferred Products Inc.

MRS. MURTHA'S - Salad dressings–bottled - Mrs. Murtha's Italian Dressing

MRS. NEUSIHIN'S - Pickles - Steinfeld's Products Co.

MRS. NICKELS PICKLES - Food products - J & R Food Products, Inc.

MRS. O'SHEA'S - Cakes - O'Shea Ltd.

MRS. OWEN'S - Jams and jellies - Owen & Mowrey Inc.

MRS. PANGBURN'S PREFERENCE - Candy - Pangburn Candy Co.

MRS. PATTERSON'S - Food products - Hormel Foods Corp.

MRS. PAUL'S - Frozen foods - CSC Brands, Inc.

MRS. PAUL'S - Seafood products–fresh or frozen - Mrs. Paul's Kitchen

MRS. PAUL'S LIGHT - Seafood products–fresh or frozen - Mrs. Paul's Kitchen

MRS. PENNYDOODLE - Video production - Amy Miller Schwartz

MRS. PENNYPACKER - Food products ☆ - Little Crow Foods

MRS. POTATO HEAD - Toys - Playskool, Inc.

MRS. PURE'S - Cookies - Pure's Food Specialities Inc.

MRS. RENFRO'S - Food products - Renfro Foods Inc.

MRS. RICHARDSON - Confections - Richardson-T Foods Corp.

MRS. RINCK'S - Food products - King's Food Products Inc.

MRS. SANTA CLAUS - Dolls ☆ - Effanbee Doll Corp.

MRS. SCHLORER'S - Pickles - Venice Maid Co. Inc.

MRS. SCHULER'S - Candy ☆ - Brock Candy Co. Inc.

MRS. SHEARER'S - Candy - Tastysnack Inc.

MRS. SHWOM'S - Candy ☆ - Eddyleon Chocolate Co. Inc.

MRS. SLABY'S - Noodles - Kosto Food Products Co.

MRS. SMITH SMART STYLE - Pies–frozen ☆ - Kellogg Co.

MRS. SMITH'S - Desserts - Mrs. Smith's Inc.

MRS. STEWART'S - Laundries–coin-operated - Luther Ford & Co.

MRS. STOVER'S - Candy ☆ - Russell Stover Candies, Inc.

MRS. SULLIVAN'S - Pastries - Mrs. Sullivan's Pies Inc.

MRS. TAKI'S KIDS - Apparel stores–sports - Mrs. Taki's Kids

MRS. TIGGY-WINKLE - Puzzles - Frederick Warne & Co., Inc.

MRS. TONE - Food flavorings - Tone Brothers, Inc.

MRS. T'S - Food products - Ateeco, Inc.

MRS. T'S COOKIES - Gourmet cookies - HDS Services

MRS. TUCKER'S - Salad dressings–bottled - Kraft Food Ingredients Corp.

MRS. TURRI'S - Food products - Turri's Italian Foods Inc.

MRS. VESLEY - Noodles - Vesley Foods Inc.

MRS. WAGES - Food products - Dacus Food Group Inc.

MRS. WARREN'S - Frozen-food products - Island Poultry Farm Inc.

MRS. WEAVERS - Food products - Dean Foods Co.

MRS. WEBER'S - Macaroni - Western Globe Products Inc.

MRS. WEINBERG'S - Food products - Mrs. Weinberg's Food Products Corp.

MRS. WEINBERG'S - Meat products - Shofar Kosher Foods, Inc.

MRS. WEINSTEIN'S TOFFEE SANTA BARBARA - Candy - Lotte Weinstein

MRS. WIGGLES ROCKET JUICES - Juices - Garratt & Gunn Ltd.

MRS. WILSON'S - Doughnuts - Holsum Bakers

MRS. WINNER'S SUPER CINNAMON SWIRL - Rolls–dinner - Mrs. Winner's

MRS. WOODS - Pickles - Pikle-Rite Co. Inc.

MRS. WRIGHT'S - Bakery products - Safeway Stores Inc.

MRS. WRIGHT'S WINNERS - Breads - Safeway Inc.

MRSAUNA - Controls–heating systems - Sussman-Automatic Corp.

MRT MORAL RECONATION THERAPY - Educational materials - Eagle Wing Books, Inc.

MRTI - Telephones - Motorola, Inc. (Land Mobile Products Sector)

MRTV - Cameras–video - Video Link

MRV - Vitamins and nutritional supplements - Health Products Corp.

MRVL - Musical instrument accessories - Success Enterprises Inc.

MRX - Antiseptics - Gena Laboratories Inc.

MRX - Skin care products - Mahdeen Laboratory

MRX HYDRATING LOTION - Skin care products - Gena Laboratories Inc.

MS - Adhesives and sealants - Synthetic Surfaces Inc.

MS - Bins - Mobile Storage Group, Inc.

MS - Cigarettes - G.A. Georgopulo & Co. Inc.

MS - Computer software - Island Software

MS - Floor coverings - Congoleum Corp.

M.S. - Frames–eyeglass - Zylo Ware Corp.

MS - Golfing equipment - Pinseeker Golf Corp.

MS. - Handbags ☆ - Hazan Imports Corp.

M.S. - Locks–door - Adams Rite Manufacturing Co.

MS - Recording label - Jazz Composer's Orchestra Association Inc.

MS 7 - Golfing equipment - Mizuno Corp. of America

MS-179 - Health care products - Wholesale Medical Import

MS-1000X BASE - Clamps–metal - Sign-Up Corp.

MS-2000X BASE - Clamps–metal - Sign-Up Corp.

MS.-AIDS - Health care products - Medique Products

MS. B - Recording label - Vision Records Inc.

MS. BARCO - Uniforms–tailored ☆ - Barco of California

MS. BESTIEN - Handbags - Robert Bestien

MS BIOSCIENCE - Chemical preparations - Milk Specialties Co.

MS. CHEESECAKE - Cakes - Boyer Printing Co.

MS CONTIN - Analgesics - Purdue Frederick Co.

MS. D. - Prophylactics - Finley Co.

MS DESIGN - Apparel–women's - M.S. Design, Inc.

MS. DESSERTS - Bakery products - Boyer Printing Co.

MS DIANE'S MUSCADINE JAM - Jams and jellies - Old South Winery

MS DIANE'S MUSCADINE WINE JELLY - Jams and jellies - Old South Winery

MS. DINGO - Footwear - Acme Boot Co., Inc.

MS-DOS - Computer software ☆ - Microsoft Corp.

MS. ENDURO - Bicycles - Schwinn Cycling & Fitness Inc.

MS. ENERGY PLUS - Orthopedic products - Foot Levelers, Inc.

MS ENTERTAINMENT - Recording label - GP Records & Tapes

MS. EXECUTIVE - Toys–stuffed ☆ - Commonwealth Toy and Novelty Co. Inc.

MS. FITNESS ACTIVEWEAR - Apparel–athletic - Wally Boyko Productions, Inc.

MS. FITNESS DIET PROGRAM - Food products - Wally Boyko Productions, Inc.

MS. FITNESS EXERCISE EQUIPMENT - Exercising equipment - Wally Boyko Productions, Inc.

MS. FLAIR - Dolls - Totsy Manufacturing Co., Inc.

MS. FROSTY - Shirts - Commander Garment Co.

MS. GOLDBERG - Greeting cards ☆ - Shulsinger Sales Inc.

MS INTERNATIONAL - Cigarettes - G.A. Georgopulo & Co. Inc.

MS. JANE'S FAVORITES - Cookies - New Success International, Inc.

MS. JIBBA JABBER - Toys - ERTL Co., Inc.

MS. KAY - Hair care products - Tu-K Industries Inc.

MS. KAY BIONIC - Hair care products - Tu-K Industries Inc.

MS. KNITS - Apparel and accessories - Burton Manufacturing Co.

MS. LEE - Jeans–women's ☆ - Lee Apparel Co. Inc.

MS. LEE RIDERS - Jeans–women's - Lee Apparel Co. Inc.

MS. LOVELADY - Greeting cards - Todd Warner Graphics Inc.

MS. LUBBABLE - Toys–stuffed - Russ Berrie and Co., Inc.

MS. MARISSA - Apparel and accessories - Goodman Knitting Co. Inc.

MS MEDICAL SOLUTIONS, INC. - Computer software - Medical Solutions, Inc.

MS. MEGA - Vitamins and nutritional supplements - Randal Nutritional Products Inc.

MS. MICHELLE - Apparel and accessories - Fritzi California

MS. MODEM - Posters - Elizabeth M. Ferrarini

MS. PAC-MAN - Chewing gum ☆ - Fleer Corp.

MS PERC - Drums–musical instruments ☆ - Reunion Blues Corp.

MS. PRO AERO-CIZERS - Footwear–athletic - Wal-Mart Stores Inc.

MS RACING - Motorcycle parts and accessories - Ed Tucker Distributor, Inc.

MS. RUSS - Apparel–women's - Russ Togs Inc.

MS/RV - Motor vehicles - Jervis B. Webb Co.

MS. SKINNY WAIST - Apparel and accessories - Strouse, Adler Co.

MS. SNEAKY - Cleaning preparations - Ronald A. Stielau

MS. SPORTS - Socks - Adams-Millis Corp.

MS. TEEN - Brassieres (Bras) - Gelmart Industries Inc.

MS. VALUE - Underwear and nightwear ☆ - Lovable Co.

MS. VICTORIA ROSE - Chocolate candy - Superior Fruit & Confections

MS. WEAR - Apparel–women's - Workwear Corp. Inc.

MS2 - Cables - Minnesota Mining & Manufacturing Co.

MS100 - Frames–eyeglass - Rozin Optical Export Corp.

MS234NEC - Measuring instruments - Humidial Corp.

MSA - Coatings - Sherwin-Williams Automotive Finishes Corp.

MSA - Pet products - Nekton USA Inc.

MSA - Sporting goods ☆ - MSA

MSA COMFO - Plugs–ear - MSA

MSA MIDI - Sound equipment - Castiglione Accordion

MSB - Recording label - Sonic Group Ltd.

MSB PLUS REV 2 - Electronic equipment - J.L. Cooper Electronics

MSC - Compressors - Dunham Bush, Inc.

MSC/ARIES - Computer software - Macneal-Schwendler Corp.

MSC/DYTRAN - Computer software - Macneal-Schwendler Corp.

MSC/EMC - Computer software - Macneal-Schwendler Corp.

MSC TECHNOLOGIES - Computer software - Mouse Systems Corp.

MSC/XL - Computer software - Macneal-Schwendler Corp.

MSD - Diamond powder - General Electric Co.

MSD - Pumps - Sulzer Bingham Pumps Inc.

☆ = Now out of production

MSDIMAGE - Computer software - Nuparadigm Imaging, Inc.
MSDS ACCESS - Computer software - Resource Consultants, Inc.
MSDS AUTHOR - Computer software - Resource Consultants, Inc.
MSE - Coatings - Sherwin-Williams Automotive Finishes Corp.
MSE - Sealing devices - Greene, Tweed of Delaware, Inc.
M.S.F. - Frames–picture ☆ - A.P.F. Master Framemaker
MSG-600 - Pharmaceutical preparations ☆ - Roberts/Hauck Pharmaceuticals Inc.
MSI - Computer software - MSI Software, Inc.
MSI - Labels–paper - Media Solutions, Inc.
MSI - Trailers - Mobile Structures, Inc.
MSI/MICRO STAR - Computer software - Softeasy Software, Inc.
MSIR - Analgesics - Purdue Frederick Co.
MSL - Handbags - Michael Stevens Ltd.
MSL - Hearing aids - Mid-States Laboratories Inc.
MSL - Mufflers–motor vehicle - Goerlich's
MSL MAXIMUM - Mufflers–motor vehicle - Goerlich's
MSM CRYSTALS - Health care products - Frye Co.
MSNBC - Computer software - MSNBC Cable LLC
MSOE - Paper–writing - Milwaukee School of Engineering
MSOFTWARE - Computer software - MSoftware Inc.
MSP - Computer hardware - Analog Devices, Inc.
MSP - Cylinders - American Cylinder Co., Inc.
MSP - Hearing aids - Audiotone, Inc.
MSR - Motorcycle parts and accessories - Ed Tucker Distributor, Inc.
MSRS - Cleaning preparations - Morris Morgan
MSS - Computer software - Gulf State Computer Services Inc.
MSST - Deodorizers ☆ - Lumi-Lite Candle Co. Inc.
MST - Shoes–athletic - Mizuno Corp. of America
MSTERA - Papier-mache articles - Siamese Imports Co.
MSU - Coatings - Sherwin-Williams Automotive Finishes Corp.
MSV - Motor vehicles–buses - Mauck Special Vehicles, Inc.
MT - Doors–glass - Monarch Shower Doors & Glass, Inc.
M.T. - Frames–eyeglass - May Optical Co. Inc.
MT - Golfing equipment - MacGregor Golf Co.
M.T. 150 - Tobacco products - Alfred & Christian Petersen U.S. Ltd.
M.T. FEEDER - Bird feeds - John A. Van Den Bosch Co.
MTA - Automotive parts and accessories - GHI Automotive Services, Inc.
MTA - Computer equipment - Specialix, Inc.
MTA SERIES - Electronic equipment ☆ - RMS Electronics, Inc.
MTC - Computer hardware - Micro Technology Concepts, Inc.
MTC - Computer storage devices - Modern Technologies Corp.
MTC - Electronic equipment - Monitoring Technology Corp.
MTC - Electronics equipment - Windmere Corp.
MTC - Medical apparatus - Collins Mobile-Tech Corp.
MTC - Pet products - RT 4 Marine Technology Inc.
MTD - Antennas - Alliance Telecommunications Corp.
MTD - Archery equipment ☆ - Martin Archery Inc.
MTD - Guitars - Michael Tobias Design
MTD - Tractors–lawn - MTD Products Inc.
MTD YARD MACHINES - Tractors–lawn - MTD Products Inc.
MTE - Recording label - Master-Trak Sound Recorders
MTE CORPORATION - Electronic equipment - MTE Corp.
MTF - Transmission fluids - Torco International Corp.
MTG GOLF - Apparel and accessories - MTG Golf, Inc.
MTI - Cameras–television - Dage-Mti, Inc.
MTI - Machine parts - Machine Technology, Inc.
MTI - Soccer equipment - Maxima Trading Co.
MTI MATHEMATICAL TECHNOLOGIES INC. - Computer software - Mathematical Technologies Inc.
MTI OASIS - Computer software - MTI Technology Corp.
M.T.IT - Motor vehicle parts and accessories - TCI Environmental Services, Inc.
MTK 80 - Polishing rouge - Pacific Piano Supply Co.
MTL - Electrical equipment - MTL, Inc.
MTM - Electron tubes - American International Technologies, Inc.
MTM - Window coverings - Levolor Inc.
MTM10/20 - Gauging instruments - Krautkramer-Branson Inc.
MTN. PEAK - Bicycles - Columbia Manufacturing Inc.
MTN TAMER - Bicycles - Dynacraft Industries Inc.
MTN TEK - Bicycles - Pederson Development Co.
MTO INTERNATIONAL - Apparel and accessories - Venture Stores, Inc.
MTR - Computer software - Manufacture Technology Resource Corp.
MTR - Thermostats - Windmere Corp.
MTRC - Wheelchairs - Labac Systems, Inc.
MTROPOLIS - Computer software - MFactory, Inc.

MTRPOWERIO - Computer peripheral equipment - Manufacture Technology Resource Corp.
MTS - Electronic equipment - Seal Products Inc.
MTS - Hobby kits ☆ - Fidelity Electronics International Inc.
MTS - Pallets–wood - Recyclable Containers Co.
MTS - Tool boxes - Mechanic's Time Savers, Inc.
MTS 2000 - Water purification systems - Shaklee Corp.
MTS SEATING - Chairs–wood - Michigan Tube Swagers and Fabricators, Inc.
MTSSOFTWARE - Computer software - Multiple Teaching Systems, Inc.
MTU - Apparel and accessories - Board of Control of Michigan Technological University
MTU - Containers - Computer Aided Systems, Inc.
MTV - Sunglasses ☆ - Riviera Trading, Inc.
MTV MUSIC TELEVISION BOOKS - Publisher's imprints - Viacom International Inc.
MTV MUSIC TELEVISION HOME VIDEO - Recording label - Viacom International Inc.
MTV SPORTS - Apparel and accessories - Viacom International Inc.
MTW - Apparel–athletic - Minnesota Professional Basketball Ltd.
MTX - Tires - Michelin Tire Corp.
MTX-2000 - Chemical preparations - Klm Products, Inc.
MTX-MAGNUM - Bicycles ☆ - Kent International Inc.
MTX SOUNDCRAFTSMEN - Audio equipment - MTX
M.U. - Thread ☆ - Perfect Thread Co. Inc.
MU INC. - Electron tubes ☆ - ARS Electronics
MU-JUICE - Fuel - Mugen USA, Ltd.
MU MU - Confections ☆ - R.L. Albert & Son, Inc.
MU-PSYCH - Recording label - Futurehealth Inc.
MU-TRON - Electronic equipment - Fender Musical Instruments
MUC-X - Medical apparatus - Utah Medical Products, Inc.
MUCAID - Health care products - Vygon Corp.
MUCH CLUTCH - Wallets - Buxton Inc.
MUCHA - Apparel and accessories - Mucha, Ltd.
MUCHO - Candy ☆ - Topps Co., Inc.
MUCHO GUSTO - Beverages–carbonated - Globe International Inc.
MUCHO MEALS - Food products - Zuzu, Inc.
MUCHO NACHO - Nuts–salted, roasted, cooked, or canned ☆ - Sonne Laboratories
MUCHOS - Snack foods - MFC
MUCILOSE - Laxatives ☆ - Winthrop Pharmaceuticals
MUCILTEX - Pharmaceutical preparations ☆ - Veratex Group
MUCK MASTER - Sporting goods - Equestrian International Products
MUCKER - Machinery - Baker-Bohnert/Service Group
MUCKY DUCK - Mustard - Mucky Duck Mustard
MUCO-FEN-LA - Expectorant - Wakefield Pharmaceuticals, Inc.
MUCODIL - Pharmaceutical preparations ☆ - Jones Medical Industries, Inc. (Medical Div.)
MUCOMYST - Pharmaceutical preparations - Bristol-Myers Squibb Co.
MUCOPLEX - Vitamins and nutritional supplements ☆ - Zeneca Inc.
MUCOSOL - Pharmaceutical preparations ☆ - Dey Laboratories, Inc.
MUCOSPERSE - Surgical supplies - Marlen Manufacturing & Developing Co.
MUCOTIN - Antacids ☆ - Warner-Lambert Co.
MUCOTUSS - Pharmaceutical preparations ☆ - Jones Medical Industries, Inc. (Medical Div.)
MUD BRUTE - Tires - Dunlop Tire Corp.
MUD-BUG - Fishing lures - Fred Arbogast Co. Inc.
MUD CAMPAIGNER - Tires - Dunlop Tire Corp.
MUD CLIMBER - Bicycles - Kent International Inc.
MUD CRUNCHERS - Footwear - SRL, Inc.
MUD FLATS - Shoes - Smith & Hawken, Ltd.
MUD GLOVE, THE - Gloves–work - Little's Good Gloves, Inc.
MUD HAWG, THE - Wheelbarrows - Trallfa U.S. Inc.
MUD HOG - Pumps - ITT Marlow
MUD JUMPER - Toys ☆ - Today's Kids Inc.
MUD KING XT - Tires - Uniroyal Goodrich Licensing Services, Inc.
MUD MASTER - Toys - Tonka Corp.
MUD MIRACLE - Hair care products - St. Ives Laboratories, Inc.
MUD PACK - Skin care products - Para Laboratories Inc.
MUD PIE - Vegetables–dried - Mud Pie Frozen Foods, Inc.
MUD PUPPIES - Apparel–athletic - K.C. Thomas
MUD PUPPY - Bicycles ☆ - Huffy Corp.
MUD RUNNER PICKUP - Toys - Tonka Corp.
MUDAN - Musical instruments - Multivox/Sorkin Music Co. Inc.
MUDBUSTER - Machinery - Textron Inc.
MUDD - Cosmetics - Chattem Inc.
MUDD - Hats - HYP

☆ = Now out of production

MUDD RACK - Shoe trees - Clairson International Corp.
MUDD SPA TREATMENT MASKS - Skin care products - Chattem Inc.
MUDDLER MINNOW - Sporting goods - Weber Industries Inc.
MUDDSLINGER - Toys–automobiles - Nikko America, Inc.
MUDDY BUDDY - Motor vehicle parts and accessories - Uretech International Inc.
MUDDY PUDDY - Clay–modeling - Hebo, Inc.
MUDHUT HAND CRAFTED CERAMICS - Tiles–ceramic - Altman Specialty Plants, Inc.
MUDMAX - Bicycles - Ritchey Design Inc.
MUDMISER - Containers–metal - Robert E. Bode
MUDRANE - Pharmaceutical preparations - ECR Pharmaceuticals
MUDRANE GG - Pharmaceutical preparations - ECR Pharmaceuticals
MUDSHARK PORTER - Beverages–malt - Fish Brewing Co.
MUDSLIDE - Coffee - Cameron Coffee Co. Inc.
MUDSLIDE - Spices and extracts - Reeves Enterprises, Inc.
MUDSLINGER - Bicycles ✩ - Huffy Corp.
MUELLER - Cold remedies - Mueller Sports Medicine Inc.
MUELLER - Food products - John Sommer Inc.
MUELLER - Furniture - Haworth, Inc.
MUELLER - Tanks–storage - Paul Mueller Co.
MUELLER KOLD - Cold remedies - Mueller Sports Medicine Inc.
MUELLER REFRIGERATION PRODUCTS CO. - Air conditioning equipment - Mueller Industries, Inc.
MUELLERGESIC - Analgesics - Mueller Sports Medicine Inc.
MUELLER'S - Macaroni - Best Foods/Mueller Co.
MUENCHENER - Beverages–malt - Anheuser-Busch Companies Inc.
MUENSTER MOUSE - Toys–stuffed - Russ Berrie and Co., Inc.
MUESLI - Cereal - Ralston Purina Co.
MUESLI - Cereal ✩ - New Morning
MUESLIX - Cereal - Kellogg Co.
MUFFABLE MUFFANIMALS - Prerecorded video cassettes - Cinnamuffs, Inc.
MUFFELT - Musical instrument accessories - Eric J. Behrenfeld
MUFFIES - Crocheted and knitted items ✩ - Reliable of Milwaukee
MUFFIN - Dolls - Alexander Doll Co. Inc.
MUFFIN-A-DAY - Muffins - American Marketplace Foods, Inc.
MUFFIN BATTER IN POUCH PAKS - Bakery products–frozen - Dawn Food Products Inc.
MUFFIN BEAR - Toys–stuffed ✩ - Dakin Inc.
MUFFIN PATCH - Bakery products - Muffin Patch, Inc.
MUFFIN QUICK BREAD MIX - Breads–mixes - Dawn Food Products Inc.
MUFFIN TIN, THE - Bakery products - AMT Inc.
MUFFIN TOP PAN - Housewares - C.M. Products, Inc.
MUFFIN TOPPERS - Bakery products - Seymour's Bakery, Inc.
MUFFIN TOPS - Bakery products - Prairie City Bakery Co.
MUFFIN WORKS - Cookware - Amco Corp.
MUFFINS - Slippers - Magic Slipper Co.
MUFFINS - Socks - Fischer Hosiery Co.
MUFFINS & MORE - Muffins - Interstate Brands Corp.
MUFFIT - Musical instrument accessories ✩ - XL Specialty Percussion
MUFFKIN COLLECTION, THE - Dolls and toys - Cinnamuffs, Inc.
MUFFLE-GARD - Marine rigging - W.H. Salisbury & Co.
MUFFLEKOTE - Coatings - Henry Co.
MUFFLING - Infant product ✩ - S. Schwab Co., Inc.
MUFFUNS - Bakery products - Pillsbury Co.
MUFFY - Toys–stuffed - North American Bear Co. Inc.
MUFFY CHEERLEADER - Dolls ✩ - Dakin Inc.
MUG - Beverages–carbonated - Pepsi-Cola Co.
#L'MUG - Containers–glass - Gritman Corp.
MUG AND KISSES - Glassware–household ✩ - Four Score Inc.
MUG-BUOY - Housewares - Orbex Inc.
MUG COLLECTION - Giftware - Waterford Wedgewood USA, Inc.
MUG 'EMS - Dishes–earthenware - Mug Shanty
MUG GREETINGS - Glassware–household - Four Score Inc.
MUG MAT - Hardware - Devon Corp.
MUG MATES - Kitchenware–earthenware - Natural Products Corp.
MUG-O-LUNCH - Food products ✩ - General Mills, Inc.
MUG OLD FASHIONED - Beverages–carbonated - Pepsico, Inc.
MUG PEOPLE - Glassware–household ✩ - Papel Freelance, Inc.
MUG + PLUSH - Giftware ✩ - National Housewares
MUG RUG - Hardware - Devon Corp.
MUG RUGS - Containers–insulated - Michael L. Meier
MUG RUGS - Housewares ✩ - Ludlow Composites Corp.
MUG SHANTY - Dishes–earthenware - Mug Shanty
MUG SHOT - Glass products ✩ - Eagle Glass Products
MUG SHOTS - Games - Flying Buffalo Inc.

MUG SHOTS - Labels–paper - William J. Motovick
MUG SLANTS - Glassware–household - Papel Freelance, Inc.
MUG TALK - Glassware–household ✩ - Papel Freelance, Inc.
MUG WAMP INK - Decals and transfers - Kim Stankey
MUGALOON - Glassware–household - Staci-Lisa Enterprises Inc.
MUGGER - Hardware - Devon Corp.
MUGGER - Wood mug rack ✩ - Interdesign, Inc.
MUGGER STOPPER - Alarm systems–burglar - Safety Technology International, Inc.
MUGGER, THE - Novelty items–glass - Elkhart Door Inc.
MUGGLES - Dolls - Margaret Lynden
MUGGS - Pet products ✩ - Best Feeds and Farm Supplies Inc.
MUGHLAI ZAIKA FINE CUISINE - Meat products - Abdul Hafiz Ismail
MUGHUL-E-AZAM - Spices and extracts - Pexco, Inc.
MUGLEY - Dishes–earthenware - Mug Shanty
MUGLIPPERS - Dishes–earthenware - Mug Shanty
MUGMAKER - Cups–paper - Marla B. Liebling
MUGMASTER - Machine parts - Stahls' Inc.
MUGMATCH - Computer software - Infotec Development, Inc.
MUGRAPS - Dishes–earthenware - Mug Shanty
MUGS BY DEFINITION - Mugs - Fitz & Floyd, Inc.
MUGS-N-TOPS - Glassware–household - Peter Pan Industries
MUGS UNLIMITED - Tableware–earthenware ✩ - Seymour Mann Inc.
MUGSET - Glassware–household - Bartlett-Collins Co.
MUGSY MUTT - Toys–stuffed - Russ Berrie and Co., Inc.
MUGUET - Talcum powders ✩ - Houbigant, Inc.
MUGUET DES BOIS - Perfume, talc, bubble bath, etc. - Coty Inc.
MUHAMMAD ALI - Candy ✩ - Cocoline Chocolate Co.
MUIR - Hoists - South Pacific Associates
MUIR - Marine rigging - Imtra Corp.
MUIRA PUAMAX - Vitamins and nutritional supplements - Organic Diversions, Inc.
MUIRFIELD - Wallpaper ✩ - Wallquest, Inc.
MUIRFIELD VILLAGE - Fabrics–tapestry ✩ - Columbus Coated Fabrics Co.
MUIRFIELD VILLAGE II - Floor coverings–carpet and rugs ✩ - Walter Carpet Mills
MUIRHEAD'S - Beverages–alcohol - Blair Importers Ltd.
MUIRHEAD'S - Whiskey - David Sherman Corp.
MUIRHEAD'S - Whiskey ✩ - Marie Brizard Wines & Spirits, USA
MUIRWOODS - Bicycles - Marin Mountain Bikes, Inc.
MUJER ELEGANTE - Hosiery - Triumph Hosiery Corp.
MUK-LUKS - Crocheted and knitted items - Reliable of Milwaukee
MUKLUK - Pet products ✩ - Rae's Harness Shop
MUL-EN-OL - Antiseptics - Specialty Products Co.
MUL-T-LITE - Glass–safety - Buchmin Industries
MUL. T. PAD - Health care products - Gaymar Industries, Inc.
MULA - Bedding–linen - Dan River Inc.
MULASTICOAT - Coatings - Multicoat Corp.
MULBERRY - Artists' materials - Andrews/Nelson/Whitehead
MULBERRY - Electrical equipment - Mulberry Metal Products Inc.
MULBERRY - Glassware–household ✩ - Fenton Art Glass Co.
MULBERRY - Publisher's imprints - William Morrow and Co. Inc.
MULBERRY PRINTS - Wallpaper - Borden, Inc.
MULBERRY STREET - Yogurt - Sunberry Farms
MULBURRY - Pottery ✩ - Rubens Originals
MULCH GUARD - Garden equipment - Teknor Apex Co.
MULCH-MASTER - Lawn and garden mulcher - Cotter & Co.
MULCH-MAT - Pesticides–agricultural - Dalen Products Inc.
MULCH-N-BAG - Lawn mowers - Murray, Inc.
MULCH-N-RIDE - Machinery - Murray, Inc.
MULCH-R-CATCH - Lawn mowers ✩ - Lawn-Boy
MULE - Beverages–alcohol - Heublein, Inc.
M.U.L.E. - Computer software ✩ - Electronic Arts Inc.
MULE - Fencing–plastic - Geotek, Inc.
MULE ANCHOR - Fencing–gates and posts - Common Sense Fence
MULE CAMP SPRINGS - Cups–plastic - City of Gainesville, Georgia
MULE-HIDE - Adhesives and sealants - Lehon Co.
MULE-TEX - Sporting goods - Muehleisen Manufacturing Co.
MULEEZE - Slippers ✩ - Stanford Professional Products Corp.
MULES - Work gloves - Marmon Holdings, Inc.
MULESKINS - Work clothes - Carhartt, Inc.
MULHAUSEN - Jams and jellies - Westdale Foods Co.
MULHOLLAND - Health care products - Mulholland Positioning Systems Inc.
MULHOLLAND GROWTH - See **GGS**
MULHOLLAND POSITIONING SYSTEMS, INC. - Health care products - Mulholland Positioning Systems Inc.

MULKEY'S - Snack foods - Jac Hes & Co.
MULLEIN - Health care products - Equinox Botanicals, Inc.
MULLEIN - Pharmaceutical preparations - Luyties Pharmacal Co.
MULLEN - Machinery - Standex International Corp.
MULLEN - Sporting goods ☆ - Powell Skateboards
MULLER - Spices and extracts ☆ - C. & J. Willenborg Inc.
MULLER - Wines - Seagram's Chateau & Estate Wines Co.
MULLER SEON - Fabrics ☆ - Leimtex Corp.
MULLET BAY - Apparel—men's - Neutral, Inc.
MULLIGAN - Flowers, plants, and seeds - Jacklin Seed
MULLIGAN FITNESS - Exercising equipment - Precision Machine, Inc.
MULLIGAN NET, THE - Golfing equipment - Keith A. Doyle
MULLINS - Water–distilled - Mullins Spring Water Co.
MULSANNE - Motor vehicles–automobiles ☆ - Bentley Motors Inc.
MULT-A-RANGE - Sights–gun - Horton Manufacturing Co. Inc.
MULT-O - Office machines - Standex International Corp.
MULT-O-MATIC - Guns ☆ - Ponsness-Warren
MULT-O-RING - Notebooks and notepads - Rediform
MULTA-HUE - Candles ☆ - Candle-Lite Co.
MULTABEN - Vitamins and nutritional supplements ☆ - United Food & Fitness Inc.
MULTAGENS + E - Vitamins and nutritional supplements - JMI-Canton Pharmaceuticals
MULTAKOLOR - Paints - Tenax Finishing Product
MULTALAN - Vitamins and nutritional supplements - Lannett Co. Inc.
MULTEE VITAMIN - Vitamins and nutritional supplements - Tawn Ltd.
MULTEEJET - Nozzles - Spraying Systems Co.
MULTEX PUBLISHER - Computer software - Multex Systems, Inc.
MULTEXNET - Computer software - Multex Systems, Inc.
MULTI - Computer software - Green Hills Software Inc.
MULTI - Floor coverings–carpet and rugs ☆ - Rugby Rugs Inc.
MULTI - Strollers–baby - Reebok International Ltd.
MULTI - Toys - Peg Perego USA Inc.
MULTI-75 - Vitamins and nutritional supplements - Fibertone Co.
MULTI-ACCESS - Health care products ☆ - Marquest Medical Products Inc.
MULTI-ACTIVE - Pharmaceutical preparations ☆ - Dermalogica Inc.
MULTI-ACTIVE PROTECTOR - Hair care products - Wella Corp. (Consumer Products Div.)
MULTI-ACTIVITY SHAPES - Toys - Lauri Inc.
MULTI-AD SEARCH - Computer software - Multi-Ad Services Inc.
MULTI-ADD - Latex - Mapei East Corp.
MULTI-APP - Computer software - Membership Collaborative Services, Inc.
MULTI-AXIS - Pipes - Dow Chemical Co.
MULTI AXIS DAMPING - Snowboards - K-2 Corp.
MULTI-BALANCE SYSTEM - Orthopedic products - Accu-Fit, Inc. (Multi-Balance System)
MULTI BAND - Antennas - Wintenna Inc.
MULTI-BEAT - Vacuum cleaners and accessories - Montgomery Ward & Co. Inc.
MULTI-BILLION DOPHILUS - Vitamins and nutritional supplements - Solgar Co. Inc.
MULTI-BOND - Hair care products - L'anza Research International
MULTI-BOT - Toys - Mattel, Inc.
MULTI-BRITE - Paints ☆ - Devoe & Raynolds Co.
MULTI-CALK - Nuts and bolts - Rawlplug Co., Inc.
MULTI CARE - Bandages - Tillotson Healthcare Corp.
MULTI CAT - Pet products - Waverly Mineral Products Co.
MULTI-CAULK - Adhesives and sealants ☆ - Sika Corp.
MULTI-CHROME - Pencils - General Pencil Co.
MULTI-CLEAN - Cleaning preparations - Hako Minuteman Inc.
MULTI COAT - Adhesives and sealants - Multi Coat Corp.
MULTI-COAT - Paints - Waterlox Coatings Corp.
MULTI-COOKER - Kitchen appliances ☆ - Sunbeam-Oster Household Products
MULTI-COPY - Envelopes–paper ☆ - Specialty Envelopes Inc.
MULTI-CRYLIC - Paints - Sophir Morris Paint
MULTI-CULTURALISM A WORLD OF SIMILARITIES - T-shirts–women's - Joyce L. Freeman
MULTI-CURE - Adhesives and sealants - Dymax Corp.
MULTI-DAK - Mats ☆ - U.S. Mat & Rubber Co. Inc.
MULTI-DAY - Electrodes - Uni-Patch
MULTI-DAY - Pharmaceutical preparations - Nature's Bounty, Inc.
MULTI DIET - Vitamins and nutritional supplements ☆ - United Food & Fitness Inc.
MULTI DRUM-VAC - Filters–air - Luwa Bahnson Inc.
MULTI-DUTY - Machine parts - Gates Rubber Co. (Automotive Aftermarket/ Hardware Sales Div.)

MULTI-DUTY - Paints - Perry & Derrick Co.
MULTI-EASE - Artists' materials - Perimeters
MULTI-EDIT - Publisher's imprints - American Cybernetics, Inc.
MULTI-ESSENTIALS - Vitamins and nutritional supplements - MXM Essential Formulas Inc.
MULTI-FACET - Jewelry - Sterling Inc.
MULTI FILE - Boxes ☆ - Newell Office Products
MULTI-FILL - Lighters - Ronson Consumer Products Corp.
MULTI-FILL - Machinery - Multi-Fill, Inc.
MULTI-FLEX - Garden equipment ☆ - Pro-Mark Corp.
MULTI-FLEX - Health care products - Cramer Products Inc.
MULTI-FLEX - Medical apparatus - Safariland Ltd., Inc.
MULTI-FLUSH - Toilets–enameled ☆ - Premier Plastics
MULTI-FOLDS - Ophthalmic goods ☆ - Luxottica
MULTI-FRESH - Soap - Minuteman International, Inc.
MULTI FRESH POTPOURRI - Deodorizers - Sterling Drug Inc.
MULTI-FRI - Kitchen appliances ☆ - Nordic Ware
MULTI-FUEL - Lanterns–kerosene - Coleman Co., Inc.
MULTI-GAGE - Electronic equipment - Flexbar Machine Corp.
MULTI GARD - Locks–door - Truth Hardware Corp.
MULTI-GEL - Vitamins and nutritional supplements - J.R. Carlson Laboratories Inc.
MULTI-GERM - Pharmaceutical preparations ☆ - Viobin U.S.A.
MULTI-GINSENG - Vitamins and nutritional supplements - General Nutrition Investment Co.
MULTI GRAIN CHEERIOS - Cereal - General Mills, Inc.
MULTI-GRAPHIC - Electronic equipment - Bogen Communications, Inc.
MULTI GREEN - Food processors - White Consolidated Industries, Inc.
MULTI GREEN - Soap - Gojo Industries, Inc.
MULTI GRIP - Exercising equipment - Self-Image Sports & Fitness Co.
MULTI-GRIP - Paints - Jones Blair Co.
MULTI GRIPPER - Adhesives and sealants - Golden Grip Products Inc.
MULTI-GUARD - Paints - Martin Paint Stores
MULTI-GUARD - Vinyl backing - Tarkett, Inc.
MULTI GUIRO - Drums–musical instruments - LP Music Group
MULTI IMAGE - Containers–plastic - Gelardi Design & Development, Inc.
MULTI-JECTOR - Hardware - B & G Equipment Co.
MULTI-JET - Erasers ☆ - Bright Boy Abrasives
MULTI-JUST - Archery equipment ☆ - Bear Archery Inc.
MULTI-KRAFT16 - Fabrics - Wangner Systems Corp.
MULTI-LAB - Toys - Tyco Toys
MULTI-LAYER - Skin care products - Frances Denney
MULTI-LENS - Lenses–optical - J.B. Holden Co.
MULTI-LIFT - Clutches–industrial - Access Unlimited
MULTI-LINEAR - Editing equipment–photographic - Editing Technologies Corp.
MULTI-LINK - Computers - Western Telematic Inc.
MULTI-LITE - Lighting fixtures ☆ - Prestigeline Inc.
MULTI-LOC - Identification tags - Bock's Cattle-Identi Co.
MULTI-LOK - Clamps - Band-It-Idex Inc.
MULTI-LUBE - Lubricants - Ronson Consumer Products Corp.
MULTI-MAG - Eyeglasses - Paralax, Inc.
MULTI MAGIC - Game machines - WMS Gaming Inc.
MULTI MARKER - Markers–felt-tip - Gillette Co.
MULTI-MARX - Self-inking stamps - Consolidated Stamp Manufacturing Co. Inc.
MULTI-MASTER - Ladders–metal - Werner Co.
MULTI-MASTIC - Finishing agents - Witco Corp.
MULTI-MAT - Floor coverings - Ludlow Composites Corp.
MULTI-MATO - Food products - Pet Inc.
MULTI-MAX - Vitamins and nutritional supplements ☆ - Makers of Kal, Inc.
MULTI-MED - Home health care products - Baxter International Inc.
MULTI MEDIA - File folders - Supreme Equipment & Systems Corp.
MULTI-MEDIA EXPRESS - Office supplies - McBee Loose Leaf Binders
MULTI-MEDIA SCINTILLA - Glass products ☆ - Hunt Manufacturing Co.
MULTI-METALS - Tools - Multt Metals
MULTI-MIL - Paints - Hempel Coatings USA Inc.
MULTI-MILE - Tires - TBC Corp.
MULTI MILER - Antennas - Wintenna Inc.
MULTI-MINERALS - Vitamins and nutritional supplements - Fibertone Co.
MULTI-MINERALS - Vitamins and nutritional supplements - Freeda Vitamins Inc.
MULTI-MIRROR - Projectors–photographic - General Electric Co.
MULTI-MIST - Hair care products - L'anza Research International
MULTI-MIX - Giftware - Highland Laboratories Inc.
MULTI-MODAL - Laboratory equipment and supplies - Toxi-Lab, Inc.

☆ = Now out of production

MULTI-MODE - Office furniture—metal ☆ - Marvel Group Inc.

MULTI-MODEM - Computers - Multi-Tech Systems, Inc.

MULTI MOP - Mops - Ardel of America Inc.

MULTI-NATIONAL POLICE AGAINST CRIME AND TURMOIL - Toys - Toymax Inc.

MULTI-NET - Electronic equipment - Siltron Illumination, Inc.

MULTI-NET - Radio communications equipment - E.F. Johnson Co.

MULTI NUTRIENTS - Vitamins and nutritional supplements - Ethical Nutrients

MULTI-OILSTONE - Abrasive products - Norton Co.

MULTI-OP - Cameras–video - Bio-Dental Technologies, Inc.

MULTI-ORBIT - Dishwashers–household - General Electric Co.

MULTI PAC - Substance detector - National Draeger, Inc.

MULTI-PACK - Medical apparatus - Apex Medical Corp.

MULTI-PAK - Contact lenses - Evans Case Co.

MULTI-PAK - Hairpins - Almar Sales Co., Inc.

MULTI/PAK - Heating equipment - Slant/Fin Corp.

MULTI-PALETTE - Paper - Hunt Manufacturing Co.

MULTI PASTEL - Pencils - General Pencil Co.

MULTI-PAY PLUS - Video games - WMS Gaming Inc.

MULTI-PAY POKER - Video games - WMS Gaming Inc.

MULTI PET - Pet products - Mardel Laboratories, Inc.

MULTI PHOENIX - Vitamins and nutritional supplements - Concord Chemists

MULTI-PHONE - Electronic equipment - Hamilton Electronics Corp.

MULTI-PIC - Photographic equipment - Heindl Masks 'n' Mounts

MULTI-PITCH - Cupolas ☆ - Aluminum Co. of America

MULTI-PLANE - Computer software - Spectra-Physics Laserplane, Inc.

MULTI-PLEX - Fertilizers - Jonathan Green, Inc.

MULTI-PLIER - Tools–hand-operated - Fiskars Inc.

MULTI-PLIER MULTI-PURPOSE - Tools - Gerber Legendary Blades

MULTI-POD - Photographic equipment - SP Systems/Saratons

MULTI POINT - Computer software ☆ - CAP Automation

MULTI POLLEN QUEST - Vitamins and nutritional supplements - Nutri-West

MULTI-POST - Paper ☆ - Master Products Manufacturing Inc.

MULTI POWER - Vitamins and nutritional supplements - United Food & Fitness Inc.

MULTI-POWER - Wire - General Cable Corp.

MULTI-POWER 3 - Oils–lubricating - Marathon Oil Co.

MULTI POWER FORMULA L - Vitamins and nutritional supplements ☆ - United Food & Fitness Inc.

MULTI-PRO - Photographic equipment - Berkey Marketing Cos.

MULTI PRO - Tools–power-driven - Dremel

MULTI-PULSE - Water heaters–household - Hydrotherm

MULTI-PUMP - Pumps - Zoeller Co.

MULTI-PUNCH - Tools - Robert Upthegrove

MULTI-PURPOSE ODO - SHIELD - Cleaning preparations - Ameri-Net Industries Inc.

MULTI PURPOSE PRIMERS - Primers - Zynolyte Products Co.

MULTI-PURPOSE THIN-SET - Cement ☆ - Custom Building Products

MULTI-RANGE - Oils–lubricating - Arkla Chemical Corp. (Petroleum Div.)

MULTI-RITE - Office supplies - Steego Corp.

MULTI-ROC - Toys–models ☆ - Estes Industries

MULTI-SCAN - Office supplies - Vemco Corp.

MULTI-SCRUB - Cleaning preparations - Knight Marketing Corp.

MULTI SEAL - Adhesives and sealants - Advetech International, Inc.

MULTI SEAL - Adhesives and sealants - Comstar International Inc. (IPC Div.)

MULTI SEAL - Caulking compounds - Allpro Corp.

MULTI-SEP - Dental compounds - GC America Inc.

MULTI-SERVICE 303 - Motor vehicle parts and accessories - Sunland Refining Corp.

MULTI-SET - Anchors - ITW Ramset/Red Head

MULTI-SET - Fishing rods - Big Jon, Inc.

MULTI-SHEAR - Scissors–hand-operated - Imperial Schrade Corp.

MULTI-SHEEN - Cleaning preparations - Hako Minuteman Inc.

MULTI-SHEEN II - Adhesives and sealants - Hako Minuteman Inc.

MULTI-SIZE - Hardware - Arfco Products, Inc.

MULTI-SIZE - Medical apparatus - Comfort Products Inc.

MULTI-SOCKET - Tools - American-International Tools Industries, Inc.

MULTI-SOUND - Recording label - Multi-Sound Records International

MULTI-SPACE - Containers–metal - Ernst Home Center Inc.

MULTI-SPORT - Braces–orthopedic - Swede-O, Inc.

MULTI-STATION - Exercising equipment - Nautilus Acquisition Inc.

MULTI-STRENGTH - Paints - Hempel Coatings USA Inc.

MULTI-STYLER - Manicure preparations - Larry P. Salvino

MULTI-SURFACE CLEANING GEL - Cleaning preparations - Conklin Co., Inc.

MULTI-SWIVEL - Faucets - Kohler Co.

MULTI-SYSTEM - Office supplies - Georgia-Pacific Corp.

MULTI/TC - Toys ☆ - Peg Perego USA Inc.

MULTI-TECH - Furniture - Ideal Creations Products, Inc.

MULTI-TECH - Water filtration systems - Culligan International Co.

MULTI-TECH 2000 - Steel products - Copperweld Steel Co.

MULTI-TEMP - Curling irons - Windmere Corp.

MULTI-TEMP - Water heaters–household ☆ - Hydrotherm

MULTI-TEX - Wallpaper ☆ - Decorative Coverings Inc.

MULTI-TEX STUCCO SYSTEMS - Plaster–wallboard - Multicoat Corp.

MULTI-THERA - Pharmaceutical preparations - Nature's Bounty, Inc.

MULTI-TOOL - Electrical equipment - GB Electrical Inc.

MULTI-TOTE - Cases–musical instrument - McCormick's

MULTI-TRAC - Surgical instruments - Acufex Microsurgical, Inc.

MULTI-TRACIN & DESIGN - Chemical preparations - Georgia-Pacific Corp.

MULTI-TRACK MAGNETICS - Electronic equipment - Rangertone Research Inc.

MULTI-TRAN - Voltmeters - A.W. Sperry Instruments, Inc.

MULTI-TWIN/2 - Computer software - Andrew Corp.

MULTI-USE - Electrodes - Uni-Patch

MULTI-USE - Welding equipment - Twenty First Century Manufacturing Co.

MULTI-USE PLAY BAR - Infant product - Summer Infant Products Inc.

MULTI V - Vitamins and nutritional supplements - James Fobair

MULTI-VAPOR - Electrical equipment - General Electric Co.

MULTI-VENDOR INTEGRATION PROTOCOL - Pet products - Natural Microsystems

MULTI-VENT - Health care products - Hudson Respiratory Care Inc.

MULTI-VENTS - Hearing aids - Qualitone

MULTI VIEW - Motor vehicle parts and accessories - Carebuild Construction, Inc.

MULTI VIT - Pharmaceutical preparations - Barre-National, Inc.

MULTI-VITA - Vitamins and nutritional supplements - H.R. Cenci Laboratories Inc.

MULTI-VITE - Vitamins and nutritional supplements - Vita-Vista

MULTI-VITE-FLOR - Pharmaceutical preparations ☆ - Par Pharmaceutical Inc.

MULTI-VUE 53 - Contact lenses - Preferred Optics, Inc.

MULTI WAVE - Antennas - Wintenna Inc.

MULTI-WRAP - Health care products - Cramer Products Inc.

MULTI-WRAP - Sporting goods - Trace Athletic Corp.

MULTI-X - Firearms, accessories, and parts - Bausch & Lomb Inc.

MULTI-ZONE - Mattress pads - Bio Clinic Corp.

MULTIA - Computer software - Digital Equipment Corp.

MULTIARRAYIII - Computer hardware - Multi-Tech Systems, Inc.

MULTIAXIS AUTO ALIGNMENT SYSTEM - Automotive equipment - Chisum Products

MULTIBAND PLUS - Computer peripheral equipment - Ascend Communications, Inc.

MULTIBANK - Integrated circuits - Monolithic System Technology, Inc.

MULTIBAR - Furnaces–industrial - Surface Combustion, Inc.

MULTIBILL - Computer software - Electronic Data Systems Corp.

MULTIBIN - Artists' materials - Loew-Cornell Inc.

MULTIBINDER - Binders - Radmar Inc.

MULTIBLITZ - Lighting equipment - Sureguard, Inc.

MULTIBLITZ - Photographic equipment - R.T.S. Inc.

MULTIBLITZ - Photographic equipment ☆ - H.P. Marketing Corp.

MULTIBLOCK - Paints - Triangle Coatings Inc.

MULTIBOND - Paints - Franklin International, Inc.

MULTIBRITE - Electronic equipment - EIT, Inc.

MULTIBROM - Water purification systems - Western Water Management, Inc.

MULTIBUCKER - Musical instrument accessories - Dimarzio, Inc.

MULTICAP - Capacitors - Constant Velocity Transmission Lines, Inc.

MULTICARD - Circuit boards - Apex Data, Inc.

MULTICEBRIN - Vitamins and nutritional supplements - Eli Lilly and Co.

MULTICIPHER - Transmitting apparatus–television - California Amplifier

MULTICLUSTERU - Computer hardware - Multi-Tech Systems, Inc.

MULTICOLOR - Lighters - Colibri Inc.

MULTICOLOR - Paper - Permalin Products Co.

MULTICOLOR BY DESIGN - Computer integrated systems design services - Multicolor Specialties Inc.

MULTICOM - Computer software - Multicom Publishing, Inc.

MULTICOM PC - Computers - Multi-Tech Systems, Inc.

MULTICOMASYNCGATEWAY - Computer hardware - Multi-Tech Systems, Inc.

MULTICOMASYNCGATEWAYII - Computer software - Multi-Tech Systems, Inc.

MULTICOMASYNCGATEWAYTSR - Computer software - Multi-Tech Systems, Inc.

MULTICOMBRIDGE - Computer software - Multi-Tech Systems, Inc.

MULTICOMRNGATEWAY - Computer software - Multi-Tech Systems, Inc.

☆ = Now out of production

MULTICURL - Curling irons–electric - Helene Curtis Industries Inc.
MULTICUT - Abrasive products - Minnesota Mining & Manufacturing Co.
MULTICUT - Paper cutters ☆ - Standard Duplicating Machines Corp.
MULTIDART - Toys ☆ - Placo Products Co.
MULTIDATA - Electronics equipment - Barco Inc.
MULTIDEX - Office supplies - ACCO USA, Inc.
MULTIDEX - Pharmaceutical - Lange Medical Associates
MULTIDOC - Computer software - Foundation Solutions, Inc.
MULTIDODGE - Photographic equipment - LogEtronics Corp.
MULTIDOPHILUS - Vitamins and nutritional supplements - Solaray
MULTIDSU - Computer hardware - Multi-Tech Systems, Inc.
MULTIEXPRESS - Computer software - Multi-Tech Systems, Inc.
MULTIEXPRESSFAX - Computer hardware - Multi-Tech Systems, Inc.
MULTIEXPRESSPCS - Computer software - Multi-Tech Systems, Inc.
MULTIFACE - Audio equipment - Pro-Co. Sound Co. Inc.
MULTIFASTENER - Hardware - Multifastener Corp.
MULTIFAX - Computer software and hardware - William G. Schwittek
MULTIFELT - Fabrics - Car Del
MULTIFEX - Calcium compounds - Minerals Technologies Inc.
MULTIFEX - Digital encoders - Peavey Electronics Corp.
MULTIFIBER - Particle board - Georgia-Pacific Corp.
MULTIFILTER - Cigarettes - Philip Morris Companies Inc.
MULTIFINDER - Computer software - Apple Computer Inc.
MULTIFIT - Machinery parts - Tripac International, Inc.
MULTIFIT - Vaporizers - Medical Molding Corp. of America
MULTIFLEC - Floor coverings - Mannington Resilient Floors
MULTIFLEX - Builders' hardware - H.B. Ives
MULTIFLEX - Glass–window - Croft Metals Inc.
MULTIFLEX - Health care products - Medtronic Nortech
MULTIFLEX - Sprinklers–lawn - Orbit Irrigation Products, Inc.
MULTIFLOR - Floor coverings - Tarkett, Inc.
MULTIFOCUS - Hearing aids - Oticon Corp.
MULTIFOODS - Food products - Semple Co.
MULTIFOODS BAKERY - Flour–blended - International Multifoods Corp.
MULTIFORM - Medical apparatus - Alimed, Inc.
MULTIFORT - Pharmaceutical preparations - Eastern Research Laboratories
MULTIFRAD - Computer hardware - Multi-Tech Systems, Inc.
MULTIFRADII - Computer hardware - Multi-Tech Systems, Inc.
MULTIFRUIT - Cosmetics - Brooks Industries, Inc.
MULTIGARD - Adhesives and sealants - Advanced Chemical Technologies, Inc.
MULTIGEN - Vitamins and nutritional supplements - Great Life Laboratories Inc.
MULTIGESIC - Pharmaceutical preparations - Alva-Amco Pharmacal Co.
MULTIGRADE III RC RAPID - Paper–photographic - ILFORD Photo Corp.
MULTIGRADE 500 SYSTEM - Photographic equipment - ILFORD Photo Corp.
MULTIGRADE FB WARMTONE - Paper–photographic - ILFORD Photo Corp.
MULTIGRADE IV - Paper–photographic - ILFORD Photo Corp.
MULTIGRADE IV FB - Paper–photographic - ILFORD Photo Corp.
MULTIGRADE RC PORTFOLIO - Paper–photographic - ILFORD Photo Corp.
MULTIGRADE RC WARMTONE - Paper–photographic - ILFORD Photo Corp.
MULTIGRADE XPRESS - Paper–photographic - ILFORD Photo Corp.
MULTIGRAIN CUTLETS - Food products - Worthington Foods Inc.
MULTIGUARD - Epoxy - Sigma Coatings USA BV.
MULTIGUARD - Medical apparatus - Sorenson Bioscience, Inc.
MULTIHELP - Computer software - Davis Technologies, Inc.
MULTIKINO - Electronics equipment - Marty Bahn & Co.
MULTILABEL - Labels - Uarco Inc.
MULTILABMASTER - Photographic equipment - Houston Fearless 76 Inc.
MULTILANA - Jewelry boxes - Ilana Issacow
MULTILEC - Oils–lubricating - Lubrication Engineers, Inc.
MULTILEX - Computer software - Hearst Corp.
MULTILEX - Pharmaceutical preparations - Rugby Laboratories Inc.
MULTILIGHT - Lighting equipment - Applied Color Systems, Inc.
MULTILIMINAL - Recording label - Futurehealth Inc.
MULTILIN - Pharmaceutical preparations ☆ - American Hygienic Laboratories Inc.
MULTILINE - Machinery - Franklin Imprinting Machines
MULTILINE - Rope - New England Ropes Inc.
MULTILINK - Computer hardware - Multilink, Inc.
MULTILINK - Educational materials - Nes Arnold Inc.
MULTILINK - Facsimile equipment - T4 Systems Inc.
MULTILOCK - Orthopedic products - Zimmer, Inc.
MULTILOG - Office supplies ☆ - Charvoz
MULTILUME - Lighting fixtures - Holophane Corp.
MULTIMAGE - Photographic equipment - SP Systems/Saratons

MULTIMARK - Lasers - Lumonics Corp.
MULTIMASTIC - Epoxy - Sigma Coatings USA BV.
MULTIMAT - Product description unknown - International Products Trading Inc.
MULTIMATCH - Games - Kadon Enterprises Inc.
MULTIMATE - Computer software - Borland International, Inc.
MULTIMATIC - Electrical equipment - ABB Metallurgy Inc.
MULTIMATIC - Lighting fixtures - Swivelier Co. Inc.
MULTIMATIC - Medical apparatus - General Physiotherapy, Inc.
MULTIMATRX - Nozzles - Toro Co.
MULTIME-D-YOU! - Computer software - TLC Professionals, Inc.
MULTIMEALS - Dinners–frozen - J & J Foods, Inc.
MULTIMEDIA - Projectors–photographic - Columbia Scientific Industries Corp.
MULTIMEDIA CD-ROM COMPATIBLE - Shelving units–plastic - Creative Point Inc.
MULTIMEDIA CLOAKING - Computer software - Helix Software Co., Inc.
MULTIMEDIA DATA DISCMAN - Electronic equipment - Sony Corp. of America
MULTIMEDIA EXTENSIONS - Computer software - Arkay Technologies Inc.
MULTIMEDIA GALLERY - Electronic equipment ☆ - NEC Technologies, Inc.
MULTIMEDIA LITERATURE - Computer storage devices–optical - McGraw-Hill Companies, Inc.
MULTIMEDIA MAKE YOUR POINT - Computer software ☆ - Asymetrix Corp.
MULTIMEDIA PEOPLE, THE - Computers - Media On, Inc.
MULTIMEDIA PLAYERS - Computer software - Simon & Schuster, Inc.
MULTIMEDIA SMARTHELP - Computer software - Lotus Development Corp.
MULTIMEDIA TOOLBOOK 3.0A - Computer software - Asymetrix Corp.
MULTIMEDIA UNIVERSITY - Computer software - Success Holdings Co. LLC
MULTIMEDIA WORKS - Computer software - Lenel Systems International, Inc.
MULTIMEDIA WORKSHOP, THE - Computer software - Knowledge Adventure
MULTIMEDIA ZONE - Computer software - School Zone Publishing Co.
MULTIMESH - Metals - Keene Corp. (Penn Metal Div.)
MULTIMIN - Vitamins and nutritional supplements - Republic Drug Co. Inc.
MULTIMIN JR. - Vitamins and nutritional supplements - Republic Drug Co. Inc.
MULTIMOBILE - Computer hardware - Multi-Tech Systems, Inc.
MULTIMOCEZPX - Computer hardware - Multi-Tech Systems, Inc.
MULTIMODE - Wheelchairs - DUFCO Electronics Inc.
MULTIMODEMII - Computer hardware - Multi-Tech Systems, Inc.
MULTIMODEMISI - Computer hardware - Multi-Tech Systems, Inc.
MULTIMODEMLAN - Computer hardware - Multi-Tech Systems, Inc.
MULTIMODEMLT - Computer hardware - Multi-Tech Systems, Inc.
MULTIMODEMMANAGER - Computer hardware - Multi-Tech Systems, Inc.
MULTIMODEMPC - Computer hardware - Multi-Tech Systems, Inc.
MULTIMODEMPCS - Computer hardware - Multi-Tech Systems, Inc.
MULTIMODEMPS - Computer hardware - Multi-Tech Systems, Inc.
MULTIMODEMX25 - Computer hardware - Multi-Tech Systems, Inc.
MULTIMODEMZDXV - Computer hardware - Multi-Tech Systems, Inc.
MULTIMODEMZPW - Computer hardware - Multi-Tech Systems, Inc.
MULTIMUX - Computer hardware - Digital Voice Systems, Inc.
MULTIMUX - Computers - Multi-Tech Systems, Inc.
MULTIMUX800 - Computer hardware - Multi-Tech Systems, Inc.
MULTINET - Computer software - Process Software Corp.
MULTINODE - Computer software - Alloy Computer Products Inc.
MULTIPAC - Medical apparatus - Intersurgical Inc.
MULTIPACK - Ribbons - Stephen Lawrence Co.
MULTIPAD - Computer peripheral equipment - Hitachi Digital Graphics, Inc.
MULTIPAK - Cameras–video - Dotronix Inc.
MULTIPAK - Pharmaceutical preparations - Pro Cap
MULTIPAN - Housewares - Amana Refrigeration Inc.
MULTIPAX - Computer storage devices - Indotronix International Corp.
MULTIPAX - Shell shot measures - Joel M. Odom
MULTIPDA - Measuring instruments - Dantec Measurement Technology Inc.
MULTIPETTE - Laboratory apparatus - Saigian, Inc.
MULTIPHASE - Recording label - Jazz Composer's Orchestra Association Inc.
MULTIPLAN - Computer software - Microsoft Corp.
MULTIPLE ACTION - Pens - Astro Pen Co.
MULTIPLE ACTION - Pens - Eversharp Pen Co.
MULTIPLE ARRAYED GEOMETRIC INDUCTIVE COUPLING - Audio equipment - Sergio Hamernik
MULTIPLE B-C - Pharmaceutical preparations ☆ - Vitarine Pharmaceuticals Inc.
MULTIPLE CHOICE - Computer software - Lotus Development Corp.
MULTIPLE CHOICE - Wallcovering - Wall Trends, Inc.
MULTIPLE CHOICE III - Wallcovering - Wall Trends, Inc.
MULTIPLE DIAMOND DESIGN - Office supplies - Georgia-Pacific Corp.
MULTIPLE MAKER, THE - Jewelry - Vine Products Manufacturing Co.
MULTIPLE MEANINGS - Computer software - Hartley Courseware Inc.

☆ = Now out of production

MULTIPLE OBLIQUE - Microscopes - Edge Scientific Instrument Corp.
MULTIPLE, THE - Cosmetics - Francois Nars
MULTIPLES - Apparel—women's - Jerell, Inc.
MULTIPLES - Handbags - Bagland
MULTIPLES - Wallpaper ☆ - Royson's Corp.
MULTIPLEX - Chemical preparations - Baker Hughes Inc.
MULTIPLEX - Vitamins and nutritional supplements - The Lifestar Millennium, Inc.
MULTIPLEX TECHNOLOGY, INC. - Communications equipment - Multiplex Technology, Inc.
MULTIPLICATION BRIGADE - Computer software - Gamco Industries Inc.
MULTIPLICATION OF WHOLE NUMBERS - Computer software - Orange Cherry Software
MULTIPLICATION ROCK - Video tapes—blank - ABC Inc.
MULTIPLIER - Electronic equipment - Multiplier Industries Corp.
MULTIPLY - Electrodes - E.I. Dupont de Nemours and Co.
MULTIPLY - Glass products - Floral Glass & Mirror Inc.
MULTIPLY - Wood products - Multiply Plywood
MULTIPLY SERIES II - Mattresses - Mason Medical Products
MULTIPOINT - Monitors—electronic - Svedala Industries, Inc.
MULTIPOINT DRIVERS - Computer software - LCS/Telegraphics Inc.
MULTIPORT - Electronic equipment - Silicon Valley Bus Co., Inc.
MULTIPRINT - Ribbons—inked - Leedall Products Manufacturing Co.
MULTIPRO - Tools—power-driven - S-B Power Tool Co.
MULTIPROBE - Laboratory apparatus - Packard Instrument Co., Inc.
MULTIQUE - Paper products - Lewis Paper Place, Inc.
MULTIRAIL - Tools—hand-operated - Gabriel M. McCubbin
MULTIREACH - Computer software - MediaPlan, Inc.
MULTIROUTER - Computer hardware - Multi-Tech Systems, Inc.
MULTISAFE - Floor coverings - Tarkett, Inc.
MULTISCAN - Cameras - Gatan, Inc.
MULTISCAN - Door openers—electronic ☆ - Kawneer Co., Inc.
MULTISCOPE - Photographic equipment ☆ - Heitz Service Corp.
MULTISCRUB - Skin care products - Bristol-Myers Squibb Co.
MULTISEAL - Machinery - Seal Products Inc.
MULTISEAL - Wire - Keystone Manufacturing Co., Inc.
MULTISEALER - Office machines - Standard Register Co.
MULTISET - Electronic equipment - Genlyte Group Inc.
MULTISHARE - Computer peripherals - D.E.W. International Corp.
MULTISOFT - Napkins—paper - Georgia-Pacific Corp.
MULTISONIC - Hearing aids - Qualitone
MULTISONIC - Recording label - Americatone Records International
MULTISPAN - Computer software - NetFRAME Systems Inc.
MULTISPEC 86 - Paints - Multicolor Specialties Inc.
MULTISPEC FINE FLECK - Paints - Multicolor Specialties Inc.
MULTISPEC WATERBORNE - Paints - Multicolor Specialties Inc.
MULTISPEED - Computers—personal ☆ - NEC Technologies, Inc.
MULTISPEED HD - Computers—personal ☆ - NEC Technologies, Inc.
MULTISPIN - Computer storage devices—optical - NEC Technologies, Inc.
MULTISPOT - Bond paper - Calcomp Inc.
MULTISTAR - Alarm system, loudspeaker, telephone - Auditron Corp.
MULTISTEP - Floor coverings - Forbo Industries, Inc.
MULTISUMMA 24 - Calculators ☆ - Olivetti North America Inc. (Consumer Products Div.)
MULTISYNC - Computer peripheral equipment ☆ - NEC Technologies, Inc.
MULTISYNC 3D - Computer peripheral equipment ☆ - NEC Technologies, Inc.
MULTITAINER - Containers - Radmar Inc.
MULTITAP - Screws - VSI Fasteners, Inc.
MULTITECH - Electronic equipment - Indala Corp.
MULTITEMP - Adhesives and sealants - Atlan Plastics Inc.
MULTITEST: COPPER - Pet products - Seachem Laboratories
MULTITEST: FREE & TOTAL AMONIA - Pet products - Seachem Laboratories
MULTITEST: IODINE & IODIDE - Pet products - Seachem Laboratories
MULTITEST: IRON - Pet products - Seachem Laboratories
MULTITEST: MARINE BASIC - Pet products - Seachem Laboratories
MULTITEST: MARINE PH & ALKALINITY - Pet products - Seachem Laboratories
MULTITEST: NITRITE & NITRATE - Pet products - Seachem Laboratories
MULTITEST: PHOSPHATE - Pet products - Seachem Laboratories
MULTITEST: REEF SPECIAL - Pet products - Seachem Laboratories
MULTITEST: SILICATE - Pet products - Seachem Laboratories
MULTITEX - Thread - Belding Heminway Co. Inc.
MULTITINT - Paints ☆ - Colony Paints Div.
MULTITONE - Toners - Pierce Companies, Inc.
MULTITRAC - Lubricating oils - Coastal Unilube, Inc.
MULTITRAC8 - Distance measuring equipment—aeronautical - Garmin Corp.

MULTITRACE - Pharmaceutical preparations - American Regent Laboratories, Inc.
MULTIUSER BASIC - Computer software - THEOS Software Corp.
MULTIVAULT - Firearms, accessories, and parts - Gunvault, Inc.
MULTIVERSE GIFT BOX - Trading cards and stamps - Wizards of the Coast, Inc.
MULTIVIEW - Computer peripheral equipment - Radius Inc.
MULTIVIEW - Window shades - Draper Shade and Screen Co. Inc.
MULTIVIEW 5+1 - Televisions, amplifiers, and speakers - Court Technologies, Inc.
MULTIVOICE - Circuit boards - Voiceboard Corp.
MULTIVOICE - Speech synthesizer for the handicapped - C.H.M.C. Otolaryngologic Foundation
MULTIVOX - Pianos - Multivox/Sorkin Music Co. Inc.
MULTIVUE - Humphrey Systems
MULTIWARE - Computer software - TGV, Inc.
MULTIWAVE - Communications equipment - Ciena Corp.
MULTIWAY - Computer software - Kenan Systems Corp.
MULTIWAY - Vitamins and nutritional supplements - Multiway Associates
MULTIWORKS - Computer software - WizardWorks Group Inc.
MULTNOMAH - Publisher's imprints - Questar Publishers, Inc.
MULTO-RING - Office supplies - C-Line Products, Inc.
MULTRIUM - Vitamins and nutritional supplements - Winning Laboratories Corp.
MULTUM - Animal feed supplements - Hubbard Milling Co.
MULTUM - Computer software - Multum Information Services, Inc.
MULTUM - Office supplies - R.A. Stewart Superior
MULTYDE ACTION - Pens ☆ - Eversharp Pen Co.
MULVIDREN F - Pharmaceutical preparations ☆ - Zeneca Inc.
MULVITAB - Pharmaceutical preparations - Solvay Pharmaceuticals Inc.
MUM - Deodorants—personal - Bristol-Myers Squibb Co.
MUMBO - Eyeglasses - Oakley, Inc.
MUMM VSOP - Beverages—alcohol - Joseph E. Seagram & Sons, Inc.
MUMMATO - Toys - Mattel, Inc.
MUMMIES AND DEADIES - Candy - Fleer Corp.
MUMM'S - Beverages—alcohol - Seagram's Chateau & Estate Wines Co.
MUMMY BLIND - Sporting goods - Evans Land Co.
MUMMY FOOD - Food products - Home Health Products, Inc.
MUMMY MOUTH - Candy - Glenn Confections Inc.
MUMMY PLANT - Novelty items - Dynamic Development
MUMMY RUMMY - Games - Gamewright, Inc.
MUMMY'S CHARIOT - Toys—automobiles - Thomas Lowe Ventures, Inc.
MUMPSVAX - Vaccines - Merck & Co., Inc. (Merck Research Laboratories)
MUMSIES - Apparel—women's - Southwest Mercantile Corp.
MUMTAZ BLACK - Teas—herbal - M.I.M.T. Corp. of USA
MUN-CHEE - Food products - Beatrice Cheese Co.
MUNCH-A-ROOS - Snack foods - Variety Foods, Inc.
MUNCH BOX - Apparel and accessories - Tyke Corp.
MUNCH BOX - Lunch boxes ☆ - Newell Office Products
MUNCH 'EMS - Crackers - Keebler Co.
MUNCH-ITS - Cookies ☆ - Sunshine Biscuits, Inc.
MUNCH KING - Food products - Bruce Foods Corp.
MUNCH MATES - Toys—stuffed ☆ - Kenner Products
MUNCH MOUTH - Candy ☆ - Nellson Candies Inc.
MUNCH 'N-GO - Nuts—salted, roasted, cooked, or canned - Planters LifeSavers Co.
MUNCH-NAKS - Meat products - Saramar Corp.
MUNCH-NAKS - Snack foods - Design Foods
MUNCH PEANUT BRITTLE - Candy - Mars, Inc.
MUNCH RIGHTS - Snack foods - Wyandot, Inc.
MUNCHEE BEAR - Food products - Bake-Line Products Inc.
MUNCHEES - Food products - Health is Wealth
MUNCHER, THE - Grinders - Dresser Industries, Inc.
MUNCHERS - Pet products - Chilmar Inc.
MUNCHERS - Pickles - Curtice-Burns Foods, Inc.
MUNCHETTES - Containers - Rubbermaid Inc.
MUNCHIE - Magnets ☆ - Dakin Inc.
MUNCHIE BUNNY - Toys—stuffed - Russ Berrie and Co., Inc.
MUNCHIE CUP - Food containers - Sweetheart Cup Co. Inc.
MUNCHIE LIGHTS - Fishing lures - Area Rule Engineering Inc.
MUNCHIE MIX - Snack foods ☆ - Hershey Import Co. Inc.
MUNCHIE POPS - Pet products - Ethical Products Inc.
MUNCHIES - Pet products - Penn-Plax, Inc.
MUNCHIES - Pet products ☆ - RHB Enterprises
MUNCHIES - Publisher's imprints - Antioch Publishing Co.
MUNCHIES, THE - Snack food ☆ - Pelican Bay Ltd. Inc.

MUNCHIN' BUNNIES - Toys–stuffed - Fun World Inc.
MUNCHIN' MORSELS - Food products - Kraft Food Ingredients Corp.
MUNCHIN' U.S.A. - Clay–modeling - Tonka Corp.
MUNCHKINS - Doughnuts - Dunkin' Donuts of America Inc.
MUNCHMATES - Snack foods - Wyandot, Inc.
MUNCHOS - Potato chips - Frito-Lay, Inc.
MUNCHPUMP - Sewerage systems - Dresser Industries, Inc.
MUNCHSKINS - Vegetables–frozen ☆ - Lamb-Weston, Inc.
MUNCHSTRIPS - Vegetables–frozen ☆ - Lamb-Weston, Inc.
MUNCHY - Key rings, magnets, etc. - Iwasaki Images of America
MUNCHY MALT BAR - Chocolate candy ☆ - Ghirardelli Chocolate Co.
MUNCHY MUMMIES - Candy ☆ - Topps Co., Inc.
MUNDI - Artichokes–canned - A. Sargenti Co. Inc.
MUNDI - Wallets - Westport Corp.
MUNDI-VISION - Metals - Herman Joseph Pieters
MUNDIAL - Cutlery - Mundial Inc.
MUNGO CUM LAUDE - Toys–stuffed - Russ Berrie and Co., Inc.
MUNGO MONKEY - Toys–stuffed - Russ Berrie and Co., Inc.
MUNI IRIS - Computer software - Disclosure Progress Corp.
MUNICH - Soccer and rugby balls - Audero Sports Supply
MUNICH OCKTOBERFEST - Beer - Miller Brewing Co.
MUNIEMAKER - Tobacco products - F.D. Grave & Son, Inc.
MUNILAW - Computer software - Legal Information Solutions, Inc.
MUNK - Chore gloves - Boss Manufacturing Co.
MUNKEE - Inks - Specialty Ink Co. Inc.
MUNKEFACE - Chore gloves - Boss Manufacturing Co.
MUNRO - Footwear - Munro & Co., Inc.
MUNRO SPORT AMERICAN FOOTWEAR - Shoes–athletic - Munro & Co., Inc.
MUNROE DAIRY - Milk - Munroe Dairy Inc.
MUNSELL - Artists' materials - Munsell Color
MUNSEY - Appliance parts - Munsey Products Inc.
MUNSINGWEAR - Apparel and accessories - Munsingwear, Inc.
MUNSON HAMMERHEAD - Boats - Hammerhead Corp.
MUNSTER - Floor coverings–carpet and rugs - Concepts International
MUNSTER ALT - Beverages–alcohol - Merchant du Vin Corp.
MUNSTER-CHRIS - Cheese - Haram-Christensen Corp.
MUNSTON - Electronic equipment - Comspace Corp.
MUNTERS - Dehumidifiers - Munters Corp.
MUNTING BOTANICALS - Posters - One-of-a-Kind Workshop
MUNTU - Recording label - Jazz Composer's Orchestra Association Inc.
MUNTZ - Television equipment ☆ - Muntz Electronics Inc.
MUPI - Furniture - Marana Unique Products Inc.
MUPPET BABIES - Diapers–disposable ☆ - Mount Vernon Mills Inc.
MUPPET BABIES - Games - Milton Bradley Co.
MUPPET BABIES - Toys - Jim Henson Productions, Inc.
MUPPET BABIES BIG STEPS BOOK, A - Publisher's imprints - Jim Henson Productions, Inc.
MUPPET BABY PEEK 'N PLAY - Toys - Playskool, Inc.
MUPPET BABY TUMBLE WHEEL - Toys - Playskool, Inc.
MUPPET LEARNING KEYS - Computer software ☆ - Sunburst Communications, Inc.
MUPPET PARODIES - Posters - Raleigh Studios
MUPPET WORD BOOK - Computer software ☆ - Sunburst Communications, Inc.
MUPPETS - Bathroom accessories ☆ - Tsumura International Inc.
MUPPETS - Umbrellas - Shaw Creations Inc.
MUPPETS ON STAGE - Computer software ☆ - Sunburst Communications, Inc.
MUPPETVILLE - Computer software ☆ - Sunburst Communications, Inc.
MURA - Audio equipment - Mura Corp.
MURA - Cold remedies ☆ - Polam Wholesale Inc.
MURA - Waxes–sealing ☆ - Freund-Mayer & Co. Inc.
MURA 5 - Plastics–laminated ☆ - Plaskolite Inc.
MURA-EAR - Pharmaceutical preparations - Polam Wholesale Inc.
MURA RED SET - Headphones - Mura Corp.
MURAD - Skin care products - Murad Skin Research Laboratories, Inc.
MURAD SKIN RESEARCH LABORATORY - Skin-care products - Murad Skin Research Laboratories, Inc.
MURAFLOC - Wallpaper ☆ - Bonar & Flotex Inc.
MURAL - Paper–photographic - Luminos Photo Corp.
MURAL - Puzzles ☆ - Warren Industries Inc.
MURAL MOUNTS - Photographic equipment - CODA Inc.
MURALO - Paints - Muralo Co. Inc.
MURALS - Tiles–ceramic - Summitville Tiles, Inc.
MURALTEX - Wallpaper - Wall Fashion Inc.

MURAMASA KUDO - Posters - Icart Vendor Graphics Inc.
MURAMATSU - Musical instruments - Custom Music Co.
MURANITE - Floor coverings–tile ☆ - Walker and Zanger Inc.
MURANO - Floor coverings ☆ - Congoleum Corp.
MURANO - Floor coverings–carpet and rugs - Couristan Inc.
MURANO - Giftware - Alice Sturzinger Ltd.
MURANO - Wallpaper ☆ - Marburg Wallcoverings Inc.
MURANO GLASS - Home furnishings - Italia Collections
MURAPHONE - Communications equipment–mobile - Mura Corp.
MURASAKI - Cosmetics - Shiseido Cosmetics (America) Ltd.
MURASAN - Colognes ☆ - Polam Wholesale Inc.
MURASOME - Cosmetics - Murad Skin Research Laboratories, Inc.
MURASUN - Sun screen - Murad Skin Research Laboratories, Inc.
MURAT - Fabrics - Gretchen Bellinger Inc.
MURATA - Office supplies - Erie North America Inc.
MURATEC - Cellular phones, home fax machines - Murata Bus Systems Inc.
MURATONE - Wallpaper - Koroseal Wallcoverings
MURATTI AMBASSADOR - Cigarettes - G.A. Georgopulo & Co. Inc.
MURATTI AMBASSADOR - Cigarettes - Philip Morris Companies Inc.
MURAWSKI'S ALLER-DRYL - Skin care products - Polam Wholesale Inc.
MURAWSKI'S ASTHMA TABS - Pharmaceutical preparations - Polam Wholesale Inc.
MURAWSKI'S FIRST AID - Skin care products - Polam Wholesale Inc.
MURAWSKI'S FORMULA 44 - Cold remedies - Polam Wholesale Inc.
MURAWSKI'S IBUPROFEN - Analgesics - Polam Wholesale Inc.
MURAWSKI'S IVY-TOX - Skin care products - Polam Wholesale Inc.
MURAWSKI'S PEDIATRIC FORMULA - Cough medicines - Polam Wholesale Inc.
MURAWSKI'S PHARMACIST'S CREME - Analgesics - Polam Wholesale Inc.
MURAWSKI'S RECOFEN - Cough medicines - Polam Wholesale Inc.
MURAWSKI'S RECOFEN D - Cough medicines - Polam Wholesale Inc.
MURAWSKI'S RECOFEN PLUS - Cough medicines - Polam Wholesale Inc.
MURAWSKI'S RECORT PLUS - Skin care products - Polam Wholesale Inc.
MURAWSKI'S REDACON DX - Cold remedies - Polam Wholesale Inc.
MURAWSKI'S REPHENYL - Cold remedies - Polam Wholesale Inc.
MURAWSKI'S SUPER 28 FORMULA - Vitamins and nutritional supplements - Polam Wholesale Inc.
MURAWSKI'S TETRA CAPS - Cold remedies - Polam Wholesale Inc.
MURAWSKI'S TRIM ELLM - Pharmaceutical preparations - Polam Wholesale Inc.
MURBLE - Games - Murray E. Kramer
MURBO - Recording label - Bourne Co.
MURCH'S - Fruit drinks–bottled or canned - J.M. Smucker Co.
MURDER A LA CARTE - Games - Lombard Marketing, Inc.
MURDER AT MALINDI - Computer software ☆ - Earthware Computer Services
MURDER AT THE MISSION - Games ☆ - Milton Bradley Co.
MURDER BY PROXY - Games ☆ - Milton Bradley Co.
MURDER BY THE DOZEN - Computer software - CBS Software
MURDER IN DISGUISE - Games - Tonka Corp.
MURDER IN PARADISE - Games ☆ - Milton Bradley Co.
MURDER INK - Puzzles ☆ - International Polygonics Ltd.
MURDER MAGIC - Apparel and accessories - Through the Looking Glass Filmworks
MURDER MYSTERY PARTY - Novelty items - University Games Corp.
MURDER MYSTERY THEATRE - Watches - Constance J. Gay
MURDER ON THE ATLANTIC - Computer software ☆ - Capstone Software
MURDER TO GO - Games - CBS Toys
MURDOCH RACING ENTERPRISES - Motorcycles - Murdoch Racing Enterprises
MURDOCH'S PERFECTION - Liquors - Cameron Craig Ltd.
MURDUCK - Toys–electronic - Video Technology U.S. Inc.
MUREDALE - Golf umbrellas - Proactive Sports
MURESCO - Finishing agents - Benjamin Moore & Co.
MUREXIDE - Pharmaceutical preparations - City Chemical Corp.
MURI - Cheese - New England Import Co. Inc.
MURI-LUBE - Oils–mineral - Lyphomed Inc.
MURIEL - Cigar boxes–wood - Consolidated Cigar Corp.
MURIEL - Handbags - Regal Bag Corp.
MURIEL MATES - Cigar boxes–wood - Consolidated Cigar Corp.
MURIEL SWEETS - Cigar boxes–wood - Consolidated Cigar Corp.
MURIETTA'S WELL - Wines ☆ - Shaw-Ross International Importers
MURILLO - Artists' materials - Andrews/Nelson/Whitehead
MURILLO - Artists' materials ☆ - M. Grumbacher Inc.
MURINE - Plugs–ear - Murine Co.
MURINE PLUS - Eyes–glass - Murine Co.
MURINE TEARS - Pharmaceutical preparations - Abbott Laboratories

☆ = Now out of production

MURIPSIN - Pharmaceutical preparations ☆ - Norgine Laboratories Inc.

MURITIBA - Cigarettes - Gesty Trading & Manufacturing Corp.

MURJANTI SPECIALLY FORMULATED FOR HAIR SYSTEMS - Hair care products - Joseph A. Curcio

MURK WORKS - Computer software ☆ - Murkworks, Inc.

MURLIN - Wallpaper - K.M.L. Industries

MURLOK - Containers - Weyerhaeuser Co.

MURMANSK - Vodka - East-West Distributing Co.

MURO - Pharmaceutical preparations - Muro Pharmaceuticals Inc.

MURO - Wallpaper - Winfield Design Associates, Inc.

MURO II - Wallpaper - Winfield Design Associates, Inc.

MUROCEL - Ophthalmic goods - Bausch & Lomb Inc.

MUROCOLL - Ophthalmic goods - Bausch & Lomb Inc.

MURO'S - Ophthalmic goods - Bausch & Lomb Inc.

MURPHY - Furniture - Murphy Bed Co. Inc.

MURPHY - Toys–stuffed - Russ Berrie and Co., Inc.

MURPHY BED CENTERS OF AMERICA - Furniture - VSS, Inc.

MURPHY CIRCUITS - Electrical equipment - Advanced Interconnections Corp.

MURPHY-GOODE - Wines - Murphy-Goode Estate Winery

MURPHY MACKALL - Apparel–children's - Grace Co.

MURPHY MILLER - Furniture ☆ - Hon Co.

MURPHY'S - Tires - JTM Products Inc.

MURPHY'S IRISH STOUT - Beverages–malt - Van Munching and Co. Inc.

MURPHY'S KITCHEN CARE - Cleaning preparations–household - Colgate-Palmolive Co.

MURPHY'S OIL SOAP - Cleaning preparations–household - Colgate-Palmolive Co.

MURRAY - Bicycles - Murray, Inc.

MURRAY - Cold remedies ☆ - Murray Drug Corp.

MURRAY - Electrical equipment - Siemens Energy & Automation, Inc.

MURRAY - Hardware - Gordon Associates

MURRAY & LANMAN - Perfumes - Lanman & Kemp-Barclay & Co. Inc.

MURRAY BRONZE - Bicycles - Murray, Inc.

MURRAY-CON - Pharmaceutical preparations ☆ - Murray Drug Corp.

MURRAY FEISS - Lanterns–electric - Murray Feiss

MURRAY-GESIC - Pharmaceutical preparations ☆ - Murray Drug Corp.

MURRAY GOLD - Bicycles - Murray, Inc.

MURRAY HILL - Fabrics - Stroheim & Romann, Inc.

MURRAY HILL - Flatware ☆ - W.M.F. of America Inc.

MURRAY HILL - Recording label - Crown Publishers Inc.

MURRAY HILL - Wallpaper ☆ - Wolf-Gordon Inc.

MURRAY MOLE - Dolls - Mattel, Inc.

MURRAY O. CLEVE. O. USA - Toys - Murray, Inc.

MURRAY SILVER - Bicycles - Murray, Inc.

MURRAY TRX - Bicycles - Murray, Inc.

MURRAY'S - Fruit drinks–bottled or canned - Murray Cider Co. Inc.

MURRAY'S - Hair care products - Murray's Worldwide Inc.

MURRAY'S OLYMPIC - Bicycles - Murray, Inc.

MURRAY'S ON PLYMOUTH ROAD - Housewares stores - Murray's Bargain Center, Inc.

MURRIETA'S WELL - Wines - Wente Bros.

MURRIETA'S WELL - Wines ☆ - Wilson Daniels Ltd.

MURRINI - Vases–glass - Nourot Glass Studio

MURRYHILL - Prefabricated buildings–metal - Arrow Group Industries

MURRY'S MAKES IT A MEAL - Frozen foods - Murry's Inc.

MURRY'S STEAKS - Food products - Murry's Inc.

MURSULI CIGARS - Cigars - Oscar Mursuli

MURTUSS GG - Cough medicines ☆ - Murray Drug Corp.

MUS-L BLAST 2000+ - Vitamins and nutritional supplements - MLO Products, Inc.

MUS-L-TONE - Pharmaceutical preparations - High Chemical Co.

MUSA - Beverages–alcohol - Musa Inc.

MUSA-PHYSICS - Recording label - Jazz Composer's Orchestra Association Inc.

MUSARDE - Yarn ☆ - Joseph Galler Inc.

MUSCA-DOOM - Insecticides - Farnam Companies, Inc.

MUSCAL CANELLI ESTATE - Wines ☆ - Glen Ellen Winery

MUSCAT DE BEAULIEU - Wines - IDV Wines (Beaulieu Vineyard)

MUSCATO - Apparel - FSC (USA) Inc.

MUSCATO CANELLI - Wines - Renwood Winery, Inc.

MUSCLAX - Veterinary pharmaceutical preparations ☆ - Zirin Laboratories International

MUSCLE - Bicycles - Columbia Manufacturing Inc.

MUSCLE - Computer software - Bourbaki Inc.

M.U.S.C.L.E. - Toys - Mattel, Inc.

MUSCLE BONES - Dog food - Pet Center, Inc.

MUSCLE-BUILDING AEROBICS - Exercising equipment - Soloflex, Inc.

MUSCLE B.U.M. - Apparel–men's - Chauvin International Ltd.

MUSCLE BUZZ - Apparel and accessories - Endorphin Warriors

MUSCLE CHARGE II - Vitamins and nutritional supplements - Universal Protein Supplements, Inc.

MUSCLE DYNAMICS - Health care products - Euro-Care Products & Services Co.

MUSCLE DYNAMO - Vitamins and nutritional supplements - Source Naturals

MUSCLE DYNAMO II - Vitamins and nutritional supplements - Source Naturals

MUSCLE EDGE - Vitamins and nutritional supplements - Nutri Science Inc.

MUSCLE FIRE - Nutritional supplement - Strength Systems USA

MUSCLE FLEX - Vitamins and nutritional supplements - Unipro Inc.

MUSCLE FUEL - Pharmaceutical preparations - Proteins Inc.

MUSCLE FUEL - Protein supplement ☆ - Jackson Enterprises Inc.

MUSCLE IMPACT - Vitamins and nutritional supplements - Vitol Health Products

MUSCLE LSE - Automotive parts and accessories - Pullman Co.

MUSCLE MAGIC - Analgesics - Mission Pharmacal Co.

MUSCLE MAKER - Health care products - Nature Health

MUSCLE MAKER - Vitamins and nutritional supplements ☆ - Naturade Inc.

MUSCLE MAKER AMINOS PLUS - Health care products - Nature Health

MUSCLE MASS - Vitamins and nutritional supplements - Source Naturals

MUSCLE MASTERS - Vitamins and nutritional supplements - Nature's Plus

MUSCLE MAXX - Vitamins and nutritional supplements - Sportpharma USA, Inc.

MUSCLE MINDER - Health care products - Remington Products Co.

MUSCLE MIX - Vitamins and nutritional supplements - D.A.S.H. Products Inc.

MUSCLE NITRO - Vitamins and nutritional supplements - Champion Nutrition

MUSCLE OCTANE - Health care products - Anabol Naturals

MUSCLE ON - Food products ☆ - Health is Wealth

MUSCLE PASTA - Pasta - Muscle Pasta, Inc.

MUSCLE PEP - Vitamins and nutritional supplements - Caroline Owens

MUSCLE PEP - Vitamins and nutritional supplements ☆ - Natural Balance, Inc.

MUSCLE PIG - Animal feeds - MFA Inc.

MUSCLE PLUS - Vitamins and nutritional supplements ☆ - Eriss Corp.

MUSCLE POW'R - Skin care products - Alacer Co.

MUSCLE PUMP - Pharmaceutical preparations ☆ - Bricker Laboratories

MUSCLE PUNCH - Beverages - Smoothie King Franchises, Inc.

MUSCLE RUB - Orthopedic products - Gustave Rick Rinz

MUSCLE SHOALS - Recording label - Malaco Records Inc.

MUSCLE TREAT - Health care products - Heritage Store Inc.

MUSCLEBIKE - Motorcycles - Surgical-Steeds, Classic American Motorcycles, Inc.

MUSCLEEASE - Animal feed supplements - Trade One Inc. (Equine Specialty Feed Co.)

MUSCLEFLEX - Exercising equipment - Adam Jofi Mclean

MUSCLEMAN - Computer software - Data Consultants, Inc.

MUSCLEMAN - Toys - Mattel, Inc.

MUSCLEMAXX - Exercising equipment - Wholesale Fitness Inc.

MUSCLES IN A MINUTE - Apparel and accessories - Fitness Wholesale

MUSCLES IN A MINUTE - Exercising equipment - Future Dynamics, Inc.

MUSCLES IN A MINUTE - Exercising equipment - Future Dynamics, Inc.

MUSCLESENSE - Electromedical apparatus - Smith & Nephew DonJoy Inc.

MUSCLESPORT USA - Apparel–athletic - Musclesport USA

MUSCLIN' MAGIC - Toys - Tonka Corp.

MUSCLIN' MOVER - Toys - Tonka Corp.

MUSCO - Olives–pickled or brined - Musco Olive Products Inc.

MUSCULAR WEIGHT GAIN - Vitamins and nutritional supplements - Healthy 'N Fit Nutritionals

MUSE - Apparel and accessories - Kellwood Co.

MUSE - Computer software - Muse Software

MUSE - Pianos ☆ - Ford Piano Supply Co.

MUSE - Recording label - Creav Inc. USA

MUSE, THE - Headphones - PS Engineering

MUSEES NATIONAUX - Postcards - Fotofolio Inc.

MUSEO - Statuary ☆ - Seymour Mann Inc.

MUSEO - Wallcoverings - Stretchwall Fabrics Co.

MUSEO DEL PRADO - Postcards - Fotofolio Inc.

MUSETTE - Dinnerware–glass ☆ - Lenox, Inc.

MUSETTE - Floor coverings–carpet and rugs - Monticello Carpet Mills

MUSETTE - Glass–leaded - Seneca Glass Co.

MUSETTE - Pianos - Aeolian Pianos Inc.

MUSETTE - Rings–jewelry - Artcarved Inc.

MUSETTE - Seafood products–canned or cured - Tidelands Sales Co. Inc.

MUSETTE - Watches - Bulova Corp.

MUSEUM - Doors - Super Millwork, Inc.

MUSEUM - Watches - Movado Time Corp.
MUSEUM CARDS - Notebooks and notepads - GMG Publishing Inc.
MUSEUM CHINTZ - Craft supplies ☆ - VIP/VIP Crafts
MUSEUM CITY - Video production - V.I.E.W. Video Inc.
MUSEUM CLASSIC REPROS - Frames—picture - De Ville Galleries Inc.
MUSEUM CLASSICS - Craft supplies ☆ - VIP/VIP Crafts
MUSEUM COLLECTION - Apparel and accessories - Revillon, Inc.
MUSEUM COLLECTION - Carpet - Shaw Industries Inc.
MUSEUM COLLECTION, THE - Artists' materials ☆ - Artisan House Inc.
MUSEUM COLLECTION, THE - Wallpaper ☆ - J. Josephson, Inc.
MUSEUM EDITION COVER - Paper—lithograph - ANW-Crestwood Paper Co.
MUSEUM EDITIONS - T-shirts—men's - Gouda Inc.
MUSEUM GUILD - Dolls - Glassmasters
MUSEUM LEGACY COLLECTION - Book ends - Children's Museum of Indianapolis Inc.
MUSEUM MADNESS - Educational materials - Softkey International Inc.
MUSEUM MASTERPIECES - Canvas—artists' - Fabulous Forgeries Ltd.
MUSEUM MINIATURES - Toys ☆ - Reeves International, Inc.
MUSEUM OF CONTEMPORARY ARTS, LA - Postcards - Fotofolio Inc.
MUSEUM OF HEALTH MEDICAL SCIENCE - Apparel and accessories - Foundation for the Museum of Medical Science
MUSEUM OF JEWELRY - Jewelry - Facets Inc.
MUSEUM OF MODERN ART - Postcards - Fotofolio Inc.
MUSEUM OF MODERN ART, THE - Paper—writing - Museum of Modern Art
MUSEUM PIECES - Figurines - Marv Art Designs Inc.
MUSEUM PUBLISHING COMPANY - Publisher's imprints - Bill-Kell Inc.
MUSEUM PUZZLE - Puzzles - GMG Publishing Inc.
MUSEUM RECREATORS - Giftware - Godinger Silver Art Ltd.
MUSEUM REPRODUCTIONS - Museums - The Jewish Museum Cooper Shop
MUSEUM SE - Watches - Movado Time Corp.
MUSGRAVE HB - Pencils - Musgrave Pencil Co. Inc.
MUSHER - Crocheted and knitted items - Schuessler Knitting Mills Inc.
MUSHROOM - Glassware—household ☆ - Lotus Glass Co.
MUSHROOM - Loudspeakers - Soundscape Speakers, Inc.
MUSHROOM - Tools ☆ - Regent Sheffield, Ltd.
MUSHROOM 1 - Handlebars—bicycle - Organizational Dynamics Inc. (ODI)
MUSHROOM HOUSE U.S.A. - Agricultural products - Mushroom House USA
MUSHROOM II - Handlebars—bicycle - Organizational Dynamics Inc. (ODI)
MUSHROOM MOUNTAINEER - Handlebars—bicycle - Organizational Dynamics Inc. (ODI)
MUSHROOMS - Footwear - United States Shoe Corp.
MUSI-DEX - Office supplies - Southern Music Co.
MUSI-KEY - Music—sheet - Musi-Key
MUSI-POE - Labels—paper - Five Star Entertainment
MUSIC - Candy - Uniconfis Corp.
MUSIC - Computer software ☆ - Performance Products Inc.
MUSIC - Floor coverings—carpet and rugs ☆ - Foreign Accents
MUSIC - Semiconductors - Music Semiconductors Inc.
MUSIC - Water—mineral - Music Mountain Water Co.
MUSIC ACE - Computer software - Harmonic Vision, Inc.
MUSIC & ARTS - Recording label - Music and Arts Programs of America Inc.
MUSIC & MOTION - Music boxes ☆ - National Artcraft Co.
MUSIC & SOUND - Audio equipment - M and S Systems Inc.
MUSIC APPRECIATION: A STUDY GUIDE - Computer software - Electronic Courseware Systems Inc.
MUSIC BLOCKS - Cases—plastic - RF Products Inc.
MUSIC BOX - Computer software - Trantor Systems Ltd.
MUSIC BOX MEMORIES - Music boxes - Corners of the World Inc.
MUSIC BOX MOBILE - Toys - Fisher-Price, Inc.
MUSIC BOX MOON - Toys - Fisher-Price, Inc.
MUSIC BOX RADIO - Toys - Fisher-Price, Inc.
MUSIC BOX RECORD PLAYER - Toys - Fisher-Price, Inc.
MUSIC BOX SHOP - Music boxes - Schmid Inc.
MUSIC BOX TEACHING CLOCK - Toys - Fisher-Price, Inc.
MUSIC BOX TEDDY BEAR - Toys - Fisher-Price, Inc.
MUSIC BOX TV - Toys - Fisher-Price, Inc.
MUSIC CENTER - Musical instrument accessories - Mininome Inc.
MUSIC CITY - Recording label ☆ - Caprice International Records
MUSIC CLUB - Apparel and accessories - Michael Wilkerson Jones
MUSIC COMPOSER QUIZ - Computer software - Electronic Courseware Systems Inc.
MUSIC CONCEPTS - Computer software - Ventura Educational Systems
MUSIC CONNECTION, THE - Educational materials - Silver Burdett Ginn Inc.
MUSIC CONSTRUCTION SET - Computer software - Electronic Arts Inc.
MUSIC DICE - Games - Friendship House
MUSIC EXPRESS - Audio equipment - Royal Sound Co. Inc.

MUSIC FACTORY, THE - Computer software - Music Factory, Inc.
MUSIC FLASH CARDS - Computer software - Electronic Courseware Systems Inc.
MUSIC FOR LITTLE PEOPLE - Recording label - Music for Little People
MUSIC FOR YOUR EYES - Computer software - Forte' Advanced Management Software, Inc.
MUSIC FOR YOUR EYES - Sweatshirts - Malibu Comics Entertainment, Inc.
MUSIC GALLERY EDITION - Recording label - Jazz Composer's Orchestra Association Inc.
MUSIC-GRAPH - Fabrics—flannel ☆ - Ohio Flock-Cote Co.
MUSIC GUILD - Recording label - MCA Universal Studios
MUSIC HISTORY: A STUDY GUIDE - Computer software - Electronic Courseware Systems Inc.
MUSIC HISTORY REVIEW: COMPOSERS - Computer software - Electronic Courseware Systems Inc.
MUSIC HOUSE PRODUCTIONS - Recording label - Music House Records
MUSIC IN MOTION - Recording label ☆ - Fit Net
MUSIC IN THE ROUND - Music boxes - Century Designs
MUSIC-LINK - Recording label - Select Music Systems Inc.
MUSIC-LITER - Lamps - GRK Manufacturing
MUSIC LOCKER - Cases—plastic - Ryka, Inc.
MUSIC LOVERS - Microphones ☆ - Shure Brothers, Inc.
MUSIC LOVIN' - Dolls - Mattel, Inc.
MUSIC MACHINE - Recording label ☆ - Caprice International Records
MUSIC MACHINE - Toys—musical - Proll Toy Co.
MUSIC MACHINE BOOKS, THE - Publisher's imprints - Joybug Teaching Aids Inc.
MUSIC MAKER - Computer software - Magix Computer Products International Corp.
MUSIC MAKERS - Toys—musical - Imperial Toy Corp.
MUSIC MAN - Guitars, basses, accessories, amplifiers ☆ - Ernie Ball Inc.
MUSIC MANAGEMENT - Computer software ☆ - Ancott Associates
MUSIC MANAGEMENT ASSOCIATES - Publisher's imprints - SCP Records
MUSIC MASTER - Accordions - Atlas Accordions Inc.
MUSIC MASTERS - Recording label - Essex Entertainment Inc.
MUSIC-MATES - Audio equipment - CSI/Speco
MUSIC MATH - Computer software - Dunamis Inc.
MUSIC MATS - Placemats ☆ - Straight Edge Inc.
MUSIC MERCHANT - Phonographs ☆ - Fantasy Inc.
MUSIC MINUS ONE - Recording label - MMO Music Group Inc.
MUSIC MISS - Apparel—women's - Wacoal America Inc.
MUSIC MOUSE - Computer software - Dr. T's Music Software Inc.
MUSIC 'N LIGHTS PARADE - Toys - Mattel, Inc.
MUSIC NETWORK - Musical instrument accessories - Heritage Industries
MUSIC OF POLYNESIA - Recording label - Music of Polynesia Inc.
MUSIC OF THE WORLD - Recording label - Music of the World Ltd.
MUSIC ONE - Musical instruments - Roberto Ciarfella Inc.
MUSIC PEN - Computer software - Music Pen Inc.
MUSIC PLANT - Recording label - Music Music, Ltd.
MUSIC PRODUCT DIRECTORY - Directories - Ancott Associates
MUSIC RECYCLERY, THE - Department stores - Progressive Storm
MUSIC ROOM - Computer software - Electronic Courseware Systems Inc.
MUSIC SCREENERS - Computer software - Sony Music Entertainment Inc.
MUSIC SOUTH - Recording label - Allan Kaplan Enterprises
MUSIC STANDS - Music stands - Ardsley Musical Instrument Co.
MUSIC STORE, THE - Recording label - Ichiban Records, Inc.
MUSIC STUDIO, THE - Computer software - Activision, Inc.
MUSIC SUITE, THE - Computer software - Yamaha Corp. of America
MUSIC TECH MIDI - Sound equipment - Castiglione Accordion
MUSIC TERMINOLOGY - Computer software - Electronic Courseware Systems Inc.
MUSIC TIME - Computer software - Passport Designs Inc.
MUSIC TO GO - Audio equipment - Royal Sound Co. Inc.
MUSIC TO YOUR CHEERS - Music boxes - Silverdale Inc.
MUSIC TRAVELLER - Audio equipment - Royal Sound Co. Inc.
MUSIC TUTOR - Computer software ☆ - Passport Designs Inc.
MUSIC UNLIMITED - Recording label - Jazz Composer's Orchestra Association Inc.
MUSIC WEAR - Musical instrument accessories - Slobeat Industries
MUSIC WERKS - Recording label - Jazz Composer's Orchestra Association Inc.
MUSIC WEST - Recording label - Music West Records
MUSIC WORLD - Recording label - Ralph L. Seltzer
MUSICA - Cables - Esoteric Audio USA Inc.
MUSICA - Glassware—household - Oneida Ltd.
MUSICA - Musical instruments - Ideal Musical Merchandise Co.

☆ = Now out of production

MUSICAL - Cases–musical instrument - Alco Carrying Cases Inc.
MUSICAL BIRDS - Figurines ☆ - Gorham Inc.
MUSICAL BUBBLE MAKER - Toys - Imperial Toy Corp.
MUSICAL BUNNIES - Toys–stuffed - Fun World Inc.
MUSICAL BUSY BOX - Toys–musical - CBS Toys
MUSICAL CHAIRS - Furniture - Lynn Walker
MUSICAL DREAM WEDDING - Dolls - Mattel, Inc.
MUSICAL EXPEDITIONS - Recording label - Relaxation Co., Inc.
MUSICAL JOLLY CHIMP - Toys - Tyco Toys
MUSICAL LEARNING EXPERIENCES - Musical instrument accessories ☆ - Hal Leonard Corp.
MUSICAL MAP-ATLAS - Maps - Riconstabob's Co.
MUSICAL MEMORIES - Music boxes - American Music Box Co.
MUSICAL PRINCESS - Dolls - Mattel, Inc.
MUSICAL PRODUCTIONS - Recording label - Sonotone Corp.
MUSICAL PRODUCTIONS (M.P.) - Publisher's imprints - Audiorama Records Corp.
MUSICAL STAIRS - Computer software - Electronic Courseware Systems Inc.
MUSICAL TERMINOLOGY - Electronic Courseware Systems Inc.
MUSICAL TREASURES - Music boxes - Mangelsen's (VDI)
MUSICAL WIND-UPS - Music boxes - National Artcraft Co.
MUSICAL WORLD OF PROFESSOR PICCOLO, THE - Computer software - Opcode Systems, Inc.
MUSICALLY GIFTED - Paper–gift wrap - Nancy Drew, Inc.
MUSICAM - Cameras - John Reynolds Tipton, Jr.
MUSICARD - Greeting cards - Dickens Co.
MUSICARDS - Games ☆ - Cramer Products Co.
MUSICARDS - Novelty items - Pro Set Inc.
MUSICASTER - Amplifiers ☆ - Electro-Voice, Inc.
MUSICAT - Computer software - Viking Software Services, Inc.
MUSICBYTES - Computer software - Rosemead Music Productions, Inc.
MUSICENTER - Stereos ☆ - Sanyo Fisher (USA) Corp.
MUSICIAN'S LIFE - Percussion caps - Musician's Repair & Supply
MUSICLINK - Cables–coaxial - Transparent Audio Marketing, Inc.
MUSICLOTHES - Apparel and accessories - Edgerton Enterprises
MUSICMAN - Computer software ☆ - Zephyr Services
MUSICMASTER - Computer hardware - Record-Rama Sound Archives
MUSICMASTER - Guitars - Fender Musical Instruments
MUSICMASTERS - Recording label - Musicmasters
MUSICMATE - Electronic equipment - A.L.S. Industries Inc.
MUSICMOVERS - Giftware - A.L.S. Industries Inc.
MUSICOLA - Giftware - Agent Andy Inc.
MUSICOM - Computer software ☆ - Rolandcorp US
MUSICOMP - Computers ☆ - Apple Computer Inc.
MUSICOMP - Electronic equipment - MB Quart Electronics USA, Inc.
MUSICOR - Recording label - Musicor Records Inc.
MUSICORP - Musical instrument accessories - MBT International, Inc.
MUSICPOWER - Computer software - Mpower, Inc.
MUSICROM - Recording label ☆ - Selectware Technologies, Inc.
MUSICSAFARI - Educational materials - Judy Knudson
MUSICSTAR - Musical instruments - Reveal Computer Products Co.
MUSICTRACK - Compact discs–prerecorded - TRF Production Music Libraries
MUSICUS - Computer software - Electronic Courseware Systems Inc.
MUSICWEAR - Shirts - Musictime Specialties Corp.
MUSICWORKS - Computer software - Spinnaker Software Corp.
MUSICWRITER - Computer software - Mindscape Software Inc.
MUSICWRITER - Typewriters - Music Print Co.
MUSIFLEX - Audio equipment - Connectronics Corp.
MUSIKFEST - Apparel and accessories - Bethlehem Musikfest Association
MUSIKINS - Dolls - Uneeda Doll Co., Inc.
MUSIMA - Musical instruments ☆ - Castiglione Accordion
MUSIMATIC - Musical instruments - Musimatic Electronics Inc.
MUSIMEX - Recording label - Musimex Inc.
MUSIQUE - Computer software - Electronic Courseware Systems Inc.
MUSIQUE - Floor coverings–carpet and rugs - Evans-Black Carpet Mills
MUSIQUICK - Computer storage devices–optical - Jim Long Companies, Inc.
MUSIQUICK+CLIPZ - Computer storage devices–optical - Jim Long Companies, Inc.
MUSIRANMA - Publisher's imprints - Afterschool Publishing Co.
MUSITRONICS - Audio equipment - Fender Musical Instruments
MUSK BY ENGLISH LEATHER - Colognes - Mem Co., Inc.
MUSK FEVER - Fragrance ☆ - Cosrich Inc.
MUSK FOR MEN - Colognes - Avon Products, Inc.
MUSK FOR MEN - Fragrance - Coty Inc.
MUSK LITE - Colognes - Romane Inc.
MUSK #II - Perfumes - Ritornelle Inc.

MUSKADINE - Recording label ☆ - Roots and Rhythm
MUSKET - Tobacco–chewing or smoking - 1776 Tobacco Co.
MUSKETEER - Aircraft–airplanes ☆ - Beech Aircraft Corp.
MUSKETEER - Bicycles - Columbia Manufacturing Inc.
MUSKETEER - Dolls ☆ - Effanbee Doll Corp.
MUSKETTEER - Cutlery ☆ - Liberty Mountain Sports
MUSKIE - Motors–outboard - Jetco Inc.
MUSKIE PIKE - Fishing tackle ☆ - Gladding Braided Products Inc.
MUSKIE PRO - Boats–fishing ☆ - Crestliner Boats Inc.
MUSKIN - Filters–water - Muskin Leisure Products Inc.
MUSKOKA LAKES - Apparel and accessories - Muskoka Lakes U.S.A., L.C.
MUSKOKA LAKES - Apparel and accessories - Muskoka Trading Co.
MUSKOL - Insecticides - Schering-Plough Healthcare Products
MUSKY KILLER - Fishing lures - Sheldons', Inc.
MUSKY MASTER - Fishing lines - Cortland Line Co., Inc.
MUSKY ROLLER - Fishing lures - Lindy Little Joe Inc.
MUSO - Food products - Eden Foods, Inc.
MUSSELMAN'S - Food products - Musselman Fruit Products
MUSSELMAN'S - Fruits–canned - Knouse Foods Cooperative, Inc.
MUSSELTONE - Vitamins and nutritional supplements - Bio San Laboratories Inc.
MUSSER - Musical instrument accessories ☆ - Selmer Co. Inc.
MUSSER'S - Potato chips ☆ - Charles Chip Corp.
MUSSETTE - Luggage ☆ - French Co.
MUSSINI - Artists' materials ☆ - M. Grumbacher Inc.
MUSSON - Floor coverings - R.C. Musson Rubber Co.
MUSSO'S - Bakery products - Gourmet Bakery, Inc.
MUST - Jewelry - Cartier Inc.
MUSTACHE COMBS & FOLDING SCISSORS - Combs - Estus Export-Import
MUSTACHE MASQUERADE - Costumes - Russ Berrie and Co., Inc.
MUSTACHIO - Candy - Glenn Confections Inc.
MUSTANG - See GRASS PLUS
MUSTANG - Apparel–children's - Blue Bird Knitwear Co.
MUSTANG - Apparel–men's - Haggar Apparel Co.
MUSTANG - Audio equipment - Mustang Electronics
MUSTANG - Badminton equipment ☆ - National Sporting Goods Corp.
MUSTANG - Beverages–malt - Pittsburgh Brewing Co.
MUSTANG - Bicycles - Columbia Manufacturing Inc.
MUSTANG - Blankets - MTC
MUSTANG - Boats ☆ - Correct Craft Inc.
MUSTANG - Boats–motor - Ebbtide Corp.
MUSTANG - Boats–motor ☆ - Century Boat Co.
MUSTANG - Cameras ☆ - Edixa Camera Co.
MUSTANG - Cigarettes - R.J. Reynolds Tobacco Co.
MUSTANG - Cigars ☆ - Phillies Cigar Co.
MUSTANG - Eyeglasses - Joy Enterprises
MUSTANG - Fishing tackle - Shakespeare Fishing Tackle
MUSTANG - Fishing tackle ☆ - South Bend Sporting Goods Inc.
MUSTANG - Floor coverings - Congoleum Corp.
MUSTANG - Footwear–children's - Lvichiny Destroy Imports Inc.
MUSTANG - Guitars - Fender Musical Instruments
MUSTANG - Hardware - Allpro Corp.
MUSTANG - Hats - Bailey Hat Co.
MUSTANG - Knives ☆ - Precise International/Wenger
MUSTANG - Lawn mowers - Mowett Sales Co. Inc.
MUSTANG - Mops ☆ - Piedmont Mop Co.
MUSTANG - Motor vehicles–automobiles - Ford Motor Co.
MUSTANG - Musical instrument accessories - Carpenter Co.
MUSTANG - Musical instrument accessories - Sottile Manufacturing Co.
MUSTANG - Oils–lubricating - Cedar Enterprises, Inc.
MUSTANG - Pens - Micropoint Inc.
MUSTANG - Pet products - Mustang Products, Inc.
MUSTANG - Pistols - Colt's Manufacturing Co. Inc.
MUSTANG - Seats–automobile - Al Simmons Co., Inc.
MUSTANG - Staplers ☆ - ITW Paslode
MUSTANG - Tools - Great Neck Saw Manufacturers, Inc.
MUSTANG - Tools ☆ - Litton Industries Inc. (New Britain Tool Div.)
MUSTANG - Toy vehicle replicas - 1992 Mathre Family Trust
MUSTANG - Toys–models - Comet Montrose Ltd.
MUSTANG - Truck caps - Jackson Enterprises Inc.
MUSTANG - Underwear and nightwear - Youthcraft-Charmfit
MUSTANG - Video production - Conwest Resources, Inc.
MUSTANG - Watches - Croton Watch Co., Inc.
MUSTANG - Wheelbarrows - Ames Lawn & Garden Tool Co.
MUSTANG - Wire–barbed - Burly Corp. of North America
MUSTANG 30 ANNIVERSARY - Apparel and accessories - Ford Motor Co.

☆ = Now out of production

MUSTANG BY HAGGAR - Slacks–men's ☆ - Haggar Corp.
MUSTANG GHIA - Motor vehicles–automobiles ☆ - Ford Motor Co.
MUSTANG II - Motor vehicles–automobiles ☆ - Ford Motor Co.
MUSTANG MACH 1 - Motor vehicles–automobiles ☆ - Ford Motor Co.
MUSTANG MOUNTAIN - Horseradish - C.V. Finer Foods Inc.
MUSTARD OF CHAMPIONS, THE - Mustard - Sun and Earth Co.
MUSTARD SEED - Dresses–girls' - T.P. Industries Inc.
MUSTARD SEED CO. - T-shirts–men's - Steven J. Neeves
MUSTARDS GRILL - Apparel and accessories - Mustards, Inc.
MUSTARGEN - Pharmaceutical preparations - Merck & Co., Inc. (Merck Research Laboratories)
MUSTEK PARAGON - Computer peripheral equipment - Mustek, Inc.
MUSTELA - Skin care products - Mustela USA
MUSTELA M-9 - Skin care products - Mustela USA
MUSTER - Ophthalmic goods - Foremost Optical Products
MUSTER MOUSE - Measuring instruments - Ross Industries Inc.
MUSTEROLE - Analgesics - Schering-Plough Healthcare Products
MUSTEVIC - Recording label - Jazz Composer's Orchestra Association Inc.
MUSTIQUE - Beverages - Juba Beverages Corp.
MUSTIQUE - Shoes ☆ - Allen-Edmonds Shoe Corp.
MUSTISES - Chocolate candy ☆ - Casino North America
MUSTNUTO - Sauces - T.K. Vodrey
MUSTO-HYDE - Boats - Fore 'n Aft
MUTALIN - Pharmaceutical preparations - G.O. Spanner Inc.
MUTAMYCIN - Pharmaceutical preparations - Bristol-Myers Squibb Co.
MUTANOID - Computer software - Legacy Software
MUTANT LEAGUE - Computer games and manuals - Electronic Arts Inc.
MUTANT LEAGUE - Toys - Lewis Galoob Toys, Inc.
MUTANTS - Toys - Spearhead Industries Inc.
MUTATOX - Chemical products - Microbics Corp.
MUTE - Recording label - Enigma Entertainment
MUTE FORCE - Tools ☆ - Thor Power Tools
MUTEC - Musical instrument accessories - Music Industries Inc.
MUTED GOLD - Melamine product - Boonton Molding Co. Inc.
MUTINEER - Ships–sailing vessels - Cardinal Yachts
MUTINY - Boats–motor ☆ - Bayliner Marine Corp.
MUTINY - Colognes - Brandy Harvest
MUTINY - Frames–eyeglass - Zylo Ware Corp.
MUTOID - Hobby kits - Mattel, Inc.
MUTSCHLER - Cabinets - Triangle Pacific Corp. (Cabinet Division)
MUTSHLER EUROPEAN - Cabinets ☆ - Triangle Pacific Corp. (Cabinet Division)
MUTT & JEFF - Apparel and accessories - Mutt & Jeff Lures
MUTT MAT-TRESS - Pet products - Zerick Co.
MUTT MATS - Pet products - Zerick Co.
M.U.T.T., THE - Tools - Village Blacksmith
MUTTON BUTTONS - Cookies - Upper Crust Bakery
MUTTSY - Toys–stuffed - Gund, Inc.
MUTUAL - Craft supplies - Dunn Manufacturing Corp.
MUTUAL CERTIFIED - Apparel and accessories - Styl-land Inc.
MUY BUENO - Food products - Stone Mill Kitchens, Inc.
MUY FRESCO - Snack foods - Real Fresh, Inc.
MUY MUCHO - Food products - Ham I Am, Inc.
MUZ - Motorcycles - American Jawa Ltd.
MUZA - Recording label - Polish Record & Video Center of America
MUZZLELOADER - Pet products - 3-D Investment, Inc.
MUZZLER - Mufflers–motor vehicle - Sears, Roebuck and Co.
MUZZLES THE MANATEE - Novelty items - Jazz Angel Productions
MUZZY - Archery equipment - Archer Sports Inc.
MV AGUSTA - Motorcycles ☆ - Commerce Overseas Corp.
MV ALERT! - Computer software - MVIS Corp.
MV EZ KLEEN - Filters–air - Research Products Corp.
MV PAGE DISPLAY - Computer software - MVIS Corp.
MV PICS - Frames–picture - Stewart Industries, Inc.
MV QUOTE LINK - Computer software - MVIS Corp.
MV SPORT - Apparel - David Peyser Sportswear Inc.
MVCP - Lighting fixtures - Solar Kinetics, Inc.
MVE - Machinery - Mississippi Valley Equipment Co.
M.V.I. - Vitamins and nutritional supplements - Rhone-Poulenc Rorer Pharmaceuticals Inc.
M.V.M. - Vitamins and nutritional supplements ☆ - Integrated Health, Inc.
M.V.P. - Apparel–men's - Barrow Manufacturing Co., Inc.
MVP - Balls - General Sportcraft Co. Ltd.
MVP - Dictating machines - Dictaphone Corp.
MVP - Electric lighting equipment - Solar Kinetics, Inc.
MVP - Electronic equipment - General Electric Co.

MVP - Electronic equipment - Micro Mo Electronics, Inc.
M.V.P. - Grass seed - Wetsel Seed Co. Inc.
MVP - Guitars - M.V. Pedulla Guitars
MVP - Locks–padlocks - Medeco Security Locks, Inc.
MVP - Ophthalmic goods - Karlen Manufacturing, Inc.
MVP - Orthopedic products - Ortho-Kinetics, Inc.
M.V.P. - Pens - Bic Corp.
MVP - Pharmaceutical preparations - Standard Textile Co., Inc.
MVP - Pizzas–frozen ☆ - Mr. Z's Fund Raising Corp.
MVP - Recording label - Polygram Records, Inc.
MVP - Toys - Jak-Pak Inc.
MVP BREAKFAST - Doughnuts - Super Bakery, Inc.
M.V.P. FLEECE - Fabrics–flock - Minnetonka Mills Inc.
MVP-II - Basketball shoes ☆ - Jaclar
MVP MEMBER VALUE PACK - Checkbooks - Clarke American Corp.
MVP MOST VALUED PATRON - Advertising agencies - C. & J. Clark America, Inc.
MVP MOUSE - Computer peripheral equipment ☆ - Curtis Manufacturing Co., Inc.
MVP NUTRITION - Doughnuts - Super Bakery, Inc.
MVP POWER - Doughnuts - Super Bakery, Inc.
MVP SPORTSTARS - Toys–stuffed - Ace Novelty Co. Inc.
MVPOWER - Computer hardware - Datacube, Inc.
MVS GOLD - Computer software - MVS Gold, Inc.
MVT - Floor tiles - Allstate Rubber Corp.
MVX - Telephone answering machines - Macrovoice Corp.
MW - Apparel and accessories - Musictime Specialties Corp.
MW - Computer software - Mobile Ware Corp.
MW - Watches - Tempus International Corp.
MW - Wines - Martine's Wines Inc.
MW - Wire - Mize & Co.
MW COLLECTION - Shoes ☆ - Montgomery Ward & Co. Inc.
MW MICHELE - Watches - Tempus International Corp.
MW SELECT - Oils–lubricating - Northland Products Co.
MW/SS - Blankets - Ty Mawr Classics
MW STUDIO - Apparel–children's - Monkey Wear, Inc.
MWAVE - Circuit boards - International Business Machines Corp.
MWC - Apparel - Ronon Enterprises, Ltd.
MWD-1000 - Golfing equipment - Golfsmith International Inc.
MWS - Electrical wiring system - Cooper Industries, Inc.
MX - Bowling balls - P.J. Trading Co.
MX - Cosmetics - Atlanta Center for Aesthetics, Inc.
MX - Filters–industrial - Surface Combustion, Inc.
MX - Jewelry - Marvalex Jewelry Inc.
MX - Thread ☆ - SCT Yarns Inc.
MX-1 - Frames–eyeglass - Rozin Optical Export Corp.
MX-2 - Electric organs - Lowrey Organ Co.
MX-2 - Frames–eyeglass - Rozin Optical Export Corp.
MX-2 CLIP ON - Frames–eyeglass - Rozin Optical Export Corp.
MX-2 DELUXE - Frames–eyeglass - Rozin Optical Export Corp.
MX-3 - Frames–eyeglass - Rozin Optical Export Corp.
MX-3 - Motor vehicles–automobiles - Mazda Motor of America Inc.
MX-4 - Frames–eyeglass - Rozin Optical Export Corp.
MX-5 MIATA - Motor vehicles–automobiles - Mazda Motor of America Inc.
MX-6 - Motor vehicles–automobiles - Mazda Motor of America Inc.
MX-7 PLUS - Cleaning preparations - Eddie's Auto Detail Clinic, Inc.
MX-7 ULTRA - Cleaning preparations - Eddie's Auto Detail Clinic, Inc.
MX 40 - Lawn mowers - Qualcast USA
MX-86 - Flowers, plants, and seeds - Jacklin Seed
MX-200 SERIES HOME USE BENCHES - Exercising equipment - Maximus Fitness Products
MX-500 SERIES SINGLE STATION MACHINES - Exercising equipment - Maximus Fitness Products
MX-1800 HOME GYM - Exercising equipment - Maximus Fitness Products
MX-2800 LIGHT COMMERCIAL MULTI GYM - Exercising equipment - Maximus Fitness Products
MX-4800 4 STACK MULTI GYM-COMMERCIAL - Exercising equipment - Maximus Fitness Products
MX MISSILE - Toys–models ☆ - Estes Industries
MX/PF - Respirators - Glendale Protective Technologies Inc.
MX-POSED - Video production - Michael Bryant
MX SERIES - Elevators - Montgomery Kone Inc.
MX SPACE LAMP - Fireworks - American Promotional Events, Inc.
MX/T - Drums–musical instruments - Marc Inc.
MX93 - Hardware - Vertilux-Louverlux Inc.
MXBUS - Electronic equipment - Mizar Inc.

☆ = Now out of production

MXBUS II - Electronic equipment - Mizar Inc.
MXC - Audio equipment - ADA Signal Processors Inc.
MXG - Computer software - Merrill Consultants
M.X.I. - Apparel–athletic - Shomi, Inc.
MXI - Orthodontic equipment - TP Orthodontics, Inc.
MXL - Bicycles - Columbia Manufacturing Inc.
MXL - Sporting goods ☆ - MXL Industries Inc.
MXM BOTANICALS - Hair care products - MXM Essential Formulas Inc.
MXO - Fuel additives - Bell Additives, Inc.
MXP - Automotive parts and accessories - Malco Products, Inc.
MXR - Audio equipment - MXR Innovations Inc.
MXR - Musical instrument accessories - Dunlop Manufacturing, Inc.
MXV4 - Tires - Michelin Tire Corp.
MY - Dental equipment - Austenal, Inc.
MY - Pet products - Martin M. Vega
MY-A-MULTI - Vitamins and nutritional supplements - Leiner Health Products Inc.
MY ADVANCED MAILLIST - Computer software - My Software Co.
MY AGE IS CONSEALED - Skin care products - Cosmetically Sealed Industries Inc.
MY ARMORED BANK - Toys–automobiles - Nylint Toy Corp.
MY BABY - Apparel–children's - Star Baby Inc.
MY BABY FLOAT - Swim rings - Intex Recreation Corp.
MY BABY LOVES HER BATH - Dolls - Davis Brothers & Madison Ltd.
MY BABY PUPPY - Toys - Marchon, Inc.
MY BACKPACK SET - Toys - Fisher-Price, Inc.
MY BAG IS CANDY - Candy - Harry London's Candies Inc.
MY BATHING BABY - Dolls - Fisher-Price, Inc.
MY BEAUTIFUL NAILS - Electrical equipment - Medicool Inc.
MY BEAUTIFUL SWAN - Toys–stuffed ☆ - Commonwealth Toy and Novelty Co. Inc.
MY BEEPER - Electronic equipment - Electronic Systems Co., Inc.
MY BEST BUDDIES - Toys–stuffed ☆ - Fun World Inc.
MY BEST FRIEND - Leather pet supplies - Auburn Leathercrafters Inc.
MY BEST FRIEND - Toys - Eugene Doll & Novelty Co. Inc.
MY BEST FRIEND'S - Toys - Pro-Line Winning Ways Inc.
MY BIG SISTER - Fashion dolls - Kid Kore International Ltd.
MY BODY - Publisher's imprints - Thomas M. Mitchell
MY BODY AND ME - Apparel and accessories - Barbara Ann Diskin
MY BOTTLE BABY - Toys–stuffed ☆ - CBS Toys
MY BOY - Diapers–disposable - Paragon Trade Brands, Inc.
MY BRANDS - Condiments - My Brands Inc.
MY BREST FRIEND - Pillows - Andrew R. Zenoff
MY BUDDY - Candy - Tom's Foods Inc.
MY BUDDY - Pet products - Bacon Products Corp.
MY BUDDY - Sporting goods ☆ - Hedstrom Corp.
MY BUDDY - Tobacco products - Sterling Tobacco Co.
MY BUDDY - Tool boxes - Disston Co.
MY BUDDY - Toys - Playskool, Inc.
MY BUNDLE - Dolls - Mattel, Inc.
MY BUSY CAR - Infant product - Playskool Baby Inc.
MY CADDY - Golf carts - Bag Boy Inc.
MY CADDY - Sports rackets and accessories - Gexco Enterprises
MY CAFE - Coffee makers–electric ☆ - Toshiba America Consumer Products, Inc. (Consumer Products Business Sector)
MY CARE - Flower care labels - World Wide Growers, Inc.
MY CHAIR - Infant product - Pansy Ellen Products, Inc.
MY CHATTY PATTY - Dolls - Mattel, Inc.
MY CHECKS & BALANCES - Computer software - My Checks & Balances Corp.
MY CHILD - Cosmetics for children ☆ - Cosrich Inc.
MY CHILD - Dolls - Mattel, Inc.
MY CHILD - Footwear ☆ - Mercury International Trading Corp.
MY CHILD POSITIVE INFANT IDENTIFICATIONKIT - Identification tags ☆ - Prosec Protection Systems Inc.
MY CHOICE - Floor coverings–carpet and rugs ☆ - Gulistan Carpet Inc.
MY CHRISTMAS BABY - Toys - Eugene Doll & Novelty Co. Inc.
MY CLASSIC PIZZA - Food products ☆ - Pillsbury Co.
MY COLOR 2 - Floor coverings–carpet and rugs ☆ - Royalweve Carpet Mills
MY COLORING SHIRT - Apparel–children's - Creative Intellectual Properties, Inc.
MY COMB & CARE BABY - Dolls - Fisher-Price, Inc.
MY COOKBOOK, LTD. - Publisher's imprints - My Cookbook, Ltd.
MY-CORT - Health care products ☆ - Scrip-Physician Supply Co.
MY COUNTRY - Mustard - Nancy's Specialty Foods
MY COUNTRY SITTERS - Dolls - Evelyn Hanson Sabourin

MY CRAZY LIFE - Apparel and accessories - My Crazy Life
MY CUBBY - Furniture ☆ - Superior Storage Systems, Inc.
MY DAD DRESSED ME - Apparel stores–children's - Richard P. Proctor, Jr.
MY DANCING MEMORIES - Scrapbooks - Favorite Memories, Inc.
MY DARLING - Cutlery ☆ - Lifetime Hoan Corp.
MY DEBUT - Invitations - Southwest Announcements
MY DESIRE - Candles - Circle of Beauty, Inc.
MY DISH - Pet products ☆ - Penn-Plax, Inc.
MY DOG SPOT - Pillows - My Dog Spot, Inc.
MY DOGGIE'S BAG - Dog food - Pet Life Foods Inc.
MY DOLLY - Dolls - Imperial Toy Corp.
MY DREAM - Skin care products - Goubaud
MY EPIL - Skin care products - Ella Bache Inc.
MY EUREKA! - Computer software - Information Advantage, Inc.
MY EVERYTHING TREATMENT - Skin care products - Flori Roberts Inc.
MY EXCEL - Sewing machines–household - New Home Sewing Machine Co.
MY EYES - Frames–eyeglass ☆ - Universal/Univis Inc.
MY FACE - Cosmetics ☆ - Avon Products, Inc.
MY FAIR LADY - Furniture - Pulaski Furniture Corp.
MY FAIR LADY IX - Wallpaper - Norwall Wallcoverings
MY FANCY - Frames–eyeglass - Zylo Ware Corp.
MY FANTASTIC FRAGRANCES - Toys - Toymax Inc.
MY FANTASY - Floor coverings–carpet and rugs ☆ - Patcraft Mills Inc.
MY FATHER'S BEST - Pizzas–frozen - Nation Pizza Products L.P.
MY FATHER'S BUSINESS - Giftware - Walnut Valley Printery
MY FAVORITE - Brassieres (Bras) - Vanity Fair Mills Inc.
MY FAVORITE - Ice cream - Dunkirk Ice Cream Co., Inc.
MY-FAVORITE - Paper–carbon - Eaton Allen Ko-Rec-Type Corp.
MY FAVORITE - Vitamins and nutritional supplements - Natrol, Inc.
MY FAVORITE BAGELS - Bagels - My Favorite Muffin, Too, Inc.
MY FAVORITE BAKERY - Gingerbread–mixes - American Specialty Foods Inc.
MY FAVORITE CAPPUCCINO - Coffee - My Favorite Muffin, Too, Inc.
MY FAVORITE ESPRESSO - Coffee - My Favorite Muffin, Too, Inc.
MY FAVORITE FANTASY - Brassieres (Bras) - Vanity Fair Mills Inc.
MY FAVORITE GAL - Vitamins and nutritional supplements - Natrol, Inc.
MY FAVORITE LATTE - Coffee - My Favorite Muffin, Too, Inc.
MY FAVORITE MONSTER - Video games - Schoolscape Inc.
MY FAVORITE MUFFIN - Baked-goods franchise - My Favorite Muffin
MY FAVORITE PASTA - Food products - My Own Meals Inc.
MY FAVORITE PEN - Pens - Tops Pen Co.
MY FAVORITE PICKED AT THE RIPE TIME - Fruits and vegetables - Favorite Products, Inc.
MY FAVORITE RECIPES - Receipt books - Wahlman Publishing
MY FAVORITE SCHOOL MEMORIES - Photo albums - Minnesota American, Inc.
MY FAVORITE SCHOOL MEMORIES - Scrapbooks - Favorite Memories, Inc.
MY FAVORITE THINGS - Christmas tree ornaments - Cracker Box Inc.
MY FAVORITE THINGS - Hobby kits ☆ - Blumenthal/Lansing Co.
MY FAVORITE THINGS - Music boxes - William Hammerstein and Philip Zimet
MY FAVORITE THINGS - Music boxes - Rodgers Family Partnership
MY FAVORTIE DELITES - Sandwiches - My Favorite Muffin
MY FEET ARE HEADED FOR... - Footwear–children's - Vision Imports Inc.
MY FINANCES - Office supplies - Boorum & Pease Co.
MY FIRST ANIMAL BOOK - Electronic equipment ☆ - Texas Instruments Inc.
MY FIRST BABY - Dolls - Doll Factory, Inc.
MY FIRST BABY DOLL - Dolls ☆ - Fun World Inc.
MY FIRST BACKSEAT BOOKS - Publisher's imprints - Rand McNally & Co.
MY FIRST BARBIE - Dolls - Mattel, Inc.
MY FIRST BASEBALL - Toys - Bantam Collections Inc.
MY FIRST BEAR - Toys ☆ - Those Characters from Cleveland, Inc.
MY FIRST BRA - Apparel–women's - Wacoal America Inc.
MY FIRST BUDDYS - Toys - Buddy L Inc.
MY FIRST BUSTER - Footwear ☆ - Brown Shoe Co.
MY FIRST CAMERA - Cameras - Eastman Kodak Co.
MY FIRST CAMERA - Cameras - Sakar International Inc.
MY FIRST CHRISTMAS - Toys–stuffed - Dan-Dee International Ltd.
MY FIRST COLGATE - Toothbrushes - Colgate-Palmolive Co.
MY FIRST COLORFORMS - Games - Colorforms
MY FIRST CRAYON - Pencils - Dixon Ticonderoga Co.
MY FIRST DRIVER - Toys - Mattel, Inc.
MY FIRST ELECTRIC CAR - Toys ☆ - Combi International Corp.
MY FIRST ELECTRIC TRIKE - Toys ☆ - Combi International Corp.
MY FIRST FAIRY TALE - Video production - Saban Entertainment, Inc.
MY FIRST FISHING POLE - Toys - Playskool, Inc.
MY FIRST FOOTBALL - Toys - Bantam Collections Inc.

☆ = Now out of production

MY FIRST FRISBEE - Toys - Mattel, Inc.

MY FIRST GAME - Games - CBS Toys

MY FIRST GOLDEN SOUND STORY - Publisher's imprints - Western Publishing Co., Inc.

MY FIRST HELLO READER! - Publisher's imprints - Scholastic Inc.

MY FIRST HOCKEY - Hockey equipment - Mattel, Inc.

MY FIRST ID - Identification tags - Textron Inc.

MY FIRST ID - Jewelry - Hirsch Speidel Inc.

MY FIRST ID BY SPEIDEL - Identification tags - Textron Inc.

MY FIRST INLAY - Puzzles - Milton Bradley Co.

MY FIRST KEYBOARD - Computer hardware - Kidtech Inc.

MY FIRST KWAANZA - Toys–stuffed - Prestige Toy Corp.

MY FIRST MARKER - Writing utensils - Dixon Ticonderoga Co.

MY FIRST MODEL - Toys - Monogram Models Inc.

MY FIRST PENCIL - Pencils - Dixon Ticonderoga Co.

MY FIRST PHOTO BOOK - Publisher's imprints - Chilcote Co.

MY FIRST PONY - Toys ☆ - Sun Products Corp. (Wellington)

MY FIRST PUPPY - Toys ☆ - Those Characters from Cleveland, Inc.

MY FIRST READ-ALONG - Recording label - Walt Disney Co.

MY FIRST SANTA - Toys–stuffed - Dan-Dee International Ltd.

MY FIRST SING-ALONG - Recording label - Walt Disney Co.

MY FIRST SNOWMAN - Toys–stuffed - Dan-Dee International Ltd.

MY FIRST SONY - Tape players–cassette - Sony Corp. of America

MY FIRST STEPS TO MATH - Computer software - Hopkins Technology LLC

MY FIRST TEE-BALL - Balls - Mattel, Inc.

MY FIRST TIGER - Toys–electronic - Tiger Electronics, Inc.

MY FIRST TONKA - Toys - Tonka Corp.

MY FIRST TRAVELIN' SET - Luggage - Kingport International Corp.

MY FIRST WASHABLE WATER COLORS - Paint sets–hobby - Dixon Ticonderoga Co.

MY FOOTBALL MONSTER - Toys ☆ - Those Characters from Cleveland, Inc.

MY FRIEND - Dolls - Fisher-Price, Inc.

MY FRIEND JENNY - Dolls - Fisher-Price, Inc.

MY FRIEND MANDY - Dolls - Fisher-Price, Inc.

MY FRIENDS AND ME - Toys–models - Shipping Shop, Inc.

MY GANG - Wallpaper - Old Deerfield Fabrics Inc.

MY GANG - Wallpaper - Piedmont Collections

MY GANG - Wallpaper - Seabrook Wallcoverings, Inc.

MY GARDEN WINDOW - Furniture - Garden Window Network, Inc.

MY GIRL - Diapers–disposable - Paragon Trade Brands, Inc.

MY GIRL - Eyeglasses - Art-Craft Optical Co.

MY GIRL - Pet products - Glo-Marr Products Inc.

MY GLORIA - Fruits and vegetables - William E. McBryde, Inc.

MY GOODNESS - Candy - Eddyleon Chocolate Co. Inc.

MY GRANDMA'S OF NEW ENGLAND COFFEE CAKE - Bakery products - R & E, Inc.

MY GRANDMOTHER'S HOUSE - Wallpaper ☆ - Glidden Co.

MY-GRIP - Handles–plastic - Smith & Nephew Inc. (Rehabilitation Div.)

MY HAIR - Hair care products - My Hair, Inc.

MY HANDS - Artists' materials - Frances Meyer, Inc.

MY HEALTH - Diaries - Favorite Memories, Inc.

MY HEART - Pencils ☆ - Dakin Inc.

MY HEART HAS WINGS - Figurines - Lifelike Birds, Inc.

MY HOMETOWN - Wallpaper - Hunting Valley Prints

MY HOSIERY BAG - Hosiery - Noe-Equal Hosiery Corp.

MY HOUSE - Computer programming services - Berta-Max Inc.

MY HOUSE - Computer software - Designware, Inc.

MY HOUSE - Tableware–earthenware - Anacapa Corp.

MY HOUSE BILINGUAL - Computer software - Laureate Learning Systems Inc.

MY HOUSE: LADL - Computer software - Laureate Learning Systems Inc.

MY INCREDIBLE CASE - Markers–felt-tip - Panline USA, Inc.

MY INNER CHILD - Novelty items - MicroGlyphics

MY ISLANDS - Colognes - Gillette Co.

MY JILLY - Linen - Jill Stewart Williams

MY-K - Pharmaceutical preparations ☆ - Morton Grove Pharmaceuticals

MY-K FORMULA 77 - Pharmaceutical preparations ☆ - Morton Grove Pharmaceuticals

MY-K FORMULA 77D - Pharmaceutical preparations ☆ - Morton Grove Pharmaceuticals

MY KIND OF CHICKEN - Food products - My Own Meals Inc.

MY KIND OF COOKIE - Cookies - Cookies by Cedric Inc.

MY KIT AND KABOODLE - Medical apparatus - My Kit and Kaboodle

MY KITTY CAT TREATS - Cat food - Cosmic Cat Corp.

MY LADY - Eyeglasses - Art-Craft Optical Co.

MY-LADY - Hosiery–children's - Gerber Products Co.

MY LADY - Wines - Duplin Wine Cellars

MY LIL BAT - Toys - A.J. Renzi Plastic Corp.

MY LIL SWING - Toys - A.J. Renzi Plastic Corp.

MY LINES ARE CONSEALED - Cosmetics - Cosmetically Sealed Industries Inc.

MY-LITE - Lamps–desk - Mobilite-Spartus

MY LITTER - Pet products - My Litter Products

MY LITTLE ANGEL - Dolls - Kid Kore International Ltd.

MY LITTLE BED - Beds–wood - Newborne Co.

MY LITTLE COMPUTER - Electronic equipment - Texas Instruments Inc.

MY LITTLE COMPUTER - Games - Tiger Electronics, Inc.

MY LITTLE CRADLE - Toys - Today's Kids Inc.

MY LITTLE CRIB - Cribs–wood - Newborne Co.

MY LITTLE LAUNDRY SET - Toys - Playskool, Inc.

MY LITTLE LOCKET PET - Toys–stuffed - Dan-Dee International Ltd.

MY LITTLE MARINA - Infant product - Century Products Co.

MY LITTLE ONE NURSERY - Toys - Today's Kids Inc.

MY LITTLE PONY - Footwear ☆ - Pony Sports & Leisure Inc.

MY LITTLE PONY - Games - Milton Bradley Co.

MY LITTLE PONY - Toys - Hasbro, Inc.

MY LITTLE PONY - Toys ☆ - A.R.C. Toys Inc.

MY LITTLE PONY - Wallpaper ☆ - Priss Prints Inc.

MY LITTLE PONY FLUTTER PONIES - Puzzles - Milton Bradley Co.

MY LITTLE PONY MERRY-GO-ROUND - Games ☆ - Milton Bradley Co.

MY LITTLE PUZZLES - Puzzles ☆ - Lauri Inc.

MY LITTLE RED WAGON - Fabrics–tapestry ☆ - Columbus Coated Fabrics Co.

MY LITTLE REINDEER - Toys–stuffed - Rothkopf Enterprises, Inc.

MY LITTLE ROCKER - Rocking chairs - Newborne Co.

MY LITTLE SHOWER - Games - Century Products Co.

MY LOVE - Flatware ☆ - Wallace International Silversmiths, Inc.

MY LUCKY LOTTERY - Paper products - Ibbafhahs International Inc.

MY LUV-EY BALL - Balls - Marge L. Mead

MY LUVIN' HEART - Toys–stuffed ☆ - Fun World Inc.

MY MAGIC MARBLE - Kaleidoscopes - Gemini Kaleidoscopes

MY MAP - Maps - Gentle Giant Publishing, Inc.

MY MASTERPIECE - Musical instrument accessories - French American Reeds Manufacturing

MY MEATBALLS & SHELLS - Food products - My Own Meals Inc.

MY MELODY - Floor coverings–carpet and rugs - Capel, Inc.

MY MERMAID - Snack foods - Street Kids

MY MICHELLE - Apparel and accessories - Fritzi California

MY MOMMY'S PURSE - Toys - Tonka Corp.

MY MOM'S NUTS - Kitchenware–china - Jan Ellen Adams

MY MOTHERS KNISH - Bakery products - Dairy Fresh Products Co.

MY NAILS ARE SEALED - Manicure preparations - Cosmetically Sealed Industries Inc.

MY-NAME - Pens ☆ - Sakura of America

MY-NAME - Stamp sets - Consolidated Stamp Manufacturing Co. Inc.

MY NANA'S - Tortillas - La Canasta Food Products

MY NEW BOOK - Books - Silver Seahorse Press

MY NEWBORN NANCY - Dolls - Nationsbank of North Carolina, N.A.

MY NIK IS SEALED - Skin care products - Cosmetically Sealed Industries Inc.

MY NONNA'S - Confections - Ann C. Taylor

MY OFFICE - Computer software ☆ - DataPak Software Inc.

MY OFFICE - Office accessories - Diamond Y, Inc.

MY ONE AND ONLY - Decals and transfers - TMT North America Inc.

MY OWN - Pharmaceutical preparations - Schering-Plough Healthcare Products

MY OWN BRAND - Coffee - Papanicholas Coffee

MY OWN BUNNY - Chocolate candy - Brach and Brock Confections Inc.

MY OWN JEWELRY - Jewelry - Hirsch Speidel Inc.

MY OWN MEALS - Food products - My Own Meals Inc.

MY OWN STORIES - Computer software - Softkey International Inc.

MY OWN TUNES - Novelty items - Kidselebration Inc.

MY PAD - Infant product - Pansy Ellen Products, Inc.

MY PADS - Musical instrument accessories - Enzo Pizzi

MY PAINT & CIRCUS - Computer software - Laureate Learning Systems Inc.

MY PAINT & FIRST WORDS COLOR BOOK - Computer software - Laureate Learning Systems Inc.

MY PAL - Gloves - Knoxville Glove Co.

MY PASSION - Colognes - Renee Distributors

MY PET - Bathroom accessories - Luu Corp.

MY PET BEAR - Toys–stuffed - Mattel, Inc.

MY PET BUNNY - Toys–stuffed - Mattel, Inc.

MY PET KITTEN - Toys–stuffed - Mattel, Inc.

MY PET MONSTER - Games ☆ - Ben Cooper Inc.

MY PET MONSTER - Toys - Those Characters from Cleveland, Inc.

☆ = Now out of production

MY PET PONY - Toys ☆ - Hedstrom Corp.
MY PET PUPPY - Toys–stuffed - Mattel, Inc.
MY PET SPERM - Novelty items - Angel Agency
MY PETER RABBIT PLAY BOX - Recording label - Frederick Warne & Co., Inc.
MY PIZZA RAVIOLIS - Food products ☆ - My Own Meals Inc.
MY PLAY A TUNE - Publisher's imprints - JTG of Nashville
MY PLAY CD BOOK - Publisher's imprints - Reader's Digest Association, Inc.
MY POTTY GAME - Infant product - Rock-A-Bye Baby Inc.
MY PRECIOUS PETS COLLECTABLES - Toys - Jasman, Inc.
MY PRECIOUS PUFFS - Dolls - Matchbox Toys USA
MY-PREFERENCE - Spices and extracts - Herbert Marmorek & Son, Inc.
MY PREGNANCY JOURNAL - Books–blank - Informative Amenities Inc.
MY PRESCHOOL PROGRAM - Computer software - Debran Software, Inc.
MY PRETTY BALLERINA - Novelty items–paper ☆ - Unique Industries, Inc.
MY PRETTY DOLLHOUSE - Dolls - Lewis Galoob Toys, Inc.
MY PRETTY PURSE - Toys - Fisher-Price, Inc.
MY PRINCESS BY GIOVANNI - Jewelry - Giovanni Jewelry Co.
MY PRIVATE STOCK - Fruits and vegetables - William G. Roe & Sons, Inc.
MY PUPPY LOVES ME - Toys - Those Characters from Cleveland, Inc.
MY REAL PETS - Toys - Hasbro, Inc.
MY ROMANCE - Floor coverings–carpet and rugs - Lees Carpets
MY ROOM - Wallcovering ☆ - Fashon Wallcoverings
MY ROOM III - Wallcovering ☆ - Fashon Wallcoverings
MY SATIN FANTASY - Apparel–women's - Vanity Fair, Inc.
MY SATIN FANTASY - Brassieres (Bras) - Vanity Fair Mills Inc.
MY SCHOOL - Computer software - Laureate Learning Systems Inc.
MY SCHOOL BILINGUAL - Computer software - Laureate Learning Systems Inc.
MY SECRET - Colognes ☆ - CTS Laboratories Inc.
MY SECRET - Floor coverings–carpet and rugs - Evans-Black Carpet Mills
MY SECRET POWER LOCKET - Jewelry - Helen McCrea
MY SHADOW - Postcards - Exclusive Co.
MY SHAPE 'N STIR POT - Toys - Playskool, Inc.
MY SIN - Frames–eyeglass - Zylo Ware Corp.
MY SISTER'S - Candy - My Sister's Caramels
MY SIZE - Dolls - Mattel, Inc.
MY SIZE BARBIE - Dolls - Mattel, Inc.
MY SKIN - Apparel and accessories - Warnaco Inc.
MY SKIN - Skin care products - Dena Corp.
MY SLEEPOVER PARDNER - Pajamas–women's - Finetex International, Inc.
MY SLUMBER PARTY - Dolls - Justin Products, Inc.
MY SNUGGLE PILLOW - Pillows - Bibb Co.
MY SOLE - Footwear–women's - Famolare Inc.
MY SON THE DOCTOR - Games ☆ - CFC Games
MY SPORT! - Furniture - My Sport! Products, Inc.
MY SPORTS MEMORIES - Photo albums - Minnesota American, Inc.
MY SPOTS ARE CONSEALED - Cosmetics - Cosmetically Sealed Industries Inc.
MY STARS - Girls' clothing - Montgomery Ward & Co. Inc.
MY STICKER ALBUM BOOK - Decals and transfers ☆ - Creative Teaching Press
MY STORIES - Publisher's imprints - Western Publishing Co., Inc.
MY STORY - Computer software - E. David & Associates
MY STUFF - Candy - Ross Acquisitions, Inc.
MY SWEET - Frames–eyeglass - Hudson Optical Corp.
MY SWEET NOTHINGS - Underwear and nightwear - Scentique Ltd.
MY-T-CHEWS - Candy - Gerrit J. Verburg Co.
MY-T-FINE - Desserts - Nabisco Foods Group
MY-T-GOOD - Seafood products–canned or cured ☆ - Dejean Packing Co.
MY-T-MITE - Veterinary pharmaceutical preparations - Hartz Mountain Corp.
MY-T-MOIST - Cakes–mixes - J.W. Allen & Co.
MY-T-ONE - Vitamins and nutritional supplements - Brite Years Vitamins
MY-T-SIREN - Toys - Gerrit J. Verburg Co.
MY-T-TUFF - Socks - Leininger Mills Inc.
MY-TE - Winches - My-Te Products Inc.
MY-TE-FINE - Food products - West Coast Grocery
MY TEAM - Decals - DRL Enterprises, Inc.
MY THREE SONS - Apparel and accessories - CBS Inc.
MY TIME FOR YOU - Greeting cards - M.S. Strong, LLC
MY TIME MANAGER - Computer storage devices - PowerCore Inc.
MY TINY SEFER - Educational materials - Shurgee Creations
MY-TOWEL - Towels - Kirk Enterprises
MY TOWN - Computer software - Laureate Learning Systems Inc.
MY TOWN - Toys - Montgomery Ward & Co. Inc.
MY TOWN BILINGUAL - Computer software - Laureate Learning Systems Inc.

MY TRAIN - Toys–trains - Montgomery Schoolhouse
MY TREASURE - Perfumes ☆ - Treasure Masters
MY TREAT - Fruits and vegetables - George F. Joseph Orchard Siding Inc.
MY TURKEY MEATBALLS - Food products - My Own Meals Inc.
MY TURN - Floor coverings–carpet and rugs - Burlington House Carpets
MY TWINN - Dolls - My Twinn
MY TWO HOMES - Calendars - Ladybug Press
MY-TYME SUCCESS PLANNER - Educational materials - Smi International, Inc.
MY VERY FIRST BABY - Dolls - Fisher-Price, Inc.
MY VERY OWN - Tools–hand-operated ☆ - Atlas Tool
MY VERY OWN - Toys - Mattel, Inc.
MY VERY OWN BOOK - Paper–writing - Kurtz Bros.
MY VERY OWN CALENDAR - Computer software - Learning Well
MY VERY OWN PUPPY - Toys - Mattel, Inc.
MY VERY SOFT BABY - Toys - Playskool, Inc.
MY VILLAGE - Bedding–linen - Dan River Inc.
MY WATCH - Watches - Medana Watch Corp.
MY WATCHDOG - Dolls - Mattel, Inc.
MY WAY - Cosmetics - Christine Valmy, Inc.
MY WAY - Floor coverings–carpet and rugs ☆ - Mohawk Carpet Corp.
MY WAY - Toys - Russ Berrie and Co., Inc.
MY WAY - Wall tile - Integrity Tile Co.
MY WIFE'S FORMULA - Skin care products ☆ - Lee Pharmaceuticals
MY WINDOWS - Bedding–linen - Dan River Inc.
MY WORD! - Computer software - TNT Software Inc.
MY WORKSHOP - Frames–picture - My Workshop Inc.
MY YELLOW PAGES - Telephone directories - Gift Creations, Inc.
MYA - Whirlpools - Jacuzzi Inc.
MYACHT - Boats–motor - Tracker Marine, L.P.
MYAD - Labels–gummed - Chicago Show Printing Co.
MYADEC - Vitamins and nutritional supplements - Warner-Wellcome
MYAPAP - Pharmaceutical preparations ☆ - Morton Grove Pharmaceuticals
MYBACKUP - Computer software - My Software Co.
MYBALS - Toys - Mybals, Inc.
MYBRO - Office supplies - Molded Rubber Co.
MYCADEC DM - Pharmaceutical preparations ☆ - Morton Grove Pharmaceuticals
MYCAL GROUP - Tofu - Nichii Co. of America, Inc.
MYCASEPTIC - Veterinary pharmaceutical preparations - Vetoquinol USA, Inc.
MYCEL - Vitamins and nutritional supplements - Ethical Nutrients
MYCEL - Vitamins and nutritional supplements - Metagenics, Inc.
MYCEL BABY VITES - Vitamins and nutritional supplements - Ethical Nutrients
MYCEL MULTI VITES - Vitamins and nutritional supplements - Ethical Nutrients
MYCELEX - Pharmaceutical preparations - Bayer Corp. (Consumer Care Div.)
MYCHESS - Computer software ☆ - Software Toolworks, Inc.
MYCHRON - Timers–appliance - Stokes Publishing Co., Inc.
MYCI SPRAY - Pharmaceutical preparations - Misemer Pharmaceuticals Inc.
MYCIFRADIN - Pharmaceutical preparations - Upjohn Co.
MYCIGUENT - Pharmaceutical preparations ☆ - Upjohn Co.
MYCINAIRE - Pharmaceutical preparations - Pfeiffer Pharmaceuticals Inc.
MYCINETTES - Cough drops - Pfeiffer Pharmaceuticals Inc.
MYCINEX - Aquatic pharmaceutical preparations ☆ - Aquatronics-Filtronics
MYCITRACIN - Pharmaceutical preparations - Upjohn Co.
MYCO-ARICIN - Prescription drug - IDE-Interstate Inc.
MYCO-KOTE - Chemical preparations - Encore Technologies, Inc.
MYCO SILENCER - Veterinary nutritional supplements - Oxford Veterinary Laboratories, Inc.
MYCO TRIACET - Pharmaceutical preparations - Lemmon Co.
MYCOBUTIN - Antibiotics - Adria Laboratories
MYCOCIDE NS - Nail care products - Woodward Laboratories, Inc.
MYCODEX - Pet products - SmithKline Beecham Animal Health Products
MYCODYN URITEC - Biological reagents and test kits - DynaGen Inc.
MYCOGARD - Veterinary pharmaceutical preparations - Protatek International, Inc.
MYCOGEN - Flowers, plants, and seeds - Mycogen Corp.
MYCOGEN - Pharmaceutical preparations - Goldline Laboratories, Inc.
MYCOLOG - Pharmaceutical preparations - Bristol-Myers Squibb Co.
MYCOMIST - Shoe accessories - Gordon Laboratories
MYCONOS - Floor coverings–carpet and rugs - Couristan Inc.
MYCOPUR - Pet products ☆ - Sera Aquaristik USA Inc.
MYCOSTATIN - Pharmaceutical preparations - Bristol-Myers Squibb Co.
MYCOTROL - Pesticides–agricultural - Mycotech Corp.
MYCOTUSSIN - Cold remedies ☆ - Morton Grove Pharmaceuticals
MYCOZOL - Pharmaceutical preparations ☆ - Parke-Davis
MYCROCLEAN - Towels - Apollo Environmental Corp.

☆ = Now out of production

MYDATABASE - Computer software - My Software Co.

MYDFRIN - Ophthalmic goods - Alcon Laboratories, Inc.

MYDIET - Computer software ☆ - Software Toolworks, Inc.

MYDLAND - Milk - Mydland Dairy Farms

MYDOR - Chemical preparations - Mydor Industries Inc.

MYDOR - Pet products - Blalock Wholesale Distributors

MYDRAPRED - Ophthalmic goods ☆ - Alcon Laboratories, Inc.

MYDRIACYL - Ophthalmic goods - Alcon Laboratories, Inc.

MYDRIVE - Computer storage devices - Oakleigh Systems, Inc.

MYE - Yeast - Gist-Brocades Food Ingredients Inc.

MYER - Wedding gowns - Dewiani

MYER 1890 - Beverages–carbonated - Canada Dry Corp.

MYERLAKE - Computer peripheral equipment - Tech Data Corp.

MYERS - Chickens - Myers Foods Inc.

MYERS - Pumps - F.E. Myers Co.

MYER'S - Rum - House of Seagram

MYERS COUNTRY FRESH - Soups–canned - Myers Foods Inc.

MYERS CRAFT - Canvas–artists' - Myers Craft Manufacturing Co.

MYERS LIMITED RESERVE - Wines - White Oak Vineyards & Winery

MYFED - Pharmaceutical preparations - Morton Grove Pharmaceuticals

MYFEDRINE - Pharmaceutical preparations ☆ - Morton Grove Pharmaceuticals

MYFEDRINE PLUS - Pharmaceutical preparations ☆ - Morton Grove Pharmaceuticals

MYGEL - Pharmaceutical preparations - Geneva Generics Inc.

MYHISTINE - Pharmaceutical preparations ☆ - Morton Grove Pharmaceuticals

MYHISTINE DH - Pharmaceutical preparations ☆ - Morton Grove Pharmaceuticals

MYHOUSE - Computer software - Designware, Inc.

MYHYDROMINE - Pharmaceutical preparations ☆ - Morton Grove Pharmaceuticals

MYIDYL - Pharmaceutical preparations ☆ - Morton Grove Pharmaceuticals

MYINVOICES - Computer software - My Software Co.

MYKEY - Computer peripheral equipment - Ergonomixx, Inc.

MYKO - Frames–eyeglass - May Optical Co. Inc.

MYKONOS - Vegetables–canned - Devanco Foods, Inc.

MYLABELDESIGNER - Computer software - My Software Co.

MYLAGEN - Pharmaceutical preparations - Goldline Laboratories, Inc.

MYLANTA - Antacids - McNeil Pharmaceuticals

MYLAR - Film - E.I. Dupont de Nemours and Co.

MYLAR RADIANCE - Wallpaper - Fine Art Wallcoverings Ltd.

MYLAR SENSATION - Wallpaper - Fine Art Wallcoverings Ltd.

MYLAST - Yarn - Clarence L. Meyers Inc.

MYLATEX - Pharmaceutical preparations ☆ - Veratex Group

MYLAXEN - Pharmaceutical preparations ☆ - Wallace Laboratories

MYLEC - Sporting goods - Pennsylvania Sporting Goods Co.

MYLEOGEN - Vitamins and nutritional supplements - Great Life Laboratories Inc.

MYLERAN - Pharmaceutical preparations - Burroughs Wellcome Co.

MYLEX - Computer hardware - Mylex Corp.

MYLICON - Health care products - McNeil Pharmaceuticals

MYLICON-125 - Health care products - McNeil Pharmaceuticals

MYLINKA - Handbags - Mylinka Inc.

MYLINKA - Leather goods - Accessories to the Fact

MYLITE - Electric lighting equipment - Lutron Electronics Co., Inc.

MYLO FLEX - Dentifrices - Outer Limits Research, Inc.

MYLOCAINE - Pharmaceutical preparations ☆ - Morton Grove Pharmaceuticals

MYLORAL - Pharmaceutical preparations - Autoimmune, Inc.

MYM - Computer software - Meca Software, Inc.

MYMAILLIST - Computer software - My Software Co.

MYMARX - Crockery - Source Northwest, Inc.

MYMEDIA SERIES - Computer software - Unitrendix Corp.

MYMETHASONE - Pharmaceutical preparations ☆ - Morton Grove Pharmaceuticals

MYMIC - Computer software - Meca Software, Inc.

MYMINIC - Cold remedies ☆ - Morton Grove Pharmaceuticals

MYMINICOL - Pharmaceutical preparations ☆ - Morton Grove Pharmaceuticals

MYNAP - Napkins–paper - Fort Howard Corp.

MYO-LOGIC - Medical apparatus - Harold G. McCoy

MYO MANAGER - Medical apparatus - Gish Biomedical, Inc.

MYO RUB - Pharmaceutical preparations - Home Health Products, Inc.

MYO-STATIN - Vitamins and nutritional supplements - Primequest International, Inc.

MYO-SYSTEM XL - Vitamins and nutritional supplements - Metagenics, Inc.

MYO-TONE - Health care products - Enzymatic Therapy, Inc.

M.Y.O.B. - Computer software - Best! Ware, Inc.

MYOBID - Pharmaceutical preparations ☆ - Laser Inc.

MYOCALM - Analgesics - Parmed Pharmaceuticals, Inc.

MYOCHRYSINE - Pharmaceutical preparations - Merck & Co., Inc. (Merck Research Laboratories)

MYOEXERCISER - Health care products - Verimed Inc.

MYOFLEX - Analgesics - Rhone-Poulenc Rorer Pharmaceuticals Inc.

MYOKO - Skin care products - Gillette Co.

MYOLIN - Pharmaceutical preparations - Roberts/Hauck Pharmaceuticals Inc.

MYOMINDER - Health care products - Verimed Inc.

MYONNE - Apparel–athletic - I. Appel Corp.

MYONNE PANTIES - Undergarments - I. Appel Corp.

MYOPACK - Scientific apparatus - Clonetics Corp.

MYOPRO - Vitamins and nutritional supplements - Experimental and Applied Sciences

MYOPTER - Glass–optical - Ridgeview Enterprises Inc.

MYOPULSE - Electromedical apparatus - TH Charters, Inc.

MYORUB - Analgesics - Parmed Pharmaceuticals, Inc.

MYORX - Pharmaceutical preparations - Myorx Corp.

MYOSAL - Pharmaceutical preparations ☆ - Seatrace Co.

MYOSPORT - Pharmaceutical preparations - Myorx Corp.

MYOSSAGE - Skin care products - Chattanooga Group, Inc.

MYOSTAR - Vitamins and nutritional supplements - Victor Poletajev

MYOTALIS-EC - Pharmaceutical preparations - Vita Elixir Co. Inc.

MYOTONACHOL - Pharmaceutical preparations - Glenwood LLC

MYOTONOLOGY - Skin care products - Universal Health Products Inc.

MYOTROL - Pharmaceutical preparations - Legere Pharmaceuticals Inc.

MYOTROPHIN PMG - Vitamins and nutritional supplements - Standard Process Inc.

MYPHENTOL - Pharmaceutical preparations ☆ - Morton Grove Pharmaceuticals

MYPHETANE - Pharmaceutical preparations - Morton Grove Pharmaceuticals

MYPHONEBOOK - Computer software - My Software Co.

MYRIAD - Compact discs–prerecorded - Myriad Entertainment

MYRIAD - Computer software - Adobe Systems Inc.

MYRIAD - Computer software - Informative Graphics Corp.

MYRIAD - Fabric - Herman Miller, Inc.

MYRIAD - Floor coverings–carpet and rugs ☆ - Kelly Group Inc.

MYRIAD - Floor coverings–carpet and rugs ☆ - Masland Corp.

MYRIAD - Loudspeakers - International Jensen Inc.

MYRIAD - Wallpaper ☆ - Koroseal Wallcoverings

MYRIAD II - Floor coverings–carpet and rugs ☆ - Kelly Group Inc.

MYRIAH JUN - Recording label - I AM Records

MYRIAL - Floor coverings–carpet and rugs - Ashley Commercial Carpets

MYRINGACAINE - Pharmaceutical preparations ☆ - Upjohn Co.

MYRISTOL - Skin care products - Concord Chemists

MYRO - Caulking compounds - Myro, Inc.

MYRO DRYBACK - Molding compounds–plastics - Myro, Inc.

MYRO NO-SLIP - Shower stalls–plastic - Myro, Inc.

MYRON - Health care products - Meiller Co.

MYRON COPE'S OFFICIAL THE TERRIBLE TOWEL - Towels - Allegheny Valley School

MYRRH - Recording label - Word, Inc.

MYRTLE - Furniture - Haworth, Inc.

MYRTLE BEACH FACTORY STORES - Department stores - R.R. Myrtle Beach, Inc.

MYRTLE THE TURTLE - Furniture–children's - Maze Inc.

MYSAMA - Frames–eyeglass - Mysama Inc.

MYSAN - Fungicides - Daywell Laboratories Corp.

MYSELF - Apparel and accessories - Marble Sportswear, Inc.

MYSELLA - Oils–lubricating - Shell Oil Co.

MYSOLINE - Pharmaceutical preparations - Wyeth-Ayerst Laboratories

MYSORE - Soap ☆ - Auromere Inc.

MYSOTROL - Skin-care products - Sunshine Products

MYSPEX - Eyeglasses - Myspex, Inc.

MYSPORT - Bottles–plastic - U.S. Poly Enterprise, Inc.

MYST - Computer game - Cyan, Inc.

MYST - Computer software - Broderbund Software, Inc.

MYSTARA - Publisher's imprints - Tsr, Inc.

MYSTECLIN-F - Pharmaceutical preparations - Bristol-Myers Squibb Co.

MYSTEE-MOLY - Lubricants - Pep Boys Manny, Moe & Jack

MYSTERE - Apparel stores–lingerie - Goddess Bra

MYSTERE DE LYS - Fabric stores - Jaunty Textile Div.

MYSTERIES OF THE BIBLE - Video production - A & E Television Network

MYSTERIOUS - Frames–eyeglass - Zylo Ware Corp.

MYSTERIOUS AIR - Flowers, plants, and seeds - National Card 'n Gift Co.

MYSTERIOUS ENCOUNTER - Christmas tree ornaments - Cracker Box Inc.

MYSTERIOUS EYES - Frames–eyeglass ☆ - Universal/Univis Inc.

☆ = Now out of production

MYSTERIOUS HOURS - Jewelry - Van Cleef & Arpels, Inc.
MYSTERIOUS MAUVE - Cosmetics - Elizabeth Arden Inc.
MYSTERY - Frames—eyeglass - Rozin Optical Export Corp.
MYSTERY AND POWER OF TAI CHI, THE - Recording label - Positive Response Television, Inc.
MYSTERY BALL WITH MAGIC BAT - Toys ☆ - A.J. Renzi Plastic Corp.
MYSTERY DATE - Games ☆ - Milton Bradley Co.
MYSTERY DATE - Publisher's imprints - Kensington Publishing Corp.
MYSTERY DICE - Games - Hasbro, Inc.
MYSTERY EGGS - Hobby kits ☆ - Hinkle Easter Products
MYSTERY HOUSE - Computer software ☆ - Gessler Publishing Co., Inc.
MYSTERY MANSION - Games ☆ - Milton Bradley Co.
MYSTERY MOUNTAIN - Computer software - Knowledge Adventure, Inc.
MYSTERY MOUTH - Confections - Wells' Dairy, Inc.
MYSTERY PITCH - Chewing gum - Philadelphia Chewing Gum Corp.
MYSTERY ROCK - Hobby kits - Educational Insights, Inc.
MYSTERY SHIFTER - Automotive parts and accessories ☆ - Hurst Performance Inc.
MYSTERYEZ - Recording label - Marco Antonio Benitez
MYSTEX - Girdles - Character Foundations Inc.
MYSTIC - Bicycles - Columbia Manufacturing Inc.
MYSTIC - Boats—motor ☆ - Bayliner Marine Corp.
MYSTIC - Clocks ☆ - General Time Corp. (Westclox/Seth Thomas Div.)
MYSTIC - Cookies - Nabisco Foods Group
MYSTIC - File folders - Kole Industries Inc.
MYSTIC - Floor coverings—carpet and rugs - Kelly Group Inc.
MYSTIC - Floor coverings—carpet and rugs - Regal Rugs Inc.
MYSTIC - Insecticides - Mystic Chemical Products
MYSTIC - Potato chips - Mystic Chips
MYSTIC - Vases - Lenox Crystal, Inc.
MYSTIC - Wallpaper - Koroseal Wallcoverings
MYSTIC - Watches - A.P. Imports Inc.
MYSTIC BAY - Bathing suits - Finals
MYSTIC CLIFFS - Beverages—alcohol - Canandaigua Wine Co. Inc.
MYSTIC COLLECTION - Giftware - Lenox, Inc.
MYSTIC COTTAGE - Apparel—children's - Tot Inc.
MYSTIC CRYSTAL - Games - Mattel, Inc.
MYSTIC EYE - Apparel and accessories - Icon
MYSTIC EYES - Frames—eyeglass ☆ - Universal/Univis Inc.
MYSTIC FARMS - Fruit drinks—bottled or canned - Ocean Spray Cranberries Inc.
MYSTIC HARBOR - Furniture - Universal Flooring
MYSTIC HEART, THE - Games - Robert S. Reinish
MYSTIC IMPRESSIONS - Colognes - Delagar
MYSTIC INK - Inks ☆ - Ramstar Mills, Inc.
MYSTIC IV - Wallpaper ☆ - Mirage Wallcovering Co.
MYSTIC LAKE - Food products - Mystic Lake Dairy Inc.
MYSTIC LAKE - Health care products - Little Six, Inc.
MYSTIC LIGHTS - Photo albums - Kleer-Vu Plastics Inc.
MYSTIC-MANICARE - Nail care products - Magic Nails
MYSTIC MASQUES - Hobby kits - Mangelsen's (VDI)
MYSTIC MIDWAY - Laser disc game - Philips Interactive Media of America
MYSTIC MOON - Toiletries - Natural Body Bath Aroma Art
MYSTIC MOVIES - Film—motion picture - Mystic Records
MYSTIC NAILS - Nail care products - Magic Nails
MYSTIC PRODUCTIONS - Books—comic - Mystic Productions, Inc.
MYSTIC/RAZER - Guitars - Peavey Electronics Corp.
MYSTIC SEAPORT - Giftware - Virginia Metalcrafters Inc.
MYSTIC SHADOWS - Floor coverings—carpet and rugs - Philadelphia Carpets
MYSTIC SMOKE - Novelty items - S.S. Adams Co.
MYSTIC TEMPLE - Incense - Matchless Gifts Inc.
MYSTIC USA - Recording label - Mystic Records
MYSTIC VALLEY - Floor coverings—carpet and rugs - Evans-Black Carpet Mills
MYSTIC WARRIORS WRATH OF THE NINJAS - Computer software ☆ - Konami (America) Inc.
MYSTIC WHEEL - Melamine product - Boonton Molding Co. Inc.
MYSTIC WHITE - Sand and stone - U.S. Silica Co.
MYSTIC WIZARD MAGIC CARDS - Playing cards - United States Playing Card Co.
MYSTIC WOOD, THE - Games ☆ - Avalon Hill Game Co.
MYSTICA - Hardware ☆ - Mystica & Co. Inc.
MYSTICAL - Cleaning preparations—carpet and rug - Pyramid Development Inc.
MYSTICAL - Floor coverings—carpet and rugs - Burtco Enterprises Inc.
MYSTICAL - Floor coverings—carpet and rugs ☆ - Downs Carpet Co. Inc.

MYSTICAL - Floor coverings—carpet and rugs ☆ - Heuga USA
MYSTICAL EYE, THE - Jewelry - Le Grande Productions Inc.
MYSTICAL FRIENDS - Apparel and accessories - RMR Distributors,Inc
MYSTICAL GUM REMOVER - Cleaning preparations - Pyramid Development Inc.
MYSTICAL MOMENTS - Underwear and nightwear - Exquisite Design Distributors Inc.
MYSTICAL MONKS - Statuary - Patricia Gagliardo
MYSTICAL MOODS - Cosmetics - Cosmania, Inc.
MYSTICAL MORNING DUE - Cleaning preparations - Pyramid Development Inc.
MYSTICAL MULTI-PURPOSE CLEANER - Cleaning preparations - Pyramid Development Inc.
MYSTICAL PASSION - Bicycles - Dynacraft Industries Inc.
MYSTICAL UNION - Rings—jewelry - Cana-Nuptial
MYSTICOTE - Paints - Shaheen Paint Co.
MYSTIFYING ORACLE - Toys - Tonka Corp.
MYSTIK - Adhesives and sealants - Mystik Corp.
MYSTIK EL-6 - Lubricants - Kerr-McGee Chemical Corp.
MYSTIKLEER - Tape—adhesive - Mystik Corp.
MYSTIQUE - Apparel—women's - Newton Manufacturing Corp.
MYSTIQUE - Bags—duffel - Dunlop Maxfli Sports Corp.
MYSTIQUE - Beverages—alcohol - Heublein, Inc.
MYSTIQUE - Christmas tree ornaments - Cracker Box Inc.
MYSTIQUE - Contact lenses - Cooper Companies Inc.
MYSTIQUE - Dinnerware—glass - Nikko Ceramics Inc.
MYSTIQUE - Dishes—china - Pickard Inc.
MYSTIQUE - Floor coverings—carpet and rugs - Regal Rugs Inc.
MYSTIQUE - Floor coverings—carpet and rugs ☆ - Blue Ridge Carpet Mills
MYSTIQUE - Floor coverings—carpet and rugs ☆ - Mohawk Industries Inc.
MYSTIQUE - Furniture - Thomasville Furniture Industries Inc.
MYSTIQUE - Furniture ☆ - Bassett Furniture Industries, Inc.
MYSTIQUE - Furniture ☆ - Hammary Furniture Co. Inc.
MYSTIQUE - Glass products ☆ - Crisa Corp.
MYSTIQUE - Golfing equipment ☆ - Wilson Sporting Goods Co.
MYSTIQUE - Mats ☆ - LaVelle Textile Marketing Inc.
MYSTIQUE - Motor vehicles—automobiles - Ford Motor Co. (Lincoln-Mercury Div.)
MYSTIQUE - Paints ☆ - Star Bronze Co. Inc.
MYSTIQUE - Paper—writing - Champion International Corp.
MYSTIQUE - Rackets—tennis - Slazengers
MYSTIQUE - Recording label - Rising Star Productions
MYSTIQUE - Silverware - Imperial Schrade Corp.
MYSTIQUE - Skin care products - Rudolph International, Inc.
MYSTIQUE - Socks - Ben Berger LLC.
MYSTIQUE - Thread ☆ - Perfect Thread Co. Inc.
MYSTIQUE - Vaccines - Bayer Corp.
MYSTIQUE - Wallpaper ☆ - Mirage Wallcovering Co.
MYSTIQUE - Watches - Invasion Time Corp.
MYSTIQUE - Wigs - Jean Paree Weegs Inc.
MYSTIQUE BY MAGGIE - Cosmetics - Maggie Sparks
MYSTIQUE GLAMOUR - Toys—stuffed - Fun World Inc.
MYSTIQUE V - Wallpaper ☆ - Mirage Wallcovering Co.
MYSTIQUE VI - Wallpaper - Mirage Wallcovering Co.
MYSTIQUES - Footwear—children's - Step Master Shoes
MYSTIS - Cosmetics - Donald R. Bernard
MYSTIX - Toys - Infinity, Inc.
MYSTOLENE - Deodorizers - Imperial Manufacturing Co. Inc.
MYSTON - Artists' materials - M. Grumbacher Inc.
MYSTY EYES - Frames—eyeglass ☆ - Universal/Univis Inc.
MYTEE - Water heaters—household - Mytee Products
MYTEE-LITE - Eyeglass lenses - Soderberg Inc.
MYTEE SWING CREATES A MIGHTY SWING - Sporting goods - Daniel V. Regan
MYTEL - Communications equipment—mobile - K & K Merchandise Group Inc.
MYTELASE - Pharmaceutical preparations - Winthrop Pharmaceuticals
MYTER MITE - Pet products - Glo-Marr Products Inc.
MYTH - Apparel and accessories - Van Raalte Gloves
MYTH FORTUNES - Games - Mayfair Games, Inc.
MYTHICAL CHARACTERS - Figurines ☆ - Doranne
MYTHOLOGIQUE - Giftware - Gorham Inc.
MYTHOS - Computer software - Adobe Systems Inc.
MYTHOS - Games - Chaosium Inc.
MYTREX - Pharmaceutical preparations - Savage Laboratories Inc.
MYTUSSIN - Pharmaceutical preparations - Morton Grove Pharmaceuticals
MYTUSSIN AC - Pharmaceutical preparations - Morton Grove Pharmaceuticals

---

☆ = Now out of production

MYTUSSIN DAC - Pharmaceutical preparations - Morton Grove
  Pharmaceuticals
MYTUSSIN DM - Pharmaceutical preparations - Morton Grove Pharmaceuticals
MYVATEM - Photographic equipment - Eastman Kodak Co.
MYX - Lighting fixtures - Designs by Desart

MYX MAKE YOUR MARK - Furniture - Designs by Desart
MZ - Recording label - Jazz Composer's Orchestra Association Inc.
MZ AMIGA - Computer software - Interface Technologies Inc.
MZF - Jewelry - Pride Jewelry Co.
MZM - Pharmaceutical preparations - Ciba-Geigy Corp.
MZM SPORT - Apparel and accessories - MZM Sport, Inc.

N

Addresses and phone numbers for the companies cited in the brands below
are available in the Company Listings section immediately following the brands listings.

N - Computer peripheral equipment - Netpower, Inc.
N - Fresh vegetables - Nunes Co.
N - Gloves - Neumann Tackified Glove Co.
N - Jewelry - Bernard Nacht & Co. Inc.
N - Jewelry - National Jewelry Direct Inc.
N - Jewelry - Ne'eman Industries Ltd.
N - Jewelry - Nuco Jewels Ltd.
N - Juices - Ben Hill Griffin, Inc.
N - Publisher's imprints - Moody Bible Institute of Chicago
N - Railings—metal - Natare Corp.
N - Toys - Tyco Toys
N 2 CARS - Shirts - Jeffrey L. Herrington
N-3 - Solder - La-Co Industries, Inc.
N-A-G - Vitamins and nutritional supplements - Source Naturals
N A W - Windows - Gentek Building Products, Inc.
N & A - Publisher's imprints - Nautical & Aviation Publishing Co. of America Inc.
N & N - Food products - Milfico Foods Inc.
N B T - Nail care products - JST Marketing, Inc.
N-CAL - Fertilizers - Pfi Corp.
N-CAP - Veterinary nutritional supplements ☆ - Prince Agri Products, Inc.
N CAPE - Apparel and accessories - Roytex, Inc.
N CAROLINE - Wines - Duplin Wine Cellars
N D - Computer software - Neuron Data, Inc.
N. D. CROWDER - Musical-instrument bows - Howard Core & Co. Inc.
N' DA DOG HOUSE - Apparel and accessories - Deborah Jean Saunders
N/DYM - Microphones - Electro-Voice, Inc.
N-E-WAZ - Apparel and accessories - Janet K. Ledford
N-ERGETIC - Electronic equipment - K & R Precision Instruments Inc.
N-ESTED - Filters—air - CECO Filters Inc.
N HELPCARE - Medical apparatus - Nelmed Corp.
N HUSKERS - Shirts - Board of Regents of the University of Nebraska
N + I - Trade journals - Softbank Exposition and Conference Co.
N J W - Jewelry - N.J. Wintrup
N. JANE TAN - Publisher's imprints - Willis Music Co.
N-JOY - Food products - Dale Foods Inc.
N JOY - Food products - Sugar Foods Corp.
N' JOY - Sweeteners—artificial - Sugar Foods Corp.
N-L - Cleaning preparations—household - L & F Consumer Products
N-LARGITS - Frames—eyeglass - May Optical Co. Inc.
N-LOC - Nuts and bolts - Lok-Mor, Inc.
N-M - Flowers—artificial - North Hollywood Manufacturing Co.
N-N - Cough medicines ☆ - Vitarine Pharmaceuticals Inc.
N-N-TWO - Apparel—women's - Nora Noh, Inc.
N NANAMOUSA - Skin care products - Nanamo, Inc.
N NATIONAL SEMICONDUCTOR - Integrated circuits - National Semiconductor Corp.
N NETWORKING - Audio tapes—blank - Internet Services Corp.
N NIGHTPRO - Sound equipment - Night Technologies, Inc.
N NITRO TRAK - Computer hardware - Micro-Trak Systems, Inc.
N NORTHEASTERN - Electrical equipment - Northeastern Plastics, Inc.
N NOVA SPRING - Computer peripheral equipment - Vic Tokai, Inc.
N NU-TEK FOODS - Cheese - Nu-Tek Foods Inc.
N-O-DOR - Deodorizers - Atsko Inc.
N O V I T - Vitamins and nutritional supplements - Waldemar Vonkeczely
N-PLEX - Computer software - ISOCOR

N-R - Garden equipment ☆ - Nelson Roanoke Corp.
N/R - Skin care products - N-R Laboratories Inc.
N-R-G - Paints - Jones Blair Co.
N-R-G - Vitamins and nutritional supplements - Naturade Inc.
N-RICH - Food products - Beatrice Cos. Inc.
N-RT - Pharmaceutical preparations - Hayes Separation, Inc.
N/S - Washing machines—commercial - N/S Corp.
N SEE - Computer software - Microcompatibles, Inc.
N SIGHT - Computer software ☆ - Topographic Mapping Co.
N-SL-PK - Concrete products - Reef Industries, Inc.
N-SUL 32 - Fertilizers - Agway Country Foods Inc.
N-SURE - Fertilizers - Hickson Kerley, Inc.
N-TECH - Computer software - Nailco, Inc.
N-TIFEBRIN - Veterinary product ☆ - American Equine Products Inc.
N V - Apparel and accessories - N V Sportswear
N-VIROMULCH - Wood chips - Craig Group Inc.
N-VISION - Electrical equipment - n-Vision Inc.
N-VISION/TPX - Computer software - Legent Corp.
N. WAGMAN - Beauty shop equipment - N. Wagman & Co.
N-ZONE - Fertilizers - AG Spectrum Co.
N-ZYME FRESH - Deodorizers - Ryter Corp.
N1 - Golfing equipment - Golden Bear International, Inc.
N2 - Vitamins and nutritional supplements - Nikken Inc.
N2 LIGHTS - Laces—boot and shoe - Jan T. Martinez
N50 - Cameras - Nikon Inc.
N64 - Video games - Nintendo of America Inc.
N90 - Cameras - Nikon Inc.
N94 - Safety products - Snell Memorial Foundation, Inc.
N100 - Hoops—wood - Gibbs Manufacturing Co.
N1000 DELUXE STAND WITH THE FOLLOWING - Hoops—wood - Gibbs Manufacturing Co.
N5200 - Pens - Zebra Pen Corp.
N6006 - Cameras - Nikon Inc.
N8008S - Cameras ☆ - Nikon Inc.
NA - Beverages—malt - Pearl Brewing Co.
NA-CHURS - Fertilizers - Na-Churs Plant Food Co.
NA-NOR - Floor waxes - C.A. Nash & Son Inc.
NA-PCA - Skin care products - Twinlab
NA-X - Fire extinguishers - Ansul, Inc.
NA-ZONE - Pharmaceutical - Snuva Inc.
NAAS - Food products - RHM Industrial Specialty Foods Inc.
NAB-EM - Fishing lures - Den Manufacturing Co.
N.A.B. NURSERY - Toys—stuffed - North American Bear Co. Inc.
NABCO - Pennants - Flags International Inc.
NABCO - Pennants - National Banner Co., Inc.
NABHOLZ - Apparel—athletic ☆ - Regina Imports
NABID - Pharmaceutical preparations ☆ - Hyrex Pharmaceuticals
NABILENE - Bandages ☆ - Beiersdorf Inc.
NABISCO - Cookies - Nabisco Foods Group
NABISCO - Eggs - Nabisco Brands Co.
NABISCO - Puddings—mixes - Nabisco Holdings Corp.
NABISCO SABE DE GRAN SABOR - Cookies - Nabisco Foods Group
NABPLAW - Computer storage devices—optical - National Association of Boards of Pharmacy
NAC - Soap ☆ - National Chemical Laboratories of Pennsylvania Inc.
NAC - Vitamins and nutritional supplements - M.M.R.C., Ltd. Co.

☆ = Now out of production

1467

NAC FUEL - Vitamins and nutritional supplements - Twin Laboratories, Inc.

NACAP - Pharmaceutical preparations ☆ - Hyrex Pharmaceuticals

NACDA - Pens - National Association of Collegiate Directors of Athletics

NACET - Shaving preparations - Gillette Co.

NACH-OS - Food products ☆ - World Finer Foods, Inc.

NACH-R-L KRISPY CHIPS - Snack foods - Nach, Inc.

NACHACHO - Snack foods - Sabatasso Foods Inc.

NACHACHOS - Mexican food - Sabatasso Foods Inc.

NACHI - Cutlery - Nachi American Co. Ltd.

NACHI - Floor coverings - Toli International

NACHIPS - Snack foods - Pet Inc.

NACHO AMIGO - Snack foods - Mexican Food Manufacturing of Omaha Inc.

NACHO CHEESIER - Food products - Recot, Inc.

NACHO CHEESIER - Snack foods - Frito-Lay, Inc.

NACHO CRISPERS! - Food products - Ore-Ida Foods, Inc.

NACHO FLAVORED - Tortillas - Guiltless Gourmet, Inc.

NACHO MAMA - Fruits–dried - Steven C. Rickun

NACHO 'N CORN - Crackers - Nabisco Foods Group

NACHO NUGGETS - Snack foods - Fred's Frozen Foods Inc.

NACHO PRIMA - Tortillas - La Suprema

NACHO THINS - Publisher's imprints - Nabisco Holdings Corp.

NACHO'S BRAVO - Food products ☆ - Taco John's International Inc.

NACHOS NOW! - Snack foods - Golden Valley Microwave Foods, Inc.

NACHOS PRONTO - Snack foods - Pet Inc.

NACHO'S RED INTENSIVE - Bird coloring - Sunshine Bird Supplies, Inc.

NACHTIGAL - Fish–canned or cured - Haram-Christensen Corp.

NACHTIGAL - Seafood products–fresh or frozen - Kreiner Imports

NACIONALES - Cigars - Faber, Coe & Gregg Inc.

NACLONE - Machinery - Pengwyn

NACO - Bulletin boards–wood - A. Lawer Corp.

NACRA - Ships–sailing vessels - Performance Catamarans Inc.

NAD - Audio equipment - Nad USA Inc.

NADA - Health care products - Nada Concepts Inc.

NADA-CHAIR - Braces–orthopedic - Nada-Chair

NADA HAT - Hats - Franklin W. Wakefield

NADA NUFF - Apparel and accessories - Neiman Marcus Co.

NADEX - Coin sorter and packager - Nadex Industries Inc.

NADIA - Dinnerware–glass ☆ - Cyclamen Studio

NADIA - Frames–eyeglass - Pathway Optical Prods.

NADIA - Wines - Banfi Vintners

NADIM USA - Belts–apparel - Belts by Nadim, Inc.

NADINA'S - Skin care products - Nadina's Cremes

NADINE - Frames–eyeglass - Hudson Optical Corp.

NADINE - Glassware–household ☆ - Crystal Clear Importing Co. Inc.

NADINE - Rings–jewelry - Artcarved Inc.

NADINOLA - Skin care products - J. Strickland & Co.

NADJA - Glassware–household ☆ - Oneida Ltd.

NADJA CHENILLE - Yarn ☆ - Tahki Imports Ltd.

NADY - Microphones - Nady Systems Inc.

NAF-NAF - Frames–eyeglass - Euro-Frames Inc.

NAFAZAIR - Ophthalmic goods - Bausch & Lomb Inc.

NAFCIL - Pharmaceutical preparations - Bristol-Myers Squibb Co.

NAFCO - Adhesives and sealants - National Floor Products Co., Inc.

NAFCO - Fencing–chain link - Merchants Metals Inc.

NAFFA - Games - Boardroom Sports Inc.

NAFGLO - Floor coverings - National Floor Products Co., Inc.

NAFLON - Fabrics–broadcloth ☆ - Chris-Craft Industrial Products Inc.

NAFRINSE - Health care products - Medical Products Laboratories

NAFTIN - Skin care products - Allergan, Inc.

NAG - Jewelry - North American Gold Inc.

NAG CHAMPA - Incense - Excelsior Incense Works

NAG NEIGHBORS AGAINST GRAFFITI - Apparel and accessories - Marnel Dice

NAGA - Seafood products–fresh or frozen ☆ - Penguin Frozen Foods, Inc.

NAGAOKA - Audio equipment - Bell & Howell Co.

NAGEL - Meat product - Nagel Inc.

NAGEL KG GERMANY - Glassware–household - Nordic Trading Inc.

NAGEL'S - Food products - Nagel's Spic 'n Span Pastry Shop Inc.

NAGLER - Lenses–optical - Tele Vue Optics Inc.

NAGOYA - Guitars - European Crafts/USA

NAGOYA SUZUKI - Musical instruments - Meisel Music Inc.

NAGRAND - Cosmetics - Pacific Corp. of America

NAHC - Health care products - National Association for Home Care

NAHDREE SUITS - Apparel–women's - Nah Nah Collections Inc.

NAHEMA - Perfumes - Guerlain Inc.

NAI - Vitamins and nutritional supplements - Natural Alternatives International, Inc.

NAIF - Tableware–china - Villeroy and Boch Tableware Ltd.

NAIF CHRISTMAS - Tableware–china - Villeroy and Boch Tableware Ltd.

NAIGAI 8X ZOOM - Cameras ☆ - Edixa Camera Co.

NAIL-A-CAIN - Health care products - Medtech Laboratories Inc.

NAIL ADVANCE - Manicure preparations - Del Pharmaceuticals, Inc.

NAIL AID - Vitamins and nutritional supplements - Ray Drug Co.

NAIL-AIDE - Cosmetics - Beauty Aids Inc.

NAIL AIDS - Nail-care products ☆ - Cosrich Inc.

NAIL BASICS - Manicure preparations - Creative Nail Design, Inc.

NAIL BOARDS - Nail care products - Nailmate Inc.

NAIL BRITE - Nail care products - Gena Laboratories Inc.

NAIL BURRO - Leather goods - Wendy Prather

NAIL-CAPS - Nail care products - SRA Industries Inc.

NAIL CARE PLUS - Electrical equipment - Medicool Inc.

NAIL CARE SYSTEM BY WINDMERE, THE - Manicure preparations - Windmere Corp.

NAIL CAVIAR - Nail care products ☆ - Gena Laboratories Inc.

NAIL CLEAN - Nail care products - Worldwide Cosmetics

NAIL COMPLEX - Nail care products - Pavion Ltd.

NAIL CRAFT - Cosmetics - Classic Laboratories Inc.

NAIL DAZZLER - Nail care products ☆ - Philips Electronics North America Corp.

NAIL DESIGNER - Manicure preparations - Customcraft Nails Inc.

NAIL DRIVER - Tools–hand-operated - Goodell, Inc.

NAIL DRY - Manicure preparations ☆ - Gena Laboratories Inc.

NAIL EATER II - Drill bits - Greenlee Textron Inc.

NAIL EXPRESSIONS - Nail-care products - International Beauty Design, Inc.

NAIL FACTOR - Manicure sets ☆ - London International U.S. Holdings

NAIL FAME - Nail care products - Orly International Inc.

NAIL FAST - Shingles - Tamko Roofing Products, Inc.

NAIL FETISH - Cosmetics - Cosmar Corp.

NAIL FIX - Adhesives and sealants - Delore International

NAIL FRESH - Manicure preparations - Creative Nail Design, Inc.

NAIL GEMS BY CARA - Manicure preparations - Nail Gems by Cara

NAIL GENIE - Beauty shop equipment - Protec International

NAIL GENIE - Manicure preparations - Sunjeen, Inc.

NAIL GENIE JR. - Beauty shop equipment - Protec International

NAIL GLASS - Nail care products - Sebastian International, Inc.

NAIL GRINDER - Skin care products - Rudolph International, Inc.

NAIL GRIP - Cosmetics - Ardell International Inc.

NAIL GRO - Nail care products - Mennen Co.

NAIL GRO - Skin care products - Fruit of the Earth, Inc.

NAIL HOLE FILLER - Plaster–patching - American Art Clay Co. Inc.

NAIL HORN - Novelty items - Nailco, Inc.

NAIL ILLUSIONS - Nail care products - Orly International Inc.

NAIL-KNEAD - Medical apparatus - Charles G. Wagner

NAIL LADY - Nail care products - SRA Industries Inc.

NAIL LAST - Nail care products - Nu-Tress Laboratories Inc.

NAIL LESS - Building materials - Gibson-Homans Co.

NAIL-LINE - Insulating panels - Apache Products Co.

NAIL LINERS - Nail care products - Showcase Cosmetics Inc.

NAIL LIT - Golfing equipment - Stuart Industries, Inc.

NAIL LOCK - Adhesives and sealants - Pratt & Lambert, Inc.

NAIL LUCK - Adhesives and sealants - Miracle Adhesives

NAIL LUMANENTS - Nail care products - Galaxy Nail Products of the Future, Inc.

NAIL MACHINE USA - Nail care products - RBI Distributors

NAIL MART - Nail care products - Nail Mart, Inc.

NAIL MASTER 45 SECOND TOP COAT SEALER - Nail care products - Naturally Beautiful Nails, Inc.

NAIL MASTER NAIL WHITENER - Nail care products - Naturally Beautiful Nails, Inc.

NAIL MENDER - Nail care products - Revlon Consumer Products Corp.

NAIL NEATS - Manicure preparations - Backscratchers, Inc.

NAIL NECESSITIES - Manicure preparations - Avon Products, Inc.

NAIL-NO-MORE - Adhesives and sealants - Gibson-Homans Co.

NAIL ODYSSEY - Nail care products - International Nail Manufacturers

NAIL PALES - Cosmetics - Garden Botanika, Inc.

NAIL PATCH - Hardware - Sherwin-Williams Automotive Finishes Corp.

NAIL POLISH REMOVER - Nail care products - RTS Laboratories, Inc.

NAIL POWER - Adhesives and sealants - Magic Seal Corp.

NAIL POWER - Adhesives and sealants - Ohio Sealants Inc.

NAIL POWER - Adhesives and sealants - OSI Sealants, Inc.

NAIL PRIME - Manicure preparations - Universal Biologics, Inc.

☆ = Now out of production

NAIL RADIANCE - Nail care products - Backscratchers, Inc.

NAIL RADIENCE - Manicure preparations - Backscratchers, Inc.

NAIL RAISERS - Nail care products - Hair Raisers Inc.

NAIL RENEWAL - Nail care products - Worldwide Cosmetics

NAIL RESTORE - Nail care products - RTS Laboratories, Inc.

NAIL SAFE - Cosmetics - Monaco Import/Export Inc.

NAIL SAUNA - Nail-care products - Cabot Laboratories Inc.

NAIL-SAVER - Bandages - D & L Industries, Inc.

NAIL SHIELD - Nail care products - Para Laboratories Inc.

NAIL SILK - Nail care products - Nu-Tress Laboratories Inc.

NAIL SMOOTH - Nail care products - Revlon Consumer Products Corp.

NAIL SPRITZ - Nail care products - Orly International Inc.

NAIL STARTER - Nail care products - Revlon Consumer Products Corp.

NAIL STRONG - Cosmetics - Monaco Import/Export Inc.

NAIL STUFF - Cosmetics ☆ - Modern Research Laboratories

NAIL TECH'S CHOICE - Manicure preparations - Carolina Absorbent Cotton

NAIL THERAPY - Cosmetics ☆ - Sally Hansen

NAIL THICK - Manicure preparations - Max Factor & Co.

NAIL TIP - Cosmetics - Ardell International Inc.

NAIL-TONE - Vitamins and nutritional supplements - Vita-Fore Products Co.

NAIL TRAIL - Bicycles - Marin Mountain Bikes, Inc.

NAIL TRIAGE MAXIMUM - Nail care products - Claire Topper Enterprises

NAIL UNDERGUARDS - Manicure preparations - Customcraft Nails Inc.

NAIL WEAVER - Cosmetics - Colour Grow Cosmetics Intl.

NAIL WIPES - Manicure preparations - W.R. Rayson Co., Inc.

NAIL WIPES - Nail care products - Opi Products, Inc.

NAIL ZAP - Nail care products - Pacer Technology

NAIL ZONE - Nail care products - Pavion Ltd.

NAILAMINS - Manicure preparations - Cosmetics International

NAILBOARD - Nail care products - Palette Ventures Inc.

NAILBOMB - Apparel and accessories - Nailbomb

NAILBOND - Adhesives and sealants - Magic Seal Corp.

NAILCATCHERS - Clippers–nail - Douglas Johnson and Mark Adelman Partnership

NAILCOVER - Cosmetics - Sheila Brit Ltd.

NAILCURE - Nail care products ☆ - Purepac Pharmaceutical Co.

NAILE CLASSICS - Nail-care product - Cabot Laboratories Inc.

NAILERS - Belts–apparel - Nailers Inc.

NAILERY BY JOYART - Nail care products - Joyart Jewelry Co.

NAILFRIEND - Nail care products - H & H Products

NAILGUN - Fasteners–snap - ACCO USA, Inc.

NAILIPID - Cosmetics - Ray Hayes Inc.

NAILIT - Tools - Seatek Co. Inc.

NAILLURE - Nail care products - Claire Topper Enterprises

NAILMAKERS - Nail care products - Kristy Wells Inc.

NAILMATE - Cosmetics - Hair Doc Co.

NAILOGICS - Cosmetics - Clairol Inc.

NAILS 2000 - Nail care products - Nails 2000 International

NAILS AGAIN - Nail care products - La Parfumerie Inc.

NAILS BEAUTIFUL - Nail care products - Nails Beautiful International

NAILS BY NATURE - Vitamins and nutritional supplements - CD&R of Meridian, Inc.

NAILS BY SAGA - Shoes - Saga House Inc.

NAILS FOR MALES - Nail care products - Orly International Inc.

NAILS, NAILS, NAILS - Vitamins and nutritional supplements - Health Products Corp.

NAILS NATURALLY - Manicure preparations - Nails Naturally, Inc.

NAILS NOW! - Cosmetics - Nails Now Inc.

NAILS OF COLOR - Cosmetics ☆ - E.O.H. Industries, Inc.

NAILS OF STEEL - Nail care products - Jacqueline A. Sabal

NAILS OR NOT - Nail care products - Ruthe Z. Inc.

NAILS PLEASE - Nail-care products - International Beauty Design, Inc.

NAILS PLUS - Nail care products - Donna Lee Cosmetics Inc.

NAILS POWER - Manicure preparations - Nailtech

NAILS TO GO - Nail care products - E.O.H. Industries, Inc.

NAILS UNLIMITED - Hardware - C. Itoh Building Products

NAILSCRUB - Cleaning preparations - Pedinol Pharmacal Inc.

NAILSEPTIC - Cosmetics - Aristocrat Hairseptic Co.

NAILSLICKS - Nail care products - Noxell Corp.

NAILTEINS - Nail care products - Finger Mates Inc.

NAILTEX - Nail care products - Nailtex Inc.

NAILTIQUES - Nail care products - Dominguez and Co. Inc.

NAILTIQUES - Nail care products - Nailtiques Cosmetic Corp.

NAIN BLEU - Frames–eyeglass - Hoya Corp. USA

NAIR - Depilatories - Carter-Wallace, Inc.

NAIR ORIENTAL ESSENCE FORMULA - Skin care products - Carter Products Co.

NAIRN - Bulletin boards–cork - Gerbert Ltd.

NAIRN FLOCK ROYALE - Wallpaper ☆ - Kingfisher Wallcoverings

NAIROBI - Motor vehicle parts and accessories - Precision Design & Engineering, Inc.

NAITRE - Hair care products - Pala Laboratories, Inc.

NAIVE - Frames–eyeglass - Zylo Ware Corp.

NAJ OLEARI - Wallcoverings - Worldwalls International Inc.

NAKAMICHI - Audio equipment - Nakamichi America Corp.

NAKANO - Rice vinegar - American Foods Corp.

NAKED - Juices - Naked Juice

NAKED - Salad dressings–mixes - Robert's American Gourmet

NAKED - Teas - Chiquita Brands, Inc.

NAKED CONCRETE - Coatings - Color-Crown Corp.

NAKED EARTH - Recording label - Naked Earth Productions

NAKED EARTH - Soap - Naked Earth Inc.

NAKED FRUIT - Food products - Chiquita Brands, Inc.

NAKED LANGUAGE - Recording label - Ichiban Records, Inc.

NAKED MOUNTAIN - Wines - Naked Mountain Vineyard

NAKED PIZZA - Pizzas–frozen - Chiquita Brands, Inc.

NAKED SUPER JUICE - Juices - Chiquita Brands, Inc.

NAKED TRUTH, THE - Cosmetics - Cosmedic Concepts, Inc.

NAKEDS, THE - Apparel stores–lingerie - Formfit Rogers

NAKEDS, THE - Cosmetics - Charles Revson Inc.

NAKINA - Ophthalmic goods - Styl-Rite Optical Manufacturing Co., Inc.

NAL BOOKS - Publisher's imprints - New American Library

NALA-CURE - Pet products - Silco Pet Products

NALA-GRAM - Pet products - Aquarium Pharmaceuticals, Inc.

NALADIN - Pet products ☆ - Aquatronics-Filtronics

NALAN - Waterproofing compounds - E.I. Dupont de Nemours and Co.

NALASOL - Pet products - Aquatrol, Inc.

NALATE - Health care products ☆ - Kay Pharmacal Co. Inc.

NALCO - Sunglasses - Nassau Lens Co. Inc.

NALDECON - Pharmaceutical preparations - Bristol-Myers Squibb Co.

NALDECON-CX - Pharmaceutical preparations - Bristol-Myers Squibb Co.

NALDECON-DX - Cold remedies - Bristol-Myers Squibb Co.

NALDECON-EX - Cold remedies - Bristol-Myers Squibb Co.

NALDEGESIC - Pharmaceutical preparations - Bristol-Myers Squibb Co.

NALDELATE - Pharmaceutical preparations - Barre-National, Inc.

NALDETUSS - Cold remedies ☆ - Bristol-Myers Squibb Co.

NALE NO AZIDE - Chemical preparations - Pharmingen

NALEPAPER - Nail care products - Yellowbird Inc.

NALEWAY - Perogies - International Food Products Inc.

NALFON - Pharmaceutical preparations - Dista Products Co.

NALGESIC - Pharmaceutical preparations - Harvey Laboratories Inc.

NALLEY - Food products - Curtice-Burns Foods, Inc.

NALLEY'S - Food products - Nalley's Fine Foods

NALLI - Recording label - Continental Communications Corp.

NALLPEN - Antibiotics - Smithkline Beecham Corp.

NALR - Recording label - Epoch Universal Publications Inc.

NALR-FIRM - Health care products - Halsey Drug Co. Inc.

NALREX - Pharmaceutical preparations - C.S. Ruckstuhl Co. Inc.

NALT - Food products - North American Laboratory Co.

NALTEX PIPE-GUARD - Resins–polyethylene - U.S. Netting, Inc.

NALTEX S - Seasonings - North American Laboratory Co.

NALTEX T - Seasonings - North American Laboratory Co.

NALU - Apparel and accessories - Nalu Kauai

NAM-A-LAC - Paints - Mobile Paint Manufacturing Co.

NAM JAM - Apparel and accessories - Vietnam Veterans of America, Tucson Chapter #106, Inc.

NAM NORTH AMERICAN MERCHANDISING - Hosiery - Hampshire Hosiery, Inc.

NAM TIME - Watches - Nam Time Inc.

NAMA - Soy sauce - Gold Mine Natural Food

NAMA LISTED - Vending machines - National Automatic Merchandising Association

NAMAM - Cooking equipment–household - Primex International Corp.

NAMARCO - Watches - Hampden Corp.

NAMBE - Trays - Nambe Mills Inc.

NAMBY PAMBY - Fabrics - Dan River Inc.

NAMDAR - Jewelry - Namdar Inc.

NAME DATES - Footwear–children's - Livonia Catalog

NAME DROPPER - Giftware - Scott/Franklin International

NAME DROPPERS - Apparel–women's - Perry Manufacturing Co.

NAME DROPPERS - Candy ☆ - Topps Co., Inc.

NAME DROPPERS - Paper ☆ - Gallant Greetings Corp.
NAME FRAMES - Sunglasses - Sungold Enterprises Ltd.
NAME GAME, THE - Novelty items - The Name Game
NAME IN GAMES, THE - Sporting goods - Regent Sports Corp.
NAME IT - Jewelry - F.A.F., Inc.
NAME N EGG - Candy - R.M. Palmer Co.
NAME-O-GRAMER - Embossing machines - Roberts, Cushman & Co. Inc.
NAME ORIGINS - Glassware–household - Papel Freelance, Inc.
NAME-SAKE - Rings–jewelry - CJC Holdings, Inc.
NAME SAVER - Telephone directories - Rediform
NAME SAYS IT ALL, THE - Vitamins and nutritional supplements - Ultimate Life, Inc.
NAME THAT TUNE - Video game - Bally Sente Inc.
NAME YOUR POISON - Glassware–household - Ceraglass Inc.
NAMEASE - Computer software - Names and Planes, Inc.
NAMEBUILDER - Computer software - Ideawerks
NAMEDAY - Greeting cards - Nameday Registry, Inc.
NAMEDROPPER - Floor coverings - Devon Corp.
NAMELESS RECORDS - Recording label - Zod Music Productions
NAMELY ART DESIGNS - Jewelry - Carmen D. Caserta
NAMELY YOU! - Toys - Chimeric, Inc.
NAMELY YOURS - Apparel–athletic - Robert's Folly Inc.
NAMELY YOURS - Name plaques - Maxelin L. Wiebe
NAMEMAKERS - Jewelry–precious - Michael Joseph, Inc.
NAMEPLATER - Photographic equipment - Max Concepts Inc.
NAMEPRO - Computer software - Intrinsic, Inc.
NAMES - Apparel stores–sports - Names Sportswear Inc.
NAMES - Toilets–porcelain - Friendship Designs
NAMES GUARD - Computer software - National Association for Medical Equipment Services
NAMES 'N DATES - Office supplies ☆ - Mead Corp.
NAMESAKE BABY - Dolls - Effanbee Doll Corp.
NAMESAKES - Bookmarks - Greg Caulton
NAMESPAC - Political organizations - National Association for Medical Equipment Services
NAMI - Building materials–asbestos - National Accreditation & Management Institute, Inc.
NAMI - Jewelry - Limpid Jewelry Inc.
NAMIC U.S.A. - Medical apparatus - NAMIC USA Corp.
NAML-OFF - Nail care products - Unique Products Co.
NAMM - Educational materials - National Association of Music Merchants, Inc.
NAMOR - Publisher's imprints ☆ - Marvel Entertainment Group, Inc.
NAMPA CHIEF - Trailers–travel - King Co.
NAMSCO - Salt - Namsco Inc.
NAMZ - Rubber stamps - All Night Media, Inc.
NAN DORSEY - Blouses–women's - Kaufman Knitting Co. Inc.
NAN-FLOWER - Apparel–women's - Nan-Flower Lingerie
NAN IV - Slacks–men's - H.R. Kaminsky & Sons Inc.
NANA - Shoes - Na Na Trading Co., Inc.
NANA BANANA - Cookies - Nabisco Foods Group
NANA NUTMEG - Toys–stuffed ☆ - Gund, Inc.
NANABERRY RITA - Beverages–alcohol - Chi-Chi's, Inc.
NANAK'S - Cookies ☆ - Nanak's Gourmet Cookies
NANAPEER - Finishing agents - Wampler Chemical Corp.
NANA'S COCIAN - Food products - Abuelita Mexican Foods
NANA'S HOUSE - Jewelry - Karen Proft
NANCE'S - Relishes - Richardson-T Foods Corp.
NANCI - Bags - Nanci Industries
NANCI - Dishes–earthenware - Advantage Marketing Group, Inc.
NANCI - Publisher's imprints - Designs by Nanci Inc.
NANCI'S FRUCTOSE FREEZER - Yogurt–frozen - Nanci's Frozen Yogurt
NANCI'S FRUCTOSE GRANITA - Beverages - Nanci's Frozen Yogurt
NANCI'S FRUCTOSE SMOOTHIE - Beverages - Nanci's Frozen Yogurt
NANCI'S FRUIT DRINK MIX - Beverages - Nanci's Frozen Yogurt
NANCY - House furnishings - Dan River Inc.
NANCY - Shirts - United Feature Syndicate, Inc.
NANCY - Shoes–athletic - Coast Shoes Inc.
NANCY - Wallpaper - Lin-Gor Wallcoverings
NANCY - Watches - Bulova Corp.
NANCY - Window coverings - Vertilux-Louverlux Inc.
NANCY II - Apparel and accessories - H.L. Miller and Son, Inc.
NANCY & DAVID - Jewelry - Designs by Nancy & David Ltd.
NANCY & SLUGGO - Toys ☆ - Knickerbocker Toy Co. Inc.
NANCY ANNE BAKERY - Jams and jellies - Schnuck Markets, Inc.
NANCY CALHOUN - Tableware–china - Nancy Calhoun Inc.
NANCY COTTON - Baked goods - Cotton Bros. Baking Co. Inc.

NANCY DREW - Publisher's imprints - Grosset & Dunlap Inc.
NANCY DREW NOTEBOOKS, THE - Publisher's imprints - Simon & Schuster, Inc.
NANCY FROCK - Apparel and accessories - H.L. Miller and Son, Inc.
NANCY HANKS - Fruits and vegetables - Comstock Michigan Fruit
NANCY JOHNSON - Clothing - Nancy Johnson
NANCY KEEGAN - Apparel–women's - Arveebee Co. Ltd.
NANCY KNOX - Shoes - Roger & Barbara Bowman
NANCY LOPEZ - Shoes ☆ - Endicott Johnson Corp.
NANCY LYNN - Food products - Grand Union Co.
NANCY MARSHALL ANTIQUE COLLECTION - Jewelry - Nancy Marshall Antique Collection
NANCY MARTIN - Food products - Dominick's Finer Foods, Inc.
NANCY NONSENSE - Toys–stuffed ☆ - Kenner Products
NANCY NURSE BEAR - Toys–stuffed - Dakin Inc.
NANCY PRENTISS - Giftware - Westmorland Sterling Co.
NANCY PREVO COLLECTION - Greeting cards ☆ - Woodbridge Graphics
NANCY SCOT - Knit goods ☆ - Three by Three
NANCY SMITH - Crocheted and knitted items - La Femme Knitting Mills Inc.
NANCY VALENTINE - Dresses–women's - Anne Klein & Co.
NANCY VOLIN'S PAMPERED PETS CUISINE - Pet treats - Pampered Pets Cuisine, Ltd.
NANCY'S - Dairy products - Springfield Creamery
NANCY'S - Food products - Marco Food Products Inc.
NANCY'S - Food products ☆ - Prepco
NANCY'S - Meat products–poultry - Lynden Farm and Garden
NANCY'S - Pastries - Nancy's Specialty Foods
NANCY'S CHINA - Ships–sailing vessels - Devlin Designing Boat Builders Inc.
NANCY'S COFFEE CAFE' - Coffee - NBW Corp.
NANCY'S FANCY - Apparel–women's - Burlington Coat Factory Warehouse Corp.
NANCY'S GOURMET APPETIZERS - Food products - Nancy's Specialty Foods
NANCY'S PETITE DESSERTS THAW & SERVE - Bakery products - Nancy's Specialty Foods
NANCY'S PETITE QUICHE - Food products - Nancy's Specialty Foods
NANCY'S PRIDE - Meat products–poultry - Brakebush Brothers Inc.
NANDI - Hair care products - Roux Laboratories, Inc.
NANDROBOLIC - Forest Pharmaceuticals Inc.
NANDROLIN - Pharmaceutical preparations ☆ - Solvay Pharmaceuticals Inc.
NANETTE - Apparel–women's - Nanette Undies Co. Inc.
NANETTE - Eyeglasses - Art-Craft Optical Co.
NANETTE - Pickles ☆ - Aunt Jane's Foods
NANIK - Blinds–venetian - Endisco Supply Co.
NANIK - Blinds–vertical - Nanik Div.
NANIK - Window coverings - Nelson Beck of Washington
NANIK - Window coverings - Vertical Blind Factory
NANIK - Window shades - Ace Blinds Inc.
NANITO - Fruits and vegetables - International Fruit Importers USA Inc.
NANKANG - Tires - Nankang Rubber Tire Corp. Ltd.
NANKEE - Cleaning preparations - Nankee Co. Inc.
NANKING - Tableware–china - Villeroy and Boch Tableware Ltd.
NANN-KNITS - Apparel–children's - Nannette Manufacturing Co. Inc.
NANNER TANNER TROPICAL OIL - Sun tanning oil - Donnie M. Naramore
NANNETTE - Apparel–children's - Nannette Manufacturing Co. Inc.
NANNETTE - Dolls ☆ - Effanbee Doll Corp.
NANNIE WALKER - Health care products - Winnie Walker Co.
NANNY AND WEBSTER - Blankets - Laurie Oki
NANNY'S - Shampoos - Aldi Inc.
NANNY'S BEST SOAP - Soap - L.A.F. Enterprises
NANO-MASTER - Measurement equipment - Nano-Master USA, Inc.
NANO2 - Fuses–electric - Littelfuse, Inc.
NANOCARB - Industrial coatings - Nanodyne Inc.
NANODYNE - Chemicals - Nanodyne Inc.
NANOGRAIN - Industrial powders - Nanodyne Inc.
NANOLITE - Antennas - Allen Telecom Group, Inc.
NANOORANGE - Chemical preparations - Molecular Probes, Inc.
NANOPATH - Computer software - Rank Taylor Hobson, Inc.
NANOSEP - Centrifuges–laboratory - Filtron Technology Corp.
NANOSHOOTER - Nozzles - Wet Labs Inc.
NANOSTEP - Motors - Oriental Motor USA Corp.
NANOTEK - Industrial chemicals - Nanophase Technologies Corp.
NANOTEK WARRIOR - Computer software - Virgin Interactive Entertainment, Inc.
NANOTOR - Connectors–electrical - Whitaker Corp.
NANOTRAK - Computer software - Rank Taylor Hobson, Inc.

☆ = Now out of production

NANOVISION - Microscopes - Topometrix Corp.
NANPING - Wallcoverings - Stretchwall Fabrics Co.
NANTICOKE - Motor vehicles–motor homes - Nanticoke Homes Inc.
NANTUCKET - Apparel–women's - Nantucket Industries Inc.
NANTUCKET - Boats–motor ☆ - Larson Boat Div.
NANTUCKET - Cabinets ☆ - American Woodmark Corp.
NANTUCKET - Clocks - General Time Corp. (Westclox/Seth Thomas Div.)
NANTUCKET - Cooking utensils–enameled ☆ - National Housewares
NANTUCKET - Dishes–china - Waterford Wedgewood USA, Inc.
NANTUCKET - Flatware - Washington Forge Inc.
NANTUCKET - Floor coverings–carpet and rugs - Langhorne Carpet Co. Inc.
NANTUCKET - Furniture–wood - Flexsteel Industries Inc.
NANTUCKET - Luggage - American Tourister, Inc.
NANTUCKET - Tables–wood - Koch & Lowy Inc.
NANTUCKET - Yarn ☆ - American Crewel & Canvas Studio
NANTUCKET BASKET - Giftware - Waterford Wedgewood USA, Inc.
NANTUCKET BUOY - Bells - North Country Wind Bells Inc.
NANTUCKET CHERRY - Tobacco products - 1776 Tobacco Co.
NANTUCKET COUNTRY CHARM - Wallpaper ☆ - Sanitas Wallcoverings
NANTUCKET GOLD - Lobster - Steve Connolly Seafood
NANTUCKET GOLD - Sunblocks - Mercer Group Ltd.
NANTUCKET HOSIERY MILLS - Hosiery ☆ - Nantucket Industries Inc.
NANTUCKET NECTARS - Beverages–carbonated - Nantucket Allserve, Inc.
NANTUCKET SLEIGH RIDE, THE - T-shirts–men's - Nantucket Sleigh Ride, Inc.
NANTUCKET TAVERN - Furniture ☆ - Bassett Furniture Industries, Inc.
NANTUCKETER'S - Food products - Nantucket Specialty Foods, Inc.
NANTUCKETT - Floor coverings - Anderson Hardwood Floors Inc.
NANZ - Hardware - Nanz Custom Hardware Inc.
NAO - Figurines ☆ - Lladro USA, Inc.
NAOMI - Food products ☆ - Empire Kosher Poultry Inc.
NAOMI - Ophthalmic goods - Foremost Optical Products
NAOMI - Perfume - Yaba International, Ltd.
NAOMI GALE - Cabinets - Naomi Gale Wall Systems
NAOMI SHURE-FIT - Rings–jewelry - Naomi Findings Manufacturers
NAOMI SIMS - Cosmetics - Yaba International, Ltd.
NAOMI SIMS - Wigs - N. Wagman & Co.
NAP - Clocks - General Time Corp. (Westclox/Seth Thomas Div.)
$NAP - Computer software - Consolidated Nutrition, L.C.
NAP - Infant product - Prince Lionheart, Inc.
NAP-EZZZZZZ - Eyeglasses - K & M Inc.
NAP KING - Napkins–paper - Pack All, Inc.
NAP-LAM - Plastics–laminated - General Binding Corp.
NAP-LOK - Metals ☆ - Roberts
NAP MATES - Toys–stuffed - Animal Fair Inc.
NAP PAC - Beds–wood ☆ - Century Products Co.
NAP-PACKS - Apparel–women's - Nap, Inc.
NAP PALS - Backpacks - Playskool Baby Inc.
NAP PILLOW - Pillow - Pillowtex Corp.
NAP SAC - Sanitary napkins - Compac Industries Inc.
NAP SACK - Sleeping bags - Nap Sack, Inc.
NAP-STAIN - Paints ☆ - Fuller-O'Brien Paints Inc.
NAP-TIME - Mattresses - Evenflo Juvenile Furniture Co.
NAPA - Automotive replacement parts - National Automotive Parts Association
NAPA - Floor coverings–carpet and rugs ☆ - Royalweve Carpet Mills
NAPA - Frames–eyeglass - U.S. Optical Frame Co.
NAPA - Furniture - Landes Manufacturing Co.
NAPA - Massage products - Everett Associates Inc.
NAPA - Occasional tables - JDI Group, Inc.
NAPA - Orthodontic equipment - Peter T. George
NAPA - Paper - Paper Corp. of America
NAPA - Stationery - Terragrafics Inc.
NAPA AND SONOMA WINE PROFESSOR, THE - Computer software - E-8 Publications, Inc.
NAPA CELLARS - Wines - San Francisco Wine Exchange
NAPA CITY - Cider - Napa Valley Wines
NAPA COUNTRY - Glassware–household - Owens-Illinois Inc. (Libbey Div.)
NAPA CREEK WINERY - Wines - Bronco Wine Co.
NAPA CREEK WINERY - Wines - Napa Creek Winery
NAPA ECHLIN - Automotive parts and accessories - Echlin Inc.
NAPA GOLD - Motor vehicle parts and accessories - National Automotive Parts Association
NAPA QUALITY - Bedspreads - MTC
NAPA RIDGE - Wines - Wine World Inc.
NAPA SERIES - Wines - IDV Wines (Beaulieu Vineyard)
NAPA SILVER - Filters–air - National Automotive Parts Association

NAPA SPRINGS - Wines - Delicato Vineyards
NAPA UNITED - Automotive parts and accessories - Echlin Inc.
NAPA UNITED - Automotive replacement parts - National Automotive Parts Association
NAPA VALLEY - Apparel–women's - Koret North America
NAPA VALLEY - Bicycles - Columbia Manufacturing Inc.
NAPA VALLEY - Coffee - Paupaiz Inc.
NAPA VALLEY - Floor coverings–carpet and rugs - Mandate-Dawn Carpet Mills
NAPA VALLEY - Furniture - Bernhardt Industries
NAPA VALLEY - Mustard - Beaverton Foods
NAPA VALLEY - Wines - Napa Valley Wines
NAPA VALLEY BY SARA BARNES - Dinnerware–glass ☆ - Block China Co.
NAPA VALLEY GOURMET - Sauces - Napa Valley Salsa, Inc.
NAPA VALLEY KITCHENS - Oils–edible - De Medici Imports Ltd.
NAPA VALLEY PANTRY - Food products - Kelly P. Wheeler
NAPA VALLEY PRINTS - Wallpaper ☆ - J.M. Lynne Co. Inc.
NAPA VALLEY RESERVE - Wines - Napa Valley Reserve Certification Board
NAPA VALLEY WINE CO. - Wines - Napa Valley Wines
NAPA VALLEY WINE TRAIN - Wines - Napa Valley Wine Train
NAPA-VILLAGES - Wines - Newlan Vineyards & Winery Inc.
NAPA VINEYARDS - Wines - Napa Valley Wines
NAPA VINTNERS - Wines - Napa Valley Wines
NAPA WINE CELLARS - Wines - Napa Wine Cellars
NAPAKKA - Bedding–linen - Dan River Inc.
NAPANOOK VINEYARD - Wines - Dominus Estate Corp.
NAPAT-D - Pharmaceutical preparations ☆ - Hyrex Pharmaceuticals
NAPCA - Skin care products - Orjene Natural Cosmetics
NAPCA LITE - Skin care products - Jason Natural Products, Inc.
NAPCO - Aluminum products - National Aluminum Products Co.
NAPCO - Beef ☆ - Edmac Foods Inc.
NAPCO - Glassware–household - Napco Inc.
NAPCO AMERICAN HERITAGE - Vinyl ☆ - National Aluminum Products Co.
NAPCO SECURITY SYSTEMS - Alarm systems - Napco Security Systems Inc.
NAPCOWARE - Giftware - National Potteries
NAPEEZ - Diapers - Braha Industries Inc.
NAPHCON - Ophthalmic goods - Alcon Laboratories, Inc.
NAPHCON-A - Ophthalmic goods - Alcon Laboratories, Inc.
NAPHCON FORTE - Ophthalmic goods - Alcon Laboratories, Inc.
NAPIER - Jewelry - Napier Co.
NAPIER GALLERY, THE - Jewelry ☆ - Napier Co.
NAPKIN WINGS - Tableware–plastic - Landmark Graphics, Inc.
NAPKINS OF DISTINCTION - Napkins–paper - Beach Products
NAPLES - Brushes–paint - Corona Brushes Inc.
NAPLES - Cabinets ☆ - Marsh Furniture Co.
NAPLES - Furniture - Hammary Furniture Co. Inc.
NAPLES - Lighting equipment–motorcycle - C. Bruno & Son Inc.
NAPLES VALLEY - Wines - Widmer's Wine Cellars Inc.
NAPLOPAN - Pharmaceutical preparations ☆ - Vortech Pharmaceuticals
NAPMAT - Blankets - Llumar Star Kites Inc.
NAPMATE - Pillows - Pillowtex Corp.
NAPOLEAN - Furniture - Lyon-Shaw Inc.
NAPOLEAN - Toys–stuffed ☆ - Gund, Inc.
NAPOLEN GOLD - Vitamins and nutritional supplements - Cernitin America Inc.
NAPOLEON - Artichokes–canned - Napoleon Co.
NAPOLEON - Cabinets - Vinotemp International
NAPOLEON - Candles - Empire Manufacturing Co.
NAPOLEON - Flowers–artificial - Napoleon USA Inc.
NAPOLEON - Frames–eyeglass - Hudson Optical Corp.
NAPOLEON - Furniture - Williams-Sonoma, Inc.
NAPOLEON - Games - Avalon Hill Game Co.
NAPOLEON AT BAY - Games ☆ - Avalon Hill Game Co.
NAPOLEON CAPS - Pastries - Joey's Fine Foods
NAPOLEON HILL - Recording label - Napoleon Hill Foundation
NAPOLEON IVY - Dishes–china - Waterford Wedgewood USA, Inc.
NAPOLEON SOLO - Shirts - 88 International, Inc.
NAPOLEONS - Cigars - General Cigar Co., Inc.
NAPOLEON'S BATTLES - Games - Avalon Hill Game Co.
NAPOLI - Cabinets - Aristokraft, Inc.
NAPOLI - Cookies - Pez Candy Inc.
NAPOLI - Floor coverings–carpet and rugs - Milliken & Co. Inc.
NAPOLI - Furniture ☆ - Lane Co. Inc.
NAPOLI - Tables–wood - Riverside Furniture Corp.
NAPOLI - Tableware–china - Pfaltzgraff Investment Co.
NAPOLI GRANDE - Glassware–household - Owens-Illinois Inc. (Libbey Div.)

☆ = Now out of production

NAPOLINO - Breads - La Piccolina and Co. Inc.
NAPOLI'S - Food products - Wal-Bon of Ohio, Inc.
NAPOLITAINS - Candy ☆ - Brocks Candy Co.
NAPPA FLEX - Shoes - Bally of Switzerland
NAPPCO - Pens - National Pen & Pencil Co.
NAPPE-BABCOCK - Cushions - Gold Medal Inc.
NAPPY - Bags - Gold Medal Inc.
NAPRIL - Pharmaceutical preparations - Marion Merrell Dow
NAPRO - Meat products - North American Processing Co.
NAPROSYN - Pharmaceutical preparations - Syntex USA, Inc.
NAPS - Medical apparatus - Druzak Medical Inc.
NAPSACK - Apparel and accessories - Harry N. Dunnington
NAPSAK - Baby carrier - International Design Manufacturing Inc.
NAPSURE - Paper products - Harold L. Krainin
NAPTIME - Blankets - Llumar Star Kites Inc.
NAPTRATE - Pharmaceutical preparations ☆ - Vortech Pharmaceuticals
NAQUA - Diuretics - Schering-Plough Healthcare Products
NAQUALIFT - Mufflers–motor vehicle - Marine Muffler Corp.
NAQUIVAL - Pharmaceutical preparations - Schering-Plough Healthcare Products
NARA - Furniture - National/Mt. Airy Furniture
NARADA - Recording label - Narada Productions Inc.
NARAMURA'S - Incense - Darwell Import Co. Inc.
NARAWCO - Banjos - National Rawhide Manufacturing Co.
NARBETH - Floor coverings ☆ - Tarkett, Inc.
NARCAL - Bricks - North American Refractories Co.
NARCAN - Pharmaceutical preparations - Du Pont Pharmaceuticals
NARCISSE - Candy bars ☆ - Brocks Candy Co.
NARCISSUS - Giftware - Sasaki
NARCISSUS - Glassware–household - Spiegelau Inc.
NARCISSUS CLEAR - Giftware - Sasaki
NARCO - Bricks - North American Refractories Co.
NARCO - Fabrics–rayon - North American Rayon Corp.
NARCO - Hobby kits - National Artcraft Co.
NARCO STRIPS - Cosmetics - National Artcraft Co.
NARCOCAST - Bricks - North American Refractories Co.
NARCOGUN - Gunpowder - North American Refractories Co.
NARDA COLLECTION, THE - Handbags - East-West Designs
NARDALERT - Alarm systems - Narda Microwave Corp.
NARDIL - Pharmaceutical preparations - Parke-Davis
NARDIS - Apparel–women's - Nardis, Inc.
NARELLE - Ophthalmic goods - Swank Optical
NAREOB - Real estate agencies - National Association of Reo Brokers
NARGAOKA - Electronic equipment - Bell & Howell Co.
NARIN - Floor coverings–linoleum ☆ - Forbo Industries, Inc.
NARLIGATOR - Toys - Tonka Corp.
NARLIHOG - Toys - Tonka Corp.
NARLIPHANT - Toys - Tonka Corp.
NARLIZARD - Toys - Tonka Corp.
NARLY NOGGINS HELMUT STUFF - Decals and transfers - GBH Inc.
NARMAG - Bricks - North American Refractories Co.
NARO-X - Corner bead for plaster - Bostwick Steel Lath Co.
NARON - Candy - Naron Candy Co. Inc.
NARONE - Pharmaceutical preparations ☆ - Ulmer Pharmacal Co.
NARPHOS - Plastics - North American Refractories Co.
NARRAGANSETT - Apparel–men's - Omnisport Inc.
NARRAGANSETT - Beverages–alcohol - Falstaff Brewing Corp.
NARRAGANSETT - Drawing paper - Boston Paper Board Corp.
NARRAGANSETT - Frames–eyeglass ☆ - Universal/Univis Inc.
NARRAGANSETT GOLD - Flatware - Gorham Inc.
NARRATOR - Projectors–photographic - Montage Productions Inc.
NARRO-TEX - Siding–metal ☆ - GAF Corp.
NARROLINE - Window frames - Andersen Corp.
NARROW - Recording label - Refuge Music Group
NARROWOOD - Floor coverings ☆ - Robbins Inc.
NARSPAN - Pharmaceutical preparations ☆ - Coast Laboratories Inc.
NARTAR - Bricks - North American Refractories Co.
NARTURALL - Infant product - Diaperwhere Inc.
NARUMI - Dishes–china - Mikasa Co.
NARVI - Saunas - Cedarbrook Sauna Inc.
NARVIK - Floor coverings–carpet and rugs ☆ - Eurotex Inc.
NARWHAL - Watches - Gruen Marketing Corp.
NAS - Leather goods - Nas Import Corp.
N.A.S. 99 - Nail care products - Opi Products, Inc.
NASA - Toys–automobiles - ERTL Co., Inc.
NASA PEGASUS - Toys–models ☆ - Estes Industries

NASA SHUTTLE - Toys–models ☆ - Estes Industries
NASA X-15 - Toys–models ☆ - Estes Industries
NASABID - Cough medicines - Abana Pharmaceuticals, Inc.
NASABID - Pharmaceutical preparations - Jones Medical Industries, Inc. (Medical Div.)
NASACON - Pharmaceutical preparations - Consolidated Midland Corp.
NASACORT - Pharmaceutical preparations - Rhone-Poulenc Rorer Pharmaceuticals Inc.
NASADENT - Toothpaste ☆ - Schering-Plough Healthcare Products
NASAFED - Pharmaceutical preparations - Whitby Pharmaceuticals, Inc.
NASAGUARD-B - Pharmaceutical preparations - Pfizer Inc.
NASAHIST - Pharmaceutical preparations - Keene Pharmaceuticals Inc.
NASAL-D - Pharmaceutical preparations - Shaklee Corp.
NASAL MIST - Pharmaceutical preparations - Jess Clarke & Sons Inc.
NASAL MOIST - Health care products - Blairex Laboratories, Inc.
NASAL MOISTURIZER - Cold remedies - Bayer Corp. (Consumer Care Div.)
NASAL SPRAY - Cold remedies - Reese Chemical Co.
NASALCROM - Health care products - Fisons Corp.
NASALIDE - Pharmaceutical preparations - Syntex USA, Inc.
NASALINE - Health care products ☆ - Scandinavian Natural Health & Beauty Products, Inc.
NASALSPAN - Pharmaceutical preparations - Rotex Pharmaceuticals Inc.
NASALTONE - Pharmaceutical preparations - Luyties Pharmacal Co.
NASALUBE - Skin care products - Professional Aids Corp.
NASAPAP - Pharmaceutical preparations ☆ - Whitby Pharmaceuticals, Inc.
NASAREL - Pharmaceutical preparations - Syntex USA, Inc.
NASATAB - Cough medicines - ECR Pharmaceuticals
NASATAB LA - Pharmaceutical preparations - ECR Pharmaceuticals
NASATUSS - Cough medicines - Abana Pharmaceuticals, Inc.
NASATUSS - Pharmaceutical preparations - Jones Medical Industries, Inc. (Medical Div.)
NASCAR - Colognes - Wilshire Fragrance Corp.
NASCAR - Housewares ☆ - Blue Ridge International Products Co., Inc.
NASCAR - Metals - National Association for Stock Car Auto Racing, Inc.
NASCAR - Toys - ERTL Co., Inc.
NASCAR - Wallets - Westport Corp.
NASCAR RACE CAR - Toys–automobiles - Kingsbury Mini Motors of America Inc.
NASCO - Giftware ☆ - National Housewares
NASCO - Paints - Nasco Industries, Inc.
NASCO-HAND 'N HAND CLEANER - Cleaning preparations - Nasco Industries, Inc.
NASCO-ONE MINUTE CONTRACTOR'S PAINT & VARNISH REMOVER - Varnish removers - Nasco Industries, Inc.
NASCO-PAINT REMOVERS & REFINISHERS - Varnish removers - Nasco Industries, Inc.
NASCO-ULTRA SAFE STRIPPER - Varnish removers - Nasco Industries, Inc.
NASCOBAL B - Pharmaceutical preparations - Nastech Pharmaceutical Co., Inc.
NASCOTE II - Wood products - Nasco Industries, Inc.
NASE - Apparel–athletic - National Association for the Self Employed, Inc.
NASEC - Pharmaceutical preparations ☆ - Roberts/Hauck Pharmaceuticals Inc.
NASEEM - Canned meat - MF Group, Inc.
NASH - Apparel–women's - Nash Designs, Inc.
NASH - Motor vehicles ☆ - DaimlerChrysler
NASH GOREY - Toys - Tonka Corp.
NASHBORO RECORDS - Compact discs–prerecorded - SSRE
NASHCO - Toys ☆ - Nashco Products Inc.
NASHEEN - Yarn ☆ - National Spinning Co., Inc.
NASHOBA NETWORKS - Computer hardware - Nashoba Networks Inc.
NASHOBA VALLEY - Wines - Nashoba Valley Winery
NASHUA - Adhesives and sealants - Phil Marano Inc.
NASHUA - Cabinets - Triangle Pacific Corp. (Cabinet Division)
NASHUA - Labels–paper - Nashua Corp.
NASHUA - Mobile homes ☆ - Wescon Products Co.
NASHUA - Stoves–wood-burning - Ohio Steel Industries Inc.
NASHVILLE - Cigarettes - Brown & Williamson Tobacco Corp.
NASHVILLE - Thread - Threads USA Div.
NASHVILLE 400 - Amplifiers–musical instrument - Peavey Electronics Corp.
NASHVILLE ALLSTAR - Recording label - Rains Recording Co.
NASHVILLE BLUEGRASS - Recording label - Jack Lynch Music Group
NASHVILLE BRASS, THE - Recording label - Danny Davis Productions
NASHVILLE COUNTRY - Recording label - Jack Lynch Music Group
NASHVILLE CUSTOM - Musical instrument accessories - Sound Post Inc.
NASHVILLE INTERNATIONAL - Recording label - Nashville International Entertainment Group

☆ = Now out of production

NASHVILLE ON STAGE - Musical instruments - Opryland USA Inc.
NASHVILLE SOUND - Musical instrument accessories - Cromwell & Co. Inc.
NASHVILLE SOUNDS - Paper products - Nashville Sounds Baseball Club
NASHVILLE STRAIGHTS - Musical instrument accessories ☆ - Washburn International
NASIXX - Health care products - Pharma Botanixx
NASO-ENTERIC - Medical apparatus ☆ - Biosearch Medical Products Inc.
NASO FORM - Eyeglasses - Art-Craft Optical Co.
NASO-MIST - Cold remedies ☆ - Vitarine Pharmaceuticals Inc.
NASON - Jewelry - Nason Trading Co. Inc.
NASOYA - Food products - Nasoya Foods Inc.
NASSA - Lubricating oils ☆ - Shell Oil Co.
NASSAU - Bicycles - Murray, Inc.
NASSAU - Boats—motor ☆ - Four Winns Inc.
NASSAU - Brushes—paint - Corona Brushes Inc.
NASSAU - Clocks - Timex Corp.
NASSAU - Floor coverings—carpet and rugs ☆ - Masland Corp.
NASSAU - Flowers, plants, and seeds - Jacklin Seed
NASSAU - Frames—eyeglass ☆ - Universal/Univis Inc.
NASSAU - Goggles—safety - Aearo Co.
NASSAU - Thread - Threads USA Div.
NASSAU - Tools - Great Neck Saw Manufacturers, Inc.
NASSAU - Toys ☆ - Strombecker Corp.
NASSAU - Watches - Nicolet International Inc.
NASSAU BLUE - Glassware—household ☆ - Lenox Crystal, Inc.
NASSAU HALL - Floor coverings—tile ☆ - Kentile Floors Inc.
NASSAU PLUS - Goggles—safety - Cabot Safety Intermediate Corp.
NASSAU ROYALE - Beverages—alcohol - Bacardi Imports Inc.
NASSAU SUIT - Waterproof outerwear ☆ - Helly-Hansen Inc.
NASSCOR - Saunas - Cedarbrook Sauna Inc.
NASTA - Games - Playtime Corp.
NASTIES - Candy ☆ - Ce De Candy Inc.
NASTOFF - Firearms, accessories, and parts - Nastoff's .45 Shop
NASTRIX - Watches - Centier Corp.
NASTURTIUM - Cosmetics - Shiseido Cosmetics (America) Ltd.
NASTY - Air purification systems - Medo Industries, Inc.
NASTY - Wireless instrument transmitters - Nady Systems Inc.
NASTY CHILD - Apparel and accessories - Jay Spear
NASTY JIGS - Sporting goods - Gapen Co.
NASTY TRICKS - Candy - Confex Inc.
NAT - Jewelry - National Chain Co.
NAT - Jewelry - United Air Lines, Inc.
NAT - Wallpaper - Carlton-Metro Wallcoverings
NAT KING COLE - Recording label - King Cole Partners, L.P.
NAT NAST - Shirts ☆ - Swingster Co.
NAT ROBBINS - Cosmetics - Nat Robbins Ltd.
NAT SHERMAN - Tobacco products - Nat Sherman, Inc.
NAT-TROP - Health care products - Top of the Line
NATA-FAUVE - Veterinary pharmaceutical preparations - Nutra-Vet Research Corp.
NATA-KEY - Vitamins and nutritional supplements ☆ - J.R. Carlson Laboratories Inc.
NATA-PAR - Pharmaceutical preparations - Pharmics Inc.
NATABEC - Vitamins and nutritional supplements ☆ - Parke-Davis
NATACYN - Ophthalmic goods - Alcon Laboratories, Inc.
NATAFORT - Pharmaceutical preparations ☆ - Parke-Davis
NATAGRAMS - Posters - Natalie Sehn
NATAL-MAT - Pharmaceutical preparations - Tetra Medical Supply Corp.
NATALAC - Pharmaceutical preparations ☆ - U.S. Ethicals Inc.
NATALCARE - Vitamins and nutritional supplements - KV Pharmaceutical Co.
NATALE - Dinnerware ☆ - Corning Inc.
NATALIA - Rings—jewelry - Artcarved Inc.
NATALIA'S FLOWER - Bedding—linen - Dan River Inc.
NATALIE - Bedding—linen - Dan River Inc.
NATALIE - Frames—eyeglass - U.S. Optical Frame Co.
NATALIE - Lamps - Natalie Lamp and Shade Corp.
NATALIE - Wallcovering - The Creative Edge, Inc.
NATALIE ROBYN - Sleepwear - D.B. Royalty Inc.
NATALIE'S KITCHEN WITH JASPER WHITE - Video and audio tapes - Dawn Productions, Inc.
NATALIE'S ORCHARD ISLAND JUICE CO. - Fruit drinks—bottled or canned - Orchid Island Juice Co.
NATALINX - Vitamins and nutritional supplements - Bristol-Myers Squibb Co.
NATASHA - Dolls - Russ Berrie and Co., Inc.
NATASHA - Dolls ☆ - Dakin Inc.
NATASHA KAYN - Jewelry - Hughes-Ruiz, Inc.

NATASHA YAR - Toys - Paramount Pictures Corp.
NATASHKA - Vodka - Gaetano Specialties Ltd.
NATC/SDT - Electrical equipment - Triangle Wire & Cable, Inc.
NATCH - Crocheted and knitted items ☆ - Puritan Sportswear Corp.
NATCH MAN - Combs ☆ - Summit Laboratories
NATCHEZ - Cabinets - Belwood Inc.
NATCHEZ - Dolls ☆ - Effanbee Doll Corp.
NATCHEZ - Firearms, accessories, and parts - High Standard Manufacturing Corp.
NATCHEZ - Floor coverings—carpet and rugs ☆ - Masland Corp.
NATCHEZ - Frames—eyeglass - U.S. Optical Frame Co.
NATCHEZ - Furniture - Henredon Furniture Industries Inc.
NATCHEZ - Furniture ☆ - Bassett Furniture Industries, Inc.
NATCHEZ CLASSIC - Furniture - Henredon Furniture Industries Inc.
NATCHEZ COLLECTION, THE - Dining room furniture - The Davis Co.
NATCHEZ PILGRIMAGE TOURS - Apparel and accessories - Pilgrimage Garden Club
NATCO - Maps - Natural Color Cards Co.
NATCOL - Artists' materials - Natcol Crafts & Hobbies
NATCRACKER - Giftware - Enesco Corp.
NATGO - Engines - Natgo, Inc.
NATHA - Apparel and accessories - Mynet America Inc.
NATHAN - Games ☆ - Reeves International, Inc.
NATHAN - Horns—motor vehicle - Windham Machine Co., Inc.
NATHAN FAMOUS - Food products - Chiquita Brands, Inc.
NATHANIEL - Apparel stores—sports ☆ - Gillman Knitwear Co.
NATHAN'S - Mustard - Gold Pure Food Products Inc.
NATHAN'S FAMOUS - Restaurants—fast food - Nathan's Famous Inc.
NATHANSON CREEK - Wines - Estates Group
NATHERA - Pharmaceutical preparations - Harmony Laboratories, Inc.
NATICO - Clocks - Natico Originals Inc.
NATION - Pizzas—frozen - Nation Pizza Products L.P.
NATION - Thread - Quality Thread Co.
NATION WIDE - Modular homes - Insilco Corp.
NATION-WIDE - Motor vehicles—personnel carriers - Nation-Wide General Rental Centers Inc.
NATIONAL - Adhesives and sealants - Federal-Mogul Corp.
NATIONAL - Audio equipment - National Brand Outlet
NATIONAL - Beverages - National Fruit Flavor Co.
NATIONAL - Biscuits - Nabisco Foods Group
NATIONAL - Blinds—vertical - Amsterdam Fabricators
NATIONAL - Blinds—vertical - National Vertical Blind Co. Inc.
NATIONAL - Brushes—hair - Capitol Novelty Co.
NATIONAL - Burial caskets - National Casket Co.
NATIONAL - Calendars - Keith Clark Inc.
NATIONAL - Cat food ☆ - National Scent Co.
NATIONAL - Christmas tree ornaments - Santa's Best
NATIONAL - Christmas tree stands - National Metal Industries (Utility Metal Products Div.)
NATIONAL - Clocks - National Timepieces Ltd. Inc.
NATIONAL - Cooking equipment—household - Rival Manufacturing Co.
NATIONAL - Cooking utensils—enameled ☆ - National Housewares
NATIONAL - Dog food - Milk Specialties Co.
NATIONAL - Drums—musical instruments - National Rawhide Manufacturing Co.
NATIONAL - Eyeglasses - Martin-Copeland Eyewear Corp.
NATIONAL - Fencing—gates and posts - National Fence Corp.
NATIONAL - Food products - National Tea Co.
NATIONAL - Food products - Universal Foods Corp.
NATIONAL - Frames—eyeglass - Creative Optiks
NATIONAL - Fruits and vegetables - Orchard Foods
NATIONAL - Furniture - Kimball International, Inc.
NATIONAL - Garbage disposal units—household - Hobart Corp.
NATIONAL - Guitar picks ☆ - International Music Corp.
NATIONAL - Hardware - National Manufacturing Co.
NATIONAL - Inks - National Ink Inc.
NATIONAL - Kitchen appliances - Nozawa Inc.
NATIONAL - Labels—paper - National Sales Co.
NATIONAL - Ladders—wood - John S. Tilley Ladders Co. Inc.
NATIONAL - Ledgers - Dennison National Co.
NATIONAL - Oats—rolled or meal - National Oats Co. Inc.
NATIONAL - Pencils - National Pen & Pencil Co.
NATIONAL - Pianos - Universal Player Piano Co.
NATIONAL - Railroad equipment - National Castings, Inc.
NATIONAL - Rulers—metal - Bates Manufacturing Co.
NATIONAL - Seasonings - National Products Co.

NATIONAL - Seating accessories - Austin Athletic Equipment Corp.

NATIONAL - Soap - National Chemical Laboratories of Pennsylvania Inc.

NATIONAL - Sporting goods - Minstar Inc.

NATIONAL - Straws–drinking - Clear Shield National Inc.

NATIONAL - Syrup - B. Westergaard & Co. Inc.

NATIONAL - Tires - Target Tire and Automotive Corp.

NATIONAL - Tools–hand-operated - General Tools Manufacturing Co. Inc.

NATIONAL - Vinegar - National Vinegar Co.

NATIONAL - Water–bottled or canned - National Spring Water Co.

NATIONAL ACME - Machine tools - Devlieg-Bullard Services Group

NATIONAL AEROSPACE PLANE - Toys–models ✫ - Estes Industries

NATIONAL ATHLETIC TRAINERS' ASSOCIATIONNATA 1950 - Publisher's imprints - National Athletic Trainers' Association, Inc.

NATIONAL AUDUBON SOCIETY - Bird feeds - Duncraft, Inc.

NATIONAL AUDUBON SOCIETY - Computer software - National Audubon Society, Inc.

NATIONAL AUDUBON SOCIETY - Giftware ✫ - Enesco Corp.

NATIONAL BASKETBALL ASSOCIATION - Apparel stores–children's - D. Glasgow & Sons Inc.

NATIONAL BASKETBALL ASSOCIATION - Socks - Fuqua Industries Inc.

NATIONAL BEAUTIFICATION - Flowers, plants, and seeds ✫ - Seaboard Seed Co.

NATIONAL BOHEMIAN - Beverages–malt - The Stroh Brewery Co.

NATIONAL BRAND FORMULA - Vitamins and nutritional supplements ✫ - Leiner Health Products Inc.

NATIONAL CANOLA - Oils–edible - California Olive Oil Corp.

NATIONAL CATHEDRAL - Jewelry - Protestant Episcopal Cathedral Foundation

NATIONAL CIRCUS LEAGUE - Apparel and accessories - Ringling Bros.-Barnum & Bailey Combined Shows, Inc.

NATIONAL CLASSICS CLOTHING - Apparel and accessories - Newstar Group, Inc.

NATIONAL COMING OUT DAY - Apparel and accessories - Good Catch

NATIONAL COMPUTERIZED BUSINESS SERVICES - Computer software - National Computerized Business Services, Inc.

NATIONAL CONEY ISLAND - Chili–canned - National Coney Island Chili Co.

NATIONAL CUP - Coffee - Tetley Inc.

NATIONAL CURRICULUM & TRAINING INSTITUTE - Educational materials - National Curriculum & Training Institute, Inc.

NATIONAL DECOR - Mirrors ✫ - National Products Inc.

NATIONAL DEFENSE - Novelty items–paper - National Defense, Inc.

NATIONAL DELI - Meat products–beef - Hebrew Foods Inc.

NATIONAL EMBROIDERY - Badges–uniform ✫ - Needlecraft Industries

NATIONAL EMPLOYMENT SCREENING SERVICES - Directories - Transportation Information Services Inc.

NATIONAL EN-AR-CO - Lubricants ✫ - Ashland Oil, Inc.

NATIONAL EN-AR-CO SOLV - Lubricants ✫ - Ashland Oil, Inc.

NATIONAL EN-AR-CO TUNE - Lubricants ✫ - Ashland Oil, Inc.

NATIONAL ESSENTIAL COLLECTION - Apparel and accessories - Jaclyn, Inc.

NATIONAL FARM & SHOP - Hose repair kits - National Welders Supply Co. Inc.

NATIONAL FITNESS - Weightlifting equipment - Bell Foundry Co.

NATIONAL FLARE COMPANY - Signal flares - Calvin B. Chang

NATIONAL FLEXWAY - Plastics–laminated - DHJ Plastics (USA), Inc.

NATIONAL FOOTBALL LEAGUE - Apparel and accessories - Garan, Inc.

NATIONAL FOOTBALL LEAGUE - Socks - Fuqua Industries Inc.

NATIONAL FORGE COMPANY - Steel products - National Forge Co.

NATIONAL GALLERY (LONDON) - Greeting cards - Kensington Cards

NATIONAL GALLERY OF ART - Postcards - Fotofolio Inc.

NATIONAL GALLERY OF LONDON, THE - Posters ✫ - Graphic Arts Unltd. Inc.

NATIONAL GOLD FLAKE - Cigarettes - G.A. Georgopulo & Co. Inc.

NATIONAL GYPSUM - Furniture ✫ - National Gypsum Co.

NATIONAL HOCKEY LEAGUE - Apparel stores–children's - D. Glasgow & Sons Inc.

NATIONAL HOME HEALTH - Health care products - National Home Health Care Exposition

NATIONAL HOME PRODUCTS - Housewares ✫ - Daily Dryer Co. Inc.

NATIONAL IMPORT RACING ASSOCIATION - Apparel and accessories - Gene's Auto Dynamics, Inc.

NATIONAL INSTRUMENTS - Computer hardware - National Instruments Corp.

NATIONAL INTERCLUB INVITATIONAL - Apparel - Robert Trent Jones Golf Club, Inc.

NATIONAL KEYLINE PRODUCTS - Paper products - National Blueprinters Supply Co. Inc.

NATIONAL KEYPRINT - Copying paper - National Blueprinters Supply Co. Inc.

NATIONAL KING - Balls–baseball ✫ - National Sporting Goods Corp.

NATIONAL LAMPOON'S CHESS MANIAC 5 BILLION AND 1 - Computer software - J2 Communications

NATIONAL LEAGUE FOR NURSING - Video production - National League for Nursing

NATIONAL LEASING AND FINANCIAL CORPORATION - Office supplies - National Leasing and Financial Corp.

NATIONAL LIBRARY SERVICE - Catalogs - Pages Book Fairs, Inc.

NATIONAL LIGHTWEIGHTS - Wallpaper - National Wallcovering

NATIONAL LOCK - Locks–door - National Lock Hardware

NATIONAL LOST AND FOUND FOR PETS - Computer programming services - D & D Enterprises

NATIONAL-MT. AIRY - Furniture ✫ - Bassett Furniture Industries, Inc.

NATIONAL MUSEUMS OF FRANCE - Postcards - Fotofolio Inc.

NATIONAL PAINT - Paints - Surface Protection Industries, Inc.

NATIONAL PARK EXPLORER - Recording label - Beaumonde Production Co.

NATIONAL PARKS - Tiles–ceramic - American Marazzi Tile, Inc.

NATIONAL PC SYSTEMS - Computers - AKOA, Inc.

NATIONAL PEN - Pens - National Pen Co.

NATIONAL PET ACCESSORIES - Pet products ✫ - Linda Sanicola

NATIONAL PORTRAIT GALLERY LONDON - Postcards - Fotofolio Inc.

NATIONAL POWER CORPORATION - Batteries - National Power Corp.

NATIONAL PREMIUM - Beverages–malt - The Stroh Brewery Co.

NATIONAL PRIDE - Doors–storm - National Nail Corp.

NATIONAL PRIDE - Patterns–clothing - Square Stitchers

NATIONAL PRO - Badminton equipment ✫ - National Sporting Goods Corp.

NATIONAL RING - Jewelry - National Ring & Leather Corp.

NATIONAL SAFE PET - Pet products - Safe Pet USA

NATIONAL SCALE SCOOPS - Scales–bathroom - National Scoop & Equipment Co.

NATIONAL SCENT - Pet products - National Scent Co.

NATIONAL SEA - Seafood products–fresh or frozen ✫ - National Sea Products U.S. Corp.

NATIONAL SEMICONDUCTOR - Games ✫ - National Semiconductor Corp.

NATIONAL SPECIALITY ALLOYS - Metals - National Speciality Alloys, Inc.

NATIONAL SPORTS NETWORK - Camps–recreational - Pinellas Association for Retarded Children, Inc.

NATIONAL SPORTWHEELS - Bicycles ✫ - National Sporting Goods Corp.

NATIONAL SUEDES - Wallpaper - National Wallcovering

NATIONAL SUNGLASS LEAGUE - Sunglasses ✫ - Riviera Trading, Inc.

NATIONAL TEXTBOOK COMPANY - Publisher's imprints - NTC Contemporary Publishing Group

NATIONAL TOTS AND TEENS, INC. TOTS AND TEENS 1954 - T-shirts–children's - National Tots and Teens, Inc.

NATIONAL TOURNAMENT - Sporting goods - Macon Manufacturing

NATIONAL TRUST - Giftware - Virginia Metalcrafters Inc.

NATIONAL TRUST COLLECTION, THE - Furniture–upholstered ✫ - Hickory Chair Co.

NATIONAL VALUE LINE, THE - Candy - Sathers Inc.

NATIONAL VEHICLE POPULATION PROFILE - Computer software - R.L. Polk & Co.

NATIONAL VELVET - Floor coverings–carpet and rugs - West Point-Pepperell Mill Store

NATIONAL VERTICAL BLIND - Blinds–vertical - National Vertical Blind Co. Inc.

NATIONAL WILDLIFE FEDERATION - Holiday greeting cards, calendars - National Wildlife Federation

NATIONAL WILDLIFE FEDERATION CONSERVATION SUMMITS - Bags–duffel ✫ - National Wildlife Federation

NATIONS HISTORY - Furniture - Vaughan Furniture Co. Inc.

NATIONS PRIDE - Food products - Nations Pride Distributors Inc.

NATION'S TREASURES - Christmas tree ornaments - Jackson-Pacific, Inc.

NATION'S WIPER SOURCE, THE - Paper–toweling - IFC Disposables, Inc.

NATIONWIDE - Gloves–safety - Midwest Glove Co.

NATIONWIDE - Mobile homes - Nationwide Homes Inc.

NATIONWIDE - Paper–writing - Champion International Corp.

NATIONWIDE - Pennants - Flags International Inc.

NATIONWIDE BLACK RADIO - Recording label - CDE Records & Tapes

NATIONWIDE EXTERMINATING - Pesticides–household - Nationwide Chemical Products, Inc. (Nationwide Exterminating Div.)

NATIONWIDE HOMES - Mobile homes - Nationwide Homes Inc.

NATIVA - Jewelry - Deborah West Accessory Art Collection

NATIVE - See **GARDNER'S**

NATIVE - Food products ✫ - Universal/Univis Inc.

NATIVE ACCENTS - Wood products - BARD International, Inc.

✫ = Now out of production

NATIVE AMERICA - Apparel–men's - Alps Sportswear Manufacturing Co.

NATIVE AMERICA - Bird cages - John E. Potente

NATIVE AMERICA - Wallpaper ☆ - David Merritt Handprints Inc.

NATIVE AMERICAN - Luggage - New England Leather Accessories

NATIVE AMERICAN FISH & WILDLIFE SOCIETY - Apparel–athletic - Native American Fish & Wildlife Society

NATIVE BOTANICAL CO., THE - Lip balms - Brian Toogood

NATIVE COLLECTION - Dinnerware ☆ - Corning Inc.

NATIVE DIAMOND - Games - International Gamco, Inc.

NATIVE FILE EXCHANGE - Computer software - Essential Technical Services, Inc.

NATIVE FROG WAX COOL - Surfboard wax - Eurosurf Inc.

NATIVE GAME CO., THE - Publisher's imprints - Native Game Co., Inc.

NATIVE GROUND - Fabrics - Interface, Inc.

NATIVE HABITAT PLANET EARTH - Apparel stores–sports - Amy Zhang Industries Inc.

NATIVE INSTINCTS - Ophthalmic goods - Foremost Optical Products

NATIVE INTERNATIONALE - Luggage - Euro Surf, Inc.

NATIVE KJALII FOODS - Food products - Jeremy Bret

NATIVE LEGEND TEA - Teas–herbal - Enrich Corp.

N8TIVE NITS - Apparel–women's - N8tive Nits Inc.

NATIVE PACIFIC - Apparel and accessories - Maureen D. Manos

NATIVE S-U-N - Apparel and accessories - Rock N' Roll Custom Screened Shirts, Inc.

NATIVE SON - Agricultural products - Anthony Vineyards, Inc.

NATIVE TRAILS - Greeting cards - Amberley Greeting Card Co.

NATIVE WEST - Frames–picture - Coan Woodworks, Inc.

NATIVE WOOD - Giftware - Native Wood Products Inc.

NATIVEARTH - Cosmetics - For Earth's Sake Inc.

NATIVEGRAINS - Breads–mixes - Nativegrains, Inc.

NATIVEGRAINS OF FOSSTON IN MINNESOTA - Breads–mixes - Nativegrains, Inc.

NATIVELANDS - Apparel and accessories - Orange You Glad Inc.

NATIVITY-ART - Greeting cards ☆ - Nu-Art Inc.

NATIVITY VIGNETTES - Giftware - Lenox, Inc.

NATO - Games - Avalon Hill Game Co.

NATO - Recording label - Jazz Composer's Orchestra Association Inc.

NATORI - Apparel–women's - Natori Co. Inc.

NATORI - Perfumes - Avon Products, Inc.

NATORI II - Apparel–women's - Natori Co. Inc.

NATORIOUS - Apparel and accessories - Natori Co. Inc.

NATRA - Pet products - Natra Pet Inc.

NATRA-BIO - Health care products - Botanical Laboratories Inc.

NATRA DERM - Pet products - Natra Pet Inc.

NATRA DERM PLUS - Pet products - Natra Pet Inc.

NATRA FLEA - Pet products - Natra Pet Inc.

NATRA GROOM - Pet products - Natra Pet Inc.

NATRA-LOOK - Archery targets - McKenzie Supply

NATRA PET - Pet products - Natra Pet Inc.

NATRA PET MITE MIST - Pet products - Natra Pet Inc.

NATRA PET WAY - Pet products - Natra Pet Inc.

NATRA TASTE - Food products - Cumberland Packing Corp.

NATRA TASTE - Sweeteners–artificial - Stadt Corp.

NATRAJ - Floor coverings–carpet and rugs - American of Lynchburg, Inc.

NATRAPEL - Repellent - Tender Corp.

NATRASOLVE - Cleaning preparations - S.C. Johnson & Son, Inc.

NATRECOR - Pharmaceutical preparations - Scios Nova Inc.

NATREL PLUS - Deodorants–personal - Gillette Co.

NATREX - Pharmaceutical preparations - Mikeco., Inc.

NATRI-PAS - Pharmaceutical preparations ☆ - Glenwood LLC

NATRICE - Licorice - Finn Foods

NATRIUM - Chemical preparations - Natrium Products, Inc.

NATROGEN - Pharmaceutical preparations - Bennett Pharmaceutical Corp.

NATROL HIGH, A - Vitamins and nutritional supplements - Natrol, Inc.

NATROLEUM - Fireplace logs–treated - Benjamin R. Ross

NATRUM - Vitamins and nutritional supplements - Garcoa Labs/Vitamin Classics

NATSCO - Cookies - Commerce Foods Inc.

NATSUME - Artists' materials - Andrews/Nelson/Whitehead

NATTI - Yarn ☆ - National Spinning Co., Inc.

NATTY THREADS - Apparel and accessories - Jerman Design Inc.

NATUARY, THE - Aquariums–household - Lawrence I. Wechsler

NATUR - Apparel and accessories - Wongas International Textiles, Ltd.

NATUR - Beverages–alcohol ☆ - Cedar Hill Wine Co.

NATUR - Fabrics–terrycloth - Guilford Mills, Inc.

NATUR-CLEAN - Soap - Natural Foods Inc.

NATUR-EARTH - Vitamins and nutritional supplements - Lifeline, Inc.

NATUR-ESCENT - Lighting equipment ☆ - Duro-Lite Lamps Inc.

NATUR PERLE - Cigars - Gesty Trading & Manufacturing Corp.

NATURA - Cosmetics - Spornette International, Inc.

NATURA - Deodorizers - Forty Fifty Three Corp.

NATURA - Fishing lures - Uncle Josh Bait Co.

NATURA - Floor coverings–carpet and rugs - Cumberland Mills Inc.

NATURA - Floor coverings–carpet and rugs - Foreign Accents

NATURA - Pet products - Virbac, Inc.

NATURA - Plant-hanger bracket ☆ - Interdesign, Inc.

NATURA - Skin care products - Avon Products, Inc.

NATURA - Tiles–ceramic - Florida Tile Industries, Inc.

NATURA - Yarn - National Spinning Co., Inc.

NATURA CHAR - Vitamins and nutritional supplements - Char-Care Inc.

NATURA CLEANSE - Skin care products - Pharmagel Corp.

NATURA CURL - Hair coloring preparations - Stylors Inc.

NATURA DESIGNER SERIES - Tiles–ceramic - Florida Tile Industries, Inc.

NATURA GRANITE SERIES - Tiles–ceramic - Florida Tile Industries, Inc.

NATURA HAYASHI - Hair-care products - Hayashi for Hair Inc.

NATURA LATCH HOOK KITS - Thread - Caron International Inc.

NATURA-LUX - Lighting equipment - Penn-Plax, Inc.

NATURA MEDICA - Vitamins and nutritional supplements - Dolisos America, Inc.

NATURA QUALITY YARN - Yarn - National Spinning Co., Inc.

NATURA SEAWEED - Hair care products - Hayashi for Hair Inc.

NATURA SEAWEED RECONSTRUCTOR - Hair care products - Hayashi for Hair Inc.

NATURA SHAPE - Hair care products - Hayashi for Hair Inc.

NATURA VOLUME + - Hair care products - Hayashi for Hair Inc.

NATURA-WEAVE - Hair care products - Alfa Services USA Inc.

NATURABATH - Skin care products ☆ - ABRA Inc.

NATURACTIVES - Vitamins and nutritional supplements - Starwest Botanicals Inc.

NATURADE - Health care products - Naturade Inc.

NATURADE-ALOE VERA 80 - Health care products - Naturade Inc.

NATURAFED - Health care products ☆ - Pacific BioLogic Inc.

NATURAFED PLUS - Health care products - Pacific BioLogic Inc.

NATURAL - Apparel and accessories - Foster Industries, Inc.

NATURAL - Apparel and accessories - Grieder Sales and Brokerage, Inc.

NATURAL - Cleaning preparations ☆ - Paxon Manufacturing Co.

NATURAL - Computer peripheral equipment - Microsoft Corp.

NATURAL - Floor coverings–carpet and rugs ☆ - Daltonian Carpet & Cushion Inc.

NATURAL - Hair care products - Waverly Beauty Products

NATURAL - Health care products - Heritage Store Inc.

NATURAL - Infant product - Evenflo Co.

NATURAL - Pencils - Faber-Castell Corp.

NATURAL - Pet products - Classic Products

NATURAL - Pet products - The Crab Connection

NATURAL - Rugbacking - Rug-Hold Co., Inc.

NATURAL - Skateboards - Jason L. Austin, Jr. & Mike F. Metzger

NATURAL 3D DESIGN - Computer software - Metatools, Inc.

NATURAL 100 - Cereal - Sovex Foods, Inc.

NATURAL ACCENT - Mulch - GSO America, Inc.

NATURAL ACCENTS - Cosmetics - Intellectual Property Holding Co.

NATURAL ACCENTS - Cosmetics - Maybelline Co.

NATURAL ACCENTS - Dinnerware–glass - Lenox, Inc.

NATURAL ACCENTS - Fabrics–tapestry - Coloroll Inc.

NATURAL ACCESS ALL-TERRAIN WHEELCHAIRS-INNOVATIVE PRODUCTS - Wheelchairs - John Egan

NATURAL ACTION - Apparel–women's ☆ - Q-T Foundations Co. Inc.

NATURAL ACTION - Bottles–plastic - Johnson & Johnson

NATURAL ACTION - Infant product - Playtex Beauty Care, Inc.

NATURAL AFFINITY - Postmastectomy breast form - Coloplast Corp.

NATURAL AIR - Cosmetics - Naturelle, Inc.

NATURAL-AIRE - Cosmetics - Revlon-Realistic Professional Products Inc.

NATURAL ALTERNATIVE - Pet products - Brewers Yeast Specialist

NATURAL ALTERNATIVES - Pharmaceutical preparations - Pro Cap

NATURAL AMERICAN SPIRIT - Tobacco products - Santa Fe Natural Tobacco Co.

NATURAL & NICE - Hair care products - Wella Corp. (Consumer Products Div.)

NATURAL ANIMAL - Pet products - Natural Animal Health Products, Inc.

NATURAL ANIMAL - Pet products - Natural Animal Nutrition Inc.

NATURAL ANIMAL - Pharmaceutical preparations - Wayne Ellison

NATURAL ANIMALS - Glassware–household ☆ - Fenton Art Glass Co.

NATURAL APPLE - Cosmetics - Naturelle, Inc.
NATURAL ARCHITECT - Computer software - Software AG of North America, Inc.
NATURAL ART - Surfboards - Natural Art, Inc.
NATURAL ASSETS - Neckties ☆ - Randa Corp.
NATURAL ATTACHMENTS - Hobby kits - JCA, Inc.
NATURAL BABY - Baby product - Aubrey Organics, Inc.
NATURAL BABY - Dolls - Doll Factory, Inc.
NATURAL BACK, THE - Pillows - Natural Back
NATURAL BALANCE - Skin care products - Sally Beauty Co., Inc.
NATURAL BALANCE - Vitamins and nutritional supplements - Natural Balance, Inc.
NATURAL BALANCE - Vitamins and nutritional supplements - Caroline Owens
NATURAL BALANCE - Water purification systems - Fiberstars, Inc.
NATURAL BASICS - Health care products - Smith & Vandiver, Inc.
NATURAL BATH - Bathroom accessories - Carolina Designs Ltd.
NATURAL BEAUTIES - Frames—eyeglass ☆ - Universal/Univis Inc.
NATURAL BEAUTY - Apparel—women's - Wacoal America Inc.
NATURAL BEAUTY - Dishes—china - Mikasa Co.
NATURAL BEAUTY - Floor coverings—carpet and rugs - Catalina Carpet Mills Inc.
NATURAL BEAUTY - Floor coverings—carpet and rugs ☆ - Downs Carpet Co. Inc.
NATURAL BEAUTY - Giftware - Delfino Products Inc.
NATURAL BEAUTY - Hair care products ☆ - Carson Products Co.
NATURAL BEAUTY - Pajamas—women's - Bentley Lingerie, Inc.
NATURAL BEAUTY - Stains - Servistar Corp.
NATURAL BEAUTY FENCE - Fencing—wood - Natbefco Inc.
NATURAL BEAUTY FROM WITHIN - Vitamins and nutritional supplements - Marine Biotherapies
NATURAL BEAUTY INDIGO - Apparel and accessories - Bentley Lingerie, Inc.
NATURAL BEDROOM, THE - Bedding—linen - Eliana Judith Jantz
NATURAL BEGINNINGS - Skin care products - Hewitt Soap Co., Inc.
NATURAL BEHAVIOR MANAGEMENT SYSTEM, THE - Veterinary medical equipment - Ameri-Pet Inc.
NATURAL BLACKBERY - Lipsticks - Honey & Spice Toiletries
NATURAL BLEND - Durable-press cotton fabrics - Cotton Inc.
NATURAL BLEND - Siding - Heartland Building Products Inc.
NATURAL BLUE DIAMOND ALMONDS - Nuts - California Almond Growers Exchange
NATURAL BLUSH - Cosmetics - Almay Inc.
NATURAL BODY - Apparel and accessories - Bradley Weller Buck
NATURAL BODY - Hair care products - Vancar Research Inc.
NATURAL BODY HIGHLIGHTER - Hair-care product - Aubrey Organics, Inc.
NATURAL BOUNCE - Hair care products - Helene Curtis Industries Inc.
NATURAL BREW - Paper - Rockline Industries Inc.
NATURAL BRUSH COLLECTION - Brushes - Rally Accessories, Inc.
NATURAL BRUSH-ON SATIN BLUSH - Cosmetics - Noxell Corp.
NATURAL BRUSH, THE - Brushes—paint - Min Hung Enterprise Co., Ltd.
NATURAL BUFF - Manicure preparations - W.E. Bassett Co.
NATURAL BUTTERY - Margarine - Nature's Hearth
NATURAL CANESUGAR UNREFINED - Sugar—granulated, refined, or powdered - Montgomery Sugar
NATURAL CARE - Health-care product - Iodent Co.
NATURAL CARIBBEAN - Seafood products—fresh or frozen - Bluewater Aquaculture, Inc.
NATURAL CATHETER, THE - Medical apparatus - Rochester Medical Corp.
NATURAL CHAMBERS - Pillows - Pacific Coast Feather Co.
NATURAL CHARM - Cosmetics - Pavcom, Inc.
NATURAL CHARM - Floor coverings—carpet and rugs - Queen Carpet Corp.
NATURAL CHEMISTRY - Water purification systems - Natural Chemistry Inc.
NATURAL CHILD CARE - Infant product - Natural Child Care Inc.
NATURAL CHOICE - Cream - Vendors Supply Co., Inc.
NATURAL CHOICE - Cups—plastic - Nyman Manufacturing Co.
NATURAL CHOICE - Dog food - Nutro Products, Inc.
NATURAL CHOICE - Health care products ☆ - Rockline Industries Inc.
NATURAL CHOICE - Hosiery - Renfro Corp.
NATURAL CHOICE - Meat products—poultry - Jennie-O Foods, Inc.
NATURAL CHOICE - Snack foods - Frontier Foods International
NATURAL CHOICE - Water purification systems - Natural Choices Inc.
NATURAL CHOICE ORGANIC CERTIFIED - Fruits and vegetables - Nationwide Produce Co.
NATURAL CHOICE, THE - Dairy products - Foremost Farms USA
NATURAL CHOICE, THE - Insulating materials - International Cellulose Corp.
NATURAL CHOICE, THE - Molasses - Mid-Eastern Molasses Co. Inc.
NATURAL CHOICE, THE - Flooring—hardwood - Triangle Pacific Corp.

NATURAL CHOICES - Vitamins and nutritional supplements - Swanson Health Products, Inc.
NATURAL CLASSIC - Floor coverings—carpet and rugs - Mohawk Carpet Corp.
NATURAL CLASSICS - Cosmetics - Merle Norman Cosmetics
NATURAL CLEAR - Chemical preparations - Great Lakes Biochemical Co., Inc.
NATURAL COLLAGEN COMPLEX - Cosmetics - Revlon Consumer Products Corp.
NATURAL COLLECTION, THE - Pillows - Pillowtex Corp.
NATURAL COLORS - Aquariums—household - Jungle Laboratories Corp.
NATURAL COMFORT - Mattresses - Spring Air Co.
NATURAL COMFORTS - House furnishings - Kellwood Co.
NATURAL CONNECTION - Computer software - Software AG of North America, Inc.
NATURAL CONTROL - Hair care products - Sebring Products Inc.
NATURAL CORD - Floor coverings - Bellbridge Carpets
NATURAL COUNTRY - Juices - Natural Country Farms Inc.
NATURAL COVER - Cosmetics - L S Cosmetics Inc.
NATURAL CRADLE - Furniture - Infant Advantage
NATURAL CURL - Hair curlers - Helene Curtis Industries Inc.
NATURAL-CURV - Knives ☆ - United Cutlery Corp.
NATURAL CUSHION - Shoe accessories - Leif J. Ostberg Inc.
NATURAL CUTS - Vegetables—frozen ☆ - Lamb-Weston, Inc.
NATURAL CYCLE CLUB - T-shirts - NCC
NATURAL DECAF - Coffee - Cain's Coffee Co.
NATURAL DECORATIONS - Fabrics - Natural Decorations Inc.
NATURAL DELITES - Pet products ☆ - American Cat Emporium
NATURAL DENTIST, THE - Mouthwashes - Victor Zeines
NATURAL DESIGN - Floor coverings—carpet and rugs - Design Materials, Inc.
NATURAL DIMENSIONS - Wallpaper - Maharam Vertical Surfaces
NATURAL E - Food products ☆ - Chex Co.
NATURAL EFFECTS - Skin care products - Marianna Imports, Inc.
NATURAL EFFECTS I - Wallpaper - J. Josephson, Inc.
NATURAL EFX - Vitamins and nutritional supplements - Natural Efx, Inc.
NATURAL ELEGANCE - Floor coverings—carpet and rugs - Evans-Black Carpet Mills
NATURAL ELEGANCE - Flowers—artificial - Winward International
NATURAL ELEGANCE - Pet products - Carfore Ltd.
NATURAL ELEGANCE - Skin care products - Kiwi Brands, Inc.
NATURAL ELEGANCE - Wallcoverings - Cork Products Co. Inc.
NATURAL ELEGANCE - Wallpaper - Pageant Wallpaper Corp.
NATURAL ELEGANCE - Wallpaper ☆ - Pickhardt & Siebert USA Inc.
NATURAL ELEMENTS - Floor coverings—carpet and rugs - Dan River Inc.
NATURAL ENEMY - Garden equipment - Dalen Products Inc.
NATURAL ENERGY - Beverages ☆ - Veryfine Products, Inc.
NATURAL ENERGY - Dietary supplement - Action Product Marketing
NATURAL ENERGY - Hair care products - GOLDWELL Cosmetics (USA) Inc.
NATURAL ESPECIAL - Shampoos - Zerran International Corp.
NATURAL ESSENCE - Deodorizers - R.B. Howell Co.
NATURAL ESSENCE - Soap - Delagar
NATURAL ESSENTIALS - Apparel - Jansport Inc.
NATURAL EXCHANGE BY ALEXANDER LLOYD - Apparel and accessories - JBI, Inc.
NATURAL EXPOSURES - Photographic equipment - Daniel J. Cox
NATURAL EXPRESSIONS - Wallpaper - H & S Sales Inc.
NATURAL EXPRESSIONS - Wallpaper - Wall Fashion Inc.
NATURAL FACE GLOW - Cosmetics - Dr. Babor Natural Cosmetics
NATURAL FACIAL LIFT - Skin tightening cream - Naturechem International
NATURAL FINISH - Hair care products - Matrix Essentials, Inc.
NATURAL FIRE - Sporting goods ☆ - Gold Eagle/Arnold Palmer
NATURAL FIRE - Stoves ☆ - Earth Stove Inc.
NATURAL-FIT - Jewelry - Astoria Jewelry Manufacturing Co., Inc.
NATURAL FLARE - Cosmetics - Beautee Sense Inc.
NATURAL FLARE - Floor coverings—carpet and rugs ☆ - Walter Carpet Mills
NATURAL FLATS - Sporting goods - Woods & Brooks, Ltd.
NATURAL FLEX - Footwear - E.S. Originals, Inc.
NATURAL FLEX - Gloves—rubber - Mapa Pioneer Corp.
NATURAL FLEX - Gloves—work - Pioneer Industrial Products Co.
NATURAL FLEX - Nipples—rubber - Gerber Products Co.
NATURAL FLOW - Grain products—corn - Agco Corp.
NATURAL FLOWER - Craft supplies - Ziabicki Import Co.
NATURAL FOCUS - Lenses—magnifying - Community Vision Clinic
NATURAL FOOD STORE - Margarine - Kettle Foods
NATURAL FOODS VEGETARIAN CUISINE - Video production - Ten Talents Distributors

☆ = Now out of production

NATURAL FOOT SHAPE - Footwear–athletic ☆ - Prince Sports Group, Inc.

NATURAL FORMATIONS - Furniture - Synsor Corp.

NATURAL FORMULA - Health care products - Acis, Inc.

NATURAL FRUIT DELIGHTS - Food products - Liberty Orchards Co., Inc.

NATURAL GAS FOR VEHICLES - Natural gas - Mountain Fuel Supply Co.

NATURAL GIRL - Frames–eyeglass ☆ - Universal/Univis Inc.

NATURAL GLO - Animal feeds - Wolcott Farms Inc.

NATURAL GLORY FASHIONS - Apparel–men's - Perm Inc.

NATURAL GLOW - Cosmetics - Del Pharmaceuticals, Inc.

NATURAL GOLD - Popcorn ☆ - Weaver Popcorn Co. Inc.

NATURAL GOLD - Shampoos - Kim Laube & Co. Inc.

NATURAL GOLF - Golfing equipment - Natural Golf Corp.

NATURAL GOODNESS FROM CALIFORNIA - Food products - Hickory Farms, Inc.

NATURAL GOURMET - Oils–edible - Liberty Natural Products

NATURAL GRACE - Health care products - Himalayan Laboratories

NATURAL GREEN LEAF BRAND - Teas - Prestige Chinese Teas Co.

NATURAL GRILL FLAVOR - Spices and extracts - Kraft Food Ingredients Corp.

NATURAL GUARD - Fertilizers - Voluntary Purchasing Group Inc.

NATURAL HABITAT - Housewares - May Department Stores Co.

NATURAL HABITAT - Wallpaper - James Seeman Studios

NATURAL HARMONY - Wallpaper ☆ - ICI Americas Inc.

NATURAL HARVEST - Food products - Jewel Food Stores Inc.

NATURAL HARVEST - Jewelry - Titusville Dairy Products Co.

NATURAL HEALTH CARE PRODUCTS - Health care products ☆ - Nature's Herbs

NATURAL HEALTH PILLOW, THE - Pillows - Pacific Coast Feather Co.

NATURAL HEARTH - Bread - Roush Products Co., Inc.

NATURAL HENNA LIFE - Hair care products ☆ - Freeman Cosmetics Corp.

NATURAL HERBAL - Pet collars - Natural Research People, Inc.

NATURAL HIGH - Juices - Natural High Products

NATURAL HIGH-FIVE - Calendars - Manning Enterprises

NATURAL HISTORY AND GUIDEBOOK - Publisher's imprints - Syracuse University Press

NATURAL HOLD - Hair care products - Nexxus Products Co.

NATURAL HONEY - Hair care products - Revlon Consumer Products Corp.

NATURAL HORIZONS - Wallpaper ☆ - Mirage Wallcovering Co.

NATURAL HORIZONS III - Wallpaper ☆ - Mirage Wallcovering Co.

NATURAL HORIZONS IV - Wallpaper - Mirage Wallcovering Co.

NATURAL HUES - Tiles–ceramic - Quarry Tile Co.

NATURAL ICE - Beverages–malt - Anheuser-Busch Companies Inc.

NATURAL ICE - Medicated lip balms - Mentholatum Co.

NATURAL IMAGE - Frames–eyeglass - Pathway Optical Prods.

NATURAL IMAGE - Hair care products - Natural Image Industries Inc.

NATURAL IMAGE BOTANICALS - Incense - Natural Image Botanicals Inc.

NATURAL IMAGES - Dinnerware - Corning Inc.

NATURAL INTELLIGENCE - Computer software - Ricorso

NATURAL INTRIGUE - Floor coverings–carpet and rugs - Downs Carpet Co. Inc.

NATURAL ISSUE - Apparel–men's - Supreme International Corp.

NATURAL JUICES - Juices - Dellwood Foods, Inc.

NATURAL KEYBOARD - Computer peripheral equipment - Microsoft Corp.

NATURAL KIDS - Jeans–men's - Salant/Manhattan Industries

NATURAL KNIT - Fabrics–broadcloth - Desire Mills Co. Inc.

NATURAL LABS - Vitamins and nutritional supplements - American Supplement Technologies

NATURAL LASAGNA CHEESE, THE - Cheese - Sargento Cheese Co. Inc.

NATURAL LASH - Cosmetics - Noxell Corp.

NATURAL LASHDARKENER - Cosmetics - Noxell Corp.

NATURAL LATCH - Hobby kits - Caron International Inc.

NATURAL LEAF - Tobacco–chewing or smoking - Swedish Math North America Inc.

NATURAL LEAGUE, THE - Apparel and accessories - Salamander

NATURAL LEMON - Coffee - Tetley Inc.

NATURAL LIFE - Skin care products - Leiner Health Products Inc.

NATURAL LIFE - Wallpaper - Warner Co.

NATURAL LIFE ADULT DOG FORMULA - Pet products - Natural Life Pet Products Inc.

NATURAL LIFE C-FLEX CANINE VITAMIN SUPPLEMENT - Pet products - Natural Life Pet Products Inc.

NATURAL LIFE CONDITION DOG FORMULA - Pet products - Natural Life Pet Products Inc.

NATURAL LIFE FELINE ADULT FORMULA - Pet products - Natural Life Pet Products Inc.

NATURAL LIFE FELINE CHICKEN MENU - Pet products - Natural Life Pet Products Inc.

NATURAL LIFE FELINE MEAT MENU - Pet products - Natural Life Pet Products Inc.

NATURAL LIFE HEALTHY SNACKS DOG BISCUITS BAKED - Pet products - Natural Life Pet Products Inc.

NATURAL LIFE HEALTHY SNACKS DOG BISCUITS ORIGINAL - Pet products - Natural Life Pet Products Inc.

NATURAL LIFE KITTEN FELINE FORMULA - Pet products - Natural Life Pet Products Inc.

NATURAL LIFE LAMADERM DOG BISCUITS - Pet products - Natural Life Pet Products Inc.

NATURAL LIFE LAMADERM DOG FORMULA - Pet products - Natural Life Pet Products Inc.

NATURAL LIFE LAMADERM FELINE FORMULA - Pet products - Natural Life Pet Products Inc.

NATURAL LIFE LAMADERM PUPPY FORMULA - Pet products - Natural Life Pet Products Inc.

NATURAL LIFE PUPPY DOG FORMULA - Pet products - Natural Life Pet Products Inc.

NATURAL LIFE SENIOR DOG FORMULA - Pet products - Natural Life Pet Products Inc.

NATURAL LIFE VEGETARIAN DOG FORMULA - Pet products - Natural Life Pet Products Inc.

NATURAL LIFESTYLES - Cooking equipment–household - Nordic Ware

NATURAL LIGHT - Beverages–malt - Anheuser-Busch Companies Inc.

NATURAL LIGHT - Skin care products - Vivant, Inc.

NATURAL LIGHTS - Cigarettes - Nat Sherman, Inc.

NATURAL LINE - Hearing aids - Rexton Inc.

NATURAL LINE - Novelty items ☆ - Arthur Court Designs Inc.

NATURAL LINENS & WEAVES - Wallpaper - Wallpaper Imports Inc.

NATURAL-LITE - Candles - Empire Manufacturing Co.

NATURAL LIVING - Apparel and accessories - Tropical Sportswear International Corp.

NATURAL LIVING - Pharmaceutical preparations - Natural Living, Inc.

NATURAL LIVING - Wallpaper ☆ - Mayfair Wallcoverings

NATURAL LIVING 4 - Wallpaper ☆ - Mayfair Wallcoverings

NATURAL LOOK - Fabrics–tapestry ☆ - Coloroll Inc.

NATURAL LOOK - Hair care products - Almay Inc.

NATURAL LOOK - Wallpaper - Hunting Valley Prints

NATURAL LOOK 4 - Fabrics–tapestry - Coloroll Inc.

NATURAL LUSTRE - Lipsticks - Prince Matchabelli

NATURAL MAGIC - Deodorizers - Osmegen Inc.

NATURAL MAID - Juices - Ludford Fruit Products Inc.

NATURAL MAN - Apparel–men's ☆ - Jantzen Inc.

NATURAL MAN - Hair care products - Electronic Hair Styling, Inc.

NATURAL MANICURE, THE - Fingernail polish - Jonel Inc.

NATURAL MARROW BONE - Dog food - Fieldhaven, Inc.

NATURAL MEDICINE CENTER - Vitamins and nutritional supplements - King Bio Pharmaceuticals, Inc.

NATURAL MOIST - Cosmetics - Dr. Babor Natural Cosmetics

NATURAL MOISTURE - Hair care products ☆ - Tressa, Inc.

NATURAL MOISTURE FACTOR - Hair care products - Helene Curtis Industries Inc.

NATURAL MOTHER - Health care products - Evenflo Co.

NATURAL MOVES - Hosiery–women's - Sara Lee Corp.

NATURAL MYSTIQUE - Floor coverings–carpet and rugs - Downs Carpet Co. Inc.

NATURAL NAIL FILE - Emery products - Ramona Enterprises Inc.

NATURAL NAILS - Artificial fingernails - International Beauty Design, Inc.

NATURAL NECTAR - Ice cream - Natural Nectar Corp.

NATURAL NEEDS - Vitamins and nutritional supplements - Pay Less Drug Stores Northwest Inc.

NATURAL NEW DIMENSION - Computer software - Software AG of North America, Inc.

NATURAL NUTRITION CENTER - Vitamins and nutritional supplements - Natural Nutrition Center Inc.

NATURAL NYLON - Fabrics–nylon - Lortex, Inc.

NATURAL OILEGGS - Fishing lures - Brown Bear Bait Co.

NATURAL ONE, THE - Hair care products - Alberto-Culver Co.

NATURAL ORDER OF THINGS - Infant product - Marks Designs

NATURAL OVENS OF MANITOWOC - Oats–rolled or meal ☆ - Natural Ovens of Manitowoc Inc.

NATURAL PAK - Fruits and vegetables - Natural Pak Produce Inc.

NATURAL PASSAGES - Floor coverings–carpet and rugs ☆ - J and J Industries Inc.

☆ = Now out of production

NATURAL PEOPLE - Vitamins and nutritional supplements - Anthony Didonato

NATURAL PERFORMER - Apparel and accessories - Tropical Garment Manufacturing Co.

NATURAL PET-PALS - Pet products - Florida East Atlantic Pet Products, Inc.

NATURAL PH - Hair care products - Image Laboratories, Inc.

NATURAL PHASES - Pharmaceutical preparations - Boiron Inc.

NATURAL PILSNER - Beverages–malt - Anheuser-Busch Companies Inc.

NATURAL PINK - Nail care products - Orly International Inc.

NATURAL PLAN - Pet food - Schell & Kampeter, Inc.

NATURAL PLEASURES - Pillows - Pacific Coast Feather Co.

NATURAL PLEASURES - Snack foods - Fairmont Snacks Group Inc.

NATURAL PLUS - Apparel–women's - Cupid Foundations Inc.

NATURAL POPS - Candy ☆ - Tootsie Roll Industries, Inc.

NATURAL POWER - Cleaning preparations - Tifco Industries Inc.

NATURAL POWER - Vitamins and nutritional supplements ☆ - Mueller Sports Medicine Inc.

NATURAL POWER OF ENDORPHINS - Food supplements - Biotech Health Research Corp.

NATURAL PREFERENCES - Breads - Rubschlager Baking Corp.

NATURAL PRINTS - Wallpaper - Sherburne Ewing Wallcovering Co.

NATURAL PRINTS & TEXTURES - Wallpaper - Sherburne Ewing Wallcovering Co.

NATURAL PROGESTERONE BODY CREAM - Vitamins and nutritional supplements - Vitamin Research Products Inc.

NATURAL QUERY - Computer software - FairCom Corp.

NATURAL RADIANCE - Cosmetics - Avon Products, Inc.

NATURAL REFLECTIONS - Cosmetics ☆ - New England Natural Sponge, Inc.

NATURAL REFLECTIONS - Floor coverings - Bruce Hardwood Floors

NATURAL REFLECTIONS - Flooring–hardwood - Triangle Pacific Corp.

NATURAL REFLECTIONS - Mirrors ☆ - Interdesign, Inc.

NATURAL RELIEF-1222 - Pharmaceutical preparations - Mikeco., Inc.

NATURAL REMEDY - Soap ☆ - Carolina Designs Ltd.

NATURAL RESOURCES - Health care products - Quality Formulation Laboratories Inc.

NATURAL RESOURCES - Wallpaper ☆ - Wallquest, Inc.

NATURAL RESOURCES BY GOSSAMER WINGS - Wallpaper ☆ - Old Deerfield Fabrics Inc.

NATURAL RESOURCES II - Wallpaper ☆ - Imperial Wallcoverings, Inc.

NATURAL RESOURCES MELATONIN - Vitamins and nutritional supplements - Scandinavian Natural Health & Beauty Products, Inc.

NATURAL RESPONSE - Mattresses - King Koil Licensing Co., Inc.

NATURAL RESPONSE TO THE SUN, A - Outlook Eyewear Co.

NATURAL RESULT - Hair care products ☆ - Roberts Research Laboratories, Inc.

NATURAL RICE - Wallcoverings - Stretchwall Fabrics Co.

NATURAL RIVER - Apparel and accessories - Horizon Screen Printing, Inc.

NATURAL ROCKS GOURMENT SPRING WATER ICE - Ice - Natural Rocks Spring Water Ice Co. Inc.

NATURAL RUSH - Honey - Alveole Foods

NATURAL SCIENCE BOOK CLUB, THE - Publisher's imprints - MacMillan Publishing Co. Inc.

NATURAL SCIENCE CORPORATION OF AMERICA - Chalk - Natural Science Corp. of America

NATURAL SCIENCE OF WATER PURITY, THE - Water purification systems - Fountainhead Technologies, Inc.

NATURAL SEAL PLUS - Waterproofing compounds - Behr Process Corp.

NATURAL SEASONS - Wallpaper ☆ - Wallquest, Inc.

NATURAL SEAT - Apparel stores–lingerie - Goddess Bra

NATURAL SELECT - Cheese - Kraft Foods, Inc.

NATURAL SELECT - Pet products - American Colloid Co.

NATURAL SELECTION - Floor coverings–carpet and rugs - Mohawk Carpet Corp.

NATURAL SELECTION - Floor coverings–carpet and rugs - Regal Rugs Inc.

NATURAL SELECTION FOODS - Fruits and vegetables - Earthbound Farms, Inc.

NATURAL SELECTIONS - Soap - David Reynolds

NATURAL SELECTIONS COVENTRY GARDENS - Cosmetics - David Reynolds

NATURAL SEX - Vitamins and nutritional supplements - Life Extension Foundation

NATURAL SEX FOR MEN - Vitamins and nutritional supplements - Life Extension Foundation

NATURAL SEX FOR WOMEN - Vitamins and nutritional supplements - Life Extension Foundation

NATURAL SHADOW - Roofing shingles - GAF Corp.

NATURAL SHINE - Hair care products - Gefden International Inc.

NATURAL SLEEP - Pharmaceutical preparations - Life Extension Foundation

NATURAL SLEEP SYSTEM - Pillows - Pillowtex Corp.

NATURAL SLICES - Vegetables–frozen ☆ - Lamb-Weston, Inc.

NATURAL SLUMBER - Pillows ☆ - J.C. Penney Co., Inc.

NATURAL SMOOTHIE - Apparel and accessories - Strouse, Adler Co.

NATURAL SOLUTIONS - Cleaning preparations - Dan Kilgore

NATURAL SOLUTIONS - Pet products - Mason Distributing

NATURAL SOLUTIONS - Pet products - Natural Solutions

NATURAL SOLUTIONS - Vitamins and nutritional supplements - Natural Solutions

NATURAL SORB - Peat moss - Walker Environmental Products, Inc.

NATURAL SOURCES - Pet products - TK Enterprises

NATURAL SPLASH - Juices - Goodlife Beverages, Inc.

NATURAL SPLENDOR - Floor coverings–carpet and rugs ☆ - Walter Carpet Mills

NATURAL SPORT - Footwear - Brown Shoe Co.

NATURAL SPRING - Mattresses - Boyd Flotation, Inc.

NATURAL SPRINGS - Beverages–carbonated - BCB USA Corp.

NATURAL SPRINGS - Deodorizers - S.C. Johnson & Son, Inc.

NATURAL STATEMENT - Floor coverings–carpet and rugs - Wunda Weve Carpet Co.

NATURAL STONE AND CERAMIC W/C - Tiles–ceiling - Wallpaper Imports Inc.

NATURAL STONES - Wallpaper - I. Gottlieb & Associates

NATURAL STRESS - Pharmaceutical preparations - Republic Drug Co. Inc.

NATURAL STYLE - Pet products - ALPO Petfoods Inc.

NATURAL STYLING - Hair care products - Schwarzkopf Inc.

NATURAL SUN - Citrus product - Bordo Products Co.

NATURAL SURROUNDINGS - Wallpaper ☆ - Eisenhart Wallcoverings Co.

NATURAL S'WHEAT - Bakery products - American White Wheat Producers Association

NATURAL SYNERGY - Cosmetics ☆ - Prince Matchabelli

NATURAL TAMARI - Soy sauce - San-J International Inc.

NATURAL TEMPTATIONS - Candy - Edward & Sons Trading Co., Inc.

NATURAL TEXTURE - Artists' materials - Duncan Enterprises

NATURAL TEXTURES - Floor coverings–carpet and rugs - Design Materials, Inc.

NATURAL TEXTURES - Wallpaper ☆ - J.M. Lynne Co. Inc.

NATURAL, THE - Sponges - Acme Sponge & Chamois Co., Inc.

NATURAL, THE - Tape–adhesive - American Tape Co.

NATURAL, THE - Snack foods - Bagel Place, Inc.

NATURAL, THE - Floor coverings–carpet and rugs - Calladium & Marglen

NATURAL, THE - Manicure preparations - Creative Nail Design, Inc.

NATURAL, THE - Infant product - Leachco Inc.

NATURAL, THE - Lighting fixtures - Natural Skylights Inc.

NATURAL, THE - Brushes - Plaid Enterprises, Inc.

NATURAL, THE - Towels - Professional Towel Mills, Inc.

NATURAL, THE - Fertilizers - Seacoast Laboratories Inc.

NATURAL, THE - Chickens - Tidewater Marketing, Inc.

NATURAL, THE - Hair care products - Waverly Beauty Products

NATURAL TINT - Artists' materials - Duncan Enterprises

NATURAL TOUCH - Artists' materials - Duncan Enterprises

NATURAL TOUCH - Contact lenses - Pilkington Visioncare, Inc.

NATURAL TOUCH - Deodorizers - Nilodor Inc.

NATURAL TOUCH - Disposable washcloths - James River Corp.

NATURAL TOUCH - Floor coverings–carpet and rugs - Tuftex Carpet Mills, Inc.

NATURAL TOUCH - Food products - Worthington Foods Inc.

NATURAL TOUCH - Prosthetic apparatus - Nearly Me

NATURAL TOUCH - Sporting goods ☆ - Jantzen, Inc.

NATURAL TOUCH - Wallpaper ☆ - Mayfair Wallcoverings

NATURAL TOUCH 3 - Wallpaper ☆ - Mayfair Wallcoverings

NATURAL TOUCH VEGE - Frankfurters - Worthington Foods Inc.

NATURAL TRACKS - Apparel and accessories - Natural Tracks LLC

NATURAL TRANQUILITY - Vitamins and nutritional supplements - Marine Biotherapies

NATURAL TRANSITIONS - Furniture - Harden Furniture Co. Inc.

NATURAL TREASURES - Jewelry - Lucoral Co., Inc.

NATURAL TRIM - Vegetables–frozen ☆ - Lamb-Weston, Inc.

NATURAL TRIM - Vitamins and nutritional supplements - Natural Dietary Products, Inc.

NATURAL VETERINARY PHARMACEUTICAL CENTER - Vitamins and nutritional supplements - King Bio Pharmaceuticals, Inc.

NATURAL VIGOR - Fertilizers - Jonathan Green, Inc.

NATURAL VISION - Computer software - Software AG of North America, Inc.

NATURAL VISIONS - Recording label - The SOAR Corp.

☆ = Now out of production

NATURAL VUE - Lenses–optical - Titmus Optical, Inc.

NATURAL-WARE - Wood products ☆ - Knobler International Ltd.

NATURAL WARM MOISTURE - Humidifiers - Duracraft Corp.

NATURAL WAY - Cereal - Natural Way Mills

NATURAL WEALTH - Vitamins and nutritional supplements - Natural Wealth Nutrition Corp.

NATURAL WELLNESS - Recording label - J.R. Andorin, Inc.

NATURAL WHIRL - Salad dressings–bottled - John E. Cain Co.

NATURAL WHITES - Tiles–ceramic - H & R Johnson Inc.

NATURAL WONDER - Cosmetics - Revlon Consumer Products Corp.

NATURAL WONDER - Dryers–hair - Dazey Corp.

NATURAL WONDER ART & CRAFTY EYES - Cosmetics - Revlon Consumer Products Corp.

NATURAL WONDERS - Brooms - O-Cedar/Vining Household Products Co.

NATURAL WORLD - Vitamins and nutritional supplements - Locus L.P.

NATURALAMB - Health care products - Carter-Wallace, Inc.

NATURALAMP - Lamps ☆ - Interdesign, Inc.

NATURALASH - Cosmetics - Beautee Sense Inc.

NATURALCARE ALERT - Vitamins and nutritional supplements - Healthcare Laboratories, Inc.

NATURALCARE APPETITE - Vitamins and nutritional supplements - Healthcare Laboratories, Inc.

NATURALCARE INTERNAL CLEANSER - Vitamins and nutritional supplements - Healthcare Laboratories, Inc.

NATURALCARE MIGRAINE - Vitamins and nutritional supplements - Healthcare Laboratories, Inc.

NATURALCRISP - Food products - J.R. Simplot Co.

NATURALE - Floor coverings–carpet and rugs ☆ - Karastan-Bigelow Inc.

NATURALE 90 - Beverages–carbonated ☆ - Liberty Richter Inc.

NATURALE GRILLS - Fish–fresh or frozen - Market Day Corp.

NATURALEAF - Apparel and accessories - Avid Outdoor LLC

NATURALEAN - Vitamins and nutritional supplements - Desert Health Products, Inc.

NATURALGLO - Inks - Sun Chemical Corp.

NATURALIA - Health care products - Maison Naturelle USA Inc.

NATURALIFE - Apparel - Northwear Fashions (USA) Inc.

NATURALIFE LABORATORIES - Turbines–hydraulic ☆ - Paragon Laboratories

NATURALINE - Flowers–artificial - Caffco International

NATURALIS - Food products - Adamba Imports International Inc.

NATURALIST - Drafting supplies - Mayline/Hamilton

NATURALITE - Candles - Lumi-Lite Candle Co. Inc.

NATURALITE - Doors–garage ☆ - McKee Door, Inc.

NATURALITE - Lenses–magnifying - Midwest Labs, Inc.

NATURALIZER - Floor coverings–carpet and rugs - Barrett Carpet Mills Inc.

NATURALIZER - Footwear - Brown Shoe Co.

NATURALIZER - Mattresses - Land and Sky Manufacturing Inc.

NATURALLY - Crackers ☆ - Fort Biscuit Co.

NATURALLY - Craft supplies - Yarn Kits Inc.

NATURALLY - Floor coverings–carpet and rugs - Edgecrest Carpet Mills

NATURALLY - Floor coverings–carpet and rugs - Shaheen Carpet Mills

NATURALLY - Seasonings - Modern Products, Inc.

NATURALLY - Wallpaper ☆ - Mt. Diablo Hand Prints Inc.

NATURALLY BEAUTIFUL NAILS - Nail care products - Naturally Beautiful Nails, Inc.

NATURALLY BENEFICIAL - Skin care products - Beneficial International

NATURALLY BLONDE - Hair care products - Clairol Inc.

NATURALLY BOYS - Apparel–children's - May Department Stores Co.

NATURALLY CAJUN - Seasonings - Modern Products, Inc.

NATURALLY CRANBERRY - Juices - Apple and Eve Inc.

NATURALLY ENHANCE - Vitamins and nutritional supplements - Marine Biotherapies

NATURALLY EXOTIC - Health-care products ☆ - Aura Cacia Inc.

NATURALLY FARM FRESH - Eggs - Crystal Farms Inc.

NATURALLY FAT-FREE - Crackers ☆ - Fort Biscuit Co.

NATURALLY FEMININE - Deodorants–personal ☆ - Johnson & Johnson

NATURALLY FRESH - Food products - American Culinary Foods, Inc.

NATURALLY FRESH - Salad dressings–bottled - Eastern Foods, Inc.

NATURALLY FRESH - Sauces - Naturally Fresh

NATURALLY FRESH LITE - Salad dressings–bottled - Eastern Foods, Inc.

NATURALLY GLAMOROUS - Cosmetics - Revlon Consumer Products Corp.

NATURALLY GOOD - Food products - SPADA enterprise, ltd.

NATURALLY GOOD - Fruits and vegetables - Comstock Michigan Fruit

NATURALLY GOOD - Snack foods - Curtice-Burns Foods, Inc.

NATURALLY GOOD FROM NASOYA - Salad dressings–bottled - Nasoya Foods, Inc.

NATURALLY GREAT - Floor coverings–carpet and rugs ☆ - Cabin Crafts Carpets

NATURALLY HEALTHY HAIR - Hair care products - Hoffman Beauty & Barber Supply Co. Inc.

NATURALLY INSPIRED - Vitamins and nutritional supplements - United Vitamin Manufacturing Corp.

NATURALLY IT'S BEELER'S - Meat products - Beeler Brothers, Inc.

NATURALLY JUICEE'S - Vitamins and nutritional supplements - Naturally Vitamin Supplements Inc.

NATURALLY LEAN - Meat products–beef - Armour Swift-Eckrich

NATURALLY LITE - Vegetable oil - Creative Products Inc. of Rossville

NATURALLY ME - Apparel–women's ☆ - Bali Co. Inc.

NATURALLY MORE - Fabrics - More Corp.

NATURALLY NINE - Frozen dessert - Gise Creme Glace Inc.

NATURALLY NORTHWEST - Marmalade - Pacific Food Products Co.

NATURALLY PRECIOUS CRAFTSTONES - Jewelry - Stanislaus Imports, Inc.

NATURALLY PURE SUNNY HONEYSTIKS - Snack foods - Josef Rosenfeld

NATURALLY RELAXED - Cosmetics - Almay Inc.

NATURALLY RISING PIZZA - Pizza - Jack's Frozen Pizza Co.

NATURALLY SLENDER - Cheese - Northfield Foods Inc.

NATURALLY TEXAS - Leather goods - Texas Department of Agriculture

NATURALLY TOFU - Milk - Sovex Foods, Inc.

NATURALLY TRIM - Veterinary pharmaceutical preparations - Fit Pet, Inc.

NATURALLY VANILLA - Perfumes - Del Pharmaceuticals, Inc.

NATURALLY VITAMINS - Vitamins and nutritional supplements - Naturally Vitamin Supplements Inc.

NATURALLY WHITE - Shampoos - Image Laboratories, Inc.

NATURALLY YOU - Underwear and nightwear - Rago Foundations Inc. LLC

NATURALLY YOURS - Apparel and accessories - Alpha-Sylray Co., Inc.

NATURALLY YOURS - Cosmetics - Coe & Dru Inc.

NATURALLY YOURS - Floor coverings–carpet and rugs ☆ - Gulistan Carpet Inc.

NATURALLY YOURS - Yogurt - Mathis Dairy

NATURALOG - Fireplace logs–treated - Magee Co.

NATURALON - Bandages - Kendall Co.

NATURALS - Baby foods - Beech-Nut Nutrition Corp.

NATURALS - Cigar boxes–wood - Consolidated Cigar Corp.

NATURALS - Cigarettes - Nat Sherman, Inc.

NATURALS - Eyeglasses - Bausch & Lomb Inc.

NATURALS - Floor coverings–carpet and rugs - Galaxy Carpet Mills Inc.

NATURALS - Fruit drinks–bottled or canned - Coca-Cola Co.

NATURALS - Microwave cookware - Corning Inc.

NATURALS & FOILS - Wallpaper ☆ - Sanitas Wallcoverings

NATURALS BY COMARE, THE - Combs - Windmere Corp.

NATURALS BY SILVER TOE, THE - Hosiery - GAKM Resources Corp.

NATURALS, THE - Dog food - Concord Pet Products

NATURALS, THE - Floor coverings–carpet and rugs - Galaxy Carpet Mills Inc.

NATURALS, THE - Finishing agents - Masury Paint Co.

NATURALS, THE - Toys–stuffed - Princess Soft Toys

NATURALS, THE - Mats - Tenex Corp.

NATURALSCENT - Deodorizers - Lumi-Lite Candle Co. Inc.

NATURALSILK - Flowers–artificial - Caffco International

NATURALTONE - Drums–musical instruments - Eames Drum Co.

NATURALTUFF - Inks - Sun Chemical Corp.

NATURALUBE - Lubricating oils - Tosco Corp.

NATURALURE - Animal feeds - Arkansas County Seed Co., Inc.

NATURALWEAR - Prosthetic apparatus ☆ - Camp, Inc.

NATURALWEAR BY AMY - Apparel–children's - Biscayne Apparel International, Inc.

NATURALWEAVE - Wicking - Caffco International

NATURALYTE - Health care products - UBI

NATURALYTE - Pharmaceutical preparations - Dowelanco

NATURALYTE - Pharmaceutical preparations ☆ - Reese Chemical Co.

NATURALYTE INSECT CONTROL - Compost - Dowelanco

NATURAVA - Fruits and vegetables - Highland Hills Ventures, Inc.

NATURCARE - Cleaning preparations - Nature Plus, Inc.

NATURE - Puzzles - Milton Bradley Co.

NATURE - Skin care products - Avanza Corp.

NATURE - Skin care products ☆ - Nature Cosmetics

NATURE - Yarn ☆ - Tahki Imports Ltd.

NATURE 2 - Water purification systems - Fountainhead Technologies, Inc.

NATURE AND THE GAME - Apparel and accessories - Underground Screenprinting, Inc.

NATURE APPROVED - Bags–paper - Rocco D'Antonio

NATURE BABIES - Toys–stuffed - Dakin Inc.

NATURE BABY - Mattresses - California Concepts

NATURE BAKE - Bakery products - AVB, Inc.
NATURE BAY - Food products - Golden Dipt Co.
NATURE BLEND - Hair care products - Helene Curtis Industries Inc.
NATURE BLUE - Hair care products - Hemingway Unimpex Corp.
NATURE BOY - Apparel and accessories - Gorilla Graphic Design Studio
NATURE BOY - Novelty items - On the Ball
NATURE BOY - Pet products - Rexotic Products Co.
NATURE BOY - Salad dressings—bottled - Nature Boy Natural Food Inc.
NATURE BRIGHT - Detergents - Shaklee Corp.
NATURE BY DESIGN - Greeting cards - Kristin Elliott Inc.
NATURE CAKE - Cakes - Great Cakes
NATURE CALLS - Pet food supplements - Omnitrition International, Inc.
NATURE CAMPSITE - Toys - Fisher-Price, Inc.
NATURE CHAIR - Pet products - Maine Nature Products
NATURE CLEANSE - Vitamins and nutritional supplements - Natural Organics, Inc.
NATURE CLUB - Bicycles ☆ - Huffy Corp.
NATURE COLLECTION - Footwear - E.S. Originals, Inc.
NATURE COLLECTORS KIT - Toys - Natural Science Industries, Ltd.
NATURE CONSERVE - Fruit butters - Cascadian Farm, Inc.
NATURE CREST WOODWORKS - Furniture—wood - Nature Crest
Woodworks, Inc.
NATURE CURL - Hair care products - Apex Products Co.
NATURE DE FRANCE - Deodorants—personal - Para Laboratories Inc.
NATURE DISCOVERY WINDOWS - Toys - Mattel, Inc.
NATURE EAR - Amplifiers - Walker's (Game Ear), Inc.
NATURE ETCHINGS - Statuary - Iminac Inc.
NATURE EXPLORERS KIT - Hobby kits - Natural Science Industries, Ltd.
NATURE EYES - Cosmetics ☆ - Nature Cosmetics
NATURE FIRST SINCE 1974 FIRST PLACE 1 - Pet products - Natural
Research People, Inc.
NATURE FOOD CENTRES - Health care products - Nature Food Centers Inc.
NATURE FORCE - Vitamins and nutritional supplements - Sundown Vitamins,
Inc.
NATURE FRESH - Air freshener, etc. - Vaportek, Inc.
NATURE FRESH - Cleaning preparations - Grandma Wheaton
NATURE FRESH - Deodorizers - Surco Products Inc.
NATURE FRESH - Pet products - Golden Cat Corp.
NATURE FRESH - Sewage treatment and odor counteraction additives -
Edwards Laboratories Inc.
NATURE FRESH - Vitamins and nutritional supplements ☆ - Pharmavite Corp.
NATURE GARD - Fertilizers - Security Product Co.
NATURE GEMS - Statuary - Iminac Inc.
NATURE GIRL - Underwear and nightwear ☆ - Kiki International
NATURE-GRAIN - Cereal - Wholly Cow Foods
NATURE GRAM 1 - Vitamins and nutritional supplements - Garcoa Labs/
Vitamin Classics
NATURE - GREEN - Drain pipe cleaners - J.A. Sexauer, Inc.
NATURE GROWTH - Shampoos - Ampro Industries, Inc.
NATURE GUARD - Chemical preparations - Edge Development, Inc.
NATURE GUARD - Roofing materials - Louisiana-Pacific Corp.
NATURE GUARD - Sanitary paper - Cleveland Cotton Products Co.
NATURE GUARD ADVANTAGE - Insulating materials - Louisiana-Pacific Corp.
NATURE HOUSE - Prefabricated buildings—wood - Better Building Systems
NATURE IMPRESSIONS - Stamps—hand - Nature Impressions
NATURE IN HARMONY - Giftware - Enesco Corp.
NATURE IN YOUR NEIGHBORHOOD - Binoculars ☆ - Swift Instruments, Inc.
NATURE ISLAND - Cereal - Nature Island, Inc.
NATURE ISLAND - Fruits and vegetables - Nature Island Ltd.
NATURE JET - Bathroom fixtures - Pacific Spirit Corp.
NATURE KIST - Nuts—salted, roasted, cooked, or canned - Quality Packaging
Inc.
NATURE KNITS - Apparel and accessories - Salant/Manhattan Industries
NATURE LITE - Candles - Empire Manufacturing Co.
NATURE MADE - Vitamins and nutritional supplements - Pharmavite Corp.
NATURE MILK - Vitamins and nutritional supplements ☆ - Pharmavite Corp.
NATURE-MIN - Vitamins and nutritional supplements - Aloe Vera of America,
Inc.
NATURE MINT - Toothpaste - Bob Barker Co., Inc.
NATURE NAILS - Nail care products ☆ - Nature Cosmetics
NATURE NOTES - Notebooks and notepads ☆ - Recycled Paper Products, Inc.
NATURE NOTES BY VERONICA - Stationery - Ten Talents Distributors
NATURE ONE - Audio equipment - Northword Press, Inc.
NATURE-ONE - Vitamins and nutritional supplements - Earth Industries Inc.
NATURE OPTICS - Lighting equipment ☆ - Creative Concepts
NATURE O'S - Cereal - Arrowhead Mills, Inc.

NATURE PAK - Nuts—salted, roasted, cooked, or canned ☆ - Kettle Foods
NATURE PLEX - Vitamins and nutritional supplements - Natural Organics, Inc.
NATURE PLUS - Soil—potting - Womack Nursery Co.
NATURE PLUS - Tiles—ceramic - Porcelanite, Inc.
NATURE POINT - Vitamins and nutritional supplements - La Chasse Corp.
NATURE PRESERVATION GALLERY, THE - Figurines - CHLC Ltd.
NATURE PUFFS - Cereal ☆ - Arrowhead Mills, Inc.
NATURE QUEEN - Vitamins and nutritional supplements - CRA International,
Co.
NATURE QUEST - Vitamins and nutritional supplements - Eileen F. Bowman
NATURE REST - Heaters—space - Perfect Dreamer
NATURE RULES - Housewares - Tom Hatton Ceramics
NATURE SAC FOR NATURE'S SAKE - Tote bags - Naturesac, Inc.
NATURE SAFE - Fertilizer - Griffin Industries Inc.
NATURE SAFE - Pet products - Bark Industries Inc.
NATURE SAVER - Envelopes - S.P. Richards Co.
NATURE SCENT - Deodorizers - Surco Products Inc.
NATURE SCENT - Sporting goods ☆ - Wright & McGill Co.
NATURE SCENTS - Soap - Andrew Jergens Co.
NATURE SEAL OF APPROVAL - Food products - Edible Coatings
Development Corp.
NATURE SHAPE - Publisher's imprints - Western Publishing Co., Inc.
NATURE SHOWER - Skin care products - Amway Corp.
NATURE SLEEP - Mattresses - Nature Sleep
NATURE-SLIM - Teas - Connex Enterprises Inc.
NATURE SOFT - Diapers—disposable - Weyerhaeuser Co.
NATURE SOOTHE - Cough medicines - Prince of Peace Enterprises Inc.
NATURE STAIN - Paints - Lilly Perfection Paint
NATURE STEEL TOE - Shoes - Interco Inc.
NATURE STONE - Lighting fixtures - Adjusta-Post Manufacturing Co.
NATURE STUDIES - Wallcovering ☆ - Colortree Designs
NATURE TANK, THE - Filters—water - Carl M. Hulick
NATURE-THROID - Pharmaceutical preparations - Jones Medical Industries,
Inc. (Medical Div.)
NATURE-TIME - Vitamins and nutritional supplements - Nutrition Enterprises
NATURE-TONE - Food products - Beatrice Cos. Inc.
NATURE TONE - Paints - Sophir Morris Paint
NATURE TOOLS - Vitamins and nutritional supplements - APIC USA, Inc.
NATURE TRANSFER - Wallets - Le Baron Manufacturing Corp.
NATURE TREE - Grain, nut, vegetable, and fruit products - Nature Tree, Inc.
NATURE VALLEY - Granola bars - General Mills, Inc.
NATURE VEAL - Meat products—beef - Nathan Schweitzer & Co.
NATURE VISION - Kaleidoscopes - Gemini Kaleidoscopes
NATURE WAVE - Hair care products - Lustrasilk Corp. of America Inc.
NATURE WEAVE - Blankets - Crown Crafts, Inc.
NATURE WORLD - Figurines - Arnart Imports Inc.
NATURE ZONE, THE - Apparel and accessories - Michael S. Kofman
NATUREAL - Cosmetics - Dynamica International
NATUREBARK - Pet products - Four Paws Products Ltd.
NATURECRAFT - Cooking utensils—stoneware - Exquisite China & Crystal Inc.
NATURECRATE - Paperboard - Rock-Tenn Co.
NATUREDECK - Wood products - Madison Wood Preservers, Inc.
NATUREGRAPH PUBLISHERS INC. - Publisher's imprints - Naturegraph
Publishers Inc.
NATUREGRO - Garden equipment - Austram, Inc.
NATUREHOUSE - Vitamins and nutritional supplements - Phoenix
Laboratories, Inc.
NATUREL - Wood products ☆ - Masonite Corp.
NATUREL SEAL - Cleaning preparations—household - JDH Distribution
NATURELITE - Statuary - Iminac Inc.
NATURELL - Vitamins and nutritional supplements - Halsey Drug Co. Inc.
NATURELLE - Floor coverings—carpet and rugs - Couristan Inc.
NATURELLE - Hair care products - Naturelle, Inc.
NATURELLE - Pillows - E.R. Carpenter Co.
NATURELLE 10 - Health care products - Alta Health Products
NATURELLE AIRE - Hair care products ☆ - Naturelle, Inc.
NATURELLE PLUS - Wallpaper - Capital Carousel Inc.
NATURELLES - Apparel—women's ☆ - Camp, Inc.
NATURELLES - Cooking equipment—household ☆ - Rival Manufacturing Co.
NATUREMADE - Paper—tissue - Monaco Import/Export Inc.
NATUREMOST - Vitamins and nutritional supplements - Naturemost
Laboratories Inc.
NATURENCYCLOPEDIA - Publisher's imprints - Stemmer House Publishers
Inc.
NATUREQUEST - Recording label - Northword Press, Inc.
NATURE'S - Beverages - Archibald Bros. Fine Beverages, Inc.

☆ = Now out of production

NATURE'S - Blush and lipstick - Coty Inc.
NATURES - Paper–writing - P.H. Glatfelter Co.
NATURE'S 170 - Pet products - Applied Industrial Materials
NATURE'S ACCENTS - Deodorizers - Dial Corp.
NATURE'S ACRES - Vegetables–canned - Furman Foods, Inc.
NATURE'S ADVANTAGE - Shampoos - Marianna Imports, Inc.
NATURE'S AIR FRESHENER - Deodorizers - Reckitt & Colman, Inc.
NATURE'S ALCHEMY - Health care products - Lotus Brands Inc.
NATURE'S ALMANAC - Food products - Ultramar Marketing Corp.
NATURE'S ANSWER - Cleaning preparations - Golden Pride-Rawleigh, Inc.
NATURE'S ANSWER - Health care products - Nature's Answer (Bio Botanica)
NATURE'S ANTISEPTIC - Health care products - Natural Laboratories Corp.
NATURES APPLE - Hair coloring preparations - Stylors Inc.
NATURE'S ART - Stationery - Current, Inc.
NATURE'S ARTESIAN SPRING WATER - Water–bottled or canned - Tahquamenon Artesian Well Water Co.
NATURE'S BABIES - Infant product ☆ - Edison Industries Inc.
NATURE'S BABY - Diapers–disposable - Weyerhaeuser Co.
NATURE'S BABY - Hair care products - Arctic Pak, Inc.
NATURE'S BALANCE - Chemical preparations - Soil Mate, Inc.
NATURE'S BALANCE - Skin care products - Beneficial International
NATURE'S BALANCE - Skin-care products - Garcoa Labs/Vitamin Classics
NATURE'S BALANCE - Vitamins and nutritional supplements - Nature's Balance, Inc.
NATURE'S BALANCE - Vitamins and nutritional supplements - Vitamin Classics, Inc.
NATURE'S BEAUTY - Hair care products - Garcoa Labs/Vitamin Classics
NATURE'S BEAUTY - Stationery - Sangamon Co.
NATURE'S BED - Mattresses - Hillside Bedding Inc.
NATURE'S BEST - Agricultural products - Hess Brothers Fruit Co.
NATURE'S BEST - Flooring–hardwood - Buffalo Hardwood Floor Center, Inc.
NATURE'S BEST - Food products - Super Valu Inc.
NATURE'S BEST - Garden equipment ☆ - Vigoro Consumer & Professional Products Group
NATURE'S BEST - Jams and jellies - Wetterau Inc.
NATURE'S BEST - Pet collars - Natural Research People, Inc.
NATURE'S BEST - Shampoos - Blue Cross Laboratories Inc.
NATURE'S BEST - Vitamins and nutritional supplements - Nature's Best Inc.
NATURE'S BETA BLAST - Food products - Farm-Pak Products
NATURE'S BLEND - Pet products - Western Reserve Farm Cooperative
NATURE'S BLEND - Vitamins and nutritional supplements - Enrich Corp.
NATURES BLESSING - Hair care products - Mystic Essence
NATURE'S BODYCARE - Food products - Australian Bodycare Enterprises, Inc.
NATURE'S BOUNTY - Clocks - General Time Corp. (Westclox/Seth Thomas Div.)
NATURE'S BOUNTY - Cooking utensils–earthenware ☆ - Anchor Hocking Glass, Inc.
NATURE'S BOUNTY - Vitamins and nutritional supplements - Nature's Bounty, Inc.
NATURE'S BOUNTY ANTIOXIDANT 4000 - Vitamins and nutritional supplements - Nature's Bounty, Inc.
NATURE'S BOUNTY SLIM - Vitamins and nutritional supplements - Nature's Bounty, Inc.
NATURE'S BOUNTY SLIM QUICK - Vitamins and nutritional supplements - Nature's Bounty, Inc.
NATURE'S BOUQUET - Fruit drinks–bottled or canned ☆ - San Antonio Winery Inc.
NATURE'S BREATH - Health care products - Healthwatchers System
NATURES BREATH - Pet products - Rexotic Products Co.
NATURE'S BURGER - Preserved foods–prepackaged - Fantastic Foods Inc.
NATURE'S BURGER MIX - Food products - Fantastic Foods Inc.
NATURE'S CAFE - Bird feeds - Animal Supply Co.
NATURE'S CALCIUM PLUS - Milk - Creamland Dairies Inc.
NATURE'S CAMPFIRE - Camping products - Natures Fire, Inc.
NATURES CANDY - Fruits–dried - California Hi-Lites, Inc.
NATURE'S CANVAS - Apparel - Environmental Artwear, Inc.
NATURE'S CARE - Diapers–disposable - Weyerhaeuser Co.
NATURE'S CHARM - Stationery - Sangamon Co.
NATURE'S CHOICE - Animal feed supplements - Auburn Bean & Grain Companies
NATURE'S CHOICE - Bags–storage - Earle Industries, Inc.
NATURE'S CHOICE - Basket liners - Cobraco Manufacturing, Inc.
NATURE'S CHOICE - Deodorizers - Fuller Brush Co.
NATURE'S CHOICE - Flowers, plants, and seeds - Fuller Brush Co.
NATURE'S CHOICE - Garden equipment ∑ - NK Lawn & Garden Co.

NATURE'S CHOICE - Oils–lubricating - Hicks Oil and Hicks Gas Inc.
NATURE'S CHOICE - Paper–toilet - Plainwell Tissue
NATURE'S CHOICE - Pastries - Barbara's Bakery, Inc.
NATURE'S CHOICE - Rice - AC Humko Rice Specialties
NATURE'S CHOICE - Yarn ☆ - Lion Brand Yarn Co.
NATURE'S CHOICE ORIGINAL RECIPE BREADS - Bakery products - Roush Products Co., Inc.
NATURE'S CHOICE PERFECT - Cakes–mixes - Sunmark Inc.
NATURE'S CLASSICS - Vitamins and nutritional supplements - Vitamin Classics, Inc.
NATURE'S CLEANSE - Health care products - Melaleuca, Inc.
NATURES CLUB - Snack foods - A.L. Bazzini Co. Inc.
NATURE'S COLDCARE - Vitamins and nutritional supplements - Nature's Way Products, Inc.
NATURE'S COMFORT - Vitamins and nutritional supplements - TSN Labs, Inc.
NATURES COMPOSTER - Chemical preparations - Palmer Fixture Co.
NATURE'S COSMETICS - Skin care products - Junker
NATURE'S COURSE - Dog food - Ralston Purina Co.
NATURE'S CREATION - Hair- and skin-care products, fragrance, etc. - Benjamin Ansehl Co.
NATURE'S CRISPY RYES - Snack foods - Creative Foods Corp.
NATURE'S CUISINE - Food products - Nature's Best
NATURE'S CURE - Skin care products - Amulet Partners, Inc.
NATURE'S DEFENSE - Vitamins and nutritional supplements - Vitamin Classics, Inc.
NATURE'S DELITES - Jams, syrups, vegetables - Inorex Inc.
NATURE'S DETOX - Health care products - Natural Laboratories Corp.
NATURE'S DIGEST-EASE - Health care products - Natural Laboratories Corp.
NATURE'S DREAM - Vitamins and nutritional supplements - Nature's Dream
NATURE'S ECHO - Calendars - Natures Echo
NATURE'S EDGE - Vitamins and nutritional supplements - Tishcon Corp.
NATURE'S EEEZZ - Cushions - Winona M. Langrud
NATURE'S ELEMENTS - Cosmetics - Nature's Elements International Ltd.
NATURE'S ENSEMBLE - Wood products - Vermillion Inc.
NATURE'S ESSENCE - Incense - E. Davis Inc.
NATURE'S ESSENCE NATURAL WASH - Cleaning preparations–household - Nature's Essence Co., Inc.
NATURE'S FAMILY - Cosmetics - Dep Corp.
NATURES FAMILY IS NATURAL SKIN THERAPY - Skin care products - Dep Corp.
NATURE'S FARMS - Peanut butter - Clements Food Co. Inc.
NATURE'S FEMALE - Health care products - Healthwatchers System
NATURE'S FINEST - Agricultural products - Scrivner, Inc.
NATURE'S FINEST - Mattresses - Englander Licensing Limited Liability Co.
NATURE'S FINEST - Olive oil - California Olive Oil Corp.
NATURE'S FINEST - Skin care products - Walgreen Co.
NATURE'S FIRE - Camping products - Natures Fire, Inc.
NATURE'S FIRESTARTER - Wood products - Natures Fire, Inc.
NATURE'S FIRST - Milk–canned or powdered - MMI International Corp.
NATURE'S FISH FOOD - Fish food - Buford Bait, Inc.
NATURE'S FLAVORS - Soft drinks - Corr's Natural Beverages Inc.
NATURE'S FLOWERS - Flowers, plants, and seeds - Nature's Flowers
NATURE'S FRIEND - Cleaning preparations - Massco, Inc.
NATURE'S FRIEND - Diapers–disposable - Weyerhaeuser Co.
NATURE'S FRIENDS - Figurines - American Greetings Corp.
NATURE'S FRUIT - Confections - La Perla
NATURES GALLERY - Boxes - Natures Gallery
NATURES GALLERY - Dishes–earthenware - Mikasa Co.
NATURES GALLERY - Fertilizers ☆ - United Design Corp.
NATURE'S GALLERY - Flowers, plants, and seeds - Gerson Co.
NATURES GAR - Garlic tablets - Country Life
NATURE'S GARDEN - Bird feeds - Cole's Wild Bird Products Co.
NATURES GARDEN - Dishes–china - Mikasa Co.
NATURE'S GARDEN - Incense - Auroma International Inc.
NATURE'S GARDEN BAKERY - Bakery products - Rockaway Garden Bakery, Inc.
NATURE'S GATE - Skin care products - Levlab, Inc.
NATURE'S GEM - Deodorants–personal - Acts II Enterprises, Inc.
NATURES GIFT - Fruits and vegetables - Gillette Citrus Co.
NATURES GIFTS - Bird feeds - New Creative Enterprises, Inc.
NATURES GIFTS - Giftware - Delfino Products Inc.
NATURE'S GIRL - Health care products ☆ - Nature Cosmetics
NATURE'S GLORY - Skin care products - Garcoa Labs/Vitamin Classics
NATURE'S GOLD - Bird feeds - L/M Animal Farms, Inc.
NATURE'S GRAINS - Skin care products - Oakmont Investments Co.

☆ = Now out of production

NATURE'S GRANITE - Counter tops–laminated - Marble Source Unlimited, Inc.

NATURE'S GYM SET - Bird feeders - South Hill Ventures

NATURE'S HAIR - Hair care products - GSK Products, Inc.

NATURE'S HAND - Cereal - Nature's Hand, Inc.

NATURE'S HARMONY - Compact discs–prerecorded - Metacom Inc.

NATURE'S HARVEST - Breads–mixes - Nature's Harvest

NATURE'S HARVEST - Fruit drinks–bottled or canned - Farmland Dairies Inc.

NATURE'S HARVEST - Processed nuts - Ann's House of Nuts, Inc.

NATURE'S HEALTH - Hair care products - Tom's Trade Inc.

NATURE'S HEAT - Pet products - Four Paws Products Ltd.

NATURE'S HERB COMPANY - Teas - San Francisco Herb & Natural Food Co.

NATURE'S HERBS - Cosmetics - Rainco Co. Inc.

NATURE'S HERBS - Vitamins and nutritional supplements - Natur-Pharma, Inc.

NATURES HERITAGE - Giftware ☆ - Munro Enterprises Inc.

NATURE'S HILIGHTS - Food products - Nature's Hilights, Inc.

NATURE'S IMAGINATION - House furnishings - Laurie North Corp.

NATURE'S INSPIRATIONS - Greeting cards - American Greetings Corp.

NATURE'S KEY - Cleaning preparations–household - American Eco Systems

NATURE'S KINGDOM - Apparel and accessories - Busch Entertainment Corp.

NATURE'S KISS - Cosmetics - Arthur Matney Co., Inc.

NATURES KISS - Skin care products - Gold Medal Hair Products Inc.

NATURE'S KITTY - Food products - Health Valley Food

NATURE'S LAB - Health care products - Enrich International, Inc.

NATURE'S LEGACY - Giftware - Service Merchandise Co. Inc.

NATURE'S LEGACY - Pillows - Service Merchandise Co., Inc.

NATURE'S LIFE - Vitamins and nutritional supplements - M.K. Health Food Distributors, Inc.

NATURES LIP RENEWEL STICK - Lipsticks - Isla Cosmetique

NATURE'S LITTLE GREENHOUSE - Pet products - Four Paws Products Ltd.

NATURE'S MAGIC - Health care products - Natural Laboratories Corp.

NATURE'S MAJESTY - Water–bottled or canned - Chatham Imports, Inc.

NATURE'S MALE - Health care products - Healthwatchers System

NATURES MARKET - Bird feeders - Cedar Works Inc.

NATURE'S MEDICINE CABINET - Oils–essential - Sybaritic, Inc.

NATURE'S MEDICINES - Health care products ☆ - Nature's Herbs

NATURE'S MENDER - Skin care products - American Salon Products

NATURE'S METHOD - Computer software - Mercedes Arzu Wilson

NATURE'S MILK TREAT - Beverages - Milk Made Inc.

NATURE'S MINS - Vitamins and nutritional supplements - Natural Organics, Inc.

NATURE'S MIRACLE - Cleaning preparations - PETS 'N PEOPLE, INC.

NATURE'S MIRACLE - Vitamins and nutritional supplements - Nu-Wave Health Products, Inc.

NATURE'S NAILS - Nail care products ☆ - E.O.H. Industries, Inc.

NATURES NATURALS BOTANICALS - Deodorizers - Lumi-Lite Candle Co. Inc.

NATURES NEST - Pet products - Pets International, Ltd.

NATURE'S NET - Netting - Jetnet Corp.

NATURE'S NUTRIENTS - Fertilizers ☆ - Albion Laboratories, Inc.

NATURE'S NUTRITION - Food products - Alliance USA Inc.

NATURE'S OIL - Hair care products - Home Health Products, Inc.

NATURE'S ONE - Perfumes - La Parfumerie Inc.

NATURES OPTION - Cleaning preparations–household - Kafko International Ltd.

NATURE'S ORANGE - Cleaning preparations - Blue Coral, Inc.

NATURE'S ORCHARD - Air freshener - Dial Corp.

NATURES OVEN - Cooking utensils–earthenware - Reco International Corp.

NATURE'S OWN - Bakery products - Flowers Industries Inc.

NATURE'S OWN - Deodorizers - New Ideas International, Inc.

NATURE'S OWN - Fruit drinks–bottled or canned - Brooklyn Bottling Co.

NATURE'S OWN - Honey ☆ - Miller's Honey Co.

NATURE'S OWN - Juices - Brooklyn Bottling Corp.

NATURE'S OWN - Juices - Hudson Valley Apple Products Co. Inc.

NATURES OWN - Pet products - Farnam Cos. Inc.

NATURES OWN - Pet products - R.A.F. Trading Inc.

NATURE'S OWN - Pharmaceutical preparations - Michigan Pharmaceutical

NATURE'S OWN - Shampoos ☆ - Naturelle, Inc.

NATURE'S OWN - Vitamins and nutritional supplements - Nature's Own Inc.

NATURE'S OWN - Vitamins and nutritional supplements - VMC Corp.

NATURE'S OWN - Water treating compounds - Kalium Chemicals, Ltd.

NATURE'S OWN CHUNK CHARWOOD - Briquettes - Treestock Ltd.

NATURE'S OWN LIGHT - Breads - Flowers Industries Inc.

NATURE'S PAL - Food products - Health Valley Food

NATURE'S PARADISE FACE & BODY CARE - Skin care products - Nature's Paradise by Joanna International, Inc.

NATURE'S PASTA - Pasta - Remlik Foods Inc.

NATURE'S PH - Cosmetics - House of Winslow

NATURE'S PICNIC - Bird feeders - South Hill Ventures

NATURES PLANK - Wood products - Kwaterski Bros. Wood Products Inc.

NATURES PLANTAPLEX CLEAR - Skin care products - Isla Cosmetique

NATURE'S PLAYLAND - Cages–wire - Penn-Plax, Inc.

NATURE'S PLEASURES - Massage products - Nature's Touch Inc.

NATURE'S PLUMBER - Water treating compounds - Palmer Fixture Co.

NATURE'S PLUS - Vitamins and nutritional supplements - Natural Organics, Inc.

NATURE'S PRIDE - Flowers, plants, and seeds - L.E. Cooke Co.

NATURES PRIDE - Fruits and vegetables - DNE World Fruit Sales

NATURE'S PRIDE - Pet products ☆ - Emsco Inc.

NATURE'S PRIDE - Vegetables–canned - Nature's Pride Inc.

NATURE'S PROMISE - Vitamins and nutritional supplements - Nature's Promise Inc.

NATURE'S RAIN - Pet products - Four Paws Products Ltd.

NATURE'S RECIPE - Pet products - Nature's Recipe

NATURES RECIPE INNOVATIVE PET FOODS - Dog food - Nature's Recipe

NATURE'S RELAXING SOUNDS - Recording label - Thomas Nelson, Inc.

NATURE'S REPTILE VITA-SPRAY - Vitamins and nutritional supplements - Four Paws Products Ltd.

NATURE'S RESCUE - Health care products - Ellon Bach USA Inc.

NATURE'S RHYTHM - Statuary - Apple & Pear Ltd.

NATURE'S RICHEST - Soil–potting - Michigan Peat Co.

NATURE'S RITUALS - Cosmetics - CBI Laboratories, Inc.

NATURE'S SCENTS - Incense ☆ - Olfactory Corp.

NATURE'S SEASONS - Garden equipment - South St. Paul Feed Inc.

NATURE'S SEASONS - Seasonings - Morton International Inc. (Morton Salt Div.)

NATURE'S SECOND SKIN - Skin care products - Lansinoh Laboratories Inc.

NATURE'S SECOND SUN - Novelty items - Nature's Second Sun

NATURE'S SECRET - Health care products - Energen Products Inc.

NATURE'S SECRET - Oils–edible - Columbus Foods Co.

NATURE'S SECRET SKIN REJUVENATOR - Hair-care products and skin care products - Arizona Naturals, Inc.

NATURE'S SELECT - Beverages - Orange-Co, Inc.

NATURE'S SERENADE - Jewelry - Serenade Graphics, Inc.

NATURE'S SHIELD - Vitamins and nutritional supplements - Kaire International, Inc.

NATURE'S SKETCHBOOK - Greeting cards - Hallmark Cards Inc.

NATURE'S SMALL WONDERS - Candy - Homestead, Inc.

NATURE'S SNACKS - Snack foods - Mexi-Snax Inc.

NATURE'S SONG - Dishes–earthenware - Mikasa Co.

NATURE'S SOUND - Health care products - Healthwatchers System

NATURE'S SOURCE - Skin care products - Barcolene Inc.

NATURE'S SOURCE - Vitamins and nutritional supplements - Nature's Source Corp.

NATURE'S SPICE BIJOUX DE BAIN - Skin care products - Savonnerie, Inc.

NATURE'S SPLASH - Containers–plastic - Robbie S. Lee

NATURE'S SPRING - Water purification systems - Lifetrends International

NATURE'S STEROLS - Vitamins and nutritional supplements - Healthy 'N Fit Nutritionals

NATURE'S STOP - Sewage treatment equipment - Kay Cor Enterprises Ltd.

NATURE'S STOREHOUSE - Cereal - Sovex Foods, Inc.

NATURE'S STRIKE - Health care products - Apothecary Products, Inc.

NATURE'S SUNSHINE - Herbal products - Lifetrends International

NATURE'S SUPER GRO - Hair care products - All Ways Natural Industries Inc.

NATURE'S SUPER NATURALS - Wallpaper - Snap & Sell Corp.

NATURE'S SWEETEST - Pipes - Missouri Meerschaum Co.

NATURES TALC POWER - Deodorizers - Krueger Enterprises

NATURE'S TEA - Teas–herbal - Enrich Corp.

NATURE'S THREADS - Apparel and accessories - Fortune Fashions Inc.

NATURE'S TOUCH - Beverages–carbonated ☆ - Certified Grocers Midwest Inc.

NATURES TOUCH - Pet products - Gentle Touch Corp.

NATURES TOUCH - Pillows - Pacific Coast Feather Co.

NATURE'S TOUCH - Sponges - Acme Sponge & Chamois Co., Inc.

NATURE'S TOYLAND - Cages–wire - Penn-Plax, Inc.

NATURE'S TREASURES - Greeting cards - American Greetings Corp.

NATURE'S TREATS - Pet foods - Triumph Pet Industries, Inc.

NATURE'S TRUST - Vitamins and nutritional supplements - Natural Organics, Inc.

NATURE'S VALUE - Fruits–canned - Hess and Associates, Inc.

NATURE'S WALKING - Pharmaceutical preparations - D.R. Little

NATURE'S WALL - Floor coverings–carpet and rugs - Milliken & Co. Inc.

☆ = Now out of production

NATURE'S WAREHOUSE - Bakery products - Nature's Warehouse Inc.
NATURE'S WASH - Cleaning preparations - C2L Corp.
NATURE'S WASH - Skin care products - Geritrex Corp.
NATURE'S WASH - Sponges - Acme Sponge & Chamois Co., Inc.
NATURES WAVE - Cleaning preparations - Garcoa Labs/Vitamin Classics
NATURE'S WAY - Bait - Nature's Way
NATURE'S WAY - Floor coverings–carpet and rugs ☆ - Mohawk Carpet Corp.
NATURES WAY - Paints - True-Tagg Paint Co.
NATURE'S WAY - Shoes ☆ - Hoy Shoe Co. Inc.
NATURE'S WAY - Varnishes - Perry & Derrick Co.
NATURE'S WAY ANIMALS - Novelty items - Totsy Manufacturing Co., Inc.
NATURE'S WEALTH - Cosmetics - Nature's Wealth Co.
NATURES WHEY - Beverages–malt - Carr Products Co. Inc.
NATURE'S WINDOW - Aquariums–household - Wolverton Krislin, Inc.
NATURE'S WINDOWS - Vases - Two's Co. Inc.
NATURE'S WONDERLAND - Teas–herbal - Penn Herb Co. Ltd.
NATURE'S WONDERS - Chimes - Edward Rodriguez & Co., Inc.
NATURE'S WORKSHOP - Cosmetics - CBI Laboratories, Inc.
NATURE'S YIELD - Spices and extracts - Royal-Souders Inc.
NATURE'S YOUNG'UNS - Decals and transfers - Morehead, Inc.
NATURESAFE - Cosmetics - Naturesafe Corp.
NATURESAFE - Posters - De La Fuente, Inc.
NATURESCAPE - Flowers, plants, and seeds ☆ - Applewood Seed & Garden Group
NATURESCAPES - Pharmaceutical preparations - Naturescapes Inc.
NATURESEAL - Cooking equipment–household - Lifetrends International
NATURESLIM - Health care products - Fairhill Foods
NATURESONG - Transmitting apparatus - FBA Sales Co. Inc.
NATURE'SONS - Chimes - Joyful Noise
NATURESSENCE - Skin care products - Nature Cosmetics
NATURETEX - Fabrics–polyethylene - Starensier, Inc.
NATURETIN - Pharmaceutical preparations - Bristol-Myers Squibb Co.
NATURETONE - Food products - Beatreme Foods, Inc.
NATURETONES - Tiles–ceramic - American Olean Tile Co.
NATUREVELDT - Shoes - Clarks of England Inc.
NATUREVIEW - Binoculars - Bausch & Lomb Inc.
NATUREWALK - Sandals - Red Wing Shoe Co. Inc.
NATUREWEAVE COLLECTION, THE - Floor coverings–carpet and rugs - Daltonian Carpet & Cushion Inc.
NATUREWISE - Fabrics - Dixie Yarns, Inc.
NATUREWISE - Office supplies ☆ - Esselte Corp.
NATUREWISE - Recycled shipping and mailing products - International Rotex Inc.
NATUREWOOD - Lumber - Madison Wood Preservers, Inc.
NATUREWORKS - Playground equipment - Miracle Recreation Equipment Co.
NATUREWORKS - Skin care products - Abkit, Inc.
NATUREWORKS - Soap - Natureworks Inc.
NATUREWRAP - Paper–gift wrap ☆ - Abbeville Press, Inc.
NATURFARM - Flowers, plants, and seeds - Johrei Fellowship
NATURFRESH - Wheat germ - Fearn Natural Foods, Division of Modernproducts, Inc.
NATURICE - Confections - Vita Chlor Corp.
NATURIN - Vitamins and nutritional supplements - Healthcare Laboratories, Inc.
NATURIPE - Fruits and vegetables - Naturipe Berry Growers
NATURISTICS - Skin care products - Del Pharmaceuticals, Inc.
NATURISTICS SHOP - Skin care products - Del Pharmaceuticals, Inc.
NATURITE - Vitamins and nutritional supplements ☆ - Columbia Laboratories Inc.
NATURITE - Vitamins and nutritional supplements ☆ - Leiner Health Products Inc.
NATURMADE - Food products - Tri Valley Growers, Inc.
NATUROL - Fuel additives - Buckley & Scott Co., Inc.
NATURONICS HAIR COMPLEX - Hair care products - Redmond Products, Inc.
NATUROSE - Health care products - Cyanotech Corp.
NATUROTHERAPY - Bath salts ☆ - Essential Aromatics
NATURPLEX - Vitamins and nutritional supplements ☆ - Naturade Inc.
NATURSLIM - Beverages - Pro-Form Laboratories
NATURSPAN - Botanical extracts - Zuellig Botanicals, Inc.
NATURVET - Pet products - Garmon Corp.
NATURVUE - Publisher's imprints - Sharon Helmann
NATUS BORN - Beverages - Natus Corp.
NATUS BORN OF NATURE PURE INDULGENCE - Bath salts - Natus Corp.
NATUSPATCH - Pharmaceutical preparations - Natus Corp.
NATY - Skin care products - Beneficial International
NAUDET - Navigational instruments - Weems & Plath, Inc.
NAUDET - Perfumes - Essential Products Co. Inc.

NAUGA-PLUS - Fabrics ☆ - Uniroyal Engineered Products
NAUGAFORM - Fabrics - Uniroyal Engineered Products
NAUGAHYDE - Fabrics - Uniroyal Engineered Products
NAUGALITE - Fabrics - Uniroyal Engineered Products
NAUGALON - Fabrics ☆ - Uniroyal Engineered Products
NAUGATHANE - Fabrics ☆ - Uniroyal Engineered Products
NAUGHTY & NICE - Sleepwear and intimate apparel - Home Shopping Club, Inc.
NAUGHTY BAKER AND CANDY MAKER, THE - Cakes - John O'Neill
NAUGHTY BUT NICE - Cookies - Creative Cookie Inc. (American Dream Enterprises)
NAUGHTY BUT NICE - Shoes - Styles Inc.
NAUGHTY DOG - Video games - Naughty Dog, Inc.
NAUGHTY DONKEY, THE - Coffee - Royal Aloha Coffee, Tea, & Spice Co., Inc.
NAUGHTY GIRL! - Apparel and accessories ☆ - Warnaco Inc.
NAUGHTY MARIETTA - Brassieres (Bras) - Valmont Inc.
NAUGHTY NAKEDS, THE - Cosmetics - Charles Revson Inc.
NAUGHTYHEDRON - Games - Gamescience
NAUS-A-WAY - Pharmaceutical preparations - Roberts/Hauck Pharmaceuticals Inc.
NAUS-EASE - Pharmaceutical preparations - Pharos Health Products
NAUSATROL - Pharmaceutical - Medique Products
NAUSET - Powerboat ☆ - Boston Whaler, Inc.
NAUT-O-LINE - Sporting goods ☆ - Hedstrom Corp.
NAUTA - Tanks–water - Imtra Corp.
NAUTACOM - Electronic equipment ☆ - Three-Five Systems Inc.
NAUTAMATIC MARINE SYSTEMS, INC. - Automatic pilots - Nautamatic Marine Systems, Inc.
NAUTECH - Fabrics - Nautica Enterprises Inc.
NAUTI-KAT - Boats - Nautical Boats Ltd.
NAUTI-KOTE - Cement - Passonno Paints
NAUTI MAR - Marine rigging - Nauti-Mar, Inc.
NAUTI-VIEW - Cameras - Leisure Components Inc.
NAUTIC - Paints - Hempel Coatings USA Inc.
NAUTICA - Bathing suits - Collette Manufacturing Co.
NAUTICA - Boats - Nautica International Inc.
NAUTICA - Colognes - Revlon Consumer Products Corp.
NAUTICA - Electronic equipment - Pioneer Electronics USA Inc.
NAUTICA - Flatware - Reed and Barton Corp.
NAUTICA - Footwear - Nautica Enterprises Inc.
NAUTICA - Recording label - Luke Records Inc.
NAUTICA - Seafood products–canned or cured - Stevens Industries Inc.
NAUTICA - Watches - Timex Corp.
NAUTICA COMPETITION - Cosmetics - Nautica Enterprises Inc.
NAUTICA EYEWEAR - Frames–eyeglass - Zylo Ware Corp.
NAUTICA MARINE DENIM CO. - Apparel and accessories - Nautica Enterprises Inc.
NAUTICA SUNGLASSES - Sunglasses - Zylo Ware Corp.
NAUTICA SWIMWEAR - Bathing suits - Apparel Ventures, Inc.
NAUTICA VILLAGER - Motor vehicles–automobiles - Ford Motor Co. (Lincoln-Mercury Div.)
NAUTICAL - Floor coverings–carpet and rugs ☆ - Regal Rugs Inc.
NAUTICAL - Paints - Nautical Marine Paint Corp.
NAUTICAL AMERICANA - Wallpaper ☆ - Evergreen Press
NAUTICAL BEARS - Infant product - Kids II, Inc.
NAUTICAL BLUE - Dinnerware ☆ - Corning Inc.
NAUTICALWAY - Cosmetics - Jerry Karst
NAUTICO INTERNATIONAL - Pet products ☆ - Africana Gifts & Shells Inc.
NAUTICOLORS - Chemical preparations - Woolsey Marine Industries
NAUTICUS - Apparel and accessories - National Maritime Center
NAUTIGUARD - Marine-security systems - Nauta Inc.
NAUTIL - Paints - Hempel Coatings USA Inc.
NAUTILIS - Seafood products–fresh or frozen - G.F. Higgins
NAUTILUS - Bathroom accessories - Monarch Metal Products Corp.
NAUTILUS - Battery chargers - Exide Corp.
NAUTILUS - Dinnerware–glass - Franciscan by Johnson Brothers, USA, Inc.
NAUTILUS - Exercising equipment - Nautilus Acquisition Inc.
NAUTILUS - Floor coverings - American Floor Products Co. Inc.
NAUTILUS - Floor coverings–carpet and rugs - Regal Rugs Inc.
NAUTILUS - Floor coverings–carpet and rugs ☆ - Catalina Carpet Mills Inc.
NAUTILUS - Giftware - World of Porcelain & Glassware
NAUTILUS - Health care products - Euro-Care Products & Services Co.
NAUTILUS - Jewelry - Jacoby-Bender Inc.
NAUTILUS - Lubricating oils ☆ - Shell Oil Co.
NAUTILUS - Mops - Geerpres Wringer Co.

☆ = Now out of production

NAUTILUS - Pet products - Tetra Sales USA
NAUTILUS - Playground equipment - Learning Products Inc.
NAUTILUS - Seafood products–fresh or frozen - State Fish Co., Inc.
NAUTILUS - Seafood salads - Golden Beach, Inc.
NAUTILUS - Telephones - Motorola, Inc. (Land Mobile Products Sector)
NAUTILUS - Ventilation equipment - Nautilus Industries
NAUTILUS - Vitamins and nutritional supplements ☆ - Dr. Pepper/Seven Up, Inc.
NAUTILUS - Watches ☆ - SMH (US) Inc.
NAUTILUS - Water heaters–household - Mor-Flo Industries Inc.
NAUTILUS - Water purification systems ☆ - Flint & Walling Industries, Inc.
NAUTILUS FOR WOMEN - Exercising equipment - Nautilus Acquisition Inc.
NAUTILUS MICROMATE - Stoves - Nautilus Industries
NAUTIQUE SUPER SPORT - Boats - Correct Craft Inc.
NAUTITOOL - Hand tools - Stephen J. Rountree
NAUTOLEX - Floor coverings–carpet and rugs - Gencorp Polymer Products
NAUTROL - Pharmaceutical preparations ☆ - Solvay Pharmaceuticals Inc.
NAUVOO - Cheese - Nauvoo Cheese Co.
NAUVOO BLUE CHEESE - Cheese - Raskas Foods, Inc.
NAUZENE - Pharmaceutical preparations - Jeffery H. Gerchenson
NAV 5000 - Navigational instruments - Magellan Corp.
NAV 5000 PRO - Navigational instruments - Magellan Corp.
NAV-FINDER - Electronic equipment - John Eric Richardson
NAV-O - Spices and extracts - Ottens Flavors
NAV-STARTGUARD - Power switching equipment - ROI Development Corp.
NAVA NAVA - Floor coverings–carpet and rugs ☆ - Regal Rugs Inc.
NAVAGRID - Compasses–gyroscopic - Rule Industries, Inc.
NAVAHO - Floor coverings–carpet and rugs ☆ - Quaker Inc.
NAVAHO - Pet collars ☆ - Leatherite-Nylorite Manufacturing Inc.
NAVAHO - Polishing cloths ☆ - Beverly Manufacturing Corp.
NAVAHO - Radios - Tandy Corp.
NAVAJO - Automotive parts and accessories - Lancaster Colony Automotive Group
NAVAJO - Clocks ☆ - General Time Corp. (Westclox/Seth Thomas Div.)
NAVAJO - Darts and dart games - Dart World Inc.
NAVAJO - Dinnerware–glass ☆ - Nikko Ceramics Inc.
NAVAJO - Floor coverings - American Floor Products Co. Inc.
NAVAJO - Frames–picture - Terragrafics Inc.
NAVAJO - Motor vehicles–automobiles - Mazda Motor of America Inc.
NAVAJO - Truck bodies - Gem Top Manufacturing Inc.
NAVAJO - Wallpaper ☆ - Wall-Pride Inc.
NAVAJO CO-OP, THE - Tables–wood - Navajo Coop
NAVAJO PINE - Lumber - Navajo Forest Products Industries
NAVAL BATTLE - Games - Smethport Specialty Co.
NAVAL JELLY - Adhesives and sealants - Loctite Corp.
NAVAL JELLY - Rust removers - Naval Jelly Co. Inc.
NAVAL ORANGE - Sporting goods - Voit Corp.
NAVAL WAR - Games - Avalon Hill Game Co.
NAVALLE - Wines - Heublein, Inc.
NAVAMAR - Waterproofing compounds ☆ - Sigma Coatings USA BV.
NAVAN - Floor coverings–carpet and rugs - Navan Carpets Inc.
NAVANE - Pharmaceutical preparations - J.B. Roerig & Co.
NAVAPAK HANDICUT - Lumber - Navajo Forest Products Industries
NAVAPINE - Particle board ☆ - Navajo Forest Products Industries
NAVARA - Floor coverings - Congoleum Corp.
NAVARRE - Dishes–china - Pickard Inc.
NAVARRE - Flatware - Couzon USA
NAVARRE - Furniture ☆ - Bassett Furniture Industries, Inc.
NAVARRE - Glassware–household ☆ - Lenox Crystal, Inc.
NAVARRE - Guitars ☆ - Guild Music Corp.
NAVARRO - Cleaning preparations - Navarro Discount Pharmacies No.1, Inc.
NAVARRO BROTHERS - Footwear - Navarro Brothers
NAVARRO CELLARS - Wines - Navarro Vineyards and Winery
NAVARRO CORREAS - Beverages–alcohol - Tosi Vintners International
NAVARRO CORREAS WINES FROM ARGENTINA - Wines - Palm Bay Imports, Inc.
NAVARRO VINEYARDS - Wines - Navarro Vineyards and Winery
NAVASOTA - Jewelry - Gotcha Covered
NAVATRIM - Moldings–plaster of paris - Navajo Forest Products Industries
NAVCIS - Computer software - Dvorak Development & Publishing Corp.
NAVCO INTERNATIONAL IMPORTS - Flowers, plants, and seeds - Vans, Inc.
NAVCOM - Audio equipment - Sumiko Inc.
NAVEJO - Furniture - Bean Station Furniture Factory Inc.
NAVETTE - Motor vehicles–motor homes - BBC RV, Inc.
NAVFURL - Engines ☆ - Navtec Inc.
NAVI GUIDE - Electronic equipment - Galileo Corp.

NAVI PESANDA - Blankets - Boucher Boys & The Indian, Inc.
NAVIA - Watches ☆ - Tag-Heuer Time & Electronics Corp.
NAVID O NADIA - Shoes - Demfon International Trading Network Inc.
NAVIERA - Coffee - Naviera Coffee Mills, Inc.
NAVIFLEX NT - Dental equipment - Brasseler USA, Inc.
NAVIG-AIDER 50 - Door openers–electronic - Besam Inc.
NAVIGATA - Apparel and accessories - Bugle Boy Industries, Inc.
NAVIGATE - Computer software - Chicago Data Destruction Corp.
NAVIGATE - Herbicides - Applied Biochemists, Inc.
NAVIGATION BOAT WORKS - Sportswear - David Peyser Sportswear Inc.
NAVIGATION SERVER - Computer software - Sybase, Inc.
NAVIGATOR - Bicycles - Murray, Inc.
NAVIGATOR - Boats–motor ☆ - Cobia Boat Co.
NAVIGATOR - Braces–orthopedic - Tecnol Medical Products, Inc.
NAVIGATOR - Cleaning equipment - H-Tech, Inc.
NAVIGATOR - Computers - Telesensory Systems Inc.
NAVIGATOR - Doors - Hufcor Inc.
NAVIGATOR - Electronic equipment - Babson Bros. Co.
NAVIGATOR - Electronic equipment - Galileo Corp.
NAVIGATOR - Games - Great Time Software
NAVIGATOR - Golfing equipment - Pro Select Sports USA
NAVIGATOR - Leather - Horween Leather Co.
NAVIGATOR - Motor vehicles–motor homes - Holiday Rambler Corp.
NAVIGATOR - Nautical instruments - Datamarine International Inc.
NAVIGATOR - Pencils ☆ - Koh-I-Noor, Inc.
NAVIGATOR - Safety products - Plastic Safety Systems, Inc.
NAVIGATOR - Watches - Bulova Corp.
NAVIGATOR 2000 - Compasses–magnetic - E.S. Ritchie & Sons Inc.
NAVIGATOR COMICS - Books–comic - Jerome Glasser
NAVIGATOR MARK I - Binoculars ☆ - Swift Instruments, Inc.
NAVIGATOR SERIES - Lighting fixtures - Holophane Corp.
NAVIGATORS - Waterproof footwear - Kaysam Corp. of America
NAVIGRAPH - Computer software - Landmark Systems Corp.
NAVIGUIDE - Computer software - Sales Navigation Systems, Inc.
NAVILEX-T - Pharmaceutical preparations ☆ - Vita-Fore Products Co.
NAVILUX - Electronic equipment ☆ - Navitar, Inc.
NAVIMATIC - Navigational instruments - Raytheon Co.
NAVISTAR - Motor vehicles–automobiles - Navistar International Transportation Corp.
NAVISTAR INTERNATIONAL - Motor vehicles–trucks ☆ - Navistar International Transportation Corp.
NAVITAR - Projectors–photographic - Navitar, Inc.
NAVITAR BRIGHTLIGHT - Photographic equipment - Navitar, Inc.
NAVITRACK - Computer software - Northpoint Software
NAVITRON - Television equipment ☆ - Navitar, Inc.
NAVIX - Computer software - Navix Soft Wares, Inc.
NAVLINK - Computer software - Tideland Signal Corp.
NAVMAP - Computer software - Paragon Technologies, Inc.
NAVNET - Computer hardware - Ilmorrow, Inc.
NAVOO - Cheese - Raskas Foods, Inc.
NAVPAK - Computer software - San Francisco Marketing Group, Inc.
NAVPAK - Nautical instruments ☆ - Signet Marine
NAVQUEST - Computer software - American Technologies, Inc.
NAVSAFE - Computer software - Navsys Corp.
NAVSTAR - Computer software - Dvorak Development & Publishing Corp.
NAVTEC - Boats - Navtec Inc.
NAVTEC SHEET STOPPER - Boats ☆ - Navtec Inc.
NAVTEK - Cables–signal - Harrison Ward
NAVTERM - Computer software - Tideland Signal Corp.
NAVY - Apparel and accessories - Naval Academy Athletic Association
NAVY - Colognes - Noxell Corp.
NAVY - Colognes - Procter & Gamble Co.
NAVY - Tobacco - American Tobacco Co.
NAVY 1851 - Guns - Euroarms of America
NAVY ARMS - Guns - Navy Arms Co.
NAVY BLUE - Apparel–men's - Chauvin International Ltd.
NAVY BY COVER GIRL - Colognes - Noxell Corp.
NAVY NURSE - Watches - Bulova Corp.
NAVY ONE - Binoculars - Pioneer Marketing & Research, Inc.
NAVY PLAIN - Snuff - American Maize-Products Co.
NAVY PRIDE - Calendars - Mach 1, Inc.
NAVY SEAL - Computer software - Cosmi Corp.
NAVY SWEET - Snuff - American Maize-Products Co.
NAVY TOUGH - Enamels - Masury Paint Co.
NAVY WHITE - Colognes - Procter & Gamble Co.
NAWICO - Wines - Gibson Wine Co.

☆ = Now out of production

NAWLA TRADERS MARKET - Trade Associations - North American Wholesale Lumber Association, Inc.

NAWLINS LADY - Apparel and accessories - Charles T. Collazo

NAYA - Water–bottled or canned - Canada Dry Corp.

NAYAD - Pharmaceutical preparations ☆ - Dermalab Ltd.

NAYADERM - Skin care products - Byron A. Donzis

NAYADIC - Water purification systems - Nayadic, Inc.

NAYCO - Wood products - Nathan Cohen Inc.

NAZARE - Fabrics - Dan River Inc.

NAZARETH - Crocheted and knitted items - Nazareth Kentury Mills

NAZARETH SPEEDWAY - Apparel and accessories - Pennsylvania International Raceway, Inc.

NAZDRAVE - Wines - Farlow & MacPhail, Inc.

NB - Computer software - American Circuit Breaker Corp.

NB-1 - Sporting goods - Tonka Corp.

NBA - Apparel and accessories - G-III Apparel Group, Ltd.

NBA - Apparel and accessories - Pyramid Handbags Inc.

NBA - Chewing gum - NBA Properties, Inc.

NBA - Cocktail tables ☆ - JDI Group, Inc.

NBA - Frames–eyeglass - Creative Optiks

NBA - Games ☆ - Avalon Hill Game Co.

NBA - Sporting goods - Hutch Sports USA Inc.

NBA - Umbrellas - Shedrain Corp.

NBA ACTION - Clothing - NBA Properties, Inc.

NBA ARENA CLUB - Apparel - NBA Properties, Inc.

NBA BAS-KET - Games - Cadaco Div.

NBA COMMEMORATIVE COLLECTION - Jewelry - NBA Properties, Inc.

NBA EASTERN CONFERENCE - Trading cards and stamps - NBA Properties, Inc.

NBA HOOPS - Trading cards - NBA Properties, Inc.

NBA IN THE ZONE - Computer storage devices–optical - Konami (America) Inc.

NBA INSIDE STUFF - Printed materials - NBA Properties, Inc.

NBA PLAYOFFS - Apparel and accessories - NBA Properties, Inc.

NBA STUFF - Apparel and accessories - NBA Properties, Inc.

NBA VIDEO - Video production - NBA Properties, Inc.

NBA WESTERN CONFERENCE - Apparel and accessories - NBA Properties, Inc.

NBAF - Apparel - National Black Arts Festival Inc.

NBASE SWITCH COMMUNICATIONS - Computer peripheral equipment - MRV Communications, Inc.

NBC - Medical apparatus - National Biological Corp.

NBC-1 - Briefcases - ACCO USA, Inc.

NBC-600 - Food products - Universal Foods Corp.

NBC TRUCK EQUIPMENT - Motor vehicles - NBC Truck Equipment Inc.

NBF - Butter flavor - American Flavor & Fragrance Corp.

NBK - Jewelry - NBK Co.

NBL - Coatings - Formwood Industries, Inc.

NBM - Stone products - Natural Building Materials, Inc.

NBNSOFT - Computer software - Nbnsoft Corp.

N.B.P. - Health care products - Forest Pharmaceuticals Inc.

NBPA - Games ☆ - Tudor Inc.

NBRC - Vitamins and nutritional supplements - Viva Nutrient Research Co.

NBS - Compact discs–prerecorded - Walter Fields

NBS-AV - Vitamins and nutritional supplements - Lifetrends International

N.B.T. - Thread - New Bedford Thread Co. Inc.

NC - Circuit breakers - American Circuit Breaker Corp.

NC+ - Flowers, plants, and seeds - NC+ Hybrids Cooperative

NC - Pharmaceutical preparations - American Cultures & Enzyme Systems, Inc.

NC - Wines - Duplin Wine Cellars

NC-80 - Penetrating oil - Contact Industries Inc.

NCA - Footwear - Summit Footwear Inc.

NCA COMPUTER PRODUCTS - Computer peripheral equipment - Inverse Corp.

NCAA - Handbags - Pyramid Handbags Inc.

NCAA - Shoes - Interco Inc.

NCAA CHAMPIONSHIP - Balls - Brine Inc.

NCAA INTERNATIONAL - Recording label - National Collegiate Athletic Association

NCADMIN - Computer software - Cummings Group, Inc.

NCAP - Liquid crystal displays - Raychem Corp.

NCAR GRAPHICS - Computer software - University Corp. for Atmospheric Research

N.C.B. - Canned hams - J & M Universal Sales Co.

NCC - Jewelry - OroCal Manufacturing Co. Inc.

NCC COMPUTER - Computer stores - Thuan Thi Doan Nguyen

NCFI 2020 PLUS - Insulating materials–foam - North Carolina Foam Industries, Inc.

NCFR - Wood products - Homasote Co.

NCH REPORTRIGHT - Computer software - NCH Promotional Services, Inc.

NCI - Building materials - NCI Building Systems, Inc.

NCNP - Chemical preparations - State Chemical Manufacturing Co.

NCP - Pet products - Neuhaus Chemical Products, Inc.

NCP - Thread - Gudebrod, Inc.

NCP-2 - Cleaning preparations - Noco Co.

NCR - Paper - Appleton Papers Inc.

NCS WORKS - Computer software - National Computer Systems, Inc.

NCTI - Educational materials - Versacom, Inc.

NCW - All-purpose cleaner - Mirachem Corp.

ND - Musical instrument accessories - New Day Christian Distributors, Inc.

ND-914 - Boots - Wellco Enterprises Inc.

ND CLEAR - Pharmaceutical preparations - Seatrace Co.

ND-GESIC - Pharmaceutical preparations - Hyrex Pharmaceuticals

ND-HIST - Pharmaceutical preparations - Hyrex Pharmaceuticals

ND INDUSTRIES - Waxes–mineral - Nd Industries, Inc.

ND MICROSPHERES - Epoxy - Nd Industries, Inc.

ND-STAT - Pharmaceutical preparations - Hyrex Pharmaceuticals

NDC CAPTURE - Computer software - Nationsbank of North Carolina, N.A.

NDC LASER - Electronic equipment - Nationsbank Corp.

NDESTRUKT - Shoes–athletic ☆ - Nike, Inc.

NDIS - Computer software - PC-Plus Communications Lp

NDM - Surgical supplies - NDM Acquisition Corp.

NDP - Computer peripheral equipment - Microway, Inc.

N.D.Q. - Candy ☆ - Marshmallow Products

NDS - Vitamins and nutritional supplements - Shaperite Concepts, Ltd.

NDT - Water treating compounds - Gurtler Chemicals Inc.

NDT-II - Automotive parts and accessories - Paul E. Hawkinson Co.

NDX - Apparel–men's - Cottage Mills, Inc.

NDX - Computers - Tandem Computers Inc.

NE-MO'S - Bakery products ☆ - Ne-Mo's Bakery Inc.

NE PLUS ULTRA - Guitars ☆ - Fred Gretsch Enterprises

NE-PRIME - Coatings - Sherwin-Williams Automotive Finishes Corp.

NEA HELP - Banks–commercial - National Education Association

NEA HIGHER EDUCATION LOAN PROGRAM - Banks–commercial - National Education Association

NEA HOMEOWNERS - Insurance agencies–life - National Education Association

NEA MEMBERCARE - Insurance agencies–health - National Education Association

NEAL FEHEMAN - Bedding–linen - Red Calliope and Associates Inc.

NEAL-FERROGRAPH - Audio equipment ☆ - Connectronics Corp.

NEAL MCCOY - Recording label - Neal McCoy Enterprises, Inc.

NEAL'S - Cookies - Neal's

NEALSON DISTRIBUTORS - Jewelry - Lawrence Neal

NEAPOLITAN - Beverages–alcohol - Consolidated Distilled Products Inc.

NEAPOLITAN - Floor coverings–carpet and rugs ☆ - Whitecrest Carpet Mills

NEAPOLITAN - Furniture ☆ - Stanley Furniture Co. Inc.

NEAPOLITAN ESPRESSO - Coffee - Mr. Espresso

NEAR EAST - Food products - Golden Grain Co.

NEAR EAST - Food products - Near East Food Products Inc.

NEAR SHEER - Underwear and nightwear ☆ - Lovable Co.

NEARLY ME - Bathing suits ☆ - Nearly Me

NEARLY ME BRA - Underwear and nightwear ☆ - Nearly Me

NEARLY ME EQUALIZER - Prosthetic apparatus - Nearly Me

NEARLY ME III - Prosthetic apparatus - Nearly Me

NEARLY ME LITE - Prosthetic apparatus ☆ - Nearly Me

NEARLY ME REST BREAST - Prosthetic apparatus ☆ - Nearly Me

NEARLY ME SUPER V - Prosthetic apparatus ☆ - Nearly Me

NEARLY ME TENDER TOUCH - Medical apparatus - Spenco Medical Corp.

NEARLY ME TOO - Prosthetic apparatus ☆ - Nearly Me

NEARLY NUDE - Manicure preparations - Del Pharmaceuticals, Inc.

NEARLY NUDES - Apparel–women's - Cacique, Inc.

NEARLY YOU - Underwear and nightwear - Maidenform Inc.

NEARRANGER - Antennas - Communications & Energy Corp., Inc.

NEAS - Motorcycles - Suzuki of America Automotive Corp.

NEAT - Adhesives and sealants ☆ - Desert Enterprises

NEAT - Computer software - Matrix Real Estate Advisors, Inc.

NEAT AND CLEAN - Paints - Standard Brands Paint Co.

NEAT & UNTIDY - Apparel and accessories - William Sivers, Sr.

NEAT-CLEAT - Sporting goods - C. Sherman Johnson Co. Inc.

NEAT ERASER - Erasers ☆ - Sakura of America

NEAT FEET BY DIVINE DESIGN - Jewelry - Harriet Marcus

NEAT-FLO - Stamps–hand - Avery Dennison Corp.
NEAT IDEAS - File folders - Fellowes Manufacturing Co.
NEAT-JET - Toners - Sercomp Corp.
NEAT KITTY - Pet products - Applied Industrial Materials
NEAT-LAC - Leather goods - Tandy Leather Co.
NEAT 'N' EASY - Bags–storage - E-Z-Por Corp.
NEAT N EASY - Garden equipment - Carefree Garden Products
NEAT NEON - Jewelry - Imperial Toy Corp.
NEAT-O-MOSAICS - Decals and transfers - A + A
NEAT PLEAT - Blinds–venetian - Spring Window Fashions Division, Inc.
NEAT SCOOP - Pet products - Applied Industrial Materials
NEAT-SEAT - Apparel and accessories - Cherokee Group
NEAT SEAT - High chairs - Graco Children's Products
NEAT SEAT - Paper–toilet - Sanitor Manufacturing Co.
NEAT SHEETS - Office supplies ☆ - Dixon Ticonderoga Co.
NEAT SWEEP - Dusters ☆ - Zorbite Corp.
NEAT, SWEET, READY TO EAT! - Fruits and vegetables - Grimmway
     Enterprises, Inc.
NEAT TEEN - Toys - Eugene Doll & Novelty Co. Inc.
NEAT-TOUCH - Nail care products - Revlon Consumer Products Corp.
NEATFORM - Napkins–paper - Georgia-Pacific Corp.
NEATGARDS - Aprons - Handgards, Inc.
NEATIP - Laces–boot and shoe ☆ - St. Louis Braid Co.
NEATO - Computer peripheral equipment - MicroPatent L.L.C.
NEATSFOOT - Pet products ☆ - Glo-Marr Products Inc.
NEATSLENE - Shoe accessories - Bickmore Inc.
NEATSOPE - Soap - Shore Chemical Co. Inc.
NEB-U-LITE - Medical apparatus - Graham-Field Inc.
NEBBIA - Cabinets ☆ - Lane Co. Inc.
NEBBIOLO - Wines - Renwood Winery, Inc.
NEBCIN - Pharmaceutical preparations - Eli Lilly and Co.
NEBCO - Laces–boot and shoe ☆ - Hickory Industries, Inc.
NEBLOT - Biochemical kits - New England Biolabs Inc.
NEBRALIN - Health care products - Dorsey Laboratories
NEBRASKA - Meat products–beef ☆ - Central Nebraska Packing Inc.
NEBU-SOL - Health care products ☆ - Dey Laboratories Inc.
NEBULA - Apparel–women's - R. & A. Collections Inc.
NEBULA - Doors–storm - Canyon Creek Cabinet Co.
NEBULA - Exercising equipment - Proto Weld Inc.
NEBULA - Floor coverings - American Floor Products Co. Inc.
NEBULA - Recording label ☆ - Centaur Records
NEBULA RUBRA AROMATICA - Pharmaceutical preparations - Sherwood
     Laboratories Inc.
NEBULIZER - Medical apparatus - Blairex Laboratories, Inc.
NEBULO - Nebulizers ☆ - Specialty Health Care Products Inc.
NEBULON WARRIOR - Toys–models ☆ - Estes Industries
NEBUTACH HDN - Medical apparatus - Salter Labs
NEBWORTH - Floor coverings–carpet and rugs - Daltonian Carpet & Cushion
     Inc.
NEC - Computers - Enterprise Computer Systems Inc.
NEC - Computers–personal ☆ - NEC Technologies, Inc.
NEC - Health care products - Power Plus Systems Inc.
NEC AVENUE - Recording label - J/L Entertainment Group
NEC EXPERT - Video tapes–blank - National Fire Protection Association
NEC ULTRALITE - Computers–personal ☆ - NEC Technologies, Inc.
NECC - Electrical brushes - New England Carbon Corp.
NECCO - Fruits–canned - New Era Canning Co.
NECCO PEACH BLOSSOMS - Candy ☆ - New England Confectionery Co.
NECCO WAFERS - Candy - New England Confectionery Co.
NECESS-A-TEES - Apparel–women's - SM Acquisition Sub, Inc.
NECESS-A-TEES YOU GOTTA HAVE ONE - Leotards - SM Acquisition Sub,
     Inc.
NECESSARY ORGANICS - Insecticides - Necessary Organics Inc.
NECESSITIES - Vitamins and nutritional supplements - Bayer Corp.
NECHLORIN - Prescription drug - IDE-Interstate Inc.
NECK - Jewelry - Peter Brams Designs, Ltd.
NECK COOLER - Bandana - Earl Campbell
NECK EZE - Pillows ☆ - Alger Creations Inc.
NECK F/X - Neckties - Pamela L. Kafka
NECK-HUGGAR - Health care products - Bodyline Comfort Systems
NECK JOY - Pillows - Linda H. Dixon
NECK KNOT - Gloves - Totes, Inc.
NECK NOOGIES - Medical apparatus - Positive Touch Therapists, Inc.
NECK-PIL-O - Pillows ☆ - E.R. Carpenter Co.
NECK-PRO-TECH - Sporting goods - Powersports Safety Co., LLC

NECK PROTEC/WEATHER SHIELD - Hats - Talako Products and Services
     Inc.
NECK RESCUE, THE - Pillows - Pacific Spirit Corp.
NECK $AFE - Wallets ☆ - Apothecary Products, Inc.
NECK SAVER - Musical instrument accessories - Rico International
NECK SOCK - Apparel and accessories - Jerry Alcorn
NECK STRIPS - Hair care products - W.R. Rayson Co., Inc.
NECK-UPS - Apparel–athletic - Reliable of Milwaukee
NECKAR - Glassware–household - Oneida Ltd.
NECKLACE - Pens ☆ - Sheaffer Inc.
NECKLACES - Candy - Ce De Candy Inc.
NECKLETS - Neckwear - Byzantium Inc.
NECKPAK - Musical instrument accessories - Kiwi Wind Products
NECKSAVER - Skin care products - Niche Research Inc.
NECKSET - Television equipment - Television Equipment Associates
NECKTRAC - Traction apparatus–medical - Lossing Orthopedic Co.
NECKWRAP - Pillows - Perfect Fit Industries, Inc.
NECKWRAP PLUS - Pillows - Perfect Fit Industries, Inc.
NECKY KAYAK - Boats–kayaks - Johnson Worldwide Associates, Inc.
NECON - Electrical equipment - Applied Power Inc.
NECRODOME - Games - Strategic Simulations, Inc.
NECTA SWEET - Food products - Procter & Gamble Co.
NECTA SWEET - Spices and extracts ☆ - NutraSweet Co.
NECTAR - Granola bars - Natural Nectar Corp.
NECTAR COLLECTOR - Games - Animal Town
NECTAR DREAMS - Confections - Natural Nectar Corp.
NECTAR FREEZE - Snack foods - Natural Nectar Corp.
NECTAR LOVE - Pottery ☆ - Rubens Originals
NECTAR NOVELTIES - Desserts - Natural Nectar Corp.
NECTAR NUGGET - Candy - Natural Nectar Corp.
NECTAR PIE - Snack foods - Natural Nectar Corp.
NECTAR SODA SYRUP - Soft drink syrup - Nectar Soda Co., Inc.
NECTARADE - Fruit drinks–bottled or canned - Fliinko, Inc.
NECTARBERRY - Fruit drinks - Everfresh Beverages, Inc.
NECTAREL - Fruit flavored drinks - Nectarel Co.
NECTAROSE - Wines - Seagram's Chateau & Estate Wines Co.
NECTARSWEET - Food products - Breadshop's Natural Foods
NECTARVILLE POPS - Juices–frozen ☆ - Natural Nectar Corp.
NECTARYL - Health care products ☆ - Halsey Drug Co. Inc.
NECTOSE - Corn syrup ☆ - Penford Products Co.
NED-U-MASK - Health care products - Hudson Respiratory Care Inc.
NED-U-MIST - Health care products - Hudson Respiratory Care Inc.
NED-U-TENT - Health care products - Hudson Respiratory Care Inc.
NEDERBURG - Wines - Dreyfus Ashby Inc.
NEDERDAM - Cheese - Swissrose International Inc.
NEDERLANDS VITA - Bird feeds - Sunshine Bird Supplies, Inc.
NEDICKS - Beverages–carbonated - Canada Dry Corp.
NEDLAND - Watches - Gruen Marketing Corp.
N.E.E. 1/35 - Pharmaceutical preparations - Lexis Laboratories Inc.
N.E.E. 1/50 - Pharmaceutical preparations - Lexis Laboratories Inc.
N.E.E. 5/35 - Pharmaceutical preparations - Lexis Laboratories Inc.
N.E.E. 10/11 - Pharmaceutical preparations - Lexis Laboratories Inc.
NEE DE PROVENCE - Mayonnaise - Stache Foods
NEECHI - Fruit drinks–bottled or canned - Occanneechi Inc.
NEED A LITTLES - Toys–stuffed - Matchbox Toys USA
NEED ACCESS - Computer software - Law Access, Inc.
NEED-L-EEL - Fishing lures - Acme Tackle Co.
NEED TO KNOW LIBRARY, THE - Publisher's imprints - Rosen Publishing
     Group & Pelion Press
NEEDLE & THREADS - Apparel and accessories - Folette Design, Inc.
NEEDLE ART - Hobby kits - Rosewood Products Inc.
NEEDLE CASE - Cases–plastic - Caro Creations Inc.
NEEDLE CHECK - Mats ☆ - Ludlow Composites Corp.
NEEDLE-EASE - Needlework products - American Crewel & Canvas Studio
NEEDLE-EASEL - Roll frames and table stands - American Crewel & Canvas
     Studio
NEEDLE-EZE - Fabrics–cotton - Barnhardt Manufacturing Co.
NEEDLE-EZE - Thread - Needlecraft Industries
NEEDLE-LUBE - Housewares - Sewing Organizer
NEEDLE MASTER - Fasteners–hook and eye - Boye Needle
NEEDLE-MATE - Recording label - Rains Recording Co.
NEEDLE MINDER - Electronics equipment - L & M Auto Supply
NEEDLE NICHES - Wood products - Daphne Grad
NEEDLE ODYSSEY - Hobby kits ☆ - Accent Studios Inc.
NEEDLE PIN - Mats - Ludlow Composites Corp.
NEEDLE POINT - Slippers, socks - Allen D. Everitt Knitting Co.

☆ = Now out of production

NEEDLE-RIB - Mats - Ludlow Composites Corp.
NEEDLE SAFE - Medical apparatus - Biotronix Laboratories, Inc.
NEEDLE TREASURES - Hobby kits - Carilorz Corp.
NEEDLE TREASURES - Hobby kits - JCA, Inc.
NEEDLE TREASURES CHRISTMAS - Hobby kits - JCA, Inc.
NEEDLECRAFT CHEST - Toys - Coloron Industries
NEEDLECRAFT SHOP, THE - Yarn - Needlecraft Shop, Inc.
NEEDLEFISH - Sporting goods - Boone Bait Co. Inc.
NEEDLEFORM - Cross-stitch kits - Needleform
NEEDLEGARD - Veterinary medical equipment - Ideal Instruments Inc.
NEEDLEPOINT - Dinnerware and counter saver ☆ - Corning Inc.
NEEDLEPOINT - Dinnerware—glass ☆ - Nikko Ceramics Inc.
NEEDLEPOINT CAT - Clocks - General Time Corp. (Westclox/Seth Thomas Div.)
NEEDLEPRINT - Fabrics - It's Polite to Point, Inc.
NEEDLER'S - Candy - S.L. Kaye Co., Inc.
NEEDLES AND PINS - Apparel and accessories - Judy Bond Inc.
NEEDLES READY - Hobby kits - Patricia P. Punton
NEEDLETECH PRODUCTS, INC. - Medical apparatus - Needletech Products, Inc.
NEEDLEWEB - Fabrics ☆ - West Point-Pepperell Inc.
NEEDLEXPRESS - Hobby kits - Lawrence E. Nerheim
NEEDLYZER - Electronics equipment - Bio-Safety Instruments, Inc.
NEEDS... - Skin care products - By Casey, Inc.
NEEDS. - Skin care products - By Casey, Inc.
NEEGARDS - Hardware - The Centro Co. Inc.
NEELIS & SONS - Bakery products - Neelis & Son Orchard & Cider Mill
NEELIX - Toys - Paramount Pictures Corp.
NEELON - Automotive parts and accessories - Echlin Inc.
NEELY - Garment storage bags - Neely Manufacturing Co. Inc.
NEELY'S BAR-B-Q SAUCE - Barbecue sauce - Neely's Bar-B-Que, Inc.
NEEMADENT - Dentifrices - Herbaceuticals Inc.
NEEMAZAD - Pesticides—agricultural - W.R. Grace & Co.
NEEMGARD - Fungicides - W.R. Grace & Co.
NEEN - Recording label - Jazz Composer's Orchestra Association Inc.
NEENAH BOND - Paper—bond - Neenah Paper Co.
NEENAH FOUNDRY CO. - Iron - Neenah Corp.
NEENAH LASER - Paper - Neenah Paper Co.
NEEPLE - Jewelry - Claire's Boutiques, Inc.
NEERA'S - Food products - Cinnabar Specialty Foods, Inc./Neera's Products
NEESE INDUSTRIES - Apparel and accessories - Neese Industries, Inc.
NEESE RAINWEAR - Waterproof outerwear - Neese Industries, Inc.
NEET - Archery equipment - Neet Products Inc.
NEET - Skin care products - Whitehall Laboratories
NEET - Watchbands and straps - Jacoby-Bender Inc.
NEET FEET - Sandals - Neet Feet, Inc.
NEET SLEEPER - Linen - Bentley Bedding
NEET STREETER - Toys—automobiles - Mattel, Inc.
NEETLINE - Pens ☆ - Faber-Castell Corp.
NEFA+ - Shampoos - KMS Research Inc.
NEFAX - Facsimile equipment - NEC America, Inc.
NEFCO - Seafood products—fresh or frozen - New England Fish Co.
NEFCO - Water purification systems - Nefco
NEFE PRESS - Publisher's imprints - National Endowment for Financial Education
NEFERTARI - Cosmetics - Houria Iderkou
NEFERTARI - Perfumes ☆ - Aloe Creme Laboratories
NEFERTITI - Apparel and accessories ☆ - Swatch Watch USA
NEFERTITI - Cigarettes - G.A. Georgopulo & Co. Inc.
NEFF'S - Cigars - A.J. Golden Inc.
NEGA-FILE - File folders - Negafile Systems Inc.
NEGA GUARD - Photographic equipment - Light Impressions Corp.
NEGASOL - Sunblocks ☆ - Covermark Cosmetics
NEGATIVE NEGATIVE - Bath salts - Lauren Bird
NEGATRANS - Photographic equipment - Charles Beseler Co.
NEGATRON - Antistatic mats, now out of production - American Floor Products Co. Inc.
NEGAWATT METER - Temperature sensors - John Mark Dempsey
NEGEV - Footwear - Yaleet Inc.
NEGEV CERAMIC - Tiles—ceramic ☆ - Maxsam Sales, Inc.
NEGGRAM - Antibiotics - Winthrop Pharmaceuticals
NEGOTIATE SMART - Publisher's imprints - Princeton Review Publishing, LLC
NEGRA MODELO - Beverages—malt - Barton Brands, Ltd.
NEGRA MODELO - Beverages—malt - Canandaigua Wine Co. Inc.
NEGRAR - Beverages—alcohol - Trebon Wine & Spirit Corp.

NEGRO LEAGUES BASEBALL MUSEUM - Clothing - Negro Leagues Baseball Museum, Inc.
NEHALEM - Yarn - Oregon Worsted Co.
NEHALEM BAY - Wines - Nehalem Bay Wine Co.
NEHEMIAH - Educational materials - Daniel J. Smithwick
NEHEMIAH - Recording label - Whirlwind Records
NEHI - Beverages—carbonated - Royal Crown Cola Co.
NEHI FROOT - Beverages—carbonated - Royal Crown Cola Co.
NEHI LOCKJAW - Beverages—carbonated - Royal Crown Cola Co.
NEHI NATURAL - Beverages—carbonated - Royal Crown Cola Co.
NEHI ORIGINALS - Beverages—carbonated - Royal Crown Cola Co., Inc.
NEHPEM - Pharmaceutical preparations ☆ - Wendt-Bristol Co.
NEI - Asphalt - Northern Elastomeric, Inc.
NEI - Jewelry - Nanasi Enterprises Inc.
NEIDECKEN - Plumbing fixtures—enameled - Kohler Co.
NEIGHBORHOOD ADVENTURES - Publisher's imprints - Kenneth T. Gerew
NEIGHBORHOOD KIDS - Dolls - Mattel, Inc.
NEIGHBORS - Coffee ☆ - Chase Collection, Inc.
NEIGHBORS - Computer software - E. David & Associates
NEIGHBORS QUALITY HOUSE - Coffee - Executive Coffee Service Co.
NEIL DEFALCO - T-shirts—men's - Neil Defalco
NEIL EMPSON - Beverages—alcohol ☆ - Trebon Wine & Spirit Corp.
NEIL STANLEY COLLECTION, THE - Neckties - Newsub Services, Inc.
NEILSON - Trailers—boat - Neilson Wheel Co. Inc.
NEIMAN MARCUS FOR ALL SEASONS - Raincoats - Neiman Marcus Co.
NEJAIME'S LAVASCH - Breads - Nejaime's of the Berkshires
NEK/CDT - Wire - Cable Design Technologies, Inc.
NEK-EZE - Cushions ☆ - Better Sleep, Inc.
NEK-L-O - Orthopedic products - Gustave Rick Rinz
NEK-L-O - Pillows - Rinz-L-O Pillow Co.
NEK-LOK - Cosmetics - Hydro-Tex Corp.
NEK TRACKER - Shelving units—metal - Mead Corp.
NEKER - Glass vases, perfume bottles - Israeli Accents
NEKO - Soap ☆ - Parke-Davis
NEKOOSA - Paper—bond - Georgia-Pacific Corp.
NEKSESSORY - Jewelry - Meryl Designs, Inc.
NEKTAR PLUS - Pet products - Nekton USA Inc.
NEKTON - Pet products - Nekton USA Inc.
NEL-SCRIPT - Paints - Nelson Paint Co., Inc.
NEL SPOT - Guns - Nelson Paint Co., Inc.
NEL-STAIN - Stains - Nelson Paint Co., Inc.
NELCO - Ashtrays—glass ☆ - AAA Glass Corp.
NELCO - Sewing machines—household - Nelco Sewing Machine Sales Corp.
NELINE - Hosiery ☆ - Signal Knitwear Co.
NELIZ - Recording label - Combo Records
NELKIN - Health care products - Nelkin/Piper Health Products
NELKIN/PIPER INTERNATIONAL - Health care products - Nelkin/Piper Health Products
NELL FLOWERS - Apparel stores—children's - J.G. Hook, Inc.
NELLIE - Dolls - Mattel, Inc.
NELLIE - Food products - NC Acquisitions Inc.
NELLIE - Health care products - Nellson Candies Inc.
NELLIE & JOE'S - Juices - Castle Food Products
NELLIE STICKS - Fruits—candied - Nellson Candies Inc.
NELLY COW - Toys—stuffed ☆ - Dakin Inc.
NELLY DE VUYST OLEASLIM - Skin care products - Nelly de Vuyst USA
NELO OF SWITZERLAND - Fabrics ☆ - Leimtex Corp.
NEL'S - Shaving preparations - Nel's Laboratories Inc.
NELSON - Artists' materials - Hunt Manufacturing Co.
NELSON - Cigars - E. Regensburg & Sons
NELSON - Meat products—beef ☆ - Melson Meat Co. Inc.
NELSON - Snowboards - Nelson Sports, Inc.
NELSON - Sprinklers—lawn - L.R. Nelson Corp.
NELSON BEAD - Giftware - Luminiere Corp.
NELSON CANDLES - Candles - Nelson Candles, Inc.
NELSON PAINTBALLS - Sporting goods - Nelson Paint Co., Inc.
NELSON-RICKS - Food products - Nelson-Ricks Creamery Co.
NELSON SEATREATS - Shrimp—canned or cured - Nelson Crab Inc.
NELSONIC - Watches - M.Z. Berger & Co. Inc.
NELSONITE - Coatings - Nelsonite, Inc.
NELSON'S - Seafood products—fresh or frozen - Bon Secour Fisheries Inc.
NELSON'S CLASSY BASKETS - Food products - Nelson Floral Co. Inc.
NELSON'S INSTITUTIONAL MARKETPLACE ON-DISK - Computer software - Nelson Publications
NELSONS OF AINTREE - Jams and jellies - Europa Foods Ltd.
NELSONS OF ENGLAND - Food products ☆ - Gourmet America

NELSON'S QUICK-REFERENCE - Publisher's imprints - Thomas Nelson, Inc.

NELSON'S TOKELAND - Seafood products–canned or cured - Nelson Crab Inc.

NELSONX - Garden equipment ☆ - Nelsonite, Inc.

NEM - Hardware - National Extrusion and Manufacturing Co.

NEMA - Apparel and accessories - Jennifer E. McNabb

NEMA - Flowers, plants, and seeds - Petoseed Co., Inc.

NEMACUR - Insecticides - Bayer Corp. (Agriculture Div.)

NEMARC - Audio equipment - Nemarc Inc.

NEMASKET - Soybean oil - Belmont Springs Water Co. Inc.

NEMASOL - Agricultural products - Platte Chemical Co.

NEMBU-DONNA - Pharmaceutical preparations ☆ - Abbott Laboratories

NEMBUDEINE - Analgesics ☆ - Abbott Laboratories

NEMBUTAL - Pharmaceutical preparations - Abbott Laboratories

NEMCO - Flour–blended - New Era Milling Co.

NEMCO - Musical instrument accessories - Newark Musical Merchandise Co.

NEMCO - Wastebaskets ☆ - F.H. Lawson Co.

NEMDI - Skin care products - Nemectron Skin Care Inc.

NEMEAN LINE, THE - Paints - Tufco International, Inc.

NEMECTRON - Skin care products - Nemectron-Belmont Inc.

NEMECTRON-BELMONT - Cosmetics - Nemectron-Belmont Inc.

NEMESIS - Alarm systems - Whistler Acquistion Corp.

NEMESIS - Books–comic - Harvey Comics Entertainment, Inc.

NEMESIS - Footwear–athletic - L.A. Gear, Inc.

NEMESIS - Rackets–racquetball - Ektelon

NEMESIS - Toys - Tonka Corp.

NEMESIS-A WIZARDLY ADVENTURE - Computer software - Sir-Tech Software, Inc.

NEMESIS II - Computers - Cochran Undersea Technology Div.

NEMESPRAY - Skin care products - Nemesis Inc.

NEMO - Food products - Bob Ostrow Co.

NEMO - Games - Lakeside Games

NEMO - Nautical instruments ☆ - Watrous & Co. Inc.

NEMO'S - Food products - Dairy Fresh Products Co.

NEMPEROR - Tape players–cassette - Sony Music Entertainment Inc.

NENS - Cosmetics - New England Natural Sponge, Inc.

NENUCHOS - Dolls - Mattel, Inc.

NEO - Computer software - Sun Microsystems, Inc.

NEO - Curtain rods - Spring Window Fashions Division, Inc.

NEO - Frames–eyeglass - Hoya Corp. USA

NEO - Toys - Duncan Toys Co.

NEO 7 - Office furniture–plastic - Domore/DO3

NEO-ANGLE - Shower stalls–plastic - Plaskolite Inc.

NEO-AQUA-DRIN - Health care products - McKesson Home Health Care

NEO-BALANCE - Pharmaceutical preparations - Via Natura Inc.

NEO BAU - Furniture - Hodkinson Associates, Inc.

NEO-BETALIN 12 - Pharmaceutical preparations ☆ - Eli Lilly and Co.

NEO-CALGLUCON - Pharmaceutical preparations - Dorsey Laboratories

NEO CANVAS - Compact discs–prerecorded - Neo Custom Painted Environments, Inc.

NEO CARE - Catheters - Klein-Baker Medical, Inc.

NEO CARNIVAL - Game machines - Snk Corp. of America

NEO-CASTADERM - Pharmaceutical preparations - Lannett Co. Inc.

NEO-CHROME - Hinges - Coburn Corp.

NEO-CITRUN - Cold remedies - Sandoz Pharmaceuticals Corp.

NEO-CLASSIC - Wallpaper - Signature Wallcoverings

NEO CLASSIC STYLE - Wallpaper - Sterling Prints

NEO-CLASSICAL COLLECTION - Wallpaper - Bradbury & Bradbury Wallpapers

NEO-CORTEF - Pharmaceutical preparations - Upjohn Co.

NEO-CUTAWAY - Fretted instruments ☆ - International Music Corp.

NEO-DELTA-CORTEF - Pharmaceutical preparations ☆ - Upjohn Co.

NEO-DELTEF - Pharmaceutical preparations ☆ - Upjohn Co.

NEO DEO - Deodorants–personal - Neoquest, Inc.

NEO-DIARAL - Pharmaceutical preparations - Roberts/Hauck Pharmaceuticals Inc.

NEO-DOMEFORM-HC - Cribs–metal ☆ - Miles Inc.

NEO-DURABOLIC - Pharmaceutical preparations ☆ - Roberts/Hauck Pharmaceuticals Inc.

NEO-GENIC-DA - Health care products ☆ - Kay Pharmacal Co. Inc.

NEO GEO - Video games - Snk Corp. of America

NEO-GERASTAN - Health care products - Halsom Home Care

NEO GLAZE - Cleaning preparations ☆ - Chemical Products Co.

NEO-GRID - Signs - Data Display Corp.

NEO HYDELTRASOL - Ophthalmic goods ☆ - Merck & Co., Inc. (Merck Research Laboratories)

NEO MAX - Bathing suits ☆ - Jonathan Logan Inc.

NEO-MAX - Braces–orthopedic - Royce Medical Co.

NEO-MEDROL - Pharmaceutical preparations - Upjohn Co.

NEO-NAIL - Hardware - Deniston Co.

NEO-NYSTA-CORT - Antibiotics ☆ - Miles Inc.

NEO-OXYLONE - Pharmaceutical preparations ☆ - Upjohn Co.

NEO-PARCORT - Pharmaceutical preparations ☆ - Parmed Pharmaceuticals, Inc.

NEO PHENYLINE - Pharmaceutical preparations ☆ - Chase Laboratories Inc.

NEO-PHN - Health-care products ☆ - Inter-Cal Corp.

NEO-PLASTIC - Paints ☆ - Wescon Products Co.

NEO-PLASTIQUE - Wallpaper - Aresda Design Associates

NEO-POLY - Caulking compounds - Sav-Cote Chemical Laboratories Inc.

NEO-POLYCIN - Pharmaceutical preparations - Marion Merrell Dow

NEO-PREDEF - Veterinary pharmaceutical preparations - Upjohn Co.

NEO-PRIME - Cosmetics - Ladyfingers

NEO-PROMAR - Electronic equipment - Leica USA Inc.

NEO-PROPISOL - Pharmaceutical preparations ☆ - Wyeth-Ayerst Laboratories

NEO-PROTEC - Vitamins and nutritional supplements - J.R. Carlson Laboratories Inc.

NEO-PYRANISTAN - Health care products - Halsom Home Care

NEO-QUAD - Veterinary pharmaceutical preparations - Gerard-Pellham Co.

NEO-RADIAL TECHNOLOGY - Amplifiers - Aura Systems, Inc.

NEO-RADIUS - Shower stalls–plastic ☆ - Plaskolite Inc.

NEO SAC - Bags–duffel - Markuson Group Inc.

NEO-SCOUR - Antibiotics ☆ - Farnam Cos. Inc.

NEO-SEAL - Sealing devices ☆ - Robert Manufacturing Co.

NEO-SHOK - Building materials - Midwest Sport Floors, Inc.

NEO-SHOK - Floor covering - Continental Hardwood Floor Distributors Inc.

NEO-SPONGE - Floor coverings - American Floor Products Co. Inc.

NEO-SPORT - Sporting goods - Henderson Aquatics Inc.

NEO-SPRAY - Health care products - Halsey Drug Co. Inc.

NEO-SULFALYTE - Veterinary pharmaceutical preparations - Greever's

NEO-SYNALAR - Pharmaceutical preparations - Syntex USA, Inc.

NEO-SYNEPHRINE - Cold remedies - Bayer Corp. (Consumer Care Div.)

NEO SYNTHETIC - Enamels ☆ - Wescon Products Co.

NEO-TAB - Pharmaceutical preparations ☆ - Pal-Pak Inc.

NEO-TEARS - Ophthalmic goods - Barnes-Hind Inc.

NEO-TEN - Pharmaceutical preparations - Barrows Pharmacal Inc.

NEO-TERRAMYCIN - Restaurants–ice cream parlors ☆ - Pfizer Inc.

NEO-TEX - Floor coverings - American Floor Products Co. Inc.

NEO-THERM - Thermometers - Respiratory Support Products, Inc.

NEO-THRYCEX - Antibiotics ☆ - Del Pharmaceuticals, Inc.

NEO-TITE - Washers–leather - J.A. Sexauer, Inc.

NEO TO GO - Pharmaceutical preparations - Warner-Wellcome

NEO-TRAK - Health care products - Corometrics Medical Systems Inc.

NEO-TYPE - Band-saw blades - American Saw & Manufacturing Co.

NEO-WRITER - Typewriters - Brother International Corp.

NEO-XU - Pencils - Pilot Pen Corp. of America

NEOACCESS - Computer software - Neologic Systems, Inc.

NEOASMA - Pharmaceutical preparations - Tarmac Products Inc.

NEOBAKASAL - Food products - Sterling Winthrop Inc.

NEOBASE - Pharmaceutical preparations ☆ - Burroughs Wellcome Co.

NEOBIOTIC - Antibiotics - W.A. Butler Co.

NEOBOOK - Computer software - Neosoft Corp.

NEOBOOK PROFESSIONAL - Computer software - Neosoft Corp.

NEOBOR - Insecticides - U.S. Borax Inc.

NEOCAD PRISM - Computer software - Neocad, Inc.

NEOCAR - Latex - Union Carbide Corp.

NEOCARBON - Pharmaceutical preparations ☆ - U.S. Ethicals Inc.

NEOCET - Pharmaceutical preparations ☆ - Pal-Pak Inc.

NEOCHAIR - Furniture - Haworth, Inc.

NEOCHOLAN - Pharmaceutical preparations - Marion Merrell Dow

NEOCHROME II - Fabrics - Uniroyal Engineered Products

NEOCLASSIC - Furniture - Harter

NEOCLASSIC - Furniture - Jami, Inc.

NEOCLASSIC COLLECTION - Wallcovering - Gilford Corp.

NEOCOLD - Pharmaceutical preparations - Bruder Healthcare Co.

NEOCOLOR - Crayons - Caran D'Ache of Switzerland Inc.

NEOCOMPLEX - Pharmaceutical preparations ☆ - U.S. Ethicals Inc.

NEOCORD - Mats - Cactus Mat Manufacturing Co.

NEOCRETE - Setting and bonding agent - Construction Adhesives Co.

NEOCURB - Pharmaceutical preparations - Pasadena Research Laboratories, Inc.

NEOCURTASAL - Salt ☆ - Winthrop Pharmaceuticals

NEOCUSSOR - Medical apparatus - General Physiotherapy, Inc.

☆ = Now out of production

NEOCYLATE - Analgesics ☆ - Central Pharmaceutical Inc.
NEOCYTEN - Pharmaceutical preparations ☆ - Central Pharmaceutical Inc.
NEODATA - Computer software - Metasoft Systems, Inc.
NEODECADRON - Ophthalmic goods - Merck & Co., Inc. (Merck Research Laboratories)
NEODEX - Pharmaceutical preparations ☆ - U.S. Ethicals Inc.
NEODEXAIR - Ophthalmic goods - Bausch & Lomb Inc.
NEODRAW - Computer software - Neosoft Corp.
NEOFAX-PC - Computer software - Neofax PC, Inc.
NEOFED - Pharmaceutical preparations ☆ - Pal-Pak Inc.
NEOFLEECE - Apparel and accessories - Seirus Innovative Accessories, Inc.
NEOFLEECE - Fabrics - Seirus Innovative Accessories, Inc.
NEOGEN - Chemical preparations - Neogen Corp.
NEOGEN - Pigments - Dry Branch Kaolin Co.
NEOGESIC - Pharmaceutical preparations ☆ - Pal-Pak Inc.
NEOGLOBIN - Pharmaceutical preparations - Northfield Laboratories, Inc.
NEOGRAB - Computer software - Neosoft Corp.
NEOGRAPHICS I - Wallpaper - J. Josephson, Inc.
NEOGRAPHIX - Wallpaper - K.M.L. Industries
NEOGRAPHIX - Wallpaper - Manuscreens
NEOGRIP - Grip enhancer - NEOCARE Laboratories Inc. (International Daleco)
NEOLAX - Laxatives ☆ - Central Pharmaceutical Inc.
NEOLET - Medical apparatus - Sherwood Medical Co.
NEOLITE - Magnets - SPS Technologies, Inc.
NEOLITE - Shoe soles - Goodyear Tire & Rubber Co.
NEOLOID - Health care products - Kenwood Laboratories Inc.
NEOLOZ-B - Pharmaceutical preparations ☆ - Cameron Medical Corp.
NEOLT - Drawing furniture - Martin Universal Design Inc.
NEOMARK - Pharmaceutical preparations ☆ - C&M Pharmacal, Inc.
NEOMISSION - Furniture - Custom Woodcarving, Inc.
NEOMIX - Veterinary pharmaceutical preparations - Upjohn Co.
NEOMIX PLUS - Veterinary pharmaceutical preparations - Upjohn Co.
NEOMIXIN - Pharmaceutical preparations - Roberts/Hauck Pharmaceuticals Inc.
NEOMYCIN - Pet products ☆ - Aquatronics-Filtronics
NEON - Apparel and accessories - Oxford Industries, Inc.
NEON - Floor coverings - American Floor Products Co. Inc.
NEON - Floor coverings–carpet and rugs - Ashley Commercial Carpets
NEON - Furniture - Haworth, Inc.
NEON - Motor vehicle parts and accessories - DaimlerChrysler
NEON - Motor vehicles–automobiles - Chrysler Corp. (Chrysler-Plymouth Div.)
NEON - Paper–bond - Riverside Paper Corp.
NEON - Recording label - Guajiro Records Inc.
NEON ART - Writing product ☆ - Binney & Smith Inc.
NEON BANDITS - Candy - Uniconfis Corp.
NEON BEACH - Chewing gum ☆ - Amurol Confections Co.
NEON BLAST - Beverages–carbonated - Topco Associates, Inc.
NEON BLASTER - Toys–automobiles - Tyco Industries, Inc.
NEON BUBBLE STRIPS - Chewing gum - Amurol Confections Co.
NEON CLASSICS - Office supplies - Datacom Inc.
NEON EFFECTS - Lighting equipment–automotive - Rally Accessories, Inc.
NEON HEAT - Air purification systems ☆ - Medo Industries, Inc.
NEON KING AMERICA - Signs - A Cube Inc.
NEON LASERS - Candy - R.L. Albert & Son, Inc.
NEON LITES - Pens - Faber-Castell Corp.
NEON NAMES - Key rings - Wald Designs Acrylic Idea Factory
NEON NERDS - Candy - Willy Wonka Brands
NEON NIGHT - Kites ☆ - Hi-Flier Manufacturing Co.
NEON PAC - Computer disks - Cenna Technology Inc.
NEON PLUS - Signs - Clearr Corp.
NEON POWER DRIVE - Transformers–electric - Marshall Electric Corp.
NEON PURPLE - Nail care products - Pavion Ltd.
NEON RAINBOW - Fireworks - Ingram Enterprises, Inc.
NEON RAYS - Yarn - Rainbow Gallery, Inc.
NEON RECORDS, INC. - Recording label - Neon Records, Inc.
NEON ROCKET - Toys–automobiles - Tyco Industries, Inc.
NEON SPECIFIER, THE - Neon - Tecnolux, Inc.
NEON SPORTSWEAR, USA - Apparel–men's - Oxford Industries, Inc.
NEONATAL MONITOR - Medical apparatus - Nellcor Puritan Bennett
NEONATE - Dog food ☆ - Central Soya Co. Inc.
NEONIZE - Electronic equipment - Neonize Corp.
NEONLITE - Signs - Jewelite Sign Co.
NEONS - Balls - Sipa Sipa Games
NEONS - Flowers–artificial - Penn-Plax, Inc.
NEONS - Paints - House of Kolor, Inc.
NEOPAINT - Computer software - Neosoft Corp.

NEOPAP SUPPRETTES - Pharmaceutical preparations ☆ - M. Polymedica Corp.
NEOPAQUE - Paints - Ivy Imports Inc.
NEOPASTEL - Artists' materials - Caran D'Ache of Switzerland Inc.
NEOPATH - Computer software and hardware - Neopath Inc.
NEOPERL - Faucets - Neoperl Inc.
NEOPERSIST - Computer software - Neologic Systems, Inc.
NEOPHIL - Thread - Premier Thread Co.
NEOPHYLLINE - Pharmaceutical preparations ☆ - Bolan Pharmaceutical Inc.
NEOPLEX - Pet products - Seachem Laboratories
NEOPROFILE - Housewares - Bammental Wallcoverings Inc.
NEOPTX - Lenses–optical - OPTX 20/20
NEOQUESS - Pharmaceutical preparations - Forest Pharmaceuticals Inc.
NEORHYTHMS - Floor coverings–carpet and rugs - Karastan-Bigelow Inc.
NEORION - Health care products - Johnson & Johnson
NEOROM - Spices and extracts - Dragoco Inc.
NEOS - Machinery ☆ - Prince Sports Group, Inc.
NEOSCAN - Computer hardware - Spacelabs Medical, Inc.
NEOSCREEN - Window shades ☆ - John Dixon Inc.
NEOSHARE - Computer software - Neologic Systems, Inc.
NEOSHO - Barbecues and grills ☆ - Sunbeam Outdoor Products Inc.
NEOSHOW - Computer software - Neosoft Corp.
NEOSHOW PRO - Computer software - Neosoft Corp.
NEOSOCU - Footwear - Seirus Innovative Accessories, Inc.
NEOSOFT - Computer software - Neosoft Corp.
NEOSOFT - Computer software - Neosoft, Inc.
NEOSOLV - Chemical preparations - Shell Oil Co.
NEOSONE - Pharmaceutical preparations ☆ - Upjohn Co.
NEOSORB PLUS - Pharmaceutical preparations ☆ - Lemmon Co.
NEOSPECT - Pharmaceutical preparations ☆ - Lemmon Co.
NEOSPHERE - Lighting equipment - Kim Lighting Inc.
NEOSPORIN - Antibiotics - Warner-Wellcome
NEOSPORIN PLUS - Pharmaceutical preparations - Warner-Wellcome
NEOSPUN - Thread ☆ - SCT Yarns Inc.
NEOSTAR MEDICAL - Catheters - Neostar Medical Technologies, Inc.
NEOSTATIC - Starch–laundry ☆ - Faultless Starch/Bon Ami Co.
NEOSTATS - Computer software - Neoglyphics Media Corp.
NEOSTYLE - Faucets - Masco Corp. (Plumbing Products Div.)
NEOSULFEX - Aquatic pharmacuetical preparations ☆ - Aquatronics-Filtronics
NEOSYNEPHRINOL - Cold remedies ☆ - Winthrop Pharmaceuticals
NEOTAL - Pharmaceutical preparations ☆ - Roberts/Hauck Pharmaceuticals Inc.
NEOTEC - Floor coverings–carpet and rugs - Mannington Carpets, Inc.
NEOTEK - Automobile parts - Neotek Corp. Inc.
NEOTEK - Lighting fixtures - Neotek, Inc.
NEOTERIC - Recording label - Jazz Composer's Orchestra Association Inc.
NEOTHYLLINE - Pharmaceutical preparations ☆ - Lemmon Co.
NEOTRIZINE - Pharmaceutical preparations - Eli Lilly and Co.
NEOTUBE - Water treating compounds - Mearl E. Ellison
NEOVA - Cooking equipment–household - Vita-Mix Corp.
NEOVAL - Vitamins and nutritional supplements - Halsey Drug Co. Inc.
NEOVIDEO - T-shirts–women's - Neon Shirtworks
NEOVIDEO INTERACTIVEWEAR - Apparel and accessories - Neon Shirtworks
NEOWELD - Adhesives and sealants - Imperial Adhesives Inc.
NEOXYN - Pharmaceutical preparations ☆ - Rhone-Poulenc Rorer Pharmaceuticals Inc.
NEOZYME - Chemical preparations - Neozyme International, Inc.
NEOZYMES - Paper–newsprint - Neozyme International, Inc.
NEPAL - Floor coverings–carpet and rugs - Couristan Inc.
NEPAL - Floor coverings–carpet and rugs ☆ - Orian Rugs Inc.
NEPCO - Paper–gift wrap - Georgia-Pacific Corp.
NEPCO-DRI - Pet products - Northeastern Products Corp.
NEPHILIM - Games - Chaosium Inc.
NEPHPLEX RX - Vitamins and nutritional supplements - Nephro-Tech, Inc.
NEPHROCAPS - Vitamins and nutritional supplements - Fleming & Co.
NEPHRON - Dental equipment - Nephron Corp.
NEPHRON - Inhalers - Nephron Pharmaceuticals
NEPHRON FA - Vitamins and nutritional supplements - Nephro-Tech, Inc.
NEPHROSOL - Pharmaceutical preparations - Minntech Corp.
NEPHROSOLID - Health care products - Bioforce of America Ltd.
NEPHROX - Antacids - Fleming & Co.
NEP#100 - Oils–lubricating - Parkin Chemical Co.
NEPO - Markers–felt-tip ☆ - Sanford Corp.
NEPON PEARL - Toilets–enameled - Ecos/Water Conservation System Inc.
NEPRO - Health care products - Abbott Laboratories
NEPSEAL - Insulating materials - National Engineering Products, Inc.

☆ = Now out of production

NEPTONE - Food products - NV Aquaculture
NEPTUNA - Tuna–canned - Mitsui & Co. Inc.
NEPTUNE - Aquarium thermometers ☆ - American Thermometer Co.
NEPTUNE - Bathtubs–enameled ☆ - Lasco Products Group
NEPTUNE - Binoculars ☆ - Swift Instruments, Inc.
NEPTUNE - Boats - Goldeneye Products, Inc.
NEPTUNE - Boats–motor ☆ - Huckins Yacht Corp.
NEPTUNE - Chemical preparations - Woolsey Marine Industries
NEPTUNE - Chickens - Bil Mar Foods
NEPTUNE - Filters–air - Aquaria Inc.
NEPTUNE - Fishing lures - Sunset Line and Twine Co.
NEPTUNE - Flatware - Washington Forge Inc.
NEPTUNE - Flatware ☆ - Anacapa Corp.
NEPTUNE - Floor coverings–carpet and rugs ☆ - Galaxy Carpet Mills Inc.
NEPTUNE - Food products - Acme Continental Foods Inc.
NEPTUNE - Frozen shrimp - Neptune Fisheries Inc.
NEPTUNE - Generators - Sonicstar International, Ltd.
NEPTUNE - Giftware ☆ - Dansk International Designs, Ltd.
NEPTUNE - Glassware–household - Durand International
NEPTUNE - Insulating materials - Branton Industries, Inc.
NEPTUNE - Paper - Strathmore Paper Co.
NEPTUNE - Pet products - Tetra Sales USA
NEPTUNE - Recording label - Gamble Huff Music Productions
NEPTUNE - Sardines–canned - Stinson Seafood Co.
NEPTUNE - Ships–sailing vessels - Capital Yachts Inc.
NEPTUNE - Shrimp–fresh or frozen - Neptune Sea Food Co.
NEPTUNE - Sinks–porcelain - Neptune
NEPTUNE - Soap - Lever Brothers Co. Inc.
NEPTUNE - Stationery ☆ - Superior Marking Equipment Co.
NEPTUNE - Thread - Threads USA Div.
NEPTUNE - Toys–models ☆ - Estes Industries
NEPTUNE - Vitamins and nutritional supplements - Kroeger Herb Products Co.
    Inc.
NEPTUNE - Watches - Bulova Corp.
NEPTUNE - Water–distilled - Neptune Water Co.
NEPTUNE - Wet mops - Bouras Mop Manufacturing Co.
NEPTUNE - Wire products - Trefilarbed Inc.
NEPTUNE 66 - Beverages–malt - Bonton Manufacturing Corp.
NEPTUNE FANTASY - Dolls - Mattel, Inc.
NEPTUNE PLUNGE - Playground equipment - Miracle Recreation Equipment
    Co.
NEPTUNE SPORT DIVING ACCESSORIES - Diving equipment - Underwater
    Diving Inc.
NEPTUNE U - Beverages–malt - Bonton Manufacturing Corp.
NEPTUNES ARCH - Pet products - Penn-Plax, Inc.
NEPTUNES GOLD - Vitamins and nutritional supplements - Great Life
    Laboratories Inc.
NEPTUNE'S SEASCAPE - Pet products - Aquarium Decor
NEPTUNITE - Varnishes - Sherwin-Williams Automotive Finishes Corp.
NEPTURE - Bathing suits - Ocean Pool Co.
NER-VITA DE HUXLEY - Health care products - Etna Products Co. Inc.
NERD PRIDE - Apparel and accessories - Massachusetts Institute of
    Technology
NERD TESTER - Novelty items - Adams Apple Distributing L.P.
NERDS - Candy - Willy Wonka Brands
NERDS - Cereal - Ralston Purina Co.
NERDS - Pens - Pentech International Inc.
NEREX - Rope - New England Ropes Inc.
NERF - Toys - Tonka Corp.
NERF BALL - Toys - Tonka Corp.
NERF BLAST-A-BALL - Toys - Tonka Corp.
NERF BLAST-A-MATIC - Toys - Tonka Corp.
NERF-MOBILES - Toys - Tonka Corp.
NERF NERF - Fabrics - Dan River Inc.
NERF TO THE NEXT POWER - Toys–guns - Tonka Corp.
NERF-TRUCK - Toys ☆ - Tonka Corp.
NERF TURBO SCREAMER - Toys - Tonka Corp.
NERFMAN - Toys - Tonka Corp.
NERFOOP - Toys - Tonka Corp.
NERFULS - Toys - Tonka Corp.
NERFULS BOPPER - Toys - Tonka Corp.
NERGECO BY CHASE - Doors - Chase Industries, Inc.
NERINA - Cooking equipment–household - Primex International Corp.
NERI'S - Wines - Neri's Wine Cellar
NERI'S WINE CELLAR - Wines - Neri's Wine Cellar
NERISONE - Pharmaceutical preparations ☆ - Stiefel Laboratories, Inc.

NERITA - Lubricants ☆ - Shell Oil Co.
NERO - Cigars ☆ - General Cigar Co., Inc.
NEROMAX - X-ray apparatus - Victoreen, Inc.
NERVE TWISTER - Toys - Maryland Toy Corp.
NERVEMASTER - Hearing aids ☆ - United Hearing Systems Inc.
NERVES BREAK DOWN - Playing cards - Ernesto X. Mendoza
NERVO - Wines ☆ - Geyser Peak Winery
NERVOCAINE - Pharmaceutical preparations - Keene Pharmaceuticals Inc.
NERVOSAN - Pharmaceutical preparations - Bioforce of America Ltd.
NERVOSAN - Teas–herbal - Herb Products Co.
NERVOUS - Furniture repair shops - Creatnetics
NERVOUS - Recording label - Max Entertainment Inc. (Nervous, Inc.)
NERVOUS RECORDS - Recording label - Max Entertainment Inc. (Nervous,
    Inc.)
NERVOUSNESS - Pharmaceutical preparations ☆ - Boiron Inc.
NERVSOL - Analgesics - Polam Wholesale Inc.
NES - Jewelry–precious - New England Sterling, Inc.
N.E.S. 33 - Apparel and accessories - Stevens Sportwear
NES NESTECH - Machinery - Nestech Machine Systems Inc.
NESAK - Recording label - Nesak International
NESBITT - Heating equipment - Mestek Inc.
NESBITT'S - Beverages–carbonated - Monarch Co., Inc.
NESCAFE - Coffee - Nestle Beverage Co.
NESCAFE CAPPUCCINO - Coffee - Nestle Beverage Co.
NESCAFE CLASSIC - Coffee - Nestle Beverage Co.
NESCO - Backpacks - American Camper
NESCO - Batteries - Nesco Battery Systems
NESCO - Binders - Polar Manufacturing Co.
NESCO - Housewares - Metal Ware Corp.
NESCO - Sporting goods ☆ - Fuqua Industries Inc.
NESCO 101 - Flour–blended - New Era Milling Co.
NESCOTE - Coatings - Metal Ware Corp.
NESHEEKA - Apparel and accessories - Nesheeka, Inc.
(NESLIHAN) - Women's sportswear - Neslihan Danisman Ltd.
NESS - Vitamins and nutritional supplements - International Enzyme
    Foundation, Inc.
NESS ADVENTURES - Board games - Ness Adventures, Inc.
NESS-TECH - Motorcycle parts - Arlen Ness Enterprises, Inc.
NESSA - Recording label - Jazz Composer's Orchestra Association Inc.
NESSIE - Golf clubs - Renaissance Golf Products, Inc.
NEST EGG - Pet products - Nest Egg Manufacturing Co.
NEST EGGS - Eggs - Food Animal Concerns Trust
NEST ENTERTAINMENT - Video production - Nest Entertainment Inc.
NEST-KLEEN - Veterinary pharmaceutical preparations ☆ - Vineland
    Laboratories Inc.
NEST WITH THE BEST - Computer software - Sigmatek Corp.
NESTABS - Vitamins and nutritional supplements - Fielding Pharmaceutical Co.
NESTABS FA - Vitamins and nutritional supplements - Fielding Pharmaceutical
    Co.
NESTACK - Boxes - Stackbin Corp.
NESTAR - Photographic equipment - SP Systems/Saratons
NESTEA - Iced tea–bottled or canned - Coca-Cola Co.
NESTEA - Teas - Nestle Beverage Co.
NESTEA COOL - Iced tea–bottled or canned - Nestle Beverage Co.
NESTEA FREE - Teas - Nestle Beverage Co.
NESTECH - Machinery - Nestech Machine Systems Inc.
NESTER - Water purification systems ☆ - Aquaculture Research/Environmental
    Associates Inc.
NESTERS - Cookware - Peregrine Outfitters, Inc.
NESTIBENCHES - Furniture - The Tramble Co.
NESTING BEAR FAMILY - Toys - Fisher-Price, Inc.
NESTLE - Chocolate candy - Nestle USA
NESTLE - Hair care products ☆ - All Clubman
NESTLE - Syrup - Made in France
NESTLE BUNCHA CRUNCH - Chocolate candy - Nestle USA
NESTLE CRUNCH - Chocolate candy - Nestle USA
NESTLE CRUNCH LITE - Ice cream - Nestle USA
NESTLE MORSELS - Chocolate candy - Nestle USA
NESTLE-QUIK - Dairy products - Ryan Foods Co.
NESTLETS - Pet products - Ancare Corp.
NESTORONE - Pharmaceutical preparations - Population Council, Inc.
NESTRAY - Stacking letter trays ☆ - Corry Hiebert
NESTREX - Pharmaceutical preparations - Fielding Pharmaceutical Co.
NESTYLE - Cups–paper - Sealright Co., Inc.
NESW - Computer software - Lantec Inc.
NESW - Footwear - Eastland Shoe Manufacturing Corp.

☆ = Now out of production

NET - Publisher's imprint - God's Word to the Nations Bible Society
NET - Video tapes–blank - Net International Inc.
NET/AUDITOR - Computer peripheral equipment - Emcom Corp. of Delaware
NET CHECK - Jewelry - Ronnie DaVinci Inc.
NET/DACS - Computer software ☆ - Utimaco Mergent
NET/DAQ - Computers - Fluke Corp.
NET EFFECT - Hair care products - Sally Beauty Co., Inc.
NET EXPLORATIONS - Computer software ☆ - Sunburst Communications, Inc.
NET FORTRESS - Computer software - DSN Technology, Inc.
NET-GARD - Talcum powders - Powell-Esco Co.
NET LITES - Electronic equipment - J. Kinderman & Sons, Inc.
NET/OVERVIEW - Computer software - Enterprise Software Corp.
NET-PATH - Computer software - Teltronics, Inc.
NET-PERFECT - Computer software - Ward Systems Group, Inc.
NET PHONE - Computer storage devices–optical - Pro CD Inc.
NET PRO-FIT - Computer software - Tem-Pro, Inc.
NET/QC - Computer software - Emcom Corp. of Delaware
NET RESULTS SPORTSWEAR - Athletic apparel - Phoenix Suns
NET-SCORE - Computer software - Salem Gymnastics Center, Ltd.
NET SHIELD - Computer software - Secure Transactions Solutions, LLC
NET SOAK - Aquariums–household - Jungle Laboratories Corp.
NET SOLUTION - Computer peripheral equipment - Applied Creative Technology, Inc.
NET STIK - Traps–animal - Fuhrman Diversified
NET STIK QC - Traps–animal - Fuhrman Diversified
NET TO YOU - Advertising agencies - Net to You, Inc.
NET TOOLS - Computer software - Mcafee Associates, Inc.
NET TRUE - Sporting goods - Gold Medal Recreational Products
NET-WORKS - Computer software ☆ - Integrated Medical System
NET-WORKS - Sporting goods - Forster Inc.
NET WORKSHOP - Computer software - Tennecon Services, Inc.
NET WORTH - Apparel–athletic ☆ - Winning Ways Inc.
NET WORTH - Financial journal - Informative Amenities Inc.
NET WORTH - Floor coverings–carpet and rugs - Eagle Carpets Inc.
NET/WRK - Computer software - KnowledgeNet Inc.
NET2NET - Communications equipment - Net2net Corp.
NETACCESS - Computer hardware - Xircom, Inc.
NET+ARM - Computer hardware - Netsilicon, Inc.
NETASSISTANT - Computer software - Ungermann-Bass, Inc.
NETATTACHE - Computer software - Tympani Development Inc.
NETAXCESS - Computer software - Andrew Corp.
NETBASE - Computer software - Quest Software Inc.
NETBASIC - Computer software ☆ - High Technology Software Corp., Inc.
NETBASIC COMPILER - Computer software - High Technology Software Corp., Inc.
NETBASIC PRO - Computer peripheral equipment - High Technology Software Corp., Inc.
NETBEAMIR - Computer peripheral equipment - Hewlett-Packard Co.
NETBUILDER II - Computer storage devices - 3Com Corp.
NETCARE - Cleaning preparations - Network Associates Inc.
NETCERT - Computer software - Transcender Corp.
NETCHE - Paper - Network Graphics Inc.
NETCLOAK - Computer peripheral equipment - Microlink Technologies, Inc.
NETCLOAK - Computer software - Maxum Development Corp.
NETCO - Tape–adhesive - McNett Corp.
NETCO - Watches - SKL Co. Inc.
NETCOM - Computer software - Netcom On-Line Communication Services, Inc.
NETCOMM - Computer hardware - Icon Medical Systems, Inc.
NETCOMPILE - Computer software - Netpower, Inc.
NETCONNECT - Electrical equipment - Whitaker Corp.
NETCONTROL - Computer software - Executive Systems, Inc.
NETCRUISER PLUS - Computer software - Netcom On-Line Communication Services, Inc.
NETDOOR - Computer software - International Business Machines Corp.
NETDRAW - Computer software - International Data Group, Inc.
NETEXPERT - Computer software - Objective Systems Integrators, Inc.
NETFRONT - Computer software - Netfront Communications, Inc.
NETFUNDS NAVIGATOR - Computer software - No-Load Fund Shareholders Association, Inc.
NETGAIN - Computer software - North Communications, Inc.
NETGATE - Computer software - Smallworks, Inc.
NETGEAR - Computer peripheral equipment - Bay Networks, Inc.
NETHAPRIN - Pharmaceutical preparations ☆ - Marion Merrell Dow
NETHEAD - Apparel stores–sports - Dorothea A. Lorber
NETHEADS INTERNATIONAL - Novelty items - Laid Back Enterprises, Inc.
NETHERLAND - Milk - Byrne Dairy, Inc.

NETHERLAND NATURAL - Wallpaper - PCI Industries Inc.
NETHERLANDER - Cheese ☆ - Crowley Foods, Inc.
NETHERLANDS - Floor coverings–carpet and rugs ☆ - Callaway Carpets
NETHERLANDS NAT LINENS - Wallpaper - Advance Wallcoverings
NETHOPPER - Computer software - AllPen Software Inc.
NETHOPPER - Computer software - AllPen Software Inc.
NETIQ - Computer peripheral equipment - Netiq Corp.
NETIS - Computer peripheral equipment - Netis Technology, Inc.
NETJET - Printers–computer - Emulex Corp.
NETLABS/DISCOVERY - Computer software - NetLabs Inc.
NETLENS - Data communications equipment - Telecommunications Techniques Corp.
NETLINE N - Computers - Netline, Inc.
NETMAGIC - Computer software - Netmagic Systems Inc.
NETMANAGE - Computer software - Netmanage, Inc.
NETMATICS - Computer hardware - Netmatics, Inc.
NETMAXER - Computer software - BMC Software, Inc.
NETMON - Computer software - Systems Enhancement Corp.
NETOBJECTS - Computer software - Netobjects, Inc.
NETOLE - Computer software - Intuitive Technology Corp.
NETOSSA - Toys - Mattel, Inc.
NETPAC - Laboratory apparatus - Kaye Instruments Inc.
NETPAGER - Telephones - John M. Keagy
NETPAK - Computer software - Crescent Software, Inc.
NETPAKS - Recording label - Kimbo Educational
NETPERFORMER - Computer software - Act Networks, Inc.
NETPLAN - Radio communications equipment - Motorola, Inc. (Land Mobile Products Sector)
NETPLEX - Computer peripheral equipment - ISOCOR
NETPLUS - Computer software - American Computer and Electronics Corp.
NETPODIUM - Computer software - Metabridge, Inc.
NETPOINT - Computer software - SourceView Software International
NETPOWER - Computer hardware - Netpower, Inc.
NETPUBLISHER - Computer software - Ameritech Corp.
NETQUE - Printers–computer - Emulex Corp.
NETQUE MATE - Printers–computer - Emulex Corp.
NETREACH - Computers - Leemah Datacom Security Corp.
NETRIX - Computer software - Netrix Corp.
NETROAD - Computer software - Ukiah Software, Inc.
NETROAD FIREWARE - Computer software - Ukiah Software, Inc.
NETROM - Computer software - XInt, Inc.
NETROMYCIN - Antibiotics - Schering-Plough Healthcare Products
NETRPC - Computer software - Banyan Systems Inc.
NETRUNNER - Novelty items–paper - Wizards of the Coast, Inc.
NETS - Apparel and accessories - Meadowlands Basketball Associates
NETSAVERS - Electrical surge protectors - Sutton Designs, Inc.
NETSCAPE - Computer software - Netscape Communications Corp.
NETSCAPE NAVIGATOR - Computer software - Netscape Communications Corp.
NETSHELTER - Safety products - American Power Conversion Corp.
NETSKIN - Tights–stockings - Danskin, Inc.
NETSOFT - Computer software - Netsoft
NETSPACE - Computer software - Avail Systems Corp.
NETSPAN - Computer networking products - NetSpan Corp.
NETSPEAK - Computer software - Netspeak Corp.
NETSQUEEZE - Computer software - Lan Support Group, Inc.
NETSTART - Computer software - Netstart, Inc.
NETSTREAM - Computer hardware - Danpex Corp.
NETSURFER - Apparel and accessories - Mark A. Maidenburg
NETSURFER - Computer software - Netsurfer, Inc.
NETT'EM - Cages–wire - A Thru Z Consulting and Distributing, Inc.
NETTEXT - Computer diskettes - International Data Group, Inc.
NETTIE'S - Jams and jellies ☆ - Nettie's Home Preserving Co.
NETTLE CREEK - Retail franchise - Pillowtex Corp.
NETTLETON - Footwear - 313 East Willow Street Corp.
NETVANTAGE - Computer peripheral equipment - Netvantage
NETVISION - Computer peripheral equipment - Symbol Technologies, Inc.
NETWALKER - Computer software - Fujitsu Open Systems Solutions, Inc.
NETWARE - Computer software - Novell, Inc.
NETWARE CONNECT - Computers - Novell, Inc.
NETWARE HOSTPRINT - Computer software - Novell, Inc.
NETWATS RECOVER - Telephone apparatus - CRG International, Inc.
NETWAVE - Computer software - Xircom, Inc.
NETWISE - Computer hardware - Coherent Communications Systems Corp.
NETWIZARD - Computer software - Microlink Technologies, Inc.
NETWORK - Adhesives and sealants - Network Associates Inc.

NETWORK - Floor coverings–carpet and rugs ☆ - Kelly Group Inc.

NETWORK - Recording label - I.R.S. Records

NETWORK - Switches–power - Lutron Electronics Co., Inc.

NETWORK 2000 - Computer peripheral equipment - CDG, Inc.

NETWORK 9000 - Electronic equipment - Xyplex Inc.

NETWORK ADVICE - Computer software - Integrated Decision Support Corp.

NETWORK BANKER - Computer software - Stockholder Systems, Inc.

NETWORK BROKER - Computer software - Ideas, Inc.

NETWORK DETECTIVE'S ASSISTANT, THE - Computer software - Empirical Tools and Technologies, Inc.

NETWORK DISCUSSION GUIDES - Publisher's imprints ☆ - Harold Shaw Publishers

NETWORK EXCHANGE - Computer software - Netrix Corp.

NETWORK FRAMEXCHANGE - Computer software - Telematics International, Inc.

NETWORK H.Q. - Computer software - Magee Enterprises, Inc.

NETWORK INTEGRITY - Computer software - Network Integrity, Inc.

NETWORK LTC - Computer software - Toro Co.

NETWORK MANAGEMENT FORUM - Publisher's imprints - Network Management Forum

NETWORK MANAGER II - Computer software - Para Systems, Inc.

NETWORK NAVIGATOR DISPATCHER - Computer software - American International Communications Corp.

NETWORK OF BUSINESS OPPORTUNITY ENTREPRENEURS - Audio tapes–blank - Internet Services Corp.

NETWORK SECURITY GUARD - Computer software - Michael Robertson

NETWORK SECURITY ORGANIZER - Computer software - Leprechaun Software International Ltd.

NETWORKER - Binders - Dennison National Co.

NETWORKMCI - Pagers - MCI Communications Corp.

NETWORKMCI BUSINESS - Computer software - MCI Communications Corp.

NETWORKS - Machinery - Powerflow, Inc.

NETWORLD - Computer software - World Game Institute

NETWORX - Furniture - Hon Co.

NETX - Conveyors - Dynamic Air, Inc.

NETXRAY - Computer software - Cinco Networks, Inc.

NETZIP - Computer software - Software Builders International, Inc.

NEU - Cheese ☆ - Cook-Boynton and Hilton Inc.

NEU BLEU - Salad dressings–bottled - Sandoz Pharmaceuticals Corp.

NEU-CITI - Bicycles - Schwinn Cycling & Fitness Inc.

NEU-GEL - Bicycle parts and accessories - Serfus, Inc.

NEU-TAK - Hammers and staples - Automation Fastening Co. Inc.

NEU-TECH - Paper - Gilbert Paper Co.

NEU-VUE - Liquid crystal displays - Neumade Products Corp.

NEUBALANCE - Hair care products - Helene Curtis Industries Inc.

NEUBERG - Sporting goods - Moody & Co. Inc.

NEUBURGER - Fabrics ☆ - Leimtex Corp.

NEUCALM 50 - Pharmaceutical preparations - Legere Pharmaceuticals Inc.

NEUCHATEAU - Floor coverings - Mannington Resilient Floors

NEUCUE - Electronic equipment - Neumade Products Corp.

NEUDENKO - Computer peripheral equipment - Cadscan Electronics USA, Inc.

NEUDESIGNS - Publisher's imprints - National Plan Service

NEUDOERFER - Musical-instrument bows ☆ - International Violin Co. Ltd.

NEUE - Cosmetics - Neue Cosmetic Co., Inc.

NEUFUNDLAND - Floor coverings–carpet and rugs ☆ - Capel, Inc.

NEUHARTH - Wines ☆ - Olympic Cellars

NEULAR - Electronic equipment - Neumade Products Corp.

NEULITE - Electronic equipment - Neumade Products Corp.

NEUMAN - Breads - Dairy Fresh Products Co.

NEUMAN SEED CO. - Seeds - Neuman Seed International Inc.

NEUMED - Medical apparatus - Neurotron Inc.

NEUPAC - Electronic equipment - Neumade Products Corp.

NEUPOGEN - Prescription drug - Amgen Inc.

NEURA - Pet products - Old Mother Hubbard Dog Food Co., Inc.

NEURA FORMULA 200 - Dog food - Old Mother Hubbard Dog Food Co., Inc.

NEURA FORMULA 400 - Animal feeds - Old Mother Hubbard Dog Food Co., Inc.

NEURACTOR - Computer hardware and peripherals - United States Cyberlab, Inc.

NEURAL - Controls–heating systems - Neural Applications Corp.

NEURAL CONNECTION - Computer software - SPSS, Inc.

NEURAL LEDGER - Computer software - Jeff S. Eder

NEURALOGIX - Computers - American NeuraLogix Inc.

NEURAY - Medical apparatus - Martland Healthcare, Inc.

NEUREGULIN - Pharmaceutical preparations - Cambridge Neuroscience, Inc.

NEURO-EMOTIONAL REMEDIES - Vitamins and nutritional supplements - Theresa Dale

NEURO FUZZY - Kitchen appliances - Zojirushi America Corp.

NEURO-PULSER - Electromedical apparatus - TH Charters, Inc.

NEURO SCIENCE MONITOR, THE - Pamphlets - Moberg Research, Inc.

NEURO WINDOWS - Computer software - Microsoft Corp.

NEUROAID - Health care products - Medtronic Nortech

NEUROBASE - Computer software - Arbor Publishing Corp.

NEUROBICS - Computer software - SRA/McGraw-Hill (Div. of The McGraw-Hill Companies)

NEUROBION - Vitamins - Benard Industries Inc.

NEUROCARE GROUP - Medical apparatus - Heyer-Schulte Neurocare, LP

NEUROCORDER - Medical apparatus - Del Mar Avionics

NEURODEP COPS - Pharmaceutical preparations ☆ - Medical Products Panamericana Inc.

NEURODEP PLUS - Pharmaceutical preparations ☆ - Medical Products Panamericana Inc.

NEURODEPINT. - Pharmaceutical preparations - Medical Products Panamericana Inc.

NEUROEASE - Health care products - Medtronic Nortech

NEUROEDUCATOR - Medical apparatus - Therapeutic Alliances, Inc.

NEUROFORCE - Spices and extracts ☆ - Bioforce of America Ltd.

NEUROGENIC - Vitamins and nutritional supplements - Natural Organics, Inc.

NEUROLOGY REVIEWS - Paper–newsprint - Clinicians Publishing Group Inc.

NEURON-LINE - Computer software - Gensym Corp.

NEURONTIN - Pharmaceutical preparations - Parke-Davis

NEUROPAGE - Prosthetic apparatus - Hersh & Treadgold

NEUROPEDIC - Beds–wood - Neuropedic

NEUROPHONICS - Audio tapes–blank - Progressive Awareness Research, Inc.

NEUROPULSER 2 - Electromedical apparatus - TH Charters, Inc.

NEUROSCANNER - Medical apparatus - Del Mar Avionics

NEUROSINE - Pharmaceutical preparations ☆ - Walker Pharmacal Co.

NEUROSTATION - Computer software - Stealth Technologies Inc.

NEUROTIC RECORDS - Apparel and accessories - Thump Records, Inc.

NEUROTROPHIN PMG - Vitamins and nutritional supplements - Standard Process Inc.

NEUROVEU - Pharmaceutical preparations - Bristol-Myers Squibb Co.

NEUROVIEW - Surgical supplies - Neuro Navigational Corp.

NEUROVITE M - Pharmaceutical preparations - Medical Chemical Corp.

NEUSCALE - Electronic equipment ☆ - Neumade Products Corp.

NEUSE RIVER - Seafood products–fresh or frozen - Sound Packing Co.

NEUT - Skin care products - GOLDWELL Cosmetics (USA) Inc.

NEUTAPE - Film–motion picture - Neumade Products Corp.

NEUTAPER - Film–motion picture - Neumade Products Corp.

NEUTERSOL - Veterinary pharmaceutical preparations - Pet Healthcare International Inc.

NEUTICLES - Implants–surgical - CTI Corp.

NEUTOL - Photographic equipment - Miles Inc. (Agfa Div.)

NEUTONE - Floor waxes - Hillyard Enterprises, Inc.

NEUTRA FOAM - Shampoos - Ampro Industries, Inc.

NEUTRA FRESH - Deodorizers - S.C. Johnson & Son, Inc.

NEUTRA-FRESH - Perfumes ☆ - Knight Marketing Corp.

NEUTRA-GREEN - Cleaning preparations - Cello Chemical Co.

NEUTRA KLEEN - Cleaning preparations - Analab Inc.

NEUTRA PAC - Cleaning preparations - PortionPac Chemical Corp.

NEUTRA-PHOS - Vitamins and nutritional supplements - Willen Drug Co.

NEUTRA-PHOS-K - Vitamins and nutritional supplements - Willen Drug Co.

NEUTRA QUAT - Disinfectants - Pioneer/Eclipse Corp.

NEUTRA-STAT - Pharmaceutical preparations - Damon Industries, Inc.

NEUTRACOLOR - Hair coloring preparations - Schieffelin & Co. (Pharmaceutical Laboratories Div.)

NEUTRADERM - Gloves–rubber - Aladan Corp.

NEUTRAL - Recording label - Jazz Composer's Orchestra Association Inc.

NEUTRAL BALANCE - Health care products - Colgate-Palmolive Co.

NEUTRAL-C PLUS - Health care products - Integrated Health Network

NEUTRAL GEAR - Apparel and accessories - Neutral, Inc.

NEUTRAL PROTEIN FILLER - Hair care products - Colorful Products Corp.

NEUTRAL REGLATOR - Pet products - Seachem Laboratories

NEUTRAL SPRAY - Fungicides ☆ - Stoner Inc.

NEUTRAL TERRITORY - Cosmetics - Chesebrough-Pond's USA Co.

NEUTRAL ZONE - Apparel and accessories - Bugle Boy Industries, Inc.

NEUTRALIN - Pharmaceutical preparations - Dover Pharmaceutical Inc.

NEUTRALITE - Window insulating film - Madico, Inc.

NEUTRALIZER - Laboratory apparatus - CSP International, Inc.

NEUTRALIZER - Medical apparatus - Smith & Nephew DonJoy Inc.

☆ = Now out of production

NEUTRALIZER - Sporting goods - Archery Horizons, Inc.
NEUTRALLE - Cleaning preparations - Scentex Inc.
NEUTRALLY - Wallpaper - Royaleigh Designs Ltd.
NEUTRALS COLORS BY NUMBER, THE - Cosmetics - American Makeup Inc.
NEUTRALS GO BEHIND THE SCENES - Cosmetics - Revlon Consumer Products Corp.
NEUTRALUX - Window insulating film - Madico, Inc.
NEUTRAPLEX - Hair care products - Johnson Products Co., Inc.
NEUTRAPOLLEN - Vitamins and nutritional supplements - International Medical Research, Inc.
NEUTRASCENT - Pet products ☆ - Trophy Animal Health Care
NEUTRESCA - Lubricants ☆ - Aarhus Inc.
NEUTREX - Deodorizers - Aroma Tech, Inc.
NEUTREX - Glass–laboratory - Chase Instruments Corp.
NEUTREXIN - Pharmaceutical preparations - U.S. Bioscience, Inc.
NEUTRIFF - Chemical preparations - International Flavors & Fragrances Inc.
NEUTRIFFUSIONS - Chemical preparations - International Flavors & Fragrances Inc.
NEUTRIK - Connectors–electrical - ARS Electronics
NEUTRIK SPEAKON - Connectors–electrical - Electro-Voice, Inc.
NEUTRINO - Computer software - Corel USA
NEUTRIX - Audio equipment ☆ - Rapco International
NEUTRO - Soldering equipment - M.W. Dunton Co.
NEUTRO-CLENE - Cleaning preparations ☆ - Flo-Pac Corp.
NEUTRO-STAT - Static eliminator ☆ - Simco
NEUTRO VAC - Air purification systems - Simco
NEUTRODA POWDER - Deodorizers - Stewart-Hall Chemical Corp.
NEUTROGENA - Skin care products - Neutrogena Corp.
NEUTROGENA CLEAR PORE TREATMENT - Skin care products - Neutrogena Corp.
NEUTROGENA COMBINATION SKIN MOISTURE - Skin care products - Neutrogena Corp.
NEUTROGENA DAILY MOISTURE SUPPLY - Lotions - Neutrogena Corp.
NEUTROGENA DEEP PORE TREATMENT - Skin care products - Neutrogena Corp.
NEUTROGENA GLOW - Sun protection preparation - Neutrogena Corp.
NEUTROGENA HAND CREAM - Skin care products - Neutrogena Corp.
NEUTROGENA HEALTHY SCALP ANTI-DANDRUFF SHAMPOO - Shampoos - Neutrogena Corp.
NEUTROGENA INTENSIFIED DAY MOISTURIZER - Skin care products - Neutrogena Corp.
NEUTROGENA INTENSIFIED EYE MOISTURE - Skin-care products - Neutrogena Corp.
NEUTROGENA NO-STICK SUNSCREEN - Suntan lotions - Neutrogena Corp.
NEUTROGENA NON-DRYING CLEANSING LOTION - Skin care products - Neutrogena Corp.
NEUTROGENA RAINBATH - Skin care products - Neutrogena Corp.
NEUTROGENA SKINCLEARING - Skin care products - Neutrogena Corp.
NEUTROGENA SUNBLOCK - Sunblocks - Neutrogena Corp.
NEUTROGRAPHY - Electronic equipment - General Electric Co.
NEUTRON - Computer software - Nucleus Interactive, Inc.
NEUTRON - Sporting goods - Dunlop Maxfli Sports Corp.
NEUTRONIC - Electronic equipment - Neumade Products Corp.
NEUTROX - Dental compounds ☆ - Richardson-Vicks USA
NEUVAL - Computer software - Neurotron Inc.
NEUVATOR - Electronic equipment - Neumade Products Corp.
NEUVEX - Watches - Hampden Corp.
NEUVILLE - Faucets - Kohler Co.
NEUVILLE - Glassware–household - Durand International
NEUWEILER'S ALE & BEER LOUIS E. NEUWEILER'S SONS ALLENTOWN, PA. - Toys–automobiles - Barbara S. Barbara
NEV-A-SLIP - Crutches - Harvy Surgical Supply Corp.
NEV-R-KURL - Paper–carbon - Phillips Process Co. Inc.
NEV-R-SPOT - Wallpaper - Athena Products Corp.
NEV-R-WARP - Metallic doors - Northern Classic Door Inc.
NEVA CRUSH - Carpet underlay - PMC, Inc.
NEVA-RUST - Aluminum products ☆ - Florida Wire Products
NEVADA - Bicycles ☆ - Huffy Corp.
NEVADA - Briefcases - United States Luggage Corp.
NEVADA - Floor coverings–carpet and rugs - Rugby Rugs Inc.
NEVADA - Wallpaper - Capital Carousel Inc.
NEVADA - Window shades ☆ - Kenney Manufacturing Co.
NEVADA CEMENT - Cement - Centex Corp.
NEVADA CITY CELLARS - Wines ☆ - Nevada City Winery
NEVADA CITY MOUNTAIN SPRING WATER - Bottled water - Nevada City Mountain Spring Water, Inc.

NEVADA CITY WINERY - Wines - Nevada City Winery
NEVADA CRAPS - Games ☆ - Milton Bradley Co.
NEVADA DIAMONDS - Games - Universal Manufacturing Co., Inc.
NEVADA HIGH DESERT - Vegetables - Peri & Sons Farms Inc.
NEVADA JACKS - Beer - Nevada Jacks Brewing Co.
NEVADA N OMEGA APPAREL COMPANY - Apparel–men's - Omega Apparel Limited
NEVADA NICKELS - Game machines - IGT - North America
NEVADA ONE - Playing cards - Gemaco Playing Card Co.
NEVADA SILVER BONANZA - Silver products - Golden Triangle Distributors, Ltd.
NEVADA SILVER GLASSWORKS - Doors–glass - Kohler Co.
NEVADA TOURING - Apparel and accessories - Intersport Fashions West
NEVADA WESTERN - Wire products - Thomas & Betts Holdings, Inc.
NEVADA'S BEST - Fertilizers - Lawn & Garden Supply Co.
NEVADOS - Footwear–athletic - American Sporting Goods Corp.
NEVAMAR - Counter tops–laminated - International Paper (Decorative Products Division)
NEVAMAR IMPRESSIONS - Plastics–laminated - Nevamar Corp.
NEVAQUA - Pet products - Nevaqua Corp.
NEVASTANE - Lubricants - Elf Lubricants North America, Inc.
NEVATAK - Carbon and graphite products ☆ - Curtis-Young Corp.
NEVAWIND - Watches - Gruen Marketing Corp.
NEVCO - Furniture–wood - Hansen Industries Inc. (Nevco Div.)
NEVCO COMFORT HOLD - Medical apparatus - Nevco International Inc.
NEVENT - Jewelry - Ventura Gem & Pearl Co. Inc.
NEVER A DULL MOMENT - Knives ☆ - Lifetime Hoan Corp.
NEVER BITE - Nail care products - Naturally Beautiful Nails, Inc.
NEVER-BURN-DOWN - Candles - Chace Candles, Inc.
NEVER-CLOG - Bags - Pullman/Holt Corp.
NEVER DULL APRON COMPANY, THE - Aprons - Never Dull Apron Co.
NEVER ENOUGH - Shoes - MSF Corp.
NEVER FADE - Cosmetics - Top Ten Cosmetics, Inc.
NEVER-FLIP - Mattressess - Schottenstein Stores Corp.
NEVER FREEZE - Oils–lubricating - Frederickseal, Inc.
NEVER GO HUNGRY - Recording label - Jayne Benkendorf
NEVER HAVE SUN WITHOUT PROTECTION - Cosmetics - Biocycle Laboratories, Inc.
NEVER LUBE JANDY - Valves–intake - Jandy Industries, Inc.
NEVER MAR - Adhesives and sealants ☆ - Consolidated Coatings Corp.
NEVER-MIST - Cleaning preparations - Schnapp Enterprises Inc.
NEVER RE-ROOF AGAIN - Roofing materials - Sa-Bon Enterprises Inc.
NEVER ROLL DUO TROL MEASURETTE - Apparel–women's - Cupid Foundations Inc.
NEVER-SEEZ - Epoxy - Bostik Inc.
NEVER SLIP - Kitchen appliances - Vaughan Manufacturing Co. Inc.
NEVER STOP GROWING - Footwear - SR Holdings Inc.
NEVER SUMMER NS - Sporting goods - Never Summer Industries, Inc.
NEVER TAME! - Apparel and accessories - Richard Trevino
NEVER TEACH A PIG TO SING!! - Apparel and accessories - Michael B. Lange
NEVER TO PART - Jewelry - Something Old, Something New, Inc.
NEVER UNARMED - Video production - Cold Steel Inc.
NEVER WETTER - Lipsticks - Charles Revson Inc.
NEVER-WILT - Containers - John Henry Co.
NEVEREVERDIET - Pharmaceutical preparations - Save-A-Life Today, Inc.
NEVERGLARE - Eyeglasses - National Vision Associates, Ltd.
NEVERHOOD, THE - Computer software - Neverhood, LLC
NEVERINKLE - Rubber cement ☆ - Dick Blick Co.
NEVERIP - Erasers ☆ - Quartet Manufacturing Co.
NEVERLEAK - Motor vehicle parts and accessories - R.M. Hollingshead Corp.
NEVERLOOSE - Rubber-stamp supplies - Consolidated Stamp Manufacturing Co. Inc.
NEVERMORE - Recording label - Joseph Smalkowski
NEVERS OAK - Wines - Seagram's Chateau & Estate Wines Co.
NEVERSOFT ENTERTAINMENT - Computer software - J.C.M. Productions, Inc.
NEVERTREE - Toys - Mattel, Inc.
NEVERUST - Hair care products ☆ - Fromm Industries
NEVERUST - Nails–horseshoe - Dickson Weatherproof Nail Co.
NEVILLE - Cabinets - Actua
NEVIN - Publisher's imprints - Willis Music Co.
NEVO - Games - Artdeco Games USA Inc.
NEVR-DULL - Housewares - George Basch Co. Inc.
NEV'R-LUBE - Wheels - Round I Sales, Co.
NEVROTOSE - Pharmaceutical preparations ☆ - Pal-Pak Inc.

☆ = Now out of production

N.E.W. - Animal feeds - Stevens Industries Inc.
NEW - Apparel–women's - Kellwood Co.
NEW 2 - Apparel–women's - Nuvogue Creations
NEW ACE - Nuts–salted, roasted, cooked, or canned - Sunshine Pecan Co.
NEW ACT - Recording label - O.L. Records
NEW ADDITION - Paper–writing - C'est Papier Inc.
NEW ADVENTURE - Floor coverings–carpet and rugs ☆ - Lees Carpets
NEW ADVENTURE II - Floor coverings–carpet and rugs - Lees Carpets
NEW AGAIN - Stain removers - Colgate-Palmolive Co.
NEW AGE - Accordions - Italo-American Accordion Manufacturing Co.
NEW AGE - Beverages–carbonated - Markstein Importers
NEW AGE - Cheese - Kraft Food Ingredients Corp.
NEW AGE - Floor coverings–carpet and rugs - Mohawk Carpet Corp.
NEW AGE - Hair coloring preparations - Roux Laboratories, Inc.
NEW AGE - Health care products ☆ - Medical Science Products Inc.
NEW AGE - Jackets–leather ☆ - A & K Inc.
NEW AGE - Skin care products - Revlon Consumer Products Corp.
NEW AGE - Wallpaper - Marburg Wallcoverings Inc.
NEW AGE BOOKS - Publisher's imprints - Bantam Doubleday Dell Publishing Group, Inc.
NEW AGE CREATIONS - Herbal products - Jeanne Rose
NEW AGE NATURALS - Skin care products - Revlon Consumer Products Corp.
NEW AKRON - Tiles–ceramic - Kowa Texas Inc.
NEW ALBANY STABLES - Toiletries - Bath & Body Works, Inc.
NEW ALBION - Recording label - Jazz Composer's Orchestra Association Inc.
NEW AMERICAN - Publisher's imprints - Penguin USA
NEW AMERICAN BUSINESS SYSTEM, THE - Boxes - Fax Communications Inc.
NEW AMERICAN CITY, THE - Publisher's imprints - Cleveland Bicentennial Commission, Inc.
NEW AMERICAN CUISINE - Dinners–frozen - Campbell Soup Co.
NEW AMERICAN DREAM - Bedding–linen - Dan River Inc.
NEW AMERICAN SPIRIT - Wallpaper ☆ - Eisenhart Wallcoverings Co.
NEW AMERICAN STANDARD BIBLE - Publisher's imprints - Lockman Foundation
NEW AMERICAN STANDARD ELECTRONIC BIBLE LIBRARY - Computer software - Lockman Foundation
NEW AMERICA'S FUNNIEST PEOPLE, THE - Music–sheet - Gina Communications Corp.
NEW ANGLE ON SNACKING, A - Potato chips ☆ - Keebler Co.
NEW ANGLES - Lighting fixtures - Swivelier Co. Inc.
NEW ANTIQUES - Posters - Andrew Kolb and Son Ltd.
NEW ARRIVAL - Dolls - Horsman
NEW ARRIVAL - Dolls - Mattel, Inc.
NEW ARRIVALS - Infant product - Eden LLC
NEW ART - Paints–artists' ☆ - Winsor & Newton
NEW ARTISTS - Recording label - Jazz Composer's Orchestra Association Inc.
NEW ATTITUDE - Apparel and accessories - Russ Togs Inc.
NEW ATTITUDE - Bicycles - Kent International Inc.
NEW ATTITUDE - Bicycles ☆ - Hedstrom Corp.
NEW ATTITUDE - Wallpaper - Fine Art Wallcoverings Ltd.
NEW ATTITUDES - Wallpaper ☆ - Imperial Wallcoverings, Inc.
NEW AURA - Apparel–women's - Bandini Inc.
NEW AVENUES - Housewares ☆ - Treasure Craft Co.
NEW BABY - Dolls - Doll Factory, Inc.
NEW BABY - Strollers–baby - Aimtex International Inc.
NEW BABY COLLECTION, THE - Toys - Pleasant Co.
NEW BALANCE - Footwear–athletic - New Balance Athletic Shoe, Inc.
NEW BASIC - Fabrics–cotton - P & B Fabrics, Inc.
NEW BEAT - HIHATS - Cymbals - Avedis Zildjian Co.
NEW BEDFORD - Floor coverings - Arthur J. Beacom & Co.
NEW BEDFORD - Floor coverings - Congoleum Corp.
NEW BEGINNINGS - Apparel–children's - Gerber Products Co.
NEW BEGINNINGS - Floor coverings–carpet and rugs - Gulistan Carpet Inc.
NEW BEGINNINGS - Glassware–household - Noah's Art Inc.
NEW BEGINNINGS - Toys–stuffed - Gund, Inc.
NEW BEGINNINGS - Vitamins and nutritional supplements - Schiff Products, Inc.
NEW BEGINNINGS - Wallpaper - Regency Mills Inc.
NEW BELGRADE - Floor coverings–carpet and rugs ☆ - Callaway Carpets
NEW BEST - Floor coverings–carpet and rugs - Daltonian Carpet & Cushion Inc.
NEW BIRD - Dishes–earthenware - Hadley Pottery Co. Inc.
NEW BIRTH - Recording label ☆ - Benson Music Group

NEW! B.K. HEUERMANN'S EXCLUSIVE POPPINGCORN - Popcorn - B.K.H. Popcorn, Inc.
NEW BLOOD - Books–comic - Warp Graphics, Inc.
NEW BLOSSOM - Deodorizers - W.W. Grainger, Inc.
NEW BODY - Dietary food supplements ☆ - Optimum Lifestyles, Inc.
NEW BODY, THE - Apparel and accessories ☆ - Warnaco Inc.
NEW BOSTON SEAFOOD CO. - Shrimp–fresh or frozen - Meg International, Inc.
NEW BOUTIQUE - Ophthalmic goods - Foremost Optical Products
NEW BREED - Dog food ☆ - Nestle USA
NEW BRIGHT - Toys - New Bright Industries Inc.
NEW BRITAIN TOOL - Tools ☆ - Litton Industries Inc. (New Britain Tool Div.)
NEW BRITIAN MACHINE - Machinery - Devlieg-Bullard Services Group
NEW BROWN LINER - Adhesives and sealants - Phil Marano Inc.
NEW CADENCE - Floor coverings–carpet and rugs ☆ - Karastan-Bigelow Inc.
NEW CALYPSO - Floor coverings–carpet and rugs ☆ - Trans-Ocean Import Co. Inc.
NEW CAPE COD - Tobacco products - Shepherd Tobacco Co.
NEW CASTLE - Floor coverings - Mannington Resilient Floors
NEW CASTLE - Floor coverings–carpet and rugs - Criterion Mills Inc.
NEW CASTLE LAMPS - Furniture - Atico International Inc.
NEW CENTURY - Floor coverings–carpet and rugs - Mohawk Industries Inc.
NEW CENTURY 2000 PLUS - Vitamins and nutritional supplements - John Driscoll
NEW CENTURY SUPPRESS - Pharmaceutical preparations - John Driscoll
NEW CHAMPION BY RI - Rackets–racquetball ☆ - Rackets International (Racket Sports Div.)
NEW CHAMPION GUIDE GRIP - Tires - Bridgestone/Firestone, Inc.
NEW CHAPTER - Food supplements - New Moon Extracts, Inc.
NEW CHAPTER EVERY WOMAN - Vitamins and nutritional supplements - New Moon Extracts, Inc.
NEW CHARM - Flatware - Wallace International Silversmiths, Inc.
NEW CHATEAU - Floor coverings ☆ - Congoleum Corp.
NEW CHICAGO - Greeting cards - Remigraphics, State of the Heart
NEW CLASSICS - Clocks - Sunbeam Corp.
NEW CLASSICS - Fabrics–tapestry ☆ - Coloroll Inc.
NEW CLASSICS - Floor coverings–carpet and rugs - Philadelphia Carpets
NEW CLEAN - Cleaning preparations - Ardex Laboratories, Inc.
NEW CLOTHING COMPANY - Apparel and accessories - Kellwood Co.
NEW CLOUD - Wallpaper ☆ - Maya Romanoff Corp.
NEW CLUB - Ammunition ☆ - Remington Arms Co., Inc.
NEW COAT - Paints - Montgomery Ward & Co. Inc.
NEW COLLECTIONS - Wallpaper - Andover Wallcovering
NEW COLOR HORIZONS - Finishing agents - Rust-Oleum Corp.
NEW COM - Computers - Aura Systems, Inc.
NEW COMPLEXION - Cosmetics - Revlon Consumer Products Corp.
NEW COMPLEXION MAKEUP - Cosmetics - Revlon Consumer Products Corp.
NEW CONCEPT - Floor coverings–carpet and rugs - Specialty Carpets
NEW CONCEPT - Floor waxes - Multi-Care Corp.
NEW CONCEPT - Toothpaste - Shaklee Corp.
NEW CONCEPT '80 - Furniture - Thayer Coggin Inc.
NEW CONCEPTS - Furniture ☆ - Bassett Furniture Industries, Inc.
NEW CONCEPTS - Wallpaper - Pantasote Inc. (Wallcovering Div.)
NEW CONNECTIONS - Apparel and accessories - American Argo Corp.
NEW CONSOL - Health care products - Care-Tech Laboratories Inc.
NEW CONSOL 20 - Skin care products - Care-Tech Laboratories Inc.
NEW COUNTRY - Fabrics–tapestry ☆ - Coloroll Inc.
NEW COUNTRY GEAR - House furnishings - Gear Holdings, Inc.
NEW COUNTRY STORY - Wallpaper - J. Josephson, Inc.
NEW COVENTRY - Motor vehicle parts and accessories - Lancaster Colony Automotive Group
NEW CREATION - Floor coverings–carpet and rugs - World Carpets, Inc.
NEW CROP - Apparel and accessories - Newstar Group, Inc.
NEW CROP - Fruits–pickled or brined - Safeway Inc.
NEW CYCLE - Health care products ☆ - Seventh Generation Wholesale Inc.
NEW DAWN - Food products - Wetterau Inc.
NEW DAWN - Furniture - Adam Wuest Inc.
NEW DAWN - Hair care products - Alberto-Culver Co.
NEW DAY - Clocks ☆ - General Time Corp. (Westclox/Seth Thomas Div.)
NEW DAY - Contact lenses - Bausch & Lomb Inc.
NEW DAY - Recording label - QCA Inc.
NEW DAY - Wallpaper ☆ - Imperial Wallcoverings, Inc.
NEW DAY CREATIONS - Figurines - V.I.P. Enterprises LLC
NEW DAY'S CHOICE - Sanitary napkins - Total Marketing Co. Inc.
NEW DEAL - Computer software - Nuco, Inc.
NEW DEAL, THE - Skateboards - P.S. Stix Inc.

☆ = Now out of production

NEW DECADE - Apparel and accessories - Campus Casuals of California
NEW DECOR - Tiles–ceramic - Dal-Tile Corp.
NEW DEFINITION - Cosmetics - Max Factor & Co.
NEW DEFINITIONS - Apparel and accessories - Image International, Inc.
NEW DELHI DILLY - Spices and extracts ☆ - Jodie's Kitchen Inc.
NEW DELHI SPICES - Spices and extracts - Ranjan Dey
NEW DEPARTURE - Floor coverings–carpet and rugs - Barrett Carpet Mills Inc.
NEW DEPARTURE - Floor coverings–carpet and rugs - Capel, Inc.
NEW DEX - Tools - Newcomer Products, Inc.
NEW DIMENSION - Apparel and accessories - Warnaco Inc.
NEW DIMENSION - Computer software - Software AG of North America, Inc.
NEW DIMENSION - Faucets - Sterling Plumbing Group Inc.
NEW DIMENSION - Floor coverings - Congoleum Corp.
NEW DIMENSION - Floor coverings–carpet and rugs - Galaxy Carpet Mills Inc.
NEW DIMENSION - Shirts - Horace Small Apparel Co.
NEW DIMENSION - Sporting goods ☆ - Outdoor Technologies Group
NEW DIMENSION GOLD - Animal feeds - Land O'Lakes, Inc.
NEW DIMENSION GOLD - Veterinary nutritional supplements - Land O'Lakes, Inc.
NEW DIMENSION SILVER - Animal feeds - Land O'Lakes, Inc.
NEW DIMENSIONS - Bedding–linen - Fieldcrest Cannon, Inc.
NEW DIMENSIONS - Computer software - Sealy Development Corp.
NEW DIMENSIONS - Floor coverings–carpet and rugs - Whitecrest Carpet Mills
NEW DIMENSIONS - Food products - Beatrice Cheese Co.
NEW DIMENSIONS - Furniture ☆ - Bassett Furniture Industries, Inc.
NEW DIMENSIONS - Greeting cards - Sunrise Publications, Inc.
NEW DIMENSIONS - Luggage ☆ - American Tourister, Inc.
NEW DIMENSIONS - Mats ☆ - U.S. Mat & Rubber Co. Inc.
NEW DIMENSIONS - Publisher's imprints ☆ - And/Or Press
NEW DIMENSIONS - Wallpaper - Advance Wallcoverings
NEW DIMENSIONS - Wallpaper - Fine Art Wallcoverings Ltd.
NEW DIMENSIONS II - Floor coverings–carpet and rugs - Galaxy Carpet Mills Inc.
NEW DIMENSIONS IN HANGER DESIGN - Garment hangers–wood - Carlisle Plastics, Inc.
NEW DIRECTION - Floor coverings–carpet and rugs - Cabin Crafts Carpets
NEW DIRECTION - House furnishings ☆ - Lea Industries Inc.
NEW DIRECTIONS - Fans–electric - Nutone Inc.
NEW DIRECTIONS - Floor coverings–carpet and rugs - J and J Industries Inc.
NEW DIRECTIONS - Floor coverings–carpet and rugs - Mohawk Carpet Corp.
NEW DIRECTIONS - Floor coverings–carpet and rugs ☆ - Callaway Carpets
NEW DIRECTIONS - Furniture ☆ - Universal Flooring
NEW DIRECTIONS - Handbags - Sarne Co. Inc.
NEW DIRECTIONS - Patterns–clothing ☆ - Simplicity Pattern Co., Inc.
NEW DIRECTIONS - Publisher's imprints - New Directions Publishing Corp.
NEW DIRECTIONS - Wallpaper ☆ - Wallquest, Inc.
NEW DIRECTIONS II - Floor coverings–carpet and rugs - Milliken & Co. Inc.
NEW DISCOVERIES - Electronic equipment - Texas Instruments Inc.
NEW DIVISION - Robes - Periphery Loungewear Inc.
NEW DUNES - Fabrics - Vertilux-Louverlux Inc.
NEW DUOTRON AM - Floor coverings–carpet and rugs - Mohawk Carpet Corp.
NEW DYNASTY - Furniture - Mersman Furniture Co.
NEW EAR 150 - Pet products - Francodex Labs
NEW EARTH - Food products ☆ - Clean Foods Inc.
NEW ECHOTA - Water–mineral - Lithia Springs Water Co., Inc.
NEW EDEN - Dishes–earthenware ☆ - Royal China & Porcelain Companies Inc.
NEW EDGEWOOD - Manufactured homes - Redman Industries, Inc.
NEW EDITION - Floor coverings–carpet and rugs - Mohawk Carpet Corp.
NEW EDITION - Floor coverings–carpet and rugs ☆ - Hollytex Carpet Mills Inc.
NEW EDITION - Ophthalmic goods - Foremost Optical Products
NEW ELEGANCE - Jewelry - Ostbye & Anderson, Inc.
NEW ELITE - Markers–felt-tip ☆ - Zebra Pen Corp.
NEW EMISSARY - Floor coverings–carpet and rugs - Mohawk Carpet Corp.
NEW ENAMELS - Tea kettles–nonelectric ☆ - Robinson Knife & Fiddlers Plastics
NEW ENGLAND - Clocks - New England Clock Co.
NEW ENGLAND - Coffee - New England Coffee Co.
NEW ENGLAND - Cosmetics - New England Natural Sponge, Inc.
NEW ENGLAND - Disinfectants ☆ - New England Serum Co.
NEW ENGLAND - Floor coverings–tile - Interface, Inc.

NEW ENGLAND - Food products ☆ - Veryfine Products, Inc.
NEW ENGLAND - Glass products - Taylor Building Products Co.
NEW ENGLAND - Granola bars ☆ - New England Natural Bakers Inc.
NEW ENGLAND - Honey - Gourmet Products Inc.
NEW ENGLAND - Safes ☆ - Boston Lock & Safe Co.
NEW ENGLAND - Soups–canned - Bay State Chowda
NEW ENGLAND - Twine - Geo. B. Carpenter Co.
NEW ENGLAND ASSOCIATES - Hair care products - Fearino's, Inc.
NEW ENGLAND BRASS GLASSWORKS - Doors–glass - Kohler Co.
NEW ENGLAND BREWING CO. - Beer - New England Brewing Co. Inc.
NEW ENGLAND BUTTER COMPANY, THE - Butter - Cabot Creamery Cooperative, Inc.
NEW ENGLAND COFFEE - Coffee - New England Coffee Co.
NEW ENGLAND COUNTRY PIES HOME OF THE MILE HIGH APPLE PIE - Pies–frozen - New England Country Pies, Inc.
NEW ENGLAND DAIRIES - Milk - New England Dairies Inc.
NEW ENGLAND DECK & WOOD FINISH - Cleaning preparations - Chemique Inc.
NEW ENGLAND FARMHOUSE PANCAKE SYRUP - Syrup - Maple Grove Farms of Vermont, Inc.
NEW ENGLAND FARMS - Milk - Nature's Best Dairy
NEW ENGLAND FEEDS - Animal feed supplements - United Co-Operative Farmers, Inc.
NEW ENGLAND GENTLEMAN - Apparel and accessories - Oxford Industries, Inc.
NEW ENGLAND HEIRLOOMS - Furniture ☆ - Hickory Chair Co.
NEW ENGLAND NATIONAL - Cookies ☆ - New England Natural Bakers Inc.
NEW ENGLAND NATURAL BAKERS - Cereal - New England Natural Bakers Inc.
NEW ENGLAND NATURAL SPONGE - Cosmetics - New England Natural Sponge, Inc.
NEW ENGLAND POTTERY - Garden equipment ☆ - Lawn & Garden Supply Co.
NEW ENGLAND REVOLUTION - Potash - Major League Soccer, LLC
NEW ENGLAND RUSTICS - Novelty items - D.A. Glassco Inc.
NEW ENGLAND SEAFOOD & LOBSTER CO. - Seafood products–fresh or frozen - Prospect Enterprises, Inc.
NEW ENGLAND SEASHORE - Furniture - Bassett Furniture Industries, Inc.
NEW ENGLAND SHRIMP CO. - Shrimp–fresh or frozen - New England Shrimp Co. Inc.
NEW ENGLAND STUDIES - Publisher's imprints - Northeastern University Press
NEW ENGLAND SUPERNATURAL - Food products - Breadshop's Natural Foods
NEW ENGLAND TRAVELER - Games - World Traveler Ltd.
NEW ENGLAND VILLAGE SERIES - Figurines - Department 56 Inc.
NEW ENGLAND YANKEE - Fruit and vegetable markets - J.P. Sullivan & Co.
NEW ENGLANDER - Desk sets - Stanton's Quills
NEW ENGLANDER - Leather–chamois - Beverly Manufacturing Corp.
NEW ENGLANDER - Rifles - Thompson/Center Arms
NEW ENGLANDER - Safes ☆ - Boston Lock & Safe Co.
NEW ENTITIES - Apparel and accessories - Frederick Atkins, Inc.
NEW ENTITIES PETITE - Apparel stores–women's - Frederick Atkins, Inc.
NEW ENTITIES WOMAN - Apparel stores–women's - Frederick Atkins, Inc.
NEW ERA - Apparel–athletic - New Era Knitting Mills
NEW ERA - Bedding–linen - Thomaston Mills Inc.
NEW ERA - Caps–baseball - New Era Cap Co., Inc.
NEW ERA - Cooking equipment–household - New Era Co.
NEW ERA - Door frames - S.D.S. Industries, Inc.
NEW ERA - Food products - New Era Canning Co.
NEW ERA - Musical instruments ☆ - Selmer Co. Inc.
NEW-ERA - Oils–illuminating - New-Era Trading Group, Inc.
NEW ERA - Pet products - Francodex Labs
NEW ERA - Wallpaper - Pantasote Inc. (Wallcovering Div.)
NEW ERA ALL DAY ENERGY! - Fruit drinks–bottled or canned - Everfresh Beverages, Inc.
NEW ESSENTIALS - Cosmetics - New Essentials Ltd.
NEW ESSENTIALS SUNCARE - Skin care products - Revlon Consumer Products Corp.
NEW EXPERIENCE IV - Mattresses ☆ - Kingsdown, Inc.
NEW EXPERIENCE VI - Mattresses ☆ - Kingsdown, Inc.
NEW EXPRESSIONS - Apparel and accessories - Bobbie Brooks Inc.
NEW EXPRESSIONS - Wallpaper - Regency Mills Inc.
NEW EXPRESSIONS FABRICS - Fabrics - Troy Mills Inc.
NEW FACES - Fabrics - Dan River Inc.
NEW FADE RESISTANT PREFERENCE - Hair care products - Cosmair Inc.

☆ = Now out of production

NEW FALMOUTH - Fabrics ☆ - Greenwood Mills Inc.
NEW FAMILY MOVIES - Video production - Simitar Entertainment, Inc.
NEW FAVORITE - Lawn mower - American Lawn Mower Co.
NEW FEELINGS - Apparel and accessories - Warnaco Inc.
NEW FIGURAMA - Apparel–women's ☆ - Maidenform Inc. (True Form Foundations Div.)
NEW FOLD - Bird feeders - Walter L. Loggins
NEW FOREST - Tiles–ceramic ☆ - Latco Products
NEW FORM - Ophthalmic goods - Foremost Optical Products
NEW FORM B-12 - Health care products - Resurrection Laboratories
NEW FREEDOM - Sanitary napkins - Kimberly-Clark Corp.
NEW FRESHNESS - Health care products ☆ - C.B. Fleet Co. Inc.
NEW FRIENDS - Jeans–women's ☆ - Gabriel Manufacturing Co.
NEW FRONTIER - Bags - New Frontier Outdoor Ltd.
NEW FRONTIER - Beverages–malt - Frontier Brewing Co.
NEW FRONTIER - Floor coverings–carpet and rugs - Queen Carpet Corp.
NEW FRONTIER - Revolvers ☆ - Colt's Manufacturing Co. Inc.
NEW FRONTIER AMBER LAGER - Beverages–malt - Frontier Brewing Co.
NEW FRONTIER COLLECTION - Furniture–upholstered - Hickory Hill Furniture Corp.
NEW-GARG - Pharmaceutical preparations - Lustol Co.
NEW GENERATION - Automotive parts and accessories - Westling Manufacturing Co.
NEW GENERATION - Bird cages - Ameriguard Corp.
NEW GENERATION - Detergents - Imperial Manufacturing Co. Inc.
NEW GENERATION - Floor coverings - Congoleum Corp.
NEW GENERATION - Floor coverings–carpet and rugs - Regal Rugs Inc.
NEW GENERATION - Floor coverings–carpet and rugs ☆ - Columbus Mills, Inc.
NEW GENERATION - Oils–lubricating ☆ - Conoco Inc.
NEW GENERATION - Paints - Ponderosa Paint Manufacturing Co. Inc.
NEW GENERATION - Shirts - Horace Small Apparel Co.
NEW GENERATION - Towels - Fieldcrest Cannon, Inc.
NEW GENERATION - Trading cards and stamps - Pinnacle Brands, Inc.
NEW GENERATION - Vitamins and nutritional supplements - Pure Planet Products
NEW GENERATION - Wallpaper - Sunnyside Prints
NEW GENERATION - Wallpaper ☆ - Pickhardt & Siebert USA Inc.
NEW GENERATION - Yarn ☆ - Lion Brand Yarn Co.
NEW GENERATION 40 - Adhesives and sealants - Spartan Chemical Co., Inc.
NEW GENERATION 50 - Adhesives and sealants - Spartan Chemical Co., Inc.
NEW GENERATION NUTRITION - Animal feed supplements - Moorman Manufacturing Co.
NEW GENERATION OUTERWEAR - Jackets - Horace Small Apparel Co.
NEW GENERATION STAIN CONTROL FIBER - Yarn - Dry Corp.
NEW GENERATION, THE - Bird feeders - Droll Yankees, Inc.
NEW GENERATION, THE - Water purification systems - Eagle Spring Filtration, Inc.
NEW GENERATION WORKWHEEL - Propellers - Bird-Johnson Co.
NEW GENERATIONS - Recliners ☆ - Action Industries Inc.
NEW-GLASS - Wood products - Newcourt, Inc.
NEW GOLDEN COLLECTION - Wigs - Sun Taiyang Co. Ltd.
NEW GOODIES - Apparel–children's - Good Lad Co.
NEW GRAMAPHONE SOCIETY - Recording label - Stanyan Record Co.
NEW GRANGE - Floor coverings–carpet and rugs - Atlas Carpet Mills Inc.
NEW-GRIP - Tools - Newcomer Products, Inc.
NEW GROWTH - Hair care products ☆ - J. Strickland & Co.
NEW GUTENBERG SOFTWARE - Computer software - New Gutenberg Press, Inc.
NEW HAMPSHIRE SOAP - Soap - Sally Sherrard
NEW HAMPTON - Cabinets–wood ☆ - Kemper
NEW HAMPTON CATHEDRAL - Cabinets–wood ☆ - Kemper
NEW HARD - Mats–wire ☆ - Zebra Pen Corp.
NEW HARMONY - Chimes ☆ - Nutone Inc.
NEW HARVEST ORGANICS - Fruits and vegetables - Philip S. Ostrom
NEW HAVEN - Clocks - Burwood Products Co.
NEW HAVEN - Furniture - O'Sullivan Industries, Inc.
NEW HAVEN - Ramps - GRK Manufacturing
NEW HAVEN - Recording label - Skylite-Sing Inc.
NEW HAVEN - Rifles - O.F. Mossberg & Sons, Inc.
NEW HEIGHTS - Wallpaper - Four Seasons
NEW HOLLAND - Cheese - Bongrain Cheese USA
NEW HOLLAND - Floor coverings - Congoleum Corp.
NEW HOLLAND BULB CO. - Flowers, plants, and seeds - Foster and Gallagher Inc.
NEW HOLSTEIN - Cheese - AMPI/Morning Glory Farms

NEW HOME - Sewing machines–household - New Home Sewing Machine Co.
NEW HOPE - Floor coverings–carpet and rugs ☆ - Regal Rugs Inc.
NEW HOPE - Furniture - Lineage Home Furnishings, Inc.
NEW HOPE - Wallpaper ☆ - Sandpiper Studios
NEW HOPE MILLS - Pancakes–mixes - New Hope Mills
NEW HOPE MILLS GOLD DUST - Flour–blended - New Hope Mills
NEW HOPE STENCIL - Wallpaper ☆ - Sandpiper Studios
NEW HORIZON - Faucets - Sterling Plumbing Group Inc.
NEW HORIZON - Floor coverings–carpet and rugs - Colonial Mills Inc.
NEW HORIZON - Meat products–beef - New Horizon
NEW HORIZON - Trailers–travel ☆ - Shasta Industries Inc.
NEW HORIZONS - Floor coverings–carpet and rugs ☆ - Mandate-Dawn Carpet Mills
NEW HORIZONS - Mattresses ☆ - Sealy Inc.
NEW HORIZONS - Oils–edible - Rose Acre Farms, Inc.
NEW HORIZONS - Paints–artists' - Celex Group, Inc.
NEW HORIZONS - Posters - Successories, Inc.
NEW HORIZONS - Ships–sailing vessels - Ray Greene Industries
NEW HORIZONS - Wallpaper ☆ - Schooner Prints Inc.
NEW HORIZONS - Wallpaper ☆ - Wallpaper Imports Inc.
NEW HORIZONS 3000 - Office supplies ☆ - McDonald Products
NEW HORIZONS SWIMWEAR - Swimwear - Grand Knitting Mills, Inc.
NEW HYGIENE - Bathroom fixtures - Crane Plumbing/Fiat Products
NEW IDEA - Agricultural machinery - Allied Products Corp.
NEW IDEA - Housewares - Agco Corp.
NEW IDEAS INTERNATIONAL - Deodorizers - New Ideas International, Inc.
NEW IMAGE - Apparel and accessories - Scharpf's Identity Apparel, Inc.
NEW IMAGE - Bicycles - Kent International Inc.
NEW IMAGE - Cleaning preparations–window - Analab Inc.
NEW IMAGE - Contact lenses - Universal Contact Lenses, Inc.
NEW IMAGE - Floor coverings–carpet and rugs ☆ - Regal Rugs Inc.
NEW IMAGE - Food products - Enzo-Pac Inc.
NEW IMAGE - Hair care products - Dial Corp.
NEW IMAGE - Wallpaper - Bill Villetto Designs Inc.
NEW IMAGE ONE COAT - Paints ☆ - Pratt & Lambert United, Inc.
NEW IMPRESSIONS - Skin-care products - Fair Lady Video
NEW INALTERA UNIS - Wallpaper ☆ - Wallquest, Inc.
NEW INFINITY JR. - Cameras ☆ - Olympus America Inc.
NEW INVITATION - Educational materials - United Methodist Publishing House
NEW IRRESISTIBLE - Floor coverings–carpet and rugs ☆ - Durkan Patterned Carpets
NEW IVORY - Soap - Procter & Gamble Co.
NEW JAMESTOWN - Floor coverings–carpet and rugs - Couristan Inc.
NEW JAZZ - Phonographs - Fantasy Inc.
NEW JERSEY AMERICANS - Apparel and accessories - NBA Properties, Inc.
NEW JERUSALEM - Audio tapes–blank - New Jerusalem
NEW JERUSALEM JEWELRY - Jewelry - Springer Russell
NEW JEWEL - Floor coverings–carpet and rugs - Galaxy Carpet Mills Inc.
NEW KID - Ophthalmic goods - Foremost Optical Products
NEW KID ON THE BLOCK - Computer software - Hartley Courseware Inc.
NEW KIDS ON THE BLOCK - Candy - Topps Co., Inc.
NEW KIDS ON THE BLOCK - Puzzles ☆ - Milton Bradley Co.
NEW LEAF - Food products - Quong Hop & Co.
NEW LEAF - Giftware - Doranne
NEW LEGACY, A - Wallpaper - Beachwood Wallcoverings
NEW LEGENDS - Apparel–children's - Kids R Us Co.
NEW LENGTHS - Cosmetics - Sally Hansen
NEW LIBERTY - Floor coverings–carpet and rugs - Barrett Carpet Mills Inc.
NEW LIFE - Apparel and accessories - New Life Industries, Inc.
NEW LIFE - Peanut butter - Producers Peanut Co. Inc.
NEW LIFE - Prosthetic apparatus ☆ - Camp, Inc.
NEW LIFE BOOKS - Publisher's imprints ☆ - Standard Publishing Co.
NEW LIFE CABINET SOLUTIONS - Cabinets - Dura-Craft Kitchens
NEW LIFE DECAFE - Coffee - Try Coffee Group Ltd.
NEW LIFE DESIGN - Vitamins and nutritional supplements - High Life Formulas Inc.
NEW LIFE KITCHENS - Cakes - New Life Bakery Inc.
NEW LIFE TO LIVE, A - Computer software - A New Life to Live, Inc.
NEW LINE - Motion picture distributors–prerecorded - Turner Broadcasting System Inc.
NEW LINK CUISINE, THE - Food products - FAF Associates Inc.
NEW-LOCK - Tools - Newcomer Products, Inc.
NEW LOGIC - Filters–industrial - New Logic International, Inc.
NEW LONDON STYLE - Wallpaper ☆ - ICI Americas Inc.
NEW LONDONER - Fabrics ☆ - Beverly Manufacturing Corp.
NEW LOOK - Floor coverings–carpet and rugs ☆ - Quaker Inc.

☆ = Now out of production

NEW LOOK - Patterns–clothing - Simplicity Pattern Co., Inc.
NEW LOOK FOR HEALTH PROFESSIONALS, A - Apparel and accessories -
   Avery Medical Fashions, Inc.
NEW LOOKS - Paper–gift wrap - Flowers, Inc. Balloons
NEW-LUBE - Metal-cutting-tool lubricant - New Tech Cutting Tools Inc.
NEW LUCCA - Food products ✰ - Homestead Ravioli Co.
NEW MAN - Hair-care products, wigs, hair-replacement product - International
   Hairgoods Inc.
NEW MAN - Vitamins and nutritional supplements - Barth-Spencer Corp.
NEW MAN HAIR ADDITION - Hair-care products, wigs, and hairpieces -
   International Hairgoods Inc.
NEW MANOR - Floor coverings - Congoleum Corp.
NEW MARKET - Floor coverings - Mannington Resilient Floors
NEW MATH BLASTER PLUS - Computer software ✰ - Knowledge Adventure
NEW MAUVE - Lipstick ✰ - Cosrich Inc.
NEW MEDIA SCHOOLHOUSE - Computer storage devices - New Media
   Schoolhouse, Inc.
NEW MEDIUM - Recording label - Strafe Entertainment/New Medium Records
NEW MIDDLE - Frames–eyeglass ✰ - Kenmark Optical Co.
NEW MILL - Noodles - Borden Pasta Group
NEW MILL - Pasta - Borden, Inc.
NEW MILLENNIUM - Christmas tree ornaments - Prosperity Tree International
NEW MILLENNIUM RECORDS - Recording label - New Millennium Records
NEW MILLENNIUM WORLD ATLAS DELUXE - Computer software - Rand
   McNally & Co.
NEW MILLERS CREEK COLLECTION - Furniture ✰ - American Drew
NEW MOOD - Ophthalmic goods - Foremost Optical Products
NEW MOON - Floor coverings–carpet and rugs - John D. Kurtz
NEW MOON - Health care products - New Moon Extracts, Inc.
NEW MOON - Manufactured homes - Redman Industries, Inc.
NEW MOON LIMITED - Manufactured homes - Redman Industries, Inc.
NEW MORGAN, THE - Tableware–plastic ✰ - Kraftware Corp. (Morgan Div.)
NEW MORNING - Cereal - New Morning
NEW MORNING - Food products - New Morn, Inc.
NEW MOTHERHOOD - See PRE-MOTHERHOOD
NEW MOUSE - Computer peripheral equipment - Mouse Systems Corp.
NEW MOVES - Apparel–children's - J.C. Penney Co., Inc.
NEW MOWN HAY - Skin care products ✰ - Avon Products, Inc.
NEW MURALS COLLECTION - Wallpaper - Charles Barone Inc.
NEW MUSIC CIRCLE - Recording label - Jazz Composer's Orchestra
   Association Inc.
NEW N' EXCITING - Floor coverings–carpet and rugs ✰ - Prestige Mills Inc.
NEW NAME IN TOWN - Apparel–athletic - International Sourcing Concepts,
   Inc.
NEW NATIVE - Infant product - Nancy Scrivens
NEW NATURAL CLASSICS - Fabrics - Valley Forge Fabrics Inc.
NEW NATURALS, THE - Lipsticks - Orjene Natural Cosmetics
NEW NINETIES - Footwear - Sam & Libby, Inc.
NEW NOTCH - Tools - Newcomer Products, Inc.
NEW NOTE - Recording label - Jazz Composer's Orchestra Association Inc.
NEW NOVELTY - Earthenware - Scio Pottery Co.
NEW OASIS - Hair care products - New Oasis Inc.
NEW OIL - Pharmaceutical preparations ✰ - Lustol Co.
NEW ONYX - Nail care products - Onyx Corp.
NEW ORGANIC - Nuts–salted, roasted, cooked, or canned ✰ - Walnut Acres
   Inc.
NEW ORIGINAL - Bowling balls - Ebonite International, Inc.
NEW ORLEANS - Candy ✰ - Elmer Candy Corp.
NEW ORLEANS - Dolls ✰ - Effanbee Doll Corp.
NEW ORLEANS - Fans–electric ✰ - Sunbeam-Oster Household Products
NEW ORLEANS - Radios - Robert Bosch Corp.
NEW ORLEANS - Recording label - Sharon Productions Inc.
NEW ORLEANS - Seasonings - Carnival Seasonings
NEW ORLEANS BEST - Beverages–malt - Dixie Brewing Co.
NEW ORLEANS BEST LIGHT - Beverages–malt - Dixie Brewing Co.
NEW ORLEANS BLEND - Coffee - Community Coffee Co., Inc.
NEW ORLEANS CHEF CREATIONS - Food products - Diversified Foods, Inc.
NEW ORLEANS JAZZ - T-shirts–men's - Jazz Basketball Investors, Inc.
NEW ORLEANS JAZZ BRUNCH - Video production - GCI Inc. (Great Chefs
   Television/Publishing Div.)
NEW ORLEANS JUBILEE - Food products - Dolefam Corp.
NEW ORLEANS MIX - Nuts–salted, roasted, cooked, or canned - SCT Corp.
NEW ORLEANS RHYTHM KINGS - Recording label - Frank R. Naundorf
NEW ORLEANS SAINTS - Trading cards and stamps - New Orleans Louisiana
   Saints L. P.
NEW ORLEANS SOUL - Labels–paper - King Walk Inc.

NEW ORLEANS SOUND - Recording label - Great Southern Record Co. Inc.
NEW ORLEANS STYLE - Food products ✰ - McIlhenny Co.
NEW PARADIGM - Bicycles - Wilderness Trail Bikes Inc.
NEW PARAGON - Floor coverings ✰ - Congoleum Corp.
NEW PARENT PRODUCTIONS - Recording label ✰ - American Baby
   Concepts
NEW PERFECTION - Cosmetics ✰ - Chem Spray Aerosols Inc.
NEW PERFORMING PREFERENCE - Hair coloring preparations - Cosmair Inc.
NEW PERIOD - Lacquers - New Period Lacquer Corp.
NEW PERSPECTIVE - Apparel and accessories - Colonial Textile
   Manufacturing Corp.
NEW PERSPECTIVES - Wallpaper - Capital Carousel Inc.
NEW PERSPECTIVES - Wallpaper - Roger Nicholson Designs Ltd.
NEW PHOENIX - Fabrics - Vertilux-Louverlux Inc.
NEW PLANT LIFE - Insecticides ✰ - New Plant Life
NEW POINSET - Floor coverings–carpet and rugs ✰ - Masland Corp.
NEW POINT - Computer peripheral equipment - Mouse Systems Corp.
NEW POINTE - Burial caskets - Batesville Casket Co., Inc.
NEW PORT - Giftware - Sasaki
NEW-POS - Tools - Newcomer Products, Inc.
NEW POTATOES - Apparel–children's - Sweet Potatoes, Inc.
NEW PRECIOUS - Floor coverings–carpet and rugs ✰ - Patcraft Mills Inc.
NEW PRESS - Publisher's imprints - McGraw-Hill Companies, Inc.
NEW PRICE IS RIGHT - Games ✰ - Milton Bradley Co.
NEW PRINT SHOP COMPANION, THE - Computer software ✰ - Broderbund
   Software, Inc.
NEW PRINT SHOP, THE - Computer software ✰ - Broderbund Software, Inc.
NEW PROFILE - Apparel and accessories - Brazabra Corp.
NEW PROFILE - Health care products - Conklin Co., Inc.
NEW PROTOLAB 4.0 - Computer software - Interplex Electronics Inc.
NEW PROVINCIAL - Floor coverings - Tarkett, Inc.
NEW RAPID TAP - Lubricating oils - Relton Corp.
NEW RECORDS - Recording label ✰ - J.R. Records
NEW REFELECTIONS - Mirrors ✰ - Bassett Furniture Industries, Inc.
NEW REVELATION - Floor coverings–carpet and rugs - Barrett Carpet Mills
   Inc.
NEW REVENUE - Advertising agencies - Edith Ann Howard
NEW RHYTHM - Floor coverings–carpet and rugs ✰ - Karastan-Bigelow Inc.
NEW RIVAL - Ammunition ✰ - Olin Corp. (Winchester Div.)
NEW RIVER - Apparel–men's - Edison Brothers Stores, Inc.
NEW RIVER - Furniture - Vaughan Furniture Co. Inc.
NEW ROMANCE - Floor coverings–carpet and rugs ✰ - Zenith Carpets
NEW ROMANTICS, THE - Apparel stores–lingerie - Formfit Rogers
NEW RULES. NEW GAMES. - Computer software - Iwn, Inc.
NEW SAFARI 80 - Floor coverings–carpet and rugs ✰ - Hollytex Carpet Mills
   Inc.
NEW SCENE - Floor coverings–carpet and rugs - Alexander Smith Carpets
NEW SCIENCE LIBRARY - Publisher's imprints ✰ - Shambhala Publications
   Inc.
NEW SCIMITAR - Cymbals - Avedis Zildjian Co.
NEW SEASONS - Vitamins and nutritional supplements - Home Health
   Products, Inc.
NEW SENSATION - Bicycles - Kent International Inc.
NEW SENSATIONS - Floor coverings–carpet and rugs - Philadelphia Carpets
NEW SERENADE - Floor coverings–carpet and rugs - Karastan-Bigelow Inc.
NEW SERVICE - Firearms, accessories, and parts ✰ - Colt's Manufacturing Co.
   Inc.
NEW SHAPE - Ophthalmic goods - Foremost Optical Products
NEW-SKIN - Health care products - Medtech Laboratories Inc.
NEW SOLUTIONS DESIGNWEAVE - Carpet - Tuftex Carpet Mills, Inc.
NEW SONGS FOR WORSHIPING CHURCHES - Recording label - Integrity
   Music, Inc.
NEW SOUND - Recording label ✰ - Accent Records
NEW SOUND OF COMPUTING - Electronic equipment - Monolith Technologies
   Corp.
NEW SPICE - Cooking equipment–household ✰ - General Housewares Corp.
NEW SPIRIT - Floor coverings–carpet and rugs ✰ - Karastan-Bigelow Inc.
NEW SPIRIT - Floor coverings–carpet and rugs ✰ - Masland Corp.
NEW SPIRIT - Juices–frozen - New Age Foods, Inc.
NEW SPIRIT - Wallpaper ✰ - Eisenhart Wallcoverings Co.
NEW SPIRIT - Window coverings - Viking Distributors
NEW SPIRIT ACCENTS - Floor coverings–carpet and rugs ✰ - Karastan-
   Bigelow Inc.
NEW SPLENDOR - Wallpaper - Advent Industries Inc.
NEW SPLENDOUR - Floor coverings–carpet and rugs ✰ - World Carpets, Inc.
NEW SQUARE - Milk - Ahava Dairy Products Corp.

NEW STANDARD - Publisher's imprints - Standard Educational Corp.

NEW STANDARD OF EXCELLENCE, THE - Telephones - Code-a-Phone Corp.

NEW STAR - Blankets - New Star Oriental Corp.

NEW STAR - Floor coverings–carpet and rugs ☆ - Karastan-Bigelow Inc.

NEW STAR - Seafood products–fresh or frozen - Seafood Resources, Ltd.

NEW STAR ACCENTS - Floor coverings–carpet and rugs ☆ - Karastan-Bigelow Inc.

NEW START - Cosmetics - New Start Cosmetics Inc.

NEW STEP - Hair-texturizing shears - B.W. Boyd Shears Inc.

NEW STYLE - Recording label - Lite Album Publishing Co.

NEW SUPERTRON - Floor coverings–carpet and rugs - Mohawk Carpet Corp.

NEW SURROUNDINGS - Floor coverings ☆ - B.F. Goodrich Co.

NEW SYLVA - Sleepwear - Meltzer Industries Corp.

NEW SYMPHONY - Floor coverings–carpet and rugs - Karastan-Bigelow Inc.

NEW TALKING STICKYBEAR ALPHABET, THE - Computer software ☆ - Optimum Resource, Inc.

NEW TALKING STICKYBEAR OPPOSITES, THE - Computer software ☆ - Optimum Resource, Inc.

NEW TALKING STICKYBEAR SHAPES, THE - Computer software ☆ - Optimum Resource, Inc.

NEW TAMPRUF - Hardware ☆ - Allegheny Bolt & Screw

NEW TECH KITES - Kites and related products - New Tech Sports

NEW TEMPO - Floor coverings–carpet and rugs - Karastan-Bigelow Inc.

NEW TERRAIN - Bicycles - Roadmaster Corp.

NEW TERRAIN - Footwear - Track 'n Trail

NEW TESTAMENT MATCH - Computer software - Hartley Courseware Inc.

NEW TESTAMENT ODYSSEY - Computer software - Hartley Courseware Inc.

NEW TEXTILE - Wallpaper ☆ - Combo Industries

NEW TEXTURE - Hair care products - Kenra, Inc.

NEW-THIGH - Dermatological preparations - Rebeka, Inc.

NEW THRILL FOR THE GRILL, THE - Meat products - Tav Brands Inc.

NEW TIA - Colognes ☆ - CTS Laboratories Inc.

NEW TIMES - Floor coverings–carpet and rugs ☆ - Masland Corp.

NEW TITANS - Games ☆ - Mayfair Games, Inc.

NEW TOMORROW - Paper products - New Tomorrow Inc.

NEW TOMORROW - Photographic equipment - Magic Garden Products (New Tomorrow, Inc.)

NEW-TONIC - Vitamins and nutritional supplements - Newton Laboratories, Inc.

NEW TOP NOTCH - Floor coverings–carpet and rugs - Mohawk Carpet Corp.

NEW TOY CLASSICS - Toys - Laurence Jay Shaw

NEW TRACERY - Wallpaper ☆ - Maya Romanoff Corp.

NEW TRADITIONAL PLANK - Floor coverings - Robbins Inc.

NEW TRADITIONS - Beverages - Scotty's Naturals, LLC

NEW TRADITIONS - Christmas decorations - MJ Designs

NEW TRADITIONS - Desk sets ☆ - Newell Office Products

NEW TRADITIONS - Dinnerware–glass - Arita Sales Co. Inc.

NEW TRADITIONS - Floor coverings–carpet and rugs - Gulistan Carpet Inc.

NEW TRADITIONS - Meat products–pork ☆ - Hormel Foods Corp.

NEW TRADITIONS - Shelving units–metal - Dorfile Manufacturing Co.

NEW TRADITIONS - Wallpaper - Capital Carousel Inc.

NEW TRADITIONS - Wallpaper - Roger Nicholson Designs Ltd.

NEW TRAIL - Snack foods - Hershey Chocolate USA

NEW TRENDS - Floor coverings–carpet and rugs ☆ - Carpet Crafts Inc.

NEW TRENDS - Ophthalmic goods - Foremost Optical Products

NEW TWIST - Rings–jewelry - Artcarved Inc.

NEW VALUES IN INFUSION - Pumps - McKinley, Inc.

NEW VELVET - Floor coverings–carpet and rugs ☆ - Fieldturf & Carpet Inc.

NEW VENTURE GEAR - Automotive parts - New Venture Gear Inc.

NEW VIGOR - Fertilizers - Jonathan Green, Inc.

NEW VINTAGE - Apparel and accessories - Marble Sportswear, Inc.

NEW VINTAGE - Giftware ☆ - Great Graphic Originals

NEW VISION - Floor coverings–carpet and rugs ☆ - Regal Rugs Inc.

NEW VISION - Vitamins and nutritional supplements - New Vision International, Inc.

NEW VISION SERIES - Loudspeakers Now out of production - International Jensen Inc.

NEW VISIONS FROM WILD WINGS - Posters - Wild Wings, Inc.

NEW VISTA - Finishing agents - Blue Ridge Talc Co. Inc.

NEW VISTA - Floor coverings–carpet and rugs - Masterpiece Finishing Co.

NEW VISTA - Hair care products - Scruples Professional Salon Products, Inc.

NEW VOGUE - Cooking utensils–aluminum ☆ - General Housewares Corp.

NEW VOLT - Power transformers - Sergio Hamernik

NEW VYCON - Wallcoverings - Vycon Contract

NEW WARMTH - Cosmetics - Almay Inc.

NEW WARPS & WEAVES - Wallcoverings - Cork Products Co. Inc.

NEW WARRIORS, THE - Publisher's imprints ☆ - Marvel Entertainment Group, Inc.

NEW WASHINGTON SQUARE - Floor coverings ☆ - Robbins Inc.

NEW WATER - Chlorine - King Technology, Inc.

NEW WATERFALL - Fountains–drinking - Crane Plumbing/Fiat Products

NEW WAVE - Archery equipment - Pro Line Co.

NEW WAVE - Audio equipment - Pyle Industries Inc.

NEW WAVE - Blinds–venetian ☆ - Hunter Douglas, Inc.

NEW WAVE - Floor coverings–carpet and rugs - J and J Industries Inc.

NEW WAVE - Hair care products - Drake-Bluestein, Inc.

NEW WAVE - Hair care products - Willat Co.

NEW WAVE - Ovens–convection - Fairsound USA Corp.

NEW WAVE - Rings–jewelry - Artcarved Inc.

NEW WAVE - Sporting goods ☆ - Outdoor Technologies Group

NEW WAVE - Toys - Maui Toys

NEW WAVE - Wallpaper ☆ - David & Dash

NEW WAVE - Watches - Delta Impex Watch Corp.

NEW WAVE - Water purification systems - GKG Corp.

NEW WAVE AQUAFARMS - Herbal products - Fisheries Development Foundation of North Carolian

NEW WAVES - Wallpaper - Marburg Wallcoverings Inc.

NEW WAVES - Wallpaper - Wolf-Gordon Inc.

NEW WAVEZ - Goggles–safety - Sellstrom Manufacturing Co.

NEW WAY - Erasers - Empire Berol USA

NEW WAY TO TELL, A - Clocks - By Design Corp.

NEW WAY TO TELL TIME, A - Clocks - Charles S. Coster

NEW WAYS TO KNOW - Computer software - Houghton Mifflin Co.

NEW WEAVE - Bandages - Tillotson Healthcare Corp.

NEW WEST - Bicycles - Huffy Corp.

NEW WEST - Cosmetics - Aramis Inc.

NEW WEST - Fruits–dried ☆ - Ross Packing Co.

NEW WEST - Fruits–frozen - New West Foods Inc.

NEW WEST - Hats - Bailey Hat Co.

NEW WINDSOR - Fabrics ☆ - Greenwood Mills Inc.

NEW WINGS - Music–sheet - Lorenz Creative Services Corp.

NEW WOMAN - Hair-replacement product and wigs - International Hairgoods Inc.

NEW WONDER - Floor coverings–carpet and rugs - World Carpets, Inc.

NEW WORLD - Bicycles ☆ - Huffy Corp.

NEW WORLD - Cages–wire - Mid-West Metal Products Co. Inc.

NEW WORLD - Food products - Levin Distributing

NEW WORLD - Games - Avalon Hill Game Co.

NEW WORLD - Recording label - Recorded Anthology of American Music

NEW WORLD - Seasonings - Nat-Trop

NEW WORLD - Yogurt ☆ - Cass-Clay Creamery Inc.

NEW WORLD BOTANICALS - Vitamins and nutritional supplements - New World Enterprizes, Inc. (New World Entertainment)

NEW WORLD COFFEE - Coffee - New World Coffee, Inc.

NEW WORLD COLLECTION - Floor coverings ☆ - Azrock Commercial Flooring

NEW WORLD COMPUTING INC. - Toys–electronic - New World Computing Inc.

NEW WORLD FOODS - Food products - VPS, Inc.

NEW WORLD METALLICS - Floor coverings ☆ - Azrock Commercial Flooring

NEW WORLD OF OLD TIME - Jewelry - Authentic Models, Inc.

NEW WORLD ORDER - Apparel and accessories - Brawn of California, Inc.

NEW WORLD PAPERBACKS - Publisher's imprint - International Publishers Co. Inc.

NEW WORLD PARTY MIX - Snack foods - Keystone Food Products

NEW WORLD TILE - Floor coverings–tile - Winnington Corp.

NEW YEAR'S BLEND - Coffee - Saramar Corp.

NEW YORK - Breads - Stroehmann Bakeries Inc.

NEW YORK - Breads–frozen - T. Marzetti Co.

NEW YORK - Computer software - Apple Computer Inc.

NEW YORK - Faucets - Kallista Inc.

NEW YORK - Flooring–hardwood - Mannington Wood Floors

NEW YORK - Guitars ☆ - Fred Gretsch Enterprises

NEW YORK - Mustard - Arbor Hill Associates, Inc.

NEW YORK - Stepladders - W.W. Babcock Co. Inc.

NEW YORK - Wallpaper - Bayview Wallcoverings

NEW YORK - Wallpaper - Edward Laurence & Co.

NEW YORK - Window coverings ☆ - Vertilux-Louverlux Inc.

NEW YORK ALE - Beverages–malt - Chatham Imports, Inc.

NEW YORK AMBER - Beverages–malt - Chatham Imports, Inc.

NEW YORK BAGEL BOYS - Bakery products - General Bagels, Inc.

NEW YORK BAKERY - Bakery products - New York Bakery Inc.

☆ = Now out of production

NEW YORK CABLE - Floor coverings–carpet and rugs ☆ - Porter Carpet Mills Inc.

NEW YORK CHAIN - Cables–steel - Kryptonite Corp.

NEW YORK CHEESECAKE, THE - Candy - David Glass

NEW YORK CITY - Footwear - New York City Shoes Inc.

NEW YORK CITY BLOUSE CO. - Apparel and accessories - MSB International, Ltd.

NEW YORK CITY CUSTOM LEATHER - Apparel and accessories - NYC Custom Leather

NEW YORK CITY LIGHTS - Cigarettes ☆ - Nat Sherman, Inc.

NEW YORK CITY SEPARATES CO. - Apparel and accessories - MSB International, Ltd.

NEW YORK CITY SEWER RAT - Toys - Russ Berrie and Co., Inc.

NEW YORK CONSTRUCTION COMPANY, THE - Apparel–men's - Glen Shoe Co. Inc.

NEW YORK DELI - Frankfurters - Tobin Packing

NEW YORK DELI - Potato chips - Borden, Inc.

NEW YORK DELI - Potato chips - Wise Foods

NEW YORK DELI BRAND PREMIUM - Frankfurters - John Morrell & Co.

NEW YORK DIAMOND DISTRICT MUSEUM - Museums - Almod Diamonds Ltd.

NEW YORK DIZZY IZZY'S BAGELS - Bagels - Jimmy Chang

NEW YORK FIREFIGHTER'S FRIEND - Apparel - New York Firefighter's Friend, Inc.

NEW YORK FLATBREADS - Breads - New York Flats Acquisition Corp.

NEW YORK GIANTS - Apparel and accessories - New York Football Giants, Inc.

NEW YORK II - Wallpaper - Bayview Wallcoverings

NEW YORK KNIT - Floor coverings–carpet and rugs ☆ - Porter Carpet Mills Inc.

NEW YORK KNITWORKS - Knitting machines - Fortune Knits Inc.

NEW YORK LITES - Footwear - R & S Sales Co. Inc.

NEW YORK LOCK - Cables–steel - Kryptonite Corp.

NEW YORK NETS - Apparel and accessories - Meadowlands Basketball Associates

NEW YORK NEW YORK - Cigars - Consolidated Cigar Corp.

NEW YORK NEW YORK - Handbags - L.J.S. Accessory Collection Inc.

NEW YORK, NEW YORK - Wallpaper - Capital Carousel Inc.

NEW YORK NEW YORK HOTEL & CASINO LAS VEGAS - Apparel and accessories - New York New York Hotel, LLC

NEW YORK, N.Y. - Floor coverings–carpet and rugs ☆ - World Carpets, Inc.

NEW YORK, NY - Wallpaper - Edward Laurence & Co.

NEW YORK PAJAMA DEPT. N.Y.P.D. - Underwear and nightwear - Bentley Lingerie, Inc.

NEW YORK PHOTOGRAPHERS DAYBOOK, THE - Books–blank - Photographers Daybook, Inc.

NEW YORK PROUD! - Beverages - Hondo Inc.

NEW YORK PUBLICITY OUTLETS - Publisher's imprints - Public Relations Plus, Inc.

NEW YORK ROASTED DALTON COFFEE LTD. - Coffee - Dalton Coffee Ltd.

NEW YORK SOCK EXCHANGE - Socks - Sockyard Co. Inc.

NEW YORK SOCK EXCHANGE, THE - Shoe accessories - Glen Shoe Co. Inc.

NEW YORK SOPHISTICATES - Nail care products - Orly International Inc.

NEW YORK STATE STUDIES - Publisher's imprints - Syracuse University Press

NEW YORK STEAK ON A STICK - Meat products - Zachary Shalvarjian

NEW YORK STREET ACTION - Footwear–athletic - E.S. Originals, Inc.

NEW YORK STRINGS - Musical instrument accessories - E. & O. Mari Inc.

NEW YORK STRIPZ - Dog food - Ralston Purina Co.

NEW YORK STUDIO - Jewelry - Lerner New York, Inc.

NEW YORK STYLE - Bagels - New York Style Bagel Chip Co. Inc.

NEW YORK STYLE - Wallpaper - Capital Carousel Inc.

NEW YORK STYLE - Wallpaper - Edward Laurence & Co.

NEW YORK STYLE - Watches - Lerner New York, Inc.

NEW YORK STYLE HARBOR ALE - Beverages–malt - Old World Brewing Co.

NEW YORK SUPER FUDGE CHUNK - Ice cream - Ben and Jerry's Homemade, Inc.

NEW YORK SUPER JUMBOS - Pretzels - J & J Snack Foods Corp.

NEW YORK TIME - Clocks - Marble Masterpieces Inc.

NEW YORK TIMES EXECUTIVE - Diaries - Distinctive Diaries Ltd.

NEW YORK TRAFFIC TREATS - Cookies - Tina L. Blumenthal

NEW YORK TRAVELER - Games - World Traveler Ltd.

NEW YORK VIEW - Wallpaper - Edward Laurence & Co.

NEW YORK VIEWS - Wallpaper - Capital Carousel Inc.

BREW YORK WHIRLWINDS - Caps–baseball - EDS West, Inc.

NEW YORK WINE PROFESSOR, THE - Computer software - E-8 Publications, Inc.

NEW YORK ZOOLOGICAL SOCIETY - Umbrellas - Shaw Creations Inc.

NEW YORKER - Air conditioning equipment ☆ - Burnham Corp.

NEW YORKER - Applesauce - Bowman Apple Products Co. Inc.

NEW YORKER - Cabinets–wood - Kinzee Industries Inc.

NEW YORKER - Cheese - Northfield Foods Inc.

NEW YORKER - Cigars - General Cigar Co., Inc.

NEW YORKER - Fabrics ☆ - Beverly Manufacturing Corp.

NEW YORKER - Jewelry - Jacoby-Bender Inc.

NEW YORKER - Mats - Cactus Mat Manufacturing Co.

NEW YORKER - Musical instrument accessories ☆ - C.F. Martin & Co., Inc.

NEW YORKER 5TH AVENUE - Motor vehicles–automobiles - Chrysler Corp. (Chrysler-Plymouth Div.)

NEW YORKER CHUNKY - Food products - RHM Holdings (USA) Inc.

NEW YORKER FALCON 660 - Batteries ☆ - Bridgestone/Firestone, Inc.

NEW YORKER, THE - Bagels - Big Apple Baking Co.

NEW YORKER, THE - Alarm systems ☆ - Maxi-Guard

NEW YORKER, THE - Apparel–men's ☆ - Michaels/Stern & Co. Inc.

NEW YORKER, THE - Luggage ☆ - Universal Trav-ler Inc.

NEW YORK'S MICRO-BREW - Beverages–malt - Chatham Imports, Inc.

NEW YORK'S TURF - Food products - Turf Cheesecake Corp.

NEW YOU - Apparel–women's - Cupid Foundations Inc.

NEW YOUTH - Hair-replacement product and wigs - International Hairgoods Inc.

NEW Z - Labeling machinery - Farnam Cos. Inc.

NEW ZEALAND - Floor coverings–carpet and rugs - Mandate-Dawn Carpet Mills

NEW ZEALAND - Food products - New Zealand Lamb Co., Inc.

NEW ZEALAND FARMS - Cheese - Swissrose International Inc.

NEW ZEALAND OUTBACK - Apparel–athletic - Cooper Sportswear Manufacturing Co., Inc.

NEW ZEALAND QUALITY WATERS - Water–mineral - Pacific Resources International

NEW ZELAND LAMB CO. - Food products - Pioneer Food Sales Inc.

NEWARK - Apparel and accessories - Negro Leagues Baseball Museum, Inc.

NEWARK FORGE - Tools - Newark Specialty Co.

NEWAVE - Artists' materials - Artoptic International Corp.

NEWAVE - Beauty shop equipment ☆ - JRC Products Inc.

NEWAVE - Dryers–hair - Drake-Bluestein, Inc.

NEWAVES IN PERSONAL COMMUNICATIONS - Communications equipment - Personal Communications Industry Association

NEWAY GENUINE LIGHT - Autoclaves–laboratory - Nai Neway, Inc.

NEWBERRY - Wines - Cedar Creek Winery Inc.

NEWBERY AWARD - Recording label - Random House, Inc.

NEWBOLD - Typesetting machines - Newbold Corp.

NEWBORN - Caulking guns - Newborn Brothers & Co., Inc.

NEWBORN PINK - Lipstick ☆ - Cosrich Inc.

NEWBORNE CRADLE, THE - Infant product - Newborne Co.

NEWBORNE TRAVELER, THE - Cribs–wood - Newborne Co.

NEWBORNS - Stationery - Vagabond Creations Inc.

NEWBURGH - Clocks ☆ - General Time Corp. (Westclox/Seth Thomas Div.)

NEWBURGH - Prefabricated buildings–metal - Arrow Group Industries

NEWBURGH BRICK - Floor coverings ☆ - Tarkett, Inc.

NEWBURY - Cabinets - Aristokraft, Inc.

NEWBURY - Cabinets ☆ - Decora

NEWBURY - Cabinets–wood ☆ - Kemper

NEWBURY - Clocks ☆ - General Time Corp. (Westclox/Seth Thomas Div.)

NEWBURY - Floor coverings–carpet and rugs - Karastan-Bigelow Inc.

NEWBURY - Furniture ☆ - Bassett Furniture Industries, Inc.

NEWBURY - Office furniture–metal - Haskell of Pittsburgh, Inc.

NEWBURY GUILD - Greeting cards - Paper Magic Group Inc.

NEWBURY SQUARE - Dinnerware–glass - Lenox, Inc.

NEWBURY STREET - Fans–electric - Duracraft Corp.

NEWBURYPORT - Dinnerware–glass - Royal China & Porcelain Companies Inc.

NEWCAST - Computer software - Sendit, LLC

NEWCASTLE - Occasional tables - JDI Group, Inc.

NEWCASTLE - Wallpaper - Capital Carousel Inc.

NEWCASTLE BROWN ALE - Beverages–malt - Scottish & Newcastle Importers Co.

NEWCASTLE NATURALS - Wallpaper - Newcastle Fabrics Corp.

NEWCELL - Fibers–cellulose - Akzo America Inc.

NEWCLIME - Air conditioning equipment - Upstate Parts & Supply, Inc.

NEWCO - Drills–electric - New England Workholding Co., Inc.

NEWCOM - Computers - Aura Systems, Inc.

☆ = Now out of production

NEWCOMER - Brassieres (Bras) ☆ - Lovable Co.
NEWCOMER - Cigars - A.J. Golden Inc.
NEWCOMER - Floor coverings–carpet and rugs - Cabin Crafts Carpets
NEWCOMER II - Floor coverings–carpet and rugs ☆ - Walter Carpet Mills
NEWE FRYE - Shortening - Kraft Food Ingredients Corp.
NEWELL - Curtain rods - Newell Operating Co.
NEWELL - Drapery hardware - Newell Window Furnishing Co.
NEWELL, THE - Trailers–travel - Newell Coach Corp.
NEWEN - Engines–motor vehicle - Brice Harmand
NEWER - Computer peripheral equipment - Spectrum Engineering, Inc.
NEWEST AND PUREST WATER FILTERING SYSTEM, THE - Water
   purification systems - H2 Go, Inc.
NEWEST HORIZONS - Wallpaper - Bayview Wallcoverings
NEWEST HORIZONS II - Wallpaper - Bayview Wallcoverings
NEWFANGLED - Crocheted and knitted items - Heritage Sportswear
NEWFILER - Tools - Granberg International
NEWFOUNDLAND IMPERIAL - Seafood products–fresh or frozen - Fishery
   Products International USA
NEWGATE - Computers–personal - Avant Technologies of Puerto Rico Inc.
NEWGATE - Furniture ☆ - Riverside Furniture Corp.
NEWGEN SYSTEMS CORPORATION - Computer peripheral equipment -
   NewGen Imaging Systems Corp.
NEWHALL - Dinnerware–glass - Andrew D. Darvas Inc.
NEWHAVEN - Awnings - Alcan Aluminum Corp. Alcan Building Products Div.
NEWHOUSE - Traps–animal ☆ - Woodstream Corp.
NEWK'S MOUSTACHE GEAR - Apparel and accessories ☆ - Catalina
NEWLAN VINEYARDS & WINERY - Wines - Newlan Vineyards & Winery Inc.
NEWLEAF - Flowers, plants, and seeds - Hybritech Seed International, Inc.
NEWLIFE - Cooking equipment–household - New Era Co.
NEWLIFE - Flowers–artificial - Natural Decorations Inc.
NEWLIFE - Skin care products - Giesee International
NEWLIFE KITCHENS - Bakery products - New Life Bakery Inc.
NEWLIME - Fertilizers - Blue Circle Inc.
NEWLOC - Metals - Newage Industries, Inc.
NEWLOK - Floor coverings–carpet and rugs ☆ - Heuga USA
NEWLY WEDS - Bakery products - Newly Weds Foods, Inc.
NEWMAN - Boats–motor - Jarvis Newman Boats
NEWMAN'S OWN - Salad dressings–bottled - Newman's Own Inc.
NEWMAN'S OWN ORGANICS - Pretzels - Newman's Own Inc.
NEWMAN'S SARATOGA BRAND - Beverages–malt - Wm. S. Newman
   Brewing Co, Inc.
NEWMARKET - Puddings–mixes - Newmarket Foods, Inc.
NEWMARKET FOODS - Chocolate candy - Newmarket Foods, Inc.
NEWMATIC - Toilets–portable - Mag Aerospace Industries, Inc.
NEWMATIC II - Toilets–portable - Monogram Sanitation Co.
NEWMATIC III - Toilets–portable - Monogram Sanitation Co.
NEWMENU - Food products - Nasoya Foods, Inc.
NEWMETRICS - Computer software - Newmetrics Corp.
NEWNET - Computer software - Newnet, Inc.
NEWPAK - Vitamins and nutritional supplements - O'Brien
NEWPAX - Recording label ☆ - Benson Music Group
NEWPLAST - Plastics film - Prize Plastics and Chemicals, Inc.
NEWPOINT - Computer peripheral equipment - Newpoint Corp.
NEWPORT - Beverages–alcohol - Marie Brizard Wines & Spirits, USA
NEWPORT - Bicycles - American Recreation Co., Inc.
NEWPORT - Bicycles ☆ - Huffy Corp.
NEWPORT - Boats–motor ☆ - Lund Boat Co.
NEWPORT - Brushes - Perfex Corp.
NEWPORT - Cabinets - American Woodmark Corp.
NEWPORT - Cabinets - Classic Bath Products
NEWPORT - Cabinets - Grandview Products Co.
NEWPORT - Cabinets - Riviera Cabinets Inc.
NEWPORT - Cabinets - Trendlines Inc.
NEWPORT - Cabinets–wood ☆ - Kemper
NEWPORT - Ceramic floor tile - Interceramic Inc.
NEWPORT - Christmas tree ornaments - Cracker Box Inc.
NEWPORT - Cigarettes - Lorillard Tobacco Co.
NEWPORT - Clocks - Chelsea Clock Co. Inc.
NEWPORT - Colognes - Caswell-Massey Co. Ltd.
NEWPORT - Dinnerware–glass - Nikko Ceramics Inc.
NEWPORT - Doors–glass - Peachtree Doors and Windows Inc.
NEWPORT - Fabrics ☆ - Beverly Manufacturing Corp.
NEWPORT - Floor coverings - American Floor Products Co. Inc.
NEWPORT - Floor coverings - Anderson Hardwood Floors Inc.
NEWPORT - Floor coverings–carpet and rugs - Barrett Carpet Mills Inc.
NEWPORT - Floor coverings–carpet and rugs - Capel, Inc.

NEWPORT - Floor coverings–carpet and rugs - Mandate-Dawn Carpet Mills
NEWPORT - Floor coverings–carpet and rugs - Masland Corp.
NEWPORT - Floor coverings–carpet and rugs - Rugby Rugs Inc.
NEWPORT - Floor coverings–carpet and rugs - V & B Carpet
NEWPORT - Floor coverings–carpet and rugs ☆ - Blue Ridge Carpet Mills
NEWPORT - Floor coverings–carpet and rugs ☆ - Colonial Mills Inc.
NEWPORT - Floor coverings–carpet and rugs ☆ - Regal Rugs Inc.
NEWPORT - Flowers, plants, and seeds - Jacklin Seed
NEWPORT - Frames–eyeglass ☆ - Universal/Univis Inc.
NEWPORT - Furniture - Bassett Furniture Industries, Inc.
NEWPORT - Furniture - Teak Traders Inc.
NEWPORT - Furniture ☆ - Lexington Furniture Industries, Inc.
NEWPORT - Furniture–children's ☆ - Child Craft Industries Inc.
NEWPORT - Giftware ☆ - Doranne
NEWPORT - Giftware ☆ - Gorham Inc.
NEWPORT - Giftware ☆ - Kraftware Corp. (Morgan Div.)
NEWPORT - Glass–leaded - Seneca Glass Co.
NEWPORT - Glassware–household - Anchor Hocking Glass, Inc.
NEWPORT - Guitars ☆ - International Music Corp.
NEWPORT - Hammocks - E-Z Sales & Manufacturing, Inc.
NEWPORT - Luggage - Airway Industries, Inc.
NEWPORT - Mats - Cactus Mat Manufacturing Co.
NEWPORT - Meat products–poultry ☆ - Louis Rich Co.
NEWPORT - Motor vehicles–automobiles ☆ - Chrysler Corp. (Chrysler-
   Plymouth Div.)
NEWPORT - Motor vehicles–motor homes - Forest River, Inc.
NEWPORT - Musical instrument accessories - Sottile Manufacturing Co.
NEWPORT - Paints - Commercial Chemical Co. Inc.
NEWPORT - Powerboat ☆ - Boston Whaler, Inc.
NEWPORT - Seafood products–fresh or frozen - Newport Shrimp Co.
NEWPORT - Ships–sailing vessels - Capital Yachts Inc.
NEWPORT - Shoes - Allen-Edmonds Shoe Corp.
NEWPORT - Sporting goods - Acushnet Co.
NEWPORT - Sporting goods ☆ - Midwest Sporting Goods Manufacturing Co.
NEWPORT - Tape–adhesive - Crowell Corp.
NEWPORT - Thread - Cincinnati Thread Co.
NEWPORT - Tiles–ceramic - Monarch Tile Inc.
NEWPORT - Trailers–travel ☆ - Fleetwood Enterprises, Inc.
NEWPORT - Underwear and nightwear - Youthcraft-Charmfit
NEWPORT - Vases ☆ - Lenox Crystal, Inc.
NEWPORT - Vegetables–canned - Stokely USA, Inc.
NEWPORT - Windows–plastic - Beckson Marine Inc.
NEWPORT - Windows–vinyl - Care-Free Windows
NEWPORT BEACH - Floor coverings–carpet and rugs - Cabin Crafts Carpets
NEWPORT BEACH - Floor coverings–carpet and rugs ☆ - Walter Carpet Mills
NEWPORT BEACH BREWING COMPANY - Apparel and accessories -
   Newport Beach Brewing Co., Inc.
NEWPORT BLUE - Apparel and accessories - Mass Transit
NEWPORT CATHEDRAL - Cabinets - Grandview Products Co.
NEWPORT CLASSIC - Apparel–athletic - Reebok International Ltd.
NEWPORT CLASSIC - Recording label - Newport Classic Ltd.
NEWPORT CLASSIC PREMIER - Recording label - Newport Classic Ltd.
NEWPORT COLLECTION GILDED AGE, THE - Art reproductions -
   Preservation Society of Newport County
NEWPORT GILDED AGE COLLECTION, THE - Wallpaper - Scalamandre
   Silks Inc.
NEWPORT II - Floor coverings–carpet and rugs - Karastan-Bigelow Inc.
NEWPORT IMPRESSIONS USA - Soft luggage - Newport Impressions, Inc.
NEWPORT LIGHTS - Cigarettes - Lorillard Tobacco Co.
NEWPORT MANOR - Furniture ☆ - Bassett Furniture Industries, Inc.
NEWPORT NATURALS - Figurines ☆ - Rawcliffe Corp.
NEWPORT NEWS - Apparel–women's - Hampton Acquisition Corp.
NEWPORT NEWS - Apparel–women's - New Hampton, Inc.
NEWPORT NEWS CATALOG CLOSEOUTS - Publisher's imprints - Newport
   News, Inc.
NEWPORT PATENTSEARCH - Computer software - Newport Data Associates,
   Inc.
NEWPORT SCROLL - Dishes–china - Gorham Inc.
NEWPORT SLIM LIGHTS - Cigarettes ☆ - Lorillard Tobacco Co.
NEWPORT STRIPES - Cigarettes - Lorillard Tobacco Co.
NEWPORT SYSTEMS SOLUTIONS - Computer hardware - Newport Systems
   Solutions, Inc.
NEWPORT TELL-TALE - Weather tracking equipment - Davis Instruments
   Corp.
NEWPORT UPPER CRUST GOURMET WHITE MEAT CHICKEN PIE - Bakery
   products - Newport Upper Crust, Inc.

☆ = Now out of production

NEWPORT VILLA - Dining-room furniture ☆ - American Drew
NEWPORTER III - Foul-weather gear - Bliss Marine
NEWS - Detergents - Dial Corp.
NEWS 600 - Pencils - Musgrave Pencil Co. Inc.
NEWS AGENT - Computer peripheral equipment - IDD Enterprises, L.P.
NEWS & VIEWS - Posters - Clement Communications Inc.
NEWS, CO. - Apparel and accessories - International News, Inc.
NEWS IN MOTION - Computer software - WalkSoft Corp.
NEWS KING II - Printing presses - King Press Corp.
NEWS-LINC - Computer peripheral equipment - I.D.A.B. Inc.
NEWS-WRITER - Pencils ☆ - Faber-Castell Corp.
NEWSBASE - Computer software - Profound
NEWSBOY SPECIAL - Bicycles - Columbia Manufacturing Inc.
NEWSCARD - Radio communications equipment - Motorola, Inc. (Land Mobile Products Sector)
NEWSCASTER - Bulletin boards–cork - Dick Blick Co.
NEWSCASTER - Ophthalmic goods - Foremost Optical Products
NEWSCATCHER - Computer hardware - Global Village Communication, Inc.
NEWSCOLOR IV - Printing presses - King Press Corp.
NEWSCUTTER - Computer peripheral equipment - Avid Technology, Inc.
NEWSENGIN - Computer software - Newsengin Inc.
NEWSENTRY - Computer software - Motorola, Inc. (Land Mobile Products Sector)
NEWSEVENT - Computer software - National Digital Corp.
NEWSFIRST VIDEO - Transmitting apparatus - Baron Tech; LLC
NEWSHAM - Pork - Newsham Hybrids (USA) Inc.
NEWSHOE - Footwear - Cool Feet Inc.
NEWSIE - Advertising agencies - Knoxville News-Sentinel Co.
NEWSIE - Apparel–children's - Kidwise, Inc.
NEWSOFT - Computer software - Maxsoft-Ocron, Inc.
NEWSPAC - Paper - Chicago Tribune Co.
NEWSPRINT - Pencils ☆ - National Pen & Pencil Co.
NEWSSTREAM - Electronic equipment - Motorola, Inc. (Land Mobile Products Sector)
NEWSTAND - Bookcases–metal ☆ - Trepte Wire and Metal Works
NEWSTAND - Computer software - Imagina, Inc.
NEWSTAR - Drafting supplies - Puretech International Inc.
NEWSTONE - Building materials–concrete - Phenix Composites, Inc.
NEWSTROKE - Brushes–paint - Minnesota Mining & Manufacturing Co.
NEWSVISION - Computer software - Earthwatch Communications, Inc.
NEWSWEEK - Office supplies - Newsweek Inc.
NEWTEC - Packaging machines - Newtech Packing Equipment Corp.
NEWTECH - Pet products - Newtech Enterprises Inc.
NEWTEX - Wallcovering - Newtex Industries Inc.
NEWTON - Bond paper - Boston Paper Board Corp.
NEWTON - Computer software ☆ - CONDUIT
NEWTON - Computers - Apple Computer Inc.
NEWTON - Pianos - Kohler & Campbell Inc.
NEWTON - Wines - Newton Vineyard
NEWTON MESSAGEPAD - Computer software - Apple Computer Inc.
NEWTON SQUARE - Furniture ☆ - Bassett Furniture Industries, Inc.
NEWTON VINEYARD - Wines - Newton Vineyard
NEWTONE - Colognes - Lustol Co.
NEWTONIAN - Wines ☆ - Newton Vineyard
NEWTONMAIL - Computer software - Apple Computer Inc.
NEWTONS - Cookies - Nabisco Foods Group
NEWTON'S YO-YO - Toys - Fascinations Toys and Gifts Inc.
NEWTRITION - Vitamins and nutritional supplements - O'Brien
NEWTRO - Food products - F & L Packing Corp.
NEWTROGEL - Pharmaceutical preparations ☆ - Murray Drug Corp.
NEWTYPE - Computer software - Metro Software Inc.
NEWVICON - Electronic equipment - Panasonic Co.
NEWYORK CENTRAL SYSTEM - Toys–automobiles - Paul R. McDonald
NEWZONOPHONE - Recording label - Acoustographic Records
NEX SYS - Audio equipment - Crest Audio Inc.
NEXCELL - Battery chargers - Electrochem Automation, Inc.
NEXEN - Computer software - Ascom Nexion Inc.
NEXES - Analyzers–amino acid - Ventana Medical Systems, Inc.
NEXFLASH - Integrated circuits - Nexcom Technology, Inc.
NEXGEN - Computer hardware - Nexgen Microsystems
NEXGEN - Medical apparatus - Zimmer, Inc.
NEXGEN/ADE - Publisher's imprint - Next Computer, Inc.
NEXO - Footwear - Viniul International Corp.
NEXPAC - Batteries - Electrochem Automation, Inc.
NEXPERT OBJECT - Computer software - Neuron Data, Inc.
NEXPRO - Computer software - Taxware International, Inc.

NEXPROM - Circuit breakers - Nexcom Technology, Inc.
NEXT - Bicycles - Dynacraft Industries, Inc.
NEXT - Cigarettes - Philip Morris Companies Inc.
NEXT - Computer software - Next Computer, Inc.
NEXT - Watches - MMC
NEXT DAY - Herbicides - Enforcer Products Inc.
NEXT DESIGN - Paper - Next Design Associates Ltd.
NEXT DIMENSION - Cleaning preparations–window - Amrep Inc.
NEXT DIMENSION - Computers and accessories - Next Computer, Inc.
NEXT DIMENSION - Windows–vinyl - Woodgrain Millwork
NEXT ERA - Apparel - L'Koral Inc.
NEXT EXIT - Apparel–women's - Trendmasters Inc.
NEXT GENERATION - Exercise equipment - Nautilus Acquisition Inc.
NEXT GENERATION - Fans–electric - Casablanca Fan Co.
NEXT GENERATION - Floor waxes ☆ - Harley Chemicals
NEXT GENERATION - Lubricants - Coastal Corp.
NEXT GENERATION - Paper - Butler Paper Co.
NEXT GENERATION - Soups–canned - Next Generation, Inc.
NEXT GENERATION, THE - Office furniture–wood - ABCO Office Furniture Inc.
NEXT GENERATION, THE - Saws–power - DBNA Trademarks Holding Inc.
NEXT GENERATION, THE - Sporting goods - SSK America Inc.
NEXT IN LINE - Trading cards and stamps - Upper Deck Co.
NEXT LEVEL - Video production - Next Level, LLC
NEXT NUTRITION - Vitamins and nutritional supplements - Next Nutrition
NEXT-OF-SKIN - Cosmetics - Matrix Essentials, Inc.
NEXT PLATEAU - Recording label - Next Plateau Records Inc.
NEXT STEP - Baby foods - Mead Johnson & Co.
NEXT STEP - Toys - Simmons Juvenile Products Co., Inc.
NEXT TO NATURE - Figurines - United Creasian Co. of North America Inc.
NEXT TO NATURE - Pet products - Next to Nature
NEXT TO NATURE - Pet products - Petguard, Inc.
NEXT WAVE - Apparel–athletic - Nazareth Kentury Mills
NEXT WORD, THE - Games ☆ - Decipher Inc.
NEXTCUBE - Computer equipment - Next Computer, Inc.
NEXTEC - Fabrics - Nextec Applications, Inc.
NEXTECH - Automatic pilots - Valvtechnologies, Inc.
NEXTEL - Building materials - Minnesota Mining & Manufacturing Co.
NEXTGEN ENTERPRISES, INC. - Computers - Nexgen Microsystems
NEXTIME - Computer software - Next Computer, Inc.
NEXTON - Pet products - Morton Jones Co.
NEXTSTEP - Electrical equipment - Reltec Corp.
NEXTSTEP - Health care products - NobleMotion Inc.
NEXTWAVE - Electronic equipment - C.R.E., Inc.
NEXUS - Audio equipment - Comrex Corp.
NEXUS - Cushions - Roho, Inc.
NEXUS - Dental compounds - Kerr Corp.
NEXUS - Electronic equipment - J.L. Cooper Electronics
NEXUS - Footwear ☆ - Wolverine World Wide, Inc.
NEXUS - Infant product - Century Products Co.
NEXUS - Prosthetic apparatus - Wright Medical Technology, Inc.
NEXUS - Scales - Polyproducts Corp.
NEXUS PLUS - Electronic equipment ☆ - J.L. Cooper Electronics
NEXXT GENERATION - Shampoos - Nexxus Products Co.
NEXXUS - Hair care products - Nexxus Products Co.
NEY - Circuit boards–printed - J.M. Ney Co.
NEY YORK STYLE MICROWAVEABLE SANDWIDHES - Sandwiches–prepackaged - Raybern Foods, Inc.
NF - Chemical preparations - Zecol Inc.
NF - Computer peripheral equipment - NetFRAME Systems Inc.
NF - Jewelry - Chapal-Zenray Inc.
NFC FOOTBALL - Toys ☆ - Tyco Toys
NFL - Apparel and accessories - Fabry Glove & Mitten Co.
NFL - Apparel and accessories - G-III Apparel Group, Ltd.
NFL - Apparel and accessories - National Football League Properties, Inc.
NFL - Apparel and accessories ☆ - Kellwood Co.
NFL - Apparel stores–sports ☆ - Rugged Wear Ltd.
NFL - Colognes - Shiara
NFL - Handbags - Pyramid Handbags Inc.
NFL - Sporting goods - Hutch Sports USA Inc.
NFL - Sporting goods - Wilson Sporting Goods Co.
NFL - Trunks ☆ - Seward Luggage Co.
NFL - Waterproof outerwear - Essex Manufacturing Inc.
NFL-AMERICAN CONFERENCE - Games - Tudor Inc.
NFL BEAN BAG HEADS - Figurines - Kamar International Inc.
NFL COACHES CLUB - Apparel - National Football League Properties, Inc.

☆ = Now out of production

NFL CRUNCHIT! - Popcorn - National Football League Properties, Inc.

NFL FLEX - Apparel and accessories - National Football League Properties, Inc.

NFL FOOTBALL - Pencils ☆ - Faber-Castell Corp.

NFL FOOTBALL DOLLS - Figurines - Kamar International Inc.

NFL FULL CONTACT - Computer storage devices–optical - Konami (America) Inc.

NFL GAME PLAN - Games ☆ - Tudor Inc.

NFL GAMEDAY - Apparel and accessories - National Football League Properties, Inc.

NFL GAMEDAY - Computer software - National Football League

NFL KIDS - Apparel–children's - Barrel-Marvin Apparel, Inc.

NFL LADIES - Apparel and accessories - Regent International Corp.

NFL/MNF SPORT BAGS - Backpacks - La Rue International, Inc.

NFL-NATIONAL CONFERENCE - Games - Tudor Inc.

NFL PLAYING CARDS - Playing cards ☆ - Hoyle Products

NFL POCKET FOOTBALL - Toys - Hirsch Co.

NFL PUPPETS - Figurines - Kamar International Inc.

NFL QUARTERBACK - Product description unknown - Tudor Inc.

NFL QUARTERBACK CLUB - Apparel–athletic - National Football League Properties, Inc.

NFL REGIMIN - Vitamins and nutritional supplements - Pharmavite Corp.

NFL ROCKS - Shirts - National Football League Properties, Inc.

NFL STRATEGY - Games - Tudor Inc.

NFL SUPPERS - Food products - Kamar International Inc.

NFO SMARTSYSTEM - Computer software - NFO Research, Inc.

NFOG - Antennas–satellite - KVH Industries, Inc.

NFS - Seafood products–canned or cured - Natural Food Systems Inc.

NFS PRINCE - Footwear ☆ - Prince Sports Group, Inc.

NFT - Cables–coaxial - Vanco International, Inc.

NGC - Jewelry - Northern Pearl Co. Inc.

NGE - Irrigation equipment ☆ - Hardie-Toro Irrigation

NGL - Jewelry - Angel's Jewelry Manufacturing Co. Inc.

NGOMA - Beverages–malt - Bulunda Import-Export Co.

NGS PICTURESHOW - Recording label - National Geographic Society

NGT - Pharmaceutical preparations - Geneva Generics Inc.

NH-5 - Chemicals–photographic - Brandess Kalt Aetna

NH THE NAPOLEAN HILL FOUNDATION - Video equipment - Napoleon Hill Foundation

NHBB - Machine parts - New Hampshire Ball Bearings, Inc.

N.H.C. - Food supplements - N.H.C. Natural Health Centers Inc.

NHFR - Chemical preparations - Environmental Products Inc.

NHL - Apparel and accessories - G-III Apparel Group, Ltd.

NHL - Apparel and accessories - National Hockey League

NHL - Games ☆ - American Toy & Furniture Co.

NHL - Handbags - Pyramid Handbags Inc.

NHL BREAKOUT '95 - Apparel and accessories - National Hockey League

NHL COOLAIR - Sporting goods - National Hockey League

NHL GAME ONE - Athletic associations - National Hockey League

NHL STREET - Apparel and accessories - National Hockey League

NHLPA - Games ☆ - Tudor Inc.

NI - Novelty items - National Imprint Corp.

NI-CHROME - Vitamins and nutritional supplements - Shaperite Concepts, Ltd.

NI-CO - Apparel and accessories - Nightingale Uniform Co. Inc.

NI-DX - X-ray apparatus - New Image Industries, Inc.

NI-DX DIGITAL RADIOGRAPHY - X-ray apparatus - New Image Industries, Inc.

NI-HYD - Rechargeable battery - Arista Enterprises Inc.

NI-MATRIX - Welding equipment - Alloy Rods Global, Inc.

NI PAK - Power transformers ☆ - VDO Pak Batteries

NI-TEES INTIMATES - Women's loungewear ☆ - Julius Corn & Co.

NIA - Dolls - Mattel, Inc.

NIA-BID - Vitamins and nutritional supplements - Geriatric Pharmaceutical Corp.

NIA-C - Vitamins and nutritional supplements ☆ - Nutritional Research Associates Inc.

NIAC - Pharmaceutical preparations - Forest Pharmaceuticals Inc.

NIACAL - Pharmaceutical preparations ☆ - JMI-Canton Pharmaceuticals

NIACELS - Pharmaceutical preparations - Roberts/Hauck Pharmaceuticals Inc.

NIACHROM - Health care products - Physicians Choice

NIACIN-TIME - Vitamins and nutritional supplements ☆ - J.R. Carlson Laboratories Inc.

NIACINAMATE - Health care products - Natural Organics, Inc.

NIACOR - Pharmaceutical preparations - Upsher-Smith Laboratories, Inc.

NIACOR SR - Pharmaceutical preparations - Upsher-Smith Laboratories, Inc.

NIADOX - Ophthalmic goods ☆ - Barnes-Hind Inc.

NIAGARA - Abrasive products ☆ - Carborundum Abrasives North America

NIAGARA - Bathing suits - Ocean Pool Co.

NIAGARA - Beds–wood - Niagara Therapy Manufacturing Corp.

NIAGARA - Bicycles - Columbia Manufacturing Inc.

NIAGARA - Faucets - Kallista Inc.

NIAGARA - Flatware - Washington Forge Inc.

NIAGARA - Insecticides - FMC Corp.

NIAGARA - Locks–door - Harloc, Inc.

NIAGARA - Medical instruments and apparatus - Cabot Technology Corp.

NIAGARA - Paper - Consolidated Papers, Inc.

NIAGARA - Pet products - Oscar Enterprises Inc.

NIAGARA - Photographic equipment - Eastman Kodak Co.

NIAGARA - Shower rods ☆ - Trayco, Inc.

NIAGARA - Skin care products - Imperial Inc.

NIAGARA - Starch–laundry - CPC International Inc.

NIAGARA - Trailers–travel - Fleetwood Enterprises, Inc.

NIAGARA - Water–bottled or canned - Niagara Drinking Waters Inc.

NIAGARA - Water–distilled - Ching Construction, Inc.

NIAGARA - Windows–storm - Duo-Temp

NIAGARA - Wines - Bully Hill Vineyards, Inc.

NIAGARA - Wines - Lukens Vineyard Inc.

NIAGARA - Wines - Widmer's Wine Cellars Inc.

NIAGARA CHOCOLATES - Candy - Niagara Candy, Inc.

NIAGARA CROWN - Business cards - Niagara Envelope Co., Inc.

NIAGARA OVERFLOW SYSTEM - Bathroom fixtures - Kohler Co.

NIAGARA RECYCLE TEF - Paper–bond - Niagara of Wisconsin Paper Corp.

NIAGARA SOLINE - Air conditioning equipment - Thomason Solar Homes

NIAGARA SPRINGS - Food products - Rim View Trout Co.

NIAGARA TEXTILES - Apparel–athletic - Can Am Textiles Inc.

NIAGRA - Cigarettes - Brown & Williamson Tobacco Corp.

NIAGRA - Wines - Heritage Wine Cellars

NIALEXO-C - Pharmaceutical preparations ☆ - Roberts/Hauck Pharmaceuticals Inc.

NIAPEN - Pharmaceutical preparations ☆ - Hyrex Pharmaceuticals

NIAPENT - Health care products ☆ - Ferndale Laboratories, Inc.

NIARD - Drain pipe cleaners - Roto-Rooter Corp.

NIASPAN - Pharmaceutical preparations - Wesley Pharmacal Co. Inc.

NIAX - Textiles and fabrics - Nissho Iwai Textiles (USA), Inc.

NIAZOLE IMPROVED - Pharmaceutical preparations - Wesley Pharmacal Co. Inc.

NIB BASE - Pharmaceutical preparations - H.R. Cenci Laboratories Inc.

NIB-L-SKITS - Crackers - Vista Bakery, Inc.

NIB NAX - Candy ☆ - Y & S Candies Inc.

NIBAN - Pesticide bait - Nisus Corp.

NIBBITS - Snack foods - Old Dutch Foods, Inc.

NIBBL - Apparel and accessories - Thomas LaGarde

NIBBLE PACK COOKIES - Cookies ☆ - Sathers Inc.

NIBBLE STICKS - Pet products - Petland, Inc.

NIBBLE-STIK - Cheese - Welcome Dairy Inc.

NIBBLENIKS - Pastries - L. Karp & Sons, Inc.

NIBBLER - Food products ☆ - Erbrich Products Co. Inc.

NIBBLE'R'PECK - Nipples–rubber - Precision Products, Inc.

NIBBLERS - Cookies - Mrs. Fields Cookies

NIBBLES - Candy ☆ - R.M. Palmer Co.

NIBBLES - Cheese ☆ - Kolb-Lena Cheese Co.

NIBBLES - Toys–stuffed - Fun World Inc.

NIBBLES - Toys–stuffed - Gund, Inc.

NIBCO - Valves–industrial - Nibco Hardware Marketing

NIBGARDS - Markers–felt-tip - M.J.F. Design

NIBLACK - Wheat germ - Niblack

NIBLETS - Vegetables–canned - Green Giant Co.

NIBLIC - Candy - Swizzels Matlow (USA) Ltd.

NIBO - Sporting goods - Pompanette Inc.

NIBRAL - Propellers - Columbian Bronze Corp.

NIBS - Licorice - Y & S Candies Inc.

NIC - Trees - Brandt's Fruit Trees, Inc.

NIC INTERNATIONAL (SEATTLE) LTD. - Helmets–athletic - NIC International Ltd.

NIC NAC - Fabrics - Greenwood Mills Inc.

NIC NAC - Toys–stuffed ☆ - Gund, Inc.

NIC:NO IRON COTTON - Shirts - Cluett, Peabody & Co.

NICA - Seafood products–canned or cured - Ludwig Shrimp Co.

NICAD - Batteries - Saft America Inc.

NICALEX - Pharmaceutical preparations ☆ - Marion Merrell Dow

NICAMAKA YOUR GENTLE REST ALTERNATIVE - Hammocks - Nicamaka Distributors, Inc.

☆ = Now out of production

NICARAGUA ESPECIAL - Cigars - Lignum-2, Inc.
NICARB - Veterinary pharmaceutical preparations - Merck & Co., Inc. (Merck Agvet Division)
NICC - Golfing equipment - Nassau Precision Casting Co., Inc.
NICCO - Women's apparel - U.S. Fashions Inc.
NICE - Bicycles - Nissho Iwai American Corp.
N'ICE - Cough drops - SmithKline Beecham Consumer Healthcare
N'ICE - Pharmaceutical preparations - Smithkline Beecham Corp.
NICE - Sardines—canned - Arnold Sorensin Inc.
NICE AIRE - Deodorizers - Coughlan Products Corp.
NICE & CLEAN - Cleaning preparations - Everyday Products Inc.
NICE & ICY - Ice - Campbell Manufacturing Inc.
NICE & NATURAL - Juices - Knudsen & Sons Inc.
NICE & NEAT - Cosmetics - Chem Spray Aerosols Inc.
NICE & STRAIGHT - Hair care products - Nutrine Ltd.
NICE APPROACH - Fabrics—tapestry - Comark Wallcoverings
NICE CARD COMPANY, THE - Envelopes—paper - Nice Card Co., Inc.
NICE CHANGE - Hair coloring preparations - Roux Laboratories, Inc.
NICE CREAM CONE - Toys—stuffed ✰ - Gund, Inc.
NICE DICE - Novelty items - Koplow Games
NICE IMPRESSIONS - Mattel, Inc.
NICE MAN - Shirts - Nice Man Merchandising
NICE MICE - Candy ✰ - Stark Candy Co.
NICE MICE - Housewares - Doranne
NICE N CLEAN - Cleaning preparations - Coughlan Products Corp.
NICE 'N CLEAN - Paper—toweling - Nice-Pak Products, Inc.
NICE-N-CLEAR - Chemical preparations - Aqua Clear Industries Inc.
N'ICE 'N CLEAR - Cough drops - SmithKline Beecham Consumer Healthcare
N'ICE 'N CLEAR - Cough medicines - Smithkline Beecham Corp.
NICE N' COLD - Pharmaceutical preparations - Tetra Medical Supply Corp.
NICE 'N EASY - Cleaning preparations - Alumin-Nu Corp.
NICE 'N EASY - Floor coverings—carpet and rugs ✰ - Walter Carpet Mills
NICE 'N EASY - Hair coloring preparations - Clairol Inc.
NICE-N-EASY - Paint removers ✰ - Seneca Research Inc.
NICE-N-EASY - Publisher's imprints - Research and Education Assn.
NICE 'N EASY BRIGHTS - Hair coloring preparations - Clairol Inc.
NICE 'N EASY KNITS - Fabrics - Minnetonka Mills Inc.
NICE 'N FRESH - Cosmetics - Pearl Collection, Inc.
NICE 'N FRESH - Sanitary napkins - Arquest, Inc.
NICE-N-KLEEN - Skin care products - Kutol Products Co.
NICE N LIGHT - Dairy products - Knudsen Dairy Products
NICE 'N NATURAL - Yogurt—frozen - Circle K Corp.
NICE N' NEAT - Apparel—children's - Camptown Togs Inc.
NICE 'N SLIM - Sweeteners—artificial - F.D.C. Wholesale Corp.
NICE 'N SOFT - Toilet paper, facial tissue - James River Corp.
NICE 'N SPICY - Underwear and nightwear - Maidenform Inc.
NICE' N THICK - Hair care products - Palm Beach Beauty Products
NICE 'N' TITE - Veterinary pharmaceutical preparations - Uptite Co., Inc.
NICE N'EASY - Frames—eyeglass - May Optical Co. Inc.
NICE OVER ICE - Teas—herbal ✰ - R.C. Bigelow, Inc.
NICE PAD, MAN - Computer peripheral equipment - Intergroup Business Systems, Inc.
NICE SHOT - Guns - Nice Shot LLC
NICE TOUCH - Cleaning preparations - No Touch North America Corp.
NICE TOUCH - Hosiery - Sears, Roebuck and Co.
NICE TOUCH - Shoes - Chi-Shun Associates
NICE TOUCH 2 - Camera ✰ - Nikon Inc.
NICE TOUCH ZOOM - Cameras - Nikon Inc.
NICE WORK - Skin care products - Gillette Co.
NICERASE - Pharmaceutical preparations - DynaGen Inc.
NICETY - Frames—eyeglass - Pathway Optical Prods.
NICHALLOY - Garden equipment ✰ - Nichols-Homeshield Inc.
NICHCO - Communications equipment—mobile - Nichco Inc.
NICHE - Frames—eyeglass - Zylo Ware Corp.
NICHE - Hair care products ✰ - Duart Industries Ltd.
NICHE AUDIO CONTROL MODULE - Audio equipment - Russ Jones Marketing
NICHE AUTOMATION STATION - Audio equipment - Russ Jones Marketing
NICHE COMPUTER SUPPLY - Ribbons—inked - Niche Computer Supply, Inc.
NICHELINI VINEYARD - Wines - Nichelini Winery
NICHELLE - Dolls - Mattel, Inc.
NICHIREI - Seafood products—fresh or frozen - Nichirei Foods America
NICHOLAS - Dolls - Mattel, Inc.
NICHOLAS - Glassware—household - Crisa Corp.
NICHOLAS - Hardware - McGuire-Nicholas Co., Inc.
NICHOLAS - Ophthalmic goods - Styl-Rite Optical Manufacturing Co., Inc.

NICHOLAS GRAHAM - Apparel and accessories - Nicholas Graham
NICHOLSON - Saws, files, burrs - Cooper Industries, Inc.
NICHOLSON'S PEERLESS - Water colors - Peerless Color Laboratories
NICK AND NORA - Apparel and accessories - Shady Character Ltd.
NICK & NORA - Apparel and accessories - Shady Character Unlimited, Ltd.
NICK & PULL - Pencils - Empire Berol USA
NICK BLADE - Apparel and accessories - Converse Pointe
NICK LUCAS - Musical instrument accessories - Grover/Trophy Musical Products Inc.
NICK N SHEAR - Machinery - Betaram, Inc.
NICK SANDER - Sanders and grinders - Nicsand, Inc.
NICK TEDDY - Toys—stuffed - Dakin Inc.
NICK THE GREEK - Games ✰ - A.R.C. Toys Inc.
NICKABOOD'S FISHERMAN'S WHARF - Salad dressings—bottled - Nickabood's Inc.
NICKEL KNIT - Scouring pads ✰ - Purex Industries Inc. (Kurly Kate Div.)
NICKEL-NU - Cleaning preparations - Kester Solder Co.
NICKEL PLUS - Musical instrument accessories - Gibson Strings & Accessories
NICKEL PRESS - Publisher's imprints - Nichols Industries, Ltd.
NICKEL-RICH - Lubricants - Rectorseal Corp.
NICKEL ROCKERS - Musical instrument accessories - GHS Strings
NICKEL SUPRA - Riflescopes - Continental Arms Corp.
NICKEL WRAPPERS - Musical instrument accessories - E. & O. Mari Inc.
NICKLODEON - Eyeglasses - Art-Craft Optical Co.
NICKELODEON - Jars—glass ✰ - Crisa Corp.
NICKELODEON - Video production - Viacom International Inc.
NICKELODEON BOOKS - Publisher's imprints - Putnam Publishing Group
NICKELODEON VIDEO - Video production - Viacom International Inc.
NICKELS - Musical instrument accessories - Kaman Music Corp.
NICKELS - Shoes - Intershoe Inc.
NICKELS - Toys—stuffed - CTI Industries Corp.
NICKERSNAX - Horse treats - White Horse Trading Co., Inc.
NICKERSON'S ANTIOXIDANT FORMULA - Vitamins and nutritional supplements - Nickers International Ltd.
NICKI - Frames—eyeglass - U.S. Optical Frame Co.
NICKI & ZOEY - Apparel - Chabot Freres, Inc.
NICKLAD - Coatings for structures - JWI, Inc.
NICKLAUS - Socks - Golden Bear International, Inc.
NICKLAUS SPIRIT - Apparel and accessories - Golden Bear International, Inc.
NICKLEPLAST - Medical apparatus - Alimed, Inc.
NICKLES - Food products - Alfred Nickles Bakery Inc.
NICKLOGRIT - Floor coverings - Wooster Products Inc.
NICKNAMES - Games ✰ - Twinson Co.
NICKNAMES - GUESSINE CARD GAME - Games - Twinson Co.
NICK'S - Meat products - Ferrante, Inc.
NICK'S LITE ALCOHOL - Beverages - Nick's Lite Alcohol
NICK'S MIX - Snack food - Big Steer Enterprises
NICK'S NACKS - Stationery - Impact International Inc.
NICKS OF TIME, THE - Dolls - The Nicks of Time
NICKSIKO - Beverages—malt ✰ - S & J Importing Co. Inc.
NICKTOONS - Posters - Viacom International Inc.
NICKY & MANDY'S - Dog food - Westie Industries
NICLOCIDE - Pharmaceutical preparations - Miles Inc.
NICO - Pharmaceutical preparations - Jones Medical Industries, Inc. (Medical Div.)
NICO-400 - Vitamins and nutritional supplements - Marion Merrell Dow
NICO-CLEAN - Perfumes - Isis Absorption Technologies Inc.
NICO-FREE - Health care products - Natural Laboratories Corp.
NICO-METRAZOL - Pharmaceutical preparations ✰ - Knoll Pharmaceutical Co.
NICO-STOP - Pharmaceutical preparations - Enzymatic Therapy, Inc.
NICO-TABS - Health care products ✰ - Enzymatic Therapy, Inc.
NICO-VERT - Pharmaceutical preparations - Edwards Pharmaceuticals, Inc.
NICODERM - Pharmaceutical preparations - Marion Merrell Dow
NICOLA - Cosmetics - NDG Cosmetics
NICOLA - Lenses—optical - National Optical Co.
NICOLA MANCINI - Apparel—men's - Hartmarx Corp.
NICOLA MANCINI - Shirts - Yorke Shirt Corp.
NICOLAS - Wines - Remy Martin Amerique Inc.
NICOLAS ALLEN - Apparel and accessories ✰ - Edison Brothers Stores, Inc.
NICOLAS FEUILLATTE - Wines - Blair Importers Ltd.
NICOLAS NAPOLEON - Wines - Leonard Kreusch Inc.
NICOLA'S PASTA PAIL - Food products - Nicola Pizza, Inc.
NICOLE - Dinnerware—glass - Johnson Brothers, USA, Inc.
NICOLE - Dinnerware—glass - WMF/USA
NICOLE - Dolls - Uneeda Doll Co., Inc.

✰ = Now out of production

NICOLE - Dolls ☆ - Effanbee Doll Corp.
NICOLE - Footwear - Consolidated Shoe Co., Inc.
NICOLE - Frames—eyeglass - Rozin Optical Export Corp.
NICOLE - Frames—eyeglass - U.S. Optical Frame Co.
NICOLE - Furniture - Singer Furniture Co.
NICOLE - Glassware—household - Dansk International Designs, Ltd.
NICOLE - Pajamas—women's - Jennifer Dale Inc.
NICOLE - Rings—jewelry - Artcarved Inc.
NICOLE - Skin care products - Nicole Research Inc.
NICOLE - Tableware—china ☆ - Lenox, Inc.
NICOLE & CHILLI - Apparel—children's - Sutton Creations, Inc.
NICOLE DESIGN - Skin care products - Nicole Research Inc.
NICOLE MARX - Apparel and accessories - Forgotten Woman
NICOLE MILLER - Apparel and accessories - Gordon & Ferguson of Delaware, Inc.
NICOLE MILLER - Eyeglasses - California Design Studio Inc.
NICOLE MILLER - Hosiery - Paul Lavitt Mills, Inc.
NICOLE MILLER - Jewelry - Kobra International, Ltd.
NICOLE PERRY - Underwear and nightwear - Spirite Industries Inc.
NICOLE REED - Cosmetics - New England Natural Sponge, Inc.
NICOLE STEVENS - Apparel and accessories - MJT Imports Corp.
NICOLE SUMMERS - Apparel—women's - DM Management Co.
NICOLE WIOR - Apparel—women's - Wior Corp.
NICOLE'S - Mustard - Nicole Inc.
NICOLET - Watches - Nicolet International Inc.
NICOLET PERE ET FILS - Wines - Classic Wine Imports Inc.
NICOLETTE - Floor coverings—carpet and rugs ☆ - World Carpets, Inc.
NICOLETTES - Children's shoes - Consolidated Shoe Co., Inc.
NICOLLA BELLA - Food products - San Benito Foods
NICOLLET - Magnetic tape—blank - Nicollet Technologies Corp.
NICOLMELT - Adhesives and sealants - Malcolm Nicol & Co. Inc.
NICOLO ALFIERI - Neckties - Ram Tiemakers Inc.
NICOLSEAL - Adhesives and sealants - Malcolm Nicol & Co. Inc.
NICOM - Compressors - J. Gerber & Co., Inc.
NICOMB - Vitamins and nutritional supplements ☆ - Freeda Vitamins Inc.
NICON - Industrial chemicals - Nebraska Irrigation
NICONYL - Pharmaceutical preparations ☆ - Parke-Davis
NICOQUIT II - Health care products - Futurebiotics
NICOREST - See NICO-TABS
NICORETTE - Pharmaceutical preparations - Marion Merrell Dow
NICORETTE - Pharmaceutical preparations - SmithKline Beecham Consumer Healthcare
NICOSCORB - Pharmaceutical preparations ☆ - Shannon Chemical Co. Inc.
NICOSINE - Pharmaceutical preparations - Wesley Pharmacal Co. Inc.
NICOSTRAL - Pharmaceutical preparations ☆ - U.S. Ethicals Inc.
NICOTAL - Pharmaceutical preparations ☆ - Hyrex Pharmaceuticals
NICOTEX - Health care products - Healthwatchers System
NICOTINE - Apparel and accessories - E.C.U., Inc.
NICOTINE BUSTERS - Filters—air - Lifetrend, Inc.
NICOTINEX - Vitamins and nutritional supplements - Fleming & Co.
NICOTROL - Pharmaceutical preparations - McNeil Pharmaceuticals
NICOTYM - Health care products ☆ - Everett Laboratories Inc.
NICOZIN-C - Pharmaceutical preparations - Misemer Pharmaceuticals Inc.
NICOZOL - Pharmaceutical preparations ☆ - Hyrex Pharmaceuticals
NICRO - Coffee makers—electric - ARA Services
NICRO - Wire ☆ - Outdoor Technologies Group
NICRO/FICO - Hardware - Nicro Corp.
NICROMIUM - Rings—jewelry - Student Services Co.
NICRON - Chemical preparations - Luzenac America Inc.
NICSAND - Paper—sand - Nicsand, Inc.
NIDACE - Apparel—women's - Horace Grant
NIDAR - Chocolate candy - Haram-Christensen Corp.
NIDEGGEN - Artists' materials - Andrews/Nelson/Whitehead
NIDO SHERPA - Peg Perego USA Inc.
NIDOS - Footwear—women's ☆ - Nina Footwear Co., Inc.
NIEBAUM-COPPOLA - Wines - Niebaum-Coppola Estate Winery
NIECO - Windows—screen ☆ - Nieco Corp.
NIEDEREGGER - Bakery products - C. & J. Willenborg Inc.
NIEHOFF - Automotive parts and accessories - Echlin Inc.
NIELSEN - Aluminum products - Letraset USA Inc.
NIELSEN - Food products machinery - Food Associates Inc.
NIELSEN MASSEY - Spices and extracts - De Choix Specialty Foods Co.
NIELSEN-MASSEY VANILLAS INC. - Food products - Nielsen-Massey Vanillas Inc.
NIELSEN'S - Vitamins and nutritional supplements - Peter N. Nielsen Enterprises Ltd.

NIELSTONE - Dishes—earthenware ☆ - Dansk International Designs, Ltd.
NIEMOLLER - Clocks - Sara Lee Corp.
NIEPOORT - Wines - W.J. Deutsch & Sons Ltd.
NIEU AMSTERDAM - Floor coverings ☆ - Congoleum Corp.
NIF-T-FILE - Desk sets ☆ - Hunt Manufacturing Co.
NIFDA - Food products - Cirelli Foods Inc.
NIFEREX - Pharmaceutical preparations - Central Pharmaceutical Inc.
NIFEREX-150 - Pharmaceutical preparations - Central Pharmaceutical Inc.
NIFEREX-150 FORTE - Pharmaceutical preparations - Central Pharmaceutical Inc.
NIFEREX FORTE - Pharmaceutical preparations - Central Pharmaceutical Inc.
NIFEREX PN - Pharmaceutical preparations - Central Pharmaceutical Inc.
NIFEREX-PN FORTE - Pharmaceutical preparations - Central Pharmaceutical Inc.
NIFITSA KLOSTI - Thread - New Bedford Thread Co. Inc.
NIFLINS CHOICE - Cigars - M. Marsh & Son
NIFREE - Jewelry - Studex USA Inc.
NIFTEE - Door openers—electronic ☆ - LCN Closers
NIFTEES - Stationery ☆ - Joli Greeting Card Co.
NIFTIES - Apparel—women's ☆ - Vesta Intimate Apparel
NIFTY - Animal feeds - Foster Canning Inc.
NIFTY - Apparel and accessories ☆ - Fritzi California
NIFTY - Food products - Le Frois Foods Corp.
NIFTY - Food products - B. Sessler Co.
NIFTY - Frames—eyeglass ☆ - Universal/Univis Inc.
NIFTY - Notebooks and notepads - Carolina Pad and Paper Co.
NIFTY - Paper clips - Noesting Inc.
NIFTY BOGGLER - Notebooks and notepads - Cavert Wire Co. Inc.
NIFTY DRIFTY - Artists' materials ☆ - Donald Art Co.
NIFTY FIFTY - Amplifiers - Evets Corp.
NIFTY FIFTY - Trading cards and stamps - Score Group, Inc.
NIFTY NOTIONS - Needles—sewing - Quilters' Resource Inc.
NIFTY NURSER - Infant product - Sharie A. Fried
NIFTY THRIFTY - Goggles—safety - Aearo Co.
NIGEL QUINEY - Paper—gift wrap - H. George Caspari Inc.
NIGEL'S - Apparel—men's - Pincus Bros., Inc.
NIGEL'S WORLD - Computer software ☆ - Knowledge Adventure
NIGHT - Cosmetics - Dr. Babor Natural Cosmetics
NIGHT - Frames—eyeglass ☆ - Universal/Univis Inc.
NIGHT - Recording label - Virgin Records
NIGHT - Stoneware dinnerware - Iron Mountain Stoneware Inc.
NIGHT - Vitamins and nutritional supplements - Natural Organics, Inc.
NIGHT & DAY - Clocks - Sunbeam Precision Measurement
NIGHT & NOON - Fabrics - Concord Fabrics Inc.
NIGHT ASSAULT PARACHUTE - Fireworks - American Promotional Events, Inc.
NIGHT AT THE OPERA - Dolls ☆ - Effanbee Doll Corp.
NIGHT BEACON - Glass—illuminating - Richlore Home Products Inc.
NIGHT BEFORE CHRISTMAS - Christmas tree ornaments - Cracker Box Inc.
NIGHT BEFORE CHRISTMAS - Paper—gift wrap - Gift Wrap Co.
NIGHT BLEU - Cosmetics - Cosmair Inc.
NIGHT BLOOMING JASMINE - Perfumes - Quintessence Inc.
NIGHT BURNERS - Toys—automobiles - Mattel, Inc.
NIGHT BY LIZ - Apparel—women's - Liz Claiborne Inc.
NIGHT CAP - Health care products - East Earth Herb Inc.
NIGHT-CAPS - Pharmaceutical preparations ☆ - JMI-Canton Pharmaceuticals
NIGHT CAST - Health care products ☆ - Seres Laboratories Inc.
NIGHT CRAWLER - Automotive parts and accessories ☆ - Allied Wholesale Inc.
NIGHT CRAWLER LINKS - Fishing lures - Strike King Lure Co.
NIGHT CREW - Pajamas—men's ☆ - J.C. Penney Co., Inc.
NIGHT DAZZLE - Dolls - Mattel, Inc.
NIGHT DEVIL - Fireworks - American Promotional Events, Inc.
NIGHT DIMENSIONS - Nightgowns - Warnaco Inc.
NIGHT DRIVER - Video games - Atari Games Corp.
NIGHT ENFORCER - Goggles - ITT Corp.
NIGHT EYES - Health care products - Arizona Natural Products
NIGHT EYES - Lighting fixtures - Point Electric
NIGHT FLIGHT - Bicycles - Columbia Manufacturing Inc.
NIGHT FLOWER - Rings—jewelry - Artcarved Inc.
NIGHT-FRIGHT - Toys - Tonka Corp.
NIGHT FRIGHT BATS - Novelty items - Russ Berrie and Co., Inc.
NIGHT FROST - Toilets—enameled - Kohler Co.
NIGHT GLOW - Clocks - General Time Corp. (Westclox/Seth Thomas Div.)
NIGHT-GUARD - Electrical equipment - Cable Electric Products
NIGHT HAWK - Archery equipment ☆ - High Country American

☆ = Now out of production

NIGHT HAWK - Bicycles ☆ - Roadmaster Corp.
NIGHT HAWK - Frames—eyeglass ☆ - Universal/Univis Inc.
NIGHT HAWK - Golfing equipment - Golfsmith International Inc.
NIGHT HAWK - Kites ☆ - Hi-Flier Manufacturing Co.
NIGHT HAWK - Toys - Tyco Toys
NIGHT HAWK'S - Food products - Night Hawk Foods Inc. (Frozen Foods Div.)
NIGHT HEROES - Shirts - R. Drew Fezzey
NIGHT HERON MUSIC - Recording label - Night Heron Music
NIGHT IN GOTHAM - Games ☆ - Mayfair Games, Inc.
NIGHT INTENSITY - Skin-care products ☆ - California SunCare, Inc.
NIGHT LARK - Lighting fixtures - Big Beam Emergency Systems Inc.
NIGHT LIFE - Apparel—women's - Hooper Associates Ltd.
NIGHT LIFE - Beds—wood - Richards Quality Bedding
NIGHT LIFE - Floor coverings—carpet and rugs ☆ - Hollytex Carpet Mills Inc.
NIGHT LIFE - Footwear - Brown Shoe Co.
NIGHT LIFE - Hosiery - Sheffield Industries Inc.
NIGHT LIFE - Recording label - Sea Breeze Record Co.
NIGHT LIGHT - Computer software - GTE Service Corp.
NIGHT LIGHTER - Lighting equipment - Marketing Insights, Inc.-Frank Luppino Jr., and Associates
NIGHT LIGHTERS - Shoes - KangaROOS USA Inc.
NIGHT LIGHTS - Greeting cards - Image Ad Graphics
NIGHT-LITES - Frames—eyeglass - Liberty Optical Manufacturing Co.
NIGHT LOOKS - Ophthalmic goods - Foremost Optical Products
NIGHT MAGIC - Apparel—women's - Milco Industries, Inc.
NIGHT MAGIC - Apparel—women's - Movie Star, Inc.
NIGHT MAGIC - Bedding—linen - Dan River Inc.
NIGHT MAGIC - Giftware - Avon Products, Inc.
NIGHT MAJIC - Bedding—linen - Dreamtex Corp.
NIGHT MAN, THE - Books—comic - Malibu Comics Entertainment, Inc.
NIGHT MARINER - Goggles - ITT Corp.
NIGHT MISSION - Computer software - SubLogic Corp.
NIGHT-MODE - Watches and watch parts - Timex Corp.
NIGHT MOODS - Cosmetics - Alexandra De Markoff, Ltd.
NIGHT MOODS - Floor coverings—carpet and rugs ☆ - World Carpets, Inc.
NIGHT MOODS - Lighting fixtures ☆ - Hubbell Lighting, Inc. (Lighting Div.)
NIGHT MOVES - Frames—eyeglass ☆ - Universal/Univis Inc.
NIGHT MOVES - Shoes - Genesco Inc.
NIGHT MOVES - Underwear and nightwear - L.V. Myles
NIGHT N' DAY - Mirrors - Salton/Maxim Housewares, Inc.
NIGHT NIP - Health care products - Old Amish Herbs
NIGHT OF OLAY - Skin care products - Richardson-Vicks USA
NIGHT OF PASSION - Skin care products - J. Gaunt Woodman Co.
NIGHT-OFF - Computers - Western Telematic Inc.
NIGHT ON THE HUDSON, A - Dolls ☆ - Effanbee Doll Corp.
NIGHT ORCHID - Lipsticks - Elysee Scientific Cosmetic Co.
NIGHT OUT - Perfumes - Allanco
NIGHT OWL - Colognes - Brandy Harvest
NIGHT OWL - Greeting cards - David Neal Dewitt
NIGHT OWL - Recording label - American Music Co.
NIGHT OWL - Teas - Eastern Shore Tea Co.
NIGHT OWL - Teas ☆ - San Francisco Herb & Natural Food Co.
NIGHT PAL - Lamps - Unisar, Inc.
NIGHT PATROL - Floodlights ☆ - RAB Electric
NIGHT PRO - Bicycle parts and accessories - Union Frondenberg USA Co.
NIGHT QUEST - Binoculars - ITT Industries, Inc.
NIGHT QUEST - Floor coverings—carpet and rugs ☆ - World Carpets, Inc.
NIGHT RANGER - Toys - Tonka Corp.
NIGHT REFLECTIONS - Calendars ☆ - House of Doolittle
NIGHT REFLEX - Cosmetics ☆ - Shiseido Cosmetics (America) Ltd.
NIGHT REPAIR - Skin care products - Estee Lauder Inc.
NIGHT REPLENISHING COMPLEX - Skin care products - Viviane Woodard Industries, Ltd.
NIGHT REST - Pillows - Finger Furniture Co., Inc.
NIGHT REST - Vitamins and nutritional supplements - Source Naturals
NIGHT RHYTHM - Perfumes - Prince Matchabelli
NIGHT RIDER - Eyeglasses - Art-Craft Optical Co.
NIGHT ROVER - Pet products - Nancy M. Nasser
NIGHT SCAN - Masts—wood - Will-Burt Co.
NIGHT SCENE - Frames—eyeglass ☆ - Universal/Univis Inc.
NIGHT SENSATION - Dolls - Mattel, Inc.
NIGHT SHADOW - Bicycles - Murray, Inc.
NIGHT SHADOWS - Lighting fixtures ☆ - Thomas Industries Inc.
NIGHT SHAPERS - Apparel stores—lingerie ☆ - Formfit Rogers
NIGHT SHIFT - Frames—eyeglass - May Optical Co. Inc.
NIGHT SHIFT - Insecticides - United Industries Corp.

NIGHT SHIFTS - Pens - Bic Corp.
NIGHT SHOT - Frames—eyeglass ☆ - Universal/Univis Inc.
NIGHT SKY - Hobby kits - Creative Art Activities Inc.
NIGHT SKY - Kaleidoscopes - Gemini Kaleidoscopes
NIGHT SKY - Recording label - DA Music USA
NIGHT SONG - Floor coverings—carpet and rugs ☆ - Zenith Carpets
NIGHT SONG - Mattresses - King Koil Licensing Co., Inc.
NIGHT SONG - Vitamins and nutritional supplements - Organic Diversions, Inc.
NIGHT SPARKLES - Corn—flour or meal ☆ - Halston Borghese Inc. (North America Div.)
NIGHT SPICE - Health care products - Procter & Gamble Co.
NIGHT SPOTTERS - Decals and transfers - Paper Magic Group Inc.
NIGHT STALKER - Electronic equipment - CCS Communication Control Systems of NY, Ltd.
NIGHT STALKER - Firearms, accessories, and parts - James W. Teetzel
NIGHT STALKER - Toys - Mattel, Inc.
NIGHT STAR - Artists' materials ☆ - Artoptic International Corp.
NIGHT STAR - Beverages—malt - G. Heileman Brewing Co., Inc.
NIGHT STAR - Beverages—malt - The Stroh Brewery Co.
NIGHT STAR - Floor coverings—carpet and rugs ☆ - World Carpets, Inc.
NIGHT STAR - Motor vehicles ☆ - General Motors Corp. (Chevrolet Motor Div.)
NIGHT STOCKER - Video game - Bally Sente Inc.
NIGHT STRIPE - House furnishings - Dan River Inc.
NIGHT STYLES - Glassware—household - Durand International
NIGHT SUPPORT - Skin care products ☆ - Avon Products, Inc.
NIGHT-TEA - Apparel and accessories ☆ - Edison Brothers Stores, Inc.
NIGHT TEE - Underwear and nightwear - Continnuus
NIGHT TIME BY FOREVER YOURS - Dresses—women's - Forever Yours International Corp.
NIGHT-TIME INTENSIVE BODY SCULPTING TREATMENT - Skin care products - Rebeka.
NIGHT TIMER - Lighting fixtures ☆ - Thomas Industries Inc.
NIGHT-TIMER - Novelty items - Francine S. Moraff
NIGHT TRAIN EXPRESS - Wines - Ernest and Julio Gallo Winery
NIGHT TRAIN TO CHICAGO - Wallpaper - Jack Denst Designs
NIGHT TRIM - Pharmaceutical preparations - Quantum, Inc.
NIGHT WASH - Jeans - Blue Bell, Inc.
NIGHT WATCH-5 - Searchlights - Bright Star Industries Inc.
NIGHTBLASTER - Automotive parts and accessories - Optronics Inc.
NIGHTCAP - Tobacco—chewing or smoking - Alfred Dunhill of London Inc.
NIGHTCYCLE - Pet products - Tetra Sales USA
NIGHTFALL - Window shades ☆ - Spring Window Fashions Division, Inc.
NIGHTFIGHTER - Citronella oil - Wisconsin Pharmacal Co. Inc.
NIGHTFLIGHT - Mattresses - Land and Sky Manufacturing Inc.
NIGHTFORCE - Spotlights - Lightforce USA, Inc.
NIGHTGUARD - Reflective fencing - Leucadia, Inc.
NIGHTHAWK - Archery equipment ☆ - Martin Archery Inc.
NIGHTHAWK - Bicycles - Commonwealth Inc.
NIGHTHAWK - Binoculars ☆ - Swift Instruments, Inc.
NIGHTHAWK - Communications equipment - Flightcom Corp.
NIGHTHAWK - Firearms, accessories, and parts - Welsh Sporting Goods Corp. (Boyt Div.)
NIGHTHAWK - Machine tools - Cincinnati Machine
NIGHTHAWK - Motor vehicles—taxicabs - Magline Inc.
NIGHTHAWK - Motorcycles - American Honda Motor Co. Inc. (Acura Div.)
NIGHTHAWK - Trailers—truck ☆ - Sun-Lite Inc.
NIGHTHAWK 2000 - Measuring instruments - Nighthawk Industries, Inc.
NIGHTHAWK, THE - Knives—hunting - Buck Knives, Inc.
NIGHTIME - Candy - Silver Palate Kitchen
NIGHTIME - Pharmaceutical preparations ☆ - Whitby Pharmaceuticals, Inc.
NIGHTINGALE - Fabrics - Greenwood Mills Inc.
NIGHTINGALE - Flour—blended - Star of the West Milling Co
NIGHTINGALE - Medical apparatus - Comfortex Inc.
NIGHTINGALE - Recording label - Harmonia Mundi U.S.A. Inc.
NIGHTINGALE - Recording label ☆ - Higher Octave Music, Inc.
NIGHTINGALE - Tea kettles—nonelectric - Metrokane
NIGHTINGALE - Watches - Bulova Corp.
NIGHTINGALE I - Wallpaper - Four Seasons
NIGHTLIFE - Barrettes - Originalities
NIGHTLIFE - Lighting fixtures - Hadco
NIGHTLIFE - Outdoor-light fixtures - Genlyte Group Inc.
NIGHTLIFE - Serving carts - Svend Jensen of Denmark Inc.
NIGHTLIGHT - Marble products - Kohler Co.
NIGHTLY - Recording label - Nightly Records
NIGHTMARE - Toys - Tonka Corp.
NIGHTMARE ON ELM STREET, A - Games - Avalon Hill Game Co.

☆ = Now out of production

NIGHTMARE WARRIORS - Toys - Multi Toys Corp.
NIGHTMOIST - Skin care products - Key West Aloe Inc.
NIGHTOWL - Frames–eyeglass - Liberty Optical Manufacturing Co.
NIGHTRIDER - Condoms - LRC North America, Inc.
NIGHTSCAPES - Books–comic - Andrew M. Vaughan
NIGHTSCAPING - Lighting fixtures ☆ - Hubbell Lighting, Inc. (Lighting Div.)
NIGHTSHADE - Computer software - Atemi Corp.
NIGHTSHADOWS - Ornamental products–glass - Markee Products Co.
NIGHTSHIELD - Optical machinery - Korry Electronics Co.
NIGHTSHIFT - Computer software - Bridgeware Systems
NIGHTSIGHT - Computer peripheral equipment - Sensor Dynamics, Inc.
NIGHTSIGHT - Lanterns–kerosene - Coleman Co., Inc.
NIGHTSIGHT - Lighting equipment ☆ - Tork Inc.
NIGHTSONG - Dolls - Tonka Corp.
NIGHTSPIKER - Sporting goods - Nightspiker Fluorescent Volleyball, Inc.
NIGHTSPOTS - Sunglasses - Face 2 Face Corp.
NIGHTSTAR - Recording label - Nightstar Records Inc.
NIGHTSTICK - Golfing equipment - Adams Golf, Inc.
NIGHTSTICK AUTOBAR - Engines–internal combustion - Kraco Enterprises Inc.
NIGHTSTREAKER - Toys–automobiles - Mattel, Inc.
NIGHTTIME FOOT RENEWAL - Skin care products - Benchmark Brands
NIGHTTIME PAMPRIN - Health care products - Chattem Inc.
NIGHTVIEW MARKERS - Hardware - Premax L.P.
NIGHTVIEWERS - Lenses–optical - OSP Laboratories Corp.
NIGHTVISION - Video production - Atlantic Records
NIGHTVISION - Watches - Helbros International
NIGHTWARE - Communications equipment - Micro Energetics Corp.
NIGHTWATCH - Books–comic ☆ - Marvel Entertainment Group, Inc.
NIGHTWATCH - Electronic equipment - Polaroid Corp.
NIGHTWATCHER - Lighting equipment–automotive - Peterson Manufacturing Co.
NIGHTWIND - Recording label - Fireball Records
NIGHTWING - Guitars - Silver St. Inc.
NIGHTY NIGHT - Pharmaceutical preparations - Traditional Medicinals, Inc.
NIGHTY NIGHT - Toys–stuffed - Russ Berrie and Co., Inc.
NIGHTY NIGHT BEARS - Toys - Securitag Corp.
NIGLYCON - Pharmaceutical preparations ☆ - Consolidated Midland Corp.
NIGROIDS - Cough drops - Consolidated Midland Corp.
NIJI - Artists' materials - Yasutomo
NIJI HI-BALL - Pens ☆ - Yasutomo
NIJI STYLISTS - Pens - Yasutomo
NIK-NAK - Frames–eyeglass - Hudson Optical Corp.
NIK NAKS - Candy - Brock Candy Co. Inc.
NIK NAKS - Snack foods - Cornnuts Inc.
NIK-NIK - Neckties ☆ - Randa Corp.
NIK STOP - Pet products ☆ - Tomlyn Products
NIK STOP II - Pet products - Tomlyn Products
NIKE - Binders - BRS, Inc.
NIKE - Bricks - North American Refractories Co.
NIKE - Floor coverings–carpet and rugs ☆ - Hollytex Carpet Mills Inc.
NIKE - Food products - Landshire Food Service Inc.
NIKE - Footwear–athletic - Nike, Inc.
NIKE - Frames–eyeglass ☆ - Universal/Univis Inc.
NIKE - Nail care products - Sculptured Nails by Nike Inc.
NIKE AEROBICS - Footwear - BRS, Inc.
NIKE-AJAX - Bicycles - Ross Bicycles USA, Ltd.
NIKE APACHE - Toys–models ☆ - Estes Industries
NIKE F.I.T. - Apparel–athletic - Nike, Inc.
NIKE GOLF - Bags–duffel - Nike, Inc.
NIKE INTERNATIONAL - Apparel–athletic ☆ - Nike, Inc.
NIKE REGRIND - Footwear - BRS, Inc.
NIKE REGRIND RECYCLED OUTSOLE - Footwear - BRS, Inc.
NIKE SOUND - Electronic equipment - Adar Import and Distributing Corp.
NIKE TOUR - Umbrellas - Nike, Inc.
NIKE-X - Toys–models ☆ - Estes Industries
NIKI - Fruits–dried - Takari International, Inc.
NIKI - Toys - Tonka Corp.
NIKI DE SAINT PHALLE - Perfumes - Alfin Fragrances Inc.
NIKI DE SAINT PHALLE - Perfumes ☆ - Major/Advance International
NIKI WIOR - Apparel–women's - Wior Corp.
NIKIT - Paints - Reliable Plastics
NIKITA - Apparel–women's - N.Y.F. (U.S.) Inc.
NIKKA - Whiskey - JFC International, Inc.
NIKKA DORI - Apparel and accessories - I.J. Piccolo, Inc.
NIKKEYS - Diapers–cloth - Family Clubhouse

NIKKI - Dolls - Mattel, Inc.
NIKKI - Ophthalmic goods ☆ - Luxottica
NIKKI - Shoes - Daniel Green Co.
NIKKI - Wigs - Jean Paree Weegs Inc.
NIKKI CAT - Toys–stuffed - Russ Berrie and Co., Inc.
NIKKI-D - Cosmetics ☆ - Majestic Drug Co., Inc.
NIKKI HELMET - Helmets–athletic - Edward M. Tetterton
NIKKI YOUNG - Apparel and accessories - Nikki Young, Inc.
NIKKI'S - Cookies - Nikki's Cookies, Inc.
NIKKI'S COOKIES - Cookies - Nikki's Cookies, Inc.
NIKKO - Dinnerware–glass - Nikko Ceramics Inc.
NIKKO - Electronic equipment ☆ - JTG of Nashville
NIKKO - Finepoint marker ☆ - Itoya of America, Ltd.
NIKKO - Watches - Noorallah Rahim
NIKKO TEC - Toys - Nikko America, Inc.
NIKKOR - Photographic equipment - Nikon Inc.
NIKKORMAT - Electronics equipment - Nikon Inc.
NIKLAD - Chemical preparations - Macdermid, Inc.
NIKO - Blinds–vertical - NIKO Vertical Blinds Inc.
NIKO NIKO - Food products - Seasia
NIKOBAN - Pharmaceutical preparations ☆ - Smithkline Beecham Corp.
NIKOLAI - Gin ☆ - Sazerac Co. Inc.
NIKON - Cameras - Nikon Inc.
NIKON COOLPRINT - Photographic equipment - Nikon Inc.
NIKON COOLSCAN - Photographic equipment - Nikon Inc.
NIKON LITE III HARD CLEAR COAT - Lenses–optical - Nikon Inc.
NIKON ONE-TOUCH - Cameras - Nikon Inc.
NIKON WAVE - Frames–eyeglass - Nikon Inc.
NIKONOS - Photographic equipment - Nikon Inc.
NIKOR - Photographic equipment ☆ - The Tiffen Co.
NIKOS SAFETY BRAKES - Brake parts - Nikos Safety Brakes
NIKS - Jeans–women's - Crane Manufacturing Co. Inc.
NIKSICKO - Beverages–malt - Stanley Stawski Distributing Co.
NIKURIZE - Cleaning preparations ☆ - Rukin Industries Inc.
NIL-DUST - Sweeping compounds - Paxon Manufacturing Co.
NIL-O-FRESH - Pet products - Nilodor Inc.
NIL-O-LITTER - Pet products - Nilodor Inc.
NIL-O-NAL - Health care products - Fleetwood Co.
NIL-O-SAN - Disinfectants ☆ - Nilodor Inc.
NIL-O-WIK - Deodorizers - Nilodor Inc.
NIL-O-ZYME - Cleaning preparations–household - Nilodor Inc.
NILADE - Pharmaceutical preparations - Blair Pharmacal
NILATUS - Pharmaceutical preparations ☆ - JMI-Canton Pharmaceuticals
NILCOL - Antihistamine preparations - Health Care Industries Inc.
NILDA - Frames–eyeglass - Hudson Optical Corp.
NILE - Chimes ☆ - J.W. Stannard Co.
NILE - Clocks ☆ - General Time Corp. (Westclox/Seth Thomas Div.)
NILE - Erasers ☆ - Bright Boy Abrasives
NILE - Flatware ☆ - Dansk International Designs, Ltd.
NILE - Games ☆ - Milton Bradley Co.
NILE BLOSSOM - Lipsticks ☆ - Aloe Creme Laboratories
NILE SPICE - Soups–mixes - Golden Grain Co.
NILE SPICE - Soups–mixes - Nile Spice Foods Inc.
NILE SPICE FOODS - Soups–mixes - Nile Spice Foods Inc.
NILECHO - Deodorizers - Nilodor Inc.
NILES - Amplifiers - Niles Audio Corp., Inc.
NILES - Novelty items - Darwell Import Co. Inc.
NILES AUDIO - Amplifiers - GNP Audio Video Inc.
NILIUM - Deodorizers - Nilodor Inc.
NILLA - Cookies - Nabisco Foods Group
NILO - Rope - Wellington Leisure Products, Inc.
NILO BONDED - Cordage and twine - Wellington Leisure Products, Inc.
NILODOR - Candles - Carolina Designs Ltd.
NILODOR - Pet products - Nilodor Inc.
NILODOR TAP-A-DROP - Deodorizers - Nilodor Inc.
NILODORIZER - Deodorizers ☆ - Nilodor Inc.
NILORIC - Pharmaceutical preparations ☆ - B.F. Ascher & Co. Inc.
NILOSOL - Deodorizers - Nilodor Inc.
NILOSORB - Deodorizers - Nilodor Inc.
NILOTEX - Stain removers - Nilodor Inc.
NILOTRON - Deodorizers - Nilodor Inc.
NILSPASM - Pharmaceutical preparations ☆ - Parmed Pharmaceuticals, Inc.
NILSPIN - Rope - MacWhyte Co.
NILSTAT - Air purification systems - Ion Systems
NILTON - Music stands - M & M Distributing Co.
NILVA - Recording label - Jazz Composer's Orchestra Association Inc.

☆ = Now out of production

NIMA - Medical apparatus - Critical Device Corp.
NIMBEX - Surgical supplies - Glaxo Wellcome Inc.
NIMBLE - Bicycles ☆ - Roadmaster Corp.
NIMBLE - Computer peripheral equipment - BJMT Technology Corp.
NIMBLE - Ships–sailing vessels - Nimble Boats Inc.
NIMBLE FINGERS - Gloves - Pioneer Industrial Products Co.
NIMBLE-LITE - Lighting fixtures - Swivelier Co. Inc.
NIMBLE NUMBER NED - Toys–electronic ☆ - Philips Consumer Electronics Co.
NIMBUS - Chairs–folding - Cramer Inc.
NIMBUS - Computer peripheral equipment - Ariel Corp.
NIMBUS - Floor coverings–carpet and rugs ☆ - Bellbridge Carpets
NIMBUS - Floor coverings–tile - ECC International
NIMBUS - Frames–eyeglass ☆ - Universal/Univis Inc.
NIMBUS - Gauging instruments - Airguide Instrument Co.
NIMBUS - Recording label - Jazz Composer's Orchestra Association Inc.
NIMBUS - Sunglasses ☆ - Outlook Eyewear Co.
NIMBUS - Tiles–ceramic ☆ - H & R Johnson Inc.
NIMBUS - Toys–models ☆ - Estes Industries
NIMBUS - Wallpaper - Seabrook Wallcoverings, Inc.
NIMBUS 4 SAILPLANE - Toys - North Pacific Products Inc.
NIMROD - Backpacks - Nimrod Co.
NIMROD - Boats - Glen-L Marine Designs
NIMROD - Footwear - Tucuru
NIMROD - Frames–eyeglass ☆ - Universal/Univis Inc.
NIMROD - Toys - Tonka Corp.
NIN - Compact discs–prerecorded - J. Artist Management, Inc.
NINA - Cosmetics - Nina International, Inc.
NINA - Footwear–women's - Nina Footwear Co., Inc.
NINA - Frames–eyeglass - U.S. Optical Frame Co.
NINA - Whirlpools - Jason International, Inc.
NINA - Wigs - Nina America, Inc.
NINA AUSTIN - Women's apparel - Oggi Ltd.
NINA CAPRI - Apparel and accessories - Pacific Teaze
NINA DE SCREAMIN MIMI'S - Vegetable sauces - Screamin' Mimi's Salsa, Inc.
NINA DOLL - Footwear–women's - Nina Footwear Co., Inc.
NINA D'ORO - Beverages - Tropicana Products, Inc.
NINA RICCI - Apparel and accessories - Jerry Kohn Inc.
NINA RICCI - Jewelry - Nina Ricci Jewelry-Pierre Balmain
NINA RICCI - Skin care products - Parfums Nina Ricci
NINA ROSSINI - Jewelry - Bentley Industries Inc.
NINA SCOTT - Jewelry - Astoria Jewelry Manufacturing Co., Inc.
NINA STUDIO - Statuary - Campania Imports Inc.
NINE - Recording label - Westbound Records Inc.
NINE BEAN LOAF - Food products - Specialty Foods Investment Co.
NINE FLAGS - Shaving preparations - Gillette Co.
NINE GATES INSTITUTE - Apparel and accessories - Nine Gates Institute
NINE GINSENGS - Health care products - East Earth Herb Inc.
NINE KEYS - Publisher's imprints - John H. Richards
NINE LIVES - Fabrics - Dan River Inc.
NINE LIVES - Safety products - AAA Uniforms, Inc.
NINE LIVES OF CLAW - Apparel and accessories - Pilla-Scheetz Productions
NINE MONTH BRA - Apparel–women's ☆ - Bali Co. Inc.
NINE MONTH MIRACLE - Computer software - A.D.A.M. Software, Inc.
NINE ONE SIX - Apparel and accessories - Nine One Six Snowboard Wear
NINE/QUARTZ - Watches - North American Watch Corp.
NINE TO FIVE - Coffee makers–electric - Amway Corp.
NINE TO FIVE - Frames–eyeglass - Liberty Optical Manufacturing Co.
NINE TO FIVE SCREEN GEMS - Computer software - Nine to Five Software Co., Inc.
NINE WEST - Apparel and accessories - G-III Apparel Group, Ltd.
NINE WEST - Handbags and purses - Nine West Group Inc.
NINE WEST - Shoes - Fisher Camuto Corp.
NINE WEST - Sunglasses - Riviera Trading, Inc.
NINE WEST KIDS - Footwear–children's - Nine West Group Inc.
NINE WEST NW SPORT - Footwear - Nine West Group Inc.
NINEBALL SHOOTOUT - Video games - Supervision, Inc.
NINER - Medical apparatus - Microvena Corp.
NINETEEN-TWENTY - Wines - World Shippers & Importers
NINETTE - Glassware–household - Van Dow-Fenton Inc.
NINETY-EIGHT - Pens - Paper Mate Co.
NINETY-EIGHT REGENCY - Motor vehicles–automobiles - General Motors Corp. (Oldsmobile Div.)
NINETY-EIGHT REGENCY BROUGHAM - Motor vehicles–automobiles ☆ - General Motors Corp. (Oldsmobile Div.)

NINETY-ONE - Recording label - Creav Inc. USA
NINETY-TWO - Guns ☆ - Weatherby Inc.
NINEVEH - Recording label - Thomas Wiggins Associates
NINEWINDS - Recording label - Jazz Composer's Orchestra Association Inc.
NINFARITA - Beverages–alcohol - Ninfa's Inc.
NINFARITA LITE - Beverages–alcohol - Ninfa's Inc.
NING COLLECTION - Pet products - Michelle International Ltd.
NING-HSIA - Floor coverings–carpet and rugs - Artistic Rugs Inc.
NINGSIA - Lenses–optical ☆ - Nassau Lens Co. Inc.
NINJA - Bowling balls - AMF Bowling Worldwide
NINJA - Computers - Mitsuba Corp.
NINJA - Darts and dart games - Dart World Inc.
NINJA - Fireworks - Red Rock Trading Co. Inc.
NINJA - Motors–outboard - Zebco Corp.
NINJA - Perfumes - Parfum de Coeur Ltd.
NINJA - Pet products - Marketech
NINJA - Scissors–hand-operated - Burmax Co. Inc.
NINJA - Toy swords - Just Toys, Inc.
NINJA - Toys - Azrak-Hamway International, Inc.
NINJA - Toys–models - Estes Industries
NINJA AEROSLED - Bobsleds and toboggans - Flexible Flyer Co.
NINJA GOLF - Video games - Atari Games Corp.
NINJA HIGH SCHOOL - T-shirts–children's - Malibu Comics Entertainment, Inc.
NINJA MADDNESS - Games - Colleen T. Curtin
NINJA MEGAFALCONZORD - Toys–electronic - Saban Entertainment, Inc.
NINJA SPIRIT - Toys–electronic - ABC International Traders Inc.
NINJA STICKS - Candy - Confex Inc.
NINJA TROLLS - Candy - Brock Candy Co. Inc.
NINJA TUNE - Recording label ☆ - Instinct Records Corp.
NINJA TURTLES - Pasta - American Home Food Products Inc.
NINJA TURTLES - Umbrellas - Essex Manufacturing Inc.
NINJA ULTRAZORD - Toys - Saban Entertainment, Inc.
NINJA UNDERGROUND BRIGADE, THE - Toys - Imperial Toy Corp.
NINJA WARRIOR - Video games - Taito America Corp.
NINKIE - Dolls - C.V. Gambina Inc.
NINNO-VELA - Apparel–men's - Intrep Imports, Inc.
NINO - Cosmetics - Nino Originals
NINO - Ophthalmic goods - Styl-Rite Optical Manufacturing Co., Inc.
NINO CERRUTI - Apparel–men's - Hartmarx Corp.
NINO CERRUTI RUE ROYALE - Apparel–men's - Hartmarx Corp.
NINO FRANCO PROSECCO - Wines ☆ - Pellegrini Bros. Wines Inc.
NINO PANDOLFI - Footwear–athletic - Atsco Footwear Inc.
NINO POOF - Cosmetics - Nino Originals
NINO RAZOR BLADES - Razor blades - Nino Originals
NINO SEGURINI - Footwear–men's - Shore Imports, Inc.
NINO VALENTINO - Apparel and accessories ☆ - Braxton Jeans Inc.
NINOI - Food products - Tucuru
NINOS - Cigar boxes–wood - Consolidated Cigar Corp.
NINO'S - Salads–prepackaged - Demma Fruit Co., Ltd.
NINTENDO - Candy - Topps Co., Inc.
NINTENDO - Frames–eyeglass - Ambassador Eyewear Group
NINTENDO - Snack foods - Lipton Investments, Inc.
NINTENDO - Socks ☆ - High Point Knitting Inc.
NINTENDO - Trunks ☆ - Seward Luggage Co.
NINTENDO - Umbrellas - Shaw Creations Inc.
NINTENDO CEREAL SYSTEM - Cereal - Ralston Purina Co.
NINTENDO POWER - Video games - Nintendo of America Inc.
NINTENDO SUPER SYSTEM - Video games - Nintendo of America Inc.
NINTENDO WORLD CUP - Video games - Nintendo of America Inc.
NIOBRARA - Firearms, accessories, and parts - Welsh Sporting Goods Corp. (Boyt Div.)
NIONET - Electrical equipment - Fire-Lite Alarms, Inc.
NIONG - Pharmaceutical preparations - U.S. Ethicals Inc.
NIOSOME - Cosmetics - Cosmair Inc.
NIOSPRAY - Hair care products - Nioxin Research Laboratories Inc.
NIP - Pet products ☆ - Sera Aquaristik USA Inc.
NIP & TUCK - Dog food - Blue Seal Feeds Inc.
NIP & TUCK - Frames–eyeglass ☆ - Universal/Univis Inc.
NIP AND TUCK - Wallpaper - Carlton-Metro Wallcoverings
NIP CHIP - Motor vehicle parts and accessories - D.D. Designs, Inc.
NIP-CO - Pesticides–agricultural - Roccorp, Inc.
NIP-ET - Mouthwashes ☆ - Stanback Co.
NIP-GUARD - Vitamins and nutritional supplements - Albion Laboratories, Inc.
NIP-I-DIDDEE - Sporting goods ☆ - Gladding Braided Products Inc.
NIP 'N FOLD - Nail care products - Revlon Consumer Products Corp.

NIP-NAKS - Crackers - Daimaru New York Corp.
NIP TITE - Window coverings - Conso Products Co.
NIP, TUCK AND BOOST - Apparel and accessories - Warnaco Inc.
NIPAZ - Computer software - Henry Townsend
NIPENT - Pharmaceutical preparations - Parke-Davis
NIPIGON - Boats–motor ☆ - Lund Boat Co.
NIPON STUDIO - Apparel and accessories - Leslie Fay Companies Inc.
NIPPED IN THE BUD - Spices and extracts - Fitzgerald Fairfield, Inc.
NIPPER - Pliers - ACCO USA, Inc.
NIPPER - Wire - North and Judd Inc.
NIPPER AND SKIPPER - Candy - R.M. Palmer Co.
NIPPER/SLIPPER - Boats–pontoons ☆ - Rebel Industries Inc.
NIPPET - Toys–stuffed - Lucasfilm Ltd.
NIPPLE - Crackers - Umeya Rice Cake Co.
NIPPLES - Jewelry - Michelle Danica Gordon
NIPPON - Cameras - Archer Worldwide
NIPPON - Cameras - Arrow Trading Co. Inc.
NIPPON - Glass–flat - Orient Glass Inc.
NIPPON - Guitars - European Crafts/USA
NIPPON - Pet products - Nippon Pet Food
NIPPON - Television equipment - Fortune Star Products Corp.
NIPPON AMERICA - Radios - Caribbean Export Appliances, Inc.
NIPPON KOGAKU - Cameras - Nikon Inc.
NIPPON RAILS - Games - Mayfair Games, Inc.
NIPRIDE - Pharmaceutical preparations - Roche Laboratories
NIPSEY MUZZLES - Pet products - Aaronco Grooming Products
NIR - Electronic equipment - JPS Communications, Inc.
NIRAM - Health care products ☆ - J.H. Guild Co. Inc.
NIRO PETERSEN - Marine fittings - International Yachting Center
NIRU - Floor coverings - American Floor Products Co. Inc.
NIRU - Floor coverings - Superior Manufacturing Group/Notrax Floor Matting
NIRU - Mats - Wear Proof Mat Co.
NIRVANA - Apparel - Nirvana
NIRVANA - Floor coverings–carpet and rugs - American of Lynchburg, Inc.
NIRVANA - Ophthalmic goods ☆ - Luxottica
NIRVANA - Salad dressings–bottled - Stache Foods
NIRVANA FLAV-O-RAMA - Ice cream - Jack & Jill Ice Cream Co.
NISA - Salad dressings–bottled - Nisa Gourmet Food Inc.
NISAVAL - Pharmaceutical preparations ☆ - Pal-Pak Inc.
NISENTIL - Analgesics - Roche Laboratories
NISEO - Ice cream - Louis Trauth Dairy Inc.
NISERT - Needles–sewing - Foster Needle Co. Inc.
NISH TROPICALE - Beverages - Nish Distributors, Inc.
NISHE - Ophthalmic goods ☆ - Luxottica
NISHICO - Food products - Nishimoto Trading Co. Ltd.
NISHIKI - Bicycles - Raleigh USA Bicycle Co.
NISHIKI BICYCLES - Bicycles - Derby Cycle Corp.
NISO - Paints - Sherwin-Williams Automotive Finishes Corp.
NISQUALLY - Boats–motor ☆ - Bayliner Marine Corp.
NISSAN - Motor vehicles–automobiles - Nissan Motor Corp. USA
NISSAN GTP - Toys–automobiles - Kingsbury Mini Motors of America Inc.
NISSEN - Bakery products - John J. Nissen Bakeries
NISSEN - Beverages–alcohol - Dieter Steinmann Inc.
NISSEN - Sporting goods - Nissen Corp.
NISSEN - Wood products - IDG-International Designers Group Inc.
NISSIN - Photographic equipment - R.T.S. Inc.
NISSKO - Jewelry - Nissko Jewelry Trading Co.
NISSLEY VINEYARDS - Wines - Nissley Vineyards
NISSWA GUIDE - Boats–motor ☆ - Lund Boat Co.
NIST - Measurement devices - National Institute of Standards & Technology
NISTKA - Dresses–women's - Nicola Scalisi and Daniel Scalisi Partnership
NITE-AIR - Ventilation equipment ☆ - Lau Industrial and Commercial Fans Div.
NITE ALERT - Lighting fixtures ☆ - Hubbell Lighting, Inc. (Lighting Div.)
NITE AND DAY - Frames–eyeglass - May Optical Co. Inc.
NITE-BEAM BEDLITE - Electric lighting equipment - Eagle Electric Manufacturing Co., Inc.
NITE BREAKER - Lenses–optical - D.O.C. Optics Corp.
NITE-BRITE - Paints - United Gilsonite Laboratories
NITE CALL - Telephone accessories - Toshiba America Consumer Products, Inc. (Consumer Products Business Sector)
NITE CAP - Health care products - Nutratech Inc.
NITE CHAIR - Chairs–upholstered - La-Z-Boy Chair Co.
NITE CLUB - Housewares - Zim Manufacturing Co.
NITE-EYES - Frames–eyeglass - May Optical Co. Inc.
NITE FIGHTER - Frames–eyeglass - May Optical Co. Inc.
NITE FLITE - Balls–basketball - Voit Corp.

NITE-GLO - Electronic equipment - Thomson Consumer Electronics, Inc.
NITE GUARD - Lighting equipment - Lectro Science, Inc.
NITE HAWK - Flashlights ☆ - Rayovac Corp.
NITE IMAGES - Underwear and nightwear - Alan Komack
NITE JEWELS - Jewelry–costume - Phillips International Jewelry & Souvenirs Inc.
NITE KAPS - Health care products - Rex Research Laboratories
NITE KRAZE - Dresses–women's - Jamie Brooke Inc.
NITE LIGHT - Cold remedies - Sandoz Pharmaceuticals Corp.
NITE LITE - Bedding–linen - Thomaston Mills Inc.
NITE-LITE - Electrical equipment - Gem Electric Manufacturing Co. Inc.
NITE LITE - Lighting equipment - Mr. Mutt Pet Products Inc.
NITE-LITE - Lighting equipment–bicycles ☆ - Raleigh USA Bicycle Co.
NITE-LITE - Pet products - ID Store
NITE LITE - Watches - Timex Corp.
NITE LITE I & II - Safety products - Plastic Safety Systems, Inc.
NITE N' DAY - Apparel–women's - Maidenform Inc. (True Form Foundations Div.)
NITE NITE - Sleep aid - Fields of Nature
NITE NITE - Vitamins and nutritional supplements - American Vitamin Products, Inc.
NITE NOTE - Paper–writing - Mkg, Inc.
NITE OWL - Lamps–desk - Lumatec Industries, Inc.
NITE OWL - Lighting fixtures ☆ - Rayovac Corp.
NITE OWL - Pajamas–men's ☆ - J.C. Penney Co., Inc.
NITE OWL - Spotlights - United States Stove Co. Inc.
NITE PIERCER - Rechargeable lights - Coon Den
NITE READER - Electric lighting equipment - Barnes & Noble, Inc.
NITE-REST - Sleeping aid, sedative - American Pharmaceutical Co.
NITE SLIM - Vitamins and nutritional supplements - Creative Nutritional Concepts, Inc.
NITE SPOTTERS SAFETY STICKERS - Decals and transfers - Paper Magic Group Inc.
NITE STAND - Health care products - Nephron Pharmaceuticals
NITE-TIME - Cold remedies - Rexall Nutritional Products Inc.
NITE-TO-LITE - Lighting fixtures - Hubbell Lighting, Inc. (Lighting Div.)
NITE-TOGS - Crocheted and knitted items ☆ - Tultex Corp.
NITE TRAIN'R - Medical apparatus - Nite Train'r
NITE WATCH - Alarm systems ☆ - Regent Lighting Corp. (Consumer Products Div.)
NITE WHITE - Cosmetics - Discus Enterprises Inc.
NITECAP - Teas–herbal - Nature's Design Ltd.
NITEGARD - Electronic equipment - Thomson Consumer Electronics, Inc.
NITELEES - Apparel–children's - Kid Duds
NITELINE - Fishing tackle ☆ - Outdoor Technologies Group
NITELITE - Clocks ☆ - General Time Corp. (Westclox/Seth Thomas Div.)
NITELITE - Health care products - Healthwatchers System
NITELITE - Toys - Pick Point Sports
NITELITE - Toys - Tonka Corp.
NITEMAPPER - Computer software - Zephyr Services
NITEMATE - Electronic equipment - Intevac, Inc.
NITENAIL - Skin care products - Allercare Inc.
NITEOWL - Alarm systems–burglar - Gentec Equipment Co.
NITEQUARTZ - Lighting fixtures ☆ - Hubbell Lighting, Inc. (Lighting Div.)
NITESHIELD - Lighting fixtures ☆ - Hubbell Electrical Products
NITESHIELD - Lighting fixtures ☆ - Hubbell Lighting, Inc. (Lighting Div.)
NITESPOT - Pens - Autopoint Inc.
NITETIME - Sanitary napkins - Confab, Inc.
NITETORCH - Lighting fixtures - Hubbell Lighting, Inc. (Lighting Div.)
NITETRACKER - Spotlights - Lectro Science, Inc.
NITEWRITER - Pens - Electro-Optix Inc.
NITEX - Fabrics - Tetko Inc.
NITEY NITE - Apparel–children's ☆ - Mount Vernon Mills Inc.
NITEY NITE-GLOWS IN THE DARK - Toys–stuffed ☆ - Commonwealth Toy and Novelty Co. Inc.
NITIL - Pet food supplements - C & C Environmental, Inc.
NITOBOND - Epoxy - Fosroc Inc.
NITOCOTE - Epoxy - Fosroc Inc.
NITOFLOR - Floor coverings - Fosroc Inc.
NITOPRIME ZINCRICH 2 - Primers - Fosroc Inc.
NITORA - Pharmaceutical preparations - Merz Inc.
NITRAN - See **MINITRAN**
NITRASAFE - Gloves - Ansell Edmont Industrial Inc.
NITREX - Gloves–rubber - Delta Group
NITREX - Oils–lubricating - BP America Inc.
NITREX - Pharmaceutical preparations - Star Pharmaceuticals Inc.

☆ = Now out of production

NITREX - Water treating compounds - Aquarium Products Inc.

NITREX RIFLE - Ammunition - Blount International, Inc. (Sporting Equipment Group)

NITRIN - Pharmaceutical preparations ☆ - Pal-Pak Inc.

NITRO - Bats–baseball - Pacers Sports

NITRO - Bicycles ☆ - Huffy Corp.

NITRO - Boats - Tracker Marine Corp.

NITRO - Floor coverings–carpet and rugs - Trend Carpet

NITRO - Guitars - Peavey Electronics Corp.

NITRO - Recording label - Multi-Sound Records International

NITRO - Sporting goods - Outboard Marine Corp.

NITRO - Wheelchairs - Everest and Jennings International Ltd.

NITRO 27 - Ammunition - Remington Arms Co., Inc.

NITRO-AID - Bandages - Carolon Co.

NITRO-BITE - Deicing fluid - Vigoro Industries, Inc.

NITRO CLUB - Ammunition ☆ - Remington Arms Co., Inc.

NITRO-DUR PATCH - Nitroglycerin - Key Pharmaceuticals Inc.

NITRO EXPRESS - Ammunition ☆ - Remington Arms Co., Inc.

NITRO FIRE - Dietary supplement - Weider Health and Fitness

NITRO-FRESH - Medical apparatus ☆ - Apothecary Products, Inc.

NITRO FUEL - Vitamins and nutritional supplements - Twinlab

NITRO-LOK - Coatings - Teledyne Industries Inc.

NITRO-MAG - Sporting goods - Remington Arms Co., Inc.

NITRO MAGNUM - Ammunition - Remington Arms Co., Inc.

NITRO-PAR - Pharmaceutical preparations - Parmed Pharmaceuticals, Inc.

NITRO-PUR - Pesticides–agricultural - Rosen's Inc.

NITRO-QUIK - Pet products - Hawaiian Marine Imports Inc.

NITRO-RETARD - Pharmaceutical preparations - U.S. Ethicals Inc.

NITRO SERIES - Marine rigging - Outboard Marine Corp.

NITRO SYSTEM - Soil–potting - Track III Inc.

NITRO WATER - Water–mineral - Richard D. Bristow

NITRO40 - Computer peripheral equipment - Heurikon Corp.

NITRO60 - Computer peripheral equipment - Heurikon Corp.

NITROBLADE - Skates–roller - Rollerblade, Inc.

NITROCAP TD - Pharmaceutical preparations ☆ - Vortech Pharmaceuticals

NITROCINE - Pharmaceutical preparations ☆ - Schwarz Pharma

NITROCOT - Pharmaceutical preparations - C.O. Truxton Inc.

NITROD - Toys - Mattel, Inc.

NITRODISC - Pharmaceutical preparations - G. D. Searle & Co.

NITRODOSE - Liquid crystal displays - Vacuum Barrier Corp.

NITROFOR - Pharmaceutical preparations ☆ - Kenyon Drug Co. Inc.

NITROFURA-G - Pet products ☆ - Aquatronics-Filtronics

NITROFURAZONE - Veterinary pharmaceutical preparations ☆ - Aquarium Products Inc.

NITROFURE X - Aquatic pharmacuetical preparations ☆ - Aquatronics-Filtronics

NITROGAIN - Food supplement - Advanced Nutrition Inc.

NITROGARD - Pharmaceutical preparations - Forest Pharmaceuticals Inc.

NITROGEN/ES - Footwear - Ryka, Inc.

NITROGEN ULTRA-LITE - Shoes - Ryka, Inc.

NITROGLYN - Nitroglycerin - Kenwood Laboratories Inc.

NITROGOLD - Agricultural chemicals - Chemical Dynamics, Inc.

NITROIL - Chemical preparations - Performance Chemicals International Corp.

NITROLIN - Pharmaceutical preparations - Schein Pharmaceutical Inc.

NITROMED - Pharmaceutical preparations - U.S. Ethicals Inc.

NITRONET - Pharmaceutical preparations - U.S. Ethicals Inc.

NITRONG - Pharmaceutical preparations - U.S. Ethicals Inc.

NITRONGIN - Pharmaceutical preparations ☆ - U.S. Ethicals Inc.

NITRONGPLAST - Pharmaceutical preparations - U.S. Ethicals Inc.

NITRONOW - Medical apparatus - Apex Medical Corp.

NITROPHASE - Vitamins and nutritional supplements - Metaphaz Sports Nutrition Inc.

NITROREX - Pharmaceutical preparations - C.S. Ruckstuhl Co. Inc.

NITROSPAN - Pharmaceutical preparations - Rhone-Poulenc Rorer Pharmaceuticals Inc.

NITROSTAT - Pharmaceutical preparations - Parke-Davis

NITROSTEEL - Steel products - Quanex Corp.

NITROSULF - Pharmaceutical preparations - Misemer Pharmaceuticals Inc.

NITROTYM - Health care products ☆ - Everett Laboratories Inc.

NITROX-RETARD - Pharmaceutical preparations - U.S. Ethicals Inc.

NITRUS - Recording label - Gary Richards

NITTA CASINGS - Iron - Nitta Casings Inc.

NITTAKU - Balls ☆ - Martin-Kilpatrick Table Tennis Co.

NITTAKU - Sporting goods ☆ - General Sportcraft Co. Ltd.

NITTNAY MOUNTAIN - Water–bottled or canned ☆ - Hanover Foods Corp.

NITTO - Tires - Nissho Iwai American Corp.

NITTOH - Floor coverings - Nittoh Tile Corp.

NITTY-GRITTY - Abrasive products ☆ - Marson Creative Fastener Group

NITTY GRITTY - Audio equipment - GNP Audio Video Inc.

NITTY GRITTY - Publisher's imprints - Bristol Publishing Enterprises Inc.

NITWIT - Sporting goods - Weber Industries Inc.

NITZ - Pharmaceutical preparations - Sterling Winthrop Inc.

NITZA - Ophthalmic goods - Swank Optical

NIV - Computer software - Zondervan Publishing House

NIV KIDS' CLUB, THE - Video production - Blair Music

NIVA - Ophthalmic goods - Swank Optical

NIVEA - Skin care products - Beiersdorf Inc.

NIVEA OPTIMALE - Cosmetics - Beiersdorf Inc.

NIVEA SHOWER & BATH - Skin care products - Beiersdorf Inc.

NIVEA SUN - Skin care products - Beiersdorf Inc.

NIWI - Games - Niwi Game Co.

NIX - Fabrics–linen ☆ - Oakhurst Co.

NIX - Pharmaceutical preparations - Burroughs Wellcome Co.

NIX - Veterinary pharmaceutical preparations - Nix Co.

NIX-STIX - Chemical preparations - BDJ Two, Inc.

NIX STIX - Chemical preparations - Dwight Products Inc.

NIXALITE - Fabricated metal products - Nixalite of America Inc.

NIXDORF - Computers–personal - Nixdorf Computer Corp.

NIXIT - Apparel and accessories - Edison Brothers Stores, Inc.

NIXIT - Paint rollers - Garon Products Inc.

NIZORAL - Antifungal products - Janssen Pharmaceutica Inc.

NIZOREX - Pharmaceutical preparations - C.S. Ruckstuhl Co. Inc.

NIZZA BELLA - Food products - Continental Food Corp.

NJ - Jewelry - Norma Jewelers

NJ - Sportswear - Meadowlanders Inc.

NJB NATIONAL JUNIOR BASKETBALL - Balls–basketball - National Junior Basketball League

NJD - Luggage - NJD Enterprises

NJOY PIZZA DELIVERY & COUNTERANT - Food products - N-Joy Pizza Co. Int'l., LLC

NK - Flowers, plants, and seeds - NK Lawn & Garden Co.

NK - Paints ☆ - Shiva Inc.

NK-2 - Musical instrument accessories - Alembic Inc.

NK-4 - Musical instrument accessories - Alembic Inc.

NK L & G - Publisher's imprints - National Plan Service

NK RANCH - Shirts - Nak Corp.

NKD - Apparel and accessories - Nygard, Inc.

NKD EXPRESS - Apparel and accessories - Nygard, Inc.

NKI - Tools–hand-operated - Nelson King Inc.

NKL - Apparel and accessories - NKL Apparel Inc.

NKL SAFE - Safes - NKL Industries, Ltd.

NKOTB - Recording label - Nkotb, Inc.

NKP - Pet products - Ancare Corp.

NL - Computers - American NeuraLogix Inc.

NL CHAMPIONS - Apparel and accessories - National League of Professional Baseball Clubs

NLB - Apparel and accessories - Tomato, Inc.

NLF - Apparel–men's - Nulook Fashions Menswear Inc.

NM - Containers–glass - Neiman-Marcus Group, Inc.

NM - Key rings - Neiman Marcus Co.

NM - Wines - Binns Vineyards & Winery

NM-E - Trading cards and stamps - Malibu Comics Entertainment, Inc.

NM GUARANTEED-PURITY-POTENCY-RELEASE - Vitamins and nutritional supplements - Pharmavite Corp.

NM STRIPPER - Tools - Seatek Co. Inc.

NM UNIFORM - Apparel and accessories - Neiman Marcus Co.

NMCO - Garment storage bags ☆ - Neely Manufacturing Co. Inc.

N.M.I. - Jewelry - Nugget Manufacturers Inc.

NMI - Recording label - 3 G's Industries Inc.

NMW ROLL MASTER - Dolly for vehicles - NMW Products, Inc.

NN - Jewelry - Nelson and Nelson Inc.

NN - Nail care products - Nailtiques Cosmetic Corp.

NNCC CHECKMATE - Publisher's imprints - National Nurses Career Connection, Inc.

NO. - See also NUMBER

NO - Cookies - Sugar Shop

N.O. - Deodorizers - SCI Marketing Inc.

NO 3 MORE 9 CHICAGO - Clothing - Sandra Myria Reed

NO ACCIDENT - Pet products - R.A.F. Trading Inc.

NO-AD - Skin care products - Solar Cosmetic Labs, Inc.

NO-AD HAWAIIAN STYLE - Tanning agents - Solar Cosmetic Labs, Inc.

NO-AD WHITE COAT - Skin care products ☆ - Solar Cosmetic Labs, Inc.

NO AGE LIMIT - Apparel and accessories - Bennett Talsky

☆ = Now out of production

NO AGE MUSIC - Recording label - John Greenfield
NO ANIMAL TESTING - Cosmetics - Levlab, Inc.
NO APOLOGIE - Apparel–women's - Allan & Marcy, Inc.
NO-BACK - Apparel–women's - Lady Marlene
NO-BACK - Underwear and nightwear - Exquisite Form Industries
NO-BAKE - Cakes - Nabisco Foods Group
NO BAKE ONE TONIGHT. - Desserts - Kraft Foods, Inc.
NO BAKES - Desserts ☆ - Pillsbury Co.
NO-BEND - Mailing envelopes - American Fiber-Velope Manufacturing Co.
NO BETTER BREAD - Baked goods - I Can't Believe It's Health Food, Inc.
NO BETTER CHAIR FOR THE MONEY - Office furniture–metal - JSJ Seating Corp.
NO BLACKBALL - Apparel and accessories - Bettina Carnahan
NO BLOT - Office supplies - Faber-Castell Corp.
NO-BLOW BALL POPS - Candy ☆ - Dorval Trading Co., Ltd.
NO B.O. - Deodorizers - Focus Sports
NO BOGEY - Golfing equipment - Consumer Financial Services, Inc.
NO BONE - Pet products - Hill Top Enterprises
NO BONES - Apparel–athletic - CND Sports
NO BONES ABOUT IT - Greeting cards ☆ - American Greetings Corp.
NO BONES ABOUT IT - Pet products - Hill Top Enterprises
NO BONES WHEAT MEAT - Food products - Today's Tamales
NO BOUNDARIES - Apparel and accessories - Wal-Mart Stores Inc.
NO BOUNDRIES - Floor coverings–carpet and rugs ☆ - World Carpets, Inc.
NO-BOWZ - Laces–boot and shoe - T.H.Inc Corp.
NO BRAINER - Erasers - Sanford Corp.
NO-BRAINER DRAINER - Automotive parts and accessories - Robert A. Andersen
NO BRAINS NO GAINS - Apparel - Reality Fitness Services
NO BS - Apparel and accessories - Victor Des Prez
NO BUGS - Paper - Kittrich Corp.
NO BUGS M'LADY - Paper - Kittrich Corp.
NO BULL RECORDS - Recording label - Thomas Wiggins Associates
NO BURN NO BITE - Suntan lotions - Chesebrough-Pond's USA Co.
NO BURST - Plumbing fixtures - Fluidmaster, Inc.
NO-C-UM - Sporting goods - Weber Industries Inc.
NO-CAF - Beverages–carbonated - A.J. Canfield Co.
NO-CAL - Beverages - Canada Dry Corp.
NO CAL - Beverages–carbonated - Dr. Pepper/Seven Up, Inc.
NO-CAL - Spices and extracts - H. Fox & Co., Inc.
NO CALK - Adhesives and sealants - Oatey Co.
NO CHAR - Paints - Parker Paint Manufacturing Co.
NO-CHARGE - Battery chargers - Solar Usage Now Inc.
NO-CHEW - Pet products - Farnam Cos. Inc.
NO CHILD LABOR - Floor coverings–carpet and rugs - Couristan Inc.
NO-CHOL - Cheese - Swissrose International Inc.
NO CLING EVER! - Underwear and nightwear - Warnaco Inc.
NO-CLOG 4 IN 1 - Fertilizers - Scotts Miracle-Gro Products, Inc.
NO CLOG AIRSTONE - Aquariums–household ☆ - Jungle Laboratories Corp.
NO-CLUE - Markers–felt-tip ☆ - Craft World International Inc.
NO COAX - Electronic equipment - Paso Sound Products Inc.
NO COLOR - Cosmetics - Research Council of Make-Up Artists Inc.
NO COLOR LINES - Broadcasting stations–television - Evergreen Media Corp.
NO COMMENT - Belts, handbags, hair accessories, jewelry, etc. - Querelle Inc.
NO COMPROMISE - Vitamins and nutritional supplements - Abundant Life Custom-Made Food Supplements
NO-COP - Paints - Sav-Cote Chemical Laboratories Inc.
NO CRAWL - Artists' materials ☆ - M. Grumbacher Inc.
NO-CRUSH - Corrugated mailers - American Fiber-Velope Manufacturing Co.
NO CURVE NO COOL - Novelty items - Perfect Curve, Inc.
NO DAMP - Dehumidifiers - Star Brite
NO DELIVERY CHARGE - Apparel and accessories - Breton Industries
NO DENT - Office supplies - Master Caster Co.
NO DEPOSIT - Shampoos - Origins Natural Resources Inc.
NO DICE - Games ☆ - Decipher Inc.
NO-DIG - Pet products - Nala Barry Laboratories
NO DISCRIMINATION! - Apparel–women's - America Enterprises, Inc.
NO DOUBT - Frames–eyeglass ☆ - Universal/Univis Inc.
NO DOUBT ABOUT A BITE - Dental compounds - J. Morita USA, Inc.
NO DOZ - Pharmaceutical preparations - Bristol-Myers Squibb Co.
NO DOZE - Automotive parts and accessories - Save-a-Life
NO-DRIP - Faucets - Tomlinson Industries
NO-DRIP - Furniture - International Colorcast Corp.
NO DRIP - Hair care products - Luster Products, Inc.
NO-DRIP - Pipe-joint compound - Vibe Records Inc.
NO DRIP - Tape–masking - Mortite Inc.

NO DRIP STRIP - Paint removers - Parks Corp.
NO EMPTY PROMISES - Skin care products - Michelle Yvonne Ltd.
NO ENDS - Toys - No Ends
NO EQUAL - Fishing lures - Hopkins Fishing Lures Co. Inc.
NO ESCAPE - Pesticides–household - Bonide Products, Inc.
NO EXAGGERATION - Apparel and accessories - Warnaco Inc.
NO EXCEPTION TO THE RULE - Apparel and accessories - No Exception, Inc.
NO EXCUSES - Apparel - New Retail Concepts Inc.
NO EXCUSES - Belts–apparel ☆ - Pyramid Handbags Inc.
NO FADE - Candy - Heads-Up Sports
NO-FADE - Machine parts - Previte Enterprises, Inc.
NO-FAIL MAGIC IN MINUTES - Toys - Hasbro, Inc.
NO FAIL PAIL - Recording label - Stylette Plastics Inc.
NO-FALL - Cases–eyeglass - Snugfit Eye Patch Co.
NO FAT CHANCE - Cookies - Jeremy Wiesen
NO-FAT LAND O' LAKES - Cheese - Land O'Lakes Inc.
NO FAT PLUS - Cottage cheese - Purity Dairies, Inc.
NO FAT TRIM - Meat products–beef - Fleming Companies, Inc.
NO FAULT - Frames–eyeglass ☆ - Universal/Univis Inc.
NO-FAULT - Heating equipment - Watkins Manufacturing Corp.
NO FEAR - Toys–automobiles - No Fear, Inc.
NO-FLAME - Hardware - Amalgamated Chemical Inc.
NO-FLAME - Varnish removers - James B. Day and Co.
NO FLAME SISAL - Wallpaper - Design Materials, Inc.
NO FLATS - Bicycle parts and accessories - C.T.M. Master
NO-FLEAS - Pesticides–household ☆ - Athena Products Corp.
NO-FLUSH - Vitamins and nutritional supplements - Source Naturals
NO-FLUSH NIACIN - Vitamins and nutritional supplements - Twinlab
NO-FOAM - Cleaning preparations–carpet and rug - Uncle Sam Chemical Co., Inc.
NO-FOG - Apparel and accessories - MST Corp.
NO FOG - Cleaning preparations–window - Cadie Products Corp.
NO FOG - Goggles–underwater - Scott USA Inc.
NO-FOG - Medical apparatus - Crosstex
NO-FREEZ - Heat-transfer fluid - Vibe Records Inc.
NO-FREEZE - Deicing fluid - Aeroil Products Co. Inc.
NO FRIES - Snack foods - Pacific Grain Products, Inc.
NO FRILLS - Cardboard - Michael Lee Associates
NO FRILLS - Hair care products - Schnapp Enterprises Inc.
NO-FRILLS - Toys–stuffed ☆ - Dakin Inc.
NO FRIZZ - Hair care products - St. Ives Laboratories, Inc.
NO FUR NO EARS - Agricultural products - Nunes Co.
NO GAP - Recording label - Zim Records
NO-GLOVE - Hardware ☆ - Sculp-Metal Co.
NO GO - Pet products - Nala Barry Laboratories
NO GRAVITY - Bedding–linen - Dan River Inc.
NO GRIT - Sweeping compounds - Frank Miller and Sons Inc.
NO-GRO - Herbicides - J. & L. Adikes Inc.
NO GRUB INSECT KILLER - Insecticides - Seacoast Laboratories Inc.
NO GUTS NO GALAXY - Games - Fasa Corp.
NO GUTS NO GLORY - Shirts - Rugby & Soccer Supply
NO H2O2 - Hair care products - Scruples Professional Salon Products, Inc.
NO HAMMERS! E-Z SHELF SHELF BRACKET SYSTEM NO SCREWS! - Brackets - Arizona Enterprises, Industries & Opportunities Unlimited, Inc.
NO HANDS SOFTWARE - Computer software - No Hands Software, Inc.
NO HEADACHE - Visors - Gexco Enterprises
NO-HIST - Pharmaceutical preparations - Dunhall Pharmaceuticals Inc.
NO HITCH PITCH - Tents - North Face
NO HOE - Garden equipment - Warp Bros.
NO HOLDS BAR - Food products - Nature's Best Inc.
NO-HOP - Veterinary pharmaceutical preparations - Happy Jack, Inc.
NO HOT SHOTS - Regulators–power - Kermode Concepts
NO-ICE - Antifreeze - Illinois Oil Products Inc.
NO IFS ANDS OR BUTTER - Food products - Topco Associates, Inc.
NO ISSUE - Cleaning preparations - State Chemical Manufacturing Co.
NO-ITCH - Pet shops - Sergeant's Pet Products, Inc.
NO JOKE - Sauces - J.I. Zavala
NO JOKE - Sweatshirts - Steve Allan Productions Inc.
NO JUDGEMENTS - Apparel–athletic - Crunch World, Inc.
NO JUSTICE - Apparel and accessories - R. Cousins Ltd.
NO-K-RODE - Automotive parts and accessories ☆ - Berryman Products Inc.
NO KINK - Aquariums–household ☆ - Jungle Laboratories Corp.
NO-KINK - Telephone apparatus ☆ - Lewis-Frank Corp.
NO-KLIK - Electrical equipment - Challenger Circle F Inc.
NO KLOR - Paint removers ☆ - Charles Paint Research Inc.

☆ = Now out of production

NO KNOTS NECESSARY - Apparel and accessories - Descent Control Inc.

NO KOOKS - Novelty items–paper - Jack Adams

NO LADDER NEEDED - Paint rollers - Mr. Longarm Inc.

NO LEAK - Bathroom accessories - Pini Lipski & Associates

NO LIFT - Manicure preparations - Face Up Professional Skin Centers Inc.

NO LIMITZ - Desks ☆ - Leelo Industries, Inc.

NO LINE - Eyeglasses - Cole Vision

NO LINE PLUS - Skin care products - Victoria Vogue, Inc.

NO-LINES - Skin care products - Victoria Vogue, Inc.

NO-LITE - Cosmetics - Worldwide Cosmetics

NO-LOK DOWN - Apparel and accessories - New Line Designs, Inc.

NO-LOSE SCREWS - Garage door openers - Gmi Holdings, Inc.

NO-LYE RELAXER - Hair care products - Image Laboratories, Inc.

NO MAN DOWN - Bulletproof vests - 21st Century Hard Armor Protection, Inc.

NO-MAR - Epoxy - Colony Paints Div.

NO-MAR - Furniture ☆ - Bassick Casters

NO-MAR - Hammers - Plus Manufacturing Co.

NO MARR - Locks–door - M.A.G. Engineering & Manufacturing Co. Inc.

NO MAYO - Compact discs–prerecorded - No Mayo

NO MERCY SURF & SPORTS GEAR - Apparel and accessories - Max S. Moran

NO MESS DOUGH DISC - Brushes–hair - Wood Family Enterprise

NO-MESS HALL - Pet products - Penn-Plax, Inc.

NO MISTAKE - Hair care products - Aminco Inc.

NO-MO RUST - Paints - Sampson Coatings Inc.

NO MONOX - Electronic equipment - Harvey-Westbury Corp.

NO MOR DUST - Adhesives and sealants ☆ - Consolidated Coatings Corp.

NO-MOR FLATS - Adhesives and sealants - Cyclo Manufacturing Co.

NO MOR FLATS - Sporting goods - No Mor Flats by Cyclo Manufacturing

NO MORE ALGAE - Aquariums–household - Jungle Laboratories Corp.

NO MORE BLIND SPOT - Motor vehicle parts and accessories - Reflectory

NO MORE BORING BIKES - Bicycle parts and accessories - Dynacraft Industries Inc.

NO MORE BUMPS - Shaving preparations - ADM Tronics Unlimited, Inc.

NO MORE BURN - Antiseptics - Johnson & Johnson

NO MORE GERMIES - Soap - Johnson & Johnson

NO MORE GREEN WATER - Filters–water - Pond Filtration Inc.

NO MORE ITCHIES - Pharmaceutical preparations - Johnson & Johnson

NO MORE OUCHIES - Antiseptics - Johnson & Johnson

NO MORE PAIN GOD'S MIRACLE HERBAL HEALER - Skin care products - GMH Products, LLC

NO MORE PLUMBER! - Drain pipe cleaners - Randolph M. Reynolds

NO MORE RUNS - Hosiery - Volt USA Inc.

NO MORE SNEEZES - Linen - Levinsohn Textile Co., Inc.

NO MORE TANGLES - Hair care products - Johnson & Johnson

NO MORE TEARS - Suntan lotions - Johnson & Johnson

NO MORE WEEDS! - Flowers, plants, and seeds - Ausam Horticultural Enterprises, Inc.

NO MORE WIRE - Brass products - J.C. Penney Co., Inc.

NO MORE YELLOW - Cleaning preparations - Whink Products Co.

NO-MUV - Floor coverings–carpet and rugs - No-Muv Corp., Inc.

NO-NAIL - Housewares ☆ - Slip Seal Co.

NO NAIL - Sheet metal products ☆ - Genova Products Inc.

NO NAME - Eyeglasses - Orrb Corp.

NO NAME - Skin care products - W.E.A.R. Laboratories Inc.

NO-NECK - Metals - Dormont Manufacturing Co.

NO NEEDLE - Electrical equipment - Removatron International

NO-NIK - Glassware–household - Owens-Illinois Inc. (Libbey Div.)

NO-NIK - Tools - Clauss Cutlery Co.

NO-NIP - Rodenticides ☆ - Roccorp, Inc.

NO-NIP TIP - Razor blades - Jatai International

NO NIX - Pharmaceutical preparations - Requa Manufacturing Co. Inc.

NO-NO - Cookies - Wedgie Dietetic Foods

NO-NO - Locks–door ☆ - M.A.G. Engineering & Manufacturing Co. Inc.

NO NO - Pet products - John Ewing Co.

NO NONSENSE - Footwear - S. Goldberg and Co. Inc.

NO NONSENSE - Hosiery - Kayser-Roth Corp.

NO NONSENSE - Luggage - Welsh Sporting Goods Corp. (Boyt Div.)

NO NONSENSE - Panty hose - No Nonsense Fashions Inc.

NO NONSENSE - Pens - Sheaffer Inc.

NO NONSENSE AMERICAN WOMAN - Hosiery - Kayser-Roth Corp.

NO-O-DOR - Deodorizers ☆ - Flo-Pac Corp.

NO ONE DARES COME CLOSE - Alarm systems - Directed Electronics, Inc.

NO-OX - Chromium compounds ☆ - DecoArt, Inc.

NO-OX ID - Rustproofing compounds - Sanchem

NO-OX-ID - Rustproofing compounds - Sanchem

NO-OX TUBING - Oxygen - Systec, Inc.

NO PARKING - Shoes - Edison Brothers Stores, Inc.

NO PEAK - Tape–adhesive - Orcon Corp.

NO-PEEK - Envelopes - Massachusetts Envelope Co.

NO PEEKEY - Playing cards - Charlotte M. Paul

NO-PEEL, NO-SPLIT - Cosmetics - Avon Products, Inc.

NO PEST - Insecticides - Chesebrough-Pond's USA Co.

NO-PICK - Pet products - Natra Pet Inc.

NO-POP - Fabrics–polyester - Lubash Fabrics, Inc.

NO POTENTIAL LOST - Comforters - Griggs Productions Inc.

NO PROBLEM - Cleaning preparations - Linview Corp.

NO PROBLEM - Computer software - Thomson Legal Publishing Inc.

NO PROBLEM - Games - Winters Enterprises

NO-PROFILE - Electronic equipment - Stow-Away Controls, Inc.

NO-PULL - Pet supplies - Four Paws Products Ltd.

NO-PULL HALTER - Pet products - Four Paws Products Ltd.

NO PUMPING - Sprayers - Root-Lowell Manufacturing Co.

NO REGRETS - Perfumes - Alexandra De Markoff, Ltd.

NO REGRETS - Wallpaper - Advance Wallcoverings

NO REGRETS - Wallpaper - Southland Wallcoverings

NO RESERVATIONS - Wallpaper - Southland Wallcoverings

NO RESPECT - Games ☆ - Milton Bradley Co.

NO RESTRICTIONS - Apparel–women's - Kohl's Department Stores, Inc.

NO RETREAT - Animal feed supplements - Triple F, Inc.

NO-RIDE - Underwear and nightwear - Maidenform Inc.

NO-RINSE - Shampoos - N-R Laboratories Inc.

NO RISK - Apparel and accessories - No Fear, Inc.

NO-RIVL - Paper–toweling ☆ - Fort Howard Corp.

NO RODS JUST ROLLERS - Hair care products - Revlon Consumer Products Corp.

NO ROLL - Apparel–women's ☆ - Bali Co. Inc.

NO-ROLL - Crayons ☆ - Milton Bradley Co.

NO-ROLL - Hams - June Tailor Inc.

NO-ROLL - Signal flares - Orion Safety Products (Signal Products Operation)

NO-ROT - Roofing materials–clay - L.D. Sterns Corp.

NO ROTATE - Thermostats - Kirkhill Inc.

NO-RUB - Automotive parts and accessories ☆ - Stoner Inc.

NO RUB - Hair care products - Fromm Industries

NO RULES - Apparel and accessories - R & S Trading Co., Inc.

NO RULES - Paper - Mead Corp.

NO RUN - Adhesives and sealants - Comstar International Inc. (IPC Div.)

NO SAINT - Apparel–athletic - No Saint

NO SALT - Seasonings - RCN Products Inc.

NO SALT - Seasonings - Smithkline Beecham Corp.

NO-SALT CHIPPLES - Potato chips - Bell Brand Foods Inc.

NO-SAND - Cleaning preparations - Klean-Strip

NO SAND 4 - Sweeping compounds - Paxon Manufacturing Co.

NO-SCENT SOAP - Sporting goods - Lindy Little Joe Inc.

NO SCORCH - Irons–electric - Hamilton Beach/Proctor-Silex Inc.

NO-SCRATCH - Pet products - Nala Barry Laboratories

NO SCRATCH - Photographic equipment - Edwal Scientific Products Corp.

NO-SCRUB - Cleaning preparations–household - Stanson Corp.

NO SEAMS - Floor coverings–carpet and rugs - Galaxy Carpet Mills Inc.

NO SEARCH - Plumbing supplies - Zin-Plas Corp.

NO-SEIZE - Oils–lubricating - J.C. Whitlam Manufacturing Co.

NO SET - Hair care products - Helene Curtis Industries Inc.

NO SEW - Glue–household or industrial - Aleene's

NO-SEW - Lace - M.E. Heuck Co. Inc.

NO-SHAG - Golf courses - Gold Medal Recreational Products

NO-SHEEN - Sporting goods - Weber Industries Inc.

NO-SHOCK - Uncle Sam Chemical Co., Inc.

NO-SHOCK - Fibers–synthetic - Monsanto Polymer Products

NO SHOCK - Lighting equipment - Noma International, Inc.

NO SHORTCUTS! - Educational materials - United Way of Minneapolis Area

NO SHOT B-12 - Vitamins and nutritional supplements - CVC Specialties

NO SHOW - Apparel stores–lingerie - Formflex Foundations Inc.

NO SHOW - Cosmetics - Sassaby Inc.

NO-SHOW - Underwear and nightwear - Maidenform Inc.

NO-SHOW BODY TALK - Underwear and nightwear - Maidenform Inc.

NO-SHOW FANCY - Underwear and nightwear - Maidenform Inc.

NO-SHOW SILKIES - Underwear and nightwear - Maidenform Inc.

NO-SHOW TRICOT - Underwear and nightwear - Maidenform Inc.

NO-SHRINK - Plaster–wallboard ☆ - Reliable Finishing Products, Inc.

NO-SIT - Pet products - Custom Cable Co.

NO-SKID - Office supplies - Quality Circle Products

NO SKIP - Cosmetics - Del Pharmaceuticals, Inc.

NO SLIME STRIP - Chemicals - Gold Coast Chemical Corp.
NO-SLIP - Lawn product - Coughlan Products Corp.
NO-SLIP - Pet products - Pet Lift
NO-SLIP - Sporting goods - Rip Flag
NO SLIP STRIP - Abrasive products - Garelick Manufacturing Co.
NO SLIP TIP - Screws - S-B Power Tool Co.
NO-SLIPS - Shoes - Premier Brands of America
NO-SMEAR - Cosmetics - Hazel Bishop International
NO-SMELL - Pet products - Nala Barry Laboratories
NO SMOKE - Ashtrays–metal - Pollenex Corp.
NO SMOKE - Deodorizers - Surco Products Inc.
NO SMOKING - Air purification systems - Medo Industries, Inc.
NO-SNORE - Medical apparatus - Derrill J. Heiland
NO-SOIL - Housewares - Amalgamated Chemical Inc.
NO-SOL - Climate-control product - Ayling & Reichert Co.
NO SPEAK - Recording label - I.R.S. Records
NO SPILL CLEAN AND FILL - Pet products - Python Products
NO SPOT - Sweeping compounds - Frank Miller and Sons Inc.
NO STAIN - Pet products - St. Aubrey
NO STAT - Chemical preparations - Windsor Wax Co. Inc.
NO STAY - Pet products - Nala Barry Laboratories
NO STINKIN' BAGS - Repellent - Robinson Laboratories, Inc.
NO-STIR - Peanut butter - Curtice-Burns Foods, Inc.
NO STITCH 2000 - Adhesives and sealants - Best Buys Direct, Inc.
NO STOOP - Weed and grass pullers - Invention Prototypes & Marketing Corp.
NO-STOP - Pet products - Farnam Cos. Inc.
NO STRANGER TO DANGER - Apparel and accessories - Mediamax
NO-STRAW DEAL - Games - International Gamco, Inc.
NO-STREAK - Housewares - TR Industries
NO STREEK - Cleaning preparations–window - R-H, Inc.
NO-STRIKE - Static eliminator - W. Gregg Fawthrop
NO STRING - Dental equipment - T-4 Corp.
NO STRINGS ATTACHED - Coats - S. Rothschild & Co., Inc.
NO STRINGS ATTACHED - Computer software - Elastic Reality, Inc.
NO-SUEDE - Wallpaper - Carlton-Metro Wallcoverings
NO SUGAR/SALT DIP-IDY-DILL - Spices and extracts - Jodie's Kitchen Inc.
NO SURRENDER - Apparel and accessories ☆ - Edison Brothers Stores, Inc.
NO-SWAY - Ladders–wood - Rich Ladder Co.
NO SWAY - Sporting goods - Iso-Drive Co., Inc.
NO SWEAT - Broadcasting stations–television - Tower Productions Inc.
NO SWEAT - Cleaning preparations - Puritan-Churchill Chemical Co.
NO SWEAT - Glassware–household - Michael J. Rappold
NO SWEAT - Health care products - Revlon Consumer Products Corp.
NO SWEAT KITS - Exercising equipment - Food For Thought Inc.
NO SWET - Apparel and accessories - Bette Appel Inc.
NO TACK - Artists' materials - Badger Air-Brush Co.
NO-TAIR - Hair care products - N.B. Cohen Co.
NO-TANGLE - Pet products - Lambert-Kay
NO TANGLES - Crochet hooks - Rands Industry
NO-TAPE - Hair care products - Vapon, Inc.
NO TAPE RULER - Tools ☆ - Jobar International Inc./Bibi Products
NO-TAR-IN - Finishing agents - Rutland Products
NO-TARNISH - Bags–storage - Accurate Flannel Bag Co.
NO TEARS - Onions - Ready Pac Produce, Inc.
NO TEARS - Sportswear - Peter Johnson
NO TENSION - Skin care products - L'anza Research International
NO THIEVES GOTCHALOK - Cable locks - Gotchalok Corp.
NO TIES - Footwear–children's - Right Stuff, Inc.
NO TIES - Shoes - Kinney Shoe Corp.
NO-TIME NAIL DRY - Nail care products - Cosmair Inc.
NO TIP LUGGAGE - Luggage - Bernard D. Sadow
NO-TONE - Telephone apparatus - Inventures, Inc.
NO-TOUCH - Medical apparatus - Natalie Levy
NO TOUCH - Polishes - No Touch North America Corp.
NO-TOX - Firearms, accessories, and parts - Bismuth Cartridge Co.
NO-TRACK - Electrical equipment - Utility Solutions, Inc.
NO TRAKS - Bicycle parts and accessories - Retraks USA, Inc.
NO TRAX - Mats - Superior Manufacturing Group/Notrax Floor Matting
NO TRUMP - Thread ☆ - SCT Yarns Inc.
NO-TUG - Health care products - Louis M. Gerson Co. Inc.
NO-TURN - Bins - Russell W. Lold
NO TURN PLUS - Mattresses - Wickline Bedding Co. Inc.
NO-TWEEZE - Depilatories - Kenra Laboratories, Inc.
NO-TWIST - Archery equipment - Saunders Archery Co.
NO-TWIST - Telephone apparatus - Pacific Electricord Co.
NO-TYE - Wallets ☆ - ACCO USA, Inc.

NO US NO THEM - Apparel and accessories - Zubaz, Inc.
NO-VEL - Dental compounds - Degussa Corp.
NO-VENT - Heaters–gas - Suburban Manufacturing Co.
NO-VEX - Detergents - Falls Chemical Products Co.
NO-VOC - Varnishes - Williams-Hayward Protective Coatings Inc.
NO-WAIT - Soil testing kits - Security Products Co.
NO WARNING - Sporting goods - Kellwood Co.
NO-WASH - Paint removers - Wilson Imperial Co.
NO-WASTE - Pet products - Kellogg Inc.
NO WASTE, BETTER TASTE - Coffee makers–electric - Manufacturers Components, Inc.
NO WASTED YARN - Crochet hooks - Rands Industry
NO WEIGH! APPETITE CONTROL SPRAY - Dietary supplement - Flair Image, Inc.
NO-WELD - Lubricants - Elf Lubricants North America, Inc.
NO WHIFF'S OF BUTTS - Deodorizers - Surco Products Inc.
NO WHINERS - Apparel and accessories - Mark Taverniti
NO-WOOD - Adhesives and sealants - Kwik-Affix Products
NO YOLKS - Noodles - Foulds Inc.
NOAA - Computer software - Nortel-Networks
NOACK - Meat extracts - Roth & Liebmann Inc.
NOAH - Chemical preparations - Griffin Corp.
NOAH & NELLIE'S ARK - Toys–stuffed - Tomy America, Inc.
NOAH 'N FRIENDS - Snack foods - Glenn Foods Inc.
NOAH'S - Candy - Salem's Old Fashioned Candies Inc.
NOAH'S - Soft drinks - Varni Brothers Corp.
NOAH'S ARK - Dishes–china ☆ - Gorham Inc.
NOAH'S ARK - Fruits–dried ☆ - Vacu-Dry Co.
NOAH'S ARK - Games - Cadaco Div.
NOAH'S ARK - Puzzles ☆ - Milton Bradley Co.
NOAH'S ARK - Toys - Coloron Industries
NOAH'S ARK - Toys - Tupperware Co.
NOAH'S ARK COLLECTION - Jewelry - Dedeian Enterprises, Inc.
NOAH'S ARKIVE - Computer software - Board of Regents of the University System of Georgia
NOAH'S ART - Desks - Wilderness Cards
NOAH'S ART - Greeting cards - Faylor Studios, Inc.
NOAH'S BAGELS - Bagels - Noah's New York Bagels, Inc.
NOAH'S BAGELS - Slicing machines - Noah's New York Bagels, Inc.
NOAH'S BLACK CHERRY BEAR CHERRY SODA - Beverages–carbonated - Varni Brothers Corp.
NOAHS CALIFORNIA SPRING WATER - Water–bottled or canned - Barni Bothers Corp.
NOAH'S COUGAR COLA - Soft drinks - Varni Brothers Corp.
NOAH'S ELEPHANT ORANGE SODA - Beverages–carbonated - Varni Brothers Corp.
NOAH'S HIPPOPOTAMUS PUNCH - Soft drinks - Varni Brothers Corp.
NOAH'S NEIGHBORS - Toys - Heaven Knows Inc.
NOAH'S NEW YORK BAGELS - Glassware–household - Noah's New York Bagels, Inc.
NOAH'S PITCH - Roofing materials - Celotex Corp.
NOAH'S PORCUPINE PINEAPPLE SODA - Beverages–carbonated - Varni Brothers Corp.
NOAH'S SHIPMATES - Pharmaceuticals - Paul Schell
NOALA - Thread ☆ - SCT Yarns Inc.
NOATAK - Bags–duffel - Kinney Shoe Corp.
NOB HILL - Cabinets ☆ - Nutone Inc.
NOB HILL - Chocolate candy ☆ - Price Candy Co. Inc.
NOB HILL - Coffee - Safeway Stores Inc.
NOB HILL - Fabrics - Thompson of California Inc.
NOB HILL - Floor coverings - Mannington Resilient Floors
NOB HILL - Floor coverings–carpet and rugs - Galaxy Carpet Mills Inc.
NOB HILL - Floor coverings–carpet and rugs ☆ - Blue Ridge Carpet Mills
NOB HILL - Footwear - Nob Hill Sales Inc.
NOB HILL - Fruits and vegetables - Vanguard Trading Services, Inc.
NOB HILL - Glassware–household - Owens-Illinois Inc. (Libbey Div.)
NOB HILL - Neckties - Cornell of California Inc.
NOB HILL CLASSICS - Food products - Golden Whisk Pasta Partners
NOBACK - Jewelry - Jaime Shechter
NOBEL - Automotive parts and accessories - Echlin Inc.
NOBEL - Automotive parts and accessories ☆ - Hyundai Motor America
NOBEL - Cigars - James B. Russell Inc.
NOBEL - Food products - Nobel-Sysco Food Services Co.
NOBEL - Pet products - Univier International Corp.
NOBEL - Thread - Threads USA Div.
NOBEL - Tiles–ceramic ☆ - American Marazzi Tile, Inc.

☆ = Now out of production

NOBEL HALL - Paper–writing - Cherrydale Farms Inc.

NOBELLA - Wines - Seagram's Chateau & Estate Wines Co.

NOBELT - Apparel and accessories - Nobelt Co.

NOBEMA - Artists' materials - Riebe's Artist Materials Inc.

NOBIALLO - Perfumes - Nobiallo USA

NOBILE - Yarn - William Unger & Co. Inc.

NOBILETTE - Handlebars–bicycle - Nobilette Cycles

NOBILITO - Agricultural products - Hogan Associates

NOBILITY - Envelopes - New York Envelope Corp.

NOBILITY - Floor coverings–carpet and rugs - Karastan-Bigelow Inc.

NOBILITY - Floor coverings–carpet and rugs - Trans-Ocean Import Co. Inc.

NOBILITY - Food products - Mitsui & Co. Inc.

NOBILITY - Rings–jewelry - Artcarved Inc.

NOBILITY - Thread - Imperial Threads Inc.

NOBILITY - Towels - Dillard Department Stores Inc.

NOBILITY - Watches - Hampden Corp.

NOBILLIS - Wallpaper - Winfield Design Associates, Inc.

NOBILLIS MICA - Wallpaper - Winfield Design Associates, Inc.

NOBILLIS OF FRANCE - Wallpaper - Winfield Design Associates, Inc.

NOBIS - Amplifiers–public address - S.I.L./Silver Spring Corp.

NOBLE - Accordions ☆ - Harris-Teller, Inc.

NOBLE - Golfing equipment - Noble Golf Co.

NOBLE - Herbicides - Estes, Inc.

NOBLE - Oils–edible - U.S. Trading Enterprise, Inc.

NOBLE - Popcorn - Noble Distributors, Inc.

NOBLE - Sugar–granulated, refined, or powdered - Ustov, Inc.

NOBLE - Wines - Old South Winery

NOBLE & COOLEY - Drums–musical instruments ☆ - J.D. Calato Manufacturing Inc.

NOBLE & LOCKE FIBER MERCHANTS - Apparel and accessories - Passport International Ltd.

NOBLE CHARM - Floor coverings–carpet and rugs ☆ - Blue Ridge Carpet Mills

NOBLE CHOICE - Floor coverings–carpet and rugs - Lees Carpets

NOBLE CHOICE - Pillows - Pillowtex Corp.

NOBLE CROWN - Mattresses and box springs - Ohio Mattress Co.

NOBLE ELEMENTS - Floor coverings–carpet and rugs - Dillard Department Stores Inc.

NOBLE ESTATE - Floor coverings–carpet and rugs - Evans-Black Carpet Mills

NOBLE EXCELLENCE - Floor coverings–carpet and rugs - Regal Rugs Inc.

NOBLE FARMS - Food products - Ray Brothers and Noble Canning Inc.

NOBLE GINSENG - Vitamins and nutritional supplements ☆ - Ethical Nutrients

NOBLE GOLD - Jewelry - Leach & Garner Co.

NOBLE HOUSE - Floor coverings–carpet and rugs - Lees Carpets

NOBLE HOUSE - Wallpaper - Advance Wallcoverings

NOBLE II - Motor vehicles–motor homes - Commodore Corp.

NOBLE IMAGE - Floor coverings–carpet and rugs - Karastan-Bigelow Inc.

NOBLE MANOR - Floor coverings–carpet and rugs - Evans-Black Carpet Mills

NOBLE PHEASANTS - Glassware–household - Ceraglass Inc.

NOBLE PLANNER - Paper–writing - Noble Publishing Associates

NOBLE ROSE - Wines - Old South Winery

NOBLE SAVAGE - Wallpaper - Kirk-Brummel

NOBLE SUPREME - Pillows - Pillowtex Corp.

NOBLES - Cigars - Faber, Coe & Gregg Inc.

NOBLES - Vacuum cleaners and accessories - Nobles Manufacturing Inc.

NOBLESEAL - Sheet waterproofing - Noble Co.

NOBLESEAL CIS - Crack-isolation sheet - Noble Co.

NOBLESEAL SIS - Noble Co.

NOBLESEAL TS - Noble Co.

NOBLESEAL TS - Waterproofing compounds - American Olean Tile Co.

NOBLESSE - Cookware - Kaiser Bakeware, Inc.

NOBLESSE - Glassware–household - Durand International

NOBLESSE - Pens ☆ - Koh-I-Noor, Inc.

NOBLESSE - Rings–jewelry ☆ - Artcarved Inc.

NOBLESSE - Skin care products - Pharmacaps Inc.

NOBLESSE - Tableware–china ☆ - Lenox, Inc.

NOBLESSENCE - Bronze products - Mark Hopkins Sculpture, Inc.

NOBLESSENCE - Figurines - Mark Hopkins Sculpture Inc.

NOBLET - Wines - Heaven Hill Distilleries, Inc.

NOBLET/NORMANDY - Musical instruments - G. Leblanc Corp.

NOBLEX - Cameras - R.T.S. Inc.

NOBLIA - Watches - Citizen Watch Co. of America Inc.

NOBLUR - Fishing lures ☆ - Bay De Noc Lure Co.

NOBLVAC-DART - Veterinary pharmaceutical preparations - Nobl Laboratories, Inc.

NOBO - Bakery products - Campbell Soup Co.

NOBODY CAN SAY NO! - Cereal - General Mills, Inc.

NOBODY DOES HOCKEY LIKE UPPER DECK - Trading cards and stamps - Upper Deck Co.

NOBODY FAMOUS DRINKS IT - Beverages–carbonated - Razcal Corp.

NOBODY MAKES A CARD FOR THAT EXCEPT ME! - Computers - Creatacard, Inc.

NOBODY'S GONNA KNOCK MY SOX OFF - T-shirts–men's - River North Records, Inc.

NOBRUZE - Padding–foam - Connecticut Valley Corp.

NOBURST - Noble Co.

N.O.C. - Deodorizers - Krueger Enterprises

N.O.C. - Pet products - Professional Pet Products

NOC IT DOWN - Apparel and accessories - Rickey White

N.O.C.-PLUS - Deodorizers - Krueger Enterprises

NOCERA UMBRA - Water–mineral - New Horizon

NOCHE BUENA - Beverages–malt - All Brand Importers

NOCHIP - Skin care products - Allercare Inc.

NOCISOUTH - See LA PICCOLINA

NOCKS - Pencils - Sakura of America

NOCONA - Boots - Nocona Boot Co. Inc.

NOCONA BELTMAKER COLLECTION - Belts–apparel - Nocona Boot Co. Inc.

NOCORD RECHARGEABLE SHAVER - Razors - Peter Wong

NOCORE - Thread ☆ - Perfect Thread Co. Inc.

NOCTAGEL - Vitamins and nutritional supplements - Tishcon Corp.

NOCTEC - Pharmaceutical preparations - Bristol-Myers Squibb Co.

NOCTILUX - Photographic equipment - Leica USA Inc.

NOCTOSOME - Skin care products - Lancome

NOCTULAR - Lenses–optical - Nesty/Chafin Partnership

NOCTURNA - Toys - Mattel, Inc.

NOCTURNAL NAVIGATION SYSTEMS - Flashlights - Liston Concepts, Inc.

NOCTURNE - Chimes - J.W. Stannard Co.

NOCTURNE - Chocolate candy - Nestle USA

NOCTURNE - Christmas tree ornaments - Cracker Box Inc.

NOCTURNE - Dinnerware - Corning Inc.

NOCTURNE - Dishes–china ☆ - Gorham Inc.

NOCTURNE - Dishes–china ☆ - Pickard Inc.

NOCTURNE - Floor coverings–carpet and rugs - Lees Carpets

NOCTURNE - Floor coverings–carpet and rugs ☆ - Regal Rugs Inc.

NOCTURNE - Glass–leaded - Seneca Glass Co.

NOCTURNE - Mattresses - Sealy Inc.

NOCTURNE - Watches - Bulova Corp.

NOCTURNE - Window coverings - Joanna Western Mills Co.

NOCTURNO - Glassware–household ☆ - WMF/USA

NOCTUSOM - Vitamins and nutritional supplements ☆ - Tishcon Corp.

NOD-A-WAY - Furniture - Okla Homer Smith Furniture Manufacturing Co.

NODAMPOFF - Garden equipment - Deli, Inc.

NODE CONNECTION, THE - Computer hardware - Node Connection

NODEBUILDER - Computer peripheral equipment - Echelon Corp.

NODERUNNER - Computer software - Artisoft, Inc.

NODILANS - Pharmaceutical preparations ☆ - P.J. Noyes Co., Inc.

NODINE'S SMOKEHOUSE - Meat products–pork - Nodine's Smokehouse Inc.

NODKIN - Dolls - Donna Poulson

NODO - Apparel–men's - Ellegi, Inc.

NODOR - Darts and dart games - General Sportcraft Co. Ltd.

N'ODOR - Deodorants–personal - Banner-Pharmacaps Inc. (Advanced Nutritional Technology Division)

NODROG - Aquariums–household - R.A.F. Trading Inc.

NODULAR - Pharmaceutical preparations - Hoffmann-La Roche Inc.

NO'EAST - Boats–motor - Thurston Co.

NOEL - Beverages - Noel Corp.

NOEL - Christmas tree ornaments - Cracker Box Inc.

NOEL - Dinnerware–glass ☆ - WMF/USA

NOEL - Frames–eyeglass - Rozin Optical Export Corp.

NOEL - Sporting goods ☆ - Continental Sports Supply Inc.

NOEL-COHOL - Nonalcoholic beer - Miller Brewing Co.

NOEL NATURALS - Giftware - Enesco Corp.

NOEL PORCELLE - Dinnerware–glass - Salem China Co.

NOEL YOUNG BOOKS - Publisher's imprints - Capra Press Inc.

NOELFS - Figurines - Ricke Charles Foster

NOEVIR 95 - Skin care products - Noevir

NOFIRE - Chemical preparations - No Fire Technologies, Inc.

NOFLASH - Cleaning preparations - LPS Laboratories, Inc.

NOFOAM - Chemical preparations - Oil Chem Technologies, Inc.

NOFS - Computer software - Cranel Inc.

NOG - Food products - Nog Inc.

NOG - Wines - Willamette Valley Vineyards
NOGA - Thread ☆ - SCT Yarns Inc.
NOGALES CLIP POINT - Knives–hunting - Cold Steel Inc.
NOGENIC - Pharmaceutical preparations - Syosset Laboratories Inc.
NOGGINS - Hobby kits ☆ - Libby Lee Toys Inc.
NOGGY - Candy - Ferrero U.S.A Inc.
NOH - Audio equipment - Adriana M. Vick
NOH - Food products - Noh Foods International
NOHANDS - Furniture - Samsonite Furniture Co. (Consumer Products Div.)
NOI - Food products - Tucuru
NOID - Automotive parts and accessories - Patrick A. McFadden
NOID - Candy ☆ - Amurol Confections Co.
NOILLY PRAT - Beverages–alcohol - Brown-Forman Corp.
NOIRO - Computer software - Apple Computer Inc.
NOIROT-CARRIERE - Wines - Seagram's Chateau & Estate Wines Co.
NOISE BRAKER - Sporting goods - Hocks Laboratories
NOISE BUSTER - Fans–electric - Ranco North America
NOISE-BUSTERS - Plugs–ear - Affirmed Medical, Inc.
NOISE CANCELLING - Musical instrument accessories - Seymour Duncan
   Pickups
NOISE CONTROL - Audio equipment - Eclectic Co.
NOISE FILTER - Plugs–ear - Aearo Co.
NOISE MAGNET - Insulating materials - Watermaker RV Specialties
NOISEBLOTTER - Insulating materials - B. Stanley Lynn
NOISEBUSTER - Electronic equipment - Noise Cancellation Technologies, Inc.
NOISEEATER - Electronic equipment - Noise Cancellation Technologies, Inc.
NOISEFOE - Plugs–ear - MSA
NOISEGARD - Health care products ☆ - Shoplyne Safety Products
NOISEGARD - Tools - Fibre-Metal Products Co.
NOISEMASTER - Audio equipment - The Proudfoot Co. Inc. (Architectural
   Acoustics Div.)
NOISET - Candy ☆ - Bahlsen Inc.
NOISY CARD - Greeting cards - Beyond Tomorrow Inc.
NOISY NUMBER ROBOTS, THE - Electronic equipment ☆ - Texas Instruments
   Inc.
NOIZAY - Glassware–household - Durand International
NOJO - Infant product - Noel Joanna, Inc.
NOJO BABY COVER-UP - Covers–seat - Noel Joanna, Inc.
NOK-HOCKEY - Games - Carrom Co.
NOK-OFF - Cleaning preparations - Lil-Tec Laboratories, Inc.
NOK-OFF - Cleaning preparations - Travaco Laboratories Inc. ,
NOK SET - Archery equipment - Saunders Archery Co.
NOKA - Belts, hair accessories, jewelry, etc. - Honey Fashions Ltd.
NOKAOI - Suntan lotions - Major International Inc.
NOKIA - Tires - Stateside International Inc.
NOKKELOST - Cheese - Land O'Lakes Inc.
NOKOMIS FARMS, INC. - Food products - Nokomis Farms, Inc.
NOKORODE - Automotive parts and accessories - Tosco Corp.
NOKORODE - Soldering equipment - M.W. Dunton Co.
NOKRUST - Oils–lubricating - Shaler Co.
NOLA - Shrimp–canned or cured ☆ - Robinson Canning Co. Inc.
NOLAHIST - Antihistamine preparations - Carnick Laboratories Inc.
NOLAMINE - Antihistamine preparations - Carnick Laboratories Inc.
NOLAN - Bicycles ☆ - XLM Corp.
NOLAN & HANKS - Music–sheet - Jackman Music Corp.
NOLAN POOLIFT - Health care products - Guardian Products Inc.
NOLAN TUBLIFT - Health care products - Guardian Products Inc.
NOLARO - Rope - Columbian Rope Co.
NOLA'S GOURMET - Fruits–dried - ACB/Richard Watson
NOLATEX - Chemical preparations - Karlen Manufacturing, Inc.
NOLAVAX - Waterproofing compounds - Suheil S. Rayes
NOLEX LA - Antihistamine preparations - Carnick Laboratories Inc.
NOLIKO - Food products - ABA Management & Development Inc.
NOLO PRESS - Recording label - Nolo Press/Folklaw Inc.
NOLUDAR - Pharmaceutical preparations - Roche Laboratories
NOLVADEX - Pharmaceutical preparations - Zeneca Inc.
NOLVASAN - Veterinary product - American Home Products Corp.
NOMA - Christmas tree lights - Noma International, Inc.
NOMA - Lawn mowers - Murray, Inc.
NOMA EXACT - Hardware - Murray, Inc.
NOMA GARDENWARE - Pottery ☆ - Noma International, Inc.
NOMAD - Bicycles ☆ - Roadmaster Corp.
NOMAD - Binders - ACCO USA, Inc.
NOMAD - Boats - Glen-L Marine Designs
NOMAD - Compasses–magnetic - Airguide Instrument Co.
NOMAD - Electronic equipment - Omega Engineering, Inc.

NOMAD - Floor coverings - American Floor Products Co. Inc.
NOMAD - Floor coverings–carpet and rugs - S and S Mills Inc.
NOMAD - Floor coverings–carpet and rugs - Superior Manufacturing Group/
   Notrax Floor Matting
NOMAD - Floor coverings–carpet and rugs ☆ - Foreign Accents
NOMAD - Floor coverings–carpet and rugs ☆ - Interloom Ltd.
NOMAD - Floor coverings–carpet and rugs ☆ - Regal Rugs Inc.
NOMAD - Golfing equipment - Harris International Inc.
NOMAD - Knives - Precise International/Wenger
NOMAD - Motor vehicles ☆ - General Motors Corp. (Chevrolet Motor Div.)
NOMAD - Motor vehicles–motor homes - Skyline Homes Inc.
NOMAD - Oxygen ☆ - Caire
NOMAD - Telephones - At&T Corp.
NOMAD - Telescopes - Northern Telecom, Inc.
NOMAD - Tents - Coleman Co., Inc.
NOMAD - Toys–models ☆ - Estes Industries
NOMAD - Video games - Sega of America, Inc.
NOMAD PELLET-MATIC - Barbecues and grills - TSD Industries Inc.
NOMADE - Apparel and accessories - Hunza Inc.
NOMADIC - Office supplies - Nomadic Structures, Inc.
NOMADIC DISPLAY - Display cases–metal - Nomadic Structures, Inc.
NOMADS - Luggage - J.C. Penney Co., Inc.
NOMALOCK - Insulating materials - Nomaco Inc.
NOMANCO - Sporting goods - Nomanco Inc.
NOMAR - Erasers ☆ - Empire Berol USA
NOMAR - Hardware - Nomar Inc.
NOMAR - Hose pipes - Parker-Hannifin Corp.
NOMAR - Musical instruments ☆ - Kansas Music Co. Inc.
NOMASTYL - Moldings–plaster of paris - NMC Decoration Inc.
NOME - Brushes–paint - Corona Brushes Inc.
NOMELLE - Apparel and accessories - United Hosiery Corp.
NOMELLE - Yarn - E.I. Dupont de Nemours and Co.
NOMEM - Batteries - Lenmar Enterprises, Inc.
NOMETA - Pharmaceutical preparations - New Idea Chemical Co.
NOMEX - Apparel and accessories - Spray Sok Co. Inc.
NOMEX - Craft supplies - A. Meyers & Sons Corp.
NOMEX - Fabrics–felt - E.I. Dupont de Nemours and Co.
NOMEX OMEGA - Firefighting suits - E.I. Dupont de Nemours and Co.
NOMEX THERMACOLOR - Textile fibers - E.I. Dupont de Nemours and Co.
NOMIE - Christmas tree lights ☆ - Noma International, Inc.
NOMINEE - Steel springs–railroad - Needlecraft Industries
NOMINEE - Wines - Luneau USA, Inc.
NOMINETTE - Trimmings–fabric ☆ - Hollcar Trading Co.
NOMIS - Vegetables–canned - Furman Foods, Inc.
NOMIX - Cement - Nomix Corp.
NOMO-100 - Chemical preparations - Noco Co.
NOMOGRIP - Medical apparatus - Nomos Corp.
NOMONUTS - Key rings - Weerok Ranch
NOMOUSE - Computer software ☆ - Abacus Software, Inc.
NON-ADHERA - Bandages - American White Cross Laboratories
NON-CLIMB - Fencing–steel - Keystone Steel & Wire Co.
NON-FLAM - Adhesives and sealants - Imperial Adhesives Inc.
NON GLAS - Glass products ☆ - Hunt Manufacturing Co.
NON-LIFT - Manicure preparations - Customcraft Nails Inc.
NON LINEAR LOAD - Electrical equipment ☆ - Acme Electric Corp.
NON-METH - Paints - Grow Group, Inc.
N.O.N. NO OTHER NAME - Apparel and accessories - Lucretia Batten
NON NOBIS DOMINE, SED NOMINE TUO DA GLORIAM. - Wines - Sovereign
   Military Order of the Temple of Jerusalem, Inc.
NON-PARTICIPATING ATHLETE NPA - Slippers - Universal Footwear, Inc.
NON-REPRO - Pencils ☆ - Faber-Castell Corp.
NON-REQUIRED READING - Greeting cards - Recycled Paper Products, Inc.
NON SCENTS - Pet products - NSI Industries
NON SENSE - Napkins–paper ☆ - Pratt & Austin Co.
NON-SKID FLEX DECK - Floor coverings–carpet and rugs - Flex Deck Corp.
NON-SKUFF - Floor waxes - Uncle Sam Chemical Co., Inc.
NON SLIP LINE IT - Plastics - L & P Property Management Co.
NON STINK - Sporting goods - Wellington Leisure Products, Inc.
NON-STOP NACHO - Corn chips - Recot Inc.
NON STOP WARDROBE - Patterns–clothing - Mccall Pattern Co.
NON-STOP WOMAN - Patterns–clothing ☆ - Mccall Pattern Co.
NON-TAMP - Electrical equipment - Eagle Electric Manufacturing Co., Inc.
NONA MORELLI - Pasta - The Pasta Fresca Co. Inc.
NONAMIN - Pharmaceutical preparations - Western Research Laboratories
NONA'S - Pasta ☆ - Food City USA Inc.
NONCHALANCE - Underwear and nightwear - NCC Industries, Inc.

☆ = Now out of production

NONCHALANT - Apparel and accessories - Louis Barasch, Inc.
NONCO - Rope - Columbian Rope Co.
NONE-BETR - Doughnuts–mixes - L. Karp & Sons, Inc.
NONE FINER - Fencing–gates and posts - National Fence Corp.
NONE SUCH - Mincemeat - Borden, Inc.
NONEBETTER - Thread - Threads USA Div.
NONESUCH - Recording label - Warner Music International
NONEX - Glass products - Corning Inc.
NONG KHAI - Marinade - C.V. Finer Foods Inc.
NONHEX - Skin care products - Pettibone Laboratories Inc.
NONI - Vitamins and nutritional supplements - Matrix Health Products, Inc.
NONIN - Medical apparatus - Nonin Medical, Inc.
NONINI VINTNERS SELECT - Wines - A. Nonini Winery
NONION - Deodorizers - 5K Enterprises
NONNA D'S - Sauces - Victoria's Treasure Inc.
NONNA'S KITCHEN - Meat products–beef ☆ - Normark & Associates
NONNI'S - Bakery products - Nonni's, Corp.
NONO PMS - Beverages - Original Smoothie Co., Inc.
NONOVITES PLUS - Vitamins and nutritional supplements ☆ - Concord Chemists
NONPAREIL - Fabrics - A. Wimpfheimer & Brother Inc.
NONPAREIL - Fruits and vegetables - Nonpareil Processing Corp.
NONPAREIL - Sporting goods ☆ - Gared Sports, Inc.
NONPAREIL BOOKS - Publisher's imprints - David R. Godine Publisher Inc.
NONSCENTS - Candles ☆ - Carolina Designs Ltd.
NONSCENTS - Deodorizers - Krueger Enterprises
NONSPI - Deodorants–personal ☆ - Numark Laboratories Inc.
NONSTOP - Dialing devices–telephone - Baltimore Luggage Co.
NONY NEW YORK WEAR - Apparel and accessories - Nony New York
NOODLE LOOP - Door mats - Royal Rubber & Manufacturing Co.
NOODLE NEST - Soups–canned - Campbell Soup Co.
NOODLE-RONI - Food products ☆ - Golden Grain Co.
NOODLE TRIO - Pasta - Best Foods/Mueller Co.
NOODLES BY LEONARD - Noodles - Noodles by Leonardo Inc.
NOODLES-N-NUTS - Pet food - Judee K. Creations, Inc. (Crazy Corn Division)
NOODLES-N-NUTS - Pet products - Crazy Corn
NOODLES PLUS - Food products - Union Foods
NOODNIX - Apparel and accessories - Mary W. Wells
NOOK & CRANNY - Brooms - O-Cedar/Vining Household Products Co.
NOOKIES - Snack foods - Glenn Foods Inc.
NOON HOUR - Food products - Noon Hour Food Products
NOONAN'S - Meat products - Noonan's Specialties, Inc.
NOONDAY PRESS - Publisher's imprints - Farrar, Straus and Giroux Inc.
NOOOODLES - Plastics - Toner Plastics Inc.
NOPELTS - Apparel and accessories - Paws International Inc.
NOPILES - Vitamins and nutritional supplements ☆ - Pilex Corp.
NOPROFILE - Catheters - Meadox Medicals, Inc.
NOR - Playing cards ☆ - United States Playing Card Co.
NOR AM TECH - Detergents - Noramtech Corp.
NOR-CAL - Food products - Eureka Fisheries
NOR-GUARD - Doors–glass - Norandex, Inc.
NOR-LIEF - Pharmaceutical preparations ☆ - Vortech Pharmaceuticals
NOR-MIL - Pharmaceutical preparations ☆ - Vortech Pharmaceuticals
NOR-PRED S - Pharmaceutical preparations ☆ - Vortech Pharmaceuticals
NOR-PRED T.B.A. - Pharmaceutical preparations ☆ - Vortech Pharmaceuticals
NOR-QD - Pharmaceutical preparations - Syntex USA, Inc.
NOR-TET - Pharmaceutical preparations ☆ - Vortech Pharmaceuticals
NOR-TWIST - Hardware - Northwestern Steel and Wire Co.
NORA - Floor coverings - Nora Rubber Flooring
NORA - Glassware–household ☆ - Crisa Corp.
NORA - Rice - Connell Co.
NORA TOP SET - Floor coverings ☆ - Nora Rubber Flooring
NORADRYL - Pharmaceutical preparations ☆ - Vortech Pharmaceuticals
NORAFED - Pharmaceutical preparations ☆ - Vortech Pharmaceuticals
NORALAC - Pharmaceutical preparations ☆ - Vortech Pharmaceuticals
NORAM - Cleaning preparations ☆ - Emsco Inc.
NORAM - Clutches–industrial - North American Clutch Corp.
NORAMENT - Floor coverings - Nora Rubber Flooring
NORAMENT 925B DUO - Floor coverings ☆ - Nora Rubber Flooring
NORAMENT GRANO - Floor coverings ☆ - Nora Rubber Flooring
NORAMENT SPECIAL ESD CONTROL - Floor coverings - Nora Rubber Flooring
NORAMINIC - Pharmaceutical preparations ☆ - Vortech Pharmaceuticals
NORAND - Computer software - Norand Corp.
NORANDA - Doors–storm - Noranda Building Products Co.
BRANDEX - Building materials - Norandex, Inc.

NORAPLAN - Floor coverings - Nora Rubber Flooring
NORAPLAN DECO - Floor coverings ☆ - Nora Rubber Flooring
NORAPLAN DUO - Floor coverings ☆ - Nora Rubber Flooring
NORAPLAN ESD CONTROL - Floor coverings - Nora Rubber Flooring
NORATUSS II - Pharmaceutical preparations ☆ - Vortech Pharmaceuticals
NORBERT BELEER - Lighting fixtures - Lighting World Inc.
NORBEST - Turkeys - Norbest Inc.
NORBEST BARBEQUE DELITE - Meat products–poultry - Norbest Inc.
NORBEST TENDER-TIMED - Meat products–poultry - Norbest Inc.
NORBIDE - Dressing sticks - Norton Co.
NORBOOTS - Footwear–athletic - Norski of America Ltd.
NORCARE - Skin care products ☆ - Nortrade International, Inc.
NORCET - Analgesics ☆ - Abana Pharmaceuticals, Inc.
NOR'CLAD - Windows–storm - Norco Windows, Inc.
NORCO - Automotive parts and accessories - Norco Industries, Inc.
NORCO - Fruits and vegetables - Mike Norinsberg Manufacturing Inc.
NORCO - Pharmaceutical preparations - Watson Laboratories, Inc.
NORCOM - Cables–coaxial - Nordx/CDT-IP Corp.
NORCOM - Communications equipment–satellite - Norcom Networks Corp.
NORCOM NETWORKS CORPORATION - Communications equipment–satellite - Norcom Networks Corp.
NORCRAFT - Cabinets - Norcraft Companies Inc.
NORCRAFT - Fencing–wood ☆ - MacGillis and Gibbs Co.
NORCREST - Giftware ☆ - Norcrest China Co.
NORCROSS - Greeting cards - Norcross Inc.
NORCROSS KITTENS - Greeting cards - Norcross Inc.
NORCURON - Pharmaceutical preparations - Organon Inc.
NORD - Glassware–household ☆ - Knobler International Ltd.
NORD - Ships–sailing vessels - Nord Yachts
NORD HAVEN - Boats - Pacific Asian Enterprises Inc.
NORDA - Seafood products–fresh or frozen - Kreiner Imports
NORDAN - Seafood products–fresh or frozen - Gloucester Corp.
NORDANTIN - Pharmaceutical preparations - Norwich-Eaton Pharmaceuticals
NORDBAK - Paints ☆ - Rexnord Corp.
NORDCHOKLAD - Candy - Products-from-Sweden Inc.
NORDCO - Machinery - Nordco Inc.
NORDEL - Rubber–synthetic - E.I. Dupont de Nemours and Co.
NORDEN LABS - Pet products - SmithKline Beecham Animal Health Products
NORDETTE - Pharmaceutical preparations - Wyeth-Ayerst Laboratories
NORDEVCO - Puzzles - Nordevco, Inc.
NORDFEIL - Floor coverings–carpet and rugs - Marks International Oriental Rugs & Carpets
NORDIC - Boats–motor ☆ - Crestliner Boats Inc.
NORDIC - Breads ☆ - A.V. Olsson Trading Co., Inc.
NORDIC - Cabinets - American Woodmark Corp.
NORDIC - Cabinets - Triangle Pacific Corp. (Cabinet Division)
NORDIC - Doors–storm - Quik-Fab Aluminum Manufacturing Co. Inc.
NORDIC - Electronic equipment ☆ - Ercona Corp.
NORDIC - Flatware ☆ - Anacapa Corp.
NORDIC - Floor coverings–carpet and rugs - Regal Rugs Inc.
NORDIC - Floor coverings–carpet and rugs ☆ - Colonial Mills Inc.
NORDIC - Food products - Wally Sea Products Corp.
NORDIC - Frames–eyeglass - Nordic Eyewear Inc.
NORDIC - Fruits and vegetables - Northern Fruit Co.
NORDIC - Glassware–household - Federal Glass
NORDIC - Glassware–household - Svend Jensen of Denmark Inc.
NORDIC - Heating equipment - Mastex Industries, Inc.
NORDIC - Paper–coated - Unisource Brands, Inc.
NORDIC - Saunas - Cedarbrook Sauna Inc.
NORDIC - Seafood products–fresh or frozen - Nordic Fisheries
NORDIC - Ships–sailing vessels - Nordic Sailing Yachts Inc.
NORDIC - Sporting goods - Nordictrack, Inc.
NORDIC - Stoves - American Road Equipment Co.
NORDIC - Tape–adhesive - Malow Corp.
NORDIC - Tires - Stateside International Inc.
NORDIC - Waterproof outerwear - Seaway Importing Co.
NORDIC - Yarn ☆ - Caron International Inc.
NORDIC BLOCKS - Bedding–linen - Dan River Inc.
NORDIC CHALLENGE, THE - Educational materials - JM Perry Corp.
NORDIC FITNESS CHAIR - Sporting goods - Nordictrack, Inc.
NORDIC FLEECE - Apparel and accessories - Santana Ltd.
NORDIC FLOWERS - Bedding–linen - Dan River Inc.
NORDIC GEAR - Blankets - Nordic Gear Inc.
NORDIC GNOME - Apparel and accessories - Derrick Partnership
NORDIC GOLD - Sporting goods - Nordictrack, Inc.
NORDIC GOLD - Yarn - Rainbow Gallery, Inc.

NORDIC GRID - Mattresses - Paramount Industrial Companies Inc.
NORDIC MIDNIGHT - Glassware–household - Federal Glass
NORDIC MIST - Water–bottled or canned - Coca-Cola Co.
NORDIC MORN - Tableware–plastic ☆ - Washington Forge Inc.
NORDIC MYSTIQUE - Skin care products - Finn Imports
NORDIC OAK - Cabinets - Del Mar Cabinets
NORDIC PRINCE - Cutlery ☆ - Lifetime Hoan Corp.
NORDIC QUARRY - Floor coverings ☆ - Tarkett, Inc.
NORDIC SKY - Bedding–linen - Dan River Inc.
NORDIC SPA - Toiletries - Nordictrack, Inc.
NORDIC TRAIL - Boots and shoes - Track 'n Trail
NORDIC WARE - Cooking equipment–household - Nordic Ware
NORDIC XC - Exercising equipment - Icon Health & Fitness, Inc.
NORDICA - Door frames - Canyon Creek Cabinet Co.
NORDICA - Floor coverings–carpet and rugs - Karastan-Bigelow Inc.
NORDICA - Furniture - Thomasville Furniture Industries Inc.
NORDICA COLLECTION - Bedding–linen - Dan River Inc.
NORDICARE - Sporting goods - Nordictrack, Inc.
NORDICARE RESISTOR - Sporting goods - Nordictrack, Inc.
NORDICARE STRIDER - Sporting goods - Nordictrack, Inc.
NORDICFLEX - Sporting goods - Nordictrack, Inc.
NORDICFLEX GOLD - Sporting goods - Nordictrack, Inc.
NORDICGOLD - Sporting goods - Nordictrack, Inc.
NORDICPOWER - Sporting goods - Nordictrack, Inc.
NORDICPOWER PLUS - Sporting goods - Nordictrack, Inc.
NORDICPOWER PRO - Sporting goods - Nordictrack, Inc.
NORDICROW TBX - Sporting goods - Nordictrack, Inc.
NORDICSPORT - Sporting goods - Nordictrack, Inc.
NORDICTRACK - Sporting goods - Nordictrack, Inc.
NORDICTRACK 505 - Sporting goods - Nordictrack, Inc.
NORDICTRACK 900 - Exercising equipment - Nordictrack, Inc.
NORDICTRACK ADVENTURER - Exercising equipment - Nordictrack, Inc.
NORDICTRACK PRO - Sporting goods - Nordictrack, Inc.
NORDICTRACK PRO JR. - Exercising equipment - Nordictrack, Inc.
NORDIK - Finishing agents - Coronado Paint Co.
NORDIK-NIFE - Knives–carving - Deke-Ware Co.
NORDISK OF DENMARK - Health care products - Oakmont Investments Co.
NORDISKA MUSIKFORLAGET - Music–sheet - MMB Music Inc.
NORDQUEST - Apparel and accessories - Edward Sanders
NORDRYL - Pharmaceutical preparations ☆ - Vortech Pharmaceuticals
NORDSHIP - Ships–sailing vessels - Scandinavian Yachts
NORDSTAR WOOD FLOORING - Floor coverings - Pantim Wood Products
NORDSTROM BEST - Candy - Nordstrom, Inc.
NORDX/CDT - Cables–fiber optic - Cable Design Technologies, Inc.
NOREAST FRESH - Fruits and vegetables - Noreast Fresh, Inc.
NOR'EASTER - Gloves - Dakota Corp.
NOR'EASTER - Roofing materials–clay - GAF Corp.
NOREEN - Hair coloring preparations - L & F Consumer Products
NOREFMI - Pharmaceutical preparations ☆ - C.O. Truxton Inc.
NOREL - Cold remedies - U.S. Pharmaceutical Corp.
NOREL PLUS - Pharmaceutical preparations - U.S. Pharmaceutical Corp.
NORELCO - Dictating machines - Philips Business Systems Co.
NORELCO - Razors–electric - Philips Electronics North America Corp.
NORELCO POINT - Hair care products - Philips Electronics North America Corp.
NORELCO TRIPLEHEADER - Razors–electric - Philips Electronics North America Corp.
NORELL - Perfumes - Revlon Consumer Products Corp.
NORELL II - Perfumes - Revlon Consumer Products Corp.
NOREX - Pharmaceutical preparations - Scott Medical Products
NORFERAN - Pharmaceutical preparations ☆ - Vortech Pharmaceuticals
NORFIELD - Blankets–electric ☆ - Sunbeam-Oster Household Products
NORFIELD - Tools - Norfield Manufacturing Co.
NORFIELDS EQUINEBAND - Bandages - Norfields Corp.
NORFIELDS EQUINEHOCKWRAP - Horse bandages - Norfields Corp.
NORFIELDS EQUINEPAD - Bandages - Norfields Corp.
NORFIELDS EQUINEPATCH - Bandages - Norfields Corp.
NORFIELDS EQUINESTRIP - Bandages - Norfields Corp.
NORFIELDS EQUINEWRAP - Veterinary products - Norfields Corp.
NORFIN - Toy trolls - EFS Marketing Associates Inc.
NORFLEET - Apparel–men's - Donald Matthew Daley
NORFLEET HAWAII - Apparel and accessories - Donald Matthew Daley
NORFLEX - See **HART & COOLEY**
NORFLEX - Abrasive products - Norton Co.
NORFLEX - Health care products - Minnesota Mining & Manufacturing Co.
NORFOLK - Clocks - General Time Corp. (Westclox/Seth Thomas Div.)

NORFOLK DELIGHT - Beverages ☆ - Traditional Products Inc.
NORFOLK-INTERNATIONAL - Recording label - Rockmasters International
NORFOLKWIRE & ELECTRONICS - Computer peripheral equipment - Norfolk Wire & Electronics, Inc.
NORFORMS - Health care products - Procter & Gamble Co.
NORFRANIL - Pharmaceutical preparations ☆ - Vortech Pharmaceuticals
NORGANIC - Health care products - REVELATION LLC
NORGE - Hosiery ☆ - Wigwam Mills Inc.
NORGE - Kitchen appliances - Norge Co.
NORGE - Ovens–microwave ☆ - Maytag Corp.
NORGESIC - Health care products - Minnesota Mining & Manufacturing Co.
NORIA - Cosmetics - Noria, Inc.
NORIC - Pharmaceutical preparations - Lardon Laboratories
NORICA - Pencils ☆ - Staedtler, Inc.
NORIMAT - Projectors–photographic ☆ - Heitz Service Corp.
NORIMOOR CO. INC. - Skin care products - Norimoor Co.
NORINA BALLERINA - Toys–stuffed - Russ Berrie and Co., Inc.
NORINCO - Firearms, accessories, and parts - International Armament Corp.
NORINYL - Pharmaceutical preparations - Syntex USA, Inc.
NORIS-COLOR - Pens - Staedtler, Inc.
NORISC - Skin care products - FNC Medical Corp.
NORISODRINE AEROTROL - Pharmaceutical preparations - Abbott Laboratories
NORISODRINE SULFATE - Pharmaceutical preparations ☆ - Abbott Laboratories
NORITAKE - Dinnerware–glass - Noritake Co. Inc.
NORITRON - Pens ☆ - Staedtler, Inc.
NORIVITEL - Vitamins and nutritional supplements - Norimoor Co.
NORJAC - Housewares - Norjac Manufacturing Corp.
NORKA - Ordnance ☆ - B.F. Goodrich Co.
NORKON - Pharmaceutical preparations - Norkon Pharmacal Inc.
NORLAC - Vitamins and nutritional supplements ☆ - Solvay Pharmaceuticals Inc.
NORLAN - Cables–signal - Cable Design Technologies, Inc.
NORLANDER - Boats–skiffs ☆ - Nord Yachts
NORLESTRIN - Pharmaceutical preparations ☆ - Parke-Davis
NORLINE TRAFFIC MARKINGS - Paints - Morton International Traffic Markings
NORLUND - Axes - E-Z Sales & Manufacturing, Inc.
NORLUTATE - Pharmaceutical preparations ☆ - Parke-Davis
NORLUTIN - Pharmaceutical preparations ☆ - Parke-Davis
NORLUX - Enamels ☆ - Morton International Traffic Markings
NORMA - Ammunition ☆ - Federal Cartridge Co.
NORMA B - Shoes - Norma B Inc.
NORMA B SPORT - Shoes, boots, etc. - Norma B Inc.
NORMA KAMALI - Apparel and accessories - Norma Kamali, Inc.
NORMA KAMALI - Frames–eyeglass - Carrera Eyewear Corp.
NORMA KAMALI - Hosiery–women's - Camp Hosiery
NORMA KAMALI BEAUTY - Cosmetics - Norma Kamali, Inc.
NORMA VIRGIN - Cosmetics - Beauty for All Seasons Inc.
NORMA WORK DRIVE - Hoses ☆ - CRP Industries, Inc.
NORMACID - Pharmaceutical preparations ☆ - Zeneca Inc.
NORMADERM - Skin care products ☆ - Doak Dermatologics
NORMAG - Motors–hydraulic - Northern Magnetics Inc.
NORMAL-AID - Computer software - SourceView Software International
NORMAL PEOPLE - Greeting cards ☆ - Kersten Bros. Studios
NORMALAID - Vitamins and nutritional supplements - Home Health Products, Inc.
NORMALINE - Pharmaceutical preparations - Apothecary Products, Inc.
NORMALIPID - Pharmaceutical preparations ☆ - Edom Laboratories Inc.
NORMAN - Binders - Dennison National Co.
NORMAN - Cosmetics - Merle Norman Cosmetics
NORMAN - Kilns - Kiln Supply & Service Corp.
NORMAN - Mops ☆ - Helen Keller Services for the Blind
NORMAN BAER I - Wallpaper - Norman/Baer Associates
NORMAN BATES - Furniture ☆ - Hon Co.
NORMAN LABS - Audio equipment - Norman Laboratories Inc.
NORMAN LURES - Fishing lures - Howe Now Inc.
NORMAN PERRY - Lamps - Norman Perry Co.
NORMAN ROCKWELL - Figurines - Dave Grossman Creations Inc.
NORMAN ROCKWELL - Figurines ☆ - Goebel of North America
NORMAN ROCKWELL - Furniture - Stanley Furniture Co. Inc.
NORMAN ROCKWELL - Postcards ☆ - Classico San Francisco Inc.
NORMAN ROCKWELL CLASSICS - Puzzles ☆ - Parker Brothers
NORMAN S. GUTERMAN - Jewelry - Norman S. Guterman
NORMAN VANCE - Apparel and accessories ☆ - Edison Brothers Stores, Inc.

☆ = Now out of production

NORMANDI - Wallpaper ✩ - Wolf-Gordon Inc.
NORMANDIE - Cabinets - American Woodmark Corp.
NORMANDIE - Chocolate candy - Normandie Chocolate Ltd.
NORMANDIE - Furniture ✩ - Bassett Furniture Industries, Inc.
NORMANDIE - Furniture ✩ - Tropitone Furniture Co. Inc.
NORMANDIE - Tiles–ceramic ✩ - Metropolitan Ceramics
NORMANDIE - Wallcovering - Fashon Wallcoverings
NORMANDIE CLASSIC FRENCH - Wallcovering ✩ - Fashon Wallcoverings
NORMANDIE CRUISLINER - Chocolate candy - Normandie Chocolate Ltd.
NORMANDIE 'NACHE - Chocolate candy - Normandie Chocolate Ltd.
NORMANDY - Boats - McKenzie Boat Manufacturing Co.
NORMANDY - Cabinets - Markus Cabinet Manufacturing Co.
NORMANDY - Cabinets - Schrock
NORMANDY - Cabinets ✩ - Yorktowne Inc.
NORMANDY - Dinnerware and counter saver ✩ - Corning Inc.
NORMANDY - Dishes–china - Viletta China Co.
NORMANDY - Dishes–china ✩ - WMF/USA
NORMANDY - Eyeglasses - Willson/Dalloz Safety
NORMANDY - Floor coverings–carpet and rugs - Hartford Carpet Mills
NORMANDY - Furniture ✩ - Bassett Furniture Industries, Inc.
NORMANDY - Furniture ✩ - Hammary Furniture Co. Inc.
NORMANDY - Furniture ✩ - Hooker Furniture Corp.
NORMANDY - Furniture–upholstered - Maharam Vertical Surfaces
NORMANDY - Jewelry - Samuel Kamsly Inc.
NORMANDY - Musical instruments - G. Leblanc Corp.
NORMANDY - Occasional tables ✩ - JDI Group, Inc.
NORMANDY - Silverware - Imperial Schrade Corp.
NORMANDY - Thread ✩ - United Thread Mills Corp.
NORMANDY - Trailers–travel ✩ - Coachmen Industries, Inc.
NORMANDY - Trailers–travel ✩ - Shasta Industries Inc.
NORMANDY - Vases - Crisa Corp.
NORMANDY COLLECTION - Furniture ✩ - Southern Furniture Co. of Conover
NORMANDY FARMS - Snack foods - Art Hendley Sales & Marketing Inc.
NORMANDY GUMS - Candy ✩ - Maillard Corp.
NORMANDY LINEN - Yarn - Henry's Attic
NORMANDY MANOR - Furniture ✩ - Hooker Furniture Corp.
NORMANDY PLAZQUE - Frames–picture ✩ - Sureguard, Inc.
NORMAN'S - Food products - Norman Inc.
NORMAN'S OF SALISBURY - Window coverings - Norman's of Salisbury
NORMARK - Sporting goods - Normark Corp.
NORMATANE - Pharmaceutical preparations ✩ - Vortech Pharmaceuticals
NORMAX - Abrasive products - Norton Co.
NORMIFLO - Pharmaceuticals - American Home Food Products Inc.
NORMIN - Pharmaceutical preparations - Deleon Laboratories Inc.
NORMLSHIELD - Pharmaceutical preparations - MPM Medical, Inc.
NORMODYNE - Pharmaceutical preparations - Schering-Plough Healthcare Products
NORMOFORM - Pharmaceutical preparations - G.O. Spanner Inc.
NORMOL - Ophthalmic goods ✩ - Alcon Laboratories, Inc.
NORMOLAX - Pharmaceutical preparations - Boehringer Ingelheim Pharmaceuticals Inc.
NORMOSAN - Pharmaceutical preparations - Herb Products Co.
NORMOZIDE - Pharmaceutical preparations - Schering-Plough Healthcare Products
NORO - Yarn - Knitting Fever Inc.
NOROCAINE - Pharmaceutical preparations ✩ - Vortech Pharmaceuticals
NOROTEK - Perfumes - Lumi-Lite Candle Co. Inc.
NOROXIN - Pharmaceutical preparations - Merck & Co., Inc. (Merck Research Laboratories)
NORPAC - Lumber - North Pacific Lumber Co.
NORPAC - Vegetables–canned - Norpac Services, Inc.
NORPACE - Pharmaceutical preparations - G. D. Searle & Co.
NORPACE CR - Pharmaceutical preparations - G. D. Searle & Co.
NORPANTH - Pharmaceutical preparations ✩ - Vortech Pharmaceuticals
NORPHYL - Pharmaceutical preparations - Vita Elixir Co. Inc.
NORPINE - Sporting goods - Jarvinen USA
NORPLANT - Pharmaceutical preparations - Wyeth-Ayerst Laboratories
NORPLANT SYSTEM - Contraceptives - Population Council, Inc.
NORPRAMIN - Pharmaceutical preparations - Marion Merrell Dow
NORRE - Glassware–household - Dansk International Designs, Ltd.
NORRELL - Employment agencies–temporary help - Norrell Corp.
NORREN'S - Cabinets - Norren Manufacturing Inc.
NORRGREVE - Cheese - A.V. Olsson Trading Co., Inc.
NORRHOIDS - Pharmaceutical preparations - Pan American Laboratory, Inc.
NORRIS - Milk ✩ - Land O' Lakes, Inc. (Fluid Dairy Division)
NORRIS - Plumbing fixtures–metal ✩ - Mansfield Plumbing Products, Inc.

NORRIS - Shirts ✩ - Umbro USA
NORRIS CASUALS - Apparel and accessories ✩ - Umbro USA
NORRUTH MUSIC - Music–sheet - MMB Music Inc.
NORSE - Fish–canned or cured - B. Westergaard & Co. Inc.
NORSE BY NORSEWEST - Computer software - Interplay Productions
NORSE MAN - Snuff ✩ - Swedish Math North America Inc.
NORSE-NET - Apparel and accessories ✩ - Duofold Inc.
NORSE PEARL - Fish–canned or cured - B. Westergaard & Co. Inc.
NORSEA - Seafood products–fresh or frozen - Iceland Seafood Corp.
NOR'SEA - Ships–sailing vessels - Nor'sea Marine
NORSEMAN - Bicycles - Ross Bicycles USA, Ltd.
NORSEMAN - Boats–motor ✩ - Crestliner Boats Inc.
NORSEMAN - Footwear–athletic ✩ - Seaway Importing Co.
NORSEMAN - Motors–outboard ✩ - Outboard Marine Corp.
NORSEMAN - Musical instrument accessories - Viking Cases
NORSEMAN - Ships–sailing vessels - Loos and Co. Inc.
NORSEMAN - Tires - Armtec Industries Inc.
NORSET - Apparel and accessories - Champion Products Inc.
NORSHIELD - Doors–metal - W.S.A., Inc.
NORSK - Air purification systems - Medo Industries, Inc.
NORSK - Beverages–malt - Heaven Hill Distilleries, Inc.
NORSK-DISK - Recording label - Lindberg Records
NORSK MUSIKFORLAG - Music–sheet - MMB Music Inc.
NORSKE - Skin care products - Norske Product Development Corp.
NORSKE II - Fishing lures ✩ - Triple Teazer Co.
NORSKOLORS - Enameled ware - Norwegian Silver Corp.
NORSTAR - Airplane parts - Nordam
NORT - Apparel–athletic ✩ - Regina Imports
NORTAC - Bicycles - Nova Cycles Inc.
NORTELLE - Bedding–linen - Dan River Inc.
NORTEX - Apparel–men's - Arnav Industries Inc.
NORTEX - Office supplies - Potlatch Corp.
NORTH - Apparel and accessories - Nordstrom, Inc.
NORTH - Cement - Centex Corp.
NORTH - Cleaning preparations - Hastings Plastics Co.
NORTH - First aid kits - Rockford Medical & Safety Co.
NORTH - Sporting goods ✩ - Nelson Paint Co., Inc.
NORTH 40 - Beef - Cattleman's Inc.
NORTH ALABAMA LIONS - Apparel and accessories - University of North Alabama Board of Trustees
NORTH AMERICA - Belts–apparel - S.C. Import & Export Ltd.
NORTH AMERICAN - Doors–wood - Wayne-Dalton Corp.
NORTH AMERICAN - Flooring–hardwood - North American Hardwood Flooring
NORTH AMERICAN - Fruits–canned - Aslesen Co.
NORTH AMERICAN - Honey - Sioux Honey Association
NORTH AMERICAN - Salad dressings–bottled - Hudson Industries, Inc.
NORTH AMERICAN - Sporting goods - Henri Salaun Sports Inc.
NORTH AMERICAN - Telescopes - North American Foreign Trading Corp.
NORTH AMERICAN ANGLER VIDEO ADVENTURE - Video production - North American Outdoor Group, Inc.
NORTH AMERICAN ARMS - Firearms, accessories, and parts - North American Arms, Inc.
NORTH AMERICAN BEDDING COMPANY - Mattresses - Ohio Mattress Co.
NORTH AMERICAN BIOTECHNOLOGY DIRECTORY - Publisher's imprints - International Exhibitions, Inc.
NORTH AMERICAN BOWHUNTER - Apparel and accessories - Image Marketing Alternatives
NORTH AMERICAN CERAMIC PRODUCTS - Adhesives and sealants - Color Tile, Inc.
NORTH AMERICAN CHALLENGE - Men's apparel - Melville Corp.
NORTH AMERICAN HUNTING ODYSSEY VIDEO COLLECTION - Video production - North American Outdoor Group, Inc.
NORTH AMERICAN ORIGINAL - Food products - John W. Taylor Packing Co. Inc.
NORTH AMERICAN PHARMACAL - Pharmaceutical preparations ✩ - Vortech Pharmaceuticals
NORTH AMERICAN RECIPE - Pie crusts - Philchic, Inc.
NORTH AMERICAN RECREATION - Pool tables - Sport Supply Group, Inc.
NORTH AMERICAN SAFE PET - Pet products - Safe Pet USA
NORTH AMERICAN SPORTSWEAR PORSHA - Apparel and accessories - Winer Industries Inc.
NORTH AMERICAN WILD BIRD - Bird feeds - Pine Tree Farms, Inc.
NORTH AMERICAN WILDLIFE - Figurines ✩ - Goebel of North America
NORTH & JUDD - Hardware - Sea Spike Marine Supply Co. Inc.
NORTH & SOUTH - Video games - Data East USA Inc.

NORTH ATLANTIC - Fish–fresh or frozen - North Atlantic Fish Co.

NORTH ATLANTIC CONVOY RAIDER - Games ✩ - Avalon Hill Game Co.

NORTH ATLANTIC FISHERIES - Seafood products–fresh or frozen - Prelude Corp.

NORTH BAY - Floor coverings–carpet and rugs - Gulistan Carpet Inc.

NORTH BAY PRODUCE - Fruits and vegetables - North Bay Produce, Inc.

NORTH BEACH - Leather and sheep-lined clothing - North Beach Leather International Inc.

NORTH BRANCH - Paper–construction - Cascade School Supplies

NORTH BY NORTHEAST - Apparel and accessories - North By Northeast

NORTH CAPE - Seafood products–canned or cured - Frionor USA Inc.

NORTH CAROLINA CENTRAL UNIVERSITY - Stationery - North Carolina Central University

NORTH CAROLINA MOTOR SPEEDWAY - Apparel and accessories - North Carolina Motor Speedway, Inc.

NORTH CASTLE - Crackers - Norseland Foods Inc.

NORTH COAST - Fruit drinks–bottled or canned - Manzana Products Co. Inc.

NORTH COAST - Seafood products–fresh or frozen - North Coast Sea-Foods Corp.

NORTH COAST CARDS - Greeting cards - American Greetings Corp.

NORTH COAST CELLARS - Wines - The Beverage Source Inc.

NORTH COAST CELLARS - Wines - Fred Bofird Co.

NORTH COAST CLOTHING CO. - Apparel and accessories - Tony Marterie & Associates

NORTH COAST JAZZ - Recording label - Jazz Composer's Orchestra Association Inc.

NORTH COAST ROCKETRY - Toys–models - Estes Industries

NORTH COLLINS - Meat products–poultry - Nathan Schweitzer & Co.

NORTH COUNTRY - Food products - Butler Trading Co. Inc.

NORTH COUNTRY - Pancakes–mixes ✩ - ConAgra Grain Co.

NORTH COUNTRY - Water–mineral - North Country Natural Spring Water

NORTH COUNTRY BOTANICALS - Spices and extracts ✩ - North Country Botanicals, Ltd.

NORTH COUNTRY FARMS - Chicken - Gold'n Plump Poultry, Inc.

NORTH COUNTY CLASSICS - Luggage - New England Leather Accessories

NORTH DAKOTA MILLS - Food products - Semple Co.

NORTH DAKOTA STATE UNIVERSITY OF AGRICULTURE AND APPLIED SCIENCE 1890-1990 - Playing cards - North Dakota State University of Agriculture and Applied Science

NORTH EAST - Ships–sailing vessels ✩ - A. Le Comte Co. Inc.

NORTH END CLASSICS - Spaghetti sauces - Cains Foods, Inc.

NORTH FACE - Apparel–athletic - North Face

NORTH FORK NOUVEAU BLANC - Wines - Osprey's Dominion Vineyards, Ltd.

NORTH FORK NOUVEAU ROUGE - Wines - Osprey's Dominion Vineyards, Ltd.

NORTH GLOVES - Gloves–rubber - Rockford Medical & Safety Co.

NORTH HILL COLLECTION - Greeting cards ✩ - Stevenson Industries Inc.

NORTH HILLS - Fruits and vegetables - Cascade Fruit Co.

NORTH HILLS - Furniture ✩ - Bassett Furniture Industries, Inc.

NORTH HILLS - Wallpaper - Lawrence Wallcoverings

NORTH IDAHO ENERGY LOGS - Fireplace logs–treated - North Idaho Energy Logs, Inc.

NORTH LIGHT - Bicycles - Columbia Manufacturing Inc.

NORTH MARKET - Kitchen utensils–aluminum - Wilton Industries, Inc.

NORTH PACIFIC - Toys–airplanes - North Pacific Products Inc.

NORTH PACIFIC SEAFOODS - Salmon–smoked, salted, dried, or pickled - North Pacific Seafoods

NORTH PASS - Footwear–men's - JBI, Inc.

NORTH PEAK - Apparel–men's - C.J. Two Brothers, Inc.

NORTH PENN - Candy ✩ - L.C. Good Candy Co. Inc.

NORTH POLE - Ice cream - Reinhold Ice Cream

NORTH POLE - Ice cream - Taylor All Star Dairy

NORTH POLE CRITTER CO. - Toys–stuffed ✩ - Spearhead Industries Inc.

NORTH POLE GREETINGS - Greeting cards - Bradford Novelty Co., Inc.

NORTH POLE HOTLINE - Toy telephone - Trendmasters, Inc.

NORTH POLE INDUSTRIES - Watches - Fada Industries Inc.

NORTH POLE SERIES - Figurines - Department 56 Inc.

NORTH POLE TAE KWON DO BLEDSAW MARTIAL ARTS ACADEMIES - Badges–uniform - Marcus L. Bledsaw

NORTH POLE VILLAGE - Figurines ✩ - Enesco Corp.

NORTH POLES - Cookies - Mother's Cake & Cookie Co.

NORTH RANGE - Bags–duffel - Pacific Market, Inc.

NORTH RESPIRATORY - Pharmaceutical preparations - Rockford Medical & Safety Co.

NORTH RIVER - Apparel and accessories - Foria International, Inc.

NORTH RIVER - Furniture - H.W. Hull & Sons Inc.

NORTH SAILS - Leather goods - North Sails Group, Inc.

NORTH SALEM GALLERY - Statuary - North Salem Gallery Ltd.

NORTH SALEM VINEYARD - Wines - North Salem Vineyard Inc.

NORTH SEA - Waterproof outerwear ✩ - Helly-Hansen Inc.

NORTH SHORE - Fabrics - Valley Forge Fabrics Inc.

NORTH SHORE - Floor coverings–carpet and rugs - Galaxy Carpet Mills Inc.

NORTH SHORE - Floor coverings–carpet and rugs - Philadelphia Carpets

NORTH SHORE - Floor coverings–carpet and rugs ✩ - Catalina Carpet Mills Inc.

NORTH SHORE NATIVE - Shirts - Design Tees Hawaii Inc.

NORTH SHORE SUNRISE - Water–bottled or canned - Upper Ridge, Inc.

NORTH SHORE UNDERGROUND HAWAII - Apparel and accessories - N.S.U. North Shore Underground Corp.

NORTH SOUND CELLARS - Wine - Brown & Cole, Inc.

NORTH STAR - Beverages–malt - Cold Spring Brewing Co.

NORTH STAR - Bicycles - Roland Distributing

NORTH STAR - Blankets - Chatham Manufacturing Co.

NORTH STAR - Cigarettes - R.J. Reynolds Tobacco Co.

NORTH STAR - Compasses–magnetic ✩ - Sherrill Corp.

NORTH STAR - Dairy products - Mid-America Dairymen Inc. Southern Div.

NORTH STAR - Envelopes–paper ✩ - Smead Manufacturing Co.

NORTH STAR - Finishing agents - Hillyard Enterprises, Inc.

NORTH STAR - Floor coverings–carpet and rugs - Southern Carpet Mills

NORTH STAR - Floor coverings–carpet and rugs ✩ - Galaxy Carpet Mills Inc.

NORTH STAR - Food products - Corvallis Packing Co.

NORTH STAR - Food products - North Star Foods Inc.

NORTH STAR - Food products - Topline Foods Inc.

NORTH STAR - Ice cream - Ice Cream Specialties Inc.

NORTH STAR - Oils–lubricating - Citgo Petroleum Corp.

NORTH STAR - Recording label - Starman Records

NORTH STAR - Rings–jewelry - Artcarved Inc.

NORTH STAR - Shoes - Desa Shoe Co. Inc.

NORTH STAR - Steel products - S-B Manufacturing Co. Ltd.

NORTH STAR ADVANTAGE - Computers–personal - Northstar

NORTH STAR DIMENSION - Computers–personal - Northstar

NORTH STAR FARMS - Meat products–beef - North Star Foods Inc.

NORTH STAR HORIZON - Computers–personal - Northstar

NORTH STATES - Infant product - North States Industries Inc.

NORTH WALES - Crocheted and knitted items - Gillman Knitwear Co.

NORTH WEST BLUE - Apparel and accessories - Montgomery Ward & Co. Inc.

NORTH WIND - Handles–wood - Hartwell Brothers Handle Co.

NORTH WIND BOOKS - Publisher's imprints - Harold Shaw Publishers

NORTH WOODS - Bicycles - North Woods Performance Bikes, Inc.

NORTH WOODS - Fruits and vegetables ✩ - Walnut Acres Inc.

NORTH WOODS TRAILBLAZER - Toys - Fisher-Price, Inc.

NORTHAMPTON MEDICAL INC. - Health care products - Northampton Medical, Inc.

NORTHANE - Varnishes ✩ - Morton International Traffic Markings

NORTHBILT - Waterproof outerwear - Gordon & Ferguson of Delaware, Inc.

NORTHBROOK - Floor coverings–carpet and rugs ✩ - Karastan-Bigelow Inc.

NORTHBROOK - Lamps - Stiffel Co.

NORTHBROOK - Playing cards ✩ - United States Playing Card Co.

NORTHBROOK - Wallpaper - Shelbourne Wallcoverings

NORTHBROOK COURT - Wallpaper - Shelbourne Wallcoverings

NORTHBROOK PRINTS - Fabrics–tapestry - Comark Wallcoverings

NORTHBURY - Clocks ✩ - General Time Corp. (Westclox/Seth Thomas Div.)

NORTHCOLITE - Paints - North Jersey Paint Co. Inc.

NORTHCOTE BOOKS - Publisher's imprints - Harold Shaw Publishers

NORTHCREST - Apparel and accessories - Shopko Stores, Inc.

NORTHEAST - Ships–sailing vessels - Cabo Rico Yachts Inc.

NORTHEAST HARBOR - Soups–canned - New Atlantic Foods Ltd. Partnership

NORTHEAST KNITTING - Sweaters - Northeast Knitting Mills Inc.

NORTHEAST OUTFITTERS - Apparel and accessories - Dick's Clothing & Sporting Goods, Inc.

NORTHEAST TIME - Watches - SKL Co. Inc.

NORTHEAST VINEYARD - Wines - Northeast Vineyard

NORTHEASTERN - Fruits–frozen ✩ - Agvest, Inc. (Northeastern Packing Div.)

NORTHEASTERN - Recording label - Northeastern Records

NORTHEASTERN - Sawdust - Northeastern Products Corp.

NORTHEASTERN CLASSICS - Publisher's imprints - Northeastern University Press

NORTHEN LIGHTS - Toys ✩ - B & N Companies, Inc.

NORTHERN - Beverages–malt - Cold Spring Brewing Co.

✩ = Now out of production

NORTHERN - Flooring–hardwood - Maple Flooring Manufacturers Association, Inc.

NORTHERN - Health care products - Sunbeam-Oster Household Products

NORTHERN - Manufactured homes - Northern Homes Inc.

NORTHERN - Tissues and towels - James River Corp.

NORTHERN - Trailers–travel - Custom Trailers Ltd.

NORTHERN - Wet suits–rubber - Parkway Systems

NORTHERN BACKYARD - Bird feeds - Petco Pet Food & Supplies

NORTHERN BRIGHTS - Paper–bond - Badger Paper Mills, Inc.

NORTHERN CHEF - Sauces - Tai Foong USA Inc.

NORTHERN COMFORT - Syrup - American Maple Products Corp.

NORTHERN COVE - Chowders–canned - Quality Food Centers, Inc.

NORTHERN DELIGHTS - Food products - Northern Delights, Inc.

NORTHERN DESIGN BY QUEST - Tents - Jinwoong Inc.

NORTHERN EXPLORER - Apparel and accessories - Elder-Beerman Stores Corp.

NORTHERN EXPOSURE - Floor coverings–tile - Interface, Inc.

NORTHERN EXPOSURE - Flowers, plants, and seeds - W. Atlee Burpee and Co.

NORTHERN EXPOSURE - Ski apparel - Inside Edge

NORTHERN FOREST - Trees–artificial - Bradford Novelty Co., Inc.

NORTHERN GLACIER - Water–bottled or canned - Taormina Foods & Beverages

NORTHERN ISLES - Apparel and accessories - Goodman Knitting Co. Inc.

NORTHERN ISLES - Apparel and accessories - Kellwood Co.

NORTHERN ISLES II - Apparel and accessories - Kellwood Co.

NORTHERN ITALIAN - Bathroom fixtures - Kohler Co.

NORTHERN KING - Seafood products–fresh or frozen - Tai Foong USA Inc.

NORTHERN LIGHT - Boats–canoes - Old Town Canoe Co.

NORTHERN LIGHT - Furniture - Gardener's Supply Co.

NORTHERN LIGHT - Rings–jewelry - Artcarved Inc.

NORTHERN LIGHT - Whiskey - Hiram Walker & Sons, Inc.

NORTHERN LIGHTS - Bedding–linen - Dan River Inc.

NORTHERN LIGHTS - Beverages–malt - James Page Brewing Co., LLC

NORTHERN LIGHTS - Christmas tree ornaments - Cracker Box Inc.

NORTHERN LIGHTS - Floor coverings–carpet and rugs - Bellbridge Carpets

NORTHERN LIGHTS - Floor coverings–carpet and rugs - Couristan Inc.

NORTHERN LIGHTS - Floor coverings–carpet and rugs - Quaker Inc.

NORTHERN LIGHTS - Floor coverings–carpet and rugs - Regal Rugs Inc.

NORTHERN LIGHTS - Housewares - Bammental Wallcoverings Inc.

NORTHERN LIGHTS - Liquors - Canandaigua Wine Co. Inc.

NORTHERN LIGHTS - Pillows - Pacific Coast Feather Co.

NORTHERN LIGHTS - Sleeping bags - Northern Lights, Inc.

NORTHERN LIGHTS - Sunglasses ✩ - Bolle' America, Inc.

NORTHERN LIGHTS - Tableware–china ✩ - Lenox, Inc.

NORTHERN LIGHTS - Toilets–enameled - Kohler Co.

NORTHERN LIGHTS - Vegetables–canned - Olivia Canning Co.

NORTHERN LIGHTS - Yogurt - Golden Swirl

NORTHERN LITES - Beverages - Triax, Inc.

NORTHERN LITES - Pancakes–mixes - Homestead Mills

NORTHERN LITES - Popcorn - Old Dutch Foods, Inc.

NORTHERN LITES - Seafood products–canned or cured - Alaskan Harvest

NORTHERN LITES - Shovels - Emsco Inc.

NORTHERN LITES - Windows - M.S.E. Investment Group, Inc.

NORTHERN MAID - Horseradish - Fisher Food Products

NORTHERN MAPLE - Floor coverings - Anderson Hardwood Floors Inc.

NORTHERN MICHIGAN UNIVERSITY - Apparel and accessories - Northern Michigan University

NORTHERN MYSTIC - Apparel and accessories - Mystic Lane America Inc.

NORTHERN NECTAR - Food products - Euro-Can Products, Inc.

NORTHERN NIGHTS - Pillows - Pacific Coast Feather Co.

NORTHERN OUTFITTERS - Apparel and accessories - Katharyn Gonzales, Inc.

NORTHERN PENINSULA - Footwear - Kobacker Co.

NORTHERN PLAINS - Beverages–malt - The Stroh Brewery Co.

NORTHERN PLAINS - Food products ✩ - Sleepy Eye Foods

NORTHERN PRESERVE - Food products - Harbour Foods, Ltd.

NORTHERN PRIDE - Salmon–smoked, salted, dried, or pickled - Wards Cove Packing Co.

NORTHERN QUEEN - Seafood products–fresh or frozen ✩ - Arctic King Trading Corp.

NORTHERN REFLECTIONS - Apparel - Northern Reflections

NORTHERN REFRIGERATOR - Refrigerators - Northern Refrigerator Co.

NORTHERN RIDGE - Bicycles - Dynacraft Industries Inc.

NORTHERN ROCKIES NUTRITION - Vitamins and nutritional supplements - Montana Naturals Int'l. Inc.

NORTHERN RUGGED - Gloves - Fabry Glove & Mitten Co.

NORTHERN SEA - Flatware - Washington Forge Inc.

NORTHERN SKY - Bedding–linen ✩ - Dan River Inc.

NORTHERN STAR - Food products - Northern Star Co.

NORTHERN STAR - Office supplies - Light Opera Studios Inc.

NORTHERN STAR - Seafood products–fresh or frozen ✩ - Wilbur-Ellis Co.

NORTHERN STAR GAME - Pharmaceutical preparations - Trailer Craft

NORTHERN STATES - Food products - Conagra, Inc.

NORTHERN STRETCH FLEECE - Apparel and accessories - Norm Thompson Outfitters, Inc.

NORTHERN TELECOM - Telescopes - Northern Telecom, Inc.

NORTHERN TRAILS - Shoes - MSF Corp.

NORTHERN TREAT - Fruits and vegetables - Per-Clin Orchards Inc.

NORTHERN VALLEY - Fruits and vegetables - Magi Inc.

NORTHERN WHITE CEDAR - Log cabins–prefabricated - Ward Log Homes

NORTHERN WIND'S OCEAN REQUESTS - Seafood products–fresh or frozen - Northern Wind, Inc.

NORTHERN WOODS - Furniture - Zenith Products Corp.

NORTHERNAIRE - Apparel and accessories - Buster Brown Apparel Inc.

NORTHERNAIRE - Fans–electric ✩ - Sunbeam-Oster Household Products

NORTHERNER - Boots - Servus Footwear Co.

NORTHFIELD - Apparel and accessories ✩ - Kellwood Co.

NORTHFIELD - Cabinets - American Woodmark Corp.

NORTHFIELD - Conveyors - York International Corp.

NORTHFIELD - Floor coverings–carpet and rugs - Gulistan Carpet Inc.

NORTHFIELD - Furniture ✩ - Bassett Furniture Industries, Inc.

NORTHFIELD - Looms - Northfield Loom

NORTHFIELD TRADING - Apparel and accessories - B.W. Harris Manufacturing Co.

NORTHFIRE - Trees - Bailey Nurseries, Inc.

NORTHGATE - Furniture ✩ - Athens Furniture Industries Inc.

NORTHGLEN - Floor coverings–carpet and rugs ✩ - Olympic Carpets Inc.

NORTHIA - Lubricating oils ✩ - Shell Oil Co.

NORTHLAKE - Boots - Georgia Boot Inc.

NORTHLAND - Air purification systems ✩ - Medo Industries, Inc.

NORTHLAND - Antifreeze - Northland Products Co.

NORTHLAND - Fireplace logs–treated - Conros Corp.

NORTHLAND - Flatware - Oneida Ltd.

NORTHLAND - Flowers, plants, and seeds - NK Lawn & Garden Co.

NORTHLAND - Food products - M.A. Gedney Co.

NORTHLAND - Food products - Northland Frozen Foods Inc.

NORTHLAND - Hockey equipment - Christian Brothers, Inc.

NORTHLAND - Hockey equipment - Life Industries Inc.

NORTHLAND - Juices - Northland Cranberries Inc.

NORTHLAND - Seafood products–canned or cured - Maloney Seafood Corp.

NORTHLAND CRANBERRIES - Fruits and vegetables - Northland Cranberries Inc.

NORTHLAND EXPRESS - Toys–trains - Mattel, Inc.

NORTHLAND PRESS - Publisher's imprints - Northland Publishing

NORTHLINE - Toilets–enameled - Kohler Co.

NORTHMAN - Snowblowers - Northman Snowplows

NORTHMAN NOTES - Greeting cards - Northman Co.

NORTHPAW - Firearms, accessories, and parts - Texas Longhorn Arms, Inc.

NORTHPLAINS - Cabinets - Fieldstone Cabinetry

NORTHPOINT - Apparel–women's - Robi-Lou Ltd.

NORTHRIDGE - Floor coverings–carpet and rugs - Burlington House Carpets

NORTHRIDGE - Furniture ✩ - Landes Manufacturing Co.

NORTHRIDGE VALVE - Valves–industrial - Seismic Safety Products, Inc.

NORTHROP GRUMMAN - Aircraft - Northrop Corp.

NORTHROP OASYS - Electronic equipment - Northrop Corp.

NORTHRUP KING - Flowers, plants, and seeds - NK Lawn & Garden Co.

NORTHSHORE - Siding–metal - Reynolds Metals Co.

NORTHSHORE COFFEE ROASTERS - Coffee - Dan T. Davis

NORTHSIDE BRAND - Meat products - M & V Provisions

NORTHSPECK CARTS - Sporting goods - Northspeck Carts

NORTHSTAR - Doors–glass - Jeld-Wen, Inc.

NORTHSTAR - Radios - Wireless Marketing Corp.

NORTHSTAR - Truck campers - R.C. Willett Co. Inc.

NORTHSTAR - Water purification systems - Ecowater Systems, Inc.

NORTHSTAR INDUSTRIES - Air conditioning equipment - Northstar Industries, Inc.

NORTHSTAR LEGAL TRUST ACCOUNTING SYSTEM - Computer software - Northstar Business Solutions, Inc.

NORTHVIEW - Cheese - Northfield Foods Inc.

NORTHWAY - Cabinets ✩ - Universal-Rundle Corp.

NORTHWEAR - Apparel–men's - Nordstrom, Inc.

NORTHWEST - Bedspreads - Layton Home Fashions
NORTHWEST - Envelopes ☆ - Western States Envelope Co.
NORTHWEST - Floor coverings–tile - Quarry Tile Co.
NORTHWEST - Paper - Northwest Blueprint and Supply
NORTHWEST - Pizzas–frozen - Pietro's Corp.
NORTHWEST - Rice - Grey Owl Foods
NORTHWEST BEANPOT - Baked beans–canned - Buckeye Beans & Herbs, Inc.
NORTHWEST BEST PLACES - Publisher's imprint - Sasquatch Books
NORTHWEST COUNTRY - Rice - Buckeye Beans & Herbs, Inc.
NORTHWEST DELIGHTS - Fruits–dried - Le-An Sales
NORTHWEST FUTON COMPANY - Furniture - Northwest Futon Co.
NORTHWEST GRAIN COUNTRY - Breads - Original Oatmeal Baking Co.
NORTHWEST GROWN - Flowers, plants, and seeds - Smith Gardens Inc.
NORTHWEST HORIZON - Wines - Worden's Washington Winery
NORTHWEST NATURAL PRODUCTS - Vitamins and nutritional supplements - Nutrition Now, Inc.
NORTHWEST NAUTIX - Publisher's imprints - Northwest Nautix
NORTHWEST OUTFITTERS - Apparel - Lamonts Apparel Inc.
NORTHWEST PASSAGE - Sports apparel - Medalist Apparel Inc.
NORTHWEST SELECT - Sauces - Greg Bolen
NORTHWEST SPECIALTY - Ice cream - Danken's Gourmet Ice Creams
NORTHWEST TERRITORY - Tents - Kmart Corp.
NORTHWEST TRAILS - Luggage - Skyway Luggage Co.
NORTHWESTERN - Golfing equipment - Northwestern Golf Co.
NORTHWESTERN - Wire - Northwestern Steel and Wire Co.
NORTHWESTERN GOURMET - Meats–luncheon - Jerome Foods Inc.
NORTHWESTERN KNITTING COMPANY, THE - Apparel–children's ☆ - Munsingwear, Inc.
NORTHWESTERN OIL - Lubricants - McCollister & Co.
NORTHWESTERN PRESS, THE - Publisher's imprints ☆ - T.S. Denison and Co.
NORTHWESTWOOD - Manufactured homes - Redman Industries, Inc.
NORTHWIND - Jackets - Eddie Bauer Inc.
NORTHWIND - Motor vehicles–motor homes - Coachmen Industries, Inc.
NORTHWIND - Tobacco products - Philip Morris Companies Inc.
NORTHWINDS - Tableware–earthenware - Pfaltzgraff Investment Co.
NORTHWOODS - Dinnerware–glass - Charles I. Moore
NORTHWOODS - Food products - W.B. Roddenbery Co., Inc.
NORTHWOODS - Kitchenware–china - Dansk International Designs, Ltd.
NORTHWOODS - Luggage - Lexi International Inc.
NORTHWOODS - Pizzas–frozen - Northwoods Bar
NORTHWOODS - Toilet seats ☆ - Bemis Manufacturing Co.
NORTHWOODS BLEND - Soap - Botanicare, Inc.
NORTHWOODS CHRISTMAS - Christmas tree ornaments - Seasonal Specialties Electrics, Inc.
NORTHWOODS COLLECTION, THE - Toys–automobiles - Charlie's Woodshop
NORTON - Abrasive products - Norton Co.
NORTON - Locks–door - Scovill Inc.
NORTON - Machinery - Yale Security Inc.
NORTON - Musical instrument accessories - Dimarzio, Inc.
NORTON COMMANDER, THE - Computer software - Peter Norton Computing Inc.
NORTON EDITOR, THE - Computer software - Peter Norton Computing Inc.
NORTON GUIDES, THE - Computer software - Peter Norton Computing Inc.
NORTON MCNAUGHTON - Apparel - Norton Mcnaughton of Squire, Inc.
NORTON SG - Abrasive products - Norton Co.
NORTON UTILITIES, THE - Computer software - Peter Norton Computing Inc.
NORTON WINES OF ARGENTINA - Wines - Pastene Companies Ltd.
NORTUSSIN - Pharmaceutical preparations ☆ - Vortech Pharmaceuticals
NORVA - Flatware - Royal Silver Manufacturing Co. Inc.
NORVALINE - Pharmaceutical preparations - City Chemical Corp.
NORVELL - Brassieres (Bras) - Designs by Norvell Inc.
NORVIR - Pharmaceutical preparations - Abbott Laboratories
NORVY - Paints - Norvy, Inc.
NORWALK - Floor coverings ☆ - Durable Corp.
NORWALK - Furniture - Norwalk Furniture Corp.
NORWAY - Floor coverings–carpet and rugs ☆ - Olympic Carpets Inc.
NORWAY GOURMET - Fish–fresh or frozen - Frionor USA Inc.
NORWEGIAN BEAUTY - Food products - Zaloom Brothers Co. of New Jersey
NORWEGIAN FORMULA - Skin care products - Neutrogena Corp.
NORWESCO - Containers - Norwesco, Inc.
NORWESCO - Spices and extracts - Northwestern Extract Co.
NOR'WESTER - Beverages–malt - Willamette Valley Co.
NORWESTERN - Meat products–poultry - Jerome Foods Inc.

NORWESTERN FRESH DELI MEATS - Meat products–poultry - Jerome Foods Inc.
NORWICH - Apparel and accessories - Champion Products Inc.
NORWICH - Bathroom fixtures - Crane Plumbing/Fiat Products
NORWICH - Cabinets ☆ - Serway Brothers Inc.
NORWICH - Clocks ☆ - General Time Corp. (Westclox/Seth Thomas Div.)
NORWICH - Health care products - Procter & Gamble Co.
NORWICH - Tableware–earthenware ☆ - Robinson Knife & Fiddlers Plastics
NORWICH BUSINESS PRINTING - Forms, labels, printed products - Lumi-Lite Candle Co. Inc.
NORWICH INN - Furniture ☆ - Bassett Furniture Industries, Inc.
NORWICH NAVIGATORS - Apparel and accessories - Minor League Sports Enterprises
NORWOOD - Beverages–alcohol - Standard Distillers Products Inc.
NORWOOD - Brushes - Wright-Bernet
NORWOOD - Cabinets - American Woodmark Corp.
NORWOOD - Cabinets - Marsh Furniture Co.
NORWOOD - Cassette-tape recorders, blank cassette tapes, etc. - Audio Books on Cassette Distributors, Inc.
NORWOOD - Chimes ☆ - Nutone Inc.
NORWOOD - Guitars ☆ - Grossman Music Corp.
NORWOOD - Music stands ☆ - Norwood Co.
NORWOOD - Photo albums ☆ - Esselte Corp.
NORWOOD - Siding–insulating - Norandex, Inc.
NORWOOD - Wood products - Aspen Valley Lumber Co. Inc.
NORWOOD AND TUX - Greeting cards - Current, Inc.
NORWOOD XLP - Cassette-tape recorder - Audio Books on Cassette Distributors, Inc.
NORYL - Resins–synthetic - General Electric Co.
NORZINE - Pharmaceutical preparations - Purdue Frederick Co.
NOS-EASE - Cushions - Chaska Inc./Medihome-Doctors Podiatry
NOS NITROUS OXIDE SYSTEMS - Fuel systems–motor vehicle - Nitrous Oxide Systems, Inc.
NOSCOTUSS - Cough syrup ☆ - Iodent Co.
NOSDRI - Pharmaceutical preparations - Physician Sales & Service
NOSE BETTER - Health care products - Lee Pharmaceuticals
NOSE BONE - Sporting goods - Powell Skateboards
NOSE GLOWS - Christmas tree lights ☆ - Norstar Enterprises
NOSE GUARDS - Sporting goods - Surfco Hawaii Inc.
NOSE HOOK - Fishing tackle - Banjo Buddies, Inc.
NOSE MATCH-UPS - Games - Smethport Specialty Co.
NOSE PADS - Ophthalmic goods - Karlen Manufacturing, Inc.
NOSE SHOW - Toys - Russ Berrie and Co., Inc.
NOSEDIVE - Toys - Mattel, Inc.
NOSEGAY - Clocks ☆ - General Time Corp. (Westclox/Seth Thomas Div.)
NOSEY - Toys–stuffed ☆ - Gund, Inc.
NOSHI - Furniture - Hickory Manufacturing Co.
NOSKOTE - Sunblocks - Schering-Plough Healthcare Products
NOSPAZ - Pharmaceutical preparations ☆ - Solvay Pharmaceuticals Inc.
NOSQUITO - Electrical equipment - Theodore-James Mizzo
NOSQUITO - Veterinary pharmaceutical preparations ☆ - Farnam Cos. Inc.
NOSTAIN - Stain removers - Matrix Essentials, Inc.
NOSTALGIA - Bags - Howard Decorative Packaging Inc.
NOSTALGIA - Christmas tree ornaments - Cracker Box Inc.
NOSTALGIA - Floor coverings–carpet and rugs - Calladium & Marglen
NOSTALGIA - Floor coverings–carpet and rugs ☆ - Royalweve Carpet Mills
NOSTALGIA - Floor coverings–carpet and rugs ☆ - Southern Carpet Mills
NOSTALGIA - Food products - Nostalgia Products Corp.
NOSTALGIA - Furniture ☆ - Evenflo Juvenile Furniture Co.
NOSTALGIA - Glassware–household ☆ - Lancaster Colony Corp.
NOSTALGIA - Housewares - Gemco Ware, Inc.
NOSTALGIA - Jewelry - Marketing Insights, Inc.-Frank Luppino Jr., and Associates
NOSTALGIA - Leather goods - AR Accessories Group Inc.
NOSTALGIA - Pens - Sheaffer Inc.
NOSTALGIA - Puzzles - Franklin Merchandising Co.
NOSTALGIA - Recording label - Sonic Arts Corp.
NOSTALGIA - Stationery ☆ - Joli Greeting Card Co.
NOSTALGIA - Toilets–porcelain - Universal-Rundle Corp.
NOSTALGIA - Watch fobs - Jacoby-Bender Inc.
NOSTALGIA 200'S - Novelty items ☆ - West Coast Wood Specialties
NOSTALGIA CLASSICS - Lighting fixtures - Meyda Tiffany Inc.
NOSTALGIA CYCLE - Motorcycle parts and accessories - Nostalgia-Cycle, Inc.
NOSTALGIA EYEWEAR - Eyeglasses - Sungold Enterprises Ltd.
NOSTALGIA RECORDS - Compact discs–prerecorded - William A. Nicholas
NOSTALGIAS - Dolls - Bradley Import Co.

☆ = Now out of production

NOSTALGIC WAREHOUSE - Hardware - Nostalgic Warehouse, Inc.
NOSTALGIQUE - Floor coverings–carpet and rugs ☆ - Karastan-Bigelow Inc.
NOSTAT - Cleaning preparations ☆ - Charleswater
NOSTEALUM - Fishing lures ☆ - Eppinger Manufacturing Co.
NOSTRAPHON - Health care products - ConsultingPlan USA
NOSTRIL - Pharmaceutical preparations - Boehringer Ingelheim
Pharmaceuticals Inc.
NOSTRILLA - Pharmaceutical preparations - Boehringer Ingelheim
Pharmaceuticals Inc.
NOSTRISOL - Health care products ☆ - D'Franssia Corp.
NOSY BEARS - Bathroom accessories ☆ - Tsumura International Inc.
NOSY BEARS - Toys - Those Characters from Cleveland, Inc.
NOSY BEARS - Toys–stuffed - Playskool, Inc.
NOSY RHINO - Puppets - Dakin Inc.
NOT-A-KNOT - Fishing tackle - Outdoor Technologies Group
NOT-A-STITCH-ON - Apparel and accessories - Warnaco Inc.
NOT ACTIVE - Shirts - Stadium Sports
NOT-ALL-THAT-BODY-BRIEFER - Apparel and accessories ☆ - Warnaco Inc.
NOT-ALL-THAT-BRA - Apparel and accessories - Warnaco Inc.
NOT DOGS - Food products - Northern Soy
NOT EVEN THE RAIN - Apparel and accessories - Not Even the Rain, Inc.
NOT EXACTLY GREETINGS - Greeting cards - Imagine That! Corp.
NOT FADE AWAY - Apparel and accessories - Not Fade Away Graphics, Inc.
NOT IN OUR HOUSE - Apparel and accessories - Seattle Supersonics, Inc.
NOT JUST A CUP, BUT A JUST CUP - Coffee - Thanksgiving Coffee Co.
NOT JUST ANOTHER JUICE - Juices - Ultravit Enterprises, Inc.
NOT JUST BLUE JEANS - Artists' materials - Duncan Enterprises
NOT JUST DONUTS - Bakery products - IM Vending, Inc.
NOT JUST FOR KIDS - Publisher's imprints - College Street Publishing
NOT JUST JOHNS - Apparel and accessories - Karyn Lewandowski
NOT JUST SEEDS - Flowers, plants, and seeds - Boxbook Media
NOT JUST SEXY - Apparel–women's - Exquisite Form Industries
NOT NAUGHTY - Apparel–women's - Exquisite Form Industries
NOT ORDINARY TROUSERS - Apparel and accessories - American Design
Intelligence Group
NOT PLAIN CHERRY - Fruit drinks–bottled or canned - Tree Top, Inc.
NOT POLITICALLY CORRECT COMPANY, INC., THE - Toys–banks - James
Earl Sweeney
NOT-SCRAPE - Traps–animal - Wildlife Research Center, Inc.
NOT SO BASIC STUFF - Apparel - Children's Place Retail Stores, Inc.
NOT SO INNOCENT NUDES - Brassieres (Bras) - Warnaco Inc.
NOT-SO-SLOPPY-JOE - Meat sauces - Hormel Foods Corp.
NOT SO TIGHT - Apparel–women's - Bette Appel Inc.
NOT-THE-NORM - Apparel - Not the Norm
NOT TONIGHT DEER! - Repellent - Robert Lind
NOT-TOO-BIG - Calendars - Antioch Publishing Co.
NOT YET - Recording label - Winners Circle Records
NOTA BENE PARIS-MILAN NEW YORK-TOKYO - Apparel and accessories -
Renee Lehner
NOTABLE - Computer software - Notable Technologies, Inc.
NOTABLE - Floor coverings - Aladdin Mills, Inc.
NOTABLE - Floor coverings–carpet and rugs - Philadelphia Carpets
NOTABLE - Floor coverings–carpet and rugs - S and S Mills Inc.
NOTABLE - Office supplies - Rubbermaid Office Products Inc.
NOTABLE DIFFERENCE - Health care products - Nature's Design Ltd.
NOTABLE PHANTOM, THE - Computer peripheral equipment - Compton's
NewMedia
NOTABLE TECHNOLOGIES - Computer software - Notable Technologies, Inc.
NOTABLES - Apparel–women's - Koret of California, Inc.
NOTABLES - Shoes - Viner Brothers Inc.
NOTABLES - Wallpaper - Gencorp Polymer Products
NOTAC - Health care products - Tecnol Medical Products, Inc.
NOTANGLE - Fishing lures - Eppinger Manufacturing Co.
NOTARE - Hair care products - Cosway Co., Inc.
NOTARE - Thread - A. Lewis Thread Co. Inc.
NOTARY - Paper–bond - Esleeck Manufacturing Co., Inc.
NOTATION - Pencils - General Pencil Co.
NOTCH - Trading cards and stamps - Malibu Comics Entertainment, Inc.
NOTCH LOC - Wood products - Daniel L. Christensen
NOTCHOS - Games - Serigraph, Inc.
NOTE-A-DATE - Calendars ☆ - Southworth Co.
NOTE-A-LOON - Paper - CTI Industries Corp.
NOTE CAN - Paper products - Paper Conversions Inc.
NOTE CARDS AND - Greeting cards - Edna Hibel Studio
NOTE CUBE - Paper products - Paper Conversions Inc.
NOTE DETECTIVE - Computer software - Electronic Courseware Systems Inc.

NOTE-IT - Computer software - Symantec Corp.
NOTE JAC - Office supplies - Pen-Tab Industries
NOTE POSTER - Office supplies ☆ - Park Sherman
NOTE SKETCH - Artists' materials - Hunt Manufacturing Co.
NOTE SPELLER - Computer software - Electronic Courseware Systems Inc.
NOTE STIX - Notebooks and notepads - Rediform
NOTE-TAKER'S DELIGHT - Notebooks and notepads - People Systems Inc.
NOTE TOTE - Computer carrying bag - Mark Ogne
NOTE-TOTE - Notebooks and notepads - Ampad Corp.
NOTE WRITER - Markers–felt-tip - Liqui-Mark
NOTEAR - Office supplies - Boorum & Pease Co.
NOTEAR - Office supplies ☆ - Esselte Corp.
NOTEBOARD - Computer peripheral equipment - Darwin Keyboards, Ltd.
NOTEBOOK COMPANION - Computer software - WizardWorks Group Inc.
NOTEBOOK GAMES - Games - Tyco Toys
NOTEBOOK II - Computer software - Digital Marketing Corp.
NOTEBOOK TRAVELERS - Computers - Kensington
NOTEBRICK - Computers–personal - The Brick Computer Co.
NOTECORDER 100 - Electronic equipment - Olympus America Inc.
NOTECORDER 200 - Electronic equipment - Olympus America Inc.
NOTECORDER 300 - Electronic equipment - Olympus America Inc.
NOTEGUN RECORDS - Recording label - Virginia Arts Records
NOTEKEEPER - Computer software - Systems Center Inc.
NOTEMASTER - Counting devices - Federated Banknote Co.
NOTEMAX - Computer peripheral equipment - Panamax
NOTEPAD PLUS - Audio equipment - Telequest Inc.
NOTERY - Office supplies - Rubbermaid Office Products Inc.
NOTES - Computer software - Lotus Development Corp.
NOTES - Floor coverings–tile - Interface, Inc.
NOTES - Paper products ☆ - Paper Conversions Inc.
NOTES & QUOTES - Bulletin boards - Coordinated Products Corp.
NOTES FROM HOME - Computer storage devices–optical ☆ - Literally Lisa's
Literature
NOTES FROM THE HEART - Recording label - Muhyi Shakoor
NOTES/FX - Computer software - Lotus Development Corp.
NOTES-N-FILES - Computer software ☆ - DataPak Software Inc.
NOTES 'N STUFF - Paper–writing - Mattel, Inc.
NOTES OF HAPPINESS - Stationery - Happiness Inc.
NOTES OF JOY - Music–sheet - Samuel S. Kelly
NOTES READY - Computer software - Lotus Development Corp.
NOTESAVER - Locks–padlocks - Compu-Lock, Inc.
NOTESAVERS - Office supplies - Moore Business Forms, Inc.
NOTESCAN - Computer software - Grande Software, Inc.
NOTESMAIL - Computer software - Lotus Development Corp.
NOTESSQL - Computer software - Lotus Development Corp.
NOTESSUITE - Computer software - Lotus Development Corp.
NOTESTERS - Office accessories - Universal Cork, Inc.
NOTESTRAP - Desks - Rolf O. Anderson
NOTESTRIPS - Forms–preprinted - Moore Business Forms, Inc.
NOTETAKERS - Desk sets - Lasercraft, Inc.
NOTETAPE - Office supplies - Lee Products Co.
NOTETAPE TRANSPARENT NOTES - Tape–adhesive ☆ - Lee Products Co.
NOTEWORK - Computer software - On Technology Corp.
NOTEWORKS - Notebooks and notepads - Rediform
NOTEWORTHY - Computer peripheral equipment - Toshiba America
Information Systems, Inc.
NOTEWORTHY - Telephones - At&T Corp.
NOTEWRITER - Computer software ☆ - Passport Designs Inc.
NOTHIN' BUT JUICE - Juices - Apple and Eve Inc.
NOTHIN' BUT ORGANICALLY GROWN - Flour–blended - Cochran Mill Inc.
NOTHING - Lamps - Roxter Lighting
NOTHING BUT BLUE - Apparel and accessories - Tomato, Inc.
NOTHING BUT NET - Sandwiches–prepackaged - Mcdonald's Corp.
NOTHING CLEANS LIKE THE CLAM - Machine parts - Clam Industries, Inc.
NOTHING ELSE EVEN COMES CLOSE - Nail care products - Nailtiques
Cosmetic Corp.
NOTHING MORE TO PROVE - Footwear ☆ - E.S. Originals, Inc.
NOTHING REAL - Computer software - Nothing Real, LLC
NOTHING-TO-IT-LETTERS - Greeting cards - Thought Factory
NOTICEABLY NEW - Colognes ☆ - Avon Products, Inc.
NOTIFF - Apparel and accessories ☆ - Conic Enterprises Ltd.
NOTIFY! - Computer software - EX Machina, Inc.
NOTNUTS - Food products - Morton Scott, Ltd.
NOTO - Jewelry - Noto Jewelry Co. Inc.
NOTORIOUS - Apparel and accessories ☆ - Edison Brothers Stores, Inc.
NOTORIOUS - Perfumes - Cosmair Inc.

NOTOSE - Pharmaceutical preparations - Alto Pharmaceuticals Inc.

NOTOX - Tubes–plastic - Aquarium Pump & Piping Systems

NOTRAX FLOOR MATTING VISUAL WARNING MATTING SYSTEM - Floor coverings–linoleum - Superior Manufacturing Group, Inc.

NOTRAX STAGES - Floor coverings - Superior Manufacturing Group/Notrax Floor Matting

NOTRE DAME - Food products - Crystal Food Import Corp.

NOTRIX - Computer software - Percussion Software, Inc.

NOTTAWAY PINE - Furniture ☆ - Bassett Furniture Industries, Inc.

NOTTE GIORNO - Lingerie - Mel-Lin Lingerie Inc.

NOTTINGHAM - Bicycles - Kent International Inc.

NOTTINGHAM - Floor coverings - Mannington Resilient Floors

NOTTINGHAM - Furniture - Haworth, Inc.

NOTTINGHAM - Furniture ☆ - Hammary Furniture Co. Inc.

NOTTINGHAM - Mushrooms - L.K. Bowman & Co. Inc.

NOTT'S - Insecticides - Nott Manufacturing Co. Inc.

NOTUS 500 - Pencils–mechanical - Zebra Pen Corp.

NOTWAX - Sporting goods - Ramer Products, Ltd.

NOUGAT FLUFFS - Candy - Miss Saylor's Candies

NOUGAT PECAN LOGS - Candy ☆ - Judson-Atkinson Candies

NOUGATON - Cheese - Swissrose International Inc.

NOUGLES - Ice cream - H.P. Hood & Sons Inc.

NOUMENAL BOOKS - Publisher's imprints - Panjandrum Books

NOUN ENDINGS - Electronic equipment ☆ - Texas Instruments Inc.

NOUR - Candy - Karabetian Import & Export

NOURISH - Skin care products ☆ - Mastey De Paris

NOURISH - Vitamins and nutritional supplements - G. D. Searle & Co.

NOURISHING - Hair care products - ABBA Products Inc.

NOURISHMENT - Hair care products - Amethyst Investment Group, Inc.

NOURISHMENT - Nail care products - RTS Laboratories, Inc.

NOURISHMENT FOR LIFE - Vitamins and nutritional supplements - Intracell Nutrition Inc.

NOUROT GLASS STUDIOS - Glassware–household - Nourot Glass Studio

NOUVAGE - Nail care products - Quintessence Inc.

NOUVEATE - Fabric stores - Streamline Industries, Inc.

NOUVEAU - Bedding–linen ☆ - Dan River Inc.

NOUVEAU - Cabinets - Merillat Industries, Inc.

NOUVEAU - Clocks - General Time Corp. (Westclox/Seth Thomas Div.)

NOUVEAU - Cooking utensils–china - Princess House, Inc.

NOUVEAU - Dishes–china - Pickard Inc.

NOUVEAU - Display cases–plastic - Claridge Products and Equipment Inc.

NOUVEAU - Flatware ☆ - Gorham Inc.

NOUVEAU - Floor coverings - Beaulieu of America, Inc.

NOUVEAU - Footwear ☆ - Brooks Shoe Inc.

NOUVEAU - Furniture ☆ - Hammary Furniture Co. Inc.

NOUVEAU - Labels–paper - K-Tel International, Inc.

NOUVEAU - Rings–jewelry - Artcarved Inc.

NOUVEAU - Tablecloths - Cascade Fibers Co.

NOUVEAU - Tableware–china - Susquehanna Glass Co.

NOUVEAU - Tiles–ceramic - Monarch Tile Inc.

NOUVEAU - Wallpaper - Royson's Corp.

NOUVEAU - Wine ☆ - Ingleside Plantation Winery

NOUVEAU DEBUT - Furniture ☆ - Romweber Co.

NOUVEAU HOBO - Luggage ☆ - Hartmann Luggage Co.

NOUVEAU II - Furniture ☆ - Hammary Furniture Co. Inc.

NOUVEAU MONDE - Apparel and accessories - Mevisions International Inc.

NOUVEAU MONDE SPORT - Apparel and accessories - Mevisions International Inc.

NOUVEAU ROYALTY - Apparel - Indus Imports, Inc.

NOUVEAU, THE - Recliners - Lane Co. Inc.

NOUVEAU USA - Apparel–women's - ABS Clothing Collection Inc.

NOUVEAU VISAGE - Skin care products - Finelle Industries Inc.

NOUVEAUTE - Hosiery - Virginia Maid Hosiery Mills Inc.

NOUVEAUTEK - Floor coverings–carpet and rugs ☆ - Customweave Carpets Inc.

NOUVEAUX RICHE - Wines - Horizon Wines

NOUVEL - Artists' materials ☆ - Sakura of America

NOUVELLA - Floor coverings–carpet and rugs - Whitecrest Carpet Mills

NOUVELLE - Floor coverings–carpet and rugs ☆ - Customweave Carpets Inc.

NOUVELLE - Floor coverings–carpet and rugs ☆ - Regal Rugs Inc.

NOUVELLE - Furniture - National/Mt. Airy Furniture

NOUVELLE - Furniture ☆ - Pulaski Furniture Corp.

NOUVELLE - Furniture–upholstered - Maharam Vertical Surfaces

NOUVELLE - Giftware - Incolay Studios Inc.

NOUVELLE - Health care products - Coloplast Corp.

NOUVELLE - Perfumes ☆ - Parfum de Coeur Ltd.

NOUVELLE - Seafood products–fresh or frozen ☆ - Homarus Inc.

NOUVELLE - Soups–frozen ☆ - Oregon Freeze Dry Inc.

NOUVELLE - Wallpaper ☆ - Imperial Wallcoverings, Inc.

NOUVELLE - Window coverings - Del Mar Window Coverings

NOUVELLE - Women's shoes - Ipanema Shoe Corp.

NOUVELLE CUISINE - Food products ☆ - Nutri-Metics International (USA) Inc.

NOUVELLE FASHIONS - Eyeglasses - Martin-Copeland Eyewear Corp.

NOUVELLE FOODS - Fruits and vegetables - Nouvelle Foods, Inc.

NOUVELLE GENERATION - Infant product ☆ - Couzon USA

NOUVELLE GRENI - Seasonings - Castle Food Products

NOUVELLE SORBET - Ice cream - Nouvelle Ice Cream Corp.

NOUVELLETTE - Glassware–household - Crystal Clear Importing Co. Inc.

NOUVIR - Lighting equipment - Design Technology Corp.

NOUVO - Cabinets - Contempri Kitchens

NOVA - Air cushions - Nova Health Systems Inc.

NOVA - Audio equipment ☆ - John Marovskis Audio Systems

NOVA - Blenders - Waring Products Div.

NOVA - Blinds–venetian - Craftsman Window Coverings Inc.

NOVA - Boats - Wellcraft Marine Corp.

NOVA - Brushes - Wright-Bernet

NOVA - Cabinets - Canyon Creek Cabinet Co.

NOVA - Cabinets - Dewils Industries Inc.

NOVA - Cabinets ☆ - Quality Cabinets

NOVA - Candy - Nova Chocolate Co., Inc.

NOVA - Computer software - Astrolabe Software

NOVA - Deicing fluid - Ossian, Inc.

NOVA - Electric lighting equipment - Lutron Electronics Co., Inc.

NOVA - Electrical equipment ☆ - Bass Products

NOVA - Fabrics - Superior Shade & Blind Co. Inc.

NOVA - Fabrics–spandex - Haggar Corp.

NOVA - Fans–electric - Encon Industries Inc.

NOVA - Faucets - Sterling Plumbing Group Inc.

NOVA - Fishing rods - Zebco Corp.

NOVA - Flags - Annin and Co.

NOVA - Floor coverings - Congoleum Corp.

NOVA - Floor coverings–carpet and rugs - Mohawk Carpet Corp.

NOVA - Floor coverings–carpet and rugs - Porter Carpet Mills Inc.

NOVA - Floor coverings–carpet and rugs - Quaker Inc.

NOVA - Floor coverings–carpet and rugs ☆ - Regal Rugs Inc.

NOVA - Floor coverings–tile - Daltonian Carpet & Cushion Inc.

NOVA - Furniture - U.S. Furniture Industries Inc.

NOVA - Furniture ☆ - Bassett Furniture Industries, Inc.

NOVA - Glassware–household - Owens-Illinois Inc. (Libbey Div.)

NOVA - Hair-cutting shears - B.W. Boyd Shears Inc.

NOVA - Hardware - Shepherd Products U.S. Inc.

NOVA - Headphones - Tandy Corp.

NOVA - Health care products - ETAC USA Inc.

NOVA - Herbicides - Rohm and Haas Co.

NOVA - Jewelry - Nova Stylings Inc.

NOVA - Lighting fixtures - Kenall Manufacturing Co.

NOVA - Marine rigging ☆ - Windline Marine

NOVA - Mops - Piedmont Mop Co.

NOVA - Motor vehicles ☆ - General Motors Corp. (Chevrolet Motor Div.)

NOVA - Motor vehicles–motor homes - Commodore Corp.

NOVA - Musical instrument accessories ☆ - Rico International

NOVA - Paints - Josten's Sportswear

NOVA - Pens - Empire Berol USA

NOVA - Pillows - Pillowtex Corp.

NOVA - Pipes–tobacco - S.M. Frank & Co. Inc. (Kaywoodie-Yello-Bole-Medico)

NOVA - Plywood - States Industries Inc.

NOVA - Portable partition - Brewster Corp.

NOVA - Projection screens - Claridge Products and Equipment Inc.

NOVA - Projectors–photographic - Buhl Industries, Inc.

NOVA - Recording label - Nova Records Inc.

NOVA - Rings–jewelry - Artcarved Inc.

NOVA - Seafood products–fresh or frozen - St. Joseph Fisheries

NOVA - Skates–roller ☆ - Seneca Sports, Inc.

NOVA - Sporting goods - Wellington Leisure Products, Inc.

NOVA - Tables–wood - Riverside Furniture Corp.

NOVA - Telescopes - WGBH Educational Foundation

NOVA - Trailers–travel - Starcraft Corp.

NOVA - Wallpaper ☆ - Wolf-Gordon Inc.

NOVA - Whirlpools - Jacuzzi Inc.

NOVA - Wood products - Homasote Co.

NOVA 3 - Computer software - Corel USA

☆ = Now out of production

NOVA-8 - Night vision apparates - Night Vision Corp.
NOVA A-STAR - Electric lighting equipment - Lutron Electronics Co., Inc.
NOVA AUDIO BOOKS - Recording label - Brilliance Corp. Inc.
NOVA CHROME - Hardware ☆ - Genova Products Inc.
NOVA CLASSIC - Motor vehicles—motor homes - Commodore Corp.
NOVA COLOR - Paints - Artex Manufacturing Co.
NOVA COLOR - Paints—artists' - Nova Color
NOVA-DEC - Pharmaceutical preparations - Rugby Laboratories Inc.
NOVA DER - Cosmetics - Ya-Man Ltd.
NOVA DERM - Bandages - Cramer Products Inc.
NOVA DESIGNS - Statuary - Nova Designs
NOVA ERA - Beverages—alcohol - New Age Wine & Spirits
NOVA FISHERIES - Seafood products—fresh or frozen - Nova Fisheries, Inc.
NOVA FLEX - Circuit boards - Sheldahl, Inc.
NOVA FUTURA - Wallcovering - Wall Trends, Inc.
NOVA-LITE - Construction equipment ☆ - Novi American Inc.
NOVA MACHINE PRODUCTS CORP. - Nuts and bolts - Nova Machine
  Products Corp.
NOVA MAGIC MARBLE - Kaleidoscopes - Gemini Kaleidoscopes
NOVA NOVA DESIGNS - Wallpaper - Jones Blair Co.
NOVA-PAC - Health care products - Wholesale Medical Import
NOVA PAINT - Paints - Artex Manufacturing Co.
NOVA PAYLOADER - Toys—models - Estes Industries
NOVA PEARLS - Pet products - Tomlyn Products
NOVA-PHONE - Headphones ☆ - Tandy Corp.
NOVA PLUS - Jewelry - Nova Stylings Inc.
NOVA PRESS - Music—sheet - Lorenz Creative Services Corp.
NOVA SCOUT SHIP - Toys—models ☆ - Estes Industries
NOVA SHEERS - Hosiery—women's - Hampshire Hosiery, Inc.
NOVA SOFT - Water treating compounds ☆ - Genova Products Inc.
NOVA SPRING - Computer software - Vic Tokai, Inc.
NOVA T-STAR - Electric lighting equipment - Lutron Electronics Co., Inc.
NOVA VENT - Plumbing fixtures - Genova Products Inc.
NOVABEAM - Video equipment - AmPro Corp.
NOVABELL - Floor coverings—tile - Federal Tile Imports Inc.
NOVABOND - Chemical preparations - Georgia-Pacific Corp.
NOVACEBRIN - Pharmaceutical preparations ☆ - Eli Lilly and Co.
NOVACLAD - Plastics—laminated - Sheldahl, Inc.
NOVACLEAN - Cleaning equipment - Genova Products Inc.
NOVACOLOR - Pencils - Blackfeet Writing Instruments Inc.
NOVACOMM - Alarm systems - Novacomm, Inc.
NOVACOTE - Chemical preparations - Georgia-Pacific Corp.
NOVACOTE PC - Chemical preparations - Georgia-Pacific Corp.
NOVACRYLIC - Floor coverings - Nova Sports USA Inc.
NOVADIGM - Computer software - Novadigm Inc.
NOVADIGM ENTERPRISE DESKTOP MANAGER - Computer software -
  Novadigm Inc.
NOVADYNE - Computer software - Novadyne Computer Systems Inc.
NOVAERA - Sanitary napkins - Kimberly-Clark Corp.
NOVAFAX - Facsimile equipment - Novacore Technologies, Inc.
NOVAFED - Pharmaceutical preparations - Marion Merrell Dow
NOVAFLO - Chemical preparations - Georgia-Pacific Corp.
NOVAFLOR - Pharmaceutical preparations - Medical Products Panamericana
  Inc.
NOVAGARD - Silicon products - Foam Seal, Inc.
NOVAGATEWAY - Computer software - Novasoft Systems, Inc.
NOVAGRAPH - Computer software - Novagraph, Inc.
NOVAGUARD - Epoxy - Sigma Coatings USA BV.
NOVAHISTINE - Pharmaceutical preparations - Marion Merrell Dow
NOVAHISTINE DMX - Pharmaceutical preparations - Marion Merrell Dow
NOVAHISTINE DMX - Pharmaceutical preparations - SmithKline Beecham
  Consumer Healthcare
NOVAK - Accordions - Castiglione Accordion
NOVAL - Blinds—venetian - Baumann Inc.
NOVALENE - Colognes ☆ - Avon Products, Inc.
NOVALIN - Laundry starch - Ecolab Inc.
NOVALIN - Wallcoverings - Designtex Fabrics Inc.
NOVALINK - Circuit boards - Sheldahl, Inc.
NOVALIS - Recording label - Creav Inc. USA
NOVALOCK - Hardware - Detroit Tool Industries Corp.
NOVALON - Musical instrument accessories - Ernest Deffner Inc.
NOVAMINE - Pharmaceutical preparations - Kabi Pharmacia Inc.
NOVAMOR - Pharmaceutical preparations ☆ - Moore Medical Corp.
NOVAMURA - Wallpaper - ICI Americas Inc.
NOVANEX - Amplifiers—musical instrument - Novanex (USA) Inc.
NOVANTA-90 - Dryers—hair ☆ - Nino Originals

NOVAPAK - Modems - Novalink Technologies, Inc.
NOVAPAK - Musical instrument accessories - Rico International
NOVAPET - Dog food ☆ - Novapet, Inc.
NOVAPET CANOLLY - Dog food ☆ - Novapet, Inc.
NOVAPET CHIPS - Pet products - Novapet, Inc.
NOVAPET COMPACT STICKS - Pet products - Novapet, Inc.
NOVAPET COW EARS - Pet products - Novapet, Inc.
NOVAPET DINO BONE - Dog food ☆ - Novapet, Inc.
NOVAPET DONUTS - Pet products - Novapet, Inc.
NOVAPET GRISSINI - Pet products - Novapet, Inc.
NOVAPET HEAVY PRIME BONES - Pet products - Novapet, Inc.
NOVAPET LEG BONE - Pet products - Novapet, Inc.
NOVAPET MINI COMPACT STICKS - Pet products - Novapet, Inc.
NOVAPET MINI ROLLS - Pet products - Novapet, Inc.
NOVAPET MULTIFLAVOR PACKS - Pet products - Novapet, Inc.
NOVAPET PETITE BAKERY - Pet products - Novapet, Inc.
NOVAPET PRETZELS - Pet products - Novapet, Inc.
NOVAPET RETRIEVER ROLLS - Pet products - Novapet, Inc.
NOVAPET VALUE PACKS - Pet products - Novapet, Inc.
NOVAPET VANILLA BAKERY - Pet products ☆ - Novapet, Inc.
NOVAPLUS - Chemical preparations - Georgia-Pacific Corp.
NOVAPULSE - Medical apparatus - Luxar Corp.
NOVAQUA - Aquarium accessories - Kordon
NOVAQUA - Water treating compounds - Novalek, Inc.
NOVARA - Furniture ☆ - Lane Co. Inc.
NOVARA - Shoes ☆ - Allen-Edmonds Shoe Corp.
NOVARES - Resins—polymer - Georgia-Pacific Corp.
NOVASERVER - Computer software - Resnova Software, Inc.
NOVASIZE - Chemical preparations - Georgia-Pacific Corp.
NOVASPERSE - Chemical preparations - Georgia-Pacific Corp.
NOVASPHERE - Cosmetic - Estee Lauder Inc.
NOVASPORT - Apparel—athletic ☆ - Regina Imports
NOVASYNC - Electronics equipment - Nova Systems Inc.
NOVATEL - Telephones—cellular - Muntz Electronics Inc.
NOVATERM - Computer software - Resnova Software, Inc.
NOVATEUR - Apparel—men's - York East Merchandise, Inc.
NOVATOPE - Chemical preparations - Novagen, Inc.
NOVATRIN - Pharmaceutical preparations ☆ - Wyeth-Ayerst Laboratories
NOVATUSS - Pharmaceutical preparations ☆ - Blaine Co. Inc.
NOVAWALL - Building materials - Novawall Systems, Inc.
NOVAWARE - Computer software - NovaStor Corp.
NOVAWELD - Cement - Genova Products Inc.
NOVAX-14 - Detergents - Ecolab Inc.
NOVEAU - Cosmetics - Madeleine Mono Ltd.
NOVEEN - Health care products ☆ - Nova Health Systems Inc.
NOVEL - Cookies ☆ - Dainty Cookies Inc.
NOVEL ALTERNATIVE, A - Publisher's imprints - Adams Book Co., Inc.
NOVEL APPROACH - Recording label - Harper Audio
NOVEL WASH - Cleaning preparations - Novel Wash Co. Inc.
NOVELETTE - Toys—stuffed - Novelette Industries Inc.
NOVELL - Computer software - Novell, Inc.
NOVELL PRESS - Computer software ☆ - Novell, Inc.
NOVELLA - Floor coverings - Congoleum Corp.
NOVELLE - Fabrics - Greenwood Mills Inc.
NOVELLE - Floor coverings—carpet and rugs - Providence Rug Co.
NOVELLE - Watches - Accuitme Watch Corp.
NOVELLE ARCH - Cabinets—wood - Kemper
NOVELLE SQUARE - Cabinets—wood - Kemper
NOVELLI - Shoes - Hess's Department Stores Inc.
NOVELLO - Furniture - Dinaire Corp.
NOVELLO - Music—sheet - Theodore Presser Co.
NOVELLO GRAPH - Pencils ☆ - Faber-Castell Corp.
NOVELOSE - Starch—edible - Indopco, Inc.
NOVELTIES ACCENT - Flowers - Southern Rainbow Corp.
NOVELTY - Floor coverings ☆ - Congoleum Corp.
NOVELTY - Paper - Mactac Inc. (Packaging Closures Systems Div.)
NOVELTY BLUE - Apparel—athletic - Regaliti Inc.
NOVELTY CREATIONS - Pens, pencils, and paper goods - Novelty Creations,
  Inc.
NOVELTY SPECIALTIES - Candy - ACB/Richard Watson
NOVELTY STUFF - Toys - Knickerbocker Toy Co. Inc.
NOVELTYE - Yarn ☆ - W.F.R. Ribbon Corp.
NOVEMBER - Apparel and accessories - Carnival Manufacturing, Inc.
NOVEMBER HARVEST - Wines - Americana Vineyards Estate Winery
NOVEMBER RECORDS - Recording label - November Records, Inc.
NOVERA - Computer software - Novera Software, Inc.

NOVEROX - Stain removers ☆ - Faultless Starch/Bon Ami Co.
NOVERT - Pharmaceutical preparations ☆ - Abana Pharmaceuticals, Inc.
NOVEX - Chemical preparations - Novel Experimental Technology
NOVEX - Ships–sailing vessels ☆ - Lewmar Marine Inc.
NOVEXX - Office machines - Avery Dennison Corp.
NOVI - Bathtubs–enameled - Novi American Inc.
NOVI KIDS - Novelty items - Novi International
NOVICTIM - Alarm systems - Novictim Inc.
NOVIE - Seafood products–fresh or frozen - Tri-Novie Distributors Corp.
NOVIPLEX - Pharmaceutical preparations ☆ - ICN Pharmaceuticals Inc.
NOVIS - Computer hardware - Modcomp/Cerplex L.P.
NOVITA - Yarn - Knitting Fever Inc.
NOVITAS - Lighting equipment - Novitas, Inc.
NOVITIATE - Wines - Novitiate Wines
NOVLIB - Computer software - Assembler Software Manufacturers, Inc.
NOVO - Greeting cards ☆ - Moderne Card Co. Inc.
NOVO ARTS INC. - Recording label - Novo Arts, Inc.
NOVO-POXI - Epoxy coatings - Rock-Tred Corp.
NOVOBORD - Lumber - Georgia-Pacific Corp.
NOVOCAIN - Anesthetics - Sterling Winthrop Inc.
NOVOCOL - Anesthetics - Septodont, Inc.
NOVOCOM - Video tapes–blank - Novocom, Inc.
NOVOCORE - Particle board - Georgia-Pacific Corp.
NOVOCS - Water purification systems - EG&G Environmental, Inc.
NOVODECK - Wood products - Georgia-Pacific Corp.
NOVODENT ACCU-T - Toothbrushes–electric ☆ - Robert Krups North America
NOVODENT PULSAR - Toothbrushes ☆ - Robert Krups North America
NOVODOR - Wood products - Georgia-Pacific Corp.
NOVOFLEX - Photographic equipment - Aetna Optix Inc.
NOVOFLOR - Wood products - Georgia-Pacific Corp.
NOVOFOLD - Wood products - Georgia-Pacific Corp.
NOVOGRAIN - Wood products - Georgia-Pacific Corp.
NOVOLIN L - Insulin - Novo Nordisk Pharmaceuticals Inc.
NOVOLIN N - Insulin - Novo Nordisk Pharmaceuticals Inc.
NOVOLIN N PENFILL - Insulin - Novo Nordisk Pharmaceuticals Inc.
NOVOLIN R - Insulin - Novo Nordisk Pharmaceuticals Inc.
NOVOLIN R PENFILL - Insulin - Novo Nordisk Pharmaceuticals Inc.
NOVOLITE - Doors - Georgia-Pacific Corp.
NOVON - Detergents - Shaw's Supermarkets, Inc.
NOVONETTE - Fabrics - Veratec
NOVOPAN - Particle board - Georgia-Pacific Corp.
NOVOPEN - Insulin - Novo Nordisk Pharmaceuticals Inc.
NOVOPHEN - Skin care products - Luyties Pharmacal Co.
NOVOPLY - Particle board - Georgia-Pacific Corp.
NOVOPLY - Wood products - Champion International Corp.
NOVOPRINT USA - Publisher's imprints - Novoprint USA, Inc.
NOVOSHELF - Particle board - Georgia-Pacific Corp.
NOVOSTEP - Lumber - Georgia-Pacific Corp.
NOVOSTRAND - Lumber - Georgia-Pacific Corp.
NOVOTEX - Lumber - Georgia-Pacific Corp.
NOVOTEX - Yarn - New World Textiles, LLC
NOVOTILE - Particle board - Georgia-Pacific Corp.
NOVOWALL - Wood products - Georgia-Pacific Corp.
NOVOWELD - Lumber - Georgia-Pacific Corp.
NOVOWOOD - Lumber - Georgia-Pacific Corp.
NOVRAD - Pharmaceutical preparations ☆ - Eli Lilly and Co.
NOVRONG - Floor coverings–linoleum - Lucky America Inc.
NOVUS - Automotive repair shops–glass - Novus Inc.
NOVUS - Calculators ☆ - National Semiconductor Corp.
NOVUS - Computer hardware - Novus Technologies, Inc.
NOVUS - Medical apparatus - Coherent, Inc.
NOVUS - Water treatment chemicals - Betz Laboratories, Inc.
NOVX - Health care products ☆ - Nova Health Systems Inc.
NOW - Books - Now Entertainment Corp.
NOW - Cigarettes - R.J. Reynolds Tobacco Co.
NOW - Detergents - Blue Cross Laboratories Inc.
NOW - Dishcloths - Now Designs
NOW - Dresses–women's - Anne Klein & Co.
NOW - Recording label - Original Sound Record Co. Inc.
NOW - Vitamins and nutritional supplements - Fruitful Yield, Inc.
N.O.W. - Vitamins and nutritional supplements - Reliv' International, Inc.
NOW 100S - Cigarettes - R.J. Reynolds Tobacco Co.
NOW AGE - Publisher's imprints - Pendulum Press Inc.
NOW & FOREVER - Floor coverings–carpet and rugs - Philadelphia Carpets

NOW AND FOREVER - Floor coverings–carpet and rugs ☆ - Mohawk Carpet Corp.
NOW AND FOREVER BY FOREVER YOURS - Wedding gowns - Forever Yours International Corp.
NOW & LATER - Candy - Phoenix Confections Inc.
NOW AND LATER RADBERRY - Candy - Phoenix Confections Inc.
NOW AND THEN - Fabrics–tapestry - Comark Wallcoverings
NOW & THEN - Wallpaper - Riverside Silkscreen
NOW COMPRESS - Computer software - Now Software, Inc.
NOW CONTACT - Computer software - Now Software, Inc.
NOW COUNTRY - Wallpaper - Sanitas Wallcoverings
NOW FLOOR - Floor coverings - Congoleum Corp.
NOW FLOWER - Floor coverings ☆ - Congoleum Corp.
NOW FOODS - Food products - Now Foods Corp.
NOW FUN! - Computer software - Now Software, Inc.
NOW HIRING - Publisher's imprints - International Employment Group
NOW I CAN LOOK SLIMMER IN ANYTHING - Underwear and nightwear - NCC Industries, Inc.
NOW I'M COOKING - Receipt books - Wahlman Publishing
NOW LOOK - Fabrics–tapestry - Comark Wallcoverings
NOW LUGGAGE - Luggage ☆ - Universal Trav-ler Inc.
NOW NYLON - Pet products - Now Pet Products
NOW SPORT - Apparel–women's - May Department Stores Co.
NOW THATS BODY - Hair care products ☆ - Protege Corp.
NOW THAT'S ITALIAN - Sausages - Johnsonville Foods Co.
NOW THAT'S KEY - Food processors - Key Technology, Inc.
NOW USA - Photographic equipment - Sidetrack, Inc.
NOW UTILITIES - Computer software - Now Software, Inc.
NOW VOYAGER - Floor coverings–carpet and rugs ☆ - Mohawk Carpet Corp.
NOW WEDDING LINE, THE - Greeting cards ☆ - Regency Thermographers Inc.
NOW WHAT SOFTWARE - Computer storage devices–optical - Now What Software
NOW YOU FEEL IT, NOW YOU DON'T - Underwear and nightwear ☆ - Lovable Co.
NOW YOU KNOW WHY I WEAR RED - Shirts - Tortoize Productions, Inc.
NOW YOU SEE IT - Games ☆ - Milton Bradley Co.
NOW YOU'RE STYLIN' - Hair care products - Blue Cross Laboratories Inc.
NOWA LI - Footwear - Imex International Inc.
NOWATA - Cleaning preparations ☆ - Golden Star Inc.
NOWLINE - Answering machines ☆ - Groupcom, Inc.
NOWMEDIA1 - Computer storage devices–optical - Penton Publishing Inc.
NOWTRITION - Vitamins and nutritional supplements - Nikken Inc.
NOX-ICH - Pet products - Weco Products Inc.
NOX OUT - Chemical preparations - Crown Technology, Inc.
NOXACORN - Health care products ☆ - E. Fougera & Co. Inc.
NOXALL - Paints ☆ - Nowstar
NOXELL - Skin care products ☆ - Noxell Corp.
NOXIDENE - Hair care products - L.T. York Co.
NOXIT - Health care products ☆ - CTS Laboratories Inc.
NOXOL - Chemical preparations - CORPEX Technologies Inc.
NOXON - Furniture polish and wax - Boyle-Midway
NOXON - Tools–hand-operated - Spring Line, Inc.
NOXZEMA - Skin care products - Noxell Corp.
NOXZEMA SENSITIVE - Skin care products - Noxell Corp.
NOYANTAL - Pharmaceutical preparations ☆ - P.J. Noyes Co., Inc.
NOYCE ALLWAY - Hooks - G.W. Witte Co.
NOYES 107 - Pharmaceutical preparations ☆ - P.J. Noyes Co., Inc.
NOYES ISLAND - Seafood products–fresh or frozen - E.C. Phillips & Son, Inc.
NOYMER - Leather goods - Noymer Leather and Gifts Ltd.
NOYO - Wood products - Boise Cascade Corp.
NOYO PRIDE - Food products machinery ☆ - FoodSalesWest Inc.
NOYO RIVER CELLARS - Wines - House of Daniels, Inc.
NOYO RIVER REDWOOD - Lumber - Georgia-Pacific Corp.
NOYO TRAWLER - Boats - Glen-L Marine Designs
NOZ-L-JET - Electronic equipment - The Fogmaster Corp.
NOZARK - Publisher's imprints - Nozark Products International, Inc.
NOZ'L GUN - Nozzles ☆ - Proen Products Co.
NOZONE - Toys - Troma, Inc.
NOZOVENT - Health care products - Scandinavian Natural Health & Beauty Products, Inc.
NOZZ-ALL - Hoses ☆ - L.R. Nelson Corp.
NOZZLE - Recording label - Jazz Composer's Orchestra Association Inc.
NOZZOLE - Wines - Kobrand Corp.
N.P. - Cleaning preparations - National Purity Inc.
NP-10 COOLPRINT - Computer printer - Nikon Inc.

☆ = Now out of production

NP 27 - Antiseptics - Procter & Gamble Co.
NP-27 - Health care products - Thompson Medical Co., Inc.
NPAC - Surgical supplies - National Service Industries, Inc.
NPD POWERVIEW - Computer software - NPD Group, Inc.
NPE - Paper - Lionel Smith
NPF - Gauging instruments - Uniweld Products, Inc.
NPF - Meat products–poultry - Sanderson Farms Inc.
NPG - Computer peripheral equipment - Teknow, Inc.
NPH - Pharmaceutical preparations - Bristol-Myers Squibb Co.
NPK - Fertilizers - International AG Labs, Inc.
NPM - First aid kits - National Patent Medical
NPOWER - Computer terminals - ACMA Computers Inc.
NPP - Polyethylene film sheets - Atlantis Plastics
NPR - Forklifts - Clark Material Handling Co.
N.P.S. - Cleaning preparations - National Purity Inc.
NPS - Pharmaceutical preparations - NPS Pharmaceuticals, Inc.
NPS - Publisher's imprints - National Plan Service
NPS - Vitamins and nutritional supplements ☆ - Shaklee Corp.
NPS PHARMACEUTICALS - Pharmaceutical preparations - NPS
   Pharmaceuticals, Inc.
NQS/MVS - Computer software - International Business Machines Corp.
NR - Pharmaceutical preparations - Mikeco., Inc.
N.R.C. - Vitamins and nutritional supplements - Raway Pharmacal Inc.
N.R.C. NOISE REDUCTION CONCEPTS - Construction equipment - Unique
   Concepts, Inc.
NRF-250 - Tubes–plastic - Noco Co.
NRG - Bowling balls - Track, Inc.
NRG - Insulation - NRG Barriers, Inc.
NRG - Laces–boot and shoe - NRG Inc.
NRG - Lighting fixtures - Hubbell Lighting, Inc. (Lighting Div.)
NRG-BRAID - Rope - Wellington Leisure Products, Inc.
NRG IN-LINE SKATES - Sporting goods - NRG In-Line Skates, Inc.
NRG NATURAL RESOURCES GROUP - Fertilizers - Tom Hrncirik
NRG PLUS - Soft drink - Bottlers International Ltd.
N.R.G. ULTRATEK - Filters–water - N.R.G. Enterprises, Inc./Mistra Inc.
NRG2 - Isotonic - Bottlers International Ltd.
N'RICH - Cream–canned or powdered - Hunt-Wesson, Inc.
NRL GOLD BANNER - Pharmaceutical preparations - Xcel Laboratories Inc.
NRM EXTRUSION - Machinery - Crompton and Knowles Corp.
NRP - Cleaning preparations - National Refrigeration and Air Conditioning
   Products, Inc.
NRP'S ORIGINAL - Pet products - Natural Research People, Inc.
NRS - Pharmaceutical preparations - Rugby Laboratories Inc.
NRS NATIONAL ROPERS SUPPLY DECATUR, TEXAS - Saddles - DRI
   Enterprises, Inc.
NRT - Recording label - Musical Productions, Inc.
NRV - Vitamins and nutritional supplements - Vital Energy
NS - Christmas tree ornaments - Premier Sydell, Ltd.
NS - Furniture - Nordic Line, Inc.
NS - Hammers - Ennis Manufacturing Co.
NS - Jewelry - Nova Stylings Inc.
NS - Sporting goods - Never Summer Industries, Inc.
N.S. CO - Jewelry - N S Co., Inc.
NS/COMMANDER CL - Computer software - Netsoft
NS/FOLDERS - Computer software - Netsoft
NS/FTS - Computer software - Netsoft
NS/HUB - Computer software - Netsoft
NS/MIDRANGE BUNDLE - Computer software - Netsoft
NS/MIDRANGE CLIENT SERVICES - Computer software - Netsoft
NS NORTH SAILS - Leather goods - North Sails Group, Inc.
NS/PREMIER - Computer software - Netsoft
NS/QUEUES - Computer software - Netsoft
NS/TECHNOLOGY - Computer software - Netsoft
NS/TOOLS - Computer software - Netsoft
NS/TRANSFER - Computer software - Netsoft
NS/VIRTUAL PRINT - Computer software - Netsoft
NSA - Beverage dispensers, water and air filters - National Safety Associates
NSA SPARKLING WATER SYSTEM - Beverage carbonator - National Safety
   Associates
NSC - Adhesives and sealants ☆ - Walton March
NSC - Bags - NSC Corp. (Johnson Tent Div.)
N.S.C. - Jewelry - Navajo Shopping Center
NSD - Recording label - Nationwide Sound Distributors
NSF - Building materials - NSF International
NSM - Office supplies - Faber-Castell Corp.
NSP - Herbal products - Lifetrends International

NSR - Electronic equipment - Nikon Inc.
N.S.T. - Thread ☆ - Signal Thread Co. Inc.
NSU - Motor vehicles–automobiles - Overseas Motors Inc.
NSWA - Water–bottled or canned - National Spring Water Assoc., Inc.
NT - Food products - Nash-Finch Co.
NT - Skin care products - Opi Products, Inc.
NT - Telescopes - Northern Telecom, Inc.
NT-CERT - Computer software ☆ - Transcender Corp.
NT-ENTERPRISE-CERT - Computer software ☆ - Transcender Corp.
NT RO-GRO - Fertilizers - Crop Builders Plus, Inc.
NT-SERVERCERT - Computer software ☆ - Transcender Corp.
NTC BUSINESS BOOKS - Publisher's imprints - NTC Contemporary Publishing
   Group
NTC LEARNING WORKS - Publisher's imprints - NTC Contemporary
   Publishing Group
NTERFORT - Computer software - Hughes Aircraft Co.
N.T.F. - Pet products - Richard Hanau Pet Foods Corp.
N.T.F. NATURAL TANNING FORMULA - Skin-care products - Natural Tanning
   Formula, Inc.
NTGARGIULO - Fruits and vegetables - Ntgargiulo, L.P.
NTH DEGREE NUTRITION - Vitamins and nutritional supplements -
   Renussance MM
NTIS FEDWORLD - Publisher's imprints - National Technical Information
   Service U.S. Department of Commerce
NTM SALT - Animal feeds - Redmond Clay & Salt Co.
NTP - Electronic equipment - G Prime Limited
NTP - Fixtures–plastic - Advanced Technology Inc.
NTSI - Publisher's imprints - NTSI Corp.
NTVT - Tubes–plastic - Aquaculture Research/Environmental Associates Inc.
NTWINE - Containers - TPS Package Engineering, Inc.
NTZ - Antihistamine preparations - Winthrop Pharmaceuticals
NU - Apparel and accessories - Northwestern University-Purchasing Dept.
NU - Skin care products ☆ - Francosmetics International Inc.
NU-A/B - Food products - Christian Hansen's Laboratory Inc.
NU-ACE - Office supplies - Ace Art Co.
NU/ALPHA - Labels–paper - Filing Equipment Inc.
NU-AQUA - Paints ☆ - Valspar Corp.
NU-ART - Greeting cards - Nu-Art Inc.
NU-BALL - Balls–tennis - Rebound Systems Inc.
NU-BEAT - Recording label - Priority Records
NU-BLANCO - Cheese - Irwin L. Gold & Assoc.
NU BORN TIME CAPSULES - Novelty items - Nu Born Time Capsules
NU-BRASS - Faucets - Franke, Inc. (Kitchen Systems Division)
NU-BREDE - Bandages - Johnson & Johnson
NU-BRIEF - Girdles - Nuvogue Creations
NU-BRITE - Cleaning preparations - Nu-Calgon Wholesaler, Inc.
NU-BRITE - Paints - Nu-Brite Chemical Co. Inc.
NU BROOM - Vacuum cleaners and accessories ☆ - Bissell Inc.
NU-CAM-PAQ - Brakes–motor vehicle - Maintenance-Free Brakes, Inc.
NU CAR - Defrosters and climate control products - Interdynamics, Inc.
NU-CHALKS - Toys - Coloron Industries
NU-CHECK - Check valves - Aladco
NU-CHECKERS - Games - Peter A. & Nathalie Belpulsi Partnership
NU CLEAN - Cleaning preparations - Bronner Enterprises, Inc.
NU-CLEAR - Carbons - American Coated Products Inc.
NU CLIP - Eyeglasses - Nu-Clip by Okayama
NU-CLO - Water treating compounds - Alden Leeds Corp.
NU-COLD - Frames–picture - Framemica Co.
NU-COLOR - Audio equipment - Oneida Electronics Manufacturing Co. Inc.
NU-COTE - Hardware - Sherwin-Williams Automotive Finishes Corp.
NU-CRAFT - Adhesives and sealants - Nu-Brite Chemical Co. Inc.
NU-CRETE - Building materials - Nucrete Corp.
NU CRISPS - Snack foods - Burns and Ricker Inc.
NU-CRYLIC - Turpentine - Sterling-Clark-Lurton Corp.
NU-D - Novelty items - Poly Tech Development, Inc.
NU-DA - Paints - Schulte Paint & Lacquer Manufacturing Co., Inc.
NU-DE - Brassieres (Bras) - Finebrand Inc.
NU-DEAL - Paints - Payson Corp.
NU-DECK - Paints - Evans Paint
NU-DEK 6-SUIT - Playing cards - SECOBRA
NU DELUXE - Antennas - Recoton Corp.
NU-DIMENSION - Furniture - Stratford Co.
NU DIMENSIONS - Novelty items - Fordick Corp.
NU DIMENSIONS - Wallcoverings - Cork Products Co. Inc.
NU DIMENSIONS - Wallpaper - K.M.L. Industries
NU ERA - Music stands - Krauth & Benninghofen Inc.

NU-ERA - Tools - Rack Engineering Co.
NU-EZE - Health care products ☆ - CTS Laboratories Inc.
NU-FAB - Dyes and pigments ☆ - Adhesive Products, Inc.
NU-FIT - Padding–foam - Gholamali Khamneipur
NU-FITS - Sporting goods - Hocks Laboratories
NU FLEX - Wheels - Hamilton Caster & Manufacturing Co.
NU-FLOW M - Fungicides - Wilbur-Ellis Co.
NU-FOAM - Cushions - Better Sleep, Inc.
NU FORM - Medical apparatus - Physicians Appliance Co.
NU FORM - Prophylactics - Schmid Laboratories
NU-GARD - Hardware ☆ - Macklanburg-Duncan Co.
NU-GENIC - Hair care products ☆ - Designer's Edge International
NU-GLAZE - Finishing agents - Star Finishing Products Inc.
NU-GLAZE - Weather stripping ☆ - Macklanburg-Duncan Co.
NU-GLO - Finishing agents - Star Finishing Products Inc.
NU GOLD - Watches - Enchanted Gold, Inc.
NU-GOLD - Wire - Sax Arts & Crafts
NU-HAIRTRITION - Shampoos - Hobe Labs Inc.
NU-HANDS - Soap ☆ - Grace Construction Products
NU HOUSE - Fruits and vegetables ☆ - Snokist Growers
NU-HUE - Paints - Krylon/Dupli-Color
NU-IRON - Pharmaceutical preparations - Merz Inc.
NU-J - Knives–hunting ☆ - Hunt Manufacturing Co.
NU-JOY - Girdles - Nuvogue Creations
NU JUICE - Juices - Nujuice Corp.
NU-JR. BELT - Girdles - Nuvogue Creations
NU-KANE - Caning–rattan - Wendell Fabrics Corp.
NU-KAR SCENT - Deodorizers - Surco Products Inc.
NU-KILL - Insect repellents - Nu-Calgon Wholesaler, Inc.
NU-KOIL - Weather stripping ☆ - Macklanburg-Duncan Co.
NU-KUT - Skin care products ☆ - Hess Hair Milk Laboratories Inc.
NU-KUTZ - Hair care products - Nu-Kutz Ltd.
NU LAST - Wheels - Hamilton Caster & Manufacturing Co.
NU-LIFE - Milk - Chris Hansen, Inc.
NU-LIFE - Smoke detectors - Filter Tip Research Co.
NU-LIFT - Apparel–women's ☆ - Bali Co. Inc.
NU-LINE - Furniture ☆ - Gerry Wood Products
NU-LIQUID - Cleaning preparations ☆ - Grace Construction Products
NU-LITE - Fuses - Dependable Electric Manufacturing Co.
NU-LOAF - Cheese - Irwin L. Gold & Assoc.
NU LOCK - Rings–jewelry - Feature Enterprises
NU-LOOK - Adhesives and sealants ☆ - Atlas Chemical Co.
NU-LOOK - Cleaning preparations - Knight Marketing Corp.
NU LOOK - Jewelry - Weingeroff Enterprises, Inc.
NU MADE - Food products ☆ - Safeway Stores Inc.
NU-MAID - Margarine - Miami Margarine Co. Inc.
NU MAR - Margarine ☆ - Wilsey Foods, Inc.
NU MASCA - Cosmetics, skin-care products ☆ - Cosrich Inc.
NU-MATIC - Brushes–hair - Magic Distributing Ltd.
NU-MERICAN - Cheese - Irwin L. Gold & Assoc.
NU-METAL - Door frames ☆ - Macklanburg-Duncan Co.
NU METAL - Metals - Advanced Technology Inc.
NU-METRIC - Hair care products ☆ - Designer's Edge International
NU-METRICS - Measuring instruments - Nu-Metrics, Inc.
NU-MIRROR - Mirrors - Yerger Industries, Inc.
NU-NAILS - Nail care products - Nu-Nails
NU-NAP - Napkins–paper - Fort Howard Corp.
NU-NOIR - Hair care products ☆ - Designer's Edge International
NU-NUT - Peanut butter - Nalley's Fine Foods
NU-OZ GROUP, THE - Apparel and accessories - Timely Trends, Inc.
NU-PAK - Food products - Hungerford Packing Co. Inc.
NU-PARTS - Automotive parts and accessories - Nu-Parts Automotive Products, Inc.
NU-PHALT - Cement–asphalt ☆ - Macklanburg-Duncan Co.
NU-PLASTIX - Paints - Sampson Coatings Inc.
NU-PLUS - Filters–water - Nu-Calgon Wholesaler, Inc.
NU-POLAR - Lenses–optical - Younger Optics
NU-POLY - Paneling - Nudo Products Inc.
NU-PORCE - Adhesives and sealants - Nu-Porce Inc.
NU POWER - Battery chargers - Remington Products Co.
NU-POWER - Vitamins and nutritional supplements - Nu-Power
NU PRIDE - Tools–hand-operated - Marshalltown Trowel Co.
NU PRIDE BLT - Tools–hand-operated - Marshalltown Trowel Co.
NU-RAIL - Rails–aluminum - Hollaender Manufacturing Co.
NU-ROPE - Jewelry - Adrienne Designs
NU-SALT - Food products - Cumberland Packing Corp.

NU SASH - Windows–vinyl - Louisiana-Pacific Corp.
NU-SCREW - Hinges - Sir-C
NU-SEATER - Tools - Edward O'Malley Valve Co.
NU-SEN-SATION - Paints - Republic Powdered Metals, Inc.
NU SENSATIONS - Underwear and nightwear - Wells Fargo Bank, N.A.
NU-SET - Hair care products - Nexxus Products Co.
NU-SET - Hardware - Kwan Y. Ng
NU-SHINE - Musical instrument accessories - Micro Musical Products Corp.
NU-SHU-PAQ - Brakes–motor vehicle ☆ - Maintenance-Free Brakes, Inc.
NU-SILVER - Frames–picture - Framemica Co.
NU-SKIN HANDS - Toys - Topstone Industries Inc.
NU-SLANT - Pillows - Better Sleep, Inc.
NU-SNACK - Cheese - Irwin L. Gold & Assoc.
NU-SNO - Napkins–paper - Erving Paper Products Inc.
NU SOFT - Fabric softeners - First Preference Products Corp.
NU-SOUR - Detergents - Ecolab Inc.
NU SPARKLE - Detergents - Clo White Co.
NU-STAG - Knives–carving ☆ - Kirk & Matz Ltd.
NU-STAIR - Pigments - Garon Products Inc.
NU-STRIP - Paint removers - Autre Products, Ltd.
NU STUD - Fabrics - Greenwood Mills Inc.
NU/SYSTEM CUISINE - Food products - Nutri/System L.P.
NU TECH PERFORMANCE SUSPENSIONS - Automotive parts and accessories - Nu Tech Performance Suspensions, Inc.
NU-TECH POLYMER BUSHING SYSTEM - Machinery - Truk-Align, Inc. of Florida
NU-TEK - Electronic equipment - Everquest, Inc.
NU TEMP - Antifreeze - Prestone Products Corp.
NU-TEMPERA - Paints ☆ - Shiva Inc.
NU THENA - Computer software - Nu Thena Systems
NU-THRED - Tools - JAW Manufacturing Co.
NU-TILE - Cleaning preparations - Hertron International Inc.
NU-TIP - Medical apparatus - Marlow Surgical Technologies Inc.
NU TOFU - Food products - Cemac Foods Corp.
NU-TONE - Musical instrument accessories - E. & O. Mari Inc.
NU-TONE - Paints ☆ - M.A. Bruder & Sons Inc.
NU-TONE - Paper–sand - Canson-Talens Inc.
NU-TOP - Fixtures–plastic ☆ - ICI Acrylics Inc.
NU-TRAC - Cables–aluminum - Smiths Industries Aerospace & Defense Systems Inc.
NU TREASURE - Fabrics–satin - Rosebar Textile Co.
NU-TRED - Mats, matting - American Floor Products Co. Inc.
NU-TREND - Giftware ☆ - Anchor Hocking Glass, Inc.
NU-TRENZ - Jewelry - Nicole Mintzes
NU TRESS - Hair care products - Nu-Tress Laboratories Inc.
NU-TREX - Hair care products ☆ - Gabel's Cosmetics Inc.
NU-TRISH - Food products - Christian Hansen's Laboratory Inc.
NU-TRISH A/B - Milk - Hygeia Dairy Products
NU-V - Girdles - Nuvogue Creations
NU-VISION - Automotive parts and accessories - Trico Products Corp.
NU-VITA - Detergents - Nu-Vita Foods
NU VITA - Hair care products ☆ - Framesi USA/Roffler Industries Inc.
NU-VOLONE - Cheese - Irwin L. Gold & Assoc.
NU-VU II - Glass–window ☆ - Remington Building Products
NU-VUES - Building materials - Entol Industries Inc.
NU-WAL - Coatings - Specification Chemicals, Inc.
NU-WALK - Sealing compounds - Garon Products Inc.
NU WAVE - Bathtubs–enameled - Lyons Industries Inc.
NU-WAVE - Building materials - BHP Steel Building Products USA, Inc.
NU-WAVE - Finishing agents - Rudd Co. Inc.
NU-WAX - Paints ☆ - Klean-Strip
NU-WAX - Varnishes - Nu-Brite Chemical Co. Inc.
NU WAY - Containers–plastic - Laclede Chain Manufacturing Co.
NU WAY - Footwear - Sam Brilliant Sporto
NU-WAY - Weather stripping ☆ - Macklanburg-Duncan Co.
NU-WELL - Cleaning equipment - US Filter/Johnson Screens
NU-WORLD - Musical instrument accessories ☆ - French American Reeds Manufacturing
NU YOLKS - Stationery - Binkerton
NU-ZONE - Fungicides - Wilbur-Ellis Co.
NU-ZZARELLA - Cheese - Irwin L. Gold & Assoc.
NUAGE - Health care products - Nuage Laboratories Ltd.
NUAGE - Tiles–ceramic - Latco Products
NUAGE D'OR - Skin care products - Emboy Co.
NUAGES - Floor coverings–carpet and rugs ☆ - Columbus Mills, Inc.
NUAIR - Doors–glass - Nu-Air Manufacturing Co.

☆ = Now out of production

NUAIR - Windows–storm - Nu-Air Manufacturing Co.
NUANCE - Beverages - Shasta Beverages, Inc.
NUANCE - Cabinets - Actua
NUANCE - Calculators - Texas Instruments Inc.
NUANCE - Christmas tree ornaments - Cracker Box Inc.
NUANCE - Floor coverings–carpet and rugs - Cumberland Mills Inc.
NUANCE - Floor coverings–carpet and rugs - Whitecrest Carpet Mills
NUANCE - Footwear - White Lights Inc.
NUANCE - Fragrance ☆ - Coty Inc.
NUANCE - Furniture - Tomlinson of High Point Inc.
NUANCE - Pigments–paint - Paragon Paint & Varnish Corp.
NUANCE - Tiles–ceramic - Latco Products
NUANCE - Wallpaper - Robert Crowder & Co.
NUANCE - Wallpaper - Surface Industries Inc.
NUANCE II - Tiles–ceramic ☆ - Latco Products
NUANCE ACCENTS - Tiles–ceramic - Latco Products
NUANCE ACCENTS - Tiles–ceramic - Los Angeles Tile Co., Inc.
NUANCE BASICS - Tiles–ceramic ☆ - Latco Products
NUANCE STONEWARE - Tiles–ceramic ☆ - Latco Products
NUANCES - Hair care products - Clairol Inc.
NUANCES - Wallcovering - Wall Trends, Inc.
NUANCES - Wallpaper ☆ - Capital Carousel Inc.
NUARAMID - Gloves - PR Industries, Inc.
NUART - Clothing - Nuart Fashions, Inc.
NUART - Greeting cards - Royal Stationery Co.
NUART - Nail care products - Nu-Art Beauty Products
NUB-HANDLES - Bicycles - Schwinn Cycling & Fitness Inc.
NUB HILL - Fabrics - Dan River Inc.
NUBA BY SKIVERTEX - Paper products - REXAM DSI
NUBAIN - Pharmaceutical preparations - Du Pont Pharmaceuticals
NUBASICS VHP - Vitamins and nutritional supplements - Clintec Nutrition Co.
NUBBIES - Golf shoes and gloves - Austad Co.
NUBBIES - Sandals ☆ - Swenson Imports
NUBBIES - Toys–stuffed - Harvey Herman Associates, Inc.
NUBBINS - Candy - Brach and Brock Confections Inc.
NUBBINS - Dolls - Laura White
NUBBLE - Toys - Sonoma Trading Co., Inc.
NUBBY - Yarn ☆ - William Unger & Co. Inc.
NUBBY DAN - Fabrics - Dan River Inc.
NUBEECOMP - Pharmaceutical preparations ☆ - Vitarine Pharmaceuticals Inc.
NUBEL - Electrical equipment - Edwards Co. Inc.
NUBELE - Fabrics - Dan River Inc.
NUBLACK - Ammunition ☆ - Olin Corp. (Winchester Div.)
NUBLEND - Blenders - Dynamics Corp. of America
NUBLUE - Flowers, plants, and seeds - Jacklin Seed
NUBODY - Bath salts - Joico Laboratories, Inc.
NUBOLIC - Pharmaceutical preparations - Seatrace Co.
NUBONNET - Cleaning preparations–carpet and rug - Bronner Enterprises, Inc.
NUBOX - Safes - Nutech Fire and Security, Inc.
NUBREEZE - Electrical equipment - Nutone Inc.
NUBRITE - Wood products - Georgia-Pacific Corp.
NUBRUSH - Toothbrushes - Applied Microdontics
NUBTEX - Fabrics - International Paper Co.
NUBTEX - Fabrics - Veratec
NUBU - Computer software and hardware - Utility Systems, Inc.
NUBWALL - Wallpaper - PCI Industries Inc.
NUCANOLA - Vegetable oil ☆ - GFA Brands Inc.
NUCAP WORKS - Paints - OEM Paints, Inc.
NUCELLE - Skin care products - Dermaceutical Labs, Inc.
NUCELLE 31 - Skin care products - Dermaceutical Labs, Inc.
NUCHIEF - Food products - Nuchief Sales Inc.
NUCKEME - Milk ☆ - Ryan Foods Co.
NUCLEAR - Thread ☆ - American & Efird, Inc.
NUCLEAR ESCALATION - Games - Flying Buffalo Inc.
NUCLEAR FREEZE - Food products - Garden of Eatin', Inc.
NUCLEAR HELL - Sauces - Gib's Classics, Inc.
NUCLEAR PROLIFERATION - Games - Flying Buffalo Inc.
NUCLEAR SICILIAN SUB ROSA - Food products - Mission Control
NUCLEAR WAR - Games - Flying Buffalo Inc.
NUCLEIC A - Recording label - Dowbrands L.P.
NUCLEIC COMPLEX - Vitamins and nutritional supplements ☆ - Fibertone Co.
NUCLEIC PAK - Hair care products - Joico Laboratories, Inc.
NUCLEIC PLUS - Hair care products - Palm Beach Beauty Products
NUCLEOPROTEIN - Hair care products - KMS Research Inc.
NUCLEUS - Apparel–men's - Montgomery Ward & Co. Inc.

NUCLEUS - Dictating machines - Dictaphone Corp.
NUCLEUS - Recording label - Nucleus Records
NUCLEUS - Stereos - Gallo Acoustics, Inc.
NUCLEUS - Transmitting apparatus–television - Motorola, Inc. (Land Mobile Products Sector)
NUCLEUS - Vitamins and nutritional supplements - Amrion, Inc.
NUCLEUS - Wallpaper - Seabrook Wallcoverings, Inc.
NUCOA - Margarine ☆ - CPC International Inc.
NUCOFED - Pharmaceutical preparations - Smithkline Beecham Corp.
NUCOIL - Cleaning preparations - Skasol Corp.
NUCOL - Coatings ☆ - Sigma Coatings USA BV.
NUCONCEPT - Coffee - El Dorado Coffee
NUCOR - Paperboard - Savage Universal Corp.
NUCOR - Screws - Nucor Corp.
NUCORD - Cording ☆ - Samson Cordage Works
NUCORK - Bulletin boards–cork - Claridge Products and Equipment Inc.
NUDE - Apparel–women's ☆ - Carnival Creations
NUDE - Perfumes - Revlon Consumer Products Corp.
NUDE FOOD - Snack foods - Robert's American Gourmet
NUDECK - Cement - United Gilsonite Laboratories
NUDERMA - Skin care products - Joico Laboratories, Inc.
NUDES & DUDES - Pens - Tops Pen Co.
NUDESSE - Depilatories - Normajean Fusco
NUDESSE - Depilatories - Total Woman Salon
NUDGE - Game machines - Sigma Game Inc.
NUDIT - Skin care products - Medtech Laboratories Inc.
NUDITUDE - Apparel and accessories - Gary M. Saville
NUDOX - Pharmaceutical preparations ☆ - Ulmer Pharmacal Co.
NUDRY - Chemical preparations - OSI Specialties, Inc.
NUECO - Varnish removers ☆ - Foy-Johnston Inc.
NUECO - Varnishes - Perry & Derrick Co.
NUEVA CREACION - Publisher's imprints - Wm. B. Eerdmans Publishing Co.
NUEVA SALUD - Pharmaceutical preparations - Pennex Products
NUEVE PROPOSTE - Product description unknown - Durawall Inc.
NUEVO - Recording label ☆ - Rangel Record Distributors
NUEVO GLAS - Sporting goods - Cut 'n Jump Ski Corp.
NUFF SAID - Footwear - Shoe Carnival, Inc.
NUFFY - Apparel - Hub Distributing Inc.
NUFFY CLOTHIERS - Apparel and accessories - Hub Distributing Inc.
NUFLOOR - Flooring–parquet - Victoria's Dance-Theatrical Supply
NUFORM - Giftware - European Imports of California Inc.
NUFORM - Jewelry - Ultralite Technology Inc.
NUFORM - Yogurt - H.P. Hood & Sons Inc.
NUFREE - Depilatories - Normajean Fusco
NUFRESH - Cleaning preparations–carpet and rug - Bronner Enterprises, Inc.
NUGANIA - Hair care products - Willat Co.
NUGARD - Locks–door - Sunico Industries, Inc.
NUGEN - Pharmaceutical preparations - Barrows Pharmacal Inc.
NUGGET - Coffee - Park Corp.
NUGGET - Eggs - Almark Inc.
NUGGET - Fabrics ☆ - Dan River Inc.
NUGGET - Fishing lures - Hildebrandt Corp.
NUGGET - Flowers, plants, and seeds - Jacklin Seed
NUGGET - Food products - Davis-Le Grand Co.
NUGGET - Food products - Lombardi Foodservice
NUGGET - Nuts and nut products - Nugget Distributors Inc.
NUGGET - Preserved foods–prepackaged - Anchor Food Products, Inc.
NUGGET - Pumps–water - Beckett Corp.
NUGGET - Tobacco–chewing or smoking - Amar Blends Co.
NUGGET - Tools - Goldblatt Tool Co.
NUGGET - Toys - Tonka Corp.
NUGGET - Turkeys - Watson Quality Foods Inc.
NUGGET & MEAL - Dog food - Star Feeds Inc.
NUGGET NUTRI-GOLD - Fruit drinks–bottled or canned - Nugget Distributors Inc.
NUGGET ORO FINO - Olive oil - Nugget Distributors Inc.
NUGGETS - Candy - Hershey Chocolate USA
NUGGETS - Dog food ☆ - Agway Country Foods Inc.
NUGGETS - Laxatives - Endovations Inc.
NUGGETS - Marble products - Vitro Agate Corp.
NUGGETS - Salt - Akzo America Inc.
NUGGETS O'GOLD - Candy ☆ - Donruss Co.
NUGGIT - Toys - Tonka Corp.
NUGLADE - Flowers, plants, and seeds - Jacklin Seed
NUGRAPE - Beverages–carbonated - Monarch Co., Inc.
NUGUARD - Cleaning preparations–carpet and rug - Bronner Enterprises, Inc.

☆ = Now out of production

NUGUARD - Footwear - Lehigh Safety Shoe Co.
NUGUARD 75 - Footwear - Lehigh Safety Shoe Co.
NUGUN - Dental equipment - Centrix, Inc.
NUHEALTH - Food products - Park Corp.
NUHIDE - Apparel and accessories - Glove Source, Inc.
NUISANCE PREVENTION - Alarm systems - Directed Electronics, Inc.
NUIT - Dresses—women's - Jonathan Logan Inc.
NUITS INDIENNES - Perfumes - Conopco, Inc.
NUJAWS - Tubes—steel ☆ - FasTest Inc.
NUJAZ - Beverages - At Your Convenience Stores Inc.
NUJOL - Oils—mineral ☆ - Schering-Plough Healthcare Products
NUJOY - Candy - Standard Candy Co. Inc.
NUK - Nipples—rubber - Gerber Products Co.
NUKE - Waterproof outerwear ☆ - Distributors Service Corp.
NUKE BOOT - Galoshes - Distributors Service Corp.
NUKE SUIT - Waterproof outerwear - Distributors Service Corp.
NUKE THE BEAR - Pillows - Ann E. Sanders
NUKERZ - Toys—guns - Mattel, Inc.
NUKEWAR - Games ☆ - Avalon Hill Game Co.
NUKRAF - Paperboard - Fairfield Recycled Papers Inc.
NULAST - Bandages ☆ - Glenwood LLC
NULCERS - Pharmaceutical preparations - Health Alternative Products, Inc.
NU'LEVEN - Pharmaceutical preparations ☆ - Lemmon Co.
NULICAINE - Health care products - Kay Pharmacal Co. Inc.
NULIFE - Floor waxes - AmeriPlus Inc.
NULIFE - Shampoos ☆ - ICN Pharmaceuticals Inc.
NULL - Toys - Mattel, Inc.
NULL-A-FIRE & DESIGN - Gypsum products - Georgia-Pacific Corp.
NULLO - Pharmaceutical preparations - Chattem Inc.
NULLO - Pharmaceutical preparations - Monticello Drug Co.
NULOK - Tools ☆ - Nupla Corp.
NULOX - Hair care products - Samlo
NULOX HAIR FOOD - Hair care products - Samlo
NULOY NAIL DRIVE - Hardware - Barrett Manufacturing Co.
NULUX - Lighting fixtures - Nulux
NULYTELY - Medical apparatus - Braintree Laboratories, Inc.
NUM-RITE - Sporting goods ☆ - Olin Corp. (Winchester Div.)
NUM-ZIT - Infant product - Purepac Pharmaceutical Co.
NUMA LUBE - Oils—lubricating - Numa
NUMANO - Wines ☆ - Takara Sake USA
NUMAR - Food products - Chiquita Brands, Inc.
NUMARK - Audio and video equipment - Numark Industries, Inc.
NUMARK PPD - Audio equipment - Numark Electronics Corp.
NUMB-GUMS - Analgesics - Business Medical Supply, Inc.
NUMB-SCULL - Toys - Maryland Toy Corp.
NUMBATABS - Office supplies ☆ - The Tiffen Co.
NUMBER - See also NO.
NO.1 - Recording label - Sony Disco Inc.
NUMBER 1 - Tires - Bridgestone/Firestone, Inc.
NO. 1 SELECT ESTRUS - Hunting equipment - Wildlife Research Center, Inc.
NO. 1 WHITE - Calcium compounds - ECC International
NO. 5 - Firearms, accessories, and parts - Texas Longhorn Arms, Inc.
NUMBER 7 - Cigarettes - Tobacco Exporters International (USA) Ltd.
NUMBER 7-FORMULA R - Vitamins and nutritional supplements - Nima Products Inc.
NO. 11 - Fishing lures - Uncle Josh Bait Co.
NUMBER 13 - Lubricants - Ashland Oil, Inc.
NO. 13 - Skin care products ☆ - Avigal Henna
NO. 14 GRENADIERS - Cigars - G.W. Van Slyke & Horton
NUMBER 88 - Tobacco products - Brick-Hanauer Co.
NO. 119 - Beverages—malt - Riverside Brewing Co.
NO. 1939 - Apparel and accessories - Moray, Inc.
NUMBER CHASE - Computer software ☆ - SRA/McGraw-Hill (Div. of The McGraw-Hill Companies)
NUMBER CRUNCHER - Computer programming services - Berta-Max Inc.
NUMBER EXPRESS - Games - Smethport Specialty Co.
NUMBER EXPRESS - Toys - Lauri Inc.
NUMBER FACT SHEETS - Computer software - Gamco Industries Inc.
NUMBER FACTORY - Computer software ☆ - Queue Inc.
NUMBER FACTS - Computer software - Gamco Industries Inc.
NUMBER FARM - Computer software - SRA/McGraw-Hill (Div. of The McGraw-Hill Companies)
NUMBER FUN - Electronic equipment - Texas Instruments Inc.
NUMBER-INOS - Games ☆ - Teaching Concepts Inc.
NUMBER-IT - Hardware - Number-It, Inc.
NUMBER JUNGLE - Games - World Traveler Ltd.

NUMBER MATCH IT - Computer programming services - Berta-Max Inc.
NUMBER MUNCHERS - Computer software - Softkey International Inc.
NUMBER NINE - Computer hardware - Number Nine Visual Technology Corp.
NUMBER ONE - Floor coverings—carpet and rugs - Philadelphia Carpets
NUMBER ONE BAR - Frozen confectioneries - International Ice Cream Corp.
NUMBER PLAQUES - Toys - Lauri Inc.
NUMBER PLAY - Toys - Lauri Inc.
NUMBER PUZZLE BOARDS AND PEGS - Toys - Lauri Inc.
NUMBER QUEST - Computer software ☆ - Sunburst Communications, Inc.
NUMBER QUEST - Games ☆ - Decipher Inc.
NUMBER SEA HUNT - Computer software - Gamco Industries Inc.
NUMBER SIX - Deodorants—personal - Caswell-Massey Co. Ltd.
NUMBER WISE - Games - Tiger Electronics, Inc.
NUMBER WON - Trophies—metal - Tropar Manufacturing Co., Inc.
NUMBER WORKSHOP - Computer software - Jostens Learning Corp.
#1 SADDLE OIL - Cleaning preparations - Bee Natural Leathercare Inc.
#6 DIET - Pet products - Breeder's Choice Pet Foods, Inc.
#76 SOUTHPAW - Hair care products - Dubl Duck/Jet Set Inc.
#502 FAMILY - Underwear and nightwear - Exquisite Form Industries
#916 FAMILY - Underwear and nightwear - Exquisite Form Industries
NUMBERGRAPHS - Nameplates—engraved - Metalcraft Inc.
NUMBERLAND - Games ☆ - Milton Bradley Co.
NUMBERS - Apparel—women's ☆ - Jonathan Logan Inc.
NUMBERSCOPE - Computer software - Zephyr Services
NUMBERTIME - Infant product ☆ - Ming Ta Supply
NUMBERZ - Packaging—paper - Z-Barten Productions
NUMBLER - Games - William N. Rheams
NUMBSKUL - Apparel and accessories - John Emrich
NUMED - Pharmaceutical preparations - Dorex International Corp.
NUMER-RING - Binders - Dennison National Co.
NUMER UNO - Cigars - Tropical Tobacco, Inc.
NUMERIC - Clocks ☆ - By Design Corp.
NUMERO DOS - Cigars - Tropical Tobacco, Inc.
NUMERO-O-SAURUS - Puzzles - Lauri Inc.
NUMERO UNO - Colognes - Luzier Personalized Cosmetics, Inc.
NUMERO UNO - Sporting goods - Cut 'n Jump Ski Corp.
NUMERO UNO ENTRE FAMILIAS - Food products ☆ - Ruiz Food Products Inc.
NUMEROLOGY: THE KEY TO YOUR INNER SELF - Computer software - Spectrum Universal
NUMEROUNO - Olive oil - De Medici Imports Ltd.
NUMICA - Blackboards—wood - Arcana Products Co.
NUMISMATIC DEALER DIRECTORY - Publisher's imprints - CDN, Inc.
NUMISMATICS - Giftware - Franklin Mint
NUMO - Health care products - Respironics, Inc.
NUMONYL SR - Pharmaceutical preparations - Teral Laboratories
NUMORPHAN - Analgesics - Dupont Merck Pharmaceutical Co.
NUMORPHAN HCL - Analgesics - Du Pont Pharmaceuticals
NUMOTIZINE - Pharmaceutical preparations - Hobart Laboratories Inc.
NUMS - Computer software - SourceView Software International
NUMZIDENT - Denture materials - Purepac Pharmaceutical Co.
NUN-BETTER - Cleaning preparations - Kleen-Rite Products
NUN CHACKUN - Video games - Taito America Corp.
NUNES - Nuts—salted, roasted, cooked, or canned - Nunes Farms
NUNN BETTER - Flour—blended - Nunn & Sons Milling Co. Inc.
NUNN BETTER - Fruit drinks—bottled or canned - Ron Nunn Farms
NUNN-BUSH - Footwear—men's - Nunn Bush Shoe Co.
NUNN BUSH - Shoes - Weyco Group Inc.
NUNN MORE NATURAL - Meat products - Leslie E. Nunn
NUN'S SAUCE, THE - Food products - Kendall-Brown Foods
NUNSUN - Insulating materials - National Metallizing
NUNSUN II - Insulating materials - National Metallizing
NUNUS - Apparel and accessories - Fred Meyer, Inc.
NUON KLOCKS - Clocks - Gemini Display Ltd.
NUONS - Women's sportswear - Interstyle Inc.
NUORI - Vitamins and nutritional supplements - Finlandia Ltd.
NUOVA - Water purification systems ☆ - Aquarium Products Inc.
NUOVA AMORE - Pasta ☆ - Fred Montesi Super Markets
NUOVALON - Water purification systems ☆ - Aquarium Products Inc.
NUOVO - Jewelry, hair ribbons, etc. - County Seat Stores Inc.
NUOVO - Ophthalmic goods - Foremost Optical Products
NUOVO - Sporting goods - Exel Marketing Inc.
NUOVO COUNTY SEAT - Apparel - County Seat Stores Inc.
NUOVO CURL - Hair care products - Modafini Inc.
NUPAK - Food products - Connell Co.
NUPASTEL - Chalk - Faber-Castell Corp.

☆ = Now out of production

NUPERCAINAL - Analgesics - Ciba-Geigy Corp.
NUPLA CUSH-N-GRIP - Tools ☆ - Nupla Corp.
NUPLABOND - Epoxy ☆ - Nupla Corp.
NUPLAFLEX - Hammers - Nupla Corp.
NUPLAGLAS - Tools - Nupla Corp.
NUPON N - Computers - Nupon Computing Corp.
NUPOP - Computer software - Northwestern University-Purchasing Dept.
NUPREP - Cleaning preparations–carpet and rug - Bronner Enterprises, Inc.
NUPRIME - Hardware ☆ - Season-all Industries Inc.
NUPRIN - Analgesics - Bristol-Myers Squibb Co.
NUPRO - Kitchen utensils–aluminum - Nupro Co.
NUPTIALS - Napkins–paper - Erving Paper Products Inc.
NUQULTURE - Apparel–men's - Subquifure
NURAP - Paper–gift wrap ☆ - Mosinee Paper Corp.
NUREALITY - Electronic equipment - Atlantis Computers, Inc.
NURETEC - Containers–trash - Nu-Recycling Technology, Inc.
NURICA - Cigar boxes–wood - Consolidated Cigar Corp.
NURIT - Cash registers - Lipman USA, Inc.
NURMIKKO - Bedding–linen - Dan River Inc.
NURNBERG - Thermometers - Nurnberg Thermometer Co. Inc.
NUROLL - Scoops - Zeroll Co.
NUROOF - Metals - Metal Building Components, Inc.
NURSE COMFORT - Footwear - Southern Shoe Importers Inc.
NURSE FLORENCE - Watches - Elgin Watch Co.
NURSE HOPE - Dolls - Russ Berrie and Co., Inc.
NURSE MATES - Apparel and accessories ☆ - Kellwood Co.
NURSE MATES - Footwear - H.H. Brown Shoe Co., Inc.
NURSE MATES - Shoes - Lowell Shoe, Inc.
NURSE RUTH - Watches - Elgin Watch Co.
NURSE SUNNY - Toys–stuffed - Russ Berrie and Co., Inc.
NURSERY BIRDS - Toys ☆ - Kenner Products
NURSERY BLEND - Fertilizers - Pursell Industries, Inc.
NURSERY CLASSICS - Apparel–women's - Eden LLC
NURSERY FOAM - Infant product - Nurserytyme Products/Doppelt Industries
NURSERY NEEDS - Infant product - Sanitoy Inc.
NURSERY NOVEL, THE - Toys - Wimmer-Ferguson Inc.
NURSERY ODOR KLEEN - Deodorizers - G.G. Bean Inc.
NURSERY PEDIC - Bedding–linen - Nurserytyme Products/Doppelt Industries
NURSERY PETS - Toys–stuffed ☆ - Kenner Products
NURSERY PRO - Fountains - Water Creations
NURSERY RHYME - Games ☆ - World Traveler Ltd.
NURSERY RHYME COLLECTION, THE - Jewelry - Harry Winston, Inc.
NURSERY TALES - Games - CBS Toys
NURSERYTECH ID SYSTEMS - Computer software - Electronic Label Technology Inc.
NURSERYTEX - Infant product - Nurserytyme Products/Doppelt Industries
NURSES AUDIO NEWS - Recording label - Charles Vincent Sicola
NURSES BOOK SOCIETY, THE - Publisher's imprints - MacMillan Publishing Co. Inc.
NURSE'S CHOICE - Home-health-care products - Ivex Corp.
NURSES CHOICE - Panty hose - Nurses Choice Corp.
NURSES P.A.L. - Medical apparatus - Med Works Inc.
NURSES RINSELESS - Shampoos - Nephron Pharmaceuticals
NURSETTA - Brassieres (Bras) ☆ - Carmen Foundations Inc.
NURSING STOOL, THE - Furniture - Ortho-Stools, Inc.
NURSOY - Infant product - Wyeth-Ayerst Laboratories
NURTURALL - Veterinary nutritional supplements - Veterinary Products Laboratories
NURTURE - Computer software - Perceptive Solutions, Inc.
NURTURING NURSE COMPANY, THE - Recording label - Nurturing Nurse Co.
NURTURY - Infant product ☆ - Teledyne Water Pik
NURTZ - Playing cards - United States Playing Card Co.
NUSAL T - Veterinary pharmaceutical preparations - DVM Pharmaceuticals, Inc.
NUSED - Computers - Rumarson Technologies, Inc.
NUSHOE - Shoe polish - Top Brass Metal, Inc.
NUSPORT - Apparel–athletic - Donald James Polley Inc.
NUSTAR - Flowers, plants, and seeds - Jacklin Seed
NUSTAR - Fungicides - E.I. Dupont de Nemours and Co.
NUSTEEL - Cleaning preparations - Nusteel Co.
NUSTEP - Medical apparatus - Life Plus, Inc.
NUSURF - Adhesives and sealants - Sinclair Paint Co.
NUSURG MEDICAL - Surgical instruments - Nusurg Medical, Inc.
NUSWITCH - Computer hardware - Network Peripherals Inc.
NUT & HONEY CRUNCH - Cereal ☆ - Kellogg Co.
NUT BARREL - Nuts–candied - Trophy Nut Co.

NUT BOWL - Nuts - S & W Fine Foods, Inc.
NUT-BUSH - Flowers, plants, and seeds - New Tomorrow Inc.
NUT BUTTER BALLS - Snack foods - Betty Lou's Inc.
NUT CARAMELS - Candy - Cultural Survival, Inc.
NUT CHEWS - Candy - Squirrel Brand Co.
NUT-CHOCOLATE CLUSTER - Candy - Cultural Survival, Inc.
NUT CLUB - Snack foods - A.L. Bazzini Co. Inc.
NUT COAT'N - Seasonings - Andre Prost Inc.
NUT DUDS - Candy ☆ - Leaf, Inc.
NUT GEMS - Candy ☆ - Gilliam Candy Co. Inc. (Gilliam Candy Brands)
NUT HARVEST - Nuts–salted, roasted, cooked, or canned - Frito-Lay, Inc.
NUT HOUSE - Pet products - JungleTalk Inc.
NUT HUT - Bird feeders - Alden Lewis
NUT KETTLE - Confections - Nut Kettle East Inc.
NUT LOAF - Candy ☆ - Glade Taffy Town, Inc.
NUT LUNCH - Food products - Hoody Corp.
NUT MAZE - Pet products - JungleTalk Inc.
NUT-N-WOOD - Pet products - JungleTalk Inc.
NUT QUARTET, THE - Mixed nuts - MT OSO Trading Co.
NUT ROYAL - Candy - Glade Taffy Town, Inc.
NUT-SHELF - Nuts–salted, roasted, cooked, or canned ☆ - CPC International Inc.
NUT THINS - Crackers ☆ - Blue Diamond Growers
NUT-TREE - Flowers, plants, and seeds - New Tomorrow Inc.
NUT ZIPPERS - Candy - Squirrel Brand Co.
NUTAB - Electrodes - Ludlow Technical Products
NUTBERRY ROYALE - Bakery mixes - DCA Food Industries, Inc.
NUTCRACKER - Chocolate candy - Superior Fruit & Confections
NUTCRACKER - Coffee - Santa Cruz Coffee Roasting Co.
NUTCRACKER - Computer software - Datafocus Inc.
NUTCRACKER - Ice cream - Pierre's French Ice Cream Distributing Co. of Akron
NUTCRACKER - Nuts–salted, roasted, cooked, or canned - Nutcrackers Snacks Inc.
NUTCRACKER FESTIVAL ALE SEASONAL - Beverages–malt - Brew Moon Enterprises Inc.
NUTCRACKER SUITE - Pet products - JungleTalk Inc.
NUTCRACKER SWEETS - Food products - Homestyle Foods
NUTCRACKER, THE - Dolls ☆ - Effanbee Doll Corp.
NUTCRACKERS - Giftware - Whitehurst Imports
NUTEK - Computers - Nutek Inc.
NUTELLA - Chocolate candy - Ferrero U.S.A Inc.
NUTEX - Mold release - Adhesive Products, Inc.
NUTEX - Shortening - Procter & Gamble Co.
NUTKINS - Candy - Frederick Warne & Co., Inc.
NUTLETTES - Cereal - Dixie, USA, Inc.
NUTMEG - Christmas tree ornaments - Cracker Box Inc.
NUTMEG - Clothing - Nutmeg Mills, Inc.
NUTMEG - Dinnerware ☆ - Corning Inc.
NUTMEG - Glassware–household ☆ - Lenox Crystal, Inc.
NUTMEG - Wallpaper - Capital Carousel Inc.
NUTMEG FARM - Colognes ☆ - Avon Products, Inc.
NUTMEG RACING - Apparel and accessories - Nutmeg Mills, Inc.
NUTMEG TEDDY - Toys–stuffed - Russ Berrie and Co., Inc.
NUT'N BETTER - Candy ☆ - Leaf, Inc.
NUT'N GRAIN - Pet products - L/M Animal Farms, Inc.
NUTONE - Heaters–space - Nutone Inc.
NUTONE-HALLMACK - Bathroom accessories - Nutone Inc.
NUTRA - Skin care products - CCA Industries, Inc.
NUTRA IV - Vitamins and nutritional supplements - Nutra-Source Corp.
NUTRA 60 - Skin care products - CCA Industries, Inc.
NUTRA AEROBIC PHASES - Vitamins and nutritional supplements - Nature's Plus
NUTRA ALOE - Vitamins and nutritional supplements - Nutra-Source Corp.
NUTRA-BEAUTY - Skin care products - Marlyn Nutraceuticals, Inc.
NUTRA BETIC - Vitamins - Home Shopping Club, Inc.
NUTRA BLEND - Pet food - Topper Bird Ranch West
NUTRA BREAK - Granola bars - Holland American Wafer Co.
NUTRA-CARE - Pet products - Kaytee Products Inc.
NUTRA CARE - Shampoos - CCA Industries, Inc.
NUTRA-CHEW - Pet products - Petpro Products Inc.
NUTRA-CHUNK - Dog food ☆ - Stevens Industries Inc.
NUTRA-COA - Cosmetics ☆ - Pharmavite Corp.
NUTRA-E - Skirts–women's - Pharmavite Corp.
NUTRA-FARMED - Rice - Wehah Farm, Inc.
NUTRA FIG - Fruits–dried - San Joaquin Figs, Inc.

☆ = Now out of production

NUTRA FIN - Pet products - Rolf C. Hagen (USA) Corp.
NUTRA-FIT - Bakery products - B.I. Bakery Products Inc.
NUTRA FIX - Cosmetics - Alleghany Pharmacal Corp.
NUTRA FIX - Cosmetics - CCA Industries, Inc.
NUTRA FRESH BOX - Containers–paper - NBTY, Inc.
NUTRA FRESH PACK - Containers–paper - NBTY, Inc.
NUTRA GLOSS - Cosmetics - Alleghany Pharmacal Corp.
NUTRA-GRILL - Shortening - Bunge Foods Corp.
NUTRA NAIL - Cosmetics - CCA Industries, Inc.
NUTRA NAIL PLUS - Cosmetics - CCA Industries, Inc.
NUTRA NUGGET - Dog food - Diamond Feeds
NUTRA NUGGET PRODIET - Dog food - Diamond Feeds
NUTRA-PAL - Pet products - Champion Pet Foods Inc.
NUTRA-PHOS - Flowers, plants, and seeds - Pace International Corp.
NUTRA-PLEX - Vitamins and nutritional supplements - ECR Pharmaceuticals
NUTRA-PLEX - Vitamins and nutritional supplements - Natural Organics, Inc.
NUTRA-PLUS - Veterinary pharmaceutical preparations - Nutra-Vet Research Corp.
NUTRA PORTION - Food products - Zartic, Inc.
NUTRA PRO USA - Vitamins and nutritional supplements - Robert V. Rossitto
NUTRA-RINSE - Floor waxes - Hillyard Enterprises, Inc.
NUTRA SCIENCE NATURALS - Animal feed supplements - Vita Bran
NUTRA/SHAKE - Vitamins and nutritional supplements - Nutra/Balance Products
NUTRA SILK - Cosmetics - CCA Industries, Inc.
NUTRA SOOTHE - Skin care products - Brimms Inc.
NUTRA SOUP - Broth - Barth-Spencer Corp.
NUTRA SOUP - Soups–canned - Barth's Nutra Products
NUTRA-SPRAY - Flowers, plants, and seeds - Pace International Corp.
NUTRA SPRAY - Vitamins and nutritional supplements - Source Naturals
NUTRA-SUPPORT - Vitamins and nutritional supplements - J.R. Carlson Laboratories Inc.
NUTRA SWEET - Drink mixes - American Instants Inc.
NUTRA TRIM 7 - Vitamins and nutritional supplements - Vitamin Power Inc.
NUTRA-TRIM SYSTEM - Vitamins and nutritional supplements - Vitamin Power Inc.
NUTRA VITA - Vitamins and nutritional supplements - Fibertone Co.
NUTRA-ZYME - Surgical instrument cleaner - Snowden Pencer, Inc.
NUTRABALANCE - Pet food - Ralston Purina Co.
NUTRABLAST - Vitamins and nutritional supplements - S.L.I.M.
NUTRABOLICS - Vitamins and nutritional supplements - Twinlab
NUTRACANE - Natural sweetener - Nutracane, Inc.
NUTRACHEM - Containers–plastic - Equipment for the Graphic Arts, Inc.
NUTRACID - Coatings - Garon Products Inc.
NUTRACID - Plant growth regulators - Pro-Sol, Inc.
NUTRACORT - Pharmaceutical preparations - Owen/Galderma Laboratories Inc.
NUTRADERM - Skin care products - Owen/Galderma Laboratories Inc.
NUTRADIET - Food products - S & W Fine Foods, Inc.
NUTRAFLEX - Animal feed supplements - Reichhold Chemicals, Inc.
NUTRAGEOUS - Candy bars - Hershey Chocolate USA
NUTRALAX - Health care products - Futurebiotics
NUTRALICIOUS - Vitamins and nutritional supplements - Crystal Springs
NUTRALIFE - Vitamins and nutritional supplements - Lifessence Labs
NUTRAMENT - Health care products - Drackett Co.
NUTRAMENT THE ENERGY AND FITNESS DRINK - Vitamins and nutritional supplements - Mead Johnson & Co.
NUTRAMIGEN - Pharmaceutical preparations - Bristol-Myers Squibb Co.
NUTRAPATHIC - Vitamins and nutritional supplements - Parametric Associates Inc.
NUTRAPLUS - Skin care products - Owen/Galderma Laboratories Inc.
NUTRASLEEP - Vitamins and nutritional supplements - Source Naturals
NUTRASOLV - Cleaning preparations - Laun-Dry Supply Co., Inc.
NUTRASOME - Cosmetics - Revlon Consumer Products Corp.
NUTRASPA - Skin care products ☆ - Owen/Galderma Laboratories Inc.
NUTRASSIST - Pharmaceutical preparations - Chronimed Inc.
NUTRASWEET - Sweeteners–artificial ☆ - NutraSweet Co.
NUTRASWEET SPOONFUL - Sweeteners–artificial - NutraSweet Co.
NUTRASWIS - Skin care products - Gordon Cosmetic Enterprises Inc.
NUTRATABS - Vitamins and nutritional supplements - Great Life Laboratories Inc.
NUTRATEEM - Yeast - Early Times Distillery Co.
NUTRATURF - Fertilizers - Coe W. Fischer
NUTRATWIST - Ice cream - Dessert Marketing Corp.
NUTRE-MOIST 21 - Beauty shop equipment - Focus 21 International Inc.
NUTREA - Cosmetics ☆ - Shaklee Corp.

NUTRELIXIR - Vitamins and nutritional supplements - Intelligent Nutrients, Inc.
NUTRELLE - Soap - Dial Corp.
NUTRENA - Dog food - Stevens Industries Inc.
NUTRESS - Hair care products - Nutress Laboratories Inc.
NUTREX - Cereal - Nutrex Inc.
NUTREX - Food products - Universal Foods Corp.
NUTREX - Vitamins and nutritional supplements - Cyanotech Corp.
NUTREX - Vitamins and nutritional supplements ☆ - Abana Pharmaceuticals, Inc.
NUTRI-AN - Bird feeds ☆ - Lafeber Co.
NUTRI-BERRIES - Bird feeds - Lafeber Co.
NUTRI-BEV - Beverages - Archer Daniels Midland Co.
NUTRI-BLEND - Flour–blended - Nylander's Vantage Products
NUTRI-BODY - Hair care products - Playtex Beauty Care, Inc.
NUTRI-BONE - Dog food - Hartz Mountain Corp.
NUTRI-BROIL - Barbecues and grills - Dazey Corp.
NUTRI-BYTE - Computer software - I.S.C. Consultants Inc.
NUTRI-CAL - Veterinary pharmaceutical preparations - Evsco Pharmaceuticals
NUTRI-CANE - Sugar–granulated, refined, or powdered - Nylander's Vantage Products
NUTRI-CELL - Vitamins and nutritional supplements - Nutri-Cell Inc.
NUTRI-CELL COMPLEX - Skin care products - Viviane Woodard Industries, Ltd.
NUTRI CEPT - Vitamins and nutritional supplements - Natural Organics, Inc.
NUTRI-CLEANSE - Vitamins and nutritional supplements - The Lifestar Millennium, Inc.
NUTRI-COOKIE - Cookies - Nutrition Express Corp.
NUTRI-CORN - Snack foods ☆ - Garden of Eatin', Inc.
NUTRI DIET - Bird feed - Seed Factory, Inc.
NUTRI-DOPHILUS - Pharmaceutical preparations ☆ - Nylander's Vantage Products
NUTRI-DRENAL - Health care products - Healthwatchers System
NUTRI-DRENCH - Animal feed supplements - Bovidr Laboratories, Inc.
NUTRI-DRINK - Beverages ☆ - Nylander's Vantage Products
NUTRI-DROPS - Animal feed supplements - Bovidr Laboratories, Inc.
NUTRI-EGG - Eggs - Tollefson Farms Inc.
NUTRI-EGG - Eggs ☆ - Sleepy Eye Foods
NUTRI-FLAKES - Veterinary nutritional supplements - Gimborn U.S., Inc.
NUTRI-FLAX - Vitamins and nutritional supplements - Omega Nutrition USA Inc.
NUTRI-FLOW - Food dehydrators - American Enterprises Inc.
NUTRI-FRESH - Eggs - Chino Valley Ranchers
NUTRI FRESH - Eggs - Chino Valley Ranchers
NUTRI-FRUIT - Juices - Nutri-Fruit, Inc.
NUTRI-GAME - Vitamins and nutritional supplements - Hillestad International, Inc.
NUTRI-GAR - Vitamins and nutritional supplements - Nylander's Vantage Products
NUTRI-GENIC - Vitamins and nutritional supplements - Natural Organics, Inc.
NUTRI-GEST - Health care products - Healthwatchers System
NUTRI GLOW - Vitamins and nutritional supplements - Natural Organics, Inc.
NUTRI-GOLD - Food products - Park Corp.
NUTRI-GRAIN - Cereal - Kellogg Co.
NUTRI-GRAIN CORN - Cereal - Kellogg Co.
NUTRI-GRAIN NUGGETS - Cereal ☆ - Kellogg Co.
NUTRI-GRAIN WHEAT - Cereal - Kellogg Co.
NUTRI GUARD - Fertilizers - Howard Fertilizer Co., Inc.
NUTRI-HOMO - Vitamins and nutritional supplements - NH Products
NUTRI-JECT - Fertilizers - Tree Technology Systems, Inc.
NUTRI-JOINT - Vitamins and nutritional supplements - Vitamin Research Products Inc.
NUTRI-JUICE - Beverage dispensing equipment - Better Beverages
NUTRI-LABEL - Labels–paper - Nashua Corp.
NUTRI-LIFE - Hair care products ☆ - Monique Quality Products Co. Inc.
NUTRI-LIP - Lipsticks - Janet Sartin, Inc.
NUTRI-LOCK - Animal feed supplements - Vit-E-Men Co., Inc. (Life Products)
NUTRI-MAC - Pasta - Nylander's Vantage Products
NUTRI-MANNAN - Vitamins and nutritional supplements - Alleghany Pharmacal Corp.
NUTRI-MATIC - Vending machines - Royal Apples, Inc.
NUTRI-MATTE - Lipsticks - Janet Sartin, Inc.
NUTRI-METICS - Vitamins and nutritional supplements - Nutri-Metics International (USA) Inc.
NUTRI-MIST - Vitamins and nutritional supplements - Mayor Pharmaceutical Laboratories
NUTRI NATAL - Vitamins and nutritional supplements - Nutrition Center, Inc.

☆ = Now out of production

NUTRI-OPTICS - Vitamins and nutritional supplements - National Institute of Nutrition

NUTRI-OSTEO SYSTEM - Vitamins and nutritional supplements - Joseph M. Esposito

NUTRI PACK - Vitamins and nutritional supplements - Healthy 'N Fit Nutritionals

NUTRI-PAK - Food products - Park Corp.

NUTRI-PAK - Vitamins and nutritional supplements - Vita-Vista

NUTRI-PAN - Health care products - Healthwatchers System

NUTRI-PEARL - Vitamins and nutritional supplements ✰ - Optimal Nutrients

NUTRI PHITE - Fertilizers - Biagro Western Sales, Inc.

NUTRI-PLEX - Cooking equipment–household - Rena-Ware Distributors, Inc.

NUTRI-POP - Beverages ✰ - ICN Pharmaceuticals Inc.

NUTRI-PRO - Fish food ✰ - Superior Brands Inc.

NUTRI PUNCH - Beverages - Gonzalez and Tapanes Foods, Inc.

NUTRI QUEST RX - Vitamins and nutritional supplements - Nutri-West

NUTRI QUEST RX - Vitamins and nutritional supplements - Nutrition Center, Inc.

NUTRI-QUICK - Health care products - Natural Organics, Inc.

NUTRI SENSOR BY RENA WARE - Cooking equipment–household - Rena-Ware Distributors, Inc.

NUTRI-SMART FORMULA - Vitamins and nutritional supplements - Better Health Products

NUTRI-SOFT - Soap - Nutri-Metics International (USA) Inc.

NUTRI-SOL EFA - Veterinary pharmaceutical preparations - SmithKline Beecham Animal Health Products

NUTRI-SOURCE - Compost - Nutri-Source, Inc.

NUTRI-SOURCE - Health care products ✰ - Enzymatic Therapy, Inc.

NUTRI-SPORT - Vitamins and nutritional supplements ✰ - Pharmavite Corp.

NUTRI-START - Bird feeds - Lafeber Co.

NUTRI STAT - Vitamins and nutritional supplements - Tomlyn Products

NUTRI-STRESSR - Pet products ✰ - BenePet Pet Care Products

NUTRI/SYSTEM - Food products - Nutri/System L.P.

NUTRI/SYSTEM 2000 FOODS OF THE FUTURE - Food products ✰ - Nutri/System L.P.

NUTRI-TECH - Housewares - Carico International Inc.

NUTRI-TIME - Vitamins and nutritional supplements - Nutrition Enterprises

NUTRI-TONE - Skin care products - Fanie International

NUTRI-TONIC - Hair care products - Del Pharmaceuticals, Inc.

NUTRI-TONIC LIFE - Hair care products - Del Pharmaceuticals, Inc.

NUTRI-TOX - Health care products - Healthwatchers System

NUTRI-TREAT - Animal feeds - Camp-Cap Products

NUTRI-TREAT - Pet products - BenePet Pet Care Products

NUTRI-TRIM - Vitamins and nutritional supplements - Nutri-Metics International (USA) Inc.

NUTRI-VEG - Vitamins and nutritional supplements - NH Products

NUTRI-VITALE FORMULA - Vitamins and nutritional supplements ✰ - Nutri-Metics International (USA) Inc.

NUTRI VIVE - Skin care products ✰ - Columbia Laboratories Inc.

NUTRI-WAVE - Fertilizers - Biotherm International, Inc.

NUTRI-WEST - Vitamins and nutritional supplements - Nutri-West

NUTRI-WOMAN - Vitamins and nutritional supplements - Women's International Pharmacy, Inc.

NUTRIBATH - Skin care products - The Nutribath Co.

NUTRIBEL - Skin care products - Lancome

NUTRIBIOTIC - Antiseptics - NutriBiotic

NUTRIBITS - Animal feeds - Hubbard Milling Co.

NUTRIBIX - Dog food - Mardel Laboratories, Inc.

NUTRICARE - Health care products - Dean Distributors, Inc.

NUTRICARE - Health care products - Nutricare

NUTRICELL - Skin care products ✰ - Gordon Cosmetic Enterprises Inc.

NUTRICOAT - Animal feed supplements - 8 in 1 Pet Products Inc.

NUTRICOAT - Pet products - St. Aubrey

NUTRICOL - Flour–blended - FMC Corp.

NUTRICOM - Vitamins and nutritional supplements - Nutricom Inc.

NUTRICON - Vitamins and nutritional supplements - Pasadena Research Laboratories, Inc.

NUTRICULTURE - Fertilizers - Plant Marvel Laboratories

NUTRIDERM - Veterinary pharmaceutical preparations - SmithKline Beecham Animal Health Products

NUTRIEDGE - Vitamins and nutritional supplements - Nutrilite, Div. of Amway Corp.

NUTRIENT BUFFER - Vitamins and nutritional supplements - Vita Royal Products, Inc.

NUTRIENT PLUS - Pet products - St. Jon Pet Care Products Inc.

NUTRIENT PRECISION - Dog food - Colgate-Palmolive Co.

NUTRIFASTER - Juice extracting devices - C2L Corp.

NUTRIFIC - Cereal ✰ - Kellogg Co.

NUTRIFIL - Frosting - Beatrice Cheese Co.

NUTRIFIT - Vitamins and nutritional supplements - Nutrifit International Corp.

NUTRIFLEX - Vitamins and nutritional supplements - Health-Flex Industries International, Inc.

NUTRIFLO - Hoses - Goodyear Tire & Rubber Co.

NUTRIFORCE - Cosmetics - Lancome

NUTRIFORM - Computer software - Nutrition and Food Associates, Inc.

NUTRIGEL - Veterinary nutritional supplements - Gimborn U.S., Inc.

NUTRIGENIE - Computer software - Nutrigenie

NUTRIGUARD E - Pharmaceutical preparations - Guthy-Renker Corp.

NUTRIHANCE - Vitamins and nutritional supplements - Nutri/System L.P.

NUTRILITE - Snack foods - Nutrilite, Div. of Amway Corp.

NUTRILOGIC - Vitamins and nutritional supplements - Trans Mins by Nutrilogic

NUTRIMALT - Beverages–carbonated - Florida Brewing Co.

NUTRIMALT - Pet products - St. Jon Pet Care Products Inc.

NUTRIMASTER - Cookware - Farberware Inc.

NUTRIMATO - Frames–eyeglass - Mott's Inc.

NUTRIMIN - Pet products - 8 in 1 Pet Products Inc.

NUTRIMIX - Pharmaceutical preparations - Abbott Laboratories

NUTRIMIX 500 - Dairy products - Foremost Farms USA

NUTRINE - Skin care products - Nutrine Ltd.

NUTRINE FINISH UP - Cosmetics - Nutrine Ltd.

NUTRINE FOR TRESS - Cosmetics - Nutrine Ltd.

NUTRINET - Computer software - Nutrinet Corp.

NUTRION 800 - Vitamins and nutritional supplements - Geri-Nutritional Co.

NUTRIPEAT - Soil–potting - Foster Brothers Farm, Inc.

NUTRIPHARMA - Health care products - Bioenergy Inc.

NUTRIPHASE - Animal feeds - Petsmart, Inc.

NUTRIPHASE - Pet food - Weisheimer Companies Inc.

NUTRIPLAN - Computer software - Micromedx Computer Software Corp.

NUTRIPLAZ - Animal feed supplements - Swiss Bank Corp.

NUTRIPLENISH - Hair care products - Paje Products

NUTRIPLEXX - Hair care products - Aramis Inc.

NUTRIPRIME - Vitamins and nutritional supplements ✰ - Hess & Clark, Inc.

NUTRIPURE - Water purification systems - Atlantic Ultraviolet Corp.

NUTRIQUEST SPORTS - Vitamins and nutritional supplements - Nutri-West

NUTRISAN - Food products ✰ - Recsei Laboratories

NUTRISEA - Crab meat–canned or cured - Fox and Co.

NUTRISEAL COMPLEX - Hair care products - Aguste Personal Care Products, Inc.

NUTRISHAKE - Beverages–malt - Carr Products Co. Inc.

NUTRISHAPE - Vitamins and nutritional supplements - Shara Laboratories, Inc.

NUTRISHIELD - Hair care products - Paje Products

NUTRISILK - Vitamins and nutritional supplements - Highland Laboratories

NUTRISNACKS - Dog food - Merrick Petfoods Inc.

NUTRISOURCE - Pet food - Nutrisource Pet Products of Stewart, Inc.

NUTRISOURCE MODULAR SYSTEM - Vitamins and nutritional supplements - Novartis Nutrition Corp.

NUTRISOY - Soybean product - Archer Daniels Midland Co.

NUTRISPAN - Vitamins and nutritional supplements - Phoenix Laboratories, Inc.

NUTRISTAR - Computer software - Hopkins Technology LLC

NUTRISTYLE - Food supplements - Nutristyle, Inc.

NUTRISURGE - Nutritional food supplement - Magni Co.

NUTRITE - Fertilizers - Nutrite Corp.

NUTRITEK - Computer software - Dentek Systems Inc.

NUTRITEK - Dairy products - Foremost Farms USA

NUTRITION COMPANY OF AMERICA - Vitamins and nutritional supplements - Nutrition 21

NUTRITION EXPRESS - Catalogs - Nutrition Express Corp.

NUTRITION FARM, THE - Vitamins and nutritional supplements - Polyionics Inc.

NUTRITION FOR LIFE - Vitamins and nutritional supplements - Nutrition Express Corp.

NUTRITION FOR NAILS - Health care products - Futurebiotics

NUTRITION HEADQUARTERS - Vitamins and nutritional supplements - Nutrition Headquarters, Inc.

NUTRITION PRO! - Computer software - ESHA Research Inc.

NUTRITION SOLUTION, THE - Fertilizers - Dyna-Gro Nutrition Solutions

NUTRITIONAL ADVANTAGE - Pet products - Brewers Yeast Specialist

NUTRITIONAL ADVANTAGE TREAT PETS LOVE TO EAT, THE - Pet products - Brewers Yeast Specialist

NUTRITIONAL BONE BUILDER BLOCKS - Pet products - Nutritional Research Associates Inc.

NUTRITIONAL BRIDGE TO THE 21ST CENTURY - Fruits and vegetables - W.E. Bailey & Son, Inc.
NUTRITIONAL CARE - Food products - Idle Wild Farm
NUTRITIONAL DYNAMICS - Vitamins and nutritional supplements - Natural Organics, Inc.
NUTRITIONAL FACTORS - Health care products ☆ - ICN Pharmaceuticals Inc.
NUTRITIONAL FRUIT FORMULAS - Beverages - Smoothie King Franchises, Inc.
NUTRITIONAL RECOVERY FORMULA - Pet food - Iams Co.
NUTRITIONAL YOU - Vitamins and nutritional supplements - Nutritional You, Inc.
NUTRITIONALS - Animal feeds - Federal Foods, Inc.
NUTRITIONALS-ALL - Vitamins and nutritional supplements - Horizon Worldwide Export Corp.
NUTRITIONALYSIS - Vitamins and nutritional supplements - Old Fashioned Natural Products, Inc.
NUTRITIOUS - Skin care products - Estee Lauder Inc.
NUTRITIOUS TREAT THAT'S FUN TO EAT, THE - Veterinary nutritional supplements - Brewers Yeast Specialist
NUTRITOL - Vitamins and nutritional supplements - Sukrol Laboratories Inc.
NUTRIUM - Cleaning preparations ☆ - Tempo Chemical Co. Inc.
NUTRIVALS - Vitamins and nutritional supplements - Vita-Fore Products Co.
NUTRIVANCE - Pet products - Ralston Purina Co.
NUTRIVED - Vitamins and nutritional supplements - Vedco, Inc.
NUTRIVENTION - Vitamins and nutritional supplements - Inner Health Group, Inc.
NUTRIVISION - Vitamins - Bronson Pharmaceuticals
NUTRIX - Food products - Gold Kist Inc.
NUTRIX - Skin care products - Lancome
NUTRIZYME - Pharmaceutical preparations - Enzyme Process Co. Inc.
NUTRO - Milk–canned or powdered - Diehl Inc.
NUTRO - Pet food - Nutro Products, Inc.
NUTRO - Toys - Homecall, Inc.
NUTRO - Vitamins and nutritional supplements - Nutro Laboratories, Inc.
NUTRO BASIC - Dog food - Nutro Products, Inc.
NUTRO MAX - Dog food - Nutro Products, Inc.
NUTRO PREMIUM - Dog food - Nutro Products, Inc.
NUTRO TRAIL - Dog food ☆ - Nutro Products, Inc.
NUTROFEM - Vitamins and nutritional supplements - Nutrition Headquarters, Inc.
NUTROPIN LIQUID - Pharmaceutical preparations - Genentech, Inc.
NUTRO'S NATURAL CHOICE - Dog food - Nutro Products, Inc.
NUTROX - Vitamins and nutritional supplements - Tyson & Associates, Inc.
NUTROX - Vitamins and nutritional supplements ☆ - Integrated Health, Inc.
NUTRVIEW - Paper products - Nutrinform, Inc.
NUTS ! - Nuts–salted, roasted, cooked, or canned - Palmer Candy Co.
NUTS ABOUT FRUIT - Chocolate candy - That's My Favorite Inc.
NUTS ABOUT NUTS - Nuts–salted, roasted, cooked, or canned - United Snacks, Inc.
NUTS ABOUT VEGAS - Nuts–salted, roasted, cooked, or canned - Del Rey Nut Co.
NUTS 'N MORE - Nuts–salted, roasted, cooked, or canned - Planters LifeSavers Co.
NUTS 'N NUGGETS - Bird feeds - Lafeber Co.
NUTS OFF - Lubricating oils - Spray Products Corp.
NUTS TO DRUGS - Food products - Kar Nut Products Co.
NUTS TO YOU - Candy - Nuts to You
NUTSERTS - Fasteners - Auto Vehicle Parts Co.
NUTSHELL - Computer software - Quantum Micro Systems
NUTSO - Snack foods - Fairmont Snacks Group Inc.
NUTSOS - Food products ☆ - Thin's Inn Inc.
NUTTER BUTTER - Cookies - Nabisco Foods Group
NUTTER BUTTER BITES - Cookies - Nabisco Foods Group
NUTTIN' - Cereal - Ralston Purina Co.
NUTTIN - Novelty items - Nuttin Special
NUTTIN' BETTER - Snack foods ☆ - Maranatha! Natural Foods
NUTTIN' LIKE IT - Candy bars - Auburn Farms, Inc.
NUTT'N BETTER - Ice cream - Wells' Dairy, Inc.
NUTTY BAVARIAN NUTS, THE - Roasted nuts and confections - Nutty Bavarian, Inc.
NUTTY BONE - Dog food - Williamsburg Foods, Inc.
NUTTY BROTHERS - Snack foods - Health Foods, Inc.
NUTTY CHARACTERS - Statuary - Star Imports, Inc.
NUTTY CRUNCH - Chocolate bars - Nabisco Foods Group
NUTTY HO HOS - Snack cakes - Interstate Brands Corp.
NUTTY HUMPS - Candy ☆ - Brock Candy Co. Inc.

NUTTY KNAVES - Cookies - Simmers Products
NUTTY NOLAGRAN - Bakery products - Gretchen K. Lupinacci
NUTTY NUGGETS - Snack foods - Sycamore Creek Co. (INARI, Ltd.)
NUTTY NURSERY RHYMES - Greeting cards - Gibson Greetings, Inc.
NUTTY PUTTY - Toys - Tonka Corp.
NUTTY RICE - Cereal - Pacific Grain Products, Inc.
NUTTY RUGGY - Pastries - Nutty Ruggy Inc.
NUTTY SNACK - Seeds–salted, roasted, cooked, or canned ☆ - David and Sons Inc.
NUTTY ZONKERS - Popcorn ☆ - Novartis Nutrition Corp.
NUTTYEST OF ALL - Crackers, etc ☆ - Bowlby Candy Co. Inc.
NUTURA-CURL - Hair coloring preparations - Stylors Inc.
NUTURELITE - Lamps - Angelo Brothers Co.
NUTUSSIN - Cough medicines ☆ - Nature's Herbs
NUTZELS - Pretzels - Bachman Co.
NUTZIES - Candy - Murray-Allen International Inc.
NUVA-SIL - Silicon products - Loctite Corp.
NUVA-SIL 5076 - Adhesives and sealants - Loctite Corp.
NUVA-SIL 5083 - Adhesives and sealants - Loctite Corp.
NUVA-SIL 5084 - Adhesives and sealants - Loctite Corp.
NUVA-SIL 5088 - Adhesives and sealants - Loctite Corp.
NUVA-SIL 5091 - Adhesives and sealants - Loctite Corp.
NUVEG - Vitamins and nutritional supplements - Nature's Herbs
NUVEG - Vitamins and nutritional supplements - Twinlab
NUVEG HERB - Vitamins and nutritional supplements ☆ - Nature's Herbs
NUVEL - Construction equipment - Formica Corp.
NUVERB - Audio equipment ☆ - Lexicon, Inc.
NUVISION - Optical-services franchise - NuVision Inc.
NUVISTA - Frames–picture - LaVista Industries Inc.
NUVO - Belts–apparel ☆ - Kleinert's Inc.
NUVO - Bulletin boards–wood ☆ - Scentex Inc.
NUVO SPORT - Stationery ☆ - Scentex Inc.
NUVOLCELLE - Moisturizers - Omnitrition International, Inc.
NUVOS - Men's slacks - Levi Strauss & Co.
NUVOX - Audio equipment - Nuvox Electronics Corp.
NUVOX - Telephone answering machines - Hal-Hen Co. Inc.
NUWAVE - Health care products - Staodyn, Inc.
NUWAVE - Water–bottled or canned - Collegiate Water Co.
NUWAY - Chemical preparations - N. Jonas and Co. Inc.
NUWAY - Trailers–travel - Martin Industries, Inc.
NUWEAVE - Socks ☆ - Signal Knitwear Co.
NUWITE - Brushes - Wright-Bernet
NUWOOD - Varnishes - Mobile Paint Manufacturing Co.
NUYENS - Cordials - White Rock Distilleries Inc.
NUZINE - Pharmaceutical preparations - Hobart Laboratories Inc.
NUZZLES - Toys–stuffed - Dakin Inc.
NUZZLETIME NURSERY - Toys–stuffed - Tonka Corp.
NV - Fabrics - Carlton-Metro Wallcoverings
N.V. PLEIADES - Wines - Diamond Wine Merchants
NVG - Posters - Nvision Grafix, Inc.
NVIDIA - Integrated circuits - Nvidia Corp.
NVIEW - Electronic equipment - nVIEW Corp.
NVP NICOLAUS PAPER - Paper - Nicolaus Paper Inc.
NVPP - Computer software - R.L. Polk & Co.
NW - Boats–motor - NWTX Controls Inc.
NW - Containers - Norwesco, Inc.
NW - Jewelry - Northwest Jewelers
NW - Wood products - Weyerhaeuser Co.
NW BERRY GROWERS - Jams and jellies - Pacific Westcoast Foods
NW GOLD - Golfing equipment - Pro Select Sports USA
NW1000 - Computer peripheral equipment - 3Com Corp.
NWA QUALITY MONITOR - Computer software - Northwest Analytical, Inc.
NWCONNECT - Computer software ☆ - Northwest Airlines
NWO - T-shirts–men's - World Championship Wrestling, Inc.
NX - Gold products - Surface Combustion, Inc.
NX586 - Computer software - Nexgen Microsystems
NXPCI - Computer hardware - Nexgen Microsystems
NXT - Games - NXT Games, Inc.
NXT ONE - Golfing equipment - Pro Select Sports USA
NXT TECH - Golfing equipment - Pro Select Sports USA
NXT TWO - Golfing equipment - Pro Select Sports USA
NXVL - Computer hardware - Nexgen Microsystems
NY - Switches–electric - Knorr Brake Holding Corp.
NY 10018 - Apparel and accessories - New York, Inc.
NY APPEAL - Apparel–women's - Crossland Associate, Inc.
N.Y. BEAT - Footwear - Diesse Shoes Inc.

☆ = Now out of production

N.Y. CAPTOR - Video games ☆ - Taito America Corp.
N.Y. GIRL - Coats–children's - Braetan Kids
NY-GLIS - Pharmaceutical preparations ☆ - Lexis Laboratories Inc.
NY-GOLD - Cording ☆ - Samson Cordage Works
NY ISLANDERS - Apparel - Nassau Sports
NY-LACE - Apparel–women's - Jezebel-Renee of Hollywood
NY LINE - Apparel - Lerner New York, Inc.
NY-LO - Looms ☆ - Lily Craft Products
NY-LONG - Apparel–women's - Jezebel-Renee of Hollywood
NY-LUBE - Lubricants ☆ - Stoner Inc.
N.Y. LUG CO. - Apparel and accessories - Jack Schwartz Shoes, Inc.
NY-PRO - Bags ☆ - Innovo Inc.
N.Y. STRAMI - Food products ☆ - Lightlife Foods, Inc.
NY TIMES - Puzzles - Ben Cooper Inc.
NY-TRO PRO-40 - Vitamins and nutritional supplements - AST Research, Inc.
NYAANZA NATURALS - Hair- and skin-care products ☆ - Aubrey Organics, Inc.
NYAC - Apparel and accessories - New York Athletic Club
NYACK - Apparel and accessories - Nyack Runner International Inc.
NYAD - Chemical preparations - Nyco Minerals, Inc.
NYALIC - Resins–polymer - HBI, Inc.
NYALOX - Tools–power-driven - Dico Products Corp.
NYATLAS - Maps - Vandam Inc.
NYB - Apparel and accessories - NYB Corp.
NYBLOC - Electrical equipment - Pass & Seymour, Inc.
NYBORG - Pet products - Vo-Toys Inc.
NYBRO - Glass products - Arnold Larson Inc.
NYC: THE BIG APPLE - Games - S. Alden Inc.
N.Y.C.A.C. - Recording label - Jazz Composer's Orchestra Association Inc.
NYCLAD - Ammunition - Federal Cartridge Co.
NYCOAT - Cables - MacWhyte Co.
NYCOFF - Pharmaceutical preparations - Dover Pharmaceutical Inc.
NYCOR - Sporting goods - Edwards Sports Products
NYCORE - Thread - Threads USA Div.
NYCRALAN - Pharmaceutical preparations - Lannett Co. Inc.
NYDRAZID - Pharmaceutical preparations - Bristol-Myers Squibb Co.
NYDURA - Steel springs–railroad - Needlecraft Industries
NYDURA - Uniforms–tailored ☆ - Angelica Uniform Group
NYE - Jewelry - Stuart Nye Hand Wrought Jewelry
NYE DOGWOOD - Jewelry - Stuart Nye Hand Wrought Jewelry
NYE TRAYS - Distilling apparatus–laboratory - Nye Trays, Inc.
NYECO - Food products - New York Extract Co. Inc.
NYEMATIC III - Tape recorders - Lanier Voice Products
NYESTA - Yarn - Roselon Industries, Inc.
NYFLON 25 - Paints - Armoloy Corp.
NYFORM - Latex - Bergquists
NYG - Jewelry - New York Gem Corp.
NYGLOS - Chemical preparations ☆ - Nyco Minerals, Inc.
NYGRAN - Gloves - Granet Inc.
NYGUARD - Zippers - Scovill Inc.
NYK - Headwear - Madison Square Garden Corp.
NYL BRAID - Rope - Wellington Leisure Products, Inc.
NYL BRAND - Musical instrument accessories - Fender Musical Instruments
NYL-D'ESPRIT - Fabrics–nylon - Gehring Textiles Inc.
NYL-FLOSS - Thread - United Thread Mills Corp.
NYL-GLO - Flags - Annin and Co.
NYL-LAST - Thread - United Thread Mills Corp.
NYL MEX - Thread - Belding Heminway Co. Inc.
NYL-O-PAK - Fishing tackle ☆ - Mason Tackle Co.
NYL-O-TAPE - Hardware - HDI/Hardware Designers Inc.
NYL-SOFT - Thread - United Thread Mills Corp.
NYL-TAZ - Thread - United Thread Mills Corp.
NYLA - Labels–gummed - New York Label & Box Corp.
NYLABALL - Pet products ☆ - Nylabone Products
NYLABIRD - Pet products ☆ - Nylabone Products
NYLABONE - Pet products - Nylabone Products
NYLABONE - Pet products - T.F.H. Publications, Inc.
NYLABONE EDIBLES - Pet food - T.F.H. Publications, Inc.
NYLAC - Cleaning preparations–carpet and rug - Tonka Mills Inc.
NYLAFLOSS KNOT - Veterinary pharmaceutical preparations - Nylabone Products
NYLAIRE - Zippers ☆ - Scovill Inc.
NYLAKRIMP - Electrical equipment - Molex-Etc Inc.
NYLAMB - Yarn - Brunswick Yarns
NYLANIN - Flags ☆ - Annin and Co.
NYLARIB - Underwear and nightwear - Munsingwear, Inc.

NYLARING - Pet products - Nylabone Products
NYLATEX - Bandages - Chattanooga Group, Inc.
NYLATWIST - Thread ☆ - A.H. Rice Co.
NYLBLEND - Thread - United Thread Mills Corp.
NYLBLOC - Electrical surge protectors - Pass & Seymour, Inc.
NYLBOND - Thread - Belding Heminway Co. Inc.
NYLCLEAR - Thread - Belding Heminway Co. Inc.
NYLENE - Paints - Epoca Corp.
NYLENE - Shortening - Kraft Food Ingredients Corp.
NYLENE - Water treating compounds - Century Chemical Co.
NYLEX - Thread - Advance Thread Corp.
NYLFLOOR - Fabrics - Interface, Inc.
NYLFOAM - Sponges - Padco Companies, Inc.
NYLFUSE - Thread - United Thread Mills Corp.
NYLGLOV - Thread ☆ - Belding Heminway Co. Inc.
NYLIDE - Fabrics ☆ - Fiber Mark, Inc.
NYLINT - Toys - Nylint Toy Corp.
NYLITE - Luggage - Airway Industries, Inc.
NYLO - Thread - Cincinnati Thread Co.
NYLO-FLEX - Electrical equipment - GB Electrical Inc.
NYLO-GRIT - Brushes - Flo-Pac Corp.
NYLO-TEX - Thread - Threads USA Div.
NYLO-WISP - Apparel–women's - Jezebel-Renee of Hollywood
NYLOC - Electrical equipment - McGill Manufacturing Co. Inc.
NYLOGLIDE - Office supplies - Warshaw Manufacturing Co. Inc.
NYLOK - Bags–duffel - Safariland Ltd., Inc.
NYLOMAT - Mats ☆ - U.S. Mat & Rubber Co. Inc.
NYLON -
NYLON 44 - Ribbons–inked ☆ - Curtis-Young Corp.
NYLON 55 - Ribbons–inked ☆ - Curtis-Young Corp.
NYLON 66 - Ammunition - Remington Arms Co., Inc.
NYLON-BRITE - Detergents ☆ - Household Research Corp.
NYLON CLASSICS - Furniture–upholstered - Maharam Vertical Surfaces
NYLON DELIGHTS - Apparel stores–women's - Ithaca Industries, Inc.
NYLON/GOLDEN - Rope - Tubbs Cordage Co.
NYLON II - Life preservers - Parkway Systems
NYLON NAIL-IN - Anchors - Rawlplug Co., Inc.
NYLONAIRE - Tires ☆ - Bridgestone/Firestone, Inc.
NYLONFLEX - Furniture ☆ - Walker and Zanger Inc.
NYLORFI - Fishing tackle ☆ - Cortland Line Co., Inc.
NYLORITE - Pet products - Leatherite-Nylorite Manufacturing Inc.
NYLOSTRAND - Fishing tackle - Mason Tackle Co.
NYLOTILE - Floor coverings–carpet and rugs ☆ - Lees Carpets
NYLOUR - Paper - Creative Coatings Corp.
NYLOWARE - Frames–eyeglass - Zylo Ware Corp.
NYLQUILT - Thread - Belding Heminway Co. Inc.
NYLSEAM - Thread ☆ - Belding Heminway Co. Inc.
NYLSET - Thread - Perfect Thread Co. Inc.
NYLSEW - Thread - Belding Heminway Co. Inc.
NYLSHU - Thread - Belding Heminway Co. Inc.
NYLSLIDES - Hardware - HDI/Hardware Designers Inc.
NYLSPUN - Thread - United Thread Mills Corp.
NYLSTRETCH - Thread - United Thread Mills Corp.
NYLTEX - Thread - Blue Mountain Industries, Inc.
NYLTEX - Thread - A. Lewis Thread Co. Inc.
NYLTITE - Hardware - Nyltite Corp. of America
NYLU - Costume jewelry ☆ - Robert Rose
NYLYNN - Cosmetics - Nylynn Cosmetic Inc.
NYLYNN GLYCOLIC ACID TREATMENT - Pharmaceutical preparations - Nylynn Cosmetic Inc.
NYLYNN HOT STUFF - Skin care products - Nylynn Cosmetic Inc.
NYLYNN LACTIC ACID TREATMENT - Pharmaceutical preparations - Nylynn Cosmetic Inc.
NYMAN - Containers–paper - Nyman Manufacturing Co.
NYMAN MARINE - Power-operated lifts - Nyman Marine, Inc.
NYMO - Orthopedic products - Smith & Nephew Inc. (Rehabilitation Div.)
NYMO - Thread - Belding Heminway Co. Inc.
NYMO-EX - Thread - Belding Heminway Co. Inc.
NYMO INTIMA - Thread - Belding Heminway Co. Inc.
NYMO-PLETT - Thread - Belding Heminway Co. Inc.
NYMO SET - Thread - Belding Heminway Co. Inc.
NYMO SILFREE - Thread - Belding Heminway Co. Inc.
NYMO SOTITE - Thread - Belding Heminway Co. Inc.
NYMO STRINGLAST - Thread - Belding Heminway Co. Inc.
NYMOLEX - Thread - Belding Heminway Co. Inc.

☆ = Now out of production

NYMOLON - Thread - Belding Heminway Co. Inc.

NYMOMATIC - Thread - Belding Heminway Co. Inc.

NYMPH - Ophthalmic goods ☆ - Luxottica

NYMPH MASTER - Apparel and accessories - Nymph Master

NYMPHE - Hydrotherapy equipment - Setma, Inc.

NYNEX - Telephones–cellular - Nynex Corp.

NYNEX USACCESS - Computer software - Nynex Corp.

NYOIL - Oils–lubricating - TAI Lubricants, Inc.

NYOIL - Oils–lubricating ☆ - William F. Nye Inc.

NYOMIN - Pharmaceutical preparations ☆ - ICN Pharmaceuticals Inc.

NYOTHENE - Sporting goods - Sport Supply Group, Inc.

NYPER - Publisher's imprints - Eric D. Randall

NYQUIL - Cold remedies - Richardson-Vicks USA

NYQUIL HOT THERAPY - Medicine - Richardson-Vicks USA

NYRACORD - Floor coverings - Superior Manufacturing Group/Notrax Floor Matting

NYRACORD - Mats - JCH International Inc.

NYRACORD - Thread - Lancaster Colony Automotive Group

NYRAL - Pharmaceutical preparations ☆ - Pal-Pak Inc.

NYREE - Ophthalmic goods ☆ - Luxottica

NYRIM - Ophthalmic goods - Vista Optical Corp.

NYS CHARDONNAY - Wines - Schloss Doepken Winery

NYS GEWURZTRAMINER - Wines - Schloss Doepken Winery

NYS JOHANNISBERG RIESLING - Wines - Schloss Doepken Winery

NYSE PRIME - Consulting services - New York Stock Exchange, Inc.

NYST-OLONE - Pharmaceutical preparations - Schein Pharmaceutical Inc.

NYSTEX - Pharmaceutical preparations - Savage Laboratories Inc.

NYSTROM - Doors–metal - Nystrom, Inc.

NYTCOLD - Pharmaceutical preparations - Rugby Laboratories Inc.

NYTELLE - Yarn ☆ - Bridgestone/Firestone, Inc.

NYTEMP - Hardware - Nylok Fastener Corp.

NYTETIME - Cold remedies - Schein Pharmaceutical Inc.

NYTEX - Cordage and twine - Monofilaments International Inc.

NYTILAX - Laxatives - Mentholatum Co.

NYTOL - Health care products - Block Drug Co., Inc.

NYTOL NATURAL - Vitamins and nutritional supplements - Block Drug Co., Inc.

NYTROL - Lighting equipment - Precision Multiple Controls, Inc.

NYTYE - Connectors–electrical - Heyco Products, Inc.

NYU PRESS - Publisher's imprints - New York University Press

NYVEL - Packaging–paper - Crowell Corp.

NYWARE - Hardware - Heyco Products, Inc.

NYZIN - Batteries ☆ - Yardney Technical Products Inc.

N.Z. - Sporting goods - Americal Ltd.

NZ ALUNDUM - Abrasive products - Norton Co.

NZE - Tanks–storage - Baron Blakeslee, Inc.

☆ = Now out of production

O

Addresses and phone numbers for the companies cited in the brands below
are available in the Company Listings section immediately following the brands listings.

O-3 - Cleaning preparations ☆ - Scentex Inc.

O A OCEAN - Apparel and accessories - Ocean Athlete Inc.

O & C - Vegetables–canned - Hanover Foods Corp.

O & H DANISH BAKERY - Pastries - O & H Danish Bakery

O & O - Watches ☆ - Luxury International Inc.

O-AT-KA - Milk–canned or powdered ☆ - O-AT-KA Milk Products Cooperative Inc.

O-B - Cleaning preparations - Bison Laboratories (Central OB Products Division)

O-B - Containers - Owens-Illinois Inc.

O/B/C - Cushions - Commander-Omni Co. Inc.

O-B-E-C - Pharmaceutical preparations ☆ - Morton Pharmaceuticals Inc.

O-BABY - Apparel–children's - Happy Kids Ltd.

O-BAC - Binders - The Union Group

O-BACK - Underwear and nightwear - Jennifer Mirya Collections

O-BEAD - Automotive parts and accessories - Bridgestone/Firestone, Inc.

O-BRITE-O - Hardware - Selig Co. Inc.

O-CAL-ETTE - Pharmaceutical preparations - Pharmics Inc.

O-CAL-FA - Pharmaceutical preparations - Pharmics Inc.

O-CEDAR - Cleaning preparations - Drackett Co.

O-CEDAR - Toys ☆ - A.R.C. Toys Inc.

O-CEDAR 2000 - Scouring pads - O-Cedar/Vining Household Products Co.

O-CEDAR-HOUSEKEEPING - Toys - Libby Lee Toys Inc.

O-CEDAR LIGHT & EASY - Mops - Drackett Co.

O-CEDAR POWER STRIP - Mops - Drackett Co.

O-CEL-O - Scouring pads - Minnesota Mining & Manufacturing Co.

O' CHRISTMAS TREE - Trees–artificial - Amlings Flowerland

O CONNOR'S - Liqueurs - American Stores Co.

O DE LANCOME - Perfumes - Lancome

O DESIGN - Eyeglasses - Oakley, Inc.

O! EUCLID - Games - Ampersand Press

O-JAY - Fruit drinks–bottled or canned - O-Jay Inc.

O-K PAPER CENTER - Paper - Olmsted-Kirk Paper Co.

O-KAY - Cereal ☆ - U.S. Mills, Inc.

O-LOC - Nuts and bolts - Lok-Mor, Inc.

O M E G A - Seafood products–fresh or frozen - Pan Fish Sales, Inc.

O MATIC - Bakery machines - A.M. Manufacturing Co., Inc.

O-MATIC, A - Key cases - Cool-Ray Inc.

O MATRIX - Computer software - Harmonic Software Inc.

O-N-D - Animal feeds - Blue Seal Feeds Inc.

O-NEH-DA - Wines - Eagle Crest Vineyard Inc.

O OBJECT DESIGN - Computer software - Object Design, Inc.

O OHIO STATE - Key rings - Ohio State University

O OLDS - Musical instruments - LuRey Indsutries Inc.

O-P-S - Hair care products - Paula Payne Products Co. Inc.

O-PERM - Lenses - Optical Polymer Research, Inc.

O-POI-ZO - Pharmaceutical preparations ☆ - Childs Co.

O-RIGINALS - Brooms and mops - O-Cedar/Vining Household Products Co.

O-RING LOCKS - Archery equipment - Saunders Archery Co.

O-RING SECURITY SYSTEM - Tool boxes - Frederickseal, Inc.

O-RINGS - Transmission equipment–motor vehicle - Fenner Drives

O/S PROJECT - Golfing equipment - Golfsmith International Inc.

O/S PROJECT II - Golfing equipment - Golfsmith International Inc.

O SCAN - Computer software - Oasis Systems, Inc.

O-SO-GUD - Peanut butter - Nabisco Foods Group

O-TWO - Pet products - Lake Products Co. Inc.

O-U GLATTBEEF - Food products ☆ - Empire Kosher Poultry Inc.

O-U MATIC - Sporting goods ☆ - O-U Sports Inc.

O U NO U LIKE IT! - Apparel and accessories - Patrick J. Maloney

O-UTH - Girdles - Form-O-Uth

O-V STATIN - Pharmaceutical preparations - Bristol-Myers Squibb Co.

O VITESSE CONCENTRIC - Catheters - Spectranetics Corp.

O VITESSE ECCENTRIC - Catheters - Spectranetics Corp.

O WEAR - Environmentally correct apparel - O Wear

O/Z SWISS WINDS - Deodorizers - Surco Products Inc.

O1 - Chemicals - Olin Corp.

O2 AIRE APPAREL - Apparel and accessories - Thomas Henriques

O2 T.V. - Broadcasting stations–television - Omni 2000 Inc.

O2O - Recording label - Progressive Awareness Research, Inc.

O2XY-WASH - Cleaning preparations - Bioxy, Inc.

O2XYGEN - Colognes - James Paul Miller

O2XYGEN - Sunblocks - California North

O3 - Automotive parts and accessories - Tempress, Inc.

O3 THE HAPPY OZONE MOLECULE - Automotive parts and accessories - Tempress, Inc.

OA - Machinery - OA Inc.

OA - Publisher's imprints - Overeaters Anonymous, Inc.

O.A. PLUS - Vitamins and nutritional supplements - International Medical Research, Inc.

OACES - Golfing equipment ☆ - John Rouzee Green Co., Inc.

O.A.D. - Deodorants–personal - Sween Corp.

OAHU - Frames–eyeglass - May Optical Co. Inc.

OAK - Music–sheet - Music Sales Corp.

OAK - Novelty items - Oak Rubber Co.

OAK - Wood products - Vermillion Inc.

OAK & CLAY - Apparel and accessories - Tricots St. Raphael, Inc.

OAK & IVORY - Handbags - Oak & Ivory

OAK APPLE - Dishes–earthenware - Denby USA Limited

OAK AVENUE - Furniture ☆ - Cochrane Furniture Co. Inc.

OAK BARREL WINECRAFT - Beverage dispensing equipment - Oak Barrel Winecraft Inc.

OAK BLUFFS - Wines - Vintwood International Ltd.

OAK BREEZE - Furniture ☆ - Bassett Furniture Industries, Inc.

OAK-BRIDGE - See **COFFMAN SPIRAL**

OAK BRIDGE - Wines - Delicato Vineyards

OAK BROOK - Furniture - Kincaid Furniture Co. Inc.

OAK CANYON - Furniture - Oak Canyon Inc.

OAK CARRELATES - Furniture - Brill Manufacturing Co.

OAK CITY BY JASCO - Cabinets ☆ - Jasco Products Co. Inc.

OAK COLLECTIBLES - Furniture - Hooker Furniture Corp.

OAK COLLECTION - Bathroom fixtures - Leigh

OAK COLLECTION - Cutting boards ☆ - Regent Sheffield, Ltd.

OAK COUNTRY - Furniture ☆ - Lane Co. Inc.

OAK CREEK - Desks - Riverside Furniture Corp.

OAK CREEK - Meat products - LMG Investments, Inc.

OAK CREEK COLLECTION, THE - Office furniture–wood - Riverside Furniture Corp.

OAK CREST - Cabinets - Wellborn Cabinet, Inc.

OAK CREST - Mobile homes - Kit Manufacturing Co.

OAK ESTATES - Furniture - Bassett Furniture Industries, Inc.

OAK EXPRESS - Furniture - Big Sur Waterbeds, Inc.

OAK FALLS - Wines - European Beverage Co., Inc.

OAK FALLS - Wines ☆ - Maison Jomere Ltd.
OAK FARMS - Milk - Oak Farms Dairies
OAK FREQUENCY CONTROL GROUP - Electronic equipment - Oak
  Frequency Control Group
OAK GROVE - Food products - Roberts Bros. Inc.
OAK GROVE - Lumber - Georgia-Pacific Corp.
OAK GROVE - Milk - Oak Grove Dairy
OAK GROVE - Trailers–travel - Fleetwood Enterprises, Inc.
OAK HALL - Furniture - Lineage Home Furnishings, Inc.
OAK HARBOR - Furniture ☆ - Universal Flooring
OAK HILL - Cabinets - Riviera Cabinets Inc.
OAK HILL - Furniture ☆ - Bassett Furniture Industries, Inc.
OAK HILL - Furniture ☆ - Southern Furniture Co. of Conover
OAK HILL - Tableware–plastic ☆ - Oak Hill Industries Corp.
OAK HILL COLLECTION - Furniture - BDO Seidman
OAK HILL FARM - Iced tea–bottled or canned - Oak Hill Farm
OAK KNOLL - Trailers–travel - Fleetwood Enterprises, Inc.
OAK KNOLL - Wines - Oak Knoll Winery Inc.
OAK LEAF - Lumber - Georgia-Pacific Corp.
OAK LEAF - Recording label - Artifex Records Inc.
OAK LEAF BRAND COWHIDE - Leather tanning and finishing - Leather
  Factory Inc.
OAK LEAVES - Tableware–china - Pfaltzgraff Investment Co.
OAK-LIN - Tables–metal - Teledyne Post
OAK-LOK - Wood products - Aspen Valley Lumber Co. Inc.
OAK MANOR - Furniture - Bean Station Furniture Factory Inc.
OAK MANOR - House furnishings ☆ - Lexington Furniture Industries, Inc.
OAK MATE - Flooring–hardwood ☆ - Biwood Flooring
OAK MATE - Wood products ☆ - Gossen Corp.
OAK MICROSYSTEMS - Computers - Oak Microsystems
OAK MOSS - Shampoos - Holistic Laboratories
OAK MOTIF - Furniture ☆ - Bassett Furniture Industries, Inc.
OAK-N-IVY ARMOR - Health care products - Tec Laboratories, Inc.
OAK 'N PATCHWORK - Furniture ☆ - Bassett Furniture Industries, Inc.
OAK ORIGINALS - Hardware - Marley Mouldings Inc.
OAK-OVER - Moldings and trim - Contact Lumber Co.
OAK PARK - Cabinets ☆ - Nutone Inc.
OAK PARK - Cabinets–wood - Kemper
OAK PARK - Cutlery ☆ - Lifetime Hoan Corp.
OAK PARK - Food products - Richelieu Trading Co.
OAK PARK - Furniture - Hammary Furniture Co. Inc.
OAK PARK - Furniture ☆ - Universal Flooring
OAK PARK - Trailers–travel - Fleetwood Enterprises, Inc.
OAK PARK CATHEDRAL - Cabinets–wood - Kemper
OAK PARK COLLECTION - Furniture - Brady Furniture Co. Inc.
OAK PARK PLAID - Bedding–linen - Dan River Inc.
OAK PLAZA - Furniture ☆ - Bassett Furniture Industries, Inc.
OAK POINTE - Apparel and accessories - Cummington-Ford, Inc.
OAK PROFILES - Mirrors - Hoyne Industries Inc.
OAK RIDGE - Furniture - Avon Co.
OAK RIDGE - Furniture ☆ - Bassett Furniture Industries, Inc.
OAK RIDGE II - Furniture - Universal Flooring
OAK RIDGE VINEYARDS - Wines - Oak Ridge Vineyards
OAK RIVER FOODS - Baked goods - Greenfield Healthy Foods Co.
OAK RIVER FOODS - Desserts - Natural Food Systems Inc.
OAK ROYALE - Furniture - Keller Manufacturing Co.
OAK-SEAL - Weather stripping - KEL-EEZ
OAK-TEX - Floor coverings - Mannington Resilient Floors
OAK TOWNE - Cabinets - Markus Cabinet Manufacturing Co.
OAK TRAIL - Tables–wood - Riverside Furniture Corp.
OAK TRANSITIONS - Furniture ☆ - Kincaid Furniture Co. Inc.
OAK TREE - Apparel and accessories - Edison Brothers Stores, Inc.
OAK TREE - Dairy products - Oak Tree Farm Dairy, Inc.
OAK TREE - Publisher's imprints - Oak Tree Publications Inc.
OAK TREE CABINETS & WOODWORKING - Furniture–wood - Rohloff
  Builders, Inc.
OAK-UMMS - Pet products - Penn-Plax, Inc.
OAK VALLEY - Furniture - Stratford Co.
OAK VALLEY - Manufactured homes - Redman Industries, Inc.
OAK VALLEY - Turkeys - Sunday House Foods Inc.
OAK VALLEY FARMS - Meat products–poultry - El Jay Poultry Corp.
OAK VINEYARDS - Wines - Cannon Wines Ltd.
OAK WAINSCOT - Wood products - Gibco Services Inc.
OAK WIND - Clocks ☆ - Ridgeway Clock Co.
OAKBROOK - Bathroom fixtures ☆ - Crane Plumbing/Fiat Products
OAKBROOK - Doors–wood - ODL, Inc.

OAKBROOK - Furniture ☆ - Bassett Furniture Industries, Inc.
OAKBROOK - Furniture ☆ - Brooks Furniture Manufacturing Inc.
OAKBROOK - Tables–wood - Riverside Furniture Corp.
OAKBROOKE - Flatware - General Mills, Inc.
OAKBROOKE - Floor coverings–carpet and rugs ☆ - Whitecrest Carpet Mills
OAKCRAFT - Frames–picture ☆ - Intercraft Industries
OAKCRAFT - Spiral staircases - American General Products Inc.
OAKCREST - Cabinets - Triangle Pacific Corp. (Cabinet Division)
OAKCREST - Chimes - Nutone Inc.
OAKCREST - Clocks ☆ - General Time Corp. (Westclox/Seth Thomas Div.)
OAKCREST - Doors–wood ☆ - Visador Co.
OAKCREST - Health care products ☆ - Sunrise Medical
OAKCREST COLLECTION - Furniture - Oakwood Interiors
OAKDALE - Clocks ☆ - General Time Corp. (Westclox/Seth Thomas Div.)
OAKDALE - Floor coverings ☆ - Tarkett, Inc.
OAKDALE - Floor coverings–carpet and rugs ☆ - Blue Ridge Carpet Mills
OAKDALE - Furniture - Pilliod Co.
OAKDALE - Housewares - Himark Enterprises Inc.
OAKDALE - Mattresses - Simmons USA
OAKDALE SQUARE - Furniture ☆ - Bassett Furniture Industries, Inc.
OAKDSPCORE - Computer software - DSP Group, Inc.
OAKEN KEG - Pickles - Aunt Jane's Foods
OAKFORD - Floor coverings - Mannington Resilient Floors
OAKGROVE - Floor coverings ☆ - Tarkett, Inc.
OAKHILL COLLECTION - Furniture ☆ - Hedstrom Corp.
OAKHURST - Floor coverings ☆ - Congoleum Corp.
OAKHURST - Furniture ☆ - Bassett Furniture Industries, Inc.
OAKHURST - Salad dressings–bottled - Oakhurst Dairy
OAKITE - Cleaning preparations - Oakite Products, Inc.
OAKITE ABC - Cleaning preparations - Oakite Products, Inc.
OAKITE BACTERICIDE - Disinfectants - Oakite Products, Inc.
OAKLAND - Cabinets - Aristokraft, Inc.
OAKLAND - Shoes ☆ - Allen-Edmonds Shoe Corp.
OAKLAND - Trailers–travel - Fleetwood Enterprises, Inc.
OAKLAND - Veterinary pharmaceutical preparations - Oakland Corp.
OAKLAND HILLS - Furniture - Pilliod Co.
OAKLAND MIST - Cabinets ☆ - Aristokraft, Inc.
OAKLAND OAKS - Apparel and accessories - John A. Busch
OAKLAND PARK - Furniture - Athens Furniture Industries Inc.
OAKLAND RAIDERS - Apparel–athletic - National Football League Properties,
  Inc.
OAKLANDON - Furniture - Thomasville Furniture Industries Inc.
OAKLAWN - Floor coverings - Tarkett, Inc.
OAKLAWN - Furniture ☆ - Hooker Furniture Corp.
OAKLEAF - Lard ☆ - Swift Edible Oil Co.
OAKLEIGH - Cabinets - Belwood Inc.
OAKLEIGH - Cabinets–wood - Parcraft Distinctive Cabinetry
OAKLEY - Decals and transfers - Oakley, Inc.
OAKLEY - Ophthalmic goods - Styl-Rite Optical Manufacturing Co., Inc.
OAKLEY'S CAR WASH - Apparel and accessories - 230 Car Wash Corp.
OAKMONT - Cabinets - Triangle Pacific Corp. (Cabinet Division)
OAKMONT - Clocks ☆ - General Time Corp. (Westclox/Seth Thomas Div.)
OAKMONT - Floor coverings - Bruce Hardwood Floors
OAKMONT - Frames–eyeglass ☆ - Universal/Univis Inc.
OAKMONT - Furniture - Universal Flooring
OAKMONT - Furniture ☆ - Cochrane Furniture Co. Inc.
OAKMONT - Furniture ☆ - Southern Furniture Co. of Conover
OAKMONT FEATURE STRIPS - Floor coverings - Bruce Hardwood Floors
OAKPRO - Wood products - P & M Cedar Products, Inc.
OAKQUEST - Furniture - Simon Corp.
OAKRIDGE - Cabinets - Leedo Manufacturing Co.
OAKRIDGE - Cabinets ☆ - Quality Cabinets
OAKRIDGE - Floor coverings–carpet and rugs ☆ - Criterion Mills Inc.
OAKRIDGE - Occasional furniture ☆ - JDI Group, Inc.
OAKRIDGE - Recording label - Oakridge Music Recording Service
OAKRIDGE - Shingles - Owens Corning
OAKRIDGE II - Shingles - Owens Corning
OAKRIDGE PLUS - Shingles - Owens Corning
OAKRIDGE PLUS - Shingles–asphalt or tar - Owens Corning Fiberglass
  Technology Inc.
OAKRIDGE SERIES - Shingles - Owens Corning
OAKS - Concrete products - Lafarge Corp.
OAKSPRINGS - Greeting cards - Oaksprings Impressions
OAKTON - Furniture ☆ - Bassett Furniture Industries, Inc.
OAKTON - Furniture ☆ - Lane Co. Inc.
OAKTON - Laboratory apparatus - Cole-Parmer Instrument Co.

☆ = Now out of production

OAKTOWN - Apparel and accessories - Isaac Haynie

OAKTOWN - Recording label - Isaac B. Haynie

OAKTOWNE - Furniture - Keller Manufacturing Co.

OAKTREE - Cabinets - Starmark, Inc.

OAKTREE - Dairy products - Oak Tree Farm Dairy, Inc.

OAKTREE - Recording label - Credence Records

OAKTREE PACKAGING - Packaging–paper - Oak Tree Packaging Corp.

OAKTRON - Amplifiers–musical instrument - MTX Oaktron

OAKVIEW - Furniture - Stanley Furniture Co. Inc.

OAKVIEW - Mobile homes ☆ - Kit Manufacturing Co.

OAKVILLE - Bedding–linen - Dan River Inc.

OAKVILLE - Office supplies - Labelon Corp.

OAKVILLE ESTATE - Wines - Franciscan Vineyards, Inc.

OAKVILLE GRADE - Wines - Merryvale Vineyards

OAKVILLE RANCH - Beverages–alcohol - Oakville Ranch Vineyard, LP

OAKWIND - Furniture ☆ - Singer Furniture Co.

OAKWOOD - Bakery products - Oakwood Bakery

OAKWOOD - Bathroom accessories ☆ - Nutone Inc.

OAKWOOD - Fabrics - Uniroyal Engineered Products

OAKWOOD - Footwear - G.H. Bass and Co.

OAKWOOD - Furniture - Mersman Furniture Co.

OAKWOOD - Glassware–household ☆ - Wallace International Silversmiths, Inc.

OAKWOOD - Housewares - Winsome Trading, Inc.

OAKWOOD - Mobile homes - Oakwood Homes Corp.

OAKWOOD - Thread - A. Lewis Thread Co. Inc.

OAKWOOD BRIDGE - Wines - Glenora Wine Cellars, Inc.

OAKWOOD COLLECTION - Footwear–men's - Thom McAn Shoe Co.

OAKWOOD FROST - Cabinets - Del Mar Cabinets

OAKWOOD INTERIORS - Furniture - Oakwood Interiors

OAKWOOD VILLAGE - Wallpaper - Taylor Wallcoverings Inc.

OAKWOODE - Windows–plastic ☆ - Aluminum Co. of America

OAKWORKS - Furniture - Stacor Corp.

OAM - Apparel and accessories - Chris E. Malloy

OAO - Recording label - Jazz Composer's Orchestra Association Inc.

OAPI - Pharmaceutical preparations - Otsuka America, Inc.

OAR MOLDWORKS - Moldings and trim - O.A.R. Tool and Die, Inc.

OARMASTER - Boats - Alden Ocean Shells Inc.

OARSTIR - Bar fixtures–plastic - Spir-it Inc.

OAS - Computer software - Coda Inc.

O.A.S. - Veterinary pharmaceutical preparations - Grease Eater International Inc.

OASIS - Audio cables and accessories - Wireworld by David Salz, Inc.

OASIS - Awnings - Dometic Corp.

OASIS - Bicycles - Columbia Manufacturing Inc.

OASIS - Bicycles - Dynacraft Industries Inc.

OASIS - Breads - Healthbreads Inc.

OASIS - Cigarettes ☆ - Liggett Group Inc.

OASIS - Cleaning preparations - Ecolab Inc.

OASIS - Computer software - International Family Entertainment, Inc.

OASIS - Computer software - Orion Automation, Inc.

OASIS - Containers–insulated - E-Z Sales & Manufacturing, Inc.

OASIS - Craft supplies - Smithers-Oasis USA

OASIS - Dehumidifiers - Oasis Corp.

OASIS - Exchangers–heat - Aavid Laboratories, Inc.

OASIS - Figurines - Master Mark Plastic Products

OASIS - Film for insulation - E.I. Dupont de Nemours and Co.

OASIS - Floor coverings–carpet and rugs - Foreign Accents

OASIS - Floor coverings–carpet and rugs - Quaker Inc.

OASIS - Floor coverings–carpet and rugs ☆ - Couristan Inc.

OASIS - Floor coverings–carpet and rugs ☆ - Richmond Carpet Mills

OASIS - Floor coverings–carpet and rugs ☆ - S and S Mills Inc.

OASIS - Frames–eyeglass - Zylo Ware Corp.

OASIS - Fruits–canned - Oasis Foods Inc.

OASIS - Health care products - Procter & Gamble Co.

OASIS - Hobby kits ☆ - Brittoys

OASIS - Medical apparatus - Oasis Medical, Inc.

OASIS - Motor vehicles–automobiles - American Isuzu Motors Inc.

OASIS - Novelty items ☆ - Cobbs Manufacturing Co.

OASIS - Office supplies - Alvin and Co. Inc.

OASIS - Oxygen ☆ - Caire

OASIS - Pet products ☆ - Novalek, Inc.

OASIS - Plastics–laminated - Madico, Inc.

OASIS - Religious organizations - Phil Waldrep Evangelist Association

OASIS - Saunas ☆ - Trayco, Inc.

OASIS - Telecommunications apparel - Promptus Communications Inc.

OASIS - Tents - Coleman Co., Inc.

OASIS - Wallpaper - Secrest Handprints Inc.

OASIS - Watches - Golden State Imports International, Inc.

OASIS - Water–bottled or canned - Ozark Water Co.

OASIS - Water–bottled or canned - Perrier Group of America Inc.

OASIS - Window shades - Comfortex Corp.

OASIS 3 - Wallpaper - Secrest Handprints Inc.

OASIS CHEMICAL CORP. - Chemical preparations - Oasis Chemical U.S.A. Corp.

OASIS FLOWER - Shaving preparations - S.C. Johnson & Son, Inc.

OASIS HOT'N COLD - Ice chests–plastic - Oasis Corp.

OASIS, THE - Fireplaces - Heat-N-Glo Fireplace Products, Inc.

OASISPORTS - Apparel–men's - Sea-Bell Sportswear, Inc.

OASYS - Computer software - Oasys Software, Inc.

OASYS - Musical instruments - Korg, USA, Inc.

OASYS - Synthesizers–musical instrument - Korg USA

OASYS OPEN ARCHITECTURE SYNTHESIS SYSTEM - Synthesizers– musical instrument - Korg, USA, Inc.

OAT BRAN 1000 - Vitamins and nutritional supplements - Source Naturals

OAT BRAN 1000 - Vitamins and nutritional supplements ☆ - Lifessence Labs

OAT BRAN CRUNCH - Cereal ☆ - Edward & Sons Trading Co., Inc.

OAT BRAN DELITE - Breads ☆ - Natural Ovens of Manitowoc Inc.

OAT BRAN MUESLI - Cereal - Breadshop's Natural Foods

OAT BRAN O - Cereal - Health Valley Food

OAT BRAN OPTIONS - Cereal - Ralston Purina Co.

OAT CHEX - Cereal - Ralston Purina Co.

OAT HOOPS - Food products - Kraft Food Ingredients Corp.

OAT-RAGEOUS - Cookies - Greenfield Healthy Foods Co.

OAT SQUARES - Cereal - Quaker Oats Co.

OAT THINS - Crackers - Nabisco Foods Group

OATBAKE - Cereal ☆ - Kellogg Co.

OATEY - Adhesives and sealants - Oatey Co.

OATFIELD - Candy - Pennsylvania Dutch Candies

OATFIELD - Confections - Dae Julie, Inc.

OATI ETS - Computer peripheral equipment - Open Access Technology International, Inc.

OATIOLA - Cereal - New Morn, Inc.

OATIOLA - Cereal - New Morning

OATIOS - Cereal - New Morn, Inc.

OATIOS - Cereal - New Morning

OATIOS-FAMILY SIZE - Cereal - New Morn, Inc.

OATIOS POLY BAG - Cereal - New Morn, Inc.

OATLANDS FARM - Magnets ☆ - Chase Collection, Inc.

OATMEAL CRANBERRY MOUNTAINS - Cakes - Sweet Street Desserts, Inc.

OATMEAL CREAM - Cosmetics ☆ - Comfort Manufacturing Co.

OATMEAL CRISP - Cereal - General Mills, Inc.

OATMEAL CRUNCH - Cereal - Quaker Oats Co.

OATMEAL CRUNCH - Crackers - Nabisco Holdings Corp.

OATMEAL GOODNESS - Bread - Interstate Brands Corp.

OATMEAL LIGHTS - Snack foods - McKee Foods Corp.

OATMEAL RAISIN CRISP - Cereal - General Mills, Inc.

OATMEAL RAISIN RINGS - Cookies ☆ - Sunshine Biscuits, Inc.

OATMEAL STOUT - Beer - New England Brewing Co. Inc.

OATMEAL SWEET CHIPPIES - Cookies - Peachtree Specialties Ltd.

OATMEAL SWIRLERS - Cereal - General Mills, Inc.

OATMEAL XMAS COOKIES - Pet products - Francodex Labs

OATS & MORE - Cereal - Ralston Foods, Inc.

OATS FUR COATS - Shampoos - Kim Laube & Co. Inc.

OATS 'N GROATS - Bird feeds - Petland, Inc.

OAURA - Juices - Curt Grob Jr.

OAXAKA WILLIE - Apparel and accessories - Pletz Imports

O.B. - Tampons - Johnson & Johnson

OB 1 - Medical apparatus - Healthdyne Technologies, Inc.

OB/MASCO - Drapery hardware - Masco Corp.

OB-MX - Musical instruments - Gibson Guitar Corp.

OB-NATAL - Vitamins and nutritional supplements - Armenpharm Ltd.

OB-NATAL - Vitamins and nutritional supplements - Pharmeral Inc.

OB-NATAL PLUS - Vitamins and nutritional supplements - Armenpharm Ltd.

O.B.-THERA - Vitamins and nutritional supplements ☆ - Legere Pharmaceuticals Inc.

OB-TINIC - Pharmaceutical preparations ☆ - Roberts/Hauck Pharmaceuticals Inc.

OB-VIT - Vitamins and nutritional supplements ☆ - Scrip-Physician Supply Co.

OBACIN - Pharmaceutical preparations ☆ - Kenyon Drug Co. Inc.

OBAGI - Cosmetics - Zein E. Obagi

OBAI - Apparel and accessories ☆ - Jasper Textiles Inc.

☆ = Now out of production

OBALAN - Pharmaceutical preparations - Lannett Co. Inc.

OBAN - Deodorizers - Nationwide Chemical Products, Inc.

OBBLIGATO - Blinds–venetian ☆ - Hunter Douglas, Inc.

OBCON SUB BASS - Acoustical speakers - Andrew Oberbillig

O.B.C.T. - Pharmaceutical preparations ☆ - Vita-Fore Products Co.

OBE-DEL - Pharmaceutical preparations ☆ - Marlop Pharmaceuticals Inc.

OBE-MAR - Pharmaceutical preparations ☆ - Marlop Pharmaceuticals Inc.

O'BEARIGAN - Toys–stuffed ☆ - Gund, Inc.

OBECYN - Vitamins and nutritional supplements - Fleming & Co.

OBEDIENCE - Hair care products - Lori Davis Hair, Inc.

OBELISK - Audio equipment - Shahinian Acoustics Ltd.

OBELISK - Publisher's imprints - E.P. Dutton Inc.

OBENIX - Pharmaceutical preparations - Abana Pharmaceuticals, Inc.

OBENIX - Pharmaceutical preparations - Jones Medical Industries, Inc. (Medical Div.)

OBEPAR - Pharmaceutical preparations ☆ - Parmed Pharmaceuticals, Inc.

OBEPHEN - Pharmaceutical preparations - Roberts/Hauck Pharmaceuticals Inc.

OBERDORFOR WEISEE - Beverages–malt ☆ - HDT Importers Inc.

OBERFRANKISCHE - Glassware–household - Whitehurst Imports

OBERG - Automotive filters - Oberg USA, Inc.

OBERGLAS - Glassware–household - Primex International Corp.

OBERHELLMANN VINEYARDS - Wines - Bell Mountain Vineyards Inc.

OBERHOF - Wines - Bell Mountain Vineyards Inc.

OBERLE - Food products - Oberle Meats, Inc.

OBERLE DOG - Sausages - Oberle Meats, Inc.

OBERLIN FARMS - Milk - Oberlin Farms Dairy Inc.

OBERMEYER - Apparel–athletic - Sport Obermeyer Ltd.

OBERMINE - Pharmaceutical preparations - Forest Pharmaceuticals Inc.

OBERON - Building materials - TCT

OBERON - Dishes–china - Waterford Wedgewood USA, Inc.

OBERON - Ophthalmic goods - Swank Optical

OBERON - Rings–jewelry - Artcarved Inc.

OBERON PROSPERO - Computer peripheral equipment - Oberon Software, Inc.

OBERTI - Olives–canned - Oberti Olive Co.

OBERTO - Meat products–beef - Bob Ostrow Co.

OBERTO - Wines - C. Daniele & Co., Inc.

OBERWEIS DAIRY - Milk - Oberweis Dairy Inc.

OBESAN - Pharmaceutical preparations - Dunhall Pharmaceuticals Inc.

OBESBLETS - Pharmaceutical preparations ☆ - Chase Laboratories Inc.

OBESE I - Pharmaceutical preparations ☆ - Legere Pharmaceuticals Inc.

OBESITY BELL - Pharmaceutical preparations - Hollings-Smith Co. Inc.

OBESTAT - Pharmaceutical preparations ☆ - Lemmon Co.

OBESTER - Wines - Obester Winery

OBESTROL - Pharmaceutical preparations ☆ - ICN Pharmaceuticals Inc.

OBETROL - Pharmaceutical preparations - Rexar Pharmacal Corp.

OBEVAL - Pharmaceutical preparations ☆ - Pal-Pak Inc.

OBEX - Computer software - Borland International, Inc.

OBEY - Frames–eyeglass - Liberty Optical Manufacturing Co.

OBEZINE - Pharmaceutical preparations - Western Research Laboratories

O.B.I. - Buckles ☆ - Erich M. Reich Inc.

OBI - Frames–eyeglass - May Optical Co. Inc.

OBI - Soft drinks - International Beverages Inc.

OBI APFELSAFT - Fruit juices - International Beverages Inc.

OBI-WAN KENOBI - Publisher's imprints - Lucasfilm Ltd.

OBIE'S - Bakery products - Jeffrey A. Caden

OBIE'S COOKIE JAR - Bakery products - Jeffrey A. Caden

OBJECT CORE - Computer software - American Management Systems, Inc.

OBJECT-ENGINE - Computer software ☆ - DataPak Software Inc.

OBJECT-FAX - Facsimile equipment - Traffic Software, Inc.

OBJECT GALLERY - Computer software - Intek Technologies, Inc.

OBJECT GAME, THE - Educational game - Object International, Inc.

OBJECT GT ENGINE - Computer software - Lavelle Associates Inc.

OBJECT INTEGRATION SERVER - Computer software - Ontos, Inc.

OBJECT-MENU - Computer software - Island Systems Inc.

OBJECT-ORIENTED RECORDING - Computer software - SQA, Inc.

OBJECT POWER - Computer software - Philip J. Campaigne

OBJECT TECHNOLOGY EVERYWHERE - Computer software - Ontos, Inc,

OBJECT WINDOWS - Computer software - Microsoft Corp.

OBJECTBANK - Computer software - Sun Software Corp.

OBJECTBENCH - Computer software - Scientific and Engineering Software, Inc.

OBJECTBROKER - Computer software - Digital Equipment Corp.

OBJECTCARD - Computer hardware - Horizon Technologies, Inc.

OBJECTCATALOG - Computer software - Objectspace, Inc.

OBJECTCENTER - Computer software - Saber Software Corp.

OBJECTCONTROL/SYSTEM - Computer software - Hardy Software Systems, Inc.

OBJECTEXPRESS - Computer software - I-Kinetics, Inc.

OBJECTGRAPHICS - Computer software - Whitewater Group Inc.

OBJECTIONS OVERRULED!!! - Video production - Where Magazine

OBJECTIVE - Wallcoverings - Sherman & Associates International

OBJECTIVE-C - Computer software - Stepstone Corp.

OBJECTIVE COMMUNICATIONS - Computer hardware - Objective Communication Software

OBJECTIVES AND TEXTILE - Wallcoverings - Worldwalls International Inc.

OBJECTIVITY/DB - Computer programs - Objectivity, Inc.

OBJECTPUMP - Computer software - I-Kinetics, Inc.

OBJECTRIEVE - Computer software - Coromandel Industries Inc.

OBJECTS D'HEART - Jewelry - Crystal Brands Inc.

OBJECTS OF DESIRE - Skin care products - Cosmedic Concepts, Inc.

OBJECTSTORE - Computer software - Object Design, Inc.

OBJECTTELLER - Computer software - Sun Software Corp.

OBJECTUTILITIES - Computer software ☆ - OTG Software

OBJECTVAULT - Computer software - Sun Software Corp.

OBJECTWIRE - Computer software - Sun Software Corp.

OBJECTWORKS SMALLTALK - Audio tapes–blank - ParcPlace Systems Inc.

OBJET NATURA - Skin care products - Alba Products Group Inc.

OBJEX - Computer software ☆ - Auto-Trol Technology Corp.

OBJIX - Computer hardware - Objix Multimedia Corp.

OBL - Electrical equipment - Gibson Guitar Corp.

OBL - Guitars - Hamer Guitars

OBLINA - Toys - Mattel, Inc.

OBLIO - Beverages–alcohol - Dear, Inc.

OBLIQO - Games - Charlie's Woodshop

OBLIQUE - Dinnerware–plastic - Plastics Manufacturing Co.

OBLIQUE - Office supplies - Oblique Filing Systems

OBLIQUE SHELF - Office supplies - Oblique Filing Systems

OBNOXIOUS YOUTH - Apparel - Obnoxious Youth

OBO THE CLOWN - Infant product - Eden LLC

O'BOISIES - Potato chips ☆ - Keebler Co.

OBOTAN - Pharmaceutical preparations ☆ - Wallace Laboratories

O'BOY - Housewares ☆ - Utikem Products

OBRA+ - Computer software - Medical Communications Software Inc.

OBREGON - Shoes - Royal Footwear Co., Inc.

O'BRIEN - Paints - Fuller-O'Brien Paints Inc.

O'BRIEN - Sporting goods - O'Brien International

O'BRIEN - Toys–stuffed - Russ Berrie and Co., Inc.

O'BRIEN SMOK-KIST - Meat products–beef - Louies Wholesale Meats

O'BRIEN'S - Beef - O'Brien & Co., Inc.

OBRION - Skin care products - Ron Peaker

OBRITE - Ophthalmic goods - Whitby Pharmaceuticals, Inc.

OBRUS - Software - Brent Collins

OBSCURITY EDITIONS - Artists' materials - Charles J. Katz Jr.

OBSERV-O-SCOPE - Hardware - Baldwin Hardware Corp.

OBSERVATION GUARD STAND - Swimming pools - Recreonics, Inc.

OBSERVATORY WATCH, THE - Watches - Longines-Wittnauer Watch Co.

OBSERVER - Binoculars - Swift Instruments, Inc.

OBSERVER - Clocks ☆ - General Time Corp. (Westclox/Seth Thomas Div.)

OBSERVER - Eyeglasses - Martin-Copeland Eyewear Corp.

OBSERVER - Health care products - Omron Healthcare, Inc.

OBSERVER - Laser systems–medical - Kentek Corp.

OBSERVER-OBSERVED - Apparel–athletic - Lois Teicher

OBSERVISION - Photographic equipment - Ultrak, Inc.

OBSESSION - Colognes - Calvin Klein Ltd.

OBSESSION - Floor coverings–carpet and rugs - Tuftex Carpet Mills, Inc.

OBSESSION - Floor coverings–carpet and rugs ☆ - Regal Rugs Inc.

OBSESSION - Floor coverings–carpet and rugs ☆ - Royalweve Carpet Mills

OBSESSION - Jewelry - B. Tekel

OBSESSION - Wallpaper - Bayview Wallcoverings

OBSESSION FOR MEN - Colognes - Calvin Klein Ltd.

OBSESSION MOUNTAIN VINEYARDS - Wines - Kautz Vineyards, Inc.

OBSESSION TELESCOPES - Telescopes - David Thomas Kriege

OBSESSIONS - Floor coverings–carpet and rugs - Patcraft Mills Inc.

OBSIDIAN - Hair care products - Luxor Corp.

OBSIDIAN IMAGING - Cameras - Obsidian Imaging

OBSIDIAN STOUT - Beverages–malt - Deschutes Brewery

OBSOLETE - Recording label - International Record Corp.

OBSTREPEROUS LETTER, THE - Games - Obstreperous Letter, Inc.

OBTUNDIA ANTISEPTIC - Anesthetics - Buffington

OBTUNDIA ANTISEPTIC - Skin care products - Otis Clapp & Son Inc.

☆ = Now out of production

OBTUNDIA CALAMINE - Anesthetics - Buffington
OBTUNDIA CALAMINE - Pharmaceutical preparations - Otis Clapp & Son Inc.
OBTUNDIA CREAM - Anesthetics - Buffington
OBTUNDIA CREAM - Pharmaceutical preparations - Otis Clapp & Son Inc.
OBUS FORME - Health care products - Camp, Inc.
OBV - Tools - Liberty Distributors Group
OBVIOUS LE VALUE - Apparel and accessories - Lillie Rubin Affiliates, Inc.
OBVIOUSLY ONION - Spices and extracts - Jodie's Kitchen Inc.
OBVIOUSLY YOU - Underwear and nightwear - Maidenform Inc.
OBY-REX - Pharmaceutical preparations ☆ - Parmed Pharmaceuticals, Inc.
OBY-TRIM - Pharmaceutical preparations - Rexar Pharmacal Corp.
OBZONE - Pet products - Sandpoint Aquarium Products
OC - Pharmaceutical preparations - Brown Manufacturing Co.
OC-7 - Vitamins and nutritional supplements - TSN Labs, Inc.
OC-10 - Research–chemical - Bushwacker Backpack & Supply Co.
OC SHAKE SHINGLES - Shingles–shakes ☆ - Owens Corning
OCA 19 - Deodorants–personal - Hinstlblon Ltd.
OCALA CONE - Flowers, plants, and seeds - Lake Ferns, Inc.
OCAMPO - Cigars ☆ - Tropical Tobacco, Inc.
OCB - Beverages–malt - Otter Creek Brewing, Inc.
OCB - Cigarette paper - Republic Tobacco L.P.
OCCASION - Floor coverings–carpet and rugs ☆ - Porter Carpet Mills Inc.
OCCASION GALLERIE FROM BLUE MOUNTAIN ARTS, THE - Greeting cards - Blue Mountain Arts Inc.
OCCASIONAL CHOCOLATE BY NAVOY - Candy - Occasional Chocolate by Navoy
OCCASIONAL COLLECTION - Trays–wood ☆ - All-Luminum Products Inc.
OCCASIONALS - Underwear and nightwear - Alba-Waldensian, Inc.
OCCASIONS - Contact lenses - Bausch & Lomb Inc.
OCCASIONS - Dinnerware and servingware - Corning Inc.
OCCASIONS - Glassware–household - ACC
OCCASIONS - Glassware–household - Svend Jensen of Denmark Inc.
OCCELLI - Butter - Crystal Food Import Corp.
OCCIGEMS - Diamonds - Occidental Gems Inc.
OCCLUSAL - Health care products - Genderm Corp.
OCCLUSAL-HP - Health care products - Genderm Corp.
OCCO - Pet food - Archer Daniels Midland Co.
OCCODEGEN - Computer software - Object International, Inc.
OCCUMITTS - Gloves–safety - Occunomix International Inc.
OCCUPATIONAL HAZARD - Apparel and accessories - Hazardous Materials, Inc.
OCCUPATIONAL HAZARDS - Glassware–household - Papel Freelance, Inc.
OCCUR! - Colognes ☆ - Avon Products, Inc.
OCCUR - Eyeglasses - Martin-Copeland Eyewear Corp.
OCCURRENCE - Floor coverings–carpet and rugs ☆ - Callaway Carpets
OCCUVUE - Optical scanners–computer - Titmus Optical, Inc.
OCEAN - Electronic equipment - Centennial Electric Sound Co. Ltd.
OCEAN - Finishing agents ☆ - Fire Research Laboratories, Inc.
OCEAN - Freezers - Frigibar Industries Inc.
OCEAN - Hardware ☆ - Tubbs Cordage Co.
OCEAN - Health care products - Fleming & Co.
OCEAN - Insecticides - Ocean Coffee Co. Inc.
OCEAN 50 SEAMIX - Aquariums–household ☆ - Jungle Laboratories Corp.
OCEAN-200 - Toys ☆ - Transcience Corp.
OCEAN ADVENTURE - Pasta - CPC International Inc.
OCEAN AIR - Fans–electric - JBS Enterprises, Inc.
OCEAN ANIMAL - Snack foods - Kristine's Foods
OCEAN BABIES - Craft supplies ☆ - VIP/VIP Crafts
OCEAN BASKET - Cat food - Ralston Purina Co.
OCEAN BAY - Apparel and accessories - Jonbil Inc.
OCEAN BEACH - Furniture - Lane Co. Inc.
OCEAN BEAUTY - Food products - Seattle Seafoods Inc.
OCEAN BEAUTY - Seafood products–fresh or frozen - Ocean Beauty Seafood, Inc.
OCEAN BISTRO - Seafood products–fresh or frozen - Aqua Star, Inc.
OCEAN BLEND - Cat food - Ralston Purina Co.
OCEAN BLOOM - Dinnerware ☆ - Corning Inc.
OCEAN BLUE - Apparel and accessories - J.C. Penney Co., Inc.
OCEAN BLUE - Apparel and accessories - Oceantours, Ltd.
OCEAN BLUE - Recording label - Ace Records
OCEAN BLUE - Shrimp–fresh or frozen - Price Seafood Inc.
OCEAN BREEZE - Cleaning preparations–household - Harley Chemicals
OCEAN BREEZE - Eyeglasses - Art-Craft Optical Co.
OCEAN BREEZE - Seafood products–fresh or frozen - Morgan City Freezer & Cold Storage Inc.
OCEAN BUFFET - Cat food - Mardel Laboratories, Inc.

OCEAN BUFFET OCEANSNAX - Cat food - Mardel Laboratories, Inc.
OCEAN B.U.M. - Apparel–men's - Chauvin International Ltd.
OCEAN CHAMPION - Bathing suits - Ocean Pool Co.
OCEAN CHEF - Seafood products–fresh or frozen - Nanticoke Seafood Corp.
OCEAN CLEAR - Apparel trimmings - Red Sea Fish Farms
OCEAN CLIPPER - Seafood - American Seafood International Inc.
OCEAN CLIPPER - Watches - Bulova Corp.
OCEAN COFFEE ROASTERS - Coffee - Excellent Coffee Co. Inc.
OCEAN CREEK - Furniture ☆ - Lexington Furniture Industries, Inc.
OCEAN CREST - Coffee - Ocean Coffee Co. Inc.
OCEAN CREST - Seafood products–fresh or frozen - Ocean Crest Seafoods Inc.
OCEAN CRUISER - Ships–sailing vessels ☆ - A. Le Comte Co. Inc.
OCEAN CURVES - Surfboards - Amtec Global Inc.
OCEAN DAWN - Seafood products–fresh or frozen - Arrowac Fisheries Inc.
OCEAN DELIGHT - Seafood products–fresh or frozen - Seastar Inc.
OCEAN DELITES - Herring, sardines, mussels - Inorex Inc.
OCEAN DIAMOND - Seafood products–fresh or frozen ☆ - Gourmet Club Corp.
OCEAN DRIVE - Apparel and accessories - Barrow Manufacturing Co., Inc.
OCEAN EAGLE - Sporting goods ☆ - Wright & McGill Co.
OCEAN EDGE - Apparel and accessories - Lashdell Underwater Partners
OCEAN EDGE - Bedding–linen - Dan River Inc.
OCEAN EQUIPMENT - Outerwear - David Peyser Sportswear Inc.
OCEAN FARMS - Shrimp–fresh or frozen ☆ - Neptune Sea Food Co.
OCEAN FIRE - Finishing agents ☆ - Fire Research Laboratories, Inc.
OCEAN FRESH - Fish–fresh or frozen - Detroit City Dairy Inc.
OCEAN GARDEN - Shrimp–fresh or frozen - Stavis Seafoods Inc.
OCEAN GEM - Scallops - Sea-Rich Seafoods, Inc.
OCEAN GEMS - Aquariums–household - Marine Fauna & Flora Co.
OCEAN GLEN - Seafood products–fresh or frozen - New England Fish Co.
OCEAN GOLD - Crab meat–canned or cured - Coast to Coast Seafood Inc.
OCEAN GOLD - Seafood - Clouston Foods USA
OCEAN GOURMET - Seafood products–fresh or frozen - Aptco Inc.
OCEAN GRANGER - Sporting goods - Wright & McGill Co.
OCEAN GROUP, LUXURY YACHT CO-OWNERSHIP, THE - Hotels and motels - Giant Marine Group, Ltd.
OCEAN HARVEST - Shrimp–fresh or frozen - Caleb Haley and Co. Inc.
OCEAN HAVEN - Seafood products–fresh or frozen - C.E. Lixie Fisheries Inc.
OCEAN IMAGES - House furnishings - Ocean Images
OCEAN ISLE - Furniture ☆ - Hooker Furniture Corp.
OCEAN ISLE SOFTWARE - Computer software - Ocean Isle Software
OCEAN JACK - Life preservers - Parkway Systems
OCEAN JEWEL - Shrimp–fresh or frozen - Kirad Importing Corp.
OCEAN JEWELS - Jewelry - Scassis Originals, Inc.
OCEAN KAYAK - Boats–kayaks - Johnson Worldwide Associates, Inc.
OCEAN KAYAK INC. - Boats–kayaks - Ocean Kayak, Inc.
OCEAN KING - Shrimp–fresh or frozen - Transpac Food
OCEAN LEE - Seafood products–fresh or frozen - Ocean Pearl Foods Inc.
OCEAN LIFE - Computer storage devices–optical - Cuneiform Corp.
OCEAN LOTION - Cosmetics - Jenefer Palmer Denberg
OCEAN M-L - Pet products - Mei Lan Aquarium
OCEAN MAGIC - Seafood - Jana Brands
OCEAN MAID - Seafood products–fresh or frozen - Fishery Products International USA
OCEAN MAJESTY - Fish–fresh or frozen - Ruggiero Seafood, Inc.
OCEAN MASTER - Boats - Ocean Master Marine Inc.
OCEAN MASTIC - Finishing agents - Fire Research Laboratories, Inc.
OCEAN MERMAID - Bathing suits - Ocean Pool Co.
OCEAN MIST - Antiseptics - Waverly Beauty Products
OCEAN MIST - Cleaning preparations - Ocean Coffee Co. Inc.
OCEAN MIST - Skin care products - Crabtree & Evelyn, Ltd.
OCEAN MIST BLUE - Dolls - Mattel, Inc.
OCEAN MOTION - Apparel–women's - Cape Cod Cricket Lane
OCEAN MOTION - Electrical equipment - J.P. Burleson Inc.
OCEAN NUTRITION - Pet products - Ocean Nutrition Corp.
OCEAN OCEAN - Apparel–women's - Cape Cod Cricket Lane
OCEAN OF WEALTH - Herbal products - Golden Temple Natural Foods Bakery
OCEAN OPTICS - Binoculars - Pioneer Marketing & Research, Inc.
OCEAN OPTIQUE - Eyeglasses - Ocean Optique Distributors Inc.
OCEAN PACIFIC - Bathing suits - Lunada Bay Corp.
OCEAN PACIFIC SPORT - Apparel and accessories - Mass Transit
OCEAN PALS - Toys–stuffed - Dakin Inc.
OCEAN PARTY - Apparel and accessories - Laurick Clothing Ltd.
OCEAN PEARL - Hair care products - Redmond Products, Inc.

OCEAN PLATTER - Food products - Specialty Foods Investment Co.

OCEAN PREMIUM - Shrimp—fresh or frozen - Harrison Pierce & Co. Inc.

OCEAN PRINCE - Sardines—canned - Crown Prince Inc.

OCEAN PRO - Automotive parts and accessories - Ocean Pro Engineering

OCEAN PRO - Sporting goods - Oceanic

OCEAN PURE SEA CUCUMBER + - Vitamins and nutritional supplements - Barth-Spencer Corp.

OCEAN QUEEN - Toys - Tonka Corp.

OCEAN RACER - Belts—automotive - Defender Industries

OCEAN RACER - Ships—sailing vessels ☆ - A. Le Comte Co. Inc.

OCEAN RACERS - Boats—canoes - Howmar Boat Corp.

OCEAN REEF CLUB - Shrimp - Continental Seafoods Inc.

OCEAN REEF CLUB - Stationery - Ocean Reef Club, Inc.

OCEAN-RITE - Pet products - Lake Products Co. Inc.

OCEAN SANCTUARY - T-shirts—men's - Ocean Sanctuary Productions

OCEAN SANS - Computer storage devices - Monotype Corp.

OCEAN SEAMAID - Bathing suits - Ocean Pool Co.

OCEAN SHADOWS - Floor coverings—carpet and rugs ☆ - Catalina Carpet Mills Inc.

OCEAN SPARKLE - Seafood products—fresh or frozen - Ocean Garden Products, Inc.

OCEAN SPLASH - Deodorizers - Linden Corp.

OCEAN SPRAY - Fruit drinks—bottled or canned - Ocean Spray Cranberries Inc.

OCEAN SPRAY - Insecticides - Ocean Coffee Co. Inc.

OCEAN SPRAY LIGHTSTYLE - Juices - Ocean Spray Cranberries Inc.

OCEAN SPRAY ON A STICK - Confections - Ocean Spray Cranberries Inc.

OCEAN SPRAY SPLASH - Fruit drinks—bottled or canned - Pepsico, Inc.

OCEAN STATE - Beverages—alcohol - Jenkins Spirits Corp., Ltd.

OCEAN SUPREME - Food products - VS Tampa Inc.

OCEAN SUPREME - Seafood products—canned or cured - California Shellfish Co. Inc.

OCEAN SURGE - Skin moisturizers - Aramis Inc.

OCEAN TANK - Ice chests—plastic - Victor I. Podd

OCEAN TECHNOLOGY - Apparel and accessories - W.L. Gore & Associates, Inc.

OCEAN THINGS - Toys ☆ - Lauri Inc.

OCEAN TIDE - Seafood products—fresh or frozen ☆ - J.F. Clarke Corp.

OCEAN TRACE BLOCKS - Aquariums—household ☆ - Jungle Laboratories Corp.

OCEAN TREASURES - Jewelry - Town & Country Fine Jewelry Group, Inc.

OCEAN TRENDS - Apparel and accessories - Mass Transit

OCEAN TRIBE - Apparel - David Nicholas DiGirolamo

OCEAN TROPIC - Apparel and accessories - Gitz-It Inc.

OCEAN TROVE - Seafood products—fresh or frozen - Lighthouse Inc.

OCEAN VIEW BRAND CALIFORNIA FLOWERS - Flowers, plants, and seeds - Ocean View Flowers

OCEAN VILLAGE - Salt - National Oats Co. Inc.

OCEAN WATER WONDER - Sporting goods - Ocean Pool Co.

OCEAN-ZOO - Aquariums—household - Transcience Corp.

OCEANA - Colognes - A.K.A. Saunders, Inc.

OCEANA - Floor coverings—carpet and rugs ☆ - Catalina Carpet Mills Inc.

OCEANA - Food products ☆ - Tupman Thurlow Co. Inc.

OCEANA PUBLICATIONS INC. - Publisher's imprints - Oceana Publications Inc.

OCEANBLUE - Dyes and pigments - Ken's Farms Inc.

OCEANBREEZE - Fabrics - Greenwood Mills Inc.

OCEANCO - Boats - Oceanco (USA) Inc.

OCEANDAWN - Food products - Marketing Services Inc.

OCEANEERS - Eyeglasses - Martin-Copeland Eyewear Corp.

OCEANESCE - Toiletries - Fuller Brush Co.

OCEANGLO - Sporting goods - American Underwater Products

OCEANIA - Teas - Caribbean Coffee Co.

OCEANIC - Aquariums—household - Jewel Industries Inc.

OCEANIC - Binoculars - Swift Instruments, Inc.

OCEANIC - Boats—motor - Lyn-Craft Boat Co.

OCEANIC - Boats—motor ☆ - Huckins Yacht Corp.

OCEANIC - Floor coverings—carpet and rugs ☆ - Royalweve Carpet Mills

OCEANIC - Mops - O-Cedar/Vining Household Products Co.

OCEANICS - Paper products - Clarke American Checks, Inc.

OCEANIS - Sporting goods - Beneteau USA Inc.

OCEANLIFE - Compact discs—prerecorded - Sumeria, Inc.

OCEANNA SEA WEES - Toys - Tonka Corp.

OCEANNA TROPIGAL - Toys - Tonka Corp.

OCEANOGRAPHER - Watches - Bulova Corp.

OCEANOGRAPHY - Computer software - Orange Cherry Software

OCEANOLA OCEANOLA - Greeting cards - Originals by Maris (O.B.M. Publishing)

OCEANPRO - Seafood products—fresh or frozen - Profish, Ltd.

OCEANRUNNER - Engines - Outboard Marine Corp.

OCEANS AMERICA - Food products - Shore Lobster & Shrimp Corp.

OCEANS AND DREAMS - Artists' materials - Oceans and Dreams

OCEANS BELOW - Computer software - Amazing Media, Inc.

OCEAN'S BOUNTY - Food products - Seafood Packers Representatives Inc.

OCEANS CUISINE - Fish—fresh or frozen - Oceans Cuisine, Ltd.

OCEANS ELEVEN - Watches - Hampden Corp.

OCEANSIDE - Apparel and accessories - Rockaway Beach Surf Shop Inc.

OCEANSIDE - Dishes—china - Waterford Wedgewood USA, Inc.

OCEANSIDE - Eyeglasses - Art-Craft Optical Co.

OCEANSIDE - Floor coverings—carpet and rugs - Hollytex Carpet Mills Inc.

OCEANSIDE - Furniture - Kmart Corp.

OCEANSIDE - Furniture - Singer Furniture Co.

OCEANSIDE - Furniture ☆ - Riverside Furniture Corp.

OCEANSIDE - Motor vehicles—motor homes ☆ - Georgie Boy Manufacturing, Inc.

OCEANSIDE - Wallcovering - Seabrook Wallcoverings, Inc.

OCEANSIDE - Yarn ☆ - Caron International Inc.

OCEANSIDE STRIP - Floor coverings - Bruce Hardwood Floors

OCEANSNAX - Cat food - Mardel Laboratories, Inc.

OCEANSPORT - Apparel and accessories - Oceansport Design, Inc.

OCEANTIMER - Watches - Bulova Corp.

OCEANTRAWL - Seafood products—canned or cured - Oceantrawl Inc.

OCEANUS - Toilets—enameled - Kohler Co.

OCEANUS - Wines - Chicama Vineyards

OCEANUS SYSTEMS - Pet products - Oceans for Real

OCEANWAY - Seafood products—fresh or frozen - King & Prince Seafood Corp.

OCELET - Archery equipment - Martin Archery Inc.

OCELOT - Golfing equipment - Golfsmith International Inc.

OCEM - Computer software - DSP Semiconductors, Inc.

OCEM - Computer software - DSP Semiconductors, Inc.

OCENS - Computer integrated systems design services - Ocean and Coastal Environmental Sensing, Inc.

OCHMAN - Office supplies - Edward Ochman Systems

OCHOA - Shrimp—fresh or frozen - Darik Enterprises Inc.

OCHSNER - Bicycles - Ochsner International, Inc.

OCILLA - Ophthalmic goods - Styl-Rite Optical Manufacturing Co., Inc.

OCIS - Computer software - Computer Aided Systems, Inc.

OCK SUL SUN SIK - Vitamins and nutritional supplements - Bi-Sung USA

OCKIE - Electronic equipment - Edward Ochman Systems

OCL - Locks—padlocks - Olympus Lock, Inc.

O'CLAIR - Juices - Eau Claire Packing Co.

OCLV - Helmets—athletic - Trek Bicycle Corp.

OCM - Apparel and accessories - O.C.M. Productions Inc.

OCM24 - Computer software - SDM International Inc.

OCMS - Computer software - Mitratech Inc.

OCOEE - Boats - Phoenix Products Inc.

OCOEE - Medical apparatus - Ocoee, Inc.

OCOMA - Food products - Tyson Foods Inc.

OCOS - Audio equipment - Sumiko Inc.

OCOTILLO - Floor coverings—carpet and rugs - Catalina Carpet Mills Inc.

OCOTILLO SOUTHWEST FLAVORS - Seasonings - Ocotillo Southwest Foods

OCRON - Computer software - Ocron Inc.

OCS - Computer software - Outcome Concept Systems, Inc.

OCT - Computers - Phoenix Technologies, Ltd.

OCTA 2000 - Vitamins and nutritional supplements - Unipro Inc.

OCTA-FASHION - Frames—eyeglass ☆ - Universal/Univis Inc.

OCTA-FEM - Frames—eyeglass ☆ - Universal/Univis Inc.

OCTA-GAL - Frames—eyeglass ☆ - Universal/Univis Inc.

OCTA GRANDE - Stone products - E.P. Henry Corp.

OCTA-PAC - Transformers—electric - Coiltronics, Inc.

OCTA-POLLEN - Health care products - Foodscience Laboratories Inc.

OCTA POWER - Vitamins and nutritional supplements - Solaray

OCTA-PROTEIN - Health care products ☆ - Foodscience Laboratories Inc.

OCTA-SHAPE - Frames—eyeglass ☆ - Universal/Univis Inc.

OCTA-THERM - Fireplaces - Martin Industries, Inc.

OCTA-TRADITIONAL - Lighting fixtures - National Service Industries, Inc.

OCTABALL - Games - Jerry P. Maley

OCTACOSANOL - Vitamins and nutritional supplements - Freeda Vitamins Inc.

OCTAD - Floor coverings—tile ☆ - Kentile Floors Inc.

OCTAGON - Detergents - Colgate-Palmolive Co.

OCTAGON - Giftware - Octagon Gifts Inc.

☆ = Now out of production

OCTAGON - Golfing equipment - Carl T. Wagner
OCTAGON - Radios ☆ - RELM Communications Inc.
OCTAGON ADF-PLUS - Aircraft parts - Octagon Process Inc.
OCTAGON BOOKS - Publisher's imprints - Farrar, Straus and Giroux Inc.
OCTAGON RECORDS - Audio equipment - Octagon Products Inc.
OCTAGON, THE - Artists' materials - Visual Design Manufacturing Co. Inc.
OCTAGONAL - Ophthalmic goods ☆ - Luxottica
OCTALINE - Frames–eyeglass - Pathway Optical Prods.
OCTAMAX - Chemical preparations - Chevron USA Inc.
OCTAMETER - Floor coverings–carpet and rugs - Masland Corp.
OCTANE PLUS - Fuel additives - PJH Brands
OCTAPLANTERS - Giftware - Artisans Stained Glass
OCTARORA - Floor coverings - Mannington Resilient Floors
OCTAVE - Electronic equipment - AudioControl
OCTAVE - Floor coverings - Mannington Resilient Floors
OCTAVE - Frames–eyeglass - May Optical Co. Inc.
OCTAVIA - Whirlpools - Lasco Products Group
OCTAVIAN - Floor coverings–tile ☆ - Kentile Floors Inc.
OCTAVIAN - Frames–eyeglass - Hudson Optical Corp.
OCTAVIEW - Containers–plastic - De Ster Corp.
OCTEL - Computers - Octel Communications Corp.
OCTET - Floor coverings - Congoleum Corp.
OCTET STATION - Computer peripheral equipment - Promise Technology
OCTIAMOND RING - Puzzles - Kadon Enterprises Inc.
OCTIC PLUS - Electric lighting equipment - Magnetek, Inc.
OCTILES - Games - Kadon Enterprises Inc.
OCTIME - Glassware–household - Durand International
OCTIVA - Pagers - Matsushita Electric Corp. of America
OCTIVE - Apparel–women's - Lynne Praver and Jennifer Brown
OCTO - Chalk ☆ - Faber-Castell Corp.
OCTO-BLIMP - Toys–automobiles - Mattel, Inc.
OCTOBER - Dinnerware–glass - Franciscan by Johnson Brothers, USA, Inc.
OCTOBER - Furniture - Haworth, Inc.
OCTOBER - Insecticides - U.S. Borax Inc.
OCTOBER BOX - Audio cabinets–wood - Design Direct Sound
OCTOBER! BRILLIANCE - Trees - Willet N. Wandell
OCTOBER HARVEST - Wines - Meredyth Vineyard
OCTOBER NIGHT - Wines - J. Lohr Winery
OCTOBERFEST - Beverages–malt ☆ - St. Killian Importing Co.
OCTOBLEN - Bonding agent - IPA Systems Inc.
OCTOCIDE - Aquatic pharmacuetical preparations ☆ - Aquatronics-Filtronics
OCTOCRETE - Patching mortar - IPA Systems Inc.
OCTOGRIP - Surfboard coating - Donald Stone
OCTOLUME - Lamps - Philips Lighting Co.
OCTONEK - Sweaters - Centralia Knitting Mills Inc.
OCTOPACK - Packaging machines - Hartness International, Inc.
OCTOPLUG - Cement water plug - IPA Systems Inc.
OCTOPOIDS - Toys - Toymax Inc.
OCTOPUS - Computer software - Octopus Technologies, Inc.
OCTOPUS - Fasteners–snap - American Octopus Inc.
OCTOPUS - Medical apparatus - Medtronic, Inc.
OCTOPUS - Novelty items - Cobbs Manufacturing Co.
OCTOPUS ARMY - Apparel - I.M. Mugen Trading, Inc.
OCTOPUS GARDEN - Seasonings - Goat Yogurt
OCTOPUS SOLING - Sandals - ALP Sport Sandals
OCTOPUSSY ADVENTURE - Games - Avalon Hill Game Co.
OCTOSEAL - Sealant - IPA Systems Inc.
OCTOSHIELD - Waterproof coating - IPA Systems Inc.
OCTOSKIM - Concrete resurfacer - IPA Systems Inc.
OCTOTROPIC - Footwear–athletic - Henderson Aquatics Inc.
OCTOWELD - Vinyl bonding agent - IPA Systems Inc.
OCTRELLE - Floor coverings ☆ - Azrock Commercial Flooring
OCTRILLON - Jewelry–costume - Diamond Essence Co.
OCTRON - Gasoline ☆ - BP America Inc.
OCTS - Computer software - AT&T Global Information Solutions
OCTURA - Toys–electronic - Octura Models Inc.
OCTUS - Computer peripheral equipment - Office Automation Systems, Inc.
OCTY-ROUND - Tablecloths - Converting, Inc.
OCTYCINE-100 - Pharmaceutical preparations - C.O. Truxton Inc.
OCU CAPS - Pharmaceutical preparations ☆ - Akorn Inc.
OCU-CARE - Vitamins and nutritional supplements - Natural Organics, Inc.
OCU-CEL XL - Medical apparatus - Mentor O & O Inc.
OCU-FILM - Medical apparatus - Mentor O & O Inc.
OCU-GUARD MB - Vaccines - Boehringer Ingelheim Animal Health, Inc.
OCU-GUARD SUPPLE - Medical apparatus - Bio-Vascular, Inc.

OCU-MAX 20/20 - Vitamins and nutritional supplements - Garcoa Labs/Vitamin Classics
OCUCLEAR - Pharmaceutical preparations - Schering-Plough Healthcare Products
OCUCLENZ - Eye-care product - Storz Instrument Co.
OCUCOAT PF - Pharmaceutical preparations - Storz Instrument Co.
OCUDERMA - Cosmetics - Medical Cosmetics Corp.
OCUFEN - Ophthalmic goods - Allergan, Inc.
OCUFLOX - Pharmaceutical preparations - Allergan, Inc.
OCUGEN - Vitamins and nutritional supplements ☆ - Tishcon Corp.
OCUHIST - Lenses–optical - Pfizer Inc.
OCULARVISION - Lenses - Ocularvision, Inc.
OCULID - Health care products ☆ - Halsey Drug Co. Inc.
OCULON - Pharmaceutical preparations - Oculon Corp.
OCULOTROPHIN PMG - Vitamins and nutritional supplements - Standard Process Inc.
OCULUS - Golfing equipment - Del-Com Facilities, Inc.
OCUPLEX - Pharmaceutical preparations - Tishcon Corp.
OCUSERT - Medical apparatus - Alza Corp.
OCUSHIELDS - Glass–laboratory - Dioptics Medical Products, Inc.
OCUSOFT - Ophthalmic goods - Blairex Laboratories, Inc.
OCUSOL - Health care products - Procter & Gamble Co.
OCUSURG - Surgical supplies - Allergan, Inc.
OCUTEIN - Vitamins and nutritional supplements - Tishcon Corp.
OCWORKBENCH - Computer software - Object International, Inc.
OD-R-ADE - Animal feed supplements - Loveland Industries, Inc.
ODA - Chemicals - Chevron Chemical Co.
ODAAT - Candy - Enthusiasts Unlimited
ODALATE - Pharmaceutical preparations ☆ - Kenyon Drug Co. Inc.
ODALISQUE - Perfumes - Nettie Rosenstein Inc.
ODARA - Dental compounds - Lorvic Corp.
O'DARBY - Cordials ☆ - Marie Brizard Wines & Spirits, USA
ODD BALLS - Chewing gum ☆ - Leaf, Inc.
ODD BALLS - Toys ☆ - Jak-Pak Inc.
ODD-BOUNDER - Pet products - Fundex Inc.
ODD ONE OUT - Computer software - Sunburst Communications, Inc.
ODD RODS - Candy ☆ - Donruss Co.
ODDBALLZ - Video games - Pf. Magic, Inc.
ODDITY - Candlesticks - Root Candle Co.
ODDO BOOKS - Publisher's imprints - Oddo Publishing Inc.
ODDO PUBLISHING INC. - Publisher's imprints - Oddo Publishing Inc.
ODDS & ENDS BASKET - Baskets–wood - Longaberger Co.
ODDS 'N' ENDS - Enamels - Plasti-Kote Co. Inc.
ODDS-N-N'Z - Apparel–women's - Jockey International, Inc.
ODE - Banjos ☆ - Fred Gretsch Enterprises
ODE - Dishes–earthenware - Denby USA Limited
ODE - Hearing aids - Beltone Electronics Corp.
ODE - Tape players–cassette - Sony Music Entertainment Inc.
O'DELL - Aquariums–household ☆ - O'Dell Industries
ODELL DOWN UNDER - Computer software - Softkey International Inc.
ODELL'S EASY ST. WHEAT - Beverages–malt - Odell Brewing Co., Inc.
ODEN - Cabinets - Triangle Pacific Corp. (Cabinet Division)
ODENSE - Almond pastes - Holland-American Importing Co. Inc.
ODENSE - Candy - Andre Prost Inc.
ODENSE - Floor coverings–carpet and rugs - V & B Carpet
ODENWALD - Fruits and vegetables - Haram-Christensen Corp.
ODENWALD - Fruits–canned - Kreiner Imports
ODENWALDER - Marzipan - Westdale Foods Co.
ODEON - Liquors ☆ - Sidney Frank Importing Co., Inc.
ODEON - Recording label ☆ - Penco Industries Inc.
ODER ELIMINATOR - Disinfectants ☆ - Outdoor Technologies Group
ODESSA - Apparel stores–sports - Gotcha Covered
ODESSA - Athletic shoes - Converse Inc.
ODESSA - Bicycles - Fuji America, Inc.
ODESSA - Computer software ☆ - Odessa Engineering, Inc.
ODESSA - Cooking utensils–aluminum ☆ - Reston Lloyd Ltd.
ODESSA - Fixtures - Universal-Rundle Corp.
ODESSA - Glassware–household - Durand International
ODESSA - Hardware - Baldwin Hardware Corp.
ODESSA - Toys–musical ☆ - Davitt and Hanser Music Co.
ODESSA MAID - Bathroom accessories - Action Products Co.
ODESSE - Gin - Majestic Distilling Co.
ODESSEY - Travel accessories - Austin House Inc.
ODETTE - Cigars - Gesty Trading & Manufacturing Corp.
ODEUM - Integrated circuits - Odeum Microsystems
ODEVE - Colognes - Fragranhaus

ODI - Jewelry - Famor Inc.
ODIE - Candy ☆ - Amurol Confections Co.
ODIE - Stationery ☆ - Medo Industries, Inc.
ODIE - Toys–stuffed - Dakin Inc.
ODIE EYES - Ophthalmic goods - Foremost Optical Products
ODIE IN SHEEP'S CLOTHING - Toys–stuffed - Dakin Inc.
ODIE LOVE STRUCK - Toys–stuffed - Dakin Inc.
ODIE PARTY TIME - Toys–stuffed - Dakin Inc.
ODIE STUCK ON YOU - Toys–stuffed - Dakin Inc.
ODIN - Cigars - National Cigar Corp.
ODIN - Flatware - Dansk International Designs, Ltd.
ODIN LTD. - Fabrics–linen - Odin Ltd.-Scan Am Imports Inc.
ODINEX - Pharmaceutical preparations - Hawaiian Marine Imports Inc.
ODIN'S RUNE CARDS - Publisher's imprints - Narada Media
ODL - Doors–wood - ODL, Inc.
ODLO - Sports apparel ☆ - Gerry Sportswear Corp.
ODO - Video games - Paramount Pictures Corp.
ODO-HEX - Cosmetics ☆ - Alvin Last Inc.
ODO-MISTER - Deodorizers - Surco Products Inc.
ODO VINYL FIGURE - Toys - ERTL Co., Inc.
ODO-WAY - Insecticides ☆ - Uncle Sam Chemical Co., Inc.
ODOKILL - Deodorizers - Greentree Laboratories, Inc.
ODOKLEEN - Deodorizers - Greentree Laboratories, Inc.
ODOL - Mouthwashes - Odol Chemical Corp.
ODOMASTER - Deodorizers - Surco Products Inc.
ODOMATIC - Deodorizers - Surco Products Inc.
ODOM'S - Meat products–beef - Odom's Tennessee Pride Sausage Co.
ODOM'S TENNESSEE PRIDE - Sausages - Odom's Tennessee Pride Sausage Co.
O'DONNELL RACING FUEL - Fuel systems–motor vehicle - Pro-Blend, Inc.
ODONTIC - Dentifrices ☆ - Balas Dental Supply Co.
ODOR - Toys - Tonka Corp.
ODOR-ARMOR - Deodorizers - John Ablon
ODOR ATTACKERS - Shoe accessories - Schering-Plough Healthcare Products
ODOR B GONE - Disinfectants - Gannons Inc.
ODOR BAN - Deodorizers ☆ - Columbia Laboratories Inc.
ODOR-BANE - Deodorizers - Certified International
ODOR BLASTER - Deodorizers - Osmegen Inc.
ODOR-BLOC - Deodorizers - Distributors Processing Inc.
ODOR BLOCKS - Deodorizers - Unit Chemical Corp.
ODOR CONTROL - Deodorizers - Dualle Products
ODOR CONTROL - Deodorizers ☆ - Mackwin Co.
ODOR CRUSH - Pet products - Best n' Show Pet Products Inc.
ODOR CURE - Deodorizers - Atmosphere Products Co. Inc.
ODOR DISPOSERS - Deodorizers - Mardel Laboratories, Inc.
ODOR-EATERS ANTIFUNGAL FOOT SPRAY - Footcare products - Combe Inc.
ODOR-EATERS ANTIFUNGAL POWDER - Footcare products - Combe Inc.
ODOR-EATERS DEODORANT FOOT POWDER - Footcare products - Combe Inc.
ODOR-EATERS FOOT & SNEAKER SPRAY - Footcare products - Combe Inc.
ODOR-EATERS WITH BAKING SODA - Shoe insoles - Combe Inc.
ODOR ERASER - Deodorizers - Gold Eagle Co.
ODOR EXTERMINATOR - Deodorizers - Griot's Garage
ODOR-EXX - Air deordorizing unit - AAA Auto-Tech Limited
ODOR EZE - Deodorizers - International Marketing Group, Inc.
ODOR FREE - Pharmaceutical preparations - Basic Organics, Inc.
ODOR-GUARD - Floor coverings–carpet and rugs ☆ - Maxxon Corp.
ODOR GUARD - Sporting goods - Camp-Cap Products
ODOR GUN - Housewares - Medo Industries, Inc.
ODOR HANDLER - Pet products - Senproco Inc.
ODOR-KIL - Deodorizers - Imperial Manufacturing Co. Inc.
ODOR KNOTROLLER - Filters–air - Air Kontrol Inc.
ODOR KONTROLLER - Filters–air - Air Kontrol Inc.
ODOR LAUNCHER - Deodorizers - Osmegen Inc.
ODOR NET - Deodorizers - AmeriPlus Inc.
ODOR NEUTRALIZER - Deodorizers - Vaportek, Inc.
ODOR NIX - Deodorizers - Atmosphere Products Co. Inc.
ODOR OFF - Deodorizers - Washington Homeopathic Products
ODOR-OFF - Pet products - Farnam Cos. Inc.
ODOR OUT - Cleaning preparations–carpet and rug ☆ - Hako Minuteman Inc.
ODOR-OUT - Pet products - Universal Marketing
ODOR OUTLAW - Deodorizers - Geo-Environmental Resources, Inc.
ODOR-PLEX - Perfumes - Revere Manufacturing
ODOR-PLEX - Veterinary nutritional supplements - Petco Animal Supplies, Inc.

ODOR-RASER - Pet products ☆ - Vaportek, Inc.
ODOR RELIEF - Deodorizer - Intex Chemical Inc.
ODOR RID - Pet products - Vo-Toys Inc.
ODOR SCRIP - Health care products ☆ - Scrip-Physician Supply Co.
ODOR SHUTER - Toilet seats - Microphor Inc.
ODOR SOL - Deodorizers - Circle K Industries Inc.
ODOR STOP - Deodorizers - Geritrex Corp.
ODOR STOPPERS - Apparel and accessories - Megas Beauty Care, Inc.
ODOR STOPPERS - Shoes - Premier Brands of America
ODOR-X - Deodorizers - Unit Chemical Corp.
ODOR-X PAINT ODOR REMOVER - Deodorizers - Enviro-Chem Inc.
ODOR ZAPPERS - Shoe accessories - Coin Gallery of San Francisco, Inc.
ODORCHECK - Air purification systems ☆ - Airomax Corp.
ODORCIDE - Deodorizers - Thornell Corp.
ODORETTES - Deodorizers - Perky-Pet Products Co.
ODOREX - Deodorizers - Surco Products Inc.
ODOREX - Insecticides ☆ - Cenol Co. Inc.
ODORGON - Deodorizers - Stewart-Hall Chemical Corp.
ODORID - Deodorizers - Analab Inc.
ODORLESS FORMULA - Hunting equipment - Wildlife Research Center, Inc.
ODORLOK - Water treating compounds - Eaglebrook, Inc.
ODORMUTE - Deodorizers - Ryter Corp.
ODORMUTE C - Deodorizers - Ryter Corp.
ODORONO - Deodorants–personal - Chesebrough-Pond's USA Co.
ODORS AWAY - Deodorizers - Wrap-On Co. Inc.
ODORSORB - Fire- and smoke-damage odor eliminator - Advance Cleaning Products Inc.
ODORTROL - Deodorants–personal - Hill Manufacturing Co. Inc.
ODORVENT - Skin care products - Electrocorp
O'DOUL'S - Beverages–malt - Anheuser-Busch Companies Inc.
ODOUR-BAN - Surgical supplies - Marlen Manufacturing & Developing Co.
ODOUR-GUARD - Surgical supplies - Marlen Manufacturing & Developing Co.
ODP - Computer diskettes–blank - Eastman Kodak Co.
ODP - Optical lenses - Optical Diamond Products
ODR 2000 - Computer peripheral equipment - Monsanto Co.
ODRINIL - Pharmaceutical preparations - Fox Pharmacal Inc.
ODS - Computer hardware - Optical Data Systems, Inc.
ODS - Electrical equipment ☆ - Wiremold Co.
ODWALLA - Juices - Odwalla, Inc.
ODYSSEA - Boats - Glen-L Marine Designs
ODYSSEUS - Watches - Jaeger-Le Coultre SA
ODYSSEY - Apparel and accessories - Odyssey Apparel, Inc.
ODYSSEY - Automotive parts and accessories - Midwest Sunroofs
ODYSSEY - Batteries - Hawker Energy Products Inc.
ODYSSEY - Boats - Outboard Marine Corp.
ODYSSEY - Boats–motor ☆ - Cobia Boat Co.
ODYSSEY - Bowls ☆ - Lenox Crystal, Inc.
ODYSSEY - Cabinets - Triangle Pacific Corp. (Cabinet Division)
ODYSSEY - Cleaning preparations - Hillyard Enterprises, Inc.
ODYSSEY - Clocks - General Time Corp. (Westclox/Seth Thomas Div.)
ODYSSEY - Colognes - Avon Products, Inc.
ODYSSEY - Dryers–hair ☆ - Sunbeam-Oster Household Products
ODYSSEY - Fireplace equipment - Design Specialties Inc.
ODYSSEY - Floor coverings–carpet and rugs - Colonial Mills Inc.
ODYSSEY - Floor coverings–carpet and rugs - Providence Rug Co.
ODYSSEY - Floor coverings–carpet and rugs - Whitecrest Carpet Mills
ODYSSEY - Floor coverings–carpet and rugs ☆ - Hollytex Carpet Mills Inc.
ODYSSEY - Floor coverings–carpet and rugs ☆ - Regal Rugs Inc.
ODYSSEY - Flowers, plants, and seeds - Jacklin Seed
ODYSSEY - Furniture - Expo Displays
ODYSSEY - Game machines - Silicon Gaming, Inc.
ODYSSEY - Games - Tsr, Inc.
ODYSSEY - Glassware–household ☆ - Wallace International Silversmiths, Inc.
ODYSSEY - Greeting cards - American Artists Group Inc.
ODYSSEY - Hardware - Alside Div.
ODYSSEY - Hot tubs–fiberglass - Trayco, Inc.
ODYSSEY - Luggage ☆ - Samsonite Corp.
ODYSSEY - Marinas–prefabricated - Odyssey Marine Systems, LLC
ODYSSEY - Medical apparatus - Mentor O & O Inc.
ODYSSEY - Meters–electric - Futurestar Corp.
ODYSSEY - Motor vehicles–minivans - American Honda Motor Co. Inc. (Acura Div.)
ODYSSEY - Occasional tables - JDI Group, Inc.
ODYSSEY - Swimming pool covers ☆ - Odyssey Systems
ODYSSEY - Synthesizers–musical instrument - Fender Musical Instruments
ODYSSEY - Tape players–cassette - Sony Music Entertainment Inc.

☆ = Now out of production

ODYSSEY - Telescopes - Murnaghan Instruments, Inc.

ODYSSEY - Tents - Coleman Co., Inc.

ODYSSEY - Tires - Laramie Tire Distributors, Inc.

ODYSSEY - Toys ☆ - Wham-O Manufacturing Co.

ODYSSEY - Toys–electronic - Philips Consumer Electronics Co.

ODYSSEY - Toys–models ☆ - Estes Industries

ODYSSEY - Trailers–travel ☆ - Viking Recreational Vehicles Inc.

ODYSSEY - Valves–industrial ☆ - Dixie, USA, Inc.

ODYSSEY - Wallpaper - K.M.L. Industries

ODYSSEY 2 - Toys–electronic - Philips Consumer Electronics Co.

ODYSSEY-4 - Veterinary pharmaceutical preparations - Agri Laboratories, Ltd.

ODYSSEY CHIMES - Chimes - Woodstock Percussion, Inc.

ODYSSEY II - Cabinets ☆ - Triangle Pacific Corp. (Cabinet Division)

ODYSSEY SOLAR BLANKET REEL SYSTEMS - Swimming pool covers - Odyssey Systems

ODYSSEY, THE - Exercising equipment ☆ - California Gym Equipment

ODYSSEY WINDSOR BONE CLASSIC - Dinnerware–glass - Block China Co.

OE - Automotive oil, air and fuel filters - Import Brokers, Inc.

OE - Mufflers–motor vehicle - Walker Manufacturing Co.

O.E. BRAND - Motor vehicle parts and accessories - Foreign Parts Distributors Inc.

OE JUNIOR - Oxygen - Oxygen Enrichment Co. Ltd.

OE OMEGA - Electronic equipment - Omega Engineering, Inc.

OE PLUS - Oxygen - Oxygen Enrichment Co. Ltd.

OEBEL - Breads - John Sommer Inc.

OEBEL STOLLEN - Cakes - Haram-Christensen Corp.

OECO - Oxygen - Oxygen Enrichment Co. Ltd.

O.E.D. - Hair care products - A.R. Winarick Inc.

OEHME - Bakery products - Specialty Bakers Inc.

O.E.I. - Business forms - Office Electronics Inc.

OEM - Microphones - Scott Music Supply Inc.

O.E.M. - Paint removers ☆ - Klean-Strip

OEM - Tools - Great Neck Saw Manufacturers, Inc.

OEM APPROVED - Ribbons–inked - Astro-Med Inc.

OEM ORIGINAL EQUIPMENT MANUFACTURER - Lamps - Osram Sylvania Inc.

OEM PAINTS - Paints - OEM Paints, Inc.

OEMG - Publisher's imprints - Kelly Properties, Inc.

OEMTECH - Medical apparatus - Meadox Medicals, Inc.

OE+ - Health care products - Gulfstream Medical Products Inc.

OES - Deodorizers - C & M Group, Inc.

OESLAUER MANUFAKTUR - Dinnerware–glass ☆ - Goebel of North America

OETKER - Food products - John Sommer Inc.

OEV - Endoscopic equipment - Olympus America Inc.

OF THE FOUR SEASONS - Mustard - Victoria Pantry

O'FARRELL ENTERTAINMENT - Recording label - MCA Universal Studios

OFC - Beverages–alcohol - Schenley Industries Inc.

OFF - Insecticides - S.C. Johnson & Son, Inc.

OFF & RUNNING - Games ☆ - Milton Bradley Co.

OFF BROADWAY - Furniture - Romweber Co.

OFF BROADWAY - Paint removers - Calgon Vestal Laboratories

OFF-BROADWAY - Paints - Rosco Laboratories Inc.

OFF BROADWAY - Shoes - Soft Shoe, Inc.

OFF-DUTY - Guns - Charter Arms

OFF-EZY - Pharmaceutical preparations - Del Pharmaceuticals, Inc.

OFF-HAND - Paper–toweling - Liquid Paper Corp.

OFF-KEY - Apparel and accessories - Bonnie Bracy

OFF LIMITS - Apparel and accessories - Eileen M. O'Donnell

OFF ROAD - Bicycles ☆ - J.C. Penney Co., Inc.

OFF-ROAD CHAMPIONSHIP GRAN PRIX - Decals and transfers - Mickey Thompson Entertainment Group

OFF-ROAD HOPPERS - Toys–automobiles - Tyco Toys

OFF-ROADENT - Toys–automobiles - Mattel, Inc.

OFF RODEO - Apparel and accessories - Bernini, Inc.

OFF SEASON - See SMALL ENGINE

OFF-SET - Screw drivers - Atlas Copco Electric Tools Inc.

OFF-SHOOT-T - Chemical preparations - Procter & Gamble Co.

OFF-SHORE - Fishing tackle - Mason Tackle Co.

OFF! SKINTASTIC - Insecticides - S.C. Johnson & Son, Inc.

OFF THE BENCH - Apparel and accessories - Majestic Athletic Wear, Ltd.

OFF THE COAST - Apparel - D.B. Royalty Inc.

OFF THE DEEP END - Jewelry - R. Drew & Co. Inc.

OFF THE FLOOR - Racks - Butler Enterprises

OFF THE NET SPORTSWEAR - Sportswear - Phoenix Suns

OFF THE WALL - Footwear–athletic - Vans, Inc.

OFF-THE-WALL - Furniture ☆ - American Toy & Furniture Co.

OFF THE WALL - Musical instrument accessories - Barry W. Bross

OFF THE WALL - Musical instrument accessories - David Wexler & Co.

OFF THE WALL - Video game - Bally Sente Inc.

OFF THE WALL STREET - Apparel and accessories - Theodore Perednia

OFFBEAT - Calendars - Day Dream Publishing, Inc.

OFFBEAT - Cosmetics - Big M, Inc.

OFFBRAND - Apparel and accessories - Offbrand

OFFENSIVE FORCE - Apparel and accessories - Logan Knitting Mills, Inc.

OFFERDAHL'S BAGEL GOURMET - Bakery products - John Offerdahl

OFFHAND - Wallpaper - Armor & Tabler

OFFICE - Computer software - Microsoft Corp.

OFFICE 1 SUPERSTORE - Paper products - Office 1 Superstores L.P.

OFFICE 2000 - Typewriters - Smith Corona Corp.

OFFICE-AIDE - Paper–looseleaf - Colonial Co.

OFFICE ANGLIN' - Pet products - Wannabe

OFFICE ANTICS - Calendars ☆ - American Greetings Corp.

OFFICE BASICS - Desk sets - Newell Office Products

OFFICE BUDDIES - Labels - Dennison Manufacturing Co.

OFFICE CENTRAL - Computer software - Panther Software, Inc.

OFFICE COMPANION, THE - Computer software - Braddock Communications, Inc.

OFFICE CONVERSIONS - Motor vehicles–buses - Turtle Top Specialty Products

OFFICE COSMETICS - Cleaning preparations - Liquid Paper Corp.

OFFICE DATE - Clocks ☆ - General Time Corp. (Westclox/Seth Thomas Div.)

OFFICE DESIGNS - Filing cabinets–metal - Steelworks, Inc.

OFFICE DESKING - Furniture - Haworth, Inc.

OFFICE EDGE - Paper products - Bowater Communication Papers Inc.

OFFICE ENVIRONMENT SERIES - Air purification systems - Hunt Holdings, Inc.

OFFICE FRESH - Deodorizers - Surco Products Inc.

OFFICE FRIENDLY - Office supplies - JBC Design Group, Inc.

OFFICE-GRADE - Electrical equipment - Proxima Corp.

OFFICE IMAGE - Office furniture–wood - HON Industries Inc.

OFFICE IMPRESSIONS - Office furniture–metal - United Stationers Inc.

OFFICE-IN-A-BOX - Computer peripheral equipment - Alacrity Systems Inc.

OFFICE LAYOUT - Computer software - Autodesk Inc.

OFFICE LINER - Cushions - Manco, Inc.

OFFICE LUBE, INC. - Lubricating oils - Office Lube, Inc.

OFFICE MAILER - Office machines - Standard Register Co.

OFFICE MANAGER - File folders - Igloo Products Corp.

OFFICE MANAGER - Office supplies - Sangamon Co.

OFFICE MANAGER PLUS - File folders - Igloo Products Corp.

OFFICE MATE - Projectors–photographic ☆ - Apollo Audiovisual Div.

OFFICE-MATE - Tools - Esselte Corp.

OFFICE MINI-MART - Vending machines - Orion Products Corp.

OFFICE MLS - Computer software - Moore Business Forms, Inc.

OFFICE ORGANIZER'S CHOICE - Shelving units–metal - Metro Industries Inc.

OFFICE PALS - Pencil sharpeners - General Time Corp. (Westclox/Seth Thomas Div.)

OFFICE PARK - Floor coverings–carpet and rugs - Milliken & Co. Inc.

OFFICE PARK II - Floor coverings–carpet and rugs - Porter Carpet Mills Inc.

OFFICE PLUS - Office supplies - Independent Stationers, Inc.

OFFICE POWER - Extension cords - Crown Wire & Cable (Carol Div.)

OFFICE POWER - Extension cords - General Cable Corp.

OFFICE PROTOCOL - Computer software - Physicians Practice Management Inc.

OFFICE-RITER - Pens ☆ - Empire Berol USA

OFFICE ROLLER - Office supplies - Scripto-Tokai Corp.

OFFICE SELECT - Magnets - Kmart Properties, Inc.

OFFICE SOLUTIONS - Computer software - Ikon Office Solutions

OFFICE SPECIAL - Ribbons–inked - Buckeye Business Products Inc.

OFFICE STAR PRODUCTS - Chairs–plastic - Blumenthal Distributing, Inc.

OFFICE TO EVENING - Jewelry - Esther Fuhrman Designs, Ltd.

OFFICE TROLLEY - Luggage - Skyway Luggage Co.

OFFICE VALET - Garment racks–metal - Vogel Peterson Furniture Co.

OFFICE WAGON - Trailers–travel - Wells Cargo Inc.

OFFICE WORKS - Office furniture–plastic - Newell Office Products

OFFICE WORKS - Paper - Fred Meyer, Inc.

OFFICEJET - Computer peripheral equipment - Hewlett-Packard Co.

OFFICEMATE - Computer peripheral equipment - Marchon and Marcolin Eyewear Inc.

OFFICEMAX - Paper products - Officemax, Inc.

OFFICEPORTE - Modems - Microcom Systems, Inc.

OFFICER ABLE - Toys - Those Characters from Cleveland, Inc.

☆ = Now out of production

OFFICER BEAR - Toys–stuffed - Dakin Inc.
OFFICER BOB - Toys - Tonka Corp.
OFFICER BOOKUM - Toys - Mattel, Inc.
OFFICER CORPS - Men's apparel - Levi Strauss & Co.
OFFICER'S ACP - Firearms, accessories, and parts - Colt's Manufacturing Co. Inc.
OFFICER'S CLUB - Apparel and accessories - Londontown Corp.
OFFICESYNERGY - Audio and video tapes - Abel Associates, Inc.
OFFICETECH - Computer peripheral equipment ☆ - Hunt Manufacturing Co.
OFFICEWRITER - Computer software - Software Publishing Corp.
OFFICIAL - Computer software now out of production - Konami (America) Inc.
OFFICIAL - Stationery ☆ - Mead Corp.
OFFICIAL BABY WATCHER - Dolls - Raymond Guerra Gatica
OFFICIAL BASEBALL BLAZER - Coats - Kobra International, Ltd.
OFFICIAL BINGO CLUB, THE - Giftware ☆ - Enesco Corp.
OFFICIAL BOWLING CLUB, THE - Giftware ☆ - Enesco Corp.
OFFICIAL CARD OF THE '90'S - Trading cards and stamps - Score Group, Inc.
OFFICIAL CELEBRITY REGISTRY, THE - Publisher's imprints - General Publishing Group, Inc.
OFFICIAL COLLECTOR - Computer software now out of production - Konami (America) Inc.
OFFICIAL COLLECTOR SERIES - Computer software now out of production - Konami (America) Inc.
OFFICIAL COOKIE BOUQUET COOKIE SURVIVAL KIT, THE - Cookies - Cookie Bouquet Franchising Corp.
OFFICIAL COOKIES BY DESIGN COOKIE SURVIVAL KIT, THE - Cookies - Cookie Bouquet Franchising Corp.
OFFICIAL EXPRESS MANAGEMENT GUIDE - Publisher's imprints - Kelly Properties, Inc.
OFFICIAL FAN - Sportswear - Salem Screen Printers Inc.
OFFICIAL FILM OF SUMMER - Film - Konica USA Inc.
OFFICIAL FIREFIGHTERS PLAY EQUIPMENT - Toys - Manley Toys (USA) Ltd.
OFFICIAL FOOTBALL BLAZER - Coats - Kobra International, Ltd.
OFFICIAL GARDENS - Sporting goods ☆ - Outdoor Technologies Group
OFFICIAL GOLF BLAZER - Coats - Kobra International, Ltd.
OFFICIAL JOE NAMATH - Games - Munro Games Inc.
OFFICIAL JOHNNY BENCH - Games - Munro Games Inc.
OFFICIAL LAWYER BLAZER - Apparel and accessories - Kobra International, Ltd.
OFFICIAL LICENSED PRODUCT FORD MOTOR COMPANY - Safety products - Ford Motor Co.
OFFICIAL MAIL MANAGEMENT GUIDE - Publisher's imprints - Kelly Properties, Inc.
OFFICIAL NFLPA - Games - Munro Games Inc.
OFFICIAL PIZZA OF SUMMER, THE - Pizzas–frozen - Papa John's International, Inc.
OFFICIAL PLAY - Sporting goods - Schutt Manufacturing Co.
OFFICIAL SCOUT - Harmonicas - Hohner Inc.
OFFICIAL SEASON TICKET HOLDER - Hats - Joseph A. Lanza
OFFICIAL SEGA SEAL OF QUALITY - Video games - Sega of America, Inc.
OFFICIAL SOCCER BLAZER - Coats - Kobra International, Ltd.
OFFICIAL TENNIS BLAZER - Apparel and accessories - Kobra International, Ltd.
OFFICIAL TOURNAMENT - Outdoor Technologies Group
OFFICIAL TROV TROUNCER - Games - Trov USA, Inc.
OFFICIAL UNIVERSAL STUDIOS MONSTERS - Toys - Universal City Studios, Inc.
OFFICIAL WEDDING ORGANIZER & KEEPSAKE, THE - Publisher's imprints - D. Diane Hill
OFFICIAL WILLIS REED-WALT FRAZIER PRO - Games - Munro Games Inc.
OFFISTAMP - Stamps–hand - Base Type, Inc.
OFFIX - Computer software ☆ - Emerging Technology Consultants Inc.
OFFLEY - Beverages–alcohol - Bacardi Imports Inc.
OFFLEY PORT - Beverages–alcohol - Blair Importers Ltd.
OFF'N ON - Floor waxes ☆ - Demert & Dougherty, Inc.
OFFNET-ACCESS - Computer software - Morgan Software, Inc.
OFFROAD - Bicycles - OSI Sports
OFFSHOOTS - Jewelry - Steven A. Rosendorf
OFFSHORE - Binoculars - Tasco Sales, Inc.
OFFSHORE - Boats–fishing - Klamath Boat Co. Inc.
OFFSHORE - Boats–motor - Sport-Craft Inc.
OFFSHORE - Boats–motor ☆ - Grady-White Boats, Inc.
OFFSHORE - Marine paint - Interlux Yacht Finishes
OFFSHORE - Powerboat - Boston Whaler, Inc.

OFFSHORE - Ships–sailing vessels - Offshore Yachts
OFFSHORE - Waterproof outerwear ☆ - Helly-Hansen Inc.
OFFSHORE FISHERMAN - Boats - Lanness K. McKee & Co.
OFFSHORE MATRIX - Computer software - Lucian Spataro, Jr.
OFFSHORE PRO - Boats–motor ☆ - Grady-White Boats, Inc.
OFFSHORE S - Boats–fishing - Klamath Boat Co. Inc.
OFFSHOREMAN - Boats ☆ - Lanness K. McKee & Co.
OFFSPRING - Bicycle parts and accessories - Softride, Inc.
OFIR - Recording label ☆ - Penco Industries Inc.
OFIS - Stationery ☆ - Litton Systems, Inc. (Airtron Division)
O'FISH'L - Sporting goods - Melvin C. Ross
OFL - Lighting equipment - General Electric Co.
O'FLEX - Pharmaceutical preparations - Seatrace Co.
OFP ODOR FREE PAINT - Paints - Mautz Paint Co.
O.F.T - Apparel and accessories - Montbell America Inc.
OFTANOL - Insecticides - Bayer Corp. (Agriculture Div.)
OFTC STUDIO - Apparel - CFTC Group Inc.
O'FUDGE CHEEZ STIK - Cheese - Arpin Dairy Inc.
OG VATO JAM - Broadcasting stations–radio - Baka Boyz Productions, Inc.
O.G. WEAR - Clothing - John S. Woodward
OGCI - Computer software - Ogci Software, Inc.
OGEE - Skin care products - Waverly Beauty Products
OGEE MISTY - Hair care products - Highpoint Chemicals Inc.
OGEE WAVE - Hair care products - Waverly Beauty Products
OGEN - Pharmaceutical preparations - Abbott Laboratories
OGEN - Pharmaceutical preparations - Upjohn Co.
OGGELI - Hair care products - Gelle-International Ltd.
OGGI DOMANI - Handbags - B.H. Smith, Inc.
OGGI DOMANI ITALY - Handbags - B.H. Smith, Inc.
OGI - Brushes–paint - Rubberset Co.
OGILVIE - Hair care products - Tussy Cosmetics Inc.
OGILVIE - Musical instruments ☆ - United Musical Instruments USA Inc.
OGILVIE SPIRAL WAVES - Hair care products - Personal Care Group, Inc.
OGIO - Apparel and accessories - Ogio International, Inc.
OGIO SPORT - Apparel–athletic - Ogio International, Inc.
OGIVE NET - Traps–animal - Fuhrman Diversified
OGIVES - Vases - Durand International
OGLALA SIOUX - Moccasins - Oglala Sioux Products Inc.
OGLEBAY - Paper–toilet - Wheeling Park Commission
OGLERS - Apparel and accessories - Darrel J. Snyder
OGLETHORPE POWER - Electronic equipment - Oglethorpe Power Corp.
OGLIO - Video production - Oglio Entertainment Group, Inc.
O'GLUE - Paper glue - Itoya of America, Ltd.
OGORE - Toys - Mattel, Inc.
OGP - Video equipment - Optical Gaging Products, Inc.
O'GRADY BEAR - Toys–stuffed - Russ Berrie and Co., Inc.
O'GRADY CONTAINERS - Containers - Union Camp Corp. (Fine Paper Division)
O'GRADYS - Potato chips - Pepsico, Inc.
OGRE - Games - Steve Jackson Games Inc.
OGRE - Toys–models - Grenadier Models
OGRE - Video games - Origin Systems, Inc.
OGRE BATTLE - Video games - Enix America Corp.
O'GREGORY'S - Liqueurs - Ginger Spirits, Inc.
O'GREGORY'S - Wines - Black Prince Distillery, Inc.
O'GUIN - Air purification systems ☆ - Medo Industries, Inc.
OGURA - Artists' materials - Andrews/Nelson/Whitehead
OH BABOL - Chewing gum ☆ - Ferrara Pan Candy Co., Inc.
OH! BABY - Greeting cards - American Greetings Corp.
OH-BE-JOYFUL - Cereal - Firefly Foods
OH, BE JOYFUL - Wines - Bully Hill Vineyards, Inc.
OH! BERRY - Cookies - Sunshine Biscuits, Inc.
OH BOK FOODS - Tofu - Young Gi Park
OH BOY - Apparel and accessories - American Argo Corp.
OH BOY - Food products - Oh Boy Corp.
OH BOY - Food products - W.B. Roddenbery Co., Inc.
OH BOY - Recording label - Al Bunetta Management
OH! BOY - Syrup - W.B. Roddenbery Co., Inc.
OH BOY OATMEAL - Cookies - Vermont Country Foods Inc.
OH-DEAR - Deodorants–personal ☆ - Uncommon Conglomerates
OH DEARS - Licorice - Dutchess Licorice
OH EWE - Slippers - Acorn
OH FUDGE - Candy - Oh Fudge Inc.
OH HEAVENLY - Candy - That's My Favorite Inc.
OH HELL - Games - Twinson Co.
OH HENRY! - Candy - Nestle USA

☆ = Now out of production

OH, LOOK OUT LORETTA!! - T-shirts–men's - Michael B. Lange

OH! MAMMA - Apparel–women's - I.E. Industries Fashions, Inc.

OH MY! - Apparel–children's - Oh My!

OH NO! - Deodorizers - Pestco, Inc.

OH NUTS! - Games - Cadaco Div.

OH! OH! - Cleaning preparations - National Interchem Corp.

OH REALLY - Apparel and accessories - James Carrington Rodden

OH RYANS - Candy - Bewley Irish Imports

OH SCRUD! - Games - Martin & Associates

OH, SHIRT! - Apparel and accessories - Christopher S. Erickson

OH SO BLUE - Men's apparel - Levi Strauss & Co.

OH SO COCOA - Hot chocolate - Gourmet Coffees of America, Inc.

OH SO CRISPY - Fish–fresh or frozen - Harker's Distribution Inc.

OH SO CUTE - Stationery - Novelty Creations, Inc.

OH SO GENTLE - Hair care products - KMS Research Inc.

OH SO TENDER - Meat products–pork - Seaboard Corp.

OH! SO VERY VANILLA! - Frozen foods - Weight Watchers International, Inc.

OH-WAH-REE - Games ☆ - Avalon Hill Game Co.

OH, WHAT A DUCK!!! - Games - Universal Manufacturing Co., Inc.

OH, WHAT A DUCK!!! - Games - Uvex Safety LLC

OH, WHAT A MOUNTAIN - Games ☆ - Milton Bradley Co.

OH WILDERNESS - Games - Ampersand Press

OH ZONE! - Bicycles ☆ - Hedstrom Corp.

OH ZONE - Toys - Hummingbird Toy Co. Ltd.

OHANA - Beverages–carbonated - Faygo Beverages, Inc.

OHANYAN'S BASTIRMA & SOUJOUK CO - Meat products–dried - Ohanyan's Bastirma & Soujouk Co.

O'HARA - Paints–artists' - Art Supply & Instrument Co.

O'HARES - Apparel and accessories - Cara Marks

O'HARES BY CARA MARKS - Giftware - Roman, Inc.

OHAUS - Weights and measures - Ohaus Corp.

O'HENRY - Frames–eyeglass - Zylo Ware Corp.

OHH SOO GOOD - Fireworks - Ingram Enterprises, Inc.

OHIO - Brushes–paint - Wooster Brush Co.

OHIO - Sweatshirts - Ohio University

OHIO - Thermometers - Taylor Environmental Instruments

OHIO - Thread - Cincinnati Thread Co.

OHIO AWNING - Awnings - Ohio Awning & Manufacturing Co.

OHIO CRAFTSMAN - Floor coverings–tile ☆ - Kepcor, Inc./SSI Tiles

OHIO PET - Dog food - Ohio Pet Foods Inc.

OHIO REPORTS - Computer storage devices–optical - West Publishing Co.

OHIO VALLEY - Wines - McIntoshs Ohio Valley Wines

OHM - Amplifiers–musical instrument - Ohm Acoustics Corp.

OHMEDA - Health care products - Home Care Instruments Inc.

OHMEDA BIOX - Health care products ☆ - Datex-Ohmeda, Inc.

OHMPROBE - Voltmeters - A.W. Sperry Instruments, Inc.

O'HOIR - Shutters–plastic - Endisco Supply Co.

OHP - Barbituates - Faber-Castell Corp.

OH'S - Cereal - Quaker Oats Co.

OHSAWA - Macrobiotic foods - Gold Mine Natural Food

OHSAWA AMERICA - Rice-syrup powder - Gold Mine Natural Food

OHSE - Meat products–cured - R.W. Zant Co.

OHSEE - Fruits and vegetables - Gold Digger Apple Inc.

OHTSU - Tires - Chatani Enterprises Inc.

OHVI - Engines–marine - Generac Corp.

OH'YES - Footwear - Pegasus Co.

OI - Glassware–household - Owens-Illinois Inc. (Libbey Div.)

OI - Hardware - Orchard International, Inc.

O.I. - Jewelry - Oro International, Inc.

OI BUILD - Computer software - Eason Technology, Inc.

OI-LIN - Skin care products - Sunrider Corp.

OIA - Apparel and accessories - Only in America

OIDS - Computer software - FTL Games

OII - Intraocular lenses - Ophthalmic Innovations International, Inc.

OIL-B-GON DRIVEWAY CLEANER - Chemical preparations - Gordon Feron & Co., Inc.

OIL-B-GON PARTS CLEANER - Chemical preparations - Gordon Feron & Co., Inc.

OIL BOSS - Filters–oil - Abanaki Corp.

OIL CONCENTRATOR - Oils–edible - Abanaki Corp.

OIL CUB - Boats - Thomas Marine, Inc.

OIL CURED OLIVES - Olives–canned - Europa Foods Ltd.

OIL-DRI - Automotive parts and accessories - Oil-Dri Corp. of America

OIL-DRI SOAKES - Paper–toweling - Paxon Manufacturing Co.

OIL-DRI WIPES - Paper–toweling - Paxon Manufacturing Co.

OIL DROPS - Candy - Texas Brags, Inc.

OIL-D'VINE - Oils–edible - Clanel Inc.

OIL EATER - Degreasing solvents - Kafko International Ltd.

OIL-FIELD SAUSAGE - Sausages - Hoffman Locker Plant, Inc.

OIL-FLO - Degreasing solvents - KC Products, Inc. (Sharon D. Spence)

OIL-FLO - Degreasing solvents - Titan Laboratories

OIL FORTE - Pharmaceutical preparations - Doak Dermatologics

OIL FRANCAIS - Health care products ☆ - Spruce Foods Inc.

OIL GARD - Lubricants - Gard Corp.

OIL HARDENED - Golfing equipment - Texas Golf Co.

OIL HAWG - Chemical preparations - Dry-Sorbents, Inc.

OIL MASK - Mats - Poly-Tak Protection Systems

OIL-O-SOL - Pharmaceutical preparations - Health Care Industries Inc.

OIL OF EMU - Cosmetics - Transmex Supply Co., Inc.

OIL OF LIFE - Cosmetics ☆ - Quintessence Inc.

OIL OF MELALEUCA - Pharmaceutical preparations - Melaleuca, Inc.

OIL OF MINK - Skin care products - King Research, Inc.

OIL OF OLAY - Cosmetics - Olay Co., Inc.

OIL OF OLAY - Skin care products - Procter & Gamble Co.

OIL OF OLAY HYDRO-GEL - Skin care products - Procter & Gamble Co.

OIL OF OLAY MOISTURIZING BODY WASH - Skin care products - Procter & Gamble Co.

OIL OF OLAY RENEWAL - Skin care products - Procter & Gamble Co.

OIL-OFF - Cosmetics - Worldwide Cosmetics

OIL-OUT - Chemical preparations - Bio-Dex Laboratories

OIL-PRIME - Sealing compounds - Garon Products Inc.

OIL SENTRY - Automotive parts and accessories - Kohler Co.

OIL SOAKER, THE - Insulating materials - Buffalo Industries, Inc.

OIL SPILL - Board game - NewHagy Inc.

OIL-STAIN-IT - Brushes–paint - Corona Brushes Inc.

OIL STONES - Soap - Retail Products Corp.

OIL SYSTEM CLEANER - Fuel additives - Engine Muscle

OIL THE BEAUTIFUL FUEL OF CHOICE - Oil burners - R.W. Beckett Corp.

OIL-VAC - Pumps–vacuum - Thomas Industries Inc. (Power Air Div.)

OIL WELL IN A BOTTLE - Oils–lubricating - Fiske Brothers Refining Co.

OILATUM - Soap - Stiefel Laboratories, Inc.

OILBAR - Paints–artists' - Winsor & Newton

OILEX - Oils–lubricating - Exxon Corp.

OILFIELD - Brushes–paint ☆ - PPG Industries, Inc.

OILFIELD MANAGER - Computer software - Ogci Software, Inc.

OILILY - Eyeglasses - Windsor Optical Inc.

OILILY - Lenses–optical ☆ - Ambassador Eyewear Group

OILITE - Bearings–industrial ☆ - GKN Sinter Metals

OILLOCK - Measuring and dispensing pumps - Tuthill Corp.

OILMASTER - Oil burner - Ducane Corp. Inc.

OILOMATIC - Lubricants - Stihl Inc.

OILS BY OMAR - Flowers, plants, and seeds ☆ - Flower Essence Services

OILS OF THE WORLD - Oils–edible ☆ - Liberty Richter Inc.

OIL'S WELL - Computer software ☆ - Sierra On-Line, Inc.

OILSKIMMERS, INC. - Machinery - Oil Skimmers, Inc.

OILSTAIN BUSTER - Cleaning equipment - Metro Industries

OILWICK - Wicking - Oilwick Co.

OILY BIRD - Lubricants ☆ - Ronson Consumer Products Corp.

OILZUM - Oils–lubricating - Castrol Heavy Duty Lubricants Inc.

OINKERS - Pet treats - Oink, Oink, Inc.

OINKERS BBQ SAUCE - Barbecue sauce - Barnyard Enterprises, Inc.

OINKLETTES - Candy - Nutrisource Pet Products of Stewart, Inc.

OINT EASE - Health care products ☆ - J.H. Guild Co. Inc.

OISHII - Soy sauce - California Olive Oil Corp.

OISMET LTD. - Apparel and accessories ☆ - Roxanne Swim Suits Co. Inc.

O.J. - Doughnuts–mixes - Dawn Food Products Inc.

O.J. - Ophthalmic goods - Embassy Creations Inc.

OJ - Skateboards - NHS, Inc.

OJ - Skateboards - Santa Cruz Skateboards

OJAI COOK - Food products - Sweet Adelaide Enterprises

OJAI COOK, THE - Food products - Baeder Co., Inc.

OJC - Beverages–alcohol - Conrad Inc.

O.J.C. SNACK CONTROL - Vitamins and nutritional supplements - American Vitamin Products, Inc.

OJIBWAY - Boats–canoes ☆ - Old Town Canoe Co.

OJII - Skateboards - NHS, Inc.

OJL - Recording label - Origin Jazz Library

OJM - Jewelry–precious - OTG, Inc.

OJ'S - Skin care products - Block Drug Co., Inc.

O.K. - Automotive parts and accessories ☆ - Ashland Oil, Inc.

OK - Beverages–carbonated - Coca-Cola Co.

OK - Brushes–paint ☆ - PPG Industries, Inc.

O.K. - Cleaning preparations ☆ - Albatross USA Inc.
OK - Contact lenses - Contex, Inc.
OK - Cosmetics - Major International Inc.
O.K. - Food products - Sea Snack Foods Inc.
O.K. - Frames–eyeglass - Hudson Optical Corp.
OK - Hair-texturizing shears - B.W. Boyd Shears Inc.
O.K. - Meat products–poultry - O.K. Foods Inc.
O.K. - Seafood products–fresh or frozen - Otto L. Kuehn Co. Inc.
O.K. - Thread - Sea Island Thread Corp.
OK-2 - Apparel and accessories - Barrel-Marvin Apparel, Inc.
OK 4 KIDS - Cough syrup - Bronson Pharmaceuticals
OK 2000 - Deodorizers - E.E.C., Inc.
OK, A - Candy - Auburn Farms, Inc.
OK COLA - Beverages–carbonated - Coca-Cola Co.
OK DINGHY - Ships–sailing vessels - Clark Boat Co.
OK! GARLIC - Mouthwashes - Ark-Ell Corp.
OK HARRIS - Postcards ☆ - Fotofolio Inc.
O.K. KIDS! - Wallpaper - Taylor Wallcoverings Inc.
OK MIKADO - Brushes–paint ☆ - PPG Industries, Inc.
O.K. MULTISTAR - Tires ☆ - Ashland Oil, Inc.
O.K. SNOWSTAR - Tires ☆ - Ashland Oil, Inc.
OK-WATER - Water treating compounds - Iceaway, Inc.
OKA - Food products - Tour Eiffel
OKABASHI - Footwear - Okabashi US Corp.
OKABASHI - Footwear - Relaxers Comfort Footwear, L.C.
OKAPI - Sunglasses and accessories ☆ - Corning Inc.
OKASA SILVER - Health care products - Alfred L. Ettlinger Inc.
OKAVANGO CHUNK - Cookies ☆ - Michael D's Cookies
OKAWARA - Artists' materials - Andrews/Nelson/Whitehead
OKAY - Soap - Prestige Products Inc.
O'KAYE - Candy - S.L. Kaye Co., Inc.
OKAY'S - Key rings - Hill Security Products
OKCO - Paper products - Olmsted-Kirk Paper Co.
OKE DOKE - Snack foods - Jays Foods LLC
OKEECHOBEE SPECIAL - Fishing lures - Hildebrandt Corp.
O'KEEFE - Beverages–alcohol - Century Importers Inc.
O'KEEFE & MERRITT - Kitchen appliances - White Consolidated Industries, Inc.
O'KEEFE CELLARS - Wines - Chateau Grand Traverse Ltd.
O'KEEFE EXTRA GOLD STOCK - Beverages–malt - The Stroh Brewery Co.
O'KEEFE LIGHT - Beverages–alcohol ☆ - Century Importers Inc.
O'KEEFE MARKETING - Advertising agencies - Cadmus/O'keefe Marketing Group, Inc.
O'KEEFE MARKETING - Advertising agencies - Cadums/O'Keefe Marketing Group, Inc.
OKEH - Recording label - Sony Music Entertainment Inc.
OKEH - Tape measures ☆ - Keuffel & Esser Co.
OKG - Vitamins and nutritional supplements - Source Naturals
OKG CAPSULES - Vitamins and nutritional supplements - Vitamin Research Products Inc.
OKG DRINK - Vitamins and nutritional supplements - Vitamin Research Products Inc.
OKG FUEL - Vitamins and nutritional supplements - Twinlab
OKHOTNICHYA - Vodka - Monsieur Henri Wines Ltd.
OKI - Printers–computer - Okidata
OKIDATA - Printers–computer - Okidata
OKIE - Jewelry - White Products Co. Inc.
OKIE-DOKIE - Apparel–children's - J.C. Penney Co., Inc.
OKIE GIRL BREWERY - Beer - Okie Girl Corp.
OKIE SNO - Ice - Snowonder Distributing, Inc.
OKIELITE SLOW FALL - Fishing tackle - Okielite Lures, Inc.
OKIFAX - Facsimile equipment - Okidata
OKIJET - Printers–computer - Okidata
OKIMATE - Printers–computer ☆ - Okidata
OKIO - Eyewear - Okio International, Inc.
OKIPAGE - Printers–computer - Okidata
OKKUPASHUNAL PRYDE - Apparel and accessories - Williams E. Samuels
OKLA HOMER SMITH - Furniture - Okla Homer Smith Furniture Manufacturing Co.
OKLAHOMA - Trailers–travel ☆ - Trailers by Dorsey, Inc.
OKO BONJOUR - Yarn - Henry's Attic
OKOCIM - Beverages–malt - Stanley Stawski Distributing Co.
OKOSHEATH - Insulators–electrical - Okonite Co. Inc.
OKOUME - Plywood - Harbor Sales Co.
OKRA PINNACLE 2000 - Computer software - Okra Marketing Corp.
OKRAY - Vegetables–frozen - J.R. Simplot Co.

OKTOBER - Beverages–malt - HDT Importers Inc.
OKTOBERFEST - Beverages–malt - Geyer Bros. Brewing Co.
OKTOBERFEST - Beverages–malt - Merchant du Vin Corp.
OKTOBERFEST - Beverages–malt - Sprecher Brewing Co. Inc.
OKTOBERFEST PRETZELS - Pretzels - Samuel John Moser
OKUN - Hair care products - Major International Inc.
OKURA - Electronic equipment - Caribbean Export Appliances, Inc.
O.L. - Recording label - O.L. Records
OL' BLUE JAY WINERY - Wines - Girard Winery Inc.
OL' BUBBA - Video production - Myriad Licensing, Inc.
OL' BUBBA HOUND - Glassware–household - Myriad Licensing, Inc.
OL' FAVORITE, THE - Horns–motor vehicle - Anes Electronics Burglar Alarm Systems
OL' LONELY - Appliance parts - Maytag Corp.
OL' PAINT - Apparel - Guntersville Outlet Inc.
OL' SAVANNAH - Wainscotting - Georgia-Pacific Corp.
OL SMOKY - Coats - Sew Fine Inc.
OL' SOFTY - Video production - Nalpak Video Sales, Inc.
OL' SOUTH - Mayonnaise - Piknik Products Co. Inc.
OL' SOUTH WHITETAIL MAGIC - Hunting equipment - Ol'South Distributing Co., Inc.
OL' SPRINGHILL - Corn dogs - Griffith Packing Plant, Inc.
OL' TEXAS - Food products ☆ - Stegner Food Products Co.
OL' TIME WASHERS - Games - Heritage Sports
OL-VITUM - Vitamins and nutritional supplements - Wyeth-Ayerst Laboratories
OL WIVE - Fishing lures ☆ - Bay De Noc Lure Co.
OL' YALLOW - Hot-dog sandwiches - Southeast Food Systems, Inc.
OL' YELLA - Gloves - Knoxville Glove Co.
OLAF ORANGUTAN - Puppets - Dakin Inc.
OLAFO EL TERRIBLE - Computer software - Gessler Publishing Co., Inc.
OLAFSEN - Pharmaceutical preparations - Walgreen Co.
OLAIANCE - Hair care products - Redken Laboratories, Inc.
OLAMTOV - Ceramics ☆ - Israeli Accents
OLAND'S EXPORT - Beverages–malt ☆ - Labatt Importers Inc.
OLAND'S EXTRA - Beverages–malt ☆ - Labatt Importers Inc.
OLAND'S LITE - Beverages–malt ☆ - Labatt Importers Inc.
OLATHE - Footwear - Olathe Boot Co.
OLAY - Skin care products - Richardson-Vicks USA
OLAY BODY WASH - Skin care products - Procter & Gamble Co.
OLBAS - Cough medicines - Penn Herb Co. Ltd.
OLC - Computer software - Massachusetts Institute of Technology
OLD 97 - Colognes - Old 97 Co.
OLD 1889 - Beverages–alcohol - Old Boone Distillery Co.
OLD ACE - Wines ☆ - Bully Hill Vineyards, Inc.
OLD AGE STIPPLE - Cosmetics - Research Council of Make-Up Artists Inc.
OLD AMERICAN - Food products - Tyson Foods Inc.
OLD AMERICAN - Wines - American Vineyards Co. Inc.
OLD AMERICAN DUNGAREES - Apparel and accessories - Lucky Brand Dungarees, Inc.
OLD AND MODERN MASTERS - Postcards - Geme Art Inc.
OLD ARBOR - Wines - Gibson Wine Co.
OLD ARMY - Revolvers - Sturm, Ruger & Co., Inc.
OLD ATLANTA - Flatware - Wallace International Silversmiths, Inc.
OLD BACHELOR - Card games - Eisel-Johnston Games
OLD BALL YARD, THE - Toys - Donald Erickson
OLD BARDSTOWN - Beverages–alcohol - Pure Kentucky Distilling Co.
OLD BAWDY - Beverages–malt - The Pike Brewing Co.
OLD BAY - Seasonings - McCormick & Co., Inc.
OLD BAY - Seasonings - Old Bay
OLD BENNINGTON - Dinnerware–glass ☆ - Bennington Potters
OLD BETSY - Toys–guns - Parris Manufacturing Co.
OLD BIDDY - Novelty items - Beyond Creative, Inc.
OLD BLUE - Dog food - Old Blue Inc.
OLD BLUE - Fabric softeners - Malco Products, Inc.
OLD BLUE SPECK - Cooking utensils–enameled ☆ - General Housewares Corp.
OLD BOHEMIA - Food products - Jewel Food Stores Inc.
OLD BOHEMIAN - Beverages–malt ☆ - Eastern Brewing Corp.
OLD BOSTON - Recording label - R.T.P. International
OLD BOURBON HOLLOW - Whiskey - Jim Beam Brands Co.
OLD BRITISH CASTLE - Dinnerware–glass ☆ - Johnson Brothers, USA, Inc.
OLD BROADWAY - Apparel–women's - Andrew Assael
OLD BROOKVILLE - Wines - Banfi Vintners
OLD BRUSSELS - Cookies - Venus Wafers, Inc.
OLD BULL - Lubricants - L.J. Hogwood & Associates
OLD CABIN STILL - Whiskey ☆ - United Distillers of North America

OLD CALHOUN - Beverages–alcohol - Safeway Stores Inc.

OLD CALIFORNIA - Tomato pastes and sauces - Northwest Packing Co.

OLD CALIFORNIA - Wines - Rapides Grocery Co.

OLD CAPE HARBOR - Seafood products–fresh or frozen - Carmine N. Romano

OLD CAPITOL - Furniture ☆ - Keller Manufacturing Co.

OLD CAROLINA - Bricks - Dudley Inc.

OLD CASTEEL VINEYARDS - Wines - Old Casteel Vineyards

OLD CASTLE - House furnishings ☆ - S.P. Skinner Co. Inc.

OLD CHARTER - Whiskey - Schenley Industries Inc.

OLD CHICAGO - Beverages - Logret Import & Export Co.

OLD CHICAGO - Beverages–malt - Joseph Huber Brewing Co., Inc.

OLD CHICAGO - Glassware–household - Rock Bottom Restaurants, Inc.

OLD CHICAGO - Greeting cards - Remigraphics, State of the Heart

OLD CHICAGO - Pizzas–frozen - Old Chicago Pizza

OLD CHICAGO SELTZER PLUS - Water–bottled or canned - Old Chicago Seltzer Co.

OLD CHURCH - Wines ☆ - Bully Hill Vineyards, Inc.

OLD CLASSICS - Wallpaper ☆ - Old Deerfield Fabrics Inc.

OLD CLASSICS - NEW STYLES - Fabrics - Piedmont Collections

OLD CLOTHES - Fabrics - Dan River Inc.

OLD COCO BAY TRADING CO., THE - Beverages–alcohol - Sazerac Co. Inc.

OLD COINS - Glassware–household ☆ - Ceraglass Inc.

OLD COLONY - Gasoline - Circle K

OLD COLONY - Gin - David Sherman Corp.

OLD COLONY - Locks–door ☆ - Dexter Lock

OLD COLONY - Maple candy and syrup - American Maple Products Corp.

OLD COLONY - Metals ☆ - Sheffield Silver Co.

OLD COLONY - Syrup - CPC International Inc.

OLD COLONY - Wines - Canandaigua Wine Co. Inc.

OLD COMISKEY - Beverages - National Fruit Flavor Co.

OLD COMMONWEALTH - Beverages–alcohol - Commonwealth Distillery

OLD CONCORD - Paper–bond ☆ - Southworth Co.

OLD CONSTITUTION - Wines - Monarch Wine Co. of Georgia

OLD COOT - Canes - Beyond Creative, Inc.

OLD CORRAL - Food products - Paramount Foods Inc.

OLD COUNCIL TREE - Paper–bond - Kimberly-Clark Corp.

OLD COUNCIL TREE BOND - Paper–bond - Neenah Paper Co.

OLD COUNTRY - Flatware - Utica Cutlery Co.

OLD COUNTRY - Food products - Old Country Bakery

OLD COUNTRY FORMULA - Health care products - Barcolene Inc.

OLD COUNTRY ROAD LEMONADE - Lemonade - Cincinnati Ice Machine Co. Inc.

OLD COUNTRY RYE - Breads–mixes - L. Karp & Sons, Inc.

OLD COUNTY - Paper ☆ - Southworth Co.

OLD COURT PRESS - Publisher's imprints - William Fox Eckbert

OLD COURTHOUSE - Bacon - Sugar Creek Packing Co.

OLD COURTHOUSE PORTER TRAILHEAD BREWINGCO - Beverages–malt - Trailhead Brewing Co., LLC

OLD CRAFTSMAN - Frames–picture - Decorel Inc.

OLD CRAFTSMAN - Plywood - Georgia-Pacific Corp.

OLD CRAFTSMEN - Tin products ☆ - Fox Run Craftsmen

OLD CREEK - Apparel and accessories - Woods & Gray, Ltd.

OLD CREEK RANCH WINERY - Wines - Old Creek Ranch Winery

OLD CROW - Whiskey - Jim Beam Brands Co.

OLD CUMBERLAND - Furniture–upholstered ☆ - Webb Furniture Enterprises Inc.

OLD CUTLER - Knives–pocket - Colonial Knife Co. Inc.

OLD DAN TUCKER - Liquors - Paramount Distillers Inc.

OLD DEERFIELD - Wallpaper ☆ - Old Deerfield Fabrics Inc.

OLD DENMARK - Flatware - Yamazaki Tableware Inc.

OLD DETROIT - Beer - Frankenmuth Brewery, Inc.

OLD DEVONSHIRE - Food products - US Foodservice

OLD DISTILLER - Whiskey - Old Boone Distillery Co.

OLD DOBBIN - Food products - H.H. Dobbins Inc.

OLD DOG - Wines ☆ - David Bruce Winery

OLD DOMINICK - Biscuits–mixes - D. Canale Food Services Inc.

OLD DOMINION - Furniture - Bassett Furniture Industries, Inc.

OLD DOMINION - Furniture ☆ - Virginia House Furniture Corp.

OLD DOMINION - Giftware ☆ - Gorham Inc.

OLD DOMINION - Tobacco products - 1776 Tobacco Co.

OLD DOMINION - Varnishes - Perrow Chemical Co.

OLD DOMINION BARN DANCE - Apparel and accessories - Old Dominion Barn Dance Inc.

OLD DUBLIN WINE CO. - Wines - Bardenheier Wine Cellars

OLD DUKE - Beverages–alcohol - Canandaigua Wine Co. Inc.

OLD DUTCH - Beverages ☆ - Vess Beverages Inc.

OLD DUTCH - Beverages–malt - Pittsburgh Brewing Co.

OLD DUTCH - Cleaning preparations - Tri-Par Inc.

OLD DUTCH - Housewares - Old Dutch International Ltd.

OLD DUTCH - Margarine - Miami Margarine Co. Inc.

OLD DUTCH - Paints - A. Flohr Co. Inc.

OLD DUTCH - Salad dressings–bottled - Old Dutch Co.

OLD DUTCH - Snack foods - Old Dutch Foods, Inc.

OLD DUTCH - Soil–potting - F.H. Von Damm Inc.

OLD DUTCH - Vinegar - Old Dutch Mustard Co. Inc.

OLD DUTCH BRICK - Tiles–mosaic - Capitol Tile Import Co.

OLD DUTCH FARM - Wines ☆ - Clinton Vineyards Inc.

OLD E-Z DOZ IT - Oils–lubricating - Berryman Products Inc.

OLD EL PASO - Vegetables–canned - Pet Inc.

OLD EL PASO FIRECRACKERS - Food products - Pet Inc.

OLD EL PASO SHIRT WORKS - Apparel–women's - Ruddock Manufacturing Co.

OLD ELK - Whiskey ☆ - United Distillers of North America

OLD ELM - Bird feeders - Reinders, Inc.

OLD ENGLAND TRIFLE - Food products - Antique Mall & Crown

OLD ENGLISH - Breads–mixes - J.W. Allen & Co.

OLD ENGLISH - Cheese - Kraft Foods, Inc.

OLD ENGLISH - Fans–electric - Nutone Inc.

OLD ENGLISH - Flowers, plants, and seeds - Stanford Seed Co.

OLD ENGLISH - Food products machinery ☆ - Fort Lupton Canning Co.

OLD ENGLISH - Furniture polish and wax - Boyle-Midway

OLD ENGLISH - Lighting fixtures - National Service Industries, Inc.

OLD ENGLISH 800 - Beverages–malt - Pabst Brewing Co.

OLD ENGLISH C - Metals ☆ - Carson Industries, Inc.

OLD ENGLISH COUNTRYSIDE - Dinnerware–glass ☆ - Johnson Brothers, USA, Inc.

OLD ENGLISH PEWTER - Jewelry - Michael Ricker Pewter, Inc.

OLD ENGLISH TIPT - Flatware - Gorham Inc.

OLD ENGLISH WHITE - Dishes–china - Waterford Wedgewood USA, Inc.

OLD EUROPEAN BREWERY COMPANY - Beverages–malt - Old European Brewery Co.

OLD FAITHFUL - Brooms ☆ - Suburbanite Industries

OLD FAITHFUL - Candy - Idaho Candy Co.

OLD FAITHFUL - Dog food - Eagle Roller Mill Co.

OLD FAITHFUL - Handles–metal - Dare Products Inc.

OLD FAITHFUL - Mats - Akro Corp.

OLD FAITHFUL - Meats - Bea Hall

OLD FAMILY RECIPE - Food products - Martin Gillet and Co. Inc.

OLD FARM - Jams and jellies ☆ - Owen & Mowrey Inc.

OLD FARM - Sausages ☆ - Formico Food Co.

OLD FART CORK - Novelty items - JOCO

OLD FASHION - Candy - Bobs Candies Inc.

OLD FASHION - Candy - Marshmallow Products

OLD FASHION - Corn–flour or meal - House-Autry Mills, Inc.

OLD FASHION - Meat extracts - Reelfoot Packers

OLD FASHION - Wines - Bardenheier Wine Cellars

OLD FASHION CHIX-STIX - Meat products–poultry - Pierce Foods Corp.

OLD FASHIONABLES - Jewelry ☆ - Pakula & Co.

OLD FASHIONED - Bait ☆ - Siberian Salmon Egg Co.

OLD FASHIONED - Beef - Pioneer Sausage

OLD FASHIONED - Cakes - Hazelwood Farms

OLD FASHIONED - Candy - Brock Candy Co. Inc.

OLD FASHIONED - Candy - Fritz Co., Inc.

OLD FASHIONED - Candy - Hooper's Chocolates

OLD FASHIONED - Chocolate candy ☆ - Hunt-Wesson, Inc.

OLD FASHIONED - Cocoa–powders or mixes - Nestle Beverage Co.

OLD FASHIONED - Health care products - Old Amish Herbs

OLD FASHIONED - Horseradish - Morehouse Foods

OLD FASHIONED - Pet products - Pet Supply Imports Inc.

OLD FASHIONED - Veterinary pharmaceutical preparations ☆ - Vital Nutrition Products

OLD FASHIONED BABY - Dolls - Uneeda Doll Co., Inc.

OLD-FASHIONED CALICO BEAN SOUP - Soups–canned - Country Hospitality Corp.

OLD-FASHIONED COUNTRY BEAR - Calendars - Dakin Inc.

OLD-FASHIONED CREAMS - Chocolate candy - Tom and Sally's Handmade Chocolates, Inc.

OLD FASHIONED EGG CREAM COMPANY, THE - Beverages–carbonated - Original Fashioned Egg Cream Co., Inc.

OLD-FASHIONED FOODS YOU'LL REMEMBER - Food products - Old Fashioned Enterprises Inc.

☆ = Now out of production

OLD-FASHIONED GARDEN POTATO CASSEROLES - Food products - Old Fashioned Enterprises Inc.

OLD FASHIONED HAMS - Hams - Fischer Packing Co.

OLD FASHIONED KITCHEN - Bakery products ☆ - Old Fashioned Kitchen Inc.

OLD FASHIONED KITCHEN GOLDEN - Bakery products - Old Fashioned Kitchen Inc.

OLD FASHIONED LOLLYPOPS - Candy - BRC Corp.

OLD FASHIONED MUSTARD - Food products - Europa Foods Ltd.

OLD FASHIONED NAST SANTA - Dolls ☆ - Effanbee Doll Corp.

OLD FASHIONED PENNSYLVANIA DUTCH - Candy - Keppel's Inc.

OLD FASHIONED ROADSIDE VIRGIN - Lemonade - Newman's Own Inc.

OLD FASHIONED SHOE BUTTONS - Candy ☆ - New England Confectionery Co.

OLD FASHIONED TEDDIES - Toys–stuffed - Russ Berrie and Co., Inc.

OLD FASHIONED TIC-TAC-TOE - Games - Mardi Gras Enterprises

OLD FASHIONED TOMATOES - Tomato pastes and sauces - Norden Fruit Co. Inc.

OLD FAVORITE - Candy - Variety Foods, Inc.

OLD FAVORITES - Wallpaper ☆ - Longwood Wallcovering

OLD FETTERCAIRN - Whiskey - Jim Beam Brands Co.

OLD FIDDLER - Musical instrument accessories - Super-Sensitive Musical String Co.

OLD FITZGERALD - Gin - Old Fitzgerald Distillery Inc.

OLD FITZGERALD 1849 - Beverages–alcohol - Old Fitzgerald Distillery Inc.

OLD FITZGERALD BOND - Beverages–alcohol - Old Fitzgerald Distillery Inc.

OLD FITZGERALD PRIME - Beverages–alcohol - Old Fitzgerald Distillery Inc.

OLD FLAME - Fireplace logs–treated - James A. Walmsley

OLD FOGHORN - Beverages–malt - Anchor Brewing Co.

OLD FOLKS - Sausages - F.P. Purnell Sausage Co.

OLD FOLKS DIETER'S DELIGHT - Sausages ☆ - F.P. Purnell Sausage Co.

OLD FORESTER - Whiskey - Brown-Forman Corp.

OLD FORESTER - Whiskey - Early Times Distillery Co.

OLD FORGE - Cutlery - Washington Forge Inc.

OLD FORGE - Floor coverings ☆ - Congoleum Corp.

OLD FORGE - Hooks - Melard Manufacturing Corp.

OLD FORGE - Knives–pocket ☆ - W.R. Case & Sons Cutlery Co.

OLD FORGE COLLECTIBLES - Figurines - Vaughn Communications, Inc.

OLD FORT - Rice - Gourmet House Inc.

OLD FRENCH - Flatware - Gorham Inc.

OLD FRIAR - Wine - Italian and French Wine Co. of Buffalo Inc.

OLD FRIENDS - Dolls ☆ - Fibre-Craft Materials Corp.

OLD FROST PLACE - Furniture - Vaughan Furniture Co. Inc.

OLD GERMAN - Beverages–malt ☆ - Eastern Brewing Corp.

OLD GLORY - Ice cream - Deconna Ice Cream Co., Inc.

OLD GLORY FIREWORKS - Fireworks - Freedom Fireworks, Inc.

OLD GOLD - Cigarettes - Lorillard Tobacco Co.

OLD GOLD - Lubricants ☆ - Ashland Oil, Inc.

OLD GOLD LIGHTS - Cigarettes - Lorillard Tobacco Co.

OLD GRAND DAD - Beverages–alcohol - Jim Beam Brands Co.

OLD GRAND-DAD 114 - Beverages–alcohol - Jim Beam Brands Co.

OLD GRAND-DAD CAVENDISH - Cigar boxes–wood - Consolidated Cigar Corp.

OLD GRIMES - Vegetables–canned - Faribault Foods Inc.

OLD GUASTI - Wines - Brookside Enterprises Inc.

OLD GUIDE'S SECRET - Breads–mixes - Sportsman's Recipes Inc.

OLD HAMPDEN - Paper ☆ - Parsons Paper Co.

OLD HAMPSHIRE - Stationery - Pratt & Austin Co.

OLD HARBOR - Candles - Old Harbor Candles

OLD HARDESTY - Gin - Old Boone Distillery Co.

OLD HAT - Recording label - Old Hat Records

OLD HAWAII RECIPES - Jams and jellies - Hawaiian Plantations Inc.

OLD HEAVEN HILL - Liquors - Heaven Hill Distilleries, Inc.

OLD HEIDELBERG - Beverages–malt - The Stroh Brewery Co.

OLD HEIDELBERG - Meats–luncheon - Groezinger Provision Inc.

OLD HERBALISTS - Health care products - Equinox Botanicals, Inc.

OLD HEURICH - Beverages–malt - Pittsburgh Brewing Co.

OLD HICKORY - Dog food - Gimborn U.S., Inc.

OLD HICKORY - Handles–wood - Hartwell Brothers Handle Co.

OLD HICKORY - Knives - Ontario Knife Co.

OLD HICKORY BRAND - Meat products–cured - Wright Brand Foods, Inc.

OLD HOLBORN - Tobacco–chewing or smoking - James B. Russell Inc.

OLD HOME - Bakery products - Metz Baking Co.

OLD HOME - Food products - Old Home Foods Inc.

OLD HOME - Syrups - American Maple Products Corp.

OLD HOME KITCHENS - Cakes - Bensons Inc. (Bakery Div.)

OLD HOME LIGHT - Puddings–canned - Old Home Foods Inc.

OLD HOME ORCHARDS - Food products - Fred L. Glaize

OLD HOMEPLACE COLLECTION, THE - Furniture - Vaughan Furniture Co. Inc.

OLD HOME'S PRIDE - Dairy products - Old Home Foods Inc.

OLD HOMESTEAD - Candy ☆ - New England Confectionery Co.

OLD HOMESTEAD - Cutlery - Lifetime Hoan Corp.

OLD HOMESTEAD - Floor coverings–carpet and rugs - Capel, Inc.

OLD HOMESTEAD - Glassware–household - Mayflower Glass Works

OLD HOMESTEAD - Recording label - Old Homestead Record Co.

OLD HOMESTEAD - Wines - Canandaigua Wine Co. Inc.

OLD HOMESTEAD - Wood products - Old Homestead, Inc.

OLD HONESTY - Paints - Farrell-Calhoun Inc.

OLD HUNDRED - Pajamas–men's - Knothe Corp.

OLD IMARI - Giftware ☆ - Seymour Mann Inc.

OLD INDIAN - Vitamins and nutritional supplements - Planetary Formulas

OLD INDIAN SPIRIT - Skin care products ☆ - CTS Laboratories Inc.

OLD IRONSIDES - Apparel and accessories ☆ - Melton Shirt Co., Inc.

OLD IRONSIDES - Cans–metal - New Delphos Manufacturing

OLD IRONSIDES - Computer software ☆ - Optimum Resource, Inc.

OLD IRONSIDES - Handles–metal - Dare Products Inc.

OLD IRONSIDES - Paper ☆ - Mead Corp.

OLD ISLAND RUM - Colognes ☆ - Key West Aloe Inc.

OLD ITALIAN BRAND - Pizzas–frozen - A.M. Gilardi and Sons, Inc.

OLD JACKSONVILLE - Fans–electric - Gulf Coast Fan & Light

OLD JOCK - Beverages–malt - Phoenix Imports Ltd.

OLD JOE TWIST - Tobacco products - Scott Tobacco Co.

OLD JUDGE - Coffee - Chock Full O'Nuts Corp.

OLD JUDGE - Trading cards and stamps - Collector's Club, Inc.

OLD KENT - Musical instrument accessories ☆ - Deltex Music Corp.

OLD KETTLE - Butter ☆ - Roanoke Apple Products Co.

OLD KING COLE - Dolls ☆ - Effanbee Doll Corp.

OLD LATROBE - Beverages–malt - Latrobe Brewing Co.

OLD LEATHER BY BOSCA - Leather goods and gifts - Hugo Bosca Co., Inc.

OLD LONDON - Sandwiches–prepackaged - Old London Foods Inc.

OLD LONDONER - Baskets–wood - Coe & Dru Inc.

OLD LYME BRICK - Floor coverings ☆ - Tarkett, Inc.

OLD LYME PINE - Furniture - Vaughan Furniture Co. Inc.

OLD MACDONALD - Dolls ☆ - Effanbee Doll Corp.

OLD MACDONALD'S FARM - Puzzles ☆ - Natural Science Industries, Ltd.

OLD MACDONALD'S TALKING FARMYARD FRIENDS - Toys–stuffed - Metacom Inc.

OLD MAID ARCADE - Games ☆ - Warren Industries Inc.

OLD MAID BOARD - Games - Warren Industries Inc.

OLD MAIDS - Snack foods ☆ - Harold Cunningham & Co.

OLD MAINE TROTTERS - Shoes - Penobscot Shoe Co.

OLD MAMMY'S - Food products - Morgan Foods Inc.

OLD MAN EMU - Shock absorbers–motor vehicle - Air Locker, Inc.

OLD MANSION - Coffee - Old Mansion Foods Inc.

OLD MAP - Glassware–household - Ceraglass Inc.

OLD MARIETTA WHITE - Paints - Vanguard Paints & Finishes Inc.

OLD MARKET DELI - Food products ☆ - Hunt-Wesson, Inc.

OLD MARKET PRODUCE - Fruits and vegetables ☆ - Omaha Steaks International

OLD MARTINIQUE - Liquors - United States Distilled Products Co.

OLD MARYLAND - Flatware - Kirk Stieff Co.

OLD MASKER CORONAS - Cigars - T.E. Brooks & Co.

OLD MASTER - Brushes–paint - Baker Brush Co. Inc.

OLD MASTER - Coffee - Euclid Coffee Co.

OLD MASTER - Floor coverings–carpet and rugs - Barrett Carpet Mills Inc.

OLD MASTER - Glass–leaded - Seneca Glass Co.

OLD MASTER - Golfing equipment - John Rouzee Green Co., Inc.

OLD MASTER - Musical instruments - Ernest Deffner Inc.

OLD MASTER - Postcards - Geme Art Inc.

OLD MASTER - Silver products - Towle Silversmiths

OLD MASTER GRIP - Golfing equipment - John Rouzee Green Co., Inc.

OLD MASTERPIECE - Liquors - Hughes Markets Inc.

OLD MASTERS - Handbags - Accessories International

OLD MASTERS - Paint removers - Master Products Inc.

OLD MASTERS BLACK OIL - Art supplies - Old Masters Paint Co.

OLD MC CALL - Beverages–alcohol - Montebello Brands, Inc.

OLD MCDONALD'S - Fertilizers - Aquila Group Inc.

OLD MEDFORD - Rum - M.S. Walker Inc./Seacoast

OLD MEISTER - Meat products–beef - Schweigert Foods

OLD MELTON'S - Bourbon - William Grant & Sons, Inc.

OLD MERCHANT - Fabrics - Dan River Inc.

OLD MILL - Apparel–women's - Hartmarx Corp.

☆ = Now out of production

OLD MILL - Fruits and vegetables - Old Mill Storage

OLD MILL - Furniture - A.A. Laun Furniture Co.

OLD MILL - Furniture - Pilliod Co.

OLD MILL - Siding–insulating - Weyerhaeuser Co.

OLD MILL - Stationery ☆ - Pratt & Austin Co.

OLD MILL - Toys - Greene Plastics Corp.

OLD MILL BROWN - Dinnerware–glass ☆ - Johnson Brothers, USA, Inc.

OLD MILWAUKEE - Beverages–malt - The Stroh Brewery Co.

OLD MILWAUKEE FINE PREMIUM BEER - Beer - The Stroh Brewery Co.

OLD MILWAUKEE GENUINE DRAFT - Beverages–malt - The Stroh Brewery Co.

OLD MILWAUKEE GENUINE DRAFT LIGHT - Beverages–malt - The Stroh Brewery Co.

OLD MILWAUKEE ICE - Beverages–malt - The Stroh Brewery Co.

OLD MILWAUKEE LIGHT - Beverages–malt - The Stroh Brewery Co.

OLD MILWAUKEE N.A. - Beverages–malt - The Stroh Brewery Co.

OLD MILWAUKEE RED - Beverages–malt - The Stroh Brewery Co.

OLD MISSION - Tiles–ceramic - Kraftile Co.

OLD MISSION VINEYARDS - Wines - Chateau Grand Traverse Ltd.

OLD MISSION WINERY - Wines - Chateau Grand Traverse Ltd.

OLD MISSOURI - Meats–luncheon - John Morrell & Co.

OLD MONASTERY - Stationery ☆ - Pratt & Austin Co.

OLD MONEY - Paper products - Crane & Co. Inc.

OLD MONK - Olive oil - Dolefam Corp.

OLD MONTECITO - Wines - Gibson Wine Co.

OLD MONTEREY BAY - Potato chips ☆ - Kettle Foods

OLD MOTHER HUBBARD - Dog food - Old Mother Hubbard Dog Food Co., Inc.

OLD MOTHER HUBBARD BITZ - Pet food - Old Mother Hubbard Dog Food Co., Inc.

OLD MULL - Whiskey - Cameron Craig Ltd.

OLD MUSKETEER - Liquors - Longs Drug Stores Corp.

OLD NAVY - Apparel and accessories - GPS, Inc.

OLD NAVY - Apparel and accessories - GPS, Inc.

OLD NAVY CLOTHING CO. - Apparel and accessories - Gap Inc.

OLD NAVY DUNGAREES SAN FRANCISCO NEW YORK - Jeans–women's - GPS, Inc.

OLD NAVY JEANS - Apparel and accessories - GPS, Inc.

OLD NAVY KHAKIS - Slacks - GPS, Inc.

OLD NAVY KIDS - Apparel and accessories - GPS, Inc.

OLD NEIGHBORHOOD - Food products - Old Neighborhood Foods

OLD NEIGHBORHOOD THIN 'N TRIM - Meats–luncheon - Old Neighborhood Foods

OLD NEW ENGLAND - Eggnog - M.S. Walker Inc./Seacoast

OLD NEW ORLEANS STYLE - Beverages–carbonated - Acadiana Bottling Co., Inc.

OLD NEWBURY CRAFTERS - Flatware - Old Newbury Crafters Inc.

OLD NORMAN'S CONQUEST - Beverages–malt - Humboldt Brewing Co.

OLD NORTH STATE - Tobacco–chewing or smoking - Brown & Williamson Tobacco Corp.

OLD NUMBER 5 - Toys–automobiles - Mattel, Inc.

OLD NO. 38 STOUT NORTH COAST BREWING CO. HANDMADE SINCE 1987 MENDOCINO COUNTY - Beverages–malt - North Coast Brewing Co., Inc.

OLD OAK - Musical instrument accessories - Super-Sensitive Musical String Co.

OLD OAK - Rum - Angostura

O.L.D. OLIVIA LEEDS DESIGN - Handbags - S. Lee Joffe

OLD ORANGE BLOSSOM - Flatware - Gorham Inc.

OLD ORCHARD - Fruit drinks–bottled or canned - Apple Valley International, LLC

OLD ORCHARD - Fruits and vegetables - Old Orchard Brands Inc.

OLD OREGON TRAIL MIXES - Snack foods - Orchard Crest Farms

OLD ORIGINAL - Flooring–hardwood - Joinery Co.

OLD ORIGINAL - Varnishes ☆ - Kyanize Paint Co.

OLD ORIGINAL LEVIS - Food products - Amazing Beverages, Inc.

OLD OVERHOLT - Whiskey - Jim Beam Brands Co.

OLD PADUKE STICKS - Candy - Gilliam Candy Co. Inc. (Gilliam Candy Brands)

OLD PAINTING PRESS - Greeting cards - Workshop Cards

OLD PAL - Pet products - Woodstream Corp.

OLD PARR - Beverages–alcohol - Guinness Import Co.

OLD PENNSYLVANIA RECIPE DUTCHIE PRETZELS - Snack foods - LDI, Inc.

OLD PHILADELPHIA ROASTING CO - Coffee - East Indies Coffee & Tea Co.

OLD PLANTATION - Candy - Nuts to You

OLD PLANTATION - Food products - Leon's Fine Foods Inc.

OLD PLANTATION - Syrup - W.B. Roddenbery Co., Inc.

OLD PORT ARTISANS - Posters - Old Port Artisans

OLD PRIDE - Breads - Big Star Food Stores

OLD PRO - Brushes–paint - Rubberset Co.

OLD PRO - Tools - Goldblatt Tool Co.

OLD PUEBLO - Soups–mixes ☆ - Mannons Chocolates, Inc.

OLD PUEBLO RANCH ALL NATURAL - Food products - Anita's Mexican Food Corp.

OLD PULTENEY - Liquors - Canandaigua Wine Co. Inc.

OLD QUEBEC - Cheese - Crystal Food Import Corp.

OLD QUILT - Glass products - Westmoreland Glass Co.

OLD RANCHERS - Meat products–beef - Old Ranchers Canning Co. Inc.

OLD RANGER - Food products - J.C. Wright Sales Co.

OLD RECIPE - Beverages - James B. Kaufmann & Associates

OLD RED - Beverages - 4% Co.

OLD REGENCY - Bakery products - Community Bakeries

OLD RELIABLE - Cigars - M. Marsh & Son

OLD RELIABLE - Firearms, accessories, and parts - John R. Schoffstall

OLD RELIABLE - Fishing lures - Shannon Lure Co.

OLD RELIABLE - Gloves–work - Shelby Group International, Inc.

OLD RELIABLE MECHANICAL SEALS - Sealing devices - Fredrickseal, Inc.

OLD RIP VAN WINKLE - Beverages–alcohol - Commonwealth Distillery

OLD ROYAL - Beverages–alcohol - Black Prince Distillery, Inc.

OLD ST. CROIX - Rum - Marie Brizard Wines & Spirits, USA

OLD ST. JOHN - Liquors - United States Distilled Products Co.

OLD ST. NICK'S - Alcoholic beverage - NWS, Inc.

OLD SALEM - Brooms ☆ - Suburbanite Industries

OLD SALEM - Giftware - Virginia Metalcrafters Inc.

OLD SALEM - Housewares - Old Salem, Inc.

OLD SALEM - Varnishes - Pettit Paint Co. Inc.

OLD SALEM COLLECTION - Furniture - Lexington Furniture Industries, Inc.

OLD SALEM NC - Giftware - Virginia Metalcrafters Inc.

OLD SALT - Brushes–paint - Wooster Brush Co.

OLD SALT - Cleaning preparations - Douglas Products and Packaging Co.

OLD SALT - Furniture ☆ - Ridgeway Clock Co.

OLD SALT - Seafood products–fresh or frozen - Sea Watch International Ltd.

OLD SAN FRANCISCO STYLE - Pretzels - Sunshine Biscuits, Inc.

OLD SAN FRANCISCO STYLE - Snack foods - Granny Goose Foods Inc.

OLD SANTA FE - Corn chips ☆ - Barbara's Bakery, Inc.

OLD SAVANNAH - Flour–blended - Community Mill & Bean Crusoe Island Natural Foods

OLD SCHOOL - Chocolate candy - Harry London's Candies Inc.

OLD SCHOOL - Recording label - Thump Records, Inc.

OLD SCHOOL BRAND - Food products - Old School Meal

OLD SCOTIA - Beverages–malt ☆ - Labatt Importers Inc.

OLD SETTER - Beverages–alcohol - Majestic Distilling Co.

OLD SETTLER - Flour–blended - The Wall-Rogalsky Milling Co.

OLD SETTLERS - Meat products–beef - Old Settlers Jerky Co., Inc.

OLD SHAY - Beverages–malt ☆ - Jones Brewing Co.

OLD SHELL GAME, THE - Now out of production ☆ - Milton Bradley Co.

OLD SKOOL - Footwear - Vans, Inc.

OLD SLATER MILL - Food products ☆ - Tarpy's

OLD SLAVE MART - Candy - Stephan's Candy Co.

OLD SLAVONIC - Computer software - Philip B. Payne and Nancy C. Payne

OLD SMOKEHOUSE - Meat products–pork - Hormel Foods Corp.

OLD-SMOKY - Gloves - Knoxville Glove Co.

OLD SMUGGLER - Beverages–alcohol - Hiram Walker & Sons, Inc.

OLD SOAK - Wet mops ☆ - American Textile Products Co.

OLD SOCK PURSE - Handbags - St. Thomas Inc.

OLD SOUTH - Flatware - Oneida Ltd.

OLD SOUTH - Food products - Bridgford Foods Corp.

OLD SOUTH - Food products - Martin Gillet and Co. Inc.

OLD SOUTH - Food products ☆ - State Fair Foods, Inc.

OLD SOUTH - Fruits–pickled or brined - Bryant Preserving Co.

OLD SOUTH - Juices–frozen - Lykes Services Co.

OLD SOUTH - Meat products–poultry - Plantation Foods, Inc.

OLD SOUTH - Paints - Spencer-Adams Paint Co. Inc.

OLD SOUTH LOG ROLLS - Candy - Standard Candy Co. Inc.

OLD SOUTH PASCO - Fruit drinks–bottled or canned ☆ - Lykes Services Co.

OLD SOUTH TRADING COMPANY SOUTHERN TRAILS - Meat products–beef - Highland Beefalo Farms, Inc.

OLD SOUTHERN - Food products - Garden Complements Inc.

OLD SPICE - Health care products - Procter & Gamble Co.

OLD SPICE - Sauces - Beaverton Foods

OLD SPICE SOOTHING GEL - Shaving preparations - Procter & Gamble Co.

OLD SPRUCE MOUNTAIN - Building materials–concrete - Connecticut Stone Supplies, Inc.

OLD STANDBY - Harmonicas - Hohner Inc.

OLD STONE MILL - Food products - Tree of Life, Inc.

OLD STONE MILL - Wallpaper - Old Stone Mill

OLD STURBRIDGE VILLAGE - Giftware - Virginia Metalcrafters Inc.

OLD STYLE - Beverages–malt - The Stroh Brewery Co.

OLD STYLE - Breads ☆ - Roman Meal Co.

OLD STYLE - Food products - Beatrice Cos. Inc.

OLD STYLE - Liquors - Heaven Hill Distilleries, Inc.

OLD STYLE - Musical instrument accessories - Kyser Musical Products, Inc.

OLD STYLE - Spices and extracts - Shank's Extracts Inc.

OLD STYLE DRAFT LIGHT - Beverages–malt - The Stroh Brewery Co.

OLD STYLE DRY - Beverages–malt - The Stroh Brewery Co.

OLD STYLE ICE - Beverages–malt - The Stroh Brewery Co.

OLD STYLE L.A. - Beverages–malt - The Stroh Brewery Co.

OLD STYLE LIGHT - Beverages–malt - The Stroh Brewery Co.

OLD STYLE LIGHT ICE - Beverages–malt - The Stroh Brewery Co.

OLD STYLE ROOT BEER - Beverages–alcohol - Joseph E. Seagram & Sons, Inc.

OLD STYLE ROOT BEER - Beverages–malt - The Stroh Brewery Co.

OLD STYLE ROYAL AMBER - Beverages–malt - The Stroh Brewery Co.

OLD SUNNY BROOK - Beverages–alcohol ☆ - Jim Beam Brands Co.

OLD TANKARD - Beverages–malt ☆ - Pabst Brewing Co.

OLD TANNER - Shoe polish - Whittemore Polish Co.

OLD TAP - Beverages–malt ☆ - Pabst Brewing Co.

OLD TAVERN - Beverages–alcohol - Jim Beam Brands Co.

OLD TAVERN - Cheese - Old Tavern Food Products Inc.

OLD TAVERN - Coffee - Quality Containers of New England

OLD TAVISTOCK - Furniture–upholstered - Mersman Furniture Co.

OLD TAYLOR - Chewing tobacco - Conwood Co. L.P.

OLD TAYLOR - Whiskey - Jim Beam Brands Co.

OLD TESTAMENT ODYSSEY - Computer software - Hartley Courseware Inc.

OLD TIME - Candy - Crystal Pure Candy Co.

OLD TIME - Coffee - Old Time Enterprises Inc.

OLD TIME - Food products - Roundy's Inc.

OLD TIME - Putties - Sterling-Clark-Lurton Corp.

OLD TIME - Whiskey - Jack Daniel's Distillery

OLD TIME - Wood products - E.B. Frye & Son Inc.

OLD TIME BODY & AGE - Beverages–alcohol - David Michael & Co.

OLD TIME WOODENWARE - Boxes ☆ - Charles Zahn-Import Merchant

OLD TIMER - Cutlery - Imperial Schrade Corp.

OLD-TIMER - Knives–pocket - Hard Hat Inc.

OLD TIMER HOT SAUCE - Sauces - Ronnie Arthur Cottrill

OLD TIMER SALSA - Sauces - Ronnie Arthur Cottrill

OLD TIMER, THE - Shirts - Adtees Corp.

OLD TIMERS - Sausages - Loveland Foods

OLD TIMERS - Toys - Lancaster Toy Co.

OLD TIMES - Flour–blended - Wolcott Argentine Milling

OLD TIMEY - Candy - Bobs Candies Inc.

OLD TIMEY - Recording label ☆ - Arhoolie Productions Inc.

OLD TOWN - Apparel–women's ☆ - Lucia, Inc.

OLD TOWN - Boats - Old Town Canoe Co.

OLD TOWN - Boats–canoes - Johnson Worldwide Associates, Inc.

OLD TOWN - Breads - Old Town

OLD TOWN - Coffee - Old Town Coffee & Tea Co.

OLD TOWN - Fans–electric ☆ - Aluminum Co. of America

OLD TOWN BLUE - Dinnerware - Corning Inc.

OLD TOWNE - Beverages - RC Cola Bottling Co., Inc.

OLD TOWNE - Beverages - Royal Crown Cola Co.

OLD TOWNE - Magnets - Russ Berrie and Co., Inc.

OLD TRADER - Paper–carbon - Kores Nordic USA Corp.

OLD TRAPPER - Meat products–beef - Bob Ostrow Co.

OLD TRAPPERS - Hunting equipment - Wildlife Research Center, Inc.

OLD TRAVEN - Floor coverings - Mannington Resilient Floors

OLD TRAWLER - Wines - Bully Hill Vineyards, Inc.

OLD TRUSTY - Brushes–paint - Wooster Brush Co.

OLD TYME - Breads - Schmidt Baking Co., Inc.

OLD TYME - Ice cream ☆ - Alta-Dena Certified Dairy, Inc.

OLD TYME - Meat products–pork - Hormel Foods Corp.

OLD VERMONT - Syrup - Conagra, Inc.

OLD VERMONTER - Breads - Fassetts Bakery Inc.

OLD VIENNA - Beverages–alcohol - Century Importers Inc.

OLD VIENNA - Dolls ☆ - Effanbee Doll Corp.

OLD VIENNA LIGHT - Beverages–alcohol ☆ - Century Importers Inc.

OLD VIRGINIA - Apple butter, preserves, juices - Bowman Apple Products Co. Inc.

OLD VIRGINIA - Glassware–household ☆ - Wilson Marketing Concepts

OLD VIRGINIA - Wallpaper - Surface Industries Inc.

OLD W. L. WELLER - Whiskey - United Distillers of North America

OLD WARDEN - Sporting goods - O Dee Mac Inc.

OLD WARSAW - Meat products–pork - John Hofmeister & Son, Inc.

OLD WELLER 107 - Whiskey - United Distillers of North America

OLD WESSEX - Oats–rolled or meal - Old Wessex Ltd.

OLD WEST - Greeting cards ☆ - Thought Factory

OLD WEST COLLECTOR'S - Postcards - Kustom Quality

OLD WEST GUNFIGHT - Games ☆ - Gamescience

OLD WESTBURY - Giftware ☆ - Towle Silversmiths

OLD WEYMOUTH - Floor coverings–carpet and rugs - Weymouth Braided Rug Co.

OLD WINDMILL - Food products - Old Windmill, Inc.

OLD WINE CELLAR - Wines - Old Wine Cellar Winery

OLD WISCONSIN - Sausages - Carl Buddig & Co.

OLD WISCONSIN - Sausages - Dairy Fresh Products Co.

OLD WISCONSIN SWISS TRADITION - Cheese - Carl Buddig and Co.

OLD WOMAN IN THE SHOE - Dolls ☆ - Effanbee Doll Corp.

OLD WORK - Switches–power - Power Controls Corp.

OLD WORLD - Bakery products - Plantation Baking Co. Inc.

OLD WORLD - Barbecue sauce - Gold Pure Food Products Inc.

OLD WORLD - Beads - Greene Plastics Corp.

OLD WORLD - Bread - Iversen Baking Co.

OLD WORLD - Breads - Lebanon Baking Co. Inc.

OLD WORLD - Christmas tree lights - Old World Christmas

OLD WORLD - Coffee - Pearl Coffee Co.

OLD WORLD - Crackers ☆ - Elam's

OLD WORLD - Food products - Ener-G Foods Inc.

OLD WORLD - Food products - Ommy Imports International Inc.

OLD WORLD - Furniture ☆ - Baker, Knapp & Tubbs

OLD WORLD - Furniture ☆ - A. Brandt Co. Inc.

OLD WORLD - Games ☆ - Pacific Game Co.

OLD WORLD - Glassware–household - Whitehurst Imports

OLD WORLD - Hams - Hansel 'n Gretel Brand, Inc.

OLD WORLD - Meats–luncheon - Dinner Bell Foods Inc.

OLD WORLD - Mobile homes ☆ - Wick Building Systems Inc. (Manufactured Home Div./North)

OLD WORLD - Novelty items ☆ - Easter Unltd. Inc.

OLD WORLD - Pastries - Strossner's Bakery

OLD WORLD - Pizzas–mixes - Burke Marketing Corp.

OLD WORLD - Skin care products - Old World Honey

OLD WORLD - Tiles–ceramic - KPT Inc.

OLD WORLD - Wallpaper ☆ - S.R. Wood Inc.

OLD WORLD ART - Foil–gold - Old World Art

OLD WORLD ARTISANS - Leather goods - S and S Leather Goods

OLD WORLD CHARM PICTURES - Scrapbooks - Jo-An Imports

OLD WORLD CREATIONS - Statuary - Old World Creations

OLD WORLD ELEGANCE - Wallpaper - Sterling Prints

OLD WORLD GLASS - Christmas tree ornaments - Old World Christmas

OLD WORLD II - Wainscotting - Georgia-Pacific Corp.

OLD WORLD II - Wallpaper ☆ - S.R. Wood Inc.

OLD WORLD II TELFAIR - Wainscotting - Georgia-Pacific Corp.

OLD WORLD II WHITEHALL - Wainscotting - Georgia-Pacific Corp.

OLD WORLD RECIPE - Candy ☆ - Eddyleon Chocolate Co. Inc.

OLD WORLD SPICES & SEASONINGS - Spices and extracts - Industrial Ingredient Sales, Inc.

OLD WORLD STEW - Food products - My Own Meals Inc.

OLD WORLD TREASURES - Furniture - Ethan Allen, Inc.

OLD ZANZIBAR - Enamels - Rudd Co. Inc.

OLDBRIDGE - Wood products - Georgia-Pacific Corp.

OLDCASTLE - Roofing materials–concrete - Oldcastle, Inc.

OLDE AMERICAN TRADITIONS - Wallpaper ☆ - Imperial Wallcoverings, Inc.

OLDE BOSTON - Leather goods - Noymer Leather and Gifts Ltd.

OLDE BOSTON - Paints - Parks Paint & Varnish Co., Inc.

OLDE BRICK - Lighting fixtures - L.D. Kichler Co.

OLDE CHAPP - Candles - Olde Chapp Candle Co.

OLDE CITY SPECS - Frames–eyeglass - Windsor Optical Inc.

OLDE COUNTRY - Craft supplies - Ports of Scandinavia Inc.

OLDE ENGLISH - Cabinets - Just Cabinets Inc.

OLDE ENGLISH - Craft supplies - Ohio Ceramic Supply Inc.

OLDE ENGLISH LUXURY - Paper–gift wrap - Gift Wrap Co.

OLDE ENGLISH PORTER BREWSACK - Home-brewed beer - Brewking

OLDE FARM - Syrup - Gem Inc.

☆ = Now out of production

OLDE FASHIONED RECIPE - Ice cream - Borden, Inc.

OLDE FASHIONED TENNESSEE BOAR'S BREATH THE THICKER PEPPER UPPER - Sauces - Porky's Gourmet Foods, Inc.

OLDE FAYETTEVILLE - Fans–attic ☆ - Fasco Industries Inc. (Consumer Products Div.)

OLDE FORGE - Furniture - Hammary Furniture Co. Inc.

OLDE FROTHINGSLOSH - Beverages–malt - Pittsburgh Brewing Co.

OLDE GEORGETOWN - Beverages–malt - Olde Heurich Brewing Co.

OLDE GREENWICH COBBLE - Construction equipment - Hengestone Holdings, Inc.

OLDE HOMESTEAD - Jams and jellies ☆ - Richardson-T Foods Corp.

OLDE MILL - Hobby kits ☆ - Janlynn Corp.

OLDE NEW ENGLAND - Candy - Burnham and Brady Inc.

OLDE NEW ENGLANDER - Cabinets - Just Cabinets Inc.

OLDE NUT - Ice cream - Good Humor Corp.

OLDE NUT SUNDAE CONE - Ice cream - Good Humor Corp.

OLDE NUT SUNDAE CONES - Confections - Good Humor Corp.

OLDE PHILADELPHIA - Meat products - Medfords, Inc.

OLDE PINE - Wood products - Three Mountaineers Inc.

OLDE PINE COLLECTION, THE - Furniture - J. Kenneth Zahn

OLDE RED EYE - Beverages–malt - Southern California Brewing Co.

OLDE RED EYE RED ALE A HIGH QUALITY MICRO BEER BREWED BY HAND IN THE SOUTH BAY - Beverages–malt - Southern California Brewing Co.

OLDE SOUTH - Vitamins and nutritional supplements - Phillips Gulf Corp.

OLDE SOUTH, THE - Fans–ceiling ☆ - Fasco Industries Inc. (Consumer Products Div.)

OLDE STONE MILL - Floor coverings–carpet and rugs - Capel, Inc.

OLDE STYLE - Peanut butter - Try-Angle Foods

OLDE TANKARD WARE - Statuary ☆ - Seymour Mann Inc.

OLDE THOMPSON - Housewares - Olde Thompson

OLDE TOWER - Waxes–sealing ☆ - E.M.I. Inc.

OLDE TOWNE - Sandwiches–prepackaged - Golden Valley Farms Commodity Group, Inc.

OLDE TOWNE BRICK - Tiles–ceramic - Summitville Tiles, Inc.

OLDE TOWNE OAK COLLECTION - Furniture - Brady Furniture Co. Inc.

OLDE TOWNE QUARRY - Tiles–ceramic - Summitville Tiles, Inc.

OLDE TYME - Labels–paper ☆ - Cleo Inc.

OLDE TYME - Popcorn - Detroit Popcorn Co.

OLDE TYME BUGGY - Balsa-wood model kits - Country Lane Dutch Supply

OLDE TYME CHRISTMAS - Spices and extracts - Scentex Inc.

OLDE TYME TEDDIES - Giftware - JDM, Inc.

OLDE VILLAGE BRICK - Floor coverings–tile - Kentile Floors Inc.

OLDE WAYE - Teas - Olde Time Tea Co.

OLDE WHALER'S SCENTED CANDLES - Candles - Cavedon Co., Inc.

OLDE WINDJAMMER - Jewelry - Olde Windjammer

OLDE WORLD - Furniture ☆ - Bassett Furniture Industries, Inc.

OLDE WORLD GOURMET GUMMIES - Candy - Brock Candy Co. Inc.

OLDE WORLD ICE CREAM MIX - Food products - Instantwhip Foods Inc.

OLDE WORLD PILAF - Food products - Lundberg Family Farms

OLDE YANKEE TOWNE - Epoxy coatings - Sterling-Clark-Lurton Corp.

OLDE YORK TOWNE - Food products - Smith Enterprises Inc.

OLDEN - Paints - Impervious Paint Industries Ltd.

OLDER KIDS IN FASHON - Wallcovering ☆ - Fashon Wallcoverings

OLDER KIDS TOO - Wallpaper - Gencorp Polymer Products

OLDER THAN GOD - Greeting cards - Diploma Mill

OLDEROL - Pharmaceutical preparations - Doral Pharmamedics Inc.

OLDESIGN - Computer software - AMX Corp.

OLDFORGE - Tools–hand-operated - Oldforge Tools Corp.

OLDHAM - Saw blades - Oldham Saw Co., Inc.

OLDHAM - Wallpaper - Koroseal Wallcoverings

OLDIES BUT GOODIES - Recording label - Original Sound Record Co. Inc.

OLDSMOBILE - Motor vehicles–automobiles - General Motors Corp. (Oldsmobile Div.)

OLDSTYLE PICTURE SHOW - Popcorn - Newman's Own Inc.

OLDTOWNE - Wainscotting - Georgia-Pacific Corp.

OLDWICK SQUARE - Floor coverings ☆ - Tarkett, Inc.

OLE - Calendars - Candy Lop Calendars

OLE' - Cigars ☆ - General Cigar Co., Inc.

OLE - Crocheted and knitted items - Puritan Sportswear Corp.

OLE - Fruit drinks–bottled or canned - Orange Bang Inc.

OLE - Liquors ☆ - Sazerac Co. Inc.

OLE - Paper–transfer ☆ - Staff Supermarket Associates, Inc.

OLE - Pens ☆ - Sanford Corp.

OLE' - Stationery ☆ - Stuart Hall Co., Inc.

OLE - Vegetable sauces ☆ - S & W Fine Foods, Inc.

OLE - Yarn - Tahki Imports Ltd.

OLE AMIGOS! - Sauces - Karen Orazi

OLE BLUE - Dog food - MFC Services

OLE DIZ - Charcoal - Hood Charcoal Co.

OLE DIZ - Charcoal - Royal Oak Enterprises, Inc.

OLE FASHION - Nuts–salted, roasted, cooked, or canned - Nut Bar Co. Inc.

OLE FASHUN - Seasonings - Flavorite Laboratories Inc.

OLE-IKES - Meat products–pork - Hot Springs Packing Co.

OLE JOE'S - Candy ☆ - Ruth Hunt Candy Co.

OLE MILL - Saunas ☆ - Miller Sausage Co. Inc.

OLE NASHVILLE - Clocks ☆ - General Time Corp. (Westclox/Seth Thomas Div.)

OLE POWDER KEG - Rocking horses - Dawn 'til Dusk Inc.

OLE REB - Cigars - Tampa Sweetheart Cigar Co.

OLE REB - Dog food - Stevens Industries Inc.

OLE RIPE - Fruits and vegetables - Mission Produce, Inc.

OLE RUFF - Dog food - Big V Feeds Inc.

OLE SMOKEY - Barbecue sauce ☆ - Sigma Quality Foods Corp.

OLE SMOKY - Candy - Ole Smoky Candy Kitchen

OLE TIME WOODSMAN - Pesticides–household ☆ - Ole Time Woodsman

OL'E TIMER - Gloves - Knoxville Glove Co.

OLE WYE - Vegetables–canned - S.E.W. Friel

OLE YAZOO BREAD - Spices - American Mercantile Co.

OLEAN - Food products - Procter & Gamble Co.

OLE'BOND - Adhesives and sealants - Uncommon Conglomerates

OLEC - Lighting equipment - Olec Corp.

OLEFIN - Pet collars - Leatherite-Nylorite Manufacturing Inc.

OLEFIN ONE - Wallcovering ☆ - Technique Textiles Inc.

OLEG CASSINI - Apparel and accessories - Esskay Manufacturing Co.

OLEG CASSINI - Apparel and accessories ☆ - Dame Belt Co. Inc.

OLEG CASSINI - Apparel–men's ☆ - Burma-Bibas, Inc.

OLEG CASSINI - Belts–apparel - Lyntone Belts Inc.

OLEG CASSINI - Floor coverings–carpet and rugs - Oleg Cassini Inc.

OLEG CASSINI - Hosiery–women's ☆ - Sara Lee Corp.

OLEG CASSINI - Leather and sheep-lined clothing - Excelled Sheepskin Leather Inc.

OLEG CASSINI - Manicure sets - London International U.S. Holdings

OLEG CASSINI - Neckties ☆ - Randa Corp.

OLEG CASSINI - Perfumes - Quintessence Inc.

OLEG CASSINI - Photographic equipment - Phoenix Corp. of America

OLEG CASSINI - Shoes ☆ - Atsco Footwear Inc.

OLEG CASSINI - Sunglasses - Nassau Lens Co. Inc.

OLEG CASSINI - Umbrellas - Shaw Creations Inc.

OLEG CASSINI - Watches - Marcel Watch Corp.

OLENDER - Margarine - Philip Olender & Co.

OLEO-FIT - Vitamins and nutritional supplements - Tishcon Corp.

OLEOCAP - Hair care products - Cosmair Inc.

OLEOGARD - Filters–air - W.L. Gore & Associates, Inc.

OLEOLUX - Oils–edible ☆ - Omega Nutrition USA Inc.

OLEOPASTO - Paints–artists' - Winsor & Newton

OLEVIA ST. - Slacks ☆ - Duck Head Apparel Co., Inc.

OLFA - Tools - Olfa Products Corp.

OLFACTORY - Incense - Olfactory Corp.

OLFISCO - Cheese - Olfisco Inc.

OLGA - Apparel–women's - Olga Co.

OLGA - Sandwiches–prepackaged - Olga's Kitchen Licensing, Inc.

OLGA CULTURED PEARLS - Underwear and nightwear - Warnaco Inc.

OLGA FROSTED EMBROIDERIES - Brassieres (Bras) - Warnaco Inc.

OLGA HOLIDAY HOLOGRAM - Underwear and nightwear - Warnaco Inc.

OLGA HOLIDAY VELVETS - Underwear and nightwear - Warnaco Inc.

OLGA INSPIRATION - Foundation garments–women's - Warnaco Inc.

OLGA LACY TEXTURES - Apparel–women's - Warnaco Inc.

OLGA TAILORED SHEERS - Apparel–women's - Warnaco Inc.

OLGA TOUCH, THE - Apparel–women's - Olga Co.

OLGA TREASURES - Underwear and nightwear - Warnaco Inc.

OLGA WONDER-WEAR - Underwear and nightwear - Warnaco Inc.

OLGALON - Apparel–women's - Olga Co.

OLGALURE - Brassieres (Bras) - Olga Co.

OLGA'S CHRISTINA - Apparel–women's - Olga Co.

OLGA'S FRESH FRIES - Food products - Olga's Kitchen Licensing, Inc.

OLGURT - Desserts - Olga's Kitchen Licensing, Inc.

OLHAUSEN - Pool tables - Olhausen Billiard Manufacturing, Inc.

OLI - Sauces - Otto Knuper

OLIANCE - Shampoos - Redken Laboratories, Inc.

OLICAMP - Sporting goods - Liberty Mountain Sports

OLIGO-MAJOR - Skin care products - Cosmair Inc.

OLIGOMEX - Chemical preparations - Boehme Filatex, Inc.
OLIGOPROBE - Diagnostic substances - Enzo Biochem, Inc.
OLIGREEN - Chemical preparations - Molecular Probes, Inc.
OLIGRO - Fertilizers - Laurent G. Guez
OLIMP-R - Ammunition - B-West Imports, Inc.
OLIN - Chemical preparations - Olin Corp.
OLIN - Skis, ski equipment - Olin Skis
OLINA - Underwear and nightwear - Carolina Underwear Co.
OLINDA - Olive oil - Orland Olive Oil Co.
OLIO CARLI - Oils–edible - Crystal Food Import Corp.
OLIO CARLI EXTRA VIRGIN OLIVE OIL - Olive oil - Crystal Food Import Corp.
OLIO SANTO - Olive oil - De Medici Imports Ltd.
OLIVA - Olive oil - Atlas Enterprises, Inc.
OLIVA - Shampoos - Home Health Products, Inc.
OLIVE - Relishes - Olive Co.
OLIVE BLOSSOM - Olive oil - Carother's Research Laboratories
OLIVE HILL VINEYARD - Wines - B.R. Cohn Winery
OLIVE-IT - Olive oil - Derse Olive-It, Inc.
OLIVE MIST - Oils–edible - Par-Way Group
OLIVER - Balls - Oliver Sporting Goods, Inc.
OLIVER - Fabrics - Dan River Inc.
OLIVER - Knives ☆ - Oliver Products Co.
OLIVER - Thread ☆ - Perfect Thread Co. Inc.
OLIVER - Toys - Agco Corp.
OLIVER - Toys–stuffed ☆ - Gund, Inc.
OLIVER - Toys–stuffed ☆ - Russ Berrie and Co., Inc.
OLIVER - Wines - Oliver Wine Co. Inc.
OLIVER ALES - Beverages–malt - Oliver Breweries Ltd.
OLIVER BLADES - Knives - Oliver Products Co.
OLIVER BREWERIES LTD. - Apparel and accessories - Oliver Breweries Ltd.
OLIVER CANTRELL - Apparel and accessories - Oliver Cantrell Inc.
OLIVER DITSON - Music–sheet - Theodore Presser Co.
OLIVER OCTOPUS FRANCESCA - Toys–stuffed - Dakin Inc.
OLIVER PEOPLES LOS ANGELES - Ophthalmic goods - Kenneth Lorence Opticians, Inc.
OLIVER SHEEPDOG - Puppets ☆ - Dakin Inc.
OLIVER WINSTON - Frames–eyeglass - Styl-Rite Optical Manufacturing Co., Inc.
OLIVERI - Musical instrument accessories - CTC Music Inc.
OLIVES D'AQUILA - Olives–canned - Giant Eagle, Inc.
OLIVET LANE - Wines - Pellegrini Bros. Wines Inc.
OLIVET LANE ESTATE - Wines - Pellegrini Bros. Wines Inc.
OLIVETO - Oils–edible - Santini Foods
OLIVETTI - Typewriters - Olivetti North America Inc. (Consumer Products Div.)
OLIVETTI ET - Typewriters - Olivetti North America Inc. (Consumer Products Div.)
OLIVETTI PRAXIS - Typewriters ☆ - Olivetti North America Inc. (Consumer Products Div.)
OLIVETTI SPORT - Leather goods - Olivet International Inc.
OLIVIA - Dolls ☆ - Effanbee Doll Corp.
OLIVIA - Recording label - Olivia Records Inc.
OLIVIA - Tableware–china - Pfaltzgraff Investment Co.
OLIVIA - Toys–stuffed ☆ - Russ Berrie and Co., Inc.
OLIVIA - Wigs - Paula Young
OLIVIA GOLD - Dinnerware–glass - WMF/USA
OLIVIA OWL - School supplies - Premier Agendas, Inc.
OLIVIA RHODES - Apparel and accessories - Silk Empire Inc.
OLIVIA STREET - Apparel and accessories - Stanwood Corp.
OLIVIA THE STRETCH OCTOPUS - Toys ☆ - Kenner Products
OLIVIA VALERE - Apparel–women's - Reflex Manufacturing Inc.
OLIVIA'S OWN - Bakery products - Garden City Foods, Inc.
OLIVIA'S TEARS - Jewelry - Olive Leaf, Inc.
L'OLIVIER, A - Olive oil - De Medici Imports Ltd.
OLIVIER LEFLAIVE FRERES - Wines - Frederick Wildman and Sons Ltd.
OLIVIERO - Dinnerware–glass - Crate and Barrel
OLIVIO - Oils–edible - Nicola Corp.
OLLERRER - Accordions - Castiglione Accordion
OLLIE COASTER - Toys - Little Tikes Co.
OLLIE GRAB - Toys - Mattel, Inc.
OLLIE LOLLIES - Candy - Wilkinson-Spitz Ltd.
OLLIE MCTWIST - Toys - Mattel, Inc.
OLLIE OCTOPUS - Toys–stuffed ☆ - Dakin Inc.
OLLIE OTTER - Toys–stuffed - Russ Berrie and Co., Inc.
OLLIE PEOPLES - Lenses–optical - Kenneth Lorence Opticians, Inc.
OLLIE THE CLOWN - Toys ☆ - Blue Ridge International Products Co., Inc.
OLLIE WEAR - Apparel and accessories - Amy Greenwood

OLLIES - Syrup - Good Food Inc.
OLLIFONT - Toys–stuffed ☆ - Gund, Inc.
OLLO - Sporting goods ☆ - Easton Sports Inc.
OLLY - See **QUINCY DRAGON**
OLLY - Filters–industrial - P-T Templet Co. Inc.
OL'MAN - Hunting equipment - L & L Enterprises, Inc.
OLMEC - Dolls - Olmec Toys, Inc.
OLMEC - Floor coverings–carpet and rugs ☆ - Regal Rugs Inc.
OLMECA GOLD - Liquors - House of Seagram
OLMECTOYS - Dolls - Olmec Toys, Inc.
OLMOS - Tiles–terrazzo - Imperial Tile and Marble Corp.
OLO-LUX - Paints ☆ - Waterlox Coatings Corp.
OLO-SEAL - Paints ☆ - Waterlox Coatings Corp.
OLOF - Pens ☆ - Anson Inc.
OLOFDAUGHTERS - Footwear - Arizona Mail Order Co., Inc.
OLOFF - Depilatories - Oloff Cosmetics Ltd.
OLOGY - Cigars - Reiss Dabney Cigar Co.
OLSEN LINE, THE - Stationery - Olde Towne Artisans Inc.
OLSEN'S - Seafood products–fresh or frozen - Olfisco Inc.
OLSON - Saw blades - Foredom Electric Co.
OLSON FARMS - Food products - Olson Farms Inc. (Liquid Egg Div.)
OLSON INTERNATIONAL - Metals - Olson International Ltd.
OLSONITE - Toilet seats - Olsonite Corp.
OLSS - Drapery hardware - Candace K. Deming
OLSTEN KIMBERLY QUALITYCARE - Vitamins and nutritional supplements - Olsten Service Corp.
OLT - Sporting goods - Philip S. Olt Co.
OLTONAR - Boats–canoes - Old Town Canoe Co.
OLYLOG - Screws - Olympic Manufacturing Group, Inc.
OLYMEX - Tools - Olympia Industrial Inc.
OLYMPADE - Beverages–carbonated - United States Olympic Committee
OLYMPIA - Beverages–malt - Pabst Brewing Co.
OLYMPIA - Brushes–paint - Corona Brushes Inc.
OLYMPIA - Campers - American Sterling Corp.
OLYMPIA - Cheese - Olympia Cheese Co. LLC
OLYMPIA - Curtain rods - Newell Window Furnishing Co.
OLYMPIA - Cutlery ☆ - Lifetime Hoan Corp.
OLYMPIA - Flatware ☆ - Wallace International Silversmiths, Inc.
OLYMPIA - Floor coverings - Applied Radiant Energy Corp.
OLYMPIA - Footwear - Olympia Industrial Inc.
OLYMPIA - Furniture - Weiman Co.
OLYMPIA - Giftware - Joseph Berland
OLYMPIA - Glass–leaded - Seneca Glass Co.
OLYMPIA - Glassware–household - Denby USA Limited
OLYMPIA - Gloves - Olympia Sports Co. Inc.
OLYMPIA - Housewares - Shuford Mills Inc. (Diversified Products Division)
OLYMPIA - Office machines - AEG Olympia Inc.
OLYMPIA - Playing cards ☆ - United States Playing Card Co.
OLYMPIA - Recording label - Universal Record
OLYMPIA - Rings–jewelry - Artcarved Inc.
OLYMPIA - Wallpaper - Winfield Design Associates, Inc.
OLYMPIA - Wallpaper ☆ - Capital Carousel Inc.
OLYMPIA - Yarn ☆ - William Unger & Co. Inc.
OLYMPIA DRY - Beverages–malt - Pabst Brewing Co.
OLYMPIA GOLD - Beverages–malt - Pabst Brewing Co.
OLYMPIA-GOLD - Dinnerware–glass ☆ - Lenox, Inc.
OLYMPIA II - Wallpaper - Winfield Design Associates, Inc.
OLYMPIA LIGHT - Beverages–malt - Pabst Brewing Co.
OLYMPIA LINEN - Cabinets ☆ - American Woodmark Corp.
OLYMPIA NATURALS - Cheese - Olympia Cheese Co. LLC
OLYMPIA-PLATINUM - Tableware–china ☆ - Lenox, Inc.
OLYMPIAD - Bicycles - Murray, Inc.
OLYMPIAD - Cheese - Alpine Lace Brands, Inc.
OLYMPIAD - Wallpaper ☆ - Wall-Pride Inc.
OLYMPIAN - Floor coverings–carpet and rugs - Coronet Carpets Inc.
OLYMPIAN - Guns ☆ - Weatherby Inc.
OLYMPIAN - Mats–rattan ☆ - Golden Star Inc.
OLYMPIAN - Rings–jewelry - Artcarved Inc.
OLYMPIAN - Sporting goods ☆ - Bridgestone/Firestone, Inc.
OLYMPIAN - Trailers–travel - Marathon Homes Corp.
OLYMPIAN - Windows–vinyl - Care-Free Windows
OLYMPIC - Bathroom fixtures - Crane Plumbing/Fiat Products
OLYMPIC - Bicycles - Ross Bicycles USA, Ltd.
OLYMPIC - Boats–motor ☆ - Duracraft Boats Inc.
OLYMPIC - Brushes–paint ☆ - PPG Industries, Inc.
OLYMPIC - Cleaning preparations - Chemical Products Co.

☆ = Now out of production

OLYMPIC - Electronics equipment - Burgess Inc.
OLYMPIC - Floor coverings–carpet and rugs - Stephen-Leedom Carpet Co.
OLYMPIC - Floor coverings–carpet and rugs ☆ - Southern Carpet Mills
OLYMPIC - Glassware–household ☆ - Lenox Crystal, Inc.
OLYMPIC - Milk - H.P. Hood & Sons Inc.
OLYMPIC - Paints - Olympic Paint & Varnish Co.
OLYMPIC - Pencils - Reliance Pen & Pencil Corp.
OLYMPIC - Pharmaceutical preparations - Vartex Pharmaceuticals Inc.
OLYMPIC - Pistols - High Standard Manufacturing Corp.
OLYMPIC - Recording label - Everest Record Group
OLYMPIC - Skin care products ☆ - Utikem Products
OLYMPIC - Sponges - Acme Sponge & Chamois Co., Inc.
OLYMPIC - Sporting goods - York Barbell Co., Inc.
OLYMPIC - Tents - Coleman Co., Inc.
OLYMPIC - Thread - United Thread Mills Corp.
OLYMPIC - Toys - Creative Playthings Ltd.
OLYMPIC - Toys - Peg Perego USA Inc.
OLYMPIC - Window coverings - Vertilux-Louverlux Inc.
OLYMPIC - Wines - Olympic Cellars
OLYMPIC - Yarn ☆ - Caron International Inc.
OLYMPIC 12 - Bicycles ☆ - Raleigh USA Bicycle Co.
OLYMPIC 1000 - Dryers–hair ☆ - Sunbeam-Oster Household Products
OLYMPIC ASH - Floor coverings ☆ - Harris-Tarkett, Inc.
OLYMPIC DREAM - Floor coverings–carpet and rugs - Karastan-Bigelow Inc.
OLYMPIC FREEDOM MACHINE - Sporting goods - Olympic Enterprises Inc.
OLYMPIC GOLD METAL - Paints - Olympic Paint & Varnish Co.
OLYMPIC ISU - Firearms, accessories, and parts - High Standard Manufacturing Corp.
OLYMPIC JON - Boats - O.M.C. Aluminum Boat Group
OLYMPIC JR. - Rifles - Redfield Co.
OLYMPIC KIDS - Breads - Metz Baking Co.
OLYMPIC OVERCOAT - Paints - PPG Industries, Inc.
OLYMPIC PET - Pet products - Sutton Corp.
OLYMPIC PRIDE - Frankfurters ☆ - Olympic Foods Inc.
OLYMPIC REGAL - Motor vehicles–automobiles - General Motors Corp. (Buick Motor Div.)
OLYMPIC SR. - Rifles - Redfield Co.
OLYMPIC SHOPPER - Toys - Peg Perego USA Inc.
OLYMPIC SPLENDOR - Floor coverings–carpet and rugs - Karastan-Bigelow Inc.
OLYMPIC STAIN - Paints - PPG Industries, Inc.
OLYMPIC-SUPRA - Yarn ☆ - Joseph Galler Inc.
OLYMPIC VALLEY - Crocheted and knitted items - Towne & King Inc.
OLYMPICS, THE - Games - S. Alden Inc.
OLYMPIKIDS - Binoculars - United States Olympic Committee
OLYMPION - Bicycles - Ross Bicycles USA, Ltd.
OLYMPUS - Audio tapes–blank - Adams Magnetic Products Inc.
OLYMPUS - Bathroom fixtures - Crane Plumbing/Fiat Products
OLYMPUS - Cabinets - Del Mar Cabinets
OLYMPUS - Cameras - Olympus America Inc.
OLYMPUS - Dinnerware–glass - Nikko Ceramics Inc.
OLYMPUS - Exercising equipment - Little River Marine Co.
OLYMPUS - Floor coverings - Mannington Resilient Floors
OLYMPUS - Food products ☆ - The Ostrom Co. (Ostrom Mushroom Farms Div.)
OLYMPUS - Glassware–household ☆ - Lenox Crystal, Inc.
OLYMPUS - Glassware–household ☆ - Rosenthal USA Ltd.
OLYMPUS - Pens ☆ - K-9 Pen Co.
OLYMPUS - Rings–jewelry - Artcarved Inc.
OLYMPUS - Tiles–ceramic ☆ - H & R Johnson Inc.
OLYMPUS - Volleyballs and soccer equipment - Audero Sports Supply
OLYMPUS - Wallpaper ☆ - Wolf-Gordon Inc.
OLYMPUS II - Floor coverings–carpet and rugs ☆ - Hollytex Carpet Mills Inc.
OLYMPUS II - Wallpaper ☆ - Wolf-Gordon Inc.
O.M. - Dinnerware–glass ☆ - Goebel of North America
OM - Jewelry - Modern Importers Inc.
OM - Skin care products ☆ - KMS Research Inc.
OM-3TI - Cameras - Olympus America Inc.
OM-4T - Cameras ☆ - Olympus America Inc.
OM-4TI - Cameras ☆ - Olympus America Inc.
OM FORMULAS - Pet products - Ralston Purina Co.
OM GENUINE DRAFT - Beverages–malt - The Stroh Brewery Co.
OM TOWN - Recording label - Higher Octave Music, Inc.
O'MA - Milk - Princess Bay Ltd.
OMABOND - Floor coverings–carpet and rugs - Omalon
OMAG - Photographic equipment ☆ - Heitz Service Corp.

OMAGGIO - Food products - Axiom Enterprises, LLC
OMAGGIO - Neckties - Robert Talbott Inc.
OMAHA - Fabrics - Dan River Inc.
OMAHA - Trailers–travel ☆ - Marathon Homes Corp.
OMAHA BEACHHEAD - Games - Avalon Hill Game Co.
OMAHA JEAN COMPANY - Apparel and accessories - Pamida, Inc.
OMAHA STEAKS - Meat products–beef - Omaha Steaks International
OMAHA STEAKS ANGUS - Meat products–beef - Omaha Steaks International
OMAHA STEAKS ANGUS THE BEST CHOICE - Meat products–beef - Omaha Steaks International
OMAHA STEAKS FOODSERVICE - Meat products - Omaha Steaks International
OMAHA STEAKS INTERNATIONAL - Meat products - Omaha Steaks International
OMALA - Lubricating oils - Shell Oil Co.
OMALON - Floor coverings–carpet and rugs - Omalon
OMANHENE THE COCOA BEAN COMPANY EHO YE NA IT IS RARE - Candy - Wifely Sprockets Co.
OMANTI - Apparel and accessories - Apparel Associates, Inc.
OMAR - Floor coverings–carpet and rugs ☆ - Couristan Inc.
OMAR - Pencils ☆ - Faber-Castell Corp.
OMAR - Perfumes - Hartz Mountain Corp.
OMARI - Shoes - Chanley Inc.
OMAR'S - Imported delicacies ☆ - Continental Crafts Co.
OMB-91 - Chemical preparations - Rapid Cast, Inc.
OMBRE - Blinds–venetian ☆ - Hunter Douglas, Inc.
OMBRE - Motor vehicles–automobiles - American Isuzu Motors Inc.
OMBRE BLEUE BY JEAN-CHARLES BROSSEAU - Perfumes - Alfin Fragrances Inc.
OMBRE CONTRASTE - Cosmetics - Chanel Inc.
OMBRE CRISTALLINE - Cosmetics - Chanel Inc.
OMBRE LUMIERE - Cosmetics - Chanel Inc.
OMBRE OASIS - Bathing suits ☆ - Jantzen Inc.
OMBRE ROSE BY JEAN-CHARLES BROSSEAU - Perfumes - Alfin Fragrances Inc.
OMBRELLA - Waterproofing compounds ☆ - Flood Co.
OMC - Boat sterns - American Marine Ltd.
OMC - Boats–pontoons - Weeres Industries Corp.
OMC - Engines - Outboard Marine Corp.
OMC II - Disinfectants - Cottrell, Ltd.
OMC COBRA - Marine rigging - Outboard Marine Corp.
OMC EXPRESS - Boats - Outboard Marine Corp.
OMC KING COBRA - Marine rigging - Outboard Marine Corp.
OMC OMNIVISION - Computer software - Outboard Marine Corp.
OMC PREMIUM - Lubricants - Outboard Marine Corp.
OMC SEA DRIVE - Marine rigging - Outboard Marine Corp.
OMC SILVER LABEL - Water–bottled or canned - Stonebridge Co.
OMC SYSTEMATCHED - Marine rigging - Outboard Marine Corp.
OMC TRACKER - Electronic equipment ☆ - Outboard Marine Corp.
OMC TRACKER 100 - Electronic equipment ☆ - Outboard Marine Corp.
OMC TRACKER 200 - Electronic equipment ☆ - Outboard Marine Corp.
OMCO - Food products - Oscar Mayer Foods Corp.
OMD - Chains - Lestage Manufacturing Co.
OME - Banjos - OME Co. Inc.
OME - Computer software - Princenet, Inc.
OMEGA - Air cushions ☆ - Nova Health Systems Inc.
OMEGA - Archery equipment and accessories - Indian Industries Inc.
OMEGA - Belts–apparel - Omega Fashions Ltd.
OMEGA - Boats–motor ☆ - Dolphin Boats Ltd.
OMEGA - Burial caskets - Batesville Casket Co., Inc.
OMEGA - Cabinets–wood - Kemper
OMEGA - Chalk - Quartet Manufacturing Co.
OMEGA - Cigars - Havatampa Inc.
OMEGA - Coatings - Omega Optical, Inc.
OMEGA - Computer software - Alexander & Alexander Services Inc.
OMEGA - Computer software - Western Atlas International Inc.
OMEGA - Doughs–frozen - S & J Importing Co. Inc.
OMEGA - Electronic equipment - Omega Engineering Inc.
OMEGA - Electronics equipment - RTI Research Technology International
OMEGA - Floor coverings - Congoleum Corp.
OMEGA - Floor coverings ☆ - Aladdin Mills, Inc.
OMEGA - Floor coverings–carpet and rugs - Regal Rugs Inc.
OMEGA - Floor coverings–carpet and rugs ☆ - Omega Pattern Works, Inc.
OMEGA - Food products - California-Omega Foods Inc.
OMEGA - Footwear - Polo International Inc.
OMEGA - Gasoline - Omega Oil Co.

OMEGA - Glassware–household - Crisa Corp.
OMEGA - Hair care products - William Marvy Co., Inc.
OMEGA - Hair-cutting shears - B.W. Boyd Shears Inc.
OMEGA - Health care products - Block Drug Co., Inc.
OMEGA - Health care products ☆ - Allergy Resources/Ecologic
OMEGA - Hearing aids ☆ - Starkey Labs Inc.
OMEGA - Juice extracting devices - Omega Products
OMEGA - Ladders–wood - John S. Tilley Ladders Co. Inc.
OMEGA - Lamps–ultraviolet - QDM Co.
OMEGA - Lighting fixtures - Thomas Industries Inc.
OMEGA - Lighting fixtures - Thomas Lighting (Accent Division)
OMEGA - Medical apparatus - Invivo Research, Inc.
OMEGA - Medical apparatus - Osteoimplant Technology, Inc.
OMEGA - Motor vehicles–automobiles ☆ - General Motors Corp. (Oldsmobile Div.)
OMEGA - Musical instruments ☆ - Selmer Co. Inc.
OMEGA - Neckties - Resisto Tie Makers
OMEGA - Office supplies - Wescosa Inc.
OMEGA - Pet products - Hoegh Industries Inc.
OMEGA - Photographic equipment - Omega/Arkay
OMEGA - Pipes–tobacco - Dr. Grabow Pre-Smoked Pipes Inc.
OMEGA - Recording label ☆ - Joey Records International Inc.
OMEGA - Spices and extracts - Herbert Marmorek & Son, Inc.
OMEGA - Sporting goods - Bausch & Lomb Inc.
OMEGA - Sporting goods - Climb High Inc.
OMEGA - Sporting goods - Montgomery Ward & Co. Inc.
OMEGA - Sporting goods - Oceanic
OMEGA - Strollers–baby - Aprica Kassai USA Inc.
OMEGA - Tents - Coleman Co., Inc.
OMEGA - Tiles–ceramic - Federal Tile Imports Inc.
OMEGA - Tiles–ceramic - United Ceramic Tile Corp.
OMEGA - Typewriters - Corpex International, Ltd.
OMEGA - Video games - Origin Systems, Inc.
OMEGA - Vitamins and nutritional supplements - Vitamex America
OMEGA - Wallpaper - Koroseal Wallcoverings
OMEGA - Wallpaper ☆ - Capital Carousel Inc.
OMEGA - Watches - Omega Watch Corp.
OMEGA 3 - Oils–edible ☆ - Grifair Co.
OMEGA-3 - Vitamins and nutritional supplements - Makers of Kal, Inc.
OMEGA-3 - Vitamins and nutritional supplements - Schiff Products, Inc.
OMEGA 5000 - Medical apparatus ☆ - Spenco Medical Corp.
OMEGA BAR - Food products - Omega-Life Inc.
OMEGA BOND - Vitamins and nutritional supplements ☆ - Schiff Products, Inc.
OMEGA BOOSTER - Oils–mineral - Aquafauna Bio-Marine, Inc.
OMEGA BOYS CLUB - Apparel and accessories - Omega Boys Club
OMEGA CENTURY - Musical instrument accessories - Kaman Music Corp.
OMEGA CLASSICS - Musical instrument accessories - Kaman Music Corp.
OMEGA ENVIRONMENTAL TECHNOLOGIES - Air conditioning equipment - Auto Air Export, Inc.
OMEGA-FLAX - Vitamins and nutritional supplements - Source Naturals
OMEGA FRAME - Doors–metal ☆ - Peachtree Doors and Windows Inc.
OMEGA II - Computer software - Dr. T's Music Software Inc.
OMEGA III - Vitamins and nutritional supplements - Allergy Resources/Ecologic
OMEGA LIFT EQUIPMENT - Tools - Shinn Fu Co. of America, Inc.
OMEGA MOTION - Furniture - Omega Motion, LLC
OMEGA NUTRIPHARM - Vitamins and nutritional supplements - Omega Pharmaceutical, Inc.
OMEGA NUTRITION - Flour–blended ☆ - Omega Nutrition USA Inc.
OMEGA OIL - Analgesics - Block Drug Co., Inc.
OMEGA (ONE - 10) - Targets - Johnson Matthey Inc.
OMEGA PET - Vitamins and nutritional supplements - Omega Nutrition USA Inc.
OMEGA PLEX - Health care products - American Biologics
OMEGA PLUS - Vitamins and nutritional supplements - Omega Nutrition USA Inc.
OMEGA-REFLECTA - Photographic equipment - Berkey Marketing Cos.
OMEGA RUG WORKS - Floor coverings–carpet and rugs - Omega Pattern Works, Inc.
OMEGA SIGNBOARD - Plywood - Harbor Sales Co.
OMEGA SUN - Vitamins and nutritional supplements - New Algae Co.
OMEGA SUPREME - Mattresses ☆ - California Concepts
OMEGABITE - Bicycles - Ritchey Design Inc.
OMEGACLAD - Wines - Omega Engineering, Inc.
OMEGADYNE - Electronic equipment - Omegadyne, Inc.
OMEGAEPA - Vitamins and nutritional supplements - Source Naturals
OMEGAFEED - Animal feeds - Omegatech Inc.

OMEGAFLO - Vitamins and nutritional supplements - Omega Nutrition USA Inc.
OMEGAGLASS - Resins–synthetic - Alpha & Omega Fiberglass Finishes
OMEGAKRON - Games ☆ - Avalon Hill Game Co.
OMEGALASKA - Vitamins and nutritional supplements - Health Products Corp.
OMEGAPHONE - Electronic equipment - Omega Engineering, Inc.
OMEGAPLUS - Computer software - Gas Research Institute
OMEGARICH - Animal feeds - Omegatech Inc.
OMEGASAYS - Electrical testing instruments - Omega Engineering, Inc.
OMEGASCOPE - Electrical testing instruments - Omega Engineering, Inc.
OMEGASOFT - Computer software - Omega Engineering, Inc.
OMEGASOURCE - Vitamins and nutritional supplements - Source Food Technology, Inc.
OMEGAVIEW II - Computer software - Candle Corp.
OMEGURT - Yogurt ☆ - Natural Ovens of Manitowoc Inc.
OMELET MASTER - Egg substitutes - Hormel Foods Corp.
OMELIA - Jams and jellies - Ommy Imports International Inc.
OMETIN - Vitamins and nutritional supplements - Winning Laboratories Corp.
OMF - Computer software - Avid Technology, Inc.
OMF INTERCHANGE - Computers - Avid Technology, Inc.
OMG - Chemical preparations - Mooney Chemicals, Inc.
OMG - Jewelry - Omega Casting Corp.
O.M.H. - Dog food - Old Mother Hubbard Dog Food Co., Inc.
OMI SPORT - Shoes - Open Minds, Inc.
OMICHRON - Giftware - Simon Golub & Sons Inc.
OMIDERM - Health care products - Doak Dermatologics
OMIGA - Computer peripheral equipment - Oxford Molecular Group
OMIKRON - Hearing aids - Omikron Hearing Aid Corp.
OMINCRON CONSPIRACY - Computer software - First Star Software Inc.
OMINO - Apparel and accessories - Hering North America Inc.
OMINVET - Computer software - Sungard Business Systems Inc.
OMIRON - Pharmaceutical preparations ☆ - U.S. Ethicals Inc.
OMIT - Cleaning preparations - Century Labs Inc.
OMITE - Insecticides - Uniroyal Chemical Co. Inc. (Crop Protection Div.)
OMLOID - Toys–models - Estes Industries
OMMG - Publisher's imprints - Kelly Properties, Inc.
OMNET - Computer software - Omnet Inc.
OMNI - Adhesives and sealants - Quikrete Cos.
OMNI - Blinds–venetian - Chelsea House Fabrics
OMNI - Blinds–venetian ☆ - Hunter Douglas, Inc.
OMNI - Cabinets - Merillat Industries, Inc.
OMNI - Cabinets–wood - Parcraft Distinctive Cabinetry
OMNI - Computer software - Haverly Systems Inc.
OMNI - Cording - M.W. Kasch Co.
OMNI - Dinnerware–glass - Prolon Dinnerware
OMNI - Draperies - Maharam Vertical Surfaces
OMNI - Electronics equipment - RTI Research Technology International
OMNI - Flatware - Oneida Ltd.
OMNI - Floor coverings–carpet and rugs - Regal Rugs Inc.
OMNI - Floor coverings–carpet and rugs ☆ - Patcraft Mills Inc.
OMNI - Food products - Wonder Bar Products Inc.
OMNI - Food products machinery - American National Can Co.
OMNI - Footwear–men's - Milo Inc.
OMNI - Furniture ☆ - Avant Industries
OMNI - Furniture–wood ☆ - Charvoz
OMNI - Gutters–metal - ZMC, Inc.
OMNI - Handbags - Buxton Inc.
OMNI - Health care products - Commander-Omni Co. Inc.
OMNI - Hearing aids - Omni Hearing Systems
OMNI - Heaters–space - Kero-Sun Inc.
OMNI - Hobby kits ☆ - Unicraft Products
OMNI - Hotels and motels - Omni Hotels Management Corp.
OMNI - Housewares - Scott Paper Co.
OMNI - Machinery - Pacific Steamex Cleaning System Inc.
OMNI - Mattresses - Omni Futon Furniture, Inc.
OMNI - Medical apparatus - Arjo-Century Inc.
OMNI - Motor vehicles ☆ - Chrysler Corp. (Dodge Car Div.)
OMNI - Notebooks and notepads - Norcom Inc.
OMNI - Ophthalmic goods - American Optical Corp.
OMNI - Paper - M. Grumbacher Inc.
OMNI - Publisher's imprints - Scholastic Inc.
OMNI - Recording label - Island Records Inc.
OMNI - Sporting goods - Shakespeare Fishing Tackle
OMNI - Strollers–baby ☆ - Evenflo Co.
OMNI - Synthesizers–musical instrument - Fender Musical Instruments
OMNI - Thread - Lewis Threads Inc.

☆ = Now out of production

OMNI - Valves–industrial - Aquaculture Research/Environmental Associates Inc.

OMNI - Watches - Omni Quartz Ltd.

OMNI - Water purification systems - Omni Corp.

OMNI - Water treating compounds - Bio-Lab, Inc.

OMNI - Water–distilled - Chronomite Laboratories Inc.

OMNI - Wet suits–rubber - Parkway Systems

OMNI - Whirlpool bath ☆ - Jacuzzi Inc.

OMNI - Zippers - Talon Inc.

OMNI-4 - Space heaters ☆ - Cool Attic

OMNI 100'S - Cigarettes - Eve Holdings Inc.

OMNI ADVANCE - Electronic equipment - Projectapix-II

OMNI AQUA - Water–bottled or canned - Omnitrition International, Inc.

OMNI AUDIO - Audio equipment - Republic Distributors, Inc.

OMNI BASIC - Water purification systems - Omni Corp.

OMNI CASE - Palettes - Plaid Enterprises, Inc.

OMNI-CEPTOR - Antennas - Winegard Co.

OMNI CONVERTER - Computer software - Compu-Tations Inc.

OMNI CUSTOM - Motor vehicles ☆ - Chrysler Corp. (Dodge Car Div.)

OMNI-DEX - Office supplies - Esselte Corp.

OMNI FAUCET - Water purification systems - Omni Corp.

OMNI-FEED - Pet products - Omni Feed Parrot Diet

OMNI-FIT - Nutritional drink - Omnitrition International, Inc.

OMNI FLEX - Diaphragms - Milex Products Inc.

OMNI-FLEX - Sporting goods - Shakespeare Fishing Tackle

OMNI-FLEXOR - Exercise device - Omni-Flexor Corp.

OMNI-FLEXOR - Exercising equipment - Body Care Inc.

OMNI-FLO - Whirlpools ☆ - Aqua Glass Corp.

OMNI-FORM - Pillows ☆ - Lumex, Inc.

OMNI-GAIN - Antennas - Valor Enterprises, Inc.

OMNI-GARD - Auto bug deflector - G.T. Styling Inc.

OMNI GUARD - Health care products - Omni Group Inc.

OMNI HEARING SYSTEMS - Hearing aids - Omni Hearing Systems

OMNI HOUSE - Water purification systems - Omni Corp.

OMNI II - Furniture–wood - Johnston-Tombigbee

OMNI-KEY - Electronics equipment - Grass Valley Group Inc.

OMNI-KOLOR - Daylight lamps - Boyd Lighting Co.

OMNI LIFT - Health care products - Arjo Manufacturing Co.

OMNI-LIGHT - Lighting equipment - Lowel-Light Manufacturing Inc.

OMNI-LINK - Antennas - Kaul-Tronics, Inc.

OMNI-LITE - Flashlights - Fulton Industries Inc.

OMNI-LOC - Electronic equipment - Arion Corp.

OMNI-LOCK - Machinery - Jakob Systems, Inc.

OMNI LUXURY LIGHTS - Cigarettes - Liggett Group Inc.

OMNI-M-TABS - Health care products - Halsey Drug Co. Inc.

OMNI-MATE - Electronic equipment - Arion Corp.

OMNI-MEGA - Vitamins and nutritional supplements - Bio San Laboratories Inc.

OMNI MITE - Water purification systems ☆ - Omni Corp.

OMNI MOUNT - Audio equipment - GNP Audio Video Inc.

OMNI MOUSE II - Computer peripheral equipment - Mouse Systems Corp.

OMNI-MUL - Chemical preparations - Baker Hughes Inc.

OMNI-ODOR-GUARD - Deodorizers - ICD Industries, Inc.

OMNI PAPERMAKER - Computer storage devices - Omnipress

OMNI-POINTE - Floor coverings–carpet and rugs ☆ - Couristan Inc.

OMNI PRO - Ophthalmic goods - American Optical Corp.

OMNI-PROFILE - Computer chassis - Tandy Corp.

OMNI-PURPOSE - Brackets - Atlas/Soundolier

OMNI-PURPOSE - Office supplies - Radmar Inc.

OMNI QUANTA - Computer software - American Trading and Production Corp.

OMNI QUICK - Water purification systems ☆ - Omni Corp.

OMNI-RAIL - Musical instrument accessories - XL Specialty Percussion

OMNI REGULAR - Water purification systems - Omni Corp.

OMNI SCOUT - Insecticides - Hercon Environmental Corp.

OMNI SET - Adhesives and sealants - Quikrete Cos.

OMNI SINK - Water purification systems ☆ - Omni Corp.

OMNI SITTING BENCH - Benches–plastic - Pacific Spirit Corp.

OMNI SOURCE PLUS - Battery chargers - Lenmar Enterprises, Inc.

OMNI-STIK - Decorations - A.J. Ganz Co. Inc.

OMNI SUPER - Water purification systems - Omni Corp.

OMNI-TEC - Chemical preparations - Baker Hughes Inc.

OMNI TECH - Televisions - Projectapix-II

OMNI TOTAL - Water purification systems - Omni Corp.

OMNI-TRAK - Medical apparatus - Invivo Research, Inc.

OMNI TROL - Insecticides - Vedco, Inc.

OMNI TWO - Vitamins and nutritional supplements - Natural Organics, Inc.

OMNI-VIEW - Mirrors - Ram Products Co.

OMNI-VISION - Antennas - Kaul-Tronics, Inc.

OMNI VITE - Vitamins and nutritional supplements - Natural Organics, Inc.

OMNI VUFONE - Computer peripheral equipment - Verifone, Inc.

OMNI WAND - Electronics equipment - Videx, Inc.

OMNIA - Floor coverings - Mannington Resilient Floors

OMNIACCESS - Computer software - Sungard Business Systems Inc.

OMNIALON E - Yarn - Hohenberg Co. Inc.

OMNIARRAY - Computer software - Northgate Computer Systems Inc.

OMNIBAR - Pumps–vacuum - Danielson Vacuum Products, Inc.

OMNIBEAM - Lighting equipment - General Electric Co.

OMNIBOND - Inks - Sun Chemical Corp.

OMNIBOOK - Computers - Hewlett-Packard Co.

OMNIBUS - Floor coverings–carpet and rugs ☆ - Porter Carpet Mills Inc.

OMNIBUS - Wallpaper - Textile Wallcoverings International Ltd.

OMNIBUS PRESS - Publisher's imprints - Music Sales Corp.

OMNIC - Computer software - Nicolet Instrument Corp.

OMNICAP - Computer peripheral equipment - Verifone, Inc.

OMNICAPS - Health care products - Halsey Drug Co. Inc.

OMNICART - Racks - Omnimed Inc.

OMNICEF - Pharmaceutical preparations - Warner-Lambert Co.

OMNICEL - Recording label - Functional Foods Corp., Inc.

OMNICENTER - Computer software - Omnicell Technologies, Inc.

OMNICHORD - Musical instrument accessories - Suzuki Corp.

OMNICLEAN - Cleaning preparations - Eastwater Scientific Products, Inc.

OMNICOM - Computer software - Omni Flow Computers, Inc.

OMNICORE - Computer software - Prentice-Hall, Inc.

OMNICRAFT - Electronic equipment - C-T Audio Marketing Inc.

OMNICRYL - Pigments - Engelhard Corp.

OMNICSR PROFESSIONAL - Computer software - Sungard Business Systems Inc.

OMNIDATACONNECTION - Computer software - Sungard Business Systems Inc.

OMNIDBEN - Computer software - Sungard Business Systems Inc.

OMNIDESK - Furniture - Omni International Inc.

OMNIDIRECTIONAL FOOT - Metals - Wenger Corp.

OMNIDYNE - Electronic equipment - Shure Brothers, Inc.

OMNIFEX - Musical instrument accessories - SLM Marketplace

OMNIFILE - File folders ☆ - National Metal Industries (Utility Metal Products Div.)

OMNIFILM - Plastic wrap - Goodyear Tire & Rubber Co.

OMNIFLEX - Electrical equipment ☆ - Monster Cable Products, Inc.

OMNIFLO - Soldering equipment - Electrovert USA Corp.

OMNIFLOOD - Lighting equipment - ProLight

OMNIFLOX - Antibiotics - Abbott Laboratories

OMNIFOAM - Foam rubber - Omnifoam, Inc.

OMNIFORCE - Washing machines–commercial - Stoelting, Inc.

OMNIFORM - Computer software - Caere Corp.

OMNIGLOW - Lighting equipment - General Electric Co.

OMNIGO 100 - Electronic equipment - Hewlett-Packard Co.

OMNIGRAPHIC - Electronic equipment ☆ - Houston Instrument

OMNIGRAPHIC - Projectors–photographic - Elmo Manufacturing Corp.

OMNIGRAPHICS BOOKS - Publisher's imprints - Omnigraphics Inc.

OMNIGREEN - Vitamins and nutritional supplements - Bioenergy Nutrient's Inc.

OMNIGRIP - Health care products - Maddak Inc.

OMNIGRIP - Medical apparatus ☆ - Apothecary Products, Inc.

OMNIGUARD/ENTERPRISE ACCESS CONTROL - Computer software - Raxco Software Inc.

OMNIGUARD/ENTERPRISE SECURITY MANAGER - Computer software - Raxco Software Inc.

OMNIGUARD/INTRUDER ALERT - Computer software - Raxco Software Inc.

OMNIGUIDE - Catheters - Micro Interventional Systems, Inc.

OMNIHIB - Pharmaceutical preparations - Smithkline Beecham Corp.

OMNIHIST - Antihistamine - We Pharmaceuticals, Inc.

OMNII C-Z - Pharmaceutical preparations - Dunhall Pharmaceuticals Inc.

OMNIKITE - Kites ☆ - Avionics Plastics Corp.

OMNILERT - Computer hardware - Baron Services, Inc.

OMNILIB - Electronic equipment - Computer Upgrade Corp.

OMNILINK - Computer peripheral equipment - Symbol Technologies, Inc.

OMNILITE - Fabrics–wool - King of the Mountain Sports Inc.

OMNIMAIL - Computer software - Sungard Business Systems Inc.

OMNIMARK - Pencils ☆ - Empire Berol USA

OMNIMAX - Health care products - Graham-Field Inc.

OMNIMIX - Fertilizers - NovAgra Inc.

OMNIMODELS - Radio controlled vehicles - Hobbico Inc.

OMNIMOUNT - Hardware - Electro-Voice, Inc.

OMNINAC - Computer hardware - Verifone, Inc.

OMNINOTE - Transceivers - D.I. Systems, Inc.

OMNIPANEL - Heated bath towel racks - Runtal North America Inc.

OMNIPAY - Computer software - Sungard Business Systems Inc.

OMNIPED - Filing cabinets—metal - Omni International Inc.

OMNIPEN - Computer peripheral equipment - Wintime Corp.

OMNIPEN - Pharmaceutical preparations - Wyeth-Ayerst Laboratories

OMNIPERM - Hair care products - Naturelle, Inc.

OMNIPHONICS - Recording label - Progressive Awareness Research, Inc.

OMNIPLAN/400 - Computer software - Sungard Business Systems Inc.

OMNIPLUS - Computer software - Sungard Business Systems Inc.

OMNIPOINT - Electronic equipment - Omnipoint Corp.

OMNIPRESSOR - Electronic equipment - Eventide Inc.

OMNIPRO - Computer hardware - Trippe Manufacturing Co. Inc.

OMNIPULSE - Telecommunication equipment - At&T Corp.

OMNIREADER - Computer software - Nestor, Inc.

OMNISAN - Pet products ☆ - Sera Aquaristik USA Inc.

OMNISCOPE - Medical apparatus - Simmons Outdoor Corp.

OMNISCRIBE - Electronic equipment ☆ - Houston Instrument

OMNISEARCH MULTIMEDIA CONTROL SOFTWARE - Computer software - Knowledge Access International, Inc.

OMNISENSE - Alarm systems - System Innovations, Inc.

OMNISHARE CONFERENCER - Office supplies - Hewlett-Packard Co.

OMNISHEARS - Scissors—hand-operated - Sammann Co. Inc.

OMNISLIDE - Electric lighting equipment - Lutron Electronics Co., Inc.

OMNISPACE - Furniture - Omni International Inc.

OMNISPACE CLASSIC - Furniture - Omni International Inc.

OMNISPACE FLEX - Furniture - Omni International Inc.

OMNISPACE MAX - Fabrics - Omni International Inc.

OMNISPORT 1000 - Electronic equipment - Daktronics Inc.

OMNISPORT 6000 - Electronic equipment - Daktronics Inc.

OMNISPORT HS-100 - Electronic equipment - Daktronics Inc.

OMNISSAGE - Skin care products ☆ - Comare Corp.

OMNISTAR - Hobby kits - Avionics Plastics Corp.

OMNISTAR - Navigational instruments - Omnistar, Inc.

OMNISTAT - Electrical equipment - Julie Associates, Inc.

OMNISTATION - Computers—micro - Northgate Computer Systems Inc.

OMNISTATION - Furniture - Omni International Inc.

OMNISTIM - Medical apparatus - Physio Technology Inc.

OMNISTREAM - Computers - Mercury Computer Systems Inc.

OMNISUPPLIER - Computer hardware - Omnicell Technologies, Inc.

OMNISURROUND - Audio equipment - Audio-Video Technologies Inc.

OMNISWITCH - Computer hardware - Xylan Corp.

OMNITABS - Health care products - Halsey Drug Co. Inc.

OMNITEAM - Computer software - Island Way Corp.

OMNITHERM - Fabrics—wool - King of the Mountain Sports Inc.

OMNITIME - Watches ☆ - Realtime Corp.

OMNITOOLS - Computer software - Nestor, Inc.

OMNITRACE - Chemical preparations - EM Industries, Inc.

OMNITRACS - Printed materials - Qualcomm Inc.

OMNITRAIN - Video production - Safety Short Production Inc.

OMNITRAK - Computer software - Timetrak Systems, Inc.

OMNITRONIC - Heaters—swimming pool ☆ - Teledyne Laars

OMNIUM - Vitamins and nutritional supplements - Solgar Vitamin and Herb Co., Inc.

OMNIVAC - Vacuum cleaners and accessories - Metropolitan Vacuum Cleaner Co. Inc.

OMNIVBA - Computer software - Sungard Business Systems Inc.

OMNIVIEW - Electronic equipment - Telerobotics International, Inc.

OMNIVISION - Electronic equipment - Panasonic Co.

OMNIVOICE - Computer software - Sungard Business Systems Inc.

OMNIVOICE 2000 - Computer software - Sungard Business Systems Inc.

OMNIWRITER - Computer software - Medical Equipment Distributors, Inc.

OMNIWRITER - Pens - Accutec Inc.

OMNIZOLE - Veterinary pharmaceutical preparations ☆ - Merck & Co., Inc. (Merck Agvet Division)

OMO GYM - Apparel—athletic - Norma Kamali, Inc.

OMO NORMA KAMALI - Apparel and accessories - Norma Kamali, Inc.

OMOHUNDRO - Boating equipment and accessories - Omohunro Co., Inc.

OMOTE / URA AIKIDO - T-shirts - Manuel Vargas

OMOTREX - Health care products - Altana, Inc. (Savage Laboratories, Div.)

OMOWOMAN - Apparel—women's - Norma Kamali, Inc.

OMR - Cleaning preparations - Kwick Kleen Industrial Solvents, Inc.

OMR - Paper—writing - Dur-O-Lite Inc.

OMS - Computer software - Opcode Systems, Inc.

OMS - Medical apparatus - Sunrise Medical (Respiratory Products Division)

OMS OPTICAL MARK SYSTEM - Computer software - Rovak, Inc.

OMSTAR D-1208X - Fuel additives - D-1280-X Inc.

OMSTEAD - Food products - John Labatt Foods

OMX - Paint sprayers - Ransburg Corp.

ON - Statuary - Meriwether Capital

ON A CLEAR DAY - Skin care products - Cosmedic Concepts, Inc.

ON A GREEN BUS - Computer software - Don Johnston Inc.

ON ANIMAL PROTECTION - Pet products - HTZ Investment Corp.

ON BALANCE - Computer software ☆ - Broderbund Software, Inc.

ON-BOARD - Health care products ☆ - Invacare Corp.

ON BOARD - Luggage - York Luggage Co.

ON-BOARD - Pumps—vacuum - Helix Technology Corp.

ON CALL - Apparel - Frederick Atkins, Inc.

ON CALL - Floor coverings—carpet and rugs ☆ - Lees Carpets

ON-CALL PHOTOGRAPHER - Computers - Boston Imaging, Inc.

ON CONTACT - Apparel and accessories - H.H. Cutler Co.

ON-COR - Food products - On-Cor Frozen Foods, Inc.

ON-COR LITE - Food products - On-Cor Frozen Foods, Inc.

ON COURSE - Apparel and accessories - Montgomery Ward & Co. Inc.

ON COURSE - Sporting goods - J.A. Cissel Manufacturing Co.

ON-CUE - Garage door openers ☆ - Frantz Manufacturing Co.

ON DASHER - Christmas tree ornaments - Cracker Box Inc.

ON DECK - Baseball batting apparatus - Diversified Products Corp.

ON DECK POWER SWING - Sporting goods - Markwort Sporting Goods Co.

ON DEMAND - Automotive parts and accessories - Subaru of America, Inc.

ON-DEMAND TECHNOLOGIES - Computer peripheral equipment - On-Demand Technologies, Inc.

ON DUTY - Health care products ☆ - Avon Products, Inc.

ON FOOT - Apparel and accessories - Lady Love

ON-GARD - Weather stripping ☆ - Macklanburg-Duncan Co.

ON-GLASS - Antennas - Allen Telecom Group, Inc.

ON-GUARD - Archery equipment - Saunders Archery Co.

ON GUARD - Chemical preparations - N. Jonas and Co. Inc.

ON GUARD - Lighting equipment - Dura Electric Lamp Co. Inc.

ON GUARD! - Scissors - Hoechst Celanese Corp.

ON-GUARD - Sporting goods - Gexco Enterprises

ON GUARD DOOR CANE - Metals - Irvin N. Ferverda

ON HAND - Computer software - Softbank Inc.

ON HER MAJESTY'S SECRET SERVICE - Games - Avalon Hill Game Co.

ON LEVEL - Publisher's imprints - Evangelical Lutheran Good Samaritan Society

ON-LINE - Skates—roller - National Sporting Goods Corp.

ON-LINE - Yarn - Knitting Fever Inc.

ON-LINE CATALOG EXPANDED - Computer software - Right on Programs

ON-LINE CATALOG PLUS + - Computer software ☆ - Right on Programs

ON-LINE EXPRESS 14.4 - Computer peripheral equipment - Boca Research, Inc.

ON-LINE MACCATALOG + - Computer software - Right on Programs

ON LINE...ALL THE TIME - Golf balls - WPI Acquisition Corp.

ON MY OWN - Footwear - Toddler University

ON MY WAY - Infant product - Lisco, Inc.

ON PAROLE - Apparel and accessories - On Parole Streetwear

ON POINT - Glassware—household - Owens-Illinois Inc. (Libbey Div.)

ON-POINT - Meat products—beef - Willamette Valley Co.

ON Q - Faucets - Sloan Valve Co.

ON-RITE - Brushes—hair - On-Rite Men's Hairpiece Co.

ON-SCHEDULE - Computer software - Odyssey Computing Inc.

ON-SERT - Fasteners—snap - American Engineer Components

ON-SETS - Games - Wff'n Proof Learning Games Associates

ON-SITE - Finishing agents - Rudd Co. Inc.

ON SPEC - Epoxy coatings - Torginol, Inc.

ON STAGE - Cosmetics - On Stage Cosmetics, Inc.

ON STAGE - Ophthalmic goods - Foremost Optical Products

ON STAGE STANDS - Musical instrument accessories - Music People Inc.

ON-TAP - Beverages—carbonated - Pepsi-Cola Co.

ON TAP - Vending machines - Saniserv Inc.

ON TARGET - Floor coverings—carpet and rugs - Philadelphia Carpets

ON TARGET - Games ☆ - Milton Bradley Co.

ON TARGET EYEDROP DELIVERY SYSTEM - Eyeglasses - Peter Michalos

ON TECHNOLOGY - Computer software - On Technology Corp.

ON THE BALL - Coatings - Merix Chemical Co.

ON-THE-BALL - Lubricants - Reese Products, Inc.

ON THE BALL - Pipes—plastic - Donald L. Spears

ON THE BEACH - Calendars - Swim Publishing Corp.

ON THE BEACH SURF SHOP - Apparel and accessories - Kelly Sorensen

ON THE BRINK - Apparel and accessories - Tex Venture Holding Ltd.

ON THE CUTTING EDGE - Greeting cards - Gallant Greetings Corp.

☆ = Now out of production

ON THE EDGE - Watchbands–leather - On the Edge, Inc.

ON THE GO - Juices - Coca-Cola Co.

ON THE GO - Luggage - Mattel, Inc.

ON THE GO - Luggage - Shalam Imports Inc.

ON-THE-GO - Salad dressings–bottled - Borden, Inc.

ON-THE-GO - Toothbrushes - Fountain Fresh

ON-THE-GO - Toys - Fisher-Price, Inc.

ON-THE-GO DESK - Toys - Manco, Inc.

ON-THE-JOB - Containers - Samsonite Corp.

ON THE LEVEL - Tools - On the Level Co., Inc.

ON-THE-LINE - Sporting goods - Brine Inc.

ON THE MARK - Fabrics–tapestry - Christopher Prints

ON THE MARK - Wallpaper ☆ - Old Deerfield Fabrics Inc.

ON THE MONEY - Golfing equipment - Pro's Edge Wholesale Inc.

ON THE MOVE - Cosmetics ☆ - Avon Products, Inc.

ON THE MOVE - Umbrellas - Totes, Inc.

ON THE PORCH - Dolls - Seymour Mann Inc.

ON THE PRAIRIE - Dolls - Effanbee Doll Corp.

ON THE QT BY QUILTEX - Apparel–children's ☆ - Quiltex

ON THE RAMP TO THE INTERNET - Publisher's imprints - Parsons
Technology, Inc.

ON THE RIGHT TRACK - Apparel and accessories - Future Enterprises Inc.

ON THE ROAD - Automotive parts and accessories - Big Beam Emergency
Systems Inc.

ON THE ROAD - Motor vehicle parts and accessories - Kmart Properties, Inc.

ON THE ROAD AGAIN - Automotive parts and accessories ☆ - Unival Corp.

ON THE ROAD OF LIFE THERE ARE PASSENGERS AND THERE ARE
DRIVERS - Advertising agencies - Volkswagen of America Inc.

ON THE ROCKS - Apparel and accessories - T.S. Designs Inc.

ON-THE-ROCKS - Cosmetic bags - Millennium Frozen Assets, Inc.

ON-THE-ROCKS - Ice chests - Reliable Plastics

ON THE ROCKS - Novelty items - Edda O. Gilbert

ON THE SIDE - Publisher's imprints - Aluminum Co. of America

ON-THE-SPORT - Pharmaceutical preparations - Neutrogena Corp.

ON THE SPOT - Adhesives and sealants - Super Glue Corp.

ON-THE-SPOT - Pharmaceutical - Neutrogena Corp.

ON-THE-SPOT - Pharmaceutical preparations ☆ - Noxell Corp.

ON THE SPOT - Recording label - Private, Inc.

ON THE SQUARE - Bedding–linen - Dan River Inc.

ON THE STREET - Apparel and accessories - Mlk Inc.

ON THE TRACK - Electronic equipment - Texas Instruments Inc.

ON THE WALL - Dolls - On the Wall Productions Inc.

ON THE WATCH - Medical identification tag - SLB Enterprises Inc.

ON THE WIND - Cologne, bath product ☆ - Bourjois Ltd.

ON TIME - Apparel–athletic - Made in the Shade by Prime Time

ON TIME - Recording label - DNA International Inc.

ON TIME - Watches - Hugo Maxx Inc.

ON TIME DELIVERY FOR LESS - Courier services–land - Express
Messenger Systems, Inc.

ON-TITE - Paints - Perry & Derrick Co.

ON-TITE - Paints ☆ - Foy-Johnston Inc.

ON TOP - Flowers, plants, and seeds - Golden State Bulb Growers

ON TOP - Whipped topping–frozen - Rich Products Corp.

ON TOUR - Luggage - Paris Presents Ltd.

ON TRACK - MRNA isolation diagnostic kit - Biotecx Laboratories, Inc.

ON TRACK SNACKS - Snack foods - John Hein

ON VIEW - Snack foods ☆ - Avon Products, Inc.

ON-WALL - Electrical equipment ☆ - Wiremold Co.

ON WHEELS - Skates–roller - On Wheels Roller Skates

ON WHEELS STAXX BY A-BEE - Plastic drawers and rolling carts - A-Bee
Syndicate Inc.

ON-WORDS - Games - Wff'n Proof Learning Games Associates

ON WORLD - Computer software - Jeff Kreegar

ON/X - Computer software - Shared Systems Corp.

ON-X - Medical apparatus - Medical Carbon Research Institute, LLC

ON YOUR MARK - Apparel and accessories - Dillard Department Stores Inc.

ON YOUR TOES - Bedding–linen - Dan River Inc.

ON YOUR WAY - Food products - Wesco, Inc.

ONACCOUNT - Computer software - White Crow Software, Inc.

ONADIME - Brake parts ☆ - Hawkhead Automotive Inc.

ONALERT - Audio equipment - Warning Systems, Inc.

ONAMIA - Rice - Gourmet House Inc.

ONANO - Apparel and accessories - Kathryn Kamifuji

ONARGA - Office supplies ☆ - Louis Melind Co.

ONAWA - Computer hardware - PRW Trading, Inc.

ONAYA - Fruits and vegetables - Troy Fresh Commodities Inc.

ONBASE - Computer software - Hyland Software, Inc.

ONBOARD YACHT MANAGEMENT SOFTWARE - Computer software - Force
Ten Software

ONC - Flatware - Old Newbury Crafters Inc.

ONCE-A-DAY - Surco Products Inc.

ONCE-A-DAY, ALL DAY SUNSCREEN, THE - Suntan lotions - Block Drug
Co., Inc.

ONCE-A-MONTH - Pet products - Hartz Mountain Corp.

ONCE-A-WEEK TARRY - Chemical preparations - Coastal Industries Inc.

ONCE AGAIN - Paint dryers - Syndet Products, Inc.

ONCE AGAIN - Paper - French Paper Co.

ONCE AGAIN - Toys - Howard McDonald

ONCE AGAIN NUT BUTTER - Nuts–salted, roasted, cooked, or canned -
Once Again Nut Butter Inc.

ONCE & FOR ALL - Adhesives and sealants ☆ - Roman Adhesives, Inc.

ONCE DAILY - Vitamins and nutritional supplements - Vita-Vista

ONCE OVER - Brassieres (Bras) - Maidenform Inc.

ONCE-OVER - Hair care products - Master Chemical Co.

ONCE OVERS - Cleaning preparations - Kimberly-Clark Corp.

ONCE UPON A CHRISTMAS - Figurines - American Greetings Corp.

ONCE UPON A DREAM - Toys - Fisher-Price, Inc.

ONCE UPON A PILLOW - Pillows - PSE Concepts, Inc.

ONCE UPON A PLANET - Greeting cards - Once Upon a Planet Inc.

ONCE UPON A POTTY - Publisher's imprints - Child Matters

ONCE UPON A RHYME - Toys–stuffed ☆ - Gund, Inc.

ONCE UPON A ROSE - Cosmetics - Enchante Slippers, Inc.

ONCE UPON A TALE - Puzzles - Natural Science Industries, Ltd.

ONCE UPON A TIME - Dolls ☆ - Effanbee Doll Corp.

ONCE UPON A TIME - Wallpaper - Pickhardt & Siebert USA Inc.

ONCE UPON A TIME - Watches - E. Gluck Corp.

ONCE UPON A TUNE - Recording label - Discovery Music

ONCE UPON A WALL - Wallcoverings - WallCapers Ltd.

ONCE UPON AN ARK - Giftware - Roman, Inc.

ONCO - Cleaning preparations ☆ - Onthank Co.

ONCOFILE - File folders - Saxonville Industrial Park

ONCOFIX - Diagnostic substances - Oncodiagnostic Laboratory, Inc.

ONCOJECT - Medical apparatus - Adria Laboratories

ONCOLOGY THERAPEUTICS NETWORK - Pharmaceutical preparations -
Access Biotechnology Inc.

ONCOLYSIN - Pharmaceutical preparations - Immunogen, Inc.

ONCOMEMBRANE, INC. - Pharmaceutical preparations - Oncomembrane, Inc.

ON!CONTACT - Computer software - On!Contact Software Corp.

ONCOR - Laboratory apparatus - Oncor, Inc.

ONCORE - Computer peripheral equipment - Chipcom Corp.

ONCORMED - Computer software - Oncormed, Inc.

ONCOVIN - Pharmaceutical preparations - Eli Lilly and Co.

ONCOVITE - Vitamins and nutritional supplements - Mission Pharmacal Co.

ONCRETE - Concrete products - Sandstrom Products Co.

ONCSTATION - Computer software - Clinical Information Advantages, Inc.

ONCYTE - Medical products - Grace Bio-Labs Inc.

ONDAFIX - Hair care products - IT&LY Hairfashion NA Inc.

ONDAFORM - Hair care products - IT&LY Hairfashion NA Inc.

ONDAWAVE - Hair care products - IT&LY Hairfashion NA Inc.

ONDE - Giftware - Sasaki

ONDINE - Apparel–women's - Wacoal America Inc.

ONDINE - Fabrics–spandex - Dan River Inc.

ONDINE - Floor coverings–carpet and rugs - Masland Corp.

ONDINE I - Personal-care shower - Interbath, Inc.

ONDINE II - Personal-care shower - Interbath, Inc.

ONDREX - Food products - Shaffer, Clark & Co. Inc.

ONDROX - Health care products - LifeScience Inc.

ONDULATION - Hair care products - Revlon Consumer Products Corp.

ONDULINE - See ONDURA

ONDURA - Roofing materials–slate - Ondura Inc.

ONDURALINE - Roofing materials - Nuline Industries, Inc.

O.N.E. - Dog food - Ralston Purina Co.

ONE - Rice - On-Net, Inc.

ONE - Sporting goods - Carmate, Inc.

ONE 2 ONE - Hair care products - Cosmair Inc.

ONE-4-ALL - Electronic equipment - Signal Transformer Co., Inc.

ONE 4 ALL - Lubricants - Corrosion Solutions, Inc.

ONE 212 - Apparel–women's - Hanover Direct Inc.

ONE-A-DAY - Vitamins and nutritional supplements - Bayer Corp. (Consumer
Care Div.)

ONE-ALL - Paints - Olympic Paint & Varnish Co.

ONE ALTERNATIVE - Recording label - Jazz Composer's Orchestra Association Inc.

ONE & ONE - Hair care products - Helene Curtis Industries Inc.

ONE AND ONLIES - Greeting cards - Advantage/Aurora Publications

ONE ARM BANDIT - Golfing equipment - Walter S. Bush

ONE-AT-A-TIME - Paper products - Interstate Label Co.

ONE BAD APPLE - Games ☆ - Pressman Toy Corp.

ONE BAD CAT! - Rodenticides - Hacco, Inc./Loveland Industries, Inc.

ONE BALL JAY - Clothing - Faction, Ltd.

ONE BETTER - Hair care products - Helene Curtis Industries Inc.

ONE BETTER - Interior paints - Insilco Corp.

ONE BUTTON MAIL - Computer software - Sigea Systems, Inc.

ONE-BY-ONE - Bags–trash - Olympic General Corp.

ONE-CALL - Computer software - Atwork Corp.

ONE CALL - Remote control devices - Universal Electronics Inc.

ONE COAT - Cosmetics - Almay Inc.

ONE COAT - Nail care products - Prince Matchabelli

ONE COAT - Rubber cement - Union Rubber, Inc.

ONE-COAT-IT - Automotive parts and accessories ☆ - Fibre Glass-Evercoat Co. Inc.

ONE COAT MAGIC - Paints ☆ - Sequa Corp.

ONE COAT PLUS - Paint rollers - Adams Brush Manufacturing Co., Inc.

ONE COATER - Brushes–paint - E-Z Paintr Corp.

ONE CREATION - Jewelry - Barbara Wolinski

ONE CUP - Coffee - Raisonne Inc.

ONE-DAILY - Vitamins and nutritional supplements - Bio San Laboratories Inc.

ONE-DAR-GLOS - Paints - C.M. Athey Paint Co.

ONE-DAR-WITE - Paints ☆ - C.M. Athey Paint Co.

ONE DAY AT A TIME - Calendars ☆ - American Greetings Corp.

ONE-DER - Skin care products - Waverly Beauty Products

ONE-DER-KOTE - Paints - Washington Paint Products

ONE-DERS - Ice milk - H.J. Heinz Co.

ONE DISK SOLUTION - Computer software - BlumbergExcelsior, Inc.

ONE DOG ONE BONE - Decals and transfers - Jeff Eaton

ONE DROP - Deodorizers - Cadie Products Corp.

ONE DROP - Deodorizers - Fast Industries, Inc.

ONE DROP - Deodorizers ☆ - Spellman & Zenon Products Corp.

ONE DROP - Nail care products - Orly International Inc.

ONE EARTH - Pet products - Eight-In-One Pet Products, Inc.

ONE EARTH CORPORATION - Cardboard - One Earth Corp.

ONE ELEVEN MAIN - Handbags - JLN Inc.

ONE-EYED JACK - Fishing lures ☆ - Fred Arbogast Co. Inc.

ONE EYED JACKS - Watches - Oscar F. Dykes

ONE EYED JOHN - Toys - Imperial Toy Corp.

ONE EYED PETE - Tobacco products - Don Pedro Garcia - Moreno, Inc.

ONE-FIFTY - Pens ☆ - Paper Mate Co.

ONE FISH, TWO FISH, RED FISH, BLUE FISH - Puzzles - Dr. Seuss Enterprises, L.P.

ONE FITS ALL - Pet collars - Leatherite-Nylorite Manufacturing Inc.

ONE FOOT IN - ONE FOOT OUT - Prepared entrees - W & C Inc.

ONE FOR ALL - Remote control devices - Universal Electronics Inc.

ONE FOR ALL - Universal remote control - One For All

ONE-FOR-ALL/FIVE-IN-ONE - Cosmetics - Colour Grow Cosmetics Intl.

ONE FOR ALL LITE - Remote control devices - Universal Electronics Inc.

ONE-FOR-ONE - Washcloths - Mark One Healthcare Products Inc.

ONE FOR THE ROAD - Vitamins and nutritional supplements ☆ - J.R. Carlson Laboratories Inc.

ONE FORMULA ULTRA SHINE - Hair care products ☆ - Gefden International Inc.

ONE FOUR YOU TWO - Apparel and accessories - Rainbow Garment Contracting Inc.

ONE-GRAM-C - Vitamins and nutritional supplements - J.R. Carlson Laboratories Inc.

ONE GROOVE CITY - Apparel and accessories - M. Benjamin Designs

ONE GUN - Glue–household or industrial - New Pendulum Corp.

ONE-HANDED QUICK CHANGE CAPO, THE - Musical instrument accessories - Kyser Musical Products, Inc.

ONE HECK OF A SHINE - Hair care products - Giovanni Cosmetics Inc.

ONE HOT TOMATO - Spices and extracts - R.G.E. Inc.

ONE HOUR - Finishing agents - Benjamin Moore & Co.

ONE HOUR - Shelving units–wood - Action Sales & Marketing, Inc.

ONE HOUR - Spices and extracts - Aldo's Spices

ONE HOUSE - Apparel and accessories - N.A. Fashion, Ltd.

ONE HUNDRED DEGREES - Bathing suits - A and H Sportswear Co., Inc.

ONE HUNDRED MILLION B.C. - Apparel and accessories - Village Originals, Inc.

ONE INDUSTRIES - Seat covers - Ludovic Boinnard

ONE LIFE - Filters–air - A C Engineering, Inc.

ONE LIFE - Vitamins and nutritional supplements - One Life, Inc.

ONE-LINERS - Greeting cards - Joli Greeting Card Co.

ONE LINERS - Lipsticks - Sassaby, Inc.

ONE-LINERS - Novelty items - GRK Manufacturing

ONE-LITE - Lighting fixtures - Acme-Lite Manufacturing Co.

ONE LOVE - Colognes ☆ - Avon Products, Inc.

ONE LOVE - Footwear - Fred E. Goldstein

ONE MAIN PLACE - Apparel–athletic ☆ - Lorch Co.

ONE MARK - Fruits and vegetables - D'Arrigo Brothers Co.

ONE MATCH - Fireplace logs–treated - Rutland Products

ONE MINUTE - Washing machines–household ☆ - Midwest Manufacturing Co.

ONE-MINUTE BIBLE, THE - Publisher's imprints - Garborg's Heart 'n Home, Inc.

ONE MINUTE DIET - Apparel–women's - Maidenform Inc. (True Form Foundations Div.)

ONE MIX - Lubricants - Mark Macline Inc.

ONE 'N ONLY - Hair care products - Jheri Redding Products Inc.

ONE NATION - Puzzles ☆ - Parker Brothers

ONE NIGHT - Enamels - Bridges Smith & Co.

ONE-O-ONE - Novelty items ☆ - Key Novelty Manufacturing Co.

ONE OBJECT ORIENTED ENVIRONMENT - Computer software - Visible Systems Corp.

ONE O'CLOCK - Paints - Graham Paint and Varnish Co.

ONE OF A KIND - Candles - Candle Corp. of America

ONE-OF-A-KIND - Stoneware dinnerware ☆ - Iron Mountain Stoneware Inc.

ONE OF A KIND FLAVOR - Publisher's imprints - HVR Co.

ONE-OF-A-KIND-WONDERS - Jewelry–precious - Romancing The Stone

ONE OF EACH - Candy - That's My Favorite Inc.

ONE ON ONE - Apparel–athletic - Finish Line, Inc.

ONE-ON-ONE - Games - Tsr, Inc.

ONE ON ONE - Greeting cards - Russ Berrie and Co., Inc.

ONE ON ONE - Shoes–athletic - Trans-World Shoe Import Corp.

ONE ON ONE - Skin care products - Robert Gura

ONE-ON-ONE - Toys - Tonka Corp.

ONE OS - Computer software - At&T Corp.

ONE PACPUFF - Inks - Flexible Products Co.

ONE PAGE SOFTWARE, THE - Computer software - INFOTRAC, Inc.

ONE-PASS - Machine parts - Wespatt, Inc.

ONE PERFECT - Cosmetics - Revlon Consumer Products Corp.

ONE PERFECT SHADOW - Cosmetics ☆ - Bonne Bell, Inc.

ONE PERSON, ONE NUMBER - Computer software - Accessline Technologies, Inc.

ONE PHONE - Radio communications equipment - Interdigital Communications Corp.

ONE PIE - Fruit pie mixes - One Pie Canning Co.

ONE PIECE - Clamps–metal - Sign-Up Corp.

ONE PLANET - Apparel - One Planet Inc.

ONE PLANET - ONE PEOPLE - Posters - Benihana Inc.

ONE PLUS - Cleaning preparations - Hillyard Enterprises, Inc.

ONE POT COFFEE - Coffee - Tree of Life, Inc.

ONE POWDER - Cosmetics - Merle Norman Cosmetics

ONE PREP - Adhesives and sealants - Kyanize Paint Co.

ONE RING CIRCUS - Toys - Fisher-Price, Inc.

ONE SHINING MOMENT - Apparel and accessories - David Barrett

ONE SHOT - Containers - Universal Electronics Inc.

ONE SHOT - Lighter fluid ☆ - Tubed Products Inc.

ONE SHOT - Lubricants - McCulloch Corp.

ONE SHOT - Pesticides–household - Bonide Products, Inc.

ONE-SHOT - Rodenticides - Security Product Co.

ONE SHOT PLUMBERS HELPER - Drain pipe cleaners - AmeriPlus Inc.

ONE SIXTY SEVEN BARS - Candy - Klein Chocolate Co.

ONE SIZE FITS MOST - Towels - Susan Dunn Inc.

ONE SLOT - Computer peripheral equipment - Star-Gate Technologies, Inc.

ONE SOLUTION - Ophthalmic goods - Barnes-Hind Inc.

ONE SPORT - Shoes–athletic - Climb High Inc.

ONE SQUEEZE - Medical apparatus - James Alexander Inc.

ONE STAR - Food products - US Foodservice

ONE STAR - Footwear–athletic - Converse Inc.

ONE STAR SUPREME SAND - Garden equipment - Patio Industries

ONE-STEP - Adhesives and sealants - Super-Tek Products Inc.

ONE STEP - Cameras - Polaroid Corp.

ONE STEP - Cleaning preparations - Bissell Inc.

ONE STEP - Cleaning preparations - Knight Marketing Corp.

ONE STEP - Cleaning preparations–household - Penn Champ Inc.

☆ = Now out of production

ONE-STEP - Dental compounds - Bisco, Inc.

ONE STEP - Food products - CPC International Inc.

ONE-STEP - Infant product - Evenflo Co.

ONE STEP - Nail care products - Orly International Inc.

ONE-STEP - Paints - Happy Painter Products

ONE-STEP - Pet products - Purepet Co.

ONE-STEP - Traps–animal - Trius Products Co.

ONE STEP - Water purification systems - Aquacide

ONE STEP - Wood-floor wax - Intex Chemical Inc.

ONE STEP ABOVE - Wallpaper - Sunnyside Prints

ONE STEP ADVANTAGE, THE - Garden equipment - Garden Way Inc.

ONE STEP AT A TIME - Smoke detectors - Teledyne Water Pik

ONE STEP ENTREES - Food products - Wehah Farm, Inc.

ONE STEP FORMMANAGER - Computer software ☆ - Communication Intelligence Corp.

ONE STEP HDL CHOLESTEROL TEST STRIP - Pharmaceutical preparations - Technical Chemicals and Products, Inc.

ONE STEP LH TEST STRIP - Pharmaceutical preparations - Technical Chemicals and Products, Inc.

ONE STEP, THE - Cleaning preparations - Cleaning Systems, Inc.

ONE STEP WASH 'N WAX - Automotive parts and accessories - Turtle Wax, Inc.

ONE STOP - Aquariums–household ☆ - Jungle Laboratories Corp.

ONE STOP - Sprinklers–lawn - Misti Maid Inc.

ONE STOP FENCING - Fencing–gates and posts - North Central Plastics Inc.

ONE STOP FERN SHOP, THE - Flowers, plants, and seeds - Casa Flora, Inc.

ONE STRIP - Paint removers ☆ - Fibre Glass-Evercoat Co. Inc.

ONE STROKE - Brushes–paint - Winsor & Newton

ONE STROKE - Manicure preparations - Max Factor & Co.

ONE STROKE - Paints - D.I.Y. Products

ONE TABLET DAILY - Pharmaceutical preparations - Goldline Laboratories, Inc.

ONE TEN - Recording label - Jazz Composer's Orchestra Association Inc.

ONE THAT WORKS, THE - Skin care products - Cox Industries

ONE, THE - Rubber–molded - Boston Metal Products Corp.

ONE, THE - Glassware–household - Gemco Ware, Inc.

ONE, THE - Vitamins and nutritional supplements - Nature's Concept Inc.

ONE THING TODAY - Educational materials - James R. Casazza, Jr.

ONE-TIME - Paper–carbon - Frye Copysystems Inc.

ONE TO NINE - Apparel and accessories ☆ - Edison Brothers Stores, Inc.

ONE-TO-ONE - Computer software - Ja-Dal Technologies, Ltd.

ONE TO ONE - Greeting cards - Freedom Greeting Card Co. Inc.

ONE TOUCH - Automotive parts and accessories - Skylite Sunroofs and Motoring Accessories Inc.

ONE TOUCH - Blinds–venetian ☆ - Spring Window Fashions Division, Inc.

ONE TOUCH - Cameras - Nikon Inc.

ONE TOUCH - Cleaning preparations–upholstery - No Touch North America Corp.

ONE TOUCH - Depilatory, skin-care products - Inverness Corp.

ONE TOUCH - Furniture - RMF/DLO Group, Inc.

ONE-TOUCH - Gaskets ☆ - General Electric Co.

ONE TOUCH - Hardware - DIG Corp.

ONE TOUCH - Medical apparatus - LifeScan Inc.

ONE TOUCH - Pepper mills - Chef Specialties Co.

ONE TOUCH - Thermostats - Hunter Fan Co.

ONE-TOUCH 200 - Cameras - Nikon Inc.

ONE TOUCH BASIC - Medical apparatus - LifeScan Inc.

ONE-TOUCH DOOR - Doors–metal - Tsubaki Conveyor of America, Inc.

ONE TOUCH FINEPOINT - Medical apparatus - LifeScan Inc.

ONE-TOUCH PLUS - See WEBER MASTER-TOUCH

ONE TOUCH PROFILE - Medical apparatus - LifeScan Inc.

ONE TOUCH SELECT 'N SAVE - Thermostats - Hunter Fan Co.

ONE TRIBE - Computer software - Virgin Sound and Vision, Inc.

ONE TWO THREE - Cosmetics ☆ - Shiseido Cosmetics (America) Ltd.

ONE UNLIMITED - Perfumes - Perlier La Parfumerie

ONE-UP - See FOLD 'N GO DIRECTOR'S CHAIR

ONE UP - Display cases–metal - Rose Displays, Ltd.

ONE UP - Gloves - Grandoe Corp.

ONE UP - Snack foods - One-Up Corp.

ONE-UPS - Power transformers - Exide Electronics Corp.

ONE WAY OUT - Apparel and accessories - Church Art Works

ONE WAY STREET - Clothing - Silk Screen Inc.

ONE WEEK FROM SEED TO SALAD - Garden equipment - Sprout House

ONE WEIGH - Computer software - International Agricultural & Food Industries, Ltd.

ONE-WIPE - Cleaning preparations - Joseph Parmet Co. Inc.

ONE-WIPE - Cleaning preparations–household - Guardsman Products, Inc.

ONE WITH THE WORM, THE - Beverages–alcohol - Barton Brands, Ltd.

ONE WOMAN IN A MILLION - Women's apparel - Countess Mara Inc.

ONE WOMAN, ONE VOTE - Video production - Educational Film Center

ONE WOMAN'S STORY - Bags - Desires Chardas

ONE WORLD - Dinnerware–glass - Sango Co. Ltd. (Sango USA Div.)

ONE WORLD - Dolls ☆ - Effanbee Doll Corp.

ONE WORLD - Posters - One World, Inc.

ONE WORLD - Toys - Marlon Creations

ONE WORLD ATLAS - Computer software - Virgin Sound and Vision, Inc.

ONE WORLD ONE HEART - T-shirts–men's - Ben & Jerry's Homemade Holdings, Inc.

ONE XCEL - Medical apparatus - One Xcel, Inc.

ONE ZIP SLIDER - Bags–plastic - Mobil Oil Corp.

ONEAC - Electrical equipment - Oneac Corp.

ONECLEAN - Cleaning preparations–carpet and rug - Chemspec, Inc.

ONECOFLAT - Paints - Paragon Paint & Varnish Corp.

ONECOMM - Radio communications equipment - Onecomm Corp.

ONECONAMEL - Paints - Paragon Paint & Varnish Corp.

ONEDERFUL - Breads - Garden of Eatin', Inc.

ONEDRIVER - Computer software - Noblenet, Inc.

ONEIDA - Fishing lures ☆ - Bay De Noc Lure Co.

ONEIDA - Flatware - Oneida Ltd.

ONEIDA - Floor coverings - American Floor Products Co. Inc.

ONEIDA - Footwear–men's - W.C. Russell Moccasin Co.

ONEIDA - Photographic equipment - Eastman Kodak Co.

ONEIDA - Traps–animal ☆ - Woodstream Corp.

ONEIDA ARTISTRY - Flatware - Oneida Ltd.

ONEIDA BEAUTYCARE - Jewelry - Connoisseurs Products Corp.

ONEIDA COMMUNITY - Flatware - Oneida Ltd.

ONEIDA DELUXE - Flatware - Oneida Ltd.

ONEIDA PROFILE - Flatware - Oneida Ltd.

ONEIDA ROGERS - Cleaning preparations - Malco Products, Inc.

ONEIDA SILVERSMITHS - Flatware - Oneida Ltd.

O'NEILL - Apparel and accessories - Bayly Corp.

O'NEILL - Coffee - O'Neill Coffee Co.

ONEITA POWER-SWEATS - Apparel and accessories - Oneita Industries Inc.

ONEITA POWER T - T-shirts–children's - Oneita Industries Inc.

ONEITA'S KIDS - Apparel–children's - Oneita Industries Inc.

ONELID - Housewares - Amoco Fabrics and Fibers Co.

ONENET - Computer software - Jostens Learning Corp.

ONENET - Computers - Onenet International Communications, Inc.

ONESEAL - Automotive parts and accessories - IQ Products Co.

ONESIES - Apparel–children's - Gerber Products Co.

ONESOURCE - Vitamins and nutritional supplements - L. Perrigo Co.

ONESTEP - Office supplies - Cardinal Products

ONESTEP FLASH - Cameras - Polaroid Corp.

ONETIME - Caulking compounds - Red Devil Inc.

ONETIME LITE - Stucco - Red Devil Inc.

ONETRAK - Publisher's imprints - Dearborn Financial Publishing, Inc.

ONE.TWO.TREE. - Trees - Wildtree Products, Inc.

ONEUP - Alarm systems - Overhead Door Corp.

ONEVISION - Computer peripheral equipment - Computer Task Group, Inc.

ONEWORLD - Computer peripheral equipment - Global Village Communication, Inc.

ONEX - Tools - O.P. Link Handle Co. Inc.

ONEX - Veterinary pharmaceutical preparations - Happy Jack, Inc.

ONEX-SEAL II - Waxes–sealing - Hillyard Enterprises, Inc.

ONEZIP - Bags–plastic - Mobil Oil Corp.

ONFIRE! - Computer software - Wizard's Toybox Inc.

ONGARD - Skin care products - Gainshare Inc.

ONGARD-SYSTEMS - Containers - On-Gard Systems, Inc.

ONGARD SYSTEMS - Medical apparatus - On-Gard Systems, Inc.

ONGUARD - Plastics–laminated - Laminated Glass Corp.

ONI BEAN - Dolls - Golden Ribbon Playthings, Inc.

ONICA - Cosmetics ☆ - Redken Laboratories, Inc.

ONIIJIT - Lighting fixtures - Acme-Lite Manufacturing Co.

ONION CREEK - Furniture ☆ - Bassett Furniture Industries, Inc.

ONION MAGIC - Seasonings - Modern Products, Inc.

ONION PEEL - Computer software - Onion Peel Software

ONION RINGERS - Food products - Ore-Ida Foods, Inc.

ONION RINGS - Snack foods ☆ - Holland American Wafer Co.

ONION SOUP-ER BOWL - Fruits and vegetables - Stockyard Steakhouse, Inc.

ONION TAMS - Crackers - B. Manischewitz Co.

ONION, THE - Paper–newsprint - Onion, Inc.

ONIONEZE - Food products ☆ - Rubenstein Foods Inc.

☆ = Now out of production

ONIONSKINS - Apparel and accessories - Brawn of California, Inc.

ONIX - Ceramic floor tile - Interceramic Inc.

ONIXOL - Pharmaceutical preparations ☆ - Schering-Plough Healthcare Products

ONKYO - Stereos - Onkyo USA Corp.

ONLEE - Hair care products ☆ - Nutrine Ltd.

ONLI-ONE - Hosiery - Perfect Plus, Inc.

ONLINE - Apparel stores–men's - Castlewood Apparel Corp.

ONLINE - Office supplies - Scripto-Tokai Corp.

ONLINE GOLF PRODUCTS - Golfing equipment - On Line Golf Products, Inc.

ONLINE HEALTH LIBRARY - Computer software - Geoaccess, Inc.

ONLINE JOURNAL OF CURRENT CLINICAL TRIALS - Computer software - American Association for the Advancement of Science

ONLINE SOFTWARE LABS - Computer software - On-Line Software Labs, Inc.

ONLINE SOI - Computer software - M & M Systems, Inc.

ONLINEABG - Medical apparatus - Marquette Electronics, Inc.

ONLINELAB - Computer storage devices - Antrim Corp.

ONLISAFE - Computer peripheral equipment - Exide Electronics Corp.

ONLIWON - Brushes–paint - Wooster Brush Co.

ONLIWON - Napkins–fabric - Georgia-Pacific Corp.

ONLIWON - Paper napkins - Statler Industries, Inc.

ONLY 8 - Food products - Dessert Marketing Corp.

ONLY A PINCH - Soups–mixes - Fantastic Foods Inc.

ONLY A ROSE - Stationery - Mead Corp.

ONLY A SECOND - Nail care products - E.O.H. Industries, Inc.

ONLY BY JULIO - Colognes - Frances Denney

ONLY FOR BABIES - Paper–gift wrap - Gift Wrap Co.

ONLY FOR KIDS - Paper–gift wrap - Gift Wrap Co.

ONLY IN YOUR DREAMS - Apparel–athletic - Wormser Co.

ONLY IN YOUR WILDEST DREAMS - Teas - Village Herbalist

ONLY KRAFT PAPER FOR COLOR, THE - Office supplies - Georgia-Pacific Corp.

ONLY NAME TO CARRY, THE - Luggage - Recyco

ONLY ONE - Oils–lubricating - Blount, Inc.

ONLY OREO MOMENTS - Cookies - Nabisco Brands Co.

ONLY PLACE TO CALL, THE - Adhesives and sealants - Dymax Corp.

ONLY THE BEST - Coffee - Ahh-Some Gourmet Coffee, Inc.

ONLY THE BEST IS BRANDED BAR-S - Meat products - Bar-S Foods Co.

ONLY THE BEST ...ONLY IN HEALTH FOOD STORES - Health care products - Nature's Bounty, Inc.

ONLY WATER - Water purification systems ☆ - Coleman Powermate, Inc.

ONLY YOU - Footwear–children's - Granton Shoe Imports

ONNIES - Statuary - Austin Productions, Inc.

ONO - Crackers ☆ - American Roland Food Corp.

ONO - Fish–fresh or frozen - Yamasa Enterprises

O'NO 99 - Card game - International Games

ONO SHIRT, THE - Shirts - Liberty House, Inc.

ONOX - Pharmaceutical preparations - Onox Inc.

ONPA - Audio equipment - ONPA International Co.

ONPOINT - Computer software - Research Institute of America Inc.

ONPOINT SYSTEM - Computer software - Research Institute of America Inc.

ONQ MUSIC - Recording label - QVC, Inc.

ONSCREEN SCIENCE, INC. - Computer software - Onscreen Science, Inc.

ONSEMBLE - Computer software - Chipcom Corp.

ONSET - Lighting fixtures - Genlyte Group Inc.

ONSET-5 - Pharmaceutical preparations ☆ - Bock Pharmacal Co.

ONSLOW'S - Candy - Stephan's Candy Co.

ONTARIO - Brushes–paint - Corona Brushes Inc.

ONTARIO - Cabinets ☆ - Decora

ONTARIO - Recording label - Terock Records

ONTARIO COUNTY - Knives–hunting - Queen Cutlery Co.

ONTARIO ORCHARDS - Fruits and vegetables - Ontario Orchards Inc.

ONTHANK - Window coverings - Onthank Co.

ONTIME ENTERPRISE - Computer software - Campbell Services, Inc.

ONTOS - Computer software - Ontos, Inc.

ONTOS DB - Computer software - Ontos, Inc,

ONTOS OBJECT SQL - Computer software - Ontos, Inc,

ONTOS OIS - Computer software - Ontos, Inc,

ONTRA - Food products - Seymour Canning Co.

ONTRACK - Braces–orthopedic - Ortho Rx, Inc.

ONVIEW - Electrical equipment - ViewSonic Corp.

ONWARD - Colognes ☆ - Avon Products, Inc.

ONWARD - Floor coverings–carpet and rugs ☆ - Cabin Crafts Carpets

ONWATCH - Electrical equipment - John E. Bunting

ONWORD PRESS - Computer software - Design & Systems Research Publishing Co. Inc.

ONY-CLEAR SPRAY - Health care products ☆ - Pedinol Pharmacal Inc.

O.N.Y.S. - Beverages–alcohol - Anthony Distributors Inc.

ONYUMS - Snack foods ☆ - General Mills, Inc.

ONYX - Apparel and accessories - Gobic Inc.

ONYX - Audio speakers - Kintek, Inc.

ONYX - Cigars - Lane Ltd.

ONYX - Colognes - Old 97 Co.

ONYX - Computer software - Silicon Graphics, Inc.

ONYX - Cooking utensils–aluminum ☆ - Revere Ware Corp.

ONYX - Dyes and pigments - C.A. Zoes Manufacturing Co. Inc.

ONYX - Electrical equipment - Angstrom Sciences

ONYX - Eyeglasses - Bausch & Lomb Inc.

ONYX - Flatware - Denby USA Limited

ONYX - Floor coverings–carpet and rugs - Trans-Ocean Import Co. Inc.

ONYX - Frames–picture - North American Enclosures Inc.

ONYX - Fruit drinks–bottled or canned - Amazing Beverages, Inc.

ONYX - Furniture - American Furniture Co. Inc.

ONYX - Golfing equipment ☆ - Square Two Golf

ONYX - Mat boards - Onyx Mat Board

ONYX - Medical apparatus - Nonin Medical, Inc.

ONYX - Office supplies - Faber-Castell Corp.

ONYX - Paper–photographic ☆ - Keuffel & Esser Co.

ONYX - Plastics - American Premier, Inc.

ONYX - Skin care products - Becky Lynn Co.

ONYX - Tables–metal - Alvin and Co. Inc.

ONYX 1000 - Mattresses - DLM Plastics Corp.

ONYX 1000LS - Mattresses - DLM Plastics Corp.

ONYX CAT - Toys–stuffed - Russ Berrie and Co., Inc.

ONYX COLLECTION, THE - Computer peripheral equipment - Daubert Industries - ECP

ONYX COLLECTION, THE - Jackets - Felco Athletic Wear Co.

ONYX DCC - Telephones - TIE Communications Inc.

ONYX GOLD - Dinnerware–glass ☆ - Nikko Ceramics Inc.

ONYX ITALIA - Floor coverings ☆ - Azrock Commercial Flooring

ONYX KISS - Jewelry - Avon Products, Inc.

ONYX MOP - Artists' materials - Stangren Co.

ONYX ORIGINALS - Crocheted and knitted items - Heritage Sportswear

ONYX-R - Dental equipment - Moyco Industries, Inc.

ONYX TONGUE - Artists' materials - Stangren Co.

ONZA - Archery equipment ☆ - Martin Archery Inc.

O+O - Computer software - O+O Inc.

OO LA LA! - Apparel–children's - Sasson Jeans Inc.

OO-LA-LA! - Apparel–women's - Wacoal America Inc.

OO LA LA - Colognes - Key West Aloe Inc.

OO LA LA - Colognes - Key West Fragrance & Cosmetics Inc.

OO-LA-LA - Flowers, plants, and seeds - Monrovia Nursery Co.

OO LA LA! - Watches - Sasson Licensing Corp.

OO-LA-LACE - Laces–boot and shoe ☆ - Design Circle Ltd.

OO-ZOO - Bulletin boards–cork - Jason Art Productions

OO4GL - Computer software - Interactive Software Engineering Inc.

OOBE - Apparel and accessories - Oobe, Inc.

OOBE - Apparel and accessories - Xomed Surgical Products, Inc.

OOCHA BREW - Teas - Teapilz, Inc.

OODINOPUR - Pet products ☆ - Sera Aquaristik USA Inc.

OODLES - Hobby kits - Bostik Inc.

OODLES - Hobby kits ☆ - Hazel Pearson Handicrafts

OODLES OF DOODLES - Markers–felt-tip - Dri Mark Products, Inc.

OODLES OF NOODLES ORIENTAL - Soups–canned - Nissin Foods USA Co. Inc.

OODLES OF OATS - Bird feeds - Petland, Inc.

OODWAE - Brushes–hair - Goody Products, Inc.

OOE - Fabrics and accessories - American Crewel & Canvas Studio

OOF - Apparel–athletic - Robert S. Nenniger

OOGLY - Modeling kits - Myrin Enterprises

OOGLY EYES - Candy - Confex Inc.

OOH CHILD JEANS RUGGED WEAR - Apparel and accessories - Roosevelt M. Norris, Jr.

OOH-LA-BRA - Apparel–women's - Jezebel-Renee of Hollywood

OOH LA LIFT - Cosmetics - Benefit Cosmetics

OOKAMI GOLD - Scissors–hand-operated - Wolff Industries Inc.

OOKEYMAN - Computer software - Secure Transactions Solutions, LLC

OOLA - Looms - Northfield Loom

OOLONG - Thread - Threads USA Div.

OOMPAS - Candy ☆ - Willy Wonka Brands

OOMPH - Chocolate bars - Betco Corp.

OOMPH - Hair care products - Roux Laboratories, Inc.

☆ = Now out of production

OOMPH! - Slippers - Oomphies Inc.
OOMPHIES - Slippers - Oomphies Inc.
OON - Toys - Mattel, Inc.
OONA - Apparel–women's - China Trade & Research, Inc.
OOOH! WHAT A COLOR - Lipsticks - MGM Cosmetics
OOOZY POP - Candy - Cap Toys, Inc.
OOPS! - Health care products - Hot Springs Thermalsoft, Inc.
OOPS! - Pet product - ISE Inc.
OOPS! - Pet products - Farnam Cos. Inc.
OOPS - Posters - Wry Idea Co.
OOPS! - Recording label - Pandisc Records
OOPS - Stain removers - D.I.Y. Products
OOPS & DOWNS - Games - Mattel, Inc.
OOPS HOLEY - Socks - Maddak Inc.
OOPS! PAINTER'S SWIPES - Paint and wallpaper cleaners - D.I.Y. Products
OOPS! PROOF - Bowls - Little Kids, Inc.
OOPS! SCOOP - Pet product - ISE Inc.
OOPSIE DAISY - Dolls - Tyco Toys
OOPSY DAISY - Deodorizers - Oopsy Daisy
OORGANIK - Health care products - Biotics Research Corp.
OOSINK - Seafood products–fresh or frozen - Osmar's Ocean Specialties
OOTP - Computer peripheral equipment - Client Server Computing, Inc.
OOWIN - Computer software - Logic Works, Inc.
OOXI-BILBERRY - Vitamins and nutritional supplements - Marlyn Nutraceuticals, Inc.
OOZE - Putties - Ritam International Ltd.
OOZE - Skin care products - Paul Mazzotta Inc.
OOZE POP - Candy ✰ - Amurol Confections Co.
OOZ'N ORANGE - Beverages - Premiere Innovations, Inc.
OP - Apparel and accessories - Ocean Pacific Sunwear Ltd.
OP - Forklifts - Clark Material Handling Co.
OP - Watches - Ocean Pacific Apparel Corp.
OP ART - Kaleidoscopes - Gemini Kaleidoscopes
O.P. GIRLS - Apparel–women's - Lee Thomas Inc.
O.P. JUNIORS - Apparel–women's - Lee Thomas Inc.
O.P. KIDSWEAR - Apparel–children's - Just Like Dad's Inc.
OP LUCENT - Toys - Skitters
OP OFFICE PLUS - Office supplies - Independent Stationers, Inc.
OP-SEC - Labels–paper - Optical Security Industries, Inc.
OP/TECH - Photographic equipment - Butler Creek Corp.
OP/TECH USA - Photographic equipment - Butler Creek Corp.
OP-THAL-ZIN - Ophthalmic goods ✰ - Alcon Laboratories, Inc.
OP-TICS - Cosmetics - I-Tech Laboratories Inc.
OP-TIQUE - Apparel–women's - Wacoal America Inc.
OP-WRAP - Paper–gift wrap ✰ - Stephen Lawrence Co.
(OP)2 - Computer hardware - Bricmanage, Inc.
OPACEDRIN - Pharmaceutical preparations ✰ - ICN Pharmaceuticals Inc.
OPACICOAT - Calcium compounds - ECC International
OPACITRAC - Medical apparatus - Oculon Corp.
OPACITRIQUE - Apparel and accessories - ShadowLine Inc.
OPAK - Food products ✰ - Robert W. Hayman Inc.
OPAL - Apparel–women's - Hot Property, Inc.
OPAL - Brushes–paint ✰ - Linzer Products Corp.
OPAL - Cabinets - Schrock
OPAL - Dolls ✰ - Effanbee Doll Corp.
OPAL - Fireplaces ✰ - Malm Fireplaces Inc.
OPAL - Flatware - Denby USA Limited
OPAL - Floor coverings–carpet and rugs - Trans-Ocean Import Co. Inc.
OPAL - Lasers - Spectra-Physics Lasers, Inc.
OPAL - Office supplies - Alvin and Co. Inc.
OPAL - Ophthalmic goods ✰ - Fidelity Case Corp.
OPAL - Plumbing fixtures - National Fiber Glass Products
OPAL - Wallcovering - Wall Trends, Inc.
OPAL - Wallpaper - Maya Romanoff Corp.
OPAL ARK, THE - Jewelry ✰ - Opal Supply Inc.
OPAL BUNNY - Figurines - Dakin Inc.
OPAL NERA - Beverages–alcohol - Hiram Walker & Sons, Inc.
OPAL SPRINGS - Water–bottled or canned - Shown & Sons Vineyards
OPAL SQUARE - Floor coverings - Congoleum Corp.
OPAL SYSTEMS PERFORMANCE COMPUTERS - Computer peripheral equipment - Opal Technologies, Inc.
OPALART - Glass products - Spectrum Glass Co.
OPALAX - Glass products ✰ - Corning Inc.
O'PALE - Skin care products - Smyre & Chambers, Inc.
OPALE GLACE - Lipsticks - Cosmair Inc.
OPALENE - Games - Pacific Game Co.

OPALESCE - Yarn ✰ - JCA, Inc.
OPALESCENCE - Apparel–women's - Lorraine Wardy Enterprises
OPALESCENCE - Toothpaste - Ultradent Products, Inc.
OPALESQUE - Ribbons - Berwick Industries, Inc.
OPALFINA - Dental products - Excelco International, Inc.
OPALIA - Whirlpools - Jacuzzi Inc.
OPALINE - Artists' materials - MacPherson Sales Co.
OPALINE - Christmas tree ornaments - Cracker Box Inc.
OPALITE - Gas machinery - Humphrey Products Co.
OPALS - Candy - Mars, Inc.
OPALURE - Film - Eastman Kodak Co.
OPALUX - Paper ✰ - Canson-Talens Inc.
OPALYS - Skin care products - Lever Brothers Co. Inc.
OPAQUE - Inks - Crown Art Products
OPAQUE-FORM - Paper ✰ - Northwest Paper Co.
OPAQUER - Markers–felt-tip - Illustrator Pen Products Inc.
OPASAL - Pharmaceutical preparations ✰ - ICN Pharmaceuticals Inc.
OPAX - Rolling pins–wood - SCI Scandicrafts Inc.
OPB - Machinery - Western Litho Plate & Supply Co.
OPC - Laboratory apparatus - Applied Biosystems Inc.
OPDB - Computer software - Office Products Update Service, Inc.
OPECTO - Pharmaceutical preparations ✰ - JMI-Canton Pharmaceuticals
OPEL - Motor vehicles ✰ - General Motors Corp. (Buick Motor Div.)
OPEL - Surveillance equipment - Combi International Corp.
OPEL - Surveillance equipment - Philips Communication & Security Systems Inc.
OPELINE - Porcelain tile ✰ - Integrity Tile Co.
OPELLA - Plumbing fixtures - Opella, Inc.
OPELLE - Glass ornaments - Corning Inc.
OPEN - Horse feed - McCauley Brothers Inc.
OPEN - Recording label - Loadstone, Lock & Open Record Co.
OPEN/A - Computer software - Asgard Software Inc.
OPEN ACTIVE WEAR - Apparel and accessories - Edwin Gomez
OPEN ADMINISTRATOR - Computer software - Peregrine Systems, Inc.
OPEN ADVANTAGE - Computer software - Digital Equipment Corp.
OPEN AIR - Housewares ✰ - Shell Oil Co.
OPEN-AIR - Sandals - ALP Sport Sandals
OPEN-ALL - Can openers–electric - Sunbeam-Oster Household Products
OPEN CHANNEL SOUND - Recording label - SRI Records & Tapes
OPEN CHINESE - Computer software - Jao Laboratories, Inc.
OPEN CLINICAL FOUNDATION/POWER CHART - Computer software - Cerner Corp.
OPEN COMMUNICATIONS - Video production - Open Communications, Inc.
OPEN COUNTRY - Cooking utensils–aluminum - Metal Ware Corp.
OPEN COURT - Weightlifting equipment - Lifetime Products, Inc.
OPEN DOOR - Wallpaper - Pantasote Inc. (Wallcovering Div.)
OPEN DOOR II - Wallpaper - Pantasote Inc. (Wallcovering Div.)
OPEN FIELDS - Giftware ✰ - Giordano Art, Ltd.
OPEN FIRE - Games - Avalon Hill Game Co.
OPEN FOR BUSINESS - Greeting cards - Nu-Art Inc.
OPEN-GRIP - Metals - Morton Manufacturing Co.
OPEN HEARTH - Bread - Lewis Bakeries, Inc.
OPEN HEARTH - Cooking equipment–household - Farberware Inc.
OPEN HEARTH - Furniture polish and wax - Sears, Roebuck and Co.
OPEN HOME - Housewares - Sears, Roebuck and Co.
OPEN HOUSE - Fabrics–tapestry ✰ - Columbus Coated Fabrics Co.
OPEN HOUSE - Floor coverings–carpet and rugs ✰ - Lees Carpets
OPEN HOUSE - Food products - M & K Foods Inc.
OPEN HOUSE 12 - Fabrics–tapestry ✰ - Columbus Coated Fabrics Co.
OPEN HOUSE 14 - Fabrics–tapestry ✰ - Columbus Coated Fabrics Co.
OPEN ICE - Computer software - Midway Manufacturing Co.
OPEN II, THE - Sporting goods - Nine Eagles Golf Co.
OPEN INTERFACE ELEMENTS - Computer software - Neuron Data, Inc.
OPEN KEEL DELTA - Kites - Kite Factory
OPEN KETTLE - Vegetables–pickled or brined ✰ - Paisley Farm
OPEN KOTE - Paper–sand - Norton Co.
OPEN/LIMS - Computer software - Talem, Inc.
OPEN ME FIRST - Photographic equipment - Eastman Kodak Co.
OPEN MEDIA FRAMEWORK - Computer software - Avid Technology, Inc.
OPEN MIND - Computer software - Digital Communications Associates, Inc.
OPEN MIND - Deodorizers - Origins Natural Resources Inc.
OPEN MUSIC SYSTEM - Computer storage devices–magnetic - Opcode Systems, Inc.
OPEN ONE AND SAVOR - Candles - Smoky Mountain Products
OPEN PANTRY - Grocery stores - Open Pantry Food Marts Inc.

✰ = Now out of production

OPEN PERFORMANCE - Computer software - Belvedere Financial Systems, Inc.

OPEN PERSON FOUNDATION/OPEN PERSON IDENTIFIER - Computer software - Cerner Corp.

OPEN PIT - Food products - Vlasic Foods Inc.

OPEN PLAN - Computer software - Welcom

OPEN PLAN DESKTOP - Computers–personal - Welcom

OPEN PLAN PROFESSIONAL - Computer software - Welcom

OPEN PORT - Computer software - Open Port Technology, Inc.

OPEN PORT HARMONY - Computer software - Open Port Technology, Inc.

OPEN-RING - Office supplies - Faber-Castell Corp.

OPEN ROAD - Bicycles - Montgomery Ward & Co. Inc.

OPEN SEA - Food products - Milfico Foods Inc.

OPEN SECRET - Underwear and nightwear - NCC Industries, Inc.

OPEN SESAME - Snack foods - Faris Co.

OPEN SESAME - Tape–adhesive - H.B. Fuller Co. (North American Adhesives, Sealants and Coatings Group)

OPEN SKY - Recording label - Open Sky Records

OPEN-STITCH WITCHERY - Underwear and nightwear ☆ - Lovable Co.

OPEN SYSTEMS - Computer software - Open Systems, Inc.

OPEN TOURNAMENT GOLF - Video games - Nintendo of America Inc.

OPEN TRAILS - Backpacks - Dolgencorp

OPEN UP - Electrical equipment - Appliance Science Corp.

OPEN-WEB - Computer software - Open Software Associates, Inc.

OPEN WIDE - Cabinets - Sally Designs, Ltd.

OPEN WIDE - Tools–plumbing - Folkrod Specialty Tool Co.

OPEN WIDE - Toys–automobiles - Mattel, Inc.

OPEN WINDOWS - Jewelry–precious - Peter J. Malnekoff

OPEN WINDOWS COLLECTION - Jewelry–precious - Peter J. Malnekoff

OPEN WORKSHOP - Computer software - Thoroughbred Software International, Inc.

OPEN+ACCEL - Computer software - Open+Voice, Inc.

OPENADA - Computer software - Aetech Inc.

OPENAIR - Garden furniture–metal - Samsonite Furniture Co. (Consumer Products Div.)

OPENARC - Computer software - McGraw-Hill Companies, Inc.

OPENBOOK - Computer software - Cadence Design Systems, Inc.

OPENBRIDGE - Computer software - Informatica Corp.

OPENDOC - Computer software - Apple Computer Inc.

OPENEDITION - Educational materials - International Business Machines Corp.

OPENEND - Yarn - Parkdale Mills, Inc.

OPEN+ENTRY - Computer software - Open+Voice, Inc.

OPENER, THE - Kitchen utensils–aluminum - Bonny Products Inc.

OPENFLIGHT - Computer software - Software Systems

OPENGL - Computer software - Silicon Graphics, Inc.

OPENGUIDE - Computer software - Elan Associates (GreenLight Software Division)

OPEN!INFO MANAGER - Computer storage devices–optical ☆ - Horizons Technology, Inc.

OPENING DAY ALE - Beverages–malt - The Pike Brewing Co.

OPENING EYES TO MATHEMATICS - Textbooks - Math Learning Center

OPENING NIGHT - Computer software - Minnesota Educational Computing Corp.

OPENING NIGHT - Computer software - Softkey International Inc.

OPENING NIGHT - Figurines ☆ - Enesco Corp.

OPENING NIGHT - Floor coverings–carpet and rugs - Calladium & Marglen

OPENING NIGHT - Floor coverings–carpet and rugs - Lees Carpets

OPENING NIGHT 1993 INAUGURAL GAME - Apparel and accessories - Florida Panthers Hockey Club, Ltd.

OPENING NIGHT BARBIE - Dolls - Mattel, Inc.

OPENINSIGHT - Computer software - Revelation Technologies, Inc.

OPENMAC - Computer software - Data General Corp.

OPENNOTE - Computers - Kiwi Computer, Inc.

OPENPLUS DISTRIBUTION - Computer software - Openplus International, Inc.

OPENQUEST - Computer software - Openquest Technologies, Inc.

OPENQUEST TECHNOLOGIES - Computer software - Openquest Technologies, Inc.

OPENRDA - Computer software - Automation Technology, Inc.

OPENS ALL - Kitchen appliances ☆ - Vaughan Manufacturing Co. Inc.

OPENSERIES ADVISOR - Computer software - Dodge Group Inc.

OPENUP - Computer software - Openconnect Systems, Inc.

OPENUSE - Computer peripheral equipment - Honeywell Inc.

OPENVISION - Computer software - Openvision Technologies, Inc.

OPERA - Cigars - Gesty Trading & Manufacturing Corp.

OPERA - Hearing aids - Beltone Electronics Corp.

OPERA - Vases ☆ - Lenox Crystal, Inc.

OPERA - Watches - Elgin Watch Co.

OPERAND - Pharmaceutical preparations - Redi Products Laboratories

OPERATION - Games - Milton Bradley Co.

OPERATION: ALIENS - Lunch boxes - Twentieth Century Fox Film Corp.

OPERATION: ATLANTIS - Games ☆ - Mayfair Games, Inc.

OPERATION C - Video games ☆ - Konami (America) Inc.

OPERATION CARMARK - Automobile burglar-alarm accessory - Auto Alarm Supply Corp.

OPERATION CRUSADER - Computer software - Monarch Avalon, Inc.

OPERATION DEEP FREEZE - Apparel and accessories ☆ - Duofold Inc.

OPERATION: FIREFIGHT - Computer software - Sphere Inc.

OPERATION: FROG - Computer software - Scholastic Software Inc.

OPERATION LOGIC BOMB - Games - Jaleco USA, Inc.

OPERATION NEPTUNE - Computer software - The Learning Co., Inc.

OPERATION WHIRLWIND - Computer software ☆ - Broderbund Software, Inc.

OPERATION WOLF - Video games ☆ - Taito America Corp.

OPERATIONS OPTIMIZER - Computer software - Bricmanage, Inc.

OPERATOR ASSIST - Computer software - EG&G Astrophysics

OPERETTA - Floor coverings–carpet and rugs ☆ - Zenith Carpets

OPERETTA - Rings–jewelry - Artcarved Inc.

OPERON - Chemical preparations - Operon Technologies, Inc.

OPEX - Rackets–racquetball - Ektelon

OPFAMILY - Computer software - Woodward Governor Co.

OPHELIA - Apparel and accessories ☆ - Edison Brothers Stores, Inc.

OPHIR - Craft supplies - Tivian Laboratories Inc.

OPHTHA-LIPO - Pharmaceutical preparations - Misemer Pharmaceuticals Inc.

OPHTHA P/S - Ophthalmic goods - Misemer Pharmaceuticals Inc.

OPHTHACET - Pharmaceutical preparations ☆ - Vortech Pharmaceuticals

OPHTHAINE SOLUTION - Pharmaceutical preparations - Bristol-Myers Squibb Co.

OPHTHALGAN - Pharmaceutical preparations - Wyeth-Ayerst Laboratories

OPHTHALMIC PURCHASING NETWORK - Ophthalmic apparatus - Hayes Marketing, Inc.

OPHTHALMOLOGY INTERACTIVE - Educational materials - CD-Stat, Inc.

OPHTHAMOL - Pharmaceutical preparations ☆ - Schering-Plough Healthcare Products

OPHTHASONIC - Medical apparatus - Mentor O & O Inc.

OPHTHEL - Pharmaceutical preparations ☆ - ICN Pharmaceuticals Inc.

OPHTHETIC - Ophthalmic goods - Allergan, Inc.

OPHTHOCHLOR - Antibiotics ☆ - Parke-Davis

OPHTHOCORT - Pharmaceutical preparations ☆ - Parke-Davis

OPI - Nail care products - Opi Products, Inc.

OPICI - Wines - Opici Wine Co.

OPIE - Vegetables–pickled or brined - Europa Foods Ltd.

OPINEL - Knives–pocket ☆ - Gutmann Cutlery Inc.

OPINION POLE - Computer hardware - Gregory R. Chumbley

OPINION SEEKR - Computer software - Wimbush & Associates of Michigan, Inc.

OPIUM - Floor coverings–carpet and rugs ☆ - Kelly Group Inc.

OPIUM - Perfumes - Yves St. Laurent Parfum Corp.

O.P.M. - Dinnerware–glass ☆ - Goebel of North America

O.P.M. - Tobacco products - Brick-Hanauer Co.

OPM RECORDS - Recording label - Music People, Inc.

OPMAN - Computer software - Mobius Management Systems, Inc.

OPMS/32 - Computer software - Softeasy Software, Inc.

OPN-WINDO - Office supplies ☆ - Office Products Inc.

OPNET MODELER - Computer software - Mil 3, Inc.

OPNET PLANNER - Computer peripheral equipment - Mil 3, Inc.

OPOCO - Food products - Ogden Poultry Co.

OPOLO - Glass products - Gillinder Brothers Inc.

OPORSLIDE - Electronic equipment ☆ - Charles Beseler Co.

OPORTO COLLECTION - Giftware - Block China Co.

OPPAMA - Tachometers - Kanematsu USA Inc. (High-Tech Div.)

OPPORTUNITY - Paper products - Georgia-Pacific Corp.

OPPORTUNITY IS MOUNTING - Frames–picture - Byers Industries, Inc.

OPPORTUNITY MINE-ING - Paper–book - Career Systems, Inc.

OPPTICOAT - Packaging films - Borden Brands Foodservice Co.

OPPTIWRAP - Packaging–foam - BDH Two, Inc.

OPS - Office furniture–metal - GF Office Furniture Ltd.

OPS 'N POPS - Pens ☆ - Paper Mate Co.

OPSOLAR - Sunglasses - Opsales, Inc.

OPT - Hair care products ☆ - Stephan Co.

OPT 4 - Furniture–upholstered - August Inc.

OPT-FOR-HEALTH - Vitamins and nutritional supplements - Richard M. Dealany

OPTA - Hair care products - Wella Corp. (Consumer Products Div.)

☆ = Now out of production

OPTA-FLOW - Machinery - Sno-Way International, Inc.

OPTACON II - Audio equipment - Telesensory Systems Inc.

OPTACRYL - Contact lenses - Paragon Optical Industries Inc.

OPTAFIL - Pacific Coast Feather Co.

OPTAFIL - Food products - Opta Food Ingredients, Inc.

OPTAFRY - Oils—edible - Opta Food Ingredients, Inc.

OPTAGRADE - Food additives - Opta Food Ingredients, Inc.

OPTALAC - Chemical preparations - Opta Food Ingredients, Inc.

OPTAPHONE PLUS - Transceivers - Carlson Communications, Inc.

OPTAPHONE STAR - Antennas - Carlson Communications, Inc.

OPTAPHONE SYSTEMS - Communications equipment - Carlson Communications, Inc.

OPTARE - Bicycles - Applied Tectonics Inc.

OPTCALC - Computer programs - Systems Development Corp.

OPTEF - Pharmaceutical preparations ☆ - Upjohn Co.

OPTEGRA - Computer software - Computervision Corp.

OPTEK - Sunglasses - Optek Sunglass Corp.

OPTEK MUSIC SYSTEMS - Recording label - Optek Music Systems, Inc.

OPTEM - Insecticides - Whitmire Research Laboratories, Inc.

OPTEMA - Goggles - Glendale Protective Technologies Inc.

OPTEON - Limb implant devices - Exactech, Inc.

OPTEX - Food products - Opta Food Ingredients, Inc.

OPTHAMEND - Sutures - Deknatel Inc.

OPTI - Packaging machines - Marlen Research Corp.

OPTI - Vitamins and nutritional supplements - Metagenics, Inc.

OPTI-2 - Lubricating systems—motor vehicle - Interlube International, Inc.

OPTI-4 - Lubricating systems—motor vehicle - Interlube International, Inc.

OPTI-ACETYL CARNITINE - Vitamins and nutritional supplements - Optimal Nutrients

OPTI-ACTIVE - Vitamins and nutritional supplements - Optimal Nutrients

OPTI-AID - Optical services - Bradley Corp.

OPTI-BALANCE - Textile machinery - White Consolidated Industries, Inc.

OPTI-BARLEY - Vitamins and nutritional supplements - Optimal Nutrients

OPTI-BILBERRY - Vitamins and nutritional supplements - Optimal Nutrients

OPTI-BON - Pharmaceutical preparations - Barrows Pharmacal Inc.

OPTI-BORAGE - Vitamins and nutritional supplements - Optimal Nutrients

OPTI-BRITE - Shampoos - Farnam Cos. Inc.

OPTI-C - Vitamins and nutritional supplements - Performance Labs Inc.

OPTI-CAL - Vitamins and nutritional supplements - Twinlab

OPTI-CDCACHE - Computer software - Online Computer Systems, Inc.

OPTI-CHARGE - Electrical equipment - Chipco, Inc.

OPTI CHECK - Computer software - Micrographic Services Corp.

OPTI CLAD - Coatings - Optical Polymer Research, Inc.

OPTI-CLEAN - Ophthalmic goods - Alcon Laboratories, Inc.

OPTI CLEAN II - Ophthalmic goods - Alcon Laboratories, Inc.

OPTI-COOL ILLUSIONS - Binders - Avery Dennison Corp.

OPTI-COQ10 - Vitamins and nutritional supplements - Optimal Nutrients

OPTI-CORD - Eyes—glass ☆ - Jobar International Inc./Bibi Products

OPTI-CORDS - Ophthalmic goods - Karlen Manufacturing, Inc.

OPTI-CURRANT - Vitamins and nutritional supplements - Optimal Nutrients

OPTI-CURVE - Health care products - AnaMed Healthcare

OPTI-CYSTEINE - Vitamins and nutritional supplements - Optimal Nutrients

OPTI-DROP - Health care products - Afassco

OPTI-ECHINACEA - Vitamins and nutritional supplements - Optimal Nutrients

OPTI-EPA - Vitamins and nutritional supplements - Optimal Nutrients

OPTI-FIBER - Vitamins and nutritional supplements - Optimal Nutrients

OPTI-FILM - Chemical preparations - Betz Laboratories, Inc.

OPTI-FLAX - Vitamins and nutritional supplements - Optimal Nutrients

OPTI-FLEX - Surgical instruments - Flexbar Machine Corp.

OPTI-FLEX - Vitamins and nutritional supplements - Optimal Nutrients

OPTI-FLUX - Machinery - Ultrasonic Systems, Inc.

OPTI-FREE - Vitamins and nutritional supplements - Optimal Nutrients

OPTI-FREE ENZYMATIC CLEANER - Health care products - Alcon Laboratories, Inc.

OPTI-FREE LENS CASE - Health care products - Alcon Laboratories, Inc.

OPTI-FREE REWETTING DROPS - Health care products - Alcon Laboratories, Inc.

OPTI-FREE RINSING, DISINFECTING AND STORAGE SOLUTION - Health care products - Alcon Laboratories, Inc.

OPTI FUEL II - Vitamins and nutritional supplements - Twinlab

OPTI-GARLIC 4000 - Vitamins and nutritional supplements - Optimal Nutrients

OPTI-GERMANIUM - Vitamins and nutritional supplements - Optimal Nutrients

OPTI-GINKO - Vitamins and nutritional supplements - Optimal Nutrients

OPTI-GOLDEN SEAL - Vitamins and nutritional supplements - Optimal Nutrients

OPTI-GRIP - Cases—eyeglass - Durasol Drug & Chemical Co.

OPTI-GS 500 - Vitamins and nutritional supplements - Optimal Nutrients

OPTI-GS 750 - Vitamins and nutritional supplements - Optimal Nutrients

OPTI-GS 1000 - Vitamins and nutritional supplements - Optimal Nutrients

OPTI-GUARANA - Vitamins and nutritional supplements - Optimal Nutrients

OPTI-GUARD - Vitamins and nutritional supplements - Optimal Nutrients

OPTI HEAT - Dryers—hair - Conair Corp.

OPTI-HEAT - Ophthalmic goods - Alcon Laboratories, Inc.

OPTI-HORSETAIL - Vitamins and nutritional supplements - Optimal Nutrients

OPTI-INDEX - Bicycles - Huffy Corp.

OPTI-INTESTINE - Vitamins and nutritional supplements - Optimal Nutrients

OPTI-KIT - Ophthalmic goods - Apex Medical Corp.

OPTI-KIT - Ophthalmic goods - Karlen Manufacturing, Inc.

OPTI-KLEEN - Electronic equipment - Bell & Howell Co.

OPTI-KOREAN - Vitamins and nutritional supplements - Optimal Nutrients

OPTI-LENS - Ophthalmic goods - Alcon Laboratories, Inc.

OPTI LIFE - Vitamins - HSN Lifeway Health Products Inc.

OPTI-LINK - Electronic equipment - Lanzar Sound Corp.

OPTI-LITE - Watches - Sharp International Corp.

OPTI LOC - Lockers—plastic - Unger Enterprises Inc.

OPTI-LUNG - Vitamins and nutritional supplements - Optimal Nutrients

OPTI-MAG - Vitamins and nutritional supplements - Vitamin Research Products Inc.

OPTI-MAG FOR KIDS - Vitamins and nutritional supplements - Vitamin Research Products Inc.

OPTI-MAN - Vitamins and nutritional supplements - Optimal Nutrients

OPTI-MAX - Chromatographs - Optimize Technologies, Inc.

OPTI-MAX - Tires - Carlisle Tire & Rubber Co.

OPTI-MCT - Vitamins and nutritional supplements - Optimal Nutrients

OPTI-MEAL - Vitamins and nutritional supplements - Vitamin Research Products Inc.

OPTI-MELATONIN - Vitamins and nutritional supplements - Optimal Nutrients

OPTI-METER - Sporting goods - Ranging Inc.

OPTI-MIST - Ophthalmic goods - Karlen Manufacturing, Inc.

OPTI-MIZER - Lubricating systems—motor vehicle - Interlube International, Inc.

OPTI-MULTI - Vitamins and nutritional supplements - Nutro Laboratories, Inc.

OPTI-NAG - Vitamins and nutritional supplements - Optimal Nutrients

OPTI-NAIL-SKIN-HAIR - Vitamins and nutritional supplements - Optimal Nutrients

OPTI-OMEGA - Vitamins and nutritional supplements - Optimal Nutrients

OPTI-ONE MULTI-PURPOSE SOLUTION - Health care products - Alcon Laboratories, Inc.

OPTI-ONE REWETTING DROPS - Health care products - Alcon Laboratories, Inc.

OPTI-PADS - Ophthalmic goods - Karlen Manufacturing, Inc.

OPTI-PASSIFLORA - Vitamins and nutritional supplements - Optimal Nutrients

OPTI-PEARL - Vitamins and nutritional supplements - Optimal Nutrients

OPTI-PHENE - Cleaning preparations - Bio-Tek Industries, Inc.

OPTI-PRIM - Vitamins and nutritional supplements - Optimal Nutrients

OPTI-PRO - Electronic equipment - Enbee Plastics, Inc.

OPTI-PRO - Lubricants - Interlube International, Inc.

OPTI-PURE - Ophthalmic goods - Alcon Laboratories, Inc.

OPTI-ROLL - Health care products - AnaMed Healthcare

OPTI RX - Food products - Republic Drug Co. Inc.

OPTI-SAFE - Dyes and pigments - Phantom Research Laboratories, Inc.

OPTI-SEAL - Chromatographs - Optimize Technologies, Inc.

OPTI-SEAL - Frames—eyeglass - U.S. Optical Frame Co.

OPTI-SEPT - Ophthalmic goods - Alcon Laboratories, Inc.

OPTI-SHARK - Vitamins and nutritional supplements - Optimal Nutrients

OPTI-SHARK OIL - Vitamins and nutritional supplements - Optimal Nutrients

OPTI-SHINE - Ophthalmic goods - Endslip Products Co.

OPTI SIGHT - Eyeglasses - BEC Distribution, Inc.

OPTI-SKIN - Skin care products - Dermacare Products, Inc.

OPTI-SLEEP - Vitamins and nutritional supplements - Optimal Nutrients

OPTI-SOAK - Cleaning preparations - Alcon Laboratories, Inc.

OPTI SOFT - Ophthalmic goods - Alcon Laboratories, Inc.

OPTI-SPRAY - Lubricating systems—motor vehicle - Interlube International, Inc.

OPTI-SQUALENE - Vitamins and nutritional supplements - Optimal Nutrients

OPTI-SUMA - Vitamins and nutritional supplements - Optimal Nutrients

OPTI-SUMAX - Vitamins and nutritional supplements - Optimal Nutrients

OPTI TEAR - Ophthalmic goods - Alcon Laboratories, Inc.

OPTI-TECH - Animal feeds - Farmland Industries Inc.

OPTI TEMP - Machinery - Opti Temp Inc.

OPTI-THISTLE - Vitamins and nutritional supplements - Optimal Nutrients

OPTI TRAC - Electronic equipment - Sanyo Fisher (USA) Corp.

OPTI-ZINC - Vitamins and nutritional supplements - Natrol, Inc.

OPTI-ZYME - Ophthalmic goods - Alcon Laboratories, Inc.

OPTIACINEUTRAL - Vitamins and nutritional supplements - Quantum Publications, Inc.

OPTIAGE - Oils—essential - Quantum Publications, Inc.

OPTIAROMA - Deodorizers - Quantum Publications, Inc.

OPTIBALANCE - Pet food - Ralston Purina Co.

OPTIBLOCK - Sunblocks - Opticell Skin Services, Inc.

OPTIBODY - Massage products - General Nutrition Investment Co.

OPTIBOND - Denture adhesive - Kerr Corp.

OPTIBOND FL - Dental compounds - Kerr Corp.

OPTIBOR - Insecticides - U.S. Borax Inc.

OPTIBRITE - Lighting fixtures - Amalco Metals, Inc.

OPTIC - Dinnerware - Corning Inc.

OPTIC - Fishing lures - Den Manufacturing Co.

OPTIC - Floor coverings—carpet and rugs - Regal Rugs Inc.

OPTIC - Glassware—household - ACC

OPTIC - Telephones - Harris Corp.

OPTIC-FIRMS - Ophthalmic goods - Karlen Manufacturing, Inc.

OPTIC NERVE EYEWEAR - Sunglasses - Mountain Shades Distributing Co.

OPTIC SHUTTLE - Computer peripheral equipment - Onset Computer Corp.

OPTIC STOWAWAY - Data loggers - Onset Computer Corp.

OPTIC TOP ☆ - Toys ☆ - Brimms Inc.

OPTICA - Cleaning preparations ☆ - Sima Products Corp.

OPTICA - Garden equipment - Luster Leaf Products Inc.

OPTICA - Glassware—household - Svend Jensen of Denmark Inc.

OPTICA - Optical scanners—computer - 3D Technology, Inc.

OPTICAID - Ophthalmic apparatus - Edroy Products Co.

OPTICAL AFFAIRS - Eyeglasses - Optical Affairs, Inc.

OPTICAL-AIDS - Frames—eyeglass - Penny Pendleton Manufacturing Inc.

OPTICAL BENCH, THE - Computer software - Digital Compositing Systems, Inc.

OPTICAL CONCLUSIONS - Puzzle game - International Games

OPTICAL DATA CORPORATION - Computer software - Optical Data Corp.

OPTICAL DESIGN COLLECTION - Ophthalmic goods - Rozin Optical Export Corp.

OPTICAL DIAMOND PRODUCTS - Lenses—optical - Optical Diamond Products

OPTICAL EXCELLENCE FOR LESS - Eyeglasses - Innotech, Inc.

OPTICAL FAIR - Frames—eyeglass - Liberty Optical Manufacturing Co.

OPTICAL GLIDE - Electrical testing instruments - Thot Technologies

OPTICAL ILLUSION - Eye makeup - Coty Inc.

OPTICAL ILLUSIONS - Cosmetics - Maybelline Co.

OPTICAL PRACTICE MANAGER - Computer software - Tralice Corp.

OPTICAL REACH - Cables—fiber optic - Comm/Scope Inc.

OPTICAL SUPERSTOR - Computerized disk storage unit - U.S. Design Corp.

OPTICALM - Herbal products - Quantum Publications, Inc.

OPTICAP - Photographic equipment - SP Systems/Saratons

OPTICARDIO - Food products - Quantum Publications, Inc.

OPTICARE - Computer hardware - Optimark Corp.

OPTICARE - Eyeglasses - Opticare Eye Health Center, P.C.

OPTICARE - Optical scanners—computer - Titmus Optical, Inc.

OPTICASE - Cases—eyeglass - Aristocraft Co.

OPTICCOLOR - Photographic equipment - Harrison & Harrison

OPTICELL-U-LITE - Skin care products - Opticell Skin Services, Inc.

OPTICHROME - Adhesive backed plastic sheets - Mactac Inc. (Packaging Closures Systems Div.)

OPTICHROME - Photographic equipment - Avcom Systems Inc.

OPTICIAN'S FORMULA - Toiletries - Puretek Corp.

OPTICLEAN - Heating equipment - Emerson Electric Co.

OPTICLEAN GLASS AND DISH RACKS - Kitchen appliances - Carlisle Foodservice Products, Inc.

OPTICLEAR - Pet products - Tomlyn Products

OPTICLEAR - Plastics film - Mactac Inc. (Packaging Closures Systems Div.)

OPTICLEAR II - Pet products ☆ - Tomlyn Products

OPTICO - Ophthalmic goods - Karlen Manufacturing, Inc.

OPTICOAT - Pet products - Natural Animal Nutrition Inc.

OPTICOAT II - Pet products - Natural Animal Nutrition Inc.

OPTICOLOR - Frames—eyeglass - Pathway Optical Prods.

OPTICONS - Computer software - Opticolor Inc.

OPTICORE - Pipes—plastic - Phillips Petroleum Co.

OPTICRAFT - Microscopes ☆ - Polk's Model Craft Hobbies, Inc.

OPTICROM - Ophthalmic goods - Fisons Corp.

OPTICS - Dinnerware—glass - Block China Co.

OPTICS POCKET - Apparel and accessories - Stephen B. Dipietro

OPTICURL - Hair care products - Matrix Essentials, Inc.

OPTIDEFINE - Computer peripheral equipment - FBC Computer Systems, Inc.

OPTIDIGEST - Vitamins and nutritional supplements - Quantum Publications, Inc.

OPTIELIM - Food products - Quantum Publications, Inc.

OPTIENERGY - Vitamins and nutritional supplements - Quantum Publications, Inc.

OPTIFACTS - Ophthalmic goods - Vision Ease

OPTIFAST - Health care products - Novartis Nutrition Corp.

OPTIFICHE - Computer software - FBC Computer Systems, Inc.

OPTIFILL-II - Computer hardware - Baxter International Inc.

OPTIFILTER - Respirators - Mine Safety Appliances Co.

OPTIFIT - Contact lenses - Wesley-Jessen Inc.

OPTIFLASH PEGLITE - Signs - Fasteners for Retail, Inc.

OPTIFLASH STRIPLITE - Signs - Fasteners for Retail, Inc.

OPTIFLEX - Computer software - Optimax Systems Corp.

OPTIFLEX - Lighting equipment - Rohm and Haas Co.

OPTIFLEX - Optical machinery - Perceptron, Inc.

OPTIFLEX SELECT - Plastics—laminated - Flexcon Co. Inc.

OPTIFLO - Paints - United Catalysts Inc.

OPTIFLO - Paper - Wangner Systems Corp.

OPTIFLOAT - Glass products - Crystal International Corp.

OPTIFLURE - Electric lighting equipment - Lutron Electronics Co., Inc.

OPTIFORM - Hair care products - Wella Corp. (Consumer Products Div.)

OPTIGAR - Vitamins and nutritional supplements - Nu Skin International, Inc.

OPTIGARD - Sunglasses - H.L. Bouton Co. Inc.

OPTIGEAR - Eyeglasses - Amcon Laboratories, Inc.

OPTIGEL - Purified clay particles - United Catalysts Inc.

OPTIGENE - Pharmaceutical preparations - Pfeiffer Pharmaceuticals Inc.

OPTIGENE III - Pharmaceutical preparations - Pfeiffer Pharmaceuticals Inc.

OPTIGLO - Lamps - BKL, Inc.

OPTIGLOW - Electronic equipment - Telex Communications, Inc.

OPTIGONE - Frames—eyeglass - Zylo Ware Corp.

OPTIGRIP - Gloves—rubber - Digitcare Corp.

OPTIHEP - Herbal products - Quantum Publications, Inc.

OPTIK - Cleaning preparations - Pace National Corp.

OPTIK-RIDALL - Cleaning preparations - Pace National Corp.

OPTIKA - Computer programs - Optika Imaging Systems, Inc.

OPTIKA - Giftware - Lenox Crystal, Inc.

OPTIKA COLLECTION - Giftware - Lenox, Inc.

OPTIKK - Toys - Mattel, Inc.

OPTIKON - Frames—eyeglass - Liberty Optical Manufacturing Co.

OPTIKWERKS - Computer software - Optikwerk, Inc.

OPTILETS - Vitamins and nutritional supplements - Abbott Laboratories

OPTILIGHT - Lighting fixtures - Optilight, Inc.

OPTILINE - Cables—fiber optic - Poly-Optical Products, Inc.

OPTILINK - Computer software - Optimark Corp.

OPTILOAD - Machinery - Opti Temp Inc.

OPTILUBE - Lubricating systems—motor vehicle - Dana Corp.

OPTIMA - Balls - Wilson Sporting Goods Co.

OPTIMA - Bicycles ☆ - Raleigh USA Bicycle Co.

OPTIMA - Coffee makers—electric - Black & Decker Corp.

OPTIMA - Computer diskettes—blank - Eastman Kodak Co.

OPTIMA! - Computer peripheral equipment - Advanedge Technologies, Inc.

OPTIMA - Dinnerware—glass - Mikasa Licensing, Inc.

OPTIMA - Electrical apparatus - Olympic Controls Corp.

OPTIMA - Fabrics - Asten, Inc.

OPTIMA - Fabrics - Industrial Coatings Group, Inc.

OPTIMA - Fabrics - E.R. Moore Co.

OPTIMA - Fertilizers - Helena Chemical Co.

OPTIMA - Film - Miles Inc. (Agfa Div.)

OPTIMA - Floor coverings - Tarkett, Inc.

OPTIMA - Frames—picture - Ammak Manufacturing Corp.

OPTIMA - Furniture ☆ - Stanley Furniture Co. Inc.

OPTIMA - Golfing equipment - Triumph Golf Co.

OPTIMA - Health care products - ETAC USA Inc.

OPTIMA - Health care products ☆ - Wheel Ring Inc.

OPTIMA - Lamp bulbs—fluorescent - Duro-Test Corp.

OPTIMA - Luggage - Airway Industries, Inc.

OPTIMA - Manicure preparations - Fromm Industries

OPTIMA - Motor oil - Atlantic Refining & Marketing Corp.

OPTIMA - Motor vehicle parts and accessories - Harnischfeger Industries

OPTIMA - Paper ☆ - Rite-Made Paper Converters Inc.

OPTIMA - Pet products - Rolf C. Hagen (USA) Corp.

OPTIMA - Plumbing fixtures - Sloan Valve Co.

OPTIMA - Power transformers - Muller Martini Corp.

OPTIMA - Rackets—racquetball - Ektelon

OPTIMA - Rings—jewelry - Artcarved Inc.

☆ = Now out of production

OPTIMA - Television equipment - Jasco Products Co. Inc.

OPTIMA - Toys–models ☆ - Estes Industries

OPTIMA - Vacuum cleaners and accessories - HMI Industries Inc.

OPTIMA - Wallcoverings - R.K. Style Inc.

OPTIMA 400 - Film - AGFA-Gevaert Inc.

OPTIMA 2000 - Bathroom fixtures ☆ - Showerlux USA

OPTIMA 2000 - Hearing aids - Beltone Electronics Corp.

OPTIMA BY KING - Fireplace equipment - Martin Industries, Inc.

OPTIMA FZ - Polishing rouge ☆ - Flitz International Ltd.

OPTIMA II - Solar cells - Novan Energy Inc.

OPTIMA PLUS - Plumbing fixtures - Sloan Valve Co.

OPTIMA PLUS - Vacuum cleaners and accessories - HMI Industries Inc.

OPTIMA RECOVER - Paper ☆ - Rite-Made Paper Converters Inc.

OPTIMA-SUPERIOR - Paper ☆ - Rite-Made Paper Converters Inc.

OPTIMAB - Biochemicals - Life Technologies, Inc.

OPTIMAGO - Puzzles - English Shopper

OPTIMAIR - Respirators - Mine Safety Appliances Co.

OPTIMAL - Floor coverings–carpet and rugs - Whitecrest Carpet Mills

OPTIMAL - Ophthalmic goods - Vision Ease

OPTIMAL CONTROL INC. - Thermometers - Vankel Industries, Inc.

OPTIMAL SCIENTIST - Computer software - Transpower Corp.

OPTIMAN - Vitamins and nutritional supplements - Quantum Publications, Inc.

OPTIMARC - Lamps - Duro-Test Corp.

OPTIMARK - Computer software - Optimark Corp.

OPTIMARMA - Oils–essential - Quantum Publications, Inc.

OPTIMASK - Publisher's imprints - E.I. Dupont de Nemours and Co.

OPTIMASSAGE - Oils–essential - Quantum Publications, Inc.

OPTIMAT - Floor coverings - American Floor Products Co. Inc.

OPTIMAT - Floor coverings - Ludlow Composites Corp.

OPTIMATCH - Computer software - Nikon Precision Inc.

OPTIMAX - Dispensers - Fluid Management

OPTIMAX - Electronic equipment - Optical Radiation Corp.

OPTIMEDIA - Cabinets - Wright Line Inc.

OPTIMETABOLIZE - Herbal products - Quantum Publications, Inc.

OPTIMEYES - Lenses–optical - Charles P. Larson

OPTIMEYES - Skin care products - Jafra Cosmetics Inc.

OPTIMIL - Pharmaceutical preparations ☆ - Wallace Laboratories

OPTIMILL - Treadmills - Pacer Fitness Systems

OPTIMIN POLYCOLLOIDAL - Health care products - Integrated Health Network

OPTIMIND - Vitamins and nutritional supplements - Quantum Publications, Inc.

OPTIMINE - Antihistamine preparations - Schering-Plough Healthcare Products

OPTIMIS - Medical apparatus - Optimed Technologies, Inc.

OPTIMISER - Electronic equipment - Motorola, Inc. (Land Mobile Products Sector)

OPTIMIST - Boats ☆ - Dynamic Plastics Inc.

OPTIMIST - Frames–eyeglass ☆ - Universal/Univis Inc.

OPTIMIST - Suntan lotions - ETS, Inc.

OPTIMIST PRAM - Ships–sailing vessels ☆ - Snug Harbor Boat Works

OPTIMIX - Asphalt felts and coatings - Optimix, Inc.

OPTIMIZE - Medical apparatus - Mentor O & O Inc.

OPTIMIZE THE EFFORT! - Apparel and accessories ☆ - Easton International

OPTIMIZER - Chemical preparations - Bio-Lab, Inc.

OPTIMIZER - Cleaning preparations - Trico Products Corp.

OPTIMIZER - Detergents - Diversey Corp.

OPTIMIZER - Insecticides - Y-Tex Corp.

OPTIMIZER - Medical apparatus - Radiation Measurements, Inc.

OPTIMIZER - Suntan lotions - Rotheudt Enterprises, Inc.

OPTIMIZER ADJUSTABLE DISH DOLLIES - Kitchen appliances - Carlisle Foodservice Products, Inc.

OPTIMIZOR BRAND FLAVOR - Seasonings - Applied Food Biotechnology, Inc.

OPTIMOIST - Pharmaceutical preparations - Colgate-Palmolive Co.

OPTIMOX PRENATAL - Health care products - Optimox Corp.

OPTIMS - Lenses–optical - Fosta-Tek Optics, Inc.

OPTIMUM - Air filtering units - Optimum Air Corp.

OPTIMUM - Bathtubs–enameled - Sterling Plumbing Group Inc.

OPTIMUM - Cat food - Nature's Recipe

OPTIMUM - Dental equipment - Milford Holding Co.

OPTIMUM - Floor coverings - Aladdin Mills, Inc.

OPTIMUM - Garden equipment - J. Thomas Distributors, Inc.

OPTIMUM - Glass products - D & L Stained Glass Supply, Inc.

OPTIMUM - Hair care products - Soft Sheen Products Co.

OPTIMUM - Sprayers - RL Flo-Master

OPTIMUM - Window coverings - M.A. Baskind Co.

OPTIMUM 6 - Vitamins and nutritional supplements - Vitamin Research Products Inc.

OPTIMUM 18 - Vitamins and nutritional supplements - Vitamin Research Products Inc.

OPTIMUM BALANCE - Golfing equipment - Golfsmith International Inc.

OPTIMUM BALANCE - Vitamins and nutritional supplements - Leiner Health Products Inc.

OPTIMUM BY LOBOB - Pharmaceutical preparations - Lobob Laboratories Inc.

OPTIMUM CHOICE - Food products - Sysco Corp.

OPTIMUM CHOICE - Food products - Sysco Food Services

OPTIMUM COMFORT - Pillows - American Fiber Industries Corp.

OPTIMUM CONSOLE - Machinery - Crest Ultrasonics Corp.

OPTIMUM D - Vitamins and nutritional supplements - Vitamin Research Products Inc.

OPTIMUM GROWTH - Veterinary nutritional supplements - Dr. Goodpet

OPTIMUM HEALTH OPTIMUM DELIVERY SYSTEM - Pharmaceutical preparations - Optimum Health International, Inc.

OPTIMUM LEVELS ANTIOXIDANT - Vitamins and nutritional supplements - Ethical Nutrients

OPTIMUM LIFESTYLE - Vitamins and nutritional supplements - Optimum Lifestyle, Inc.

OPTIMUM LIMIT - Vitamins and nutritional supplements ☆ - Pharmavite Corp.

OPTIMUM NAIL THERAPEUTICS - Nail care products - Schiff Products, Inc.

OPTIMUM PH - Detergents - Ecolab Inc.

OPTIMUM SD - Yarn - Interface, Inc.

OPTIMUM SETTINGS - Computer software - CEO Software, Inc.

OPTIMUM SILVER - Vitamins and nutritional supplements - Vitamin Research Products Inc.

OPTIMUM TRAINING SYSTEMS - Vitamins and nutritional supplements - Strength & Conditioning Technologies

OPTIMUS - Camp furniture–metal - Suunto USA

OPTIMUS - Floor coverings–carpet and rugs - Karastan-Bigelow Inc.

OPTIMUS - Headphones - Tandy Corp.

OPTIMUS PRIME - Toys–erector sets - Hasbro, Inc.

OPTIMYD - Pharmaceutical preparations - Schering-Plough Healthcare Products

OPTINEPH - Vitamins and nutritional supplements - Quantum Publications, Inc.

OPTION - Eyeglasses - Martin-Copeland Eyewear Corp.

OPTION - Floor coverings–carpet and rugs - Hollytex Carpet Mills Inc.

OPTION - Games ☆ - Parker Brothers

OPTION - Hair coloring preparations - Clairol Inc.

OPTION - Toys - Tonka Corp.

OPTION 1 - Lubricating oils - Relton Corp.

O.P.T.I.O.N. CARE - Health care products - O.P.T.I.O.N. Care

OPTION I - Chairs ☆ - EAC Integrated Furniture Solutions

OPTION-LOK - Medical apparatus - Abbott Laboratories

OPTION ONE - Veterinary medical equipment ☆ - Agrophysics Inc.

OPTION SERIES - Golfing equipment - Tiger Shark Golf Inc.

OPTION WIZ - Computer software - Builder Software Tools, Inc.

OPTIONS - Brackets - National Manufacturing Co.

OPTIONS - Burial caskets - Batesville Casket Co., Inc.

OPTIONS - Desk accessories - Coronet General Corp.

OPTIONS - Educational materials - Options, Inc.

OPTIONS - Floor coverings–carpet and rugs ☆ - Wunda Weve Carpet Co.

OPTIONS - Glass products - Service Merchandise Co. Inc.

OPTIONS - Greeting cards - Hallmark Cards Inc.

OPTIONS - Hardware - Marley Mouldings Inc.

OPTIONS - Lighting fixtures - M G Products, Inc.

OPTIONS - Paper products - Mohawk Paper Mills, Inc.

OPTIONS - Skin care products - Options International, Inc.

OPTIONS - Wallcoverings - Arthur Sanderson and Sons North America Ltd.

OPTIONS - Wallpaper ☆ - W.H.S. Lloyd

OPTIONS 5 - Infant product - Cosco, Inc.

OPTIONS & CHOICES - Computer software and equipment - Options & Choices, Inc.

OPTIONS DOCDRAW - Computer software - Wallace Computer Services, Inc.

OPTIONS FORM FRAMEWORK - Computer software - Wallace Computer Services, Inc.

OPTIONS UNLIMITED FROM MATT TOTILLO - Shirts - Southpaw Trading Ltd.

OPTIONSLINK - Credit institutions - Hambrecht & Quist LLC

OPTIONWEAR - Apparel and accessories - M.B.E International Resources, Inc.

OPTIPAK - Cases–eyeglass - Optipak, Inc.

OPTIPATCH - Optical scanners–computer - Data Switch Corp.

OPTIPATH - Computer software - CGtech

OPTIPHOTO - Film - Seattle Filmworks, Inc.

OPTIPHYLLIN - Health care products ☆ - E. Fougera & Co. Inc.

OPTIPLATE-XM - Bars–steel - Burgon Tool Steel Co. Inc.

☆ = Now out of production

OPTIPRANA - Herbal products - Quantum Publications, Inc.
OPTIPRO - Optical disks - International Memory Products of Illinois, Inc.
OPTIPURE - Pharmaceutical preparations - Sepracor Inc.
OPTIQUE - Dinnerware–glass ☆ - Nikko Ceramics Inc.
OPTIQUE - Floor coverings–carpet and rugs ☆ - J and J Industries Inc.
OPTIQUE - Glassware–household - ACC
OPTIQUE - Lamps - Fine Art Lamps
OPTIQUE - Sunglasses ☆ - Optique du Monde Ltd.
OPTIQUE 1 - Pharmaceutical preparations - Boiron Inc.
OPTIQUE BOUTIQUE - Ophthalmic goods ☆ - Optique du Monde Ltd.
OPTIQUE DE PARIS - Eyeglasses - Accessories International
OPTIQUE SOLAIRE - Ophthalmic goods - Yves St. Laurent Parfum Corp.
OPTIRHEUM - Vitamins and nutritional supplements - Quantum Publications, Inc.
OPTIS PLUS - Computer software - Options & Choices, Inc.
OPTISCOPE - Photographic equipment - Testrite Instrument Co. Inc.
OPTISCREEN - Electronics equipment - Jerome Menell Co.
OPTISCRIPT - Computer program - Dennis Zahorchak
OPTISEAL - Sealing devices - CDI Seals, Inc.
OPTISED - Pharmaceutical preparations - Steri-Med Inc.
OPTISEP - Filters–industrial - North Carolina SRT, Inc.
OPTISET - Frames–eyeglass - Zylo Ware Corp.
OPTISHAKE - Dairy products - Sysco Corp.
OPTISHIELD - Chemical preparations - Opti Temp Inc.
OPTISITE - Computer software - Microanalytics
OPTISONE - Veterinary pharmaceutical preparations ☆ - Evsco Pharmaceuticals
OPTISPACE - Furniture - Ossi
OPTISTAR - Unexposed microfilm - Eastman Kodak Co.
OPTISTORE - Medical apparatus - Mentor O & O Inc.
OPTISUB - Laboratory apparatus - Biotecx Laboratories, Inc.
OPTITOUCH - Oils–essential - Quantum Publications, Inc.
OPTITRAC - Electronic equipment - Integrated Solutions, Inc.
OPTITRAN - Laboratory apparatus - Schleicher and Schuell Inc.
OPTIVIEW - Contact lenses and eyeglasses - Texas State Optical, Inc.
OPTIVIEW - Television monitors - Poly-Optical Products, Inc.
OPTIVISION - Computer hardware - Optivision, Inc.
OPTIVISOR - Lenses–magnifying - Donegan Optical Co. Inc.
OPTIVISUAL - Compact discs–prerecorded - AVLS Profiles, Inc.
OPTIVITY - Computer software - Synoptics Communications, Inc.
OPTIVOX - Easels - Advance Products Co. Inc.
OPTIWAVE - Frames–eyeglass - Pathway Optical Prods.
OPTIWHITE - Glass products - Crystal International Corp.
OPTIWHITE - Toothpaste - Amercon, Inc.
OPTIWOMAN - Vitamins and nutritional supplements - Quantum Publications, Inc.
OPTIWRITER - Sensitized photographic film - Eastman Kodak Co.
OPTIX - Blinds–vertical - Nanik Div.
OPTIX - Floor coverings - Duramax, Inc.
OPTIX - Floor coverings–carpet and rugs - Hartford Carpet Mills
OPTIX - Hair care products - Andre Fantasies Inc.
OPTIX DOCUMENT IMAGING SYSTEM - Computer software - Blueridge Technologies, Inc.
OPTIX DOCUMENT MANAGEMENT SYSTEM - Computer software - Blueridge Technologies, Inc.
OPTIX WEB - Computer software - Blueridge Technologies, Inc.
OPTIX WORKFLOW - Computer software - Blueridge Technologies, Inc.
OPTIXX - Projection screens ☆ - Da-Lite Screen Co. Inc.
OPTIZINC - Vitamins and nutritional supplements - William Seroy Group Inc.
OPTO-PAK - Controls–heating systems - Imo Industries Inc.
OPTOBAHN - Transmitting apparatus - Optobahn Corp.
OPTOELECTRONICS - Frequency counters and universal time/counters - Optoelectronics, Inc.
OPTOFORM - Lathes - Rank Taylor Hobson, Inc.
OPTOLOW - Pharmaceutical preparations - Wesley Pharmacal Co. Inc.
OPTONE - Frames–eyeglass - Pathway Optical Prods.
OPTONICA - Stereos - Sharp Electronics Corp.
OPTOPICS - Pharmaceutical preparations - NutraMax Products Inc.
OPTOZINE - Pharmaceutical preparations - Wesley Pharmacal Co. Inc.
OPTRA - Printers–computer - Lexmark International, Inc.
OPTRALITE - Lasers - Optra, Inc.
OPTREX - Pharmaceutical preparations ☆ - Consolidated Midland Corp.
OPTRIEVE - Computer software - National Computer Systems, Inc.
OPTRIX - Cleaning preparations - John P. Murphy
OPTRONICS - Automotive parts and accessories - Optronics Inc.
OPTSTOCK - Computer software - A&O Systems, Inc.

OPTUBE - Bags–cosmetic - Risdon Corp.
OPTULLE - Bandages–surgical - Consolidated Midland Corp.
OPTUM - Frames–eyeglass ☆ - Universal/Univis Inc.
OPTUM - Polymer resin - Ferro Corp.
OPTX 20/20 - Lenses–optical - OPTX 20/20
OPTY - Medical apparatus - Del Mar Avionics
OPTYL - Frames–eyeglass ☆ - Carrera Eyewear Corp.
OPTYLITE - Optical scanners–computer - Tart Optical
OPTYX - Binoculars ☆ - Liberty Mountain Sports
OPUL - Ophthalmic goods - Styl-Rite Optical Manufacturing Co., Inc.
OPULENCE - Blinds–venetian ☆ - Hunter Douglas, Inc.
OPULENCE - Fabrics–tapestry ☆ - Coloroll Inc.
OPULENCE - Floor coverings–carpet and rugs - Calladium & Marglen
OPULENCE - Floor coverings–carpet and rugs ☆ - Regal Rugs Inc.
OPULENCE - Floor coverings–carpet and rugs ☆ - Royalweve Carpet Mills
OPULENCE - Furniture ☆ - Stanley Furniture Co. Inc.
OPULENCE - Jewelry - Marshalls, Inc.
OPULENCE - Nail care products ☆ - Noxell Corp.
OPULENCE - Ophthalmic goods - Foremost Optical Products
OPULENCE - Placemats - Now Designs
OPULENCE & ELEGANCE - Christmas tree ornaments - Seasonal Specialties Electrics, Inc.
OPULENCIAS - Cigar boxes–wood - Consolidated Cigar Corp.
OPULENT - Floor coverings–carpet and rugs - Columbus Mills, Inc.
OPULENT - Leather goods - Accessories to the Fact
OPULENT IMPRESSIONS - Wallpaper - Advent Industries Inc.
OPULENT IMPRESSIONS - Wallpaper - Capital Carousel Inc.
OPULENT ORCHIDS - Cosmetics - Elizabeth Arden Inc.
OPULENT REFLECTIONS - Wallpaper - Seabrook Wallcoverings, Inc.
OPULITE - Lighting fixtures - R & G Internationale, Inc.
OPUS - Air conditioning equipment - CTS Consolidated Technical Services Inc.
OPUS - Bicycles - Toshoku America Inc.
OPUS - Cameras - Vivitar Corp.
OPUS - Clarinets - G. Leblanc Corp.
OPUS - Computer software - Asa International, Ltd.
OPUS - Computer software - MediaShare Inc.
OPUS - Computer software - Renaissance Software Inc.
OPUS - Floor coverings - Mannington Resilient Floors
OPUS - Floor coverings–carpet and rugs - Kelly Group Inc.
OPUS - Furniture - Bassick Casters
OPUS - Garden equipment - Lawn & Garden Supply Co.
OPUS - Garden equipment ☆ - Opus Inc.
OPUS - Luggage and travel accessories - Jameslee Corp.
OPUS - Medical apparatus - Bernafon Inc.
OPUS - Power switching equipment - Onan Corp.
OPUS - Recording label ☆ - Apon Record Co., Inc.
OPUS - Toys–stuffed - Dakin Inc.
OPUS - Typewriters - Brother International Corp.
OPUS II - Furniture ☆ - Southern Furniture Co. of Conover
OPUS 3 - Synthesizers–musical instrument ☆ - EJE Research Corp.
OPUS 3 - Wallpaper ☆ - Bolta Wallcoverings
OPUS 10 - Musical instrument accessories - Glenn Davis Music Co.
OPUS 12 - Glassware–household - Coppersource/Halves Inc.
OPUS CLUB - Luggage and travel accessories - Jameslee Corp.
OPUS DANDELION SOCIETY - Toys–stuffed - Dakin Inc.
OPUS GOES TO RIO - Toys–stuffed - Dakin Inc.
OPUS I - Furniture ☆ - Southern Furniture Co. of Conover
OPUS I - Musical instruments - G. Leblanc Corp.
OPUS KIDS - Pet products - Opus Inc.
OPUS MAGNUM - Diagnostic apparatus - PB Diagnostic Systems Inc.
OPUS ONE - Cabinets ☆ - Crystal Cabinet Works Inc.
OPUS ONE - Recording label - Jazz Composer's Orchestra Association Inc.
OPUS ONE - Wines ☆ - House of Burgundy Inc.
OPUS ONE MUSIC PUBLICATIONS - Publisher's imprints - Neil A. Kjos Music Co.
OPV SOFTWARE - Computer software - OPV Software
O.P.W. - Paints ☆ - Orleans Paint Co. Inc.
OR - Apparel and accessories - Oscar De La Renta, Ltd.
OR - Jewelry - OroAmerica Inc.
OR - Nuts and bolts - Ohio Rod Products
OR BLEU - Cosmetics - Smithkline Beecham Corp.
OR CHART - Computer software - Spacelabs Medical, Inc.
OR-LAC - Pet products - Or-Lac Pet Products
OR MASCULIN - Fragrance - Bourjois Ltd.
OR-TEC - Caulking guns - Oliver Rubber Co.
ORA - Communications equipment - ORA Electronics

☆ = Now out of production

ORA - Jackets - Graff Californiawear, Inc.

ORA-PLUS - Pharmaceutical preparations - Paddock Laboratories Inc.

ORA-POPS - Vitamins and nutritional supplements - Alacer Co.

ORA-STETIC - Cold remedies - Schein Pharmaceutical Inc.

ORA-SWEET - Pharmaceutical preparations - Paddock Laboratories Inc.

ORA-SWEET SF - Pharmaceutical preparations - Paddock Laboratories Inc.

ORA-SYRINGE - Health care products - Apothecary Products, Inc.

ORA-TESTRYL - Pharmaceutical preparations - Bristol-Myers Squibb Co.

ORABASE - Pharmaceutical preparations - Colgate Oral Pharmaceuticals Inc.

ORABASE-B - Pharmaceutical preparations - Colgate Oral Pharmaceuticals Inc.

ORABASE HCA - Pharmaceutical preparations - Colgate Oral Pharmaceuticals Inc.

ORABEST - Dentifrices - Teledyne Industries Inc.

ORABEX-TF - Pharmaceutical preparations - Lunsco Inc.

ORABID - Pharmaceutical preparations ☆ - Lunsco Inc.

ORAC - Wallpaper - K.M.L. Industries

ORACIN - Pharmaceutical preparations - Richardson-Vicks USA

ORACLE - See **PRONTO**

ORACLE - Communications equipment - Circuits Maximus Co., Inc.

ORACLE - Electronic equipment - Endosonics Corp.

ORACLE - Phonographic turntables - GNP Audio Video Inc.

ORACLE - Rings—jewelry - Artcarved Inc.

ORACLE - Wallpaper ☆ - Winfield Design Associates, Inc.

ORACLE APPLICATION OBJECT LIBRARY - Computer software - Oracle Corp.

ORACLE BOOKS - Publisher's imprints - Price Stern Sloan Inc.

ORACLE CONTEXT - Computer software - Oracle Corp.

ORACLE-EAST - Computer software ☆ - Zephyr Services

ORACLE MEDIA OBJECTS - Computer software - Oracle Corp.

ORACLE MEDIA SERVER - Computer software - Oracle Corp.

ORACLE POWER OBJECTS - Computer software - Oracle Corp.

ORACLE PRESS - Publisher's imprints - Oracle Corp.

ORACLE SECURE NETWORK SERVICES - Computer software - Oracle Corp.

ORACLE TRANSPARENT GATEWAY - Computer software - Oracle Corp.

ORACLEWARE - Computers - Oracle Corp.

ORACON - Pharmaceutical preparations ☆ - Bristol-Myers Squibb Co.

ORADERM - Hair care products - Sporicidin International

ORADEX-C - Pharmaceutical preparations ☆ - Del Pharmaceuticals, Inc.

ORADRATE - Pharmaceutical preparations ☆ - Coast Laboratories Inc.

ORAFED - Pharmaceutical preparations ☆ - Lunsco Inc.

ORAFIX - Dental compounds - Smithkline Beecham Corp.

ORAFLEX - Pharmaceutical preparations ☆ - Eli Lilly and Co.

ORAFLOW PLUS - Vitamin supplements - Nutrition for Life International, Inc.

ORAGRAFIN - Pharmaceutical preparations - Bristol-Myers Squibb Co.

ORAGRIP - Denture materials - Teledyne Industries Inc.

ORAHEAL - Analgesics - Teledyne Industries Inc.

ORAHIST - Pharmaceutical preparations ☆ - Vangard Labs Inc.

ORAJEL - Analgesics - Del Pharmaceuticals, Inc.

ORAJEL COVERMED - Pharmaceutical preparations - Del Pharmaceuticals, Inc.

ORAJEL CSM - Analgesics ☆ - Del Pharmaceuticals, Inc.

ORAJEL/D - See **ORAJEL DENTURE**

ORAJEL DENTURE - Dentifrices - Del Pharmaceuticals, Inc.

ORAJEL MOUTH-AID - Analgesics - Del Pharmaceuticals, Inc.

ORAJEL PERIOSEPTIC - Health care products ☆ - Del Pharmaceuticals, Inc.

ORAL-B - Toothbrushes - Oral B Laboratories

ORAL-B ALCOHOL FREE PLAQUE RINSE - Dentifrices - Oral B Laboratories

ORAL-B ANTI-CAVITY RINSE - Dentifrices - Oral B Laboratories

ORAL-B LOW ALCOHOL ANTI-PLAQUE RINSE - Dentifrices - Oral B Laboratories

ORAL-B SENSITIVE WITH FLUORIDE - Toothpaste - Oral B Laboratories

ORAL-B TOOTH AND GUM CARE - Toothpaste - Oral B Laboratories

ORAL-EASE - Mouthwashes - Mizzy Inc.

ORAL ENGINEERING - Denture materials - Studioline Dental Laboratories, Inc.

ORAL PENTACRESOL - Pharmaceutical preparations ☆ - Upjohn Co.

ORAL PRO - Vitamins and nutritional supplements - Bio-Therapeutics, Inc.

ORAL PURE - Mouthwashes - Kmart Properties, Inc.

ORAL SAFE - Disinfectants - Great Lakes Orthodontics, Ltd.

ORALBALANCE - Skin care products - Laclede Professional Products, Inc.

ORALCHELATORX - Vitamins and nutritional supplements - Vitamin Research Products Inc.

ORALET - Pharmaceutical preparations - Abbott Laboratories

ORALGIENE - Toothbrushes—electric - Oralgiene USA, Inc.

ORALGIENE - Veterinary pharmaceutical preparations ☆ - Evsco Pharmaceuticals

ORALPHYLLIN - Pharmaceutical preparations - Consolidated Midland Corp.

ORALX-B - Veterinary nutritional supplements - Oralx Corp.

ORAM PROFESSIONAL AUDIO - Microphones - Bob White Associates

ORAMINIC - Antihistamine preparations ☆ - Vortech Pharmaceuticals

ORAMINIC SPANCAP - Pharmaceutical preparations ☆ - Vortech Pharmaceuticals

ORAN-GEL - Degreasing solvents - State Chemical Manufacturing Co.

ORAN-J - Beverages—carbonated - Original New York Seltzer

ORANDA GOLD GOLDFISH FOOD - Pet products - Hikari Sales USA Inc.

ORANGADA - Deodorizers - Surco Products Inc.

ORANGE - Brushes—paint - Corona Brushes Inc.

ORANGE - Brushes—paint - Rubberset Co.

ORANGE - Floor coverings—carpet and rugs ☆ - Regal Rugs Inc.

ORANGE - Recording label - Orange Record Co. Inc.

ORANGE-A-PEEL - Cleaning preparations - Renewable Energy Resources, Inc.

ORANGE-AIDES - Bowling balls - DBA Products Co.

ORANGE-ALL - Fruits—dried - Food Technology Inc.

ORANGE & OTHER - Beverages—alcohol ☆ - Wine Group Inc.

ORANGE-APRICOT - Marmalade - Sarabeth's Kitchen

ORANGE ASSORTMENT - Signs - Corona Brushes Inc.

ORANGE BAKERY - Bakery products - Orange Bakery Inc.

ORANGE BLAST - Beverages—carbonated - Seven-Up Bottling Co. of San Francisco

ORANGE BLOSSOM - Colognes ☆ - Old 97 Co.

ORANGE BLOSSOM - Housewares - Amaza Laboratories Inc.

ORANGE BLOSSOM - Meats—luncheon - Field Packing Co.

ORANGE BLOSSOM - Rings—jewelry - Bijouterie Inc.

ORANGE BLOSSOM - Tobacco—chewing or smoking - Amar Blends Co.

ORANGE BLOSSOM SPECIAL II - Toys ☆ - Playskool, Inc.

ORANGE BLOSSOM SPECIAL II - Toys—models ☆ - ERTL Co., Inc.

ORANGE BLOSSOM SPECIAL, THE - Honey - Leighton's Honey Inc.

ORANGE BOWL - Jewelry - Orange Bowl Committee, Inc.

ORANGE BOWL BASKETBALL CLASSIC - Paper products - Orange Bowl Committee, Inc.

ORANGE BOX - Paper clips - Majestic Staple Corp.

ORANGE BRITE - Beverages—carbonated - Snapple Beverage Corp.

ORANGE-C - Vitamins and nutritional supplements ☆ - NutriBiotic

ORANGE CASTLE - Fruits—dried - Sunny Cove Citrus Assoc.

ORANGE CHILL - Desserts - Moore Enterprises, Inc.

ORANGE CLEAN - Cleaning preparations - Appel Mountain, Inc.

ORANGE CO - Fruit drinks—bottled or canned - Orange-Co, Inc.

ORANGE-CO - Fruit drinks—bottled or canned - Orange-Co, Inc.

ORANGE-CO THE BEVERAGE COMPANY - Juices - Orange-Co, Inc.

ORANGE COLADA - Fruits and vegetables - Seald-Sweet Growers Inc.

ORANGE CORE - Tape—adhesive - Central Products Co.

ORANGE COUNTY - Apparel and accessories - Melville Corp.

ORANGE COUNTY SWEETS - Food products - Ronald M. Madura, Sr.

ORANGE COVE - Fruits and vegetables - Orange Cove-Sanger Citrus Association

ORANGE-CRETE - Brushes - Riviera Brokerage, Inc.

ORANGE CROWN - Shortening ☆ - CPC International Inc.

ORANGE CRUSH - Toys—electronic - Bird Bromiticous Inc.

ORANGE-DE-SOLVIT - Cleaning preparations - Uncle Sam Chemical Co., Inc.

ORANGE DELITE - Candy - Clasen Quality Coating Inc.

ORANGE DRIVER - Beverages - Montebello Brands, Inc.

ORANGE DRY - Beverages—carbonated - Canada Dry Corp.

ORANGE ELEPHANT, THE - Publisher's imprints - Cambridge Research Group, Ltd.

ORANGE FLOWER - Skin care products - Dorothy Gray Cosmetics Ltd.

ORANGE GLO - Cleaning preparations - Appel Mountain, Inc.

ORANGE GLO MADE WITH PURE ORANGE OIL - Cleaning preparations - Appel Mountain, Inc.

ORANGE GLOW - Food products - Pierce Foods Corp.

ORANGE GLOW/LS - Food products - Pierce Foods Corp.

ORANGE HABANERO - Vegetable sauces - GNS Spices Inc.

ORANGE-ITS - Candy ☆ - Donruss Co.

ORANGE JUNIORS - Cakes - Tasty Baking Co.

ORANGE KRISPY - Candy - See's Candy Shops, Inc.

ORANGE LANE - Fruit drinks—bottled or canned - Del Monte Corp.

ORANGE LIGHTENING - Degreasing solvents - Knight Marketing Corp.

ORANGE LIGHTNING - Cleaning preparations - Carter Enterprises

ORANGE-MAID - Deodorizers - Orange-Mate, Inc.

ORANGE MANGO ZINGER - Teas - Celestial Seasonings, Inc.

ORANGE MANIA - Cleaning preparations - Puritan-Churchill Chemical Co.

ORANGE-MATE - Deodorizers - Orange-Mate, Inc.

ORANGE MIRACLE - Cleaning preparations - Stanley Home Products Inc.

ORANGE MIST MIMOSA - Wines ☆ - H. Schmitt Soehne, Inc.

ORANGE NATURELLE - Fruit drinks—bottled or canned - Johanna Foods, Inc.

ORANGE NIP - Food products - Procter & Gamble Co.

ORANGE NIP - Juices - Ben Hill Griffin, Inc.

ORANGE PARK - Juices—frozen ☆ - Hi-Acres Inc.

ORANGE PHZZZ - Health care products ☆ - Barristo Ltd.

ORANGE PLUS - Cleaning preparations—household - Earth Friendly Products

ORANGE POP - Bath salts - GPS, Inc.

ORANGE POWER - Cleaning preparations - C.W. Parker Co.

ORANGE POWER - Pet products - Red Bell Inc.

ORANGE RING - Fruit drinks—bottled or canned - Orange Ring Inc.

ORANGE ROSE - Wine coolers ☆ - Canandaigua Wine Co. Inc.

ORANGE SLICES - Candy - Brach and Brock Confections Inc.

ORANGE SLUGGER - Juices - Chiquita Brands, Inc.

ORANGE SOLVE-CLEANER - Cleaning preparations - Analab Inc.

ORANGE SPOT - Beverages—carbonated - Canada Dry Corp.

ORANGE SQUEEZE - Candy - American Chewing Gum Inc.

ORANGE SQUEEZE - Wines - Diamond Island Cellars Inc.

ORANGE STIX - Candy - Leaf, Inc.

ORANGE STUFF - Cleaning preparations - Great American Health Foods

ORANGE SUPREME - Beverages ☆ - Snapple Beverage Corp.

ORANGE SUPREME - Cleaning preparations - Gold Coast Chemical Corp.

ORANGE TANGO - Yogurt - Haagen-Dazs Brands, Inc.

ORANGE TANGO - Yogurt—frozen - Haagen-Dazs Co. Inc.

ORANGE TOUGH - Cleaning preparations - Spartan Chemical Co., Inc.

ORANGE TREATS - Cakes ☆ - Tasty Baking Co.

ORANGE TREE - Fruit drinks—bottled or canned - Lipton Investments, Inc.

ORANGE-YA-CAN - Cleaner - Intex Chemical Inc.

ORANGE ZINGER - Teas—herbal - Celestial Seasonings, Inc.

ORANGEBOOM-PETER'S - Beverages—malt - Fred Bofird Co.

ORANGEBURG - Pipes—plastic - GS Roofing Products Co.

ORANGEHEAD - Candy - Ferrara Pan Candy Co., Inc.

ORANGEOLA - Beverages - Health Valley Food

ORANGERY - Fruit drinks—bottled or canned - Orangery Inc.

ORANGETTE - Beverages—carbonated - Grapette International

ORANGINA - Beverages—carbonated - Orangina USA Inc.

ORANGUTAN - Vitamins and nutritional supplements - Resurrection Laboratories

ORANGUTAN AMINO HIGH - Health care products - Resurrection Laboratories

ORANGUTAN MAN - Fruit drinks—bottled or canned - Homestead, Inc.

ORANGY - Apparel and accessories - Munico International Corp.

ORANJA - Beverages - Jarritos, Inc.

ORAN'S - Hair care products - Belgrave's Beauty Supplies & Cosmetics

ORANYL - Pharmaceutical preparations - Buffington

ORANYL - Skin care products - Otis Clapp & Son Inc.

ORANYL PLUS - Pharmaceutical preparations - Buffington

ORANYL PLUS - Pharmaceutical preparations - Otis Clapp & Son Inc.

ORAP - Pharmaceutical preparations - Lemmon Co.

ORAPAV - Pharmaceutical preparations ☆ - Roberts/Hauck Pharmaceuticals Inc.

ORAPIK - Dental Concepts Inc.

ORARELIEF - Health care products - Teledyne Industries Inc.

ORASEPT - Mouthwashes - Pharmakon Labs, Inc.

ORASITE - Pharmaceutical preparations - KV Pharmaceutical Co.

ORASONE - Pharmaceutical preparations - Solvay Pharmaceuticals Inc.

ORASPAN - Pharmaceutical preparations - Primedics Laboratories

ORASPAN FA - Pharmaceutical preparations - Primedics Laboratories

ORASTAT - Anesthetics - Durham Pharmacal Corp.

ORASURE - Pharmaceutical preparations - SmithKline Beecham Consumer Healthcare

ORATOR - Eyeglasses - Art-Craft Optical Co.

ORATROL - Pharmaceutical preparations ☆ - Alcon Laboratories, Inc.

ORATRONICS - Orthodontic equipment - Oratronics Inc.

ORATUSS - Pharmaceutical preparations - Barre-National, Inc.

ORAVAX - Pharmaceutical preparations - Oravax, Inc.

ORAZINC - Pharmaceutical preparations - Mericon Industries Inc.

ORAZINC 110 - Pharmaceutical preparations - Mericon Industries Inc.

ORAZINC 220 - Pharmaceutical preparations - Mericon Industries Inc.

ORB - Audio equipment - Hughes Aircraft Co.

ORB - Golfing equipment - Kenneth Smith Inc.

ORB - Jewelry - Nicholas Clements Associates

ORB-IT - Lupes ☆ - Crossbow Inc.

ORBAN - Audio equipment - Saul Mineroff Electronics Inc.

ORBAN - Broadcasting equipment - AKG Acoustics Inc.

ORBAN'S - Analgesics ☆ - Balas Dental Supply Co.

ORBAX - Veterinary pharmaceutical preparations - Schering-Plough Animal Health

ORBEAR - Toys - Mattel, Inc.

ORBEX - Glassware—household - Orbex Inc.

ORBI - Tennis rackets - Lisco, Inc.

ORBIS - Computer software ☆ - B & N Companies, Inc.

ORBIS - Fabrics—cotton - Heeksuede Inc.

ORBIS - Jewelry - Heart & Co.

ORBIS - Tea kettles—nonelectric ☆ - National Housewares

ORBIT - Cabinets - Bloch Industries Inc.

ORBIT - Chewing gum ☆ - Wm. Wrigley Jr. Co.

ORBIT - Cleaning preparations - Orbit Chemical Inc.

ORBIT - Clocks ☆ - By Design Corp.

ORBIT - Dinnerware—glass ☆ - Nikko Ceramics Inc.

ORBIT - Electronic equipment - QDM Co.

ORBIT - Floor coverings—carpet and rugs ☆ - Patcraft Mills Inc.

ORBIT - Frames—eyeglass ☆ - Universal/Univis Inc.

ORBIT - Hardware - Alumatic Corp. of America

ORBIT - Health care products ☆ - Smith and Davis Manufacturing Co.

ORBIT - Lamps - Orbit Design, Inc.

ORBIT - Milk - St. Albans Coop. Creamery

ORBIT - Photographic equipment - Hudson Photographic Industries Inc.

ORBIT - Publisher's imprints - Krieger Publishing Co.

ORBIT - Toys - Tonka Corp.

ORBIT - Wallpaper ☆ - Marburg Wallcoverings Inc.

ORBIT - Watches - Hampden Corp.

ORBIT JUICE - Vitamins and nutritional supplements - Nutra-Source Corp.

ORBIT KAPS - Vitamins and nutritional supplements - Nutra-Source Corp.

ORBIT NATURALS - Apparel and accessories - Orbit Industries, Inc.

ORBIT UNDERGROUND - Sprinklers—lawn - Orbit Irrigation Products, Inc.

ORBITAL - Frames—eyeglass ☆ - Universal/Univis Inc.

ORBITAL - Giftware - Pollenex Corp.

ORBITAL INTERCEPTOR - Toys - Tonka Corp.

ORBITAL MK PRODUCTS - Welding equipment - M.K. Products, Inc.

ORBITAL TRANSPORT - Toys—models ☆ - Estes Industries

ORBITAL WATCH - Watches - By Design Corp.

ORBITER - Computer software ☆ - Spectrum Holobyte, Inc.

ORBITER - Embossing machines - New Hermes Inc.

ORBITER - Lighting fixtures - Swivelier Co. Inc.

ORBITER - Motor vehicles ☆ - Sunline Coach Co.

ORBITER - Skates—roller ☆ - National Sporting Goods Corp.

ORBITER - Vacuum cleaners and accessories - Oreck Corp.

ORBITEX - Wet mops ☆ - American Textile Products Co.

ORBITGAMES - Games - Electro-Mech Inc.

ORBITILE - Floor coverings - American Floor Products Co. Inc.

ORBITING DIAMONDS - Tools—hand-operated - Edgecraft Corp.

ORBITIP - Pens - Accutec Inc.

ORBITOR 6 SHUTTLE COMMAND - Toys - Tonka Corp.

ORBITRED - Floor coverings - American Floor Products Co. Inc.

ORBITWHEEL - Games - Electro-Mech Inc.

ORBIX - Games - Hasbro, Inc.

ORBLITE - Lighting fixtures ☆ - Hubbell Lighting, Inc. (Lighting Div.)

ORBRITE - Cleaning preparations - Wilson Advisory Corp.

ORBS - Sunglasses - Bausch & Lomb Inc.

ORBS 100% RESPONSIBLE WEAR - Flags - Sherwood Group, Inc.

ORC - Chemical preparations - Plant Research Laboratories

ORCA - Computer software - Lunar Corp.

ORCA - Fishing rods - Johnson Fishing, Inc.

ORCA - Sewage treatment equipment - Envirovac Inc.

ORCA - Ships—sailing vessels - A.S. Fiberglass Co. Inc.

ORCA - Toys - Orca Industries, Inc.

ORCA BAY - Seafood products—canned or cured - Orca Bay Seafoods, Inc.

ORCA PATROL - Shirts - Lifeforms International, Inc.

ORCACLOR - Cleaning preparations - Envirovac Inc.

ORCAD LAYOUT - Computer software - Orcad, Inc.

ORCAD SIMULATE - Computer software - Orcad, Inc.

ORCA'S KILLER ICE CREAM - Ice cream - Lawrence Batterton

ORCHAND - Wood products - Weyerhaeuser Co.

ORCHARD - Brushes—paint ☆ - PPG Industries, Inc.

ORCHARD - Dinnerware—glass - Arita Sales Co. Inc.

ORCHARD - Dinnerware—glass - Nikko Ceramics Inc.

ORCHARD - Dinnerware—glass ☆ - Johnson Brothers, USA, Inc.

ORCHARD - Dinnerware—glass ☆ - Lenox, Inc.

ORCHARD - Fruit drinks—bottled or canned - Everfresh Beverages, Inc.

ORCHARD - Fruit drinks—bottled or canned - Orchard Foods

ORCHARD - Soap - Caswell-Massey Co. Ltd.

☆ = Now out of production

ORCHARD BIN - Candy - American Candy Co.
ORCHARD BLOSSOM - Deodorizers - L & F Products Inc.
ORCHARD BOY - Fruits–pickled or brined - National Fruit Product Co., Inc.
ORCHARD BRAN - Cereal - Ralston Purina Co.
ORCHARD CHARM - Fruits–canned - Big Star Food Stores
ORCHARD COLLECTION, THE - Wine coolers ☆ - Ernest and Julio Gallo Winery
ORCHARD CREEK - Furniture - Vaughan Furniture Co. Inc.
ORCHARD CREST FARMS - Snack foods - Orchard Crest Farms
ORCHARD CRISP - Crackers - Nabisco Foods Group
ORCHARD CRISP - Fruits and vegetables - West Breeze Orchards Inc.
ORCHARD FARM - Fruits–canned - Curtice-Burns Foods, Inc.
ORCHARD FARMS - Food products - Curtice-Burns Foods, Inc.
ORCHARD FOODS - Food products - Orchard Foods
ORCHARD FRESH - Food products ☆ - Curtice-Burns Foods, Inc.
ORCHARD FRESH - Fruit drinks–bottled or canned - Johanna Foods, Inc.
ORCHARD FRESH - Fruits and vegetables - Comstock Michigan Fruit
ORCHARD FRESH COBBLER - Fruit pie mixes - Lawrence Foods Inc.
ORCHARD GAP - Furniture - Vaughan Furniture Co. Inc.
ORCHARD GEM - Fruit and vegetable markets ☆ - Fruit Growers Marketing Association
ORCHARD GLADE - Dinnerware–glass - Franciscan by Johnson Brothers, USA, Inc.
ORCHARD GLADE - Dishes–china - Waterford Wedgewood USA, Inc.
ORCHARD GRASS HAY BALE - Pet products - Novalek, Inc.
ORCHARD GROVE - Fruit and vegetable markets - Peninsular Products Co./ Heatherwood Farms Co.
ORCHARD HARVEST - Juices - Bi-Lo, Inc.
ORCHARD HILL - Floor coverings - Mannington Resilient Floors
ORCHARD HILL PRODUCTIONS - Video production - Orchard Hill Productions
ORCHARD INN, THE - Wallpaper - Exeter Wallcoverings
ORCHARD MIST - Hair care products ☆ - Melaleuca, Inc.
ORCHARD MYSTIQUE - Jams and jellies - Mountain Maid Gourmet Jelly
ORCHARD NECTAR - Deodorizers - Reckitt & Colman, Inc.
ORCHARD OF NAZARETH - Olives–pickled or brined - Ultima Foods
ORCHARD PARK - Floor coverings ☆ - Tarkett, Inc.
ORCHARD PARK - Fruit drinks–bottled or canned - Park Corp.
ORCHARD PARK - Furniture - Dinaire Corp.
ORCHARD PARK - Wallpaper - Taylor Wallcoverings Inc.
ORCHARD ROSE - Dinnerware - Corning Inc.
ORCHARD SELECT - Fruits and vegetables - Sodus Fruit Farm Inc.
ORCHARD SELECT - Fruits–canned - Del Monte Corp.
ORCHARD SUN - Fruit drinks–bottled or canned - Pepsi-Cola Co.
ORCHARD, THE - Potpourri - Countryside Fragrances Inc.
ORCHARD, THE - Perfumes - Southern Harvest Inc.
ORCHARD TWIST - Beverages - Excellent Foods, Inc.
ORCHARD VIEW - Bakery products–frozen - Rich Products Corp.
ORCHARD VIEW FARM - Pies–frozen - Rich Products Corp.
ORCHARD VIEW FARMS - Food products - Duckwall-Pooley Fruit Co.
ORCHARDGRASSES - Flowers, plants, and seeds - Jacklin Seed
ORCHARDS - Fruit and vegetable markets - Frigid Food Products Inc.
ORCHARD'S BEST - Beverages - Coca-Cola Co.
ORCHARDSTAND - Fruit drinks–bottled or canned - Tropicana Products, Inc.
ORCHESTRA - Bedding–linen - Dan River Inc.
ORCHESTRA - Computers - Orchestra Multisystems, Inc.
ORCHESTRA - Office furniture–wood - Westinghouse Electric Corp.
ORCHESTRA COMPUTING ENVIRONMENT - Computer software - Tarek Parallel Systems
ORCHESTRATOR - Communications equipment - Compunetix, Inc.
ORCHESTRICON - Electronic equipment - Bell & Howell Co.
ORCHETTE - Frames–eyeglass - May Optical Co. Inc.
ORCHIC PMG - Vitamins and nutritional supplements - Standard Process Inc.
ORCHID - Chocolate candy - Hoffman Candy Co.
ORCHID - Frames–eyeglass ☆ - Universal/Univis Inc.
ORCHID - Fruit - Florida Fresh
ORCHID - Glassware–household - Rezler & Howell Co.
ORCHID - Glassware–household - Spiegelau Inc.
ORCHID - Watches - Rolex Watch USA, Inc.
ORCHID BOW - Candy ☆ - Burnham and Brady Inc.
ORCHID FLAMBE - Lipsticks - Honey & Spice Toiletries
ORCHID FRESH - Health care products - Care-Tech Laboratories Inc.
ORCHID FRESH II - Health care products - Care-Tech Laboratories Inc.
ORCHID GLOW - Nail care products - Cosmair Inc.
ORCHID OPALE - Cosmetics - Lancome
ORCHID PLUS - Cosmetics ☆ - Jason Natural Products, Inc.
ORCHID STRIPE - Bedding–linen - Dan River Inc.

ORCHIDEA - Dishes–china - Pasmantier Co. Inc.
ORCHIDIAN - Jewelry–precious - Christopher Designs, Inc.
ORCHIDLAND - Orchid plants - Peach State Orchids, Inc.
ORCHIDS - Fish–canned or cured - Oriental Trading Co.
ORCHIDS - Shoes - World Import Co. Inc.
ORCHIDS EXOTICA - Flowers, plants, and seeds ☆ - Security Products Co.
ORCHIDS IN THE MOONLIGHT - Hair- and skin-care products, fragrance, etc. - Benjamin Ansehl Co.
ORCHIDS OF HAWAII - Novelty items - Orchids of Hawaii Inc.
ORCIST - Swords - Atlanta Cutlery Corp.
ORCO - Cheese - Swissrose International Inc.
ORCO PD - Tires - Oliver Rubber Co.
ORCOHESION - Caulking guns - Oliver Rubber Co.
ORCOLITE - Lenses–optical - Optical Radiation Corp.
ORCON - Photographic equipment - Optical Radiation Corp.
ORDA - Toys - DGI/Buki
ORDER - Fruits and vegetables - Orange Cove-Sanger Citrus Association
ORDER OF OPERATIONS - Computer software - Gamco Industries Inc.
ORDER TAKER - Computer software - Eckart and Finard Inc.
ORDEREST - Mattresses - Park Place Corp.
ORDERFIRST - Computer software - Repository Technologies, Inc.
ORDERFLOW - Computer software - Asher Software Development
ORDERMANAGER - Computer software - Mitchum, Jones & Templeton
ORDERNET - Computer software - Donohue Consulting, Inc.
ORDERPATH - Computer software - Jefferies & Co., Inc.
ORDERPEDIC - Mattresses - Park Place Corp.
ORDERS PLUS FOR WINDOWS - Computer software - Business Systems of America Inc.
ORDERTRAK - Computer software - Software Innovations
ORDERWRITER - Computer software - Access International, Inc.
ORDRAM - Herbicides - Chesebrough-Pond's USA Co.
ORE-IDA - Food products - Ore-Ida Foods, Inc.
ORE-IDA - Potato sticks - H.J. Heinz Co.
ORE-IDA FAST FRIES - Fruits and vegetables - Ore-Ida Foods, Inc.
ORE-IDA LITES - Food products - Ore-Ida Foods, Inc.
ORE LIETE - Cookies - Perugina Chocolate & Confections Inc.
OREAQUA - Wood products - Weyerhaeuser Co.
ORECK - Vacuum cleaners and accessories - Oreck Corp.
OREFIELD - Floor coverings - Tarkett, Inc.
OREGOLD - Christmas tree ornaments - Cracker Box Inc.
OREGOLD - Eyeglasses - Art-Craft Optical Co.
OREGOLD - Fruits–canned ☆ - Harry and David Inc.
OREGON - Bicycles - Huffy Corp.
OREGON - Brushes–paint ☆ - PPG Industries, Inc.
OREGON - Clocks - Ridgeway Clock Co.
OREGON - Fencing–wood - C & D Lumber Co.
OREGON - Fireplace equipment - Design Specialties Inc.
OREGON - Food products - Oregon Fruit Products Co., Inc.
OREGON - Jams and jellies - Clearbrook Farms
OREGON 9 - Paperboard ☆ - Sanlu Art Industries Inc.
OREGON BLOSSOM - Wines - Willamette Valley Vineyards
OREGON BLUEBERRY CRUNCH - Food products - Breadshop's Natural Foods
OREGON BREAD - Bakery products - Original Oatmeal Baking Co.
OREGON CHAI - Teas - Lund Distribution, Inc.
OREGON CHIEF - Food products - Portland Provision Co.
OREGON COAST - Potato chips ☆ - Curtice-Burns Foods, Inc.
OREGON COFFEE ROASTER INC. - Coffee - Oregon Coffee Roaster, Inc.
OREGON DUNGENESS - Crab meat–fresh - Winchester Bay Seafood Inc.
OREGON FARMS - Food products - John Labatt Foods
OREGON GRAPE COLLECTION - Skin care products - Langmack Seed Co., Inc.
OREGON GROVES - Fruits–dried - Oregon Groves Inc.
OREGON HARVEST - Wines - Ponzi Vineyards
OREGON HAZELNUT BROWNIE - Cookies - Stanford's Restaurant & Bar, Inc.
OREGON HEALTH - Animal feeds - Oregon Brand Pet Foods
OREGON MIST - Wines - Hillcrest Vineyard
OREGON MOUNTAIN - Cakes - Mountain Bakery
OREGON NATURAL SPORTSTONIC - Teas–herbal - Yellow Emperor Inc.
OREGON NATURAL TEA - Teas - Pacific Westcoast Foods
OREGON NATURE CRAFTS - Statuary ☆ - Hillside House of Originals
OREGON NEVADA CALIFORNIA FAST FREIGHT - Toys - Toy Truck Lines, Inc.
OREGON RED RASPBERRY - Candy bars - Cloud Nine
OREGON SCIENTIFIC - Electronic equipment - Oregon Scientific, Inc.
OREGON SPRING - Wines - Eyrie Vineyards

☆ = Now out of production

OREGON SUET BLOCK - Pet products - Coicor
OREGON TRAIL - Beverages–malt - Brewing Northwest, Ltd.
OREGON TRAIL - Food products ☆ - Paradigm Foodworks
OREGON TRAIL - Fruits–canned - Northwest Packing Co.
OREGON TRAIL - Potato flakes - Oregon Potato Co.
OREGON TRAIL II - Computer software - Softky International Inc.
OREGON TRAIL, THE - Computer software - Softkey International Inc.
OREGON'S FINEST - Frozen foods - Agripac, Inc.
OREGON'S NOG - Beverages–alcohol - Willamette Valley Vineyards
OREGON'S OLDEST MICROBREWERY - Beverages–malt - Bridgeport Brewing Co.
OREGON'S PREMIER WINE ESTATE - Glass products - Montinore Vineyards Ltd.
OREGRO - Food products - Oregon Fruit Products Co., Inc.
O'REILLY SOFTWARE - Computer software - O'Reilly & Associates, Inc.
ORELIA - Skin care products ☆ - Frances Denney
ORELLE - Yarn - Pharr Yarns Inc.
ORELUX - Fruits–canned ☆ - Oregon Fruit Products Co., Inc.
ORENO MATIC - Fishing tackle - South Bend Sporting Goods Inc.
ORENSTEIN - Preserved foods–prepackaged - Shofar Kosher Foods, Inc.
ORENZYME - Pharmaceutical preparations ☆ - Marion Merrell Dow
OREO - Cookies - Nabisco Foods Group
OREO - Cookies - Nabisco Holdings Corp.
OREO - Skin care products - Becky Lynn Co.
OREO COOKIE CRUMBS - Cookies - Nabisco Foods Group
OREO COOKIE FACTORY - Games ☆ - Cadaco Div.
OREO COOKIES 'N CREAM - Confections - Good Humor Corp.
OREO CRUNCHIES - Ice cream - Nabisco Foods Group
OREO MINT CREME - Cookies - Nabisco Foods Group
OREO SNACKWICHES - Ice cream - Good Humor Corp.
OREOR - Hair care products - Cosmair Inc.
OREPAK - Food products ☆ - Oregon Fruit Products Co., Inc.
ORETETIC - Food products ☆ - Oregon Fruit Products Co., Inc.
ORETIC - Pharmaceutical preparations - Abbott Laboratories
ORETICYL - Pharmaceutical preparations - Abbott Laboratories
ORETON - Hormone preparations - Schering-Plough Healthcare Products
O'RETTA - Recording label - Daran Records
OREXIN - Vitamins and nutritional supplements - McNeil Pharmaceuticals
ORFED - Pharmaceutical preparations - Lunsco Inc.
ORFEO - Recording label - Koch International
ORFEON - Recording label - Sony Disco Inc.
ORFEU - Recording label ☆ - Penco Industries Inc.
ORFF-SCHULWERK - Musical instruments - MMB Music Inc.
ORFFGARAGE - Musical instrument accessories - Wenger Corp.
ORFFMOBILE - Carts - Wenger Corp.
ORFLAGEN - Pharmaceutical preparations - Goldline Laboratories, Inc.
ORFRO - Pharmaceutical preparations - C.O. Truxton Inc.
ORG - Electronic equipment - Scientific Technology, Inc.
ORG - Jewelry - Austern & Paul/Orgel-Shorr Inc.
ORG CHART BUILD - Computer software - Lois Melbourne
ORGA-SONIC - Pianos ☆ - Baldwin Piano & Organ Co.
ORGAN - Pasta - Cemac Foods Corp.
ORGAN ADVENTURE - Publisher's imprints - Hal Leonard Corp.
ORGAN-MATIC - Pianos - Organ-Matic Player Inc.
ORGAN MIDI - Electronic equipment ☆ - J.L. Cooper Electronics
ORGAN TRANSPLANTEE'S - Shirts - Steven M. Rzeczkowski
ORGANAGRO - Organic soil amendments - Bedminster Bioconversion Corp.
ORGANDY - Frames–eyeglass ☆ - Universal/Univis Inc.
ORGANETTE - Accordions - Titano Accordion Co. International
ORGANEX - Hair care products - Helene Curtis Industries Inc.
ORGANI-CURE - Veterinary pharmaceutical preparations - Aquarium Products Inc.
ORGANIC - Pet products - Lightning Products
ORGANIC AID - Hair care products - Buty-Wave Products Co., Inc.
ORGANIC BABY ORGANIC BABY - Apparel–children's - Diaperaps Limited
ORGANIC BANANA BABY - Cosmetics - Nutrine Ltd.
ORGANIC BLUE CORN TORTILLA CHIPS - Tortillas - Guiltless Gourmet, Inc.
ORGANIC BLUE TORTILLA CHIPS - Tortillas - Barbara's Bakery, Inc.
ORGANIC BOTANICALS - Health care products - McZand Herbal, Inc.
ORGANIC BRONZE LABEL SHOYU - Soy sauce - San-J International Inc.
ORGANIC CHEF - Soy sauce - Muir Glen
ORGANIC CITRUS - Pet products - Natra Pet Inc.
ORGANIC COFFEE COMPANY, THE - Coffee - Organic Coffee Co., Inc.
ORGANIC CONVENIENCE - Fruits and vegetables - Joe's Vegetables, Inc.
ORGANIC COUNTRY - Fertilizers - Jonathan Green, Inc.
ORGANIC COW OF VERMONT, THE - Milk - Linda Ferris Flint

ORGANIC FOOD MATRIX - Vitamins and nutritional supplements - The Lifestar Millennium, Inc.
ORGANIC-FULL - Hair care products - Organifyl Laboratories
ORGANIC GARDEN - Melamine product - Boonton Molding Co. Inc.
ORGANIC GIANT - Cleaning preparations - Tennstar International
ORGANIC GOLD LABEL TAMARI - Soy sauce - San-J International Inc.
ORGANIC GOURMET - Condiment - Scenario International
ORGANIC GOURMET - Soup - Scenario International
ORGANIC HARVEST - Cereal - New Harvest Grains Inc.
ORGANIC HEALTH - Health care products - Prime Natural Health Laboratories Inc.
ORGANIC MATTER MANAGEMENT - Fertilizers - Growth Products Ltd.
ORGANIC MATTERS - Publisher's imprints - Rebecca Lynch
ORGANIC MOODS - Funnels ☆ - KMS Research Inc.
ORGANIC OBOE - Recording label - Jazz Composer's Orchestra Association Inc.
ORGANIC PLANET - Teas–herbal - Organic Planet
ORGANIC PLATINUM LABEL TAMARI - Soy sauce - San-J International Inc.
ORGANIC PLUS - Shampoos - Cheveux Inc.
ORGANIC POWER - Cleaning preparations - Harvey Universal Inc.
ORGANIC RECHARGE - Juices - Knudsen & Sons Inc.
ORGANIC RECORDS - Recording label - Pamplin Music Corp.
ORGANIC RED CORN - Tortillas - Guiltless Gourmet, Inc.
ORGANIC SOLUTIONS - Chemical preparations - Luxello Properties, Inc.
ORGANIC VALLEY - Dairy products - CROPP/Organic Valley
ORGANICA - Degreasing solvents - Organica, Inc.
ORGANICS - Beverages - After the Fall Products Inc.
ORGANICS PLUS - Salad dressings–mixes - Walden Farms, Inc.
ORGANIDIN - Pharmaceutical preparations - Wallace Laboratories
ORGANIDIN NR - Pharmaceutical preparations - Wallace Laboratories
ORGANILLA - Spices and extracts - David Michael & Co.
ORGANIMALS - Personal-care product - Aubrey Organics, Inc.
ORGANIQUE CLASSIQUE - Deodorizers - Surco Products Inc.
ORGANIX - Frames–eyeglass - Diaco
ORGANIZATION AT ITS BEST - Office supplies - InteliDesign Products Inc.
ORGANIZATION BREEDS SUCCESS - Scrapbooks ☆ - Pengad, Inc.
ORGANIZATION GIRL - Fabrics - Dan River Inc.
ORGANIZATION MAP - Computer software - Pacesetter Group
ORGANIZATION MASTER - Computer software - SourceView Software International
ORGANIZATION STATION - Racks - Flambeau Products Corp.
ORGANIZE - Fertilizers - Green Garden Inc.
ORGANIZE IT - Calculators - Stuart Hall Co., Inc.
ORGANIZE YOUR NEST - Notebooks and notepads - Legal Eagle, Inc.
ORGANIZED CRIME - Games ☆ - Koplow Games
ORGANIZED SPORTS - Computer software - Pennine Computer Consulting, Inc.
ORGANIZED THINKING - Games - David Griffel
ORGANIZER - Office supplies - Mead Corp.
ORGANIZER - Wallets - Buxton Inc.
ORGANIZER III - Luggage - American Tourister, Inc.
ORGANIZER, THE - File folders - Artistic Office Products
ORGANIZER, THE - Computer software - Lotus Development Corp.
ORGANIZER, THE - Infant product - Prince Lionheart, Inc.
ORGANIZER, THE - Luggage - United States Luggage Corp.
ORGANIZERS - Hooks - Crawford Products Inc.
ORGANIZERS, THE - Luggage ☆ - Universal Trav-ler Inc.
ORGANNIZER - Boxes - Ray Gann & Co. Inc.
ORGANNIZER HANDI-KIT - Boxes - Ray Gann & Co. Inc.
ORGANO - Garden equipment - Lawn & Garden Supply Co.
ORGANO - Mulchers - Browning-Ferris Industries, Inc.
ORGANO RECYCLE - Mulchers - Browning-Ferris Industries, Inc.
ORGANO STEER MANURE - Fertilizers - Browning-Ferris Industries, Inc.
ORGANODUST - Insecticides - Green Light Co.
ORGANOGRIT - Insecticides - Green Light Co.
ORGANOSPRAY - Insecticides - Green Light Co.
ORGANOTECH - Dietary food supplements - Vitasol Inc.
ORGANOWAFERS - Nutritional supplement ☆ - Aubrey Organics, Inc.
ORGATRAX - Pharmaceutical preparations ☆ - Organon Inc.
ORGELECTRA - Power switching equipment - La Marche Manufacturing Co.
ORGILL - Paints ☆ - Orgill Brothers and Co.
ORGS - Computer peripheral equipment - Carl E. Hewitt
ORI - Jewelry - Aluma USA Inc.
ORI - Jewelry - Originalities
ORIANA - Floor coverings–carpet and rugs - Lees Carpets
ORIANA - Ophthalmic goods ☆ - Luxottica

☆ = Now out of production

ORIBETIC - Pharmaceutical preparations - H.R. Cenci Laboratories Inc.

ORIBI - Sunglasses ☆ - Corning Inc.

ORIENT - Dinnerware–glass - Royal China & Porcelain Companies Inc.

ORIENT - Floor coverings–carpet and rugs - Capel, Inc.

ORIENT - Games - Lakeside Games

ORIENT - Recording label - Rashid Sales Co.

ORIENT - Vases - Durand International

ORIENT & FLUME GLASS - Giftware - N.S. Gustin Co.

ORIENT CHEF - Food products - CTC Food International

ORIENT COLLECTIONS - Apparel and accessories - China Trade & Research, Inc.

ORIENT CONNECTION - Apparel–women's - China Trade & Research, Inc.

ORIENT/CRISTALLE - Cosmetics - Chanel Inc.

ORIENT EXPRESS - Floor coverings–carpet and rugs ☆ - Regal Rugs Inc.

ORIENT EXPRESS - Furniture - Vaughan Furniture Co. Inc.

ORIENT EXPRESS - Games - S. Alden Inc.

ORIENT EXPRESS - Leather goods ☆ - Mutterperl Group Inc.

ORIENT EXPRESS - Wallpaper - Quality House Inc.

ORIENT EXPRESS - Wallpaper ☆ - S.R. Wood Inc.

ORIENT EXPRESS - Yarn ☆ - JCA, Inc.

ORIENT EXPRESS MYSTERY DETECTIVE - Games - Just Games

ORIENT HILL - Wallpaper ☆ - Wall Fabrics Inc.

ORIENT PASSPORT - Frozen foods - Nichirei Foods America

ORIENT SELECT - Teas - Christopher Brookes Distinctive Foods

ORIENT TODAY - Wallpaper - Dekortex Inc.

ORIENTA - Cymbals - European Crafts/USA

ORIENTA - Frames–eyeglass - May Optical Co. Inc.

ORIENTA - Jewelry - Leys, Christie & Co. Inc.

ORIENTAL - Cymbals - Avedis Zildjian Co.

ORIENTAL - Floor coverings - American Floor Products Co. Inc.

ORIENTAL - Food products - Acme Continental Foods Inc.

ORIENTAL - Glassware–household - Lancaster Colony Corp.

ORIENTAL - Olives–pickled or brined - Oriental Foods Inc.

ORIENTAL - Stucco - United States Gypsum Co.

ORIENTAL - Teas - Eastern Tea Corp.

ORIENTAL - Wallpaper ☆ - Wolf-Gordon Inc.

ORIENTAL ACCENTS - Wallpaper - Enterprise Wallcoverings Inc.

ORIENTAL BASICS - Vegetables–frozen - Dean Foods Co.

ORIENTAL BEAUTIES - Dolls - Seymour Mann Inc.

ORIENTAL BEAUTY - Skin care products ☆ - Sunshine Products

ORIENTAL BEAUTY COLLECTION - Skin care products - Entre-Nous Fragrances Ltd.

ORIENTAL BLOSSOM - Skin-care products - Benjamin Ansehl Co.

ORIENTAL-CHEF - Mayonnaise - Q & B Foods, Inc.

ORIENTAL CHEF - Salad dressings–bottled - Q & B Foods, Inc.

ORIENTAL CLASSICS - Food products - General Mills, Inc.

ORIENTAL CLASSICS - Furniture ☆ - Lane Co. Inc.

ORIENTAL DAYS - Trees–artificial - H & P Sales, Inc.

ORIENTAL DYNASTY - Wallpaper - Aresda Design Associates

ORIENTAL EDGE - Scissors–hand-operated - Burmax Co. Inc.

ORIENTAL ELEGANCE - Wallpaper - Enterprise Wallcoverings Inc.

ORIENTAL ESSENCE FORMULA - Depilatories - Carter-Wallace, Inc.

ORIENTAL EXPRESS - Food products - B.V. Foods International Inc.

ORIENTAL EXPRESS - Food products - Waltham Beef & Provision Co.

ORIENTAL EXPRESSION - Wallpaper - Richard E. Thibaut, Inc.

ORIENTAL FANTASY - Bedding–linen - Dan River Inc.

ORIENTAL FANTASY - Toiletries - Minnetonka Brands

ORIENTAL FIRM - Floor coverings–carpet and rugs - Omalon

ORIENTAL FLOWER - Rice - Gulf Pacific Rice Co., Inc.

ORIENTAL FLOWERS - Dishes–china ☆ - Royal China & Porcelain Companies Inc.

ORIENTAL GAMES - Computer software ☆ - Microprose Software, Inc.

ORIENTAL GARDEN - Floor coverings–carpet and rugs - Roxbury Carpet Co.

ORIENTAL GARDEN - Giftware - Arnart Imports Inc.

ORIENTAL GARDEN - Salad dressings–bottled - China Bowl Trading Co.

ORIENTAL GARDENS - Teas - Swiss American Import Co.

ORIENTAL GINSENG CREAM - Skin care products - Entre-Nous Fragrances Ltd.

ORIENTAL ICE - Scissors–hand-operated - Burmax Co. Inc.

ORIENTAL JADE - Health care products - Saxony Products Inc.

ORIENTAL JADE TABAC - Health care products - Schnapp Enterprises Inc.

ORIENTAL LOTUS - Perfumes - Quintessence Inc.

ORIENTAL MAJESTY - Floor coverings ☆ - Congoleum Corp.

ORIENTAL MOOD - Cutlery ☆ - Lifetime Hoan Corp.

ORIENTAL MURAL PANELS - Wallpaper - Christopher Hyland

ORIENTAL NATURAL & TEXTILES - Wallpaper - Stamford Wall Paper Co. Inc.

ORIENTAL ORIGINALS - Wallpaper ☆ - Gamrod-Harman

ORIENTAL PANTRY - Food products ☆ - Liberty Richter Inc.

ORIENTAL PATCHWORK - Toilets–enameled - Kohler Co.

ORIENTAL PEARL - Floor coverings–tile - Robbins Interior Surface Inc.

ORIENTAL REIGN - Furniture ☆ - Bassett Furniture Industries, Inc.

ORIENTAL SECRETS - Skin care products ☆ - Sunshine Products

ORIENTAL SPLENDOR - Bedroom and dining-room furniture ☆ - Bassett Furniture Industries, Inc.

ORIENTAL STRINGS - Wallpaper ☆ - Capital Carousel Inc.

ORIENTAL STYLE - Rice - Riceland Foods, Inc.

ORIENTAL TEALAND - Teas–herbal - Yamamoto of Orient Inc.

ORIENTAL TEXTILES - Wallpaper - Advance Wallcoverings

ORIENTAL TRAIL MIX - Snack foods - Amsnack, Inc.

ORIENTAL TREASURES - Teas–herbal - Lipton Investments, Inc.

ORIENTAL WEAVE - Wallpaper ☆ - Capital Carousel Inc.

ORIENTAL WINDS - Wallpaper ☆ - Fairwinds Studio

ORIENTAL WOOD - Dinnerware ☆ - Corning Inc.

ORIENTAL WOODS - Giftware ☆ - Avon Products, Inc.

ORIENTALS THE DESIGNER COLLECTION 10 - Wallpaper - Pantasote Inc. (Wallcovering Div.)

ORIENTEC - Jewelry - OTC Inc

ORIENTEX - Wallpaper ☆ - Quality House Inc.

ORIENT'S CHOICE - Food products - Orient's Choice Hawaii Inc.

ORIGAMI - Wallpaper - Archetonic

ORIGAMI - Wallpaper ☆ - Koroseal Wallcoverings

ORIGI-NAILS - Nail care products - E.O.H. Industries, Inc.

ORIGI-STIK - Nail care products - E.O.H. Industries, Inc.

ORIGI-TIPS - Nail care products - E.O.H. Industries, Inc.

ORIGIN/FX - Video games - Origin Systems, Inc.

ORIGIN TACKER - Medical apparatus - Origin Medsystems, Inc.

ORIGIN TECHNOLOGIES CORPORATION - Gauging instruments - Origin Technologies Corp.

ORIGINAILS - Nail care products - E.O.H. Industries, Inc.

ORIGINAL - Beverages–carbonated - Snapple Beverage Corp.

ORIGINAL - Bowling balls - Ebonite International, Inc.

ORIGINAL - Drums–musical instruments - LP Music Group

ORIGINAL - Fireplace equipment - Thermo-Rite Manufacturing Co.

ORIGINAL - Golfing equipment - Golfsmith International Inc.

ORIGINAL - Jewelry, pencils, tote bags, etc. - Au Coton

ORIGINAL - Markers–felt-tip ☆ - K. Ogawa & Co. Inc.

ORIGINAL - Novelty items ☆ - Hortense B. Hewitt Inc.

ORIGINAL - Paper - Simpson Paper Co.

ORIGINAL - Personal-care shower - Interbath, Inc.

ORIGINAL - Saws–power - Lancaster Machinery Co.

ORIGINAL II - Fireplace equipment - Thermo-Rite Manufacturing Co.

ORIGINAL 3-D DECOUPAGE, THE - Hobby kits - Uniek, Inc.

ORIGINAL 24KT GOLD JEAN CO 1991, THE - Apparel and accessories - Allen Shevalier

ORIGINAL 1859'ER BEANS - Baked beans–canned - Sysco Services Co.

ORIGINAL 1897 - Waterproof outerwear - MacGregor Golf Co.

ORIGINAL ACCESSORIES - Crocheted and knitted items - Beldoch Industries Corp.

ORIGINAL ADULT ICE CREAM, THE - Beverages–alcohol - Ice Cream Bar, Inc.

ORIGINAL AFGHAN COMPANY, THE - Linen - Tapestry, Inc.

ORIGINAL AIR FRESHENER FOR AMENITIES PACKAGING, THE - Deodorizers - Dear Products Inc.

ORIGINAL ALL SPORTS, THE - Puzzles - Xtrax Corp.

ORIGINAL AMBIDERM RAINBOW PASTEL, THE - Gloves–rubber - Meditex Inc.

ORIGINAL AMERICAN HEALTH FOOD, THE - Meat products - Great Plains Foods Co.

ORIGINAL AMERICAN HOMMUS, THE - Food products - Hommus Factory Inc.

ORIGINAL AMERICAN SCONES - Bakery products - By Bread Alone, Inc.

ORIGINAL AMY BLOOMS - Apparel–women's - Original Amy Blooms

ORIGINAL ANGELIC SOLE, THE - Footwear - John Fluevog Shoes, Ltd.

ORIGINAL ARIZONA JEAN COMPANY, THE - Apparel and accessories - J.C. Penney Co., Inc.

ORIGINAL AUSTIN SHIRT COMPANY U.S.A. - Apparel and accessories - Texas Chic, Inc.

ORIGINAL AUTOGRAPH NETWORK, THE - Apparel and accessories - Jay Edward Jones

ORIGINAL B D BAGGIES, THE - Apparel–men's - Apparel Group, Ltd.

ORIGINAL BABY SAC - Diapers–disposable - Cudlie Diaper Bags

ORIGINAL BABY TEE - Apparel - Gitano Licensing, Ltd.

ORIGINAL BACKNOBBER, THE - Massage products - Pressure Positive Co.

ORIGINAL BACKNOBBER, THE - Massage products - The Pressure Positive Co.

ORIGINAL BAGIT SYSTEM - Racks - Bag Connection Inc.

ORIGINAL BAKERS, THE - Baked goods - Bavarian Specialty Foods

ORIGINAL BAN-A-BEE, THE - Housewares - Kantec Manufacturing Inc.

ORIGINAL BARREL, THE - Sandwiches - Barrel Sandwich Co., Inc.

ORIGINAL BASEBALL, THE - Puzzles - Xtrax Corp.

ORIGINAL BDB SOCK TIE, THE - Neckties - Damon Creations Inc.

ORIGINAL BEN'S, THE - Apparel - Ben Davis Co.

ORIGINAL BILINGUAL CARPET, THE - Floor coverings–carpet and rugs - Flagship Carpets, Inc.

ORIGINAL BLACK AND TAN - Beverages–malt - D.G. Yuengling & Son Inc.

ORIGINAL BLEND - Cat food - Ralston Purina Co.

ORIGINAL BLEND - Perfumes - Tennessee Gold Inc.

ORIGINAL BLUES CLASSICS - Phonographs - Fantasy Inc.

ORIGINAL BOBS CANDY CANES - Candy - Bobs Candies Inc.

ORIGINAL BOOGER BUSTERS, THE - Paper–tissue - Mark D. O'Neal

ORIGINAL BOOT BRACELET, THE - Accessories - Annie Oakley Enterprise Inc.

ORIGINAL BOSSMAN BARBECUE SAUCE - Barbecue sauce - Bossman Foods Corp.

ORIGINAL BOSTON COFFEE CAKE, THE - Cakes - Original Boston Coffee Cake Co., Inc.

ORIGINAL BOSTON COLA, THE - Beverages - Beverage Marketing of Pa., Inc.

ORIGINAL BOTTLE TIE - Neckties - Together Crafts Inc.

ORIGINAL BOW MAKER, THE - Ribbons - Ribbon Magic, Inc.

ORIGINAL BOYZ CLOTHING CO., THE - Apparel–children's - Girl's Will Be Girl's, Inc.

ORIGINAL BRAND - Paints - Krylon/Dupli-Color

ORIGINAL BRASS LINE, THE - Cash registers - Auer Register Co.

ORIGINAL BREAD 'N BUTTER PICKLES - Pickles - GFA Brands Inc.

ORIGINAL BREAD SIZE, THE - Meats–luncheon - Fischer Packing Co.

ORIGINAL BREAKAWAY STEAK, THE - Meat products - Heartland Beef Management, Inc.

ORIGINAL BRIMLESS CAP, THE - Caps–baseball - Sidney Richlin

ORIGINAL BT - Water treatment - RPS Products Inc.

ORIGINAL BUG COLLECTION, THE - Stuffed toys - Original Bug Collection, Inc.

ORIGINAL BUTT MAT, THE - Cushions - Trunkmat, Inc.

ORIGINAL BUTTERFLY - Chairs–folding - Algoma Net Co.

ORIGINAL C - Teas - Satori Fine Herbals

ORIGINAL CAJUN - Cooking utensils–cast iron - Lodge Manufacturing Co.

ORIGINAL CALIFORNIA - Hammocks - E-Z Sales & Manufacturing, Inc.

ORIGINAL CALIFORNIA CAR DUSTER, THE - Auto-exterior duster - California Magic Car Duster Co. Inc.

ORIGINAL CALIFORNIA CAR DUSTER, THE - Dusters - Original California Car Duster Co.,Inc.

ORIGINAL-CAMLIN - Girdles - H.F. Robbins

ORIGINAL CANTON DELIGATE - Liquors - Chatam International Inc.

ORIGINAL CARLSBAD OBLATEN WAFER, THE - Cookies - Award Baking International

ORIGINAL CELEBRATED, THE - Candy - R.J. Hirt Co.

ORIGINAL CHICAGO STYLE, THE - Frankfurters - Vienna Sausage Manufacturing Co.

ORIGINAL CHILE MADNESS - Food products - Pecos Valley Spice Co.

ORIGINAL CHILI BOWL - Frozen foods - Windsor Quality Food Co. Ltd.

ORIGINAL CHINO CASUAL - Apparel and accessories - Tropical Sportswear International Corp.

ORIGINAL CHOICE - Computer diskettes–blank - Standard Manifold Co.

ORIGINAL CHRISTMAS TREE - Dinnerware–glass - Cuthbertson Imports Inc.

ORIGINAL CHUCKLE BUCKLE, THE - Automotive parts and accessories - Chuckle Buckle Inc.

ORIGINAL CHUMS, THE - Ophthalmic goods - Chums Ltd.

ORIGINAL CIGAR CLOTHING COMPANY, THE - Apparel–women's - Original Cigar Clothing Co.

ORIGINAL CIGAR WEDGE, THE - Golfing equipment - Walter H. Brauer, Jr.

ORIGINAL COMICS - Books–comic - Idea Workshop, Inc.

ORIGINAL COMPUTER GLITCH, THE - Figurines - Nord Advertising Associates

ORIGINAL CONVERTIBLE VEST-PURSE BY ALETA MAYE, THE - Handbags - Aleta Mays

ORIGINAL COOKIE BOUQUET - Cookies - Cookie Bouquet Franchising Corp.

ORIGINAL CORN BEAN MIX - Pet food - Judee K. Creations, Inc. (Crazy Corn Division)

ORIGINAL CORN BEAN MIX - Pet products - Crazy Corn

ORIGINAL COSMIC UFO TECHNO-FLYER, THE - Kites - Thomas J. Bukur

ORIGINAL COWBOY, THE - Beverages–alcohol - Olde St. Nick Distillery Inc.

ORIGINAL CRANBERRY BY PILGRIM - Glass products - Pilgrim Glass Corp.

ORIGINAL CRESTED BUTTE, COLORADO POWERHOUSE SALSA, THE - Sauces - Crested Butte Power Co.

ORIGINAL CROWN MILL - Stationery - Oldcastle Associates Inc.

ORIGINAL CRYBABY - Musical instrument accessories - Dunlop Manufacturing, Inc.

ORIGINAL DAKOTA GOLD BLACK HILLS GOLD - Jewelry - Coleman Co.

ORIGINAL DAKOTA GOLD BLACK HILLS GOLD JEWELRY - Jewelry–precious - Coleman Co.

ORIGINAL DIET NOTES - Stationery - Ten Talents Distributors

ORIGINAL DR. DENTON, THE - Apparel and accessories - Salant/Manhattan Industries

ORIGINAL DR. MULLER QDM - Lamps–ultraviolet - QDM Co.

ORIGINAL DOOLITTLE DOODLE PAD - Calendars - House of Doolittle

ORIGINAL DOUBLE CHOCOLATE CHIP COOKIE - Cookies - Natco Sales and Marketing, Inc.

ORIGINAL DUKE'S DOG FASHIONS, THE - Pet products - Duke's Dog Fashions

ORIGINAL DUNKERS, THE - Cookies - Nabisco Foods Group

ORIGINAL EASTCOAST GYM - Sportswear - Samuel Vitrano, Jr.

ORIGINAL EMMETT KELLY, THE - Figurines - Dave Grossman Creations Inc.

ORIGINAL ENGRAVINGS - Floor coverings–carpet and rugs ☆ - Evans-Black Carpet Mills

ORIGINAL EQUIPMENT PLUS - Automotive oil, air and fuel filters - Import Brokers, Inc.

ORIGINAL FAT FREE, THE - Potato chips - Friday Harbor Snack Foods Inc.

ORIGINAL FINNISH MINNOW - Fishing lures - Normark Corp.

ORIGINAL FIREHOUSE BRAND - Sauces - Original Firehouse Products, Inc.

ORIGINAL FLAPHAPPY FLAPHAT, THE - Hats - Flap Happy

ORIGINAL FORMULA FUNNY HI BROWS - Greeting cards - American Greetings Corp.

ORIGINAL FORMULA, THE - Lipsticks - Anders Lowe Inc.

ORIGINAL FOUNTAIN OF YOUTH WATER - Drinking water - Ponce de Lleon's Fountain of Youth Archeological Park

ORIGINAL FRENCH COUNTRY PRINTS II - Wallpaper - Pelican Prints

ORIGINAL FRENCH MANICURE, THE - Nail care products - Orly International Inc.

ORIGINAL FRIDGE CARD! - Greeting cards - Under the Same Sun, Inc.

ORIGINAL GENERIC, THE - Cigarettes - G.A. Georgopulo & Co. Inc.

ORIGINAL GIANT PRETZEL, THE - Pretzels - Natco Sales and Marketing, Inc.

ORIGINAL GLIMMER - Fabrics–satin - Guilford Mills, Inc.

ORIGINAL GLOSSINE - Hair care products - Madame C.J. Walker Inc.

ORIGINAL GOURMET JELLY BEAN, THE - Candy - Herman Goelitz Candy Co., Inc.

ORIGINAL GOURMET, THE - Frozen foods - Carando Gourmet Foods Corp.

ORIGINAL GRANNY BOOZER'S - Desserts - Margaret Van Der Blom Sapp

ORIGINAL GREAT AMERICAN COMPUTER CLOTHING COMPANY, THE - Computers - Dallco Industries Inc.

ORIGINAL GREENSLEEVE - Plastics - Mer-Nel Co.

ORIGINAL HAMBURGER STAND, THE - Restaurants–fast food - Wienerschnitzel International Inc.

ORIGINAL HANDICAP SWEAT JEANS BY RICKY COX, THE - Jeans–men's - Richard Cox

ORIGINAL HEART - Labels–fabric - Original Heart Co.

ORIGINAL HERKIMER COUNTY - Cheese - Original Herkimer County Cheese Co. Inc.

ORIGINAL HEWN AMERICAN LOGS - Toys–blocks - American Wood Toys Co.

ORIGINAL HIDDEN IMAGE APPAREL, THE - Apparel and accessories - Diversified Enterprises, Inc.

ORIGINAL HOT DOG SHOP - Sandwiches–prepackaged - Original Hot Dog Shops, Inc.

ORIGINAL HOUSE ITALIAN - Salad dressings–bottled - Patch Park Foods

ORIGINAL I - Fireplace equipment - Thermo-Rite Manufacturing Co.

ORIGINAL IMPRESSIONS - Nail care products - Cosmania, Inc.

ORIGINAL INDEXKNOBBER, THE - Massage products - Pressure Positive Co.

ORIGINAL INDIAN VALLEY - Snack foods - Kolve Sawchain Co. Inc.

ORIGINAL INLINE SPORTS BAG, THE - Sporting goods - Zepter Sports International

ORIGINAL INNKEEPER'S RECIPE - Sauces - WSF L.P. of Michigan

ORIGINAL IROQUOIS QUALITY, THE - Popcorn - Iroquois Popcorn Co. Inc.

☆ = Now out of production

ORIGINAL IT'S A BABY - Apparel–children's - Robert J. Haertel

ORIGINAL JACKNOBBER, THE - Massage products - Pressure Positive Co.

ORIGINAL JALAPENO PECAN BRITTLE, THE - Candy - Windmill Candy Inc.

ORIGINAL JAMAICAN ICED TEA, THE - Iced tea–bottled or canned - B.S.W. Ventures, Inc.

ORIGINAL JAMES BOWIE, THE - Beverages–malt - Hornell Brewing Co. Inc.

ORIGINAL JAZZ CLASSICS - Phonographs - Fantasy Inc.

ORIGINAL JENASOL, INC. - Vitamins - Jenasol, Inc.

ORIGINAL JIMBO FORK, THE - Forks - Stills, Inc.

ORIGINAL K-PAUL'S - Beverages–alcohol ☆ - Sazerac Co. Inc.

ORIGINAL KACY PRODUCT - Apparel and accessories - Sunny Jung Trading, Inc.

ORIGINAL KETCHUP - Food products - Uncle Dave's Kitchen

ORIGINAL KHAKI CO., THE - Apparel and accessories - Tropical Sportswear International Corp.

ORIGINAL KINGSDOWN - Mattresses - Kingsdown, Inc.

ORIGINAL KNITS BY JEAN SWEET - Apparel - Jean S. Ehlinger

ORIGINAL KOMFY KID, THE - Infant product - Skrozco Inc.

ORIGINAL KONG, THE - Pet products - Kong Co.

ORIGINAL KOOL TIE A PRO-SURVIVAL PRODUCT, THE - Neckties - Pamela L. Kafka

ORIGINAL KROME KAP, THE - Trading cards and stamps - Signs & Glassworks, Inc.

ORIGINAL LAMPLIGHT FARMS, THE - Oils–illuminating - Lamplight Farms, Inc.

ORIGINAL LEAN LINKS, THE - Frankfurters - Classic Country Rabbit Co.

ORIGINAL LIL' DRUG STORE, THE - Health care products - Lil' Drug Store Products, Inc.

ORIGINAL LIL' POUTERS, THE - Dolls - Bonnie Wrixton

ORIGINAL LIL' REMEDY STORE, THE - Health care products - Lil' Drug Store Products, Inc.

ORIGINAL LIVE OAK - Leather goods - Tandy Leather Co.

ORIGINAL LOCALS - Apparel and accessories - Paul J. Kelly

ORIGINAL LOGGERSTAPE - Tape measures - Spencer Products Co.

ORIGINAL LOGGERSTAPE MADE BY SPENCER PRODUCTS CO. SEATTLE, WA. - Tape measures - Spencer Products Co.

ORIGINAL LOVE ME NON STOP WEAR - Apparel–children's - Power Clothing Inc.

ORIGINAL MACKY SAC, THE - Cushions - Paul Zurlini

ORIGINAL MACRAME DESIGNS - Fabrics - Decorative Aides Co. Inc.

ORIGINAL MAIL BOX COOKIE, THE - Cookies - Jody Heitner

ORIGINAL MANATEE SHIRT COMPANY, THE - Towels - Jazz Angel Productions

ORIGINAL MANATEE SHIRT COMPANY, THE - Toys–stuffed - Original Manatee Shirt Co.

ORIGINAL MASTER RECORDINGS - Recording label - Mobile Fidelity Sound Lab

ORIGINAL MCKENZIE - Medical apparatus - Positex Inc.

ORIGINAL MCKENZIE PROCESS, THE - Animal feed supplements - Animal Feed Supplement, Inc.

ORIGINAL MEGA WARHEADS, THE - Candy - Foreign Candy Co. Inc.

ORIGINAL MELTDOWN - Beverages–alcohol - Brinker Restaurant Corp.

ORIGINAL MEMORY, THE - Games - Milton Bradley Co.

ORIGINAL MESSAGE MAGNETS, THE - Magnets - Frog Prince Inc.

ORIGINAL MINK OIL - Leather tanning and finishing - Original Mink Oil Inc.

ORIGINAL MIRACLE BAG, THE - Handbags - Accessory Network Group, Inc.

ORIGINAL MOUNTAIN CHEDDAR - Cheese - Northfield Foods Inc.

ORIGINAL MOUSE COUCH, THE - Computer peripheral equipment - Sky

ORIGINAL MUDDLER - Sporting goods - Gapen Co.

ORIGINAL MUGTEE'S - Housewares - Pro Ad, Inc.

ORIGINAL MULTI-CULTURAL, MULTI-PURPOSE, AND MULTI-SKINS BODY POWDER, THE - Toiletries - Dear Products Inc.

ORIGINAL MUSCLE UP - Skin care products - P.M.A.E.S. & Body Development Inc.

ORIGINAL MUSIC - Recording label - Jazz Composer's Orchestra Association Inc.

ORIGINAL MUSICAL WATCH, THE - Clocks - Lori Industries Inc.

ORIGINAL NEW YORK EXPRESS - Coffee - Original New York Seltzer

ORIGINAL NEW YORK FOUNTAIN STYLE - Beverages–carbonated - Original New York Seltzer

ORIGINAL NEW YORK SELTZER - Beverages - Original New York Seltzer

ORIGINAL NEWBORN, THE - Dolls - Doll Factory, Inc.

ORIGINAL NORFOLK - Beverages ☆ - Traditional Products Inc.

ORIGINAL NUT HOUSE BRANDS - Nuts–salted, roasted, cooked, or canned - Morven Partners, LP

ORIGINAL NUT HOUSE, THE - Nuts–salted, roasted, cooked, or canned - Morven Partners, LP

ORIGINAL OHIO - Thermometers - Taylor Environmental Instruments

ORIGINAL OJAI FLOWER CANDLE, THE - Candles ☆ - Essential Aromatics

ORIGINAL PAPA JOE'S BUTCHER BLOCK SINCE 1892, THE - Spices and extracts - Bolner's Fiesta Products, Inc.

ORIGINAL PAWLEYS ISLAND - Hammocks - Pawleys Island Rope Hammock

ORIGINAL PAWLEYS ISLAND, THE - Hammocks - The HammockSource

ORIGINAL PENNSYLVANIA DUTCH - Candy - Keppel's Inc.

ORIGINAL PINK TAPE, THE - Adhesives and sealants - Hy-Tape Surgical Products Corp.

ORIGINAL PIZSOY, THE - Food products - Tree Tavern Products Inc.

ORIGINAL POCKETBAG, THE - Bags - The Original Pocketbag Inc.

ORIGINAL POPCORN CUISINE CARRIER, THE - Popcorn ☆ - Continental American Corp.

ORIGINAL POPCORN PARTY SACK - Popcorn ☆ - Continental American Corp.

ORIGINAL POTATO FLYERS - Snack foods - Robert's American Gourmet

ORIGINAL PREEMIE, THE - Dolls - Doll Factory, Inc.

ORIGINAL PRETTY PUNCH, THE - Hobby kits - Original Pretty Punch, Inc.

ORIGINAL PRO-FILER - Lubricants - Edge Specialties, Inc.

ORIGINAL PUB SODA, THE - Beverages–carbonated - Original Pub Soda Co.

ORIGINAL PUMPKIN CARVER - Knives–carving - Impel, Inc.

ORIGINAL RANCH - Dips–sour cream based - HVR Co.

ORIGINAL RECIPE - Breads - Roush Products Co., Inc.

ORIGINAL RECIPE - Food products - Snackmasters, Inc.

ORIGINAL RED EAGLE - Transmissions–motor vehicle - Alto Products Corp.

ORIGINAL RED VACUUM CLEANER, THE - Vacuum cleaners and accessories - Royal Appliance Manufacturing Co.

ORIGINAL RESEAT - Furniture - Norbert George Marklin

ORIGINAL RHYMING ROMPER - Apparel–children's - Mamiye Brothers, Inc.

ORIGINAL RICE CRUST PIZZA, THE - Food products ☆ - Amberwave Foods

ORIGINAL ROLLABOARD, THE - Luggage - Eiffel Design, Inc.

ORIGINAL ROUND TEA BAG, THE - Tea - Tetley Inc.

ORIGINAL SALT WATER COLOGNE - Colognes - Beach Gifts Ltd.

ORIGINAL SAMBA GUARANA - Beverages–carbonated - IBI Beverage, Inc.

ORIGINAL SAND WALKERS - Ramps - Sand Walkers, Inc.

ORIGINAL SAND WALKERS, THE - Floor coverings - Sand Walkers, Inc.

ORIGINAL SCOPE ENHANCER, THE - Electronic equipment - Scope Enhancer Inc.

ORIGINAL SCRUBBA DUCKY, THE - Toys–electronic - Video Technology U.S. Inc.

ORIGINAL SHOWER MASSAGE, THE - Hardware - Teledyne Industries Inc.

ORIGINAL SILCA SHAMPOO - Guns–pellet - Scandinavian Natural Health & Beauty Products, Inc.

ORIGINAL SILICA HIGH POTENCY FORMULA - Vitamins and nutritional supplements - Scandinavian Natural Health & Beauty Products, Inc.

ORIGINAL SILICA SILICA SILICA - Vitamins and nutritional supplements - Scandinavian Natural Health & Beauty Products, Inc.

ORIGINAL SIN - Beverages–alcohol - Original Sin Corp.

ORIGINAL SIN - Sporting goods - Skis Dynastar, Inc.

ORIGINAL SKIN - Cosmetics - Origins Natural Resources Inc.

ORIGINAL SKIN - Skin care products - Faberge Co.

ORIGINAL SMITH HOIST, THE - Machinery - Smith Hoist Engineering Corp.

ORIGINAL SMOOTHIE COMPANY - Beverages - Original Smoothie Co.

ORIGINAL SNAK-ENS - Snack foods - Gardetto's

ORIGINAL SNOW VILLAGE, THE - Figurines - Department 56 Inc.

ORIGINAL SOUND - Recording label - Original Sound Record Co. Inc.

ORIGINAL SOUND ENTERTAINMENT - Recording label - Original Sound Record Co. Inc.

ORIGINAL SOURER SODA - Beverages–carbonated - J & H Food and Beverage, Inc.

ORIGINAL SOUTHERN CINNAMON BROOM - Novelty items - Butler Imports Inc.

ORIGINAL SOUTHERN PLAYER 94 - Apparel–athletic - Charles Coleman and Timothy Yancy Partnership

ORIGINAL/SPICY DRY SEASONING - Seasonings - Guido's International Foods, LLC

ORIGINAL SPREADABLES, THE - Dairy products - Michael Seiff

ORIGINAL SPRITZA - Skin care products - Brushes by Anne Marie Inc.

ORIGINAL STATE OVALS, THE - Decals and transfers - WJL, Inc.

ORIGINAL STEP - Video tapes–blank - Fit Net

ORIGINAL STICKY FINGERS, THE - Bakery products - Port City Bakery & Deli Inc.

ORIGINAL STRAPLOCK - Musical instrument accessories - Dunlop Manufacturing, Inc.

ORIGINAL SUN CORD, THE - Cording - Michael Miroyan

ORIGINAL SUPER COIL, THE - Coils–ignition - QMP Enterprises Inc.

ORIGINAL SURPRISE BAG, THE - Candy - Foreign Candy Co. Inc.

ORIGINAL SUSPENDER T-SHIRT, THE - T-shirts–men's - Crown Imperial Promotion Corp.

ORIGINAL SWAB - Musical instrument accessories - David Wexler & Co.

ORIGINAL SWIRLED LUNCH BUNS - Sandwiches–prepackaged - Stefano's Provision

ORIGINAL TALKING MAIL ENVELOPE, THE - Envelopes - Talking Mail Envelopes

ORIGINAL TEDCO GYROSCOPE - Toys - Tedco Inc.

ORIGINAL TEXAS JACQUES TEXAS ASS KICKIN' CHILI 100% MEAT CHILI CON CARN, THE - Chili–canned - Texas Jacques Gourmet Chili Co.

ORIGINAL, THE - Magnets ☆ - Great Graphic Originals

ORIGINAL, THE - Mushrooms - Lake Erie Frozen Foods Inc.

ORIGINAL, THE - Fishing tackle - Wilderness System

ORIGINAL THIN THIGHS, THE - Cosmetics - Cosmedix Inc.

ORIGINAL TOMMY HAWK, THE - Guitars - Thomas G. Barth

ORIGINAL TOMMY'S GUN PACK, THE - Bags - Kickin' a Packs 'n Stuff

ORIGINAL TOP LOADER, THE - Paper products - PKK, Inc.

ORIGINAL TOTEM NUTS, THE - Processed nuts - Totem International Inc.

ORIGINAL TOUCHDOWN-TOWEL, THE - Towels - D & G Sports International

ORIGINAL TWIRLY GIRL, THE - Apparel–women's - Young Enterprises, Inc.

ORIGINAL U.S.S. ENTERPRISE - Toys–models - ERTL Co., Inc.

ORIGINAL WA HOO, THE - Games - Traditional Game & Toy Co.

ORIGINAL WASS GEAR, THE - Apparel and accessories - Urban Jungle Empire

ORIGINAL WEAVER MOVIE POPCORN - Popcorn - Weaver Popcorn Co. Inc.

ORIGINAL WEBBING - Paints - Carnival Arts, Inc.

ORIGINAL WILD ONES, THE - Novelty items - Boozefighters Motorcycle Club, Inc.

ORIGINAL WINGS GOURMET SAUCE FOR CHICKEN WINGS, THE - Barbecue sauce - PRH Foods, Inc.

ORIGINAL YARD VAC, THE - Tools–machine - Yard Vac Products, Inc.

ORIGINAL YELLOW PAGES, THE - Telephone directories - Southern New England Telephone Co.

ORIGINAL YOOPER PASTY, THE - Cakes - Yooper Pastry Inc.

ORIGINAL ZOOLACES - Laces–boot and shoe - Dirk Gombert II

ORIGINALA - Apparel–women's - N & I Notice Corp.

ORIGINALA - Frames–eyeglass - May Optical Co. Inc.

ORIGINALE - Eyeglasses - Martin-Copeland Eyewear Corp.

ORIGINALE BY REGAL - Floor coverings–carpet and rugs ☆ - Regal Rugs Inc.

ORIGINALIA - Wallpaper ☆ - Royaleigh Designs Ltd.

ORIGINALITIES - Jewelry - Originalities

ORIGINALS - Bakeware - Corning Inc.

ORIGINALS ASSORTMENT - Chocolate candy - Price Candy Co. Inc.

ORIGINALS BY IRMI - Lamps ☆ - Reliance Products Corp.

ORIGINALS IN CRYSTAL - Statuary ☆ - Hillside House of Originals

ORIGINALS IN KNITWEAR - Crocheted and knitted items - Hedy Knits of California

ORIGINALS INTERNATIONAL - Dolls - Pittsburgh Originals, Inc.

ORIGINALS OF ORIGINALS - Canvas–artists' - Fabulous Forgeries Ltd.

ORIGINATION STATION - Computer software - Greatland Corp.

ORIGINATOR - Breads–mixes - Dawn Food Products Inc.

ORIGINE SUISSE - Skin care products - Neutrogena Corp.

ORIGINL JELL - Shampoos ☆ - Colorful Products Corp.

ORIGINS - Cosmetics - Origins Natural Resources Inc.

ORIGINS - Floor coverings–carpet and rugs ☆ - Alexander Smith Carpets

ORIGINS - Skin care products - Estee Lauder Inc.

ORIGINS - Tableware–earthenware - Pfaltzgraff Investment Co.

ORIGINS OF WORLD WAR II - Games ☆ - Avalon Hill Game Co.

ORIGO - Tableware–china ☆ - Villeroy and Boch Tableware Ltd.

ORIKI - Computer diskettes–blank - Oriental King (USA) Inc.

ORINASE - Pharmaceutical preparations - Upjohn Co.

ORINASE DIAGNOSTIC - Pharmaceutical preparations - Upjohn Co.

ORINDA - Food products ☆ - Lindsay Olive Growers

ORINGER - Syrup - Concord Foods Inc.

ORIOLE - Brushes–paint ☆ - PPG Industries, Inc.

ORIOLE - Cookies - Mid-Atlantic Snacks Inc.

ORIOLE - Eyeglasses - Art-Craft Optical Co.

ORIOLE - Paper–writing - Butler Paper Co.

ORIOLE - Pencils - Dixon Ticonderoga Co.

ORIOLE FUN BAR - Pet products - Hummingbird Heaven

ORIOLES BALTIMORE - Metal novelty items - Orioles, Inc.

ORION - Bedding–linen - Dan River Inc.

ORION - Bicycles ☆ - XLM Corp.

ORION - Boats ☆ - Pacific Seacraft Corp.

ORION - Coated printing paper - Consolidated Papers, Inc.

ORION - Dinnerware–glass - WMF/USA

ORION - Electric lighting equipment - Lutron Electronics Co., Inc.

ORION - Electronic equipment - Hoosier Electronics

ORION - Electronic equipment - Newport Corp.

ORION - Electronic equipment - Orion Sales, Inc.

ORION - Eyewear - Willson/Dalloz Safety

ORION - Fabrics - Superior Shade & Blind Co. Inc.

ORION - Fans–electric - Hunter Fan Co.

ORION - Flatware ☆ - Svend Jensen of Denmark Inc.

ORION - Floor coverings–carpet and rugs ☆ - Hollytex Carpet Mills Inc.

ORION - Furniture - Weiman Co.

ORION - Furniture ☆ - Rosemont Office Systems Inc.

ORION - Glassware–household ☆ - Lenox Crystal, Inc.

ORION - Guitars ☆ - Pacific Music Supply Co.

ORION - Guns - Weatherby Inc.

ORION - Health care products - Neuromedics

ORION - Hearing aids - Rexton Inc.

ORION - Machinery - Kearney & Trecker Corp.

ORION - Mattresses - Ohio Mattress Co.

ORION - Musical instruments ☆ - VMI Industries

ORION - Non-metallic windows - Vinyl Therm Inc.

ORION - Ophthalmic goods - Swank Optical

ORION - Pipes–plastic - Orion Fittings, Inc.

ORION - Radios - General Electric Co.

ORION - Recording label - Ripete Music Group

ORION - Recording label ☆ - CRS Inc.

ORION - Staplers - Maruzen Co. Ltd.

ORION - Tea kettles–nonelectric ☆ - Robinson Knife & Fiddlers Plastics

ORION - Tiles–ceramic ☆ - Maxsam Sales, Inc.

ORION - Video recording label - Orion Pictures Corp.

ORION - Wines - Diamond Wine Merchants

ORION - Wines - Thackrey & Co.

ORION ATTACK CRAFT - Toys–models ☆ - Estes Industries

ORION FANS - Hobby kits - SW Marketing Associates, Inc.

ORION FOOD SYSTEMS - Food products - Orion Enterprises, Inc.

ORION OLD VINES - Wines - Diamond Wine Merchants

ORION RM 100 - Skis - Wellington Leisure Products, Inc.

ORION TEAM XTREME - Apparel and accessories - Orion Industries, Inc.

ORIONLEADS - Computer software - Orion Scientific Systems

ORIONLINK - Computer software - Orion Scientific Systems

ORION'S RED ALE - Beverages–malt - Brew Moon Enterprises Inc.

ORIONVIA - Computer software - Orion Scientific Systems

ORISSA - Computer software - Apurva Patel

ORISSA - Health care products - Lakon Herbals Inc.

ORIZZONTI - Tiles–ceramic ☆ - American Marazzi Tile, Inc.

ORJENE - Cosmetics - Orjene Natural Cosmetics

ORJENE FOR MEN - Cosmetics - Orjene Natural Cosmetics

ORJENE NATURAL - Skin care products - Orjene Natural Cosmetics

ORKIDEER - Produce - Florida Fresh

ORKNEY - Food products - Maxim Co. Ltd.

ORKNEY BROONIE - Coffee - Executive Coffee Service Co.

ORLA - Organs–musical instrument - Syn-Cordion Musical Instruments Corp.

ORLAAM - Pharmaceutical preparations - Biodevelopment Corp.

ORLAINE - Watches - Hampden Corp.

ORLANDO - Bedding–linen - Dan River Inc.

ORLANDO - Bread crumbs - Orlando Baking Co. Inc.

ORLANDO - Brushes–paint - Corona Brushes Inc.

ORLANDO - Floor coverings–carpet and rugs - Mica Inc.

ORLANDO - Food products - Orlando Food Corp.

ORLANDO - Guitars - Pacific Music Supply Co.

ORLANDO - Seafood products–canned or cured - J.G. Pieri Co. Inc.

ORLANDO - Tableware–china ☆ - Villeroy and Boch Tableware Ltd.

ORLANDO - Vegetables–pickled or brined - Pacific Choice Brands Inc.

ORLANDO - Yarn - Henry's Attic

ORLANDO COUNTY - Furniture - Singer Furniture Co.

ORLANDO ROSSI - Apparel and accessories - Shannan Inc.

ORLANDO SUN - Fruit drinks–bottled or canned - T.G. Lee Foods Inc.

ORLEANS - Bedding–linen - Dan River Inc.

ORLEANS - Brushes–paint - Corona Brushes Inc.

ORLEANS - Cabinets ☆ - Riviera Cabinets Inc.

ORLEANS - Cookies - Pepperidge Farm Inc.

☆ = Now out of production

ORLEANS - Dinnerware–glass - WMF/USA
ORLEANS - Fans–electric - Nutone Inc.
ORLEANS - Flatware - Orleans Silver Co.
ORLEANS - Floor coverings ☆ - Congoleum Corp.
ORLEANS - Floor coverings–carpet and rugs - Atlas Carpet Mills Inc.
ORLEANS - Furniture - Lane Co. Inc.
ORLEANS - Furniture - Universal Flooring
ORLEANS - Furniture ☆ - Bernhardt Industries
ORLEANS - Glass–leaded - Seneca Glass Co.
ORLEANS - Glassware–household - H. Wittur & Co.
ORLEANS - Liquors ☆ - SPAR Inc.
ORLEANS - Seafood products–canned or cured ☆ - Southland Canning & Packing Co. Inc.
ORLEANS - Sporting goods - Brunswick Corp.
ORLEANS - Tiles–ceramic - Wenczel Tile Co.
ORLEANS BLUE - Tableware–china - Lenox, Inc.
ORLEANS COLLECTION - Furniture - Evenflo Juvenile Furniture Co.
ORLEANS COLLECTION - Furniture - Oakwood Interiors
ORLEANS DIJON - Cheese - Alpine Lace Brands, Inc.
ORLENTA - Pharmaceutical preparations - Marin Pharmaceuticals
ORLIDE - Rings–jewelry - Artcarved Inc.
ORLIK - Tobacco–chewing or smoking - G.A. Georgopulo & Co. Inc.
ORLIK HURRICANE - Pipes–tobacco - Mastercraft Pipes Inc.
ORLO WOODCRAFTERS CLASSIC HEIRLOOMS - Toys - Orlo WoodCrafters Inc.
ORLOCKULA - Publisher's imprints - Robert Reed
ORLOFF PRESS - Publisher's imprints - John A. Miller
ORLON - Fibers–acrylic - E.I. Dupont de Nemours and Co.
ORLUX - Bird feeds - Active Pet Supplies
ORLY - Nail care products - Orly International Inc.
ORLY - Sunglasses ☆ - Corning Inc.
ORMAX - Computer software - Applications Plus, Inc.
ORMAZINE - Pharmaceutical preparations ☆ - Roberts/Hauck Pharmaceuticals Inc.
ORMET - Chemicals - Ormet Corp.
ORMOND BEACH - Floor coverings–carpet and rugs - Eagle Carpets Inc.
L'ORNA - Lace - Abby Riba
ORNABAC - Bird feeds - Mardel Laboratories, Inc.
ORNACYCLINE - Veterinary pharmaceutical preparations - Mardel Laboratories, Inc.
ORNACYN - Veterinary pharmaceutical preparations - Mardel Laboratories, Inc.
ORNACYN PLUS - Veterinary pharmaceutical preparations - Mardel Laboratories, Inc.
ORNADE - Antihistamine preparations - Smithkline Beecham Corp.
ORNAGUARD - Automotive parts and accessories - Harold Prunty
ORNALURES - Christmas tree ornaments - Ruby Dee
ORNALYTE - Veterinary pharmaceutical preparations - Mardel Laboratories, Inc.
ORNAM-ETTES - Sugar–granulated, refined, or powdered ☆ - Durkee French Foods
ORNAMATION - Ornamental products–glass - Midwest of Cannon Falls Inc.
ORNAMENTA - Floor coverings - Azrock Commercial Flooring
ORNAMENTAL & OVAL ART - Glass products - AWSCO
ORNAMENTAL GRASSES - Flowers, plants, and seeds ☆ - Applewood Seed & Garden Group
ORNAMENT*A*LA*CARD - Greeting cards - Joyeanna Chaudiere
ORNAMESH - Gratings–floor - Alabama Metal Industries Corp.
ORNAMINTS - Candy - Brach and Brock Confections Inc.
ORNAMITE - Insecticides - Uniroyal Chemical Co. Inc. (Crop Protection Div.)
ORNAMOTION - Electrical equipment - Ornamotor, Inc.
ORNASCALE - Veterinary pharmaceutical preparations - Mardel Laboratories, Inc.
ORNATEX - Pharmaceutical preparations ☆ - Veratex Group
ORNELLA MOLON - Wines - Pellegrini Bros. Wines Inc.
ORNELLAIA - Wines - Kobrand Corp.
ORNEN - Leather goods - Clark Leather Products Inc.
ORO - Fruits and vegetables - Gold Digger Apple Inc.
ORO ARDITO - Jewelry - Spec Imports, Inc.
ORO BLANCO - Packaged rice - Frigorifico Y Almacen Perez Hermanos, Inc.
ORO DI SOLE - Tomato pastes and sauces - Northwest Packing Co.
ORO DIAMANTE - Jewelry - Oro Diamante
ORO FINO - Meat products - Nugget Distributors Inc.
ORO FINO NUGGET - Food products - Nugget Distributors Inc.
ORO GOLD - Cleaning preparations - S.M. Arnold Inc.
ORO-MICA - Rubber–molded - Ovadia Corp.
ORO SOLO - Apparel–women's - Oro Solo

ORO-TERGENE - Pharmaceutical preparations - Richards Pharmaceutical Co.
OROAMERICA - Automotive alarms - KSP New York Inc.
OROAMERICA - Jewelry - OroAmerica Inc.
OROCO - Jewelry - Oroco Manufacturing Inc.
OROKO - Snack foods - A.L. Bazzini Co. Inc.
OROMESH - Handbags - Whiting & Davis Co.
OROMI - Jewelry - Oromi, Inc.
ORONITE - Chemical preparations - Chevron Chemical Co.
ORONOQUE ORCHARDS - Pies–frozen - Pet Inc.
ORORA - Candy - Peerless Confection Co.
OROS - Computer software - ABC Technologies, Inc.
OROTEX - Paints - Tresco Paint Co. Inc.
OROTONE - Hair coloring preparations - Form-U-La-Hair Co.
OROTOSCOPE - Health care products ☆ - Nelkin/Piper Health Products
ORPAK - Sweaters ☆ - Binghamton Knitting Co.
ORPENEED - Pharmaceutical preparations - Hanlon Drug Products
ORPHEE - Vases - Durand International
ORPHENATE - Pharmaceutical preparations - Hyrex Pharmaceuticals
ORPHEUS - Men's shaving product - Colin Ingram Co.
ORPINE WASH & WAX - Cleaning preparations - G. Whitfield Richards Co.
ORR F.I.R.S.T. - Computer peripheral equipment - Environmental Compliance Systems Corp.
ORR-LAC - Paints - Spray Products Corp.
ORR STACKDAS-CEM - Computer peripheral equipment - Environmental Compliance Systems Corp.
ORREFORS - Glass–leaded - Orrefors Inc.
ORR'S MILL BRICK - Floor coverings ☆ - Tarkett, Inc.
ORRVILLE - Pet products - ORRCO, Inc.
ORS - Chemical preparations - Oil Chem Technologies, Inc.
ORS-41 - Chemical preparations - Oil Chem Technologies, Inc.
ORSAT - Wines - Dieter Steinmann Inc.
ORSI - Musical instruments ☆ - St. Louis Music Supply Co.
ORSINI - Apparel–men's - Alan Stuart, Inc.
ORSINI - Cheese - Swissrose International Inc.
ORSINI - Wines - Gibson Wine Co.
ORSO OUMO - Apparel–athletic ☆ - Cooper Sportswear Manufacturing Co., Inc.
ORSON - Toys–stuffed - Dakin Inc.
ORSONIC - Electronic equipment ☆ - Monster Cable Products, Inc.
ORT 2000 - Elastic - Moore Co.
ORTAC - Hoses - Goodyear Tire & Rubber Co.
ORTAC - Pharmaceutical ☆ - Ion Laboratories Inc.
ORTAK - Jewelry - Kashlan Co.
ORTEGA - Cheese - Nabisco Foods Group
ORTEGA - Food products - Del Monte Corp.
ORTEGA - Sauces - Nabisco Holdings Corp.
ORTEK - Electric lighting equipment - CSL Lighting Manufacturing, Inc.
ORTEX - Chemical preparations - Alden Leeds Corp.
ORTH - Bakery products ☆ - Lotus Manufacturing Co.
ORTH - Jams and jellies - PH Orth Co.
ORTHALETIC - Tape–adhesive - Professional Medical Products, Inc.
ORTHENEX - Insecticides - Monsanto Co.
ORTHO - Chemical preparations - Monsanto Co.
ORTHO - Girdles - Bonwit Teller & Co.
ORTHO - Mattresses - Ortho Mattress Inc.
ORTHO - Pharmaceutical preparations - Ortho Pharmaceutical Corp.
ORTHO - Pharmaceutical preparations ☆ - Vortech Pharmaceuticals
ORTHO - Publisher's imprints - National Plan Service
ORTHO ADVANTAGE - Cushions - Saddleman, Inc.
ORTHO AID - Prosthetic apparatus ☆ - Camp, Inc.
ORTHO-BIOTIC - Medical apparatus - Lumex, Inc.
ORTHO BOX - Boxes–corrugated paperboard - Supportive Orthodontics Services, Inc.
ORTHO BUDDY - Medical apparatus - Marcor, Inc.
ORTHO-CANE - Medical apparatus - Lumex, Inc.
ORTHO COIL - Mattress - High Point Bedding, Inc.
ORTHO COPPER PLUS - Health care products - Alta Health Products
ORTHO DIENESTROL - Pharmaceutical preparations - Ortho Pharmaceutical Corp.
ORTHO-EASE - Medical apparatus - Lumex, Inc.
ORTHO-FLEX NEO BREAST COLLAR - Saddles - Ortho-Flex Saddle Co., Inc.
ORTHO-FLEX NEO GIRTH - Saddles - Ortho-Flex Saddle Co., Inc.
ORTHO FRESH - Cleaning preparations - Distar, Inc.
ORTHO GEL - Health care products - Cramer Products Inc.
ORTHO-GRIP - Hair care products - Fromm Industries
ORTHO-GRO - Fertilizers - Monsanto Co.

☆ = Now out of production

ORTHO-GYNOL - Pharmaceutical preparations - Ortho Pharmaceutical Corp.
ORTHO-KLOR - Insecticides - Monsanto Co.
ORTHO-LIFT - Orthopedic products - Ortho-Kinetics, Inc.
ORTHO MATE - Medical apparatus - Encore Products Inc.
ORTHO MEDIC - Mattresses - Oceanside Bedding, Inc.
ORTHO-MOLD - Health care products - Ortho-Mold Bracing Systems
ORTHO-NOVUM - Pharmaceutical preparations - Ortho Pharmaceutical Corp.
ORTHO NUTRITION - Vitamins and nutritional supplements - Sportelesis, Inc.
ORTHO-POSTURE - Bedding–linen - Rockaway Bedding, Inc.
ORTHO-PRONE - Mattresses - Ortho-Prone USA, Inc.
ORTHO-QUAD - Wheelchairs - Mason Medical Products
ORTHO RECOMBIPLASTIN - Medical equipment - Johnson & Johnson
ORTHO-REST - Health care products - Bell-Horn
ORTHO TONIC - Mattresses - U.S. Mattress Corp.
ORTHO TRI-CYCLEN - Health care products - Johnson & Johnson
ORTHO-TRICEPT - Health care products - Johnson & Johnson
ORTHO VISION - Computers - XI Vision
ORTHO WEDGE - Beds–metal - Commander-Omni Co. Inc.
ORTHOBAND 2000 SERIES - Orthodontic equipment - Orthoband Co., Inc.
ORTHOCIDE - Fungicides - Monsanto Co.
ORTHOCISER - Exercising equipment - Larry Gilbert Kennedy Partnership
ORTHODOC - Computers - Integrated Surgical Systems, Inc.
ORTHODONTIST'S BRACES BRUSH, THE - Toothbrushes - Twixt Inc.
ORTHODONTIST'S CHOICE - Dental equipment - U.S. Dentek Corp.
ORTHODYNE - Therapy equipment - Orthodyne International Ltd.
ORTHOENGINE - Computer software - PCI Remote Sensing Corp.
ORTHOFEET - Shoe insoles - Orthofeet, Inc.
ORTHOFLAVIN - Pharmaceutical preparations - Enzyme Process Co. Inc.
ORTHOFLEX - Footwear - D'Bello Shoe Corp.
ORTHOFLEX - Health care products - Medtronic Nortech
ORTHOFLEX - Health care products - Pacific BioLogic Inc.
ORTHOFORM - Medical apparatus - Atco Truelife International
ORTHOGARD - Herbicides - Monsanto Co.
ORTHOGEL - Shoe soles - Libertyville Saddle Shop, Inc.
ORTHOGOLD SERIES - Pillows - Perfect Fit Industries, Inc.
ORTHOGON - Ophthalmic goods ☆ - Bausch & Lomb Inc.
ORTHOKRAFT - Braces–orthopedic - Orthokraft Laboratories, Inc.
ORTHOLITE - Ophthalmic goods ☆ - Bausch & Lomb Inc.
ORTHOLURE - Pharmaceutical preparations - Lifecore Biomedical, Inc.
ORTHOMATIC - Chemical preparations - Monsanto Co.
ORTHOMAX - Computer software - Autometric, Inc.
ORTHONUCLEO - Pharmaceutical preparations - Enzyme Process Co. Inc.
ORTHOPAEDICS OVERNIGHT - Medical apparatus - Depuy Inc.
ORTHORIX - Fungicides - Monsanto Co.
ORTHOSCRIBE - Computer software ☆ - Report Systems, Inc.
ORTHOTECH - Footwear - Home Shopping Club, Inc.
ORTHOTOLIDINE - Chemical preparations - Coastal Industries Inc.
ORTHOVERSAL PACK - Health care products - Bruder Healthcare Co.
ORTHOVISC - Phamaceuticals - MedChem Products Inc.
ORTHOVITA - Dental compounds - Orthovita, Inc.
ORTHOXICOL - Pharmaceutical preparations ☆ - Upjohn Co.
ORTHOZYME - Health care products - Johnson & Johnson
ORTOFON - Electronic equipment - Ortofon Inc.
ORTOPEDIA - Home-health-care product - International Medical Core
ORTOVOX - Sporting goods - Climb High Inc.
ORUDIS KT - Analgesics - American Home Products Corp.
ORVAL - Skin care products - Eve Industries Inc.
ORVAL KENT - Salad dressings–mixes - Orval Kent Food Co., Inc.
ORVAL TRAPPIST - Beverages–malt - Merchant du Vin Corp.
ORVETTA - Hosiery–children's - Gerber Products Co.
ORVILLE REDENBACHER 100% POPCORN CAKES - Snack foods - Hunt-Wesson, Inc.
ORVILLE REDENBACHER'S - Popcorn - Hunt-Wesson, Inc.
ORVILLE WABBIT - Housewares - Great American Fun Corp.
ORVILLE'S PERFECT POPPIN' PARTNER - Vegetable oil ☆ - Hunt-Wesson, Inc.
ORVIS - Sporting goods - Orvis Co., Inc.
ORVIS CO., THE - Luggage - Eclipse Inc.
ORVISION - Computer hardware - Orckit Communications, Inc.
ORV'S - Pizzas–frozen - Five Star Frozen Foods, Inc.
ORYAL - Fruits and vegetables - Oryal Export Co.
ORYX - Watches - United Orient
OS - Apparel and accessories - Otterwear Inc.
OS - Chemicals–photographic - Brandess Kalt Aetna
OS/2 - Computer software - International Business Machines Corp.
OS/2 WARP - Computer software - International Business Machines Corp.

OS 172 - Golfing equipment ☆ - Hansberger Precision Golf Worldwide
O'S BABIES - Toys - Universal Manufacturing Co., Inc.
OS-CAL - Vitamins and nutritional supplements - Marion Merrell Dow
OS-CAL - Vitamins and nutritional supplements - Hoechst Marion Roussel Inc.
OS-CAL - Vitamins and nutritional supplements - SmithKline Beecham Consumer Healthcare
OS CAL 250 D - Vitamins and nutritional supplements - Hoechst Marion Roussel Inc.
OS-CAL-FORTE - Vitamins and nutritional supplements - Marion Merrell Dow
OS-CAL-GESIC - Pharmaceutical preparations - Marion Merrell Dow
OS-CAL-MONE - Pharmaceutical preparations ☆ - Marion Merrell Dow
OS-CAL-PLUS - Vitamins and nutritional supplements - Marion Merrell Dow
OS-FEO-CAL - Vitamins and nutritional supplements ☆ - Marion Merrell Dow
OS-FEO-VIM - Vitamins and nutritional supplements ☆ - Marion Merrell Dow
O'S OF OATS - Pretzels ☆ - Benzel's Bretzel Bakery, Inc.
OS SCAN - Computer software - Oberlin Scientific Corp.
OS-VIM - Vitamins and nutritional supplements ☆ - Marion Merrell Dow
O.S.A. - Apparel and accessories - Oxford Industries, Inc.
OSA - Guitars - Allparts
OSADO - Cosmetics - Darling Corp.
OSAGA - Footwear–athletic - Osaga Footwear, Inc.
OSAGA SPIDER - Footwear - Kinney Shoe Corp.
OSAGE - Brushes–paint ☆ - Linzer Products Corp.
OSAGE - Food products - Cherokee Products Co.
OSAGE - Oils–lubricating - Harrell Petroleum Co.
OSAGE - Wines - Montelle Winery
OSAGE CHIEF - Nuts–salted, roasted, cooked, or canned - Osage Pecan Co. Inc.
OSAGE RIVER - Apparel–men's - Pel Industries, Inc.
O.S.A.R. - Apparel–athletic - Talbot Street Pier, Inc.
OSATO - Jewelry ☆ - T.K.O.
O'SAUR - Air purification systems - Medo Industries, Inc.
OSAWA - Audio equipment - Bell & Howell Co.
OSBORNE - Dishes–china - Waterford Wedgewood USA, Inc.
OSBORNE - Wines ☆ - Specialty Food & Beverage Sales Inc.
OSBOURNE RABBIT - Toys–stuffed - Russ Berrie and Co., Inc.
OSBY - Glassware–household - Van Dow-Fenton Inc.
O.S.C. SPORT CLUB - Apparel–women's - Ormond Shops Inc.
OSCAL - Vitamins and nutritional supplements - Hoechst Marion Roussel Inc.
OSCAL 500+D CALCIUM WITH VITAMIN D - Vitamins and nutritional supplements - Hoechst Marion Roussel Inc.
OSCAL CHEWABLE 500 CALCIUM - Vitamins and nutritional supplements - Hoechst Marion Roussel Inc.
OSCAR - Computer hardware - Apex Pc Solutions, Inc.
OSCAR - Computer software - Ultra Trading Analytics, Inc.
OSCAR - Generators–wind-powered - Telesensory Systems Inc.
OSCAR - Ice chests–plastic - Coleman Co., Inc.
OSCAR - Pet products - Oscar Enterprises Inc.
OSCAR - Recording label ☆ - Alshire International Inc.
OSCAR - Video production - Academy of Motion Picture Arts and Sciences
OSCAR ACTION ROCKERS - Rocking chairs ☆ - Little Tikes Co.
OSCAR & BERTIE AND FRIENDS - Toys–stuffed ☆ - MonkeyPuzzle Inc.
OSCAR BEAR - Toys–stuffed ☆ - Dakin Inc.
OSCAR DE LA RENTA - Apparel and accessories - Oxford Industries, Inc.
OSCAR DE LA RENTA - Apparel and accessories - Wemco, Inc.
OSCAR DE LA RENTA - Apparel–children's - Mcgregor Corp.
OSCAR DE LA RENTA - Bathing suits - Authentic Fitness Corp.
OSCAR DE LA RENTA - Frames–eyeglass - Ambassador Eyewear Group
OSCAR DE LA RENTA - Jewelry - Weingeroff Enterprises, Inc.
OSCAR DE LA RENTA - Luggage - Pierre Cardin Electronique
OSCAR DE LA RENTA - Neckties - Randa Corp.
OSCAR DE LA RENTA - Perfumes - Sanofi Beaute Inc.
OSCAR DE LA RENTA - Scarves - Accessory Street Inc.
OSCAR DE LA RENTA - Shirts - Tica Industries Inc.
OSCAR DE LA RENTA - Umbrellas - New York Umbrella Co.
OSCAR DE LA RENTA - Umbrellas - Oscar De La Renta, Ltd.
OSCAR DE LA RENTA - Watches - Gruen Marketing Corp.
OSCAR DE LA RENTA FOR BARBIE - Dolls - Mattel, Inc.
OSCAR DE LA RENTA FOR SWIRL - Apparel and accessories - Swirl II Ltd.
OSCAR DE LA RENTA'S ESPRIT DE PARFUM - Colognes ☆ - Avon Products, Inc.
OSCAR GRAPHICS - Prints ☆ - Wm. O. Jacobson
OSCAR I-ROT - Toys - Mattel, Inc.
OSCAR JR. - Golfing equipment - Jef World of Golf
OSCAR MAYER - Meat products–beef - Oscar Mayer Foods Corp.
OSCAR ROBERTSON'S BASKETBALL - Games ☆ - A.R.C. Toys Inc.

☆ = Now out of production

OSCAR SCHMIDT - Musical instrument accessories - Washburn International
OSCAR SCHMIDT - Musical instruments - Oscar Schmidt International Inc.
OSCAR SPORT - Boots - Miura Sports Inc.
OSCAR THE GROUCH - Toys - Fisher-Price, Inc.
OSCAR THE GROUCH - Toys - Jim Henson Productions, Inc.
OSCAR THE OCTOPUS - Toys - Milton Bradley Co.
OSCAR'S DESIGNER ACCENTS - Closet organizers - Oscar's Wall & Window Treatments, Inc.
OSCARVISION - Pet products ☆ - Bardwyn Productions Inc.
OSCEOLA - Food products - Empire Butter & Egg Co.
OSCEOLA - Footwear - Osceola Shoe Co. Inc.
OSCILLOCOCCINUM - Pharmaceutical preparations - Boiron Inc.
OSCO - Marine rigging - Osco Motors Corp.
OSCO - Pharmacies - American Stores Co.
OSCO - Sausages - Palmetto Hotel Inc.
OSCODA - Boats–canoes ☆ - Sawyer Composite Products
OSCOR OMNI SPECTRAL CORRELATOR - Computer peripheral equipment - Research Electronics, Inc.
OSE - Jewelry - Old Shellback Enterprises
OSE - Perfumes - Cosmair Inc.
OSEA - Skin care products - Jenefer Palmer Denberg
OSEC - Water purification systems - Wallace & Tiernan, Inc.
OSELLA - Cheese - Bel Canto Fancy Foods Ltd.
OSEM - Food processors - SWB Co. Inc.
OSETRA CAVIAR - Caviar - Tsar Nicoulai Caviar
OSH KOSH B'GOSH - Toys–stuffed - Eden LLC
O'SHAUGHNESSY - Wines - Betty L. O'Shaughnessy
OSHAY - Exercising equipment - Carolyn G. Price
OSHIMA - Bedding–linen - Dan River Inc.
OSHKOSH - Motor vehicles–trucks - Oshkosh Truck Corp.
OSHKOSH B'GOSH - Apparel and accessories - Oshkosh B'gosh, Inc.
OSHKOSH B'GOSH - Gloves, hats, scarves, and neckwear - Hansen Knits
OSHUN - Hair care products ☆ - Summit Laboratories
OSI - Musical instruments ☆ - Oscar Schmidt International Inc.
OSI - Office furniture–wood ☆ - GF Office Furniture Ltd.
OSIRIS - Computer software - Hitachi Data Systems Corp.
OSIRIS - Computer software - McGraw-Hill Companies, Inc.
OSIRIS - Tableware–china ☆ - Villeroy and Boch Tableware Ltd.
OSKAR - Food processors - Sunbeam-Oster Household Products
OSKAR HERMANN SEIDS - Violins - Fred Gretsch Enterprises
OSKAR'S DISKS - Puzzles - Kadon Enterprises Inc.
OSLER! - Computer software - Robert Y. Oikawa
OSLO - Computer software - Science for Kids
OSLO - Floor coverings–carpet and rugs ☆ - Colonial Mills Inc.
OSMA WARS - Video games - Taito America Corp.
OSMET - Medical apparatus - Alza Corp.
OSMOCOTE - Garden equipment - Grace-Sierra Crop Protection Co.
OSMOCOTE - Plant growth regulators - Scotts Miracle-Gro Products, Inc.
OSMOCYTE - Pharmaceutical preparations - Procyte Corp.
OSMOGLYN - Ophthalmic goods - Alcon Laboratories, Inc.
OSMOLITE - Vitamins and nutritional supplements - Ross Laboratories
OSMOSALTS - Finishing agents ☆ - Osmose Wood Preserving Inc.
OSMOSE - Lumber - Osmose Wood Preserving Inc.
OSMOSIS - Recording label - Jazz Composer's Orchestra Association Inc.
OSMOSIS - Water purification systems - International Osmosis, Inc.
OSMOTICS - Skin care products - Osmotics Corp.
OSO NUTS - Cashews and almonds - MT OSO Trading Co.
OSO SWEETS - Onions - Saven Corp.
OSOLO - Wallpaper - Jolie Papier
OSOYOOS LAKE - Fruits and vegetables - Gold Digger Apple Inc.
OSP - Apparel–athletic - Charles Coleman and Timothy Yancy Partnership
OSP - Electronic equipment - Buhl Industries, Inc.
OSP INSIGHT - Computer software - Advance Fiber Optics Inc.
OSPHO - Paints - Skybryte Co.
OSPORO - Vitamins and nutritional supplements - International Medical Research, Inc.
OSPREY - Binoculars ☆ - Swift Instruments, Inc.
OSPREY - Boats–canoes - Old Town Canoe Co.
OSPREY - Boats–motor ☆ - Forester Boats Inc.
OSPREY - Computer hardware - Osprey Technologies, Inc.
OSPREY - Computer software - Active Computer Engineering, Inc.
OSPREY - Electronic equipment - Moor Electronics Inc.
OSPREY - Fishing lures - Eppinger Manufacturing Co.
OSPREY - Fruits and vegetables - Dovex Corp.
OSPREY - Tires–automobile - Greenball Corp.
OSPREY - Watches - Lynx Marketing Corp.

OSPREY'S DOMINION - Wines - Osprey's Dominion Vineyards, Ltd.
OSQ OPTIMUM SERVICE QUANTITY - Computer software - Stratman Group, Inc.
OSQL - Computer software - HyperDesk Corp.
OSRAM - Lamps - Saul Bower Inc.
OSS - Computer software - Open Systems Solutions, Inc.
OSS-I-LATION - Toys - North Pacific Products Inc.
OSS SYSTEM I - Golfing equipment - Golfsmith International Inc.
OSSA - Motor vehicles - Slater Brothers
OSSEOFIX - Surgical supplies - Implant Innovations, Inc.
OSSER & FRIEDLAND - Footwear–men's - Milo Inc.
OSSID - Labeling machinery - Ossid Corp.
OSSIDORR - Hair care products - Framesi USA/Roffler Industries Inc.
OSSINI - Hairbrushes - West Coast Beauty Supply Co.
OSSIRENE - Pharmaceutical preparations - Baker Norton Pharmaceuticals, Inc.
OSTALKIEWICZ DIAMOND IMPORTERS - Jewelry - C.J. Ostalkiewicz & Co., Inc.
OSTENBORG - Cheese - Roth Kase USA, Ltd.
OSTEO-AID - Pharmaceutical preparations - Light Force Inc.
OSTEO-ARTHRITIS PLUS - Vitamins and nutritional supplements - Desert Health Products, Inc.
OSTEO-CAL - Vitamins and nutritional supplements - TSN Labs, Inc.
OSTEO DEFENSE - Vitamins and nutritional supplements - Intracell Nutrition Inc.
OSTEO-FEM - Vitamins and nutritional supplements - Marlyn Co. Inc.
OSTEO-MED - Vitamins and nutritional supplements - Australian Bodycare Enterprises, Inc.
OSTEOBOND - Orthopedic products - Zimmer, Inc.
OSTEOCOMPLETE - Vitamins and nutritional supplements - Intracell Nutrition Inc.
OSTEOEX - Health care products - Healthwatchers System
OSTEOHEALTH - Dental equipment - Luitpold Pharmaceuticals, Inc.
OSTEON/D - Pharmaceutical preparations - Pasadena Research Laboratories, Inc.
OSTEOPOREX NEW ERA - Vitamins and nutritional supplements - New Era Natural Products, Inc.
OSTEOPREP - Medical device - Linvatec Corp.
OSTEOPRIME - Health care products - Enzymatic Therapy, Inc.
OSTEOPROCARE - Vitamins and nutritional supplements - Doctor's Signature Sales & Marketing International Corp.
OSTEOSHIELD - Vitamins and nutritional supplements - Amrion, Inc.
OSTEOSTAT - Medical apparatus - Howmedica Inc.
OSTER - Clippers–barber - Marianna Imports, Inc.
OSTER - Kitchen appliances - Sunbeam-Oster Household Products
OSTER - Pet products - Oster Professional Products
OSTERETTE - Food processors ☆ - Sunbeam-Oster Household Products
OSTERIZER - Blenders - Sunbeam-Oster Household Products
OSTERIZER BLENDERS - Blenders - Sunbeam Corp.
OSTERMOOR - Bedding–linen - Standard Mattress Co.
OSTIDERM - Pharmaceutical preparations - Pedinol Pharmacal Inc.
OSTMANN - Sausages - Haram-Christensen Corp.
OSTOBON - Deodorizers - Pettibone Laboratories Inc.
OSTOMATE CAPSULES - Deodorizers - Krueger Enterprises
OSTONE - Pharmaceutical preparations ☆ - Solvay Pharmaceuticals Inc.
OSTOSAN - Cleaning preparations ☆ - Pettibone Laboratories Inc.
OSTRAKAL - Pharmaceutical preparations ☆ - ICN Pharmaceuticals Inc.
OSTRIC KIDS - Dolls - Ostric Kids, Inc.
OSTRICH WORLD - Apparel and accessories - Ostrich World, Inc.
OSTRIGRO - Animal feeds - Purina Mills, Inc.
OSTRIM - Snack foods - Protos, Inc.
OSTROM'S - Mushrooms ☆ - The Ostrom Co. (Ostrom Mushroom Farms Div.)
OSTROPHIN PMG - Vitamins and nutritional supplements - Standard Process Inc.
OSTROVA - Vodka - Heublein, Inc.
O'SULLIVAN - Furniture - O'Sullivan Industries, Inc.
OSVANIA - Lighting fixtures ☆ - Angelo Brothers Co.
OSWEGO - Boats–canoes - Carstens Industries Inc.
OSZILLOV - Electrical equipment - Mankind Research Unltd. Inc.
O.T. - Herbicides - American Cyanamid Co.
OT - Jewelry - Religious Technology Center
OT - Recording label - On Top Records Inc.
O.T. - Thread ☆ - Perfect Thread Co. Inc.
O.T. BEARS - Cookies ☆ - Sunshine Biscuits, Inc.
OT SPORT - Apparel and accessories ☆ - Edison Brothers Stores, Inc.
OT TRAILERS - Trailers - OT Fabricating, Inc.
OTAFUK-MAGNET - Sandals - Genki USA

☆ = Now out of production

OTAFUKA - Shoe accessories - Genki USA

OTAGIRI - Giftware - Enesco Corp.

OTALGINE - Pharmaceutical preparations ☆ - Purdue Frederick Co.

OTALL - Pharmaceutical preparations ☆ - Saron Pharmacal Corp.

OTARD - Liquors ☆ - IDV Wines (Beaulieu Vineyard)

OTARI - Audio equipment - Otari Corp.

OTB ORIGINAL - Food products - Brinker Restaurant Corp.

OTC - Crackers - Original Trenton Cracker Co.

OTC - Medical apparatus - OTC Professional Appliances

OTC - Tools - Owatonna Tool Co.

O.T.C. TRENTON - Breads - Original Trenton Cracker Co.

OTCA - Boats–canoes - Old Town Canoe Co.

OTELLO - Colognes - J. Palazzolo Son Inc.

OTF - Computer software - Schenck Pegasus

OTG - Computer peripheral equipment - OTG Software

OTHELLO - Cutlery ☆ - Lifetime Hoan Corp.

OTHELLO - Games - Pressman Toy Corp.

OTHELLO - Games ☆ - Milton Bradley Co.

OTHELLO - Watches - Seville Watch Corp.

OTHELLO'S GOURMET - Pet supplies - Frederick M. Nass

OTHER BRATS, THE - Sausages ☆ - Johnsonville Foods Co.

OTHER EYE - Electronic equipment - Sharp Electronics Corp.

OTHER MUSIC - Recording label - Jazz Composer's Orchestra Association Inc.

OTHER-SONIC - Health care products - Pharmaceutical Innovations

OTHER WEAR - Apparel and accessories - Sara Lee Corp.

OTHERS, THE - Books–comic - James A. Valentino

OTHERWHERE QUEST, THE - Games ☆ - Mayfair Games, Inc.

OTHINE - Skin care products - J. Strickland & Co.

OTI-CARE - Pet products - Rich Health

OTI-CLEAN - Pet products - Rich Health

OTI-SEPT PLUS - Health care products - Phoenix Pharmaceutical, Inc.

OTIC DOMEBORO - Pharmaceutical preparations - Miles Inc.

OTIC-HC - Pharmaceutical preparations ☆ - Roberts/Hauck Pharmaceuticals Inc.

OTIC TRIDESILON - Pharmaceutical preparations - Miles Inc.

OTICIN-HC - Pharmaceutical preparations - Teral Laboratories

OTICON - Hearing aids - Oticon Corp.

OTICONGRESS - Hearing aids - Oticon Corp.

OTICOT - Pharmaceutical preparations - C.O. Truxton Inc.

OTIMAR - Pharmaceutical preparations - Marlop Pharmaceuticals Inc.

OTIS - Apparel and accessories - Spring City Knitting

OTIS - Golfing equipment - Cooper/Lindsay Corp.

OTIS PERMASOL - Fabrics - Glen Raven Mills Inc.

OTIS SPUNKMEYER - Food products - Otis Spunkmeyer, Inc.

OTIS SPUNKMEYER SPUNKIES - Cookies - Otis Spunkmeyer, Inc.

OTISOL - Pet products - Wysong Corp.

OTIX - Medical apparatus - Dewitt USA, Inc.

OTIX - Pharmaceutical preparations - Monticello Drug Co.

OTLEY - Furniture - Union National Inc.

OTM - Apparel and accessories - Moteng International, Inc.

OTNAS - Stain removers - Waverly Beauty Products

OTNEVA CREAMER - Cream - Otneva Corp.

OTO - Pharmaceutical preparations ☆ - Vortech Pharmaceuticals

OTO-LOGIC - Hearing aids - Oto-Logic Physician Services, Inc.

OTO-SONIC - Hearing aids - Beltone Electronics Corp.

OTOBIONE - Pharmaceutical preparations - Schering-Plough Healthcare Products

OTOBIOTIC - Pharmaceutical preparations - Schering-Plough Healthcare Products

OTOCAIN - Pharmaceutical preparations - Abana Pharmaceuticals, Inc.

OTOCAIN - Pharmaceutical preparations - Jones Medical Industries, Inc. (Medical Div.)

OTOCALM - Photo albums - Parmed Pharmaceuticals, Inc.

OTOCORT - Pharmaceutical preparations - Lemmon Co.

OTODYNE - Pharmaceutical preparations ☆ - Schering-Plough Healthcare Products

OTOE'S FINEST - Vegetables–canned - Faribault Foods Inc.

OTOGESIC - Pharmaceutical preparations - A.J. Bart

OTOGESIC - Pharmaceutical preparations ☆ - Lexis Laboratories Inc.

OTOGESIC HC - Pharmaceutical preparations ☆ - Lexis Laboratories Inc.

OTOGRAF - Hearing aids ☆ - Hearing Health Group Inc.

OTOGRAM - Hearing aids ☆ - Hearing Health Group Inc.

OTOKI - Apparel and accessories - Acorn Partners

OTOMEDIC - Pharmaceutical preparations ☆ - Medical Products Panamericana Inc.

OTOMIDE - Pharmaceutical preparations ☆ - Schering-Plough Healthcare Products

OTOMIX - Sportswear, footwear, hats - Otomix Inc.

OTOMYCIN - Pharmaceutical preparations - Misemer Pharmaceuticals Inc.

OTOOL COMPANY - Tools–hand-operated - Q.E.P. Co., Inc.

OTOPLASTICS - Headphones - Westone Laboratories Inc.

OTOREID-HC - Pharmaceutical preparations ☆ - Solvay Pharmaceuticals Inc.

OTOS-MOSAN - Pharmaceutical preparations ☆ - Wyeth-Ayerst Laboratories

OTOSONIC - Hearing aids - Beltone Electronics Corp.

OTOVIEW - Endoscopic equipment - Smith & Nephew Richards, Inc.

OTOZONE - Pharmaceutical preparations - R.A. McNeil Co.

O.T.P. - Apparel - Mark D. Floor

OTR - Fuel additives - Index Industries Inc.

OTRA - Food products - Europa Foods Ltd.

OTRA NO HAY! - Beer - Miller Brewing Co.

OTRIVIN - Pharmaceutical preparations - Ciba-Geigy Corp.

OTS TECHNOLOGY IN DEPTH - Communications equipment–marine - Undersea Systems International, Inc.

OTSEGO - Flour–blended - Hubbard Milling Co.

OTSUKA USA ONCOMEMBRANE - Pharmaceutical preparations - Oncomembrane, Inc.

OTT - Jewelry - Ortega's Manufacturers and Pawn, Inc.

OTTAROME - Spices and extracts - Ottens Flavors

OTTAWA - Bathroom fixtures ☆ - Crane Plumbing/Fiat Products

OTTAWA - Tractors - Ottawa Truck, Inc.

OTTAWA GUARDS - Floor coverings - American Floor Products Co. Inc.

OTTENBERG'S - Tortillas - Ottenberg's Bakers, Inc.

OTTENHEIMER - Uniforms–academic - Ottenheimer and Co. Inc.

OTTEN'S - Food products - Custom Food Products Inc.

OTTER - Boats–kayaks - Old Town Canoe Co.

OTTER - Fishing tackle - Big Jon, Inc.

OTTER - Pillows - P & P Design Inc.

OTTER CREEK - Beverages–malt - Otter Creek Brewing, Inc.

OTTER CREST - Pharmaceutical preparations ☆ - Lossing Orthopedic Co.

OTTER SLED - Sleds - Otter Sales

OTTER SOCIETY - Apparel and accessories - Otterwear Inc.

OTTER SOCIETY FOR THE PURE JOY OF LIVING, THE - Apparel and accessories - Otterwear Inc.

OTTER SPRING - Wines ☆ - Heron Hill Vineyards Inc.

OTTERLY PEACEFUL - Confections - Northern Chocolate

OTTERMATIC - Razors - C.A. Daniels & Co.

OTTERWEAR - Apparel and accessories - Foxx Industries Inc.

OTTIMO - Food products - Sysco Corp.

OTTO - Machined parts - Otto Engineering Inc.

OTTO - Patches, insignia, and emblems - Otto Printing & Entertainment Graphics

OTTO - Tools - Tools for Trades Inc.

OTTO-B-RITE - See 90/90 BACKTRAC

OTTO BASICS - Cosmetics - Galaxy Network, Inc.

OTTO BRUCKMAN - Beverages–malt - Old European Brewery Co.

OTTO BRUCKNER - Musical instruments ☆ - Scherl & Roth Inc.

OTTO ERNST FISCHER - Musical instruments - M & M Distributing Co.

OTTO ERNST FISCHER - Musical instruments - Shar Products, Inc.

OTTO GERDAU - Chairs–wood - Otto Gerdau Co.

OTTO HEINE - Musical instruments - Deltex Music Corp.

OTTO LINK - Musical instrument accessories - Otto Link Inc.

OTTO OWL - Toys–stuffed - Dakin Inc.

OTTO PAULUS - Musical-instrument bows - Howard Core & Co. Inc.

OTTO PENZLER BOOKS - Publisher's imprints - Penzler, Inc.

OTTO-RIDE - Tractors - Ottawa Truck, Inc.

OTTO ROTH - Cheese ☆ - Swissrose International Inc.

OTTO SCHMIT - Toys - Tonka Corp.

OTTOMAN - Thread - A. Lewis Thread Co. Inc.

OTTOMAN COLLECTION, THE - Floor coverings–carpet and rugs - Couristan Inc.

OTTOMAR HAUSMANN - Violins - Ideal Musical Merchandise Co.

OTTONI - Tea kettles–nonelectric - Crate and Barrel

OTTO'S - Food products - Otto W. Liebold & Co.

OTTO'S BEST - Food products - Otto W. Liebold & Co.

OTTO'S PRIDE - Food products - Otto W. Liebold & Co.

OTTOTEK - Voltmeters - International Manufacturing Enterprises

OTT'S - Salad dressings–bottled - Ott Food Products

O.T.Y. ONLY THE YOUNG - Apparel and accessories - Isfel Co. Inc.

OUBLIETTE - Computer software - SourceView Software International

OUCH - Chewing gum - Amurol Confections Co.

OUCH! - Computer software - Adobe Systems Inc.

☆ = Now out of production

OUCH KIT - First aid kits - Sentinel Consumer Products, Inc.

OUCH-LESS - Combs - Nino Originals

OUCH MOUSE - Infant product - Stephan Enterprises, Inc.

OUCH PATCH - Wound dressing - Carl J. Hafner

OUCH PREVENTION - Valves–intake - Emhart Industries Inc.

OUCH! SPOTS - Candy - Amurol Confections Co.

OUCH WEAR SO GOOD IT HURTS - T-shirts–men's - Anthony Marano

OUD DELFT - Giftware - Eastern Shore Trading Co.

OUI - Computer software - Dvorak Development & Publishing Corp.

OUI - Floor coverings–carpet and rugs - Customweave Carpets Inc.

OUI INTERNATIONAL - Coats–men's - Gallron

OUI PETITES - Apparel and accessories - Nygard, Inc.

OUICKDRAW - Headbands - Seirus Innovative Accessories, Inc.

OUIJA - Games ☆ - Parker Brothers

OUMRON - Furniture - Inwood Office Furniture

OUR ADVERTISER - Tobacco products - Republic Tobacco L.P.

OUR BABY'S FIRST SEVEN YEARS - Books–blank - C.R. Gibson Co.

OUR BEAUTY IS SKEIN DEEP - Fibers–synthetic - Monsanto Co.

OUR BEST - Axes - Snow & Nealley Co.

OUR BEST - Beverages–carbonated - Perry Drug Stores, Inc.

OUR BEST - Brooms - Hamburg Broom Works Inc.

OUR BEST - Vegetables–canned - KLM Foods Inc.

OUR BETTER OPTION - Beef - Kraft Food Ingredients Corp.

OUR BIOSPHERES - Apparel and accessories - Decisions Investment Corp.

OUR BIRD - Pet products - Animal Lovers

OUR BODIES - Computer software - Right on Programs

OUR CHILDREN - Figurines ☆ - National Potteries

OUR CHOICE - Food products - Tony's Pizza Service

OUR CHOICE - Pillows - Pacific Coast Feather Co.

OUR CLASSIC - Meat products–poultry - Louis Rich Co.

OUR COUNTRY - Seasonings - SOUPerior Bean & Spice

OUR DAIRY BEST - Cheese - The Kroger Co.

OUR DARLING - Vegetables–canned - Joan of Arc Co.

OUR DELIGHT - Floor coverings–carpet and rugs - Lees Carpets

OUR DELUXE - Meat products–poultry - Louis Rich Co.

OUR FAMILY - Books–blank - Advertisers Publishing Co.

OUR FAMILY - Food products - Nash-Finch Co.

OUR FAMILY TREE - Greeting cards - Stevenson Industries Inc.

OUR FAMOUS TEXAS - Food products - Texas Chili Co.

OUR FARM - Food products - Sugardale Foods Inc.

OUR FARM - Food products - Vanderhorst Cannery

OUR FARM BRAND - Bacon - Fresh Mark, Inc.

OUR FATHERS - Skin care products - Cosmedic Concepts, Inc.

OUR FAVORITE - Pillows - Pacific Coast Feather Co.

OUR FINEST - Food products - Culinary Foods Inc.

OUR FINEST - Meat products–poultry - Tyson Holding Co.

OUR FINEST HOUR - Floor coverings–carpet and rugs ☆ - Calladium & Marglen

OUR FINEST RECIPE - Salads–prepackaged - First National Supermarkets Inc.

OUR FLAG - Toys - Maryland Toy Corp.

OUR GANG - Apparel–children's ☆ - Health-Tex Inc.

OUR GANG - Cookies - Parco Foods, Inc.

OUR GANG - Video production - Turner Entertainment Co.

OUR GIRL - Apparel–children's ☆ - Health-Tex Inc.

OUR GOLDEN SUPREME - Meat products–poultry ☆ - Longmont Foods

OUR GOURMET - Meat products–pork - Russer Foods

OUR GREAT TASTE COMES NATURALLY - Cereal - U.S. Mills, Inc.

OUR HOME - Dinnerware–glass - Shopko Stores, Inc.

OUR HOME - Kitchen appliances ☆ - National Housewares

OUR HOME - Paints - United Coatings, Inc.

OUR HOUSE - Snack foods - Our House Inc.

OUR KEENER WEINER FRANKIES - Meat products - Fresh Mark, Inc.

OUR LADY - Paper ☆ - Nash-Finch Co.

OUR LEADER - Paints - Schulte Paint & Lacquer Manufacturing Co., Inc.

OUR LEAGUE - Apparel–women's - Loumel, Inc.

OUR LIGHT TOUCHES OTHERS - Lasers - Coherent, Inc.

OUR LITE SUPREME - Meat products–poultry ☆ - Longmont Foods

OUR LIVING HERITAGE COLLECTION - Puzzles - Crown Prince International

OUR MISS CHIPS - Computer peripheral equipment - Our Miss Chips, Inc.

OUR MISS CLOWN - Toys ☆ - Mego Financial Corp.

OUR MUSIC PAST - Recording label - Library of Congress Broadcasting

OUR NATION'S CAPITOL - Toys - Maryland Toy Corp.

OUR OLD ITALIAN - Food products - A.M. Gilardi and Sons, Inc.

OUR OWN - Lamp bulbs - Our Own Hardware Co.

OUR OWN - Nonfood products - Stop and Shop Companies Inc.

OUR OWN - Pet products - Rotanis Pet Products Inc.

OUR OWN IMPORT - Dolls - Cardinal Inc.

OUR OWN KITCHEN - Food products - Peck Foods Corp.

OUR OWN KITCHEN - Food products ☆ - Emmber Foods, Inc.

OUR OWN SILKS - Flowers–artificial - Rubens Originals

OUR PENCILS DON'T GROW ON TREES - Pencils - Watson Paper Co.

OUR PREFERRED - Pillows - Pacific Coast Feather Co.

OUR PREMIUM - Meat products–poultry - Louis Rich Co.

OUR PRIDE - Spices and extracts - Big Star Food Stores

OUR QUALITY IS IN YOUR HANDS - Fans–electric - Crest Industries Inc.

OUR RECOMMEMDED - Pillows - Pacific Coast Feather Co.

OUR SEAL IS YOUR ASSURANCE OF QUALITY SINCE 1970 - Water–bottled or canned - Pure Water Corp.

OUR SECRET AROMATHERAPY - Candles - Our Secret, Ltd.

OUR SELECT - Meat products–poultry ☆ - Longmont Foods

OUR SONG - Floor coverings–carpet and rugs - Queen Carpet Corp.

OUR SPECIAL - Bacon - Fischer Packing Co.

OUR SPECIAL - Beverages - American Ace LLC

OUR SPECIAL ALE - Beverages–malt - Anchor Brewing Co.

OUR SPECIAL GARDEN - Salad dressings–bottled - International Food Products Corp.

OUR SPECIALTY - Food - S.T. Specialty Foods, Inc.

OUR STRENGTHS ARE LEGENDARY - Cases–camera - Samsonite Corp.

OUR SUPERIOR - Meat products–poultry ☆ - Longmont Foods

OUR SUPREME - Meat products–poultry ☆ - Longmont Foods

OUR SURFACE IS YOUR EDGE - Paper - Mead Corp.

OUR TIMES - Glassware–household - Papel Freelance, Inc.

OUR TINY - Peas ☆ - American Fine Foods Inc.

OUR TOWN - Bedding–linen - Dan River Inc.

OUR TOWN - Giftware - Santa's Best

OUR TOWN - Pharmaceutical preparations - Laurel Hill Paper Co.

OUR TOWN - Recording label ☆ - Higher Octave Music, Inc.

OUR TOWN II - Wallpaper ☆ - Sanitas Wallcoverings

OUR TOWNERS - Greeting cards - Amberley Greeting Card Co.

OUR TURKEYS DON'T DO DRUGS - Meat products–poultry ☆ - Shelton's Poultry, Inc.

OUR VALLIE - Food products - Autry Greer and Sons Inc.

OUR VALUE - Food products - S.M. Flickinger Co. Inc.

OUR VALUE - Food products - Scrivner, Inc.

OUR VALUE - Food products - Tyler & Simpson Co.

OUR VERSION - Skin care products - Simply Superior Products

OUR VERY BEST - Gravy - Supreme Food Distributing Co. Inc.

OUR WEDDING DAY - Bags - Papercraft Inc.

OUR WORLD - Apparel and accessories - Our World, Inc.

OUR WORLD OUR FUTURE - Beauty shops - Joico Laboratories, Inc.

OURBROKER - Real estate agencies - Peter G. Miller

'OURGLASS - Cleaning preparations - Joseph A. Thomas Ltd.

OURO VERDE - Wines - Admiral Wine Merchants

OURPAL - Legal services - S. Pal Asija

OUSLEY FARMS - Mustard - Ousley Farms Inc.

OUST - Herbicides - E.I. Dupont de Nemours and Co.

OUT! - Pet products - Bramton Co.

OUT-A-SITE - Golfing equipment - Ralph Maltby Enterprises Inc.

OUT A TOWN - Apparel and accessories - Sharon Marie's Boutique

OUT-AND-ABOUT BOOKS - Publisher's imprints - E.P. Dutton Inc.

OUT AND ABOUT SPOUT - Hardware - Masco Corp. (Plumbing Products Div.)

OUT CAST - Sporting goods - Shakespeare Fishing Tackle

OUT COLD - Recording label - Echo Records Inc.

OUT DAM SPOT - Pet products - Goodwinol Products Corp.

OUT-DOORS - Floor coverings–carpet and rugs ☆ - American Excelsior Co.

OUT HERE ACTIONWEAR - T-shirts–men's ☆ - Andy's Tee Shirts

OUT ISLAND JAVA - Coffee - Nella Oil Co.

OUT ISLANDER - Boats–motor ☆ - Huckins Yacht Corp.

OUT LOUD - Shirts - Mary K. Turner

OUT-N-ABOUT - Medical apparatus - American Walker Inc.

OUT-N-ABOUT - Strollers–baby ☆ - Combi International Corp.

OUT 'N ABOUT COLLECTION - Dolls - Mattel, Inc.

OUT OF AMERICA - Bags–storage - Mcinternational

OUT OF CONTEXT - Games ☆ - Western Publishing Co., Inc.

OUT OF CONTROL RECORDS - Recording label - Out of Control Records, Inc.

OUT OF GAS - Video games - Fujisankei Communications International Inc.

OUT OF HAND - Pottery ☆ - Root Candle Co.

OUT-OF-SIGHT - Cosmetics - Circle of Beauty, Inc.

OUT OF SIGHT - Radios - Worldwide Marketing Group

OUT OF STEP - Postcards - Russ Berrie and Co., Inc.

☆ = Now out of production

OUT OF THE WOODS - Apparel–men's - Jay Garment Co.

OUT OF THIS WORLD - Computer software - Interplay Productions

OUT OF THIS WORLD - Toys–electronic ☆ - Philips Consumer Electronics Co.

OUT OF THIS WORLD - Wallcoverings - Wallworks

OUT OF TIME - Computer software ☆ - Earthware Computer Services

OUT-OF-WALL - Electrical equipment - Monster Cable Products, Inc.

OUT ON A LIMB PUBLISHING/BMI - Recording label - Wan Star Entertainment Group

OUT-RIDER - Health care products - Bruno Independent Living Aids Inc.

OUT-SIDER - Health care products - Bruno Independent Living Aids Inc.

OUT-STANDING IN THE FIELD - Toilets–portable - America West Service Corp.

OUT TO DRY - Racks - Artcraft Wire Works, Inc.

OUT TO LUNCH - Video games - Mindscape Software Inc.

OUT! WEAR - Apparel and accessories - M.S.N. Enterprizes

OUTA LIMITZ - Sunglasses - Solar-Mates, Inc.

OUTA-SITE - Handbags - Vanguard Military Equipment Corp.

OUTASIGHT - Wallpaper - James Seeman Studios

OUTASIGHT VII - Wallpaper - James Seeman Studios

OUTBACK - Aircraft–airplanes - SkyStar Aircraft Corp.

OUTBACK - Bakery products - Gai's Seattle French Baking Co., Inc.

OUTBACK - Beverages–alcohol ☆ - Jim Beam Brands Co.

OUTBACK - Binoculars - Olympus America Inc.

OUTBACK - Boots - KangaROOS USA Inc.

OUTBACK - Floor coverings–tile - Interface, Inc.

OUTBACK - Jewelry - Teresa Morrison

OUTBACK - Leather–chamois - Acme Sponge & Chamois Co., Inc.

OUTBACK - Sandals - ALP Sport Sandals

OUTBACK - Tape players–cassette - Sony Corp. of America

OUTBACK - Toys–stuffed - Gund, Inc.

OUTBACK CHAMOIS - Cleaning preparations - Sponge Fishing Co., Inc.

OUTBACK COUNTRY - Apparel and accessories - Saramar Corp.

OUTBACK JOEY - Video games - Heartbeat Corp.

OUTBACK LAGER - Beverages–malt - Dallas Brewing Co. Inc.

OUTBACK LEATHER - Leather goods - Outback Leather Inc.

OUTBACK PERFORMANCE - Jackets - Outback Trading Co. Ltd.

OUTBACK PRIME - Food products - Outback Steakhouse of Florida, Inc.

OUTBACK RED - Apparel and accessories - Limited Inc.

OUTBACK SERIES - Bicycle parts and accessories - Graber Products, Inc.

OUTBACK SIT-N-SNACK - Knapsacks ☆ - Durbin Industries

OUTBACK STEAKHOUSE - Novelty items - Outback Steakhouse of Florida, Inc.

OUTBACK U.S.A. COLLECTIONS BY GREAT THREADS - Apparel and accessories - Great Threads, Inc.

OUTBOUND - Computer software - Firesign Computer Co.

OUTBROOK - Coats - Wal-Mart Stores Inc.

OUTBURST - Games - Hasbro, Inc.

OUTBURST - Sporting goods - Wellington Leisure Products, Inc.

OUTBURST JUNIOR - Games - Hasbro, Inc.

OUTCOME - Skin care products - Kenra Laboratories, Inc.

OUTCOME ADVISOR - Computer software - Patrick Consult Inc.

OUTCOMES TRACKER - Computer software - Client/Server Inc.

OUTCROP - Floor coverings–carpet and rugs - Regal Rugs Inc.

OUTDOOR BOOKS & MAPS - Publisher's imprints - Outdoor Books & Maps, Inc.

OUTDOOR CHEF - Cooking equipment–household - GSW Jackes-Evans Manufacturing Co.

OUTDOOR CRAFT - Pet products - Gallo Manufacturing Co.

OUTDOOR DECOR - Finishing agents - Rust-Oleum Corp.

OUTDOOR DESIGN - Apparel stores–sports - Dorfman-Pacific Co. Inc.

OUTDOOR ENTERTAINMENT - Broadcasting stations–television - Outdoor Entertainment, Inc.

OUTDOOR ESSENTIALS - Paving materials–stone - Universal Forest Products, Inc.

OUTDOOR EXCHANGE - Apparel and accessories - Montgomery Ward & Co. Inc.

OUTDOOR FRESH - Deodorizers - S.C. Johnson & Son, Inc.

OUTDOOR GEAR - Toys - Imperial Toy Corp.

OUTDOOR GLOW - Skin care products - Polo Ralph Lauren Corp.

OUTDOOR GOURMET - Seafood - Kasilof Fish Co.

OUTDOOR HEADWEAR - Hats - Bollman Hat Co.

OUTDOOR JOURNAL, THE - Broadcasting stations–television - Scott Randell Linden

OUTDOOR LIFE - Cosmetics ☆ - Noxell Corp.

OUTDOOR LIFE - Footwear - Phil Shir Inc.

OUTDOOR LIFE - Glassware–household - Owens-Illinois Inc. (Libbey Div.)

OUTDOOR LIVING - Baskets–wood - Himark Enterprises Inc.

OUTDOOR LIVING - Furniture - General Foam Plastics Corp.

OUTDOOR PAL - Dolls - Mattel Inc.

OUTDOOR PRODUCTS - Sporting goods - Outdoor Recreation Group

OUTDOOR RECREATION - Sporting goods - Gerber Legendary Blades

OUTDOOR SOLES - Sandals - John W. Schelling

OUTDOOR SPORTS - Footwear - Benjamin Shir Inc.

OUTDOOR SPORTSMAN - Computer software - Dynamix, Inc.

OUTDOOR SPORTSMAN - Magazines - Hurricane Creek Associates Inc.

OUTDOOR SURVIVAL - Games - Avalon Hill Game Co.

OUTDOOR TORCH - Torches - Bernzomatic

OUTDOORABLES - Shoes - Daniel Green Co.

OUTDOORS INN - Barbecues and grills ☆ - Sunbeam-Oster Household Products

OUTDOORS STORE, THE - Apparel and accessories - Outdoors Store Inc.

OUTDOORS UNLIMITED - Luggage - London Fog Industries, Inc.

OUTDOORS UNLIMITED - Women's apparel - Interco Inc.

OUTDOORSMAN - Battery chargers - Exide Corp.

OUTDOORSMAN - Beverage dispensing equipment - Kraftware Corp. (Morgan Div.)

OUTDOORSMAN - Eyeglasses - Bausch & Lomb Inc.

OUTDOORSMAN - Jackets - Coleman Co., Inc.

OUTDOORSMAN - Knives - Precise International/Wenger

OUTDOORSMAN - Lighting fixtures ☆ - Big Beam Emergency Systems Inc.

OUTDOORSMAN - Orthopedic products - Chase Ergonomics Inc.

OUTDOORSMAN - Sporting goods - Outdoor Technologies Group

OUTDOORSMAN - Work shoes - Interco Inc.

OUTDOORSMAN, THE - Giftware - Fort USA

OUTDOORSTUFF - Sporting goods - F & L Packing Corp.

OUTER BANKS - Apparel and accessories - Jasper Textiles Inc.

OUTER BANKS - Bells - North Country Wind Bells Inc.

OUTER BANKS - House furnishings ☆ - Lea Industries Inc.

OUTER BANKS - Sunglasses - Style Eyes of California

OUTER BANKS HOME - Linen - Mark Azzarello

OUTER DOWN - Pillows - Pillowtex Corp.

OUTER EDGE - Blue Ridge Carpet Mills

OUTER EDGE - Markers–felt-tip - Dri Mark Products, Inc.

OUTER-KLEEN - Automotive parts and accessories - Tuff-Kote Dinol Inc.

OUTER LIMIT PRO - Sporting goods - Gared Sports, Inc.

OUTER LIMITS - Coats ☆ - Gerry Sportswear Corp.

OUTER LIMITS - Floor coverings–carpet and rugs - J and J Industries Inc.

OUTER LIMITS - Hair care products - Helene Curtis Industries Inc.

OUTER LIMITS - Office accessories - Avery Dennison Corp.

OUTER LIMITS - Recording label - Quark, Inc.

OUTER-OFFICE MAIL - Envelopes - Earth Class Mail Co.

OUTER REEF - Apparel–women's ☆ - Mount Vernon Mills Inc.

OUTER SPACE - Cosmetics ☆ - Noxell Corp.

OUTERS - Firearms, accessories, and parts - Blount International, Inc. (Sporting Equipment Group)

OUTERSPACE - Novelty items–paper - Romar Enterprises Ltd.

OUTERWEAR ESSENTIALS - Jackets - Nordstrom, Inc.

OUTERWORLDS - Novelty items–glass - Properties in Space Inc.

OUTFIT USA BY DIPORT SEEK ADVENTURE - Apparel and accessories - Lacers Sport, Inc.

OUTFITTER - Cooking equipment–commercial - Coleman Co., Inc.

OUTFITTERS - Apparel–men's - Big & Tall Associates

OUTFITTING THE VIRTUAL WORKPLACE - Furniture - MG Taylor Corp.

OUTGRO - Pharmaceutical preparations - Whitehall Laboratories

OUTLAND - Floor coverings–carpet and rugs ☆ - World Carpets, Inc.

OUTLAND - Recreational vehicle - Skyline Corp.

OUTLAND - Watches - Fada Industries Inc.

OUTLANDER - Frames–eyeglass - Denver International Eyewear Inc.

OUTLANDER - Knives–pocket ☆ - W.R. Case & Sons Cutlery Co.

OUTLANDER LTD. - Apparel–women's - Leslie Fay Companies Inc.

OUTLANDER PETITE - Apparel–women's - Leslie Fay Companies Inc.

OUTLANDER PLUS - Apparel–women's - Leslie Fay Companies Inc.

OUTLANDISH ORANGE - Candy - Nabisco Holdings Corp.

OUTLAW - Audio equipment - Devonics Corp.

OUTLAW - Bicycles - Columbia Manufacturing Inc.

OUTLAW - Bicycles ☆ - Huffy Corp.

OUTLAW - Braces–orthopedic - U.S. Action Concepts, Inc.

OUTLAW - Bumpers–motor vehicle - Wedgestone Automotive Corp.

OUTLAW - Candy ☆ - Goetze's Candy Co., Inc.

OUTLAW - Darts and dart games - Dart Mart Inc.

OUTLAW - Skates–roller - Variflex, Inc.

☆ = Now out of production

OUTLAW - Sporting goods - Outdoor Technologies Group
OUTLAW - Toys - Tonka Corp.
OUTLAW BROS. - Apparel and accessories - Joy C. Wilke
OUTLAW S/T - Automotive parts and accessories - Hurst Performance Inc.
OUTLAW SX - Boats–motor ☆ - Marathon Boat Group, Inc.
OUTLAW, THE - Fuel additives - Snap Products, Inc.
OUTLAWS - Cigars - Swisher International, Inc.
OUTLAW'S BAR-B-QUE SO GOOD IT AUGHT TO BE AGAINST THE LAW - Barbecue sauce - Mark Brundige
OUTLET - Recording label - Outlet Records
OUTLINE - Fabrics - Hong Yuan Industrial Co., Ltd.
OUTLINE - Hair care products - Redken Laboratories, Inc.
OUTLINE - Wallpaper - Charles Barone Inc.
OUTLINER - Markers–felt-tip - Sakura of America
OUTLINER II - Health care products - Andis Co.
OUTLOOK - Clocks ☆ - General Time Corp. (Westclox/Seth Thomas Div.)
OUTLOOK - Colognes ☆ - Avon Products, Inc.
OUTLOOK - Window coverings - Outlook Window Fashions
OUTLOOK - Wood products - Westvaco Corp.
OUTLOOKS - Apparel and accessories - Mcgregor Corp.
OUTLOOKS - Jewelry - Beall's, Inc.
OUTPACK - Cases–camera - The Tiffen Co.
OUTPOST - Computer software - Sierra On-Line, Inc.
OUTPOST - Playground equipment - Leisure Time Products, Inc.
OUTPUT - Shoes - Consolidated Shoe Co., Inc.
OUTPUT 315 - Adhesives and sealants - Loctite Corp.
OUTPUT 383 - Adhesives and sealants - Loctite Corp.
OUTPUT 384 - Adhesives and sealants - Loctite Corp.
OUTPUT ACTIVATOR - Adhesives and sealants - Loctite Corp.
OUTRACE - Ophthalmic goods - Foremost Optical Products
OUTRAGE - Bicycles - Murray, Inc.
OUTRAGE - Boats - Glen-L Marine Designs
OUTRAGE - Boats–canoes ☆ - Sawyer Composite Products
OUTRAGE - Lipsticks - Revlon Consumer Products Corp.
OUTRAGE - Powerboat - Boston Whaler, Inc.
OUTRAGE CUDDY - Powerboat ☆ - Boston Whaler, Inc.
OUTRAGEOUS - Hair care products - Revlon Consumer Products Corp.
OUTRAGEOUS - Handbags - Wathne Ltd.
OUTRAGEOUS - Recording label ☆ - Rounder Records Corp.
OUTRAGEOUS FAUX JEWELS - Jewelry–costume - Carolee Designs Inc.
OUTRAGEOUS ORANGE - Kites ☆ - Hi-Flier Manufacturing Co.
OUTRAGEOUS SERIES - Fishing equipment - Thomas M. Breen
OUTRAGEOUSLY DELICIOUS - Food products - Muir Glen
OUTRE - Wigs - Sun Taiyang Co. Ltd.
OUTREACH - Computer software - Intergroup, Inc.
OUTRIDER - Bicycles - American Recreation Co., Inc.
OUTRIDER - Electrical equipment - T.D. Williamson, Inc.
OUTRIDER - Toys–automobiles ☆ - Kenner Products
OUTRIGGER - Apparel and accessories - Edison Brothers Stores, Inc.
OUTRIGGER - Brushes–paint - Elder & Jenks, Inc.
OUTRIGGER - Fabrics ☆ - Charter Fabrics Inc.
OUTRIGGER - House furnishings - Lexington Furniture Industries, Inc.
OUTRIGGER - Luggage - Bernard D. Sadow
OUTRIGGER - Lumber - Georgia-Pacific Corp.
OUTRIGGER - Machine parts - R.L. Wright Co., Inc.
OUTRIGGER - Office supplies - American Trading and Production Corp.
OUTRIGGER, THE - Ships - Bay Manufacturing
OUTRIGGER USA - Apparel–men's - Edison Brothers Stores, Inc.
OUTRIGHT - Pet products - Bramton Co.
OUTRUN - Ophthalmic goods - Foremost Optical Products
OUTRUNNER - Sealing devices - Freudenberg-Nok General Partnership
OUTSDOORSMAN - Sporting goods - South Bend Sporting Goods Inc.
OUTSERT - Golfing equipment - Ram Golf Corp.
OUTSIDE - Footwear - Wolverine World Wide, Inc.
OUTSIDE - Stationery - Sunrise Publications, Inc.
OUTSIDE DESIGN - Umbrellas - Outside Design Inc.
OUTSIDE FLEA RELIEF - Veterinary pharmaceutical preparations - Dr. Goodpet
OUTSIDE IN - Computer software - Systems Compatibility Corp.
OUTSIDER - Audio equipment - Barcus-Berry Inc.
OUTSIDER - Tools - Portable Products, Inc.
OUTSIDERS - Brooms - Drackett Co.
OUTSIDEVIEW - Computer software - Crystal Point, Inc.
OUTSIDEWOOD - Lumber - Hoover Treated Wood Products Inc.
OUTSPOKEN CHANEL - Perfumes - Chanel Inc.
OUTSTAINDING - Stain removers - Pet Connection

OUTSTANDING - Floor coverings–carpet and rugs - Cabin Crafts Carpets
OUTSTANDING - Food products - Beaver Street Fisheries Inc.
OUTSTANDING - Recording label - Outstanding Records
OUTSTANDING - Wallpaper - Essex Wallcoveringss
OUTSTANDING ORANGE - Food products - Jel Sert Co.
OUTSULATION - Insulating materials - Dryvit Systems, Inc.
OUTTA HERE - Apparel–children's - Dream Baby Enterprises
OUTTA HERE - Luggage - NLDA Associates, Inc.
OUTTAKES - Greeting cards - Hallmark Cards Inc.
OUTWARD BOUND FOR SHUT INS - Computer software - Right on Programs
OUTWEST - Vegetables–canned - Haney Seed/Bean Growers
OUTWIT - Games ☆ - Parker Brothers
OUTWIT THE OWL - Computer software - Hartley Courseware Inc.
OUVERTURE - Accordions - Hohner Inc.
OUVIO - Footwear–children's - Lvichiny Destroy Imports Inc.
OUWIE! BALM - Skin care products - Liane Elise Souders-Sims
OUZOUNIS - Alcoholic beverages - Attiki Imports & Distributors
OV-CARE - Cleaning preparations - National Chemsearch Corp.
OV-N-KLEEN - Cleaning preparations–household - Harley Chemicals
OV-U-PEAK - Pharmaceutical preparations - International Canine Genetics Inc.
OVA - Pharmaceutical preparations - Rugby Laboratories Inc.
OVA-NITE - Ophthalmic goods - Whitby Pharmaceuticals, Inc.
OVA-NITER - Ophthalmic goods - Whitby Pharmaceuticals, Inc.
OVABAN - Veterinary pharmaceutical preparations - Schering-Plough Animal Health
OVACATH - Catheters - Ovamed Corp.
OVAGIN - Pharmaceutical preparations ☆ - Medical Products Panamericana Inc.
OVAH MUSIC - Recording label - Sublime Music, Inc.
OVAL - Girdles - Vanity Corset Co. Inc.
OVAL - Water treating compounds ☆ - Akzo America Inc.
OVAL-ART - Artists' materials - Gene Green's Oval Machine
OVAL FACETTE - Glassware–household - Dansk International Designs, Ltd.
OVAL/PHONE - Telephones - Action Systems Co.
OVAL V - Bathtubs–enameled - Pearl Baths Inc.
OVAL VI - Bathtubs–enameled - Pearl Baths Inc.
OVALFLOW - Fluid transfer pumps - Xolox Corp.
OVALGRAPH - Tools–hand-operated - Ovalgraph Manufacturing Co.
OVALGREY - Erasers ☆ - Faber-Castell Corp.
OVALLA - Lighting fixtures ☆ - Progress Lighting Inc.
OVALTINE - Spices and extracts - Novartis Nutrition Corp.
OVALUX - Lighting fixtures - P.L.I. Enterprises, Inc.
OVAMED - Medical apparatus - Ovamed Corp.
OVAMINS - Pharmaceutical preparations ☆ - Vita-Fore Products Co.
OVANITE - Gloves - George Glove Co. Inc.
OVARAGEN-F - Vitamins and nutritional supplements - Great Life Laboratories Inc.
OVATION - Aircraft - Mooney Aircraft Corp.
L'OVATION - Binders - Pengad, Inc.
OVATION - Clarinets ☆ - G. Leblanc Corp.
OVATION - Cleaning preparations–household - Mission Kleensweep Products, Inc.
OVATION - Dental compounds - NEY Dental International, Inc.
OVATION - Doors–wood - Simpson Timber Co.
OVATION - Eyewear - NuVision Inc.
OVATION - Figurines - Freeman Products, Inc.
OVATION - Floor coverings - Congoleum Corp.
OVATION - Floor coverings–carpet and rugs - Edgecrest Carpet Mills
OVATION - Floor coverings–carpet and rugs - Milliken & Co. Inc.
OVATION - Floor coverings–carpet and rugs - Porter Carpet Mills Inc.
OVATION - Floor coverings–carpet and rugs - S and S Mills Inc.
OVATION - Floor coverings–carpet and rugs ☆ - American Carpet Mills
OVATION - Floor coverings–carpet and rugs ☆ - Richmond Carpet Mills
OVATION - Glassware–household - Oneida Ltd.
OVATION - Guitars - Castiglione Accordion
OVATION - Guitars - Kaman Music Corp.
OVATION - Guitars - Ovation Instruments
OVATION - Helmets–athletic ☆ - Bell Sports Corp.
OVATION - Lamps ☆ - Cannon Products Inc.
OVATION - Mattresses and box springs - Ohio Mattress Co.
OVATION - Napkins–paper - Encore Paper Co., Inc.
OVATION - Pet products - Eugene G. Danner Manufacturing Inc.
OVATION - Sporting goods - Oceanic
OVATION - Stoves–gas - Pyro Industries, Inc.
OVATION - Underwear and nightwear - Bestform Foundations, Inc.

☆ = Now out of production

OVATION PREMIUM NYLON - Floor coverings–carpet and rugs - Superior Manufacturing Group/Notrax Floor Matting

OVATIONS - Floor coverings - Congoleum Corp.

OVATIONS - Wallpaper - Capital Carousel Inc.

OVATIONS - Wallpaper - Gloria Merrill Enterprises

OVATIONS FLEX - Floor coverings - Congoleum Corp.

OVATONE - Veterinary pharmaceutical preparations - BASF Corp.

OVATROPHIN PMG - Vitamins and nutritional supplements - Standard Process Inc.

OVCON - Pharmaceutical preparations - Bristol-Myers Squibb Co.

OVELMO - Antacids - Ovelmo Co.

OVEN - Thread - Lewis Threads Inc.

OVEN ACCENTS - Hobby kits - Design-Dye

OVEN-AIRE - Cooking equipment–household - Northland Aluminum Products Inc.

OVEN-AIRE - Fans–electric - Nordic Ware

OVEN ART - Bakery products - Community Bakeries

OVEN ART - Pens ☆ - Sanford Corp.

OVEN BASICS - Cooking utensils–earthenware - Anchor Hocking Glass, Inc.

OVEN BRIQUE - Cooking equipment–household ☆ - Nordic Ware

OVEN BROWNS - Vegetables–frozen ☆ - Lamb-Weston, Inc.

OVEN CRISP - Food products - Ore-Ida Foods, Inc.

OVEN EASY - Seasonings - McCormick & Co., Inc.

OVEN EXPRESS - Food products - Tyson Foods Inc.

OVEN-FRESH - Bakery products - Oven Fresh Bakery

OVEN FRESH - Cookies - Grocers Baking Co.

OVEN FRESH - Cookies and crackers - Interbake Foods Inc.

OVEN FRESH JUST BAKED AWESOME GOURMET COOKIES - Cookies - Country Home Bakers, Inc.

OVEN GOLD - Breads - American Bakeries Co.

OVEN GOOD - Vegetables–frozen - Norpac Services, Inc.

OVEN-GUIDE - Thermometers - Taylor Environmental Instruments

OVEN JOY - Flour–blended - Safeway Stores Inc.

OVEN KEY - Kitchen utensils–aluminum - Thomas A. Erickson Ovenkeys

OVEN KIST - Food products - Gold Kist Inc.

OVEN KRISP - Snack foods - Big Star Food Stores

OVEN LOVIN - Food products ☆ - Pillsbury Co.

OVEN MILL - Bakery products - Certified Grocers of California, Ltd.

OVEN-PERFECT - Frozen potatoes - Saramar Corp.

OVEN POPPERS - Seafood products–fresh or frozen - Ovenpoppers, Inc.

OVEN Q - Food products - Universal Frozen Foods Co.

OVEN QUEEN - Bakery products - Oven Fresh Bakery

OVEN-QUICK - Food products - Pierce Foods Corp.

OVEN READY - Thread ☆ - Perfect Thread Co. Inc.

OVEN SOFT - Cookies - Keebler Co.

OVEN STUFF - Bakery products - G & S Metal Products Co., Inc.

OVEN STUFFER ROASTER - Meat products–poultry - Perdue Farms Inc.

OVEN WING-DINGS - Meat products–poultry - Pierce Foods Corp.

OVENAL - Food containers - Premix Inc.

OVENCRAFT - Giftware - Wilton Industries, Inc.

OVENCRAFT - Pottery products - Laguna Clay Co.

OVENGATOR - Housewares - Hansel 'n Gretel Brand, Inc.

OVENGLO - Bakery products - Oven Fresh Bakery

OVENGOLD - Meat products - Frank Brunckhorst Co., LP

OVENMASTER - Toasters - Hamilton Beach/Proctor-Silex Inc.

OVENMATE - Paperboard - Gulf States Paper Corp.

L'OVENWARE - Cookware - Creative Specialty Manufacturing, Inc.

OVENWORKS - Pastries - Associated Grocers, Inc.

OVER - Recording label - KCTS Television

OVER 40 - Food products - Lewis Laboratories International Ltd.

OVER A CENTURY OF SKIN CARING - Cosmetics - Shiseido Cosmetics (America) Ltd.

OVER-ALL - Correction fluid - Wirth International Inc.

OVER AND OUT - Cosmetics - Circle of Beauty, Inc.

OVER AND OVER - Gloves - Knoxville Glove Co.

OVER BROOK - Eggnog - M.S. Walker Inc./Seacoast

OVER C - Vitamins and nutritional supplements ☆ - Integrated Health, Inc.

OVER EASY - Apparel–men's - Phillips-Van Heusen Corp.

OVER EASY - Exercising equipment ☆ - STL International, Inc.

OVER EASY - Toasters - Holman Cooking Equipment, Inc.

OVER FIFTY - Pharmaceutical preparations - Bretney Corp.

OVER-GUARD - Goggles–safety - Allan Enterprises

OVER-LOK - Jewelry - Jacoby-Bender Inc.

OVER 'N OUT - Games - CBS Toys

OVER N UNDER - Sporting goods - Over 'N Under, Inc.

OVER-RUST - Paints ☆ - Kelly-Moore Paint Co. Inc.

OVER-SEAS - Seafood products–fresh or frozen - Alphin Bros. Inc.

OVER-THE-AIR PROGRAMMING - Electronic equipment - AmeriCom Corp.

OVER THE EDGE - Apparel and accessories - Psychographic Design Group, Inc.

OVER THE EDGE - Hobby kits - Tri-Chem Inc.

OVER THE HILL NOVELTY - Novelty items - Laid Back Enterprises, Inc.

OVER THE HILL PILLS - Candy - Marsyl Inc. (Marsyl Enterprises, Inc.)

OVER THE HILLS - Stoneware dinnerware - Iron Mountain Stoneware Inc.

OVER THE LINE - Chairs–wood - Old Mission Beach Athletic Club Inc.

OVER THE NET - Apparel–athletic - Allen A. Sales

OVER THE RAINBOW - Apparel–women's - Leading Lady Companies Inc.

OVER THE RAINBOW - Dolls ☆ - Effanbee Doll Corp.

OVER THE RAINBOW - Floor coverings–carpet and rugs - Mohawk Industries Inc.

OVER THE RAINBOW - Games - Smethport Specialty Co.

OVER THE SHOULDER LAUNDRY HOLDER, THE - Bags–duffel - Michael Laconte

OVER THE TOP - Apparel and accessories - I.C. Isaacs & Co.

OVER-THE-TOP - Machinery - Roe Inc.

OVER THE TOP - Toy action figures - Tonka Corp.

OVER TIME - Chewing gum ☆ - Wm. Wrigley Jr. Co.

OVERALL - Adhesives and sealants - Gardner Asphalt Corp.

OVERALL - Computer software - Software Garden, Inc.

OVERALL - Paints - Parker Paint Manufacturing Co.

OVERALL - Thread - Threads USA Div.

OVERBROOK - Floor coverings - Mannington Resilient Floors

OVERBROOK - Floor coverings–carpet and rugs - Karastan-Bigelow Inc.

OVERBROOK FARMS - Dinners–frozen - Overbrook Farms, Inc.

OVERCOAT - Correction fluid - International Rotex Inc.

OVERCOAT - Skin care products - Sogo Inc.

OVERCOAT ALL - Correction fluid - International Rotex Inc.

OVERCOATS - Lipsticks - Avon Products, Inc.

OVERCOATS - Nail care products - Orly International Inc.

OVERDRIVE - Apparel and accessories - Dress Of The Month Club Inc.

OVERDRIVE - Computer hardware - Intel Corp.

OVERDRIVE - Electronic equipment - AudioControl

OVERDRIVE - Vitamins and nutritional supplements - Nu Skin International, Inc.

OVERDRIVERS - Toys - Tiger Electronics, Inc.

OVERDUE BOOKS MANAGER - Computer software - Right on Programs

OVERFLOW I - Computer software - CBS Software

OVERGEAR - Gloves - Glove Source, Inc.

OVERHAND - Skin care products - Evolve, Inc.

OVERHEAD DOOR - Remote control devices - Overhead Door Corp.

OVERHEADS - Headbands - Bernard Thomas Dlugokeski

OVERKILL - Fly sprays - Farnam Cos. Inc.

OVERKIRK - Apparel–men's - Popular Club Plan, Inc.

OVERKOTE - Concrete products - Rust-Oleum Concrete Protection Systems, Inc.

OVERLAKE - Fruits–frozen - Overlake Food Corp.

OVERLAM - Photographic equipment - CODA Inc.

OVERLAND - Bicycles - Columbia Manufacturing Inc.

OVERLAND - Cigars ☆ - Brick-Hanauer Co.

OVERLAND - Motor vehicles–motor homes - Mallard Coach

OVERLAND SHEEPSKIN - Apparel and accessories - Overland Sheepskin Co.

OVERLAND TRAIL - Snack foods - Granny Goose Foods Inc.

OVERLANDER - Trailers–travel - Airstream Inc.

OVERLAP - Computer software - William C. Chennault

OVERLAY CLIPPER CUTS - Clippers–barber - Sunbeam-Oster Household Products

OVERLAY MAKER - Computer software - Unicorn Engineering, Inc.

OVERLAY, THE - Paper ☆ - Hunt Manufacturing Co.

OVERLAY/UNDERLAY - Office supplies - MagnaPlan Corp.

OVERLOAD - Game machines - Bally Gaming International, Inc.

OVERLOAD ALERT - Measuring instruments - Beckman Industrial Corp.

OVERLOCK/SERGER - Patterns–clothing ☆ - Simplicity Pattern Co., Inc.

OVERLOOK PRESS, THE - Publisher's imprints - Overlook Press

OVERLOOKS - Eyeglasses - Opsales, Inc.

OVERLORD - Toys - Tonka Corp.

OVERMAN CUSHION - Tires–automobile - R. Castelli, Inc.

OVER'N UNDER - Sporting goods - Shield Manufacturing Inc.

OVERNIGHT - Jewelry - A.L.A. Casting Co., Inc.

OVERNIGHT - Pharmaceutical preparations - Vita Plus Industries Inc.

OVERNIGHT BUSINESS TRAVELER - Luggage - Hartmann Luggage Co.

OVERNIGHT PASSPORT - Hair and skin-care products - Aubrey Organics, Inc.

OVERNIGHT SUCCESS - Skin-care products - Coty Inc.

☆ = Now out of production

OVERNIGHTER - Boats–motor ☆ - Grady-White Boats, Inc.
OVERNIGHTER - Boats–pontoons ☆ - Harris-Kayot Inc.
OVERNIGHTER - Sofabeds - Statesville Chair Co. Inc.
OVERNIGHTER, THE - Manicure sets ☆ - London International U.S. Holdings
OVERNIGHTER, THE - Office supplies - United States Postal Service
OVERNITE - Insecticides - Enforcer Products Inc.
OVERNITE SECRETARY - Carry-on luggage, briefcases - Jameslee Corp.
OVERNITER - Boats - Glen-L Marine Designs
OVERNITES - Sanitary napkins - Kimberly-Clark Corp.
OVEROCEAN - Clocks - Overocean Clock Co. Inc.
OVERPOWER - Trading cards and stamps - Fleer Corp.
OVERQUOTA - Computer software - MJF International
OVERSEAS FACTOR - Health care products - Superior Trading Co.
OVERSHADE - Lamp shades–fabric ☆ - Vista Solutions Inc.
OVERSTOLZ - Cigarettes - R.J. Reynolds Tobacco Co.
OVERSTUFFERS - Bags–plastic - Zeta Consumer Products Corp.
OVERTEXT - Computer software - Protobyte Inc.
OVERTIME - Basketball footwear ☆ - Autry Industries Inc.
OVERTIME - Computer software - Kali Corp.
OVERTIME - Electronic equipment ☆ - GC Thorsen, Inc.
OVERTIME - Sporting goods - Lifetime Products, Inc.
OVERTIME SHADOW - Cosmetics - Revlon Consumer Products Corp.
OVERTON SQUARE - Floor coverings–carpet and rugs ☆ - Columbus Mills, Inc.
OVERTON SQUARE - Wallpaper ☆ - Somerville Designs
OVERTONE - Floor coverings–carpet and rugs ☆ - Regal Rugs Inc.
OVERTONE - Underwear and nightwear - Maidenform Inc.
OVERTONES - Wallcovering - Gencorp Inc.
OVERTURE - Apparel–women's ☆ - Bobbie Brooks Inc.
OVERTURE - Bathtubs–enameled - Kohler Co.
OVERTURE - Blinds–venetian ☆ - Hunter Douglas, Inc.
OVERTURE - Computer software - Opcode Systems, Inc.
OVERTURE - Confections - Hershey Chocolate USA
OVERTURE - Dishes–china - Pickard Inc.
OVERTURE - Electrical equipment - National Semiconductor Corp.
OVERTURE - Floor coverings–carpet and rugs ☆ - Karastan-Bigelow Inc.
OVERTURE - Glassware–scientific - Federal Glass
OVERTURE - Recording label - Ambassador Recording Corp.
OVERTURE - Rings–jewelry - Feature Enterprises
OVERTURE - Tea kettles–nonelectric ☆ - General Housewares Corp.
OVERTURE - Yarn - Rainbow Gallery, Inc.
OVERTURES - Building materials - Georgia-Pacific Corp.
OVERTURES - Tiles–ceramic - American Olean Tile Co.
OVERTURES - Wallpaper ☆ - Winfield Design Associates, Inc.
OVERUST - Paints - Epoca Corp.
OVERWETS - Bathing suits - Catalina
OVERWHELMING - Mohawk Industries Inc.
OVETTE - Bathroom fixtures ☆ - Crane Plumbing/Fiat Products
OVID - Computer software - CDP Technologies, Inc.
OVIDE - Health care products - Genderm Corp.
OVIEDO - Glassware–household ☆ - Oneida Ltd.
OVIS - Cheese - Pastene Companies Ltd.
OVL 8 - Water colors - Dixon Ticonderoga Co.
OVL-16 - Water colors - Dixon Ticonderoga Co.
OVOMAT SPECIAL - Cooking equipment–household ☆ - Robert Krups North America
OVRAL - Pharmaceutical preparations - Wyeth-Ayerst Laboratories
OVRETTE - Pharmaceutical preparations - Wyeth-Ayerst Laboratories
OVT - Varnishes - Samuel Cabot Inc.
OVUCHECK - Pregnancy test kits - Johnson & Johnson
OVULEN - Pharmaceutical preparations - G. D. Searle & Co.
OVULINDEX - Thermometers - Linacre Laboratories
OVULOMETER - Electromedical apparatus - Mankind Research Unltd. Inc.
OVURA - Chairs–upholstered - United Chair Co., Inc.
OWEGO - Oils–edible - Owego International Inc.
OWEN - Silent springs - Babcock Industries Inc. (Babcock Control Group)
OWEN ENTERPRISES - Publisher's imprints - Viking Import House Inc.
OWEN GROMME - Posters - Stanton & Lee
OWENS - Food products - Bob Evans Farms Inc.
OWENS - Food products - Owen & Mowrey Inc.
OWENS - Pharmaceutical preparations - American Cyanamid Co.
OWENS - Sausages - Owens Country Sausage Inc.
OWENS - Toothbrushes - Oral B Laboratories
OWENS BORDER BREAKFAST - Sausages - Owens Country Sausage Inc.
OWENS CORNING - Building materials - Owens Corning Fiberglass Technology Inc.

OWENS-CORNING - Shingles - Owens Corning
OWENS OVALS - Glassware–household - Owens-Illinois Inc. (Libbey Div.)
OWL - Artists' materials - Thomas C. Laipply
OWL - Fruits and vegetables - Watsonville Exchange Inc.
OWL - Glassware–household - Rezler & Howell Co.
OWL - Kites - Hi-Flier Manufacturing Co.
OWL - Lighting fixtures - General Electric Co.
OWL - Onions ☆ - Hi Quality Packing
OWL - Recording label - Jazz Composer's Orchestra Association Inc.
OWL - Thread - Threads USA Div.
OWL BOOKS - Publisher's imprints - Henry Holt and Co.
OWL CREEK - Apparel - Owl Creek Designs
OWL JR. - Lighting fixtures - General Electric Co.
OWL LIGHT - Lamps ☆ - Lamplight Farms, Inc.
OWL STEP STOOL - Stools–wood ☆ - Little Tikes Co.
OWLET PAPERBACKS - Publisher's imprints - Henry Holt and Co.
OWLETTES - Fruits and vegetables - Watsonville Exchange Inc.
OWL'S NEST - Gelatin - Lakeview Farms, Inc.
OWN A PIECE OF HOMELAND - Bookmarks - Universal Sunshine Corp.
OWN THE WEST - Apparel–women's ☆ - Shea West Manufacturing, Inc.
OWNER'S BLEND PREMIUM CONGOU - Teas - Grace Tea Co. Ltd.
O.W.S. - Ophthalmic goods - Whitby Pharmaceuticals, Inc.
OWYHEE - Candy - Idaho Candy Co.
OX - Barbed wire - BP & N Inc.
OX AND MULE - Cleaning preparations–household - Ox and Mule Co.
OX-ANGLE - Brushes–paint ☆ - Linzer Products Corp.
OX-BEST - Brushes–paint ☆ - Linzer Products Corp.
OX-CRAFT - Brushes–paint ☆ - Linzer Products Corp.
OX-CROWN - Brushes–paint ☆ - Linzer Products Corp.
OX-FLO - Brushes–paint ☆ - Linzer Products Corp.
OX GALL - Pharmaceutical preparations - City Chemical Corp.
OX-GARD - Electrical equipment - GB Electrical Inc.
OX HIDE - Apparel and accessories - J.C. Penney Co., Inc.
OX JEANS - Apparel and accessories - Robert Cho
OX-KING - Brushes–paint ☆ - Linzer Products Corp.
OX-KUTTER - Brushes–paint ☆ - Linzer Products Corp.
OX-LINE - Paints ☆ - California Products Corp.
OX-LORD - Brushes–paint ☆ - Linzer Products Corp.
OX-NAMEL - Brushes–paint ☆ - Linzer Products Corp.
OX-O-LIN - Brushes–paint ☆ - Linzer Products Corp.
OX-PRINCE - Brushes–paint ☆ - Linzer Products Corp.
OX-REGAL - Brushes–paint ☆ - Linzer Products Corp.
OX-RITE - Brushes–paint ☆ - Linzer Products Corp.
OX-ROYAL - Brushes–paint ☆ - Linzer Products Corp.
OX-SWIRL - Brushes–paint ☆ - Linzer Products Corp.
OX-TOPAZ - Brushes–paint ☆ - Linzer Products Corp.
OX-TRAN - Measuring instruments - MOCON/Modern Controls, Inc.
OXAINE M - Pharmaceutical preparations ☆ - Wyeth-Ayerst Laboratories
OXALERT - Alarm systems - Hospitak Inc.
OXALID - Analgesics - Rhone-Poulenc Rorer Pharmaceuticals Inc.
OXBOARD - Plywood - Potlatch Corp.
OXBRIDGE - Cabinets - Aristokraft, Inc.
OXBRIDGE ROMAN ARCH - Cabinets - Aristokraft, Inc.
OXECON - Office supplies - Esselte Corp.
OXEN - Fabrics - Uniroyal Engineered Products
OXEQUIP - Medical apparatus - Allied Healthcare Products Inc.
OXFORD - Amplifiers–musical instrument - Oxford Speakers Co.
OXFORD - Backpacks - Eddie Bauer Inc.
OXFORD - Bathroom accessories ☆ - F.H. Lawson Co.
OXFORD - Bathroom fixtures - Crane Plumbing/Fiat Products
OXFORD - Blinds–vertical - Newell Operating Co.
OXFORD - Cabinets - Canyon Creek Cabinet Co.
OXFORD - Cabinets - Del Mar Cabinets
OXFORD - Cabinets - Wellborn Cabinet, Inc.
OXFORD - Cabinets–wood - Parcraft Distinctive Cabinetry
OXFORD - Cabinets–wood ☆ - Kemper
OXFORD - Cooking equipment–household - Primex International Corp.
OXFORD - Cribs–wood ☆ - Welsh Co.
OXFORD - Cutlery - Washington Forge Inc.
OXFORD - Dartboards, darts ☆ - Indian Industries Inc.
OXFORD - Dinnerware–glass ☆ - Nikko Ceramics Inc.
OXFORD - Floor coverings - Congoleum Corp.
OXFORD - Floor coverings ☆ - Bruce Hardwood Floors
OXFORD - Floor coverings–carpet and rugs - Atlas Carpet Mills Inc.
OXFORD - Floor coverings–carpet and rugs - Philadelphia Carpets
OXFORD - Floor coverings–carpet and rugs ☆ - LaVelle Textile Marketing Inc.

☆ = Now out of production

OXFORD - Frames–eyeglass - U.S. Optical Frame Co.
OXFORD - Furniture - Inwood Office Furniture
OXFORD - Games - Arthur Schwartz & Co. Inc.
OXFORD - Lamps - Kaadan Ltd.
OXFORD - Leather goods - David Kirk (London)
OXFORD - Lighting fixtures ☆ - Liteway
OXFORD - Office supplies - Esselte Corp.
OXFORD - Pickles - John E. Cain Co.
OXFORD - Plumbing fixtures–metal - Sterline Manufacturing Corp.
OXFORD - Puzzles - Milton Bradley Co.
OXFORD - Shirts - Oxford Industries, Inc.
OXFORD - Tables–wood ☆ - Krueger International, Inc.
OXFORD - Tableware–china ☆ - Lenox, Inc.
OXFORD - Wallpaper - Capital Carousel Inc.
OXFORD - Watches - Bulova Corp.
OXFORD - Wood products - Georgia-Pacific Corp.
OXFORD BRITES - Office supplies ☆ - Esselte Corp.
OXFORD CLASS ALE - Beverages–malt - Oxford Brewing Co.
OXFORD COPYCALC - Office supplies - Esselte Corp.
OXFORD COPYKEEPER - Office supplies - Esselte Corp.
OXFORD CREAM - Cookies - Sunshine/Salerno Inc.
OXFORD DATALINE - Office supplies - Esselte Corp.
OXFORD DECOPOUCH - Office supplies - Esselte Corp.
OXFORD GLEN - Furniture ☆ - Bassett Furniture Industries, Inc.
OXFORD HALL - Flatware ☆ - Towle Silversmiths
OXFORD HALL - Furniture - Thomasville Furniture Industries Inc.
OXFORD HOUSE - Furniture ☆ - Bassett Furniture Industries, Inc.
OXFORD HOUSE COLLECTION, THE - Lace - Lace Lastics Co., Inc.
OXFORD IRONHIDE - Office supplies - Esselte Corp.
OXFORD M-LINE - Cabinets–metal ☆ - Esselte Corp.
OXFORD MANOR - Doors–storm - Weather Shield Manufacturing, Inc.
OXFORD MANOR - Fabrics–tapestry - Coloroll Inc.
OXFORD MANOR - Furniture - Hooker Furniture Corp.
OXFORD PINE - Furniture ☆ - Hammary Furniture Co. Inc.
OXFORD PLACE - Floor coverings–carpet and rugs - Atlas Carpet Mills Inc.
OXFORD PLUS - Office supplies - Esselte Corp.
OXFORD PORTFILE - Office supplies - Esselte Corp.
OXFORD ROLL 'EMS - Cabinets–metal ☆ - Esselte Corp.
OXFORD ROLLER CLIP - Office supplies - Esselte Corp.
OXFORD ROYAL - Fruits and vegetables - Oxford Royal Mushroom Products Inc.
OXFORD SHIRTMAKER - Shirts - Oxford Sportswear & Apparel
OXFORD STREET - Floor coverings–carpet and rugs - Milliken & Co. Inc.
OXFORD THERMAL BINDING SYSTEM - Office supplies - Esselte Corp.
OXFORD TOTE - Office supplies - Esselte Corp.
OXFORD WAVE - Office supplies - Esselte Corp.
OXFORD WEAVE - Stationery ☆ - Mead Corp.
OXFORD WIRE WORKS - Office supplies ☆ - Esselte Corp.
OXFORDON - Fabrics ☆ - Dan River Inc.
OXI-FREEDA - Vitamins and nutritional supplements - Freeda Vitamins Inc.
OXI-PRO - Vitamins and nutritional supplements - Champion Nutrition
OXI-VITA - Vitamins and nutritional supplements - Naturally Vitamin Supplements Inc.
OXI2CLEAN - Cleaning preparations - Appel Mountain, Inc.
OXIA - Motor vehicles–automobiles - Peugeot Motors of America Inc.
OXIBAK H - Bricks - Indresco Inc.
OXIFLOW - Medical apparatus - Nellcor Puritan Bennett Inc.
OXIFREE - Water purification systems - Capital Controls Co.
OXIGENTA - Hair care products - Schwarzkopf Inc.
OXILAN - Pharmaceutical preparations - Cook Imaging Corp.
OXILY - Skin care products - IT&LY Hairfashion NA Inc.
OXINA - Hair care products - Framesi USA/Roffler Industries Inc.
OXIPHEN - Pharmaceutical preparations ☆ - M. Polymedica Corp.
OXIPLEN - Pharmaceutical preparations ☆ - Medical Products Panamericana Inc.
OXIPOR VHC - Pharmaceutical preparations - Whitehall Laboratories
OXISOLV - Chemical preparations - Solv-O Corp.
OXITIVA - Vitamins and nutritional supplements - Manhattan Drug Co., Inc.
OXITRACE - Electronic apparatus - Capital Controls Co.
OXLIFE - Health care products - Medical Repair Service
OXLIN - Tablecloths - Cascade Fibers Co.
OXLINE - Paints - Wyckoff Paint & Wallpaper Co.
OXLITE - Ramps - Oxlite, Inc.
OXLITE ANGLE - Brushes–paint - Corona Brushes Inc.
OXLOPAR - See **WARNER-CHILCOTT**
OXMOOR HOUSE - Publisher's imprints - Oxmoor House Inc.

OXO - Cooking utensils–aluminum - General Housewares Corp.
OXOIDS - Pharmaceutical preparations ☆ - Lemmon Co.
OXOLIN - Varnishes - Ranbar Technology Inc.
OXONIAN - Apparel and accessories - Oxford Industries, Inc.
OXSORALEN - Pharmaceutical preparations - ICN Pharmaceuticals Inc.
OXSORALEN-ULTRA - Pharmaceutical preparations - ICN Pharmaceuticals Inc.
OXSPORT - Fabrics - Dan River Inc.
OXWALL - Hand tools - Atlas Group
OXWORD - Office supplies ☆ - Esselte Corp.
OXY - Cosmetics ☆ - Duart Industries Ltd.
OXY - Footwear - Der-Tex Corp.
OXY - Pharmaceutical preparations - Smithkline Beecham Corp.
OXY-55S - Pharmaceutical preparations - SmithKline Beecham Consumer Healthcare
OXY-90S - Pharmaceutical preparations - SmithKline Beecham Consumer Healthcare
OXY 5000 FORTE - Health care products - American Biologics
OXY BALANCE - Pharmaceutical preparations - SmithKline Beecham Consumer Healthcare
OXY-BRITE - Coatings ☆ - Seal-Krete Inc.
OXY-BRITE - Water treating compounds - Great Lakes Biochemical Co., Inc.
OXY-CADDY - Health care products - Trenton Surgical Supply Co.
OXY-CAPS - Vitamins and nutritional supplements - Matrix Health Products, Inc.
OXY-CATALYTIC - Water purification systems - Reynolds Water Conditioning Co.
OXY CLEAN - Skin care products ☆ - SmithKline Beecham Consumer Healthcare
OXY-CLEANSE - Vitamins and nutritional supplements - Matrix Health Products, Inc.
OXY-DUO-PAK - Medical apparatus - Mada Medical Products Inc.
OXY-DYE SYSTEM - Hair care products - Wella Corp. (Consumer Products Div.)
OXY-E - Dietary and nutritional supplements - Great Earth International Inc.
OXY-EFX - Pharmaceutical preparations - Natural Efx, Inc.
OXY-FRAME - Frames–eyeglass - Engineered Specialty Products
OXY FREE - Steel products - RFE Industries, Inc.
OXY FREE - Vitamins and nutritional supplements - Natural Organics, Inc.
OXY-G2 - Vitamins and nutritional supplements - Body Wise International, Inc.
OXY-GARD - Veterinary medical equipment - Ecolab Inc.
OXY-GON - Vitamins and nutritional supplements - Ameri-Pac, Inc.
OXY-LENS - Contact lenses - Contex, Inc.
OXY LIFE - Vitamins and nutritional supplements - Natural Organics, Inc.
OXY LOCK - Hair care products - Focus 21 International Inc.
OXY-MAX - Vitamins and nutritional supplements - Matrix Health Products, Inc.
OXY-MIST - Vitamins and nutritional supplements - Matrix Health Products, Inc.
OXY-NECTAR - Antitoxins - Nature's Plus
OXY-NECTAR - Food supplement - Natural Organics, Inc.
OXY NIGHT WATCH - Pharmaceutical preparations ☆ - SmithKline Beecham Consumer Healthcare
OXY-OFF - Cleaning preparations - Horizons Marketing Group, Inc.
OXY-ORAL - Health care products - Organics Corp. of America (Ambix Laboratories Div.)
OXY-OTIC - Health care products - Organics Corp. of America (Ambix Laboratories Div.)
OXY PAD LIFTER - Skin care products - Smithkline Beecham Corp.
OXY-PEP - Vitamins and nutritional supplements ☆ - Natural Balance, Inc.
OXY PET NATURES EMISSARY - Housewares - Mike Margucci
OXY PLEX - Vitamins and nutritional supplements - Natural Organics, Inc.
OXY-QUENCHERS - Vitamins and nutritional supplements - Twinlab
OXY-QUIK - Medical apparatus ☆ - Allied Healthcare Products Inc.
OXY SENSITIVE - Health care products - Smithkline Beecham Corp.
OXY SENSITIVE - Skin care products ☆ - SmithKline Beecham Consumer Healthcare
OXY-SEPT - Disinfectants - Ecolab Inc.
OXY-SHIELD - Vitamins and nutritional supplements - Pdk Labs, Inc.
OXY-SHOCK - Chemical preparations - Aqua Clear Industries Inc.
OXY-SHOT - Veterinary pharmaceutical preparations - Sanofi Animal Health, Inc.
OXY-UNI-PAK - Medical apparatus - Mada Medical Products Inc.
OXY-VISION - Vitamins and nutritional supplements - Pharmavite Corp.
OXY VITE - Vitamins and nutritional supplements - Natural Organics, Inc.
OXY WASH - Skin care products ☆ - SmithKline Beecham Consumer Healthcare
OXYBEN - Pharmaceutical preparations - Goldline Laboratories, Inc.

☆ = Now out of production

OXYBLEND - Chemical preparations - Scott Specialty Gases, Inc.

OXYBOOT - Medical apparatus - Paul A. Geary, Jr., Sean M. Geary and Joseph R. Westwood Partnership

OXYCAL - Lubricants - Calgene Chemical

OXYCAL - Vitamins and nutritional supplements - Inter-Cal Corp.

OXYCAL-M - Antiarthritic ☆ - Inter-Cal Corp.

OXYCAP - Health care products - Datex-Ohmeda, Inc.

OXYCARE - Dentifrices - Oxyfresh Worldwide, Inc.

OXYCAT - Air purification systems - Met-Pro Corp.

OXYCEL - Pharmaceutical preparations - Becton, Dickinson and Co.

OXYCELL - Reactors–nuclear - Endotronics Inc.

OXYCHINOL - Health care products - Ferndale Laboratories, Inc.

OXYCLEAR - Resins–vinyl - Occidental Chemical Corp.

OXYCOIL - Respirators - Chad Therapeutics Inc.

OXYCON - Optical scanners–computer - Oxycontact Lens Inc.

OXYCUP - Ophthalmic goods ☆ - Allergan, Inc.

OXYCUR - Skin care products - GOLDWELL Cosmetics (USA) Inc.

OXYCURE - Health care products - Hospitak Inc.

OXYDERMAL - Skin care products - Organics Corp. of America (Ambix Laboratories Div.)

OXYDESS - Pharmaceutical preparations ☆ - Vortech Pharmaceuticals

OXYDESS II - Pharmaceutical preparations ☆ - Vortech Pharmaceuticals

OXYDOL - Detergents - Procter & Gamble Co.

OXYDYNE - Medical apparatus - Oxydyne, Inc.

OXYFREE - Hair care products - Oxyfree Inc.

OXYFRESH - Toothpaste - Oxyfresh Worldwide, Inc.

OXYGARD - Health care products - Marquest Medical Products Inc.

O2XYGEN - Aquariums–household - Marine Metal Products

OXYGEN - Beverages - Juba Beverages Corp.

OXYGEN PLUS - Garden equipment - Lawn & Garden Supply Co.

OXYGEN SUPPORT - Health care products - Healthwatchers System

OXYGENATOR - Pet products - Aquarium Products Inc.

OXYGENEX - Aquatic pharmacuetical preparations ☆ - Aquatronics-Filtronics

OXYGENICS - Shower rods - Fan-Fi International Inc.

OXYGENPAC - Oxygen - Life Corp.

OXYGLAZED SYSTEM - Gloves - Safeskin Corp.

OXYGUARD - Safety products - Thermal Gas Systems, Inc.

OXYLIANCE - Skin care products - Sothys USA Inc.

OXYLITE - Contact lenses - Contact Lens Technology

OXYLITE - Respirators - Chad Therapeutics Inc.

OXYLONE - Pharmaceutical preparations ☆ - Upjohn Co.

OXYMANNA - Aquatic pharmacuetical preparations ☆ - Aquatronics-Filtronics

OXYMANNA FLAKE PLUS - Aquatic pharmacuetical preparations ☆ - Aquatronics-Filtronics

OXYMATIC - Respirators - Chad Therapeutics Inc.

OXYMAX - Machine parts - Nigrelli Systems Inc.

OXYMIZER - Respirators - Chad Therapeutics Inc.

OXYPHOTON - Air purification systems - Fusion Filter Inc.

OXYPLETH - Medical apparatus - Novametrix Medical Systems, Inc.

OXYPURE - Machinery - Arbor Research Corp.

OXYQUAT - Deodorizers - Krueger Enterprises

OXYRICH - Air purification systems - Fusion Filter Inc.

OXYRICH JR. - Air purification systems - Fusion Filter Inc.

OXYSEPT - Ophthalmic goods - Allergan, Inc.

OXYSPECTRO - Vitamins and nutritional supplements - A. Glenn Braswell

OXYSTAT - Pharmaceutical preparations ☆ - Hyrex Pharmaceuticals

OXYSTAT - Vitamins and nutritional supplements - NF Formulas, Inc.

OXYTETRACYN - Pet products ☆ - Aquatronics-Filtronics

OXYTHIN - Contact lenses - Contact Lens Technology

OXYTIME+ - Beverages - Aquagen International Inc. of Arizona

OXYTIP - Health care products - Datex-Ohmeda, Inc.

OXYTOCIN - Veterinary pharmaceutical preparations ☆ - New England Serum Co.

OXYVATINE - Pharmaceutical preparations - Dorsey Laboratories

OXYWET - Contact lenses - Contact Lens Technology

OXYZAL - Pharmaceutical preparations - Gordon Laboratories

OY! VAT A BAGEL - Bagels - Neuhauser USA Corp.

OY VEY - Apparel–athletic - El Aguila Dorada

OYAKO - Stereos - First International Corp.

OYAMA - Brushes–paint - Rubberset Co.

OYE - Apparel and accessories - Lee J. McAninch

OYLTITE-STIK - Adhesives and sealants - La-Co Industries, Inc.

OYM - Sweatshirts - Dillard Department Stores Inc.

OYSCO - Pharmaceutical preparations - Rugby Laboratories Inc.

OYST-CAL D - Pharmaceutical preparations - Goldline Laboratories, Inc.

OYSTER - Luggage - Samsonite Corp.

OYSTER - Recording label - Polygram Records, Inc.

OYSTER - Watches - Rolex Watch USA, Inc.

OYSTER BAY - Apparel and accessories - Seneca Knitting Mills Corp.

OYSTER BAY - Cutlery ☆ - Lifetime Hoan Corp.

OYSTER BAY - Floor coverings–carpet and rugs ☆ - Calladium & Marglen

OYSTER BAY - Floor coverings–carpet and rugs ☆ - Regal Rugs Inc.

OYSTER-DATE - Watches - Rolex Watch USA, Inc.

OYSTER PERPETUAL - Watches - Rolex Watch USA, Inc.

OYSTER QUARTZ - Watches - Rolex Watch USA, Inc.

OYSTER SHELL - Vitamins and nutritional supplements - Reese Chemical Co.

OYSTER SHELL WITH VITAMIN D - Vitamins and nutritional supplements - Reese Chemical Co.

OYSTER SNACKS - Crackers - Keebler Co.

OYSTERBORN - Jewelry–costume - H.S. Strygler & Co. Inc.

OYSTERETTES - Crackers - Nabisco Foods Group

OYSTERLOCK - Watches - Rolex Watch USA, Inc.

OYSTERLOOK - Watches - Rolex Watch USA, Inc.

OYSTERS & PEARLS - Floor coverings–carpet and rugs ☆ - LaVelle Textile Marketing Inc.

OYSTRON - Vitamins and nutritional supplements - Winning Laboratories Corp.

OZ - Chemical preparations - Oz Technology, Inc.

OZ - Cleaning preparations–household - H. Behlen & Bro. Inc.

OZ - Cups–paper - Andrews and McMeel

OZ - Greeting cards - House of Oz

OZ - Greeting cards - Oz

OZ - Lacrosse equipment - Brine Inc.

OZ - Peanut butter - Oz Food Corp.

OZ-12 - Chemical preparations - Oz Technology, Inc.

OZ FANTASY CLASSICS - Publisher's imprints - Random House, Inc.

OZ NATIVES - Flowers, plants, and seeds - Bill Suyeyasu Wholesale Florist, Inc.

OZ-PCE - Computer software - Videomedia, Inc.

OZ TECH - Air purification systems - Oz Tech

OZACHROME - Electronic equipment - GAF Corp.

OZALID - Electronic equipment - GAF Corp.

OZALUCENT - Electronic equipment - GAF Corp.

OZAMASTER - Electronic equipment - GAF Corp.

OZAMATIC - Electronic equipment - GAF Corp.

OZAPLASTIC - Electronic equipment - GAF Corp.

OZARK - Boats–motor - Ozark Boat Works Inc.

OZARK - Briquettes ☆ - Safeway Stores Inc.

OZARK - Food products ☆ - Gold Kist Inc.

OZARK - Housewares - Osage Products Co. Inc.

OZARK - Trailers–travel ☆ - Marathon Homes Corp.

OZARK - Vinegar - Speaco Foods Inc.

OZARK - Water–bottled or canned - Water House

OZARK - Wood products - Ozark Cedar Inc.

OZARK BEST - Food products ☆ - Gravette Shelling Co. Inc.

OZARK BLUSH - Juices - Nooncaster Vineyards, Inc.

OZARK CANOPY - Awnings - Ozark Canopy

OZARK CROOKS - Cigars - T.E. Brooks & Co.

OZARK FRY - Food products - Tyson Foods Inc.

OZARK GOURMET - Popcorn - Jasper Foods, Inc.

OZARK LIGHT - Popcorn - Jasper Foods, Inc.

OZARK MOUNTAIN - Apparel and accessories - Kayo of California

OZARK MOUNTAIN - Juices - Bardenheier Wine Cellars

OZARK MOUNTAIN - Wines - Post Winery Inc.

OZARK MOUNTAIN LOGANBERRY MIST - Juices - Bardenheier Wine Cellars

OZARK PEPPERCORN - Cheese - Alpine Lace Brands, Inc.

OZARK SUN - Suntan lotions - Ozark Sun Marketing Corp.

OZARK SWEET HICKORY - Pipes–tobacco - Buescher's Industries Inc.

OZARK TRAIL - Apparel and accessories - Wal-Mart Stores Inc.

OZARK TRAILS - Meat products - Ham I Am, Inc.

OZARK TREAT - Pickles - Green Bay Foods Co.

OZARKA - Water–bottled or canned - Distilled Water Co. of Tulsa

OZARKA - Water–mineral - Perrier Group of America Inc.

OZEKI - Food products - Ozeki San Benito Inc.

OZITE STACK BOOK - Wallpaper - Capital Carousel Inc.

OZO-DETOX - Soil and water purification units - Arctech, Inc.

OZO-ELECTRONIC - Skin care products ☆ - P.S. Pibbs Inc.

OZOKLEEN - Water purification systems - Pure Flow Water Co., Inc.

OZONA - Snuff - James B. Russell Inc.

OZONE - Apparel–children's - Jay-Zee Inc.

OZONE - Water–bottled or canned - Keystone-Ozone Water Co.

OZONE - Water–mineral - Ozone Spring Water Co.

☆ = Now out of production

OZONE FRIENDLY - Adhesives and sealants - Ultra Industries/Polycel Products

OZONE GENERATORS - Aquariums–household - Quality Marine

OZONE SAVER - Bags–plastic - Whirlpool Corp.

OZONE SAVER - Bags–plastic - Whirlpool Properties, Inc.

OZONIC - Lubricants - Hangsterfer's Labs., Inc.

OZONOLOGY O3 - Generators - Ozoteq Inc.

OZYME - Deodorizers - Waterbury Companies, Inc.

OZZEE - Toys ☆ - Revell-Monogram, Inc.

OZZERA - Recording label - Jazz Composer's Orchestra Association Inc.

OZZIE - Recording label - Digital Impact

P

Addresses and phone numbers for the companies cited in the brands below
are available in the Company Listings section immediately following the brands listings.

P - Ammunition - Remington Arms Co., Inc.
P - Animal feed supplements - Mycogen Corp.
P - Apparel and accessories - Phillies
P - Apparel–athletic ☆ - Powell Skateboards
P - Bags - Princess Hotels International, Inc.
P - Bags–plastic - Inteplast Group Ltd.
P - Bakery products - Petrofsky's Enterprises Inc.
P - Brakes–motor vehicle - Rockwell International Corp.
P - Computer software - Peterson's Guides, Inc.
P - Computer software - Soft-Logik Publishing Corp.
P - Computers and peripherals - Poqet Computer Corp.
P - Cosmetics - Mark Raphan
P - Food and beverage containers - Plaxicon Co.
P - Jewelry - Patrick Jewelers Ltd.
P - Jewelry - Premier Gem Corp.
P - Novelty items–paper - Portland Maine Baseball, Inc.
P - Packaging–paper - Paramount Packaging Corp.
P - Photo albums - Pioneer Photo Albums, Inc.
P - Prefabricated buildings–metal - Parkline, Inc.
P - Tools–hand-operated - Parts Inc.
P - Vitamins and nutritional supplements - Pride America Holdings Inc.
P - Vitamins and nutritional supplements - Pyramid Nutrition Inc.
P-10 - Abrasive products - Park Metallurgical Corp.
P-12 - Sporting goods - Lisco, Inc.
P-17 - Springs–furniture ☆ - Bingman Laboratories, Inc.
P-26 RED EDGE - Fabrics–canvas - Crown Textile Co.
P-29 - Pet products - Vortex Innerspace Products Inc.
P-30 - Insecticide - Contact Industries Inc.
P-40 WARHAWK - Toys–models ☆ - Cox Products Inc.
P-51 MUSTANG - Toys–models ☆ - Cox Products Inc.
P 76 - Caps–baseball - Philadelphia 76ers Basketball Club, Inc.
P-80 - Cleaning preparations - International Products Co.
P-91 - Fabrics–canvas - Crown Textile Co.
P-93 - Irrigation equipment - Pierce Corp.
P-105 - Flowers, plants, and seeds - Jacklin Seed
P-200 - Calendars - Transilwrap Co., Inc.
P-200 - Scales–industrial - Pelouze Scale Co.
P-1600 - Pigments - Radiant Color Div.
P-1700 - Pigments - Radiant Color Div.
P-A-C - Pharmaceutical preparations ☆ - Upjohn Co.
P. & A. LAMPS BY INDECOR - Early American lamps, weather instruments, clocks - Indecor Inc.
P & A NUTMEG - Wicking - Hooper Industries Inc.
P & B - Paints ☆ - Fibreboard Corp.
P & C - Desk sets - P & C Quality Screw Products Inc.
P & C - Grocery stores - P and C Food Markets Inc.
P & K - Lighting fixtures ☆ - Cooper Industries, Inc.
P & L - Enamels - Pratt & Lambert, Inc.
P. AND M. STAIGER - Wines - P. & M. Staiger
P & N - First aid kits ☆ - Physicians & Nurses Manufacturing Corp.
P & P - Artists' materials - Artype Inc.
P & Q REVIEW - Computer software - Teknekron Infoswitch Corp.
P & R - Pasta - Hershey Pasta Group
P & R - Pasta ☆ - Pastamania
P & S - Skin care products - Baker Cummins Dermatologicals Inc.
P & S - Wiring devices - Pass & Seymour, Inc.

P & S ALABAX - Lighting fixtures ☆ - Pass & Seymour, Inc.
P & T LAWN CHAPS - Apparel and accessories - Crack Shot Products
P. B. MAX - Candy bars - Mars, Inc.
P-B-SAL - Pharmaceutical preparations ☆ - Ulmer Pharmacal Co.
P. BUCKLEY MOSS - Giftware - Anna-Perenna Inc.
P/C ALPHASITE - Chalk - Quartet Manufacturing Co.
P/C PRIVACY - Computer software - M.C. Tel Corp.
P-CAT - Boats - Westport Pacific Boats
P. CHALLAIN - Wines - Leonard Kreusch, Inc.
P. CUCCHI U.S.A. - Tools–machine - Gosiger, Inc.
P. DOVOSOU - Whiskey - Schenley Industries Inc.
P-E-C - Food products - L. Karp & Sons, Inc.
P/E PLUS - Floor cleaning equipment - Microtron Abrasives, Inc.
P E R C S THE ULTIMATE EMPLOYEE! - Computer software - Elem Associates
P/G - Apparel and accessories - Silver/Gulfstream Inc.
P. I. JONES - Toys–guns - Daisy Manufacturing Co.
P-I-N - Pharmaceutical preparations - Lannett Co. Inc.
P-J DESIGNS - Jewelry ☆ - Peggy Sullivan-Cramer Designs
P. J. KNIGHT - Underwear and nightwear - Quitman Manufacturing Co.
P. J. MARX - Guitars - P.J. Marx Industries
P. J. SPARKLES - Dolls - Mattel, Inc.
P JAAZ - Apparel–children's - N. Edelson Sons Corp.
P-K BLEND MASTER - Electric blenders - Harsco Corp.
P-K KOTE - Adhesives and sealants - Parker-Kalon Inc.
P-M BRAND - Hardware - N.K.R. Precision Manufacturing Corp.
P. M. CHURCHILL - Briefcases - Winn International Corp.
P/M UNI-DRAW - Furnaces–industrial - Surface Combustion, Inc.
P/METER - Medical apparatus - Zertl Medical Inc.
P NEW YORK - Linen - Portico Bed and Bath
P-NUT-SO PATTY - Confections - Twang
P-NUTTIER - Pet products - Old Mother Hubbard Dog Food Co., Inc.
P-NUTTLES - Candy - Adams & Brooks, Inc.
P-O-D'S - Ostomy product - Torbot-Gricks
P-O-M-PEACE OF MIND - Shirts - Marble Sportswear, Inc.
P PAPERWORKS - Computer software - Xerox Corp.
P PARKING SYSTEMS VALET SERVICE - Motor vehicle dealers - Mark Baron
P PARTHENA - Cosmetics - Parthena Ltd.
P PEERLESS - Logging equipment - Peerless Corp.
P PELLETRON - Machinery - Pelletron Corp.
P PETERS NO. 12 VICTOR - Ammunition - Remington Arms Co., Inc.
P. PEUGEOT - Watches - Viva Time Corp.
P PHALO - Electronic equipment - Intercole, Inc.
P PHOTRONICS - Electrical equipment - Photronics, Inc.
P PLANAR - Targets - Johnson Matthey Electronics, Inc.
P. POHL - Harmonicas - Hohner Inc.
P PREMIER GAMING - Game machines - Premier Technology
P PRIMAVERA - Facial tissues - Atlas Paper Mills, Ltd.
P PRINCE MACHINE - Machinery - Prince Machine Corp.
P PROFESSIONAL CURL - Hair care products - Golden Sun Inc.
P PROLEN - Apparel and accessories - Chi Ying Chiang
P PROLINK PROGRAPHIC IMAGE SHARPENER - Computer peripheral equipment - Prolink Computer Inc.
P PSY OPS - Computer software - Rodrigo Xavier Cavazos
P P.U.R.E .5 - Apparel and accessories - Alfred Coleman Burnett, II
P PURIFIED CAPSAICIN - Analgesics - Thompson Medical Co., Inc.

☆ = Now out of production

P-Q - Disinfectant ☆ - Intex Chemical Inc.
P-R-O SERIES NAIL LAQUER - Nail care products - Cosmetco Industries Ltd.
P-ROYAL - Food products - Oceana Canning Co.
P-RYTON - Cosmetics - P-Ryton Corp.
P/S - Desk sets - Park Sherman
P/S - Jewelry - Penedo & Swiber Inc.
P/S - Lighting fixtures–stage - Tomcat USA Inc.
P. S. BARTLETT - Watches - Elgin Watch Co.
P. S. PIBBS - Hair care products - P.S. Pibbs Inc.
P. S. QUATTROCIOCHI - Pasta - US Foodservice
P. SHINE - Nail care products - P. Shine USA Inc.
P-T - Stencils - P-T Templet Co. Inc.
P. T. BARNUM'S ACROBATS - Toys–electronic ☆ - Philips Consumer
  Electronics Co.
P T S - Meters–frequency - Programmed Test Sources, Inc.
P-T100 - Pharmaceutical preparations ☆ - Hyrex Pharmaceuticals
P-TEC - Electronic equipment - Harris Corp.
P-TOUCH STICKERKID - Labeling machinery - Brother International Corp.
P-V-K - Pharmaceutical preparations ☆ - Legere Pharmaceuticals Inc.
P-V-TUSSIN - Pharmaceutical preparations - Solvay Pharmaceuticals Inc.
P-WE - Golfing equipment - Nassau Precision Casting Co., Inc.
P-WEE FLYER - Toys - Berlin Wood Products
P/X - Computer software - PSDI
P-Z-M - Pharmaceutical preparations ☆ - Wendt-Bristol Co.
P3 - Golfing equipment - Sun-Davis Golf, Inc.
P3 KEVRON - Rackets–tennis - Estusa Corp.
P3 LASER - Rackets–tennis - Estusa Corp.
P3 TURBO - Rackets–tennis - Estusa Corp.
P3N - Cameras ☆ - Pentax Corp.
P6 120 - Video tapes–blank - BASF Corp.
P7 SCANNER - Medical apparatus - Bird Products Corp.
P19 - Polishes - HMK Stone Care System
P21 - Polishes - HMK Stone Care System
P21S - Automotive parts and accessories - Brookside Import Specialities, Inc.
P23 - Polishes - HMK Stone Care System
P23/16 - Tools–garden - Sea Roy Corp.
P24 - Polishes - HMK Stone Care System
P27 - Polishes - HMK Stone Care System
P29 - Polishes - HMK Stone Care System
P30T - Cameras ☆ - Pentax Corp.
P38 - Hardware - Aqua-Tainer Co.
P53-PRIME - Chemical preparations - Novagen, Inc.
P85 - Pistols - Sturm, Ruger & Co., Inc.
P728C - Springs–mechanical - Holmes-Hally Industries
P730C - Springs–mechanical - Holmes-Hally Industries
P928C - Garages - Holmes-Hally Industries
P1200 PRECISION SERIES - Amplifiers - Electro-Voice, Inc.
P1250 PRECISION SERIES - Amplifiers - Electro-Voice, Inc.
P2000 PRECISION SERIES - Amplifiers - Electro-Voice, Inc.
P3000 PRECISION SERIES - Amplifiers - Electro-Voice, Inc.
PA - Cosmetics - Research Council of Make-Up Artists Inc.
PA - Jewelry - Pamela Ann Nolan
PA - Machinery - P/A Industries Inc.
PA - Sporting goods - Project Adventure, Inc.
PA - Vodka - Mccormick Distilling Co., Inc.
PA 2000 - Tires - Bridgestone/Firestone, Inc.
PA-CURTAGON - Lenses–photographic - Schneider Optics, Inc.
PA-DUTCH - Nuts–salted, roasted, cooked, or canned - Lancaster Nut Co. Inc.
PA DUTCH - Sausages - Hatfield, Inc.
PA. DUTCH - Soups–canned - Hanover Provision Co.
P.A. KID.S - Apparel–children's - Patsy Aiken Designs, Inc.
PA PA'S - Fruits and vegetables - M. Pagano & Sons, Inc.
PA-PAW'S - Hunting equipment - Pa-Paw's LC
P.A. PRODUCTS - Seasonings - Porfirio Aquino
PA PUR-ALL - Paints - Pur-All Paint Products Co. Inc.
PA-RISC - Integrated circuits - Hewlett-Packard Co.
PA-ZAZ - Boxes - John Henry Co.
PA ZAZZ - Paper products - J.P. Paper Shredders
PAALO CERVANTES - Perfumes ☆ - Nettie Rosenstein Inc.
PAARS - Computer software - Image Graphic Systems, Inc.
PAAS - Dyes–food - Schering-Plough Healthcare Products
PAASCHE - Artists' materials - Paasche Airbrush Co.
PABA - Vitamins and nutritional supplements - Vitamin Research Products Inc.
PABA MOIST - Cosmetics ☆ - Dep Corp.
PABAFILM - Suntan lotions ☆ - Owen/Galderma Laboratories Inc.
PABAGEL - Sunblocks ☆ - Owen/Galderma Laboratories Inc.

PABALAN - Pharmaceutical preparations - Lannett Co. Inc.
PABALATE - Pharmaceutical preparations - A.H. Robins Co. Inc.
PABANOL - Pharmaceutical preparations ☆ - ICN Pharmaceuticals Inc.
PABATECTION - Suntan lotions ☆ - Key West Aloe Inc.
PABCO SUREFIT ELBOWS - Fabricated metal products - Pabco Metals Corp.
PABERBACING - Fabrics - Custom Laminations Inc.
PABIRIN - Health care products - Dorsey Laboratories
PABIZOL - Pharmaceutical preparations ☆ - Rexall Nutritional Products Inc.
PABLITO - Food products - Camino Real Foods
PABLO - Floor coverings–carpet and rugs ☆ - American Carpet Mills
PABLO - Pencils - Caran D'Ache of Switzerland Inc.
PABLO - Phonographs - Fantasy Inc.
PABLO - Toys - DGI/Buki
PABLO COMBO - Hobby kits - Riverside Paper Corp.
PABLO LIVE - Phonographs - Fantasy Inc.
PABLO PYTHON - Recording label - New York Zoological Society
PABLO TODAY - Phonographs - Fantasy Inc.
PABLOS - Food products - Dairy Fresh Products Co.
PABST BLUE RIBBON - Beverages–malt - Pabst Brewing Co.
PABST DRY - Beverages–malt - Pabst Brewing Co.
PABST EXTRA LIGHT - Beverages–malt - Pabst Brewing Co.
PABST GOLD - Beverages–malt ☆ - Pabst Brewing Co.
PABST ICE - Beverages–malt - Pabst Brewing Co.
PABST LIGHT - Beverages–malt - Pabst Brewing Co.
PABST NA - Beverages–malt - Pabst Brewing Co.
PABST SPECIAL DARK - Beverages–malt ☆ - Pabst Brewing Co.
PABX - Electronic equipment - Da-Tel Research Co., Inc.
PAC - Air purification systems - Barnebey and Sutcliffe Corp.
PAC - Computer software - Magnetek Inc.
PAC - Hosiery ☆ - Wigwam Mills Inc.
PAC - Plastics - Pushpa America Corp.
PAC-A-DAP - Alarm systems–burglar - Litton Security Systems
PAC-A-MO - Apparel–men's - Alps Sportswear Manufacturing Co.
PAC-AX - Axes - AX International, LLC
PAC CHECK - Measuring instruments ☆ - MOCON/Modern Controls, Inc.
PAC-IT - Adhesives and sealants - W.R. Meadows Inc.
PAC KNIFE - Knives - Pacific Saw and Knife Co.
PAC-L - Bicycles ☆ - Troxel Co. Cycling and Fitness
PAC LITE - Truck bodies - Gem Top Manufacturing Inc.
PAC-MAN - Chewing gum ☆ - Fleer Corp.
PAC-MAN - Pasta - American Home Food Products Inc.
PAC-MAN - Toys - Azrak-Hamway International, Inc.
PAC-MAN - Toys–electronic - Bally Manufacturing Corp.
PAC-MAN - Vitamins and nutritional supplements - Rexall Nutritional Products
  Inc.
PAC-MOR - Luggage - Jacob E. Cloessner
PAC-SKIN - Sporting goods - Pachmayr Ltd.
PAC TRIM - Molding compounds–plastics - Pacific MDF Products, Inc.
PACAL 2000 - Machine parts - Paper, Calmenson & Co.
PACALLOY - Motor vehicle parts and accessories - Paper, Calmenson & Co.
PACAPS - Pharmaceutical preparations - Lunsco Inc.
PACCAS - Pharmaceutical preparations - Blair Pharmacal
PACCO - Food products - Chas. G. Summers, Jr. Inc.
PACE - Animal feed supplements - Morgan Manufacturing Co., Inc.
PACE - Athletic footwear - Athlete's Foot Marketing Associates Inc.
PACE - Audio cassettes - International Audio Inc.
PACE - Automotive parts and accessories - Warren Distribution, Inc.
PACE - Beverages–malt ☆ - Hudepohl-Schoenling Brewing Co.
PACE - Chemical preparations - Olin Corp.
PACE - Computer peripheral equipment - Infimed, Inc.
PACE - Dentifrices - Procter & Gamble Co.
PACE - Exchangers–heat - Maxxim Medical Inc.
PACE - Floor coverings–carpet and rugs ☆ - Southern Carpet Mills
PACE - Floor waxes ☆ - Turtle Wax, Inc.
PACE - Food products - Pace Foods, Ltd.
PACE - Food products, health-care products, household cleaners, etc. - Pace
  Membership Warehouse, Inc.
PACE - Hoses - Pace Manufacturing, Inc.
PACE - Irons–electric - Pace, Inc.
PACE - Kitchen cabinets–metal - Richwood
PACE - Locks–padlocks - Chicago Lock Co.
PACE - Occasional furniture ☆ - JDI Group, Inc.
PACE - Pool tables - Pace Collection Inc.
PACE - Posters - Pace Posters
PACE - Switches–electric - Kohler Co.
PACE - Trailers - Mobile Structures, Inc.

☆ = Now out of production

PACE 1 - Computer software - Electronic Data Systems Corp.
PACE ARROW - Motor vehicles–motor homes - Bounder & Fliar
PACE ARROW - Motor vehicles–motor homes - Fleetwood Enterprises, Inc.
PACE ARROW VISION - Motor vehicles–motor homes - Fleetwood Enterprises, Inc.
PACE COACH - Sporting goods - Nielsen-Kellerman Co.
PACE EDITIONS - Posters - Pace Posters
PACE/MACGILL - Posters - Pace Posters
PACE PILSNER - Beverages–malt ☆ - Hudepohl-Schoenling Brewing Co.
PACE PLUS SYSTEM - Computer peripheral equipment - General Electric Co.
PACE RACER - Toys–automobiles - Mattel, Inc.
PACE SALSA BASE - Sauces - Pace Foods, Ltd.
PACE SETTER - Bicycles - Columbia Manufacturing Inc.
PACE SETTER - Health care products - Unicare Health & Fitness Co.
PACE-SETTER - Paper–sand - Stanley Works
PACE-SETTER - Tools - Goldblatt Tool Co.
PACE SETTER PROFESSIONAL STANDARD - Insulating materials - Leslie-Locke, Inc.
PACE SETTERS - Cookies - Bahlsen Inc.
PACE SPORTSWEAR - Apparel and accessories - Pace/Cap-It-All
PACE TRAINER - Watches - Timex Corp.
PACE WIPES - Paper products - Georgia-Pacific Corp.
PACEBREAKER - Tools - Paratech Inc.
PACECLOX - Sporting goods - S & R Sport/Maric
PACEDRYL - Drills–electric - Paratech Inc.
PACEMAKER - Bicycles ☆ - Roadmaster Corp.
PACEMAKER - Binders - Master-Craft Corp.
PACEMAKER - Daters and numberers - Consolidated Stamp Manufacturing Co. Inc.
PACEMAKER - Floor coverings - Congoleum Corp.
PACEMAKER - Floor-maintenance machine - Advance Machine Co.
PACEMAKER - Locks–padlocks ☆ - Harloc Products Corp.
PACEMAKER - Luggage - United States Luggage Corp.
PACEMAKER - Medical apparatus - Becton, Dickinson and Co.
PACEMAKER - Medical apparatus - Evets Corp.
PACEMAKER - Motors–air - Magnetek Inc.
PACEMAKER - Recording label - Music Enterprises Inc.
PACEMAKER - Staplers - Markwell Manufacturing Co. Inc.
PACEMAKER - Watch batteries ☆ - Duracell Co. USA
PACEMAKER - Watches - Gruen Marketing Corp.
PACEMAKER - Watches - Hampden Corp.
PACEMAKER - Window frames - Yale Ogron Manufacturing Co. Inc.
PACEMAKER 3 - Toys–electronic - A-Loop Offroads
PACEMAKER II - Floor coverings - Congoleum Corp.
PACEMAKER II - Furniture–upholstered - Imperial of Morristown Inc.
PACEMAKER/STARLITE - Sinks–metal - Elkay Manufacturing Co.
PACEMASTER - Gasoline - Pacemaster Inc.
PACEMASTER - Treadmills - Aerobics, Inc.
PACEPAK - Drills–electric - Paratech Inc.
PACEPORT - Home health care products - Baxter International Inc.
PACEPUMP - Pumps - Paratech Inc.
PACER - Adhesives and sealants - Pacer Technology
PACER - Archery equipment - Welsh Sporting Goods Corp. (Boyt Div.)
PACER - Automotive parts and accessories - J.H. Heafner Co. Inc.
PACER - Bathroom fixtures - Shower-Rite Corp.
PACER - Bicycles - Ross Bicycles USA, Ltd.
PACER - Boats–motor - Duracraft Boats Inc.
PACER - Caulking compounds ☆ - Dap Products Inc.
PACER - Door openers–electronic - LCN Closers
PACER - Drafting supplies - Pierce Business Products Inc.
PACER - Electronic equipment - Da-Lite Screen Co. Inc.
PACER - Flatware - Utica Cutlery Co.
PACER - Footwear–athletic - Roller Derby Skate Corp.
PACER - Gloves–rubber - PM Gloves Inc.
PACER - Golf carts ☆ - Ajay Leisure Products Inc.
PACER - Hardware - Shepherd Products U.S. Inc.
PACER - Heart monitors ☆ - Polar Electro Inc.
PACER - Kitchen appliances ☆ - Sunbeam-Oster Household Products
PACER - Motor vehicles ☆ - DaimlerChrysler
PACER - Motors–hydraulic - Magnetek Inc.
PACER - Pagers - Pi Inc.
PACER - Pens - Faber-Castell Corp.
PACER - Seafood products–fresh or frozen - Pace Fish Co. Inc.
PACER - Sporting goods - Dacor Corp.
PACER - Sporting goods ☆ - Gill Sports Equipment, Inc.
PACER - Staplers ☆ - ITW Paslode

PACER - Toys–automobiles ☆ - Roadmaster Corp.
PACER - Video games - Taito America Corp.
PACER - Walking footwear ☆ - Autry Industries Inc.
PACER III - Sporting goods ☆ - Gill Sports Equipment, Inc.
PACER ACTIVEWEAR - Apparel–men's - Kayser-Roth Corp.
PACER FITNESS SYSTEMS - Treadmills - Pacer Fitness Systems
PACER II - Heart monitors - Polar Electro Inc.
PACER SATURN II - Sporting goods ☆ - Gill Sports Equipment, Inc.
PACERANALYZER - Medical apparatus - Del Mar Avionics
PACERCORDER - Medical apparatus - Del Mar Avionics
PACERONE - Pharmaceutical preparations - Upsher-Smith Laboratories, Inc.
PACERS - Men's shoes ☆ - Bostonian Shoe Co.
PACES - Floor coverings–carpet and rugs ☆ - Alliance Industries Inc.
PACESAVER - Medical apparatus - Leisure Lift, Inc.
PACESCOPE - Medical apparatus - Synchrotech Medical Corp.
PACESETTER - Amplifiers - Bob White Associates
PACESETTER - Apparel and accessories ☆ - Pace/Cap-It-All
PACESETTER - Archery equipment - Golden Key Futura, Inc.
PACESETTER - Boats–liferafts - Intex Recreation Corp.
PACESETTER - Chimes ☆ - Nutone Inc.
PACESETTER - Clocks - General Time Corp. (Westclox/Seth Thomas Div.)
PACESETTER - Computer software - Mind Play
PACESETTER - Curling irons–electric - Helen of Troy Corp.
PACESETTER - Desks - Art Metal-U.S. Corp.
PACESETTER - Dryers–commercial - White Consolidated Industries, Inc.
PACESETTER - Duplicators and supplies ☆ - Copy Plus Inc.
PACESETTER - Electrical equipment - Drew Hudson Edwards
PACESETTER - Electronics equipment - International Audio Inc.
PACESETTER - Floor coverings–carpet and rugs - Collins & Aikman Corp.
PACESETTER - Floor coverings–carpet and rugs - Eagle Carpets Inc.
PACESETTER - Floor coverings–carpet and rugs ☆ - Playfield International Inc.
PACESETTER - Furniture - Lane Co. Inc.
PACESETTER - Furniture - Samsonite Furniture Co. (Consumer Products Div.)
PACESETTER - Glassware–household - Owens-Illinois Inc. (Libbey Div.)
PACESETTER - Golf bags - Taylor Made Golf Co. Inc.
PACESETTER - Horseshoes - Thoro'bred Racing Plate Co., Inc.
PACESETTER - Motor vehicle parts and accessories - Budge Industries, Inc.
PACESETTER - Musical instrument accessories - E. & O. Mari Inc.
PACESETTER - Paints - Precise International/Wenger
PACESETTER - Pens ☆ - K-9 Pen Co.
PACESETTER - Plywood - Plywood & Panels Inc.
PACESETTER - Rope - Wellington Leisure Products, Inc.
PACESETTER - Underwear and nightwear - Henson-Kickernick Inc.
PACESETTER - Ventilation equipment - Leslie-Locke, Inc.
PACESETTER II - Wallpaper ☆ - Pantasote Inc. (Wallcovering Div.)
PACESETTER PRESS - Publisher's imprints - Gulf Publishing Co. (Book & Div.)
PACESETTERS - Toy cars, inflatable boots - Intex Recreation Corp.
PACESSORIES - Apparel and accessories ☆ - Pace/Cap-It-All
PACESTOR - Computer software - Pace Environs, Inc.
PACEX - Water recycling and antipollution units - Byers Industries, Inc.
PACH-PEN - Medical apparatus - Mentor O & O Inc.
PACHANGA - Boats–motor - Sea Ray Boats
PACHAWK - Fishing tackle - Ocean Tech Co. Inc., USA
PACHECO RANCH WINERY - Wines - Pacheco Ranch Winery
PACHEE - Bags - Jomil Enterprises, Inc.
PACHINKO - Toys–electronic ☆ - Philips Consumer Electronics Co.
PACHMAYR - Sporting goods - Pachmayr Ltd.
PACHYDERM PRESS - Publisher's imprints - Wallace D. Sears
PACIFIC - Artists' materials ☆ - A.I. Friedman Inc.
PACIFIC - Bedding–linen - M. Lowenstein Corp.
PACIFIC - Cabinets ☆ - Schuler Corp.
PACIFIC - Dinnerware–glass ☆ - WMF/USA
PACIFIC - Fabrics - Burlington Industries, Inc.
PACIFIC - Floor coverings–carpet and rugs ☆ - Regal Rugs Inc.
PACIFIC - Food products - Quong Hop & Co.
PACIFIC - Fruits and vegetables - Pacific Fruit Growers & Packers Inc.
PACIFIC - Furniture ☆ - Lane Co. Inc.
PACIFIC - Games - Pacific Game Co.
PACIFIC - Hardware - Servistar Corp.
PACIFIC - Hinges - Pacific Hardware Manufacturing
PACIFIC - Pencils - General Pencil Co.
PACIFIC - Pet products - Pacific Aquarium & Pet Supplies
PACIFIC - Recording label - Atlantic Records
PACIFIC - Seafood products–fresh or frozen - Southeast Foods Inc.

☆ = Now out of production

PACIFIC - Soap - Lever Brothers Co. Inc.
PACIFIC - Tobacco products - Philip Morris Companies Inc.
PACIFIC AIRBRUSH - Nail care products - Magic Touch/Pacific Airbrush
PACIFIC ARC - Drafting supplies - Pacific Arc Inc.
PACIFIC BAY - Apparel—men's - Sullcraft Industries
PACIFIC BEACH - Floor coverings—carpet and rugs ☆ - Catalina Carpet Mills Inc.
PACIFIC BEAT - Recording label - Hawaii Calls Inc.
PACIFIC BEAUTY - Food products ☆ - Pasco Foods Co.
PACIFIC BEAUTY - Fruits and vegetables - Western State Sales
PACIFIC BEST - Food products - Warrenton Deep Sea Inc.
PACIFIC BIOTECH - Immunoassay devices - Pacific Biotech Inc.
PACIFIC BLEND - Frozen foods - J.R. Simplot Co.
PACIFIC BLUE - Crab meat—fresh - Keeler
PACIFIC BLUE - Dinnerware—glass ☆ - Metlox Pottery Shoppe
PACIFIC BOOKS - Publisher's imprints - Pacific Books, Publishers
PACIFIC BREEZE - Fruit drinks—bottled or canned - John Devincenzo and Bobbie Devincenzo
PACIFIC BREEZES - Deodorizers - Reckitt & Colman, Inc.
PACIFIC CANVAS COMPANY - Luggage - Coastside Creations
PACIFIC CLIPPER - Food products ☆ - Agripac, Inc.
PACIFIC CLOTH - Bags—storage ☆ - Accurate Flannel Bag Co.
PACIFIC CLOUD - Food products - Hogan Associates
PACIFIC CLUB - Shirts - Nak Corp.
PACIFIC COAST - Deodorizers - Surco Products Inc.
PACIFIC COAST - Pillows - Pacific Coast Feather Co.
PACIFIC COAST - Salt ☆ - Great Eastern Sun Trading Co. Inc.
PACIFIC COAST FEATHER CO. SINCE 1884 - Comforters - Pacific Coast Feather Co.
PACIFIC COAST ORGANIC SCENTS - Deodorizers - Pestco, Inc.
PACIFIC COAST RESERVE - Wines - King Estate Vineyards, Inc.
PACIFIC COAST VINEYARDS - Wines - King Estate Vineyards, Inc.
PACIFIC COASTAL - Skin care products - Aramis Inc.
PACIFIC COOLER - Fruit drinks—bottled or canned - Capri Sun, Inc.
PACIFIC CREST - Wines ☆ - Weibel Vineyards
PACIFIC CROWN - Trading cards and stamps - Pacific Trading Cards, Inc.
PACIFIC CYCLE USA - Bicycle parts and accessories - Diversified Investments Corp.
PACIFIC DEEP - Seafood - B and B Fisheries Inc.
PACIFIC DESIGNS - Glassware—household - Root Candle Co.
PACIFIC DETAILS - Cleaning preparations—household - John Labarbera
PACIFIC DS - Boats—skiffs - Pacific Skiffs, Inc.
PACIFIC ELEGANCE - Wallpaper - Quality House Inc.
PACIFIC EXPRESS - Handbags - Hazan Imports Corp.
PACIFIC FASHIONS - Furniture - Leonetti Furniture Manufacturing Co.
PACIFIC FITNESS - Exercise machines, apparel, etc. - Pacific Fitness Corp.
PACIFIC FOODS - Spices and extracts - Pacific Foods Inc.
PACIFIC FRAMES INC. - Furniture - Pillow Kingdom, Inc.
PACIFIC GALA - Trees - Olsen Bros.
PACIFIC GENERAL - Computer software - Strategic Simulations, Inc.
PACIFIC GIANT, INC. - Seafood products—fresh or frozen - Pacific Giant, Inc.
PACIFIC GOLD - Chocolate candy - Grifair Co.
PACIFIC GOLD - Roasted and salted nuts; dried nuts - Pacific Gold Marketing, Inc.
PACIFIC GOLD - Shrimp - Golden Shore Food Processors, Inc.
PACIFIC GOLD FRY - Oils—edible - Rykoff-Sexton, Inc.
PACIFIC GOLF GROUP - Paper - Nick Lombardo, Inc.
PACIFIC GRAIN PRODUCTS - Food products - Pacific Grain Products, Inc.
PACIFIC GULF - Seafood products—fresh or frozen - Zaloom Brothers Co. of New Jersey
PACIFIC HARVEST - Fruits—dried - Stapleton-Spence Packing Co.
PACIFIC HARVEST - Seafood - B and B Fisheries Inc.
PACIFIC HEIGHTS KITES - Kites - Barbara J. Macaire
PACIFIC/HOE - Tools—power-driven - Pacific Saw and Knife Co.
PACIFIC HYBRID - Flower pots—plastic - Davids & Royston Bulb Co. Inc.
PACIFIC II - Finishing agents - Bonakemi USA, Inc.
PACIFIC JADE - Food products - US Foodservice
PACIFIC LIGHT - Seafood - H & N Fish Co.
PACIFIC LIGHTS - Floor coverings—carpet and rugs ☆ - Bellbridge Carpets
PACIFIC LINE, THE - Toilets—porcelain - Microphor Inc.
PACIFIC LUMBER COMPANY, THE - Lumber - Pacific Lumber Co.
PACIFIC MEDIA - Video production - Pacific Media Center, Inc.
PACIFIC MINIATURES - Mannequins - Trileen International Inc.
PACIFIC MIST - Dinnerware ☆ - Corning Inc.
PACIFIC MOUNTAIN - Jams and jellies - J.M. Smucker Co.
PACIFIC NATURALS - Skin care products - Garcoa Labs/Vitamin Classics

PACIFIC NORTH EQUIPMENT CO. - Construction machinery - Pacific North Equipment Co.
PACIFIC NORTHWEST - Food products - Bay Port Trading Corp.
PACIFIC NORTHWEST - Sausages - Pacific Northwest Venison Producers
PACIFIC ONE - Finishing agents - Bonakemi USA, Inc.
PACIFIC OVERTURES - Furniture - Lexington Furniture Industries, Inc.
PACIFIC PALACIDES - Furniture—upholstered - Clyde Pearson Inc.
PACIFIC PALISADES - Apparel and accessories - Alexander's Inc.
PACIFIC PALMS - Bicycles - Strictly BMX/Off Road
PACIFIC PARADISE - Fireworks - Ingram Enterprises, Inc.
PACIFIC PASSION - Beverages - Juice Club, Inc.
PACIFIC PEARL - Fruits—canned - CI Seafoods, Inc.
PACIFIC PEN COMPANY - Pens - By Pass Four, Inc.
PACIFIC PINK - Juices ☆ - Dole Food Co., Inc.
PACIFIC PLACE - Shoes - Fred Meyer, Inc.
PACIFIC PLANTATIONS - Fruits—dried ☆ - Grifair Co.
PACIFIC PLATINUM - Shampoos - Randall Caruso of Beverly Hills, Inc.
PACIFIC PLAZA - Floor coverings—carpet and rugs ☆ - Walter Carpet Mills
PACIFIC POINT PRESERVE - Amusement parks - Sea World, Inc.
PACIFIC POOL - Swimming pools - Pacific Industries Inc.
PACIFIC PRESS - Publisher's imprints - Pacific Press Publishing Association
PACIFIC PRIDE - Seafood products—canned or cured - California Shellfish Co. Inc.
PACIFIC PRIDE - Seafood products—fresh or frozen - G.F. Higgins
PACIFIC PRIDE - Whipped topping—frozen - Presto Food Products, Inc.
PACIFIC PRIME - Food products - New West Foods Inc.
PACIFIC PRINCESS - Bicycles - Roadmaster Corp.
PACIFIC QUEEN - Butter ☆ - Wilsey Foods, Inc.
PACIFIC RAIN GUARD - Waterproofing compounds - Dorfman-Pacific Co. Inc.
PACIFIC RAINBOW - Wallpaper - Quality House Inc.
PACIFIC RAINBOW II - Wallpaper - Quality House Inc.
PACIFIC REEF - Scuba diving equipment - Suunto USA
PACIFIC REGION MUSIC - Recording label - Hawaii Calls Inc.
PACIFIC RIDGE - First aid kits - Suunto USA
PACIFIC RIM - Dinnerware—glass ☆ - Lenox, Inc.
PACIFIC RIM - Flowers—artificial - Pacific Rim International Inc.
PACIFIC RIM EYEWEAR - Sunglasses - Mountain Shades Distributing Co.
PACIFIC ROAD - Wallpaper - Quality House Inc.
PACIFIC ROYAL - Seafood products—fresh or frozen - Demerico Corp.
PACIFIC SEACRAFT - Boats - Pacific Seacraft Corp.
PACIFIC SEAS - Canned foods - Sinco, Inc.
PACIFIC SELTZER - Beverages - Pacific Seltzer & Soda Works Inc.
PACIFIC SILK - Flowers—artificial - Pacific Sunshine Enterprises Inc.
PACIFIC SPECIAL - Adhesives and sealants ☆ - Pettit Paint Co. Inc.
PACIFIC SPORT - Finishing agents - Bonakemi USA, Inc.
PACIFIC SPRING - Animal feeds - Land O'Lakes, Inc.
PACIFIC STAR - Seafood products—fresh or frozen - Zaloom Brothers Co. of New Jersey
PACIFIC STRONG - Finishing agents - Bonakemi USA, Inc.
PACIFIC SUNSET - Trees - J. Frank Schmidt & Son Co.
PACIFIC SUNTONES - Paints - Commercial Chemical Co. Inc.
PACIFIC SURF - Food products - Young's Market Co.
PACIFIC TECH-1 - Finishing agents - Bonakemi USA, Inc.
PACIFIC TEES - Apparel and accessories - Pax Pacifica, Ltd.
PACIFIC TEE'S - Nail care products - Magic Touch/Pacific Airbrush
PACIFIC TELESIS - Publisher's imprints - Pacific Telesis Group
PACIFIC TEXTURES - Finishing agents - Dunn Edwards Corp.
PACIFIC THEATER OF OPERATIONS - Computer software - Koei Corp.
PACIFIC THEATER, THE - Computer software ☆ - Hartley Courseware Inc.
PACIFIC TRAIL - Luggage - Pacific Trail, Inc.
PACIFIC TRAIL - Shoes - Desa Shoe Co. Inc.
PACIFIC TREND - Vitamins and nutritional supplements - Peterson's Health Products
PACIFIC TRENDS - Lamps - David Wexler & Co.
PACIFIC TRIBE - Footwear - Terra Australis Inc.
PACIFIC UNIFORM - Uniforms—athletic - Pacific Uniform Manufacturing Corp.
PACIFIC VALLEY - Food products - Pacific Valley Foods
PACIFIC WAR - Games - Avalon Hill Game Co.
PACIFIC WATERS - Seafood products—fresh or frozen - Ocean Fresh Seafoods Inc.
PACIFIC WAVE - Sporting goods - Design Tees Hawaii Inc.
PACIFIC WAVE CRAFT - Apparel and accessories - Carlos Roy Sanchez
PACIFICA - Benches—metal ☆ - Artesian Industries
PACIFICA - Bicycles ☆ - Veltec Sports, Inc.
PACIFICA - Boats - Pacifica Yachts
PACIFICA - Boats—motor ☆ - Checkmate Boats Inc.

☆ = Now out of production

PACIFICA - Dinnerware ☆ - Corning Inc.
PACIFICA - Fish food - San Francisco Seamaster
PACIFICA - Floor coverings–carpet and rugs - Hollytex Carpet Mills Inc.
PACIFICA - Floor coverings–carpet and rugs ☆ - American Carpet Mills
PACIFICA - Floor coverings–carpet and rugs ☆ - Royalweve Carpet Mills
PACIFICA - Furniture ☆ - Lane Co. Inc.
PACIFICA - Giftware - Mack L. Jones
PACIFICA - Jewelry - Sultan Co.
PACIFICA - Nautical instruments ☆ - Datamarine International Inc.
PACIFICA - Occasional tables ☆ - JDI Group, Inc.
PACIFICA - Pet products - Pets Pacifica Inc.
PACIFICA - Seafood - International Pacific Seafoods, Inc.
PACIFICA - Tiles–ceramic ☆ - Quarry Tile Co.
PACIFICA - Vitamins and nutritional supplements - Cyanotech Corp.
PACIFICA - Wines - Columbia Winery
PACIFICA PRODUCE - Skin care products - Mervyn's
PACIFICAN - Giftware - Albert Kessler and Co.
PACIFICO - Beverages–malt - Canandaigua Wine Co. Inc.
PACIFICPAGE - Office supplies - Pacific Data Systems Inc.
PACIFIER PLUS - Infant temperature responsive pacifier - John Olsson
PACINI - Housewares ☆ - Royal Products
PACK - Boats–canoes - Old Town Canoe Co.
PACK-A-PUTTER - Golfing equipment - Pack-A-Putter Corp.
PACK-A-SNACK - Infant product ☆ - Newborne Co.
PACK AWAY - Dishes–plastic - Spectrum International, Inc.
PACK AWAY - Moped - Italjet USA
PACK BALM - Skin care products - Old World Honey
PACK HORSE - Trailers–travel ☆ - Coleman Co., Inc.
PACK IN - Hampers ☆ - Alger Creations Inc.
PACK-IT - Health care products - Roho, Inc.
PACK MASTER - Containers - Igloo Products Corp.
PACK MASTER - Travel accessories - American Guard-It Manufacturing Co. Inc.
PACK MULE - Pulleys–industrial - Deuer Manufacturing Inc.
PACK N' PLAY - Playpens–metal - Graco Children's Products
PACK N' SEAL - Envelopes–paper - Crystal Tissue Co. Inc.
PACK N SHACK - Sporting goods - Hector Vazquez
PACK N SHACK, THE - Sporting goods - Hector Vazquez
PACK-N-SNACK - Cookies ☆ - Archway Cookie Inc.
PACK RACK - Sporting goods - All Rite Products, Inc.
PACK RAT - Archery equipment - Martin Archery Inc.
PACK RAT - Luggage racks–automotive - Knaack Manufacturing Co.
PACK RAT - Rope - Crow Rope Industries LLC
PACK TRAIN - Syrup - Safeway Stores Inc.
PACKABLE PILLOW - Pillows - Pillowtex Corp.
PACKAGE EX - Computer software - ExacTax Inc.
PACKAGE/IT - Computer software - Platinum Technology, Inc.
PACKAGE P SIES - Crocheted and knitted items - Linda Louise Greene
PACKAGE PAVEMENT - Cement - Package Pavement Co. Inc.
PACKAGE/XPRESS - Computer software - Relational Data Services Inc.
PACKAGED FOR PROGRESS - Publisher's imprints - ABS Communications, Inc.
PACKAGED SUNSHINE - Giftware ☆ - Gessner Products Co. Inc.
PACKAGELIFT - Conveyors - Inclinator Co. of America
PACKAGEMASTER - Computer software - American Business Systems
PACKARD - Automotive parts and accessories - Packard Electric Div.
PACKARD - Motor vehicles–automobiles ☆ - Studebaker-Packard Corp.
PACKARD - Pianos ☆ - Story & Clark Piano Co.
PACKARD BELL - Computers - Packard Bell Electronics Inc.
PACKER - Boats–canoes - Black River Canoes
PACKER - Housewares - SGI Inc.
PACKER - Motor vehicle parts and accessories - Delta Consolidated Industries, Inc.
PACKER - Office supplies - Better Packages
PACKER, THE - Footwear - West Coast Shoe Co.
PACKERLAND PACKING - Meat products–beef - Packerland Packing Co., Inc.
PACKER'S BEST - Vegetables–frozen - Packers' Marketing Inc.
PACKERS OF INDIAN RIVER, THE - Grapefruit - Packers of Indian River, Inc.
PACKER'S PRIDE - Seafood products–fresh or frozen - Impex Shrimp & Fish Co.
PACKER'S SUPREME - Food products ☆ - Cap's Italian Foods Inc.
PACKET - Furniture–upholstered ☆ - Grand Rapids Leather Furniture Co.
PACKET DAIRY - Milk - Land-O-Sun Dairies, Inc.
PACKET PRINTERS INCORPORATED - Paper - Packet Printers Inc.
PACKETTE - Lenses–magnifying - Bausch & Lomb Inc.

PACKIN' PACER - Toys–automobiles - Mattel, Inc.
PACKIT - Sporting goods - Wright & McGill Co.
PACKITS - Leather goods - RGA Accessories Inc.
PACKMASTER - Backpacks - Seaway Importing Co.
PACKMASTER - Fabrics - Minnetonka Mills Inc.
PACKMASTER - Motor vehicle parts and accessories ☆ - Carefree of Colorado
PACKPACK - Apparel and accessories - California Manufacturing Co. Inc.
PACKRACK - Racks ☆ - Raleigh USA Bicycle Co.
PACKRIP - Tape–adhesive - Industrial Adhesives, Inc.
PACKSTRING - Tape–adhesive - Industrial Adhesives, Inc.
PACKTOWL - Towels - Cascade Designs, Inc.
PACKWHIP - Machinery - Weatherford U.S., Inc.
PACKY POPPLES - Toys - Those Characters from Cleveland, Inc.
PACLAN - Computer peripheral equipment - Pacific Scientific Co.
PACLIN - Pharmaceutical preparations - Armenpharm Ltd.
PACLOAN - Computer software - Notis Systems, Inc.
PACMIN - Mannequins - Trileen International Inc.
PACNET - Computer software - Data Instruments, Inc.
PACO VERA - Footwear ☆ - J. Steiner Imports Inc.
PACOM - Computers–personal - Pacom Data, Inc.
PACON - Toys–stuffed - Pacon Corp.
PACON SUPREME - Paints - Bruning Paint Co.
PACOR - Computer software ☆ - Queue Inc.
PACOSTRIP - Wallpaper - Paper Corp. of the United States
PACQUIN - Skin care products - Pfizer Inc.
PACRALON - Paints - Paris Paint & Varnish Co.
PACRALUX - Paints - Paris Paint & Varnish Co.
PACS - Audio equipment - Xantech Inc.
PACS - Electrical equipment - Peaktronics, Inc.
PACS - Electrical equipment - UtiliCorp United Inc.
PACSIM - Computer peripheral equipment - Pacific Simulation
PACSTRAP - Cordage and twine - Pacific Strapping, Inc.
PACTAINER ED - Containers - Better Agricultural Goals Corp.
PACTEL - Telephones–cellular - PacTel Personal Communications
PACTITE - Conveyors - Maryland Wire Belts, Inc.
PACTORFUME - Insecticides - Uncle Sam Chemical Co., Inc.
PACTRA PREP - Paints - Testor Corp.
PACWEST RACING GROUP - Apparel and accessories - Pacwest Racing Group
PAD - DEPAD - Pressing machines–commercial - Appalachian Controls Environmental
PAD/DOCK - Boxes - Rubbermaid Commercial Products Inc.
PAD-ETTES - Brassieres (Bras) ☆ - Lovable Co.
PAD-EX - Cleaning equipment - Pad-Ex International, Inc.
PAD-GRAB - Brushes - Flo-Pac Corp.
PAD GUARD - Veterinary pharmaceutical preparations - P R N Pharmacal, Inc.
PAD-KRAFT - Envelopes - Astro-Valcour, Inc.
PAD LOCK - Sports gloves - Figgie Licensing Corp.
PAD-LOK - Polishing cloths ☆ - Norton Co.
PAD-P-PAINT - Paints ☆ - Valspar Corp.
PAD-RITE - Vinyl - Sac Corp.
PAD, THE - Pet products - Seachem Laboratories
PAD TUFF - Pet products - Pet Biotics Inc.
PAD-TUFF - Pet products ☆ - BenePet Pet Care Products
PAD WORKS - Tape–adhesive - Kama, Inc.
PADBLOCKS - Paper - Somerset Trading Co.
PADCALL - Communications equipment - Dwyer Precision, Inc.
PADCO - Cotton batting - Absorbent Cotton Co.
PADCO - Paints - Padco Companies, Inc.
PADDED CELLS - Camping products - Outdoor Research, Inc.
PADDED SELLS - Notebooks and notepads - Hoshal Advertising, Inc.
PADDED SKINS - Apparel and accessories - Andiamo!
PADDERS - Baby bootees - Padders Inc.
PADDI MAKER - Pet products ☆ - Kane Manufacturing Co.
PADDINGTON BEAR - Buttons - JHB International Inc.
PADDINGTON BEAR - Figurines ☆ - Enesco Corp.
PADDINGTON BEAR - Infant product - Eden LLC
PADDINGTON OF CANADA - Beverages–alcohol - Paddington Corp.
PADDLE - Candy ☆ - Williams & Randolph Inc.
PADDLE BIKE - Boats ☆ - Riviera Cruiser
PADDLE DRUMS - Games - Woodstock Percussion, Inc.
PADDLE-N-CATCH! - Games - Bravo International Corp.
PADDLE PAC INC. - Sorority/fraternity paddle-making kit - Paddle Pac Inc.
PADDLE-PADS - Frames–eyeglass - J.I. Morris Co.
PADDLE PITCH - Games - Gold Medal Recreational Products
PADDLE POOL - Games ☆ - Milton Bradley Co.

☆ = Now out of production

PADDLE POPS - Candy - Williams & Randolph Inc.

PADDLE SCATCH - Games - Drybranch Inc./Sport Design

PADDLE-TAIL - Fishing tackle - Paddle Tail Fishing Lures Inc.

PADDLE TRAMPS - Product description unknown - Paddle Tramps Manufacturing Co.

PADDLE WHACKER - Fishing lures - Bomber Bait Co.

PADDLE WHEELER - Boats - DMM Industries, Inc.

PADDLE YOUR OWN CANOE - Liqueurs - Chatam International Inc.

PADDLE YOUR OWN CANOE - Wine-based beverages - Charles Jacquin et Compagnie Inc.

PADDLES BEAR - Toys - Tonka Corp.

PADDLES ELEPHANT - Toys–stuffed - Russ Berrie and Co., Inc.

PADDLEWHEEL PUBLICATIONS - Publisher's imprints - Pelican Publishing Co. Inc.

PADDOCK - Pharmaceutical preparations - Paddock Laboratories Inc.

PADDOCK DRIVE - Wallpaper - I. Gottlieb & Associates

PADDOCK PRIDE - Pet products - RHB Enterprises

PADDS - Apparel and accessories - Thor-Lo Inc.

PADDY - Rice - China Doll, Inc.

PADDY - Scouring pads - Dial Corp.

PADDY KADDY - Bags–canvas - Patricia Ann Hunter

PADDY O'BEAR - Giftware - Russ Berrie and Co., Inc.

PADDY O'CINNAMON - Toys–stuffed - Stiles-Bishop Productions Inc.

PADDY WAGON - Toys–automobiles - Mattel, Inc.

PADDYCAKES - Food products ☆ - Amberwave Foods

PADDYPAD - Fishing tackle - Charles A. Grosse

PADDY'S - Breads - Charles Freihofer Baking Co.

PADDYWACK - Pet products - Classic Products

PADETTE - Brassieres (Bras) - Bi-Flex International

PADFORM - Computer program - Padcom Inc.

PADI - Apparel and accessories - International Padi, Inc.

PADIS - Hair care products - Padis Inc.

PADKOTE - Veterinary pharmaceutical preparations - Happy Jack, Inc.

PADL-PAK - Sporting goods - General Sportcraft Co. Ltd.

PADLIFE - Computer programs - Padcom Inc.

PADLOCK - Alarm systems - William Orum

PADLOCK - Tape–adhesive - Central Products Co.

PADLOCK GUARD - Locks–padlocks ☆ - Kwikset Powdered Metal Products

PADLOCK SENTRY - Locks–padlocks - Small Products, Inc.

PADMAN - Computer software - Padcom Inc.

PADMATE - Carpet-pad reinforcements - Conwed Plastics

PADMINI - Incense - Excelsior Incense Works

PADMORE - Shoes - Clarks of England Inc.

PADMORE LITES - Shoes ☆ - Clarks of England Inc.

PADOW'S - Sandwiches–prepackaged - Padow's Deli, Inc.

PADOW'S DELI SHOPS - Sandwiches–prepackaged - Padow's Deli, Inc.

PADPAK - Pet products - Ranpak Corp.

PADPLUS RF - Computer hardware - Fujitsu Personal Systems, Inc.

PADRE - Beverages–malt ☆ - Safeway Stores Inc.

PADRE ISLAND FAN CO. - Fans–electric - Ampac Industries Inc.

PADRE ISLE - Furniture–wood ☆ - Flanders Industries Inc.

PADRINO - Footwear–men's - Harbor Footwear Group Ltd.

PADRINO - Furniture ☆ - Bassett Furniture Industries, Inc.

PADRON - Cigars - Piloto Cigars, Inc.

PADRON FABRICA DE TABACOS FUNDADA EN 1964 - Cigars - Piloto Cigars, Inc.

PADSTAR - Computer programs - Padcom Inc.

PADUA - Paper–book - Padua Franciscan High School, Inc.

PADUKE JR. - Candy - Gilliam Candy Co. Inc. (Gilliam Candy Brands)

PADUKE SR. - Candy - Gilliam Candy Co. Inc. (Gilliam Candy Brands)

PADWARE - Computer peripherals - Jones & Vining Inc.

PAECH - Breads - Allied Bakers Co.

PAESANA - Olive oil - L and S Packing Co., Inc.

PAESANO - Tires–motorcycle - John N. Wright Jr. Inc.

PAESAR - Electric lighting equipment - Lutron Electronics Co., Inc.

PAESOLO - Musical instruments - Boosey & Hawkes Buffet Crampon USA

P.A.F. - Flowers–artificial - Europa Co.

PAF - Guitars - Dimarzio, Inc.

PAF AND BACK - Computer software ☆ - Quinsept Inc.

PAF PRO - Guitars - Dimarzio, Inc.

PAG - Electronic equipment - Comprehensive Video Supply Corp.

PAGAN PINK - Wines ☆ - Ernest and Julio Gallo Winery

PAGANI - Pasta ☆ - Bascoms Corp.

PAGANI - Tomato pastes and sauces - Dean & Deluca Inc.

PAGANINI - Musical instruments - Grossman Music Corp.

PAGANI'S - Tomato pastes and sauces - Taste of the World

PAGE - Bedding–linen - Thomaston Mills Inc.

PAGE - Brushes–paint - Corona Brushes Inc.

PAGE - Fencing–chain link - Page Aluminized Steel Corp.

PAGE - Flowers, plants, and seeds - Page Seed Co.

PAGE - Napkins–paper - Fort Howard Corp.

PAGE - Paint sets–hobby ☆ - Anthes Universal

PAGE 2000 - Paging devices - SNET Paging Inc.

PAGE-A-DAY - Calendars - Workman Publishing Co., Inc.

PAGE A DAY, A - Diaries - Samuel Ward Manufacturing Inc.

PAGE ABILITY - Computer software - John Matter

PAGE ALERT - Alarm systems - Page Alert Systems

PAGE & SHAW - Candy ☆ - New England Confectionery Co.

PAGE BOY - Apparel–women's - Page Boy Co. Inc.

PAGE BOY - Tobacco products - Philip Morris Companies Inc.

PAGE BRIDGE - Telephone answering machines - Motorola, Inc. (Land Mobile Products Sector)

PAGE BRUSH - Computer software - Mouse Systems Corp.

PAGE BRUSH 256 - Computer software - Mouse Systems Corp.

PAGE DIRECTOR - Software - Managing Editor Software Inc.

PAGE FORTRESS - Fencing–gates and posts ☆ - Page Aluminized Steel Corp.

PAGE-IT - Computer software - Capital Data Systems, Inc.

PAGE MAKER - Radio communications equipment - Motorola, Inc. (Land Mobile Products Sector)

PAGE MILL WINERY - Wines - Page Mill Winery

PAGE OF LONDON - Paint sets–hobby ☆ - Winsor & Newton

PAGE ONE - Dresses–girls' - T.P. Industries Inc.

PAGE OVERTURES - Computer storage devices–optical - Form and Function

PAGE PALS - Paper - Hershy The Tin Man

PAGE SPEED - Computer software - Digital Technology International

PAGE STREAM - Computer software - Oce Printing Systems USA, Inc.

PAGE STUDIOS - Lighting fixtures–underwater - Page Lighting

PAGEANT - Colognes ☆ - Avon Products, Inc.

PAGEANT - Cosmetics ☆ - Shiseido Cosmetics (America) Ltd.

PAGEANT - Floor coverings–carpet and rugs ☆ - Galaxy Carpet Mills Inc.

PAGEANT - Glassware–household - Oneida Ltd.

PAGEANT - Photographic equipment - Eastman Kodak Co.

PAGEANTRY - Greeting cards ☆ - American Artists Group Inc.

PAGEANTRY - Paper–writing - Champion International Corp.

PAGEANTRY - Tableware–china - Pfaltzgraff Investment Co.

PAGEANTRY - Wallpaper - Payne Fabrics

PAGEANTRY - Wallpaper - Warner Co.

PAGEBOT - Computer software - Strategic Open Solutions Group

PAGEBOX - Computer software - Strategic Open Solutions Group

PAGEBOY - Pagers - Sims Communications Inc.

PAGECARD - Computers - Socket Communications, Inc.

PAGEDRAW - Computer software - Netobjects, Inc.

PAGEGUARD - Surge protectors - Harris Corp.

PAGEKEEP - Computer software - Electronic Information Exchange

PAGEKOM - Pagers - Atlas/Soundolier

PAGELOGIC - Data loggers ☆ - Senercomm Inc.

PAGEMAKER - Chemical preparations - Novagen, Inc.

PAGEMAKER - Computer software - Aldus Corp.

PAGEMASTER - Computer software - Adobe Systems Inc.

PAGEMASTER - Electronic equipment - Bogen Communications, Inc.

PAGEMASTER, THE - Apparel and accessories - Turner Pictures, Inc.

PAGEMASTER, THE - Trading cards and stamps - Twentieth Century Fox Film Corp.

PAGEMATE - Binders - Eagle Marketing

PAGEMILL PRESS - Publisher's imprints - Pagemill Press

PAGENTRY - Portable computer - RTS Electronics Inc.

PAGEPERFECT - See **IMSI PUBLISHER**

PAGEPLEX - Printers–computer - Olympus Image Systems, Inc.

PAGER LINK - Computer peripheral equipment - Casio Phonemate, Inc.

PAGER PAL - Holsters - IYP Inc.

PAGES - Confections ☆ - R.L. Albert & Son, Inc.

PAGES - Food products - Europa Foods Ltd.

PAGES BY PAGES - Computer software - Pages Software, Inc.

PAGESAVER - Plastics–laminated - D & K International, Inc.

PAGESCAN COLOR - Computer peripheral equipment - Logitech, Inc.

PAGESERVER - Computer software - Infospinner, Inc.

PAGESOFT - Computer software - Socket Communications, Inc.

PAGESTORE - Computer hardware - Gammagraphx, Inc.

PAGETHRU - Pagers - Grayson Electronics Co.

PAGEVIEW - Clipboards - Krapf Business Systems, Inc.

PAGEWATCH - Pagers - Scarsdale Security System, Inc.

☆ = Now out of production

PAGEXTRA - Radio communications equipment - Metromedia Paging Services Inc.

PAGINATION - Computer software ☆ - DataPak Software Inc.

PAGINE - Computer hardware - Pagine Corp.

PAGLIACCIO - Food products - Pastene Companies Ltd.

PAGLIANO - Apparel and accessories - Castle Apparel Group, Inc.

PAGLIARESE - Wines ☆ - IDV Wines (Beaulieu Vineyard)

PAGO PAGO - Floor coverings–carpet and rugs ☆ - Royalweve Carpet Mills

PAGO PAGO - Games - Just Games

PAGODA - Furniture - Vaughan Furniture Co. Inc.

PAGODA - Recording label - Pagoda Entertainment, Inc.

PAGODA - Shoes ☆ - Sidney Rich Associates Inc.

PAGODA - Skin care products - Paul Mazzotta Inc.

PAGODA - Wines - Takara Sake USA

PAGODA CAFE - Food products - Schwan's Sales Enterprises, Inc.

PAGODA TEMPLE - Fireworks - Great Grizzly, Inc.

PAGODA YASHIRO - Cages–wire - Ameriguard Corp.

PAI - Computer hardware - Precision America, Inc.

PAI - Electrical equipment - Augat Inc.

PAI - Nuts and bolts - Parts Associates Inc.

PAI/O DRIVER - Computer software - Performance Associates, Inc.

PAID - Recording label - Paid Records

PAID PRO ATHLETE IN DEVELOPMENT - Sporting apparel - Michael Coburn

PAIDAHUEN - Fruits and vegetables - Marglo Products Corp.

PAIDI - Furniture - World-Wide Trade Corp.

PAIGE - Computer software ☆ - DataPak Software Inc.

PAIGE - Motor vehicles–automobiles ☆ - Paige-Detroit Motor Car Co.

PAIL SACKS - Diaper-pail liners - Barna Inc.

PAILMASTER - Mixers - Fluid Management

PAILS - Glass products - Blenko Glass Co. Inc.

PAIN - Apparel and accessories - Scott Myers and Jason Aeck Partnership

PAIN-A-TRATE - Analgesics - Melaleuca, Inc.

PAIN & STRESS PUBLICATIONS - Recording label - M.M.R.C., Ltd. Co.

PAIN-AWAY - Health care products ☆ - Carter-Wallace, Inc.

PAIN-AWAY - Pharmaceutical preparations - American First Aid Co.

PAIN BUST-R 2 - Analgesic - Continental Quest Research Corp.

PAIN BUST R II - Pharmaceutical preparations - Continental Equities, Inc.

PAIN BUST RI - Pharmaceutical preparations - Continental Equities, Inc.

PAIN CHEATERS - Sporting goods - Kevin Day

PAIN DOCTOR - Analgesics ☆ - E. Fougera & Co. Inc.

PAIN DOCTOR - Pharmaceutical preparations - ABC Pharmaceuticals, Inc.

PAIN EASA MASSAGER PAD - Massage products - Gelfer Group

PAIN ERASER - Massagers - Michael Thompson

PAIN-EZE + - Pharmaceutical preparations ☆ - Reese Chemical Co.

PAIN FREE - Analgesics - Afassco

PAIN FREEZE - Analgesics - Biochemics, Inc.

PAIN GEL PLUS - Analgesics - Mentholatum Co.

PAIN IN TAC - Computer storage devices - PT Diagnostic Software, Inc.

PAIN-LESS - Health care products - Natural Laboratories Corp.

PAIN MANAGEMENT SYSTEM - Health care products - Desert Health Products, Inc.

PAIN PATCH - Pharmaceutical preparations - Mentholatum Co.

PAIN-RELIEVER-E - Analgesic - IDE-Interstate Inc.

PAIN STICK - Analgesics - Premier Nutraceuticals, Inc.

PAIN TAMER PADS - Health care products - Professional Foot Care Products Inc.

PAIN-X - Analgesics - B.F. Ascher & Co. Inc.

PAINAID - Analgesics - Zee Medical Inc.

PAINALAY - Health care products - Medtech Laboratories Inc.

PAINE - Transducers - Paine Co.

PAINLESS PUNCTUATION - Computer software - Orange Cherry Software

PAINLESS WIRING - Automotive wiring and accessories - Perfect Performance Products, Inc.

PAINT - Chewing gum - Stanico, Inc.

PAINT 4 KIDS - Paints - Van Aken International

PAINT A CARPET - Paints ☆ - Fibre Glass-Evercoat Co. Inc.

PAINT-A-FISH - Hobby kits - Snakes & Things

PAINT-A-HABITAT - Hobby kits - Pamela Drake Imports, Inc.

PAINT-A-KITE KIT - Kites - Barbara J. Macaire

PAINT-A-LOON - Decorations - National Latex Products Co.

PAINT A PILLOW - Hobby kits - Stearns Technical Textiles Co.

PAINT-A-SNAKE - Hobby kits - Snakes & Things

PAINT-A-THON - Paint rollers - Padco Companies, Inc.

PAINT-A-TURN - Lighting equipment - Country Plus

PAINT ALL - Paints - DIMC, Inc.

PAINT ALONG WITH CONNI - Artists' materials ☆ - Conni Gordon Art Method Inc.

PAINT AMERICA - Paints - M.A. Bruder & Sons Inc.

PAINT & PLAY TRAY - Toys - Romar Enterprises Ltd.

PAINT AWAY - Paperboard - Invention Co.

PAINT BOX - Rubber stamp inkpad - Clearsnap, Inc.

PAINT BRUSH - Sporting goods - Wellington Leisure Products, Inc.

PAINT BRUSH FLEX - Paints - Allway Tools Inc.

PAINT BRUSH RACK - Hardware - Aqua-Tainer Co.

PAINT BULL, THE - Primers - Colortec, Inc.

PAINT CLAY CAFE - Clay products - Paint Clay Cafe

PAINT CRAFT - Paints - Sophir Morris Paint

PAINT CRAFT - Wallpaper - Mayfair Wallcoverings

PAINT EASE - Paints - Davis Paint Co.

PAINT-EZE - Paint rollers - Pelco Industries Inc.

PAINT GLOVE - Toys - Mattel, Inc.

PAINT-GON - Paints ☆ - Turco-Purex

PAINT IT! - Paint and wallpaper stores - Great American Marketing, Inc.

PAINT IT RIGHT - Paints - Jones Blair Co.

PAINT MAKERS - Turpentine ☆ - Devoe & Raynolds Co.

PAINT MASTER - Paints - Red Spot Paint & Varnish Co., Inc.

PAINT-MATE - Paints ☆ - Larsen Products Corp.

PAINT MATES - Toys - Anthony Williams, Inc.

PAINT-ME - Dolls - Overly-Raker

PAINT ME...IN WATERCOLOR - Paints–artists' - M.A. Boysen Enterprises Inc.

PAINT N CRAFT - Gloves–work - Pioneer Industrial Products Co.

PAINT 'N DAZZLE - Toys - Mattel, Inc.

PAINT-N-DUST - Respirators - Aearo Co.

PAINT 'N PITCH - Brushes–paint - Wooster Brush Co.

PAINT N PLASTER - Paints - Graham Paint and Varnish Co.

PAINT 'N ROLL - Paint rollers - Wagner Spray Tech Corp.

PAINT 'N SPARKLE - Toys - M.&S. Shillman Inc.

PAINT-N-SWIRL - Paint sets–hobby - Natural Science Industries, Ltd.

PAINT 'N TOTE - Toys ☆ - Coloron Industries

PAINT 'N WEAR - Toys ☆ - Coloron Industries

PAINT-ON - Crayons - Dixon Ticonderoga Co.

PAINT-ON - Hobby kits - Hinkle Easter Products

PAINT-ON - Paints ☆ - Mac-O-Lac Paints Inc.

PAINT ON WOOD - Toys ☆ - Coloron Industries

PAINT PARTY - Artists' materials - Conni Gordon Art Method Inc.

PAINT PIG - Centrifugal separators - Alfa-Laval Separation, Inc.

PAINT POCKETS - Filters–industrial - Products Unlimited, Inc.

PAINT POT - Paints–artists' - Palmer Paint Products, Inc.

PAINT RATED - Brushes–paint - Wooster Brush Co.

PAINT, RATTLE & ROLL - Hobby kits - Natural Science Industries, Ltd.

PAINT RITE - Brushes–paint - E-Z Paintr Corp.

PAINT-RITE - Paints–artists' - Montrose Products Inc.

PAINT SAVER - Autoclaves–laboratory - California Dealer Accessories, Inc.

PAINT SAVER - Cans–metal ☆ - Behlen Manufacturing Co.

PAINT SAVER KEYS - Paints–artists' - Masterson Art Products, Inc.

PAINT SCENTS - Perfumes ☆ - Delagar

PAINT SMART - Paints - Sweet's Wholesale Distributors, Inc.

PAINT SPOTS - Paints–artists' ☆ - Reeves International, Inc.

PAINT STOPPER - Dropcloths - Mutual Dropcloth Co.

PAINT THE WILD - Hobby kits - Balitono, Inc.

PAINT USA - Paints - Bloch/New England, Inc.

PAINT-VISION - Paints - Talon Paint Inc.

PAINT WITH PENCILS - Pencils - Faber-Castell Corp.

PAINT, WRITE & PLAY! - Computer software - Softkey Multimedia Inc.

PAINT YOUR T - Paints - Tulip Productions

PAINT YUR OWN - Placemats - Anacapa Corp.

PAINTABLES - Wallpaper - Brewster Wallcovering Co.

PAINTABLES, THE - Window coverings - Bamboo Abbott Florida Corp.

PAINTAC - Computer software - PT Diagnostic Software, Inc.

PAINTBALL BOTTOMS - Sporting goods ☆ - Earth & Ocean Sports, Inc.

PAINTBALLS - Candy - Glico Harmony Foods Corp.

PAINTBOARD - Computer software - Rasterops Corp.

PAINTBOX - Inkpads - All Night Media, Inc.

PAINTED DESERT - Blinds–venetian ☆ - Hunter Douglas, Inc.

PAINTED DESERT - Craft supplies ☆ - VIP/VIP Crafts

PAINTED DESERT - Fireworks - Ingram Enterprises, Inc.

PAINTED DESERT - Food products - Poloni Pepper Co.

PAINTED DESERT - Glassware–household - Crisa Corp.

PAINTED DESERT - Tiles–ceramic ☆ - American Marazzi Tile, Inc.

PAINTED DESERT - Wallpaper - Marburg Wallcoverings Inc.

☆ = Now out of production

PAINTED DOOR - Cups–plastic - Painted Door Gallery, Ltd.
PAINTED DOOR GALLERY - Shirts - Painted Door Gallery, Ltd.
PAINTED FINISHES - Wallpaper - Imperial Wallcoverings, Inc.
PAINTED GLASS - Floor coverings–carpet and rugs - Quaker Inc.
PAINTED IMPRESSIONS - Decals and transfers - Wang's International, Inc.
PAINTED MOUNTAINS - Dinnerware–glass ☆ - WMF/USA
PAINTED PONY - Apparel and accessories ☆ - Polomate Corp.
PAINTED PONY - Apparel–children's - Painted Pony
PAINTED PRAIRIE - Fabrics–tapestry ☆ - Combeau Industries
PAINTED PRINTS - Yarn - Melrose Yarn Co. Inc.
PAINTER - Wallpaper ☆ - Osborne & Little
PAINTER DOWN - Paint and wallpaper stores ☆ - Wagner Spray Tech Corp.
PAINTER MAGIC - Brushes–paint - Wooster Brush Co.
PAINTER-MATE - Brushes–paint - E-Z Paintr Corp.
PAINTERS - Markers–felt-tip - Hunt Manufacturing Co.
PAINTERS ADVANTAGE - Cleaning preparations - ChemPlus
PAINTER'S CHOICE - Brushes–paint - Wooster Brush Co.
PAINTER'S CHOICE - Paints - Bruning Paint Co.
PAINTER'S DOZEN - Paints–artists' - Plaid Enterprises, Inc.
PAINTERS EDGE - Brushes–paint - American Brush Co. Inc.
PAINTERS EDGE - Paints - Jobar International Inc./Bibi Products
PAINTERS EDITION - Apparel - Mark Lunde
PAINTERS' FRIEND - Brushes–paint - Porter Paint Co.
PAINTERS' HELPER - Cleaning preparations - Klean-Strip
PAINTER'S HELPER DEGLOS - Cleaning preparations - Klean-Strip
PAINTER'S MATE - Brushes–paint - Leaktite Corp.
PAINTER'S NAIL HOLE FILLER - Adhesives and sealants - Eclectic Products Inc.
PAINTERS PAL - Brushes–paint - Embee Corp.
PAINTER'S PAL, THE - Housewares - Ladco Industries
PAINTER'S PALETTE - Dishes–earthenware - Denby USA Limited
PAINTERS PALS - Fabrics - Plezall Wipers Inc.
PAINTER'S PARTNER - Tools - Portable Products, Inc.
PAINTER'S PRIDE - Brushes–paint - Wooster Brush Co.
PAINTER'S SELECT - Brushes–paint - Plaid Enterprises, Inc.
PAINTERS SERIES, THE - Wallpaper - Blumenthal
PAINTER'S SPECIAL - Brushes–paint - Bestt-Liebco
PAINTER'S STENCIL - Artists' materials - Plaid Enterprises, Inc.
PAINTER'S TEAM - Paint sprayers - Graco Inc.
PAINTER'S TIME SAVER - Waterproofing compounds ☆ - Charles Paint Research Inc.
PAINTER'S XTRA - Adhesives and sealants - Gibson-Homans Co. (Sealant Technology)
PAINTHIDE - Paints ☆ - PPG Industries, Inc.
PAINTIN' BUDDIES - Artists' materials ☆ - Master Products Inc.
PAINTIN' FACES KID - Dolls - Mattel, Inc.
PAINTING - Wallpaper ☆ - Marburg Wallcoverings Inc.
PAINTINGS IN STONE - Wallpaper ☆ - Morton Jonap Co. Inc.
PAINTLESS PAINT - Artists' materials - Mattel, Inc.
PAINTLIFT - Paint removers - Wilson Imperial Co.
PAINTMAKER - Pigments - Applied Color Systems, Inc.
PAINTPRINTS - Hobby kits - Lisa Frank, Inc.
PAINTPRO - Hardware - Campbell Group (Wayne Home Equipment Div.)
PAINTS THE LINE - Cosmetics ☆ - Madeleine Mono Ltd.
PAINTSEED - Painters' materials - Century Autoline Inc.
PAINTSTIK - Paints - Markal Co.
PAINTSTONE - Inks - Rubber Stampede
PAINTTOOS - Paints - Palmer Paint Products, Inc.
PAINTWORKS - Toys - Mattel, Inc.
PAIR - Recording label - Essex Entertainment Inc.
PAIR O' DICE - Games - Pair O' Dice LLC
PAIR 'O' PETS - Toys–stuffed - Fun World Inc.
PAIR OF SHADES - Cosmetics - Clinique Laboratories, Inc.
PAIR-OFFS - Apparel and accessories - Koret North America
PAIR-OFFS - Sporting goods - E Enterprises
PAIR YOU WEAR, THE - Shoes - Consolidated Shoe Co., Inc.
PAIRABLES - Jewelry - Ears-R-In Inc.
PAIRPOINT - Furniture ☆ - Bassett Furniture Industries, Inc.
PAIRS - Hosiery–children's - McCubbin Hosiery Inc.
PAIRTREE - Computer software - Voice Processing Solutions, Inc.
PAIRWARE - LAN computer programs - Webcorp
PAISANO - Food products - Paisano Food Products Inc.
PAISANO - Wines - Ernest and Julio Gallo Winery
PAISANO TROPICAL - Cheese - Tropical Cheese Industries, Inc.
PAISANOS - Cigars - Consolidated Cigar Corp.
PAISLEY - Apparel–women's - Queen Casuals Inc.

PAISLEY - Ashtrays–glass ☆ - Van Guard Studios of North Carolina
PAISLEY - Floor coverings–carpet and rugs - Regal Rugs Inc.
PAISLEY - Glassware–household - Ceraglass Inc.
PAISLEY - Glassware–household - Culver Glass Inc.
PAISLEY - Glassware–household ☆ - Fenton Art Glass Co.
PAISLEY - Stationery ☆ - Berkshire Stationery Inc.
PAISLEY & LACE - Wallpaper - United Wallcoverings
PAISLEY FARM - Vegetables–pickled or brined - Paisley Farm
PAISLEYS, PLAIDS AND STRIPES - Wallpaper - Pelican Prints
PAISTE 302 - Cymbals - Paiste America, Inc.
PAISTE 402 - Cymbals - Paiste America, Inc.
PAISTE 502 - Cymbals - Paiste America, Inc.
PAISTE 802 - Cymbals - Paiste America, Inc.
PAISTE 2002 - Cymbals - Paiste America, Inc.
PAISTE LINE - Cymbals - Paiste America, Inc.
PAITUE ORCHARDGRASS - Flowers, plants, and seeds - Jacklin Seed
PAJ - Recording label - Paris Records
PAJAMA KIDS - Dolls ☆ - Effanbee Doll Corp.
PAJAMA PARTY - Pajamas–women's - J.C. Penney Co., Inc.
PAJAMA WORK SHOP - Apparel and accessories - Bentley Lingerie, Inc.
PAJAMAS - Apparel–women's - Bentley Lingerie, Inc.
PAJAMS - Apparel–women's - Bentley Lingerie, Inc.
PAJANIMALS - Underwear and nightwear - Doze Clothes, Inc.
PAJARO - Backpacks - Lois L. Olmstead
PAJE - Hair care products - Paje Products
PAK - Machinery - Akron Extruders, Inc.
PAK - Office supplies - Continental Graphics Corp. (Los Angeles Div.)
PAK 12 - Diagnostic substances - Genetic Testing Institute, Inc.
PAK-A-LUNCH SCHOOL BUS CAUTION - Food products - International Trading Co.
PAK-A-PET - Pet products - Colony Pet Goods
PAK-A-POTTI - Toilets–portable - Sears, Roebuck and Co.
PAK-A-ROBE - Blankets - Faribault Woolen Mill Co.
PAK-A-VITE - Health care products - Energen Products Inc.
PAK-ALL - Bags - Lefkowitz and Santangelo Co.
PAK & STORE - Boxes - Public Storage, Inc.
PAK-KIT - Sporting goods - Madden/USA
PAK-LOK - Plywood - Georgia-Pacific Corp.
PAK-LOK & DESIGN - Plywood - Georgia-Pacific Corp.
PAK-MOR - Bags - Lefkowitz and Santangelo Co.
PAK 'N' APPLE - Food products - Knouse Foods Cooperative, Inc.
PAK-N-CARRY - Housewares - Tupperware Co.
PAK-N-STAK - Containers ☆ - Mead-Hatcher, Inc.
PAK PAD - Sporting goods - North By Northeast
PAK PLUS - Vitamins and nutritional supplements - Jarrow Formulas
PAK RACK - Shelving units–wood - Jaken Co., Inc.
PAK RAP - Buckles - Net/Werk/USA, Inc.
PAK-TAB - Archery equipment - Saunders Archery Co.
PAK TITES - Apparel and accessories - 3 Strikes Custom Design USA
PAK-TITES - Hardware - Barrett Manufacturing Co.
PAK-TUBE - Containers–plastic - Carroll Packaging Co.
PAK-WIPES - Paper–toweling - Georgia-Pacific Corp.
PAKADERM - Recording label - Word, Inc.
PAKAPS - Cold remedies - Rogers' Drug Co.
PAKAUTO - Diagnostic substances - Genetic Testing Institute, Inc.
PAKAY BY GIBSON - Paper–crepe - Gibson Greetings, Inc.
PAKHAMMER 90 - Tools–hand-operated - Paratech Inc.
PAKKAWOOD - Drums–musical instruments ☆ - Cappella Wood Enterprises
PAKKAWOOD - Wood products - Adams Pakkawood Corp.
PAKKS - Crocheted and knitted items - Kreinik Manufacturing Co. Inc.
PAKKY - Plastics - Packaging Products Corp. of America
PAKLITE - Travel accessories ☆ - Clopay Building Products Co., Inc.
PAKMIX - Concrete–ready-mix - Pakmix Inc.
PAK'N TOTE - Bags–duffel - RonPak Inc.
PAKO - Photographic equipment - Pako Corp.
PAKO - Sewing machines–household ☆ - Fleur De Paris
PAKOR - Photographic equipment - Pakor Inc.
PAKS - Food products ☆ - Empire Kosher Poultry Inc.
PAKS-A-TIVE - Pharmaceutical preparations - Paks Drugs Inc.
PAKTITES - Apparel and accessories - 3 Strikes Custom Design USA
PAKULA - Jewelry - Pakula & Co.
PAL - Brushes - Corona Brushes Inc.
PAL - Cables–fiber optic - Texscan Corp.
PAL - Chewing gum - Leaf, Inc.
PAL - Colognes - Brandy Harvest
PAL - Computers - Dometic Corp.

☆ = Now out of production

PAL - Guns–BB - Daisy Manufacturing Co.

PAL - Home-health-care products - Infomed

PAL - Ladders–metal - Cramer Inc.

PAL - Peanut butter - Sessions Co. Inc.

PAL - Pharmaceutical preparations - American Pharmaceutical Laboratories Inc.

PAL - Razor blades - American Safety Razor Co.

PAL - Stoves–gas ☆ - Fatsco

PAL-A WARM - Bathing suits - Catalina

PAL-AT - Smoke detectors - Midwesco Inc.

PAL BLADES - Razor blades - American Safety Razor Co.

PAL JOEY - Notebooks and notepads - Riverside Paper Corp.

PAL O MINE - Pet products - Next to Nature

PAL PEER ASSISTANCE LEADERSHIP - Publisher's imprints - Orange County Superintendent of Schools

PAL PLUS - Pallets–wood - C.C. Clark, Inc.

PAL SYSTEM - Electronics equipment - Instructional Industries Inc.

PALABRAS & CONCEPTS II - Computer software - Laureate Learning Systems Inc.

PALACE - Dishes–china - Pickard Inc.

PALACE - Floor coverings - Congoleum Corp.

PALACE - Flowers, plants, and seeds - Bear Creek Gardens, Inc.

PALACE - Furniture - Universal Flooring

PALACE - Housewares - Elon Inc.

PALACE - Meat products–poultry - Palace Products Corp.

PALACE - Meats–luncheon ☆ - John Morrell & Co.

PALACE - Tableware–china ☆ - Villeroy and Boch Tableware Ltd.

PALACE - Wallpaper ☆ - Lawrence Wallcoverings

PALACE - Watches - Fortunoff Fine Jewelry and Silverware Inc.

PALACE COURT - Floor coverings - Congoleum Corp.

PALACE COURT - Floor coverings–carpet and rugs - Gulistan Carpet Inc.

PALACE COURT - Furniture ☆ - Bassett Furniture Industries, Inc.

PALACE COURT - Tableware–china ☆ - Lenox, Inc.

PALACE ELEPHANT - Figurines - Lenox, Inc.

PALACE GATE - Floor coverings–carpet and rugs ☆ - Atlas Carpet Mills Inc.

PALACE LIGHTS - Floor coverings–carpet and rugs - Milliken & Co. Inc.

PALACE OF LIGHTS - Recording label - Jazz Composer's Orchestra Association Inc.

PALACE OF POWER - Toys - Mattel, Inc.

PALACE PARK - Floor coverings–carpet and rugs ☆ - Lees Carpets

PALACE ROYALE - Dishes–china - Pickard Inc.

PALACE ROYALE - Floor coverings–carpet and rugs - Cabin Crafts Carpets

PALACE SILK - Fabrics–silk - Ian Crawford Ltd.

PALACE SUITE - Floor coverings–carpet and rugs ☆ - Customweave Carpets Inc.

PALACE TILE - Floor coverings - Congoleum Corp.

PALACE WALK - Floor coverings - Mannington Resilient Floors

PALACIO - Baskets–wood - Coe & Dru Inc.

PALACIO - Furniture ☆ - Bassett Furniture Industries, Inc.

PALACIO DE ORIENTE - Fish–canned or cured - La Cena Fine Foods Inc.

PALACIO DEL SOL - Floor coverings ☆ - Azrock Commercial Flooring

PALADAC - Pharmaceutical preparations ☆ - Parke-Davis

PALADAR - Faucets - Kohler Co.

PALADIN - Apparel–athletic - Paladin Golf USA, Inc.

PALADIN - Cheese ☆ - Swissrose International Inc.

PALADIN - Employment agencies–temporary help - Paladin Companies, Inc.

PALADIN - Furniture ☆ - Stanley Furniture Co. Inc.

PALADIN - Pharmaceutical preparations - Pal Midwest Ltd.

PALADIN - Tobacco products - Swedish Math North America Inc.

PALADIN - Waterproof outerwear - Distributors Service Corp.

PALADIN BLACKCHERRY - Smoking tobacco - American Tobacco Co.

PALADIN PRESS - Vitamins and nutritional supplements - Paladin Enterprises, Inc.

PALADINO - Luggage ☆ - Shalam Imports Inc.

PALADIN'S QUEST - Games ☆ - Enix America Corp.

PALAESTRUM - Watches - North American Watch Corp.

PALAIS - Floor coverings–carpet and rugs - Eligere Carpets

PALAIS - Wallpaper - Koroseal Wallcoverings

PALAIS DUET - Wallpaper - Koroseal Wallcoverings

PALAIS ROYAL - Apparel and accessories - Palais Royal Inc.

PALAIS ROYALE - Floor coverings–carpet and rugs ☆ - Karastan-Bigelow Inc.

PALANTIR - Computer software ☆ - Palsoft

PALAPA - Floor coverings–carpet and rugs ☆ - Foreign Accents

PALARRE - Toilets–enameled - Kohler Co.

PALASET - Glassware–household - Genin Trudeau and Co. Ltd.

PALATABS - Pet products - Toogood Laboratories

PALATE - Pasta - Silver Palate Kitchen

PALATIA - Dishes–china - Waterford Wedgewood USA, Inc.

PALATIAL - Floor coverings–carpet and rugs ☆ - Customweave Carpets Inc.

PALATIAL - Infant product - Dundee Mills, Inc.

PALATINA - Floor coverings–carpet and rugs - Karastan-Bigelow Inc.

PALATINO - Floor coverings ☆ - Azrock Commercial Flooring

PALATINO - Furniture ☆ - Singer Furniture Co.

PALATINO - Tableware–china - Villeroy and Boch Tableware Ltd.

PALAWAN - Lumber - Georgia-Pacific Corp.

PALAZA - Furniture ☆ - Hammary Furniture Co. Inc.

PALAZZO - Coffee - First Colony Coffee and Tea Co. Inc.

PALAZZO - Furniture ☆ - Lyon-Shaw Inc.

PALAZZO - Giftware ☆ - Gorham Inc.

PALAZZO - Glassware–household ☆ - Ceraglass Inc.

PALAZZO - Tiles–ceramic - American Marazzi Tile, Inc.

PALAZZO - Wallpaper - Bayview Wallcoverings

PALAZZO - Wallpaper - Blumenthal

PALAZZO - Wallpaper - Brewster Wallcovering Co.

PALAZZO BY ANSON - Jewelry ☆ - Anson Inc.

PALAZZO ROMA - Floor coverings - Mannington Resilient Floors

PALBAR - Pharmaceutical preparations ☆ - Roberts/Hauck Pharmaceuticals Inc.

PALC - Vitamins and nutritional supplements - Bodyonics, Ltd.

PALCO - Floor coverings - Pacific Lumber Co.

PALCO BEARIER - Health care products - Palmero Health Care

PALCO-LOC - Floor coverings - Pacific Lumber Co.

PALCO-PLY - Lumber ☆ - Pacific Lumber Co.

PALCO PRIME - Siding - Pacific Lumber Co.

PALCO PRIME PRE-PRIMED QUALITY LUMBER - Lumber - Pacific Lumber Co.

PALCORE - Circuit boards–printed - Parlex Corp.

PALCOTE - Lumber ☆ - Pacific Lumber Co.

PALDEK - Fabricated metal products - Paltier, Inc.

PALE ALE - Beverages–malt - Sierra Nevada Brewing Co.

PALE CREPE - Office supplies ☆ - Faber-Castell Corp.

PALE CREPE GOLD - Rubber bands - Alliance Rubber Co.

PALE DRY - Beverages–carbonated ☆ - V. & E. Kohnstamm Inc.

PALE RIDER ALE - Beverages–alcohol - Clint Eastwood

PALEBERRIE - Nail care products - Cosmair Inc.

PALED BEIGE - Cosmetics - Lancome

PALEFACE - Chili peppers–powdered - Cowboy Vittles & More

PALEKH - Papier-mache articles - Siamese Imports Co.

PALEN TILE - Floor coverings - Congoleum Corp.

PALEOVIEW - Posters - Perspective Visuals, Inc.

PALEOZENE - Skin care products - European Care Inc.

PALERMO - Candy - Perugina Chocolate & Confections Inc.

PALERMO - Floor coverings ☆ - Tarkett, Inc.

PALERMO - Floor coverings–carpet and rugs ☆ - Karastan-Bigelow Inc.

PALERMO - Furniture ☆ - Bassett Furniture Industries, Inc.

PALERMO - Furniture ☆ - Hammary Furniture Co. Inc.

PALERMO - Furniture ☆ - Lane Co. Inc.

PALERMO'S FOCACCIA - Breads - Palermo's Villa Inc.

PALESTRA - Floor coverings–carpet and rugs - Masland Corp.

PALESTRINA - Musical instruments - Kraskin Baton Co.

PALETIN - Paint rollers - Corona Brushes Inc.

PALETTE - Electronic equipment - Polaroid Corp.

PALETTE - Floor coverings–carpet and rugs - Mohawk Industries Inc.

PALETTE - Floor coverings–carpet and rugs ☆ - American Carpet Mills

PALETTE - Furniture–public buildings - JG Furniture Systems, Inc.

PALETTE - Yarn ☆ - William Unger & Co. Inc.

PALETTE ACANTA - Recording label - Creav Inc. USA

PALETTE LETTERS - Paper–writing - Mead Corp.

PALETTE MAGIQUE - Wallpaper ☆ - Decorative Coverings Inc.

PALETTE N PAL - Artists' materials ☆ - Loew-Cornell Inc.

PALETTE PAK - Paints–artists' ☆ - Palmer Paint Products, Inc.

PALETTE SEAL - Palettes - Masterson Art Products, Inc.

PALETTE SERVERS - Glassware–household - Knobler International Ltd.

PALETTE, THE - Frames–picture - Framemica Co.

PALETTES - Apparel–children's - Kohl's Department Stores, Inc.

PALETTES - Wallets - Robin Kumabe

PALFORM - Containers - Case Designers, Corp.

PALGARD - Epoxy coatings - Pratt & Lambert, Inc.

PALGESIC M - Analgesics ☆ - Pan American Laboratories, Inc.

PALGIC - Antihistamine preparations - Pan American Laboratories, Inc.

PALIGARD - Epoxy coatings - Palma Inc.

PALINEY - Dental compounds - J.M. Ney Co.
PALIO - Bedding–linen - Dan River Inc.
PALIO - Handbags - Gary Gaines, Inc.
PALIO - Hot tubs–fiberglass ☆ - Jacuzzi Inc.
PALIO - Security carry-on bag - Countess Creations
PALIRRIA - Vegetables–canned - Krinos Foods, Inc.
PALISADE - Floor coverings - Congoleum Corp.
PALISADE - Giftware - Pfaltzgraff Investment Co.
PALISADE - Sinks–metal - American Standard Inc.
PALISADE - Wood products - Georgia-Pacific Corp.
PALISADES - Fabrics - Thompson of California Inc.
PALISADES - Floor coverings–carpet and rugs - Kelly Group Inc.
PALISADES - Floor coverings–carpet and rugs ☆ - Robertex Associates Inc.
PALISADES - Furniture ☆ - Stanley Furniture Co. Inc.
PALISADES - Tableware–china ☆ - Lenox, Inc.
PALISADES - Wood products - Weyerhaeuser Co.
PALISADES CLASSICS - Wallpaper - Frankford Wallcoverings Inc.
PALISADES PARK - Furniture ☆ - Bassett Furniture Industries, Inc.
PALISANDER - Fabrics - Interface, Inc.
PALISHEEN - Adhesives and sealants - Palma Inc.
PALITAR - Adhesives and sealants - Palma Inc.
PALITE - Posters - Service Litho-Print Inc.
PALIUNIKROM - Adhesives and sealants - Palma Inc.
PALIZZIO - Shoes - Arcadia International Shoe Corp. (Palizzio Div.)
PALL MALL - Cigarettes - American Tobacco Co.
PALLACE - Pharmaceutical preparations - Bristol-Myers Squibb Co.
PALLADEX - Electronic equipment - Enthone-OMI
PALLADIA - Furniture - Haworth, Inc.
PALLADIAN - Display cases–plastic - Expostar Displays, Inc.
PALLADIAN - Floor coverings - Mannington Resilient Floors
PALLADIAN - Furniture–wood ☆ - Ficks Reed Co. Inc.
PALLADIAN COLLECTION, THE - Lamps - J.C. Penney Co., Inc.
PALLADIAN COURT - Furniture ☆ - Hooker Furniture Corp.
PALLADIAN SUNBURST - Window treatments - Midwest Curtain Co.
PALLADINO - Wines - Orion Imports Ltd.
PALLADIO - Computer storage devices - Palladio Software Corp.
PALLADIO - Tiles–ceramic ☆ - American Marazzi Tile, Inc.
PALLADIO - Wallpaper - Textile Wallcoverings International Ltd.
PALLADIO - Wines - Leonardo Lo Cascio
PALLADIUM - Drums–musical instruments ☆ - Grossman Music Corp.
PALLADIUM - Floor coverings–carpet and rugs - Mohawk Carpet Corp.
PALLADIUM - Floor coverings–carpet and rugs - Philadelphia Carpets
PALLADIUM - Floor coverings–carpet and rugs ☆ - Regal Rugs Inc.
PALLADIUM - Footwear - French Dressing Inc.
PALLADIUM - Furniture - Bassett Furniture Industries, Inc.
PALLADIUM - Hair coloring preparations - National Aerosol Products Co.
PALLADIUM - Occasional furniture ☆ - JDI Group, Inc.
PALLADIUM - Paints ☆ - General Coating Technologies, Inc.
PALLADIUM PRO - Shoes ☆ - Hyde Athletic Industries Inc.
PALLANTIS PICTURES - Film–motion picture - Stop and Shop Companies Inc.
PALLARES - Olive oil - Joseph Caragol Inc.
PALLAS - Cigarettes - G.A. Georgopulo & Co. Inc.
PALLAS - Floor coverings–carpet and rugs - Masland Corp.
PALLAS - Hockey equipment - Montreal Hockey Co.
PALLAS ATHENA - Recording label - Athena Productions
PALLAS WALLS - Wallcovering - Krueger International, Inc.
PALLAZO - Floor coverings–carpet and rugs ☆ - Alliance Industries Inc.
PALLENTONE - Paints - Whittaker Corp. (Orrville Coatings Div.)
PALLET-BUSTER - Saw blades - Simonds Industries Inc.
PALLET PALLET - Pallets–wood - Pallet Pallet Inc.
PALLET PALLET REUSABLE CONTAINER SYSTEMS - Pallets–wood - Pallet Pallet Inc.
PALLET WORLD - Motoman, Inc.
PALLETITE - Adhesives and sealants - Wilmington Trust Co.
PALLETTES - Skin care products - Plasto Tech Co. International
PALLIDO - Wines ☆ - Casa Larga Vineyards Inc.
PALLISADES - Floor coverings–carpet and rugs - Hollytex Carpet Mills Inc.
PALLISER - Wallpaper - Capital Carousel Inc.
PALLMA MUSIC CO. - Publisher's imprints - Neil A. Kjos Music Co.
PALLOWS - Infant product ☆ - Dragons Are Too Seldom Inc.
PALLTRONIC - Electrical testing instruments - Pall Corp.
PALLY - Biscuits - Holland-American Importing Co. Inc.
PALM - Coconut–shredded - Far Eastern Coconut Co.
PALM - Oils–lubricating - Emro Marketing
PALM - Recording label - Criterion Music Corp.

PALM - Seafood products–canned or cured ☆ - L. Ray Packing Co.
PALM - Shrimp–fresh or frozen - Southern Shell Fish Co.
PALM-AIR - Fans–electric - Harbor Sales Co.
PALM BAY - Furniture - Homecrest Industries Inc.
PALM BEACH - Apparel–men's - Palm Beach Co., Inc.
PALM BEACH - Cosmetics - Palm Beach Beauty Products
PALM BEACH - Floor coverings–carpet and rugs ☆ - Colonial Mills Inc.
PALM BEACH - Food products - Hudgins Fish Co.
PALM BEACH - Furniture ☆ - Bassett Furniture Industries, Inc.
PALM BEACH - Furniture ☆ - Lane Co. Inc.
PALM BEACH - Motor vehicles–motor homes ☆ - Coachmen Industries, Inc.
PALM BEACH - Roofing materials–slate - Quik-Fab Aluminum Manufacturing Co. Inc.
PALM BEACH - Shutters–wood - Hunter Douglas, Inc.
PALM BEACH - Wallpaper - Frankford Wallcoverings Inc.
PALM BEACH - Window coverings - Vertilux-Louverlux Inc.
PALM BEACH CLASSIC - Lamp posts - Palm Beach Plastics Inc.
PALM BEACH COLLECTION - Garden furniture - De Jay Corp.
PALM BEACH ENTERTAINMENT - Recording label - Front Row Entertainment, Inc.
PALM BEACH II - Wallpaper - Frankford Wallcoverings Inc.
PALM BEACH ORIGINALS - Luggage - Mercury Luggage Manufacturing Co.
PALM BEACH SHADES - Sunglasses - Sungold Enterprises Ltd.
PALM BEACH SPORTS - Apparel and accessories - Palm Beach Co., Inc.
PALM BEACH TASTE - Salad dressings–bottled - Palm Beach Taste, Inc.
PALM BEACHER - Luggage - Universal Trav-ler Inc.
PALM CANYON - Floor coverings–carpet and rugs - Monticello Carpet Mills
PALM COAST - Beverages - Juice Bowl Products Inc.
PALM COURT - Floor coverings–carpet and rugs - Queen Carpet Corp.
PALM COURT - Furniture ☆ - Bernhardt Industries
PALM DALE - Fruits–canned - S & W Fine Foods, Inc.
PALM DESERT - Floor coverings–carpet and rugs - Gulistan Carpet Inc.
PALM DESERT - Lamps - Pacific Coast Lighting
PALM DESERT - Wallpaper - Bayview Wallcoverings
PALM DESERT - Wallpaper - Madison Wallcoverings
PALM GRIP - Tools–hand-operated - GC Thorsen, Inc.
PALM GUARD - Medical apparatus - Alimed, Inc.
PALM HARBOR - Lighting fixtures - Sweet's Wholesale Distributors, Inc.
PALM HARBOR - Prefabricated buildings–wood - Magnahome Inc.
PALM HILL - Floor coverings–carpet and rugs ☆ - Calladium & Marglen
PALM LITE - Apparel and accessories - Palm Beach Co., Inc.
PALM MOUNTAIN PARADISE - Skin care products - Palm Mountain Paradise, Inc.
PALM NAILER - Tools–power-driven - Danair, Inc.
PALM PAK - Audio carrying vase - RKCO
PALM-PEDAL - Musical instrument accessories - Bigsby Accessories Inc.
PALM PET - Toys–stuffed - Dan-Dee International Ltd.
PALM SAND - Tools–hand-operated - LVS, LLC
PALM SANDER - Paper–sand - Bullard Abrasives Inc.
PALM SPRINGS - Apparel and accessories - Palm Beach Co., Inc.
PALM SPRINGS - Bathtubs–enameled - Lyons Industries Inc.
PALM SPRINGS - Dinnerware–glass ☆ - Metlox Pottery Shoppe
PALM SPRINGS - Floor coverings–carpet and rugs - Cabin Crafts Carpets
PALM SPRINGS - Floor coverings–carpet and rugs ☆ - American Carpet Mills
PALM SPRINGS - Furniture ☆ - Bassett Furniture Industries, Inc.
PALM SPRINGS - Hammocks - E-Z Sales & Manufacturing, Inc.
PALM SPRINGS - Lamps - Sperti Sunlamp
PALM SPRINGS - Shampoos - Rescue Marketing Group
PALM SPRINGS GOLD - Lotions - Palm Springs Gold
PALM SPRINGS LIGHTING - Lighting fixtures - Fredrick Ramond Inc.
PALM SPRINGS SILVER - Cosmetics - Randall Caruso of Beverly Hills, Inc.
PALMA - Ammunition ☆ - Remington Arms Co., Inc.
PALMA - Cigars - House of Windsor Inc.
PALMA - Furniture - Homecrest Industries Inc.
PALMA - Spices and extracts - Herbert Marmorek & Son, Inc.
PALMA 100'S - Cigars - F.D. Grave & Son, Inc.
PALMA CHRISTI - Soap - Home Health Products, Inc.
PALMA LITES - Cigars - House of Windsor Inc.
PALMA LOUCA - Beverages–malt - Amazon, Inc.
PALMA SOLA - Furniture ☆ - Halcyon Inc.
PALMA SUPREME - Cigars ☆ - J.C. Newman Cigar Co.
PALMA THROW OUTS - Cigars - T.E. Brooks & Co.
PALMADE - Hair care products - Image Laboratories, Inc.
PALMAIRE - Floor coverings–carpet and rugs - Whitecrest Carpet Mills
PALMAS DEL MAR - Shirts–polo - Palmas Del Mar Properties, Inc.
PALMAX II - Blood pressure apparatus ☆ - Graham-Field Inc.

☆ = Now out of production

PALMCAL - Decals - American Decal

PALMCO QUALITY PALMS - Trees - Trademark Palms Inc.

PALMCONNECT - Computer software - Palm Computing, Inc.

PALMCOT - Apparel—athletic - Tenacious Ltd.

PALMDALE - Fruits—candied - Redwood Food Packing Co.

PALMDALE - Furniture - Dinaire Corp.

PALMDSPCORE - Computer software - DSP Group, Inc.

PALME D'OR - Cosmetics - Smithkline Beecham Corp.

PALMER - Accordions - Titano Accordion Co. International

PALMER - Balls—billiard - Palmer Billiard Corp.

PALMER - Candy - R.M. Palmer Co.

PALMER - Floor coverings—carpet and rugs ☆ - Regal Rugs Inc.

PALMER - Golfing equipment - Arnold Palmer Golf Co.

PALMER - Guitars - Palmer Guitar Co.

PALMER - Musical instruments - Tropical Music and Pro Audio

PALMER - Paints—artists' - Palmer Paint Products, Inc.

PALMER - Paper—tissue - Fort Howard Corp.

PALMER - Pens - Palmer Pen Co. Inc.

PALMER - Pretzels - Palmer Candy Co.

PALMER GOLFKART - Motor vehicles - Palmer Industries

PALMER HOME COLLECTION, THE - House furnishings - Lexington Furniture Industries, Inc.

PALMER ICE PAINT - Paints—artists' - Palmer Paint Products, Inc.

PALMER JOHNSON - Ships—sailing vessels - Palmer Johnson Inc.

PALMER PHD - Golfing equipment - Arnold Palmer Golf Co.

PALMER/PLETSCH, THE FIT EXPERTS - Patterns—clothing - Mccall Pattern Co.

PALMER'S - Hair care products - E.T. Browne Drug Co. Inc.

PALMER'S - Plugs - Palmer's Plastics

PALMER'S COCOA BUTTER FORMULA - Skin care products - E.T. Browne Drug Co. Inc.

PALMER'S PEANUT CLUSTER - Candy - Palmer Candy Co.

PALMETTE - Dinnerware—glass ☆ - Nikko Ceramics Inc.

PALMETTO - Fabrics - Greenwood Mills Inc.

PALMETTO - Floor coverings - Mannington Resilient Floors

PALMETTO - Meat products—poultry - Palmetto Pigeon Plant

PALMETTO - Paints - Dozier & Gay Paint Co.

PALMETTO COUNTRY - Wines - Fruit Wines of Florida Inc.

PALMETTO POUSSIN - Meat products—poultry - Palmetto Pigeon Plant

PALMETTO PUBLISHING CO. - Publisher's imprints ☆ - Great Outdoors Publishing Co.

PALMETTO'S - Apparel and accessories ☆ - Hartwell Garment Co.

PALMFAX - Computer peripheral equipment - New Media Corp.

PALMGARD - Sporting goods - Markwort Sporting Goods Co.

PALMICO SOUND - Recording label ☆ - Sugar Hill Records Inc.

PALMIKROM - Epoxy coatings - Palma Inc.

PALMINATE - Pharmaceutical preparations ☆ - Roberts/Hauck Pharmaceuticals Inc.

PALMINATE-FA - Pharmaceutical preparations ☆ - Roberts/Hauck Pharmaceuticals Inc.

PALMIRON - Pharmaceutical preparations ☆ - Roberts/Hauck Pharmaceuticals Inc.

PALMIRON-C - Pharmaceutical preparations ☆ - Roberts/Hauck Pharmaceuticals Inc.

PALMITO - Cookies - Sunshine/Salerno Inc.

PALMLAC - Decals - American Decal

PALMLITE - Flashlights - Zelco Industries, Inc.

PALMMODEM - Computer peripheral equipment - New Media Corp.

PALMOCULAR - Binoculars - Lifetime Optics International, Inc.

PALMOL - Skin care products - Sargeant Acnoid Pharmaceutical Co.

PALMOLIVE - Soap - Colgate-Palmolive Co.

PALMOLIVE ESSENTIAL - Skin care products - Colgate-Palmolive Co.

PALMOLIVE ESSENTIALS - Skin care products - Colgate-Palmolive Co.

PALMOLIVE-GOLD - Soap - Colgate-Palmolive Co.

PALMOLIVE PLUS - Dishwashing compounds - Colgate-Palmolive Co.

PALMOLIVE RAPID SHAVE - Shaving preparations - Colgate-Palmolive Co.

PALMPRINT - Computer software - Palm Computing, Inc.

PALMPRINTER - Calculators ☆ - Canon USA, Inc.

PALMSPRINGS - Apparel and accessories - Palm Springs Golf Co.. Inc.

PALMTERM - Computer software - New Media Corp.

PALMTRONIC - Calculators ☆ - Canon USA, Inc.

PALMYRA - Dinnerware—glass ☆ - Royal China & Porcelain Companies Inc.

PALMYRA - Flatware ☆ - Kirk Stieff Co.

PALMYRA - Floor coverings - Mannington Resilient Floors

PALMYRA - Floor coverings—carpet and rugs - Ashley Commercial Carpets

PALMYRA - Tableware—china ☆ - Lenox, Inc.

PALMYRA GOLD - Flatware ☆ - Kirk Stieff Co.

PALNUT - Fasteners—snap - American Engineer Components

PALO ALTO - Furniture ☆ - Bassett Furniture Industries, Inc.

PALO PINTO - Pharmaceutical preparations - Summa Pharmaceutical Laboratories Inc.

PALO VIEJO - Rum - Joseph E. Seagram & Sons, Inc.

PALODENT - Dental equipment - Alvin Meyer

PALOMA - Figurines - Bey-Berk International

PALOMA - Shoes - Intershoe Inc.

PALOMA - Tableware—china - Durand International

PALOMA - Wines - Frank Sutton & Co.

PALOMA-MENSAJERA DE AMOR - Greeting cards - Joche Davila Studio

PALOMA PICASSO - Perfumes - Cosmair Inc.

PALOMA PICASSO - Stationery - Anne Paloma Ruiz-Picasso

PALOMA PICASSO - Sunglasses - Carrera Eyewear Corp.

PALOMA PICASSO - Wallpaper - Motif Designs, Inc.

PALOMA PICASSO-CARAVAN - Wallpaper - Motif Designs, Inc.

PALOMA PICASSO LA MAISON V.1 - Wallpaper - Capital Carousel Inc.

PALOMA PICASSO LA MAISON V.2 - Wallpaper - Capital Carousel Inc.

PALOMAR - Automotive parts and accessories ☆ - Lancaster Colony Automotive Group

PALOMAR - Floor coverings—carpet and rugs - Couristan Inc.

PALOMAR - Floor coverings—carpet and rugs - Hollytex Carpet Mills Inc.

PALOMAR - Glassware—household ☆ - Lotus Glass Co.

PALOMAR - Water—mineral - Palomar Mountain Spring Water Andice

PALOMAR - Wood products - Georgia-Pacific Corp.

PALOMAR E - Pharmaceutical preparations - Pal Midwest Ltd.

PALOMINO - Boats—motor - Century Boat Co.

PALOMINO - Candy - Pangburn Candy Co.

PALOMINO - Frames—eyeglass ☆ - Universal/Univis Inc.

PALOMINO - Rifles - O.F. Mossberg & Sons, Inc.

PALOMINO - Trailers—travel - Vanguard Industries of Michigan Inc.

PALONAD - Pharmaceutical preparations ☆ - Roberts/Hauck Pharmaceuticals Inc.

PALOOKAVILLE - Clothing - Foster Industries, Inc.

PALOOPS - Candy ☆ - Clark Gum Co.

PALOPAUSE - Pharmaceutical preparations ☆ - Roberts/Hauck Pharmaceuticals Inc.

PALOS VERDES - Floor coverings—carpet and rugs - Cabin Crafts Carpets

PALOS VERDES - Floor coverings—carpet and rugs ☆ - Royalweve Carpet Mills

PALOSEIN - Veterinary pharmaceutical preparations - DDI Pharmaceuticals Inc.

PALOUSE - Condiments - Hall-Mock Productions

PALPIN - Pins—jewelry - ADCO Inc.

PALS - Footwear - Morse Shoe, Inc.

PALS - Pharmaceutical preparations - Glenwood LLC

PALS - Recording label - Rene J. Manley

PALS - Vitamins and nutritional supplements - Bristol-Myers Squibb Co.

PALS - Whey protein-based compound ☆ - New Zealand Milk Products Inc.

PALS 'N PETS - Dolls ☆ - Fun World Inc.

PALS POSITIVE ACTION LEARNING SYSTEMS - Educational materials - Positive Action Learning Systems, Inc.

PALSA - Firearms, accessories, and parts - Palsa Outdoor Products Inc.

PALTA-PHENE - Veterinary medical equipment ☆ - Bingman Laboratories, Inc.

PALTER - Footwear - Samuels Shoe Co.

PALTRAY - Plastic palette tray ☆ - Martin Universal Design Inc.

PALUCH MEMORIALS - Greeting cards - Paluch Memorials, Inc.

PALUDRINE - Pharmaceutical preparations ☆ - Wyeth-Ayerst Laboratories

PALZONE - Garment bags, luggage, tote bags, etc. - Jameslee Corp.

PAM - Apparel—women's - Cinema Etoile

PAM - Bags—cosmetic - Adept Manufacturing Co.

PAM - Electronic equipment - Da-Tel Research Co., Inc.

PAM - Food products - Reckitt & Colman, Inc.

PAM - Medical apparatus - McKesson Home Health Care

PAM - Medical apparatus - Mentor O & O Inc.

PAM - Pan coating - American Home Food Products Inc.

PAM - Telephone answering machines - PhoneMate Inc.

PAM - Underwear and nightwear - Claxton Manufacturing Co. Inc.

PAM HAIR CARE - Dolls - Uneeda Doll Co., Inc.

PAM MARKER - Paper products - Pam Marker Inc.

PAM MARKERS COLLECTIONS, THE - Stationery - C.R. Gibson Co.

PAM TEATIME - Dolls - Uneeda Doll Co., Inc.

PAMA - Floor coverings—carpet and rugs - Concepts International

PAMA - Pharmaceutical preparations ☆ - Vortech Pharmaceuticals

PAMA I - Pharmaceutical preparations ☆ - Vortech Pharmaceuticals

☆ = Now out of production

PAMELA - Clocks - General Time Corp. (Westclox/Seth Thomas Div.)

PAMELA - Cosmetics - Ross Cosmetics Inc.

PAMELA - Dolls ☆ - Worlds of Wonder

PAMELA - Glassware–household - Oneida Ltd.

PAMELA - Yarn ☆ - Lion Brand Yarn Co.

PAMELAS - Bakery products - Pamela's Products, Inc.

PAMELA'S PANSIES - Bedding–linen - Dan River Inc.

PAMELA'S PERFECTLY POPPED POPCORN BALLS - Popcorn - Pamela's Popcorn Co.

PAMELOR - Pharmaceutical preparations - Sandoz Pharmaceuticals Corp.

PAMESA - Tiles–ceramic ☆ - Federal Tile Imports Inc.

PAMFERRELL - Skin care products - Cornrows & Co.

PAMID - Wines - Icarus International Inc.

PAMIDA - Nuts–salted, roasted, cooked, or canned - Pamida, Inc.

PAMINA - Yarn ☆ - William Unger & Co. Inc.

PAMINE - Pharmaceutical preparations - Upjohn Co.

PAMISYL - Pharmaceutical preparations ☆ - Parke-Davis

PAMKIN - Underwear and nightwear - Russell Athletic Div.

PAMLAB - Pharmaceutical preparations - Pan American Laboratories, Inc.

PAMMIE POPPIT - Dolls - Mattel, Inc.

PAMPA - Trays ☆ - Artex-Green Corp. of N.Y.

PAMPAS - Doughs–frozen - Quaker Oats Co.

PAMPAS - Frames–eyeglass - Liberty Optical Manufacturing Co.

PAMPAS - Meat products - Safra International, Inc.

PAMPER - Clocks ☆ - General Time Corp. (Westclox/Seth Thomas Div.)

PAMPER-KAT - Pet products - American Colloid Co.

PAMPER-LITE - Lamps ☆ - Cannon Products Inc.

PAMPER YOURSELF - Flowers, plants, and seeds - Florists' Transworld Delivery, Inc.

PAMPERED BABY - Dolls - Uneeda Doll Co., Inc.

PAMPERED CHEF, THE - Coffee and cocoa - Pampered Chef, Ltd.

PAMPERED FOOT, THE - Pharmaceutical preparations - New Projects Group Ltd.

PAMPERED PARTNER - Computer software - Pampered Chef, Ltd.

PAMPERED PET - Pet products - Eagle Products, Inc.

PAMPERED PET - Pet products - Pampered Pet

PAMPERING PINKS, THE - Nail care products - Schering-Plough Healthcare Products

PAMPERO - Rum - Campari USA Inc.

PAMPERS - Diapers–disposable - Procter & Gamble Co.

PAMPERS BABY-DRY - Diapers–disposable - Procter & Gamble Co.

PAMPERS PHASES - Diapers–disposable - Procter & Gamble Co.

PAMPERS PREMIUM - Diapers–disposable - Procter & Gamble Co.

PAMPERS STRETCH - Diapers–disposable - Procter & Gamble Co.

PAMPERS TRAINERS - Diapers–disposable - Procter & Gamble Co.

PAMPRIN - Pharmaceutical preparations - Chattem Inc.

PAMPRIN-IB - Pharmaceutical preparations - Chattem Inc.

PAN - Accordions - Castiglione Accordion

PAN-90 - Shampoo, etc. - American Pharmacal Laboratories Inc.

PAN-A-LUX - Lighting fixtures - Rambusch Decorating Co.

PAN AM - Food products - Pitsweet Inc.

PAN AM - Hardware - Blaine Window Hardware Inc.

PAN AM - Solar-shade cloth - Pan Am Agri Fabric

PAN AMERICAN ASSISTANCE, INC. - Air transportation–passengers - Pan American Assistance, Inc.

PAN & GRIDDLE GOLD - Shortening - Mallet and Co.

PAN-APPLE CAKES - Food products ☆ - Denny's Inc.

PAN ASIA - Food products - Seafood Packers Representatives Inc.

PAN-ASIA VIDEO - Labels–paper - Pan-Asia Video Inc.

PAN ASIAN - Furniture ☆ - Henredon Furniture Industries Inc.

PAN-ASPHERIC - Ophthalmic goods ☆ - Bausch & Lomb Inc.

PAN BARS - Photographic equipment - Egriment USA, Inc.

PAN C - Vitamins and nutritional supplements - Freeda Vitamins Inc.

PAN-CAKE - Cosmetics - Max Factor & Co.

PAN CARE - Scrapers ☆ - Flambeau Products Corp.

PAN DANDY - Bakery products - Flowers Bakeries (West Virginia Div.)

PAN DANDY - Cleaning preparations ☆ - Benckiser Consumer Products Inc.

PAN DEGREASER - Dishwashing compounds - Analab Inc.

PAN DESIGNS - Statuary - Universal Statuary Corp.

PAN DI PAN - Breads - Roth & Liebmann Inc.

PAN-DUCT - Electrical equipment - Panduit Corp.

PAN DULCE - Bathing suits - Double J of Broward Inc.

PAN-ESTRA - Pharmaceutical preparations ☆ - Pan American Laboratories, Inc.

PAN F PLUS - Film - ILFORD Photo Corp.

PAN FOR ALL REASONS - Kitchen appliances ☆ - Sunbeam-Oster Household Products

PAN FREE - Food products - Beatrice Cos. Inc.

PAN HANDL'RS - Scouring pads - Airwick Industries

PAN INSUL - Insulating materials - Manville/Schuller

PAN INTERNATIONAL - Buttons - Pan Trading Corp.

PAN-ITALIA - Accordions - Pancordion Inc.

PAN-JACK - Communications equipment - Panduit Corp.

PAN-KITS - Pancakes–mixes - Morrison Milling Co.

PAN-KRAFT - Ophthalmic goods - Eye-Kraft Optical, Inc.

PAN-L-BOND - Adhesives and sealants - W.J. Ruscoe Co.

PAN-L-MATCH - Power switching equipment ☆ - Lomar Industries Inc.

PAN LITE - Oils–edible - AHP Subsidiary Holding Corp.

PAN MAGIC - Oils–edible - Minstar Inc.

PAN-MAN-FAN - Musical instrument accessories - Fredrico Percussion

PAN MARINE WORLD - Paints ☆ - Woolsey Marine Industries

PAN MAX - Oils–edible - California Olive Oil Corp.

PAN-O-MITE - Cleaning preparations - Diversey Wyandotte Corp.

PAN-O-PLAY - Exercising equipment - Collins & Aikman Corp.

PAN-O-RAMA - Bakery products - Pan-O-Rama Baking, Inc.

PAN OB - Pharmaceutical preparations ☆ - Pan American Laboratories, Inc.

PAN OCEANIC - Frames–eyeglass - Pan Oceanic Eyewear, Ltd.

PAN-OVALS - Vitamins and nutritional supplements - Vita-Fore Products Co.

PAN PACIFIC - Giftware - Paul Marshall Products L.P.

PAN-PACIFIC - Seafood products–fresh or frozen - Tri-Union International, LLC

PAN PAL - Housewares - Blue Cross Laboratories Inc.

PAN PALS - Cooking equipment–household ☆ - Mirro Corp.

PAN PERFECT - Pizzas–mixes - Mr. Gatti's, Inc.

PAN-REDI - Seafood products–fresh or frozen - Rich-Seapak Corp.

PAN RICH - Gravy - R.T. French Co.

PAN SEAS - Food products ☆ - Ocean Beauty Seafood, Inc.

PAN-STIK - Cosmetics - Max Factor & Co.

PAN STYLE - Food products - Pepperidge Farm Inc.

PAN-T-LETTE - Girdles - Lady Marlene

PAN-TERM - Electrical equipment - Panduit Corp.

PAN-THERA 40 - Vitamins and nutritional supplements - Vita-Fore Products Co.

PAN-TY - Electrical equipment - Panduit Corp.

PAN U.S.A. - Apparel and accessories - Pan Trading Corp.

PAN VIM - Pharmaceutical preparations - Misemer Pharmaceuticals Inc.

PAN-WAY - Electrical equipment - Panduit Corp.

PAN-ZER - Pharmaceutical preparations - Old 97 Co.

PANA - Hats - Cailor SA

PANA-AMERICAN - Hats - American Hat Co. Inc.

PANA-FIT - Hosiery–women's - Mayer/Berkshire Corp.

PANA-PLUS - Exercising equipment ☆ - Fuji America, Inc.

PANA-VUE - Toys - Tyco Toys

PANABARB - Pharmaceutical preparations ☆ - Pan American Laboratories, Inc.

PANABRITE - Electronic equipment - Panasonic Co.

PANACARB - Pharmaceutical preparations - Lannett Co., Inc.

PANACCORDION - Accordions - Pancordion Inc.

PANACEA - Fillings for teeth - Zeza Inc.

PANACEA - Pharmaceutical preparations - Luyties Pharmacal Co.

PANACEA - Room dividers - Globe Business Furniture, Inc.

PANACET - Pharmaceutical preparations - ECR Pharmaceuticals

PANACHE - Bedding–linen - Dan River Inc.

PANACHE - Coffee - Coffee Bean International, Inc.

PANACHE - Coffee - Nestle USA

PANACHE - Fabrics ☆ - Gretchen Bellinger Inc.

PANACHE - Floor coverings–carpet and rugs - Karastan-Bigelow Inc.

PANACHE - Frames–eyeglass ☆ - Universal/Univis Inc.

PANACHE - Markers–felt-tip - Hunt Manufacturing Co.

PANACHE - Rice - Acme Continental Foods Inc.

PANACHE - Shoes - Benjamin Shir Inc.

PANACHE - Wallcoverings ☆ - Decorative Coverings Inc.

PANACHE - Wallpaper - Bill Villetto Designs Inc.

PANACHE - Wines ☆ - Domaine Chandon

PANACHE BY DEMA - Dishes–earthenware - Denby USA Limited

PANACHE COCOAS - Cocoa–powders or mixes - Coffee Bean International, Inc.

PANACHE GOURMET COFFEES - Coffee - Coffee Bean International, Inc.

PANACO INC. - Natural gas - Panaco, Inc.

PANACORT R-P - Health care products ☆ - Ferndale Laboratories, Inc.

PANACROSS - Games - Robert E. Barrett

☆ = Now out of production

PANADERIA MI COLONIA - Breads - Arga's Mexican Food Products, Inc.
PANADERIA MI COLONIA DESDE 1942 - Breads - Arga's Mexican Food Products, Inc.
PANADOL - Analgesics - SmithKline Beecham Consumer Healthcare
PANADOL - Analgesics - Sterling Winthrop Inc.
PANADOL JR. - Analgesics - Sterling Winthrop Inc.
PANADYL - Pharmaceutical preparations - Misemer Pharmaceuticals Inc.
PANAFIL - Pharmaceutical preparations - Rystan Co. Inc.
PANAGEN - Vitamins and nutritional supplements - Great Life Laboratories Inc.
PANAGOGGLE - Safety goggles - H.L. Bouton Co. Inc.
PANAGRAPHICS - Hats - Sportcap Inc.
PANAJA - Sporting goods - Reliable Racing Supply Inc.
PANAKOPITES - Pies–fresh - Coco's Gourmet Mediterranean Foods Inc.
PANAKTIV - Health care products ☆ - Bio-Nutritional Products
PANALENS - Safety eyewear - H.L. Bouton Co. Inc.
PANALGESIC - Analgesics - ECR Pharmaceuticals
PANALGESIC GOLD - Pharmaceutical preparations - ECR Pharmaceuticals
PANALITE - Safety eyewear - H.L. Bouton Co. Inc.
PANALURE - Paper–photographic - Eastman Kodak Co.
PANAM - Recording label - Creav Inc. USA
PANAMA - Cabinets ☆ - Merillat Industries, Inc.
PANAMA - Eyeglasses - Art-Craft Optical Co.
PANAMA - Floor coverings–carpet and rugs ☆ - Trans-Ocean Import Co. Inc.
PANAMA - Frames–eyeglass - U.S. Optical Frame Co.
PANAMA - Thread - Threads USA Div.
PANAMA BAY - Seafood products–fresh or frozen - Darik Enterprises
PANAMA CANAL - Food products - Homestead Ravioli Co.
PANAMA JACK - Suntan lotions - Panama Jack International Inc.
PANAMA JACK SUPER SPORT - Suntan lotions - Panama Jack International Inc.
PANAMA JOE - Games - Tonka Corp.
PANAMANIAN QUEEN - Shrimp–fresh or frozen - Darik Enterprises Inc.
PANAMERICANA - Sunglasses - Optyl Eyewear Fashion International Corp.
PANAMPS - Amplifiers–musical instrument - Pancordion Inc.
PANAPESCA - Seafood products–fresh or frozen - Pescafreeze Seafood Corp.
PANAPRESS - Printing presses - Panavise Products, Inc.
PANAPRINT - Paper–writing - Champion International Corp.
PANARAMIC - Amplifiers–musical instrument - Pancordion Inc.
PANARANA GOLDEN FROG - Apparel and accessories - Panarana Golden Frog
PANARAY - Loudspeaker systems - Bose Corp.
PANARAY - X-ray apparatus - Panoramic Corp.
PANARIA - Floor coverings–tile ☆ - Federal Tile Imports Inc.
PANARINA - Corn–flour or meal - Cuban-Portorican-American Products Inc.
PANASAL - Analgesics - ECR Pharmaceuticals
PANASOL - Pharmaceutical preparations - Seatrace Co.
PANASOL II - Health care products - National Biological Corp.
PANASONIC - Bicycles ☆ - Panasonic Bicycles Midwest
PANASONIC - Electronic equipment - Panasonic Co.
PANASONIC JETWRITER - Typewriters - Morse Typewriter Co. Inc.
PANASONIC REAL 3DO INTERACTIVE MULTIPLAYER - Games - 3do Co.
PANASPEC - Safety eyewear - H.L. Bouton Co. Inc.
PANATECH - Safety eyewear - H.L. Bouton Co. Inc.
PANATELAS - Cigars - House of Windsor Inc.
PANATELLA - Cigarette holders - S.M. Frank & Co. Inc. (Kaywoodie-Yello-Bole-Medico)
PANATELLA - Cigars - General Cigar Co., Inc.
PANATOMIC-X - Film - Eastman Kodak Co.
PANAVAC - Veterinary pharmaceutical preparations - Synbiotics Corp.
PANAVELLE - Crocheted and knitted items - Fab. Industries Inc.
PANAVIEW - Laser systems–medical - Kentek Corp.
PANAVIEW - Safety goggles - H.L. Bouton Co. Inc.
PANAVISE - Telephone apparatus - Panavise Products, Inc.
PANAVISE SLIM-LINE - Telephone apparatus - Panavise Products, Inc.
PANAVISION - Frames–eyeglass - Zylo Ware Corp.
PANAVUE - Doors–storm - Quaker Window Products Co.
PANAVUE - Electronic equipment - GAF Corp.
PANAWARDS - Trophies–metal - Ernest Deffner Inc.
PANAX - Fabrics–cotton - Panax, Ltd.
PANAX GINSENG - Health care products - East Earth Herb Inc.
PANCAKE - Electrical equipment - Wiremold Co.
PANCAKE - Labels–gummed - Brown-Bridge Industries
PANCAKE - Luggage ☆ - Hartmann Luggage Co.
PANCALDI - Footwear–men's - Pancaldi
PANCEBRIN - Pharmaceutical preparations ☆ - Eli Lilly and Co.

PANCET - Pharmaceutical preparations ☆ - Pan American Laboratories, Inc.
PANCHE WRAP - Paper–gift wrap - Stephen Lawrence Co.
PANCHET - Thermometers - French & Pacific Trading Corp.
PANCHO - Frames–eyeglass - Pathway Optical Prods.
PANCHO GARCIA - Cigars - Finck Cigar Co.
PANCHO VILLA - Food products - Pet Inc.
PANCHO'S TACO FACTORY - Salsa - Pancho & Sonny's, Inc.
PANCHROMATIC - Thread ☆ - Perfect Thread Co. Inc.
PANCO - Cooking equipment–commercial - Metal Masters Foodservice Equipment Co., Inc.
PANCO THE HARDER PAN - Pans - Metal Masters Foodservice Equipment Co., Inc.
PANCODER - Computer software - Applied Medical Data, Inc.
PANCOF - Pharmaceutical preparations ☆ - Pan American Laboratories, Inc.
PANCOLOR - Markers–felt-tip - Staedtler, Inc.
PANCORDION - Accordions - Ernest Deffner Inc.
PANCORDION - Accordions - Pancordion Inc.
PANCREAS SUPPORT - Health care products - Healthwatchers System
PANCREASE - Pharmaceutical preparations - McNeil Pharmaceuticals
PANCREATIN 1300 - Vitamins and nutritional supplements - Solaray
PANCREATROPHIN PMG - Vitamins and nutritional supplements - Standard Process Inc.
PANDA - Air purification systems - Quantum Electronics Corp.
PANDA - Archery equipment - Bear Archery Inc.
PANDA - Balls - Tidy International Corp.
PANDA - Candy - Finnfoods Div.
PANDA - Candy - S.L. Kaye Co., Inc.
PANDA - Chili sauce - Lee Kum Kee Inc.
PANDA - Food products - Michigan Soy Products Co. Inc.
PANDA - Food products - Perk-Up, Inc.
PANDA - Food products ☆ - Nasoya Foods, Inc.
PANDA - Footwear - C.O. Lynch Enterprises, Inc.
PANDA - Fruits and vegetables - Price Cold Storage & Packing Co.
PANDA - Health care products - Kwok Shing Import-Export Inc.
PANDA - Kites ☆ - Hi-Flier Manufacturing Co.
PANDA - Licorice - Shaffer, Clark & Co. Inc.
PANDA - Office supplies - Darwell Import Co. Inc.
PANDA - Paints–artists' - Canson-Talens Inc.
PANDA - Paper–toweling - Baer Supply Co. Inc.
PANDA - Pencils ☆ - Panda Inc.
PANDA - Trailers–travel - Leader Enterprises
PANDA - Vitamins and nutritional supplements - O'Brien
PANDA BEARSKIN - Toys–stuffed ☆ - Dakin Inc.
PANDA EXPRESS GOURMET CHINESE FOOD - Food products - Panda Management Co., Inc.
PANDA PAINTER - Puzzles - Lisa Frank, Inc.
PANDA PALS - Flatware - Bonny Products Inc.
PANDA PAWS - Mops ☆ - Baer Supply Co. Inc.
PANDA SANTA - Publisher's imprints - Lisa Frank, Inc.
PANDA-VICTORY - Paints - St. Louis Paint Manufacturing Co.
PANDABOARD - Office supplies - Krapf Business Systems, Inc.
PANDALUX - Paper–writing - Krapf Business Systems, Inc.
PANDAS - Footwear - A.G.S. of Hanover Inc.
PANDAWARE - Computer software - Pandaware
PANDEMONIUM - Frames–eyeglass - May Optical Co. Inc.
PANDEMONIUM - House furnishings - Dan River Inc.
PANDEMONIUM ADVENTURES IN TABLOID WORLD - Toys - M.I.B. Productions, Inc.
PANDEMONIUM POKER - Game machines - Universal Distributing of Nevada, Inc.
PANDIMONIUM - Pizzas–frozen - Chicago Brothers, Inc.
PANDISC - Recording label - Pandisc Records
P&N - Fruits and vegetables - Jakov P. Dulcich & Sons
PANDORA - Apparel–women's ☆ - Chic Lingerie Co.
PANDORA - Sandwiches–prepackaged - Red Robin Inc.
PANDORA - Sweaters - Pandora Sportswear Industries
PANDORA - Toys–stuffed ☆ - Dakin Inc.
PANDORA - Vegetables–canned - Pandora Canning Co.
PANDORA DIRECTIVE, THE - Computer software - Access Software Inc.
PANDORA LTD. - Jewelry - CJC Holdings, Inc.
PANDORA/SYNTHE - Recording label - Pandora/Synthe Records
PANDORABLE - Apparel and accessories ☆ - Pandora Sportswear Industries
PANDORA'S BOX - Computer software ☆ - Rose Studios, Inc.
P&P - Computer software ☆ - Visions 2000 Window Fashions, Inc.
P&S - Paper–book - Central National-Gottesman Inc.
PANDY - Chocolate candy - Shaffer, Clark & Co. Inc.

PANE - Draperies - Maya Romanoff Corp.

PANE D'ALESSANDRO - Bakery products - Gonnella Baking Co.

PANE DI PAOLO - Breads - Broadmoor Baker, Inc.

PANE E VINO DI ACAPULCO - Food products - Golden Whisk Pasta Partners

PANE E VINO DI LUCCA - Food products - Golden Whisk Pasta Partners

PANE E VINO DI SORRENTO - Food products - Golden Whisk Pasta Partners

PANE FRESCO - Bakery products - Gai's Seattle French Baking Co., Inc.

PANE IN THE GLASS - Glass products - Jill Simonson

PANE-LESS - Cleaning preparations ✰ - Elcal Enterprises Ltd.

PANE MARIANO - Breads - Campagna-Turano Bakery Inc.

PANEF - Lubricants - Panef Corp.

PANEL - Clocks ✰ - General Time Corp. (Westclox/Seth Thomas Div.)

PANEL 15 - Siding–insulating - Weyerhaeuser Co.

PANEL 32 - Plywood - Hardel Mutual Plywood Corp.

PANEL ACTION BINGO - Computer software - Fujisankei Communications International Inc.

PANEL BRIGHT - Cleaning preparations - Herbert Stanley Co.

PANEL-CAD - Computer software - Thermwood Corp.

PANEL CARE - Furniture polish and wax - Apple Polishes Inc.

PANEL CLIP - Wood products - Panel Clip Co.

PANEL GLO - Polishing rouge ✰ - Golden Star Inc.

PANEL GRAPE - Glass products - Westmoreland Glass Co.

PANEL GRAPHIC - Wallcoverings - Wallcovering Industries Inc.

PANEL-GRIP - Adhesives and sealants - Columbia Cement Co. Inc.

PANEL JACKET - Door openers–electronic - L.E. Johnson Products Inc.

PANEL-KWIK - Screws ✰ - Black & Decker Corp.

PANEL LIFE - Cleaning preparations - Byrne Plywood Inc.

PANEL-LITE - Safety products - Plastic Safety Systems, Inc.

PANEL LOCK - Adhesives and sealants - Miracle Adhesives

PANEL-LOFT - Pillows - American Fiber Industries Corp.

PANEL-LOK - Envelopes - Tension Envelope Corp.

PANEL MAGIC - Cleaning preparations - Magic American Corp.

PANEL MASTER - Saws–power - Kett Tool Co.

PANEL MATCH - Putties ✰ - Master Products Inc.

PANEL MATE - Floor coverings–carpet and rugs - Tate Access Floors Inc.

PANEL-NU - Cleaning preparations–household - Dap Products Inc.

PANEL PAK - Interior paneling - Stair-Pak Products Co. Inc.

PANEL PINE - Trees–artificial - General Foam Plastics Corp.

PANEL PRO - Adhesives and sealants - ABT Co., Inc.

PANEL QUILT - Window shades - Window Quilt

PANEL ROUTER - Saws–power - Safety Speed Cut Manufacturing Co.

PANEL SOLUTIONS - Fabrics - Gilford Corp.

PANEL SOLUTIONS - Wallpaper - Wall Fashion Inc.

PANEL STONE - Cement ✰ - GAF Corp.

PANEL SURFACES - Furniture–upholstered - Arc-Com Fabrics, Inc.

PANEL SYSTEMS - Office furniture–metal - Marvel Group Inc.

PANEL-TITE - Adhesives and sealants ✰ - Leech Products Inc.

PANEL TRACK - Heating equipment - Embassy Industries Inc.

PANEL TRIMS - Appliques ✰ - Suburbanite Industries

PANEL VIEW - Awnings–metal - Texas Aluminum Industries Inc.

PANEL-VUE - Lighting fixtures - Holophane Corp.

PANEL-WAX - Cleaning product - Wood Kote Products, Inc.

PANEL ZONE - Electrical equipment - Wiremold Co.

PANELAIRE - Wood products - Decor-Aire Inc.

PANELBILD - Wood products - Georgia-Pacific Corp.

PANELBOOK - Electronic transparency - In Focus Systems, Inc.

PANELCARVE - Wood products - Forms + Surfaces Corp.

PANELERA - Wood products - Western Sun Inc.

PANELETTE - Clocks ✰ - General Time Corp. (Westclox/Seth Thomas Div.)

PANELFOLD - Doors - Panelfold Inc.

PANELGROOVE - Siding - Masonite Corp.

PANELLA - Girdles - Formflex Foundations Inc.

PANELLED INFORMALS - Stationery ✰ - Berkshire Stationery Inc.

PANELLI - Footwear - Ideal Specialty Shoe Co.

PANELMATCH - Hardware - Panelmatch

PANELMATE - Desk sets - Safco Products Co.

PANELMATE - Fasteners–hook and eye - Elco Textron Inc.

PANELRAMA - Artists' materials - Jordan Specialty Co.

PANELRAMA - File folders - Angler's Roslyn Group Ltd.

PANELSTORE - Wood products - Plywood & Panels Inc.

PANELTRAC - Drapery hardware ✰ - Kirsch Co.

PANELWALL - Wallpaper - PCI Industries Inc.

PANELWELD - Construction equipment - Dap Products Inc.

PANENERGY - Computer software - Panenergy LNG Sales, Inc.

PANEX - Pharmaceutical preparations - Roberts/Hauck Pharmaceuticals Inc.

PANFIL - Pharmaceutical preparations ✰ - Pan American Laboratories, Inc.

PANFIL G - Pharmaceutical preparations ✰ - Pan American Laboratories, Inc.

PANFISH - Fishing lures - Brown Bear Bait Co.

PANFISH ONLY - Fishing lures - Maurice Sporting Goods, Inc.

PANFISHER - Sporting goods ✰ - Wright & McGill Co.

PANFLEX - Pharmaceutical preparations ✰ - Pan American Laboratories, Inc.

PANFORTE - Food products - Bel Canto Fancy Foods Ltd.

PANFORTE DI MENDOCINO - Confections - Cafe Beaujolais Bakery

PANFORTE DI SIENA CLASICO - Cakes - La Tempesta Bakery Confections, Inc.

PANFREDI - Food products - Panfredi Inc.

PANGAEA - Recording label - I.R.S. Records

PANGAM-15 - Pharmaceutical preparations - Nature's Bounty, Inc.

PANGASINAN - Seafood products–fresh or frozen - Roger Santander Corp.

PANGBURN'S - Candy - Pangburn Candy Co.

PANGBURN'S WESTERN STYLE - Candy - Pangburn Candy Co.

PANGEA - Apparel and accessories - Edan Products, Inc.

PANGEA - Apparel–athletic - Pangea Silkscreen Inc.

PANGEA - Cosmetics - Pangea, Ltd.

PANGO PANGO - Apparel–women's - Pango-Pango Swimwear Corp.

PANGO PEACH - Eyeglasses - Art-Craft Optical Co.

PANHANDLE - Recording label - Lamon Records

PANHANDLE SLIM - Boots - Westmoor Manufacturing Co. Inc.

PANHANDLER - Kitchen appliances ✰ - Hamilton Beach/Proctor-Silex Inc.

PANHEAD - Sandwiches–prepackaged - H-D Michigan, Inc.

PANHEMATIN - Pharmaceutical preparations - Abbott Laboratories

PANHEPRIN - Pharmaceutical preparations ✰ - Abbott Laboratories

PANIC BUTTON - Computer software - First Star Software Inc.

PANIC MASTER - Key rings - Jasco, Inc.

PANICS - Greeting cards - Paramount Cards Inc.

PANICUP - Sporting goods - Panek Precision Products

PANIER - Biscuits - Europa Foods Ltd.

PANIERS - Tiles–ceramic ✰ - Brigitte Pottery

PANINARI - Footwear–women's - Mootsies Tootsies

PANIPLEX - Chemical preparations - Archer Daniels Midland Co.

PANISET - Emulsifiers - Archer Daniels Midland Co.

PANISTAY - Icing stabilizers - Archer Daniels Midland Co.

PANITOL - Pharmaceutical preparations - Wesley Pharmacal Co. Inc.

PANITONE - Pharmaceutical preparations - Wesley Pharmacal Co. Inc.

PANIVON - Pharmaceutical preparations - Wesley Pharmacal Co. Inc.

PANJANDRUM BOOKS - Publisher's imprints - Panjandrum Books

PANJANDRUM INC. - Publisher's imprints - Panjandrum Books

PANJET - Accordions - Pancordion Inc.

PANLEX - Vitamins and nutritional supplements ✰ - Freeda Vitamins Inc.

PANLUTIN - Pharmaceutical preparations ✰ - Pan American Laboratories, Inc.

PANMASTER - Dishwashing compounds - Ecolab Inc.

PANMYCIN - Pharmaceutical preparations - Upjohn Co.

PANNACIO - Sandwiches–prepackaged ✰ - Swissrose International Inc.

PANNAZ - Pharmaceutical preparations - Pan American Laboratories, Inc.

PANNET - Spices and extracts - Europa Foods Ltd.

PANNI - Food products - R.J. Hirt Co.

PANNI - Soups–mixes - Acme Food Specialties Inc.

PANODERM - Skin care products - American Biologics

PANODIA - Electronic equipment ✰ - Leedal Inc.

PANODYNES - Pharmaceutical preparations - Keystone Laboratories Inc.

PANOLA - Sauces - Panola Pepper Corp.

PANOLA PLANTATION - Food products - Panola Pepper Corp.

PANOLI - Food products - Rich Products Corp.

PANOMAKER - Projectors–photographic - Panoram Technologies, Inc.

PANOMAT - Photographic equipment - SP Systems/Saratons

PANONEX - Soil–potting ✰ - Hydroponic Chemical Co. Inc.

PANOPTIC - Lenses–optical - Tele Vue Optics Inc.

PANOPTIK - Ophthalmic goods ✰ - Bausch & Lomb Inc.

PANORA - Wallpaper - Beachwood Wallcoverings

PANORAL - Pharmaceutical preparations ✰ - Eli Lilly and Co.

PANORAMA - Awnings - Alcan Aluminum Corp. Alcan Building Products Div.

PANORAMA - Boxes - U.S. Box Crafts Inc.

PANORAMA - Cabinets - Nutone Inc.

PANORAMA - Compact discs–prerecorded - Federation of Societies for Coatings Technology

PANORAMA - Computer software - International Software Automation, Inc.

PANORAMA - Computer software - Teletrol Systems Inc.

PANORAMA - Floor coverings–carpet and rugs - J and J Industries Inc.

PANORAMA - Floor coverings–carpet and rugs - Tate Access Floors Inc.

PANORAMA - Frames–picture ✰ - Two's Co. Inc.

PANORAMA - Fruits and vegetables - Diamond Fruit Growers

PANORAMA - Furniture ✰ - Stanley Furniture Co. Inc.

✰ = Now out of production

PANORAMA - Greeting cards - Specialty Sales Inc.
PANORAMA - Office supplies - Esselte Corp.
PANORAMA - Patio doors - American Standard Inc.
PANORAMA - Puzzles - Hasbro, Inc.
PANORAMA - Shoes - Interco Inc.
PANORAMA - Window coverings - Jencraft Corp.
PANORAMA DESIGNER FILMS - Polyester film sheets - Solar-Gard International, Inc.
PANORAMAX - Boxes - Noemi Chaparro
PANORAMIC - Aircraft–balloons - Anagram International, Inc.
PANORAMIC - Fireplaces ☆ - Superior Fireplace Co.
PANORAMIC - Paints - KCI Coatings, Inc.
PANORAMIC - Watches - Bulova Corp.
PANORAMIC - Window coverings - Vertical Blind Factory
PANORAMIC-TELESCOPE MOUNT - Telescopes - Tele Vue Optics Inc.
PANOREA - Cigars - Cigar Exchange International, Ltd
PANORGAN - Musical instruments - Pancordion Inc.
PANOSOL II - Medical apparatus - National Biological Corp.
PANOVIR - Pharmaceutical preparations - Vyrex Corp.
PANOXYL - Pharmaceutical preparations - Stiefel Laboratories, Inc.
PANOZ - Motor vehicles–automobiles - Panoz Automotive Development Corp.
PAN!PAN! - Food products - Little Caesar Enterprises, Inc.
PANPAV TP - Pharmaceutical preparations ☆ - Pan American Laboratories, Inc.
PANPECO - Artists' materials ☆ - Riebe's Artist Materials Inc.
PANPRES - Pharmaceutical preparations ☆ - Pan American Laboratories, Inc.
PANREXIN - Pharmaceutical preparations ☆ - Pan American Laboratories, Inc.
PANREXIN MTP - Pharmaceutical preparations ☆ - Pan American Laboratories, Inc.
PANRITIS - Pharmaceutical preparations ☆ - Pan American Laboratories, Inc.
PANRITIS FORTE - Pharmaceutical preparations - Pan American Laboratories, Inc.
PANROMAN - Computer software - Philip B. Payne and Nancy C. Payne
PANSCAN - Computer software - Omega Software Inc.
PANSCOL - Skin care products - Baker Cummins Dermatologicals Inc.
PANSEA - Seafood products–canned or cured - TTT International Enterprises
PANSHAPE MTP - Pharmaceutical preparations ☆ - Pan American Laboratories, Inc.
PANSIES ON CRANBERRY - Giftware - Fenton Art Glass Co.
PANSIZE - Bacon - Dubuque Foods, Inc.
PANSY - Flour–blended ☆ - ConAgra Grain Co.
PANSY - Ophthalmic goods - Styl-Rite Optical Manufacturing Co., Inc.
PANSY-ETTE - Infant product - Pansy Ellen Products, Inc.
PANSY MELODY - Cooking utensils–aluminum ☆ - General Housewares Corp.
PANSY PATCH - Apparel and accessories - Pansy's Patch Inc.
PANSY PETALS - Apparel and accessories - Pansy's Patch Inc.
PANSY PLUS - Apparel and accessories - Pansy's Patch Inc.
PANSY ROSE THRILLER - Flowers, plants, and seeds - John Bodger & Sons, Co.
PANT-A-RAMA - Apparel and accessories - Eckerd Corp.
PANT-HER - Apparel–women's - College-Town Inc.
PANT MATE - Apparel–women's - Cupid Foundations Inc.
PANT-O-MINE - Girdles - Wacoal America Inc.
PANT PLANT - Apparel and accessories - Breton Industries
PANTAC - Cold remedies ☆ - Robinette Inc.
PANTACHAR - Lenses–photographic ☆ - Ercona Corp.
PANTAFLEX - Window shades - Butler Printing and Laminating Co. Inc.
PANTAGES - Furniture ☆ - Tropitone Furniture Co. Inc.
PANTALOON - Medical apparatus - W.L. Gore & Associates, Inc.
PANTARRA - Floor coverings–carpet and rugs - Hollytex Carpet Mills Inc.
PANTASIA - Apparel–women's - Bi-Flex International
PANTASTIC - Bakery products - Procter & Gamble Co.
PANTASTIC - Kitchen appliances ☆ - Hamilton Beach/Proctor-Silex Inc.
PANTASY - Apparel–women's - Wacoal America Inc.
PANTEENS - Apparel–women's - Wacoal America Inc.
PANTEMIC - Pharmaceutical preparations ☆ - Pan American Laboratories, Inc.
PANTENE - Hair care products - Procter & Gamble Co.
PANTER - Cigars - James B. Russell Inc.
PANTER - Cigars and cigarillos - Superior Value Tobacco Co.
PANTERA - Apparel and accessories - Arctco, Inc.
PANTERA - Archery equipment ☆ - Martin Archery Inc.
PANTERA - Bicycles - Ross Bicycles USA, Ltd.
PANTERA - Eyeglasses - Hudson Universal Ltd.
PANTERA - Filters–water ☆ - Sta-Rite Industries Inc.
PANTERA - Motor vehicles–automobiles ☆ - Ford Motor Co.

PANTERA - Posters - Pantera
PANTERA - Toys–stuffed - Dakin Inc.
PANTERIC - Pharmaceutical preparations ☆ - Parke-Davis
PANTEST LA 200 - Pharmaceutical preparations ☆ - Pan American Laboratories, Inc.
PANTEX - Underwear and nightwear - Youthcraft-Charmfit
PANTEX - Wallpaper - Pantasote Inc. (Wallcovering Div.)
PANTEX II - Wallpaper ☆ - Pantasote Inc. (Wallcovering Div.)
PANTEX III - Wallpaper - Pantasote Inc. (Wallcovering Div.)
PANTHENOL - Cosmetics ☆ - Duart Industries Ltd.
PANTHEON - Glassware–household ☆ - Oneida Ltd.
PANTHEON - Publisher's imprints - Random House, Inc.
PANTHEON DESERT - Recording label ☆ - Nationwide Sound Distributors
PANTHER - Amplifiers - HSS Inc.
PANTHER - Apparel–men's - Oxford Industries, Inc.
PANTHER - Archery equipment - High Country American
PANTHER - Bicycles ☆ - Huffy Corp.
PANTHER - Blow torches - Bernzomatic
PANTHER - Boats - Nautical Boats Ltd.
PANTHER - Firearms, accessories, and parts ☆ - Welsh Sporting Goods Corp. (Boyt Div.)
PANTHER - Food products - Veronica Foods Co.
PANTHER - Gloves–rubber - Granet Inc.
PANTHER - Industrial machinery - Chicago Sewing Machine Co., Inc.
PANTHER - Jewelry - Beads & More
PANTHER - Knives–pocket - Compass Industries, Inc.
PANTHER - Lenses–optical - Kelley & Hueber
PANTHER - Skates–roller - Chicago Roller Skate Co.
PANTHER - Sporting goods - Dunlop Maxfli Sports Corp.
PANTHER - Telescopes - Swift Instruments, Inc.
PANTHER - Tires - Alpha Tire Corp.
PANTHER - Tires ☆ - Bridgestone/Firestone, Inc.
PANTHER - Tripods–photographic - Phoenix Corp. of America
PANTHER - Wheelchairs - Snug Seat, Inc.
PANTHER 35 - Lawn mowers - Qualcast USA
PANTHER COMP - Rackets–tennis ☆ - Slazengers
PANTHER CREEK - Carports - O.D. Funk Co.
PANTHER FASTRAK - Computer peripheral equipment - Prepress Solutions, Inc.
PANTHER LITTER - Pet products - Zorbite Corp.
PANTHER MARTINS - Fishing lures - Harrison-Hoge Industries Inc.
PANTHER PLAYER - Rackets–tennis - Slazengers
PANTHER POWER - Rackets–tennis - Slazengers
PANTHER PRECISION - Rackets–tennis - Slazengers
PANTHER PRO - Rackets–tennis ☆ - Slazengers
PANTHER PRO JUNIOR - Rackets–tennis ☆ - Slazengers
PANTHER VTS - Guns - Indian Creek Design, Inc.
PANTHERELLA - Hosiery–men's ☆ - S.L. Gilbert Co.
PANTHERMAL - Cosmetics - P-Ryton Corp.
PANTHERS - Footwear - Polo International Inc.
PANTHO-F - Pharmaceutical preparations ☆ - Rhone-Poulenc Rorer Pharmaceuticals Inc.
PANTHO-FOAM - Pharmaceutical preparations ☆ - Rhone-Poulenc Rorer Pharmaceuticals Inc.
PANTHOCAL - Health care products - Halsey Drug Co. Inc.
PANTHODERM - Pharmaceutical preparations - Jones Medical Industries, Inc. (Medical Div.)
PANTHODERM - Pharmaceutical preparations - Rhone-Poulenc Rorer Pharmaceuticals Inc.
PANTHOLIN - Pharmaceutical preparations - Eli Lilly and Co.
PANTHOR - Toys - Mattel, Inc.
PANTI-LEGS - Hosiery–women's - Glen Raven Mills Inc.
PANTI-SLIP - Apparel–women's ☆ - Olga Co.
PANTIERS - Flower and plant pot covers - Catherine J. Burns
PANTIQUE - Apparel–men's - Oxxford Clothes Inc.
PANTLESS PANTYHOSE - Panty hose - Aire Hosiery Inc.
PANTO - Ophthalmic goods - Rozin Optical Export Corp.
PANTOCRIN - Vitamins and nutritional supplements - Ferguson Health and Nutrition, Inc.
PANTOCRIN-F - Pharmaceutical preparations - G.O. Spanner Inc.
PANTOGRAPHS - Wood products ☆ - Anco Wood Specialties Inc.
PANTOLOGEN - Hair care products - St. Ives Laboratories, Inc.
PANTON - Pharmaceutical preparations ☆ - Pan American Laboratories, Inc.
PANTON - Recording label ☆ - Apon Record Co., Inc.
PANTON - Wallpaper - Carlton-Metro Wallcoverings
PANTONE - Apparel and accessories - Pantone, Inc.

☆ = Now out of production

PANTONE - Electronic equipment - Letraset USA Inc.
PANTONE COLORDRIVE - Computer software - Pantone, Inc.
PANTONE COLORREADY - Computer software - Pantone, Inc.
PANTONE COLORWEB PRO - Computer software - Pantone, Inc.
PANTONE CONSUMER COLOR PREFERENCE STUDY - Publisher's imprints - Pantone, Inc.
PANTONE HEXACHROME - Inks - Pantone, Inc.
PANTONE HEXWRENCH - Computer software - Pantone, Inc.
PANTONE OFFICECOLOR ASSISTANT - Computer software - Pantone, Inc.
PANTOPON - Pharmaceutical preparations - Roche Laboratories
PANTOTHEX - Pharmaceutical preparations - Enzyme Process Co. Inc.
PANTRESSE - Hair care products - Pantresse Inc.
PANTRI RESERVE - Fruits–dried - Vacu-Dry Co.
PANTRIN - Pharmaceutical preparations ☆ - Pan American Laboratories, Inc.
PANTRON - Vitamins and nutritional supplements ☆ - Vita-Fore Products Co.
PANTROPIC - Apparel and accessories - Pantropic
PANTRY - Cookies - Nabisco Foods Group
PANTRY - Food products - Mountain States Bean Co.
PANTRY - Wallpaper ☆ - Decorative Coverings Inc.
PANTRY FOODS - Breads - H.E. Butt Grocery Co.
PANTRY FRY - Food products - Golden Dipt Co.
PANTRY HERITAGE - Food products ☆ - Tripp Bakers Inc.
PANTRY HOUSE - Fruit drinks–bottled or canned - Federated Foods Inc.
PANTRY PAL - Food products - Pantry Pal, Inc.
PANTRY PICKINS - Poultry product - Pantry Inc.
PANTRY POPS - Housewares - Gemco Ware, Inc.
PANTRY PRIDE - Food products - Sunstar Foods Inc.
PANTRY PRINTS - Fabrics–tapestry - Comark Wallcoverings
PANTS KING, THE - Apparel–men's - J. Schoeneman Inc.
PANTS 'R US - Apparel–women's - Pants 'R Us
PANTS REMOVER - Perfumes - Thomas Adams
PANTSKIN - Foundation garments–women's - Merit Foundations Inc.
PANTSLINER, THE - Panty hose - Olga Co.
PANTSLIP - Fabrics - Dan River Inc.
PANTSUIT - Colognes ☆ - Avon Products, Inc.
PANTY-TOO - Hosiery ☆ - Vision Hosiery
PANTYGRAMS - Apparel–women's - Newton Manufacturing Corp.
PANTYHOSE PARTNER - Girdles - Olga Co.
PANTYHOSE SAVERS - Chemical preparations - Dexus Laboratories, Inc.
PANTZIPS - Zippers - YKK USA Inc.
PANULI - Candy - Grandma Wheaton
PANWARFIN - Pharmaceutical preparations - Abbott Laboratories
PANWICHES - Sandwiches–prepackaged - Pizza Hut Inc.
PANZ - Tiles–ceiling - United States Gypsum Co.
PANZER ARMEE AFRIKA - Games - Avalon Hill Game Co.
PANZER COMMAND - Games - Avalon Hill Game Co.
PANZER LEADER - Games - Avalon Hill Game Co.
PANZERBLITZ - Games - Avalon Hill Game Co.
PANZERGRUPPE GUDERIAN - Games - Avalon Hill Game Co.
PANZERJAGD - Games ☆ - Avalon Hill Game Co.
PANZERKRIEG - Games ☆ - Avalon Hill Game Co.
PANZERS EAST - Games ☆ - Avalon Hill Game Co.
PANZYME - Pharmaceutical preparations ☆ - Hyrex Pharmaceuticals
PAOLA - Lenses–optical - National Optical Co.
PAOLA - Tiles–ceramic - Federal Tile Imports Inc.
PAOLE - Tiles–terrazzo - Imperial Tile and Marble Corp.
PAOLI - Furniture - Paoli, Inc.
PAOLINI COLLECTION - Footwear–women's - Verden Imports Co. Ltd.
PAOLO - Watches ☆ - Nicolet International Inc.
PAOLO CELLINI COLLECTION - Apparel and accessories ☆ - Edison Brothers Stores, Inc.
PAOLO CORDERO - Wines - Wine World Inc.
PAOLO DESIGNED BY PAOLO GUCCI - Sunglasses - Status Eyes Ltd.
PAOLO DILORENZO - Eyeglasses - Hudson Universal Ltd.
PAOLO GUCCI - Watches ☆ - Nicolet International Inc.
PAOLO SOPRANI - Accordions - Castiglione Accordion
PAOLUCCI - Wines ☆ - Frank Sutton & Co.
PAP - Vitamins and nutritional supplements - Kroeger Herb Products Co. Inc.
PAPA ALDO'S - Prepared foods - Papa Aldo's International, Inc.
PAPA ALDO'S TAKE & BAKE - Food products - Papa Aldo's International, Inc.
PAPA & JUNIOR - Chocolate candy - Superior Fruit & Confections
PAPA CRISTO'S - Baked goods - C & K Importing Co., Inc.
PAPA C'S RUM PUNCH - Beverages–alcohol - Cephus Blending Corp.
PAPA DASH - Salt - Alberto-Culver Co.
PAPA GENTLY - Toys ☆ - Playskool, Inc.

PAPA GEPPETTO'S SON - Dolls - Eden Toys, Inc.
PAPA GWORK - Toys–stuffed - Russ Berrie and Co., Inc.
PAPA HEMINGWAY - Eyeglasses - Hemingway, Ltd.
PAPA JAVA - Coffee - P.J.'s USA, Inc.
PAPA JOE'S - Pizzas–frozen - Armato's Pizza Co.
PAPA JOE'S - Sauces ☆ - Barzi Foods
PAPA JOHN'S - Pizzas–mixes - Papa John's International, Inc.
PAPA LEDO'S - Pizzas–mixes - Wine & Schulz Inc.
PAPA LOUIE'S - Food products ☆ - Stilwell Foods
PAPA LYNN - Food products - Wilson Products Co. Inc.
PAPA MILANO - Pasta and sauces - Papa Milano, Inc.
PAPA MONET - Apparel–women's - St. Tropez Ltd.
PAPA PATTYS - Food products - Quality Meats and Seafood Inc.
PAPA POLINO - Food products - VanEerden Distribution Co.
PAPA PRIMO - Pizzas–frozen - Special Tees
PAPA ROMANO'S - Food products - Papa Romano's, Inc.
PAPACON - Pharmaceutical preparations - Consolidated Midland Corp.
PAPAGAYO - Beverages–alcohol - Parrott & Co.
PAPAGAYO - Tools–hand-operated - Barco Industries, Inc.
PAPAGNI VINEYARDS - Wines - Papagni Vineyards
PAPANICHOLAS - Coffee - Napco Inc.
PAPANSIN - Pharmaceutical preparations - Consolidated Midland Corp.
PAPANTONIOU - Food products - Golden Dipt Co.
PAPARAZZI - Cases–camera ☆ - Innovative Manufacturing Corp.
PAPARAZZI - Cosmetics - Max Factor & Co.
PAPARAZZI - Frames–eyeglass - Zylo Ware Corp.
PAPARELLA - Food products - Bari Importing Corp.
PAPA'S - Food products - Ore-Ida Foods, Inc.
PAPA'S PET - Dolls ☆ - Effanbee Doll Corp.
PAPA'S PIZZA TO-GO FRESH BAKED - Pizzas–frozen - Papa's Pizza To-Go, Inc.
PAPA'S PRIDE - Vegetables–frozen - Crosetti Frozen Foods Inc.
PAPA'S SAUCE - Barbecue sauce - Papa's Sauces, Inc.
PAPA'S VINEYARD - Wines - Alfred B. Menegus/Papa's Vineyard
PAPASE - Pharmaceutical preparations ☆ - Parke-Davis
PAPASTRATOS - Cigarettes - G.A. Georgopulo & Co. Inc.
PAPATOLA'S PASTA SAUCE - Food products - Papatola's Kitchen, Inc.
PAPAVERINE - Pharmaceutical preparations - United Research Laboratories, Inc.
PAPAYA - Apparel and accessories - A & H Sportswear Co., Inc.
PAPAYA DELITE - Juices ☆ - Snapple Beverage Corp.
PAPAYA EASE - Hair care products - Dena Corp.
PAPAYA PARADISE - Juices - Juice Club, Inc.
PAPAYA PLUS - Shampoos - St. Ives Laboratories, Inc.
PAPCO - Business cards - Papercraft Inc.
PAPCO - Combs ☆ - Paul A. Price Co. Inc.
PAPCO - Electronic equipment - Rothenberger USA, Inc.
PAPCO - Seafood products–fresh or frozen - Hallmark Fisheries
PAPE VERLAG - Recording label - Organ Literature Foundation
PAPENOL - Pharmaceutical preparations - Afassco
PAPER - Computer software - Paper Software Inc.
PAPER ACE - Apparel and accessories - Paper Ace, Inc.
PAPER ADVENTURES - Stationery - Leader Cards Inc.
PAPER ART - Candles - James River Paper Co.
PAPER ART - Decorations - Creative Expressions Group
PAPER ARTS MILL & STUDIO - Paper mills - C. Grey
PAPER BACK - Cardboard containers - Form Farm Inc.
PAPER BLEND - Correction fluid - Eaton Allen Ko-Rec-Type Corp.
PAPER BUSH - Housewares - Vantage Tool Inc.
PAPER CAPERS - Paper - Plaid Enterprises, Inc.
PAPER CAPERS - Puzzles - Hasbro, Inc.
PAPER CHASE - Stationery - Chase
PAPER CHINA - Plates–paper ☆ - Creative Expressions Group
PAPER CLASSICS - Stationery ☆ - Scentex Inc.
PAPER CREME - Skin care products - Liquid Paper Corp.
PAPER DECORS - Novelty items–paper ☆ - Creative Expressions Group
PAPER DOLL - Frames–eyeglass ☆ - Universal/Univis Inc.
PAPER EASY - Computer software - Pro Technologies, Inc.
PAPER-ECTH - Chemical preparations - Michele Hester
PAPER ELEGANCE - Paper party goods ☆ - American Greetings Corp.
PAPER FACES - Dolls - Kira Pratt Davis
PAPER FIX - Abrasive products - Conros Corp.
PAPER GOLF - Board game - MGtee, Inc.
PAPER KEEPERS - Office supplies ☆ - U.S. Fiberglass Inc.
PAPER KEYBOARD - Computer software - Datacap, Inc.
PAPER-KING - Office supplies - McGill Inc.

☆ = Now out of production

PAPER LANTERN - Greeting cards - Lindsay Whiting
PAPER LEAGUE - Games - Anthony D. Tidwell
PAPER LINEN - Plates–paper ☆ - Creative Expressions Group
PAPER LUXURY - Paper party goods ☆ - American Greetings Corp.
PAPER MAID - See SCI
PAPER MATE - Pens - Paper Mate Co.
PAPER MATE ANTIQUE - Pens - Paper Mate Co.
PAPER MATE CLASSIC - Pens ☆ - Paper Mate Co.
PAPER MATE GOLD - Pens ☆ - Paper Mate Co.
PAPER MATE LACQUER - Pens ☆ - Paper Mate Co.
PAPER MILL - Giftware - Faroy Sales
PAPER MILL CHANNEL, THE - Educational materials - Industrial Exchange Corp.
PAPER MILL, THE - Paper ☆ - Shiva Inc.
PAPER MOSIACS - Artists' materials - Plaid Enterprises, Inc.
PAPER PAK - Computer software - Iambic Software
PAPER-PAK - Paper - Paper-Pak Products, Inc.
PAPER PATCH, THE - Paper products - Shauna Shelby
PAPER PEDDLER - Postcards - Paper Peddler Inc.
PAPER PIC - Cosmetics ☆ - Marianna Imports, Inc.
PAPER PITCH - Office supplies - Safco Products Co.
PAPER PLANES, INC. - Publisher's imprints - W. Christopher Musselwhite
PAPER PLEASURES - Wallpaper - Warner Co.
PAPER PORT - Photo albums - K & M Co.
PAPER POWER - Stationery - Norcross Inc.
PAPER QUARRY - Wallpaper - Capital Carousel Inc.
PAPER RAINBOW - Greeting cards - Paramount Cards Inc.
PAPER RAINBOW PRESS - Greeting cards - Paramount Cards Inc.
PAPER RITER - Pens - La-Co Industries, Inc.
PAPER SAFE - Paper cutters - Dahle USA
PAPER SAFE - Safes ☆ - Meilink Safe Co.
PAPER SCRAPER - Scrapers - William Zinsser & Co. Inc.
PAPER SCULPTURE - Greeting cards ☆ - MonkeyPuzzle Inc.
PAPER SHAPERS - Scissors–hand-operated - Armada Art Inc.
PAPER SHAPES - Stationery - Impact International Inc.
PAPER SKATER - Pens - Itoya of America, Ltd.
PAPER SNIPPING DESIGNS - Decals and transfers - Christy Crafts, Inc.
PAPER STAND, THE - Electronic equipment - Screen Works
PAPER STATION, THE - Paper and paper products - Paper Direct, Inc.
PAPER TAPER - Tools–hand-operated - Minnesota Mining & Manufacturing Co.
PAPER TIGER - Scrapers - William Zinsser & Co. Inc.
PAPER TRAIL - Computer software - Wextech Systems, Inc.
PAPER TREASURES - Paper - ANW-Crestwood Paper Co.
PAPER TREASURES - Stationery - Willmann Paper Co., Inc.
PAPER TUNER - Archery equipment - Saunders Archery Co.
PAPER VISION PRESS - Publisher's imprints - Western Tanager Press
PAPER VU - Office supplies - Wallace Computer Services, Inc.
PAPER WARE - Computer software - Xerox Corp.
PAPER WEIGHT COLLECTIBLES - Giftware - Dynasty Import Co.
PAPER WELDER - Paper clips - Paper Welder Inc.
PAPER WHITE LTD. - Apparel and accessories - Paper White Ltd.
PAPER WORKS - Paneling - Georgia-Pacific Corp.
PAPER WORKS COLLECTION, THE - Wainscotting - Georgia-Pacific Corp.
PAPERA RANCH - Wines - Deloach Vineyards
PAPERBACK BOOKSMITH - Book stores - Brookline Booksmith
PAPERBOY - Video games - Atari Games Corp.
PAPERCLAY - Clay–modeling - Creative Paperclay Co., Inc.
PAPERCRAFT - Paper–gift wrap - Papercraft Corp.
PAPERCRAFT - Stationery - Papercraft Inc.
PAPERCREME - Skin care products - Lee Products Co.
PAPERDATE - Calendars ☆ - Ad-a-Day Co. Inc.
PAPERDEX - Printed office forms - Willowtree Press Inc.
PAPERDISK - Computer software - Cobblestone Software, Inc.
PAPERGRIPPER - Office supplies - Paper Direct, Inc.
PAPERKIT - Paper - Famport Co.
PAPERKIT - Paper - Paper Direct, Inc.
PAPERLESS MANAGEMENT - Computer software - Park City Group, Inc.
PAPERLINK - Computer software - Delta Computer Systems, Inc.
PAPERLUX - Paper–tissue - Fort Howard Corp.
PAPERMINT - Fabrics–tapestry ☆ - Coloroll Inc.
PAPERMOON - Wallpaper ☆ - Tattersalls
PAPEROID - Envelopes - Alvah Bushnell Co.
PAPEROLLER - Craft supplies - Rose Art Industries, Inc.
PAPEROPOLIS - Computer software - Virgin Sound and Vision, Inc.
PAPEROUTE - Computer peripheral equipment - Paperwise Inc.

PAPERPACKER - Computer peripheral equipment ☆ - QMS, Inc.
PAPERPAINT - Paints - Tulip Productions
PAPERPATH - Computer software - Medico, Inc.
PAPERPLUS - Computer peripheral equipment - QMS, Inc.
PAPERPORT - Computer hardware - Visioneer Communications, Inc.
PAPERROCKET - Computer software - Unisource Brands, Inc.
PAPERS OF LONDON - Wallpaper - Christopher Hyland
PAPERSAFE - Containers–metal - Steel City Corp.
PAPERSELECTOR - Paper swatches - Paper Direct, Inc.
PAPERSILK COLLECTION, THE - Paper–gift wrap - Marketplace America Inc.
PAPERSTAND - Electronic equipment - Screen Works
PAPERSTAR - Paper–book - Putnam Berkley Group, Inc.
PAPERTAMER - File folders - Dennison National Co.
PAPERULERS - Paper products - B & J Supply, Inc.
PAPERVIDEOS - Greeting cards - Michael Patrick Robbins
PAPERVIEW - Binoculars - Bnox, Inc.
PAPERWEIGHT - Paper - Paper Co.
PAPERWHITE PRESS, THE - Stationery - Kate Mahoney Curtsinger
PAPERWORKS - Computer software - Xerox Corp.
PAPETTE PARADISE - Floor coverings–carpet and rugs ☆ - Regal Rugs Inc.
PAPETTI'S - Food products - Papetti's Hygrade Egg Products, Inc.
PAPETTI'S SCRAMBLE - Egg substitutes - Papetti's Hygrade Egg Products, Inc.
PAPHEN - Resins–synthetic - Phenoxy Associates
PAPI - Underwear and nightwear - Tugaloo River Boxer Co.
PAPI TIME - Popcorn - Rodrigo International Commodities, Inc.
PAPIER GLACE - Floor coverings–carpet and rugs ☆ - Regal Rugs Inc.
PAPIER POTPOURRI - Wallcoverings - Authentic Reproductions
PAPIER POUDRE - Cosmetics - Caswell-Massey Co. Ltd.
PAPILLADRIN - Pharmaceutical preparations - Crazy Horse International
PAPILLON - Calendars - Papillon Airways, Inc.
PAPILLON - Cheese - Swissrose International Inc.
PAPILLON - Chimes - J.W. Stannard Co.
PAPILLON - Christmas tree ornaments - Cracker Box Inc.
PAPILLON - Dinnerware–glass ☆ - Nikko Ceramics Inc.
PAPILLON - Floor coverings–carpet and rugs - Helios Carpets
PAPILLON - Furniture ☆ - Bassett Furniture Industries, Inc.
PAPILLON - Hosiery - Sara Lee Corp.
PAPILLON - Seafood products–fresh or frozen ☆ - J.F. Clarke Corp.
PAPILLON - Wallpaper - Academy Handprints Ltd.
PAPILLON INTERNATIONAL - Decals and transfers - Papillion International Giftware Inc.
PAPILLOTE 2000 - Leather–parchment - Papillote Co.
PAPILLOTE 2000 COOKING TUBE - Cooking equipment–household - Papillote Co.
PAPILLOTE 2000 OVEN COOKING PAPER - Paper - Papillote Co.
PAPILLOTE 2000 PAPER OVEN - Paper - Papillote Co.
PAPILON - Umbrellas ☆ - Sunesta Products
PAPO PARROT - Puppets - Dakin Inc.
PAPOOCH - Pet products - Sanjo, Inc.
PAPOOSE - Guitars - Tacoma Guitar Co., Inc.
PAPOOSE - Vacuum cleaners and accessories–commercial - Advance Machine Co.
PAPOOSE CABOOSE - Bicycle parts and accessories - S. Winchester's Originals, Inc.
PAPP KIDS - Apparel–children's - Holden Development & Cos. Inc.
PAPPA G'S - Food products - A.M. Gilardi and Sons, Inc.
PAPPA MONET - Apparel–women's - St. Tropez Ltd.
PAPPAGALLO - Apparel and accessories - Pappagallo Inc.
PAPPAGALLO - Footwear - Nine West Group Inc.
PAPPALO'S - Pizzas–frozen - Pillsbury Co.
PAPPAS - Food products - Clement Pappas and Co.
PAPPAS BALKAN - Salad dressings–bottled - Ellen Pappas Balfour
PAPPILLON - Lenses–optical - Ditto Industries Inc.
PAPPY - Eyeglasses - Art-Craft Optical Co.
PAPPYLAND - Video production - Craftsman & Scribes, Inc.
P.A.P.R. - Respirators ☆ - Glendale Protective Technologies Inc.
PAPRIKAS - Doughs–frozen - Paprikas Weiss Importer
PAPRUS - Peroxides–inorganic - Keyes Fibre Co.
PAP'S - Sausages - Pap's Louisiana Cuisine, Inc.
PAQ - Paints - Perry & Derrick Co.
PAQ - Paints ☆ - Foy-Johnston Inc.
PAQEL - Fibers–synthetic - Monsanto Polymer Products
PAQRAT - Audio equipment - Rane Corp.

PAQUETAGE - Handbags, wallets, and small leather goods - Christiane Paine Accessories

PAR - Bakery products - Clements Food Co. Inc.

PAR - Chemical preparations - Kmco, Inc.

PAR - Computer software - Par Business Systems, Inc.

PAR - Fabric softeners - Safeway Stores Inc.

PAR - Frames–eyeglass - Liberty Optical Manufacturing Co.

PAR - Golfing equipment - Brandell Products, Inc.

PAR - Lens coatings - Photran Corp.

PAR - Marine pumps, boat fenders - ITT Jabsco

P.A.R. - Waterproofing compounds ☆ - Dap Products Inc.

PAR 3 - Floor coverings–carpet and rugs ☆ - Porter Carpet Mills Inc.

PAR 3 - Golfing equipment - Voit Corp.

PAR 5 - Apparel–men's - Drummond Knitwear Ltd.

PAR 5 - Pharmaceutical preparations ☆ - Parmed Pharmaceuticals, Inc.

PAR 6 - Golfing equipment - Par 6 Originals, Inc.

PAR 62 - Floor coverings–carpet and rugs ☆ - Patcraft Mills Inc.

PAR 500 - Pharmaceutical preparations ☆ - Parmed Pharmaceuticals, Inc.

PAR AIDE - Golfing equipment - Western Golf Inc.

PAR-AK - Breads - Venus Wafers, Inc.

PAR AVION - Apparel and accessories ☆ - Edison Brothers Stores, Inc.

PAR B & C - Pharmaceutical preparations - Parmed Pharmaceuticals, Inc.

PAR-B-Q - Barbecue and grill accessories - Pbq Designs, Inc.

PAR-BEAM-LITE - Swivelier Co. Inc.

PAR BUSTER - Golfing equipment - Plawood Mormac Corp.

PAR-CHEM - Waste-system chemical ☆ - ITT Jabsco

PAR CLASSICS - Golfing equipment - Green Eagle, Inc.

PAR-CREAM - Pharmaceutical preparations - Parmed Pharmaceuticals, Inc.

PAR-DECON - Pharmaceutical preparations - Par Pharmaceutical Inc.

PAR DRIX - Pharmaceutical preparations ☆ - Parmed Pharmaceuticals, Inc.

PAR E - Pharmaceutical preparations - Parmed Pharmaceuticals, Inc.

PAR-ESTRONE - Pharmaceutical preparations ☆ - Parmed Pharmaceuticals, Inc.

PAR-ETH - Pharmaceutical preparations ☆ - Par Pharmaceutical Inc.

PAR EX - Computer software - Micro Insurance Software, Inc.

PAR EX - Fertilizers - Vigoro Consumer & Professional Products Group

PAR EX - Fertilizers - Vigoro Industries, Inc.

PAR EXCELLENCE - Computer software - Joseph Dattilo

PAR EXCELLENCE - Fabrics ☆ - Gretchen Bellinger Inc.

PAR EXCELLENCE - Frames–eyeglass - Liberty Optical Manufacturing Co.

PAR-EXCELLENCE - Health care products - Brukvin Imports

PAR-F - Pharmaceutical preparations - Pharmics Inc.

PAR V - Floor coverings–carpet and rugs - Quaker Inc.

PAR-FLO - Fungicides - Amvac Chemical Corp.

PAR FOR THE COURSE - Calendars ☆ - American Greetings Corp.

PAR FOUR - Apparel–men's - J.C. Penney Co., Inc.

PAR-KEN - Food products ☆ - Parman-Kendall Corp.

PAR KEYHOLE - Frames–eyeglass - Liberty Optical Manufacturing Co.

PAR-LI-CIN - Pharmaceutical preparations - Lanpar Co.

PAR-LINE - Hats ☆ - Imperial Headwear Inc.

PAR-LITE - Frames–eyeglass - Liberty Optical Manufacturing Co.

PAR-MAG - Pharmaceutical preparations - Parmed Pharmaceuticals, Inc.

PAR-MATE - Pumps–water - ITT Jabsco

PAR-MAX - Pumps–water - ITT Jabsco

PAR-MED - Pharmaceutical preparations - Parmed Pharmaceuticals, Inc.

PAR-NATAL - Pharmaceutical preparations - Parmed Pharmaceuticals, Inc.

PAR-NINE - Frames–eyeglass - Liberty Optical Manufacturing Co.

PAR-O-PHYLLINE - Pharmaceutical preparations - Parmed Pharmaceuticals, Inc.

PAR-PH - Pharmaceutical preparations - Parmed Pharmaceuticals, Inc.

PAR PLUS - Sporting goods - Chesal Golf

PAR POWER - Lighting fixtures ☆ - Nutone Inc.

PAR PRONE - Apparel and accessories - Jeffrey J. Roberts

PAR-PROTEIN - Pharmaceutical preparations ☆ - Parmed Pharmaceuticals, Inc.

PAR PROTOTANK - Holding tank ☆ - ITT Jabsco

PAR QUEST - Sporting goods - Banner Strategies

PAR STOR - Storage units - Amcart Inc.

PAR-STRESS - Pharmaceutical preparations - Parmed Pharmaceuticals, Inc.

PAR-SUPP - Pharmaceutical preparations - Parmed Pharmaceuticals, Inc.

PAR-T - Recording label - Master-Trak Sound Recorders

PAR-T-AID - Beverages - Bev-Rich Inc.

PAR T JEL - Beverages–alcohol - Jel-Master, Inc.

PAR-T-PAK - Beverages–carbonated - Royal Crown Cola Co.

PAR TECH - Golfing equipment - Par Tech Golf, Inc.

PAR TEE - Golf wear - Lisa Alderete Handy

PAR-TI PUPS - Meat products - R.L. Ziegler Co. Inc.

PAR TOGS - Underwear and nightwear - Gerber Products Co.

PAR-UP - Pharmaceutical preparations - Lanpar Co.

PAR VAG - Pharmaceutical preparations - Parmed Pharmaceuticals, Inc.

PAR VITES - Pharmaceutical preparations - Parmed Pharmaceuticals, Inc.

PAR-X - Breads - Dupras Baking Co.

PARA - Rifles - Fie Corp.

PARA-BABE - Tofu ☆ - Paraeusal Co.

PARA-CHEM - Adhesives and sealants - Para-Chem Southern, Inc. (Parabond Adhesives Division)

PARA-DICHLOROBENZENE - Pharmaceutical preparations ☆ - Humco

PARA-DOLLS - Greeting cards - Paramount Cards Inc.

PARA DYNAMICS - Antennas - Valor Enterprises, Inc.

PARA FLOOR - Paints - Paragon Paint & Varnish Corp.

PARA FORM - Pet products - Aquatronics-Filtronics

PARA-HIST - Cold remedies - Pharmics Inc.

PARA-HIST HD - Cold remedies - Pharmics Inc.

PARA-KITE - Kites - Hi-Flier Manufacturing Co.

PARA/METRIC - Sporting goods - Outdoor Technologies Group

PARA-MOUNT - Frames–eyeglass - Hudson Optical Corp.

PARA-PAK - Medical apparatus - Meridian Diagnostics, Inc.

PARA PALL P - Pallets–metal - Paragon Packaging Products Inc.

PARA-PROTECT FACTORS - Vitamins and nutritional supplements - Consac Industries, Inc.

PARA-SONIC - Pianos - Baldwin Piano & Organ Co.

PARA-THERM - Thread ☆ - Eddington Thread Manufacturing Co.

PARA-TROOP - Thread - Threads USA Div.

PARA-VENT - Air purification systems - United Air Specialists, Inc.

PARA-WOOD - Varnishes - Kwal-Howells Inc.

PARABAL - Hardware - Woodward-Wanger Co.

PARABATH - Health care products ☆ - Thermo-Electric Co.

PARABLE - Computer software - Parable Corp.

PARABOARD - Office supplies ☆ - Charvoz

PARABODY - Exercising equipment - Parabody, Inc.

PARABODY STRENGTH BUILDING GEAR - Exercising equipment - Parabody, Inc.

PARABOLA STORYTIME, THE - Recording label - Society for the Study of Myth and Tradition Inc.

PARABOLAR - Ophthalmic apparatus - Whitby Pharmaceuticals, Inc.

PARABOLETTE - Ophthalmic apparatus - Whitby Pharmaceuticals, Inc.

PARABOLITE - Lighting fixtures - Hubbell Lighting, Inc. (Lighting Div.)

PARABOLIX 100 - Cleaning preparations - Merix Chemical Co.

PARABOND - Adhesives and sealants - Para-Chem Southern, Inc. (Parabond Adhesives Division)

PARABONE - Milking machines - Germania Dairy Automation, Inc.

PARAC - Adhesives and sealants - Georgia-Pacific Corp.

PARACET - Pharmaceutical preparations - Sagmel, Inc.

PARACHROME - Greeting cards - Paramount Cards Inc.

PARACHROME PETS - Greeting cards - Paramount Cards Inc.

PARACHUTE - Chairs–wood - Westinghouse Electric Corp.

PARACHUTE - Recording label - Jazz Composer's Orchestra Association Inc.

PARACHUTE BLASTER - Toys - Mattel, Inc.

PARACHUTE COLLECTION - Fabrics - Capital Carousel Inc.

PARACHUTE DROP - Kites ☆ - Hi-Flier Manufacturing Co.

PARACHUTE PARTS OF SPEECH - Computer software - Southwest Edpsych Services Inc.

PARACHUTE PRESS - Publisher's imprints - Parachute Press, Inc.

PARACIDE - Pet products ☆ - Aquatronics-Filtronics

PARACIDE II - Veterinary pharmaceutical preparations - Happy Jack, Inc.

PARACLEAR - Vitamins and nutritional supplements - Amrion, Inc.

PARACOM - Computers - Parsytec Inc.

PARACONE - Lighting fixtures - Thomas Industries Inc.

PARACONE - Lighting fixtures - Thomas Lighting (Accent Division)

PARACORD - Shoes - Endicott Johnson Corp.

PARACORR - Lenses–optical - Tele Vue Optics Inc.

PARACORT - Pharmaceutical preparations ☆ - Parke-Davis

PARACRYLIC - Paints - Paragon Paint & Varnish Corp.

PARADE - Christmas tree ornaments - Cracker Box Inc.

PARADE - Cigars - Gesty Trading & Manufacturing Corp.

PARADE - Detergents ☆ - Safeway Stores Inc.

PARADE - Dinnerware–glass - Nikko Ceramics Inc.

PARADE - Electric organs - Lowrey Organ Co.

PARADE - Fabrics - Gretchen Bellinger Inc.

PARADE - Floor coverings–carpet and rugs - Lees Carpets

PARADE - Floor coverings–carpet and rugs ☆ - J and J Industries Inc.

PARADE - Food products - Indian Summer

☆ = Now out of production

PARADE - Food products - Pridgen Brothers Co. Inc.
PARADE - Sunglasses - Nassau Lens Co. Inc.
PARADE - Tomato pastes and sauces - Federated Foods Inc.
PARADE - Turkeys - Watson Quality Foods Inc.
PARADE - Video tapes–blank - Peter Pan Industries
PARADE - Water–bottled or canned - Water House
PARADE - Yarn ☆ - Caron International Inc.
PARADE CLASSIC - Ice cream - Federated Group, Inc.
PARADE LEADER - Toys ☆ - A.J. Renzi Plastic Corp.
PARADE-M - Pet collars - R.A.F. Trading Inc.
PARADE OF THE WOODEN SOLDIERS - Dolls ☆ - Effanbee Doll Corp.
PARADE PETS - Toys–stuffed ☆ - Fun World Inc.
PARADE SOFTWARE - Computer software - Peter Pan Industries
PARADER - Girdles - Formflex Foundations Inc.
PARADICE - Ice - Paradice Corp.
PARADIGM - Air conditioning equipment - Climate Master, Inc.
PARADIGM - Cleaning preparations - Ecolab Inc.
PARADIGM - Computer software - Blue Chip Technologies, Inc.
PARADIGM - Fishing lures - Thomas and Thomas Rodmakers Inc.
PARADIGM - Food products ☆ - Paradigm Foodworks
PARADIGM - Golfing equipment - Golfsmith International Inc.
PARADIGM - Luggage - American Tourister, Inc.
PARADIGM - Office furniture–metal - Stow/Davis Furniture Co.
PARADIGM - Recording label - PDS-Universal Entertainment Group Inc.
PARADIGM 2000 - Cleaning preparations - Ecolab Inc.
PARADIGM COLLECTION - Sweaters - Island G Ltd.
PARADIGM HAUTE FUDGE - Food products - Paradigm Foodworks
PARADIGM PIONEERS - Video production - Charthouse International Learning Corp.
PARADIGM PLANNER - Calendars - Douglas S. Warren
PARADIGM PLUS - Computer software - Protosoft, Inc.
PARADIGM PRISM - Video production - Alternative Visions, Inc.
PARADIONE - Pharmaceutical preparations - Abbott Laboratories
PARADISA - Toys–blocks - Lego Systems Inc.
PARADISE - Beverages - Paradise Fruit Co., Inc.
PARADISE - Computer peripheral equipment - Intercontinental Enterprises, Inc.
PARADISE - Computer software - Scientific Computing Associates, Inc.
PARADISE - Cosmetics - Paradise Cosmetics
PARADISE - Floor coverings–carpet and rugs - Coronet Carpets Inc.
PARADISE - Food products - C.Q. Yee Hop & Co. Ltd.
PARADISE - Food products - Paradise Products Corp.
PARADISE - Furniture - Halcyon Inc.
PARADISE - Incense - Excelsior Incense Works
PARADISE - Kitchenware–earthenware - Arnart Imports Inc.
PARADISE - Oils–edible - James Devito
PARADISE - Olives–pickled or brined - James B. Kaufmann & Associates
PARADISE - Pencils ☆ - Faber-Castell Corp.
PARADISE - Pet products - Mason Distributing
PARADISE - Rings–jewelry - Artcarved Inc.
PARADISE - Seafood ☆ - Winter Harbor Fisheries
PARADISE - Synthetic turf - Instant Turf Industries Inc.
PARADISE - Tablecloths - Paradise Manufacturing Co. Inc.
PARADISE - Teas - Cafe Au Lait
PARADISE - Teas - Kittridge & Frederickson
PARADISE - Wallpaper ☆ - J.C. Prints
PARADISE BAY - Lotions - NHS, Inc.
PARADISE CANDLES - Candles - Paradise Candles
PARADISE COOLER - Teas ☆ - Traditional Medicinals, Inc.
PARADISE COSMETICS - Cosmetics - Laguna Brush Co.
PARADISE COURT - Floor coverings–carpet and rugs - Gulistan Carpet Inc.
PARADISE COVE - Bicycles - Dynacraft Industries Inc.
PARADISE COVE - Floor coverings–carpet and rugs ☆ - Hollytex Carpet Mills Inc.
PARADISE FARM ORGANICS - Food products - Paradise Farm Organics, Inc.
PARADISE FARMS - Candy - Killips Investment Corp.
PARADISE FOUND - Clothing - Pacific Clothing Co., Inc.
PARADISE FOUND - Floor coverings–carpet and rugs ☆ - Mohawk Carpet Corp.
PARADISE GARDEN - Glassware–household - Crystal Clear Importing Co. Inc.
PARADISE GARDEN - Wallpaper ☆ - Cherry Hill Studio
PARADISE GOLD - Fruit drinks–bottled or canned - Paradise Gold Beverages
PARADISE ISLAND - Bathing suits - Water Colors of Florida Inc.
PARADISE ISLAND - Food products - Dole Food Co., Inc.
PARADISE ISLAND - Wallpaper - Frankford Wallcoverings Inc.
PARADISE ISLAND II - Wallpaper - Frankford Wallcoverings Inc.

PARADISE KITTEN - Shoes - Valley Shoe Corp.
PARADISE NIGHT - Floor coverings–carpet and rugs - Alexander Smith Carpets
PARADISE NUGGETS - Bird feeds - Kellogg Inc.
PARADISE PASSION - Beverages - Ocean Spray Cranberries Inc.
PARADISE PASTA - Pasta - Fortune Macaroni Co.
PARADISE PLUM - Lipsticks - Cosmair Inc.
PARADISE RANCH - Fruits and vegetables - Valley Center Packing Co. Inc.
PARADISE RIDGE - Wines - Paradise Ridge Winery
PARADISE RIVER - Fruits and vegetables - Fresh Pacific
PARADISE SPRINGS - Beverages - Joseph Victori Wines Inc.
PARADISE SUITE - Floor coverings–carpet and rugs - Philadelphia Carpets
PARADISE VALLEY - Cosmetics - Arizona Natural Resources
PARADISE VALLEY - Floor coverings–carpet and rugs - Mohawk Carpet Corp.
PARADISE VALLEY - Floor coverings–carpet and rugs ☆ - Hollytex Carpet Mills Inc.
PARADISE VALLEY - Fruits and vegetables - Winnemucca Farms
PARADISE VALVERDE - Food products - Paradise Products Corp.
PARADISO - Beverages–alcohol - Robert Denton & Co., Ltd.
PARADISO - Floor coverings–carpet and rugs - Atlas Carpet Mills Inc.
PARADISO - Food products - Sun Garden Packing Co., Inc.
PARADISO - Skin care products - Drake-Bluestein, Inc.
PARADISO - Tableware–china ☆ - Villeroy and Boch Tableware Ltd.
PARADISO - Teas–herbal - Christopher Brookes Distinctive Foods
PARADISO - Tortillas - Mexican Foods
PARADISO - Tortillas - Sparta Foods, Inc.
PARADOME - Lighting fixtures - Holophane Corp.
PARADOX - Apparel - Spiegel, Inc.
PARADOX - Computer software - Borland International, Inc.
PARADOX - Hair care products - Chenice Beverly Hills
PARADOX - Ophthalmic goods - Foremost Optical Products
PARADOX - Sporting goods - Lisco, Inc.
PARADOX AND DESIGN - Leather goods - Dreher Industries Ltd.
PARADOX PRESS, THE - Books–comic - DC Comics
PARADOX SQL LINK - Computer software - Borland International, Inc.
PARADOXBOX - Truck bodies - Crysteel Manufacturing Inc.
PARADOXY - Pharmaceutical preparations - Pharmics Inc.
PARADRAFT - Office supplies ☆ - Charvoz
PARADUXX - Beverages - St. Helena Wine Co., Inc.
PARADYME - Computer software - Paradyme Learning Corp.
PARADYNE - Pharmaceutical preparations - G.O. Spanner Inc.
PARAEUSAL - Antiseptics - Paraeusal Co.
PARAFAN - Food products - Chiquita Brands, Inc.
PARAFFIN-FLO - Machine parts - Magniflo Corp.
PARAFFIN SPRINGS SPA - Skin care products - Gena Laboratories Inc.
PARAFIELD - Oils–lubricating ☆ - Witco Corp.
PARAFLECTOR - Antennas - Scala Electronic Corp.
PARAFLEX - Pharmaceutical preparations - McNeil Pharmaceuticals
PARAFLOOD - Lighting fixtures - Genlyte Group Inc.
PARAFOIL - Kites ☆ - Kite Factory
PARAFOLD - Window coverings - Paramount Fabrics Inc.
PARAFON FORTE - Pharmaceutical preparations - McNeil Pharmaceuticals
PARAFORTE - Pharmaceutical preparations - Goldline Laboratories, Inc.
PARAGAUGE - Accuset Tool Co., Inc.
PARAGE - Golf equipment - Mechanix, Inc.
PARAGESIC - Vitamins and nutritional supplements - Tishcon Corp.
PARAGLIDE - Wheelchairs - Robert Donaldson
PARAGON - Animal feeds - Continental Grain Co.
PARAGON - Aquatic pharmacuetical preparations ☆ - Aquatronics-Filtronics
PARAGON - Artists' materials - Keuffel & Esser Co.
PARAGON - Ashtrays–glass - Federal Glass
PARAGON - Bicycles - Nissho Iwai American Corp.
PARAGON - Bicycles - Ross Bicycles USA, Ltd.
PARAGON - Building materials - Texas Aluminum Industries Inc.
PARAGON - Computer software - Hotel Information Systems
PARAGON - Computer software - Paragon Systems, L.P.
PARAGON - Diapers–disposable - Paragon Trade Brands, Inc.
PARAGON - Floor coverings - Aladdin Mills, Inc.
PARAGON - Floor coverings - Permagrain Products, Inc.
PARAGON - Floor coverings ☆ - Congoleum Corp.
PARAGON - Floor coverings–carpet and rugs - J and J Industries Inc.
PARAGON - Floor coverings–carpet and rugs - Porter Carpet Mills Inc.
PARAGON - Floor coverings–carpet and rugs ☆ - Royalweve Carpet Mills
PARAGON - Floor coverings–carpet and rugs ☆ - World Carpets, Inc.
PARAGON - Frozen foods - Paragon Ice Cream L.P.

☆ = Now out of production

PARAGON - Furniture ☆ - Halcyon Inc.
PARAGON - Glassware–household - Royal Doulton-Somerset UK Ltd.
PARAGON - Glucogen replenishment - Dean Distributors, Inc.
PARAGON - Hair care products - Windmere Corp.
PARAGON - Hearing aids - Beltone Electronics Corp.
PARAGON - Kilns - Paragon Industries Inc.
PARAGON - Knives–hunting - Little River Knives
PARAGON - Lighting fixtures - Kenall Manufacturing Co.
PARAGON - Mailing machines - Pitney Bowes Inc.
PARAGON - Medical apparatus - Danek Medical, Inc.
PARAGON - Projection screens - Draper Shade and Screen Co. Inc.
PARAGON - Recording label - Paragon Associates Inc.
PARAGON - Sporting goods ☆ - Allsop, Inc.
PARAGON - Tiles–ceramic - Gloria Enterprises Inc.
PARAGON - Valves - American Granby Inc.
PARAGON - Vaporizers - Garfield Trading Co., Inc.
PARAGON II - Aquatic pharmacuetical preparations ☆ - Aquatronics-Filtronics
PARAGON CALIBRATION - Measuring instruments - Filtech Corp.
PARAGON CLASSIC - Golf carts ☆ - RE/NEW4U
PARAGON CUTLERY CO. - Knives - Little River Knives
PARAGON MEMORY CORPORATION UPGRADE TO EXCELLENCE EST.
  1989 - Computer peripheral equipment - Paragon Solutions, Inc.
PARAGON OF TARRAGON - Spices and extracts - To Market to Market
PARAGON PICTURE - Puzzles ☆ - Warren Industries Inc.
PARAGON SERIES - Fans–electric - Windmere Corp.
PARAGONA - Artists' materials - Paragon Art Products, Inc.
PARAGONA - Artists' materials - Paragona Art Products, Inc.
PARAGRAPHICS - Wallpaper - Textile Wallcoverings International Ltd.
PARAGREEN - Erasers ☆ - Faber-Castell Corp.
PARAGREY - Erasers ☆ - Faber-Castell Corp.
PARAGRID - Floor coverings–tile - Collins & Aikman Corp.
PARAGUARD - Pet products - Seachem Laboratories
PARAHAMMER - Tools–hand-operated ☆ - Paratech Inc.
PARAHAT - Apparel–athletic - Parahat
PARAHISIAN - Medical apparatus - Webster Laboratories Inc.
PARAISO - Paper–gift wrap - Paraiso Publishers, Inc.
PARAISO MARBLE - Floor coverings - Tarkett, Inc.
PARAKEET NESTING BOX - Pet products - R.A.F. Trading Inc.
PARAKIT - Health care products - Omron Healthcare, Inc.
PARAL - Pharmaceutical preparations - Forest Pharmaceuticals Inc.
PARAL-EX - Computers - Western Telematic Inc.
PARAL-LINER - Drafting supplies - Plasticoid Manufacturing Inc.
PARAL-LINER - Office supplies - Alvin and Co. Inc.
PARAL-LINER DELUX - Drafting supplies - Plasticoid Manufacturing Inc.
PARAL-LINER DELUX - Rulers–metal - Alvin and Co. Inc.
PARALAC - Adhesives and sealants - Testworth Laboratories Inc.
PARALAC - Paints - Paragon Paint & Varnish Corp.
PARALINE - Glass products - Glass Inc.
PARALINE - Sporting goods ☆ - Gladding Braided Products Inc.
PARALITE - Ophthalmic goods - Rozin Optical Export Corp.
PARALITO - Tools - Columbine International
PARALLAM - Lumber - Trus Joist MacMillan L.P.
PARALLAX - Computer software - Mindscape Software Inc.
PARALLAX - Golfing equipment - Golfsmith International Inc.
PARALLAX - Golfing equipment - Lynx Golf, Inc.
PARALLAX - Recording label - Parallax Records
PARALLEL - Apparel–women's - Francine Browner Inc.
PARALLEL - Clocks ☆ - General Time Corp. (Westclox/Seth Thomas Div.)
PARALLEL - Desks - Joyce International Inc.
PARALLEL - Flatware - Kirk Stieff Co.
PARALLEL - Floor coverings - Harris-Tarkett, Inc.
PARALLEL AXIS - Musical instrument accessories - Seymour Duncan Pickups
PARALLEL DIAMOND - Flatware - Dansk International Designs, Ltd.
PARALLEL-LINERS - Drafting supplies - Plasticoid Manufacturing Inc.
PARALLEL LINES - Apparel and accessories - Montgomery Ward & Co. Inc.
PARALLEL PACKET EXPRESS - Computer peripheral equipment - Wellfleet
  Communications, Inc.
PARALLEL TASKING - Electrical equipment - 3Com Corp.
PARALLEL TURNS - Apparel and accessories - Edison Brothers Stores, Inc.
PARALLEL WORLDS - Watches - Design Knowledge International Labs, Inc.
PARALLELE - Floor coverings–carpet and rugs - J.L. Benson Co.
PARALLELO - Tools - Martin Universal Design Inc.
PARALLELS - Floor coverings - Mannington Resilient Floors
PARALLELS - Floor coverings–carpet and rugs - Mohawk Industries Inc.
PARALLELS - Floor coverings–carpet and rugs ☆ - Regal Rugs Inc.
PARALLELS - Wallpaper - Capital Carousel Inc.

PARALLELS - Wallpaper - Motif Designs, Inc.
PARALLELS II - Wallpaper - Motif Designs, Inc.
PARALOID - Chemical preparations - Rohm and Haas Co.
PARALON - Computer hardware - Paralon Technologies, Inc.
PARALTILT - Drafting supplies - Teledyne Post
PARALUX - Backpacks - Lowe Alpine Systems, Inc.
PARALUX - Enamels - Paragon Paint & Varnish Corp.
PARALUX - Lighting equipment - Diffusa-Lite Co.
PARALYZER - Sporting goods - United Defense Industries Inc.
PARAMAGNETIC LOGGING - Measuring instruments - Paramagnetic Logging,
  Inc.
PARAMAR - Chemical preparations - Exxon Corp.
PARAMARK - Bookmarks - William Alden
PARAMAX - Chemical preparations - Dade International Inc.
PARAMED - Pet products - Gerard-Pellham Co.
PARAMENDER - Photographic equipment ☆ - Nikon Inc.
PARAMETER - Chemical preparations - Research & Diagnostic Systems, Inc.
PARAMETRIC SERIES - Elevators - Montgomery Kone Inc.
PARAMETRIC TECHNOLOGY CORPORATION - Computer software -
  Parametric Technology Corp.
PARAMOTOR - Aircraft–gliders - Paramarketing Inc.
PARAMOUNT - Artists' materials - Keuffel & Esser Co.
PARAMOUNT - Artists' materials - Paramount Brush Co.
PARAMOUNT - Barbecues and grills - Paramount Housewares
PARAMOUNT - Bicycles - Schwinn Cycling & Fitness Inc.
PARAMOUNT - Candy - Lanco Corp.
PARAMOUNT - Cleaning preparations–household - Ecolab Inc.
PARAMOUNT - Computer software - Paramount Pictures Corp.
PARAMOUNT - Cordials - Paramount Distillers Inc.
PARAMOUNT - Dialing devices–telephone - Baltimore Luggage Co.
PARAMOUNT - Fabrics - Gretchen Bellinger Inc.
PARAMOUNT - Fabrics - Paramount Fabrics Inc.
PARAMOUNT - Flatware - Kirk Stieff Co.
PARAMOUNT - Floor coverings - Matworks
PARAMOUNT - Floor coverings ☆ - Congoleum Corp.
PARAMOUNT - Food products - Pies Inc.
PARAMOUNT - Garden equipment - Allegretti & Co.
PARAMOUNT - Hair care products - Helene Curtis Industries Inc.
PARAMOUNT - Health care products - Euro-Care Products & Services Co.
PARAMOUNT - Manufactured homes - Redman Industries, Inc.
PARAMOUNT - Motion pictures - Viacom International Inc.
PARAMOUNT - Pasta - Paramount Macaroni Co. Inc.
PARAMOUNT - Pickles - Paramount Foods Inc.
PARAMOUNT - Projection screens - Claridge Products and Equipment Inc.
PARAMOUNT - Recording label - MCA Universal Studios
PARAMOUNT - Telephones - Paramount Electronic Corp.
PARAMOUNT - Tools - Bacon Felt Co. Inc.
PARAMOUNT - Wallpaper ☆ - Koroseal Wallcoverings
PARAMOUNT - Window shutters - Design House, Inc.
PARAMOUNT HEADWEAR - Apparel and accessories - Paramount Headwear,
  Inc.
PARAMOUNT LADY - Exercising equipment - Paramount Fitness Equipment
  Corp.
PARAMOUNT NOVELTIES - Novelty items - Victor H. Levy Inc.
PARAMOUNT PETS - Greeting cards - Paramount Cards Inc.
PARAMOUNT SHEARKING - Garden equipment ☆ - Allegretti & Co.
PARAMOUNT VELVET - Beverages–alcohol ☆ - Paramount Distillers Inc.
PARAMOUR - Ophthalmic goods - Foremost Optical Products
PARAMYD - Fibers–synthetic - Aramid, Ltd.
PARANA - Printers–computer - Parana Supplies Corp.
PARANET - Bandages - Glenwood LLC
PARANOL - Veterinary pharmaceutical preparations - Happy Jack, Inc.
PARAPAD - Health care products ☆ - Tecnol Medical Products, Inc.
PARAPECTOLIN - Health care products - Dooner Laboratories Inc.
PARAPIC BUG BITE - Health care products - Tucuru
PARAPINK - Erasers ☆ - Faber-Castell Corp.
PARAPORT - Computer hardware - Compex, Inc.
PARAPRO - Computer software - Optimal Engineering Solutions, Inc.
PARAQUAD - Bedding–linen - Cherry Hill Medical Inc.
PARARED - Erasers ☆ - Faber-Castell Corp.
PARARING - Tiles–ceiling - Artcrest Products Co. Inc.
PARAROUND - Lighting fixtures - Thomas Industries Inc.
PARAROUND - Lighting fixtures - Thomas Lighting (Accent Division)
PARAS - Seafood products–fresh or frozen ☆ - Robert W. Hayman Inc.
PARASCSI - Computer peripherals - D.E.W. International Corp.
PARASEAL - Candles - W and F Products Inc.

☆ = Now out of production

PARASHOOT - Guns ☆ - Harrington & Richardson Inc.
PARASITE CARE - Aquariums–household - Jungle Laboratories Corp.
PARASITE CLEAR - Aquariums–household - Jungle Laboratories Corp.
PARASITE GUARD - Aquariums–household - Jungle Laboratories Corp.
PARASITES - Toys ☆ - Matchbox Toys USA
PARASLEEVE - Hardware ☆ - Black & Decker Corp.
PARASOL - Christmas tree ornaments - Cracker Box Inc.
PARASOL - Nozzles - Spraying Systems Co.
PARASOL - Tableware–china ☆ - Lenox, Inc.
PARASOL - Window shades - Delaware Valley Solar Screens
PARASOUND - Electronic equipment - Parasound Products Inc.
PARASOX - Apparel and accessories - L.A. Sox Inc.
PARASTRAN - Rope ☆ - Samson Cordage Works
PARATA ANALYTICS RESEARCH - Computer database - Parata Analytics Research, Inc.
PARATHANE - Finishing agents - Plastics & Resins Ltd.
PARATOL - Paints - Testworth Laboratories Inc.
PARATORQ - Transmission fluids - Exxon Corp.
PARATOX - Health care products - Healthwatchers System
PARATRAC - Drafting supplies ☆ - Plan Hold Corp.
PARATROOPER - Games - Avalon Hill Game Co.
PARATROOPER - Ophthalmic goods - Foremost Optical Products
PARAVIDEO - Computer peripheral equipment - Destiny Technology Corp.
PARAVIEW - Tiles–ceiling - Artcrest Products Co. Inc.
PARAWAX - Artists' materials - Star Parts Inc.
PARAWHITE - Erasers ☆ - Faber-Castell Corp.
PARAZAN - Pet products - Nishiki Koi USA Inc.
PARAZIN - Pet products - Aquatic Biotechnologies Inc.
PARAZINE - Cleaning equipment - Restortek, Inc.
PARAZONE - Prescription drug ☆ - IDE-Interstate Inc.
PARBENEM - Pharmaceutical preparations - Parmed Pharmaceuticals, Inc.
PARBEX T - Pharmaceutical preparations - Parmed Pharmaceuticals, Inc.
PARBOCYL - Pharmaceutical preparations ☆ - ICN Pharmaceuticals Inc.
PARBOLIZADO - Rice - Goya Foods, Inc.
PARBREAKER - Gloves - Champion Glove Manufacturing Co.
PARC GRASS - Floor coverings–carpet and rugs - Conquest Carpet Mills Inc.
PARCAINE 10 - Pharmaceutical preparations - Parmed Pharmaceuticals, Inc.
PARCEL-GRAF - Scales–industrial ☆ - Pennsylvania Scale Co.
PARCELPAK - Bags–storage - Curtis 1000 Inc.
PARCH - Fungicides - State Chemical Manufacturing Co.
PARCHEESI - Games - Milton Bradley Co.
PARCHMARQUE - Paper ☆ - Fox River Paper Co.
PARCHMENT - Cosmetics - Almay Inc.
PARCHMENT - Greeting cards - Gibson Greetings, Inc.
PARCHMENT - Pajamas–women's ☆ - J.C. Penney Co., Inc.
PARCHMENT - Wallpaper - Winfield Design Associates, Inc.
PARCHMENT BRISTOL - Paper ☆ - Parsons Paper Co.
PARCHMENT DEED - Paper - Southworth Co.
PARCHTEX - Paper–writing - Sorg Paper Co.
PARCHTONE - Paper - French Paper Co.
PARCO - Cookies - Parco Foods, Inc.
PARCO - Floor coverings - Pawling Corp. (Standard Products Div.)
PARCO - Lubricants - Henkel Corp. (Functional Products Div.)
PARCO - Pens ☆ - Parker Pen USA
PARCO-LINK - Floor coverings - Pawling Corp. (Standard Products Div.)
PARCOAT F.R. - Coatings - Enersys3 Inc.
PARCOF - Cough medicines - Parmed Pharmaceuticals, Inc.
PARCORT - Pharmaceutical preparations - Parmed Pharmaceuticals, Inc.
PARCOURS - Apparel and accessories - Nygard, Inc.
PARCOURSE - Exercising equipment - Game Time, Inc.
PARCRAFT - Kitchen cabinets–metal - Parsons Floors and Cabinet Co.
PARD - Dog food - Wells Pet Foods Co.
PARDEX - Motor vehicle parts and accessories - Pardners Unlimited, Inc.
PARDIVA - Wines - Viansa Winery and Marketplace
PARDNER - Carpet cleaner - Intex Chemical Inc.
PARDNER - Dog food ☆ - Agway Country Foods Inc.
PARDNERS - Pens ☆ - Parker Pen USA
PARDNERS - Vehicle accessories - Pardners Unlimited, Inc.
PARDRYL - Pharmaceutical preparations - Parmed Pharmaceuticals, Inc.
PARDUBA - Musical instrument accessories - John Parduba
PARDUCCI - Wines - Parducci Winery Ltd.
PARDUCCI WINE CELLARS - Wines - Hill & Thoma Wines
PAREDRINE - Pharmaceutical preparations - Pharmics Inc.
PAREDRINE - Pharmaceutical preparations - Smithkline Beecham Corp.
PAREE - Thread - Threads USA Div.
PARELIXIR - Pharmaceutical preparations ☆ - Purdue Frederick Co.

PARENOGEN - Medical apparatus - Cutter Laboratories
PARENTING PUZZLE, THE - Broadcasting stations–television - Detroit Educational Television Foundation
PARENTINI - Bicycling apparel ☆ - Corso Bicycle Distributor Inc.
PARENT'S ALERT - Pharmaceutical preparations - Parent's Alert, Inc.
PARENTS AS TEACHERS - Publisher's imprints - Parents AS Teachers National Center, Inc.
PARENTS GAME POWER FOR PHONICS - Games - Spin-A-Test Publishing Co.
PARENTS LEADERSHIP INSTITUTE - Publisher's imprints - Parents Leadership Institute
PARENTS ON YOUR SIDE - Video production - Canter and Associates, Inc.
PARENT'S PAL - Infant product - Wittenstein, Susan R.
PARENTS' PRIDE - Water–bottled or canned - Absopure Water Co.
PAREO - Fibers–synthetic - Nova-Tech International Ltd.
PAREPECTOLIN - Pharmaceutical preparations - Rhone-Poulenc Rorer Pharmaceuticals Inc.
PAREST - Pharmaceutical preparations ☆ - Parke-Davis
PARET - Computer peripheral equipment - Opedia Corp.
PAREX - Automotive parts and accessories - Freudenberg-Nok General Partnership
PAREX - Corn and callus trimmers, blades ☆ - American Safety Razor Co.
PAREXCELLENCE - Rice - Producers Rice Mill, Inc.
PARFAIRE - Floor coverings–carpet and rugs - J.L. Benson Co.
PARFAIT - Fabrics - Guilford Mills, Inc.
PARFAIT - Floor coverings ☆ - Congoleum Corp.
PARFAIT - Floor coverings–carpet and rugs - Regal Rugs Inc.
PARFAIT - Floor coverings–carpet and rugs ☆ - Customweave Carpets Inc.
PARFAIT - Horseradish - H.E. Whitaker Co. Inc.
PARFAIT - Manicure preparations - Blue Cross Beauty Products Inc.
PARFAIT - Wallpaper - Bayview Wallcoverings
PARFAIT 2 - Housewares - Bammental Wallcoverings Inc.
PARFAIT COLLECTION - Lipsticks - Honey & Spice Toiletries
PARFAY - Food products - Beatrice Cheese Co.
PARFAY - Musical instrument accessories - Enzo Pizzi
PARFLEX - Wallcovering - Parex, Inc.
PARFORM - Golfing equipment ☆ - Focus Golf Systems, Inc. (Dunlop Golf)
PARFUM D'ORO - Cosmetics - Lal Rewachand
PARFUM LILLABEL - Skin care products ☆ - T.N. Dickinson Co.
PARFUMS BLANCHARD - Colognes - Del Pharmaceuticals, Inc.
PARFUMS FAMOUS - Perfumes and colognes - Suarez Corp.
PARFUMS GALANOS - Colognes - Gary Farn Ltd.
PARFURAN - Pharmaceutical preparations ☆ - Parke-Davis
PARGEL - Pharmaceutical preparations ☆ - Parke-Davis
PARGEN FORTIFIED - Pharmaceutical preparations - Goldline Laboratories, Inc.
PARGESIC - Pharmaceutical preparations - Parmed Pharmaceuticals, Inc.
PARHIST - Pharmaceutical preparations - Parmed Pharmaceuticals, Inc.
PARHISTINE - Pharmaceutical preparations - Parmed Pharmaceuticals, Inc.
PARHYDRINATE - Pharmaceutical preparations - Parmed Pharmaceuticals, Inc.
PARI - Rice - Basmati Rice Imports Inc.
PARI BABY - Medical apparatus - Pari Respiratory Equipment Inc.
PARI LC PLUS - Medical apparatus - Pari Respiratory Equipment Inc.
PARI PEP - Medical apparatus - Pari Respiratory Equipment Inc.
PARI WAX - Depilatories - Pari Helmi
PARIAGE - Apparel–women's - Wacoal America Inc.
PARIAN - Furniture ☆ - Bassett Furniture Industries, Inc.
PARIAN MARBLE - Floor coverings - Congoleum Corp.
PARIGI - Toilets–enameled - Kohler Co.
PARIOLI - Coffee - 1 Uno Espresso, Inc.
PARIS - Classic Time Watch Co.
PARIS - Artists' materials - Scratch-Art Co., Inc.
PARIS - Belts–apparel - M. Aron Corp.
PARIS - Cabinets - Kabom Kitchen & Bath Manufacturing
PARIS - Candy - Paris Chocolates, Inc.
PARIS - Cookies - Crystal Food Import Corp.
PARIS - Infant product ☆ - Paris Co. Inc.
PARIS - Skin care products - Northern Labs, Inc.
PARIS - Vases - Durand International
PARIS - Wigs - Paula Young
PARIS BISTRO - Aprons - Now Designs
PARIS BLUES - Apparel and accessories - Paris Blues, Inc.
PARIS COLLECTION, THE - Dinnerware–glass - Block China Co.
PARIS FLEUR DE PARFUM - Perfumes - Yves St. Laurent Parfum Corp.
PARIS GOURMETS - Pasta - Paris Gourmets

☆ = Now out of production

PARIS HOLIDAY - Underwear and nightwear - Youthcraft-Charmfit
PARIS IN DANGER - Games ☆ - Avalon Hill Game Co.
PARIS MAUVE - Nail care products - Cosmair Inc.
PARIS NIGHT - Hair- and skin-care products, fragrance, etc. - Benjamin Ansehl Co.
PARIS PARIS - Bakery products - Euro International
PARIS PASTRY - Bakery products - Paris Pastry, Inc.
PARIS PLEAT - Window shades - Allied Extrusions
PARIS POODLE - Toys–stuffed - Dakin Inc.
PARIS PRETTY - Dolls - Mattel, Inc.
PARIS RECORDS - Recording label - Chunkball Music, Inc.
PARIS ROMANCE - Soap - Softsoap Enterprises, Inc.
PARIS SILHOUETTE - Girdles - Magic Mold Inc.
PARIS SPLENDOR - Cutlery ☆ - Lifetime Hoan Corp.
PARIS STATION - Apparel and accessories - M. Serman & Co. Inc.
PARIS TWIRLS - Biscuits - Anco Foods Corp.
PARIS USA 1924 TEAM - Pins–jewelry - United States Olympic Committee
PARIS VALLEY RANCH - Wines - Joseph E. Seagram & Sons, Inc.
PARISA - Clothing - AFR Apparel International Inc.
PARISIAN - Apparel and accessories - Parisian, Inc.
PARISIAN - Artists' materials ☆ - Robert Simmons Inc.
PARISIAN - Bakery products - Parisian Bakeries Inc.
PARISIAN - Bicycles - Murray, Inc.
PARISIAN - Cases–eyeglass - California Optical Leather Inc.
PARISIAN - Pet products - Aspen Pet Products
PARISIAN - Rings–jewelry - Artcarved Inc.
PARISIAN - Wallpaper - Capital Carousel Inc.
PARISIAN - Yarn - Joseph Galler Inc.
PARISIAN COTTON - Yarn - Joseph Galler Inc.
PARISIAN GOURMET - Giftware - Doranne
PARISIAN KNIGHTS - Publisher's imprints - Hard Hat Records
PARISIAN MOIRE WALLCOVERING, VOL. 111 - Wallpaper - Wallpaper Imports Inc.
PARISIAN NEW DIRECTIONS - Apparel and accessories - Parisian, Inc.
PARISIAN ORIGINAL - Breads - Parisian Bakeries Inc.
PARISIAN PRINTS - Tablecloths ☆ - Sultan's Linen Inc.
PARISIAN SIGNATURE - Apparel - Parisian, Inc.
PARISIAN VELVET - Floor coverings–carpet and rugs - Roxbury Carpet Co.
PARISIEN - Furniture ☆ - Bassett Furniture Industries, Inc.
PARISIENNE - Bedding–linen - Dan River Inc.
PARISIENNE - Cigarettes - G.A. Georgopulo & Co. Inc.
PARISIENNE - Dishes–china ☆ - Gorham Inc.
PARISIENNE - Floor coverings–carpet and rugs - Alexander Smith Carpets
PARISIENNE - Frames–picture - Terragrafics Inc.
PARISIENNE - Girdles - John Wanamaker Inc.
PARISIENNE - Lighters - Colibri Inc.
PARISIENNE - Mattresses - Namaco Industries, Inc.
PARISIENNE DUET - Brassieres (Bras) - Gelmart Industries Inc.
PARISIENNE LASHGRO - Cosmetics ☆ - Palm Beach Beauty Products
PARISPEAK - Computer software - Megadyne Information Systems
PARISTONE - Gypsum products - Georgia-Pacific Corp.
PARITEX - Finishing agents ☆ - Plastics & Resins Ltd.
PARIVAL - Mustard - Anco Foods Corp.
PARK - Artists' materials - American Blueprint Co. Inc.
PARK - Cabinets - Legeis Corp.
PARK - Cheese - Park Cheese Co., Inc.
PARK - Cleaning preparations - Bicycle Tools Inc.
PARK - Flowers, plants, and seeds - Jacklin Seed
PARK - Food products - Park Corp.
PARK - Health care products - Park Surgical Co. Inc.
PARK - Kelp - Quali Tech, Inc.
PARK - Thread ☆ - Perfect Thread Co. Inc.
PARK - Tools–hand-operated - Park Tool Co.
PARK-A-CUP - Housewares - Harry Hill Mott
PARK & SHOP - Leather goods - St. Thomas Inc.
PARK & SUN - Sporting goods - Park & Sun Sports
PARK AVE. - File folders - Angler's Roslyn Group Ltd.
PARK AVE. - Fireplace equipment - Thermo-Rite Manufacturing Co.
PARK AVE. BY MAYERS - Apparel and accessories - L. Mayers & Son Inc.
PARK AVENUE - Bathroom accessories - Melard Acquisition, Inc.
PARK AVENUE - Bathroom fixtures - Melard Manufacturing Corp.
PARK AVENUE - Bicycles - Ross Bicycles USA, Ltd.
PARK AVENUE - Calendars ☆ - House of Doolittle
PARK AVENUE - Candy - Tom's Foods Inc.
PARK AVENUE - Dinnerware–plastic - Plastics Manufacturing Co.
PARK AVENUE - Dolls ☆ - Effanbee Doll Corp.

PARK AVENUE - Fencing–wood - Machalk Enterprises Inc.
PARK AVENUE - Floor coverings–carpet and rugs - Johnson's Carpets Inc.
PARK AVENUE - Fruits and vegetables - Dole Dried Fruit & Nut Co.
PARK AVENUE - Furniture - Lane Co. Inc.
PARK AVENUE - Furniture - Taylor-Ramsey Corp.
PARK AVENUE - Furniture ☆ - Bassett Furniture Industries, Inc.
PARK AVENUE - Hot tubs–plastic ☆ - Coleman Spas
PARK AVENUE - Jams and jellies - Dawn Food Products Inc.
PARK AVENUE - Motor vehicles–automobiles - General Motors Corp. (Buick Motor Div.)
PARK AVENUE - Paper–toweling - Wisconsin Tissue Mills Inc.
PARK AVENUE - Perfumes - Ruckel Manufacturing Co. Inc.
PARK AVENUE - Shoes - Allen-Edmonds Shoe Corp.
PARK AVENUE - Tables–wood ☆ - Butler Specialty Co.
PARK AVENUE - Wallpaper ☆ - Wolf-Gordon Inc.
PARK AVENUE CRYSTAL - Giftware - Crystal Clear Industries, Inc.
PARK AVENUE SEED - Flowers, plants, and seeds - Park Avenue Turf, Inc.
PARK AVENUE SUITE - Floor coverings–carpet and rugs ☆ - Durkan Patterned Carpets
PARK AVENUE TURF - Flowers, plants, and seeds - Park Avenue Turf, Inc.
PARK AVENUE ULTRA - Motor vehicles–automobiles - General Motors Corp. (Buick Motor Div.)
PARK AVENUE ULTRA - Paper–toweling - Wisconsin Tissue Mills Inc.
PARK BENCH - Benches–wood - Algoma Net Co.
PARK BENCH KIDS - Apparel and accessories - Babyfair Inc.
PARK BLOK - Fabricated metal products - E & H Concepts, Inc.
PARK CAFE - Coffee, tea and cocoa - Park Corp.
PARK CENTRAL - Floor coverings–carpet and rugs - Gulistan Carpet Inc.
PARK CENTRAL - Furniture ☆ - Bassett Furniture Industries, Inc.
PARK CENTRAL - Furniture–wood ☆ - Flanders Industries Inc.
PARK CHATEAU - Trailers–travel - Royals International
PARK CIRCLE - Furniture ☆ - Bassett Furniture Industries, Inc.
PARK CITY - Furniture–wood ☆ - Flanders Industries Inc.
PARK CITY GROUP - Computer software - Park City Group, Inc.
PARK CONSUL - Trailers–travel - Royals International
PARK CREST - Furniture - Interfurn Inc.
PARK DRIVE - Cigarettes - Philip Morris Companies Inc.
PARK EAST - Blankets - Sufolla Industries Inc.
PARK FALLS - Sinks–metal - Kohler Co.
PARK FOREST - Furniture–children's ☆ - Child Craft Industries Inc.
PARK GARDEN - Wines - Fink Winery
PARK HALL - Food products - Nature's Pride Inc.
PARK HILL - Chocolate novelties - Bortz Chocolate Co.
PARK HILL - Flatware - Wallace International Silversmiths, Inc.
PARK J TUNES - Recording label - TMA Records
PARK LANE - Adhesives and sealants ☆ - Induron Coatings Inc.
PARK LANE - Crocheted and knitted items - Gillman Knitwear Co.
PARK LANE - Fireplace equipment - Thermo-Rite Manufacturing Co.
PARK LANE - Floor coverings–carpet and rugs - Customweave Carpets Inc.
PARK LANE - Floor coverings–carpet and rugs - Galaxy Carpet Mills Inc.
PARK LANE - Floor coverings–carpet and rugs - Glen Eden Wool Carpets
PARK LANE - Floor coverings–carpet and rugs ☆ - Atlas Carpet Mills Inc.
PARK LANE - Food products - Beatrice Cos. Inc.
PARK-LANE - Furniture–upholstered ☆ - Mersman Furniture Co.
PARK LANE - Glassware–household - Spiegelau Inc.
PARK LANE - Glassware–household ☆ - Lancaster Colony Corp.
PARK LANE - Pens - Park Lane Associates Inc.
PARK LANE - Tiles–ceramic ☆ - H & R Johnson Inc.
PARK LANE - Watches - Bulova Corp.
PARK LARK - Orthopedic products - Ortho-Kinetics, Inc.
PARK LIAISON - Trailers–travel - Royals International
PARK MANOR - Floor coverings–carpet and rugs - Cabin Crafts Carpets
PARK-MANOR - Trailers–travel ☆ - Fleetwood Enterprises, Inc.
PARK MEADOW - Floor coverings–carpet and rugs - Gulistan Carpet Inc.
PARK 'N PLATES - Toys–automobiles - Mattel, Inc.
PARK N'GO - Toys ☆ - Steven Manufacturing Co.
PARK PATROL - Infant product ☆ - Ming Ta Supply
PARK PERENNIALS - Plants - George W. Park Seed Co., Inc.
PARK PERFECT - Mirrors - Bert J. Viskovich
PARK PLACE - Floor coverings - Mannington Resilient Floors
PARK PLACE - Floor coverings–carpet and rugs - Ashley Commercial Carpets
PARK PLACE - Furniture - Dinaire Corp.
PARK PLACE - Furniture - Park Place Corp.
PARK PLACE - Furniture–children's - Child Craft Industries Inc.
PARK PLACE - Mats - Cactus Mat Manufacturing Co.

☆ = Now out of production

PARK PLACE - Recording label ☆ - Amherst Records
PARK PLACE - Shoes - Kinney Shoe Corp.
PARK PLACE - Trailers–travel ☆ - Fleetwood Enterprises, Inc.
PARK PLACE - Trees–artificial - Hudson Valley Tree Inc.
PARK PLACE - Wallpaper - United Wallcoverings
PARK PLAZA - Cosmetics - Park Plaza Inc.
PARK PLAZA - Floor coverings - Mannington Resilient Floors
PARK PLAZA - Floor coverings–carpet and rugs - Coronet Carpets Inc.
PARK PLAZA - Floor coverings–carpet and rugs - Monticello Carpet Mills
PARK PLAZA - Floor coverings–carpet and rugs - Philadelphia Carpets
PARK PLAZA - Furniture - Universal Flooring
PARK REGENCY - Food products - Park Corp.
PARK RIDGE - Garden furniture - Jack-Post Corp.
PARK RIVER - Prefabricated buildings–wood - Champion Enterprises Inc.
PARK ROW - Floor coverings–carpet and rugs - Blue Ridge Carpet Mills
PARK ROYAL - Bakery products - H.E. Butt Grocery Co.
PARK SEED - Potting soil and fertilizer - George W. Park Seed Co., Inc.
PARK SHERMAN - Desk sets - Park Sherman
PARK SIDE - Furniture - Lyon-Shaw Inc.
PARK SLOPE BREWING COMPANY - Beverages–malt - Park Slope Brewing Co., Inc.
PARK SMART - Automotive parts and accessories - Auto Care Products, Inc.
PARK SOUTH - Floor coverings - Mannington Resilient Floors
PARK SQUARE BOND - Envelopes - Quality Park Products Co.
PARK STUFF - Playground equipment - Ultra Play Systems Inc.
PARK TERRACE - Floor coverings - Congoleum Corp.
PARK TERRACE - Furniture - Lane Co. Inc.
PARK TOWERS - Furniture ☆ - Bassett Furniture Industries, Inc.
PARK VIEW - Wallpaper ☆ - Benchmark Preferred Wallcoverings
PARKA PENGUIN - Toys–stuffed - Dakin Inc.
PARKAY - Margarine - Kraft Foods, Inc.
PARKAY - Margarine - Nabisco Foods Group
PARKAY GOLD - Margarine - Kraft Foods, Inc.
PARKCHESTER - Floor coverings–tile - Kentile Floors Inc.
PARKCREST - Cabinets - Leedo Manufacturing Co.
PARKDALE - Luggage - Samsonite Corp.
PARKE DAVIS - Pharmaceutical preparations - Parke-Davis
PARKEDALE - Gauze–surgical ☆ - Parke-Davis
PARKELP - Kelp - Quali Tech, Inc.
PARKER - Barbecue and grill accessories - Parker, Inc.
PARKER - Boats–motor - Parker Marine Enterprises, Inc.
PARKER - Cabinets–metal - Parker Steel Products Inc.
PARKER - Floor coverings–carpet and rugs - Karastan-Bigelow Inc.
PARKER - Garden equipment - Parker Sweeper Co.
PARKER - Hardware - S. Parker Hardware Manufacturing Corp.
PARKER - Pens - Parker Pen USA
PARKER - Toys - Tonka Corp.
PARKER - Watches - Hampden Corp.
PARKER - Watches - Parker Watch Inc.
PARKER 27 - Garden equipment - Parker Sweeper Co.
PARKER BOSS - Sporting goods - Boss Manufacturing, Inc.
PARKER BROTHERS - Games ☆ - Parker Brothers
PARKER FARMS - Food products ☆ - Woodmont Orchards Inc.
PARKER FARM'S - Peanut butter - Parker Farm
PARKER HERBEX - Shampoos - Bradco Products Inc.
PARKER HOUSE - Coffee - White Coffee Corp.
PARKER JONES - Apparel and accessories ☆ - Kellwood Co.
PARKER REORDER - Hotels and motels - Parker Reorder Corp.
PARKER TAYLOR - Skin care products - Parker Taylor, Inc.
PARKER WRITING INKS - Inks - Parker Pen USA
PARKERETTE - Garden equipment - Parker Sweeper Co.
PARKER'S - Furniture polish and wax ☆ - C.W. Parker Co.
PARKER'S - Popcorn - Glico Harmony Foods Corp.
PARKER'S PERFECT - Oils–mineral - C.W. Parker Co.
PARKER'S PRIDE - Snack foods - Glico Harmony Foods Corp.
PARKFIELD - Floor coverings–carpet and rugs - Gulistan Carpet Inc.
PARKHILL FURNITURE - Furniture–upholstered - Parkhill Furniture Co.
PARKING ZONE - Catalogs - Pacific Cascade Corp.
PARKIS MILLS - Soil–potting - High View Church Farm, Inc.
PARKLAND - Juices–frozen ☆ - Hi-Acres Inc.
PARKLAND HERITAGE - Garden furniture - Dragon Claw (U.S.A.) Inc.
PARKLANE - Fabrics ☆ - Greenwood Mills Inc.
PARKLANE - Floor coverings–carpet and rugs ☆ - Royalweve Carpet Mills
PARKLANE - Handbags ☆ - Integrated Handbags
PARKLANE - Lighting fixtures - Holophane Corp.
PARKLANE - Shoes ☆ - Allen-Edmonds Shoe Corp.

PARKLINE - Cabinets - Leedo Manufacturing Co.
PARKMASTER - Lighting fixtures ☆ - Hubbell Lighting, Inc. (Lighting Div.)
PARKMASTER - Parking meters - Schlumberger Technologies, Inc.
PARKMASTER - Stoves ☆ - Porter Athletic Equipment Co.
PARKMATIC - Prefabricated structures - Advance National Management
PARKO - Automotive parts and accessories ☆ - Park Metallurgical Corp.
PARKOLOR - Paints ☆ - Park Metallurgical Corp.
PARKPAK - Lighting fixtures - Holophane Corp.
PARKPLACE - Flowers, plants, and seeds - Land O'Lakes, Inc.
PARKRAFT - Envelopes - Quality Park Products Co.
PARKRIDGE - Floor coverings ☆ - Congoleum Corp.
PARKRIDGE - Prefabricated buildings–wood - Champion Enterprises Inc.
PARKROSE LABORATORIES LIMITED - Cosmetic products ☆ - Countryside Fragrances Inc.
PARKS - Razors–electric - Parks Products Inc.
PARKS MUSIC CO. - Publisher's imprints - Neil A. Kjos Music Co.
PARKSIDE - Lumber - Georgia-Pacific Corp.
PARKSLIDE - Playground equipment ☆ - Wonderline
PARKSTONE - Footwear - Mushiro, Inc.
PARKTOP - Concrete products - Metalcrete Industries Inc.
PARKVIEW - Floor coverings–carpet and rugs - Patrick Carpet Mills
PARKVIEW - Furniture ☆ - Athens Furniture Industries Inc.
PARKVIEW KITCHEN & BATH - Wallpaper - Parkview Designs
PARKWAY - Floor coverings - Congoleum Corp.
PARKWAY - Floor coverings–carpet and rugs - Lees Carpets
PARKWAY - Food products - Del Mar Food Products Corp.
PARKWAY - Mail boxes - Leigh
PARKWAY - Occasional tables - JDI Group, Inc.
PARKWAY - Syrup - Stevens Tropical Plantation Inc.
PARKWAY - Tires–airplane - Parkway Tire Co.
PARKWAY - Wire products - Kaspar Wire Works, Inc.
PARKWEAR ORIGINALS - Apparel and accessories - Jefferson National Expansion Historical Assoc.
PARKWOOD - Coffee - John F. Kusner Enterprises, Inc.
PARKWOOD - Floor coverings–carpet and rugs - Gulistan Carpet Inc.
PARKWOOD - Floor coverings–carpet and rugs - Queen Carpet Corp.
PARLAB - Electronic equipment - Printing Arts Research Laboratories
PARLAMINE FORTE - Pharmaceutical preparations ☆ - Parmed Pharmaceuticals, Inc.
PARLAX - Pharmaceutical preparations - Parmed Pharmaceuticals, Inc.
PARLAY - Varnishes - Petri Paint Co. Inc.
PARLEZ-VOUS PATE - Meat products–beef - Marcel & Henri Charcuterie Francaise
PARLIAMENT - Cigarettes - Philip Morris Companies Inc.
PARLIAMENT - Clocks ☆ - General Time Corp. (Westclox/Seth Thomas Div.)
PARLIAMENT - Floor coverings–carpet and rugs - Karastan-Bigelow Inc.
PARLIAMENT - Floor coverings–carpet and rugs - Philadelphia Carpets
PARLIAMENT - Furniture ☆ - Bassett Furniture Industries, Inc.
PARLIAMENT - Trailers–travel ☆ - Coachmen Industries, Inc.
PARLIAMENT COLLECTION - Mattresses - R.F. Simmons Co.
PARLIAMENT HOUSE - Gimp - Gaetano Specialties Ltd.
PARLIAMENT LIGHTS - Cigarettes - Philip Morris Companies Inc.
PARLITE + - Glass products - BP Chemicals Inc. (Filon Products Div.)
PARLODEL - Pharmaceutical preparations - Sandoz Pharmaceuticals Corp.
PARLOID - Pharmaceutical preparations - Lanpar Co.
PARLOPHONE - Recording label - Sony Disco Inc.
PARLOR HORSE - Racks - Ortho-Flex Saddle Co., Inc.
PARLOR PERFECT - Confections - Signature Brands, LLC
PARLOR PETS - Toys–stuffed - Kamar International Inc.
PARLOR PIG - Sausages - Gold Kist Inc.
PARLOR PLANTATION - Terrariums, planters, etc. - IMS Corp.
PARLOR POSIES - Flowers, plants, and seeds ☆ - Applewood Seed & Garden Group
PARLOR PUZZLES - Puzzles - David Corp.
PARLOR STONE - Floor coverings - Congoleum Corp.
PARLORMANAGER - Computer hardware - Babson Bros. Co.
PARLORSCAN - Electronic equipment - Remote AG Data, Inc.
PARLOUR FAN, THE - Fans–ceiling ☆ - Fasco Industries Inc. (Consumer Products Div.)
PARLUX - Dryers–hair ☆ - RBI Distributors
PARLYN - Cough medicines - Parmed Pharmaceuticals, Inc.
PARLYN - Hardware - Blaine Window Hardware Inc.
PARMA - Food products - A.F.I. Food Service Distributors Inc.
PARMA - Mopeds ☆ - Motor Bikes Import
PARMA - Tools–garden - Nordlie Inc.
PARMA - Toys–automobiles - Parma International, Inc.

☆ = Now out of production

PARMA INTERNATIONAL - Furniture - Parma International, Inc.
PARMA RELLA - Food products - Rella Good Cheese Co.
PARMA VIOLET - Cosmetics - Lancome
PARMALAT LONG LIFE - Milk - Parmalat USA Corp.
PARMALEE - Floor coverings ☆ - Tarkett, Inc.
PARMANO - Cheese ☆ - Supreme Foods Inc.
PARMED - Pharmaceutical preparations ☆ - Parmed Pharmaceuticals, Inc.
PARMESAN - Cheese - Grande Cheese Co.
PARMESAN - Floor coverings—carpet and rugs ☆ - Regal Rugs Inc.
PARMIGIANO - Pamesan cheese ☆ - Grande Cheese Co.
PARMINE - Pharmaceutical preparations - Parmed Pharmaceuticals, Inc.
PARMINIC - Cough medicines - Parmed Pharmaceuticals, Inc.
PARNAMI - Pet products - Parnami Co.
PARNASSUS PRESS - Publisher's imprints - Houghton Mifflin Co.
PARNATAL - Pharmaceutical preparations ☆ - Murray Drug Corp.
PARNATE - Pharmaceutical preparations - Smithkline Beecham Corp.
PARNELL - Apparel—women's - Nanwani International Ltd.
PARNELL - Fabrics - Bibb Co.
PARNELL - Pharmaceutical preparations - Parnell Pharmaceuticals Inc.
PARNELL'S PRIDE - Nuts—salted, roasted, cooked, or canned - Peanut Corp. of America
PARNESS - Rings—jewelry - Artcarved Inc.
PARODI - Cigars - Avanti Cigar Co.
PARODRAW - Toys ☆ - Small World Toys
PARODY - Wines - ASV Wines, Inc.
PAROS - Faucets - Kallista Inc.
PAROS - Tape recorders ☆ - Edixa Camera Co.
PAROTHYL - Prescription drug ☆ - IDE-Interstate Inc.
PAROVITA - Crackers - Sunshine/Salerno Inc.
PAROWAX - Waxes—paraffin ☆ - BP America Inc.
PAROX - Detergents - Steritech Laboratories, Inc.
PARQ SQUARE - Floor coverings—carpet and rugs ☆ - Cumberland Mills Inc.
PARQUET - Clocks ☆ - General Time Corp. (Westclox/Seth Thomas Div.)
PARQUET - Floor coverings—carpet and rugs ☆ - Regal Rugs Inc.
PARQUET - Floor coverings—tile - Kentile Floors Inc.
PARQUET - Furniture ☆ - Hooker Furniture Corp.
PARQUET - Jewelry - Suna Bros. Inc.
PARR - Rubber—acrylic - ACCO USA, Inc.
PARR - Skin care products - Loctite Corp.
PARRALLEX - Floor coverings—carpet and rugs - Couristan Inc.
PARRANO - Cheese puffs - Best Cheese Corp.
PARRIS REPLICAS - Toys—guns - Parris Manufacturing Co.
PARRITZ HOTEL - Pet products - Pyramid Bird Toys
PARROT - Brooms - Wright-Bernet
PARROT - Food products - S and D Foods
PARROT - Kites ☆ - Hi-Flier Manufacturing Co.
PARROT - Meat products—canned - Sun Hing Foods, Inc.
PARROT - Printers—computer - Zygo Industries Inc.
PARROT & MACAW - Printers—computer - Zygo Industries Inc.
PARROT AUDIO BOOKS - Recording label - Walberg Publishing
PARROT BEAK - Machinery - Liftomatic Material Handling, Inc.
PARROT BELL - Pet products - Hill Top Enterprises
PARROT CHEW - Bird feeds - L/M Animal Farms, Inc.
PARROT HEAD CLUB - Apparel and accessories - Jimmy Buffett
PARROT MOUNTAIN - Coffee - Thomas/Hoe Inc.
PARROT MOUNTAIN - Pet shops - Dermo Inc.
PARROT PALS - Pet products - Emerald Bird Caddy
PARROT PASSAGES - Games - Parrot Passages, Inc.
PARROT PERFORMANCE - Bird feeds - Petland, Inc.
PARROT PLEASERS - Pet products - Polly's Pleasures
PARROT POPS - Candy - Sathers Inc.
PARROT ROCK - Pet products - Hill Top Enterprises
PARROT VALLEY - Pet shops - Dermo Inc.
PARROTATS - Pet products - Next to Nature
PARROTDISE - Pet products - Pyramid Bird Toys
PARROT'S PUNCH - Fruit drinks—bottled or canned - After the Fall Products Inc.
PARROTT'S - Ice cream - Parrott Ice Cream Co.
PARRUCCA COLLECTION, THE - Tiles—ceramic - Arte D'Italia Imports
PARSADOC - Computer software - Imas Ltd.
PARSEC - Antennas - Recoton Corp.
PARSEC MODEL 2000 - Audio equipment - Recoton Corp.
PARSIDOL - Pharmaceutical preparations ☆ - Parke-Davis
PARSIFAL - Computer software - Parsifal Systems, Inc.
PARSIFAL - Watches - Seville Watch Corp.
PARSLEY PATCH - Spices and extracts - McCormick & Co., Inc.

PARSNIP PETE - Candy - R.M. Palmer Co.
PARSONAGE CROSSING - Furniture - Woodpecker
PARSONS - Cabinets—wood - Parcraft Distinctive Cabinetry
PARSONS' - Floor waxes - Dial Corp.
PARSONS - Paper - Parsons Paper Co.
PARSONS COLLECTION - Furniture - Lane Co. Inc.
PARSONS CREEK - Wines - Parsons Creek Winery
PARSONS PLACE - Apparel and accessories ☆ - Kellwood Co.
PART-EASE - Lubricants - American Grease Stick Co.
PART OF THE HEALING - Health care products - Alphatec Research Institute
PART OF THE SOLUTION - Chemical preparations - Henkel Corp.
PART OF THE SOLUTION - Kitchen appliances - Emerson Electric Co.
PART TRACKER - Computer software - Borg Enterprises
PARTAGAS - Cigars - General Cigar Co., Inc.
PARTAGAS LIMITED RESERVE - Cigars - General Cigar Co., Inc.
PARTAGER - Wines - Gold Seal Vineyards Inc.
PARTAKE - Food products - Plee-Zing Inc.
PARTANE - Cough medicines - Parmed Pharmaceuticals, Inc.
PARTAPP - Pharmaceutical preparations - Parmed Pharmaceuticals, Inc.
PARTEE - Floor coverings - Partee Flooring Mill
PARTEE - Toys—stuffed ☆ - Russ Berrie and Co., Inc.
PARTEIN - Pharmaceutical preparations - Lanpar Co.
PARTEN - Pharmaceutical preparations - Parmed Pharmaceuticals, Inc.
PARTEZE - Lubricants - Kano Laboratories Inc.
PARTHA - Figurines - Rawcliffe Corp.
PARTHENON - Adhesives and sealants ☆ - Parthenon Co. Inc.
PARTHENON - Flatware - Reed and Barton Corp.
PARTHENON - Floor coverings - Congoleum Corp.
PARTHENON - Floor coverings—carpet and rugs - Mannington Carpets, Inc.
PARTHENON - Floor coverings—carpet and rugs ☆ - Hollytex Carpet Mills Inc.
PARTHENON - Furniture ☆ - Lane Co. Inc.
PARTHIAN KINGS - Games ☆ - Avalon Hill Game Co.
PARTI-KRAFT - Boats—pontoons - Polar Kraft Manufacturing Co.
PARTI STICKS - Candy - Bobs Candies Inc.
PARTI STYLE - Meat products—beef - Armour Swift-Eckrich
PARTICIPANT - Floor coverings—carpet and rugs - Mohawk Carpet Corp.
PARTICULARES - Cigars ☆ - Tropical Tobacco, Inc.
PARTICULARS, THE - Rings—jewelry - Feature Enterprises
PARTISOL - Measuring instruments - Rupprecht & Patashnick Co., Inc.
PARTISOME - Chemical preparations - Molecular Bioquest Inc.
PARTITION EXPERT - Computer software - Platinum Technology, Inc.
PARTNER - Apparel—men's ☆ - Sampson Inc.
PARTNER - Artists' materials - Artoptic International Corp.
PARTNER - Herbicides - Monsanto Co.
PARTNER - Saws—chain ☆ - Husqvarna Forest & Garden Co.
PARTNER - Scooters—motorized - Pride Health Care, Inc.
PARTNER 2 - Telephones - At&T Corp.
PARTNER MAIL VS - Computer software - At&T Corp.
PARTNER PLUS - Dog food - Wilson Fertilizer & Grain
PARTNER WITH THE BRIGHTEST MINDS IN LAW - Computer storage devices—optical - Matthew Bender & Co., Inc.
PARTNERING FOR QUALITY - Craft supplies - Vans, Inc.
PARTNERS - Audio equipment - Teledyne Acoustic Research
PARTNERS - Crackers - Partners
PARTNERS - Wallpaper - Kingfisher Wallcoverings
PARTNERS 5 - Wallpaper ☆ - Kingfisher Wallcoverings
PARTNERS AGAINST PAIN - Educational materials - Purdue Pharma L.P.
PARTNERS IN AMERICANA - Wallpaper ☆ - Kingfisher Wallcoverings
PARTNERS IN GRIME - Filters—air - Donaldson Co., Inc.
PARTNERS IN PRINT - Video production - Creative Teaching Press
PARTNERS WITH TOMORROW - Electronic equipment - Pacific Coast Technologies
PARTNERSHIP CHESS - Games ☆ - Ridgeview Enterprises Inc.
PARTOUT - Apparel—women's ☆ - Partout International Corp.
PARTRADE - Hardware - Outdoor Sports Industries
PARTREX - Pharmaceutical preparations - Parmed Pharmaceuticals, Inc.
PARTRIDGE - Meat products—canned - Partridge Meats Inc.
PARTRIDGE KIDS TUNES, THE - Publisher's imprints - Market Place
PARTRIDGE LANE - Wallpaper ☆ - Benchmark Preferred Wallcoverings
PARTRIDGE PRESS - Publisher's imprints - Omnigraphics Inc.
PARTRIDGE SINCE 1876 - Meat products - John Morrell & Co.
PARTRON C - Pharmaceutical preparations - Parmed Pharmaceuticals, Inc.
PARTS EXPRESS - Audio equipment - Parts Express International, Inc.
PARTS-GENIE - Computer software - Computer Systems and Solutions, Inc.
PARTS-IN-MINUTES - Chemical preparations - Ciba-Geigy Corp.

☆ = Now out of production

PARTS MASTER - Automotive parts and accessories - Auto Value Associates, Inc.

PARTS NOW - Metals - Soligen, Inc. (Soligen Technologies Inc.)

PARTS PLUS - Tools–hand-operated - Parts Inc.

PARTS WASHER IN A CAN - Cleaning preparations - Mirachem Corp.

PARTSLINK - Computer peripheral equipment - Freightliner Corp.

PARTSTALK - Computer software - Digitalk, Inc.

PARTUSS - Pharmaceutical preparations - Parmed Pharmaceuticals, Inc.

PARTUSS-A - Analgesics ☆ - Parmed Pharmaceuticals, Inc.

PARTY - Artists' materials - Duncan Enterprises

PARTY - Candy - Sunset Paper Products Inc.

PARTY - Cookies - Parco Foods, Inc.

PARTY - Games ☆ - Koplow Games

PARTY ANIMAL - Costumes - Fun World Inc.

PARTY ANIMAL - Straws–drinking - Sansom, Inc.

PARTY ANIMALS - Apparel and accessories - Owen Ryan Associates, Ltd.

PARTY ANIMALS - Candy ☆ - R.M. Palmer Co.

PARTY ANIMALS - Toys–electronic - Axlon Inc.

PARTY BAKE - Toys - Mattel, Inc.

PARTY BALL, THE - Dinnerware ☆ - Ingrid

PARTY BARS - Cookies - Parco Foods, Inc.

PARTY BASKET - Candy - Home of the Hebert Candies, Inc.

PARTY BEAR - Toys–stuffed - Dakin Inc.

PARTY BROWNIES - Food products - General Mills, Inc.

PARTY CAKE - Food products - General Mills, Inc.

PARTY CAKE CENTER, THE - Cakes - Coast Novelty Manufacturing Co.

PARTY CARDS - Invitations ☆ - Morgan & Morgan

PARTY CAT - Boats - International Marine & Aviation Equipment Inc.

PARTY CAT - Toys–stuffed - Russ Berrie and Co., Inc.

PARTY CENTER, THE - Cakes - Coast Novelty Manufacturing Co.

PARTY CHEESE - Snack foods - Pepperidge Farm Inc.

PARTY CHEF - Cooking equipment–household - GSW Jackes-Evans Manufacturing Co.

PARTY CHEST - Beverages–malt ☆ - Pabst Brewing Co.

PARTY CHIEF - Computer software - Ramss, Inc.

PARTY CLUB - See **SUNNY SQUARE**

PARTY COLORS - Cosmetics ☆ - Caran D'Ache of Switzerland Inc.

PARTY COLOURS - Cosmetics - Zauder Bros. Inc.

PARTY CUBIES - Ice chests - Reliable Plastics

PARTY CUPBOARD - Toys - Little Tikes Co.

PARTY CUPS - Cups–plastic - James River Corp.

PARTY DAZZLE - Dolls - Mattel, Inc.

PARTY DECKER - Boats - H & H Molded Products

PARTY DOTS - Decals and transfers - Molly O'Brien-Smith

PARTY ELEPHANT - Toys–stuffed - Dakin Inc.

PARTY EXPRESS - Plates–paper - Hallmark Cards Inc.

PARTY EXPRESSIONS - Paper - Hallmark Cards Inc.

PARTY FACTORY - Office supplies - Impact International Inc.

PARTY FAVORITES - Meat products - John Morrell & Co.

PARTY FAVORS - Dresses–girls' - Baylis Co.

PARTY FIXXER - Vitamins and nutritional supplements - CVC Specialties

PARTY FRILLS - Toothpicks - Royal Paper Products Inc.

PARTY FROSTING - Food products - General Mills, Inc.

PARTY GEAR - Pet products ☆ - Gerard-Pellham Co.

PARTY GIRL - Health care products - New Ideas International, Inc.

PARTY GIRL - Perfume and necklace - Cosrich Inc.

PARTY GRAHAMS - Cookies - Nabisco Foods Group

PARTY HANGERS - Garment hangers - Miller Studio

PARTY HOLDEMS - Trays - Funzone Co.

PARTY HOUNDS - Pretzels - D.F. Stauffer Biscuit Co., Inc.

PARTY HOUR - Tableware–plastic ☆ - Creative Expressions Group

PARTY HOUSE - Paper goods - Van Dow-Fenton Inc.

PARTY IN A BOX - Decorations - Hollee Krizen

PARTY IN PINK - Dolls - Mattel, Inc.

PARTY ISLAND - Boats–liferafts - Coleman Co., Inc.

PARTY JELLIES - Candy - Thos. D. Richardson Co.

PARTY KENYA - Dolls - Tyco Industries, Inc.

PARTY KITCHEN - Toys - Little Tikes Co.

PARTY LACE - Dolls - Mattel, Inc.

PARTY LIGHTS - Candles - Biedermann & Sons Inc.

PARTY LIKE IT'S 1999 - Paper products - Myrna Ann Capers

PARTY LINE - Apparel–women's - Wacoal America Inc.

PARTY LINES - Games ☆ - Parker Brothers

PARTY LOUNGER, THE - Outdoor chair ☆ - Ingrid

PARTY MAGIC - Plates–paper - Gibson Greetings, Inc.

PARTY MANAGER, THE - Computer programs - Pem Software, Inc.

PARTY MANIA! - Party supplies - Factory Card Outlet of America, Ltd.

PARTY MATE - Novelty items - Pioneer Balloon Co.

PARTY MATS - Placemats - Partners in Fun

PARTY MONKEY - Toys–stuffed - Dakin Inc.

PARTY MOUNTS - Hardware - Miller Studio

PARTY 'N PLAY - Dolls - Mattel, Inc.

PARTY NIGHTS - Dolls - Mattel, Inc.

PARTY PAC - Popcorn - Atlas Biscuit Co. Inc.

PARTY PAC - Popcorn - Gilster-Mary Lee Corp.

PARTY PACK! - Food products - Little Caesar Enterprises, Inc.

PARTY PACK - Food products - Tyson Foods Inc.

PARTY-PACK - Spices and extracts - Jodie's Kitchen Inc.

PARTY PACKAGE - Cutlery ☆ - Lifetime Hoan Corp.

PARTY PAD, THE - Exercise/beach mat ☆ - Ingrid

PARTY PAK - Containers–plastic - GKG Corp.

PARTY PAK - Cups–plastic - New Wave Water Systems

PARTY PAK - Dinnerware–plastic ☆ - Plastics, Inc. (Anchor Hocking Plastics)

PARTY PAK - Novelty items ☆ - Gessner Products Co. Inc.

PARTY-PAK - Pickles - Paramount Foods Inc.

PARTY PAL - Containers - Coolers Unlimited

PARTY PAL - Dolls - Mattel, Inc.

PARTY PALETTE - Dishes–plastic - Spectrum International, Inc.

PARTY PALS - Barbecues and grills ☆ - Mr. Cheftender Products Inc.

PARTY-PATIO - Lighting fixtures - Lidco Co.

PARTY PAX - Paper ☆ - Wisconsin Tissue Mills Inc.

PARTY PENGUIN - Toys–stuffed - Dakin Inc.

PARTY PENS - Greeting cards ☆ - Amberley Greeting Card Co.

PARTY PEOPLE - Novelty items - Tilly Balloon Inc. / Center Stage Productions

PARTY PERFECT - Candy - L.E.G. Inc.

PARTY PERFECT - Dolls - Mattel, Inc.

PARTY PERFECT - Floor coverings–carpet and rugs - Alexander Smith Carpets

PARTY PET - Toys–stuffed - Dakin Inc.

PARTY PIECES - Confetti - Paper Co.

PARTY PIG - Containers–insulated - Quoin Industrial Inc.

PARTY PILL - Vitamins and nutritional supplements - Vitamin Research Products Inc.

PARTY PILLOWS - Candy - Thos. D. Richardson Co.

PARTY PINK - Dolls - Mattel, Inc.

PARTY PISTOL - Cooking equipment–household ☆ - Montgomery Ward & Co. Inc.

PARTY PITA - Breads - GDF, Inc.

PARTY PIXIES - Foil–tin ☆ - Jo-An Imports

PARTY PLAKS - Novelty items ☆ - Wry Idea Co.

PARTY PLASTICS PLUS - Dinnerware–plastic - First Phillips Manufacturing Corp.

PARTY PLATE - Dips–flea - Nyman Manufacturing Co.

PARTY PLATFORM - Boats–liferafts - Coleman Co., Inc.

PARTY PLATTER - Hotplates ☆ - Kaz Business Systems Inc.

PARTY-POPS - Ice making machinery ☆ - Flambeau Products Corp.

PARTY PREMIERE - Dolls - Mattel, Inc.

PARTY PRIDE - Ice cream cones ☆ - Safeway Stores Inc.

PARTY PRINCESS - Novelty items–paper ☆ - Unique Industries, Inc.

PARTY PRINTS - Disposable dresses ☆ - Creative Expressions Group

PARTY PUM'KINS - Chocolate candy - Superior Fruit & Confections

PARTY PUNCH - Beverages–alcohol ☆ - Wine Group Inc.

PARTY PUPS - Food products ☆ - Lightlife Foods, Inc.

PARTY SACK, THE - Picnic bag ☆ - Ingrid

PARTY SENSATION - Dolls - Mattel, Inc.

PARTY SERVER - Baking dish and wooden server ☆ - Corning Inc.

PARTY SHOT - Confetti - Leland Limited Inc.

PARTY SNACKSTER - Electrical equipment - Toastmaster Inc.

PARTY SPARKLEZ - Packaging–paper - Z-Barten Productions

PARTY SPIRIT, THE - Beverages–alcohol - Jim Beam Brands Co.

PARTY SPREAD - Cheese - Pine River Pre-Pack Inc.

PARTY SPRINKLES - Candy ☆ - Unique Industries, Inc.

PARTY STARTERS - Meats–luncheon - Field Packing Co.

PARTY STARTS HERE!, THE - Novelty items - Kuepper Favor Co., Inc.

PARTY STIX'S - Snack foods - Parco Foods, Inc.

PARTY TALK - Aprons - Now Designs

PARTY TEEN - Dolls - Mattel, Inc.

PARTY TIME - Dolls - Mattel, Inc.

PARTY TIME - Dolls ☆ - Effanbee Doll Corp.

PARTY TIME - Floor coverings–carpet and rugs - Kelly Group Inc.

PARTY TIME - Glassware–household - Durand International

PARTY TIME - Ice cream - Dairy Mart Convenience Stores, Inc.

PARTY TIME - Ice cream ☆ - Knudsen Dairy Products
PARTY TIME - Novelty items - Party Time Manufacturing Co.
PARTY-TIME - Socks - Neuville Industries Inc.
PARTY TIME - Tablecloths - Straubel Paper Co.
PARTY TO GO - Compact discs–prerecorded - Viacom International Inc.
PARTY TREAT - Beverages–carbonated - Certified Grocers of California, Ltd.
PARTY TREAT - Nuts–salted, roasted, cooked, or canned ☆ - CPC International Inc.
PARTY TREATS - Dolls - Mattel, Inc.
PARTY-TYME PLATE - Housewares - Molor Products Co.
PARTY WARE - Toys - Little Tikes Co.
PARTY WINGS - Chicken - B.C. Rogers Food Service, Inc.
PARTY WITH JEBS - Stationery - JEBS Custom Designs
PARTY ZONE - Games ☆ - Tsr, Inc.
PARTYCASE - Tableware–plastic ☆ - Oak Hill Industries Corp.
PARTYCRAFT MASTER - Hobby kits - Richard Marks
PARTYFLASH - Cameras - Eastman Kodak Co.
PARTYLINE - Novelty items–paper - Rodin Industries Inc.
PARTYLITES - Pastries - Dufour Pastry Kitchens Inc.
PARTYMATE - Mixed nuts - Azar Nut Co.
PARTYMATES - Novelty items ☆ - Gessner Products Co. Inc.
PARTYMUG - Novelty items ☆ - Oak Hill Industries Corp.
PARTY!PARTY! - Food products - Little Caesar Enterprises, Inc.
PARTYSTAR - Cameras - Eastman Kodak Co.
PARTYSTRIPE - Glassware–household ☆ - Oak Hill Industries Corp.
PARTYTIME - Cameras - Eastman Kodak Co.
PARTYTIME - Dinnerware - WNA Carthage, Inc.
PARTYTIME - Novelty items ☆ - Superior Balloon Co.
PARTYTIME - Tableware–plastic ☆ - Oak Hill Industries Corp.
PARTYTOWN USA - Toys - Party Town USA Inc.
PARURE - Perfumes ☆ - Guerlain Inc.
PARVACAL - Vitamins and nutritional supplements - Freeda Vitamins Inc.
PARVE - Cookies - Margareten Enterprises
PARVELICIOUS - Cookies - Margareten Enterprises
PARVENZYME - Vitamins and nutritional supplements - Freeda Vitamins Inc.
PARVLEX - Vitamins and nutritional supplements - Freeda Vitamins Inc.
PARVO-LAN 128 - Pet products - Glo-Marr Products Inc.
PARVOCINE - Veterinary pharmaceutical preparations - BioCor Inc.
PARVOSOL - Detergents - Hess & Clark, Inc.
PARVUS - Bathroom fixtures - Crane Plumbing/Fiat Products
PARVUSOL - Detergents - Hess & Clark, Inc.
PARYO-GUARD ML - Pet products - Thomas Veterinary Drug
PAS - Audio equipment - Professional Audio Systems
P.A.S. - Carts - Sage Products
PAS+ - Computer software - Cyma Systems, Inc.
PAS - Computers - Mercury Computer Systems Inc.
PAS - Gas machinery - MKS Instruments, Inc.
PAS III - Electrical equipment - Public Service Technologies, Inc.
PAS IIIA - Electrical equipment - Public Service Technologies, Inc.
PAS-KOTE - Finishing agents - ITW Paslode
P.A.S. PORT - Health care products - Sims Deltec, Inc.
P.A.S. PORT II - Health care products - Sims Deltec, Inc.
PAS SENTRY - Electrical equipment - Public Service Technologies, Inc.
P.A.S. SOD - Pharmaceutical preparations - Consolidated Midland Corp.
PAS-TEES - Posters - King's Art Inc.
PAS VR. - Electrical equipment - Public Service Technologies, Inc.
PASADENA - Bicycles ☆ - Huffy Corp.
PASADENA - Floor coverings ☆ - Congoleum Corp.
PASADENA - Furniture - National/Mt. Airy Furniture
PASADENA ROSE - Skin care products - Pasadena Research Laboratories, Inc.
PASAN POTTERY - Candles - Concept/Research, Concept/Development
PASCAL - Coffee - Pascal Coffee Inc.
PASCAL'S - Ice cream - Glacier Gourmet
PASCARELLA SANTE - Oils–edible - Sante Vito Trading Corp.
PASCO - Food products - Pastene Companies Ltd.
PASCO - Fruit drinks–bottled or canned ☆ - Lykes Services Co.
PASCO - Marine rigging - Pasco Marine Supply Inc.
PASCO - Paper - Paper Sales Corp.
PASCO-ERMAT - Marine rigging - Pasco Marine Supply Inc.
PASCO-FRED - Measuring instruments - Pasco Marine Supply Inc.
PASCO PURE - Water–bottled or canned ☆ - Lykes Services Co.
PASCO SCIENTIFIC - Computer software - Pasco Scientific
PASEO - Colognes - Clientele, Inc.
PASEO - Motor vehicles–automobiles - Toyota Motor Sales USA Inc.
PASER - Pharmaceutical preparations - Jacobus Pharmaceutical Co., Inc.

PASHA - Beverages–alcohol - Park Ave. Imports
PASHA - Cymbals ☆ - Grossman Music Corp.
PASHA - Fabrics - Gretchen Bellinger Inc.
PASHA - Paper–writing - Cartier Inc.
PASHA - Recording label - Pasha Music Organization Inc.
PASHI - Apparel and accessories - Elise J. Pashigian
PASIGRAM - Publisher's imprints - Paul Shoemaker
PASILLA NEGRO - Chili peppers–powdered ☆ - Frieda's, Inc.
PASIS - Computer software - Hughes Aircraft Co.
PASKALIUM - Pharmaceutical preparations - Glenwood LLC
PASLODE - Staplers - ITW Paslode
PASNA - Health care products ☆ - Barnes-Hind Inc.
PASO - Abrasive products ☆ - Charles Paint Research Inc.
PASO - Audio equipment - Paso Sound Products Inc.
PASOLINI ESTATE - Wines - Dieter Steinmann Inc.
PASQUA - Wines - Valley Cheese, Wine & Food Co.
PASQUALE CARAVETTA - Cheese - Peerless Cheese Co.
PASQUALES KITCHEN EXPRESS - Aprons - Universal Food Fork Corp.
PASQUALICHIO - Beef, pork, and poultry - Pasqualichio Brothers, Inc.
PASQUAL'S - Tortillas - San Pasqual's, Inc.
PASQUE - Fruits and vegetables - Pasquinelli Produce Co.
PASQUINI - Coffee - Pasquini Imports, Inc.
PASS - Electrotek Concepts, Inc.
P.A.S.S. - Health care products - Skil-Care Corp.
PASS - Tape players–cassette ☆ - Califone International Inc.
P.A.S.S.-III - Forms–preprinted - Personnel Systems Corp.
PASS-BACK FOOTBALL - Toys - Play Visions
PASS-IN - Paints - Solar Usage Now Inc.
PASS IT ONS - Novelty items–paper - Argus Communications
PASS-KEY - Automotive-stereo security system - Delco Electronics Corp.
PASS-LOC - Leather goods - St. Thomas Inc.
PASS N SHOOT - Games - Munro Games Inc.
PASS N THRU - Earrings and jewelry - Shube's Manufacturing, Inc.
PASS-OUT - Games - Golden's Magic Wand
PASS PAR TOUT - Apparel - Tyler Industries Inc.
PASS-PORT - Containers–paper - David Leinberger
PASS THE PIGS - Games - Milton Bradley Co.
PASS THE PIGS - Games - David Moffat Enterprises
PASS THE WORD - Greeting cards - Scott Matthew Luedtke
PASSA BROWN STUDIOS - Recording label - Wizard & Feather Brown Productions
PASSAGE - Bicycles - Schwinn Cycling & Fitness Inc.
PASSAGE - Floor coverings–carpet and rugs ☆ - Regal Rugs Inc.
PASSAGE - Furniture - Drexel Heritage Furnishings, Inc.
PASSAGE - Medical apparatus - Merit Medical Systems Inc.
PASSAGE - Motor vehicles–motor homes - Winnebago Industries, Inc.
PASSAGE - Perfumes - Gera Dist. Inc.
PASSAGE - Ships–sailing vessels - Hunter Marine Corp.
PASSAGER FUNWEAR - Apparel and accessories - M Hidary & Co., Inc.
PASSAGES - Floor coverings–carpet and rugs - Heuga USA
PASSAGES - Floor coverings–carpet and rugs - J and J Industries Inc.
PASSAGES - Frames - Intercraft Industries
PASSAGES - Luggage - AR Accessories Group Inc.
PASSAGES - Occasional tables - JDI Group, Inc.
PASSAGES - Wallpaper - Capital Carousel Inc.
PASSAGES - Wallpaper - Dekortex Inc.
PASSAGES - Wallpaper - Ozite Corp.
PASSAGES-INSPIRING THOUGHTS BY EMILY MATTHEWS - Greeting cards ☆ - American Greetings Corp.
PASSAGEWAY - Computer peripheral equipment - At&T Corp.
PASSAIC - Thread - Blue Mountain Industries, Inc.
PASSALARM - Alarm systems–burglar - Rampart Corp.
PASSAMAQUODDY TECHNOLOGY RECOVERY SCRUBBER - Gloves - Passamaquoddy Technology L.P.
PASSANTE - Wines ☆ - Jack Poust & Co. Inc.
PASSANTINO - Music–sheet - Music Sales Corp.
PASSASED - Pharmaceutical preparations ☆ - C.O. Truxton Inc.
PASSAT - Motor vehicles–automobiles - Volkswagen of America Inc.
PASSBOOK - Office supplies - R.A. Stewart Superior
PASSBOOKS - Publisher's imprints - National Learning Corp.
PASSEMENTERIE ECAL - Lace - Los Angeles Creative Embroidery, Inc.
PASSENDALE - Cheese - Swissrose International Inc.
PASSENGERS, THE - Luggage - Lake Shore Ltd.
PASSEREAUX - Tableware–china - Durand International
PASSFOLD - Leather goods - St. Thomas Inc.
PASSHIV - Pharmaceutical preparations - Verigen, Inc.

☆ = Now out of production

PASSIN THRU - Recording label - Jazz Composer's Orchestra Association Inc.
PASSING PARADE - Dolls ☆ - Effanbee Doll Corp.
PASSING ZONE - Food products - D.P. Dough, Inc.
PASSION - Beverages ☆ - Labatt Importers Inc.
PASSION - Colognes - Elizabeth Arden Inc.
PASSION - Cosmetics - Flori Roberts Inc.
PASSION - Floor coverings—carpet and rugs - Tuftex Carpet Mills, Inc.
PASSION - Razors - Image Media International, Inc.
PASSION - Toys—automobiles - Mattel, Inc.
PASSION - Wallcoverings - Ben James Ltd.
PASSION - Wallpaper - Carlton-Metro Wallcoverings
PASSION BLAST - Vitamins and nutritional supplements - Brent Laboratories, Inc.
PASSION BOUQUETS - Artificial and silk flower arrangements - Designs by Victoria, Inc.
PASSION CONTROL PILLS - Candy - Marsyl Inc. (Marsyl Enterprises, Inc.)
PASSION FOR COFFEE - Publisher's imprints - Sunset Publishing Corp.
PASSION FOR LEARNING - Toys - Passion for Learning Inc.
PASSION FOR MEN - Skin care products - Elizabeth Arden Inc.
PASSION MASSAGE LOTION - Lotions - Lawrence Research Group, Inc.
PASSION MIST - Hair care products ☆ - Peter Hantz Co.
PASSION MIST - Massage products - Lawrence Research Group, Inc.
PASSION PUNCH - Wines - Diamond Island Cellars Inc.
PASSION PYRAMIDS - Novelty items - Judith La Rue & Co.
PASSION SUPREME - Beverages—carbonated - Snapple Beverage Corp.
PASSIONATELY YOURS - Candy - Ethel M. Chocolates, Inc.
PASSIONATTA - Wines ☆ - Cadenasso Winery
PASSIONFRUIT - Teas - Eastern Shore Tea Co.
PASSIONS - Mattresses - Kingsdown, Inc.
PASSKETBALL - Sporting goods - Bruder Healthcare Co.
PASSLOCK - Automotive parts and accessories - General Motors Corp.
PASSPORT - Bedding—linen - Springs Industries, Inc.
PASSPORT - Cases—musical instrument - Shar Products, Inc.
PASSPORT - Cheese - Beatrice Cheese Co.
PASSPORT - Clocks ☆ - General Time Corp. (Westclox/Seth Thomas Div.)
PASSPORT - Computer software - Diversified Systems Resources Limited
PASSPORT - Computer software - Lane Telecommunications, Inc.
PASSPORT - Computer software ☆ - Gessler Publishing Co., Inc.
PASSPORT - Diapers—disposable - Mark One Healthcare Products Inc.
PASSPORT - Fabrics - Greenwood Mills Inc.
PASSPORT - Fabrics—tapestry ☆ - Columbus Coated Fabrics Co.
PASSPORT - Floor coverings - Congoleum Corp.
PASSPORT - Floor coverings—carpet and rugs - Coronet Carpets Inc.
PASSPORT - Frames—picture - Frame Factory
PASSPORT - Furniture - Pilliod Co.
PASSPORT - Furniture - Vogel Peterson Furniture Co.
PASSPORT - Gas machinery - Mine Safety Appliances Co.
PASSPORT - Golfing equipment - Illah California, Inc.
PASSPORT - Hearing aids - Argosy Electronics, Inc.
PASSPORT - House furnishings ☆ - Lexington Furniture Industries, Inc.
PASSPORT - Liquors - House of Seagram
PASSPORT - Luggage - Universal Trav-ler Inc.
PASSPORT - Medical apparatus - Datascope Corp.
PASSPORT - Medical apparatus - SPS Medical Supply Corp.
PASSPORT - Motor vehicles—motor homes - Forest River, Inc.
PASSPORT - Motor vehicles—sport-utility - American Honda Motor Co. Inc. (Acura Div.)
PASSPORT - Oriental rugs - Patusan Trading Co., Inc.
PASSPORT - Radar systems and equipment - Cincinnati Microwave, Inc.
PASSPORT - Recording label - Passport Records Inc.
PASSPORT - Remote control devices - Overhead Door Corp.
PASSPORT - Scooters—motorized - Leisure Lift, Inc.
PASSPORT - Ships—sailing vessels - Passport Yachts International
PASSPORT - Wallcovering - BDH Two, Inc.
PASSPORT - Wallpaper ☆ - Three Sisters Studio
PASSPORT - Wallpaper ☆ - Wallpaper Imports Inc.
PASSPORT 16 - Electrical equipment - Sun Industries, Inc.
PASSPORT, A - Food products ☆ - Flagship Foods Inc.
PASSPORT BOOKS - Publisher's imprints - NTC Contemporary Publishing Group
PASSPORT COLLECTION - Faucets ☆ - U.S. Brass Corp.
PASSPORT COLLECTION - Furniture—wood ☆ - Butler Specialty Co.
PASSPORT COLLECTION, THE - Luggage - Universal Trav-ler Inc.
PASSPORT CUISINE - Meat products - Nichirei Foods America
PASSPORT FIVESTAR - Measuring instruments - Mine Safety Appliances Co.
PASSPORT MIDI INTERFACE - Computer terminals - Passport Designs Inc.

PASSPORT TO ETERNITY WORD OF GOD ISAIAH 6:2 - Publisher's imprints - Tony L. Crisp
PASSPORT TO FRIENDSHIP - Stationery - Educational Insights, Inc.
PASSPORT TO MATH SUCCESS - Video production - Multimedia Tutorial Services, Inc.
PASSPORTGOLD - Computer software - Diversified Systems Resources Limited
PASSPORTMED - Computer software - Diversified Systems Resources Limited
PASSPORTS - Footwear—women's - Cels Enterprises Inc.
PASSPORTS - Knapsacks - Coleman Co., Inc.
PASSPROOF - Computer storage devices ☆ - Kensington
PASSWARE - Computer peripheral equipment - Spectar Solutions, Inc.
PASSWORD - Floor coverings—carpet and rugs ☆ - Walter Carpet Mills
PASSWORD - Games - Milton Bradley Co.
PASSWORD PLUS - Games ☆ - Milton Bradley Co.
PAST & PRESENT - Wallpaper - Winfield Design Associates, Inc.
PAST & PRESENT - Wallpaper ☆ - Glidden Co.
PAST IMPRESSIONS - Calendars ☆ - Amcal Inc.
PAST IMPRESSIONS - Toys - Alan G. Maley
PAST LIVES - Games - Avalon Hill Game Co.
PAST TENSE - Apparel—women's - QVC, Inc.
PAST TENSE - Syrup - Origins Natural Resources Inc.
PASTA - Apparel—women's - Paul Harris Stores, Inc.
PASTA - Floor coverings—carpet and rugs ☆ - Regal Rugs Inc.
PASTA - Food products - Golden Grain Co.
PASTA ABUNDANZA - Food products - Pometta's Italian Salsa
PASTA ACCENTS - Dinners—frozen - Green Giant Co.
PASTA ALLORA - Food products - Pasta Prospero
PASTA AMORE - Kitchen appliances - Keystone Manufacturing Co., Inc.
PASTA AVENUE - Food products - Chicago Brothers, Inc.
PASTA BAR - Food containers ☆ - Metrokane
PASTA BITES - Dog food - Thompson's Pet Pasta Products, Inc.
PASTA CHEF - Housewares - Rival Co.
PASTA CLASSICS - Food products - Del Monte Corp.
PASTA CRESPA - Snack foods - Pastabilities
PASTA CRUNCH - Noodles - Blue Bridge Enterprises, Inc.
PASTA CUISINE - Food products - Best Foods/Mueller Co.
PASTA CURLS - Pasta - Best Foods/Mueller Co.
PASTA DE FINO - Pasta - Shade Pasta Inc.
PASTA DEL GINNS - Kitchen appliances - Maverick Industries, Inc.
PASTA DEL MONDO - Pasta - Pasta Del Mondo Ltd.
PASTA DEL SOLE - Pasta - Ital Florida Foods, Inc.
PASTA DELLA VITA - Pasta - Food Services of America, Inc.
PASTA DI CICCIANO - Pasta - Marzoni Marketing
PASTA DI LUSSO - Pasta - Merlino & Sons
PASTA D'ORO - Pasta - The Pasta Fresca Co. Inc.
PASTA ELEGANTE - Pasta - Truscello & Sons Wholesalers Inc.
PASTA ESPRESSO - Ovens—roaster - Pasta Espresso USA, Inc.
PASTA FAVORITES - Dinners—frozen - Conagra, Inc.
PASTA FRESCA - Pasta - The Pasta Fresca Co. Inc.
PASTA FRESCA - Pasta ☆ - De Laurenti Specialty Food Market
PASTA FRESCA - Pasta ☆ - Homestyle Foods
PASTA GRANDE - Pasta - Pasta Grande
PASTA GROWERS - Pasta - Dakota Growers Pasta Co.
PASTA ITALIANO - Pasta - Hilton Commercial Group Inc.
PASTA KING - Cooking equipment—commercial - I.S.I. Cran, Inc.
PASTA LABELLA - Pasta - American Italian Pasta Co.
PASTA LEONARDO - Pasta - Noodles by Leonardo Inc.
PASTA LOUIGI - Spaghetti - Noodles by Leonardo Inc.
PASTA MAN, THE - Pasta - M & M RW, Inc.
PASTA MEALS - Tomato pastes and sauces - Van Den Bergh Foods Co.
PASTA MISTA - Food products - Golden Whisk Pasta Partners
PASTA PALS 'N SAUCE - Macaroni—canned - Crown Brands Inc.
PASTA PARTNERS - Food products - Golden Whisk Pasta Partners
PASTA PARTY - Food products - Golden Whisk Pasta Partners
PASTA PERFECT - Cooking equipment—commercial - Pitco Frialator, Inc.
PASTA PERFECT - Pasta - Norpac Services, Inc.
PASTA PERFECT - Pasta ☆ - Pillsbury Co.
PASTA PESTO - Salads—prepackaged - Byerly Foods Inc.
PASTA PETE - Pizzas—frozen - J.W.D., Inc.
PASTA PIPES - Toys - Mattel, Inc.
PASTA PLACE - Food products - Pasta Prospero
PASTA PLUS - Food products - Judyth's Mountain Inc.
PASTA POCKETS - Food products - Ateeco, Inc.
PASTA POUROVERS - Tomato pastes and sauces - Madison Inc.
PASTA PRIMA - Seasonings - McCormick & Co., Inc.

PASTA PRO - Kitchen appliances ☆ - National Housewares

PASTA PRONTO - Pasta - Myers Foods Inc.

PASTA RED - Wines - Knapp Farms, Inc.

PASTA REVOLUTION - Food products - Tony's Pizza Service

PASTA ROMANO - Spaghetti - Nestle USA

PASTA RONI - Food products - Golden Grain Co.

PASTA RUFFLES - Pasta ☆ - CPC International Inc.

PASTA SANITA - Pasta - Dakota Growers Pasta Co.

PASTA SECCA - Pasta - The Pasta Fresca Co. Inc.

PASTA SECRETS - Frozen foods - Dean Foods Vegetable Co.

PASTA TIME - Cooking equipment–household - Metrokane

PASTA TO GO - Pasta - Gusto Italiano

PASTA TOSS - Pasta - R.T. French Co.

PASTA TREES - Pasta - Buckeye Beans & Herbs, Inc.

PASTA USA - Pasta - Pasta USA Inc.

PASTA VALENTE FAT FREE MARINARA - Food products - Pasta Valente

PASTA VITALE - Pasta - Pasta USA Inc.

PASTA WAREHOUSE - Cheese - Jeffrey C.Villano

PASTA WITH GARDEN VEGETABLES - Food products - My Own Meals Inc.

PASTABILITIES - Food products - Golden Whisk Pasta Partners

PASTABILITIES - Food products - Pastabilities

PASTABREAD - Breads - Campione D'Italia Foods Inc.

PASTAIO - Pasta - Pasta Products

PASTAMANIA ! - Pasta - Hodgson Mill

PASTAMORE - Pasta - Glico Harmony Foods Corp.

PASTANECK - Seafood products–fresh or frozen ☆ - Atlantic LittleNeck ClamFarms Inc.

PASTAPRO - Cooking equipment–household - Farberware Inc.

PASTARIA - Pasta - Ravioli Kitchen Inc.

PASTARONI - Apparel–children's - Donna Christi Designs Inc.

PASTAVILLA - Pasta - Mira International Foods Inc.

PASTAZESTA - Pasta - Flavorzest Foods

PASTBEAM - Computer software - Georgia-Pacific Corp.

PASTE-AWAY - Paints - Reliable Finishing Products, Inc.

PASTE-EEZ - Underwear and nightwear - Mark S. Johnson

PASTE LYTE - Veterinary nutritional supplements - Purina Mills, Inc.

PASTE-MATES - Adhesives and sealants - Scratch-Art Co., Inc.

PASTE-THE-WALL - Wallpaper ☆ - Allpro Corp.

PASTE-WELL - Machinery - Paste-Well Corp.

PASTE WITHOUT PASTE - Toys ☆ - Warren Industries Inc.

PASTEL - Ceramic tile - Interceramic Inc.

PASTEL - Recording label - Orange Record Co. Inc.

PASTEL - Tiles–ceramic ☆ - KPT Inc.

PASTEL BALLET - Dinnerware - Corning Inc.

PASTEL BOUQUET - Cookware ☆ - Corning Inc.

PASTEL HEARTS CLOWN - Toys–stuffed - Dakin Inc.

PASTEL LIQUID SEQUINS - Paints ☆ - DecoArt, Inc.

PASTEL LITE - Window coverings - Evashin Wood U.S. Co.

PASTEL MAGIC MARBLE - Kaleidoscopes - Gemini Kaleidoscopes

PASTEL PARCHMENT - Greeting cards - Norcross Inc.

PASTEL PATTIES - Candy - Thos. D. Richardson Co.

PASTEL PETS - Puzzles - Milton Bradley Co.

PASTEL PLAYMATES - Toys - Pansy Ellen Products, Inc.

PASTEL POODLES - Greeting cards - Norcross Inc.

PASTEL SHAVERS - Bic Corp.

PASTEL VIOLETS - Glassware–household ☆ - Fenton Art Glass Co.

PASTELCLOTH - Canvas–artists' - New York Central Art Supply Co.

PASTELLE - Floor coverings–carpet and rugs ☆ - Heuga USA

PASTELLE - Giftware ☆ - Gorham Inc.

PASTELLE - Paper - Strathmore Paper Co.

PASTELLE - Tiles–ceramic ☆ - Latco Products

PASTELLE CAMEOS - Stationery - Burgoyne Inc./Curtis Swann

PASTELLES & PRINTS - Wallpaper ☆ - Andover Wallcovering

PASTELLO - Chalk - Dixon Ticonderoga Co.

PASTELNA - Scissors–hand-operated - Acme United Corp.

PASTELS - Baskets–wood - Coe & Dru Inc.

PASTELS - Floor coverings–carpet and rugs ☆ - Hollytex Carpet Mills Inc.

PASTELS - Skin care products - Pastels International, Inc.

PASTELS - Yogurt-based food beverages - Homestead, Inc.

PASTELS DE PAPILLONS - Cosmetics - Lancome

PASTELS FROM PARADISE - Nail care products ☆ - Noxell Corp.

PASTE'N HANG - Adhesives and sealants - Synkoloid Co.

PASTENE - Food products - Pastene Companies Ltd.

PASTFINDER - Computer software - Activision, Inc.

PASTICCINI DI BURRO - Baked goods - Dicamillo Baking Co. Inc.

PASTICHE - Floor coverings–carpet and rugs - J.L. Benson Co.

PASTICHE - Handbags - Pastiche, Inc.

PASTICHE - A LITTLE BIT OF EVERYTHING - Apparel–women's - Pastiche, Inc.

PASTICK - Markers–felt-tip - Pentel of America, Ltd.

PASTILLAS MCCOY - Health care products - McCoy's Products Inc.

PASTILLE - Fabrics - Gretchen Bellinger Inc.

PASTILLE - Floor coverings–carpet and rugs ☆ - Masland Corp.

PASTILLE FRIEZE - Floor coverings–carpet and rugs - Couristan Inc.

PASTIME - Children's craft kits - Pastime Industries Inc.

PASTIME - Computer software - Catherine Julianne Benke

PASTIME - Playing cards ☆ - United States Playing Card Co.

PASTIME - Sporting goods - Sports Doctor

PASTINE - Pasta - The Pasta Fresca Co. Inc.

PASTIROL - Cough drops - Nabisco Foods Group

PASTIZZA - Pasta - Pastizza's Inc.

PASTLANDS, B.C. - Sweaters - Esquire Knits, Inc.

PASTOR DA SERRA - Cheese - Happy Goat Farm Inc.

PASTORAL - Cooking utensils–aluminum ☆ - Reston Lloyd Ltd.

PASTORAL - Glassware–household - Durand International

PASTORALE - Dishes–china - Pasmantier Co. Inc.

PASTORALE - Floor coverings–carpet and rugs ☆ - Karastan-Bigelow Inc.

PASTORI - Wines - Pastori Winery

PASTROLI - Filled pastry ☆ - B & H Pizza Co.

PASTRY CAFE - Dolls - Mattel, Inc.

PASTRY FILS - Bakery products - Yohay Baking Co. Inc.

PASTRY GARDEN, THE - Bakeries - Diana Adams

PASTRY KING - Flour–blended - Acme-Evans/A.D.M. Milling Co.

PASTRY MAGIC.WATCH IT RISE - Pastries - PF Brands, Inc.

PASTRY POCKETS - Cakes - Tastykake Inc.

PASTRY POCKETS - Doughs–frozen ☆ - Pillsbury Co.

PASTRY POPPERS - Pastries - Auburn Farms, Inc.

PASTRY PRIDE - Whipped topping–frozen - Presto Food Products, Inc.

PASTRY RIDGE FARM - Confections - Country Cottage Bake Shop

PASTRY SHOP - Food products - Conagra, Inc.

PASTRY SHOPPE - Bakery products ☆ - Specialty Bakers Inc.

PASTRY STIX - Bakery products - Design Foods

PASTUNETTE - Underwear and nightwear ☆ - M.A. Rabinowitz Corp.

PASTURE AID - Animal feed supplements - PM AG Products Inc.

PASTURE KING - Farm machinery - Sukup Manufacturing Co.

PASTURE PARTNER - Animal feeds - Stevens Industries Inc.

PAT - Computer software - Board Room, Inc.

PAT - Dolls ☆ - Effanbee Doll Corp.

PAT 1000 - Ribbons - Roselin Manufacturing Co. Inc.

PAT-A-CAKE - Dolls ☆ - Effanbee Doll Corp.

PAT-AMARI PAPERWORKS - Greeting cards - Patricia B. Harris

PAT AUTOMATIC DOUBLES TRAP - Sporting goods - Stuart W. Patenaude

PAT BOOTH - Colognes - Pat Booth's Miami, Inc.

PAT CASH - Shoes–athletic - Diadora America

PAT FARRELL - Greeting cards - Stephen Lawrence Co.

PAT FASHIONS - Apparel–women's - Pat Fashions Industries Inc.

PAT GARRETT - Toys–guns - Daisy Manufacturing Co.

PAT HAND - Food products - Hansen Fruit & Cold Storage Co., Inc.

PAT-IT - Adhesives and sealants - Minnesota Mining & Manufacturing Co.

PAT KEY KEEPER - Key rings ☆ - Park Sherman

PAT O'BRIEN'S - Beverages–carbonated - Franco's Cocktail Products Inc.

PAT O'BRIEN'S - Novelty items - Pat O'Brien's Bar Inc.

PAT O'BRIEN'S HURRICANE - Beverages–alcohol - Pat O'Brien's Bar Inc.

PAT ON THE BACK - Dolls - Joseph Glaser

PAT PAULSEN VINEYARDS - Wines - Pat Paulsen Vineyards

PAT PIN-ON - Pencils ☆ - Park Sherman

PAT PRINTS - Greeting cards - Pat Prints Inc.

PAT REELRITER - Pens ☆ - Park Sherman

PAT STAMP KEEPER - Office supplies ☆ - Park Sherman

PATAANK - Video games ☆ - Pf. Magic, Inc.

PATAGONIA - Apparel and accessories - Patagonia, Inc.

PATAGONIA QUALITY SINCE 1975 - Apparel and accessories - Patagonia, Inc.

PATAGONIAN - Flooring–hardwood - Standard Plywood Inc.

PATAK - Food products machinery - R.T. French Co.

PATAKS - Food products - Gourmet America

PATALOHA - Shirts - Patagonia, Inc.

PATAN - Bedding–linen - Dan River Inc.

PATANOL - Pharmaceutical preparations - Alcon Laboratories, Inc.

PATAPSCO - Footwear ☆ - P.H. Volk Co.

PATARA - Floor coverings–carpet and rugs ☆ - Evans-Black Carpet Mills

PATATINA - Dolls - Cardinal Industries, Inc.

☆ = Now out of production

PATATO - Drums–musical instruments - LP Music Group
PATAY - Pumps - Parker Industries Inc.
PATCH - Puzzles - Patch Products, Inc.
PATCH AID - Chemical preparations - Coastal Industries Inc.
PATCH-ALL - Adhesives and sealants - Comstar International Inc. (IPC Div.)
PATCH-ALL - Adhesives and sealants - Synkoloid Co.
PATCH & PUMP - Automotive parts and accessories - Stop & Go International
PATCH & SEAL - Caulking compounds - Somay Products Inc.
PATCH ANTENNA, THE - Antennas - International Cellular Communications, Llc.
PATCH BALANCE - Computer software - Hunter Engineering Co.
PATCH-BOND - Cement ☆ - Atlas Chemical Co.
PATCH COMMANDER - Audio equipment - Meico Electronics
PATCH-IT - Adhesives and sealants - Pettit Paint Co. Inc.
PATCH KITS FOR PEOPLE - Gauze–surgical - Polymedica Healthcare, Inc.
PATCH-MAGIC - Adhesives and sealants ☆ - GS Roofing Products Co.
PATCH MASTER - Computer software ☆ - Voyetra Technologies Inc.
PATCH MATES - Adhesives and sealants - Bil-Dry Corp.
PATCH 'N CONTOUR - Tools - Red Devil Inc.
PATCH 'N FILL - Putties - Red Devil Inc.
PATCH-N-PAINT - Mortars–clay - Custom Building Products
PATCH OF SHADES - Musical instruments - Stick Enterprises, Inc.
PATCH PEDDLER - Bedding–linen - Goosefeathers
PATCH-RITE - Adhesives and sealants - Synkoloid Co.
PATCH STICK - Caulking compounds - Dap Products Inc.
PATCH, THE - Stickers - Randolph Joseph Biernacki
PATCH TREE - Patches, insignia, and emblems ☆ - A-B Emblem Corp.
PATCH-UPS - Novelty items–stitched ☆ - Best Emblem & Insignia Co. Inc.
PATCH USA, THE - Apparel and accessories - Nightrider Leathers
PATCHADAPS - Electronic equipment - Tower Products, Inc.
PATCHCRETE - Building materials–concrete - Lyons Distributing, Inc.
PATCH'EMS - Home product - Atlanta Sundries Inc.
PATCHES - Hobby kits ☆ - Accent Studios Inc.
PATCHES BUNNY - Toys–stuffed - Russ Berrie and Co., Inc.
PATCHES FOR LIFE - Patches, insignia, and emblems - Wet Seal Inc.
PATCHES OF JOY - Patterns–clothing - Patches of Joy
PATCHES PUP - Toys–stuffed - Russ Berrie and Co., Inc.
PATCHIT - Concrete products - Sealwall Products Inc.
PATCHIT! - Plaster–wallboard - Marshalltown Trowel Co.
PATCHITT - Dolls - Mattel, Inc.
PATCHMARK - Computer peripheral equipment - Network Assemblies Corp.
PATCHMASTER - Garden equipment - Scotts Co. (Organics Business Group)
PATCHO - Floor slabs–concrete - Roxseal Products
PATCHUP - Flowers, plants, and seeds - J. & L. Adikes Inc.
PATCHVIEW - Computer peripheral equipment - Voyetra Technologies Inc.
PATCHWORK - Floor coverings–carpet and rugs - Regal Rugs Inc.
PATCHWORK - Floor coverings–carpet and rugs ☆ - Colonial Mills Inc.
PATCHWORK - Floor coverings–carpet and rugs ☆ - Quaker Inc.
PATCHWORK & PATTERNS - Wallpaper - Milbrook Wallcoverings
PATCHWORK SQUARES - Fabrics–quilted ☆ - Mats Etc. Inc.
PATCHWORKER PLANNER, THE - Tools - Distlefink Designs, Inc.
PATCHWORKS - Chocolate bars - Silver Palate Kitchen
PATCHWORKS - Roofing materials - Master's Choice Inc.
PATCO - Automotive parts and accessories - Protective Automotive Trim Co. Inc.
PATCOMM - Transceivers - Patcomm Corp.
PATCRAFT - Floor coverings - Queen Carpet Corp.
PATCRAFT - Floor coverings–carpet and rugs - Patcraft Mills Inc.
PATCRAFT COMMERCIAL SD NYLON - Floor coverings–carpet and rugs - Queen Carpet Corp.
PATE - Gasoline - Exxon Corp.
PATE SUPREME - Dog food - Kal Kan Foods, Inc.
PATEAU - Watches ☆ - Ballandra Corp.
PATEFONAS - Recording label - Clay Pigeon Records
PATEK PHILIPPE - Watches - Henri Stern Watch Agency Inc.
PATELLALIGNER - Braces–orthopedic - JUZO
PATEL'S CASH & CARRY - Oils–essential - V. Patel and Sons, Inc.
PATENE ARTECTURA - Concrete products - Bomanite Corp.
PATENT 1 - Legal services - Joseph T. Regard, Ltd. APLC
PATENT 289 - Hair care products - Wella Corp. (Consumer Products Div.)
PATENT-CD - Computer storage devices–optical - Patentec
PATENT IT YOURSELF - Computer software - Nolo Press/Folklaw Inc.
PATENTPOWER - Computer software - MicroPatent L.L.C.
PATENTRAX - Computer software - Iris Information Systems, Inc.
PATENTWORKS - Computer storage devices - Smartpatents, Inc.
PATERNAYAN - Hobby kits - Carilorz Corp.

PATERNAYAN - Yarn - JCA, Inc.
PATERNOSTER - Wines ☆ - Orion Imports Ltd.
PATERSON - Photographic equipment - Tiffen Manufacturing Corp.
PATERSON BRONTE - Breads ☆ - Chase Collection, Inc.
PATETOE - Recording label - Jazz Composer's Orchestra Association Inc.
PATH 411 - Computer hardware - International Business Systems, Inc.
PATH BEATER - Toys–automobiles - Mattel, Inc.
PATH CLIMBER - Bicycles - Kent International Inc.
PATH LIGHT - Electrical equipment - Graham Group LLC
PATH PILOT, THE - Lighting fixtures - Kim Lighting Inc.
PATH TO FUJI - Wallpaper - Textile Wallcoverings International Ltd.
PATHDETECT - Medical apparatus - Stratagene
PATHE - Cameras–motion picture ☆ - Heitz Service Corp.
PATHE MARCONI-EMI - Recording label ☆ - Connoisseur Society Inc.
PATHFINDER - Humphrey Systems
PATHFINDER - Binoculars - Olympus America Inc.
PATHFINDER - Boats ☆ - Alumitech Inc.
PATHFINDER - Boats–canoes - Old Town Canoe Co.
PATHFINDER - Carpet cleaning equipment - Jon-Don Products, Inc.
PATHFINDER - Dog food - AGP Petfoods
PATHFINDER - Doors - Hufcor Inc.
PATHFINDER - Guns - Charter Arms
PATHFINDER - Lighting fixtures - Hubbell Lighting, Inc. (Lighting Div.)
PATHFINDER - Luggage - Paragon Luggage, Inc.
PATHFINDER - Luggage - Welsh Sporting Goods Corp. (Boyt Div.)
PATHFINDER - Meters–water - Futurestar Corp.
PATHFINDER - Motor vehicles–motor homes ☆ - Coachmen Recreational Vehicle Co.
PATHFINDER - Motor vehicles–sport-utility - Nissan Motor Corp. USA
PATHFINDER - Motors–outboard - G. & R. Industries Inc.
PATHFINDER - Musical instruments - Fred Gretsch Enterprises
PATHFINDER - Navigational instruments ☆ - Ray Jefferson
PATHFINDER - Paper–writing - Dur-O-Lite Inc.
PATHFINDER - Radar systems and equipment - Raytheon Co.
PATHFINDER - Scooters–motorized - Medical Equipment Distributors, Inc.
PATHFINDER - Searchlights - ACR, Electronics, Inc.
PATHFINDER - Shoes ☆ - Justin Cos.
PATHFINDER - Sporting goods - Precise International/Wenger
PATHFINDER - Toys - Tonka Corp.
PATHFINDER - Toys–models ☆ - Estes Industries
PATHFINDER PLUS - Medical apparatus - Utah Medical Products, Inc.
PATHFINDER TRAVELING SPRINKLER - Sprinklers–lawn - Thompson Manufacturing Co.
PATHFORWARD - Computer software - Pathfinder, Inc.
PATHGUARD - Computer peripheral equipment - American PCs, L.P.
PATHILON - Pharmaceutical preparations ☆ - Lederle Laboratories
PATHKEY - Computer hardware - Paralon Technologies, Inc.
PATHMAKER - Computer software - Applied Quality Methods Inc.
PATHMAKER - Electronic equipment - Texscan Corp.
PATHMAKER - Guitars - Abraham Wechter
PATHMARK - Fruit drinks–bottled or canned - Golden Gem Growers Inc.
PATHMARK - Pizza - Continental Food Products Inc.
PATHMARK WASH CYCLE - Fabric softeners - Supermarkets General Corp.
PATHMASTER - Navigational instruments - Rockwell International Corp.
PATHOCIDE - Computer software - Upjohn Co.
PATHOCIL - Pharmaceutical preparations - Wyeth-Ayerst Laboratories
PATHQUEST - Computer software - Automation Association, Inc.
PATHS TO FREEDOM - Computer software - Encyclopaedia Britannica Inc.
PATHWATCH - Optical machinery - Detector Electronics Corp.
PATHWAY - Cosmetics - Reliv' International, Inc.
PATHWAY MUSIC - Recording label - Church of God
PATHWAYS - Furniture - Steelcase Inc.
PATHWAYS - Furniture ☆ - Bassett Furniture Industries, Inc.
PATHWAYS FOR PEOPLE - Notebooks and notepads - Rodale Press, Inc.
PATHWAYS INTERACTIVE ELECTRONIC PUBLISHING - Computer software - Westinghouse Electric Corp.
PATHWAYS OF SOUND - Recording label - Pathways of Sound Inc.
PATHWAYS TO EXCELLENCE - Video production - Pacific Institute Inc.
PATHWAYS TO HEALING - Recording label - Roberta M. Savitt
PATHWAYS TO SUCCESS - Posters - Successories, Inc.
PATHWORDS - Computer software - CBS Software
PATI - Computer hardware - Comdial Corp.
PATI - Hair care products ☆ - RBI Distributors
PATI O BOLT - Locks–door - Perfection Products
PATIENCE - Giftware ☆ - Brushcreek Creative Co.
PATIENT ACCESS SYSTEM - Carts - Sage Products

PATIENT-AIDS - Medical apparatus - Kendall Co.
PATIENT CARE TECHNOLOGIES - Computer software - Patient Care Technologies, Inc.
PATIENT-EASE - Health care products ☆ - Invacare Corp.
PATIENT EDUCATION CENTER - Educational displays - On Target Media, Inc.
PATIENT INFORMATION MANAGER - Computer software - Emfotec Information Systems Corp.
PATIENT MATE - Medical apparatus - Hill Rom, Inc.
PATIENT MONITOR, THE - Medical apparatus - American Clicical Industries
PATIENT PEOPLE - Magnets - Russ Berrie and Co., Inc.
PATIENTGUARD - Linen - Compass Group Marketing, Inc.
PATIENT'S CHOICE - Dental equipment - Crosstex
PATILEZ - Games - Imaginations Unlimited, Inc.
PATIMA - Apparel and accessories - Pleasure-Knit Corp.
PATINA - Brass products ☆ - European Imports of California Inc.
PATINA - Cabinets - Classic Bath Products
PATINA - Fabrics - Dan River Inc.
PATINA - Floor coverings - Congoleum Corp.
PATINA - Floor coverings–carpet and rugs - Hollytex Carpet Mills Inc.
PATINA - Floor coverings–carpet and rugs - Robertex Associates Inc.
PATINA - Frames–picture - Framemica Co.
PATINA - Furniture - Patina, Inc.
PATINA - House furnishings ☆ - Ernest Sohn Creations
PATINA - Shoe polish - Trina/Genie
PATINA - Tableware–china - Pfaltzgraff Investment Co.
PATINA - Wallpaper - Capital Carousel Inc.
PATINA - Wallpaper - Maya Romanoff Corp.
PATINA - Yarn - Rainbow Gallery, Inc.
PATINA - Yarn - William Unger & Co. Inc.
PATINA ANTICO - Wallpaper - Robert Crowder & Co.
PATINA ITALIA - Furniture - Patina, Inc.
PATINA PLUS - Wallpaper - Capital Carousel Inc.
PATINA PLUS - Wallpaper - Roger Nicholson Designs Ltd.
PATINA RUB - Furniture polish and wax ☆ - H.F. Staples & Co. Inc.
PATINA SUPREME - Floor coverings–carpet and rugs - Hollytex Carpet Mills Inc.
PATINA TOO - Floor coverings–carpet and rugs - Hollytex Carpet Mills Inc.
PATINE - Dinnerware–glass ☆ - Nikko Ceramics Inc.
PATINEAU - Floor coverings–carpet and rugs - Karastan-Bigelow Inc.
PATIO - Beverages–carbonated - Pepsi-Cola Co.
PATIO - Brooms - Lighthouse Industries
PATIO - Dinnerware–glass ☆ - Johnson Brothers, USA, Inc.
PATIO - Dinnerware–glass ☆ - Sango Co. Ltd. (Sango USA Div.)
PATIO - Floor coverings - Mannington Resilient Floors
PATIO - Floor coverings–carpet and rugs ☆ - Regal Rugs Inc.
PATIO - Food products - Conagra, Inc.
PATIO - Food products - Nabisco Foods Group
PATIO - Garden equipment - The Companion Group
PATIO - Glassware–household - Culver Glass Inc.
PATIO - Synthetic turf - Instant Turf Industries Inc.
PATIO 76 - Wood products ☆ - Biltbest Windows
PATIO 500 - Fabrics - John Boyle & Co., Inc.
PATIO BUTLER - Dishes–plastic ☆ - Thermos Co.
PATIO CADDIE - Barbecues and grills - Char-Broil
PATIO COAT - Paints ☆ - Essex Specialty Products, Inc.
PATIO CONCEPTS - Furniture - Keller Industries Inc.
PATIO DELITE - Frankfurters ☆ - King Cotton Foods
PATIO DOORMISER - Doors–storm - Noranda Building Products Co.
PATIO GARDEN - Bells - Bevin Brothers Manufacturing Co.
PATIO GEAR - Forks - Chadwick-Miller, Inc.
PATIO GLO-LITE - Candles ☆ - Arizona Natural Resources
PATIO GUARD - Sealing compounds - C.M. Athey Paint Co.
PATIO HAULER - Trailers–travel - Kit Manufacturing Co.
PATIO HUGGER - Ceiling fans - Davoil, Inc.
PATIO KEEPER - Weed-control blankets, etc. - Atlantic Construction Fabrics, Inc.
PATIO KITCHEN - Barbecues and grills - Char-Broil
PATIO LUSTRE & SEALER - Chemical preparations - Thompson-Minwax Co.
PATIO MAGIC - Furniture polish and wax - Lawn Furniture Repair & Sales Co., Inc.
PATIO-MATE - Windows–screen ☆ - Care-Free Windows
PATIO MATES - Furniture - Tel-O-Post Co.
PATIO MOSAIC - Floor coverings ☆ - Tarkett, Inc.
PATIO PAINT - Paints - DecoArt, Inc.
PATIO PAL - Barbecues and grills - DTM International, Inc.

PATIO PAL - Garden equipment - Argee Corp.
PATIO-PALS - Furniture - Almet/Lawnlite
PATIO PET - Ornamental products–metal ☆ - Metal Man, Inc.
PATIO PETITE - Ceiling fans - Davoil, Inc.
PATIO PLANTER - Flowers, plants, and seeds ☆ - Applewood Seed & Garden Group
PATIO PLEASER - Chimes - Metal Man, Inc.
PATIO PLUS - Coatings ☆ - Nelsonite, Inc.
PATIO POLE - Garden furniture - Racine Tube Services Inc.
PATIO POOL GARDENS - Pet products - Maryland Aquatic Nurseries
PATIO PRO - Barbecue and grill accessories - M.E. Heuck Co. Inc.
PATIO PRODUCTS, INC. - Garden furniture–metal - Patio Products, Inc.
PATIO QUEEN - Hardware - Cardinal Home Products
PATIO SQUARES - Candy - Hooper's Chocolates
PATIO TONES - Paints - Kelley Technical Coatings Inc.
PATIO WEB - Electronic equipment ☆ - Weber-Stephen Products Co.
PATIO WOK - Cooking equipment–household - Flame Engineering Inc.
PATIOAMERICA - Garden furniture - Bernd Pasler
PATIOLIFE - Waterproofing compounds - Dap Products Inc.
PATIOLITE - Lighting equipment - Sunergy Inc.
PATIOMASTER - Barbecues and grills - Sunbeam Outdoor Products Inc.
PATIOMATES - Hardware - Cardinal Home Products
PATIOPRO - Bricks - Reemay, Inc.
PATIQUE - Siding–metal - ASC Pacific Inc.
PATISFRANCE - Pastries - Made in France
PATITA'S - Food products - Castle Rock Meats Inc.
PATIVA - Hair care products - Dowbrands L.P.
PATLON - Fabric stores - Amoco Fabrics and Fibers Co.
PATLON PLUS - Fibers–synthetic - Amoco Fabrics and Fibers Co.
PATMOS - Recording label - Parallax Records
PATNEL - Fiberboard - Kemlite Co., Inc.
PATONS - Yarn - Susan Bates Inc.
PATONS - Yarn - Coats and Clark Inc.
PATRAIKI RETSINA - Wines - S & J Importing Co. Inc.
PATRIARCHE - Wines - Chrissa Imports Ltd.
PATRIARCHE - Wines - Finest Wines Inc.
PATRIARCHE PERE ET FILS - Wines - Patriarche Pere & Fils
PATRIART - Glassware–household - Patriart LLC
PATRICE - Hobby kits - Craft World International Inc.
PATRICHS - Colognes - Chesebrough-Pond's USA Co.
PATRICIA - Dolls ☆ - Effanbee Doll Corp.
PATRICIA - Fruits and vegetables - Steven L. Gilfenbain
PATRICIA - Leather - A & A Sales
PATRICIA - Tableware–china - Lenox, Inc.
PATRICIA HOLSTINE'S COLLECTIBLE CREATIONS - Toys–stuffed ☆ - HC & E Inc.
PATRICIA KNOX - Jewelry - Patricia Knox
PATRICIA MOSS - Apparel–women's - Phoebe Co., LLC
PATRICIA NIMOCKS - Craft supplies - Plaid Enterprises, Inc.
PATRICIA PANCALDI - Footwear–women's - Pancaldi
PATRICIAN - Audio equipment ☆ - Electro-Voice, Inc.
PATRICIAN - Boxes - Kellerman Manufacturing Co. Inc.
PATRICIAN - Doors–glass ☆ - Miller Industries Inc.
PATRICIAN - Flatware - Utica Cutlery Co.
PATRICIAN - Furniture–upholstered - Patrician Furniture Co.
PATRICIAN - Giftware ☆ - Gorham Inc.
PATRICIAN - Guitars, etc. - International Music Corp.
PATRICIAN - Guns ☆ - Weatherby Inc.
PATRICIAN - Ladders–wood - John S. Tilley Ladders Co. Inc.
PATRICIAN - Luggage ☆ - Ventura Travelware Inc.
PATRICIAN - Plywood - Georgia-Pacific Corp.
PATRICIAN - Spices, herbs, and seeds - Atlantic Processing Mills Corp.
PATRICIAN - Wallcoverings - Cork Products Co. Inc.
PATRICIAN - Watches - North American Watch Corp.
PATRICIAN CUSHION - Furniture - Tropitone Furniture Co. Inc.
PATRICIAN ROLDSKINS - Prophylactics - Patrician Products Inc.
PATRICIAN SLING - Furniture - Tropitone Furniture Co. Inc.
PATRICIAN-WARE - Giftware - Terrace Ceramics Inc.
PATRICIANA - Food products - Modern Foods Inc.
PATRICK - Colognes - Elysee Scientific Cosmetic Co.
PATRICK - Footwear–athletic - Patrick Athletic Shoe Co.
PATRICK - Frames–eyeglass - U.S. Optical Frame Co.
PATRICK CARPETS - Floor coverings–carpet and rugs - Masland Carpets, Inc.
PATRICK CUDAHY - Food products - Patrick Cudahy Inc.
PATRICK CUDAHY - Meat products - Dennis J. Alba & Co.

☆ = Now out of production

PATRICK EWING - Apparel and accessories - Dream Inc.
PATRICK EWING - Shoes–athletic - Adidas USA Inc.
PATRICK HENRY'S REVOLUTIONARY BLOODY MARY MIX - Beverages - W.W. Distributors, Inc.
PATRICK KELLY - Sunglasses - Quest Eyewear Inc.
PATRICK THE PUP - Toys–stuffed - F.A.O. Schwarz
PATRICK'S PRIDE - Bacon - Patcud Investments, Inc.
PATRICK'S PRIDE - Meat products - Patrick Cudahy Inc.
PATRIOT - Animal feeds - Master Mix Feeds
PATRIOT - Antennas - Satellite Export & Engineering, Inc.
PATRIOT - Audio equipment - R & T Enterprises
PATRIOT - Automotive parts and accessories - Patriot Spot Free Cleaning Systems, Inc.
PATRIOT - Balls - A.D. Starr
PATRIOT - Beverages - Network Group
PATRIOT - Bicycles - Sears, Roebuck and Co.
PATRIOT - Boats–motor ☆ - Glassmaster Co.
PATRIOT - Boats–motor ☆ - Yar-Craft, Inc.
PATRIOT - Bowling balls - Award Skores Unlimited Inc.
PATRIOT - Concrete products - Hanover Prest Paving Co.
PATRIOT - Electrical equipment - Simplex Time Recorder Co.
PATRIOT - Electronic equipment - Best Power Technology Inc.
PATRIOT - Electronic equipment - Uniden America Corp.
PATRIOT - Fabrics - Dan River Inc.
PATRIOT - Fireworks - American Promotional Events, Inc.
PATRIOT - Floor coverings - Superior Manufacturing Group/Notrax Floor Matting
PATRIOT - Footwear - Interco Inc.
PATRIOT - Game machines - Sigma Game Inc.
PATRIOT - Golfing equipment - Golfsmith International Inc.
PATRIOT - Grindstones - Salem Distributing Co. Inc.
PATRIOT - Guitars - Peavey Electronics Corp.
PATRIOT - Hearing aids - Epic Corp.
PATRIOT - Heaters–space - Preway Industries Inc.
PATRIOT - Knives - Precise International/Wenger
PATRIOT - Locks–padlocks - ITTI Corp.
PATRIOT - Mobile homes ☆ - Wick Building Systems Inc. (Manufactured Home Div./North)
PATRIOT - Pet food ☆ - Central Soya Co. Inc.
PATRIOT - Pet products - Fermenta Animal Health
PATRIOT - Pistols ☆ - Thompson/Center Arms
PATRIOT - Safety goggles ☆ - Uvex Sports, Inc.
PATRIOT - Siding–metal - Aluminum Co. of America
PATRIOT - Skates–roller - Chicago Roller Skate Co.
PATRIOT - Sporting goods - Outdoor Technologies Group
PATRIOT - Sporting goods - Shakespeare Fishing Tackle
PATRIOT - Tables - Impact Furniture
PATRIOT - Tableware–china ☆ - Lenox, Inc.
PATRIOT - Tools - Railway Handle Corp.
PATRIOT - Toys - Hasbro, Inc.
PATRIOT - Toys–models - Estes Industries
PATRIOT - Trading cards and stamps - Treat Entertainment, Inc.
PATRIOT - Vinyl link mats ☆ - American Floor Products Co. Inc.
PATRIOT - Watches - Bulova Corp.
PATRIOT - Watches - Hampden Corp.
PATRIOT - Wheelchairs - AM Scooters
PATRIOT 80 PLUS - Heating equipment - Heat Controller Inc.
PATRIOT ALERT - Alarms–personal - Americorp International, Inc.
PATRIOT BRAND - Food products - Cambridge Farms, Inc.
PATRIOT CHIPPER BLOWER VAC - Garden equipment - Patriot Co.
PATRIOT CHIPPER SHREDDER VAC - Garden equipment - Patriot Co.
PATRIOT FEEDER - Containers - Asher Plumbing Co.
PATRIOT FILTRATION - Air purification systems - Stephen Schlesinger
PATRIOT FIREWORKS - Fireworks - Freedom Fireworks, Inc.
PATRIOT FLEECE JACKET - Jackets - Horace Small Apparel Co.
PATRIOT HOMES - Building materials - Patriot Homes, Inc.
PATRIOT HOMES, INC. SINCE 1972 - Mobile homes - Patriot Homes, Inc.
PATRIOT MISSILE - Cigars - Heaven Group, LLC
PATRIOT MISSILE - Golfing equipment - Swingline Golf Co.
PATRIOT NATURAL - Guitars - Peavey Electronics Corp.
PATRIOT POP - Candy ☆ - Spangler Candy Co.
PATRIOT PRESS - Embossing plates - Devin-Adair Co. Inc.
PATRIOTIC - Pencils - Faber-Castell Corp.
PATRIOTIC - Postcards - Schellmark, Inc. (Netlaunch, Inc. Division)
PATRIOTS - Strollers–baby ☆ - Welsh Co.
PATROL - Colognes - Brandy Harvest

PATROL - Computer software - BMC Software, Inc.
PATROL - Gas filter - Atlas Products Co.
PATROL - Medical apparatus - Abbott Laboratories
PATROL - Pencils ☆ - Empire Berol USA
PATROL 1 - Insecticides - Speer Products, Inc.
PATROLMAN - Radios - Tandy Corp.
PATRON - Greeting cards ☆ - American Artists Group Inc.
PATRON PLUS - Advertising agencies - Datamark Software, Inc.
PATRON TEQUILA IMPORTED ANEJO - Beverages–alcohol - St. Maarten Spirits, Ltd.
PATRON XO CAFE - Beverages–alcohol - St. Maarten Spirits, Ltd.
PATRON'S CHOICE - Meat products - Global Military Marketing, Inc.
PATS - Cigar boxes–wood - Consolidated Cigar Corp.
PAT'S - Snack foods - Health Plus
PAT'S GARDEN - Figurines - The Gift Hub
PAT'S HOLIDAY CRAFTS - Christmas ornaments - Intromark Inc.
PAT'S PRIDE - Leather–rawhide - Sergeant's Pet Products, Inc.
PATSON - Food products - Patterson Frozen Foods, Inc.
PATSY - Dolls ☆ - Effanbee Doll Corp.
PATSY AIKEN DESIGNS - Apparel–children's - Patsy Aiken Designs, Inc.
PATSY WALKER - Nail-care products - Walker Tool & Mold Inc.
PATSY'S PARTY - Food products - Bruce Foods Corp.
PATSY'S PR SINCE 1944 - Vegetable sauces - Patsy's Brand, Inc.
PATTEN SERVICE - Paper ☆ - Lincoln Paper Co.
PATTER TOGS - Crocheted and knitted items ☆ - Alpha Mills Corp.
PATTERN - Clocks - General Time Corp. (Westclox/Seth Thomas Div.)
PATTERN ACCENT - Dinnerware–glass ☆ - Kenro Inc.
PATTERN BEARS - Toys - Lauri Inc.
PATTERN CONTROL - Firearms, accessories, and parts - Triple G Plastics, Inc.
PATTERN MASTER - Tools–garden - Gilmour Manufacturing Co.
PATTERN PACKS - Quilts - Martingale & Co.
PATTERN PAK - Hobby kits - Oxmoor House Inc.
PATTERN-PALS - Toys - Wimmer-Ferguson Inc.
PATTERN PISTOL - Tools - Goldblatt Tool Co.
PATTERN PLANK - Plastics - Tool Chemical Co., Inc.
PATTERN-PLAY - Toys - Wimmer-Ferguson Inc.
PATTERN-PLUS - Floor coverings - Hartco Wood Flooring
PATTERN-PLY - Wood products - Weyerhaeuser Co.
PATTERN PORTFOLIO - Floor coverings–tile - Collins & Aikman Corp.
PATTERN PRETTY - Underwear and nightwear ☆ - Lovable Co.
PATTERN PUMP - Tools - Goldblatt Tool Co.
PATTERNBLOK - Flooring–hardwood ☆ - Memphis Hardwood Flooring Co.
PATTERNED CONCEPTS - Floor coverings–carpet and rugs ☆ - Karastan-Bigelow Inc.
PATTERNED FOR PERFECTION! - Crocheted and knitted items - Dickson Industries, Inc.
PATTERNMAKER - Computer software - Voyager Software Corp.
PATTERNS - Adhesives and sealants - Formica Corp.
PATTERNS - Furniture - White Furniture Co.
PATTERNS - Hair care products - Clairol Inc.
PATTERNS - Infant product ☆ - Playtex Beauty Care, Inc.
PATTERNS - Underwear and nightwear - Maidenform Inc.
PATTERNS IN PITCH - Computer software - Electronic Courseware Systems Inc.
PATTERNS IN RHYTHM - Computer software - Electronic Courseware Systems Inc.
PATTERNS PACIFICA - Patterns–clothing - Pauloa Hawaii Ltd.
PATTERSON PIAZZA - Wallpaper - Patterson Piazza
PATTERSON'S - Chili sauce - Patterson Packing Co.
PATTI - Computer software - O.I. Corp.
PATTI - Nail care products - Oloff Cosmetics Ltd.
PATTI JEAN - Food products - Tyson Foods Inc.
PATTI KLAWANS - Giftware ☆ - Schmid Inc.
PATTI LA BELLE - Cosmetics - Color Me Beautiful, Inc.
PATTI LABELLE LIP AND NAIL - Cosmetics - Posner Laboratories Inc.
PATTI PORT - Carports - Texas Aluminum Industries Inc.
PATTI PRINTS - Clay–modeling - Gregory Robert Bessert
PATTICAKE PATTICAKE - Dolls - Goldberger Doll Manufacture Co.
PATTIE CAKES - Greeting cards - American Greetings Corp.
PATTIN' PANDA BEAR - Toys–stuffed ☆ - Dakin Inc.
PATTON - Fans–electric - Patton Electric Co. Inc.
PATTON - Floor coverings–carpet and rugs - Barrett Carpet Mills Inc.
PATTON - Tiles–ceramic - Custom Crafts
PATTON - Toys–stuffed - Dakin Inc.

PATTON STRIKES BACK: THE BATTLE OF THE BULGE - Computer software ☆ - Broderbund Software, Inc.
PATTON VERSUS ROMMEL - Computer software - Electronic Arts Inc.
PATTON'S BEST - Games - Avalon Hill Game Co.
PATTOYA - Bedding–linen - Dan River Inc.
PATTY BEA - Bath salts ☆ - Mid-America Chemical Inc.
PATTY BERG - Golfing equipment - Wilson Sporting Goods Co.
PATTY BRITTLE - Snack foods - Patty Brittle
PATTY CAKE - Bakery products - Campbell Taggart Inc.
PATTY CAKE SINGS - Dolls - Vogue Dolls Inc.
PATTY JOE SKWEEL - Dolls - Meritus Industries, Inc.
PATTY MAE'S - Bakery products - Wal-Bon of Ohio, Inc.
PATTY MCMELT - Sandwiches–prepackaged - Mcdonald's Corp.
PATTY MCMELT II - Sandwiches–prepackaged - Mcdonald's Corp.
PATTY-O-CANDLE - Candles - Empire Manufacturing Co.
PATTY-O-PAIL - Candles - Empire Manufacturing Co.
PATTY PEACH - Dolls - Mattel, Inc.
PATTY POPPIT - Dolls - Mattel, Inc.
PATTY POSABLE - Dolls ☆ - Fun World Inc.
PATTY PURSE - Craft supplies ☆ - Pepperell Braiding Co. Inc.
PATTY WOODARD - Apparel–women's - Lee Thomas Inc.
PATTYCAKE - Toys–stuffed ☆ - Gund, Inc.
PATUXENT FARMS - Meat products - JP Foodservice, Inc.
PAU D'ARCO - Health care products - Alta Health Products
PAU D'ARCO - Teas - Wishing Well Video Distributing Co.
PAU D'ARCOLA - Teas - Seelect, Inc.
PAUIGRES - Tiles–ceramic ☆ - Maxsam Sales, Inc.
PAUL - Frames–eyeglass - Rozin Optical Export Corp.
PAUL ADRIAN - Shoes - JBI, Inc.
PAUL ALEXANDER - Giftware - Reco International Corp.
PAUL ALEXANDER - Women's sportswear - Irka
PAUL AZINGER, THE - Golfing equipment - Hurricane Sports, Inc.
PAUL BALL - Apparel and accessories - George Mason University
PAUL BOCUSE - Cutlery ☆ - Robinson Knife & Fiddlers Plastics
PAUL BOCUSE - Wines - Winesellers Ltd.
PAUL BRAYTON DESIGNS - Fabrics - Paul Brayton Designs
PAUL BREGUETTE - Watches - Sterling Inc.
PAUL BRISSON - Musical instruments - Ernest Deffner Inc.
PAUL BUNYAN - Apparel–men's - Brill Bros. Inc.
PAUL BUNYAN - Crocheted and knitted items - Schuessler Knitting Mills Inc.
PAUL BUNYAN - Housewares - Adam Starchild
PAUL CHENEAU - Wines - Sunbelt Beverage Corp.
PAUL CLINE - Greeting cards - Green Tiger Press
PAUL CORCELLET - Food products - Dean & Deluca Inc.
PAUL C'S - Guitars ☆ - Chandler Industries
PAUL DORE - Lighters - Park Lane Associates, Inc.
PAUL DUJARDIN - Musical instruments - C. Bruno & Son Inc.
PAUL DUPRE - Musical instruments - Hershman Musical Instrument
PAUL DUVALL - Watches - Nicolet International Inc.
PAUL ELLIOT - Apparel and accessories - Paul Levy
PAUL GARRETT VINTNER'S CHOICE - Wines - Guild Wineries
PAUL HATHCOAT - Giftware - N.S. Gustin Co.
PAUL HOGE CREATIONS - Candles - Paul Hoge Creations
PAUL J. CUTTER'S - Rum - Joseph E. Seagram & Sons, Inc.
PAUL JABOULET AINE - Wines - Frederick Wildman and Sons Ltd.
PAUL JACQUET - Paper–gift wrap - Somerset Trading Co.
PAUL JARDIN - Watches - Mira Enterprises Inc.
PAUL JAVEY - Wines ☆ - Winesellers Ltd.
PAUL JEAN BARNETT - Cheese - Churny Co., Inc.
PAUL JONES - Tobacco products - Philip Morris Companies Inc.
PAUL JONES - Whiskey - Heaven Hill Distilleries, Inc.
PAUL KLEE - Apparel and accessories - Designers in Motion, Inc.
PAUL LABRECQUE - Hair care products - Paul Labrecque Salon, Inc.
PAUL MARSHALL - Flowers–artificial - Paul Marshall Products L.P.
PAUL MASSON - Wines - Canandaigua Wine Co. Inc.
PAUL MASSON GRANDE AMBER BRANDY - Beverages–alcohol ☆ - Canandaigua Wine Co. Inc.
PAUL MILAN - Cosmetics - Eckerd Corp.
PAUL MITCHELL - Hair care products - John Paul Mitchell Systems
PAUL MITCHELL CREATIVES - Hair care products - John Paul Mitchell Systems
PAUL MITCHELL CREATIVES FINISHING RINSE - Hair care products - John Paul Mitchell Systems
PAUL MITCHELL CREATIVES GLOSS - Hair care products - John Paul Mitchell Systems
PAUL MITCHELL FACIAL FRESH - Cosmetics - John Paul Mitchell Systems

PAUL MITCHELL GENTLE EXFOLIATING SYSTEM - Cosmetics - John Paul Mitchell Systems
PAUL MITCHELL HAND & BODY - Cosmetics - John Paul Mitchell Systems
PAUL MITCHELL LIPOSOMES - Skin care products - John Paul Mitchell Systems
PAUL MITCHELL WHITE OAK FACIAL CLEANSER - Cosmetics - John Paul Mitchell Systems
PAUL MORELLI - Jewelry - Paul Morelli Design, Inc.
PAUL PENDERS - Hair care products - Paul Penders Co. Inc.
PAUL REED SMITH - Guitars - Paul Reed Smith Guitars
PAUL REVERE - Fruits and vegetables - Sierra Vista Packing Co. Inc.
PAUL REVERE - Giftware ☆ - Gorham Inc.
PAUL REVERE LIMITED EDITION - Cooking utensils–aluminum ☆ - Revere Ware Corp.
PAUL REVERE SIGNATURE - Bakery products - G & S Metal Products Co., Inc.
PAUL REVERE SIGNATURE COLLECTION - Cooking utensils–aluminum ☆ - Revere Ware Corp.
PAUL SCHULZE - Hair clippers–veterinary - Friends Imports Inc.
PAUL SELDEN - Recording label - Paul H. Selden III
PAUL SMITH - Apparel–men's - Berkley Shirt Co. Inc.
PAUL STANLEY - Women's apparel - Paul Stanley, Ltd.
PAUL THOMAS - Wines - Paul Thomas Wines Ltd.
PAUL TOURIER - Wines - European Beverage Co., Inc.
PAUL VICTORIUS - Posters - Graphic Arts Unltd. Inc.
PAUL WEAVER STUDIO - Furniture - Paul Weaver Studio
PAULA - Apparel–women's - Nuvogue Creations
PAULA - Labels–paper - Sue Records Inc.
PAULA CUTES - Posters - C.M. Paula Co.
PAULA PAYNE - Cosmetics - Paula Payne Products Co. Inc.
PAULANER - Beverages–malt ☆ - Hudepohl-Schoenling Brewing Co.
PAULA'S - Pillows - C.M. Paula Co.
PAULA'S - Salad dressings–bottled - Sweet Adelaide Enterprises
PAULA'S BEST SALAD - Vinegar - Sweet Adelaide Enterprises
PAULA'S FIESTA - Vinegar - Sweet Adelaide Enterprises
PAULA'S FISHERMAN - Vinegar ☆ - Sweet Adelaide Enterprises
PAULA'S HATBOX - Hats - SC Corp.
PAULA'S HERB GARDEN - Salad dressings–bottled - Sweet Adelaide Enterprises
PAULA'S ITALIAN GARDEN - Vinegar - Sweet Adelaide Enterprises
PAULA'S LITTLE FRIENDS - Magnets - C.M. Paula Co.
PAULA'S LUSTY - Vinegar - Sweet Adelaide Enterprises
PAULA'S NO OIL - Salad dressings–bottled - Sweet Adelaide Enterprises
PAULA'S PERFECT - Vinegar - Sweet Adelaide Enterprises
PAULA'S PICNIC - Vinegar - Sweet Adelaide Enterprises
PAULA'S RASPBERRY ROYAL - Vinegar - Sweet Adelaide Enterprises
PAULA'S TEACH EZE-L - Easels - Paula Adelman
PAULA'S TWO CHIVE - Vinegar - Sweet Adelaide Enterprises
PAULBEN - Skin care products - Hess Hair Milk Laboratories Inc.
PAULCHEN - Biscuits - Haram-Christensen Corp.
PAULEE - Mops ☆ - Harbor Manufacturing
PAULEY PLACE - Floor coverings ☆ - Tarkett, Inc.
PAULIE PENGUIN - Toys–stuffed - Dakin Inc.
PAULINA - Shoes - Morning Bird, Inc.
PAULINA CAPPUCCINO - Liqueurs - Shaw-Ross International Importers
PAULINE - Eyeglasses - Art-Craft Optical Co.
PAULINE GORDON - Brassieres (Bras) - Custom Maid Brassiere Co.
PAULINE TRIGERE - Apparel and accessories - Pauline Trigere
PAULINE TRIGERE - Cooking equipment–household ☆ - Grainware Co.
PAULINES - Seafood - Boja's Foods Inc.
PAULINGS - Analgesics - Pauling's Pharmacal Co. Inc.
PAULI'S - Skin care products - Pauli of Vienna
PAULOA - Patterns–clothing - Pauloa Hawaii Ltd.
PAUL'S - Cheese - VanEerden Distribution Co.
PAUL'S - Food products - Pierceton Foods Inc.
PAUL'S - Lamps - Edward P. Paul & Co. Inc.
PAUL'S - Nuts–salted, roasted, cooked, or canned - Paul's Peanuts
PAUL'S ADIRONDACK TACKLE - Fishing lures - Paul Alfieri
PAUL'S DERBY - Musical instrument accessories ☆ - Micro Musical Products Corp.
PAUL'S PIX - Toothpicks - Mottavation Products
PAUL'S POWDERS - Health care products - New Moon Extracts, Inc.
PAULUX - Glassware–household - Edward P. Paul & Co. Inc.
PAULY - Cheese ☆ - Hunt-Wesson, Inc.
PAUPAIZ FINE COFFEES - Coffee - Paupaiz Inc.
PAUSE - Apparel and accessories - Harcrest International, Inc.

☆ = Now out of production

PAUSE - Pharmaceutical preparations ✩ - Columbia Drug Co. Inc.
PAUSE MASTER - Electronics equipment - MPC Educational Systems Inc.
PAUSE-TO-SERVE - Coffee makers—electric ✩ - Black & Decker Corp.
PAV TEK - Construction equipment - Henry A. Crivelli
PAVA - Hair care products ✩ - Cassidy Inc.
PAVA-PAR - Pharmaceutical preparations - Parmed Pharmaceuticals, Inc.
PAVA-RX - Pharmaceutical preparations ✩ - Blaine Co. Inc.
PAVACAP - Pharmaceutical preparations ✩ - Solvay Pharmaceuticals Inc.
PAVACAP UNICELLES - Pharmaceutical preparations ✩ - Solvay Pharmaceuticals Inc.
PAVACELS - Pharmaceutical preparations ✩ - Roberts/Hauck Pharmaceuticals Inc.
PAVACELS-300 - Pharmaceutical preparations ✩ - Roberts/Hauck Pharmaceuticals Inc.
PAVACEN - Pharmaceutical preparations ✩ - Central Pharmaceutical Inc.
PAVACOT - Pharmaceutical preparations - C.O. Truxton Inc.
PAVACRON - Pharmaceutical preparations - H.R. Cenci Laboratories Inc.
PAVADYL - Pharmaceutical preparations - Bock Pharmacal Co.
PAVAGEN - Pharmaceutical preparations - Rugby Laboratories Inc.
PAVAKEY - Pharmaceutical preparations ✩ - Key Pharmaceuticals Inc.
PAVAKOR - Pharmaceutical preparations ✩ - Hyrex Pharmaceuticals
PAVALAR - Pharmaceutical preparations - Lardon Laboratories
PAVALOR - Deodorizers - Pavalor Merchandising, Inc.
PAVAN - Artists' materials ✩ - Loew-Cornell Inc.
PAVAN - Furniture - American Furniture Co. Inc.
PAVANA - Floor coverings—tile ✩ - Kentile Floors Inc.
PAVANE - Furniture - Tomlinson of High Point Inc.
PAVANE - Ophthalmic goods - Swank Optical
PAVAREX - Pharmaceutical preparations ✩ - C.S. Ruckstuhl Co. Inc.
PAVARINE - Pharmaceutical preparations ✩ - Pharmex Inc.
PAVASED - Pharmaceutical preparations ✩ - Roberts/Hauck Pharmaceuticals Inc.
PAVASULE - Pharmaceutical preparations - Misemer Pharmaceuticals Inc.
PAVATRAN - Pharmaceutical preparations ✩ - Merz Inc.
PAVATYM - Health care products ✩ - Everett Laboratories Inc.
PAVCO - Pharmaceutical preparations ✩ - Coast Laboratories Inc.
PAVCO - Plywood - Pavco Industries Inc.
PAVE - Computer software - Instructional/Communications Technology Inc.
PAVE - Floor coverings—carpet and rugs - Customweave Carpets Inc.
PAVE - Furniture ✩ - Chromcraft Corp.
PAVE - Wallpaper - CSE Designs
PAVE-FLEX - Connectors—electrical - Pave Technology Co., Inc.
PAVE-MELT - Connectors—electrical - Pave Technology Co., Inc.
PAVE-SEAL - Connectors—electrical - Pave Technology Co., Inc.
PAVE THEMES - Jewelry - Wideband Jewelry Corp.
PAVECHEK - Chemical preparations - Morton International Inc. (Morton Salt Div.)
PAVEMASTER - Electronic equipment - Laser Alignment, Inc.
PAVEMENT MUSIC - Recording label - Pavement Music, Inc.
PAVEMENT POUNDER - Toys—automobiles - Mattel, Inc.
PAVER - Pharmaceutical preparations ✩ - Legere Pharmaceuticals Inc.
PAVER CLEAR - Sealing compounds - Sealwall Products Inc.
PAVER SEAL - Adhesives and sealants - Atlas Chemical Co.
PAVERA - Tiles—ceramic ✩ - Latco Products
PAVERIL PHOSPHATE - Pharmaceutical preparations ✩ - Eli Lilly and Co.
PAVERINE SPANCAP - Pharmaceutical preparations ✩ - Vortech Pharmaceuticals
PAVEROLAN - Pharmaceutical preparations - Lannett Co. Inc.
PAVEX - Pharmaceutical preparations ✩ - Xttrium Laboratories Inc.
PAVI ELLE - Perfumes - Avon Products, Inc.
PAVIA - Dishes—china - Pasmantier Co. Inc.
PAVIA - Dishes—china ✩ - Gorham Inc.
PAVIA - Floor coverings—carpet and rugs ✩ - Atlas Carpet Mills Inc.
PAVIA - Furniture - Weiman Co.
PAVICH PRODUCE - Fruits—dried - Pavich Family Farms
PAVIEMENTO - Floor coverings—carpet and rugs - Interface, Inc.
PAVILIA - Footwear—women's ✩ - Johansen Brothers Shoe Co.
PAVILION - Computers - Hewlett-Packard Co.
PAVILION - Dishes—china - Pickard Inc.
PAVILION - Dishes—china - Waterford Wedgewood USA, Inc.
PAVILION - Floor coverings—carpet and rugs - Philadelphia Carpets
PAVILION - Frames—eyeglass - May Optical Co. Inc.
PAVILION - Furniture - Pavilion/Sunburst Furniture
PAVILION - Furniture ✩ - Drexel Heritage Furnishings, Inc.
PAVILION - Furniture ✩ - Hickory Chair Co.
PAVILION - Garden furniture—metal - Lloyd/Flanders Industries

PAVILION - Wallpaper - S.M. Hexter Co.
PAVILION SILK - Fabrics—silk - Ian Crawford Ltd.
PAVILLION - Floor coverings - Congoleum Corp.
PAVILLION - Floor coverings—carpet and rugs - Burtco Enterprises Inc.
PAVILLION - Floor coverings—carpet and rugs ✩ - Catalina Carpet Mills Inc.
PAVILLION - Floor coverings—carpet and rugs ✩ - Regal Rugs Inc.
PAVILLON - Wines ✩ - Kobrand Corp.
PAVILLON ROUGE DE CHATEAU MARGAUX - Wines - Seagram's Chateau & Estate Wines Co.
PAVION - Nail care products - Pavion Ltd.
PAVISION - Brushes—hair ✩ - Robert Simmons Inc.
PAVLIDES - Chocolates - Isma Trading Corp.
PAVLOVA - Skin care products - Frances Denney
PAVLOVA - Vodka - Glencourt Products
PAVLOV'S CAT - Pet products - Del West Enterprises
PAVON - Floor coverings - Mannington Resilient Floors
PAVONA - Beverages—alcohol - Richard Kanakaris
PAVONE - Neckties - Pavone Inc.
PAVONE - Sausages - Patrick Cudahy Inc.
PAVONINE - Floor coverings—carpet and rugs - Masland Corp.
PAVOPAQUE - Inks - CHT North America
PAVRIN - Pharmaceutical preparations ✩ - Kenyon Drug Co. Inc.
PAVULON - Pharmaceutical preparations - Organon Inc.
PAW - Golfing equipment - Golfsmith International Inc.
PAW - Golfing equipment - Lynx Golf, Inc.
PAW & CLAW - Cleaning preparations—carpet and rug - Specialty Products, Inc.
PAW CUFFS - Pet products - Pet Concepts
PAW ISLAND - Apparel and accessories - Pet Care, Inc.
PAW-LOK - Pet products - Bandit Products Equipment
PAW-MARK - Pet products - Coski's Choice Inc.
PAW OF FAME - Pet products - Paw Marketing Inc.
PAW PALS - Pet products - Petco Animal Supplies, Inc.
PAW PAW - Food products - RHM Holdings (USA) Inc.
PAW PRODUCTIONS - Video production - Paw Productions
PAW PUPPETS - Puppets - Cascade Toy, Ltd.
PAW WASH - Soap - Aire-Master of America, Inc.
PAWBELL - Door openers—electronic - John W. Soranno, Jr.
PAWCLIFF - Pet products - Picture Pets Inc.
PAWDY - Toys - Mattel, Inc.
PAWIER - Veterinary nutritional supplements - Pawier, Inc.
PAWLEYS ISLAND - Rocking chairs ✩ - Pawleys Island Rope Hammock
PAWNEE - Floor coverings - American Floor Products Co. Inc.
PAWNEE - Knives—pocket ✩ - W.R. Case & Sons Cutlery Co.
PAWNEE BILL'S PB - Meat products—dried - Pawnee Bill's Snack Food Co.
PAWNS OF TIME - Games ✩ - Mayfair Games, Inc.
PAWPRINTS CLASSICS - Greeting cards - Pawprints Greeting Cards
PAWROBICS - Pet products ✩ - Kong Co.
PAWS - Pet products - Marksman Products Inc.
PAWS - Wallpaper - Import Ltd.
PAWS & CLAWS - Cat food - Tractor Supply Co.
PAWS & EFFECT - Perfumes - Philosophy, Inc.
PAWS FOR THOUGHT - Pet products - Jowen Enterprises
PAWS 'N CLAUS - Christmas tree ornaments - Mother Moose Enterprises
P.A.W.S. PET ALERT - Signboards - P.A.W.S., Inc.
PAWS UP - Pet products - Mitsui & Co. Inc.
PAWS WITH A CAUSE - Video production - Paws with a Cause
PAWSIBLES - Clothes - L. Sacha Shapiro & Luca Coletta
PAWSITIVELY PETS - Pet products - Ames Department Stores, Inc.
PAWSOLEUM - Vases—stone - Joanne Brooks
PAWTUCKET - Apparel—women's ✩ - Rhoda Lee, Inc.
PAWTUCKET FASTENERS INC. - Screws - Pawtucket Fasteners L.P.
PAX - Fertilizers - Pax Co.
PAX - Footwear—athletic - C.O. Lynch Enterprises, Inc.
PAX - Pharmaceutical preparations ✩ - Kenyon Drug Co. Inc.
PAX - Recording label ✩ - Alcazar Productions
PAX - Skin care products - Arius-Eickert Co. Inc.
PAX - Soap - Calgon Vestal Laboratories
PAX ACTION - Fertilizers - Pax Co.
PAX BRITANNICA - Games ✩ - Avalon Hill Game Co.
PAX F.I.F. - Fertilizers - Pax Co.
PAX GLO - Paints - Wellborn-DE Corp.
PAX PLUS - Paints - Wellborn-DE Corp.
PAX PUBLISHING - Publisher's imprints - William Karneges
PAX SUPER IRON - Fertilizers - Pax Co.
PAX TOTAL - Fertilizers - Pax Co.

✩ = Now out of production

PAXAREL - Pharmaceutical preparations ☆ - Circle Pharmaceuticals Inc.
PAXIL - Pharmaceutical preparations - Smithkline Beecham Corp.
PAXIPAM - Pharmaceutical preparations - Schering-Plough Healthcare Products
PAXLITE - Fertilizers - Pax Co.
PAXMAN - Musical instruments - Custom Music Co.
PAXTON - Floor coverings–carpet and rugs - Whitecrest Carpet Mills
PAXTON - Frames–eyeglass - Pathway Optical Prods.
PAXTON - Paper - Bee Paper Co. Inc.
PAXTON - Shoes ☆ - Allen-Edmonds Shoe Corp.
PAXTON - Tobacco products - Philip Morris Companies Inc.
PAXWELL #2 - Paper–tissue ☆ - Paper Service Ltd.
PAY 7 - Games - D.B. Sales, Inc.
PAY 3000 - Computer software - SEI Corp.
PAY CAR - Tobacco–chewing or smoking - Swedish Math North America Inc.
PAY DAY - Animal feeds - Gold Kist Inc.
PAY DAY - Floor coverings–carpet and rugs - Newport Carpet Mills Inc.
PAY DAY - Floor coverings–carpet and rugs ☆ - Quaker Inc.
PAY DIRT - Floor coverings–carpet and rugs ☆ - Cumberland Mills Inc.
PAY LESS - Health care products - Pay Less Drug Stores Northwest Inc.
PAY LESS - Vegetables–canned - Clifton Canning Co.
PAY LO - Food products - J.G. Pieri Co. Inc.
PAY-LODE - Fuel additives - Index Industries Inc.
PAY-MASTER - Television equipment - Zenith Electronics Corp.
PAY' N SAVE - Health care products - Pay'N Save Drug Stores Inc.
PAYA - Toys ☆ - Reeves International, Inc.
PAYBACK - Machine parts - Coyote Electronics, Inc.
PAYBACK TO LIFE - Video production - Deano's, Inc.
PAYBILL PLUS! - Computer software - Damian Services Corp.
PAYCHECK - Computer software - Aatrix Software Inc.
PAYCHECK PARTY MACHINE - Hotels and motels - Coast Hotels & Casinos, Inc.
PAYCHEX - Computer software - Paychex, Inc.
PAYCLOCK - Computer software - Lathem Time Corp.
PAYDAE - Computer software - Pennsylvania State Employees Credit Union
PAYDAY - Candy bars - Leaf, Inc.
PAYDAY - Games - Parker Brothers
PAYDAY - Golfing equipment - Bobby Grace Golf Design, Inc.
PAYDIRT - Games - Avalon Hill Game Co.
PAYETTE FARMS - Vegetables–frozen - J.R. Simplot Co.
PAYGEL - Vitamins and nutritional supplements ☆ - General Mills, Inc.
PAYLESS SHOE SOURCE - Shoes - Payless Shoesource Worldwide, Inc.
PAYLESS SHOESOURCE - Shoe stores - Payless Shoesource Worldwide, Inc.
PAYLINK - Computer software - Paychex, Inc.
PAYLOAD - Beverages ☆ - York Barbell Co., Inc.
PAYLOAD - Fishing lures - B-17 Fly Tackle Ltd.
PAYLOAD - Motor vehicle parts and accessories - Delta Consolidated Industries, Inc.
PAYLOAD - Palettes - Gate Pallet Systems Inc.
PAYLOAD PLUS - Motor vehicle parts and accessories - Delta Consolidated Industries, Inc.
PAYLODE - Recording label - Comstock Records Ltd.
PAYMASTER - Automotive parts and accessories - Rockwell International Corp.
PAYMASTER - Leather goods - St. Thomas Inc.
PAYMATE - Computer software - Payroll 1, Inc.
PAYMATE - Leather goods - St. Thomas Inc.
PAY'N DOUBLE - Game machines - WMS Gaming Inc.
PAYNE - Air conditioning equipment - United Technologies Corp.
PAYNE - Heating equipment - Carrier Corp.
PAYOFF - Frames–eyeglass - Pathway Optical Prods.
PAYOLA - Recording label - Traditional Music Record Co.
PAYONS - Crayons - Dixon Ticonderoga Co.
PAYORATE - Computer software - MCIS, Inc.
PAYOT - Skin care products - Frances Denney
PAYROLL NAVIGATOR - Computer software - Automating Peripherals, Inc.
PAYSAGES D'INTERIERS - Wallpaper ☆ - Wallquest, Inc.
PAYSON - Hardware - Blaine Window Hardware Inc.
PAYSON CANDLE FACTORY - Candles - Root Candle Co.
PAYSOURCE - Recording label - Payroll Support Associates
PAYTRAC - Computer software - Microhealth Corp.
PAYUE STEWERT - Apparel and accessories - Pincus Bros., Inc.
PAYWRITE - Computer software - SCS/Compute, Inc.
PAYWRITE - Paper - Reynolds and Reynolds Co.
PAYZONE - Chemical preparations - Tetra Technologies, Inc.
PAZAZZ - Dryers–hair - Remington Products Co.

PAZAZZ - Food products - First Coast Foods Corp.
PAZINE - Pharmaceutical preparations ☆ - Seatrace Co.
PAZO - Pharmaceutical preparations - Bristol-Myers Squibb Co.
PAZZAZZ - Cameras - Eastman Kodak Co.
PAZZO - Footwear–women's - B. Levy & Son
PAZZO PORTFOLIO - Shoes - 700 Associates
PB - Amplifiers - Crown International, Inc.
PB - Bathing suits - Natus Corp.
PB - Hardware - Portland Bolt & Manufacturing Co., Inc.
P.B. - Peanut butter ☆ - Red Wing Co., Inc.
PB - Publisher's imprints - Professional Press Inc.
P.B. - Threads ☆ - International Thread Co.
PB-10 - Pet products - Vortex Innerspace Products Inc.
PB 286-LPT - Computer software - Teledyne Packard Bell
PB ARCHITECT - Computer software - Analytical Technologies Inc.
P.B. BANANA - Cookies - Intersweet Candy Inc.
PB COLLECTIONS - Apparel and accessories - Natus Corp.
P.B. CRISPS - Cookies - Planters LifeSavers Co.
P.B. CRUNCHERS - Candy - Leaf, Inc.
P.B. FUDGEBUTTERS - Cookies - Keebler Co.
P.B. KRUNCH - Cakes ☆ - Tasty Baking Co.
P.B. MICHAELS - Apparel–men's - I.E. Industries Fashions, Inc.
PB PLUS - Chemical preparations - Pb Plus, Inc.
PB PRIMA BELLA - Jewelry - D.M. Merchandising, Inc.
PB SELECT - Candy bars - Public Label Brands, Inc.
PB8 - Vitamins and nutritional supplements - Biotech (N.A.) Corp.
PBAC - Chemical preparations - Novagen, Inc.
PBAX-3500 - Motorized hand tools - Proficient Products Inc.
PBB - Hinges - PBB, Inc.
PBC DIMENSIONS - Computer software - Enrichment Resources, Inc.
PBDM - Wood products - Weyerhaeuser Co.
PBF - Bicycle parts and accessories - Robert L. Barnett
PBG PHILLIPS & BROOKS/GLADWIN, INC - Construction materials ☆ - Phillips and Brooks/Gladwin Inc.
PBGS+ - Vitamins and nutritional supplements - Shaperite Concepts, Ltd.
PBH - Pharmaceutical preparations - Pilkington Barnes Hind, Inc.
PBI - Hardware - Pesznecker Bros. Inc.
PBJ - Boats–dinghies - PBJ Dory Co.
PBJ SPORT - Activewear - Zimmer Enterprises Inc.
PBL - Wheels–motor vehicle - Private Brands Ltd.
PBM - Apparel and accessories - Pincus Bros., Inc.
PBM - Cleaning preparations–window ☆ - Hako Minuteman Inc.
PBM WOMEN - Apparel and accessories - Pincus Bros., Inc.
PBOX - Plastics ☆ - Maxxon Corp.
PBR - Insecticides - Mackwin Co.
P.B.S. - Pet products ☆ - Jungle Laboratories Corp.
PBS COLLECTION - Wallcovering - Interials Inc.
PBS DENTAL - Computer software - Probusiness Systems, Inc.
PBS ENDO - Construction equipment rental services - Probusiness Systems, Inc.
PBS PERIO - Construction equipment rental services - Probusiness Systems, Inc.
PBS VIDEOINDEX - Video production - Public Broadcasting Service
PBTOO - Eyeglasses - Peter Blanco & Co., Inc.
PBTOOLBOX - Computer software - Advanced Communication Resources Inc.
P.B.X. - Paints ☆ - PPG Industries, Inc.
PBX-2 - Oils–lubricating - K & W Products
PBXTRA - Computer peripheral equipment - Cobotyx Corp., Inc.
PBZ - Antihistamine preparations - Ciba-Geigy Corp.
PC - Artists' materials ☆ - LogEtronics Corp.
PC - Cameras - Pentax Corp.
PC - Cushions - Packaging Technology, Inc.
PC - Footwear - Warson Group Inc.
PC - Golfing equipment ☆ - Ben Hogan Co.
P.C. - Pharmaceutical preparations ☆ - U.S. Ethicals Inc.
PC - Sunglasses - Bolle' America, Inc.
P.C. - Toys - Tonka Corp.
PC-2 - Electronic equipment - Comprehensive Video Supply Corp.
PC-3 - Binoculars - Bausch & Lomb Inc.
PC-3 - Labeling machinery - Timemed Labeling Systems, Inc.
PC-4 - Labeling machinery - Timemed Labeling Systems, Inc.
PC-5 - Labeling machinery - Timemed Labeling Systems, Inc.
PC-7 - Epoxy - Protective Coating Co.
PC-11 - Epoxy - Protective Coating Co.
PC-30 - Cameras - Pentax Corp.
PC-50 - Cameras - Pentax Corp.

☆ = Now out of production

PC-55 - Vitamins and nutritional supplements - Twinlab
PC-100 - Cameras - Pentax Corp.
PC-205 - Cleaning preparations - Westech Products Inc.
PC-205A - Cleaning preparations - Westech Products Inc.
PC 300 - Computers–personal - International Business Machines Corp.
PC-606-W - Cameras ☆ - Pentax Corp.
PC-700 - Cameras - Pentax Corp.
PC-2500 - Computers–personal - Sharp Electronics Corp.
PC-5541 - Computers–personal - Sharp Electronics Corp.
PC ACCESS - Computer software - Computing Resources, Inc.
PC ACCESSORIES - Computer peripheral equipment - Gemini Industries, Inc.
PC/ASSURE - Computer software - Centel Federal Systems Inc.
PC ASTRO NAVIGATOR - Computer software - Davis Instruments Corp.
PC AT - Computers–personal - International Business Machines Corp.
PC-ATM - Computer software - Futuresoft, Inc.
PC BANNER - Computer software - SourceView Software International
PC BARTENDER - Computer software ☆ - Uneekware, Inc.
PC BRIDGE - Computer software - Recreational Mathemagical Software
PC-BROWSE - Computer software - Quicksoft
PC BUDDY - Office accessories - Nina Enterprises, Inc.
PC BULLET - Computer software - ADC Inc.
PC BUSINESSDISK - Computer software - Softdisk Publishing Inc.
PC-C31 ARUBA - Computer hardware - Ariel Corp.
PC CAPTURE - Computer software - Novus Credit Services Inc.
PC CARD - Computer hardware - Personal Computer Memory Card International Association
PC CINELUX - Electrical equipment - Schneider Optics, Inc.
PC CLINIC PC - Video production - Data Depot Inc.
PC COMPATIBLES - Computer peripheral equipment - Newell Office Products
PC COMPLIANCE - Computer software - RMS Systems, Inc.
PC CORE WORKS - Publisher's imprints ☆ - Roth Publishing Inc.
PC CRAYON - Computer software - PCSoftware
PC CREME - Skin care products - Gordon Laboratories
PC/DACS - Computer software - Utimaco Mergent
PC DEBIT - Computer software - Futuresoft, Inc.
PC DESIGN - Postcards - Fotofolio Inc.
PC DESIGN POSTCARDS - Postcards - Fotofolio Inc.
PC DESKGATE - Computer software - PC Deskgate, Inc.
PC DIAG - Computer software - Unicore Software, Inc.
PC-DOCTOR - Computer peripheral equipment - Watergate Software, Inc.
PC/DOCTOR - Computer software - Howmedica Inc.
PC-DRAW - Computer software - Micrografx, Inc.
PC DUAL - Golfing equipment - Precision Composites, Inc.
PC ENCLOSURE - Computer storage devices ☆ - Kennedy Manufacturing Co.
PC ENTERPRISE - Computer software - Platinum Solutions, Inc.
PC ERGONIZER - Computers–personal ☆ - Hamilton Sorter Co. Inc.
PC ERGONIZER II - Computers–personal ☆ - Hamilton Sorter Co. Inc.
PC-ETCH MAINTENANCE - Chemical preparations - Proler International Corp.
P.C. EXCALIBUR - Toys–models ☆ - Estes Industries
PC-FA - Chemical preparations - Elf Atochem North America, Inc.
PC FIFTY - Golfing equipment - Precision Composites, Inc.
PC FINANCIAL NETWORK'S MAXIMIZER - Computer software - Donaldson Lufkin & Jenrette Securities Corp.
PC FORMS - Computer software - SourceView Software International
PC FORTRESS - Computers - Mead-Hatcher, Inc.
PC FORTY - Golfing equipment - Precision Composites, Inc.
PC GATE - Computer software - PC Deskgate, Inc.
PC GEAR - Office supplies - Nina Enterprises, Inc.
PC GLASSBLOCK - Glass products - Pittsburgh Corning Corp.
PC GLOBE - Computer software ☆ - Broderbund Software, Inc.
PC GRAPHICS & VIDEO - Magazines - Advantage Communications, Inc.
P.C. HACKER - Erasers - Diener Industries Inc.
PC HELP DESK - Computer software - Blue Sky Software Corp.
PC HOME CHECKBOOK - Computer software - SourceView Software International
PC HUB - Software - National Data Corp.
PC INVISION - Computer software - First Union Corp.
PC JR. - Computers–personal ☆ - International Business Machines Corp.
PC KARAOKE - Computer software - Sirius Publishing, Inc.
PC/KPR - Electronic equipment - Xerox Corp.
PC LINKAGRAF - Computer software - Computer Associates International, Inc.
PC LONG - Golfing equipment - Precision Composites, Inc.
PC MAILER - Computer software - SourceView Software International
PC MASTER LITE - Computer software - Master Data Center Inc.
PC MATE - Computer software - Payroll 1, Inc.
PC MIRROR - Computer software - SourceView Software International

PC MOUSE 3D - Computer peripheral equipment - Mouse Systems Corp.
PC MOUSE III - Computer peripheral equipment - Mouse Systems Corp.
PC OPTION - Computer software - Boatmen's Bancshares, Inc.
PC PAINT - Computer software ☆ - Mouse Systems Corp.
PC-PAK - Computer software ☆ - Northern Computers, Inc.
PC PARTNER XL - Computers - VTech Computers Inc.
PC-PATCH - Computers - Western Telematic Inc.
PC-PAYROLL - Computer software - Pen Soft
PC-PAYROLL - Computer software - Peninsula Software, Inc.
PC PHYSICIANS CHOICE - Pillows - Thomas A. Owen III
PC PICTURE SHOW - Photofinishing laboratories - Konica Photo Service U.S.A.
P.C. POPPLE - Toys–stuffed - Mattel, Inc.
P.C. POPPLES - Toys - Those Characters from Cleveland, Inc.
PC: PRECISION CHUCK - Metal finishing equipment - Golden Lyon Investment, Inc.
PC-PRO+ - Computer software - Schlumberger Industries, Inc.
PC PRO CELEBRITY - Shirts - Tee Top of California, Inc.
PC PROGRESSIVE COMPONENTS - Building materials - Progressive Components, Inc.
PC PUCK - Computer peripheral equipment - Back Basics Ltd
PC/RADIO - Computers - International Business Machines Corp.
PC-RECORDER - Computer software ☆ - Arkay Technologies Inc.
PC RL-92 - Clothing - Polo Ralph Lauren Corp.
PC ROAD MAP - Computer software - Parsons Technology, Inc.
PC RX - Computer software - Trend Micro Inc.
PC SCANMASTER - Computer software - Netpro Computing, Inc.
PC SCREEN - Computer software - SourceView Software International
PC SECURE - Computer software - SourceView Software International
PC SOFT LENS - Filters–air - Ergo-Tech Inc.
PC SOFTSWITCH - Computer peripheral equipment - J.K. Erga Co., Inc.
PC SPRINTMAIL - Computer software - Sprint Communications Co. L.P.
PC STUDIO - Photofinishing laboratories - Skrudland Photo, Inc.
PC STYLUS - Computer software - IMSI
PC-SWITCH - Computer software - Futuresoft, Inc.
PC TAILORS - Computer peripheral equipment - PC Tailors, Inc.
PC-TAR - Hair care products - Geritrex Corp.
PC/TCP - Computer software - FTP Software, Inc.
P.C. TEE'S - Computer peripheral equipment - Dallco Industries Inc.
PC TENS - Pumps - Sterling Medical Technologies, Inc.
PC TEST - Computer software - Touchstone Software Corp.
PC THIRTY SIX - Golfing equipment - Precision Composites, Inc.
PC TRACKER - Computer software - Alk Associates, Inc.
PC-TRANSLATOR - Computer software - Linguistic Products, Inc.
PC-TRON - Fuses - Cooper Industries, Inc.
PC TRONICS - Computer hardware - PC Express, Inc.
PC VINA - Computer software - R.L. Polk & Co.
PC VIS - Computer software - R.L. Polk & Co.
P.C. VOICEWRITER - Dictating machines - Lanier Voice Products
PC WORD - Computer software - SourceView Software International
PC WORDSMITH - Computer software - Parsons Technology, Inc.
PC WORK CENTER - Computer storage devices - Wright Line Inc.
PC WORLD - Computer software - International Data Group, Inc.
PC WORLD INTERACTIVE - Computer software - International Data Group, Inc.
PC-WRITE - Computer software - Quicksoft
PC-WRITE LITE - Computer software - Quicksoft
PC-XPEDITE - Computer peripheral equipment - Xpedite Systems, Inc.
PC XT - Computers–personal - International Business Machines Corp.
PC-XWARE - Computer software - NCD Graphic Software Corp.
PC1 - Sporting goods - Donnay USA
PC2X - Computer program - UniPress Software Inc.
PC12 - Sporting goods - Donnay USA
PCA - Egg cartons - Packaging Corp. of America
PCA - Faucets - Neoperl Inc.
PCA - Machinery - C and C Manufacturing Inc.
P.C.A. - Medical apparatus - Howmedica Inc.
PCA - Pajamas–men's - PCA Apparel Industries Inc.
PCA-200 - Electronic equipment - AudioControl
PCA-CAD - Computer software - Portland Cement
PCA-FRAME - Computer software - Portland Cement
PCA LOTION CONCENTRATE - Vitamins and nutritional supplements - Vitamin Research Products Inc.
PCA-MATS - Computer software - Portland Cement
PCA ULTRA FACIAL CREAM - Vitamins and nutritional supplements - Vitamin Research Products Inc.

☆ = Now out of production

PCA ULTRA HAND & BODY LOTION - Skin care products - Vitamin Research Products Inc.

PCABEAM - Computer software - Portland Cement

PCACOL - Computer software - Portland Cement

PCBLAST - Computer software - Mark A. Fry & Associates, Inc.

PCBX - Computer peripheral equipment - PCBX Systems, Inc.

PCC - Apparel–women's - Public Clothing Co.

PCC - Containers - Pollution Control, Inc.

PCC - Electronic equipment - Tadiran Electronic Industries, Inc.

PCC - Hair care products - Trionics Systems Corp.

PCC - Jewelry - Platinum Customcraft Corp.

PCC - Pumps - ITT Corp.

PCC - Swimming pools - Paramount Leisure Industries, Inc.

PCC 160 - Microphones - Crown International, Inc.

PCC 2000 - Computers–personal ☆ - Scan-Optics, Inc.

PCC GIRLS - Apparel and accessories - Public Clothing Co.

PCD - Computer peripherals - Abovo, Inc.

P.C.E. DISPERTAB - Antibiotics - Abbott Laboratories

PCEBBC - Computer hardware - Applied Data Sciences Inc.

PCEHSD - Computers - Applied Data Sciences Inc.

PCF - Binoculars - Pentax Corp.

PCG - Glass products ☆ - Laminated Glass Corp.

PCGS - Containers–glass - Professional Coin Grading Service, Inc.

PCGS PROFILE - Trading cards and stamps - Professional Coin Grading Service, Inc.

PCGUIDE - Computer software - Elan Associates (GreenLight Software Division)

PCHSD2 - Computer hardware - Applied Data Sciences Inc.

PCI - Chemical preparations - Georgia-Pacific Corp.

PCI - Computer software - PCI Remote Sensing Corp.

PCI - Furniture - Neal B. Shamis

PCI - Medical apparatus - Physicians Consulting, Inc.

PCI - Pet food - Pet Center, Inc.

PCI-3 - Hardware - Lone Star Screw Co. of Houston Inc.

PCI TRANSAID - Machinery - Pharmaceutical Consultants, Inc.

PCITE - Chemical preparations - Novagen, Inc.

PCJ - Hair care products - Luster Products, Inc.

PCJOBBER - Computer software - JB Software

PCLAB - Computer software - Data Translation, Inc.

P'CLAY - Clay–modeling - New Century Ceramics

PCM - Computer software - McDermott Inc.

PCMALL - Publisher's imprints - Creative Computers, Inc.

PCMCIA PA PAGE CARD SOCKET - Computer hardware - Socket Communications, Inc.

PCMIM - Computer hardware - Cabletron Systems, Inc.

PCN GOLD - Film - Eastman Kodak Co.

PCO - Giftware - Present Co. Inc.

PCO - Lenses–optical - Photran Corp.

PCO PHYTOSOME - Vitamins and nutritional supplements - Enzymatic Therapy, Inc.

PCP - Health care products - PCP-Champion

PCP - Pesticides–agricultural ☆ - Roccorp, Inc.

PCP-SCAN - Radio communications equipment - Immunomedics, Inc.

PC*PRO - Computer software - NPC Freight Services

PCR - Apparel and accessories - Patagonia, Inc.

PCR - Roofing materials - Powell Electrical Manufacturing Co.

P.C.R. - Rope - New England Ropes Inc.

PCRISK - Computer software - PRC Inc.

PCRTSPY - Computer software - Productivity-Quality Systems Inc.

PCS - Asphalt - Air Products and Chemicals, Inc.

PCS-E-ZINC - Photoengraving machines - Revere Copper and Brass Inc.

PCS IN SPACE - Computer software - Jackson and Tull

PCS-SCOREKEEPER - Computer peripheral equipment - Environmental Data Resources, Inc.

PCT - Photographic equipment - Eastman Kodak Co.

PCTAXI - Computers - Applied Data Sciences Inc.

PCTEL - Integrated circuits - PC-Tel, Inc.

PCTHERM - Computer software ☆ - Data Translation, Inc.

PCTOUCH - Computer peripheral equipment - AMX Corp.

PCTOWN - Computer peripheral equipment - Computown, Inc.

PCV - Motor vehicles - Trans2 Corp.

PCVAULT - Computer software - At&T Corp.

PCW PACIFIC WAVE CRAFT - Apparel and accessories - Carlos Roy Sanchez

PCX - Golfing equipment - Square Two Golf

PD - Jewelry - Pampillonia Designs, Inc.

PD - Jewelry - Regency Diamond Corp.

PD - Pharmaceutical preparations - Warner-Lambert Co.

PD CUE BUMPER POOL - Games ☆ - Milton Bradley Co.

PD PAULA DORF - Cosmetics - Paula Dorf Cosmetics, Inc.

PD PREMIER DESIGNS - Jewelry - Premier Designs, Inc.

P.D., Q. LITE - Computer software - First Colony Life Insurance Co.

PD SPECTAR - Lenses–photographic ☆ - Photo Research, Inc.

PDC - Computer hardware - Peripheral Devices Corp.

PDC - Food products - P. Drescher Co. Inc.

PDC - Irrigation equipment - Hunter Industries Inc.

PDC-7 - Coatings - Unnatural Resources Inc.

PDC INTERNATIONAL - Apparel and accessories ☆ - Gallron

PDCM72+ THE ORIGINAL PLANT DERIVED COLLOIDAL MINERALS - Vitamins and nutritional supplements - Millennium Marketplace, Inc.

P.D.E. - Paint removers - H. Behlen & Bro. Inc.

PDE/LIB - Computer software - International TechneGroup Inc.

PDEASE - Computer software - SPDE, Inc.

PDF - Motorcycles - Suzuki of America Automotive Corp.

P.D.I. - Apparel and accessories - Product Designs International Inc.

PDI - Electronic equipment - Precision Devices, Inc.

PDI - Pharmaceutical preparations - Nice-Pak Products, Inc.

PDI - Publisher's imprints - Psychological Dimensions Inc.

PDL - Pharmaceutical preparations - Protein Design Labs, Inc.

PDL - Solder ☆ - Kester Solder Co.

PDM - Sound equipment - Gemini Sound Products Corp.

PDM-SURVEYPRO - Computer peripheral equipment - Professional Data Management Associates, Inc.

PDO - Cleaning preparations - Roebic Laboratories Inc.

PDO - Computer software - Next Computer, Inc.

P.D.P. - Pharmaceutical preparations - Wesley Pharmacal Co. Inc.

PDQ - Artists' materials ☆ - C-Thru Ruler Co.

P.D.Q. - Brushes–paint - Wooster Brush Co.

PDQ - Chemical preparations - Colonial Refining and Chemical Co.

P.D.Q. - Lubricants - CRC Chemicals USA/Siloo

P.D.Q. - Paints - Conco Paint Co.

P.D.Q. - Paints - Smiland Paint Co.

P.D.Q. - Paints - Triangle Coatings Inc.

P.D.Q. - Pregnancy test kits - Bio-Medical Products Corp.

P.D.Q. - Sealing compounds - Kwal-Howells Inc.

PDQ - Shelving units–wood ☆ - Lundia

PDQ - Spices and extracts - Novartis Nutrition Corp.

P.D.Q. - Wallpaper ☆ - Allpro Corp.

PDQ - Water purification systems - PDQ Manufacturing, Inc.

PDQ MARLIN TOOL - Machine parts - Marlin Tool, Inc.

PDQCOMM - Computer software - Crescent Software, Inc.

PDQ'S - Hair care products - Burston Inc.

PDR - Computers–personal - Me Licensing Corp.

PDRTA - Computer storage devices–optical - CD Technology, Inc.

PDS - Computer software - Lattice Semiconductor Corp.

PDS - Computer software - Parameter Driven Software Inc.

PDS - Computer software - Personnel Data Systems Inc.

PDS - Disinfectants - Medical Polymers Technologies, Inc.

PDS - Jewelry - Peggy Dempsey Inc.

PDS - Recording label - PDS-Universal Entertainment Group Inc.

PDS - Tape recorders–cassette - Matsushita Consumer Electronics Co.

PDS-ADVENT - Computer software - Parameter Driven Software Inc.

PDS-C - Computer software - Parameter Driven Software Inc.

PDS-OPEN - Computer software - Parameter Driven Software Inc.

PDT SENSOR - Dental equipment - Professional Dental Technologies, Inc.

PDX - Apparel and accessories ☆ - Jantzen Inc.

PDX SPORTSWEAR - Apparel and accessories ☆ - Jantzen Inc.

PE - Jewelry - Pacific East Trading Co. Ltd.

PE - Ophthalmic goods - Alcon Laboratories, Inc.

PE-BLETEX - Paints - Morris Paint & Varnish Co.

PE LOGIC PRACTICAL ENHANCED LOGIC, CORP. - Computer hardware - PE Logic Corp.

PE/PROCESS LIBRARY - Computer software - Learmonth & Burchette Management Systems, Inc.

PE/PROCESS MANAGER - Computer software - Learmonth & Burchette Management Systems, Inc.

PE/ROUTE 2 - Computer software - Learmonth & Burchette Management Systems, Inc.

PEII - Lenses–optical - Signet Armorlite, Inc.

PEA CHOCOLADE - Calendars - Euro-American Brands Inc.

PEA-PARA SHOOTER - Toys - Strombecker Corp.

PEA PICKER - Bicycles - Schwinn Cycling & Fitness Inc.

☆ = Now out of production

PEABERRY COFFEE - Coffee - Coffee Consultants, Inc.
PEABERRY COFFEE GROUNDS CREW - Apparel and accessories - Coffee Consultants, Inc.
PEABODY - Frames–eyeglass - May Optical Co. Inc.
PEABODY'S COFFEE CO. - Coffee - Peabody's Coffee Co.
PEACE - Balls - Tide-Rider Inc.
PEACE - Wood products - Peace Flooring Co. Inc.
PEACE-ABLE PLACE, A - Publisher's imprints - C.E. Mendez Foundation, Inc.
PEACE AND CONFLICT RESOLUTION - Publisher's imprints - Syracuse University Press
PEACE AND JOY FROM - Postcards - McCaffrey & Associates, Inc.
PEACE & QUIET - Plugs–ear - Flents Products Co. Inc.
PEACE BE STILL - Recording label - J.S. Publishing, Inc.
PEACE CULTURE - Clothing - Unity One Inc.
PEACE GEAR - Apparel and accessories - William Ferrie
PEACE ISLAND - Meat products - Prima Corp.
PEACE KEEPER - Toys - Tyco Toys
PEACE KEEPERS, THE - Toys–electronic - Jaleco USA, Inc.
PEACE LIGHT NEVER ALONE - Lighting fixtures - Cemeteries Aglow, Inc.
PEACE LOVE & CREATIVITY - Hobby kits - Creative Art Activities Inc.
PEACE LOVE & HAPPINESS - Apparel–women's - Peace, Love & Happiness Fashions, Inc.
PEACE LOVE & RESPECT - Jewelry - Jeffery Allen Rodgers
PEACE MISSILE - Golfing equipment - The Peace Missile Co.
PEACE OF MIND - Bags–plastic - Changing World Products, Inc.
PEACE OF MIND - Computer software - Spectrum Universal
PEACE OF MIND - Deodorizers - Origins Natural Resources Inc.
PEACE OF MIND - Skin care products - Estee Lauder Inc.
PEACE OF MIND FOR THE TRAVELER - Locks–padlocks - Luggage Loks Inc.
PEACE ON EARTH, OUR EARTH IN ONE PIECE - Tote bags and backpacks - XTC Products Inc.
PEACE PAD - Mattress covers - Peace Pillows, Inc.
PEACE PALS - Dolls - Lorraine Miano
PEACE PEBBLES - Novelty items - Kathy's Kovers
PEACE PILLOW - Pillows - Peace Pillows, Inc.
PEACE POPS - Ice cream - Ben and Jerry's Homemade, Inc.
PEACE THROUGH MUSIC - Recording label - Soundings of the Planet, Inc.
PEACE TREE - Coffee - Black Coffee, Inc.
PEACEABLE - Recording label - Broadbeach Records
PEACEFEATHER - Greeting cards - Ariyana Gibbon
PEACEFUL - Health care products - East Earth Herb Inc.
PEACEFUL DREAMER - Furniture–children's ☆ - Child Craft Industries Inc.
PEACEFUL GARDEN - Candles - Natural Image Botanicals Inc.
PEACEFUL PATCHOULI - Soap - Kiss My Face
PEACEFUL STREAM - Recording label - Skylite-Sing Inc.
PEACEKEEPER - Revolvers ☆ - Colt's Manufacturing Co. Inc.
PEACEKEEPER - Toilets–enameled - Kohler Co.
PEACEKEEPER, THE - Alarm systems - Protect America, Inc.
PEACEMAKER - Toy guns - Strombecker Corp.
PEACEMAKER - Toys - Peacemaker Games
PEACH - Filters–water - Perry Equipment Corp.
PEACH - Ophthalmic goods ☆ - Luxottica
PEACH - Perfumes - Tennessee Gold Inc.
PEACH - Snuff - Conwood Co. L.P.
PEACH 20/20 - Skin care products - Giovanni Cosmetics Inc.
PEACH-A-RITA - Beverages–alcohol - El Torito Restaurants Inc.
PEACH AMANTE - Wines - Bardenheier Wine Cellars
PEACH-APRICOT - Jams and jellies - Sarabeth's Kitchen
PEACH BALLAD - Pressed glassware ☆ - Indiana Glass Co.
PEACH BASKET - Rum - Joseph E. Seagram & Sons, Inc.
PEACH BLEND - Tobacco–chewing or smoking - Amar Blends Co.
PEACH BLOOM - Stoneware dinnerware - Iron Mountain Stoneware Inc.
PEACH BLOSSOM - Dinnerware–glass ☆ - Metlox Pottery Shoppe
PEACH BLOSSOM - Dolls - Mattel, Inc.
PEACH BLOSSOM - Pillows - McCarty's Sacro-Ease
PEACH BUDS - Candy - Wilson Candy Co.
PEACH CHUTNEY - Seasonings - Cinnabar Specialty Foods, Inc./Neera's Products
PEACH CLOUD - Cosmetics - Revlon Consumer Products Corp.
PEACH CREST - Glassware–household ☆ - Fenton Art Glass Co.
PEACH FLORAL - Cookware and dinnerware ☆ - Corning Inc.
PEACH FUZZ PLAYWEAR FOR LITTLE PEOPLE - Apparel–children's - Collins Graphics, Inc.
PEACH GARLAND - Dinnerware - Corning Inc.
PEACH GLO - Skin care products - Goubaud

PEACH GOBBLER - Office supplies - Brushcreek Creative Co.
PEACH GOLD - Jewelry - Dewitt Goldsmiths
PEACH KA - Beverages–alcohol - Kasser Laird Distilling Co.
PEACH LATTICE - Dinnerware ☆ - Corning Inc.
PEACH LUSTRE - Glassware–household ☆ - Anchor Hocking Glass, Inc.
PEACH MANGO FOOT SCRUB - Skin care products ☆ - Neoteric Cosmetics, Inc.
PEACH MELBA - Beverages–carbonated - Snapple Beverage Corp.
PEACH MELBA - Teas - Eastern Shore Tea Co.
PEACH NECTAR - Cosmetics - Lancome
PEACH OF THE TROPICS, THE - Food products - Chiquita Brands, Inc.
PEACH PASSION - Beverages–alcohol ☆ - David Sherman Corp.
PEACH PILLOW - Pillows - McCarty's Sacro-Ease
PEACH PIT - Clothing - David M. Goldwitz
PEACH PLEASURE - Juices - Juice Club, Inc.
PEACH PRETTY - Dolls - Mattel, Inc.
PEACH QUAKE - Juices - Tree Top, Inc.
PEACH RIDGE - Food products - Jack Brown Produce Inc.
PEACH ROYALE - Soap - R.H. Macy & Co.
PEACH SLICE PLUS - Fruit drinks–bottled or canned - Smoothie King Franchises, Inc.
PEACH STIX - Candy - Leaf, Inc.
PEACHEES - Fruits–dried ☆ - Leroux Creek Food Corp.
PEACHEROO - Apparel–women's - Wacoal America Inc.
PEACHES - Face powder ☆ - Bourjois Ltd.
PEACHES & CHERRIES - Shoes - Impo International Inc.
PEACHES & CREAM - Chewing gum ☆ - Fleer Corp.
PEACHES AND CREAM - Dolls ☆ - Effanbee Doll Corp.
PEACHES & CREAM - Fruits and vegetables - Peter Rabbit Farms, Inc.
PEACHES & CREAM - Handbags - Holiday Fair, Inc.
PEACHES AND CREAM - Lipsticks ☆ - Tinkerbell
PEACHES & CREAM - Skin care products - Kiss My Face
PEACHES & CREME - Yarn - Elmore-Pisgah, Inc.
PEACHES & DREAMS - Deodorizers - Tsumura International Inc.
PEACHES AND SCREEN - Suntan lotions - Panama Jack International Inc.
PEACHES 'N CREAM - Apparel–children's - May Apparel Group, Inc.
PEACHES 'N CREAM - Glassware–household ☆ - Fenton Art Glass Co.
PEACHES 'N CREAM CEREAL - Food products - Breadshop's Natural Foods
PEACHES 'N CREME - Hair care products - Helene Curtis Industries Inc.
PEACHEY - Tobacco - Conwood Co. L.P.
PEACHEY - Wallpaper ☆ - Ginger Tree Designs
PEACHGLOW - Dinnerware–glass - Nikko Ceramics Inc.
PEACHNUT - Cordials and liqueurs ☆ - Euromark Inc.
PEACHTREE - Baskets–wood ☆ - Royal Cathay Trading Co.
PEACHTREE - Beverages–alcohol - Jim Beam Brands Co.
PEACHTREE - Computer software - Peachtree Software Inc.
PEACHTREE - Dinnerware–glass ☆ - Lenox, Inc.
PEACHTREE - Doors–wood ☆ - Peachtree Doors and Windows Inc.
PEACHTREE CREAM - Beverages–alcohol - Jim Beam Brands Co.
PEACHTREE ORIGINALS - Toys ☆ - Mount Vernon Mills Inc.
PEACHTREE PLAYTHINGS - Balls - Southern States Marketing, Inc.
PEACHTREE PLAZA - Floor coverings–carpet and rugs - Royalty Carpet Mills, Inc.
PEACHY - Ophthalmic goods - Foremost Optical Products
PEACHY KEEN - Plastics - Krizmark Inc.
PEACHY PINK - Dinnerware–glass - Franciscan by Johnson Brothers, USA, Inc.
PEACHY PLACE TO BE, A - Postcards - Aerial Photography Services, Inc.
PEACOCK - Brushes–hair ☆ - Phillips Brush Corp.
PEACOCK - Cases–plastic - Lerner Manufacturing Inc.
PEACOCK - Cheese - Peacock Foods Inc.
PEACOCK - Containers - Hormel Corp.
PEACOCK - Cosmetics - Lancome
PEACOCK - Dishes–china ☆ - Royal China & Porcelain Companies Inc.
PEACOCK - Lenses–optical - Kelley & Hueber
PEACOCK - Looms - Nasco Handcrafters
PEACOCK - Paper - Pacon Corp.
PEACOCK - Pet products - Prevue Metal Products Inc.
PEACOCK - Recording label - MCA Universal Studios
PEACOCK - Seafood products–canned or cured - California Shellfish Co. Inc.
PEACOCK - Toilets–enameled - Kohler Co.
PEACOCK - Water colors ☆ - Binney & Smith Inc.
PEACOCK - Yarn - William Unger & Co. Inc.
PEACOCK ALLEY - Papier-mache articles ☆ - Cardinal Inc.
PEACOCK EGGS - Candy ☆ - Leaf, Inc.
PEACOCK HILL - Wines - Mark West Vineyards

☆ = Now out of production

PEACOCK PRESS - Publisher's imprints ☆ - Bantam Doubleday Dell Publishing Group, Inc.

PEACOCK TANNING SYSTEM - Sunblocks - Avex Industries Ltd.

PEACOCKS - Apparel–men's ☆ - Superba, Inc.

PEACOCK'S - Juices - Howard Foods Inc.

PEACOCKS - Shoes - Edison Brothers Stores, Inc.

PEACOCK'S BROMIDES - Pharmaceutical preparations - Natcon Chemical Co. Inc.

PEACOCKS ON PARADE - Christmas tree ornaments - Cracker Box Inc.

PEACOCKS PREMIER - Shoes - Edison Brothers Stores, Inc.

PEACOCK'S PREMIUM PET FOOD - Pet food - Northland Feed Co.

PEACOCKS SIGNATURE SERIES - Shoes - Edison Brothers Stores, Inc.

PEAK - Cutlery - Coleman Co., Inc.

PEAK - Educational materials - Digital Imaging Associates Inc.

PEAK - Food products - Horton Fruit Co.

PEAK - Gasoline ☆ - Old World Industries, Inc.

PEAK - Golfing equipment - Pro Select Sports USA

PEAK - Herbicides - Ciba-Geigy Corp.

PEAK - Pet products - Marvin Reich

PEAK - Recording label - Peak Records, Inc.

PEAK - Skates–roller - Rollerblade, Inc.

PEAK - Soups–mixes - Trinidad/Benham Holding Co.

PEAK - Toothpaste - Colgate-Palmolive Co.

PEAK - Vitamins and nutritional supplements - Hillestad International, Inc.

PEAK AIR - Medical apparatus - Omron Healthcare, Inc.

PEAK ANTIFREEZE & COOLANT - Antifreeze - Old World Industries, Inc.

PEAK FLOW METER - Medical apparatus - Blairex Laboratories, Inc.

PEAK FREAN - Cookies - Christie, Brown & Co.

PEAK FREANS - Biscuits - Nabisco Foods Group

PEAK I - Sporting goods - Coleman Co., Inc.

PEAK LOAD DISTRIBUTOR - Regulators–power - Manningtronics, Inc.

PEAK-O'BEAUTY - Brassieres (Bras) - Honor House Products Corp.

PEAK OF PAINT PERFECTION - Paints - North Jersey Paint Co. Inc.

PEAK OF QUALITY - Food products - Acme Poultry Co.

PEAK PERFORMANCE - Apparel–athletic - Tighe Industries Inc.

PEAK PERFORMANCE - Electrical surge protectors - Woods Industries, Inc.

PEAK PERFORMANCE - Floor waxes ☆ - Knight Marketing Corp.

PEAK PERFORMANCE - Vitamins and nutritional supplements - Unipro Inc.

PEAK PERFORMER - Ventilation equipment - Browning Metal Products

PEAK PHYSIQUE - Apparel–athletic - Global Fitness Apparel, LLC

PEAK POD - Tents - Coleman Co., Inc.

PEAK PREMIUM WINDSHIELD FLUID - Cleaning preparations - Old World Industries, Inc.

PEAK PRO - Pet products - Peak Pet Products

PEAK READY TO USE ANTIFREEZE - Antifreeze - Old World Industries, Inc.

PEAK RECORDS - Recording label - Peak Records, Inc.

PEAK SCIENTIFIC - Generators–gas - Peak Scientific, Inc.

PEAK-START - Toilets–enameled - Kohler Co.

PEAK, THE - Respiratory flow meters - Multispiro, Inc.

PEAK VIDEO ILLUSTRATOR - Computer software and videos - Peak Performance Technologies Inc.

PEAK WEIGHT - Glassware–household - Nourot Glass Studio

PEAKAI - Seafood products–canned or cured - Novalia, Ltd.

PEAKFIT - Computer software - Jandel Corp.

PEAKLITE - Roofing materials–concrete - Sequentia Inc. (Reinforced Plastics Div.)

PEAKLITE - Sleeping bags - Coleman Co., Inc.

PEAKLOFT - Sleeping bags - Coleman Co., Inc.

PEAKS - Apparel–men's - Alps Sportswear Manufacturing Co.

PEAKS - Beverages–malt - The Stroh Brewery Co.

PEAKS - Computer software - Cedar Creek Process Engineering

PEAKS - Footwear - Chesapeake Shoe Co. of California

PEAKS OF PERFECTION - Yogurt - Crowley Foods, Inc.

PEAK'S POINTS - Novelty items - Peak Environmental Management, Inc.

PEAKSKILL - Apparel and accessories - James A. Soucy

PEAKWOOD COLLECTION - Furniture ☆ - Hooker Furniture Corp.

PEANK - Paneling - Marlite

PEANUT - Computers - International Business Machines Corp.

PEANUT BLOSSOM - Candy - Glenn Confections Inc.

PEANUT-BONE - Pet food - T.F.H. Publications, Inc.

PEANUT BRITTLE - Cookies - Nabisco Foods Group

PEANUT BUDDY - Candy - R.M. Palmer Co.

PEANUT BUMPS - Candy ☆ - Maxfield Candy Co.

PEANUT BUTTER - Toys–stuffed ☆ - Gund, Inc.

PEANUT BUTTER & JELLY - Game - Tonka Corp.

PEANUT BUTTER & JELLY - Games ☆ - Parker Brothers

PEANUT BUTTER & JELLY - Publisher's imprints - Scholastic Inc.

PEANUT BUTTER & PEARL JAM - Ice cream - Danken's Gourmet Ice Creams

PEANUT BUTTER BARS - Candy - Atkinson Candy Co.

PEANUT BUTTER BLOCK - Candy ☆ - Ruth Hunt Candy Co.

PEANUT BUTTER BOO! BAR - Candy - Chocolate House, Inc.

PEANUT BUTTER CHEWS - Candy - Thos. D. Richardson Co.

PEANUT BUTTER CHIPS - Candy ☆ - Chex Co.

PEANUT BUTTER CRUNCH - Candy - Tom's Foods Inc.

PEANUT BUTTER CRUNCH - Candy ☆ - Brown & Haley

PEANUT BUTTER CRUNCH - Candy ☆ - Ben Myerson Candy Co.

PEANUT BUTTER CUP - Ice cream - Ben and Jerry's Homemade, Inc.

PEANUT BUTTER FACTORY - Toys ☆ - A.R.C. Toys Inc.

PEANUT BUTTER FLUFFS - Candy - Miss Saylor's Candies

PEANUT BUTTER KRUNCHIES - Candy - Nestle USA

PEANUT BUTTER LOGS - Candy - Tom's Foods Inc.

PEANUT BUTTER MELTAWAYS - Candy - Gardners Candies

PEANUT BUTTER MOUNTAIN - Candy bars - Brown & Haley

PEANUT BUTTER OOMPAS - Candy ☆ - Willy Wonka Brands

PEANUT BUTTER PALS - Candy - Tom's Foods Inc.

PEANUT BUTTER PANIC - Computer software - CBS Software

PEANUT BUTTER PARFAIT - Candy - Nabisco Foods Group

PEANUT BUTTER PETALS - Candy - D.E. Wolfgang Candy Co. Inc.

PEANUT BUTTER PIGOUTS - Chocolate bars - Linda Grishman Chocolates, Inc.

PEANUT BUTTER PUFFS - Cereal - General Mills, Inc.

PEANUT BUTTER SQUARES - Cakes - Drake Bakeries, Inc.

PEANUT BUTTER STICK - Ice cream cones - Wells' Dairy, Inc.

PEANUT BUTTER SWIRL - Candy ☆ - F.B. Washburn Candy Corp.

PEANUT BUTTER THE JELLY FISH - Publisher's imprint - Kenneth Kreisler

PEANUT BUTTER TRIUMPHS - Cookies ☆ - Keebler Co.

PEANUT BUTTER WHOPPERS - Candy ☆ - Leaf, Inc.

PEANUT BUTTER WITH NO JELLY - Candy ☆ - Peter Paul

PEANUT CHEW - Food products - Honeypot Treats

PEANUT CHEW FOR DOGS - Pet food - T.F.H. Publications, Inc.

PEANUT CHEWS - Candy - Goldenberg Candy Co.

PEANUT CITY - Hams - Pruden Packing Co. Inc.

PEANUT COUNTRY - Recording label - Rockmasters International

PEANUT CRISPS - Peanut butter - Nabisco Foods Group

PEANUT CRUNCH - Candy - Nabisco Foods Group

PEANUT CRUNCH - Candy ☆ - New England Confectionery Co.

PEANUT DELIGHTS - Candy - Russell Stover Candies, Inc.

PEANUT FACTORY - Nuts - Peanut Factory

PEANUT GALLERY - Games - Smethport Specialty Co.

PEANUT GALLERY, THE - Wallpaper - Seabrook Wallcoverings, Inc.

PEANUT JUMBO - Candy - R.L. Albert & Son, Inc.

PEANUT KIDS - Nuts–salted, roasted, cooked, or canned - Producers Peanut Co. Inc.

PEANUT KRISP - Candy ☆ - Holland American Wafer Co.

PEANUT PAK & DESIGN - Paperboard–corrugated - Georgia-Pacific Corp.

PEANUT PANIC - Games - Tonka Corp.

PEANUT PATCH - Candy - Peanut Patch

PEANUT PATCH - Food products - W.B. Roddenbery Co., Inc.

PEANUT PLANK - Candy - Tom's Foods Inc.

PEANUT POWER - Juices–frozen - Smoothie King Franchises, Inc.

PEANUT PUNCH SPORTS WEAR - Apparel and accessories - Alegre Fashions Inc.

PEANUT PUTTERS - Snack cakes ☆ - Interstate Brands Corp.

PEANUT ROLL - Candy - Tom's Foods Inc.

PEANUT ROLL - Candy bars - Standard Candy Co. Inc.

PEANUT SHACK, THE - Candy, nut and confectionery stores - Candy Candy Inc.

PEANUT SHOP, THE - Nuts–salted, roasted, cooked, or canned - Williamsburg Foods, Inc.

PEANUT SHOPPE - Nuts–salted, roasted, cooked, or canned - Peanut Products Co. Inc.

PEANUT SQUARES - Candy - Sweet Candy Co.

PEANUT WONDER - Peanut butter - Peanut Wonder Corp.

PEANUTCREME - Confections - Sunspire Foods

PEANUTS - Bedding–linen ☆ - West Point-Pepperell Inc.

PEANUTS - Christmas tree ornaments - Silvestri Corp.

PEANUTS - Frames–eyeglass - Hudson Optical Corp.

PEANUTS - Frames–eyeglass - Marine Optical, Inc.

PEANUTS - Giftware - Determined Productions, Inc.

PEANUTS - Giftware ☆ - Schmid Inc.

PEANUT'S - Glue–household or industrial ☆ - Loctite Corp.

☆ = Now out of production

PEANUTS - Infant product ☆ - La Rue International, Inc.
PEANUTS - Novelty items - Easter Unltd. Inc.
PEANUTS - Peanut butter - United Feature Syndicate, Inc.
PEANUTS - Puzzles ☆ - Milton Bradley Co.
PEANUTS - Socks - High Point Knitting Inc.
PEANUTS - Trunks ☆ - Seward Luggage Co.
PEANUTS - Watches - E. Gluck Corp.
PEANUTS HOME VIDEO - Video production - United Feature Syndicate, Inc.
PEANUTS MAZE MARATHON - Computer software - Random House, Inc.
PEANUTS PICTURE PUZZLERS - Computer software - Random House, Inc.
PEANUTS RIBBONS - Craft supplies ☆ - C.M. Offray & Son Inc.
PEANUTTY BUTTER - Food products ☆ - Natural Nectar Corp.
PEANUTTY PUTTY - Toys - Tonka Corp.
PEAR - Medical apparatus - HWE Inc.
PEAR & GRAPE - Dishes–earthenware - Hadley Pottery Co. Inc.
PEAR CARDAMOM CHUTNEY - Seasonings - Cinnabar Specialty Foods, Inc./
  Neera's Products
PEAR DE PEAR - Beverages–alcohol - Carneros Alambic Distillery
PEAR FAIR - Fruits and vegetables - Price Cold Storage & Packing Co.
PEAR SOX - Apparel and accessories - Pearsox
PEAR TREAT WASHINGTON PEARS - Fruits and vegetables - Valley Fruit
PEAR TREE - Stationery ☆ - Fran Mar Greeting cards Ltd.
PEARCE - Amplifiers–musical instrument - Pearce Amplification Ltd.
PEARCE - Blankets - Woolrich Woolen Mills Inc.
PEARCE DUFF - Food products - Universal Foods Corp.
PEARCE GRIP - Firearms, accessories, and parts - Pearce Grip, Inc.
PEARL - Belts–apparel - Accessories by Pearl Inc.
PEARL - Blinds–vertical - Louverdrape Inc.
PEARL - Brushes–paint - Corona Brushes Inc.
PEARL - Coffee - Pearl Coffee Co.
PEARL - Dinnerware–glass - Franciscan by Johnson Brothers, USA, Inc.
PEARL - Dinnerware–glass ☆ - Nikko Ceramics Inc.
PEARL - Dishwashing compounds - PLC
PEARL - Flutes - Orpheus Music Inc.
PEARL - Food products - Union Fish Co.
PEARL - Glass products ☆ - Corning Inc.
PEARL - Hearing aids - Magnatone Hearing Aid Corp.
PEARL - Paints - Polymerics, Inc.
PEARL - Paints - Tulip Productions
PEARL - Paper–bond ☆ - Southworth Co.
PEARL - Recording label - Delmark Records
PEARL - Seafood products–canned or cured - Carmine Foods Inc.
PEARL - Shrimp - Indian Ridge Shrimp Co.
PEARL - Wallpaper - Maya Romanoff Corp.
PEARL - Watches - Elgin Watch Co.
PEARL - Waxes–sealing - Cleaning Systems, Inc.
PEARL - Whirlpools - Pearl Baths Inc.
PEARL - Yarn - Brunswick Yarns
PEARL BEACH - Aquarium accessories - Kordon
PEARL BEACH - Aquarium accessories - Novalek, Inc.
PEARL BEAD HOLDER - Ophthalmic goods - Karlen Manufacturing, Inc.
PEARL BLOSSOMS - Wallcovering ☆ - Colortree Designs
PEARL BOUQUET - Dishes–china - Pickard Inc.
PEARL CARE - Jewelry - J.P. Morton Co. Inc.
PEARL CLEANER LIQUID - Cleaning preparations - Blitz Manufacturing Co.,
  Inc.
PEARL COLLECTION - Hair care products - Pearl Collection, Inc.
PEARL CORDER - Tape recorders - Saul Mineroff Electronics Inc.
PEARL COTTON - Thread - DMC Corp.
PEARL CREAM ALE - Beverages–malt ☆ - Pearl Brewing Co.
PEARL CREEK - Furniture - Homecrest Industries Inc.
PEARL CROWN - Thread - Sew-Art International
PEARL CROWN - Thread - YLI Corp.
PEARL DRIVER SERIES - Toys - Mattel, Inc.
PEARL DROPS - Christmas tree ornaments - Cracker Box Inc.
PEARL DROPS - Frames–eyeglass - May Optical Co. Inc.
PEARL DROPS - Toothpaste - Carter-Wallace, Inc.
PEARL DYE - Dyes and pigments - Lilac Enterprises, Inc.
PEARL ESSENCE - Wallpaper ☆ - J. Josephson, Inc.
PEARL II - Cameras ☆ - Konica USA Inc.
PEARL ISLAND - Shrimp–fresh or frozen - Darik Enterprises Inc.
PEARL-ITE - Jewelry - Tiara Corp.
PEARL IZUMI - Apparel–athletic - Pearl Izumi Technical Wear
PEARL JAM - Apparel and accessories - Pearl Jam
PEARL KING - Cosmetics ☆ - Dubl Duck/Jet Set Inc.
PEARL-LACE - Frames–eyeglass ☆ - Universal/Univis Inc.

PEARL LIGHT - Beverages–malt - Pearl Brewing Co.
PEARL LINEN - Fabrics - Industrial Coatings Group, Inc.
PEARL-LOOM - Fabrics - N. Erlanger, Blumgart & Co. Inc.
PEARL LYTES - Candles - Candle Corp. of America
PEARL MAE'S POTATO SALAD DRESSING - Salad dressings–bottled -
  Cleona Jeanne Gomer
PEARL MEADOWS - Floor coverings - Congoleum Corp.
PEARL PASSION - Toys - Mattel, Inc.
PEARL PREMIUM - Beverages–malt - Pearl Brewing Co.
PEARL RECORDS, INC. - Recording label - Pearl Records, Inc.
PEARL RIVER - Pianos ☆ - Kaman Music Corp.
PEARL RIVER BRIDGE - Product description unknown - Chinese Native
  Products
PEARL RIVER CLOTHING CO. - Apparel–men's - Bill's Dollar Stores Inc.
PEARL SALES - Pottery ☆ - Hillside House of Originals
PEARL SAQ - Bags - Curator
PEARL SEA WEES - Toys - Tonka Corp.
PEARL SPRING - Water–bottled or canned - Pearl Spring Water Co.
PEARL STRIPE - Wallpaper - Maya Romanoff Corp.
PEARL TOP - Lamp chimney ☆ - Corning Inc.
PEARL VALLEY - Cheese - Pearl Valley Cheese, Inc.
PEARL WHITE - Skin care products - Pearl White Cosmetics Corp.
PEARL WOOD - Cabinets - Kabom Kitchen & Bath Manufacturing
PEARLCORDER - Electronic equipment - Olympus America Inc.
PEARLCROME - Enamels ☆ - Wescon Products Co.
PEARLDIVE - Swimming accessories - North American Marketing Corp.
PEARLEE - Soap - Harley Chemicals
PEARLESCENT - Frames–eyeglass ☆ - Universal/Univis Inc.
PEARLESCENT - Paints–artists' - Palmer Paint Products, Inc.
PEARLESCENT - Pet products - Penn-Plax, Inc.
PEARLESCENT - Projection screens - Da-Lite Screen Co. Inc.
PEARLESCENTS - Wallcoverings - Elm Grounds
PEARLESQUE SPARKLE - Jewelry - Avon Products, Inc.
PEARLESSENCE FOR THE WALLS - Fabrics–tapestry ☆ - Combeau
  Industries
PEARLETTE - Frames–eyeglass ☆ - Universal/Univis Inc.
PEARLEX - Knives–carving - Kirk & Matz Ltd.
PEARLEX - Liquid soap - Country Lane Enterprises Inc.
PEARLIFE - Skin and hair care products - Universal Sunshine Corp.
PEARLINE - Skin care products ☆ - Christine Valmy, Inc.
PEARLITE - Uncle Sam Chemical Co., Inc.
PEARLITE - Clocks ☆ - Toastmaster Inc.
PEARLITES - Office supplies - P.A. Plymouth, Inc.
PEARLIZED - Paper–tissue - Crystal Tissue Co. Inc.
PEARLOXIDE - Hair care products - Redken Laboratories, Inc.
PEARLS - Candy - Ricola Inc.
PEARLS - Flatware - Ginkgo International Ltd.
PEARLS - Wallpaper - Bayview Wallcoverings
PEARLS & LACE - Perfumes - Avon Products, Inc.
PEARL'S BBQ - Barbecue sauce - Pearl's Barbecue, Inc.
PEARLS FROM THE ORIENT - Wallpaper - Decor International Wallcovering
  Inc.
PEARLS OF AUGUST, THE - Jewelry - August Gem Corp.
PEARLS OF LOVE - Greeting cards - Electric Press
PEARL'S QUALITY - Vegetables–canned - Norpac Services, Inc.
PEARLS SERIES, THE - Publisher's imprints - Hanley & Belfus, Inc.
PEARLSPUN - Cosmetics - Elizabeth Arden Inc.
PEARLTEX - Enamels ☆ - Sinclair Paint Co.
PEARLTEX - Window shades - C-Mor Co.
PEARLWRAP - Plastics film - Highland Supply Corp.
PEARLY GATES - Musical instrument accessories - Seymour Duncan Pickups
PEARLY MIST - Finishing agents - Deep Flex Plastic Molds Inc.
PEARLY SENTIMENTS - Glassware–household - Fenton Art Glass Co.
PEARS PERSONAL PLEASURES - Cosmetics - Chesebrough-Pond's USA
  Co.
PEARSON - Candy - Nestle USA
PEARSON - Educational materials - Pearson Publishing, Inc.
PEARSON - Furniture–upholstered - Clyde Pearson Inc.
PEARSON - Ships–sailing vessels - Sunfish Laser Inc.
PEARSON - Trailers–travel ☆ - Giles Industries
PEARSON - Watches - Bulova Corp.
PEARSON RESEARCH GROUP - Alarm systems - Kenneth E. Flick
PEARSON SAKRIN - Sweeteners–artificial - Pearson Products
PEARSON'S - Beef - Pearson's Preferred Stock Gourmet Beef
PEARSON'S - Snuff ☆ - Byfield Snuff Co.
PEARSON'S - Tableware–earthenware - Denby USA Limited

☆ = Now out of production

PEARSON'S SAKRIN SALT-FREE LIQUID SWEETENER - Health care products - Woolfoam Corp.

PEARTREE - Clocks - General Time Corp. (Westclox/Seth Thomas Div.)

PEAS 'N CARROTS - Infant product ☆ - Sassy Inc.

PEAS WITH HONEY - Apparel and accessories - Peas with Honey, Inc.

PEASANT VILLAGE - Dinnerware–glass - Straus Mitteldorfer Inc.

PEASANTRIES - Dishes–earthenware - Mikasa Co.

PEASE - Locks–door - Pease Industries, Inc.

PEASE - Wood products - BrowerPease Inc.

PEASE-CARBON - Doors - Pease Industries, Inc.

PEASEWAY - Wood products ☆ - BrowerPease Inc.

PEATREX - Garden equipment - Organic Conversion Corp.

PEATTITUDES - Apparel and accessories - Creative Excellence, Inc.

PEAU DE PECHE - Cosmetics - Peau Corp.

PEAU DE ROSE - Apparel–women's ☆ - Milco Industries, Inc.

PEAU DE SOIE - Skin care products - Noble Pine Products Co.

PEAU GRASSE - Cosmetics - Sothys USA Inc.

PEAU NORMAL - Cosmetics - Sothys USA Inc.

PEAU SECHE - Cosmetics - Sothys USA Inc.

PEAU SENSIBLE - Cosmetics ☆ - Sothys USA Inc.

PEAVEY - Drums–musical instruments - Peavey Electronics Corp.

PEB-TAC - Bulletin boards–wood - Marsh Chalkboard Co.

PEBBLE - Fabrics - Greenwood Mills Inc.

PEBBLE - Floor coverings ☆ - Congoleum Corp.

PEBBLE BASKET - Floor coverings–carpet and rugs ☆ - Regal Rugs Inc.

PEBBLE BEACH - Floor coverings - Mannington Resilient Floors

PEBBLE BEACH - Floor coverings–carpet and rugs - Couristan Inc.

PEBBLE BEACH - Floor coverings–carpet and rugs - Playfield International Inc.

PEBBLE BEACH - Floor coverings–carpet and rugs - Regal Rugs Inc.

PEBBLE BEACH - Glassware–household - Owens-Illinois Inc. (Libbey Div.)

PEBBLE BEACH - Hosiery - Hole-in-None Hosiery

PEBBLE BEACH - Wallpaper - Bagindd Prints

PEBBLE BEACH - Yarn ☆ - JCA, Inc.

PEBBLE BEACH CHAMPIONSHIP COURSE - Computer software ☆ - Access Software Inc.

PEBBLE BEACH FOREST COURSE - Ships–trawlers - Pebble Beach Co.

PEBBLE BRAID - Floor coverings–carpet and rugs ☆ - Regal Rugs Inc.

PEBBLE BROOK - Floor coverings–carpet and rugs - Ebsco Carpet Mills

PEBBLE BROWN - Glassware–household ☆ - Lenox Crystal, Inc.

PEBBLE CABANA - Floor coverings–carpet and rugs - Regal Rugs Inc.

PEBBLE CATCHER, THE - Truck beds - PC Safety Systems Inc.

PEBBLE CREEK - Bicycles ☆ - Huffy Corp.

PEBBLE CREEK - Floor coverings - Mannington Resilient Floors

PEBBLE CREEK - Wines - Winequest

PEBBLE-KLEERMAT - Housewares - Commercial Plastics Co.

PEBBLE KNIT - Apparel and accessories - Sally Gee Inc.

PEBBLE-LAK - Finishing agents - Lenmar Inc.

PEBBLE LEAF - Pressed glassware ☆ - Indiana Glass Co.

PEBBLE LIME - Chemical preparations - Western Lime Corp.

PEBBLE OPTIC PITCHERS - Kitchen appliances - Carlisle Foodservice Products, Inc.

PEBBLE OPTIC TUMBLERS - Glassware–household - Carlisle Foodservice Products, Inc.

PEBBLE PATH - Floor coverings–carpet and rugs - Regal Rugs Inc.

PEBBLE PEOPLE - Hobby kits - Natural Science Industries, Ltd.

PEBBLE PLAID - Floor coverings–carpet and rugs ☆ - Regal Rugs Inc.

PEBBLE POINT - Floor coverings–carpet and rugs ☆ - Catalina Carpet Mills Inc.

PEBBLE ROCK - Aquarium accessories - Kordon

PEBBLE ROCK - Aquarium accessories - Novalek, Inc.

PEBBLE SEA - Floor coverings–carpet and rugs - Regal Rugs Inc.

PEBBLE-TEX - Floor coverings–carpet and rugs ☆ - Olympic Carpets Inc.

PEBBLE-TONES - Floor coverings–carpet and rugs - Sweetwater Carpet Corp.

PEBBLE TURF - Mats ☆ - Ludlow Composites Corp.

PEBBLE TWIST - Floor coverings–carpet and rugs - Regal Rugs Inc.

PEBBLEBROOK - Apparel–women's - B.C. Moore and Sons Inc.

PEBBLEBROOK - Floor coverings–carpet and rugs - Milliken & Co. Inc.

PEBBLEBROOK - Indoor-outdoor carpet - Instant Turf Industries Inc.

PEBBLED ONYX - Floor coverings - Azrock Commercial Flooring

PEBBLEFLOR - Floor coverings ☆ - Tarkett, Inc.

PEBBLEFORD - Dishes–earthenware - Taylor, Smith & Taylor Co.

PEBBLEGATE - Floor coverings–carpet and rugs - Cabin Crafts Carpets

PEBBLEPOINT - Floor coverings–carpet and rugs ☆ - Karastan-Bigelow Inc.

PEBBLES - Candy - Bee International

PEBBLES - Ophthalmic goods - Styl-Rite Optical Manufacturing Co., Inc.

PEBBLES - Toys - Hanna-Barbera Productions, Inc.

PEBBLES - Yarn - William Unger & Co. Inc.

PEBBLES FLINTSTONE - Candy - Eileen Gilday

PEBBLES IN MY POCKET - Paper products - Pebbles in My Pocket, Inc.

PEBBLES OF THE SEA - Aquariums–household - Great American Color Co.

PEBBLESTONE - Floor coverings–carpet and rugs ☆ - Richmond Carpet Mills

PEBBLESTONE - Tiles–mosaic - Capitol Tile Import Co.

PEBBLESTONE - Wallpaper - Capital Carousel Inc.

PEBBLESTONE - Wallpaper - Ozite Corp.

PEBBLY PERLE - Yarn - Rainbow Gallery, Inc.

PEBEO - Paints - G & K Craft Industries, Ltd.

PEBL-STAK - Dinnerware–plastic - Continental/SiLite International Inc.

PEBLON - Apparel and accessories - Sally Gee Inc.

PEBLON - Floor coverings–tile - Vida Mosaic Co. Inc.

PEBS - Insulating materials - Manville/Schuller

PEC - Medical apparatus - Photoelectron Corp.

PEC-12 - Cleaning preparations - Photographic Solutions, Inc.

PEC-TRONIC - Office machines ☆ - Mead-Hatcher, Inc.

PECADINE - Pharmaceutical preparations - Wesley Pharmacal Co. Inc.

PECAN - Cookies - Nikki's Cookies, Inc.

PECAN - Floor coverings - Anderson Hardwood Floors Inc.

PECAN - Jewelry–costume ☆ - Safari Ltd.

PECAN CHEW - Food products - Honeypot Treats

PECAN CHOCOLATE CHUNKS - Bakery products - Sweet Street Desserts, Inc.

PECAN CLUSTERS - Candy - Standard Candy Co. Inc.

PECAN CRUNCH - Candy - Pecan Deluxe Candy Co.

PECAN CURLS - Sweet rolls - Interstate Brands Corp.

PECAN DELIGHT - Candy - Russell Stover Candies, Inc.

PECAN DELIGHT - Coffee - Millstone Coffee, Inc.

PECAN DIXIES - Candy - Archibald Candy Corp.

PECAN HARVEST - Cookies - Consolidated Biscuit Co.

PECAN KRISP - Candy - Pecan Deluxe Candy Co.

PECAN MEDALLIONS - Candy - Whitmans Candies, Inc.

PECAN NUTTLES - Nuts–candied - Adams & Brooks, Inc.

PECAN PASSION - Cookies - Nabisco Foods Group

PECAN PERFECTION - Candy ☆ - Cherrydale Farms Inc.

PECAN PLACE - Wainscotting - Georgia-Pacific Corp.

PECAN PLUS - Candy - McDonald Candy Co. Inc.

PECAN PUDDLE - Candy - Koeze Co.

PECAN SANDIES - Cookies - Keebler Co.

PECAN STREET SWEETS - Nuts–candied - GNS Foods, Inc.

PECAN SUPREMES - Cookies - Nabisco Holdings Corp.

PECAN TUMBLES - Candy ☆ - Sweet Candy Co.

PECAN TWIRLS - Desserts - Pet Inc.

PECANCHE - Candy ☆ - Miss Saylor's Candies

PECANEROS - Candy ☆ - Judson-Atkinson Candies

PECANOLA - Candy - Crown Candy Corp.

PECAP - Fabrics - Tetko Inc.

PECAP LE - Screen printing fabric - Tetko Inc.

PECASSO - Floor coverings–carpet and rugs ☆ - Columbus Mills, Inc.

PECATONICA RIVER - Popcorn - Trelay Farms, Inc.

PECHE D'ELYSEE - Wines ☆ - Alimar & Cie. Inc.

PECHE DREAM - Nail care products - Cosmair Inc.

PECHE LAMBIC - Beverages–malt - Merchant du Vin Corp.

PECHER MIGNON - Beverages–alcohol - Sunbelt Beverage Corp.

PECHGLO - Apparel and accessories - Vanity Fair Mills Inc.

PECHTER'S - Bakery products - Allied Bakers Co.

PECHTER'S KING SIZE - Bagels - Harrison Baking Co.

PECK A BOO - Pet products - Emerald Bird Caddy

PECK 'A' DRINK - Poultry feeds - Precision Products, Inc.

PECK ATTACK PECKSTER - Toys - Saban Entertainment, Inc.

PECK N' COO - Pet products - DD Pet Products Inc.

PECK 'N PLAY STACKER - Toys - Playskool, Inc.

PECKERHEADS - Apparel and accessories - Pan Pacific Textile Group, Inc.

PECKERWOOD - Colognes - Charleston Catalog Co.

PECO - Extension cords - Pacific Electricord Co.

PECO - Food products - Tecmar Inc.

PECO - Meat products–poultry - Peco Foods, Inc.

PECO - Uniforms–tailored - Peco, Inc.

PECO COCONUT BRITTLE - Candy - Atkinson Candy Co.

PECONIC BAY - Food products - Crescent Duck Farm, Inc.

PECONIC BAY BRAND - Seafood products–fresh or frozen - George Braun Oyster Co. Inc.

PECORA - Adhesives and sealants - Pecora Chemical Corp.

☆ = Now out of production

PECOREZ - Adhesives and sealants - Phoenix Chemical Inc.

PECOS - Boots - Red Wing Shoe Co. Inc.

PECOS - Fabrics - Greenwood Mills Inc.

PECOS - Floor coverings–carpet and rugs ☆ - Walter Carpet Mills

PECOS BILL - Games - Legends of the West, Inc.

PECOS BILL - Western boots - International Imports

PECOS HEAT - Beverages–alcohol - Black Prince Distillery, Inc.

PECOS MARCOS - Spices and extracts - William E. Vincent

PECOS PHARMACEUTICAL - Vitamins and nutritional supplements - Stuart Millheiser, Inc.

PECOS RIVERS - Food products - Universal Foods Corp.

PECOSOFT - Computer software - Paragon Electric Co., Inc.

PEC*PAD - Photographic equipment - Photographic Solutions, Inc.

PEC*PEN - Markers–felt-tip - Photographic Solutions, Inc.

PECS - Hand held weights - Body Finish, Inc.

PECTAGEL - Food products - Pectagel, Inc.

PECTALUM - Jewelry - Don Michael Herron

PECTIN BUTTONS - Candy ☆ - Maillard Corp.

PECTOCOMP - Pharmaceutical preparations - Lannett Co. Inc.

PECTOKAY - Pharmaceutical preparations ☆ - JMI-Canton Pharmaceuticals

PECTOSAN - Seasonings - Herb Products Co.

PECUNIA II - Tiles–ceramic ☆ - Latco Products

PED - Railings–metal - Scott W. Halvorsen

PED-A-STAK - Housewares ☆ - Thermo-Serv Inc.

PED SYSTEM - Kilns - Ped Technologies, Inc.

PED-X - Clippers–nail - Ped-X Corp.

PEDA - Skin care products - Benchmark Brands

PEDAL CRUISER IV - Boats–canoes - Kay Park Rec Corp.

PEDAL EXPRESS - Bicycles - Main Street Pedi-Cabs, Inc.

PEDAL PALS - Carriages–doll ☆ - AC International

PEDAL PHERNALIA - Giftware - Pedal Phernalia Bicycle Curios

PEDAL POWER - Bicycles - Kent International Inc.

PEDAL POWER - Orthopedic products - Northwest Podiatric Laboratory, Inc.

PEDAL PUSHERS - Musical instrument accessories - GRK Manufacturing

PEDALPUSHER - Tools–hand-operated - Innovations by Bueti Brothers, Inc.

PEDAMETH - Pharmaceutical preparations - Forest Pharmaceuticals Inc.

PEDASTAL - Nail care products - Opi Products, Inc.

PEDASTYLE - Bicycle-storage systems - IMS Enterprises Inc.

PEDDLARWARE - Kitchenware–earthenware - Zanesville Stoneware Co.

PEDDLER - Dolls ☆ - Effanbee Doll Corp.

PEDESTAL - Frames–eyeglass - Zylo Ware Corp.

PEDESTAL - Office supplies - Da-Lite Screen Co. Inc.

PEDESTAL PERCH - Pet products - Emerald Bird Caddy

PEDETRIN - Skin care products - Kleen Chemical Manufacturing Co.

PEDI - Infant product - Pedicraft Inc.

PEDI - Mannequins - Gaumard Scientific Co., Inc.

PEDI - Pet products - J. Narby Inc.

PEDI-4-LEGS - Elevators ☆ - Roloke Co.

PEDI BLADES - Manicure preparations - Miracle Products Co.

PEDI-BOOT - Antiseptics ☆ - Pedinol Pharmacal Inc.

PEDI-BORO - Pharmaceutical preparations - Pedinol Pharmacal Inc.

PEDI-BRAND - Pet products - J. Narby Inc.

PEDI-CAB - Bicycles - Rideable Bicycle Replicas Inc.

PEDI-CAP - Medical apparatus - Nellcor Inc.

PEDI CARE - Skin care products - Gena Laboratories Inc.

PEDI-CARE - Skin care products - Revlon Consumer Products Corp.

PEDI-CART - Pedicure products - ABAR Beauty Supply Inc.

PEDI-CAT - Manicure preparations - Professional Fabricators

PEDI CURE - Health care products ☆ - Lotus Brands Inc.

PEDI-DRI - Health care products - Pedinol Pharmacal Inc.

PEDI EXPRESS - Nail care products - Salon Service Manufacturing Inc.

PEDI-FILE - Cosmetics - Worldwide Cosmetics

PEDI-FOAM - Slippers - Medline, Industries, Inc.

PEDI FRESH - Skin care products - Gena Laboratories Inc.

PEDI ICE - Skin care products - Gena Laboratories Inc.

PEDI-PAC - Medical apparatus - Ferno Washington, Inc.

PEDI-PERFECT - Medical apparatus - Alimed, Inc.

PEDI-PORTER - Stretchers - International Biomedical, Inc.

PEDI-PRO - Health care products - Pedinol Pharmacal Inc.

PEDI PROFILE - Skin care products - Gena Laboratories Inc.

PEDI-QUETTE - Skin care products - Mennen Co.

PEDI-QUICK - Footcare products - PediFix Footcare Co.

PEDI-QUICK SAFETY CORN & CALLUS TRIMMER - Manicure preparations ☆ - PediFix Footcare Co.

PEDI REDI PLUS - Skin care products - Maxim LLC

PEDI SALTS - Skin care products - Gena Laboratories Inc.

PEDI SANDER - Skin care products - Gena Laboratories Inc.

PEDI SCRUB - Skin care products - Gena Laboratories Inc.

PEDI SEPTIC - Antiseptics - Gena Laboratories Inc.

PEDI SOAK - Skin care products - Gena Laboratories Inc.

PEDI SOFT - Skin care products - Gena Laboratories Inc.

PEDI-TOES - Cosmetic applicators - Geraldine Fardeecey

PEDI-TOT - Health care products - Halsey Drug Co. Inc.

PEDI-TRAILER - Bicycles - Rideable Bicycle Replicas Inc.

PEDI-TUBE - Medical apparatus ☆ - Biosearch Medical Products Inc.

PEDI-VIT A - Health care products ☆ - Pedinol Pharmacal Inc.

PEDIA-AIRE - Air purification systems - Pollenex Corp.

PEDIA PALS - Medical apparatus - Pedia Pals, Inc.

PEDIA-POP - Pharmaceutical preparations - LCM Pharmaceutical, Inc.

PEDIA RELIEF - Cold remedies - L. Perrigo Co.

PEDIA-THERM - Health care products - Seabrook Medical Systems, Inc.

PEDIACARE - Cough medicines ☆ - Johnson & Johnson

PEDIACOF - Pharmaceutical preparations - Sterling Winthrop Inc.

PEDIACON - Pharmaceutical preparations - Consolidated Midland Corp.

PEDIAFLOR - Pharmaceutical preparations - Ross Laboratories

PEDIALYTE - Vitamins and nutritional supplements - Ross Laboratories

PEDIAMIST - Pharmaceutical preparations - Ascent Pharmaceuticals, Inc.

PEDIAMYCIN - Antibiotics - Ross Laboratories

PEDIAPAP - Pharmaceutical preparations - Central Pharmaceutical Inc.

PEDIAPRED - Health care products - Fisons Corp.

PEDIASCAN - Medical apparatus - Sylvan Corp.

PEDIASORB - Pharmaceutical preparations ☆ - Ascent Pharmaceuticals, Inc.

PEDIASURE - Vitamins and nutritional supplements - Ross Laboratories

PEDIASURE PALS - Vitamins and nutritional supplements - Abbott Laboratories

PEDIATEMP - Pharmaceutical preparations - Ascent Pediatrics, Inc.

PEDIATRIC - Mattresses - Velsco Inc.

PEDIATRIC FORMULA - Pharmaceutical preparations - Reese Chemical Co.

PEDIATRIC PLUS - Pharmaceutical preparations ☆ - Reese Chemical Co.

PEDIATROL - Pharmaceutical preparations - Consolidated Midland Corp.

PEDIATUSS - Health care products - Dayton Laboratories, Inc.

PEDIAZOLE - Pharmaceutical preparations - Ross Laboratories

PEDIBELLE - Electrical equipment - Medicool Inc.

PEDIBUMPERS - Apparel–children's - J.C. Penney Co., Inc.

PEDICHAMPS - Footwear - Eastern Thread & Scallop Cutting Co.

PEDICIDE - Shampoos - Apothecary Products, Inc.

PEDICILLIN - Pharmaceutical preparations ☆ - Republic Drug Co. Inc.

PEDICLIP - Nail clipper ☆ - London International U.S. Holdings

PEDICRAFT - Shorts–children's - Willits Footwear Worldwide, Inc.

PEDICRAN - Pharmaceutical preparations ☆ - Schering-Plough Healthcare Products

PEDIFIX - Footcare products - PediFix Footcare Co.

PEDIFIX ARCH CRADLES - Footcare products - PediFix Footcare Co.

PEDIFIX AVOCADO CLAY FOOT MASK - Footcare products - PediFix Footcare Co.

PEDIFIX BAREFOOT SCIENCE FOOT STRENGTHENING INSOLES - Footcare products - PediFix Footcare Co.

PEDIFIX BUNION REGULATOR - Footcare products - PediFix Footcare Co.

PEDIFIX CARE SOX PLUS+ - Footcare products - PediFix Footcare Co.

PEDIFIX DEEP HEALING FOOT CREAM - Footcare products - PediFix Footcare Co.

PEDIFIX DOCTOR'S CHOICE - Footcare products - PediFix Footcare Co.

PEDIFIX FEATHERSTEP - Footcare products - PediFix Footcare Co.

PEDIFIX HEEL HUGS - Footcare products - PediFix Footcare Co.

PEDIFIX MANGO MAGIC FOOT LOTION - Footcare products - PediFix Footcare Co.

PEDIFIX NO RIDGE PLUS - Footcare products - PediFix Footcare Co.

PEDIFIX PUMPPALS - Footcare products - PediFix Footcare Co.

PEDIFIX SEA & SAND FOOT SCRUB - Footcare products - PediFix Footcare Co.

PEDIFIX SENSITIVE FEET - Footcare products - PediFix Footcare Co.

PEDIFIX SOCKLESS INSOLES - Footcare products - PediFix Footcare Co.

PEDIFIX TOE TRAINERS - Footcare products - PediFix Footcare Co.

PEDIFIX TULI'S HEEL CUPS - Footcare products - PediFix Footcare Co.

PEDIFIX VISCO-GEL TOE CAP - Footcare products - PediFix Footcare Co.

PEDIGREE - Apparel–men's ☆ - Superba, Inc.

PEDIGREE - Bedding–linen - Thomaston Mills Inc.

PEDIGREE - Crocheted and knitted items - Schuessler Knitting Mills Inc.

PEDIGREE - Dog food - Kal Kan Foods, Inc.

PEDIGREE - Eyeglasses - Art-Craft Optical Co.

PEDIGREE - Indoor-outdoor carpets and rugs, synthetic turf - Instant Turf Industries Inc.

☆ = Now out of production

PEDIGREE - Office supplies - Empire Berol USA
PEDIGREE - Paints - P.D. George Co.
PEDIGREE - Seafood products–fresh or frozen ☆ - Dejean Packing Co.
PEDIGREE CHOICE CUTS - Dog food - Kal Kan Foods, Inc.
PEDIGREE DENTABONE - Dog food - Kal Kan Foods, Inc.
PEDIGREE EXELPET - Pet products - Kal Kan Foods, Inc.
PEDIGREE EXPERT BONE - Pet food - Kal Kan Foods, Inc.
PEDIGREE HALL OF FAME - Giftware - Fort USA
PEDIGREE LITTLE CHAMPIONS - Pet food - Kal Kan Foods, Inc.
PEDIGREE MARRO BONE - Dog food - Kal Kan Foods, Inc.
PEDIGREE MARROBONE - Pet food - Kal Kan Foods, Inc.
PEDIGREE MAXI BISCUIT - Pet food - Kal Kan Foods, Inc.
PEDIGREE MEALTIME - Dog food - Kal Kan Foods, Inc.
PEDIGREE PUPPY - Pet food - Kal Kan Foods, Inc.
PEDIGREE SELECT DINNERS - Dog food - Kal Kan Foods, Inc.
PEDIGREE TANDEM - Pet food - Kal Kan Foods, Inc.
PEDIGREED DIAMOND, THE - Jewelry–precious - Charles Engelhart Co., Inc.
PEDIGREED MESSAGES - Toys–stuffed - Dakin Inc.
PEDIGRID - Mats - C/S Group/DecoGard Products
PEDIMAT - Mats - C/S Group/DecoGard Products
PEDIOTIC - Antibiotics - Burroughs Wellcome Co.
PEDIPAC - Electrical equipment - Medicool Inc.
PEDIPOCKET - Electrical equipment - Medicool Inc.
PEDIREST - Health care products - Orthopedic Products Corp.
PEDISENSO - Electrical equipment - Medicool Inc.
PEDISILK - Dermatological preparations - Durham Pharmacal Corp.
PEDISPA - Massage products - Sunbeam Products, Inc.
PEDITRED - Mats - C/S Group/DecoGard Products
PEDLAR - Exercising equipment - Battle Creek Equipment Co.
PEDMAR - Recording label - Digital Magic
PEDO JACKETS - Dental compounds - George M. Wilson
PEDO-SOL - Pharmaceutical preparations ☆ - Bock Pharmacal Co.
PEDOLATUM - Health care products - King Laboratories
PEDOLLY - Photographic equipment - Leonard Studio Equipment, Inc.
PEDONE U.S.A. - Oils–edible - Amko International Trading, Inc.
PEDRE - Watches - Pedre Co. Inc.
PEDRIC - Pharmaceutical preparations ☆ - Pal-Pak Inc.
PEDRICIN - Health care products ☆ - Halsey Drug Co. Inc.
PEDRIZZETTI - Wines - Pedrizzetti Winery
PEDRO CORTEZ - Toys - Tonka Corp.
PEDRO IGLESIAS - Cigars - Danby-Palicio
PEDRO LUGGAGE OF ST. PAUL - Leather goods - Pedro Cos. (Pedro Manufacturing Div.)
PEDRO MIRALLES - Footwear–women's ☆ - Combine Group Division Inc.
PEDRO THE MONKEY - Toys–stuffed - Animal Fair Inc.
PEDRONI - Cigars ☆ - Swisher International, Inc.
PEDROS - Tortillas - Mission Foods Corp.
PEDS - Socks - Americal Corp. (Peds Products Division)
PEDTERM - Electrical equipment - Communications Technology Corp.
PEDTERM SCS - Electrical apparatus - Communications Technology Corp.
PEDVAXHIB - Pharmaceutical preparations - Merck & Co., Inc. (Merck Research Laboratories)
PEDWIN - Footwear ☆ - Brown Shoe Co.
PEE BEE - Key rings - Perry Blackburne Inc.
PEE-CHEE - Office supplies - Mead Corp.
PEE DEE - Seasonings - Flavorite Laboratories Inc.
PEE GEE - Fabric binding - Geo. B. Carpenter Co.
PEE GEE - Fabrics - Astrup Co.
PEE-GEE - Lamps - Philip J. Greenspan Inc.
PEE GEE - Paints ☆ - Devoe & Raynolds Co.
PEE-GEE-BEE - Balls–golf - Mantua/Cosom Sporting Goods
PEE-ON-IT - Novelty items ☆ - ANTHEM Inc.
PEE WEE - Apparel–children's - Robert A. Clair Co. Inc.
PEE WEE - Battery testers - Mueller Electric Co.
PEE WEE - Boats - Glen-L Marine Designs
PEE-WEE - Diapers–disposable ☆ - Plainwell Tissue
PEE-WEE - Dolls - Uneeda Doll Co., Inc.
PEE-WEE - Life preservers ☆ - Stearns Manufacturing Co.
PEE WEE - Nuts–salted, roasted, cooked, or canned - Nut Bar Co. Inc.
PEE WEE - Toys–models - Cox Products Inc.
PEE WEE HERMAN - Games - Ben Cooper Inc.
PEE WEE HERMAN - Socks ☆ - High Point Knitting Inc.
PEE WEE TOILET LIGHT, THE - Toilet seats - Associated Technology, Inc.
PEE WEE WART - Fishing lures - Storm Manufacturing Co.
PEECE - Pharmaceutical preparations ☆ - Scrip-Physician Supply Co.
PEEK - Cleaning preparations - Tri-Peek International, Inc.

PEEK - Frames–eyeglass - May Optical Co. Inc.
PEEK-A-BABE - Apparel–children's - Shopko Stores, Inc.
PEEK-A-BEAR - Giftware - Brushcreek Creative Co.
PEEK-A-BOO - Christmas tree ornaments - Fun World Inc.
PEEK-A-BOO - Games - CBS Toys
PEEK-A-BOO - Toys–models - Russ Berrie and Co., Inc.
PEEK-A-BOO BABY - Dolls - Fisher-Price, Inc.
PEEK-A-BOO BEAR - Toys - Playskool, Inc.
PEEK-A-BOO BUNNY - Toys–stuffed - Fun World Inc.
PEEK-A-BOO CREATIONS - Apparel–children's - Peek-A-Boo Creations, Inc.
PEEK-A-BOO PALS - Toys - Mango Enterprises Inc.
PEEK-A-BOO PLAY - Toys–blocks - Wimmer-Ferguson Inc.
PEEK-A-BOO POUNDER - Toys - Mattel, Inc.
PEEK-A-BOO PRETTY - Underwear and nightwear ☆ - Lovable Co.
PEEK-A-BOO-TIQUE INC. - Giftware - Ballet Jewels Inc.
PEEK-A-BOO TUNNEL - Toys - E-Z Sales & Manufacturing, Inc.
PEEK-A-BOOK - Billing machines - Angler's Roslyn Group Ltd.
PEEK-A-BOOS - Moldings–plaster of paris ☆ - DecoArt, Inc.
PEEK-A-BOOZOO - Toys - Texas Instruments Inc.
PEEK-A-BRA - Apparel–women's - Jezebel-Renee of Hollywood
PEEK-A-BUNNY - Giftware - Brushcreek Creative Co.
PEEK-A-FLAME - Hardware - Eclipse Inc.
PEEK-A-KITTY - Giftware - Brushcreek Creative Co.
PEEK-A-LITE - Flashlights - Blue Tiger Corp.
PEEK-A-PALS - Lamps ☆ - Dolly, Inc.
PEEK-A-PALS - Toys–stuffed - Brushcreek Creative Co.
PEEK-A-PUPPY - Giftware - Brushcreek Creative Co.
PEEK-A-TOE - Infant product - S. Schwab Co., Inc.
PEEK AND SEE - Seafood products–fresh or frozen ☆ - Wally Sea Products Corp.
PEEK & SPY - Computer software - Networking Dynamics Corp.
PEEK-IN-ROLLER - Toys - Shelcore Inc.
PEEK-LITE - Eyeglasses - Art-Craft Optical Co.
PEEK 'N FETCH - Infant product ☆ - Century Products Co.
PEEK 'N PLAY - Toys - Playskool, Inc.
PEEK 'N PLAYARD - Furniture–metal ☆ - Century Products Co.
PEEK 'N SQUEEK APPLE - Games ☆ - Century Products Co.
PEEK 'N SQUEEK EGG - Games ☆ - Century Products Co.
PEEK OVER - Frames–eyeglass ☆ - Vanity Optical Manufacturing Co. Inc.
PEEK PERFORMANCE - Computer software - CECO Filters Inc.
PEEK UNDER - Frames–eyeglass ☆ - Vanity Optical Manufacturing Co. Inc.
PEEKABLUE - Toys - Mattel, Inc.
PEEKABOO - Food products - Jack Klein Trust Partnership
PEEKABOO - Invitations ☆ - Evergreen Press
PEEKABOO - Jewelry - Peekaboo Fashion Accessories, Inc.
PEEKABOOS - Ice cream ☆ - Thin's Inn Inc.
PEEKER - Balls–golf - Box Card Gifts, Inc.
PEEKING PANDA - Toys–stuffed - Dakin Inc.
PEEL & PLACE - Magnets - Norstar Enterprises
PEEL & PLAY - Toy activity sets - David C. Cook Publishing Co.
PEEL & PUT - Textbooks - Communication Skill Builders, Inc.
PEEL & SEEL - Envelopes ☆ - Kimberly-Clark Corp. (Karolton Envelope Div.)
PEEL & STICK - Decals and transfers - Bedford Industries, Inc.
PEEL & STICK - Magnets - Norstar Enterprises
PEEL & STICK - Plastics–laminated - Conolite
PEEL AWAY - Kitchen utensils–aluminum - Back to Basics Products Inc.
PEEL-AWAY - Paint removers - Dumond Chemicals Inc.
PEEL-BAK - Adhesives and sealants - Auto Vehicle Parts Co.
PEEL BLOCK - Paints - Sophir Morris Paint
PEEL E-Z EDGE - Paper - Daydots Label Co., Inc.
PEEL-KOTE - Solder - Kester Solder Co.
PEEL 'N' ETCH - Tools - Armour Products
PEEL 'N' PAT - Ornamental products–glass ☆ - W.F.R. Ribbon Corp.
PEEL-N-PAT - Paper–cloth-lined - Regency Mills Inc.
PEEL 'N PLACE - Plastics–laminated - Kent Adhesive Products Co.
PEEL-N-PLACE - Plastics–laminated ☆ - Newell Office Products
PEEL 'N PRESS - Labels–paper - Appleson Press Inc.
PEEL 'N SEAL - Weather stripping ☆ - W.J. Dennis & Co.
PEEL 'N STICK - Tape–adhesive - Selfix, Inc.
PEEL N STICK - Weather stripping - KEL-EEZ
PEEL-N'-STIK - Labels–gummed - Time Med Labeling Systems Inc.
PEEL-OFF - Erasers - Faber-Castell Corp.
PEEL-ON - Labels–gummed - Printed Systems
PEEL OUTS - Toys–automobiles - Nylint Toy Corp.
PEEL PROOF - Paints - United States Refining Co.
PEEL STICK & FLIP - Notebooks and notepads - Raul G. Garza

☆ = Now out of production

PEEL, STICK N' DROP OFFICE IN A BOX - Publisher's imprints - Egan Enterprises, Inc.
PEEL STOP - Paints - Zehrung Corp.
PEELED DELITES - Frozen foods - Kern Ridge Growers, Inc.
PEELED 'N EZ - Shrimp–fresh or frozen - Gordon Food Service, Inc.
PEELER - Milk - Peeler Jersey Farms Inc.
PEELER-PAK - Skin care products ☆ - Peeler Pak Ltd.
PEELER, THE - Kitchen utensils–aluminum - Bonny Products Inc.
PEELLE - Elevators - Peelle Co.
PEEL'N STICK - Deicing fluid - Kafko International Ltd.
PEELU - Denture cleaners - Peelu Products Corp.
PEELU - Toothpaste - Unipac Laboratories
PEELVUE SANITIZER - Health care products - Select Brands
PEELY PALS - Labels–paper - Impact International Inc.
PEELZ - Wallpaper primer ☆ - William Zinsser & Co. Inc.
PEENAMATIC - Machinery - Metal Improvement Co., Inc.
PEEP - Bird feeds - Kellogg Inc.
PEEP - Ophthalmic goods - Foremost Optical Products
PEEP SHOW - Apparel and accessories - Shane Tyler Ralston
PEEPER SWEEPERS - Cosmetics ☆ - Noxell Corp.
PEEPERS - Greeting cards - Vivian Greene Inc.
PEEPERS - Puppets - Hobart Ford
PEEPERSLEEPERS - Apparel and accessories - Marco Miehe
PEEPING TOM - Eyeglasses - Martin-Copeland Eyewear Corp.
PEEPLES - Men's shoes ☆ - Intershoe Inc.
PEEPS - Candy - Rodda Candy Co.
PEEPS FAMILY - Dolls - Monarch Toys, Ltd.
PEER - Antifreeze - Illinois Oil Products Inc.
PEER - Chains–industrial - Peer Chain Co.
PEER - Gasoline - Shelby Petroleum Corp.
PEER - Hams - Peer Food Products Co.
PEER-FLEX - Ophthalmic goods - Styl-Rite Optical Manufacturing Co., Inc.
PEER GEAR - Apparel–children's - Elder Manufacturing Co., Inc.
PEER GROUP BY JOHN WEITZ - Slacks–men's - Glen Oaks Industries Inc.
PEER GYNT - Glassware–household ☆ - Wallace International Silversmiths, Inc.
PEER IMPORTS - Giftware - Baekgaard Ltd.
PEER LEVEL STANDER - Health care products - Mulholland Positioning Systems Inc.
PEER-LITE - Ophthalmic goods - Styl-Rite Optical Manufacturing Co., Inc.
PEER ONE - Furniture - Bean Station Furniture Factory Inc.
PEER SR. - Fishing tackle ☆ - Penn Fishing Tackle Manufacturing Co.
PEER SOUTHERN CONCERT - Music–sheet - Theodore Presser Co.
PEERCO - Thread - Threads USA Div.
PEERIM - Giftware - Baekgaard Ltd.
PEERLESS - Ashtrays–glass - Richmond Pressed Metal Works Inc.
PEERLESS - Batteries - Peerless Tyre Co.
PEERLESS - Bicycles - Columbia Manufacturing Inc.
PEERLESS - Brooms - Hamburg Broom Works Inc.
PEERLESS - Brooms - F.M. Thorpe Manufacturing Co.
PEERLESS - Cleaning preparations–carpet and rug - Harvard Chemical Research, Inc.
PEERLESS - Coffee - Peerless Coffee Co.
PEERLESS - Drafting supplies - Pierce Business Products Inc.
PEERLESS - Easels ☆ - Quartet Manufacturing Co.
PEERLESS - Fabrics - Burlington Industries, Inc.
PEERLESS - Faucets - Masco Corp.
PEERLESS - Floor coverings - Congoleum Corp.
PEERLESS - Flooring–hardwood - Biwood Flooring
PEERLESS - Golfing equipment ☆ - Arnold Palmer Golf Co.
PEERLESS - Hardware - Sea Spike Marine Supply Co. Inc.
PEERLESS - Health care products - Omron Healthcare, Inc.
PEERLESS - Knives–carving - Kirk & Matz Ltd.
PEERLESS - Motor vehicles–automobiles ☆ - Peerless Motor Car Corp.
PEERLESS - Musical instrument accessories - Kansas Music Co. Inc.
PEERLESS - Office supplies ☆ - ACCO USA, Inc.
PEERLESS - Paints - Jones Blair Co.
PEERLESS - Paper clips - Noesting Inc.
PEERLESS - Plumbing fixtures - Masco Corp. (Plumbing Products Div.)
PEERLESS - Plumbing fixtures - Peerless Faucet Co. (Plumbing Products Div.)
PEERLESS - Rubber-stamp supplies - Consolidated Stamp Manufacturing Co. Inc.
PEERLESS - Scales–industrial - Triner Scale and Manufacturing Co. Inc.
PEERLESS - Shoes - Peerless Footwear Inc.
PEERLESS - Steel products - Peerless Industries, Inc.
PEERLESS - Stepladders - W.W. Babcock Co. Inc.

PEERLESS - Stones–synthetic - Charles B. Chrystal Co. Inc.
PEERLESS - Tires ☆ - Uniroyal Goodrich Tire Co.
PEERLESS - Tools - Cleveland Twist Drill Co.
PEERLESS - Tools - Great Neck Saw Manufacturers, Inc.
PEERLESS - Vegetables–canned - Lodi Canning Co.
PEERLESS (ADAMS) - Tobacco - American Tobacco Co.
PEERLESS AIRE - Furnaces–steam - Peerless Home Products
PEERLESS ANTIQUE - Fabrics - Lackawanna Leather Co. Inc.
PEERLESS COFFEE - Coffee - Peerless Coffee Co.
PEERLESS ELECTRIC - Fans–electric - Peerless-Winsmith, Inc.
PEERLESS INCENTIVES - Umbrellas - Peerless Umbrella
PEERLESS MAID - Candy - Peerless Confection Co.
PEERLESS PHD - Golfing equipment ☆ - Arnold Palmer Golf Co.
PEERLESS PUMP - Pumps - Sterling Fluid Systems, Inc.
PEERLESS RAM - Wheelbarrows - Ames Lawn & Garden Tool Co.
PEERLESS SYSTEMS - Computer software - Peerless Systems, Inc.
PEERLESS21 - Computer software - Peerless Systems, Inc.
PEERLITE - Lamps - Peerlite Manufacturing & Supply Co.
PEERLON - Ophthalmic goods - Styl-Rite Optical Manufacturing Co., Inc.
PEERMELTS - Candy - Peerless Confection Co.
PEERMINTS - Candy - Peerless Confection Co.
PEERNET - Computer software - SDM International Inc.
PEERSIGHT - Ophthalmic goods - Styl-Rite Optical Manufacturing Co., Inc.
PEERSTONE - Fireplace equipment ☆ - Majestic Co.
PEERTRAL - Ophthalmic goods - Styl-Rite Optical Manufacturing Co., Inc.
PEETERS DESIGN - Floor coverings–carpet and rugs ☆ - Hollytex Carpet Mills Inc.
PEET'S COFFEE + TEA - Coffee, tea, and spices - Peet's Coffee and Tea, Inc.
PEEWEE - Frames–eyeglass - Liberty Optical Manufacturing Co.
PEEWEE - Medical apparatus ☆ - Biosearch Medical Products Inc.
PEEWEE PUPPY - Toys–stuffed ☆ - Gund, Inc.
PEEWEEPAIL - Buckets–plastic - Romanoff Products Inc.
PEFC - Apparel and accessories - PEFC Apparel, Inc.
PEG - Educational materials - Professional Education Group, Inc.
PEG - Health care products - Entech Inc./Enteral Technology
PEG - Ophthalmic goods - Foremost Optical Products
P.E.G. - Pharmaceutical preparations - Medco Lab Inc.
PEG-24 - Medical apparatus - Wilson-Cook Medical Inc.
PEG-A-BOARD - Toys ☆ - Lauri Inc.
PEG A LITE - Toys - Toymax Inc.
PEG-A-PLANE - Toys - Lauri Inc.
PEG-A-TRAIN - Toys - Lauri Inc.
PEG-A-TRUCK - Toys - Lauri Inc.
PEG-BINS - Hardware - The Centro Co. Inc.
PEG-BOARD - Wood products - Masonite Corp.
PEG-IT - Needles–sewing ☆ - Coats and Clark Inc.
PEG-IT - Needlework supplies ☆ - Susan Bates Inc.
PEG LEGS - Food products ☆ - Goodmark Foods, Inc.
PEG-LITE - Plaything - Janex Corp.
PEG-LOK - Furniture - Thomas W. Gollick
PEG MISER - Adhesives and sealants - Loctite Corp.
PEG O' GOLD - Vegetables–canned - Reedsburg Foods Corp.
PEG O' MY HEART - Games - Edwin B. Coleman, Jr.
PEG O' SILVER - Vegetables–canned - Reedsburg Foods Corp.
PEG OUT - Games ☆ - Carrom Co.
PEG PEREGO - Scooters–children's - Peg Perego USA Inc.
PEG PLAY SET - Games - Lauri Inc.
PEG POKER - Games - Wheeler Games
PEG POP - Stamps–hand - Clearsnap, Inc.
PEG-Q - Puzzles ☆ - Milton Bradley Co.
PEG QUOITS - Games - Master Woodcraft Inc.
PEG-RAIL - Hardware ☆ - Knape and Vogt Manufacturing Co.
PEG STRIP - Hooks - VSI Fasteners, Inc.
PEG-THE-NUMBERS PUZZLE - Puzzles - Lauri Inc.
PEGA - Recording label - Sony Disco Inc.
PEGABO - Shoes - Nine West Group Inc.
PEGANONE - Pharmaceutical preparations - Abbott Laboratories
PEGASUS - Automotive parts and accessories - Bock Products Inc.
PEGASUS - Business forms - BlumbergExcelsior, Inc.
PEGASUS - Cymbals - Atlas Accordions Inc.
PEGASUS - Cymbals - Jim Atlas Cymbal Works
PEGASUS - Electrical testing instruments - Leco Corp.
PEGASUS - Fabrics - Hohenberg Co. Inc.
PEGASUS - Floor coverings–carpet and rugs ☆ - Hollytex Carpet Mills Inc.
PEGASUS - Floor coverings–carpet and rugs ☆ - Royalweve Carpet Mills
PEGASUS - Footwear - Pegasus Co.

☆ = Now out of production

PEGASUS - Footwear–athletic - Nike, Inc.
PEGASUS - Glassware–household ☆ - Lenox Crystal, Inc.
PEGASUS - Health care products - Wheel Ring Inc.
PEGASUS - Heating equipment - Blaze King Industries
PEGASUS - Jewelry - Pegasus Jewelers
PEGASUS - Ophthalmic goods - Swank Optical
PEGASUS - Paper–book - Cross Pointe Paper Corp.
PEGASUS - Pharmaceutical preparations - Alva-Amco Pharmacal Co.
PEGASUS - Recording label - The Pegasus Group, Inc.
PEGASUS - Stoves–gas - BKI, Inc.
PEGASUS - Toys–models - Estes Industries
PEGASUS - Tripods–photographic - Phoenix Corp. of America
PEGASUS - Whirlpools - Lasco Products Group
PEGASUS JR. - Automotive parts and accessories - Bock Products Inc.
PEGASUS KNEE BOARD - Skis - Wellington Leisure Products, Inc.
PEGASUS PRIME - Video games - Presto Studios, Inc.
PEGASYS - Alarm systems - Cardkey Systems, Inc.
PEGAVISION - Alarm systems - Amtech Corp.
PEGEANN - Display cases–plastic - Pegeann
PEG'EMS - Hooks - VSI Fasteners, Inc.
PEGGLEBOARD - Toys ☆ - Mego Financial Corp.
PEGGY - Frames–eyeglass - U.S. Optical Frame Co.
PEGGY - Jewelry ☆ - Peggy Sullivan-Cramer Designs
PEGGY - Ophthalmic goods - Foremost Optical Products
PEGGY & JOEL - Jewelry ☆ - Peggy Sullivan-Cramer Designs
PEGGY JANE'S - Salad dressings–bottled - Knott's Berry Farm
PEGGY JO - Ophthalmic goods - Styl-Rite Optical Manufacturing Co., Inc.
PEGGY PAGE - Crocheted and knitted items - Royal Sportswear Co.
PEGGY PAYNE - Crocheted and knitted items - Royal Sportswear Co.
PEGGY PENQUIN - Toys - Tonka Corp.
PEGGY POPPIT - Dolls - Mattel, Inc.
PEGGY SAGE - Cosmetics - Chesebrough-Pond's USA Co.
PEGGY STEWART - Teas - Eastern Shore Tea Co.
PEGGY SUE - Apparel–women's - Jeetish Imports Inc.
PEGGY'S - Pretzels ☆ - Bon Melange Inc.
PEGGY'S POWER PASTA SAUCE - Spaghetti sauces - Peggy's Power Gourmet Inc.
PEGITY - Toys - Tonka Corp.
PEGMATE - Lighting fixtures - Swivelier Co. Inc.
PEGO LAMPS - Lamps - Pego International Corp.
PEGOGRES - Tiles–ceramic - Balgres Distributing Co.
P.E.G.S. - Toys - Tonka Corp.
P.E.G.S. - Toys–electronic - Parker Brothers
PEGS IN THE PARK - Games - Sandra Fay Siefke
PEI - Telephone apparatus - Plant Equipment, Inc.
PEJIGOLD - Yarn ☆ - William Unger & Co. Inc.
PEK - Contact lenses ☆ - Wesley-Jessen Co.
PEKIN - Frames–eyeglass - May Optical Co. Inc.
PEKING - Musical instruments ☆ - St. Louis Music Supply Co.
PEKING - Novelty items - Darwell Import Co. Inc.
PEKING BLUE - Fabrics–denim - Dan River Inc.
PEKING DUK - Vegetable sauces - Saucy Susan Products Inc.
PEKING EAST - Giftware - Seymour Mann Inc.
PEKING EMBROIDERY - Tableware–earthenware - American Trading Co.
PEKING GARDENS - Wallpaper - Dekortex Inc.
PEKO FLAKES - Candy ☆ - Sweet Candy Co.
PEKOE - Thread - Coats American, Inc.
PEKOE - Thread - Threads USA Div.
PEKONI PITA PIZZA - Pizzas–frozen - Pekoni Pita Pizza, Inc.
PEL-AIRE - Fabric binding - Freudenberg Nonwovens Apparel Division
PEL-FREEZ - Meat products–cured - Pel-Freez Rabbit Meat, Inc.
PEL-LOC - Nuts and bolts - Lok-Mor, Inc.
PEL-PAK - Guns–pellet - Crosman Corp.
PEL PRINTER - Electronic equipment - GAF Corp.
PELADA - Apparel–athletic - Pelada, Inc.
PELBOX - Lasers - Ecrm Inc.
PELCO - Electronic surveillance equipment - Pelco
PELDOR - Paper–toilet - Clark Paper Converting Corp.
PELE' - Watches - I.D. Enterprises
PELHAM - Cording ☆ - Samson Cordage Works
PELHAM - Watches - Bulova Corp.
PELHAM MANOR - Floor coverings–carpet and rugs ☆ - Daltonian Carpet & Cushion Inc.
PELHAM MANOR - Floor coverings–tile ☆ - Kentile Floors Inc.
PELHAM MANOR - Wallpaper ☆ - Westchester Prints
PELI - Bedding–linen - Dan River Inc.

PELICAN - Audio equipment - Saul Mineroff Electronics Inc.
PELICAN - Bicycles - Ross Bicycles USA, Ltd.
PELICAN - Boats–dinghies ☆ - Russell Sailboats Inc.
PELICAN - Containers–plastic - Pelican Products, Inc.
PELICAN - Fishing reels - American Import Co.
PELICAN - Flashlights - Rothco Inc.
PELICAN - Fruits and vegetables - Perham Fruit Corp.
PELICAN - Garment hangers - Mission Industries Inc.
PELICAN - Pens - Pelican Products Co. Inc.
PELICAN - Pliers - Alltrade Inc.
PELICAN - Seafood products–fresh or frozen - Arctic King Trading Corp.
PELICAN - Ships–sailing vessels ☆ - Glander Boats Inc.
PELICAN - Vodka ☆ - Sazerac Co. Inc.
PELICAN 13 - Boats–canoes - Sawyer Composite Products
PELICAN BAY - Beverages - North American Beverage Co.
PELICAN BOOKS - Publisher's imprints - Penguin USA
PELICAN EGGS - Candy ☆ - Leaf, Inc.
PELICAN FAUX - Wallpaper - Pelican Prints
PELICAN GUIDE - Publisher's imprints - Pelican Publishing Co. Inc.
PELICAN HILL GOLF CLUB NEWPORT COAST - Apparel–athletic - Irvine Co.
PELICAN INTERNATIONAL - Publisher's imprints - Pelican Publishing Co. Inc.
PELICAN JEANS - Apparel and accessories - Weston
PELICAN LOUISIANA AMBER - Beverages–malt ☆ - Sazerac Co. Inc.
PELICAN LOUISIANA LAGER LIGHT - Beverages–malt ☆ - Sazerac Co. Inc.
PELICAN POINT - Furniture - Lane Upholstery (Venture Furniture Div.)
PELICAN POUCH - Publisher's imprints - Pelican Publishing Co. Inc.
PELICAN PRINTS - Wallpaper ☆ - Pelican Prints
PELICAN STATE - Recording label - Frisco Records Inc.
PELICANS - Frames–eyeglass - Zylo Ware Corp.
PELIGNA MONT PULCIAN - Beverages–alcohol - Orion Imports Ltd.
PELIGNA TREBBIANO - Beverages–alcohol - Orion Imports Ltd.
PELIKAN - Pens - Pelikan, Inc.
PELION - Tiles–ceramic - Porcelanite, Inc.
PELISIMA - Hair care products - Freeman Cosmetics Corp.
PELL HYDRASHEAR - Tools - Morse-Starrett Products Co. (Pell Cable Cutter Div.)
PELLA - Doors–glass ☆ - Pella Corp.
PELLA - Lubricating oils - Shell Oil Co.
PELLE PELLE - Luggage - Pelle Pelle, Inc.
PELLEGRINI - Wines - Pellegrini Bros. Wines Inc.
PELLEGRINI & CUDAHY - Publisher's imprints - Farrar, Straus and Giroux Inc.
PELLET PAINT - Chemical preparations - Novagen, Inc.
PELLET VENT - Ducts–metal - Simpson Dura Vent Co., Inc.
PELLETEX PLUS - Fish food ☆ - Aquatronics-Filtronics
PELLETRON - Electrical equipment - Pelletron Corp.
PELLETTI RANCH - Wines - Deloach Vineyards
PELLGUN - Rifles - Crosman Corp.
PELLGUNOIL - Lubricating oils - Crosman Corp.
PELLI-PEOPLE - Figurines - Pelli-People, Inc.
PELLINORE - Frames–eyeglass - Hoya Corp. USA
PELLISSON PINEAU DES CHARENTES - Wines - Shaw-Ross International Importers
PELLMAN - Desserts - Pellman Foods Inc.
PELLON - Fabrics - Freudenberg Nonwovens Apparel Division
PELLON - Ophthalmic goods - Freudenberg Nonwovens L.P.
PELLY - Toys - Tonka Corp.
PELMAN P - Music boxes - Pelman Corp.
PELOMIL - Hair care products - Felix B. Martinez
PELOPENESSION WAR - Games - Avalon Hill Game Co.
PELOPONNESE - Food products - Gourmet America
PELORUS - Computer software - Computervision Corp.
PELORUS - Seafood products–fresh or frozen - Tucuru
PELORUS MARINATED - Seafood products–fresh or frozen - Tucuru
PELORUS SMOKED - Seafood products–fresh or frozen - Tucuru
PELOTAS - Cigars - Gesty Trading & Manufacturing Corp.
PELOTON - Bicycles - Schwinn Cycling & Fitness Inc.
PELOUZE - Scales–industrial - Pelouze Scale Co.
PELRON - Chemical preparations - Pelron Corp.
PELSTAR - Scales–bathroom - Pelouze Scale Co.
PELSUE - Steel products - T.A. Pelsue Co.
PELT - Gauging instruments - JSR Ultrasonics, Inc.
PELTITIEOS OY - Copper products ☆ - Charles Zahn-Import Merchant
PELTONEN - Sporting goods - Exel Marketing Inc.
PELTOR - Plugs–ear - Aearo Co.
PELVIC FLOOR EXERCISER2 - Health care products - American Imex

☆ = Now out of production

PELVIC POSITIONERS - Health care products - Mulholland Positioning Systems Inc.
PEM - Fasteners–snap - Penn Engineering and Manufacturing Corp.
PEM300 - Fasteners–snap - Penn Engineering and Manufacturing Corp.
PEMA - Bakery products - C. & J. Willenborg Inc.
PEMAQUID - Bells - North Country Wind Bells Inc.
PEMAQUID - Oysters–fresh - Pemaquid Oyster Co. Inc.
PEMBERTON & OAKES - Figurines - Pemberton & Oakes Ltd.
PEMBERVILLE - Food products - Pemberville Foods
PEMBROKE - Cabinets - American Woodmark Corp.
PEMBROKE - Cabinets - Karman Kitchens Inc.
PEMBROKE - Floor coverings - Mannington Resilient Floors
PEMBROKE - Floor coverings–carpet and rugs ☆ - Atlas Carpet Mills Inc.
PEMBROKE - Frames–eyeglass ☆ - Universal/Univis Inc.
PEMBROKE - Wallpaper - Seabrook Wallcoverings, Inc.
PEMBROKE HALL - Furniture ☆ - Stanley Furniture Co. Inc.
PEMBROKE LANE - Furniture–upholstered ☆ - Webb Furniture Enterprises Inc.
PEMBROKE PINE - Furniture ☆ - Lea Industries Inc.
PEMBROOKE - Shoes ☆ - Allen-Edmonds Shoe Corp.
PEMBROOKE - Underwear and nightwear - Pembrooke Lingerie Co.
PEMCO - Aircraft parts - Precision Standard, Inc.
PEMCO ENGINEERS - Hardware - Precision Standard, Inc.
PEMHEX - Fasteners–snap - Penn Engineering and Manufacturing Corp.
PEMMICAN - Food products - Goodmark Foods, Inc.
PEMMICAN TENDER - Meat products–cured - Goodmark Foods, Inc.
PEMSERT - Fasteners–snap - Penn Engineering and Manufacturing Corp.
PEMSTUD - Fasteners–snap - Penn Engineering and Manufacturing Corp.
PEMVAR - Roofing materials - Powell Electrical Manufacturing Co.
PEN - Chemical preparations - State Chemical Manufacturing Co.
PEN 2 - Health care products - Medisense, Inc.
PEN-A-CURE - Varnishes ☆ - Devoe & Raynolds Co.
PEN-A-NOTE - Pens - Sully-Brook-Products
PEN-A-PET - Pet products - Morton Jones Co.
PEN A TIME - Pens - Hyo Sam Byun
PEN & INK - Computer software - IMSI
PEN & INK - Correction fluid - Liquid Paper Corp.
PEN AND PAINT - Toys - Placo Products Co.
PEN & QUILL - Food products - Rod's Food Products Inc.
PEN & QUILL - Frames–eyeglass - Liberty Optical Manufacturing Co.
PEN-BASED MEDICAL NETWORK - Computer software - Pen-Based Medical Network
PEN CENTRAL - Writing instruments - Pen Central
PEN-CHROME - Paints - Fuller-O'Brien Paints Inc.
PEN-CRIB - Cribs–wood ☆ - Gerry Wood Products
PEN DIRECT - Computer software - FTG Data Systems
PEN EASE - Stationery ☆ - Pratt & Austin Co.
PEN-EDGE - Drafting supplies - Plasticoid Manufacturing Inc.
PEN-G - Pharmaceutical preparations - Goldline Laboratories, Inc.
PEN HOUSE - Computer peripheral equipment - Cad Forms Technology, Inc.
PEN-IN-A-CARD - Greeting cards - Quill Co. Inc.
PEN-IT - Pet products - R.R. Manufacturing Co.
PEN KEEPERS - Automotive parts and accessories - Vacuum Supply Co.
PEN-KERA - Pharmaceutical preparations - B.F. Ascher & Co. Inc.
PEN-KOTE - Paints - Pen Paints Inc.
PEN LITE - Flashlights - Garrity Industries
PEN MATE - Computer software - Mouse Systems Corp.
PEN NOTES - Pen holders - Pen Notes Inc.
PEN-O-PAKE - Pens ☆ - Sanford Corp.
PEN-O-THANE - Paints - Pen Paints Inc.
PEN ON THE RD. - Computer software - Ruggedware Ltd.
PEN-OPAKE - Inks - Steig Products
PEN-PAL - Pens - Fun World Inc.
PEN PARTY - Pens - Sunkisses Hawaii
PEN-RAY - Lamps–ultraviolet - UVP Inc.
PEN RITE - Pens - Pen Rite Corp.
PEN SCORE - Foam stamps - Clearsnap, Inc.
PEN SEAL - Epoxy coatings - W.P. Hickman Systems
PEN SEAL #21 - Wood fillers - Hillyard Enterprises, Inc.
PEN-SONIC - Drafting supplies - Alvin and Co. Inc.
PEN SPARKLE - Cleaning preparations ☆ - Steig Products
PEN-TAB - Stationery - Pen-Tab Industries
PEN-TAB EXPERT PEN-TAB - Office accessories - Pen-Tab Industries
PEN-TAB PAPER STORE - Art supplies - Pen-Tab Industries
PEN-TAB PRO - Notebooks and notepads - Pen-Tab Industries
PEN THE PIG - Games ☆ - Western Publishing Co., Inc.

PEN TOUCH - Markers–felt-tip - Sakura of America
PEN-TRIN - Veterinary product ☆ - American Equine Products Inc.
PEN-V - Pharmaceutical preparations - Goldline Laboratories, Inc.
PEN-VEE - Pharmaceutical preparations ☆ - Wyeth-Ayerst Laboratories
PEN-VEE K - Pharmaceutical preparations - Wyeth-Ayerst Laboratories
PEN WEST - Apparel and accessories - Pendleton
PEN WORKS - Novelty items - Impact International Inc.
PENA-DRY - Firearms, accessories, and parts ☆ - Beeman Precision Airguns
PENA-LITH - Adhesives and sealants - W.R. Meadows Inc.
PENA-SEAL - Sealing devices - Uncle Sam Chemical Co., Inc.
PENADERM RUB - Health care products - Elliot Pharmacal Co.
PENALATE - Pharmaceutical preparations ☆ - Merz Inc.
PENALJO - Footwear–women's - Norwood Shoe Corp.
PENALTY BOX - Apparel–athletic - Waldron Enterprises
PENALTY GOLF - Toys - Penalty Golf Inc.
PENALTY KICK - Sporting goods - Greyhound Electronics, Inc.
PENAMIL - Cigars - Swisher International, Inc.
PENAMP - Pharmaceutical preparations - Lannett Co. Inc.
PENAPAR VK - Antibiotics ☆ - Parke-Davis
PENASCAL - Wines - Pellegrini Bros. Wines Inc.
PENATEN - Toothpaste - Johnson & Johnson
PENBERTHY - Monitors–electronic - Penberthy, Inc.
PENBRITIN - Antibiotics ☆ - Wyeth-Ayerst Laboratories
PENBROOK - Cabinets - Actua
PENBROOK - Computer software - Slate Corp.
PENBROOKE - Bathing suits - A and H Sportswear Co., Inc.
PENBROOKE LANE - Underwear and nightwear - Wal-Mart Stores Inc.
PENCAT - Chemical preparations - Penford Products Co.
PENCHANT - Floor coverings–carpet and rugs ☆ - Masland Corp.
PENCHART - Computer software - Total Healthcare Solutions, Inc.
PENCHROME - Varnishes - O'Brien Corp.
PENCHY'S - Ravioli - Solution Enterprises, Inc.
PENCIL CLASSICS - Stationery ☆ - Scentex Inc.
PENCIL GUARD - Music stands - M & M Distributing Co.
PENCIL MAGIC - Cosmetics ☆ - Honey & Spice Toiletries
PENCIL MATE - Pencils - Gillette Co.
PENCIL ME IN - Computer software - Sarrus Software, Inc.
PENCIL NECK GEEKS - Pencils - Pentech International Inc.
PENCIL PAD - Notebooks and notepads - Wellspring
PENCIL PALACE - Office supplies - Rubbermaid Office Products Inc.
PENCIL PERFECT - Cosmetics - Cosmair Inc.
PENCIL PETS - Toys–stuffed - Fun World Inc.
PENCIL POCKET - School supplies - Newell Office Products
PENCIL POINT - Floor coverings–carpet and rugs ☆ - Porter Carpet Mills Inc.
PENCIL POPS - Candy ☆ - Uniconfis Corp.
PENCIL SLIM - Girdles - Kayser-Wispese Co.
PENCILIER - Pencils–mechanical - Pilot Pen Corp. of America
PENCILIST - Office supplies - Bates Manufacturing Co.
PENCILITE - Flashlights - Accutec Inc.
PENCILS PLUS! - Furniture - Robert J. Harper
PENCILS PLUS ! - Pencils - Harper Design Co./Pencils Plus
PENCILSAVER - Pencil sharpeners - Hunt Holdings, Inc.
PENCILTEX - Drafting supplies ☆ - Teledyne Post
PENCILTIC - Pencils ☆ - Zebra Pen Corp.
PENCILUXE - Paper–carbon - Eaton Allen Ko-Rec-Type Corp.
PENCILWORKS - Pencils ☆ - Impact International
PENCO - Giftware - Penco Industries Inc.
PENCO - Guitars ☆ - Philadelphia Music Co. Inc.
PENCO - Hardware - Blaine Window Hardware Inc.
PENCO SEAL - Floor waxers–household - Cello Chemical Co.
PENCOA - Pens - Pencoa
PENCRON - Watches ☆ - J.C. Penney Co., Inc.
PEND-U-LATION - Toys - North Pacific Products Inc.
PENDAFLEX - Office supplies - Esselte Corp.
PENDAFLEX SORT PAL - Office supplies - Esselte Corp.
PENDAFLEXER - Office supplies - Esselte Corp.
PENDANT - Giftware - Accutec Inc.
PENDAPOCKET - Office supplies - Esselte Corp.
PENDASTRIP - Electronic equipment ☆ - Elmo Manufacturing Corp.
PENDAX - Electronic equipment ☆ - Elmo Manufacturing Corp.
PENDE - Hair care products - Roux Laboratories, Inc.
PENDELFIN - Figurines ☆ - British American Imports
PENDEMOMIUM - Office supplies - Jonathan Bradley Pens Inc.
PENDER - Furniture - Boling Co.
PENDIUM - Office furniture - Inwood Office Furniture
PENDLETON - Apparel–women's - Pendleton

PENDLETON - Furniture ☆ - Hammary Furniture Co. Inc.
PENDLETON - Occasional tables - JDI Group, Inc.
PENDLETON LTD. - Apparel and accessories ☆ - Pendleton
PENDLETON STUDIO - Apparel–women's - Pendleton
PENDRAFTER - Computer software - Archway Systems Inc.
PENDRAGON FICTION - Games - Chaosium Inc.
PENDULETTE - Clocks - Jaeger-Le Coultre SA
PENDULUM - Board game - Sofia Anne Shafquat
PENDULUM - Herbicides - American Cyanamid Co.
PENDULUM - Publisher's imprints - Pendulum Press Inc.
PENE-MITE - Pet products - Farnam Cos. Inc.
PENECARE - Skin-care products ☆ - Penederm Inc.
PENECINE - Medical apparatus - General Physiotherapy, Inc.
PENECORT - Skin care products - Allergan, Inc.
PENEDIT - Computer software - Advanced Pen Technologies, Inc.
PENEDRO - Wines ☆ - Safeway Stores Inc.
PENEGLAZE - Paints - Wampler Chemical Corp.
PENELACK - Inks–drawing - Boko-Undo USA Inc.
PENELOPE - Chairs–wood ☆ - Krueger International, Inc.
PENELOPE - Furniture - Haworth, Inc.
PENELOPE - Glassware–household - Durand International
PENELOPE - Jewelry - Panamerican Telemarketing
PENELOPE PUPPET - Toys–stuffed ☆ - Fun World Inc.
PENELOPE WEBB - Footwear - Shandong Inc.
PENELOPE'S - Jams and jellies - Penelope's of Evergreen
PENELOPE'S PARLOR - Wallpaper ☆ - Warner Co.
PENEPHITE - Oils–lubricating - Kano Laboratories Inc.
PENERGY - Computer software - Penergy Inc.
PENESEALTITE - Envelopes - Tension Envelope Corp.
PENESTAIN - Paints - Wampler Chemical Corp.
PENESTAT - Pharmaceutical preparations - Westwood-Squibb
  Pharmaceuticals, Inc.
PENETONE - Cleaning preparations ☆ - Penetone Corp.
PENETRAN - Pharmaceutical preparations - Transdermal Technologies, Inc.
PENETRATE - Fertilizers - C.B. Dolge Co.
PENETRATING GROUT SEALER - Adhesives and sealants - Custom Building
  Products
PENETRATING PROTEIN PACK - Hair care products - Image Laboratories,
  Inc.
PENETRATOR - Automotive parts and accessories - Tuff-Kote Dinol Inc.
PENETRATOR - Electronics equipment - RNS International, Inc.
PENETRATOR - Screws - Albany Steel & Brass Corp.
PENETRATOR - Sights–gun - Pioneer Marketing & Research, Inc.
PENETRATOR - Toys - Tonka Corp.
PENETRATOR-INFRARED - Sights–gun - Pioneer Marketing & Research, Inc.
PENETRATOR, THE - Medical apparatus - Tru-Fit Marketing Corp.
PENETRAY - Lighting fixtures - Philips Lighting Co.
PENETRAY MIRROR ON THE GO - Mirrors ☆ - Philips Electronics North
  America Corp.
PENETREME - Hair care products - Faberge Co.
PENETREX - Oils–lubricating - Quaker State Oil Refining Corp.
PENETROIL - Varnishes - Nowstar
PENETROL - Paints - Flood Co.
PENETROL - Skin care products - Home Health Products, Inc.
PENETRON - Water treating compounds - Better Packages
PENEWIPE - Wood products - Gemini Coatings, Inc.
PENFACT - Computer software - Penfact Inc.
PENFOLDS - Wines - Frederick Wildman and Sons Ltd.
PENFORD - Corn starch - Penford Products Co.
PENG WIN - Games ☆ - Milton Bradley Co.
PENGAD - Stationery - Pengad, Inc.
PENGO COMPUTER ACCESSORIES - Cleaning preparations - King Bird Inc.
PENGOLD PAYROLL - Computer software ☆ - Pen Soft
PENGRAPHIC - Pens ☆ - Faber-Castell Corp.
PENGUIN - Apparel and accessories - Meyers and Son Manufacturing Co. Inc.
PENGUIN - Apparel–men's - Munsingwear, Inc.
PENGUIN - Aquariums–household - Marineland Aquarium Products
PENGUIN - Candy - Dae Julie, Inc.
PENGUIN - Food products ☆ - Nasoya Foods, Inc.
PENGUIN - Housewares - Metrokane
PENGUIN - Industrial machinery - Penguin Industrial Products, Inc.
PENGUIN - Markers–felt-tip - Sanford Corp.
PENGUIN - Refrigerators - Springer-Penguin Inc.
PENGUIN - Shortening ☆ - Swift Edible Oil Co.
PENGUIN - Shrimp–fresh or frozen - Penguin Frozen Foods, Inc.
PENGUIN - Signal flares ☆ - Hoppe's

PENGUIN - Tarpaulins - C.R. Daniels Inc.
PENGUIN - Watches - Croton Watch Co., Inc.
PENGUIN BOOKS - Publisher's imprints - Penguin USA
PENGUIN CLUB - Apparel and accessories - Munsingwear, Inc.
PENGUIN CRYSTAL VODKA - Beverages–alcohol - Zumot and Son
PENGUIN FEET-TREET - Skin care products - Church and Dwight Co. Inc.
PENGUIN-KUN WARS - Video games - Taito America Corp.
PENGUIN MIXIPS - Straws–drinking ☆ - Premier Industries Inc.
PENGUIN PALS - Pet products - Petrapport, Inc.
PENGUIN PALS - Toys–stuffed - Fun World Inc.
PENGUIN SHUFFLE - Games - Hasbro, Inc.
PENGUIN SURFER - Toys–stuffed - Lisa Frank, Inc.
PENGUIN, THE - Measuring instruments - Mackin and Co., Inc.
PENGUINS ON ICE - Toys–stuffed ☆ - Dakin Inc.
PENHALIGON'S - Skin care products - Penhal Investments, Inc.
PENHEADS - Pencil- and pen-top ornaments - Lisa Frank, Inc.
PENHURST - Furniture - Haworth, Inc.
PENI-LUBE - Oils–lubricating - Claire Manufacturing Co.
PENICILLEX - Aquatic pharmacuetical preparations ☆ - Aquatronics-Filtronics
PENINSULA - Fireplaces ☆ - Superior Fireplace Co.
PENINSULA ENGINEERING - Telephones–cellular - Peninsula Engineering
  Group, Inc.
PENINSULA PLAYERS - Apparel and accessories - Peninsula Players Theatre
  Foundation, Inc.
PENINSULA PLAYERS THEATRE IN A GARDEN - Apparel and accessories -
  Peninsula Players Theatre Foundation, Inc.
PENINSULAR - Sugar–granulated, refined, or powdered - Savannah Foods
  and Industries Inc.
PENIT - Inks ☆ - Sanford Corp.
PENITAL - Health care products ☆ - Kay Pharmacal Co. Inc.
PENITRATE - Cough medicines ☆ - Majestic Drug Co., Inc.
PENJOY - Toys–automobiles - Penjoy Co., Inc.
PEN*KEY - Computer software - Norand Corp.
PENKOTE - Lubricants - Elf Lubricants North America, Inc.
PENLEY - Toothpicks - Penley Corp.
PENLEY RING SYSTEM - Golfing equipment - Penley Sports, LLC
PENMAC - Computer software - Communication Intelligence Corp.
PENMAN'S FRIEND, THE - Computer software - Time Being Press, Inc.
PENN - Apparel stores–sports - Gencorp Inc.
PENN - Fasteners–snap - Penn Engineering and Manufacturing Corp.
PENN - Fishing tackle - Penn Fishing Tackle Manufacturing Co.
PENN - Rackets–tennis - Penn Athletic Products
PENN - Refrigerators - Johnson Controls Inc.
PENN - Thread - Belding Heminway Co. Inc.
PENN 100 SILVER - Fishing tackle - Penn Fishing Tackle Manufacturing Co.
PENN ATP TOUR - Balls–tennis - Penn Athletic Products
PENN BAYMASTER - Fishing tackle - Penn Fishing Tackle Manufacturing Co.
PENN BOND III - Patches, insignia, and emblems - Penn Emblem Co.
PENN-C.F.S. - Thread - Blue Mountain Industries, Inc.
PENN CHAMP - Lighter fluid ☆ - Penn Champ Inc.
PENN CHAMPIONSHIP - Balls–tennis - Penn Athletic Products
PENN COPY - Paper - Willamette Industries, Inc.
PENN CORD - Floor coverings–carpet and rugs - Bloomsburg Carpet
  Industries
PENN-COT - Thread ☆ - Blue Mountain Industries, Inc.
PENN COUNTRY - Food products - Tyson Foods Inc.
PENN CRETE - Stucco finish - IPA Systems Inc.
PENN DAIRIES - Milk - Crowley Frozen Desserts Inc.
PENN DALE - Food products - Associated Wholesalers Inc.
PENN-DRAKE - Petroleum - Penreco
PENN DUTCH - Food products - Van Bennett Food Inc.
PENN ENGINEERING - Fasteners–snap - Penn Engineering and
  Manufacturing Corp.
PENN FARMS - Desserts - Crowley Frozen Desserts Inc.
PENN GLS - Fishing tackle - Penn Fishing Tackle Manufacturing Co.
PENN GRAPHITE GS SERIES - Fishing tackle - Penn Fishing Tackle
  Manufacturing Co.
PENN INTERNATIONAL II - Fishing tackle - Penn Fishing Tackle
  Manufacturing Co.
PENN-LACING - Thread ☆ - Blue Mountain Industries, Inc.
PENN LEVEL WIND - Fishing tackle - Penn Fishing Tackle Manufacturing Co.
PENN LEVELMATIC - Fishing tackle - Penn Fishing Tackle Manufacturing Co.
PENN-LIN - Thread ☆ - Blue Mountain Industries, Inc.
PENN-MADE - Thread ☆ - Blue Mountain Industries, Inc.
PENN MAID - Food products - Musselman Fruit Products
PENN MAID - Yogurt - Penn Maid Foods Inc.

☆ = Now out of production

PENN MAID PRIDE - Food products - Penn Maid Foods Inc.
PENN MANOR - Chimes ☆ - Nutone Inc.
PENN-MAR - Food products - Hepburn Orchards Inc.
PENN MULCH - Soil–potting - Lebanon Seaboard Corp.
PENN NEEDLE - Housewares - Alford Home Products Inc.
PENN-NYL - Thread ☆ - Blue Mountain Industries, Inc.
PENN-OHIO - Furnaces–electric ☆ - Will-Burt Co.
PENN-ORGANIC - Chemical preparations - Pennington Enterprises, Inc.
PENN PILSNER - Beverages–malt - Jones Brewing Co.
PENN-PLAX - Pet products - Penn-Plax, Inc.
PENN POWER GRAPH - Fishing rods ☆ - Penn Fishing Tackle Manufacturing Co.
PENN POWER STICK - Fishing tackle - Penn Fishing Tackle Manufacturing Co.
PENN PREST - Fabrics ☆ - J.C. Penney Co., Inc.
PENN RACQUETBALL - Sporting goods - Penn Athletic Products
PENN-RAY - Thread ☆ - Blue Mountain Industries, Inc.
PENN RELAYS - Paper goods and printed matter - University of Pennsylvania
PENN ROYAL - Oils–lubricating - Quaker State Oil Refining Corp.
PENN SHORE - Wines - Penn Shore Vineyards Inc.
PENN SLAMMER - Fishing tackle - Penn Fishing Tackle Manufacturing Co.
PENN SPINFISHER - Fishing rods ☆ - Penn Fishing Tackle Manufacturing Co.
PENN STAND-UP SYSTEM - Fishing tackle - Penn Fishing Tackle Manufacturing Co.
PENN STATE - Binders - Penn State Industries
PENN TAC - Gloves - Gencorp Inc.
PENN TEX - Floor coverings–carpet and rugs - Bloomsburg Carpet Industries
PENN VALLEY - Meat products–beef - Colonial Beef Co.
PENN YAN - Boats–motor - Penn Yan Boats Inc.
PENNA - Posters - Stevenson Industries Inc.
PENNANT - Balls–baseball - American Camper
PENNANT - Bicycles - Columbia Manufacturing Inc.
PENNANT - Chewing gum ☆ - Amurol Confections Co.
PENNANT - Floor coverings–carpet and rugs - Coronet Carpets Inc.
PENNANT - Floor coverings–carpet and rugs - Karastan-Bigelow Inc.
PENNANT - Maraschino cherries - Gray & Co.
PENNANT - Meat products - Saramar Corp.
PENNANT - Milk - Marigold Foods Inc.
PENNANT - Nuts–salted, roasted, cooked, or canned - Nabisco Foods Group
PENNANT - Oils–lubricating - Lyondell Petrochemical Co.
PENNANT - Thread - Threads USA Div.
PENNANT CHASE - Trading cards and stamps - Treat Entertainment, Inc.
PENNANT KEY - Publisher's imprints - Bantam Doubleday Dell Publishing Group, Inc.
PENNANT PALS - Toys–stuffed - Russ Berrie and Co., Inc.
PENNANT POWER - Trading cards - ANCO Collector Supplies, Inc.
PENNANT RACE - Games ☆ - Avalon Hill Game Co.
PENNCO - Heating equipment - Dunkirk Radiator Corp.
PENNCRAFT - Tools–power-driven - J.C. Penney Co., Inc.
PENNCREST - Appliance parts ☆ - J.C. Penney Co., Inc.
PENNCRETE - Adhesives and sealants - Penn Crete Products Co. Inc.
PENNCROSS - Flowers, plants, and seeds - Jacklin Seed
PENNEAGLE - Flowers, plants, and seeds - Jacklin Seed
PENNEEDLE - Insulin - Novo Nordisk Pharmaceuticals Inc.
PENNEYPET - Apparel and accessories - J.C. Penney Co., Inc.
PENNEY'S - Apparel and accessories - J.C. Penney Co., Inc.
PENNFIELD FARMS - Meat products–poultry - Pennfield Farms
PENNFIELD FARMS AMISH SELECT - Chickens - Pennfield Corp.
PENNGROUT - Cement grout - IPA Systems Inc.
PENNHIP - Veterinary apparatus - University of Pennsylvania
PENNHURST - Floor coverings ☆ - Congoleum Corp.
PENNI SECRETS - Dolls - Mattel, Inc.
PENNIES FROM HEAVEN - Novelty items - Pennies from Heaven, LLC
PENNINGTON - Cabinets - Yorktowne Inc.
PENNINGTON - Toilets–enameled - Kohler Co.
PENNINGTON HERITAGE DISCOVERIES - Spices and extracts - Board of Supervisors of Louisiana State University and Agricultural a Mechanical College
PENNINGTON HERITAGE DISCOVERIES SPICE TREASURES - Spices and extracts - Board of Supervisors of Louisiana State University and Agricultural a Mechanical College
PENNINGTON SQUARE - Floor coverings ☆ - Congoleum Corp.
PENNLINKS - Flowers, plants, and seeds - Jacklin Seed
PEN'N'NOTE - Stationery ☆ - Jobar International Inc./Bibi Products
PENNOPTICS - Eyeglasses - Pennsylvania Optical
PENNPRO - Garden equipment - Pennpro Corp.

PENNRAM ESS - Septic tanks–plastic - Pennram Diversified Manufacturing Corp.
PENN'S - Thread ☆ - Blue Mountain Industries, Inc.
PENN'S CHOICE GOLD LABEL COFFEE - Coffee - Rich Coast Corp.
PENN'S LANDING - Floor coverings - Mannington Resilient Floors
PENNSBURY - Floor coverings - Mannington Resilient Floors
PENNSBURY - Paints - M.A. Bruder & Sons Inc.
PENNSBURY MANOR - Tables–wood - Mersman Furniture Co.
PENNSPORT - Sporting goods - Pennsylvania Sporting Goods Co.
PENNSY - Food products - Conte Inc.
PENNSYLVANIA - See also PA.
PENNSYLVANIA - Heating equipment ☆ - Bradford-White Corp.
PENNSYLVANIA - Scales–industrial - Pennsylvania Scale Co.
PENNSYLVANIA BUCK - Novelty items - R.A. Pearson Wholesale
PENNSYLVANIA COW PIES - Chocolate candy ☆ - Tom and Sally's Handmade Chocolates, Inc.
PENNSYLVANIA DUTCH - Beverages–carbonated - Pennsylvania Dutch Birch Beer Inc.
PENNSYLVANIA DUTCH - Candy - Pennsylvania Dutch Candies
PENNSYLVANIA DUTCH - Eggnog - Charles Jacquin et Compagnie Inc.
PENNSYLVANIA DUTCH - Paints - Allentown Paint Manufacturing Co. Inc.
PENNSYLVANIA DUTCH - Pasta - Borden, Inc.
PENNSYLVANIA DUTCH - Potato chips ☆ - Herr's Inc.
PENNSYLVANIA DUTCH BIRCH BEER - Beverages–malt - Pennsylvania Dutch Birch Beer Inc.
PENNSYLVANIA DUTCH BUGGY - Balsa-wood model kits - Country Lane Dutch Supply
PENNSYLVANIA DUTCHMAN - Cigars - G.W. Van Slyke & Horton
PENNSYLVANIA DUTCHMAN - Nibs–pen - Georgio Foods Plant II
PENNSYLVANIA HOUSE - Furniture - Pennsylvania House
PENNSYLVANIA HUNTER - Sights–gun - Thompson/Center Arms
PENNSYLVANIA LAW WEEKLY - Publisher's imprints - Legal Communications, Ltd.
PENNSYLVANIA PILSNER - Beverages–malt - Pittsburgh Brewing Co.
PENNSYLVANIA PROUD! - Beverages–carbonated - Hondo Inc.
PENNSYLVANIAN - Bicycles - Ross Bicycles USA, Ltd.
PENNSYLVANIA'S BEST - Toys–automobiles - Sixth Generation
PENNTECH - Paper products - Willamette Industries, Inc.
PENNTEST - Vitamins and nutritional supplements ☆ - Pennex Products
PENNTEX - Textured acrylic coatings ☆ - IPA Systems Inc.
PENNTUSS - Health care products ☆ - Fisons Corp.
PENNVIAL - Containers–glass - Pennsylvania Glass Products Co.
PENNWOOD - Floor coverings - Penn Wood Products, Inc.
PENNWYCK - Floor coverings ☆ - Tarkett, Inc.
PENNWYCK SQUARE - Floor coverings ☆ - Tarkett, Inc.
PENNY - Racks - Penelope Products, Inc.
PENNY ANNIES - Candy ☆ - Square Shooter Candy Co.
PENNY ARCADE - Figurines - Penny Arcade
PENNY BALLS - Candy ☆ - Bobs Candies Inc.
PENNY CANDY - Shoes - Hiraoka New York Corp.
PENNY CANDY STORE - Candy ☆ - Leaf, Inc.
PENNY CURTIS - Bakery products - P and C Food Markets Inc.
PENNY CUTTER - Sporting goods - William Getz Corp.
PENNY LAINE - Chocolate candy - Madelaine Chocolate Novelties, Inc.
PENNY LANE - Floor coverings–carpet and rugs - Ashley Commercial Carpets
PENNY LANE - Footwear - Dollar General Corp.
PENNY LANE - Wallpaper - Sellers & Josephson
PENNY PENDLETON - Frames–eyeglass - Penny Pendleton Manufacturing Inc.
PENNY PEPPERMINT - Toys - Mattel, Inc.
PENNY PILE - Games - Little Harbor Corp.
PENNY PINCHER - Fruits–canned ☆ - Packers Canning Co., Inc.
PENNY PINCHER - Toys - Tyco Toys
PENNY PINCHERS - Skin care products - Lee Pharmaceuticals
PENNY PLANES - Toys ☆ - Takara USA Corp.
PENNY POPPIT - Dolls - Mattel, Inc.
PENNY POPPLES - Toys - Those Characters from Cleveland, Inc.
PENNY PRIDE - Food products - Custom Food Products Inc.
PENNY PURE - Detergents - Malco Products, Inc.
PENNY RACERS - Toys ☆ - Takara USA Corp.
PENNY RACERS STUNT N' RACE - Toys ☆ - Takara USA Corp.
PENNY ROUNDS - Tiles–mosaic - Capitol Tile Import Co.
PENNY-SAK - Exercising equipment - Penny-Sak
PENNY SAVER - Detergents ☆ - Publix Super Markets, Inc.
PENNY SHINE - Shoe polish - Turtle Wax, Inc.
PENNY SMART - Food products - Associated Grocers, Inc.

PENNY SMART - Food products - Western Family Foods, Inc.
PENNY STICKS - Pretzels ☆ - Benzel's Bretzel Bakery, Inc.
PENNY THE PONY - Toys - Tyco Toys
PENNY-WATT - Lighting fixtures ☆ - Voigt Lighting Industries Inc.
PENNY WAX - Sweeping compounds - Paxon Manufacturing Co.
PENNY-WEIGHT - Toys ☆ - Hi-Flier Manufacturing Co.
PENNY YOUNG - Apparel–women's - Anne Klein & Co.
PENNYHERB PLUS - Pet products - Hansen's Pet Products Co.
PENNYROYAL - Pharmaceutical preparations - City Chemical Corp.
PENNYROYAL LEAF - Shampoos - Kim Laube & Co. Inc.
PENNYROYAL PLUS - Pet products - Best Friend Products
PENNY'S - Sausages - Penny's Meat Products
PENNYS FORUM - Publisher's imprints - J.C. Penney Co., Inc.
PENNY'S PALS - Novelty items - Penny S. Post Inc.
PENNYSTICKS AND BENZELS - Pretzels - Benzel's Bretzel Bakery, Inc.
PENNZGRIND - Chemical preparations - Pennzoil Products Co.
PENNZKOOL - Chemical preparations - Pennzoil Products Co.
PENNZOIL - Oils–lubricating - Pennzoil Co. (Gumout Div.)
PENNZSUPPRESS - Chemical preparations - Pennzoil Products Co.
PENNZTAC BLUE STREAK - Lubricants - Pennzoil Products Co.
PENOBSCOT - Boats–canoes - Old Town Canoe Co.
PENOBSCOT - Cheese - State of Maine Cheese
PENOBSCOT - Fruits and vegetables - Penobscot Frozen Foods Inc.
PENOBSCOT - Shoes ☆ - Penobscot Shoe Co.
PENOBSCOT - Sporting goods ☆ - Shaw & Tenney Inc.
PENOTTI - Food products - Holland-American Importing Co. Inc.
PENOVATION - Computer software - Mapframe Corp.
PENOX - Medical apparatus - Penox Technologies Inc.
PENPAD - Computers–mainframe - Numonics Corp.
PENPAK! - Computer software - Mobile Computing Systems Corp.
PENQUILL PRESS - Printing presses - Jonathan David Publishers Inc.
PENRAD - Computer software - Medical Information Technologies, Inc.
PENRECO - Petroleum - Penreco
PENRIL DATABILITY NETWORKS - Computer software - Penril Datacomm Networks, Inc.
PENROD - Watches - Hampden Corp.
PENROSE - Food products - Goodmark Foods, Inc.
PENROSE - Glassware–household ☆ - Wallace International Silversmiths, Inc.
PENROSE DIAMONDS - Puzzles - Kadon Enterprises Inc.
PENROSE FIRECRACKER GIANT - Food products - Goodmark Foods, Inc.
PENROSE KITES & DARTS - Puzzles - Kadon Enterprises Inc.
PENRUST - Paints - Passonno Paints
PENRYN - Toilets–enameled - Kohler Co.
PENSA-COLA - Beverages–carbonated - William Nadler
PENSACOLA - Seafood products–fresh or frozen - Missouri Fish Co.
PENSCRIPTION - Computer software - Robert L. Swearingen
PENSEES - Skin care products ☆ - Nutri-Metics International (USA) Inc.
PENSERTER - Fasteners–snap - Penn Engineering and Manufacturing Corp.
PENSHURST - Dinnerware–glass ☆ - Royal China & Porcelain Companies Inc.
PENSIL - Resins–synthetic - General Electric Co.
PENSION BENEFITS EXPERT - Computer software - Research Institute of America Inc.
PENSION PATHWAYS - Computer software - Principal Mutual Life Insurance Co.
PENSKE - Cleaning preparations - Sears, Roebuck and Co.
PENSOFT - Computer software - Pen Soft
PENSOFT - Computer software ☆ - Pet Supply Imports Inc.
PENSOL - Adhesives and sealants - Sealmaster, Inc.
PENSTAR - Garden equipment - Grace-Sierra Crop Protection Co.
PENSTIX - Office supplies - Alvin and Co. Inc.
PENSTRUMENT - Measuring instruments - Mackin and Co., Inc.
PENSUPREME - Milk - Crowley Frozen Desserts Inc.
PENSYN - Pharmaceutical preparations ☆ - Upjohn Co.
PENT-ALL - Lubricants ☆ - Dykem Co.
PENTA - Sunglasses - McNeil Corp.
PENTA - Wood products - Dap Products Inc.
PENTA-CAL-PLUS - Vitamins and nutritional supplements - Nutrition Center, Inc.
PENTA-DIP - Wood fillers - Sterling-Clark-Lurton Corp.
PENTA FLEX - Paints - Benjamin Moore & Co.
PENTA NETS - Traps–animal - Fuhrman Diversified
PENTA-PAK - Packaging–paper - Philip Morris Companies Inc.
PENTA-PLUS - Measuring instruments - Avo Multi-Amp Corp.
PENTA-PLY - Cooking equipment–household - Vita Craft Corp.
PENTA POD - Paper products - Originetics, Inc.

PENTA-TECT - Paints - Jones Blair Co.
PENTA-WOOD-SEAL - Paints ☆ - Samuel Cabot Inc.
PENTACAM - Video equipment - Focal Point, Inc.
PENTACELL - Water purification systems - WTC Industries Inc.
PENTACIN - Pharmaceutical preparations ☆ - U.S. Ethicals Inc.
PENTACON-6 - Cameras ☆ - Edixa Camera Co.
PENTAGARD 10-1 - Finishing agents ☆ - Zehrung Corp.
PENTAGON - Herbicides - American Cyanamid Co.
PENTAGON - Paints - General Coating Technologies, Inc.
PENTAGON - Watches - Gruen Marketing Corp.
PENTAGON CORNER - Aquariums–household - Cole Enterprises
PENTAGONE - Integrated Chemistries Inc.
PENTAGRAMS - Games - Michael Carlitz
PENTAIDER - Games - Gamescience
PENTALIC - Paper - M. Grumbacher Inc.
PENTALIC BOOKS - Publisher's imprints - M. Grumbacher Inc.
PENTAMARK - Advertising agencies - BBDO Worldwide Inc.
PENTAPINE - Disinfectants - Analab Inc.
PENTAPURE - Water purification systems - WTC Ecomaster Corp.
PENTAROSE - Puzzles - Kadon Enterprises Inc.
PENTASCANNER - Electronic equipment - Microtest, Inc.
PENTASEAL - Finishing agents ☆ - Zehrung Corp.
PENTASTIC - Pens - Russ Berrie and Co., Inc.
PENTASTIC - Pens - Slencil Co.
PENTATHIN - Watches - Gruen Marketing Corp.
PENTATHLON - Fungicides - Griffin Corp.
PENTAX - Photographic equipment - Pentax Corp.
PENTAX 67 - Cameras - Pentax Corp.
PENTAX 645 - Cameras - Pentax Corp.
PENTAX A3000 - Cameras ☆ - Pentax Corp.
PENTAX AUTO SPORT - Cameras ☆ - Pentax Corp.
PENTAX IQZOOM 115 - Cameras ☆ - Pentax Corp.
PENTAX K1000 - Cameras ☆ - Pentax Corp.
PENTAX LX - Cameras ☆ - Pentax Corp.
PENTAX ME SUPER - Cameras ☆ - Pentax Corp.
PENTAX P3 - Cameras ☆ - Pentax Corp.
PENTAX P5 - Cameras ☆ - Pentax Corp.
PENTAX PRO SPORT DATE - Cameras ☆ - Pentax Corp.
PENTAX PROGRAM PLUS - Cameras ☆ - Pentax Corp.
PENTAX SUPER PROGRAM - Cameras ☆ - Pentax Corp.
PENTAX SUPER SPORT - Cameras ☆ - Pentax Corp.
PENTAX ULTRA SPORT - Cameras ☆ - Pentax Corp.
PENTAZYME - Pharmaceutical preparations ☆ - Ulmer Pharmacal Co.
PENTE - Games - Decipher Inc.
PENTE - Games - Tonka Corp.
PENTEK - Electronic equipment - Pentek Inc.
PENTEL - Stationery - Pentel of America, Ltd.
PENTELLER - Pumps - High Temperature Systems, Inc.
PENTEMP - Measuring instruments - Penberthy, Inc.
PENTENNA - Pens - Jeff M. Eliseo
PENTESTAN-80 - Health care products - Halsom Home Care
PENTET - Pharmaceutical preparations ☆ - C.O. Truxton Inc.
PENTHANE POLYURETHANE VARNISHES - Varnishes - O'Brien Corp.
PENTHOUSE - Boats–houseboats ☆ - Holiday Mansion
PENTHOUSE - Colognes - General Media International, Inc.
PENTHOUSE - Food products - Pet Inc.
PENTHOUSE - Furniture polish and wax - Star Finishing Products Inc.
PENTHOUSE - Furniture–upholstered - Simmons Upholstered Furniture Inc.
PENTHOUSE - Meat products–beef - Penthouse Meat Co.
PENTHOUSE - Padding–foam ☆ - Foamex LP
PENTHOUSE - Recording label - Penthouse International, Ltd.
PENTHOUSE - Tablecloths - Henry A. Enrich & Co. Inc.
PENTHOUSE - Wallpaper - Riverside Silkscreen
PENTHOUSE CALENDAR - Clocks ☆ - General Time Corp. (Westclox/Seth Thomas Div.)
PENTHOUSE DETANGLER - Hair care products - Penthouse for Men
PENTHOUSE FORUM - Recording label - Penthouse International, Ltd.
PENTHOUSE INTERACTIVE - Computer software - Penthouse International, Ltd.
PENTHOUSE INTIMATES INTERNATIONAL - Apparel–women's - General Media International, Inc.
PENTI - Hosiery - G & Z Trading Corp.
PENTIDE - Wood preserver ☆ - Bonide Products, Inc.
PENTIDS - Pharmaceutical preparations - Bristol-Myers Squibb Co.
PENTIUM - Computer - Intel Corp.
PENTIUM, 6MHZ-100MHZ. - See **ACM GAME CARD**

☆ = Now out of production

PENTIUM PROCESSOR - Computers - Intel Corp.
PENTO DEL - Pharmaceutical preparations ☆ - Boyle & Co.
PENTOBEE - Pharmaceutical preparations ☆ - Vitarine Pharmaceuticals Inc.
PENTON - Motorcycles ☆ - Certified Parts Corp.
PENTOSIN - Brake fluids - CRP Industries, Inc.
PENTOX - Lumber ☆ - Osmose Wood Preserving Inc.
PENTOXIL - Pharmaceutical preparations - Upsher-Smith Laboratories, Inc.
PENTRA - Machine parts ☆ - Max Daetwyler Corp.
PENTRAITT - Hair care products - Sebastian International, Inc.
PENTRAN - Health care products - Halsey Drug Co. Inc.
PENTRAX - Shampoos - Genderm Corp.
PENTREX - Fertilizers - Wilbur-Ellis Co.
PENTROX - Adhesives and sealants - Advance Cleaning Products Inc.
PENTYL-M-CRESOL - Pharmaceutical preparations - City Chemical Corp.
PENTYLAN - Pharmaceutical preparations - Lannett Co. Inc.
PENTYLENETETRAZOLE - Pharmaceutical preparations - City Chemical Corp.
PENULTIMATE - Computer software - Penultimate, Inc.
PENVISION - Computer software - Penvision Information Systems, Inc.
PENWARE - Computer software - Penware, Inc.
PENWAY - Stationery - Walgreen Co.
PENWEST - Apparel–men's ☆ - Penwest
PENX - Lubricants - Ponsness-Warren
PENZIER - Measuring instruments - Mackin and Co., Inc.
PENZOIL INDY RACER - Toys–automobiles - Kingsbury Mini Motors of America Inc.
PEONIES AND IVY - Toilets–enameled - Kohler Co.
PEONY - Dinnerware ☆ - Corning Inc.
PEONY - Food products ☆ - Curtice-Burns Foods, Inc.
PEONY - Jewelry - Peony Fine Jewelry Inc.
PEONY - Milk–canned or powdered - Sun Hing Foods, Inc.
PEONY - Recording label - Vandor Motion Pictures, Phonorecords & Music Publishing Group
PEONY - Tiles–ceramic - Monarch Tile Inc.
PEONY CLAIRE BURKE - Bathroom accessories - Tsumura International Inc.
PEONY JARDINIERE - Vases - Crisa Corp.
PEONY TREE - Bedding–linen - Dan River Inc.
PEOPLE - Apparel and accessories - People Clothing Co.
PEOPLE - Recording label - Polygram Records, Inc.
PEOPLE AND PLACES - Computer software ☆ - Knowledge Access International, Inc.
PEOPLE AT WORK - Shoes - In-Motion
PEOPLE BISCUIT, THE - Chocolate candy - Harry London's Candies Inc.
PEOPLE CRACKERS - Dog food - Pet Life Foods Inc.
PEOPLE DROPS - Candy - Golden Apples Candy Co., Inc.
PEOPLE FEEDER - Novelty items - RT Industries
PEOPLE FINDER - Telephone answering machines - Motorola, Inc. (Land Mobile Products Sector)
PEOPLE FOR PEOPLE - Computer software - People for People
PEOPLE FRIENDLY - Building materials–concrete - Burns & Russell Co.
PEOPLE GREETER - Floor coverings - Devon Corp.
PEOPLE HEATERS - Lamps - DriQuik, Inc.
PEOPLE MAKING A DIFFERENCE - Educational materials - Onolee Zwicke
PEOPLE MOVERS - Shoes - Leather 'n Things
PEOPLE MOVERS - Toys–stuffed - Kamar International Inc.
PEOPLE 'N PLACES - Toys ☆ - Creative Playthings Ltd.
PEOPLE OF COLOR - Apparel and accessories - Lavetta C. Willis
PEOPLE OF THE NEW TESTAMENT - Computer software - Hartley Courseware Inc.
PEOPLE OF THE OLD TESTAMENT - Computer software - Hartley Courseware Inc.
PEOPLE OF THE WORLD - Novelty items–paper - Possible Dreams, Ltd.
PEOPLE PALS - Dolls - Sherm 'n' Stuff
PEOPLE PENNANTS - Pennants ☆ - U.S. Fiberglass Inc.
PEOPLE PINS - Jewelry - Lucinda, Inc.
PEOPLE PLACES AND THINGS - Computer storage devices - Taligent, Inc.
PEOPLE PLEASERS - Food products - Luigino's
PEOPLE PLEASERS - Shoes - Leather 'n Things
PEOPLE PLEASING - Juices - Citrus Systems
PEOPLE POPS - Candy - Golden Apples Candy Co., Inc.
PEOPLE POSTCARDS! - Computer software ☆ - Imageware Software, Inc.
PEOPLE POSTCARDS - Postcards ☆ - Imageware Software, Inc.
PEOPLE PRODUCING PROFIT$ - Educational materials - Human Resource Management Systems, Inc.
PEOPLE PRODUCTIONS BY SUSAN FLORENCE - Greeting cards - C.R. Gibson Co.
PEOPLE ROOMS - Furniture - LADD Furniture Inc.

PEOPLE STRIPPER - Skin care products - Blue Inc.
PEOPLE SYSTEMS - Calendars - People Systems Inc.
PEOPLE TREATS - Candy - John B. Sanfilippo & Son, Inc.
PEOPLE WEEKLY - Games ☆ - Parker Brothers
PEOPLECODE - Computer software - Peoplesoft, Inc.
PEOPLES - Starch–laundry - Peoples Drug Stores Inc.
PEOPLE'S ALMANAC 2 - Games ☆ - International Polygonics Ltd.
PEOPLE'S CHOICE - Floor coverings–carpet and rugs - Barrett Carpet Mills Inc.
PEOPLE'S MARATHON - Housewares - United States of America
PEOPLE'S MEDICAL SOCIETY MED REF. - Publisher's imprints - Book Margins, Inc.
PEOPLES MUSIC - Recording label - Jazz Composer's Orchestra Association Inc.
PEOPLE'S PAGING - Pagers - People's Paging Inc.
PEOPLE'S PHARMACY WITH JOE & TERRY GRAEDON, THE - Recording label - Graedon Enterprises, Inc.
PEOPLESOFT - Computer software - Peoplesoft, Inc.
PEOPLETRACKER - Computer software - Automated Solutions
PEOPLEVISION - Mannequins - Peoplevision
PEORIA - Water–mineral - Peoria Mineral Springs
PEORIA JAVELINAS - Novelty items - Arizona Fall League, Inc.
PEP - Apparel and accessories - Pandora Sportswear Industries
PEP - Cat food - AGP Petfoods
PEP - Cereal ☆ - Kellogg Co.
PEP+ - Computer software - Stockholder Systems, Inc.
PEP - Dog food ☆ - SuperSweet Feed
PEP - Exercising equipment - Exercycle Corp.
PEP - Greeting cards - Joche Davila Studio
PEP - Vitamins and nutritional supplements - Natural Balance, Inc.
PEP 4530 - Electronic equipment ☆ - Peavey Electronics Corp.
PEP AID - Awakeners ☆ - Iodent Co.
PEP-B - Vitamins and nutritional supplements - Sundown Vitamins, Inc.
PEP-BACK - Pharmaceutical preparations - Alva-Amco Pharmacal Co.
PEP BOYS - Automotive parts and accessories - Pep Boys Manny, Moe & Jack
PEP BOYS - Towels - MMJ Corp.
PEP BOYS MANNY MOE & JACK, THE - Towels - Pep Boys Manny, Moe & Jack
PEP-CHEWS - Pharmaceutical preparations - American Hygienic Laboratories Inc.
PEP-DOUCHETTES - Pharmaceutical preparations ☆ - American Hygienic Laboratories Inc.
PEP ENGINEERING - Aquariums–household - Echo Services
PEP-O-MINT - Candy - Planters LifeSavers Co.
P.E.P. PAK - Medical apparatus - The Diagnostic Center for Men
PEP PAPERLESS ENTRY PROCESSING - Computer software - Stockholder Systems, Inc.
P.E.P. PERFORMANCE ENHANCEMENT PRODUCTSINC - Medical apparatus - Performance Enhancement Products, Inc.
PEP PLANNER - Computer software - Institute for Business Technology International, Inc.
PEP PLEX - Vitamins and nutritional supplements - Natural Organics, Inc.
PEP POPS - Candy ☆ - American Candy Co.
PEP RALLY - Footwear–athletic - L.A. Gear, Inc.
PEP STEPS - Women's shoes ☆ - Consolidated Shoe Co., Inc.
PEP TALK - Apparel–children's - Buster Brown Apparel Inc.
PEP TALK - Computer software - Communication Skill Builders, Inc.
PEP TALK - Syrup - Origins Natural Resources Inc.
PEP-TREAT - Lumber - Culpeper Wood Preservers
PEP-UP - Salt tablets ☆ - U.S. Safety Corp.
PEP UP - Vitamins and nutritional supplements ☆ - ICN Pharmaceuticals Inc.
PEPADAIN - Pharmaceutical preparations - Lanpar Co.
PEPCID - Pharmaceutical preparations - Merck & Co., Inc. (Merck Research Laboratories)
PEPCID AC - Antacids - Johnson & Johnson
PEPCID IV - Pharmaceutical preparations - Merck & Co., Inc. (Merck Research Laboratories)
PEPCO - Irrigation equipment - Nibco Inc.
PEPCOL - Pharmaceutical preparations - Quaker City Pharmacal Co.
PEPE LOPEZ - Beverages–alcohol - Brown-Forman Corp.
PEPE MUSI JEANS WEAR - Apparel and accessories - Casual Wear Manufacturers, Inc.
PEPE PAPAYA - Food products - Chiquita Brands, Inc.
PEPE RICO - Beverages–alcohol - Coca-Cola Co.
PEPE'S - Snack foods - Beatrice Cos. Inc.
PEPE'S - Snack foods - Rudolph Foods Co.

☆ = Now out of production

PEPFEST - Pickles - M.A. Gedney Co.

PEPINO PICANTE - Pickles ☆ - J.G. Van Holten & Son Inc.

PEPI'S - Food products - Beatrice Cos. Inc.

PEPITAS - Seeds–salted, roasted, cooked, or canned - Glico Harmony Foods Corp.

PEPITE D'OR - Cosmetics - Lancome

PEPITES - Crackers - Sunshine/Salerno Inc.

PEPITO - Food products - Pepito, Inc.

PEPITO - Popcorn - J.M. Rodriguez & Co. Inc.

PEPITOS - Tortillas - Borden, Inc.

PEPKIN - Meat products–beef - Armour Swift-Eckrich

PEPLOW - Dinnerware–glass ☆ - Royal China & Porcelain Companies Inc.

PEP'N ENERGY - Vitamins and nutritional supplements - CVC Specialties

PEPPAR - Palm Beach Beauty Products

PEPPAZZA - Food products - Colavita USA, Inc.

PEPPER - Bicycles - Murray, Inc.

PEPPER - Toys–stuffed ☆ - Gund, Inc.

PEPPER AID - Pharmaceutical preparations - S & B Consultant's Inc.

PEPPER BLOC - Chemical preparations - Dragon Martial Arts

PEPPER BUNNY - Toys–stuffed - Russ Berrie and Co., Inc.

PEPPER CLUB - Apparel and accessories - Veranda Marketing Co.

PEPPER FIESTA - Vegetables–canned - Bloch & Guggenheimer, Inc.

PEPPER FREE - Beverages–carbonated ☆ - Dr. Pepper/Seven Up, Inc.

PEPPER ISLAND BEACH - Sauces - Pepper Island Beach, Inc.

PEPPER-IT - Pepper mills - Sierra International Trading Co., Inc.

PEPPER JACK - Cheese - Taylor Cheese Corp.

PEPPER JAMMERS - Vegetables–frozen - Tampa Maid Seafoods, Inc.

PEPPER LADY, THE - T-shirts–women's - Jean Andrews

PEPPER-MATES - Chemical preparations - Anti-Victim Device, Inc.

PEPPER MILL - Meat products - Frank Brunckhorst Co., LP

PEPPER MILL CORNER - Housewares - Knobler International Ltd.

PEPPER MTN - Jams and jellies - Mountain Maid Gourmet Jelly

PEPPER PATCH - Food products - Pepper Patch Inc.

PEPPER PENGUIN - Puppets - Dakin Inc.

PEPPER-PEPPER - Black pepper - Frank J. Italiano Inc.

PEPPER POPS - Vegetables–canned - Desert Rose Corp.

PEPPER POWER - Pepper - Chef Specialties Co.

PEPPER RIDGE - Floor coverings–carpet and rugs ☆ - Downs Carpet Co. Inc.

PEPPER SHIELD - Chemical preparations - Degen

PEPPER SHOOTERS - Pepper - Anco Foods Corp.

PEPPER SOURCE - Fruits and vegetables - Pepper Source

PEPPER STICK - Food products ☆ - Goodmark Foods, Inc.

PEPPER TREE - Food products - Fairco, Inc.

PEPPERCHICKS - Chocolate candy - Taste Teasers

PEPPERCINI - Olive oil - Krinos Foods, Inc.

PEPPERCORN - Yarn - Clover Yarns Inc.

PEPPERCORNS - Apparel and accessories - Bryan Industries, Inc.

PEPPERED HERB - Food products - Antique Mall & Crown

PEPPERELL - Floor coverings–carpet and rugs - West Point-Pepperell Mill Store

PEPPERGAS - Chemical preparations - Guardian Royalty Corp.

PEPPERGUN - Chemical preparations - Coastal Security Products

PEPPERHYNDER'S - Mustard - Pepperhynder's Hot Beer Mustard

PEPPERIDGE FARM - Food products - Pepperidge Farm Inc.

PEPPERIDGE FARM CHOCOLATE HEAVEN - Cookies - PF Brands, Inc.

PEPPERIDGE FARM DELICE AU CHOCOLAT - Cookies - PF Brands, Inc.

PEPPERIDGE FARM FRUITFUL - Cookies - PF Brands, Inc.

PEPPERIDGE FARM HIGHLAND SHORTBREAD - Cookies - PF Brands, Inc.

PEPPERIDGE FARM HOME STYLE - Bread crumbs - Pepperidge Farm Inc.

PEPPERIDGE FARM SELECTION DE CHOIX - Cookies - PF Brands, Inc.

PEPPERIDGE FARM WHOLE NATURAL GRAIN - Breads - PF Brands, Inc.

PEPPERMATE - Spices and extracts - East Hampton Industries Inc.

PEPPERMENT STICKS - Stationery - Joli Greeting Card Co.

PEPPERMILL - Wallpaper - York Wall Coverings Inc.

PEPPERMILL GRIND - Spices and extracts - McCormick & Co., Inc.

PEPPERMINT - Beverages–alcohol - Hiram Walker & Sons, Inc.

PEPPERMINT - Dishes–earthenware ☆ - Louisville Stoneware Co.

PEPPERMINT & POPPIES FOOT LOTION - Skin care products - Freeman Cosmetics Corp.

PEPPERMINT EXPRESS - Stationery - Peppermint Express Inc.

PEPPERMINT HARVEST - Teas–herbal - Nature's Design Ltd.

PEPPERMINT ICE - Lipsticks - Elysee Scientific Cosmetic Co.

PEPPERMINT KISSES - Candy - Glade Taffy Town, Inc.

PEPPERMINT PEDICURE - Massage products - Pure Pro Massage Oils, Inc.

PEPPERMINT PEN & PENCIL - Pens - Peppermint Pen & Pencil, Inc.

PEPPERMINT PERFECT - Candy - Billy Burden

PEPPERMINT PLACE - Candy - Kencraft, Inc.

PEPPERMINT PONIES - Candy - Harbor Sweets Inc.

PEPPERMINT PONY - Apparel–children's - Little Filly Corp.

PEPPERMINT POSY - Toys ☆ - Those Characters from Cleveland, Inc.

PEPPERMINT REEF - Food products - Dearborn

PEPPERMINT ROC - Dishes–china - Taylor, Smith & Taylor Co.

PEPPERMINT ROSE - Cosmetics - Mem Co., Inc.

PEPPERMINT ROSE - Novelty items - Those Characters from Cleveland, Inc.

PEPPERMINT SCRUB - Hair care products - Brocato International

PEPPERMINT SHOPPE - Candy ☆ - American Candy Co.

PEPPERMINT STARLITES - Candy ☆ - Powers Pharmaceutical Corp.

PEPPERMINT STICK - Candy - Pecan Deluxe Candy Co.

PEPPERMINT STICK - Teas ☆ - R.C. Bigelow, Inc.

PEPPERMINT STIX - Dolls - CPG Products Corp.

PEPPERMINT SWIRL - Bicycles - Kent International Inc.

PEPPERMINT SWIRL - Christmas tree ornaments - Cracker Box Inc.

PEPPERMINT TWIST - Apparel and accessories - Compass Marketing

PEPPERMINTS - Balls–tennis - Wilson Sporting Goods Co.

PEPPERMINTS - Footwear - Kobacker Co.

PEPPERMINTS - Underwear and nightwear - Maidenform Inc.

PEPPERONI - Floor coverings–carpet and rugs ☆ - Regal Rugs Inc.

PEPPERONIBUSTER - Pizza - Mazzio's Corp.

PEPPERONI!PEPPERONI! - Food products - Little Caesar Enterprises, Inc.

PEPPERS - Shoes - Mother Goose Co.

PEPPER'S - Skin care products - Body Solutions, Inc.

PEPPERS - Vegetables–canned - Desert Rose Corp.

PEPPERS CRUSHED CHILIPEPPERS - Spices and extracts - Plinio J. Garcia, Jr.

PEPPERS ITALIA - Sausages ☆ - Johnsonville Foods Co.

PEPPER'S PRIDE - Dog food - Pepper's Pride Pet Food Co.

PEPPERTON'S CHOICE - Dog food - Pepperton's Choice Biscuit Co.

PEPPERTREE - Apparel–women's - Oxford Industries, Inc.

PEPPERTREE FARM - Candles ☆ - E.M.I. Inc.

PEPPERVINE - Food products ☆ - Gourmet Foods Inc.

PEPPERWOOD - Candles ☆ - E.M.I. Inc.

PEPPERWOOD - Computer software - Adobe Systems Inc.

PEPPERWOOD GROVE - Wines - Cecchetti Sebastiani Cellar, Inc.

PEPPI - Candy ☆ - R.M. Palmer Co.

PEPPI-CREAMS - Candy - Wilkinson-Spitz Ltd.

PEPPI'S - Food products - Gilt Edge Farms Inc.

PEPPOURI - Seasonings - Dirigo Corp.

PEPPY - Dog food - Simmons Industries Inc.

PEPPY - Nuts–salted, roasted, cooked, or canned - Miss Kings Kitchen Inc.

PEPPY MINT OOGIES - Confections ☆ - Boomer's Oogies

PEPPY PETS - Toys–stuffed - Fun World Inc.

PEPPY SALT - Pepper - Richardson-T Foods Corp.

PEPR - Electrical equipment - Shipley Co. Inc.

PEP'R'MINT - Hair care products - Nexxus Products Co.

PEPSI - Beverages ☆ - Pepsico, Inc.

PEPSI - Handbags ☆ - Holiday Fair, Inc.

PEPSI - Key rings ☆ - Gift Creations, Inc.

PEPSI - Pharmaceutical preparations - Vita Elixir Co. Inc.

PEPSI - Playing cards - United States Playing Card Co.

PEPSI - Puzzles ☆ - Ben Cooper Inc.

PEPSI A.M. - Beverages–carbonated - Pepsi-Cola Co.

PEPSI BALL - Athletic associations - Pepsico, Inc.

PEPSI-COLA - Beverages–carbonated - Pepsi-Cola Co.

PEPSI FREE - Beverages–carbonated - Pepsi-Cola Co.

PEPSI LIGHT - Beverages–carbonated - Pepsi-Cola Co.

PEPSI MAX - Beverages–carbonated - Pepsi-Cola Co.

PEPSI XL - Beverages–carbonated - Pepsi-Cola Co.

PEPSO - Water treating compounds - Jungle Laboratories Corp.

PEPSOCOLL - Pharmaceutical preparations - Western Research Laboratories

PEPSODENT - Toothpaste - Chesebrough-Pond's USA Co.

PEPSODENT - Toothpaste - Lever Brothers Co. Inc.

PEPTAVLON - Pharmaceutical preparations - Wyeth-Ayerst Laboratories

PEPTENZYME - Pharmaceutical preparations ☆ - Reed & Carnrick

PEPTICAL - Vitamins and nutritional supplements ☆ - Chronimed Inc.

PEPTO-ACID - Pharmaceutical - Jamol Laboratories Inc.

PEPTO-BISMOL - Health care products - Procter & Gamble Co.

PEPTO DIARRHEA CONTROL - Pharmaceutical preparations - Procter & Gamble Co.

PEPTO HEARTBURN CONTROL - Pharmaceutical preparations - Procter & Gamble Co.

PEPTO-LACTASE - Pharmaceutical preparations - Vartex Pharmaceuticals Inc.

PEPTO MANGAN - Pharmaceutical preparations ☆ - Oakhurst Co.

☆ = Now out of production

PEQ-1 - Electronic equipment ☆ - Polyfusion Electronics Inc.

PEQUA - Lubricants - Pequa Industries Inc.

PEQUEA - Farm machinery - Pequea Machine Inc.

PEQUOT - Bedding–linen ☆ - Springs Industries, Inc.

PEQUOT FARMS - Food products ☆ - Tarpy's

PEQUOT PHARMACEUTICAL NETWORK - Computer software -
Mashantucket Pequot Tribe

PER ANNUM ATLANTA DIARY, THE - Publisher's imprints - Per Annum, Inc.

PER ANNUM CHICAGO DIARY, THE - Publisher's imprints - Per Annum, Inc.

PER ANNUM GREATER BOSTON DIARY, THE - Publisher's imprints - Per
Annum, Inc.

PER ANNUM LOS ANGELS DIARY, THE - Publisher's imprints - Per Annum,
Inc.

PER ANNUM MANHATTAN DAILY PLAN-IT, THE - Diaries - Per Annum, Inc.

PER ANNUM MANHTTAN DIARY, THE - Publisher's imprints - Per Annum,
Inc.

PER ANNUM METROPOLITAN DIARY, THE - Publisher's imprints - Per
Annum, Inc.

PER-FIT - Hosiery - Kayser-Roth Corp.

PER-FIT - Plugs–ear - Bilsom International Inc.

PER-FIT - Thread - Signal Thread Co. Inc.

PER-FLEX - Garden equipment - Garden Pals, Inc.

PER-I-FORMER FAMILY - Coagulation agents - Peridot Chemicals, Inc.

PER LUI PER LEI - Apparel and accessories - Per Lui Per Lei Ltd.

PER LUNAM - Enamels - Kenneth G. Krukis

PER-MA-LITE - Paints - Budeke's Paint

PER-Q-CATH - Medical apparatus - Utah Medical Products, Inc.

PER-SOLVE - Cleaning preparations - Federal Mining & Manufacturing Co.

PERA-LIVER - Pharmaceutical preparations ☆ - Harvey Laboratories Inc.

PERADORO - Vegetables–canned - Lico Brands, Inc.

PERALTA - Wines ☆ - Safeway Stores Inc.

PERAMOLE - Pharmaceutical preparations - C.S. Ruckstuhl Co. Inc.

PERANTUCCI - Musical instruments - Custom Music Co.

PERATIVE - Health care products - Abbott Laboratories

PERAZINE - Pharmaceutical preparations - Wesley Pharmacal Co. Inc.

PERBUNAN - Rubber–extruded - Exxon Corp.

PERC - Food products - Tone Brothers, Inc.

PERC - Mats, runners - Ace Hose and Rubber Co.

PERCEIVA - Electric lighting equipment - National Service Industries, Inc.

PERCENT-A-CLOR - Scientific apparatus - Dexsil Corp.

PERCENT-O2-LOCK - Medical apparatus - Salter Labs

PERCENTAGE PANIC - Computer software - Unicorn Software

PERCEPTA - Lighting fixtures - Holophane Corp.

PERCEPTION - Apparel–women's ☆ - Bobbie Brooks Inc.

PERCEPTION - Floor coverings–carpet and rugs ☆ - Regal Rugs Inc.

PERCEPTION - Furniture - Tropitone Furniture Co. Inc.

PERCEPTION - Furniture - Weiman Co.

PERCEPTION II - Floor coverings–carpet and rugs - Walter Carpet Mills

PERCEPTION II - Weather tracking equipment - Davis Instruments Corp.

PERCEPTION PUZZLES - Puzzles - Lauri Inc.

PERCEPTION STRAP - Furniture - Tropitone Furniture Co. Inc.

PERCEPTIONS - Floor coverings–carpet and rugs - Richmond Carpet Mills

PERCEPTIONS - Frames–picture - Intercraft Industries

PERCEPTIONS - Hair care products - Demert & Dougherty, Inc.

PERCEPTIONS - Partitions–wood - Dowcraft Corp.

PERCEPTIONS - Publisher's imprints - Durham, Inc.

PERCEPTIONS - Tables - Impact Furniture

PERCEPTIONS - Wallpaper ☆ - Bolta Wallcoverings

PERCEPTOL - Chemical preparations - ILFORD Photo Corp.

PERCEPTOR - Electronic equipment - Thomson Consumer Electronics, Inc.

PERCH CREEK - Oysters–fresh - B.G. Smith and Sons Oyster Co. Inc.

PERCH MATE - Pet products - United Pacific Mills

PERCH PLEASERS - Pet products - Pink Parrot

PERCHERON - Watches - Bulova Corp.

PERCIVAL PUPPY - Toys–stuffed - Russ Berrie and Co., Inc.

PERCLOOP - Surgical devices - Laparomed Corp.

PERCOBARB - Analgesics ☆ - Du Pont Pharmaceuticals

PERCOCET-5 - Analgesics - Du Pont Pharmaceuticals

PERCODAN - Analgesics - Du Pont Pharmaceuticals

PERCOMP - Computer peripheral equipment - Percomp Microsystems, Inc.

PERCON - Wire - Fisk Alloy Wire, Inc.

PERCUSSION - Computer software - Percussion Software, Inc.

PERCUSSION - Dinnerware–glass ☆ - Lenox, Inc.

PERCUSSION ARTS - Drums–musical instruments - Remo, Inc.

PERCUSSION GROUP - Electronic equipment - Beyerdynamic Inc.

PERCUSSION PLUS - Musical instruments - Midco International

PERCY - Pharmaceutical preparations - Merrick Medicine Co. Inc.

PERCY P. BAKER - Brushes–paint ☆ - Charvoz

PERCY PENGUIN - Health care products - Apothecary Products, Inc.

PERDIDO - Rings–jewelry - Artcarved Inc.

PERDIEM - Laxatives - Rhone-Poulenc Rorer Pharmaceuticals Inc.

PERDUE - Boats - Perdue-Dean Inc.

PERDUE - Meat products–poultry - Perdue Farms Inc.

PERDUE - Meat products–poultry - Perdue Holdings, Inc.

PERDUE FROZEN - Meat products–poultry - Perdue Holdings, Inc.

PERE - Cheese - Besnier USA, Inc.

PERE ALESANDRO - Wines - Vintwood International Ltd.

PERE HENNEPIN - Wines - Thompson Winery

PERE JOSEPH - Cheese - Swissrose International Inc.

PERE MAGLIORE - Wines - Paterno Imports, Ltd.

PERE MAGLIORE CALVADOS - Beverages–alcohol - Shaw-Ross
International Importers

PERE MARQUETTE - Wines - Thompson Winery

PERE PATRIARCH - Wines - Peartree Imports Inc.

PEREGRINE - Beverages–malt - Mendocino Brewing Co., Inc.

PEREGRINE - Bicycles - Teel Inc.

PEREGRINE - Fishing rods - Sports Specialists of Milwaukee, Inc.

PEREGRINE - Machine parts - Peregrine Semiconductor Corp.

PEREGRINE PALE ALE - Beverages–malt - Mendocino Brewing Co., Inc.

PEREGRINE SYSTEMS - Computer software - Peregrine Systems, Inc.

PEREGRINE WHITE - Furniture - Derby & Leigh, Inc.

PEREL AND PEREL - Food products - Cuisine Perel Corp.

PERELLI-MINETTI - Wines - Pompei Winery Inc.

PERENNIAL - Bedding–linen - Dan River Inc.

PERENNIAL ADVANTAGE - Flowers, plants, and seeds - Spring Hill Nurseries
Co.

PERENNIAL FAVORITES - Flowers, plants, and seeds - Grimes Seed Co.

PERENNIAL GARDEN - Wallpaper - Sandpiper Studios

PERENNIAL GARDENS - Wallpaper - Benchmark Preferred Wallcoverings

PERENNIAL LIBRARY - Publisher's imprints - Harper & Row Publishers Inc.

PERENNIAL LINE - Flower pots–plastic - Bonar Plastics Inc.

PERENNIALS - Air fresheners - Block Drug Co., Inc.

PERENNIALS II - Wallpaper ☆ - Glidden Co.

PEREOS - Computer hardware - Datasonix Corp.

PERESTAN - Pharmaceutical - IDE-Interstate Inc.

PERESTROIKA - Meat products - Portsmouth Trading Co., Ltd.

PEREX - Pharmaceutical preparations - C.S. Ruckstuhl Co. Inc.

PERF - Detergents - Rykoff-Sexton, Inc.

PERF-A-TAPE - Tape joint reinforcement - United States Gypsum Co.

PERF-FORM - Motor vehicle parts and accessories - Perf-form Products Inc.

PERF-FORMS - Nail care products - E.O.H. Industries, Inc.

PERF-O-RITE - Paper ☆ - Rite-Made Paper Converters Inc.

PERF-OPE - Envelopes - Tension Envelope Corp.

PERF TILE - Handbags - Lumured Corp.

PERF-WRAP - Paper–gift wrap ☆ - American Greetings Corp.

PERF-X - Fabrics - Cushman and Marden, Inc.

PERFAMATCH - Thread - Perfect Thread Co. Inc.

PERFBOX - Chassis–motor vehicles - Tandy Corp.

PERFDESK - Computer software - International Business Machines Corp.

PERFEC PAK - Food products - Butler Trading Co. Inc.

PERFECLEAR - Bathroom accessories - Kinkead/Tub/Shower Doors

PERFECLITE - Electric lighting equipment - Fourth Family L.P.

PERFECOPY - Paper - Butler Paper Co.

PERFECR SCENTS - Perfumes - Richard L. Stephens

PERFECT - Artists' materials ☆ - M. Grumbacher Inc.

PERFECT - Brackets - Peerless Industries, Inc.

PERFECT - Cushions–foam - Perfect Rubber Seat Cushion Co.

PERFECT - Drill bits - Hawera Inc.

PERFECT - Fasteners–hook and eye - Perfect Fastener Inc.

PERFECT - Fishing nets ☆ - G-96 Products Co. Inc.

PERFECT - Fishing reels - American Import Co.

PERFECT - Frames–picture ☆ - Zorba Frame & Moulding

PERFECT - Hair care products - Matrix Essentials, Inc.

PERFECT - Hair care products - Orjene Natural Cosmetics

PERFECT - Musical instrument accessories - Tamarkin Co.

PERFECT - Musical instrument accessories ☆ - Micro Musical Products Corp.

PERFECT - Office furniture–metal ☆ - Joyce International Inc.

PERFECT - Paints - A. Flohr Co. Inc.

PERFECT - Paints ☆ - Rich Art Color Co., Inc.

PERFECT - Photograph albums - Webway, Inc.

PERFECT - Photographic equipment - Retouch Methods Co. Inc.

PERFECT - Recording label - Timeless Entertainment Corp.

PERFECT - Thread - Perfect Thread Co. Inc.
PERFECT - Tools - O.P. Link Handle Co. Inc.
PERFECT - Vitamins and nutritional supplements - Nature's Best Inc.
PERFECT - Wallpaper ☆ - Walldesigns
PERFECT 4 - Hosiery–men's ☆ - Keepers International
PERFECT 10 - Games - Smethport Specialty Co.
PERFECT 10 - Office supplies - C-Line Products, Inc.
PERFECT 10 - Vitamins and nutritional supplements - Thoro'bred Racing Plate Co., Inc.
PERFECT 10, THE - Golf balls - WPI Acquisition Corp.
PERFECT-A-FLO - Pet products - Perfecto Manufacturing Inc.
PERFECT-A-LAMP - Lighting fixtures - Perfecto Manufacturing Inc.
PERFECT-A-LITE - Lighting fixtures - Perfecto Manufacturing Inc.
PERFECT-A-SAFE - Pet products ☆ - Perfecto Manufacturing Inc.
PERFECT-A-SCENE - Pet products - Perfecto Manufacturing Inc.
PERFECT-A-STRIP - Lighting fixtures - Perfecto Manufacturing Inc.
PERFECT ACCENTS - Jewelry - Hills Department Store Co.
PERFECT ACTION - Skin care products - Matrix Essentials, Inc.
PERFECT ADDITION - Soups–mixes - Perfect Addition Inc.
PERFECT ANGELS - Apparel and accessories - 88 Rising Cherubs, Inc.
PERFECT ANGLE - Tools - Normark Corp.
PERFECT ANTIOXIDANT - Vitamin supplement - Rexall Sundown, Inc.
PERFECT BALANCE - Coffee - Nestle Beverage Co.
PERFECT BALANCE - Skin care products - Marilyn Miglin L.P.
PERFECT BANANA, THE - Novelty items - Perfect Products
PERFECT BEAD - Caulking compounds - Myro, Inc.
PERFECT BIND - Laminator - Bind-It Corp.
PERFECT BLEND - Cigarettes - Shurfine International, Inc.
PERFECT BLEND - Cosmetics - Noxell Corp.
PERFECT BLEND - Pasta - Noodles by Leonardo Inc.
PERFECT BODY - Apparel–athletic - Montgomery Ward & Co. Inc.
PERFECT BOND - Paper - Potomac Corp.
PERFECT BOW, THE - Ribbons - Berwick Industries, Inc.
PERFECT BREATH - Mouthwashes - Zambezi Enterprises Inc.
PERFECT BROW - Cosmetics - Revlon Consumer Products Corp.
PERFECT BROW - Skin care products ☆ - Tweezerman Corp.
PERFECT CAL - Health care products - Futurebiotics
PERFECT CALLIGRAPHY - Computer software - Social Software Inc.
PERFECT CARE - Hair care products ☆ - Avon Products, Inc.
PERFECT CHOICE - Bakery products - National Center of Nutrition, Inc.
PERFECT CHOICE - Dinnerware–plastic - Nyman Manufacturing Co.
PERFECT CHOICE - Floor coverings–carpet and rugs - Alexander Smith Carpets
PERFECT CHOICE - Floor coverings–carpet and rugs ☆ - Mohawk Carpet Corp.
PERFECT CHOICE - Indoor-outdoor carpet - Instant Turf Industries Inc.
PERFECT CHOICE - Snack foods - Amway Corp.
PERFECT CHOICE - Teas - Reeves Enterprises
PERFECT CHOICE - Toys - Liberty Diversified Industries Inc.
PERFECT CHOICE - Vitamins and nutritional supplements - Garcoa Labs/ Vitamin Classics
PERFECT CHOICE - Wallpaper - Bayview Wallcoverings
PERFECT CHOICE, THE - Publisher's imprints - Gray McPherson and Associates
PERFECT CIRCLE - Machine parts - Dana Corp. (Perfect Circle Products Div.)
PERFECT COAT - Pet products - 8 in 1 Pet Products Inc.
PERFECT COAT - Pet products - St. Aubrey
PERFECT COLOR - Putties ☆ - Bix Manufacturing Co. Inc.
PERFECT COLOR FOR EYES - Cosmetics - Chesebrough-Pond's USA Co.
PERFECT COLOR IN A PEN - Cosmetics - Chesebrough-Pond's USA Co.
PERFECT COLORS - Cosmetics ☆ - London International U.S. Holdings
PERFECT COMB-OUT - Hair care products - Zotos International Inc.
PERFECT COMFORT - Garters - Marcus & Wiesen Inc.
PERFECT COMPANION, THE - Beds–metal - Thermal Technology Inc.
PERFECT CONTROL - Cosmetics - Almay Inc.
PERFECT CONTROL - Hair care products - Wella Corp. (Consumer Products Div.)
PERFECT COORDINATE - Floor coverings–carpet and rugs - Mohawk Industries Inc.
PERFECT CORNER - Hardware ☆ - Marley Mouldings Inc.
PERFECT COVER - Tools–garden - Gilmour Manufacturing Co.
PERFECT CUT - Cigars - Concept Iv. Inc.
PERFECT CUT - Garden equipment - Uniontools, Inc.
PERFECT DEFINITION - Cosmetics - Revlon Consumer Products Corp.
PERFECT DNA - Chemical preparations - Novagen, Inc.
PERFECT DOSE - Medical apparatus ☆ - Apex Medical Corp.

PERFECT DREAMS - Pillows - Bicor Processing Corp.
PERFECT EAR - Hearing aids - Perfect Ear, Inc.
PERFECT END, THE - Meat products–pork ☆ - Harper's Country Hams
PERFECT EQUATION - Vitamins and nutritional supplements - Global Nutrition, Inc.
PERFECT FEET - Skin care products - Gena Laboratories Inc.
PERFECT FIGURE - Apparel–women's ☆ - Bali Co. Inc.
PERFECT FINISH - Frosting - J.W. Allen & Co.
PERFECT FINISH, THE - Coatings - McCloskey Corp.
PERFECT FIT - Floor coverings - Mannington Resilient Floors
PERFECT FIT - Hardware - Eagle Glass Products
PERFECT-FIT - Hardware - Vance Industries Inc.
PERFECT FIT - Hosiery - GAKM Resources Corp.
PERFECT FIT - Insulating materials - Guardian Fiberglass
PERFECT-FIT - Lamp bulbs - FFSC, Inc.
PERFECT FIT - Pillows - Perfect Fit Industries, Inc.
PERFECT FIT - Water heaters–household - Rheem Manufacturing Co.
PERFECT FOR PERMS - Hair care products - Razac Products, Inc.
PERFECT FOR TRAVEL - Games ☆ - Western Publishing Co., Inc.
PERFECT FORMULA, THE - Nail care products - Nu-Tress Laboratories Inc.
PERFECT FROTH - Coffee makers–electric - Robert Krups North America
PERFECT FUN - Bicycles - Huffy Corp.
PERFECT GAME, THE - Giftware - Papel Freelance, Inc.
PERFECT GARDENER - Hoses - Anchor Swan
PERFECT GEM - Paper clips - Noesting Inc.
PERFECT GLAZES - Wallpaper - Christopher Hyland
PERFECT GRIP ASSIST - Sporting goods - Stephen B. Rhodes
PERFECT HAIR - Hair care products - Helene Curtis Industries Inc.
PERFECT HARMONY - Apparel and accessories - Sandcastle Productions
PERFECT HARVEST - Breads - Koepplingers Bakery Inc.
PERFECT HARVEST - Vitamins and nutritional supplements - Richard Simmons
PERFECT HEIGHT - Infant product - Kolcraft Enterprises, Inc.
PERFECT HOLD - Hair care products - Paula Payne Products Co. Inc.
PERFECT HOOPER, THE - Craft supplies - Letter Perfect Inc.
PERFECT HOST - Beverages - Pro-Form Laboratories
PERFECT HOST - Beverages–alcohol - Fairhill Foods
PERFECT HOST - Food products ☆ - Oregon Freeze Dry Inc.
PERFECT IMAGE - Automotive parts and accessories - International AutoCare Services Inc.
PERFECT IMAGE - Computer storage devices - Rimage Corp.
PERFECT IMAGE - Flowers, plants, and seeds - Laduke, Bernard Jr.
PERFECT IMAGE - Infant product - Kids Basics
PERFECT IMAGE - Sunblocks - Forever Tan Inc.
PERFECT INK - Inks - Identicator Corp.
PERFECT IRON - Vitamins and nutritional supplements - Sundown Vitamins, Inc.
PERFECT-IT - Cleaning preparations - Minnesota Mining & Manufacturing Co.
PERFECT KISS - Hair care products - Maryna Cosmetics, Inc.
PERFECT KNIT - Yarn ☆ - Caron International Inc.
PERFECT LANDSCAPE - Fertilizers - Griffen Sales Corp.
PERFECT LASHES - Mascara ☆ - Coty Inc.
PERFECT LENGTH - Underwear and nightwear - Warnaco Inc.
PERFECT LENS - Lenses–optical - Benson Optical Co., Inc.
PERFECT LETTERING - Decals and transfers - Decorcal Inc.
PERFECT LIFE - Apparel and accessories - Thomas M. Anderson
PERFECT-LINE - Electrical product - American Electric
PERFECT LINK - Computer software ☆ - Penny & Giles Data Systems
PERFECT LIPSTICK - Lipsticks - Estee Lauder Inc.
PERFECT MAN, THE - Bakery products - Capital Concepts, Inc.
PERFECT MARGARITA MIX, THE - Beverages–alcohol - Nabisco Foods Group
PERFECT MATCH - Artists' materials ☆ - Loctite Corp.
PERFECT MATCH - Brushes–paint - Wooster Brush Co.
PERFECT MATCH - Cosmetics - Avon Products, Inc.
PERFECT MATCH - Games - Tonka Corp.
PERFECT MATCH - Golfing equipment - Ryobi-Toski Corp.
PERFECT MATCH - Pharmaceutical preparations - Jess Clarke & Sons Inc.
PERFECT MATCH - Pharmaceutical preparations - Winning Solutions Inc./ Miracle of Aloe
PERFECT MATCH - Putties - Master Products Inc.
PERFECT MATCH - Yarn ☆ - Caron International Inc.
PERFECT MATH - Computer software - Advanced Systems, Inc.
PERFECT MEASURE - Apparel and accessories - Warnaco Inc.
PERFECT MEASURE - Machinery - Micro Measure, Inc.
PERFECT MEASURING TAPE - Tape measures - Perfect Measuring Tape Co.

☆ = Now out of production

PERFECT MELODY - Floor coverings–carpet and rugs ☆ - Mohawk Carpet Corp.

PERFECT MENU - Cat food ☆ - Golden Cat Corp.

PERFECT MIX - Oils–lubricating - Tanaka Ltd.

PERFECT NAIL - Nail care products - Gena Laboratories Inc.

PERFECT NIGHT - Mattresses - Serta, Inc.

PERFECT ON-LINE - Computer software - Perfect Promotional Products, Inc.

PERFECT ONE - Sunblocks - Forever Tan Inc.

PERFECT OPAQUE, THE - Hosiery - Ridgeview Inc.

PERFECT PACKAGES - Furniture - Jackson Manufacturing Co.

PERFECT PAINTER - Paint rollers - Great American Marketing, Inc.

PERFECT PAINTER - Paints - MCI Quality Coatings

PERFECT PAIR, THE - Stationery ☆ - Sheaffer Inc.

PERFECT PANTS - Apparel–men's - H.R. Kaminsky & Sons Inc.

PERFECT PARTNER, THE - Cookies - De Beukelaer Corp.

PERFECT PARTNERS - Curtains - Arley Corp.

PERFECT PARTS - Automotive parts and accessories - Kem Manufacturing Co. Inc.

PERFECT PASSION - Perfumes - Carter-Wallace, Inc.

PERFECT PATCH - Building materials - Daubert Coated Products, Inc.

PERFECT PATH - Cleaning preparations - Recoton Corp.

PERFECT PATIENT CARE - Health care products - Diamond Medical Equipment Corp.

PERFECT PEN - Cosmetics - Maybelline Co.

PERFECT PERFORMANCE - Hair care products - Posner Laboratories Inc.

PERFECT PET - Pet products - Fast Industries, Inc.

PERFECT PH - Chemical preparations - Robarb Inc.

PERFECT PH - Vitamins and nutritional supplements - Amrion, Inc.

PERFECT PIANO RECITAL - Dolls - Mattel, Inc.

PERFECT PICK-UP, THE - Sports rackets and accessories - David Eddy

PERFECT PICKLE, THE - Pickles - Perfect Pickle, Inc.

PERFECT PINCH - Hair care products ☆ - Soft Sheen Products Co.

PERFECT PITCH - Recording label - Score Productions, Inc.

PERFECT PITCH - Window shades - Vertical Blind Factory

PERFECT PITCHER - Dishes–plastic ☆ - Thermos Co.

PERFECT PLAY - Games - C.G. Wood Co.

PERFECT PLAYROOM - Dolls - Mattel, Inc.

PERFECT PLEASURE - Floor coverings–carpet and rugs - Evans-Black Carpet Mills

PERFECT PLEAT - Window coverings - Conso Products Co.

PERFECT PLUMS - Lipstick and nail polish ☆ - Cosrich Inc.

PERFECT PLUS - Hosiery - Perfect Plus, Inc.

PERFECT-POINT - Artists' materials ☆ - Binney & Smith Inc.

PERFECT POINT - Cosmetics - Noxell Corp.

PERFECT POLLY - Thread - Perfect Thread Co. Inc.

PERFECT POPCORN IS OUR PASSION - Popcorn - General Mills, Inc.

PERFECT PORTIONS OF PURE - Chocolate candy - Mono-Gram Chocolates

PERFECT POSSIBILITIES - Apparel and accessories - Byrne Enterprises, Inc.

PERFECT POTATO PANCAKE MIX - Pancakes–mixes - Homestead Mills

PERFECT POTTY - Toilet seats - Evenflo Co.

PERFECT PRESENTS - Clocks - Burwood Products Co.

PERFECT PRO - Veterinary pharmaceutical preparations - Griffin Industries Inc.

PERFECT PROCESS - Hair care products - Paula Payne Products Co. Inc.

PERFECT PROPORTIONS - Apparel–women's - Perry Manufacturing Co.

PERFECT PROTECTION - Cosmetics - Yves St. Laurent Parfum Corp.

PERFECT PROTECTION - Skin care products - Elysee Scientific Cosmetic Co.

PERFECT PROTEIN - Chemical preparations - Novagen, Inc.

PERFECT PROTEIN - Vitamins and nutritional supplements - Metagenics, Inc.

PERFECT PUP - Dog food - AGP Petfoods

PERFECT PUTDOWN, THE - Floor coverings - Tec Inc.

PERFECT RATIO - Candy bars - PR Nutrition, Inc.

PERFECT RECIPE - Rice - San Francisco Spice Co. Inc.

PERFECT RESPONSE - Cosmetics - Johnson Products Co., Inc.

PERFECT RESULTS - Hair care products - Michael Kulha

PERFECT RESULTS - Paints - North Jersey Paint Co. Inc.

PERFECT RESUME, THE - Computer software - Knowledge Adventure

PERFECT RNA - Chemical preparations - Novagen, Inc.

PERFECT RX - Vitamins and nutritional supplements - Nature's Best Inc.

PERFECT SCENTS - Bags–trash - North American Plastics Corp.

PERFECT SCENTS - Perfumes - Preview Products

PERFECT SCORE, THE - Computer software - Mindscape Software Inc.

PERFECT SEAL - Caulking compounds - Super-Tek Products Inc.

PERFECT SENSE - Meat products ☆ - Agripac, Inc.

PERFECT SETTING - Floor coverings–carpet and rugs - Barrett Carpet Mills Inc.

PERFECT SHAPE - Skin care products - Monteiro's Imports Distributor

PERFECT SHAPE - Vitamins and nutritional supplements - Wakunaga of America Co., Ltd.

PERFECT SHAVE - Skin care products - Perfect Shave Inc.

PERFECT SHEEN - Hair care products - Gold Medal Hair Products Inc.

PERFECT SHINE - Nail care products ☆ - Gena Laboratories Inc.

PERFECT SHOT, THE - Electronic equipment - International Imaging Electronics, Inc.

PERFECT SLEEPER - Mattresses - Serta, Inc.

PERFECT SMILE, THE - Dental care products - Perfect Smile, Inc.

PERFECT SOLUTION - Cleaning preparations–household - Indusco, Ltd.

PERFECT SOLUTIONS - Skin care products - Jason Natural Products, Inc.

PERFECT SPA, THE - Spas–home - Southwest Spa Designs, Inc.

PERFECT SPEC - Floor coverings–carpet and rugs - Commercial Horizons

PERFECT SPEC - Floor coverings–carpet and rugs - Mohawk Industries Inc.

PERFECT SPRAY - Adhesives and sealants - National Gypsum Co.

PERFECT START - Vitamins and nutritional supplements - Nikken Inc.

PERFECT STORAGE - Containers ☆ - Huffy Plastics

PERFECT STRANDS - Hair coloring preparations - Precision Cut, Inc.

PERFECT SUPPORT - Brassieres (Bras) - Warnaco Inc.

PERFECT SUPPORT - Pillows - Hollander Home Fashions Inc.

PERFECT SWING - Sporting goods - Baseball International, Inc.

PERFECT SWING TRAINER - Golfing equipment - Perfect Swing Trainer, Inc.

PERFECT TEMP - Hair care products - Helene Curtis Industries Inc.

PERFECT TIMBRE - Musical instrument accessories - Seymour Duncan Pickups

PERFECT TIME - Cosmetics - Revlon Consumer Products Corp.

PERFECT TIMING - Apparel and accessories - L'koral, Inc.

PERFECT TIMING - Floor coverings–carpet and rugs - Burlington House Carpets

PERFECT TIMING - Floor coverings–carpet and rugs - Lees Carpets

PERFECT TOUCH - Finishing agents - Blue Ridge Talc Co. Inc.

PERFECT TOUCH - Gloves - Eve Industries Inc.

PERFECT TOUCH - Hair care products - Chase Products Co.

PERFECT TOUCH - Hair care products - Roux Laboratories, Inc.

PERFECT TOUCH - Mirrors ☆ - Sunbeam-Oster Household Products

PERFECT TOUCH - Paint rollers - United Coatings, Inc.

PERFECT TOUCH - Paints - United Coatings Inc.

PERFECT TOUCH - Staplers ☆ - Park Sherman

PERFECT TRANSITION - Hair care products - Thompson and Formby

PERFECT UNION - Housewares - Blue Magic Products Inc.

PERFECT USED CAR PACKAGE - Motor vehicles–automobiles - Enterprise Rent-A-Car Co.

PERFECT VISION - Envelopes ☆ - Kimberly-Clark Corp. (Karolton Envelope Div.)

PERFECT VISION - Sunglasses - Cliff Weil, Inc.

PERFECT WEAR - Cosmetics - Avon Products, Inc.

PERFECT WEDDING - Games - Cadaco Div.

PERFECT WIGS - Shirts - Ben Chez Inc.

PERFECT WORLD RECORDS - Recording label - Phil Giordano Jazz Orchestra, Inc.

PERFECT WRAP - Mattress pads - Perfect Fit Industries, Inc.

PERFECT WRITER - Computer software ☆ - Penny & Giles Data Systems

PERFECT-WRITING - Paper–writing - Krapf Business Systems, Inc.

PERFECTA - Floor coverings–carpet and rugs - Evans-Black Carpet Mills

PERFECTA - Floor coverings–carpet and rugs ☆ - Galaxy Carpet Mills Inc.

PERFECTA - Projection screens - Claridge Products and Equipment Inc.

PERFECTA - Prosthetic apparatus - Orthomet, Inc.

PERFECTA - Seafood - Midland Services, Inc.

PERFECTA - Watches - Hampden Corp.

PERFECTA-CUP - Kitchenware–plastic - Robbins Industries, Inc.

PERFECTA GOLD - Brushes–paint - Dunn Edwards Corp.

PERFECTAIRE - Ventilation equipment - Research Products Corp.

PERFECTED - Rice ☆ - Riceland Foods, Inc.

PERFECTEMP - Thermostats - Research Products Corp.

PERFECTFIT - Computer software - Wordperfect Corp.

PERFECTFORM - Apparel–women's - Lady Ester Lingerie Corp.

PERFECTIE - Ties - World Tie Corp.

PERFECTING - Cosmetics - Chanel Inc.

PERFECTION - See PM

PERFECTION - Beverages–carbonated - Great Western Juice Co.

PERFECTION - Candy ☆ - Glade Taffy Town, Inc.

PERFECTION - Cleaning preparations - Diversey Corp.

PERFECTION - Clocks ☆ - General Time Corp. (Westclox/Seth Thomas Div.)

PERFECTION - Containers–glass - Pennsylvania Glass Products Co.

PERFECTION - Dyes and pigments - W. Cushing & Co.

PERFECTION - Easels ☆ - Anco Wood Specialties Inc.
PERFECTION - Enamels - Masury Paint Co.
PERFECTION - Fabrics–felt - National Nonwovens
PERFECTION - Floor coverings - Arkansas Oak Flooring Co.
PERFECTION - Floor coverings–carpet and rugs - Downs Carpet Co. Inc.
PERFECTION - Floor coverings–carpet and rugs ☆ - Regal Rugs Inc.
PERFECTION - Food products - H.C. Brill Co., Inc.
PERFECTION - Food products - Seneca Foods Corp.
PERFECTION - Food products - United Pacific Packers
PERFECTION - Footwear–children's - Jumping-Jacks Shoes Inc.
PERFECTION - Games - Lakeside Games
PERFECTION - Games - Milton Bradley Co.
PERFECTION - Garden equipment - H.D. Hudson Manufacturing Co.
PERFECTION - Handles–wood - Turner, Day and Woolworth Handle Corp.
PERFECTION - Health care products ☆ - CC Pollen Co.
PERFECTION - Inks - Graphic Chemical & Ink Co.
PERFECTION - Jams and jellies ☆ - Kidd & Co.
PERFECTION - Lubricants ☆ - Ashland Oil, Inc.
PERFECTION - Macaroni - Perfection Macaroni Co.
PERFECTION - Musical instruments - C. Bruno & Son Inc.
PERFECTION - Paints - Perfection Letz Paint Co.
PERFECTION - Paper–toweling - Fort Howard Corp.
PERFECTION - Pasta - American Beauty Macaroni
PERFECTION - Pasta - Hershey Pasta Group
PERFECTION - Photographic equipment - Epson America, Inc.
PERFECTION - Post hole diggers–hand-operated - Seymour Manufacturing Co.,Inc.
PERFECTION - Razor blades ☆ - F.W. Engels Inc.
PERFECTION - Seafood products–fresh or frozen ☆ - Ocean Beauty Seafood, Inc.
PERFECTION - Shoes - Osage Footwear, Inc.
PERFECTION - Shortening - C. & T. Refinery, Inc.
PERFECTION - Thread - Perfect Thread Co. Inc.
PERFECTION - Veterinary pharmaceutical preparations - W.S. Valentine Co.
PERFECTION - Water treating compounds - Perfection Softener Co.
PERFECTION - Windows–storm - Quaker Window Products Co.
PERFECTION BY JUMPING-JACKS - Footwear–children's - Osage Footwear, Inc.
PERFECTION COLLECTION - Skin care products - Angles Beauty Care Group, Inc.
PERFECTION ENGINEERING - Phonographic turntables ☆ - GNP Audio Video Inc.
PERFECTION HY-TEST - Automotive parts and accessories - Perfection Hy-Test Co.
PERFECTION HYTEST - Automotive parts and accessories - Perfection Hy-Test Co.
PERFECTION II - Paints - Morwear Paint Co.
PERFECTION LEARNING - Computer software - Perfection Learning Corp.
PERFECTION OIL - Hair care products - Raymac Corp. Hair & Skin Technology
PERFECTION POINT - Fasteners–hook and eye - Boye Needle
PERFECTION PRINT - Floor coverings–tile - Collins & Aikman Corp.
PERFECTION SNO-WIZZER - Motor vehicles–snowplows - Perfection Softener Co.
PERFECTIONIST - Sporting goods - Perfectionist Products, Inc.
PERFECTIONIST'S - Draperies - Lederer Enterprises
PERFECTIONISTS, THE - Underwear and nightwear - Warnaco Inc.
PERFECTIONS - Jewelry - Roman Research, Inc.
PERFECTKID - Apparel–children's - Passport International Ltd.
PERFECTLY BALANCED DUO - Skin care products - Beauticontrol Cosmetics Inc.
PERFECTLY BLUNT - Chemical preparations - Novagen, Inc.
PERFECTLY CLEAR - Eyeglasses - Southern States Optical Co.
PERFECTLY EASY - Hair care products ☆ - Avon Products, Inc.
PERFECTLY EXTRAORDINARY - Teas ☆ - Rowena's Gourmet Foods Inc.
PERFECTLY FITTING - Ophthalmic goods - Foremost Optical Products
PERFECTLY NATURAL - Cosmetics - Maybelline Co.
PERFECTLY NATURAL - Floor coverings–carpet and rugs ☆ - Gulistan Carpet Inc.
PERFECTLY PIGGY - Glassware–household - Papel Freelance, Inc.
PERFECTLY PLAIN - Mayonnaise - Cortina Corp.
PERFECTLY PORTABLE - Infant product - Century Products Co.
PERFECTLY PURE - Cosmetics - Nature's Bounty, Inc.
PERFECTMOUNT - Cardboard - Crescent Cardboard Co.
PERFECTO - Aquariums–household - Perfecto Manufacturing Inc.
PERFECTO - Bags - Schott Bros. Inc.

PERFECTO - Fabrics - Dan River Inc.
PERFECTO - Jackets–leather - Schott Brothers Inc.
PERFECTO - Lamps - Lutz Superdyne Inc.
PERFECTO - Snack foods - Millner Trading Co. Inc.
PERFECTO - Stones–synthetic ☆ - Perfecto Products Co.
PERFECTO - Tools - Railway Handle Corp.
PERFECTO - Vegetable oil - Ventura Foods LLC (Lou Ana Division)
PERFECTO 100'S - Cigars - F.D. Grave & Son, Co.
PERFECTO BUBBLER - Pet products ☆ - Perfecto Manufacturing Inc.
PERFECTO EASY ACCESS REPTILE HABITATS - Pet products - Perfecto Manufacturing Inc.
PERFECTO GARCIA - Cigars ☆ - House of Windsor Inc.
PERFECTO NEW IMAGE - Pet products - Perfecto Manufacturing Inc.
PERFECTO RIVER TANK - Pet products - Perfecto Manufacturing Inc.
PERFECTO SAFE - Aquariums–household - Perfecto Manufacturing Inc.
PERFECTOFFICE - Computer software - Corel USA
PERFECTONE - Clarinet and saxophone mouthpieces - J.J. Babbitt Co. Inc.
PERFECTONE - Nautical instruments - Fiamm Technologies
PERFECTOR - Dental equipment - TP Orthodontics, Inc.
PERFECTOR - Emery products - Creative Nail Design, Inc.
PERFECTOR - Manicure preparations - Perfector Products
PERFECTOR 125 - Office supplies - Alvin and Co. Inc.
PERFECTOS - Cigar boxes–wood - Consolidated Cigar Corp.
PERFECTOS EXTRA - Cigar boxes–wood - Consolidated Cigar Corp.
PERFECTOUCH - Cosmetics - Pacific World Corp.
PERFECTPRINT - Computer peripheral equipment - Recoton Corp.
PERFECTSEAM - Thread - Blue Mountain Industries, Inc.
PERFECTSHAPE - Log measuring system - Applied Scanning Technology, Inc.
PERFECTSUN - Tanning salons - ETS, Inc.
PERFECTTEMP - Heating equipment - Research Products Corp.
PERFECTVIEW - Computer terminals - ViewSonic Corp.
PERFECTWEEZ - Cosmetics - Revlon Consumer Products Corp.
PERFECUT FLAWLESS - Jewelry–precious - Leo Pevsner & Co.
PERFELASTIC - Thread - Perfect Thread Co. Inc.
PERFELOPE - Envelopes - Mail-Well Envelope
PERFERMA COLLECTION - Mattresses - King Koil Licensing Co., Inc.
PERFETTA - Bocce balls ☆ - Berarducci Bros. Manufacturing Co. Inc.
PERFETTA - Cosmetics - Revlon Consumer Products Corp.
PERFETTI - Cough drops ☆ - R.L. Albert & Son, Inc.
PERFETTO - Olive oil - Krinos Foods, Inc.
PERFEX - Brooms - Perfex Corp.
PERFEX - Cleaning preparations - Reckitt & Colman, Inc.
PERFEX - Fabrics–broadcloth - Chicopee
PERFEX - Housewares - SCI Scandicrafts Inc.
PERFEX - Oils–lubricating - Liberty Petroleum Co.
PERFEX - Water–bottled or canned ☆ - Church and Dwight Co. Inc.
PERFICUT - Paper–bond - Georgia-Pacific Corp.
PERFIDIA - Rings–jewelry ☆ - Artcarved Inc.
PERFIK SEAL - Paints - Farrell-Calhoun Inc.
PERFIT - Window coverings - Joanna Western Mills Co.
PERFLEX - Swimming pools - Hayward Pool Products Inc.
PERFLEXION - Cleaning preparations - W.W. Grainger, Inc.
PERFMAN - Computer software - Information Systems Manager, Inc.
PERFO-FUSE - Fabrics - Handler Textile Corp.
PERFO-ROUND - Wainscotting - Georgia-Pacific Corp.
PERFO-SQUARE - Wainscotting - Georgia-Pacific Corp.
PERFORCE - Computer software - Perforce Software Inc.
PERFORM - Analgesics - Performance Health, Inc.
PERFORM - Cleaning preparations–household - Grow Group, Inc.
PERFORM - Hair care products ☆ - Smithkline Beecham Corp.
PERFORM - Insulating materials - NPS
PERFORM - Pet products - SmartPets
PERFORM GUARD - Insulating materials - AFM Corp.
PERFORMA - Bathroom fixtures - Sterling Plumbing Group Inc.
PERFORMA - Computers - Apple Computer Inc.
PERFORMA - Cutlery ☆ - Washington Forge Inc.
PERFORMA - Floor coverings - Domco Industries Ltd.
PERFORMA - Medical apparatus - Acoustic Imaging Technologies Corp.
PERFORMA - Pillows - E.I. Dupont de Nemours and Co.
PERFORMA PACKS - Luggage - Samsonite Corp.
PERFORMAIRE - Electronic equipment - Ridgewood Engineering, Inc.
PERFORMANA 1 ONE - Lubricants - QSP Marketing, Inc.
PERFORMANCE - Apparel–athletic - Tighe Industries Inc.
PERFORMANCE - Bicycles - Klein Bicycle Corp.
PERFORMANCE - Boats–motor - Starcraft Corp.
PERFORMANCE - Braces–orthopedic - Kirschner Medical Corp.

☆ = Now out of production

PERFORMANCE - Computer software - Omega B.P.
PERFORMANCE - Electronics equipment - JBL Inc.
PERFORMANCE - Fabrics–tapestry ☆ - Combeau Industries
PERFORMANCE - Floor coverings–carpet and rugs - Collins & Aikman Corp.
PERFORMANCE - Floor coverings–carpet and rugs - Johnson's Carpets Inc.
PERFORMANCE - Floor coverings–carpet and rugs ☆ - Len Dal Carpets
PERFORMANCE - Floor coverings–carpet and rugs ☆ - Southern Carpet Mills
PERFORMANCE - Greeting cards ☆ - Chase Collection, Inc.
PERFORMANCE - Meters–water - Arthur A. Hendey
PERFORMANCE - Musical instrument accessories ☆ - Shane Music Products
PERFORMANCE - Panty hose - Mayer/Berkshire Corp.
PERFORMANCE - Paper - French Paper Co.
PERFORMANCE - Paper - Strathmore Paper Co.
PERFORMANCE - Recording label - Jazz Composer's Orchestra Association Inc.
PERFORMANCE - Stationery - Diagraph Corp.
PERFORMANCE - Thread - American & Efird, Inc.
PERFORMANCE - Toys–models - Estes Industries
PERFORMANCE - Trailers–boat - Sleek-Craft Boats by Nescher Inc.
PERFORMANCE - Vitamins and nutritional supplements - Performance Nutrition, Inc.
PERFORMANCE - Vitamins and nutritional supplements - Vitamin Research Products Inc.
PERFORMANCE - Wallpaper ☆ - Fidelity Industries, Inc.
PERFORMANCE - Wiring devices - Pass & Seymour, Inc.
PERFORMANCE 1 - Lubricating oils - QSP Marketing, Inc.
PERFORMANCE 1 ONE - Antifreeze - QSP Marketing, Inc.
PERFORMANCE 2 - Fabrics–tapestry ☆ - Combeau Industries
PERFORMANCE III - Wallpaper ☆ - Wall Fashion Inc.
PERFORMANCE/7 - Computer software - Mimetics Corp.
PERFORMANCE 10 - Glass products - PPG Industries, Inc.
PERFORMANCE 10 - Nail care products - Maybelline Co.
PERFORMANCE ADVANTAGE TECHNOLOGIES - Computer software - Performance Advantage Inc.
PERFORMANCE & MEMORY BOOST BLAST OFF CAPS - Vitamins and nutritional supplements - Vitamin Research Products Inc.
PERFORMANCE ASSURANCE - Educational materials - BGS Systems, Inc.
PERFORMANCE BOBBINS - Thread - American & Efird, Inc.
PERFORMANCE CENTER - Toys ☆ - Playskool, Inc.
PERFORMANCE CHINEX - Brushes - Corona Brushes Inc.
PERFORMANCE CHROMIUN PICOLINATE - Vitamins and nutritional supplements - Weider Health and Fitness
PERFORMANCE CLUB - Hosiery - Desoto Hosiery Mills, Inc.
PERFORMANCE COACH - Computers - Omega Performance Corp.
PERFORMANCE COMPUTER SYSTEMS - Computer software - Performance Computer Systems Inc.
PERFORMANCE CONTROLS, INC. - Power switching equipment - Performance Controls, Inc.
PERFORMANCE CORE - Food products - Mars, Inc.
PERFORMANCE CRUISER - Boats–motor - Thunderbird Products
PERFORMANCE CUSHION - Apparel and accessories - Desoto Hosiery Mills, Inc.
PERFORMANCE DATA SYSTEMS, INC. - Computer software - Spears Manufacturing Co.
PERFORMANCE DESIGNS - Parachutes - P.D. of Miami, Inc.
PERFORMANCE DRAIN - Drains - Hancor Inc.
PERFORMANCE EDGE - Exercise equipment - Nordictrack, Inc.
PERFORMANCE EDGE - Vitamins and nutritional supplements - Bronson Pharmaceuticals
PERFORMANCE EFFECTS - Musical instrument accessories ☆ - Shane Music Products
PERFORMANCE ENHANCED - Printers–computer - Spring Point Corp.
PERFORMANCE FAT BURNERS - Vitamins and nutritional supplements - Weider Health and Fitness
PERFORMANCE FLEX - Golfing equipment - Lisco, Inc.
PERFORMANCE FORMULA JUNIOR - Chemical preparations - Stanadyne Automotive Corp.
PERFORMANCE GAIN - Vitamins and nutritional supplements - Performance Nutrition, Inc.
PERFORMANCE GH - Vitamins and nutritional supplements - Performance Nutrition, Inc.
PERFORMANCE GINSENG BLEND - Vitamins and nutritional supplements - Caroline Owens
PERFORMANCE GOLD - Vitamins and nutritional supplements - Weider Health and Fitness
PERFORMANCE IN A POUCH - Towels - Merisco Inc.

PERFORMANCE INSULATION - Insulating materials ☆ - NPS
PERFORMANCE KNIT - Shirts - Red Kap Apparel Corp.
PERFORMANCE LEADER, THE - Machinery - Anaheim Manufacturing Co.
PERFORMANCE LINE - Gasoline - Boardman Petroleum Inc.
PERFORMANCE LINE - Leotards - Danskin, Inc.
PERFORMANCE MATCH - Electronic equipment - AudioControl
PERFORMANCE MATCHED - Radio communications equipment - Motorola, Inc. (Land Mobile Products Sector)
PERFORMANCE MIDI - Computer software - Applied Research & Technology Inc.
PERFORMANCE NOW - Computer software - KnowledgePoint
PERFORMANCE OKG - Vitamins and nutritional supplements - Weider Health and Fitness
PERFORMANCE PACKS - Health care products - Health Maintenance Programs Inc.
PERFORMANCE PANS - Pans - Wilton Industries, Inc.
PERFORMANCE PLUS - See **SILICONE PLUS**
PERFORMANCE PLUS - Computer diskettes - Moore Business Forms, Inc.
PERFORMANCE PLUS - Dog food - Gold Kist Inc.
PERFORMANCE PLUS - Glass–window - Guardian Industries Corp.
PERFORMANCE PLUS - Joists–open web - Trus Joist MacMillan L.P.
PERFORMANCE PLUS - Musical instrument accessories - Santa Rosa Folk Guitar Co.
PERFORMANCE PLUS - Plastics film - AEP Industries, Inc.
PERFORMANCE PLUS - Sports rackets and accessories - Wilson Sporting Goods Co.
PERFORMANCE PLUS - Tools–power-driven - American Tool Companies Inc.
PERFORMANCE PLUS VIDEO - Video tapes–blank - Argus Publishers Corp.
PERFORMANCE POLY - Tires - Bridgestone/Firestone, Inc.
PERFORMANCE PRODUCTS - Fabrics - Springs Industries, Inc.
PERFORMANCE RATED - Fabrics - Guilford Mills, Inc.
PERFORMANCE RECIPE - Dog food - Kal Kan Foods, Inc.
PERFORMANCE SCORED BOARD - Insulating materials ☆ - NPS
PERFORMANCE SHAPER DIET - Vitamins and nutritional supplements - Weider Health and Fitness
PERFORMANCE SOLUTION - Computer software - Softworks Inc.
PERFORMANCE SPORT - Women's apparel - Akiba France Inc.
PERFORMANCE SYSTEM - Knives–carving - Freud USA, Inc.
PERFORMANCE TEAM - Compact discs–prerecorded - Ashland Oil, Inc.
PERFORMANCE THAT LIVES THE DREAM - Sporting goods - Nelson Paint Co., Inc.
PERFORMANCE THROUGH TECHNOLOGY - Transmissions–motor vehicle - Raybestor Products Co.
PERFORMANCE THUMB - Gloves–safety - Arbill, Inc.
PERFORMANCE TINT - Insulating materials - Madico, Inc.
PERFORMANCE TOPPINGS, THE - Sausages - Hormel Foods Corp.
PERFORMANCE UNDER PRESSURE - Plugs - National Test Plugs, Inc.
PERFORMANCE VANADYL - Vitamins and nutritional supplements - Weider Health and Fitness
PERFORMANCE WALLS IV - Wallpaper ☆ - Wall Fashion Inc.
PERFORMANCE WEIGHT GAINER - Vitamins and nutritional supplements - Weider Health and Fitness
PERFORMANCE WITHOUT LIMITS - Electronic equipment - Polk Investment Corp.
PERFORMANCE WORKS - Computer software - Landmark Systems Corp.
PERFORMANCEPAK - Containers - Wilkinson Manufacturing Co.
PERFORMANTZ - Electrical equipment - Multiple Zones International, Inc.
PERFORMAX - Dental equipment - Gillette Canada Inc.
PERFORMAX - Lubricating oils - Pennzoil Products Co.
PERFORMAXX - Adhesives and sealants - International Hairgoods, Inc.
PERFORMAZENE Z2000 - Fuel additives - Circle K Corp.
PERFORMER - Antennas - Recoton Corp.
PERFORMER - Automotive parts and accessories - Edelbrock Corp.
PERFORMER - Ballpoint pen - Zippo Manufacturing Co.
PERFORMER - Bicycles - GT Bicycles Inc.
PERFORMER - Brushes–paint - Kmart Corp.
PERFORMER - Cooking equipment–commercial - Pitco Frialator, Inc.
PERFORMER - Doughnuts–mixes - J.W. Allen & Co.
PERFORMER - Embossing tool - International Rotex Inc.
PERFORMER - Floor coverings ☆ - Congoleum Corp.
PERFORMER - Gloves - Ektelon
PERFORMER - Golfing equipment - Precision Composites, Inc.
PERFORMER - Knee braces - Orthopedic Technology, Inc.
PERFORMER - Life preservers - Coleman Co., Inc.
PERFORMER - Microphones ☆ - Lectrosonics Inc.
PERFORMER - Mops - Golden Star Inc.

☆ = Now out of production

PERFORMER - Music synthesizer ☆ - Ionic Industries Inc.
PERFORMER - Pumps - Sterling Fluid Systems, Inc.
PERFORMER - Sports rackets and accessories - Gexco Enterprises
PERFORMER - Staplers ☆ - Bates Manufacturing Co.
PERFORMER - Starch–laundry - Stevens Industries Inc.
PERFORMER - Yarn ☆ - Caron International Inc.
PERFORMER COMBOS - Sporting goods - O'Brien International
PERFORMER-ELIMINATOR - Pet products - Agri Laboratories, Ltd.
PERFORMER IAS - Shock absorbers–motor vehicle - Edelbrock Corp.
PERFORMER-LINK - Automotive parts and accessories - Edelbrock Corp.
PERFORMER-PLUS - Automotive parts and accessories - Edelbrock Corp.
PERFORMER PLUS - Carpeting - Milliken & Co.
PERFORMER RPM - Automotive parts and accessories - Edelbrock Corp.
PERFORMER, THE - Window frames ☆ - Kawneer Co., Inc.
PERFORMERS - Diapers–disposable - Shaw's Supermarkets, Inc.
PERFORMING CARE - Skin care products - Frances Denney
PERFORMING COLOR - Cosmetics - Maybelline Co.
PERFORMING PREFERENCE - Hair care products - Cosmair Inc.
PERFORMING PRIMES - Floor coverings–carpet and rugs - E.R. Carpenter Co.
PERFORMING STAR - Floor coverings–carpet and rugs ☆ - Downs Carpet Co. Inc.
PERFORMORE - Binders - U.S. Ring Binder Corp.
PERFORMOX - Printers–computer - Datasouth Computer Corp.
PERFOWOOD - Wood products - Georgia-Pacific Corp.
PERFRISA - Wainscotting ☆ - Marino/Ware
PERFSTAT - Computer software - Instrumental, Inc.
PERFUMA - Dolls - Mattel, Inc.
PERFUME GARDEN, THE - Perfumes - St. John's Herb Garden Inc.
PERFUME GIVING - Dolls - Mattel, Inc.
PERFUME PENGUIN - Animal figurine with cologne ☆ - Cosrich Inc.
PERFUME PRETTY - Dolls - Mattel, Inc.
PERFUME PUFFI - Sachets ☆ - Hazel Pearson Handicrafts
PERFUME SOPHISTICATED - Perfumes - Brukvin Imports
PERFUME SUSAN - Housewares ☆ - Larry Shaw Co.
PERFUME WANDS - Perfumes - Libby Lee Toys Inc.
PERFUMES OF HAWAII - Perfumes - House of Excellence
PERFUMEWAX - Candles ☆ - Fox Run Craftsmen
PERFUSAIRE - Cash registers - Auer Register Co.
PERGOLA - Awnings - Awnings by Sunair/Sunair Awnings
PERGOLA - Wallpaper ☆ - Osborne & Little
PERGOLA LATTICE SYSTEMS - Roofing materials - Texas Aluminum Industries Inc.
PERGONAL - Pharmaceutical preparations - Serono Laboratories Inc.
PERGONE - Beverages–alcohol - Parrott & Co.
PERHAM - Fruits and vegetables - Perham Fruit Corp.
PERHAPS - Bedding–linen - Dan River Inc.
PERHISTACON - Pharmaceutical preparations ☆ - Perry Laboratories
PERI BASEL DESIGNS - Apparel and accessories - Peri Sue Arkin
PERI-CARE - Skin care products - Sween Corp.
PERI-COLACE - Laxatives - Bristol-Myers Squibb Co.
PERI-CONATE - Pharmaceutical preparations - H.R. Cenci Laboratories Inc.
PERI-DENT - Pharmaceutical preparations - Home Health Products, Inc.
PERI-DOS - Pharmaceutical preparations - Goldline Laboratories, Inc.
PERI-K - Medical apparatus - Allegiance Corp.
PERI-KLENZ - Cleaning preparations - Polychem Corp.
PERI-ORAL - Toothpaste - Peri-Oral Dental Products, Inc.
PERI + PLUS - Medical apparatus - Hospital Marketing Service Inc.
PERI-STRIPS DRY - Medical apparatus - Bio-Vascular, Inc.
PERI-WASH - Skin care products - Sween Corp.
PERI-WASH II - Antiseptics - Sween Corp.
PERIACTIN - Antihistamine preparations - Merck & Co., Inc. (Merck Research Laboratories)
PERICARE - Health care products - Arbor Vitae Medical
PERICOL - Pharmaceutical preparations ☆ - Perry Laboratories
PERICOM - Integrated circuits - Pioneer Semiconductor Corp.
PERIDENTAL - Toothbrushes - John O.Butler Co.
PERIDEX - Dentifrices - Procter & Gamble Co.
PERIDIN - Diuretics - Moreba Pharmaceutical Corp.
PERIDIN-C - Pharmaceutical preparations - Beutlich L.P. Pharmaceuticals
PERIES - Pharmaceutical preparations ☆ - Xttrium Laboratories Inc.
PERIFOAM - Pharmaceutical preparations ☆ - Solvay Pharmaceuticals Inc.
PERIGEE - Apparel and accessories - Precision Line Industries, Inc.
PERIGEE BOOKS - Publisher's imprints - Putnam Publishing Group
PERIGON - Computers - Microcity Computer, Inc.

PERIGORD PRESS - Publisher's imprints - Bantam Doubleday Dell Publishing Group, Inc.
PERIGOURD - Mushrooms - Young's Market Co.
PERIHEMIN - Pharmaceutical preparations ☆ - Lederle Laboratories
PERIL - Perfumes ☆ - Tristar Corp.
PERILOUS LANDS - Games ☆ - Avalon Hill Game Co.
PERILS OF PRALINE - Ice cream - Baskin-Robbins Inc.
PERIM-A-TRON - Alarm systems - Universal Security Instruments Inc.
PERIMACUBE - Lighting fixtures ☆ - Hubbell Lighting, Inc. (Lighting Div.)
PERIMALITER - Lighting fixtures - Hubbell Lighting, Inc. (Lighting Div.)
PERIMALUX - Lighting fixtures - Hubbell Lighting, Inc. (Lighting Div.)
PERIMAMITE - Lighting fixtures - Hubbell Lighting, Inc. (Lighting Div.)
PERIMAPAK - Lighting fixtures - Hubbell Lighting, Inc. (Lighting Div.)
PERIMASCAPER - Lighting fixtures - Hubbell Lighting, Inc. (Lighting Div.)
PERIMASHIELD - Lighting fixtures - Hubbell Lighting, Inc. (Lighting Div.)
PERIMASQUARE - Lighting fixtures - Hubbell Lighting, Inc. (Lighting Div.)
PERIMETER DETECTION THAT SPEAKS FOR ITSELF - Electronic equipment - Electronic Security Products of California
PERIMETER EDGE CONTROL - Skis - K-2 Corp.
PERIMETER INDUSTRIES - Sporting goods - Perimeter Industries
PERIMETER TRIM SYSTEM - Tools–hand-operated - Trim USA Auto Supply, Inc.
PERIMETERS - Furniture - International Colorcast Corp.
PERIMETERS - Paneling ☆ - Marlite
PERIMIFLEX - Floor coverings - Mannington Mills, Inc.
PERIMPACK - Insecticides - Zeneca Inc.
PERINI - Watches - Prestige Enterprises, Inc.
PERIO APPRENTICE - Computer software - Jack E. Wasserstein
PERIO PIC - Dental equipment ☆ - John O.Butler Co.
PERIOCHECK - Dental equipment - Actech, Advanced Clinical Technologies Inc.
PERIOCHECK ORAL MED - Toothpaste - Actech, Advanced Clinical Technologies Inc.
PERIOD - Recording label - Everest Record Group
PERIOD PATTERNS - Patterns–clothing - Mediaeval Miscellanea
PERIOD PAVILIONS - Tents - Mediaeval Miscellanea
PERIODICAL MANAGER - Computer software - Right on Programs
PERIOGENE - Dentifrices ☆ - Noxell Corp.
PERIOGLAS - Dental equipment - U.S. Biomaterials Corp.
PERIOWISE - Medical apparatus - Periowise, Inc.
PERIPHERAL VISION - Computer software - Companion Corp.
PERIPHERY - Ophthalmic goods - Foremost Optical Products
PERIPHERY - Robes - Periphery Loungewear Inc.
PERIPHERY PLUS - Robes - Periphery Loungewear Inc.
PERIPHERY TOO - Robes - Periphery Loungewear Inc.
PERIPHEX - Batteries - Advanced Battery Systems, Inc.
PERIPRODUCER - Computer software - Periphonics Corp.
PERISCOPE - Recording label - Periscope Record Co.
PERISCOPE - Watches - Giftware Objectdesign, Inc.
PERISCOPE POT PIE - Food products - Mission Control
PERISPHERE - Furniture ☆ - Romweber Co.
PERISTUDIO - Computer software - Periphonics Corp.
PERITINIC - Pharmaceutical preparations ☆ - Lederle Laboratories
PERITRATE - Pharmaceutical preparations ☆ - Parke-Davis
PERITRODE - Surgical supplies - Neuromed, Inc.
PERITROL - Pharmaceutical preparations - Wesley Pharmacal Co. Inc.
PERITRON - Health care products - American Imex
PERIWINKLE - Apparel and accessories ☆ - Edison Brothers Stores, Inc.
PERIWINKLE - Bicycles ☆ - Kent International Inc.
PERIWINKLE - Yarn - Henry's Attic
PERK - Cleaning preparations - L & F Consumer Products
PERK - Dog food ☆ - Heinz Pet Products Co.
PERK-A-LURE - Fishing tackle - JPON Enterprises Inc.
PERK & SERVE - Coffee makers–electric - Eastern Electric Appliance Co., Inc.
PERK-IT - Hair care products - Tressa, Inc.
PERK-UP - Coffee makers–electric - Dazey Corp.
PERKBURGER - Dog food ☆ - Heinz Pet Products Co.
PERKI - Cosmetics - Paula Payne Products Co. Inc.
PERKI WHITE - Cosmetics - Paula Payne Products Co. Inc.
PERKIES - Apparel stores–lingerie - Formfit Rogers
PERKIN-ELMER - Optical products - Hughes Danbury Optical Systems Inc.
PERKINS - Engines–diesel - Perkins Engines Inc.
PERKINS - Food products - Green Bay Foods Co.
PERKINS - Machinery - Standex International Corp.
PERKINS - Toys - Tonka Corp.

☆ = Now out of production

PERKINS & SQUIER - Paper - Central National-Gottesman Inc.
PERKINS BRAILLER - Braillewriter - Howe Press
PERKINS PICKIN'S - Fruits and vegetables - Perkins Restaurants Operating Co., L.P.
PERKINS PLACE - Wallpaper ☆ - Linden Street Gallery
PERKINS PLACE II - Wallpaper ☆ - Linden Street Gallery
PERKINS TAKE HOME BAKERY - Bags–trash - Perkins Restaurants Operating Co., L.P.
PERKINS VIDEOSCOPE - Vision aid ☆ - Howe Press
PERKO - Lighting equipment - Perko Inc.
PERKS PLUS - Air transportation - United Air Lines, Inc.
PERKY - Dairy products - Sani-Dairy
PERKY - Fabrics ☆ - Greenwood Mills Inc.
PERKY - Office supplies - R & D Products Inc.
PERKY BUNNY - Candy - Keppel's Inc.
PERKY JERKY - Meat products–beef ☆ - Curtice-Burns Meat Snacks Inc.
PERKY JERKY - Snack foods ☆ - Hiland Potato Chip Co.
PERKY PANTS - Pet products - Debonair Pets of California
PERKY PENGUIN - Toys - Fisher-Price, Inc.
PERKY PENGUIN - Toys ☆ - Steven Manufacturing Co.
PERKY PENGUIN - Toys–stuffed - Russ Berrie and Co., Inc.
PERKY-PET - Bird feeds - Perky-Pet Products Co.
PERKY PIG - Candy ☆ - Keppel's Inc.
PERKY PINK - Makeup ☆ - Cosrich Inc.
PERKY POOCH - Deodorizers ☆ - Car-Freshner Corp.
PERKY PRINT - Ironing board pads - Magla Products Inc.
PERKY TURKEYS - Toys–stuffed - Russ Berrie and Co., Inc.
PERKY'S - Candy - Brach and Brock Confections Inc.
PERLA - Blinds–vertical - U.S. Polymers, Inc.
PERLA - Projection screens - Claridge Products and Equipment Inc.
PERLA DE JOJOBA - Hair care products ☆ - Hobe Labs Inc.
PERLAGE - Apparel and accessories - Central Falls Inc.
PERLAMAR - Shrimp–fresh or frozen - Darik Enterprises Inc.
PERLATOR - Faucets - Neoperl Inc.
PERLE - Glassware–scientific - Durand International
PERLE - Tobacco–chewing or smoking - Gesty Trading & Manufacturing Corp.
PERLE COTTON - Yarn - Henry's Attic
PERLE DE BRILLET - Liquors - Carillon Importers Ltd.
PERLE DI PARATI - Wallpaper - Carlton-Metro Wallcoverings
PERLE NOIRE - Perfumes - Avon Products, Inc.
PERLES DELUNE - Jewelry - Kramer Jewelry Creations Inc.
PERLES OF THE VALLEY - Produce - Jackel Farms & Cold Storage
PERLIDOS - Cigars - Gesty Trading & Manufacturing Corp.
PERLIER HONEY ALMOND - Bath salts - Perlier La Parfumerie
PERLINA - Leather - Perlina Handbags, Inc.
PERM-A-BARRIER - Partitions–wood - Grace Construction Products
PERM A BLONDE - Hair care products - Wella Corp. (Consumer Products Div.)
PERM A BROWN - Hair care products - Wella Corp. (Consumer Products Div.)
PERM-A-CLOR - Stain removers - Detrex Corp.
PERM A GRAY - Hair care products - Wella Corp. (Consumer Products Div.)
PERM-A-KLEEN - Stain removers - Detrex Corp.
PERM-A-KOOL - Beverage dispensing equipment - Kraftware Corp. (Morgan Div.)
PERM A LOCK - Tape–adhesive - Conso Products Co.
PERM-A-MATIC - Hair care products - Helene Curtis Industries Inc.
PERM-A-ROPE - Hair care products ☆ - Image Laboratories, Inc.
PERM-A-TEMP - Insulated Containers ☆ - Thermos Co.
PERM-ADJUST - Doors–glass - Contractors Wardrobe, Inc.
PERM ALLURE - Cosmetics - Perm-Allure Eyelash Co.
PERM ART - Hair care products - Redken Laboratories, Inc.
PERM BONNET - Skin care products - Tyler Creations Inc.
PERM CARE - Hair care products - Tressa, Inc.
PERM-COTE - Rust removers - Detrex Corp.
PERM-E-LASTIC - Epoxy - Perm-E-Lastic Inc.
PERM ENDURANCE - Hair care products - Joico Laboratories, Inc.
PERM ENERGY - Hair care preparation - Fermodyl Professionals Inc.
PERM/EVENT - Hair care products - Helene Curtis Industries Inc.
PERM FOR A DAY - Hair permanent - Uptown Products
PERM FRESH - Hair care products - Matrix Essentials, Inc.
PERM FRESH MOISTURE SUPPLY - Moisturizer - Matrix Essentials, Inc.
PERM GUARD - Hair care products - Helene Curtis Industries Inc.
PERM-INJECT - Epoxy - Permagile Industries Inc.
PERM-LAST - Hair care products - Para Laboratories Inc.
PERM LIFE - Hair care products - Revlon-Realistic Professional Products Inc.
PERM LIFESTYLING - Hair care products - Revlon Consumer Products Corp.

PERM-O-LAY - Concrete products - Design Masonry Systems Inc.
PERM-O-SNAP - Lamps - GKI
PERM OPTICS - Hair care products ☆ - Redken Laboratories, Inc.
PERM OVER PERM SOLUTIONS - Hair care products - Helene Curtis Industries Inc.
PERM PARTNER - Hair care products - Action Environmental Products
PERM PICK-UP - Hair care products - Revlon-Realistic Professional Products Inc.
PERM POWER - Hair care products - Raymac Corp. Hair & Skin Technology
PERM-PREP - Cosmetics ☆ - House of Lowell Inc.
PERM PRESERVER - Hair care products - Helene Curtis Industries Inc.
PERM REPAIR - Hair care products - Pro-Line Corp.
PERM RODS - Hair curlers - Alleghany Pharmacal Corp.
PERM SAVER - Hair care products ☆ - Palm Beach Beauty Products
PERM SILK - Hair care products - Sterling Winthrop Inc.
PERM SUPPORT - Hair care products - Mahdeen Laboratory
PERM SUPPORT ENHANCER - Hair care products - Mahdeen Laboratory
PERM-TICKLER - Combs - Krest Products Corp.
PERM-WALL - Electronic equipment - Da-Lite Screen Co. Inc.
PERMA - Crayons ☆ - Binney & Smith Inc.
PERMA - Office supplies - ACCO USA, Inc.
PERMA - Office supplies - Belle Cadeaux Inc.
PERMA - Pet products - Systems Go
PERMA - Window shades - Acme Awning Co.
PERMA BARK - Building materials - International Stone, Inc.
PERMA BED - Adhesives and sealants - Biddle Co.
PERMA-BIND - Binders - Duo Tang, Inc.
PERMA-BLEND - Alfalfa - Sweeney Seed Co.
PERMA BLUE - Gun blue - Birchwood Casey
PERMA BOND - Adhesives and sealants - Coronado Paint Co.
PERMA BOND - Shoes - Endicott Johnson Corp.
PERMA BRAKE - Brake parts - Primo Accessories, Inc.
PERMA-BREW - Appliance parts - Tops Manufacturing Co. Inc.
PERMA CAP - Automotive parts and accessories - Kleen Wheels Corp.
PERMA CAST - Furniture - Architectural Masterworks
PERMA CAULK - Caulking compounds - Dap Products Inc.
PERMA CELL - Batteries ☆ - Gates Energy Products Inc.
PERMA-CEMENT - Concrete products - CGM Inc.
PERMA-CHECK - Toilet seats - Sanderson Plumbing Products, Inc.
PERMA-CHINK - Adhesives and sealants - Perma-Chink Systems, Inc.
PERMA-CLAD - Door frames - V.T. Industries
PERMA-CLAD - Tape measures - Keson Industries Inc.
PERMA-CLEAN - Adhesives and sealants - Induron Coatings Inc.
PERMA-CLEAN - Filters–industrial - W.L. Gore & Associates, Inc.
PERMA-CLEAN - Stoves - Amana Refrigeration Inc.
PERMA-CLEAN - Windows–screen - Andersen Corp.
PERMA-COIF - Wigs - Richard Hartwich Inc.
PERMA-COIL - Stoves - Amana Refrigeration Inc.
PERMA COLOR - Labels–fabric - Appleson Press Inc.
PERMA COLOR - Pet products - Clifford W. Estes Co. Inc.
PERMA-COLOR - Thread - Threads USA Div.
PERMA-COOL - Air conditioning equipment - Permatron Corp.
PERMA COOL - Transmission fluids - Perma Cool
PERMA-CORD - Matting ☆ - American Floor Products Co. Inc.
PERMA CORE - Thread - American & Efird, Inc.
PERMA-COTE - Paints - Dayton Paint & Coatings Inc.
PERMA-COTE - Paper–carbon - Kores Nordic USA Corp.
PERMA-COTTA - Containers–plastic - Southern Sales & Marketing Group, Inc.
PERMA COUNTER - Cutting boards ☆ - Mills Products Inc. (Perma View Processed Glass Division)
PERMA-COVER - Film ☆ - Bemiss-Jason Corp.
PERMA CRETE - Paints - Porter Paint Co.
PERMA-CRIN - Fabric stores - Conso Products Co.
PERMA-CURVE - Sunglasses lens - Opsales, Inc.
PERMA-DIP - Pet products - Professional Pet Products
PERMA-DOOR - Steel-entry doors and patio systems - American Standard Inc.
PERMA-DRI - Waterproofing compounds - Birchwood Casey
PERMA-DRY - Footwear - Lehigh Safety Shoe Co.
PERMA-DRY - Gaskets - Fel-Pro Inc.
PERMA-DRY - Skin care products ☆ - Aquamint Laboratories Inc.
PERMA EDGE - Artists' materials ☆ - Binney & Smith Inc.
PERMA EDGE - Plastics ☆ - Ralph Wilson Plastics Co.
PERMA FILM - Cleaning preparations ☆ - Eureka Chemical Co.
PERMA FIT - Tubes–boiler - Molex-Etc Inc.
PERMA-FIT - Window frames - Andersen Corp.

☆ = Now out of production

PERMA-FLEECE - Fabrics–flannel - Gehring Textiles Inc.
PERMA-FLEX - Office supplies ☆ - Barkley Filing Supplies
PERMA-FLEX - Tires - Tirec Corp.
PERMA-FLEX FOOTING - Rubber–synthetic - Tirec Corp.
PERMA-FLEXX - Pipes - Containment Technologies Corp.
PERMA FLOW - Gutters–plastic - Crane Plastics Co. L.P.
PERMA FLOW GUTTER GUARD SYSTEM - Construction equipment - Crane Plastics Co. L.P.
PERMA-FLUTE - Fabrics–nylon - Gehring Textiles Inc.
PERMA FLUX - Flux - Comstar International Inc. (IPC Div.)
PERMA-FOAM - Insulating materials - Perma-Foam Inc.
PERMA FOCUS 2000 - Sporting goods - Bausch & Lomb Inc.
PERMA-FORM - Brassieres (Bras) - Jodee Bra Co.
PERMA-FORM - Medical apparatus - Jodee, Inc.
PERMA FROST - Alcoholic beverages - Heublein, Inc.
PERMA FUSION - Cosmetics ☆ - Alleghany Pharmacal Corp.
PERMA-GARD - Adhesives and sealants - Dallas Specialty & Manufacturing Co.
PERMA-GARD - Cages–wire - Gilbert and Bennett Manufacturing Co.
PERMA-GARD - Hardware - Centryco Inc.
PERMA-GARD - Lighting equipment - General Electric Co.
PERMA-GARD - Ophthalmic goods - Sola Optical USA, Inc.
PERMA-GEL - Gel medium - Binney & Smith Inc.
PERMA-GEL - Hair care products - Helene Curtis Industries Inc.
PERMA GIFT - Postcards - Holiday Craft
PERMA-GLAS - Blenders - Sunbeam-Oster Household Products
PERMA GLAZE - Sealing compounds - Biddle Co.
PERMA GRAPHICS - Markers–felt-tip - Dri Mark Products, Inc.
PERMA GREEN - Paints - Remien & Kuhnert Co.
PERMA-GRIP - Denture materials - Lactona Corp.
PERMA GRIT - Saws–power - S-B Power Tool Co.
PERMA-GUARD - Antifreeze - Exxon Corp.
PERMA-GUARD - Insecticides - Luxello Properties, Inc.
PERMA GUARD - Insecticides - Timcorp Environmental
PERMA HIDE - Paints ☆ - Montgomery Ward & Co. Inc.
PERMA-HINGE - Electronic equipment - GAF Corp.
PERMA-HOLD - Hooks ☆ - Selfix, Inc.
PERMA-JET - Bathroom accessories ☆ - Tub-Master Corp.
PERMA JET - Printers–computer - Codo Manufacturing Corp.
PERMA JET 9000 - Printers–computer - Codo Manufacturing Corp.
PERMA JET PLUS - Printers–computer - Codo Manufacturing Corp.
PERMA-KLEEN - Floor coverings ☆ - Ralph Wilson Plastics Co.
PERMA-KNIT - Sporting goods - AstroTurf Industries Inc.
PERMA-KOOL - Fans–exhaust - Leisure Components
PERMA-KORK - Cement - G. Leblanc Corp.
PERMA KOTE - Paints - Columbia Paint Co.
PERMA-KOTE - Toilet seats - Sanderson Plumbing Products, Inc.
PERMA LAST - Paints ☆ - Devoe & Raynolds Co.
PERMA LEVEL - Hardware ☆ - J.W. Goss Co.
PERMA-LID - Containers–trash - Sears, Roebuck and Co.
PERMA-LIFE - Knife blades - Pacific Saw and Knife Co.
PERMA-LIFT - Brassieres (Bras) - Kayser-Roth Corp.
PERMA-LITE - Watches - Bulova Corp.
PERMA-LOC - Cooking utensils–aluminum ☆ - Revere Ware Corp.
PERMA LOK - Adhesives and sealants - Paragon Paint & Varnish Corp.
PERMA-LOK - Hardware - Dap Products Inc.
PERMA-LOK - Screws - Georgia-Pacific Corp.
PERMA-LURE - Yarn - Carolina International Textiles, Inc.
PERMA MATCH - Furniture polish and wax - Put-Me-On Inc.
PERMA/MOUNT 2 - Photographic equipment - Falcon Safety Products, Inc.
PERMA-NET - Apparel stores–lingerie - Formflex Foundations Inc.
PERMA-NETTING - Fencing–steel ☆ - Gilbert and Bennett Manufacturing Co.
PERMA NYL - Flags - Valley Forge Flag
PERMA PAK - Fruits–dried - Vacu-Dry Co.
PERMA PAK - Office supplies - ACCO USA, Inc.
PERMA PANEL - Electronic equipment ☆ - Arlington Display Industries
PERMA PATCH - Concrete products - Dayton Superior Corp.
PERMA-PEL - Animal feed supplements - Georgia-Pacific Corp.
PERMA-PELENT - Waterproofing compounds - Perma Stone Co.
PERMA-PIC - Toothpicks - Perma-Pic Co., Inc.
PERMA-PITCH - Roof preserver - Coopers Creek Chemical Corp.
PERMA PLASTIC - Finishing agents ☆ - Flintkote Co.
PERMA PLASTIC - Paints ☆ - GS Roofing Products Co.
PERMA-PLATE - Coatings - Siskin Enterprises, Inc.
PERMA-PLUG - Bowling balls - Master Industries Inc.
PERMA PLUG - Electrical equipment - Gem Electric Manufacturing Co. Inc.

PERMA-PLUS - Buttons - Emsig Manufacturing Corp.
PERMA POINT - Artists' materials ☆ - Binney & Smith Inc.
PERMA POLY - Brushes - Milwaukee Dustless Brush Co.
PERMA POWER - Audio equipment - Perma Power Electronics Inc.
PERMA PRESS - Stain removers - Holloway House, Inc.
PERMA-PRESSED - Fabrics ☆ - Avondale Mills
PERMA-PREST - Housewares - Sears, Roebuck and Co.
PERMA PRIMER - Roofing materials–slate - Republic Powdered Metals, Inc.
PERMA PURE - Medical apparatus - Perma Pure, Inc.
PERMA RAISED - Stationery - Regency Thermographers Inc.
PERMA-SAF - Polyethylene film sheets - Franklin Distributors Corp.
PERMA-SCALE - Film - Dietzgen Corp.
PERMA SCENT - Fishing tackle - Bullet Weights, Inc.
PERMA SCENTS - Deodorizers - Syndet Products, Inc.
PERMA-SEA - Plastics–laminated - Rawlplug Co., Inc.
PERMA-SEAL - Adhesives and sealants - Colonial Refining and Chemical Co.
PERMA-SEAL - Concrete products - CGM Inc.
PERMA-SEAL - Index cards ☆ - Master Products Manufacturing Inc.
PERMA-SEAL - Polyvinyl sheets - General Cable Corp.
PERMA-SEAM - Rods–aluminum - Stanley Hardware Div.
PERMA-SET - Emulsifiers - Archer Daniels Midland Co.
PERMA SET - Hair care products - Richard Hartwich Inc.
PERMA SHAPE - Apparel stores–lingerie - Formflex Foundations Inc.
PERMA SHARP - Dental compounds - Hu-Friedy Manufacturing Co., Inc.
PERMA-SHEEN - Cooking utensils–aluminum ☆ - Revere Ware Corp.
PERMA SHEEN - Hair care products - Richard Hartwich Inc.
PERMA-SHIELD - Labels–paper - W.H. Brady Co.
PERMA SHIELD - Paints - Colonial Refining and Chemical Co.
PERMA-SHIELD - Varnishes ☆ - Nord-Viscount Corp.
PERMA-SHIELD - Window frames - Andersen Corp.
PERMA-SHIELD FLEXIFRAME - Window frames - Andersen Corp.
PERMA-SHIELD NARROLINE - Window frames - Andersen Corp.
PERMA SHINE - Hair care products - Amital Spinning Corp.
PERMA-SILK - Flowers, plants, and seeds - D.C. Frisbey Perma-Flora Imports
PERMA SILK - Ribbons–inked - Kores Nordic USA Corp.
PERMA-SLAAT - Sporting goods - Zenith Technologies, Inc.
PERMA-SMOCK - Fabrics–polyester - Gehring Textiles Inc.
PERMA SNAP - Buttons - Herman Pearl Button Co., Inc.
PERMA SNAP BINDR - Office supplies - ACCO USA, Inc.
PERMA SPUN - Thread - American & Efird, Inc.
PERMA-STABIL - Juices - Sunkist Growers Inc.
PERMA-STAIN - Adhesives and sealants ☆ - Induron Coatings Inc.
PERMA-STAIN - Finishing agents - Duron, Inc.
PERMA-STAMP - Stamps–hand - Carolina Marking Devices, Inc.
PERMA-STEEL - Insulating materials ☆ - Globe Building Materials Inc.
PERMA STICK - Plaster–wallboard - Sherburne Ewing Wallcovering Co.
PERMA-STIK - Artists' materials ☆ - Hunt Manufacturing Co.
PERMA-STIK - Musical instrument accessories ☆ - G. Leblanc Corp.
PERMA-STONE - Veneer - Perma Stone Co.
PERMA STOR - Office supplies - ACCO USA, Inc.
PERMA-STRATE - Hair care products - Keystone Laboratories Inc.
PERMA-STRATE - Hair care products ☆ - Perma Strate Co.
PERMA-STROKE - Artists' materials ☆ - Binney & Smith Inc.
PERMA SYSTEMS - Awnings - United Textile & Supply Co.
PERMA TABS - Abrasive products - Conros Corp.
PERMA-TECH - Varnishes - Warner Industries, Inc.
PERMA-TEE - Knit goods ☆ - Three by Three
PERMA TEK - Enamels ☆ - Ponderosa Paint Manufacturing Co. Inc.
PERMA-TEMP - Employment agencies–temporary help - T.T.C., Illinois, Inc.
PERMA-TENSION - Musical instrument accessories - Grover/Trophy Musical Products Inc.
PERMA-THANE - Coatings - Wisconsin Protective Coatings Corp.
PERMA-THINZ - Chemical preparations - Georgia-Pacific Corp.
PERMA-TILE - Epoxy coatings - Buten Paint & Wallpaper
PERMA TILE - Tiles–ceramic ☆ - American Olean Tile Co.
PERMA TITE - Combs - F. Wolkow & Sons
PERMA TORQUE - Gaskets - Fel-Pro Inc.
PERMA-TREAT - Wood products - Coastal Lumber Co.
PERMA-TRIM - Roofing materials - Benjamin Obdyke Inc.
PERMA-TUCK - Fabrics–nylon - Gehring Textiles Inc.
PERMA-TUFF - Floor coverings–tile - Kentile Floors Inc.
PERMA-TURF - Rubber–vulcanized - Tirec Corp.
PERMA TWEEZ - Electronic equipment - General Medical Corp.
PERMA-TY - Health care products - Maddak Inc.
PERMA VENEER - Enamels - Red Spot Paint & Varnish Co., Inc.
PERMA VENEER JR. - Enamels - Red Spot Paint & Varnish Co., Inc.

☆ = Now out of production

PERMA-VENT - Aluminum products - N.H. Rudeen Co.
PERMA WALK - Mats - JCH International Inc.
PERMA-WALL - Doors–glass - Kohler Co.
PERMA WASH - Chemicals–photographic - Brandess Kalt Aetna
PERMA-WELD - Adhesives and sealants - CGM Inc.
PERMA-WHITE - Paints - William Zinsser & Co. Inc.
PERMA-WICKER - Garden furniture–rattan ☆ - Lloyd/Flanders Industries
PERMA WRAP - Golfing equipment - Lamkin Corp.
PERMA-WRAP SOF-CORD - Golfing equipment - Lamkin Corp.
PERMABAC - Floor coverings - Shaw Industries Inc.
PERMABEST - Floor coverings ☆ - Congoleum Corp.
PERMABOND - Adhesives and sealants - Dap Products Inc.
PERMABOND - Coatings - Permabond Industries Inc.
PERMABOND - Padding–foam - Crain Industries Inc.
PERMABOND - Primers - Nationwide Chemical Coating Manufacturers, Inc.
PERMABRICK - Bricks ☆ - Permagrain Products, Inc.
PERMABRITES - Tiles–ceramic - Dal-Tile Corp.
PERMAC - Flatware component - JMP-Newcor International, Inc.
PERMAC PUROVA - Filters–air - Boewe Passat Drycleaning and Laundry Machinery Corp.
PERMACAD - Electronic equipment - Rollei of America Inc.
PERMACAL - Decals - Commercial Decal Inc.
PERMACAL - Paints - Triangle Coatings Inc.
PERMACAST - Pistons - Grover Piston Ring, Inc.
PERMACEL - Electrical current conductive tapes - Permacel
PERMACHEM - Wood products - Georgia-Pacific Corp.
PERMACLAD - Adhesives and sealants - Miller Purcell Co.
PERMACOASTER - Housewares ☆ - Quality House Inc.
PERMACOAT - Paints ☆ - Pella Corp.
PERMACOAT PLUS - Paints ☆ - Pella Corp.
PERMACOLOR - Antennas - TDP Electronics
PERMACOLOR - Fishing tackle - Bullet Weights, Inc.
PERMACOLOR - Photographic equipment - Mactac Inc. (Packaging Closures Systems Div.)
PERMACOTE COLORS - Paper - Permalin Products Co.
PERMACOTE LINACOUSTIC - Insulating materials - Schuller International, Inc.
PERMACOTE OFFSET - Paper - Permalin Products Co.
PERMACOTE SPIRACOUSTIC - Insulating materials - Schuller International, Inc.
PERMACRYL - Enamels - Vogel Paint and Wax Co., Inc.
PERMACRYLIC - Adhesives and sealants - Biddle Co.
PERMACUT - Cutlery - JMP-Newcor International, Inc.
PERMADEX - Leather goods ☆ - The Rytex Co.
PERMADRI - Inks–gravure - Graphic Utilities, Inc.
PERMADRYPLUS - Gaskets - Fel-Pro Inc.
PERMAFILE - Office supplies - ACCO USA, Inc.
PERMAFILL - Paints - Indopco, Inc.
PERMAFILM - Artists' materials ☆ - Hunt Manufacturing Co.
PERMAFILM - Photographic equipment ☆ - Edwal Scientific Products Corp.
PERMAFLEX - Boats - Wellington Leisure Products, Inc.
PERMAFLEX - Commercial printing - Business Records Corp.
PERMAFLEX - Contact lenses - Cooper Companies Inc.
PERMAFLEX - Fuel additives - Twin Commander Aircraft Corp.
PERMAFLEX - Gloves - Leisure Leather Ltd.
PERMAFLEX - Luggage ☆ - Lark Luggage Co. Inc.
PERMAFLEX - Mattresses - B.G. Industries Inc.
PERMAFLEX - Plastics–laminated - Mactac Inc. (Packaging Closures Systems Div.)
PERMAFLEX MEPUQUE - Contact lenses - Cooper Companies Inc.
PERMAFLEX/NATURALS - Contact lenses - Cooper Companies Inc.
PERMAFLEX/THIN - Contact lenses - Cooper Companies Inc.
PERMAFLEX/UV NATURALS - Contact lenses - Cooper Companies Inc.
PERMAFLOAT - Buoys–cork - CelloFoam North America Inc.
PERMAFLOAT - Mattresses - B.G. Industries Inc.
PERMAFOAM - Tires - Goodyear Tire & Rubber Co.
PERMAFORM THERMOSET - Spas - Tom Tabor
PERMAFRAME - Frames–picture - Permaframe, Inc.
PERMAFROST - Hobby kits ☆ - Blumenthal/Lansing Co.
PERMAFUSE - Hobby kits - Amity Inc.
PERMAFUSED - Fencing–chain link - Anchor Fence Co. Inc.
PERMAFUSED - Footwear - Lehigh Safety Shoe Co.
PERMAGARD - Plywood - Georgia-Pacific Corp.
PERMAGILE - Adhesives and sealants - Permagile Industries Inc.
PERMAGIZER - Skin care products - John Amico Expressive Hair Care Products
PERMAGLAS - Glass products - A.O. Smith Harvestore Products, Inc.

PERMAGLOSS - Dunn Edwards Corp.
PERMAGLOSS - Coatings - Kohler Co.
PERMAGRAIN - Flooring–hardwood - Permagrain Products, Inc.
PERMAGRIP - Adhesives and sealants - Imperial Adhesives Inc.
PERMAGRIP - Gloves–leather - Titleist & Foot-Joy Worldwide
PERMAGRO - Fertilizers - Sunbelt Nursery Group, Inc.
PERMAGUM - Adhesives and sealants - BASF Corp.
PERMAHOOD - Filters–air - HEPA Corp.
PERMAICE - Frosting - Parrish's Cake Decorating Supplies Inc.
PERMAID - Cosmetics ☆ - Alleghany Pharmacal Corp.
PERMAKIL - Pesticides–household - Bonide Products, Inc.
PERMAKOTE - Coatings - Nationwide Chemical Coating Manufacturers, Inc.
PERMAKOTE - Paints - Triangle Coatings Inc.
PERMAKOTE PLUS - Coatings - Nationwide Chemical Coating Manufacturers, Inc.
PERMAKOTE PLUS - Paints - Triangle Coatings Inc.
PERMALAB - Electronics equipment - American Desk Manufacturing Co.
PERMALASH - Wire - Maryland Specialty Wire Inc.
PERMALBA - Paints–artists' - Martin F. Weber Co.
PERMALEEN - Enamels ☆ - Fuller-O'Brien Paints Inc.
PERMALEX COLORS - Paper - Permalin Products Co.
PERMALEX EL-HI - Paper - Permalin Products Co.
PERMALEX END - Paper - Permalin Products Co.
PERMALIFE - Batteries - Standard Industries (Permalife Glass Fiber Div.)
PERMALIFE - Paper - Howard Paper Mills Inc.
PERMALIFE - Paper–bond - Fox River Paper Co.
PERMALIFE - Pet products ☆ - Hartz Mountain Corp.
PERMALIFE - Windows–storm - Burton Enterprises Inc.
PERMALIN COLORS - Paper - Permalin Products Co.
PERMALIN WHITES - Paper - Permalin Products Co.
PERMALINE - Wire - General Cable Corp.
PERMALINED - Waterproofing compounds - Henschel Manufacturing Co.
PERMALINS BONDED LEATHER - Leather - Permalin Products Co.
PERMALISTIC - Adhesives and sealants - Dap Products Inc.
PERMALITE - Footwear - Lehigh Safety Shoe Co.
PERMALITE - Luggage - Lark Luggage Co. Inc.
PERMALITE - Paints - Brouk Co.
PERMALITE - Paints - Fuller-O'Brien Paints Inc.
PERMALITE - Plaster–wallboard - Perm-E-Lastic Inc.
PERMALIZE - Paints - Pratt & Lambert, Inc.
PERMALOCK - Binders - Rollei of America Inc.
PERMALOCK - Golfing equipment - Perfection Corp.
PERMALOID - Waxes–paraffin - M and M Chemical Products Inc.
PERMALOK - Housewares stores - Michael E. Argent
PERMALON - Adhesives and sealants - Testworth Laboratories Inc.
PERMALON - Ironing board pads - Magla Products Inc.
PERMALON - Liners and covers–pond, pit, and landfill - Reef Industries, Inc.
PERMALON - Office supplies ☆ - Smead Manufacturing Co.
PERMALOOM - Padding–foam - Hobbs Bonded Fibers
PERMALOX - Adhesives and sealants ☆ - Bridgestone/Firestone, Inc.
PERMALUBE - Oils–lubricating ☆ - Amoco Oil Co.
PERMALUM - Paints - Seagraves Coatings
PERMALUME - Bathroom fixtures - Showerlux USA
PERMAMATIC - Luggage - Samsonite Corp.
PERMANENCE - Floor coverings–carpet and rugs - Aladdin Mills, Inc.
PERMANENT HEDGE - Fencing–plastic - National Metal Industries, Inc.
PERMANENT LIFE - Skin care products - Revlon Consumer Products Corp.
PERMANENT METALLIC - Adhesives and sealants - K & W Products
PERMANENT POWER - Markers–felt-tip - Pentech International Inc.
PERMANENT RECORD - Paper - Southworth Co.
PERMANENT SEALER - Adhesives and sealants - W.J. Ruscoe Co.
PERMANENT SOLUTION, THE - Computer peripheral equipment - Distribution Architects International, Inc.
PERMANENT SUCCESS - Hair care products - Naturelle, Inc.
PERMANENT TRIM - Paints - Perry & Derrick Co.
PERMANENT VALUE PLAN - Rings–jewelry - Artcarved Inc.
PERMANITE - Paints - Graham Paint and Varnish Co.
PERMANIZED PARCHMENT - Paper–bond ☆ - Fox River Paper Co.
PERMANONE - Insect repellents - Apex Medical Corp.
PERMANONE INSECT REPELLENT - Insect repellents - Agrevo Environmental Health, Inc.
PERMANOX - Paints - Commercial Chemical Co. Inc.
PERMAPAK - Batteries ☆ - Mamiya America Corp.
PERMAPAQUE - Markers–felt-tip - Sakura Color Products of America, Inc.
PERMAPAQUE - Markers–felt-tip ☆ - Sakura of America

☆ = Now out of production

PERMAPATCH - Adhesives and sealants - Nationwide Chemical Coating Manufacturers, Inc.

PERMAPOINT - Office supplies ☆ - Faber-Castell Corp.

PERMAPOL - Paints - Courtaulds Aerospace Inc.

PERMAQUIK - Waterproofing compounds - Permagile Industries Inc.

PERMARKINK - Indelible inks - Irwin-Hodson Co.

PERMAROLLER - Pens - Pentel of America, Ltd.

PERMAROOF - Adhesives and sealants - Republic Powdered Metals, Inc.

PERMASCAL PAK - Tubes–plastic - VisiPak

PERMASCAPE - Mats - Aquapore Moisture Systems, Inc.

PERMASEAL - Adhesives and sealants - Kimberton Enterprises, Inc.

PERMASEAL - Caulking compounds - Kelley Technical Coatings Inc.

PERMASEAL - Food products - Givaudan Roure

PERMASEAL - Pistons - Grover Piston Ring, Inc.

PERMASET - Floor coverings–carpet and rugs - Burlington House Carpets

PERMASHAPE - Trowels - Marshalltown Trowel Co.

PERMASHARP - Cutlery - Gutmann Cutlery Inc.

PERMASHARP - Pens - Dri Mark Products, Inc.

PERMASHEEN - Paints - Dunn Edwards Corp.

PERMASHEEN-DECOGLO - Paints - Dunn Edwards Corp.

PERMASHIELD - Coatings - American Marine Coatings, Inc.

PERMASHIELD - Mirrors - Metropolitan Mirror & Glass Co. Inc.

PERMA*SHINE - Badges–uniform - Best Emblem & Insignia Co.

PERMASHINE - Floor waxes - Advance Cleaning Products Inc.

PERMASHINE - Paints - Mann's Bait Co.

PERMASOL - Fabrics ☆ - Manart-Hirsch Co. Inc.

PERMASOL - Paints - Shiva Inc.

PERMASOL - Pharmaceutical ☆ - CooperVision Inc.

PERMASOLE - Shoes ☆ - Endicott Johnson Corp.

PERMASPAN - Insulating materials–foam - CelloFoam North America Inc.

PERMASSURE - Blinds–vertical - Hunter Douglas, Inc.

PERMASTABIL - Seasonings - Firmenich Inc.

PERMASTONE - Casting medium - Activa Products Inc.

PERMASTONE - Water purification systems - Aquaculture Research/ Environmental Associates Inc.

PERMASTRIP - Garden equipment - Permaloc Aluminum Edging

PERMASTYLE - Moldings and trim–automotive - Uretech International Inc.

PERMATE - Cosmetics - Revlon-Realistic Professional Products Inc.

PERMATEX - Adhesives and sealants - Loctite Corp.

PERMATEX - Photographic equipment - Eastman Kodak Co.

PERMATHAL - Bedding–linen ☆ - West Point-Pepperell Inc.

PERMATHENE - Health care products - CCA Industries, Inc.

PERMATHENE - Pharmaceutical preparations - Alleghany Pharmacal Corp.

PERMATITE - Weather stripping ☆ - Pirelli Power Transmission Corp.

PERMATONE - Cosmetics - Faberge Co.

PERMATONE - Drums–musical instruments - Fred Gretsch Enterprises

PERMATONES - Tiles–ceramic - Dal-Tile Corp.

PERMATOP - Finishing agents - Permagile Industries Inc.

PERMATRAN - Measuring instruments - MOCON/Modern Controls, Inc.

PERMATROL - Electrical equipment - Precision Multiple Controls, Inc.

PERMATUL - Dishwashers–household - General Electric Co.

PERMATWIST - Lighting fixtures - Lumatech Corp.

PERMATYPE - Decals and transfers - C-Thru Ruler Co.

PERMAVINYL - Floor coverings ☆ - Congoleum Corp.

PERMAVIS - Laboratory apparatus - Kurt J. Lesker Co.

PERMAVISION - Hair care products ☆ - Gefden International Inc.

PERMAVIVE - Hair care products - Cosmair Inc.

PERMAWALL - Wallpaper - Wolf-Gordon Inc.

PERMAWALL III - Wallpaper - Wolf-Gordon Inc.

PERMAWELD-Z - Paints - Goldblatt Tool Co.

PERMAWELT - Adhesives and sealants - Imperial Adhesives Inc.

PERMAWOOD - Plywood - Darlington Veneer Co. Inc.

PERMAX - Roofing materials - Henry Co.

PERMBLOK - Hoses - Bundy Corp.

PERMCISION - Hair care products - Mastey De Paris

PERMCLEAN - Hair care products - Tyler Creations Inc.

PERMCLIP PRODUCT EARFLAP - File folders - Permclip Products Corp.

PERMEATE GOLD - Soybean oil - Westmark AG Group, Inc.

PERMENAMEL - Key chains and tags - Crownmark Corp.

PERMERAL II - Adhesives and sealants - Rock-Tred Corp.

PERMESSENTIALS - Hair care products - Demert & Dougherty, Inc.

PERMETAGE - Marble products - Permagrain Products, Inc.

PERMETTE - Hair care products - Faberge Co.

PERMFECTION - Hair care products - Nexxus Products Co.

PERMFUR - Hair care products - Rusk Inc.

PERMGLOSS - Hair care products - Image Laboratories, Inc.

PERMI-CAULK - Caulking compounds - Permite Corp.

PERMIDENT - Luggage - Airway Industries, Inc.

PERMINATES - Hair care products - For Perms Only Inc.

PERMION - Shower stalls–metal - Sterling Plumbing Group Inc.

PERMISO - Cigars - Gesty Trading & Manufacturing Corp.

PERMISSION - Hair care products - John Amico Expressive Hair Care Products

PERMITE - Paints - Permite Corp.

PERMITIL - Pharmaceutical preparations - Schering-Plough Healthcare Products

PERMO - Audio equipment ☆ - Fidelitone Inc.

PERMO-GREEN - Paint ☆ - Continental Products Co.

PERMO-POINT - Phonographic needles ☆ - Fidelitone Inc.

PERMO-SEAL - Adhesives and sealants - Pioneer Manufacturing Co.

PERMOGGI - Hair care products - Gelle-International Ltd.

PERMON - Enamels ☆ - Lilly Perfection Paint

PERMOPLAST - Clay–modeling - American Art Clay Co. Inc.

PERMOXYN - Aquarium accessories - Kordon

PERMOXYN - Aquarium accessories - Novalek, Inc.

PERMTEC - Audio equipment - Professional Audio Systems

PERMTINE - Paint and varnish thinner - Binney & Smith Inc.

PERMUTATION - Hair care products ☆ - Gefden International Inc.

PERMUTIT - Water treating compounds - Permutit Co. Inc.

PERMY+ - Funnels ☆ - KMS Research Inc.

PERMZORB - Hair care products - W.R. Rayson Co., Inc.

PERNAEMON - Pharmaceutical preparations ☆ - Organon Inc.

PERNAVIT - Health care products ☆ - Ferndale Laboratories, Inc.

PERNOD - Liqueur - Austin, Nichols & Co., Inc.

PERNOVA - Food products machinery - SCI Scandicrafts Inc.

PERNOX - Pharmaceutical preparations - Westwood-Squibb Pharmaceuticals, Inc.

PERNUTS - Snack foods - Dolefam Corp.

PERO - Cereal - Nestle USA

PERO - Food products - Liberty Richter Inc.

PERO-CREME - Hair care products - Larkspur Group Inc.

PERO-TIPP - Hair care products - Larkspur Group Inc.

PERONE - Hydrogen peroxide - E.I. Dupont de Nemours and Co.

PERONI - Beverages–malt - Barton Brands, Ltd.

PERONI - Beverages–malt - Canandaigua Wine Co. Inc.

PEROX-OUT - Hair care products - Hair Institute

PEROXICARE - Toothpaste - Church and Dwight Co. Inc.

PEROXY - Health care products - Vital Health Products Ltd.

PEROXYCLEAR - Hydrogen peroxide - EKA Chemicals Inc.

PEROXYL - Mouthwashes - Colgate Oral Pharmaceuticals Inc.

PERPENDICULAR ARCH - Sporting goods - Patterson-Williams Manufacturing Co. Inc.

PERPETUA - Calendars ☆ - House of Doolittle

PERPETUA - Recording label - Miller & Kreisel Sound Corp.

PERPETUAL - Floor coverings–carpet and rugs ☆ - Karastan-Bigelow Inc.

PERPETUAL - Watches - Rolex Watch USA, Inc.

PERPETUAL BIRTHDAY - Calendars - Stevenson Industries Inc.

PERPETUAL CALENDAR - Computer software - SourceView Software International

PERPETUAL CALENDAR - Watches - Blancpain (Time Products Inc.)

PERPETUAL MARKERS - Tombstones - Hightower Oil Co., Inc.

PERPETUAL PINE - Doors–wood - Passages Ltd.

PERPETUAL PLATINUM - Dental equipment - Jeneric/Pentron Inc.

PERPETUAL PRESS - Publisher's imprints - Progressive Media, Inc.

PERPETUAL SYSTEMS - Computer hardware - Computer Plus, Inc.

PERPETUATOR - Hair care products - Walneir Group, Inc.

PERPETUCAL - Calendars - Success Business Industries, Inc.

PERPETUWALL - Paper–thermoplastics coated - Arden Architectural Specialties, Inc.

PERPHECT - Chemicals - Orion Research Inc.

PERPLEXING PUZZLES - Computer software - Hartley Courseware Inc.

PERPLEXX - Computer software - Spinnaker Software Corp.

PERQ - Computer peripheral equipment - Transpower Industries, Inc.

PERQ PRODUCTIVITY ERGONOMICS RELIABILITY QUALITY - Tools– power-driven - Aimco - Automotive Industrial Marketing Corporation

PERQUACKEY - Games - Lakeside Games

PERRAULT - Floor coverings–carpet and rugs ☆ - Karastan-Bigelow Inc.

PERRELLA - Gloves ☆ - La Crasia Inc.

PERRI - Sausages - Perri Sausage Inc.

PERRIER - Tableware–china - Susquehanna Glass Co.

PERRIER - Water–bottled or canned - Perrier Group of America Inc.

☆ = Now out of production

PERRIER BERRY - Water–bottled or canned ☆ - Perrier Group of America Inc.

PERRIER-JOUET - Beverages–alcohol - Co. Store

PERRIER JOUET - Wines - Seagram's Chateau & Estate Wines Co.

PERRIER VALVERT - Water–bottled or canned ☆ - Perrier Group of America Inc.

PERRIER WITH A TWIST - Water–bottled or canned - Perrier Group of America Inc.

PERRIN DE OLERON - Food products - Crystal Food Import Corp.

PERRINCRAFT - Bathroom accessories - Schwarz Bros. Plastics

PERRINE - Sporting goods - Orbex Inc.

PERROT-COLOR - Electronic equipment - Leica USA Inc.

PERRUZO - Boys' apparel - Viva L.A.

PERRY - Apparel–women's - Perry Manufacturing Co.

PERRY - Brushes–paint - Corona Brushes Inc.

PERRY - Chairs–folding - Krueger International, Inc.

PERRY - Frames–eyeglass - U.S. Optical Frame Co.

PERRY - Furniture - Charles O. Perry

PERRY - Skin care products - Perry Products

PERRY 20S LOW SMOKE - Heating equipment - Perry Fiberglass Products, Inc.

PERRY BASS - Boats–motor ☆ - Sport-Craft Inc.

PERRY CLASSICS - Apparel–women's - Perry Manufacturing Co.

PERRY ELLIS - Apparel and accessories - International Designer Accessories

PERRY ELLIS - Apparel and accessories - Salant/Manhattan Industries

PERRY ELLIS - Apparel stores–sports - Perry Ellis Sportswear Inc.

PERRY ELLIS - Apparel–men's - Greif Cos.

PERRY ELLIS - Health care products ☆ - Avon Products, Inc.

PERRY ELLIS - Hosiery–women's - Trimfit Inc.

PERRY ELLIS - Leather goods - Prince Gardner Inc.

PERRY ELLIS - Leather goods - Westport Corp.

PERRY ELLIS - Luggage - Gateway Travelware

PERRY ELLIS - Luggage - Sirco International Corp.

PERRY ELLIS - Scarves - Vera Co.

PERRY ELLIS - Sunglasses - Eyewear Designs Ltd.

PERRY ELLIS - Sunglasses - Riviera Trading, Inc.

PERRY ELLIS AMERICA - Watches - Perry Ellis Sportswear Inc.

PERRY ELLIS LEGWEAR - Apparel and accessories - Trimfit Inc.

PERRY ELLIS PORTFOLIO - Apparel and accessories - Perry Ellis International, Inc.

PERRY ELLIS PORTFOLIO - Apparel–men's - Greif Cos.

PERRY GOLSHANI - Bath salts - Brant Corp.

PERRY NEW YORK - Apparel–women's - Perry Manufacturing Co.

PERRY PERFORMANCE CLASSIC - Educational materials - JM Perry Corp.

PERRY PERISCOPE - Toys - Fisher-Price, Inc.

PERRY PRINCIPLES, THE - Educational materials - JM Perry Corp.

PERRY SPORT - Apparel–women's - Perry Manufacturing Co.

PERRYCHEWS - Vitamins and nutritional supplements ☆ - Perry Laboratories

PERRYLOK - Anchors - Securtech Co.

PERRY'S - Ice cream - Perry's Dairy

PERRY'S MAJECTIC - Beverages–malt - Riverosa

PERRY'S NON-ALCOHOLIC NO KICK BREW THREE LEGGED MULE - Beverages - Perry's Majestic Beer, Inc.

PERRY'S PLOUGHMAN'S PALE ALE - Beverages–alcohol - Perry's Majestic Beer, Inc.

PERRY'S SIX MONTHS - Beverages–malt - Riverosa

PERRY'S STEEL MULE LAGER - Beverages–alcohol - Perry's Majestic Beer, Inc.

PERRYVITE - Pharmaceutical preparations ☆ - Perry Laboratories

PERRYWARE - Containers ☆ - Clayson Co.

PERRYWINKLE - Boats–motor - National Metal Roof Services, Inc.

PERS-IN - Floor coverings–carpet and rugs ☆ - Capel, Inc.

PERSA-GEL - Pharmaceutical preparations - Ortho Pharmaceutical Corp.

PERSA-GEL W - Pharmaceutical preparations - Ortho Pharmaceutical Corp.

PERSANTINE - Pharmaceutical preparations - Boehringer Ingelheim Pharmaceuticals Inc.

PERSEPOLIS - Recording label - Thomas Wiggins Associates

PERSHING 1-A - Toys–models ☆ - Estes Industries

PERSHING PARK - Tiles–ceramic - Payless Cashways Inc.

PERSHING ROCKET - Fireworks - American Promotional Events, Inc.

PERSHORE - Dinnerware–glass ☆ - Royal China & Porcelain Companies Inc.

PERSIA - Tiles–ceramic - Monarch Tile Inc.

PERSIAN ACCENT - Floor coverings ☆ - Congoleum Corp.

PERSIAN CLAY - Plastics ☆ - Douglas & Sturgess

PERSIAN CORD - Rope - Wellington Leisure Products, Inc.

PERSIAN COURTS - Floor coverings–carpet and rugs - Roxbury Carpet Co.

PERSIAN DELIGHT - Rice ☆ - Persian Delight Inc.

PERSIAN FEATHER - Fabrics–flock - Kirk-Brummel

PERSIAN GARDEN - Apparel–women's - Wacoal America Inc.

PERSIAN JEWEL - Floor coverings–carpet and rugs ☆ - Stanton Carpet Corp.

PERSIAN LILAC - Talcum powders ☆ - Houbigant, Inc.

PERSIAN MASTERS - Floor coverings–carpet and rugs ☆ - Langhorne Carpet Co. Inc.

PERSIAN ROOM - Floor coverings–carpet and rugs - Barrett Carpet Mills Inc.

PERSIAN TILE - Floor coverings ☆ - Congoleum Corp.

PERSIAN TREASURES - Wallpaper - Sandpiper Studios

PERSIAN TREASURES II - Wallpaper - Sandpiper Studios

PERSIANA - Jewelry–costume - Royal Bead Novelty Co. Inc.

PERSIANNA - Fabrics–broadcloth - Collins & Aikman Corp.

PERSICA - Wallpaper - Capital Carousel Inc.

PERSIMMON - Lipsticks - Cosmair Inc.

PERSIST - Agricultural products - Precision Laboratories, Inc.

PERSIST-ALERT - Ammunition - Valley Products & Design Inc.

PERSISTENCE - Computer software - Persistence Software, Inc.

PERSISTENCE - Publisher's imprints - Creative Self Motivation, Inc.

PERSISTOR - Computer software - John H. Godley

PERSKE - Motors–automotive - CRP Industries, Inc.

PERSNICKETY - Chemical preparations - Syneco Systems, Inc.

PERSOL - Eyeglasses ☆ - Vangurd Sunglasses Inc.

PERSOL - Ophthalmic goods - Luxottica

PERSON TO PERSON - Games - Smethport Specialty Co.

PERSON TO PERSON - Greeting cards ☆ - American Greetings Corp.

PERSON TO PERSON/2 - Computer software - International Business Machines Corp.

PERSONA - Computer peripheral equipment - Intellivoice Communications, Inc.

PERSONA - Electronic equipment - Monster Cable Products, Inc.

PERSONA - Plumbing fixtures–metal ☆ - Barclay Products Ltd.

PERSONA - Shower stalls–metal - Kohler Co.

PERSONA ID CARD PRINTER - Printers–computer - Fargo Electronics Inc.

PERSONA PLATE - Nameplates–engraved - Namesign Corp.

PERSONA PLUS - Printers–computer - Fargo Electronics Inc.

PERSONACARD - Computer hardware - National Semiconductor Corp.

PERSONAL - Apparel–women's - Leslie Fay Companies Inc.

PERSONAL - Golfing equipment - Northwestern Golf Co.

PERSONAL ACCOMPANIST - Computer peripheral equipment - Coda Music Technology, Inc.

PERSONAL ACCOUNTANT - Computer software - Softsync Inc.

PERSONAL ADDS - Hobby kits - JCA, Inc.

PERSONAL AMPLIFIER - Hearing aids - Electone Inc.

PERSONAL ATTENDANT - Computer software - High Tech Intelligence, Inc.

PERSONAL ATTENTION - Wallpaper - Marburg Wallcoverings Inc.

PERSONAL BANKER - Calculators ☆ - Texas Instruments Inc.

PERSONAL BEST - Hair care products - Conair Corp.

PERSONAL BRANCH - Computer software - CFI Proservices, Inc.

PERSONAL BREEZE - Fans–electric - Circulair, Inc.

PERSONAL BREWERY - Beverages - G.W. Kent, Inc.

PERSONAL BUDGET SYSTEM - Computer software - SourceView Software International

PERSONAL BUSINESS CENTER - Computer software - Aegis Systems Inc.

PERSONAL BUSINESS THEATRE - Tape recorders - Jean-Philippe Gay

PERSONAL CARD FILE - Computer software - Smith Corona Corp.

PERSONAL CATHETER - Catheters - Rochester Medical Corp.

PERSONAL CHEF - Computer software - Parsons Technology, Inc.

PERSONAL CHOICE - Labels–paper - Artistic Greetings, Inc.

PERSONAL CHOICES - Tiles–ceramic - Summitville Tiles, Inc.

PERSONAL COACHING FOR RESULTS - Publisher's imprints - Pacific Institute Inc.

PERSONAL COMFORT SYSTEM - Heating equipment - York International Corp.

PERSONAL COOLING DEVICE - Air conditioning equipment - Cramer Products Co.

PERSONAL CURRENCY TABULATOR - Business forms - Holden Corp.

PERSONAL DECORATOR - Computer software - Power Solutions, Inc.

PERSONAL DEFENDERE - Alarm system - Electronic Defense Systems Corp.

PERSONAL DEFENSE - Ammunition - Federal-Hoffman, Inc.

PERSONAL DIGITAL COMPANION TOUCAN - Computers–personal - Omron Office Automation Products Inc.

PERSONAL DIGNITY - Mattresses - Care Systems Inc.

PERSONAL EAR - Hearing aids - Qualitone

PERSONAL EDITION - Calendars - Personal Edition, Inc.

PERSONAL EDITION - Computer storage devices - Ensemble Information Systems, Inc.

PERSONAL EFFECTS - Apparel and accessories - Newstar Group, Inc.

PERSONAL EFFECTS - Wallpaper ☆ - Old Deerfield Fabrics Inc.

PERSONAL ETHERNET - Computer hardware - Grand Junction Networks, Inc.

PERSONAL EXPRESS - Postcards - Argus Communications

PERSONAL EYES - Eye shadow ☆ - Cosrich Inc.

PERSONAL FINANCE FOR DUMMIE$ - Publisher's imprints - International Data Group, Inc.

PERSONAL FINISHES - Bathroom fixtures - Alsons Corp.

PERSONAL FIT - Patterns–clothing ☆ - Simplicity Pattern Co., Inc.

PERSONAL FM - Telephone apparatus - Williams Sound Corp.

PERSONAL FOOD ANALYST - Computer software - Mirical Corp.

PERSONAL HARBOR - Office furniture - Steelcase Inc.

PERSONAL HEALTH - Skin care products - Loksarang D. Hardas

PERSONAL HEALTH JOURNAL - Computer software - Parsons Technology, Inc.

PERSONAL HOME INVENTORY - Computer software - Parsons Technology, Inc.

PERSONAL HOOPER - Craft supplies - Letter Perfect Inc.

PERSONAL II - Apparel–women's - Leslie Fay Companies Inc.

PERSONAL IMPRESSIONS - Notebooks and notepads - Rediform

PERSONAL INSPIRATIONS - Greeting cards - Russ Berrie and Co., Inc.

PERSONAL INTELLIGENT COMMUNICATOR - Electronic equipment - Panasonic Co.

PERSONAL-IZED - Floor coverings ☆ - Congoleum Corp.

PERSONAL KADDY - Golfing equipment - G.G.A., Inc.

PERSONAL LAW FIRM - Computer software - IMSI

PERSONAL MAILMAN - Computer software - Reach Software Corp.

PERSONAL MAINTENANCE ASSISTANT - Computer software - Datastream Systems Inc.

PERSONAL MEDIA - Computer software - Gaia Software, Inc.

PERSONAL MODEL - Golfing equipment ☆ - Louisville Golf Club Co. Inc.

PERSONAL MODELER - Computers - BPM Technology, Inc.

PERSONAL NUTRITION PROFILE - Business forms - Nutrilite, Div. of Amway Corp.

PERSONAL/OFFICE RECEPTIONIST - Telephone answering machines ☆ - Bogen Communications, Inc.

PERSONAL ONE, THE - Beverages–malt ☆ - Dribeck Importers, Inc.

PERSONAL ORGANIZERS - Filing cabinets–metal - Hedges Manufacturing Co.

PERSONAL P.A. - Telephone apparatus - Williams Sound Corp.

PERSONAL PACE - Lawn mowers - Toro Co.

PERSONAL PARTNER, THE - Computers–personal - Panasonic Co.

PERSONAL PETITES - Apparel–women's - Leslie Fay Companies Inc.

PERSONAL PHONE SERIES - Radio communications equipment - Motorola, Inc. (Land Mobile Products Sector)

PERSONAL PLEASURES - Colognes - Conopco, Inc.

PERSONAL PLEASURES - Skin care products - Chesebrough-Pond's USA Co.

PERSONAL POST OFFICE - Office supplies - Metal Products Engineering Inc.

PERSONAL POSTAGES - Greeting cards ☆ - Amberley Greeting Card Co.

PERSONAL POSTERS - Photographic equipment - Blow Ups Inc.

PERSONAL POWER - Electric fans - Holmes Products, Corp.

PERSONAL PREFERENCE - Wallpaper ☆ - Imperial Wallcoverings, Inc.

PERSONAL PRIDE - Paints - Servistar Corp.

PERSONAL PRIVACY ZONE - Air purification systems - IEP, Inc.

PERSONAL PUNCH - Paper punches - Merrick Industries Inc.

PERSONAL RECORD - Jogging suits - Dayton Hudson Corp.

PERSONAL RECORDKEEPER - Computer software - Nolo Press/Folklaw Inc.

PERSONAL REXX - Computer software - Quercus Systems

PERSONAL ROUTING - Computer software - 3Com Corp.

PERSONAL SAFETY - Self-defense spray - Personal Safety Corp.

PERSONAL SCIENCE LABORATORY - Educational materials - Team Labs Corp.

PERSONAL SELECTION - Candy - McDonald Candy Co. Inc.

PERSONAL SELECTION - Skin care products - Fred Hayman Beverly Hills Inc.

PERSONAL SHORTHAND - Publisher's imprints - National Book Co.

PERSONAL SMART CHARGER - Battery chargers - Alexander Manufacturing Co.

PERSONAL SOUND ENVIRONMENT - Audio equipment - Sonics Associates, Inc.

PERSONAL SPA - Lotions - Conopco, Inc.

PERSONAL SPIRIT - Apparel and accessories - Marisa Christina, Inc.

PERSONAL SURROUNDINGS - Novelty items - Harold-Lawrence Associates Inc.

PERSONAL SYSTEM/1 - Computer software - International Business Machines Corp.

PERSONAL TALKER - Amplifiers - Voltronics, Inc.

PERSONAL, THE - Office machines - Park Sherman

PERSONAL TOUCH - Floor coverings–carpet and rugs - Mohawk Industries Inc.

PERSONAL TOUCH - Floor coverings–carpet and rugs ☆ - American Carpet Mills

PERSONAL TOUCH - Greeting cards - Hallmark Cards Inc.

PERSONAL TOUCH - Medical apparatus - Nedco Inc.

PERSONAL TOUCH - Razors - Schick/Wilkinson

PERSONAL TOUCH 800 SERVICE - Communications equipment–satellite - Touch 1 Communications, Inc.

PERSONAL TOUCH SLIM - Razor blades ☆ - Schick/Wilkinson

PERSONAL TOUCHES - Jewelry - Jackmail Jewelry Inc.

PERSONAL TOUCHES - Tiles–ceramic - Laufen Ceramic Tile

PERSONAL TRAINER - Exercising equipment ☆ - Maximus Fitness Products

PERSONAL TRAINING SYSTEMS - Computer software - Personal Training Systems

PERSONAL TREASURES - Display racks - Jacmel Jewelry Inc.

PERSONAL VALET - Apparel and accessories - Design Your Drawers, Inc.

PERSONAL WARES - Hobby kits - Janlynn Corp.

PERSONAL WILL WRITER - Computer software - Parsons Technology, Inc.

PERSONAL WINERY - Containers–glass - G.W. Kent, Inc.

PERSONALAIRE - Deodorizers - Health-Tech, Inc.

PERSONALASER - Lasers - RTMC Inc.

PERSONALHYB - Laboratory apparatus - Stratagene

PERSONALI-T'S - T-shirts–men's - S.A.S. Ventures Inc.

PERSONALINE - Musical instrument accessories ☆ - Selmer Co. Inc.

PERSONALINES - Vitamins and nutritional supplements ☆ - E'ola Products, Inc. (Biogenics)

PERSONALITEE - Computer peripheral equipment - Robert Waxman, Inc.

PERSONALITIES - Tiles–ceramic - American Olean Tile Co.

PERSONALITIES - Toilets–enameled - Kohler Co.

PERSONALITY - Eyeglasses ☆ - Joy Enterprises

PERSONALITY - Fruits and vegetables - Van Buren County Fruit Exchange

PERSONALITY - Shoes - Interco Inc.

PERSONALITY CHAIN, THE - Jewelry - National Chain Co.

PERSONALITY GAME - Computer software - SourceView Software International

PERSONALITY PENDANTS - Jewelry - Russ Berrie and Co., Inc.

PERSONALITY PIGGRIMS - Toys–stuffed - Russ Berrie and Co., Inc.

PERSONALITY PIGGS - Toys–stuffed - Russ Berrie and Co., Inc.

PERSONALIZATION STATION - Stationery - Inscribe, Inc.

PERSONALIZE IT! - Greeting cards - Hallmark Cards Inc.

PERSONALIZED CALCULATORS - Key rings - Stravina Inc.

PERSONALIZED FOR YOU - Greeting cards ☆ - Stephen Lawrence Co.

PERSONALIZED HIEROGRAPHICS COLLECTION - Computer software - Lori Leal Marketing

PERSONALIZED MEMORY - Candles - Old Rome Candles

PERSONALIZED NAME TALES - Novelty items - Kidselebration Inc.

PERSONALIZED PAPETERIES - Stationery ☆ - Royal Imprints Corp.

PERSONALIZER - Hair care products - Willat Co.

PERSONALLY - Health care products - Coloplast Corp.

PERSONALLY SELECTED - Food products - King Salmon Inc.

PERSONALLY SPEAKING - Tableware–earthenware - Papel/Freelance, Inc.

PERSONALLY YOURS - House furnishings ☆ - Lea Industries Inc.

PERSONALLY YOURS - Key rings - Russ Berrie and Co., Inc.

PERSONALS - Novelty items–paper - Agent Andy Inc.

PERSONALTRAC - Traction apparatus–medical - Lossing Orthopedic Co.

PERSONETIX - Computer software - Personetix Corp.

PERSONIC - Hearing aids - Oticon Corp.

PERSONNA - Razor blades ☆ - American Safety Razor Co.

PERSONNA 74 - Razor blades ☆ - American Safety Razor Co.

PERSONNA DOUBLE II - Razor blades Now out of production ☆ - American Safety Razor Co.

PERSONNA ULTRA-CHROME - Razor blades - American Safety Razor Co.

PERSONNEL ACCOUNTABILITY SYSTEM V - Bulletin boards–cork - Clemens Industries, Inc.

PERSONNEL LIFT - Machinery - JLG Industries Inc.

PERSONNEL MANAGER, THE - Computer software - Laurel Hill Software Co.

PERSONNEL SCHEDULER - Computer software - Right on Programs

PERSONNELLY YOURS - Greeting cards - G. Neil Companies

PERSONS - Bicycles - Persons-Majestic Manufacturing Co.

PERSPECT-O-METRIC - Artists' materials ☆ - Oce-Bruning Inc.

PERSPECTA - Computer software - Perspecta Software, Inc.

PERSPECTIVE - Clocks ☆ - General Time Corp. (Westclox/Seth Thomas Div.)

PERSPECTIVE - Computer software - Three D Graphics

☆ = Now out of production

PERSPECTIVE - Floor coverings–carpet and rugs - Eurotex Inc.
PERSPECTIVE - Floor coverings–carpet and rugs - Harbinger Co.
PERSPECTIVE - Floor coverings–carpet and rugs ☆ - Kelly Group Inc.
PERSPECTIVE - Furniture ☆ - Bassett Furniture Industries, Inc.
PERSPECTIVE - Giftware ☆ - Gorham Inc.
PERSPECTIVE - Nail care products - Opi Products, Inc.
PERSPECTIVE - Pencil holders - Sterling Plastics Co.
PERSPECTIVE - Video production - Christ Covenant Presbyterian Church
PERSPECTIVE COLOR GLASS - Glass–leaded - Noritake Co. Inc.
PERSPECTIVE GROUP - Floor coverings–carpet and rugs - Couristan Inc.
PERSPECTIVE POSTERS - Posters - Clement Communications Inc.
PERSPECTIVE RECORDS - Recording label - Perspective Records Inc.
PERSPECTIVE SYSTEMS - Computer software - Perspective Systems, Inc.
PERSPECTIVES - Blinds–vertical - Louverdrape Inc.
PERSPECTIVES - Wallpaper - Dekortex Inc.
PERSPECTIVES - Wallpaper - S.R. Wood Inc.
PERSPECTIVES - Wallpaper ☆ - Wall-Pride Inc.
PERSPECTIVES BY LIBRA - Computer software - Libra Corp.
PERSPECTIVES IN MUSIC HISTORY - Computer software - Electronic
   Courseware Systems Inc.
PERSPEX - Fibers–acrylic - ICI Acrylics Inc.
PERSTRIP - Abrasive products - Perstorp Compounds, Inc.
PERSUADE - Apparel stores–lingerie - Goddess Bra
PERSUADER - Boats–motor - Checkmate Boats Inc.
PERSUADER - Floor coverings–carpet and rugs ☆ - Columbus Mills, Inc.
PERSUADER - Guitars - Alembic Inc.
PERSUADER - Pens ☆ - Pentel of America, Ltd.
PERSUADER - Sporting goods - O.F. Mossberg & Sons, Inc.
PERSUADER - Telephone apparatus - Antenna Co.
PERSUADER, THE - Musical instrument accessories - Adder Plus Corp.
PERSUASION - Cleaning preparations–carpet and rug - W.W. Grainger, Inc.
PERSUASION - Floor coverings–carpet and rugs - Tuftex Carpet Mills, Inc.
PERSUASION - Glassware–household ☆ - Crisa Corp.
PERSUASION - Perfumes - All Clubman
PERSUASIONS - Wallpaper - Sunnyside Prints
PERSUASIVE PRESENTATIONS - Computer software - Hewlett-Packard Co.
PERSUIT - Floor coverings–carpet and rugs ☆ - Columbus Mills, Inc.
PERT - Hardware - Shepherd Products U.S. Inc.
PERT - Paper - Plainwell Tissue
PERT - Shampoos - Procter & Gamble Co.
PERT & PERKY - Apparel–children's - Kahn Lucas Lancaster Inc.
PERT 'N PRETTY - Dolls - Horsman
PERT PLUS - Shampoos - Procter & Gamble Co.
PERTEIN - Chemical preparations - Permethyl Specialties, LLC
PERTEX - Thread - Perfect Thread Co. Inc.
PERTINEX - Antifungal antiseptic - American Pharmaceutical Co.
PERTOFRANE - Pharmaceutical preparations - Rhone-Poulenc Rorer
   Pharmaceuticals Inc.
PERTOL - Cough medicines - Concord Chemists
PERTROPIN - Pharmaceutical preparations - Lannett Co. Inc.
PERTS - Shoes ☆ - Foot-So-Port
PERTSOVKA - Vodka - Monsieur Henri Wines Ltd.
PERTUSSIN - Cold remedies ☆ - Brimms Inc.
PERTUSSIN CS - Cold remedies ☆ - Brimms Inc.
PERTUSSIN-CS - Cough medicines - Blairex Laboratories, Inc.
PERTUSSIN-DM - Cough medicines - Blairex Laboratories, Inc.
PERUGIA - Dishes–china - Pasmantier Co. Inc.
PERUGINA - Candy ☆ - Perugina Chocolate & Confections Inc.
PERUNA - Dietary supplement - Benjamin Ansehl Co.
PERUSAL - Waterproof outerwear - Gruner & Co., Inc.
PERUVIAN - Floor coverings ☆ - Tarkett, Inc.
PERUVIAN KING - Food products - Ambassador Seafoods Inc.
PERVASIVE COMPUTING - Computer programming services - Novell, Inc.
PERVEL - Wallpaper - Pervel Industries Inc.
PERVELINE - Pet products ☆ - 8 in 1 Pet Products Inc.
PERVERT - Apparel and accessories - James George
PERVERT TESTER - Novelty items - Adams Apple Distributing L.P.
PERVINAL - Pet products - St. Aubrey
PES 828 - Analgesics - Prevo Equipment & Supply, Inc.
PESCADERO BERRIES - Fruits and vegetables - Jacobs Farm/Del Cabo Inc.
PESCADO MAS FINA - Food products - Bold Move, Inc.
PESCARA - Dinnerware–glass ☆ - WMF/USA
PESCEVINO - Wines - David Sherman Corp.
PESCEVINO-UMANI RONCHI - Beverages–alcohol - Blair Importers Ltd.
PESCHEL LIGHTING CONTROL - Regulators–voltage - Hipotronics, Inc.
PESCI - Dishes–china - Pasmantier Co. Inc.

PESENTI - Wines - Pesenti Winery
PESKANOV - Publisher's imprints - Willis Music Co.
PESKY PEEPERS - Figurines - Sandicast
PESQUERA CHILE - Food products ☆ - Darik Enterprises Inc.
PEST-ASIDE - Doors–screen - HOD International, Inc.
PEST-B-GON - Insecticides ☆ - Chevron Chemical Co.
PEST-CATCHERS, THE - Garden equipment - J.T. Eaton and Co.
PEST-DUCT - Electrical equipment - Tamaqua Cable Products Corp.
PEST FIGHTER - Hand pumped sprayers - Master Nurserymen's Association
PEST FREE - Pet products - Lynco Pet Products Inc.
PEST KILL - Pesticides–household - Jonathan Green, Inc.
PEST PATROL - Electronic equipment - Carr Products Co. Inc.
PEST-RID - Insecticides - Uncle Sam Chemical Co., Inc.
PEST TERMINATOR - Electronic device - Villapark Electronics, USA
PESTA - Food products - Green Bay Foods Co.
PESTAB - Insecticides - Zeneca Inc.
PESTAWAY - Insecticides - Uncle Sam Chemical Co., Inc.
PESTAWAY DINO - Pet products - Rainbow Laboratories
PESTCHASER - Electronic equipment - Sonic Technology Products Inc.
PESTECH - Insect repellents - Sue L. Gibson
PESTENE - Insecticides - Uncle Sam Chemical Co., Inc.
PESTEX - Pesticides–household - Mayso Chemical Co. Inc.
PESTICK - Adhesives and sealants - Phytotronics, Inc.
PESTO AND PASTABILITIES - Spices and extracts - To Market to Market
PESTO JOE'S - Sauces - Morano Associates, Inc.
PESTO PASTA BLOSSOMS - Pasta - Sunwest Foods, Inc.
PESTOID, THE - Books–comic - Alfred Juliano
PESTRAP - Pesticides–household - Phytotronics, Inc.
PESTREPELLER - Electronic equipment - Sonic Technology Products Inc.
PET - Computers–personal ☆ - Commodore Business Machines Inc.
PET - Dairy products - Pet Dairy
PET - Milk–canned or powdered - Pet Inc.
PET - Paper punches ☆ - Bates Manufacturing Co.
PET - Stoves–gas - Fatsco
P.E.T. - Thread - Gudebrod, Inc.
PET-A-MIN - Vitamins and nutritional supplements - K.C. Pharmacal Inc.
PET-A-PAL - Pharmaceutical preparations - Rugby Laboratories Inc.
PET-A-POOS - Pet products - Pet-a-Poos Inc.
PET AGREE - Pet products - Garcoa Labs/Vitamin Classics
PET-AGREE - Pet products - K-II Enterprises
PET-AGREE - Pet products - J. Narby Inc.
PET-AGREE - Pet products - R.C. Steele Co.
PET-AGREE - Pet products - WLC Co. Inc.
PET-AGREE - Vitamins and nutritional supplements - Synergy Plus
PET-AGREE-DOR - Pet products ☆ - Johnson Pet-Dor Inc.
PET AID - Pet products - Four Paws Products Ltd.
PET-AID - Veterinary pharmaceutical preparations - Vegetable Factory, Inc.
   (Sunbeam Structures Div.)
PET AIR - Deodorizers - Mia Rose Products Inc.
PET-ALOE - Pet food - Pharm-Aloe, Inc.
PET ATTIRE - Pet products - Coastal Pet Products, Inc.
PET BANDANAS - Pet products - CMI
PET BANDANAS - Pet products - Creative Gifts
PET BARRIER - Deodorizers - Petland, Inc.
PET BASICS - Pet products - Marianna Imports, Inc.
PET BEANS - Dolls - Mattel, Inc.
PET BEDS - Pet products - Heartland Futons & Fibers, Inc.
PET BLOCK - Pet products - Kaytee Products Inc.
PET BOTANICS - Pet products - Cardinal Laboratories, Inc.
PET-BRITE - Dentifrices - E & D Dental Products, Inc.
PET BUDDIES - Pet products - Keller Design, Inc.
PET BUTLER - Pet products ☆ - Farnam Cos. Inc.
PET CAB - Pet products - Doskocil Manufacturing Co., Inc.
PET CABANA - Pet products - Lazy Pet Products
PET CADDY ELITE - Pet products ☆ - Booda Products, Inc.
PET CAFE - Pet products - O.D. Funk Co.
PET CAGE FIX - Pet products - Bernard E. Ryan
PET CANTEEN - Pet products - Rich Health
PET-CAR-GO - Pet products - PR Stump & Stuff
PET CARRIER, THE - Pet products - Diverse Designs
PET CASTLE - Pet products - Pet Castle Co.
PET-CAT-LAK - Pet products ☆ - Four Paws Products Ltd.
PET CHALET - Pet products - Mapes Industries Inc.
PET CHALKBOARDS - Pet products - Mapes Industries Inc.
PET CHARMS - Pet products ☆ - Doggie Products of America
PET CHECKS - Pet products - Kansas Bank Note Co.

PET CHEF - Pet products - Pet Chef Inc.
PET CHIP - Novelty items ☆ - V.G. Industries
PET CHOICE - Pet products ☆ - Trophy Animal Health Care
PET CLEAN - Deodorizers - Ole Time Woodsman
PET-CLEAR - Deodorizers - Enviro-Dynamics Inc.
PET CLUB - Clippers–nail - Topco Associates, Inc.
PET CONNECTION, THE - Pet products - Pet Connection
PET CONTROLLER - Fencing–chain link - North Central Plastics Inc.
PET COTTAGE - Pet products ☆ - Pets International, Ltd.
PET COUCH - Pet products - O'Donnell Industries Inc.
PET CRAFT - Pet products ☆ - Mardel Laboratories, Inc.
PET CROCODILE - Candy - Herman Goelitz Candy Co., Inc.
PET CRYSTALS - Pet products - P.M. Pet Products
PET CUDIES - Toys–stuffed ☆ - Fun World Inc.
PET-D-TICK - Veterinary pharmaceutical preparations - C.J. Martin Co.
PET DEFENDER - Animal feeds - Farnam Cos. Inc.
PET DELI - Pet food - Bearinger Co., LC
PET-DERM O.M. CAPS - Veterinary nutritional supplements - Pfizer Inc.
PET DINETTE - Pet products - Penn-Plax, Inc.
PET DINOSAURS - Candy - Herman Goelitz Candy Co., Inc.
PET DISH - Pet toys and snacks - IMS Trading Inc.
PET-DOR - Pet products - Johnson Pet-Dor Inc.
PET-DOR JR. - Pet products - R.C. Steele Co.
PET-DOR JR. - Pet products ☆ - Johnson Pet-Dor Inc.
PET DOSER - Pet products - Pet Medic Corp.
PET DRYER - Pet products - Doggie Products of America
PET ELITE - Pet products - Stylette Plastics Inc.
PET ESSENTIALS - Pet food - Dayton Hudson Corp.
PET-EZE - Pet products - Pet-Eze
PET FARE - Animal feeds - Southwest Pet Products, Inc. (American Nutrition Inc.)
PET FAUCET - Pet products - Novalek, Inc.
PET FLUSH - Pet-waste-removal tool - Intromark Inc.
PET FOOD CLIP - Sealing devices - Guardsman Products, Inc.
PET FOOD SUPERMART - Toys–stuffed - Unipet Distributors, Inc.
PET-FORTE - Pet products - Schiff Products, Inc.
PET-FUN - Pet products - Loveland Pet Products
PET GALLERY - Greeting cards - American Greetings Corp.
PET-GARD - Bags–trash - Real Ideas Inc.
PET GARD - Pet products - Biological Engineering/High Tech Pet Products
PET GARD II - Pet products - Biological Engineering/High Tech Pet Products
PET GEAR BASICS - Aquariums–household - Loveland Pet Products
PET GLOW - Pet products - Valhoma Industries Inc.
PET GO-GO - Pet products ☆ - Debonair Pets of California
PET GOLD - Pet products - Revere Manufacturing
PET GUARD - Pet products - Pet Biotics Inc.
PET GUARDIAN - Pet products - Mustang Products, Inc.
PET HAIR MAGNET - Pet products - Animal Magnetism
PET HAIR PIC-UP - Pet products - Helmac Products Corp.
PET HAIR PICK-UP - Pet products - Bemistape
PET HAVEN - Pet products - Hatchbag, Inc.
PET-HEAVEN - Pet products - Bio-Pak Associates
PET HI SOCIETY - Water–bottled or canned - PI Water, Inc.
PET HOME - Pet products - Circle K Industries Inc.
PET HOOKS - Dolls - Mattel, Inc.
PET HOUSE - Pet products - Hoegh Industries Inc.
PET HQ - Pets products, toys - Southern States Cooperative Inc.
PET I.D. - Luggage - Judy Smith
PET JANITOR - Pet products - Pet Janitor
PET JOCK - Novelty items - Air Wear
PET LIFE - Dog food - Pet Life Foods Inc.
PET-LIFE - Veterinary pharmaceutical preparations - Nutri-Cell Inc.
PET LIMO - Pet products - Stylette Plastics Inc.
PET LOGS - Pet products ☆ - Zema Corp.
PET LOUNGER - Pet products - Flexi-Mat Corp.
PET LOVER'S - Pet food - Doane Products Co.
PET LOVERS - Wallets - Strand Enterprises
PET MAGIC - Pet products - Biological Engineering/High Tech Pet Products
PET MAGIC - Pet products - Petco Animal Supplies, Inc.
PET MAGIC - Pet products - Revere Manufacturing
PET MARBLE - Toys–marbles - Ancom Inc.
PET MINEER - Pet products - Animal Magnetism
PET-MOBILE ON THE GO - Toys - Mattel, Inc.
PET MOUSE - Computer software - IMSI
PET N' PURR - Pet products ☆ - Oil-Dri Corp. of America
PET NAIL SCISSORZ - Pet products - Aaronco Grooming Products

PET NAIL SCISSORZ - Scissors–hand-operated - Aaronco Pet Products, Inc.
PET NESTS - Pet products - Pet Nests
PET NET - Computer software - Sean Peter Esterhuizen
PET-NET - Pet products - Maggie Mae's Gourmet Pet Products Inc.
PET-NETS - Pet products - Double S Dog Fashions
PET-NIP-LAK - Pet products ☆ - Four Paws Products Ltd.
PET NUTRI-DROPS - Pet products - Bovidr Labs Inc.
PET O GREE - Dog food - American Stores Co.
PET O MAT - Placemats ☆ - Alger Creations Inc.
PET ODOR KLEEN - Deodorizers - G.G. Bean Inc.
PET ORGANICS - Pet products - Nala Barry Laboratories
PET PAC - Pet products - Pets Pacifica Inc.
PET PALS - Figurines ☆ - Papel Freelance, Inc.
PET PALS - Leather goods - SOS Rescue Inc.
PET PALS - Pet products - Pet Pals
PET PALS - Veterinary pharmaceutical preparations ☆ - Optimal Nutrients
PET PANACHE - Pet products - Vo-Toys Inc.
PET PANACHE - Pet products - Rebecca Solether Williams
PET PANTRY - Pet products - R.A.F. Trading Inc.
PET PARADE - Beads - Greene Plastics Corp.
PET PARTY - Toys - Mattel, Inc.
PET PASSPORT - Health journal for pets - Informative Amenities Inc.
PET PATROL - Pet products - Garcoa Labs/Vitamin Classics
PET PATTERNS - Pet products - Coastal Pet Products, Inc.
PET PATTIES - Dog food - Merrick Petfoods Inc.
PET PAWS - Apparel and accessories - Sears, Roebuck and Co.
PET-PECTILLIN - Pet products - Lambert-Kay
PET PEEVE - Pet products ☆ - Dandy Products Inc.
PET PEEVE - Vitamins and nutritional supplements - Los Angeles Stock Exchange
PET PELLETS - Pet products ☆ - Alfa-Pet Inc.
PET PEOPLE PRESS-ON - Decals and transfers ☆ - R.A.F. Trading Inc.
PET-PEP - Pet products - Alpha-Lac Inc.
PET PERSONALITIES - Dolls - Heritage Mint, Ltd.
PET PILLARS - Pet products - Trophy Animal Health Care
PET PILLOW - Pet products - Flexi-Mat Corp.
PET PIX - Frames–picture - Carolyn M. Fachinger
PET PLAYLINKS - Pet products - Blue Ribbon Pet Products, Inc.
PET-PLEASER-JERKY - Dog food - Smoke Craft
PET POCKET ID - Pet products - Diverse Designs
PET POCKET JR - Pet products - Diverse Designs
PET POPS - Pet products - Pet Pops Inc.
PET PORT - Pet products - Pattie's Pet Grooming & Pet Photique
PET PORTER - Pet products - Doskocil Manufacturing Co., Inc.
PET PORTRAITS - Jewelry - Peggy Sullivan-Cramer Designs
PET POTTY & POOP PAD - Pet products - The Uppity Puppy
PET POUCH - Pet products - Designs by Dyanne, Inc.
PET POWDER - Health care products - Healthwatchers System
PET POWDER SILVER - Health care products - Healthwatchers System
PET POWER - Pollen extracts - CC Pollen Co.
PET-PRESERVER - Pet products - Pet-Agree Co.
PET PRIDE - Dog food - The Kroger Co.
PET-PRO - Dog food - Pet Products, Inc.
PET-PRO-TEC - Cleaning preparations - Ultra-Tech Cleaning Systems, Inc.
PET PRODUCTS INTERNATIONAL CAT DIVISION - Pet products - Pet Products International, L.L.C
PET PRODUCTS PLUS - Animal feeds - RCX Holdings, Inc.
PET PROJECT - Greeting cards - Kathy Wall
PET PROOF - Stain removers ☆ - Nilodor Inc.
PET PROTECTOR - Pet products - Alert Industries
PET PRUF - Pet products - Enviro-Tech International
PET PULLEY - Pet products - Wee Waggers
PET PYRAMID - Infant product - Railnet Corp.
PET RATS - Candy - Herman Goelitz Candy Co., Inc.
PET RECORDS - Recording label - Pet Records
PET REFLECTOR - Reflectors–optical - Reflex Corp.
PET-RETREAT - Cleaning preparations–carpet and rug - Promaster
PET-RITZ - Pies–frozen - Pet Inc.
PET SAC - Pet products - Dog Wear Fashions Inc.
PET-SAC - Pet products - Pet-Agree Co.
PET-SAFE - Pet products - Molor Products Co.
PET SAFETY - Pet products - Pet Safety Products Co.
PET SAFETY SITTER - Pet products - Four Paws Products Ltd.
PET SAV-R - Decals and transfers - R.A.F. Trading Inc.
PET SAVER - Pet products - Dandy Products Inc.
PET-SAVER - Sporting goods - Jog-A-Lite Inc.

☆ = Now out of production

PET SCENTS - Deodorizers - California Scents
PET SCOOP - Pet products - Pet Star
PET SCRUB - Pet products - Bark Industries Inc.
PET SELECT - Pet collars - Mustang Products, Inc.
PET SENSE - Pet products - Revere Manufacturing
PET SHELTER - Pet products - Drew Foam Co. Inc.
PET SHIELD - Pet collars - Elexis Corp.
PET SHOP - Housewares ☆ - Treasure Craft Co.
PET SHOW - Dolls - Mattel, Inc.
PET SHOWER POWER - Sprayers - Migatz & Migatz, Inc.
PET SILK - Pet products - Pet Silk
PET SOLUTION - Agricultural products - Rosalba Emanuel-King
PET S.O.X - Pet products - Rolf C. Hagen (USA) Corp.
PET SPONGE - Pet products - V.K. Industries Inc.
PET SPOTTER - Pet products - Animal Magnetism
PET STAIN OFF! - Cleaning preparations - Harvard Chemical Research, Inc.
PET STEP - Pet products - Edemco Dryers Inc.
PET STOP - Electrical equipment - Perimeter Technologies, Inc.
PET STOP - Electrical pet containment fencing - Robert W. Wolfe
PET STOPPER - Pet products - Nala Barry Laboratories
PET SUN CHLORELLA - Pet products - Sun Wellness, Inc.
PET SWEATS - Pet products - Fashion Pet Accessories Inc.
PET SWEET - Pet products - Bramton Co.
PET TALES - Greeting cards - American Greetings Corp.
PET TARANTULA - Candy - Herman Goelitz Candy Co., Inc.
PET TAXI - Pet products - Doskocil Manufacturing Co., Inc.
PET TEAM - Pet food - Petteam, Inc.
PET-TEC - Pet products - Pet-Tec Systems Group
PET-THERM - See **TEN/CARE**
PET TIME - Pet products - IMS Trading Inc.
PET-TIP - Pet products - Bio-Pak Associates
PET TOGS - Pet products - Ben Richter Co.
PET-TOTE - Pet products ☆ - Clyde A. Dittbenner
PET TOWN - Dog food - Southwest Pet Products, Inc. (American Nutrition Inc.)
PET-TRACE 200 - Electronic equipment - General Electric Co.
PET TRACKS - Pet products - BenePet Pet Care Products
PET TRAVEL CNATEEN - Pet products - Novalek, Inc.
PET-TRAVLER - Pet products ☆ - Johnson Pet-Dor Inc.
PET TREE - Trees - Silkey & Roehl Partnership
PET VAC - Pet products - Variety International Inc.
PET VAC II - Pet products - Variety International Inc.
PET VENT - Pet products - Hamilton Products Inc.
PET-VET - Pet products - National Scent Co.
PET VOYAGEUR - Pet products - Rolf C. Hagen (USA) Corp.
PET WASHER - Housewares - Selfix, Inc.
PET WET - Water–bottled or canned - Renegade of Arizona, Inc.
PET WHIP - Whipped topping–frozen - Pet Inc.
PET WIPES - Pet products - K.O.S. Industries Inc.
PET WORM - Pet products - K.C. Pharmacal Inc.
PET-X-ERCISER - Pet products - Van Ness Plastic Molding Co. Inc.
PET XTRA - Pet products - Pet Xtra Inc.
PETABLE PUZZLES, INC. - Puzzles - Elaine Baumgartner
PETABLES & EDIBLES - Publisher's imprints - Originals by Maris (O.B.M. Publishing)
PETABLES, THE - Greeting cards - Originals by Maris (O.B.M. Publishing)
PETAG - Animal feed - Pet-Ag, Inc.
PET.A.GREE - Video production - Pet.A.Gree Tapes
PETAL - Artists' materials - Stangren Co.
PETAL - Glassware–household - Federal Glass
PETAL BRA - Brassieres (Bras) ☆ - Vanity Fair Mills Inc.
PETAL EXPRESSIONS - Paper–lithograph - Jes Originals
PETAL-FRESH - Skin care products - Levlab, Inc.
PETAL MIST - Cookware - Carlisle Foodservice Products, Inc.
PETAL-MOIST - Skin care products ☆ - Uncommon Conglomerates
PETAL PALS - Publisher's imprints - Susan K. Tate
PETAL PALS JOIN THE CLUB - Flowers, plants, and seeds - Cedar Bridge Nurseries and Greenhouses Inc.
PETAL PEDDLER - Flowers, plants, and seeds - Petal Peddler
PETAL PEOPLE - Toys - Uneeda Doll Co., Inc.
PETAL PETS - Pet products - Laid Back Enterprises, Inc.
PETAL PINK - Glassware–household ☆ - Fenton Art Glass Co.
PETAL POINT - Artists' materials - Clearsnap, Inc.
PETAL PORCELAIN - Artists' materials - Plaid Enterprises, Inc.
PETAL PORCELAIN - Fabric softeners - DKM Ltd.
PETALE - Glassware–scientific - Durand International
PETALE - Nail care products - Cosmair Inc.

PETALE - Perfumes - Revlon Consumer Products Corp.
PETALGRAM - Fresh and dried flowers and plants - Royal Rose
PETALOMA - Floor coverings–carpet and rugs - Regal Rugs Inc.
PETALS - Bicycles - Murray, Inc.
PETALS - Footwear ☆ - Saga House Inc.
PETALS - Giftware ☆ - Brushcreek Creative Co.
PETALS - Jewelry - Peter Brams Designs, Ltd.
PETALS - Soap - Colgate-Palmolive Co.
PETALS - Wallpaper - Chapters Wallcoverings
PETALS - Wallpaper - Gencorp Polymer Products
PETALS & LACE - Deodorizers - Caswell-Massey Co. Ltd.
PETALS & PEARLS - Incense - Bright of America Inc.
PETALS & PRINTS - Wallpaper ☆ - Palette Prints Inc.
PETALS EVERLASTING COLLECTION - Paper products - Custom Papers Group Inc.
PETALSKIN - Apparel and accessories - Van Raalte Gloves
PETALUMA - Wines - Dreyfus Ashby Inc.
PETALUMA CELLARS - Wines - La Crema Vinera
PETALUSTRE COLLECTION, THE - Underwear and nightwear - Classics Chicago, Inc.
PETAMINE - Pet products - Kellogg Inc.
PETASAN - Spices and extracts ☆ - Bioforce of America Ltd.
PETAVITE - Veterinary pharmaceutical preparations ☆ - Vortech Pharmaceuticals
PETBATH - Pet products - Pet Lift
PETBERRYS - Pet products - Petberrys
PETCARE - Animal feeds - Gordon's Markets
PETCARE - Pet products - Petcare Industries Inc.
PETCETERA - Pet products - Abbey Enterprises, Inc.
PETCETERA - Pet products - Aqua Stock/Petcetera Inc.
PETCETERA - Pet products - Petcetera Inc.
PETCO PETCO - Prefabricated buildings–metal - W.T. Pettit & Sons Co., Inc.
PETCRAFT - Pet products ☆ - USA-Petrx
PETCRAFT KITNIPS - Pet products ☆ - USA-Petrx
PETDEK - Pet products - Pet Lift
PETDENT - Pet products ☆ - Schering-Plough Animal Health
PETDROPS - Veterinary pharmaceutical preparations - Upjohn Co.
PETE - Frames–eyeglass - U.S. Optical Frame Co.
PETE & PAM - Toothpaste - Laclede Professional Products, Inc.
PETE & PENNY PENGUIN - Toys–stuffed ☆ - Dakin Inc.
PETE & REPEAT - Inks–gravure - Advance Business Systems & Supply Co.
PETE FOUNTAIN - Musical instrument accessories - G. Leblanc Corp.
PETE ROSE - Sunblocks - CPC Sontegra
PETE STROZIERS - Health care products - First Aids Inc.
PETE THE PERIOSAURUS - Toothpaste - Perio Products
PETE ZARIA'S PIZZA MADE FRESH - Pizzas–frozen - Deli International of Omaha, Inc.
PETE ZAROLI - Sandwiches–prepackaged - Coleman Oil Co. Inc.
PETELCO - Lighting fixtures ☆ - Hubbell Lighting, Inc. (Lighting Div.)
PETER - Jars–glass - Metro/Thebe, Inc.
PETER - Seasonings - Pam Products Inc.
PETER ALAN DESIGNS - Clocks - J. Kenneth Zahn
PETER B - Apparel–men's - Heather Hill Sportswear Co. Inc.
PETER BEDRICK BOOKS - Publisher's imprints - NTC Contemporary Publishing Group
PETER BUTTER BUNNY - Chocolate candy - Superior Fruit & Confections
PETER CANDYTAIL - Candy - R.M. Palmer Co.
PETER CHURCH - Greeting cards ☆ - Amcal Inc.
PETER DAWSON - Beverages–alcohol - Schenley Industries Inc.
PETER DE BEUKELAER - Cookies - De Beukelaer Corp.
PETER ECKRICH - Meat products–beef - Armour Swift-Eckrich
PETER ECKRICH DELI - Meat products–beef - Armour Swift-Eckrich
PETER ENGLAND FOR RICHMAN - Apparel and accessories - Richman Brothers Co.
PETER ERSKINE SIGNATURE - Musical instruments - Vic Firth Inc.
PETER FEEDERS - Pet products - Grand Champion Ranch Products, Inc.
PETER FIDUCCIA'S LOVE POTION #9 - Sporting goods - Whitetail Strategies, Inc.
PETER FRANK - Statuary ☆ - Artisan House Inc.
PETER FREUND - Knitting machines - Peter Freund Knitting Mills
PETER HAND'S - Beverages–malt - Peter Hand Brewing Co.
PETER HANTZ - Hair care products - Peter Hantz Co.
PETER HORN - Musical instrument accessories - Horn & Son String Instruments Inc.
PETER JACKSON AMERICAN - Cigarettes - Philip Morris Companies Inc.
PETER JAMES COLLECTION - Giftware - Russ Berrie and Co., Inc.

PETER JEPSEN - Giftware - Reco International Corp.

PETER KAISER - Shoes - Peter Kaiser Inc.

PETER MARINO - Lighting fixtures - Peter Marino International Ltd.

PETER MARTIN - Apparel and accessories - San Simeon, Inc.

PETER MAX - Greeting cards ☆ - Regency Thermographers Inc.

PETER MAX - Pins–jewelry - Via Max, Inc.

PETER MAX - Toys ☆ - Mego Financial Corp.

PETER MERTES - Wines ☆ - Francis A. Bonanno, Inc.

PETER N' PAL - Toys–stuffed ☆ - Dakin Inc.

PETER NORTON - Computer software - Peter Norton

PETER PAN - Dolls ☆ - Effanbee Doll Corp.

PETER PAN - Fabric stores - Henry Glass & Co.

PETER PAN - Footwear–children's - W.L. Kreider's Sons Manufacturing Co. Inc.

PETER PAN - Giftware ☆ - Gorham Inc.

PETER PAN - Peanut butter - Hunt-Wesson, Inc.

PETER PAN - Recording label - Peter Pan Industries

PETER PAN - Seafood products–fresh or frozen - Peter Pan Seafoods, Inc.

PETER PAN PLUS - Peanut butter ☆ - Hunt-Wesson, Inc.

PETER PAN SEAFOODS, INC. - Fish–canned or cured - Peter Pan Seafoods, Inc.

PETER PANDA - Publisher's imprints ☆ - Standard Publishing Co.

PETER PATCH - Candy - R.M. Palmer Co.

PETER PAUL - Candy - Hershey Chocolate USA

PETER PAUL MOUNDS - Candy - Cadbury Beverages Inc.

PETER PEANUT - Candy ☆ - R.M. Palmer Co.

PETER PEEPERS - Toys–stuffed - Associated Merchandising Corp.

PETER PEN - School supplies - Rudell Design

PETER PENGUIN - Christmas tree ornaments - Cracker Box Inc.

PETER PIPER - Pickles - Green Bay Foods Co.

PETER POLKA - Candy - R.M. Palmer Co.

PETER PRINCIPLE, THE - Games ☆ - Avalon Hill Game Co.

PETER PUMPKIN - Toys–stuffed - Russ Berrie and Co., Inc.

PETER RABBIT - Candy - R.M. Palmer Co.

PETER RABBIT - Confections - Comet Confectionery Inc.

PETER RABBIT - Jewelry - Frederick Warne & Co., Inc.

PETER RABBIT - Posters - One-of-a-Kind Workshop

PETER RABBIT - Recording label ☆ - Alshire International Inc.

PETER RABBIT - Toys ☆ - Activa Products Inc.

PETER RABBIT - Toys–stuffed - Eden LLC

PETER RABBIT - Vases–stone - Waterford Wedgwood USA, Inc.

PETER RABBIT FARMS - Agricultural products - Peter Rabbit Farms, Inc.

PETER RABBIT HOME - Cages–wire ☆ - Pets International, Ltd.

PETER REDSTONE - Musical - Peter Redstone Harpsichords

PETER REED - Fabrics–linen - Imperial Childrens Wear Inc.

PETER SCHUYLER - Cigars - G.W. Van Slyke & Horton

PETER STEINHAUS - Musical instruments - Deltex Music Corp.

PETER STERLING - Toys - Tonka Corp.

PETER STOKKEBYE/SANTA MARIA - Cigars ☆ - Swisher International, Inc.

PETER STUYVESANT - Cigarettes - House of Edgeworth

PETER THOMAS - Neckties - Superba, Inc.

PETER VELLA - Wines - Ernest and Julio Gallo Winery

PETERBILT - Motor vehicles - Peterbilt Motors Co.

PETERS - Ammunition - Remington Arms Co., Inc.

PETERS - Fertilizers - W.R. Grace & Co.

PETER'S - Seasonings - Reckitt & Colman, Inc.

PETER'S ALPHABET ADVENTURE - Computer software - Apple Computer Inc.

PETER'S BLUE MAGIC - Sporting goods ☆ - Remington Arms Co., Inc.

PETERS EDITION - Music–sheet - C.F. Peters Corp.

PETERS HIGH VELOCITY - Ammunition - E.I. Dupont de Nemours and Co.

PETER'S MAGIC ADVENTURE - Computer storage devices–optical - Apple Computer Inc.

PETER'S NUMBERS ADVENTURE - Computer software - Apple Computer Inc.

PETERS-REVINGTON - Furniture - Mohasco Corp.

PETERS SWEET SHOP - Candy ☆ - R.M. Palmer Co.

PETERSEN - Nutcrackers - Rolf Wallach Inc.

PETERSHOF ESTATE - Wines ☆ - H. Schmitt Soehne, Inc.

PETERSON - Musical instrument accessories - Peterson Electro-Musical Products

PETERSON - Nuts and bolts - Peterson American Corp.

PETERSON FARMS - Fruits–frozen - Peterson Farms Inc.

PETERSON FIELD GUIDES - Publisher's imprints - Houghton Mifflin Co.

PETERSON'S - Lubricants - Peterson Ointment Co.

PETERSON'S - Nuts–salted, roasted, cooked, or canned - Fairmont Snacks Group Inc.

PETERSON'S - Vitamins and nutritional supplements - Peterson's Health Products

PETERSON'S CAREER OPTIONS - Computer software - Peterson's Guides, Inc.

PETERSON'S OINTMENT - First aid kits - Lee Pharmaceuticals

PETERVAL - Water–bottled or canned - Water House

PETE'S BEST - Fruits and vegetables - Cascade Fruit Co.

PETES BEST - Nuts–salted, roasted, cooked, or canned ☆ - Sunshine Pecan Co.

PETE'S GOLD COAST - Beverages–malt ☆ - Pete's Brewing Co.

PETE'S GOLD COAST LAGER - Beverages–malt ☆ - Pete's Brewing Co.

PETE'S JEANS - Apparel stores–children's ☆ - Good Lad Co.

PETE'S PACIFIC DRY - Beverages–malt ☆ - Pete's Brewing Co.

PETE'S PARTNER - Apparel stores–children's - Good Lad Co.

PETE'S PLACE - Glassware–household ☆ - Pete's Place of Krebs, Inc.

PETE'S PRIDE - Food products - Al Pete Meats

PETE'S TREATS - Pet food - Pete's Inc.

PETE'S WICKED ALE - Beverages–malt - Pete's Brewing Co.

PETE'S WICKED HONEY WHEAT - Beverages–malt - Pete's Brewing Co.

PETE'S WICKED LAGER - Beverages–malt - Pete's Brewing Co.

PETE'S WICKED RED - Beverages–malt ☆ - Pete's Brewing Co.

PETE'S WICKED SUMMER BREW - Beverages–malt - Pete's Brewing Co.

PETE'S WICKED WINTER BREW - Beverages–malt - Pete's Brewing Co.

PETET POULET - Poultry feeds - Summit Pheasant Farm

PETEWICH - Plastics - Ultra Pac, Inc.

PETEX - Pet products - Leathercraft Co.

PETEX - Window coverings - Vertical Blind Factory

PETFINGERS - Pet products ☆ - Kong Co.

PETFLEX - Fabrics–polyester - Brainard Strapping

PETGUARD - Pet products - Petguard, Inc.

PETHIDOL - Health care products - Halsey Drug Co. Inc.

PETI-CLIP - Jewelry - Richelieu Corp.

PETI PLEAT - Window shades - Up & Down Shade Co.

PETICULARS - Pet shops - Star Markets Co., Inc.

PETIE - Fabrics - Dan River Inc.

PETILLION - Wines - Hilton Commercial Group Inc.

PETILLO - Guitars - Phil-Lu Inc.

PETILLO MASTERPIECE - Guitars - Phil-Lu Inc.

PETILLON - Wines - Richard Adlai Corp.

PETIPRINTS III - Wallpaper ☆ - Bob Mitchell Designs

PETIT CHERI - Colognes - Natural Fragrances Inc.

PETIT ECOLIER - Cookies - Sunshine/Salerno Inc.

PETIT ELEPHANT INTERNATIONAL - Apparel and accessories - Petit Elephant USA, Inc.

PETIT FINALES - Candy - Grand Finale Confections

PETIT FLAMENCO - Cigars - Faber, Coe & Gregg Inc.

PETIT FORS - Bakery products - Parco Foods, Inc.

PETIT MONTRACHET - Cheese - Swissrose International Inc.

PETIT PARFAIT - Cakes - Eddyleon Chocolate Co. Inc.

PETIT POINT - Floor coverings–carpet and rugs - Helios Carpets

PETIT POINT - Floor coverings–carpet and rugs - World Carpets, Inc.

PETIT POINT - Tableware–china ☆ - Lenox, Inc.

PETIT POINT - Wallpaper ☆ - Osborne & Little

PETIT-POINT CLASSICS - Floor coverings–carpet and rugs ☆ - Couristan Inc.

PETIT TAMBOUR - Cheese ☆ - Schratter Import

PETITE - Electrical equipment ☆ - Cable Electric Products

PETITE - Food products - L. Karp & Sons, Inc.

PETITE - Hearing aids - Beltone Electronics Corp.

PETITE - Liquors - Schieffelin and Somerset Co.

PETITE - Office supplies - Rolodex Corp.

PETITE - Paper clips - Noesting Inc.

PETITE - Postage meters - Pelouze Scale Co.

PETITE - Recording label - Fee Bee Record Co.

PETITE - Shrimp–canned or cured ☆ - Robinson Canning Co. Inc.

PETITE - Watches - Bulova Corp.

PETITE 150 - Food products - Chiquita Brands, Inc.

PETITE-ABLE - Patterns–clothing - Mccall Pattern Co.

PETITE AMBER - Wigs ☆ - Paula Young

PETITE & SWEET - Vegetables–canned - Stokely USA, Inc.

PETITE ANTIQUE - Hobby kits - Brocado Inc.

PETITE BEAD - Handbags - Lumured Corp.

PETITE BOUTIQUE - Giftware ☆ - Debry-Pexton Inc.

PETITE CHATEAU - Floor coverings–carpet and rugs ☆ - Customweave Carpets Inc.

PETITE CHEMISE - Apparel and accessories - Kellwood Co.

PETITE CLASSIC - Watches ☆ - SMH (US) Inc.

☆ = Now out of production

PETITE CONCEPT - Women's apparel - Interco Inc.
PETITE DAWN - Wigs - Paula Young
PETITE DAZZLEAIRE - Yarn - Caron International Inc.
PETITE DEBBIE - Wigs - Paula Young
PETITE DELITE - Wigs - Paula Young
PETITE DELUXE - Wigs - CPC Sontegra
L' PETITE DESIGNS - Jewelry - Lieberfarb, Inc.
PETITE FILET - Meat products–beef - Armour Swift-Eckrich
PETITE FILLES - Dolls ☆ - Effanbee Doll Corp.
PETITE FLEUR - Blinds–venetian ☆ - Hunter Douglas, Inc.
PETITE FLEUR - Cosmetics - NBTY, Inc.
PETITE FLEUR - Floor coverings–carpet and rugs ☆ - Stanton Carpet Corp.
PETITE FLEUR - Tableware–china - Villeroy and Boch Tableware Ltd.
PETITE FLEURETTE - Wallpaper ☆ - Fidelity Industries, Inc.
PETITE FOCUS - Apparel–women's - Focus Apparel Group Inc.
PETITE FOCUS - Apparel–women's - Nordstrom, Inc.
PETITE FUME - Wines ☆ - The Monterey Vineyard
PETITE GAMINE - Apparel–children's - Johnston Inc.
PETITE JOY - Wigs ☆ - Paula Young
PETITE LANZ - Dresses–women's - LANZ, Inc.
PETITE LE CORD - Fabrics–corduroy ☆ - Greenwood Mills Inc.
PETITE MARQUES - Trophies–metal - A-B Emblem Corp.
PETITE MISS - Cosmetics - Imperial Toy Corp.
PETITE MISS - Figurine with cologne and lipstick ☆ - Cosrich Inc.
PETITE MS - Apparel–women's - Petite MS Inc.
PETITE NATE - Cosmetics - Revlon Consumer Products Corp.
PETITE ORIGINALS - Pet products - Collar Craft/Petite Originals
PETITE PAN - Cookware - Corning Inc.
PETITE PECTIN - Candy - Maillard Corp.
PETITE P.G. - Apparel–women's - Wacoal America Inc.
PETITE POODLES - Toys–stuffed - Dakin Inc.
PETITE PRESS & GO - Nail-care products - Cosmar Corp.
PETITE PRINCESS - Toys - Imperial Toy Corp.
PETITE-PRO - Clippers–barber - Sunbeam Corp.
PETITE SEAT - Seat covers - Gold Inc.
PETITE SERAH - Wines - Cilurzo Vineyard & Winery
PETITE SOF-POT - Flowers, plants, and seeds ☆ - Applewood Seed & Garden Group
PETITE SOPHISTICATE - Apparel–women's - United States Shoe Corp.
PETITE SOPHISTICATE COLLECTION - Footwear - United States Shoe Corp.
PETITE SORBETEER - Kitchen appliances - Frosty Factory of America Inc.
PETITE SQUARES - Bathroom accessories - Wilardy Originals Inc.
PETITE STATEMENTS - Underwear and nightwear - Understatements, Inc.
PETITE STREET - Apparel and accessories - Edison Brothers Stores, Inc.
PETITE TOTE - Luggage ☆ - Samsonite Corp.
PETITE VINES - Flowers, plants, and seeds - Petite Vines
PETITES - Cosmetics - Delby System
PETITES - Greeting cards ☆ - Fran Mar Greeting cards Ltd.
PETITES FRAMBOISES - Dolls - Mattel, Inc.
PETITES (MINI) OIL-RESISTANT - Cosmetics - Delby System
PETITES PLUS - Hosiery - Mayer/Berkshire Corp.
PETITI SERAH - Wines - Cilurzo Vineyard & Winery
PETITJEAN - Food products - A & A Food Products Corp.
PETITS CHATEAUX - Wines - Parliament Import Co.
PETITS FOURS - Apparel–children's - Nannette Manufacturing Co. Inc.
PETIVA - Clothing - E. Benjamin, Inc.
PETLAND - Pet shops - Petland, Inc.
PETLOCK - Computers - Paragon Concepts Inc.
PETLOVERS - Pet food - Doane Products Co.
PETMAN - Pet products - Daniel Hauck
PETMASTER - Animal feeds - Stevens Industries Inc.
PETMATE PETDOME - Pet products ☆ - Doskocil Manufacturing Co., Inc.
PET'N DRY - Gloves–work - Pet'n Dry, Inc.
PETNAPPER - Pet products - Flexi-Mat Corp.
PETNET - Air purification systems - LifeTime Filter Inc.
PETNIKS - Pet products - Waymouth Farms Inc.
PETNIQUES - Pet products - Inkwear, Inc.
PETOILE - Rings–jewelry ☆ - Artcarved Inc.
PETOSA - Accordions - Petosa Accordions Inc.
PETOY - Pet products - Mapes Industries Inc.
PETPROTECT - Pet products - Axiom Chemical Corp.
PETPRUF - Pet products - Dri-Kleen, Inc.
PETRA - Recording label - Paul Johnson Music Productions Inc.
PETRA - Tiles–ceramic ☆ - Huntington/Pacific Ceramics Inc.
PETRAMP - Pet products - Pet Lift
PETRAPPORT - Pet products - Petrapport, Inc.

PETRELIEF - Pet products - St. Jon Pet Care Products Inc.
PETRI - Cigars - Avanti Cigar Co.
PETRI - Cookies - New Life Bakery Inc.
PETRI - Cookies - Petri Baking Products, Inc.
PETRI - Liquors - United States Distilled Products Co.
PETRI BRAVO - Wines - The Beverage Source Inc.
PETRI ROLLE - Cheese - Anco Foods Corp.
PETRIA - Olive oil - Supreme Oil Co.
PETRIBUTES BY J-C-TWIGGS - Figurines - J.C. Twiggs Co.
PETRIFYING PREHISTORICS - Toy figure molds - Toymax Inc.
PETRINI'S CLASSIC - Salad dressings–bottled ☆ - Santa Barbara Olive Co.
PETRINI'S ORIGINAL - Salad dressings–bottled ☆ - Santa Barbara Olive Co.
PETRIZZI - Apparel and accessories - Sidney T.
PETRO CAPTURE - Chemical preparations - Environmental Solutions, Inc.
PETRO-D.M. - Pet products - St. Jon Pet Care Products Inc.
PETRO GUARD - Pumps - ITT Marlow
PETRO LUBE - Oils–lubricating - Petro PSC, L.P.
PETRO PANTRY - Food-store franchise - United Oil
PETRO-PHYLIC - Soap - Doak Dermatologics
PETRO PLUS - Gasoline - Petro PSC, L.P.
PETRO POWER PLUS - Fuel additives - Petro PSC, L.P.
PETRO SORB - Cleaning preparations–household - Waverly Mineral Products Co.
PETRO STOPPING CENTER - Cleaning preparations - Petro PSC, L.P.
PETRO STOPPING CENTERS - Lighters–cigarette - Petro PSC, L.P.
PETRO-SYLLIUM - Pharmaceutical preparations ☆ - Whitehall Laboratories
PETRO:TREAD - Tires - Petro PSC, L.P.
PETRO XTRACTOR - Tools–power-driven - Abanaki Corp.
PETROCELLI - Apparel–men's - Eisenberg International Corp.
PETROCHEM - Cleaning preparations - Champions Choice Inc.
PETROCHEM ESP - Rust removers - Champions Choice Inc.
PETROCHIEF - Gloves - Jomac Products Inc.
PETRODERM - Pet products ☆ - St. Jon Pet Care Products Inc.
PETRODEX - Pet products - St. Jon Pet Care Products Inc.
PETROEX - Electrical equipment - General Electric Co.
PETROF - Pianos - Geneva International Corp.
PETROFAX - Chemical preparations - Gaines Industries, Inc.
PETROFERM - Hydrocarbon fuels - Petroferm Inc.
PETROFILTER - Filters–fuel - PDG Food Stores, Inc.
PETROFLO - Machine parts - Magniflo Corp.
PETROFSKY'S - Bagels - Petrofsky's Enterprises Inc.
PETROGALAR - Pharmaceutical preparations ☆ - Wyeth-Ayerst Laboratories
PETROL - Footwear - SBC/Sporto Corp.
PETROLATUM GAUZE - Health care products - Geritrex Corp.
PETROLUX II - Lighting fixtures - Holophane Corp.
PETROMALT - Pet products ☆ - St. Jon Pet Care Products Inc.
PETROMATE - Fuel additives - Mid-American Corp.
PETROMEDIA - Computer software - Oil and Gas Consultants International, Inc.
PETROMIZER - Automobile-mileage improver - Ament Enterprises Inc.
PETRONELLA DAUBIN - Jewelry - Kuaii & Co., Inc.
PETRONET - Chemical preparations - Cellulose Resources Corp.
PETRONOMICS - Lubricating oils - Petron International, Inc.
PETROROCKS - Ornamental products–glass - Mark R. Miller
PETROSHEEN - Pet products ☆ - St. Jon Pet Care Products Inc.
PETROSOFT - Computer software - Petrosoft, Inc.
PETROSWEEP - Water purification systems - Aqua-Net, Inc.
PETROTAPE - Measuring instruments - Metritape, Inc.
PETROTOOLS - Computer software - Petrosoft, Inc.
PETROTRADE - Computer software - Louis Dreyfus Holding Co. Inc.
PETROUCHKA - Fabrics - Gretchen Bellinger Inc.
PETROV - Beverages–alcohol - Mccormick Distilling Co., Inc.
PETROVIEW - Measuring instruments - Precision Gaging, Inc.
PETROVITE - Pet products ☆ - St. Jon Pet Care Products Inc.
PETROWAX - Waxes–mineral - U.S. Petroleum Corp.
PETROWORKS - Computer software - Landmark Graphics Corp.
PETROWORM - Pet products ☆ - St. Jon Pet Care Products Inc.
PETROZIN - Health care products ☆ - JMI-Canton Pharmaceuticals
PETRUCCELLI SUPER PRO - Dryers–hair - P.S. Pibbs Inc.
PETRUCCI MUSIC PRESS - Music–sheet ☆ - MMB Music Inc.
PETRUSHKA - Candy - Dilettante Chocolates, Inc.
PETS - Greeting cards - Paramount Cards Inc.
PETS-911 - Pet products - ID Store
PETS AND PALS - Figurines ☆ - Dave Grossman Creations Inc.
PETS CAROUSEL - Pet products - Products Carousel Inc.
PETS CHOICE - Dog food - Gimborn U.S.A., Inc.

PET'S CHOICE - Pet products - Fleming Companies, Inc.
PET'S CORNER - Pet products - Universal Cooperative Inc.
PET'S EARTH BED - Pet products ☆ - Black Sheep Inc.
PET'S NEST - Pet products ☆ - Black Sheep Inc.
PET'S ODOR GONE - Pet products ☆ - Black Sheep Inc.
PETS ON PARADE - Greeting cards ☆ - MWM Dexter Inc.
PETS ON THE MOVE - Toys - Hasbro, Inc.
PETS ON WHEELS - Toys–stuffed - Direct Connect International Inc.
PETS PACIFICA - Aquariums–household - Pets Pacifica Inc.
PET'S PAL - Pet products - Osage Products Co. Inc.
PET'S PAL - Pet products ☆ - Morton Pharmaceuticals Inc.
PET'S PET - Pet products - Pet's Pet
PETS' PRIDE - Pet products - Brower Manufacturing Co.
PETS SMELLFREE - Pet products - Pets Smellfree Inc.
PETSATIONS - Dog food ☆ - Petsations Pet Products
PETSCRIPTIONS - Animal feed supplements - Robert MacIntosh Collett
PETSHADE - Pet products ☆ - Enviroworks
PETSKOPE - Veterinary medical equipment - Techno-Optic, Inc.
PETSMARTS - Pet products - Pupperwear Inc.
PETSTERS - Toys–electronic - Axlon Inc.
PETSTUFF YOUR PETS' SUPERSTORE - Agricultural products - Petstuff, Inc.
PETT - Dog food - Hubbard Milling Co. (Landon Div.)
PETT SPICE - Sauces - Pett Spice Products, Inc.
PETTEC - Pet products - Pettec Labs
PETTI POINT - Floor coverings–carpet and rugs ☆ - Bellbridge Carpets
PETTI POINT - Jewelry ☆ - Hirsch Speidel Inc.
PETTI-PUNCH - Needle set ☆ - Susan Bates Inc.
PETTI-PUNCH - Needles–sewing ☆ - Coats and Clark Inc.
PETTICOAT - Glassware–household ☆ - Fenton Art Glass Co.
PETTICOATS PANTALOONS - Greeting cards - Specialty Sales Inc.
PETTICRISP - Fabrics–cotton - Gehring Textiles Inc.
PETTIGREW - Bakery products ☆ - American Bread Co.
PETTIJOHNS - Wheat–flour or meal - Quaker Oats Co.
PETTING FARM - Toys - Mattel, Inc.
PETTINICE - Cakes - American Bakels Inc.
PETTIPETS - Underwear and nightwear ☆ - Charles Komar and Sons Inc.
PETTIT - Paints - Pettit Paint Co. Inc.
PETTIT - Stationery - Glen W. Pettit
PETTITE-LITE - Mirrors - Monaco Import/Export Inc.
PETTITE-TRAV-LITE - Mirrors - Monaco Import/Export Inc.
PETTITROL - Paints ☆ - Pettit Paint Co. Inc.
PETTIT'S - Pharmaceutical preparations - Oakhurst Co.
PETTRELIEF PLUS - Pet products - St. Jon Pet Care Products Inc.
PETTY - Trailers–travel ☆ - Giles Industries
PETUNIA PIG - Toys–stuffed - Russ Berrie and Co., Inc.
PETVISION - Pet products - ASPC Inc.
PETWARE - Pet products - PetWare
PETXPERTS - Veterinary pharmaceutical preparations - Fleaxperts, Inc.
PETZAK - Pet music ☆ - Informative Amenities Inc.
PETZELS - Pet products - Gimborn U.S., Inc.
PETZL - Sporting goods - Climb High Inc.
PETZORB - Cleaning preparations - International Chemical Corp.
PETZYMES - Pet products - Solid Gold Holistic Animal/Equine Nutrition Center
PEUBLO - Bicycles - Raleigh USA Bicycle Co.
PEUGEOT - Housewares - SCI Scandicrafts Inc.
PEUGEOT - Kitchenware–earthenware - Charles F. La Malle
PEUGEOT - Motor vehicles–automobiles - Peugeot Motors of America Inc.
PEUGOT - Housewares - Vanderburgh & Co. Inc.
PEVELY-FRUIT-N-COTTAGE CHEESE - Cottage cheese ☆ - Pevely Dairy Co.
PEVONIA - Skin care products - Cosmopro Inc.
PEWEE THE WOODPECKER - Toys ☆ - L.K. Hecht Co. Inc.
PEWTAREX - Giftware - Olde Country Reproductions Inc.
PEWTEEL - Housewares - Shelton-Ware Corp.
PEWTER - Giftware - Garden Silversmiths Ltd.
PEWTER BY ONEIDA - Flatware ☆ - Oneida Ltd.
PEWTER FLOWERS OF THE MONTH COLLECTION - Jewelry - Kirk Stieff Co.
PEWTER OAK - Lumber - Georgia-Pacific Corp.
PEWTER PERSONALITIES - Figurines - Rawcliffe Corp.
PEWTER PORT - Giftware - WT Wilson/Limited Editions Pewter Port
PEWTER SENSATIONS - Giftware - Lawrence Neal
PEWTERLOY - Housewares - Valleau Brass Foundry
PEWTERTONE - Glassware–household - Seymour Mann Inc.
PEWTIE BITS - Figurines ☆ - E.M.I. Inc.
PEX - Cough medicines ☆ - JMI-Canton Pharmaceuticals
PEXTO - Brakes–motor vehicle - Roper Whitney of Rockford, Inc.

PEXTO - Tools - Roper Whitney Co.
PEYBEL SARGE - Pharmaceutical preparations - Enzymatic Therapy, Inc.
PEYCHAUD'S BITTER - Beverages–alcohol - Sazerac Co. Inc.
PEYOTE BIRD - Watches - Peyote Bird Designs
PEYOTE VISIONS - Apparel–women's - Nancy K. Ulmer
PEYRANO - Food products ☆ - Bel Canto Fancy Foods Ltd.
PEYTON'S - Bassoons - John Morrell & Co.
PEZ - Candy - Pez Candy Inc.
PEZA - Alcoholic beverages - Attiki Imports & Distributors
PEZAZZ - Candy - Pez Candy Inc.
PEZZULLO - Pasta - Schroeder Brothers
PF - Novelty items - Jeff Busby Magic, Inc.
P.F. - Paint rollers - Elder & Jenks, Inc.
PF - Screws - Pearson Fastener Corp.
PF - Soups–mixes - Precision Foods, Inc.
PF-2 - Lighting fixtures ☆ - Brinkmann Lighting Products
PF/2 ENERGIZER - Toilets–porcelain - W/C Technology Corp.
PF-8 - Audio equipment ☆ - C.T.I. Audio Inc.
PF 90 - Braces–orthopedic - Swanee USA Inc.
PF DISPOSA-BRUSH - Brushes ☆ - Purdue Frederick Co.
PF EXTERIOR - Paints - Synkoloid Co.
PF MAGIC - Video games - Pf. Magic, Inc.
PF PALLETTOP - Paperboard - Laminations Corp.
PF/S - Photo albums - Pacific Foto/Supply Co.
PFABULOUS PFAUCET, THE - Faucets - Emhart Inc.
PFAELZER - Food products - Conagra, Inc.
PFAFF - Sewing machines–household - Pfaff American Sales Corp.
PFALTZGRAFF - Cooking utensils–stoneware ☆ - General Housewares Corp.
PFALTZGRAFF - Dinnerware–glass - Reston Lloyd Ltd.
PFALTZGRAFF - Flatware - Pfaltzgraff Investment Co.
PFALTZGRAFF - Housewares - Himark Enterprises Inc.
PFALTZGRAFF AMERICAN ARTWARE - Housewares - Pfaltzgraff Investment Co.
PFALTZGRAFF BASICS - Tableware–china - Pfaltzgraff Investment Co.
PFALTZGRAFF COLLECTION, THE - Wallpaper - Shelbourne Wallcoverings
PFALTZGRAFF HOPSCOTCH COLLECTION - Wood products - Vermillion Inc.
PFALTZGRAFF TEAROSE COLLECTION - Wood products - Vermillion Inc.
PFALTZGRAFF YORKTOWNE COLLECTION - Wood products - Vermillion Inc.
PFANSTIEHL - Phonographic needles - Pfanstiehl Laboratories Inc.
PFANTONE - Electronic equipment - Pfanstiehl Laboratories Inc.
PFASHIONS BY PRICE PFISTER - Faucets - Emhart Inc.
PFAULOX - Animal feed supplements - George Pfau's Sons Co., Inc.
PFAUOIL - Oils–lubricating - George Pfau's Sons Co., Inc.
P.F.B. - Blades and razors - American Safety Razor Co.
PFC - Carrying case - Plastic Forming Co. Inc.
PFC - Cleaning preparations - Jelmar Industries, Inc.
PFC - Cleaning preparations–household - Jamie Industries, Inc.
PFC - Nuts and bolts - Porteous Fastener Co.
PFC - Pet products - Best Friend Products
PFC BEAR - Toys–stuffed - Dakin Inc.
PFC FIRST CLASS SERVICE - Nuts and bolts - Porteous Fastener Co.
PFC9 - Metals - Porteous Fastener Co.
PFCS-PRO FLIGHT CONTROL SYSTEM - Computer software - Thrustmaster, Inc.
PFEIFFER - Beverages–malt - The Stroh Brewery Co.
PFEIFFER - Salad dressings–bottled - T. Marzetti Co.
PFEIFFER'S - Cakes ☆ - Jac Hes & Co.
PFEIFFER'S - Pharmaceutical preparations - Pfeiffer Pharmaceuticals Inc.
PFG - Fabric - PFG
PFG - Weightlifting equipment - Personal Fitness Gear Inc.
PFG PORTABLE FORM GENERATOR - Computer hardware and software - Matrix Computer Systems, Inc.
PFI - Automotive parts and accessories - Perfect Fit Industries, Inc.
PFI FOOT SOLDIERS - Orthotic devices - Professional Foot Care International, Inc.
PFISTER - Giftware - Sasaki
PFIZER - Pharmaceutical preparations - Pfizer Inc.
PFLOP - Furniture - Glenn A. Aaron
PFOREVER PFAUCET - Faucets - Emhart Inc.
PFRETZSCHUER - Musical instruments ☆ - Scherl & Roth Inc.
PFRIEMER - Pianos - Baldwin Piano & Organ Co.
PFS - Frames–picture - North American Enclosures Inc.
PFS - Telephone accessories - Fiber Plus International
PFS-PUREMARK - Water filtering units - Puremark USA, Inc.
PFS:WINDOWWORKS - Computer software - Spinnaker Software Corp.

☆ = Now out of production

PFTREND - Computer storage devices - Multispiro, Inc.
PFV - Cables - MacWhyte Co.
PFX PLUS - Computer software - PFX USA Inc.
PG - Brake parts ☆ - Raybestos/Brake Parts Inc.
PG - Jewelry - Princess Gold Manufacturers Inc.
PG - Paper products - Paper Group Inc.
P.G. - Scissors–hand-operated - Organifyl Laboratories
PG - Windows–screen - American Management Group
PG PLUS - Brake parts - Raybestos/Brake Parts Inc.
P.G. SPORTS - Apparel and accessories - Polomate Corp.
PGA - Golfing equipment - Tommy Armour Golf Co.
PGA TOUR - Apparel and accessories - Phillips-Van Heusen Corp.
P.G.C. - Jewelry - Kaspar & Esh Inc.
P.G.C. - Playing cards - Hoyle Products
PGD - Jewelry - Phils Gold & Diamonds Inc.
PGHPF - Computer peripheral equipment - Portland Group, Inc.
PGI - Golfing equipment - Presidential Group Inc.
PGL - Computer software - Printronix, Inc.
PGL OMNI-SYSTEM - Lighting fixtures - Kim Lighting Inc.
PGM - Agricultural products - High View Church Farm, Inc.
PGM - Recording label - Quintessential Sound, Inc.
PGP - Computer software - Philip Zimmermann
PGP - Electronic equipment - Peavey Electronics Corp.
PGP - Tools–hand-operated - Pooper Getter Plus, Inc.
PGR IV - Plant growth regulators - Plant Growth Formulations, Inc.
PGREEN LANTERN - Chemical preparations - Life Technologies, Inc.
PGS - Health care products - Universal Technology Systems Inc.
PGT - Saw blades - Blackstone Industries, Inc.
PGY - Yearbooks - Scandinavian House Imports Inc.
P.H. - Pharmaceutical preparations ☆ - Scrip-Physician Supply Co.
PH-1 POWERHOUSE - Toys–trains - Kughn Enterprises
PH II - Toilets–porcelain - Raritan Engineering Co. Inc.
PH-10 - Pet products - Vortex Innerspace Products Inc.
PH ALERT - Pet products - Seachem Laboratories
PH BALANCER - Shampoos ☆ - Clairol Inc.
PH-D. - Shampoos - Wella Corp. (Consumer Products Div.)
PH DECREASER - Aquariums–household - Jungle Laboratories Corp.
PH DOWN - Chemical preparations - Great Lakes Biochemical Co., Inc.
PH DOWN - Water treating compounds - Aquarium Pharmaceuticals, Inc.
PH-EASE - Chemical preparations - Mydor Industries Inc.
PH-EASE: DECREASE - Chemical preparations - Mydor Industries Inc.
PH-EASE: INCREASE - Chemical preparations - Mydor Industries Inc.
PH FIX-IT - Water treating compounds ☆ - Aquatronics-Filtronics
PH GUARD - Aquarium accessories - Mardel Laboratories, Inc.
PH INCREASER - Aquariums–household - Jungle Laboratories Corp.
PH MINUS - Chemical preparations - Coastal Industries Inc.
PH MINUS - Water treating compounds - Mardel Laboratories, Inc.
PH NEUTRAL - Pet products ☆ - Caribsea Inc.
PH PLUS - Skin care products - Redken Laboratories, Inc.
PH PLUS - Water treating compounds - Mardel Laboratories, Inc.
P.H. SMOKE - Safety products - Condar Co.
PH-STABIL - Pharmaceutical preparations - Center Laboratories/Hermal Dermatology Group
PH STABILIZER 6.5 - Aquariums–household - Jungle Laboratories Corp.
PH STABILIZER 7.0 - Aquariums–household - Jungle Laboratories Corp.
PH STABILIZER 7.5 - Aquariums–household - Jungle Laboratories Corp.
PH TRUEBLOOD - Machinery - Resource General Corp.
PH UP - Chemical preparations - Great Lakes Biochemical Co., Inc.
PH-UP - Water treating compounds - Aquarium Pharmaceuticals, Inc.
PH WAND - Measuring instruments - Cole-Parmer Instrument Co.
PH4 - Pharmaceutical preparations - Southern Pharmacal Co. Inc.
PHA CHEK - Pharmaceutical preparations - United Biomedical Inc.
PHACES - Lighting fixtures - SPI Lighting, Inc.
PHACID - Skin care products - Baker Cummins Dermatologicals Inc.
PHACOFIT - Ophthalmic goods - Allergan, Inc.
PHACOSCRIBE - Medical apparatus - Chiron Corp.
PHADE - Pharmaceutical preparations - Alva-Amco Pharmacal Co.
PHAEDRA - Shoes - Arthur Schneider Sales, Inc.
PHAEDRUS - Watches - Robert R. Netsch
PHAETON - Shoes - Converse Inc.
PHAGEFINDER - Chemical preparations - Novagen, Inc.
PHAGIA - Cereal - Med-Diet Laboratories Inc.
PHAIDON CULTURAL GUIDES - Publisher's imprints - Simon & Schuster, Inc.
PHALANX - Guns - Phalanx Corp.
PHALANX II - Floor coverings–carpet and rugs - Trend Carpet

PHALAROPE NATURE GUIDES - Publisher's imprints - Simon & Schuster, Inc.
PHALO - Electronic equipment - Intercole, Inc.
PHALTAN - Pesticides–agricultural - Chevron Chemical Co.
PHAMOUS PHLOYD'S - Barbecue sauce - Phamous Phloyd's, Inc.
PHAN THIET - Sauces - Viet My Corp.
PHANAMINE - Pharmaceutical preparations ☆ - Jones Medical Industries, Inc. (Medical Div.)
PHANAMINE PLUS - Pharmaceutical preparations ☆ - Jones Medical Industries, Inc. (Medical Div.)
PHANASIN - Cough medicines - Pharmakon Labs, Inc.
PHANATUSS - Cough medicines - Pharmakon Labs, Inc.
PHANATUSSIN - Cough medicines ☆ - Pharmakon Labs, Inc.
PHANNYS - Chocolate candy - Phannys Chocolates Inc.
PHANNY'S PHUDGE - Candy - Phannys Chocolates Inc.
PHANO - Crayons - Dixon Ticonderoga Co.
PHANTAGRAMS - Greeting cards - Polaroid Corp.
PHANTASM - Fireworks - B.J. Alan Co. Inc.
PHANTASM - Floor coverings–carpet and rugs - Regal Rugs Inc.
PHANTASTIQUE - Girdles ☆ - Maidenform Inc. (True Form Foundations Div.)
PHANTASY STAR II - Games - Sega of America, Inc.
PHANTOM - Aquarium accessories - Rita Scott
PHANTOM - Archery equipment - Elk Mountain Archery of Colorado Ltd.
PHANTOM - Archery equipment ☆ - Martin Archery Inc.
PHANTOM - Bicycles - Schwinn Cycling & Fitness Inc.
PHANTOM - Boats - Glen-L Marine Designs
PHANTOM - Boats - New Howmar Boats Corp.
PHANTOM - Boats–motor - Alumacraft Boat Co.
PHANTOM - Boats–motor - Crestliner Boats Inc.
PHANTOM - Boats–motor - Forester Boats Inc.
PHANTOM - Cigarettes - Nat Sherman, Inc.
PHANTOM - Eyeglasses ☆ - International Tropic-Cal Inc. (I SKI Div.)
PHANTOM - Firearms, accessories, and parts ☆ - Bausch & Lomb Inc.
PHANTOM - Fireworks - B.J. Alan Co. Inc.
PHANTOM - Fishing tackle - Plano Molding Co.
PHANTOM - Girdles ☆ - Maidenform Inc. (True Form Foundations Div.)
PHANTOM - Knives - Russell Harrington Cutlery, Inc.
PHANTOM - Lenses–magnifying - C. Bennett Scopes Inc.
PHANTOM - Manicure preparations - Creative Nail Design, Inc.
PHANTOM - Mining cars - Commonwealth Inc.
PHANTOM - Model of BENELLI motorcycle ☆ - Cosmopolitan Motors Inc.
PHANTOM - Novelty items–paper ☆ - Unique Industries, Inc.
PHANTOM - Rackets–tennis - Slazengers
PHANTOM - Recording label - Phantom Productions Inc.
PHANTOM - Remote control devices - Overhead Door Corp.
PHANTOM - Ships–sailing vessels - Howmar Boat Corp.
PHANTOM - Soccer equipment - Brine Inc.
PHANTOM - Tachometers - Auto Meter Products Inc.
PHANTOM - Thread - Coats and Clark Inc.
PHANTOM - Toys–models - Estes Industries
PHANTOM - Toys–stuffed ☆ - Dakin Inc.
PHANTOM - Trailers - U.S. Cargo, Inc.
PHANTOM - Watches - Bulova Corp.
PHANTOM - Welders' hoods - Sellstrom Manufacturing Co.
PHANTOM 54 - Toys–airplanes - Paul K. Guillow Inc.
PHANTOM ACOUSTICS - Audio equipment - Threshold Corp.
PHANTOM CONNECTORS - Electronic equipment - Klyne Audio Arts, Ltd.
PHANTOM-EASE - Apparel–women's - Maidenform Inc. (True Form Foundations Div.)
PHANTOM ELECTRO - Welders' hoods ☆ - Sellstrom Manufacturing Co.
PHANTOM EXPERIENCE THE SUPER NATURAL - Manicure preparations - Creative Nail Design, Inc.
PHANTOM FENCE - Electronic equipment - Long Fence Co. Inc.
PHANTOM FIGHTER - Video games - Fujisankei Communications International Inc.
PHANTOM FLIES - Fishing tackle ☆ - Phantom Flies International, Inc.
PHANTOM FLYER - Toys - Allied Materials & Equipment Co. Inc.
PHANTOM LASER LIGHT CONTROLLER - Electronic equipment - Laser Media, Inc.
PHANTOM-LINE - Artists' materials - Phantom-Line Graphics
PHANTOM LINK - Electromechanical controls - Xantech Corp.
PHANTOM LOW PROFILE - Sporting goods - Wellington Leisure Products, Inc.
PHANTOM MESH - Screen material - Cascade Coil Drapery, Inc.
PHANTOM MOUSE - Drill presses - International Tool Co., Inc.
PHANTOM OF THE OPERA - Giftware ☆ - Enesco Corp.
PHANTOM OF THE OPERA - Jewelry - Richard A. Serbin Ltd.

PHANTOM PAD - Seats–automobile - A. Wilhelm Desser

PHANTOM PLUS - Rackets–tennis ☆ - Slazengers

PHANTOM Q - Computer software - Teksouth Corp.

PHANTOM REVOLUTION, THE - Sporting goods - Component Concepts, Inc.

PHANTOM SCRAMBLER - Bicycles - Schwinn Cycling & Fitness Inc.

PHANTOM SINGLE - Welders' hoods ☆ - Sellstrom Manufacturing Co.

PHANTOM SPORT - Boats–motor - Forester Boats Inc.

PHANTOM WALL - Doors–glass - Vistawall

PHANTOM WEIGHT - Luggage - United States Luggage Corp.

PHANTOMACHINE - Toys–automobiles - Mattel, Inc.

PHANTOMATO - Toys - Mattel, Inc.

PHANTOMS - Construction equipment - Formica Corp.

PHANTOMS NITE N' DAY - See NITE N' DAY

PHANTOMSCREEN - Computer software - Neosoft Corp.

PHAR LAP SOFTWARE - Computer software - Phar Lap Software, Inc.

PHARAOH - Apparel and accessories - Pharaoh Inc.

PHARAOH - Skin care products - Pharaoh Skin Care and Cosmetics, Limited Liability Co.

PHARAOH'S FANTASY - Game machines - Lazer-Tron Corp.

PHARAOH'S FORTUNE - Video games - WMS Gaming Inc.

PHARAOH'S TREASURE - Game machines - Bally Gaming International, Inc.

PHARM-ALOE - Veterinary pharmaceutical preparations - Pharm-Aloe, Inc.

PHARM RX, THE - Razor blades - Buckeye Discount, Inc.

PHARM, THE - Thermometers - Buckeye Discount, Inc.

PHARMA CELL - Beauty shop equipment - Focus 21 International Inc.

PHARMA CITY - Food containers - Purity Supreme Supermarkets

PHARMA GLOSS - Labels–paper - Morgan Adhesives Co.

PHARMA LAX - Vitamins and nutritional supplements - Pharmadil, Inc.

PHARMA LOGISTICS - Pharmaceutical preparations - Returns 'R' Us, Inc.

PHARMA PURE - Vitamins and nutritional supplements - D.E.F. Enterprises, Inc.

PHARMA-TURM-INC. - Springes - Pharma-Turm Inc.

PHARMACID - Antacids - Reheis Inc.

PHARMACIST BEST - Health care products - Leiner Health Products Inc.

PHARMACIST CARE - Laxatives - P. Leiner Nutritional Products, Inc.

PHARMACIST FAVORITE - Vitamins and nutritional supplements - McKesson Home Health Care

PHARMACIST FORMULA - Pharmaceutical preparations - Leiner Health Products Inc.

PHARMACIST PRIDE - Vitamins and nutritional supplements - Golden Sun Vitamins

PHARMACIST RELIEF - Vitamins and nutritional supplements - Leiner Health Products Inc.

PHARMACIST SYSTEM - Vitamins and nutritional supplements - Leiner Health Products Inc.

PHARMACIST'S CRHME - Pharmaceutical preparations - Reese Chemical Co.

PHARMACIST'S LOTION - Pharmaceutical preparations - Reese Chemical Co.

PHARMACISTS' NUTRITION CENTER - Vitamins and nutritional supplements - Pharmacists' Nutrition Center

PHARMACOSTA - Skin care products - La Costa Resort Hotel & Spa

PHARMACY CARE - Computer software - Healthcare Computer Corp.

PHARMACY CENTER - Displays - Modern Aids, Inc.

PHARMACY CLASSICS - Vitamins and nutritional supplements - Garcoa Labs/ Vitamin Classics

PHARMACY CLASSICS - Vitamins and nutritional supplements - Vitamin Classics, Inc.

PHARMADERM - Pharmaceutical preparations - Pharmaderm Inc.

PHARMAFLUR - Pharmaceutical preparations - Pharmics Inc.

PHARMAFLUR DF - Pharmaceutical preparations - Pharmics Inc.

PHARMAGENESIS - Pharmaceutical preparations - Pharmagenesis, Inc.

PHARMALITE - Labels–paper - Mactac Inc. (Packaging Closures Systems Div.)

PHARMANUTRIENTS - Vitamins and nutritional supplements - Genesis Pharmanutrients, Inc.

PHARMASEA - Bath salts - Earth Salts International, Inc.

PHARMASEAL - Sealing devices - United Associates Group Inc.

PHARMASOFT - Labels–paper - Morgan Adhesives Co.

PHARMASSISTANT - Computer software - Intellivoice Communications, Inc.

PHARMATONE - Health care products - Alpha-Lac Inc.

PHARMAVITE - Pharmaceutical preparations - Pharmavite Corp.

PHARMELAST - Silicone rubber sheeting - Chase-Walton Elastomers Inc.

PHARMEX - Pharmaceutical preparations ☆ - Pharmex Inc.

PHARMEXCRIPT - Paper–writing - Automatic Business Products, Inc.

PHARMIFIT - Surgical supplies - Larkotex Surgical Manufacturing Co.

PHARMINGEN - Chemical preparations - Pharmingen

PHARMWORKS - Health care products - Kiyo Systems Inc.

PHAROAH - Games - WMS Gaming Inc.

PHARON - Beverages - Shenmei Feilong Trading Co., Inc.

PHARYCIDIN CONCENTRATE - Antiseptics ☆ - Purdue Frederick Co.

PHAS - Pet products - Tetra Sales USA

PHASAR - Electronics equipment - RTI Research Technology International

PHASAR - Motor vehicles–motor homes - Winnebago Industries, Inc.

PHASE - Electronic equipment - Computalog USA, Inc.

PHASE 1 - Athletic shoes - Reebok International Ltd.

PHASE 6 - Fabrics–nylon ☆ - BASF Corp.

PHASE 10 - Games - Kenneth Johnson

PHASE 22 - Floor coverings–carpet and rugs - Trend Carpet

PHASE COUPLED ACTIVATOR - Electronic equipment - AudioControl

PHASE I - Apparel–men's ☆ - Sedgefield Sportswear Co.

PHASE I - Floor coverings–carpet and rugs ☆ - American Excelsior Co.

PHASE II - Hair care products - Worlds of Curls Inc.

PHASE II - Musical instruments - David Wexler & Co.

PHASE II - Recording label - Music Craftshop Inc.

PHASE II - Vitamins and nutritional supplements - More Direct Response Inc.

PHASE III - Diagnostic apparatus - Nu-Calgon Wholesaler, Inc.

PHASE III - Soap - Lever Brothers Co. Inc.

PHASE III COOLER - Coolers–electric - Hartley Controls Corp.

PHASE IV - Lighting fixtures ☆ - Hubbell Lighting, Inc. (Lighting Div.)

PHASE LINEAR - Car-stereo equipment - International Jensen Inc.

PHASE ONE - Electrical equipment - Phase One Corp.

PHASE TRAK 90 - Audio equipment ☆ - Broadcast Electronics, Inc.

PHASEAROUND - Audio equipment - Robert W. Harrison

PHASER - Printers–computer - Tektronix, Inc.

PHASER - Skates–roller - Rollerblade, Inc.

PHASER - Toys - Paramount Pictures Corp.

PHASER - Toys–models ☆ - Estes Industries

PHASES - Hair care products - Waverly Beauty Products

PHASES - High chairs - Lisco, Inc.

PHASES - Lenses–optical - Labtech Optical Corp.

PHASETRAC 12 - Measuring instruments - Garmin Corp.

PHASIR - Computer peripheral equipment - Whitaker Corp.

PHASMASTER - Welding equipment - Unitek Miyachi Corp.

PHASPHORONE - Pharmaceutical preparations ☆ - Lexis Laboratories Inc.

PHAT THREADS - Clothing - Phat Fashions

PHATNESS - Apparel and accessories - Lavance Sykes

PHAWORKS - Computer software - Primatech Inc.

PHAYZME 95 - Pharmaceutical preparations - Reed & Carnrick

PHAYZME 125 - Pharmaceutical preparations - Reed & Carnrick

PHAZER - Electrical equipment - Automax Inc.

PHAZER - Skis - Wellington Leisure Products, Inc.

PHAZER - Sporting goods - Outdoor Technologies Group

PHAZYME - Pharmaceutical preparations - Reed & Carnrick

PHB'S - Boxes - Midwest of Cannon Falls Inc.

PHBS - Vitamins and nutritional supplements - Enzyme Formulations Inc.

P.H.C. - Seasonings ☆ - All American Seasonings Inc.

PHC - Tools - Spectrum Razor Tools

PHD - Food products ☆ - Morrison Restaurants Inc.

PH.D - Overseeding mixture - International Seeds, Inc.

PHD - Vitamins and nutritional supplements - Wellness International Network, Ltd.

PHD ANALYZER - Tools–power-driven - Angus Electronics Co.

PHD PERFECT HEALTH DIET - Pet food - Jascot Products, Inc.

PH.D PRIDE - Apparel and accessories - Robert McCleave

PHE II - Toilets–porcelain - Raritan Engineering Co. Inc.

PHEASANT - Hosiery ☆ - Wigwam Mills Inc.

PHEASANT HOLLOW - Wines - Gibson Wine Co.

PHEASANT RIDGE - Wines - Pheasant Ridge Winery

PHEASANT RUN - Wallpaper - Norwall Wallcoverings

PHEASANT RUN - Wallpaper - Warner Co.

PHEASANT SUPREME - Food products - Hickory Baked Foods

PHEBE PHILLIPS - Dolls and stuffed animals - Phebe Phillips Hargrove

PHEDRAL - Pharmaceutical preparations ☆ - Vortech Pharmaceuticals

PHELANTIN - Pharmaceutical preparations ☆ - Parke-Davis

PHELONY - Apparel and accessories - Phelony

PHEMITHYN - Pharmaceutical preparations ☆ - Scrip-Physician Supply Co.

PHEN ALKA - Pharmaceutical preparations - C.S. Ruckstuhl Co. Inc.

PHEN-AMINE-25 - Pharmaceutical preparations ☆ - Scrip-Physician Supply Co.

PHEN-GESIC - Pharmaceutical preparations ☆ - Schein Pharmaceutical Inc.

PHEN-LO - Health care products - Healthwatchers System

PHENA-C - Pharmaceutical preparations - Mill-Mark Pharmaceuticals Inc.

PHENACAINE - Pharmaceutical preparations - City Chemical Corp.

PHENACON - Pharmaceutical preparations - Teral Laboratories

☆ = Now out of production

PHENADRINE - Pharmaceutical preparations - Afassco

PHENADRINE - Vitamins and nutritional supplements - Michigan Pharmaceutical

PHENADRINO FORTE - Pharmaceutical preparations - Afassco

PHENAHIST-TR - Pharmaceutical preparations - T.E. Williams Pharmaceutical Inc.

PHENAL-PLUS - Veterinary nutritional supplements - Oralx Corp.

PHENALGIN - Fertilizers - Pharmline, Inc.

PHENALGIN - Health care products - Etna Products Co. Inc.

PHENALGIN-D - Veterinary nutritional supplements - Oralx Corp.

PHENAPAP - Pharmaceutical preparations - Rugby Laboratories Inc.

PHENAPHEN - Analgesics - A.H. Robins Co. Inc.

PHENAPINE - Pharmaceutical preparations - C.S. Ruckstuhl Co. Inc.

PHENAPRO - Pharmaceutical preparations ☆ - Hyrex Pharmaceuticals

PHENASEPTIC - Pharmaceutical preparations - Barre-National, Inc.

PHENATE - Analgesics - Roberts/Hauck Pharmaceuticals Inc.

PHENATRIN - Pharmaceutical preparations ☆ - JMI-Canton Pharmaceuticals

PHENAZINE - Pharmaceutical preparations - Keene Pharmaceuticals Inc.

PHENAZODINE - Antihistamine preparations - Lannett Co. Inc.

PHENBROPHEN - Pharmaceutical preparations - L. Perrigo Co.

PHENCASET - Pharmaceutical preparations ☆ - ICN Pharmaceuticals Inc.

PHENCEN-50 - Pharmaceutical preparations ☆ - Central Pharmaceutical Inc.

PHENCOID - Pharmaceutical preparations ☆ - JMI-Canton Pharmaceuticals

PHENDIET - Pharmaceutical preparations - C.O. Truxton Inc.

PHENDOFF - Pharmaceutical preparations ☆ - Cameron Medical Corp.

PHENE-O-CLEAN - Disinfectants - Hillyard Enterprises, Inc.

PHENEREX - Pharmaceutical preparations - C.S. Ruckstuhl Co. Inc.

PHENERGAN - Pharmaceutical preparations - Wyeth-Ayerst Laboratories

PHENERGAN-D - Pharmaceutical preparations - Wyeth-Ayerst Laboratories

PHENETRON - Pharmaceutical preparations - Lannett Co. Inc.

PHENGUARD - Epoxy - Sigma Coatings USA BV.

PHENHIST - Cough medicines - Rugby Laboratories Inc.

PHENILAR - Health care products - Halsey Drug Co. Inc.

PHENINDIONE - Pharmaceutical preparations - Robinson Laboratories Inc.

PHENISTIX - Chemical preparations - Miles Inc.

PHENIX - Adhesives and sealants - Phenix Biocomposites, Inc.

PHENIX - Doors–garage - Clopay Millwork

PHENIX - Scissors - American Pin & Fastener Corp.

PHENIX - Soldering equipment - Hexacon Electric Co.

PHENO-DONNA - Prescription drug ☆ - Ion Laboratories Inc.

PHENO-SWEET - Veterinary pharmaceutical preparations ☆ - Farnam Cos. Inc.

PHENOBELLA - Health care products ☆ - Ferndale Laboratories, Inc.

PHENOBORATE - Mouthwashes - Consolidated Midland Corp.

PHENOCIDE - Aquatic pharmacuetical preparations ☆ - Aquatronics-Filtronics

PHENODAN - Pharmaceutical preparations ☆ - Jones Medical Industries, Inc. (Medical Div.)

PHENOFOAM - Insulating materials ☆ - Lewcott Corp.

PHENOGESIC - Throat spray ☆ - Iodent Co.

PHENOJECT-50 - Pharmaceutical preparations - Merz Inc.

PHENOLAX - Laxatives ☆ - Upjohn Co.

PHENOLEX - Office supplies - Oliner Fibre Co. Inc.

PHENOLITE - Plastics - NVF Co.

PHENOMANAILS - Nail care products - Phenomanails, Inc.

PHENOMENON - Floor coverings–carpet and rugs - Regal Rugs Inc.

PHENOPEP II - Pharmaceutical preparations ☆ - Legere Pharmaceuticals Inc.

PHENOSEAL - Adhesives and sealants - Gloucester Co., Inc.

PHENOXENE - Pharmaceutical preparations - Marion Merrell Dow

PHENSAL - Analgesics - Marion Merrell Dow

PHENSPRAY - Pharmaceutical preparations - Lannett Co. Inc.

PHENTABS - Analgesics - Rogers' Drug Co.

PHENTAL - Pharmaceutical preparations - Armenpharm Ltd.

PHENTERCOT - Pharmaceutical preparations - C.O. Truxton Inc.

PHENTERLOW - Pharmaceutical preparations - Wesley Pharmacal Co. Inc.

PHENTERSPAN - Pharmaceutical preparations - Wesley Pharmacal Co. Inc.

PHENTOIN SODIUM - Pharmaceutical preparations ☆ - Richie Pharmacal Co. Inc.

PHENTRA - Pharmaceutical preparations - C.S. Ruckstuhl Co. Inc.

PHENTROL - Pharmaceutical preparations ☆ - Vortech Pharmaceuticals

PHENURONE - Pharmaceutical preparations - Abbott Laboratories

PHENX, THE - Communication systems - Teknow, Inc.

PHENYL - Rubber–synthetic - General Electric Co.

PHENYLAZO - Prescription drug - American Pharmaceutical Co.

PHENYLDRINE - Cold remedies ☆ - Pharmex Inc.

PHENYLEPHRINE - Pharmaceutical preparations - Morton Grove Pharmaceuticals

PHENYLGESIC - Pharmaceutical preparations - Goldline Laboratories, Inc.

PHENYLHISTINE - Pharmaceutical preparations - H.R. Cenci Laboratories Inc.

PHENYLZONE A - Pharmaceutical preparations ☆ - Rugby Laboratories Inc.

PHENYTOIN - Pharmaceutical preparations ☆ - JMI-Canton Pharmaceuticals

PHENZINE - Pharmaceutical preparations ☆ - Roberts/Hauck Pharmaceuticals Inc.

PHEP - Electrical instrument - Hanna Instruments, Inc.

PHERAZINE - Health care products - Halsey Drug Co. Inc.

PHEROMONE - Perfumes - Marilyn Miglin L.P.

PHEYLALAN B-C - Health care products - Resurrection Laboratories

PHH EQUINOX - Computer peripheral equipment - Phh Corp.

PHI BETA BILLY BEAR - Toys–stuffed - Russ Berrie and Co., Inc.

PHI BETA FILER - Computer software - Voyager Software Corp.

PHI THETA KAPPA SOCIETY 1918 - Jewelry - Phi Theta Kappa

PHIBER - Apparel and accessories - Rosalina Leung

PHIBER OPTICS - Skin care products ☆ - Redken Laboratories, Inc.

PHIBIAN - Scuba diving equipment - American Underwater Products

PHIBRO-GUARD - Chemical preparations - Phibro-Tech, Inc.

PHICON - Pharmaceutical preparations - T.E. Williams Pharmaceutical Inc.

PHICON-E - Pharmaceutical preparations - T.E. Williams Pharmaceutical Inc.

PHICON-F - Pharmaceutical preparations - T.E. Williams Pharmaceutical Inc.

PHIFER - Blinds–vertical - A & E Blind & Awning Co.

PHIFER - Windows–screen - Phifer Wire Products Inc.

PHIFER SHADES - Window shades - Vertical Blind Factory

PHIFER SOLAR SHADES - Window shades - Bamboo Abbott Florida Corp.

PHIFERGLASS - Windows–screen - Phifer Wire Products Inc.

PHIFERTEX - Fabrics - Astrup Co.

PHIFERTEX - Fabrics - Phifer Wire Products Inc.

PHIL - Bicycles - Phil Wood & Co.

PHIL-L.A. OF SOUL - Recording label - Universal Record

PHIL LINDSEY'S ORIGINAL - Food products - Genuine Foods

PHIL MARANO - Wigs - Phil Marano Inc.

PHIL SILVERS SHOW, THE - Shirts - CBS Inc.

PHIL SPECTOR INTERNATIONAL - Recording label - Phil Spector International (Warner-Spector Records Inc.)

PHILA-DOLL-PHIAN - Apparel and accessories - Howard Garnett

PHILADELPHIA - Adhesives and sealants - Illinois Tool Works Inc.

PHILADELPHIA - Cheese - Kraft Foods, Inc.

PHILADELPHIA - Health care products - Bell-Horn

PHILADELPHIA - Medical apparatus - Philadelphia Cervical Collar Co.

PHILADELPHIA BRAND LIGHT - Dairy products - Kraft Foods, Inc.

PHILADELPHIA BULLDOGS - Apparel and accessories - Philadelphia Professional In-Line Hockey Club, Inc.

PHILADELPHIA CANDIES - Candy - Philadelphia Candies Inc.

PHILADELPHIA CERVICAL COLLAR - Medical apparatus - Philadelphia Cervical Collar Co.

PHILADELPHIA CHOCOLATE FACTORY - Candy - Williams & Randolph Inc.

PHILADELPHIA CONCEPTS - Floor coverings–carpet and rugs - Philadelphia Carpets

PHILADELPHIA DAILY NEWS - Paper–newsprint - Philadelphia Newspapers Inc.

PHILADELPHIA FAMOUS - Baked goods - Country Club Food Industries Inc.

PHILADELPHIA FREE - Cheese - Kraft Foods, Inc.

PHILADELPHIA FREEDOM - Floor coverings–carpet and rugs - Philadelphia Carpets

PHILADELPHIA INSULATED WIRE - Cables - General Cable Corp.

PHILADELPHIA INTERNATIONAL - Recording label - Gamble Huff Music Productions

PHILADELPHIA MUSEUM OF ART - Postcards - Fotofolio Inc.

PHILADELPHIA ORCHESTRA, THE - Publisher's imprints - Philadelphia Orchestra Association

PHILADELPHIA SOFT PRETZELS - Pretzels - Philadelphia Soft Pretzels, Inc.

PHILADELPHIA STYLE SYSTEM, THE - Food products - David Michael & Co.

PHILADELPHIA THI-WIDE - Health care products - Bell-Horn

PHILADELPHIA WEEKLY - Publisher's imprints - Review Publishing LP

PHILADEPHIA'S HOMETOWN BEER - Beverages–malt - Red Bell Brewing Co.

PHILATELY TODAY - Books–blank - Treat Entertainment, Inc.

PHILBIN - Exercising equipment ☆ - Exercycle Corp.

PHILCO - Electrical equipment - Phillips Electronics North America Corp.

PHILCO - Electronic equipment - Philips Consumer Electronics Co.

PHILCO - Kitchen appliances - White Consolidated Industries, Inc.

PHILCO - Video players - North American Philips Corp.

PHILCOMATIC - Televisions - Philips Consumer Electronics Co.

PHILE 13 - Snowboards - Wide Ride Inc.

PHILEAS - Perfumes - Parfums Nina Ricci

PHILESCO - Lubricants - Phillips 66 Propane Co.

PHILINEA - Lamps - Philips Lighting Co.

PHILIP & MONICA - Apparel–women's - Wide Pacific Development, Inc.

PHILIP GRAF - Wallpaper - Goffle Warehouse & Distribution Co. Inc.

PHILIP GURIAN - Dresses–women's - Anne Klein & Co.

PHILIP KRACZOWSKI - Bronze products ☆ - Rawcliffe Corp.

PHILIP KUBICKI - Guitars - Philip Kubicki Technology

PHILIP MONET - Watches ☆ - Littman Jewelers

PHILIP MORRIS - Cigarettes - Philip Morris Companies Inc.

PHILIP MORRIS COMMANDER - Cigarettes - Philip Morris Companies Inc.

PHILIP MORRIS SPECIAL RESERVE - Tobacco products - Philip Morris Companies Inc.

PHILIP MORRIS SUPER LIGHTS - Cigarettes - Philip Morris Companies Inc.

PHILIP WHITNEY LTD. - Picture frames - Philip Whitney, Ltd.

PHILIPPA - Bedding–linen - Dan River Inc.

PHILIPPE AMIEL - Watches - Overseas Time Inc.

PHILIPPE DE LANCOURT - Wine - European Beverage Co., Inc.

PHILIPPE DESHOULIERES - Dinnerware–glass - Lalique North America

PHILIPPE HERARD - Wines ☆ - Pellegrini Bros. Wines Inc.

PHILIPPE LECLERC - Wines - Wine Imports Ltd.

PHILIPPONNAT - Beverages–alcohol - Marie Brizard Wines & Spirits, USA

PHILIPS - Dictating machines - Philips Business Systems Co.

PHILIPS - Electronic equipment - Philips Consumer Electronics Co.

PHILIPS - Kitchen appliances ☆ - Philips Electronics North America Corp.

PHILIPS - Lighting fixtures - Philips Lighting Co.

PHILIPS - Recording label - Polygram Records, Inc.

PHILIPS IMPORT - Recording label - Polygram Records, Inc.

PHILIPS LABORATORIES - Computer software - Phillips Electronics North America Corp.

PHILISHAVE - Razors–electric - Philips Electronics North America Corp.

PHILLES - Recording label - Phil Spector International (Warner-Spector Records Inc.)

PHILLIES - Cigars - Havatampa Inc.

PHILLIES - Cigars - Phillies Cigar Co.

PHILLIES - Novelty items - Phillies

PHILLIES LITTLE CIGAR - Cigars - Phillies Cigar Co.

PHILLIES TIPS - Cigars - Phillies Cigar Co.

PHILLIP BRUCE - Underwear and nightwear - Quitman Manufacturing Co.

PHILLIP COURTNEY - Apparel–women's - Casual Corner of America Inc.

PHILLIP MARTIN - Footwear–men's - Univshoe Inc.

PHILLIP MARTON - Jewelry - A.P. Imports Inc.

PHILLIPPE - Handbags - IMA Fashions Inc.

PHILLIPPE NADDEF - Wines - Wine House Ltd.

PHILLIPS - Beverages–alcohol - Phillips Products Co.

PHILLIPS - Cleaning preparations - Phillips Process Co. Inc.

PHILLIPS - Electronic equipment ☆ - Fidelitone Inc.

PHILLIPS - Hair care products - Major/Advance International

PHILLIPS - Mobile homes - Phillips Products

PHILLIPS - Office supplies - Phillips Ribbon & Carbon Co.

PHILLIPS - Preserved foods–canned - Hanover Foods Corp.

PHILLIPS - Screws - Phillips Screw Co.

PHILLIPS 66 - Chemical preparations - Phillips 66 Propane Co.

PHILLIPS 66 GIANT MONSTER - Toys–electronic - Bird Bromiticous Inc.

PHILLIPS 66 SUPERCLEAN - Gasoline - Phillips 66 Propane Co.

PHILLIPS & TEMRO - Heaters–gas - Phillips & Temro Industries Inc.

PHILLIPS BROOKS - Calendars - Samuel Ward Manufacturing Inc.

PHILLIPS FAMILY - Pies–frozen - Philchic, Inc.

PHILLIPS II - Screws - Phillips Screw Co.

PHILLIPS' MILK OF MAGNESIA - Pharmaceutical preparations - Bayer Corp. (Consumer Care Div.)

PHILLIPS STREET USA - Coats - Dyersburg Fabrics Inc.

PHILLIPS STYLESAVER - Brushes–hair - Phillips Brush Corp.

PHILLIPSON - Sporting goods - Phillipson Rod Co.

PHILLY - Meat products–beef - Quaker Maid Meats Inc.

PHILLY - Medical apparatus - Philadelphia Cervical Collar Co.

PHILLY - Recording label - Jazz Composer's Orchestra Association Inc.

PHILLY FOR TOAST - Cheese - Kraft Foods, Inc.

PHILLY FREE - Cheese - Kraft Foods, Inc.

PHILLY GOURMET - Meat products–beef - Quaker Maid Meats Inc.

PHILLY GRILLERS - Sausages ☆ - Habbersett Bros. Inc.

PHILLY STEAK, THE - Meat products–beef - Quaker Maid Meats Inc.

PHILLY'S FAMOUS SOFT PRETZEL CO. - Pretzels - Philly's Famous Soft Pretzel Co.

PHILLY'S FAVORITE - Meat products - Medfords, Inc.

PHILMONT - Lighters - Colibri Inc.

PHILMORE - Computer hardware - Carter Craft Co.

PHILO - Recording label - Rounder Records Corp.

PHILOMEGA - Recording label - Universal Record

PHILOMEI - Publisher's imprints - Putnam Publishing Group

PHILOS - Hair care products - Perfector Products

PHILOSOPHY - Cosmetics - Cosmedic Concepts, Inc.

PHILOSOPHY DESIGN - Magnets - Philosophy Design Inc.

PHILSTONE - Hardware - Philstone Nail Corp.

PHILTERKOL - Water treating compounds - Reading Anthracite Co.

PHILTEX - Eyeglasses - Phillips Lens Co.

PHILTWIN - Eyeglasses - Phillips Lens Co.

PHILUBE BLUE - Lubricants - Phillips 66 Propane Co.

PHINAL PHASE - Skin care products - Redken Laboratories, Inc.

PHINE - Hair care products - Joico Laboratories, Inc.

PHINEAS - Toys–stuffed ☆ - Gund, Inc.

PHINISH - Hair care products - KMS Research Inc.

PHIREX+ - Fire extinguishing compounds - Environmental Science International Inc.

PHISH - Apparel and accessories - Phish, Inc.

PHISH - Recording label - Phish, Inc.

PHISH DOCTOR - Aquariums–household - GM Aquatics

PHISH DOCTOR - Pet products - Phish Doctor Inc.

PHISH OMEGA - Vitamins and nutritional supplements - Pharmics Inc.

PHISOAC - Pharmaceutical preparations - Winthrop Pharmaceuticals

PHISODAN - Pharmaceutical preparations - Winthrop Pharmaceuticals

PHISODERM FOR BABY - Skin care products - Sterling Winthrop Inc.

PHISOHEX - Skin care products - Winthrop Pharmaceuticals

PHISOPUFF - Skin care products - Winthrop Pharmaceuticals

PHISOSCRUB - Skin care products - Winthrop Pharmaceuticals

PHIX - Hair care products - Magic Weave

PHIX PHASE I - Hair care products - Magic Weave

PHIX PHINNISH - Hair care products - Magic Weave

PHIX PHIUNL PHINNISH - Hair care products - Magic Weave

PHK - Publisher's imprints - Clary Press

P.H.L. - Vegetable oil - Humko Products

PHLEXISPRAY - Skin care products - Chasalco Inc.

PHLOGO - Pet products - Farnam Cos. Inc.

PHLORIDZIN - Pharmaceutical preparations ☆ - City Chemical Corp.

PHM PEGASUS - Computer software - Electronic Arts Inc.

PHOBOS - Golfing equipment - Mars Golf Supply

PHOEBE - Belts–apparel - Leather Shop Inc.

PHOEBE - Eyeglasses - Art-Craft Optical Co.

PHOENICIAN - Floor coverings - Mannington Resilient Floors

PHOENIX - Air purification systems - Simco

PHOENIX - Automotive parts and accessories - James P. Wright

PHOENIX - Banjos ☆ - OME Co. Inc.

PHOENIX - Batteries - Yuasa-Exide, Inc.

PHOENIX - Bicycles - Bike Line Corp.

PHOENIX - Bicycles ☆ - Murray, Inc.

PHOENIX - Boats–kayaks - Phoenix Products Inc.

PHOENIX - Cabinets - Marsh Furniture Co.

PHOENIX - Cabinets ☆ - Medallion Kitchens of Minnesota Inc.

PHOENIX - Cabinets ☆ - H.J. Scheirich Co.

PHOENIX - Cigarettes - Brown & Williamson Tobacco Corp.

PHOENIX - Computer software - American Management Systems, Inc.

PHOENIX - Cording ☆ - Samson Cordage Works

PHOENIX - Eggs - Western Brine Shrimp, Inc.

PHOENIX - Eyeglasses - Windsor Optical Inc.

PHOENIX - Fabrics - Bradley Industrial Textiles, Inc.

PHOENIX - Fabrics - Capital Carousel Inc.

PHOENIX - Fabrics - Superior Shade & Blind Co. Inc.

PHOENIX - Fabrics - Uniroyal Engineered Products

PHOENIX - Faucets - Sterling Plumbing Group Inc.

PHOENIX - Firearms - Richard A. Voit

PHOENIX - Firearms, accessories, and parts - Welsh Sporting Goods Corp. (Boyt Div.)

PHOENIX - Fireplace equipment ☆ - Thermo-Rite Manufacturing Co.

PHOENIX - Frames–eyeglass - Pathway Optical Prods.

PHOENIX - Furniture - Herman Miller, Inc.

PHOENIX - Furniture ☆ - Hooker Furniture Corp.

PHOENIX - Furniture–wood - Chaircraft Div.

PHOENIX - Girdles - Latex Foundations Co. Inc.

PHOENIX - Glass–leaded ☆ - Charles Norman Inc.

PHOENIX - Gocarts - Manco Products, Inc.

PHOENIX - Goggles–safety - Parmelee Industries, Inc.

PHOENIX - Goggles–safety - U.S. Safety Corp.

PHOENIX - Guitars ☆ - St. Louis Music Supply Co.

PHOENIX - Hair care products - Waverly Beauty Products

PHOENIX - Hardware - Alumax Aluminum Corp.
PHOENIX - Hosiery - Kayser-Roth Corp.
PHOENIX - Juice extracting devices - Phoenix Housewares Corp.
PHOENIX - Lamp bulbs–fluorescent - Craftmade International Inc.
PHOENIX - Leather - Albert Trostel & Sons Co.
PHOENIX - Lubricants - JTM Products Inc.
PHOENIX - Machinery - DBA Products Co.
PHOENIX - Machinery - McDonald Co. Machines
PHOENIX - Marking stamps - Porelon, Inc.
PHOENIX - Massage products - Everett Associates Inc.
PHOENIX - Motor vehicles–automobiles ☆ - General Motors Corp. (Pontiac/ GMC Div.)
PHOENIX - Motor vehicles–motor homes - Forest River, Inc.
PHOENIX - Motors–hydraulic - General Electric Co.
PHOENIX - Musical instrument accessories - Mechanical Music Corp.
PHOENIX - Occasional tables ☆ - JDI Group, Inc.
PHOENIX - Oil machinery - Wayne/Scott Fetzer Co.
PHOENIX - Paints - Adelphi Coatings Co.
PHOENIX - Photographic equipment - Phoenix Corp. of America
PHOENIX - Pumps - Warren Rupp Inc.
PHOENIX - Recording label - All Star Promotions
PHOENIX - Seafood products–fresh or frozen - Robert W. Hayman Inc.
PHOENIX - Sprayers - Broyhill Co.
PHOENIX - Stamps–hand - U.S. Stamp
PHOENIX - Stoves - Precise International/Wenger
PHOENIX - Tape measures ☆ - Keuffel & Esser Co.
PHOENIX - Tiles–ceramic - Monarch Tile Inc.
PHOENIX - Tool boxes ☆ - Associated Equipment Corp.
PHOENIX - Toys–models - Estes Industries
PHOENIX - Trailers–travel - Fruehauf Trailer Corp.
PHOENIX - Wallpaper ☆ - Koroseal Wallcoverings
PHOENIX - Wallpaper ☆ - Wallquest, Inc.
PHOENIX - Window coverings ☆ - Vertilux-Louverlux Inc.
PHOENIX 3 - Computer software - 3do Co.
PHOENIX BLAU - Tableware–china ☆ - Villeroy and Boch Tableware Ltd.
PHOENIX BOOKS - Publisher's imprints - University of Chicago Press
PHOENIX CARAMELS - Candy - Phoenix Confections Inc.
PHOENIX COLORNET - Digitalis - Phoenix Color Corp.
PHOENIX COYOTES - Apparel–athletic - Bg Hockey Ventures, LP
PHOENIX DESERT DOGS - Novelty items - Arizona Fall League, Inc.
PHOENIX EDGE - Goggles–safety - Parmelee Industries, Inc.
PHOENIX EDGE - Goggles–safety - U.S. Safety Corp.
PHOENIX I - Window frames - Quaker Window Products Co.
PHOENIX II 100% RECYCLED - Pressboard - Fortifiber Corp.
PHOENIX INJECTOR - Tools–hand-operated - Phoenix Systems LLC
PHOENIX INTERNATIONAL RACEWAY - T-shirts–men's - Phoenix International Raceway, Inc.
PHOENIX PHOTOFILE - Containers - Endeavour IV, Inc.
PHOENIX RECORDS - Recording label - Nashville International Entertainment Group
PHOENIX STATIONERY PRODUCTS - Stationery products - Phoenix Stationery Products, Inc.
PHOENIX SUNS - Trading cards and stamps - Phoenix Suns
PHOENIX SYSTEM - Building materials - Inventco, Inc.
PHOENIX, THE - Floor coverings–tile ☆ - Monarch Tile Inc.
PHOENIX WILD CARDS - Apparel and accessories - Modern Thought Combine
PHOENIX WING - Barbecue sauce - Richard W. Eastman and Sarah E. Webster-Eastman Partnership
PHOENIXFELT - Fabrics–felt - National Nonwovens
PHOENIXFICTION - Publisher's imprints - Chicago Press Corp.
PHOENIXWARE - Rubber–molded - Gemco Ware, Inc.
PHOMBSTAR-7 - Puzzles - Kadon Enterprises Inc.
PHON TEK - Electrical equipment - Best Power Technology Inc.
PHONE - Pens - Micropoint Inc.
PHONE ALARM - Alarm systems - Consumer Electronics Inc.
PHONE BANK - Calculators - Texas Instruments Inc.
PHONE BILL - Electronic equipment - Estech Systems, Inc.
PHONE BLASTER - Telephone apparatus - Covox, Inc.
PHONE CENTER, THE - Telephone accessories - Syroco
PHONE CHAIR, THE - Telephone accessories - Clauder Kinnear Gardner
PHONE-CHEK - Telephone apparatus - Answer/Line Associates Inc.
PHONE CONTROL - Call screening apparatus - Phillips Home Electronics, Inc.
PHONE DIRECTOR - Computer peripheral equipment - Fiskars Inc.
PHONE-EASE - Telephone accessory - NPD Technologies, Inc.
PHONE FRAMZ - Novelty items - D.I.B. Designs

PHONE FRIENDS - Toys - Fisher-Price, Inc.
PHONE HOME - Telephone dialer - Nimrod International
PHONE HOME FOR THE HOLIDAYS - Games - Metz Baking Co.
PHONE LINK PLUS - Paper–coated - BRD Communications Inc.
PHONE MASK - Telephone apparatus - 27 Orestiados, Ltd.
PHONE MASTER - Computer software ☆ - Spectrum Universal
PHONE MATE - Office supplies ☆ - Park Sherman
PHONE ME - Eyeglasses - Martin-Copeland Eyewear Corp.
PHONE MESSENGER - Computers - International Voice Messaging Systems Inc.
PHONE-PAL - Office supplies ☆ - Bates Manufacturing Co.
PHONE PEN - Pens - Micropoint Inc.
PHONE/POINT - Computer software - Enterprise Solutions, Inc.
PHONE REST - Telephone apparatus - Bert M. Morris Co.
PHONE TOUCH - Computer software - Medtouch Inc.
PHONE-WIPE - Telephones - Texwipe Co. LLC
PHONE-Y RING PHONE - Novelty items - Cal Themes Inc.
PHONEBELT - Belts–apparel - Tune Belt, Inc.
PHONEBOARD - Telephones - Ayden F. Young
PHONECELL - Telephone apparatus - Telular Corp.
PHONEDISC - Computer storage devices–optical - Digital Directory Assistance Inc.
PHONEDUCER - Electronic equipment - Elwood Corp.
PHONEFORMS - Computer software - Spanlink Communications
PHONEKITS - Computer software - Algorhythms, Inc.
PHONELAN - Computer hardware - Performance Technologies, Inc.
PHONELOCK - Telephone apparatus - Data-Link Corp.
PHONEMASTER - Computer peripheral equipment - Netphone, Inc.
PHONEMATE - Telephone answering machines - PhoneMate Inc.
PHONEMAX - Computer software - Active Voice Corp.
PHONEPAY - Computer software - Oceana Matrix, Ltd.
PHONEPLUS - Telephone accessories - U.S. Order, Inc.
PHONESCRIBE - Electronic equipment - Ball BC, Inc.
PHONESHARE - Computer software - Xerox Corp.
PHONESPEC - Telephone accessories - D.A.S. Distributors, Inc.
PHONESPELL - Computer peripheral equipment - Siemens Business Communication Systems Inc.
PHONET - Eyeglasses ☆ - Cable Car Eyeware
PHONETREE - Telephone apparatus - Personal Communication Systems, Inc.
PHONEWARE - Computer hardware - Q.Sys International
PHONEWARE - Computer software - Q-Sys International, Inc.
PHONEWORKS - Telephone apparatus - North Supply Co.
PHONEX - Health care products - DQP
PHONEX - Wireless telephone jack - Comtrad Market Network
PHONEY BALONEY - Chewing gum ☆ - Amurol Confections Co.
PHONEY CANDY - Candy - Fleer Corp.
PHONEY PHONES - Candy ☆ - Zeebs Enterprises, Inc.
PHONIC EAR - Audio equipment - Phonic Ear, Inc.
PHONICS - Computer software ☆ - CONDUIT
PHONICS FUN - Computer software - Unicorn Software
PHONICS KIT - Recording label - Learn Phonics/Will Read Co.
PHONICS PINBALL - Computer software - Southwest Edpsych Services Inc.
PHONICS TRAVELER - Toys - Leapfrog LLC
PHONICSMART - Computer software - Steck-Vaughn Publishing Corp.
PHONIES - Fishing lures - Paul Warner Industries
PHONO - Recording label - Soundwaves Records
PHONOGRAM - Recording label - Polygram Records, Inc.
PHONOLOGICAL ZOO, THE - Video tapes–blank - Linda J. Ayres
PHONREAD - Computer storage devices - M & FC Holding Co., Inc.
PHOOL - Apparel–women's - Phool Fashion, Ltd.
PHORMULA ABC - Skin care products - Frances Denney
PHOS BRONZE - Musical instrument accessories - Gibson Strings & Accessories
PHOS-FLUR - Pharmaceutical preparations - Colgate Oral Pharmaceuticals Inc.
PHOS-FUSED - Rails–iron ☆ - Leslie-Locke, Inc.
PHOS-GOLD - Vitamins and nutritional supplements - Sports One, Inc.
PHOS-PHAID - Health care products ☆ - United-Guardian, Inc. (Guardian Laboratories Div.)
PHOS PHO LIPID - Cosmetics - Ray Hayes Inc.
PHOS-START - Vitamins and nutritional supplements - Baker Norton Pharmaceuticals, Inc.
PHOSCHOL - Vitamins and nutritional supplements - Banner-Pharmacaps Inc. (Advanced Nutritional Technology Division)
PHOSCHOL FORTE - Vitamins and nutritional supplements - Banner-Pharmacaps Inc. (Advanced Nutritional Technology Division)
PHOSGARD - Coatings - BetzDearborn Inc.

☆ = Now out of production

PHOSGUARD - Paint pigment - Mineral Pigments Corp.

PHOSGUARD - Pet products - Seachem Laboratories

PHOSH - Coffee ☆ - Cotton Club Bottling Co.

PHOSPHACAL-D - Vitamins and nutritional supplements - Lannett Co. Inc.

PHOSPHAGAIN 2 - Vitamins and nutritional supplements - Experimental and Applied Sciences

PHOSPHALJEL - Antacids - Wyeth-Ayerst Laboratories

PHOSPHATIDYL CHOLINE - Pharmaceutical preparations - Rugby Laboratories Inc.

PHOSPHATIDYLSERINE 100 PLUS - Vitamins and nutritional supplements - Vitamin Research Products Inc.

PHOSPHO-SODA - Laxatives - C.B. Fleet Co. Inc.

PHOSPHO-UROMIDE - Pharmaceutical preparations ☆ - Edwards Pharmaceuticals, Inc.

PHOSPHO-ZYME - Vitamins and nutritional supplements - Consac Industries, Inc.

PHOSPHOLIFE - Cosmetics - Ray Hayes Inc.

PHOSPHOLINE IODIDE - Pharmaceutical preparations - Wyeth-Ayerst Laboratories

PHOSPHOLIPID SV - Chemicals - Mona Industries Inc.

PHOSPHOLOBA - Vitamins and nutritional supplements - Olympian Labs, Inc.

PHOSPHOR - Musical instrument accessories - Guild Music Corp.

PHOSPHOR BRONZE - Musical instrument accessories - GHS Strings

PHOSPHORIMAGER - Computer software - Molecular Dynamics, Inc.

PHOTACT - Paper–photographic - Keuffel & Esser Co.

PHOTAGE - Hair care products - Andre Chiavelli

PHOTAR - Photographic equipment ☆ - Tiffen Manufacturing Corp.

PHOTEX - Fabrics - Veratec

PHOTILATION - Photofinishing laboratories - Larry Hamill Photography

PHOTIQUE - Novelty items–paper - Antioch Publishing Co.

PHOTO - Hair care products - Faberge Co.

PHOTO - Soap - Unopco Sub, Inc.

PHOTO-AGING SHIELD - Skin care products - Revlon Consumer Products Corp.

PHOTO ARCHIVE - Photographic equipment - Light Impressions Corp.

PHOTO ARRANGERS - Photo albums ☆ - Webway, Inc.

PHOTO BASIS - Chemicals–photographic - Merix Chemical Co.

PHOTO BROCHURE SHOP - Computer software - Moore Business Forms, Inc.

PHOTO CD - Computer storage devices–optical - Eastman Kodak Co.

PHOTO CLEAR - Photographic equipment ☆ - H.P. Marketing Corp.

PHOTO COLOR - Hair care products ☆ - Joico Laboratories, Inc.

PHOTO-CURIO - Photo albums - General Products

PHOTO DISPLAY SYSTEM - Containers - Rare Woods Inc.

PHOTO DRI - Cleaning preparations - Swiss-Tex Inc.

PHOTO-ENGRAVABLES - Giftware ☆ - Cawley Co.

PHOTO EXPRESSIONS - Greeting cards ☆ - Amberley Greeting Card Co.

PHOTO FACTORY - Photographic supply stores - Photo Factory Inc.

PHOTO FINISH - Cosmetics - Cosmania, Inc.

PHOTO-FLO - Photographic equipment - Eastman Kodak Co.

PHOTO FLOPPY - Computer peripherals - Environmental Projection Systems, Inc.

PHOTO-GOLD - Frames–eyeglass ☆ - Universal/Univis Inc.

PHOTO-GRAPHIC MARKER - Pens - Pilot Pen Corp. of America

PHOTO GREETING - Frames–picture ☆ - Papel Freelance, Inc.

PHOTO GREETING - Photographic equipment - Concord Camera Corp.

PHOTO GUARD - Photographic equipment - Light Impressions Corp.

PHOTO-IDENT - Invisible-ink pen for marking valuables - Independent Ink Inc.

PHOTO-IDENT - Jewelry ☆ - Hirsch Speidel Inc.

PHOTO ILLUSIONS - Souvenir photographs - SGL Corp.

PHOTO IMPRESSIONS - Photographic equipment - Eastman Kodak Co.

PHOTO KING, THE - Photo albums ☆ - Esselte Corp.

PHOTO LINKS - Photographic equipment - Byers Corp.

PHOTO LOG - Photo albums - McMillin Foley Publishing Co.

PHOTO LURE - Fishing lures - Fish World Inc.

PHOTO-MAN PIXTURA - Cameras - Logitech, Inc.

PHOTO MASK - Health care products - Pratt Medical Inc.

PHOTO MEMORIES - Photo albums - C.R. Gibson Co.

PHOTO MEMORY BOX - Photo albums - Holson Co.

PHOTO MESSAGE - Cameras - Concord Camera Corp.

PHOTO MOTION IMAGES - Paints–artists' - Quick Pix, Inc.

PHOTO MOUNT - Adhesives and sealants - Minnesota Mining & Manufacturing Co.

PHOTO NOTO - Labels–paper - Beaumont Products, Inc.

PHOTO ORGANIZER 200, THE - Photo albums ☆ - Esselte Corp.

PHOTO PERFECT - Paper–photographic - Onyx Mat Board

PHOTO-PIX - Photo albums - Redi-Record Industries

PHOTO-PLATE - Vitamins and nutritional supplements ☆ - Makit Products

PHOTO-RECORD - Binders ☆ - Hazel Inc.

PHOTO-RECORD - Frames–picture - Western Greeting Inc.

PHOTO-ROLL - Photo albums - Albert H Gruneisen III

PHOTO SESSION FORMULATION - Shampoos - John Frieda, Inc.

PHOTO SHARE - Computer software - TRF Systems, Inc.

PHOTO-SPREE - Frames–eyeglass ☆ - Universal/Univis Inc.

PHOTO STAR - Giftware ☆ - U.S. Fiberglass Inc.

PHOTO STAR - Photographic equipment - Byers Corp.

PHOTO STUDIO - Frames–picture - Midwest of Cannon Falls Inc.

PHOTO SWEEP - Alarm systems - Spacesaver Corp.

PHOTO SWEEP - Cleaning preparations - Electro-Chemical Products Corp.

PHOTO TREASURES - Frames–picture - Intercraft Industries

PHOTO VISOR - Book ends - Talus Corp.

PHOTO WALLET - Paper products - Rsw, Inc.

PHOTO WATCH - Computer software - Westgate Software, Inc.

PHOTO WORKS BY THOMPSON - Paper products - Thompson Paper Box Co., Inc.

PHOTO-XTRA - Lenses–optical - X-Cel Optical Co.

PHOTO ZONE - Infant apparel - Five Tees, Inc.

PHOTOBALLOON, THE - Novelty items - Amherst Technologies Inc.

PHOTOBOOSTER - Computer peripheral equipment - Radius Inc.

PHOTOBROWN EXTRA - Sunglass lenses - Corning Inc.

PHOTOBYTE - Computer software - Vertex Software, Inc.

PHOTOCAP - Hats - Edward R. Beaton

PHOTOCAPS - Computer software - Brento Corp.

PHOTOCARD - Picture frames - Aaron Lieberman

PHOTOCHE - Attache cases - Pioneer Photo Albums, Inc.

PHOTOCHROMIC - Sporting goods - Outdoor Technologies Group

PHOTOCLIP COLLECTION, THE - Computer software - Norstrilia Software Inc.

PHOTOCOVER - Makeup - American Institute of Esthetics

PHOTODERM - Medical apparatus - Esc(D), Inc.

PHOTODOC-IT - Computer software - UVP Inc.

PHOTODOOR - Posters ☆ - Scandecor Inc.

PHOTODSP - Computer software - Storm Technology, Inc.

PHOTODYNE - Cables–fiber optic - Minnesota Mining & Manufacturing Co.

PHOTOFACTS - Medical apparatus - USMS, Inc.

PHOTOFINA - Software - Ultima Electronics Corp.

PHOTOFINISH - Cleaning preparations - Photographic Solutions, Inc.

PHOTOFLAKE - Ornamental products–glass - Royal Heirlooms, Ltd.

PHOTOFLASH - Computer hardware - Apple Computer Inc.

PHOTOFLEX - Photographic equipment - Photoflex Inc.

PHOTOFLURE - Film - Eastman Kodak Co.

PHOTOFRAME - Frames–picture - Classic Frames

PHOTOFRAME - Frames–picture - MCS Industries Inc.

PHOTOFUSION - Computer software - Ultimatte Corp.

PHOTOGALLERY - Brackets ☆ - Falcon Safety Products, Inc.

PHOTOGARD - Office supplies - Minnesota Mining & Manufacturing Co.

PHOTOGENIC - Frames–eyeglass ☆ - Universal/Univis Inc.

PHOTOGENIC - Lighting equipment - Photogenic Machine Co.

PHOTOGENIX - Computer software - Firefly Software Corp.

PHOTOGLAZE - Coatings - Lord Corp. (Chemical Products Div.)

PHOTOGLOB - Calendars - Sormani Inc.

PHOTOGO - Film - Print Technology Inc.

PHOTOGRAMS - Greeting cards - Paramount Cards Inc.

PHOTOGRAPHER - Eyeglasses - Martin-Copeland Eyewear Corp.

PHOTOGRAPHIC MEMORY - Computer software - Norton-Lambert Corp.

PHOTOGRAY EXTRA - Sunglass lenses - Corning Inc.

PHOTOGRAY II - Optical product - Corning Inc.

PHOTOLAB - Computer storage devices–optical - Creative Data, Inc.

PHOTOLENE - Paper - Fox River Paper Co.

PHOTOLIFE - Batteries - Eastman Kodak Co.

PHOTOLITE - Ophthalmic goods - American Optical Corp.

PHOTOLITE - Paper - Rexam Graphics Inc.

PHOTOLOCK - Paints - Lilly Industries, Inc.

PHOTOLYNX - Software program - Vanguard Research, Inc.

PHOTOMARK - Pencils - Dixon Ticonderoga Co.

PHOTOMORPH - Computer software - North Coast Software, Inc.

PHOTON - Chocolate bars - Betco Corp.

PHOTON - Solar cells - Solar World

PHOTON - Sports rackets and accessories - Wilson Sporting Goods Co.

PHOTON DISRUPTOR - Toys–models ☆ - Estes Industries

PHOTON DISRUPTOR II - Toys–models ☆ - Estes Industries

PHOTON MICRO-LIGHT - Lighting equipment - David Allen

PHOTON PROBE - Toys–models ☆ - Estes Industries

PHOTON254 - Air purification systems - Fusion Filter Inc.

☆ = Now out of production

PHOTONIMATOR - Toys - Saban Entertainment, Inc.
PHOTOPAK - Novelty items - Oak Rubber Co.
PHOTOPC - Cameras - Epson America, Inc.
PHOTOPHONE - Electronics equipment - Image Data Corp.
PHOTOPIA IMAGES - Greeting cards - Photopia Images Inc.
PHOTOPLAST - Photographic equipment - Eastman Kodak Co.
PHOTOPLASTIC - Photographic equipment ☆ - Ilex Optical Co. Inc.
PHOTOPLAY - Ophthalmic goods - Foremost Optical Products
PHOTOPROX - Electronic equipment - Palomar Technologies Corp.
PHOTOREAL - Paper products - Beaverprints, Inc.
PHOTORENDER - Computer software - Evans & Sutherland Computer Corp.
PHOTORIAL - Novelty items - Eagle Designs!, Inc.
PHOTOSCAN - Electrical equipment - Intergraph Corp.
PHOTOSEAMLESS - Lenses–optical - Younger Manufacturing Co.
PHOTOSHOOT COSMETICS - Cosmetic kits - Photoshoot Cosmetics
PHOTOSHOP - Computer software - Adobe Systems Inc.
PHOTOSKETCH - Computer software - Infotec Development, Inc.
PHOTOSNAP - Computer software - Mages Inc.
PHOTOSOFT - Computer software - Photosoft, Inc.
PHOTOSOME - Sunblocks - Applied Genetics Inc.
PHOTOSONIX - Medical apparatus - Microfirm, Inc.
PHOTOSPHERE - Frames–picture - A and M Leatherlines Inc.
PHOTOSTACKER - Computer software - Ultima Electronics Corp.
PHOTOSTAMP - Vending machines - Gregory R. Chumbley
PHOTOSTAR - Computer software - Microtek Lab Inc.
PHOTOSTEP - Computer software - DMMS, Inc.
PHOTOSTICKS - Stickers - Paper House Productions
PHOTOSTOCK - Compact discs–prerecorded - Digital Photographic Imaging, Inc.
PHOTOSUN II - Sunglass lenses - Corning Inc.
PHOTOTONE - Computer software - DP-Tek, Inc.
PHOTOTOPE - Scientific apparatus - New England Biolabs Inc.
PHOTOTRON - Pumps–vacuum - Danielson Vacuum Products, Inc.
PHOTOUP - Computer software - Greg Merriman
PHOTOVIEW - Computer software - Tribune Publishing Co.
PHOTOWALL - Posters ☆ - Scandecor Inc.
PHOTOWARE - Computer software - DMI, Inc.
PHOTOWAVE - Digital encoders - Seavision, Inc.
PHOTOWAVE - Photofinishing laboratories - Photowave, Inc.
PHOTOWIDE - Paper–photographic - Savage Universal Corp.
PHOTOWIN35 - Computer software - Harry W. Townes
PHOTOWIPES - Paper–tissue ☆ - Sorg Paper Co.
PHOTOWORKS - Computer peripheral equipment - Seattle Filmworks, Inc.
PHOTRONICS - Electronic equipment - Photronics, Inc.
PHOX - Alarm systems - Alarm Surveillance, Inc.
PHOX - Medical apparatus - Bernafon Inc.
PHP - Vitamins and nutritional supplements - Professional Health Products, Ltd.
PHR - Medical apparatus - Raymond Mikelionis
PHRASE ALERT - Typewriters - Smith Corona Corp.
PHRASE-NASTICS - Games - William J. Jackson
PHRASEFINDER - Computer software - Seiko Instruments U.S.A., Inc.
PHRASEMAKER - Computer software ☆ - Videx, Inc.
PHRE PERM - Hair care products - Colorful Products Corp.
PHRED - Computer software - DLB Enterprises, Inc.
PHRED'S PHYDEAUX - Fishing lures - Fred Arbogast Co. Inc.
PHRED'S SHADEAUX - Fishing lures - Fred Arbogast Co. Inc.
PHREEDUMB - Apparel and accessories - Phreedumb
PHRENILIN - Pharmaceutical preparations - Carnick Laboratories Inc.
PHRENILIN FORTE - Pharmaceutical preparations - Carnick Laboratories Inc.
PHRESH - Skin care products - Minnesota Mining & Manufacturing Co.
PHROBIS - Knives–hunting ☆ - Marksman Products Inc.
PHS - Pet products - Universal Marketing
PHS PASSPORT - Insurance agencies–health - Physicians Health Services, Inc.
PHT - Computer software - Pacific Hitech, Inc.
PHTHALYSULFATHIAZOLE - Pharmaceutical preparations - City Chemical Corp.
PHUG - Lubricants - Newport Ropes Inc.
PHUKTUP - Recording label - Orange Record Co. Inc.
PHUN PHELT - Fabrics–felt ☆ - Freudenberg Nonwovens Apparel Division
PHUNN! - Recording label - CITA Communications Inc.
PHYATROMINE-H - Pharmaceutical preparations ☆ - Schwarz Pharma
PHYDOR - Cookies ☆ - Liberty Richter Inc.
PHYLISAN - Deodorizers - Pettibone Laboratories Inc.
PHYLLANTHOL - Vitamins and nutritional supplements ☆ - Nature's Herbs
PHYLLICIN - Pharmaceutical preparations ☆ - Knoll Pharmaceutical Co.

PHYLLIS - Greeting cards - Kristin Elliott Inc.
PHYLLIS DILLER'S ORIGINAL RECIPE - Food products ☆ - Stokes/Ellis Foods
PHYLLO PASTRIES - Pastries - Dufour Pastry Kitchens Inc.
PHYLLOCONTIN - Pharmaceutical preparations - Purdue Frederick Co.
PHYLLOID - Hair care products ☆ - Major/Advance International
PHYLO - Chemicals - Chemical Dynamics, Inc.
PHYLODENT - Dentifrices - Phylomed Corp.
PHYLODERM - Skin care products - Phylomed Corp.
PHYLOXATOL - Pharmaceutical preparations ☆ - JMI-Canton Pharmaceuticals
PHYNYLTROPE - Ophthalmic solution - Cooper Companies Inc.
PHYSICA - Computer software - Mystica & Co. Inc.
PHYSICA - Computer software - Physica & Co.
PHYSICAL ED'S - Apparel and accessories - Physical Ed's Personal Fitness Trainers, Inc.
PHYSICAL ELEMENTS - Apparel–athletic ☆ - Nike, Inc.
PHYSICAL FASHIONS - Apparel–athletic - Physical Fashions
PHYSICAL FASHIONS - Leotards - B.I.G. Corp.
PHYSICALC - Computer software - Zephyr Services
PHYSICIAN ACCESS LINK - Computer software - Memorial Medical Center of Jacksonville
PHYSICIANS' AESTHESTIC RESEARCH LUCRECE - Cosmetics - Physicians Aesthetic Research, Inc.
PHYSICIANS AND SURGEONS - Skin-care products - Cabot Laboratories Inc.
PHYSICIANS APPLIANCE - Medical apparatus - Physicians Appliance Co.
PHYSICIAN'S CHOICE - Hearing aids - Hocks Laboratories
PHYSICIAN'S CHOICE - Vitamins and nutritional supplements - Woodland Farms, Ltd.
PHYSICIANS' DESK REFERENCE - Computers–personal - Me Licensing Corp.
PHYSICIANS FORMULA - Cosmetics - Physicians Formula Cosmetics Inc.
PHYSICIANS FORMULA INTENSIVE THERAPY - Cosmetics - Physicians Formula Cosmetics Inc.
PHYSICIANS' GUIDE TO RARE DISEASES - Publisher's imprints - Dowden Publishing Co., Inc.
PHYSICIAN'S HEALTH AND DIET - Vitamins and nutritional supplements - Wellness International Network, Ltd.
PHYSICIANS ONLY - Neckties ☆ - Avery Medical Fashions, Inc.
PHYSICIAN'S PHARMACEUTICAL - Vitamins and nutritional supplements - General Fitness, Inc.
PHYSICIAN'S PREFERENCE - Vitamins and nutritional supplements - Steven F. Hotze
PHYSICIANS SELECT - Skin care products - Physicians Select Inc.
PHYSICIAN'S SUBSTANCE ABUSE RECOVERY - Health care products - Great American Health Foods
PHYSICIANS TOTAL CARE - Computer hardware and software - Physicians Total Care, Inc.
PHYSICS - Computer software - Estes Industries
PHYSIK VERLAG - Publisher's imprints - VCH Publishers Inc.
PHYSIO GYMNIC BALLS - Orthopedic products - Smith & Nephew Inc. (Rehabilitation Div.)
PHYSIO-ROLL - Toys - Sportime
PHYSIOLOGIC - Computer software - People-Karch International Inc.
PHYSIOLOGICS - Vitamins and nutritional supplements - Amrion, Inc.
PHYSIQUE - Health care products - Garcoa Labs/Vitamin Classics
PHYSIQUE - Vitamins and nutritional supplements - Shaklee Corp.
PHYSIQUE COUTURE - Apparel and accessories - Physique Clothing Co. Inc.
PHYSWHIZ - Computer software - College of Dupage
PHYT-ALOE - Vitamins and nutritional supplements - Emprise International, Inc.
PHYTESSENTIALS - Vitamins and nutritional supplements - Nature's Way Products, Inc.
PHYTO-BALANCE - Skin care products - Transitions for Health, Inc.
PHYTO-BEARS - Vitamins and nutritional supplements - Emprise International, Inc.
PHYTO CHEMICALS - Botanical extracts - Bio-Botanica
PHYTO DIET - Vitamins and nutritional supplements - Evan Nutraceuticals, Inc.
PHYTO-NUTRIENT - Vitamins and nutritional supplements - Leiner Health Products Inc.
PHYTO-PRO - Vitamins and nutritional supplements - NF Formulas, Inc.
PHYTO-TEIN - Vitamins and nutritional supplements - Natural Organics, Inc.
PHYTO-VEG PLUS - Vitamins and nutritional supplements - Nutri-Vision, Inc.
PHYTO-VITE - Vitamins and nutritional supplements - Wellness International Network, Ltd.
PHYTO-ZYME - Chemical preparations - Neozyme International, Inc.

PHYTO2X - Vitamins and nutritional supplements - Solgar Vitamin and Herb Co., Inc.

PHYTOACTIVES - Fertilizers - Pharmline, Inc.

PHYTOAESSENCE - Skin care products ☆ - WES Publishing

PHYTOBIODERMIE - Hair care products - Phyto USA Inc.

PHYTOCHARGED - Vitamins and nutritional supplements - Schiff Products, Inc.

PHYTOCHARGED - Vitamins and nutritional supplements - Weider Nutrition Group, Inc.

PHYTOCOPIA - Cookies - E. Excel International, Inc.

PHYTOCOSMETICS BY HELMA B. - Skin care products - Alo Pro of Chicago Inc.

PHYTOFOODS - Food products - Pharmachem Laboratories, Inc.

PHYTOGENESIS - Vitamins and nutritional supplements - Shaperite Concepts, Ltd.

PHYTOGREEN - Vitamins and nutritional supplements - Nutrition for Life International, Inc.

PHYTOLAX - Vitamins and nutritional supplements - Shaperite Concepts, Ltd.

PHYTOMED LABORATORIES - Skin care products - California Fragrance Co.

PHYTOMIN - Hair care products - Pantresse Inc.

PHYTOMYCIN - Insecticides - Olin Corp.

PHYTONOL - Vitamins and nutritional supplements - Nutrition for Life International, Inc.

PHYTOPAN - Hair care products - Aida Thibiant, Inc.

PHYTOPHENOLS - Vitamins and nutritional supplements - NF Formulas, Inc.

PHYTOPOWER GINKGO - Vitamins and nutritional supplements ☆ - Nature's Herbs

PHYTOPOWER PHYTOSOMES - Vitamins and nutritional supplements - Nature's Herbs

PHYTOPRINT - Vitamins and nutritional supplements - Triarco Industries, Inc.

PHYTORESINOIDS - Health care products - Bio-Botanica

PHYTORICH - Vitamins and nutritional supplements - Barth-Spencer Corp.

PHYTOSHIELD - Health care products - Healthwatchers System

PHYTOSTEROL COMPLEX - Vitamins and nutritional supplements - Source Naturals

PHYTOSUN' AROMS AROMATHERAPY - Oils–essential - Euro International

PHYTOTHERAPY - Teas–herbal - Yellow Emperor Inc.

PHYTOXY-ACTIN - Vitamins and nutritional supplements - Natural Organics, Inc.

PHYTOZYME - Food products - American Ingredients, Inc.

PHYTRIMAX - Vitamins and nutritional supplements - Alliance USA Inc.

PHYTRISLIM - Vitamins and nutritional supplements - Alliance USA Inc.

PHYTRON - Motors - Phytron, Inc.

PI - Computer software - Petroleum Information Corp.

PI - Lighting fixtures - Premier International Corp.

PI BEAR - Toys–stuffed - Pi Bear Co.

PI/E PRO INVOICE ESTIMATE - Computer software - RLW Concepts

PI LA - Apparel–women's - Patina International Inc.

PI-MAC - Valves - James M. Honaker

P.I. MANAGER - Computer software - Software International Group Ltd.

PI-PROCESSBOOK - Computer software - Oil Systems, Inc.

PI PROIMAGE PUBLISHING - Trading cards and stamps - Proimage Publishing Co., Inc.

PI-ROTECH - Sports rackets - Sportstech Industries Inc.

PI SERIES - Metal goods - Desert Engineering Group, Inc.

PI SYSTEM - Audio equipment - Larry Doran Enterprises Inc.

PIA - Ophthalmic goods ☆ - Luxottica

PIACERE - Dresses–women's - Jamie Brooke Inc.

PIAGET - Watches - North American Watch Corp.

PIAGGIA DEL SOLE - Wines - European Beverage Co., Inc.

PIANET - Musical instruments - Hohner Inc.

PIANETTA - Accordions - Ideal Musical Merchandise Co.

PIANI - Plumbing fixtures–metal ☆ - Barclay Products Ltd.

PIANO - Computer hardware - Donovan Data Systems, Inc.

PIANO - Tableware–china ☆ - Villeroy and Boch Tableware Ltd.

PIANO CARD - Greeting cards - Dickens Co.

PIANO DISCOVERY - Computer software - Jump! Software, Inc.

PIANO LIVE SAVER - Musical instrument accessories - Dampp-Chaser Electronics Corp.

PIANO TALK - Apparel - Dean Sanderson and Peter Cowley Partnership

PIANOLA - Pianos - Aeolian Pianos Inc.

PIANOLIGHT - Compact discs–prerecorded - Pianolight Music

PIANOSAURUS - Toys–musical - Magnus Organ Co.

PIANOWORKS - Computer software - Temporal Acuity Products Inc.

PIANTEDOSI - Bread crumbs - Piantedosi Baking Co., Inc.

PIANTEDOSI HEARTH BAKING SINCE 1916 - Bread crumbs - Piantedosi Baking Co., Inc.

PIANY - Gloves ☆ - Swany America Corp.

PIAST HONEY WINE - Liquors - Adamba Imports International Inc.

PIAT D'OR - Wines - Carillon Importers Ltd.

PIAT VARIETALS - Wines - Dreyfus Ashby Inc.

PIATNIK OF AMERICA - Playing cards - Piatnik of America Inc.

PIATTI SALUSTI - Glassware–household - Piatti Salusti

PIATTO - Dinnerware–glass ☆ - WMF/USA

PIATTO'S - Pizzas–frozen - Red Lion

PIAZZA - Cheese ☆ - Gardenia Foods

PIAZZA - Dinnerware–glass ☆ - Johnson Brothers, USA, Inc.

PIAZZA - Floor coverings–carpet and rugs ☆ - Regal Rugs Inc.

PIAZZA - Floor coverings–tile - Kentile Floors Inc.

PIAZZA - Tiles–ceramic - American Marazzi Tile, Inc.

PIAZZA - Wallpaper - Design Directions

PIAZZA - Wallpaper - Koroseal Wallcoverings

PIB - Insulating materials ☆ - Demert & Dougherty, Inc.

PIBA - Fuel additives - Shell Oil Co.

PIBBS - Hair care products - P.S. Pibbs Inc.

PIBBS-EZ SYSTEM - Hair care products - P.S. Pibbs Inc.

PIBBS GOLD - Cosmetics ☆ - P.S. Pibbs Inc.

PIBBS ICE - Hair care products ☆ - P.S. Pibbs Inc.

PIBBS LEFTY - Cosmetics ☆ - P.S. Pibbs Inc.

PIC - Blocks–chimney - Metal-Fab Inc.

PIC - Frames–picture - Two's Company

PIC - Frosting - Mallet and Co.

PIC - Insecticides - Pic Corp.

PIC - Photographic equipment - American Photographic Instrument Co.

PIC - Screws - Penrod Co.,

PIC 77 - Frosting - Mallet and Co.

PIC-100 - Remote control devices - Celadon Inc.

PIC-A-BIT - Tool boxes - A.T. & G. Co., Inc.

PIC-A-DELI - Footcare products - Sanco Foods, Inc.

PIC-A-FLIC - Video games - Melanie Joss

PIC-A-NUT - Nuts–salted, roasted, cooked, or canned - Variety Foods, Inc.

PIC-A-PAC - Games - Whitehall Inc.

PIC-A-PAC - Office supplies - Esselte Corp.

PIC-A-PART - Game ☆ - James Industries, Inc.

PIC-A-POP - Candy ☆ - Glade Taffy Town, Inc.

PIC-A-SWEET - Candy ☆ - Bobs Candies Inc.

PIC A TIP - Tools–hand-operated - Eazypower Corp.

PIC-A-WATT - Heating equipment - King Electrical Manufacturing Co.

PIC-ALL - Tools–hand-operated - Apple Picker Inc.

PIC DE VALANDON - Wines - Bercut-Vandervoort & Co.

PIC-FLO - Racks ☆ - Jarke Corp.

PIC FRESH - Food products - Richard A. Shaw Inc.

PIC HANG - Frames–picture ☆ - Franklin Picture Co.

PIC-MOUNTS - Photographic equipment - Pic-Mount Corp. (Seary Manufacturing Div.)

PIC-NIC - Breads - LaPace Imports, Inc.

PIC NIC - Chickens - Mar-Jac Processing Inc.

PIC-NIC-PAC - Sauerkraut ☆ - Rea-D-Pack Foods Inc.

PIC-O-MAINE - Food products - Sundor Brands Inc.

PIC OF THE PACK - Food products - Williamsburg Canning Co.

PIC PAC - Boxes ☆ - Alliance Rubber Co.

PIC PAK - Hardware - Hindley Manufacturing Co. Inc.

PIC PREMIER - Wines ☆ - Kobrand Corp.

PIC PRO - Photographic equipment - American Photographic Instrument Co.

PIC SAINT LOUP - Wines - Bercut-Vandervoort & Co.

PIC-SURE-STAYS - Picture stabilizers - Ed Clarke Co.

PIC-TIP - Pliers - The Petrie-Ingram Co.

PIC-UP - Pet products - Helmac Products Corp.

PIC UP HOIST - Hoists ☆ - Shur-Co. Inc.

PIC-UP STIX - Toys - Steven Manufacturing Co.

PIC WICKER - Toilets–enameled - Kohler Co.

PIC-WIN - Envelopes - Western States Envelope Co.

PICACHO - Apparel–men's - Howard Bliss

PICADILLY - Floor coverings–carpet and rugs ☆ - Atlas Carpet Mills Inc.

PICADILLY - Pickles - Randolph Pickle Corp.

PICADILLY BEAR - Toys–stuffed - Russ Berrie and Co., Inc.

!PICANTRO! - Vegetable sauces - Empacadora Tapatio

PICARDY - Fabrics ☆ - J.B. Martin Co. Inc.

PICASSO - Fishing lures - Den Manufacturing Co.

PICASSO - Floor coverings–carpet and rugs - Columbus Mills, Inc.

PICASSO - Ophthalmic goods - Styl-Rite Optical Manufacturing Co., Inc.

☆ = Now out of production

PICASSO - Window coverings - Vertilux-Louverlux Inc.
PICASSO PARTNERS - Posters - Edward Weston Fine Arts
PICATO - Frames–eyeglass - Pathway Optical Prods.
PICATO - Musical instrument accessories ☆ - Meisel Music Inc.
PICAYUNE - Cigarettes - Liggett Group Inc.
PICC-SHIELD - Medical apparatus - Menlo Care, Inc.
PICCADILLIES - Cookies - Ripon Foods, Inc.
PICCADILLY - Bath salts - Parfums Parquet
PICCADILLY - Cigarettes - Faber, Coe & Gregg Inc.
PICCADILLY - Frames–eyeglass - May Optical Co. Inc.
PICCADILLY - Potato chips ☆ - Curtice-Burns Foods, Inc.
PICCADILLY - Recording label - Organ Literature Foundation
PICCADILLY - Yarn ☆ - William Unger & Co. Inc.
PICCADILLY SQUARE - Floor coverings–carpet and rugs - Blue Ridge Carpet
 Mills
PICCALA - Liquors - White Rock Distilleries Inc.
PICCIONE - Wedding gowns - Alfred Angelo Inc.
PICCIONE SIGNATURE - Wedding gowns - Alfred Angelo Inc.
PICCOLA - Fruits and vegetables ☆ - Marin Food Specialties
PICCOLO - Apparel–children's - Kahn Lucas Lancaster Inc.
PICCOLO - Bicycle parts and accessories - Burley Design Cooperative
PICCOLO - Computer software - Cornerstone Software, Inc.
PICCOLO - Cookies - Nabisco Foods Group
PICCOLO - Cranes - Egripment USA, Inc.
PICCOLO - Dryers–hair - Nino Originals
PICCOLO - Harmonicas - Hohner Inc.
PICCOLO - Hearing aids - Rexton Inc.
PICCOLO - Musical instruments ☆ - European Crafts/USA
PICCOLO - Toys–automobiles - Lilliput Motor Co., Ltd.
PICCOLO 10A - Hearing aids - Magnatone Hearing Aid Corp.
PICCOLO CLIPPERS - Clippers–barber - Designer's Edge International
PICCOLO MOLINO - Oils–edible - Gourmet America
PICCOLO TOSCANO - Wines - Viansa Winery and Marketplace
PICES - Computer software - Visual Information Technologies Inc.
PICHARADES - Game - International Games
PICHEEZ - Diuretics - D'Lanerg Ltd.
PICHROME - Vitamins and nutritional supplements - Camall Co.
PICK - Computer software - Pick Systems
PICK - Meats–luncheon - Liberty Richter Inc.
PICK 2 - Cosmetics - Estee Lauder Inc.
PICK 6 - Lubricants - Ashland Oil, Inc.
PICK A BASKET - Toys - Tonka Corp.
PICK-A-DELI - Housewares - Tupperware Co.
PICK A FLOWER - Wallpaper - Greeff Fabrics Inc.
PICK A FLOWER IV - Wallpaper - Greeff Fabrics Inc.
PICK-A-MIX - Candy - Brach and Brock Confections Inc.
PICK-A-PACK - Snack foods - Eagle Snacks, Inc.
PICK A PACK OF PERFECT PEPPERS - Spices and extracts - To Market to
 Market
PICK-A-PAIR - Adhesives and sealants ☆ - Arsco International Inc.
PICK-A-PAL - Fabrics - Plezall Wipers Inc.
PICK-A-PARTY - Invitations - Ward Works
PICK-A-PATH - Publisher's imprints - Scholastic Inc.
PICK-A-PECKER - Playing cards - Universal Manufacturing Co., Inc.
PICK-A-PERM - Hair care products - Paula Payne Products Co. Inc.
PICK-A-POCKET - Cookware - Dazey Corp.
PICK-A-POCKET - Curtains - Kenney Manufacturing Co.
PICK-A-POUCH - Cat food - Ralston Purina Co.
PICK-A-WICK - Candles - Candles Et Cetera Inc.
PICK AXE PETE - Toys–electronic ☆ - Philips Consumer Electronics Co.
PICK CLIP - Musical instrument accessories - Silver St. Inc.
PICK FISHERIES - Food products - Pick Fisheries Inc.
PICK-IT-GARD - Nurseries and garden stores - Gilbert and Bennett
 Manufacturing Co.
PICK M UPS - Pastries - Drake Bakeries, Inc.
PICK ME CRUSH ME MAKE ME WINE - Apparel and accessories - Tara A.
 McKnight
PICK ME UP - Frames–eyeglass - May Optical Co. Inc.
PICK ME UP - Vitamins and nutritional supplements - Glamour Vitamin Labs.,
 Inc.
PICK 'N CHEWS - Chewing gum - Topps Co., Inc.
PICK N HOE - Tools–garden - Snow & Nealley Co.
PICK-N-PLACE - Labels–gummed - Pharmagraphics, Inc.
PICK 'N SAVE - Food products - Roundy's Inc.
PICK 'N STICK - Patches, insignia, and emblems - Imaginart International, Inc.

PICK O' SEA - Seafood products–fresh or frozen - Flag/Westbay Seafood
 Brokers
PICK O' THE BUSHEL - Tea - Boston Tea Co.
PICK OF THE BREED - Candles - Russ Berrie and Co., Inc.
PICK OF THE CROP - Coffee - Coffee Roasters Inc.
PICK OF THE CROP - Cooking equipment–household - Cardinal Inc.
PICK OF THE CROP - Housewares - Shafford Co. Inc.
PICK OF THE CROP - Nuts–salted, roasted, cooked, or canned - Di Mare
 Bros.
PICK OF THE GROVE - Fruit drinks–bottled or canned - Freshly Squeezed,
 Inc.
PICK-OF-THE-HARVEST - Flowers, plants, and seeds - Eldorado Trading
 Corp.
PICK OF THE LITTER - Pet products - K.C. Pharmacal Inc.
PICK OF THE PROFESSIONALS - Dryers–hair - Andis Co.
PICK PAPRIKA - Meats–luncheon - Liberty Richter Inc.
PICK POCKETS - Musical instrument accessories - Pick Pockets, Inc.
PICK PRECAUTIONARY INFECTION CONTROL KITS - First aid kits - Pick
 Enterprises, Inc.
PICK QUICK - Defoliants - Crop Production Services Inc.
PICK TWO - Games - Tah Dah Inc.
PICK UP - Fruits and vegetables - TW Apples Inc.
PICK UP - Tobacco–chewing or smoking - Brown & Williamson Tobacco Corp.
PICK-UP & PEEK - Puzzles - Fisher-Price, Inc.
PICK UP CHIPS - Games - Tyco Toys
PICK-UP-STIX - Toys - Rose Art Industries, Inc.
PICK-UP-TRICK - Toys–automobiles - Mattel, Inc.
PICK-UPS - Tools–hand-operated - Kingsbridge International, Inc.
PICK YOUR FIT - Bathing suits - Raj Manufacturing, Inc.
PICKAPEPPA - Food processors - Warbac Sales Co.
PICKASSO - Guitars - Zion Guitar Technology
PICKATOP - Metals - National Metal Shapes
PICKERING - Apparel and accessories - Kimberton Co.
PICKERING - Audio equipment - Pickering and Co. Inc.
PICKET AND POST - Apparel–women's - J.C. Penney Co., Inc.
PICKET FENCE - Paper - Bemiss-Jason Corp.
PICKET PEOPLE - Giftware - Piccadilly
PICKETS - Cosmetics - Revlon Consumer Products Corp.
PICKETT - Drafting supplies - Pickett Industries
PICKETT - Food products - RHM Industrial Specialty Foods Inc.
PICKETT - Scales–industrial - Chartpak
PICKLE BAGS - Sporting goods - Swix Sport USA, Inc.
PICKLE BRAND - Leather goods - Swix Sport USA, Inc.
PICKLE EATER'S PICKLE, THE - Pickles - New Morning
PICKLE FAIR - Pickles - Paramount Foods Inc.
PICKLE-O-PETE - Pickles - Ripon Pickle Co. Inc.
PICKLE PAL - Chemicals - Columbia Chemical Co.
PICKLE PATCH - Pickles - W.B. Roddenbery Co., Inc.
PICKLE PLANKS - Pickles - M.A. Gedney Co.
PICKLE TIME - Pickles - Freestone Pickle Co. Inc.
PICKLED GARLIC - Flavored garlic - Pikled Garlik Co.
PICKLED TINK - Greeting cards - Norcross Inc.
PICKLEFACE & OTHER STORIES - Computer software - Hartley Courseware
 Inc.
PICKLEFORK - Boats - Glen-L Marine Designs
PICKLEROONY'S INC. - Fruits and vegetables - Pickleroony's Inc.
PICKLES - Cosmetics - Caswell-Massey Co. Ltd.
PICKLES - Crocheted and knitted items - Heritage Sportswear
PICKLES TO GO - Pickles - Vlasic Foods Inc.
PICKNICK - Barbecues and grills - Kay Park Rec Corp.
PICKPOCKET - Dental floss ☆ - Sonex International Corp.
PICK'R UP'R - Hand tool - ORRCO, Inc.
PICKTURE - Computer software - Valis Group
PICKUP'N TOW - Automotive parts and accessories ☆ - Masco Corp.
PICKUPPAK - Motor vehicle parts and accessories - Kar-Rite LP
PICKWICK - Bedding–linen - Dan River Inc.
PICKWICK - Beverages–alcohol - Falstaff Brewing Corp.
PICKWICK - Housewares ☆ - Lamplight Farms, Inc.
PICKWICK - Ophthalmic goods - Styl-Rite Optical Manufacturing Co., Inc.
PICKWICK - Shirts - Phillips-Van Heusen Corp.
PICKWICK - Teas - Acme Food Specialties Inc.
PICKWICK - Teas - Sara Lee Corp.
PICKWICK - Wood products ☆ - Masonite Corp.
PICKWICK COLLECTION - Furniture ☆ - Pulaski Furniture Corp.
PICKWICK PANDA - Toys–stuffed ☆ - Dakin Inc.
PICKY PET - Dog food - Menu Foods Inc. Cadillac Foods Div.

☆ = Now out of production

PICLITE - Signs - Jewelite Sign Co.
PICMASTER - Computer hardware - Microchip Technology Inc.
PICNIC - Chili sauce - Patterson Packing Co.
PICNIC - Dinnerware–glass - Arita Sales Co. Inc.
PICNIC - Floor coverings - Congoleum Corp.
PICNIC - Fruits and vegetables ☆ - Firmenich Inc.
PICNIC - Ice chests–plastic - Coleman Co., Inc.
PICNIC - Meat products - Saramar Corp.
PICNIC - Meat products–canned - Bryan Foods, Inc.
PICNIC - Ships–sailing vessels ☆ - General Boats Corp.
PICNIC ADVENTURE - Dolls - Mattel, Inc.
PICNIC BASKET, THE - Ice-chests–plastic - Igloo Products Corp.
PICNIC BOAT - Boats–motor - The Hinckley Co.
PICNIC BUDDY - Carts - White's Marine
PICNIC CHEF - Cooking equipment–household - GSW Jackes-Evans
   Manufacturing Co.
PICNIC FOR TWO - Candles ☆ - Candle Corp. of America
PICNIC FUN! - Games - Addison-Wesley Publishing Co.
PICNIC PACK - Vegetables–pickled or brined ☆ - Pacific Choice Brands Inc.
PICNIC PRETTY - Dolls - Mattel, Inc.
PICNIC SPECIAL - Horseshoes - St. Pierre Manufacturing Corp.
PICNIC TIME - Floor coverings–carpet and rugs ☆ - Regal Rugs Inc.
PICNIC TIME - Tablecloths - Straubel Paper Co.
PICNIC!PICNIC! - Food products - Little Caesar Enterprises, Inc.
PICO - Cigar boxes–wood ☆ - Consolidated Cigar Corp.
PICO - Fuses–electric - Littelfuse, Inc.
PICO - Giftware - Pico International Corp.
PICO - Microscopes - Molecular Imaging Corp.
PICO CHICO - Sporting goods - James Heddon's Sons
PICO DE GALLO - Tomato pastes and sauces - Pace Foods, Ltd.
PICO II - Fuses–electric - Littelfuse, Inc.
PICO P - Power switching equipment - Picopower Technology, Inc.
PICO PICA - Food products - Juanita's Foods
PICO POWERED - Power switching equipment - Picopower Technology, Inc.
PICODOS - Computer software - John H. Godley
PICOFLOW - Fluid transfer pumps - Xolox Corp.
PICOJET - Printers–computer - Synergy Research Corp.
PICOLIGHT - Lamps - Fusion Lighting, Inc.
PICOMACS - Computer hardware - Peco II , Inc.
PICON - Beverages–alcohol - Cointreau America Inc.
PICONI WINERY - Wines - Piconi Wineries
PICOVERTER - Electrical equipment - RO Associates, Inc.
PICPOUL DE PINET - Wines ☆ - Bercut-Vandervoort & Co.
PICRO-BENZYL - Pharmaceutical preparations ☆ - Ulmer Pharmacal Co.
PICROLIV - Dietary supplements - Sabinsa Corp.
PICROSIL - Vitamins and nutritional supplements - Sabinsa Corp.
PICROTOXIN - Pharmaceutical preparations - City Chemical Corp.
PICS - Bicycles ☆ - Panasonic Bicycles Midwest
PICS - Computer software - NBS Consultants, Inc.
PICS - Electronic equipment - Presearch Inc.
PICS OF THE LITTER - Calendars ☆ - American Greetings Corp.
PICS SMART PANEL - Electronic equipment - Nebraska Irrigation
PICSEE - Integrated circuits - Microchip Technology Inc.
PICSOUND - Recording label - Peer-Southern Organization
PICSTART - Computer software - Microchip Technology Inc.
PICT-A-GONS - Toys - Duncan Toys Co.
PICT-O-GRAPH - Publisher's imprints - Standard Publishing Co.
PICTAR - Electronic equipment - Mast Industries Inc.
PICTIONARY - Broadcasting stations–television - Pictionary Inc.
PICTIONARY - Games - Hasbro, Inc.
PICTIONARY JUNIOR - Games - Hasbro, Inc.
PICTOGRAM - Computer software - VWS Inc.
PICTOGRAPHICS - Computer software - Pictographics International Corp.
PICTOMETRY - Computer peripheral equipment - Pictometry, Inc.
PICTORUS - Photographic lenses - ALTA Group
PICTROSTAT 200 - Photocopy machines - Fuji Photo Film USA Inc.
PICTSWEET - Food products - Pitsweet Inc.
PICTSWEET EXPRESS - Fruits and vegetables - Pitsweet Inc.
PICTURA - Binders - Key Sales Co.
PICTURA 310 - Printers–computer - Fargo Electronics Inc.
PICTURA 310E - Printers–computer - Fargo Electronics Inc.
PICTURA 310S - Printers–computer - Fargo Electronics Inc.
PICTURE - File folders - Angler's Roslyn Group Ltd.
PICTURE - Garden equipment - Scotts Co. (Organics Business Group)
PICTURE-A-DAY - Calendars - Workman Publishing Co., Inc.
PICTURE BASE - Computer software - Symmetry Corp.

PICTURE BOOK STUDIO - Publisher's imprints - Picture Book Studio
PICTURE-CRAFT - Hobby kits - Vogart Crafts Corp.
PICTURE DIALER - Toys - Wonderline
PICTURE DICTIONARY - Games ☆ - Colorforms
PICTURE ENTERTAINMENT CORPORATION - Audio equipment - Picture
   Entertainment Corp.
PICTURE FRAMES - Giftware - Sasaki
PICTURE GRAPHICS - Computer software ☆ - DataPak Software Inc.
PICTURE IT! - Computer software - Microsoft Corp.
PICTURE IT! - Computer software - Penton Overseas, Inc.
PICTURE IT TISSUE CUBE - Boxes - Goldbar Marketing LLC
PICTURE KING - Electronic equipment - Da-Lite Screen Co. Inc.
PICTURE LOTTO - Games ☆ - Milton Bradley Co.
PICTURE ME - Apparel–children's - Young Generations, Inc.
PICTURE ME BOOKS - Publisher's imprints - Picture Me Books, Inc.
PICTURE ME TALKING - Posters - Silver Capital Corp.
PICTURE PAK - Candy ☆ - Gimbel Brothers Inc.
PICTURE PEDDLER - Frames–picture - Harold-Lawrence Associates Inc.
PICTURE PERFECT - Book covers - American Companies, Inc.
PICTURE PERFECT - Cleaning preparations - Ashland Oil, Inc.
PICTURE PERFECT - Computer software - Mind Play
PICTURE PERFECT - Floor coverings–carpet and rugs ☆ - Masland Corp.
PICTURE-PERFECT - Frames–eyeglass - Liberty Optical Manufacturing Co.
PICTURE PERFECT - Frames–picture - Kohl's Department Stores, Inc.
PICTURE PERFECT - Frames–picture ☆ - Sangray Corp.
PICTURE PERFECT - Greeting cards ☆ - Thought Factory
PICTURE PERFECT - Mirrors - Conair Corp.
PICTURE PET - Dolls - Mattel, Inc.
PICTURE PICTURE - Games ☆ - Western Publishing Co., Inc.
PICTURE PLACE - Film - Melville Corp.
PICTURE PLAQUE - Artists' materials ☆ - Siphon Art Products
PICTURE PLATES - Toys - Tupperware Co.
PICTURE PLAY - Toys - Lisa Frank, Inc.
PICTURE PLAYMATES - Toys - Uneeda Doll Co., Inc.
PICTURE PRETTY - Frames–eyeglass ☆ - Universal/Univis Inc.
PICTURE PROGRESSIONS - Artists' materials - Picture Progressions, Inc.
PICTURE PROWLER - Computer software - Xing Technology Corp.
PICTURE PUFFS - Infant product - Garley Industries Inc.
PICTURE PUZZLES - Puzzles ☆ - CBS Toys
PICTURE STONES - Frames–picture - Wilderness Naturals Marketing Co.
PICTURE STORY - Notebooks and notepads - Mead Corp.
PICTURE TAKER - Computer software - Pearson Technical Software Inc.
PICTURE THE PIECES - Games - Discovery Toys, Inc.
PICTURE THIS! - Computer software - IMSI
PICTURE THIS - Decals and transfers - Plaid Enterprises, Inc.
PICTURE THIS - Frames–eyeglass - May Optical Co. Inc.
PICTURE THIS HOME! - Computer programming services - Autodesk Inc.
PICTURE THIS SING-A-LONG - Video production - Goldsholl Design and Film,
   Inc.
PICTURE TIME - Watches - Timex Corp.
PICTURE WINDOW - Binders ☆ - General Loose Leaf Bindery Co.
PICTURE WINDOW - Computer software - Digital Light & Color, Inc.
PICTURE WINDOWS - Photographic equipment - Foto Mechanic
PICTURE WORDS - Puzzles - Lauri Inc.
PICTUREADY! - Cameras - Miles Inc.
PICTUREDRIVE - Computer peripheral equipment - Polaroid Corp.
PICTUREGRADE - Printers–computer - Lexmark International, Inc.
PICTUREMAGIC - Pennants - Picturemagic Inc.
PICTUREMASTER - Electronic equipment - Telex Communications, Inc.
PICTUREMATE - Sporting goods - MascoTech Accessories
PICTUREPAGES MAKES SCIENCE SIMPLE - Learning aids ☆ - Texas
   Instruments Inc.
PICTUREPERFECT - Photograph holder - Lockermate Corp.
PICTURES & PRICES - Computer software - Drapery Service & Design Corp.
PICTURES FOR YOUR FRAME - Apparel and accessories - Marcopronto
   Productions, Inc.
PICTURES, LETTERS, AND SOUNDS - Computer software - Hartley
   Courseware Inc.
PICTURES, PLEASE! - Publisher's imprints - Psychological Corp.
PICTURESQUE - Clocks ☆ - General Time Corp. (Westclox/Seth Thomas Div.)
PICTURESQUE - Fabrics - Action International, Inc.
PICTURESQUE - Floor coverings–carpet and rugs ☆ - Lees Carpets
PICTURESQUE - Frames–eyeglass - Zylo Ware Corp.
PICTURESQUE - Giftware - Atlas Enterprises
PICTUREWINDOW - Projection screens ☆ - Da-Lite Screen Co. Inc.
PICTUREWRITER - Computer software - Voyager Software Corp.

☆ = Now out of production

PICTURLITE - Frames–eyeglass ☆ - Universal/Univis Inc.

PICUPSTIX - Video production - Nalpak Video Sales, Inc.

PID - Degreasing solvents - Perfection Industrial Distributors Inc.

PID MAX - Electronic equipment - Baker Motion Control Systems Inc.

PIDDLE PADDLES - Toys - Tyco Toys

PIDDLERS - Novelty items - Jennifer Lauer

PIDG - Electrical equipment - AMP Inc.

PIDIDDLE - Apparel–women's - Style-Craft Shirt & Blouse Co. Inc.

PIDIDDLY-LINKS - Jewelry–costume - Pididdly-Links Ltd.

PIDUCO CREEK - Wines - Parliament Import Co.

PIDY - Food products - De Choix Specialty Foods Co.

PIE FACE - Fruits and vegetables - Wapato Fruit Products Inc.

PIE FACE - Games - Tonka Corp.

PIE KING - Flour–blended - Acme-Evans/A.D.M. Milling Co.

P.I.E. PACIFIC INTERMOUNTAIN EXPRESS - Toys–automobiles - Toy Truck Lines, Inc.

PIE PATROL - Apparel and accessories - Paul Mello Jr.

PIE PIECES - Pies–frozen - Edwards Baking Co.

PIE PIPER - Bakery products–frozen - Vienna Sausage Manufacturing Co.

PIE PIPER - Food products - Pie Piper Products Ltd.

PIE-POURRI - Deodorizers - Luverne Truck Equipment, Inc.

PIE SHOPPE, THE - Glassware–household - Pie Shoppe Ltd.

PIECE 'A CAKE - Chewing gum ☆ - Fleer Corp.

PIECE AH - Pizzas–frozen - Atlantic Richfield Co.

PIECE BY PEACE CAROLYN BLAYLOCK - Greeting cards and stationery - Steve and Carolyn Blaylock Partnership

PIECE MEAL - Puzzles - Franklin Merchandising Co.

PIECE O' CAKE - Dolls - Mattel, Inc.

PIECE O'CAKE - Cakes ☆ - Edwards Baking Co.

PIECE OF MIND, A - Computer software - Floyd Victor Etienne

PIECEKEEPER - Safes - Design Annex

PIECES - Pies–frozen - Edwards Baking Co.

PIECES FROM THE PAST - Craft supplies ☆ - VIP/VIP Crafts

PIECES OF 8 - Recording label - Charles N. Mead

PIECES OF KNOWLEDGE - Puzzles - Gillette Designs

PIECEWORKS, THE - Craft supplies ☆ - VIP/VIP Crafts

PIED, A - Ballet slippers - Wolowick Shoe Co.

PIED PIPER - Fishing lures - U.S. Tackle Corp.

PIED PIPER - Pet products - Mr. Mutt Pet Products Inc.

PIED PIPER BOOKS - Publisher's imprints - E.P. Dutton Inc.

PIED PIPERS - Footwear - Consolidated Shoe Co., Inc.

PIEDMONT - Agricultural products - Ronald W. Harvey and Co.

PIEDMONT - Fans–electric - Hunter Fan Co.

PIEDMONT - Floor coverings ☆ - Azrock Commercial Flooring

PIEDMONT - Flooring–hardwood - Mannington Wood Floors

PIEDMONT - Furniture - Universal Flooring

PIEDMONT - Rope - Wellington Leisure Products, Inc.

PIEDMONT - Thread - Elmore-Pisgah, Inc.

PIEDMONT - Vinegar - Safeway Stores Inc.

PIEDMONT CHERRY - Wainscotting - Georgia-Pacific Corp.

PIEDMONT CLASSICS CAGE RAISED FISH - Fish–fresh or frozen - Coosa Valley Resource Conservation and Development Counsel, Inc.

PIEDMONT PAPER - Wallpaper ☆ - Old Deerfield Fabrics Inc.

PIEDMONT SALES - Wood products - Piedmont Sales Inc.

PIEDMONT VINEYARDS - Wines - Piedmont Vineyards & Winery

PIEDRA - Floor coverings ☆ - GS Roofing Products Co.

PIEDRA - Tiles–terrazzo ☆ - Flintkote Co.

PIEL - Leather goods - Piel, Inc.

PIEL ROJA - Cigarettes - G.A. Georgopulo & Co. Inc.

PIELS - Beverages–malt - Piel Bros. Ltd.

PIELS - Beverages–malt - The Stroh Brewery Co.

PIELS LIGHT - Beverages–malt - The Stroh Brewery Co.

PIEMASTER - Desserts - Regency Creative Foods

PIEMME - Tiles–ceramic - Capitol Tile Import Co.

PIEMME - Tiles–ceramic - Federal Tile Imports Inc.

PIEMONTE - Breads - Piemonte Foods Inc.

PIEMONTE - Dishes–china - Pasmantier Co. Inc.

PIEMONTE - Food products ☆ - Cap's Italian Foods Inc.

PIER - Fabrics - Dan River Inc.

PIER 1 - Department stores - Pier 1 Imports Inc.

PIER 10 - Shoes - Payless Shoesource Worldwide, Inc.

PIER 12 - Fish–fresh or frozen - Pappas International Foods

PIER 12 - Seafood products–fresh or frozen - Aslanis Seafoods Inc.

PIER 17 - Food products - Viking Seafoods Inc.

PIER 39 - Apparel and accessories - Pier 39 L.P.

PIER 49 SAN FRANCISCO SOURDOUGH PIZZA - Pizzas–frozen - Pizza Systems, Inc.

PIER CONNECTION - Apparel and accessories - Pier Connection

PIER EIGHT - Dips–sour cream based - Concord Foods Inc.

PIER FRANCO - Meat products–poultry - Bel Canto Fancy Foods Ltd.

PIER FRESH - Seafood products–canned or cured - Superior Seafoods Inc.

PIER POINT - Bathroom fixtures - Trayco, Inc.

PIER, THE - Fireplaces - Heat-N-Glo Fireplace Products, Inc.

PIERCE - Drafting supplies - Pierce Business Products Inc.

PIERCE - Electronic equipment ☆ - Kroy, Inc.

PIERCE - Enamels - La-Co Industries, Inc.

PIERCE - Food products - Pierce Foods Corp.

PIERCE - Key rings - Pierce Manufacturing Inc.

PIERCE - Shoe polish - C.S. Pierce Co.

PIERCE - Tableware–china ☆ - Lenox, Inc.

PIERCE-ARROW - Floor coverings - American Floor Products Co. Inc.

PIERCE-ARROW - Motor vehicles–automobiles ☆ - Pierce-Arrow Motor Car Co.

PIERCE COUNTRY - Food products - Pierce Foods Corp.

PIERCE DU JOUR - Chickens ☆ - Pierce Foods Corp.

PIERCE-GOLD - Bathmats - Pierce Foods Corp.

PIERCE TOPPERS - Meat products–poultry - Hester Industries, Inc.

PIERCE TREASURES - Food products - Hester Industries, Inc.

PIERCED - Giftware - Lenox, Inc.

PIERCELESS - Jewelry - Marvella Inc.

PIERCE'S PEANUTS BAR B-Q - Peanuts - Pierce's Pit Bar-B-Q, Inc.

PIERCINGCARE - Pharmaceutical preparations - The Hymed Group Corp.

PIERCINGCARE - Pharmaceutical preparations - Hymed Group Corp.

PIERCO - Food products - J.G. Pieri Co. Inc.

PIERCY ANN - Wines - St. Croix Winery

PIERE - Apparel and accessories - Chapeau Trading Co., Inc.

PIERGIORGIO - Handbags - Tirabasso of Florida Inc.

PIERO POLAR - Hair care products - Helene Curtis Industries Inc.

PIEROGI PRIEST - Food products - Father Edmund Nadolny Good News Fund, Inc.

PIERONI - Violins - William Lewis & Son

PIEROPAN - Wines - Wine Imports Ltd.

PIEROTTI - Fireplaces - Colonna & Co. Inc.

PIERPOINT - Apparel and accessories - Sara Lee Knit Products Inc.

PIERPOINT - Floor coverings–carpet and rugs ☆ - Atlas Carpet Mills Inc.

PIERPONT - Frames–eyeglass - May Optical Co. Inc.

PIERRE - Food products - Pierre Frozen Foods Inc.

PIERRE - Mouthwashes - Consolidated Midland Corp.

PIERRE - Shoes - Pierre Shoes Inc.

PIERRE BALMAIN - Apparel and accessories - Salant/Manhattan Industries

PIERRE BALMAIN - Colognes - Revlon Consumer Products Corp.

PIERRE BALMAIN - Handbags ☆ - Lisette Handbags Ltd.

PIERRE BALMAIN - Jewelry and watches - Nina Ricci Jewelry-Pierre Balmain

PIERRE BARGE - Wines - Wine House Ltd.

PIERRE BERNETTE - Musical instruments - M.M. Meason Inc.

PIERRE BOUREEFILS - Wines - Classic Wine Imports Inc.

PIERRE CARDIN - Apparel–men's - Burma-Bibas, Inc.

PIERRE CARDIN - Apparel–men's - Crystal Brands Inc.

PIERRE CARDIN - Apparel–men's - West Mill Clothes Inc.

PIERRE CARDIN - Colognes - Tsumura International Inc.

PIERRE CARDIN - Cutlery ☆ - Gutmann Cutlery Inc.

PIERRE CARDIN - Dinnerware–glass - WMF/USA

PIERRE CARDIN - Handbags - Beta Handbag Corp.

PIERRE CARDIN - Handbags - Koret Inc.

PIERRE CARDIN - Hosiery - Roytex, Inc.

PIERRE CARDIN - Hosiery–men's - S.L. Gilbert Co.

PIERRE CARDIN - Jewelry - Swank Inc.

PIERRE CARDIN - Luggage - Pierre Cardin Electronique

PIERRE CARDIN - Stationery - Stuart Hall Co.

PIERRE CARDIN - Sunglasses ☆ - B. Robinson Sunglasses

PIERRE CARDIN - Umbrellas - Mespo Umbrella Co. Inc.

PIERRE CARDIN - Watches - M.Z. Berger & Co. Inc.

PIERRE CARDIN CHEMISE - Crocheted and knitted items - Beldoch Industries Corp.

PIERRE CARDIN COUTURE - Watches - Nicolet International Inc.

PIERRE CARDIN ELECTRONIQUE - Calculators - Pierre Cardin Electronique

PIERRE CARDIN FOR BOYS - Apparel–children's - Crystal Brands Inc.

PIERRE CARDIN INSATIABLE - Perfumes - Tsumura International Inc.

PIERRE CARDIN SPORTIF - Apparel and accessories - Beldoch Industries Corp.

PIERRE CHAINIER - Wines - Victoire Imports Co.

PIERRE CORBEAU - Wines - Gold Seal Vineyards Inc.
PIERRE CROIZET ESTATE - Liquors - Holland St. John Ltd.
PIERRE-DEBS - Shoes ☆ - Pierre Shoes Inc.
PIERRE DEUX - Wallpaper - Capital Carousel Inc.
PIERRE DEUX - Wallpaper - Motif Designs, Inc.
PIERRE DEUX FRENCH COUNTRY - Wallpaper - Motif Designs, Inc.
PIERRE DOMINICI - Pasta - Florence Macaroni Manufacturing Co., Inc.
PIERRE DUMAS - Footwear - Olem Shoe Corp.
PIERRE DURAND - Watches - Able Time, Inc.
PIERRE FREY - Housewares - Arteriors
PIERRE GOURMET - Fuel additives ☆ - Kaadan Ltd.
PIERRE JACQUARD - Watches - Viva Time Corp.
PIERRE JEAN - Wines - Sogrape USA Inc.
PIERRE JOSEPH REDOUTE - Posters - One-of-a-Kind Workshop
PIERRE MAIN ST. DINER - Preserved foods–prepackaged - Hudson Foods, Inc.
PIERRE MARTIN - Liquors - Crestfield Importers Ltd.
PIERRE MICHEL ECOBALANCE - Hair care products - Pierre Michel Coiffure, Inc.
PIERRE NICOL - Watches - Taxor Inc.
PIERRE PONNELLE - Beverages–alcohol - Maison Portier & Fils
PIERRE RENAIR - Watches - Madison Sales Corp.
PIERRE REVAN - Musical instruments - J.M. Sahlein Music Co. Inc.
PIERRE ROJAY - Footwear - Saga House Inc.
PIERRE RUCCI - Watches - Bali Watch (L.A.) Inc.
PIERRE SANTINI - Cutlery ☆ - Lifetime Hoan Corp.
PIERRE SARDINE - Apparel and accessories - Frank A. Colonna
PIERRE VALLEE - Watches - Croton Watch Co., Inc.
PIERREPONT - Cutlery ☆ - Lifetime Hoan Corp.
PIERRE'S - Breads - Charles Freihofer Baking Co.
PIERRE'S - Desserts - Pierre's French Ice Cream Distributing Co. of Akron
PIERRE'S ORIGINAL - Cakes - Kajun Kettle Foods, Inc.
PIERROT - Dolls ☆ - Effanbee Doll Corp.
PIERROT GOURMAN D - Candy ☆ - Liberty Richter Inc.
PIERROT GOURMAND - Candy - Shaffer, Clark & Co. Inc.
PIERROT LOVE - Giftware ☆ - Schmid Inc.
PIERROT PRESS - Music–sheet - GSP
PIERSON OUTFITTERS - Apparel–women's - Pacific Trail, Inc.
PIESTENGEL - Wines - Grape Vine Winery
PIET VERDUIJN OF HOLLAND - Cookies ☆ - Dae Julie, Inc.
PIETRA - Tableware–china ☆ - Pfaltzgraff Investment Co.
PIETRA PINTA - Olive oil - Pietra Pinta U.S.A., Inc.
PIETRA SANTA - Wines - Pietra Santa Winery
PIETRAFITTA - Beverages–alcohol - Blair Importers Ltd.
PIETRO DI COMO - Neckties - World Wide Ties Inc.
PIETRO PERINI - Crocheted and knitted items - Gillman Knitwear Co.
PIETRO VILLA - Wines ☆ - Ernest and Julio Gallo Winery
PIEWORKS - Pizzas–mixes - PieWorks Development Corp.
PIEZO - Lighters - Scripto-Tokai Corp.
PIF - Binoculars - Pentax Corp.
PIFFLE - Games - Susan Ritchie
PIFKO - Food products - Van Bennett Food Inc.
PIG CREATIONS - Hobby kits - Green Apple
PIG DICE - Novelty items - Koplow Games
PIG FAMILY OF FISHING LURES, THE - Fishing lures - Odyssey Lures, Inc.
PIG-HYDE - Gloves - National Glove Inc.
PIG IN A BLANKET - Toys - Cross at the Green...Not in Between Enterprises
PIG IN A CAN - Toys–banks ☆ - Ben Cooper Inc.
PIG IN THE GARDEN - Toys - Tyco Toys
PIG IRON - Footwear - Wolverine World Wide, Inc.
PIG-NIP DRINKERS - Nipples–rubber - Precision Products, Inc.
PIG NOSE WAREHOUSE - Brooms - Fluffo Mop & Broom Co. Inc.
PIG NOSE YARDSTICK - Brooms - Fluffo Mop & Broom Co. Inc.
PIG OUT - Games - Today's Kids Inc.
PIG OUT CHOCOLATES - Confections - Robert A. Vaccarella
PIG OUT PUMPKIN - Toys - Industrial Molding Corp.
PIG PATTIE OF IOWA - Meat products–pork - Atlantic Locker
PIG-PEN-PALS - Decals and transfers - Paper Magic Group Inc.
PIG PONG - Games ☆ - Milton Bradley Co.
PIG POUNDER, THE - Beverages–malt - Gilbert-Robinson Inc.
PIG POWER FACTORS - Animal feed supplements - Agri-King Inc.
PIG SHIRT, THE - Bags–laundry - Hog Wild!
PIG TAIL TRAILER - Fishing lures - Strike King Lure Co.
PIG TIE, THE - Bags–laundry - Hog Wild!
PIGALLE - Brassieres (Bras) - Lady Marlene
PIGARILLOS - Pet food - Aries Prepared Beef Co.

PIGBITS - Animal feeds - Bluebonnet Milling Co.
PIGEON BUSTERS NIXALITE - Dishes–earthenware - Charles B. Kaufmann Trust
PIGGABLES - Patterns–clothing - Ann's Cottage
PIGGLY WIGGLY - Bakery products–frozen - Herold & Miller Inc.
PIGG'NS - Pet products - Boomer Ball
PIGGY - Food products - Associated Fruit Co.
PIGGY-BACK - Files–tools ☆ - Watson Industries Inc.
PIGGY-BACK - Ice chests ☆ - Poloron Products Inc.
PIGGY CHEWS - Pet food - Aries Prepared Beef Co.
PIGGY PUFFS - Snack foods - Old Dutch Foods, Inc.
PIGGY SUE - Dolls - Mattel, Inc.
PIGGY VAC - Vacuum cleaners and accessories - National Super Service Co.
PIGGYBACK - Bicycles ☆ - Racer-Mate, Inc.
PIGGYBACK - Envelopes - Union Envelope Co.
PIGGYBACK - Health care products ☆ - Sammons Preston
PIGGYBACK - Luggage - Lark Luggage Co. Inc.
PIGGYBACK - Luggage - Samsonite Corp.
PIGGYBACK - Pipes - Dura-Line Corp.
PIGGYBACK - Tool boxes - Artcadi Products
PIGGYPAK - Toys ☆ - Pearson Archery
PIGGZEES - Pet products - Boomer Ball
PIGHIN GRAVE - Wines - Kobrand Corp.
PIGINI - Accordions - Ernest Deffner Inc.
PIGLET - Toys–stuffed ☆ - Dakin Inc.
PIGLING BLAND - Dolls - Frederick Warne & Co., Inc.
PIGMA - Pens - Sakura of America
PIGMA 100 - Pens ☆ - K. Ogawa & Co. Inc.
PIGMA BRUSH - Pens - Sakura of America
PIGMA GRAPHIC - Pens - Sakura of America
PIGMA MICRON - Markers–felt-tip ☆ - K. Ogawa & Co. Inc.
PIGMA MICRON - Pens - Sakura of America
PIGMA PRO - Markers–felt-tip ☆ - K. Ogawa & Co. Inc.
PIGMA SUMI BRUSH - Pens–fountain - Sakura of America
PIGMAIL - Computer peripheral equipment - Cyberpuppy Software, Inc.
PIGMANIA - Games - Recycled Paper Products, Inc.
PIGMARRELLA - Stationery - Lisa Frank, Inc.
PIGMATEC - Pens ☆ - K. Ogawa & Co. Inc.
PIGMENT-O-MARK - Pens - Mark-Tex Corp.
PIGMENT + 2 - Skin care products ☆ - Redken Laboratories, Inc.
PIGMENTS OF YOUR IMAGINATION - Hair coloring preparations ☆ - Roux Laboratories, Inc.
PIGMEX - Skin care products - Lazarus Dermatologic Products
PIGMY-HIPPO - Electrical equipment - Mueller Electric Co.
PIGNOSE - Amplifiers - Pignose Industries
PIGNOSE - Plumbing fixtures–porcelain - Kirkhill Inc.
PIG'S EYE - Beverages–malt - Minnesota Brewing Co.
PIGS ONLY - Animal feeds - Stevens Industries Inc.
PIGSKIN - Apparel–men's - Jimmy Dean International Inc.
PIGSKIN PALE ALE - Beverages–malt - Super Hops!, Inc.
PIGTAIL - Cosmetics - William P. Canale
PIGTAIL - Eyeglasses - Art-Craft Optical Co.
PIGTAIL - Toys–stuffed ☆ - Gund, Inc.
PIGTAIL COTTON 175 - Yarn - Henry's Attic
PIGTAIL COTTON 770 - Yarn - Henry's Attic
PIGTAILS - Cording ☆ - Pepperell Braiding Co. Inc.
PIGTAILS - Crocheted and knitted items - Brookshire Knitting Mills Inc.
PIGTAILS AND FROGLEGS - Bags–duffel - Neiman-Marcus Group, Inc.
PIGTAILS & PONYTAILS - Games - Tonka Corp.
PIGTALES - Computer software - Pig Improvement Co., Inc.
PIGTALES INSTANT DATA SYSTEM - Computer software - Pig Improvement Co., Inc.
PIGTWIN - Gloves ☆ - Fownes Brothers & Co., Inc.
PIGZEARZ - Dog food - Pet Center, Inc.
PIK-A-PICKET - Hardware - Aluminum Hardgoods Inc.
PIK-KWIK - Food products ☆ - Pik-Kwik Stores Inc.
PIK-L-BARREL - Pickles ☆ - Whitfield Foods, Inc.
PIK 'N DRY - Hair care products ☆ - Belson Products
PIK-NIK - Peanut butter ☆ - Leavitt Corp.
PIK-NIK - Potato sticks - S & W Fine Foods, Inc.
PIK PAK - Photo albums - Holson Co.
PIK-SEE - Containers - Myers Industries, Inc.
PIK-TIPS - Electrical industrial apparatus - Pace, Inc.
PIK-UP - Erasers - Union Rubber, Inc.
PIKAROME - Food products - Europa Foods Ltd.
PIK'D RITE - Fruits–frozen - Pik'd Rite Inc.

☆ = Now out of production

PIKE - Boats–motor ☆ - Lund Boat Co.

PIKE - Posters - Aegis Entertainment, Inc.

PIKE - Ships–sailing vessels - Tedruth Plastics Corp.

PIKE IPA - Beverages–malt - The Pike Brewing Co.

PIKE-MASTER - Fishing lures - L & S Bait Co. Inc.

PIKE PLACE - Beverages–malt - Merchant du Vin Corp.

PIKE POLE ALE - Beverages–malt - The Pike Brewing Co.

PIKE PORTER - Beverages–malt - The Pike Brewing Co.

PIKE POST ALLEY AMBER - Beverages–malt - The Pike Brewing Co.

PIKE STREET XXXXX STOUT - Beverages–malt - The Pike Brewing Co.

PIKEMAN - Liquors - Canandaigua Wine Co. Inc.

PIKEPATCH - Concrete products ☆ - Fosroc Inc.

PIKE'S PEAK - Fabrics - Dan River Inc.

PIKES PEAK - Wheat–flour or meal - Conagra, Inc.

PIKES PEAK NATURAL CATTLE CO. - Beef - Pikes Peak Natural Cattle Co.

PIKE'S PEAK OR BUST - Puzzles - Niblack

PIKESVILLE - Whiskey - Standard Distillers Products Inc.

PIKITUP WHEEL BRACKET - Brackets - David M. Pigott, Jr.

PIKLE-RITE - Pickles - Pikle-Rite Co. Inc.

PIKLE-RITE-ACRE - Pickles - Pikle-Rite Co. Inc.

PIKLED GARLIK SALZA - Salsa - Pikled Garlik Co.

PIKNIK - Mayonnaise - Piknik Products Co. Inc.

PIKO HAWAIIAN LONGBOARD WEAR - Apparel and accessories - Piko Hawaiian Longboard Wear

PIKOTEK - Adhesives and sealants - Pikotek

PIKUPS - Snack foods - Salado Sales, Inc.

PIL-O-IN-A-POUCH - Quilts - Tennier Home Fashions Inc.

PILAGAN - Ophthalmic goods - Allergan, Inc.

PILAR - Eyeglasses - Art-Craft Optical Co.

PILAR FONZECA COLLECTION - Footwear–women's - Arthur Schneider Sales, Inc.

PILASITE - Pharmaceutical preparations - InSite Vision Inc.

PILATES - Apparel–athletic - Pilates, Inc.

PILBOX - Boxes - Pididdly-Links Ltd.

PILEBOND - Floor coverings–carpet and rugs - Milliken & Co. Inc.

PILED HIGH YOGURT PIE - Dessert food - Brinker International Inc.

PILES - Bean sprouts - Natraj International, Inc.

PILEX - Vitamins and nutritional supplements - Pilex Corp.

PILGRIM - Bathroom accessories - F.H. Lawson Co.

PILGRIM - Bedding–linen - Thomaston Mills Inc.

PILGRIM - Crocheted and knitted items - Pilgrim Sportswear Inc.

PILGRIM - Flatware ☆ - W.M.F. of America Inc.

PILGRIM - Food products - Pilgrim Packing Co.

PILGRIM - Frames–eyeglass ☆ - Universal/Univis Inc.

PILGRIM - Giftware ☆ - Alvin Co.

PILGRIM - Glass products ☆ - Pilgrim Glass Corp.

PILGRIM - Lamps ☆ - Lamplight Farms, Inc.

PILGRIM - Lamps ☆ - Roxter Lighting

PILGRIM - Pickles ☆ - Dean Pickle & Specialty Products Co.

PILGRIM - Publisher's imprints - Aegis Entertainment, Inc.

PILGRIM - Thread - Threads USA Div.

PILGRIM ALE 1620 OLD HARBOR BREWING COMPANY GOV. WILLIAM BRADFORD - Beverages–malt - Northern Brewers, Inc.

PILGRIM CANDLE - Candles - Pilgrim Candle Co.

PILGRIM FARMS - Food products - Dean Pickle & Specialty Products Co.

PILGRIM GUIDES - Publisher's imprint - American Life Foundation & Study Institute

PILGRIM HEIGHTS - Furniture ☆ - Kincaid Furniture Co. Inc.

PILGRIM HOUSE - Floor coverings–carpet and rugs - Pilgrim House Rug Co.

PILGRIM PLASTIC - Office supplies - Pilgrim Plastic Products Co.

PILGRIM'S - Glass products - Pilgrim Glass Corp.

PILGRIM'S BARN RED - Vases ☆ - Pilgrim Glass Corp.

PILGRIM'S CAMEO - Glass products - Pilgrim Glass Corp.

PILGRIM'S FINLANDIA - Glass products ☆ - Pilgrim Glass Corp.

PILGRIM'S GARDEN - Vases–glass ☆ - Pilgrim Glass Corp.

PILGRIM'S GLASS MENAGERIE - Glass products ☆ - Pilgrim Glass Corp.

PILGRIM'S MASTERWORK - Vases–glass - Pilgrim Glass Corp.

PILGRIM'S METROPOLIS - Vases–glass ☆ - Pilgrim Glass Corp.

PILGRIM'S NOUVEAU - Vases–glass - Pilgrim Glass Corp.

PILGRIM'S PINSTRIPE - Vases–glass - Pilgrim Glass Corp.

PILGRIM'S PLEATS - Vases - Pilgrim Glass Corp.

PILGRIM'S PRIDE - Chickens - Pilgrim Industries

PILGRIMS PRIDE - Food products - Pilgrim's Pride Corp.

PILGRIM'S PRIDE - Fruit drinks–bottled or canned - Pilgrim Foods Inc.

PILGRIM'S PRIDE - Meat products - Pilgrim's Pride Corp.

PILGRIM'S RENAISSANCE - Glass products - Pilgrim Glass Corp.

PILGRIM'S SEA - Vases–glass ☆ - Pilgrim Glass Corp.

PILGRIM'S SILHOUETTE - Trays–glass - Pilgrim Glass Corp.

PILGRIM'S TRIAD - Glassware–household ☆ - Pilgrim Glass Corp.

PILGRIM'S ZEN - Glass products - Pilgrim Glass Corp.

PILI HOT PEPPER CONDIMENT - Food products - GTL, Inc.

PILION - Floor coverings–tile - Mediterranean Marble International Inc.

PILKINGTON BARNES HIND - Contact lenses - Pilkington Barnes Hind, Inc.

PILKKE - Fishing lures - Normark Corp.

PILL - Sporting goods - Scott USA Inc.

PILL ALERT - Health care products - Elexis Corp.

PILL PAL - Containers–glass - Rupert W. Knierim

PILL PUSHER - Health care products - Maddak Inc.

PILL SPLITTER - Health care products - L.G.S. Health Products

PILLAR - Sealing compounds - Ramsey Inc.

PILLAR - Thread - New Bedford Thread Co. Inc.

PILLAR AND POST - Candles - Columbia Wax Products Inc.

PILLAR OF LITE - Candles - Empire Manufacturing Co.

PILLAR ROCK - Salmon–smoked, salted, dried, or pickled - Ocean Beauty Seafood, Inc.

PILLER - Meats–luncheon - Haram-Christensen Corp.

PILLETERI'S - Seasonings - Pilleteri's Seasoning & Marinade

PILLFINDER - Computer software - Zingery-Thrash

PILLIVUYT - Dinnerware ☆ - Franmara Co. Inc.

PILLMATE - Pharmaceutical preparations - Nature's Bounty, Inc.

PILLO - Health care products - Gaymar Industries, Inc.

PILLO-PERFECT - Orthopedic products - Gustave Rick Rinz

PILLOCORE - Artists' materials - Hunt Manufacturing Co.

PILLOMAT - Mats - Tepromark International Inc.

PILLOPLEX - Health care products - Plex Products

PILLOPRO - Pharmaceutical preparations - Procyte Corp.

PILLOT FRERES - Wines - Parliament Import Co.

PILLOW - Tiles–ceramic ☆ - Huntington/Pacific Ceramics Inc.

PILLOW BUDDIES - Pillows - KKH, Inc.

PILLOW CLOUD - Mattresses - Namaco Industries, Inc.

PILLOW COMFORT - Mattresses - Sleepwell Mattress Co. Inc.

PILLOW FACES - Craft supplies - Milton Bradley Co.

PILLOW FIGHT - Apparel and accessories - Bentley Lingerie, Inc.

PILLOW FIGHT - Toys - Tonka Corp.

PILLOW FRIENDS - Toys–stuffed - PSE Concepts, Inc.

PILLOW LITES - Footwear - Industrial Footwear Corp. of America

PILLOW MATE - Medical apparatus - Encore Products Inc.

PILLOW MOCS - Shoes - Manistee Inc.

PILLOW PACK GLIDERS - Toys–airplanes - Paul K. Guillow Inc.

PILLOW-PAK - Flower pots–plastic - G & N Landscaping & Lawn Service Ltd.

PILLOW-PAK - Toys–airplanes - Paul K. Guillow Inc.

PILLOW-PAL - Housewares - Golden West Enterprises

PILLOW PALS - Pillows - Centsable Toys Inc.

PILLOW PAWS - Slippers - Principle Business Enterprises Inc.

PILLOW PERFECT - Pillows - Rinz-L-O Pillow Co.

PILLOW PETS - Toys–stuffed - Dakin Inc.

PILLOW PETS - Toys–stuffed - Fun World Inc.

PILLOW PLAYMATES - Toys–stuffed - Mary A. Zellem

PILLOW SCULPTURES - Cushions - Mr. B Industries, Inc.

PILLOW SOFT - Paper–toilet - Cascades Industries, Inc.

PILLOW SOFT - Shoes - International Seaway Trading Corp.

PILLOW SOFT - Toys–stuffed - Dakin Inc.

PILLOW STARS - Dolls - PSE Concepts, Inc.

PILLOW TALK - Bathtubs–enameled - Kohler Co.

PILLOW TALK - Hosiery - N.S. Gustin Co.

PILLOW TALK - Pillows - C.M. Paula Co.

PILLOW, THE - Pillows - Better Sleep, Inc.

PILLOW TIP - Hair curlers - Gaylord Products Inc.

PILLOW WALK - Hosiery - Hole-in-None Hosiery

PILLOWALK - Footwear - Lyle Richards International, Ltd.

PILLOWBED - Padding–foam - Perfect Fit Industries, Inc.

PILLOWGRAMS - Linen - Turtle Productions

PILLOWLINE - First aid kits - Advertising Unlimited Inc.

PILLOWLOFT - Pillows - Stearns Technical Textiles Co.

PILLOWPLUS - Camping products - David Su

PILLOWS - Candy - M-B Candies Inc.

PILLOWS - Faucets - Kohler Co.

PILLOWS FOR POINTES - Toe pads - Pillows for Pointes, Inc.

PILLOWSACK - Bedding–linen - Perfect Fit Industries, Inc.

PILLSBURY - Flour–blended - Pillsbury Co.

PILLSBURY - Kitchen utensils–aluminum - Lifetime Hoan Corp.

PILLSBURY BAKE-OFF - Bakery products ☆ - Pillsbury Co.

☆ = Now out of production

PILLSBURY BEST - Flour–blended - Pillsbury Co.

PILLSBURY BEST SUGAR - Sugar–granulated, refined, or powdered - United Sugars Corp.

PILLSBURY COOKIES WITH M&MS - Cookies - Pillsbury Co.

PILLSBURY DELUXE - Desserts - Pillsbury Co.

PILLSBURY DINOSAURS - Cookies - Pillsbury Co.

PILLSBURY DOUGHBOY - Statuary - Benjamin & Medwin Inc.

PILLSBURY PLUS - Cakes–mixes - Pillsbury Co.

PILLSBURY TEDDY BEARS - Cookies - Pillsbury Co.

PILLTAKER - Health care products - Apothecary Products, Inc.

PILLTIMER - Medical apparatus - Nelkin/Piper Health Products

PILO-M - Ophthalmic goods - Misemer Pharmaceuticals Inc.

PILOCAR - Prescription ophthalmic - Iolab Pharmaceuticals

PILOGEL - Electrodes - Wescor, Inc.

PILOPINE HS - Pharmaceutical preparations - Alcon Laboratories, Inc.

PILOSOME - Skin care products - Lendan USA Co.

PILOT - Bicycles - Liyang USA, Inc.

PILOT - Colognes - Aeronautique Enterprises Inc.

PILOT - Computer software - Pilot Software, Inc.

PILOT - Computers - EIT, Inc.

PILOT - Dating and numbering stamps - Consolidated Stamp Manufacturing Co. Inc.

PILOT - Hardware - Shepherd Products U.S. Inc.

PILOT - Lighting equipment–automotive - Wang International

PILOT - Pens - Pilot Pen Corp. of America

PILOT - Recording label - Stark Records & Tape Co.

PILOT - Ships–sailing vessels - The Hinckley Co.

PILOT - Staplers - Ace Fastener

PILOT - Tires–airplane - Michelin Tire Corp.

PILOT - Toys ☆ - Roadmaster Corp.

PILOT BOOKS - Publisher's imprints - Pilot Books

PILOT IN COMMAND - Computer software - Digital Perceptions, Inc.

PILOT KISSES - Candy ☆ - Earl's Candy Co.

PILOT MASTER - Computer software - SourceView Software International

PILOT PUNCH - Tools - Mayhew Steel Products

PILOT-R - Ophthalmic goods - Rozin Optical Export Corp.

PILOT SYSTEMS - Computer software - Pilot Systems Inc.

PILOT WINGS - Video games - Nintendo of America Inc.

PILOTHOUSE - Boats - Marine Metals Inc.

PILOTS - Apparel–athletic - Milwaukee Brewers Baseball Club

PILOT'S AUDIO UPDATE - Recording label - Belvoir Publications, Inc.

PILOT'S PAL - Aluminum products - Lee Wolf Ltd.

PILOZ - Pillows - Owen/Garritson, Inc.

PILQ - Quilts - Sandra A. Percy

PILQUEN - Apparel–men's - Pilquen Partnership

PILSEN CALLAO - Beverages–malt - Logret Import & Export Co.

PILSENER CLUB - Beverages–malt ☆ - Pearl Brewing Co.

PILSUDSKI - Mustard - Van Bennett Food Inc.

PILY - Skin care products - Sara Lee Corp.

PILZ-SCHINDLER - Mushrooms - Kreiner Imports

PIM - Automotive parts and accessories - Precision International Manufacturing, Inc.

PIM - Pharmaceutical preparations - Vienna Beauty Products Co.

PIM POMS - Footwear ☆ - R.G. Barry Corp.

PIMA - Floor coverings–carpet and rugs - Masland Corp.

PIMA - Pharmaceutical preparations - Fleming & Co.

PIMA - Yarn - William Unger & Co. Inc.

PIMA GOLD - Fresh citrus fruits - Associated Citrus Packers, Inc.

PIMA ROYALE - Towels - Fieldcrest Cannon, Inc.

PIMALENE - Fabrics - Stylecrest Fabrics Ltd.

PIMA'S CHOICE - Citrus fruits - Associated Citrus Packers, Inc.

PIMENTEL - Cigars ☆ - James B. Russell Inc.

PIMENTO - Footwear–women's - Thom McAn Shoe Co.

PIMENTO - Rum - Carriage House Imports Ltd.

PIMLICO - Floor coverings–carpet and rugs - Queen Carpet Corp.

PIMM SHEET - Rope - Wellington Leisure Products, Inc.

PIMMS - Beverages–alcohol - Guinness Import Co.

PIMM'S CUP - Beverages–alcohol - Old Fitzgerald Distillery Inc.

PIMM'S NO.1 CUP - Beverages–alcohol - Sazerac Co. Inc.

PIMP - Apparel - Original Pimpgear

PIMPERNEL - Placemats - Pimpernel USA Inc.

PIMPLE PATCH - Pharmaceutical preparations - Transdermal Products, Inc.

PIMPLE ZAPPER - Skin care products ☆ - Christine Valmy, Inc.

PIMS - Cookies - Sunshine/Salerno Inc.

PIN-BIN - Containers - Moore Push-Pin Co.

PIN BUSTER - Firearms, accessories, and parts - Welsh Sporting Goods Corp. (Boyt Div.)

PIN CARDS - Pins–jewelry - Imprinted Products Corp.

PIN DOT - Antennas - Terk Technologies Corp.

PIN DOT - Floor coverings–carpet and rugs ☆ - Stanton Carpet Corp.

PIN-DOWN - Insect repellents - Trece, Inc.

PIN-HI - Golfing equipment - U.S. Precision Inc.

PIN-LOK - Chairs–metal ☆ - Counterpoint

PIN ME PRETTY - Novelty items - Cosrich Inc.

PIN MONEY - Pickles ☆ - John E. Cain Co.

PIN-MONEY PENNY - Toys–banks - DeLaittre Industries Inc.

PIN-N-CHAIN - Key rings - West Coast Chain Manufacturing Co.

PIN N PATCH - Stationery - N.G. Slater

PIN-NOTES - Greeting cards - Eden LLC

PIN-ON PENCIL - Pencils–mechanical ☆ - Park Sherman

PIN PAL - Bulletin boards–cork - Artistic Office Products

PIN PALS - Toys–stuffed ☆ - Fun World Inc.

PIN-POINT - Tools - Carbona Products Co.

PIN-RID - Pharmaceutical preparations - Apothecary Products, Inc.

PIN-SITE - Bandages - New Dimensions in Medicine, Inc.

PIN SPOTS - Greeting cards ☆ - Duck Press

PIN-STRIPE - Floor coverings–carpet and rugs ☆ - Porter Carpet Mills Inc.

PIN-TEC - Medical apparatus - Capintec, Inc.

PIN THE TAIL ON THE DONKEY - Games ☆ - Parker Brothers

PIN-TITE - Musical instrument accessories - Lunsford-Alden Co.

PIN-UP - Bulletin boards–cork - Evans International Inc.

PIN-UP - Trays ☆ - Fair Haven Industries Inc.

PIN-UP GIRL - Brassieres (Bras) ☆ - Gem-Dandy, Inc.

PIN-UP PINKS - Cosmetics - Chesebrough-Pond's USA Co.

PIN-UPS - Lighting fixtures - Swivelier Co. Inc.

PIN-UPS - Posters ☆ - Dolly, Inc.

PIN UPS - Shoes - International Seaway Trading Corp.

PIN WHEEL - Instruction cards - Pin Wheel, Inc.

PIN WHEEL BATONS - Candy - Creative Specialties Inc.

PIN-X - Pharmaceutical preparations - Effcon Laboratories Inc.

PINA - Beverages - Joseph Victori Wines Inc.

PINA - Food products - Liberty Fish Co.

PINA - Frames–eyeglass - Pathway Optical Prods.

PINA CALADA - Footwear - Alec Corp.

PINA COLADA - Rum - Joseph E. Seagram & Sons, Inc.

PINA COLADA WHIP - Beverages - Quick Marketing Inc.

PINA PINEAPPLE - Beverages–carbonated - Canada Dry Corp.

PINA RITA - Beverages–alcohol - Chi-Chi's, Inc.

PINACLE MOUNTAIN - Water–bottled or canned - Pinacle Mountain Waters

PINAFORE - Housewares ☆ - Lenox, Inc.

PINAFORE - Window shades - Verosol

PINAFORES - Toys - Eugene Doll & Novelty Co. Inc.

PINAID - Laboratory apparatus - Chiron Corp.

PINATA - Snack foods - Alex Foods, Inc.

PINBAK - Hardware - Scott Sign Systems, Inc.

PINBALL CONSTRUCTION SET - Computer software - Electronic Arts Inc.

PINBALL EXPRESS - Computer software - Cosmi

PINBALL MATH - Computer software - Electronic Courseware Systems Inc.

PINBALL TARGET - Game machines ☆ - Placo Products Co.

PINBALL WARRIOR - Toys - Toy Biz, Inc.

PINBALL WIZARD - Computer software ☆ - Accolade Inc.

PINCEAU ROUGE - Cosmetics - Cosmair Inc.

PINCH - Whiskey - Schenley Industries Inc.

PINCH BOTTLE - Pet products - Novalek, Inc.

PINCH HITTER - Collectible trading cards - ANCO Collector Supplies, Inc.

PINCH-ON - Sporting goods ☆ - Water Gremlin Co.

PINCH-ON-FLOAT - Fishing tackle - Palsa Outdoor Products Inc.

PINCH/SEAL - Bags - Chase Bag Co.

PINCH SHOT - Sporting goods ☆ - General Sportcraft Co. Ltd.

PINCH YOUR CHEEKS - Cosmetics - Origins Natural Resources Inc.

PINCHER - Toys - Tonka Corp.

PINCHLESS - Office supplies - Mead Corp.

PINCIO - Dishes–china - Pasmantier Co. Inc.

PINCOR - Generators–electric ☆ - Desa International, Inc.

PINDAR - Floor coverings–carpet and rugs - Bloomsburg Carpet Industries

PINDAR - Floor coverings–carpet and rugs ☆ - Masland Corp.

PINDOT - Floor coverings–carpet and rugs ☆ - Langhorne Carpet Co. Inc.

PINDOT - Health care products - Invacare Corp.

PINE - Dinnerware–glass ☆ - Nikko Ceramics Inc.

PINE - Frames–eyeglass - May Optical Co. Inc.

PINE - Socks - Pine Hosiery Mills, Inc.

☆ = Now out of production

PINE 64 - Disinfectants - W.W. Grainger, Inc.
PINE ACCENTS - Furniture ☆ - Hooker Furniture Corp.
PINE ACCENTS - Hardware ☆ - Bemis Manufacturing Co.
PINE ACTION - Cleaning preparations - Linden Corp.
PINE ACTION - Cleaning preparations—household - L & F Consumer Products
PINE-AX - Sweeping compounds - Paxon Manufacturing Co.
PINE-BOL - Cleaning preparations—household - JBI Inc.
PINE BRANCH - House furnishings ☆ - Lea Industries Inc.
PINE BRAND - Vermicelli and pasta - Summit Import Corp.
PINE-BRITE - Cleaning preparations - Analab Inc.
PINE BROOK - Wood products - Champion International Corp.
PINE BROS. - Cough drops - Leaf, Inc.
PINE BROS. - Vitamins and nutritional supplements - IVC Industries, Inc.
PINE CLASSICS - Furniture - Hammary Furniture Co. Inc.
PINE CLUB - Salad dressings—bottled - Pine Club
PINE COLLECTIBLES - Furniture - Hooker Furniture Corp.
PINE CONE - Garden equipment - North States Industries Inc.
PINE COUNTRY - House furnishings ☆ - Lea Industries Inc.
PINE CRAFTS - Furniture - Vaughan Furniture Co. Inc.
PINE CREEK - Furniture ☆ - Athens Furniture Industries Inc.
PINE CREEK GRAPHICS - Stationery - Mark Partridge
PINE CREST - Furniture ☆ - Athens Furniture Industries Inc.
PINE CREST - Wood products - Champion International Corp.
PINE CREST FARM - Desserts - Pine Crest Farm
PINE CROFT - Furniture ☆ - Kincaid Furniture Co. Inc.
PINE DEODORANT - Cleaning preparations - Analab Inc.
PINE-DRI - Pet products ☆ - Maryland Plastics Inc.
PINE FOREST - Furniture ☆ - Athens Furniture Industries Inc.
PINE FOREST 5 - Chocolate bars - Betco Corp.
PINE FRESH! - Cleaning preparations - Jennico, Inc.
PINE FROST - Cleaning preparations - Viking Manufacturing Co. Inc.
PINE GROVE - Furniture - Universal Flooring
PINE GROVE FARMS - Beef - Hoekstra Meat Co.
PINE HARBOR - Golfing equipment - Service Merchandise Co. Inc.
PINE HOLLOW - Giftware ☆ - Enesco Corp.
PINE HURST - Furniture ☆ - Hammary Furniture Co. Inc.
PINE INHERITANCE - Furniture ☆ - Kincaid Furniture Co. Inc.
PINE ISLAND - Shirts - Pine Island Sportswear, Ltd.
PINE ISLAND - Wallpaper - Seabrook Wallcoverings, Inc.
PINE KIST - Deodorizers - Ocean Coffee Co. Inc.
PINE KLEAN - Cleaning preparations—household - Malco Products, Inc.
PINE KLEEN - Disinfectants - Hexol Inc.
PINE KNOLL - Furniture - Pilliod Co.
PINE-LOK - Wood products - Aspen Valley Lumber Co. Inc.
PINE MAGIC - Cleaning preparations - Dowbrands L.P.
PINE MANOR - Cabinets—wood ☆ - Kemper
PINE MANOR - Food products - Pine Manor, Inc.
PINE MANOR - Furniture - Lane Co. Inc.
PINE MANOR - House furnishings ☆ - Lexington Furniture Industries, Inc.
PINE MILL - Wood products ☆ - Masonite Corp.
PINE MOUNTAIN - Bicycles - Marin Mountain Bikes, Inc.
PINE MOUNTAIN - Fireplace equipment - Pine Mountain Corp.
PINE MOUNTAIN - Furniture - Universal Flooring
PINE MOUNTAIN - Furniture - Vaughan Furniture Co. Inc.
PINE MOUNTAIN - Furniture - Woodland Furniture Manufacturing Co.
PINE MOUNTAIN - Shoes - Bee-Gee Shoe Corp
PINE MOUNTAIN COLLECTION - Furniture ☆ - Southern Furniture Co. of Conover
PINE NEEDLE - Paper—carbon - Eaton Allen Ko-Rec-Type Corp.
PINE NEEDLE CREATIONS - Bird cages - Pine Needle Creations
PINE-NEER - Moldings and trim - Contact Lumber Co.
PINE NOOK - Food products ☆ - R & S Pickle Co. Inc.
PINE-NU - Fertilizers - Howard Fertilizer Co., Inc.
PINE-O-CIDE II - Disinfectants - Hillyard Enterprises, Inc.
PINE O MITE - Cleaning preparations - Garcoa Labs/Vitamin Classics
PINE O PINE - Cleaning preparations - White Cap Inc.
PINE-O-QUAT - Disinfectants - Unit Chemical Corp.
PINE OIL - Disinfectants ☆ - Dowbrands L.P.
PINE OLA - Furniture polish and wax - Howard Products
PINE PEAK BLUES - Apparel—children's - Nordstrom, Inc.
PINE PLUS - Cleaning preparations - Dar-Lin Products Inc.
PINE PLUS - Moulding - ABT Co., Inc.
PINE POINT PINKS - Seafood - Bayley's Quality Seafood
PINE POWER - Disinfectants - Dowbrands L.P.
PINE Q - Disinfectants - Harley Chemicals
PINE RIDGE - Floor coverings—carpet and rugs ☆ - Hollytex Carpet Mills Inc.

PINE RIDGE - Furniture ☆ - Athens Furniture Industries Inc.
PINE RIDGE - Furniture ☆ - Bassett Furniture Industries, Inc.
PINE RIDGE - Siding—insulating - Masonite Corp.
PINE RIDGE WINERY - Wines - Pine Ridge Winery
PINE RIVER - Apparel and accessories - Aquila Inc.
PINE RIVER - Bicycles ☆ - Huffy Corp.
PINE SCRUB - Cleaning preparations - Analab Inc.
PINE-SOL - Cleaning preparations—household - Clorox Co.
PINE SPA - Bath salts ☆ - Majestic Drug Co., Inc.
PINE SPRAY - Eyeglasses - Art-Craft Optical Co.
PINE STATE - Milk - Pine State Creamery Inc.
PINE STATE CLASSIC - Sweaters - Pine State Knitwear Co.
PINE TIME - Cleaning preparations - Neutron Industries, Inc.
PINE-TIQUE KEGS - Lamps ☆ - Spaulding & Frost Co. Inc.
PINE TREASURES - Furniture ☆ - Stanley Furniture Co. Inc.
PINE TREE - Envelopes - Western States Envelope Co.
PINE TREE - Furniture - Pilliod Co.
PINE TREE - House furnishings - Lea Industries Inc.
PINE TREE SUEDE - Fabrics - Dan River Inc.
PINE VALE - Furniture ☆ - Singer Furniture Co.
PINE VALLEY - Apparel and accessories - Pine Valley Golf Club
PINE VALLEY - Furniture - Avon Co.
PINE VALLEY - Furniture - Pilliod Co.
PINE VALLEY - Water - Pine Valley Water Co. Inc.
PINE VALLEY - Wood products - Champion International Corp.
PINE VALLEY PRINTS - Wallpaper - Borden, Inc.
PINEAIR - Disinfectants - Uncle Sam Chemical Co., Inc.
PINEAPPLE - Tableware—china - Susquehanna Glass Co.
PINEAPPLE ISLAND TROPICS - Beverages—alcohol - Seagram's Chateau & Estate Wines Co.
PINEAPPLE JUICE - Clothing and sportswear - Rodney Doo
PINEAPPLE MUSIC - Publisher's imprints - Green Dog Productions
PINEAPPLE PARADISE - Juices—frozen - Del Monte Corp.
PINEAPPLE PLEASURE - Fruit drinks—bottled or canned - Smoothie King Franchises, Inc.
PINEAROMA - Disinfectant - Continental Chemical Corp.
PINEBROOK - Cabinets - Schrock
PINECONES - Footwear - Norway Footwear Corp.
PINECRAFT - Furniture - Conover Chair Co. Inc.
PINECRAFT - Wood products - Georgia-Pacific Corp.
PINECREST - Clocks ☆ - General Time Corp. (Westclox/Seth Thomas Div.)
PINECREST - Window shades - J.B. Supplies Inc.
PINECREST - Window shades - Mid-America Custom Inc.
PINEDSPCORE - Computer software - DSP Group, Inc.
PINEFIELDS - Wood products ☆ - Masonite Corp.
PINEHURST - Bedding—linen - West Point-Pepperell Inc.
PINEHURST - Cabinets—wood ☆ - Kemper
PINEHURST - Floor coverings—carpet and rugs - Burtco Enterprises Inc.
PINEHURST - Food products - Bison Canning Co. Inc.
PINEHURST - Frames—eyeglass - May Optical Co. Inc.
PINEHURST - House furnishings ☆ - Lea Industries Inc.
PINEHURST - Paper—writing - Champion International Corp.
PINEHURST - Sporting goods ☆ - Brunswick Corp.
PINEHURST CHAMPIONSHIP COURSE - Computer software - Access Software Inc.
PINEKRAFT - Envelopes - Quality Park Products Co.
PINELAND - Pickles - W.B. Roddenbery Co., Inc.
PINELLA - Bathroom fixtures - Kohler Co.
PINELLAS - Seafood products—fresh or frozen - Pinellas Seafood Co.
PINENEEDLE - Fishing tackle - Outdoor Recreation Group
PINEOLL - Disinfectants - Uncle Sam Chemical Co., Inc.
PINEPRO - Wood products - P & M Cedar Products, Inc.
PINES - Vitamins and nutritional supplements - Peterson's Health Products
PINES BROOK - Wines - Leonard Kreusch, Inc.
PINES BROOK - Wines - Leonard Kreusch Inc.
PINES, THE - Cigars - Consolidated Cigar Corp.
PINES WHEAT - Pasta - Pines International, Inc.
PINESIDE 100 - Siding—insulating - Weyerhaeuser Co.
PINESOURCE - Lumber - Pinesource, Inc.
PINETEX - Cleaning preparations—household - Alliance Consumer Industries
PINETEX - Wallpaper ☆ - H & S Sales Inc.
PINETEX III - Wallpaper ☆ - H & S Sales Inc.
PINETEX 6 - Wallpaper - H & S Sales Inc.
PINETEX V - Wallpaper - H & S Sales Inc.
PINETREE - Food products - McCain Foods Inc.
PINEWOOD - Cabinets - Belwood Inc.

☆ = Now out of production

PINEWOOD - Clocks ☆ - General Time Corp. (Westclox/Seth Thomas Div.)

PINEWOOD - Furniture - Thomasville Furniture Industries Inc.

PINEWOOD - Recording label ☆ - Fink-Pinewood Records & Productions (Pinewood Productions)

PINEWOOD DERBY RACER - Toys–automobiles - S & W Crafts Manufacturing

PINEWOOD SPRINGS - Water–bottled or canned - Hickory Springs Water Co. Inc.

PINEWOODS - Siding–insulating ☆ - Masonite Corp.

PINEWORKS - Clocks ☆ - Hunter Manufacturing Group, Inc.

PINEX - Cough medicines - Alvin Last Inc.

PINFISH - Fishing lures ☆ - Bomber Bait Co.

PINFREE - Diapers–cloth ☆ - Salk Co. Inc.

PING - Golfing equipment - Karsten Manufacturing Corp.

PING KEYS - Musical instrument accessories - Kaman Music Corp.

PING LING - Thread - Kreinik Manufacturing Co. Inc.

PING PANDA - Toys–stuffed - Russ Berrie and Co., Inc.

PING PONG - Frames–eyeglass - Hudson Optical Corp.

PING PONG - Yarn ☆ - Joseph Galler Inc.

PING PONG PANDA - Puppets - Dakin Inc.

PING-ZING - Golf clubs - Karsten Manufacturing Corp.

PINGEL - Motor vehicle parts and accessories - Pingel Enterprise, Inc.

PINGLE - Motor vehicle parts and accessories - Rivera Engineering, Inc.

PINGOBINGO - Games - Sandra Lee Adams

PINGRIP - Hardware - Star Anchors & Fasteners

PINHEAD - Apparel and accessories - Thomas Edward Wynkoop, Jr.

PINHEAD - Fishing lures - Peter J. Blicha

PINHEADS - Jewelry - Score Board Holding Corp.

PINHOLE - Construction equipment - Rald Industries, Inc.

PINHOLE SPEC - Frames–eyeglass - May Optical Co. Inc.

PINK - Hair care products - Luster Products, Inc.

PINK - Insulating materials - Owens Corning

PINK & BLUE - Apparel and accessories - Pink & Blue

PINK & GOLD - Candy ☆ - Glade Taffy Town, Inc.

PINK & WHITE - Apparel and accessories - Pink & White, Inc.

PINK ANGEL - Bicycles - Columbia Manufacturing Inc.

PINK BEAUTY - Salmon–smoked, salted, dried, or pickled - Ocean Beauty Seafood, Inc.

PINK BLOSSOM - Glassware–household ☆ - Fenton Art Glass Co.

PINK BLUSH L'ARTISTE CREME - Lipsticks - Cosmair Inc.

PINK BOUTON - Nail care products - Cosmair Inc.

PINK BROCADE PERLE - Nail care products - Cosmair Inc.

PINK CALYPSO - Beverages–carbonated - McCain Citrus, Inc.

PINK CARNATION - Erasers - Dixon Ticonderoga Co.

PINK CATABA - Wines - John Christ Winery

PINK CHAMPAGNE - Candy ☆ - Leaf, Inc.

PINK CHAMPAGNE - Christmas tree ornaments - Cracker Box Inc.

PINK CHAMPAGNE - Cosmetics ☆ - Elysee Scientific Cosmetic Co.

PINK CHIFFON - Christmas tree ornaments - Cracker Box Inc.

PINK CLOUD - Frames–eyeglass ☆ - Universal/Univis Inc.

PINK CLOUDS - Dolls - Tonka Corp.

PINK CRACKLE - Glassware–household ☆ - Fenton Art Glass Co.

PINK DAWN - Cosmetics - Merle Norman Cosmetics

PINK DOLL - Fruit and vegetable markets ☆ - Frigid Food Products Inc.

PINK DOMINO - Apparel and accessories - Pink Domino, Inc.

PINK FLAME - Trees - Wills Nursery

PINK FLAMINGO - Greeting cards - Recycled Paper Products, Inc.

PINK FOIL - Lipsticks - Revlon Consumer Products Corp.

PINK FROSTING - Colognes ☆ - Andrew Jergens Co.

PINK GARLAND - Kitchen utensils–aluminum ☆ - Reston Lloyd Ltd.

PINK GEM - Erasers ☆ - Staedtler, Inc.

PINK ICE - Lipsticks - Lancome

PINK IN THE AFTERNOON - Cosmetics - Revlon Consumer Products Corp.

PINK JUBILEE - Dolls - Mattel, Inc.

PINK-KIN - Skin care products ☆ - Kinreco Products Co. Inc.

PINK LADY - Bedding–linen - Dan River Inc.

PINK LADY - Bicycles - Columbia Manufacturing Inc.

PINK LADY - Dinnerware–glass ☆ - Metlox Pottery Shoppe

PINK LADY - Paints - A. Flohr Co. Inc.

PINK LADY - Skin care products - American Salon Products

PINK LEMON - Astringents - Elysee Scientific Cosmetic Co.

PINK LEMONADE - Apparel and accessories - Heartworks Inc.

PINK LEMONADE - Candy - Bobs Candies Inc.

PINK LEMONADE - Chewing gum ☆ - Fleer Corp.

PINK LEMONADE - Christmas tree ornaments - Cracker Box Inc.

PINK LEMONADE - Flowers, plants, and seeds - Himark Enterprises Inc.

PINK LEMONADE - Teas - Eastern Shore Tea Co.

PINK LEMONADE EUPHORIA - Fruit drinks–bottled or canned - Coca-Cola Co.

PINK LEMONADE STIX - Candy ☆ - Leaf, Inc.

PINK LIGHTNING - Bicycles - Kent International Inc.

PINK LILY - Dinnerware–glass ☆ - Lenox, Inc.

PINK LIQUID SOAP - Soap - Analab Inc.

PINK LOTION SOAP - Soap - Analab Inc.

PINK LUSTRE - Christmas tree ornaments - Cracker Box Inc.

PINK MAGIC - Detergents ☆ - Care-Tech Laboratories Inc.

PINK MAGIC - Dolls - Mattel, Inc.

PINK MINNOW - Fishing tackle - Horizon Lure Co.

PINK MYSTIQUE/ANEMONE - Cosmetics - Cosmair Inc.

PINK 'N PRETTY - Dolls - Mattel, Inc.

PINK N PRETTY - Hair coloring preparations - Stylors Inc.

PINK ON POINT - Toys - Tonka Corp.

PINK OWL - Chewing gum - Philadelphia Chewing Gum Corp.

PINK-PAKS - Pharmaceutical preparations - Paks Drugs Inc.

PINK PANTHER - Detergents - Mission Kleensweep Products, Inc.

PINK PANTHER - Dishwashing compounds - Guardian Laboratories

PINK PANTHER - Toys–stuffed ☆ - Mighty Star Inc. (Special Effects Div.)

PINK PANTHER FOOTPRINT - Chewing gum ☆ - Amurol Confections Co.

PINK PARFAIT - Christmas tree ornaments - Cracker Box Inc.

PINK PARFAIT - Dolls - Russ Berrie and Co., Inc.

PINK PARFAIT POODLE - Toys–stuffed - Russ Berrie and Co., Inc.

PINK PASSION - Beverages–alcohol ☆ - David Sherman Corp.

PINK PASSION EVERCLEAR - Beverages–alcohol ☆ - David Sherman Corp.

PINK PEARL - Erasers - Faber-Castell Corp.

PINK PEARL - Glassware–household ☆ - Fenton Art Glass Co.

PINK PEARL - Ski suits–children's ☆ - Knight Marketing Corp.

PINK PEARL - Soap - Georgia-Pacific Corp.

PINK PEONY - Dinnerware–glass - Nikko Ceramics Inc.

PINK PERFECTION - Dolls - Seymour Mann Inc.

PINK PET - Erasers - Faber-Castell Corp.

PINK PET - Erasers - Sanford Corp.

PINK PETALS - Apparel–women's - Dargani Impex International, Inc.

PINK PETE'S ABC'S - Computer software - Orange Cherry Software

PINK PETE'S WEATHER SCIENCE - Computer software - Orange Cherry Software

PINK PLANET - Pens - Pentech International Inc.

PINK PLANET!, THE - Apparel and accessories - Catherine M. Hasse

PINK PRIDE - Salmon–smoked, salted, dried, or pickled - North Pacific Seafoods

PINK PUSSYCAT - Housewares ☆ - Amaza Laboratories Inc.

PINK RANGER - Toys - Saban Entertainment, Inc.

PINK RIBBON - Cosmetics - Estee Lauder Inc.

PINK RIESLING - Wines - Staton Hills Winery Co. Ltd.

PINK SATIN - Dinnerware–glass ☆ - Nikko Ceramics Inc.

PINK SENSATION - Dolls - Mattel, Inc.

PINK SHADOWS - Bicycles - Roadmaster Corp.

PINK SPARKLES - Dolls - Mattel, Inc.

PINK SPLENDOR - Dolls - Mattel, Inc.

PINK SPORTIF - Lipsticks - Cosmair Inc.

PINK STUFF BY JINX - Cosmetics - Houston MVP Inc.

PINK TAFFETA - Christmas tree ornaments - Cracker Box Inc.

PINK TREAT - Water treating compounds - United Chemical Corp.

PINK TRIO - Dinnerware - Corning Inc.

PINK TURBO RANGER - Toys - Saban Entertainment, Inc.

PINK VERDE - Floor coverings–tile - ECC International

PINK WHISPER - Dinnerware–glass ☆ - Royal China & Porcelain Companies Inc.

PINK WILLOW - Cosmetics - Lancome

PINKEEPER - Cleaning preparations - AMF Bowling Worldwide

PINKEE'S - Hairpins - Beauty & Beauty Enterprises, Inc.

PINKEE'S - Nail care products - Beauty & Beauty Enterprises, Inc.

PINKER - Tobacco–chewing or smoking ☆ - Swedish Math North America Inc.

PINKERTON - Wallpaper - Goffle Warehouse & Distribution Co. Inc.

PINKEST - Lipsticks - Cosmair Inc.

PINKHAM - Wood products - Georgia-Pacific Corp.

PINKHEART - Dolls - Mattel, Inc.

PINKI - Grain-based prepared foods - President Foods, Ltd.

PINKIE - Fishing lures - Den Manufacturing Co.

PINKIE MOUSE - Toys–stuffed - Russ Berrie and Co., Inc.

PINKIE PANDA - Toys - M.&S. Shillman Inc.

PINKIE PUMP - Pet products - Reptilia

PINKIES - Jewelry - Ears-R-In Inc.

☆ = Now out of production

PINKIES - Jewelry–costume ☆ - Chaska Inc./Medihome-Doctors Podiatry

PINKING - Nail care products - Cosmair Inc.

PINK'N SWEET - Wines - St. James Winery

PINKPLUS - Insulating materials - Owens Corning

PINKPLUS - Insulation - Owens Corning Fiberglass Technology Inc.

PINKSEAL - Adhesives and sealants - Owens Corning

PINKUMS - Dolls - Mattel, Inc.

PINKUS ALT - Beverages–alcohol - Merchant du Vin Corp.

PINKUSSOHN'S POTPOURRI - Tobacco - American Tobacco Co.

PINKWRAP - Construction equipment - Owens Corning Fiberglass Technology Inc.

PINKWRAP - Insulating materials - Owens Corning

PINKY - Housewares - Amaza Laboratories Inc.

PINKY AND THE BRAIN - Apparel and accessories - Time Warner Entertainment Co., L.P.

PINKY & THE BRAIN - Computer storage devices–optical - Konami (America) Inc.

PINKY PIGI - Puppets - Dakin Inc.

PINKY-TAC - Bic Corp.

PINKY WOLMAN - Fabrics - Pinky Wolman Designs, Inc.

PINLIGHT MAGIC - Window coverings - Levolor Inc.

PINMAP - Computer software - Cami Research Inc.

PINMARK - Golfing equipment - Pinmark Corp.

PINMASTER - Hardware - Ambassador Industries

PINMATE - Lighting fixtures - Swivelier Co. Inc.

PINN-ACL - Surgical instruments - Linvatec Corp.

PINNACLE - Agricultural products - E.I. Dupont de Nemours and Co.

PINNACLE - Antennas–satellite - Winegard Co.

PINNACLE - Apparel and accessories - Hampton Industries, Inc.

PINNACLE - Automobile alarms - Southern Merchandising Inc.

PINNACLE - Bags–trash - Mohawk Plastics Inc.

PINNACLE - Bicycles - Klein Bicycle Corp.

PINNACLE - Bicycles - Raleigh USA Bicycle Co.

PINNACLE - Butter ☆ - Humko Products

PINNACLE - Cabinets - Grandview Products Co.

PINNACLE - Doors–garage - Pinnacle Door Co.

PINNACLE - Fishing nets - Trans-Pacific Trading, Inc.

PINNACLE - Floor coverings - Congoleum Corp.

PINNACLE - Floor coverings–carpet and rugs - Collins & Aikman Corp.

PINNACLE - Floor coverings–carpet and rugs - Criterion Mills Inc.

PINNACLE - Floor coverings–carpet and rugs ☆ - Cumberland Mills Inc.

PINNACLE - Floor coverings–carpet and rugs ☆ - J and J Industries Inc.

PINNACLE - Games ☆ - Mayfair Games, Inc.

PINNACLE - Glassware–household - Crystal Clear Importing Co. Inc.

PINNACLE - Golfing equipment - Titleist & Foot-Joy Worldwide

PINNACLE - Hearing aids - AudioScience Inc.

PINNACLE - Lamps - CBK Ltd. Inc.

PINNACLE - Motor vehicles–motor homes - Thor Industries West

PINNACLE - Musical instrument accessories - Super-Sensitive Musical String Co.

PINNACLE - Paper–toweling - Kimberly-Clark Corp.

PINNACLE - Pens - A.T. Cross Co.

PINNACLE - Plates–paper - Sweetheart Cup Co. Inc.

PINNACLE - Publisher's imprints - Windsor Publishing Corp.

PINNACLE - Razors–electric - Philips Electronics North America Corp.

PINNACLE - Regulators–voltage - Carotron, Inc.

PINNACLE - Scissors–hand-operated - Clauss Cutlery Co.

PINNACLE - Shingles - Atlas Roofing Corp.

PINNACLE - Sporting goods - Kellwood Co.

PINNACLE - Stoves–gas - Vermont Castings, Inc.

PINNACLE - Strollers–baby ☆ - Welsh Co.

PINNACLE - Stucco - Wellborn-DE Corp.

PINNACLE - Sugar - United Sugars Corp.

PINNACLE - Sweaters - Pine State Knitwear Co.

PINNACLE - Tables–wood - Krueger International, Inc.

PINNACLE - Tanks–storage - Pinnacle CNG Systems, LLC

PINNACLE - Trading cards and stamps - Score Group, Inc.

PINNACLE - Wallpaper - Camelot Design Studios

PINNACLE ADVISOR - Consulting services - Pinnacle Investors Advisory Corp.

PINNACLE BOOKS - Publisher's imprints - Pinnacle Books/Windsor Corp.

PINNACLE DIETS - Pet food - Cottonwood Distributing, Inc.

PINNACLE I - Safety eyewear - H.L. Bouton Co. Inc.

PINNACLE II - Safety eyewear - H.L. Bouton Co. Inc.

PINNACLE PAK - Vitamins and nutritional supplements - Eleva, Inc.

PINNACLE POWER - Sporting goods - Pinnacle Brands, Inc.

PINNICAL - Drapery hardware ☆ - Spring Window Fashions Division, Inc.

PINO FERRI - Footwear - Transatlantic Shoe Co. Ltd.

PINO LUONGO'S CUCINA TOSCA - Pasta - Toscorp, Inc.

PINO-MAGGIO - Pasta - Maggio Beef

PINOCCHIO - Dolls - Effanbee Doll Corp.

PINOCCHIO - Food products - Escalon Frozen Foods

PINOCCHIO - Games ☆ - Parker Brothers

PINOCCHIO'S POKER - Pool tables - Liar's Poker of America Inc.

PINOL - Cosmetics - National Products Co. Inc.

PINOL - Hair care products - William Marvy Co., Inc.

PINO'S PASTA VELOCE - Pasta - Automated Equipment, Inc.

PINOT GRIGIO DEL COLLIO - Wines - Kobrand Corp.

PINOT GRIGIO, GRAVE DEL FRIULI - Wines - Kobrand Corp.

PINOTOL - Health care products - McKesson Home Health Care

PINPOINT - Computer software - Computer Associates International, Inc.

PINPOINT - Computer software - Virage, Inc.

PINPOINT - Computer software ☆ - Pinpoint Publishing

PINPOINT - Fishing nets ☆ - G-96 Products Co. Inc.

PINPOINT - Floor coverings–carpet and rugs - Blue Ridge Carpet Mills

PINPOINT - Golf clubs - Austad Co.

PINPOINT - Insecticides - Valent USA Corp.

PINPOINT - Massage products - Healthometer

PINPOINT - Office supplies - Faber-Castell Corp.

PINPOINT - Tiles–ceramic - Quarry Tile Co.

PINPOINT FIBREOPTICS DISPLAY ILLUMINATION - Lighting equipment - Pinpoint Fiberoptics Limited

PINPOINT NAUTICAL NAVIGATION - Computer software - RJC Development Corp.

PINPOINTER - Pens - Accutec Inc.

PINPOINTFX - Paints - OEM Paints, Inc.

PINQUE - Lipsticks - Cosmair Inc.

PINQUITOS - Vegetables–canned - S & W Fine Foods, Inc.

PINS - Computer software - Chesapeake Interlink, Ltd.

PINS ARE OUR BUSINESS - Pins–jewelry - Imprinted Products Corp.

PINS E-Z - Jewelry - Champion Ideas

PINS 'N PALS - Bottles–glass - Bowling Proprietors' Association of America, Inc.

PINS TO SUIT YOU - Jewelry - Crystal Brands Inc.

PINSHOT - Golf balls - WPI Acquisition Corp.

PINSTRIPE - Floor coverings–carpet and rugs - Regal Rugs Inc.

PINSTRIPE - Maps - American Map Corp.

PINSTRIPE PETITES - Apparel and accessories - Sears, Roebuck and Co.

PINSTRIPE, THE - Apparel–athletic - Felco Athletic Wear Co.

PINSTRIPES - Dinnerware–glass ☆ - Lenox, Inc.

PINSYTE - Calculators - Sytronics, Inc.

PINT-A-FLUSH - Toilets–porcelain - Blount Industries, Inc.

PINT SIZE - Apparel and accessories - Kidfusion LLC

PINT SIZE - Apparel and accessories - Strouse, Adler Co.

PINT SIZE - Dolls ☆ - Effanbee Doll Corp.

PINT SIZE - Kitchen appliances ☆ - Sunbeam-Oster Household Products

PINTA BLUES - Corn chips ☆ - Barbara's Bakery, Inc.

PINTA CHIPS - Tortillas - Barbara's Bakery, Inc.

PINTAIL - Apparel and accessories - Pintail Corp.

PINTAIL - Food products - Robert Fierro Co. Inc.

PINTAIL - Trailers–travel ☆ - Mallard Coach

PINTAIL ALE - Beverages–malt - Bridgeport Brewing Co.

PINTAR COLIO - Wines - Tempo Imports Ltd.

PINTO - Cigarettes - Brown & Williamson Tobacco Corp.

PINTO - Flowers, plants, and seeds - Jacklin Seed

PINTO - Motor vehicles–automobiles ☆ - Ford Motor Co.

PINTO - Pens - Micropoint Inc.

PINTO - Recording label - Mark Ramos Nishita

PINTO - Wheelbarrows - Ames Lawn & Garden Tool Co.

PINTO PRESS - Publisher's imprints - Pinto Press

PINTO QUAD - Skates–roller - Seneca Sports, Inc.

PINTOLIVEIRA - Footwear ☆ - Conjac Inc.

PINTRIGUES - Rings–jewelry - Feature Enterprises

PINTS-DEDURA - Hair care products ☆ - Demert & Dougherty, Inc.

PINWEAR - Apparel and accessories - Trevor Pinnock

PINWHEEL - Glassware–household - Crystal Clear Importing Co. Inc.

PINWHEELS - Apparel–athletic - J.C. Penney Co., Inc.

PINWHEELS - Baked goods - Interstate Brands Corp.

PINWHEELS - Bicycles ☆ - Murray, Inc.

PINWHEELS - Cookies - Nabisco Foods Group

PINWHEELS - Pet products - Gimborn U.S., Inc.

PINWHEELS IN THE PARK - Christmas tree ornaments - Cracker Box Inc.

PINWRITER - Computers–personal ☆ - NEC Technologies, Inc.

☆ = Now out of production

PINX - Underwear and nightwear - Russell-Newman, Inc.
PINZETTE - Skin care products - Tweezerman Corp.
PIO CESARE - Wines - Bartolomeo Po Inc.
PIO-CORE - Doors—metal - Pioneer Industries
PIO-SONIC - Doors—metal - Pioneer Industries
PIOESTER - Resins—synthetic ☆ - Pionite Decorative Surfaces
PIONEER - Adhesives and sealants - Pioneer Manufacturing Co.
PIONEER - Agricultural machinery - Parker Hannifin Corp. (Quick Coupling Div.)
PIONEER - Archery equipment - Martin Archery Inc.
PIONEER - Artists' materials ☆ - Hamilton Industries
PIONEER - Audio equipment - Pioneer Electronics USA Inc.
PIONEER - Audio equipment - Speakerkits Inc.
PIONEER - Beef - Pioneer Snacks, Inc.
PIONEER - Bicycles - Bicycle Corp. of America
PIONEER - Bicycles - Columbia Manufacturing Inc.
PIONEER - Biscuits—mixes ☆ - Royal Cup, Inc.
PIONEER - Buffing machines - Pioneer/Eclipse Corp.
PIONEER - Cabinets - Aristokraft, Inc.
PIONEER - Cabinets - Wellborn Cabinet, Inc.
PIONEER - Cash boxes - Pioneer Steel Co.
PIONEER - Cheese - Pioneer Cheese Cooperative
PIONEER - Cigars - M. Marsh & Son
PIONEER - Clocks - Ridgeway Clock Co.
PIONEER - Cooking utensils—cast iron ☆ - National Housewares
PIONEER - Cosmetics - General Nutrition Inc.
PIONEER - Cribs—wood ☆ - Welsh Co.
PIONEER - Desks ☆ - Haskell of Pittsburgh, Inc.
PIONEER - Doors—garage - General American Door Co.
PIONEER - Fireplace equipment - Seymour Manufacturing Co.,Inc.
PIONEER - Flags - Valley Forge Flag
PIONEER - Floor coverings—carpet and rugs ☆ - American Carpet Mills
PIONEER - Floor coverings—carpet and rugs ☆ - Regal Rugs Inc.
PIONEER - Flowers, plants, and seeds - Pioneer Hi-Bred International, Inc.
PIONEER - Food products - Pioneer Packing Co.
PIONEER - Food products - Zacky Foods Co. (Los Angeles Div.)
PIONEER - Food products ☆ - Birkett Mills
PIONEER - Footwear—men's - L.B. Evans' Son Co.
PIONEER - Glassware—household - Federal Glass
PIONEER - Gloves - Pioneer Industrial Products Co.
PIONEER - Hair-cutting shears - B.W. Boyd Shears Inc.
PIONEER - Health care products ☆ - AAA Healthcare Equipment Co.
PIONEER - Housewares ☆ - Blue Mountain Industries, Inc.
PIONEER - Iron products - Lyco Enterprises, Inc.
PIONEER - Kitchen appliances ☆ - Sunbeam-Oster Household Products
PIONEER - Lubricants - Pioneer Oil Co. Inc.
PIONEER - Meat products—beef ☆ - Pioneer Coal Co.
PIONEER - Meat products—canned - Cudahy Co.
PIONEER - Metals - Pioneer Steel & Tube Corp.
PIONEER - Musical instruments ☆ - St. Louis Music Supply Co.
PIONEER - Novelty items - Pioneer Balloon Co.
PIONEER - Paper—writing ☆ - School Stationers Corp.
PIONEER - Pet products - Freeland Industries Inc.
PIONEER - Photo albums - Pioneer Photo Albums, Inc.
PIONEER - Publisher's imprints - Kalimat Press
PIONEER - Quilts - Extra Special Products Corp.
PIONEER - Recording label - Sivatt Music Productions
PIONEER - Rope - Wellington Leisure Products, Inc.
PIONEER - Sporting goods ☆ - Signature Brands, LLC
PIONEER - Sugar—granulated, refined, or powdered - Savannah Foods and Industries Inc.
PIONEER - Tools—garden - Tramontina USA, Inc.
PIONEER - Trailers—travel - Snowy Mountain Recreational Products
PIONEER - Trailers—travel - Shasta Industries Inc.
PIONEER - Wheat—flour or meal - Pioneer Flour Mills
PIONEER - Window coverings - H.J. Nieman Inc.
PIONEER 3 - Oxygen - Caire
PIONEER 3R - Oxygen - Caire
PIONEER 5 - Oxygen - Caire
PIONEER 2000 - Drycleaning machines - American Laundry Machinery, Inc.
PIONEER 2100 - Buffing machines - Pioneer/Eclipse Corp.
PIONEER 2400 STAR STRIP - Wax removers - Pioneer/Eclipse Corp.
PIONEER DAIRY - Dairy products - Pioneer Dairy Inc.
PIONEER HERITAGE - Publisher's imprints ☆ - University of Nebraska Press
PIONEER MUSIC PRESS - Music—sheet - Jackman Music Corp.
PIONEER OLD FASHIONED - Brown gravy mix - Pioneer Flour Mills

PIONEER PACKS - Jams and jellies - Knott's Berry Farm
PIONEER PINE - Furniture ☆ - Bassett Furniture Industries, Inc.
PIONEER PLUS - Toys - Newco, Inc.
PIONEER QUADRAMATIC - Paper—toweling - Georgia-Pacific Corp.
PIONEER SERIES - Placemats - Pioneer Series
PIONEER TRAIL - Furniture - Bassett Furniture Industries, Inc.
PIONEER TREASURY - Furniture - BDO Seidman
PIONEER WELLS - Water—bottled or canned - Pioneer Wells
PIONEX - Computer hardware - Pionex Technologies, Inc.
PIONEX - Plastics—laminated ☆ - Pionite Decorative Surfaces
PIONIER - Food products ☆ - Liberty Richter Inc.
PIONITE - Plastics—laminated ☆ - Pionite Decorative Surfaces
PIOREZ - Resins—synthetic ☆ - Pionite Decorative Surfaces
PIP - Adhesives and sealants - Permalite Plastics Corp.
PIP - Lighting equipment - Philips Lighting Co.
PIP-FLAM - Lighters - Park Lane Associates, Inc.
PIP II - Health care products - Vector Products Inc.
PIP-PINS - Hardware - Textron Aerospace Fasteners
PIP-SQUEEK, THE - Golfing equipment - Bobby Grace Golf Design, Inc.
PIPANOL - Pharmaceutical preparations ☆ - Winthrop Pharmaceuticals
PIPE BY LEE - Pipes—tobacco - Bradberry Briar Pipe Corp.
PIPE CLEANER ART - Hobby kits - Barry Products Co.
PIPE DRAGON - Snowblowers - Cathy A. Waugh
PIPE DREAM - Tools—hand-operated - Andrews Sales Co., Inc.
PIPE DREAMER - Toys - Tonka Corp.
PIPE DREAMS - Pet shops - Dunwishin Enterprises
PIPE DUSTER - Cleaning supplies - American Textile Products Co.
PIPE GUARD - Heat transfer fluid - Vibe Records Inc.
PIPE-GUARD - Pipes - Wrap-On Co. Inc.
PIPE HUGGERS - Pipes—tobacco - Frelen Corp.
PIPE JAMMER - Toys—automobiles - Mattel, Inc.
PIPE JOINT COMPOUND - Chemical preparations - Black Swan Manufacturing Co.
PIPE-KLEAN - Cleaning preparations - HERC, Inc.
PIPE LINE - Plumbing fixtures—metal ☆ - Stanley Hardware Div.
PIPE LINE, THE - Plumbing fixtures—metal ☆ - Stanley Hardware Div.
PIPE MAJOR - Tobacco—chewing or smoking - Brown & Williamson Tobacco Corp.
PIPE MASTER - Machinery - Teledyne Landis Machine
PIPE MATE - Machinery - Teledyne Landis Machine
PIPE MATE - Tobacco products - S.M. Frank & Co. Inc. (Kaywoodie-Yello-Bole-Medico)
PIPE N' CLIP - Pipes—tobacco - Gesty Trading & Manufacturing Corp.
PIPE 'N' HOT - Toys - Tonka Corp.
PIPE-N-HOT - Water heaters—household - Ritchie Industries, Inc.
PIPE ORGAN - Vases - Griffin Design
PIPE PEN - Metals - Richard A. Dortzbach
PIPE PLUGGERS - Pipes - Inflatable Technology Corp.
PIPE-SMOOTH - Concrete products ☆ - Tamms Industries Co.
PIPE TEMP - Thermometers - Condar Co.
PIPE, THE - Computer software - Motorola, Inc. (Land Mobile Products Sector)
PIPE WRENCH PLIER - Pliers - Wilde Tool Co. Inc.
PIPECLAD 2020 - Coatings - Lilly Industries, Inc.
PIPECONX - Adhesives and sealants - Uniseal, Inc.
PIPELASER - Tools - David White Inc.
PIPELINE - Apparel and accessories - Keepers International
PIPELINE - Bathing suits - Graphic Prints Inc.
PIPELINE - Bedding—linen - West Point-Pepperell Inc.
PIPELINE - Computer peripheral equipment - Ascend Communications, Inc.
PIPELINE - Doors—glass - Kohler Co.
PIPELINE - Ships—sailing vessels ☆ - Snark Boats
PIPELINE POWER - Sporting goods - Voit Corp.
PIPEMASTER - Metals - Hobart Brothers Co.
PIPEMASTER - Wrenches ☆ - Erie Tool Works
PIPEPLUS - Computer software - Algor, Inc.
PIPER - Clocks - General Time Corp. (Westclox/Seth Thomas Div.)
PIPER - Computer software - Fitting Solutions
PIPER - Health care products - Nelkin/Piper Health Products
PIPER ALEXANDER - Apparel and accessories - Chorus Line Corp.
PIPER COMANCHE - Toys—airplanes - Cox Products Inc.
PIPER FARMS - Pickles - Dean Foods Co.
PIPER GLEN - Floor coverings—carpet and rugs - Gulistan Carpet Inc.
PIPER HEIDSIECK - Wines - Remy Martin Amerique Inc.
PIPER PARROT - Dolls - Mattel, Inc.
PIPER SONOMA - Wines - Remy Martin Amerique Inc.
PIPER, THE - Apparel and accessories - Weathervane

☆ = Now out of production

PIPER THE PELICAN - Furniture–children's - Maze Inc.

PIPERAZOL - Pharmaceutical preparations ✩ - U.S. Ethicals Inc.

PIPERINE - Pharmaceutical preparations - City Chemical Corp.

PIPERLIN - Pharmaceutical preparations ✩ - American Hygienic Laboratories Inc.

PIPER'S CHOICE, THE - Tobacco–chewing or smoking - Sterling Tobacco Co.

PIPERS POND - Wallpaper ✩ - Carey Lind Designs

PIPER'S SUPREME - Crackers - Moran Foods, Inc.

PIPES PLATFORM - Computer programs - PeerLogic Inc.

PIPESCAN - X-ray apparatus - Eg&G Instruments

PIPESORT - Computer software - Syncsort, Inc.

PIPESPAN - Concrete–mixture - Pacific International Pipe Enterprises, Inc.

PIPESULATION - Pipes–aluminum ✩ - Gossen Corp.

PIPESULATOR - Hardware ✩ - Z-Flex U.S. Inc.

PIPET HELPER - Measuring instruments - Brinkmann Instruments, Inc.

PIPETITE-STIK - Adhesives and sealants - La-Co Industries, Inc.

PIPETTE - Lighters - Park Lane Associates, Inc.

PIPEWORKS - Computer software - Russell C. Martin

PIPEWORKS - Toys - Playskool, Inc.

PIPI - Industrial machinery - Penguin Industrial Products, Inc.

PIPIN' HOT - Breads–mixes - Pillsbury Co.

PIPIN HOT - Food warming equipment ✩ - Kenro Inc.

PIPING HOT - Plumbing fixtures–enameled - Kohler Co.

PIPING HOT - Wet suits–rubber - Deckers Outdoor Corp.

PIPING ROCK - Cordials - David Sherman Corp.

PIPING ROCK - Watches - SMH (US) Inc.

PIPIOLO - Footwear - De Osu Inc.

PIPO - Tobacco–chewing or smoking - G.A. Georgopulo & Co. Inc.

PIPOLAKI - Apparel and accessories - Skea Ltd.

PIPPIN - File folders ✩ - Hedges Manufacturing Co.

PIPPIN - Fruits and vegetables ✩ - Diamond Fruit Growers

PIPPIN - Juices ✩ - Knudsen Dairy Products

PIPPIN'S BEST - Shortening - Harrison Grocer Co., Inc.

PIPPIN'S HOLLOW - Artists' materials - National Artcraft Co.

PIPPITY - Leather - Wolverine World Wide, Inc.

PIPPSYWOGGINS - Figurines - Wee Folk Creations

PIPROTEC - Antifreeze solution - Irving Oil Corp.

PIPS - Apparel and accessories - Angel Ruedaflores

PIPS - Decals and transfers - Happiness Inc.

PIPS - Greeting cards ✩ - American Greetings Corp.

PIPSKWEEKS - Jewelry - Jordan Meryl, Inc.

PIPSQUEAK PIG - Toys–stuffed ✩ - Dakin Inc.

PIPTAL - Pharmaceutical preparations ✩ - Marion Merrell Dow

PIPZINE - Aquatic pharmaceutical preparations ✩ - Aquatronics-Filtronics

PIQUE - Musical instrument accessories ✩ - Scherl & Roth Inc.

PIQUE - Perfumes - Redken Laboratories, Inc.

PIR - Mirrors–optical - Photran Corp.

PIRA - Women's apparel - First Trading Corp.

PIRADICAL - Apparel and accessories - U.S. Care Co.

PIRAHNA II - Darts and dart games ✩ - Dart World Inc.

PIRANHA - Augers - Ardisam, Inc.

PIRANHA - Drain cleaner - Comstar International Inc. (IPC Div.)

PIRANHA - Electronic equipment - Air-Lec Industries Inc.

PIRANHA - Fire extinguishers - Ansul, Inc.

PIRANHA - Golfing equipment ✩ - Tiger Shark Golf Inc.

PIRANHA - Lighting equipment–automotive - Peterson Manufacturing Co.

PIRANHA - Liqueurs - Paddington Corp.

PIRANHA - Measuring instruments - MTI Corp.

PIRANHA - Motor vehicles - Barracuda Enterprises Inc.

PIRANHA - Paint removers - Fiberlock Technologies, Inc.

PIRANHA - Sporting goods - Columbia Industries, Inc.

PIRANHA - Tools–power-driven - Black & Decker Corp.

PIRANHA - Toys - Tonka Corp.

PIRANHA INTERACTIVE PUBLISHING - Computer software - Piranha Interactive Publishing, Inc.

PIRANHA PETE - Apparel and accessories - Design Tees Hawaii Inc.

PIRANHA PRO - Saw blades - Black & Decker Corp.

PIRANHA PROPELLERS - Propellers - Piranha Propellers, Inc.

PIRANNA - Boats–canoes - Fishin' Ski Barge

PIRASSUNUNGA 51 CACHACA - Beverages–alcohol - Sazerac Co. Inc.

PIRASTRO - Musical instrument accessories - International Violin Co. Ltd.

PIRATE - Boats ✩ - Lanness K. McKee & Co.

PIRATE - Fabrics - Gretchen Bellinger Inc.

PIRATE - Insecticides - American Cyanamid Co.

PIRATE - Salmon–smoked, salted, dried, or pickled - Wards Cove Packing Co.

PIRATE BLASTER - Toys–guns - Mattel, Inc.

PIRATE PETE - Video games - Taito America Corp.

PIRATE PETES - Cookies - Simmers Products

PIRATE PIZZA WITH CHEESE - Pizzas–frozen - Conagra, Inc.

PIRATE SURF - Apparel and accessories - Quiksilver, Inc.

PIRATEE THE GAME OF OUTRAGEOUS FORTUNE - Games - Mendocino Game Co., Inc.

PIRATEGOLF - Apparel and accessories - James P. Darling

PIRATES - Amusement parks - Sea World, Inc.

PIRATES - Candy ✩ - Leaf, Inc.

PIRATES - Computer software ✩ - Microprose Software, Inc.

PIRATE'S BOOTY - Snack foods - Robert's American Gourmet

PIRATES' BREW - Suntan lotions - Rafael Enrique Bosch

PIRATE'S FORT - Swing sets - Island Wood Products Inc.

PIRATE'S GOLD - Fruits and vegetables - Mount Konocti Growers Inc.

PIRATE'S GOLD - Games ✩ - Western Publishing Co., Inc.

PIRATE'S GOLD COINS - Chocolate candy - Sherwood Brands, Inc.

PIRATE'S KEG - Beverages–carbonated - Global Beverage Co.

PIRATE'S KEG - Beverages–carbonated - Jolt Co., Inc.

PIRATES OF DARK WATER, THE - Toy action figures - Hanna-Barbera Productions, Inc.

PIRATE'S PLEASURES - Seafood products–fresh or frozen - Sara Lee Corp.

PIRATETEX - Recording label - Piratetex Records

PIRELLI - Floor coverings–tile - Jason Industrial Inc.

PIRELLI - Mats - PRF USA Inc.

PIRELLI - Tires - Pirelli Armstrong Tire Corp.

PIRELLI TIRES - Motorcycle parts and accessories - Cosmopolitan Motors Inc.

PIRETTI - Chairs–wood - Krueger International, Inc.

PIREY - Cleaning preparations - Cleanlook Chemical

PIRF - Heating equipment - Engineering & Research Associates, Inc.

PIRF - Medical apparatus - Sebra

PIRI - Cables–fiber optic - Photonic Integration Research, Inc.

PIRI - Cables–fiber optic - Photonic Integration Research, Inc.

PIRITTA - Cigarettes - Gesty Trading & Manufacturing Corp.

PIRKATIN - Pharmaceutical preparations ✩ - Ulmer Pharmacal Co.

PIRL - Chemical preparations - Brewer Science, Inc.

PIRMI - Rice - Pacific International Rice Mills Inc.

PIROGUE - Boats - Glen-L Marine Designs

PIROLA - Harmonicas - Hohner Inc.

PIROLINE - Cookies - De Beukelaer Corp.

PIROMEN - Pharmaceutical preparations ✩ - Boots Pharmaceuticals Inc.

PIROS - Computer software - Computer Task Group, Inc.

PIROUETTE - Apparel–women's - Wacoal America Inc.

PIROUETTE - Clocks ✩ - General Time Corp. (Westclox/Seth Thomas Div.)

PIROUETTE - Construction equipment - Showerlux USA

PIROUETTE - Floor coverings - Tarkett, Inc.

PIROUETTE - Glass–leaded - Seneca Glass Co.

PIROUETTE - Glassware–household - Oneida Ltd.

PIROUETTE - Medical apparatus - Conceptus, Inc.

PIROUETTE - Stationery and envelope embosser - Consolidated Stamp Manufacturing Co. Inc.

PIROUETTE - Stools–wood - GRK Manufacturing

PIROUETTE - Window coverings ✩ - Kellwood Co.

PIROUETTE - Window shades - Sunshine Drapery Co., Inc.

PIROUETTES - Cookies - Pepperidge Farm Inc.

PIRRO - Pasta - Bel Canto Fancy Foods Ltd.

PIRTLES WEST VINEYARD - Wines - Weston Vineyards

PISA - Glassware–household ✩ - Culver Glass Inc.

PISANO - Bakery products - Pisano French Bread Baking Co. Inc.

PISCES - Computers–personal - Trans 2000 Inc.

PISCES - Floor coverings–carpet and rugs - PRF USA Inc.

PISCES - Navigational instruments - Brunswick Corp.

PISCES - Pet products - Aquatic Industries

PISCES - Recording label - Dial Records Inc.

PISCES - Teas–herbal - Calvin Thornton

PISCES - Wine - Unique Wines, Inc.

PISCES BOOKS - Publisher's imprint ✩ - Gulf Publishing Co. (Book & Div.)

PISCES SOFTWARE ANALYSIS TOOLKIT - Computer software ✩ - Reliable Software Technologies Corp.

PISCES SWIMWEAR - Apparel and accessories - Pisces Swimwear, LLC

PISHU'S - Apparel and accessories - Ramodi's

PISONI PADS - Musical instrument accessories - Ardsley Musical Instrument Co.

PISSEL THE PARAKEET - Bird cages - Opal Dunigan

PISTACHIO - Coats - M Hidary & Co., Inc.

PISTACHIO BLUES - Apparel and accessories - M Hidary & Co., Inc.

✩ = Now out of production

PISTACHIO ICE - Christmas tree ornaments - Cracker Box Inc.
PISTACHIO PETE - Nuts–salted, roasted, cooked, or canned - Zaloom Brothers Co. of New Jersey
PISTACHIO TREE RANCH - Nuts–salted, roasted, cooked, or canned - Pistachio Tree Ranch
PISTIL - Glassware–scientific - Durand International
PISTOL PAK - Guns - Daisy Manufacturing Co.
PISTOL PETE - Barbecue sauce - Young's Market Co.
PISTOL PETE - Cement - Rectorseal Corp.
PISTOL PETE - Fishing lures - Hi-Country Flies, Inc.
PISTOL POWER - Dryers–hair - Conair Corp.
PISTOLPAL - Cabinets–wood - Palmer Metal Products Inc.
PISTON HEAD - Toys - Tyco Toys
PISTON POWER - Paint sprayers - H.E.R.O. Industries Ltd.
PISTONPREP - Chemical preparations - Goldschmidt Industrial Chemical Corp.
PIT - Games ☆ - Parker Brothers
PIT BULL - Guns - Charter Arms
PIT BULLS - Knives–hunting - James F. Parker Trust
PIT BULLS - Toy boats, vehicles, and construction sets - Intex Recreation Corp.
PIT CREW - Paints - Seymour of Sycamore Inc.
PIT CREW ENGINEER - Toys - Natural Science Industries, Ltd.
PIT-FIGHTER - Video games - Atari Games Corp.
PIT-STOP - Land-vehicle bearing joints - Alloy Industries, Inc.
PIT STOP - Stain removers - Alva-Amco Pharmacal Co.
PIT STOP SPEEDWAY - Toys–automobiles ☆ - CBS Toys
PIT, THE - Computer software - SourceView Software International
PITA - Computer software - Law Office Information Systems, Inc.
PITA - Food products - Dimitria Delights Inc.
PITA CLASSICS - Health food products - Farm Foods
PITA MELTS - Food products ☆ - Health is Wealth
PITA PETITE POCKETTES - Breads - Coco's Gourmet Mediterranean Foods Inc.
PITA POCKETS - Breads - Garden of Eatin', Inc.
PITA PUFFS - Breads - Garden of Eatin', Inc.
PITA STUFFS - Sandwiches–prepackaged - Pitaria Products Co.
PITATILLA - Food products - GDF, Inc.
PITBULL - Fireworks - Neptune Wholesale, Inc.
PITBULL - Tires–automobile - Tire Mart, Inc.
PITBULL RECORDS - Recording label - Hans Buringer
PITCH - Recording label - Gusman Co.
PITCH-A-TENT - Recording label - Rough Trade Inc.
PITCH BACK - Sporting goods - Gold Medal Recreational Products
PITCH BLACK - Pencils ☆ - National Pen & Pencil Co.
PITCH IN! HELP KEEP AMERICA COOL. - Apparel and accessories - Revolutions, Ltd.
PITCH-IN ORIGINALS - Apparel and accessories - UAV Corp.
PITCH IN PAILS - Containers - Orlis E. Smith
PITCH-N-GAUGE - Tools - Granberg International
PITCH PERFECT - Containers–insulated - Aladdin Industries, Inc.
PITCH-PRO - Musical instrument accessories ☆ - Five Star Entertainment
PITCHER - Pumps–water ☆ - R & R Mill Co. Inc.
PITCHER PERFECT - Iced tea–bottled or canned - Best Flavors, Inc.
PITCHER POT - Cooking utensils–earthenware ☆ - General Housewares Corp.
PITCHERS 'N BOWLS - Pottery ☆ - Rubens Originals
PITCHERSTIR - Bar fixtures–plastic - Spir-it Inc.
PITCHFORK - Cosmetics - Capitol Novelty Co.
PITCH'R PAK - Syrup - Borden, Inc.
PITCHRIDER - Audio equipment ☆ - Dod Electronics
PITCO FRIALATOR - Cooking equipment–commercial - Pitco Frialator, Inc.
PITCOMATIC - Cooking equipment–commercial - Pitco Frialator, Inc.
PITFALL - Computer software - Activision, Inc.
PITFALL:THE MAYAN ADVENTURE - Games - Activision, Inc.
PITM - Computer software - Proteon, Inc.
PITNEY BOWES - Office machines - Pitney Bowes Inc.
PITOCIN - Pharmaceutical preparations - Parke-Davis
PITRESSIN - Pharmaceutical preparations - Parke-Davis
PITSTOP - Computer software - Epyx Inc.
PITSTOP II - Computer software - Epyx Inc.
PITT - Artists' materials - Faber-Castell Corp.
PITT BASKETBALL - Apparel and accessories - University of Pittsburgh of the Commonwealth System of Higher Education
PITT BULL - Scissors–hand-operated - Aaronco Pet Products, Inc.
PITT-CHAR XP - Paints - PPG Architectural Finishes, Inc.
PITT-GLAZE - Finishing agents - PPG Industries, Inc.

PITTABS - Water treating compounds - PPG Industries, Inc.
PITTBULL - Amplifiers–musical instrument - VHT Amplification
PITTCHLOR - Disinfectants - PPG Industries, Inc.
PITTCOMATIC - Glass–flat ☆ - PPG Industries, Inc.
PITTCOTE - Glass products - Pittsburgh Corning Corp.
PITTER PATTER - Cookies - Keebler Co.
PITTER PATTER - Footwear - Ska-Doo Sport Co. Inc.
PITTER PATTERNS - Patterns–clothing - Judy Murphy
PITTER PETS - Booties and children's slippers - Baby Gryphon
PITTER'S PANTRY - Fruits–dried - Primo Nut Co. Inc.
PITTHANE - Paints - PPG Industries, Inc.
PITTI - Dishes–china - Pasmantier Co. Inc.
PITTPON - Epoxy coatings ☆ - PPG Industries, Inc.
PITTRAK - Computer software - Precision Resource Co., LLC
PITTSBURG - Golfing equipment - Taylor Made Golf Co. Inc.
PITTSBURGH - Paints - PPG Industries, Inc.
PITTSBURGH ALLEGHENIES - Oxygen systems–aircraft - Pittsburgh Sports Heritage, Inc.
PITTSBURGH CONDORS - Apparel and accessories - NBA Properties, Inc.
PITTSBURGH STINGERS - Apparel and accessories - Pittsburgh Hockey Associates
PITTSEAL - Glass products - Pittsburgh Corning Corp.
PITTSFIELD - Clocks ☆ - General Time Corp. (Westclox/Seth Thomas Div.)
PITY PAT - Skin care products - Nails Naturally, Inc.
PITTY PATS - Apparel and accessories ☆ - Treasure Masters
PITTYPAT KITTY - Toys–stuffed - Dakin Inc.
PITU SPIRITS - Brandy - EFCO Importers
PITUAGEN - Vitamins and nutritional supplements - Great Life Laboratories Inc.
PITUITRIN - Pharmaceutical preparations ☆ - Parke-Davis
PITUITROPHIN PMG - Vitamins and nutritional supplements - Standard Process Inc.
PIUMA - Toys ☆ - Peg Perego USA Inc.
PIUS - Giftware - McConnell & Carpenter Inc.
PIVOINE - Vases - Durand International
PIVOT - Apparel and accessories - Pivot Corp.
PIVOT - Computer display monitors - Radius Inc.
PIVOT - Computer software - At&T Corp.
PIVOT - Golfing equipment - UT Golf
PIVOT - Monitors–electronic - Pivot International, Inc.
PIVOT GOLF - Games ☆ - Milton Bradley Co.
PIVOT HEALTH BOOKS - Publisher's imprints ☆ - Keats Publishing Co.
PIVOT PLUS - Shaving preparations - Gillette Co.
PIVOT POINT - Hair care products - Pivot Point International Inc.
PIVOT PRO - Bats–baseball - Markwort Sporting Goods Co.
PIVOT RULES - Apparel–athletic - Pivot Corp.
PIVOT TALK - Irrigation equipment - Lindsay Manufacturing Co.
PIVOTAL - Chairs–metal - Pivotal Suspension Seating, Inc.
PIVOTAL - Dishes–china - Mikasa Co.
PIVOTTABLE - Computer storage devices - Microsoft Corp.
PIW - Wire - General Cable Corp.
PIX - Beverages–carbonated - Publix Super Markets, Inc.
PIX' I CON' - Games - John S. Pollock
PIX-POCKETTES - Pharmaceutical preparations ☆ - JM Co.
PIX-VIEW - Electronic equipment - Advance Products Co. Inc.
PIXALL - Housewares - O.E. Clark Paper Box Co.
PIXEE - Fishing lures - Blue Fox Tackle Co.
PIXEL - Floor coverings–carpet and rugs - BASF Corp.
PIXEL - Luggage - Atchison Products, Inc.
PIXEL - Magnetic tape–blank - Pixel, Inc.
PIXEL PUTTY SOLO - Computer software - Valis Group
PIXELBURST - Circuit boards–radio - Adobe Systems Inc.
PIXELLOOM - Computer software - Three D Graphics
PIXERA - Cameras - Atlantic International Products & Services Co.
PIXI - Infant product - TL Care Inc.
PIXIANA - Tomato pastes and sauces - Swayzee Packing Co. Inc.
PIXIE - Apparel stores–lingerie - Goddess Bra
PIXIE - Chimes - J.W. Stannard Co.
PIXIE - Cosmetics - Maywood Industries Inc.
PIXIE - Flowers, plants, and seeds - Jacklin Seed
PIXIE - Food products - Curtice-Burns Foods, Inc.
PIXIE - Furniture ☆ - Evenflo Juvenile Furniture Co.
PIXIE - Giftware ☆ - Clinton Packaging Co.
PIXIE - Hobby kits - Mag-Nif Inc.
PIXIE - Ice milk - Maola Milk and Ice Cream Co.
PIXIE - Office supplies ☆ - Bates Manufacturing Co.
PIXIE - Paper–tissue - Romar International Corp.

☆ = Now out of production

PIXIE - Pet products - Universal Packers Corp.
PIXIE - Publisher's imprints ☆ - T.S. Denison and Co.
PIXIE - Seeds and bulbs - Cebeco Lilies, Inc.
PIXIE - Toys - Steven Manufacturing Co.
PIXIE - Toys–stuffed ☆ - Gund, Inc.
PIXIE BUILD-A-TOY - Toys - Steven Manufacturing Co.
PIXIE CRINKLES - Potato sticks - Ore-Ida Foods, Inc.
PIXIE DELIGHT - Flowers, plants, and seeds - J. Benjamin Williams
PIXIE DUST - Novelty items - Walt Disney Co.
PIXIE JUNIOR - Agricultural products - John Henry Co.
PIXIE PAK - Sauerkraut ☆ - Flanagan Bros. Inc.
PIXIE PENGUIN - Dolls - Mattel, Inc.
PIXIES - Florists - Denver Wholesale Florists
PIXIES - Labels–paper - John Henry Co.
PIXIETAILS - Dolls - Mattel, Inc.
PIXILITE - Lighting equipment - Bridgeport Metal Goods Manufacturing Co.
PIXIS - Computer software - Nemicron
PIXMOBILE - Photographic equipment - Advance Products Co. Inc.
PIXPAK - Generators - Sencore, Inc.
PIXSETTER - Computer software - Xerographics Laser Images Corp.
PIXTEX/EFS - Computer software and accessories - Excalibur Technologies Corp.
PIXTOOLS - Construction equipment rental services - Pixel Translations, Inc.
PIXTURA - Computer hardware - Logitech, Inc.
PIXY - Binders - Office Products Inc.
PIXY STIX - Candy - Sunline Brands
PIZ BUIN - Skin care products - Sports Access/America
PIZ BUIN - Skin care products ☆ - Hartmann Luggage Co.
PIZACCIA - Bakery products - DCB, Inc.
PIZANO - Apparel and accessories - Pizano
PIZARRO - Food products ☆ - Seaspan Products Corp.
PIZAZZ - Adhesives and sealants - Loctite Corp.
PIZAZZ - Apparel and accessories - I.C. Isaacs & Co.
PIZAZZ - Backpacks - Proteus Design Group, Inc.
PIZAZZ - Cheese - CFI of Wisconsin, Inc.
PIZAZZ - Floor coverings–carpet and rugs - Mohawk Industries Inc.
PIZAZZ - Floor coverings–carpet and rugs ☆ - J and J Industries Inc.
PIZAZZ - Greeting cards - Russ Berrie and Co., Inc.
PIZAZZ - Jewelry - Service Merchandise Co. Inc.
PIZAZZ - Paper cups and plates - Nyman Manufacturing Co.
PIZAZZ - Teas–herbal ☆ - Oakmont Investments Co.
PIZAZZ - Vitamins and nutritional supplements - Natural Organics, Inc.
PIZAZZ - Wigs ☆ - Paula Young
PIZSOY - See THE ORIGINAL PIZSOY
PIZZ-A-FUNS - Pizzas–frozen - Armato's Pizza Co.
PIZZA - Chewing gum - Philadelphia Chewing Gum Corp.
PIZZA - Floor coverings–carpet and rugs - Quaker Inc.
PIZZA ALA CART - Frozen foods - World Pizza, Inc.
PIZZA & PASTA MAGIC - Seasonings - Magic Seasoning Blends
PIZZA ASS - Shirts - TSB, LLC
PIZZA BELLA - Ovens–industrial - Keystone Manufacturing Co., Inc.
PIZZA BITES - Crackers - Barbara's Bakery, Inc.
PIZZA BONES - Food products - Eco Air Co.
PIZZA BONES - Paper - Chris Cassatt
PIZZA BUDDIES - Snack foods - Leroy A. Hughes
PIZZA BUDDY - Plastics - David A. Funk
PIZZA BY THE FOOT - Food products - Little Caesar Enterprises, Inc.
PIZZA CAPRI - Pizzas–frozen - Country's Best Pizza Inc.
PIZZA CHEEZBITS - Cheese - Fromageries Bel, Inc.
PIZZA CHEF - Pizzas - Nouveau International Inc.
PIZZ'A CHICAGO - Pizza - Glory Days Productions, Inc.
PIZZA COLORE - Pizzas–mixes - Teresa's II, Inc.
PIZZA CRUNCHABUNGAS - Corn chips - Ralston Purina Co.
PIZZA CUTTER - Novelty items - Sell-O Manufacturing Inc.
PIZZA DEL PADRONE - Pizzas–frozen - Boccone's Inc.
PIZZA DI GENOA - Food products - Golden Whisk Pasta Partners
PIZZA DI NAPOLI - Food products - Golden Whisk Pasta Partners
PIZZA DI ROMANA - Food products - Golden Whisk Pasta Partners
PIZZA DI TAVOLA - Food products - George DeLallo Co., Inc.
PIZZA DI TOSCANA - Food products - Golden Whisk Pasta Partners
PIZZA DISC - Recording label - Peter Pan Industries
PIZZA DOGS - Frankfurters - Field Packing Co.
PIZZA D'PRIMO - Food products - Tony's Pizza Service
PIZZA FINGERS - Snack foods - Matlaw's Food Products Inc.
PIZZA FIT 'N FREE - Pizza - Pizza Free, Inc.
PIZZA FORCE - Computer software - Morris Advertising Agency, Inc.

PIZZA FRACTIONS - Computer software - Queue Inc.
PIZZA FREE - Pizzas–frozen - Pizza Free, Inc.
PIZZA GARDEN - Flowers, plants, and seeds ☆ - Applewood Seed & Garden Group
PIZZA HUT - Restaurants–pizzerias - Pizza Hut Inc.
PIZZA INN - Restaurants–pizzerias - Pizza Inn, Inc.
PIZZA MAKER, THE - Pizzas–frozen - Pizza Maker Inc.
PIZZA MAN - Breads - Piemonte Foods Inc.
PIZZA-MATE - Cheese - Borden, Inc.
PIZZA MIA - Pizza - Continental Food Products Inc.
PIZZA MY WAY - Pizzas–mixes - Moran Foods, Inc.
PIZZA PAL - Cheese - Universal Foods Corp.
PIZZA PAL - Kitchen appliances - Regal Ware, Inc.
PIZZA PALACE - Toys - Cap Toys, Inc.
PIZZA PALLET - Cardboard cutouts - Interchange Products, Inc.
PIZZA PANDEMONIUM - Cooking utensils–aluminum - Anchor Hocking Glass, Inc.
PIZZA PAPA JOHN'S - Restaurants–pizzerias - Papa John's International, Inc.
PIZZA PARLOR - Cooking equipment–household ☆ - Rival Manufacturing Co.
PIZZA PARLOR - Food products - Kontos Foods
PIZZA PARLOR - Sandwiches–prepackaged - Hudson Foods, Inc.
PIZZA PARLOR - Sandwiches–prepackaged - Pierre Frozen Foods Inc.
PIZZA PARTY - Toys - Tonka Corp.
PIZZA PARTY TIME - Pizzas–mixes - Domino's Pizza Inc.
PIZZA PASTA, PLEASE - Food products ☆ - My Own Meals Inc.
PIZZA PERFECT - Pizzas–mixes - Pocino Foods Co.
PIZZA PIE - Games ☆ - Milton Bradley Co.
PIZZA PIG - Meat products–pork ☆ - Pierce Foods Corp.
PIZZA-PIX - Snack foods ☆ - Sunshine Biscuits, Inc.
PIZZA PLATTER - Hotplates - Kaz Business Systems Inc.
PIZZA POCKET - Food products ☆ - Amy's Kitchen, Inc.
PIZZA POCKETS - Food products ☆ - Lamb-Weston, Inc.
PIZZA 'POTOMUS - Potato chips ☆ - Nalley's Fine Foods
PIZZA PRETZEL STIX - Snack foods - Bachman Co.
PIZZA PUZZLE - Puzzles - Franklin Merchandising Co.
PIZZA QUICK - Tomato pastes and sauces - Van Den Bergh Foods Co.
PIZZA READY - Meat products - Burke Marketing Corp.
PIZZA READY, TORTILLA TESTED - Pizzas–frozen - Burke Marketing Corp.
PIZZA SALADS - Salads–prepackaged - Everybody's, Inc.
PIZZA SALUBRE - Food products machinery - Salubre Foods International, Inc.
PIZZA SAVER - Trays - Amoco Fabrics and Fibers Co.
PIZZA SHOPPE - Pizzas–frozen - Chicago Brothers, Inc.
PIZZA SOLO - Pizzas–frozen - Crestar Food Products, Inc.
PIZZA SPINS - Snack foods ☆ - General Mills, Inc.
PIZZA SPLASH - Sauces - Brewster's Smokehouse, Inc.
PIZZA SQUEEZE - Pizzas–mixes - Nestle USA
PIZZA STACK'R - Racks - Weidert Group, Inc.
PIZZA STATION - Restaurants–pizzerias - Little Caesar Enterprises, Inc.
PIZZA STATION EXPRESS - Restaurants–pizzerias - Little Caesar Enterprises, Inc.
PIZZA STRAWZ - Pizzas–frozen - Minnesota Foodservice, Inc.
PIZZA-TAINER - Containers–paper - Arvco Container Corp.
PIZZA-TO-BLO - Chewing gum ☆ - Fleer Corp.
PIZZA TOPPER - Meat products–beef - Foodbrands America, Inc.
PIZZA WARS - Games - Gamescience
PIZZA WHEELS - Snack foods - Wise Foods
PIZZA WORKS TAKE AND BAKE - Pizzas–frozen - Foodmaker, Inc.
PIZZABAKE - Food products - General Mills, Inc.
PIZZACAKE - Cakes - CGI Desserts Inc.
PIZZADILLA - Tortillas - Dean B. Baldwin
PIZZAGETTI N BEEF - Spaghetti and beef in pizza sauce ☆ - American Home Food Products Inc.
PIZZANET - Computer software - Assal Corp.
PIZZANO - Meat products–beef - Foodbrands America, Inc.
PIZZA!PIZZA! - Food products - Little Caesar Enterprises, Inc.
PIZZARIA DIPPER - Food products - Vienna Beef Ltd.
PIZZARIAS - Potato chips ☆ - Keebler Co.
PIZZARONI - Food products - Burke Marketing Corp.
PIZZAS OF EIGHT - Food processors - Pizzas of Eight, Inc.
PIZZATODO - Salad dressings–bottled - Essen Nutrition Corp.
PIZZAWURST - Sausages - Hillshire Farm Co.
PIZZAWURST - Sausages - Saramar Corp.
PIZZAZ - Floor coverings–carpet and rugs ☆ - Olympic Carpets Inc.
PIZZAZ - Lipsticks - Elysee Scientific Cosmetic Co.

☆ = Now out of production

PIZZAZZ! - Fabrics - International Paper Co.
PIZZAZZ - Inks ☆ - Hunt Manufacturing Co.
PIZZAZZ - Tiles–ceramic - Monarch Tile Inc.
PIZZAZZ - Wallpaper ☆ - Wallpaper Imports Inc.
PIZZAZZ - Wigs ☆ - Jean Paree Weegs Inc.
PIZZAZZ ACCENTS - Tiles–ceramic - Monarch Tile Inc.
PIZZAZZ DOG! - Pizzas–mixes - Rolly's Convenient Foods, Inc.
PIZZAZZ PANDA - Toys–stuffed - Dakin Inc.
PIZZAZZ UNICORN - Toys–stuffed ☆ - Dakin Inc.
PIZZELLE - Blinds–vertical - Tontine/VyTech Industries Inc.
PIZZELLE - Cookies - Celia's Sweets
PIZZERIA KITS - Pizzas–mixes - Nestle USA
PIZZERIA UNO - Pizzas–frozen - Uno Foods Inc.
PIZZERIA UNO - Restaurant franchise - Pizzeria Uno Corp.
PIZZERIA WHEEL - Pans ☆ - General Housewares Corp.
PIZZILLA - Prepared pizza - A.M. Gilardi and Sons, Inc.
P.J. - Dolls - Mattel, Inc.
PJ - Jewelry - Prime Jewelry Inc.
PJ - Ships–sailing vessels - Palmer Johnson Inc.
P.J. & MOORE - Apparel–women's - Kellwood Co.
P.J. LA DOIR - Recording label - La Doir Records, Inc.
PJ PENGUIN - Bedding–linen - Dan River Inc.
P.J. TROOPER BY DR. DENTON - Apparel–men's - Obion Denton
P.J. WALSH U.S.A. - Neckties - Gianfranco Ruffini
PJ1 - Motor vehicle parts and accessories - PJH Brands
PJC - Wood products - Penrod Co.,
PJCO - Jewelry - Parker Jewelry Co. Inc.
PJD - Jewelry - Asba & Dangler Designs, Inc.
PJH - Chemical preparations - PJH Brands
PJM - Jewelry - Phoenix Jewelry Manufacturing, Inc.
PJ'S COFFEE & TEA CO. - Coffee - P.J.'s USA, Inc.
P'JS WAVE - Hair care products - Waverly Beauty Products
P.K. - Chewing gum - Wm. Wrigley Jr. Co.
PK - Computer programs - Parkkware, Inc.
PK - Jewelry - Ptak Brothers Inc.
PK - Toys - Those Characters from Cleveland, Inc.
PK CLOTHING - Apparel and accessories - Premier Knits, Inc.
PK ELLIOT - Apparel–women's - Kohl's Department Stores, Inc.
PK LEMON DROP - Cleaning equipment - Woodbine Chemical Co., Inc.
P.K. PLUS - Pet products - Glo-Marr Products Inc.
PKC - Electronic equipment - Moor Electronics Inc.
PKC PLUS - Electronic equipment - Moor Electronics Inc.
PKG PLUS - Paper - Allpak Container, Inc.
PKLITE - Computer software - PKWARE Inc.
PKP - Artillery - Powell Knife Pistol, Inc.
P.K.P. - Pharmaceutical preparations - Wesley Pharmacal Co. Inc.
PKV - Wines - Strategic Capital, Inc.
PKW - Paints ☆ - Devoe & Raynolds Co.
PKWARE DATA COMPRESSION LIBRARY - Computer software - PKWARE Inc.
PKZIP V2.04G - Computer software - PKWARE Inc.
PKZMENU - Computer software ☆ - PKWARE Inc.
PL - Caulks, sealants, and adhesives - ChemRex Inc.
PL - Floor coverings–tile ☆ - Monarch Tile Inc.
PL-3 - Motor vehicles–motor homes - Vibe Records Inc.
PL 2000 - Tool belts - W.G.H., Inc.
PL EQ-40 - Electronic equipment - Peavey Electronics Corp.
PL-M - Jewel mountings–precious metal - Arly Diamond Co.
PL PRO - Communications equipment - Clear-Com Intercom Systems
PL PURE LINE - Flowers, plants, and seeds - Griffith Seed Co.
PL SUBSONIC - Electronic equipment - Peavey Electronics Corp.
P.L.A. - Jewelry - Park Lane Associates, Inc.
PLA - Paints - Testor Corp.
PLA-JAC - Shirts - Dunbrooke Sportswear Co.
PLA-KRIB - Infant product ☆ - Barden & Robeson Corp.
PLA-MOR - Playing cards - United States Playing Card Co.
PLA-O-MAPS - Games ☆ - Geo. F. Cram Co.
PLA-SHIRT - Apparel–athletic ☆ - Dunbrooke Sportswear Co.
PLA-WOOD - Toys - North Pacific Products Inc.
PLABON - Fabrics - Veratec
PLACE & PLUG CORDS - Extension cords - S.P. Wilson, Inc.
PLACE DE VOSGES - Wallpaper - Bassett & Vollum Wallpapers
PLACE FOR YOU, A - Prophylactics - Healthwise Foundation, Inc.
PLACE MAP, THE - Maps - Archar International Inc.
PLACE-MATES - Place mats - Convergence Corp.
PLACE SETTERS, THE - Silverware ☆ - Imperial Schrade Corp.

PLACE VENDOME - Floor coverings–carpet and rugs - Atlas Carpet Mills Inc.
PLACE VENDOME - Pens - Parker Pen USA
PLACEBO'S - Candy - Bissinger's Inc.
PLACEFINDER - Computer software - Rand McNally & Co.
PLACEKICK PRO - Sporting goods - Carretta Sport, Inc.
PLACEMENT - Chemical preparations - Wilfarm, LLC
PLACENTA 7 - Hair care products - Organifly Laboratories
PLACENTA MAGIC - Palm Beach Beauty Products
PLACENTA PLUS - Hair care products - Palm Beach Beauty Products
PLACENTA Q - Hair care products - Palm Beach Beauty Products
PLACENTAGEN - Skin care products - Kristine M. Schoenauer
PLACENTAL COTYLEDON - Skin care products - Xerion Import Export, Inc.
PLACENTENE - Skin care products - Para Laboratories Inc.
PLACENTONIC - Skin care products - Nailtex Inc.
PLACEPRO - Machine tools - Amistar Corp.
PLACES - Computer software - Taligent, Inc.
PLACES - Furniture - Haworth, Inc.
PLACESETTER - Plates–paper - Mobil Chemical Co. Plastics Div.
PLACETTE - Paper–toweling ☆ - Erving Paper Mills
PLACID - Blinds–venetian ☆ - Kenney Manufacturing Co.
PLACID - Paper - Encore Paper Co., Inc.
PLACIDUS - Bathroom fixtures - Crane Plumbing/Fiat Products
PLACIDYL - Pharmaceutical preparations - Abbott Laboratories
PLACKERS - Floss toothpick - L.T. Laboratories
PLACOM - Artists' materials - Alvin and Co. Inc.
PLACON - Machinery - Placon Corp.
PLACONITE - Epoxy coatings - Torginol, Inc.
PLAEBALL - Sporting goods - Fabrication Enterprises
PLAFORM - Cartons–paperboard - International Paper Co.
PLAGUE FIGHTER - Computer software ☆ - Krell Software Corp.
PLAGUES BAG - Paper–newsprint - Simon N. Jaffe
PLAID - Containers–insulated ☆ - Aladdin Industries, Inc.
PLAID - Glue–household or industrial - Plaid Enterprises, Inc.
PLAID TIDINGS - Paper–gift wrap - CPS Corp.
PLAIDBERRY - Industrial chemicals - Plaidberry Co.
PLAIN AND FANCY - Craft supplies ☆ - VIP/VIP Crafts
PLAIN & FANCY - Paints ☆ - Allentown Paint Manufacturing Co. Inc.
PLAIN AND SIMPLE - Underwear and nightwear - Maidenform Inc.
PLAIN ANTIQUE - Flatware ☆ - Kirk Stieff Co.
PLAIN BROWN PAPER WRAPPER - Greeting cards ☆ - Amberley Greeting Card Co.
PLAIN COUNTRY COLLECTION - Cabinets–wood ☆ - Manchester Wood Inc.
PLAIN JANE - Decorations - Plain Jane, Inc.
PLAIN JANES - Publisher's imprints - Strawberry Hill Press
PLAIN LANUGUAGE LAW DICTIONARY, THE - Computer software - Parsons Technology, Inc.
PLAIN POCKETS - Jeans–men's - J.C. Penney Co., Inc.
PLAIN ROLLER - Tires - Bridgestone/Firestone, Inc.
PLAIN SANE - Caps–baseball - Plain Sane, Inc.
PLAIN-TO-SEE - Craft supplies ☆ - Quiltworks
PLAIN VANILLA - Shampoos ☆ - Gena Laboratories Inc.
PLAIN-VU - Plastics–laminated ☆ - Newell Office Products
PLAIN WRAP - Recording label - Top's Records
PLAINE AUX CERFS - Floor coverings - Parquet de France Inc.
PLAINISPHARE - Recording label - Jazz Composer's Orchestra Association Inc.
PLAINJANES - Frames–picture - Cider Mill Art & Frame
PLAINLID-PROTEX - Boxes - Columbia Specialty Co. Inc.
PLAINS - Milk - Plains Dairy Products
PLAINS COLLECTION, THE - Computer software - RT Computer Graphics, Inc.
PLAINS III - Fabrics–tapestry ☆ - Clarence House Imports Ltd.
PLAINS PALS - Toys–stuffed - Russ Berrie and Co., Inc.
PLAINSMAN - Doors–garage - General Aluminum Corp.
PLAINSMAN - Doors–garage - General American Door Co.
PLAINSMAN - Firearms, accessories, and parts - Welsh Sporting Goods Corp. (Boyt Div.)
PLAINSMAN - Gloves–work - Ultra Marketing, Inc.
PLAINSMAN - Guns ☆ - Marksman Products Inc.
PLAINSMAN - Hardware ☆ - Masonite Corp.
PLAINSMAN - Knives - Marble Arms Corp.
PLAINSMAN - Shingles–asphalt or tar - Atlas Roofing Corp.
PLAINSMAN, THE - Toys–guns - Parris Manufacturing Co.
PLAINVIEW - Furniture - Taylor-Ramsey Corp.
PLAINVIEW - Milk - Plainview Milk Product Cooperative
PLAINVILLE FARMS - Meat products–poultry - Plainville Turkey Farm, Inc.

☆ = Now out of production

PLAINVU - Plastics—laminated - Alvin and Co. Inc.
PLAINWELL - Ice cream - Plainwell Ice Cream Co.
PLAISANT - Floor coverings—carpet and rugs - J.L. Benson Co.
PLAISIR - Perfumes - Revlon Consumer Products Corp.
PLAISIR DE FRANCE - Cheese - McKesson Home Health Care
PLAIZIER - Postcards - Fotofolio Inc.
PLAK ATTACK - Health care products - Salon Classics Research Laboratories, Inc.
PLAK FREE - Dental preparation - Cambridge Research Laboratories, Inc.
PLAK MASTER - Toothpaste - Plak-Master, Inc.
PLAK-MASTER - Toothpaste - Plak-Master, Inc.
PLAK MASTERS INC. - Trophies—metal - Plaque Masters Inc.
PLAK PRO - Dental equipment - Windmere Corp.
PLAK-RAK, THE - Novelty items - West Coast Wood Specialties
PLAK TRAC - Dental equipment - Windmere Corp.
PLAK-VAC - Medical apparatus - Trademark Corp.
PLAKA - Artists' materials ☆ - Koh-I-Noor, Inc.
PLAKFINDER - Mirrors - John O.Butler Co.
PLAKIE - Infant product - Plakie Inc.
PLAMATE - Vans—conversion ☆ - Seven O Seven Industries Inc.
P.LAN - Personal-computer accessory - IQ Technologies Inc.
PLAN - Toys - Small World Toys
PLAN 9 - Recording label - Caroline Records, Inc.
PLAN-A-BOARD - Paper ☆ - Newell Office Products
PLAN-A-HOME KIT - Drafting supplies - Home Planners Inc.
PLAN-A-MEAL - Housewares ☆ - Philips Electronics North America Corp.
PLAN-A-MONTH - Calendars ☆ - Keith Clark Inc.
PLAN-A-SHOW - Audio equipment - T.M. Visual Industries Inc.
PLAN A SYSTEMS - Furniture - BPI Inc.
PLAN-AWAY - Office accessories - Paradigm Plus, Inc.
PLAN FOR SUCCESS, A - Calendars - Diaco Sales, Inc.
PLAN HOLD - Binders - Plan Hold Corp.
PLAN-IT SAFE - Bags—paper - Ronald S. Mercer
PLAN MASTER PLUS - Drafting supplies - Plan Hold Corp.
PLAN-ON-IT - Office accessories - Paradigm Plus, Inc.
PLAN-V-LOPE - File folders - Angler's Roslyn Group Ltd.
PLAN WRITE - Computer peripheral equipment - Business Resource Software, Inc.
PLANADA - Fruits—canned - Oasis Foods Inc.
PLANAGLO - Lighting fixtures - Alcan Aluminum Corp. Alcan Building Products Div.
PLANALITE - Lighting fixtures - Alcan Aluminum Corp. Alcan Building Products Div.
PLANAR - Construction equipment - Alcan Aluminum Corp. Alcan Building Products Div.
PLANAR CROWN - Electrical equipment - Lucas Aerospace Communications & Electronics Inc.
PLANAR MACRO - Construction equipment - Alcan Aluminum Corp. Alcan Building Products Div.
PLANAR PLUS - Construction equipment - Alcan Aluminum Corp. Alcan Building Products Div.
PLANAT - Beverages—alcohol ☆ - Marie Brizard Wines & Spirits, USA
PLANCHER OF PARIS - Diaries - Overseas Marketing Systems
PLANDECOR - Flowers—artificial ☆ - North Hollywood Manufacturing Co.
PLANE FROM THE HEART - Greeting cards - Monica Durant
PLANE/GRIP - Wrenches - David Baker, Inc.
PLANE-TALK - Electronic equipment - Stone Technologies Corp.
PLANER BOARD TOW - Fishing lines - Cortland Line Co., Inc.
PLANER PALS - Tools—hand-operated - Woodstock International, Inc.
PLANE'S CAYUGA VINEYARD - Wines - Cayuga Ridge Estate
PLANESCAPE - Games - Tsr, Inc.
PLANESTICK - Hardware - Mohawk Finishing Products Inc.
PLANET - Brushes - Wright-Bernet
PLANET - Cleaning preparations—household - Planet Inc.
PLANET - Computer software - Mobile Systems International, Inc.
PLANET - Hardware - Shepherd Products U.S. Inc.
PLANET - Publisher's imprints - Once Upon a Planet Inc.
PLANET - Rope - Wellington Leisure Products, Inc.
PLANET - Thread - Threads USA Div.
PLANET 3 - Sporting goods ☆ - Earth & Ocean Sports, Inc.
PLANET AAHS RECORDS - Recording label ☆ - Harmoney Holdings Inc.
PLANET & CO. - T-shirts—women's - Hampshire Group, Ltd.
PLANET BAGEL - Bagels - La Parisienne Bakery
PLANET BALL - Pet products - Boomer Ball
PLANET BURGER - Food products - Good Earth Corp.
PLANET CAPS - Hats - Northern Cap Manufacturing Co.

PLANET DALLAS - Recording label - Planet Dallas, Inc.
PLANET DEXTER - Publisher's imprints - Addison-Wesley Publishing Co.
PLANET DIVA - T-shirts—women's - Planet Diva
PLANET EARTH - Bicycles ☆ - Huffy Corp.
PLANET EARTH - Cleaning preparations - John Paul Jones Dejoria
PLANET EARTH - Skateboards - K2 Inc.
PLANET FABRICS - Fabrics - Signature Fabrics, Inc.
PLANET FRIENDS - Clothing - Barbara Fowkes
PLANET GEAR - Apparel and accessories - Planet Gear, Inc.
PLANET GOLF - Apparel and accessories - Planet Golf, Inc.
PLANET GOODSTUFF - Vending machines - Planet Goodstuff, Inc.
PLANET H - Apparel and accessories - Planet Hollywood, Inc.
PLANET HALLOWEEN - Candles - Atico International, Inc.
PLANET HOLLYWOOD - Sunglasses - Planet Hollywood, Inc.
PLANET HOOPS - Apparel and accessories - Sst Marketing, Inc.
PLANET ME - Audio tapes—blank - World Disc Productions, Inc.
PLANET MINERS - Games ☆ - Avalon Hill Game Co.
PLANET MOTHERHOOD EMBRACE THE FUTURE - Skin care products - Zoomers, Inc.
PLANET NATURAL - Catalogs - Bozeman Bio-Tech, Inc.
PLANET NEW YEAR - Dance studios - Creative Artists Network, Inc.
PLANET ONE - Candy - Usher Products International, Inc.
PLANET PAK - Recyclable labels - Epsen Hillmer Graphics Co.
PLANET PLEASER - Correction fluid - Correct Solutions, Inc.
PLANET ROCK - Frames—eyeglass - United States Shoe Corp.
PLANET SACK, THE - Bags—canvas - The Planet Sack
PLANET SAVE IT - Footwear—women's - JBI, Inc.
PLANET SMASHERS - Video games - Atari Games Corp.
PLANET SNOW - Apparel and accessories - Authentic Fitness Corp.
PLANET SURVIVAL - Apparel - Scope Imports, Inc.
PLANET TAN - Apparel and accessories - Planet Tan, Inc.
PLANET TRACKS - Magnet planet locating device - Sharon Campbell Pickens
PLANET WAVES - Musical instrument accessories - Howard Silagy
PLANET WEAR (FOR A BETTER WORLD) - Shirts - Creative Dreams, Inc.
PLANET X - Bicycles - VII of California, Inc.
PLANETARY CLUBHOUSE MUSIC - Recording label - Planetary Clubhouse Music, Inc.
PLANETARY FORMULAS - Vitamins and nutritional supplements - Threshold Enterprises Ltd.
PLANETARY MANAGER - Educational materials - National Geographic Society
PLANETARY PLUM - Cosmetics ☆ - Noxell Corp.
PLANETARY PRODUCTIONS - Recording label - Continental Communications Corp.
PLANETFALL - Computer software - Activision, Inc.
PLANETHROWERS - Candy - Nabisco Foods Group
PLANETOID - Floor coverings—carpet and rugs ☆ - Royalweve Carpet Mills
PLANETOR - Machine parts - Rule Industries, Inc.
PLANETOR - Tools - Rule Industries, Inc.
PLANETS - Computer peripheral equipment - Electronic Data Systems Corp.
PLANGE TRAINER, THE - Exercising equipment - Gerstung/Gym-Thing Inc.
PLANISTER - Containers - James P. Traupman
PLANIT - Pet products - Morton Jones Co.
PLANK ROAD COLLECTION - Furniture - Brady Furniture Co. Inc.
PLANK ROAD ORIGINAL DRAUGHT - Beer - Miller Brewing Co.
PLANKTEX - Wood products - Georgia-Pacific Corp.
PLANKWELD - Wood products - Georgia-Pacific Corp.
PLANMASTER - File folders - Stacor Corp.
PLANMOBILE - Filing cabinets—metal - Stacor Corp.
PLANNING EXPRESS - Computer software - Prentice-Hall, Inc.
PLANNING GUIDE - Calendars - Memindex Inc.
PLANO - Chairs—folding ☆ - Krueger International, Inc.
PLANO - Fishing tackle - Plano Molding Co.
PLANOTYPE - Electronic equipment - GAF Corp.
PLANPERFECT - Computer software - Wordperfect Corp.
PLANSCAPE - Furniture ☆ - Vogel Peterson Furniture Co.
PLANSPEAR - Identification tags - Speedread Products, Inc.
PLANT - Skin care products - Lendan USA Co.
PLANT-A-SONG - Novelty items - DAD Enterprise
PLANT-AIR - Fans—electric - Schaefer Fan Co., Inc.
PLANT-AIR - Pet products - Penn-Plax, Inc.
PLANT AND ANIMAL CELLS - Computer software - Ventura Educational Systems
PLANT & FEED - Fertilizers - Grace-Sierra Crop Protection Co.
PLANT BOOKS FOR MODERN LIVING - Publisher's imprints - Merchants Publishing Co.

☆ = Now out of production

PLANT CADDY - Garden equipment - Cobraco Manufacturing, Inc.

PLANT CARE - Aquariums–household - Jungle Laboratories Corp.

PLANT CRITTERS - Dinnerware–glass - Childs Co.

PLANT-EFX - Vitamins and nutritional supplements - Natural Efx, Inc.

PLANT FOUNTAIN - Garden equipment - Molor Products Co.

PLANT HELPERS - Plant-care product ✩ - Corning Inc.

PLANT IDEA CENTER - Fertilizers ✩ - Stanley Hardware Div.

PLANT-IT! - Computer software - University of Florida

PLANT JACKS - Garden equipment - Basil S. Gemette

PLANT LITE - Lighting equipment - Duro-Lite Lamps Inc.

PLANT MAGIC - Garden equipment - Green Leaf Products, Inc.

PLANT MANAGER - Hardware - Hafele America Co.

PLANT MARVEL - Fertilizers - Plant Marvel Laboratories

PLANT MINDER - Water dispensers - Innovation Resources

PLANT-N-POLE - Agricultural machinery - Mark A. Maisch

PLANT NANNY - Housewares - New Creative Ways, LLC

PLANT NATURAL - Aquariums–household - Petland, Inc.

PLANT-O-TWO - Pet products - Lake Products Co. Inc.

PLANT PAK SAUCER - Housewares - Plastec Industries

PLANT PALLET - Housewares - Plastec Industries

PLANT PALS - Figurines - C.C. Farms

PLANT PATCH - Nurseries and garden stores - Bear Creek Toys, Inc.

PLANT-PLUG - Water treating compounds - Aquarium Products Inc.

PLANT PRO-TEC - Pesticides–household - Plant Pro-Tec, Inc.

PLANT PROMOTIONS - Flowers, plants, and seeds - Plant Promotions, Inc.

PLANT PURE FUME - Hair care products - A-Veda Corp.

PLANT REEL - Wood products ✩ - Liberty Ridge

PLANT REMEDIES - Flowers, plants, and seeds - Bonide Products, Inc.

PLANT-RITE - Garden equipment ✩ - Earthway Products Inc.

PLANT-SAVER - Meters–electric ✩ - AMI Medical Electronics Inc.

PLANT SCIENCES - Plants, insects, and algae - Plant Sciences, Inc.

PLANT SELECT - Flowers, plants, and seeds - Denver Botanic Gardens

PLANT SHINE - Garden equipment ✩ - Schultz Co.

PLANT SITTER - Garden equipment - Cobraco Manufacturing, Inc.

PLANT SOURCE - Vitamins and nutritional supplements - Prevail Corp.

PLANT SWING - Flower pots–plastic ✩ - Liberty Ridge

PLANT-TACK - Hardware ✩ - Black & Decker Corp.

PLANT, THE - Computer software - Ventura Educational Systems

PLANT THE EARTH - Sock and Roll Corp.

PLANT THE PLANET STERLING VINEYARDS - Wines - Sterling Vineyards, Inc.

PLANT-TONE - Flowers, plants, and seeds - Espoma Co.

PLANTABBS - Fertilizers - Plantabbs Products

PLANTAFORCE - Vegetable sauces - Bioforce of America Ltd.

PLANTAFRESH - Health care products - Nathan Export Associates, Inc.

PLANTAG - Labels–gummed - Steven M. Shapiro

PLANTAMINS - Fertilizers - Marion Stirrup

PLANTASTICS - Aquariums–household - Willinger Bros., Inc.

PLANTASTICS PLUS - Pet products - Tetra Sales USA

PLANTATION - Bakery products - Plantation Baking Co. Inc.

PLANTATION - Cabinets - Evans Cabinet Corp.

PLANTATION - Charcoal - Hood Charcoal Co.

PLANTATION - Food products - Antique Mall & Crown

PLANTATION - Food products - Dole Food Co., Inc.

PLANTATION - Food products - Gold Kist Inc.

PLANTATION - Furniture - Universal Flooring

PLANTATION - Furniture ✩ - Kincaid Furniture Co. Inc.

PLANTATION - Glassware ✩ - Indiana Glass Co.

PLANTATION - Hardware - Weslock National, Inc.

PLANTATION - Heaters–kerosene - Sunbeam-Oster Household Products

PLANTATION - Lamps - Kaadan Ltd.

PLANTATION - Manufactured homes - Redman Industries, Inc.

PLANTATION - Meat products–poultry - Plantation Foods, Inc.

PLANTATION - Meats–luncheon ✩ - John Morrell & Co.

PLANTATION - Molasses - Allied Old English, Inc.

PLANTATION - Pet products - Teaco International

PLANTATION - Recording label - Sun Entertainment Corp.

PLANTATION - Tiles–ceramic ✩ - Monarch Tile Inc.

PLANTATION - Vinegar ✩ - Keller Food Products Co.

PLANTATION - Window coverings - H.J. Nieman Inc.

PLANTATION - Yarn ✩ - JCA, Inc.

PLANTATION BEAUTY - Meat products–poultry ✩ - Plantation Foods, Inc.

PLANTATION BELLE - Dolls - Mattel, Inc.

PLANTATION BLOSSOM - Dinnerware–glass ✩ - Lenox, Inc.

PLANTATION BOUQUET - Cosmetics - May Cove Inc.

PLANTATION CLUB - Pickles - Green Bay Foods Co.

PLANTATION DELIGHT - Food products - Leon's Fine Foods Inc.

PLANTATION GARDEN - Condiment - Peachtree Specialties Ltd.

PLANTATION GATE - Furniture - Universal Flooring

PLANTATION GROVE - Juices - Lemon-X Corp.

PLANTATION II - Cabinets ✩ - Haas Cabinet Co. Inc.

PLANTATION MINT - Teas - R.C. Bigelow, Inc.

PLANTATION OF MISSISSIPPI - Furniture ✩ - Barclay Furniture Co.

PLANTATION PATTERN - Furniture–metal - General Housewares Corp.

PLANTATION PEACHES 'N CREAM - Liquors ✩ - Heublein, Inc.

PLANTATION PRIDE - Pickles - W.B. Roddenbery Co., Inc.

PLANTATION QUAIL - Quail - Quail International, Inc.

PLANTATION RUBBER - Pet products - Penn-Plax, Inc.

PLANTATIONS - Wines - Berrywine Plantations Winery

PLANTEA - Fertilizers - Marion Stirrup

PLANTECH - Computer software - Betrock Information Systems, Inc.

PLANTEES - Fabrics–cotton - G & S Enterprises

PLANTENGA - Bicycles - Dave Plantenga Custom Bicycles

PLANTER LINEN - Apparel and accessories - Palm Beach Co., Inc.

PLANTER PODS - Pet products - Penn-Plax, Inc.

PLANTER VAC - Conveyors - Christianson Systems, Inc.

PLANTERIA - Novelty items ✩ - Latham Studios

PLANTERIORS - Flowers–artificial - Planteriors by Mann's Inc.

PLANTERRA - Pet products - Enviroworks

PLANTER'S - House furnishings ✩ - Lexington Furniture Industries, Inc.

PLANTERS - Nuts–salted, roasted, cooked, or canned - Planters LifeSavers Co.

PLANTERS - Popcorn - Nabisco Foods Group

PLANTERS CARIBBEAN CRUNCH - Snack foods - Planters LifeSavers Co.

PLANTERS CHOCOLATE-COVERED PEANUTS - Chocolate candy - Ferrara Pan Candy Co., Inc.

PLANTERS CHOCOLATE CRISPS - Snack foods - Nabisco Foods Group

PLANTERS CLUB - Beverages–alcohol - Publicker Industries Inc.

PLANTERS HEAT - Food products - Nabisco Foods Group

PLANTERS HEAT - Nuts–salted, roasted, cooked, or canned - Planters LifeSavers Co.

PLANTERS HOME - Furniture–upholstered ✩ - Webb Furniture Enterprises Inc.

PLANTERS LITE - Nuts–salted, roasted, cooked, or canned - Planters LifeSavers Co.

PLANTERS NUTTY CRUNCH - Snack foods - Nabisco Foods Group

PLANTERS PENNANT - Nuts–salted, roasted, cooked, or canned - Nabisco Foods Group

PLANTERS PLUS - Garden equipment - Burkart Bros. Inc.

PLANTERS SWEET 'N CRUNCHY - Nuts–salted, roasted, cooked, or canned - Planters LifeSavers Co.

PLANTIE - Pottery - Maine Nature Products

PLANTIN - Food products - Gourmet America

PLANTIN 2001 - Hair care products - Genesis Research International

PLANTING SPOT - Signals–highway - Poly Enterprises

PLANTINOPLAN - Paper–carbon - Kores Nordic USA Corp.

PLANTIOXIDANTS - Vitamins and nutritional supplements - Source Naturals

PLANTIQUE - Posters - Windsor Collection, Ltd.

PLANTIUM SERIES PLANTS - Flowers, plants, and seeds - Windmill Nursery (L & M Farm)

PLANTLAND U.S.A. - Nurseries and garden stores - Forrest-Keeling Nursery

PLANTLIGHTER - Lighting fixtures - Fleco Industries Inc.

PLANTMOBILE - Housewares - Plantmobile, Inc.

PLANTO - Furniture - Planto Furniture Manufacturing Co., Inc.

PLANTRAY - Hardware - The Centro Co. Inc.

PLANTRONICS - Hearing aids - Harc Mercantile Ltd.

PLANTRONICS - Telephone apparatus - Plantronics, Inc.

PLANTS & HOW THEY GROW - Computer software - Right on Programs

PLANTS-AT-A-GLANCE - Boxes ✩ - Plants-at-a-Glance Corp.

PLANT'S CHOICE - Compost - Organic Recycling West, Inc.

PLANTS FOR A BETTER WORLD - Flowers, plants, and seeds - Monrovia

PLANTSCAPE HOUSE - Horticultural product - J.T. Inman Co. Inc.

PLANTSPACE - Computer software - Bentley Systems, Inc.

PLANTSTERS - Tools–garden - Libby Lee Toys Inc.

PLANTSWEAR - Uniforms–tailored - Angelica Uniform Group

PLANTVAX - Garden equipment - Uniroyal Chemical Co. Inc. (Crop Protection Div.)

PLANTWARE - Computer software - EnviroMetrics Software Inc.

PLANVIEW - Computer software - Planview, Inc.

PLANXPERT - Computer software - Information Management Services, Inc.

PLAPER - Office supplies - Kaiser Poly Kreations, Ltd.

PLAQ-ETTES - Giftware - Gibson Greetings, Inc.

✩ = Now out of production

PLAQUE ATTACKER - Pet products - T.F.H. Publications, Inc.
PLAQUE ATTACKER - Veterinary pharmaceutical preparations - Nylabone Products
PLAQUE CONTROL 3000 - Toothbrushes–electric - Teledyne Water Pik
PLAQUE ENDER - Dental equipment - Etna Products Co. Inc.
PLAQUE OUT - Pet products - T.F.H. Publications, Inc.
PLAQUE WHACKER - Pet products - Richard W. Hoagland
PLAQUENIL - Pharmaceutical preparations - Winthrop Pharmaceuticals
PLAS-DRILL - Drill bits - Craftics Inc.
PLAS-STAKES - Garden equipment - Middlesex Paper Tube Co. Inc.
PLAS-STICK - Office supplies - Wesco Industries Inc.
PLAS-STICK - Window coverings ☆ - Hunter Douglas, Inc.
PLAS-T-CAP - Signal flares - Orion Safety Products (Signal Products Operation)
PLAS-T-LOUVER - Hardware - Leslie-Locke, Inc.
PLAS-T-RIDGE - Ventilation equipment ☆ - Leslie-Locke, Inc.
PLAS-T-VENT - Ventilation equipment ☆ - Leslie-Locke, Inc.
PLAS TEC - Doors - Harann, Inc.
PLAS TECH - Musical instrument accessories - HQ Percussion Products
PLAS-TEX - Garden furniture - Maytex Mills
PLASA DERM - Pet products ☆ - Trophy Animal Health Care
PLASCRON - Paints - Vanex Inc.
PLASDEX - Playing cards ☆ - United States Playing Card Co.
PLASENCIA - Cigars - Nestor J. Plasencia
PLASHEATER - Heaters–kerosene - Craftics Inc.
PLASKITE - Wheels - Faultless Caster Co.
PLASKOLITE - Plastics–laminated - Plaskolite Inc.
PLASMA CUTTING EQUIPMENT - Tools–machine - Esterline Technologies Corp.
PLASMA-JET - Industrial machinery - Corotec Corp.
PLASMA WORLD - Industrial robots - Motoman, Inc.
PLASMADOT - Electronic equipment - Cherry Corp.
PLASMAL - Medical apparatus - Plasma Processing Corp.
PLASMANATE - Medical apparatus - Cutter Laboratories
PLASMARC - Pharmaceutical preparations - American National Red Cross
PLASMAROTOR - Medical apparatus - Statspin Technologies
PLASMATEIN - Pharmaceutical preparations - Alpha Therapeutic Corp.
PLASMATRON - Computer software ☆ - Accolade Inc.
PLASMATRONICS - Audio equipment - Plasmatronics Inc.
PLASPAC - Frames–picture ☆ - A.P.F. Master Framemaker
PLASSMAN PACK - Skin care products - Hanah Beauty & Health Inc.
PLASSWARE - Dinnerware–plastic ☆ - Plastics, Inc. (Anchor Hocking Plastics)
PLAST-A-VANE - Valves - Dwyer Instruments, Inc.
PLAST-DEC - Paint, thinner, lacquer - Automotive Finishes Inc.
PLAST-EDGE - Fertilizers - Reliance Plastic & Chemical Corp.
PLAST-I-CLAY - Clay–modeling - American Art Clay Co. Inc.
PLAST-I-KEG - Containers - Greif Bros. Corp.
PLAST-N-GLAS - Cleaning preparations - Chemtronics Inc.
PLAST-O-GLOSS - Varnishes - Sinclair Paint Co.
PLAST-O-LIFE - Paints - Sinclair Paint Co.
PLAST-O-MAT - Plastics–laminated - Warp Bros.
PLAST-O-SHIELD - Hardware - Anchor Wire Corp.
PLASTA REEL - Garden equipment ☆ - Dare Products Inc.
PLASTA-STONE - Hardware ☆ - Dare Products Inc.
PLASTA-TYTE - Cement - J.C. Whitlam Manufacturing Co.
PLASTABS - Packaging–foam - Northern Technologies International Corp.
PLASTAKOT - Lacquers - Snyder Brothers Co.
PLASTALUME - Health care products - Brown Medical Industries
PLASTAMOLD - Shoes - Thermal-Moldable Shoes Inc.
PLASTAPS - Tools - New England Tap Corp.
PLASTAR - Coatings - Viratec Thin Films, Inc.
PLASTAWRAP - Plastics film - Burrows Paper Corp.
PLASTAZOTE - Orthopedic products - Smith & Nephew Inc. (Rehabilitation Div.)
PLASTECO - Windows–plastic - Plasteco, Inc.
PLASTECOLOGY - Containers - Plastican, Inc.
PLASTELENE - Clay–modeling - Van Aken International
PLASTER CAST, THE - Plaster–wallboard ☆ - Mangelsen's (VDI)
PLASTER-IN-A-ROLL - Fabrics - Flexi-Wall Systems
PLASTER KRAFT - Building materials–concrete - Leatherback Industries Inc.
PLASTER-STIK - Coatings - Embee Corp.
PLASTER-WELD - Adhesives and sealants - Larsen Products Corp.
PLASTER WHITE 'N BRITE - Chemical preparations - Bio-Dex Laboratories
PLASTERED PEOPLE - Figurines ☆ - Cal Themes Inc.
PLASTEREX - Paints ☆ - Mac-O-Lac Paints Inc.

PLASTERTEX - Paints - Martin Paint Stores
PLASTEX - Plastex Inc.
PLASTEX - Wheels - Hamilton Caster & Manufacturing Co.
PLASTI-BILT - Boxes - Frick-Gallagher Manufacturing Co.
PLASTI-BOND - Paints - Wellborn-DE Corp.
PLASTI-CAL - Measuring instruments - MTI Corp.
PLASTI-CAL - Photo albums - Callen Photo Mount Corp.
PLASTI-CAP - Nails–horseshoe - National Nail Corp.
PLASTI-CARE - Cleaning preparations - Beckson Marine Inc.
PLASTI-CHROME - Electronic equipment ☆ - Charles Beseler Co.
PLASTI CLEAR - Cleaning preparations - Marine Development & Research Corp.
PLASTI-COOL - Curling irons–electric - Helene Curtis Industries Inc.
PLASTI-DEK - Cement–asphalt - L.D. Sterns Corp.
PLASTI-DEX - Office supplies ☆ - JM Co.
PLASTI-DRAIN - Fertilizers - Reliance Plastic & Chemical Corp.
PLASTI-FLOR - Varnishes ☆ - Hy-Klas Paints Inc.
PLASTI FOLIO - Musical instrument accessories - United Musical Instruments USA Inc.
PLASTI-FUSE - Adhesives and sealants - Pacer Technology
PLASTI-GLAS - Building materials–concrete - Joanna Western Mills Co.
PLASTI-GLAZE - Putties ☆ - Gibson-Homans Co.
PLASTI GLEAM - Enamels ☆ - Frazee/Deer-O Paints
PLASTI-GOOP - Toys - Toymax Inc.
PLASTI-GRIP - Electrical equipment - AMP Inc.
PLASTI-KLAMPS - Clamps - Baumgarten's
PLASTI-KLEEN - Cleaning preparations–household - Schnapp Enterprises Inc.
PLASTI-KOTE - Paints - Plasti-Kote Co. Inc.
PLASTI-LINER - Denture materials - Brimms Inc.
PLASTI LYRE - Musical instrument accessories - United Musical Instruments USA Inc.
PLASTI MARK - Markers–felt-tip ☆ - Red Eagle Industries
PLASTI MEND - Sealing compounds ☆ - Roccorp, Inc.
PLASTI-NAMEL - Paints - Kelly-Moore Paint Co. Inc.
PLASTI-PAK - Greeting cards ☆ - American Greetings Corp.
PLASTI RACE - Erasers ☆ - Faber-Castell Corp.
PLASTI-REED - Window shades ☆ - C-Mor Co.
PLASTI-SCENT - Air freshener - Allison Corp.
PLASTI-SEAL - Sealing compounds ☆ - Hy-Klas Paints Inc.
PLASTI-SHIELD - Glass products - Owens-Illinois Inc. (Libbey Div.)
PLASTI-SPRAY - Glassware–household - Kranson Industries, Inc.
PLASTI-SWAT - Fly swatters - Laidlaw Corp.
PLASTI-TAK - Adhesives and sealants - Brooks Manufacturing Co.
PLASTI-TEX - Coatings - Schulte Paint & Lacquer Manufacturing Co., Inc.
PLASTI-THANE - Varnishes - Kelly-Moore/Preservative Paints
PLASTI-TOP - Nails–horseshoe - National Nail Corp.
PLASTI-VELLUM - Paper - A.I. Friedman Inc.
PLASTI-ZAP - Adhesives and sealants - Pacer Technology
PLASTI-ZIP - Zippers ☆ - Talon Inc.
PLASTIBANDS - Rubber bands - Baumgarten's
PLASTIBOX - Boxes - Lewisystems
PLASTIC ARMOR - Epoxy coatings - Permagile Industries Inc.
PLASTIC BACK - Carbon paper - American Coated Products Inc.
PLASTIC CARDS - Identification tags - Schaffer Laboratories
PLASTIC/CRAFT - Plastics ☆ - Postcraft Co.
PLASTIC DOT - Cotton gloves - Boss Manufacturing Co.
PLASTIC FANTASTIC SURFBOARDS - Apparel and accessories - Kevin Andrew Doyon
PLASTIC-JAZ - Pole supports - Michael J. Jasinsky
PLASTIC JUNIOR - Plaything - James Industries, Inc.
PLASTIC KOTE - Paints - Duron, Inc.
PLASTIC-LUG - Bottle caps - Aluminum Co. of America
PLASTIC MASK - Plastics film - Aqua-Tainer Co.
PLASTIC-MASTER - Computer software - X-Rite, Inc.
PLASTIC MEDLEY - Dishes–plastic ☆ - Dansk International Designs, Ltd.
PLASTIC MOUSSE - Craft supplies ☆ - Clayton Corp.
PLASTIC NAME BADGES - Identification tags - Schaffer Laboratories
PLASTIC PARCHMENT - Plastics - Alta Industries Inc.
PLASTIC PLANET - Apparel–women's - Golden Touch Imports, Inc.
PLASTIC PLASTER - Plaster–wallboard - Schulte Paint & Lacquer Manufacturing Co., Inc.
PLASTIC POLISH-1 - Cleaning preparations - Novus Inc.
PLASTIC POLISH-2 - Polishing rouge - Novus Inc.
PLASTIC SEAL - Caulking compounds - Hercules Chemical Co. Inc.
PLASTIC SEAL-ALL - Hardware ☆ - Boatlife Inc.

☆ = Now out of production

PLASTIC SHEEN - Cosmetics ☆ - Majestic Drug Co., Inc.

PLASTIC SHIELD - Paints - Triangle Coatings Inc.

PLASTIC STEEL - Epoxy repair material - Devcon Consumer Products (ITW Devcon)

PLASTIC SURGEONS SKIN RESURFACING SYSTEM - Skin care products - Research Institute for Plastic, Cosmetic and Reconstructive Surgery, Inc.

PLASTIC VARNISH - Cleaning preparations - Travaco Laboratories Inc.

PLASTIC-VIEW - Window shades - Luckel Co. Inc.

PLASTIC-VIEW - Window shades - Plastic-View A.T.C.

PLASTIC WELD - Craft supplies - Plastruct Inc.

PLASTIC WELDER - Repair compound - Devcon Consumer Products (ITW Devcon)

PLASTIC WOOD - Fibers–cellulose - Boyle-Midway

PLASTIC WOVEN - Furniture - Wellington Home Products (Plastic Woven Products Div.)

PLASTICAD - Plastic coatings - Arthur Blank and Co. Inc.

PLASTICAL - Garden equipment ☆ - L.J. Rench & Co.

PLASTICATOR - Cement - Craftics Inc.

PLASTICDOR - See **CRITERION**

PLASTICEL - Office supplies ☆ - Faber-Castell Corp.

PLASTICLEAR - Hardware ☆ - Boatlife Inc.

PLASTICO - Plastics - Douglas & Sturgess

PLASTICOAT - Enamel - Interstate Paint Corp.

PLASTICOAT - Musical instrument accessories ☆ - Micro Musical Products Corp.

PLASTICOAT - Publisher's imprints - Colad Group Inc.

PLASTICOIL - Heating equipment - Plasticool, Inc.

PLASTICON - Concrete products - Maintenance Inc.

PLASTICOOL - Heating equipment - Plasticool, Inc.

PLASTICOTE - Caulking compounds - Lasting Paints Inc.

PLASTICOVER - Musical instrument accessories - Rico International

PLASTICS UNIVERSITY - Computer peripheral equipment - D-M-E Co.

PLASTICURE - Inks–letterpress - Borden Chemical Investments, Inc.

PLASTICURE - Resins–polymer - Peter Yang

PLASTICUTTER - Hardware - Astralite Inc.

PLASTICUTTER - Plastics - Craftics Inc.

PLASTICVILLE - Toys - Bachmann Industries Inc.

PLASTIFLEX - Pigments–paint - Scott Paint Corp.

PLASTIFOIL - Foil–aluminum - Highland Supply Corp.

PLASTIGAGE - Measuring instruments - Dana Corp. (Perfect Circle Products Div.)

PLASTIGARD - Finishing agents - Celotex Corp.

PLASTIGLASS - Plastics film - Warp Bros.

PLASTIGLIDE - Casters - Young's

PLASTIGLIDE - Furniture - Illinois Tool Works Inc.

PLASTIK - Clay–modeling - Van Aken International

PLASTIKLIP - Paper clips - Baumgarten's

PLASTIKO - Paints - Morwear Paint Co.

PLASTIKWORKS - Automotive parts and accessories - Fibre Glass-Evercoat Co. Inc.

PLASTILURE - Paints - Lilly Industries, Inc.

PLASTIMAYD - Apparel and accessories - Plastimayd Corp.

PLASTIMOUNT+ - Frames–picture - Byers Photo Equipment Co.

PLASTINAMEL - Enamels - Kelly-Moore/Preservative Paints

PLASTINAMEL - Paints - Sig Manufacturing Inc.

PLASTINE - Adhesives and sealants ☆ - Nowstar

PLASTINE - Film and print preservers - Reeves Photo Sales Inc.

PLASTIP - Pens - Accutec Inc.

PLASTIPAK - Brushes–paint ☆ - Robert Simmons Inc.

PLASTIPORE - Tubes–plastic - Aquaculture Research/Environmental Associates Inc.

PLASTIQUE - Paints - Graham Paint and Varnish Co.

PLASTIQUE - Wallcoverings - Sherman & Associates International

PLASTISEAL - Nail care products - SRA Industries Inc.

PLASTISHAKE - Siding–insulating ☆ - Certainteed Corp. (Roofing Products Group)

PLASTITE - Roof cement - Coopers Creek Chemical Corp.

PLASTITE - Screws - Research Engineering & Manufacturing Inc.

PLASTIVAR - Paints - Seagraves Coatings

PLASTIVIEW - Housewares - Plastiview Literature Display Systems, Inc.

PLASTIX - Pencils ☆ - Empire Berol USA

PLASTMO - Gutters–plastic - Plastmo Inc.

PLASTO - Toys ☆ - Small World Toys

PLASTO-JOINT STIK - Adhesives and sealants - La-Co Industries, Inc.

PLASTODERM - Skin care products - Chanel Inc.

PLASTOGRAPH - Paper–carbon - Kores Nordic USA Corp.

PLASTOID - Putties ☆ - Gibson-Homans Co.

PLASTOL - Cleaning preparations - Sherwood Laboratories Inc.

PLASTOLAC - Paints ☆ - Klean-Strip

PLASTOLITE - Tools - Toledo Pressed Steel Co.

PLASTOLYN - Tablecloths ☆ - Columbus Coated Fabrics Co.

PLASTONE - Cooking utensils–glass ☆ - Flambeau Products Corp.

PLASTONE - Plastics - EFP Corp.

PLASTOSEAL - Elastomers - Universal Protective Coatings

PLASTRAWS - Straws–drinking ☆ - Lustro-Ware Housewares Inc.

PLAST'RCRAFT - Paper - Bemiss-Jason Corp.

PLASTREES - Craft supplies - Plastruct Inc.

PLASTRON - Curtains ☆ - United Merchants and Manufacturers Inc.

PLASTURF - Landscaping ground foam - Plastruct Inc.

PLASTYLE - Cups–plastic - Sealright Co., Inc.

PLAT MAT, THE - Mattresses - Kingsdown, Inc.

PLAT MONCLAIR - Glass products - Tiffin Glass Co. Inc.

PLATANO - Glassware–household - Villeroy and Boch Tableware Ltd.

PLATANOS MADUROS - Food products - Goya Foods, Inc.

PLATE CRATE - Containers - Menasha Corp.

PLATE-LOK - Brackets - HPA Monon Corp.

PLATE MATE - Cooking equipment–household - Nordic Ware

PLATE MATE - Housewares - Larry Shaw Co.

PLATE PAL - Dinnerware - Invenetics LLC

PLATE-STOP 1 - Tape–adhesive ☆ - Permacel

PLATE-STOP 2 - Tape–adhesive ☆ - Permacel

PLATE-WELD - Denture materials - Smithkline Beecham Corp.

PLATEAU - Fabrics - Vertilux-Louverlux Inc.

PLATEAU - Floor coverings–carpet and rugs ☆ - Patrick Carpet Mills

PLATEAU - Floor coverings–carpet and rugs ☆ - Regal Rugs Inc.

PLATEAU - Floor coverings–tile - National Floor Products Co., Inc.

PLATEAU - Furniture - Lane Co. Inc.

PLATEAU - Gasoline - Suburban Propane Gas Corp.

PLATEAU - Herbicides - American Cyanamid Co.

PLATEAU - Sachets - Reminessence, Inc.

PLATEMAKER 3 - Printers–computer - Xante Corp.

PLATEOSAURUS-PUNCH - Beverages - Givaudan Rare Flavors

PLATEPRO - Printing presses - Halm Industries Co., Inc.

PLATES-A-PLENTY - Furniture - Collectable Images, Inc.

PLATEWORKS - Hardware - Pro-Co. Sound Co. Inc.

PLATFORM - Toys - Wonderline

PLATFORM GRAPHICS - Computer software - FormAtion Technologies Inc.

PLATFORM PLUS - Mattresses ☆ - Kingsdown, Inc.

PLATFORM, THE - Mattresses - Kingsdown, Inc.

PLATFORM TO PERFECTION - Golfing equipment - Timothy R. Nicholls

PLATH - Marine rigging - R.C. Plath Co.

PLATIGNUM - Artists' materials - Koh-I-Noor, Inc.

PLATIGNUM - Pens–fountain ☆ - Canson-Talens Inc.

PLATINA - Floor coverings–carpet and rugs - Couristan Inc.

PLATINA - Ribbons - W.F.R. Ribbon Corp.

PLATINE - Colognes ☆ - Dana Perfumes Corp.

PLATINOL - Pharmaceutical preparations - Bristol-Myers Squibb Co.

PLATINUM - Cigarettes - Brown & Williamson Tobacco Corp.

PLATINUM - Dolls - Mattel, Inc.

PLATINUM - Lenses - Navitar, Inc.

PLATINUM - Luggage - York Luggage Co.

PLATINUM - Paper - Fox River Paper Co.

PLATINUM - Tires - Price Co.

PLATINUM - Toiletries - Chanel Inc.

PLATINUM - Toothpaste - Colgate Oral Pharmaceuticals Inc.

PLATINUM - Wallpaper - Textile Wallcoverings International Ltd.

PLATINUM II - Photographic equipment ☆ - Edwal Scientific Products Corp.

PLATINUM 16 - Computer hardware - Multiwave Innovation, Inc.

PLATINUM ACCENT - Dishes–china ☆ - Pickard Inc.

PLATINUM ACCENTS - Jewelry - OE Design Inc.

PLATINUM & SILVER - Hair care products ☆ - Freeman Cosmetics Corp.

PLATINUM ATHLETE - Jewelry - OE Design Inc.

PLATINUM BARBIE - Dolls - Mattel, Inc.

PLATINUM BY CAESAR - Toys - Dart World Inc.

PLATINUM CAT, THE - Heaters–gas - Thermal Systems Inc.

PLATINUM COLLECTION - Medical apparatus - Lumex, Inc.

PLATINUM COLLECTION - Reading glasses - AAI/ACCESSORIES Associates Inc.

PLATINUM DATABASE ANALYZER - Computer software - Platinum Technology, Inc.

PLATINUM DETECTOR - Computer storage devices–magnetic - Platinum Technology, Inc.

☆ = Now out of production

PLATINUM EDITION - Razors–electric ☆ - Philips Electronics North America Corp.

PLATINUM F3 - Electronic equipment - American Terminal Supply Co., Inc.

PLATINUM FAST RECOVER - Computer software - Platinum Technology, Inc.

PLATINUM FX SERIES - Game machines ☆ - WMS Gaming Inc.

PLATINUM HERITAGE - Glassware–household ☆ - Crisa Corp.

PLATINUM ID, THE - Electronic equipment - Techsonic Industries, Inc.

PLATINUM II OXYGEN SENSORS - Automotive parts and accessories - Tomco, Inc.

PLATINUM LOG ANALYZER - Computer software - Platinum Technology, Inc.

PLATINUM LOOK, THE - Decorated soap - Country Lane Enterprises Inc.

PLATINUM LORELEI - Glassware–household - ACC

PLATINUM MASTERPIECE COLLECTION - Watches - Blancpain (Time Products Inc.)

PLATINUM #2 - Paper–tissue - Paper Service Ltd.

PLATINUM OBJECT ADMINISTRATOR - Computer software - Platinum Technology, Inc.

PLATINUM PETALS - Flowers, plants, and seeds - International Floral Corp.

PLATINUM PLAN ANALYZER - Computer storage devices–magnetic - Platinum Technology, Inc.

PLATINUM PLEASURES - Jewelry - OE Design Inc.

PLATINUM PLUS - Bags–trash - Maynard Plastics

PLATINUM PLUS - Floor waxes - Smith Chemical & Wax, Inc.

PLATINUM-PLUS - Razor blades - Gillette Co.

PLATINUM PLUS - Solar energy collectors - Courtaulds Performance Films Inc.

PLATINUM PLUS - Toys–stuffed - Dan-Dee International Ltd.

PLATINUM POWER - Trading cards and stamps - Upper Deck Co.

PLATINUM RECOVERY ANALYZER - Computer software - Platinum Technology, Inc.

PLATINUM ROLLER - Golfing equipment - Golfsmith International Inc.

PLATINUM RX - Advertising agencies - Financial Direct, Inc.

PLATINUM SERIES - Footwear - E.S. Originals, Inc.

PLATINUM SERIES - Toys - Bullseye Paint Pellet Co.

PLATINUM SERIES - Video production - Atlantic Steel Vision Inc.

PLATINUM SUZY - Glassware–household - ACC

PLATINUM TECHNOLOGY - Computer software - Platinum Technology, Inc.

PLATINUM VISION - Computer software - Platinum Technology, Inc.

PLATINUM WEAVES - Wallpaper - Wall-Pride Inc.

PLATINUM WHITE GOOSE DOWN - Comforters - Co. Store

PLATO - Floor coverings–carpet and rugs ☆ - Eurotex Inc.

PLATON - Computer software - IMS Business System Corp.

PLATONIC - Apparel and accessories - Platonics

PLATOON - Clocks - General Time Corp. (Westclox/Seth Thomas Div.)

PLATO'S CAVE - Computer software - Krell Software Corp.

PLATT - Tool boxes - Platt Luggage Inc.

PLATT & MUNK - Publisher's imprints - Grosset & Dunlap Inc.

PLATTE VALLEY - Fruits and vegetables - Westin Inc.

PLATTE VALLEY - Vinegar - Haarmann Vinegar & Pickle Co.

PLATTE VALLEY - Whiskey - Mccormick Distilling Co., Inc.

PLATTER FRIES - Vegetables–frozen ☆ - Lamb-Weston, Inc.

PLATTER POPS - Candy ☆ - Spangler Candy Co.

PLATYPUS - Candy - Tpl, Inc.

PLATYPUS - Goggles–sun - Eye Communications

PLATYPUS - Water bottles–rubber - Cascade Designs, Inc.

PLAUBEL - Cameras - Harrison Camera Corp.

PLAUDIT - Floor coverings–carpet and rugs ☆ - Regal Rugs Inc.

PLAUDIT - Furniture - Taylor-Ramsey Corp.

PLAUDIT - Tables–wood - Riverside Furniture Corp.

PLAX - Mouthwashes - Pfizer Inc.

PLAX RINSE BEFORE BRUSHING PATENTED FORMULA CLINICALLY PROVEN - Mouthwashes - Pfizer Inc.

P.L.A.Y. - Apparel and accessories - P.L.A.Y., Inc.

PLAY - Garden equipment - Scotts Co. (Organics Business Group)

PLAY-A-BOUT - Sporting goods - Habitat International Inc.

PLAY-A-SONG - Toys–musical - Fisher-Price, Inc.

PLAY-A-TUNE - Toys - Tonka Corp.

PLAY-A-WAY - Games ☆ - Carrom Co.

PLAY ABOUT - Toys - Little Tikes Co.

PLAY-ABOUTS - Bathing suits - Catalina

PLAY ACTION - Fishing tackle - Play Action Products Inc.

PLAY ALONG WITH ME - Tape recorders - Musicor Records Inc.

PLAY AND CARRY - Dolls - Mattel, Inc.

PLAY & DISCOVER - Toys–trains - Mattel, Inc.

PLAY & LEARN - Antennas - Recoton Corp.

PLAY AND LEARN - Toys - Larami Limited, Inc.

PLAY & LEARN - Toys - Samuel Lowe Co.

PLAY & SPELL - Toys - Bettoy Co. Inc.

PLAY AROUND TOWN - Toys - Fisher-Price, Inc.

PLAY BABY - Dolls - Uneeda Doll Co., Inc.

PLAY BALL! - Eagle-Picher Minerals, Inc.

PLAY BALL - Apparel–athletic - Jeffrey Evans Nelson

PLAY BALL - Balls ☆ - Kewaunee Equipment Co.

PLAY BALL - Chewing gum - Leaf, Inc.

PLAY BALL - Pet products - Petland, Inc.

PLAY BOOSTER - Playground equipment - Landscape Structures Inc.

PLAY BRICKS - Swimming pools - Recreonics, Inc.

PLAY BRIDGE - Games - Games Group International Inc.

PLAY BY PLAY - Apparel and accessories - Nak Corp.

PLAY BY PLAY - Toys - Play by Play Toys and Novelties, Inc.

PLAY CHEWY - Dog treats - American Leather Specialties

PLAY CITY - Pet products - HTZ Investment Corp.

PLAY CITY - Pet products - Longlife Pet Products

PLAY CUBES - Toys ☆ - Little Tikes Co.

PLAY CUTTERS - Clay–modeling - Playskool, Inc.

PLAY DAY - Golfing equipment - Bag Boy Inc.

PLAY DAY, THE - Vacuum cleaners and accessories ☆ - Sunbeam-Oster Household Products

PLAY DECKER - Boats–houseboats - H & H Molded Products

PLAY DIRTY - Apparel–men's - Built USA

PLAY-DOH - Clay–modeling - Playskool, Inc.

PLAY-DOH ANIMAL ARK - Clay–modeling - Playskool, Inc.

PLAY-DOH BAKE'N CAKE SHOP - Clay–modeling - Playskool, Inc.

PLAY-DOH SMART STARTERS - Clay–modeling - Playskool, Inc.

PLAY E-Z KENO - Games - Rafsco Nevada, Inc.

PLAY GEL - Hair care products - Dellaria International Inc.

PLAY GEL COLORS - Hair care products - Dellaria International Inc.

PLAY GROUND - Footwear–athletic - Elan-Polo, Inc.

PLAY GROUND KIDS - Toys - Those Characters from Cleveland, Inc.

PLAY GYM - Toys - Fisher-Price, Inc.

PLAY HARMONICA OVERNIGHT - Recording label - Xebec Productions, Inc.

PLAY/HIDE-AWAY - Pet products - Penn-Plax, Inc.

PLAY-HUT - Tents - Play Hut, Inc.

PLAY-IN-KNIT - Apparel–children's ☆ - Brill Bros. Inc.

PLAY IT AGAIN - Game machines - Sigma Game Inc.

PLAY IT AGAIN SAM - Fans–electric ☆ - Leslie-Locke, Inc.

PLAY IT AGAIN SAM - Recording label ☆ - Caroline Records, Inc.

PLAY IT SAFE - Infant product - Summer Infant Products Inc.

PLAY J SHORTIES - Apparel–children's - Playskool Baby Inc.

PLAY LIGHTS - Publisher's imprints - Reader's Digest Association, Inc.

PLAY LIKE A PRO - Toys ☆ - Sight & Sound Inc.

PLAY, LISTEN & LEARN - Games - Aristoplay, Ltd.

PLAY LIVELIER LONGER - Sporting goods - Ferrari Importing Co.

PLAY-MATES - Audio equipment - CSI/Speco

PLAY MONEY KITS - Toys ☆ - Strombecker Corp.

PLAY-MOR - Motor vehicles–motor homes - Play-Mor Trailers Inc.

PLAY MORE - Cleaning preparations ☆ - Kafko International Ltd.

PLAY MUNCHY - Dog treats - American Leather Specialties

PLAY 'N CARRY - Toys - Tyco Toys

PLAY 'N CARRY - Toys–trains - Mattel, Inc.

PLAY N FIT - Toys ☆ - Lauri Inc.

PLAY 'N FUN - Toys - Tyco Toys

PLAY 'N GO - Toys - Fisher-Price, Inc.

PLAY 'N JANE - Boats - Glen-L Marine Designs

PLAY 'N' LEARN - Dolls ☆ - Dakin Inc.

PLAY 'N POP - Toys - Mattel, Inc.

PLAY 'N PRETEND - Toys - Imperial Toy Corp.

PLAY 'N' WASH - Footwear - Chadwick Industries

PLAY NOW - Publisher's imprints - Warner Bros. Publications

PLAY NOW LIBRARY - Publisher's imprints - Warner Bros. Publications

PLAY-O - Games - Joe Bonomo Associates, Inc.

PLAY ONE - Crocheted and knitted items - Puritan Sportswear Corp.

PLAY PAINTS - Paints - DecoArt, Inc.

PLAY PAKS - Dolls - Mattel, Inc.

PLAY PANELS - Toys - Childcraft Education Corp.

PLAY PEN - Boats - Glen-L Marine Designs

PLAY PEN PALS - Toys–stuffed - Russ Berrie and Co., Inc.

PLAY PIANO - Computer software - Midisoft Corp.

PLAY PICTURES - Publisher's imprints - Play-Tech, Inc.

PLAY PLANES - Toys–airplanes - Paul K. Guillow Inc.

PLAY PLAY BY SYSTEMS - Computer software - Play by Play Systems

PLAY RIDER - Toys ☆ - Roadmaster Corp.

PLAY-RITE - Computer software - Play-Rite Software Inc.
PLAY SAFE - Paper cups with safety messages - James River Corp.
PLAY-SCANTS - Bathing suits - Catalina
PLAY SCREEN - Toys - Noanne S. Gwynn
PLAY SCUFFS - Footwear - Alta Products Corp.
PLAY SET - Trading cards and stamps - Kenner Products
PLAY SHAPES - Construction toys - James Industries, Inc.
PLAY SKINS - Sports apparel - Medalist Apparel Inc.
PLAY SQUARES - Floor coverings - Studio RTA, Inc.
PLAY STACKER - Furniture–children's - Selfix, Inc.
PLAY STATION - Electronic equipment - Sony Corp. of America
PLAY-STONE - Toys - Tonka Corp.
PLAY STREET - Toys - Knickerbocker Toy Co. Inc.
PLAY SYSTEMS - Toys - Stainless Inc.
PLAY TECH BABY - Toys–electronic - Play-Tech, Inc.
PLAY-TECH LEARNING - Toys–electronic - Play-Tech, Inc.
PLAY TELL TIME - Clocks - Vitos Products
PLAY THE BEATS - Games - Friendship House
PLAY THE GAME FROM THE NECK UP - Apparel and accessories - Trent Tucker
PLAY THE PLANET! - Computer software - Outland, Inc.
PLAY-THRU - Golf cart covers - Play-Thru, Inc.
PLAY-TIMER - Infant product ✰ - Welsh Co.
PLAY TIMERS - Footwear - Alta Products Corp.
PLAY TO WIN - Computer software - ATS Consultants, Inc.
PLAY TRANSPORTS - Toys ✰ - Little Tikes Co.
PLAY TRAYS - Games - Smethport Specialty Co.
PLAY UNTIL YOU WIN - Game machines - Advanced Games & Engineering, Inc.
PLAY VILLAGE - Playground equipment - Rainbow Play Systems, Inc.
PLAY VISIONS - Toys - Play Visions
PLAY WIPES - Infant product - AZ Product Co.
PLAY WITH A PURPOSE - Sporting goods - Prophet Corp.
PLAY WITH IT - Computer software - Lyrrus Inc.
PLAY WITH ME - Toys ✰ - Today's Kids Inc.
PLAY-YARDS - Playpens–wood ✰ - Gerry Wood Products
PLAYA - Drums–musical instruments - LPD Music International
PLAYA - Frames–picture - Terragrafics Inc.
PLAYA - Sandals ✰ - Playazul International Inc.
PLAYA BLANCO - Furniture ✰ - Bassett Furniture Industries, Inc.
PLAYA DEL SOL - Beverages - Pett Spice Products, Inc.
PLAYARD - Flowers, plants, and seeds ✰ - J. & L. Adikes Inc.
PLAYARD - Furniture–metal - Century Products Co.
PLAYARIUM - Infant product - Leachco Inc.
PLAYATWILL - Computer software - International Business Machines Corp.
PLAYBACK - Recording label - Continental Communications Corp.
PLAYBACK - Recording label - Gallery II Records Inc.
PLAYBALL! - Computer software - Microbase, Inc.
PLAYBALL - Sporting goods - Marty Gilman Inc.
PLAYBALL - Toy - Invention Prototypes & Marketing Corp.
PLAYBALLS - Toys–stuffed - Russ Berrie and Co., Inc.
PLAYBOOK PUBLISHING - Computer software - Cramer Products Inc.
PLAYBOUND - Floor coverings - Dodge-Regupol Inc.
PLAYBOX - Toys - Mary Murray Englehart
PLAYBOY - Apparel and accessories - Harwood Companies Inc.
PLAYBOY - Apparel and accessories - Playboy Enterprises, Inc.
PLAYBOY - Apparel–women's ✰ - Sanmark-Stardust Inc.
PLAYBOY - Bicycles - Columbia Manufacturing Inc.
PLAYBOY - Books and puzzles ✰ - American Publishing Corp.
PLAYBOY - Footwear–men's - Harbor Footwear Group Ltd.
PLAYBOY - Frames–eyeglass ✰ - Carrera Eyewear Corp.
PLAYBOY - Handkerchiefs ✰ - Carolina Manufacturing Inc.
PLAYBOY - Hats - Arlington Hat Co. Inc.
PLAYBOY - Hosiery–men's - S.L. Gilbert Co.
PLAYBOY - Motor vehicle parts and accessories - Allison Corp.
PLAYBOY - Recording label - Brilliance Corp. Inc.
PLAYBOY - Tobacco–chewing or smoking - Gesty Trading & Manufacturing Corp.
PLAYBOY SATIN - Bedding–linen - Dan River Inc.
PLAYBOY: THE GAME OF ELEGANT LIFESTYLES - Games ✰ - Avalon Hill Game Co.
PLAYCET - Hair care products - Deilaria International Inc.
PLAYCHECKS - Toys - Laurie North Corp.
PLAYCOLOR - Pens - Schwan-STABILO USA Inc.
PLAYCRAFT - Boats–motor - Playcraft Pontoon Co.
PLAYCRAFT - Furniture - Little Tikes Co.

PLAY'EM - Toys - Play'em, LLC
PLAYER - Furniture–upholstered ✰ - Mersman Furniture Co.
PLAYER - Shoes–athletic - Sam Brilliant Sporto
PLAYER, A - Sporting goods ✰ - Dunlop Maxfli Sports Corp.
PLAYER PREFERRED - Games - Arrow International, Inc.
PLAYERPACK - Audio cabinets–plastic - K-Tel International, Inc.
PLAYERPANT - Slacks - Nike, Inc.
PLAYERS - Apparel and accessories - Phillips-Van Heusen Corp.
PLAYERS - Cigarettes - Philip Morris Companies Inc.
PLAYERS - Footwear–women's - Norwood Shoe Corp.
PLAYERS - Wallpaper ✰ - Sanitas Wallcoverings
PLAYERS 100'S - Cigarettes - Philip Morris Companies Inc.
PLAYERS CHAMPIONSHIP - Apparel and accessories - PGA Tour, Inc.
PLAYERS CHOICE - Dartboard - General Sportcraft Co. Ltd.
PLAYERS CHOICE - Games ✰ - Milton Bradley Co.
PLAYER'S CHOICE - Shampoos ✰ - Hobe Labs Inc.
PLAYER'S CHOICE - Sporting goods - Jeffrey Lee Enterprises Inc.
PLAYERS CHOICE - Water–bottled or canned - Fun City Popcorn, Inc.
PLAYERS CHOICE POKER - Games - New Vision Gaming and Development, Inc.
PLAYERS EDGE, THE - Sporting goods - Kinney Shoe Corp.
PLAYERS HOCKEY - Games ✰ - Tudor Inc.
PLAYERS INC. - Apparel and accessories - Joy Athletic, Inc.
PLAYERS KIT - Hair care products ✰ - Pro-Line Corp.
PLAYERS LIGHTS - Cigarettes - Philip Morris Companies Inc.
PLAYER'S NAVY CUT - Cigarettes - Philip Morris Companies Inc.
PLAYERS PASTA - Pasta - Fortune Macaroni Co.
PLAYER'S PERFORMANCE - Hosiery - Desoto Hosiery Mills, Inc.
PLAYER'S PRIDE - Socks - Desoto Hosiery Mills, Inc.
PLAYERSHORT - Apparel–athletic - Nike, Inc.
PLAYETTE - Apparel–children's - Geoffrey Inc.
PLAYETTE - Apparel–children's - Kids R Us Co.
PLAYETTES - Toys - M.&S. Shillman Inc.
PLAYFACES - Pillows - Play by Play Toys and Novelties, Inc.
PLAYFLEX - Footwear–children's - W.L. Kreider's Sons Manufacturing Co. Inc.
PLAYFUL MINDS - Games - Darrin Adams
PLAYFUL PAWS - Dolls - Mattel, Inc.
PLAYFUL PETS - Toys–stuffed - Kamar International Inc.
PLAYFUL POUNCER - Pet products - Maggie Mae's Gourmet Pet Products Inc.
PLAYFUL SANTA - Toys–stuffed - Fun World Inc.
PLAYGIRL - Cosmetics - Playgirl Industries, Inc.
PLAYGOERS - Shoes ✰ - Edison Brothers Stores, Inc.
PLAYGRAS - Floor coverings–carpet and rugs - Playfield International Inc.
PLAYGROUND - Computer software - Object International, Inc.
PLAYGROUND - Computer software - Science for Kids
PLAYGROUND - Footwear - Colonial Shoe Co.
PLAYGROUND - Puzzles - Warren Industries Inc.
PLAYGROUND - Recording label - DLM Records
PLAYGROUND - Recording label - Playground
PLAYGROUND EARTH - Apparel and accessories - Playground Earth
PLAYGROUND KIDS - Toys - ERTL Co., Inc.
PLAYGROUND KIDS - Toys - Those Characters from Cleveland, Inc.
PLAYGROUND LEGENDS - Pens - Upper Deck Co.
PLAYGROUND PALS - Ornamental products–glass - Russ Berrie and Co., Inc.
PLAYGROUND POCKETS - Apparel–children's - Mary Kathleen Lenart
PLAYGROUP PRESCHOOL - Toys - TCA Ground Inc.
PLAYHOUSE - Paints - Valspar Corp.
PLAYHOUSE PROP - Playset - Angeles Group, Inc.
PLAYING IS AS MUCH FUN AS WINNING - Toys - Craig Candelaria
PLAYING IT SMART - Toys - Henry Gordy International Inc.
PLAYING TO LEARN - Computer software - Queue Inc.
PLAYLAB - Playground equipment ✰ - Game Time, Inc.
PLAYLAND - Cookies - Keebler Co.
PLAYLAND - Fabrics–tapestry ✰ - Coloroll Inc.
PLAYLAND - Toys ✰ - Sun Products Corp. (Wellington)
PLAYLAND BOOKS - Publisher's imprints - Putnam Publishing Group
PLAYLEARN - Playground equipment - Sports Play Equip. Inc.
PLAYLEARN - Sporting goods - PCA Industries Inc.
PLAYLOON - Toys - National Latex Products Co.
PLAYMAKER - Electronic equipment - NTN Communications, Inc.
PLAYMAKER - Sporting goods - Rawlings Sporting Goods Co., Inc.
PLAYMAKER FOOTBALL - Computer software ✰ - Broderbund Software, Inc.
PLAYMAKER! GEAR - Apparel and accessories - David F. Gallanosa

✰ = Now out of production

PLAYMASTER - Sporting goods ☆ - J. De Beer & Son Inc.
PLAYMASTER - Toys ☆ - Roadmaster Corp.
PLAYMATE - Apparel–women's - Playboy Enterprises, Inc.
PLAYMATE - Boats–motor - Glastex Co.
PLAYMATE - Boats–motor - H & H Molded Products
PLAYMATE - Boats–motor ☆ - Checkmate Boats Inc.
PLAYMATE - Boats–motor ☆ - Dolphin Boats Ltd.
PLAYMATE - Boats–motor ☆ - Glassmaster Co.
PLAYMATE - Electronic equipment ☆ - Thomson Consumer Electronics, Inc.
PLAYMATE - Footwear ☆ - Americal Corp.
PLAYMATE - Golf carts ☆ - Ajay Leisure Products Inc.
PLAYMATE - Ice chests–plastic - Igloo Products Corp.
PLAYMATE - Infant product ☆ - Welsh Co.
PLAYMATE - Lighting fixtures - Swivelier Co. Inc.
PLAYMATE - Motor vehicle parts and accessories - Allison Corp.
PLAYMATE - Sporting goods - Metaltek
PLAYMATE ELITE - Ice chests - Igloo Products Corp.
PLAYMATE PLUS - Ice chests–plastic - Igloo Products Corp.
PLAYMATE TODAY. A TREASURE TOMORROW, A - Toys - Robin Woods Inc.
PLAYMATES - Dishes–china - Mikasa Co.
PLAYMATES - Floor coverings–carpet and rugs - Mohawk Carpet Corp.
PLAYMATES - Greeting cards - Paramount Cards Inc.
PLAYMATES - Pet products - Cardinal Laboratories, Inc.
PLAYMATTERS - Hobby kits - Playmatters, Inc.
PLAYMOBIL - Toys - Tyco Toys
PLAYMORE - Playground equipment - Playmore Design Corp.
PLAYMORE INC. PUBLISHERS - Publisher's imprints - Playmore Inc. Publishers
PLAY'N LEARN - Puzzles ☆ - Warren Industries Inc.
PLAY'N POS'M - Apparel and accessories - Critter Gitter
PLAYNTS - Paint sets–hobby ☆ - Kenner Products
PLAYNTS - Toys - Tonka Corp.
PLAYOFF - Soccer equipment - Mikasa Sports
PLAYOFF - Trading cards - Playoff Corp.
PLAYOFF CLASSIC - Balls - Mikasa Sports
PLAYOFF CLUB - Trading cards and stamps - Playoff Corp.
PLAYOFF CONTENDERS SERIES - Trading cards and stamps - Playoff Corp.
PLAYOFFS - Apparel and accessories ☆ - Wrangler Co.
PLAYONAIR - Musical instrument accessories - M & M Distributing Co.
PLAYONAIR - Musical instrument accessories - Shar Products, Inc.
PLAYONS - Craft supplies - Mokee's Inc.
PLAYOTARD - Leotards ☆ - Danskin, Inc.
PLAYPANELS - Window coverings - Children's Factory, Inc.
PLAYPARK - Toys ☆ - Wonderline
PLAYPATH - Toys - Johnson & Johnson
PLAYPEN - Footwear–children's - K-P Shoe Co. Inc.
PLAYPEN PALS - Toys–stuffed ☆ - Fun World Inc.
PLAYPEN PUPPY - Toys–stuffed ☆ - Dakin Inc.
PLAYPETS TO CUDDLE & LOVE KELLYTOY - Toys–stuffed - Kellytoy (USA), Inc.
PLAYPOD - Playground equipment - Miracle Recreation Equipment Co.
PLAYPOWER - Playground equipment - Playpower, Inc.
PLAYROOM, THE - Computer software - Broderbund Software, Inc.
PLAY'S THE THING, THE - Games - Aristoplay, Ltd.
PLAYSAFE - Cribs–metal ☆ - HARD Manufacturing Co. Inc.
PLAYSCAPE - Playground equipment - Sports Play Equip. Inc.
PLAYSCENES - Toys - Playworld Systems, Inc.
PLAYSCUFFS BY PLAYTIMER - Apparel and accessories - Playtimer Industries Ltd.
PLAYSENSE - Playground equipment - Landscape Structures Inc.
PLAYSET - Bubble-blowing game - Toy Originators Inc.
PLAYSHAPER - Playground equipment - Landscape Structures Inc.
PLAYSKOOL - Footwear - Pagoda Trading Co.
PLAYSKOOL - Infant product - La Rue International, Inc.
PLAYSKOOL - Toys - Playskool, Inc.
PLAYSKOOL FLASHLIGHT - Toys - Playskool, Inc.
PLAYSKOOL PLAY PEOPLE - Toys - Playskool, Inc.
PLAYSKOOL PLAYSTORE - Toys - Playskool, Inc.
PLAYSMART - Playground equipment - Playsmart, Inc.
PLAYSTATION - Video games - Sony Corp. of America
PLAYTALKIN' - Toys–stuffed - Mighty Star Inc. (Special Effects Div.)
PLAYTANGLE - Playground equipment - Kimotion, Inc.
PLAYTENTIALS - Toys - Tonka Corp.
PLAYTEX - Toiletries - Playtex Beauty Care, Inc.
PLAYTEX DISPOSABLES - Gloves–rubber - Playtex Beauty Care, Inc.

PLAYTIME - Chalk ☆ - Binney & Smith Inc.
PLAYTIME - Computer software - SourceView Software International
PLAYTIME - Containers ☆ - Poloron Products Inc.
PLAYTIME - Floor coverings–carpet and rugs - Couristan Inc.
PLAYTIME - Food products - Universal Packers Corp.
PLAYTIME - Paints - California Products Corp.
PLAYTIME - Pet products - Falmon Falls Pet Products
PLAYTIME - Playing cards - United States Playing Card Co.
PLAYTIME - Toys - Hasbro, Inc.
PLAYTIME - Wallpaper ☆ - Palette Prints Inc.
PLAYTIME 2 - Wallpaper - Surface Industries Inc.
PLAYTIME BLANKET - Toys ☆ - Those Characters from Cleveland, Inc.
PLAYTIME CHOO-CHOO - Toys - Flexible Flyer Co.
PLAYTIME COOLER - Ice chests–plastic ☆ - Life-Like Products Inc.
PLAYTIME KALEIDOSCOPE - Novelty items - Steven Manufacturing Co.
PLAYTIME PALS - Toys–stuffed - Fun World Inc.
PLAYTIME PARADE - Wallpaper ☆ - Imperial Wallcoverings, Inc.
PLAYTIME PARADE II - Wallpaper - Imperial Wallcoverings, Inc.
PLAYTIME PUPPETS - Toys–stuffed - Russ Berrie and Co., Inc.
PLAYTOONS - Toys–electronic - Bright Star Technology Inc.
PLAYTREK - Shoes ☆ - Clarks of England Inc.
PLAYTRIUM - Playground equipment - Atrox Systems Inc.
PLAYVENTURE - Playground equipment - Landscape Structures Inc.
PLAYWEATHER - Fabrics - Dan River Inc.
PLAYWELL - Toys - Playwell Toy Inc.
PLAYWIPES - Towels ☆ - Mount Vernon Mills Inc.
PLAYWRITE - Audio equipment - KK Microboards
PLAYZONE - Computer software - Knowledge Adventure
PLAYZONE - Infant product - Warren Eugene Gilbert
PLAYZOOKIT - Toys ☆ - Reliance Products Corp.
PLAZA - See **PARADISE**
PLAZA - Baskets–wood ☆ - Burlington Basket Co. Inc.
PLAZA - Bathroom accessories - Plaza Towel Holder Co.
PLAZA - Bathroom fixtures - American Standard Inc.
PLAZA - Bedding–linen - Pillowtex Corp.
PLAZA - Bicycles - Sears, Roebuck and Co.
PLAZA - Cabinets–wood - Decora
PLAZA - Cigarettes - Philip Morris Companies Inc.
PLAZA - Clocks - General Time Corp. (Westclox/Seth Thomas Div.)
PLAZA - Easels - American Blueprint Co. Inc.
PLAZA - Fans–electric - Hunter Fan Co.
PLAZA - Floor coverings–carpet and rugs - Criterion Mills Inc.
PLAZA - Floor coverings–carpet and rugs - Edgecrest Carpet Mills
PLAZA - Floor coverings–carpet and rugs - Hartford Carpet Mills
PLAZA - Floor coverings–carpet and rugs - Quaker Inc.
PLAZA - Floor coverings–carpet and rugs - Shaheen Carpet Mills
PLAZA - Food products - H.E. Butt Grocery Co.
PLAZA - Furniture ☆ - Hammary Furniture Co. Inc.
PLAZA - Furniture–upholstered - Sherrill Furniture Co.
PLAZA - Glassware–household ☆ - Anchor Hocking Glass, Inc.
PLAZA - Occasional furniture ☆ - JDI Group, Inc.
PLAZA - Polishes - S.C. Johnson & Son, Inc.
PLAZA - Rings–jewelry - Artcarved Inc.
PLAZA - Tables–wood - Riverside Furniture Corp.
PLAZA - Thread - Threads USA Div.
PLAZA - Tiles–ceramic ☆ - Amsterdam Corp.
PLAZA - Wallpaper - Marburg Wallcoverings Inc.
PLAZA - Watches ☆ - Swatch Watch USA
PLAZA 3 - Wallpaper ☆ - Wolf-Gordon Inc.
PLAZA BRICK - Floor coverings–tile - National Floor Products Co., Inc.
PLAZA CHIP - Floor coverings ☆ - Tarkett, Inc.
PLAZA COURT - Floor coverings–carpet and rugs ☆ - World Carpets, Inc.
PLAZA DEPS - Footwear - Southern Leather & Shoe Co.
PLAZA GAME, THE - Games - S. Alden Inc.
PLAZA LIGHTS - Candy - Annedore's Fine Chocolates, Ltd.
PLAZA MARBLE - Floor coverings - Tarkett, Inc.
PLAZA MAYOR - Cheese - Crystal Food Import Corp.
PLAZA ONE - Cabinets–wood ☆ - Kitchen Kompact Inc.
PLAZA SANDURN - Ashtrays–metal ☆ - F.H. Lawson Co.
PLAZA SESAMO - Footwear - S. Goldberg and Co. Inc.
PLAZA SOUTH - Apparel and accessories - Kellwood Co.
PLAZA SOUTH PETITES - Apparel and accessories - Kellwood Co.
PLAZA SOUTH PLUS - Apparel and accessories - Kellwood Co.
PLAZA SQUARE - Floor coverings–carpet and rugs ☆ - Lees Carpets
PLAZA STONE - Floor coverings ☆ - Tarkett, Inc.
PLAZA SUITE - Floor coverings - Congoleum Corp.

☆ = Now out of production

PLAZA SUITE - Floor coverings–carpet and rugs ☆ - Gulistan Carpet Inc.
PLAZA SUITE - Hats - Chatom Collection
PLAZA SWEETS - Bakery products - Plaza Sweets Bakery
PLAZA, THE - Furniture ☆ - Bassett Furniture Industries, Inc.
PLAZA WHITE - Cabinets–wood ☆ - Kitchen Kompact Inc.
PLAZAMATE - Insulation materials - Dow Chemical Co.
PLAZCHEMCHEK - Chemical preparations - Abtox, Inc.
PLAZGAS - Gas machinery - Abtox, Inc.
PLAZVAX - Vaccines - Mallinckrodt Veterinary, Inc.
PLC - Musical instruments - Tropical Music and Pro Audio
PLC DIRECT - Computer peripheral equipment - PLC Direct by Koyo, Inc.
PLD DESIGNER - Computer software - Cadence Design Systems, Inc.
PLEASANCE - Dolls - Mattel, Inc.
PLEASANT BAY - Seafood products–fresh or frozen - Alaskan Seafood Co.
   Inc.
PLEASANT DREAMS - Christmas tree ornaments - Cracker Box Inc.
PLEASANT DREAMS - Pillows - Pillowtex Corp.
PLEASANT GROVE - Furniture ☆ - Bassett Furniture Industries, Inc.
PLEASANT HILL - Cabinets - Haas Cabinet Co. Inc.
PLEASANT HILL - Floor coverings–carpet and rugs - Eagle Carpets Inc.
PLEASANT HILL - Furniture - Thomasville Furniture Industries Inc.
PLEASANT HILL COLLECTION - Office furniture–wood - O'Sullivan
   Industries, Inc.
PLEASANT HILL FARMS - Coffee - Coffee & Tea Ltd.
PLEASANT LIVING - Floor coverings–carpet and rugs ☆ - Lees Carpets
PLEASANT LIVING - Wallpaper ☆ - Decorative Coverings Inc.
PLEASANT MOMENTS - Cookies - Mille Lacs Maple Products Corp.
PLEASANT-PLAY - Toys ☆ - Tracies Co.
PLEASANT RIDGE - Furniture ☆ - Bassett Furniture Industries, Inc.
PLEASANT THOUGHTS - Greeting cards - Pleasant Thoughts Inc.
PLEASANT VIEW - Milk - Pleasant View Dairy Corp.
PLEASANTDALE - Floor coverings–carpet and rugs ☆ - Masland Corp.
PLEASANTIME - Games - Pacific Game Co.
PLEASANTVILLE FARMS - Candy - Reader's Digest Association, Inc.
PLEASCENT - Deodorizers - Thornell Corp.
PLEASCENT - Hair care products - Helene Curtis Industries Inc.
PLEASE LET US LIVE - Apparel and accessories - Sabra International, Inc.
PLEASE MOM - Footwear - Southern Shoe Importers Inc.
PLEASE UNDERSTAND ME - Computer software - Cambridge Educational
PLEASER - Cameras - Eastman Kodak Co.
PLEASMOR - Dairy products ☆ - Nash-Finch Co.
PLEASON - Recording label - Pleason Records
PLEASONING - Seasoning - Frank J. Italiano Inc.
PLEASURABLE PIERCINGS - Jewelry - Pleasurable Piercings Inc.
PLEASURE - Floor coverings–carpet and rugs ☆ - Columbus Mills, Inc.
PLEASURE + - Grass seed - Ampac Seed Co.
PLEASURE - Rings–jewelry - Artcarved Inc.
PLEASURE DECKER - Boats–houseboats - H & H Molded Products
PLEASURE-KNIT - Apparel and accessories - Pleasure-Knit Corp.
PLEASURE LOK - Marine engine control apparatus - Andre L. Richard
PLEASURE MITT - Massage products - E.T.C., Inc.
PLEASURE PLUS - Prophylactics - Reddy Health Care Inc.
PLEASURE PUFF - Bath sponges - Sunshine Industries Inc.
PLEASURE-REST - Mattresses - Intex Recreation Corp.
PLEASURELAND - Candy ☆ - Shenandoah Candy Co. L.L.C.
PLEASURES - Floor coverings–carpet and rugs - Calladium & Marglen
PLEASURES - Underwear and nightwear - Maidenform Inc.
PLEASURES - Wallpaper - David & Dash
PLEASUREST - Bedding–linen - Kinder Manufacturing Corp.
PLEASURETONE - Enamels - Star Bronze Co. Inc.
PLEAT-A-STATIC - Filters–air - Genvac
PLEAT LAMP, THE - Hanging lamp ☆ - Interdesign, Inc.
PLEAT SEAT - Infant product ☆ - Gerry Baby Products Co.
PLEATED ELEGANCE - Underwear and nightwear - Maidenform Inc.
PLEATED IMPRESSIONS - Window coverings - Joanna Western Mills Co.
PLEATED MASTERPIECES - Window shades - Lafayette Venetian Blind, Inc.
PLEATEX - Window coverings ☆ - ESI
PLEATPAK - Multiple ply textile fabric - Southern Mills Inc.
PLEATS - Underwear and nightwear - Maidenform Inc.
PLEBEX - Pharmaceutical preparations ☆ - Wyeth-Ayerst Laboratories
PLECOMIN - Pet products - Tetra Sales USA
PLEDGE - Dust cloths - S.C. Johnson & Son, Inc.
PLEDGE EXTRA CARE - Furniture polish and wax - S.C. Johnson & Son, Inc.
PLEDGE WOOD RICH - Cleaning preparations–household - S.C. Johnson &
   Son, Inc.
PLEDGED PERFORMANCE - Paints ☆ - Devoe & Raynolds Co.

PLEE-ZING - Food products - Plee-Zing Inc.
PLEES - Jewelry - PJL Designs
PLEETSKIRT - Apparel–women's - Koret North America
PLEETWAY - Pajamas–men's - Knothe Corp.
PLEGINE - Pharmaceutical preparations - Wyeth-Ayerst Laboratories
PLEI-TECH - Automotive parts and accessories - Pleiger Plastics Co.
PLEIADES - Cigars - Swisher International, Inc.
PLEIADES - Recording label - Southern Illinois University Press
PLEIADES - Wines - Thackrey & Co.
PLEIADES RESEARCH - Computer software - Pleiades Research Corp.
PLEKX - Water purification systems - KX Industries, L.P.
PLEN-T-FUL - Fruits–canned - Cascadian Fruit Shippers
PLEN TEE COLOR - Fruit - Inland Fruit and Produce Co. Inc.
PLEN TEE GOLD - Apples - Inland Fruit and Produce Co. Inc.
PLENAIR PLUS - Dishes–earthenware - Teledyne Industries Inc.
PLENAMINS PLUS - Vitamins and nutritional supplements - Rexall Nutritional
   Products Inc.
PLENDELOR - Pharmaceutical preparations ☆ - U.S. Ethicals Inc.
PLENITUDE - Skin care products - Cosmair Inc.
PLENIUM - Vitamins and nutritional supplements - Millennium Marketplace, Inc.
PLENOS - Cigarettes - G.A. Georgopulo & Co. Inc.
PLENOZYME - Pharmaceutical preparations ☆ - U.S. Ethicals Inc.
PLENTIFUL PEA - Soups–canned - Buckeye Beans & Herbs, Inc.
PLENTITUDE ACTIVE DAILY MOISTURIZER - Skin care products - Cosmair
   Inc.
PLENTITUDE ADVANCED OVERNIGHT REPLENISHER - Skin care products
   - Cosmair Inc.
PLENTITUDE EXCELL-A3 - Skin care products - Cosmair Inc.
PLENTITUDE REVITALIFT - Cosmetics - Cosmair Inc.
PLENTY GOOD - Peanut butter ☆ - E.F. Lane & Son
PLENTY OF NOTHING - Underwear and nightwear ☆ - Lovable Co.
PLENTY TOUGH - Backpacks - Topwin Corp.
PLENTY TOUGH SPORT - Backpacks - Topwin Corp.
PLENUM FLEX 910 - Electrical equipment - Bicc Cables Corp.
PLENUM-GARD - Conduits - Lamson & Sessions Co.
PLENUM MASK - Construction equipment - Alcan Aluminum Corp. Alcan
   Building Products Div.
PLESSE PLUS - Wallpaper - Carlton-Metro Wallcoverings
PLESSEY - Radar systems and equipment - Plessey Electronics Corp.
PLETZ - Sandals - Pletz Imports
PLEURAL CAVITY - Health care products - Medi Inc.
PLEWS - Lubricating oils - Stantz Corp. (Plews Div.-Parker Automotive Group)
PLEX - Vitamins and nutritional supplements - Natural Organics, Inc.
PLEX-A-SEAL - Adhesives and sealants - Klein & Co.
PLEX ENCORE 1 - Broadcasting stations–cable television - Encore Media
   Corp.
PLEX-GRIP - Tape–adhesive - Chevron Chemical Co.
PLEXAFIL - Fibers–synthetic - E.I. Dupont de Nemours and Co.
PLEXCO BLUESTRIPE - Pipes–plastic - Chevron Chemical Co.
PLEXCOTE - Paints - Magnet Paint & Shellac Co. Inc.
PLEXERS AND MORE PLEXERS - Computer software ☆ - Ventura
   Educational Systems
PLEXI FLOWER - Desks - Wilderness Cards
PLEXI-GLASS GRAVERS - Tools - Armour Products
PLEXI-VIEW - Mirrors - Ram Products Co.
PLEXICHROME - Finishing agents - California Products Corp.
PLEXICOURT - Paints - California Products Corp.
PLEXICUSHION - Paints - California Products Corp.
PLEXIDECK - Paints ☆ - California Products Corp.
PLEXIDOR - Pet products - Petdoors USA
PLEXIES - Statuary ☆ - Creative Concepts
PLEXIFAIRING - Motorcycles ☆ - National Cycle Inc.
PLEXIFLOR - Coatings - California Products Corp.
PLEXIGLAS - Plastics–laminated - Rohm and Haas Co.
PLEXIPAVE - Paints - California Products Corp.
PLEXIPULSE - Medical apparatus - Kinetic Concepts, Inc.
PLEXIS - Computer software - Information Technologies Group, Inc.
PLEXISTAR - Motorcycles ☆ - National Cycle Inc.
PLEXLINK - Computer software - ISOCOR
PLEXO - Deodorants–personal - Alvin Last Inc.
PLEXO MOISTURE MAGIC - Cosmetics - Alvin Last Inc.
PLEXOLAN - Cosmetics - Alvin Last Inc.
PLEXON PIGTAIL - Flowers, plants, and seeds - Lifesake Faster-Form Co.
PLEXONAL - Pharmaceutical preparations ☆ - Sandoz Pharmaceuticals Corp.
PLEXUS - Alarms–personal - Plexus International, Inc.
PLEXUS - Cleaning preparations - Blake Schwartzman

☆ = Now out of production

PLEXUS - Cleaning preparations–window ☆ - John Dixon Inc.
PLEXUS WORD WEAVER - Computer software - Variety Games, Inc.
PLEXVENT - Venting system - Plexco
PLEYBEN - Bakery products - Campbell Soup Co.
PLEZALL WIPERS - Fabrics - Plezall Wipers Inc.
PLI-DRI - Dryers–hair ☆ - JRC Products Inc.
PLI-N-DRI - Paints ☆ - Foy-Johnston Inc.
PLI-N-DRI - Varnishes - Perry & Derrick Co.
PLI-SEAL - Paints ☆ - Watson-Standard Co.
PLI-SOL - Blinds–vertical - Coast to Coast Window Covering Fabricators Inc.
PLIA - Chairs–folding - Krueger International, Inc.
PLIA - Furniture - Haworth, Inc.
PLIAGEL - Ophthalmic goods - Alcon Laboratories, Inc.
PLIANCE - Hair care products - Tressa, Inc.
PLIANT WOOD - Wallpaper - Laminating Services Inc.
PLIANT WOOD II - Wallpaper - Laminating Services Inc.
PLIATEX - Artists' materials - Sculpture House Inc.
PLICORD - Hoses - Goodyear Tire & Rubber Co.
PLIKO MATIC - Toys - Peg Perego USA Inc.
PLIMATIC - Beauty shop equipment ☆ - JRC Products Inc.
PLIMED - Medical apparatus - Plicon Corp.
PLIMPTON'S - Labeling machinery ☆ - Litton Systems, Inc. (Airtron Division)
PLINK-KIT - Sporting goods ☆ - Safety Direct Inc.
PLINKSTER - Sporting goods - O.F. Mossberg & Sons, Inc.
PLIO-CALK - Caulking compounds - W.J. Ruscoe Co.
PLIO-MAGIC - Tape recorders–reels - Plastic Reel Corp. of America
PLIO-NAIL - Adhesives and sealants - W.J. Ruscoe Co.
PLIO-SEAM - Sealing compounds - W.J. Ruscoe Co.
PLIO-TAC - Adhesives and sealants - W.J. Ruscoe Co.
PLIO-TAC 38 - Adhesives and sealants - W.J. Ruscoe Co.
PLIOBOND - Adhesives and sealants ☆ - Goodyear Tire & Rubber Co.
PLIOCON - Adhesives and sealants - L.D. Sterns Corp.
PLIOFILM - Transparent sheet material ☆ - Goodyear Tire & Rubber Co.
PLIOFLEX - Enamels - Deboom Paint Co.
PLION - Sporting goods - Cortland Line Co., Inc.
PLIOSOFT - Floor coverings ☆ - Goodyear Tire & Rubber Co.
PLIOTEC - Resins–synthetic - Goodyear Tire & Rubber Co.
PLIOTONE - Waterproofing compounds - Fosroc Inc.
PLISSOL - Window coverings - Draco Corp.
PLISTOPUR - Pet products ☆ - Sera Aquaristik USA Inc.
PLIZZETTAS - Pizza - Pizzeria Uno Corp.
PLO - Thread - Belding Heminway Co. Inc.
PLOBANT - Veterinary nutritional supplements - Garmon Corp.
PLOCHMAN'S - Mustard - Plochman, Inc.
PLOCKY'S - Popcorn - Naturestar Foods, Inc.
PLOGIC - Computer software - Microsim Corp.
PLOP - Sporting goods - Plop Golf Co.
PLOPPSY BEAR - Toys–stuffed ☆ - Gund, Inc.
PLOPPSY PUPPY - Toys–stuffed ☆ - Gund, Inc.
PLOSSL - Lenses–optical - Tele Vue Optics Inc.
PLOT - Pens - Staedtler, Inc.
PLOT-COPIER BY ROTOLITE - Photocopy machines - Rotolite/Owen Manufacturing
PLOT'EM - Computer software - TFC Systems Corp.
PLOTFAST - Paper - National Printfast
PLOTMIUTIL - Computer software - Donald Argintar Associates Inc.
PLOTMIVIEW - Computer software - Donald Argintar Associates Inc.
PLOTPLUS - Computer peripheral equipment ☆ - QMS, Inc.
PLOTSTAR - Computer software - Structural Research and Analysis Corp.
PLOTTER PERFECT - Office supplies - Alvin and Co. Inc.
PLOUFFE'S - Food products - R.P. Foods
PLOVER - Binoculars - Swift Instruments, Inc.
PLOVER - Paper–bond ☆ - Fox River Paper Co.
PLOW BOY - Food products - Whitfield Foods, Inc.
PLOW BOY - Sportswear ☆ - Levi Strauss & Co.
PLOW HOSS - Garden equipment - Maxim Manufacturing Co.
PLOWEASE - Motor vehicle parts and accessories - MTS
PLOWRIGHT - Anchors ☆ - Woolsey Marine Industries
PLOWSHARES - Juices - Sunshower
PLOYSAFE - Vinyl - HPG International, Inc.
PLP - Flag poles - Flags International Inc.
PLP - Hand tools - Preformed Line Products Co.
PLP - Paints - Perfection Letz Paint Co.
P.L.S. - Computer software - Autograph USA, Inc.
PLS - Thread - Belding Heminway Co. Inc.
PLS-2 - Adhesives and sealants - Federal Process Co.

PLS-100 - Electronic equipment - General Electric Co.
PLT - Chemical preparations - Jones-Hamilton Co.
PLTK - Jewelry - Stanley Robin Inc.
PLUCK - Plant growth regulators - Cedar Chemical Corp.
PLUCK-IT - Skin care products - F.W. Engels Inc.
PLUCKETT - Toys–stuffed - Original Appalachian Artworks, Inc.
PLUCKETTS - Toys–stuffed - Original Appalachian Artworks, Inc.
PLUCKIE - Skin care products ☆ - Tweezerman Corp.
PLUCKY POPPLES - Toys ☆ - Those Characters from Cleveland, Inc.
PLUG - Recording label - P.M. Records Inc.
PLUG-A-JUG - Games ☆ - Parker Brothers
PLUG-A-LITE - Lighting fixtures - Swivelier Co. Inc.
PLUG-A-LOG - Animal feeds - Guy J. Loiselle
PLUG-ALL - Automotive parts and accessories - Thexton Manufacturing Inc.
PLUG & PUMP - Automotive parts and accessories - Stop & Go International
PLUG-CHECK - Electronic equipment - Hubbell Inc.
PLUG-IN OUTLET CENTER - Electrical equipment - Wiremold Co.
PLUG-INS - Deodorizers - S.C. Johnson & Son, Inc.
PLUG LOCK - Locks–padlocks - E.J. Brooks Co.
PLUG-MOUNTS - Lighting fixtures - Swivelier Co. Inc.
PLUG-N-GO - Electronic equipment - David Mcguire
PLUG RACK - Lighting fixtures - Swivelier Co. Inc.
PLUG-SEAL - Office supplies - Trend-Pak of Atlanta Inc.
PLUG-SEALS - Automotive parts and accessories - Manlee Industries Inc.
PLUG SNUGGERS - Electrical equipment - Frelen Corp.
PLUG-TITE - Hardware - American Stone-Mix Inc.
PLUGBOX - Electrical equipment - Hubbell Inc.
PLUGG - Apparel and accessories - Joel Auerbach, Craig Lackow, and Andrewkirplani Partnership
PLUGG-ITT - Adhesives and sealants ☆ - United Coatings Inc.
PLUGGED-IN - Hair care products ☆ - Dep Corp.
PLUGGER - Electrical equipment - Bowers Manufacturing Corp.
PLUGGO - Candy ☆ - Topps Co., Inc.
PLUGMATE - Lighting fixtures - Swivelier Co. Inc.
PLUGMOLD - Electrical equipment - Wiremold Co.
PLUG'N POWER - Remote control devices - Tandy Corp.
PLUG'N TALK - Remote control devices - Tandy Corp.
PLUGOUT - Plugs–electric - Hubbell Inc.
PLUG'R - Electrical equipment - Design and Development, Inc.
PLUGRA - Butter - Hotel Bar Foods Inc.
PLUGS - Pipes ☆ - Inflatable Technology Corp.
PLUGSTATION - Plugs–ear - Moldex-Metric Inc.
PLUGTRIM - Electrical equipment ☆ - Wiremold Co.
PLUM - Apparel and accessories - Plum Pudding, Ltd.
PLUM - Dinnerware–glass ☆ - Nikko Ceramics Inc.
PLUM - Giftware - Fenton Art Glass Co.
PLUM - Glass products - Blenko Glass Co. Inc.
PLUM - T-shirts–children's - Plum
PLUM & PUMICE FOOT SCRUB - Skin care products - Freeman Cosmetics Corp.
PLUM AVENUE - Apparel and accessories - Nordstrom, Inc.
PLUM BEAUTIFUL - Lipsticks - Schering-Plough Healthcare Products
PLUM BLOSSOM - Tableware–china ☆ - Lenox, Inc.
PLUM BROWN - Finishing agents - Birchwood Casey
PLUM CHERRY - Jams and jellies - Sarabeth's Kitchen
PLUM CRAZY - Christmas tree ornaments - Cracker Box Inc.
PLUM CRAZY - Pork - Minnesota Foodservice, Inc.
PLUM CRAZY - Wines - Heritage Wine Cellars
PLUM CREAM RINSE - Shampoos - Kim Laube & Co. Inc.
PLUM CREEK - Fiberboard - Plum Creek Lumber Co.
PLUM CREEK - Food products ☆ - Schwan's Sales Enterprises, Inc.
PLUM DELIGHT - Flowers, plants, and seeds - Hines Horticulture, Inc.
PLUM DUFF - Tobacco–chewing or smoking - Amar Blends Co.
PLUM FLOWER - Teas - Mayway Corp.
PLUM GARNET - Lipsticks - Lancome
PLUM GOLD - Nail care products ☆ - Cosmair Inc.
PLUM GOOD - Teas - Eastern Shore Tea Co.
PLUM HALL - Computer software - Plum Hall Inc.
PLUM INSUL-TRAC - Drapery hardware ☆ - Rockland Industries Inc.
PLUM LOCO - Jams and jellies - Sarabeth's Kitchen
PLUM PASSION - Flowers, plants, and seeds - Monrovia Nursery Co.
PLUM PERFECT - Toys - Tonka Corp.
PLUM PUDDING - Candles - San Francisco Candle Co.
PLUM PUDDING - Tobacco–chewing or smoking - Amar Blends Co.
PLUM PUDDY - Dolls - Susan Sona
PLUM RED - Stoneware dinnerware - Iron Mountain Stoneware Inc.

PLUM RUBY - Cosmetics - Lancome
PLUM SURPRISE - Nail care products - Cosmair Inc.
PLUM TOE - Socks - Synergy Enterprises Inc.
PLUM WHITE - Shampoos - Kim Laube & Co. Inc.
PLUM XL - Medical apparatus - Abbott Laboratories
PLUM XL3 - Medical apparatus - Abbott Laboratories
PLUMA - Apparel and accessories - Pluma Inc.
PLUMA - Computer software - Pluma, Inc.
PLUMB - Axes and hammers - Cooper Industries, Inc.
PLUMB CLEAN - Cleaning preparations - Kinzie & Payne Biochemical Corp.
PLUMB FINISH - Handles—wood - Sequatchie Handle Works Inc.
PLUMB FLO - Water filtration products - American Granby Inc.
PLUMB KITS - Hardware - Plumb Shop
PLUMB-LIGHT - Optical machinery ☆ - HD Electric Co.
PLUMB PAL - Hardware - Melard Manufacturing Corp.
PLUMB-PRO - Lawn mowers - Tee & Gee Sales
PLUMB QWIK - Pipes - Fernco Inc.
PLUMB RITE - Plumbing fixtures—metal - Sterling Plumbing Group Inc.
PLUMB SHOP - Hardware - Plumb Shop
PLUMBALLS - Health care products - Eden Foods, Inc.
PLUMBCRAFT - Hardware - Plumbcraft Manufacturing Corp.
PLUMBCRAFT - Plumbing fixtures—plastic - Waxman Industries Inc.
PLUMBER ONE - Drain pipe cleaners - Envirocare Distributors, Inc.
PLUMBER SEAL - Plumbing supplies, moldable putty - Atlas Minerals & Chemicals, Inc.
PLUMBERS ACTION - Drains - Ramco Chemical Inc.
PLUMBER'S CHOICE - Plumbing products - Waxman Industries Inc.
PLUMBERS CHORE - Solder - Fry Technology
PLUMBERS-EEL - Drain pipe cleaners ☆ - Elcal Enterprises Ltd.
PLUMBERS FAUCET, THE - Faucets - Brass Craft Manufacturing Co.
PLUMBER'S FORMULA - Hardware - A & V, Inc.
PLUMBER'S GOLD - Cleaning preparations - Paramount Distributing Co., Inc.
PLUMBER'S GOOP - Adhesives and sealants - Eclectic Products Inc.
PLUMBER'S HELPER - Drain pipe cleaners - AmeriPlus Inc.
PLUMBER'S KIT - Torches - Bernzomatic
PLUMBER'S PILLOW, THE - Pillows - Ron Stadum Co.
PLUMBERS PLUNGER - Drain cleaner - Comstar International Inc. (IPC Div.)
PLUMBLINE - Tools—hand-operated - Waxman Industries Inc.
PLUMBSET - Putties - La-Co Industries, Inc.
PLUMBTRIM - Plumbing fixtures - Brasstech, Inc.
PLUME - Computer software - University of Chicago
PLUME - Cutlery ☆ - Lifetime Hoan Corp.
PLUME - Publisher's imprints - Penguin USA
PLUME - Skin care products - Ella Bache Inc.
PLUME - Toys - Tonka Corp.
PLUME DE VEAU - Veal - Beatrice Cos. Inc.
PLUMLINE - Apparel and accessories - Alpenlite Inc.
PLUM!LINE - Floor coverings - P.W. Plumly Lumber Corp.
PLUMLINE DESIGN - Clocks - Plumline Design, Inc.
PLUMMY - Hair care products - Cosmair Inc.
PLUMOR - See ROATAN
PLUMP - Recording label - Plump Records, Inc.
PLUMP & JUICY - Meat products—poultry - Campbell Soup Co.
PLUMP & MEATY - Raisins ☆ - Dole Dried Fruit & Nut Co.
PLUMP AND TENDER - Meat products—poultry ☆ - Stevens Industries Inc.
PLUMP 'N' TASTY - Frankfurters ☆ - Hudson Foods, Inc.
PLUMP-PETS - Toys—stuffed ☆ - Fun World Inc.
PLUMP PLAYMATES - Toys—stuffed - Centsable Toys Inc.
PLUMP RECORDS - Recording label - AGF Entertainment Ltd.
PLUMPEES - Dolls - Uneeda Doll Co., Inc.
PLUMPERS - Frankfurters - Dubuque Foods, Inc.
PLUMPJACK - Apparel and accessories - Gavin G. Newsom
PLUMPKINS - Candy - R.M. Palmer Co.
PLUMPS - Bakery products - Alvin Burger
PLUMPY PIG - Toys—stuffed - Russ Berrie and Co., Inc.
PLUMRITE - Pipes—brass ☆ - Olin Corp.
PLUMROSE - Bacon - Plumrose Inc.
PLUMSTONE - Cosmetics - Cosmair Inc.
PLUMTREE - Giftware ☆ - Plumtree Products
PLUNGE - Cleaning preparations ☆ - Drackett Co.
PLUNGE DIVERS - Shorts—men's - Chums Ltd.
PLUNGER - Dust-mop handles and ferrules - American Textile Products Co.
PLUNGEREST - Archery equipment - New Archery Products Corp.
PLUNGING PEARLS - Jewelry - Richelieu Corp.
PLUNKETT - Toys—stuffed ☆ - Gund, Inc.
PLUNKETTE - Toys—stuffed ☆ - Gund, Inc.

PLUQUET - Food products - Europa Foods Ltd.
PLURA-COAT - Photographic equipment - SP Systems/Saratons
PLURACOL - Chemical preparations - BASF Corp.
PLURACOL HP - Chemical preparations - BASF Corp.
PLURAFOAM - Machinery - Nordson Corp.
PLURAZYME - Biological products ☆ - Kinzie & Payne Biochemical Corp.
PLURI-B - Pharmaceutical preparations - Pasadena Research Laboratories, Inc.
PLURI-BEX - Pharmaceutical preparations ☆ - Pasadena Research Laboratories, Inc.
PLUS - Adhesives and sealants - Maxus Energy Corp.
PLUS - Boats—motor - Duracraft Boats Inc.
PLUS! - Computer software - Microsoft Corp.
PLUS - Computer software - Pierce Leahy Corp.
PLUS - Electronics equipment - Ampex Corp.
PLUS - Floor coverings—carpet and rugs - Columbus Mills, Inc.
PLUS - Furniture - Ben Big Group America Inc.
PLUS - Health care products - Leisure Lift, Inc.
PLUS - Musical instrument accessories - American Way Marketing Inc.
PLUS - Paper—tissue ☆ - Plainwell Tissue
PLUS - Pet products - Nekton USA Inc.
PLUS - Radios—citizens' band - Cobra Electronics Corp.
PLUS - Tobacco products - Philip Morris Companies Inc.
PLUS - Wheelchairs - Fortress Inc.
PLUS 1 - Golf equipment - MasterGrip Inc.
PLUS 3 - Chemical preparations - United States Gypsum Co.
PLUS 3 - Cooking utensils—aluminum - Wilton Industries, Inc.
PLUS 3 - Cosmetics ☆ - Noxell Corp.
PLUS 4 - Socks - Adams-Millis Corp.
PLUS 5 - Marble products - Georgia Marble Co.
PLUS 10 - Medical apparatus - Essex PB&R Corp.
PLUS 19 - Pens ☆ - Empire Berol USA
PLUS 30 - Skin care products ☆ - Bonne Bell, Inc.
PLUS-50 - Electronic equipment - Reeves Soundcraft
PLUS-50 - Oils—lubricating - Deere & Co.
PLUS 111 - Scooters—motorized - Leisure Lift, Inc.
PLUS 128 - Disinfectant ☆ - Intex Chemical Inc.
PLUS 256 - Disinfectant ☆ - Intex Chemical Inc.
PLUS, A - Gasoline ☆ - Ashland Oil, Inc.
PLUS, A - Frames—eyeglass - May Optical Co. Inc.
PLUS ACTIVE NEW CELL - Skin care products ☆ - Jason Natural Products, Inc.
PLUS/AIDA - Fabrics - E Z International, Inc.
PLUS CLASS - Women's apparel - India Garments Inc.
PLUS DATA - Computer peripheral equipment - Comark, Inc.
PLUS DESIGN - Wallpaper - Planox
PLUS-FIFTY - Fire extinguishers - Ansul, Inc.
PLUS FOUR - Darts and dart games - Great Lakes Dart Distributors, Inc.
PLUS GOLD COLLECTION, THE - Jewelry - Aurafin Corp.
PLUS HEAD - Gypsum wallboard nails - Independent Nail Inc.
PLUS III - Floor coverings—carpet and rugs ☆ - Heuga USA
PLUS LEAN - Animal feed - Vigortone AG Products Inc.
PLUS MARK - Greeting cards - American Greetings Corp.
PLUS MATIC - Blenders - Sunbeam-Oster Household Products
PLUS 'N MINUS - Toys - Tyco Toys
PLUS-N-PRETTY - Pet products - Richard Hanau Pet Foods Corp.
PLUS-ONE - Apparel—men's - Nordstrom, Inc.
PLUS ONE - Games ☆ - Milton Bradley Co.
PLUS-PAK - Luggage ☆ - Samsonite Corp.
PLUS PLATINUM - Razor blades ☆ - Schick/Wilkinson
PLUS + POCKETS - Stationery - Stuart Hall Co., Inc.
PLUS POWER - Microphones ☆ - Lectrosonics Inc.
PLUS PREFERRED - Apparel and accessories - Wal-Mart Stores Inc.
PLUS SERIES - Computer hardware - Jo-Dan International, Inc.
PLUS TL - Medical apparatus - Cordis Corp.
PLUS USA - Furniture—public buildings - Plus Office Systems Corp.
PLUS VALUE, A - Cleaning preparations - AmeriPlus Inc.
PLUS + WHITE - Toothpaste - CCA Industries, Inc.
PLUS-X - Film - Eastman Kodak Co.
PLUS+3 - Fruit drinks—bottled or canned - Kiko Foods, Inc.
PLUS4 - Hand tools - Vermont American Corp.
PLUSCAPS - Pharmaceutical preparations - Extracts Plus, Inc.
PLUSH - Apparel and accessories - Real Chill, Inc.
PLUSH - Brassieres (Bras) ☆ - Lovable Co.
PLUSH - Furniture - Haworth, Inc.
PLUSH - Pet products - Nickers International Ltd.

☆ = Now out of production

PLUSH GLIDER - Recliners - Sheffield Chair Co.
PLUSH LIFE - Floor coverings ☆ - General Felt Industries, Inc.
PLUSH LIQUID - Paints ☆ - Fuller-O'Brien Paints Inc.
PLUSH, LUSH'N LIVELY - Synthetic turf - Instant Turf Industries Inc.
PLUSH PALS - Slippers - Venture Stores, Inc.
PLUSH PARADE - Toys—stuffed - Ace Novelty Co. Inc.
PLUSH-PELT - Fabrics - Mangelsen's (VDI)
PLUSH POMS - Novelty items - Wellington Leisure Products, Inc.
PLUSH PUPPIES - Pet products - Mason Distributing
PLUSH RECESS - Floor coverings ☆ - American Floor Products Co. Inc.
PLUSH SPLENDOR - Floor coverings—carpet and rugs ☆ - Karastan-Bigelow Inc.
PLUSH TOP - Floor coverings—carpet and rugs - Ludlow Composites Corp.
PLUSH TUFF - Floor coverings - Apache Mills Inc.
PLUSH-TUFT - Cushions - Klear-Vu Corp.
PLUSH TURF I - Floor coverings—carpet and rugs ☆ - Playfield International Inc.
PLUSH-TWIST - Floor coverings - American Floor Products Co. Inc.
PLUSHE - Floor coverings—carpet and rugs ☆ - Gulistan Carpet Inc.
PLUSHETTE - Novelty items—stitched - Santa's Best
PLUSHPUPS - Toys—stuffed - MT & B Corp.
PLUSHTEC TEXTURE - Moccasins - Acorn
PLUSHTEX - Floor mats - U.S. Rubber Recycling Inc.
PLUSHY - Floor coverings—carpet and rugs ☆ - Royalweve Carpet Mills
PLUSNET - Computer terminals - Hadax Electronics, Inc.
PLUS+TWO - Golf clubs - Fred Pelzer Golf Supplies
PLUSWOOD - Wood products ☆ - Pluswood Inc.
PLUT STATION - Computer software - Cadnet Corp.
PLUTARCH PRESS - Publisher's imprints - Omnigraphics Inc.
PLUTO - Floor coverings - American Floor Products Co. Inc.
PLUTO - Pencils - Koh-I-Noor, Inc.
PLUTO - Tools - Pluto Tool Co.
PLUTO - Underwear and nightwear ☆ - M.A. Rabinowitz Corp.
PLUTO PET - Pet products - J. Narby Inc.
PLUTOMAT - Pet products - Rolf C. Hagen (USA) Corp.
PLUTONITE - Eyeglasses - Oakley, Inc.
PLUTOX - Computer software - SourceView Software International
PLUVIMIN - Vitamins and nutritional supplements - Phoenix Laboratories, Inc.
PLUVIUS - Pencils ☆ - Koh-I-Noor, Inc.
PLV - Health care products - Respironics, Inc.
PLY - Skin care products - Milburn Co.
PLY-BEAD - Siding—insulating - Georgia-Pacific Corp.
PLY-BRIK - Veneer - R. Wayne Newsome
PLY-CLIPS - Hardware - Gordon Machinery & Supply Co. Inc.
PLY FRAME - Plywood - Georgia-Pacific Corp.
PLY-GEMS - Plywood - Ply-Gem Manufacturing Corp.
PLY-LASTIC - Paints - M.A. Bruder & Sons Inc.
PLY-LITE - Insulating glass - American Tempering Inc. (Laminating Div.)
PLY-MASTIC - Paints - M.A. Bruder & Sons Inc.
PLY-TEX - Travel accessories - American Guard-It Manufacturing Co. Inc.
PLY-THANE - Paints - M.A. Bruder & Sons Inc.
PLY-TILE - Paints - M.A. Bruder & Sons Inc.
PLY-TILER - Floor coverings—tile ☆ - Tec Inc.
PLY TRIM - Garden equipment - Plastigage Corp. (Gordon Plastics Div.)
PLY-VENEER - Wood products - Weyerhaeuser Co.
PLY X-100 FR - Fire retardant film - Reef Industries, Inc.
PLYARC - Tape—adhesive - Plymouth Rubber Co., Inc.
PLYBOND - Adhesives and sealants - North Jersey Paint Co. Inc.
PLYCAST - Epoxy - Plymouth Rubber Co., Inc.
PLYCOM - Tape—adhesive - Plymouth Rubber Co., Inc.
PLYCOMFORT - Furniture—upholstered ☆ - Selig Manufacturing Co.
PLYCRAFT - Doors—garage - Plycraft Fabricating Corp.
PLYCRAFT - Furniture ☆ - J. Kenneth Zahn
PLYDEK - Plywood - Harbor Sales Co.
PLYDUCT - Tape—adhesive - Plymouth Rubber Co., Inc.
PLYEX - Canvas—artists' ☆ - M. Grumbacher Inc.
PLYEX - Paper—thermoplastics coated - K & M Co.
PLYFLASH - Wood products - Nichols-Homeshield Inc.
PLYFLEX - Electrical equipment - Plymouth Rubber Co., Inc.
PLYFLEX - Strapping - Brainard Strapping
PLYFOLD - Insulating materials - Tenneco Packaging Inc.
PLYFOLD - Paper—toweling - Fort Howard Corp.
PLYGLAS - Tape—adhesive - Plymouth Rubber Co., Inc.
PLYJOINT - Electrical equipment - Plymouth Rubber Co., Inc.
PLYLON - Enamels - Pratt & Lambert United, Inc.
PLYMARK - Wire products - Plymouth Rubber Co., Inc.

PLYMOUTH - Brooms - Lighthouse Industries
PLYMOUTH - Cabinets - Imperial Cabinet Co. Inc.
PLYMOUTH - Clocks - General Time Corp. (Westclox/Seth Thomas Div.)
PLYMOUTH - Daters and numberers - Consolidated Stamp Manufacturing Co. Inc.
PLYMOUTH - Dinnerware ☆ - Corning Inc.
PLYMOUTH - Fabrics - Superior Shade & Blind Co. Inc.
PLYMOUTH - Flatware ☆ - Kirk Stieff Co.
PLYMOUTH - Fruits and vegetables - Plymouth Citrus Products Cooperative
PLYMOUTH - Giftware ☆ - Gorham Inc.
PLYMOUTH - Hardware - Gordon Associates
PLYMOUTH - Meat products—beef - Plymouth Beef Co.
PLYMOUTH - Men's shoes ☆ - Bostonian Shoe Co.
PLYMOUTH - Motor vehicles - Chrysler Corp. (Chrysler-Plymouth Div.)
PLYMOUTH - Motor vehicles - DaimlerChrysler
PLYMOUTH - Rope - Columbian Rope Co.
PLYMOUTH - Tools - Great Neck Saw Manufacturers, Inc.
PLYMOUTH BRICK - Floor coverings - Congoleum Corp.
PLYMOUTH COLONY - Flatware ☆ - Wallace International Silversmiths, Inc.
PLYMOUTH DOWNEASTER - Rope - Columbian Rope Co.
PLYMOUTH FARMS - Cheese ☆ - Sargento Cheese Co. Inc.
PLYMOUTH HOLLOW - Clocks ☆ - General Time Corp. (Westclox/Seth Thomas Div.)
PLYMOUTH LANDING - Dolls ☆ - Effanbee Doll Corp.
PLYMOUTH MANOR - Wallpaper ☆ - Stonebridge Co.
PLYMOUTH PANTRY - Bakery products - Log House Foods Inc.
PLYMOUTH PLANK - Floor coverings - National Floor Products Co., Inc.
PLYMOUTH PRIDE - Turkeys - Norbest Inc.
PLYMOUTH ROCK - Beverages—carbonated ☆ - American 76 Co.
PLYMOUTH ROCK - Furniture ☆ - Athens Furniture Industries Inc.
PLYMOUTH ROCK - Gelatin - Adit Corp.
PLYMOUTH ROCK - Seafood products—fresh or frozen - Plymouth Rock Trout
PLYMOUTH SHELL - Cutlery ☆ - Lifetime Hoan Corp.
PLYMOUTH SLIP-ON - Mops ☆ - Helen Keller Services for the Blind
PLYMOUTH SUPREME - Water purification systems - Ametek, Inc.
PLYOBALL - Sporting goods - Metapro, Inc.
PLYON - Ribbons—inked - Buckeye Business Products Inc.
PLYOTHOL - Skin care products - Milburn Co.
PLYPAK - Electrical equipment - Plymouth Rubber Co., Inc.
PLYPAK - Envelopes - U.S.A. Direct, Inc.
PLYRON - Siding—insulating ☆ - Forestex Co.
PLYSCAF - Construction equipment - Plyscaf Corp.
PLYSCULPTURE - Wood products - Easi-Bild Directions Simplified Inc.
PLYSEAL - Tape—adhesive - Plymouth Rubber Co., Inc.
PLYSIL - Tape—adhesive - Plymouth Rubber Co., Inc.
PLYSTAIN - Paints - Fulton Co.
PLYSTICK - Health care products - Larkotex Surgical Manufacturing Co.
PLYSTRAN - Plywood ☆ - Potlatch Corp.
PLYSTRING - Tape—adhesive - Industrial Adhesives, Inc.
PLYTAPE - Tape—adhesive - Industrial Adhesives, Inc.
PLYTERM - Electrical equipment - Plymouth Rubber Co., Inc.
PLYTEX - Paints - Mac-O-Lac Paints Inc.
PLYTUFF - Tape—adhesive - Plymouth Rubber Co., Inc.
PLYVOLT - Tape—adhesive - Plymouth Rubber Co., Inc.
PLYWALL - Lumber - Hoover Treated Wood Products Inc.
PLYWELD - Abrasive products - Norton Co.
PLYWOOD TOTER - Tools ☆ - Metaltek
PLYWOODIE'S - Plywood - Harbor Sales Co.
PLYWRAP - Tape—adhesive - Plymouth Rubber Co., Inc.
PM - Phoenix Mecano, Inc.
PM - Amplifiers - Pacific Monolithics
PM - Boats—motor - Starcraft Corp.
PM - Gasoline - Petroleum Marketers Inc.
PM - Motorcycle parts and accessories - Performance Machine, Inc.
PM - Paper - PM Co. (Office Products Div.)
P.M. - Recording label - P.M. Records Inc.
PM - Watches - A.P. Imports Inc.
P.M. - Whiskey - Jim Beam Brands Co.
PM BLUES - Cigarettes - Philip Morris Companies Inc.
PM BROWNS - Tobacco products - Philip Morris Companies Inc.
PM CHURCHILL - Luggage - Winn International Corp.
P.M. COLD FORMULA - Cold remedies ☆ - Church and Dwight Co. Inc.
PM COLLECTION - Apparel and accessories - Montgomery Ward & Co. Inc.
PM COLLECTIONS - Apparel and accessories - Rated P.G. Apparel, Inc.
PM CRAFTSMAN - Giftware - P.M. Craftsman
P.M. EDITION STREET UPDATE - Apparel—men's - Dino DiMilano Corp.

☆ = Now out of production

PM/FOCUS - Computer software - Information Builders, Inc.
PM GOLDLINE - Tobacco products - Philip Morris Companies Inc.
PM JR. - Medical apparatus - Hill Rom, Inc.
PM-MED - Electronic equipment - Paul-Munroe Engineering International
PM MONITER - Audio cabinets–wood - Design Direct Sound
PM SLIM LINE - Hair care products - Paul Mazzotta Inc.
PM SPORTS - Apparel - PM Enterprises, Inc.
PMA - Computer peripheral equipment - Prosthetic Memory Aid Systems Inc.
PMA - Contact lenses - Cooper Companies Inc.
PMA - Cosmetics - Research Council of Make-Up Artists Inc.
PMA PENCIL MAKERS ASSOCIATION CERTIFIED CONFORMS TO ASTM STANDARD D4236 - Pencils - Pencil Makers Association, Inc.
PMADVISOR - Computer software - Risk Data Corp.
PMAX - Mirrors–optical - Photran Corp.
PMB - Pharmaceutical preparations - Wyeth-Ayerst Laboratories
PMC - Adhesives and sealants - IDL Manufacturing & Sales Corp.
PMC - Jewelry–precious - Patterson Manufacturing
P.M.C. - Paints - Kwal-Howells Inc.
PMC - Pet products - Petmanco International Inc.
PMC - Skin care products - Face Up Professional Skin Centers Inc.
P.M.C. - Toiletries - Thomas & Thompson Co. Inc.
PMD - Computer software ☆ - Welcom
PMD - Tape players–cassette - Superscope Technologies, Inc./Marantz Professional
PMI - Gloves - Pigeon Mountain Industries, Inc.
PMI - Hardware - Product Merchandisers, Inc.
PMI - Toys–trains - Model Power
PMIO - Cosmetics - Ray Hayes Inc.
PML - Lenses–photographic - Ercona Corp.
PML - Skin care products - Dynex International
PML - Watches ☆ - SMH (US) Inc.
PMLINK - Computer software - Fluke Corp.
PMO - Electronics equipment ☆ - Pinnacle Micro, Inc.
PMP COMPOUND - Pharmaceutical preparations ☆ - Mericon Industries Inc.
PMR 2000 - Telephone answering machines - Motorola, Inc. (Land Mobile Products Sector)
PMS - Amplifiers–musical instrument - Pacific Music Supply Co.
PMS - Food products - Adweek L.P.
PMS - Vitamins and nutritional supplements - Marlyn Co. Inc.
PMS - Vitamins and nutritional supplements - Schiff Products, Inc.
PMS BALANCE - Vitamins and nutritional supplements - Rexall Nutritional Products Inc.
PMS ESCAPE - Vitamins and nutritional supplements - Internutria, Inc.
PMS FORMULA - Herbal products - 21st Century Manna
PMS FORTE - Health care products - Futurebiotics
PMS PLUS - Health care products - Futurebiotics
PMS RELEAF - Health care products - Lake Consumer Products
PMS SOLUTION - Health care products - Advantage Life Products Inc.
PMS SOOTHER - Vitamins and nutritional supplements - Barth-Spencer Corp.
PMS-STOP - Health care products - Natural Laboratories Corp.
PMSTER - Apparel and accessories - Stephen Thomas Clark and Carolyn Louise Clark Partnership
PMSTER - Apparel and accessories - Stephen Thomas Clark and Carolyn Louise Clark Partnership
PMT - Photographic equipment - Eastman Kodak Co.
PMT - Tires - Dico Tire Inc.
PMVISUALS - Computer software - PMVisuals, Inc.
PMX - Sound equipment - Gemini Sound Products Corp.
PN - Computer software - Progressive Networks, Inc.
PN 8D - Skin care products - Nemectron Skin Care Inc.
PN 700 - Cleaning preparations ☆ - Joan Maroney
PN-STIM-KATH - Medical apparatus - Medical Evaluation Devices & Instruments Corp.
PNA - Computer software - Esq Business Services, Inc.
PNA - Jewelry - Pranda North America, Inc.
PNB NATION - Apparel and accessories - PNB Nation, Inc.
PNC - Nutritional product ☆ - Ion Laboratories Inc.
PNC - Vitamins and nutritional supplements - Pharmacists' Nutrition Center
PNEU-CARE - Beds–hospital - Humanetics Inc.
PNEU-CHOICE - Screws - H. Belmer Co.
PNEU-FLUSH - Chemical preparations - Nu-Calgon Wholesaler, Inc.
PNEU-LIFT - Exercising equipment - Quinton Instrument Co.
PNEU TOUCH - Labeling machinery - PTI, Inc.
PNEU-TRAC - Medical apparatus - United States Manufacturing Co.
PNEUBACK - Sporting goods - Marty Gilman Inc.
PNEUFLEX - Hardware - Oliver Rubber Co.

PNEUMANT - Tires - Intersceptyre Tyres Inc.
PNEUMATIC - Apparel and accessories - Patagonia, Inc.
PNEUMATIC - Drills–electric - Rock Hog Rock Drilling Products USA
PNEUMO PULSSOR - Respirators - Strom Corp.
PNEUMOMIST - Cough medicines - ECR Pharmaceuticals
PNEUMONIA KNOCKER - Veterinary pharmaceutical preparations - Friona Industries, LP
PNEUMOPATTER - Skin care products - Nemectron Skin Care Inc.
PNEUMOTOX - Veterinary pharmaceutical preparations - Sanofi Animal Health, Inc.
PNEUMOTUSSIN - Cough medicines - ECR Pharmaceuticals
PNEUMOTUSSIN HC - Pharmaceutical preparations - ECR Pharmaceuticals
PNEUMOVAX 23 - Vaccines - Merck & Co., Inc. (Merck Research Laboratories)
PNEUPARAPAC - Veterinary pharmaceutical preparations - Schering-Plough Animal Health
PNM SWINE CENTER - Animal feed supplements - Pro-Edge Ltd.
PNPVIEW - Computer software ☆ - Systemsoft Corp.
PNTCO - Luggage - Purdy Neat Things Co., Inc.
PNU-LIGHT - Tools–power-driven - Pnu-Light Tool Works, Inc.
PO BOLLI - Analgesics - Polam Wholesale Inc.
PO BOY FARMS - Fruits and vegetables - Purepak, Inc.
PO-DO - Doughnuts–mixes - L. Karp & Sons, Inc.
PO-GO - Fishing lures - Fish World Inc.
PO-KE-NO - Games - United States Playing Card Co.
PO-POLSKU - Pickles - Ripon Pickle Co. Inc.
POA ALPINA - Flowers, plants, and seeds - Jacklin Seed
POA TRIVIALIS - Flowers, plants, and seeds - Jacklin Seed
POAKALANI - Patterns–clothing - Pauloa Hawaii Ltd.
POATUS - Audio equipment - Unizeal Trading Inc.
POAUL EUROPEAN - Toiletries - Poaul European, Inc.
POB BOOKS - Publisher's imprints - Stanyan Record Co.
POBLANO - Sauces - Poblano Hot Sauce Co.
POC A BALL - Apparel–athletic - Georgia's Tennis
POC-A-BALL - Apparel–women's - Milaca Mills, Inc.
POC-IT-FILE - Office supplies - Dome Publishing Co., Inc.
POC-KIT - Tools - Precision Brand Products, Inc.
POC PEOPLE OF COLOR - Apparel and accessories - Lavetta C. Willis
POCAHONTAS - Boats–canoes - Nautical Boats Ltd.
POCAHONTAS - Food products - Pocahontas Foods USA Inc.
POCAHONTAS - Footwear - Wolverine World Wide, Inc.
POCAHONTAS - Preserved foods–prepackaged - Anchor Food Products, Inc.
POCAHONTAS - Toothbrushes - Zooth Inc.
POCAHONTAS - Turkeys - Watson Quality Foods Inc.
POCAI - See **BALLENTINE**
POCANBID - Pharmaceutical preparations - Parke-Davis
POCCO BAGS - Handbags - Architraders Inc.
POCE - Computer software - Pantone, Inc.
POCINO - Food products - Pocino Foods Co.
POCINO FITNESS - Food products - Pocino Foods Co.
POC'IT HOPPER - Fishing lure - Mister Twister, Inc.
POCK-A-ROOS! - Computer peripheral equipment - Focal Point Marketing, Inc.
POCK-IT - Handbags - Steven Wayne Gallegos
POCKARAT - Scales - Polyproducts Corp.
POCKET - Toys - Tonka Corp.
POCKET ACCENT - Pens - Sanford Corp.
POCKET APPRAISER - Calculators - Calculated Industries, Inc.
POCKET BAG - Leather goods - AR Accessories Group Inc.
POCKET BASEBALL - Card game - Pocket Baseball, Inc.
POCKET BAT - Toys - James P. O'Rourke
POCKET BEN - Watches - General Time Corp. (Westclox/Seth Thomas Div.)
POCKET BINDER - Binders - Victor Cornelius, Inc.
POCKET BOGGLE - Games ☆ - Parker Brothers
POCKET BOOK - Photo albums - Holson Burnes Group
POCKET BOOKS - Publisher's imprints - Simon & Schuster, Inc.
POCKET BOOKS SOFTWARE - Computer software - Simon & Schuster, Inc.
POCKET BORDER - Hobby kits - Pocket Poster, Inc.
POCKET CADDY - Tape recorders–cassette ☆ - Lanier Voice Products
POCKET CAMERA - Toys - Fisher-Price, Inc.
POCKET CHAIN SAW - Saws–hand-operated - Supreme Products, Inc.
POCKET CHANGE - Infant product ☆ - Newborne Co.
POCKET CHARADES - Games - Brown and Bigelow Inc.
POCKET CLASSIC - Radio communications equipment - Motorola, Inc. (Land Mobile Products Sector)
POCKET CLASSICS - Food products - Lamb-Weston, Inc.
POCKET CLIP - Pens - Sheaffer Inc.

☆ = Now out of production

POCKET COFFEE - Candy - Ferrero U.S.A Inc.
POCKET COMICS - Toys - Toy Biz, Inc.
POCKET COMMUNICATIONS SYSTEM - Telephones - Spectralink Corp.
POCKET CRITTERS - Pet products - Dynamic Development
POCKET CRITTERS - Toys - Fun Stuff, Inc.
POCKET DRIVE - Boats - Action Craft, Inc.
POCKET DRUGSTORE - Pharmaceutical preparations - Nirvana Labs
POCKET DUAL AFP - Camera - Chinon America Inc.
POCKET DUAL P - Camera - Chinon America Inc.
POCKET ESCORT - Dictating machines - Lanier Voice Products
POCKET EXECUTOR - Publisher's imprints - Keith E. Schubert
POCKET FISHERMAN - Sporting goods - RonCo Inc.
POCKET FOOTBALL - Football game - A.W. Vidmer & Co.
POCKET FRUIT - Snack foods - David and Sons Inc.
POCKET GOURMET - Novelty items–paper - Antioch Publishing Co.
POCKET HANDYMAN - Calculators - Calculated Industries, Inc.
POCKET HARTMANN - Luggage - Hartmann Luggage Co.
POCKET II - Stoves - Coleman Co., Inc.
POCKET INK - Inks - A Quill in Time
POCKET-IT - Pouches - CCH Novelty Co.
POCKET JET II - Printers–computer - Pentax Technologies Corp.
POCKET LAWYER - Toys - Victoria Thomas
POCKET LIBERATOR - Leather goods - Opus 63 Design Lab Inc.
POCKET LOCK-IT - Locks–door ☆ - Lori Lock
POCKET LOCKER - Stationery - Stuart Hall Co., Inc.
POCKET-LOK - Stake pocket anchor systems - JS Products
POCKET LUNCH - Sandwiches–prepackaged - Denny's Inc.
POCKET MANAGERS - Office supplies - Wallace Computer Services, Inc.
POCKET MANIA - Paper products - Elmer's Investments, Inc.
POCKET-MATE - Flashlights ☆ - Streamlight, Inc.
POCKET-MATIC - Cameras ☆ - Keystone Camera Corp.
POCKET MESSENGER - Pagers - Bell Atlantic Corp.
POCKET MINDER - Calendars ☆ - Keith Clark Inc.
POCKET MUSEUM - Toys - Uncle Milton Industries Inc.
POCKET NACHO - Snack foods - Chili Chips Inc.
POCKET NAIL GENIE - Beauty shop equipment - Protec International
POCKET NURSE - Computer software - Physix Inc.
POCKET OF DREAMS - Pillows - Robin B. Powell
POCKET OF LOVE - Clothing - Rad Marketing Services, Inc.
POCKET OFFICE - Furniture - Pocket Office
POCKET PAC - Candy - Bradley Candy Manufacturing Co.
POCKET PACK - Rope - Wellington Leisure Products, Inc.
POCKET PACKER - Stationery - Stuart Hall Co., Inc.
POCKET-PADS - Paper products - Paper Conversions Inc.
POCKET PAGER - Pagers - Page Alert Systems
POCKET-PAK - Ammunition - Olin Corp. (Winchester Div.)
POCKET PAK - Ammunition ☆ - Crosman Corp.
POCKET-PAK - Plugs–ear - Moldex-Metric Inc.
POCKET PAK - Sporting goods - Camp-Cap Products
POCKET PAL - Electronic equipment - Newport Electronic, Inc.
POCKET PAL - Harmonicas - Hohner Inc.
POCKET PAL - Maps ☆ - CIR Products Inc.
POCKET PAL - Novelty items - Mitchener & Upton Games, Inc.
POCKET PAL - Stationery ☆ - Diagraph Corp.
POCKET PALS - Apparel–children's - Pocket Pals Ltd.
POCKET PALS - Footwear–athletic - E.S. Originals, Inc.
POCKET PALS - Novelty items - Risto Inc.
POCKET PARTNER - Screw drivers - Alexander Manufacturing Co.
POCKET PARTY - Novelty items–paper - Pocket Party
POCKET PDR - Computers–personal - Me Licensing Corp.
POCKET PEN - Pens - Creative Promotional Products, Ltd.
POCKET PENGUIN - Fans–electric - Circulair, Inc.
POCKET PENS - Pens - Gift Creations, Inc.
POCKET PENTE - Games ☆ - Parker Brothers
POCKET PERFECT - Dog food - Charlee Bear Farms, Inc.
POCKET PET SERIES - Video production - Bear Valley Productions International
POCKET PIANO - Toys–musical - Mattel, Inc.
POCKET PILLOW - Pillows - Cascade Designs, Inc.
POCKET PISTOL - Dryers–hair ☆ - Sunbeam-Oster Household Products
POCKET PLAY - Toys - Lewis Galoob Toys, Inc.
POCKET PLAYERS GUIDE - Publisher's imprints - Wizards of the Coast, Inc.
POCKET POP-UPS - Publisher's imprints - Heian International Inc.
POCKET POPPLES - Toys–stuffed - Mattel, Inc.
POCKET PORTABLE - Medical apparatus - Eagle Medical Equipment Co.
POCKET POSITIVE - Pistols ☆ - Colt's Manufacturing Co. Inc.

POCKET POSTER - Containers–paper - Pocket Poster, Inc.
POCKET POWER - Chewing gum - Philadelphia Chewing Gum Corp.
POCKET PRETZELS - Snack foods - Maxim Marketing Corp.
POCKET PRINCIPLES - Games - Brown and Bigelow Inc.
POCKET-PRO - Tape recorder - L & M Auto Supply
POCKET PRO - Voltmeters - A.W. Sperry Instruments, Inc.
POCKET PROFESSIONAL - Computer software - da Vinci Technologies Group, Inc.
POCKET PROS - Games - Tiger Electronics, Inc.
POCKET PROTEGE - Tape recorders–cassette - Lanier Voice Products
POCKET PUFFERS - Pipes–tobacco - Gesty Trading & Manufacturing Corp.
POCKET PULSE - Medical apparatus - Lynn Medical Instrument Co.
POCKET PUMP - Pumps - Robert F. Lange and Charles W. Davey Partnership
POCKET/PURSE - Medical apparatus - Apex Medical Corp.
POCKET PUSHER - Housewares - Pocket Pusher, Inc.
POCKET PUZZLE - Puzzles - Fink & Co. Inc.
POCKET QUICKEN - Computer software - Intuit Inc.
POCKET QUICKEN CONNECT - Computer software - Intuit Inc.
POCKET QUICKEN ON BOOKMAN - Computer software - Franklin Electronic Publishers, Inc.
POCKET RACERS - Toy cars - Intex Recreation Corp.
POCKET RECORDER - Computer software - Media Vision Technology Inc.
POCKET REF - Diaries ☆ - ACCO USA, Inc.
POCKET RETRIEVER - Golf equipment - Dennco, Inc.
POCKET ROCKERS - Toys - Fisher-Price, Inc.
POCKET ROCKET - Snack foods - Natural Balance, Inc.
POCKET ROCKET - Vitamins and nutritional supplements - Caroline Owens
POCKET ROD - Tape measures - Keson Industries Inc.
POCKET-SAVER - File folders - Angler's Roslyn Group Ltd.
POCKET SCANNER - Radiofrequency measuring equipment - Bio Medic Data Systems Inc.
POCKET SCIENCE - Apparel–children's - Montgomery Ward & Co. Inc.
POCKET SHAPER - Toys - Richard L. Greene
POCKET SHOTS - Toy guns - Parris Manufacturing Co.
POCKET SIMON - Games - Milton Bradley Co.
POCKET SONGS - Recording label - MMO Music Group Inc.
POCKET SPORT - Mats–wire - Astro Pen Co.
POCKET SPORT - Pens - Eversharp Pen Co.
POCKET STIX - Frozen foods - Chef America, Inc.
POCKET STUFF - Toys - Imperial Toy Corp.
POCKET SUCCESS - Novelty items–paper - Antioch Publishing Co.
POCKET SWEDE - Knives–pocket - Normark Corp.
POCKET TELEPHONE - Telephones - Spectralink Corp.
POCKET TOOL CHEST - Knives–pocket - Precise International/Wenger
POCKET TOTE - Bags–cosmetic ☆ - Gift Creations, Inc.
POCKET TRAKKER - Boats–kayaks - Ocean Kayak, Inc.
POCKET TRIVIA - Games - Brown and Bigelow Inc.
POCKET UNGAMES - Games - Talicor Inc.
POCKET VAULT, THE - Credit card cases - Michigan Jewelers, Ltd.
POCKET VISION TEST - Medical apparatus - Paul E. Runge
POCKET WAD, THE - Candy - Ripe Design, Inc.
POCKET WORN - Knives–pocket - W.R. Case & Sons Cutlery Co.
POCKETAB - Vitamins and nutritional supplements - Mercantile Food Co.
POCKETALES - Toys - Price Stern Sloan Inc.
POCKETALKER - Telephone apparatus - Williams Sound Corp.
POCKETBOOK CUTIES - Dolls with cologne and lip gloss ☆ - Cosrich Inc.
POCKETBOOKLETS - Publisher's imprints - EZ Kare Good Health Systems, Inc.
POCKETBRELLA - Umbrellas ☆ - Haas-Jordan Co.
POCKETCALL - Computer software - EX Machina, Inc.
POCKETCASE - Cases–eyeglass - Aristocraft Co.
POCKETCHIEF - Neckties - Patricia Kutza
POCKETCOOLER - Ice chests–plastic - Thermos Co.
POCKETDSP - Computer peripheral equipment - Jodfrey Associates, Inc.
POCKETE - Screws - Epic Products Inc.
POCKETFILE - Computer software - Integral Peripherals Inc.
POCKETFOLD - Napkins–paper - Wisconsin Tissue Mills Inc.
POCKETFRUIT - Granola bars ☆ - Barbara's Bakery, Inc.
POCKETFULL OF QUOTABLES - Publisher's imprints ☆ - Stevenson Industries Inc.
POCKETFULS - Games - Milton Bradley Co.
POCKETLENS - Plastic magnifier - Itoya of America, Ltd.
POCKETLINE - Electronic equipment - Rollei of America Inc.
POCKETLITE - Pistols - Colt's Manufacturing Co. Inc.
POCKETMAIL - Computer software - Cogent Business Systems, Inc.
POCKETNET - Telephone apparatus - Pilot Technologies, Inc.

☆ = Now out of production

POCKETOOL - Toys - Toymax Inc.
POCKETOTOSCOPE - Medical apparatus - Notoco
POCKETPAC BOOKS - Publisher's imprints - Harold Shaw Publishers
POCKETPOD - Tripods–photographic - Huey P. Savage
POCKETPRO - Projectors–photographic - Kopin Corp.
POCKETRONIC - Calculators ☆ - Canon USA, Inc.
POCKETS - Sandwiches–prepackaged - Maple Leaf Farms Inc.
POCKETS - Toys–stuffed - Gund, Inc.
POCKETS PLUS - Notebooks and notepads - Roaring Spring Blank Book Co.
POCKETSCOPE - Electronics equipment - Network General Holding Corp.
POCKETSCOPE - Microscopes - Learning Things Inc.
POCKETSHOP - Tools - Giro Sport Design
POCKETTE - Postage meters - Wescosa Inc.
POCKETWATCH - Medical apparatus - Pacific Pharmaceuticals, Inc.
POCKETWIZARD - Electronic equipment - Lab Partners Associates Inc.
POCKETWORKS - Apparel trimmings - Stephanie Rose
POCKITOS - Snack foods - Schwan's Sales Enterprises, Inc.
POCKITS - Magazine racks - Display Products N.A., Inc.
POCLEAR - Cosmetics - One World, Inc.
POCO - Underwear and nightwear - Jockey International, Inc.
POCO MARINE SAFETY CLEAN - Cleaning preparations - R & G Chemical Co.
POCO-MAS - Food products ☆ - State Line Potato Chip Co.
POCO 'PENOS - Food products - International Multifoods Corp.
POCO-PICO - Apparel–children's - Eleni C. Frantzides
POCO POSADA - Mexican appetizers - International Multifoods Corp.
POCOHONTAS - Food products - J.W. Wood
POCONO - Food products - Birkett Mills
POCONO - Photographic equipment - Eastman Kodak Co.
POCONO - Siding–metal - GAF Corp.
POCONO MOUNTAIN - Water–bottled or canned - Pocono Springs Co.
POCONO PLACE - Floor coverings ☆ - Tarkett, Inc.
POCONO SPRINGS - Water–bottled or canned - Pocono Springs Co.
POCORAY - Fabrics ☆ - Dan River Inc.
POCQUET - Fabrics - Handler Textile Corp.
POCSEC - Computers - Motorola, Inc. (Land Mobile Products Sector)
POCUS - Chemical preparations - Novagen, Inc.
POD - Computers - Zadian Technologies, Inc.
POD - Playground equipment - Miracle Recreation Equipment Co.
P.O.'D - T-shirts–women's - Ronald L. Paradoski
POD-BEN-25 - Pharmaceutical preparations ☆ - Glenwood LLC
POD-LOK - Playground equipment - Miracle Recreation Equipment Co.
POD PERFECT ESPRESSO - Coffee - Thomas A. Campbell Co.
POD PLUGS - Plugs–ear - Cabot Safety Intermediate Corp.
PODACTIN - Pharmaceutical preparations - Reese Chemical Co.
PODACTIN POWDER - Pharmaceutical preparations - Reese Chemical Co.
PODAN CO. - Giftware ☆ - Baekgaard Ltd.
PODEES - Shoes–orthopedic - Edward A. Martin, Evelyn D. Gliege and Dorothy A. Harris Partnership
PODERE DELLA SALA - Wines - European Beverage Co., Inc.
PODGOR - Artists' materials - Joseph E. Podgor Co. Inc.
PODIATRIST'S CHOICE, THE - Orthopedic products - PediFix Footcare Co.
PODIATRIST'S SECRET - Skin care products - Benchmark Brands
PODILIQUID - Pharmaceutical preparations ☆ - Rotex Pharmaceuticals Inc.
PODOBEN - Pharmaceutical preparations - Maurry Biological Co. Inc.
PODOFIN - Pharmaceutical preparations - Syosset Laboratories Inc.
PODRACK - Photographic equipment - Acme-Lite Manufacturing Co.
P.O.D.S. - Scientific apparatus - Sanofi Diagnostics Pasteur Inc.
PODUA - Wallpaper - Capital Carousel Inc.
PODUNK - Recording label - Podunk, Inc.
POEM COMPU-DESIGNS - Computer software - Aisin World Corp. of America
POEM FINDER - Computer software - Roth Publishing Inc.
POEMATION - Video production - Roger Blonder
POEMS - Women's apparel - Mona Lisa Fashions, Inc.
POEMS OF THE HEART - Greeting cards - Kim Conrad
POE'S SUPER CEDAR - Fishing lures - Yakima Bait Co.
POET - Blouses–women's - Protrend Ltd.
POET - Health care products - Criticare Systems Inc.
POET-WARRIOR - Teas - Eastern Shore Tea Co.
POETA MODA - Apparel and accessories - World Marketing Inc.
POETIC EXPRESSIONS - Frames–picture - Intercraft Industries
POETIC LICENSE - Games ☆ - Recycled Paper Products, Inc.
POETIC NAME 'N FRAME - Novelty items–paper - Artistic Greetings, Inc.
POETICA - Computer software - Adobe Systems Inc.
POETRY - Apparel stores–lingerie - Goddess Bra
POETRY - Dishes–china ☆ - Pickard Inc.

POETRY - Floor coverings - Congoleum Corp.
POETRY - Tableware–china ☆ - Pfaltzgraff Investment Co.
POETRY ANTHOLOGY PRESS - Publisher's imprints - Roth Publishing Inc.
POETRY EXPRESS - Computer software - Learning Well
POETRY FOR YOUR WALLS - Decals and transfers - Alice Mastrangelo
POETRY IN MOTION - Greeting cards - Paper Animation Design
POETRY INDEX PRESS - Publisher's imprints - Roth Publishing Inc.
POETRY OF FLOWERS - Soap - Twinscents
POETRY PALETTE - Computer software - Mind Play
POETRYSLAM - Games - Found Objects, Inc.
POET'S JOURNAL, THE - Computer software - Hartley Courseware Inc.
POG - Fruit drinks–bottled or canned - Orchards Hawaii Inc.
POG - Juices - Haleakala Dairy
POG WILD JEWELRY CO. - Jewelry - Weingeroff Enterprises, Inc.
POGENS - Breads - Pogens Family Bakery
POGGIO ALLE GAZZE - Wines - Kobrand Corp.
POGGIO DI SOTTO - Beverages–alcohol - Trebon Wine & Spirit Corp.
POGGIO SALVI - Wines - Wilson Daniels Ltd.
POGGIO SAN POLO - Wines ☆ - Parliament Import Co.
POGI - Slabs–concrete - Colonna & Co. Inc.
POGO - Skin care products ☆ - B & B Distributors
POGO - Steel springs–railroad - Needlecraft Industries
POGO - Tools - Miracle Products
POGO CLUB OF NY - Apparel–children's - Isfel Co. Inc.
POGO POLE - Candy - Earl's Candy Co.
POGO STICK - Antennas - Shakespeare Fishing Tackle
POGOBALL - Toys - Tonka Corp.
POGON - Wheelchairs - Theradyne Healthcare Product Div.
POGONIP - Flags - Pogonip Inc.
POGS - Diagnostic substances - Healthpoint, Ltd.
POI BOY'S - Apparel and accessories - Maureen D. Manos
POI-POI - Educational materials - Twinson Co.
POILANE - Breads - Deborah's Country French Bread
POINSETT - Fabrics ☆ - Greenwood Mills Inc.
POINSETTA & PEARLS - Candles - Carolina Designs Ltd.
POINSETTIA - Dinnerware–glass ☆ - Cuthbertson Imports Inc.
POINSETTIA - Fruits and vegetables - Fillmore-Piru Citrus Association
POINT - Apparel and accessories - Flywear International Inc.
POINT - Computer software - Calyx Software
POINT - Electronic equipment - Intevac, Inc.
POINT - Oils–lubricating - Tosco Corp.
POINT - Publisher's imprints - Scholastic Inc.
POINT - Tweezers - Tweezerman Corp.
POINT 5 - Pencils ☆ - Faber-Castell Corp.
POINT-AND-PERFORM - Computer software - Linked Solutions Inc.
POINT BLANK - Archery equipment - Pro Line Co.
POINT BLANK - Golfing equipment - Golfsmith International Inc.
POINT BLANK - Toy vehicle - Trinity Products Inc.
POINT BOCK - Beverages–malt - Stevens Point Beverage Co.
POINT CLASSIC AMBER - Beverages–malt - Stevens Point Beverage Co.
POINT DE HONGRIE - Floor coverings - Parquet de France Inc.
POINT D'ESPRIT - Rings–jewelry - Artcarved Inc.
POINT DREAD - Toys–erector sets - Mattel, Inc.
POINT ELECTRIC - Lighting fixtures - Point Electric
POINT GUARD - Alarm systems–burglar - Litton Security Systems
POINT GUARD - Detergent - Protein Technologies
POINT GUARD - Pens - Paper Mate Co.
POINT JUDITH - Seafood products–fresh or frozen - Blount Seafood Corp.
POINT JUDITH FISHERMEN'S COOP - Seafood products–fresh or frozen ☆ - Stavis Seafoods Inc.
POINT LABELLING SOLUTIONS - Computer software - Autograph USA, Inc.
POINT LIGHT - Beverages–malt - Stevens Point Beverage Co.
POINT LIGHTING CORPORATION - Lighting fixtures–airport - Point Lighting Corp.
POINT LOC - Hardware - Gary Johnson
POINT LUBRICANTS - Oils–lubricating - Tosco Corp.
POINT MAPLE WHEAT - Beverages–malt - Stevens Point Beverage Co.
POINT 'N SPRAY - Compressed air sprayer - Melnor Inc.
POINT-O-MATIC - Pencil sharpeners - Matsushita Consumer Electronics Co.
POINT OF ENTRY - Apparel–men's ☆ - Michaels/Stern & Co. Inc.
POINT OF LAW - Games ☆ - Avalon Hill Game Co.
POINT OF SALE - Computer software - Passport Software, Inc.
POINT OF SALE - Pet products - Rainbow Record Keeping Systems
POINT OF SALE RIBBONS - Paper products - Best Ribbon Corp.
POINT-OF-VIEW - Computer software - Christopher L. Farias
POINT PALE ALE - Beverages–malt - Stevens Point Beverage Co.

☆ = Now out of production

POINT PLEASANT - Floor coverings–carpet and rugs ☆ - Patcraft Mills Inc.
POINT PLEASANT - Vegetables–canned - B.G.S. Jourdan & Sons
POINT PULLER - Archery equipment - Saunders Archery Co.
POINT REYES - Bicycles - Marin Mountain Bikes, Inc.
POINT ST. GEORGE - Seafood products–canned or cured - California Shellfish Co. Inc.
POINT SEASONAL WINTER SPICE - Beverages–malt - Stevens Point Beverage Co.
POINT SIGHT - Guns - Daisy Manufacturing Co.
POINT SPECIAL - Beverages–malt - Stevens Point Beverage Co.
POINT SUR - Floor coverings–carpet and rugs ☆ - Catalina Carpet Mills Inc.
POINT TO POINT - Wallpaper ☆ - Bolta Wallcoverings
POINT-TWO - Pharmaceutical preparations - Colgate Oral Pharmaceuticals Inc.
POINT V - Pens ☆ - Itoya of America, Ltd.
POINT V LTD. - Golfing equipment - Pointfive Golf Co.
POINT VIEW - Vegetables–canned - Furman Foods, Inc.
POINT WINTER SPICE - Beverages–malt ☆ - Stevens Point Beverage Co.
POINT5 - Fabric appliques - High Voltage Graphics, Inc.
POINTE OF VIEW - Paper–gift wrap - Gift Box Corp. of America
POINTE PEARL - Furniture - Homecrest Industries Inc.
POINTED ANTIQUE - Flatware - Reed and Barton Corp.
POINTED SOFT POINT BULLET - Bullets - Olin Corp. (Winchester Div.)
POINTER - Animal feeds - Bush Brothers and Co.
POINTER - Apparel and accessories - L.C. King Manufacturing Co.
POINTER - Binoculars ☆ - Swift Instruments, Inc.
POINTER - Crocheted and knitted items - Schuessler Knitting Mills Inc.
POINTER - Publisher's imprints - Hal Leonard Corp.
POINTER - Transmitting apparatus - Pointer, Inc.
POINTER CHECKER PLUS - Computer software - BMC Software, Inc.
POINTES PLUS - Manicure preparations - Creative Nail Design, Inc.
POINTFORE - Rackets–badminton ☆ - Rackets International (Racket Sports Div.)
POINTGARD - Computers–micro - National Draeger, Inc.
POINTILIST - Floor coverings–carpet and rugs - Customweave Carpets Inc.
POINTILLIST PALETTE - Fabrics - Robert Kaufman Co., Inc.
POINTKEEPER - Pencils - Itoya of America, Ltd.
POINTMAKER - Cameras–video - Boeckeler Instruments, Inc.
POINTMAKER - Easels ☆ - Quartet Manufacturing Co.
POINTMASTER - Electronic equipment - Recoton Corp.
POINTMASTER - Frames–picture - Markwell Manufacturing Co. Inc.
POINTPRO - Medical apparatus ☆ - INRAD, Inc.
POINTS OF INTEREST - Apparel and accessories - Frederick Atkins, Inc.
POINTS OF INTEREST - Craft supplies - Points of Interest
POINT'S WEST - Jeans–women's - Lane Bryant, Inc.
POIRIER - Food products - Nuchief Sales Inc.
POIS - Electronic equipment - Pois, Inc.
POIS BLACK - Floor coverings–carpet and rugs ☆ - Regal Rugs Inc.
POISE - Clocks - General Time Corp. (Westclox/Seth Thomas Div.)
POISE - Sanitary napkins - Kimberly-Clark Corp.
POISE 'N IVY - Wallpaper ☆ - Three Sisters Studio
POISON - Apparel and accessories - Cyanide Merchandising Co., Inc.
POISON - Games - Metal Art of California, Inc.
POISON - Glassware–household ☆ - Kraftware Corp. (Morgan Div.)
POISON - Perfumes - Christian Dior Perfumes Corp.
POISON - Perfumes - Parfums Christian Dior U.S. Corp.
POISON GAS RESEARCH - Recording label - Jazz Composer's Orchestra Association Inc.
POISON PAX - Games - Metal Art of California, Inc.
POISON RING - Recording label - TNA Records
POISON TUBE - Games - Metal Art of California, Inc.
POISONIVI - Health care products - Cutter Laboratories
POISONOK - Health care products - Cutter Laboratories
POISSON - Dinnerware–glass - Durand International
POIVRE D'OR - Cosmetics - Lancome
POIVRE NORMAND - Dairy products ☆ - Besnier USA, Inc.
POJARSKY - Food products ☆ - Acme Continental Foods Inc.
POJER & SANDRI - Wines - Wine Imports Inc.
POK-IT - Tools - Band-It-Idex Inc.
POKE - Boats - Phoenix Products Inc.
POKE - Toys - Tonka Corp.
POKE-N-PULL - Bathroom accessories ☆ - Willert Home Products, Inc.
POKE-R - Apparel–men's - Shirtsmith Corp.
POKE'M - Candy ☆ - Amurol Confections Co.
POKER - Computer software - Capstone Software
POKER - Pizzas–frozen ☆ - Mr. Z's Fund Raising Corp.
POKER BINGO - Games ☆ - Milton Bradley Co.

POKER COASTER - Cardboard cutouts - Falcon Paper Co.
POKER-KEENO - Games - Cadaco Div.
POKER-MATIC - Games ☆ - Milton Bradley Co.
POKER ODDS - Novelty items - Wry Idea Co.
POKER POOL - Balls–billiard - George B. Emery III
POKEY - Toys–stuffed ☆ - Gund, Inc.
POKKA - Iced tea–bottled or canned - Pokka, Inc.
POL - Cleaning preparations - SCI Scandicrafts Inc.
POL D'ARGENT - Wines - Monarch Wine Co.
POL-E-LAWN - Floor coverings–carpet and rugs ☆ - Len Dal Carpets
POL PEREAUX - Beverages–alcohol ☆ - Warner Vineyards Inc.
POL-VI PRIM - Paints - Diamond/Kuhn Paint Co.
POL X - Vitamins and nutritional supplements - Kroeger Herb Products Co. Inc.
POLA - Food products - Pola Foods Inc.
POLA-GLARE - Photographic equipment ☆ - Da-Lite Screen Co. Inc.
POLA-SCREEN - Photographic equipment - Eastman Kodak Co.
POLAC - Spices and extracts - Pexco, Inc.
POLACAV - Adhesives and sealants - Plastics & Resins Ltd.
POLACHROME - Film - Polaroid Corp.
POLACLEAN - Cleaning preparations - Polaroid Corp.
POLACLEAR - Photographic equipment - Polaroid Corp.
POLACOAT - Projectors–photographic - Da-Lite Screen Co. Inc.
POLACOLOR - Film - Polaroid Corp.
POLACOLOR 2 - Film - Polaroid Corp.
POLACOTE - Adhesives and sealants - Plastics & Resins Ltd.
POLAFLOOR - Floor coverings - Andek Corp.
POLAFLOOR - Floor coverings - Plastics & Resins Ltd.
POLAFLOOR P.D. - Finishing agents - Plastics & Resins Ltd.
POLAFOCUS - Eyeglasses ☆ - Cable Car Eyeware
POLAGARD - Finishing agents - Plastics & Resins Ltd.
POLAGRAPH - Film - Polaroid Corp.
POLAJOINT - Caulking compounds - Andek Corp.
POLAMP-PILA - Lamp bulbs - Amceco International Corp.
POLAND SPRING - Liquors - Poland Spring Bottling Co.
POLAND SPRING - Water–mineral - Perrier Group of America Inc.
POLANER - Vegetables–dried - M. Polaner Inc.
POLAPAN - Film - Polaroid Corp.
POLAPRIME - Paints - Andek Corp.
POLAPULSE P100 - Batteries - Polaroid Corp.
POLAR - Antifreeze - Warren Distribution, Inc.
POLAR - Beverages–malt - Polar Corp.
POLAR - Boots - Reliable of Milwaukee
POLAR - Fruits and vegetables - J.R. Simplot Co.
POLAR - Heating equipment - Yukon Energy Corp.
POLAR - Saunas - Cedarbrook Sauna Inc.
POLAR - Scuba diving equipment - JWA Scubapro Undersea Industries, Inc.
POLAR - Shovels - Cole Consumer Products Inc.
POLAR - Sporting goods - Kolpin Manufacturing, Inc.
POLAR - Swimming pool covers - Century Products, Inc.
POLAR - Water–bottled or canned - Polar Water Co.
POLAR 10 - Apparel and accessories - Malden Mills Industries, Inc.
POLAR 25 - Shingles - Owens Corning Fiberglass Technology Inc.
POLAR BAR - Beverages–alcohol - Black Prince Distillery, Inc.
POLAR BAR - Ice cream - Kraft Foods, Inc.
POLAR BEAN - Desserts - White Wave
POLAR BEAR - Chemical preparations - Frank Miller and Sons Inc.
POLAR BEAR - Coffee - Coffee Consultants, Inc.
POLAR BEAR - Envelopes - Quality Park Products Co.
POLAR BEAR - Flour–blended - Scott's Auburn Mills Inc.
POLAR BEAR - Food products ☆ - Griffin Food Co.
POLAR BEAR - Ice cream - Reinhold Ice Cream
POLAR BEAR - Ice cream - Taylor All Star Dairy
POLAR BEAR - Water–mineral - Polar Bear Water Co.
POLAR BEAR ASHBURN'S - Restaurants–ice cream parlors - Polar Bear Ice Cream Co.
POLAR BEAR PEABERRY COFFEE - Coffee - Peaberry Coffee Ltd.
POLAR BLONDE - Floor coverings–carpet and rugs - Glen Eden Wool Carpets
POLAR BOMBER - Hats - Mad Bomber Co.
POLAR BRAND - Sporting goods - Kellwood Co.
POLAR BREEZE - Confections - 3-D Corp.
POLAR COLLAR - Chemical preparations - Northeast Florida Trading Co.
POLAR DARE - Games - Milton Bradley Co.
POLAR EXTREME - Fabrics - Malden Mills Industries, Inc.
POLAR FILM - Plastics film - Printpack, Inc.
POLAR FLEX - Gloves–work - Cofish International Inc.

POLAR FORCE - Apparel–athletic - Malden Mills Industries, Inc.

POLAR GARD - Gloves–work - Saf-T-Gard International, Inc.

POLAR GEL - Veterinary pharmaceutical preparations - Traileze Veterinary Products Inc.

POLAR GEL STARCH - Pie fillings - American Maize-Products Co.

POLAR GRIP - Tires - Bridgestone/Firestone, Inc.

POLAR HOOD - Hats - Cold Front

POLAR ICE - Paints - Bondex International Inc.

POLAR ICE - Pharmaceuticals - Lander Co., Inc.

POLAR ICER - Insulating materials - Harrison Direct, Inc.

POLAR KING - Coats–men's - Key Industries, Inc.

POLAR KING - Flour–blended - New Era Milling Co.

POLAR KIST - Food products machinery - Frionor USA Inc.

POLAR KRAFT - Boats - Polar Kraft Manufacturing Co.

POLAR LIGHTS - Toys - Thomas Lowe Ventures, Inc.

POLAR LIGHTS - Toys–models - Playing Mantis

POLAR LTD. - Sporting goods ☆ - Bear Archery Inc.

POLAR-LITE - Apparel–athletic - Red Head Brand Corp.

POLAR LITES - Eyeglasses ☆ - Style Eyes of California

POLAR MASK - Apparel and accessories - Go-Pro Ltd.

POLAR MOC - Slippers - Acorn

POLAR N' ICE CUBES - Pet products - Boomer Ball

POLAR PAD - Filters–air - Research Products Corp.

POLAR PAD - Health care products - Vesture Corp.

POLAR PAIRS - Slippers - Acorn

POLAR PAK - Ice cream - The Kroger Co.

POLAR PATCH - Cement - L.D. Sterns Corp.

POLAR PATCH - Repair patch for coolers and freezers - Pioneer Manufacturing Co.

POLAR PERFECTION - Cups–paper - Polar Plastics Inc.

POLAR POPS - Flavored liquid - Delicious Cookies

POLAR POWER - Extension cords - General Cable Corp.

POLAR QUEEN - Hardware - Reliance Plastic & Chemical Corp.

POLAR-READ - Photographic polarizer lenses ☆ - American Polarizers Inc.

POLAR SEAS - Aquarium accessories - Novalek, Inc.

POLAR SEAS - Aquarium accessories ☆ - Kordon

POLAR SPORT - Fabrics - Malden Mills Industries, Inc.

POLAR STAR - Seafood products–fresh or frozen - F.W. Bryce Inc.

POLAR STAR - Watches - Elgin Watch Co.

POLAR STEAM - Saunas - Cedarbrook Sauna Inc.

POLAR STICK - Sausages - Trappers Creek Inc.

POLAR SWEET - Ice cream - Fort Dodge Creamery Co.

POLAR TRAC - Tires ☆ - Bridgestone/Firestone, Inc.

POLAR TREADS - Motor vehicle parts and accessories - Henry B. Lewin

POLAR TREATS - Ice cream - Wells' Dairy, Inc.

POLAR TREDS - Boots - SGI Inc.

POLAR TROOPER - Hats - Mad Bomber Co.

POLAR WAVE GOURMET ICED TEA - Iced tea–bottled or canned - Ronnoco Coffee Co.

POLAR WIND - Bedding–linen - Meijer, Inc.

POLAR XL - Cups–paper - Polar Plastics Inc.

POLAR ZONE - Apparel and accessories - C.S.F. Corp.

POLAR ZONE - Ice chests - Coleman Co., Inc.

POLARA - Floor coverings ☆ - Congoleum Corp.

POLARA - Luggage ☆ - American Tourister, Inc.

POLARA - Motor vehicles ☆ - Chrysler Corp. (Dodge Car Div.)

POLARA - Recording label - Edwin C. Ackerson

POLARA - Whirlpool spa ☆ - Jacuzzi Inc.

POLARAMINE - Pharmaceutical preparations - Schering-Plough Healthcare Products

POLARCHROMATIC - Lenses–optical - Capo, Inc.

POLARFLEX 2 - Gloves - Jomac Products Inc.

POLARGEN - Pharmaceutical preparations - Goldline Laboratories, Inc.

POLARIC ELLIPSOD - Eyeglasses - Oakley, Inc.

POLARICE - Fabrics - Greenwood Mills Inc.

POLARIS - Air conditioning equipment ☆ - Nordyne Inc.

POLARIS - Amplifiers - Matao Corp.

POLARIS - Apparel and accessories ☆ - Eagle Knitting Mills Inc.

POLARIS - Audio cables and accessories - Wireworld by David Salz, Inc.

POLARIS - Bicycles ☆ - Murray, Inc.

POLARIS - Cabinets–wood - J.T. Wood Products, Inc.

POLARIS - Computer software - Martel Group, Inc.

POLARIS - Dinnerware–glass ☆ - Nikko Ceramics Inc.

POLARIS - Drums–musical instruments ☆ - St. Louis Music Supply Co.

POLARIS - Electronic equipment - Uniden America Corp.

POLARIS - Fabrics - Graniteville Co.

POLARIS - Fabrics - Superior Shade & Blind Co. Inc.

POLARIS - Fishing tackle - South Bend Sporting Goods Inc.

POLARIS - Flashlights - Accutec Inc.

POLARIS - Floor coverings - American Floor Products Co. Inc.

POLARIS - Floor coverings - Mannington Resilient Floors

POLARIS - Floor coverings ☆ - Tarkett, Inc.

POLARIS - Floor coverings–carpet and rugs ☆ - Regal Rugs Inc.

POLARIS - Furniture ☆ - Bassett Furniture Industries, Inc.

POLARIS - Glassware–household ☆ - Lenox Crystal, Inc.

POLARIS - Health care products - Smith and Davis Manufacturing Co.

POLARIS - Hoists - Columbus Mckinnon Corp.

POLARIS - Ophthalmic goods ☆ - Fidelity Case Corp.

POLARIS - Paper–coated - Consolidated Papers, Inc.

POLARIS - Perfumes - Hartz Mountain Corp.

POLARIS - Pet products ☆ - Hess Hair Milk Laboratories Inc.

POLARIS - Recording label - Jazz Composer's Orchestra Association Inc.

POLARIS - Snowmobiles - Pacific Kinematics, Inc.

POLARIS - Snowmobiles - Polaris Industries Partners LP

POLARIS - Soccer balls - Audero Sports Supply

POLARIS - Sporting goods - Voit Corp.

POLARIS - Tiles–ceramic - Dal-Tile Corp.

POLARIS - Tiles–ceramic ☆ - Laufen Ceramic Tile

POLARIS - Toys–models ☆ - Estes Industries

POLARIS - Vials–glass - Taito America Corp.

POLARIS - Wallcoverings - Cork Products Co. Inc.

POLARIS - Watches ☆ - SMH (US) Inc.

POLARIS - Water heaters–household - S.A.B.H. U.S. Water Heaters

POLARIS - Windows–vinyl - Modern Builders Supply Inc.

POLARIS COLLECTION - Wallpaper - Dekortex Inc.

POLARIS CYCLONE - Snowmobiles ☆ - Polaris Industries Partners LP

POLARIS EDGE - Windows–vinyl - Modern Builders Supply Inc.

POLARIS SCRAMBLER - Snowmobiles ☆ - Polaris Industries Partners LP

POLARIS/SHEPHERD - Photographic equipment - Tiffen Manufacturing Corp.

POLARIS TRAIL BOSS 4 X - Snowmobiles - Polaris Industries Partners LP

POLARITY - Apparel and accessories - Babette, Inc.

POLARITY - Floor coverings–carpet and rugs - Regal Rugs Inc.

POLARITY - Skin care products - California SunCare, Inc.

POLARITY MANAGEMENT - Computer software - Polarity Management Associates, LLC

POLARIX - Graphics software for personal computers - RIX SoftWorks Inc.

POLARIZED - Meat products–beef - Maid-Rite Steak Co. Inc.

POLARIZED - Sunglasses - Bolle' America, Inc.

POLARIZER PLUS - Televisions ☆ - Avnet, Inc.

POLARKIDS - Fabrics - Malden Mills Industries, Inc.

POLARKNIT - Apparel and accessories - Americal Corp.

POLARLINE - Backpacks ☆ - Mountain Equipment, Inc.

POLARLINK - Computer peripheral equipment - Quadron Service Corp.

POLARLITE - Fabrics - Malden Mills Industries, Inc.

POLARMAX - Apparel and accessories - Longworth Industries, Inc.

POLARMOC - Footwear - H.H. Brown Shoe Co., Inc.

POLARMOTION - Display cases–plastic - American Polarizers Inc.

POLAROID - Cameras - Polaroid Corp.

POLAROID 600 PLUS - Film - Polaroid Corp.

POLAROID DRYJET - Computer software - Polaroid Corp.

POLAROID HELIOS - Film - Polaroid Corp.

POLAROID HELIOS AND DESIGN - Medical equipment - Polaroid Corp.

POLAROID MICROCAM - Camera for microscope - Polaroid Corp.

POLAROID PHOTOPAD - Computer peripheral equipment - Polaroid Corp.

POLAROID SILHOUETTE - Video equipment - Polaroid Corp.

POLAROOF - Finishing agents - Plastics & Resins Ltd.

POLAROOF FIREGARD - Adhesives and sealants - Plastics & Resins Ltd.

POLARPAC - Cartons–paperboard - Weyerhaeuser Co.

POLARPANE - Glass products - HGP Industries Inc.

POLARPANE I/ST - Windows–storm - HGP Industries Inc.

POLARPLUS - Fabrics - Malden Mills Industries, Inc.

POLARPLUS - Tools - Yeoman Co.

POLARPRIME - Adhesives and sealants - Plastics & Resins Ltd.

POLARQUEST - Fabrics - Malden Mills Industries, Inc.

POLARSEAL - Hoses - Gates Rubber Co. (Automotive Aftermarket/Hardware Sales Div.)

POLARSEAL - Wood products - Remington Building Products

POLARSKINS - Underwear and nightwear - Kenyon Consumer Products Inc.

POLARSOFT - Computer software - David M. Fisher

POLARSTRETCH - Floor coverings - ADS Properties Corp.

POLARSYSTEM - Fabrics - Malden Mills Industries, Inc.

POLARTEC - Blankets - Acorn

☆ = Now out of production

POLARTEC - Fabrics - ADS Properties Corp.
POLARTEX - Fabrics - Malden Mills Industries, Inc.
POLARTUFF - Tools - Yeoman Co.
POLARWAVE - Refrigerator repair shops - College Rent-A-Fridge
POLARYARN - Apparel and accessories - Pleasure-Knit Corp.
POLASCAN - Computer software - Polaroid Corp.
POLASEAL - Waterproofing compounds - Plastics & Resins Ltd.
POLASHARP - Computer software - Polaroid Corp.
POLASIL - Adhesives and sealants ✩ - Plastics & Resins Ltd.
POLATRON - Automotive parts and accessories - Scott Associates Inc.
POLATRONIC - Photographic equipment - Polaroid Corp.
POLAVIEW - Liquid crystal displays - Polaroid Corp.
POLAVISION - Cameras - Polaroid Corp.
POLAWALL - Wallpaper - Andek Corp.
POLAWARTZ - Epoxy coatings - Plastics & Resins Ltd.
POLAZE - Skin care products - L'anza Research International
POLDER - Housewares - Polder Inc.
POLE BAG - Welcon
POLE-KAT - Golfing equipment - M2 Capital Corp.
POLE-MASTER - Shelving units–wood ✩ - Quaker Industries Ltd.
POLE PAKERS - Fishing nets - Four Rivers Tackle Co.
POLE POSITION - Computer software - Atari Games Corp.
POLE POSITION - Prophylactics - Jeffrey J. Rodrigues
POLE SAK - Welcon
POLE SANDER - Abrasive products - Allway Tools Inc.
POLEAN - Hams - Dennis J. Alba & Co.
POLEAN IMPORTED CANADIAN HAM - Pork - Polean Foods, Inc.
POLEAN IMPORTED POLSKA HAM - Pork - Polean Foods, Inc.
POLECAT - Brushes–paint - Wooster Brush Co.
POLECAT - Free-standing ceiling supports ✩ - Brewster Corp.
POLECAT - Hardware ✩ - Quik-Tape
POLECI - Apparel–women's - Danilo'r, Inc.
POLENGHI MASCARPONTE CHEESE - Cheese - Crystal Food Import Corp.
POLENTA CHIPS - Crackers - Select Harvest of California Inc.
POLENTA EXPRESS - Food products - Tipiak
POLEROUTER - Watches ✩ - Holzerwatch Co. Inc.
POLESTAR - Lighting fixtures - Holophane Corp.
POLESTAR - Medical apparatus - Current Concepts Corp.
POLESTAR - Window shades - Protech Shading Inc.
POLESTAR-8 - Electrical equipment - Alta Research Corp.
POLESTRON - Paints - Tenax Finishing Product
POLETERM - Connectors–electrical - Communications Technology Corp.
POLETTI - Apparel and accessories - Bushnell Associates
POLEX - Chemical preparations - Etrac Inc.
POLEY - Toys–stuffed ✩ - Russ Berrie and Co., Inc.
POLI - Hockey equipment ✩ - Dita USA
POLI-AIRE - Pillows - Regency Products
POLI COLLECTION - Novelty items - Chrishawn Associates Inc.
POLI-GRIP - Health care products - Block Drug Co., Inc.
POLI-KALA - Food products - Indo-European Foods, Inc.
POLI-KRAFT KORDE - Craft supplies - Textile Enterprises Inc.
POLI ORIGINALS - Figurines - Neuwirth Co.
POLI-X - Veterinary medical equipment - Engler Engineering Corp.
POLICE - Bicycles ✩ - Huffy Corp.
POLICE - Pharmaceutical preparations ✩ - Majestic Drug Co., Inc.
POLICE - Recording label - Peak Records, Inc.
POLICE ACADEMY - Games - Milton Bradley Co.
POLICE & FIREMAN'S - Skin care products - Camphorole Inc.
POLICE ATHLETIC LEAGUE PAL N.Y.C. - Apparel - Police Athletic League, Inc.
POLICE BLOTTER - Games - Avalon Hill Game Co.
POLICE BULLDOG - Guns - Charter Arms
POLICE CYCLE - Scooters–children's - Peg Perego USA Inc.
POLICE ENFORCEMENT - Automotive parts and accessories - BIA Marketing Co., Inc.
POLICE ESCORT - Toys–models - Diversified Specialists, Inc.
POLICE PATROL SQUAD - Toys - Fisher-Price, Inc.
POLICE POSITIVE - Pistols ✩ - Colt's Manufacturing Co. Inc.
POLICE PROTECTOR - Gloves - Dakota Corp.
POLICE PROTECTOR, THE - Leather gloves - Dakota Corp.
POLICIES NOW - Computer software - KnowledgePoint
POLICYWARE - Computer software - Wheatley Group, Ltd.
POLIDENT - Health care products - Block Drug Co., Inc.
POLIER - Adhesives and sealants ✩ - Flitz International Ltd.
POLIFAN - Tools–power-driven - Pferd Inc.
POLIGNAL - Liquors ✩ - Frank Sutton & Co.

POLIPLEET - Filters–water - Mac Equipment, Inc.
POLISH - Liquors ✩ - Adamba Imports International Inc.
POLISH AWAY - Cosmetics - Remington Products Co.
POLISH DRY - Nail care products - Worldwide Cosmetics
POLISH 'N DRY - Toys - Mattel, Inc.
POLISH NATURALS - Food products - Adamba Imports International Inc.
POLISH OFF - Manicure preparations - Barristo Ltd.
POLISH POPPER - T-shirts–men's - Jim Beam Brands Co.
POLISH PRIDE - Meat products–pork - Canada Packers (USA), Inc.
POLISH YOUR WOOD FLOOR - Floor waxes ✩ - Klean-Strip
POLISHED AMBER - Cosmetics - Revlon Consumer Products Corp.
POLISHED IMAGE - Nail care products - Encore Nails Franchising LLC
POLISHED OPAQUE - Hosiery - Danskin, Inc.
POLISHED PAWS - Dolls - Mattel, Inc.
POLISHED PERFORMANCE - Cosmetics - Estee Lauder Inc.
POLISHED PORCELAIN - Floor coverings–tile - KPT Inc.
POLISHED TILE - Adhesives and sealants - Midland Chicago Corp.
POLISHINE - Adhesives and sealants - Klein & Co.
POLISHING BAR - Skin care products - Nu Skin International, Inc.
POLISHING PEN - Nail care products ✩ - Prince Matchabelli
POLISI - Musical instruments - Ardsley Musical Instrument Co.
POLITE - Flashlights - Warren E. Gilson
POLITE-O-METER - Novelty items - MCI Communications Corp.
POLITE SOCIETY - Games - Polite Society Partners
POLITICAL PROFILES - Publisher's imprints - Facts on File Inc.
POLITICS - Toys - Tonka Corp.
POLITIX - Cigarettes - R.J. Reynolds Tobacco Co.
POLITO'S SPRAY-ON NAIL POLISH SYSTEM - Nail care products - Phil Polito
POLK - Audio equipment - Polk Audio Inc.
POLK MONITOR - Audio equipment - Polk Audio Inc.
POLKA - Fabrics - Gretchen Bellinger Inc.
POLKA - Hams ✩ - Dennis J. Alba & Co.
POLKA - Harmonicas - Hohner Inc.
POLKA - Tape–adhesive ✩ - Andek Corp.
POLKA DOT - Fabrics - Gretchen Bellinger Inc.
POLKA DOT - Fasteners–snap - American Engineer Components
POLKA DOT - Food products - Tom Thumb Stores, Inc.
POLKA DOT CIRCLE - Pet chews - Items Inc.
POLKA DOT KIDS - Wallpaper ✩ - Eisenhart Wallcoverings Co.
POLKA DOT PALS - Toys–stuffed - Dakin Inc.
POLKA KING - Accordions - Castiglione Accordion
POLKA KW6 - Recording label - Record-Rama Sound Archives
POLKA TONE - Recording label - Jay Jay Record & Tape Co.
POLK'S - Hams - Polk's Meat Products, Inc.
POLL PARROT - Shoes - Interco Inc.
POLLACK DRUMS - Cigars - M. Marsh & Son
POLLAK AND SKAN GROUP, THE - Employment agencies–temporary help - Pollak and Skan Inc.
POLLARD PLACE - Floor coverings ✩ - Tarkett, Inc.
POLLCAT II+ - Telephone answering machines - Western Telematic Inc.
POLLE-SENG - Vitamins and nutritional supplements - Great Life Laboratories Inc.
POLLEN - Recording label - Robert D. Hoag, III
POLLEN-EZE - Air purification systems - Air Kontrol Inc.
POLLEN GUARD - Safety products - Pentax Precision Instrument Corp.
POLLEN HEARTS - Diet supplements - Natur-Pharma, Inc.
POLLEN-TECTOR - Bags–paper - Butler Paper Co.
POLLENERGY - Pollen extracts - CC Pollen Co.
POLLENEX - Hair curlers - Pollenex Corp.
POLLEPOWER PLUS - Vitamins and nutritional supplements ✩ - Great Life Laboratories Inc.
POLLEY - Meat products–beef - Bob Ostrow Co.
POLLI - Food products ✩ - Liberty Richter Inc.
POLLI-MORE - Insecticides - Troy Biosciences, Inc.
POLLICIS - Screw drivers - Moody Tools Inc.
POLLINATION GAME, THE - Games - Ampersand Press
POLLINIL - Pharmaceutical preparations - Dolisos America, Inc.
POLLINOSAN - Health care products ✩ - Bioforce of America Ltd.
POLLITABS SPORT - Vitamins and nutritional supplements - Cernitin America Inc.
POLLIWOG - Infant product ✩ - Playing Mantis
POLLIWOGS - Apparel and accessories - Barrow Manufacturing Co., Inc.
POLLMAN - Musical instruments ✩ - Meisel Music Inc.
POLLO PICU - Meat products–poultry - Industrias Avicolas De Puerto Rico, Inc.

POLLUTION FREE - Hair care products - Helene Curtis Industries Inc.

POLLUTION PROTECTORS - Vitamins and nutritional supplements ☆ - Ethical Nutrients

POLLUTION SOLUTION - Cleaning preparations - Ardex Laboratories, Inc.

POLLUTROL - Vitamins and nutritional supplements - Sukrol Laboratories Inc.

POLLY - Brushes - Wright-Bernet

POLLY - Flowers–artificial - C & C Florists Supplies Inc.

POLLY - Food products ☆ - Taormina Co.

POLLY - Toys - Design Works Crafts

POLLY - Wigs - Jean Paree Weegs Inc.

POLLY AMI - Bakery products - Rawl Engineering & Manufacturing Co. Inc.

POLLY & CO. - Dresses–girls' - Baylis Co.

POLLY & FRIENDS - Apparel–children's - Baylis Brothers Inc.

POLLY-ANN - Cakes - Rawl Engineering & Manufacturing Co. Inc.

POLLY B - Footwear - Polly Bergen Shoes Inc.

POLLY BENEDICT - Bedding–linen - Dan River Inc.

POLLY BERGEN - Footwear - Polly Bergen Shoes Inc.

POLLY CRACKERS - Pet products - Hill Top Enterprises

POLLY ELLERMAN - Apparel–women's - Polly Ellerman Inc.

POLLY FLINDERS - Dresses–girls' - Baylis Co.

POLLY GOURMET - Pet products - Pyramid Bird Toys

POLLY JEAN'S PANTRY - Food products ☆ - Cal-Gar Corp.

POLLY LOGS - Pet products - Pet-Ag, Inc.

POLLY-O - Cheese - Kraft Foods, Inc.

POLLY-O-FREE - Cheese - Pollio Dairy Products Corp.

POLLY-O LITE - Cheese - Pollio Dairy Products Corp.

POLLY-O OLD FASHIONED - Cheese - Pollio Dairy Products Corp.

POLLY-O QUALITY - Food products - Kraft Food Ingredients Corp.

POLLY-O ULTRA - Food products - Kraft Food Ingredients Corp.

POLLY OF CALIFORNIA - Footwear–women's - Polly of California

POLLY ON THE GO - Dolls - Mattel, Inc.

POLLY ORCHARD - Candy ☆ - Powers Pharmaceutical Corp.

POLLY PAL - Dolls - Jason Art Productions

POLLY PAL - Dolls ☆ - Goldberger Doll Manufacture Co.

POLLY PAL - Hair care products ☆ - A.R.C. Toys Inc.

POLLY-PELLETS - Fabrics–polypropylene - Fairfield Processing Corp.

POLLY PERFECT - Thread - Perfect Thread Co. Inc.

POLLY POCKET - Bicycles - Kent International Inc.

POLLY POPS - Pet products - Picture Perfect Parrot

POLLY PRESTON - Shoes - Craddock-Terry Inc.

POLLY PRETEND - Doll ☆ - South Bend Toy Manufacturing Co.

POLLY PULL-EEZE - Pet products - Emerald Bird Caddy

POLLY ROSBOROUGH - Fishing lures - A.D. Schneider & Associates

POLLY S - Paints - Floquil-Polly S Color Corp.

POLLY SCALE - Paints - Floquil-Polly S Color Corp.

POLLY SPINWHEEL - Pet products - Emerald Bird Caddy

POLLY TACO - Pet products - Emerald Bird Caddy

POLLY TEELS - Ice cream - Vitarich Ice Cream Co.

POLLY VISION - Pet products - Emerald Bird Caddy

POLLY WANTS A COOKIE - Pet products - Picture Perfect Parrot

POLLYANA - Dolls ☆ - Uneeda Doll Co., Inc.

POLLYANNA - Dolls ☆ - Effanbee Doll Corp.

POLLYANNA - Toys - Tonka Corp.

POLLYPASTA - Pet food - Judee K. Creations, Inc. (Crazy Corn Division)

POLLYPASTA - Pet products - Crazy Corn

POLLY'S - Bird cages - Knick Enterprises

POLLY'S - Bird cages - Polly's Pet Products, Inc.

POLLY'S PLEASURES - Pet products - Parrot Paradise

POLLY'S SPORT - Dresses–girls' - Baylis Co.

POLLY'S TREASURES - Pet products - Parrot Paradise

POLLYWOG - Thread ☆ - American & Efird, Inc.

POLLYWOOD - Exercising equipment - Teknacord, Inc.

POLNETACP, THE - Computer software - Multi-Link, Inc.

POLO - Apparel and accessories - Bristol Jeans Inc.

POLO - Apparel and accessories - Polo Ralph Lauren Corp.

POLO - Boots ☆ - Acme Boot Co., Inc.

POLO - Floor coverings–tile - Federal Tile Imports Inc.

POLO - Glassware–household - Ceraglass Inc.

POLO - Napkins–paper - Erving Paper Products Inc.

POLO - Novelty items - Chukker Co.

POLO - Pencils - Staedtler, Inc.

POLO - Pet products - Dell Manufacturing

POLO - Recording label - Paris Records

POLO - Shoes ☆ - Allen-Edmonds Shoe Corp.

POLO - Sunglasses - Optique du Monde Ltd.

POLO - Thread - Threads USA Div.

POLO - Wines ☆ - Ernest and Julio Gallo Winery

POLO BAY - Wallpaper - Frankford Wallcoverings Inc.

POLO BAY - Wallpaper - K.M.L. Industries

POLO BY RALPH LAUREN - Apparel–men's - Polo Ralph Lauren Corp.

POLO BY RALPH LAUREN - Hosiery - Hot Sox Co. Inc. Ralph Lauren Hosiery Div.

POLO BY RALPH LAUREN - Perfumes - Cosmair Inc.

POLO CALENDAR - Calendars - Chukker Co.

POLO CLUB - Colognes ☆ - Caswell-Massey Co. Ltd.

POLO FOR BOYS - Apparel and accessories - Oxford Industries, Inc.

POLO-LITE - See **MARQUIS**

POLO-MATES - Furniture - Stanley Furniture Co. Inc.

POLO RALPH LAUREN - Apparel–children's - Polo Ralph Lauren Corp.

POLO RALPH LAUREN - Gloves - Swany America Corp.

POLO/RALPH LAUREN - Scarves - Echo Design Group

POLO SPORT - Eyeglasses - Polo Ralph Lauren, LP

POLO SPORT SKIN FITNESS - Skin care products - Polo Ralph Lauren Corp.

POLO UNIVERSITY CLUB BY RALPH LAUREN - Apparel–men's - Greif Cos.

POLOBIKE - Bicycles - Ross Bicycles USA, Ltd.

POLOMYX - Paints - Surface Protection Industries, Inc.

POLONAISE COLLECTION - Christmas tree ornaments - Kurt S. Adler Inc.

POLORIS - Health care products - Block Drug Co., Inc.

POLORON - Ice chests ☆ - Poloron Products Inc.

POLSKA - Sausages - Bil Mar Foods

POLSKA PUP - Frankfurters - Fircrest Farms

POLSKAS - Sausages - Sara Lee Corp.

POLSKI-ORZEL - Pickles - Benjamin Lipitz Co.

POLSKI WYROB - Pickles - Paramount Foods Inc.

POLTECO INC. - Dental floss - Polteco Inc.

POLTERGEIST - Recording label - Metro-Goldwyn-Mayer Inc.

POLTERGRILL - Toys–automobiles - Mattel, Inc.

POLY - Brooms - Zephyr Manufacturing Co.

POLY - Rope - Wellington Leisure Products, Inc.

POLY-1/2 BARREL - Containers - James T. Warring Sons Inc.

POLY-2 - Rakes - Rugg Manufacturing Co. Inc.

POLY-5 - Puzzles - Kadon Enterprises Inc.

POLY-AIR - Tires–bicycles - Poly-Air Inc.

POLY-ALL - Adhesive anchoring system - Ackerman Johnson Fastening Systems Inc.

POLY-AMERICA - Polyethylene film sheets - Poly-America, Inc.

POLY-AQUA - Paints - Valspar Corp.

POLY BINDER, THE - Binders - General Loose Leaf Bindery Co.

POLY-BIO-MARINE - Water purification systems - Poly-Bio-Marine Inc.

POLY-BLOK - Floor coverings - Morrison Molded Fiber Glass Co.

POLY-BOARD - Paper cutters - Premier

POLY-BON - Pharmaceutical preparations - Barrows Pharmacal Inc.

POLY-BOND - Thread - Belding Heminway Co. Inc.

POLY BOND CLEAR - Caulking compounds - VIP/Lighthouse Products

POLY BRAID 8 - Rope ☆ - Columbian Rope Co.

POLY-BRUSH - Brushes–paint - Jen Manufacturing Inc.

POLY-BRUTE - Plastics film ☆ - Carlysle Plastics

POLY C - Office supplies - C-Line Products, Inc.

POLY CAP - Packaging–paper - Sealed Air Corp.

POLY-CAP - Tubes–plastic - Baughman Tile Co., Inc.

POLY/CARB - Aquariums–household - Ginger, Inc.

POLY CARE - Cleaning preparations - Absolute Coatings Inc.

POLY CATCH - Fasteners–snap - Acry Fab Inc.

POLY-CHECK SEAL - Plastics - E.J. Brooks Co.

POLY CHOKE - Shotguns - Marble Arms Corp.

POLY-CIDE II - Chemical preparations - Aqua Clear Industries Inc.

POLY CLAD JR. - Skates–roller - Globe United Inc.

POLY-CLEAR - Varnish - Interlux Yacht Finishes

POLY-CLIP - Pet products - U.S. Clip Corp.

POLY/COAT - Fabrics - Kappler Safety Group

POLY COBALT - Safety products - Aearo Co.

POLY-COMP - Wood products - Sylvan Forest Products, Inc.

POLY-CONS - Electronic equipment - Richard Manufacturing Co.

POLY-CONS - Pet products - Lee's Aquarium Products

POLY-COVER - Plastics film - Warp Bros.

POLY COVER - Thread ☆ - SCT Yarns Inc.

POLY-CRON - Rope - Wall Industries Inc.

POLY CUBES - Furniture ☆ - SES Industries Inc.

POLY CURL - Hair care products - Paula Payne Products Co. Inc.

POLY-D - Gloves - Edmont

POLY D - Juice extracting devices - Valley Research, Inc.

POLY DART - Foil–aluminum - Highland Supply Corp.

☆ = Now out of production

POLY-DAX - Finishing agents - Davis Paint Co.
POLY DECK - Roofing materials–slate ☆ - Colonial Refining and Chemical Co.
POLY DIAMOND - Kites - Spectra Star Kites
POLY-DOCK - Wood products - Sylvan Forest Products, Inc.
POLY-DOLLY - Carts - ENPAC Corp.
POLY DOT - Sporting goods - Poly Enterprises
POLY DRIER - Rope - Wellington Leisure Products, Inc.
POLY-DRIP-PAN - Containers - ENPAC Corp.
POLY-EM - Fungicides ☆ - Stoner Inc.
POLY ENVELOPES - Plastic envelopes - Amko Plastics Inc.
POLY-EPOXY - Finishing agents - Pratt & Lambert United, Inc.
POLY FEND - Boating equipment and accessories - Ultra Poly, Inc.
POLY-FIL - Fibers–polyester - Fairfield Processing Corp.
POLY-FIL - Tire inflators - American Polymer Corp.
POLY-FIL SUPREME - Fibers–polyester - Fairfield Processing Corp.
POLY-FILTER - Water purification systems - Poly-Bio-Marine Inc.
POLY-FLAKE - Paints - Glitterex Corp.
POLY FLEECE - Scuba diving equipment - Parkway Systems
POLY-FLEX - Polyethylene film sheets - Poly-America, Inc.
POLY-FLOR - Pharmaceutical preparations - Goldline Laboratories, Inc.
POLY-FLUFF - Thread - Staple Sewing Aids Corp.
POLY/FOLD - Chairs–folding - Krueger International, Inc.
POLY-FRESH - Health care products - Inbrand Corp.
POLY-GARD - Car-care and rustproofing system, automotive accessories - Auto-One Accessories & Glass Inc.
POLY GEL - Electrical equipment - GB Electrical Inc.
POLY-GLAZE - Caulking compounds - Schnee-Morehead, Inc.
POLY GLIDE - Trailers–travel - Moeller Products Co. Inc.
POLY-GLO - Paints - United Paint Co.
POLY GLO GUARD - Finishing agents - Sperry Owens Inc.
POLY GLOSS - Cleaning preparations - S & S Car Care, Inc.
POLY-GONE - Chemical preparations - Schaner's Waste Water Products, Inc.
POLY-GRID - Floor coverings - American Floor Products Co. Inc.
POLY GRIP - Apparel–women's ☆ - Barnhart Industries Inc.
POLY GRIPPER - Adhesives and sealants - Golden Grip Products Inc.
POLY-GUARD - Adhesives and sealants - Midwest Polychem, Ltd.
POLY-GUARD - Bedding–linen - Workwear Corp. Inc.
POLY HI-GRO - Fertilizers - Kugler Oil Co.
POLY-HISTINE - Pharmaceutical preparations - Bock Pharmacal Co.
POLY-HISTINE CS - Pharmaceutical preparations - Bock Pharmacal Co.
POLY-HISTINE-D - Pharmaceutical preparations - Bock Pharmacal Co.
POLY-HISTINE DM - Pharmaceutical preparations - Bock Pharmacal Co.
POLY HOT POT - Kitchen appliances - Regal Ware, Inc.
POLY-INK - Printing trades machinery - Lincoln Coders, Inc.
POLY-JET - Adhesives and sealants - W.R. Meadows Inc.
POLY JR. - Binders ☆ - General Loose Leaf Bindery Co.
POLY-K - Adhesives and sealants - Key Laboratories Inc.
POLY KING - Fabrics - Dan River Inc.
POLY KING - Toothpicks - Goldmax Industries, Inc.
POLY KLEAR OUTLOOK - Wood products - Westvaco Corp.
POLY KLEER - Seat covers - Rubbermaid Inc.
POLY KNIT - Health care products ☆ - Barnhart Industries Inc.
POLY KNOB - Floor coverings–carpet and rugs - JCH International Inc.
POLY-KOR - Doors–wood - Rubbair Door
POLY LAMB - Paint rollers - Bestt-Liebco
POLY-LASTIC - Paints - C.M. Athey Paint Co.
POLY-LIN - Paints ☆ - Dean and Barry Co.
POLY LINE - Sporting goods - Poly Enterprises
POLY-LITE - Bats–baseball - Jen Cel Lite Corp.
POLY-LITE - Ice chests–plastic - Coleman Co., Inc.
POLY-LITE - Insulating materials - Hubbell Inc.
POLY LITE - Mops - Zephyr Manufacturing Co.
POLY-LOC - Rope - Hooven Allison
POLY-LOCK - Hardware - Plumb Shop
POLY-LOCK - Health care products - Consumer Care Products, Inc.
POLY-LOCK - Paints - C. De Santis Paint Manufacturing Co.
POLY-LOUR - Fabrics - Guilford Mills, Inc.
POLY-LOX - Thread ☆ - Blue Mountain Industries, Inc.
POLY MAID - Food processors - Key Laboratories Inc.
POLY-MAN - Rope - Outdoor Technologies Group
POLY MASKER - Novelty items - PC Manufacturing Corp.
POLY-MED - Aprons - United Plastic Products
POLY-NAG - Vitamins and nutritional supplements - Lescarden, Inc.
POLY-O - Thread - Staple Sewing Aids Corp.
POLY ONE - Fabrics–terrycloth - Guilford Mills, Inc.

POLY-OPTICALS - Television equipment ☆ - Poly-Optical Products, Inc.
POLY-PACK - Envelopes - Quality Park Products Co.
POLY PACK - Packaging machines - Polypack, Inc.
POLY PAD - Mats - Poly Enterprises
POLY-PAK - Tubes–plastic - VisiPak
POLY PALS - Office supplies - Globe-Weis
POLY-PANE - Plastics film - Warp Bros.
POLY-PELLER - Epworth Morehouse-Cowles
POLY PELT - Slip covers - Reeves Brothers Inc.
POLY PERK - Coffee makers–electric - Regal Ware, Inc.
POLY PERM - Filters–water ☆ - Muskin Leisure Products Inc.
POLY PIC - Toothpicks - Washburn Laboratories
POLY PIG - Toys–banks - A.J. Renzi Plastic Corp.
POLY-PIPE - Irrigation pipe - Poly Pipe Industries Inc.
POLY PITCHER - Plastics - Lerner Manufacturing Inc.
POLY PLASTIC - Finishing agents - Master Products Inc.
POLY-PLEX - Rope - Wellington Leisure Products, Inc.
POLY PLUS - Fertilizer - Lesco, Inc.
POLY-PLUS - Floor finish and reconditioner ☆ - Intex Chemical Inc.
POLY-PLUS - Rope - Wall Industries Inc.
POLY PLUSH - Mats - JCH International Inc.
POLY/PLY - Bags - Chase Bag Co.
POLY-POLY - Thread ☆ - SCT Yarns Inc.
POLY POM POMS - Rope - Wellington Leisure Products, Inc.
POLY POP - Kitchen appliances ☆ - Regal Ware, Inc.
POLY POT - Kitchen appliances ☆ - Regal Ware, Inc.
POLY PRED LIQUIFILM - Ophthalmic goods - Allergan, Inc.
POLY PREP - Paints - Perry & Derrick Co.
POLY PREP - Paints ☆ - Foy-Johnston Inc.
POLY PRESS - Wigs - Rescue Marketing Group
POLY-PRIDE - Mattress pads - Pillowtex Corp.
POLY PRINT - Toys - Empire of Carolina Inc.
POLY-PRO - Combs - Capitol Novelty Co.
POLY PRO - Lighting fixtures ☆ - Hubbell Lighting, Inc. (Lighting Div.)
POLY PRO - Office supplies - JM Co.
POLY-PRO - Polysheeting - Up North Plastics Inc.
POLY-PRO - Roofing materials - Tamko Roofing Products, Inc.
POLY-PRO - Shampoos - House of Lowell Inc.
POLY-PRO - Vitamins and nutritional supplements - Welcon
POLY PRO 6 - Rope - Columbian Rope Co.
POLY PRO POP-UP - Handles–plastic - Roberts Systems, Inc.
POLY PROFILE - Office supplies - Globe-Weis
POLY PTO - Mats - JCH International Inc.
POLY-R - Paints - Standard T Chemical Co. Inc.
POLY-R - Thread - Blue Mountain Industries, Inc.
POLY RED TOP - Food containers ☆ - Thermos Co.
POLY RIB - Mats - JCH International Inc.
POLY-RIB - Plastics film ☆ - Warp Bros.
POLY RICH - Cream - Rich Products Corp.
POLY-RITE - Bulletin boards–wood - Marsh Chalkboard Co.
POLY-ROLL - Paint and wallpaper stores - Great American Marketing, Inc.
POLY RUMBLE - Strips–Highway - Poly Enterprises
POLY-S - Brushes–paint ☆ - Wooster Brush Co.
POLY-S - Fertilizers - Scotts Co. (Organics Business Group)
POLY SCRIM - Plastics film - Raven Industries Inc.
POLY SCRUB - Ski suits–children's - Knight Marketing Corp.
POLY-SEAL - Cement - L.D. Sterns Corp.
POLY-SET - Anchor fasteners - ITW Ramset/Red Head
POLY-SHARPS - Medical apparatus - Polymer Systems Engineering
POLY SHIELD - Finishing agents - Cadie Products Corp.
POLY SHINE - Hardware - Boatlife Inc.
POLY-SI - Paints - PPG Industries, Inc.
POLY-SIBONNE PLUS - Fabrics–canvas ☆ - Crown Textile Co.
POLY SLIK - Paper–coated - Rexam Release
POLY-SMASHER - Bats–baseball - Markwort Sporting Goods Co.
POLY SMOOTH - Putties ☆ - Fibre Glass-Evercoat Co. Inc.
POLY-SORB-SPONGE - Cleaning preparations - Swiss-Tex Inc.
POLY SPOT - Sporting goods - Poly Enterprises
POLY SQUARES - Sporting goods - Poly Enterprises
POLY START - Sporting goods - Poly Enterprises
POLY STATIC - Filters–air - American Products Brokerage
POLY STIK - Fabrics–polyester - Jelliff Corp.
POLY STONE - Building materials - Arizona Cultured Stone Products, Inc.
POLY-STONE - Cutting boards - Katchall Industries International, Inc.
POLY-STRESS - Pharmaceutical preparations ☆ - Xttrium Laboratories Inc.
POLY SUEDE - Fabrics–polyester - Guilford Mills, Inc.

☆ = Now out of production

POLY SYSTEM ONE - Cleaning preparations - Star Brite
POLY-TACH - Office supplies ☆ - Avery Label Systems
POLY TAPE - Roofing materials–concrete - Consolidated Coatings Corp.
POLY-TEC - Plastics - Walk-Winn Co.
POLY-TECH - Wheels - Hamilton Caster & Manufacturing Co.
POLY-TEK - Varnishes - Passonno Paints
POLY-TEX - Christmas tree ornaments - Union Wadding Co.
POLY THRIFT - Mats ☆ - Ludlow Composites Corp.
POLY TILER - Cement-adhesive additive - Construction Adhesives Co.
POLY TILER 707 - Ceramic-tile adhesive - Construction Adhesives Co.
POLY-TIN - Containers - All-Pak, Inc.
POLY-TITE - Caulking compounds - Sandell Manufacturing Co. Inc.
POLY-TOGGLE - Anchors - Rawlplug Co., Inc.
POLY-TONE - Ribbons - Gaylord Specialties Corp.
POLY-TONER - Photographic equipment - Eastman Kodak Co.
POLY TOP - Truck bodies - Gem Top Manufacturing Inc.
POLY TOTE - Garden equipment - Eaton Brothers Corp.
POLY TOUGH - Office supplies - International Rotex Inc.
POLY-TRAK - Footwear - Iron Age Corp.
POLY TRAZ - Latex binder for floor toppings - Construction Adhesives Co.
POLY TUFF - Farm machinery - Behlen Manufacturing Co.
POLY-TUFF - Paints - Chilton Paint Co.
POLY-TUNG - Varnishes - Red Devil Paints
POLY-TWILL - Fabrics–polyester - Stahls' Inc.
POLY TWILL - Thread ☆ - Staple Sewing Aids Corp.
POLY-TWIN - Labels–paper - Christopher C. Campbell
POLY URN - Kitchen appliances ☆ - Regal Ware, Inc.
POLY-V - Belts–automotive - Goodyear Tire & Rubber Co.
POLY V-RIB - Mats - JCH International Inc.
POLY-VI-FLOR - Vitamins and nutritional supplements - Bristol-Myers Squibb Co.
POLY-VI-SOL - Vitamins and nutritional supplements - Bristol-Myers Squibb Co.
POLY-VITA - Vitamins and nutritional supplements - H.R. Cenci Laboratories Inc.
POLY-VU - Paper–thermoplastics coated - K & M Co.
POLY-VUE - Electronic equipment - Richard Manufacturing Co.
POLY WALL - Coatings - Poly-Wall International, Inc.
POLY WEAVE - Mats - JCH International Inc.
POLY-WINDOWS - Computer software - Polytron
POLY-WIRE - Wire products - A-Porcel Corp.
POLY WOOL - Brushes–paint - Imperial Paint Applicators Ltd.
POLY-WRAP - Plastics film - Warp Bros.
POLY-X - Paints ☆ - Fuller-O'Brien Paints Inc.
POLY-XL - Welding equipment - Electron Beam Technologies, Inc.
POLY ZAP - Adhesives and sealants - Pacer Technology
POLYALL - Thread - Sewing Market Industries Inc.
POLYAQUA - Aquarium accessories - Kordon
POLYAQUA - Aquarium accessories - Novalek, Inc.
POLYARAMID - Sporting goods - Outdoor Technologies Group
POLYART - Artists' materials - Polyart Products Co.
POLYART - Paper - Arjobex America
POLYBAC - Floor coverings–carpet and rugs - Amoco Fabrics and Fibers Co.
POLYBAR - Pantograph accessories - Graphicraft
POLYBASE - Pharmaceutical preparations - Paddock Laboratories Inc.
POLYBASE - Roofing materials - GS Roofing Products Co.
POLYBIND - Diagnostic substances - International Enzymes, Inc.
POLYBLEND - Grouting material - Custom Building Products
POLYBOND 007 - Adhesives and sealants - VIP/Lighthouse Products
POLYBOR - Insecticides - U.S. Borax Inc.
POLYBRA - Thread - Perfect Thread Co. Inc.
POLYBRADE - Skin care products - Texas Pharmacal Co.
POLYBRAID - Thread - Advance Thread Corp.
POLYBRANE - Finishing agents - Polymer Plastic Corp.
POLYBRITE - Enamels - Commercial Chemical Co. Inc.
POLYBUSTER - Paints - E-Z Paintr Corp.
POLYCAP - Packaging–blisterwrap - Mason Box Co. Inc.
POLYCARB TABLETS - Laxatives ☆ - Breckenridge Pharmaceutical, Inc.
POLYCARE - Bags–plastic - Fortune Plastics, Inc.
POLYCARE - Health care products - Inbrand Corp.
POLYCAST - Automotive parts and accessories - Motor Wheel Corp.
POLYCAST - Gypsum products - Georgia-Pacific Corp.
POLYCEL - Adhesives and sealants - W.R. Grace & Co.
POLYCEL - Mattress pads - Simmons USA
POLYCEL - Plastic bags - Phytotronics, Inc.
POLYCEL ONE - Insulating materials - Ultra Industries/Polycel Products

POLYCELL - Loudspeakers - Infinity Systems, Inc.
POLYCENTER - Computer peripheral equipment - Digital Equipment Corp.
POLYCERAMIC - Pottery - Rubens Originals
POLYCHARGE - Fencing–steel - E.S. Robbins Corp.
POLYCHROME - Chemicals–photographic - Sun Chemical Corp.
POLYCHRON - Envelopes - Light Impressions Corp.
POLYCILLIN - Antibiotics - Bristol-Myers Squibb Co.
POLYCILLIN-PRB - Antibiotics - Bristol-Myers Squibb Co.
POLYCITRA - Pharmaceutical preparations - Willen Drug Co.
POLYCITRA K - Pharmaceutical preparations - Willen Drug Co.
POLYCITRA-K CRYSTALS - Pharmaceutical preparations - Willen Drug Co.
POLYCITRA LC - Pharmaceutical preparations - Willen Drug Co.
POLYCLAD - Vinyl - HPG International, Inc.
POLYCLEAN - Cleaning preparations - Wilshire Technologies, Inc.
POLYCLEAR - Thread ☆ - American & Efird, Inc.
POLYCLEAR II - Filters–air - Beach Filter Products, Inc.
POLYCLIPS - Hardware ☆ - Pan Am Agri Fabric
POLYCOAT - Wallpaper - Polycoat Wallcoverings
POLYCOAT AQUAGARD - Waterproofing compounds - American Polymer Corp.
POLYCOAT-AQUASEAL - Adhesives and sealants - American Polymer Corp.
POLYCOLOR - Pencils ☆ - Koh-I-Noor, Inc.
POLYCOM - Computers - Polycom Corp.
POLYCON - Roofing materials–concrete - Consolidated Fiber Glass Products Co.
POLYCON CLASS I - Roofing materials - Consolidated Fiber Glass Products Co.
POLYCON-POSITE - Roofing materials - Consolidated Fiber Glass Products Co.
POLYCONTRAST - Photographic equipment - Eastman Kodak Co.
POLYCOPY - Computer software - Joseph M. Albanese
POLYCOR COVERS - Paint rollers - Corona Brushes Inc.
POLYCOR JUMBO COVERS - Paint rollers - Corona Brushes Inc.
POLYCORD - Thread - Advance Thread Corp.
POLYCORE - Ribbons - Ben Clements & Sons Inc.
POLYCOSE - Vitamins and nutritional supplements - Ross Laboratories
POLYCOT - Thread ☆ - Belding Heminway Co. Inc.
POLYCRAFT - Moldings–plaster of paris ☆ - Polyform Products Inc.
POLYCRETE - Mortars–clay ☆ - Mapei East Corp.
POLYCRETE PLUS - Mortars–clay - Mapei East Corp.
POLYCRETE U.S.A. - Building materials - Robert D. Holmes
POLYCRYL - Paints - Triangle Coatings Inc.
POLYCURA - Hair care products - Paula Payne Products Co. Inc.
POLYCURE - Hair care products - Revlon Consumer Products Corp.
POLYCUSHION - Foam rubber - Alimed, Inc.
POLYCUSHION - Orthopedic products - Smith & Nephew Inc. (Rehabilitation Div.)
POLYCYCLE - Plastics - Polycycle, Inc.
POLYDAX - Audio equipment - Polydax Speaker Corp.
POLYDERM - Astringents ☆ - Prince Matchabelli
POLYDINE - Pharmaceutical preparations - Century Pharmaceuticals Inc.
POLYDOL - Photographic equipment - Eastman Kodak Co.
POLYDOR - Recording label - Polygram Records, Inc.
POLYDRAFT - Paper - National Printfast
POLYDROP - Bottles–plastic ☆ - Chase Instruments Corp.
POLYDYN - Automotive parts and accessories - Polymer Dynamics Inc.
POLYEDGE - Adhesives and sealants - Woodtape Co.
POLYENVELOPE - Transparent polypropylene envelopes - Itoya of America, Ltd.
POLYERECTA - Shelving - InterMetro Industries Corp.
POLYESTER JEWELS - Floor coverings - Meadowbrook Inventions Inc.
POLYESTER Q EPOXY - Adhesives and sealants ☆ - Fibre Glass-Evercoat Co. Inc.
POLYESTOL - Bandages - Glenwood LLC
POLYFAB - Adhesives and sealants - Plastics & Resins Ltd.
POLYFAB - Housewares - Karen Carson Creations
POLYFAC - Chemical preparations - Westvaco Corp.
POLYFAST - Adhesives and sealants - Barrett Varnish Co.
POLYFIBER - Paper–photographic - Eastman Kodak Co.
POLYFIBER COILS - Pillows - Pacific Coast Feather Co.
POLYFIL - Adhesives and sealants - Induron Coatings Inc.
POLYFILE - File folders - Itoya of America, Ltd.
POLYFILE - File folders - K & M Co.
POLYFILLER - Cosmetics - Ladyfingers
POLYFIRE - Doors - Fenestra Corp.
POLYFLAX - Canvas–artists' - Fredrix Artist Canvas Inc.

☆ = Now out of production

POLYFLEX - Chemical preparations - American Cyanamid Co.

POLYFLEX - File folders - K & M Co.

POLYFLEX - Film - Plastic Suppliers, Inc.

POLYFLEX - Paints - Jones Blair Co.

POLYFLEX - Pharmaceutical preparations ☆ - Abana Pharmaceuticals, Inc.

POLYFLEX - Plastics film ☆ - Monsanto Co.

POLYFLEX II - Orthopedic products - Smith & Nephew Inc. (Rehabilitation Div.)

POLYFLEX LIGHT - Splints - Smith & Nephew Inc. (Rehabilitation Div.)

POLYFLEX XT - Pipes - Markel Corp.

POLYFLO - Chemical preparations - Consolidated Recycling Co, Inc.

POLYFLOCK - Labeling machinery ☆ - Polymark Corp.

POLYFLOR - Vinyl - HPG International, Inc.

POLYFLOW - Catheters - Sims Deltec, Inc.

POLYFLUTE - Sheet plastic - Coroplast Inc.

POLYFOAM - Craft supplies - Isle Laboratories Inc.

POLYFOAM - Furniture - Lowy Group Inc.

POLYFORM - Artists' materials - Polyform Products Inc.

POLYFORM - Contact lenses - O.S.I. Corp.

POLYFORM - Orthopedic products - Smith & Nephew Inc. (Rehabilitation Div.)

POLYFREE - Chemical preparations - Baker Hughes Inc.

POLYFUSE - Thread - United Thread Mills Corp.

POLYFUSION - Labels–paper - Kaumagraph Co. Inc.

POLYGARD - Apparel and accessories - Professional Medical Products, Inc.

POLYGARD II - Apparel and accessories - Professional Medical Products, Inc.

POLYGASKET REDLINE - Gaskets - Frederickseal, Inc.

POLYGEN - Paints - Hirshfield's Paint Manufacturing

POLYGINS - Vitamins and nutritional supplements - Grand Stone Corp.

POLYGLOSS - Flags - Metro Flag Inc.

POLYGONET COMMANDERS - Video games - Konami (America) Inc.

POLYGONZO - Toys - Polygonzo Unlimited Ltd.

POLYGRAM - Audio equipment - Polygram Records, Inc.

POLYGRANITE HD - Cases–vanity - Santana Products, Inc.

POLYGRAPH - Computer software - Pursell Industries, Inc.

POLYGUARD - Chemical preparations - William S. Litwin

POLYGUARD - Paints - Vanguard Paints & Finishes Inc.

POLYGUARD - Pet products - Seachem Laboratories

POLYGUN - Adhesives and sealants - Minnesota Mining & Manufacturing Co.

POLYHEED - Concrete–mixture - Master Builders Inc.

POLYHINGE - Waterproof plastic hinge - Atlas Minerals & Chemicals, Inc.

POLYKINS - Footwear ☆ - R.G. Barry Corp.

POLYLAST - Wheels - Hamilton Caster & Manufacturing Co.

POLYLASTOMER - Fixtures–plastic - Bruce Plastics Inc.

POLYLECTRIC - Kitchen appliances ☆ - Regal Ware, Inc.

POLYLENS - Projection screens ☆ - Da-Lite Screen Co. Inc.

POLYLETS - Chemical preparations - Chusei USA Inc.

POLYLITE - Cases–plastic - PowerMark Case Corp.

POLYLITE - Cutting boards - Read Products, Inc.

POLYLITE - Eyeglasses - Sunlink Corp.

POLYLITE - Footwear - Stride Rite Corp.

POLYLOCK - Thread - Threads USA Div.

POLYLOK - Fabrics - Polylok Corp.

POLYLOK - Window coverings ☆ - Vertical Blind Factory

POLYLURE - Crocheted and knitted items - Marcrest Knitting Mills

POLYLURE - Paints - Lilly Industries, Inc.

POLYLURE - Paints ☆ - Glidden Co.

POLYLUXE - Ribbons ☆ - C.M. Offray & Son Inc.

POLYMAGMA - Pharmaceutical preparations ☆ - Wyeth-Ayerst Laboratories

POLYMAIL - Stationery - Poly Pak America Inc.

POLYMAILER - Envelopes - Amko Plastics Inc.

POLYMAR - Paints - Diamond/Kuhn Paint Co.

POLYMARK - Paints - Tulip Productions

POLYMARS - Ventilation equipment - Mars Sales Co., Inc.

POLYMAT - Floor coverings - Devon Corp.

POLYMAT - Mats - U.S. Mat & Rubber Co. Inc.

POLYMATCH - Thread - Perfect Thread Co. Inc.

POLYMATIC - Thread - Belding Heminway Co. Inc.

POLYMAX - Luggage - Airway Industries, Inc.

POLYMAX - Nozzles - Spraying Systems Co.

POLYMAX - Pencils - Koh-I-Noor, Inc.

POLYMAX - Photographic equipment - Eastman Kodak Co.

POLYMERIC - Hair care products - Nexxus Products Co.

POLYMID - Sutures - Anchor Products Co.

POLYMIX - Concrete additives - Tycon Inc.

POLYMNIA BLEND - Teas–herbal - P.J.'s USA, Inc.

POLYMO - Thread - Belding Heminway Co. Inc.

POLYMOL - Hair care products ☆ - Majestic Drug Co., Inc.

POLYMONOCORD - Thread - Belding Heminway Co. Inc.

POLYMOX - Antibiotics - Bristol-Myers Squibb Co.

POLYNAISE - Floor coverings–carpet and rugs - Orian Rugs Inc.

POLYNESIA - Furniture ☆ - A.A. Laun Furniture Co.

POLYNESIAN - Food products - Allied Old English, Inc.

POLYNESIAN PAPER - Paper - Paul Marshall Products L.P.

POLYNESIAN PASSION - Fruit drinks–bottled or canned - Chiquita Brands, Inc.

POLYNESIAN PUNCH - Beverages - Logret Import & Export Co.

POLYNIB - Mats - Sagaz Industries Inc.

POLYON - Fertilizers - Pursell Industries, Inc.

POLYON NPK - Fertilizers - Pursell Industries, Inc.

POLYOPTICON - Microscopes ☆ - Small World Toys

POLYOXIDE - Hair care products - Redken Laboratories, Inc.

POLYPANEL - Wood products ☆ - Homasote Co.

POLYPAVE - Epoxy - Key Laboratories Inc.

POLYPELLET SYSTEM - Kitchen appliances - Carlisle Foodservice Products, Inc.

POLYPHARM - Home health care products - Edward D. Weinberger

POLYPHASE - Rulers–wood ☆ - Keuffel & Esser Co.

POLYPHASER - Electronic equipment - Polyphaser Corp.

POLYPHEN - Medical apparatus - Minntech Corp.

POLYPHONIA - Harmonicas - Hohner Inc.

POLYPLANK - Padding–foam - Astro-Valcour, Inc.

POLYPLASTIC - Enamels - Standard T Chemical Co. Inc.

POLYPLATES - Sporting goods - Denali International Inc.

POLYPLEAT - Window shades ☆ - Cooper Industries, Inc.

POLYPLEX - Audio equipment - MTX

POLYPLEX - Radio communications equipment - Telephonics Corp.

POLYPLEZ - Varnishes - Gilbert Spruance Co.

POLYPLONI - Fabrics - Loomtex Retail Fabrics

POLYPLY - Plastic/plywood paneling - Buckeye Pacific Corp.

POLYPOKITS - Envelopes - Taylor-Merchant Corp.

POLYPOLE - Drapery poles - Capps' Customs

POLYPORE - Batteries - Intertech Group, Inc.

POLYPORE - Medical apparatus - Mentor O & O Inc.

POLYPORT - File folders - K & M Co.

POLYPORTABLES - Toilets–portable - Polyportables, Inc.

POLYPOXY - Varnishes - Pettit Paint Co. Inc.

POLYPRINT - Paper–photographic - Eastman Kodak Co.

POLYPRINT - Plastics–laminated - B & F Graphics, Inc.

POLYPRO - Laundry tubs–plastic ☆ - Kinkead/Tub/Shower Doors

POLYPRO - Thread - Threads USA Div.

POLYPRO - Trowels - Clark Tile Co.

POLYPRODUCTS - Artists' materials - Polyproducts Corp.

POLYPSORALEN - Pharmaceutical preparations ☆ - ICN Pharmaceuticals Inc.

POLYPUFF - Fabric stores - M-Tex Corp.

POLYPURE - Machinery - Fluoroware, Inc.

POLYRAIL - Construction equipment - Alexander Construction, Inc.

POLYSAFE - Bags - Curtis 1000 Inc.

POLYSAFE - Thread ☆ - American & Efird, Inc.

POLYSCORE - Computer software - Johns Hopkins University

POLYSCULPT - Ribbons ☆ - Bridon Cordage LLC

POLYSEAL - Insulating materials - General Electric Co.

POLYSEAL - Tape–adhesive ☆ - Central Products Co.

POLYSEAL - Weather stripping - A.A.S.R. Inc.

POLYSEAL WRAPS - Skin care products ☆ - Salon Essentials

POLYSEAMSEAL - Adhesives and sealants - Ensign-Bickford Industries Inc.

POLYSEAMSEAL - Caulking compounds - OSI Sealants, Inc.

POLYSEIS - Seismographs - Environmental Technology, Inc.

POLYSERGE - Thread - Threads USA Div.

POLYSERT - Machine parts - Lako Tool & Manufacturing, Inc.

POLYSET - Machinery - Polyfoam Products, Inc.

POLYSET - Thread - Threads USA Div.

POLYSEW - Thread - Belding Heminway Co. Inc.

POLYSHADES - Varnishes - Minwax Co., Inc.

POLYSHEATH - Insulating materials - E.R. Carpenter Co.

POLYSHIELD - Paper–coated - Ahlstrom Filtration Inc. Industrial Products Group

POLYSHOP - Computer software - University of Central Florida

POLYSILK - Hobby kits ☆ - Kool Pak

POLYSINE - Laboratory apparatus - Erie Scientific Co.

POLYSITE - Fencing–steel - E.S. Robbins Corp.

POLYSKIM - Cement–asphalt - Dependable Chemical Co., Inc.

POLYSOME - Encapsulated chemicals - Fuisz Technologies Ltd.

POLYSORB - Health care products - E. Fougera & Co. Inc.

POLYSORB - Medical apparatus - Spenco Medical Corp.
POLYSORBATE 80 - Vitamins and nutritional supplements - Twinlab
POLYSORBIN - Vitamins and nutritional supplements ☆ - Solvay Pharmaceuticals Inc.
POLYSPORIN - Pharmaceutical preparations - Warner-Wellcome
POLYSPRAY - Bottles–plastic ☆ - Chase Instruments Corp.
POLYSPUN - Thread ☆ - SCT Yarns Inc.
POLYSPUN 300 - Fabrics - Landmaster Products Inc.
POLYSPUN II - Thread ☆ - SCT Yarns Inc.
POLYSPUN V - Thread ☆ - SCT Yarns Inc.
POLY+STAIN - Varnishes - Tru-Test Manufacturing
POLYSTAR - Greases - Texaco, Inc.
POLYSTEEL - Fencing–steel - E.S. Robbins Corp.
POLYSTEEL - Lamps - Rotocast Plastic Products
POLYSTEL - Batteries - Standard Industries (Permalife Glass Fiber Div.)
POLYSTIM - Health care products - Medical Science Products Inc.
POLYSTINGER - Flashlights - Streamlight, Inc.
POLYSTONE - Laundry tubs–plastic ☆ - Kinkead/Tub/Shower Doors
POLYSTONE 600 - Plaster–wallboard - Applied Texture Inc.
POLYSTOR - Batteries - Polystor, Corp.
POLYSTRIPE - Toys - Empire of Carolina Inc.
POLYSTYREX - Resins–synthetic - Berkley C. Badger
POLYSULFIDE - Caulking compounds - Sav-Cote Chemical Laboratories Inc.
POLYSURF - Chemical preparations - Hercules Inc.
POLYSWEPE - Brooms - Hamburg Broom Works Inc.
POLYSYNTEX - Thread - Synthetic Thread Co. Inc.
POLYTAC - Oils–lubricating - Phillips Petroleum Co.
POLYTAINE - Electronics equipment - American Sound & Video
POLYTAK - Adhesives and sealants - Imperial Adhesives Inc.
POLYTAR - Shampoos - Stiefel Laboratories, Inc.
POLYTECH - Fixtures–plastic - Bruce Plastics Inc.
POLYTEF - Medical apparatus - Mentor O & O Inc.
POLYTENSILE - Welding equipment - Weld Mold Co.
POLYTEX - Film - Chase Bag Co.
POLYTEX - Lamp shades–fabric - Nolarec Industries, Inc.
POLYTEX - Paints - Colonial Refining and Chemical Co.
POLYTEX - Sports rackets and accessories - Victor Sports
POLYTEX - Thread - Belding Heminway Co. Inc.
POLYTEX - Thread - A. Lewis Thread Co. Inc.
POLYTEX - Tires ☆ - Bridgestone/Firestone, Inc.
POLYTEXTURE - Wood products - Medalist Industries Inc.
POLYTHERM - Sports apparel - Medalist Apparel Inc.
POLYTINIC - Pharmaceutical preparations - Pharmics Inc.
POLYTIRE USA - Tires - Polytire, Inc.
POLYTISSUE - Tablecloths - Wisconsin Tissue Mills Inc.
POLYTITE - Caulking compounds - Polytite Manufacturing Corp.
POLYTONATOR - Hearing aids - Siemens Hearing Instruments Inc.
POLYTONE - Accordions - Italo-American Accordion Manufacturing Co.
POLYTONE - Finishing agents - Polymer Plastic Corp.
POLYTONE - Musical instrument accessories - Polytone Musical Instruments Inc.
POLYTOP - Finishing agents - Polymer Plastic Corp.
POLYTOUGH - File folders - Esselte Corp.
POLYTRACH - Bandages - Ferris Corp.
POLYTRACIN - Pharmaceutical preparations - Consolidated Midland Corp.
POLYTRANS - Film - Eastman Kodak Co.
POLYTRED - Vinyl - HPG International, Inc.
POLYTREE - Trees–artificial - Polytree Co., Ltd.
POLYTRIBOLATE - Lubricants - American Cyanamid Co.
POLYTRIX - Floor coverings - Polymer Plastic Corp.
POLYTRON - Lubricants - Epco Corp.
POLYTROP SEATING - Chairs–upholstered - GF Office Furniture Ltd.
POLYTUSS-DM - Cold remedies - J.G. Rhode Co. Inc.
POLYTWILL - Fabrics - QST Industries, Inc.
POLYTWINE EG - Twine - Blue Mountain Industries, Inc.
POLYTWIST - Thread - Threads USA Div.
POLYURE - Paints - McCloskey Corp.
POLYVAC - Medical apparatus - Poly-Vac, Inc.
POLYVELVA - Apparel and accessories - ShadowLine Inc.
POLYVEX - Flags - Annin and Co.
POLYVIAL - Medical apparatus ☆ - Olympic Plastics Co. Inc.
POLYVINYLPYRROLIDONE - Pharmaceutical preparations - City Chemical Corp.
POLYVISION - Hardware - Polytronix, Inc.
POLYVU - Wallets ☆ - Kleer-Vu Plastics Inc.
POLYWASH - Brushes - Wright-Bernet

POLYWEAVE - Labels–paper ☆ - International Paper Co.
POLYWELD - Lamps - Metro Mark, Inc.
POLYWIPE-C INSPECTR - Cleaning equipment - Contec, Inc.
POLYWOODE - Drums–musical instruments ☆ - LP Music Group
POLYWOOL - Paint rollers - Karmichael Industries Inc.
POLYWRAP - Twine - Blue Mountain Industries, Inc.
POLYWRITER - Computer software ☆ - Passport Designs Inc.
POLYWUD - Finishing agents ☆ - Kwal-Howells Inc.
POLYWYP - Paper–toweling - Cleveland Cotton Products Co.
POLYZINC - Adhesives and sealants ☆ - Master Builders Inc.
POM - Paper–toilet - Fort Howard Corp.
POM FLUFF - Toys–stuffed - Dakin Inc.
POM-MALE - Hair care products - Form-U-La-Hair Co.
POM POM - Fruits and vegetables - Orange Cove-Sanger Citrus Association
POM POM - Nail care products - Troika International Inc.
POM POM - Paper–gift wrap - American Greetings Corp.
POM POM OPERA - Cigars - Swisher International, Inc.
POM POM PALS - Lamps ☆ - Reliance Products Corp.
POM POM WUZZY - Toys–stuffed ☆ - Gund, Inc.
POM POMS - Candy - Tootsie Roll Industries, Inc.
POM STAMPER - Stamps–hand - Sanford Corp.
POM TAMS - Crocheted and knitted items ☆ - Reliable of Milwaukee
POMA - Floor coverings ☆ - Tarkett, Inc.
POMADES - Skin care products - Custom Cosmetics Co.
POMANDER - Deodorizers ☆ - Caswell-Massey Co. Ltd.
POMANDER - Ophthalmic goods - Swank Optical
POMANDER - Teas - Eastern Shore Tea Co.
POMATONE - Hair care products - Gold Medal Hair Products Inc.
POMEGRANATE - Artists' materials - Pomegranate Publications
POMEGRANATE - Teas - Eastern Shore Tea Co.
POMEROY - Bacon - Peer Food Products Co.
POMEROY - Windows - Pomeroy Inc.
POMEROY, THE - Ophthalmic goods - Styl-Rite Optical Manufacturing Co., Inc.
POMFRET - Yarn - Brunswick Yarns
POMI - Tomato product - Parmalat USA Corp.
POMME - Sporting goods - Thomas R. Olson
POMME D'AMOUR - Coffee - Executive Coffee Service Co.
POMME PRISSONIERE - Beverages–alcohol ☆ - Twelve Stone Flagons Ltd.
POMMEAU SAINTE ANNE - Beverages–alcohol ☆ - Twelve Stone Flagons Ltd.
POMMERAIE - Wines - Pommeraie Winery
POMMERELLE - Wines - Gibson Wine Co.
POMMERY - Mustard ☆ - Liberty Richter Inc.
POMMERY - Vinegar - Source Atlantique
POMODORI DELLA VITA - Tomato pastes and sauces - Food Services of America, Inc.
POMODORO - Dinnerware–glass - Crate and Barrel
POMON-O-LOK - Pipes - Pomona Pipe Products Co.
POMONA - Earthenware - Portmeirion USA
POMONA - Food products - Pomona Products Co.
POMONA - Occasional tables - JDI Group, Inc.
POMONA - Tiles–ceramic ☆ - American Olean Tile Co.
POMONA - Wallpaper ☆ - Wolf-Gordon Inc.
POMONA'S UNIVERSAL PECTIN - Food products - Workstead Industries
POMOUSSE - Hair care products - Matrix Essentials, Inc.
POMP - Communications equipment - Lucent Technologies Inc.
POMP - Ophthalmic goods - Embassy Creations Inc.
POMPA MAS - Cigarettes ☆ - James B. Russell Inc.
POMPADOUR - Floor coverings - Parquet de France Inc.
POMPADOUR - Floor coverings–carpet and rugs ☆ - Kelly Group Inc.
POMPADOUR - Glassware–household - Durand International
POMPADOUR - Teas - C. & J. Willenborg Inc.
POMPANETTE - Sporting goods - Pompanette Inc.
POMPANO - Motor vehicles–motor homes ☆ - Coachmen Industries, Inc.
POMPANO - Shoes - Daniel Green Co.
POMPANO 2 - Furniture - Tropitone Furniture Co. Inc.
POMPEI - Dishes–china - Pasmantier Co. Inc.
POMPEI - Frames–eyeglass - Zylo Ware Corp.
POMPEI - Wines - Pompei Winery Inc.
POMPEIAN - Olive oil - Pompeian Inc.
POMPEII - Floor coverings - Mannington Resilient Floors
POMPEII - Floor coverings–carpet and rugs - Couristan Inc.
POMPEII - Floor coverings–carpet and rugs ☆ - Karastan-Bigelow Inc.
POMPEII - Floor coverings–carpet and rugs ☆ - Trans-Ocean Import Co. Inc.
POMPEII - Giftware - N.S. Gustin Co.
POMPEII - Wallcovering - Wall Trends, Inc.

☆ = Now out of production

POMPEIIAN COLLECTION - Jewelry - Mazza/Bartholomew Ltd.

POMPIS - Diapers–disposable - Key-Met Traders, Inc.

POMPOSA - Wines ☆ - Wines of the World Inc.

POMPS - Paper–tissue - Crystal Tissue Co. Inc.

POMPTON - Floor coverings–carpet and rugs - Milliken & Co. Inc.

POMS - Computer storage devices–magnetic - Kaden Arnone, Inc.

POMS - Pharmaceutical preparations - Pulsair Inc.

POMS 20 - Pharmaceutical preparations - Pulsair Inc.

POMS 50 - Pharmaceutical preparations - Pulsair Inc.

POMTON - Toys - Lancaster Toy Co.

POMUX - Electronic equipment - Applied Digital Electronics Inc.

PONARIS - Nasal emollient - Jamol Laboratories Inc.

PONCAR - Twine - Sunshine Cordage Corp.

PONCE - Brushes–paint - Corona Brushes Inc.

PONCE - Cosmetics - Ponce Cosmetics

PONCE'S CREATIONS - Craft supplies - Ponce's Creations

PONCHO - Cookies - Sunshine/Salerno Inc.

PONCHO - Frames–eyeglass - May Optical Co. Inc.

PONCHO BALLS - Waterproof outerwear - Decision Point, Inc.

PONCHY PANDA - Toys–stuffed ☆ - Dakin Inc.

POND 1 - Water treating compounds - Mardel Laboratories, Inc.

POND 2 - Water treating compounds - Mardel Laboratories, Inc.

POND 3 - Water treating compounds - Mardel Laboratories, Inc.

POND 4 - Water treating compounds - Mardel Laboratories, Inc.

POND ACID BUFFER - Pet products - Seachem Laboratories

POND BLOCK - Water treating compounds - Jungle Laboratories Corp.

POND CARE - Fish food - Aquarium Pharmaceuticals, Inc.

POND CARE CENTER - Water treating compounds - Jungle Laboratories Corp.

POND-CLEAR - Water treating compounds - Weco Products Inc.

POND CLEAR-ZYME - Water treating compounds - Jungle Laboratories Corp.

POND: EXPLORATIONS IN PROBLEM SOLVING, THE - Computer software - Sunburst Communications, Inc.

POND FISH FOOD - Water treating compounds - Mardel Laboratories, Inc.

POND FLOURISH - Pet products - Seachem Laboratories

POND FLOURISH TABS - Pet products - Seachem Laboratories

POND FOOD - Water treating compounds - Jungle Laboratories Corp.

POND FUNGUS ELIMINATOR - Water treating compounds - Jungle Laboratories Corp.

POND GUARD - Water treating compounds - Jungle Laboratories Corp.

POND HEALTH GUARD - Pet products - Seachem Laboratories

POND ICK GUARD - Water treating compounds - Jungle Laboratories Corp.

POND LILY - Lamps - Meyda Tiffany Inc.

POND MAGIC - Fountains - Rena Corp.

POND MATRIX - Pet products - Seachem Laboratories

POND MOUNTAIN - Stoneware dinnerware ☆ - Iron Mountain Stoneware Inc.

POND PARASITE GUARD - Water treating compounds - Jungle Laboratories Corp.

POND PH BUFFER - Pet products - Seachem Laboratories

POND PH DECREASER - Water treating compounds - Jungle Laboratories Corp.

POND PH INCREASER - Water treating compounds - Jungle Laboratories Corp.

POND PLANT FOOD SPIKES - Water treating compounds - Mardel Laboratories, Inc.

POND PLANT SAVER - Water treating compounds - Jungle Laboratories Corp.

POND PREP - Aquarium accessories - Kordon

POND PREP - Aquarium accessories - Novalek, Inc.

POND PRIME - Pet products - Seachem Laboratories

POND-RITE - Pet products - Lake Products Co. Inc.

POND SCUM - Candy - Creative Confection Concepts, Inc.

POND SEAL - Liners and covers–pond, pit, and landfill - Redmond Clay & Salt Co.

POND SLIME AWAY - Water treating compounds - Jungle Laboratories Corp.

POND START - Water treating compounds - Jungle Laboratories Corp.

POND STARTER KIT - Water treating compounds - Jungle Laboratories Corp.

POND T.E.N. - Fish food - Wardley Corp.

POND TEST KIT - Water treating compounds - Mardel Laboratories, Inc.

POND TIME KIT - Water treating compounds - Mardel Laboratories, Inc.

POND WATER CLEAR - Water treating compounds - Jungle Laboratories Corp.

POND WATER SHADE - Water treating compounds - Jungle Laboratories Corp.

POND-ZYME - Chemical preparations - Aquarium Pharmaceuticals, Inc.

PONDCLEAR - Pet products ☆ - Sera Aquaristik USA Inc.

PONDER STONES - Novelty items - Squire Boone Caverns, Inc.

PONDERA - Molding compounds–plastics ☆ - Gossen Corp.

PONDEROSA - Banjos - OME Co. Inc.

PONDEROSA - Bicycles - REI

PONDEROSA - Boots - Georgia Boot Inc.

PONDEROSA - Canvas–artists' - New York Central Art Supply Co.

PONDEROSA - Charcoal - Steak & Ale Corp.

PONDEROSA - Furniture ☆ - Evenflo Juvenile Furniture Co.

PONDEROSA - Furniture–wood - Johnston-Tombigbee

PONDEROSA - Heating equipment ☆ - Birmingham Stove & Range Co.

PONDEROSA - Paints - Ponderosa Paint Manufacturing Co. Inc.

PONDEROSA - Pet products - L/M Animal Farms, Inc.

PONDEROSA - Salad dressings–bottled - Ponderosa Inc.

PONDEROSA - Shoes - Endicott Johnson Corp.

PONDEROSA GOLD - Lumber - Boise Cascade Corp.

PONDEROSA NUTRI-MAX - Animal feeds - Conagra, Inc.

PONDEROSA PALE ALE - Beverages–malt - Reno Brewing Co.

PONDEROSA PRAIRIE ONIONS - Onions - Steak & Ale Corp.

PONDEROSA PRIDE - Paints - Ponderosa Paint Manufacturing Co. Inc.

PONDEROSA PRO - Paints - Ponderosa Paint Manufacturing Co. Inc.

PONDEROSA PROGUARD - Paints - Ponderosa Paint Manufacturing Co. Inc.

PONDEROSA STEAKHOUSE - Restaurants–fast food - Ponderosa Inc.

PONDGLOW - Lighting fixtures–underwater - Little Giant Pump Co.

PONDMORENA - Pet products ☆ - Sera Aquaristik USA Inc.

POND'S - Cosmetics - Chesebrough-Pond's USA Co.

POND'S - Skin care products - Conopco, Inc.

POND'S AGE DEFYING COMPLEX - Skin care products - Chesebrough-Pond's USA Co.

POND'S DRAMATIC RESULTS - Skin care products - Chesebrough-Pond's USA Co.

PONDS INSTITUTE - Skin care products - Chesebrough-Pond's USA Co.

PONDS INSTITUTE - Skin care products - Conopco, Inc.

POND'S PREVENT & CORRECT - Skin care products - Conopco, Inc.

PONDSEAL - Clay products - Redmond Clay & Salt Co.

PONDTABBS - Fertilizers - Plantabbs Products

PONG - Video games - Atari Games Corp.

PONG-MASTER - Sporting goods - Joseph E. Newgarden, Jr.

PONG PANDA - Toys–stuffed - Russ Berrie and Co., Inc.

PONGEE - Frames–eyeglass - Zylo Ware Corp.

PONGO - Sporting goods - Panek Precision Products

PONGO - Waxes–mineral - Adica Pongo Inc.

PONSNESS-WARREN - Sporting goods - Ponsness-Warren

PONSTEL - Analgesics ☆ - Warner-Lambert Co.

PONSTEL - Pharmaceutical preparations - Parke-Davis

PONTE - Fabrics - Minnetonka Mills Inc.

PONTE - Food products - Paisano Food Products Inc.

PONTE - Wines - Joseph Victori Wines Inc.

PONTE DE MARANTE - Wines - Admiral Wine Merchants

PONTE HANES HER WAY Y YA VERAS - Apparel and accessories - Sara Lee Corp.

PONTE VECCHIO - Dishes–china - Pasmantier Co. Inc.

PONTE VECCHIO - Shoes–athletic - Alfa Shoe Corp.

PONTE VECCHIO COLLECTION - Tiles–ceramic ☆ - Huntington/Pacific Ceramics Inc.

PONTEVECCHIO - Neckties - World Wide Ties Inc.

PONTHIER - Nuts–salted, roasted, cooked, or canned ☆ - Jaret Specialties Inc.

PONTIAC - Doors–garage - Taylor Building Products Co.

PONTIAC - Motor vehicles–automobiles - General Motors Corp. (Pontiac/GMC Div.)

PONTIAC - Thread - Threads USA Div.

PONTIGGIA - Crackers - Bell'amore Imports Inc.

PONTOCAINE - Pharmaceutical preparations - Sterling Winthrop Inc.

PONTOON RUNABOUT - Boats–pontoons - Lakes Manufacturing Inc.

PONTUS - Fabrics–broadcloth - Jack Lenor Larsen, Inc.

PONY - Apparel and accessories - Pony Sports & Leisure Inc.

PONY - Bicycles - Columbia Manufacturing Inc.

PONY - Bicycles - Todson Inc.

PONY - Boats–canoes - Black River Canoes

PONY - Cameras ☆ - Eastman Kodak Co.

PONY - Cigarette holders - S.M. Frank & Co. Inc. (Kaywoodie-Yello-Bole-Medico)

PONY - Cigarettes - Star Tobacco Corp.

PONY - Combs - Accessories International

PONY - Computers–personal - Pony Computer, Inc.

PONY - Firearms, accessories, and parts ☆ - Colt's Manufacturing Co. Inc.

PONY - Frames–eyeglass ☆ - Universal/Univis Inc.

PONY - Health care products - Snug Seat, Inc.

☆ = Now out of production

PONY - Medical apparatus - Ortho-Kinetics, Inc.
PONY - Motor vehicles–automobiles ☆ - Hyundai Motor America
PONY - Pens - Faber-Castell Corp.
PONY - Pistols - Iver Johnson Arms Co.
PONY - Shovels - Ames Lawn & Garden Tool Co.
PONY - Staplers ☆ - Hunt Manufacturing Co.
PONY - Tiles–asphalt - Garden Way Inc.
PONY - Tools - Adjustable Clamp Co. Inc.
PONY - Toys–banks - A.J. Renzi Plastic Corp.
PONY - Yarn ☆ - Joseph Galler Inc.
PONY 2 PLY - Yarn - Henry's Attic
PONY BOY - Toys–guns - Esquire Novelty Corp.
PONY BOY - Toys–guns - Strombecker Corp.
PONY EXPRESS - Apparel and accessories - Hunting World, Inc.
PONY EXPRESS - Coffee - Thanksgiving Coffee Co.
PONY EXPRESS - Craft supplies - Scott Publishing Co. Inc.
PONY EXPRESS - Security system for the home - Borg-Warner Automotive Inc. (Transmission Systems Div.)
PONY EXPRESS - Toys–guns - Daisy Manufacturing Co.
PONY EXPRESS - Wigs - Look of Love International
PONY EXPRESS RANCH - Food products - Jayhawk Packaging, Inc.
PONY FLIPS - Hairpins - Telebrands Corp.
PONY GO ROUN - Toys - Marlin Toy Products Inc.
PONY II - Orthopedic products - Ortho-Kinetics, Inc.
PONY KNOTS - Hair ornaments - TLS Acquisition Inc.
PONY-'N-A-PAK - Toys–stuffed ☆ - Bradley Import Co.
PONY OH'S - Barrettes - Sta-Rite Ginnie Lou Inc.
PONY PAL - Infant product - Sanitoy Inc.
PONY PALS - Publisher's imprints - Scholastic Inc.
PONY PARADE - Toys - Mattel, Inc.
PONY PET - Rocking horses - Mapes Industries Inc.
PONY POINT HOUSE - Candles - Diane S. Dawson
PONY POUCH - Craft supplies - Milton Bradley Co.
PONY RIDERS - Footwear ☆ - Pony Sports & Leisure Inc.
PONY TAILS - Toys - Henry Gordy International Inc.
PONY TRAILS - Toys - Henry Gordy International Inc.
PONY TRAINER - Infant product - Sanitoy Inc.
PONYBAND - Apparel and accessories - Athletic Images, Inc.
PONYSHOES - Games - Clifford Warren Peterson
PONYTAIL - Ophthalmic goods - Embassy Creations Inc.
PONYTAIL - Skin care products - Delby System
PONYTAIL PORT - Helmets–athletic - Troxel-West
PONYWRAP - Hairpins - American Greetings Corp.
PONZA HUMMER - Pitching machine - Grand Slam USA
PONZI - Wines - Ponzi Vineyards
PONZI VINEYARDS - Wines - Wilson Daniels Ltd.
PONZU - Rice - Edward & Sons Trading Co., Inc.
POO POURRI - Deodorizers - Lou Ann Loebig
POOCH - Dog food - Safeway Stores Inc.
POOCH PACK - Pet products - Lazy Pet Products
POOCH PAK - Pet products - K-9 Pet Products
POOCH PICK-UP - Pet products - Mason Distributing
POOCH PILLOW - Pet products - Lazy Pet Products
POOCH PILLOW - Pet products - R.C. Steele Co.
POOCH PRESERVER - Pet products - Lazy Pet Products
POOCHI - Pet products - Petcetera Inc.
POOCHI - Pet shops - Sergeant's Pet Products, Inc.
POOCHIE - Toys - Tonka Corp.
POOCHO PONCHO - Pet products - City Dog Designed Co., Inc.
POODLE PARFUM - Animal figurine with cologne ☆ - Cosrich Inc.
POODLE SOCK - Footwear - Brown Wooten Mills Inc.
POOF - Cleaning preparations - Trina/Genie
POOF ELEPHANT - Toys–stuffed - Russ Berrie and Co., Inc.
POOF'S PATIO - Furniture - Donald G. Vatthauer
POOH - Handbags - Pyramid Handbags Inc.
POOH - Infant product - The First Years Inc.
POOH & PALS BATHTIME BUDDIES - Shampoos - Johnson & Johnson
POOKEY - Toys–stuffed - Gund, Inc.
POOKINS - Pottery products - Duncan Enterprises
POOKY - Candy ☆ - Amurol Confections Co.
POOKY - Toys–stuffed - Dakin Inc.
POOKY PENGUIN - Toys–stuffed ☆ - Gund, Inc.
POOL AID - Chemical preparations - Coastal Industries Inc.
POOL BALL - Chewing gum ☆ - Amurol Confections Co.
POOL BREEZE - Chlorine - Zeneca Inc.
POOL BRIDGE, THE - Swimming pools - Doughboy Recreational Inc.

POOL BUTLER BOTTOM VAC - Swimming pools - Coastal Industries Inc.
POOL CHOICE - Chemical preparations - Olin Corp.
POOL CLEAR - Swimming pool covers - Aqua Fab Industries Inc.
POOL-COAT - Coatings - Garon Products Inc.
POOL CUSHION - Swimming pools - W.R. Grace & Co.
POOL FLO - Swimming-pool gauges, sealing tape, etc. - American Granby Inc.
POOL-KEM - Swimming pools ☆ - Utikem Products
POOL LIFE - Paints - Bruning Paint Co.
POOL MATES - Chlorine - Chem Lab Products, Inc.
POOL MIX - Marble products - Georgia Marble Co.
POOL NOTES - Pens - Allen C. Kincheloe
POOL PALS - Books–blank - Leonard F. Jaszewski
POOL PALS - Sporting goods - Patricia N. King
POOL PARTY - Toys - Mattel, Inc.
POOL PARTY ON THE GO - Toys–automobiles - Mattel, Inc.
POOL PATCH - Concrete products - CGM Inc.
POOL-PATCH - Sealing compounds - Garon Products Inc.
POOL PATROL - Alarm systems - Danbury Marketing Corp.
POOL PEBBLES - Floor coverings - Southern Aggregates
POOL POWER PAK - Pumps–water - Doughboy Recreational Inc.
POOL PROOF - Bathing suits - Binghamton Savings Bank
POOL PULSE - Vacuum cleaners and accessories - Baracuda International Corp.
POOL-QUILT - Swimming pool covers - Aqua Fab Industries Inc.
POOL RX - Chemical preparations - Enviro Holdings, Inc.
POOL SCHOOL - Toys–stuffed - Intex Recreation Corp.
POOL SHIELD - Swimming pools - Pratt & Lambert, Inc.
POOL SHINE - Chemical preparations - Coastal Industries Inc.
POOL STOOL - Sporting goods - Leisure Products Inc.
POOL TABLE TIFFANY - Lighting fixtures - Meyda Tiffany Inc.
POOL TIME - Water treating compounds - Bio-Lab, Inc.
POOL VAC PLUS - Machinery - H-Tech, Inc.
POOLBRELLA - Swimming pool covers - Jenkins Manufacturing
POOLCOTE - Swimming pools - Premix-Marbletite Manufacturing Co.
POOLCOTE RE-DO - Swimming pools - Premix-Marbletite Manufacturing Co.
POOLE - Flatware ☆ - Poole Silver Co.
POOLE - Pianos - Aeolian Pianos Inc.
POOLE'S - Seafood products–fresh or frozen - Poole's Fish Inc.
POOLE'S LTD. - Food products ☆ - Orth Co. (Bruce)
POOLGUARD - Alarm systems - PBM Industries, Inc.
POOLIE - Toys–stuffed ☆ - Russ Berrie and Co., Inc.
POOLIFT - Health care products - Guardian Products Inc.
POOLLINK - Electronics equipment - Link Automation, Inc.
POOLMASTER - Aquariums–household - Eugene G. Danner Manufacturing Inc.
POOLPOXY II - Coatings - Nelsonite, Inc.
POOLPOXY HI-BILD - Coatings - Nelsonite, Inc.
POOL'S EYE - Alarm systems - Splash Industries, Inc.
POOLSAVER - Trowels - Marshalltown Trowel Co.
POOLSIDE - Frames–eyeglass - U.S. Optical Frame Co.
POOLSIDE - Mats - JCH International Inc.
POOLSIDE - Mats - Southern Aggregates
POOLSIDE NO SHAG - Games - Ziffco
POOLSIDE RIB - Mats - JCH International Inc.
POOLTRINE - Chemical preparations - Applied Biochemists, Inc.
POOLTRINE 60 - Herbicides ☆ - Applied Biochemists, Inc.
POOMPS - Toys - Mattel, Inc.
POOMSIES - Footwear - Ideal Specialty Shoe Co.
POONIE - Fishing lures - Robert D. Plewniak
POOPATROOPERS - Toys - Imperial Toy Corp.
POOPER SCOOPERS OF AMERICA - Pet products ☆ - Noble Beasts Graphics
POOPSCOOP - Pet products - California Flexrake Corp.
POOR CINDERELLA - Dolls - Effanbee Doll Corp.
POOR LU'S - Food products - Access Food & Beverage, Inc.
POOR RICHARD'S SMOKEHOUSE - Fresh processed beef - Poor Richard's Smokehouse, Inc.
POORE BROTHERS - Potato chips - Poore Brothers Southeast, Inc.
POORE BROTHERS - Potato chips - Poore Brothers Southeast, Inc.
POORMANS DOWNRIGGER - Sporting goods - Gapen Co.
POOSHBALL - Sporting goods - Fabrication Enterprises
POOT - Apparel and accessories - Foundation Super Co.
POOTIE TAT - Toys - Horsman
POOZ - Containers - Plastics, Inc. (Anchor Hocking Plastics)
POP - Floor coverings–carpet and rugs - Calladium & Marglen
P*O*P - Health care products - HealthCom Services/Summit Haus Comm. Ltd.

POP - Skin care products - Laguna Brush Co.
POP - Tools–power-driven - Black & Decker Corp.
POP A CHU - Candy - S.L. Kaye Co., Inc.
POP A FRUIT - Candy - S.L. Kaye Co., Inc.
POP-A-GO-GO - Beverages–carbonated ☆ - Towne Club Beverage Corp.
POP-A-LOT - Toys - Tupperware Co.
POP A MINT - Candy - S.L. Kaye Co., Inc.
POP-A-MIST - Beverages–carbonated - Vess Beverages Inc.
POP-A-TOP - Toys - Bravo International Corp.
POP & CLEAN - Can openers–electric - Sunbeam Corp.
POP & GO - Sandwiches - Entertainment Foods, Inc.
POP & LOCK - Automotive parts and accessories - Steadfast Corp.
POP ART - Decorations - Gerald Demartin
POP ART - Jigsaw puzzles ☆ - American Publishing Corp.
POP BOTTLE - Candles - Concept/Research, Concept/Development
POP BOTTLES - Candy ☆ - Topps Co., Inc.
POP CITY - Games - Bloomco
POP COIN BANK-A-ROO - Popcorn ☆ - Weaver Popcorn Co. Inc.
POP CORN CRISPS - Popcorn - Snack Factory Inc.
POP CREAM - Ice cream - Tavemo Inc.
POP CULTURE - Yogurt–frozen - Simco Sales Service of Pennsylvania, Inc.
POP-DOWN - Building materials - RFR Industries, Inc.
POP DROPS - Candy - Tootsie Roll Industries, Inc.
POP EM CHOO CHOO - Toys - Playskool, Inc.
POP 'EMS - Bakery products - Entenmann's Inc.
POP EXPRESS - Popcorn ☆ - Golden Valley Microwave Foods, Inc.
POP GUN - Popcorn poppers - Nordic Ware
POP-ICE - Fruit pops–frozen - Jel Sert Co.
POP ICON DESIGNS - Apparel and accessories - Heriberto Velez
POP IN PILLOW - Pillows - Fairfield Processing Corp.
POP-INS - Baby foods - Abbott Laboratories
POP INTO PHONICS - Publisher's imprints - McClanahan Book Co., Inc.
POP-IT - Containers - Ultrapac, Inc.
POP-IT - Machinery - Robert F. Ganley
POP-IT MUG - Containers - Kids USA, Inc.
POP-IT PEARLS - Toys - Milton Bradley Co.
POP-ITS - Deodorizers - Lumi-Lite Candle Co. Inc.
POP-ITS - Fireworks - Pyrodyne American Corp.
POP KIDS - Apparel–children's - Holden Development & Cos. Inc.
POP MACHINE - Candy - Uniconfis Corp.
POP 'MMNS - Cookies - Deer Park Baking Co.
POP N - Fishing tackle - Skyline Industries Inc.
POP N FIZZ - Candy - Carbonated Candy Ventures
POP 'N FLAVOR - Popcorn ☆ - Golden Grain Co.
POP 'N HEAR - Publisher's imprints - Yes! Entertainment Corp.
POP N HOP - Apparel–children's - TSK-Whispers Inc.
POP 'N JOT - Office supplies - Minnesota Mining & Manufacturing Co.
POP 'N LITE - Vegetable oil - Ventura Foods LLC (Lou Ana Division)
POP 'N NUTTY - Candy - Sterling Candy Corp.
POP 'N PICK UP - Toys–automobiles - Mattel, Inc.
POP 'N PICK UPS - Toys - Mattel, Inc.
POP 'N PLAY - Toys - Mattel, Inc.
POP-N-PLUNK - Sporting goods - Gapen Co.
POP N SCORE - Toys - Diversified Specialists, Inc.
POP 'N SHOOT CAMERA - Toys - Playskool, Inc.
POP 'N SNAK - Popcorn - Jasper Foods, Inc.
POP N' SOK - Toys ☆ - A.J. Renzi Plastic Corp.
POP 'N SPIN TOP - Toys - Playskool, Inc.
POP 'N TOP IT - Popcorn ☆ - TV Time Foods Inc.
POP-N-WIPE - Paper–toweling - Cleveland Cotton Products Co.
POP-O-MATIC - Games - CBS Toys
POP-O-MATIC BINGO - Games - CBS Toys
POP-O-MATIC HEADACHE - Games - Milton Bradley Co.
POP-ON - Prophylactics - Rochester Medical Corp.
POP ON PADS - Shoulder pads - Shoulders To Go
POP OVER - Apparel and accessories - Stefan Schinzinger
POP PERFECT - Pork rinds - Pop Perfect
POP PILLOWS - Pillows - Centsable Toys Inc.
POP POLISH - Cosmetics - Chesebrough-Pond's USA Co.
POP POPS - Candy - Crystal Pure Candy Co.
POP PORTS - Stationery ☆ - Scentex Inc.
POP POSTERS - Posters ☆ - Faber-Castell Corp.
POP QWIZ - Popcorn - General Mills, Inc.
POP RIVETS - Rivets–metal - Auto Vehicle Parts Co.
POP ROCKET - Computer software - Pop Rocket, Inc.
POP ROCKS - Candy - Carbonated Candy Ventures

POP-SECRET - Popcorn - General Mills, Inc.
POP SECRET BUTTERY BURST - Popcorn - General Mills, Inc.
POP-SECRET CHOCOLATE POPCORN - Chocolate bars - General Mills, Inc.
POP SECRET JUMBO POP - Popcorn - General Mills, Inc.
POP SECRET POPCORN BARS - Popcorn - General Mills, Inc.
POP SHOCKS - Toys - Processed Plastic Co.
POP STAR - Bicycles - Huffy Corp.
P.O.P. SUPER - Floor coverings - Devon Corp.
POP-TAIL - Fishing lures ☆ - Lindy Little Joe Inc.
POP TALKER - Labels–paper - Data Documents, Inc.
POP-TARTS - Bakery products - Kellogg Co.
POP-TARTS CRUNCH - Cereal ☆ - Kellogg Co.
POP-TARTS MINIS - Snack foods ☆ - Kellogg Co.
POP THE JUICY - Candy ☆ - Topps Co., Inc.
POP-TITE - Containers - E.S. Robbins Corp.
POP TOOBS - Toys - James Industries, Inc.
POP TOP - Containers - Creative Specialty Manufacturing, Inc.
POP-TOP - Containers–insulated ☆ - Aladdin Industries, Inc.
POP TOP - Sockets–electric - Advanced Interconnections Corp.
POP TOP STORABLES - Containers - Plastics, Inc. (Anchor Hocking Plastics)
POP-TOP STORABLES - Cooking utensils–earthenware ☆ - Anchor Hocking Glass, Inc.
POP TOPPERS - Seasonings - McSteven's
POP TOPS - Cages–wire - Blue Ribbon Pet Products, Inc.
POP TOPS - Frozen confections - The Kroger Co.
POP TREATS - Dog food - Petcetera Inc.
POP-UP - Boating equipment and accessories - Accon Marine, Inc.
POP UP - Computer software - John J. Mauro
POP-UP - Fishing tackle - Worth Co.
POP UP - Furniture - Barcalounger Co.
POP-UP - Ice chests - Krieg Boys Ice Corp.
POP UP - Sponges - Cadie Products Corp.
POP-UP - Stationery - Chris Crowell & Co. Inc.
POP UP - Timers–appliance - Volk Enterprises, Inc.
POP UP BABY CABANA - Infant product - Fisher-Price, Inc.
POP-UP BUNNY - Toys - Fisher-Price, Inc.
POP-UP CALCULATORS - Computer software - Popular Programs Inc.
POP-UP DESKSET - Computer software - Popular Programs Inc.
POP-UP DESKSET PLUS - Computer software - Popular Programs Inc.
POP-UP DIRECTORY ASSISTANT - Computer software ☆ - Popular Programs Inc.
POP-UP DOCUTRIEVE - Computer software ☆ - Popular Programs Inc.
POP UP FOOTBALL - Toys - Fisher-Price, Inc.
POP-UP GRAPH - Computer software ☆ - Popular Programs Inc.
POP-UP MINIWORLD - Toys - Party Play, Inc.
POP-UP PAL - Office supplies - Cornell Concepts Corp.
POP UP PALS - Toys - Playskool, Inc.
POP-UP PALS PIANO - Computer software - Tiger Electronics, Inc.
POP-UP PC-12C - Computer software - Popular Programs Inc.
POP-UP PETS - Toys - Small World Toys
POP-UP PINBALL - Games - CBS Toys
POP UP PLAY SEAT - Toys - Fisher-Price, Inc.
POP UP PLAYHOUSE - Toys - Fisher-Price, Inc.
POP-UP STAR CARD - Paper–die-cut - William F. Brunt, II
POP-UP STORY - Key rings - Takara USA Corp.
POP-UP STORY BOOK THEATER - Publisher's imprints - Ottenheimer Publishers, Inc.
POP-UP TELECOMM - Computer software - Popular Programs Inc.
POP-UP-TENT - Toys - Playskool, Inc.
POP-UP TODAY - Computer software - Popular Programs Inc.
POP-UP VEST POCKET AGENDA - Computer software ☆ - Popular Programs Inc.
POP UPS - Computer software - Popular Programs Inc.
POP UPS - Infant product - Prince Lionheart, Inc.
POP WARNER - Sporting goods - Shield Manufacturing Inc.
POP WEAVER - Popcorn - Weaver Popcorn Co. Inc.
POP-ZIT - Toys - Empire of Carolina Inc.
POPALOT - Popcorn poppers - Gold Medal Products Co.
POPBACK - Sporting goods - Marty Gilman Inc.
POPBALL - Balls - Toyvision, Inc.
POPCITY - Beverages–carbonated - Klarbrunn Inc.
POPCORN - Footwear - International Seaway Trading Corp.
POPCORN - Toys–stuffed ☆ - Gund, Inc.
POPCORN & CRANBERRIES - Christmas tree ornaments - Cracker Box Inc.
POPCORN BOWL - Housewares stores - Daugherty Studio, Inc.
POPCORN CONNECTION - Popcorn - Popcorn Connection

POPCORN EXPLOSION - Popcorn - Popcorn Explosion Inc.
POPCORN FACTORY, THE - Popcorn - Coastin'
POPCORN NOW - Popcorn poppers - National Presto Industries, Inc.
POPCORN PRETTIES - Dolls - Mattel, Inc.
POPCORN PUMPER - Popcorn poppers - Hamilton Beach/Proctor-Silex Inc.
POPCORN SLIPPER SOX - Socks - Acorn
POPCORN UNLIMITED - Popcorn - Popcorn Unlimited Inc.
POPCORN WORLD - Popcorn - Popcorn World Inc.
POPCUBES - Publisher's imprints - Educational Teaching Aids
POPDOWN - Binoculars - Brunton Co.
POPE - Bicycles - Columbia Manufacturing Inc.
POPE - Food products - Pope Food Sales Inc.
POPE - Vegetables–canned - Borelli International, Inc.
POPE VALLEY WINERY - Wines ☆ - Pope Valley Winery
POPEE - Paper - Kimberly-Clark Corp.
POPEIL - Kitchen appliances - RonCo Inc.
POPEMUSIC - Compact discs–prerecorded - Gene Pope
POPERS - Frozen foods - Intermission Productions
POPES 1880 - Beverages–malt - Mission Imports Inc.
POPEYE - Buttons - Strand Enterprises
POPEYE - Chewing gum ☆ - Amurol Confections Co.
POPEYE - Erasers - Diener Industries Inc.
POPEYE - Eyeglasses - Art-Craft Optical Co.
POPEYE - Melamine product - Boonton Molding Co. Inc.
POPEYE - Popcorn - Curtice-Burns Foods, Inc.
POPEYE - Popcorn - National Oats Co. Inc.
POPEYE - Publisher's imprints - Hearst Corp.
POPEYE - Watches - I.D. Enterprises
POPEYE/MIGHTY MOUSE PRESTO PAINTS - Paint sets–hobby ☆ - Kenner Products
POPEYE POPS - Candy ☆ - Beacon Sweets, Inc.
POPEYE SHAKE - Candy ☆ - Phoenix Confections Inc.
POPEYES - Restaurants–fast food - Popeye's Famous Fried Chicken & Biscuits Inc.
POPEYE'S - Spinach pizza - Jack's Frozen Pizza Co.
POPEYE'S PASSION - Spices and extracts - To Market to Market
POPI - Footwear - Wadiwalkers Inc.
POPINI - Chairs–upholstered - United Chair Co., Inc.
POPINS - Candy - Murray-Allen International Inc.
POPIT - Popcorn ☆ - Malt-O-Meal Co.
POPKINS - Snack food - ITC Products
POPKOFF'S - Food products - Popkoff's Frozen Food
POPLAR - Computer software - Adobe Systems Inc.
POPLAR - Thread - Elmore-Pisgah, Inc.
POPLAR RIDGE VINEYARDS - Wines - Poplar Ridge Vineyards
POPLIKOSH - Popcorn - Brown & Haley
POPLITE - Popcorn poppers - National Presto Industries, Inc.
POPLOCKET - Candy - Uniconfis Corp.
POP'N CRUNCH - Popcorn - Standard Candy Co. Inc.
POP'N PECAN - Popcorn - Standard Candy Co. Inc.
POP'N POP - Pens - Pentel of America, Ltd.
POP'N PUNCH - Beverages - Premiere Innovations, Inc.
POPO RECORDS - Recording label - Antonio O. Lopez
POPOF BY GILBERT OUAKNINE - Apparel–women's - Gilbert Ouaknine
POPOLO - Hair care products - Major International Inc.
POPOLY - Binders - John Christian Co.
POPOV - Vodka - Heublein, Inc.
POPOVER - Cosmetics - Andre Fantasies Inc.
POPOVITCH - Dresses–women's - Mishy Sportswear Inc.
POPPA-DOODLE - Fishing lures - Wood Lures of Arkansas
POPPA VETTE - Toys–automobiles - Mattel, Inc.
POPPA'S PACIFIER - Infant product ☆ - Grandpa Brand Co. (Par Beverage Co.)
POPPED INDULGENCE - Popcorn - Premium Idaho Popcorn
POPPEN - Beverages–malt ☆ - Simmers Products
POPPER - Fishing lures - Bomber Bait Co.
POPPER - Fishing lures - Boone Bait Co. Inc.
POPPER JAMM - Sauces - Anchor Food Products, Inc.
POPPER-LOAD - Ammunition - Olin Corp. (Winchester Div.)
POPPER TIME - Fruits and vegetables - Anchor Food Products, Inc.
POPPER TOPPER - Pens - Russ Berrie and Co., Inc.
POPPERS - Frames–eyeglass - Hudson Optical Corp.
POPPERS - Fruits and vegetables - Poppers Supply Co.
POPPETS - Cereal - U.S. Mills, Inc.
POPPETS - Papier-mache articles ☆ - Cardinal Inc.
POPPIES - Bakery products - Poppies Restaurant and Delicatessen

POPPIES - Chocolate candy - Progressive Bagel Concepts, Inc.
POPPIES - Cookies - FCW Imports
POPPIES - Cookies ☆ - Liberty Richter Inc.
POPPIES - Pet products - Hamilton Products Inc.
POPPIES - Shorts–women's - J. Steiner Imports Inc.
POPPIES CHRISTMAS - Tableware–earthenware - Lenox, Inc.
POPPIES ON BLUE - Dinnerware–glass - Lenox, Inc.
POPPIN' FARM TRUCK - Toys–automobiles - Mattel, Inc.
POPPIN' FRESH - Biscuits - Pillsbury Co.
POPPIN' LOCO - Toys - Mattel, Inc.
POPPIN' PALS - Games - CBS Toys
POPPIN' PESTS - Toys - Toymax Inc.
POPPIN' PIANO - Toys - Playskool, Inc.
POPPIN' PLAY PISTOL - Toys–guns - Mattel, Inc.
POPPIN' PLAY RIFLE - Toys–guns - Mattel, Inc.
POPPIN' SOUNDS - Toys - Mattel, Inc.
POPPIN' STICK - Fishing rods - Zebco Corp.
POPPIN TOPPIN - Margarine - Ventura Foods
POPPITY POP - Toys–automobiles - Fisher-Price, Inc.
POPPLES - Bathroom accessories ☆ - Tsumura International Inc.
POPPLES - Games ☆ - Ben Cooper Inc.
POPPLES - Toys - Those Characters from Cleveland, Inc.
POPPLES - Toys–stuffed - Mattel, Inc.
POPPRINT - Calendars ☆ - Stephen Lawrence Co.
POPP'S SWISS - Teas–herbal - Wunderlich-Diez Corp.
POPPUP - Pet food - T.F.H. Publications, Inc.
POPPY - Bathing suits - LANZ, Inc.
POPPY - Cooking utensils–enameled ☆ - National Housewares
POPPY - Cosmetics - Lancome
POPPY - Dinnerware–glass ☆ - Nikko Ceramics Inc.
POPPY - Glassware–household - Crisa Corp.
POPPY - Glassware–household ☆ - Spiegelau Inc.
POPPY - Patterns–clothing ☆ - Poppy Fabric
POPPY - Perfumes - Saxony Products Inc.
POPPY - Sprinklers–lawn - L.R. Nelson Corp.
POPPY - Wheelbarrows ☆ - Kelley Manufacturing Co.
POPPY BEAR - Tools–hand-operated - White Swan, Ltd.
POPPY BEAR - Toys–stuffed ☆ - Dakin Inc.
POPPY GOOD - Pasta - Buckeye Beans & Herbs, Inc.
POPPY HILL - Wines - Mont St. John Cellars Inc.
POPPY LOVE - Salad dressings–bottled ☆ - Johnny's Enterprises Inc.
POPPY MUSK - Perfumes ☆ - Carme Inc.
POPPY PATCH - Flowers, plants, and seeds - Ampro Industries, Inc.
POPPY PENGUIN - Chests–wood ☆ - Little Tikes Co.
POPPY PUPPY - Toys–stuffed - Russ Berrie and Co., Inc.
POPPY SEA'D - Salads–prepackaged - Buckeye Beans & Herbs, Inc.
POPPYCOCK - Popcorn - Novartis Nutrition Corp.
POPPYFIELD DREAMS - Craft supplies - Tamay Design Co., Inc.
POPPYTRAIL - Dinnerware–glass ☆ - Metlox Pottery Shoppe
POP'R SPELL/POP'R SPELL CHALLENGE - Computer software ☆ - Milliken Publishing Co. (Computer Software Div.)
POPRICE - Snack foods ☆ - Energy Food Factory Inc.
POP'S - Barbecue sauce - D & D Foods Inc.
POPS - Cereal ☆ - Kellogg Co.
POPS - Computer software - Derrick Keith Lewis
POPS - Musical instruments - Vitali Import Co. Inc.
POPS ALMIGHTY - Popcorn - Pops Almighty
POPS DELIGHT - Popcorn - Pops Delight
POP'S HOMEMADE WATER ICE SINCE 1932 A SOUTH PHILADELPHIA TRADITION - Ice - Pop's Homemade Water Ice, Inc.
POPS-ON - Cardboard - Chesapeake Fiber Packaging Corp.
POPS-ON - Computer software - Southern Datacomm, Inc.
POP'S PAL - Apparel and accessories - Barrow Manufacturing Co., Inc.
POPS-RITE - Popcorn - Curtice-Burns Foods, Inc.
POPS-RITE - Popcorn - National Oats Co. Inc.
POPSET - Computer peripheral equipment - QMS, Inc.
POPSHOTS - Greeting cards - Popshots Inc.
POPSI - Snack foods - GWB Imports
POPSICLE - Ice cream - Good Humor Corp.
POPSICLE FANTASTIC FRUITY - Ice cream - Good Humor Corp.
POPSICLE PLAYWEAR - Apparel–children's - Popsicle Playwear Ltd.
POPSICLE TWISTER - Ice cream - Good Humor Corp.
POPSIE - Ice cream ☆ - Good Humor Corp.
POPSIT - Food products - Colfax Inc.
POPSTARS - Watches - Temlex/Jupiter Watch Corp.
POPTERM - Computer software - Rational Data Systems

☆ = Now out of production

POPTIME - Fabrics - Greenwood Mills Inc.
POPTOP - Valves - Erie Controls
POPTOP RECORDS - Recording label - Clay Pigeon Records
POPTOPS - Infant product - Two Little Girls Inc.
POPTOPS - Kitchen utensils–aluminum - Bonny Products Inc.
POPULAIRE - Musical instrument accessories - French American Reeds Manufacturing
POPULAR - Accordions - Castiglione Accordion
POPULAR - Brushes–paint - Wright-Bernet
POPULAR - Paper cutters ☆ - Milton Bradley Co.
POPULAR - Thread - Lewis Threads Inc.
POPULAR CHOICE - Dinnerware–plastic - Nyman Manufacturing Co.
POPULAR DEMAND - Footwear - Simon's Co. Inc.
POPULAR GIRL - Eyeglasses - Art-Craft Optical Co.
POPULAR MECHANICS - Publisher's imprints - Hearst Corp.
POPULAR MECHANICS - Toys - Natural Science Industries, Ltd.
POPULAR METAPHYSICS - Recording label - 415 Records Ltd.
POPULAR PET - Pet products - Hacht Sales and Marketing, Ltd.
POPULAR RECORDS - Recording label - Lollipop Productions, Inc.
POPULAR TECHNOLOGY - Publisher's imprints - Branden Publishing Co., Inc.
POPULARITY - Apparel and accessories - Bee Hat Co.
POPULARITY - Floor coverings–carpet and rugs ☆ - Columbus Mills, Inc.
POPULARITY II - Floor coverings–carpet and rugs - Gulistan Carpet Inc.
POPULENE - Telephones ☆ - Hitachi Home Electronics America Inc.
POPULOUS - Video games - Nintendo of America Inc.
POPWISE - Food products - Stevens Industries Inc.
POPWISE - Oils–edible - Cargill, Inc.
POPYKINS - Footwear - Bentley International
POR 2OX - Adhesives and sealants - United Catalysts Inc.
POR 15 - Paints - Por-15, Inc.
POR 15 INC. - Rustproofing compounds - Por-15, Inc.
POR-COLD - Adhesives and sealants - L.D. Sterns Corp.
POR-CRAX - Building materials - Pioneer Manufacturing Co.
POR-FLOR - Concrete products - Sosroc Inc.
POR LARRANAGA - Cigar boxes–wood - Consolidated Cigar Corp.
POR-LASTIC - Sporting goods - Bike Athletic Co.
POR-ROK - Adhesives and sealants - L & F Products Inc.
PORCE-U-GLAZE - Cosmetics - Morris-Flamingo Inc.
PORCEL - Plastics - A-Porcel Corp.
PORCELAIN - Dishes–china - Mikasa Co.
PORCELAIN - Paints - Buten Paint & Wallpaper
PORCELAIN - Wallpaper - Capital Carousel Inc.
PORCELAIN & LACE - Floor coverings ☆ - Tarkett, Inc.
PORCELAIN DOLL - Underwear and nightwear - Henson-Kickernick Inc.
PORCELAIN EXPRESSIONS - Dolls - Adelco International Inc.
PORCELAIN FLOOR TILE - Tiles–ceramic - Monarch Tile Inc.
PORCELAIN GARDEN - Bedding–linen - Dan River Inc.
PORCELAIN GARDENS - Craft supplies ☆ - VIP/VIP Crafts
PORCELAIN GLAZE - Cosmetics ☆ - Hazel Bishop International
PORCELAIN GLOSS - Paper - Copco Papers Inc.
PORCELAIN IMPRESSIONS - Bathroom fixtures - Melard Manufacturing Corp.
PORCELAIN LIFE - Adhesives and sealants - Restore-X
PORCELAIN ON STEEL - Cooking utensils–aluminum - Reston Lloyd Ltd.
PORCELAIN PETITES - Toys–stuffed - Dan-Dee International Ltd.
PORCELAIN TOUCH-UP - Coatings - Sheffield Bronze Paint Corp.
PORCELAIN TREASURES - Clocks - Godinger Silver Art Ltd.
PORCELAIN TREASURES - Dolls - Mattel, Inc.
PORCELAINCOTE - Fabrics–coated - Fosroc Inc.
PORCELAINE GEORGES BOYER - Tableware–china ☆ - Bernard W. Bernthal Inc.
PORCELAINE H. VIREBAUT - Glassware–household ☆ - Avitra Corp.
PORCELAINIZE IT - Artists' materials - Aleene's
PORCELAITES - Floor coverings–tile ☆ - Kepcor, Inc./SSI Tiles
PORCELANA - Cosmetics - Dep Corp.
PORCELANA - Tiles–ceramic - Dal-Tile Corp.
PORCELANA SCHMIDT - Cooking equipment–household - Primex International Corp.
PORCELANATO - Ceramic floor tile - Interceramic Inc.
PORCELANOSA - Tiles–ceramic - Amsterdam Corp.
PORCELETTES - Tiles–ceramic - Summitville Tiles, Inc.
PORCELL - Dry erase boards - Quartet Manufacturing Co.
PORCELLANA - Blackboards–wood - Arcana Products Co.
PORCELLANE D'ARTE - Figurines ☆ - National Potteries
PORCELLE - Dinnerware–glass - Salem China Co.
PORCH - Fabrics - Gretchen Bellinger Inc.
PORCH & FLOOR - Enamels - Devoe ∑ Raynolds Co.

PORCH & HAMMOCK - Perfumes - Robert Sisk
PORCH FAN, THE - Fans–electric - Fasco Industries Inc. (Consumer Products Div.)
PORCH-LIFT - Platform lift - Access Industries, Inc.
PORCH 'N PET - Pet products - Mapes Industries Inc.
PORCH POSIES - Flowers, plants, and seeds ☆ - Applewood Seed & Garden Group
PORCHE - Ophthalmic goods - Styl-Rite Optical Manufacturing Co., Inc.
PORCHLIGHT ENTERTAINMENT - Video production - Pacific Mediaworks, Inc.
PORCIMUNE - Veterinary pharmaceutical preparations - Schering-Plough Animal Health
PORCINI - Apparel and accessories - Brigata International, Inc.
PORCINI TOSCANINI - Food products - Golden Whisk Pasta Partners
PORCRASTINATOR'S GUIDES - Publisher's imprints - Bandanna Books
PORCUPENCIL - Pencils - Securitag Corp.
PORCUPINE - Paint rollers - Wooster Brush Co.
PORCUPINE BOUNCER - Balls ☆ - Imperial Toy Corp.
PORCUPINE PROVISIONS - Spices and extracts - Porcupine Provisions, Inc.
PORE-O-PAC - Wood fillers - H. Behlen & Bro. Inc.
PORE PURGE - Skin care products - Circle of Beauty, Inc.
PORE REDUCER - Skin care products - Fanie International
POREBA - Lathes - Toolmex Corp.
PORGY AND BESS - Apparel and accessories - Porgy and Bess Enterprises
PORIDON - Insecticides - Fearing Manufacturing Co. Inc.
PORILOFF - Caviar ☆ - Purepak Foods Inc.
PORINO'S - Spaghetti sauces - Damien Corp.
PORK BY GEORGE - Meat products–pork - Hormel Foods Corp.
PORK CHOPETTES - Meat patties ☆ - J.T.M. Provisions Co.
PORK CLASSICS - Food products - Chiquita Brands, Inc.
PORK HOUSE - Pet food - Universal Product Marketing, Inc.
PORK MASTER - Animal feeds - Bluebonnet Milling Co.
PORK PLACE - Pet products - Hacht Sales and Marketing, Ltd.
PORK RIBS PONTCHARTRAIN - Food products - My Favorite Year Inc.
PORKCHOP PIG - Toys–stuffed - Dakin Inc.
PORKEATERS - Meat products–pork ☆ - Blue Diamond Meat Co.
PORKER - Motor vehicle parts and accessories - White Bros. Cycle Specialties, Inc.
PORKER PIPES - Motorcycle parts and accessories - White Bros. Cycle Specialties, Inc.
PORKER, THE - Fishing lures - Uncle Josh Bait Co.
PORKIE POTION - Sporting goods - Shawn Gregorie McDowell
PORKIES - Pork rinds - Savory Foods Inc.
PORKLINS - Pork rinds - Bachman Co.
PORKY JOE RIBLET - Food products - Janson's Foods Inc.
PORKY JOE RIBLETEER - Food products - Janson's Foods Inc.
PORKY-PATTY - Food products - Whitaker Foods Inc.
PORKY PIG - Film–motion picture - Time Warner Entertainment Co., L.P.
PORKY'S LAST STAND - Barbecue sauce - Salad Werks
PORNO - Cosmetics - Hard Candy, Inc.
POROFILL - Hair care products - Faberge Co.
POROMET - Filters–industrial - Purolator Products Co.
POROSITY CONTROL - Hair care products - Roux Laboratories, Inc.
POROWRAP - Paper–cigarette - Kimberly-Clark Corp.
POROX - Handbags - Porox International Co., Inc.
PORPHYRINDENE - Pharmaceutical preparations - City Chemical Corp.
PORPLASTIC - Coatings - APT Advanced Polymer Technology Corp.
PORPOISE - Bicycles - Ross Bicycles USA, Ltd.
PORPOISE - Watches - Croton Watch Co., Inc.
PORPRO - Computer software - Resources Engineering Systems, Inc.
PORSCHE - Furniture - Haworth, Inc.
PORSCHE - Ophthalmic goods ☆ - Carrera Eyewear Corp.
PORSCHE 356 - Motor vehicles–automobiles ☆ - Porsche Cars North America Inc.
PORSCHE 911 - Motor vehicles–automobiles - Porsche Cars North America Inc.
PORSCHE 924 - Motor vehicles–automobiles ☆ - Porsche Cars North America Inc.
PORSCHE 928 - Motor vehicles–automobiles - Porsche Cars North America Inc.
PORSCHE 944 - Motor vehicles–automobiles - Porsche Cars North America Inc.
PORSCHE 968 - Motor vehicles–automobiles - Porsche Cars North America Inc.
PORSELIN - Epoxy - Metalcrete Industries Inc.
PORSGRUND - Dinnerware–glass - Foge Jensen Imports
PORSHA - Apparel and accessories - Winer Industries Inc.

PORSIBAC - Veterinary product - American Home Products Corp.

PORT - Cases–plastic - Cocobana Inc.

PORT-A-BAR - Luggage ☆ - Maximillian Luggage Corp.

PORT-A-BAR - Serving carts ☆ - Artex-Green Corp. of N.Y.

PORT-A-BASS - Musical instruments - Original Musical Instruments Co. Inc.

PORT-A-BATH - Infant product - Century Products Co.

PORT-A-BOWL - Skin care products - Belgrave's Beauty Supplies & Cosmetics

PORT-A-CAR - Automotive parts and accessories - S. Ronald Barnette

PORT-A-CARE - Furniture - Little Tikes Co.

PORT-A-CATH - Catheters - Sims Deltec, Inc.

PORT-A-CATH II - Catheters - Sims Deltec, Inc.

PORT-A-CATH NEEDLES - Health care products - Sims Deltec, Inc.

PORT-A-CHALK - Electronic equipment - Telex Communications, Inc.

PORT-A-CORT - Sporting goods - Gold Medal Recreational Products

PORT-A-CRUSH - Tools–hand-operated - Marco B. Gonzalez

PORT A CURL - Curling irons–electric ☆ - Helen of Troy Corp.

PORT-A-FILE - Paper products - Agora Int. Ltd.

PORT-A-FOLD, THE - Furniture - Barricks Manufacturing Co. Inc.

PORT-A-HEAT - Heating pads–electric ☆ - Nesco Battery Systems

PORT-A-HORSE - Hardware - Northwestern Wood Products

PORT-A-JUST - Toys - Sport Supply Group, Inc.

PORT-A-LIFT - Hoists - Venture Marine Inc.

PORT A MATE 128 - Tools–power-driven - HTC Products, Inc.

PORT-A-METER - Electrical equipment - General Electric Co.

PORT-A-PIG - Ovens–convection - Nelgo Manufacturing Corp.

PORT-A-PILLOW - Pillows ☆ - Celeste Industries Corp.

PORT-A-POCKET - Notebooks and notepads - Wirth International Inc.

PORT-A-POUR - Concrete–mixture - Port-A-Pour, Inc.

PORT-A-PUNCH - Computers - International Business Machines Corp.

PORT-A-SHELF - Furniture - A-Zak Wood Specialties

PORT-A-STALL - Prefabricated buildings–metal - Port-a-Stall

PORT-A-STUDIO - Electronic equipment - Blonder-Tongue Laboratories Inc.

PORT-A-SWING - Infant product - Fisher-Price, Inc.

PORT-A-TAP - Kegs–wood - Brockway Standard Inc.

PORT-A-VAC - Medical apparatus - Erie Medical (Div. of Ocenco Incorporated)

PORT-A-WELL - Tanks–water - John C. Kirkmyer

PORT ARTHUR - Food products - Gourmet Award Foods

PORT AU PRINCE - Floor coverings–carpet and rugs ☆ - LaVelle Textile Marketing Inc.

PORT AUSTIN - Hardware - Port Austin Level & Tool Manufacturing Co.

PORT AUTHORITY - Electronic equipment - ASP Computer Products Inc.

PORT AUTHORITY - Floor coverings–carpet and rugs ☆ - Porter Carpet Mills Inc.

PORT BERBER - Floor coverings–carpet and rugs - Porter Carpet Mills Inc.

PORT DA BLANCA - Porcelain - Porta

PORT HURON - Paper - Port Huron Paper Co.

PORT INJECTION - Marine rigging - Outboard Marine Corp.

PORT MAC - Shrimp–fresh or frozen ☆ - Penguin Frozen Foods, Inc.

PORT MAR - Floor coverings–carpet and rugs ☆ - Porter Carpet Mills Inc.

PORT-O-BELT - Conveyors - Rotec Industries, Inc.

PORT-O-CALL - Eyeglasses - Art-Craft Optical Co.

PORT-O-CALL - Floor coverings–tile ☆ - Kepcor, Inc./SSI Tiles

PORT-O-HEAT - Health care products - Optima Medical Technologies Inc.

PORT-O-LID - Toilet seats - Barton E. Kay

PORT O'CALL - Fabrics - Pago Fabrics Corp.

PORT OF ENTRY - Cheese - Beatrice Cheese Co.

PORT OF NAPLES - Apparel and accessories - Port of Naples Ltd, Inc.

PORT OF NEW YORK - Colognes - Brandy Harvest

PORT PHILLIP MANUFACTURING - Apparel and accessories - Mariner Resource Corp.

PORT ROYAL - Floor coverings–carpet and rugs - Evans-Black Carpet Mills

PORT ROYAL - Furniture ☆ - Bassett Furniture Industries, Inc.

PORT ROYAL - Rum - Majestic Distilling Co.

PORT ROYAL - Seafood - Clouston Foods USA

PORT ROYAL EXPORT - Beverages–malt - Diversified Imports

PORT ROYALE - Floor coverings–carpet and rugs - Lees Carpets

PORT VUE - Occasional furniture ☆ - Bassett Furniture Industries, Inc.

PORT WEST - Apparel and accessories - Tropical Sportswear International Corp.

PORT WEST - Apparel–men's - Tropical Garment Manufacturing Co.

PORTA - Health care products - Crump Products Inc.

PORTA - Steel products - Porta Marketing Associates Ltd.

PORTA - Tableware–china - Porta

PORTA-BAG - Bags ☆ - Dan Dee Belt and Bag Co. Inc.

PORTA-BENCH - Benches–wood ☆ - Hirsh Co.

PORTA-BOTE - Boats - Porta-Bote International

PORTA BOX - Dust-mop cleaning tool - American Textile Products Co.

PORTA-BRACE - Cases–camera - K & H Products Ltd.

PORTA BRAZIL - Bathing suits ☆ - Apparel Ventures, Inc.

PORTA CAGE - Cages–wire - Fuhrman Diversified

PORTA CALL - Communications equipment–satellite - Murdock Corp.

PORTA-CASE - Cases–musical instrument ☆ - Selmer Co. Inc.

PORTA-CASH - Cash boxes - Major Metalfab Co.

PORTA-COOL - Air conditioning equipment - General Electric Co.

PORTA COOL - Insulated beverage bags ☆ - International Paper Co.

PORTA COPY - Duplicating machines ☆ - Silver Reed (USA) Inc.

PORTA-CUT - Tools - Seatek Co. Inc.

PORTA-DESK - Notebooks and notepads - Dennison National Co.

PORTA-DESKS - Musical instrument accessories ☆ - Selmer Co. Inc.

PORTA DOCK - Docks - Porta-Dock, Inc.

PORTA-FAX - Electronic equipment - Buhl Industries, Inc.

PORTA-FEED - Electrical equipment - Hobart Brothers Co.

PORTA-FICHE - Projectors–photographic - Radmar Inc.

PORTA-FILE - Briefcases - S and S Leather Goods

PORTA-FIT - Exercising equipment - Atlantic Fitness Products

PORTA FLAME - Garden equipment ☆ - H.D. Hudson Manufacturing Co.

PORTA-FLOW - Contact-lens storage and cleaning kit ☆ - CooperVision Inc.

PORTA-FRAME - Electronic equipment ☆ - Da-Lite Screen Co. Inc.

PORTA-GATE - Infant product ☆ - Welsh Co.

PORTA-GEN - Generators–power - Mercantile Manufacturing Co. Inc.

PORTA-GRAPH - Electronic equipment - Richard Manufacturing Co.

PORTA-GRILL - Barbecues and grills - Riccar America Co.

PORTA GRILL - Barbecues and grills ☆ - General Housewares Corp.

PORTA GRIP 2000 - Telephone accessories - Panavise Products, Inc.

PORTA HAMACA - Hammocks ☆ - Algoma Net Co.

PORTA-HEAT - Heaters–space - Lawn-Boy

PORTA-JIFFY - Housewares - Ballonoff Home Products

PORTA-LAB - Electronic equipment ☆ - Charles Beseler Co.

PORTA-LITE - Electronic equipment - GAF Corp.

PORTA-LITE - Lamps–table ☆ - Prestigeline Inc.

PORTA-LITE - Lighting equipment - Cable Electric Products

PORTA-MATIC - Office machines - Mead-Hatcher, Inc.

PORTA-MOBILE - Infant product - Rock-A-Bye Baby Inc.

PORTA-MUSIC - Cases–musical instrument ☆ - Selmer Co. Inc.

PORTA PAC - Electronic equipment - Avid Corp.

PORTA-PAIR - Appliance parts ☆ - Maytag Corp.

PORTA-PAK - Cameras - Radmar Inc.

PORTA-PAK - Novelty items ☆ - Aladdin Industries, Inc.

PORTA-PERCH - Pet products - Goodden Enterprises

PORTA PLAY - Toys - Tot Inc.

PORTA-POD - Tripods–photographic - SP Systems/Saratons

PORTA-POOCH - Pet products - Earthwhile Endeavors, Inc.

PORTA POTTI - Health care products - Thetford Corp.

PORTA PRINTER I - Telephone apparatus - Krown Research

PORTA PRINTER II - Telephone apparatus ☆ - Krown Research

PORTA PRINTER IV - Telephone apparatus - Krown Research

PORTA PRINTER PLUS - Telephone apparatus ☆ - Krown Research

PORTA-PRO - Backpacks - Porta-Pro

PORTA-PULS - Medical apparatus - General Physiotherapy, Inc.

PORTA PUMP - Pumps - Warren Rupp Inc.

PORTA-PUMP - Pumps–water - Campbell Group (Wayne Home Equipment Div.)

PORTA-QUICK - Oil machinery - ITT Jabsco

PORTA-SCRIBE - Electronic equipment ☆ - Charles Beseler Co.

PORTA-SHADE - Sporting goods ☆ - Harold Cunningham & Co.

PORTA SIESTA - Toys - Evenflo Co.

PORTA-SLEEPER - Welsh Co.

PORTA-SNACK - Tables–wood - Kessler Products Ltd.

PORTA-SONIC - Medical apparatus ☆ - Sunrise Medical (Respiratory Products Division)

PORTA-STUDIO - Artists' materials - Martin Universal Design Inc.

PORTA STUDIO - Audio equipment - Teac America, Inc.

PORTA-TECH - Electronic equipment - GWW Inc.

PORTA-TILE - Saws–power - DBNA Trademarks Holding Inc.

PORTA-TORQUE - Wrenches - Bolttech, Inc.

PORTA-TRACE - Electronic equipment - GAF Corp.

PORTA TRACE - Tables–metal - Gagne Associates Inc.

PORTA-VAC - Health care products - Equi-Tron Inc.

PORTA-VEL - Electronic equipment - Richard Manufacturing Co.

PORTA VELHA - Wines - Admiral Wine Merchants

PORTA-VIEW - Photographic equipment - Logan Electric Specialty Manufacturing Co.

☆ = Now out of production

PORTA VIEW JUNIOR - Telephone apparatus - Krown Research
PORTA-WASH - Hoses ✩ - Lawn-Boy
PORTA-WELD - Sports equipment - Austin Athletic Equipment Corp.
PORTABENE BY BERNARDO - Footwear–women's - Bernardo Brands
PORTABIRD - Medical apparatus - Bird Products Corp.
PORTABLE BALL RACKS - Sporting goods - Dacon Manufacturing
PORTABLE EASY UP - Cushions - Alimed, Inc.
PORTABLE ELECTRIC INFLATOR - Sporting goods - Dacon Manufacturing
PORTABLE GLASS SHOP - Glassware–household - Morton Glass Works Inc.
PORTABLE INSTAPURE - Water–distilled ✩ - Teledyne Water Pik
PORTABLE KITCHEN - Barbecues and grills - Char-Broil
PORTABLE OF PORTABLES, THE - Soccer equipment - Orofrio F. Pavonetti
PORTABLE OXYGEN/MAPP GAS TORCH KIT - Welding equipment - Bernzomatic
PORTABLE POP-UPS - Toys - Mattel, Inc.
PORTABLE PROPERTIES - Soil–potting - Andyland Concepts Inc.
PORTABLE, THE - Computers–personal - Hewlett-Packard Co.
PORTABLES - Tampons - Playtex Beauty Care, Inc.
PORTABOLT - Luggage ✩ - Ronde
PORTABON - Deodorizers - Pettibone Laboratories Inc.
PORTABUTLER - Vacuum cleaners and accessories - Sanyo Fisher (USA) Corp.
PORTACARDESK - Notebooks and notepads - Robert C. Kauffman
PORTACAST - Medical apparatus - Diacor Inc.
PORTACRIB - Cribs–wood - Graco Children's Products
PORTAFLOOR - Flooring–parquet - Teletek Industries, Inc.
PORTAFRIDGE - Refrigerators ✩ - General Thermetics Inc.
PORTAGE - Frames–eyeglass - U.S. Optical Frame Co.
PORTAGE - Tires - Bridgestone/Firestone, Inc.
PORTAGE - Wallpaper - Koroseal Wallcoverings
PORTAGE PACKING - Beef - Hoekstra Meat Co.
PORTAGE PATH - Wallpaper - Koroseal Wallcoverings
PORTAGEN - Pharmaceutical preparations - Bristol-Myers Squibb Co.
PORTAGER - Boats–motor - Smoker-Craft Inc.
PORTAGRIP - Telephone apparatus - Panavise Products, Inc.
PORTAL - Apparel and accessories - Portal Publications, Ltd.
PORTAL - Floor coverings–carpet and rugs - Atlas Carpet Mills Inc.
PORTAL - Publisher's imprints ✩ - Warner Press, Inc.
PORTAMAT - Racks - Cactus Mat Manufacturing Co.
PORTAMATE - Medical apparatus - Graham-Field Inc.
PORTAPAC - Rug cleaning machines–commercial - Castex Industries Inc.
PORTAPAD - Toys–models - Estes Industries
PORTAPAGE - Amplifiers–public address - Sound-Craft Systems Inc.
PORTAPOINT - Computer peripherals - Interlink Electronics, Inc.
PORTAPOWER - Vacuum cleaners and accessories - The Hoover Co.
PORTARAD - Measuring instruments ✩ - Victoreen, Inc.
PORTASCOPE - Microscopes - Bausch & Lomb Inc.
PORTASEW - Rubber product ✩ - Ace Hose and Rubber Co.
PORTASIGN - Signs - Vinylworks, Inc.
PORTASOFT - Water–bottled or canned - Portasoft Co.
PORTASOL - Tools–soldering - GC Thorsen, Inc.
PORTASTAR - Audio-video products - Cornerstone/Clearlight
PORTATABS - Denture cleaners ✩ - Warner-Lambert Co.
PORTATOUCH - Telephone apparatus - Metro-Tel Corp.
PORTATRAK - Shelves - Gaylord Bros. Inc.
PORTATRINE - Sewage treatment equipment ✩ - Applied Biochemists, Inc.
PORTAVIEW PLUS - Telephone apparatus - Krown Research
PORTAVIEW SENIOR - Telephone apparatus - Krown Research
PORTAVISION - Televisions - Tandy Corp.
PORTAWARE - Computer software - Callahan/Roach Products & Publications, Inc.
PORTE - Music–sheet - Jackman Music Corp.
PORTEGE - Computers - Toshiba America Information Systems, Inc.
PORTELLA - Floor coverings–carpet and rugs - Alexander Smith Carpets
PORTER - Floor coverings–carpet and rugs - Porter Carpet Mills Inc.
PORTER - Sewing machines - Porter Sewing Machines, Inc.
PORTER CABLE - Tools–power-driven - Porter-Cable Corp.
PORTER CASE - Suitcases - Porter Case Inc.
PORTER-FLEX - Finishing agents - Porter Paint Co.
PORTER GRAPHICS INC. 77 - Pipes–aluminum - Porter Graphics Inc.
PORTER GUARD - Paints - Porter Paint Co.
PORTER PRO - Sporting goods - Porter Athletic Equipment Co.
PORTER'S - Skin care products - Porter's Products
PORTER'S FRIEND - Polishing rouge - North American Polish Corp.
PORTERSEPT - Paints - Porter Paint Co.
PORTFILEO - File folders - Angler's Roslyn Group Ltd.

PORTFOLIO - Computer software - Micro-Frame Technologies, Inc.
PORTFOLIO - Computers–personal - Atari Games Corp.
PORTFOLIO - Dishes–china - Pfaltzgraff Investment Co.
PORTFOLIO - Display cases–metal - Nomadic Structures, Inc.
PORTFOLIO - Floor coverings–carpet and rugs ✩ - J and J Industries Inc.
PORTFOLIO - Frames–picture - M.W. Carr & Co. Inc.
PORTFOLIO - Games - Paul Douglas, Inc.
PORTFOLIO - Radio communications equipment - Motorola, Inc. (Land Mobile Products Sector)
PORTFOLIO - Wallcoverings - Coral of Chicago
PORTFOLIO - Wallcoverings - Arthur Sanderson and Sons North America Ltd.
PORTFOLIO - Wallpaper ✩ - Morton Jonap Co. Inc.
PORTFOLIO II - Furniture - National/Mt. Airy Furniture
PORTFOLIO MASTER - Computer software - SourceView Software International
PORTFOLIO OF TEXTURES - Wallpaper - Warner Co.
PORTFOLIO TECHNOLOGIES, INC. - Computer software - Portfolio Technologies, Inc.
PORTFOLIOMAKER - Software - Carl A. Schuetz
PORTFOLIOMATCH - Publisher's imprints - FMR Corp.
PORTIA - Ophthalmic goods ✩ - Styl-Rite Optical Manufacturing Co., Inc.
PORTICO - Computer software - Summa Four, Inc.
PORTICO - Floor coverings - Mannington Resilient Floors
PORTICO - Floor coverings–carpet and rugs - Regal Rugs Inc.
PORTICO - Furniture - Pavilion/Sunburst Furniture
PORTICO - Furniture–children's ✩ - Child Craft Industries Inc.
PORTICO - Glassware–household ✩ - Oneida Ltd.
PORTICO - Hardware - Emhart Inc.
PORTICO - Tableware–china ✩ - Pfaltzgraff Investment Co.
PORTICO CUSHION - Furniture - Tropitone Furniture Co. Inc.
PORTICO III NEW YORK - Cosmetics - Portico Bed and Bath Ltd.
PORTICO SLING - Furniture - Tropitone Furniture Co. Inc.
PORTILLA - Floor coverings - Kentile Floors Inc.
PORTILLA II - Floor coverings–tile - Kentile Floors Inc.
PORTION OF CHAPTER FIVE, A - Calendars - Gabby D. Gaborik
PORTION PAC GERMICIDAL DETERGENT - Cleaning preparations - PortionPac Chemical Corp.
PORTION PERFECT - Bacon - Patcud Investments, Inc.
PORTION PERFECT - Meat products - Patrick Cudahy Inc.
PORTION PICTURES - Publisher's imprints - Michelle R. Saari
PORTION POUR - Cookware - Carlisle Foodservice Products, Inc.
PORTIONS - Kitchen canisters and dispensers - Concepts Plus
PORTIPLAY - Radios - Tandy Corp.
PORTLAND - Bicycles - Ross Bicycles USA, Ltd.
PORTLAND - Brushes–paint - Corona Brushes Inc.
PORTLAND - Eyeglasses - Art-Craft Optical Co.
PORTLAND - Fireplace equipment - Thomas Industries Inc. (Portland Willamette Div.)
PORTLAND - Televisions - Daewoo International (America) Corp.
PORTLAND BAGEL BAKERY - Food products - Portland Bagel Bakery and Delicatessen, Ltd.
PORTLAND BREWING - Beverages–malt - Portland Brewing Co.
PORTLAND MIST - Umbrellas - Shedrain Corp.
PORTLAND SEA DOGS - Decals and transfers - Portland Maine Baseball, Inc.
PORTLAND STOVE - Stoves - Portland Franklin Stove Foundry Inc.
PORTLAND WILLAMETTE - Fireplace equipment - Thomas Industries Inc. (Portland Willamette Div.)
PORTLIGHTS - Ships–sailing vessels - Lewmar Marine Inc.
PORTLOCK - Computer software - Portcullis, Ltd.
PORTLOCK - Seafood products–fresh or frozen - Port Chatham Packing Co.
PORTMAN - Vials–glass - Taito America Corp.
PORTMAN SEASIDE - Footwear ✩ - Conjac Inc.
PORTMANN'S - Salad dressings–bottled - Moran Foods, Inc.
PORTMANTEAU - Computer software - Information Management Group, Inc.
PORTMASTER - Electronic equipment - International Business Machines Corp.
PORTMEIRION - Earthenware - Portmeirion USA
PORTO - Floor coverings–carpet and rugs ✩ - Rugby Rugs Inc.
PORTO - Stationery - Dennison National Co.
PORTO-ARC - Electronic equipment - Thomson Consumer Electronics, Inc.
PORTO BEIGE - Building materials ✩ - Walker and Zanger Inc.
PORTO BLANCO - Dinnerware - JMP-Newcor International, Inc.
PORTO CINCO - Wines - Robert Mondavi Winery
PORTO FERREIRA - Cooking equipment–household - Primex International Corp.
PORTO FINO - Sinks–metal - Kohler Co.
PORTO GRANADA - Floor coverings - Mannington Resilient Floors

PORTO GRANDA - Floor coverings - Mannington Resilient Floors

PORTO II - Oxygen ☆ - Caire

PORTO-LIFT - Patient-lifting device - Porto-Lift Corp.

PORTO RAMOS PINTO - Beverages–alcohol - World Shippers & Importers

PORTO VINO - Portable wine tote and cooler ☆ - Ingrid

PORTOBELLO - Tableware–china ☆ - Villeroy and Boch Tableware Ltd.

PORTOCRUZ - Apparel and accessories - Natus Corp.

PORTOFINO - Apparel and accessories - Brigata International, Inc.

PORTOFINO - Boats - Wellcraft Marine Corp.

PORTOFINO - Christmas tree ornaments - Cracker Box Inc.

PORTOFINO - Cigars - General Cigar Co., Inc.

PORTOFINO - Cribs–metal - Evenflo Juvenile Furniture Co.

PORTOFINO - Dishes–china - Pasmantier Co. Inc.

PORTOFINO - Fabrics ☆ - Charter Fabrics Inc.

PORTOFINO - Fans–electric - Seattle Lighting Fixtures Co.

PORTOFINO - Floor coverings - Congoleum Corp.

PORTOFINO - Floor coverings–carpet and rugs - Atlas Carpet Mills Inc.

PORTOFINO - Floor coverings–carpet and rugs - Couristan Inc.

PORTOFINO - Floor coverings–carpet and rugs ☆ - Catalina Carpet Mills Inc.

PORTOFINO - Footwear - Portofino Footwear Inc.

PORTOFINO - Furniture ☆ - Akko Inc.

PORTOFINO - Luggage - York Luggage Co.

PORTOFINO - Pillows - Perfect Fit Industries, Inc.

PORTOFINO COLLECTION - Handbags - Accessories by Austin Designs, Inc.

PORTOFINO COLLECTION - Neckties - Cornell of California Inc.

PORTOLA HILLS - Wines - Cronin Vineyards

PORTOVISTA - Spaghetti sauce - American Home Food Products Inc.

PORTRA - Photographic equipment - Eastman Kodak Co.

PORTRAGON - Lenses–photographic - SP Systems/Saratons

PORTRAIT - Adhesives and sealants - Betco Corp.

PORTRAIT - Bathtubs–enameled - Kohler Co.

PORTRAIT - Cabinets ☆ - Nutone Inc.

PORTRAIT - Clocks ☆ - General Time Corp. (Westclox/Seth Thomas Div.)

PORTRAIT - Eyeglasses ☆ - Carl Zeiss Optical Inc.

PORTRAIT - Furniture ☆ - Riverside Furniture Corp.

PORTRAIT - Herbicides - Green Light Co.

PORTRAIT - Luggage - American Tourister, Inc.

PORTRAIT - Photographic equipment ☆ - Ilex Optical Co. Inc.

PORTRAIT - Tape players–cassette - Sony Music Entertainment Inc.

PORTRAIT - Underwear and nightwear - Bestform Foundations, Inc.

PORTRAIT AND WEDDING MANAGER - Computer software - Epix, Inc.

PORTRAIT BEARS - Toys–stuffed - Happy Tymes Collectibles

PORTRAIT CLOTHES BY BARCO - Uniforms–tailored ☆ - Barco of California

PORTRAIT DISPLAYS, INC. - Computer peripheral equipment - Portrait Displays, Inc.

PORTRAIT IN TAFFETA - Dolls - Mattel, Inc.

PORTRAIT PALS - Dolls - Portrait Pals, Inc.

PORTRAIT PETITES - Photographs - Consumer Programs Inc.

PORTRAIT POSING WHEEL - Photographic equipment - Creativity International

PORTRAIT SUPREME - Prosthetic apparatus - OTC Professional Appliances

PORTRAITS - Computer software ☆ - Ventura Educational Systems

PORTRAITS - House furnishings - Carolina Designs Ltd.

PORTRAITS BY NORTHERN ISLES - Apparel and accessories - Kellwood Co.

PORTRAITS BY NORTHERN ISLES II - Apparel and accessories - Kellwood Co.

PORTRAITS BY VANITY FAIR - Underwear and nightwear - Vanity Fair, Inc.

PORTRAITS IN COTTON - Lingerie - Ithaca Industries Inc.

PORTRAITS IN NYLON - Lingerie - Ithaca Industries Inc.

PORTRAITS OF NATURE - Cosmetics - E.B. Botanicals Inc.

PORTRAITS OF PERFECTION - Dolls - Georgetown Collection, Inc.

PORTRAITS OF SUCCESS - Apparel and accessories - Hispanic Development Corp.

PORTRAITS OF THE NATIONS - Publisher's imprints - Harper Junior Books Group

PORTRALURE - Paper–photographic - Eastman Kodak Co.

PORTRAYAL - Frames–eyeglass ☆ - Universal/Univis Inc.

PORTRAYT - Paints - M. Grumbacher Inc.

PORTROLIO - Artists' materials - Multiple Choice

PORTS O'CALL - Floor coverings–carpet and rugs ☆ - Catalina Carpet Mills Inc.

PORTS OF CALL - Wallpaper - Imperial Wallcoverings, Inc.

PORTSERVER - Computer hardware - Digi International Inc.

PORTSIDE - Fish–fresh or frozen - Moran Foods, Inc.

PORTSIDE - Frames–eyeglass - Ben-Glo Optical Ltd.

PORTSIDER - Footwear - P.H. Volk Co.

PORTSMOUTH - Boats–motor - Sunfish Laser Inc.

PORTSMOUTH - Cabinets - American Woodmark Corp.

PORTSMOUTH - Cabinets - Imperial Cabinets Inc.

PORTSMOUTH - Clocks - General Time Corp. (Westclox/Seth Thomas Div.)

PORTSMOUTH - Clocks ☆ - Chelsea Clock Co. Inc.

PORTSMOUTH - Clocks ☆ - Ridgeway Clock Co.

PORTSMOUTH - Floor coverings - Mannington Resilient Floors

PORTSMOUTH - Frames–eyeglass ☆ - Universal/Univis Inc.

PORTSMOUTH - Giftware ☆ - Gorham Inc.

PORTSMOUTH - Wainscotting - Georgia-Pacific Corp.

PORTSMOUTH COLLECTION - Furniture–upholstered - Clyde Pearson Inc.

PORTSMOUTH INN - Furniture ☆ - Bassett Furniture Industries, Inc.

PORTUGUESE FISHERMAN - Yarn ☆ - JCA, Inc.

PORTUGUESE TILES - Wallpaper - Stamford Wall Paper Co. Inc.

PORTUS - Computer software - Livermore Software Laboratories, Inc.

PORTVELOPS - Artists' materials - Multiple Choice

PORVENE DOORS - Doors–garage - Porvene Doors, Inc.

P.O.S. - Apparel and accessories - Pen-Tab Industries

POS-A-TRACTION - Tires–automobile - Pos-A-Traction, Inc.

POS-ALIGN - Sights–gun - Burris Co., Inc.

POS EQUIPE - Shoe accessories - Pos Equipe Corp.

POS-I-CHEK - Envelopes - Mail-Well Envelope

POS-I-TABS - File folders - Professional Office Services, Inc.

POS-I-TORQUE - Clutches–industrial - Hoffco Inc.

POS-O-TITE - Drains - LSP Specialty Products Co.

POS ONE - Cameras - Graphline, Inc.

POS-PARTNER - Cash registers - Upper Midwest Industries, Inc.

POS-PARTNER - Computer software - Visa USA Inc.

POSA - Motor vehicle parts and accessories - Summit Industries, Inc.

POSADA - Food products - Multifoods Inc.

POSADA DELI-FEST - Food products - International Multifoods Corp.

POSAFIT - Wheelchairs - Adaptive Engineering Lab Inc.

POSALINK - Wheelchairs - Adaptive Engineering Lab Inc.

POSCA - Markers–felt-tip - Faber-Castell Corp.

POSE - Hosiery ☆ - Hampshire Hosiery, Inc.

POSE - Perfumes - Eurostar Corp.

POSE AND PLAY FRIENDS - Dolls - Fanny's Play House, Inc.

POSE CARDS - Paper–writing - Crannog No. 1 L.P.

POSE-ME BUNNY - Toys–stuffed ☆ - Fun World Inc.

POSE ME PRETTY - Toys - Mattel, Inc.

POSEABLES - Toys–stuffed ☆ - Gund, Inc.

POSEIDON - Beverages–malt - Fish Brewing Co.

POSEIDON - Floor coverings–carpet and rugs ☆ - Eurotex Inc.

POSEIDON - Ophthalmic goods ☆ - Luxottica

POSEIDON - Recording label - Crystal Records Inc.

POSEIDON - Shrimp–fresh or frozen - Kitchens of the Oceans Inc.

POSEIDON PRESS - Publisher's imprints - Simon & Schuster, Inc.

POSEIDON REGULATOR - Scuba diving equipment - Parkway Systems

POSER - Computer software - Fractal Design Corp.

POSEY - Bicycles ☆ - Murray, Inc.

POSH - Apparel and accessories - Salant/Manhattan Industries

POSH - Colognes - Renee Distributors

POSH BOY - Recording label - Chameleon Music Group Inc.

POSH PET PLACE - Pet products - Posh Pet Products Inc.

POSH POOCH - Pet products - Pet Concepts

POSH PUFF KITTENS - Toys - Tonka Corp.

POSH PUFFS - Facial tissues - Procter & Gamble Co.

POSH WASH - Cleaning preparations - Flair Image, Inc.

POSI CACHE - Safes - Armor Safe Technologies

POSI-CAT - Computers - Positrak

POSI-CLAMP - Tools–garden - Gilmour Manufacturing Co.

POSI-DRY - Photographic equipment - Magic Garden Products (New Tomorrow, Inc.)

POSI-DRY - Photographic equipment - New Tomorrow Inc.

POSI-FEED - Machinery - William Goodyear Co.

POSI-FLEX - Footwear - Lehigh Safety Shoe Co.

POSI-FLO II - Water purification systems - Sta-Rite Industries Inc.

POSI-FLOW - Air ducts - Berner International Corp. (Miniveil Air Curtain Div.)

POSI-FLOW - Conveyors - Carrier Vibrating Equipment, Inc.

POSI-FUSE - Pipes–tobacco - Dresser Industries, Inc.

POSI GLIDE - Hardware - National Manufacturing Co.

POSI-GRIP - Fasteners - S & S Construction Fasteners, Inc.

POSI-GRIP - Pencils - Zebra Pen Corp.

POSI-GROUND - Electrical equipment - General Electric Co.

POSI-HOLD - Pipes–tobacco - Dresser Industries, Inc.

POSI-LOCK - Housewares - Aptargroup, Inc.

☆ = Now out of production

POSI-LOCK - Plumbing fixtures—enameled - Kohler Co.
POSI-LOCK - Sights—gun - Burris Co., Inc.
POSI-LOK - Clamps - Sta-Rite Industries Inc.
POSI-PEN - Pens - Zebra Pen Corp.
POSI-POUR - Containers - Magnuson Industries Inc.
POSI STOP - Pencil sharpeners - Park Sherman
POSI-TEMP - Plumbing fixtures—metal - Moen Inc.
POSI-TRAK - Electronic equipment - AVL
POSI-TRAK - Machine tools - Chief Automotive Systems, Inc.
POSI-TRAK - Microfiche equipment - Systems Technology
POSI-TRAP - Machine parts - Mass-Vac, Inc.
POSI-VU - Electrical equipment - General Electric Co.
POSIE - Lenses—optical - Kelley & Hueber
POSIE POTS - Garden equipment - Visual Design Manufacturing Co. Inc.
POSIEDON - Fabrics - Dan River Inc.
POSIES - Dresses—women's - Posies
POSIES - Footwear—children's - JBI, Inc.
POSIES - House furnishings - Dan River Inc.
POSILOCK - Electronics equipment - Multivision Systems Inc.
POSILOK - Machine tools - Esco Corp.
POSIPRINTER - Office supplies - Esselte Corp.
POSITANO - Floor coverings—carpet and rugs - Atlas Carpet Mills Inc.
POSITANO - Floor coverings—carpet and rugs - Couristan Inc.
POSITANO - Wallpaper ☆ - Jolie Papier
POSITANO NEUTRALS - Floor coverings—carpet and rugs - Atlas Carpet Mills Inc.
POSITCOMM - Communications equipment - Titan Information Systems Corp.
POSITECH - Transmission equipment—industrial - Positech International, Inc.
POSITIF - T-shirts—men's - New World Wear Ltd.
POSITILT - Window coverings ☆ - Hunter Douglas, Inc.
POSITION-AIRE - Mattresses - Position-Aire, Inc.
POSITION CONTROL NAVIGATOR - Computer software - Automating Peripherals, Inc.
POSITION-PERFECT - Therapeutic air mattresses - EHOB Inc.
POSITIVE - Nail care products - Trina/Genie
POSITIVE ACTION - Educational materials - Positive Action Co.
POSITIVE ACTION SCHOOL - Educational materials - Positive Action Co.
POSITIVE & NEGATIVE CONTROLS - Pharmaceutical preparations - Wampole Laboratories Div.
POSITIVE BALANCE - Hair care products - Helene Curtis Industries Inc.
POSITIVE-BREAK - Electrical equipment - Schmersal LLC, Inc.
POSITIVE COMMUNICATIONS, INC. - Pagers - Positive Communications, Inc.
POSITIVE DEODORANT - Deodorizers - Definitive Deodorant Co.
POSITIVE EXPANDING POINT - Ammunition - Olin Corp. (Winchester Div.)
POSITIVE GROWTH - Fertilizer - Ecolawn, Inc.
POSITIVE HEROES - Dolls - For Penny's Sake, Inc.
POSITIVE I.D. SECURITY CHECKS - Checkbooks - Hub Checking Division Corp.
POSITIVE IMAGE - Figurines - Norman A. Hughes
POSITIVE IMAGE - Frames—eyeglass ☆ - Universal/Univis Inc.
POSITIVE IMAGE - Medical apparatus - Positive Image Orthotics
POSITIVE LOCK - Window shades - California Designs
POSITIVE MEDICINE - Video production - Michael Magee
POSITIVE MOVES - Educational materials - CWD International, Inc.
POSITIVE MUSIC - Recording label - Positive Music Records Inc.
POSITIVE OUTLOOK - Vitamins and nutritional supplements - Highland Laboratories
POSITIVE PAYLINK - Computer software - Bottomline Technologies, Inc.
POSITIVE PEOPLE KACY WORLD COLORS - Apparel and accessories - Sunny Jung Trading, Inc.
POSITIVE REACTION - Hair care products - Clairol Inc.
POSITIVE RED - Eyeglasses - Oakley, Inc.
POSITIVE REINFORCEMENT APPAREL - Shirts - Greater Than, Inc.
POSITIVE RESULTS - Skin care products - American Consumer Products, Inc.
POSITIVE SEALS 4 - Couplings - Tylok International, Inc.
POSITIVE STATE - Apparel and accessories - Michael A. Williams
POSITIVE THINKING - Posters - Graphic Arts Unltd. Inc.
POSITIVE THINKING BALLS - Golfing equipment - Todd P. Cain
POSITIVE VIBES - Crock pots - Wonderknit
POSITIVELY! - Greeting cards - American Greetings Corp.
POSITIVELY DOTTY - Fabrics - Gretchen Bellinger Inc.
POSITIVELY FOR KIDS - Publisher's imprints - Positively for Kids
POSITIVELY PECAN - Candy bars - Chocolate House, Inc.
POSITIVELY PEER - Games - Creative Development, Inc.
POSITIVELY PEPPERS - Footwear—women's - B. Levy & Son
POSITIVELY PEPPERS - Shoes - 700 Associates

POSITIVELY POSH - Mirrors - Erwin-Lambeth Inc.
POSITIVELY PRALINE CRUNCH - Frozen foods - Weight Watchers International, Inc.
POSITIVELY PURPLE - Toiletries - GPS, Inc.
POSITIVELY SINFUL - Food products - Northfield Foods Inc.
POSITIVELY STRETCH - Apparel and accessories - Joan Walters
POSITIVITY 2000 - Apparel and accessories - Bernard Terrill McDuel, Sr.
POSITRAC - Golfing equipment - Golfsmith International Inc.
POSITRACE - Electrodes - Medtronic Andover Medical, Inc.
POSITRACTION - Paints - Triangle Coatings Inc.
POSITRAX - Footwear - Lehigh Safety Shoe Co.
POSITREAD - Epoxy coatings - Metalcrete Industries Inc.
POSITRED - Shoe-repair products - Chicago Sole Leather Distributors Inc.
POSITRIM - Food products - Nutrilite, Div. of Amway Corp.
POSITRIM - Vitamins and nutritional supplements - Amway Corp.
POSITROL - Vitamins and nutritional supplements - Vitamin Research Products Inc.
POSIXWORKS - Computer software - Lynx Real-Time Systems, Inc.
POSLAM - Skin care products - Alvin Last Inc.
POSNER - Hair care products - Posner Laboratories Inc.
POSNER PRO - Hair care products - Posner Laboratories Inc.
POSPRO - Business forms - Cutting USA Inc.
POSS - Meat products—canned - Castleberry's Food Co.
POSSE - Firearms, accessories, and parts - High Standard Manufacturing Corp.
POSSE, THE - Alarm systems - Adaptive Vehicle Systems, Inc.
POSSELT - Giftware - Ebeling and Reuss Co.
POSSESSED - Apparel and accessories - B.M.Y. International
POSSESSING THE POSSESSIVES - Computer software ☆ - Right on Programs
POSSESSIVE BLINDFOLD RECORDINGS - Recording label - Scott Beebe
POSSI - Electronic equipment - Checkpoint Security Systems Group, Inc.
POSSIBILITIES - Dresses—women's - R. & M. Kaufmann
POSSIBILITIES - Wallpaper ☆ - Gilford Corp.
POSSIBLE DREAMS - Figurines - Possible Dreams, Ltd.
POSSIBLE WEAR - Apparel and accessories - Gobeco Enterprises, LLC
POSSON - Wines - Sierra Wine Corp.
POSSUM - Alarm systems - Opossum Inc.
POSSUM - Sardines—canned - Stinson Seafood Co.
POSSUM TROT VINEYARDS - Wines ☆ - Possum Trot Vineyards
POST - Boats—motor - Post Marine Co. Inc.
POST - Drafting supplies ☆ - Teledyne Post
POST A CARD - Novelty items - Flowers, Inc. Balloons
POST-A-CARD - Stationery ☆ - Mead Corp.
POST ALLEY PALE ALE - Beverages—malt - The Stroh Brewery Co.
POST AVE. - Apparel and accessories - Todd Number 1
POST BANANA NUT CRUNCH - Cereal - General Mills, Inc.
POST CARD FEVER - Greeting cards ☆ - Vintage Images
POST CARD PARADE - Greeting cards - Russ Berrie and Co., Inc.
POST COLOR - Hair care products - Framesi USA/Roffler Industries Inc.
POST FAMILIE - Wines - Post Winery Inc.
POST-GARD - Garden equipment - Weed Whip International
POST GRADUATE - Floor coverings—carpet and rugs - J and J Industries Inc.
POST HOST - Brackets - Dec-Kor, Inc.
POST HOUSE - Paints - Paragon Paint & Varnish Corp.
POST IMPRESSIONS - Hair care products - Helene Curtis Industries Inc.
POST-IT - Computer software - Minnesota Mining & Manufacturing Co.
POST-L-POST - Mail boxes - Steel City Corp.
POST-LITE - Packaging—blisterwrap - Avery Dennison Corp.
POST-LOC - Shelving - Library Bureau Inc.
POST-LOCK - Office supplies - Panter Co. Inc.
POST MASTER - Shelving units—metal - William Hodges & Co.
POST-MASTERS - Bulletin boards—wood - Master Woodcraft Inc.
POST N PLAY - Magnets - Trend Enterprises, Inc.
POST-NATE - Vitamins and nutritional supplements - KV Pharmaceutical Co.
POST NO BILLS - Apparel and accessories - Post No Bills, Inc.
POST-O-GRAF - Scales—industrial ☆ - Pennsylvania Scale Co.
POST-OP SKIN CARE PRODUCTS - Cosmetics - M. W. Laboratories, Inc.
POST-PLUS - Computer software - M.C. Tel Corp.
POST POPPER - Tools—hand-operated - McClarin Manufacturing
POST-R-PACK - Nuts and bolts ☆ - Rockford Products Corp. (International Group)
POST-RITE - Paper - Reynolds and Reynolds Co.
POST ROAD - Floor coverings—carpet and rugs ☆ - Lees Carpets
POST ROAD - Furniture ☆ - Bassett Furniture Industries, Inc.
POST ROAD - Wallpaper - Hunting Valley Prints

☆ = Now out of production

POST-ROUTING - Computer software - Geotel Communications Corp.

POST RX - Pharmaceutical preparations - Joseph L. Giampaolo, Jr.

POST SCRIPT - Toys - Post Script Inc.

POST SEASON - Apparel stores–sports - Athlete's Foot Marketing Associates Inc.

POST SUN - Skin care products - Westwood-Squibb Pharmaceuticals, Inc.

POST TIME - Animal feeds - McCauley Bros., Inc.

POST TIME - Games - Gang, Inc.

POST-UP! - Anchors - Gordon Corp.

POST WHIP - Beverage dispensing equipment - Orange Bang Inc.

POSTABLOCKS - Paints–artists' ☆ - Winsor & Newton

POSTABOUT - Footwear - Mason Shoe Manufacturing Co.

POSTACNE - Pharmaceutical preparations ☆ - Dermik Laboratories Inc.

POSTAFIX - Office machines - Data-Link Corp.

POSTAL - Pencils - Faber-Castell Corp.

POSTAL PARTNER - Packaging–blisterwrap - Tesa Tape Inc.

POSTAL POLICE - Jewelry - Frank J. Deleo

POSTAL-TRIEVER - Machinery - Kardex Systems, Inc.

POSTAL.GIF - Computer diskettes–blank - Thomas W. Kolter

POSTALIA COLLECTION, THE - Stationery - Loli Designs

POSTALSOFT ADDRESS DICTIONARY - Computer software - Postalsoft, a Firstlogic Technology

POSTALSOFT DESKTOP MAILER - Computer software - Postalsoft, a Firstlogic Technology

POSTALSOFT DESKTOP POSTALCODER - Computer peripheral equipment - Postalsoft, a Firstlogic Technology

POSTAMATIC - Desk sets - Postamatic Co. Inc.

POSTAR - Posters - Merryland Corp.

POSTBLOK - Blocks–concrete - R. Imdorf Post Supports

POSTBOX - Computer software - Postbox Technology, Inc.

POSTBOX - Video equipment - Matsushita Electric Corp. of America

POSTCARD GREETINGS - Greeting cards - Joli Greeting Card Co.

POSTCARD PRAYER - Magnets ☆ - Sangray Corp.

POSTCARD PROMOTIONS - Custom printed promotional goods - Postcard Promotions, Inc.

POSTCARDS FROM THE PARK - Postcards - Jo Anne Kiser

POSTCARE - Dental equipment - John O.Butler Co.

POSTCONFORM - Computer software - Digidesign Inc.

POSTECH - Furniture - Services, Inc. of Baudette, Minnesota

POSTED - Posters - Posted Communications L.P.

POSTED COMMUNICATIONS - Graphic posters - Posted Communications L.P.

POSTER ART - Posters - Brite-Tone Co.

POSTER BORDERS - Wallpaper - Studio IV Graphics Inc.

POSTER MOUNTS - Tape–adhesive - Miller Studio

POSTER PERFECT - Artists' materials ☆ - Hunt Manufacturing Co.

POSTER PETS - Posters - Fancy Publications, Inc.

POSTER PRINTER - Electronic equipment - Varitronic Systems, Inc.

POSTER PRINTS - Photographic equipment - Blow Ups Inc.

POSTER PUTTY - Adhesives and sealants - Manco, Inc.

POSTER PUZZLE - Puzzles - International Polygonics Ltd.

POSTER TACK - Adhesives and sealants - Bostik Inc.

POSTERBADGE - Bar fixtures–plastic - Spir-it Inc.

POSTERELLE - Inks - Crown Art Products

POSTERISAN - Health care products ☆ - Kenwood Laboratories Inc.

POSTERM - Electrical equipment - Communications Technology Corp.

POSTERMAKER PLUS - Computer software ☆ - Broderbund Software, Inc.

POSTERMATIC - Hardware ☆ - Danalco

POSTGARD - Rubber–molded - Tedford M. Randolph, Jr.

POSTILLION - Frames–eyeglass ☆ - Universal/Univis Inc.

POSTIRPIN - Bar fixtures–plastic - Spir-it Inc.

POSTIRS - Bar fixtures–plastic - Spir-it Inc.

POSITIVE IMAGE - Jewelry - Positive Image Products

POSTLAB - Computer software - Nineveh Software Corp.

POSTMAN - Mail boxes - Signlite Services, Inc.

POSTMARK AMERICA - Metals - United States Postal Service

POSTMASTER - Computer software - America.Dbf, Inc.

POSTMAX - Mail boxes - Flambeau Products Corp.

POSTMIN - Computer software - Glick Associates, Inc.

POSTMODERN ANXST - Books–comic - Greg Beda

POSTNOTES - Stationery ☆ - Printworks Inc.

POSTOBON - Beverages–carbonated - Brooklyn Bottling Corp.

POSTOSCOPE - Projectors–photographic ☆ - F.D. Kees Power Equipment LLC

POSTPRO - Computers - SOC Associates, L.P.

POST'S - Wines - Post Winery Inc.

POSTSCRIPT - Frames–eyeglass - Liberty Optical Manufacturing Co.

POSTSCRIPTS - Neckties - Superba, Inc.

POSTSET - Cement - Nomix Corp.

POSTUFIRM - Pillows - Hollander Home Fashions Inc.

POSTUP - Wines - Stanley Stawski Distributing Co.

POSTUR-CENTER - Mattresses - Spring Air Bedding Inc.

POSTURCORE - Insulating materials - Conwed Bonded Fiber

POSTURE - Brooms - Lighthouse Industries

POSTURE - Corsets - Spencer Supports Ltd.

POSTURE - Mattresses - Bemco Associates, Inc.

POSTURE - Vitamins and nutritional supplements - Whitehall Laboratories

POSTURE BRACE - Braces–orthopedic - Jamison Bedding Inc.

POSTURE BRIDGE - Mattresses - R.F. Simmons Co.

POSTURE CARE - Mattresses - Medallion Sleep Products Inc.

POSTURE CARE - Wheelchairs ☆ - Theradyne Healthcare Product Div.

POSTURE CLOUD - Mattresses - Classic Corp.

POSTURE COMFORT - Mattresses - Spring Air Bedding Inc.

POSTURE CORRECTOR - Mattresses - Spring Air Bedding Inc.

POSTURE CRAFT - Beds–wood ☆ - Classic Corp.

POSTURE CURVE - Health care products - Body Care Inc.

POSTURE CUSHION - Mattresses - Spring Air Bedding Inc.

POSTURE-D - Vitamins and nutritional supplements - Whitehall Laboratories

POSTURE FLOW - Mattresses - Mason Medical Products

POSTURE-GLIDE - Medical apparatus - Lumex, Inc.

POSTURE GUARD - Orthopedic products - Kathy L. Basque

POSTURE GUARD - Wheelchairs - Luxury Liners

POSTURE KNIGHT - Mattresses - Sleepwell Mattress Co. Inc.

POSTURE LINER - Wheelchairs - Luxury Liners

POSTURE PLEASER - Medical apparatus - Brentham Enterprises, Inc.

POSTURE-RITE - Chairs–wood - Wells Industries

POSTURE-RITE - Desk sets ☆ - Hoyle Products Inc.

POSTURE ULTIMATE - Mattresses - J.C. Penney Co., Inc.

POSTURE WEDGE - Health care products - Body Care Inc.

POSTURE X - Apparel - Comfortably Yours Inc.

POSTURE X-PERTS - Apparel and accessories - Beautiful Images, Inc.

POSTUREMATIC - Beds–hospital - Ohio Mattress Co.

POSTUREMATIC COMFORT COMMAND BED - Beds–metal - Ohio Mattress Co.

POSTUREMOTION - Adjustable beds - Hillside Bedding Inc.

POSTUREPEDIC SUPPORT ONLY FROM SEALY - Mattresses - Ohio Mattress Co.

POSTUREPLATFORM - Mattresses - Sealy Inc.

POSTUREST - Health care products - Bell-Horn

POSTURFOLD - Chairs–folding - Wenger Corp.

POSTURITE - Pillows - Cervical Support Pillow Co.

POSY - Dinnerware–glass ☆ - Johnson Brothers, USA, Inc.

POSY CORNERS - Wall fixture - Paul G. Kosky

POSY-COZY - Yarn ☆ - William Unger & Co. Inc.

POSY PATCH, THE - Flowers–artificial - It's Polite to Point, Inc.

POSY POWER - Soil–potting - Nea Enterprises, Inc.

POT & PAN PAC - Detergents - PortionPac Chemical Corp.

POT BELLIES - Cooking utensils–cast iron - Coleman Co., Inc.

POT BELLIES - Novelty items - Decorator and Craft Corp.

POT BELLY BLACK - Paints - Sheffield Bronze Paint Corp.

POT CHLORIDE - Pharmaceutical preparations - Geneva Generics Inc.

POT LIPPER - Brackets - Dec-Kor, Inc.

POT LIPPERPLUS - Brackets - Dec-Kor, Inc.

POT LUCK - Coffee - First Colony Coffee and Tea Co. Inc.

POT LUCK - Fabrics - Dan River Inc.

POT 'N ALL - Seeds–salted, roasted, cooked, or canned ☆ - Asgrow Seed Co.

POT 'N SPOON - Games - CBS Toys

POT O' GOLD - Honey - Western Commerce Corp.

POT-O-SAURS - Garden equipment - Cobraco Manufacturing, Inc.

POT-OF-LITE - Candles ☆ - Candle-Lite Co.

POT POURRI - Cooking equipment–household ☆ - Sunbeam-Oster Household Products

POT POURRI - Dishes–china - Waterford Wedgewood USA, Inc.

POT POURRI - Perfumes - FMG/Tsumara Medical

POT PROPS - Kitchen appliances ☆ - H.P. Stran & Co.

POT-ROD - Giftware - Stewart Co. Inc.

POT SHOT - Deodorizers - Unit Chemical Corp.

POT-SHOTS - Publisher's imprints - Brilliant Enterprises

POT STICKER - Decals and transfers - John Harmony Products

POT STICKERS - Flower pots–earthenware - Pot Stickers

POT, THE - Flower pots–earthenware - K-5 Coatings Inc.

POT-TO - Pottery products - Karsulyn Corp. (Novelty Gift Division)

☆ = Now out of production

POTABA - Pharmaceutical preparations - Glenwood LLC
POTABLE-AQUA - Chemical preparations - Wisconsin Pharmacal Co. Inc.
POTAGE - Potassium compounds ☆ - Lemmon Co.
POTAGES USA - Food products - Zursun Ltd.
POTASALAN - Pharmaceutical preparations - Lannett Co. Inc.
POTASSA-CAL - Calcium compounds - Magic Green Corp.
POTASSINE - Pharmaceutical preparations ☆ - Recsei Laboratories
POTASSIUM CAPS - Vitamins and nutritional supplements - Vitamin Research Products Inc.
POTASSIUM FUEL - Vitamins and nutritional supplements - Twinlab
POTASSIUM HYDROXIDE - Pharmaceutical preparations - Gordon Laboratories
POTATO ALIVE - Salad dressings–bottled - Barcelona Nut
POTATO BLAST - Spices and extracts - Brewster's Smokehouse, Inc.
POTATO BOATS - Vegetables–frozen ☆ - J.R. Simplot Co.
POTATO BUDS - Food products - General Mills, Inc.
POTATO CHEEZSKINS - Vegetables–frozen - Promark International, Inc.
POTATO CHIPSTERS - Snack foods - Nabisco Foods Group
POTATO CHOP - Food products - Mesopotamia Food Inc.
POTATO HEAD FAMILY - Puzzles ☆ - Milton Bradley Co.
POTATO HEAD KIDS - Games ☆ - Milton Bradley Co.
POTATO MEDLEYS - Food products - General Mills, Inc.
POTATO 'N SESAME - Crackers - Nabisco Foods Group
POTATO OLES - Fruits and vegetables - Taco John's International Inc.
POTATO OLE'S BRAVO - Food products - Taco John's International Inc.
POTATO PEARLS EXCEL - Potato flakes - Basic American, Inc.
POTATO PLANKS - Vegetables–frozen - Ore-Ida Foods, Inc.
POTATO POP - Snack foods - Energy Food Factory Inc.
POTATO PRIDE - Food products - Affiliated Foods, Inc.
POTATO PUFF - Pet food - T.F.H. Publications, Inc.
POTATO QUICK - Food products - Zebbie's Inc.
POTATO REAL - Food products - Idahoan Foods Inc.
POTATO REPUBLIC - Food products - Mark Ginsburg
POTATO SHAKERS - Seasonings - General Mills, Inc.
POTATO SMASH - Food products - Nancy Hope Gallo
POTATO WIDGETS - Frozen foods - Horns Poultry Inc.
POTATOE FACTORY - Computer software - CBS Software
POTATOES EXPRESS - Food products - General Mills, Inc.
POTAVITE - See QUINTABS-M
POTEET STRAWBERRY FESTIVAL - Apparel and accessories - Poteet Strawberry Festival Association, Inc.
POTEN SKIN KARE - Skin care products - Kare Inc.
POTENCY PATCH - Pharmaceutical preparations - Transdermal Products, Inc.
POTENCYN 10000 FOR MEN - Vitamins and nutritional supplements - Pharmed Group Corp.
POTENCYN 10000 FOR WOMEN - Vitamins and nutritional supplements - Pharmed Group Corp.
POTENSAN - Vitamins and nutritional supplements - Polam Wholesale Inc.
POTENT - Apparel and accessories - Todd Kenneth Williams
POTENT - Chemical preparations - Pennyrile AG Oil, Inc.
POTENT - Perfumes - Hartz Mountain Corp.
POTENT - Pumps - Little Giant Pump Co.
POTENT 6 PAK - Pet product - B-Elegant Products
POTENT C - Vitamins and nutritional supplements ☆ - Natrol, Inc.
POTENT-PAK - Pet shampoo - B-Elegant Products
POTENT POTION - Vitamins and nutritional supplements - New World Enterprizes, Inc. (New World Entertainment)
POTENT RODENT - Rodenticides - Herb Works
POTENTIAL - Lenses–optical - Ditto Industries Inc.
POTENTIAL - Window coverings - Fashion Tech, Inc.
POTENTIALS - Magazines - Lakewood Publications Acquisition Corp.
POTENTIALS UNLIMITED - Recording label - I.M.P.A.C.T. Publishing, Inc.
POTENZA - Tires - Bridgestone/Firestone, Inc.
POTION - Hair care products - Philip Pelusi, Inc.
POTLATCH - Lumber - Woodex Lumber Corp.
POTLUCK - Boats - Glen-L Marine Designs
POTLUCK - Vegetables–canned - Chevalier International USA Inc.
POTOCKY NEEDLE - Retractable needle - Cooper Companies Inc.
POTOMAC - Boats–canoes ☆ - Old Town Canoe Co.
POTOMAC - Cabinets - American Woodmark Corp.
POTOMAC - Furniture - Singer Furniture Co.
POTOMAC - Lumber - Georgia-Pacific Corp.
POTOMAC - Occasional tables ☆ - JDI Group, Inc.
POTOMAC - Tableware–china ☆ - Lenox, Inc.
POTOMAC BAKERY MIXES - Food products - Frank A. Serio and Sons Inc.
POTOMAC MANOR - Bedroom furniture ☆ - American Drew

POTOMAC RIVER - Food products - Keyser Bros. Inc.
POTOMAC, THE - Fans–electric - Hunter Fan Co.
POTOSI - Beverages–malt ☆ - Joseph Huber Brewing Co., Inc.
POTPOURRI - Candles - Hanna's Potpourri Specialties, Inc.
POTPOURRI - Correction fluid - Sk Merchandising Corp.
POTPOURRI - Dishes–earthenware - Denby USA Limited
POTPOURRI - Floor coverings ☆ - Tarkett, Inc.
POTPOURRI - Furniture - American Furniture Co. Inc.
POTPOURRI - Lenses–optical - Kelley & Hueber
POTPOURRI - Pesticides–household - Enforcer Products Inc.
POTPOURRI - Puzzles ☆ - Warren Industries Inc.
POTPOURRI - Skin care products ☆ - Prince Matchabelli
POTPOURRI - Teas - Eastern Shore Tea Co.
POTPOURRI - Wallets ☆ - Enger-Kress Co.
POTPOURRI BY ADRIENNE - Deodorizers - Herbal Holding Co.
POTPOURRI COLLECTION - Floor coverings–carpet and rugs - Colonial Mills Inc.
POTPOURRI DESIGNS - Silverware - Potpourri Press, Inc.
POTPOURRI EMPORIUM - Glass products - Beatrice Head
POTPOURRI GARDENS - Deodorizers - Gilbertie's Herb Gardens, Inc.
POTPOURRI HEARTS - Candles - Carolina Designs Ltd.
POTPOURRI OF GAMES - Computer software - SourceView Software International
POTPOURRI PALS - Figurines - Gilbertie's Herb Gardens, Inc.
POTPOURRI PEARLS - Spices and extracts - Scentex Inc.
POTPOURRI PEBBLES - Spices and extracts - Scentex Inc.
POTPOURRI PETS - Toys - Design Works Crafts
POTPOURRI PIE - Deodorizers - Oopsy Daisy
POTPOURRI PRESERVES - Deodorizers - Willert Home Products, Inc.
POTPOURRI STYLE - Wallcoverings - Cork Products Co. Inc.
POTPOURRI STYLE - Wallpaper - Pageant Wallpaper Corp.
POTS 'N PANS BAND - Toys - Mattel, Inc.
POTS-N-PEPPERS - Cooking utensils–aluminum ☆ - General Housewares Corp.
POTSTICKERS - Food products - Health is Wealth
POTTER & SMITH - Frames–picture - Caldor Corp.
POTTER VALLEY - Wines - California Wine Co.
POTTER VALLEY GROWERS PRODUCE - Fruits and vegetables - Richard Leamon
POTTERS ART - Dinnerware–glass - Franciscan by Johnson Brothers, USA, Inc.
POTTER'S ART - Dishes–china - Mikasa Co.
POTTER'S MILL - Cabinets ☆ - Medallion Kitchens of Minnesota Inc.
POTTER'S PEN - Chemical preparations - Minnesota/Midwest Clay Co.
POTTERS WHEEL - Dishes–earthenware - Denby USA Limited
POTTERY CRAFT - Housewares ☆ - Treasure Craft Co.
POTTERY NEST - Flower pots–plastic ☆ - Liberty Ridge
POTTERY SCHOONHOVEN - Pottery - Blue Delft Co. Inc.
POTTERY WHEEL WORKSHOP - Toys - Natural Science Industries, Ltd.
POTTERYCRAFT - Games - CBS Toys
POTTI-PIC - Robots–grinding - Jeb Products, Inc.
POTTI PRINCESS - Medical apparatus - Jeb Products, Inc.
POTTING SHED, THE - Publisher's imprints - Smith & Hawken, Ltd.
POTTY BEAR - Toys–stuffed ☆ - Russ Berrie and Co., Inc.
POTTY CHAIR - Toys - Hasbro, Inc.
POTTY CHARMS - Paper products - Potty Pals, Inc.
POTTY-CHEM - Cleaning preparations - Douglas Products and Packaging Co.
POTTY FRESH - Deodorizers - Surco Products Inc.
POTTY GAME, THE - Toilets–portable - Stopher Inc.
POTTY GUARD, THE - Toilet seats - Wayne S. Ouzounian
POTTY HUGGER - Stools–metal - Mininome Inc.
POTTY PALS - Paper products - Potty Pals, Inc.
POTTY POSTERS - Posters - Concept/Research, Concept/Development
POTTY SAFE - Hardware - Gary Cooper
POUCH - Uniforms–academic ☆ - Jockey International, Inc.
POUCH PAKS - Bakery products - Dawn Food Products Inc.
POUCH PERFECT - Beverages - Drink Mates
POUCH PETS - Toys–stuffed - Dakin Inc.
POUCHBAG - Golfing equipment - Bennington Golf Co.
POUCHEE - Office supplies ☆ - Datacom Inc.
POUCHERS - Bags–plastic - Xonex International, Inc.
POUCHETTE - Cases–eyeglass - California Optical Leather Inc.
POUCHMATE - Camping accessories - Campcraft Ltd.
POUDRE COMPACTE - Cosmetics - Sothys USA Inc.
POUDRE D'OR - Cosmetics - Lancome
POUDRE FINE - Cosmetics - Sothys USA Inc.

POUDRE LUMIERE - Cosmetics - Chanel Inc.
POUDRE VALLEY - Milk - Poudre Valley Creamery
POUF-ETTE - Machinery - Nuage Flowers, Inc.
POUF PLUS - Fibers–polyester - Morning Glory Products
POUFF - Furniture ✩ - Bean Station Furniture Factory Inc.
POUILLY-FUME LA MOYNERIE - Wines - Kobrand Corp.
POULAIN - Food products - Universal Foods Corp.
POULAN - Hardware - Poulan/Weed Eater
POULAN PRO - Saws–chain - White Consolidated Industries, Inc.
POULTRY IN-THE-PAN - Meat products–poultry - Colonna Brothers Inc.
POULTRY PRIZE - Food products - Chiquita Brands, Inc.
POULTRY SOLUTIONS - Seasonings - Early Times Distillery Co.
POULVAC - Poultry feeds - Solvay Animal Health, Inc.
POUNCE - Dog food - Heinz Pet Products Co.
POUNCE - Toys - Tonka Corp.
POUND - Apparel–men's - Royce Apparel, Inc.
POUND - Recording label - James Bigelow McIntyre Jr.
POUND-A-BALL - Toys ✩ - Creative Playthings Ltd.
POUND-A-PICTURE - Toys ✩ - Creative Playthings Ltd.
POUND-A-TRUCK - Toys–automobiles - Mattel, Inc.
POUND N PLAY - Games - Little Harbor Corp.
POUND O MATIC - Machinery - Bridge Machine Co., Inc.
POUND OF PADS - Notebooks and notepads ✩ - Recycled Paper Products, Inc.
POUND OF POMS - Hobby kits - Chenille Kraft Co.
POUND OF PONS - Yarn - Chenille Kraft Co.
POUND OF VEG' - Vegetables–frozen ✩ - California & Washington Co.
POUND PETS - Stationary - Marie Staddon Designs
POUND PUPPIES - Footwear - Chadwick Industries
POUND PUPPIES - Games ✩ - Ben Cooper Inc.
POUND PUPPIES - Hobby kits ✩ - Distinctive Design
POUND PUPPIES - Toys–stuffed - Tonka Corp.
POUND PUPPIES FURRIES - Toys–stuffed - Tonka Corp.
POUND PUPPIES NEWBORNS - Toys–stuffed - Tonka Corp.
POUND PUPPIES OUTFITS - Toys–stuffed - Tonka Corp.
POUND PUR-R-RIES - Toys–stuffed - Tonka Corp.
POUND PUR-R-RIES FURRIES - Toys–stuffed - Tonka Corp.
POUNDER - Audio equipment ✩ - Pyle Industries Inc.
POUNDLESS CAKES - Pharmaceutical preparations - First Fitness International, Inc.
POUNDLETTE - Bakery products - LTS Baking, Inc.
POUNDS OFF - Granola bars - Future Fit Co., LLC
POUR-A-PATCH - Hardware - Dowman Products
POUR-A-PIE - Fruit pie mixes - Snyder Corp.
POUR-A-QUICHE - Food products - Flowers Family Bakeries, Inc.
POUR-A-QUICHE - Food products - Snyder Corp.
POUR & SAVE - Food products - Patterson Frozen Foods, Inc.
POUR AND WHIP - Food products - Avoset Food Corp.
POUR FREE - Cookware - Carlisle Foodservice Products, Inc.
POUR HOMME - Perfumes - Yves St. Laurent Parfum Corp.
POUR LA FEMME - Apparel and accessories - Beldoch Industries Corp.
POUR MONSIEUR - Perfumes - Chanel Inc.
POUR 'N BAKE - Pie fillings ✩ - Specialty Bakers Inc.
POUR 'N CHILL - Toys - Mattel, Inc.
POUR 'N SEAL - Engines - Auto-Marine Tech Inc.
POUR-N-WALK - Coatings - Garon Products Inc.
POUR 'N WHIP - Food products - Kraft Food Ingredients Corp.
POUR-O-MATIC - Coffee makers–electric - Bunn-O-Matic Corp.
POUR-O-TEX - Craft supplies ✩ - Tulip Productions
POUR-POURRI - Deodorizers - Lumi-Lite Candle Co. Inc.
POUR-RITE - Cookware - Carlisle Foodservice Products, Inc.
POUR SHUN 'PAK' - Cream–canned or powdered - Ready Food Products, Inc.
POUR-SPOUT - Containers - Seal Spout Corp.
POUR-STONE - Cement - Custom Building Products
POUR THE BOAR - Vodka - United Distillers of North America
POUR YOURSELF A CANDLE - Candlemaking kit ✩ - Corning Inc.
POURABLE PLASTIC - Paints - Van Aken International
POUR'N MIST - Garden equipment - The Fountainhead Group, Inc.
POURSTER - Containers–trash - Modern Welding, Inc.
POURTHANE - Adhesives and sealants - W.R. Meadows Inc.
POV - Pet products - Hinton & Co. Inc.
POVAN - Pharmaceutical preparations ✩ - Parke-Davis
POVI-CLENS - Cleaning preparations - Purdue Frederick Co.
POVI-DOUCHE - Pharmaceutical preparations ✩ - Vortech Pharmaceuticals
POVIDERM - Pharmaceutical preparations ✩ - Vortech Pharmaceuticals

POVIDINE - Pharmaceutical preparations - Barre-National, Inc.
POW! - Cleaning preparations - Vibe Records Inc.
POW - Cleaning preparations - Viking Manufacturing Co. Inc.
POW - Drain pipe cleaners ✩ - Penn Champ Inc.
POW - Pet products ✩ - Natural Animal Health Products, Inc.
POW-R-BAK - Automotive parts and accessories ✩ - Marvel Oil Co. Inc.
POW-R CONTROL - Switches–power - Power Controls Corp.
POW-R DIM-R - Switches–power - Power Controls Corp.
POW-R-JET - Electronic equipment - The Fogmaster Corp.
POW-R-LIFT - Door openers–electronic - Wayne-Dalton Corp.
POW R PAIL - Electrical equipment - William D. Frank, Sr.
POW-R-PED - Footwear - California Pow-R-Ped Inc.
POW-R-PLUS - Gasoline - Quincy Oil Inc.
POW R PROFILE - Compressors–air - American IMC Inc.
POW-R-STIK - Communications equipment–mobile - Van Ordt Inc.
POW-R-TONE - Paints - Adelphi Coatings Co.
POW-R-TRAK - Window shades - Four Seasons Solar Products
POW-R-TRONS - Toys ✩ - ERTL Co., Inc.
POW-R-VAC - Vacuum cleaners and accessories - Brinkmann Corp.
POW-R-VENT - Cooling systems - Four Seasons Solar Products
POW-R-VITE - Vitamins and nutritional supplements - Vita-Fore Products Co.
POW-R-WRISTER - Sporting goods - Dyer Products Co.
POW' RIVETER - Tools ✩ - Klein Tools Inc.
POW WOW - Frames–eyeglass ✩ - Universal/Univis Inc.
POW WOW - Games ✩ - Parker Brothers
POW WOW - Snack foods - Wyandot, Inc.
POW WOW RECORDS INC. - Recording label - Pow Wow Records Inc.
POW WOWS - Shoes ✩ - Donato Marrone Ltd.
POWASERT - Tools–power-driven - Black & Decker Corp.
POWDAROMA - Perfumes - Intercontinental Fragrances, Inc.
POWDEN ROCKET - Sleds - Mad River Rocket Co. Inc.
POWDER BAR - Cosmetics - Max Factor & Co.
POWDER BOUQUET - Deodorizers - S.C. Johnson & Son, Inc.
POWDER BRUSH - Cosmetics - Viviane Woodard Industries, Ltd.
POWDER CHUTE - Skis - Golconda Industries
POWDER CONCENTRATE PINES - Spices and extracts ✩ - Pines International, Inc.
POWDER EYE PEARLS - Cosmetics - Maybelline Co.
POWDER FORMULA DISPENSER - Infant product - Prince Lionheart, Inc.
POWDER FREE PLUS - Gloves - Tillotson Healthcare Corp.
POWDER HORNE MILL COLLECTION - Housewares - Desoto, Inc.
POWDER KEG - Detergents - Calgon Vestal Laboratories
POWDER LYTE - Vitamins and nutritional supplements - Purina Mills, Inc.
POWDER 'N GLOSS - Face powder and lip gloss ✩ - Cosrich Inc.
POWDER-ON - Cosmetics - Revlon-Realistic Professional Products Inc.
POWDER PAL - Cosmetics - Gloria Levisohn
POWDER PENCIL - Cosmetics ✩ - Prince Matchabelli
POWDER PERFECTION - Cosmetics - Elizabeth Arden Inc.
POWDER PLUS - Deodorizers - Mem Co., Inc.
POWDER/PLUS - Paint removers - H.F. Staples & Co. Inc.
POWDER-POUR - Dispensers - American Belt Co.
POWDER POUT - Lipsticks - Pavion Ltd.
POWDER PRETTY PINK - Dolls - Mattel, Inc.
POWDER PRINTS - Greeting cards - Christine D. Martin
POWDER PRO - Sporting goods - Blount International, Inc. (Sporting Equipment Group)
POWDER PUFF - Bicycles ✩ - Murray, Inc.
POWDER PUFF - Christmas tree ornaments - Cracker Box Inc.
POWDER PUFF - Dolls - Uneeda Doll Co., Inc.
POWDER PUFF - Eyeglasses - Art-Craft Optical Co.
POWDER-PUFF - Girdles - Wacoal America Inc.
POWDER PUFF - Insecticides - Amrep Inc.
POWDER PUFF KIDS - Dolls - Uneeda Doll Co., Inc.
POWDER PUFF PEOPLE - Dolls - Uneeda Doll Co., Inc.
POWDER PUFF RACER - Bicycles - Columbia Manufacturing Inc.
POWDER PUP - Dolls - Susan Sona
POWDER ROOM - Deodorizers - Dial Corp.
POWDER ROOM - Paper–toilet - Georgia-Pacific Corp.
POWDER SOFT - Deodorants–personal - Mennen Co.
POWDER SPECIAL - Snowmobiles - Arctco, Inc.
POWDER STYPTIC - First aid kits - Flents Products Co. Inc.
POWDER UP - Sachets - Andre Richard
POWDER WINGS - Snowshoes - Wing Enterprises, Inc.
POWDER XPRESS - Food products machinery - Par-Way Group
POWDERBIBS - Apparel and accessories ✩ - Mother Karens
POWDERCREME - Cosmetics - Beauty for All Seasons Inc.

✩ = Now out of production

POWDERESSENCE - Makeup and mascara - Coty Inc.
POWDERFUL - Cosmetics - Charles of the Ritz Group Ltd.
POWDERHORN - Computer hardware - Storage Technology Corp.
POWDERHORN - Lenses–optical - Bausch & Lomb Inc.
POWDERJACKET - Apparel and accessories ☆ - Mother Karens
POWDERKEG - Toys - Tonka Corp.
POWDERLINE - Apparel and accessories - Outdoor Recreation Group
POWDERMATE - Chemical preparations - Troy Corp.
POWDERPANTS - Apparel and accessories ☆ - Mother Karens
POWDERPUFF - Furniture - Flexible Flyer Co.
POWDERSCENT - Sporting goods - Camp-Cap Products
POWDERSHIRT - Apparel and accessories ☆ - Mother Karens
POWDERSTROKE - Cosmetics - Max Factor & Co.
POWDERVEST - Apparel and accessories ☆ - Mother Karens
POWDERZ - Craft supplies - Z-Barten Productions
POWELL - Eyeglasses - Art-Craft Optical Co.
POWELL - Giftware - L. Powell Co.
POWELL & HYDE - Candy - Powell & Hyde Streets Chocolates, Inc.
POWELL COLLECTION, THE - Giftware - L. Powell Co.
POWELL PERALTA - Sporting goods ☆ - Powell Skateboards
POWELL PERALTA THREES - Sporting goods ☆ - Powell Skateboards
POWELL - SKATEBOARDS - Skateboards - Powell Skateboards
POWELL'S - Candy ☆ - Sathers Inc.
POWER - Adhesives and sealants - Bradley Paint Co.
POWER - Cleaning preparations - Alumin-Nu Corp.
POWER! - Computer software - Computing!
POWER - Computer software - CONDUIT
POWER - Computer software - Prospects of Wealth & Resources, Inc.
POWER + - Cord connectors–electric - Unitech Industries, Inc.
POWER - Detergents - Lever Brothers Co. Inc.
POWER - Detergents - Unilever United States Inc.
POWER - Fabrics - Greenwood Mills Inc.
POWER - Footwear - Bata Shoe Co. Inc.
POWER - Frames–eyeglass ☆ - Universal/Univis Inc.
POWER - Games - Specialties Inc.
POWER - Oils–lubricating ☆ - Kerr-McGee Chemical Corp.
POWER - Pet products - President Trading USA Inc.
POWER - Sporting goods - Outdoor Technologies Group
POWER - Sporting goods - Ridmark Corp.
POWER - Thread - Goldin Thread Co. Inc.
POWER 4 - Vacuum cleaners and accessories ☆ - Sunbeam-Oster Household Products
POWER 90 - Pet products - Nala Barry Laboratories
POWER ACCESS - Door openers–electronic - Power Access Corp.
POWER/ACCOUNTANT - Computer software - Software America, Inc.
POWER-ACTIN - Vitamins and nutritional supplements - Natural Organics, Inc.
POWER ACTIVATOR - Battery chargers - Power Products Inc.
POWER ADZE - Tools–woodworking ☆ - Unnatural Resources Inc.
POWER-AIRE - Air conditioning equipment - Heat Controller Inc.
POWER-AIRE - Electronic equipment ☆ - EWC Controls Inc.
POWER AMPLIFIER - Electronic equipment - Polyfusion Electronics Inc.
POWER ANALYST - Computer software - J.D. Power and Associates
POWER & PRECISION - Video production - Baptiste Power Yoga Institute, Inc.
POWER ARTISTS - Recording label - Ichiban Records, Inc.
POWER AT SEA - Computer software ☆ - Accolade Inc.
POWER AT YOUR FINGERTIPS - Computer software - Operation Technology, Inc.
POWER AUTHORITY - Electrical surge protectors - Belkin Components
POWER B-12 - Vitamins and nutritional supplements - Fanie International
POWER-BAC - Floor coverings–carpet and rugs - Trend Carpet
POWER-BACKER - Power switching equipment - Kensington
POWER BAIT - Fishing lures - Outdoor Technologies Group
POWER BAITER - Sporting goods ☆ - Wright & McGill Co.
POWER BALANCE - Window coverings - Zegers Inc.
POWER BALL - Balls - Oddzon Products, Inc.
POWER BALL - Electrical equipment - Sunbeam-Oster Household Products
POWER BALL - Fireworks - Melrose Pyrotechnics, Inc.
POWER BALL - Massage products - Sunbeam Corp.
POWER BALL, THE - Golf balls - Hi-Tech Golf, Inc.
POWER BAND - Girdles - Vanity Corset Co. Inc.
POWER BANK, THE - Jump starter - Exide Corp.
POWER BAR - Sporting goods - Nordictrack, Inc.
POWER BARONS - Games ☆ - Milton Bradley Co.
POWER-BASE - Amplifiers - Crown International, Inc.
POWER BASE - Nail care products - Cosmair Inc.
POWER BASE, THE - Electrical equipment - Haworth, Inc.

POWER BATH - Bath salts - Bare Escentuals
POWER-BATH - Pet products - Hydrosurge, Inc.
POWER BEAM - Bicycle parts and accessories - Wilderness Trail Bikes Inc.
POWER BEAM - Flashlights - Bridgeport Metal Goods Manufacturing Co.
POWER BEAM SHINE & HOLD - Hair care products - Fantasia Industries Corp.
POWER BELLOW - Batteries - Condar Co.
POWER BELT - Golfing equipment - Ajay Leisure Products Inc.
POWER-BILT - Golfing equipment - Hillerich & Bradsby Co.
POWER BINGO - Toys–electronic - Power Bingo, Ltd.
POWER BINGO KING - Furs–artificial - Stuart Entertainment, Inc.
POWER BIRD - Health care products - Theradyne Healthcare Product Div.
POWER BLASTER - Toys–guns - Diversified Specialists, Inc.
POWER BLASTERS - Toys–automobiles - Matchbox Toys USA
POWER BLENDER - Blenders ☆ - Sunbeam-Oster Household Products
POWER BLOCK - Housewares - Positive Response Marketing, Inc.
POWER BLOCKS - Educational materials - Center for Innovation in Education, Inc.
POWER BLOOM - Fertilizers - Garden Party Products, LLC
POWER BLUE LEMON - Beverages - SonRay Industries Inc.
POWER-BOARD - Exercising equipment - Zoma Design, Inc.
POWER BODY STIK - Exercising equipment - Power Pulleze, Inc.
POWER BODY SYSTEM - Exercising equipment - Power Pulleze, Inc.
POWER BOOKS - Publisher's imprints - Fleming H. Revell Co.
POWER BOOSTER - Lamp bulbs - Matsushita Consumer Electronics Co.
POWER BOOSTER - Tools–pruning - Village Blacksmith
POWER BOOSTER DELICIOUS - Cereal - Shaklee Corp.
POWER BOTTLE USA - Containers - Power Bottle USA
POWER BOX - Fans–electric - Holmes Products, Corp.
POWER BOX RAKE - Machine parts - Glenmac Inc.
POWER BREAK - Circuit breakers - General Electric Co.
POWER BREAK - Food bars - J & J Snack Foods Corp.
POWER BREEZE - Dryers–hair ☆ - Sunbeam-Oster Household Products
POWER BRIGHT - Lighting equipment - Bright Star Industries Inc.
POWER-BRITE - Cleaning preparations - Grace Construction Products
POWER BRUSH - Brushes - Easy Day Manufacturing Co.
POWER BRUSH - Cleaning preparations–carpet and rug - Castex Industries Inc.
POWER BUDDY - Golfing equipment - Southwest Aes, Inc.
POWER BUILT - Alternators–automotive - Automotive Supply Co. of Southern California
POWER BUILT - Garden equipment - Emsco Inc.
POWER-BUILT - Pharmaceutical preparations - Bricker Laboratories
POWER BULL - Hardware - CYW, Inc.
POWER BUTT - Fishing rod butts - Star Rods, Inc.
POWER CANNON - Toys - Saban Entertainment, Inc.
POWER CAP - Sporting goods - Unique Sports Products Inc.
POWER CARB - Vitamins and nutritional supplements ☆ - E'ola Products, Inc. (Biogenics)
POWER CARDS - Textbooks - Communication Skill Builders, Inc.
POWER CAT - Fans–attic - Fasco Industries Inc. (Consumer Products Div.)
POWER CATCH - Fishing nets - Frabill Inc.
POWER CATS - Computer software - Vertel Corp.
POWER-CELL - Clamps–metal - Sign-Up Corp.
POWER CELL - Shoes - Kinney Shoe Corp.
POWER CENTER - Steering mechanisms–motor vehicle - River City Investments, Inc.
POWER CHAMP - Veterinary nutritional supplements - Hubbard Milling Co.
POWER CHARGER - Toys - Mattel, Inc.
POWER CHARGER - Toys–electronic ☆ - Playskool, Inc.
POWER CHARGER - Toys–trains - Life-Like Products Inc.
POWER CHEATER - Photographic equipment - Avant Inc.
POWER CHEM - Cleaning preparations - Richard E. Trickett, Sr. & Marie C. Trickett Partnership
POWER CHIP - Electrical power resistors - Ohmite Manufacturing Co.
POWER CHUB - Fishing lures - Outdoor Technologies Group
POWER CIRCLE - Golfing equipment - Square Two Golf
POWER CIRCUIT - Exercising equipment - Universal Gym Equipment, Inc.
POWER CLAMP - Clamps - H.B. Sherman Manufacturing Co.
POWER CLASS - Computer peripheral equipment - Motorola, Inc. (Land Mobile Products Sector)
POWER CLEAN - Cleaning equipment - Leland Limited Inc.
POWER CLEAN - Cleaning preparations - Pioneer Manufacturing Co.
POWER CLEAN - Dishwashers–household - Whirlpool Properties, Inc.
POWER CLIP - Fishing tackle - Ultimate Fishing Products
POWER CLOSE - Gloves - Mizuno Enterprises USA Inc.

☆ = Now out of production

POWER CLUB - Games - International Gamco, Inc.

POWER COBIE - Audio equipment - Five Star Car Audio Svs. Inc.

POWER-COFFEE - Vitamins and nutritional supplements - Natural Organics, Inc.

POWER COLUMN - Retrieval systems - White Storage and Retrieval Systems Inc.

POWER COMMAND - Toys - Azrak-Hamway International, Inc.

POWER COMMAND - Toys–electronic - MRC

POWER COMMAND - Transmitting apparatus - Cable Electric Products

POWER COMMANDER - Electrical equipment - Perma Power Electronics Inc.

POWER COMMANDER - Motors - Power Efficiency Corp.

POWER COMMANDER - Regulators–voltage - Controlled Power Corp.

POWER CONNECTOR COMPANY, THE - Connectors–electrical - High Voltage Engineering Corp.

POWER CONSOLE - Computer peripheral equipment - American Megatrends, Inc.

POWER CONTROLS - Switches–electric - Pass & Seymour, Inc.

POWER CONVECTION - Air conditioning equipment - Surface Combustion, Inc.

POWER COOLER - Automotive parts and accessories - Vortech Engineering, Inc.

POWER COPTERS - Toys - Mattel, Inc.

POWER CORD - Drafting supplies - Pierce Business Products Inc.

POWER CORD - Ophthalmic goods - Capo, Inc.

POWER CORDUROY - Apparel–children's - Montgomery Ward & Co. Inc.

POWER CORE - Golfing equipment - Golfsmith International Inc.

POWER CORE II - Drill bits - SDI Operating Partners

POWER-CORR - Paper - Servants Inc.

POWER COURT - Sporting goods - Lifetime Products, Inc.

POWER CRANK - Bait - Outdoor Technologies Group

POWER CRANK - Batteries - Beebe Batteries Inc.

POWER CREATINE - Vitamins and nutritional supplements - Champion Nutrition

POWER CRIMPER - Wire products - Vector Enterprises

POWER-CRUNCH - Exercising equipment - Kenneth W. Stearns

POWER CRYSTAL - Quartz crystals - Psychic Discovery Network, Inc.

POWER CUSHION - Automotive parts and accessories ☆ - Gabriel Ride Control Products Div.

POWER CUSHION - Footwear - Lehigh Safety Shoe Co.

POWER-CUSHIONED - Socks - Crescent Hosiery Mills

POWER CUSTOM - Tires - Bridgestone/Firestone, Inc.

POWER-CUT - Cutlery - Bergman Tool Manufacturing Co. Inc.

POWER CYCLES - Toy cycles - Intex Recreation Corp.

POWER D-ICER - Chemical preparations - Monson Companies, Inc.

POWER DEET 25 - Insect repellents - Tec Laboratories, Inc.

POWER DEMOS - Video production - Corporate Visions Inc.

POWER DENIMS - Apparel and accessories - Montgomery Ward & Co. Inc.

POWER DIGGER - Garden tools - Fiskars Inc.

POWER DISC - Lamp bulbs–incandescent - Garon Products Inc.

POWER DIVIDER 100 - Batteries ☆ - Preco Inc.

POWER DRAIN - Pumps - Hilo Industries

POWER DRI - Dryers–hair ☆ - Helen of Troy Corp.

POWER DRIVE - Batteries - Club Car, Inc.

POWER DRIVE - Fasteners–hook and eye - VSI Fasteners, Inc.

POWER DRIVE - Hammers - Nupla Corp.

POWER DRIVE - Tires - Bridgestone/Firestone, Inc.

POWER DRIVE - Vacuum cleaners and accessories - The Hoover Co.

POWER DRIVE PLUS - Batteries - Club Car, Inc.

POWER DRIVERS - Toys–automobiles - Buddy L Inc.

POWER DRY - Fabrics - Malden Mills Industries, Inc.

POWER EAGLE - Rug cleaning machines–commercial - Castex Industries Inc.

POWER EAGLE - Sporting goods ☆ - Wright & McGill Co.

POWER EDGE - Vitamins and nutritional supplements - Nutri Science Inc.

POWER EDI - Computer software ☆ - Edi Able, Inc.

POWER EFFECTS - Exhaust systems–motor vehicle - Lawrence-Keech Inc.

POWER EGGS - Fishing lures - Outdoor Technologies Group

POWER-END - Bats–baseball - Hillerich & Bradsby Co.

POWER EXPRESS - Catalogs - Battery Express, Inc.

POWER EXPRESS - Tires - Uniroyal Goodrich Tire Co.

POWER EXTERIOR - Cleaning preparations - Alumin-Nu Corp.

POWER-EXTRACT - Vitamins and nutritional supplements ☆ - Nature's Herbs

POWER FACTORY - Video games - Sony Electronic Publishing Co.

POWER FALCON - Tires - Bridgestone/Firestone, Inc.

POWER FI - Audio equipment - Kaman Music Corp.

POWER FILL - Pillows - Pacific Coast Feather Co.

POWER FILTER - Electrical surge protectors ☆ - iEPS Electronic Inc.

POWER FIN - Appliance parts - Maytag Corp.

POWER FINGERS - Exercising equipment - Battle Creek Equipment Co.

POWER FIRM - Boxes - Simmons USA

POWER FISTER - Tools–hand-operated - Alltrade Inc.

POWER FITNESS CHUTE - Parachutes - Kytec Innovative Sports Equipment

POWER FLANGE - Sporting goods ☆ - Dunlop Maxfli Sports Corp.

POWER FLEX - Archery equipment ☆ - Martin Archery Inc.

POWER-FLEX - Cables–signal - GC Thorsen, Inc.

POWER FLEX - Cases–musical instrument ☆ - Kaman Music Corp.

POWER FLEX - Exercise device - STEP Co.

POWER-FLEX - Frames–eyeglass - Liberty Optical Manufacturing Co.

POWER-FLEX - Hoses - Tru-Flex Metal Hose Corp.

POWER FLEX - Medical apparatus - Homedics, Inc.

POWER FLEX - Paints - Ponderosa Paint Manufacturing Co. Inc.

POWER FLEX - Rope - Amsted Industries Inc.

POWER FLEX - Ships–patrol boats - T.G. Sports Co.

POWER FLEX 19 - Cables - MacWhyte Co.

POWER-FLEXOR - Sporting goods - Rebound Systems Inc.

POWER FLIPPERS - Toy vehicles - Intex Recreation Corp.

POWER FLITE - Sporting goods - Marshall-Clark Manufacturing Corp.

POWER-FLO - Cleaning preparations - Diversified Dynamics Corp.

POWER-FLO - Pumps - Hayward Pool Products Inc.

POWER-FLO PAINT STICK - Paint rollers - Diversified Dynamics Corp.

POWER FLOSS BRUSH - Toothbrushes–electric - Matsushita Consumer Electronics Co.

POWER FLUSH - Cleaning preparations ☆ - Gold Eagle Co.

POWER FLUSH - Drain pipe cleaners - Nadex Industries Inc.

POWER FLUSH 100-102 - Pumps - Hilo Industries

POWER FOAM - Cleaning preparations - American Direct Marketing, Inc.

POWER FREEZ - Cosmetics - Jheri Redding Products Inc.

POWER FRESH FREE - Detergents - Church and Dwight Co. Inc.

POWER FRUIT - Snack foods - Farley Candy Co.

POWER FUNNEL CLR - Sporting goods - Powertron

POWER-GARD - Audio equipment ☆ - Renkus-Heinz Inc.

POWER GARDENER - Tools–garden - Natural Earth Technologies, Inc.

POWER GAUGE - Integrated circuits - Benchmarq Microelectronics, Inc.

POWER GEAR - Tools–power-driven - Versa Technologies, Inc.

POWER GEAR - Toys - S.R. Mickelberg Co., Inc.

POWER GEARS - Toys - Natural Science Industries, Ltd.

POWER GEL - Cleaning preparations - Red Devil Inc.

POWER GEL - Cleaning preparations - Wilbur Products, Inc.

POWER GEL - Hair care products - Hair Care Products, Inc.

POWER GEL - Vitamins and nutritional supplements - Powerfood Inc.

POWER GELS - Footwear - Pittsburgh Plastics Manufacturing, Inc.

POWER GIANT - Motor vehicles–automobiles ☆ - DaimlerChrysler

POWER GLADIATORS - Games - Hasbro, Inc.

POWER GLIDE - Toys–models - Borin Manufacturing Co.

POWER GLOVE - Toys–electronic - Mattel, Inc.

POWER GLOW - Cosmetics - Yves St. Laurent Parfum Corp.

POWER GLOW - Heating equipment - Alltrade Inc.

POWER GLX - Batteries - Exide Corp.

POWER GOLD - Cleaning preparations - Gojo Industries, Inc.

POWER GRAN - Chlorine - Brothers Three Inc.

POWER GRAVEL - Pet products - Rolf C. Hagen (USA) Corp.

POWER GREASE & TAR CUTTER - Cleaning preparations - Harvey Universal Inc.

POWER GRID - Computer software - Queue Inc.

POWER GRIP - Bowling balls - Master Industries Inc.

POWER GRIP - Clamps–metal - Counterpoint

POWER-GRIP - Exercising equipment - All Pro Exercise Products, Inc.

POWER GRIP - Gloves–work - Red Steer Glove Co.

POWER GRIP - Polishing rouge - Williams-Hayward Protective Coatings Inc.

POWER GRIP - Skin care products - DBA Products Co.

POWER GRIP - Sporting goods - Robert M.T. Kramer

POWER GRIP - Sporting goods - Minstar Inc.

POWER GRIP - Tape–adhesive - Conso Products Co.

POWER GRIP - Tires - Montgomery Ward & Co. Inc.

POWER GRO - Hair care products - Gold Medal Hair Products Inc.

POWER GROOM - Razors–electric - Andis Co.

POWER GROOVE - Hockey equipment - Christian Brothers, Inc.

POWER GROOVE - Lamps - General Electric Co.

POWER GRUBS - Fishing lures - Outdoor Technologies Group

POWER GUARD - Oil machinery - Detroit Diesel Corp.

POWER HAILER - Marine rigging ☆ - Ray Jefferson

POWER HANDWHEEL - Measuring instruments - H.L. Ledeen Associates

POWER HANGNAIL - Hair care products - Tweezerman Corp.

☆ = Now out of production

POWER HAULER - Toys–trains - Life-Like Products Inc.
POWER HAWK - Tools–power-driven - Curtis Wright Flight Systems, Inc.
POWER HD - Computer software - Megahaus, Inc.
POWER HEAD - Golfing equipment - Anthony J. Antonious
POWER HEAT - Oils–illuminating - Candle Lamp Co.
POWER-HERBS - Health care products - Nature's Herbs
POWER HITTER! - Video laser disc game - Philips Interactive Media of America
POWER HOLD - Hair care products - Chenice Beverly Hills
POWER HOUR & DESIGN - Dolls - Mattel, Inc.
POWER HOUSE - Candy bars - Peter Paul
POWER HOUSE - Cleaning preparations ☆ - Servaas Laboratories Inc.
POWER-HOUSE - Housewares ☆ - Crow Rope Industries LLC
POWER HOUSE - Ice chests–plastic - Life-Like Products Inc.
POWER HOUSE - Magnets - Alexander Manufacturing Co.
POWER HOUSE - Ophthalmic goods - Embassy Creations Inc.
POWER HOUSE - Pet products - Rapid Electric/R & R Manufacturing
POWER II - Vacuum cleaners and accessories - Montgomery Ward & Co. Inc.
POWER IN MOTION - Railroad equipment - Trackmobile Inc.
POWER INCLINE - Exercising equipment - Icon Health & Fitness, Inc.
POWER INDEX - Computer software - Thomas Publishing Co.
POWER INTEGRATIONS - Semiconductors - Power Integrations Inc.
POWER INVESTOR - Computer software - Investors Alliance, Inc.
POWER JAM - Balls–basketball - Mikasa Sports
POWER JAPANESE - Computer software - Bayware Inc.
POWER JERKY - Meat products–dried - Robert Fritz
POWER JET - Games - American Toy & Furniture Co.
POWER JET - Sprinklers–lawn - H.B. Sherman Manufacturing Co.
POWER JUICE - Vitamins and nutritional supplements - Re-Vita Manufacturing Co., Inc.
POWER JUICE COMPANY, THE - Apparel and accessories - Tara Evans,
POWER KICK - Computer software - Cramer Products Inc.
POWER KICK - Golfing equipment - Northwestern Golf Co.
POWER KIDS - Bakery products - Quality Bakers of America Cooperative Inc.
POWER KING - Flour–blended ☆ - Stevens Industries Inc.
POWER KING - Tractors - Engineering Products Co.
POWER KINGS - Toys–automobiles - Matchbox Toys USA
POWER KITS - Recording label - Comprehensive Health Education Foundation
POWER KLEEN - Paints - Valspar Corp.
POWER-KNIT - Underwear and nightwear - Jockey International, Inc.
POWER LAZER DRILL - Toys - Saban Entertainment, Inc.
POWER LEADER - Electrical equipment - General Electric Co.
POWER LEASH - Pet products - Signal Consulting Inc.
POWER LEVELING - Tools–power-driven - Wenger Corp.
POWER-LEVER - Tools–garden - Wallace Manufacturing Corp.
POWER LIFT - Golfing equipment - Dunlop Maxfli Sports Corp.
POWER-LIFT - Skin care products - Sterling Winthrop Inc.
POWER LIFT - Vitamins and nutritional supplements - Exerhealth, Inc.
POWER LIFTER - Medical apparatus - Omnimed Inc.
POWER LIGHTS - Footwear - BBC International Ltd.
POWER LINE - Animal feeds - Hubbard Milling Co.
POWER-LINE - Exercising equipment - Body-Solid, Inc.
POWER LINE - Guns - Daisy Manufacturing Co.
POWER LINE - Musical instrument accessories - Gibson Strings & Accessories
POWER LINE, THE - Exercising equipment - California Gym Equipment
POWER LINES - Musical instrument accessories - Music People Inc.
POWER LINK - Golfing equipment - Golfsmith International Inc.
POWER-LINK - Tools–garden - Wallace Manufacturing Corp.
POWER-LINK I - Machinery - Scandura, Inc.
POWER-LINK II - Machinery - Scandura, Inc.
POWER LITE - Batteries - Exide Corp.
POWER LITE - Flashlights - Garrity Industries
POWER LITE - Lamp bulbs–fluorescent - Duro-Test Corp.
POWER-LITE - Paints - Sherwood Medical Co.
POWER LITE - Toilets–enameled - Kohler Co.
POWER-LITT - Lasers - Ceramoptec, Inc.
POWER LIZARD - Fishing lures - Outdoor Technologies Group
POWER LOC - Floor coverings - Capitol Adhesives Inc.
POWER-LOC - Toys–trains - Life-Like Products Inc.
POWER-LOCK - Abrasive products - Merit Abrasive Products, Inc.
POWER LOCK - Audio equipment ☆ - Electro-Voice, Inc.
POWER-LOCK - Musical instrument accessories ☆ - Herco Products
POWER LOCK - Sporting goods - Wilson Sporting Goods Co.
POWER LOCK - Tape–adhesive - Conso Products Co.
POWER-LOCK - Tricycles ☆ - Peg Perego USA Inc.
POWER LOCKOUT - Electronic equipment - Honeywell Inc.

POWER LOG - Lumber - Anthony Forest Products Co.
POWER-LOKT - Ammunition - Remington Arms Co., Inc.
POWER LOOK - Eyeglasses - Art-Craft Optical Co.
POWER LOOP - Motors–outboard - Eska Co.
POWER LORDS - Toys ☆ - Revell-Monogram, Inc.
POWER LORDS BEAST MACHINE - Toys ☆ - Revell-Monogram, Inc.
POWER LUBE - Cleaning preparations - Midwest Engineered Products Corp.
POWER-LUGS - Garden equipment - Union Fork and Hoe Co.
POWER LUNCH - Games - Mayfair Games, Inc.
POWER MAC - Saws–chain - McCulloch Corp.
POWER MACINTOSH - Computers - Apple Computer Inc.
POWER MAG - Archery equipment - Archer Sports Inc.
POWER MAG - Audio equipment - Electronic Industries Inc.
POWER MAG - Tools–hand-operated - Sportlite, Inc.
POWER MAKER - Vitamins and nutritional supplements - Vitamin Research Products Inc.
POWER MARCHERS - Toys - Tonka Corp.
POWER MARK - Audio equipment - Electronic Industries Inc.
POWER MASSAGE - Giftware - Pollenex Corp.
POWER MASTER - Amplifiers - Cleveland Motion Controls, Inc.
POWER MASTER - Amplifiers ☆ - Shure Brothers, Inc.
POWER MASTER - Benches–metal ☆ - Sunbeam Outdoor Products Inc.
POWER MASTER - Cleaning preparations–household - A1A Authorized Vacuum & Sewing Center Inc.
POWER MASTER - Electrical equipment - SL Waber Inc.
POWER MASTER - Gasoline - Maxus Energy Corp.
POWER MASTER - Stereos - Sunbow Industries, Inc.
POWER MASTER - Toys - Benjamin Sheridan Corp.
POWER MATCH - Rackets–badminton - Rackets International (Racket Sports Div.)
POWER MATE - Degreasing solvents - Conklin Co., Inc.
POWER MATE - Hammers - Desa International, Inc.
POWER-MATIC - Guns ☆ - Remington Arms Co., Inc.
POWER MATRIX - Fishing tackle - Orvis Co., Inc.
POWER-MAX - Deodorizers - Surco Products Inc.
POWER MAX - Electronic equipment - Molectron Detector Inc.
POWER MAX - Fencing–gates and posts - Common Sense Fence
POWER MAX - Gasoline - Kerr-McGee Chemical Corp.
POWER MAX - Radios–citizens' band - Midland International Corp.
POWER MEDIC - Skin care products - Electro-Medical Corp.
POWER MENU - Computer software - Brown Bag Software Inc.
POWER MERGE - Computer software - Greatland Corp.
POWER METER - Diagnostic computer program - Diagsoft, Inc.
POWER MINDER - Heat pumps ☆ - Lennox Industries Inc.
POWER MISSION - Video games - Nintendo of America Inc.
POWER MIST - Fabrics ☆ - Vanity Fair Mills Inc.
POWER-MITE - Cultivators–agricultural - Murray, Inc.
POWER-MITE - Electrical equipment - Hot-Shot Products Co.
POWER-MITE - Microphones - Hamilton Electronics Corp.
POWER MIX - Kitchen appliances - Robert Krups North America
POWER MIX - Recording label - Power Productions International, Inc.
POWER MIX PLUS - Kitchen appliances - Robert Krups North America
POWER MIZER - Electrical equipment - Miracle Products
POWER MODELER - Toys–models - Revell-Monogram, Inc.
POWER-MODULE - Generators–electric - Kohler Co.
POWER MOUSE - Computer software ☆ - Don Johnston Inc.
POWER MOUTH - Audio equipment - PRO Manufacturing
POWER MOVERS - Toys - Tonka Corp.
POWER MOVES - Games - Sports Concept LLC
POWER MULCH - Lawn mowers - Lawn-Boy
POWER MUNCH - Bakery products - Bon Appetit Specialty, Inc.
POWER N - Computer software - Dunamis Inc.
POWER NAIL - Hair care products - Tweezerman Corp.
POWER NICK-SANDER - Sanders and grinders - Nicsand, Inc.
POWER NUGGETS - Vitamins and nutritional supplements - Better Way Foods
POWER-NUT - Saws–power - Power Tool Holders Inc.
POWER OF A GIRL, THE - Apparel and accessories - Coed Sportswear, Inc.
POWER OF CHOICE, THE - Contact lenses - Sunsoft Corp.
POWER OF CONTINUOUS NUTRIENT DELIVERY, THE - Veterinary nutritional supplements - Hubbard Milling Co.
POWER OF ONE, THE - Apparel and accessories - Garan Services Corp.
POWER OF SCIENCE - Educational materials - Learning Resources, Inc.
POWER OF THE SPOKEN WORD, THE - Electrical equipment - Bolt Beranek and Newman, Inc.
POWER OF THREE, THE - Pharmaceutical preparations - Medicis Pharmaceutical Corp.

☆ = Now out of production

POWER OF TWO - Puzzles - Kadon Enterprises Inc.
POWER OF WANT, THE - Apparel and accessories - Michael John Kent
POWER OF WIRELESS, THE - Electronic equipment ☆ - C & K Systems, Inc.
POWER OFF - Cleaning preparations - Amway Corp.
POWER ON DEMAND - Computer peripheral equipment - Picopower Technology, Inc.
POWER ONE - Detergents - Topco Associates, Inc.
POWER ONE - Egg substitutes - Power One Inc.
POWER PAC - Food products ☆ - Love Natural Foods
POWER PAC - Hair care products - Clairol Inc.
POWER PAC - Vacuum cleaners and accessories - Royal Appliance Manufacturing Co.
POWER PACK - Archery equipment - Martin Archery Inc.
POWER PACK - Automotive parts and accessories - Packard Electric Div.
POWER PACK - Bats–baseball - Figgie International Inc.
POWER-PACK - Dialing devices–telephone - Baltimore Luggage Co.
POWER PACK - Food products - Omega-Life Inc.
POWER PACK - Lamps - Bentley Gifts Inc.
POWER PACK PC - Games - Tiger Electronics, Inc.
POWER PACK, THE - Vitamins and nutritional supplements - United Food & Fitness Inc.
POWER-PACKED - Food products - Design Foods
POWER PAD - Apparel and accessories - Portable Products, Inc.
POWER PAD - Bathing suits - Beach Patrol, Inc.
POWER PAD - Cleaning preparations - DBA Products Co.
POWER PAINT CARTRIDGE - Paints - Fox Valley Systems Inc.
POWER PAINTERS - Paint sprayers - Wagner Spray Tech Corp.
POWER-PAK - Exercising equipment - Universal Gym Equipment, Inc.
POWER-PAK - Machine parts - Esco Corp.
POWER PAK - Machinery ☆ - Odyssey Systems
POWER PAK - Plant food - Kemmer Agricultural Manufacturing Co. Inc.
POWER PAK - Recording label - Gusto Records Inc.
POWER PAK - Tape–adhesive - Central Products Co.
POWER PAK - Tools–garden - Structron Corp.
POWER PAKT - Ammunition - E.I. Dupont de Nemours and Co.
POWER PAL - Compressors–air - Campbell Group (Wayne Home Equipment Div.)
POWER PANEL - Siding–metal - Granite City Steel Co.
POWER PAR - Floodlights - Duro-Test Corp.
POWER PARK - Motorcycle parts and accessories - Power Park, Inc.
POWER PARTNER - Vacuum cleaners and accessories - Bissell Inc.
POWER PASTA - Food products ☆ - Champion Nutrition
POWER PATCH BAG - Packaging material - Viskase Corp.
POWER PATROL - Batteries - John Willemsen Corp.
POWER PATTERN - Guns - Remington Arms Co., Inc.
POWER PAWS - Pet products - Nirmala Enterprises, Inc.
POWER PAY - Computer software - Pro Business Centers, Inc.
POWER PEELER - Chemical preparations - Blue Lustre, LLC
POWER PEG - Hooks - Hempe Manufacturing Co.
POWER PENZ - Sound equipment - Yes! Entertainment Corp.
POWER-PERFECT BODY - Sporting goods - Nordictrack, Inc.
POWER PICKS, THE - Trading cards and stamps - Bonus Games Inc.
POWER PIERCE - Can openers–electric - Sunbeam Corp.
POWER PIERCE - Can openers–electric - Sunbeam-Oster Household Products
POWER PILL, THE - Vitamins and nutritional supplements - Gold Power Supplements Inc.
POWER PILOT - Marine rigging - Outboard Marine Corp.
POWER PISTON - Ammunition - E.I. Dupont de Nemours and Co.
POWER PISTON - Exercising equipment - MBI Inc.
POWER PLAIDS - Jackets–children's ☆ - Montgomery Ward & Co. Inc.
POWER PLANES - Marine rigging - Hynautic Inc.
POWER PLANK - Lumber - Anthony Forest Products Co.
POWER PLANNER - Calendars - Health & Safety Publications
POWER PLANNER - Electrical equipment - Coast Energy Management, Inc.
POWER PLANT - Batteries ☆ - Bright Star Industries Inc.
POWER PLATE - Refrigerators - Kenyon Marine, Inc. (Adler/Barbour Div.)
POWER PLAY - Collectible trading cards - ANCO Collector Supplies, Inc.
POWER PLAY - Computer software - Cramer Products Inc.
POWER PLAY - Footwear - Brown Wooten Mills Inc.
POWER PLAY - Games - Neil Kinder
POWER PLAY - Hockey equipment - Mantua/Cosom Sporting Goods
POWER PLAY - Ophthalmic goods - Foremost Optical Products
POWER PLAY - Prophylactics - Ansell Inc. (Personal Products Div.)
POWER PLAY - Recording label - Gusto Records Inc.
POWER PLAY - Sporting goods - Lisco, Inc.

POWER PLEX - Toys - Centuri Corp.
POWER PLEX - Toys - Estes Industries
POWER PLEX - Vitamins and nutritional supplements - Natural Organics, Inc.
POWER PLIER - Pliers - Sog Specialty Knives, Inc.
POWER PLOWER - Toys–automobiles - Mattel, Inc.
POWER PLUG - Games - Nationsbank of North Carolina, N.A.
POWER PLUGS - Automotive parts and accessories - G.H. Meiser & Co.
POWER PLUNGER - Tools–hand-operated - John David Rau
POWER PLUS - See **X2N**
POWER PLUS - Animal feeds - Bluebonnet Milling Co.
POWER PLUS - Apparel stores–sports - Jefferies Socks
POWER PLUS - Candy - Brock Candy Co. Inc.
POWER PLUS - Detergents - Margo International II, Inc.
POWER PLUS - Drain pipe cleaners - AmeriPlus Inc.
POWER PLUS - Electronic equipment ☆ - GC Thorsen, Inc.
POWER PLUS - Exercising equipment - Avante Fitness Systems, Inc.
POWER PLUS - Food processors - Sunbeam-Oster Household Products
POWER PLUS - Gasoline - Getty Petroleum Marketing, Inc.
POWER PLUS - Health care products - Power Plus Systems Inc.
POWER PLUS - Lighting equipment–automotive - General Electric Co.
POWER PLUS+ - Motor vehicle parts and accessories - Mike Mantel
POWER PLUS - Motors–outboard - Zebco Corp.
POWER PLUS - Pet products - Rolf C. Hagen (USA) Corp.
POWER PLUS - Vacuum cleaners and accessories - Montgomery Ward & Co. Inc.
POWER POCKET - Pet products - Aquarium Pharmaceuticals, Inc.
POWER POINT - Audio equipment - Electro-Voice, Inc.
POWER-POINT - Bullets - Olin Corp. (Winchester Div.)
POWER POINT - Caulking compounds - Dap Products Inc.
POWER POINT - Computer software - Microsoft Corp.
POWER POINT - Firearms, accessories, and parts - Horton Manufacturing Co. Inc.
POWER POINT - Golfing equipment - Allied Golf Co.
POWER POINT - Tools–boring ☆ - Century Drill & Tool Co.
POWER POINT PROPS - Toys–models - Top Flite Models
POWER POINTER - Marine rigging - Outboard Marine Corp.
POWER POINTS - Darts and dart games - Dart World Inc.
POWER POLE - Hardware - Truth Hardware Corp.
POWER POLE - Sporting goods - Outdoor Technologies Group
POWER POLLEN - Vitamins and nutritional supplements ☆ - Ethical Nutrients
POWER PORT - Electrical equipment - Hubbell Inc.
POWER PORTABLE - Audio equipment - Recoton Corp.
POWER PORTED - Marine rigging - Outboard Marine Corp.
POWER POUCHES - Detergents - Procter & Gamble Co.
POWER POWDER - Water treating compounds - Leslie's Poolmart
POWER POWDER 50+ - Engine oil additive - Rust Evader Corp.
POWER PREMIUM - Tires ☆ - Bridgestone/Firestone, Inc.
POWER PREP - Dishwashing compounds - Sysco Corp.
POWER PRESENTER - Remote control devices - General Parametrics Corp.
POWER PRESS - Tools - American Tool Companies Inc.
POWER PRIME - Paints - Ponderosa Paint Manufacturing Co. Inc.
POWER PRO - Automotive parts and accessories - Valley Forge Flag
POWER PRO - Electrical surge protectors - West Associates
POWER PRO - Fasteners–snap - National Holding Corp.
POWER-PRO - Housewares - Black & Decker Corp.
POWER PRO - Pet food - Land O'Lakes, Inc.
POWER PRO - Sporting goods - Prince Manufacturing Inc.
POWER-PRO - Tools–soldering - Wahl Clipper Corp.
POWER PRO STARTER KIT - Computer software - Dunamis Inc.
POWER PROBE - Batteries - Exide Corp.
POWER PROBES - Computer software - McCormick Systems Inc.
POWER PROCESSOR - Power transformers - Controlled Power Corp.
POWER PROJECTION - Calendars - Mach 1, Inc.
POWER PROPS - Toys–models ☆ - Top Flite Models
POWER PROTECTOR - Telephone apparatus - Cobra Electronics Corp.
POWER PUCK - Ice cream - Natural Nectar Corp.
POWER PUFF - Deodorizers ☆ - Atmosphere Products Co. Inc.
POWER-PULL - Cable puller - American Gage & Manufacturing Co.
POWER-PULL - Hitches–trailer - Valley Industries, Inc.
POWER PULSE - Thermostats ☆ - Nordyne Inc.
POWER PULSE - Tools–power-driven - Ingersoll-Rand Co.
POWER PULSE - Toys ☆ - Estes Industries
POWER PUMICE - Soap - Stahl Soap Corp.
POWER PUMP - Pumps–water ☆ - Odyssey Systems
POWER PUMP - Sprayers - United Industries Corp.
POWER PUMPER - Toys–automobiles ☆ - Hart Enterprises, Inc.

☆ = Now out of production

POWER PUNCH - Lubricating oils - Power Punch Distributors
POWER PUNCH II - Video games - Nintendo of America Inc.
POWER PUNCH MISSILES - Toys - Saban Entertainment, Inc.
POWER PUNCH PLUS - Beverages - Smoothie King Franchises, Inc.
POWER PUNCHERS - Toys - Tonka Corp.
POWER PUREE'N RICER - Food processors ☆ - Sunbeam-Oster Household Products
POWER PURGE - Cleaning preparations - Wynn Oil Co.
POWER PURIFIER - Power transformers - Controlled Power Corp.
POWER PUTTY - Exercising equipment - Sportshealth Products
POWER PYLON - Tools–hand-operated - Nupla Corp.
POWER PYRAMIDS - Game - Independent Ink Inc.
POWER RACER - Toys ☆ - Combi International Corp.
POWER RAKE - Machine parts - Glenmac Inc.
POWER RAM - Computer peripheral equipment - Technology Works Inc.
POWER RANGERS - Breads - Franz Bakery
POWER RANGERS - Socks - High Point Knitting Inc.
POWER RESPONSE - Audio equipment - Larry Doran Enterprises Inc.
POWER RESPONSE - Audio equipment - Professional Audio Systems
POWER RIB - Tires - Bridgestone/Firestone, Inc.
POWER RIBTUBE - Bait - Outdoor Technologies Group
POWER RIDE - Bicycles - Kent International Inc.
POWER RIDER - Exercising equipment - Guthy-Renker Corp.
POWER RIDGE - Golfing equipment - Besco USA
POWER RIG - Toy trucks - Intex Recreation Corp.
POWER RISE - Remote control devices - Hunter Douglas, Inc.
POWER RODS - Toys–electronic - Playskool, Inc.
POWER ROLLER PLUS - Paint rollers - Wagner Spray Tech Corp.
POWER-SAK - Trash bags - Power-Sak, Inc.
POWER SANDWORM - Bait - Outdoor Technologies Group
POWER SAVER - Heat pumps - Lennox Industries Inc.
POWER SCENT - Air freshener - Fresh Line Corp.
POWER-SCOPE - Toys ☆ - Steven Manufacturing Co.
POWER SCORE - Pet products ☆ - Aqua Stock/Petcetera Inc.
POWER SCOUR - Cleaning equipment - Petcetera Inc.
POWER SCOUR - Scouring pads - Magla Products Inc.
POWER SCRAPPER - Fishing lures - Outdoor Technologies Group
POWER SCRUBBER - Carpet cleaning machines - Regina Co.
POWER SEAL - Adhesives and sealants - Surebond, Inc.
POWER-SEAL - Clamps–hose - Breeze Industrial Products
POWER SEAL - Window coverings - Zegers Inc.
POWER SEARCH - Computer software ☆ - Horizons Technology, Inc.
POWER SELLER - Computer software - Associated Software Consultants, Inc.
POWER SENSOR - Battery tester - Midtronics Inc.
POWER SENSOR - Electronic equipment - General Electric Co.
POWER SENTRY - Electrical equipment - Power Sentry, Inc.
POWER SENTRY - Power switching equipment - Onan Corp.
POWER SENTRY - Television equipment - Zenith Electronics Corp.
POWER SEPTIC - Cleaning preparations - Alumin-Nu Corp.
POWER SERIES 400 - Computer peripheral equipment - International Business Machines Corp.
POWER SHAFT - Hockey equipment - Mantua/Cosom Sporting Goods
POWER SHAKE - Vitamins and nutritional supplements - Naturade Inc.
POWER SHAPE - Food products ☆ - Natural Balance, Inc.
POWER SHAVE - Shaving preparations - Gold Medal Hair Products Inc.
POWER SHIFT - Marine rigging - Outboard Marine Corp.
POWER SHINE - Automotive parts and accessories - Turtle Wax, Inc.
POWER SHINER - Bait - Outdoor Technologies Group
POWER SHOOTER - Toys–stuffed - Toy Biz, Inc.
POWER SHOP - Tools–power-driven - Black & Decker Corp.
POWER SHOT - Batteries - Bright Star Industries Inc.
POWER SHOT - Drums–musical instruments - Steve Clayton Inc.
POWER SHOT - Sporting goods - Porter Athletic Equipment Co.
POWER SHOT - Water heaters–household - A.O. Smith Corp.
POWER SHOWER - Dishwashers–household - General Electric Co.
POWER SHOWER, THE - Colognes - Cosmedic Concepts, Inc.
POWER SHRIMP - Fishing lures - Outdoor Technologies Group
POWER SKATERS - Toys–stuffed - Ace Novelty Co. Inc.
POWER SKIFF - Boats - Glen-L Marine Designs
POWER SLAMS - Musical instrument accessories - Shane Music Products
POWER SLAMS 5 - Guitars ☆ - Shane Music Products
POWER SLAMS ACOUSTIC BASS - Guitars ☆ - Shane Music Products
POWER SLED - Sleds - Kytec Innovative Sports Equipment
POWER-SLEEVE - Musical instrument accessories - Aquarian Accessories Corp.
POWER SLEUTH - Computer software - Sola

POWER SLICE - Pizzas–frozen - Schwan's Sales Enterprises, Inc.
POWER SLICE - Tools–garden - F.D. Kees Power Equipment LLC
POWER-SLIDE - Frames–eyeglass ☆ - Universal/Univis Inc.
POWER-SLIM - Health care products ☆ - Fox Pharmacal Inc.
POWER SLOT - Engines–marine - Master Craft Boat Co.
POWER SMASH - Rackets–squash - Dunlop Slazenger Corp.
POWER SMOOTHIE - Fruit drinks–bottled or canned - Power Smoothie Inc.
POWER SNACKS - Vitamins and nutritional supplements - Synergy Plus
POWER-SNEAKER - Motors–outboard ☆ - Outboard Marine Corp.
POWER SOAK - Power transformers ☆ - Scholz Research & Development, Inc.
POWER SOL II - Degreasing solvents - KC Products, Inc. (Sharon D. Spence)
POWER SOLUTION, THE - Switches–electric - Power Solutions Inc.
POWER-SONIC - Batteries - Power-Sonic Corp.
POWER SONIC - Pet products - Biological Engineering/High Tech Pet Products
POWER SOUP - Soups–mixes ☆ - Sahara Natural Foods, Inc.
POWER SOURCE - Batteries - Lynn Vick Products Inc.
POWER SOURCE - Computer software - Pro Business Centers, Inc.
POWER SOURCE - Hair care products - Helene Curtis Industries Inc.
POWER SOURCE - Nutritional supplement for horses - Paul Murdock
POWER SOURCE PACK - Health care products ☆ - Bios
POWER SPARK - Toys - Tonka Corp.
POWER SPHERE - Garden equipment - HSP
POWER SPIKE - Balls ☆ - Mikasa Sports
POWER-SPLIT - Tools - Seatek Co. Inc.
POWER-SPOT - Floodlights - General Electric Co.
POWER SPRAY - Sprinklers–lawn - H.B. Sherman Manufacturing Co.
POWER SQUEEZ - Exercising equipment - Fastrac Communication, Inc.
POWER SQUID - Fishing lures - Outdoor Technologies Group
POWER STANCE, THE - Sporting goods - Richard D. Cagney Jr.
POWER START - Batteries - Exide Corp.
POWER-START - Engines - Power Lawnmower Parts Inc.
POWER STATION - Battery chargers - Rayovac Corp.
POWER STATION - Computer software - Operation Technology, Inc.
POWER STATION - Exercising equipment ☆ - CSA, Inc.
POWER STEAMER - Wallpaper - Wagner Spray Tech Corp.
POWER STICK - Batteries - Gates Energy Products Inc.
POWER STICK - Batteries - General Electric Co.
POWER STICK - Deodorants–personal - Faberge Co.
POWER STITCH - Floor coverings–carpet and rugs - Masland Carpets, Inc.
POWER-STIX - Golfing equipment ☆ - J.C. Penney Co., Inc.
POWER STOP - Security products - Power Stop, Inc.
POWER STOPPER - Electrical equipment - Pacific Electricord Co.
POWER-STRIDE - Weightlifting equipment - All Pro Exercise Products, Inc.
POWER-STRIP - Wax removers - Hillyard Enterprises, Inc.
POWER STRIPPER - Paint removers - Wagner Spray Tech Corp.
POWER STRIPS - Medical apparatus - Acutek Adhesive Specialties, Inc.
POWER STROKE - Golfing equipment - Golfsmith International Inc.
POWER SUITS - Toys - Tonka Corp.
POWER SUPPORT - Orthopedic products - Reb Steel Equipment Co.
POWER SURGE - Pharmaceutical preparations - Dener Management Inc.
POWER SURGE - Vacuum cleaners and accessories - The Hoover Co.
POWER SWAMPER - Toys - Toymax Inc.
POWER SWEEP - Brooms - Ekco Housewares, Inc.
POWER SWEEP - Garden equipment - Parker Sweeper Co.
POWER SWING - Bats–baseball - Markwort Sporting Goods Co.
POWER SYSTEMS - Electrical industrial apparatus - Power Systems, Inc.
POWER SYSTEMS - Exercising equipment - Futurepro, Inc.
POWER TAMER - Electrical equipment - Hunt Holdings, Inc.
POWER TANK - Vacuum cleaners and accessories - Royal Appliance Manufacturing Co.
POWER-TAPE - Tape measures - L.S. Starrett Co. Inc. (Consumer Products Div.)
POWER TAPER - Golfing equipment - Golfsmith International Inc.
POWER TAX - Computer software - Pro Business Centers, Inc.
POWER TEACHING - Educational materials - Gannett Co., Inc.
POWER TEAM - Tricycles ☆ - Hedstrom Corp.
POWER TEAM - Vacuum cleaners and accessories - The Eureka Co.
POWER TECH - Toys–automobiles - Imperial Toy Corp.
POWER-TECTOR - Measurement equipment - Sensidyne Inc.
POWER TENDER - Electrical equipment - Perma Power Electronics Inc.
POWER TEST - Gasoline - Getty Petroleum Marketing, Inc.
POWER-TEX - Apparel and accessories - Glamorise Foundations Inc.
POWER THAW - Heaters–space - Klenatron Co. Inc.
POWER, THE - Publisher's imprints - Alfred A. Knopf Inc.
POWER THIN-HER - Apparel–women's - Weekend Exercise Co., Inc.

POWER-TIGHT - Drills–electric - Milwaukee Electric Tool Corp.
POWER-TILL - Tools–garden - Desa International, Inc.
POWER TIME - Teas - Laci Le Beau Corp.
POWER-TIME - Watches - Power of Rest Unlimited
POWER TO CHOOSE, THE - Integrated circuits - Necx
POWER TO CREATE, THE - Computer software - JASC, Inc.
POWER TO MANAGE, THE - Computer software - Accugraph Corp.
POWER TO PERFORM - Tractors–lawn - MTD Products Inc.
POWER TO START - Battery chargers ☆ - Japlar Acquisition Co. (Japlar/Schauer)
POWER TO SUCCEED, THE - Videos and audio recordings - Anthony J. Robbins
POWER TO TAKE CONTROL - Computer software - Autosimulations, Inc.
POWER TO THE PEOPLE - Apparel and accessories - Kinetic Multimedia, Inc.
POWER TOOL - Bicycle parts and accessories - Schwinn Cycling & Fitness Inc.
POWER TOOL - Tools–garden - Structron Corp.
POWER TOOL BOX - Video production - Plus Communications, Inc.
POWER TOOLS - Apparel and accessories - Combined Apparel Corp.
POWER TOOLS - Bicycle parts and accessories - KHS Inc.
POWER TOOLS - Bicycle parts and accessories - Kung Hsue She, Inc.
POWER TOOLS - Cleaning preparations - Blue Coral, Inc.
POWER TOOLS FOR INDEPENDENT INVESTORS - Computer software - Accutrade, Inc.
POWER TORQ - Bowling balls - Columbia Industries, Inc.
POWER TORQUE - Automotive parts and accessories - Perfection Hy-Test Co.
POWER TORQUE - Tires - Goodyear Tire & Rubber Co.
POWER TOUCH - Gloves–work - Red Steer Glove Co.
POWER TOUCH - Vacuum cleaners and accessories - The Eureka Co.
POWER TOUCH PLUS - Electrical equipment - Proxima Corp.
POWER TOUGH - Floor coverings–carpet and rugs - Miles Carpets Inc.
POWER TOW - Infant product - Fisher-Price, Inc.
POWER TOWER - Dishwashers–household - General Electric Co.
POWER TOWER - Exercising equipment - CSA, Inc.
POWER-TRAC - Fertilizers ☆ - Haban Manufacturing, Inc.
POWER TRAC - Lighting - Cooper Industries, Inc.
POWER TRACE - Cables - Delta-Therm Corp.
POWER TRACK - Golfing equipment - Golf Design USA
POWER-TRAK - Door openers–electronic - Robertson-Ceco Corp.
POWER-TRAK 600 - Door openers–electronic - Robertson-Ceco Corp.
POWER TRANSPORT - Toy-auto-carrier set - Intex Recreation Corp.
POWER TRAVELER - Computer peripheral equipment - Kensington Microware Ltd.
POWER-TRAX - Machine parts - Nook Industries, Inc.
POWER TREAD - Tires ☆ - Bridgestone/Firestone, Inc.
POWER TREE - Power switching equipment - Kensington
POWER TRIKE - Tricycles - Radio Flyer Inc.
POWER TRIM - Vitamins and nutritional supplements - Enrich International, Inc.
POWER TRIM 'N' TILT - Marine rigging - Outboard Marine Corp.
POWER TRIO - Sound equipment - DCM Corp.
POWER TRIP - Bicycles - Roadmaster Corp.
POWER TUBE - Fishing lures - Outdoor Technologies Group
POWER-TUNED - Marine rigging - Outboard Marine Corp.
POWER TWIN - Vacuum cleaners and accessories - The Eureka Co.
POWER-TWIST - Lamp bulbs–fluorescent - Duro-Test Corp.
POWER TWO - Cleaning preparations - Seymour of Sycamore Inc.
POWER UP - Beverages - Bunge Foods Corp.
POWER-UP - Chewing gum - Stanico, Inc.
POWER UP - Golfing equipment - Golfsmith International Inc.
POWER UP - Recording label - Omni 2000 Inc.
POWER UP - Skin care products - Gold Medal Hair Products Inc.
POWER-UP - Toys - Trendmasters, Inc.
POWER-UPHAUL - Sporting goods - Poweruphaul Corp.
POWER USA - Automotive parts - FCC Export Inc.
POWER USER - Computer peripheral equipment - Micro Warehouse, Inc.
POWER VALVE - Containers - Coca-Cola Co.
POWER-VEE - Tools–power-driven - General Wire Spring Co.
POWER VEST - Weightlifting equipment - All Pro Exercise Products, Inc.
POWER VIEW - Computer hardware - First Pacific Networks
POWER VIEW - Vacuum cleaners and accessories - The Eureka Co.
POWER-VIEW I - Mechanic's creeper - South Jersey Tool & Supply Inc.
POWER VISION - Tools - Alert Mobile Repair Inc.
POWER VISUALIZATION SYSTEM - Computer peripheral equipment - International Business Machines Corp.
POWER WALK PLUS - Treadmill exercise equipment ☆ - CSA, Inc.
POWER-WAND - Housewares - Advance Machine Co.

POWER WASH - Dishwashers–household - General Electric Co.
POWER WATCH - Batteries ☆ - Tempo Products Co.
POWER WATCH - Electrical equipment - Pennsylvania Power & Light Co.
POWER WATCH - Fencing–chain link - Common Sense Fence
POWER WAVE - Audio equipment - Recoton Corp.
POWER WEB-ULTIMATE HAND EXERCISER - Exercising equipment - Turner Enterprises
POWER WHEELS - Machine parts - Auburn Gear, Inc.
POWER WHEELS - Toys - Kransco Manufacturing Inc.
POWER WHEELS - Toys–automobiles - Fisher-Price, Inc.
POWER WIGGLERS - Fishing lures - Outdoor Technologies Group
POWER WINCH - Toys - Tonka Corp.
POWER WING - Bicycles - Softride, Inc.
POWER WIPES - Cleaning preparations ☆ - Gent-L-Kleen Products Inc.
POWER WISE - Lighting fixtures - American Power Products, Inc.
POWER WITHIN, THE - Footwear - JBI, Inc.
POWER WIZARD - Electronic equipment - Synrad, Inc.
POWER WOOL - Tools - Nicsand, Inc.
POWER WORK BELT - Safety products - Champion Ergonomics, Inc.
POWER WORKSHOP - Toys - Fisher-Price, Inc.
POWER WORMS - Fishing lures - Outdoor Technologies Group
POWER ZORDS - Toys - Saban Entertainment, Inc.
POWER2 - Vitamins and nutritional supplements - Askon Corp.
POWER2GO - Power switching equipment - D.E.W. International Corp.
POWER10 - Hair care products - Tressa, Inc.
POWERADA - Computer software - OC Systems, Inc.
POWERADE - Health care products - Coca-Cola Co.
POWERADMIN - Computer software - Unified Research Laboratories, Inc.
POWERADZ - Computer software - Poweradz Corp.
POWERAIN - Washing machines–commercial - Husky Manufacturing Co.
POWERAKE - Rakes - F.D. Kees Power Equipment LLC
POWERALBUM - Computer software - Power Up Software Corp.
POWERALL - Generators - Mobile Tool International, Inc.
POWERATED - Belts–industrial - Gates Rubber Co. (Automotive Aftermarket/Hardware Sales Div.)
POWERBACK - Shovels - True Temper Hardware Co.
POWERBANK - Electrical equipment - Arco Electric Products Corp.
POWERBANKER - Computer peripheral equipment - Adtek Information Systems, Inc.
POWERBAR - Candy bars - Powerfood Inc.
POWERBAR - Motor vehicle parts and accessories - Warn Industries, Inc.
POWERBASE - Generators - Coleman Powermate, Inc.
POWERBEAM - Flashlights - Garon Products Inc.
POWERBEAM - Furniture - Haworth, Inc.
POWERBILT - Batteries ☆ - TBC Corp.
POWERBLADE - Skates–roller ☆ - Rollerblade, Inc.
POWERBLEND - Gasoline - Amoco Oil Co.
POWERBLOCK - Batteries - Powercell Corp.
POWERBLOCK - Exercising equipment - Parabody, Inc.
POWERBLOCK - Weightlifting equipment - Intellbell, Inc.
POWERBOARD - Computer software - Nuiq Software, Inc.
POWERBOND - Floor coverings–carpet and rugs - Collins & Aikman Corp.
POWERBOND 200 - Foam rubber - Foamex LP
POWERBOOK - Computers - Apple Computer Inc.
POWERBOOK DUO - Computer peripheral equipment - Apple Computer Inc.
POWERBOOST - Regulators–voltage - Kohler Co.
POWERBORE - Cylinders - Kohler Co.
POWERBRAILLE 40 - Computers - Telesensory Systems Inc.
POWERBREED - Batteries - GNB Inc. (Automotive Battery Div.)
POWERBRICK - Computers - The Brick Computer Co.
POWERBRIDGE - Battery chargers - Hobart Corp.
POWERBRIDGE - Musical instrument accessories - Lawrence Fishman Transducers, Inc.
POWERBRIGHT - Orthopedic products - Chase Ergonomics Inc.
POWERBRITE - Electrical equipment - Belden Wire & Cable Co.
POWERBURST - Beverages ☆ - Crystal Geyser Water Co.
POWERBURST - Computer software - Airsoft, Inc.
POWERBURST SPORTS BARS - Confections - Frozfruit Corp.
POWERCACHE - Computer peripheral equipment - Daystar Digital, Inc.
POWERCACHE - Computer software - Maxwell Technologies, Inc.
POWERCARD 601 - Computer peripheral equipment - Daystar Digital, Inc.
POWERCAT - Footwear–athletic - Puma Inc.
POWERCD - Computer software - ZCI Inc.
POWERCELL - Bats–baseball - Worth Inc.
POWERCET - Hair clippers–veterinary - PowerCet Corp.
POWERCHARGE RACEWAY - Toys–automobiles - Mattel, Inc.

☆ = Now out of production

POWERCHECK - Batteries - Duracell Co. USA

POWERCISE - Exercising equipment ☆ - Maxxim Medical Inc.

POWERCLIENT - Computer storage devices–optical - Unisys Corp.

POWERCLIP - Computer hardware - Spectrum Engineering, Inc.

POWERCOAT - Adhesives and sealants - Pettit Paint Co. Inc.

POWERCOATS - Paints ☆ - Pratt & Lambert United, Inc.

POWERCOM 2000 - Computer software - Powercom-2000, Inc.

POWERCOMM - Tables–wood - Krueger International, Inc.

POWERCONNECTION - Computer software - Performance Solutions - Biocon, Inc.

POWERCOR - Water heaters–household - Bradford-White Corp.

POWERCORE - Archery equipment - McKenzie Sports Products Inc.

POWERCORE - Computer software - PowerCore Inc.

POWERCRAFT - Automotive parts and accessories - Stant Corp.

POWERCRISP - Cookware - National Presto Industries, Inc.

POWERCUT - Saws–power - Atlas Copco Electric Tools Inc.

POWERDATA - Computer software - Incremental Systems Corp. Dba Incremental Systems

POWERDECK - Roofing materials–slate - Reb Steel Equipment Co.

POWERDESK - Computer software - Microhelp, Inc.

POWERDIAL - Electrical equipment - Lutron Electronics Co., Inc.

POWERDIGM - Electrical equipment - Baltimore Gas and Electric Co.

POWERDOC - Computer software - Catapult Systems Corp.

POWERDOCK - Amplifiers - Mark IV Audio, Inc.

POWERDRIVE - Computer diskettes–blank - Insight Direct, Inc.

POWERDRIVE - Hair clippers–veterinary - Wahl Clipper Corp.

POWERDROME - Toys–automobiles - Mattel, Inc.

POWERED BY IMAGINATION - Toys - BRIO Corp.

POWERED BY NEXTSTEP NEXT - Computer software - Next Computer, Inc.

POWERED BY PROGRESS - Computer software - Progress Software Corp.

POWERED RACERS - Toy cars - Intex Recreation Corp.

POWERED SUBWOFFERS - Sound equipment - DCM Corp.

POWEREDGE - Computer hardware - Dell Computer Corp.

POWEREDGE - Electrical equipment - WCI Outdoor Products, Inc.

POWEREXPRESS - Computer storage devices - Analogy, Inc.

POWERFACTORS - Electronic equipment - Pioneer Magnetics, Inc.

POWERFAIDS - Computer software - College Entrance Examination Board

POWERFAST - Tools–power-driven - Desa International, Inc.

POWERFILE - Tools–power-driven - Black & Decker Corp.

POWERFIX - Hair care products - Brocato International

POWERFIZZ - Beverages - Healthlife LLC

POWERFLASH M-S - Photographic equipment ☆ - Dura Electric Lamp Co. Inc.

POWERFLEX - Abrasive products - Merit Abrasive Products, Inc.

POWERFLEX - Musical instrument accessories - Kaman Music Corp.

POWERFLEX - Sporting goods - Nordictrack, Inc.

POWERFLEX 90 - Cables - Triangle Wire & Cable, Inc.

POWERFLEX FLYER - Computer peripheral equipment - Advanced Logic Research Inc.

POWERFLO - Automotive parts and accessories - Purolator Products N.A., Inc.

POWERFLOOD - Floodlights - General Electric Co.

POWERFOLD - Folding machines–paper - International Machinery Sales, Inc.

POWERFORMS - Computer software - Lee Huang

POWERFPU - Computer software - John Neil & Associates

POWERFUL BOSS - All-purpose cleaner - Powerful Boss Inc.

POWERFUL DEGRIMER CUTS GREASE - Cleaning preparations - Bioenvirotech, Inc.

POWERFUL FANCY CLEAR - Flour–blended - ConAgra Grain Co.

POWERFUL FORCES - Floor coverings - Aladdin Mills, Inc.

POWERFUL IMPRESSIONS - Perfumes - Jean Philippe Fragrances, Inc.

POWERGARD - Calculators - Sanyo Fisher (USA) Corp.

POWERGEAR - Lubricating oils - Century Lubricants Co.

POWERGELS - Shoe soles - Pittsburgh Plastics Manufacturing, Inc.

POWERGENICS USA - Vitamins and nutritional supplements - Powergenics USA Inc.

POWERGLAZE - Cleaning preparations - Powerglaze USA Inc.

POWERGLIDE - Apparel and accessories - Christopher Foreman

POWERGLIDE - Bearings–industrial - L & S Bearing Co.

POWERGLIDE - Door openers–electronic - Sargent Manufacturing Co.

POWERGLIDE - Shelving units–wood ☆ - Lundia

POWERGLIDE - Tape measures - Keson Industries Inc.

POWERGLO - Water heaters–household - Rheem Manufacturing Co.

POWERGLOVE - Exercising equipment - Mattel, Inc.

POWERGOLD - Computer software - Micropower Corp.

POWERGRID - Computer software - Open Software Associates, Inc.

POWERGRIP - Adhesives and sealants - STO Corp.

POWERGRIP - Automotive parts and accessories - Gates Rubber Co. (Automotive Aftermarket/Hardware Sales Div.)

POWERGRIP - Medical apparatus - Joint Technology Enterprises

POWERGRIP - Tools–hand-operated - Fiskars Inc.

POWERGUARD - Roofing materials - Powerlight Corp.

POWERGUIDE - Cables–fiber optic - Fitel General, Inc.

POWERGUIDE - Computer software - Elan Associates (GreenLight Software Division)

POWERGUN 1000 - Staples - ACCO USA, Inc.

POWERHANDS - Medical apparatus - Bosco Lee and Yvonne H.C. Lee Partnership

POWERHEAD - Musical instrument accessories - Eric J. Behrenfeld

POWERHELP - Computer software - Astea International Inc.

POWERHORN - Radios - Tandy Corp.

POWERHORSE - Generators–electric - Kohler Co.

POWERHOUSE - Amplifiers - Earthquake Sound Corp.

POWERHOUSE - Audio equipment ☆ - Artisticover

POWERHOUSE - Converters–electric - Waukesha-Pearce Industries, Inc.

POWERHOUSE - Fabrics - Greenwood Mills Inc.

POWERHOUSE - Lanterns–electric - Coleman Co., Inc.

POWERHOUSE - Musical instruments - Atlas Accordions Inc.

POWERHOUSE - Projectors–photographic - Rangertone Research Inc.

POWERHOUSE - Recording label - Ichiban Records, Inc.

POWERHOUSE - Toys - Bachmann Industries Inc.

POWERHOUSE - Vacuum cleaners and accessories - Miele Appliances, Inc.

POWERHOUSE BOUTIQUE STUDIOS - Video production - Omni 2000 Inc.

POWERHOUSE FITNESS - Exercising equipment - Impex Inc.

POWERIDE! - Computer hardware - Future Domain Corp.

POWERIMAGE - Computer software - Desktop Advantage Development Group, Inc.

POWERIMAGING - Recording label - Progressive Awareness Research, Inc.

POWERINE - Gasoline - Powerine Oil Co.

POWERIZED FORMULA - Cleaning preparations - Drackett Co.

POWERJET XT-7 - Toys–automobiles - Mattel, Inc.

POWERJUMP - Toys–automobiles - Mattel, Inc.

POWERKEY - Computer software - Sophisticated Circuits, Inc.

POWERKING - Antennas - Recoton Corp.

POWERKUT - Abrasive products - SIA America

POWERLEADS - Computer software - Pyramid Data, Inc.

POWERLET - Cylinders - Crosman Corp.

POWERLETTE - Hardware - Nar Laboratories, Inc.

POWERLIFT - Cleaning preparations - Flood Co.

POWERLIFT - Golfing equipment - Dunlop Maxfli Sports Corp.

POWERLIFT - Vitamins and nutritional supplements - M.M.R.C., Ltd. Co.

POWERLIFT PROGRAM - Prerecorded video cassettes - Risk Management Consultants, Inc.

POWERLIGHT - Fishing rods - Wright & McGill Co.

POWERLIGHT RODS - Sporting goods - Wright & McGill Co.

POWERLINE - Electrical equipment - Cantex Inc.

POWERLINE - Electrical equipment - Computer Accessories Corp.

POWERLINE - Hardware - Emerson Electric Co.

POWERLINE - Musical instrument accessories - Selmer Co. Inc.

POWERLINE - Office machines - Martin Yale Industries, Inc.

POWERLINE - Pumps - Hypro Corp.

POWERLINE - Sporting goods - Outdoor Technologies Group

POWERLINE - Toys–automobiles - Maisto International, Inc.

POWERLINE GOLD - Vacuum cleaners and accessories - The Eureka Co.

POWERLINER - Apparel stores–sports - Champion Jogbra

POWERLINK - Electrical equipment - Cobbs Manufacturing Co.

POWERLITE - Bicycles - GT Bicycles Inc.

POWERLITE - Computers - RDI Computer Corp.

POWERLITE - Flashlights - Accutec Inc.

POWERLITE - Projection screens - Da-Lite Screen Co. Inc.

POWERLITE - Projectors–photographic - Epson America, Inc.

POWERLOK - Screws - Research Engineering & Manufacturing Inc.

POWERLORDS - Toys - F.J. Strauss Co. Inc.

POWERLUBE - Oils–lubricating - United Refining Co.

POWERMAD - Computer software - 21st Century Innovations, Inc.

POWERMAKER - Engines–motor vehicle - Bonded Motors, Inc.

POWERMAP - Electronic equipment - EIT, Inc.

POWERMAPS - Maps - Maps & Facts Unlimited, Inc.

POWERMARK - Electrical equipment - General Electric Co.

POWERMARK PLUS - Electrical equipment - General Electric Co.

POWERMASTER - Automotive parts and accessories - Key Components, Inc.

POWERMASTER - Beverages–malt - The Stroh Brewery Co.

POWERMASTER - Communications equipment–mobile - Gamber-Johnson Inc.

POWERMASTER - Dishwashers–commercial - Kleer Flo Co. Inc.

POWERMASTER - Rifles–pneumatic - Crosman Corp.

POWERMASTER - Tools–hand-operated - Atlas Tool

POWERMASTER - Toys ☆ - Wham-O Manufacturing Co.

POWERMAT - Fabrics–resin-coated - Certainteed Corp. (Roofing Products Group)

POWERMATCH - Computer software - Warren E. Wicke

POWERMATE - Computers - NEC Technologies, Inc.

POWERMATE - Electrical equipment - AG-Tronic Inc.

POWERMATE - Electrical equipment - General Electric Co.

POWERMATE - Generators - Coleman Powermate, Inc.

POWERMATE - Lenses–optical - Tele Vue Optics Inc.

POWERMATE - Marine rigging - Powerwinch Co.

POWERMATE - Television equipment - Jerrold General Instrument Corp.

POWERMATE - Vitamins and nutritional supplements - Green Turtle Bay Vitamin Co., Inc.

POWERMATIC - Electronic equipment - Apollo Audiovisual Div.

POWERMATIC - Guns–BB ☆ - Crosman Corp.

POWERMATIC - Staples ☆ - ACCO USA, Inc.

POWERMATIC - Vacuum cleaners and accessories - The Hoover Co.

POWERMATIC - Woodworking machinery - Powermatic Div.

POWERMAX - Batteries - Two Wheel Traveler, Inc.

POWERMAX - Battery chargers - Sima Products Corp.

POWERMAX - Electrical surge protectors - Panamax

POWERMAX - Gloves–work - Red Steer Glove Co.

POWERMAX - Solar cells - Siemens Solar Industries, L.P.

POWERMAX - Sporting goods - Dunlop Maxfli Sports Corp.

POWERMAX - Vacuum cleaners and accessories - The Hoover Co.

POWERMAX POWERPOCKET - Electronic equipment - Sima Products Corp.

POWER!MEDIA - Computer software ☆ - Horizons Technology, Inc.

POWERMIGHT - Generators–electric - Renewable Energy Ventures

POWERMISER - Air conditioning equipment - Nordyne Inc.

POWERMISER - Air conditioning equipment ☆ - Friedrich Air Conditioning Co.

POWERMODEL - Computer software - Brian P. Woolf

POWERMODEM - Computer equipment - PSI Integration, Inc.

POWERMONITOR-PLUS - Computer software - Clary Corp.

POWERMOW - Lawn mowers ☆ - F.D. Kees Power Equipment LLC

POWERNAIL - Floor coverings - Virginia Hardwood Co.

POWERNAILER - Woodworking machinery - Powernail Co.

POWERNECK - Exercising equipment - Larry W. Barnett

POWERNET - Computer software - American Power Conversion Corp.

POWERNET PROCESS MANAGEMENT ENGINE - Computer software - Powernet, Inc.

POWERNEWS - Computer software - Pentekk Software Technologies, Inc.

POWERNIC - Computer hardware - CNet Technology Inc.

POWEROD - Sporting goods - Shakespeare Fishing Tackle

POWERPACK - Computer peripheral equipment - Microtek International Development Systems Division, Inc.

POWERPACK - Tools–power-driven ☆ - Disston Co.

POWERPACK 7 - Publisher's imprints - Investment Training Institute - Nash, Inc.

POWERPAD - Computers - Sophisticated Circuits, Inc.

POWERPAIL - Buckets–plastic - Romanoff Products Inc.

POWERPAK - Computer peripheral equipment ☆ - CE Software, Inc.

POWERPAK - Electrical equipment - Gem Electric Manufacturing Co. Inc.

POWERPAK - Insulating materials - Manville/Schuller

POWERPAK - Meat products - LMG Investments, Inc.

POWERPARALLEL - Computer hardware - International Business Machines Corp.

POWERPASS - Electronic equipment - Exide Electronics Corp.

POWERPATH - Diagnostic apparatus - Laura Weisel

POWERPC - Computers - International Business Machines Corp.

POWERPC 601 - Electronic equipment - International Business Machines Corp.

POWERPERFORMANCE - Computer software - Powercerv Technologies Corp.

POWERPICKUP - Computer software - Federal Express Corp.

POWERPIPES - Computer hardware - Networth, Inc.

POWERPIPES - Toys - Mattel, Inc.

POWERPITCH - Propellers - Nautical Development Corp.

POWERPLAY - Floor coverings–carpet and rugs - Calladium & Marglen

POWERPLAY - Generators - Kohler Co.

POWERPLAY - Recording label - Boom/Powerplay Records

POWERPLAY - Stereos - Craig Consumer Electronics

POWERPLAY II - Floor coverings–carpet and rugs ☆ - Calladium & Marglen

POWERPLAY PLUS - Audio equipment - Berel Industries Inc.

POWERPLAYERS - Computer software - Mindscape Software Inc.

POWERPLEX - Electronic equipment - Bitronics, Inc.

POWERPLUG - Tools–garden - F.D. Kees Power Equipment LLC

POWERPLUS - Batteries - Celair Corp.

POWERPLUS - Gelatin - Vyse Gelatin Co.

POWERPLUS - Lamps - Electronic Lighting, Inc.

POWERPLUS - Tools - Senco Products, Inc.

POWERPLY - Skateboards - NHS, Inc.

POWERPOINT - Pens - Paper Mate Co.

POWERPORT - Modems - Global Village Communication, Inc.

POWERPRACTICE - Computer software - Softeasy Software, Inc.

POWERPREP - Computer storage devices–optical - Educational Testing Service

POWERPRO - Computer peripheral equipment - Daystar Digital, Inc.

POWERPRO - Computer software - Peco II , Inc.

POWERPRO - Kitchen appliances - Black & Decker Corp.

POWERPRO - Lawn mowers - H.H. Scott, Inc.

POWERPRO - Tools - Smith Equipment

POWERPRO 601 - Computer peripheral equipment - Daystar Digital, Inc.

POWERPRODUCTS - Motor vehicle parts and accessories - Parts Distributing Co., Inc.

POWERPROFILER - Electronic equipment - Basic Measuring Instruments

POWERPUMP - Medical apparatus - Arthrotek, Inc.

POWERQ - Computer software - APPX Software, Inc.

POWERQUAD - Electronic equipment - Amkor Electronics, Inc.

POWERQUEST - Vitamins and nutritional supplements - Douglas R. Casey

POWERREADY - Computer software - Powerpay Software, Inc.

POWERRIDER - Frames–eyeglass ☆ - Universal/Univis Inc.

POWERRINGS NATURE'S BUILDING BLOCKS - Toys–blocks - Ernesto D. Gyurec

POWERRIP - Computer software - Birmy Graphics Corp.

POWERRISE - Remote control devices - Hunter Douglas Window Fashions

POWERRRR TUFFS! - Toys - Azrak-Hamway International, Inc.

POWERRULES - Computer software - Beyond, Inc.

POWERS - Cough drops ☆ - Powers Pharmaceutical Corp.

POWERS - Epoxy - Powers Products, LLC

POWERS & PERILS - Games ☆ - Avalon Hill Game Co.

POWERS COUGH SUPPRESENT DROPS - Cough drops - Powers Pharmaceutical Corp.

POWERS DESIGN LINE - Furniture - Creative Powers, Inc.

POWERS MODEL - Apparel–women's ☆ - Movie Star Lingerie

POWERS OF GRAYSKULL - Toys - Mattel, Inc.

POWER'S RX ASTHMA RELIEF - Health care products ☆ - J.H. Guild Co. Inc.

POWERSAGE - Medical apparatus - Wahl Clipper Corp.

POWERSAVE - Computer software - Performance Solutions - Biocon, Inc.

POWERSCAN - Chemical preparations - Third Wave Technologies, Inc.

POWERSCAN - Computer hardware - Intrafed, Inc.

POWERSCAN - Machinery - GE Fanuc Automation North America, Inc.

POWERSCAPE - Playground equipment - Game Time, Inc.

POWERSCOPE - Computer software - PC-Kwik Corp.

POWERSCOPE - Electrical testing instruments - Microtek International Development Systems Division, Inc.

POWERSCOPE - Electronic equipment - Basic Measuring Instruments

POWERSCOURT - Earthenware ☆ - Waterford Wedgeood USA, Inc.

POWERSCREEN - Computer hardware - RDI Computer Corp.

POWERSCRIBE - Computers - Articulate Systems Inc.

POWERSCRIPT - Computer software - Comprehensive Video Supply Corp.

POWERSCROLL - Computer hardware - Mouse Systems Corp.

POWERSCRUB - Dishwashers–household - General Electric Co.

POWERSEAL - Machinery - TCC Enterprises, Inc.

POWERSECRETARY - Computer software - Articulate Systems Inc.

POWERSENSE - Loudspeakers - Community Light & Sound, Inc.

POWERSENTRY - Computer peripheral equipment - Tricord Systems, Inc.

POWERSERVER - Computers - BUM International Inc.

POWERSHARE - Computer software - Apple Computer Inc.

POWERSHIP - Computer software - Federal Express Corp.

POWERSHIP PLUS - Computer software - Federal Express Corp.

POWERSHOP - Computer hardware - Adaptive Solutions, Inc.

POWERSHOT - Fuel systems–motor vehicle - Nitrous Oxide Systems, Inc.

POWERSHOT - Sporting goods ☆ - Porter Athletic Equipment Co.

POWERSHOT - Tools–power-driven - Black & Decker Corp.

POWERSHRED - Paper - Fellowes Manufacturing Co.

POWERSIGHT - Electrical testing instruments - Summit Technology, Inc.

POWERSIM - Computer software - Systems Science Inc.

POWERSLIDE - Exercising equipment - Athletic Acceleration, Inc.

POWERSOFT - Computer software - Powersoft Corp.

☆ = Now out of production

POWERSONIC - Hearing aids - Qualitone

POWERSONIC PERCUSSION - Drums–musical instruments ☆ - On-Site Music Group

POWERSOP - Electronic equipment - Amkor Electronics, Inc.

POWERSOUND - Compact discs–prerecorded - TRF Production Music Libraries

POWERSOUND - Microphones - Westheimer Corp.

POWERSOURCE - Computer software - Powersource Software, Inc.

POWERSPEC - Computers–personal - Micro Electronics, Inc.

POWERSPEC - Lighting fixtures - Genlyte Group Inc.

POWERSTAR - Converters–electric - Power Star Products, Inc.

POWERSTAR - Hoists - Columbus Mckinnon Corp.

POWERSTAR - Vitamins and nutritional supplements - Powerstar Corp.

POWERSTAT - Transformers–electric - Warner Electric/Superior Electric

POWERSTATION - Batteries - Coleman Co., Inc.

POWERSTATION - Gypsum products - Air Products and Chemicals, Inc.

POWERSTEEL - Cables - MacWhyte Co.

POWERSTEEL - Computer software - Broderick & Bascom Rope Co.

POWERSTEP - Printers–computer - Texas Instruments Inc.

POWERSTIK - Sporting goods - Power Pulleze, Inc.

POWERSTONE, THE - Computer software - Multi-Link, Inc.

POWERSTOP - Brakes–electromagnetic - EPCO Products Inc.

POWERSTORE - Computer software - DST Systems, Inc.

POWERSTREAM - Computers - Mercury Computer Systems Inc.

POWERSTROKE - Exercising equipment - Englehart Products Inc.

POWERSUB - Circuit breakers - Square D Co.

POWERSWORD - Toys - Mattel, Inc.

POWERSYNC - Computer software - Linkpro Inc.

POWERSYSTEM - Computer software - Kelley Blue Book

POWERTABLE - Furniture–wood - Scanco

POWERTALK - Computer software - Apple Computer Inc.

POWERTEC - Electrical equipment - Powertec Industries Inc.

POWERTEL - Switches–electric - Donald P. Dattilo

POWERTEL - Telephones–cellular - Tessco Technologies Inc.

POWERTEST - Computer software - Alcatel Titn Inc.

POWERTEX - Cleaning preparations–household - Puritan-Churchill Chemical Co.

POWERTEX - Gloves–work - Red Steer Glove Co.

POWERTEXT - Computer software - Beaman Porter Inc.

POWERTONE - Vitamins and nutritional supplements - Robert V. Rossitto

POWERTOP - Mortars–clay - STO Corp.

POWERTOUCH - Recording label - Action Industries Inc.

POWERTRAC - Bicycles - 2 bi 2 Inc.

POWERTRACKER - Electrical equipment - EFI Electronics Corp.

POWERTRACKER - Electrical equipment - Niles Audio Corp., Inc.

POWERTRAK - Motor vehicles–all-terrain - TRAK International Inc.

POWERTRAP - Computer software - Professional Software Technologies, Inc.

POWERTRAX - Recording label - Zapset, Inc.

POWERTROL - Paint sprayers - Speeflo Manufacturing Corp.

POWERTRONIX - Electronic products - Powertronix Corp.

POWERTUNE - Golfing equipment - Golfsmith International Inc.

POWERTUTOR - Computer software - Roger E. Dunn

POWERTV - Computer software - Powertv, Inc.

POWERTWIST - Belts–apparel - Fenner Drives

POWERTYE - Cargo nets - Diversified Trading

POWERUPP - Pumps - Warren Rupp Inc.

POWERVALUE - Solar energy collectors - Photocomm, Inc.

POWERVESCENT - Cleaning preparations - Lockhart Jewelry Co.

POWER!VIDEO - Software ☆ - Horizons Technology, Inc.

POWERVIEW - Binoculars - Bausch & Lomb Inc.

POWERVISA - Electronic equipment - Basic Measuring Instruments

POWERVISION - Recording label - Powervision Dynamics

POWERWALKER - Exercising equipment - Battle Creek Equipment Co.

POWERWARE - Computer software - Exide Electronics Corp.

POWERWATCHER - Electrical equipment - General Electric Co.

POWERWAY - Computer software - Integrated Technologies

POWERWELL - Health care products - Cell Technologies

POWERWELL - Health care products - Union Battery USA

POWERWINCH - Hoists - Powerwinch Co.

POWERWINDOWS - Computer software - Microsoft Corp.

POWERWIZARD - Computer software - Breckenridge Software, Inc.

POWERWORDS - Recording label - Sennet & Sarnoff Learning Systems, Inc.

POWERWORKS - Hot tubs–plastic - Coleman Spas

POWERWORKS - Lawn mowers - Frederick Manufacturing Corp.

POWERWORKS, THE - Cleaning preparations–household - Blue Coral, Inc.

POWERXSTREAM - Computers - Mercury Computer Systems Inc.

POWERXTREME - Toys - Tonka Corp.

POWERZOOM - Electronic equipment - Tocad America, Inc.

POWHATAN - Boats–canoes - Nautical Boats Ltd.

POWHATAN - Floor coverings - American Floor Products Co. Inc.

POWHATAN - Food products - Pocahontas Foods USA Inc.

POWL-VAC AR - Electrical equipment - Powell Electrical Manufacturing Co.

POWLVAC - Electrical equipment - Powell Electrical Manufacturing Co.

POWLVIEW - Computer software - Powell Electrical Manufacturing Co.

POWR-CENTER - Extension cords - General Cable Corp.

POW'R CLAW - Jacks–hydraulic - Templeton, Kenly and Co., Inc.

POWR-EASEL - Tools - Tolegian Powr-Easel

POWR-FLITE - Sewing machines–household - Tacony Corp.

POWR-FLITE FAST DRY - Backpacks - Southwest Manufacturers & Distributors, Inc.

POWR-FOAM - Cables - General Cable Corp.

POWR-GAP - Automotive parts and accessories ☆ - Pacific Lubricants

POWR-GARD - Lighting equipment - General Electric Co.

POW'R-GEAR - Clamps–metal - Epicor Industries, Inc.

POW'R-GRIP - Adhesives and sealants - Tec Inc.

POW'R-HATCH - Health care products ☆ - Bruno Independent Living Aids Inc.

POWR HOUSE - Electrical equipment - GB Electrical Inc.

POWR-JACK - Tools - Klein Tools Inc.

POWR-KRAFT - Tools - Montgomery Ward & Co. Inc.

POWR-LINE - Sporting goods - Porter Athletic Equipment Co.

POWR LOOP - Amplifiers–musical instrument ☆ - Williams Sound Corp.

POWR-NET - Games - Porter Athletic Equipment Co.

POWR-PAK - Electrical equipment - GB Electrical Inc.

POWR-PAK - Vacuum cleaners and accessories - Southwest Manufacturers & Distributors, Inc.

POWR-PANL - Lighting fixtures ☆ - Hubbell Lighting, Inc. (Lighting Div.)

POW'R POST - Circuit boards - Zierick Manufacturing Corp.

POWR-PRO - Fuses–electric - Littelfuse, Inc.

POW'R PRO - Spray washers - W.W. Grainger, Inc.

POW'R PUMP - Adhesives and sealants - Indopco, Inc.

POWR-RIB - Sporting goods - Porter Athletic Equipment Co.

POW'R SLAM - Bicycles ☆ - Huffy Corp.

POWR SLIDER - Windows - C.R. Laurence Co. Inc.

POW'R STIX - Glue–household or industrial - H.B. Fuller Co. (North American Adhesives, Sealants and Coatings Group)

POW'R TROLLING RIG - Fishing lures ☆ - Lindy Little Joe Inc.

POWR TWIN - Paint sprayers - Speeflo Manufacturing Corp.

POWR-WINCH - Sporting goods - Porter Athletic Equipment Co.

POW.R.BASS - Musical instrument accessories - Gibson Strings & Accessories

POWRBELLS - Weightlifting equipment ☆ - Sinclair & Rush, Inc.

POWRCAULK - Caulking guns - Wagner Spray Tech Corp.

POWRCOMM - Electrical equipment - Specialty Lighting Inc.

POWRDRENCH - Cookware - Red Arrow Products Co., Inc.

POWREDGE - Tape–adhesive - Coating Sciences Inc.

POWRLITE - Generators–electric - Goodall Manufacturing Co.

POWRPAGE - Audio equipment - University Sound

POWRR BAND - Rails–iron - Mitek Industries, Inc.

POX-E-COTE - Epoxy - Key Laboratories Inc.

POXI-ROCK - Floor coverings - Rock-Tred Corp.

POXIE PATCH - Rubber–acrylic - C & S Tackle Manufacturing Co.

POXIMUNE - Veterinary pharmaceutical preparations - Biomune Co.

POXPLUG - Adhesives and sealants - Argosy International (USA), Inc.

POXY - Paints - Permalite Plastics Corp.

POXY-FRESH - Adhesive - Power Poxy Adhesives, Inc.

POXY HESIVE - Epoxy - Permalite Plastics Corp.

POXY MARINE - Epoxy - Power Poxy Adhesives, Inc.

POXY-MORTAR - Tiles–concrete - Dur-A-Flex Inc.

POXY PLUS - Epoxy coatings - Dayton Superior Corp.

POXY POUCHES - Adhesives and sealants - Loctite Corp.

POXY PUTTY - Epoxy - Permalite Plastics Corp.

POXY QUICK - Epoxy - Permalite Plastics Corp.

POXY STEEL - Epoxy - Power Poxy Adhesives, Inc.

POZIDRIV - Screws - Phillips Screw Co.

POZIFORM - Fencing–chain link - Southwestern Pipe Inc. (P. & H. Tube Div.)

POZITUBE - Fencing–chain link - Southwestern Pipe Inc. (P. & H. Tube Div.)

POZNANSKI - Horseradish - Brede Inc.

POZO PETE - Beef and turkey jerky and smoked and cured meats - Cattaneo Brothers Inc.

POZZA-LITE - Building materials - Pozza-Lite Corp.

POZZI - Tableware–earthenware ☆ - Villeroy and Boch Tableware Ltd.

POZZI - Windows–plastic - Bend Millwork Systems Inc.

POZZOLITH - Concrete–mixture - Master Builders Inc.

POZZUTEC 20 - Concrete–mixture - Master Builders Inc.
PP - Books–comic - DC Comics
P.P. - Cases–vanity - Jason Art Productions
PP - Jewelry - Penny Preville, Inc.
PP - Pumps–water - Sterling Fluid Systems, Inc.
PP III - Sporting goods ☆ - Powell Skateboards
PP 20 - Hair care products - Raymac Corp. Hair & Skin Technology
PP PATE POSTE ADCARDS - Greeting cards - Mullen & Morgan
   Communications, Inc.
P.P.A. - Vitamins and nutritional supplements ☆ - Alleghany Pharmacal Corp.
PPAS - Publisher's imprints - Applied Aeronautical Systems, Inc.
PPC - Cables–coaxial - John Mezzalingua Associates, Inc.
PPC - Computer software - Practitioners Publishing Co. Inc.
PPC - Giftware - Princess Pride Creations
PPC - Novelty items - Pickled Products Collection, Inc.
P.P.C. - Office supplies - General Chemical Corp.
PPC - Veterinary pharmaceutical preparations - Schering Corp.
PPG - Paints - PPG Industries, Inc.
PPG AIRCRAFT PRODUCTS: WE BUILD CONFIDENCE - Air transportation -
   PPG Industries, Inc.
PPG HIGH FIDELITY - Mirrors - PPG Industries, Inc.
PPK - Firearms, accessories, and parts - International Armament Corp.
PPL - Electronic equipment ☆ - E.F. Johnson Co.
PPL - Recording label - Credence Records
PPM - Hoists - Pro Products and Marketing
P.P.M.USA. - Jewelry–precious - J.T.S (Jersey) Inc.
PPO - Resins–synthetic - General Electric Co.
PPP - Jewelry - Pamela Park Proctor
PPP - Machine parts - Navistar International Transportation Corp.
PPP - Pet products - Professional Pet Products
PPP - Steel products - Pennock Corp.
PPP - Veterinary pharmaceutical preparations - Professional Pet Products
P.P.S. - Air purification systems - IEP, Inc.
PPS - Electronic equipment ☆ - J.L. Cooper Electronics
PPS - Footwear - Wolverine World Wide, Inc.
PPS - Motor vehicles–construction - Louis Berkman Co.
PPS - Telephones - Motorola, Inc. (Land Mobile Products Sector)
PPS 1 - Telephones - Motorola, Inc. (Land Mobile Products Sector)
PPS-2 - Electronic equipment - J.L. Cooper Electronics
PPS-100 - Electronic equipment - J.L. Cooper Electronics
PPS POLARIZED PROTECTION SYSTEMS - Adhesives and sealants - Pro-
   Tech Laboratories, Inc.
PPS-PROFESSIONAL PRACTICE SERIES ADULT EDUCATION - Publisher's
   imprints - Krieger Publishing Co.
PPT - Health care products - Las Vegas Discount Golf & Tennis, Inc.
P.P.T. S-77 - Hair care products - Redken Laboratories, Inc.
PPX - Computer peripheral equipment - Wellfleet Communications, Inc.
PPX FORMULA 7 - Lubricants - Petron International, Inc.
PQ - Thread - Advance Thread Corp.
PQM PLUS - Computer software - Union Pacific Technologies Inc.
PQNODE - Monitors–electronic - Basic Measuring Instruments
PQSENTRY - Electronic equipment - Basic Measuring Instruments
PQVIEW - Computer software - Electrotek Concepts, Inc.
PQWEB - Computer software - Electrotek Concepts, Inc.
P.R. - Drums–musical instruments - Paul A. Real Sales
PR-3 - Thread - Advance Thread Corp.
PR 6 - Tires - Uniroyal Goodrich Tire Co.
$P=R-E - Computer software - Peter A. Barris
PR RECORDS - Compact discs–prerecorded - Richard Preuss
PR SOLUTION - Food products - PR Nutrition, Inc.
PRA-STAT - Chemical preparations - Sangstat Medical Corp.
PRACTA-PERM - Office supplies ☆ - Faber-Castell Corp.
PRACTIBILT - Binders ☆ - Stationers Loose Leaf Co.
PRACTICA - Prosthetic apparatus - Smith & Nephew Richards, Inc.
PRACTICA - Soccer balls - Audero Sports Supply
PRACTICAL CHOICE - Radio communications equipment ☆ - E.F. Johnson
   Co.
PRACTICAL DESIGNERS - Pencils - A. Meyers & Sons Corp.
PRACTICAL MAGIC - Toys - D. Robbins & Co. Inc.
PRACTICAL MAN - Men's hairpieces - International Hairgoods Inc.
PRACTICAL MODEM 1200 - Modems - Hayes Microcomputer Products Inc.
PRACTICAL PERIPHERALS - Computer peripheral equipment - Practical
   Peripherals, Inc.
PRACTICAL PET - Pet food - Blue Seal Feeds, Inc.
PRACTICAL PORTIONS - Labels–paper - Four Lakes Label & Printing Co.
   Inc.

PRACTICAL PRODUCTS - Appliance parts - Practical Products, Inc.
PRACTICAL SOFTWARE - Educational software - Practical Software, Inc.
PRACTICAL SYNTHETIC - Paints - Dunn Edwards Corp.
PRACTICALARM - Alarm systems–fire - Simplex Time Recorder Co.
PRACTICALITY - Hair care products - Helene Curtis Industries Inc.
PRACTICE BUDDY - Golfing equipment - Southwest Regional Sports Inc.
PRACTICE FORECASTER, THE - Computer software - First Strategies for
   Healthcare, Inc.
PRACTICE MADE PERFECT - Sporting goods - Rammers-Roadbusters
PRACTICE PERFECT - Compact discs–prerecorded - Hadda Little Production
   Co.
PRACTICE STATION - Sporting goods - Robert E. Marier, Jr.
PRACTICE WORKS - Computer software - Integrated Dental Technologies,
   Inc.
PRACTICEMASTER - Computer software - Baldwin Piano & Organ Co.
PRACTICHEF - Electrical equipment - West Bend Co.
PRACTIDOSE - Containers - Apothecary Products, Inc.
PRACTIJUMPS - Portable dog jumps - J & J DCG Supplies Inc.
PRACTIMIN B - Vitamins and nutritional supplements - Great Life Laboratories
   Inc.
PRACTIMIN C - Vitamins and nutritional supplements - Great Life Laboratories
   Inc.
PRACTIPAC - Hardware - C. Itoh Building Products
PRACTIPAN - Vitamins and nutritional supplements - Great Life Laboratories
   Inc.
PRACTO - Crocheted and knitted items ☆ - Reliable of Milwaukee
PRADO - Dinnerware–glass ☆ - Johnson Brothers, USA, Inc.
PRADO - Doors–glass - Peachtree Doors and Windows Inc.
PRADO - Electronic equipment - Leica USA Inc.
PRADO - Floor coverings–carpet and rugs - Eurotex Inc.
PRADO - Glassware–household ☆ - Culver Glass Inc.
PRADO CLASSIC - Doors–glass - Peachtree Doors and Windows Inc.
PRADOLUX - Electronic equipment - Leica USA Inc.
PRADOVIT - Photographic equipment - Leica USA Inc.
PRAECEPTA - Publisher's imprints - Amrita Foundation, Inc.
PRAECEPTUM - Publisher's imprints - Amrita Foundation, Inc.
PRAEFECTA - Aquariums–household - William Tricker Inc.
PRAGER - Wines - Prager Winery & Port Works
PRAGMATAR - Skin care products ☆ - SmithKline Beecham Consumer
   Healthcare
PRAGMATAR - Veterinary pharmaceutical preparations - SmithKline Beecham
   Animal Health Products
PRAGMATIC - Electronics equipment - Pragmatic Instruments Inc.
PRAIRIE - Building supplies - J & W Fence Supply Co. Inc.
PRAIRIE - Cement - Prairie Material Sales, Inc.
PRAIRIE - Doors - Harloc, Inc.
PRAIRIE - Food products - Ranch Hand Foods Inc.
PRAIRIE - Nuts–salted, roasted, cooked, or canned ☆ - Prairie Products Inc.
PRAIRIE AIR - Compressors–air - Hedahls Inc.
PRAIRIE BEARWORKS - Toys–stuffed - Anne E. Rogers
PRAIRIE BELT - Meat products–canned - Bryan Foods, Inc.
PRAIRIE BLOSSOMS - Dinnerware–glass - Lenox, Inc.
PRAIRIE BOOKS - Publisher's imprints - Albert Whitman and Co.
PRAIRIE CITY BAKERY - Bakery products - Prairie City Bakery Co.
PRAIRIE CLIPPER - Farm machinery - M & W
PRAIRIE COLLECTION, THE - Furniture - Riverside Furniture Corp.
PRAIRIE CREEK - Fertilizers - Tyler Enterprises of Elwood Inc.
PRAIRIE CRUNCH - Snack foods - Prairie Products Inc.
PRAIRIE DOME - Trees - NDSU Research Foundation
PRAIRIE DUST - Recording label ☆ - Nationwide Sound Distributors
PRAIRIE FARMS - Milk - Prairie Farms Dairy Inc.
PRAIRIE FIRE - Apparel–men's - Lord Daniel Sportswear, Inc.
PRAIRIE FLOWER - Cooking utensils–earthenware ☆ - General Housewares
   Corp.
PRAIRIE FLOWER - Cooking utensils–enameled ☆ - National Housewares
PRAIRIE FLOWERS - Dinnerware–glass - Franciscan by Johnson Brothers,
   USA, Inc.
PRAIRIE FLOWERS - Toilets–enameled - Kohler Co.
PRAIRIE FUME - Wines - Wollersheim Winery, Inc.
PRAIRIE GARDEN - Popcorn - Swiss American Import Co.
PRAIRIE GARDENS - Flowers, plants, and seeds - Prairie Gardens Inc.
PRAIRIE GEM - Trees - NDSU Research Foundation
PRAIRIE GOLD - Glassware–household - Lenox, Inc.
PRAIRIE HEARTH - Fireplace equipment - ACI International, Inc.
PRAIRIE LANDSCAPE - Floor coverings–carpet and rugs - Regal Rugs Inc.
PRAIRIE MICROCHIPS - Cookies - Prairie Products Inc.

☆ = Now out of production

PRAIRIE MUSIC - Recording label - Traditional Music Record Co.
PRAIRIE NIGHTS - Dolls ☆ - Effanbee Doll Corp.
PRAIRIE PACKAGING - Cutlery - Prairie Packaging, Inc.
PRAIRIE PEACH - Food products - Jardine's Texas Foods
PRAIRIE PETE - Toys–stuffed - Dakin Inc.
PRAIRIE PREMIUM - Meat products–beef - Long Prairie Packing Co., Inc.
PRAIRIE PRINTS - Wallpaper ☆ - Wiffle Hill Studio
PRAIRIE ROCK - Beverages–malt - Prairie Rock Brewing Co.
PRAIRIE ROSE - Wines - Minnesota Winegrowers Cooperative
PRAIRIE SCHOONER - Candy ☆ - Glade Taffy Town, Inc.
PRAIRIE SCHOONER - Motor vehicles–all-terrain - Mallard Coach
PRAIRIE SCHOONER - Trailers–travel - Prairie Schooner Inc.
PRAIRIE SHIRT - Underwear and nightwear - Munsingwear, Inc.
PRAIRIE SMOKE - Wines - Minnesota Winegrowers Cooperative
PRAIRIE SPINNER - Windmills - Thompson Ornamental Windmills
PRAIRIE SPIRE - Live plants - NDSU Research Foundation
PRAIRIE STATE - Nuts–salted, roasted, cooked, or canned ☆ - John B. Sanfilippo & Son, Inc.
PRAIRIE STATE - Recording label - Prairie State Records, Inc.
PRAIRIE STATE BOOKS - Publisher's imprints - University of Illinois Press
PRAIRIE STONE TRADING CO. - Apparel and accessories ☆ - Kellwood Co.
PRAIRIE SUIT - Underwear and nightwear - Munsingwear, Inc.
PRAIRIE WIND - Apparel stores–sports - Gotcha Covered
PRAIRIE WINDS - Health care products ☆ - Avon Products, Inc.
PRAIRIEFIELD - Doors - Simpson Timber Co.
PRAIRIEWARE - Cutlery - Prairie Packaging, Inc.
PRAISE - Dog food - Ralston Purina Co.
PRAISE - Jewelry - Magnolia Diamonds Inc.
PRAISE - Occasional tables ☆ - JDI Group, Inc.
PRAISE - Recording label - Lift Him Up Music
PRAISE - Rug and upholstery cleaner - Contact Industries Inc.
PRAISE - Salad dressings–bottled ☆ - Nalley's Fine Foods
PRAISE - Soap - Lever Brothers Co. Inc.
PRAISE NOTES - Paper - Trend Enterprises, Inc.
PRAISE TEAM - Pre-recorded audio cassettes - Integrity Music, Inc.
PRAISE! WALK - Recording label - Integrity Music, Inc.
PRAISEWORTHY - Floor coverings - Aladdin Mills, Inc.
PRAISEWORTHY - Music–sheet - Jackman Music Corp.
PRAK-T-KAL - Vaporizers ☆ - Purepac Pharmaceutical Co.
PRAKTI - Cameras ☆ - Edixa Camera Co.
PRAKTINA - Cameras ☆ - Edixa Camera Co.
PRAKTISIX - Cameras ☆ - Edixa Camera Co.
PRALINE DREAM - Ice cream - Baskin-Robbins USA Co.
PRALINE LIQUER - Liquors - Sazerac Co. Inc.
PRALINE PANDEMONIUM - Ice cream - Haagen-Dazs Inc.
PRALINE PASSION - Coffee ☆ - Boyd Coffee Co.
PRAMEGEL - Health care products - Genderm Corp.
PRAMET - Vitamins and nutritional supplements - Ross Laboratories
PRAMET FA - Pharmaceutical preparations - Ross Laboratories
PRAMOSONE - Skin care products - Ferndale Laboratories, Inc.
PRANA-POT - Incense - Madu Lamar, Inc.
PRANCE - Car wash and wax ☆ - Benjamin Ansehl Co.
PRANCER - Artists' materials - Stangren Co.
PRANCER - Fishing lures - Fred Arbogast Co. Inc.
PRANCER - Toys - Mattel, Inc.
PRANCY NANCY - Dolls - Mattel, Inc.
PRANG - Water colors - Dixon Ticonderoga Co.
PRANG CRAYONS - Crayons - Dixon Ticonderoga Co.
PRANG SKIN TONES OF THE WORLD - Paints–artists' - Dixon Ticonderoga Co.
PRANKSTERS - Novelty items - Pressman Toy Corp.
PRANTAL - Pharmaceutical preparations - Schering-Plough Healthcare Products
PRARIE DANCER NATURAL GRAINS - Corn meal and cereals - Montana Merchandising Inc.
PRARIE LIGHTS - Candles - D'Adant and Sons Inc.
PRAS - Recording label ☆ - Combo Records
PRASTARA - Cosmetics - Douglas Hopkins
PRATECS - Computer hardware - YBM Technologies, Inc.
PRATER'S - Food products - Prater's Inc.
PRATIK - Footwear ☆ - Conjac Inc.
PRATT - Garden equipment - Seymour Manufacturing Co.,Inc.
PRATT & AUSTIN - Stationery - Pratt & Austin Co.
PRATT & LAMBERT - Paints - Pratt & Lambert, Inc.
PRATT'S GUIDE TO VENTURE CAPITAL SOURCES - Publisher's imprints - Securities Data Publishing Inc.

PRAVATA - Neckties - Salem Neckwear Corp.
PRAX - Health care products - Ferndale Laboratories, Inc.
PRAXIS - Typewriters - Olivetti North America Inc. (Consumer Products Div.)
PRAXISOFT - Computer software - Praxisoft, Inc.
PRAY FOR DEATH - Video games - Virgin Interactive Entertainment, Inc.
PRAY/VIRTUE - Recording label - Parr-X Corp.
PRAYER BEAR - Giftware - Brushcreek Creative Co.
PRAYER BLOCK - Statuary–wood - Paula F. Hart
PRAYER PAL, THE - Pillows - World Point Corp.
PRAYERFUL IMAGE - Paper products - Dedra J. Thomas
PRAYERWALKERS - Shoe accessories - Amelia D. Jarmon
PRAYFUL MOMENTS - Novelty items - Russ Berrie and Co., Inc.
PRAYING HANDS - Craft supplies - Leisure Arts, Inc.
PRAYING HANDS - Paper–gummed ☆ - Park Sherman
PRAZIONTEK - See PRECISION SLIDES
PRB LINE - Cleaning preparations - Projector-Recorder Belt Corp.
PRB: PEARL RIVER BRAND - Food products - Golden Lyon Investment, Inc.
PRBAR - Vitamins and nutritional supplements - PR Nutrition, Inc.
PRC - Caulking compounds ☆ - Courtaulds Aerospace Inc.
PRC - Electronic equipment ☆ - Plastic Reel Corp. of America
PRC - Siding–insulating - Bird Inc.
PRC PRECIS - Computer software - PRC Inc.
PRCA PRORODEO - Knives–hunting - Professional Rodeo Cowboys Association, Inc.
PRD PREMIUM RED DIESEL - Chemical preparations - Central Oil & Supply Corp.
PRE: - Computer software - Solon Consulting Group, Ltd.
PRE - Sporting goods - Scott USA Inc.
PRE - Tote bags - K-2 Corp.
PRE-17 - Health care products - Halsom Home Care
PRE/AFT - Shaving preparations - Parks Products Inc.
PRE-AFT - Skin care products ☆ - Sunbeam-Oster Household Products
PRE-ATTAIN - Health care products - Sherwood Medical Co.
PRE B-1 - Musical instrument accessories - Dimarzio, Inc.
PRE BASE - Roofing materials - Consolidated Fiber Glass Products Co.
PRE-CAT - Finishing agents - Lenmar Inc.
PRE-CON - Hair care products - Summit Laboratories
PRE-CON COCCI-X - Animal feeds - Bluebonnet Milling Co.
PRE-COTE - Paints - Kelly-Moore/Preservative Paints
PRE-COTE - Skin care products ☆ - DL/Banite
PRE CREAM - Cosmetics - Ampro Industries, Inc.
PRE DE PROVENCE - Bath salts - European Soaps Ltd.
PRE-DEP - Pharmaceutical preparations ☆ - Solvay Pharmaceuticals Inc.
PRE-DESIGNED DISPLAYS - Racks - E and E Display Group
PRE-EMINENT - Mattresses - Ohio Mattress Co.
PRE-EMPT - Skin care products - Phoenix Unlimited, Inc.
PRE FINISHER - Finishing agents - Parks Corp.
PRE-FIT - Guns - Pachmayr Ltd.
PRE-FIX - Apparel–men's ☆ - MMG Corp.
PRE-FIX - Games - Merriment, Inc.
PRE-GAGED - Blood pressure apparatus - Trimline Medical Products Corp.
PRE-GAMER, THE - Jackets - Howe K. Sipes Co.
PRE GLOVE - Skin care products - Sharpe Lines, Inc.
PRE GOLD - Veterinary pharmaceutical preparations - Alcide Corp.
PRE-H CAL - Vitamins and nutritional supplements - T.E. Williams Pharmaceutical Inc.
PRE-HON - Skin care products - Gigi Laboratories
PRE-INE - Health care products ☆ - Kay Pharmacal Co. Inc.
PRE JOWL - Prosthetic apparatus - Implantech Associates, Inc.
PRE-KUT - Clay products - East Coast Millwork Distributors, Inc.
PRE-LURE - Chemical preparations ☆ - Elcal Enterprises Ltd.
PRE MATT 800 - Mattresses - Span-America Medical Systems, Inc.
PRE-MAX - Animal feeds - Bluebonnet Milling Co.
PRE MAX - Cleaning preparations–carpet and rug - Imperial Manufacturing Co. Inc.
PRE-MED - Oxygen - Turner Industries Ltd.
PRE-MENS FORTE - Health care products ☆ - Blair Laboratories Inc.
PRE-MENSES - Vitamins - Country Life
PRE MIRROR - Metals - Lorin Industries, Inc.
PRE-MISS - Ophthalmic goods - Foremost Optical Products
PRE MONDE ALPINE LACE - Cheese - Alpine Lace Brands, Inc.
PRE MONDE ALPINE LACE FREE N' LEAN - Cheese - Alpine Lace Brands, Inc.
PRE MONDE LITE - Cheese - Alpine Lace Brands, Inc.
PRE-MOTHERHOOD - Health care products - Natural Laboratories Corp.
PRE-PACK - Electric lighting equipment - Lutron Electronics Co., Inc.

☆ = Now out of production

PRE-PAIR - Cleaning preparations - Polychem Corp.
PRE-PANEL - Insulating materials - Manville/Schuller
PRE-PARED - Food products - Pre-Pared Foods Inc.
PRE-PEN - Antigens - Schwarz Pharma
PRE PERM - Hair care products - Nino Originals
PRE-POSAL - Jewelry - Plainville Stock Co.
PRE-POST - Hair care products - Helene Curtis Industries Inc.
PRE-POUR - Waterproofing compounds - W.R. Grace & Co.
PRE-REQUISITE - Hair care products - Helene Curtis Industries Inc.
PRE-ROUTING - Computer software - Geotel Communications Corp.
PRE-SATE - Pharmaceutical preparations ☆ - Parke-Davis
PRE-SCHOOL - Easels - Anco Wood Specialties Inc.
PRE-SEEDER WEEDER - Hebicive - National Chelating Corp.
PRE-SET - Marine rigging - Outboard Marine Corp.
PRE-SET TRIM - Marine rigging - Outboard Marine Corp.
PRE-STRESS - Vitamins and nutritional supplements - Hillestad International, Inc.
PRE-STRESS - Vitamins and nutritional supplements ☆ - Weider Health and Fitness
PRE TAC - Health care products - Pharmaceutical Innovations
PRE TECT - Pet products - George Basch Co. Inc.
PRE-TENS - Skin care products - Uni-Patch
PRE-TESTED - Paints–artists' - Koh-I-Noor, Inc.
PRE-THANE - Paints - Kelly-Moore/Preservative Paints
PRE-TREAT - Cleaning preparations–carpet and rug ☆ - Hako Minuteman Inc.
PRE-V-ENT - Vitamins and nutritional supplements ☆ - Nature's Concept Inc.
PRE-VENT - Herbicides - J. & L. Adikes Inc.
PRE-VUE - Chimes ☆ - Nutone Inc.
PRE-WASH - Detergents - Conklin Co., Inc.
PREACHER MAN - Recording label - Derrick Lamont Miller
PREACTER - Skin care products - Hanah Beauty & Health Inc.
PREAKNESS - Binders - Steego Corp.
PREAKNESS - Flowers, plants, and seeds - Jacklin Seed
PREAM LITE - Cream - Rich Products Corp.
PREAMBLE - Recording label - Fifth Continent Music Corp.
PREAMBLE INSTRUMENTS - Electronic equipment - Preamble Instruments, Inc.
PREART - Hair care products - Cosmair Inc.
PREBON - Vitamins and nutritional supplements - Alba Pharmacal
PREBOND - Wire products - Camden Wire Co., Inc.
PRECARE FA - Vitamins and nutritional supplements - Whitby Pharmaceuticals, Inc.
PRECAST PATCH - Cement - Blackthorn, Inc.
PRECEDENCE - Bathtubs–enameled - Kohler Co.
PRECEDENCE - Electronic equipment - Rauland-Borg Corp.
PRECEDENCE - Floor coverings–carpet and rugs - Criterion Mills Inc.
PRECEDENCE - Floor coverings–carpet and rugs ☆ - Lees Carpets
PRECEDENT - Blankets–electric - Sunbeam-Oster Household Products
PRECEDENT - Computer software - Precedent Systems, Inc.
PRECEDENT - Cutlery ☆ - Carvel Hall Inc.
PRECEDENT - Floor coverings - Congoleum Corp.
PRECEDENT - Floor coverings–carpet and rugs - Calladium & Marglen
PRECEDENT - Furniture–upholstered - Sherrill Furniture Co.
PRECEDENT - Remote control devices - Draper Shade and Screen Co. Inc.
PRECEDENT - Vans–conversion ☆ - Turtle Top Specialty Products
PRECEDO - Apparel–men's ☆ - Michaels/Stern & Co. Inc.
PRECEF - Antibiotics - Bristol-Myers Squibb Co.
PRECENTOR - Computer software - GIA Publications, Inc.
PRECEPT - Boats - Powerquest Boats, Inc.
PRECEPT - Computer and electronics equipment - National Computer Systems, Inc.
PRECEPT - Food products - Central Soya Co. Inc.
PRECEPT - Furniture ☆ - Fancher Furniture Co. Inc.
PRECEPT - Goggles–safety - Ektelon
PRECEPT - Orthodontic equipment - Biomet, Inc.
PRECEPT CORDUROY - Floor coverings–carpet and rugs ☆ - Mohawk Carpet Corp.
PRECEPT P - Surgical supplies - White Knight Healthcare, Inc.
PRECEPTOR - Electronic equipment - Thomson Consumer Electronics, Inc.
PRECIMETER - Measuring instruments - Rolatape Corp.
PRECIOUS - Cheese - Sorrento Cheese Co. Inc.
PRECIOUS - Cosmetics - Jean Philippe Fragrances, Inc.
PRECIOUS - Dishes–plastic - Allied IMEX Inc.
PRECIOUS - Mattresses - King Koil Licensing Co., Inc.
PRECIOUS - Paper–toweling - Von Drehle Corp.
PRECIOUS - Toys–stuffed - Dakin Inc.

PRECIOUS - Wallpaper - Thomas Ray Designs Inc.
PRECIOUS - Yarn - William Unger & Co. Inc.
PRECIOUS BABY - Dolls - Horsman
PRECIOUS BABY - Dolls ☆ - Effanbee Doll Corp.
PRECIOUS BEGINNINGS - Jewelry - QVC, Inc.
PRECIOUS CARE - Infant product - Gerber Products Co.
PRECIOUS CARGO - Apparel–children's - Nazareth Kentury Mills
PRECIOUS CAT - Pet products - Durable Ralph, Inc.
PRECIOUS ENGRAVEABLES - Jewelry ☆ - Hirsch Speidel Inc.
PRECIOUS FEET - Jewelry - Heritage House '76 Inc.
PRECIOUS FIBERS - Apparel and accessories - QVC, Inc.
PRECIOUS FORM - Underwear and nightwear - Splendor Form International Inc.
PRECIOUS GEMS - Lip balms - Del Pharmaceuticals, Inc.
PRECIOUS GIFT - Floor coverings–carpet and rugs - Monticello Carpet Mills
PRECIOUS GIFT COLLECTION - Figurines - Michigan Artistic Creations
PRECIOUS JEWELS BY MILANO - Jewelry–costume - Donald Bruce & Co.
PRECIOUS KUTS - Wigs - Eva Gabor International, Ltd.
PRECIOUS LACE - Jewelry - Hobe Cie. Ltd.
PRECIOUS LIE - Golfing equipment - Silvermania Inc.
PRECIOUS LITE - Health care products - Vista Medical Products
PRECIOUS LITTLES - Underwear and nightwear - Maidenform Inc.
PRECIOUS MEMORIES - Floor coverings–carpet and rugs ☆ - Callaway Carpets
PRECIOUS MEMORIES - Hobby kits - Panline USA, Inc.
PRECIOUS MEMORIES - Lighting fixtures - Meyda Tiffany Inc.
PRECIOUS METALS - Cosmetics - Pavcom, Inc.
PRECIOUS METALS - Ophthalmic goods - Foremost Optical Products
PRECIOUS METALS - Paints–artists' - Duncan Enterprises
PRECIOUS METALS - Wallpaper - Carlton-Metro Wallcoverings
PRECIOUS METALS - Wallpaper - Illuminations Wallcoverings & Fabrics Inc.
PRECIOUS METALS - Wallpaper - Maya Romanoff Corp.
PRECIOUS METALS - Yarn - Rainbow Gallery, Inc.
PRECIOUS MINI PETS - Pet products - Precious Paws
PRECIOUS MOMENT - Floor coverings–carpet and rugs - Eagle Carpets Inc.
PRECIOUS MOMENTS - Bedding–linen - Quiltex
PRECIOUS MOMENTS - Dolls - Applause, Inc.
PRECIOUS MOMENTS - Footwear - S. Goldberg and Co. Inc.
PRECIOUS MOMENTS - Giftware ☆ - Enesco Corp.
PRECIOUS MOMENTS - Greeting cards - Jonathan & David Inc.
PRECIOUS MOMENTS - Handbags - Pyramid Handbags Inc.
PRECIOUS MOMENTS - Jewelry - Precious Moments, Inc.
PRECIOUS MOMENTS - Toys - Coloron Industries
PRECIOUS MOMENTS - Watches - Rosie Wells Enterprises Inc.
PRECIOUS MOMENTS BABY COLLECTION - Infant product - Precious Moments, Inc.
PRECIOUS MOMENTS COLLECTORS' CLUB - Figurines - Precious Moments, Inc.
PRECIOUS MOMENTS III - Wallpaper ☆ - Imperial Wallcoverings, Inc.
PRECIOUS MOMENTS MINIATURES - Figurines - Goebel of North America
PRECIOUS 'N FEW - Apparel–children's - Swat Fame, Inc.
PRECIOUS PEAR - Jewelry - Avon Products, Inc.
PRECIOUS PEAR - Toys–stuffed - Del Monte Corp.
PRECIOUS PEARLS - Bicycles - Dynacraft Industries Inc.
PRECIOUS PEE WEE - Dolls - Uneeda Doll Co., Inc.
PRECIOUS PETITES - Dolls ☆ - Bradley Import Co.
PRECIOUS PETS - Pet products - Precious Paws
PRECIOUS PLACES - Toys - Fisher-Price, Inc.
PRECIOUS PLUSH - Toys–stuffed ☆ - Gerber Products Co.
PRECIOUS PONY - Rocking horses - Flexible Flyer Co.
PRECIOUS POSTURE - Furniture–children's ☆ - Child Craft Industries Inc.
PRECIOUS POUTIES - Dolls - Bradley Import Co.
PRECIOUS PRECIOUS - Jewelry - OroAmerica Inc.
PRECIOUS PRINTS III - Wallpaper ☆ - Warner Co.
PRECIOUS PUP - Pet products - Durable Ralph, Inc.
PRECIOUS SCENTS - Cleaning preparations - Scentex Inc.
PRECIOUS STONES - Chewing gum ☆ - Leaf, Inc.
PRECIOUS STONES - Wallpaper - Capital Carousel Inc.
PRECIOUS STONES - Wallpaper - I. Gottlieb & Associates
PRECIOUS TIME - Jewelry - Smith & Co.
PRECIOUS TWINS NURSERY SET - Toys - Playskool, Inc.
PRECIS - Jewelry ☆ - Edison Brothers Stores, Inc.
PRECIS - Manicure preparations - Fromm Industries
PRECIS - Motor vehicles–automobiles - Mitsubishi Motor Sales of America Inc.
PRECIS - Rackets–racquetball - Ektelon
PRECISA - Cameras ☆ - Edixa Camera Co.

☆ = Now out of production

PRECISE - Cleaning preparations - Babson Bros. Co.

PRECISE - Cosmetics - Johnson Products Co., Inc.

PRECISE - Floor coverings–carpet and rugs ☆ - Bloomsburg Carpet Industries

PRECISE - Lamps - General Electric Co.

PRECISE - Medical apparatus - Minnesota Mining & Manufacturing Co.

PRECISE - Pens - Pilot Pen Corp. of America

PRECISE - Rice - China Doll, Inc.

PRECISE DESIGN - Fabrics - Badger Air-Brush Co.

PRECISE ELEMENT IN VICTORY, THE - Golf balls - WPI Acquisition Corp.

PRECISE ENDURANCE FORMULA - Dog food - Texas Farm Products Co.

PRECISE ENDURANCE FORMULA FOR DOGS WITH INCREASED ENERGY REQUIREMENTS - Dog food - Texas Farm Products Co.

PRECISE FELINE FOUNDATION FORMULA - Cat food - Texas Farm Products Co.

PRECISE FELINE FOUNDATION FORMULA FOR KITTENS AND CATS - Cat food - Texas Farm Products Co.

PRECISE FELINE GROWTH FORMULA - Pet food - Texas Farm Products Co.

PRECISE FELINE LIGHT - Cat food - Texas Farm Products Co.

PRECISE FELINE LIGHT FORMULA FOR LESS ACTIVE/OLDER OR OVERWEIGHT CATS - Cat food - Texas Farm Products Co.

PRECISE FOUNDATION FORMULA FOR MODERATELY ACTIVE ADULT DOGS - Dog food - Texas Farm Products Co.

PRECISE GROWTH FORMULA FOR PUPPIES FROMWEANING TO MATURITY - Dog food - Texas Farm Products Co.

PRECISE JOGGER - Exercising equipment - Precise International/Wenger

PRECISE LASH - Cosmetic applicators - Del Pharmaceuticals, Inc.

PRECISE LIGHT FORMULA FOR LESS ACTIVE/OLDER OR OVERWEIGHT DOGS - Dog food - Texas Farm Products Co.

PRECISE POWER PRODUCTS - Generators - Libby Corp.

PRECISE RUNNER - Exercising equipment - Precise International/Wenger

PRECISE SENSICARE FORMULA - Dog food - Texas Farm Products Co.

PRECISE SENSICARE FORMULA WITH LAMB MEAL & RICE FOR ADULT DOGS - Dog food - Texas Farm Products Co.

PRECISE TWEEZE - Tweezers - Del Pharmaceuticals, Inc.

PRECISE V5 - Pens - Pilot Pen Corp. of America

PRECISE V7 - Pens - Pilot Pen Corp. of America

PRECISE VR - Pens - Pilot Pen Corp. of America

PRECISE WALKER - Exercising equipment - Precise International/Wenger

PRECISECARE - Computer software - Medintell Systems Corp.

PRECISELY RIGHT - Coffee - Precise Packaging

PRECISELY RIGHT - Hair care products - Tussy Cosmetics Inc.

PRECISION - Air purification systems - Prym Dritz Corp.

PRECISION - Cooking equipment–household ☆ - Mirro Corp.

PRECISION - Cosmetics - Ardell International Inc.

PRECISION - Fence product - U.S. Tape Co.

PRECISION - Furniture ☆ - Bassett Furniture Industries, Inc.

PRECISION - Games - Nelson Paint Co., Inc.

PRECISION - Guitars - Fender Musical Instruments

PRECISION - Luggage - American Tourister, Inc.

PRECISION - Medical apparatus - Kendall Co.

PRECISION - Office supplies - Alvin and Co. Inc.

PRECISION - Office supplies ☆ - Seal-O-Matic Corp.

PRECISION - Ophthalmic goods - New Era Optical Co.

PRECISION - Pencils - Staedtler, Inc.

PRECISION - Rackets–racquetball ☆ - Prince Sports Group, Inc.

PRECISION - Rackets–tennis - Prince Manufacturing Inc.

PRECISION - Scissors–hand-operated - Armada Art Inc.

PRECISION - Ships–sailing vessels - Precision Boat Works Inc.

PRECISION - Staircases–metal - Precision Stair Corp.

PRECISION - Televisions - Precision Trading Corp.

PRECISION - Thread - Perfect Thread Co. Inc.

PRECISION - Tiles–terrazzo ☆ - Monarch Tile Inc.

PRECISION - Toothbrushes - Colgate-Palmolive Co.

PRECISION - Vacuum cleaners and accessories - The Eureka Co.

PRECISION - Vitamins and nutritional supplements - Novartis Nutrition Corp.

PRECISION - Watches - Gruen Marketing Corp.

PRECISION-AIR - Agricultural machinery - DMI, Inc.

PRECISION-ANGLE - Brooms - Libman Co.

PRECISION ARTU USA - Tools–hand-operated - Hamster Inc.

PRECISION BALANCED - Wire brushes - Boston Wire Brush Co. Inc.

PRECISION BILLING SYSTEM - Computer software - Base One International Corp.

PRECISION CLASSICS - Toys–automobiles - Deere & Co.

PRECISION CLUTCH - Clutches–industrial - White Consolidated Industries, Inc.

PRECISION COLOR MATCH - Machinery - Precision Color Match, Inc.

PRECISION CORPS - Sporting goods ☆ - Aquarian Accessories Corp.

PRECISION CRUSH - Machinery - M-Tal, Inc.

PRECISION DATAQUEST - Computer software - Precision Dataquest

PRECISION DEVICES - Audio equipment - AKG Acoustics Inc.

PRECISION DOLLY TRACK - Photographic equipment - Peterson/Holt Productions, Inc.

PRECISION EAR - Hearing aids - E.B. Brown Optical Co.

PRECISION EDGE - Flatware - JMP-Newcor International, Inc.

PRECISION EDGE - Surgical instruments - Microaire Surgical Instruments

PRECISION FITTING & GAUGE COMPANY - Gauging instruments - Precision Fitting & Gauge Co.

PRECISION FLO - Hobby kits - Floquil-Polly S Color Corp.

PRECISION GARDEN - Garden equipment - Earthway Products Inc.

PRECISION GEAR - Motor vehicle parts and accessories - Precision Gear, Inc.

PRECISION GOLD - Golf accessories - Striker Golf Club Co. Inc.

PRECISION I - Fishing leaders - Cortland Line Co., Inc.

PRECISION INTERNATIONAL AUTOMATIC TRANSMISSION KIT - Transmission kit - MGW Manufacturing Corp.

PRECISION K+ - Aluminum products - Kaiser Aluminum & Chemical Corp.

PRECISION LASH CURLER - Cosmetics - Japonesque

PRECISION LINE - Photographic equipment - Eastman Kodak Co.

PRECISION LITE - Golfing equipment - Golfsmith International Inc.

PRECISION LITE - Golfing equipment - Lynx Golf, Inc.

PRECISION-LITE - Photographic equipment - Eastman Kodak Co.

PRECISION MARKETING - Computer software - Claritas Inc.

PRECISION MICRO - Medical equipment - Glen Smith

PRECISION MONO - Sporting goods ☆ - Prince Sports Group, Inc.

PRECISION MOUNTAINEERING - Apparel and accessories - David Pedersen

PRECISION ONE - Hair care products - Marianna Imports, Inc.

PRECISION PAD TECHNOLOGY - Soldering equipment - Mask Technology, Inc.

PRECISION PAINT - Paints ☆ - Wattyl Paint Corp.

PRECISION PAVEMENTS - Asphalt - Duval Asphalt Products, Inc.

PRECISION PEARLS - Scissors–hand-operated - Magic Distributing Ltd.

PRECISION PORK - Veterinary pharmaceutical preparations - Pfizer Inc.

PRECISION POWER - Vitamins and nutritional supplements - L & S Research Corp.

PRECISION Q-I-D - Chemical preparations - Medisense, Inc.

PRECISION ROLLED STRIP - Metals - Allegheny Ludlum Corp.

PRECISION SC - Air purification systems - Ion Systems

PRECISION SELECT SERIES - Golfing equipment - Brunswick Bowling & Billiards Corp.

PRECISION SERIES - Amplifiers - Electro-Voice, Inc.

PRECISION SERIES - Toys–automobiles - ERTL Co., Inc.

PRECISION SLIDES - Hardware - HDI/Hardware Designers Inc.

PRECISION SUPER-DUTY - Wheels - Hamilton Caster & Manufacturing Co.

PRECISION-TORQUE - Dental equipment - Henry Schein, Inc.

PRECISION TORQUE PRODUCTS - Power wrenches - Barnes Group Inc.

PRECISION TOUCH - Golfing equipment - Components Plus, Inc.

PRECISION TOUR DESIGN - Golfing equipment - John Rouzee Green Co., Inc.

PRECISION TUNE - Automotive repair shops - Precision Tune Inc.

PRECISION WELDING & FABRICATION - Steel products - Precision Welding & Fabrication

PRECISION WORKSTANDS PW - Scaffolds–metal - Precision Metals, Inc.

PRECISIONPLUS - Prosthetic apparatus - Tecnol Medical Products, Inc.

PRECISIONSPLINT - Prosthetic apparatus - Tecnol Medical Products, Inc.

PRECISIONVIEW - Computer peripheral equipment - Radius Inc.

PRECISOR - Medical apparatus - C.R. Bard, Inc.

PRECIV - Jewelry - Bomac International Corp.

PRECLAIM - Paper–writing - Lincoln Pulp and Paper Co. Inc.

PRECLEANSE - Vitamins and nutritional supplements - Royal Source, Inc.

PRECO - Footwear - Preco Products Inc.

PRECO-LIKE MAGIC - Footwear ☆ - Mag Shoe Corp.

PRECO-MATIC - Alarm systems - Preco Inc.

PRECO-PATCH - Concrete products - Fosroc Inc.

PRECO-PLUG - Concrete products - Fosroc Inc.

PRECOMP - Health care products - McKesson Home Health Care

PRECOMPUTER GRADUATE - Game machines - Vtech Industries, Inc.

PRECOMPUTER POWER PAD - Toys–electronic - Vtech Industries, Inc.

PRECOMPUTER PRESTIGE - Games - Vtech Industries, Inc.

PRECOMPUTER THINKBOOK - Toys–electronic - Vtech Industries, Inc.

PRECORSIN - Vitamins and nutritional supplements ☆ - Pharmacaps Inc.

PRECOSE - Pharmaceutical preparations - Bayer Corp. (Pharmaceutical Division)

PRECOTE - Coatings - Precote USA, Inc.

PRECOTE 5 - Waxes–sealing - Precote USA, Inc.

PRECOTE 80 - Adhesives and sealants - Precote USA, Inc.

PRECYCLE - Paper–writing ☆ - Nicolaus Paper Inc.

PRED-5 - Pharmaceutical preparations ☆ - Saron Pharmacal Corp.

PRED 50 - Pharmaceutical preparations ☆ - R.A. McNeil Co.

PRED FORTE - Ophthalmic goods - Allergan, Inc.

PRED MILD - Ophthalmic goods - Allergan, Inc.

PREDACORTEN - Pharmaceutical preparations - Bolan Pharmaceutical Inc.

PREDAJECT-50 - Pharmaceutical preparations ☆ - Merz Inc.

PREDALONE - Pharmaceutical preparations - Forest Pharmaceuticals Inc.

PREDALONE R.P. - Pharmaceutical preparations - Forest Pharmaceuticals Inc.

PREDATE - Pharmaceutical preparations - Legere Pharmaceuticals Inc.

PREDATOR - Archery equipment - High Country American

PREDATOR - Batteries - Crischell Automotive Products, LLC

PREDATOR - Bicycles - Schwinn Cycling & Fitness Inc.

PREDATOR - Boats–motor - Alumacraft Boat Co.

PREDATOR - Boats–motor ☆ - Lund Boat Co.

PREDATOR - Computer hardware - Voyager VGA

PREDATOR - Computer software - Twentieth Century Fox Film Corp.

PREDATOR - Fabrics–cotton - WFJM Enterprises, Inc.

PREDATOR - Floor cleaning equipment - Southwest Manufacturers & Distributors, Inc.

PREDATOR - Footwear - Predator Industries, Inc.

PREDATOR - Games - Ampersand Press

PREDATOR - Golfing equipment - Golfsmith International Inc.

PREDATOR - Golfing equipment - Lynx Golf, Inc.

PREDATOR - Guitars - Peavey Electronics Corp.

PREDATOR - Hoses - Pullman Co.

PREDATOR - Lighting fixtures - Holophane Corp.

PREDATOR - Machinery - Perfection Gear, Inc.

PREDATOR - Pesticides–household - Dexol Industries

PREDATOR - Pumps - McNeil (Ohio) Corp.

PREDATOR - Shoes–athletic - Adidas USA Inc.

PREDATOR - Sporting goods - Zebco Corp.

PREDATOR - Sunglasses - Bausch & Lomb Inc.

PREDATOR - Tools–power-driven - Cooper Industries, Inc.

PREDATOR - Toys–automobiles - Mattel, Inc.

PREDATOR - Toys–automobiles - North American 4 Wheel Drive Center, Inc.

PREDATOR CAMOUFLAGE - Fabric - WFJM Enterprises, Inc.

PREDATOR CRO-MO - Bicycles - Schwinn Cycling & Fitness Inc.

PREDATOR FRIENDLY - Fabrics–wool - Predator Friendly, Inc.

PREDATOR G - Golfing equipment - Lynx Golf, Inc.

PREDATOR MAG - Bicycles - Schwinn Cycling & Fitness Inc.

PREDATOR MODEL ENGINE FUEL - Gasoline - Trinity Manufacturing, Inc.

PREDATOR PLUS - Golfing equipment - Lynx Golf, Inc.

PREDATOR SERIES - Computer hardware - Colorgrahic Communications Corp.

PREDATOR TIGER - Bicycles - Schwinn Cycling & Fitness Inc.

PREDATOR TIGRESS - Bicycles - Schwinn Cycling & Fitness Inc.

PREDATOR Z - Bicycles - Schwinn Cycling & Fitness Inc.

PREDCOR - Pharmaceutical preparations - Roberts/Hauck Pharmaceuticals Inc.

PREDCOR-TBA - Pharmaceutical preparations ☆ - Roberts/Hauck Pharmaceuticals Inc.

PREDEC - Gypsum products - Georgia-Pacific Corp.

PREDEF - Veterinary pharmaceutical preparations - Upjohn Co.

PREDICAMENTS - Toys–electronic - Mattel, Inc.

PREDICT - Computer software - Software AG of North America, Inc.

PREDICT - Diagnostic apparatus - Editek, Inc.

PREDICT - Microscopes - DLI Engineering Corp.

PREDICT/DLI - Microscopes ☆ - DLI Engineering Corp.

PREDICTA - Computer software - Pipkins, Inc.

PREDICTAKEY - Computer hardware - International Business Machines Corp.

PREDICTION - Floor coverings–carpet and rugs ☆ - Downs Carpet Co. Inc.

PREDICTOR - Boats–motor ☆ - Checkmate Boats Inc.

PREDICTOR - Pregnancy test kits - Whitehall Laboratories

PREDISOL - Pharmaceutical preparations ☆ - Hyrex Pharmaceuticals

PREDNASOL - Pharmaceutical preparations - Wesley Pharmacal Co. Inc.

PREDNASPAN - Pharmaceutical preparations - Wesley Pharmacal Co. Inc.

PREDNICEN-M - Pharmaceutical preparations - Central Pharmaceutical Inc.

PREDNICOT - Pharmaceutical preparations - C.O. Truxton Inc.

PREDNIS - Pharmaceutical preparations ☆ - Rhone-Poulenc Rorer Pharmaceuticals Inc.

PREDNISOL - Pharmaceutical preparations - Pasadena Research Laboratories, Inc.

PREDNOID - Pharmaceutical preparations - Wesley Pharmacal Co. Inc.

PREE - Hair care products - L'anza Research International

PREE - Thread - Cincinnati Thread Co.

PREE-CONDITIONER - Hair care products - Waverly Beauty Products

PREE-LEE - Beverages - Leetov

PREE-PERM - Hair care products - Waverly Beauty Products

PREE-ZERV - Trees - Lake Products Co. Inc.

PREEFER JP BOUTIQUE - Apparel–women's - Judy Preefer

PREEMICARE - Health care products - Infrasonics Inc.

PREEMIE HUGO GORILLA - Toys–stuffed - Dakin Inc.

PREEMIES - Toys - Coloron Industries

PREEMINENCE - Wallpaper - Stamford Wall Paper Co. Inc.

PREEMINENCE COM SUEDES - Wallpaper - Stamford Wall Paper Co. Inc.

PREEMO - Yarn ☆ - SCT Yarns Inc.

PREEMPTIVE DIALER - Computer hardware - Martel Group, Inc.

PREEN - Coats–children's - Brand & Puritz

PREEN - Fertilizers - Greenview Lawn & Garden Products

PREEN - Fertilizers - Lebanon Seaboard Corp.

PREEN GLEEM - Pet products - Tomlyn Products

PREEN 'N GREEN - Fertilizers - Greenview Lawn & Garden Products

PREETCH - Paints - Triangle Coatings Inc.

PREFACE - Cosmetics - Dial Corp.

PREFECT - Floor coverings–carpet and rugs ☆ - Porter Carpet Mills Inc.

PREFER - Detergents - Prefer North America, Inc.

PREFER - Diapers–cloth - Salk Co. Inc.

PREFERABLES - Bakery products - Richland Bakeries, Inc.

PREFERENCE - Contact lenses - Cooper Companies Inc.

PREFERENCE - Floor coverings - Tarkett, Inc.

PREFERENCE - Floor coverings–carpet and rugs - Hollytex Carpet Mills Inc.

PREFERENCE - Floor coverings–carpet and rugs ☆ - Regal Rugs Inc.

PREFERENCE - Furniture - Tomlinson of High Point Inc.

PREFERENCE - Hair care products - Cosmair Inc.

PREFERENCE - Jewelry - Elgin Watch Co.

PREFERENCE - Paper–writing - Dur-O-Lite Inc.

PREFERENCE - Plastics–laminated - Plaskolite Inc.

PREFERENCE - Wallpaper - Surface Industries Inc.

PREFERENCE - Yarn - Coats and Clark Inc.

PREFERENCE 2000 - Wallcovering - Gilford Corp.

PREFERENCE AFTER-COLOR - Hair care products - Cosmair Inc.

PREFERENCE PACK - Pharmaceutical preparations - Allergan, Inc.

PREFERENCE ROYALE - Bedding–linen - E.I. Dupont de Nemours and Co.

PREFERENCES - Wallpaper ☆ - Capital Carousel Inc.

PREFERRED - Automotive parts and accessories - Echlin Inc.

PREFERRED - Food products - Super Valu Inc.

PREFERRED - Girdles - Preferred Foundations

PREFERRED - Paper–writing - Dur-O-Lite Inc.

PREFERRED - Pet products - Bluebonnet Milling Co.

PREFERRED - Ribbons–inked - Aetna Products Co. Inc.

PREFERRED - Stainless steel ☆ - Latama Inc.

PREFERRED - Vacuum cleaners and accessories - The Hoover Co.

PREFERRED - Vitamins and nutritional supplements - Reese Chemical Co.

PREFERRED 1ST - Health care products - Scott Specialties, Inc.

PREFERRED 800 - Pagers - Cape Fear Paging Co.

PREFERRED BRUSHSTROKES - Wallpaper - Preferred Prints

PREFERRED BY MEN - Wallpaper - Preferred Prints

PREFERRED BY MEN II - Wallpaper - Andover Wallcovering

PREFERRED CANDIES - Candy - Super Valu Inc.

PREFERRED CARE - Medical apparatus - Lumex, Inc.

PREFERRED CARE - Veterinary nutritional supplements - Great Lakes Biochemical Co., Inc.

PREFERRED CHOICE - Pies–frozen - Edwards Baking Co.

PREFERRED CHOICES - Dinnerware–plastic ☆ - Nyman Manufacturing Co.

PREFERRED CHOLESTEROL SUPPORT - Vitamins and nutritional supplements - Reese Chemical Co.

PREFERRED COMFORT - Pillows - American Fiber Industries Corp.

PREFERRED COMMUNICATIONS - Department stores - Preferred Communications

PREFERRED ELEMENTS - Jewelry - Kinney Shoe Corp.

PREFERRED FUELS - Gasoline - Preferred Fuels, Inc.

PREFERRED GLUCOSAMINE PLUS CHONDROITIN - Vitamins and nutritional supplements - Reese Chemical Co.

PREFERRED GREEN TEA - Vitamins and nutritional supplements - Reese Chemical Co.

PREFERRED HARVEST - Nuts–salted, roasted, cooked, or canned - Preferred Harvest Co.

PREFERRED KIDS - Wallpaper ☆ - Preferred Prints

PREFERRED KITCHEN & BATH - Wallpaper - Preferred Prints

☆ = Now out of production

PREFERRED LIGHT - Cheese - Sargento Cheese Co. Inc.
PREFERRED MINI PRINTS - Wallpaper ✫ - Preferred Prints
PREFERRED PACK VIAL SYSTEM - Medical apparatus - Pac-Tec Inc.
PREFERRED PARTNER - Computer software - BMC Software, Inc.
PREFERRED PARTNER CONSULTING - Computer software - BMC Software, Inc.
PREFERRED PARTNER SOLUTIONS - Computer software - BMC Software, Inc.
PREFERRED PROGESTERONE CREAM - Vitamins and nutritional supplements - Reese Chemical Co.
PREFERRED PROSTATE SUPPORT - Vitamins and nutritional supplements - Reese Chemical Co.
PREFERRED PYCNOGENOL PLUS - Vitamins and nutritional supplements - Reese Chemical Co.
PREFERRED REMEDIES ACHES & PAIN MEDICINE - Health care products - Reese Chemical Co.
PREFERRED REMEDIES ALLERGY MEDICINE - Health care products - Reese Chemical Co.
PREFERRED REMEDIES ANTACID MEDICINE - Health care products - Reese Chemical Co.
PREFERRED REMEDIES COLD & FLU MEDICINE - Health care products - Reese Chemical Co.
PREFERRED REMEDIES DETOXIN MEDICINE - Health care products - Reese Chemical Co.
PREFERRED REMEDIES FATIGUE MEDICINE - Health care products - Reese Chemical Co.
PREFERRED REMEDIES SINUS MEDICINE - Health care products - Reese Chemical Co.
PREFERRED REMEDIES SLEEP MEDICINE - Health care products - Reese Chemical Co.
PREFERRED REMEDIES STRESS MEDICINE - Health care products - Reese Chemical Co.
PREFERRED SELECTION - Food products - Super Valu Inc.
PREFERRED SELECTIONS K & B - Wallpaper - Preferred Prints
PREFERRED SHIRTS BY MARTIN - Apparel–men's - Martin Manufacturing Co. Inc.
PREFERRED SILKS & SATINS - Wallpaper - Preferred Prints
PREFERRED SMALL PRINTS - Wallpaper - Preferred Prints
PREFERRED SPICE - Seasonings - Continnuus
PREFERRED STOCK - Floor coverings–carpet and rugs ✫ - Karastan-Bigelow Inc.
PREFERRED STOCK - Hosiery - Monarch Hosiery Mills, Inc.
PREFERRED STOCK - Men's fragrance - Coty Inc.
PREFERRED SUEDE - Fabrics - Milliken & Co.
PREFERRED ZINC LOZENGES - Cough medicines - Reese Chemical Co.
PREFERRED ZINC MENTHOL LOZENGES - Cough medicines - Reese Chemical Co.
PREFIN - Coatings - Absolute Coatings, Inc.
PREFINISHED STRIP - Floor coverings - Bruce Hardwood Floors
PREFIX - Office furniture–metal - Panel Concepts, Inc.
PREFLEX - Building materials–concrete - American Premier, Inc.
PREFLEX - Ophthalmic goods - Alcon Laboratories, Inc.
PREFLEX - Water purification systems - Arrowhead Industrial Water, Inc.
PREFRAX - Tiles–ceramic - Carborundum Co.
PREFRIN-A - Ophthalmic goods ✫ - Allergan, Inc.
PREFURAN - Pet products - Golden Pond Inc.
PREGAME WARM-UP - Trading cards and stamps - Treat Entertainment, Inc.
PREGENT - Pharmaceutical preparations - Beutlich L.P. Pharmaceuticals
PREGESTIMIL - Infant product - Bristol-Myers Squibb Co.
PREGNA-DAY - Vitamins and nutritional supplements ✫ - Tishcon Corp.
PREGNADAY - Vitamins and nutritional supplements ✫ - Tishcon Corp.
PREGNAGEN - Pet products ✫ - Aquamint Laboratories Inc.
PREGNAGEN - Pregnancy test kits - Biogenex Laboratories Inc.
PREGNANCY ONE STEP - Pregnancy test kits - Technical Chemicals and Products, Inc.
PREGNANCY ONE STEP TEST STRIP - Pharmaceutical preparations - Technical Chemicals and Products, Inc.
PREGNANCY SURVIVAL KIT, THE - Apparel–women's - Belly Basics, Inc.
PREGNASLIDE - Pregnancy test kits ✫ - Wampole Laboratories Div.
PREGNAVITES - Vitamins and nutritional supplements ✫ - Tishcon Corp.
PREGNECAL - Pharmaceutical preparations ✫ - Ulmer Pharmacal Co.
PREGNENOLONE - Pharmaceutical preparations - City Chemical Corp.
PREGNENOLONE - Vitamins and nutritional supplements - Vitamin Research Products Inc.
PREGNYL - Pharmaceutical preparations - Organon Inc.
PREGO - Dinnerware - Corning Consumer Products Co.

PREGO - Dinnerware - Corning Inc.
PREGO - Footwear - Mag Shoe Corp.
PREGO - Hair-care products - Tri-Institute of Trichology
PREGO - Luggage ✫ - Samsonite Corp.
PREGO - Spaghetti sauces - Campbell Soup Co.
PREGO - Sweaters - Northeast Knitting Mills Inc.
PREGO - Wines - Joseph E. Seagram & Sons, Inc.
PREGO AL FRESCO - Spaghetti sauces ✫ - Campbell Soup Co.
PREGO EXTRA CHUNKY - Spaghetti sauces - Campbell Soup Co.
PREGO II - Sweaters - Northeast Knitting Mills Inc.
PREGO NEW MUSHROOM SUPREME - Spaghetti sauces - Campbell Soup Co.
PREGO PLUS - Spaghetti sauces ✫ - Campbell Soup Co.
PREHISTORIC ARTIFACTS OF EARLY MAN - Trading cards and stamps - Ross Collector Card Co.
PREHISTORIC BABIES - Toys–stuffed ✫ - Dakin Inc.
PREHISTORIC MUSEUM DINOSAURS - Toys–models - Small World Toys
PREHISTORIC PALS - Giftware - Russ Berrie and Co., Inc.
PREHISTORIC PETS - Pet products - Educational Insights, Inc.
PREHISTORIK MAN - Video games - Titus Software Corp.
PREHUE - Computer software - F and S Inc.
PREISNER - Flatware - Preisner Co. Inc.
PREISS-HENNY - Wines - House of Burgundy Inc.
PREISSLER - Music–sheet - GSP
PRELAC - Animal feed supplements - Moorman Manufacturing Co.
PRELAN - Vitamins and nutritional supplements - Lannett Co. Inc.
PRELATE - Salmon–smoked, salted, dried, or pickled - Trident Seafoods Corp.
PRELAXER - Skin care products - Revlon-Realistic Professional Products Inc.
PRELESTONE - Pharmaceutical preparations - Pasadena Research Laboratories, Inc.
PRELGAN - Pharmaceutical preparations - Pasadena Research Laboratories, Inc.
PRELIEF - Vitamins and nutritional supplements - Akpharma Inc.
PRELL - Shampoos - Procter & Gamble Co.
PRELONE - Pharmaceutical preparations - Muro Pharmaceuticals Inc.
PRELU-2 - Pharmaceutical preparations - Boehringer Ingelheim Pharmaceuticals Inc.
PRELUDE - Aluminum compounds ✫ - Regal Ware, Inc.
PRELUDE - Bicycles - Schwinn Cycling & Fitness Inc.
PRELUDE - Blinds–venetian ✫ - Hunter Douglas, Inc.
PRELUDE - Cabinets - Aristokraft, Inc.
PRELUDE - Cabinets - General Marble Co.
PRELUDE - Cabinets ✫ - HomeCrest Corp.
PRELUDE - Clocks - Ridgeway Clock Co.
PRELUDE - Dinnerware–glass - Tienshan, Inc.
PRELUDE - Display cases–plastic - Channel-Kor Systems, Inc.
PRELUDE - Doors–wood - Morgan Products Ltd.
PRELUDE - Flatware - Wallace International Silversmiths, Inc.
PRELUDE - Floor coverings - Mannington Resilient Floors
PRELUDE - Floor coverings–carpet and rugs - Criterion Mills Inc.
PRELUDE - Floor coverings–carpet and rugs ✫ - Regal Rugs Inc.
PRELUDE - Food products - Cantare, Inc.
PRELUDE - Furniture - Hammary Furniture Co. Inc.
PRELUDE - Furniture - Harden Furniture Co. Inc.
PRELUDE - Glassware–household ✫ - Crisa Corp.
PRELUDE - Glassware–household ✫ - Lotus Glass Co.
PRELUDE - Glassware–household ✫ - National Housewares
PRELUDE - Health care products - Windmere Corp.
PRELUDE - Insecticides - Zeneca Inc.
PRELUDE - Motor vehicles–automobiles - American Honda Motor Co. Inc. (Acura Div.)
PRELUDE - Motor vehicles–motor homes - Eldorado Motor Corp.
PRELUDE - Musical instrument accessories ✫ - J. D'Addario & Co. Inc.
PRELUDE - Musical instrument accessories ✫ - United Musical Instruments USA Inc.
PRELUDE - Musical instruments - Hyer Percussion Products
PRELUDE - Musical instruments - VMI Industries
PRELUDE - Rackets–racquetball - Head Sports USA
PRELUDE - Rings–jewelry - Artcarved Inc.
PRELUDE - Stationery ✫ - Nu-Art Inc.
PRELUDE - Underwear and nightwear - Maidenform Inc.
PRELUDE - Wines - Merryvale Vineyards
PRELUDE CONTEMPORARY - Dishes–china - Tienshan, Inc.
PRELUDE CREATIONS - Figurines ✫ - Ideal Originals

✫ = Now out of production

PRELUDE SCRAPE CLEAN - Floor coverings–carpet and rugs - Superior Manufacturing Group/Notrax Floor Matting

PRELUDIN - Pharmaceutical preparations - Boehringer Ingelheim Pharmaceuticals Inc.

PREM - Meat products–beef - Armour Swift-Eckrich

PREM - Water bottles–rubber - Prem Bicycle Components Co.

PREM/ACLAVE - Bedding–linen - Postcraft Co.

PREM ROYALE - Health care products - Premier One Products, Inc.

PREMAIR - Air conditioning equipment - Engelhard Corp.

PREMARIN - Pharmaceutical preparations - Wyeth-Ayerst Laboratories

PREMASPEC - Electrical equipment - Challenger Circle F Inc.

PREMATEX - Paper–toweling - Cleveland Cotton Products Co.

PREMAX - Hardware - Premax L.P.

PREMENTROL - Pharmaceutical preparations ☆ - Cameron Medical Corp.

PREMERA - Vegetables–dried - Basic American, Inc.

PREMERE - Hair care products - Cosmair Inc.

PREMERE - Soccer equipment - Brine Inc.

PREMESCO COMFORT FIT - Rings–jewelry - Tessler & Weiss/Premesco,Inc.

PREMEX - Oils–lubricating ☆ - BP America Inc.

PREMIAT - Wines - Monsieur Henri Wines Ltd.

PREMICIDE - Deodorizers - J & J Chemical Co., Inc.

PREMIER - Amplifiers - Multivox/Sorkin Music Co. Inc.

PREMIER - Apparel–men's - Supreme International Corp.

PREMIER - Apparel–women's - Jezebel-Renee of Hollywood

PREMIER - Artists' materials ☆ - Hunt Manufacturing Co.

PREMIER - Audio equipment - Pioneer Electronics USA Inc.

PREMIER - Automobile covers - Budge Industries, Inc.

PREMIER - Bags–plastic - Poly-America, Inc.

PREMIER - Boats–pontoons - Premier Marine, Inc.

PREMIER - Brass products - Endisco Supply Co.

PREMIER - Cabinets - H.J. Scheirich Co.

PREMIER - Chemical preparations - Premier Refractories and Chemicals Inc.

PREMIER - Cigarettes ☆ - R.J. Reynolds Tobacco Co.

PREMIER - Cigars ☆ - General Cigar Co., Inc.

PREMIER - Cleaning preparations - Bickmore Inc.

PREMIER - Computer peripheral equipment - Avus Systems and Peripherals, Inc.

PREMIER - Cradles ☆ - Colgate Mattress Co.

PREMIER - Deicing fluid ☆ - Cargill Salt

PREMIER - Desk sets - Premier Metal Products Co.

PREMIER - Diapers–cloth - Salk Co. Inc.

PREMIER - Doors - Hufcor Inc.

PREMIER - Doors–storm ☆ - Gerkin Windows & Doors

PREMIER - Drapery hardware - Newell Window Furnishing Co.

PREMIER - Fabrics - Handler Textile Corp.

PREMIER - File folders - Fellowes Manufacturing Co.

PREMIER - Firearms, accessories, and parts - Remington Arms Co., Inc.

PREMIER - Fireplace equipment - Thomas Industries Inc. (Portland Willamette Div.)

PREMIER - Fireplaces - Dyna Corp.

PREMIER - Fishing tackle - Fo-Mac Inc.

PREMIER - Flags - Annin and Co.

PREMIER - Floor coverings - Beaulieu of America, Inc.

PREMIER - Floor coverings - Searcy Flooring Inc.

PREMIER - Floor coverings–carpet and rugs - Cabin Crafts Carpets

PREMIER - Floor coverings–carpet and rugs - Calladium & Marglen

PREMIER - Floor coverings–carpet and rugs - Criterion Mills Inc.

PREMIER - Floor coverings–carpet and rugs - LaVelle Textile Marketing Inc.

PREMIER - Floor coverings–carpet and rugs - Regal Rugs Inc.

PREMIER - Floor coverings–carpet and rugs ☆ - Burtco Enterprises Inc.

PREMIER - Floor coverings–carpet and rugs ☆ - Ebsco Carpet Mills

PREMIER - Flooring–hardwood - Biwood Flooring

PREMIER - Folding doors and partitions - American Door Co. Inc.

PREMIER - Food products - Gerawan Foods Inc.

PREMIER - Food products - Houba Inc.

PREMIER - Footcare products - Premier Malt Products, Inc.

PREMIER - Furniture - Vaughan Furniture Co. Inc.

PREMIER - Game machines - Premier Technology

PREMIER - Games - American Toy & Furniture Co.

PREMIER - Gasoline - Amoco Oil Co.

PREMIER - Giftware - Airguide Instrument Co.

PREMIER - Glassware–household - Oneida Ltd.

PREMIER - Glassware–household - Owens-Illinois Inc. (Libbey Div.)

PREMIER - Guns ☆ - Weatherby Inc.

PREMIER - Hair care products - Carolina Absorbent Cotton

PREMIER - Health care products - American Imex

PREMIER - Heating equipment - Hix Corp.

PREMIER - Heating equipment - Waterfurnace International, Inc.

PREMIER - Housewares - Scentex Inc.

PREMIER - Lighting fixtures - Premier International Corp.

PREMIER - Luggage - Apollo Handbag Co.

PREMIER - Mats - Matworks

PREMIER - Motor vehicles ☆ - DaimlerChrysler

PREMIER - Musical instruments - Entertainment Music Marketing Corp.

PREMIER - Musical instruments - Premier Percussion USA

PREMIER - Nozzles - La Fayette Brass Co. Inc.

PREMIER - Office supplies - Alvin and Co. Inc.

PREMIER - Paper clips - U-File-M Binder Manufacturing Co. Inc.

PREMIER - Paper cutters - Premier

PREMIER - Pencil sharpeners - Empire Berol USA

PREMIER - Pens ☆ - Parker Pen USA

PREMIER - Pet products - Fromm Industries

PREMIER - Pet products - Geo. W. Hill and Co., Inc.

PREMIER - Phonographs ☆ - Sumiko Inc.

PREMIER - Photographic equipment - Eastman Kodak Co.

PREMIER - Pipes–tobacco - S.M. Frank & Co. Inc. (Kaywoodie-Yello-Bole-Medico)

PREMIER - Plumbing fixtures–metal - Barnett Brass & Copper, Inc.

PREMIER - Projection screens - Draper Shade and Screen Co. Inc.

PREMIER - Pumps - Tokheim Corp.

PREMIER - Puzzles - Warren Industries Inc.

PREMIER - Rice - Wholesale Trading Corp.

PREMIER - Saw blades - DBNA Trademarks Holding Inc.

PREMIER - Scissors–hand-operated - Miller's Forge Inc.

PREMIER - Scrapbooks - The Union Group

PREMIER - Sealing compounds - Monsey Products Co.

PREMIER - Sporting goods and fishing tackle - American Import Co.

PREMIER - Sporting goods ☆ - Allsop, Inc.

PREMIER - Staplers - Martin Yale Industries, Inc.

PREMIER - Tables–wood - Krueger International, Inc.

PREMIER - Thread ☆ - Premier Thread Co.

PREMIER - Tires - Uniroyal Goodrich Tire Co.

PREMIER - Toilet seats - Alton Industries Inc.

PREMIER - Towels - Dundee Mills, Inc.

PREMIER - Vacuum cleaners and accessories - Scott Fetzer Co.

PREMIER - Watches - Elgin Watch Co.

PREMIER - Wheelchairs - Everest and Jennings International Ltd.

PREMIER - Window shades - Colony Corp.

PREMIER - Wines - Maison Portier & Fils

PREMIER II - Motor vehicle parts and accessories - Lancaster Colony Automotive Group

PREMIER 99 - Cleaning preparation - Gold Coast Chemical Corp.

PREMIER 99 - Meat products–poultry ☆ - Hudson Foods, Inc.

PREMIER 2000 - Fabrics - Astrup Co.

PREMIER ASIAN CHANNEL, THE - Broadcasting stations–television - Fouce Amusement Enterprises

PREMIER BARBECUE PRODUCTS - Barbecues and grills - Greene Manufacturing, Inc.

PREMIER BY DEKA - Batteries - East Penn Manufacturing Co., Inc.

PREMIER CHOICE - Vitamins and nutritional supplements - Albion Laboratories, Inc.

PREMIER CLUB COLLECTION - Whiskey - Joseph E. Seagram & Sons, Inc.

PREMIER COLLECTION - Apparel–women's - Nordstrom, Inc.

PREMIER COLLECTION - Cabinets - Yorktowne Inc.

PREMIER COLLECTION - Dolls - TCA Ground Inc.

PREMIER COLLECTION - Hardware - National Lock Cabinet Hardware

PREMIER COLLECTION - Rocking chairs ☆ - La-Z-Boy Chair Co.

PREMIER COLLECTION - Wallpaper - Wolf-Gordon Inc.

PREMIER COLLECTION, THE - Pens ☆ - Parker Pen USA

PREMIER COTTON CLASSICS - Apparel–men's - One-K Plus, Inc.

PREMIER CRU - Tobacco–chewing or smoking - James B. Russell Inc.

PREMIER DESIGN - Seafood - American Seafood International Inc.

PREMIER EDITION - Floor coverings–carpet and rugs ☆ - Hollytex Carpet Mills Inc.

PREMIER EDITIONS - Vans–conversion - Kentron Motor Coach Inc.

PREMIER ENERGY - Vitamins and nutritional supplements - Tea Garden Products, Inc.

PREMIER FASTTRAC - Publisher's imprints - Premier Entrepreneur Programs, Inc.

PREMIER FAUCETS - Faucets - Waxman Industries Inc.

PREMIER FEEDS - Pet food - Sabina Farmers Exchange Inc.

☆ = Now out of production

PREMIER FORMS PROCESSOR PRO - Computer software - Mitek Systems, Inc.

PREMIER GAMING - Computer peripheral equipment - Premier Technology

PREMIER IX - Floor coverings–carpet and rugs - Alexander Smith Carpets

PREMIER JAPAN - Food products - Edward & Sons Trading Co., Inc.

PREMIER LEATHER - Office supplies - McDonald Products

PREMIER LINE - Blocks–concrete - E. Dillon and Co.

PREMIER MID PLUS - Sporting goods ✩ - Gold Eagle/Arnold Palmer

PREMIER MOUNTAIN - Ice - Brookshire Grocery Co.

PREMIER NATURALS - Vitamins and nutritional supplements ✩ - Pay Less Drug Stores Northwest Inc.

PREMIER OBITUARY CARD, THE - Greeting cards - Howard Henson & Associates, Inc.

PREMIER ONE - Caulking compounds - Allpro Corp.

PREMIER ONE - Pollen extracts - Premier One Products, Inc.

PREMIER PAK - Publisher's imprints - Valassis Communications Co.

PREMIER PERFORMANCE - Music boxes - Ardleigh Elliot & Sons Ltd.

PREMIER PLASTICS - Containers–plastic - Premier Industries, Inc.

PREMIER PLUS - Motor vehicle parts and accessories - Budge Industries, Inc.

PREMIER PROSPECTS - Trading cards and stamps - Upper Deck Co.

PREMIER RED - Paper–sand - Carborundum Abrasives North America

PREMIER RED DRI-LUBE - Paper–sand - Carborundum Abrasives North America

PREMIER SERIES - Electronic equipment - Thomson Consumer Electronics, Inc.

PREMIER SHAKE - Shingles–asphalt or tar - Globe Building Materials Inc.

PREMIER SPEED TAPER - Tools - Premier Drywall Tool Co.

PREMIER SPORT - Apparel–women's - Nordstrom, Inc.

PREMIER STIK-ON - Office supplies - Office Products Inc.

PREMIER TECHNOLOGY - Game machines - Premier Technology

PREMIER UOMO - Apparel–men's - One-K Plus, Inc.

PREMIER VELOUR - Seat covers - Saddleman, Inc.

PREMIER WHITE - Thermostats - Honeywell Inc.

PREMIER WORLDWIDE EXPRESS - Courier services–air - Premier Worldwide Express, Inc.

PREMIERE - Blankets–electric - Sunbeam-Oster Household Products

PREMIERE - Cabinets ✩ - Aristokraft, Inc.

PREMIERE - Cameras - Rollei of America Inc.

PREMIERE - Christmas tree ornaments - Cracker Box Inc.

PREMIERE - Clocks - General Time Corp. (Westclox/Seth Thomas Div.)

PREMIERE - Colognes - Tristar Corp.

PREMIERE - Cooking utensils–aluminum - West Bend Co.

PREMIERE - Display cases–wood - Claridge Products and Equipment Inc.

PREMIERE - Fireplace equipment - Hearth Craft

PREMIERE - Floor coverings - Azrock Commercial Flooring

PREMIERE - Floor coverings–carpet and rugs - Patrick Carpet Mills

PREMIERE - Floor coverings–carpet and rugs - S and S Mills Inc.

PREMIERE - Furniture–upholstered - Kinder Manufacturing Corp.

PREMIERE - Giftware - World of Porcelain & Glassware

PREMIERE - Hair care products - Windmere Corp.

PREMIERE - Helmets–athletic - Bell Sports Corp.

PREMIERE - Housewares ✩ - Baum Bros. Imports Inc.

PREMIERE - Indoor-outdoor carpet - Instant Turf Industries Inc.

PREMIERE - Lawn mowers - Sales Force

PREMIERE - Musical instrument accessories - Hite Mouthpieces

PREMIERE - Pens - Micropoint Inc.

PREMIERE - Perfumes - Frances Denney

PREMIERE - Shorts–women's - Cr/LP, LLC

PREMIERE - Wallpaper ✩ - Capital Carousel Inc.

PREMIERE - Wallpaper ✩ - Morton Jonap Co. Inc.

PREMIERE - Wigs ✩ - Paula Young

PREMIERE - Window coverings - Outlook Window Fashions

PREMIERE - Window frames - Yale Ogron Manufacturing Co. Inc.

PREMIERE CLASSE - Ophthalmic goods - Foremost Optical Products

PREMIERE COLLECTION - Cosmetics - Retail Cosmetic Concepts Inc.

PREMIERE COLLECTION - Giftware ✩ - Christhomas Corp.

PREMIERE COLLECTION, THE - Paper–gift wrap - Gibson Greetings, Inc.

PREMIERE COLLECTION, THE - Flowers–artificial - Mangelsen's (VDI)

PREMIERE CUVEE - Wines ✩ - Domecq Importers Inc.

PREMIERE EDITION - Floor coverings–carpet and rugs - Evans-Black Carpet Mills

PREMIERE GLIDE - Furniture - Action Industries Inc.

PREMIERE OCCASION - Floor coverings–carpet and rugs - Porter Carpet Mills Inc.

PREMIERE PET - Pet products - Dallas Manufacturing Inc.

PREMIERE PLUS - Deodorizers - J & J Chemical Co., Inc.

PREMIERE SELECTION - Wallpaper - Pervel Industries Inc.

PREMIERE SHOWMOBILE - Trailers ✩ - Wenger Corp.

PREMIERE'S - Candy - Premiere Candy Co.

PREMIERHDR - Telescopes - Bushnell Corp.

PREMIERS - Cigars - Faber, Coe & Gregg Inc.

PREMIERS - Cigars - E. Regensburg & Sons

PREMIO - Beverages–carbonated ✩ - Monarch Co., Inc.

PREMIO AL SABOR - Corn chips - Tree of Life, Inc.

PREMIS - Bicycles - Schwinn Cycling & Fitness Inc.

PREMISE - Floor coverings–carpet and rugs - Mohawk Industries Inc.

PREMISE - Furniture - Haworth, Inc.

PREMISE - Insecticides - Bayer Corp. (Agriculture Div.)

PREMISE - Ophthalmic goods - Foremost Optical Products

PREMISE PAGER SYSTEM - Pagers - Jtech Inc.

PREMISES WIRING ADMINISTRATOR - Computer software - Telco Research Corp.

PREMISORB - Health care products ✩ - Premium Plastics, Inc.

PREMIUM - Ammunition - Federal Cartridge Co.

PREMIUM - Audio tapes–blank - Hamilton Electronics Corp.

PREMIUM - Beverages - Daily Juice Products Inc.

PREMIUM - Cheese - H.P. Hood & Sons Inc.

PREMIUM - Converters–electric - Premium Coffee

PREMIUM - Crackers - Nabisco Foods Group

PREMIUM - Detergents - Tri-Par Corp.

PREMIUM - Fabrics - Greenwood Mills Inc.

PREMIUM - Floor coverings ✩ - Congoleum Corp.

PREMIUM - Flour–blended - Morrison Milling Co.

PREMIUM - Food products - Castleberry's Food Co.

PREMIUM - Furniture–factory ✩ - Clayton Marcus Co. Inc.

PREMIUM - Greeting cards ✩ - Cleo Inc.

PREMIUM - Hardware - Alside Div.

PREMIUM - Ice cream - Nestle USA

PREMIUM - Insulating materials - Rockwool Industries Inc.

PREMIUM - Kitchen appliances - Precision Trading Corp.

PREMIUM - Lawn product - Bruner Ivory Handle Co.

PREMIUM - Meat products–pork - Lykes Services Co.

PREMIUM - Mirrors - Hoyne Industries Inc.

PREMIUM - Motor vehicle parts and accessories - Custom Chrome, Inc.

PREMIUM - Oats–rolled or meal ✩ - Edward & Sons Trading Co., Inc.

PREMIUM - Padding–foam - Crain Industries Inc.

PREMIUM - Paint removers - Sunnyside Corp.

PREMIUM - Paints - Somay Products Inc.

PREMIUM - Paints - Standard Brands Paint Co.

PREMIUM - Paints - Zynolyte Products Co.

PREMIUM - Paper - Butler Paper Co.

PREMIUM - Paper–toilet - Georgia-Pacific Corp.

PREMIUM - Pencils ✩ - Faber-Castell Corp.

PREMIUM - Pet products - Lambert-Kay

PREMIUM - Pet products ✩ - Decker Manufacturing Co.

PREMIUM - Rum - Joseph E. Seagram & Sons, Inc.

PREMIUM - Sausages - Hormel Foods Corp.

PREMIUM - Seasonings - Pacific Foods Inc.

PREMIUM - Seasonings ✩ - Williams Foods Inc.

PREMIUM - Shirts - Signal Art Wear

PREMIUM - Spices and extracts - Scentex Inc.

PREMIUM - Sprayers - RL Flo-Master

PREMIUM - Strollers–baby - Century Products Co.

PREMIUM - Syrup - W.B. Roddenbery Co., Inc.

PREMIUM - Tools - O.P. Link Handle Co. Inc.

PREMIUM - Water-filtering units - Premium Drinking Water Inc.

PREMIUM 37 - Tape–adhesive - Plymouth Rubber Co., Inc.

PREMIUM 111 - Tape–adhesive - Plymouth Rubber Co., Inc.

PREMIUM ALTBIER LONG TRAIL ALE - Beverages–malt - Long Trail Brewing Co.

PREMIUM ALTBIER LONG TRAIL ALE - Beverages–malt - Mountain Brewers, Inc.

PREMIUM AMERICA - Popcorn - Great Western Products Inc.

PREMIUM BAND - Rubber bands - B.F. Goodrich Co.

PREMIUM BLADES - Fishing lures - Hildebrandt Corp.

PREMIUM-BLEND - Adhesives and sealants ✩ - Custom Building Products

PREMIUM BLEND - Deicing fluid - Pasvalco

PREMIUM BLEND - Oils–lubricating - Pep Boys Manny, Moe & Jack

PREMIUM BOVA CHOICE - Animal feeds - Carl S. Akey Inc.

PREMIUM BRINE SHRIMP EGGS - Pet food - Prime Artemia Inc.

PREMIUM BUY - Cigarettes - Philip Morris Companies Inc.

PREMIUM CARD - Sporting goods - Super Marketing Associates

PREMIUM CHACHIES SALSA - Sauces - Chachies, Inc.

PREMIUM CHOICE - Juices - Minute Maid Foodservice Group

PREMIUM CHOICE - Pet products - American Colloid Co.

PREMIUM CHOICE EXTRA - Pet products - American Colloid Co.

PREMIUM CLASSIC - Frozen dairy products - Smith's Food & Drug Centers, Inc.

PREMIUM COLONY - Wines - The Beverage Source Inc.

PREMIUM CREAM POLISH - Leather tanning and finishing - Bickmore Inc.

PREMIUM DAIRY FORTIFIER CRUMBLES - Animal feeds - Carl S. Akey Inc.

PREMIUM DURALITE 2000 - Roofing materials - Monierlifetile

PREMIUM EDGE - Pet food - Schell & Kampeter, Inc.

PREMIUM EDITION - Apparel and accessories - Haggar Corp.

PREMIUM EMBERS QUALITY - Briquettes - Embers Charcoal Co., Inc.

PREMIUM ENTRANCE - Locks–padlocks - Kwikset Powdered Metal Products

PREMIUM ESD - Tires - Bridgestone/Firestone, Inc.

PREMIUM FARMS - Milk–canned or powdered - M.W. Salomon & Son Inc.

PREMIUM FLEX - Hunting equipment - Hunter's Specialties, Inc.

PREMIUM FRANCE DELUXE FRENCH BRIDGES - Musical instrument accessories - Deltex Music Corp.

PREMIUM GOLD - Crackers - B. Manischewitz Co.

PREMIUM GOLD - Pet products - Wardley Corp.

PREMIUM GOLDEN ARROW - Office supplies - Arrow Rubber Products Inc.

PREMIUM HC303 - Cleaning preparations - Expert Products

PREMIUM HEALTH - Animal feeds - Petcare Plus, Inc.

PREMIUM HOUSE - Vegetables–frozen - Ore-Ida Foods, Inc.

PREMIUM I - Paints - Sophir Morris Paint

PREMIUM KOI - Pet food - Wardley Corp.

PREMIUM LIGHT - Ice milk - Cass-Clay Creamery Inc.

PREMIUM MCT GOLD - Vitamins and nutritional supplements - Prostar, Inc.

PREMIUM MIX - Pet products - Ginger, Inc.

PREMIUM MIXED - Nuts–salted, roasted, cooked, or canned - Western Family Foods, Inc.

PREMIUM MULTI-MIX - Pet products ☆ - Jungle Laboratories Corp.

PREMIUM NAIL CONCEPTS - Nail care products - Impact Media

PREMIUM PAK - Food products - Stilwell Foods

PREMIUM PERM - Hair care products - KMS Research Inc.

PREMIUM PESENTI - Wines - Pesenti Winery

PREMIUM PIG 1300 - Animal feeds - Carl S. Akey Inc.

PREMIUM PIG 2000 - Animal feeds - Carl S. Akey Inc.

PREMIUM PLUS - Brushes–paint - Behr Process Corp.

PREMIUM PLUS - Building materials - MS International, Inc.

PREMIUM PLUS - Cement - Custom Building Products

PREMIUM PLUS - Crackers - Nabisco Foods Group

PREMIUM PLUS - Electrodes - EGL Co. Inc.

PREMIUM PLUS - Mattresses - Classic Corp.

PREMIUM PLUS - Oils–lubricating - Primrose Oil Co., Inc.

PREMIUM POOL, THE - Swimming pools - Fort Wayne Plastics, Inc.

PREMIUM POP - Popcorn - Princeton Farms

PREMIUM POWER PRODUCTS - Motor vehicle parts and accessories - Navistar International Transportation Corp.

PREMIUM PRINT - Paper - Butler Paper Co.

PREMIUM PRO - Computer software - Tritech Software Development Corp.

PREMIUM QUALITY - Pet products - Ginger, Inc.

PREMIUM QUALITY ODYSSEY SEAFOODS - Seafood products–canned or cured - Odyssey Corp.

PREMIUM QUALITY WAKEFIELD - Shrimp–fresh or frozen - Rich-Seapak Corp.

PREMIUM RADIAL RIDE PLUS - Automotive repair shops–tires - Summit Tire and Battery, Inc.

PREMIUM RATTLESNAKE - Beverages–malt - Kershenstine's Diamond Beer

PREMIUM RECIPE - Bakery products - Roush Products Co., Inc.

PREMIUM RECIPE - Food products - Pocahontas Foods USA Inc.

PREMIUM ROCK - Salt - Gunther Salt Co.

PREMIUM RUNBRITE - Paper–writing - Mead Corp.

PREMIUM RUT - Sporting goods - Ole Time Woodsman

PREMIUM SELECT - Fruit drinks–bottled or canned - Lykes Services Co.

PREMIUM SELECT - Oils–lubricating - Primrose Oil Co., Inc.

PREMIUM SELECT - Pet food - Eagle Products, Inc.

PREMIUM SELECT - Vegetables–frozen - Ore-Ida Foods, Inc.

PREMIUM SELECTIONS - Meat products–poultry - Tyson Foods Inc.

PREMIUM SERIES, THE - Moldings and trim - Saroyan Lumber Co.

PREMIUM SK - Cleaning preparations - Expert Products

PREMIUM SOW PLUS - Animal feeds - Carl S. Akey Inc.

PREMIUM STANDARD FARMS - Meat products–pork - PSF Finance L.P.

PREMIUM STANDARDS - Vitamins and nutritional supplements - McZand Herbal, Inc.

PREMIUM STONE GROUND - Food products - Morrison Milling Co.

PREMIUM SWINE 5S - Animal feeds - Carl S. Akey Inc.

PREMIUM THE GREEN LINE - Vitamins and nutritional supplements - Ultravit Enterprises, Inc.

PREMIUM THERMOLITE - Paints - Standard Brands Paint Co.

PREMIUM TIME - Paper–writing - George H. Stevenson

PREMIUM TOUCH - Yarn - Peck Manufacturing Co.

PREMIUM ULTRA STUFF - Pillow stuffing - American Fiber Industries Corp.

PREMIUM WASHINGTON CHEESE - Cheese - Washington Farms Distribution Inc.

PREMIUM WILDFLOWER GARDENS - Flowers, plants, and seeds - Applewood Seed & Garden Group

PREMIXX - Health care products - Pharma Botanixx

PREMO - Chairs–metal - Alvin and Co. Inc.

PREMO - Yarns and threads - Fil-Tec, Inc.

PREMOFAST - Yarn - Fil-Tec, Inc.

PREMOSE - Beverages–alcohol - Premier Malt Products, Inc.

PREMOULDED MEMBRANE - Adhesives and sealants - W.R. Meadows Inc.

PREMPHASE - Pharmaceutical preparations - American Home Products Corp.

PREMSYN PMS - Pharmaceutical preparations - Chattem Inc.

PREMULATUM - Cosmetics - Canyon Global Corp.

PRENAL - Pharmaceutical preparations ☆ - Lemmon Co.

PRENATAL-B - Pharmaceutical preparations - Blair Pharmacal

PRENATE - Animal feed supplements - Feed Specialties Co. Inc.

PRENATE 90 - Pharmaceutical preparations - Bock Pharmacal Co.

PRENAVITE - Pharmaceutical preparations - Rugby Laboratories Inc.

PRENDIVILLE LOOPS - Medical apparatus - Utah Medical Products, Inc.

PRENTICE HALL PRESS - Publisher's imprints - Prentice-Hall, Inc.

PRENTISS - Apparel–men's - Prentiss Manufacturing Co. Inc.

PREP - Cleaning preparations - Fabulon Products

PREP - Cleaning preparations–carpet and rug - Host/Racine Industries Inc.

PREP - Computer software - American Academy of Pediatrics

PREP - Shaving preparations - Mark Allen Co.

PREP - Shaving preparations - Parks Products Inc.

PREP - Shortening - Procter & Gamble Co.

PREP - Sporting goods - Schutt Manufacturing Co.

PREP-AID - Laboratory apparatus - Spex CertiPrep, Inc.

PREP & PAINT - Paints - United States Refining Co.

PREP & PAPER - Paints - United States Refining Co.

PREP CREW - Tools - Wooster Brush Co.

PREP-IT-ALL - Wallpaper ☆ - Reliable Finishing Products, Inc.

PREP KIT - Laxatives - C.B. Fleet Co. Inc.

PREP-KLEEN - Cleaning preparations - Sterling-Clark-Lurton Corp.

PREP-MIX - Cement - Synkoloid Co.

PREP N' HANG - Tools - Warner Manufacturing Co.

PREP 'N SIZE - Wallpaper - California Products Corp.

PREP N' STAY - Health care products - Pharmaceutical Innovations

PREP PEN - Cleaning preparations - Pro Motorcar Products Inc.

PREP-PLANE - Brushes - Wooster Brush Co.

PREP-PLUS - Animal feed - Purina Mills, Inc.

PREP-RITE - Archery equipment - Bohning Co. Ltd.

PREP SEAL - Paints - Wikel Manufacturing Co. Inc.

PREP STEP - Paints - Valspar Corp.

PREP TEAM - Automotive parts and accessories - Minnesota Mining & Manufacturing Co.

PREP-WALL - Sealing compounds - Synkoloid Co.

PREP WIPES - Polishing cloths - Mainline Industries Inc.

PREPAIR - Pharmaceutical preparations - Trimensa Corp.

PREPARATION 77 - Veterinary product ☆ - American Equine Products Inc.

PREPARATION H - Pharmaceutical preparations - Whitehall Laboratories

PREPARE - Animal feed - Purina Mills, Inc.

PREPARED - Prerecorded video tapes - Healthcare Works

PREPCORT - Pharmaceutical preparations - Whitehall Laboratories

PREPIDIL - Pharmaceutical preparations - Upjohn Co.

PREPJET - Dental equipment - American Dental Technologies, Inc.

PREPKOTE - Paint removers - Morris Paint & Varnish Co.

PREPMASTER - Educational materials - Prepmaster Review

PREPOL - Chemical preparations - Karlen Manufacturing, Inc.

PREPPIE! - Video games - Atari Games Corp.

PREPPY - House furnishings - Dan River Inc.

PREPPY PAL - Dolls - Mattel, Inc.

PREPPY PUPPY - Pet products - Debra Girard

PREPRIDER - Frames–eyeglass ☆ - Universal/Univis Inc.

PREPRUFE - Building materials - W.R. Grace & Co.

PREPTRODE - Health care products - Pharmaceutical Innovations

PREPZ - Sealant - Masterchem Industries, Inc.

☆ = Now out of production

PREQ 3 - Amplifiers - Night Technologies, Inc.
PRES-A-PLY - Office supplies - Avery Dennison Corp.
PRES DE CHAMONIX - Apparel–women's - Moonstone Mountaineering, Inc.
PRES-ON - Adhesives and sealants - Pres-On Merchandising Corp.
PRES-R-CUFF - Medical apparatus - Marquette Electronics, Inc.
PRES-STIK - Envelopes - Western States Envelope Co.
PRES-TO-HEAT - Tools–soldering - Esico Triton
PRES-TO-SEAL - Adhesives and sealants - IDL Manufacturing & Sales Corp.
PRES-TOCK - Mats - Weyerhaeuser Co.
PRESADIL - Pharmaceutical preparations ☆ - Econo Med Pharmaceuticals Inc.
PRESALIN - Pharmaceutical preparations - Roberts/Hauck Pharmaceuticals Inc.
PRESAMINE - Pharmaceutical preparations - Rhone-Poulenc Rorer Pharmaceuticals Inc.
PRESARIO - Computers–personal - Compaq Computer Corp.
PRESARIO - Slacks - Corbin Ltd.
PRESAT - Electrical equipment - Preventative Maintenance Corp.
PRESBIFLEX - Ophthalmic goods - Breger Mueller Welt Corp.
PRESCALE - Mouthwashes - J. Coleman, Inc.
PRESCENT - Deodorizers - Jerome Flax
PRESCHOOL EXPRESS, THE - Publisher's imprints - Creative Teaching Press
PRESCHOOL PARADE - Computer software - Nordic Software, Inc.
PRESCHOOL PRESS - Publisher's imprints - Playmore Inc. Publishers
PRESCHOOLERS BIBLE, THE - Publisher's imprints - Scripture Press Publications Inc.
PRESCLIP - Paper clips - Charles Leonard Inc.
PRESCO - Spices and extracts - Presco Food Seasonings Inc.
PRESCOLITE - Lighting fixtures - Hanson Lighting Group
PRESCOTT - Cabinets–wood ☆ - Kemper
PRESCOTT - Furniture - Haworth, Inc.
PRESCOTT PENGUIN - Dolls - Mattel, Inc.
PRESCRIBED CARE - Skin care products - Almay Inc.
PRESCRIPTION - Paints - Red Spot Paint & Varnish Co., Inc.
PRESCRIPTION - Recording label - Prescription Co.
PRESCRIPTION - Sunglasses ☆ - Bolle' America, Inc.
PRESCRIPTION ART - Containers–plastic - Patricia F. Kussin
PRESCRIPTION DIET - Pet products - Hill's Pet Nutrition Inc.
PRESCRIPTION DIET A/D - Veterinary pharmaceutical preparations - Colgate-Palmolive Co.
PRESCRIPTION DIET HEALTHBLEND - Pet products - Hill's Pet Nutrition Inc.
PRESCRIPTION DIET T/D - Veterinary nutritional supplements - Colgate-Palmolive Co.
PRESCRIPTION FLEX - Orthopedic products - Northwest Podiatric Laboratory, Inc.
PRESCRIPTION FOR NAILS - Nail-care products - Cabot Laboratories Inc.
PRESCRIPTION ONE - Vitamins and nutritional supplements - Bionutritional Research Group, Inc.
PRESCRIPTION PACK - Exercising equipment - Hygenic Corp.
PRESCRIPTION PACKAGING - Cardboard - Liberty Diversified Industries Inc.
PRESCRIPTION PLUS - Skin-care products, makeup - American Institute of Esthetics
PRESCRIPTION SLEEP SYSTEM - Mattresses - Amana Bedding Co.
PRESCRIPTIONS - Vinyl - Tarkett, Inc.
PRESCRIPTIVES - Skin care products - Estee Lauder Inc.
PRESCRIPTOR - Hearing aids - Hearing Health Group Inc.
PRESCUT - Glassware–household - Anchor Hocking Glass, Inc.
PRESDWOOD - Wood products - Masonite Corp.
PRESEASON - Footwear and clothing - Reebok International Ltd.
PRESEIS - Hydrophones - I/O Exploration Products (U.S.A.), Inc.
PRESENCE - Diapers–disposable - Inbrand Corp.
PRESENCE - Electronic equipment - Shure Brothers, Inc.
PRESENCE - Ophthalmic goods - Foremost Optical Products
PRESENCE - Perfumes - Houbigant, Inc.
PRESENCE OF ANGELS, THE - Figurines - Presence of Angels, Inc.
PRESENCE SENSE - Lighting fixtures - Hubbell Lighting, Inc. (Lighting Div.)
PRESENT CO. - Apparel–women's ☆ - Bobbie Brooks Inc.
PRESENT-IT - Notebooks and notepads - Riverside Paper Corp.
PRESENT-O-FOLIO - Calendars - Design-A-Day, Inc.
PRESENT PERFECT - Ribbons - Stephen Lawrence Co.
PRESENTATION - Easels - Anco Wood Specialties Inc.
PRESENTATION - Floor coverings–carpet and rugs - Philadelphia Carpets
PRESENTATION - Hair care products - Wella Corp. (Consumer Products Div.)
PRESENTATION - Servingware - Indiana Glass Co.
PRESENTATION - Sporting goods - Normark Corp.
PRESENTATION ELECTRICS - Cooking equipment–household ☆ - Farberware Inc.

PRESENTATION ENVIRONMENTS - Furniture - Bretford Manufacturing, Inc.
PRESENTATION I - Fishing leaders ☆ - Cortland Line Co., Inc.
PRESENTATION LINE, THE - Leather goods - Helm Leathercraft Inc.
PRESENTATION MODEL - Recoil pads - Pachmayr Ltd.
PRESENTATION SHOWCASE - Artists' materials - Custom Case Co.
PRESENTATION SOLUTIONS - Video equipment - Presentation Solutions, Inc.
PRESENTATIONPAK - Paper products - Unicover Corp.
PRESENTATIONS - Computer software - Corel USA
PRESENTATIONS - Furniture ☆ - Bassett Furniture Industries, Inc.
PRESENTATIONS - Magazines - Lakewood Publications Acquisition Corp.
PRESENTENSE - Dishes–earthenware - MGP Corp.
PRESENTER - Easels - Pierce Business Products Inc.
PRESENTER - Lighting equipment - Cornerstone/Clearlight
PRESENTERPAD - Computer software - Avalon Engineering, Inc.
PRESENTIT - Computer software - Shoreline Electronics, Inc.
PRESENTS - Giftware ☆ - Enesco Corp.
PRESERV-A-PAK - Bags–storage - Curtis 1000 Inc.
PRESERV-A-SHOE - Shoe polish ☆ - Classic Plaques Inc.
PRESERV-O-SOTE - Wood preservative - Crowley Tar Products Co. Inc.
PRESERV-WOOD - Wood products ☆ - Fibreboard Corp.
PRESERVA CLEANSE - Vitamins and nutritional supplements ☆ - Kroeger Herb Products Co. Inc.
PRESERVA-COAT - Paints ☆ - Lilly Perfection Paint
PRESERVATION - Pressure cookers ☆ - National Presto Industries, Inc.
PRESERVATION KRAFT - Envelopes - Niagara Envelope Co., Inc.
PRESERVATION STONE - Envelopes - Niagara Envelope Co., Inc.
PRESERVATION WORLD BLUES TRUST - Museums - Robinson Property Group LP
PRESERVATONE - Automotive parts and accessories - U.S. Chemical and Plastics Inc.
PRESERVE - Chemical preparations - McCulloch Corp.
PRESERVE - Paper–toweling - Von Drehle Corp.
PRESERVE - Toothbrushes - Recycline, Inc.
PRESERVE - Wood products - Chemical Specialties, Inc.
PRESERVE-A-TAX - Binders - Remington Products
PRESERVE THE MOMENT - Florists - Faster-Form Corp.
PRESERVED BAITS - Fishing lures - Brown Bear Bait Co.
PRESERVED PERSONALITIES - Dolls - Russ Berrie and Co., Inc.
PRESERVER'S - Fruits–canned - Swiss American Import Co.
PRESERVEX - Paints - K & S Marketing Services Inc.
PRESERVO - Sealing compounds - Champion Products Inc.
PRESFILM - Plastics film - Prestype Inc.
PRESIDENT - Boats–motor - Seajay Boats Inc.
PRESIDENT - Boats–motor ☆ - Lund Boat Co.
PRESIDENT - Boots - Willert Home Products, Inc.
PRESIDENT - Cheese - Besnier USA, Inc.
PRESIDENT - Cosmetics ☆ - Dubl Duck/Jet Set Inc.
PRESIDENT - Envelopes - Western States Envelope Co.
PRESIDENT - Fishing tackle - Shakespeare Co.
PRESIDENT - Floor coverings–carpet and rugs ☆ - Navan Carpets Inc.
PRESIDENT - Guns ☆ - Armsport Inc.
PRESIDENT - Industrial pumps - Graco Inc.
PRESIDENT - Jewelry - Jacoby-Bender Inc.
PRESIDENT - Leather goods - St. Thomas Inc.
PRESIDENT - Motor vehicles–motor homes ☆ - Coachmen Industries, Inc.
PRESIDENT - Motor vehicles–motor homes ☆ - Honey Recreational Vehicles Inc.
PRESIDENT - Musical instruments ☆ - Fred Gretsch Enterprises
PRESIDENT - Office furniture–metal - Joyce International Inc.
PRESIDENT - Pencils ☆ - Faber-Castell Corp.
PRESIDENT - Pet products - President Trading USA Inc.
PRESIDENT - Projectors–photographic - Toshiba America Medical Systems Inc.
PRESIDENT - Rackets–tennis - Fischer
PRESIDENT - Thread - Lewis Threads Inc.
PRESIDENT - Watches - Rolex Watch USA, Inc.
PRESIDENT BAKING - Bakery products - President Baking Co., Inc.
PRESIDENT BOND - Envelopes ☆ - Quality Park Products Co.
PRESIDENT I - Boats–motor - Seajay Boats Inc.
PRESIDENT IS MISSING, THE - Computer software - Cosmi Corp.
PRESIDENT MAJOR - Floor coverings–carpet and rugs - Navan Carpets Inc.
PRESIDENT PELL - Toys - Mattel, Inc.
PRESIDENT RIVERBOAT CASINO, THE - Metal accessories - Connelly Group
PRESIDENT, THE - Wigs - New Image
PRESIDENT, THE - Notebooks and notepads - Riverside Paper Corp.
PRESIDENTE - Brandy - Domecq Importers Inc.

PRESIDENTE - Cigars - General Cigar Co., Inc.
PRESIDENTE - Cigars - Tropical Tobacco, Inc.
PRESIDENTE BEER - Beverages–malt - Martlet Importing Co.
PRESIDENTE PILSENER - Beverages–malt - The Stroh Brewery Co.
PRESIDENTIAL - Electronic equipment - George R. Snell Associates, Inc.
PRESIDENTIAL - Firearms, accessories, and parts - Welsh Sporting Goods Corp. (Boyt Div.)
PRESIDENTIAL - Flags - Annin and Co.
PRESIDENTIAL - Floor coverings - American Floor Products Co. Inc.
PRESIDENTIAL - Floor coverings–carpet and rugs - Blue Ridge Carpet Mills
PRESIDENTIAL - Glassware–household - Federal Glass
PRESIDENTIAL - Glassware–household - Owens-Illinois Inc. (Libbey Div.)
PRESIDENTIAL - Glassware–household - Rhinehart Glass
PRESIDENTIAL - Health care products - Sunrise Medical
PRESIDENTIAL - Hearing aids - Electone Inc.
PRESIDENTIAL - Horseshoes - St. Pierre Manufacturing Corp.
PRESIDENTIAL - Lecturn - Van San Corp.
PRESIDENTIAL - Luggage - United States Luggage Corp.
PRESIDENTIAL - Manufactured homes - Redman Industries, Inc.
PRESIDENTIAL - Mattresses - High Point Bedding, Inc.
PRESIDENTIAL - Motor vehicle parts and accessories - Raymark Friction Co.
PRESIDENTIAL - Office supplies - Alvin and Co. Inc.
PRESIDENTIAL - Paints - MCI Quality Coatings
PRESIDENTIAL - Pens - Parker Pen USA
PRESIDENTIAL - Portfolio covers - Pajco Products Inc.
PRESIDENTIAL - Tableware–china - Lenox, Inc.
PRESIDENTIAL - Water heaters–household - State Industries, Inc.
PRESIDENTIAL - Wines - Jack Poust & Co. Inc.
PRESIDENTIAL 500 - Luggage - Ventura Travelware Inc.
PRESIDENTIAL BURLS - Frames–picture - Framemica Co.
PRESIDENTIAL COLLECTION - Lamps - Rembrandt Lamps
PRESIDENTIAL COLLECTION - Office supplies ☆ - McDonald Products
PRESIDENTIAL FACTS - Toys–electronic - Mattel, Inc.
PRESIDENTIAL LEATHER - Office supplies - McDonald Products
PRESIDENTIAL PARCHMENT - Paper–bond ☆ - Marvin Envelope & Paper Co.
PRESIDENTIAL ROCKER - Rocking chairs - P and P Chair Co.
PRESIDENTIAL SHAKE - Shingles–asphalt or tar - Celotex Corp.
PRESIDENTIAL STRIPE - Wallpaper - Blumenthal
PRESIDENTIAL SUITE - Floor coverings–carpet and rugs - Durkan Patterned Carpets
PRESIDENTIAL TASTER - Glassware–household ☆ - Crisa Corp.
PRESIDENT'S - Wines - Seagram's Chateau & Estate Wines Co.
PRESIDENT'S CHOICE - Floor coverings–carpet and rugs - American Carpet Mills
PRESIDENTS CHOICE - Flooring–hardwood - Permagrain Products, Inc.
PRESIDENT'S CHOICE - Food products - American Stores Co.
PRESIDENT'S CHOICE - Pillows - Pacific Coast Feather Co.
PRESIDENT'S CHOICE, THE - Whiskey - Brown-Forman Corp.
PRESIDENTS CHOICE, THE - Siding, paneling, and accessories - Heartland Building Products Inc.
PRESIDENT'S COLLECTION - Furniture - Evenflo Juvenile Furniture Co.
PRESIDENT'S COLLECTION - Giftware - Koeze Co.
PRESIDENTS CUP, THE - Apparel and accessories - PGA Tour, Inc.
PRESIDENT'S LADY - Wigs ☆ - Paula Young
PRESIDENT'S LUNCH, THE - Pollen extracts - CC Pollen Co.
PRESIDENTS OF THE UNITED STATES OF AMERICA, THE - Video production - Presidents of the United States of America
PRESIDENTS PHYSICAL FITNESS - Computer software - Hartley Courseware Inc.
PRESIDENTS PRIDE - Food products - Bar S Food Co. Inc.
PRESIDENT'S SIGNATURE - Shrimp–fresh or frozen - New England Shrimp Co. Inc.
PRESIDENT'S SNACK BAR - Vitamins and nutritional supplements ☆ - CC Pollen Co.
PRESIDENTS, THE - Dolls - Effanbee Doll Corp.
PRESIDIO - Fabrics - Dan River Inc.
PRESIDIO - Floor coverings–carpet and rugs ☆ - Hollytex Carpet Mills Inc.
PRESIDIO - Furniture - Tropitone Furniture Co. Inc.
PRESIDIO - Incense - Gps, Inc.
PRESIDIO - Leather and sheep-lined clothing - Sawyer of Napa, Inc.
PRESIDIO - Rings–jewelry - Artcarved Inc.
PRESIDIO - Vegetable sauces ☆ - Sauces Unlimited Inc.
PRESIDIO II - Furniture - Tropitone Furniture Co. Inc.
PRESIDO - Hardware ☆ - Masonite Corp.
PRESIDOR - Cookies - GWB Imports

PRESIDOR WAFEROLLS - Confections - GWB Imports
PRESOLVE - Cleaning preparations - LPS Laboratories, Inc.
PRESQUE ISLE WINE CELLARS - Wines - Presque Isle Wine Cellars
PRESS - Recording label - Jazz Composer's Orchestra Association Inc.
PRESS 2 GO - Computer software - Atex Publishing Systems Corp.
PRESS-A-NUMBER - Housewares - Barnhart Industries Inc.
PRESS-A-PATTERN - Housewares - Barnhart Industries Inc.
PRESS - A - PRINT - Printing trades machinery - Press A Print
PRESS-ABC'S - Housewares - Barnhart Industries Inc.
PRESS ACTION TRUCKS - Toys - Tonka Corp.
PRESS AND CLOSE - Office supplies - Uniflex, Inc.
PRESS & GO NAIL KITS - Nail-care products - Cosmar Corp.
PRESS & PRINT - Novelty items - Paper Magic Group Inc.
PRESS-BAK - Furniture - Super Sagless Corp.
PRESS BOOK - Binders - Jordan Bondstar
PRESS-BOOT - Gaskets - Press-Seal Gasket Corp.
PRESS CLUB BLEND - Beverages–alcohol - Kasser Laird Distilling Co.
PRESS-ETTE - Ironing boards ☆ - Duchess Royale Inc.
PRESS-EVAC FLUID SYSTEMS - Machinery - Pure Technology, Inc.
PRESS-FELT - Housewares - Barnhart Industries Inc.
PRESS FLASH - Photographic equipment ☆ - Dura Electric Lamp Co. Inc.
PRESS GRIP - Weightlifting equipment - Steven B. Carter
PRESS-GUARD - Binders - Fiber Mark, Inc.
PRESS-IN-PLACE - Caulking compounds - Minnesota Mining & Manufacturing Co.
PRESS LOCK CHECKERS - Games - Warren Industries Inc.
PRESS MASTER - Electronic equipment - Rollei of America Inc.
PRESS-MATE - Iron products - June Tailor Inc.
PRESS MOUNT - Paperboard - Salwen Paper Co. Inc.
PRESS 'N DAB - Glue–household or industrial - Manco, Inc.
PRESS-N-GO - Cosmetics - Ardell International Inc.
PRESS 'N' HANG - Housewares - Molor Products Co.
PRESS 'N HOLD - Manicure preparations - Barristo Ltd.
PRESS 'N' LISTEN - Electronic equipment - Western Publishing Co., Inc.
PRESS 'N PAINT - Paints–artists' - Manco, Inc.
PRESS 'N PLAY - Toys - Little Tikes Co.
PRESS 'N PLAY - Toys - Tonka Corp.
PRESS N SAND - Paper–sand - Minnesota Mining & Manufacturing Co.
PRESS-N-SET - Tiles–ceramic ☆ - American Olean Tile Co.
PRESS N' SEW - Quilts - Extra Special Products Corp.
PRESS-N-STICK - Photo albums ☆ - Webway, Inc.
PRESS N TEAR - Fabrics - Sew-Art International
PRESS 'N' TELL BUNNY - Toys - Great American Fun Corp.
PRESS-ON - Apparel and accessories - Associated Bag Co.
PRESS ON BODY TATTOOS - Decals and transfers - Lee Pharmaceuticals
PRESS-ON COLOR - Nail care products - Orly International Inc.
PRESS-OUTS - Toys - Tonka Corp.
PRESS-PACK - Pet products - L/M Animal Farms, Inc.
PRESS PASS - Trading cards - Press Pass
PRESS PLUS - Ironing boards - Design Trend, Inc.
PRESS PRETTY - Toys - Mattel, Inc.
PRESS QUEEN - Ironing board pads - Magla Products Inc.
PRESS-SIDE - Paints - Vergason Technology, Inc.
PRESS-SURE - Adhesives and sealants - Pressure Graphics Inc.
PRESS-T0-SEAL - Caulking compounds - Mortite Inc.
PRESS-TAPE - Rubber cement - Garon Products Inc.
PRESS-TO-LOCK - Binders - Dennison National Co.
PRESS TO PLAY - Computer software - Don Johnston Inc.
PRESSA C - Juice extracting devices - Robert Krups North America
PRESSA MINI - Juice extracting devices - Robert Krups North America
PRESSALIT - DANSK toilet seats ☆ - Jaclo Inc.
PRESSCAR - Health care products - Tecnol Medical Products, Inc.
PRESSCO TECHNOLOGY INC. - Computer integrated systems design services - Pressco Technology, Inc.
PRESSDIRECTOR - Computer peripheral equipment - T/R Systems, Inc.
PRESSDOWN - Decals - American Decal
PRESSEAL - Boxes - Cavert Wire Co. Inc.
PRESSED FLOWER - Clocks - General Time Corp. (Westclox/Seth Thomas Div.)
PRESSED IN THE USA - Apple juice - Bowman Apple Products Co. Inc.
PRESSED PETALS - Giftware - Pressed Petals, Inc.
PRESSED POWDER COMPACT - Cosmetics - Viviane Woodard Industries, Ltd.
PRESSED TIONESTA - Floor coverings–tile ☆ - Kepcor, Inc./SSI Tiles
PRESSING MATTERS - Neckties - Patricia Kutza
PRESSING ON - Greeting cards - Warner Press, Inc.

☆ = Now out of production

PRESSION - Health care products - Chattanooga Group, Inc.
PRESSIT SEALIT - Office supplies - Mead Corp.
PRESSMAN - Tape players–cassette - Sony Corp. of America
PRESSMAN - Toys - Pressman Toy Corp.
PRESSMAN'S BEST FRIEND - Gloves–safety - Guards Corp.
PRESSMASTER - Paper - Copco Papers Inc.
PRESS'N COLOR - Games - Lakeside Games
PRESS'N CURL - Curling irons–electric - Windmere Corp.
PRESS'N SEAL - Caulking compounds ☆ - Sika Corp.
PRESSNAP - Binders - Charles Leonard Inc.
PRESST - Housewares - Ironees Co.
PRESST-O-CEL - Rubber–acrylic - BASF Corp.
PRESSTAPE - Photographic equipment - Eastman Kodak Co.
PRESSTEX - Binders - ACCO USA, Inc.
PRESSTIGHT - Office supplies - Charles Leonard Inc.
PRESSTIK - File folders - Charles Leonard Inc.
PRESSTO - Office supplies - Warshaw Manufacturing Co. Inc.
PRESSTO - Pens - Accutec Inc.
PRESSTO - Wallcovering - D.W. Wallcovering, Inc.
PRESSUR-FORMD - Hardware ☆ - Holo-Krome Co.
PRESSUR-LO - Health care products - Futurebiotics
PRESSURE ALERT - Health care products - Medical Industries America, Inc.
PRESSURE-BACK - Pistons - Outboard Marine Corp.
PRESSURE CARE - Agricultural machinery - Custom Marketing
PRESSURE CLEAN - Plumbing fixtures–enameled - Kohler Co.
PRESSURE DROP - Computer software - Rocket Science Games, Inc.
PRESSURE EEZ - Health care products - Med Foam
PRESSURE FRESH - Fruits and vegetables - PCP Partnership
PRESSURE KING - Water-pressure systems ☆ - Attwood Corp.
PRESSURE LIFT - Padding–foam - Juanita Carver
PRESSURE LITE - Toilets–enameled - Kohler Co.
PRESSURE-LOCK - Electrical equipment - Thomas Industries Inc. (Tool & Fastener Div.)
PRESSURE-LOCK - Electronic equipment - General Electric Co.
PRESSURE MAID - Paint sprayers ☆ - Campbell Group (Wayne Home Equipment Div.)
PRESSURE MAX - Marine pumps ☆ - ITT Jabsco
PRESSURE PAINTER - Paint rollers - Padco Companies, Inc.
PRESSURE POINT - Bicycles - Roadmaster Corp.
PRESSURE PRINCESS - Water-pressure systems ☆ - Attwood Corp.
PRESSURE PROOFED - Pencils - Faber-Castell Corp.
PRESSURE QUEEN - Water-pressure systems ☆ - Attwood Corp.
PRESSURE RELEASE FLUTES - Sporting goods - O'Brien International
PRESSURE RELIEF - Adhesives and sealants ☆ - W.R. Meadows Inc.
PRESSURE RISER - Electronic equipment - Schaffer Test Products, Inc.
PRESSURE STIK - Office supplies - Avery Label Systems
PRESSUREATER - Valves - M & FC Holding Co., Inc.
PRESSUREFLEX - Hoses - Hose Master, Inc.
PRESSUREGUARD - Health care products - HealthFLEX Inc.
PRESSURESCAN - Medical apparatus - Del Mar Avionics
PRESSUREWASHERPLUS - Sprayers - Ryobi America Corp.
PRESSUREWOUND - Musical instrument accessories - GHS Strings
PRESSUROMETER - Medical apparatus - Del Mar Avionics
PRESSVIEW - Computer software - Supermac Technology
PRESSWELD - Welding equipment - Colson Caster Corp.
PRESSWISE - Computer software - Aldus Corp.
PREST-4-LIFE - Apparel and accessories - Barrow Manufacturing Co., Inc.
PREST-O-FLEX - Jewelry - Jacoby-Bender Inc.
PREST-O-SLIDE - Jewelry - Jacoby-Bender Inc.
PREST-ON - Hardware - Prest-On Co.
PRESTAPE - Office supplies - Prestype Inc.
PRESTART 700 - Animal feeds - Carl S. Akey Inc.
PRESTAX - Paperboard - Savage Universal Corp.
PRESTE - Floor coverings - Compass Concepts
PRESTIGE - Apparel–women's - Cape Cod Cricket Lane
PRESTIGE - Audio cabinets–wood - Luxor
PRESTIGE - Automotive parts and accessories - Lancaster Colony Automotive Group
PRESTIGE - Benches–metal - Artesian Industries
PRESTIGE - Bicycles ☆ - Roadmaster Corp.
PRESTIGE - Blankets - Chatham Manufacturing Co.
PRESTIGE - Cabinets - Prestige Inc.
PRESTIGE - Candy - McDonald Candy Co. Inc.
PRESTIGE - Candy ☆ - Pet Inc. (Whitman's Chocolates Div.)
PRESTIGE - Car-security systems - Audiovox Corp.
PRESTIGE - Cheese - Anco Foods Corp.

PRESTIGE - Cheese - Churny Co., Inc.
PRESTIGE - Cleaning preparations–household - Gem Inc.
PRESTIGE - Clocks - General Time Corp. (Westclox/Seth Thomas Div.)
PRESTIGE - Coffee - S & D Coffee, Inc.
PRESTIGE - Cutlery ☆ - Lifetime Hoan Corp.
PRESTIGE - Desk sets - Artistic Office Products
PRESTIGE - Dishes–plastic - Plastics, Inc. (Anchor Hocking Plastics)
PRESTIGE - Doughnuts - Prestige American Foods
PRESTIGE - Drinkware - Indiana Glass Co.
PRESTIGE - Faucets - Kallista Inc.
PRESTIGE - Floor coverings - Congoleum Corp.
PRESTIGE - Floor coverings–carpet and rugs - J and J Industries Inc.
PRESTIGE - Floor coverings–carpet and rugs - Johnson's Carpets Inc.
PRESTIGE - Floor coverings–carpet and rugs ☆ - Regal Rugs Inc.
PRESTIGE - Floor coverings–carpet and rugs ☆ - Robertex Associates Inc.
PRESTIGE - Floor coverings–carpet and rugs ☆ - Walter Carpet Mills
PRESTIGE - Flowers, plants, and seeds - Abbott Laboratories
PRESTIGE - Food products - Cap's Italian Foods Inc.
PRESTIGE - Furniture - Thomasville Furniture Industries Inc.
PRESTIGE - Furniture–upholstered ☆ - Bassett Furniture Industries, Inc.
PRESTIGE - Glassware–household - Federal Glass
PRESTIGE - Glassware–household - Oneida Ltd.
PRESTIGE - Greeting cards ☆ - American Artists Group Inc.
PRESTIGE - Hair care products ☆ - Astra International Corp.
PRESTIGE - Hair care products ☆ - Stevley International
PRESTIGE - Leather goods - St. Thomas Inc.
PRESTIGE - Luggage - Whitmor Manufacturing Co. Inc.
PRESTIGE - Luggage ☆ - Universal Trav-ler Inc.
PRESTIGE - Makeup brushes and manicure tools ☆ - London International U.S. Holdings
PRESTIGE - Manila paper - Boston Paper Board Corp.
PRESTIGE - Mattresses - Lisco, Inc.
PRESTIGE - Napkins–paper - Scott Paper Co.
PRESTIGE - Office supplies - JM Co.
PRESTIGE - Office supplies ☆ - Esselte Corp.
PRESTIGE - Paints - Servistar Corp.
PRESTIGE - Paper ☆ - Esleeck Manufacturing Co., Inc.
PRESTIGE - Paper ☆ - Union Camp Corp. (Fine Paper Division)
PRESTIGE - Paper–gift wrap - Gift Wrap Co.
PRESTIGE - Pet products - Roccorp, Inc.
PRESTIGE - Phonographs - Fantasy Inc.
PRESTIGE - Puzzles - Warren Industries Inc.
PRESTIGE - Sporting goods - Outdoor Technologies Group
PRESTIGE - Stoves–gas ☆ - Caloric Corp.
PRESTIGE - Tiles–ceramic - AGA Corp.
PRESTIGE - Toys–models - ERTL Co., Inc.
PRESTIGE - Vaccines - Bayer Corp.
PRESTIGE - Watches - Nicolet International Inc.
PRESTIGE - Water heaters–household - Mor-Flo Industries Inc.
PRESTIGE - Wheelchairs - Jaken Co., Inc.
PRESTIGE - Window coverings - Bamboo-Abbott Inc.
PRESTIGE - Windows - Louisiana-Pacific Corp.
PRESTIGE - Wines - Prestige Wine Co.
PRESTIGE & CREATION - Hair care products - Prestige & Creation, Inc.
PRESTIGE AUDIO - Stereos - House of Imports Inc.
PRESTIGE BOND - Paper–bond - Saxon Nuco Inc.
PRESTIGE BOOKS - Publisher's imprints - Advent Books Inc.
PRESTIGE BOOKS INC. - Publisher's imprints ☆ - Playmore Inc. Publishers
PRESTIGE COLLECTION - Apparel and accessories - Kellwood Co.
PRESTIGE COLLECTION - Wallpaper - Prestige Wallcoverings
PRESTIGE COLLECTION - Wallpaper - S.R. Wood Inc.
PRESTIGE COMFORT PRODUCTS INT'L INC. - Recliners - Prestige Comfort Products Int'l, Inc.
PRESTIGE CUSTOM - Drums–musical instruments - Pearl Corp.
PRESTIGE DOLL COLLECTION, THE - Dolls - Kingstate Corp.
PRESTIGE EDITIONS - Posters ☆ - Class Posters
PRESTIGE GIFT BOX SYSTEMS - Boxes - Gift Box Corp. of America
PRESTIGE MAT - Mat boards - Callen Photo Mount Corp.
PRESTIGE PLASTIC - Boxes - U.S. Box Crafts Inc.
PRESTIGE PLATE - Giftware - Nobility-Prestige Co.
PRESTIGE PLUS - Sinks–metal - Franke, Inc.
PRESTIGE PLUSH - Floor coverings–carpet and rugs - Prestige Mills Inc.
PRESTIGE PRINTS - Greeting cards - American Artists Group Inc.
PRESTIGE PROFILES - Frames–picture - Acme Frame Products, Inc.
PRESTIGE SESSION - Drums–musical instruments - Pearl Corp.
PRESTIGE STUDIO - Drums–musical instruments - Pearl Corp.

PRESTIGE VELOUR - Floor coverings–carpet and rugs ☆ - Karastan-Bigelow Inc.

PRESTINI - Musical instrument accessories - Prestini Reed Corp.

PRESTINI PADS - Musical instrument accessories - Ardsley Musical Instrument Co.

PRESTISSIMO - Preserved foods–prepackaged ☆ - Sanwa Foods Inc.

PRESTO - Apparel and accessories - School Apparel, Inc.

PRESTO - Briefcases ☆ - Art Craft Wallets Inc.

PRESTO - Brushes–paint - Imperial Paint Applicators Ltd.

PRESTO - Cameras ☆ - Edixa Camera Co.

PRESTO - Chimes ☆ - J.W. Stannard Co.

PRESTO - Cigarette lighters ☆ - New Method Manufacturing Co.

PRESTO - Computer software - Kendall Square Research Corp.

PRESTO - Connectors–electrical - Richland Manufacturing Co.

PRESTO - Cotton–balls - Presto Products Co.

PRESTO - Decals and transfers - Visu-Com Inc.

PRESTO - Dinnerware ☆ - Corning Inc.

PRESTO - Fabrics - Greenwood Mills Inc.

PRESTO - Gun blue - Birchwood Casey

PRESTO - Knives–butcher ☆ - M.E. Heuck Co. Inc.

PRESTO - Paint removers ☆ - H. Behlen & Bro. Inc.

PRESTO - Paints ☆ - Hampton Paint Manufacturing Co.

PRESTO - Paper–gummed ☆ - Webway, Inc.

PRESTO - Pharmaceutical preparations - University Drug Co. Inc.

PRESTO - Pressure cookers - National Presto Industries, Inc.

PRESTO - Recording label - Presto Records

PRESTO - Rubber cement - Columbia Cement Co. Inc.

PRESTO - Screws, nails, carpet tacks ☆ - American Tack & Hardware Co., Inc.

PRESTO - Seafood products–canned or cured - Frank's Seafood Inc.

PRESTO - Shoes - J.E. Moore & Associates

PRESTO - Soldering equipment - L.B. Allen Co. Inc.

PRESTO - Stamps–hand - PrestoGraphics Corp.

PRESTO AMINO - Hair care products ☆ - Freeman Cosmetics Corp.

PRESTO! BIZCARD - Computer software - Newsoft America Inc.

PRESTO BLACK - Paints - Black & Puryear Paint Manufacturing Co. Inc.

PRESTO CASES - Cases–musical instrument ☆ - D'Andrea Manufacturing Co. Inc.

PRESTO FIX - Adhesives and sealants - Presto Products Co.

PRESTO ID CARD SYSTEM - Printers–computer - Fargo Electronics Inc.

PRESTO-KLEEN - Cleaning preparations - Birchwood Casey

PRESTO KOTE - Adhesives and sealants - Presto Products Co.

PRESTO-KOTE - Rustproofing compounds - Birchwood Casey

PRESTO-LOK - Binders - The Union Group

PRESTO! LOOP-N-CUSHION - Shoe accessories - PediFix Footcare Co.

PRESTO MAGIC CREAM - Paint removers ☆ - H. Behlen & Bro. Inc.

PRESTO MAGIX - Dry-transfer sets - American Publishing Corp.

PRESTO MAGIX RUB-ONS - Decals and transfers - Warren Industries Inc.

PRESTO-MATIC - Steel springs–railroad - Needlecraft Industries

PRESTO MATS - Photograph-mounting mats - Presto Mats Inc.

PRESTO-MOLDER - Toys - Tonka Corp.

PRESTO-NAMEL - Enamels - Perry & Derrick Co.

PRESTO! OCR PRO 3.0 - Computer software - Newsoft America Inc.

PRESTO! PAGEMANAGER 98 GOLD EDITION - Computer software - Newsoft America Inc.

PRESTO-PAINTS - Paint sets–hobby ☆ - Kenner Products

PRESTO PATCH - Building materials - Bondex International Inc.

PRESTO PATCH - Rubber–acrylic - C & S Tackle Manufacturing Co.

PRESTO PATCH - Wood fillers ☆ - Savogran Co.

PRESTO PESTO - Salads–prepackaged - Buckeye Beans & Herbs, Inc.

PRESTO PETE - Candy ☆ - R.M. Palmer Co.

PRESTO! PHOTOALBUM - Computer software - Newsoft America Inc.

PRESTO PLEASERS! - Food products - Carfagna's Inc.

PRESTO POCKETS - Snack foods - St. Jacques

PRESTO POP - Popcorn ☆ - National Oats Co. Inc.

PRESTO QUARTO - Printers–computer - Fargo Electronics Inc.

PRESTO-SEAL - Adhesives and sealants - James B. Day and Co.

PRESTO SET - Adhesives and sealants ☆ - Champion International Corp.

PRESTO SHIELD - Plastics–laminated - Visu-Com Inc.

PRESTO-STICK - Decals and transfers - Paper Magic Group Inc.

PRESTO-STICK BOOKS - Decals and transfers - Paper Magic Group Inc.

PRESTO STIK - Adhesives and sealants - Presto Products Co.

PRESTO STIK - Decals and transfers - Visu-Com Inc.

PRESTO STRAWS - Candy ☆ - Topps Co., Inc.

PRESTO SWEEP - Cosmetics ☆ - Marianna Imports, Inc.

PRESTO UNO - Printers–computer - Fargo Electronics Inc.

PRESTO VAR - Varnishes - Presto Products Co.

PRESTOBOX - Boxes–paperboard - The Flatbow Co.

PRESTOBURGER - Kitchen appliances - National Presto Industries, Inc.

PRESTOBURGER/2 - Cooking equipment–household - National Presto Industries, Inc.

PRESTOCAL - Decals - Commercial Decal Inc.

PRESTODOOR - Doors–wood - Maywood Inc.

PRESTOFLATE - Sporting goods ☆ - Hedstrom Corp.

PRESTOLITE - Batteries - Exide Corp.

PRESTOLITE - Motor vehicle parts and accessories - Prestolite Electric Inc.

PRESTOLOCK - Locks–padlocks - Presto Lock Co. Inc.

PRESTOLOCK - Locks–padlocks - Prestolock International, Ltd.

PRESTOLOGS - Fireplace logs–treated - Weyerhaeuser Co.

PRESTOMIST - Atomizers - Irving W. Rice & Co. Inc.

PRESTOMIX - Paints ☆ - Mac-O-Lac Paints Inc.

PRESTON - Blinds–vertical - Tontine/VyTech Industries Inc.

PRESTON - Cabinets - Merillat Industries, Inc.

PRESTON - Floor coverings–carpet and rugs ☆ - Barrett Carpet Mills Inc.

PRESTON - Lighting fixtures - Liteway

PRESTON - Pressure-sensitive personalized labels - Bolind Inc.

PRESTON - Sporting goods - Ride Snowboard Co.

PRESTON - Wines - Preston Vineyards

PRESTON BINDINGS - Snowboards - Ride Snowboard Co.

PRESTON CREW - Wallpaper - York Wall Coverings Inc.

PRESTON CROSSING - Floor coverings–carpet and rugs - Gulistan Carpet Inc.

PRESTON DAIRY - Milk - Preston Dairy Products Inc.

PRESTON FARMS - Food products ☆ - Preston Farms Inc.

PRESTON HALL - Furniture ☆ - Bassett Furniture Industries, Inc.

PRESTON PANTHER - Toys–stuffed - Russ Berrie and Co., Inc.

PRESTON PARK - Furniture ☆ - Lane Co. Inc.

PRESTON PREMIUM WINES - Wines - Preston Premium Wines

PRESTON SMITH - Shirts - Career Club Shirt Co.

PRESTONE - Automotive parts and accessories - First Brands Corp.

PRESTONE - Chemicals - First Brands Properties Inc.

PRESTONE HI-TEMP - Brake fluids - First Brands Corp.

PRESTONE PROCHEM - Chemical preparations - Prestone Products Corp.

PRESTONE RECYCLING FORMULA - Chemicals - First Brands Properties Inc.

PRESTONG - File folders - Charles Leonard Inc.

PRESTOTILE - Tiles–ceramic - Commercial Decal Inc.

PRESTOWIPES - Towels - IFC Disposables, Inc.

PRESTWICK - Bathroom fixtures - Trayco, Inc.

PRESTWICK - Doors–glass - Therma-Tru Corp.

PRESTYPE - Office supplies - Prestype Inc.

PRESULIN - Skin care products - Schieffelin & Co. (Pharmaceutical Laboratories Div.)

PRESUMARK - Labels–paper - Kaumagraph Co. Inc.

PRESUMED GUILTY! - Computer software - Cosmi Corp.

PRESUN - Tanning agents - Westwood-Squibb Pharmaceuticals, Inc.

PRESUN 39 - Tanning agents - Westwood-Squibb Pharmaceuticals, Inc.

PRESUN KIDS - Dermatological preparations - Westwood-Squibb Pharmaceuticals, Inc.

PRESUN PRO TAN - Tanning agents - Westwood-Squibb Pharmaceuticals, Inc.

PRET-A-PORTE - Apparel–women's - Howard B. Wolf Inc.

PRET-A-PORTER - Wallpaper - Jack Foley Associates Inc.

PRET'E - Apparel and accessories - HMJ Clothing Co. Ltd.

PRETEC - Computer peripheral equipment - Pretec Electronics Corp.

PRETEEN - Underwear and nightwear ☆ - Youthform Co.

PRETEL - Altimeters - Suunto USA

PRETENDER - Apparel–women's - Wacoal America Inc.

PRETENDER - Ophthalmic goods - Foremost Optical Products

PRETERM FOSC - Electrical equipment - Raychem Corp.

PRETEXT - Ophthalmic goods - Foremost Optical Products

PRETREAT - Cleaning preparations–carpet and rug - Castex Industries Inc.

PRETTI-PAKS - Bags ☆ - Plus Mark Inc.

PRETTI PAWS - Cosmetics - Only Natural Cosmetics, Inc.

PRETTIEAR - Jewelry - Jeanie Hearring, Inc.

PRETTIES - Apparel and accessories ☆ - Warnaco Inc.

PRETTS - Railroad transportation–passenger - Milance Laboratories Inc.

PRETTY - Dolls - Bradley Import Co.

PRETTY - Flatware - Utica Cutlery Co.

PRETTY ACTIVE - Brassieres (Bras) - Lovable Co.

PRETTY AND ME - Dolls - Toy Biz, Inc.

PRETTY AS A PICTURE - Deodorizers - L & F Consumer Products

PRETTY AS A PICTURE - Dolls ☆ - Effanbee Doll Corp.

☆ = Now out of production

PRETTY AS A PICTURE - Dresses–women's - Gerson and Gerson Inc.
PRETTY AS A PICTURE - Games ☆ - Western Publishing Co., Inc.
PRETTY BABY - Diapers–disposable - Whitestone Products Inc.
PRETTY BABY - Dolls - Doll Factory, Inc.
PRETTY BABY - Dolls - Uneeda Doll Co., Inc.
PRETTY BABY - Floor coverings–carpet and rugs ☆ - Mohawk Carpet Corp.
PRETTY BABY LTD. - Apparel–children's - Tena Ellen McDonald
PRETTY BALI - Apparel–women's - Bali Co. Inc.
PRETTY BELLE - Fruits and vegetables - Sunwest Fruit Co., Inc.
PRETTY BIGS - Watches - Timex Corp.
PRETTY BIRD - Toys - North Pacific Products Inc.
PRETTY BUNNIES - Sporting goods - Mattel, Inc.
PRETTY CHOICES - Dolls - Mattel, Inc.
PRETTY CLOSETS - Dolls - Mattel, Inc.
PRETTY COLLECTION, THE - Underwear and nightwear - Maidenform Inc.
PRETTY COOL - Ophthalmic goods - Foremost Optical Products
PRETTY COOL, PRETTY CUTE, PRETTY YOU - Toys - Imperial Toy Corp.
PRETTY CRIMP 'N CURL - Dolls - Hasbro, Inc.
PRETTY EYE - Vitamins and nutritional supplements - Kroeger Herb Products Co. Inc.
PRETTY FACE - Cosmetics ☆ - Chemway Corp.
PRETTY FEET - Footwear–women's - Diesse Shoes Inc.
PRETTY FEET & HANDS - Skin care products - Smithkline Beecham Corp.
PRETTY FINGERNAIL GAME - Games - Rapid Mounting and Finishing Co.
PRETTY FINGERS - Manicure preparations - Nailtex Inc.
PRETTY FLOWERS - Bedding–linen - Dan River Inc.
PRETTY FLYER - Toys - Meritus Industries, Inc.
PRETTY GIRL - Girdles - Maidenform Inc. (True Form Foundations Div.)
PRETTY GOOD - Computer software - Philip Zimmermann
PRETTY GOOD - Recording label - Sparrow Corp.
PRETTY GOOD PRIVACY - Computer software - Philip Zimmermann
PRETTY GOOD U.S.A. - Apparel–women's - Paul U. Kye
PRETTY HEARTS - Dolls - Mattel, Inc.
PRETTY IN PINK - Bicycles - Dynacraft Industries Inc.
PRETTY IN PINK - Christmas tree ornaments - Cracker Box Inc.
PRETTY IN PINK - Cosmetics ☆ - Prince Matchabelli
PRETTY IN PLAID - Dolls - Mattel, Inc.
PRETTY IN PURPLE - Dolls - Mattel, Inc.
PRETTY KITTY - Deodorizers ☆ - Car-Freshner Corp.
PRETTY LADY - Fruits and vegetables - Jakov P. Dulcich & Sons
PRETTY LADY - Jewelry - International Importers and Liquidators, Inc.
PRETTY LIPS - Lip gloss ☆ - Cosrich Inc.
PRETTY-LITE - Mirrors - Monaco Import/Export Inc.
PRETTY LITE DIET SKINNY WAIST - Apparel and accessories - Strouse, Adler Co.
PRETTY LOOKS - Apparel and accessories - Charles Komar and Sons Inc.
PRETTY ME - Toys - Alvimar Manufacturing Co. Inc.
PRETTY ME - Underwear and nightwear - Maidenform Inc.
PRETTY MISS - Hairpins - Diane Products Inc.
PRETTY MORNING VANITY SET - Toys - Playskool, Inc.
PRETTY NATURAL - Bird feeds - Pretty Bird International, Inc.
PRETTY NEAT - Trays - Goody Products, Inc.
PRETTY ONE - Recording label - S.W. & A. Associates Co.
PRETTY PAIRS - Hair care products - Durlacher & Co., Inc.
PRETTY PANDAS - Dolls - Mattel, Inc.
PRETTY PANTS - Dolls - Uneeda Doll Co., Inc.
PRETTY PARTY - Dolls - Mattel, Inc.
PRETTY PASTEL SUPER BLOCKS - Toys–blocks - Nationsbank of North Carolina, N.A.
PRETTY PASTELS - Napkins–paper - American Tissue Mills of New York Inc.
PRETTY PATTY - Toys ☆ - Henry Gordy International Inc.
PRETTY PENNY - Postcards ☆ - S.J. Miller Co.
PRETTY PERFECT - Apparel–women's - Wacoal America Inc.
PRETTY PETALS - Christmas tree ornaments - Cracker Box Inc.
PRETTY PETALS - Flowers–artificial - Sirocraft
PRETTY PETS - Pet products - Pretty Bird International, Inc.
PRETTY PETS - Toys - Azrak-Hamway International, Inc.
PRETTY PICKS - Flowers, plants, and seeds - Joan Baker Designs
PRETTY PIERROTS - Dolls ☆ - Delfino Products Inc.
PRETTY PINAFORE - Dolls and doll accessories - TCA Ground Inc.
PRETTY PINK - Toys–stuffed ☆ - Gund, Inc.
PRETTY PLEASE - Apparel–women's - Wacoal America Inc.
PRETTY PLEASE - Housewares - Athena Products Corp.
PRETTY PLEASE - Ophthalmic goods - Foremost Optical Products
PRETTY PLEATS - Window shades - Levolor Inc.
PRETTY PLUNGE - Apparel–women's - Exquisite Form Industries

PRETTY PLUS - Apparel and accessories - Sears, Roebuck and Co.
PRETTY POPS - Novelty items - Larry Eckler
PRETTY PORCUPINE - Jewelry ☆ - Imperial Toy Corp.
PRETTY POSE MODEL - Toys ☆ - Those Characters from Cleveland, Inc.
PRETTY POWDER - Perfumes - Carter-Wallace, Inc.
PRETTY PUCKER - Apparel–women's ☆ - Bali Co. Inc.
PRETTY PURSE - Tampons - Johnson & Johnson
PRETTY QUICK - Electric hair curling irons - Andis Co.
PRETTY-QUIKS - Cosmetics - Reina Claire
PRETTY ROOMS - Wallpaper - Cynthia Gibson Inc.
PRETTY SECRET - Brassieres (Bras) - Exquisite Form Industries
PRETTY SHAPELY - Underwear and nightwear - Maidenform Inc.
PRETTY SHOES S.L. - Footwear–women's - J.R. Carus Inc.
PRETTY SLICK - Cooking utensils–aluminum ☆ - General Housewares Corp.
PRETTY SLICK - Wallpaper - Carlton-Metro Wallcoverings
PRETTY SLIMMING - Underwear and nightwear ☆ - Lovable Co.
PRETTY SMOOTH - Apparel and accessories ☆ - Glamorise Foundations Inc.
PRETTY SMOOTH - Razors ☆ - Standard Products Corp.
PRETTY SPECIAL - Apparel–children's - Montgomery Ward & Co. Inc.
PRETTY SURPRISE - Dolls - Mattel, Inc.
PRETTY TEEN - Apparel–women's - Wacoal America Inc.
PRETTY TEEN - Dolls - Mattel, Inc.
PRETTY THINGS - Apparel–women's ☆ - Bali Co. Inc.
PRETTY THINGS - Wallpaper - Frankford Wallcoverings Inc.
PRETTY TIME - Hosiery–women's - Shogren Industries, Inc.
PRETTY-TRAV-LITE - Mirrors - Monaco Import/Export Inc.
PRETTY TREASURES - Dolls - Mattel, Inc.
PRETTY TRIM - Apparel and accessories ☆ - Glamorise Foundations Inc.
PRETTY UP - Barrettes, lipstick, and perfume ☆ - Cosrich Inc.
PRETTY UP - Nail care products - Maji Nail Inc.
PRETTY UP MAGIC - Nail care products - Maji Nail Inc.
PRETTY WAIST - Belts–apparel - CLC Enterprises
PRETTY YOU - Apparel and accessories - Montgomery Ward & Co. Inc.
PRETTYBOY - Bird feeds - Audubon Park Co.
PRETTYCARDS - Greeting cards - American Greetings Corp.
PRETTY.SMART. - Nightgowns - Vanity Fair, Inc.
PRETTYSPORTY - Apparel and accessories - P. Cheryl Flanagan and John S. Treworgy
PRETY PET - Toys ☆ - A.R.C. Toys Inc.
PRETZ - Health care products - Parnell Pharmaceuticals Inc.
PRETZ-D - Health care products - Parnell Pharmaceuticals Inc.
PRETZ-L NUGGETS - Pretzels - Old London Foods Inc.
PRETZ-L RINGS - Pretzels - Old London Foods Inc.
PRETZEL BAKER - Pans ☆ - General Housewares Corp.
PRETZEL BEND - Toys–automobiles - Mattel, Inc.
PRETZEL B'S - Pretzels ☆ - Bachman Co.
PRETZEL DUNK - Dips–sour cream based - Summit Food Sales, Inc.
PRETZEL FRESH BAKED HAUS - Pretzels - Pretzel Haus, Inc.
PRETZEL JOYS - Snack foods - Harry London's Candies Inc.
PRETZEL LITE - Crackers ☆ - Keebler Co.
PRETZEL MILL - Bakery products - Blue Ribbon Development Group, LLC
PRETZEL OVEN, THE - Pretzels - Mrs. Fields' Original Cookies, Inc.
PRETZEL PEOPLE - Confections - Chocolicious Chocolatier, Inc.
PRETZEL PUFFS - Pretzels - Snack Factory Inc.
PRETZEL TWISTER, THE - Pretzels - Mister Twister Pretzels, Inc.
PRETZELETTES - Pretzels - Nabisco Foods Group
PRETZELS-4-U - Food products - Bagels-4-U, Inc.
PRETZL LITE - Flashlights - Universal Security Instruments Inc.
PRETZLCONES - Ice cream cones - Ian Cooper
PREVACID - Ulcer treatment - Tap Pharmaceuticals Inc.
PREVACTIN - Skin care products - MJ Marketing, Ltd.
PREVACTIN F.A. - Skin care products - MJ Marketing, Ltd.
PREVAIL - Computer software - Cadence Design Systems, Inc.
PREVAIL - Floor coverings–carpet and rugs - Dorsett Carpet Mills Inc.
PREVAIL - Floor coverings–carpet and rugs ☆ - J and J Industries Inc.
PREVAIL - Flowers, plants, and seeds - NK Lawn & Garden Co.
PREVAIL - Insecticides - Gustafson Inc.
PREVAIL - Vitamins and nutritional supplements - Prevail Corp.
PREVAIL - Water purification systems - King Technology, Inc.
PREVAILER - Batteries ☆ - East Penn Manufacturing Co., Inc.
PREVAILING WORD, THE - Recording label - Way International
PREVAL - Bottles–plastic - Precision Valve Corp. (Preval Sprayer Div.)
PREVAL SPRAYMAKER - Bottles–plastic - Precision Valve Corp. (Preval Sprayer Div.)
PREVALITE - Pharmaceutical preparations - Upsher-Smith Laboratories, Inc.

☆ = Now out of production

PREVAM - Pharmaceutical preparations ☆ - Rhone-Poulenc Rorer Pharmaceuticals Inc.

PREVEENT - Cleaning preparations—carpet and rug - Multi-Care Corp.

PREVENANCE - Health care products - Sanofi Beaute Inc.

PREVENT - Chewing gum - Philadelphia Chewing Gum Corp.

PREVENT - Lubricants - Precision Brand Products, Inc.

PREVENT - Medical apparatus - C.R. Bard, Inc.

PREVENT - Toothbrushes - Johnson & Johnson

PREVENT PLUS - Water purification systems - Great Lakes Biochemical Co., Inc.

PREVENTECH - Dental compounds - Preventive Technologies, Inc.

PREVENTILATOR - Ventilation equipment - Tamarack Technologies, Inc.

PREVENTIME - Vitamins and nutritional supplements - Nutrition Enterprises

PREVENTION IN A DROP - Adhesives and sealants - Medlogic Global Corp.

PREVENTION SERUM - Skin care products - Chanel Inc.

PREVENTIVE AGE TREATMENT - Skin care products - Clientele, Inc.

PREVENTIVE NUTRITION - Vitamins - General Nutrition Investment Co.

PREVENTIVE NUTRITION FORMULA - Vitamins and minerals - General Nutrition Investment Co.

PREVENTOLOGY - Massage products - Nicholas M. Brecher

PREVENTOR - Educational materials - Harry R. McClellan

PREVENZYME - Pharmaceutical preparations - Legere Pharmaceuticals Inc.

PREVETTS - Health care products ☆ - Fox Pharmacal Inc.

PREVEX - Resins—synthetic - General Electric Co.

PREVEX IMPROVED - Pharmaceutical preparations ☆ - Vita-Fore Products Co.

PREVIA - Motor vehicles—automobiles - Toyota Motor Sales USA Inc.

PREVIDENT - Pharmaceutical preparations - Colgate Oral Pharmaceuticals Inc.

PREVIEW - Artists' materials - Jordan Specialty Co.

PREVIEW - Clocks - General Time Corp. (Westclox/Seth Thomas Div.)

PREVIEW - Floor coverings—carpet and rugs - Milliken & Co. Inc.

PREVIEW - Furniture ☆ - Singer Furniture Co.

PREVIEW COLLECTION - Apparel—women's - Nordstrom, Inc.

PREVIEWER - Projectors—photographic - Apollo Audiovisual Div.

PREVIEWER - Projectors—photographic - Brumberger Co. Inc.

PREVIEWS - Apparel—women's - Montgomery Ward & Co. Inc.

PREVIEWS - Food products - Alberto-Culver Co.

PREVIMIN - Pharmaceutical preparations - Legere Pharmaceuticals Inc.

PREVISION - Ophthalmic goods - Foremost Optical Products

PREVISTAN - Toothpaste ☆ - Colgate Oral Pharmaceuticals Inc.

PREVOST - Machine parts - Staubli Corp.

PREVOST - Projectors—photographic - Xetron

PREVOX - Paints - Lasting Paints Inc.

PREVOX - Rustproofing compounds - Kano Laboratories Inc.

PREVU - Jewelry—costume - Buy-Rite Costume Jewelry, Inc.

PREVUE - Computer software - Micro*D, Inc.

PREVUE - Pet products - Prevue Metal Products Inc.

PREWAY - Fireplaces - Preway Industries Inc.

PREWORX - Skin care products - Scott Paper Co.

PREXPORT - Leather goods - Intersport, Inc.

PREY - Health care products - 1st American Medical Inc.

PREYFISH - Fishing lures - James Heddon's Sons

PREZZIES! - Coffee - R.D. Ryan & Associates, Inc.

PREZZURGARD - Gauging instruments - Alnor Instrument Co.

PRG - Publisher's imprints - Patent Resources Group, Inc.

PRI - Coating - W.W. Grainger, Inc.

PRI - Medical apparatus - American Clicical Industries

PRI-ANDRIOL LA - Pharmaceutical preparations ☆ - Primedics Laboratories

PRI-CORTIN - Pharmaceutical preparations - Primedics Laboratories

PRI-DEXTRA - Pharmaceutical preparations ☆ - Primedics Laboratories

PRI-METHYLATE - Pharmaceutical preparations ☆ - Primedics Laboratories

PRI-SEAL - Paints - Frazee Paint

PRIATTI - Wallets - Phillips-Van Heusen Corp.

PRICE - Fruits and vegetables - Price Cold Storage & Packing Co.

PRICE - Glassware—household - Albert E. Price, Inc.

PRICE - Ice cream - Dean Foods Co.

PRICE - Pumps - Price Pump Manufacturing Co.

PRICE & KENSINGTON - Giftware - Ebeling and Reuss Co.

PRICE & KENSINGTON - Tea kettles—nonelectric - Elite Design

PRICE CHECK SHOPPING CART - Toys - Fisher-Price, Inc.

PRICE-CHEK PC - Computer software - Medi-Span, Inc.

PRICE CHOPPER - Pizza - Continental Food Products Inc.

PRICE CLUB SIGNATURE - Bags—trash - Price Co.

PRICE IS RIGHT - Games ☆ - Milton Bradley Co.

PRICE KIDS - Toys - Price Co.

PRICE KUTTER - Food products - Paris Food Corp.

PRICE KUTTER - Macaroni - Borden, Inc.

PRICE-LESS - Recording label - Random House, Inc.

PRICE-LESS PREMIUM - Recording label - Random House, Inc.

PRICE MASTER - Cigarettes - R.J. Reynolds Tobacco Co.

PRICE MASTER - Furniture - Seal-O-Matic Corp.

PRICE MASTER PLUS - Computer software - Software Plus, Inc.

PRICE PFISTER - Bathroom fixtures - Price Pfister Co.

PRICE-RITE - Floor coverings ☆ - American Floor Products Co. Inc.

PRICE SAVER - Food products - Shurfine International, Inc.

PRICE SAVERS - Brassieres (Bras) - Lovable Co.

PRICE WISE - Fabric softeners - Greenbax Enterprises, Inc.

PRICED-RITE - Meat products—beef - Ottman & Co.

PRICED SEW RIGHT COLLECTION - Containers - FCA Financial, Inc.

PRICELESS - Flour—blended ☆ - Orth Co. (Bruce)

PRICELESS - Fruits and vegetables - Price Cold Storage & Packing Co.

PRICELESS - Games - Winning Moves Inc.

PRICELESS - Wallpaper - Lawrence Wallcoverings

PRICELESS VELVET - Floor coverings—carpet and rugs - Alexander Smith Carpets

PRICELINK - Computer software - Goodin Co.

PRICEMAX - Computer software - Applied Information for Marketing, Inc.

PRICEPAK - Computer software - Mead Corp.

PRICEPOINT - Displays - Pricepoint, Inc.

PRICEPOINT, INC. - Electrical equipment - Pricepoint, Inc.

PRICER - Electronic equipment - Pricer, Inc.

PRICERIGHT - Computer software - Sterling Software, Inc.

PRICE'S - Candy - Price Candy Co. Inc.

PRICE'S - Cheese - Dean Foods Co.

PRICES - Cheese - Fromageries Bel, Inc.

PRICE'S - Cheese - Nestle USA

PRICE'S CANDLELIGHT COLLECTION - Candy - Price Candy Co. Inc.

PRICES CREAMERY - Milk - Country Classic Dairies Inc.

PRICILLA - Floor coverings—carpet and rugs ☆ - Concord/Aldon Industries Inc.

PRID - Pharmaceutical preparations - Walker Pharmacal Co.

PRIDDY'S - Food products - Sara Lee Corp.

PRIDE - Apparel—athletic ☆ - MacGregor Sport Products Inc.

PRIDE - Apparel—women's - Wacoal America Inc.

PRIDE - Beer - Miss Mess, Inc.

PRIDE - Cleaning preparations—window - Uncle Sam Chemical Co., Inc.

PRIDE - Dishes—earthenware - Denby USA Limited

PRIDE - Fabrics - Dan River Inc.

PRIDE - Flypaper - Haylon Corp.

PRIDE - Furniture polish and wax ☆ - S.C. Johnson & Son, Inc.

PRIDE - Gasoline - Pride Oil Co.

PRIDE - Glassware—household ☆ - Wills Co.

PRIDE - Health care products - Pride Plastics

PRIDE - Lubricants - Activist Products

PRIDE - Oils—lubricating - Northland Products Co.

PRIDE - Paints - Jones Blair Co.

PRIDE - Paper—gift wrap ☆ - CPS Corp.

PRIDE - Pet products - Z Industries

PRIDE - Pharmaceutical preparations - Trigg Advertising Inc.

PRIDE - Underwear and nightwear - Bestform Foundations, Inc.

PRIDE - Watchbands—leather - Westerman Manufacturing Co. Inc.

PRIDE - Yarn - Dixie Yarns, Inc.

PRIDE AND JOY - Floor coverings—carpet and rugs - Mohawk Industries Inc.

PRIDE BINDER - Binders ☆ - General Loose Leaf Bindery Co.

PRIDE CRAFT - Tools - Pollard Brothers Manufacturing Co. Inc.

PRIDE GENTLE LIFT - Health care products - Pride Health Care, Inc.

PRIDE IN AMERICA - Checkbooks - Clarke American Corp.

PRIDE IN EXCELLENCE - Medical diagnostic kit - Greer Laboratories Inc.

PRIDE IN EXCELLENCE - Window coverings - Presidential Window Products Inc.

PRIDE IN GROOM - Dolls ☆ - Uneeda Doll Co., Inc.

PRIDE IN PRINT - Jewelry - Printing Industry of the Carolinas Foundation, Inc.

PRIDE MOUNTAIN VINEYARDS - Wines - Pride Mountain Vineyards

PRIDE 'N JOEY - Toys—stuffed ☆ - Gund, Inc.

PRIDE 'N JOY - Infant wear - Frederick Atkins, Inc.

PRIDE N' JOY - Pet products - ORRCO, Inc.

PRIDE 'N PASTRY FILLINGS - Bakery products - Dawn Food Products Inc.

PRIDE O' TEXAS - Fruits and vegetables - Pride of the Citrus of Texas Inc.

PRIDE O' THE FARM - Bakery products - J & J Snack Foods Corp.

PRIDE O' THE FARM - Cookies - Pride of the Farm

PRIDE OF AFRICA - Apparel and accessories - Pride of Africa, Inc.

PRIDE OF ALABAMA - Fruits and vegetables - Schermer Potato Co.

PRIDE OF ALASKA - Food products - Unisea Foods Inc.

☆ = Now out of production

PRIDE OF ALBERMARLE - Seafood products–fresh or frozen - Chowan River Fishery Inc.

PRIDE OF AMERICA - Fabrics–cotton ☆ - Dan River Inc.

PRIDE OF AMERICA - Toy stores - Douglas Co. Inc.

PRIDE OF AMERICA 80 PROOF VODKA - Vodka - Montebello Brands, Inc.

PRIDE OF CALIFORNIA - Snack foods - Variety Foods, Inc.

PRIDE OF CALIFORNIA - Wines - California Wine Co.

PRIDE OF CAROLINA - Food products - Bruce Foods Corp.

PRIDE OF CHAS DEVIL - Seafood products–canned or cured - Taylor's Frozen Foods & Cold Storage Inc.

PRIDE OF CHESAPEAKE - Seafood products–fresh or frozen - Carol Dryden & Co. Inc.

PRIDE OF DENMARK - Bakery mixes - Westco Products Inc.

PRIDE OF GEORGIA - Food products ☆ - Harrison Poultry Inc.

PRIDE OF GERMACK - Nuts–salted, roasted, cooked, or canned - Germack Pistachio Co.

PRIDE OF GOLD KIST - Fertilizers - Gold Kist Inc.

PRIDE OF GUATEMALA - Seafood products–fresh or frozen - Ocean Garden Products, Inc.

PRIDE OF HILBERT - Cheese ☆ - Swiss American Import Co.

PRIDE OF HOLLAND - Onions - A. Camacho Inc.

PRIDE OF HUNGARY - Food products - Spiceco

PRIDE OF ILLINOIS - Vegetables–canned - Faribault Foods Inc.

PRIDE-OF-INDIA - Pepper - Food Trading Corp. of America

PRIDE OF INDIA - Seafood products–fresh or frozen - Ocean Garden Products, Inc.

PRIDE OF LIFE - Food products - Wilsey Foods, Inc.

PRIDE OF NEBRASKA - Meat products - Omaha Steaks International

PRIDE OF NEW ORLEANS - Shrimp–canned or cured - Deepsouth Packing Co. Inc.

PRIDE OF OREGON - Maraschino cherries ☆ - Gray & Co.

PRIDE OF PHILLY - Paints - Impervious Paint Industries Ltd.

PRIDE OF ST. LOUIS, THE - Meat products–pork - Double G Brands Inc.

PRIDE OF SPAIN - Olives–pickled or brined - A. Camacho Inc.

PRIDE OF STERLING - Tobacco–chewing or smoking - Sterling Tobacco Co.

PRIDE OF SZEGED - Spices and extracts - Spiceco

PRIDE OF THE FARM - Catsup ☆ - Hunt-Wesson, Inc.

PRIDE OF THE FARM - Meat products–poultry - Rocco Turkeys Inc.

PRIDE OF THE FLOCK - Yarn ☆ - Pride of the Flock Woolen Mills Inc.

PRIDE OF THE HOME - Artists' materials - Standard Stamping Co. Inc.

PRIDE OF THE LAKES - Seafood products–fresh or frozen - Weyand Fisheries Inc.

PRIDE OF THE NATION - Sporting goods - Tel-O-Post Co.

PRIDE OF THE NEST - Eggs - Century Acres Eggs

PRIDE OF THE OCEAN - Food products - Ocean-Wide Food Industries Inc.

PRIDE OF THE ORCHARD - Food products - Barzi Foods

PRIDE OF THE PRINTWORKS - Craft supplies ☆ - VIP/VIP Crafts

PRIDE OF THE ROCKIES - Food products - Ogden Poultry Co.

PRIDE OF THE SOUTH - Dolls ☆ - Effanbee Doll Corp.

PRIDE OF THE SOUTH - Food products ☆ - Gol-Pak Corp.

PRIDE OF THE SOUTH - Meat products - Gol-Pak Corp.

PRIDE OF THE VALLEY - Bird feeds - Wagner Bros. Feed Corp.

PRIDE OF THE WEST - Potato sticks - Farwest Foods Corp.

PRIDE OF THE WORKSHOP - Tools ☆ - Carborundum Abrasives North America

PRIDE OF WISCONSIN, THE - Cheese - Fromageries Bel, Inc.

PRIDE OF WRENS - Flour–blended - Wrens Grocery Co.

PRIDE O'MAINE - Potato flakes - Taterstate Frozen Foods

PRIDE PRO-SERIES - Cases–plastic - Pride Plastics

PRIDE SPECIAL - Golfing equipment - Eaton Corp. (Golf Grip Div.)

PRIDE, THE - Dog food - Hyland Co.

PRIDE XRG - Archery equipment - Martin Archery Inc.

PRIDECO - Pipes–steel - Prideco, Inc.

PRIDELINE - Jewelers' tools and supplies - Vigor Co.

PRIDES CROSSING - Crocheted and knitted items - Valor

PRIDE'S CROSSING - Rocking chairs - Oak Land Furn. Manufacturing, Inc.

PRIDGENS PRIDE - Brooms - Pridgen Brothers Co. Inc.

PRIENTE - Printers–computer - Seikosha America Inc.

PRIESTESS - Candles - Merrill-West Publishing

PRIFERON - Pharmaceutical preparations ☆ - Primedics Laboratories

PRIFORM - Prosthetic apparatus ☆ - Camp, Inc.

PRIGEST-R - Pharmaceutical preparations ☆ - Primedics Laboratories

PRIM - Clocks - General Time Corp. (Westclox/Seth Thomas Div.)

PRIM - Hardware - Shepherd Products U.S. Inc.

PRIM - Musical instrument accessories - Ideal Musical Merchandise Co.

PRIM - Musical instrument accessories - International Violin Co. Ltd.

PRIM - Paper–toilet - Fort Howard Corp.

PRIMA - Artists' materials - Adams Creative Products, Inc.

PRIMA - Boats - Wellcraft Marine Corp.

PRIMA - Cabinets - HomeCrest Corp.

PRIMA - Calculators ☆ - Olivetti North America Inc. (Consumer Products Div.)

PRIMA - Chairs–upholstered ☆ - Northwest Blueprint and Supply

PRIMA - Combs - Fromm Industries

PRIMA - Cookware - Tramontina USA, Inc.

PRIMA - Cutlery ☆ - National Housewares

PRIMA - Floor coverings–carpet and rugs - Collins & Aikman Corp.

PRIMA - Frames–eyeglass - Rozin Optical Export Corp.

PRIMA - Furniture ☆ - Singer Furniture Co.

PRIMA - Glassware–household ☆ - Anchor Hocking Glass, Inc.

PRIMA - Hearing aids - Beltone Electronics Corp.

PRIMA - Kitchen utensils–aluminum - General Housewares Corp.

PRIMA - Machinery - Muller Martini Corp.

PRIMA - Ophthalmic goods - American Optical Corp.

PRIMA - Pet products - Rolf C. Hagen (USA) Corp.

PRIMA - Photographic equipment - Hudson Photographic Industries Inc.

PRIMA - Seafood products–fresh or frozen ☆ - Ocean Beauty Seafood, Inc.

PRIMA - Telephones - Conair Corp.

PRIMA - Underwear and nightwear ☆ - M.A. Rabinowitz Corp.

PRIMA - Whirlpool bath ☆ - Jacuzzi Inc.

PRIMA 20 - Calculators ☆ - Olivetti North America Inc. (Consumer Products Div.)

PRIMA BOND - Adhesives and sealants - A.I. Technology Inc.

PRIMA BOND - Nail care products - E.O.H. Industries, Inc.

PRIMA COAT - Caulking compounds - A.I. Technology Inc.

PRIMA COLLEZIONE - Belts–apparel - Leather Luster Inc.

PRIMA-CRYLIC - Turpentine - Sterling-Clark-Lurton Corp.

PRIMA DONNA - Christmas tree ornaments - Cracker Box Inc.

PRIMA DONNA - Fabrics - Gretchen Bellinger Inc.

PRIMA DONNA - Floor coverings–carpet and rugs ☆ - World Carpets, Inc.

PRIMA DONNA - Food products - Scally Imperial Importing Co.

PRIMA DONNA - Toys ☆ - Roadmaster Corp.

PRIMA DONNA - Underwear and nightwear - Carole Hochman Designs Inc.

PRIMA DONNA - Watches - Hampden Corp.

PRIMA FACIE - Electronic equipment - Prima Facie, Inc.

PRIMA-FLEX - Jewelry - Aurafin Corp.

PRIMA GOLD - Jewelry - Pranda North America, Inc.

PRIMA GRAPHICS LTD. - Cameras - Atlantic International Products & Services Co.

PRIMA-LOFT - Pillows ☆ - American Fiber Industries Corp.

PRIMA NORA #20 - Cigars - Gesty Trading & Manufacturing Corp.

PRIMA OIL - Vitamins and nutritional supplements - Bioenergy Nutrient's Inc.

PRIMA PAD - Diapers–disposable - Salk Co. Inc.

PRIMA PORTA - Sausages - Hatfield, Inc.

PRIMA PUBLISHING - Publisher's imprints - Prima Communications, Inc.

PRIMA ROMA - Fruits and vegetables - Mike Mendenhall

PRIMA ROSA! - Frozen foods - Ruiz Food Products Inc.

PRIMA SALSA - Spaghetti sauces ☆ - Hunt-Wesson, Inc.

PRIMA SHIELD - Paints - A.I. Technology Inc.

PRIMA SOLDER - Adhesives and sealants - A.I. Technology Inc.

PRIMA SWAG - Drapery hardware ☆ - Spring Window Fashions Division, Inc.

PRIMA TERRA CALIFORNIA PREMIUM QUALITY - Fruits–canned - Pacific Coast Producers

PRIMA VERA - Wines - Banfi Vintners

PRIMA VISTA - Furniture - National/Mt. Airy Furniture

PRIMA VOCE - Recording label - Nimbus Records Ltd.

PRIMABALT - Pharmaceutical preparations - Primedics Laboratories

PRIMABALT RP - Pharmaceutical preparations ☆ - Primedics Laboratories

PRIMABENE BY BERNARDO - Footwear–women's ☆ - Bernardo Brands

PRIMABOND - Nail care products - E.O.H. Industries, Inc.

PRIMACARE - Diapers–cloth - Salk Co. Inc.

PRIMACIDE - Manicure preparations - Creative Nail Design, Inc.

PRIMACLASSICS - Socks - Kayser-Roth Corp.

PRIMAD - Manicure preparations - Creative Nail Design, Inc.

PRIMADERM - Pharmaceutical preparations - Sparta Surgical

PRIMADERM-B - Pharmaceutical preparations - Arrow Medical Co. Inc.

PRIMADONE - Pharmaceutical preparations ☆ - Murray Drug Corp.

PRIMADORO - Food products - Lico Brands, Inc.

PRIMAFIL - Wood fillers - Pratt & Lambert, Inc.

PRIMAFORT - Pharmaceutical preparations ☆ - Primedics Laboratories

PRIMAGE - Printers–computer - Primages Inc.

PRIMAGE 90-GT - Printers–computer - Primages Inc.

PRIMAGEST - Vitamins and nutritional supplements - Mickey A. Hall

PRIMAHEMIN - Pharmaceutical preparations ☆ - Primedics Laboratories
PRIMAL CARE - Hair care products - Helene Curtis Industries Inc.
PRIMAL ELEMENTS - Skin care products - Scott Freeman
PRIMAL IMPULSE - Apparel and accessories - Primal Impulse Inc.
PRIMALE - Vitamins and nutritional supplements - Trace Minerals Research
PRIMALINE - Shoe insoles - Milliken & Co.
PRIMALITE - Detonating compounds - Ensign-Bickford Industries Inc.
PRIMALOFT - Fibers, fabrics and felts - Albany International Corp.
PRIMALOFT - Fibers–synthetic - United Feather & Down Inc.
PRIMALON - Fabrics–broadcloth - Collins & Aikman Corp.
PRIMALT - Pet products - Tomlyn Products
PRIMAPAK - Containers–paper - Ensign-Bickford Industries Inc.
PRIMAPLEX - Pharmaceutical preparations - Primedics Laboratories
PRIMAPLEX II - Pharmaceutical preparations ☆ - Primedics Laboratories
PRIMAQUINE PHOSPHATE - Pharmaceutical preparations - Winthrop Pharmaceuticals
PRIMARILY HEALTH - Video production - Comprehensive Health Education Foundation
PRIMARILY KIDS - Wallcovering - Colortree Designs
PRIMARILY PRIMARY - Paper–gift wrap - Stephen Lawrence Co.
PRIMARITE - Paints - Standard T Chemical Co. Inc.
PRIMARK - Labels–paper - National Sales Co.
PRIMARK - Office supplies - Esselte Corp.
PRIMAROSA! BY RUIZ - Food products - Ruiz Food Products Inc.
PRIMARY - Dinnerware–glass - Franciscan by Johnson Brothers, USA, Inc.
PRIMARY - Fans–electric - Duracraft Corp.
PRIMARY - Floor coverings–carpet and rugs ☆ - Porter Carpet Mills Inc.
PRIMARY - Toilets–enameled - Kohler Co.
PRIMARY ACCESS - Computers and accessories - Primary Access Corp.
PRIMARY BENEFIT - Hair care products - Helene Curtis Industries Inc.
PRIMARY BLOCKS - Bedding–linen - Dan River Inc.
PRIMARY COLORS - Greeting cards - Signprint, Inc.
PRIMARY COMFORT - Pillows - American Fiber Industries Corp.
PRIMARY GREENS - Vitamins and nutritional supplements - Vitamin Research Products Inc.
PRIMARY MAX - Glassware–household - Heller Inc.
PRIMARY NURSERYMATES - Furniture ☆ - Hedstrom Corp.
PRIMARY PLAYMATES - Furniture ☆ - Hedstrom Corp.
PRIMARY POSES - Bedding–linen - Dan River Inc.
PRIMARY SOURCES - Wallcovering ☆ - Colortree Designs
PRIMARY SOURCES - Wallpaper ☆ - Eisenhart Wallcoverings Co.
PRIMASCRIPT - Computer hardware - Raster Graphics, Inc.
PRIMASET - Resins–synthetic - Alliedsignal Inc.
PRIMASHEET - Explosives - Ensign-Bickford Industries Inc.
PRIMASPORT - Socks - Kayser-Roth Corp.
PRIMASTER - Apparel and accessories - Big Entertainment, Inc.
PRIMASTICK - Detonators - Ensign-Bickford Industries Inc.
PRIMASTONE - Dinnerware–glass - Noritake Co. Inc.
PRIMATAN - Leather tanning agent - Genencor International, Inc.
PRIMATENE - Pharmaceutical preparations - Whitehall Laboratories
PRIMATIV PEEPUL INTERNATIONAL - Jewelry - John Francis Mason
PRIMATIVE PAPAYA - Beverages - Wiman Beverage Co., Inc.
PRIMATIZED - Pharmaceutical preparations - IDEC Pharmaceuticals Corp.
PRIMATO - Pizzas–frozen - Design Foods
PRIMATONE - Pharmaceutical preparations ☆ - Primedics Laboratories
PRIMATUSS - Pharmaceutical preparations - Rugby Laboratories Inc.
PRIMAVERA - Computer software - Primavera Systems, Inc.
PRIMAVERA - Desserts - Bell'amore Imports Inc.
PRIMAVERA - Fabrics - Dan River Inc.
PRIMAVERA - Fabrics–linen - Stylecrest Fabrics Ltd.
PRIMAVERA - Floor coverings–carpet and rugs - Artistic Rugs Inc.
PRIMAVERA - Floor coverings–carpet and rugs - Eligere Carpets
PRIMAVERA - Food products - US Foodservice
PRIMAVERA - Fruits and vegetables - Primavera Marketing, Inc.
PRIMAVERA - Fruits and vegetables - Marglo Products Corp.
PRIMAVERA - Furniture - Walker and Zanger Inc.
PRIMAVERA - Glassware–household - Royal Crystal Rock Inc.
PRIMAVERA - Jewelry - Danecraft, Inc.
PRIMAVERA - Luggage - Airway Industries, Inc.
PRIMAVERA - Olives–canned ☆ - Marin Food Specialties
PRIMAVERA - Pastries ☆ - Jaret Specialties Inc.
PRIMAVERA - Wallpaper - Sellers & Josephson
PRIMAVERA CHAMOIS - Knitting machines - Collins & Aikman Corp.
PRIMAVERA FLORAL - Shampoos ☆ - Jason Natural Products, Inc.
PRIMAX - Electronics equipment - Primax Electronics
PRIMAXIN - Antibiotics - Merck & Co., Inc. (Merck Research Laboratories)

PRIMAZINE - Pharmaceutical preparations ☆ - Primedics Laboratories
PRIME - Cables - Gehr Industries, Inc.
PRIME - Caulking compounds - Lasting Paints Inc.
PRIME - Filters–oil - Alliedsignal Inc.
PRIME - Floor coverings ☆ - Tarkett, Inc.
PRIME - Floor coverings–carpet and rugs ☆ - World Carpets, Inc.
PRIME - Food products - Givaudan Roure
PRIME - Glass–window - Remington Building Products
PRIME - Leather - Prime Tanning Co., Inc.
PRIME - Mushrooms - Quincy Farms
PRIME - Pet products - Prime Pet Products
PRIME - Pet products - Ralston Purina Co.
PRIME - Pet products - Rolf C. Hagen (USA) Corp.
PRIME - Pet products - Seachem Laboratories
PRIME - Pharmaceutical preparations - Rothkopf & Associates Inc.
PRIME - Prophylactics - Ansell Inc. (Personal Products Div.)
PRIME - Tires–bicycles - Klein Bicycle Corp.
PRIME - Whiskey - John Gross & Co.
PRIME 1 - Vitamins and nutritional supplements - Primequest International, Inc.
PRIME-1-TIME - Primers - Evans Adhesive Corp.
PRIME ACCESS - Meat products - Old Farm, Inc.
PRIME AGAIN - Vitamins and nutritional supplements - Sunrider Corp.
PRIME ALPACA - Yarn - Henry's Attic
PRIME AMERICAN VALUE SELECTION AVS - Cigarettes - American Tobacco Co.
PRIME & BOND - Dental compounds - Dentsply International Inc.
PRIME & SEAL - Paints - Somay Products Inc.
PRIME & SHINE - Nail care products ☆ - Victoria Vogue, Inc.
PRIME A.P.E. AUTOMATED PRODUCTION ENVIRONMENT WEB PUBLISHING TOOLS - Computer software - Iguide, Inc.
PRIME A.P.E. WEB PUBLISHING TOOLS - Computer software - News Internet Services
PRIME ART - Jewelry - PAJ, Inc.
PRIME ARTEMIA - Fish food - Prime Artemia Inc.
PRIME ASSET - Floor coverings–carpet and rugs ☆ - Columbus Mills, Inc.
PRIME ATTRACTION - Floor coverings–carpet and rugs - Evans-Black Carpet Mills
PRIME BOX - Jewelry - Rocket Jewelry Box, Inc.
PRIME CATCH - Tuna–canned - Star-Kist Foods, Inc.
PRIME CHOICE - Dog food - Superior Brands Inc.
PRIME CHOICE - Meat sauces - House of Herbs Inc.
PRIME CONNECTION - Apparel and accessories - Aljar Industries II
PRIME CONTENDER - Floor coverings–carpet and rugs ☆ - Cumberland Mills Inc.
PRIME CONTROLS, INC. - Electronic equipment - Prime Controls, Inc.
PRIME COTE - Paints - Carnival Arts, Inc.
PRIME CUISINE - Dog food - Tapf, Inc.
PRIME CUISINE - Pet products - ALPO Petfoods Inc.
PRIME CUT - Floor coverings–carpet and rugs ☆ - Interloom Ltd.
PRIME CUT - Welding equipment - Broco, Inc.
PRIME ELEMENTS - Apparel and accessories - Bob's Inc.
PRIME FIBER - Vitamins and nutritional supplements - Primequest International, Inc.
PRIME FILE - Filing cabinets–metal - Steelworks, Inc.
PRIME FIT - Exercising equipment - Diversified Products Corp.
PRIME FITNESS - Skates–roller - Chicago Roller Skate Co.
PRIME FROZEN - Food products - Pitsweet Inc.
PRIME FRY - Shortening - Mallet and Co.
PRIME GRIND - Cleaning preparations - Hertron International Inc.
PRIME GRIND - Coffee - HDS Services
PRIME GRO - Chemical preparations - Therm-O-Rock East, Inc.
PRIME GUARD - Paints - Parker Paint Manufacturing Co.
PRIME HEART - Vitamins and nutritional supplements - McZand Herbal, Inc.
PRIME IMAGE - Cameras–video - Prime Image Inc.
PRIME-IT - Paints - Sterling-Clark-Lurton Corp.
PRIME-IT 2000 - Paints - Brod-Dugan Co./Sherwin Williams Co.
PRIME-KLIP - Fasteners–snap - C.O. Tools, Inc.
PRIME LIFE - Food products - Wilsey Foods, Inc.
PRIME-LIFE - Vitamins and nutritional supplements ☆ - Klaire Laboratories Inc.
PRIME LINE - Automotive parts and accessories - Echlin Inc.
PRIME LINER - Wallpaper - Gencorp Inc.
PRIME-MATE - Paints - Zynolyte Products Co.
PRIME-MATES - Glassware–household - Owens-Illinois Inc. (Libbey Div.)
PRIME MERIDIAN - Seafood products–fresh or frozen - Meridian Products
PRIME MERIDIAN - Seafood products–fresh or frozen - Meridian Products, Inc.

☆ = Now out of production

PRIME MINERALS - Vitamins and nutritional supplements - Bioenergy Nutrient's Inc.

PRIME MINISTER - Floor coverings–carpet and rugs ☆ - Porter Carpet Mills Inc.

PRIME MOULDING - Moldings and trim - ABT Co., Inc.

PRIME 'N FILL - Paint and wallpaper stores - Synkoloid Co.

PRIME NATURAL HEALTH - Pharmaceutical preparations - Prime Natural Health Laboratories Inc.

PRIME NUMBER EXPLORER - Toys–models ☆ - Estes Industries

PRIME ODD WILD SQUARE MISS - Games - Interactive Dimensions

PRIME OF YOUR LIFE - Cups–plastic - Russ Berrie and Co., Inc.

PRIME PAC - Veterinary pharmaceutical preparations - Schering Corp.

PRIME PAK - Pharmaceutical preparations - Primequest International, Inc.

PRIME PARTS - Food products - Perdue Holdings, Inc.

PRIME PATTIES - Food products - Specialty Foods Investment Co.

PRIME PERFECT - Vitamins and nutritional supplements - Primequest International, Inc.

PRIME-PHOS - Paints - Valspar Corp.

PRIME PIT - Food products - Pierce Foods Corp.

PRIME PLACE - Floor coverings–carpet and rugs - Barrett Carpet Mills Inc.

PRIME PLUS - Fishing tackle - E.I. Dupont de Nemours and Co.

PRIME PLUS - Vitamins and nutritional supplements - Primequest International, Inc.

PRIME QUALITY - Fish–fresh or frozen - Mountaire Farms Inc.

PRIME RATE - Floor coverings–carpet and rugs - Karastan-Bigelow Inc.

PRIME REEF - Pet products - Ocean Nutrition Corp.

PRIME RELIEF - Health care products - East Earth Herb Inc.

PRIME RESCUE - Health care products - East Earth Herb Inc.

PRIME RESERVE - Vegetables–frozen ☆ - Lamb-Weston, Inc.

PRIME RESIN - Laboratory apparatus - PLC Corp.

P.R.I.M.E. RESOURCE GROUP - Publisher's imprints - P.R.G., Inc.

PRIME RESPONSE - Health care products - East Earth Herb Inc.

PRIME RIB - Computer software - Valis Group

PRIME RITE - Glue–household or industrial - Synkoloid Co.

PRIME RITE - Paints - Valspar Corp.

PRIME SECURITY - Motor vehicle parts and accessories - Avital Technologies, Inc.

PRIME SELECTA - Shrimp–fresh or frozen - Selecta Seafoods, Inc.

PRIME SHIELD - Metal primer - Interstate Paint Corp.

PRIME-SHINE - Cleaning preparations - Aiken Chemical Co., Inc.

PRIME SHINE - Floor waxes - Hako Minuteman Inc.

PRIME SHINE - Leather–chamois - Acme Sponge & Chamois Co., Inc.

PRIME SHINE RSB - Floor waxes - Hako Minuteman Inc.

PRIME SIRLOIN BUFFET - Restaurants–fast food - WSMP Inc.

PRIME SOURCE - Animal feed - Purina Mills, Inc.

PRIME SOURCE - Cleaning preparations - Bunzl Plastics, Inc.

PRIME-STAR - Floor waxes - Pioneer/Eclipse Corp.

PRIME TAN - Tools - Wells Lamont Corp.

PRIME TANNING - Leather - Prime Tanning Co., Inc.

PRIME TEST - Pharmaceutical preparations - Mark Lovendale

PRIME TIME - Agricultural products - Sun and Sands Enterprises

PRIME TIME - Apparel and accessories - Salant/Manhattan Industries

PRIME TIME - Apparel–men's - Made in the Shade by Prime Time

PRIME TIME - Chemical preparations - Construction Forms, Inc.

PRIME TIME - Cookies - Prime Time America Health Foods

PRIME TIME - Floor coverings–carpet and rugs - Queen Carpet Corp.

PRIME TIME - Jewelry - Komor Manufacturing

PRIME TIME - Lipsticks - Preview Products

PRIME TIME - Meat products - CTD, Inc.

PRIME TIME - Popcorn - Nature Kist Snacks

PRIME TIME - Recording label - Koch International

PRIME TIME - Vitamins and nutritional supplements ☆ - Natural Balance, Inc.

PRIME TIME - Wallpaper - Riverside Silkscreen

PRIME TIME - Watches - Elgin Watch Co.

PRIME TIMER - Metronomes - Stringer Industries Inc.

PRIME TIMERS - Leather goods - St. Thomas Inc.

PRIME TREATS - Pet food - St. Jon Laboratories, Inc.

PRIME ULTRAVERSE - Shirts - Malibu Comics Entertainment, Inc.

PRIME VALUE - Bags–trash - Innovative Packaging Group, Inc.

PRIME WEATHER SHIELD - Weather stripping ☆ - The Standard Products Co.

PRIME WEIGH - Scales - Fairbanks Inc.

PRIME YEARS - Pharmaceutical preparations - McZand Herbal, Inc.

PRIMEAU - Floor coverings–carpet and rugs ☆ - Karastan-Bigelow Inc.

PRIMECOAT - Paints - Devoe & Raynolds Co.

PRIMECOAT - Rustproofing compounds - Cortec Corp.

PRIMECRETE - Coatings - Pioneer Paint of Arizona

PRIMEDECK - Wood products - Chemco, Inc.

PRIMEENTERTAINMENT - Broadcasting stations–television - Primestar Partners LP

PRIMEFORM - Homeopathic remedies - Nature's Sunshine Products, Inc.

PRIMEGRIP - Adhesives and sealants - Prime Source Building Products, Inc.

PRIMEGUARD - Screws - Prime Source Building Products, Inc.

PRIMEHIDE - Pet food - Abbey Enterprises, Inc.

PRIMEHIDE USA - Pet products - Aqua Stock/Petcetera Inc.

PRIMEKOTE - Roofing materials–concrete - Prime Source Building Products, Inc.

PRIMEKOTE-DUBLX - Paints ☆ - Everseal International Sales Co. Inc.

PRIMELINE - Cabinets - Prime Wood, Inc.

PRIMELINE - Paints - Cook and Dunn Paint Corp.

PRIMELINE-OIL LEATHER - Sporting goods - Lisco, Inc.

PRIMENE - Chemical preparations - Rohm and Haas Co.

PRIMENOL - Pharmaceutical preparations ☆ - Primedics Laboratories

PRIMEOL - Leather goods - Prime Leather Finishes Co.

PRIMEPAC - Veterinary pharmaceutical preparations - Schering-Plough Animal Health

PRIMEQUEST - Skin care products - Primequest International, Inc.

PRIMER - Pharmaceutical preparations - Glenwood LLC

PRIMER-1 - Primers - Aexcel Corp.

PRIMER 83 - Computer software - Dynacomp Inc.

PRIMER ALL 20 - Paints - Lanci Industries, Inc.

PRIMER PAK - Toys - Lauri Inc.

PRIMER-X - Cosmetics - Monaco Import/Export Inc.

PRIMERA - Curling irons–electric - Windmere Corp.

PRIMERA - Furniture - Telescope Casual Furniture Inc.

PRIMERA - Paper - Mead Corp.

PRIMERA - Printers–computer - Fargo Electronics Inc.

PRIMERA - Printing trades machinery - E.I. Dupont de Nemours and Co.

PRIMERA - Rice - Town Fiesta Trading, Inc.

PRIMERA CLASE - Recording label - Musical Productions, Inc.

PRIMERA DE ARIZONA - Food products - Ash Enterprises, Inc.

PRIMERA LUZ - Candles - Cathedral Candle Co.

PRIMERA SLING COLLECTION - Furniture - Telescope Casual Furniture Inc.

PRIMERAPRO - Printers–computer - Fargo Electronics Inc.

PRIMERAPRO ELITE - Printers–computer - Fargo Electronics Inc.

PRIMERITE - Primers - Sigma Coatings USA BV.

PRIMERO - Floor coverings–carpet and rugs ☆ - American Carpet Mills

PRIMERO - Liquors - Wine Imports Ltd.

PRIMERO - Pickles - H.E. Butt Grocery Co.

PRIMEROS VERBOS - Computer software - Laureate Learning Systems Inc.

PRIMERRO - Pizzas–frozen - Little Lady Foods Inc.

PRIMERS TO PROTEIN - Chemical preparations - Novagen, Inc.

PRIMESEAL - Paints - Perma-Chink Systems, Inc.

PRIMESPACER - Gypsum products - Panelfold Inc.

PRIMESTAR RACING - Bags–duffel - Primestar Partners LP

PRIMESTRIN - Pharmaceutical preparations ☆ - Primedics Laboratories

PRIMETCH - Primers - Atlas Coatings Corp.

PRIMETHASONE - Pharmaceutical preparations ☆ - Primedics Laboratories

PRIMETHASONE LA - Pharmaceutical preparations ☆ - Primedics Laboratories

PRIMETIME - Floor coverings–carpet and rugs ☆ - American Carpet Mills

PRIMETIME - Health care products - Inbrand Corp.

PRIMETIME - Sporting goods - Hunter's Specialties, Inc.

PRIMETIME - Trading cards and stamps - Impel Marketing Inc.

PRIMETIME - Video tapes–blank ☆ - E.I. Dupont de Nemours and Co.

PRIMETIME 24 - Broadcasting stations–television - Primetime 24 Joint Venture

PRIMETIME PLAYTHINGS - Toys - International Playthings Inc.

PRIMETINIC - Aquarium accessories - Rainbow Lifegard Aquarium Products

PRIMETRIM - Wood products - Georgia-Pacific Corp.

PRIMETTA - Eyeglasses ☆ - Private Eyes Sunglass Corp.

PRIMETTA - Vegetables–canned - Lico Brands, Inc.

PRIMEVALUE - Broadcasting stations–television - Primestar Partners LP

PRIMEVIEW - Computer peripheral equipment - Futuretel, Inc.

PRIMEWOOD - Veneer - Prime Wood, Inc.

PRIMEWRAP - Door frames - Prime Wood, Inc.

PRIMEX - Boating equipment and accessories - Marine Muffler Corp.

PRIMEX - Shortening - Procter & Gamble Co.

PRIMEX B & C - Shortening - Procter & Gamble Co.

PRIMI - Pasta - Schwan's Sales Enterprises, Inc.

PRIMI PASSI - Footwear - Wadiwalkers Inc.

PRIMIATO - Spaghetti sauces - Red Wing Co., Inc.

PRIMIDONE - Pharmaceutical preparations - Rugby Laboratories Inc.

PRIMIS - Automotive parts and accessories - IQ Products Co.

PRIMISSIMI - Food products machinery - Bertolli USA, Inc.

PRIMISSIMO - Meat products–pork - Hormel Foods Corp.

PRIMITIVE - Tiles–ceramic ☆ - American Olean Tile Co.

PRIMITIVE ART - House furnishings - Dan River Inc.

PRIMITIVE ENCORE - Tiles–ceramic ☆ - American Olean Tile Co.

PRIMITIVE FOLK - Posters - Teresa Ann Kogut

PRIMITIVE FROG - Apparel and accessories - Lee N. Bishop

PRIMITIVE, INK. - Apparel and accessories - Primitive, Ink.

PRIMITIVE PUCKS - Apparel–athletic - Tim Bedison Co., Inc.

PRIMITIVE STITCHERY - Hobby kits - Sign of the Sunflower

PRIMITIVO - Wines - Hop Kiln Winery

PRIMIZIA - Olive oil - Venetian Import & Export Co.

PRIMKOTE - Paints - Abatron, Inc.

PRIMLOK - Floor coverings–carpet and rugs ☆ - Heuga USA

PRIMO - Beverages–malt - The Stroh Brewery Co.

PRIMO - Biscuits ☆ - Haddon House Food Products Inc.

PRIMO - Cheese - Land O'Lakes Inc.

PRIMO - Colognes - Parfum de Coeur Ltd.

PRIMO - Flashlights - Zelco Industries, Inc.

PRIMO - Flutes ☆ - Selmer Co. Inc.

PRIMO - Food products - Avico Distributing Inc.

PRIMO - Health care products - Tip Wholesaler Distributing

PRIMO - Motor vehicle parts and accessories - Rivera Engineering, Inc.

PRIMO - Motorcycle parts and accessories - Primo Products, Inc.

PRIMO - Ophthalmic goods - Foremost Optical Products

PRIMO - Sausages - Perri Sausage Inc.

PRIMO - Tables–metal ☆ - Teledyne Post

PRIMO - Tiles–ceramic ☆ - Huntington/Pacific Ceramics Inc.

PRIMO 40 - Dog food - Happy Jack, Inc.

PRIMO CAR KLEEN - Cleaning preparations - JMH International, Inc.

PRIMO COLLECTION - Eyeglasses - Wal-Mart Stores Inc.

PRIMO DEANO - Sporting goods ☆ - Powell Skateboards

PRIMO DEL REY - Cigar boxes–wood - Consolidated Cigar Corp.

PRIMO DEL REY - Cigars - Moro Cigar Co.

PRIMO DONNA - Toys–stuffed - Dakin Inc.

PRIMO I - Bicycles - Gallop Cycle

PRIMO-L - Lenses–photographic - Panavision International L.P.

PRIMO POLISH - Cleaning preparations - Total Marketing Co. Inc.

PRIMO SCREE - Recording label - Caroline Records, Inc.

PRIMO-SEAL - Lumber - Georgia-Pacific Corp.

PRIMO SPARKLE - Cleaning preparations - JMH International, Inc.

PRIMO-TRAP - Fishing lures - Sports Design and Development, Inc.

PRIMO ZOOM - Lenses–photographic - Panavision International L.P.

PRIMOLITH - Oils–lubricating - Kerr-McGee Chemical Corp.

PRIMORTALS - Apparel and accessories - Big Entertainment, Inc.

PRIMO'S - Food products - Primo's Italian Foods

PRIMOS - Hunting equipment - Primos, Inc.

PRIMO'S ESPRESSO AMERICANA - Coffee - Primo's Coffee, Inc.

PRIMP 'N PRETTY - Lip gloss, nail polish, and face powder ☆ - Cosrich Inc.

PRIMROSE - Computer storage devices - Tesseract Corp.

PRIMROSE - Dinnerware–glass ☆ - Royal China & Porcelain Companies Inc.

PRIMROSE - Flatware ☆ - Kirk Stieff Co.

PRIMROSE - Girdles - Primrose Undergarment Co.

PRIMROSE - Glassware–household - Gorham Inc.

PRIMROSE - Lipsticks - Cosmair Inc.

PRIMROSE - Luggage - Airway Industries, Inc.

PRIMROSE - Serving carts ☆ - National Housewares

PRIMROSE - Snack foods - Bell'amore Imports Inc.

PRIMROSE - Vases - Crisa Corp.

PRIMROSE - Yarn - William Unger & Co. Inc.

PRIMROSE BORDIER - Bedding–linen - Descamps

PRIMROSE HILL - Wallpaper - Warner of London

PRIMSOL - Pharmaceutical preparations - Ascent Pharmaceuticals, Inc.

PRIMUCELL FIP - Veterinary pharmaceutical preparations - SmithKline Beecham Animal Health Products

PRIMULA - Coffee makers–electric - Epoca, Inc./Ballarini

PRIMUS - See **ACROBASE**

PRIMUS - Computer peripheral equipment - Symbologic Corp.

PRIMUS - Pens ☆ - Pelikan, Inc.

PRIMUS - Recording label - Les Claypool

PRIMUS - Rings–jewelry - Artcarved Inc.

PRIMUS - Wines - Franciscan Vineyards, Inc.

PRIMWAY - Food products ☆ - Tommy's Foods Inc.

PRIMZ - Finishing agents - O'Brien Corp.

PRIMZ - Paints - Fuller-O'Brien Paints Inc.

PRIN-SETTES - Jewelry–costume - Preferred Products Inc.

PRINCE - Bats–baseball - Toshiba America Medical Systems Inc.

PRINCE - Brushes–hair - Wright-Bernet

PRINCE - Brushes–paint - Corona Brushes Inc.

PRINCE - Candy - American Chewing Gum Inc.

PRINCE - Chemical preparations - Philipp Brothers Chemical Inc.

PRINCE - Cigars ☆ - Havatampa Inc.

PRINCE - Computer software - Baudville, Inc.

PRINCE - Dog food - Simmons Industries Inc.

PRINCE - Dolls - Mattel, Inc.

PRINCE - Footwear - Angel-Etts of California, Inc.

PRINCE - Office supplies - Monarch Industries Inc.

PRINCE - Pet products - Glo-Marr Products Inc.

PRINCE - Pet products - L & H Packing Co.

PRINCE - Rackets–tennis - Prince Sports Group, Inc.

PRINCE - Recording label - Criterion Music Corp.

PRINCE - Recording label - TMC Productions

PRINCE - Ribbons ☆ - Princess Ribbon Corp.

PRINCE - Sauces - Borden/Prince Foods (Canning Div.)

PRINCE - Sporting goods - Dart Mart Inc.

PRINCE - Sporting goods - Prince Manufacturing Inc.

PRINCE - Watches - Bulova Corp.

PRINCE - Watches - Rolex Watch USA, Inc.

PRINCE - Welding equipment - M.K. Products, Inc.

PRINCE - Wigs - Jean Paree Weegs Inc.

PRINCE - Wines - Seagram's Chateau & Estate Wines Co.

PRINCE ADAM - Toys - Mattel, Inc.

PRINCE ALBERT - Tobacco products - John Middleton Inc.

PRINCE ALBERT - Watches - Bulova Corp.

PRINCE ALEXIS - Beverages–alcohol - James A. Robertson Co.

PRINCE & PRINCESS - Skin care products - Chris C. Maduka

PRINCE AVENUE - Floor coverings–carpet and rugs - Gulistan Carpet Inc.

PRINCE BIANCA - Jewelry - Preferred Products Inc.

PRINCE CASTLE INC. - Baskets–steel - Prince Castle Inc.

PRINCE CASTLE INC. WORLDWIDE - Metals - Prince Castle Inc.

PRINCE CHARMING - Dolls - Effanbee Doll Corp.

PRINCE CHARMING - Toys–stuffed ☆ - Dakin Inc.

PRINCE CONSORT - Neckties - A. Schreter & Sons Co. Inc.

PRINCE D'ARMAGNAC - Liquors - Crestfield Importers Ltd.

PRINCE FREDERIC - Apparel–men's ☆ - Dunleigh Tuxton Inc.

PRINCE GARDNER - Leather goods - Prince Gardner Inc.

PRINCE GARDNER ACCESSORIES - Leather - J.S.B. Jenkins

PRINCE GOLD PREMIUM - Beverages–malt - Prince-Wiest Brewing

PRINCE HAMLET - Cigars ☆ - Phillies Cigar Co.

PRINCE IGOR - Apparel–men's ☆ - Burma-Bibas, Inc.

PRINCE KITTY - Toys–stuffed ☆ - Dakin Inc.

PRINCE KUHIO - Shoes - Scott Hawaii

PRINCE MARCO BORGHESE - Beauty shop equipment - N. Wagman & Co.

PRINCE MATCHABELLI - Cosmetics - Prince Matchabelli

PRINCE MICHEL DE RAPIDAN - Wine - Omni Services, Inc.

PRINCE MICHEL DE VIRGINIA - Beverages–alcohol - Omni Services, Inc.

PRINCE OBOLENSKI - Shaving preparations - Schnapp Enterprises Inc.

PRINCE OF DENMARK - Vegetables–frozen - Dan Trade, Inc.

PRINCE-OF-EASE - Furniture - Kittinger Co.

PRINCE OF PEACE - Teas ☆ - Prince of Peace Enterprises Inc.

PRINCE OF PERSIA - Computer software ☆ - Broderbund Software, Inc.

PRINCE OF PERSIA 2'S THE SHADOW AND THE FLAME - Computer software - Broderbund Software, Inc.

PRINCE OF WALES - Floor coverings–carpet and rugs ☆ - Regal Rugs Inc.

PRINCE OF WALES - Furniture - National/Mt. Airy Furniture

PRINCE OF WALES - Leather–chamois - S.M. Arnold Inc.

PRINCE OF WALES - Liquors - Paramount Distillers Inc.

PRINCE PALAVICINI - Wines - Kobrand Corp.

PRINCE PAUL - Fish–canned or cured ☆ - Safeway Stores Inc.

PRINCE PHILIP - Cigars - General Cigar Co., Inc.

PRINCE PHILIP - Colognes - Ritornelle Inc.

PRINCE PIRATE - Wines - Admiral Wine Merchants

PRINCE PIRATE - Wines - Maison Jomere Ltd.

PRINCE REGENT - Dishes–earthenware ☆ - Royal China & Porcelain Companies Inc.

PRINCE RUBY - Fruits and vegetables - Corrin

PRINCE SOLMS - Wines ☆ - Moyer Texas Champagne Co.

PRINCE VALIANT - Games ☆ - Chaosium Inc.

PRINCE WILLIAM ON THE POTOMAC RIVERFEST & BOAT SHOW - Apparel and accessories - Prince William County of Virginia Chamber of Commerce, Inc.

PRINCECRAFT/SPRINGBOK - Boats–motor - Outboard Marine Corp.

☆ = Now out of production

PRINCEDOR - Chocolate candy - Casino North America
PRINCELLA - Salads–prepackaged - Joan of Arc Co.
PRINCELY COURT - Floor coverings–carpet and rugs ☆ - Gulistan Carpet Inc.
PRINCESAS - Cigars - G.A. Georgopulo & Co. Inc.
PRINCESS - Athletic shoes - Reebok International Ltd.
PRINCESS - Bathroom fixtures ☆ - Alsons Corp.
PRINCESS - Boats–motor ☆ - Regal Marine Industries Inc.
PRINCESS - Cabinets ☆ - Akro-Mils Inc.
PRINCESS - Candy ☆ - Brady Enterprises Inc.
PRINCESS - Candy ☆ - F.B. Washburn Candy Corp.
PRINCESS - Christmas tree ornaments - Cracker Box Inc.
PRINCESS - Copper compounds ☆ - Regal Ware, Inc.
PRINCESS - Cutlery - Maryland Plastics Inc.
PRINCESS - Doors–metal ☆ - Remington Building Products
PRINCESS - Doughnuts–mixes ☆ - Dawn Food Products Inc.
PRINCESS - Floor coverings ☆ - Teak International
PRINCESS - Floor coverings–carpet and rugs - Regal Rugs Inc.
PRINCESS - Floor coverings–carpet and rugs - Rugby Rugs Inc.
PRINCESS - Food products - Whipple Co.
PRINCESS - Footwear - Angel-Etts of California, Inc.
PRINCESS - Frames–picture ☆ - Acme Frame Products, Inc.
PRINCESS - Furniture - Weiman Co.
PRINCESS - Furniture ☆ - Lane Co. Inc.
PRINCESS - Glassware–household - Crystal Clear Importing Co. Inc.
PRINCESS - Glassware–household - Svend Jensen of Denmark Inc.
PRINCESS - Glassware–household ☆ - Lotus Glass Co.
PRINCESS - Hair care products - Carolina Absorbent Cotton
PRINCESS - Hair care products ☆ - Le Pages Inc.
PRINCESS - Harmonicas - Hohner Inc.
PRINCESS - Headsets–telephone - Hamilton Electronics Corp.
PRINCESS - Hosiery–children's ☆ - Kaz Business Systems Inc.
PRINCESS - Housewares ☆ - Knobler International Ltd.
PRINCESS - Jewelry - S.H. Clausin & Co.
PRINCESS - Lamps ☆ - Tensor Corp.
PRINCESS - Manicure preparations - Nailtex Inc.
PRINCESS - Motor vehicles–motor homes ☆ - Honey Recreational Vehicles Inc.
PRINCESS - Opera glasses - Swift Instruments, Inc.
PRINCESS - Paperware, disposable diapers - American Stores Co.
PRINCESS - Pens ☆ - Faber-Castell Corp.
PRINCESS - Pet supplies - Ginger, Inc.
PRINCESS - Polishing cloths ☆ - Fair Haven Industries Inc.
PRINCESS - Ribbons - Princess Ribbon Corp.
PRINCESS - Signs - Hy-Ko Products Co.
PRINCESS - Slippers - Daniel Green Co.
PRINCESS - Snack foods ☆ - Bremner Inc.
PRINCESS - Soldering equipment - Eldon Industries Inc. (Ungar Div.)
PRINCESS - Stationery ☆ - Pratt & Austin Co.
PRINCESS - Tableware–china ☆ - Lenox, Inc.
PRINCESS - Telephones - At&T Corp.
PRINCESS - Thread - Threads USA Div.
PRINCESAS - Toys - Princess Soft Toys
PRINCESS - Vacuum cleaners and accessories - Health-Mor Inc.
PRINCESS - Watches - Bulova Corp.
PRINCESS - Watches - Rolex Watch USA, Inc.
PRINCESS - Window coverings - Conso Products Co.
PRINCESS ADORA - Toys - Mattel, Inc.
PRINCESS & THE CRAB, THE - Computer software - Knowledge Adventure
PRINCESS ANN - Lamps - Lamplight Farms, Inc.
PRINCESS ANN MARIE - Jewelry - Ann Marie Borhgese
PRINCESS ANNE - Cutlery - Carvel Hall Inc.
PRINCESS ANNE - Dresses–girls' - Baylis Co.
PRINCESS ANNE - Furniture - Pilliod Co.
PRINCESS ASTRID - Food products ☆ - Haram-Christensen Corp.
PRINCESS BED - Beds–wood - Lisco, Inc.
PRINCESS CAT - Footwear–athletic - Puma Inc.
PRINCESS CHIC - Underwear and nightwear - Kayser-Roth Corp.
PRINCESS CONSORT - Scarves ☆ - A. Schreter & Sons Co. Inc.
PRINCESS CRUISER - Boats–motor - Lyn-Craft Boat Co.
PRINCESS CRUISES - Apparel and accessories - Princess Cruises, Inc.
PRINCESS-CUT ROPE - Jewelry - Grando, Inc.
PRINCESS DI - Air purification systems - Athena Products Corp.
PRINCESS DIANE - Beauty shop equipment - Diane Products Inc.
PRINCESS EUGENIE - Watches - Bulova Corp.
PRINCESS FAIRA - Toys - Mattel, Inc.

PRINCESS FEATHER - Glass products - Westmoreland Glass Co.
PRINCESS GARDNER - Leather goods - Prince Gardner Inc.
PRINCESS GRACE - Luggage - Grace Luggage Co.
PRINCESS GWENEVERE AND THE JEWEL RIDERS - Cosmetics - Libby Lee Toys Inc.
PRINCESS HERITAGE - Glassware–household - Princess House, Inc.
PRINCESS HOTELS - Bags - Princess Hotels International, Inc.
PRINCESS HOUSE - Jewelry - Princess House, Inc.
PRINCESS HOUSE PETS - Figurines - Princess House, Inc.
PRINCESS IMPERIAL COLLECTION - Dolls - Uneeda Doll Co., Inc.
PRINCESS IN PINK - Dolls - Mattel, Inc.
PRINCESS IRENE - Glassware–household - ACC
PRINCESS KAIULANI - Shoes - Scott Hawaii
PRINCESS KITTEN - Shampoos - Summit Laboratories
PRINCESS KITTY - Toys–stuffed - Dakin Inc.
PRINCESS KNEESAA - Toys - Lucasfilm Ltd.
PRINCESS KNIT SET - Craft supplies - Milton Bradley Co.
PRINCESS LACE - Tablecloths - Cascade Fibers Co.
PRINCESS LEIA - Publisher's imprints - Lucasfilm Ltd.
PRINCESS LEIA ORGANA - Toys–stuffed - Kenner Products
PRINCESS LORI - Hosiery ☆ - Staff Supermarket Associates, Inc.
PRINCESS LORI - Knives - Trans Western Polymers Inc.
PRINCESS MARCELLA BORGHESE - Apparel–women's - Borghese Trademarks Inc.
PRINCESS MARCELLA BORGHESE - Fragrance - Borghese Cosmetics Inc.
PRINCESS MARCELLA BORGHESE IL BACIO - Hair care products - Revlon Consumer Products Corp.
PRINCESS MERRYBELL - Toys ☆ - Those Characters from Cleveland, Inc.
PRINCESS MID PLUS - Sporting goods ☆ - Gold Eagle/Arnold Palmer
PRINCESS NEW WAVES - Apparel and accessories - Princess Cruises, Inc.
PRINCESS NYLA - Skin care products - United Enterprises Inc. (Nyla Laboratories)
PRINCESS OF POWER - Dolls - Mattel, Inc.
PRINCESS OF POWER - Games ☆ - Ben Cooper Inc.
PRINCESS OF THE FLOWERS - Toys - Yes! Entertainment Corp.
PRINCESS PAM BY STEPHEN - Apparel and accessories ☆ - Ed-Burt Corp.
PRINCESS PAT - Watches - Bulova Corp.
PRINCESS PEARLS - Novelty items–paper - Lisa Frank, Inc.
PRINCESS PERSIAN - Toys–stuffed - Dakin Inc.
PRINCESS PET - Ice cream ☆ - Pet Dairy
PRINCESS POPPY - Dinnerware–glass ☆ - Franciscan by Johnson Brothers, USA, Inc.
PRINCESS PUP - Toys–stuffed - Julie Sturma
PRINCESS PURITAN - Crocheted and knitted items ☆ - Puritan Sportswear Corp.
PRINCESS REBECCA - Dolls - Rebecca Mance
PRINCESS ROYAL - Watches - Bulova Corp.
PRINCESS RYAN'S STAR MARINES - Games - Mark G. Mclaughlin .
PRINCESS SARINA - Caviar - King Oscar Inc.
PRINCESS SMART - Natural dyestuffs - Diversified Products Corp.
PRINCESS SNUGGLELINA - Toys ☆ - Playskool, Inc.
PRINCESS TENKO - Dolls - Mattel, Inc.
PRINCESS TENKO - Footwear ☆ - S. Goldberg and Co. Inc.
PRINCESS TOMATO IN THE SALAD KINGDOM - Video games - Hudson Soft USA Inc.
PRINCESS VANESSA - Dolls - Tonka Corp.
PRINCESS VANESSA AND HER ROYAL FAMILY - Dolls - Tonka Corp.
PRINCESS WISHING STAR - Dolls - Hasbro, Inc.
PRINCESSA - Candy ☆ - Super Valu Inc.
PRINCESSA - Jewelry–costume - Preferred Products Inc.
PRINCESSA - Wallpaper - Jolie Papier
PRINCESSWOOD - Cabinets ☆ - H.J. Scheirich Co.
PRINCETON - Bicycles - Columbia Manufacturing Inc.
PRINCETON - Brushes - Wright-Bernet
PRINCETON - Cabinets - Marsh Furniture Co.
PRINCETON - Cabinets ☆ - Canyon Creek Cabinet Co.
PRINCETON - Cribs–wood - Welsh Co.
PRINCETON - Crocheted and knitted items - Princeton Knitting Mills
PRINCETON - Desks ☆ - Domore/DO3
PRINCETON - Dinnerware ☆ - Corning Inc.
PRINCETON - Fireplace equipment - Design Specialties Inc.
PRINCETON - Flatware - Washington Forge Inc.
PRINCETON - Floor coverings–carpet and rugs - Atlas Carpet Mills Inc.
PRINCETON - Floor coverings–carpet and rugs ☆ - Barrett Carpet Mills Inc.
PRINCETON - Floor coverings–carpet and rugs ☆ - Colonial Mills Inc.
PRINCETON - Frames–eyeglass - U.S. Optical Frame Co.

☆ = Now out of production

PRINCETON - Furniture - Homecrest Industries Inc.
PRINCETON - Occasional tables ☆ - JDI Group, Inc.
PRINCETON - Ophthalmic goods - Rozin Optical Export Corp.
PRINCETON - Paints–artists' ☆ - Winsor & Newton
PRINCETON - Watches - Temlex/Jupiter Watch Corp.
PRINCETON 105 - Flowers, plants, and seeds - Jacklin Seed
PRINCETON BOOK CO. - Textbooks - Princeton Book Co., Publishers
PRINCETON BRICK - Floor coverings–tile - Kentile Floors Inc.
PRINCETON FARMS - Popcorn - Princeton Farms
PRINCETON FARMS - Popcorn - Princeton Mining Co. Inc.
PRINCETON GALLERY - Statuary - Lenox, Inc.
PRINCETON PLANK - Floor coverings - Robbins Inc.
PRINCETON SQUARE - Floor coverings–carpet and rugs ☆ - Mohawk Carpet Corp.
PRINCETON SQUARE - Shoes - Kobacker Co.
PRINCETON TEC - Flashlights - Princeton Tectonics, Inc.
PRINCETREE - Nursery products - Princeton Nurseries
PRINCIPAL - Music stands ☆ - Ferree's Tools Inc.
PRINCIPAL'S TOOLBOX - Computer software - Learning Systems Consultants, Inc.
PRINCIPATO - Wines - Palm Bay Imports, Inc.
PRINCIPATO ITALIAN TABLE WINES - Wines - Palm Bay Imports, Inc.
PRINCIPE - Bicycles - Ross Bicycles USA, Ltd.
PRINCIPE - Leather goods - Italian Classics Inc.
PRINCIPE - Neckties ☆ - Randa Corp.
PRINCIPE REGENERANT NO. 1 - Skin care products - Chanel Inc.
PRINCIPEN - Pharmaceutical preparations - Bristol-Myers Squibb Co.
PRINCIPESSA GAVI - Wines - Banfi Vintners
PRINCIPLE - Golfing equipment - Tonkin Inc.
PRINCIPLE WAY, THE - Posters - Thomas E. Ford
PRINCIPLES - Chairs ☆ - EAC Integrated Furniture Solutions
PRINCO - Ribbons ☆ - Princess Ribbon Corp.
PRINCRAFT - Ribbons ☆ - Princess Ribbon Corp.
PRINDELO - Wines - Viansa Winery and Marketplace
PRINDLE - Ships–sailing vessels - Performance Catamarans Inc.
PRINDLE, WEBER & SCHMIDT - Publisher's imprints - PWS Publishing
PRINDLES - Underwear and nightwear - Prindles, Inc.
PRINGLE - Apparel and accessories - Warnaco Inc.
PRINGLE - Toys–stuffed ☆ - Gund, Inc.
PRINGLE OF SCOTLAND - Apparel and accessories - Dawson International
PRINGLES - Potato chips - Procter & Gamble Co.
PRINGLES LIGHT - See PRINGLES RIGHT CRISPS
PRINGLES PLUS - Potato chips - Procter & Gamble Co.
PRINGLES POP UMS - Snack foods - Procter & Gamble Co.
PRINGLES RANCH - Potato chips - Procter & Gamble Co.
PRINGLES RIGHT CRISPS - Potato chips - Procter & Gamble Co.
PRINI U.S. - Fabrics–silk - Joscar Industries Inc.
PRINIVIL - Pharmaceutical preparations - Merck & Co., Inc. (Merck Research Laboratories)
PRINSSECA - Dresses–girls' - Kloz for Girls Corp.
PRINT 90 - Paper - Strathmore Paper Co.
PRINT-A-MARK - Inks - Matthews International Corp.
PRINT-AID - Fabrics–broadcloth - Chicopee
PRINT-ALL - Photographic equipment - SP Systems/Saratons
PRINT BAZAAR - Women's apparel - Country Miss Inc.
PRINT CENTRAL - Computer software - Aldus Corp.
PRINT/CLAMP - File folders - Stacor Corp.
PRINT COLLECTION - Floor coverings–carpet and rugs - Masterpiece Finishing Co.
PRINT COLLECTION, THE - Floor coverings–carpet and rugs ☆ - Galaxy Carpet Mills Inc.
PRINT CONDITIONER - Photographic equipment - Retouch Methods Co. Inc.
PRINT CONTRACT MANAGER - Computer software - ZML Software Systems, Inc.
PRINT FAX COPY IT IMAGING TECHNOLOGY - Toners - QC Group Corp.
PRINT FILE - Photographic equipment - Pacific Foto/Supply Co.
PRINT FRAME - Framing supplies - Clearr Corp.
PRINT GLO - Chemical preparations - John H. Olenik
PRINT GLOSS - Photo albums ☆ - Andrew Jeri Co. Inc.
PRINT GUARD - Electronic equipment - Seal Products Inc.
PRINT KING IV - Printing presses - King Press Corp.
PRINT MASTER - Computer peripheral equipment - Interactive Products Corp.
PRINT MATE - Paperboard - Gulf States Paper Corp.
PRINT-ME - Novelty items - Shirts Illustrated, Inc.
PRINT MEDIA SERVICE - Computer software - Dynamic Graphics Inc.
PRINT MUSIC - Computer software - Coda Music Technology, Inc.

PRINT-OFF - Cleaning preparations - Rite-Off Inc.
PRINT PAKS - Computer software - Printpaks, Inc.
PRINT PARADE, THE - Floor coverings–carpet and rugs ☆ - Evans-Black Carpet Mills
PRINT PHONE - Facsimile equipment ☆ - Cobra Electronics Corp.
PRINT-PLAST - Paper products - Cadillac Plastic Group, Inc.
PRINT PLUS - Paper–rolls - Willamette Industries, Inc.
PRINT PRESSION - Apparel and accessories - Prolific Screen Printing Co.
PRINT Q - Computer software - Software Directions Inc.
PRINT SHOP - Computer software - Broderbund Software, Inc.
PRINT SHOP DELUXE CD ENSEMBLE - Computer software - Broderbund Software, Inc.
PRINT SHOP DELUXE COMPANION - Computer software - Broderbund Software, Inc.
PRINT SHOP DELUXE ENSEMBLE II - Computer software - Broderbund Software, Inc.
PRINT SHOP, THE - Computer software ☆ - Gessler Publishing Co., Inc.
PRINT THE PLANET - Apparel and accessories - Print the Planet, Inc.
PRINT WOVE - Envelopes - Paper Corp. of America
PRINT WRITE - Paper–writing - Kurtz Bros. Inc.
PRINT YOUR OWN BINGO - Computer software - Hartley Courseware Inc.
PRINT YOUR OWN CALENDAR - Computer software - Hartley Courseware Inc.
PRINT2GETHER - Computer software - Transkrit Corp.
PRINTBRIDGE - Computer hardware - Alexicon Consultants
PRINTCHECK - Computer software - X-Rite, Inc.
PRINTCHEF - Computer software - Mindgate Technologies Inc.
PRINTCOMMANDER - Computer software - Image Sciences Inc.
PRINTEC - Blankets - Explan International Trade Inc.
PRINTED DECALS - Decals and transfers - Glover Advertising Inc.
PRINTED TEE - Fabrics–broadcloth - Desire Mills Co. Inc.
PRINTED VELOUR FINGERTIPS - Needlework towels - Charles Craft Inc.
PRINTELLE - Yarn ☆ - Lion Brand Yarn Co.
PRINTEMPS - Floor coverings–carpet and rugs ☆ - Regal Rugs Inc.
PRINTEMPS - Giftware - Sasaki
PRINTER MUFFLER - Printers–computer ☆ - Kensington
PRINTER STACK - Computer-printer stands - Atlantic Furniture Systems
PRINTERLINK - Computer components - Primax Electronics
PRINTER'S CALENDAR LINE - Paper - Goes Lithographing Co.
PRINTERS RESEARCH PRO PRODUCTS - Chemicals - Printers Research Co.
PRINTEX - Wallpaper ☆ - H & S Sales Inc.
PRINTFAST - Paper - National Printfast
PRINTFORM - Computer software - Postalsoft, a Firstlogic Technology
PRINTGINE - Integrated circuits - Chips and Technologies, Inc.
PRINTHEAD SAVER - Ribbons - Advent Corp.
PRINTHOUSE - Computer software - Corel USA
PRINTING - Printers–computer - Rosie Wells Enterprises Inc.
PRINTING CORNER PRESS - Publisher's imprints - Beck-Drennan, Inc.
PRINTING STUDIO 3-D - Postcards - Fotofolio Inc.
PRINTIQUE - Fabrics - Dan River Inc.
PRINTKOTE COVER - Paper - Westvaco Corp.
PRINTKOTE EAGLE - Paperboard - Westvaco Corp.
PRINTKOTE EASYSEAL - Paper–coated - Westvaco Corp.
PRINTKRAFT - Paperboard - Westvaco Corp.
PRINTLINK - Computer peripheral equipment - QMS, Inc.
PRINTMAKERS, THE - Artists' materials - The Printmakers
PRINTMASTER - Computer software - Infotec Development, Inc.
PRINTMASTER - Envelopes - Union Envelope Co.
PRINTMASTER - Ribbons–inked - Curtis-Young Corp.
PRINTMATE - Computer software - Micro Logic Corp.
PRINTMAX - Computer hardware - American Commercial Terminals, Inc.
PRINTOSEAL - Sealing compounds - Fel-Pro Inc.
PRINTPACK - Wallpaper - Printpack, Inc.
PRINTPAKS - Paper products - Printpaks, Inc.
PRINTPDF - Computer storage devices - Bell Data Network Communications, Inc.
PRINTPROTECT - Alarm systems - Allison Systems, Inc.
PRINTRAID - Computer hardware - Indata Corp.
PRINTRAK - Computer software - National Film Service, Inc.
PRINTRITE - Printing trades machinery - B.F. Goodrich Co.
PRINTS & STENCILS - Wallpaper - Seabrook Wallcoverings, Inc.
PRINTS AND WEAVES - Wallpaper - Sellers & Josephson
PRINTS CHARMING - Pencils ☆ - Faber-Castell Corp.
PRINTS CHARMING - Stationery ☆ - Coronet General Corp.

☆ = Now out of production

PRINTS FROM DOWN UNDER - Wallpaper - Decor International Wallcovering Inc.

PRINTS OF TAILS - T-shirts—men's - Nachman Corp.

PRINTS-PRO - Computer software - Media Cybernetics, L.P.

PRINTS ROYAL COLLECTION - Floor coverings—carpet and rugs - Trend Carpet

PRINTSMITH - Computer software - M Data Inc.

PRINTSMITH COPY SHOP - Computer software - M Data Inc.

PRINTSTATION - Electronics equipment - AZTEK Inc.

PRINTSTUDIO - Apparel—women's - Printmaker International Ltd.

PRINTVIEWER - Computer peripheral equipment ☆ - Lee Products Co.

PRINTVISION - Computer software - Oce Printing Systems USA, Inc.

PRINTY - Office supplies - IDL Manufacturing & Sales Corp.

PRINTYPE - Decals and transfers - Letraset USA Inc.

PRINZ - Electronic equipment - Amcam International, Inc.

PRINZENGARDE - Cigars - Gesty Trading & Manufacturing Corp.

PRIODERM - Pharmaceutical preparations ☆ - Purdue Frederick Co.

PRIOR - Apparel and accessories - Miller Stockman Western Wear

PRIOR - Crackers - Sunshine/Salerno Inc.

PRIORA P.F. - Pharmaceutical preparations ☆ - Xttrium Laboratories Inc.

PRIORE & ASSOCIATES - Wine - International Wine & Spirits Inc.

PRIORITE - Skin care products - Dana Perfumes Corp.

PRIORITE - Skin care products - Les Parfums De Dana, Inc.

PRIORITIES - Wallpaper - Artisan Handprints Inc.

PRIORITIES BY VAN HEUSEN - Shirts - Phillips-Van Heusen Corp.

PRIORITY - Furniture - Vaughan Furniture Co. Inc.

PRIORITY - Pizzas—frozen - Lou Malnati's Pizzeria

PRIORITY - Skin care products - Lancome

PRIORITY 1 PUBLISHING - Publisher's imprints - Priority One International Inc.

PRIORITY I - Apparel—women's - Lane Bryant, Inc.

PRIORITY MANUFACTURING - Carpet cleaning equipment - Jon-Don Products, Inc.

PRIORITY ONE EMERGENCY KIT - Pharmaceutical preparations - Priority One Marketing International

PRIORITY POWER - Computer software - Day-Timers, Inc.

PRIORITY ROCKS - Recording label - Priority Records

PRIORITY SEATING BY SHUFORD - Furniture—wood - Century Furniture Co.

PRIPPS PLUSS - Vitamins and nutritional supplements ☆ - Mueller Sports Medicine Inc.

PRISAR - Apparel and accessories - Big Entertainment, Inc.

PRISCILLA - Dolls - Effanbee Doll Corp.

PRISCILLA - Fabrics—felt - Roberts Colonial House Inc.

PRISCILLA - Housewares ☆ - General Housewares Corp.

PRISCILLA - Thread - Threads USA Div.

PRISCILLA - Watches - Bulova Corp.

PRISCILLA - Wedding gowns - Priscilla of Boston Inc.

PRISCILLA COUTURE - Wedding gowns - Priscilla of Boston Inc.

PRISCILLA HAUSER - Artists' materials - Robert Simmons Inc.

PRISCILLA HAUSER - Paints—artists' ☆ - Martin F. Weber Co.

PRISCILLA PILGRIM - Toys—stuffed - Russ Berrie and Co., Inc.

PRISCILLA PRESLEY - Colognes - Frances Denney

PRISCILLA TURNER - Floor coverings—carpet and rugs - KMM Corp.

PRISCILLA'S GARDEN - Giftware - Charles Zahn-Import Merchant

PRISCO ENVIROKLENE - Cleaning preparations - Printers' Service, Inc.

PRISCOLINE - Pharmaceutical preparations - Ciba-Geigy Corp.

PRISM - Adhesives and sealants - Loctite Corp.

PRISM - Audio equipment ☆ - Telequest Inc.

PRISM - Batteries - CSB Battery of America Corp.

PRISM - Bricks - North American Refractories Co.

PRISM - Cabinets - Zenith Products Corp.

PRISM - Cables - Tara Labs, Inc.

PRISM - Chimes - Nutone Inc.

PRISM - Computer software - Goulds Pumps, Inc.

PRISM - Computer software - Princeton University Press

PRISM - Computer software - Quality Visions, Inc.

PRISM - Computer software - Spectrum Universal

PRISM - Computer storage devices—magnetic - Prism Magnetics, Inc.

PRISM - Dinnerware ☆ - Corning Inc.

PRISM - Envelopes - Western States Envelope Co.

PRISM - Fabrics - Vertilux-Louverlux Inc.

PRISM - Fireplace equipment - Thermo-Rite Manufacturing Co.

PRISM - Floor coverings - Azrock Commercial Flooring

PRISM - Floor coverings—carpet and rugs - Blue Ridge Carpet Mills

PRISM - Floor coverings—carpet and rugs ☆ - Regal Rugs Inc.

PRISM - Furniture ☆ - Bassett Furniture Industries, Inc.

PRISM - Glassware—household - Dansk International Designs, Ltd.

PRISM - Golfing equipment - Pro Select Sports USA

PRISM - Inks - Rubber Stampede

PRISM - Lamp bulbs - Halco Lighting

PRISM - Luggage - Samsonite Corp.

PRISM - Medical apparatus - Depuy Inc.

PRISM - Musical instrument accessories - J. D'Addario & Co. Inc.

PRISM - Occasional furniture ☆ - JDI Group, Inc.

PRISM - Office supplies - Wallace Computer Services, Inc.

PRISM - Office supplies ☆ - Faber-Castell Corp.

PRISM - Paints - Palmer Paint Products, Inc.

PRISM - Publisher's imprints ☆ - Chronicle Books

PRISM - Reagent chemical kits - Applied Biosystems Inc.

PRISM - Skin care products - Eurostar Inc.

PRISM - Skin care products - Veeco Manufacturing Co.

PRISM - Sporting goods - Prince Manufacturing Inc.

PRISM - Stains - Rudd Co. Inc.

PRISM - Vacuum cleaners and accessories - Clarke Industries, Inc.

PRISM - Vases ☆ - Lenox Crystal, Inc.

PRISM - Wallpaper - Southport

PRISM - X-ray apparatus - Princeton Gamma-Tech Inc.

PRISM 401 - Adhesives and sealants - Loctite Corp.

PRISM 403 - Adhesives and sealants - Loctite Corp.

PRISM 405 - Adhesives and sealants - Loctite Corp.

PRISM 406 - Adhesives and sealants - Loctite Corp.

PRISM 408 - Adhesives and sealants - Loctite Corp.

PRISM 410 - Adhesives and sealants - Loctite Corp.

PRISM 411 - Adhesives and sealants - Loctite Corp.

PRISM 447 - Adhesives and sealants - Loctite Corp.

PRISM 454 - Adhesives and sealants - Loctite Corp.

PRISM 455 - Adhesives and sealants - Loctite Corp.

PRISM 460 - Adhesives and sealants - Loctite Corp.

PRISM COLOR-FAST DYES - Cleaning preparations—carpet and rug - Von Schrader Co.

PRISM COLOR GROUP - Electronic equipment - Dayton Tech Art Co.

PRISM EDITIONS - Publisher's imprints ☆ - Naturegraph Publishers Inc.

PRISM I - Wallpaper - Ozite Corp.

PRISM II - Wallpaper - Bayview Wallcoverings

PRISM II - Wallpaper - Ozite Corp.

PRISM-LEVEL - Sextants—surveying - Davis Instruments Corp.

PRISM LINERS - Tiles—ceramic - Monarch Tile Inc.

PRISM LT - Dental compounds - Derby Dental Laboratory, Inc.

PRISM MAGIC - Decals and transfers - Prism Magic, Inc.

PRISM PIGMENTS - Pigments - Mix Manufacturing, Inc.

PRISM PRESS BOOKS - Publisher's imprints - Blaine Ethridge Books

PRISM TARGET MARKETING - Video production - Mobil Oil Corp.

PRISM TECHNOLOGIES - Medical apparatus - Prism Enterprises, Inc.

PRISM, THE - Optical device - Cary Hodous

PRISMA - Bedding—linen - Dan River Inc.

PRISMA - Cabinets ☆ - Aristokraft, Inc.

PRISMA - Cabinets ☆ - Mutschler European

PRISMA - Cleaning preparations—carpet and rug - Chembond

PRISMA - Cosmetics - Rich On, Inc.

PRISMA - Floor coverings - Mannington Resilient Floors

PRISMA - Floor coverings—carpet and rugs ☆ - Lowe's Carpet Corp.

PRISMA - Furniture - Thayer Coggin Inc.

PRISMA - Glassware—household ☆ - National Housewares

PRISMA - Glassware—household ☆ - Sasaki

PRISMA - Greeting cards - Kensington Cards

PRISMA - Mirrors - National Products Inc.

PRISMA - Molding compounds—plastics ☆ - Gossen Corp.

PRISMA - Rings—jewelry - Artcarved Inc.

PRISMA - Stools—metal - Krueger International, Inc.

PRISMA BY PREDICTIONS - Shoes ☆ - Edison Brothers Stores, Inc.

PRISMA CRAFT - Tiles—ceramic ☆ - Huntington/Pacific Ceramics Inc.

PRISMA DECORATOR - Molding compounds—plastics - Gossen Corp.

PRISMA GEM - Molding compounds—plastics ☆ - Gossen Corp.

PRISMA MIRROR - Wallcoverings - Wallcovering Industries Inc.

PRISMA OFFICE - Computer software - Crandell Group, Inc.

PRISMA TRIO LIGHTS - Lamps - Lamplight Farms, Inc.

PRISMACOLOR - Office supplies - Empire Berol USA

PRISMAIRE - Lighting fixtures - Holophane Corp.

PRISMALUME - Lighting fixtures - Holophane Corp.

PRISMAROUND - Lighting fixtures - Guth Lighting

PRISMASPHERE - Lighting fixtures - Holophane Corp.

PRISMAT - Seat covers - Rubbermaid Inc.

PRISMATIC - Floor coverings—carpet and rugs - Patcraft Mills Inc.

☆ = Now out of production

PRISMATIC - Skis - Collins Ski Products Inc.
PRISMATIC - Sporting goods - Oceanic
PRISMATIC ILLUSIONS - Paperboard - Pennsylvania Pulp and Paper Co.
PRISMATICS - Toys - Learning Materials Workshop
PRISMATITE - Lighting fixtures - Holophane Corp.
PRISMBEAM II - Lighting fixtures - Holophane Corp.
PRISMEX - Signs - Illumination Research Group, Inc.
PRISMGEAR - Speedometers - Rexnord Corp.
PRISMGLO - Lighting fixtures - Holophane Corp.
PRISMPACK V - Lighting fixtures - Holophane Corp.
PRISMPAY - Computer software - Spectrum Human Resource Systems Corp.
PRISMPIC - Bar fixtures–plastic - Spir-it Inc.
PRISMS - Cosmetics - Revlon Consumer Products Corp.
PRISMS - Floor coverings–carpet and rugs - Lotus Carpets
PRISMS - Floor coverings–carpet and rugs - Quaker Inc.
PRISMS - Floor coverings–carpet and rugs ☆ - Heuga USA
PRISMS IOS - Computer software - Prisms Products
PRISMS/IOS - Computer software - Prisms Products Partners
PRISMSTATS - Computer software - TLG Corp.
PRISMSTIR - Bar fixtures–plastic - Spir-it Inc.
PRISMWARE - Computer software - Spectrum Universal
PRISNERDS - Toys ☆ - Those Characters from Cleveland, Inc.
PRISONER OF LOVE - Dolls - Mattel, Inc.
PRISONER OF LOVE PANDA - Toys–stuffed - Mattel, Inc.
PRISONER OF SCHOOL - Stationery ☆ - Scentex Inc.
PRISS PRINTS - Wallpaper - Priss Prints Inc.
PRISSY MISS - Fishing lures - Mr. Bob's
PRIST - Fuel additives - PPG Industries, Inc.
PRISTEEN - Cleaning preparations ☆ - Warner-Lambert Co.
PRISTEEN - Health care products - Lee Pharmaceuticals
PRISTENE WATER - Water–bottled or canned - Pristene Water, Inc.
PRISTINE - Agricultural products - American Cyanamid Co.
PRISTINE - Bathtubs–enameled - Kohler Co.
PRISTINE - Dinnerware - Homer Laughlin China Co.
PRISTINE - Floor coverings–carpet and rugs - Regal Rugs Inc.
PRISTINE - Floor coverings–carpet and rugs - Robertex Associates Inc.
PRISTINE - Handbags - Design by Pristine Inc.
PRISTINE - Paper–writing - Lincoln Pulp and Paper Co. Inc.
PRISTINE CHECK - Chemical preparations - Earth Science Laboratories Inc.
PRISTINE WHITE - Tableware ☆ - Corning Inc.
PRITCHARD HILL - Beverages–alcohol - Chappellet Vineyard
PRITIKIN - Bread, muffins - Interstate Brands Corp.
PRITIKIN PROMISE - Exercising equipment ☆ - Trotter Inc.
PRITT - Adhesives and sealants ☆ - The Lockrey Co. Inc.
PRITT TACK-UPS - Abrasive products - Conros Corp.
PRITT TACK-UPS - Adhesives and sealants - Loctite Corp.
PRITUSSIN - Pharmaceutical preparations ☆ - Legere Pharmaceuticals Inc.
PRITZI - Luggage - TJX Companies, Inc.
PRIV-A-SEE - Blankets - Priv-A-See
PRIVA - Incontinence product - Med-I-Pant Inc. (Priva Homecare Div.)
PRIVACY BLIND, THE - Blinds–venetian - Phase II Inc.
PRIVACY GUARD - Telephone accessories - Conair Corp.
PRIVACY PHONE FILTER - Telephone answering machines - Comprehensive Software, Inc.
PRIVACY PLUS - Building materials - Blue Mountain Industries, Inc.
PRIVAFAX - Cellular Services Group Inc.
PRIVAFONE - Telecommunications equipment ☆ - Cellular Services Group Inc.
PRIVASEE - Apparel and accessories - Dorothy Wolfe
PRIVATA - Alarm systems - Philippe Sebrechts
PRIVATE AFFAIR - Underwear and nightwear - Maidenform Inc.
PRIVATE BLEND - Hair care products - Helene Curtis Industries Inc.
PRIVATE BLEND - Waxes–sealing - Summit-Naked Furniture Inc.
PRIVATE CALL - Telephones - Cobra Electronics Corp.
PRIVATE CALL - Toys - Hasbro, Inc.
PRIVATE CLOTHING COMPANY - Apparel–women's - Public Clothing Co.
PRIVATE CLUB - Cosmetics - Kmart Corp.
PRIVATE COLLECTION - Coffee - Maxwell House
PRIVATE COLLECTION - Dolls - Mattel, Inc.
PRIVATE COLLECTION - Meat products - Fresh Mark, Inc.
PRIVATE COLLECTION - Ophthalmic goods - Foremost Optical Products
PRIVATE COLLECTION - Perfumes - Estee Lauder Inc.
PRIVATE COLLECTION - Wallcoverings - Beverly Stevens Ltd.
PRIVATE COLLECTIONS - Footwear - Dyeables Inc.
PRIVATE DELIVERY - Computer software - Geoff Phillips
PRIVATE DISK - Computer software - Private Data, LLC
PRIVATE EAR - Amplifiers ☆ - LP Music Group

PRIVATE EXPRESSIONS - Lingerie - Peebles Inc.
PRIVATE-EYE - Electrical equipment ☆ - Precision Multiple Controls, Inc.
PRIVATE EYES - Frames–eyeglass - Private Eyes Sunglass Corp.
PRIVATE GARDEN - Candles - Private Gardens, L.C.
PRIVATE GRADE - Floor coverings–carpet and rugs - Columbus Mills, Inc.
PRIVATE ISLAND - Wallpaper - Charterhouse Ltd.
PRIVATE ISSUE - Sanitary napkins - Bob Barker Co., Inc.
PRIVATE LABEL - Apparel and accessories - Gottschalks Inc.
PRIVATE LABEL - Apparel–men's - Weekendz-Off, Inc.
PRIVATE LABEL - Apparel–women's - Wilkins Industries Inc.
PRIVATE LABEL - Hats - Bollman Hat Co.
PRIVATE LABEL - Jewelry ☆ - Hirsch Speidel Inc.
PRIVATE LABEL COFFEE - Coffee - C.S.A. Inc.
PRIVATE LABELINE - Botanical extracts - Bio-Botanica
PRIVATE LABELING - Food products - Golden Specialty Foods Inc.
PRIVATE LINES - Paper goods - John H. Lee
PRIVATE LINES - Wallpaper ☆ - Wallpaper Imports Inc.
PRIVATE LIVES - Floor coverings–carpet and rugs - Barrett Carpet Mills Inc.
PRIVATE LIVES - Wallpaper ☆ - Mirage Wallcovering Co.
PRIVATE LIVES III - Wallpaper ☆ - Mirage Wallcovering Co.
PRIVATE LOCKER - Giftware - Agent Andy Inc.
PRIVATE MOMENTS - Bath salts - Colgate-Palmolive Co.
PRIVATE MOMENTS COLLECTION - Cosmetics - Revlon Consumer Products Corp.
PRIVATE PARADISE - Floor coverings–carpet and rugs - Evans-Black Carpet Mills
PRIVATE PARTS - Toys–stuffed - Russ Berrie and Co., Inc.
PRIVATE PIZZA - Toys - Mattel, Inc.
PRIVATE PLEASURES - Apparel–women's - Warnaco Inc.
PRIVATE PRO - Golfing equipment - Ajay Leisure Products Inc.
PRIVATE RESERVE - Candy - Pangburn Candy Co.
PRIVATE RESERVE - Potato sticks - M.C. Snack Inc.
PRIVATE RESERVE - Vegetables–frozen ☆ - Lamb-Weston, Inc.
PRIVATE ROASTERS - Coffee - Richard Saunders International, Inc.
PRIVATE SCREENING - Furniture - Ring King Visibles, Inc.
PRIVATE SECRETARY - Leather goods - St. Thomas Inc.
PRIVATE SELECTION - Food products - Ralphs Grocery Co.
PRIVATE STOCK - Apparel and accessories - Toll-Gate Garment Co.
PRIVATE STOCK - Beverages–alcohol - Laird and Co.
PRIVATE STOCK - Cigar boxes–wood - Consolidated Cigar Corp.
PRIVATE STOCK - Crocheted and knitted items - Beldoch Industries Corp.
PRIVATE STOCK - Floor coverings–carpet and rugs - Porter Carpet Mills Inc.
PRIVATE STOCK - Floor coverings–carpet and rugs ☆ - Kelly Group Inc.
PRIVATE STOCK - Food products - Stache Foods
PRIVATE STOCK - Seafood products–fresh or frozen - Mar-Lees Seafood Co.
PRIVATE STOCK - Stationery ☆ - Berkshire Stationery Inc.
PRIVATE SYSTEMS - Office furniture–plastic - Rosemont Office Systems Inc.
PRIVATE TOUCHES - Apparel and accessories - Mallory and Kraft Ltd.
PRIVATE TUTOR - Computer software - James D. Mason
PRIVATE WORLD - File folders ☆ - Jesse Jones Box Corp.
PRIVATE WORLD - Underwear and nightwear - Bestform Foundations, Inc.
PRIVATEER - Boats–canoes ☆ - Kenner Manufacturing Co. Inc.
PRIVATEER - Computer software - Origin Systems, Inc.
PRIVATEERS - Cigar boxes–wood - Consolidated Cigar Corp.
PRIVATELINE SECURE E-MAIL - Computer software - Stellarsoft
PRIVATENET - Computer software - Nec Systems Laboratory, Inc.
PRIVATEPAGE - Treadmills - Command Communications, Inc.
PRIVATETAILOR BY OXXFORD - Apparel and accessories - Fine Clothing International, Inc.
PRIVATEWEAR - Apparel–athletic - Michael Thomas S.C., Ltd.
PRIVATINE - Window coverings - Joanna Western Mills Co.
PRIVEE - Beverages - Private Cellars Ltd.
PRIVIET - Vodka - Monsieur Henri Wines Ltd.
PRIVIET - Vodka - Pepsico, Inc.
PRIVILEGE - Apparel–women's - Mystere, Inc.
PRIVILEGE - Floor coverings–carpet and rugs - Monticello Carpet Mills
PRIVILEGE - Printers–computer - Eltron International, Inc.
PRIVILEGED ACCESS - Banks–commercial - Bear, Stearns & Co. Inc.
PRIVILEGIO RIOJA - Wines ☆ - Domecq Importers Inc.
PRIVINE - Pharmaceutical preparations - Ciba-Geigy Corp.
PRIX - Rings–jewelry - Artcarved Inc.
PRIX BLANC - Wines - Joseph E. Seagram & Sons, Inc.
PRIX DE SAUTE - Saddles - Big Horn, Inc.
PRIX ROUGE - Wines - Joseph E. Seagram & Sons, Inc.
PRIYA - Fruits and vegetables - V.R.S. International, Inc.
PRIZE - Doughnuts - R.S. Prewitt Co.

☆ = Now out of production

PRIZE - Food products ☆ - Birkett Mills
PRIZE - Pet products - Certified Grocers of California, Ltd.
PRIZE BOXES - Candy ☆ - Phoenix Confections Inc.
PRIZE CROP - Food products ☆ - Seasia
PRIZE ENTRY - Floor coverings–carpet and rugs ☆ - Karastan-Bigelow Inc.
PRIZE KANT STICK - Lubricants - Kerr-McGee Chemical Corp.
PRIZE OF IOWA - Milk–canned or powdered - Mid-America Dairymen Inc. Southern Div.
PRIZE PERFECT - Awards, plaques and medals - Art Promotions Pacific
PRIZE PETAL - Dolls - Mattel, Inc.
PRIZE PRINTZ - Fabrics - Valley Forge Fabrics Inc.
PRIZE PROPERTY - Games ☆ - Milton Bradley Co.
PRIZE STATEMENT - Floor coverings–carpet and rugs ☆ - Karastan-Bigelow Inc.
PRIZE-WINNER - Water colors - Peerless Color Laboratories
PRIZED ORCHID - Nail care products ☆ - Noxell Corp.
PRIZED POSSESIONS - Fabrics - Arc-Com Fabrics, Inc.
PRIZED POSSESSIONS - Fabrics - Arc-Com Fabrics, Inc.
PRIZELAWN - Garden equipment - Porcelain Steel Buildings Co.
PRIZELAWN BIG FOOT - Machinery - White Castle System, Inc.
PRIZEWINNERS - Flowers, plants, and seeds - W. Atlee Burpee and Co.
PRIZM - Electronic equipment - Texscan Corp.
PRIZM - Motor vehicles - General Motors Corp. (Chevrolet Motor Div.)
PRIZM - Office supplies ☆ - Esselte Corp.
PRIZMATE - Lighting fixtures - Kenall Manufacturing Co.
PRIZZWALLERS - Greeting cards - Victoria Dodd, Ltd.
PRJ - Jewelry–precious - Polynesian Resources, Inc.
PRL - Golfing equipment - Tiger Shark Golf Inc.
PRM - Musical instrument accessories - Berkshire Instruments Inc.
PRM - Recording label - Rustron Music Productions
PRM-PLL - Computer software - Preferred Resource Management, Inc.
PRMS - Computer software - IEX Corp.
PRN+ - Health care products - PRN Services Inc.
PRN - Health care products - PRN Services Inc.
PRN - Veterinary pharmaceutical preparations - P R N Pharmacal, Inc.
PRNT SCRN - Computer software - Mitnor Software
PRNTSCRN - Computer software - Mitnor Software
PRO - Amplifiers - Fender Musical Instruments
PRO - Amplifiers ☆ - Electro-Voice, Inc.
PRO# - Apparel and accessories - Snake Creek Manufacturing Co., Inc.
PRO - Audio equipment - Pyle Industries Inc.
PRO - Automotive parts and accessories - Baf Industries
PRO - Bicycles ☆ - Huffy Corp.
PRO - Boats–motor - Lund Boat Co.
PRO - Boats–motor - Pro-Line Boats Inc.
PRO - Boats–motor ☆ - Marathon Boat Group, Inc.
PRO - Caulking compounds ☆ - Resources Park
PRO - Clippers–barber - Sunbeam-Oster Household Products
PRO - Computer software - Calera Recognition Systems Inc.
PRO - Computer software - Electrifier, Inc.
PRO - Disinfectants ☆ - Coughlan Products Corp.
PRO - Display cases–metal - Professional Displays, Inc.
PRO - Dog food - Simmons Industries Inc.
PRO - Door openers–electronic - The Genie Co.
PRO - Electronic equipment - Telex Communications, Inc.
PRO - Exercising equipment - Professional Gym Inc.
PRO - Flatware ☆ - Towle Silversmiths
PRO! - Floor coverings - L.D. Brinkman & Co. Inc.
PRO - Housewares ☆ - All State Industries Inc. (Hue Chemical Div.)
PRO - Leather goods - Tandy Leather Co.
PRO - Lighting fixtures–stage - Ranging Inc.
PRO+ - Motor vehicle parts and accessories - Import Brokers, Inc.
PRO - Oils–lubricating - Witco Corp.
PRO - Orthodontic equipment - Professional Positioners, Inc.
PRO - Paints - Paragon Paint & Varnish Corp.
PRO - Photographic equipment - Photographic Research Organization Inc.
PRO - Skin care products - State Chemical Manufacturing Co.
PRO - Sporting goods - Prince Manufacturing Inc.
PRO - Sprayers - RL Flo-Master
PRO - Stereos - Recoton Corp.
PRO - Sunglasses - Sunglass Products, Inc.
PRO - Tape–adhesive - Pro Tapes & Specialties, Inc.
PRO - Tools–garden ☆ - Pro Inc.
PRO - Toothbrushes - Milor
PRO - Water colors - Steig Products
PRO-1 - Lenses–projection - Projectapix-II

PRO-1 - Paint rollers - Bestt-Liebco
PRO-2 - Lenses–projection - Projectapix-II
PRO 2 O - Mops - Golden Star Inc.
PRO-4-MER - Propellers - Brunswick Corp.
PRO 4 MOR - Engines - Ryobi America Corp.
PRO 8 - Electronic equipment - Thomson Consumer Electronics, Inc.
PRO-10 - Paints - Universal Protective Coatings
PRO 10 NAIL CARE - Nail-care products - Cosmar Corp.
PRO-12 - Nautical instruments ☆ - Falcon Safety Products, Inc.
PRO-16 - Boats–motor - Tracker Marine Corp.
PRO-16 - Tools - Vaughan & Bushnell Manufacturing Co.
PRO 20 - Vitamins and nutritional supplements ☆ - Schiff Products, Inc.
PRO 24 - Computer software - Steinberg/Jones Corp.
PRO 25 RATION - Dog food - Jim Dandy Co.
PRO-35 - Office supplies - Ballantyne of Omaha Inc.
PRO 35 - Saws–power - DBNA Trademarks Holding Inc.
PRO 40 - Saws–power - DBNA Trademarks Holding Inc.
PRO 65 - Saws–power - DBNA Trademarks Holding Inc.
PRO 90 - Skin care products - GOLDWELL Cosmetics (USA) Inc.
PRO 90 SYSTEM, THE - Chemical preparations - Triple T Marketing
PRO-100 - Athletic footwear - International Seaway Trading Corp.
PRO 100 - Photographic equipment ☆ - Yashica Inc.
PRO 100 - Sporting goods ☆ - National Sporting Goods Corp.
PRO 100 - Welding equipment - Lincoln Electric Co.
PRO 100 XL - Balls–golf ☆ - National Sporting Goods Corp.
PRO 155 - Welding equipment - Lincoln Electric Co.
PRO 250 - Sports rackets and accessories ☆ - Victor Sports
PRO/400 - Aquariums–household - Vortex Innerspace Products Inc.
PRO-500 - Health care products ☆ - Care-Tech Laboratories Inc.
PRO 500 - Shoes ☆ - Endicott Johnson Corp.
PRO 750 - Computer software - Intel Corp.
PRO 900 - Shoes ☆ - Endicott Johnson Corp.
PRO 1000 - Dryers–hair - Conair Corp.
PRO-2000 - Mattress pads - CH Administration, Inc.
PRO 5000 - Shirts - Wilson Sporting Goods Co.
PRO-ACT - Shampoos - KMS Research Inc.
PRO ACTION - Games - Munro Games Inc.
PRO ACTION - Golfing equipment - Northwestern Golf Co.
PRO ACTION - Helmets–athletic - Troxel-West
PRO ACTION - Sporting goods ☆ - Randall May International
PRO-ACTION BY CAMPUS - Men's apparel - Interco Inc.
PRO ADVANTAGE - Dental equipment - Midwest Dental Equipment & Supply
PRO ADVANTAGE - Fishing rods - Sunbelt Sales
PRO AERO - Bicycles - Columbia Manufacturing Inc.
PRO-AIR - Marine accessories - Charger Inc.
PRO-AIR - Sporting goods - Bike Athletic Co.
PRO-AIRBRUSH - Blasting compounds - W.R. Brown Co.
PRO AIRE - Dryers–hair ☆ - Sunbeam-Oster Household Products
PRO-AIRE - Lawn mowers - Ariens Co.
PRO AL - Pans - Polar Ware Co.
PRO-ALIGN - Computer software - Hunter Engineering Co.
PRO-ALO CREME - Health care products - Healthwatchers System
PRO-AM - Antennas - Valor Enterprises, Inc.
PRO AM - Bicycles - Columbia Manufacturing Inc.
PRO AM - Coatings - Smiland Paint Co.
PRO AM - Exercising equipment - Little River Marine Co.
PRO/AM - Musical instrument accessories - Kyser Musical Products, Inc.
PRO/AM - Pens - Pentel of America, Ltd.
PRO-AM - Socks - Leininger Mills Inc.
PRO AM - Sporting goods - Wellington Leisure Products, Inc.
PRO AM TC - Bicycles - Columbia Manufacturing Inc.
PRO AM TEAM - Bicycles - Columbia Manufacturing Inc.
PRO AM XP - Bicycles - Columbia Manufacturing Inc.
PRO-AMATINE - Pharmaceutical preparations - Roberts Laboratories Inc.
PRO-AMINO FORMULA - Health care products - Healthwatchers System
PRO-ANALYZER - Computer software - Automation Sciences Corp.
PRO & AM - Paints - Fredericks/Hansen Paint Manufacturing Co.
PRO ANGLE - Toothbrushes - Milor
PRO ANGLER - Boats–motor ☆ - Lund Boat Co.
PRO APPROVED - Toothbrushes - Milor
PRO-AQUA - Pet products ☆ - Aquatronics-Filtronics
PRO-ARC - Arc welders - Lincoln Automotive
PRO ART - Artists' materials - Arthur Brown and Bros. Inc.
PRO ART - Dental equipment - Ivoclar North America, Inc.
PRO ARTE - Musical instrument accessories - J. D'Addario & Co. Inc.
PRO ATHLETIC - Recreational apparel - Pro-Athletic

PRO AUDIO - Audio equipment - Royal Sound Co. Inc.
PRO AUDIO POWERPAK - Computer software - Media Vision Technology Inc.
PRO AUDIO SPECTRUM - Computer software - Media Vision Technology Inc.
PRO AUDIO STUDIO - Computer hardware - Media Vision Technology Inc.
PRO AVENGER - Rackets–tennis - Wilson Sporting Goods Co.
PRO AVIGAL - Health care products - Avigal Henna
PRO BABY - Dryers–hair ☆ - Conair Corp.
PRO-BANTHINE - Pharmaceutical preparations - G. D. Searle & Co.
PRO BAR - Chocolate bars ☆ - Weider Health and Fitness
PRO BAR - Ice cream ☆ - Good Humor Corp.
PRO BAR - Preserved foods–prepackaged - Pro Bar, Inc.
PRO BASEBALL - Games - Just Games
PRO BASS - Boats–fishing - Glasstream Boats Inc.
PRO BASS - Boats–motor - Forester Boats Inc.
PRO-BATCH - Computer peripheral equipment - Pro-Log Corp.
PRO-BEAD - Wainscotting - Aluminum Co. of America
PRO-BEARING - Archery equipment - Tru-Fire Corp.
PRO BEAT - Drums–musical instruments - Telexport, Inc.
PRO-BEAUTEE - Cosmetics - Beautee Sense Inc.
PRO-BENCHES - Hardware - Alum-A-Pole Corp.
PRO BLACK - Water colors - Steig Products
PRO BLAZER - Bicycles ☆ - Murray, Inc.
PRO-BLEND - Stains - Rudd Co. Inc.
PRO-BOARD - Tables–metal - Pro-Flex, Inc.
PRO-BOND - Electronic equipment - Seal Products Inc.
PRO-BOOM - Sporting goods - Electric Fishing Reel Systems Inc.
PRO BOOST - Cables - General Cable Corp.
PRO BOTANIXX - Herbal products - Brion Corp.
PRO-BOUND - Sporting goods - Thomas Mahoney
PRO BOX - Carrying cases for collector cards - Pro Box
PRO-BRED - Dog food - Happy Jack, Inc.
PRO-BRELLA - Umbrellas - Reising International Inc.
PRO-BRELLA - Umbrellas ☆ - Double Products Co.
PRO-BRITE - Toothpaste - Amwhite Labs, Inc.
PRO BRUSH - Toothbrushes - Milor
PRO-BUILD - Tools - U.S.E. Diamond Inc.
PRO BUSINESS SYSTEM - Calendars - Day Runner, Inc.
PRO-BUZZ - Fishing lures - Strike King Lure Co.
PRO-C - Skin care products - Esta Kronberg
PRO C SNACKS - Potato chips - Michael David Day
PRO-C1 - Sporting goods - Lisco, Inc.
PRO CADDY RAX - Musical instrument accessories - Mechanical Music Corp.
PRO CALIBER - Balls - Lisco, Inc.
PRO-CALK - Caulking compounds - Synkoloid Co.
PRO CAPS - Vitamins and nutritional supplements - Winning Combination
PRO CARBO FORCE 500 - Vitamins and nutritional supplements - American Body Building Products, Inc.
PRO CARE - Soap - Sani-Fresh International Inc.
PRO CASE - Barber shop equipment - Kim Laube & Co. Inc.
PRO CAST - Cooking equipment–household - Nordic Ware
PRO-CAST - Cooking utensils–stoneware - Northland Aluminum Products Inc.
PRO CAVITY - Golfing equipment - Golfsmith International Inc.
PRO CEL - Housewares - S.M. Arnold Inc.
PRO-CELLSIUS - Hair care products - Tressa, Inc.
PRO CHALLENGER - Game machines - Custom Manufacturing, Inc.
PRO CHAMP - Sporting goods - Action Sports
PRO CHANGE - Containers–plastic - Pro Change Products Inc.
PRO-CHASTE - Novelty items - Charles William Dealy III
PRO-CHECK - Games - Ken-Tech, Inc.
PRO-CHEF - Kitchen appliances - John Boos and Co. Inc.
PRO-CHOICE - Garden equipment ☆ - Bond Manufacturing Co. Inc.
PRO CHOICE - Paints - Buten Paint & Wallpaper
PRO-CHOICE - Tools ☆ - Goldblatt Tool Co.
PRO CHOICE - Tools–hand-operated - Great Neck Saw Manufacturers, Inc.
PRO-CIDE - Insecticides - Hub States Corp.
PRO-CINELUX - Lenses–projection - Schneider Optics, Inc.
PRO CIRCUIT - Apparel–men's - Honolulu T-Shirt Co.
PRO CIRCUIT - Sporting goods - O'Brien International
PRO-CITE - Computer software - Personal Bibliographic Software Inc.
PRO-CLASS - Guns - Tasco Sales, Inc.
PRO CLASS - Sporting goods - Mill Run Products Co.
PRO CLASSIC - Bicycles - Columbia Manufacturing Inc.
PRO CLASSIC - Brushes–paint - Wooster Brush Co.
PRO CLASSIC - Golfing equipment - Ajay Leisure Products Inc.
PRO CLASSIC - Golfing equipment - Northwestern Golf Co.
PRO CLASSIC - Paints - Sherwin-Williams Automotive Finishes Corp.

PRO CLASSIC - Sporting goods - Prince Manufacturing Inc.
PRO CLASSIC FITNESS EQUIPMENT - Exercising equipment - Bi-Com Industries, Inc.
PRO-CLEAN - Soap ☆ - CRC Chemicals USA/Siloo
PRO-CLEAR - Adhesives and sealants - Allpro Corp.
PRO-CLEARZ - Medical apparatus - Professional Product Research, Inc.
PRO-CLERK - Computer software - Sally Starling
PRO CLUB - Balls - Brine Inc.
PRO-CO SOUND - Cables - Pro-Co. Sound Co. Inc.
PRO COACH - Video games - Atari Games Corp.
PRO COAT - Paints - Buten Paint & Wallpaper
PRO-COAT - Pet products - Lambert-Kay
PRO COIL - Hair care products - Marianna Imports, Inc.
PRO-COLD - Cold remedies - Vita-Fore Products Co.
PRO COM - Pagers - Darco of Texas Inc.
PRO COMBO - Sporting goods ☆ - Hedstrom Corp.
PRO COMFORT - Shoe accessories ☆ - Schering-Plough Healthcare Products
PRO-COMMANDER - Remote control devices - Matsushita Consumer Electronics Co.
PRO CON - Chemical preparations - Patrick Buehring
PRO-CON PLUS - Hair care products - Summit Laboratories
PRO-CONTENDER - Footwear - Summit Footwear Inc.
PRO CONTROL - Golfing equipment - Leroy P. Rosasco
PRO-CONTROL - Insecticides - Micro-Gen Equipment Corp.
PRO-CONTROL - Motor vehicle parts and accessories - Finks Racing Enterprises
PRO-CONTROL DUAL CHOICE - Insecticides - Micro-Gen Equipment Corp.
PRO COOL - Automotive parts and accessories - Valley Industries, Inc.
PRO-CORD/CORDLESS - Hair clippers–veterinary - Sunbeam Corp.
PRO-CORDER/PRO-DISSOLVE - Audio equipment ☆ - Tiffen Manufacturing Corp.
PRO-CORT - Health care products - Barnes-Hind Inc.
PRO-COTE - Paints - Pen Paints Inc.
PRO COURT - Sporting goods - Lifetime Products, Inc.
PRO-CRAFT - Chemical preparations - Grobet File Co. of America, Inc.
PRO-CRAFT ULTIMA - Cleaning preparations - Grobet File Co. of America, Inc.
PRO CT-400 - Brushes–hair - Phillips Brush Corp.
PRO CUP - Sporting goods - Hillerich & Bradsby Co.
PRO CURL - Hair care products - Belson Products
PRO CURVE - Cleaning equipment - Mr. Longarm Inc.
PRO-CUSHION - Socks - Neuville Industries, Inc.
PRO CUT - Cutlery - Stanley Roberts, Inc.
PRO CUT - Machinery - Ingersoll-Rand Co.
PRO-CUT - Paper cutters - Swaneck Graphic Equipment, Inc.
PRO-CUT - Tools - Great Neck Saw Manufacturers, Inc.
PRO-CUT - Tools - Lancaster Machinery Co.
PRO-CUT THROAT - Skin care products - Dome Cosmetics
PRO CUTE - Health care products - Ferndale Laboratories, Inc.
PRO-CUTTER - Knives–pocket ☆ - Keson Industries Inc.
PRO DART - Sporting goods - Pennsylvania Sporting Goods Co.
PRO-DAX 21 - Pharmaceutical preparations ☆ - Columbia Laboratories Inc.
PRO-DEC - Coatings - Premier Coatings, Inc.
PRO DECK - Computer peripheral equipment - Curtis Manufacturing Co., Inc.
PRO DECORATOR - Brushes–paint - Adams Brush Manufacturing Co., Inc.
PRO DELUXE - Archery equipment - Tru-Fire Corp.
PRO DELUXE - Boats–fishing - Glasstream Boats Inc.
PRO-DENTX - Mouthwashes - Professional Dental Technologies, Inc.
PRO-DEPO - Pharmaceutical preparations ☆ - Vortech Pharmaceuticals
PRO DESIGN - Hair care products - Pro Design International, Inc.
PRO DESIGN - Ophthalmic goods - Optic Studio Inc.
PRO DESIGN - Paint rollers - Mr. Longarm Inc.
PRO DESIGN, THE - Golfing equipment - Allied Golf Co.
PRO DESIGNED FITNESS - Exercise equipment - Pro Designed Fitness
PRO-DETOX - Vitamins and nutritional supplements - Organic Diversions, Inc.
PRO DEUCE - Fishing lures - Hildebrandt Corp.
PRO/DGX - Synthesizers–musical instrument - Fender Musical Instruments
PRO-DHEA - Vitamins and nutritional supplements - Organic Diversions, Inc.
PRO-DIAL - Computer software - Prolyx Data Systems, Inc.
PRO DIAMOND - Firearms, accessories, and parts - Blount International, Inc. (Sporting Equipment Group)
PRO-DIATOM - Pet products - Vortex Innerspace Products Inc.
PRO-DIET - Pet products - Pro-Diet Pet Foods
PRO-DIET - Veterinary medical equipment - Minnesota Pet Breeders, Inc.
PRO-DIET - Vitamins and nutritional supplements - Michigan Pharmaceutical
PRO DIGIT - Motor vehicle parts and accessories - Dirt Digits

☆ = Now out of production

PRO DIP 50 - Pet products - Zoecon Corp.

PRO DIP II - Pet products - Zoecon Corp.

PRO DIVE - Apparel and accessories - Professional Diving Schools of Florida, Inc.

PRO/DOO-Z - Paint rollers - Wooster Brush Co.

PRO DOPE - Air conditioning equipment - Hercules Chemical Co. Inc.

PRO DOUBLE DUTY - Toothbrushes - Milor

PRO-DOWN - Medical apparatus - Sport Supply Group, Inc.

PRO DRAFT - Games ☆ - Parker Brothers

PRO-DRIVER - Screw drivers ☆ - Plasticrafters

PRO-DUCT - Tape–adhesive - Pro Tapes & Specialties, Inc.

PRO-DUOSTERONE - Pharmaceutical preparations ☆ - Roussel-Uclaf Corp.

PRO DUST H2O - Cleaning preparations–household - Wilen Companies, Inc.

PRO-DUSTER - Brushes–paint - Corona Brushes Inc.

PRO-DUTY - Adhesives and sealants - White Lightning Products Corp.

PRO-DUTY - Paint sprayers - Wagner Spray Tech Corp.

PRO EARS - Electrical equipment - Ridgeline, Inc.

PRO-EARTH - Cleaning preparations - Blue Coral, Inc.

PRO-ECO - Coffee - Pro-Eco Coffee, Inc.

PRO EDGE - Apparel and accessories - Chinin USA, Inc.

PRO EDGE - Bicycles ☆ - Roadmaster Corp.

PRO EDGE - Brushes–paint - American Brush Co. Inc.

PRO EDGE - Hair care products - Perfector Products

PRO-EDGE - Pet products - Tapco Products Co. Inc.

PRO EDI - Computer software - Randall O. Smith

PRO-ELIMINATE - Hair care products - Gelle-International Ltd.

PRO ELITE - Footwear–athletic - Head Sports USA

PRO ENERGE FEMME - Apparel–women's - Gallini Designs, Inc.

PRO ENERGY - Pet products - Stevens Industries Inc.

PRO ENERGY RESEARCH - Health care products - Alpha Pak Inc.

PRO-EPA - Vitamins and nutritional supplements - Pharmavite Corp.

PRO-ESCAPE - Animal feed supplements - Baker Commodities, Inc.

PRO-EST - Pharmaceutical preparations - Physician Sales & Service

PRO-EST BALANCE - Vitamins and nutritional supplements - Crystal Star Herbal Nutrition, Inc.

PRO-ESTRIN - Pharmaceutical preparations ☆ - C.O. Truxton Inc.

PRO-ESTRUGEN - Pharmaceutical preparations - Wesley Pharmacal Co. Inc.

PRO-EX - Plastics film - AEP Industries, Inc.

PRO EXTREME - Balls - Lisco, Inc.

PRO EZGC - Computer software - Analytical Innovations, Inc.

PRO-F1 - Sporting goods - Lisco, Inc.

PRO-FAME - Chemical preparations - M & M Livestock Products Co., Inc.

PRO-FECTED - Sporting goods - Ashaway Line & Twine Manufacturing Co.

PRO-FEED - Industrial machinery - U.S. Baird Corp.

PRO-FEX - Electronics equipment - Peavey Electronics Corp.

PRO FIBRE - Musical instrument accessories ☆ - Carpenter Co.

PRO FILE - Beauty aids - Flowery Beauty Products, Inc.

PRO-FILE - File folders ☆ - Yawman and Erbe of California Corp.

PRO-FILE - Filing cabinets–metal - Desert Enterprises

PRO-FILE #2 - Nail-care products - International Beauty Design, Inc.

PRO-FILM - Decals and transfers - Dalco Athletic Lettering Inc.

PRO FILTER - Air conditioning equipment - Monroe Gas Equipment, Inc.

PRO-FINALIST - Goggles ☆ - Bausch & Lomb Inc.

PRO FINE FEMME - Apparel–women's - Gallini Designs, Inc.

PRO-FINISH - Cosmetics ☆ - Divina Products Co.

PRO FINISH - Health care products - Pro Finish USA, Ltd.

PRO-FINISHER - Laundry machines–commercial - Leonard Automatics, Inc.

PRO-FIRE - Garden equipment - Echo, Inc.

PRO-FISHERMAN - Knives–hunting ☆ - Cole Consumer Products Inc.

PRO-FIT - Exercising equipment ☆ - Exercycle Corp.

PRO FIT - Floor coverings - Congoleum Corp.

PRO-FIT - Furniture hardware fittings - Pro-Fit Distributing of California

PRO-FIT - Gutters–plastic - Aluminum Co. of America

PRO/FIT - Jackets - King Louie International Inc.

PRO-FIT - Whirlpools ☆ - Mansfield Plumbing Products, Inc.

PRO-FIT INTERNATIONAL - Cellular telephone accessories - Pro-Fit International, Inc.

PRO FITNESS - Toiletries - Avon Products, Inc.

PRO-FLASH - Photographic equipment ☆ - Dura Electric Lamp Co. Inc.

PRO-FLAT - Paints - Parker Paint Manufacturing Co.

PRO FLEECE - Blankets - GPS, Inc.

PRO FLEET - Coatings - Specialty Chemical Resources, Inc.

PRO FLEX - Bicycles - Girvin Inc.

PRO-FLEX - Bicycles - Ocean State International Inc.

PRO-FLEX - Controls–heating systems - Cobra Products Inc.

PRO-FLEX - Hoses - Tru-Flex Metal Hose Corp.

PRO-FLEX - Paints - Parker Paint Manufacturing Co.

PRO FLEX - Pipes–plastic - Fernco Inc.

PRO FLEX - Wood products - Flexible Materials Inc.

PRO FLEX ADJUSTABLE PLATE - Sporting goods - O'Brien International

PRO-FLITE - Sporting goods - Spalding Sports Worldwide

PRO-FLO - Air conditioning equipment - Mission Marketing Corp.

PRO-FLO - Automotive parts and accessories - Edelbrock Corp.

PRO-FLO - Faucets - Pro-Flo Products

PRO-FLOAT - Building materials–concrete - Laticrete International Inc.

PRO FLOAT COAT - Waterproof outerwear ☆ - Helly-Hansen Inc.

PRO FLOORING ASSOCIATION - Floor coverings–carpet and rugs - L.D. Brinkman & Co. Inc.

PRO-FLOW - Brushes–paint - Bestt-Liebco

PRO FLOW POWER PLENUM R&D RACING PRODUCTS U.S.A. - Fire extinguishers - R & D Racing Products USA, Inc.

PRO FLY - Boomerangs - Gutmann Cutlery Inc.

PRO-FLYER - Buttons - Strand Enterprises

PRO-FOAM - Automotive parts and accessories - Turtle Wax, Inc.

PRO FOLIO - Office supplies - Light Impressions Corp.

PRO FORCE - Oils–lubricating - J.D. Streett & Co. Inc.

PRO FORCE - Tools–hand-operated - Union Fork and Hoe Co.

PRO FORCE - Uniforms–athletic - Asian World of Martial Arts, Inc.

PRO-FORM - Antennas - Kaul-Tronics, Inc.

PRO-FORM - Apparel and accessories - Answer Products Inc.

PRO-FORM - Cases–musical instrument - Capsule Inc.

PRO-FORM - Counter tops–laminated - Vangura Surfacing Products

PRO-FORM - Dog food - Alliance Foods, Inc.

PRO-FORM - Musical instruments cases - TKL Products Corp.

PRO-FORM - Vitamins and nutritional supplements - Fairhill Foods

PRO-FORMANCE - Animal feeds - American Agco, Inc.

PRO FORMANCE - Eyeglasses - Cable Car Eyeware

PRO-FORMANCE - Oils–edible - Bunge Foods Corp.

PRO-FORMANCE - Vitamins and nutritional supplements ☆ - Marlyn Co. Inc.

PRO-FORMANCE SERIES - Hardware - Allpro Corp.

PRO FORMS - Office supplies ☆ - CFI Pro Services, Inc.

PRO FORMULA - Musical instrument accessories ☆ - GHS Strings

PRO-FORMULA - Sanders and grinders ☆ - S-B Power Tool Co.

PRO-FOTO FOOTBALL - Games - Cadaco Div.

PRO-FRAME - Shower stalls–metal - Sterling Plumbing Group Inc.

PRO-FRAMER'S - Tape–adhesive - Pro Tapes & Specialties, Inc.

PRO-FREQUENCY - Skin care products - Proteus Inc.

PRO-G-YAM - Skin care products - Nature's Sunshine Products, Inc.

PRO-GAFF - Tape–adhesive - Pro Tapes & Specialties, Inc.

PRO-GAFFER - Tape–adhesive - Pro Tapes & Specialties, Inc.

PRO-GAGE - Brake parts - Adams Machine & Tool Co.

PRO-GAME - Games ☆ - Precision Silk Screen Co. (Pro Game Div.)

PRO-GAP - Measuring instruments - CTA Manufacturing Corp.

PRO-GARD - Adhesives and sealants - Gardner Asphalt Corp.

PRO-GARD - Coatings - Guardsman Products, Inc.

PRO-GEL - Athletic gloves - Champion Glove Manufacturing Co.

PRO-GEN - Pharmaceutical preparations ☆ - Chex Co.

PRO-GEST - Cosmetics - Professional & Technical Services, Inc.

PRO-GLASS - Water purification systems - Aquaculture Research/Environmental Associates Inc.

PRO GLIDE - Cookware - Regal Ware, Inc.

PRO-GLIDE - Cosmetics - Noxell Corp.

PRO GLIDE - Irons–electric - Bernina of America Inc.

PRO GLIDE - Transmissions–motor vehicle - Ati Performance Products, Inc.

PRO GLIDE PLUS - Irons–electric - Bernina Sewing Machine Co. Inc.

PRO-GLO - Automotive parts and accessories - Answer Products Inc.

PRO-GLO - Pet products - Glo-Marr Products Inc.

PRO-GLOS - Paints - California Products Corp.

PRO GLOW - Cleaning preparations ☆ - Klean-Strip

PRO GOAL - Sporting goods - Porter Athletic Equipment Co.

PRO-GOLD - Animal feeds - Hubbard Milling Co.

PRO GOLF - Games - Avalon Hill Game Co.

PRO-GRADE - Adhesives and sealants - Monsey Products Co.

PRO GRADE - Extension cords - General Cable Corp.

PRO-GRADE - Roofing materials - Kimberton Enterprises, Inc.

PRO GRADE - Tools–hand-operated - Allied Wholesale Inc.

PRO GRADE AND DESIGN - Extension cords - General Cable Corp.

PRO GRAIN - Cereal ☆ - Kellogg Co.

PRO GRAPHICS - Greeting cards ☆ - Thought Factory

PRO-GRASS - Fertilizers - IMC Agribusiness Inc.

PRO GRILL - Barbecues and grills - Kingsford Co.

PRO GRIP - Adhesives and sealants - Fel-Pro Inc.

PRO GRIP - Flashlights - Brinkmann Corp.

PRO GRIP - Flashlights - Brinkmann Lighting Products

PRO-GRIP - Tools - Vaughan & Bushnell Manufacturing Co.

PRO GRIP-CLEAN - Golfing equipment - Trio Johnson, Inc.

PRO-GRIP NON-SLIP - Skin care products - DBA Products Co.

PRO-GRO - Fungicides ☆ - Uniroyal Chemical Co. Inc. (Crop Protection Div.)

PRO-GROOM - Pet products - Lambert-Kay

PRO-GROUT 90 - Sealing compounds - CGM Inc.

PRO GROW - Bird feeds - Sunshine Bird Supplies, Inc.

PRO GUARD - Alarm systems - Directed Electronics, Inc.

PRO-GUARD - Audio equipment ☆ - Renkus-Heinz Inc.

PRO-GUARD - Cleaning preparations - Sysco Corp.

PRO-GUARD - Electronic equipment - General Electric Co.

PRO-GUARD - Goggles–safety - Allan Enterprises

PRO-GUARD - Safety equipment - Klein Tools Inc.

PRO GUARD - Sporting goods - Schutt Manufacturing Co.

PRO GUARD - Sporting goods - Trace Athletic Corp.

PRO-GUARD, GIGBAGS - Cases–musical instrument - Deg Music Products Inc.

PRO-GUARD SOFTIE - Pet products - Custom Cable Co.

PRO-GUIDE - Silverware - Imperial Schrade Corp.

PRO GUN - Dryers–hair ☆ - Remington Products Co.

PRO-GUN - Nozzles - Hydro-Chem Systems, Inc.

PRO HAIR2 - Vitamins and nutritional supplements - IVC Industries, Inc.

PRO-HAIRMIN - Skin care products - Hanah Beauty & Health Inc.

PRO HAWK - Bicycles ☆ - Roadmaster Corp.

PRO HEALTH - Health care products - Pro Health Co.

PRO-HEALTH DINING - Food products ☆ - Morrison Restaurants Inc.

PRO-HEAR - Computer software - Starkey Labs Inc.

PRO-HEPATONE - Vitamins and nutritional supplements ☆ - Marlyn Co. Inc.

PRO-HIDE - Paints - Pratt & Lambert, Inc.

PRO-HIDE - Varnishes - Parker Paint Manufacturing Co.

PRO HIGH WHEEL MOWERS - Lawn mowers - Pro Inc.

PRO-HOLD - Cosmetics ☆ - Divina Products Co.

PRO-HOOKER - Pipes - Anderson-Barrows Metals Corp.

PRO ICE - Medical cold packs - Sports Products Inc.

PRO-IDA - See **IDAHO PACIFIC**

PRO II - Cymbals - Jim Atlas Cymbal Works

PRO II - Guitars - Music Distributors Inc.

PRO IMAGE - Floor finishing machines–commercial ☆ - Basic Coatings, Inc.

PRO IMPACT - Golfing equipment - Spalding & Evenflo Companies, Inc.

PRO/INDUSTRIAL - Steel wool - Allpro Corp.

PRO-IONIC QUENCH - Hair care products - Pro Design International, Inc.

PRO ISO - Pharmaceutical preparations ☆ - Zenith Laboratories, Inc.

PRO-JACKS - Hardware - Alum-A-Pole Corp.

PRO-JAM - Hair care products - Carson Products Co.

PRO JAZZ - Recording label - Counter Culture

PRO-JECT - Epoxy adhesive - American Synthetics Co.

PRO-JEX - Paints - Miller Paint Co., Inc.

PRO-JOGGS - Footwear - Pro-Joggs International Inc.

PRO JON - Boats - O.M.C. Aluminum Boat Group

PRO-KADIMA - Games - Drybranch Inc./Sport Design

PRO-KAGE - Paint rollers - E-Z Paintr Corp.

PRO-KAL - Food containers - Fabri-Kal Corp.

PRO KARE - Golfing equipment - DBA Products Co.

PRO-KART PK - Gocarts - Central Purchasing Inc.

PRO-KART PK - Motor vehicles - Central Purchasing Inc.

PRO-KEDS - Footwear - SR Holdings Inc.

PRO-KEDS - Footwear - Stride Rite Corp.

PRO-KEN 16 - Pet products ☆ - Glo-Marr Products Inc.

PRO-KENNEX - Rackets–tennis - Century Sports Inc.

PRO-KERATEIN - Hair care products - Peter Hantz Co.

PRO KILL - Pesticides–household - Nationwide Chemical Products, Inc. (Nationwide Exterminating Div.)

PRO KING - Flooring–hardwood - Horner Flooring Co. Inc.

PRO KIT-1000 - Cosmetics - Ladyfingers

PRO-KOAT - Coatings - Coronado Paint Co.

PRO-KOLLAR - Bicycles - Moth Studios

PRO KOTE - Paints - Duron, Inc.

PRO-KOTE - Paints - Tuff-Kote Co. Inc.

PRO KRAFT - Paints - C.M. Athey Paint Co.

PRO-LABEL - Polyethylene film sheets - Atlantis Plastics

PRO LACER - Health care products - Cramer Products Inc.

PRO LAM - Giftware - Adams Products Co.

PRO-LAM - Paint rollers - Panda Brush Co.

PRO-LANCE - Hoses - Rogan & Shanley, Inc.

PRO-LAX - Pharmaceutical preparations ☆ - Vangard Labs Inc.

PRO LEAGUE - Balls - Mikasa Sports

PRO LEAGUE - Games - Munro Games Inc.

PRO-LEAGUE - Sporting goods - T.G. Sports Co.

PRO-LECIN - Vitamins and nutritional supplements - Shaklee Corp.

PRO-LECIN NIBBLERS - Vitamins and nutritional supplements - Shaklee Corp.

PRO-LEDGE - Fishing lures - Strike King Lure Co.

PRO LEGEND - Rackets–badminton - Rackets International (Racket Sports Div.)

PRO LIFE - Liquid protein, vitamin and mineral tablets ☆ - Iodent Co.

PRO-LINC - Computer peripheral equipment - Dator Corp.

PRO LINE - Adhesives and sealants - Fel-Pro Inc.

PRO-LINE - Apparel stores–sports ☆ - Terramar Sports Worldwide, Ltd.

PRO LINE - Apparel–athletic - National Football League Properties, Inc.

PRO LINE - Batteries - Rayovac Corp.

PRO-LINE - Boats–motor - Pro-Line Boats Inc.

PRO-LINE - Brushes–hair - Phillips Brush Corp.

PRO-LINE - Chemical preparations - Barristo Ltd.

PRO-LINE - Control valves - Fillpro Products Inc.

PRO LINE - Cooking utensils–aluminum - Revere Ware Corp.

PRO LINE - Electrical equipment - General Electric Co.

PRO LINE - Electronic equipment - Fairtron Corp.

PRO LINE - Faucets - Webstone Co. Inc.

PRO-LINE - Footwear - Top Line Manufacturing Co.

PRO-LINE - Hair care products - Pro-Line Corp.

PRO LINE - Musical-instrument accessories - International Music Corp.

PRO-LINE - Paint sprayers - H.E.R.O. Industries Ltd.

PRO-LINE - Paints - Bruning Paint Co.

PRO-LINE - Paints - Kwal-Howells Inc.

PRO LINE - Paints - Martin-Senour Co.

PRO-LINE - Photo albums - Kleer-Vu Plastics Inc.

PRO LINE - Rope - Wellington Leisure Products, Inc.

PRO-LINE - Scissors–hand-operated - Arius-Eickert Co. Inc.

PRO-LINE - Shower stalls–metal - Sterling Plumbing Group Inc.

PRO LINE - Soldering equipment - Victor Equipment Co.

PRO LINE - Swimming pools - Spectrum Pool Products

PRO LINE - Tanks–storage - Hughes Supply, Inc.

PRO LINE - Tape measures - Keson Industries Inc.

PRO LINE - Tools ☆ - D & L Stained Glass Supply, Inc.

PRO LINE - Tools ☆ - GC Thorsen, Inc.

PRO-LINE - Vitamins and nutritional supplements - Lance Dreher

PRO LINE - Wallcoverings adhesives, mineral spirits, etc. - Porter Paint Co.

PRO-LINE BUSINESS FURNITURE - Office furniture–metal - Blumenthal Distributing, Inc.

PRO LINE PREMIUM - Paints - Martin-Senour Co.

PRO LINER - Leather goods - Casecraft Inc.

PRO-LINER - Truck beds - Plas-Tech Unlimited Inc.

PRO-LINING - Cosmetics - Noxell Corp.

PRO-LINING PERFECT BLEND - Cosmetics - Procter & Gamble Co.

PRO-LINK - Liners and covers–pond, pit, and landfill - Moulder-Oldham Co.

PRO-LINK 9000 - Computer peripheral equipment - Micro Processor Systems, Inc.

PRO LINKS - Floor coverings–carpet and rugs - Milliken & Co. Inc.

PRO-LITE - Bathing suits - Gulbenkian Swim Inc.

PRO-LITE - Eyeglasses - Art-Craft Optical Co.

PRO-LITE - Hair care products - Revlon Consumer Products Corp.

PRO-LITE - Health care products - Trenton Surgical Supply Co.

PRO LITE - Padding–foam - National Foam Cushion Manufacturing Inc.

PRO-LITE - Sporting goods - Bike Athletic Co.

PRO-LITES - Footwear - E.S. Originals, Inc.

PRO LOC - Fishing tackle - SNL Corp.

PRO-LOC - Roofing materials - Metal Sales Manufacturing Corp.

PRO-LOCK - Adhesives and sealants - Fel-Pro Inc.

PRO-LOCK - Motor vehicle parts and accessories ☆ - Cobra Electronics Corp.

PRO LOCKER - Sporting goods - RSM, Inc.

PRO-LOG - Fireplaces ☆ - Thermal Systems Inc.

PRO-LOK - Floor coverings–tile - Pawling Corp. (Standard Products Div.)

PRO LOK - Hardware - Pro Seal Products

PRO-LOK - Sporting goods ☆ - O'Brien International

PRO-LONG - Filters–fuel - J. Thomas Distributors, Inc.

PRO-LOUPE - Lenses–magnifying - Edroy Products Co.

PRO-MA NUTRITION - Vitamins and nutritional supplements - Pro-Ma Systems (USA), Inc.

PRO-MA SYSTEMS - Fuel additives - Pro-Ma Systems (USA), Inc.

PRO MAC - Saws–chain - McCulloch Corp.

☆ = Now out of production

PRO-MAG - Electromedical apparatus - Cob Industries, Inc.
PRO MAG - Fertilizers - Martin Marietta Magnesia Specialties, Inc.
PRO-MAG - Musical instrument accessories - Dean Markley Strings, Inc.
PRO-MAG - Window coverings - Magnetic Specialty Inc.
PRO MAGIC - Animal feeds - American Nutritional Laboratories, Inc.
PRO MANAGER - Games ✩ - Avalon Hill Game Co.
PRO MARINE - Batteries - GNB Inc. (Automotive Battery Div.)
PRO-MARK - Doors–garage - Overhead Door Corp.
PRO MARK - Musical instrument accessories - Pro-Mark Corp.
PRO-MARK - Pharmacies - Pro-Mark Pharmacies, Inc.
PRO-MARKERS - Paints - Star Finishing Products Inc.
PRO-MASK - Tape–adhesive - Custom Tapes, Inc.
PRO MASS - Vitamins and nutritional supplements - E'ola Products, Inc. (Biogenics)
PRO-MASTER - Cleaning preparations - Mega Manufacturing Co. Inc.
PRO-MASTER - Computer software - SourceView Software International
PRO-MASTER - Fertilizers - PBI/Gordon Corp.
PRO MASTER - Golfing equipment ✩ - Northwestern Golf Co.
PRO MASTER - Knives ✩ - Tru-Balance Knife Co.
PRO MASTER - Lawn mowers - Kato Equipment Co.
PRO MASTER - Musical instrument accessories ✩ - Carpenter Co.
PRO-MASTER GRIP - Medical apparatus - John D. Wiggins
PRO MASTER INDUSTRIES - Golf carts - Plastics Manufacturing, Inc.
PRO-MASTER PROFESSIONAL SERIES SOUTHERNRIDING - Saddles - Alexander Industries
PRO-MAT - Artists' materials - Polyform Products Inc.
PRO MATE - Boats–motor ✩ - Commander Marine
PRO MATE - Fertilizers - Helena Chemical Co.
PRO-MATIC 2 - Automotive parts and accessories - Hurst Performance Inc.
PRO-MATTE - Paints - Sophir Morris Paint
PRO MAVICA - Electronic equipment - Sony Corp. of America
PRO MAX - Automotive parts and accessories - John G. Callies
PRO MAX - Flashlights - Brinkmann Lighting Products
PRO-MAX - Hardware - The Genie Co.
PRO-MAX - Outward motors - Brunswick Corp.
PRO-MAX - Photographic equipment - Climax, Ltd.
PRO MAX - Pumps - Patterson Pump Co.
PRO-MAX - Skates–roller ✩ - Rollerblade, Inc.
PRO-MAX - Work clothes - Vallen Safety Supply Co.
PRO-MAX 3 - Heels–boot and shoe - Professional Product Research, Inc.
PRO MAX 32 - Cleaning preparations–carpet and rug - Imperial Manufacturing Co. Inc.
PRO MEDALIST - Archery equipment ✩ - Hoyt
PRO-MESH - Glass products - Custom Tapes, Inc.
PRO MIDI - Computer software - MusicWriter Inc.
PRO-MIN - Pet products - SuperSweet Feed
PRO MIST - Hair care products ✩ - Image Laboratories, Inc.
PRO-MIST - Photographic equipment - Tiffen Manufacturing Corp.
PRO MISTETTE - Cosmetics ✩ - Delta Industries International, Inc.
PRO-MITT - Golfing equipment - Daiwa Corp.
PRO-MITT - Paints - E-Z Paintr Corp.
PRO MIX - Dog food ✩ - Pet Products Plus
PRO-MIX - Paints - Atlas Chemical Co.
PRO-MIX - Pet products - Vo-Toys Inc.
PRO MIX DAIRY BLEND - Food products - All American Foods, Inc.
PRO MIX DESSERTS - Food products - All American Foods, Inc.
PRO MLB - Sporting goods ✩ - Apsco Enterprises
PRO-MODEL - Fishing lures - Strike King Lure Co.
PRO-MONE - Hair care products - Pro-Capa Products Inc.
PRO-MOTION - Medical apparatus - Sutter Corp.
PRO-MOTION THIRST QUENCHER - Beverages - Sports Beverage, Inc.
PRO MOUND - Soil supplement and additive - Pro's Choice Products, Inc.
PRO-MOUNTAIN - Bicycles - Columbia Manufacturing Inc.
PRO MOVIE - Photographic equipment - Kalart Victor Corp.
PRO MOVIE SPECTRUM - Computer storage devices - Media Vision Technology Inc.
PRO MS - Socks - Russell National Sport Socks
PRO-MULCH - Garden equipment ✩ - Dalen Products Inc.
PRO MUSCLE - Vitamins and nutritional supplements ✩ - ICN Pharmaceuticals Inc.
PRO-N-30 - Pharmaceutical preparations - Graci Research, Ltd.
PRO-NAILER - Tools–hand-operated - Viking Tool Works, Ltd.
PRO NAMEL - Paints - Kwal-Howells Inc.
PRO-NASYL - Pharmaceutical preparations ✩ - American Pharmacal Inc.
PRO-NATURE - Bags–paper - Simon Miller Sales Co.
PRO NEB - Medical apparatus - Pari Respiratory Equipment Inc.

PRO-NEC - Sanitary paper - Willat Co.
PRO NERF - Toys - Tonka Corp.
PRO-NET - Hair care products - Domestic & International Trade Corp.
PRO-NEURIN - Pharmaceutical preparations ✩ - Nutrition Control Products
PRO NFL - Sporting goods ✩ - Apsco Enterprises
PRO NIQ - Racquetball equipment - Hawe Yue Inc.
PRO-NORM - Pet products - Berolina Imports
PRO-NU - Hair care products - John Amico Expressive Hair Care Products
PRO-NU - Health care products - Cyanotech Corp.
PRO-NUTRA - Shampoos - John Capra
PRO-NUTS - Snack foods ✩ - Solnuts Inc.
PRO-OFFSET - Golfing equipment - Spalding & Evenflo Companies, Inc.
PRO-OIL - Musical instrument accessories - Musichem
PRO ONE - Motor vehicle parts and accessories - Demert & Dougherty, Inc.
PRO-ONE - Screen-printing machines - Precision Screen Machines Inc.
PRO OPTIBOL - Vitamins and nutritional supplements - Next Nutrition
PRO-OPTIC - Binoculars - Emblem Corp.
PRO-OPTICS - Lenses–optical - Bausch & Lomb Inc.
PRO-ORE - Pet products ✩ - Aquatronics-Filtronics
PRO/OX - Brushes–paint - Wooster Brush Co.
PRO-OX - Vitamins and nutritional supplements - Health Products Corp.
PRO/OXCO - Brushes ✩ - Milor
PRO PAC - Cases–musical instrument - Protec International
PRO PAC - Tools ✩ - Granberg International
PRO PAC CAT - Cat food - Midwestern Pet Foods Inc.
PRO PAC DOG - Dog food - Midwestern Pet Foods Inc.
PRO PAC SERIES - Construction machinery - Ingersoll-Rand Co.
PRO PACK - Batteries - Rayovac Corp.
PRO-PACK - Water treating compounds - Stevens Industries Inc.
PRO PAD - Apparel and accessories - Portable Products, Inc.
PRO PAD - Sporting goods - Porter Athletic Equipment Co.
PRO PAD BY THORNBERG - Apparel and accessories ✩ - Etonic Inc.
PRO PAIL - Balls–tennis - Edgeroy Co. Inc.
PRO-PAIN - Pharmaceutical preparations - Vita-Fore Products Co.
PRO PAINT - Paints - California Products Corp.
PRO PAIR - Water bottles–rubber - Connelly Skis, Inc.
PRO PAK - Beauty shop equipment - Focus 21 International Inc.
PRO PAK - Crystal-chandelier cleaner - Contact Industries Inc.
PRO/PAK - Fire extinguishers - Task Force Tips, Inc.
PRO-PAK - Flowers, plants, and seeds ✩ - Akin Seed Co.
PRO-PAK - Health care products - Physician Engineered Products
PRO-PAK - Insulating materials - Manville Corp.
PRO PAK - Motor vehicle parts and accessories - Navistar International Transportation Corp.
PRO PAK - Uniforms–athletic - Speedline Athletic Wear, Inc.
PRO-PAK - Wood products - Giles and Kendall Inc.
PRO PAK AGAIN - Stainless-steel cleaner - Contact Industries Inc.
PRO PAL - Paints - Geo. Sproull Co. Inc.
PRO-PANEL II - Siding–metal - Metal Sales Manufacturing Corp.
PRO-PANT - Diapers–cloth - Salk Co. Inc.
PRO-PAR - Trailers–travel - Fruehauf Trailer Corp.
PRO-PARTS - Musical instrument accessories ✩ - Davitt and Hanser Music Co.
PRO-PATCH - Adhesives and coatings - American Synthetics Co.
PRO-PAV SERIES - Machine parts - Ingersoll-Rand Co.
PRO PEDALS - Computer peripheral equipment - Joystick Technologies (CH Products Division)
PRO PEN PRO BALL - Office supplies - Country Club Industries (U.S.A) Corp.
PRO PENN - Sporting goods - Penn Athletic Products
PRO-PEP - Pharmaceutical preparations - Alva-Amco Pharmacal Co.
PRO-PERFECT - Paints - Thomas Paint Applicators
PRO-PERM - Health care products - CCA Industries, Inc.
PRO/PF-1 - Water purification systems - Vortex Innerspace Products Inc.
PRO-PHILE - Loudspeakers - Harman-Motive, Inc.
PRO PHUSION - Hair care products - Peter Hantz Co.
PRO PIKE - Boats–motor ✩ - Lund Boat Co.
PRO PISTOL - Dryers–hair ✩ - Sunbeam-Oster Household Products
PRO PITCH BASEBALL TRAINER - Sporting goods - Aluminum Hardgoods Inc.
PRO PLAN - Pet products - Ralston Purina Co.
PRO PLASTIC - Paints - Gray Seal Paint Manufacturing Co. Inc.
PRO PLATINUM - Sporting goods - Porter Athletic Equipment Co.
PRO PLAYER - Apparel and accessories - Daniel Young International Corp.
PRO PLAYGOLF - Computer software - Thrustmaster, Inc.
PRO PLEAT - Bases–baseball - Wilson Sporting Goods Co.
PRO-PLUG - Adhesives and coatings - American Synthetics Co.

PRO PLUS - Cutlery - Stanley Roberts, Inc.
PRO PLUS - Hardware - Allpro Corp.
PRO PLUS - Pet products - Breeder's Choice Pet Foods, Inc.
PRO-PLUS - Screws - Angeles Metal Trim Co.
PRO PLUS - Socks - Chipman-Union Inc.
PRO PLUS - Sprayers - RL Flo-Master
P.R.O. POCKET - Bags - Bonnie Reese
PRO POCKETS - Aprons - Home Entertainment & Decor Systems Inc.
PRO POINT - Darts and dart games - Dart World Inc.
PRO-POINT - Inks - Matthews International Corp.
PRO-POINT - Optical scanners–computer - Tasco Sales, Inc.
PRO-POLE - Steel basketball posts - Jack-Post Corp.
PRO POLICE - Helmets and accessories - NJL Helmets, Inc.
PRO POLY - Firefighting apparatus - Pro Poly of America, Inc.
PRO POLY GUARD - Floor coverings - Apache Mills Inc.
PRO-POND - Pet products - Vortex Innerspace Products Inc.
PRO-PORTION - Food products ☆ - Pro-Portion Industries
PRO-PORTIONED TO FIT - Apparel and accessories - Sutton Shirt Corp.
PRO-POUR - Beverage dispensing equipment - International Manufacturing Enterprises
PRO POWER EDGERS - Lawn mowers - Pro Inc.
PRO POWER STEAMER - Wallpaper - Wagner Spray Tech Corp.
PRO POX - Pharmaceutical preparations ☆ - Kenyon Drug Co. Inc.
PRO-POXY 20 - Epoxy - Hercules Chemical Co. Inc.
PRO PREMIUM - Animal feeds - Stevens Industries Inc.
PRO PRICER - Computer software - Executive Business Services, Inc.
PRO-PRIME - Paints - Parker Paint Manufacturing Co.
PRO PRO WATCH - Clocks - Wai Kin Ng
P.R.O. PROFORMANCE RESEARCH ORGANIZATION - Sports clubs - World Associates, Inc.
PRO PROLUX - Lenses–projection - Schneider Optics, Inc.
PRO PROOF - Computer software - DRG Consults, Inc.
PRO PUCK - Skates–roller ☆ - Rollerblade, Inc.
PRO PUMP - Generators ☆ - Clinton Engines Corp.
PRO PUP - Dog food - Jim Dandy Co.
PRO PURE - Chemical preparations - Benson Pump Co.
PRO PUSH - Manicure tools - International Beauty Design, Inc.
PRO-PUTT - Golfing equipment - Wittek Golf Supply Co., Inc.
PRO-Q BY CENTURY - Coatings - Century Industries Corp.
PRO-Q10 - Vitamins and nutritional supplements - Organic Diversions, Inc.
PRO QUALIFIER - Fishing tackle - Bass Pro Shops Inc.
PRO QUALITY - Caulking compounds - Dap Products Inc.
PRO QUEEN - Bowling balls - Master Industries Inc.
PRO QUIP - Lubricants - First Union Corp.
PRO RACING - Apparel–athletic - Nichols Motorcycle Supply, Inc.
PRO-RAIDER - Boats–fishing - DJ's Fiberglass Products Inc.
PRO-REEL - Electrical equipment - Alert Stamping and Manufacturing Co., Inc.
PRO RIDER - Exercising equipment - Dynamic Classics Ltd.
PRO-RINSE - Hair care products - Gelle-International Ltd.
PRO-RITE - Hockey equipment - Christian Brothers, Inc.
PRO-RITE - Markers–felt-tip - Marsh Chalkboard Co.
PRO ROADSTER - Skates–roller ☆ - Chicago Roller Skate Co.
PRO ROCKER - Tools - Vaughan & Bushnell Manufacturing Co.
PRO ROLLER - Archery equipment - Pro Release, Inc.
PRO ROLLER - Golf bag covers - Dennco, Inc.
PRO ROLLING TRIMMER/MOWER - Lawn mowers - Pro Inc.
PRO ROSE - Sunglasses - Style Eyes of California
PRO/RX - Computer software - Freedom Data Systems, Inc.
PRO-SAFE - Medical apparatus - Dimension Corp.
PRO SAFETY - Apparel and accessories - Falcon Specialities, Inc.
PRO SALT - Pet products - Mid Jersey Pet Supply
PRO-SAN - Skin care products - Hillcrest Laboratories Inc.
PRO-SAND - Tools - Great Neck Saw Manufacturers, Inc.
PRO-SATIN - Paints - Parker Paint Manufacturing Co.
PRO SCALE - Veterinary medical equipment - Integrated Health Products Corp.
PRO-SCAN - Antennas - Valor Enterprises, Inc.
PRO SCAPER - Garden equipment - McCulloch Corp.
PRO SCRATCH FADER - Electronic equipment - Gemini Sound Products Corp.
PRO-SCRIPTION - Hair care products - John Frieda, Inc.
PRO SD - Cameras ☆ - Mamiya America Corp.
PRO SEAL - Adhesives and sealants - Pacer Technology
PRO SEAL - Housewares stores - Recpro, Inc.
PRO SEAL - Motor vehicle parts and accessories - Pro Seal Products
PRO-SEAL - Nonporous-surface sealant - Trade & Marketing Inc.

PRO SEAL - Weather stripping ☆ - Resources Park
PRO-SEARCH - Computer software - Personal Bibliographic Software Inc.
PRO-SECT - Publisher's imprints - Nasco International, Inc.
PRO SECT - Sporting goods - 2-N-1 Grip Inc.
PRO-SELECT - Building materials - Aluminum Co. of America
PRO SELECT - Golfing equipment - Pro Select Sports USA
PRO-SELECT - Lubricants - Benz Oil Inc.
PRO SELECT - Photo albums - 20th Century Plastics
PRO SELECT - Rackets–tennis - Wilson Sporting Goods Co.
PRO-SELECT - Tools–power-driven - Disston Co.
PRO-SELECT - Veterinary pharmaceutical preparations - Epoc Veterinary Laboratories
PRO-SELECT ALOE - Veterinary pharmaceutical preparations - Epoc Veterinary Laboratories
PRO SELECT STAFF - Golfing equipment - Pro Select Sports USA
PRO SELECT SUNDAY - Golfing equipment - Pro Select Sports USA
PRO-SENTRY-IMS - Monitors–electronic - Molecular Analytics, LLC
PRO-SERIES - Adhesives and sealants - Ohio Sealants Inc.
PRO SERIES - Adhesives and sealants - OSI Sealants, Inc.
PRO SERIES - Clippers–barber - Wahl Clipper Corp.
PRO SERIES - Computer software - National Education Training Group, Inc.
PRO SERIES - Engines - Kohler Co.
PRO SERIES - Garage doors - Clopay Millwork
PRO SERIES - Kitchen appliances - Emerson Electric Co.
PRO SERIES - Locks–padlocks - Master Lock Co.
PRO-SERIES - Paints - Wagner Spray Tech Corp.
PRO-SERIES - Photo albums - 20th Century Plastics
PRO SERIES - Photofinishing laboratories - Konica Photo Service U.S.A.
PRO SERIES - Pistons - Sealed Power Technologies LP
PRO SERIES - Tires - Sand Tires Unlimited Inc.
PRO SERIES - Tools–soldering - Lincoln Electric Co.
PRO SERIES - Toys–automobiles - Hasbro, Inc.
PRO SERIES - Vacuum cleaners and accessories - Royal Appliance Manufacturing Co.
PRO-SET - Cosmetics ☆ - Monique Quality Products Co. Inc.
PRO SET - Golfing equipment - Ram Golf Corp.
PRO SET - Paint rollers - Corona Brushes Inc.
PRO-SET - Personal stereos - Memtek Products
PRO-SET - Programmable punch press controller - Weldotron Corp.
PRO SET - Shoes ☆ - Endicott Johnson Corp.
PRO SET POWER - Trading cards and stamps - Pro Set Inc.
PRO SET RACING - Trading cards and stamps - Pro Set Inc.
PRO SHAKE - Beverages - Weider Health and Fitness
PRO-SHAVE - Shaving preparations - Pro-Capa Products Inc.
PRO-SHEEN - Paints - California Products Corp.
PRO-SHEEN - Paints - Parker Paint Manufacturing Co.
PRO-SHELL - Paints - Parker Paint Manufacturing Co.
PRO SHIELD - Automotive parts and accessories - National Interchem Corp.
PRO-SHIELD - Coatings - Interstate Paint Corp.
PRO-SHIELD INTERNATIONAL - Chemical protectant - Pro-Shield International
PRO SHOP - Cleaning preparations - National Interchem Corp.
PRO SHOP - Floor coverings - R.W. Beattie Carpet Industries Inc.
PRO SHOT - Pigments - Pro Shot Aerosol Corp.
PRO SHOT - Sporting goods - Collette Manufacturing Co.
PRO SHOT GOLF - Golfing equipment - Proshot Golf, L.P.
PRO-SHOW DIRECTOR - Photographic equipment - SP Systems/Saratons
PRO SIDE SPORTS - Golfing equipment - Tanglewood Holdings, Inc.
PRO SKILL NET - Sporting goods - Roy Justin Thomas Enterprises
PRO-SKIN - Vitamins and nutritional supplements - Marlyn Co. Inc.
PRO SKINS - Sports apparel - Medalist Apparel Inc.
PRO SLEEPER - Motor vehicles–trucks - Navistar International Transportation Corp.
PRO SLEEVE - Crocheted and knitted items - Towne & King Inc.
PRO-SLIDE - Music stands - Super Star Products
PRO-SLING - Musical instrument accessories - Micro Musical Products Corp.
PRO SLOT - Sporting goods - Johnston's Golf Innovations Inc.
PRO-SNOWBIE - Sleds - Empire Industries
PRO SOCCER - Computer software ☆ - Microprose Software, Inc.
PRO-SOF - Pharmaceutical preparations - Vangard Labs Inc.
PRO-SOL - Fertilizers - Frit Industries, Inc.
PRO-SOLE - Socks - Adams-Millis Corp.
PRO SOLOIST - Synthesizers–musical instrument - Fender Musical Instruments
PRO SONIC - Dental equipment - Sultan Chemists, Inc.
PRO SOURCE - Deodorizers - Unisource Worldwide, Inc.

☆ = Now out of production

PRO SOURCE - Golfing equipment - Global Edge, Inc.
PRO-SOY - Animal feeds - Wholesale Feeds, Inc.
PRO-SP - Lenses–photographic - Photographic Research Organization Inc.
PRO-SPAN - Pharmaceutical preparations ☆ - Primedics Laboratories
PRO SPAN - Roofing materials–slate - ASC Pacific Inc.
PRO-SPARKLE IT - Cleaning preparations - Pro Sun Industries
PRO SPATIALIZER - Electronics equipment - Desper Products, Inc.
PRO-SPEC - Enamels - Commercial Chemical Co. Inc.
PRO-SPEC - Eyeglasses - Uvex Safety LLC
PRO-SPEC - Lighting fixtures - Genlyte Group Inc.
PRO-SPEC - Petroleum - Texas Refinery Corp. (Lubricants Div.)
PRO-SPEC - Shutters–wood - Design House, Inc.
PRO SPECIAL - Cymbals - Jim Atlas Cymbal Works
PRO-SPECIAL - Paint rollers - Florida Roller, Inc.
PRO SPECS - Golfing equipment - Donald Jeen Chang Sun
PRO SPECS - Sporting goods - Unique Sports Products Inc.
PRO SPECWARE - Computer software - Rust-Oleum Corp.
PRO-SPEED - Paints - Pen Paints Inc.
PRO SPEED - Toys - Hasbro, Inc.
PRO-SPENSE - Laboratory apparatus - Cole-Parmer Instrument Co.
PRO-SPIKE - Exercising equipment - American Athletic Inc.
PRO-SPIKE - Flooring–hardwood - Horner Flooring Co. Inc.
PRO-SPLICE - Electronics equipment - Pro Tapes & Specialties
PRO-SPLICE - Tape–adhesive - Pro Tapes & Specialties, Inc.
PRO SPORT - Bicycles - Otasco
PRO SPORT - Bicycles - Service Merchandise Co. Inc.
PRO SPORT - Boats–motor - Master Craft Boat Co.
PRO SPORT - Dryers–hair - Windmere Corp.
PRO SPORT - Games - Jaleco USA, Inc.
PRO SPORT - Locks–door - Master Lock Co.
PRO SPORT - Motorcycle parts and accessories - Nichols Motorcycle Supply, Inc.
PRO SPORT - Scoreboards - Daktronics Inc.
PRO SPORTS - Athletic shoes ☆ - Garrison Industries
PRO-SPORTS - Vitamins and nutritional supplements - MLO Products, Inc.
PRO SPOT - Audio equipment ☆ - Galaxy Audio
PRO SPOT - Welding equipment - Pro Spot International, Inc.
PRO SPRAY - Cosmetics - Delta Industries International, Inc.
PRO SPRINTS - Shoes–athletic - Kobacker Co.
PRO SQUEEZE - Exercising equipment - Pro Orthopedic Devices, Inc.
PRO-SSK - Sporting goods - SSK America Inc.
PRO STAFF - Rackets–tennis - Wilson Sporting Goods Co.
PRO STAFF LITE - Rackets–tennis - Wilson Sporting Goods Co.
PRO STAFF TOUR - Footwear–athletic - Wilson Sporting Goods Co.
PRO STAGS - Footwear–athletic - Osceola Shoe Co. Inc.
PRO-STAIN-IT - Brushes–paint - Corona Brushes Inc.
PRO STAK - Electronics equipment - Pacific Innovations
PRO STAMP - Stamps–hand - Newell Office Products
PRO STANDARD - Audio equipment - Sony Electronics Inc.
PRO STAR - Boats–motor - Master Craft Boat Co.
PRO STAR - Fishing rods - Pro Tackle Industries, Inc.
PRO STAR - Hair care products - Windmere Corp.
PRO STAR - Video equipment - Daktronics Inc.
PRO STAR SPORTS - Exercising equipment - Pro Star Sports, Inc.
PRO STARR - Water purification systems - Blue Devil Industries, Inc.
PRO-STARS - Games - Hasbro, Inc.
PRO START - Engines–motor vehicle - BWD Automotive Corp.
PRO-STAT - Thermostats - Harper-Wyman Co.
PRO STEAM - Iron - Salton/Maxim Housewares, Inc.
PRO-STENCIL - Stencils - Ideal Stencil Machine and Tape Co.
PRO STICK - Adhesives and sealants - Adhesive Technologies, Inc.
PRO-STICK - Dryers–hair ☆ - Sunbeam-Oster Household Products
PRO STICK - Sporting goods - Unique Sports Products Inc.
PRO-STIX - Abrasive products - Woodstock International, Inc.
PRO STIX - Skateboards - Nash Manufacturing Inc.
PRO STOCK - Adhesives and sealants - Gibson-Homans Co. (Sealant Technology)
PRO STOP - Brake parts - Raybestos/Brake Parts Inc.
PRO-STOP - Clocks ☆ - General Time Corp. (Westclox/Seth Thomas Div.)
PRO-STOP - Metals - Prosec, Inc.
PRO STREAM II - Hair care products - Redken Laboratories, Inc.
PRO-STRENGTH - Cleaning preparations–household - Pro-Strength
PRO STRIDER - Shoe insoles - L & A, Inc.
PRO STRIKE - Fishing tackle - Kmart Properties, Inc.
PRO STRIKE CROSS-TRAIN SYSTEM - Sporting goods - Pete Incaudo & Associates, Inc.

PRO STRIPPER - Paint removers - Parks Corp.
PRO STRIPPER II - Paint removers - Parks Corp.
PRO STRONG - Manicure preparations - Pro Strong, Inc.
PRO STYL - Hair care products - Ampro Industries, Inc.
PRO-STYLE - Footwear–athletic ☆ - American Athletic Shoe Co.
PRO STYLE 1500 - Dryers–hair - Dubl Duck/Jet Set Inc.
PRO SUIT - Waterproof outerwear ☆ - Helly-Hansen Inc.
PRO-SUM - Footwear - Summit Footwear Inc.
PRO-SWEEP - Brushes ☆ - Felton Brush Inc.
PRO SWING SYSTEM, THE - Golfing equipment - Sports Sciences, Inc.
PRO SYSTEM - Personal-care product - Cotter & Co.
PRO TACH - Exercising equipment - Precise International/Wenger
PRO-TACK - Gloves - Champion Glove Manufacturing Co.
PRO TACK - Golfing equipment - Golfsmith International Inc.
PRO-TAMRON - Projectors–photographic ☆ - Tamron Industries Inc.
PRO-TAPER - Office supplies - Spray Sok Co. Inc.
PRO TARP - Tarpaulins - Lewis Hyman, Inc.
PRO TE - Pharmaceutical preparations ☆ - ICN Pharmaceuticals Inc.
PRO TEAM - Beverages–carbonated - Ultimate Strength Systems Labs, Inc.
PRO TEC - Cases–musical instrument - Protec International
PRO TEC - Chemical preparations - Pro Tec USA, Inc.
PRO-TEC CLASSIC - Shovels - Nupla Corp.
PRO-TEC PLUS - Adhesives and sealants - Klein & Co.
PRO-TEC-TOR, THE - Extension cords - Alert Safety Lite Products, Inc.
PRO-TECH - Apparel and accessories ☆ - Horace Small Apparel Co.
PRO-TECH - Audio equipment - Parts Express International, Inc.
PRO TECH - Cooking equipment–household - Jacksonville Manufacturing
PRO-TECH - Hair care products - European Tanning Systems Inc.
PRO TECH - Knives–hunting - Colonial Knife Co. Inc.
PRO TECH - Motor vehicles–snowplows - Pro-Tech Welding & Fabrication, Inc.
PRO TECH - Paints - Fuller-O'Brien Paints Inc.
PRO TECH - Paints ☆ - Duron, Inc.
PRO-TECH - Plugs–ear - Apex Medical Corp.
PRO-TECH - Siding–insulating - Aluminum Co. of America
PRO TECH 2000 - Lubricants - Witco Corp.
PRO TECH FINS - Sporting goods - Surfco Hawaii Inc.
PRO-TECH-ION - See **EASTON**
PRO-TEC'S - Pet products ☆ - King of All Manufacturing, Inc.
PRO TECT - Dropcloths - Pro Tect Associates, Inc.
PRO-TECT - Enamels ☆ - Atlas Chemical Co.
PRO-TECT - Paints - Pen Paints Inc.
PRO-TECT - Pet products ☆ - Aquatronics-Filtronics
PRO-TECT - Repellent - Petcare Plus, Inc.
PRO-TECTA - Construction equipment - Hoffinger Industries, Inc.
PRO-TECTA-COTE - Paints - Sureguard, Inc.
PRO-TECTIT - Video production - Nalpak Video Sales, Inc.
PRO-TECTIVE - Electronic equipment - Tiffen Manufacturing Corp.
PRO-TECTOR - Goggles–safety - Allan Enterprises
PRO-TECTOR - Pet products ☆ - Lazy Pet Products
PRO-TEE - Fabrics ☆ - Veratec
PRO-TEEN TREET - Vitamins and nutritional supplements - Hillestad International, Inc.
PRO TEES - Apparel and accessories - Adtees Corp.
PRO-TEK - Hair care products - Vigorol Inc.
PRO-TEK - Hardware - Bulldog Home Hardware
PRO-TEK - Housewares ☆ - Thermwell Products Co. Inc.
PRO-TEK - Insecticides - J. & L. Adikes Inc.
PRO-TEK - Paints - Dutch Boy Group
PRO-TEK - Plaster–wallboard - Pawling Corp. (Standard Products Div.)
PRO-TEK - Skin care products - E.I. Dupont de Nemours and Co.
PRO-TEK EYE - Frames–eyeglass - Spotlight Industries Inc.
PRO-TEKT - Mats - Ludlow Composites Corp.
PRO-TEKT - Plant growth regulators - Dyna-Gro Nutrition Solutions
PRO-TEMP GOO - Glass products ☆ - D & L Stained Glass Supply, Inc.
PRO-TEN - Fabrics–broadcloth - Collins & Aikman Corp.
PRO TENNIS - Games - Avalon Hill Game Co.
PRO-TENS - Electrodes - Uni-Patch
PRO-TENSIVE - Hair care products - Helene Curtis Industries Inc.
PRO-TEX - Closet and travel accessories ☆ - Clopay Building Products Co., Inc.
PRO-TEX - Finishing agents - Proko Industries Inc.
PRO-TEX - Housewares - Ballonoff Home Products
PRO-TEX - Paints - Dayton Paint & Coatings Inc.
PRO-TEX - Safety products - Pro-Tex International Inc.
PRO TEXXION - Sporting goods - Knight Golf, Inc.

PRO, THE - Pens ☆ - K-9 Pen Co.
PRO, THE - Staplers - Markwell Manufacturing Co. Inc.
PRO, THE - Sunglasses - Style Eyes of California
PRO, THE - Floor coverings—carpet and rugs - Tec Inc.
PRO-THICKS - Hosiery - Moretz Hosiery Mills Inc.
PRO-THIK - Hair care products - Syosset Laboratories Inc.
PRO THRASH - Integrated circuits - Nationsbank of North Carolina, N.A.
PRO THROTTLE - Computer peripheral equipment - Joystick Technologies (CH Products Division)
PRO THUNDER 500 - Bicycles ☆ - Huffy Corp.
PRO THUNDER 3000 - Bicycles - Huffy Corp.
PRO TICKET - Apparel—men's - Vehon & Associates
PRO-TINT - Paints - Briner Paint Manufacturing Co. Inc.
PRO-TIP - Industrial machinery - Settles Precision Manufacturing, Inc.
PRO TIP - Manicure preparations ☆ - Gena Laboratories Inc.
PRO-TITAN - Housewares ☆ - Geerpres Wringer Co.
PRO-TONE - Brushes—paint - Wooster Brush Co.
PRO-TONE - Coatings - Vogel Paint and Wax Co., Inc.
PRO TONE - Egg substitutes - Willamette Egg Farms
PRO TOOLS - Computer hardware - Digidesign Inc.
PRO-TOP - Cement - American Stone-Mix Inc.
PRO TOUCH - Cleaning preparations - No Touch North America Corp.
PRO TOUCH - Hair curlers - Windmere Corp.
PRO TOUCH - Massage products - Pure Pro Massage Oils, Inc.
PRO-TOUCH - Paint sprayers - E-Z Paintr Corp.
PRO-TOUCH - Paints - OEM Paints, Inc.
PRO TOUCH - Sporting goods - Shakespeare Fishing Tackle
PRO TOUR - Apparel—athletic - Stage II Apparel Corp.
PRO TOUR - Bags—duffel - Ektelon
PRO TOUR - Balls - Brine Inc.
PRO TOUR - Balls - Mikasa Sports
PRO TOUR - Bicycles ☆ - Roadmaster Corp.
PRO TOUR - Glassware—household - Papel Freelance, Inc.
PRO-TOUR - Golfing equipment - Suarez Corp.
PRO TOURNEY - Boats - Warrior Fiberglass Products Inc.
PRO-TOW - Trailer jacks - Atwood Mobile Products
PRO TRAC - Bicycles ☆ - J.C. Penney Co., Inc.
PRO TRAC TRICK - Sporting goods - O'Brien International
PRO-TRACER - Electronics equipment - Imatronic Inc.
PRO-TRACK - Electronic equipment - Shure Brothers, Inc.
PRO TRAINER - Exercising equipment - Tunturi, Inc.
PRO/TRAINER - Heart monitors - Polar Electro Inc.
PRO TRAINER - Pet products - R.C. Steele Co.
PRO-TRAINER - Scissors—hand-operated - L.B.D., Inc. (Medco Supply Co.)
PRO-TRAINER SADDLE LINE BY THORNHILL - English saddles - Thornhill Enterprises, Inc.
PRO TRAJECTORY - Golfing equipment - Acjshnet Co.
PRO TRAVLER - Electronic equipment - AVL
PRO TRICKS - Water bottles—rubber - Connelly Skis, Inc.
PRO-TRIM - Knives - United Manufacturers Supplies Inc.
PRO-TRONIX - Thermostats - General Signal Corp.
PRO TUBE - Insulating materials - Pepco Sales of Dallas, Inc.
PRO-TUFF - Tools - KP Industries
PRO TUFF SOLE - Hosiery - GAKM Resources Corp.
PRO-TUFT - Chemical preparations ☆ - Bemis Co. Inc.
PRO TUNE UP TARGET LINE - Golfing equipment - Clear Perceptions, Inc.
PRO TURBO - Oils—lubricating - Witco Corp.
PRO TURBO 1600 - Dryers—hair - Dubl Duck/Jet Set Inc.
PRO TURF - Floor coverings—carpet and rugs - Conquest Carpet Mills Inc.
PRO TYPE - Paints - Perry & Derrick Co.
PRO TYPE PLUS - Paints - Perry & Derrick Co.
PRO TYPE PREMIUM - Paints - Perry & Derrick Co.
PRO ULTIMATE - Bicycles - Recreational Equipment, Inc.
PRO USA - Balls—golf - Hawaii Calls Inc.
PRO USA - Golfing equipment - Palm Springs Golf, Inc.
PRO V - Bicycles - Raycon Technology
PRO-V - Hair care products - Procter & Gamble Co.
PRO V - Windows—vinyl - SNE Enterprises Inc.
PRO VAC - Lawn mowers - Kato Equipment Co.
PRO VAC - Vacuum cleaners and accessories—commercial - Ariens Co.
PRO-VAL - Paints - Rubberset Co.
PRO VANIC - Skin care products - Proteus Inc.
PRO VANTAGE - Archery equipment ☆ - Hoyt
PRO VENT - Air conditioning equipment - Quest/U.S. Brass
PRO VET - Pet food - Lextron, Inc.
PRO-VIBE - Mallets - Mike Balter Mallets

PRO/VIDE - Vitamins and nutritional supplements - M & D Sales Co., Inc.
PRO-VIDEO - Cameras—video - CSI/Speco
PRO VIDEO - Computer software - Shereff Systems Inc.
PRO/VIEW - Binders ☆ - Samsill Corp.
PRO-VIEW - Computer peripheral equipment - Gusdorf Corp.
PRO-VIEW - Lenses—optical - Bausch & Lomb Inc.
PRO-VIEW - Phototransmission equipment - Luxor
PRO VIEW - Sporting goods - Unique Sports Products Inc.
PRO-VISION - Trading cards and stamps - Sports Flipp Tipps Inc.
PRO-VISIONS - Pet products - Ralston Purina Co.
PRO-VITA - Pet products - Pro-Diet Pet Foods
PRO-VITA - Veterinary medical equipment - Minnesota Pet Breeders, Inc.
PRO-VITE - Vitamins and nutritional supplements - Pharmavite Corp.
PRO-VUE - Electronic equipment - Pro-Vue, Inc.
PRO-VUE - Goggles ☆ - Bausch & Lomb Inc.
PRO-VYN-AL - Paints - Benjamin Moore & Co.
PRO WALL - Plastics—laminated - Plaskolite Inc.
PRO-WATCH - Computer software - Northern Computers, Inc.
PRO-WAY - Animal feeds - Southern States Cooperative Inc.
PRO-WEAR BY WEAR-EVER - Cookware - Anchor Hocking Glass, Inc.
PRO/WEAVE - Paint rollers ☆ - Wooster Brush Co.
PRO WEIGHT - Fishing tackle ☆ - South Bend Sporting Goods Inc.
PRO WELD - Adhesives and sealants - Pro Seal Products
PRO-WHACKER - Fishing lures - Bomber Bait Co.
PRO-WHITE - Manicure preparations - Professional Foot Care Products Inc.
PRO-WHITE - Medical apparatus ☆ - Professional Product Research, Inc.
PRO WHITE - Water colors - Steig Products
PRO-WICK - Fabrics—felt - Wildlife Research Center, Inc.
PRO WINCH 90 - Winches - Superior Lubricants Co., Inc.
PRO WINCH 200 - Winches - Superior Lubricants Co., Inc.
PRO-WINNER I - Hair care products ☆ - Dubl Duck/Jet Set Inc.
PRO WONDER - Electronic equipment - Thomson Consumer Electronics, Inc.
PRO WOOD - Knives—putty - Hyde Manufacturing Co.
PRO/WOOL - Paint rollers - Wooster Brush Co.
PRO-WRAP - Hair care products - Willat Co.
PRO-WRAP - Sporting goods - Bike Athletic Co.
PRO WRESTLING AMERICA - Athletic associations - Pro Wrestling America Inc.
PRO WYERS - Musical instrument accessories - PRO Manufacturing
PRO-X - Pet products - Pet Lift
PRO X 10 - Archery equipment ☆ - Martin Archery Inc.
PRO X100 - Sunglasses - Style Eyes of California
PRO XCEL FEMME - Apparel—women's - Gallini Designs, Inc.
PRO-XL - Men's hairpieces - International Hairgoods Inc.
PRO YAPER - Skin care products - Proteus Inc.
PRO YO - Toys - Playmaxx Inc.
PRO ZEMA - Pet products - Zema Corp.
PRO-ZONE - Sporting goods ☆ - Bike Athletic Co.
PRO ZONE - Vitamins and nutritional supplements - NutriBiotic
PRO ZONE, THE - Toys - Playmates Toys Inc.
PRO2 - Fertilizers - Plant Research Laboratories
PRO2 - Oxygen - Precise International/Wenger
PRO3700 - Electronic equipment ☆ - J.L. Cooper Electronics
PRO*ACCT - Computer software - Data Systems Inc.
PROACE - Shirts - ProAce Inc.
PROACT - Computer hardware - Weisman Enterprises, Inc.
PROACT - Computer software - Electronic Data Systems Corp.
PROACTAZYME - Pharmaceutical preparations - Lifetrends International
PROACTION - Bicycles - Troxel Co. Cycling and Fitness
PROACTION MAINTENANCE MANAGER - Computer software - Diagnetics, Inc.
PROACTIV - Health care products - KR Dermatologics
PROACTIVE - Electronic equipment - Noise Cancellation Technologies, Inc.
PROACTIVE - Lenses—optical - O.S.I. Corp.
PROACTIVE - Paper products - Howard E. Sproull III
PROACTIVE TECHNOLOGIES - Computer software - Proactive Technologies, Inc.
PROAGIO - Computer hardware - Mouse Systems Corp.
PROAIR - Safety products - National Draeger, Inc.
PROAMERICA - Computer software - Proamerica, Inc.
PROAMINO - Animal feeds - Vita Plus Corp.
PROANIDIN 50 - Vitamins and nutritional supplements - Source Naturals
PROANIDIN 100 - Vitamins and nutritional supplements - Source Naturals
PROANIMAL - Veterinary pharmaceutical preparations - Time Span Research, Inc.
PROANTHODYN - Vitamins and nutritional supplements - Source Naturals

☆ = Now out of production

PROANTHOGEN-LS - Vitamins and nutritional supplements - Better Health Products
PROAQUA - Pharmaceutical preparations ☆ - Solvay Pharmaceuticals Inc.
PROARTE - Recording label - Counter Culture
PROAXON - Hair care products - Lombardi Research Group, LLC
PROB SIM - Computer software - Clifford Konold
PROBABILITY TOOLKIT - Computer software - Ventura Educational Systems
PROBAC - Floor coverings - Mannington Mills, Inc.
PROBACON - Pharmaceutical preparations ☆ - Legere Pharmaceuticals Inc.
PROBADDILITY - Games - Wff'n Proof Learning Games Associates
PROBAHIST - Pharmaceutical preparations - Legere Pharmaceuticals Inc.
PROBAK - Razor blades - Gillette Co.
PROBALAN - Pharmaceutical preparations - Lannett Co. Inc.
PROBALANCED - Pet food - Gold Kist Inc.
PROBALLS - Doughnuts - Granny's Kitchens Ltd.
PROBALOTO - Computer software - Gary Olander
PROBAMIDE - Pharmaceutical preparations ☆ - Roberts/Hauck Pharmaceuticals Inc.
PROBANA - Infant product ☆ - Bristol-Myers Squibb Co.
PROBAND - Identification tags - Michel & Washer Enterprises, Inc.
PRO+BAR - Medical apparatus - Almac Consumer Products, Inc.
PROBASE - Computer software - Probase Group, Inc.
PROBASS 1000 - Amplifiers–musical instrument - Peavey Electronics Corp.
PROBATE - Pharmaceutical preparations - Vita Elixir Co. Inc.
PROBATH - Bathroom accessories - Kinkead/Tub/Shower Doors
PROBATH - Shower stalls–metal - Sterling Plumbing Group Inc.
PROBAX - Lip balms - T/I Pharmaceuticals, Inc.
PROBE - Audio equipment - Probe Audio Laboratories, Inc.
PROBE - Coils–ignition ☆ - St. Pierre Manufacturing Corp.
PROBE - Computer terminals - Autotote Systems, Inc.
PROBE - Floor coverings–carpet and rugs - Mohawk Industries Inc.
PROBE - Games ☆ - Parker Brothers
PROBE - Lighting fixtures - Swivelier Co. Inc.
PROBE - Motor vehicles–automobiles - Ford Motor Co.
PROBE - Scooters–children's ☆ - Hedstrom Corp.
PROBE 2000 - Toys–electronic - Philips Consumer Electronics Co.
PROBE-CLIP - Medical apparatus - Grace Bio-Labs Inc.
PROBE-GUARD - Medical apparatus - Carter-Wallace, Inc.
PROBE NET - Computer storage devices ☆ - Landmark Systems Corp.
PROBE ONE - Dental equipment - Dental Probe, Inc.
PROBEAM - Lighting fixtures–street - Holophane Corp.
PROBEC T - Vitamins and nutritional supplements - McNeil Pharmaceuticals
PROBENCH - Work benches - Clarke Power Products, Inc.
PROBER VISION - Computer software - Electroglas, Inc.
PROBESTAR - Circuit boards - Proteus Corp.
PROBEVEL - Canvas–artists' - Wolsey Co.
PROBIATA - Vitamins and nutritional supplements - Kyolic/Wakunaga
PROBILAGOL - Pharmaceutical preparations ☆ - Purdue Frederick Co.
PROBILIFE PROBIOTICS - Animal feeds - Vit-E-Men Co., Inc. (Life Products)
PROBIONIC - Vitamins and nutritional supplements - Enrich Corp.
PROBIOTIC SOLUTIONS ACTIVOL - Chemical preparations - Bio Huma Netics, Inc.
PROBIOTIC SOLUTIONS BIO GENESIS - Chemical preparations ☆ - Bio Huma Netics, Inc.
PROBIOTIC SOLUTIONS NATURE'S LIGHT PROBIOTIC - Grain products–oats ☆ - Bio Huma Netics, Inc.
PROBIOTIC SOLUTIONS NUTRIPLEX - Chemical preparations ☆ - Bio Huma Netics, Inc.
PROBIT - Tools–machine - Spencer Products Co.
PROBITA - Computer software - Probita, Inc.
PROBITAL - Pharmaceutical preparations ☆ - G. D. Searle & Co.
PROBLADE - Skates–roller ☆ - Rollerblade, Inc.
PROBLEM SOLVER - Health care products ☆ - Futurebiotics
PROBLEM SOLVER - Varnishes - Samuel Cabot Inc.
PROBLEM SOLVERS - Publisher's imprints - Research and Education Assn.
PROBLEM SOLVERS, THE - Plumbing fixtures–metal ☆ - Moen Inc.
PROBLEM SPOTTER, THE - Skin care products - Estee Lauder Inc.
PROBLOCK - Athol Corp.
PROBLOCK - Paints - Sherwin-Williams Automotive Finishes Corp.
PROBLOCK - Tools–hand-operated - Pro Motorcar Products Inc.
PROBOARD - Medical apparatus - Proboard, Inc, Llc.
PROBOCON - Pharmaceutical preparations ☆ - Legere Pharmaceuticals Inc.
PROBOLIC - Pharmaceutical preparations - Hyrex Pharmaceuticals
PROBOND - Dental compounds - Dentsply International Inc.
PROBOND - Electronic equipment - Seal Products Inc.
PROBOTECH - Industrial machinery - Probotech, Inc.

PROBRIDGE - Headphones - Unex Corp.
PROBUILD - Paints - Sherwin-Williams Automotive Finishes Corp.
PROBUY - Computer software - Trade Service Corp.
PROCABIN 67Z - Photographic equipment - Mamiya America Corp.
PROCABLE - Sound and lighting Multicables - TMB Associates
PROCAINE CREME ONE - Skin care products - Fanie International
PROCAINE CREME TWO - Skin care products - Fanie International
PROCALC - Calculators ☆ - Texas Instruments Inc.
PROCALIBER - Musical instruments ☆ - Deg Music Products Inc.
PROCALL - Computer storage devices - AVL
PROCALLUS - Medical apparatus - Amei Technologies Inc.
PROCAM - Cameras - Polaroid Corp.
PROCAM - Computer software - Prime Site Inc.
PROCAM - Greeting cards - Salvatore Gurrieri
PROCAN - Aluminum lighting fixtures - TMB Associates
PROCAN - Containers - American National Can Co.
PROCAN SR - Pharmaceutical preparations - Parke-Davis
PROCANBID - Pharmaceutical preparations - Warner-Lambert Co.
PROCARDIA - Pharmaceutical preparations - Pfizer Inc.
PROCARDIA XL - Pharmaceutical preparations - Pfizer Inc.
PROCARE - Bandages - 1st Defense Safety Corp.
PROCARE - Pet products - Melaleuca, Inc.
PROCARE - Pet products - Professional Pet Products
PROCAREX - Pharmaceutical preparations - C.S. Ruckstuhl Co. Inc.
PROCART - Carts - Central Supply of America, Corp.
PROCASE - Computer software - Procase Corp.
PROCASTER - Sporting goods - Daiwa Corp.
PROCASTER MAGFORCE - Sporting goods ☆ - Daiwa Corp.
PROCASTER TOURNAMENT - Sporting goods - Daiwa Corp.
PROCAULK - Caulking compounds - Devan Sealants Inc.
PROCD - Computer software - Procd, Inc.
PROCD - Computer storage devices–optical - Pro CD Inc.
PROCEA - Dietary supplement - L. Perrigo Co.
PROCEED - Computer software - Salesoft, Inc.
PROCEED - Digital encoders - GNP Audio Video Inc.
PROCEEDINGS ON DISK - Publisher's imprints - Omnipress
PROCEL - Bandages - W.L. Gore & Associates, Inc.
PROCEPTION - Medical apparatus - Milex Products Inc.
PROCESS - Ovens–convection - Fostoria Industries Inc.
PROCESS - Recording label - Country Star International
PROCESS ARCHITECT - Computer software - Viewstar Corp.
PROCESS BREAKTHROUGH - Computer software - Qualpro, Inc.
PROCESS COMPANY, THE - Publisher's imprints - Andrulis Research Corp.
PROCESS E - Abrasive products - Norton Co.
PROCESS IDS - Disinfectants - E.R. Squibb & Sons, Inc.
PROCESS INNOVATOR - Computer software - Cimtelligence Systems, Inc.
PROCESS INSIGHTS - Computer software - Pavilion Technologies, Inc.
PROCESS KING - Printing presses - King Press Corp.
PROCESS LCS - Disinfectants - E.R. Squibb & Sons, Inc.
PROCESS NPD - Germicide - Merck & Co., Inc. (Merck Research Laboratories)
PROCESS PERFECTER - Computer software - Pavilion Technologies, Inc.
PROCESS PRO - Computer software - Gineric Corp.
PROCESS PROBE - Silicon products - Sensarray Corp.
PROCESS PROTECTOR - Hair care products - KMS Research Inc.
PROCESS PUTTY - Toys - Quality Process Consultants, Inc.
PROCESS QDS - Disinfectants - E.R. Squibb & Sons, Inc.
PROCESS SELLING - Publisher's imprints - Management Development Corp.
PROCESS SOFTWARE - Computer software - Process Software Corp.
PROCESS THERAPY - Software - Shirley Spicer
PROCESS WINDOWS - Computer software - Total Control Products, Inc.
PROCESSBASE - Computer software ☆ - Leadership 2000, Inc.
PROCESSING POWER - Computer software - Instructional/Communications Technology Inc.
PROCESSION - Laboratory apparatus - Genetic Systems Corp.
PROCESSION - Tableware–china - Pfaltzgraff Investment Co.
PROCESSIONAL - Floor coverings–carpet and rugs ☆ - World Carpets, Inc.
PROCESSLOGIC - Construction equipment rental services - Media Logic, Inc.
PROCESSOR 1 - Computer software - Electronic Data Systems Corp.
PROCESSWATCH - Electrical testing instruments - Teradyne, Inc.
PROCHAIN - Jewelry - Providence Chain Co.
PROCHARGER - Solar energy collectors - Siemens Solar Industries, L.P.
PROCHECK - Drug testing kits - DynaGen Inc.
PROCHEF - Barbecues and grills - Prochef, Inc.
PROCHLOR - Chemical preparations - Aqua Clear Industries Inc.
PROCHLOR - Pharmaceutical preparations ☆ - Vita-Fore Products Co.
PROCHOICE - Laces–boot and shoe - Mitchellace Inc.

☆ = Now out of production

PROCIL - Pharmaceutical preparations ☆ - Vita-Fore Products Co.

PROCIRCUIT - Shoes - Ektelon

PROCISE - Computer software - Setpoint Inc.

PROCISION LURES - Fishing tackle - Procision Lures

PROCLAIM - Floor coverings - Tarkett, Inc.

PROCLAIM - Floor coverings–carpet and rugs ☆ - Downs Carpet Co. Inc.

PROCLAIM - Floor coverings–carpet and rugs ☆ - Karastan-Bigelow Inc.

PROCLAIM - Hair- and skin-care products, fragrance, etc. - Benjamin Ansehl Co.

PROCLAIM - High-protein bread ☆ - Interstate Brands Corp.

PROCLAIM - Insecticides - Merck & Co., Inc. (Merck Research Laboratories)

PROCLAIM - Paper–writing - Lincoln Pulp and Paper Co. Inc.

PROCLAIM - Pet products - Hubbard Milling Co.

PROCLAIM - Pet products - Supreme Pet Food

PROCLAIM PEN - Computer software - Curtis Software Inc.

PROCLAMATION - Clocks ☆ - General Time Corp. (Westclox/Seth Thomas Div.)

PROCLAMATION - Floor coverings–carpet and rugs - Coronet Carpets Inc.

PROCLAMATION - Floor coverings–carpet and rugs ☆ - Walter Carpet Mills

PROCLASS - Computer hardware - Practical Peripherals, Inc.

PROCLEARZ - Manicure preparations - Professional Foot Care Products Inc.

PROCLIMB - Ladders–wood - Bauer Corp.

PROCLINCH - Tools–power-driven - Vertex Fasteners Inc.

PROCLIP - Alarm systems - Protex International Corp.

PROCLIPS - Computer software - AOTR Inc.

PROCLN - Furniture–metal - NTA Industries

PROCOAT - Fabrics–resin-coated ☆ - Fibre Glass-Evercoat Co. Inc.

PROCOLIM - Pharmaceutical preparations ☆ - JMI-Canton Pharmaceuticals

PROCOLLAGEN - Cosmetics - Revlon Consumer Products Corp.

PROCOLLAGEN - Skin care products - Charles Revson Inc.

PROCOLOR - Hair care products - Rocco Altobelli, Inc.

PROCOMP HIGH PERFORMANCE WHEELS - Automotive parts and accessories - Big O Tires, Inc.

PROCON - Contact lenses - O.S.I. Corp.

PROCON - Food products - Central Soya Co. Inc.

PROCON - Pumps - Standex International Corp.

PROCONNECT - Couplings - Colder Products Co.

PROCONNECT - Electrical equipment - D.E.W. International Corp.

PROCOOL - Motor vehicle parts and accessories - Pep Boys Manny, Moe & Jack

PROCORE - Fabrics - Hind, Inc.

PROCORT - Skin care products - Roberts Laboratories Inc.

PROCOST - Computer software - Procomp Software, Inc.

PROCOTE - Coatings ☆ - Regal Ware, Inc.

PROCRAFT - Gloves–leather - United American Sales, Inc.

PROCREATIN 7 - Animal feed supplements - SAF Product Corp.

PROCRIMP - Machinery - Aeroquip Corp.

PROCTER & GAMBLE - Health care products - Procter & Gamble Co.

PROCTO CREAM-HC - Pharmaceutical preparations - Reed & Carnrick

PROCTO-KIT - Health care products - American Generics Inc.

PROCTOCAINE - Pharmaceutical preparations - Wesley Pharmacal Co. Inc.

PROCTOCORT - Pharmaceutical preparations - Solvay Pharmaceuticals Inc.

PROCTODON - Pharmaceutical preparations ☆ - Solvay Pharmaceuticals Inc.

PROCTOFOAM-HC - Pharmaceutical preparations - Reed & Carnrick

PROCTOFOAM-NS - Pharmaceutical preparations - Reed & Carnrick

PROCTOR - Hardware - Proctor Products Co. Inc.

PROCTOR - Publisher's imprints - National Association of Securities Dealers, Inc.

PROCTOR-SILEX - Kitchen appliances - Hamilton Beach/Proctor-Silex Inc.

PROCTOSOL-HC - Health care products - American Generics Inc.

PROCURE - Fungicides - Uniroyal Chemical Co. Inc. (Crop Protection Div.)

PROCURE - Veterinary pharmaceutical preparations - Miles Inc.

PROCURVE - Cleaning equipment - Mr. Longarm Inc.

PROCUSSION - Synthesizers–musical instrument - E-Mu Systems, Inc.

PROCUT - Pet products - Fromm Industries

PROCUT ELITE - Cutting machine - Seal Products Inc.

PROCYCLE - Bicycles - Fitness Innovations

PROCYCLE - Paper–coated - Consolidated Papers, Inc.

PROCYON'S ULTRAENERGY - Beverages - Procyon Industries Inc.

PRODEA SYNERGY - Computer software - Information Synthesis

PRODEAN - Pet products - Twinlab

PRODECK - Scaffolds–metal - Stinson Sales Corp.

PRODERM - Pharmaceutical preparations - Dow B. Hickam Inc.

PRODERNA - Skin care products - Westwood-Squibb Pharmaceuticals, Inc.

PRODEX - Pharmaceutical preparations ☆ - Whitby Pharmaceuticals, Inc.

PRODICUS - Computer software - Eagle International Institute Inc.

PRODIGAL - Recording label - Motown Record Co. L.P.

PRODIGIES - Sporting goods ☆ - O'Brien International

PRODIGIOUS PESTS - Toys - Toymax Inc.

PRODIGITAL RECORDS - Recording label - Peter Hatch

PRODIGY - Booklets, postcards, posters, etc. - Prodigy Services Co.

PRODIGY - Dental compounds - Kerr Corp.

PRODIGY - Doors–wood - Stanley Hardware Div.

PRODIGY - Electronics equipment - Videotek Inc.

PRODIGY - Hair care products - Fromm Industries

PRODIGY - Helmets–athletic - Giant Bicycle, Inc.

PRODIGY - Occasional tables - JDI Group, Inc.

PRODIGY - Tires - Yokohama Tire Corp.

PRODIGY - Toys ☆ - Decipher Inc.

PRODIGY 21 - Heating equipment - Slant/Fin Corp.

PRODIGY PLUS - Printing presses ☆ - Fargo Electronics Inc.

PRODIGY SWING SYSTEM - Playground equipment - Roadmaster Corp.

PRODIS - Computer storage devices - Clinical Multiphase Research, Inc.

PRODIUM - Laxatives - Breckenridge Pharmaceutical, Inc.

PRODOCS - Computer software - Lotus Development Corp.

PRODOK - Rope ☆ - Tubbs Cordage Co.

PRODOS - Computer software - Apple Computer Inc.

PRODOSA - Clothing - Summit Ridge Corp.

PRODOTTI VILLA - Ravioli - Prodotti Villa Ltd. Inc.

PRODRIVER - Electronic equipment - Detroit Diesel Corp.

PRODROX - Pharmaceutical preparations - Legere Pharmaceuticals Inc.

PRODTRADCO - Meat products–pork - Produce Trading Corp.

PRODUCE IMPORTERS INC. - Agricultural products - Produce Importers, Inc.

PRODUCE KOUNTRY - Fruit and vegetable markets - Produce Kountry

PRODUCE PARTNERS - Seasonings - McCormick & Co., Inc.

PRODUCE PLUS - Soups–mixes - Bri-AL, Inc.

PRODUCE PLUS - Soups–mixes - Bri-Al, LP

PRODUCED WITH PRIDE BY TEAM DITTLER - Games - Dittler Brothers, Inc.

PRODUCER - Computer software - Dow Chemical Co.

PRODUCER - Cooking equipment–commercial - Pitco Frialator, Inc.

PRODUCER - Eyeglasses - Art-Craft Optical Co.

PRODUCER - Flour–blended - ConAgra Grain Co.

PRODUCERS - Furniture ☆ - Bassett Furniture Industries, Inc.

PRODUCERS CHOICE - Fertilizers - Gold Kist Inc.

PRODUCERS DAIRY - Milk - Producers Dairy Delivery

PRODUCER'S EDGE - Computer software - Advanced Marketing, Inc.

PRODUCING TODAY AND THINKING FOR TOMORROW - Cement - Baker Hughes Inc.

PRODUCON - Golfing equipment - Allied Golf Co.

PRODUCT 19 - Cereal - Kellogg Co.

PRODUCT BACKPLANE SYSTEM - Computer software - American Computer and Electronics Corp.

PRODUCT DATA MANAGEMENT - Computer software - Microdynamics, Inc.

PRODUCT DEVELOPMENT - Botanical extracts - Bio-Botanica

PRODUCT EXPERT - Computer software - Interpose, Inc.

PRODUCT MONITOR - Computer software - A.B. Kelley Corp.

PRODUCT OF SIMPLICITY, THE - Computer peripheral equipment - Multi/Point, Inc.

PRODUCT OF USA - Vegetables–frozen - United Foods, Inc.

PRODUCT PERFECT - Skin care products - Nylynn Cosmetic Inc.

PRODUCT PLUS - Electronic equipment - Delta Management Co., Inc.

PRODUCT PLUS - Hair care products - Apollo Products, Inc.

PRODUCT PRESERVERS - Machine parts - A.O. Smith Corp.

PRODUCT TECHKNOWLEDGY - Computer software - Northpoint Software Ventures Inc.

PRODUCTBASE - Computer software - MediaShare Inc.

PRODUCTION - Abrasive products - Minnesota Mining & Manufacturing Co.

PRODUCTION - Computer peripheral equipment - PPG Industries, Inc.

PRODUCTION - Paper–writing - P.H. Glatfelter Co.

PRODUCTION - Scales–industrial - Triner Scale and Manufacturing Co. Inc.

PRODUCTION CAR CARE - Cleaning preparations - Production Chemical Manufacturing, Inc.

PRODUCTION MASTER - Machine parts - Esco Corp.

PRODUCTION PAINTER - Brushes–paint - Wooster Brush Co.

PRODUCTION PLUS - Flowers, plants, and seeds - Production Seeds Plus, Inc.

PRODUCTION SCHEDULING ADVISOR - Computer software - Stone & Webster Advanced Systems Development Services, Inc.

PRODUCTION SYSTEM 2 - Computer software - Computer Language Research Inc.

PRODUCTIVE PC'S - Computer software - Carrie Torme

PRODUCTIVITY PLUS - Display cases–plastic - Gibson Greetings, Inc.

☆ = Now out of production

PRODUCTLINE - Computer software - MCIS, Inc.

PRODUCTMAKERS - Cooking equipment–household ☆ - Grainware Co.

PRODUCTPAC - Computer software - International Business Machines Corp.

PRODUCTPRO INTERACTIVE - Computer software - Georgia-Pacific Corp.

PRODUCTS BY MARBILL - Fencing–gates and posts - Priefert Manufacturing Co., Inc.

PRODUCTS FOR OCCUPATIONAL ATHLETES - Sporting goods - Ergodyne Corp.

PRODUCTS OF DISTINCTION - Garment racks–plastic - Tamor Corp. (HPI Company)

PRODUCTS PLUS - Housewares - Rolnick Helman

PRODUCTS THAT THINK FOR THEMSELVES - Magnetic recording equipment - Intercard, Inc.

PRODUPESA - Seafood products–fresh or frozen - Purcell International

PROEAR - Veterinary pharmaceutical preparations - New England Serum Co.

PROEDGE - Sporting goods - Ridmark Corp.

PROEDIT - Electronic equipment - Thomson Consumer Electronics, Inc.

PROEDITOR - Computer software - International Software Systems, Inc.

PROEN - Garbage disposal units–household - Thompson Manufacturing Co.

PROEST - Computer software - Jeffrey D. Gerardi

PROEX FLASH, THE - Cameras - Proex Photo Systems, Inc.

PROF - Frames–eyeglass ☆ - Universal/Univis Inc.

PROF. OLIVER'S BERRY - Beverages–alcohol ☆ - Oliver Wine Co. Inc.

PROF. OLIVER'S PEACH - Beverages–alcohol ☆ - Oliver Wine Co. Inc.

PROFAC - Health care products - Kay Pharmacal Co. Inc.

PROFALAC - Pet products ☆ - Bingman Laboratories, Inc.

PROFASI - Pharmaceutical preparations - Serono Laboratories Inc.

PROFAST - Footwear - Jiun Tay USA Corp.

PROFECTION - Cutlery - J.A. Henckels Zwillingswerk Inc.

PROFEDA - Pet products - Vitakraft Pet Products Co., Inc.

PROFEDRIN - Pharmaceutical preparations - Bio-Factor Laboratories

PROFELT - Fabrics - Rubie's Costume Co., Inc.

PROFEN LA - Pharmaceutical preparations - Wakefield Pharmaceuticals, Inc.

PROFENAL - Surgical supplies - Alcon Laboratories, Inc.

PROFERAL - Primers ☆ - Sigma Coatings USA BV.

PROFERA'S - Pizzas–frozen - Proferas Pizza Bakery Inc.

PROFESSIONAIRE - Dryers–hair ☆ - Sunbeam-Oster Household Products

PROFESSIONAL - Wright & McGill Co.

PROFESSIONAL - Adhesives and sealants - Roman Adhesives, Inc.

PROFESSIONAL - Apparel–athletic - E-Z Gard Industries, Inc.

PROFESSIONAL - Artists' materials - M. Grumbacher Inc.

PROFESSIONAL - Clippers–barber - Sunbeam-Oster Household Products

PROFESSIONAL - Cosmetics - Noxell Corp.

PROFESSIONAL - Cosmetics ☆ - Lachine Inc.

PROFESSIONAL - Cutlery - Imperial Schrade Corp.

PROFESSIONAL - Fishing tackle - South Bend Sporting Goods Inc.

PROFESSIONAL - Garden equipment - Valley View Specialties Co.

PROFESSIONAL - Golfing equipment - Harrison Sports, Inc.

PROFESSIONAL - Housewares - Smyth Manufacturing Co.

PROFESSIONAL - Lawn mowers - MTD Products Inc.

PROFESSIONAL - Leather goods - St. Thomas Inc.

PROFESSIONAL - Musical instrument accessories - E. & O. Mari Inc.

PROFESSIONAL - Paints - Somay Products Inc.

PROFESSIONAL - Pencils ☆ - Koh-I-Noor, Inc.

PROFESSIONAL - Rackets–badminton ☆ - Rackets International (Racket Sports Div.)

PROFESSIONAL - Rackets–tennis - Head Sports USA

PROFESSIONAL - Safety glasses ☆ - Bilsom International Inc.

PROFESSIONAL - Sewing machines–household - Singer Co.

PROFESSIONAL - Skates–roller - Chicago Roller Skate Co.

PROFESSIONAL - Snow making machinery - Sullivan Manufacturing & Sales Corp.

PROFESSIONAL - Sporting goods - Avon Marine

PROFESSIONAL - Sporting goods - Jobe Ski Corp.

PROFESSIONAL - Sports rackets and accessories - Victor Sports

PROFESSIONAL - Staples - ACCO USA, Inc.

PROFESSIONAL - Tables–metal - Alvin and Co. Inc.

PROFESSIONAL - Toys - Duncan Toys Co.

PROFESSIONAL - Waterproofing compounds - Professional Products of Kansas, Inc.

PROFESSIONAL 1 - Hair care products - Paula Payne Products Co. Inc.

PROFESSIONAL 30 - Photographic equipment - Richard Manufacturing Co.

PROFESSIONAL 486 SYSTEMS - Computers - Mitsuba Corp.

PROFESSIONAL 920 - Adhesives and sealants - Geocel Corp.

PROFESSIONAL ADVANCED PACKAGING SYSTEM - Computer software - Professional Software Technologies, Inc.

PROFESSIONAL ADVANTAGE - Hair care products - Amole Inc.

PROFESSIONAL ALI-GATOR-GRIT - Abrasive products - Ali Industries, Inc.

PROFESSIONAL APPOINTMENT - Calendars ☆ - Rediform

PROFESSIONAL BASKETBALL - Games - Munro Games Inc.

PROFESSIONAL BOWLERS TOUR PBA - Giftware - Professional Bowlers Association of America

PROFESSIONAL BRAKE PARTS CLEANER - Cleaning preparations - Pennzoil Co. (Gumout Div.)

PROFESSIONAL BRUSH CLEANER - Cosmetics - Victoria Vogue, Inc.

PROFESSIONAL CHEF COLLECTION - Housewares - Syracuse China Corp.

PROFESSIONAL CHEF'S SECRET - Housewares ☆ - Ontario Knife Co.

PROFESSIONAL CHEF'S, THE - Cookbooks - Thomson Publishing Corp.

PROFESSIONAL CHOICE - Hardware - Stanley Hardware Div.

PROFESSIONAL CLASSICS - Jewelry - Sandra S. Feder & Jack S. Feder

PROFESSIONAL COLOR SHAMPOO - Hair care products - Hayashi for Hair Inc.

PROFESSIONAL COLORMATCH - Cosmetics - Noxell Corp.

PROFESSIONAL COMPOUNDING CENTERS OF AMERICA, INC. - Pharmaceutical preparations - Professional Compounding Centers of America, Inc.

PROFESSIONAL CURL - Hair care products - Golden Sun Vitamins

PROFESSIONAL DEALER'S CHOICE, THE - Hardware - John D. Roba Co., Inc.

PROFESSIONAL DRY 1600 - Dryers–hair - Dubl Duck/Jet Set Inc.

PROFESSIONAL EDGE - Fishing lures - All Outdoor Marketing, Inc.

PROFESSIONAL EDGE, THE - Tools–power-driven - Porter-Cable Corp.

PROFESSIONAL EDGE, THE - Sporting goods - SSK America Inc.

PROFESSIONAL EDIT - Computer software - Buzzwords International Inc.

PROFESSIONAL EXPRESSIONS - Cosmetics - Chem Spray Aerosols Inc.

PROFESSIONAL EYELASH - Cosmetics - Ardell International Inc.

PROFESSIONAL EYES - Cosmetics ☆ - Noxell Corp.

PROFESSIONAL FILE - Computer software - Software Publishing Corp.

PROFESSIONAL FINISH - Cosmetics - Alexandra De Markoff, Ltd.

PROFESSIONAL FLEXOSCREEN - Computer peripheral equipment - Professional Software Technologies, Inc.

PROFESSIONAL FLEXOSYSTEM - Computer software - Professional Software Technologies, Inc.

PROFESSIONAL FORMULA - Pet products - Manna Pro Corp.

PROFESSIONAL GRADE - Brake parts ☆ - Raybestos/Brake Parts Inc.

PROFESSIONAL GREETINGS - Greeting cards - Professional Greetings Co., Inc.

PROFESSIONAL GROWTH SERIES - Publisher's imprints - Linworth Publishing, Inc.

PROFESSIONAL ICE MELTER - Chemical preparations - Vogel Seed & Fertilizer, Inc.

PROFESSIONAL IMAGEEXCHANGE - Computer software - Professional Software Technologies, Inc.

PROFESSIONAL KIDS - Apparel–children's - Haddad Apparel Group Ltd.

PROFESSIONAL M - Cosmetics - Beauty Products International, Inc.

PROFESSIONAL MEDICAL PRODUCTS - Medical apparatus - Professional Medical Products, Inc.

PROFESSIONAL METABOLICS - Health care products - Light Force Spirulina Co.

PROFESSIONAL ONE - Hair care products - Demert & Dougherty, Inc.

PROFESSIONAL ONECOAT - Nail care products - Noxell Corp.

PROFESSIONAL PAINTER - Paints - Evans Paint

PROFESSIONAL PERCUSSION - Musical instruments - Santa Rosa Folk Guitar Co.

PROFESSIONAL PERFORMANCE - Cooking utensils–aluminum - Amco Corp.

PROFESSIONAL PERFORMANCE - Hair care products - Smap Manufacturing, Inc.

PROFESSIONAL PERFORMANCE - Novelty items - Imagineering Inc.

PROFESSIONAL PICK-PROOF POCKET POUCH - Wallet - Howard N. Geschwind

PROFESSIONAL POWER AUDIO - Audio equipment - George Technology

PROFESSIONAL PREPRESS SYSTEM - Computers - Professional Software Technologies, Inc.

PROFESSIONAL PRESS - Publisher's imprints - Professional Press Inc.

PROFESSIONAL PRIDE - Paints - Major Paint Co.

PROFESSIONAL PRODUCTS - Agricultural products - Terra International, Inc.

PROFESSIONAL PROFOOT PRODUCTS - Footcare products - Professional Product Research, Inc.

PROFESSIONAL QUEUEMANAGER - Computer software - Professional Software Technologies, Inc.

PROFESSIONAL REMEDIES - Vitamins and nutritional supplements - Jones Products International, Inc.

PROFESSIONAL RIVER BOATMAN - Sandals - ALP Sport Sandals

PROFESSIONAL RIVER GUIDE - Sandals - ALP Sport Sandals

PROFESSIONAL RODEO COWBOYS ASSOCIATION - Knives–pocket - Professional Rodeo Cowboys Association, Inc.

PROFESSIONAL RUBBER REROOF - Roofing materials - Master's Choice Inc.

PROFESSIONAL SALON - Computer software - Selectcomputer, Inc.

PROFESSIONAL SALON STYLE - Nail care products - Lee Pharmaceuticals

PROFESSIONAL SCHEDULER - Calendars - House of Doolittle

PROFESSIONAL SECRETS - Cosmetics - Cinema Secrets Inc.

PROFESSIONAL SECRETS - Dryers–hair - Caruso International, Inc.

PROFESSIONAL SERIES - Compressors–air - Campbell Group (Wayne Home Equipment Div.)

PROFESSIONAL SERIES - Electrical equipment - West Bend Co.

PROFESSIONAL SERIES - Electronic equipment - Sharp Electronics Corp.

PROFESSIONAL SERIES - Office supplies - McBee Loose Leaf Binders

PROFESSIONAL SERIES - Vitamins and nutritional supplements - Hi-Vidomin Laboratories Inc.

PROFESSIONAL SERIES - Water purification systems - Bruner Corp.

PROFESSIONAL SHELL - Computer software - Professional Software Technologies, Inc.

PROFESSIONAL SIGN MAKER, THE - Computer software ☆ - Sunburst Communications, Inc.

PROFESSIONAL SP STERLING - Plumbing fixtures–metal - Sterling Plumbing Group Inc.

PROFESSIONAL SPORTING GOODS - Water additives - Professional Sporting Goods, Inc.

PROFESSIONAL STEPS - Shoes - Lowell Shoe, Inc.

PROFESSIONAL STYLE NAIL GENIE - Beauty shop equipment - Protec International

PROFESSIONAL SUPREME - Shampoos - House of Lowell Inc.

PROFESSIONAL, THE - Brackets - Crawford Products Inc.

PROFESSIONAL, THE - Sporting goods - Outdoor Technologies Group

PROFESSIONAL, THE - Garbage disposal units–commercial - Roberts-Hamilton Co.

PROFESSIONAL TOWEL MILLS - Towels - Professional Towel Mills, Inc.

PROFESSIONAL WALNEIR INTERNATIONAL CORP. - Hair care products - Walneir International Corp.

PROFESSIONAL WOOD TONE PUTTY - Wood fillers - H.F. Staples & Co. Inc.

PROFESSIONAL WRITE - Computer software - Software Publishing Corp.

PROFESSIONAL WRITE PLUS - Computer software - Software Publishing Corp.

PROFESSIONAL WRITER'S PACKAGE, THE - Computer software - Emerging Technology Consultants Inc.

PROFESSIONALLY YOURS - Greeting cards - One Write Systems, Inc.

PROFESSIONALS - Cutlery - J.A. Henckels Zwillingswerk Inc.

PROFESSIONALS - Footwear–athletic - Wolverine World Wide, Inc.

PROFESSIONALS - Greeting cards ☆ - Thought Factory

PROFESSIONAL'S BRAND, THE - Eyeglasses - Logo Paris, Inc.

PROFESSIONAL'S CHOICE - Automotive parts and accessories - Automotive Parts Assoc., Inc.

PROFESSIONALS' CHOICE - Garden equipment - Emsco Inc.

PROFESSIONAL'S CHOICE - Hair care products ☆ - Jason Natural Products, Inc.

PROFESSIONAL'S CHOICE - Hardware - Allpro Corp.

PROFESSIONALS CHOICE - Sporting goods - Gerry Cosby & Co., Inc.

PROFESSIONALS' CHOICE, THE - Uniforms–athletic - Gerry Cosby & Co., Inc.

PROFESSIONAL'S CHOICE, THE - Pumps - Little Giant Pump Co.

PROFESSIONAL'S CHOICE, THE - Solder - Taracorp, Inc.

PROFESSIONAL'S PHORMULA - Cosmetics ☆ - Jason Natural Products, Inc.

PROFESSIONAL'S, THE - Artificial-fingernail glue - International Beauty Design, Inc.

PROFESSOR - Candy - R.M. Palmer Co.

PROFESSOR - Computer software - Individual Software Inc.

PROFESSOR CAYENNE'S - Health care products - Christopher Enterprises Inc.

PROFESSOR CONFIDENCE - Exercising equipment - Jugglebug

PROFESSOR DOS - Computer software - Individual Software Inc.

PROFESSOR PEP - Vitamins and nutritional supplements ☆ - Natural Balance, Inc.

PROFESSOR PROMPT - Computer software - Information Handling Services Inc.

PROFESSOR X - Books–comic ☆ - Marvel Entertainment Group, Inc.

PROFESSOR'S FRENCH, THE - Computer software - Professor Corp.

PROFESSOR'S PHYSICS, THE - Computer software - Professor Corp.

PROFFITT - Floor coverings–carpet and rugs ☆ - Proffitt Manufacturing Co.

PROFIBER - Health care products - Sherwood Medical Co.

PROFICIENCY - Floor coverings–carpet and rugs - Karastan-Bigelow Inc.

PROFICIENT - Cleaning preparations–household - Uncle Sam Chemical Co., Inc.

PROFICOLOR - Glass products - Seaply International

PROFIL D'AFRIK - Apparel–women's - Rothmour Investments, Inc.

PROFILATE - Pharmaceutical preparations - Alpha Therapeutic Corp.

PROFILATE H.P. - Pharmaceutical preparations - Alpha Therapeutic Corp.

PROFILE - Appliance parts - General Electric Co.

PROFILE+ - Automotive parts and accessories - G.T. Styling Inc.

PROFILE - Bread ☆ - Interstate Brands Corp.

PROFILE - Cables–fiber optic - W.L. Gore & Associates, Inc.

PROFILE - Clocks - General Time Corp. (Westclox/Seth Thomas Div.)

PROFILE - Computer peripheral equipment - Apple Computer Inc.

PROFILE - Computer software - Tandy Corp.

PROFILE - Cosmetics - Morris-Flamingo Inc.

PROFILE - Electronic equipment - Profile Systems

PROFILE - Eyeglasses - Art-Craft Optical Co.

PROFILE - Floor coverings - L.D. Brinkman & Co. Inc.

PROFILE - Floor coverings - Congoleum Corp.

PROFILE - Floor coverings–carpet and rugs - Patrick Carpet Mills

PROFILE - Floor coverings–tile - Collins & Aikman Corp.

PROFILE - Frames–picture ☆ - Art Americana

PROFILE - Furniture - Haworth, Inc.

PROFILE - Glassware - Garcia Group Inc.

PROFILE - Hair care products - European Tanning Systems Inc.

PROFILE - Hardware - Alumatic Corp. of America

PROFILE - Hearing aids - Beltone Electronics Corp.

PROFILE - Housewares - Oneida Ltd.

PROFILE - Luggage - Samsonite Corp.

PROFILE - Office furniture–wood - Anderson Desk Inc.

PROFILE - Pens - Paper Mate Co.

PROFILE - Pet products - Bioglan Animal Products Inc.

PROFILE - Plugs–ear - Vallen Safety Supply Co.

PROFILE - Projection screens - Draper Shade and Screen Co. Inc.

PROFILE - Rackets–tennis - Wilson Sporting Goods Co.

PROFILE - Sanitary napkins - Kimberly-Clark Corp.

PROFILE - Shaving preparations ☆ - Schick/Wilkinson

PROFILE - Shower stalls–metal - Kohler Co.

PROFILE - Skis - Nash Manufacturing Inc.

PROFILE - Toys–models - Morris Hobbies

PROFILE - Vitamins and nutritional supplements - Mcgaw, Inc.

PROFILE - Wheelchairs ☆ - Everest and Jennings International Ltd.

PROFILE - Window coverings ☆ - Hunter Douglas, Inc.

PROFILE - Wines - Merryvale Vineyards

PROFILE 2000 - Electronic equipment - Profile Systems

PROFILE 2002 - Lighting equipment - Profile Systems

PROFILE COMPETITION - Bicycles - Profile Racing Inc.

PROFILE EVALUATION SYSTEM - Computer software - Enrichment Resources, Inc.

PROFILE FORMULA XL - Cleaning preparations - Church and Dwight Co. Inc.

PROFILE GALLERY - Frames–picture - Acme Frame Products, Inc.

PROFILE INTIMATES - Apparel–women's - Jezebel-Renee of Hollywood

PROFILE PAVER - Blocks–paving - Britlin Co., Inc.

PROFILE PERFORMANCE - Pet products - Bioglan Animal Products Inc.

PROFILE SYSTEMS - Electronic equipment - Profile Systems

PROFILE, THE - Office supplies - Globe-Weis

PROFILE TWENTY - Furniture–public buildings - Myrtle Desk Co.

PROFILE V - Automotive parts and accessories - G.T. Styling Inc.

PROFILER - Measuring instruments - MOCON/Modern Controls, Inc.

PROFILER - Office supplies - Esselte Corp.

PROFILER, THE - Meters–water - Exidyne Instrumentation Technologies, Inc.

PROFILES - Apparel and accessories - Phillips-Van Heusen Corp.

PROFILES - Beauty aids - Windmere Corp.

PROFILES - Binders - Stephen R. Classe

PROFILES - Furniture - Drexel Heritage Furnishings, Inc.

PROFILES - Furniture - Stanley Furniture Co. Inc.

PROFILES - Furniture ☆ - Bassett Furniture Industries, Inc.

PROFILES - Furniture–children's ☆ - Child Craft Industries Inc.

PROFILES - Glassware–household ☆ - National Housewares

PROFILES - Hair care products - Belson Products

PROFILES - Jewelry - Alviti Tool & Die Inc.

PROFILES - Paper products - Georgia-Pacific Corp.

☆ = Now out of production

PROFILES - Sunglasses - Bonneau Co.
PROFILES - Uniforms–tailored - Angelica Uniform Group
PROFILES CAREER SEARCH SYSTEM - Computer software - Starpine Telepictures
PROFILEVIEW - Computer software - Extrude Home Corp.
PROFILEWOOD - Wood products - Ostermann & Scheiwe USA Inc.
PROFILM - Markers–felt-tip - Staedtler, Inc.
PROFILNINE HEAT - Pharmaceutical preparations - Alpha Therapeutic Corp.
PROFILVER - Glass products - Seaply International
PROFIN - Finishing agents - Daly's Inc.
PROFIND - Health care products ✰ - Medical Data Institute
PROFINE - Animal feed supplements ✰ - Central Soya Co. Inc.
PROFINESSE - Surgical instruments - Allergan, Inc.
PROFINISH - Iron - Black & Decker Corp.
PROFINISH - Paints - Wattyl Paint Corp.
PROFIT - Computer software ✰ - Performance Products Inc.
PROFIT ADVISORS, THE - Computer software - Profit Advisors, Inc.
PROFIT BOOSTER - Animal feeds - Alceco Inc.
PROFIT LOGIC - Computer software - Serex Information Systems, Inc.
PROFIT MANAGER - Calculators - Texas Instruments Inc.
PROFIT MENTOR - Computer software - Moss Adams L.L.P.
PROFIT PELLETS - Snack foods - Crispy Snacks
PROFIT PLUS - Printing presses - E.I. Dupont de Nemours and Co.
PROFIT-POWER SYSTEMS - Computer software - International Food Service Foundation
PROFIT RULER - Computer software - Prosolutions, Inc.
PROFIT SHARE - Computer software - SourceView Software International
PROFIT TOOLS - Educational materials - Bill Main & Associates
PROFIT TRACK - Animal feeds - Cargill, Inc.
PROFIT WARE - Computer software - Marvin W. Plunkett
PROFIT WATCH SYSTEM - Electrical industrial apparatus - Interface Systems, Inc.
PROFIT WATCH SYSTEMS - Electrical industrial apparatus - Interface Systems, Inc.
PROFIT-WHEEL - Calculators - Wescosa Inc.
PROFITRADER - Computer software - Sungard Investment Ventures, Inc.
PROFITTER - Computer software - Viewlogic Systems, Inc.
PROFLAM - Plastic molding compounds - Plastex Inc.
PROFLAVANOL - Vitamins and nutritional supplements - Usana, Inc.
PROFLAVINE SULFATE - Pharmaceutical preparations - City Chemical Corp.
PROFLEET - Computer software - Translogic Group
PROFLEX - Adhesives and sealants - Geocel Corp.
PROFLEX - Cleaning preparations - Worcester Brush Co.
PROFLEX - Electronics equipment - RTI Research Technology International
PROFLEX - Exercising equipment - Universal Gym Equipment, Inc.
PROFLEX - Golfing equipment - Northwestern Golf Co.
PROFLEX - Ink - Maxtek Inc.
PROFLEX - Paints ✰ - Wallauer Paint & Wallpaper
PROFLEX - Slippers - Atlas Trading Associates, Inc.
PROFLEX - Sporting goods - Wellington Leisure Products, Inc.
PROFLEX 5000 - Tools - Dico Products Corp.
PROFLEX HIGH VOLTAGE - Wet suits–rubber - Casad Manufacturing Corp.
PROFLICK - Cardboard - Mgwhiz, Inc.
PROFLIFIC MAX - Fertilizers ✰ - Terra Chemicals International
PROFLINE - Antennas–satellite ✰ - Antenna Technology Communications, Inc.
PROFLINE - Computer software - Schaffner EMC, Inc.
PROFLUX - Electronic equipment - Amicon, Inc.
PROFLY - Toy - GCI Products
PROFOAM - Medical apparatus - Dome Publishing Co., Inc.
PROFOLIO - Presentation folders, photo albums - Itoya of America, Ltd.
PROFONO - Recording label - Sony Disco Inc.
PROFORCE - Microphones - Sennheiser Electronic Corp.
PROFORM - Adhesives and sealants - National Gypsum Co.
PROFORM - Automotive parts and accessories - Polyproducts Corp.
PROFORM - Computer software - Wysong and Miles Co.
PROFORM - Condoms - Eckerd Corp.
PROFORM - Fabrics - Athol Corp.
PROFORM - Siding - Amerimark Building Products, Inc.
PROFORM - Sporting goods - Weider Health and Fitness
PROFORMA - Hair care products - Matrix Essentials, Inc.
PROFORMA-12 - Animal feeds - Farmers Feed Mill Inc.
PROFORMA-COMPLEX - Skin care products - Orjene Natural Cosmetics
PROFORMANCE - Chairs–wood ✰ - EAC Integrated Furniture Solutions
PROFORMANCE - Paints - Duron, Inc.
PROFORMANCE PLUS - Musical instruments - E-Mu Systems, Inc.

PROFORMER - Toys–automobiles - Mattel, Inc.
PROFORMIX - Computers - Proformix, Inc.
PROFORX - Bicycles parts - Proforx, Inc.
PROFOTO - Electronic equipment ✰ - Leedal Inc.
PROFOTO ACUTE FLASH GENERATOR - Photographic equipment - Mamiya America Corp.
PROFOTO COMPACT SELF-CONTAINED UNIT - Photographic equipment - Mamiya America Corp.
PROFOUND - Floor coverings–carpet and rugs ✰ - Walter Carpet Mills
PROFOUND - Lenses–optical - Ditto Industries Inc.
PROFOUND FRENCH VANILLA - Ice cream - Neal's
PROFOUND PARCHMENTS - Frames–picture - Walnut Valley Printery
PROFREE - Paints - Sherwin-Williams Automotive Finishes Corp.
PROFREE/GP - Ophthalmic goods - Allergan, Inc.
PROFRESH - Mouthwashes - Jon L. Richter
PROFUMI D' ITALIA - Wallpaper - Winfield Design Associates, Inc.
PROFUNDOL - Pharmaceutical preparations ✰ - Norgine Laboratories Inc.
PROFUSE - Medical apparatus - Lake Region Manufacturing Co., Inc.
PROFUSION - Computer peripheral equipment - Corollary, Inc.
PROFUSION - Tiles–ceramic - H & R Johnson Inc.
PROFUSION 21 - Hair care products - Protege Corp.
PROGAINE - Shampoos - Upjohn Co.
PROGARD - Fabrics - Athol Corp.
PROGARD - Footwear - Hershberg Shoe Co. Inc.
PROGARD - Laboratory apparatus - Elkay Products Co. Inc.
PROGARD - Photographic equipment - Enor Corp. Inc.
PROGARD - Veterinary pharmaceutical preparations - Intervet, Inc.
PROGARD PROMISE - Insurance agencies–health - Intervet, Inc.
PROGEAR 21 - Lubricant - Aerospace Lubricants Inc.
PROGELAN - Pharmaceutical preparations - Lannett Co. Inc.
PROGEN - Hair care products - Pro-Gen Corp.
PROGENA - Vitamins and nutritional supplements - Meditrend, Inc.
PROGENITOL - Pharmaceutical preparations - Wesley Pharmacal Co. Inc.
PROGENY - Computer software - Leeds and Northrup Co.
PROGENY - Office furniture–wood - Haskell of Pittsburgh, Inc.
PROGEST - Pharmaceutical preparations - C.O. Truxton Inc.
PROGEST-L - Pharmaceutical preparations - Lanpar Co.
PROGESTA - Pharmaceutical preparations ✰ - C.O. Truxton Inc.
PROGESTAJECT-50 - Pharmaceutical preparations ✰ - Merz Inc.
PROGESTAMATE - Hormone preparations - Ciba-Geigy Corp.
PROGESTASERT - Medical apparatus - Alza Corp.
PROGESTERONE - Health care products - Reese Chemical Co.
PROGESTRA - Pharmaceutical preparations - Andropharm Inc.
PROGESTRALATE - Pharmaceutical preparations - Wesley Pharmacal Co. Inc.
PROGESTRONAQ-LA - Pharmaceutical preparations ✰ - Central Pharmaceutical Inc.
PROGIATRIC - Vitamins and nutritional supplements ✰ - Nutrition Control Products
PROGIENIC - Clippers–barber - Sunbeam-Oster Household Products
PROGLIDE - Coatings - Regal Ware, Inc.
PROGLO - Pet products - New England Serum Co.
PROGLOVES - Gloves–rubber - Playtex Apparel, Inc.
PROGLYCEM - Pharmaceutical preparations - Medical Market Specialities Inc.
PROGLYCEM - Pharmaceutical preparations - Schering-Plough Healthcare Products
PROGLYDE - Chemical preparations - Dow Chemical Co.
PROGRAM - Nail care products - RTS Laboratories, Inc.
PROGRAM - Ophthalmic goods - Foremost Optical Products
PROGRAM I BASIC - Analgesics - Worldwide Products, Inc.
PROGRAM I CLEAR - Analgesics - Worldwide Products, Inc.
PROGRAM II BASIC - Cosmetics - Worldwide Products, Inc.
PROGRAM II CLEAR - Skin care products - Worldwide Products, Inc.
PROGRAM II SUNFADER - Sun screen preparations - Worldwide Products, Inc.
PROGRAM MANAGER - Computer software ✰ - Lassen Software Inc.
PROGRAM MANAGER PLUS - Computer software - Lassen Software Inc.
PROGRAM MASTER - Computer peripheral equipment - Mark Force Ltd.
PROGRAM SAVER - Irrigation equipment - Glen-Hilton Products, Inc.
PROGRAMAP - Computer software - Barnard Systems Co.
PROGRAMASTER - Photographic equipment - SP Systems/Saratons
PROGRAMATIX - Computer software - Lee S. Tannenbaum
PROGRAMAX 10 - Amplifiers–musical instrument - Peavey Electronics Corp.
PROGRAMIX - Computer peripheral equipment - Programix Corp.
PROGRAMMA BUHL - Electronic equipment - Buhl Industries, Inc.
PROGRAMME HOMME - Skin care products - Lancome
PROGRAMME MARTIN - Apparel and accessories - Programme Martin Inc.

PROGRAMMED MOTION - Electronics equipment - Grass Valley Group Inc.
PROGRAMMERS PRESS - Publisher's imprints - International Data Group, Inc.
PROGRAMMING THE POWER WITHIN - Publisher's imprints - Davenport Agency, Inc.
PROGREENS - Vitamins and nutritional supplements - James Cassidy
PROGRES - Skin care products - Lancome
PROGRES PLUS - Skin care products - Lancome
PROGRESS - Apparel and accessories - Utility Clothing Co. Warehouse, Ltd.
PROGRESS - Floor coverings–carpet and rugs ☆ - Walter Carpet Mills
PROGRESS - Frames–eyeglass - Pathway Optical Prods.
PROGRESS - Ice chests–metal - Louisville Tin and Stove
PROGRESS - Lighting fixtures - Progress Lighting Inc.
PROGRESS - Office supplies - Datacom Inc.
PROGRESS - Recording label - F & L Records
PROGRESS - Toys–models ☆ - Cox Products Inc.
PROGRESS - Vitamins and nutritional supplements - American Home Products Corp.
PROGRESS PALS - Toys ☆ - Trend Enterprises, Inc.
PROGRESSION - Computer software - Macola, Inc.
PROGRESSION - Cooking equipment–household - Noritake Co. Inc.
PROGRESSION - Floor coverings–carpet and rugs - Robertex Associates Inc.
PROGRESSION - Ophthalmic goods - Foremost Optical Products
PROGRESSION IV - Audio equipment - Pioneer Electronics USA Inc.
PROGRESSIONS + - Office furniture–metal - Rosejohnson
PROGRESSIONS II - House furnishings ☆ - Lea Industries Inc.
PROGRESSIV R - Optical machinery - Coburn Optical Industries Inc.
PROGRESSIVE - Floor coverings–carpet and rugs - Alexander Smith Carpets
PROGRESSIVE - Golfing equipment - Wilson Sporting Goods Co.
PROGRESSIVE - Labels–paper - Jazzology-GHB Records
PROGRESSIVE - Medical apparatus - Smith & Nephew Rolyan, Inc.
PROGRESSIVE - Office supplies - McDonald Products
PROGRESSIVE - Ophthalmic goods - Foremost Optical Products
PROGRESSIVE - Wallpaper - Hamilton Adams Imports Ltd.
PROGRESSIVE DIAGNOSTICS CO - Computer software - Progressive Diagnostics Co.
PROGRESSIVE ELEGANCE - Lenses–optical - Signet Armorlite, Inc.
PROGRESSIVE INTERNATIONAL - Kitchen utensils–aluminum - Progressive International Corp.
PROGRESSIVE SUSPENSION - Motorcycle parts and accessories - Progressive Suspension, Inc.
PROGRESSIVES - Musical instrument accessories - GHS Strings
PROGRESSO - Soups–canned - Progresso Quality Foods
PROGRESSO HEALTHY CLASSICS - Soups–canned - Pet Inc.
PROGRESSO SODIUM WATCH - Soups–canned - Pet Inc.
PROGRESSO TO:GO - Food products - Pet Inc.
PROGRESSOR - Optical scanners–computer - Titmus Optical, Inc.
PROGRESSUS - Kitchen utensils–aluminum - Progressus Co.
PROGRIP - Musical instrument accessories - D'Andrea Manufacturing Co. Inc.
PROGRO - Garden equipment - Austram, Inc.
PROGROW STEP - Fertilizers - Scotts Co. (Organics Business Group)
PROGUARD - Computer software - Vasco Data Security, Inc.
PROGUARD - Dryers–hair - Helen of Troy Corp.
PROGUARD - Fungicides - Proguard, Inc.
PROGYNON - Hormone preparations ☆ - Schering-Plough Healthcare Products
PROHEAL - Pharmaceutical preparations - Johnson & Johnson
PROHEAT - Fuel fired preheaters - Teleflex Inc.
PROHEAT - Heaters–space - Master Appliance Corp.
PROHEAT - Heating pads–electric - Prism Technologies
PROHEAT - Massage products - Pollenex Corp.
PROHIBIT - Surgical supplies - Medline, Industries, Inc.
PROHIBIT - Veterinary pharmaceutical preparations - Agri Laboratories, Ltd.
PROHIM - Pharmaceutical - Baker Norton Pharmaceuticals, Inc.
PROHIST-8 - Pharmaceutical preparations - Econo Med Pharmaceuticals Inc.
PROHOLD - Hardware - Proprietary Main, Inc.
PROHOOK - Bowling balls - Columbia 300 Inc.
PROHORSE - Sawhorses - Prohorse Inc.
PROHOST - Carts - Hostar International Inc.
PROHUNTER - Sporting goods - Simmons Acquisition Corp.
PROIMAGE - Printers–computer - Varitronic Systems, Inc.
PROINI - Paper–newsprint - Petallides Publishing, Inc.
PROINVERSION - Health care products - Unicare Health & Fitness Co.
PROJAR - Electrical equipment - Schneider Optics, Inc.
PROJECT - Audio equipment - Sumiko Inc.
PROJECT - Chimes ☆ - Nutone Inc.
PROJECT 3 - Recording label - Essex Entertainment Inc.
PROJECT-A-MARK - Markers–felt-tip ☆ - Marsh Co.

PROJECT-A-SCOPE - Projection screens - Arthur Brown and Bros. Inc.
PROJECT-A-SCOPE - Toys - Brumberger Co. Inc.
PROJECT-A-TYPE - Decals and transfers ☆ - Letraset USA Inc.
PROJECT AXIS - Computer software - Frontrunner, LLC
PROJECT-BOARD - Computer software ☆ - Tandy Corp.
PROJECT BRIDGE - Computer storage devices - Applied Business Technology Corp.
PROJECT BRIDGE MODELER - Computer software - Applied Business Technology Corp.
PROJECT BUDDY - Ladders–wood - Werner Co.
PROJECT CONVERTER - Computer software - Selfware, Inc.
PROJECT E - Apparel and accessories - Project E
PROJECT E EVOLUTION IN CLOTHING - Apparel and accessories - Project E, Inc.
PROJECT EARTH - Educational toy - TCA Ground Inc.
PROJECT FINISHERS - Pottery products - Duncan Enterprises
PROJECT GEMINI - Toys - Park Plastics Co.
PROJECT GREEN - Paper–tissue - Ashdun Inc.
PROJECT HABITAT - Pamphlets - American Cyanamid Co.
PROJECT INVESTIGATOR - Computer software - Independent Project Analysis, Inc.
PROJECT KOM 10 - Bicycles - Schwinn Cycling & Fitness Inc.
PROJECT LEAD: HIGH EXPECTATIONS ! - Educational kits - Links Foundation Inc.
PROJECT LIFE - Programmed-instruction equipment - Instructional Industries Inc.
PROJECT MANAGEMENT DIRECTOR - Computer software ☆ - Welcom
PROJECT MASTER - Computer software - SourceView Software International
PROJECT-O-STAND - Electronic equipment ☆ - Da-Lite Screen Co. Inc.
PROJECT OVERKILL - Computer storage devices–optical - Konami (America) Inc.
PROJECT PACKS - Hydrogen peroxide - Black & Decker Corp.
PROJECT PAK - Steel-wool pads ☆ - International Steel Wool Corp.
PROJECT PAPER - Paper - Loose Ends
PROJECT PARTNERS - Tools–hand-operated - Allied Wholesale Inc.
PROJECT PROMETHEUS - Games ☆ - Mayfair Games, Inc.
PROJECT SAFETY - Educational materials - Board of Regents of the University of Texas
PROJECT: SPACE STATION - Computer software ☆ - Accolade Inc.
PROJECT STAR - Computer software - Hartley Courseware Inc.
PROJECT TIME - Computer software - Selfware, Inc.
PROJECTACARTRIDGE - Electronic equipment ☆ - AVES Audio Visual Systems Inc.
PROJECTACHROME - Pens - Faber-Castell Corp.
PROJECTAPIX - Televisions - Projectapix-II
PROJECTAVISION - Video equipment - Projectavision, Inc.
PROJECTEXCHANGE - Computer software - Information Management Services
PROJECTINA - Projectors–photographic ☆ - Heitz Service Corp.
PROJECTION - Chalk ☆ - Binney & Smith Inc.
PROJECTION - Floor coverings–carpet and rugs ☆ - Walter Carpet Mills
PROJECTO-AID - Electronic equipment - GAF Corp.
PROJECTO-BOARD - Electronic equipment - Telex Communications, Inc.
PROJECTO-CARBON - Electronic equipment - GAF Corp.
PROJECTO-COLOR - Pencils ☆ - Koh-I-Noor, Inc.
PROJECTO-EDITOR - Projectors–photographic - Kalart Victor Corp.
PROJECTO-LITE - Electronic equipment - GAF Corp.
PROJECTO MAT - Projectors–photographic - Brumberger Co. Inc.
PROJECTO-O-MATIC - Electronic equipment - Apollo Audiovisual Div.
PROJECTO-O-MOUNT - Electronic equipment - GAF Corp.
PROJECTO PERMOUNT - Electronic equipment - GAF Corp.
PROJECTO-PRINTER - Electronic equipment - GAF Corp.
PROJECTO-ROLL - Electronic equipment - GAF Corp.
PROJECTO-SCREEN - Electronic equipment - GAF Corp.
PROJECTO-VIEWFOIL - Electronic equipment - GAF Corp.
PROJECTOR - Golf clubs - UT Golf
PROJECTORS - Toys - Toy Biz, Inc.
PROJECTPAK - Computer software - Tradesoft, Inc.
PROJECTRAK - Computer software - Eden Communications
PROJECTS - Frames–picture - Markuse Corp.
PROJECTS FOR PRESCHOOLERS - Publisher's imprints - McClanahan Book Co., Inc.
PROJECTS ON-LINE - Computer software - Projects On-Line, LLC
PROJECTSERVER - Computer software - Micro-Frame Technologies, Inc.
PROJECTTEAM - Computer software - Micro-Frame Technologies, Inc.
PROJECTWISE - Computer software - Bentley Systems, Inc.

☆ = Now out of production

PROJECTWORKS - Computer software - Bechtel Group, Inc.
PROJEK - Furniture - Acme-Lite Manufacturing Co.
PROJEKTRIX 42 - Furniture - Acme-Lite Manufacturing Co.
PROJET - Boats - Zodiac of North America
PROJEX - Tools ☆ - Bondex International Inc.
PROJX - Fabric softeners - Berkshire Corp.
PROKART - Containers–trash - Aggressive Industries Inc.
PROKEDS - Apparel–athletic - Fuqua Industries Inc.
PROKER - Hair coloring preparations ☆ - Ladds-Nessler Co. Inc.
PROKETAZINE - Pharmaceutical preparations ☆ - Wyeth-Ayerst Laboratories
PROKEY - Computer software - CE Software, Inc.
PROKEY - Computer software - Prohome, Inc.
PROKEY - Computer software - Rosesoft
PROKINE - Pharmaceutical preparations - Hoechst-Roussel Pharmaceuticals Inc.
PROKLAR - Pharmaceutical preparations - Forest Pharmaceuticals Inc.
PROKLENE - Cleaning preparations ☆ - Stoner Inc.
PROKNIT - Shirts - Cintas Corp.
PROKNITS - Crocheted and knitted items - Beldoch Industries Corp.
PROKO-LITE - Paints ☆ - Proko Industries Inc.
PROKOTE - Paints - Dunn Edwards Corp.
PROKOTE - Paper products - Georgia-Pacific Corp.
PROKUT 788 - Abrasive products ☆ - Park Metallurgical Corp.
PROLAB - Nutritional supplements - Prolab Nutrition, Inc.
PROLACE - Pharmaceutical preparations - Vita-Fore Products Co.
PROLAGEN-C - Pharmaceutical preparations - Metra Biosystems, Inc.
PROLAMINE - Vitamins and nutritional supplements ☆ - Thompson Medical Co., Inc.
PROLASTIC - Asphalt - Gardner Asphalt Corp.
PROLECTRIC - Heating equipment - Surface Combustion, Inc.
PROLEEN - Health care products - Ray Drug Co.
PROLENE - Fertilizers - Omnicology, Inc.
PROLENE - Thread - Blue Mountain Industries, Inc.
PROLEUKIN-PEG - Pharmaceutical preparations - Cetus Corp.
PROLIANT - Computers - Compaq Computer Corp.
PROLIB - Computer software - Interface Technologies Inc.
PROLIFE - Nail care products - Revlon Consumer Products Corp.
PROLIFE 28 - Flowers, plants, and seeds - Armenpharm Ltd.
PROLIFICS - Computer software - Jyacc, Inc.
PROLIFIXX - Shampoos - KMS Research Inc.
PROLIFORCE - Hair care products - KMS Research Inc.
PROLIFREE - Hair care products - KMS Research Inc.
PROLIFT - Medical apparatus - Hartwell Medical Corp.
PROLIMAXX - Hair care products - KMS Research Inc.
PROLIMIN GOLD - Hair care products - KMS Research Inc.
PROLIMIST - Hair care products ☆ - KMS Research Inc.
PROLIMIST PURE - Hair care products - KMS Research Inc.
PROLIN - Insecticides - Cenol Co. Inc.
PROLINE - Apparel and accessories - Signal Knitwear Co.
PROLINE - Bathroom accessories - Kinkead/Tub/Shower Doors
PROLINE - Building materials - Hoffman
PROLINE - Cases–musical instrument - Calzone Case Co.
PROLINE - Garden equipment - Permaloc Aluminum Edging
PROLINE - Garden equipment - Permaloc Corp.
PROLINE - Hair care products - A. Eickert Co., Inc.
PROLINE - Medical apparatus - Smith & Nephew Dyonics, Inc.
PROLINE - Milk - Borden, Inc.
PROLINE - Plastics - George C. Oelrich
PROLINE - Rakes - North American Marketing Corp.
PROLINE - Shingles–asphalt or tar - Georgia-Pacific Corp.
PROLINE - Sporting goods - Lee Tennis Products
PROLINE - Stoves–wood-burning - Daka Corp.
PROLINE - Tripods–photographic - Sima Products Corp.
PROLINE - Vacuum cleaners and accessories - General Floorcraft Inc.
PROLINE - Water-ski equipment - Connelly Skis, Inc.
PROLINE - Windows–plastic - Rolscreen Co.
PROLINE II - Cases–musical instrument - Calzone Case Co.
PROLINE BILLIARD TABLES - Pool tables - Altamonte Billiard Factory Inc.
PROLINE COVER - Sporting goods - Kach Ka
PROLINE II - Amplifiers ☆ - BGW Systems Inc.
PROLINE SERIES 5 - Computer software - Printronix, Inc.
PROLINE SHADOW - Shingles–asphalt or tar - Georgia-Pacific Corp.
PROLINE USA - Golfing equipment ☆ - John Rouzee Green Co., Inc.
PROLINER - Plastics film - Mobil Oil Corp.
PROLINK - Computer software - Micro Motion Inc.
PROLINK - Computer software - Northland Strategics, Inc.

PROLINK - Electronic equipment - David Levy Co., Inc.
PROLINK - Electronic equipment - Monster Cable Products, Inc.
PROLINX - Computer hardware - Dowelanco
PROLINX - Golfing equipment - Landmark Golf Products, Inc.
PROLITE - Bicycles - Ritchey Design Inc.
PROLITE - Flashlights - Accutec Inc.
PROLITE - Hardware - McGuire-Nicholas Co., Inc.
PROLITE - Jewelry - Providence Chain Co.
PROLITE - Shoes ☆ - Hyde Athletic Industries Inc.
PROLITE WAFER BUTTERSCOTCH - Health care products - Healthwatchers System
PROLIXIN - Pharmaceutical preparations - Bristol-Myers Squibb Co.
PROLL - Toys–musical - Proll Toy Co.
PROLL-O-TONE - Toys–musical - Proll Toy Co.
PROLOC - Lockers–metal - Phelps-Tionton Millwork, Llc.
PROLOC - Vinyl - Variform, Inc.
PROLOG-CRS - Computer software - E.R. Squibb & Sons, Inc.
PROLOGUE - Apparel–women's ☆ - Bobbie Brooks Inc.
PROLOGUE - Floor coverings–carpet and rugs ☆ - Masland Corp.
PROLOGUE - Microphones - Shure Brothers, Inc.
PROLOGUE - Tires–bicycles - Schwinn Cycling & Fitness Inc.
PROLOID - Pharmaceutical preparations ☆ - Parke-Davis
PROLON - Apparel and accessories - Duofold Inc.
PROLON - Cooking equipment–household ☆ - Smart Kids
PROLON - Nail care products - Revlon Consumer Products Corp.
PROLON - Plastics - Teknor Color Co.
PROLON - Trays - National Plastics Corp.
PROLON - Yarn - Ronile, Inc.
PROLONG - Chemical preparations - Molecular Probes, Inc.
PROLONG - Chemical preparations - Resource Recovery Systems, Inc.
PROLONG - Christmas-tree preservative - Plantabbs Products
PROLONG - Fertilizers ☆ - J.R. Simplot Co.
PROLONG - Sporting goods - Major Racquet Strings International
PROLONWARE - Dinnerware–glass - Prolon Dinnerware
PROLOPRIM - Antiseptics - Burroughs Wellcome Co.
PROLOX - Security equipment ☆ - Intercontinental Enterprises Ltd.
PROLUTIN - Pharmaceutical preparations ☆ - Hyrex Pharmaceuticals
PROLUX - Lenses–projection - Schneider Optics, Inc.
PROLUX - Paints - Lasting Paints Inc.
PROLUX - Pet products - Classic Products
PROLUX - Projectors–photographic - Prolux, Corp.
PROLUX LCD LIGHT ENGINE - Electrical equipment - Prolux, Corp.
PROLYNX - Computer hardware - Varitronic Systems, Inc.
PROM - Hair care products - Gillette Co.
PROMACHLOR - Tranquilizers ☆ - Geneva Generics Inc.
PROMACOT - Pharmaceutical preparations - C.O. Truxton Inc.
PROMACSYS - Computer software - Promedex Technologies, Inc.
PROMADELER - Hobby kits - Revell-Monogram, Inc.
PROMAGIC - Electronic equipment - Sima Products Corp.
PROMAGIC - Pet products ☆ - National Scent Co.
PROMAGNA - Footwear - Fila USA, Inc.
PROMAKER - Golfing equipment - Ram Golf Corp.
PROMAN - Computer software - Midstream Inc.
PROMANAGER - Computer software - Detroit Diesel Corp.
PROMAP - Computer software ☆ - TSR Technologies, Inc.
PROMAPAR - Tranquilizers ☆ - Parke-Davis
PROMAPPING - Computer software - Software Solutions of Illinois, Inc.
PROMAR - Paints - Sherwin-Williams Automotive Finishes Corp.
PROMAR - Rodenticides - Hacco, Inc./Loveland Industries, Inc.
PROMAR - Vitamins and nutritional supplements - Marlop Pharmaceuticals Inc.
PROMARK - Automotive parts and accessories - APS Big A
PROMARK - Pet products - Doane Products Co.
PROMARK - Sporting goods - Promark
PROMASK - Paper goods - Advocate Printing, Inc.
PROMASTER - Computer software - Pro Series Software, Inc.
PROMASTER - Gloves - Alenax Corp.
PROMASTER - Lawn mowers - Ariens Co.
PROMASTER - Photographic equipment - Photographic Research Organization Inc.
PROMASTER - Semiconductors - Data I/O Corp.
PROMASTER - Watches - Citizen Watch Co. of America Inc.
PROMASTER PLUS - Exercising equipment - Ovation Inc.
PROMASTER SPECTRUM 7 - Photographic equipment - Photographic Research Organization Inc.
PROMASTERS - Knives–hunting ☆ - Camillus Cutlery Co.
PROMAT - Archery equipment - Impact Industries Inc.

PROMATE - Tools - Truecraft Tools
PROMATE - Tranquilizers - Kay Pharmacal Co. Inc.
PROMATEK - Health care products - Promatek Medical Systems Inc.
PROMATRON - Health care products - Promatek Medical Systems Inc.
PROMATS - Sporting goods - Promats, Inc.
PROMAX - Food products - Central Soya Co. Inc.
PROMAX MOLDED HEEL CUSHIONS - Health care products - Professional Foot Care Products Inc.
PROMAXX - Tools–stonecutting - Ingersoll-Rand Co.
PROMAZ - Pharmaceutical preparations ☆ - Keene Pharmaceuticals Inc.
PROMECTANE - Hair care products - Helene Curtis Industries Inc.
PROMED - First aid kits - Monaco Import/Export Inc.
PROMED - Video production - U.S. Magnetics Corp.
PROMEDIX - Stretchers - Pro Med, Inc.
PROMEGA - Pumps–water - Lomart Industries
PROMEGA - Vitamins and nutritional supplements ☆ - Parke-Davis
PROMENA - Vitamins and nutritional supplements - Bioenergy Nutrient's Inc.
PROMENADE - Cleaning preparations - S.C. Johnson & Son, Inc.
PROMENADE - Computer software - Quantum Computer Services Inc.
PROMENADE - Flatware - Utica Cutlery Co.
PROMENADE - Floor coverings ☆ - Congoleum Corp.
PROMENADE - Floor coverings–carpet and rugs ☆ - Karastan-Bigelow Inc.
PROMENADE - Floor coverings–tile ☆ - Monarch Tile Inc.
PROMENADE - Furniture - Krueger International, Inc.
PROMENADE - Furniture - Lyon-Shaw Inc.
PROMENADE - Furniture ☆ - Halcyon Inc.
PROMENADE - Furniture ☆ - Stanley Furniture Co. Inc.
PROMENADE - Kitchenware–earthenware ☆ - Arita Sales Co. Inc.
PROMENADE - Organs–musical instrument - Midi Music Center, Inc.
PROMENADE - Rings–jewelry - Artcarved Inc.
PROMENADE - Wallpaper - Capital Carousel Inc.
PROMENADE - Wallpaper - K.M.L. Industries
PROMENADE II - Walking footwear - Autry Industries Inc.
PROMENAIRE II - Wallpaper ☆ - Manuscreens
PROMENAIRE III - Wallpaper - Manuscreens
PROMEND - First aid kits - Altaire Pharmaceuticals, Inc.
PROMENE - Pharmaceutical preparations ☆ - Hyrex Pharmaceuticals
PROMENSIN-F - Pharmaceutical preparations - G.O. Spanner Inc.
PROMENU - Computer software - Cain International Corp.
PROMESA - Candles - Miracle Candle Co.
PROMESH - Apparel–athletic - InSport International Inc.
PROMESSE - Flatware - Couzon USA
PROMET - Cold remedies - Legere Pharmaceuticals Inc.
PROMETABS - Pharmaceutical preparations - Viobin U.S.A.
PROMETAL - Computer software - Extrude Home Corp.
PROMETH - Pharmaceutical preparations - Barre-National, Inc.
PROMETHAPAR - Pharmaceutical preparations - Parmed Pharmaceuticals, Inc.
PROMETHEAN - Burial caskets - Batesville Casket Co., Inc.
PROMETHEGAN - Health care products - G and W Laboratories Inc.
PROMETHIAN - Furniture ☆ - White Furniture Co.
PROMETHYASUL - Pet products ☆ - Wardley Corp.
PROMETOL - Pharmaceutical preparations - Viobin U.S.A.
PROMETRIUM - Pharmaceutical preparations - Schering Corp.
PROMEX - Pharmaceutical preparations ☆ - Lemmon Co.
PROMID - Rackets–racquetball - Head Sports USA
PROMIDI - Electronic equipment - Systems Design Associates, Inc.
PROMIGAN - Pharmaceutical preparations ☆ - Hyrex Pharmaceuticals
PROMINAR - Lenses–photographic ☆ - Navitar, Inc.
PROMINE - Food products - Central Soya Co. Inc.
PROMINENCE - Beds, mattresses, and box springs - King Koil Licensing Co., Inc.
PROMINENCE - Floor coverings - Congoleum Corp.
PROMINENCE - Shingles - Owens Corning
PROMINENCE - Shingles - Owens Corning Fiberglass Technology Inc.
PROMINENCE - Tiles–ceramic - GTE Products Corp.
PROMINENCE - Tiles–ceramic ☆ - American Olean Tile Co.
PROMINENCE COUNTRY LIFE - Wallpaper - J. Josephson, Inc.
PROMINENT - Floor coverings–carpet and rugs - Columbus Mills, Inc.
PROMINENT - Floor coverings–carpet and rugs ☆ - World Carpets, Inc.
PROMINIC - Pharmaceutical preparations - Republic Drug Co. Inc.
PROMINICAL - Pharmaceutical preparations - Republic Drug Co. Inc.
PROMIRA - Cameras - Lucht Engineering Inc.
PROMISE - Bags–laundry - Joe Boxer Corp.
PROMISE - Clocks - General Time Corp. (Westclox/Seth Thomas Div.)
PROMISE - Dinnerware - Corning Inc.

PROMISE - Floor coverings–carpet and rugs ☆ - Masland Corp.
PROMISE - Floor waxes - Twi-Laq Industries Inc.
PROMISE - Health care products - Scott Health Care
PROMISE - House furnishings - Dan River Inc.
PROMISE - Margarine - Lever Brothers Co. Inc.
PROMISE - Ophthalmic goods - Foremost Optical Products
PROMISE - Recording label - QCA Inc.
PROMISE - Tableware–china ☆ - Lenox, Inc.
PROMISE - Toothpaste - Block Drug Co., Inc.
PROMISE EXTRA LIGHT - Margarine - Lever Brothers Co. Inc.
PROMISE ULTRA - Margarine - Lever Brothers Co. Inc.
PROMISE ULTRA - Oils–edible - Van Den Bergh Foods Co.
PROMISE ULTRA FAT-FREE - Margarine - Van Den Bergh Foods Co.
PROMISED LAND - Cheese ☆ - Churny Co., Inc.
PROMISED LAND - Turkeys - Sunday House Foods Inc.
PROMISED LAND D-A-I-R-Y - Ice cream - Promised Land Dairy, Inc.
PROMISES - Floor coverings–carpet and rugs - Calladium & Marglen
PROMISES - Floor coverings–carpet and rugs ☆ - Galaxy Carpet Mills Inc.
PROMISES - Furniture - Bean Station Furniture Factory Inc.
PROMISES - Furniture - Stanley Furniture Co. Inc.
PROMISES OF PRAYER - Glassware–household - Shirley A. Felice
PROMIST - Cough medicines - Whitby Pharmaceuticals, Inc.
PROMIX, THE - Apparel–women's - Won Young Kim
PROMJET - Computer peripheral equipment - Westec Research Corp.
PROM'NAID - Traction apparatus–medical ☆ - Lossing Orthopedic Co.
PROMO - Bicycles ☆ - Raleigh USA Bicycle Co.
PROMO ACCENTS - Figurines - Promo Accents by Val, Ltd.
PROMO COLLECTION, THE - Recording label - Megatrax Production Music, Inc.
PROMO ONLY - Recording label - Promo Only, Inc.
PROMO-PLUS - Vinyl - Spartan International, Inc.
PROMO SEEDS - Flowers, plants, and seeds - Panta Co.
PROMOCAST - Publisher's imprints - Radyne Comstream Corp.
PROMOCHLOR - Pharmaceutical preparations ☆ - Legere Pharmaceuticals Inc.
PROMODEL - Pet products ☆ - Pet Lift
PROMOFORM - Pharmaceutical preparations - G.O. Spanner Inc.
PROMOLD - Manicure preparations - Professional Foot Care Products Inc.
PROMONTORY - Railings–wood - Mansion Industries Inc.
PROMOPRO - Games - D. Allan Such & Associates, Inc.
PROMOSOY - Food products - Central Soya Co. Inc.
PROMOSUITE - Computer software - Broadcast Manager, Inc.
PROMOSYSTEM - Computer software - Crawford Communications, Inc.
PROMOTER - Frames–eyeglass ☆ - Universal/Univis Inc.
PROMOTER - Pens - National Pen & Pencil Co.
PROMOTION - Integrated circuits - Alliance Semiconductor Corp.
PROMOTION PLUS - Signs - Fasteners for Retail, Inc.
PROMOTOR - Dryers–hair - Andis Co.
PROMOUNT - Lubricants - Stoner Inc.
PROMOUNT - Television cabinets - Luxor
PROMOVES - Footwear - Promoves, Inc.
PROMOW - Lawn mowers - Promow, Inc.
PROMOX - Health care products - Suppositoria Laboratories
PROMPT - Computer software ☆ - Gessler Publishing Co., Inc.
PROMPT - Health care products ☆ - Procter & Gamble Co.
PROMPT MASTER - Computer software - Comprehensive Video Supply Corp.
PROMPT PAYMASTER - Computer software - Genesis Software, Inc.
PROMPTUS - Computer software and hardware - Promptus Communications Inc.
PROMPTUS 99 - Filing cabinets–metal - Kardex Systems, Inc.
PROMS AND PROMISES - Apparel and accessories ☆ - Edison Brothers Stores, Inc.
PROMSTAR FUN - Toys - Tonka Corp.
PROMYLIN - Pharmaceutical preparations - Shear Kershman Laboratories Inc.
PROMYLIN HL 4 - Pharmaceutical preparations - Shear Kershman Laboratories Inc.
PROMYLIN HL 10 - Pharmaceutical preparations - Shear Kershman Laboratories Inc.
PROMYLIN HL 16 - Pharmaceutical preparations - Shear Kershman Laboratories Inc.
PRONAC - Astringents ☆ - E. Fougera & Co. Inc.
PRONAIL - Nail care products - Pronail Manufacturing
PRONEL - Paint rollers - E-Z Paintr Corp.
PRONESTYL - Pharmaceutical preparations - Bristol-Myers Squibb Co.
PRONET - Computer software ☆ - Cerner Corp.
PRONG - Archery equipment - Martin Archery Inc.

☆ = Now out of production

PRONGHORN HUNTER - Archery equipment ☆ - Bear Archery Inc.
PRONIC - Computer peripheral equipment - Zenith Electronics Corp.
PRONIT - Recording label - Polish Record & Video Center of America
PRONO - Desserts - Dietary Specialties
PRONOUNCER - Sound equipment - Microlog Corp.
PRONT-O-RONI - Pizzas–mixes - Pronto Food Kitchens Inc.
P.R.O.N.T.I. - Apparel–men's - Phita International Corp.
PRONTO - Adhesives and sealants - Smith & Nephew Inc. (Rehabilitation Div.)
PRONTO - Apparel–women's - Sportswear by Pronto
PRONTO - Bicycles - Ross Bicycles USA, Ltd.
PRONTO - Block anchors ☆ - ITW Ramset/Red Head
PRONTO - Brushes–paint ☆ - Charles Paint Research Inc.
PRONTO - Cabinets - Joyce International Inc.
PRONTO - Cameras ☆ - Polaroid Corp.
PRONTO - Cameras–video - Good Times Home Video Corp.
PRONTO - Concrete products - Sika Corp.
PRONTO - Cosmetics - Spornette International, Inc.
PRONTO - Food products - Ferrara Food Co., Inc.
PRONTO - Food products ☆ - Borden/Prince Foods (Canning Div.)
PRONTO - Locks–padlocks ☆ - Fort Lock Corp.
PRONTO - Measuring and dispensing pumps - B. Braun Medical Inc.
PRONTO - Meat products–canned - Burke Marketing Corp.
PRONTO! - Pencils - Faber-Castell Corp.
PRONTO - Pharmaceutical preparations - Del Pharmaceuticals, Inc.
PRONTO - Pizzas–mixes - Pronto Food Kitchens Inc.
PRONTO - Plastics–laminated ☆ - Plaskolite Inc.
PRONTO - Refried beans - Inland Empire Foods
PRONTO - Telescopes - Tele Vue Optics Inc.
PRONTO - Tools–garden - True Temper Hardware Inc.
PRONTO - Track lighting ☆ - Cooper Industries, Inc.
PRONTO CAFFE - Beverages ☆ - Conair Corp.
PRONTO DRAFTER - Computer software - Vision Systems, Inc.
PRONTO FAST PATCH - Adhesives and sealants ☆ - Consolidated Coatings Corp.
PRONTO FORNO - Pizza mix - Parmalat USA Corp.
PRONTO GEL - Analgesics ☆ - Del Pharmaceuticals, Inc.
PRONTO II - Toys ☆ - Nylint Toy Corp.
PRONTO SONAR - Cameras ☆ - Polaroid Corp.
PRONTO SPANISH - Computer software - Bilingual Software Co.
PRONTO V - Wallpaper - Norwall Wallcoverings
PRONTORONI - Food products - Burke Marketing Corp.
PRONUTRIENTS - Vitamins and nutritional supplements - Vyrex Corp.
PROOF - Pet products - Handley Corp.
PROOF & BAKE - Bakery products–frozen - Quaker Oats Co.
PROOF IS IN THE PASTRY, THE - Pies–fresh - Razzleberry Foods Corp.
PROOF PACK - Adhesives - Permacel
PROOFILE - Photographic equipment - SP Systems/Saratons
PROOFPOSITIVE - Printing trades machinery - Supermac Technology
PROOFREADER - Computer software - E. David & Associates
PROP - Shaving preparations - Mennen Co.
PROP-A-BYE BABY - Pillows - Lorne Jason Clute
PROP-A-HIST - Pharmaceutical preparations - Bolan Pharmaceutical Inc.
PROP-A-SEAT - Infant product ☆ - Evenflo Co.
PROP AND PLAY - Toys - Calapitter Creations, Inc.
PROP-IT - Collapsible stand - S.A. Richards, Inc.
PROP-MASTER - Automotive parts and accessories - Rockwell International Corp.
PROP N POCKETS - Infant product - Leachco Inc.
PROP-O-SURG - Antiseptics ☆ - Gena Laboratories Inc.
PROP-O'S - Infant product - Leachco Inc.
PROP-STOP - Outboard motor part - K & C Industries Inc.
PROP STOW - Propellers - Mercury Hi-Performance Group
PROPA PH - Pharmaceutical preparations - Del Pharmaceuticals, Inc.
PROPABLES - Playground equipment - Calapitter Creations, Inc.
PROPAC - Computer software - Notis Systems, Inc.
PROPAC - Health care products - Sherwood Medical Co.
PROPACAST GT - Packaging materials - Borden Brands Foodservice Co.
PROPACET 100 - Pharmaceutical preparations - Lemmon Co.
PROPACK - Faucets - Masco Corp. (Plumbing Products Div.)
PROPACK - Film - Fuji Photo Film USA Inc.
PROPACK - Lead products - Hybrivet Systems, Inc.
PROPACK - Machinery - Polyfoam Products, Inc.
PROPADRINE - Pharmaceutical preparations ☆ - Merck & Co., Inc. (Merck Research Laboratories)
PROPAEDIA - Computer software - Encyclopaedia Britannica Inc.
PROPAFED - Pharmaceutical preparations ☆ - Whitby Pharmaceuticals, Inc.

PROPAGANDA - Games - Wff'n Proof Learning Games Associates
PROPAGE - Business forms and stationery - Moore Business Forms, Inc.
PROPAGE - Paper - Rediform
PROPAGEST - Antihistamine preparations - Carnick Laboratories Inc.
PROPAGON-S - Pharmaceutical preparations - G.O. Spanner Inc.
PROPAHIST - Pharmaceutical preparations - Glaxo Wellcome Inc.
PROPAK - Amplifiers - AMS Industries Calrec
PROPAK - Packaging material - W.R. Grace & Co.
PROPALETTE - Computer software - Kollmorgen Instruments Corp.
PROPAN - Pharmaceutical preparations - C.O. Truxton Inc.
PROPANADE - Health care products - Halsey Drug Co. Inc.
PROPAQ ENCORE - Medical apparatus - Protocol Systems, Inc.
PROPARTNER - Labeling machinery - Varitronic Systems, Inc.
PROPASTA - Pasta - Pasta Pacifica Inc.
PROPATCH - Adhesives and sealants ☆ - Eclectic Products Inc.
PROPAY - Computer software - Kennedy and Coe, LLC
PROPDOC PERSONAL PROPERTY DOCUMENTATION - Video production - Affordable Video Services
PROPECIA - Pharmaceutical preparations - Merck & Co., Inc.
PROPEL - Artists' materials - Badger Air-Brush Co.
PROPEL - Medical device - Linvatec Corp.
PROPEL - Pencils–mechanical - Sanford Corp.
PROPELL - Vitamins and nutritional supplements - Tishcon Corp.
PROPELLER - Bicycles - Wheelsmith Fabrications Inc.
PROPELLER PLUM - Cosmetics ☆ - Noxell Corp.
PROPENN - Rackets–racquetball - Gencorp Inc.
PROPER - Ventilation equipment - Poly Foam Inc.
PROPER ENGLISH - Wallpaper ☆ - Carey Lind Designs
PROPER ENGLISH SCONES - Bakery products - Proper English Products, Ltd.
PROPER ENGLISH VILLAGE - Wallpaper ☆ - Raintree Designs Inc.
PROPER PALS - Infant product - KN Industries
PROPER POPPER - Popcorn poppers - Nordic Ware
PROPER POSITION - Infant product - Leachco Inc.
PROPER SIZE. PERFECT FIT. - Footwear - Munro & Co., Inc.
PROPER SOX - Hosiery - Talisman Group Licensing Corp.
PROPERT'S - Cleaning preparations - Kiwi Brands, Inc.
PROPERTY - Apparel and accessories - Sears, Roebuck and Co.
PROPERTY MATE - Publisher's imprints - Little, Brown and Co., Inc.
PROPERTY OF GOD - Apparel and accessories - Property of God
PROPERTY PREDICTOR - Computer software - Pavilion Technologies, Inc.
PROPERTY TRACKER - Computer software - Spectar Solutions, Inc.
PROPEX - Plumbing fixtures - Wirsbo Co.
PROPFLECTOR - Sporting goods - Brad Billington
PROPHARMA - Pharmaceutical preparations - Propharma Inc.
PROPHECY - Apparel and accessories - Kellwood Co.
PROPHECY - Colognes - Prince Matchabelli
PROPHECY - Floor coverings–carpet and rugs ☆ - Regal Rugs Inc.
PROPHECY - Frames–eyeglass ☆ - Universal/Univis Inc.
PROPHECY - Games ☆ - Regina Products Inc.
PROPHECY PETITES - Apparel and accessories - Kellwood Co.
PROPHECY TAROT ASTROLOGY NUMEROLOGY - Games - Roy Worley
PROPHECY WOMEN - Apparel and accessories - Kellwood Co.
PROPHESY - Computer software - Prophesy Transportation Software, Inc.
PROPHET - Hearing aids - Qualitone
PROPHET - Software - Essential Management Systems, Inc.
PROPHET - Trading cards and stamps - Rob Liefeld, Inc.
PROPHET UX - Hearing aids - Qualitone
PROPHETISIMA - Skin care products - Santa Fe Fragrance Inc.
PROPHETLINE - Computer software - Robert A. Brown
PROPHILE - Detergents - Laun-Dry Supply Co., Inc.
PROPHONE - Recording label - Pro CD Inc.
PROPHY CHOICE - Toothpaste - Princeton Dental Products LLC
PROPHY PAIR - Dental equipment - John O.Butler Co.
PROPHYDENT - Toothpaste - Orachem Pharmaceuticals
PROPHYLLIN - Pharmaceutical preparations - Rystan Co. Inc.
PROPHYMAX - Dental equipment - Centrix, Inc.
PROPIC - Musical instrument accessories - Micro Musical Products Corp.
PROPIK - Musical instrument accessories - Mapson Engineering Inc.
PROPILE - Underwear and nightwear - Helly-Hansen Inc.
PROPINE - Ophthalmic goods - Allergan, Inc.
PROPINK - Insulating materials - Owens Corning
PROPION GEL - Pharmaceutical preparations ☆ - Wyeth-Ayerst Laboratories
PROPLD - Computer software - Viewlogic Systems, Inc.
PROPLEX - Cables - TMB Associates
PROPLOCK - Marine rigging - Nautilus Marine Engineering

☆ = Now out of production

PROPLOT - Computer software - Houston Instrument
PROPLUS - Faucets - Barnett, Inc.
PROPLUS - Paints - Sherwin-Williams Automotive Finishes Corp.
PROPLUS TULIP - Umbrellas ☆ - Chase Collection, Inc.
PROPLY - Plywood - Pro Shop Co.
PROPOD - Cameras - Acme-Lite Manufacturing Co.
PROPOFF - Tools - Buck-Algonquin Marine Hardware
PROPOINT - Computer peripheral equipment - Interlink Electronics, Inc.
PROPOINTE - Plastics film - AEP Industries, Inc.
PROPOLIS - Toothpaste - Beehive Botanicals Inc.
PROPOLIS DERMA - Health care products - P-Bee Products
PROPOLIS EXTRACT - Vitamins and nutritional supplements - Vitamin Research Products Inc.
PROPOLIS LOZENGES - Cough drops - Holistic Products Corp.
PROPOLIS PLUS - Vitamins and nutritional supplements - Solaray
PROPORE - Plastics–laminated - Minnesota Mining & Manufacturing Co.
PROPORTION PLUS - Underwear and nightwear ☆ - Alba-Waldensian, Inc.
PROPORTIONAL MULTI-PRESSURE PAK - Valves - Mac Valves, Inc.
PROPORTIONED RISE - Jeans–men's - Sheplers, Inc.
PROPOSALS - Wallpaper - Gencorp Inc.
PROPOSTE - Suits–men's - Segye International, Inc.
PROPOXY - Coatings - Nelsonite, Inc.
PROPOXY - Pharmaceutical preparations ☆ - Legere Pharmaceuticals Inc.
PROPOXYCON - Pharmaceutical preparations - Consolidated Midland Corp.
PROPOXYPHENE - Health care products - Halsey Drug Co. Inc.
PROPP-O-PLAST - Plugs–ear - Bilsom International Inc.
PROPPER CHOPPER - Toys–automobiles - Mattel, Inc.
PROP'R TOES - Footwear - PediFix Footcare Co.
PROPREP - Knives - Pacific Handy Cutter Inc.
PROPREP - Knives - Spectrum Razor Tools
PROPREP - Paint removers - Nac Industries Inc.
PROPRINT - Paper products - Georgia-Pacific Corp.
PROPRINTER - Printers–computer - International Business Machines Corp.
PROPRYLEN - Pharmaceutical preparations - Richards Pharmaceutical Co.
PROPULSID - Anti-reflux - Janssen Pharmaceutica Inc.
PROPULSION KICKRIDER - Sporting goods - Aqua-Leisure Industries, Inc.
PROPURE - Saunas - Benson Pump Co.
PROPYL-P HYDROBENZOATE - Pharmaceutical preparations - City Chemical Corp.
PROPYLENE GLYCOL - Chemical preparations - Consolidated Recycling Co, Inc.
PROQUALITY - Paints - PPG Architectural Finishes, Inc.
PRORAB - Vaccines - Intervet, Inc.
PRORACK - Racks - Stinson Sales Corp.
PRORAK - Golfing equipment - Edge Technologies Inc.
PRORAMP - Ramps - Stinson Sales Corp.
PRORECO - Adhesives and sealants - Courtaulds Aerospace Inc.
PRORELIEF - Massage products - Healthometer
PROREP - Computer software - Spalding Software, Inc.
PROREP - Pharmacies - Deecorp. Inc.
PROREX - Pharmaceutical preparations - Hyrex Pharmaceuticals
PROROM - Computer hardware - Programix Corp.
PRO'S - Key rings ☆ - Dakin Inc.
PROS-AIDE - Adhesives and sealants - ADM Tronics Unlimited, Inc.
PRO'S BEST - Steel-wool pads - International Steel Wool Corp.
PROS-CARE - Vitamins and nutritional supplements - Gateway Nutrition, Inc.
PRO'S CHOICE - Asphalt felts and coatings - Gibson-Homans Co.
PRO'S CHOICE - Cleaning preparations - Flo-Pac Corp.
PRO'S CHOICE - Electronic equipment - Il Shin International Inc.
PRO'S CHOICE - Floor coverings–carpet and rugs - LaVelle Textile Marketing Inc.
PRO'S CHOICE - Floor coverings–carpet and rugs - Playfield International Inc.
PROS CHOICE - Socks - Adams-Millis Corp.
PRO'S CHOICE - Sporting goods - Comfort Cushion Mills, Inc.
PRO'S CHOICE, THE - Insulating materials - Guardian Fiberglass
PRO'S FIRST CHOICE, THE - Caulking compounds - Dap Products Inc.
PROS KNOW - Socks - Russell National Sport Socks
PRO'S ONLY - Wallpaper ☆ - Rainbow Creations Inc.
PROS TALK FOX, THE - Computer software - Pinnacle Publishing, Inc.
PROS' TEACHING TOOL, THE - Golfing equipment - Goyen International Inc.
PROSAGE - Food products - Worthington Foods Inc.
PROSAND 7 - Floor sander - Bonakemi USA, Inc.
PROSAND 8 - Floor finishing machines–commercial - Bonakemi USA, Inc.
PROSAND SUPER 8 - Floor finishing machines–commercial - Bonakemi USA, Inc.
PROSAT CUSTOM - Cleaning equipment - Contec, Inc.

PROSAT STERILE - Cleaning equipment - Contec, Inc.
PROSCAN - Cameras–video - Thomson Consumer Electronics, Inc.
PROSCAPE - Computer software - Blanchard-Healy, Inc.
PROSCENIUM - Cameras - Sonora Manufacturing Group
PROSCIUTTO OF PARMA - Food products - Bel Canto Fancy Foods Ltd.
PROSCREEN - Machinery - Knight Manufacturing Corp.
PROSCREEN - Sunblocks - Golfers 911, Inc.
PROSE - Computer software - Digital Equipment Corp.
PROSE - Computer software - Ingram Industries Inc.
PROSE PEN - Novelty items - Agent Andy Inc.
PROSEAL - Adhesives and sealants - Gardner Asphalt Corp.
PROSEAL - Paints - Dunn Edwards Corp.
PROSECA - Pharmaceutical preparations - Westwood-Squibb Pharmaceuticals, Inc.
PROSED - Pharmaceutical preparations - Star Pharmaceuticals Inc.
PROSED/DS - Pharmaceutical preparations - Star Pharmaceuticals Inc.
PROSEK - Wines - Stanley Stawski Distributing Co.
PROSELECT - Computer peripheral equipment - Zenith Electronics Corp.
PROSELL - Computer software ☆ - Lowell Corp.
PROSENSE - Computers - Radius Inc.
PROSENTIAL - Hair care products - Vogue Laboratories
PROSENTRY - Computer software - Bytex Corp.
PROSENTRY-IMS - Monitors–electronic - Environmental Technologies Group, Inc.
PROSERIES - Computer software - Intuit Inc.
PROSERIES - Fishing tackle - Rubbermaid Inc.
PROSERIES - Game machines - Bally Gaming International, Inc.
PROSERV - Apparel - ProServ Inc.
PROSGUARD - Pet products ☆ - Seachem Laboratories
PROSHAPE - Vitamins and nutritional supplements - John A Shannon
PROSHIELD - Chemical preparations - Betz Process Chemicals, Inc.
PROSHIELD - Cleaning preparations - Cleaning Systems, Inc.
PROSHIELD - Electrical surge protectors - Atlantic Scientific Corp.
PROSHOVEL - Motor vehicles–snowplows - Superior Lubricants Co., Inc.
PROSIGNIA - Computers - Compaq Computer Corp.
PROSIL - Hair care products - Matrix Essentials, Inc.
PROSINGLE - Paints - Sherwin-Williams Automotive Finishes Corp.
PROSLANT - Game machines - Bally Gaming International, Inc.
PROSLATE - Building materials–concrete ☆ - Bird Inc.
PROSLCSE - Computer software - International Software Systems, Inc.
PROSLEEVE - Cases–plastic - Case Logic, Inc.
PROSLEEVES - Apparel and accessories - Protectit, Inc.
PROSLOT - Game machines - Bally Gaming International, Inc.
PROSMS - Computer software - Boole & Babbage, Inc.
PROSNAP - Computer software - Yvette L. Kimmel
PROSNIP - Tools - American Tool Companies Inc.
PROSOBESE - Food products - Bristol-Myers Squibb Co.
PROSOCIAL ALTERNATIVES INCORPORATED - Publisher's imprints - Prosocial Alternatives, Inc.
PROSOLUTIONS - Computer peripheral equipment - Sector Group
PROSOLV - Tools–hand-operated - Katec
PROSONIX - Audio equipment ☆ - Meteor Light & Sound Co.
PROSONUS - Recording label - Rosemead Music Productions, Inc.
PROSORT - Computer software - Group 1 Software, Inc.
PROSORT - Research kits - Applied Biosystems Inc.
PROSOURCE - Floor coverings–carpet and rugs - Leading Edge Marketing, Inc.
PROSPARK - Wire–insulated - General Cable Corp.
PROSPEC - Audio equipment - Prospec Inc.
PROSPEC - Binoculars - J.C. Penney Co., Inc.
PROSPEC - Building materials - Illbruck, Inc.
PROSPEC - Goggles–safety - Uvex Safety LLC
PROSPEC - Paints ☆ - Surface Protection Industries, Inc.
PROSPECT - Ophthalmic goods - Embassy Creations Inc.
PROSPECT DIE & MOLD CO. - Metal finishing equipment - Clifford A. Moberg
PROSPECT FARMS - Food products - Prospect Farms
PROSPECT HOUSE - Fabrics - Gretchen Bellinger Inc.
PROSPECT PARK - Bicycles - Ross Bicycles USA, Ltd.
PROSPECT PLACE - Floor coverings - Congoleum Corp.
PROSPECT PRESS - Publisher's imprints - Gorsuch Scarisbrick Publishers
PROSPECTING PARTNER - Telephone accessories - Eagles Nest Marketing Group, Inc.
PROSPECTOR - Animal feed supplements - Consolidated Nutrition, L.C.
PROSPECTOR - Computer software - Shared Data Systems, Inc.
PROSPECTOR - Fireplace equipment - George Mayer Manufacturing Inc.
PROSPECTOR - Footwear - H.H. Brown Shoe Co., Inc.

☆ = Now out of production

PROSPECTOR - Frames–eyeglass - Pathway Optical Prods.
PROSPECTOR - Jeans–men's - Kellwood Co.
PROSPECTOR - Pet products - Rae's Harness Shop
PROSPECTOR - Seat covers - Alco Manufacturing Co. Inc.
PROSPECTOR - Trailers–travel ✩ - Shasta Industries Inc.
PROSPECTOR, THE - Games - McJay Game Co.
PROSPECTOR'S CHOICE - Computer software - The Gale Group
PROSPECTOR'S PARADISE - Video equipment - New Gaming Systems
PROSPECTS - Floor coverings–carpet and rugs - Criterion Mills Inc.
PROSPECTUS - Floor coverings–carpet and rugs - Lees Carpets
PROSPECTUS - Frames–eyeglass ✩ - Universal/Univis Inc.
PROSPEED - Computers–personal ✩ - NEC Technologies, Inc.
PROSPER - Computer software - Ernst & Young LLP
PROSPER FOODS - Rice - Excel Mass Merchandiser, Inc.
PROSPERA - Computer software - Edi Able, Inc.
PROSPERITY - Board game ✩ - Intromark Inc.
PROSPERITY - Candy ✩ - American Candy Co.
PROSPERITY - Floor coverings–carpet and rugs - S and S Mills Inc.
PROSPERITY - Lenses–optical - Ditto Industries Inc.
PROSPERITY - Thread - A. Lewis Thread Co. Inc.
PROSPERITY ANGELS - Christmas tree ornaments - Prosperity Tree International
PROSPERITY BRAND - Rice - Gia Dong Market
PROSPERO - Juices ✩ - Ariel Vineyards
PROSPEROCK - Novelty items - Arthur Richard Stout, Jr.
PROSPEROUS FARMER - Health care products - East Earth Herb Inc.
PROSPIN - Fabrics - Prospin Industries, Inc.
PROSPONSE - Animal feeds - Consolidated Nutrition, L.C.
PROSPORT - Heart monitors - Sensor Dynamics, Inc.
PROSPORT - Sunblocks - Solar Gear Inc.
PROSQUARE - Milking machines - IBA Inc.
PROSSAGE - Medical apparatus ✩ - General Physiotherapy, Inc.
PROSSER FALLS - Wines - Wallfam Inc.
PROST-ADE - Health care products ✩ - Enzymatic Therapy, Inc.
PROST-TECH - Vitamins and nutritional supplements - Highland Laboratories
PROSTA CAPS - Health care products ✩ - Oakmont Investments Co.
PROSTA-FORTE - Vitamins and nutritional supplements - Matrix Health Products, Inc.
PROSTA-GEL - Vitamins and nutritional supplements - Tishcon Corp.
PROSTA-METTO - Vitamins and nutritional supplements - Nutrition Warehouse, Inc.
PROSTA-PLUS - Vitamins and nutritional supplements - Ultravit Enterprises, Inc.
PROSTABS - Health care products - Futurebiotics
PROSTABS PLUS - Vitamins and nutritional supplements - Pdk Labs, Inc.
PROSTACARE - Vitamins and nutritional supplements - Ayurvedic Concepts Ltd.
PROSTACOL - Vitamins and nutritional supplements - Vitamin Research Products Inc.
PROSTAGEUM - Vitamins and nutritional supplements - Solaray
PROSTAHELP - Pharmaceutical preparations - Food & Health Services, Inc.
PROSTALL - Pharmaceutical preparations - Metabolic Products Corp.
PROSTAPHLIN - Penicillin preparations - Bristol-Myers Squibb Co.
PROSTAPLEX - Vitamins and nutritional supplements - Home Health Products, Inc.
PROSTAR - Antennas - Winegard Co.
PROSTAR - Microphones - Telex Communications, Inc.
PROSTAR PROFESSIONAL - Cutlery ✩ - Lifetime Hoan Corp.
PROSTART - Batteries - MMJ Corp.
PROSTASAN - Health care products - Bioforce of America Ltd.
PROSTASUPREME - Vitamins and nutritional supplements - Million Minks, Corp.
PROSTASYN - Vitamins and nutritional supplements - Great Life Laboratories Inc.
PROSTAT - Electronics equipment - Prostat Corp.
PROSTATE PLUS - Vitamins and nutritional supplements ✩ - Ethical Nutrients
PROSTATE PMG - Vitamins and nutritional supplements - Standard Process Inc.
PROSTATE SUPPORT - Vitamins and nutritional supplements - Reese Chemical Co.
PROSTAY HEALTHY PLUS - Health care products - Alta Health Products
PROSTEK 3000 - Medical apparatus - Thermal Therapeutics, Inc.
PROSTEP - Pharmaceutical preparations - American Cyanamid Co.
PROSTEP - Pharmaceutical preparations - Lederle Laboratories
PROSTEX - Pharmaceutical preparations - Metabolic Products Corp.
PROSTIGMIN BROMIDE - Pharmaceutical preparations - Roche Laboratories

PROSTIGMIN METHYLSULFATE - Pharmaceutical preparations - Roche Laboratories
PROSTIN - Pharmaceutical preparations ✩ - Upjohn Co.
PROSTIN F2 ALPHA - Veterinary pharmaceutical preparations - Upjohn Co.
PROSTIX - Tape–adhesive - Olympian Tape Sales Inc.
PROSTOFIT - Vitamins and nutritional supplements - Tishcon Corp.
PROSTOGEN - Vitamins and nutritional supplements - Tishcon Corp.
PROSTOID - Health care products - Healthwatchers System
PROSTONE - Dietary supplements - Sportron International, Inc.
PROSTOP - Automotive parts and accessories - Pep Boys Manny, Moe & Jack
PROSTOSAN - Pharmaceutical preparations - Herb Products Co.
PROSTREAM - Medical apparatus - Micro Therapeutics, Inc.
PROSTRETCH - Health care products - Prism Enterprises, Inc.
PROSTRIP - Hardware - Illinois Tool Works Inc.
PROSTRIP - Hardware - ITW Paslode
PROSTRIPE - Automotive parts and accessories - Spartan International, Inc.
PROSTRUCTOR - Cameras–video - Columbia Audio/Video, Inc.
PROSTSAFE - Vitamins and nutritional supplements - Whitewing Labs, Inc.
PROSTYLE - Paints - Yenkin Majestic Paint Corp.
PROSUN - Electrical equipment - Florida Tanning Systems, Inc.
PROSWEET - Chemical preparations - Betz Process Chemicals, Inc.
PROSYNTHESIS - Computer software - Viewlogic Systems, Inc.
PROSYS - Prophylactics - E.R. Squibb & Sons, Inc.
PROSYSTEM - Exercising equipment - Parabody, Inc.
PROSYSTEM - Paints - Sherwin-Williams Automotive Finishes Corp.
PROSYSTEM FX - Computer software - CCH Inc. (Wolters Kluwer)
PROT-EGE - Sunblocks - Mastey De Paris
PROTABOLIN - Pharmaceutical preparations ✩ - Pasadena Research Laboratories, Inc.
PROTABS - Pharmaceutical preparations - Wesley Pharmacal Co. Inc.
PROTAC - Health care products - Republic Drug Co. Inc.
PROTAC SF - Cold remedies - Republic Drug Co. Inc.
PROTAG - Identification tags - ProTag America Inc.
PROTAGE - Hair care products - Tressa, Inc.
PROTAL - Blinds–venetian - Baumann Inc.
PROTALBA-R - Pharmaceutical preparations - Marion Merrell Dow
PROTALK - Audio equipment - Jing Lu Gu
PROTALK - Audio equipment - Vostech Corp.
PROTAN - Gloves - Leisure Leather Ltd.
PROTANK - Cleaning preparations - Cenex/Land O'Lakes Agronomy Co.
PROTAPE - Rubber bands - Alliance Rubber Co.
PROTAPE - Sports rackets and accessories - Wilson Sporting Goods Co.
PROTAPER - Brushes–paint ✩ - Porter Paint Co.
PROTEAM - Chemical preparations - John Girvan Co., Inc.
PROTEAM - Computer software - Automation Control Inc.
PROTEAM - Computer software - Scopus Technology, Inc.
PROTEAR - Measuring instruments - Thwing-Albert Instrument Co.
PROTEC - Envelopes - Trigon Packaging Corp.
PROTEC - Fabrics - John Boyle & Co., Inc.
PROTEC - Pet products - Golden Pond Inc.
PROTEC - Polypropylene sheets - Compression Polymers Group
PROTEC - Weightlifting equipment - Bollinger Industries
PROTEC-HER - Alarm systems ✩ - ITC, Inc.
PROTEC KING - Bolts–door - S-B Manufacturing Co. Ltd.
PROTEC SOC - Apparel–athletic - Match-Fit Athletic Apparel Ltd.
PROTEC-TOP - Pharmaceutical preparations - Rugby Laboratories Inc.
PROTECH - Cabinets ✩ - Wright Line Inc.
PROTECH - Computer software - Vicon Industries Inc.
PROTECH - Denture cleaners - Protech Professional Products, Inc.
PROTECH - Electronic equipment - Woodward Governor Co.
PROTECH - Examination and surgical gloves - Avista International Inc.
PROTECH - Industrial machinery - Parker Coatings Inc.
PROTECH - Mattress pads - E.R. Carpenter Co.
PROTECH - Medical apparatus - Karlen Manufacturing, Inc.
PROTECH - Pans - Regal Ware, Inc.
PROTECH - Tubes–plastic - Loom Products, Inc.
PROTECH - Water treating compounds - Windo
PROTECHTOR - Cases–musical instrument - XL Specialty Percussion
PROTECHTOR - Packaging machines - E.R. Carpenter Co.
PROTECHTOR - Windows - Extech/Exterior Technologies, Inc.
PROTECRETE CONCRETE'S BEST SOLUTION - Chemical preparations - Applied Concrete Technology, Inc.
PROTECRITE - Tape–masking - American Biltrite Tape Products
PROTECT - Air purification systems - Barnebey and Sutcliffe Corp.
PROTECT - Frames–eyeglass - Zylo Ware Corp.
PROTECT - Hair care products - Hayashi for Hair Inc.

PROTECT - Hardware - Calterm, Inc.
PROTECT - Manicure preparations - Creative Nail Design, Inc.
PROTECT - Medical apparatus - American Disposables, Inc.
PROTECT - Paints - Magicolor Co.
PROTECT - Toothpaste - John O.Butler Co.
PROTECT-A-BIKE - Bicycles - Technical Packaging Corp.
PROTECT-A-BLOCK - Paints - U.S. Protective Coatings Inc.
PROTECT-A-CLEAR - Silicon products - U.S. Protective Coatings Inc.
PROTECT-A-CRETE - Paints - U.S. Protective Coatings Inc.
PROTECT-A-CRYPT - Pillows - Central States Fiber Corp.
PROTECT-A-FLOOR - Paints ☆ - U.S. Protective Coatings Inc.
PROTECT-A-GLAZE - Plastics - General Electric Co.
PROTECT A GUARD - Hardware - Windor Security Manufacturing Inc.
PROTECT-A-KLEEN ETCH - Cleaning preparations ☆ - U.S. Protective
  Coatings Inc.
PROTECT-A-PAK - Bags - Curtis 1000 Inc.
PROTECT A PART - Chemical preparations - Brock Supply Co.
PROTECT-A-PET - Identification tags - Weiss Works
PROTECT-A-PET - Pet products - Protect-A-Pet Inc.
PROTECT-A-PLUG - Cement - U.S. Protective Coatings Inc.
PROTECT-A-POOL - Swimming-pool paint - U.S. Protective Coatings Inc.
PROTECT-A-PUMP - Machine parts - Process Systems, Inc.
PROTECT-A-ROD - Sporting goods - Plano Molding Co.
PROTECT-A-SEAL - Sealing devices - U.S. Protective Coatings Inc.
PROTECT-A-SHIELD - Adhesives and sealants - Blue Coral, Inc.
PROTECT-A-SHINE - Adhesives and sealants - Ziebart International Corp.
PROTECT-A-SOLVE - Thinner ☆ - U.S. Protective Coatings Inc.
PROTECT-A-TERMINAL - Automotive-circuit tester - M. Eagles Tool
  Warehouse Inc.
PROTECT-A-TOT - Hardware - Shur-Lok Corp.
PROTECT-A-WELD - Acrylic bonding agent - U.S. Protective Coatings Inc.
PROTECT-ALL - Cleaning preparations - Bio-Dex Laboratories
PROTECT ALL - Cleaning preparations - Champions Choice Inc.
PROTECT ALL - Doors–metal - Vanguard Manufacturing Co.
PROTECT-ALL - Outdoor furniture protectant and preservative - Keromate
  Products Inc.
PROTECT & RECOVER - Skin care products - Skin Biology, Inc.
PROTECT & RESTORE - Skin care products - Skin Biology, Inc.
PROTECT & TAN - Skin care products - Schering-Plough Healthcare Products
PROTECT-EASE - Chemical preparations - Mydor Industries Inc.
PROTECT-N-SHINE - Cosmetics - Cici Cosmetic Co.
PROTECT-O - Cleaning preparations–carpet and rug - Certified International
PROTECT-O-BOARD - Bulletin boards–wood - Marsh Chalkboard Co.
PROTECT-O-COM - Amplifiers–public address ☆ - Fasco Industries Inc.
  (Consumer Products Div.)
PROTECT-O-DISC - Cases–plastic - Video Store Shopper
PROTECT-O-FILM - Electronics equipment - RTI Research Technology
  International
PROTECT O FILM - Stencils - Heyer Inc.
PROTECT-O-GUARD - Garden equipment ☆ - Bridgestone/Firestone, Inc.
PROTECT-O-LITE - Glass–safety - Buchmin Industries
PROTECT-O-MATIC - Kitchen appliances - Rival Manufacturing Co.
PROTECT-O-SHUTTER - Shutters–metal - Green Hammer Metal Products
  Co.
PROTECT-O-SILL - Window frames - Green Hammer Metal Products Co.
PROTECT-O-SLEEVES - Electrical equipment - McGill Manufacturing Co. Inc.
PROTECT-O-SOFFIT - Aluminum products - Green Hammer Metal Products
  Co.
PROTECT-O-STAT - Trays ☆ - Olympic Plastics Co. Inc.
PROTECT PLUS - Paints - Magicolor Co.
PROTECT YOUR LIFE - Health care products - Apothecary Products, Inc.
PROTECT YOUR PET - Pet products - Valco International Inc.
PROTECTA - Automotive parts and accessories - Lancaster Colony Automotive
  Group
PROTECTA - Pesticides–household - Bell Laboratories Inc.
PROTECTA-CARD - Leather goods - AR Accessories Group Inc.
PROTECTA COAT - Coil/metal coating - Comstar International Inc. (IPC Div.)
PROTECTA-LITE - Lighting equipment–bicycles - Protecta Corp.
PROTECTA-PAD - Pet products - Tomlyn Products
PROTECTA-PAD - Veterinary pharmaceutical preparations - Evsco
  Pharmaceuticals
PROTECTA POXY - Exterior protective coating - A.G.P. Surface Control
  Systems Inc.
PROTECTA PRODUCT - Paper - Kleer-Vu Plastics Inc.
PROTECTA-VUE - Awnings ☆ - APC Corp.
PROTECTA-WELL - Awnings ☆ - APC Corp.

PROTECTACAP - Vitamins and nutritional supplements - Tishcon Corp.
PROTECTACIDE - Disinfectants - Horizons Marketing Group, Inc.
PROTECTAGEL - Vitamins and nutritional supplements - Tishcon Corp.
PROTECTALL - Cases–plastic - Medicool Inc.
PROTECTALL - Medical apparatus - Cin Med Associates
PROTECTEAR - Plugs–ear - Aural Tech Inc.
PROTECTED BY 100+ SECURITY - Alarm systems - Coyote Enterprises, Inc.
PROTECTED BY INFOSAFE - Computer software - Infosafe Systems, Inc.
PROTECTERCISE - Recording label - Karen Sheperd
PROTECTEYE - Goggles–safety ☆ - Shoplyne Safety Products
PROTECTING THE ENVIRONMENT THAT PROTECTS YOU - Floor
  coverings–carpet and rugs - Interface, Inc.
PROTECTINT - Cleaning preparations - Sunpoint Products, Inc.
PROTECTION ONE - Alarm systems - Protection One Alarm Services Inc.
PROTECTION PLUS - Electrical equipment - Eaton Corp.
PROTECTION PLUS - Health care products - Medline, Industries, Inc.
PROTECTION PRO - Computer software - Wayne D. Storkman
PROTECTIVE CLOTHING CO. - Waterproof outerwear - Wippette International,
  Inc.
PROTECTIVE HAND & BODY THERAPY - Skin care products - Viviane
  Woodard Industries, Ltd.
PROTECTIVE MEASURE - Skin care products - Georgette Klinger, Inc.
PROTECTIVES - Skin care products - Almay Inc.
PROTECT'N SHINE - Hair care products - Electronic Hair Styling, Inc.
PROTECTO - Copper products - Kester Solder Co.
PROTECTO - Deodorants–personal - Willert Home Products, Inc.
PROTECTO - Firearms, accessories, and parts - Hoppe's
PROTECTO - Giftware ☆ - Artex-Green Corp. of N.Y.
PROTECTO - Hair care products - Avlon Industries Inc.
PROTECTO - Organs–musical instrument - Schaff Piano Supply Co.
PROTECTO - Sports clubs - Penguin Industries of Delaware, Inc.
PROTECTO - Tools ☆ - Budge Industries, Inc.
PROTECTO - Toys ☆ - Reliance Products Corp.
PROTECTO CARD GUARDS - Trading cards and stamps - Sportworld
  Distributing Inc.
PROTECTO-CLEAR - Irrigation equipment - Natco Products Corp.
PROTECTO DECK - Floor coverings–carpet and rugs - Protecto Wrap Co.
PROTECTO-DOME - Display cases–plastic - Wasco Products, Inc.
PROTECTO FILM - Vinyl - Bemiss-Jason Corp.
PROTECTO-GLO - Novelty items - Carl J. Abraham
PROTECTO GUARD - Fans–ceiling - Northwest Envirofan
PROTECTO JR. - Glass products - Crystal Glass Tube & Cylinder Co.
PROTECTO-MASK - Tape–adhesive - Mystik Corp.
PROTECTO PAGER - Novelty items - Wainwright Industries, Inc.
PROTECTO-SEAL - Adhesives and sealants - Kokem Products Inc.
PROTECTO-SEAL - Adhesives and sealants ☆ - Consolidated Coatings Corp.
PROTECTO SEAL 45 - Roofing materials - Protecto Wrap Co.
PROTECTO SR. - Glass products - Crystal Glass Tube & Cylinder Co.
PROTECTOL - Pharmaceutical preparations - Jones Medical Industries, Inc.
  (Medical Div.)
PROTECTONE - Ceiling panels - Celotex Corp.
PROTECTONGUE - Harmonicas - Fred Gretsch Enterprises
PROTECTOR - Alarm systems–burglar - Radatron Corp.
PROTECTOR - Bicycles - Graber Products, Inc.
PROTECTOR - Document covers - Label Plus
PROTECTOR - Electronic equipment - General Binding Corp.
PROTECTOR - Floor coverings–carpet and rugs - Collins & Aikman Corp.
PROTECTOR - Floor coverings–carpet and rugs - Karastan-Bigelow Inc.
PROTECTOR - Flypaper - S.C. Johnson & Son, Inc.
PROTECTOR - Footwear - Distributors Service Corp.
PROTECTOR - Frames–eyeglass - Zylo Ware Corp.
PROTECTOR - Gelatin - Vyse Gelatin Co.
PROTECTOR - Lighting fixtures - Kenall Manufacturing Co.
PROTECTOR - Office supplies - Mead Corp.
PROTECTOR - Paper–toweling - Scott Paper Co.
PROTECTOR - Pet products - Four Paws Products Ltd.
PROTECTOR - Ribbons–inked ☆ - Standard Manifold Co.
PROTECTOR - Vitamins and nutritional supplements ☆ - J.R. Carlson
  Laboratories Inc.
PROTECTOR COVERS - Motor vehicle parts and accessories - Dowco, Inc.
PROTECTOR MATS - Floor coverings–carpet and rugs - Garon Products Inc.
PROTECTOR PLUS - Locks–padlocks - National Manufacturing Co.
PROTECTOR PLUS - Remote control devices - X-10 Inc.
PROTECTOR PLUS - Transparency holders - Winslow Manufacturing Corp.
PROTECTOR PLUS - Wire - Wilson-Cook Medical Inc.
PROTECTOR, THE - Doors–storm ☆ - A-J Manufacturing

☆ = Now out of production

PROTECTOR, THE - Ladders–metal - Aluminum Ladder Co.
PROTECTOR, THE - Medical apparatus - Camp, Inc.
PROTECTOR, THE - Electrical equipment - Challenger Circle F Inc.
PROTECTOR, THE - Cables - Crown Industries, Inc.
PROTECTOR, THE - Computer peripheral equipment - Daubert Industries - ECP
PROTECTOR, THE - Pet products - Four Paws Products Ltd.
PROTECTOR, THE - Fireplace equipment ☆ - O.D. Funk Co.
PROTECTOR, THE - Paints - Mautz Paint Co.
PROTECTOR, THE - Chemical preparations - Roark-Davis International Corp.
PROTECTOR, THE - Motor vehicles–trucks - Superior Industries International, Inc.
PROTECTORING - Flowers, plants, and seeds - Paga Corp.
PROTECTORS - Hardware - National Manufacturing Co.
PROTECTORS - Vitamins and nutritional supplements - Shaklee Corp.
PROTECTORS - Waterproof footwear - Kaysam Corp. of America
PROTECTORS OF INNER SPACE - Boilers–hot water - Marcham Laboratories, Inc.
PROTECTORS, THE - Publisher's imprints - Scholastic Inc.
PROTECTPRO - Computer software - Wayne D. Storkman
PROTECTRON - Electronics equipment - RTI Research Technology International
PROTECTS TO THE MAX - Oils–lubricating - Pennzoil Products Co.
PROTECTWARE - Computer software - Wayne D. Storkman
PROTEEN 25 - Bird feeds - Sunshine Bird Supplies, Inc.
PROTEEN COLOR - Bird feeds - Sunshine Bird Supplies, Inc.
PROTEF - Amplifiers ☆ - Electro-Voice, Inc.
PROTEF - Veterinary pharmaceutical preparations ☆ - Upjohn Co.
PROTEFERM - Cattle feed additive - Ajinomoto USA, Inc.
PROTEGE - Floor coverings–carpet and rugs - Coronet Carpets Inc.
PROTEGE - Floor coverings–carpet and rugs ☆ - Mohawk Carpet Corp.
PROTEGE - Floor waxes - W.W. Grainger, Inc.
PROTEGE - Furniture - Thomasville Furniture Industries Inc.
PROTEGE - Golfing equipment - Daiwa Corp.
PROTEGE - Machinery - Bernard L. Miles
PROTEGE - Mattresses and box springs - Ohio Mattress Co.
PROTEGE - Microscopes - Global Surgical Corp.
PROTEGE - Motor vehicles–automobiles - Mazda Motor of America Inc.
PROTEGE - Pencils–mechanical - Pilot Pen Corp. of America
PROTEGE - Rackets–racquetball - Ektelon
PROTEGE - Sewing machines–household - Tacony Corp.
PROTEGE VITESSE - Sporting protective equipment - Protege Vitesse
PROTEGEE - Floor coverings–carpet and rugs - Hollytex Carpet Mills Inc.
PROTEGRA MEANS PROTECTION - Vitamins and nutritional supplements - American Cyanamid Co.
PROTEI-NAIL - Nail care products - Nu-Tress Laboratories Inc.
PROTEIMER - Pharmaceutical preparations - Protein Delivery, Inc.
PROTEIN 5 - Pet products - Vo-Toys Inc.
PROTEIN 8X - Pet products - Glo-Marr Products Inc.
PROTEIN 21 - Hair care products - Mennen Co.
PROTEIN 29 - Hair care products - Mennen Co.
PROTEIN 1000 - Health care products - Pierson Co.
PROTEIN-AIDE - Oils–edible ☆ - Loriva Supreme Foods Inc.
PROTEIN-AIDE SUPREME - Oils–edible ☆ - Loriva Supreme Foods Inc.
PROTEIN BODIFIER - Hair-care products - Tri-Institute of Trichology
PROTEIN CREME - Skin care products - Fanie International
PROTEIN DESIGN LABS - Pharmaceutical preparations - Protein Design Labs, Inc.
PROTEIN ENGINEERED FOR THE HUMAN RACE - Vitamins and nutritional supplements - Kevin Lawrence
PROTEIN-G - Vitamins and nutritional supplements ☆ - Fibertone Co.
PROTEIN MASQUE - Skin care products ☆ - Joico Laboratories, Inc.
PROTEIN NUGGETS - Vitamins and nutritional supplements ☆ - Pharmavite Corp.
PROTEIN PLUS - Cereal ☆ - General Mills, Inc.
PROTEIN PLUS - Pharmaceutical preparations - Schein Pharmaceutical Inc.
PROTEIN PLUS - Shampoos ☆ - Palm Beach Beauty Products
PROTEIN POWDER - Food products - Twinlab
PROTEIN POWER - Pet products - Biologic Pet
PROTEIN ROYALE - Fish food ☆ - Aquatronics-Filtronics
PROTEIN SKIMMERS - Aquariums–household - Quality Marine
PROTEIN-SNAX - Candy ☆ - Chex Co.
PROTEIN SYNTHESIS/CODON - Computer software - Queue Inc.
PROTEIN TREAT - Hair care products - Para Laboratories Inc.
PROTEINSPRAY - Hair care products - Sacha International
PROTEK - Adhesives and sealants - Kohler Co.

PROTEK - Electronic equipment ☆ - Da-Lite Screen Co. Inc.
PROTEK - Hair care products - I. Sekine Co. Inc.
PROTEK - Pet products - Pet's Corner
PROTEK DIV. - Alarms–personal ☆ - Amtek Pet Behavior Products
PROTEK-LENS - Optical scanners–computer - Titmus Optical, Inc.
PROTEK PRODUCTS - Cleaning equipment - Protek Products
PROTEK-TOE - Shoe accessories - Stein's Health Industries, Inc.
PROTEK-TOE - Sporting goods - Duro Med Industries Inc.
PROTEKT - Insulating materials - Madico, Inc.
PROTEKT2 - Floor coverings–carpet and rugs - Interface, Inc.
PROTEL - Fabric stores ☆ - Amoco Fabrics and Fibers Co.
PROTEL - Telephone apparatus - Protel, Inc.
PROTEMA - Goggles ☆ - Glendale Protective Technologies Inc.
PROTEMP - Automotive parts and accessories - Pep Boys Manny, Moe & Jack
PROTENERGY - Pharmaceutical preparations ☆ - Vita-Fore Products Co.
PROTENSION - Pharmaceutical preparations ☆ - Blaine Co. Inc.
PROTENTIAL - Golfing equipment - RD Max Co.
PROTEO BARISTA - Coffee makers–electric - Starbucks Corp.
PROTEO GRANDE - Coffee makers–electric - Starbucks Corp.
PROTEOGLUCOSEAL - Hair care products - Tiro Industries, Inc.
PROTERNOL - Health care products ☆ - Key Pharmaceuticals Inc.
PROTERRA - Paper - Georgia-Pacific Corp.
PROTEST - Frames–eyeglass - Zylo Ware Corp.
PROTEUS - Barometers - Maximum Inc.
PROTEUS - Games - Kadon Enterprises Inc.
PROTEUS - Gasoline - Southern Union Co.
PROTEUS - Musical instrument accessories - E-Mu Systems, Inc.
PROTEUS - Publisher's imprints - Prima Communications, Inc.
PROTEUS - Skin care products - Proteus Inc.
PROTEVITE - Pharmaceutical preparations ☆ - Vitarine Pharmaceuticals Inc.
PROTEX - Cases–musical instrument - Harptone
PROTEX - No-scratch base pads - Aetna Felt Corp.
PROTEX - Office supplies - Warshaw Manufacturing Co. Inc.
PROTEX - Paints - Passonno Paints
PROTEX - Prophylactics - Protex
PROTEX - Soap - Colgate-Palmolive Co.
PROTEX - Soap - Dial Corp.
PROTEX - Sporting goods - Comfort Cushion Mills, Inc.
PROTEX - Ultrasonic testing equipment - Technodyne Research International Inc.
PROTEX - Veterinary pharmaceutical preparations - Intervet, Inc.
PROTEX-IT - Shelf liner, etc. - ADPI Enterprises Inc.
PROTEX-RAY - Pharmaceutical preparations - Uniflex, Inc.
PROTEX-ZIP - Protective envelopes - Curtis 1000 Inc.
PROTEXALL - Apparel and accessories - Protexall Inc.
PROTEXIT - Plastics–laminated - John Boyle & Co., Inc.
PROTEXORGAN - Organ-pedal protectors - Paul L. Jansen & Son
PROTEXTURE - Hardware - United Manufacturers Supplies Inc.
PROTHAZINE - Pharmaceutical preparations ☆ - Vortech Pharmaceuticals
PROTHERM - Chemical preparations - Georgia Gulf Corp.
PROTHINS - Snack foods ☆ - Sovex Foods, Inc.
PROTICALL - Schering-Plough Animal Health
PROTICULEEN - Pharmaceutical preparations - G.O. Spanner Inc.
PROTID - Pharmaceutical preparations - Lunsco Inc.
PROTIES - Crackers ☆ - Commerce Foods Inc.
PROTIME - Medical apparatus - International Technidyne Corp.
PROTIMER - Computer software - Chronotech
PROTINA - Hair care products - Revlon Consumer Products Corp.
PROTINI - Footwear - Protini Group International
PROTINI - Pasta - Quaker Oats Co.
PROTINOL - Chemical preparations - Advanced Instruments, Inc.
PROTISS - Computer software - Simulation Sciences Inc.
PROTITE - Paints - Gray Seal Paint Manufacturing Co. Inc.
PROTO - Hair care products - Faberge Co.
PROTO 2000 - Toys–models - Life-Like Products Inc.
PROTO & TYPE - Jewelry - B. Tekel
PROTO-BISKIT - Pet products - Triumph Pet Industries, Inc.
PROTO-CHOL - Pharmaceutical preparations - Bristol-Myers Squibb Co.
PROTO-CINO - Vitamins and nutritional supplements - Bionutritional Research Group, Inc.
PROTO-COUPLER - Toys–trains - Mike's Train House, Inc.
PROTO-DIET - Pet products - Triumph Pet Industries, Inc.
PROTO-MITE - Health care products - Health Products Corp.
PROTO-PLUS - Hair care products - Renbow International Ltd. USA
PROTO-REEL - Electronic equipment - Johanson Dielectrics, Inc.
PROTO-SPOT - Cleaning preparations–carpet and rug - Certified International

☆ = Now out of production

PROTO VSI - Skates–roller - Dare Development Group, Inc.

PROTO WHEY - Vitamins and nutritional supplements - Bionutritional Research Group, Inc.

PROTOBASE - Computer software - Southern Datacomm, Inc.

PROTOBOL - Pharmaceutical preparations - Wesley Pharmacal Co. Inc.

PROTOCALL - Electronic equipment - Harris Corp.

PROTOCOL - Dog food - Simmons Industries Inc.

PROTOCOL - Floor coverings–carpet and rugs - Roxbury Carpet Co.

PROTOCOL - Paper–writing - Simpson Paper Co.

PROTOCOP - Computer peripheral equipment - Ods Networks, Inc.

PROTOGEL - Chemical preparations - National Diagnostics

PROTOGEN LITE - Breads - Best Foods Baking Group

PROTOGENIC - Hair care products - Helene Curtis Industries Inc.

PROTOLAB - Computer software - Interplex Electronics Inc.

PROTOLAN - Pharmaceutical preparations - Lannett Co. Inc.

PROTOLIGHT - Lamps - Durel Corp.

PROTOLYZER - Computer software - Protools Inc.

PROTOMONE - Hormone preparations ☆ - J.N. Michell Co.

PROTON - Agricultural machinery - Kelly McNichols

PROTON - Audio equipment - Proton Corp.

PROTON - Dinnerware–glass - Prolon Dinnerware

PROTON DANCE - Recording label - Echo Records Inc.

PROTON PRO - Computer peripheral equipment - Nucleus Interactive, Inc.

PROTON SAGA - Toys–models - Proton America Inc.

PROTONE - Containers–trash - Victor Stanley, Inc.

PROTONIC - Sporting goods - Protonic Inc.

PROTOP - Hardware - Proto Corp.

PROTOPAM CHLORIDE - Pharmaceutical preparations - Wyeth-Ayerst Laboratories

PROTOPLAST - Paper–thermoplastics coated - Unnatural Resources Inc.

PROTORIC - Contact lenses - RLI Vision Corp.

PROTOSAN - Vitamins and nutritional supplements - Recsei Laboratories

PROTOSILK - Hair care products ☆ - Demert & Dougherty, Inc.

PROTOSMOKE - Toys–trains - Mike's Train House, Inc.

PROTOSTAR - Computer hardware - Dick K. Pine

PROTOSTAT - Pharmaceutical preparations - Ortho Pharmaceutical Corp.

PROTOTABS - Pharmaceutical preparations ☆ - Vortech Pharmaceuticals

PROTOTYPE - Books–comic - Malibu Comics Entertainment, Inc.

PROTOTYPE MACHENING - Firearms, accessories, and parts - Evolution Gun Works

PROTOUCH - Computer peripheral equipment - Key Tronic Corp.

PROTOUCH - Hair care products - Belson Products

PROTOUCH - Splints - Smith & Nephew Inc. (Rehabilitation Div.)

PROTOUCH 1000 - Electrical equipment - Medicool Inc.

PROTOUCH STEAM SUPREME - Electric hairsetters - Windmere Corp.

PROTOUR MEMORABILIA AUTHENTIC COLLECTABLES - Golfing equipment - Pro Tour Memorabilia, LLC

PROTOVIR - Pharmaceutical preparations - Protein Design Labs, Inc.

PROTOZIME - Pharmaceutical preparations - Wesley Pharmacal Co. Inc.

PROTOZOA - Computer software - Ventura Educational Systems

PROTRAINER - Pet products - Biological Engineering/High Tech Pet Products

PROTRAK - Database management system - Marmen Computing, Inc.

PROTRAN-PLUS - Pharmaceutical preparations ☆ - Vangard Labs Inc.

PROTRAQ - Computer software - Quaker Chemical Corp.

PROTREES - Trees–artificial - Plastruct Inc.

PROTRON SKIMMER - Pet products ☆ - Aquatronics-Filtronics

PROTRUDE - Shoes - Easy Luck Co., Inc.

PROTTER'S HAWAIIAN HONEY NUTS - Nuts–salted, roasted, cooked, or canned - Honey Nuts Inc.

PROTURA - Hair care products ☆ - Modern Research Laboratories

PROTURBO - Sporting goods - Jobe Ski Corp.

PROTUSS-D LIQUID C-III - Pharmaceutical preparations - Horizon Pharmaceutical Corp.

PROTUSS DM - Pharmaceutical preparations ☆ - Vangard Labs Inc.

PROTUSS-DM TABLETS RX - Pharmaceutical preparations - Horizon Pharmaceutical Corp.

PROTUSS LIQUID C-III - Pharmaceutical preparations - Horizon Pharmaceutical Corp.

PROTWIN - Machinery - Knight Manufacturing Corp.

PROTX PLUS - Dietary supplement - Life Plus

PROTYPE - Office supplies - Phillips Process Co. Inc.

PROTZMANN - Furniture - Domore/DO3

PROUD - Ophthalmic goods - Foremost Optical Products

PROUD 1 - Goggles–safety ☆ - U.S. Safety Corp.

PROUD COCK - Labels–paper - King Walk Inc.

PROUD EAGLE COLLECTION - Barbecue and grill accessories - M.E. Heuck Co. Inc.

PROUD FOX - Glassware–household - Ceraglass Inc.

PROUD HERITAGE - Floor coverings–carpet and rugs - Lees Carpets

PROUD HERITAGE - Furniture ☆ - Bassett Furniture Industries, Inc.

PROUD LADY - Ophthalmic goods - Foremost Optical Products

PROUD LINE - Floor coverings–carpet and rugs ☆ - Alexander Smith Carpets

PROUD MARY - Beverages - Romanoff International Inc.

PROUD PAWS PET FRAMES - Frames–picture - Cascom International, Inc.

PROUD TO SERVE - Food products ☆ - Pierre Frozen Foods Inc.

PROUDFIT - Office supplies - Grand Rapids Loose Leaf Inc.

PROUT SNOWGOOSE ELITE - Ships–sailing vessels - Prout USA

PROV-U-SEP - Pharmaceutical preparations ☆ - Solvay Pharmaceuticals Inc.

PROVA - Hair care products - S Mark Enterprise

PROVACATIVE - Perfumes - Avon Products, Inc.

PROVADO - Insecticide - Miles Inc.

PROVADO - Insecticides - Bayer Corp. (Agriculture Div.)

PROVAKAS - Containers - Martha Miller

PROVAL - Computer peripheral equipment - Winklevoss Consultants, Inc.

PROVAL - Metal valves - Tuson Corp.

PROVAL - Pharmaceutical preparations ☆ - Solvay Pharmaceuticals Inc.

PROVALUE - Safety products - McGuire-Nicholas Co., Inc.

PROVALUE SERVICES - Computer software - Procard, Inc.

PROVALVE, PROLITE, PROMAX - Belts–apparel - McGuire-Nicholas Co., Inc.

PROVANE - Adhesives and sealants - Kwik-Affix Products

PROVANTA - Computer hardware - Provantage Corp.

PROVANTAGE - Vitamins and nutritional supplements - Reliv' International, Inc.

PROVATI - Pizzas–frozen - Crestar Food Products, Inc.

PROVE IT! - Computer software - American Society of Consultant Pharmacists

PROVE IT - Hair care products ☆ - Vigorol Inc.

PROVECHO - Snack foods - La Familia Latina Corp.

PROVECTOR - Computer software - Stylus Inc.

PROVEIL - Fabrics ☆ - Veratec

PROVEN - Housewares - Pro Hardware Inc.

PROVEN DEFENSE, THE - Skin care products - Tec Laboratories, Inc.

PROVEN PERFORMANCE - Cosmetics - Elizabeth Arden Inc.

PROVEN POWER - Fuel systems–motor vehicle - Proven Propane Products and Accessories, Inc.

PROVEN RELEASE - Health care products - Leiner Health Products Inc.

PROVENCAL - Furniture–upholstered - Hickory Tavern Furniture

PROVENCAL - Giftware - Seymour Mann Inc.

PROVENCAL - Glassware–household - Svend Jensen of Denmark Inc.

PROVENCE - Wallace International Silversmiths, Inc.

PROVENCE - Dinnerware–glass - Crate and Barrel

PROVENCE - Dinnerware–glass - Dansk International Designs, Ltd.

PROVENCE - Dishes–china - Waterford Wedgewood USA, Inc.

PROVENCE - Faucets - Kohler Co.

PROVENCE - Flatware - Anacapa Corp.

PROVENCE - Floor coverings ☆ - Kentile Floors Inc.

PROVENCE - Floor coverings–carpet and rugs - Bloomsburg Carpet Industries

PROVENCE - Floor coverings–carpet and rugs ☆ - Hollytex Carpet Mills Inc.

PROVENCE - Furniture - Hickory Manufacturing Co.

PROVENCE - Furniture - Tropitone Furniture Co. Inc.

PROVENCE - Furniture ☆ - Lyon-Shaw Inc.

PROVENCE - Hardware ☆ - Masonite Corp.

PROVENCE - Tiles–ceramic - American Marazzi Tile, Inc.

PROVENCE - Vases - Durand International

PROVENCE - Wallpaper - Newmarket Designs Ltd.

PROVENCE ARCH - Cabinets–wood - Kemper

PROVENCE COUNTRY - Cooking utensils–aluminum - Joyce Chen, Inc.

PROVENCE GREEN - Tableware–china ☆ - Lenox, Inc.

PROVENCE SANTE - Bath salts - Baudelaire Inc.

PROVENCE SQUARE - Cabinets–wood - Kemper

PROVENCE-THE COUNTRY - Wallpaper - Newmarket Designs Ltd.

PROVENCER - Giftware ☆ - Gorham Inc.

PROVENCIAL - Glassware–household - Owens-Illinois Inc. (Libbey Div.)

PROVENTIL - Pharmaceutical preparations - Schering-Plough Healthcare Products

PROVENWORTH - Paper–bond - P.H. Glatfelter Co.

PROVENZA - Floor coverings–tile - Federal Tile Imports Inc.

PROVERA - Pharmaceutical preparations - Upjohn Co.

PROVEST - Pharmaceutical preparations ☆ - Upjohn Co.

PROVHDL - Computer software - Viewlogic Systems, Inc.

PROVI - Fruits and vegetables - Europa Foods Ltd.

☆ = Now out of production

PROVI-TABS - Pet products - Nutra-Vet Research Corp.
PROVICO-BIG H - Animal feeds - Hubbard Milling Co.
PROVICTOR - Extension cords - Victor Electric Wire & Cable Corp.
PROVIDE - Computer software - Telephone Response Technologies
PROVIDE - Diapers–disposable - Weyerhaeuser Co.
PROVIDE - Hair care products - Stanley Home Products Inc.
PROVIDE - Incontinence products - Scott Health Care
PROVIDE - Vitamins and nutritional supplements - Solaray
PROVIDENCE - Clocks ☆ - Ridgeway Clock Co.
PROVIDENCE - Fireplace equipment - Majestic Co.
PROVIDENCE - Flatware - Pfaltzgraff Investment Co.
PROVIDENCE - Giftware ☆ - Lenox Crystal, Inc.
PROVIDENCE - Occasional tables ☆ - JDI Group, Inc.
PROVIDENCE - Watches - Bulova Corp.
PROVIDENCE PINE - Furniture ☆ - Kincaid Furniture Co. Inc.
PROVIDENT INDUSTRIES, INC. - Circuit breakers - American Circuit Breaker Corp.
PROVIDEO - Game machines - Bally Gaming International, Inc.
PROVIDER - Communications equipment - Jeron Electronic Systems, Inc.
PROVIDER - Fireplaces - Preway Industries Inc.
PROVIDER - Vitamins and nutritional supplements - Abbott Ambulatory Infusion Systems
PROVIDER - Water purification systems - Norwalk Sales & Service
PROVIDER BRIEFCASE - Computer software - Total Healthcare Solutions, Inc.
PROVIDER CENTRAL - Computer software - Total Healthcare Solutions, Inc.
PROVIDERMATCH - Computer software - Geoaccess, Inc.
PROVIDEX - Pharmaceutical preparations ☆ - Solvay Pharmaceuticals Inc.
PROVIDIA - Computer hardware - Trident Microsystems, Inc.
PROVIDING SUPERIOR QUALITY - Water–bottled or canned - Water Store Network
PROVIEW - Audio and video storage accessories ☆ - Innovative Concepts Inc.
PROVIEW - Cameras–video - Thomson Consumer Electronics, Inc.
PROVIEW - Computer hardware - EMC Monitor Corp.
PROVIEW - Golfing equipment - Finch and Dupaix, Inc.
PROVIEW - Trading cards and stamps - Upper Deck Co.
PROVIGAN - Pharmaceutical preparations ☆ - Solvay Pharmaceuticals Inc.
PROVIGIL - Pharmaceutical preparations - Cephalon, Inc.
PROVIM - Veterinary pharmaceutical preparations - Nutra-Vet Research Corp.
PROVIMALT - Health care products ☆ - C.B. Fleet Co. Inc.
PROVIMI - Meat products–beef - Provimi Veal Corp.
PROVINCE - Floor coverings–carpet and rugs - Blue Ridge Carpet Mills
PROVINCE - Hardware - Harloc, Inc.
PROVINCE - Manufactured homes - Redman Industries, Inc.
PROVINCETOWN - Siding–insulating - Georgia-Pacific Corp.
PROVINCETOWN BANNER - Publisher's imprints - Provincetown Banner, Inc.
PROVINCIA GRANDE - Floor coverings ☆ - Tarkett, Inc.
PROVINCIAL - Copper compounds ☆ - Regal Ware, Inc.
PROVINCIAL - Dinnerware–glass ☆ - Sango Co. Ltd. (Sango USA Div.)
PROVINCIAL - Dishes–china - Waterford Wedgewood USA, Inc.
PROVINCIAL - Doors - Jeld-Wen, Inc.
PROVINCIAL - Doors–glass - Therma-Tru Corp.
PROVINCIAL - Floor coverings ☆ - Bruce Hardwood Floors
PROVINCIAL - Floor coverings ☆ - Tarkett, Inc.
PROVINCIAL - Floor coverings–carpet and rugs - Mohawk Industries Inc.
PROVINCIAL - Frames–eyeglass - May Optical Co. Inc.
PROVINCIAL - Furniture ☆ - Keller Manufacturing Co.
PROVINCIAL - Furniture polish and wax ☆ - Martin-Senour Co.
PROVINCIAL - Glassware–household - Crisa Corp.
PROVINCIAL - Hobby kits ☆ - Craft World International Inc.
PROVINCIAL - Melamine product - Boonton Molding Co. Inc.
PROVINCIAL - Rings–jewelry ☆ - Artcarved Inc.
PROVINCIAL - Shelving units–wood - Naomi Gale Wall Systems
PROVINCIAL - Toilets–enameled - Kohler Co.
PROVINCIAL BLUE - Dinnerware - Corning Inc.
PROVINCIAL BLUE - Dinnerware–glass ☆ - Metlox Pottery Shoppe
PROVINCIAL BLUE - Glassware–household ☆ - Fenton Art Glass Co.
PROVINCIAL BOUQUET - Glassware–household ☆ - Fenton Art Glass Co.
PROVINCIAL DESIGNS - Dinnerware–glass - Nikko Ceramics Inc.
PROVINCIAL FRUIT - Dinnerware–glass ☆ - Metlox Pottery Shoppe
PROVINCIAL GARDENS - Fabrics–tapestry ☆ - Christopher Prints
PROVINCIAL HONEY - Toiletries - Nordstrom, Inc.
PROVINCIAL PINE - Wood products - Three Mountaineers Inc.
PROVINCIAL SQUARE - Floor coverings ☆ - Tarkett, Inc.
PROVINCIAL TREASURES - Furniture ☆ - Stanley Furniture Co. Inc.
PROVING EVERYDAY THAT: QUALITY CAN INDEED EXIST WITHIN A VACUUM! - Paper products - Gavin Manufacturing Corp.

PROVING GROUND - Apparel–men's - Edison Brothers Stores, Inc.
PROVING GROUNDS OF THE MAD OVERLORD - Computer software - Sir-Tech Software, Inc.
PROVIS - Computer software - American Management Systems, Inc.
PROVISC VISCOELASTIC MATERIAL - Surgical supplies - Alcon Laboratories, Inc.
PROVISION - Eyeglasses - Uvex Safety LLC
PROVISIONS - Slacks–men's - Glen Oaks Industries Inc.
PROVITA - Vitamins and nutritional supplements - Biochemics, Inc.
PROVITA PLUS - Shampoos - Beauty Brands Group
PROVIVID - Photographic equipment - Polaroid Corp.
PROVNET - Computer peripheral equipment - Usable Systems, Inc.
PROVO-LO - Cheese - Alpine Lace Brands, Inc.
PROVO-LOVER - Cheese - Irwin L. Gold & Assoc.
PROVOC FITNESS APPAREL - Apparel–athletic - Kimberlie A. Peterson
PROVOCATEUR - Frames–eyeglass ☆ - Universal/Univis Inc.
PROVOCATIVE - Floor coverings - Aladdin Mills, Inc.
PROVOICE - Computer software - First Byte Inc.
PROVOKER - Fishing jigs - American Import Co.
PROVOL - Vitamins and nutritional supplements - Upsher-Smith Laboratories, Inc.
PROVOSIL - Insulating materials - Redco II
PROVOX - Electronic equipment - Fisher Controls International, Inc.
PROVUE - Computer software - Digital Equipment Corp.
PROWALKER - Footwear–athletic - Rockport Co. Inc.
PROWALL 2000 - Paints - Hirshfield's Paint Manufacturing
PROWALL 4000 - Paints - Hirshfield's Paint Manufacturing
PROWALL 6000 - Paints - Hirshfield's Paint Manufacturing
PROWARE - Computer software - Curtis Software Inc.
PROWASH - Cleaning equipment - DBNA Trademarks Holding Inc.
PROWELD - Hardware - Ambroid Co.
PROWESS - Medical apparatus ☆ - Intercontinental Enterprises Ltd.
PROWESS SYSTEM - Health care products ☆ - Intercontinental Enterprises Ltd.
PROWEVE - Floor coverings–carpet and rugs - Sweetwater Carpet Corp.
PROWICKETS - Desks - TEI, Inc.
PROWL - Computer software programs - Legent Corp.
PROWLER - Archery equipment - Martin Archery Inc.
PROWLER - Bicycles - Ross Bicycles USA, Ltd.
PROWLER - Frames–eyeglass - May Optical Co. Inc.
PROWLER - Golfing equipment - Components Plus, Inc.
PROWLER - Golfing equipment - Lynx Golf, Inc.
PROWLER - Kites - Gayla Industries Inc.
PROWLER - Motor vehicles–automobiles - Chrysler Corp. (Chrysler-Plymouth Div.)
PROWLER - Sporting goods - James Heddon's Sons
PROWLER - Trailers–travel - Fleetwood Enterprises, Inc.
PROWLER GROWLER - Alarm systems - Astro-Guard Industries Inc.
PROWLER LITE - Motor vehicles–motor homes ☆ - Fleetwood Enterprises, Inc.
PROWLER LYNX - Trailers–travel ☆ - Fleetwood Enterprises, Inc.
PROWLER PARK TRAILERS - Trailers–travel - Fleetwood Enterprises, Inc.
PROWLER REGAL - Trailers–travel ☆ - Fleetwood Enterprises, Inc.
PROWOOD - Hardware - Universal Forest Products Inc.
PROWOOD - Wood products - Universal Forest Products, Inc.
PROWORKS - Computer software - Sun Microsystems, Inc.
PROWRITER - Printers–computer - C-TECH Electronics Inc.
PROX - Golfing equipment - Allied Golf Co.
PROX-O-LITE - Electronic equipment - Rollei of America Inc.
PROXABRUSH - Toothbrushes - John O.Butler Co.
PROXACOL - Pharmaceutical preparations - Warner-Wellcome
PROXAPIC - Dental equipment ☆ - John O.Butler Co.
PROXENE - Pharmaceutical preparations ☆ - JMI-Canton Pharmaceuticals
PROXGATE - Computer software - Proxima Inc.
PROXIFAR - Lenses–photographic - SP Systems/Saratons
PROXIGEL - Health care products - Reed & Carnrick
PROXIMA - Electronics equipment - Computer Accessories/Proxima
PROXIMA OVATION - Computer peripheral equipment - Proxima Corp.
PROXIMAGE & PRAT - Stationery - Press Book Prat, Inc.
PROXIMAT - Lenses–photographic - SP Systems/Saratons
PROXIMATE ACCESS - Medical apparatus - Johnson & Johnson
PROXIMELLE - Luggage - Chia Tai Inc., Ltd.
PROXIMITY - Computer software - Decisionmark Corp.
PROXIMITY - Measuring instruments - Dwyer Instruments, Inc.
PROXISCOPE - Photographic equipment - SP Systems/Saratons
PROXITEL - Lenses–photographic - SP Systems/Saratons

☆ = Now out of production

PROXIVAR - Lenses–photographic - SP Systems/Saratons

PROXPRESS - Iron - Black & Decker Corp.

PROXRITE - Electronic equipment - Allsafe Co. Inc.

PROXTAG - Electric equipment - Checkpoint Systems Inc.

PROXUS - Golfing equipment - Donald Jeen Chang Sun

PROXY - Frames–eyeglass - Liberty Optical Manufacturing Co.

PROXY - Shoes - Arcadia International Shoe Corp. (Palizzio Div.)

PROXYCARB - Bleach - Riverside Products Corp.

PROXYCERT - Computer software - Transcender Corp.

PROXYNET - Computer software - WM Applications Inc.

PROZAP - Rodenticides - Hacco, Inc./Loveland Industries, Inc.

PROZAP AGRI-BRAND - Rodenticides - Hacco, Inc./Loveland Industries, Inc.

PROZINE-50 - Pharmaceutical preparations ☆ - Roberts/Hauck
   Pharmaceuticals Inc.

PROZIP - Computer software - RT Computer Graphics, Inc.

PROZONE - Insecticides - Eight-In-One Pet Products, Inc.

PROZORB - Cleaning equipment - Contec, Inc.

PROZYDE - Pharmaceutical preparations ☆ - Tracy Pharmacal Co.

PROZYME - Pharmaceutical preparations ☆ - Ulmer Pharmacal Co.

PRP - Oil machinery - Petrol Rem, Inc.

PRP - Resins–polymer - Hamilton Co.

PRS - Computer software - C-Way Systems Inc.

PRS - Guitars - Paul Reed Smith Guitars

PRSC - Novelty items–glass - PRSC

PRSM - Optical fibers and couplers - Corning Inc.

PRT - Tools - Paratech Inc.

PRUDEN - Hams - Pruden Packing Co. Inc.

PRUDENCE - Floor coverings–carpet and rugs ☆ - Regal Rugs Inc.

PRUDENCE - Meat products–canned - Bunker Hill Foods

PRUDENCE - Publisher's imprints - Child Matters

PRUDENCE ISLAND - Screws - American Mussel Harvesters Inc.

PRUDENCE ISLAND VINEYARDS - Wines - Prudence Island Vineyards

PRUDENT - Gloves–rubber - American Health & Hospital Supplies Inc.

PRUDENTIAL - Cooking utensils–aluminum - West Bend Co.

PRUDENTIAL - Paints - Sullivan Co.

PRUDENTIAL - Screws - Prudential Building Materials

PRUF - Starch–laundry - Colgate-Palmolive Co.

PRUFACRYL - Paints ☆ - Devoe & Raynolds Co.

PRUFAST - Nails–horseshoe - Prudential Building Materials

PRUFCOAT - Paints ☆ - Devoe & Raynolds Co.

PRUFENAMEL - Paints ☆ - Devoe & Raynolds Co.

PRUFGLO - Paints ☆ - Devoe & Raynolds Co.

PRUFLEX - Adhesives and sealants ☆ - Geocel Corp.

PRUFTONE - Paints ☆ - Devoe & Raynolds Co.

PRUITT'S PEANUTS - Snack foods - David and Sons Inc.

PRULET - Laxatives ☆ - Mission Pharmacal Co.

PRULOSE COMPLEX - Laxatives - Standard Laboratories

PRUN-EVAC - Laxatives - Pharmex Inc.

PRUNA-MATE - Tools–garden - Kinsman Co. Inc.

PRUNE POWER - Health care products - Healthwatchers System

PRUNE TREAT WASHINGTON PRUNES - Fruits and vegetables - Valley Fruit

PRUNELLE - Lipsticks - Lancome

PRUNELLE GLACE - Lipsticks - Cosmair Inc.

PRUNERPLUS - Tools–garden - Ryobi America Corp.

PRUNICODEINE - Cold remedies - Eli Lilly and Co.

PRUNVAR (LEKVAR) - Prunes ☆ - Mallet and Co.

PRURILO - Pharmaceutical preparations - Whorton Pharmaceuticals Inc.

PRUSSIAN BLUE - Tools ☆ - Loctite Corp.

PRV - Vending machines - Nicola, Gudbranson, and Cooper

PRV-MUNE - Veterinary pharmaceutical preparations - Oxford Veterinary
   Laboratories, Inc.

PRY-AXE - Tools–hand-operated - Paratech Inc.

PRYDON - Pharmaceutical preparations - Smithkline Beecham Corp.

PRYDONNAL - Pharmaceutical preparations - Smithkline Beecham Corp.

PRYER - Mopeds - Palmer Industries

PRYFON - Insecticides ☆ - Bayer Corp. (Agriculture Div.)

PRYLAC - Hardware - Sherwin-Williams Automotive Finishes Corp.

PRYM - Craft supplies - Prym Dritz Corp.

PRYME - Varnishes - Pratt & Lambert, Inc. (Specialty Products Div.)

PRYME TYME - Recording label - PDS-Universal Entertainment Group Inc.

PRYMEX - Food products - Universal Foods Corp.

PRYMUS - Veterinary pharmaceutical preparations - Nutra-Vet Research Corp.

PRYNE - Fans–exhaust - Emerson Electric Co.

PRYOYL - Hardware - Sherwin-Williams Automotive Finishes Corp.

PRYPHEN - Hardware - Sherwin-Williams Automotive Finishes Corp.

PRYSYN - Hardware - Sherwin-Williams Automotive Finishes Corp.

P.S. - Cigars ☆ - G.W. Van Slyke & Horton

PS - Computer software - Medical Systems, Inc.

PS - Deodorizers - Surco Products Inc.

PS - Fishing tackle - P/S Engineering and Manufacturing Co.

PS - Fragrance - Paul Sebastian, Inc.

PS - Hair care products - Dowbrands L.P.

PS - Jewelry–precious - Prime Source Int'l Corp.

P.S. - Lacquers - Sherburne Ewing Wallcovering Co.

P.S. - Paper–newsprint - MBNA America Bank, National Association

PS - Permanently-set pantograph - Graphicraft

P.S. - Pressure-sensitive adhesives - Aetna Felt Corp.

P.S. - Water–bottled or canned - Poland Spring Bottling Co.

PS 1 - Apparel–women's - Gitano Licensing, Ltd.

PS/1 - Computer software - International Business Machines Corp.

PS-2 - Golfing equipment - Pro Select Sports USA

PS-360 SERIES - Electronic equipment ☆ - Da-Lite Screen Co. Inc.

PS AUDIO - Audio equipment - PS Audio

P.S. COLLECTION - Girls' lingerie and sleepwear - Inner World Inc.

PS FOR WOMEN - Health care products - Brite Years Vitamins

PS GITANO - Footwear - G.G. Licensing, Inc.

P.S. IT'S FAT FREE - Cookies - Sherwood Brands, Inc.

PS JET + - Computer peripheral equipment - QMS

PS (PERFORMANCE SERIES) - Audio equipment - ESS Laboratory Inc.

PS PLANTINUM SERIES - Sound equipment - Gemini Sound Products Corp.

P.S. PRODUCT SATISFACTION - Cleaning preparations - Cello Corp.

PS/VALUEPOINT - Computers - International Business Machines Corp.

PS1 - Golfing equipment - Pro Select Sports USA

PS45 - Contact lenses - Chariotstar Inc.

PS89 - Camera - Vivitar Corp.

PS250 - Contact lenses - Chariotstar Inc.

P.S.A. - Nail care products - DeEnterprises Inc.

PSALMS - Recording label - American Music Co.

PSC - Jewelry - Peter Storm Co.

PSC - Pumps - Franklin Electric Co.

PSC-24 - Electronic equipment - Ideal Stencil Machine and Tape Co.

PSCAP - Electronic equipment - Econd International, Inc.

PSCLONE - Computer software - Pipeline Associates Inc.

PSCO - Jewelry - Plainville Stock Co.

PSCREEN - Chemical preparations - Novagen, Inc.

PSD - Machine parts - Lako Tool & Manufacturing, Inc.

PSD4042 - Printers–computer - Comtec Information Systems, Inc.

PSE - Audio equipment - Sonics Associates, Inc.

PSE - Bottling machinery - Plant Service and Equipment Corp.

PSENNER PEARL WILLIAM - Liquors - Crestfield Importers Ltd.

PSEUDO BID - Pharmaceutical preparations ☆ - Abana Pharmaceuticals, Inc.

PSEUDO HIST - Pharmaceutical preparations ☆ - Abana Pharmaceuticals, Inc.

PSEUDO-MAL - Pharmaceutical preparations - Rugby Laboratories Inc.

PSEUDOCILLIN - Antibiotics ☆ - Lexis Laboratories Inc.

PSEUDOCOT - Pharmaceutical preparations ☆ - C.O. Truxton Inc.

PSG - Skin care products - PSG, LLC

PSG - Sporting goods - Pennsylvania Sporting Goods Co.

PSG PEPPER SPRAY GEAR - Self-defense spray - Anti-Victim Device, Inc.

PSI - Adhesives and sealants - Polymeric Systems, Inc.

PSI - Bearings–industrial - Rexnord Corp.

PSI - Electronics equipment - Photonic Systems Inc.

PSI - Plants, insects, and algae - Plant Sciences, Inc.

PSI FLEX-GEL - Surgical supplies - Pelton Shepherd Industries

PSI-LORDS - Books–comic - Voyager Communications Inc.

PSI METERVIEW - Computer software - Process Systems, Inc.

PSI ORIGEN - Computer software - Preferred Systems, Inc.

PSI PROCESS SYSTEMS - Electrical industrial apparatus - Process Systems,
   Inc.

PSII - Spectrometers - Analytical Spectral Devices Inc.

PSIONICS - Games ☆ - Mayfair Games, Inc.

PSITTIMUNE - Veterinary nutritional supplements - Biomune Co.

PSL - Binders - Majestic Penn State Inc.

P.S.L. - Cosmetics ☆ - Divina Products Co.

PSL - Educational materials - Team Labs Corp.

PSL 300 - Lumber - Trus Joist MacMillan L.P.

P'SLIP - Clay–modeling - New Century Ceramics

PSM - Animal feed supplements - Moorman Manufacturing Co.

PSM - Medical apparatus - Sarcos, Inc.

PSM - Sewing machines - Porter Sewing Machines, Inc.

PSM - Sporting goods - NDL Products Inc.

PSMSOURCE - Computer software - Primatech Inc.

PSORA-LENS - Goggles ☆ - ICN Pharmaceuticals Inc.

☆ = Now out of production

PSORA-SHIELDS - Eyes—glass ☆ - ICN Pharmaceuticals Inc.
PSORANIDE - Prescription drug ☆ - ICN Pharmaceuticals Inc.
PSORANIL - Pharmaceutical preparations - Sabinsa Corp.
PSORCON - Pharmaceutical preparations - Dermik Laboratories Inc.
PSORELIEF - Pharmaceutical preparations - Unipharma International (USA), Inc.
PSORI CLEAR - Pharmaceutical preparations - Royal Products, Inc.
PSORIA-GARD - Skin care products - Hobe Labs Inc.
PSORIASIS RELIEF - Pharmaceutical preparations - Consolidated Midland Corp.
PSORIASKIN - Health care products - ConsultingPlan USA
PSORIATROL - Pharmaceutical preparations - Roosa & Ratliff Drug Co.
PSORIGEL - Shampoos - Owen/Galderma Laboratories Inc.
PSORINAIL - Nail care products ☆ - Summers Laboratories Inc.
PSORIZIDE - Pharmaceutical preparations - Plymouth Pharmaceuticals, Inc.
PSOS - Computer software - Integrated Systems, Inc.
PSP - Fittings—cast iron - Fab-Tech Inc.
P.S.P. IV - Pharmaceutical preparations ☆ - Solvay Pharmaceuticals Inc.
P.S.Q. - Food products - US Foodservice
PSQ - Golfing equipment - International Golf Enterprises, Inc.
PSS - Audio equipment - Paso Sound Products Inc.
PSS - Computer software - Advanced Systems Concepts
PSSR - Hand tools - Richard N. Padgett
PSSSSSST - Shampoos - Clairol Inc.
PSSSSST - Frames—eyeglass - Zylo Ware Corp.
PSSST - Apparel—children's ☆ - Kellwood Co.
PST - Heating equipment - Loctite Corp.
P.S.T. - Paper - Marcal Paper Mills, Inc.
PST PIPE SEALANT 565 - Adhesives and sealants - Loctite Corp.
PST PIPE SEALANT 567 - Adhesives and sealants - Loctite Corp.
PST PIPE SEALANT 580 - Adhesives and sealants - Loctite Corp.
PST PIPE SEALANT 592 - Adhesives and sealants - Loctite Corp.
PSTER - Jewelry - Pace Enterprises
PSTIMATE - Computer software - Graphic Systems Technology, Inc.
PSU - Deodorizers - West Sanitation Services, Inc.
PSW - Computer software - PSW Technologies, Inc.
PSX - Computers - Tandem Computers Inc.
PSX - Softball bats - Pro Select, Inc.
PSY-DYE - Filters—water - High End Systems, Inc.
PSYBERNET - Computer software - Psybernetics, Inc.
PSYCH-O-LITE - Lighting equipment - National Artcraft Co.
PSYCH-OUT - Games - Wry Idea Co.
PSYCHE - Games - Inner Productions
PSYCHE - Perfumes - Gila Parfums
PSYCHEDELIC - Incense - Excelsior Incense Works
PSYCHEDELIC EYES - Decals and transfers - Wry Idea Co.
PSYCHEDELIC SATELLITE NETWORK - Apparel and accessories - Sterling Grant Hazen
PSYCHEDELIC SCENTS - Incense - Adams Apple Distributing L.P.
PSYCHEDILIA - Publisher's imprints - Ronin Publishing, Inc.
PSYCHIC CIRCLE - Games - Monte Farber
PSYCHIC I - Games - High Tech Marketing
PSYCHLONE - Sporting goods - Seneca Sports, Inc.
PSYCHO - Food products - Rapazzini Winery
PSYCHO - Pencils - Pentech International Inc.
PSYCHO - Toys - Tonka Corp.
PSYCHO-LOCK - Hardware ☆ - Graham-Field Inc.
PSYCHO NUMBERS - Toys - Maryland Toy Corp.
PSYCHO SPAGHETTI - Puzzles ☆ - Koplow Games
PSYCHO STICK - Skateboards - Vision Sports Holding Corp.
PSYCHOACOUSTIC SOUND - Recording label - T.E.C. Tones/Ralph Records
PSYCHOETRY - Educational materials - Brian Philip Wohlmuth
PSYCHOFFICE - Computer software - AdvantaCare, Inc.
PSYCHOLOGICAL METHODS - Publisher's imprints - American Psychological Association
PSYCHOLOGY OF VISION - Publisher's imprints - Charles Lee Spezzano
PSYCHOPATH MATH - Games - Smart Alec Toys, Inc.
PSYCHOSONIC COMIC - Books—comic ☆ - Marvel Entertainment Group, Inc.
PSYCHRO-NOMIC - Coolers—electric - Baltimore Aircoil Co. Inc.
PSYCLING - Apparel and accessories - No Fear, Inc.
PSYDATA - Publisher's imprints - Kenneth R. Frankel
PSYTEST - Computer software - Psychological Corp., Inc.
PT - Apparel—athletic - Powers Manufacturing Co.
PT - Buttons - Scandinavian House Imports Inc.
PT - Exercising equipment - Schwinn Cycling & Fitness Inc.
PT - Hardware - PT Coupling Co., Inc.

PT - Jewelry - Pearl Trend Ltd.
PT-19 FLIGHT TRAINER - Toys—airplanes - Cox Products Inc.
PT 90 PLUS - Golfing equipment - Suarez Corp.
PT 105 - Pharmaceutical preparations - Legere Pharmaceuticals Inc.
PT-109 - Computer software ☆ - Spectrum Holobyte, Inc.
P.T. JR. - Paint sprayers - Speeflo Manufacturing Corp.
PT/MC NAVIGATOR - Computer peripheral equipment - Power Transmission Distributors Association
PT PERFORMANCE TOOL - Tools—hand-operated - Wilmar Corp.
P.T. SCOUT - Paint sprayers - Speeflo Manufacturing Corp.
PT7 - Cleaning preparations - W.W. Grainger, Inc.
PTA - Computer software - Office Automation Systems, Inc.
PTA - Paints - Penn Crete Products Co. Inc.
PTACH - Computer software - Jeffrey Newman
PTB - Headwear - Trail Blazers, Inc.
P.T.C. - Chemical preparations - Monogram Sanitation Co.
PTC - Computers - Physicians Total Care, Inc.
PTC - Wheelchairs - Labac Systems, Inc.
PTC 9000 MEDICATION MANAGEMENT SYSTEM - Computer hardware and software - Physicians Total Care, Inc.
PTC INDUSTRIES - Carts - PTC Industries, Inc.
PTD - Communications equipment - GTE Service Corp.
PTE - Computer software - Custom Software Services, Inc.
PTERODACTYL SIDE CAR - Toys—automobiles - Saban Entertainment, Inc.
PTEX - Computer software - Paul A. Knaplund
P.T.G. - Automotive parts and accessories - Echlin Inc.
PTI - Computer software - Pinestar Technology, Inc.
PTL - Hardware - Maze Nails
P.T.M. - Drafting supplies ☆ - Teledyne Post
PTNY - Apparel stores—women's - Prime Time Sportswear NY, Inc.
PTO - Computer software ☆ - Koei Corp.
PTO - Garden equipment - Garden Way Inc.
PTOOEY - Candles - American Eagle Co., Inc. (Dedo Gargoyles)
PTOPE - Chemical preparations ☆ - Novagen, Inc.
PTOTER'S CHOICE - Tiles—ceramic - Florida Tile Industries, Inc.
PTOTER'S TOUCH - Tiles—ceramic - Florida Tile Industries, Inc.
PTP - Cold remedies ☆ - Concord Chemists
PTP - Computer software - Tandem Computers Inc.
PTP - Health care products - Vector Products Inc.
PTP - Paper - Ludlow Corp.
PTP I - Health care products - Vector Products Inc.
PTR-OH - Computer software - Barrie Adsett Computer Services, Inc.
PTR-US - Computer software - Barrie Adsett Computer Services, Inc.
P.T.S - Liquors - White Rock Distilleries Inc.
PTS CORPORATE - Computer software - Burr Wolff, LP
PTS TOTAL BODY TURBO - Exercising equipment - California Sports Equipment
PTS TURBO - Exercising equipment - California Sports Equipment
PTW - Varnishes - Samuel Cabot Inc.
PTX - Telescopes ☆ - Nutone Inc.
PUA - Apparel—men's - Surf Line Hawaii, Ltd.
PUB - Colognes - Revlon Consumer Products Corp.
PUB - Glassware—household ☆ - Lancaster Colony Corp.
PUB - Ice chests—plastic ☆ - Glacier Ware Inc.
PUB CHEESE - Cheese - Churny Co., Inc.
PUB CLUB - Beverages—alcohol - Majestic Distilling Co.
PUB CRAWL - Housewares - Lindy Promotions Inc.
PUB MASTER - Darts and dart games - General Sportcraft Co. Ltd.
PUB MUGS - Giftware - Charles Zahn-Import Merchant
PUB-NUTS - Food products - Willman Cookie & Nut Co.
PUB PARAPHANALIA - Novelty items - English Shopper
PUB RING TOSS - Games - S.J. Miller Co.
PUB SODA - Beverages—carbonated - Original Pub Soda Co.
PUBERTY 101 - Games - Borgardt & Bishop
PUBLIC - Thread - A. Lewis Thread Co. Inc.
PUBLIC ALLIES - Shirts - Public Allies: The National Center For Careers in Public Life
PUBLIC ASSISTANCE - Game tables - Hammerhead Enterprises, Inc.
PUBLIC CLOTHING CO. - Apparel—women's - Public Clothing Co.
PUBLIC DEBT - Apparel and accessories - Michael D. Thies
PUBLIC DOMAIN - Apparel and accessories - Systems Affiliates, Ltd.
PUBLIC ENEMY - Recording label - Bring the Noise, Inc.
PUBLIC FORUM - Computer software - Owen Michael Wilkerson
PUBLIC HISTORY - Publisher's imprints - Krieger Publishing Co.
PUBLIC IMAGE - Apparel and accessories - Pi Clothing, Inc.
PUBLIC IMAGE - Skin care products - Clientele, Inc.

PUBLIC NOTICE - Apparel and accessories - Fishman and Tobin Inc.
PUBLIC PANT - Slacks - Tommy Hilfiger Licensing, Inc.
PUBLIC PLACES - Disinfectants - Microgen Inc.
PUBLIC SAFETY - Chemical preparations - Monson Companies, Inc.
PUBLIC UTILITIES - Computer software - Fifth Generation Systems Inc.
PUBLIK - Floor coverings–carpet and rugs ☆ - Patrick Carpet Mills
PUBLISH ANYTHING! ONDISK & CD-ROM - Computer software - Brandel Communications, Inc.
PUBLISH CARD - Computer peripheral equipment - New Media Corp.
PUBLISH IT! - Computer software - Timeworks International Inc.
PUBLISH MATE - Machinery - Banner American Products Inc.
PUBLISHER'S ADVANTAGE COMPUTING SYSTEM - Computer software - T and B Computing, Inc.
PUBLISHERS CHOICE VIDEO - Recording label - National Syndications, Inc.
PUBLISHERS GROUP INTERNATIONAL - Publisher's imprints - Publishers Group International, Inc.
PUBLISHERS' PARADISE - Computer software - Data Conversion Specialists, Inc.
PUBLIX - Food products - Publix Super Markets, Inc.
PUBLIX PREMIER - Yogurt - Publix Super Markets, Inc.
PUBLIX PREMIUM - Ice cream - Publix Super Markets, Inc.
PUC - Apparel and accessories - Hering North America Inc.
PUCCI - Figurines - Arnart Imports Inc.
PUCCI AIR ORTHOTICS - Medical apparatus - D'mannco, Inc.
PUCHNER/COOPER - Musical instruments - Custom Music Co.
PUCK - Cleaning preparations - Super Brands, Inc.
PUCK OFF ROLLER HOCKEY WARE - Apparel and accessories - John L. Lyman
PUCK WEAR - Apparel and accessories - Puck Wear, Inc.
PUCKEE UP LINGERIE - Underwear and nightwear - Julius Corn & Co.
PUCKER BEARS - Candy - Brach Van Houten Holding Inc.
PUCKER-BRIEF - Apparel–women's - Nuvogue Creations
PUCKER HUSTLE - Candy - Brock Candy Co. Inc.
PUCKER PANTY - Apparel–women's - Wacoal America Inc.
PUCKER PUSS - Candy - Farley Candy Co.
PUCKER ROOS - Candy - Tom's Foods Inc.
PUCKER SUCKERS - Candy - Square Shooter Candy Co.
PUCKER-UPS - Candy - American Chewing Gum Inc.
PUCKERETTE PANTY - Apparel–women's - Wacoal America Inc.
PUCKERFREE - Thread - Belding Heminway Co. Inc.
PUCKERS - Candy - Leaf, Inc.
PUCKERS - Crackers ☆ - Sweet Adelaide Enterprises
PUCKERS PIG - Toys–stuffed ☆ - Russ Berrie and Co., Inc.
PUCKERUPPER - Exercising equipment - Matthews Management Inc.
PUCKHEAD - Novelty hats - Puckhead International
PUCKMASTER - Hockey equipment - Christian Brothers, Inc.
PUCKMASTER - Uniforms–athletic - Stall & Dean Manufacturing Co. Inc.
PUD - Chewing gum - Fleer Corp.
PUD-L-SCOOP - Pumps - Simer Pump Co.
PUDDIN - Dolls - Alexander Doll Co. Inc.
PUDDIN' CREMES - Cookies ☆ - Keebler Co.
PUDDIN' IN THE MIDDLE - Cakes–frozen - Sara Lee Corp.
PUDDIN ON THE RITZ - Food products - Food Pak Inc.
PUDDIN' ON THE RITZ - Food products ☆ - VIP Sales Co. Inc.
PUDDIN' PAWS - Recording label - Lawrence Enterprises
PUDDIN' THINGS - Ice cream - Vroman Foods Inc.
PUDDING ON A STICK - Frozen foods - J & J Snack Foods Corp.
PUDDING PLUS - Puddings–canned - Dean Foods Co.
PUDDING POCKETS - Desserts ☆ - Pillsbury Co.
PUDDING ROLL-UPS - Snack foods - General Mills, Inc.
PUDDING SHOP - Handbags - ACC Enterprises, LLC
PUDDING TO GO - Puddings–canned - Kozy Shack Inc.
PUDDLE BOOKS - Computer software ☆ - Knowledge Adventure
PUDDLE BUSTERS - Footwear - Max Merchandising, Inc.
PUDDLE D. DUCK - Chocolate candy - Superior Fruit & Confections
PUDDLE JUMPER PRESS - Greeting cards - Puddle Jumper Press, Inc.
PUDDLE JUMPERS - Footwear - Lowell Shoe, Inc.
PUDDLE JUMPERS - Recording label - Rick Vartian
PUDDLE PADS - Health care products - Americare Products
PUDDLE PAN - Washing machine parts - Moss Enterprises Inc.
PUDDLE QUESTIONS - Educational materials - Ideal School Supply Corp.
PUDDLEDUCK - Boats–dinghies - New England Skiff Builders
PUDDLES PUP - Toys–stuffed - Russ Berrie and Co., Inc.
PUDGE BROS. PIZZA, HOME OF THE MONSTER - Pizzas–mixes - Pudge Bros. Pizza, Home of the Monster LLC
PUDGIE BABY - Dolls - Horsman

PUDGIE POSERS - Toys–stuffed ☆ - Mighty Star Inc. (Special Effects Div.)
PUDGIES - Stationery ☆ - Joli Greeting Card Co.
PUDGIES NATURAL - Paper–toweling - Nice-Pak Products, Inc.
PUDGY BEAR - Toys–stuffed - Dakin Inc.
PUDGY PAL - Toys–stuffed - Eden LLC
PUDGY PALS - Statuary - Russ Berrie and Co., Inc.
PUDGY WUDGIES - Toys–stuffed - Fun World Inc.
PUD'N-CREAM CAKE MIX - Cake mix - Westco Products Inc.
PUEBLA - Shower stalls–metal - Kohler Co.
PUEBLA FOODS INC. - Tortillas - Puebla Foods, Inc.
PUEBLA FOODS INC. MEXICAN CORN TORTILLAS - Tortillas - Puebla Foods, Inc.
PUEBLA GLASSWORKS - Doors–glass - Kohler Co.
PUEBLO - Bicycles - Raleigh USA Bicycle Co.
PUEBLO - Clocks ☆ - General Time Corp. (Westclox/Seth Thomas Div.)
PUEBLO - Fencing–steel - CF and I Steel L.P.
PUEBLO - Floor coverings–carpet and rugs - Artistic Rugs Inc.
PUEBLO - Floor coverings–carpet and rugs ☆ - Regal Rugs Inc.
PUEBLO - Housewares ☆ - Treasure Craft Co.
PUEBLO - Occasional tables - JDI Group, Inc.
PUEBLO - Pencils - Empire Berol USA
PUEBLO DOMINICANO - Cigars - Rafael A. Lopez
PUEBLO GUARDS - Floor coverings - American Floor Products Co. Inc.
PUEBLO PIE - Frozen foods - SSE Foods, Inc.
PUEBLO SHADES - Tiles–ceramic - Summitville Tiles, Inc.
PUEBLO STONES - Tiles–ceramic - Summitville Tiles, Inc.
PUEBLOWARE - Dinnerware–plastic - Mallek Kay Studios
PUER DOG - Apparel and accessories - Sternheimer Bros., Inc.
PUERINGER - Meats - International Multifoods Corp.
PUERTA DEL SOL - Recording label ☆ - Champs-Elysees Inc.
PUERTO AZUL - Footwear - First International Corp.
PUERTO VALLARTA - Glassware–household - Crisa Corp.
PUF-N-PIE - Frosting - Brokay Products Inc.
PUFF - Bicycles - Schwinn Cycling & Fitness Inc.
PUFF - Sporting goods - Pennsylvania Sporting Goods Co.
PUFF - Toys–stuffed ☆ - Gund, Inc.
PUFF - Yarn ☆ - Plymouth Yarn Co.
PUFF BALL - Candy - Claeys Candy Inc.
PUFF DRAGON - Toys ☆ - Imperial Toy Corp.
PUFF-IT-CLEAN - Cooking equipment–household - Maywood Industries Inc.
PUFF-N-CORN - Snack foods - Snyder of Berlin
PUFF 'N GLO - Archery equipment - Kwikee-Kwiver Co., Inc.
PUFF 'N PLAY - Doll and children's furniture, tents, etc ☆ - Intex Recreation Corp.
PUFF PASTRY - Pastries - Dufour Pastry Kitchens Inc.
PUFF PETS - Toys–stuffed ☆ - Fun World Inc.
PUFF POOL - Games ☆ - Carrom Co.
PUFF PRINT - Apparel stores–sports - Challenger-General
PUFF PUFF - Toys–stuffed - Russ Berrie and Co., Inc.
PUFF TOYS - Toys - Petco Animal Supplies, Inc.
PUFFALOONS - Novelty items ☆ - Pacific Balloon Co., Inc.
PUFFALUMPS, THE - Hobby kits - Distinctive Design
PUFFALUMPS, THE - Toys–stuffed - Fisher-Price, Inc.
PUFFEAZE - Apparel and accessories - Pleasure-Knit Corp.
PUFFED KASHI - Cereal - Kashi Co.
PUFFER - Ships–sailing vessels - Sunfish Laser Inc.
PUFFER HUBBARD - Freezers - Revco Scientific, Inc.
PUFFERS - Fans–electric - Davoil, Inc.
PUFFETS - Christmas tree ornaments - Carousel Crafts Co.
PUFFIES - Decals and transfers - Scanner Badges, Inc.
PUFFIN - Bedding–linen - Welsh Co.
PUFFIN - Boats–canoes - Old Town Canoe Co.
PUFFIN - Doughs–frozen - Bridgeford Foods (Superior Div.)
PUFFIN BOOKS - Publisher's imprints - Penguin USA
PUFFIN DOWN - Apparel and accessories - Schuessler Knitting Mills Inc.
PUFFING DRAGON - Tea kettles–nonelectric - Metrokane
PUFFINS - Cereal - Barbara's Bakery, Inc.
PUFFINS - Fruits–dried ☆ - Paradigm Foodworks
PUFFINS - Novelty items - Pacific Balloon Co., Inc.
PUFFINS CRUNCHY CORN CEREAL - Cereal - Barbara's Bakery, Inc.
PUFFLE - Toys–stuffed - Cozy's Inc.
PUFFPAINT - Paints - Tulip Productions
PUFFS - Archery equipment - Archer Sports Inc.
PUFFS - Deodorizers - Candle Station, Ltd.
PUFFS - Facial tissues - Procter & Gamble Co.
PUFFS - Pet products - 8 in 1 Pet Products Inc.

☆ = Now out of production

PUFFS AU PRALINE - Candy - Premier Gourmet Products Inc.
PUFFS 'N HONEY - Cereal - Breadshop's Natural Foods
PUFFS O'LOVE - Toys–stuffed ☆ - Fun World Inc.
PUFFS O'SPRING - Toys–stuffed ☆ - Fun World Inc.
PUFFS PLUS - Facial tissues - Procter & Gamble Co.
PUFFS TO GO! - Facial tissues - Procter & Gamble Co.
PUFFY - Paints - Tulip Productions
PUFFY - Sporting goods ☆ - Schutt Manufacturing Co.
PUFFY - Toilet seats - Magnolia Products
PUFFY BEAR - Toys–stuffed ☆ - Gund, Inc.
PUFFY BRUSH - Makeup brush ☆ - Cosrich Inc.
PUFFY HEART - Deodorizers - Quality of Life Associates
PUFFY PALS - Toys–models ☆ - Century Products Co.
PUFFY PETS - Christmas tree ornaments - Fun World Inc.
PUFFY POMS - Novelty items - Aldastar Corp.
PUFFY PRODUCTS - Toys ☆ - Henry Gordy International Inc.
PUFFY STICKERS - Toys–stuffed - Fun World Inc.
PUF'N'TUF - Novelty items - Oak Rubber Co.
PUG - Pipes–tobacco - S.M. Frank & Co. Inc. (Kaywoodie-Yello-Bole-Medico)
PUG-NOSE - Fishing lures ☆ - Fred Arbogast Co. Inc.
PUGET - Wood products - Georgia-Pacific Corp.
PUGET FREE - Wood products - Georgia-Pacific Corp.
PUGET SOUND - Oxygen tents - Olympia Oyster Co.
PUGETSOL - Chemical preparations - Georgia-Pacific Corp.
PUGG - Sporting goods - Pugg Co., Inc.
PUGH - Gasoline - W.H. Pugh Oil Co.
PUHL - Soap ☆ - Freund-Mayer & Co. Inc.
PUHLS - Bath salts ☆ - European Soaps Ltd.
PUIFORCAT - Giftware - Puiforcat
PUIFORCAT - Silverware - Lalique North America
PUIG - Nuts–salted, roasted, cooked, or canned - Joseph Caragol Inc.
PUISSANCE - Golfing equipment - Pro Sports USA Co.
PUJA - Correction fluid - Sk Merchandising Corp.
PUKEBERG - Glass–safety ☆ - Leland Limited Inc.
PUKLIGHT - Lighting fixtures - Lucifer Lighting Co.
PUL-A-NAP - Napkins–paper - Fort Howard Corp.
PULASKI - Audio equipment ☆ - Pulaski Furniture Corp.
PULASKI - Axes ☆ - True Temper Hardware Co.
PULASKI - Pickles - Pikle-Rite Co. Inc.
PULGINI - Pasta - Made in France
PULICI - Food products ☆ - Old Ranchers Canning Co. Inc.
PULINEAL - Plastic structural beams - Pultrusions Corp.
PULITZ-HER - Apparel–women's - McCrory Corp.
PULITZER - Computer software - Naji A. Jurdi
PULITZER - Floor coverings–carpet and rugs - World Carpets, Inc.
PULITZOR PIZE - Pies–fresh - Buck's Desert Co.
PULL - Chocolate bars - Betco Corp.
PULL-A-LONG - Toys ☆ - Little Tikes Co.
PULL-A-PART - Toys - Uniquity
PULL A STRING LACE - Ribbon - Bowmaster Inc.
PULL-A-TUNE - Toys–musical - Fisher-Price, Inc.
PULL-ALL - Hoists - Griphoist Inc.
PULL-ALONG PLANE - Toys - Fisher-Price, Inc.
PULL & TEAR - Tape–adhesive ☆ - Permacel
PULL-APARTS - Apparel and accessories - Nesheeka, Inc.
PULL BOARD - Swimming pools - Recreonics, Inc.
PULL BOW - Ribbons ☆ - Equality/Stribbons
PULL BUOYS - Swimming pools - Recreonics, Inc.
PULL CUT - Saws–hand-operated - Takagi Tools, Inc.
PULL EASY - Thread - Cincinnati Thread Co.
PULL-MAN - Scrapers - Wooster Brush Co.
PULL-OUT PLAYHOUSE - Dolls - Mattel, Inc.
PULL-OUT POUCHES - Tool boxes - Reading Body Works, Inc.
PULL-PAC - Electrical equipment - General Cable Corp.
PULL PACK - Housewares - King Cotton Cordage Co.
PULL-PIN - Magnets - Aster Enterprises Inc.
PULL POPPERS - Toy cycles ☆ - Intex Recreation Corp.
PULL-PRUF - Health care products ☆ - Sammons Preston
PULL-R-HOIST - Lawn mowers - Porcelain Steel Buildings Co.
PULL SAW - Saws–hand-operated - Takagi Tools, Inc.
PULL-TAB PAK - Tubes–plastic - VisiPak
PULL TAB POKER - Games - Universal Manufacturing Co., Inc.
PULL THE DOT - Fasteners–snap - American Engineer Components
PULL TITE - Screws - Fastec Industrial Corp.
PULL-UMS - Toys - Marlin Toy Products Inc.
PULL UP - Cleaning preparations–carpet and rug - W.W. Grainger, Inc.

PULL-UP PETS - Toys ☆ - Playskool, Inc.
PULL-UPS - Diapers–disposable - Kimberly-Clark Corp.
PULL-X - Staple removers - Multi-Pro., Inc.
PULLAR BLUE - Chemical preparations - GC Thorsen, Inc.
PULLED BARBECUES - Sandwiches–prepackaged - Webber Farms
PULLER - Tires ☆ - Bridgestone/Firestone, Inc.
PULLER'S PRIDE - Trailers - Murphy's Welding Service
PULLETMATE - Animal feeds - Cenex/Land O'Lakes AG Services
PULLI-POPS - Candy ☆ - Y & S Candies Inc.
PULLITA - Rice - La Cena Fine Foods Inc.
PULLMAN - Beverages–malt - Riverside Brewing Co.
PULLMAN - Daters and numberers - Consolidated Stamp Manufacturing Co. Inc.
PULLMAN - Hardware - Blaine Window Hardware Inc.
PULLMAN - Trailers–travel - Pullman Camper Manufacturing Co. Inc.
PULLMAN - Trailers–travel ☆ - Carriage, Inc.
PULLMAN CLOTH - Fabrics - Gretchen Bellinger Inc.
PULLMAN/HOLT - Vacuum cleaners and accessories - Pullman/Holt Corp.
PULLSTONE - Hardware - Elizabeth M. Waldorf and Jennifer L. Isbill Partnership
PULLTARPS - Tarpaulins - Lynn Chenowth
PULM 300 - Pharmaceutical preparations ☆ - Saron Pharmacal Corp.
PULMA-GEL - Cough medicines - Metagenics, Inc.
PULMO-AIDE - Compressors–air - Sunrise Medical (Respiratory Products Division)
PULMO-AIDE TRAVELER - Compressors–air - Sunrise Medical (Respiratory Products Division)
PULMO-GRAPH - Medical apparatus ☆ - Sunrise Medical (Respiratory Products Division)
PULMO-NEB - Medical apparatus - Sunrise Medical (Respiratory Products Division)
PULMO-VENT - Respirators - National Medical Care
PULMO-WRAP - Health care products - Respironics, Inc.
PULMOHIST - Pharmaceutical preparations - G.O. Spanner Inc.
PULMOL FORTE - Pharmaceutical preparations - Vartex Pharmaceuticals Inc.
PULMONEX - Mattresses - Hill Rom, Inc.
PULMOSIN - Pharmaceutical preparations - G.O. Spanner Inc.
PULMOSONIC - Vaporizers ☆ - Sunrise Medical (Respiratory Products Division)
PULMOTOL - Pharmaceutical preparations - D'Franssia Corp.
PULMOTOSS - Cough medicines - Pharmakon Labs, Inc.
PULMOVITAL - Cough medicines - Benard Industries Inc.
PULP - Apparel and accessories - Origin America, LLC
PULPAID - Chemical preparations - Dow Corning Corp.
PULPARTNERS - Computer software - Pulpartners, LLC
PULSAIR - Alternating-pressure pad - International Medical Core
PULSAIR - Pharmaceutical preparations - Pulsair Inc.
PULSAIR OMS I - Oxygen - Pulsair Inc.
PULSAIR OMS II - Oxygen - Pulsair Inc.
PULSAPHEN - Pharmaceutical preparations - Wesley Pharmacal Co. Inc.
PULSAR - Cabinets - Schrock
PULSAR - Chemical preparations - Olin Corp.
PULSAR - Dental equipment - Mti Precision Products, Inc.
PULSAR - Electronic equipment - Avo Multi-Amp Corp.
PULSAR - Electronics equipment - RTI Research Technology International
PULSAR - Fabrics - Herman Miller, Inc.
PULSAR - Floor coverings–carpet and rugs ☆ - Royalweve Carpet Mills
PULSAR - Furniture - Avant Industries
PULSAR - Golfing equipment - Lisco, Inc.
PULSAR - Hot tubs–fiberglass ☆ - Jacuzzi Inc.
PULSAR - Machinery - Warrender, Ltd.
PULSAR - Mattresses - Ohio Mattress Co.
PULSAR - Motor vehicles–automobiles - Nissan Motor Corp. USA
PULSAR - Toys ☆ - Estes Industries
PULSAR - Wallpaper - S.R. Wood Inc.
PULSAR - Watches - Pulsar Time Inc.
PULSAR CONTROL - Door openers–electronic - Pulsar Control Corp.
PULSAR III - Aircraft–airplanes - SkyStar Aircraft Corp.
PULSAR NX - Motor vehicles–automobiles - Nissan Motor Corp. USA
PULSAR ST 200 - Skis - Wellington Leisure Products, Inc.
PULSARE - Boats–motor - Checkmate Boats Inc.
PULSATION - Plumbing fixtures–metal - Moen Inc.
PULSATOR - Irrigation equipment - Wade Manufacturing Co.
PULSAVAC - Surgical tubing - Zimmer, Inc.
PULSE - Audio equipment - Yorkville Sound
PULSE - Bicycles - Dynacraft Industries Inc.

☆ = Now out of production

PULSE - Bicycles - Klein Bicycle Corp.
PULSE - Boats - Lanness K. McKee & Co.
PULSE - Boats–motor - Checkmate Boats Inc.
PULSE - Bowling balls - Columbia Industries, Inc.
PULSE - Furnaces–electric - Lennox Industries Inc.
PULSE - Games - Proplan, Inc.
PULSE - Generators - Coleman Powermate, Inc.
PULSE - Watches - Precise International/Wenger
PULSE I - Deodorizers - Technical Concepts, L.P.
PULSE 21 - Heaters–gas - Lennox Industries Inc.
PULSE BAR - Air purification systems - Simco
PULSE GUN - Air purification systems - Simco
PULSE I - Cleaning preparations - Scentex Inc.
PULSE IV - Office furniture–plastic - La-Z-Boy Chair Co.
PULSE KLEENER - Filters–air - Exijet Inc.
PULSE-LITE - Electrical testing instruments - Pulse-Lite Inc.
PULSE-LOK - Connectors–electronic - Alden Products Co.
PULSE OXIMETER - Medical apparatus - Nellcor Puritan Bennett
PULSE-PAK - Circuit boards - Pulse Charge Systems, Inc.
PULSE PERCUSSION - Drums–musical instruments - Semita Corp.
PULSE POINTER - Printers–computer - D'San Corp.
PULSE SPECTRUM - Communications equipment - Pulse Engineering, Inc.
PULSE STAR - Exercising equipment - Battle Creek Equipment Co.
PULSE TECHNOLOGIES - Computer software - Saint Francis, Inc.
PULSE TOUCH - Dictating machines ☆ - Dictaphone Corp.
PULSE WATCH II - Exercising equipment - Precise International/Wenger
PULSEAGILE - Laboratory apparatus - Cyto Pulse Sciences, Inc.
PULSECHECK - Health care products - Elexis Corp.
PULSECOACH - Health care products - Elexis Corp.
PULSECOACH II - Health care products - Elexis Corp.
PULSEMINDER - Heart monitors ☆ - Polar Electro Inc.
PULSETIME - Health care products - Elexis Corp.
PULSETRACK - Sporting goods - Nordictrack, Inc.
PULSETRONIX - Hardware ☆ - Graham-Field Inc.
PULSEWATCH - Health care products - Elexis Corp.
PULSEWEAR - Brassieres (Bras) - Lovable Co.
PULSOAR - Refrigerators - Calmac Manufacturing Corp.
PULSOR - Medical apparatus - JB Research, Inc.
PULSOX-7 - Health care products ☆ - Marquest Medical Products Inc.
PULSTAR - Electronic equipment - Pulse Dynamics Manufacturing Corp.
PULVER-EYES - Toys - Tonka Corp.
PULVERIZADOR - Skin care products - Dynex International
PULVERIZOR - Toys - Tonka Corp.
PULVEX - Pet products - Zema Corp.
PULVEX CHRYSANTHEMUM EXTRACT - Dips–pets - Zema Corp.
PUMA - Archery equipment - High Country American
PUMA - Footwear–athletic - Puma Inc.
PUMA - Mats - Matworks
PUMA TX-3 - Footwear–athletic - Puma Inc.
PUMICE PRO - Soap - Miracle Line Inc.
PUMIE - Housewares - United States Pumice Co.
PUMIE CHAR ROCK - Outdoor-living product - United States Pumice Co.
PUM'KIN HEADS - Chocolate candy - Superior Fruit & Confections
PUMKINS - Candy - Rodda Candy Co.
PUMP-A-DRINK - Containers - Aladdin Industries, Inc.
PUMP GUARD - Electronic equipment - R.E. Prescott Co., Inc.
PUMP IT - Air fresheners - E. Davis Inc.
PUMP IT - Medical apparatus - Genesis Industries Inc.
PUMP IT UP! - Footwear–athletic - Reebok International Ltd.
PUMP 'N PLAY - Toys - Tonka Corp.
PUMP 'N POWER - Apparel–athletic - Age Group Ltd.
PUMP-N-SEAL - Machinery - Pioneering Concepts Inc.
PUMP-N-SHOOT - Pesticides–household - Bonide Products, Inc.
PUMP OMNI ZONE - Athletic footwear - Reebok International Ltd.
PUMP PACK - Pharmaceutical preparations - Bricker Laboratories
PUMP PAL - Cosmetics ☆ - Delta Industries International, Inc.
PUMP PAL - Pumps–water ☆ - Jacuzzi Brothers
PUMP-PETS - Pottery products - Duncan Enterprises
PUMP STATION - Brackets - Gojo Industries, Inc.
PUMP, THE - Adhesives and sealants - Ashland Oil, Inc.
PUMP, THE - Apparel and accessories - Reebok International Ltd.
PUMP-UP - Toothpaste - Polyproducts Corp.
PUMP UP YOUR LASH - Cosmetics - Select Brands
PUMP-X53 - Cement - Edison Coatings, Inc.
PUMPAK - Water purification systems - MP Pumps Inc.
PUMPBALL - Balls - Weiss Twice Toys, Inc.

PUMPED WITH ATTITUDE - Apparel–athletic - S. Kathleen Cowan
PUMPENCIL - Pencils - Dur-O-Lite Inc.
PUMPERNIBBLES - Snack foods ☆ - Pepperidge Farm Inc.
PUMPERNICKEL - Wallpaper - Seabrook Wallcoverings, Inc.
PUMPERS - Socks - Jobst Institute Inc.
PUMPHOUSE - Sporting goods - Daniel Timmes
PUMPHREY'S BLEND - Teas - Peet's Coffee and Tea, Inc.
PUMPING CURLS - Hair care products - Cosmair Inc.
PUMPING IRONS - Hair care products - Conair Corp.
PUMPIT - Cement - Refractory Technology, Inc.
PUMPKIN - Dolls - Alexander Doll Co. Inc.
PUMPKIN - Games ☆ - Koplow Games
PUMPKIN - Recording label - Empty Sky Records
PUMPKIN BUDDIES - Giftware - Russ Berrie and Co., Inc.
PUMPKIN DELIGHTS - Cakes - McKee Foods Corp.
PUMPKIN FACE - Chewing gum - Fleer Corp.
PUMPKIN FACES - Novelty items - At the Zoo
PUMPKIN JOYS - Seeds–salted, roasted, cooked, or canned - Glico Harmony Foods Corp.
PUMPKIN KISS - Dishes–earthenware - Homestead, Inc.
PUMPKIN LITE - Candles - Candle-Lite Co.
PUMPKIN MAGIC - Decorations - Highgate Products, Inc.
PUMPKIN MASTERS - Hobby kits - Pumpkin Masters, Inc.
PUMPKIN MONSTER - Batteries - Fun World Inc.
PUMPKIN PACK - Flashlights ☆ - Mag Instrument Inc.
PUMPKIN PAIRS - Candy ☆ - R.M. Palmer Co.
PUMPKIN PALS - Candy ☆ - Deran Holding Co., Inc.
PUMPKIN PARTY - Novelty items - Paper Magic Group Inc.
PUMPKIN PATCH - Amusement parks - Sellner Manufacturing Co., Inc.
PUMPKIN PATCH - Candy ☆ - R.M. Palmer Co.
PUMPKIN PATCH - Craft supplies ☆ - VIP/VIP Crafts
PUMPKIN PATCH - Magnets - Russ Berrie and Co., Inc.
PUMPKIN PLACE - Toys–stuffed - Russ Berrie and Co., Inc.
PUMPKIN POP-UPS - Toys–stuffed - Fun World Inc.
PUMPKIN PRETENDERS - Decorations - Sunstar Industries Inc.
PUMPKIN RIDGE GOLF CLUB - Apparel and accessories - Pumpkin Ridge Golf Club
PUMPKIN TIME - Candles - Kmart Properties, Inc.
PUMPKINS & SPICE - Deodorizers - Reynolds Consumer Products, Inc.
PUMPMASTER - Rifles–pneumatic - Crosman Corp.
PUMPMINDER, THE - Pumps - West Coast Tank, Piping & Construction Inc. (Pumpminder Div.)
PUMP'N JUMP - Exercising equipment - William T. Wilkinson
PUMPPALS - Shoe accessories - PediFix Footcare Co.
PUMPQUICK - Novelty items - International Venture Capital Inc.
PUMP+RUN - Apparel–athletic - Schweizer's Therapy and Rehabilitation
PUMPS-A-LOT - Pumps–water - G.T. Water Products Inc.
PUN-CHEE PANDA - Toys–stuffed - Russ Berrie and Co., Inc.
PUN 'KIN SEAT - Infant product - Welsh Co.
PUNA - Food products - Amfac Tropical Products
PUNCH - Audio equipment - Rockford Corp.
PUNCH - Candy - Murray-Allen International Inc.
PUNCH - Cigars - Danby-Palicio
PUNCH - Detergents - Colgate-Palmolive Co.
PUNCH - Fungicides - E.I. Dupont de Nemours and Co.
PUNCH AND DIE DETAILS - Tools–machine - Esterline Technologies Corp.
PUNCH-DRAIN - Nautical instruments - Daniel Gabison
PUNCH-IT OUT - Labels–paper - Charles Strickland
PUNCH KISSES - Candy ☆ - Glenn Confections Inc.
PUNCH LINE - Apparel and accessories - Kellwood Co.
PUNCH LINE - Beverages - Sundor Brands Inc.
PUNCH 'N' FILE - Office furniture–plastic - Merrick Industries Inc.
PUNCH N FRUITY - Beverages - White Rock Products Corp.
PUNCH 'N GRO - Flowers, plants, and seeds ☆ - NK Lawn & Garden Co.
PUNCH 'N JUICY - Candy ☆ - American Chicle Co.
PUNCH-O-BALLS - Novelty items - Oak Rubber Co.
PUNCH OUT - Cleaning preparations–carpet and rug - Punchline Products
PUNCH POPS - Fruit pops–frozen - Consolidated Flavor Corp.
PUNCH-PRO - Tools–power-driven - Hougen Manufacturing, Inc.
PUNCH-RITE - Punches–tool - P.J. Mieth Manufacturing Co. Inc.
PUNCH-UATION! - Fruit drinks–bottled or canned - Juice Pac, Inc.
PUNCH UP - Food products - Marbo, Inc.
PUNCHBOWLE - Tobacco products ☆ - House of Edgeworth
PUNCHEES - Fruit drinks–bottled or canned - Vines Enterprises, Inc.
PUNCHERS - Toys - Tonka Corp.
PUNCHIN' JIMMY - Ribbons - Z-Barten Productions

☆ = Now out of production

PUNCHINELLO - Bedding–linen - Dan River Inc.
PUNCHMASTER - Paper punches ☆ - Markwell Manufacturing Co. Inc.
PUNCHODEX - Paper punches - Rolodex Corp.
PUNCTUAL - Clocks ☆ - General Time Corp. (Westclox/Seth Thomas Div.)
PUNCTUATION BASEBALL - Computer software - Gamco Industries Inc.
PUNCTUATION CHECK - Ribbons–inked - Smith Corona Corp.
PUNCTUATION + STYLE - Computer software ☆ - Software Heaven
PUNCTUATION PUT-ON - Computer software ☆ - Sunburst Communications, Inc.
PUNCTUATION RULES - Computer software - Optimum Resource, Inc.
PUNCTURE GUARD - Adhesives and sealants - Puncture Guard, LLC
PUNCTURE PROOF - Liquid tire sealant - Puncture Proof, Inc.
PUNGEN - Pet products - Seachem Laboratories
PUNISHER, THE - Toys - Marvel Entertainment Group, Inc.
PUNISHER, THE - Guitars - Gene Simmons
PUNJA - Fabrics - Dan River Inc.
PUNJAB - Fabrics - Dan River Inc.
PUNJAB JUTE - Wallpaper ☆ - Wolf-Gordon Inc.
PUNJAB VICTOR - Abrasive products ☆ - American Hone Co.
PUNJIM - Fabrics - Dan River Inc.
PUNK - Toys - Tonka Corp.
PUNKIES - Greeting cards ☆ - Fran Mar Greeting cards Ltd.
PUN'KIN - Dolls ☆ - Effanbee Doll Co.
PUNKIN & P. J. - Greeting cards - Kersten Bros. Studios
PUNKIN HEAD - Toys–stuffed - Dakin Inc.
PUNKIN PATCH - Seeds–salted, roasted, cooked, or canned ☆ - David and Sons Inc.
PUNKINHEAD - Figurines - Anna-Perenna Inc.
PUNKINHEAD PEGS - Toys - Lauri Inc.
PUNKY - Cosmetics - Jerome Russell Cosmetics, Inc.
PUNKY - Toys–stuffed - Gund, Inc.
PUNKY - Toys–stuffed - Russ Berrie and Co., Inc.
PUNKY BREWSTER - Puzzles ☆ - Milton Bradley Co.
PUNKYS - Candy - Willy Wonka Brands
PUNNY BUSINESS - Greeting cards - American Greetings Corp.
PUNOS - Recording label - Jazz Composer's Orchestra Association Inc.
PUNT - Insecticides - Vectec, Inc.
PUNTA BRAVA - Seafood products–fresh or frozen - Kitchens of the Oceans Inc.
PUNTA CLARA KITCHEN - Candy - Punta Clara Kitchen, Inc.
PUNTINI - Confections - Chipurnoi Inc.
PUNTOONS - Greeting cards - Mack Rowe Visual Communications, Ltd.
PUP CHIPS - Dog food - Superior Brands Inc.
PUP CORN - Dog food - Bruce W. Brown
PUP DESIGN - Dog food - Stevens Industries Inc.
PUP E. LUV - Pet products - Alpha Innovative Products Inc.
PUP HUT - Pet products - Pet Castle Co.
PUP-JAMAS - Pet products - Debonair Pets of California
PUP LINKS - Dog food ☆ - Gimborn U.S., Inc.
PUP-O - Dog food ☆ - Central Nebraska Packing Inc.
PUP PAK - Pet products - Aero/Byne Co.
PUP-PERONI - Dog food - Heinz Pet Products Co.
PUP-PET - Pet products ☆ - Bardwyn Productions Inc.
PUP SHELL - Trailers–travel - Rancho Trailers Inc.
PUPA - Cosmetics - The Wilkes Group
PUP'KIN PATTERN - Novelty items–paper - National Child Safety Council
PUPKORN - Pet product - Items Inc.
PUPMITT - Pet products - Marilyn A. Englund
PUPP-KITS - Breads–mixes ☆ - Morrison Milling Co.
PUPPERMINT - Pet products - Petkin Pet Care Systems
PUPPET-GO-ROUND - Toys–models ☆ - Century Products Co.
PUPPET PALS - Puppets - Kencraft, Inc.
PUPPET PARADE - Toys–stuffed - Russ Berrie and Co., Inc.
PUPPET PARTNERS - Puppets - Gregory A. Frank Co.
PUPPET PETS - Toys - Toy Originators Inc.
PUPPET SHOW - Computer software - Laureate Learning Systems Inc.
PUPPET TALES - Puppets - Native Art Trading Co.
PUPPET THEATER - Educational materials - Twinson Co.
PUPPETDEARS - Sponges - Delby System
PUPPI PAL - Candy ☆ - L.E.G. Inc.
PUPPIES' ADVENTURE - Toys - Mattel, Inc.
PUPPIES AND BEARS - Toys–models ☆ - Century Products Co.
PUPPIES KNOW - Dog food - Nabisco Foods Group
PUPPIES, THE - Recording label ☆ - Joey Boy Records Corp.
PUPPIZZA - Dog food - Best Bred Products
PUPPY - Hot-dog sandwiches - Southeast Food Systems, Inc.

PUPPY - Loudspeakers - Wilson Audio Specialties, Inc.
PUPPY-AID - Pet food - Hunte Corp.
PUPPY ALIVE - Toys–stuffed - Kenner Products
PUPPY BOOSTER - Pet products - Natra Pet Inc.
PUPPY CARE - Dog food - Bailes Pet Food Co. Inc.
PUPPY CHECK-UP - Toys–stuffed - Tonka Corp.
PUPPY CHOW - Dog food - Ralston Purina Co.
PUPPY DROPS - Vitamins and nutritional supplements - Tomlyn Products
PUPPY GUNDS - Toys–stuffed ☆ - Gund, Inc.
PUPPY IN MY POCKET - Footwear–children's ☆ - S. Goldberg and Co. Inc.
PUPPY IN MY POCKET - Toys - Morrison Entertainment Group
PUPPY KIST - Dog food - Gold Kist Inc.
PUPPY LOVE - Calendars - American Greetings Corp.
PUPPY LOVE - Candy - Fleer Corp.
PUPPY LOVE - Dog food - Jim Dandy Co.
PUPPY LOVE - Perfumes - Philosophy, Inc.
PUPPY MAGIC - Pet products - Bluebonnet Milling Co.
PUPPY OS - Dog food - Pet Products Plus
PUPPY PACK - Pet products ☆ - Black Sheep Inc.
PUPPY PAD - Pet products - Dallas Manufacturing Inc.
PUPPY PAK - Pet products ☆ - Black Sheep Inc.
PUPPY PAL - Dog food ☆ - Central Soya Co. Inc.
PUPPY PAPER - Pet products - Rolf C. Hagen (USA) Corp.
PUPPY PARK - Pet products - Country Puppy
PUPPY PIDDLE PADS - Pet products - Spellman & Zenon Products Corp.
PUPPY PIECES - Dog food - Heinz Pet Products Co.
PUPPY PLAY - Bicycles ☆ - Huffy Corp.
PUPPY PLUS - Dog food - Bailes Pet Food Co. Inc.
PUPPY PRESERVER - Pet products - Black Sheep Inc.
PUPPY PROTECTOR - Radiation shielding equipment - Agri Laboratories, Ltd.
PUPPY PUDDLERS - Pet products - Teach Your Pet Inc.
PUPPY PUPPY - Toys–stuffed - Shoot the Moon Products, Inc.
PUPPY RUFF - Toys–stuffed - Mattel, Inc.
PUPPY SHIELD - Pet products - Lambert-Kay
PUPPY SURPRISE - Toys - Hasbro, Inc.
PUPPY TALES - Calendars - American Greetings Corp.
PUPPY TUG & TWIRL - Pet products - HMH Productions
PUPPYLAC - Veterinary nutritional supplements - Landco
PUPPY'S FIRST YEAR - Pet products - Media West Home Video Inc.
PUPPYVITE - Veterinary pharmaceutical preparations - Evsco Pharmaceuticals
PUPUCE - Apparel–children's - Trend Associates, Inc.
PUR - Water purification systems - Recovery Engineering, Inc.
PUR-A-GOLD - Electronic equipment - Enthone-OMI
PUR-ADE - Beverages - Tropicana Products, Inc.
PUR-AIR - Air purification systems - Barnebey and Sutcliffe Corp.
PUR-AIR - Air purification systems - OK Industries Inc.
PUR-AMEL - Enamels - Pur-All Paint Products Co. Inc.
PUR-BRITE - Paints - Pur-All Paint Products Co. Inc.
PUR-DECK - Paints - Pur-All Paint Products Co. Inc.
PUR-FLO - Filters–industrial - Standard-Keil Hardware Manufacturing Co.
PUR-LAST - Paints - Pur-All Paint Products Co. Inc.
PUR-O-PAK - Water purification systems - Akzo America Inc.
PUR-POOL - Paints - Pur-All Paint Products Co. Inc.
PUR PORTABLE - Water purification systems - Recovery Engineering, Inc.
PUR SILVER - Motor vehicle parts and accessories - BASF Corp.
PUR-VAR - Varnishes - Pur-All Paint Products Co. Inc.
PURA - Vitamins and nutritional supplements - D'Franssia Corp.
PURA - Water–bottled or canned - Triangle Distilled Water
PURA-BAND - Hearing aids - Moldex-Metric Inc.
PURA-FIT - Plugs–ear - Moldex-Metric Inc.
PURA LOPEZ - Footwear - Academia Inc.
PURA MASK - Tools ☆ - Moldex-Metric Inc.
PURAFILTER - Air purification systems - Purafil, Inc.
PURAFYZIT - Cleaning preparations - Royal Source, Inc.
PURAIRE - Air purification systems - Sperti Sunlamp
PURALKYD - Enamels ☆ - Adelphi Coatings Co.
PURALUBE - Health care products - E. Fougera & Co. Inc.
PURASAN - MARINE SANITATION DEVICE - Toilets–portable - Raritan Engineering Co. Inc.
PURAWATER - Pet products - Rudducks USA Inc.
PURBASE - Software - Public Utilities Reports Inc.
PURCELL - Floor coverings - Virginia Hardwood Co.
PURCHASESQL - Computer software - Commerce Software, Inc.
PURCHASING AT A GLANCE - Computer software - Charleston Financial Services Inc.
PURDU POP - Popcorn - Ramsey Popcorn

☆ = Now out of production

PURDUE BOILERMAKERS - Apparel and accessories - Purdue University
PURDUE UNIVERSITY - Apparel and accessories - Purdue University
PURDUM'S - Paints - Purdum Paint Co. Inc.
PURDY - Brushes–paint - Purdy Corp.
PURDY NEAT STUFF - Luggage - Purdy Neat Things Co., Inc.
PURE - Cookies - Nabisco Foods Group
PURE - Linen - Springs Industries, Inc.
PURE - Magazines - Taylor Made Golf Co. Inc.
PURE - Vegetable oil ☆ - Catania-Spagna Corp.
PURE - Water–bottled or canned - Ozark Water Co.
PURE - Wheels–motor vehicle - Progressive Custom Wheels
PURE-3-THREE - Paint ☆ - Continental Products Co.
P.U.R.E. .5 - Apparel and accessories - Alfred Coleman Burnett, II
PURE-A-PHY - Health care products - Alta Health Products
PURE ADVANTAGE - Gloves - Tillotson Healthcare Corp.
PURE ADVANTAGE POWDER FREE - Gloves - Tillotson Healthcare Corp.
PURE AIR 99 - Air purification systems - Pollenex Corp.
PURE AIR BY RGF - Air purification systems - RGF 03 Systems, Inc.
PURE AIRE 1000 - Air purification systems - Pollenex Corp.
PURE AIRE 2000 - Cleaning preparations–household - Pollenex Corp.
PURE AMERICAN - Water–mineral - Aquapenn Spring Water Co., Inc.
PURE & BASIC - Hair care products - Head Shampoo, Inc.
PURE & GENTLE - Shampoos - Almay Inc.
PURE & LIGHT - Juices ☆ - Dole Food Co., Inc.
PURE & NATURAL - Cosmetics ☆ - Jason Natural Products, Inc.
PURE & NATURAL - Finishing agents ☆ - Siphon Art Products
PURE & NATURAL - Paints - Triangle Coatings Inc.
PURE & NATURAL - Soap - Dial Corp.
PURE & NATURAL - Syrup - Lollipop Tree
PURE & NATURAL - Teas–herbal - Nature's Design Ltd.
PURE & PERFECT - Food products - Aloha Produce Corp.
PURE & SIMPLE - Blankets - Faribault Woolen Mill Co.
PURE & SIMPLE - Recording label - Pure & Simple Records
PURE & SIMPLE - Vitamins and nutritional supplements - MLO Products, Inc.
PURE ANGST - Apparel and accessories - Thermal Die Cutters, Inc.
PURE ART - Apparel and accessories - Pure Art USA, Inc.
PURE AS GOLD - Lubricants - Pep Boys Manny, Moe & Jack
PURE ASSAM IRISH BREAKFAST - Teas - Grace Tea Co. Ltd.
PURE ATTRACTION - Skin care products - Giorgio Beverly Hills
PURE BALANCE - Golfing equipment - Golfsmith International Inc.
PURE BASIX - Apparel–men's - BUM International Inc.
PURE-BIND - Corn starch - Grain Processing Corp.
PURE BLISS - Perfumes - Mary Kay Inc.
PURE-BRAND - Pet products - Petrapport, Inc.
PURE BREW - Paper coffee filters - Little Rapids Corp.
PURE BRIGHT - Computer software - Maxwell Technologies, Inc.
PURE BRIGHT - Lighting fixtures - Foodco Corp.
PURE CAL - Water purification systems - Western Lime Corp.
PURE CARE - Pet products - Purepet Co.
PURE CARE - Skin care products - Avon Products, Inc.
PURE CHECK - Pet products - Precision Aquarium Testing Inc.
PURE-CIDE - Water treating compounds - Bio-Dex Laboratories
PURE CLASIX - Apparel and accessories - BUM International Inc.
PURE CLEAN - Cleaning preparations - Ecolab Inc.
PURE CLOVER - Pet products - Purepet Co.
PURE COCKTAIL NECKS - Seafood products–fresh or frozen - Galilean Seafood, Inc.
PURE COMFORT - Brassieres (Bras) - Montgomery Ward & Co. Inc.
PURE COTTON HAGGAR CLOTHING CO. - Apparel and accessories - Haggar Apparel Co.
PURE COUNTRY - Apparel and accessories - Karman Western Apparel
PURE COUNTRY - Cider ☆ - Veryfine Products, Inc.
PURE CRAW - Fishing tackle - James Kelch Taube II
PURE CREAM - Skin care products - Origins Natural Resources Inc.
PURE CULTURE - Health care products - Pure Culture Products
PURE DECEIT - Perfumes - Proverbial Inc.
PURE DEFENSE - Health care products - Healthwatchers System
PURE-E - Health care products - Health Maintenance Programs Inc.
PURE EBONY - Fabrics - Dan River Inc.
PURE EFFECT - Water purification systems - Pure Effect
PURE ELEGANCE - Infant product ☆ - Ming Ta Supply
PURE ENERGY - Herbal supplement - Montana Naturals Int'l. Inc.
PURE ESSENTIALS - Skin-care products - Ilona Moldavon
PURE EYES - Contact lenses - Ciba-Geigy Corp.
PURE-FACT - Water–bottled or canned - Pure-Fact Inc.
PURE FISH - Pet products - Marketech

PURE FIT - Hardware - Pure Fit, Inc.
PURE FLAME - Fireplaces - Majestic Co.
PURE FLOW - Monitors–electronic - Tri-Gas, Inc.
PURE FLUID INTELLIGENCE - Skin care products ☆ - Warner-Lambert Co.
PURE FOREST - Hunting equipment - Pure Chem, Inc.
PURE FRESH - Lobster - Steve Connolly Seafood
PURE-GAR - Vitamins and nutritional supplements - Pure-Gar
PURE GOLD - Cosmetics ☆ - Revlon Consumer Products Corp.
PURE GOLD - Fabrics–tapestry - Coloroll Inc.
PURE GOLD - Food products - W.B. Roddenbery Co., Inc.
PURE GOLD - Food products - J. Weller Co.
PURE GOLD - Skin care products - Sun-Pro of California Inc.
PURE GOLD 13 OZ. - Apparel–children's - Mark Trouser Inc.
PURE-GREEN - Fertilizers - Crop Production Services Inc.
PURE GROW WOOL - Comforters - Natural Bedroom Corp.
PURE HANDS - Soap - Friendly Systems, Inc.
PURE HEALTH - Air purification systems - Pure Health, Inc.
PURE HERBS LTD. - Spices and extracts - Pure Herbs Ltd.
PURE I - Chickens - Hillcrest Foods Inc.
PURE INDULGENCE - Frozen foods - Dannon Co., Inc.
PURE INSANITY - Apparel and accessories - Michael Luongo
PURE INSTINCT - Containers - Pure Instinct Sportswear, Inc.
PURE-IT - Water purification systems - Ecomaster Corp.
PURE KENTUCKY - Whiskey - Pure Kentucky Distilling Co.
PURE LECI-THIN - Pharmaceutical preparations - Bretney Corp.
PURE LIQUID INK PILOT - Pens - Pilot Pen Corp. of America
PURE LITE - Oils–illuminating - Candle Lamp Co.
PURE-LOCK - Bottles–plastic - Coca-Cola Co.
PURE LUBE - Lubricants - Grignard Co., Inc.
PURE LUXURY - Women's and girls' undergarments - Montgomery Ward & Co. Inc.
PURE MAGIC - Apparel and accessories ☆ - Warnaco Inc.
PURE MAGIC - Craft supplies - Sig Manufacturing Inc.
PURE MAGIC - Floor coverings–carpet and rugs ☆ - Karastan-Bigelow Inc.
PURE MAGIC - Water-purification product - Constellation Inc.
PURE MAID - Food products - Detroit City Dairy Inc.
PURE MAID - Juices–frozen - Tropicana Products, Inc.
PURE METAL - Recording label - Refuge Music Group
PURE METALS - Furniture–metal - International Paper (Decorative Products Division)
PURE MILK - Glassware–household - Ceraglass Inc.
PURE MIST - Heaters–gas - Holmes Products, Corp.
PURE MOTION - Shoes - Wal-Mart Stores Inc.
PURE MOTIVATION - Computer software - Insights Software
PURE MOUNTAIN WATER - Water–bottled or canned - Deer Park Spring Water Inc.
PURE N GENTLE - Health care products - Rockline Industries Inc.
PURE 'N NATURAL - Towels - Jay Franco and Sons Inc.
PURE 'N PERFECT - Deodorants–personal - Perfect Natural Products, Inc.
PURE NATURAL - Varnishes - Behr Process Corp.
PURE NATURAL COLOR - Paints - Behr Process Corp.
PURE NATURE - Skin care products ☆ - Nature Cosmetics
PURE-O-LAN - Skin care products ☆ - Purepac Pharmaceutical Co.
PURE O'FLEE - Pet products - Purepet Co.
PURE OXI - Hair care products - Scruples Professional Salon Products, Inc.
PURE PACK - Meat products–poultry - Puritan Food Co. Inc.
PURE PARIAN - Glassware–household ☆ - Seeley's Ceramics Inc.
PURE PEARL - Pet products - Purepet Co.
PURE PEPPERMINT - Teas - Grace Tea Co. Ltd.
PURE PERFECTION - Cosmetics - Alba Products Group Inc.
PURE PERFORMANCE - Hair care products - Rajoc International
PURE PETROLEUM JELLY - Petroleum - Blue Cross Laboratories Inc.
PURE PLANET - Health care products - Pure Planet Products
PURE PLATINE - Cosmetics - Cosmair Inc.
PURE PLEASURE - Frozen yogurt - International Yogurt Co.
PURE POWER - Deodorants–personal - Gillette Co.
PURE POWER - Detergents - Amsoil, Inc.
PURE PRO - Food products - Papetti's Hygrade Egg Products, Inc.
PURE PRO - Massage products - Pure Pro Massage Oils, Inc.
PURE RADIANCE - Cosmetics - Revlon Consumer Products Corp.
PURE-RED - Pet products - Rael Co.
PURE ROCK - Water–bottled or canned - White Rock Products Corp.
PURE ROMANCE - Wedding gowns - Jim Hjelm a Private Collection, Inc.
PURE ROSE - Pet products - Purepet Co.
PURE SCENT - Cleaning preparations - Cleaning Systems, Inc.
PURE SCIENCE - Skin care products - Life Extension International, Inc.

☆ = Now out of production

PURE SENSATIONS - Floor coverings–carpet and rugs ☆ - World Carpets, Inc.

PURE SHAMPOO - Pet products - Dr. Goodpet

PURE SHINE - Hair care products - Gold Medal Hair Products Inc.

PURE SILK - Shaving preparations - Pfizer Inc.

PURE SILK 2 - Fabrics–tapestry - Coloroll Inc.

PURE SLUMBER - Pillows - Medline, Industries, Inc.

PURE SOFT - Pet products - Purepet Co.

PURE SOUL - Recording label - University Records, Inc.

PURE SOUL OF ICELAND, THE - Water–bottled or canned - Akva, USA, Inc.

PURE SOUND - Telephones - Columbia Telecommunications Group, Inc.

PURE SPICE - Pet products - Purepet Co.

PURE SPRING - Drink flavors and mixes - Procter & Gamble Co.

PURE STRENGTH - Cleaning preparations - Rust-Oleum Corp.

PURE STRUCTURE - Wallpaper - Pickhardt & Siebert USA Inc.

PURE SUGAR - Apparel stores - Wright's Knitwear Corp.

PURE SUGAR PUFFS - Candy - Helms Candy Manufacturing Co. Inc.

PURE SUGAR TWIST - Candy - Bobs Candies Inc.

PURE SUN - Fruit drinks–bottled or canned - Paramount Citrus Association

PURE SUNSHINE - Fruit drinks–bottled or canned - Ventures-East, Inc.

PURE SWEAT - Apparel–athletic - JBI, Inc.

PURE SWEET - Sweeteners–artificial - Allen Sugar Co.

PURE-TECH - Antifreeze - Pure Technology, Inc.

PURE THERAPY - Lip balms - Solaray

PURE THOUGHT - Vitamins and nutritional supplements - Organic Diversions, Inc.

PURE TO GO - Containers–plastic - Richard Simmons Living Trust

PURE TONE - Musical instrument accessories ☆ - Herco Products

PURE TONE - Skin care products - Matrix Essentials, Inc.

PURE VIOLET - Lipsticks ☆ - Honey & Spice Toiletries

PURE VITAL - Skin care products - A-Veda Corp.

PURE VITE - Vitamins and nutritional supplements - Pharmavite Corp.

PURE WATER - Apparel–men's - Roytex, Inc.

PURE WATER - Mattresses - Dreamland Waterbedzzz Inc.

PURE WATER - Shampoos ☆ - Smithkline Beecham Corp.

PURE WATER - Water–bottled or canned - Pure Water Corp.

PURE WATER 99 - Water purification systems - Pollenex Corp.

PURE WATER A12 - Water purification systems - Pure Water Inc.

PURE WATER CLEAN AIR GROUP, N.A., THE - Air purification systems - Pure Water Clean Air Group, N.A.

PURE WATER CONCEPTS - See **FILTERCOLD**

PURE WATER CORP. - Water–bottled or canned - Pure Water Corp.

PURE WESTERN ALFALFA - Animal feeds - Agri-Marketing Inc.

PURE WINNERS - Pollen extracts - CC Pollen Co.

PURE WORLD - Vitamins and nutritional supplements - Pure World, Inc.

PURE ZONE - Toiletries - CRS International, Inc.

PUREAGAIN - Water–bottled or canned - Mangold Enterprises, Inc.

PUREBODY - Sparkling water and sports drinks - Bancar Health

PUREBRED - Pet products - Purebred Co. Inc.

PUREBRED PETS - Giftware ☆ - Enesco Corp.

PUREBRED PUPS - Figurines - Brennan Studio Inc.

PUREBRIGHT - Medical apparatus - Purepulse Technologies, Inc.

PUREBROM - Pharmaceutical preparations - Purepac Pharmaceutical Co.

PUREBURN - Wood pellets - Pure Burn, Inc.

PURECELL - Medical apparatus - Pall Corp.

PURECELL - Sponges - Merocel Corp.

PURECOVERAGE - Computer software - Pure Software, Inc.

PURECYCLE - Automotive parts and accessories - Certified Technologies Corp.

PUREDDTS - Publisher's imprints - Pure Software, Inc.

PUREDIGITAL SELECT - Electrical equipment - Emerson Electric Co.

PUREE ENTREE - Spices and extracts - North American Laboratory Co.

PUREE PLUS - Food products - Diamond Crystal Specialty Foods Inc.

PUREE SHAPE & SERVE - Farm machinery - Menu Magic Foods Inc.

PUREED PERFECT - Food products - Sysco Corp.

PUREFLOW - Air purification systems - Amway Corp.

PUREFUME - Perfumes - A-Veda Corp.

PUREGOLD - Clay products - Amcol International Corp.

PUREGRO - Fertilizers - Crop Production Services Inc.

PUREHEAT - Fireplaces - Superior Fireplace Co.

PUREHOLD QTS - Hair care products - Beauty Brands Group

PUREKNIT - Fabrics–broadcloth - Collins & Aikman Corp.

PUREL - Soap - Go-Jo Industries Inc.

PURELAX - Health care products ☆ - FutureMed America Inc.

PURELEAN - Meat products–beef - Kohler Co.

PURELIN - Paper–toweling - Georgia-Pacific Corp.

PURELINE - Hair care products - Pureline, Inc.

PURELINK - Computer software - Pure Software, Inc.

PURELY ALASKAN - Water–bottled or canned - Purely Alaskan Water Co.

PURELY AMERICAN - Soups–mixes - Purely American

PURELY DELICIOUS - Juices - Langan Associates

PURELY DELICIOUS-NATURALLY NUTRITIOUS! - Meat products–poultry - Plainville Turkey Farm, Inc.

PURELY HAWAIIAN - Sun tan lotion - Purely Hawaiian Inc.

PURELY NATURAL - Hair care products - Rajoc International

PURELY PEPPERMINT - Teas–herbal - R.C. Bigelow, Inc.

PURELY PERFECT - Cosmetics - Chem Spray Aerosols Inc.

PURELY PISTACHIO - Ice cream - Dogwood Restaurants, Inc.

PURELY POLLEN - Health care products - Naturally Vitamin Supplements Inc.

PURELY SILVER - Jewelry - Erwin Pearl, Inc.

PURE'N NATURAL - Fruit drinks–bottled or canned - Everfresh Beverages, Inc.

PURENE - Paints - Whittaker Corp. (Orrville Coatings Div.)

PURENESS - Skin care products - Shiseido Cosmetics (America) Ltd.

PURENOGENOL - Vitamins and nutritional supplements - Health Products Corp.

PUREPAC - Analgesics - Purepac Pharmaceutical Co.

PUREPAK - Caviar - Purepak Foods Inc.

PUREPAK - Caviar - Quality Bakery Co.

PUREPRO - Water purification systems - Matrix Desalination, Inc.

PUREPULSE - Electrical equipment - Purepulse Technologies, Inc.

PURERESULTS - Cleaning preparations–household - Quick 'n Brite, Inc.

PURESCRIPTIONS - Hair care products - A-Veda Corp.

PURESPEECH - Computer software - Integrated Speech Solutions, Inc.

PURETAN - Sunblocks - Puretan International Inc.

PURETANE - Pharmaceutical preparations - Purepac Pharmaceutical Co.

PURETE DE LA SOURCE - Cosmetics - Dermacel Research Laboratories, Inc.

PURETEK - Pharmaceutical preparations - Puretek Corp.

PURETREATS - Candy - Lehman SUGARFREE Confections

PURETTE - Antacids ☆ - Robinette Inc.

PURETTES - Chewing gum - Philadelphia Chewing Gum Corp.

PUREVEG - Fruits and vegetables - Purepak, Inc.

PUREX - Bleach - Dial Corp.

PUREX - Salt - Morton International Inc. (Morton Salt Div.)

PUREX ALL-CLEAN - Cleaning preparation - Dial Corp.

PUREX RAIN DROPS - Cleaning preparations - Dial Corp.

PUREX RINSE 'N SOFT - Fabric softeners - Dial Corp.

PUREX SUPREME - Detergents - Dial Corp.

PUREX TOSS'N SOFT - Fabric softeners - Dial Corp.

PUREX2 - Detergents - Dial Corp.

PURFECT PUFF - Yarn ☆ - Caron International Inc.

PURFIK - Sporting goods - Thomas A. Bursik

PURGE - Health care products - Fleming & Co.

PURGE - Herbicides - Security Products Co.

PURGE FIRE - Insecticides - Waterbury Companies, Inc.

PURGE FIRE - Vitamins and nutritional supplements - Ethical Nutrients

PURGE PUMP PROPHY ANGLE - Apparel–athletic - Brahler Products, Inc.

PURGE SAVER - Water purification systems - QED Environmental Systems, Inc.

PURGED SLED COMPANY - Apparel and accessories - Johnson B. Thomas

PURGEOMATIC - Cleaning preparations - Stewart-Hall Chemical Corp.

PURGEX - Cleaning preparations - Neutrex, Inc.

PURGRAIN - Pet products - Scarlett Co.

PURI-BLEND - Teas–herbal - Puri-Clean Enterprises, Inc.

PURI-CLEAR - Air purification systems - Slant/Fin Corp.

PURI-CLENS - Deodorizers - Sween Corp.

PURIBATH - Manicure preparations - Flowery Beauty Products, Inc.

PURICIT - Housewares - Tryson Co.

PURIDYNE - Air purification systems - Clinitex Holdings, Inc.

PURIFAST 30 - Vitamins and nutritional supplements - Talk America, Inc.

PURIFIED H20 - Water–bottled or canned - Modesto Bottled Water Co.

PURIFIER PLUS - Position emission tomography apparatus - American Standard Inc.

PURIFIER PURGE - Gastroscopes - American Standard Inc.

PURIFIER, THE - Water purification systems - Besttest

PURIFILES - Manicure preparations - Flowery Beauty Products, Inc.

PURIFIX - Hair care products - Lombardi Research Group, LLC

PURIFRY - Chemical preparations - Square Deal Development, LLC

PURIFY - Hair care products - Hayashi for Hair Inc.

PURILENS - Contact lens cleaner - American Vision, Inc.

PURINA - Pet products - Ralston Purina Co.

PURINA 100 - Cat food - Ralston Purina Co.

☆ = Now out of production

PURINA CANINE CASH - Pet products - Ralston Purina Co.
PURINA GRRRAVY - Dog food - Ralston Purina Co.
PURINA NUTRIENT MANAGEMENT - Pet food - Ralston Purina Co.
PURINA ONE - Pet products - Ralston Purina Co.
PURINA PREMIUM - Pet products - Ralston Purina Co.
PURINA SELECT - Cat food - Ralston Purina Co.
PURINETHOL - Pharmaceutical preparations - Burroughs Wellcome Co.
PURIPHYING - Hair care products - Amethyst Investment Group, Inc.
PURIST - Bathroom accessories - Kohler Co.
PURIST - Bicycles ✩ - Roadmaster Corp.
PURIST - Fishing lures - Den Manufacturing Co.
PURIST - Sporting goods ✩ - Shakespeare Fishing Tackle
PURIST SKIN THERAPY - Skin care products - Cosmericana, Inc.
PURISYS - Air purification systems - Purisys Inc.
PURITAN - Apparel–athletic - Puritan Sportswear Corp.
PURITAN - Brooms - Hamburg Broom Works Inc.
PURITAN - Dishes–china ✩ - Pickard Inc.
PURITAN - Floor coverings–carpet and rugs - Masland Corp.
PURITAN - Food products - Birkett Mills
PURITAN - Food products - Cudahy Co.
PURITAN - Food products - National Preserve Co.
PURITAN - Giftware ✩ - Gorham Inc.
PURITAN - Glass–leaded - Seneca Glass Co.
PURITAN - Oils–edible - Procter & Gamble Co.
PURITAN - Paints ✩ - California Products Corp.
PURITAN - Pottery products - United States Gypsum Co.
PURITAN - Rope - Columbian Rope Co.
PURITAN - Rope - Wellington Leisure Products, Inc.
PURITAN - Tables–wood ✩ - Quaker Industries Ltd.
PURITAN - Tobacco products - Philip Morris Companies Inc.
PURITAN CLASSICS - Apparel–men's - Warnaco Inc.
PURITAN MAID - Confections ✩ - Geo. Melhado & Co.
PURITAN MAID - Rope - Wellington Leisure Products, Inc.
PURITAN MATES - Crocheted and knitted items ✩ - Puritan Sportswear Corp.
PURITAN OPTI-BRITE - Twine - Wellington Leisure Products, Inc.
PURITAN PANTS - Apparel–women's - Anne Klein & Co.
PURITAN VIP CLASSICS - Apparel–men's - Warnaco Inc.
PURITANOS FINOS - Cigar boxes–wood - Consolidated Cigar Corp.
PURITANS PRIDE - Vitamins and nutritional supplements - Nature's Bounty, Inc.
PURITE - Pharmaceutical preparations - Allergan Elite, Inc.
PURITEA - Teas–herbal - Unitea Herbs
PURITEX - Thread - Belding Heminway Co. Inc.
PURITRON - Kitchen appliances ✩ - Hamilton Beach/Proctor-Silex Inc.
PURITY - Candy ✩ - Chiodo Candy Co.
PURITY - Dinnerware–glass ✩ - Nikko Ceramics Inc.
PURITY - Food containers - Purity Products Inc.
PURITY - Gloves–rubber - Duracraft Corp.
PURITY - Ice cream - Purity Dairies, Inc.
PURITY - Jewelry - Purity Ring Co.
PURITY - Juices - Rich Harvest Juice Co.
PURITY - Pet products ✩ - United Feeds Inc.
PURITY - Rope - Wellington Leisure Products, Inc.
PURITY - Salt - Akzo America Inc.
PURITY - Water–bottled or canned - Purity Bottling Co.
PURITY FARMS - Bacon - Purity Group Inc.
PURITY MILLS - Popcorn - National Oats Co. Inc.
PURITY-PLUS - Water purification systems - Cuno Inc.
PURITY PROCESSED SHELLFISH - Seafood products–fresh or frozen - Our Delight Seafood, Inc.
PURITY SEAFOOD - Seafood products–fresh or frozen - Almex USA, Inc.
PURITY SUPREME - Pizzas–frozen - Purity Supreme Supermarkets
PURLITE - Vegetable oil - CPC International Inc.
PURLSTITCH - Thread ✩ - American & Efird, Inc.
PURLY POPS - Candy - Dorval Trading Co., Ltd.
PURNACIDE - Disinfectants - Sporicidin International
PURO - Water–bottled or canned - Puro Corp. of America
PURO CAFF ESPRESSO MACHINE CLEANER - Cleaning preparations - Timothy Joseph O'Connor
PURO LISO - Skin care products - Landau Skincare Products
PURO PLEAT - Filters–air - Purolator Products Co.
PUROCLEAN - Cleaning preparations–carpet and rug - Puroclean Inc.
PURODENT - Mouthwashes ✩ - Purepac Pharmaceutical Co.
PURODIGIN - Pharmaceutical preparations ✩ - Wyeth-Ayerst Laboratories
PUROLATOR - Motor vehicle parts and accessories - Purolator Products Co.

PUROLATOR PROFORMANCE - Motor vehicle parts and accessories - Purolator Products Co.
PUROS INDIOS - Cigars - Puros Indios Cigars, Inc.
PUROSEPTIC 511 - Mouthwashes ✩ - Purepac Pharmaceutical Co.
PURPLE - Skin care products - USA Enterprises Miami Co., Inc.
PURPLE 100-GRIT - Skin care products - Backscratchers, Inc.
PURPLE BLAST - Cosmetics ✩ - Prince Matchabelli
PURPLE BLUSH - Flowers, plants, and seeds - W. Atlee Burpee and Co.
PURPLE HAZE - Skin care products - Trimco International
PURPLE HAZE - Sunglasses - Gatorz Sport Optiks
PURPLE HEART - Games - Avalon Hill Game Co.
PURPLE JESTER - Flowers, plants, and seeds - Panamerican Seed
PURPLE LAVA - Chewing gum ✩ - Leaf, Inc.
PURPLE MARTIN QUADPLEX - Games - Vitos Products
PURPLE MOUNTAIN - Vegetables–pickled or brined - Del Monte Fresh Produce N.A., Inc.
PURPLE PASSION - Beverages–alcohol - David Sherman Corp.
PURPLE PASSION - Toys ✩ - Tonka Corp.
PURPLE PASSION - Toys–automobiles - Mattel, Inc.
PURPLE PASSION EVERCLEAR - Beverages–alcohol - David Sherman Corp.
PURPLE PASSIONS - Candy - Stanico, Inc.
PURPLE PAWS - Dolls - Mattel, Inc.
PURPLE PEPPER, THE - Sauces - Purple Pepper, Inc.
PURPLE PLUS - Cleaning preparations - Knight Marketing Corp.
PURPLE QUEEN - Flowers, plants, and seeds - Monrovia Nursery Co.
PURPLE RAIN - Fireworks - American Promotional Events, Inc.
PURPLE RAIN - Flowers, plants, and seeds - Panamerican Seed
PURPLE ROYAL - Brooms - Fluffo Mop & Broom Co. Inc.
PURPLE ROYAL TRITON - Oils–lubricating ✩ - Unocal Corp.
PURPLE STAR - Game machines - Purple Star, Inc.
PURPLE TIGER - Cleaning preparations - Chemco Corp.
PURPLE VALLEY TEDDY BEARS - Toys–stuffed - Samantha J. Dedivitis
PURPLE VINES - Candy - American Licorice Co.
PURPLE WILDBERRY - Candy - Phoenix Confections Inc.
PURPLE WOODY - Apparel–men's - Gary David Johnson
PURPLEPOWER - Cleaning preparations - Aiken Chemical Co., Inc.
PURPLES - Jewelry - Replicas, Inc.
PURPOM FRENCH APPLE CIDER - Cider - Palm Bay Imports, Inc.
PURPOSE - Skin care products - Johnson & Johnson
PURPOSE M LIFE: ETHICS & ORGANIZATIONAL SUCCESS - Video production - Pacific Institute Inc.
PURQUIK - Automotive parts and accessories - Wasser High-Tech Coatings, Inc.
PURR - Fruits and vegetables - Van Buren County Fruit Exchange
PURR FECT CHRISTMAS - Figurines - Flambro Imports, Inc.
PURR-FECT PUNCH - Craft supplies - Plaid Enterprises, Inc.
PURR-MALT - Pet products - Petland, Inc.
PURR-TENDERS - Toys - Fisher-Price, Inc.
PURRFECT - Pet products - Vee Enterprises
PURRFECT CAT BRUSH - Pet products - Aaronco Grooming Products
PURRFECT CIRCLE - Pet products - Pupperwear Inc.
PURRFECT FEATHER - Pet products - Vee Enterprises
PURRFECT HERBS FOR CATS - Seeds–salted, roasted, cooked, or canned - Kingfisher Inc.
PURRFECT PET - Figurines - Marty Sculpture
PURRFECTION - Pet products - Virbac, Inc.
PURRFECTION - Toys–stuffed ✩ - Gund, Inc.
PURRFECTLY YOURS - Novelty items–paper ✩ - Antioch Publishing Co.
PURRFICURL - Eyelash curler - Sepralash Co.
PURRR-FECT PAW - Toys–electronic - Bandai America Inc.
PURRRFECT PRESENTS - Pet products - Hills Department Store Co.
PURRS - Toys–stuffed ✩ - Dakin Inc.
PURRS & GRRRS - Notebooks and notepads - Mead Corp.
PURRSACK - Pet products - Cedarsack Pet Products, Inc.
PURRSONALITIES - Greeting cards - Pat's Printing
PURRTY KITTY - Toys–stuffed ✩ - Russ Berrie and Co., Inc.
PURSABLES - Handbags - Burdal Corp.
PURSALLET - Bags–duffel - Koltov Inc.
PURSE-N-ABLE - Hobby kits - Accento Plastic Manufacturing Inc.
PURSE-N-ALITY - Coin purses - Norstar Enterprises
PURSE-N-POCKET - Atomizers - Irving W. Rice & Co. Inc.
PURSE-O-NALITY PLUS - Toys–stuffed ✩ - Fun World Inc.
PURSE PAK - Telephone accessories - Motorola, Inc. (Land Mobile Products Sector)
PURSE PALLETTE - Mirrors - Diane Products Inc.

✩ = Now out of production

PURSE PRETTIES - Toys - Toymax Inc.
PURSELL'S - Fertilizers - Pursell Industries, Inc.
PURSE'NL LITE - Paper - Dawn's Designs & Imports Inc.
PURSESTRINGS - Computer software - Jon R. Pearce
PURSIN - Health care products - McKesson Home Health Care
PURSUE - Disinfectants - Amway Corp.
PURSUIT - Bicycles - Columbia Manufacturing Inc.
PURSUIT - Car-security systems - Audiovox Corp.
PURSUIT - Cleaner ☆ - Intex Chemical Inc.
PURSUIT - Floor coverings–carpet and rugs - Columbus Mills, Inc.
PURSUIT - Motor vehicles–motor homes - Georgie Boy Manufacturing, Inc.
PURSUIT - Occasional tables - JDI Group, Inc.
PURSUIT - Sporting goods - Troxel-West
PURSUIT - Sunglasses - Capo, Inc.
PURSUIT OF EXCELLENCE - Recording label - Silver Bells Music
P.U.R.T. - Deodorizer - Harris Research, Inc.
PURTEX - Apparel–women's - Anne Klein & Co.
PURTON - Bathroom fixtures - Crane Plumbing/Fiat Products
PURTY - Dolls ☆ - Uneeda Doll Co., Inc.
PURVEYOR - Computer software - Process Software Corp.
PURVEYOR'S OF FUN - Beverages–malt - Technically Leading Consultants Co.
PUSH - Chocolate bars - Betco Corp.
PUSH-A-MALT - Ice cream - Nestle USA
PUSH ABOUT - Toys - Little Tikes Co.
PUSH-ALONG CLOWN - Toys - Fisher-Price, Inc.
PUSH-BUTTON - Locks–door - ILCO Unican Corp. (Unican Lock Division)
PUSH LITE - Chimes ☆ - Nutone Inc.
PUSH N' GLOW - Toys - Steven Manufacturing Co.
PUSH 'N PEEK - Toys - Mattel, Inc.
PUSH 'N POP - Toys ☆ - Playskool, Inc.
PUSH N' POP - Toys ☆ - Steven Manufacturing Co.
PUSH 'N' PULL - Umbrellas - Storm Hero Umbrella Co. Inc.
PUSH 'N RIDE - Toys - Little Tikes Co.
PUSH-N-SEAL - Sinks–plastic - Guarantee Specialties Inc.
PUSH N SIP DOME LID - Housewares - Arthur J. Kaufman Sales Co.
PUSH 'N WATER - Pet products - Farnam Cos. Inc.
PUSH OVER - Toys ☆ - Parker Brothers
PUSH-PAL - Racks ☆ - Jarke Corp.
PUSH PERFORMANCE - Vitamins and nutritional supplements - Push Performance Inc.
PUSH POINT - Office supplies ☆ - Scripto-Tokai Corp.
PUSH POP - Candy - Topps Co., Inc.
PUSH-PULL - Wagons–children's - Radio Flyer Inc.
PUSH THE LIMITS - T-shirts - Graphic Prints Inc.
PUSH THE ROCK - Apparel and accessories - Brendan J. Kelly
PUSH-UP - Apparel–women's - Carnival Creations
PUSH UP - Feather dusters - Texas Feathers Inc.
PUSH UP - Ladders–wood - John S. Tilley Ladders Co. Inc.
PUSH-UP BAG, THE - Handbags - Suzan Briganti Inc.
PUSH-UP PLUS - Apparel–women's - Carnival Creations
PUSH UP PRETTY - Brassieres (Bras) ☆ - Lovable Co.
PUSH-UPS - Ice cream - Nestle USA
PUSHBACK - Sporting goods - Marty Gilman Inc.
PUSHBANK - Racks - L.B. International, Inc.
PUSHBUTTON - Locks–padlocks - Weil Service Products Corp.
PUSHBUTTON BINGO - Games ☆ - Milton Bradley Co.
PUSHBUTTON LANDLORDING - Computer software - Leigh Robinson
PUSHBUTTON SOFTWARE - Computer software - Pushbutton Software Inc.
PUSHCART - Pretzels - New England Pretzel & Popcorn Co.
PUSHCART MUSIC - Publisher's imprints - San Juan Music Group
PUSHER - Motor vehicles–motor homes - Tiffin Motor Homes, Inc.
PUSHER - Pencils–mechanical - National Pen & Pencil Co.
PUSHIN CUSHION - Toys - Evenflo Juvenile Furniture Co.
PUSH'N PLAY - Toys–stuffed - Gerber Products Co.
PUSHNUT - Fasteners–snap - American Engineer Components
PUSHNUTS - Nuts and bolts - Auto Vehicle Parts Co.
PUSHPALENE - Plastics - Pushpa America Corp.
PUSS IN BOOTS - Deodorizers ☆ - Blue Ridge International Products Co., Inc.
PUSS IN CHUTES - Bedding–linen - Dan River Inc.
PUSS PALS - Pet products - Mason Distributing
PUSSER'S - Rum - Jim Beam Brands Co.
PUSSICAT - Pet product - Interwood Marketing
PUSSY - Artists' materials - Stangren Co.
PUSSY CAT - Dolls - Alexander Doll Co. Inc.
PUSSY-CAT - Thread ☆ - Perfect Thread Co. Inc.

PUSSY CAT - Toys–stuffed - Pussy Cat Toy Co. Inc.
PUSSY CAT POOL - Pet products - Gillians Jungle
PUSSY LAWN - Pet products - Colony Pet Goods
PUSSYCAT - Games - Dollsandreams
PUSSYFLATS - Shoes - Cypress Shoes
PUSSYFOOTS - Shoes ☆ - Penobscot Shoe Co.
PUSSYWILLOW - Food products ☆ - Seneca Foods Corp.
PUT A CORK IN IT! - Corks - Stephen R. Garavatti
PUT A HALT TO RUST - Rust removers - Elsco, Inc.
PUT A LID ON IT! - Apparel and accessories - Lids, Inc.
PUT A LID ON IT - Carts ☆ - Contico International Inc.
PUT AMERICA FIRST - Locks–door ☆ - Fort Lock Corp.
PUT & PLAY - Games ☆ - Western Publishing Co., Inc.
PUT & TAKE - Games - Tyco Toys
PUT-LINES - Office supplies - Put-Lines Manufacturing Co.
PUT ON THE DOG - Pet products - Put on the Dog
PUT-ONS - Clip-in hair extensions - International Hairgoods Inc.
PUT OUT GEAR - Apparel and accessories - Imac, Inc.
PUT THE STING ON CRIME - Automotive parts and accessories - Directed Electronics, Inc.
PUT US IN PLAY - Balls–basketball - Voit Corp.
PUTAH CREEK RED - Wines - Winters Winery Inc.
PUTAH CREEK WHITE - Wines - Winters Winery Inc.
'PUTER POWER - Apparel and accessories - Dewey Makem & Howe, Inc.
PUTNAM AND GROSSET GROUP - Publisher's imprints - Putnam Gift Products
PUTNAM LEATHER COMPANY - Leather goods - Putnam Industries
PUTNAM LEATHER GOLD - Apparel and accessories ☆ - Putnam Industries
PUTNAM NEW MEDIA - Computer storage devices–optical - Putnam Berkley Group, Inc.
PUTNAM PUBLISHING - Publisher's imprints ☆ - Chase Collection, Inc.
PUTNEY - Music synthesizer ☆ - Ionic Industries Inc.
PUTNEY KNITS - Crocheted and knitted items ☆ - Hampshire Hosiery, Inc.
PUTNEY PASTA - Food products - Putney Pasta Co., Inc.
PUTNEY'S - Food products ☆ - Paradigm Foodworks
PUTPAL - Sporting goods - Dar Products Corp.
PUTRID POTIONS - Beverages - Tyco Industries, Inc.
PUTT-A-BOUT - Golfing equipment - Habitat International Inc.
PUTT-A-LINER - Golf putting aids - Fairview Products, Inc.
PUTT N PAR - Hosiery ☆ - Wigwam Mills Inc.
PUTT PARTNER - Golfing equipment - Harold Brent Arnett
PUTT PRO - Games - Jeron Technology Inc.
PUTT-PUMP - Tools - Molex-Etc Inc.
PUTT-PUTT. - Tools–garden - Olympia Industrial Inc.
PUTT-PUTT - Toys–models - Mattel, Inc.
PUTT-PUTT FOR FUN - Toys - G.M. Inc.
PUTT PUTT PETE - Candy - R.M. Palmer Co.
PUTT-R-GOLF - Golf courses ☆ - SGD Co.
PUTTER - Flowers, plants, and seeds - Jacklin Seed
PUTTER BOY - Golfing equipment - Triumph Golf Co.
PUTTER COVER - Crocheted and knitted items - Reliable of Milwaukee
PUTTER-ER - Golf training devices - Slim-Gym
PUTTER GIRL - Golfing equipment - Triumph Golf Co.
PUTTER PAL - Golfing equipment - K & M Wholesale Co., Inc.
PUTTER POOL - Games - PGI Golf Inc.
PUTTERS - Candy - Brach and Brock Confections Inc.
PUTTER'S TOUCH, THE - Golfing equipment - A. James Owen, Jr.
PUTTIN' ON THE DOGG! - Pet products - Petcetera Originals Inc.
PUTTIN' ON THE GLITZ! - Apparel–women's - Glitz Inc.
PUTTIN' ON THE GLITZ - Hobby kits - Mangelsen's (VDI)
PUTTIN' ON THE GLITZ - Lipsticks - Maybelline Co.
PUTTIN' ON THE POOCH - Pet products - Pet Concepts
PUTTIN' ON THE RITZ - Dolls - Effanbee Doll Corp.
PUTTING CHALLENGE - Miniature-golf game sets and accessories - G.L. Technology Inc.
PUTTING CLIENT/SERVER TO WORK - Catalogs - Christopher Evans
PUTTING ON THE DOG - Pet products - Double S Dog Fashions
PUTTING ON THE RITZ - Floor coverings–carpet and rugs ☆ - Regal Rugs Inc.
PUTTING ON THE RITZ - Wallpaper - Pantasote Inc. (Wallcovering Div.)
PUTTING STICK - Golfing equipment - Pro Form Golf
PUTTING THE ONE MINUTE MANAGER TO WORK - Computer software - Spinnaker Software Corp.
PUTTRON - Golfing equipment - Stephen G. Wash
PUTTY FACE - Toys–stuffed - Chuck Frankhouse, Celebrations of America
PUTTY PENCILS - Wood fillers - H.F. Staples & Co. Inc.

PUTTY SLICK - Paints - Sherburne Ewing Wallcovering Co.
PUTTY STIK - Caulking compounds ☆ - OSI Sealants, Inc.
PUTZ - Perfumes - Burnishine Products
PUZZL-FOLD - Toys - Nathan Polsky
PUZZLE BUFFS INT'L. - Games - Scramb-L-Gram, Inc.
PUZZLE COLLECTION, THE - Puzzles - Warren Industries Inc.
PUZZLE CRAFT - Furniture - Instant Products, Inc.
PUZZLE EXPRESS! - Greeting cards - Sunbelt International, Inc.
PUZZLE FUN - Puzzles - Warren Industries Inc.
PUZZLE IT - Computer software ☆ - Right on Programs
PUZZLE LOCK - Adhesives and sealants - Dupey Management Corp.
PUZZLE LOGIC - Computer software - Ventura Educational Systems
PUZZLE MACHINE, THE - Computer software - Hartley Courseware Inc.
PUZZLE-MAN, THE - Toys - Charlie's Woodshop
PUZZLE MATH - Games - Leisure Learning Products
PUZZLE 'N PAINT - Toys - Tonka Corp.
PUZZLE PAK - Puzzles - Lauri Inc.
PUZZLE PEACE - Jewelry - Zan Design, Inc.
PUZZLE PERFECTION - Games - Lakeside Games
PUZZLE PETS - Jigsaw puzzles ☆ - American Publishing Corp.
PUZZLE PIE - Puzzles - Jim Kelly
PUZZLE PIECE DESIGN - Audio equipment - Someday Baby, Inc.
PUZZLE PIX - Computer software - Zephyr Services
PUZZLE PLACE, THE - Toys - Community Television of Southern California
PUZZLE PLACE, THE - Publisher's imprints - Lancit Media Productions, Ltd.
PUZZLE PLACE, THE - Lunch boxes - Thermos Co.
PUZZLE PLEX THE 3-D PUZZLE - Puzzles - Telebrands Corp.
PUZZLE PLUS - Video games - Sergey K. Aityan
PUZZLE PUPPY - Toys - Fisher-Price, Inc.
PUZZLE SQUARES - Puzzles - International Polygonics Ltd.
PUZZLE STICKS - Games ☆ - Avalon Hill Game Co.
PUZZLE STORYBOOK - Computer software - First Byte Inc.
PUZZLE TANKS - Computer software - Sunburst Communications, Inc.
PUZZLE TIN - Puzzles - Andrew M. Gole
PUZZLE TOTE, THE - Game tables ☆ - Ceaco, Inc.
PUZZLE-UPS - Puzzles - Milton Bradley Co.
PUZZLE WORKS - Games - Continental Press, Inc.
PUZZLEBOOKS - Publisher's imprints - Price Stern Sloan Inc.
PUZZLED EGGS - Puzzles - Compoz-A-Puzzle Inc.
PUZZLEMINT - Teas - San Francisco Herb & Natural Food Co.
PUZZLEPATCH - Puzzles - Patch Products, Inc.
PUZZLEPATCH SHARP PUZZLES - Puzzles - Patch Products, Inc.
PUZZLER - Toys - Tonka Corp.
PUZZLER, THE - Puzzles - Go Images Inc.
PUZZLER, THE - Computer software ☆ - Sunburst Communications, Inc.
PUZZLES D'ART - Puzzles ☆ - Chase Collection, Inc.
PUZZLES PEOPLE LOVE - Puzzles - Coburn Designs
PUZZLETTER - Puzzles ☆ - Joslin Photo Puzzle Co.
PUZZLING EGG - Puzzles - Bleyer Industries (Peoria Plastics Div.)
PUZZLING PEN PAL MYSTERIES - Puzzles ☆ - Lombard Marketing, Inc.
PUZZLING PENTAGON - Puzzles - Kadon Enterprises Inc.
PUZZLING STATIONERY - Puzzles - Compoz-A-Puzzle Inc.
PUZZLING SURPRISE, A - Puzzles - Henry J. Legendre, Jr.
PUZZNIK - Puzzles ☆ - Warren Industries Inc.
P.V. - Dinnerware—glass - Straus Mitteldorfer Inc.
PV - Electrical surge protectors - Powervar, Inc.
PV - Golfing equipment - S.E.G., Inc.
PV - Microphones - Peavey Electronics Corp.
PV 4 MASTER - Shock absorbers—motor vehicle - Bridgestone/Firestone, Inc.
PV-BOND - Clay products - Polymer Valley Chemicals, Inc.
PV-BRIGHT - Clay products - Polymer Valley Chemicals, Inc.
P.V. CARBACHOL - Ophthalmic goods ☆ - Allergan, Inc.
P.V. CARPINE LIQUIFILM - Ophthalmic goods ☆ - Allergan, Inc.
PV-FLOAT - Clay products - Polymer Valley Chemicals, Inc.
P.V. LANE - Underwear and nightwear - LANZ, Inc.
PV SYSTEM 27 - Electrical equipment - Powell Electrical Manufacturing Co.
PV SYSTEM 38 - Electrical equipment - Powell Electrical Manufacturing Co.
PV2 - Computer hardware - Compression Labs, Inc.
PVA - Hobby kits - Environmental Technology, Inc.
PVA - Paints - Muralo Co. Inc.
P.V.A. - Paints - Somay Products Inc.
PVC - Blinds—venetian ☆ - Hunter Douglas, Inc.
PVC - Recording label - Passport Records Inc.
PVC-3 - Siding—insulating - Aluminum Co. of America
PVC-EX - Vinyl tape - C and H Distributors Inc.
PVCS - Computer software - Intersolv, Inc.

PVG - Ventilation equipment - Field Controls Co.
PVK - Pharmaceutical preparations ☆ - Legere Pharmaceuticals Inc.
PVM - Microphones - Peavey Electronics Corp.
PVM - Pharmaceutical preparations ☆ - Smithkline Beecham Corp.
PVO - Computer software - Mpsi Systems Inc.
PVO - Ventilation equipment - Field Controls Co.
PVP - Iodine - Consolidated Midland Corp.
PVP - Rings—jewelry - Artcarved Inc.
PVP - Veterinary pharmaceutical preparations - Walco International, Inc.
PVS - Computer peripheral equipment - Hekimian Laboratories Inc.
P.V.SEE. - Vinyl - Robeco, Inc.
PVT - Liquid crystal displays - American Consolidated Manufacturing Co., Inc.
PVT - Measuring instruments - Wilcoxon Research, Inc.
PVT - Pet products - Economy Distributors
PVT - Vinyl - Patrician Products Inc.
PVT SYSTEMS - Cleaning equipment - PVT Systems Inc.
PVTV - Video production - Peavey Electronics Corp.
PVX - Amplifiers ☆ - Gemini Sound Products Corp.
PW - Computer software - Price Waterhouse Llp
PW - Jewelry - Philip Wolman & Co.
P.W. - Wines - Pompei Winery Inc.
PW-15 - Hair care products ☆ - Image Laboratories, Inc.
PW-ASSIST - Computer software - Price Waterhouse Llp
P.W. SPORT - Apparel—women's - Lee Thomas Inc.
PWC - Electrical equipment - Triangle Wire & Cable, Inc.
PWD - Forklifts - Clark Material Handling Co.
PWJ - Jewelry - Paul Winston Jewelry Corp.
PWK DESIGNS - Sewing machines—household - Pat Wilkie Keene Designs
PWP - Typewriters - Smith Corona Corp.
PWP START-RITE - Typewriters - Smith Corona Corp.
PWRLINK - Communications equipment - Harmonic Lightwaves, Inc.
PWS/KENT PUBLISHING - Textbooks - Wadsworth, Inc.
PWT - Water treating compounds - Aquacide
PWTN - Liquid crystal displays - Polytronix, Inc.
PXL - Cameras - Photometrics Ltd.
PXL 2000 - Toys - Fisher-Price, Inc.
PXPLUS - Telephone apparatus - ADC Telecommunications, Inc.
PY-CO-PAY - Toothbrushes - Block Drug Co., Inc.
PY-CO-TWIN - Toothbrushes - Block Drug Co., Inc.
PY FORMULA SCALP CLEANSER - Shampoos - Paula Young
PY-O-MY - Food products - Gilster-Mary Lee Corp.
PY2 - Pet products - Wysong Corp.
PYAC - Shortening ☆ - Swift Edible Oil Co.
PYCNOGENOL PLUS - Vitamins and nutritional supplements - Reese Chemical Co.
PYCO - Flour—blended ☆ - Cahokia Flour Co.
PYE - Recording label ☆ - Telemark Dance Records
PYE QUICK - Food products - General Mills, Inc.
PYENO-PLUS - Health care products - Healthwatchers System
PYEWCH - Electrical equipment - T.G.M., Inc.
PYGEUM-POWER - Dietary supplements ☆ - Nature's Herbs
PYGMAL - Pharmaceutical preparations ☆ - Consolidated Midland Corp.
PYGMY - Plugs—nose - Studex Corp.
PYGMY SPIN - Fishing lures - Storm Manufacturing Co.
PYKE & GILBERT - Pet products ☆ - Pet Supply Imports Inc.
PYKE LTD. - Apparel and accessories - Pyke Manufacturing Co.
PYKETTES - Apparel—women's - Pyke Manufacturing Co.
PYKETTES PLUS - Apparel—women's - Pyke Manufacturing Co.
PYLA-CERT - Dyes—food - Pylam Products Co. Inc.
PYLA-WAX - Candles - Pylam Products Co. Inc.
PYLAKLOR - Chemical preparations - Pylam Products Co. Inc.
PYLAKROME - Oils—edible - Pylam Products Co. Inc.
PYLE DRIVER - Audio equipment - Pyle Industries Inc.
PYLON - Tape—adhesive - Ben Clements & Sons Inc.
PYLORA - Pharmaceutical preparations ☆ - Hyrex Pharmaceuticals
PYLORITEK - Paper punches - Serim Research Corp.
PYLUMIN - Paints - Fyr-Fyter Co.
PYMATUNING DAM - Beverages—malt - Crooked Creek Brewery, Inc.
PYNAMMO - Cleaning preparations ☆ - Flo-Pac Corp.
PYNCLENE - Cleaning preparations ☆ - Flo-Pac Corp.
PYNNACLE - Hair care products - Treslure Hair Cosmetics
PYOBEN - Skin care products - Allerderm Inc.
PYOCIDIN - Pharmaceutical preparations - Forest Pharmaceuticals Inc.
PYOPEN - Pharmaceutical preparations ☆ - Smithkline Beecham Corp.
PYOTT - Cookies - Europa Foods Ltd.
PYRACORT - Pharmaceutical preparations ☆ - Lemmon Co.

☆ = Now out of production

PYRADYNE - Pharmaceutical preparations ☆ - Lemmon Co.

PYRAL - Electronic equipment ☆ - G Prime Limited

PYRALUX - Lacquers - E.I. Dupont de Nemours and Co.

PYRAM - Games - Pyram Enterprises, Inc.

PYRAM - Glass wall panels ☆ - Corning Inc.

PYRAMAN - Publisher's imprints - Roger Cecil Philip

PYRAMAT - Garden equipment - Synthetic Industries, Inc.

PYRAMID - Batteries - Star Struck Inc.

PYRAMID - Beer and ale - Hart Brewing, Inc.

PYRAMID - Cigarettes - Liggett Group Inc.

PYRAMID - Compact discs–prerecorded - TRF Production Music Libraries

PYRAMID - Deodorizers - Quality of Life Associates

PYRAMID - Envelopes - Melo Envelope Co. Inc.

PYRAMID - Fabrics - Greenwood Mills Inc.

PYRAMID - Floor coverings ☆ - Tarkett, Inc.

PYRAMID - Fruits and vegetables - Pyramid Orchards

PYRAMID - Game machines - Ramparts Inc.

PYRAMID - Handbags - Pyramid Handbags Inc.

PYRAMID - Health care products - Temco Health Care

PYRAMID - Lamps ☆ - Lamplight Farms, Inc.

PYRAMID - Lighting fixtures - Thomas Lighting (Accent Division)

PYRAMID - Mats ☆ - U.S. Mat & Rubber Co. Inc.

PYRAMID - Musical instrument accessories - Ideal Musical Merchandise Co.

PYRAMID - Paints–artists' ☆ - Riebe's Artist Materials Inc.

PYRAMID - Printing trades machinery - Nama Graphics, Inc.

PYRAMID - Publisher's imprints - Berkley Publishing Corp.

PYRAMID - Recording label - All Star Promotions

PYRAMID - Rings–jewelry - Artcarved Inc.

PYRAMID - Sealing compounds - Monsey Products Co.

PYRAMID - Storage files ☆ - Convoy Inc.

PYRAMID - Trays - Pyramid Gift Collection

PYRAMID - Watches - Nationwide Time Inc.

PYRAMID - Water–bottled or canned - Pyramid Spring Water Co.

PYRAMID A - Brushes–paint - Wooster Brush Co.

PYRAMID ALES - Beverages–malt - Pyramid Breweries Inc.

PYRAMID CHALLENGE - Computer software - Dine Systems, Inc.

PYRAMID DIGESTER - Pet products - Ryter Corp.

PYRAMID ELECTRONICS - Electronic equipment - Bob Bartlett & Associates Inc.

PYRAMID HEFEWEIZEN - Beverages–malt - Hart Brewing, Inc.

PYRAMID KALSCH BEER - Beverages–malt - Pyramid Breweries Inc.

PYRAMID LAKE - Floor coverings–carpet and rugs ☆ - Hollytex Carpet Mills Inc.

PYRAMID MYSTERY TOP - Novelty items - Andrews Manufacturing Co. Inc.

PYRAMID OF MODERN CIVILIZATION - Apparel and accessories - Kirkland Properties, Inc.

PYRAMID OF THE SUN - Mayonnaise - Stache Foods

PYRAMID OPTICAL CORPORATION - Optical scanners–computer - Pyramid Optical Corp.

PYRAMID PLAN, THE - Publisher's imprints - Riviana Foods Inc.

PYRAMID SPHINX SERIES - Beverages–malt - Pyramid Breweries Inc.

PYRAMID STANDARD - Pharmaceutical preparations - Duro Med Industries Inc.

PYRAMID, THE - Cups–plastic - Public Building Authority of Memphis and Shelby County, Tennessee

PYRAMID TOP - Mats - Superior Manufacturing Group/Notrax Floor Matting

PYRAMID TRIM PRODUCTS INC. - Fabrics - Pyramid Trim Products, Inc.

PYRAMIDS - Games - Universal Manufacturing Co., Inc.

PYRAMIDS - Windmills - Whitehurst Imports

PYRAMIND - Mats ☆ - JCH International Inc.

PYRAMOD - Prefabricated buildings–wood - Mansion Industries Inc.

PYRANEE BOOKS - Publisher's imprints ☆ - Zondervan Publishing House

PYRANEURIN - Vitamins and nutritional supplements ☆ - Nutrition Control Products

PYRANISTAN - Health care products - Halsom Home Care

PYRAPEX - Hair care products ☆ - Designer's Edge International

PYRAPEX USA - Hair care products ☆ - Designer's Edge International

PYRAPHED - Pharmaceutical preparations ☆ - Lemmon Co.

PYRATUSS - Cough medicines - Vita-Fore Products Co.

PYRAWA - Boats–canoes ☆ - Sea Eagle

PYRAZODINE - Pharmaceutical preparations - H.R. Cenci Laboratories Inc.

PYRE-ML - Varnishes - E.I. Dupont de Nemours and Co.

PYRECHLOR - Pharmaceutical preparations ☆ - C.O. Truxton Inc.

PYREGESIC - Pharmaceutical preparations - C.O. Truxton Inc.

PYREHISTSAL - Pharmaceutical preparations ☆ - C.O. Truxton Inc.

PYRENETTE - Cheese - Zausner Foods Corp.

PYRENNES - Floor coverings–carpet and rugs ☆ - Robertex Associates Inc.

PYRENONE - Pet products - Roussel-Uclaf Corp.

PYRENONE LIVESTOCK SPRAY & INSECT SPRAY - Insecticides - Uncle Sam Chemical Co., Inc.

PYREX - Glassware - Corning Inc.

PYREXPLUS - Glassware–scientific - Corning Inc.

PYRICIDE - Pharmaceutical preparations ☆ - Pharmex Inc.

PYRIDAMIDE - Pharmaceutical preparations - Western Research Laboratories

PYRIDIN - Pharmaceutical preparations - C.S. Ruckstuhl Co. Inc.

PYRIDIUM - Pharmaceutical preparations - Parke-Davis

PYRIDOREX - Pharmaceutical preparations - Rex Research Laboratories

PYRIDOX - Vitamins and nutritional supplements - Oxford Laboratories Inc.

PYRIDOX - Vitamins and nutritional supplements ☆ - Integrated Health, Inc.

PYRIDOXINE - Pharmaceutical preparations - Roberts/Hauck Pharmaceuticals Inc.

PYRILINKS - Medical apparatus - Metra Biosystems, Inc.

PYRINEX - Health care products - Organics Corp. of America (Ambix Laboratories Div.)

PYRO - Pharmaceutical preparations ☆ - Hyrex Pharmaceuticals

PYRO BLASTER - Fireworks - American Promotional Events, Inc.

PYRO COVER - Ironing board pads - Pyrotex Corp.

PYRO-GEL - Sporting goods ☆ - Perfection Tip Co.

PYRO-GUARD - Lumber - Hoover Treated Wood Products Inc.

PYRO-HIDE - Sealing compounds - Harrison Paint Corp.

PYRO-JET - Cleaning preparations–household - Puritan-Churchill Chemical Co.

PYRO-KLEEN - Furnaces–electric - Detrex Corp.

PYRO OBSESSION - Fireworks - American Promotional Events, Inc.

PYRO-PAD - Insulating materials - MM Systems Corp.

PYRO-PLY - Copper compounds ☆ - Regal Ware, Inc.

PYRO-POWER - Pharmaceutical preparations - Bricker Laboratories

PYRO PRINTZ - Fabrics - Valley Forge Fabrics Inc.

PYRO-SEAL - Photographic equipment - Heindl Masks 'n' Mounts

PYRO WH-1 - Lubricants - Texaco, Inc.

PYROBAR - Partition tile ☆ - United States Gypsum Co.

PYROBATCH - Incinerators–metal - Surface Combustion, Inc.

PYROBLOCK - Laboratory apparatus - Associates of Cape Cod, Inc.

PYROCAINE - Pharmaceutical preparations - Medical Chemical Corp.

PYROCAL - Decals - Commercial Decal Inc.

PYROCERAM - Glass products - Corning Inc.

PYROCOOL - Fire extinguishing compositions - Metro Fire & Rescue, Inc.

PYROCORD - Braiding - Pyrotex Corp.

PYROCURE - Decals and transfers - Philadelphia Ceramics Inc.

PYRODEX - Firearms, accessories, and parts - Hodgdon Powder Co. Inc.

PYRODWARF - Flowers, plants, and seeds - Tree Connection, Inc.

PYROFLAM - Housewares - Corning Inc.

PYROGALLIC - Pharmaceutical preparations - Gordon Laboratories

PYROGARD - Firefighting suits - Kimberly-Clark Corp.

PYROGEL - Insulating materials–foam - Aspen Systems, Inc.

PYROGUENT - Pharmaceutical preparations ☆ - Republic Drug Co. Inc.

PYROIL - Motor vehicle parts and accessories - Pyroil Co. Inc.

PYROIL PERFORMANCE PRODUCTS - Fuel additives - Ashland Oil, Inc.

PYROKNIT - Fabrics - Asheboro Knitting Mills, Inc.

PYROKURE - Fire extinguishers - Fortifiber Corp.

PYROLANE - Tiles–ceramic - Amsterdam Corp.

PYROLECTRIC - Pens - Post Electric Co. Inc.

PYROLITE - Glass–safety ☆ - O'Keeffe's, Inc.

PYROLUBE - Lubricants - Kano Laboratories Inc.

PYROMANIAC - Fireworks - American Promotional Events, Inc.

PYROMANIAC - Fireworks - China Pyrotechnics, Inc.

PYROPACK - Health care products - Medi Inc.

PYROPLATE - Laboratory apparatus - Associates of Cape Cod, Inc.

PYROPLEX PLUS - Lubricants - HDL, Inc.

PYROS - Vials–glass ☆ - Taito America Corp.

PYROSAN - Pharmaceutical preparations - Herb Products Co.

PYROSCAN - Electronic equipment - Credence Technologies, Inc.

PYROSEAL - Cement - Stewart-Hall Chemical Corp.

PYROSENTRY - Kilns - Cole Ceramic Laboratories

PYROSET - Siding–insulating ☆ - GS Roofing Products Co.

PYROSET - Siding–metal ☆ - Flintkote Co.

PYROSTOP - Glass products - Crystal International Corp.

PYROTECTOR - Smoke detectors ☆ - Walter Kidde Aerospace

PYROTHERM - Incinerators–metal - Surface Combustion, Inc.

PYROTONE - Awnings - United Textile & Supply Co.

PYROVENT - Hardware - Wasco Products, Inc.

PYROXINE - Health care products - Kay Pharmacal Co. Inc.

PYRRALAN - Cold remedies - Lannett Co. Inc.
PYRROXATE - Pharmaceutical preparations ☆ - Upjohn Co.
PYRYD - Cough medicines - Vita-Fore Products Co.
PYTHAGORAS AND THE DRAGON - Computer software ☆ - Krell Software Corp.
PYTHIA - Computer software - Pythia Corp.
PYTHON - Alarm systems - Directed Electronics, Inc.
PYTHON - Computer-data storage system - Archive Corp.
PYTHON - Gloves - Granet Inc.
PYTHON - Insecticides - Y-Tex Corp.
PYTHON - Pistols - Colt's Manufacturing Co. Inc.
PYTHON - Plastics - Premier Python Systems, Inc.
PYTHON PORTER - Pet products - Python Products

PYXIS - Electronics equipment - ALTA Group
PYXIS - Navigational instruments - Sony Corp. of America
PYXIS-E - Electronics equipment - ALTA Group
PZ-1 - Cameras ☆ - Pentax Corp.
PZ-10 - Cameras ☆ - Pentax Corp.
PZ-44 - Food products - Foremost Farms USA
PZ 3900 - Lenses–optical - Capo, Inc.
PZ-IP - Cameras - Pentax Corp.
PZ PACIFIC ZONE - Clothing - Pacific Zone
PZ1 - Tools–hand-operated - Phillips Screw Co.
PZ2 - Tools–power-driven - Phillips Screw Co.
PZ3 - Tools–power-driven - Phillips Screw Co.
PZLSAURUS - Puzzles - Dongeo, Inc.
PZM - Microphones - Crown International, Inc.

Q

Addresses and phone numbers for the companies cited in the brands below
are available in the Company Listings section immediately following the brands listings.

Q - Computer peripheral equipment - Qsystem Computers, Inc.
Q - Detergents - Burge Chemical Products Inc.
Q - Fans–electric - Davoil, Inc.
Q - Floor cleaning equipment - Windsor Industries, Inc.
Q - Tools - Q.E.P. Co. Inc.
Q 3DQ - Loudspeakers - Hitachi Instruments, Inc.
Q-ALERT - Dictating machines - Dictaphone Corp.
Q-ALKA - Pharmaceutical preparations ☆ - Hyrex Pharmaceuticals
Q AMBIENT WEAR - Apparel and accessories - Q-Ambient Wear
Q-AMP - Machine parts - Eaton Corp.
Q & A - Computer software - Symantec Corp.
Q & B - Salad dressings–bottled - Q & B Foods, Inc.
Q AT WORK AND WIN - Broadcasting stations–radio - Evergreen Media
    Corp. of the Great Lakes
Q ATHLETIC - Apparel–athletic - Reza Shakoori
Q-B II - Chemical preparations - Georgia-Pacific Corp.
Q B SQUARE - Notebooks and notepads - Crayon Cube, Inc.
Q-BEAM - Lighting equipment - Brinkmann Corp.
Q-BEE - Apparel and accessories ☆ - Winer Industries Inc.
Q-BEE - Candy - Queen Bee Gardens
Q BERT - Games ☆ - Ben Cooper Inc.
Q-BERT - Toys–electronic ☆ - Parker Brothers
Q-BIC - Paint rollers - E-Z Paintr Corp.
Q BILLION - Electronic game - SETA USA Inc.
Q-BLE - Bouncing toy - Marv Lee Inc.
Q-BOND - Cement - JTL Co.
Q-BRITE - Electronic equipment - Acme-Lite Manufacturing Co.
Q-BRON - Pharmaceutical preparations ☆ - Hyrex Pharmaceuticals
Q-CALL - Telephone answering machines ☆ - Dictaphone Corp.
Q CANARY BY QUEST - Computer software - Quest Consultants Inc.
Q CARD - Computer hardware - Quantum Corp.
Q-CARD - Electrical equipment - Q-Card, Inc.
Q CARDS - Playing cards - Zolo Inc.
Q CARE - Health care products - Unimed, Inc.
Q-CEE'S - Decals and transfers - Mountain Corp.
Q-CHAN - Pet products - Nippon Pet Food
Q-CHARTS - Dry erase boards - Quartet Manufacturing Co.
Q-CHECK - Computer software - Optical Gaging Products, Inc.
Q-CLEAN - Chemical preparations - Quaker Chemical Corp.
Q DAMON - Soap - Damon Industreis, Inc.
Q-DEC II - Paints - Fulton Co.
Q-DECON - Pharmaceutical preparations ☆ - Hyrex Pharmaceuticals
Q-ETCH - Chemical preparations - Printing Developments Inc.
Q-FON FORTE - Pharmaceutical preparations ☆ - Hyrex Pharmaceuticals
Q FRESH - Breads - Arizona Supermarkets Inc.
Q G - Apparel and accessories - Gary David Johnson
Q-GEL - Vitamins and nutritional supplements - Tishcon Corp.
Q GRILL - Barbecues and grills - Hapco
Q-HALT - Cleaning preparations - Platte Chemical Co.
Q-JET - Industrial machinery - Q-JET DSI Inc.
Q-LACE - Pharmaceutical preparations ☆ - Hyrex Pharmaceuticals
Q-LENOL - Pharmaceutical preparations ☆ - Hyrex Pharmaceuticals
Q-LIGHT - Photographic equipment - Polaroid Corp.
Q LINE - Shelving units–metal - Tennsco Corp.
Q-LOCK - Computer software - Quintet, Inc.
Q-LUX - Lighting equipment - ProLight

Q-LUX - Lighting fixtures ☆ - Guth Lighting
Q MANUAL - Games - Avalon Hill Game Co.
Q-MARIN - Pharmaceutical preparations ☆ - Hyrex Pharmaceuticals
Q-MART - Food containers - Q-Mart Food Stores
Q-MASTER - Nozzles - Mark Ettere
Q-MATE - Remote control devices - AVL
Q MENU - Computer software - W. Quinn Associates, Inc.
Q-MIX - Swimming-pool plaster - U.S. Silica Co.
Q-NET - Traps–animal - Fuhrman Diversified
Q PACK - Packaging–paper - Queens Group, Inc.
Q-PACK - Paper products - Queens Group, Inc.
Q-PADS - Audio equipment - Fibre Glass-Evercoat Co. Inc.
Q-PAQ - Sheet metal products ☆ - Alltrista Corp.
Q-PET - Electronic equipment - Samco Scientific Inc.
Q-POINTE - Golfing equipment - Vulcan Golf Technology
Q-PONGEE - Cosmetic applicators - CHK International, Inc.
Q QUAKER STATE FOR LONGER ENGINE LIFE - Oils–lubricating - Quaker
    State Oil Refining Corp.
Q QUARTERDECK - Computer software - Quarterdeck Corp.
Q QUARTERS - Apparel and accessories - Ames Department Stores, Inc.
Q QUORUM - Computer software - Quorum Software Systems Inc.
Q-RAIL - Office supplies - Quartet Manufacturing Co.
Q-RAP - Recording label - Quark, Inc.
Q-REFRES-KO LACTA - Confections - R.L. Albert & Son, Inc.
Q-RELEASE - Health care products - Bioenergy Inc.
Q S - Racks - Hein-Werner Corp.
Q-SAFE - Computer software - Quintet, Inc.
Q-SANTIN - Pharmaceutical preparations ☆ - Hyrex Pharmaceuticals
Q-SEP - Pharmaceutical preparations ☆ - Hyrex Pharmaceuticals
Q-SEPT - Disinfectants - Damon Industries, Inc.
Q SERIES CONTROLERS - Computer hardware - Proprietary Controls
    Systems Corp.
Q-SMOOTH - Paperboard - Jefferson Smurfit Corp.
Q-SPONDER - Electronic equipment - Bell & Howell Co.
Q-STAR - Air conditioning equipment - Friedrich Air Conditioning Co.
Q-STATS II - Computer software - Derby Associates International Limited
    Liability Co.
Q-STICK - Pens ☆ - Faber-Castell Corp.
Q-STOR - Furniture stores - Mallard Manufacturing Corp.
Q SYSTEM DATABASE - Computer software - Honeywell Loveland Controls
    Co.
Q-SYSTEMS - Electronics equipment - Reactive Systems Inc.
Q-T - Apparel–women's - Q-T Foundations Co. Inc.
Q T. - Disinfectants - Hillyard Enterprises, Inc.
Q-T - Food products - Gloria Marshall Figure Salons Ltd.
Q-TECH - Pencils - Quill Corp.
Q-TEE-CLOWN - Dolls - Star Imports, Inc.
Q-TEE-MAG-EE - Magnets - Star Imports, Inc.
Q-TEE NOTES - Office supplies - Exclusive Co.
Q TEST - Pharmaceutical preparations - Becton, Dickinson and Co.
Q-TEST - Prophylactics - Ansell Inc. (Personal Products Div.)
Q-TILE SYSTEM - Tools - Q.E.P. Co. Inc.
Q-TILE TRIM - Molding compounds–plastics - Q.E.P. Co. Inc.
Q-TIPS - Cotton–balls - Chesebrough-Pond's USA Co.
Q TLC - Framing and face plates - Quaker Plastic Corp.
Q-TONE - Electronics equipment - AZTEK Inc.

☆ = Now out of production

Q-TRACKER - Measuring instruments - Badger Meter, Inc.
Q TRAN - Transformers–electric - Q Tran, Inc.
Q-T'S - Ostomy product - Torbot-Gricks
Q-VEEV - Firearms, accessories, and parts - Q-Veev Speciality Gear
Q-VEL - Pharmaceutical preparations - Ciba-Geigy Corp.
Q-VI-FLOR - Pharmaceutical preparations ☆ - Hyrex Pharmaceuticals
Q-VIBE - Pharmaceutical preparations - Pfizer Inc.
Q-VON 65 - Pharmaceutical preparations ☆ - Hyrex Pharmaceuticals
Q WALL STATWALL SYSTEMS BY HPI - Plaster–wallboard - HPI Inc.
Q WHITE - Water colors - Steig Products
Q-WRAP - Packaging–paper ☆ - Daubert Coated Products, Inc.
Q2 PLUS - Mattresses - Kinetic Concepts, Inc.
Q32000 - Filters–air - HEPA Corp.
QA - Confections - Q & A Products Inc.
QA+ - Hardware - Century Fasteners, Inc.
QA-40 - Disinfectants - Unit Chemical Corp.
QA ADVISOR - Computer software - Quality Assurance Systems, Inc.
QA DIRECTOR - Computer software - Compuware Corp.
Q.A. INSPECTOR - Chemical preparations - Sherwin-Williams Automotive Finishes Corp.
QA PARTNER - Computer software - Segue Software, Inc.
QA QUALITY ASSURANCE - Apparel and accessories - J.C. Penney Co., Inc.
QA RADAR - Computer software - Segue Software, Inc.
QA SCAN - Medical apparatus - Clintec Nutrition Co.
QA21 - Building materials - Senergy, Inc.
QABBALY - Jewelry - Capucine Osman-Li
QAD.INC - Computer software - Qad.Inc
Q&V HEAVENLY! - Bakery products - BCB USA Corp.
Q&V PEACH MIST - Beverages–carbonated - BCB USA Corp.
QANTAR - Watches - Elgin Watch Co.
QAPLUS/FACTORY - Diagnostic computer programs - Diagsoft, Inc.
QARX - Computer software - Cygnus Systems Development, Inc.
QAS - Disinfectants - PVT Systems Inc.
QAYLAR - Hair-replacement product ☆ - International Hairgoods Inc.
QAYLAR NOVA - Hair-replacement product ☆ - International Hairgoods Inc.
QB - Fabrics - Quality Braid Corp.
QB - Nuts and bolts - Quality Bolt and Screw Co.
QB - Printing trades machinery - Gestetner Corp.
QB - Thread - WesekPalley Tile Inc.
QB2 - Irrigation equipment - Pepco Water Conservation Products Inc.
QBC - Apparel and accessories - National Football League Properties, Inc.
QBC - Cables - Quality Microwave Interconnects, Inc.
QBC - Projectors–photographic ☆ - Buhl Optical Co.
QBL - Computer software - Jerry D. Lloyd
QBOX - Computer software - Bowman Merritt and Associates, Inc.
QBR - Soups–mixes - Arrowhead Mills, Inc.
QC - Chemical preparations - Ciba Corning Diagnostics Corp.
QC - Microphones ☆ - Electro-Voice, Inc.
QC - Semiconductors - Quadrant Components, Inc.
QC - Shoes - Edison Brothers Stores, Inc.
QC-2 - Dairy products - Quality Chekd Dairy Products Association
QC-7 - Aluminum products - Aluminum Co. of America
QC CALC - Calculators - Calculated Industries, Inc.
Q.C. EROTICA - Hair care products - Quick Cut Inc.
QC-GAGE - Computer software - Prolink, Inc.
QC GROUP, A - Toners - AQC Group Corp.
QC GROUP, A - Toners - AQC Group Corp.
QC-PLAN - Computer software - Qualcomm Inc.
QC PLEX - Pharmaceutical preparations ☆ - Solaray
QC QUAL CRAFT - Scaffolds–metal - Qual-Craft Industries
QC QUALITY CABINETS - Cabinets - Texwood Industries, Inc.
QC SERIES, THE - Drill bits - Precision Twist Drill Co.
QC1 - Automotive parts and accessories - Blue Chip Products Inc.
QC3 - Apparel and accessories ☆ - Edison Brothers Stores, Inc.
Q=C3E - Laboratory apparatus - Charles River Laboratories, Inc.
QC61 - Coatings for storage tanks - Quick Tanks, Inc.
QCA - Recording label - QCA Inc.
Q'CASE - Computer software - Curtis Hill Publishing Co.
QCB PLEX - Pharmaceutical preparations - Solaray
QCC - Machine parts - Harsco Corp.
QCC - Welding equipment - Electron Beam Technologies, Inc.
QCF - Film - Eastman Kodak Co.
QCI QUALITY CLOTHING - Apparel and accessories - Goody's Family Clothing, Inc.
QCOLOR - Printers–computer - QMS, Inc.
QCOM - Computer software - Quadron Service Corp.

QCP - Computer software - Biological Simulators, Inc.
QCP - Paper–photographic - Eastman Kodak Co.
QCP-2700 - Communications equipment - Qualcomm Inc.
QCPILOT - Computer software - Qualcomm Inc.
QCS - Computer software - QCS Corp.
QCS-NET - Computer software - QCS Corp.
QCT - Animal feeds - Classic Pet Products, Inc.
QD - Hair care products - Stanley Fay Co.
QD+ - Jewelry - Quality Designs Plus Corp.
QD-3 ROBOT - Hair- and skin-care products, fragrance, etc. - Benjamin Ansehl Co.
QD 30 - Paints - Benjamin Moore & Co.
Q.D. PRIMER - Paints - Dunn Edwards Corp.
QDA - Bandages–orthopedic - Cramer Products Inc.
QDIVISION - Recording label - Q Division Records, Inc.
QDM - Feed grinders - Quincy Design & Manufacturing, Inc.
QDM - Photographic film - Eastman Kodak Co.
QDS - Machinery - Helicoflex Co.
QDS QUALITY DESIGN SERIES - Sewing machines–household - Union Special Corp.
QDSP - Electronic equipment - Advanced Mos Technology, Inc.
Q+E - Publisher's imprints - Q+E Software, Inc.
QE TEA - Teas - Sakina Brunk
Q.E.2 - Yarn - Henry's Attic
QEA - Computer hardware - Quality Engineering Associates, Inc.
QED - Printers–computer - Zygo Industries Inc.
QED - Watches ☆ - SMH (US) Inc.
QEDESIGN - Computer software - Qualcomm Inc.
QELIB - Computer software - Pioneer Software, Inc.
QEST - Hardware - U.S. Brass Corp.
QEVB - Software manuals - Pioneer Software, Inc.
QEX - Audio equipment - Alaron Inc.
QFAST - Communications equipment - Probe Science, Inc.
QFD/CAPTURE - Computer software - International TechneGroup Inc.
QFLASH - Photographic flash units - Quantum Instruments, Inc.
QFORM - Computer software - QMS, Inc.
QFS - Tents - Academy Broadway Corp.
QGC - Jewelry - Quality Gold of Cincinnati, Inc.
QH - Coffee - Coffee Butler Service Inc.
QI - Shirts - Silk Skyway, Ltd.
QI TO HEALTH - Food products - Master Hong
QIANA - Fibers–nylon ☆ - E.I. Dupont de Nemours and Co.
QIC - Medical apparatus - Quantum Imaging Corp.
QIC-EXTRA - Computer peripheral equipment - Verbatim Corp.
QIC-STAND - Computer storage devices - Microplas Inc.
QICDRAW - Computer peripheral equipment - Competitive Technologies International Inc.
QICVAULT - Computer software - Rexon/Tecmar Inc.
QIG/400 - Computer software ☆ - Strategic Information Solutions
QIK-FRY - Seafood products–canned or cured - Rose Frozen Shrimp Inc.
QIKALERT - Watches - Image Watches, Inc.
QING - Teas - Chinese Native Products
QING - Teas - Eastrise Trading Corp.
QINGEN - Electronic equipment - Qintar, Inc.
QINN CHAPEL - Wines - Pliska Winery
QISMET LTD. - Apparel–women's - Milady Brassiere & Corset Co., Inc.
QIX - Video games - Nintendo of America Inc.
QJ - Jewelry - Jordana Creations, Inc.
QJ - Nozzles - Spraying Systems Co.
QJJ - Nozzles - Spraying Systems Co.
QJP - Jewelry - Leer Gem Ltd.
QL - Computer peripheral equipment - Infimed, Inc.
QL - Golfing equipment - Tourshot Golf Co. Inc.
QLAT - Computer software - Mark Chang
QLC - Cheese - Leprino Foods
QLIKVIEW - Computer software - Qlik Tech Inc.
QLN - Heating equipment - Coen Co., Inc.
QLS - Laboratory apparatus - Point Plastics Inc.
QLT - Tools–masonry - Marshalltown Trowel Co.
QM-NOTIFY! - Computer software - EX Machina, Inc.
QMB - Coats–fur - Quality Furs-Manos & Block Inc.
QMB - Scales–industrial - Fairbanks Scales Inc.
QMB2 - Coats–fur - Quality Furs-Manos & Block Inc.
QMQB - Switches–power - American Circuit Breaker Corp.
QM'S - Apparel–athletic ☆ - Cross Creek Apparel Inc.
QMS COLORGRAFIX - Printers–computer - QMS, Inc.

☆ = Now out of production

QMS COLORSCRIPT - Printers–computer - QMS, Inc.
QMS CROWN - Computer software - QMS, Inc.
QMS CROWN TECHNOLOGY - Computer software - QMS, Inc.
QMS DELUX FONT PACKAGE - Computer software - QMS, Inc.
QMS LASERGRAFIX - Printers–computer - QMS, Inc.
QMS-PS - Printers–computer - QMS, Inc.
QMS WRITER - Printers–computer - QMS, Inc.
QNEZ - Meat products–beef ☆ - Quaker Maid Meats Inc.
QO - Circuit breakers - Square D Co.
QO - Fabrics - Dan River Inc.
Q.O.D. - Skin care products - Perry Products
QOLI - Publisher's imprints - Michael B. Frisch
QORK CYLINDER - Garden equipment - Visual Design Manufacturing Co. Inc.
QORK QUBE - Garden equipment - Visual Design Manufacturing Co. Inc.
QORO - Sporting goods - Rodel, Inc.
QORPAK - Bottles–plastic - All-Pak, Inc.
QOSMEDIX - Pharmaceutical preparations - Qosina Corp.
Q.P. - Eggs - Milton G. Waldbaum Co.
QPORT - Computer peripheral equipment - New Generation Software, Inc.
QPS - Computer software - Quark, Inc.
QQ - Compressors–air - Coltec Industries Inc.
QQEST - Computer software - Qqest Software Systems
QQQQ - Ovens–convection - Quadlux, Inc.
QR - Chemical preparations - Precision Labs, Inc.
QR - Lighting equipment - Precision Multiple Controls, Inc.
Q.R. - Medical apparatus - Minimed Inc.
QR-1R - Heating equipment - Quartz Radiation Corp.
QR-25 - Air compressor - Coltec Industries Inc.
QRANC - Apparel–athletic - Qranc Usa, Inc.
QRB - Paints - Qrb Industries
QRC - Cleaning equipment - Tweco Products, Inc.
QRC - Toys–airplanes - Cox Products Inc.
QRS - Electronic equipment - Quick Response Systems Inc.
Q.R.S. - Pianos - Q-R-S Music Rolls Inc.
QRS PIANOMATION - Electronic equipment - QRS Music Rolls, Inc.
QRUZE - Beverages–malt - Joseph L. Owades
QRX - Bakery products - International Paper Co.
QRYLIC - Frames–picture - Ammak Manufacturing Corp.
Q'S - Bakery products - Q's No Frills Catering Inc.
QS - Jewelry - Greenberg & Shaw, Inc.
QS/1 - Health care products - QS/1 Data Systems
Q'S BILLIARD CLUB - Apparel and accessories - David Houston
QS QUIET SERIES - Vacuum cleaners and accessories ☆ - The Hoover Co.
QS3000 - Antennas - Checkpoint Systems Inc.
QS3000 PLUS - Surveillance equipment - Checkpoint Systems Inc.
QSC - Audio equipment - QSC Audio Products Inc.
QSOURCE - Electronic equipment - Qsource, Inc.
QSP - Vacuum cleaners and accessories - Shop Vac Corp.
QSTAR IV - Medical apparatus - Medline, Industries, Inc.
QSWITCH - Switches–electric - Quintech, Inc.
QSYSTEM - Computer storage devices - Qsystem Computers, Inc.
QT - Air compressor - Coltec Industries Inc.
QT - Bags–cosmetic - Monaco Import/Export Inc.
QT - Cakes - Frank Foods Co.
Q.T. - Dinners–frozen - Design Foods
QT - Food products - Quiktrip Corp.
QT - Publisher's imprints - Qualtec Quality Services, Inc.
Q.T. - Suntan lotions - Schering-Plough Healthcare Products
QT VIDEO - Photographic equipment ☆ - GMI Photographic Inc.
QTA - Electronic equipment - QTA
QTC - Watches ☆ - SMH (US) Inc.
QTECH - Watches - Luxury International Inc.
QTEKPLOT - Computer software - QMS, Inc.
QTEST - Computer and electronics equipment - MTS Systems Corp.
QTEX - Wigs - Louis Ferre, Inc.
QTG - Valves - Keystone International Holdings Corp.
QTICA - Cosmetics - Zoya Co.
QTOWELS - Paper–toweling - Sanitor Manufacturing Co.
QTR - Welding equipment - Tweco Products, Inc.
QTROFF - Computer software - QMS, Inc.
QTS - Air compressor - Coltec Industries Inc.
Q.T.S. SATIN SEAL - Adhesives and sealants - Mapei East Corp.
QTZ-X - Yarn - Clark-Schwebel Fiber Glass Corp.
QUA-BID - Pharmaceutical preparations - Quaker City Pharmacal Co.
QUA-GO - Pharmaceutical preparations - Quaker City Pharmacal Co.
QUA-LITE - Lighting fixtures - Galaxy Electrical Manufacturing, Inc.

QUABBIN - Paper–writing - Hinkson Paper Co.
QUABOAG - Paper–writing - Hinkson Paper Co.
QUACHARBEL - Pharmaceutical preparations - Quaker City Pharmacal Co.
QUACK - Fabrics - Veratec
QUACK ALONG DUCKS - Toys - Tomy America, Inc.
QUACK-'N-A-SACK - Toys–stuffed ☆ - Bradley Import Co.
QUACK PACK - Giftware - Great American Duck Races, Inc.
QUACK TRACK - Computer software - Great American Duck Races, Inc.
QUACKENBUSH - Nut-lobster cracker - Cook Things
QUACKERS - Crackers - Nabisco Foods Group
QUACKERS - Exercising equipment - Lisco, Inc.
QUACKERS - Fabrics ☆ - Greenwood Mills Inc.
QUACKERS DUCK - Toys–stuffed - Russ Berrie and Co., Inc.
QUACKETTE - Recording label - Electricity Enterprises Inc.
QUACKETTE DUCK - Puppets - Dakin Inc.
QUACKLES - Toys ☆ - Little Tikes Co.
QUAD - Adhesives and sealants - Ohio Sealants Inc.
QUAD - Cameras ☆ - Avant Inc.
QUAD - Floor coverings–carpet and rugs ☆ - Regal Rugs Inc.
QUAD - Graffitti remover - Little Tokyo Leasing & Sales
QUAD - Hardware - Southco, Inc.
QUAD - Pens - Astro Pen Co.
QUAD - Pens - Eversharp Pen Co.
QUAD ARM - Photographic equipment - SP Systems/Saratons
QUAD BENDER - Tools–hand-operated - Greenlee Textron Inc.
QUAD CITY RIVER BANDITS - Paper products - Quad City Professional Baseball, Inc.
QUAD CITY THUNDER - Athletic associations - Jay Gellerman
QUAD CURE - Concrete products - Symons Corp.
QUAD-CUT 4X4 - Drill bits - Barnes Group Inc.
QUAD-DRIVER - Tools–power-driven - Jore Corp.
QUAD FINGER - Locks–door - Powerbrace Corp.
QUAD FOLD - Kitchen appliances - Vaughan Manufacturing Co. Inc.
QUAD GAS - Monitors - Mine Safety Appliances Co.
QUAD-GRIP - Hand tools - Olympia Industrial Inc.
QUAD HOCKEY - Games - General Sportcraft Co. Ltd.
QUAD-LITE - High-intensity lamps - Control Research Inc.
QUAD/LOK - Hunting equipment - Dwight M. Jennings
QUAD-PAK - Brushes–hair - Nailtex Inc.
QUAD/PAK - Insulating materials - Manville/Schuller
QUAD-QUILL - Drill presses - Russell T. Gilman, Inc.
QUAD QUIP - Health care products ☆ - Sammons Preston
QUAD-RAIL - Photographic equipment - SP Systems/Saratons
QUAD-RATED - Electrical equipment - Triangle Wire & Cable, Inc.
QUAD-REX - Games - Eugene Kisielowski
QUAD-RULE - Artists' materials ☆ - Graphic Products Corp.
QUAD STAR - Antennas–satellite ☆ - Winegard Co.
QUAD-TIP - Soldering equipment - Hexacon Electric Co.
QUAD TUBE - Bumpers–motor vehicle - Wedgestone Automotive Corp.
QUAD TUBE - Lamps - Wiko Ltd.
QUADATA - Computer software - Rockford Map Publishers, Inc.
QUADBLOCK - Animal feed supplements - Moorman Manufacturing Co.
QUADCAP - Capacitors - AVX Corp.
QUADETTES - Prescription drug ☆ - Iodent Co.
QUADETTS - Pharmaceutical preparations ☆ - ICN Pharmaceuticals Inc.
QUADFLEXTRA - Computer software - Quadram Corp.
QUADINE - Pharmaceutical preparations ☆ - Hyrex Pharmaceuticals
QUADJET - Printers–computer - Quadram Corp.
QUADLAB - Toys ☆ - Revell-Monogram, Inc.
QUADLINK - Spectrometers - Ametek, Inc. (Process-Analytical Division)
QUADLOG - Microscopes–electron - Moore Products Co.
QUADLUX - Ovens–convection - Quadlux, Inc.
QUADMED, INC. Q QUALITY INNOVATION VALUE SERVICE - Medical apparatus - Quadmed Inc.
QUADMETICS - Nail care products - Rudolph International, Inc.
QUADPACER - Toothbrushes–electric - Optiva Corp.
QUADPLEX RECEPTACLES - Wiring devices - Bryant Electric Co.
QUADPUTER - Computer peripheral equipment - Microway, Inc.
QUADRA - Floor cleaning equipment - Windsor Industries, Inc.
QUADRA - Glassware–household - Villeroy and Boch Tableware Ltd.
QUADRA - Radio tower amplifier - Allen Telecom Group, Inc.
QUADRA - Tires - Bridgestone/Firestone, Inc.
QUADRA - Wheelchairs ☆ - Ortho-Kinetics, Inc.
QUADRA CHAIN - Chains - St. Pierre Manufacturing Corp.
QUADRA-COIL - Medical apparatus - Cabot Technology Corp.
QUADRA COIL - Motor vehicle parts and accessories - DaimlerChrysler

QUADRA-FLEX - Audio equipment - Thermodyne International Ltd.
QUADRA-FLEX - Jewelry - Aurafin Corp.
QUADRA FOIL - Sealing devices - Slade, Inc.
QUADRA-GRIP - Toys—trains - K-Line
QUADRA-MATIC - Office supplies - Vanguard Corp.
QUADRA MAXX - Alarm systems - Maxi-Guard
QUADRA MULTIACTION - Pens - Staedtler, Inc.
QUADRA-PLATE - Motorcycle parts and accessories - ABC
QUADRA-POD - Photographic equipment - Steven P. Jones
QUADRA SHADOW - Cosmetics - Chanel Inc.
QUADRA-THERM - Fireplaces - Martin Industries, Inc.
QUADRA-TRAC - Motor vehicle parts and accessories - DaimlerChrysler
QUADRA-VERSION - Automotive parts and accessories - Quigley Motor Co. Inc.
QUADRA XT2 - Tires - Bridgestone/Firestone, Inc.
QUADRACER - Motorcycles - Suzuki of America Automotive Corp.
QUADRACOLOR - Office supplies - Transfertech Inc.
QUADRACUT - Tools—machine - Threading Systems Inc.
QUADRACYCLE INC - Motor vehicles - Quadracycle, Inc.
QUADRAFLEX - Vacuum cleaners and accessories - The Hoover Co.
QUADRAKEY - Electrical equipment - Westinghouse Electric Corp.
QUADRAKLEEN - Filters—industrial - Baker Hughes Inc.
QUADRAMA - Hardware - Merchandising Inventives, Inc.
QUADRAMATE - Audio equipment ☆ - Telephonics Corp.
QUADRAMED CORPORATION - Computer software - Quadramed Corp.
QUADRAMIN - Pharmaceutical preparations - Wesley Pharmacal Co. Inc.
QUADRAMOID - Pharmaceutical preparations ☆ - ICN Pharmaceuticals Inc.
QUADRANGLE - Recording label - Jazz Composer's Orchestra Association Inc.
QUADRANT - Electronic equipment - Quadrant Components, Inc.
QUADRANT - Floor coverings—carpet and rugs - Mohawk Industries Inc.
QUADRANT - Floor coverings—carpet and rugs ☆ - Regal Rugs Inc.
QUADRANT - Shoulder braces - Smith & Nephew DonJoy Inc.
QUADRAPLEXER - Photographic equipment ☆ - Buhl Optical Co.
QUADRAPOD - Electronic equipment - Hudson Photographic Industries Inc.
QUADRAPOINT - Floor coverings—carpet and rugs - Criterion Mills Inc.
QUADRASHIFT - Motor vehicle parts and accessories - Agco Corp.
QUADRASPEC - Floor coverings—carpet and rugs - Karastan-Bigelow Inc.
QUADRASPENSE - Medical device - Ultradent Products, Inc.
QUADRASPERSE - Computer hardware - ChemTreat, Inc.
QUADRASTRETCH - Apparel and accessories - Four Seasons Design Group
QUADRASYNTH - Musical instruments - Alesis Corp.
QUADRATA - Floor coverings—tile ☆ - Vida Mosaic Co. Inc.
QUADRATECH - Radar systems and equipment - TT Systems Corp.
QUADRECTIFIER - Filters—air - Technical Dynamics Inc.
QUADREL - Machinery - QLS, Inc.
QUADRI-CUT - Saws—power - Mitek Industries Inc.
QUADRIFID - Electrical product - Augat Inc.
QUADRIFLEX - Health care products - Medtronic Nortech
QUADRIGA - Greeting cards - Reproducta Co., Inc.
QUADRILLE - Candles - Colonial Candle of Cape Cod
QUADRILLE - Dinnerware—glass - Nikko Ceramics Inc.
QUADRILLE - Floor coverings - Mannington Resilient Floors
QUADRILLE - Floor coverings—carpet and rugs ☆ - Masland Corp.
QUADRILLE - Rings—jewelry - Artcarved Inc.
QUADRILLE BY SANGO - Dinnerware—glass - Sango Co. Ltd. (Sango USA Div.)
QUADRILLION - Masonry drill bits - Credo Co.
QUADRINAL - Health care products - Knoll Pharmaceutical Co.
QUADRINO - Dinnerware—glass - Sango Co. Ltd. (Sango USA Div.)
QUADRIPOD - Photographic equipment ☆ - Heitz Service Corp.
QUADRO - Antennas—satellite - KVH Industries, Inc.
QUADRO - Drill bits - Hawera Inc.
QUADRO - Toys - DGI/Buki
QUADROTEX - Fabrics - Albany International Corp.
QUADROVENT - Fabrics - Albany International Corp.
QUADRUM - Golfing equipment - P & S Golf Management Co. Inc.
QUADRUM TELECOM - Telephones - Quadrum Telecommunications, Inc.
QUADRUNNER - Computer peripheral equipment - Vinca Corp.
QUADRUNNER - Motorcycles - Suzuki of America Automotive Corp.
QUADRUPED, THE - Footwear - Jeffrey S. Hoot
QUADRUPLEX - Clocks ☆ - General Time Corp. (Westclox/Seth Thomas Div.)
QUADRYL - Pharmaceutical preparations ☆ - U.S. Ethicals Inc.
QUADS - Roller skates - Seneca Sports, Inc.
QUADSCAN - Computer software - PC Video Conversion
QUADSCORE - Games - Little Harbor Corp.

QUADSCORE2 - Games - Little Harbor Corp.
QUADSCREEN - Computers—mainframe - Union Pacific Technologies Inc.
QUADSEAL - Electronic equipment - Advantek, Inc.
QUADSEAL - Rubber—molded - Performance Plastics Products Inc.
QUADSPORT - Motorcycles - Suzuki of America Automotive Corp.
QUADSTAR - Medical apparatus - Medserv Group, Inc.
QUADSTONE - Floor coverings ☆ - Tarkett, Inc.
QUADTRO - Cushions - Roho, Inc.
QUADTRODE - Medical apparatus - Invivo Research, Inc.
QUADTRUSS - Shelving units—metal - Metal Masters Foodservice Equipment Co., Inc.
QUADY - Wines - Quady Winery
QUAIL - Fruits and vegetables - Upland Lemon Co.
QUAIL HOLLOW - Slacks - Duck Head Apparel Co., Inc.
QUAIL HUNTER - Footwear - G.H. Bass and Co.
QUAIL IRONSTONE - Dinnerware—glass - S.P. Skinner Co. Inc.
QUAIL RIDGE - Dinnerware—glass - Metlox Pottery Shoppe
QUAIL RIDGE - Floor coverings ☆ - Congoleum Corp.
QUAIL RIDGE - Wines - Quail Ridge Cellars & Vineyards
QUAIL RUN - Manufactured homes - Redman Industries, Inc.
QUAIL RUN - Slacks—men's - Spencer Industries Inc.
QUAIL RUN - Wines - Quail Run Cellars & Vintners
QUAIL VALLEY - Furniture ☆ - Bassett Furniture Industries, Inc.
QUAILRIDGE - Trailers—travel - Forest River, Inc.
QUAKE - Bicycles - Marin Mountain Bikes, Inc.
QUAKE - Computer software - Adobe Systems Inc.
QUAKE - Computer software - ID Software, Inc.
QUAKE - Sporting goods - Dunlop Maxfli Sports Corp.
QUAKE BREAKER - Valves—industrial - UMAC Inc.
QUAKE SECURE! - Glue—household or industrial - DCOR Inc.
QUAKEBEDS - Furniture - Douglas Steven Jackman
QUAKEDRIN - Pharmaceutical preparations - Quaker City Pharmacal Co.
QUAKEGARD - Packaging—foam - Dean Doser
QUAKELOCK - Hardware - Quakelock Inc.
QUAKER - Cheese - Bongrain Cheese USA
QUAKER - Floor coverings—carpet and rugs - Quaker Inc.
QUAKER - Hardware - Quaker City Manufacturing Co.
QUAKER - Health care products ☆ - CTS Laboratories Inc.
QUAKER - Insulating materials - Quaker Window Products Co.
QUAKER - Paints ☆ - Colony Paints Div.
QUAKER - Spices and extracts - Ottens Flavors
QUAKER - Stoves—wood-burning ☆ - Quaker Stove Co. Inc.
QUAKER - Sugar—granulated, refined, or powdered - Savannah Foods and Industries Inc.
QUAKER - Thread - Threads USA Div.
QUAKER CHAMBRAY - Fabrics—cotton ☆ - Dan River Inc.
QUAKER CHEWY - Granola bars - Quaker Oats Co.
QUAKER CITY - Chemical preparations - Malco Products, Inc.
QUAKER CITY - Oils—lubricating - Pennsylvania Petroleum Products Co.
QUAKER DEX - Pharmaceutical preparations - Quaker City Pharmacal Co.
QUAKER HILL FARMS - Cookies and snacks - Atlas Biscuit Co. Inc.
QUAKER IN-STORE BAKERY - Breads - Quaker Oats Co.
QUAKER INSTANT OATMEAL - Cereal - Quaker Oats Co.
QUAKER KOAT - Motor vehicle parts and accessories - Quaker State Oil Refining Corp.
QUAKER LACE - Tablecloths - Lorraine Linens, Inc.
QUAKER LACE(BLUE RIBBON) - Tablecloths - Quaker Lace Co.
QUAKER MAID - Cabinets - White Consolidated Industries, Inc.
QUAKER MAID - Meat products—poultry - Quaker Maid Meats Inc.
QUAKER MAID - Oils—lubricating - Quaker State Oil Refining Corp.
QUAKER MAID - Pickles - Venice Maid Co. Inc.
QUAKER MARINE SUPPLY - Hats - Quaker Marine Supply Co. Inc.
QUAKER OAT LIFE - Cereal - Quaker Oats Co.
QUAKER PUFFED RICE - Cereal - Quaker Oats Co.
QUAKER PUFFED WHEAT - Cereal - Quaker Oats Co.
QUAKER QRUNCH'UMS - Snack foods - Quaker Oats Co.
QUAKER ROAD - Furniture - Dinaire Corp.
QUAKER STATE - Lubricants - Quaker State Oil Refining Corp.
QUAKER STATE - Paper—writing - Kurtz Bros. Inc.
QUAKER STATE 4X4 - Oils—lubricating - Quaker State Oil Refining Corp.
QUAKER TEX - Yarn - Quaker Textile Corp.
QUAKER TOASTED OATMEAL - Cereal - Quaker Oats Co.
QUAKERDONAL - Pharmaceutical preparations - Quaker City Pharmacal Co.
QUAKERETTE - Apparel—women's - Wm. Rifkin & Sons
QUAKERTOWN - Dinnerware—glass ☆ - Lenox, Inc.
QUAKERWARE - Tables—wood - Quaker Industries Ltd.

☆ = Now out of production

QUAKES - Apparel and accessories - Valley Baseball Club, Inc.
QUAKKE - Toys - Mattel, Inc.
QUAL-A-LITE - Insulating materials - Jen Cel Lite Corp.
QUAL CARE - Medical apparatus - Alimed, Inc.
QUAL-CORD - Musical instrument accessories - Distex Corp.
QUAL-CRAFT - Scaffolds–wood - Qual-Craft Industries
QUAL-PAK - Agricultural products - Hill Bros. Inc.
QUAL PET - Dog food - National By-Products, Inc.
QUAL PRO - Animal feed supplements - National By-Products, Inc.
QUALABAR - Printers–computer - RJS, Inc.
QUALALACQ - Lacquers - H. Behlen & Bro. Inc.
QUALAPAD - Lacquers - H. Behlen & Bro. Inc.
QUALASOLE - Lacquers - H. Behlen & Bro. Inc.
QUALATEX - Novelty items - Pioneer Balloon Co.
QUALATEX - Pillows - E.R. Carpenter Co.
QUALATONE - Adhesives and sealants - H. Behlen & Bro. Inc.
QUALAX - Pharmaceutical preparations - Quaker City Pharmacal Co.
QUALCO - Deicing fluid - Qualco Products Co.
QUALCO - Watches - Hampden Corp.
QUALCON - Bandages - Professional Medical Products, Inc.
QUALCRAFT - Medical apparatus - Alimed, Inc.
QUALEST - Pharmaceutical preparations ☆ - Hyrex Pharmaceuticals
QUALFOAM - Wire–insulated - General Cable Corp.
QUALI-BAKE - Shortening - Alliant Foodservice, Inc.
QUALI-PRO - Food containers - Fearn Natural Foods, Division of Modernproducts, Inc.
QUALI-QUICK - Medical apparatus - Solopak Pharmaceuticals Inc.
QUALI-TEA - Ice cream - Al-Rite Fruits & Syrups
QUALI-TECH - Paint rollers - Panda Brush Co.
QUALI-TEE - Hardware ☆ - Leslie-Locke, Inc.
QUALICHEK - Vitamins and nutritional supplements - Tishcon Corp.
QUALICO - Cleaning preparations–window ☆ - Ulmer Pharmacal Co.
QUALICO - Thread - Quality Thread Co.
QUALICON - Chemical preparations - E.I. Dupont de Nemours and Co.
QUALICORE - Thread - Quality Thread Co.
QUALICRAFT - Shoes - Edison Brothers Stores, Inc.
QUALICRAFT JUNIORS - Shoes ☆ - Edison Brothers Stores, Inc.
QUALIFIED - Paper–rolls ☆ - Central Products Co.
QUALIFIER - Bicycles - Schwinn Cycling & Fitness Inc.
QUALIFIER - Bicycles ☆ - Murray, Inc.
QUALIFIER - Golfing equipment - Northwestern Golf Co.
QUALIFIER - Shoes - Kinney Shoe Corp.
QUALIFIER - Tires - Dunlop Tire Corp.
QUALIFIER PLUS - Calculators - Calculated Industries, Inc.
QUALIFIER PRESS - Calendars - A.D. Productions, Inc.
QUALIFIER, THE - Computer software - Integrated Credit Services
QUALIFLEX - Sporting goods - Texon Inc.
QUALIFLO - Filters–oil - Reemay, Inc.
QUALIPAK - Food products - Great Western Sugar Co.
QUALIPUR - Resins–synthetic - Advanced Polymer Technology Corp.
QUALISPUN - Thread - Quality Thread Co.
QUALISURE - Vitamins and nutritional supplements - Tishcon Corp.
QUALITEA - Toys - Chilton-Globe, Inc.
QUALITECH - Wallpaper - Quality House Inc.
QUALITEX - Ribbons–inked - Leedall Products Manufacturing Co.
QUALITEX - Thread - Toowain Co. Inc.
QUALITITE - Sealing compounds - APT Advanced Polymer Technology Corp.
QUALITONE - Hearing aids - Qualitone
QUALITONE CANAL - Hearing aids - Qualitone
QUALITY - Candy ☆ - Elmer Candy Corp.
QUALITY - Containers–insulated - Aladdin Industries, Inc.
QUALITY - Cooking utensils–aluminum - B. Aronson Inc.
QUALITY - Fencing–chain link - Bell Fence Co.
QUALITY - Floor coverings–carpet and rugs ☆ - Masland Corp.
QUALITY - Flowers, plants, and seeds - Caffco International
QUALITY - Food products - Shurfine International, Inc.
QUALITY - Garden equipment - Ace Hardware Corp.
QUALITY - Ice cream - Dean Foods Co.
QUALITY - Office supplies - Quality Park Products Co.
QUALITY - Rubber-stamp inks - Consolidated Stamp Manufacturing Co. Inc.
QUALITY - Sausages - Van Den Bergh Foods Co.
QUALITY - Seafood products–fresh or frozen - Atlantic Coast Fisheries Corp.
QUALITY - Seafood products–fresh or frozen - Standard Fisheries Corp.
QUALITY - Soups–mixes - Campbell Soup Co.
QUALITY - Thread - Quality Thread Co.
QUALITY - Water–distilled - Absopure Water Co.

QUALITY AMERICA - Food containers - Purity Foods Inc.
QUALITY AND PRIDE WORLD-WIDE - Automotive components - Borg-Warner Automotive Inc. (Transmission Systems Div.)
QUALITY ASSURANCE - Flowers, plants, and seeds - Illinois Crop Improvement Association, Inc.
QUALITY BEARING - Electronic equipment - Fidelitone Inc.
QUALITY BY DESIGN - Electronics equipment - Carlingswitch Inc.
QUALITY BY DESIGN - Tools–hand-operated - Fuller Tool Corp.
QUALITY CARE - Dental floss - Topco Associates, Inc.
QUALITY CARE PLUS - Animal feeds - Classic Pet Products, Inc.
QUALITY-CHECKED - Hair care products ☆ - Cumberland-Swan, Inc.
QUALITY CHEKD - Dairy products - Sinton Dairy Foods Co. Inc.
QUALITY CHOICE - Meat products - Shurfine International, Inc.
QUALITY CIRCLE - Computer software - Orr & Associates Corp.
QUALITY CLASSIC SELECTION - Beverages–carbonated - Southland Corp.
QUALITY COACH - Computer software - Quality Coach Inc.
QUALITY COMPASS - Publisher's imprints - National Committee for Quality Assurance
QUALITY COPY - Duplicating machines - Dietzgen Corp.
QUALITY COVER - Paper–bond - Fox River Paper Co.
QUALITY CRAFT - Lighting fixtures - Remcraft Lighting Products
QUALITY CUISINE - Food products - Culinary Foods Inc.
QUALITY DAIRY - Milk - Quality Dairy Co.
QUALITY DISPLAYS. IN JUST DAYS. - Display cases–plastic - American Fastsigns, Inc.
QUALITY DOORS - Doors - Texwood Industries, Inc.
QUALITY EXPEDITION PRODUCTS - Sporting goods - Thomas C. Ritchie
QUALITY FARMS - Frozen potatoes - Interstate Potato Packers
QUALITY FIT FOR PRESIDENTS - Sauces - TR's Great American
QUALITY FOR HEALTH - Vitamins and nutritional supplements - Ultravit Enterprises, Inc.
QUALITY FOR LIFE - Medical products - Medrad, Inc.
QUALITY GRAINS - Coffee - Quality Grains, SA De C.V.
QUALITY GRASS - Floor coverings–carpet and rugs - Value Carpets Inc.
QUALITY GUARANTEED SCHNUCKS - Cleaning preparations - Schnuck Markets, Inc.
QUALITY HIGHLAND BEEF - Meat products–beef - American Highland Cattle Association
QUALITY HOUSE - Food products ☆ - J.G. Van Holten & Son Inc.
QUALITY HOUSE - Pet products - Monroe Specialty Co.
QUALITY INDICATOR - Thermometers - Oscar Mayer Foods Corp.
QUALITY INNS - Hotels and motels - Choice Hotels International Inc.
QUALITY IS OUR TRADITION - Life preservers - Stearns Manufacturing Co.
QUALITY KITCHEN - Juices–frozen - Quality Kitchen Corp.
QUALITY KOSHER - Cheese - Cheese Smokers Inc.
QUALITY LOCKED - Cheese - Leprino Foods
QUALITY MARK - Lighting fixtures - American Lantern Co.
QUALITY MILLS - Apparel and accessories - Donnkenny Inc.
QUALITY MOVES AROUND THE WORLD - Transportation vehicles and equipment - United Van Lines, Inc.
QUALITY OF LIGHT, THE - Lighting fixtures–stage - Altman Stage Lighting Co. Inc.
QUALITY PAK - Fasteners–hook and eye - VSI Fasteners, Inc.
QUALITY PAK - Rubber bands - Alliance Rubber Co.
QUALITY PAPERBACKS - Publisher's imprints - Littlefield, Adams & Co.
QUALITY PARK - Envelopes - Paper Corp. of America
QUALITY PLUS - Food products ☆ - Super Valu Inc.
QUALITY PLUS - Garden equipment - Emsco Inc.
QUALITY PLUS - Hand tools - Great Neck Saw Manufacturers, Inc.
QUALITY PLUS - Lumber - Quality Wood Treating Co. Inc.
QUALITY-PLUS - Machine parts - Amco Corp.
QUALITY-PLUS - Tools–hand-operated - Liberty Distributors Group
QUALITY PRODUCTS THAT PERFORM BEAUTIFULLY - Cleaning preparations - Quickie Manufacturing Corp.
QUALITY QUEEN - Cushions - Schaff Piano Supply Co.
QUALITY SCREW & NUT - Screws - QSN Industries, Inc.
QUALITY SEAL - Cigarettes - Liggett Group Inc.
QUALITY SEAL - Paper–toilet - Georgia-Pacific Corp.
QUALITY SELECT - X-ray apparatus - Dharmesh D. Parikh
QUALITY SELECTED - Dairy products - Affiliated Funding, Inc.
QUALITY SINCE 1860 - Cleaning products - Shaw's Supermarkets, Inc.
QUALITY SPIRIT TEAM - Computer software - Hj Ford Associates Inc.
QUALITY SPUD - Food products - Universal Frozen Foods Co.
QUALITY STANDARD - Moldings and trim - PCS Co.
QUALITY STREET - Wallpaper - Raintree Designs Inc.
QUALITY SUITES - Hotels and motels - Choice Hotels International Inc.

QUALITY TELECOMMUNICATIONS FOR BUSINESS - Communications equipment - Total-Tel USA Communications, Inc.

QUALITY TIME - Beverages–malt - Beck's North America

QUALITY TIME TOYS - Toys - Quality-Time Toys

QUALITY TRADE MARK - Tools–hand-operated - C.S. Osborne and Co.

QUALITY TRAILER PRODUCTS, INC. - Motor vehicle parts and accessories - Quality Trailer Products, Inc.

QUALITY VALUE - Veterinary pharmaceutical preparations - Beach Pharmaceuticals, Inc.

QUALITY VALUES QV INC. - Educational materials ☆ - B-Row

QUALITY VIDEO - Video production - Quality Video, Inc.

QUALITY WOOD - Lumber - Quality Wood Treating Co. Inc.

QUALITY WORKBENCH - Computer software - Productivity-Quality Systems Inc.

QUALITY YOU CAN SEE - Antennas - Winegard Co.

QUALITY YOU CAN TOUCH - Shelving units–metal - Lee-Rowan Co.

QUALITYCOPY - Paper - Dietzgen Corp.

QUALITYFIRST - Computer software - International Software Automation, Inc.

QUALITYTEAM - Computer software - Scopus Technology, Inc.

QUALIVIEW - Computer hardware - Compression Telecommunications Corp.

QUALLA - Hair care products - Palm Beach Beauty Products

QUALLA BIOLOGICAL - Hair care products - Palm Beach Beauty Products

QUALLOCLASSIC - Fiberfill pillows - E.I. Dupont de Nemours and Co.

QUALLOFIL - Fibers–nylon - E.I. Dupont de Nemours and Co.

QUALLOFLEX - Pillows - E.I. Dupont de Nemours and Co.

QUALLOLOFT - Fibers–polyester - E.I. Dupont de Nemours and Co.

QUALLOMAGIC - Pillows - E.I. Dupont de Nemours and Co.

QUALLOPLUSH - Pillows and mattress pads - E.I. Dupont de Nemours and Co.

QUALLOREST - Pillows - E.I. Dupont de Nemours and Co.

QUALLOSPUN - Pillows - E.I. Dupont de Nemours and Co.

QUALLOWARM - Comforters - E.I. Dupont de Nemours and Co.

QUALM - Pharmaceutical preparations ☆ - Perry Laboratories

QUALPETH - Cables - General Cable Corp.

QUALTEX - Watches - Hampden Corp.

QUAM-NICHOLS - Audio equipment - Quam-Nichols Co.

QUAMAGRA - Tiles–mosaic - WesekPalley Tile Inc.

QUAMM - Disinfectants - C.J. Martin Co.

QUAMOPHET - Pharmaceutical preparations - Quaker City Pharmacal Co.

QUANGLES - Potato chips ☆ - Keebler Co.

QUANTA - Calculators ☆ - Olivetti North America Inc. (Consumer Products Div.)

QUANTA - Meters - Newport Electronic, Inc.

QUANTA LITE - Chemical preparations - Inova Diagnostics, Inc.

QUANTA LITH - Printing trades machinery - Flint Ink Corp.

QUANTAM - Air purification systems - Pacific Spirit Corp.

QUANTAM - Amplifiers - CTC Music Inc.

QUANTAMATIC - Electrical equipment - General Electric Co.

QUANTAR - Communications equipment - Motorola, Inc. (Land Mobile Products Sector)

QUANTECH - Computer storage devices - Corbel

QUANTEM - Computer software - Emory University

QUANTEX - Computer hardware - Quantex Microsystems, Inc.

QUANTEX - Computer software - Investment Technology Group Inc.

QUANTEX - Wallpaper - Epko Industries Inc.

QUANTI-TRAY - Laboratory apparatus - Idexx Laboratories, Inc.

QUANTIFY - Computer software - Pure Software, Inc.

QUANTITREE - Computer software ☆ - Davey Tree Expert Co.

QUANTIX - Chemical preparations - Idetek, Inc.

QUANTREX - Cleaning preparations - L & R Manufacturing Co.

QUANTRO - Radios - Motorola, Inc. (Land Mobile Products Sector)

QUANTUM - Apparel–athletic - Milady Brassiere & Corset Co., Inc.

QUANTUM - Barbecues and grills - Thermos Co.

QUANTUM - Beverage dispensing equipment - Nicola, Gudbranson, and Cooper

QUANTUM - Bicycles - Klein Bicycle Corp.

QUANTUM - Bowling balls - Brunswick Bowling & Billiards Corp.

QUANTUM - Briefcases - Samsonite Corp.

QUANTUM - Chassis–motor vehicles - Pierce Manufacturing Inc.

QUANTUM - Cleaning preparations - Ecolab Inc.

QUANTUM - Computer peripheral equipment - Quantum Corp.

QUANTUM - Electrical equipment - Ingersoll-Rand Co.

QUANTUM - Fans–electric - Hunter Fan Co.

QUANTUM - Filing cabinets–metal - GF Office Furniture Ltd.

QUANTUM - Floor coverings ☆ - Tarkett, Inc.

QUANTUM - Floor coverings–carpet and rugs - Ashley Commercial Carpets

QUANTUM - Fuel additives - Gold Eagle Co.

QUANTUM - Furniture - Expo Displays

QUANTUM - Furniture ☆ - Stanley Furniture Co. Inc.

QUANTUM - Games - Kadon Enterprises Inc.

QUANTUM - Guitars - Modulus Graphite Products

QUANTUM - Hair care products - Helene Curtis Industries Inc.

QUANTUM - Lighters - Colibri Inc.

QUANTUM - Lighters - Park Lane Associates, Inc.

QUANTUM - Logging equipment - Wood-Mizer Products, Inc.

QUANTUM - Machine parts - Joseph W. Kozora

QUANTUM - Metals - White's Electronics, Inc.

QUANTUM - Monitors–electronic - Westlock Controls Corp.

QUANTUM - Motor vehicles–automobiles ☆ - Volkswagen of America Inc.

QUANTUM - Musical instrument accessories - J. D'Addario & Co. Inc.

QUANTUM - Office supplies - Georgia-Pacific Corp.

QUANTUM - Paints - Sherwin-Williams Automotive Finishes Corp.

QUANTUM + - Plastics film - MSC Specialty Films Inc.

QUANTUM - Plastics film - MSC Specialty Films Inc.

QUANTUM - Projectors–photographic - Dukane Corp.

QUANTUM - Sewing machines–household - Singer Co.

QUANTUM - Skates–roller - Rollerblade, Inc.

QUANTUM - Strollers–baby ☆ - Aprica Kassai USA Inc.

QUANTUM - Telephone accessories - Columbia Ultimate Business Systems, Inc.

QUANTUM - Tiles–ceramic - Buchtal USA

QUANTUM - Toilets–porcelain - Mansfield Plumbing Products, Inc.

QUANTUM - Tools–power-driven - Black & Decker Corp.

QUANTUM - Vitamins and nutritional supplements - Quantum Natural Vitamin Co.

QUANTUM - Whirlpools - Jacuzzi Inc.

QUANTUM BUZZ AWAY - Insect repellents - Quantum, Inc.

QUANTUM CHESS - Chessboards - Quantum Development, Inc.

QUANTUM CLARIFYING - Hair care products - Helene Curtis Industries Inc.

QUANTUM CRAFT - Computer software - Quantum Leap Research, Inc.

QUANTUM DECISIONS - Computer software - Quantum Leap Research, Inc.

QUANTUM DRYER CONTROLLER - Electronic equipment - Beard Industries, Inc.

QUANTUM ENTREE SPECIALISTS - Meat products–canned - Quantum Foods Inc.

QUANTUM GATE - Computer storage devices–optical - Hyperbole Studios, Inc.

QUANTUM IMAGING - Medical apparatus - Quantum Imaging Corp.

QUANTUM IV - Telephone accessories - Columbia Ultimate Business Systems, Inc.

QUANTUM JET - Toys - Saban Entertainment, Inc.

QUANTUM LEAP - Computer software - Quantum Leap Research, Inc.

QUANTUM LEAP - Computer software - Quantum Software Inc.

QUANTUM LEAP - Drills–electric - Ingersoll-Rand Co.

QUANTUM LEAP - Flowers, plants, and seeds - Jacklin Seed

QUANTUM MAGNETICS - Magnetic resonance imaging devices - Quantum Magnetics, Inc.

QUANTUM OUTERWEAR SYSTEM - Coats ☆ - Horace Small Apparel Co.

QUANTUM PAU D'ARCO - Vitamins and nutritional supplements - Quantum, Inc.

QUANTUM Q-CARD - Computer peripheral equipment - Quantum Corp.

QUANTUM SIROCCO - Computer storage devices - Quantum Corp.

QUANTUM SUFFICT - Pharmaceutical preparations - Western Research Laboratories

QUANTUM VIEW - Computer software - Quantum Leap Research, Inc.

QUANTUM VIKING - Computer hardware - Quantum Corp.

QUANTUM VISION - Computer software - Quantum Leap Research, Inc.

QUANTUM WORKS - Computer software - Quantum Leap Research, Inc.

QUANTUM YIELD - Diagnostic reagents - Promega Corp.

QUANTUS - Rackets–racquetball - Ektelon

QUAR-A-POXY - Adhesives and sealants - Tec Inc.

QUARANTINE - Video games - Gametek, Inc.

QUARITE - Acrylic materials - Aristech Chemical Corp.

QUARITE PLUS - Plastics–laminated - Aristech Chemical Corp.

QUARK - Toys - Paramount Pictures Corp.

QUARK PUBLISHING SYSTEM - Computer software - Quark, Inc.

QUARK VINYL FIGURE - Toys - ERTL Co., Inc.

QUARKCONNECT - Computer software - Quark, Inc.

QUARKCOPYDESK - Computer software - Quark, Inc.

QUARKSTYLE - Computer software ☆ - Quark, Inc.

QUARKXPOGURE - Computer software - Quark, Inc.

QUARKXPRESS - Computer software - Quark, Inc.

☆ = Now out of production

QUARKXPRESS PASSPORT - Computer software - Quark, Inc.

QUARKXTENSIONS - Computer software - Quark, Inc.

QUARLES HARRIS - Wines - Remy Martin Amerique Inc.

QUARMBY - Novelty items ☆ - Chase Collection, Inc.

QUARRY - Floor coverings ☆ - Azrock Commercial Flooring

QUARRY - Floor coverings–tile - Kentile Floors Inc.

QUARRY COLLECTION - Frames–picture - Framemica Co.

QUARRY HILL WINERY - Wines - Quarry Hill Winery

QUARRY INTERNATIONAL - Desks ☆ - Gilbert Stone Enterprises Inc.

QUARRY MESA - Tiles–ceramic ☆ - American Olean Tile Co.

QUARRY MESA GRANDE - Tiles–ceramic - American Olean Tile Co.

QUARRY NATURALS - Tiles–ceramic - American Olean Tile Co.

QUARRY ROAD COLLECTION - Furniture - Moosehead Manufacturing Co.

QUARRY STREAM - Tiles–ceramic - American Olean Tile Co.

QUARRY STRIPE - Fabrics - Dan River Inc.

QUARRY, THE - Bathroom fixtures ☆ - Trayco, Inc.

QUARRYBASICS - Tiles–ceramic - Metropolitan Ceramics

QUARRYBASICS - Tiles–ceramic - Metropolitan Industries, Inc.

QUARRYETTES - Tiles–ceramic - Summitville Tiles, Inc.

QUARRYSTONE - Tiles–ceramic ☆ - Quarry Tile Co.

QUARRYSTREAM - Tiles–ceramic - American Olean Tile Co.

QUARRYTONES - Floor coverings - Mannington Resilient Floors

QUART - Apparel and accessories - MB Quart Electronics USA, Inc.

QUARTACH - Tachometers - Outboard Marine Corp.

QUARTER BUCKET - Furniture - John Rinehart Industries

QUARTER CORD - Craft supplies - Synthetic Textiles Inc.

QUARTER DUNK - Video games - Prime Video, Inc.

QUARTER HORSE - Hats - Bailey Hat Co.

QUARTER-POUND - Musical instrument accessories - Seymour Duncan Pickups

QUARTER POUNDER - Sandwiches–prepackaged - Mcdonald's Corp.

QUARTER ROUNDER - Pet products - Gimborn U.S., Inc.

QUARTER STICK - Automotive parts and accessories - Hurst Performance Inc.

QUARTER TO MIDITE - Window coverings - Duratex Inc.

QUARTER TO MIDNITE - Window coverings - Duratex Inc.

QUARTERBACK - Apparel and accessories - Esskay Manufacturing Co.

QUARTERBACK - Fishing lures - Howe Now Inc.

QUARTERBACK CRUNCH - Cereal - General Mills, Inc.

QUARTERBACK CRUNCH - Chewing gum - Leaf, Inc.

QUARTERBACK'S CHOICE - Sausages - Sparrer Sausage Co., Inc.

QUARTERCAM - Camera recorders - Broadcast Television Systems

QUARTERDECK - Computer software - Quarterdeck Corp.

QUARTERDECK TEAK - Floor coverings–tile - National Floor Products Co., Inc.

QUARTERHORSE - Apparel–women's ☆ - Jonbil Inc.

QUARTERMAINE - Coffee - West Bertona Group, Inc.

QUARTERMASTER - Boats–motor ☆ - Bayliner Marine Corp.

QUARTERMASTER - Furniture ☆ - Stanley Furniture Co. Inc.

QUARTERS DELUXE - Game machines - IGT - North America

QUARTERTURN - Pliers - Milbar Corp.

QUARTET - Office supplies - Georgia-Pacific Corp.

QUARTET - Recording label - Bainbridge Entertainment Co. Inc.

QUARTET - Respirators - Respironics, Inc.

QUARTET - Wallpaper ☆ - Wolf-Gordon Inc.

QUARTET DURAMAX - Easels - Alvin and Co. Inc.

QUARTET OF ANGELS - Glassware–household ☆ - Fenton Art Glass Co.

QUARTEX - Watches - Delta Impex Watch Corp.

QUARTEZ - Floor coverings–carpet and rugs ☆ - Zenith Carpets

QUARTILE - Floor coverings - Congoleum Corp.

QUARTZ - Flowers, plants, and seeds - Panamerican Seed

QUARTZ - Wallpaper ☆ - Marburg Wallcoverings Inc.

QUARTZ BEAM - Electronic equipment - Comprehensive Video Supply Corp.

QUARTZ CRYSTAL - Tiles–ceramic - American Olean Tile Co.

QUARTZ-LITE - Floodlights - Regent Lighting Corp. (Consumer Products Div.)

QUARTZ NAILS - Nail care products - Orly International Inc.

QUARTZ VOL. 2 - Wallpaper - I. Gottlieb & Associates

QUARTZELL - Scales–industrial - Weigh-Tronix, Inc.

QUARTZFLOOD - Floodlights - General Electric Co.

QUARTZLINE - Lamps–table - General Electric Co.

QUARTZLITER - Lighting fixtures - Hubbell Lighting, Inc. (Lighting Div.)

QUARTZMATIC - Clocks ☆ - General Time Corp. (Westclox/Seth Thomas Div.)

QUARTZMISER - Lighting fixtures - Hubbell Lighting, Inc. (Lighting Div.)

QUARZAN - Pharmaceutical preparations - Roche Laboratories

QUARZITE - Paints ☆ - Dryvit Systems, Inc.

QUARZPUTZ - Finishing agents - Dryvit Systems, Inc.

QUASAR - Electronic equipment ☆ - Quasar Co.

QUASAR - Floor coverings - American Floor Products Co. Inc.

QUASAR - Recording label - Starbound Publishing

QUASAR - Toys–models ☆ - Estes Industries

QUASAR - Watches - E. Gluck Corp.

QUASAR - Whirlpools - Jacuzzi Inc.

QUASAR ZX - Shoes–athletic - Etonic Inc.

QUASECT - Grinders - Grinders Clearing House Inc.

QUASI - Apparel and accessories - Salant/Manhattan Industries

QUASI BORE - Golfing equipment - Kin Taka Golf Works, Inc.

QUAT TB - Disinfectants - C.B. Dolge Co.

QUATALIS - Pharmaceutical preparations - Quaker City Pharmacal Co.

QUATECH - Computer hardware - Quatech, Inc.

QUATHINUX - Pharmaceutical preparations - Quaker City Pharmacal Co.

QUATRADERM - Pharmaceutical preparations - Barrows Pharmacal Inc.

QUATRAM - Pharmaceutical preparations ☆ - C.O. Truxton Inc.

QUATRESAL - Antiseptics ☆ - Miles Inc.

QUATRINE - Furniture–upholstered - Quatrine Furniture, Inc.

QUATRO - Hair accessories - Fantasia Accessories Ltd.

QUATRO - Pesticides–agricultural - Helena Chemical Co.

QUATRO - Thread ☆ - Perfect Thread Co. Inc.

QUATRO - Tires ☆ - Bridgestone/Firestone, Inc.

QUATSYL - Disinfectants - Sterling Winthrop Inc.

QUATTRA - Skin care products - Veeco Manufacturing Co.

QUATTRO - Computer software - Corel USA

QUATTRO - Fishing tackle - Hi-Seas Industries, Inc.

QUATTRO - Hearing aids - Widex Hearing Aid Co., Inc.

QUATTRO - Model of BENELLI motorcycle ☆ - Cosmopolitan Motors Inc.

QUATTRO - Motor vehicles–automobiles - Audi of America Inc.

QUATTRO - Motor vehicles–automobiles - Volkswagen of America Inc.

QUATTRO - Occasional tables - JDI Group, Inc.

QUATTRO - Tiles–ceramic - Monarch Tile Inc.

QUATTRO - Toys - Kal Kan Foods, Inc.

QUATTRO - Weightlifting equipment ☆ - CSA, Inc.

QUATTRO FORMAGGI - Pasta ☆ - Ferrara Food Co., Inc.

QUATTRO KID - Strollers–baby - MTS Products

QUATTRO PRO - Computer software - Borland International, Inc.

QUATTRODE - Medical equipment - Neuromed, Inc.

QUATTROPORTE - Motor vehicles–automobiles - Maserati Automobiles Inc.

QUATTROPRO - Computer software - Corel USA

QUATZAR - Ophthalmic goods - Rozin Optical Export Corp.

QUAY - Thread ☆ - Imperial Threads Inc.

QUAZAR - Rackets–racquetball - Ektelon

QUAZINE - Pharmaceutical preparations - Quaker City Pharmacal Co.

QUBE - Clear malt beverage - Miller Brewing Co.

QUBE - Computer software - Qube Software, Inc.

QUBE - Storage racks - Qube, Inc.

QUBE - Television equipment–cable - Warner Cable Communications Inc.

QUBE PAK - Electrical testing instruments - EJ Systems, Inc.

QUBIC - Games ☆ - Parker Brothers

QUBIT - Video equipment - Quvis, Inc.

QUE - Apparel and accessories - Quiksilver, Inc.

QUE BUEN CAFE - Coffee - Compass Foods Inc.

QUE PASA - Tortillas ☆ - Nalley's Fine Foods

QUE PRO - Barbecue and grill accessories - Jonathon J. Weber

QUEASYAIDE - Home health care products - Mayday, Inc.

QUEBEC - Floor coverings–carpet and rugs ☆ - Stanton Carpet Corp.

QUEBEC - Mattresses - Simmons USA

QUEBEC - Window coverings - Vertilux-Louverlux Inc.

QUEBLO - Computer software - Regency Thermographers of California, Inc.

QUEBRACHO - Pharmaceutical preparations ☆ - C.O. Truxton Inc.

QUECHEE - Footwear - Hershberg Shoe Co. Inc.

QUED - Sporting goods - Seaway Mats Inc.

QUEEN - Bags–plastic - Interstate Packaging Corp.

QUEEN - Floor coverings–carpet and rugs ☆ - Queen Carpet Corp.

QUEEN - Glassware–household - Svend Jensen of Denmark Inc.

QUEEN - Hair care products - J. Strickland & Co.

QUEEN - Knives–pocket - Queen Cutlery Co.

QUEEN - Polishing cloths ☆ - Fair Haven Industries Inc.

QUEEN - Recording label - Gusto Records Inc.

QUEEN - Rubber product ☆ - Ace Hose and Rubber Co.

QUEEN - Sporting goods ☆ - Gold Eagle/Arnold Palmer

QUEEN - Tools - Swan Handle Corp.

QUEEN AIR - Aircraft–airplanes ☆ - Beech Aircraft Corp.

QUEEN AIR - Fireplaces - George Mayer Manufacturing Inc.

QUEEN-ANN - Apparel stores–lingerie - Formflex Foundations Inc.

QUEEN ANN - Candy - Koppers Chocolate Specialty Co. Inc.

☆ = Now out of production

QUEEN ANN - Pasta - Queen Ann Macaroni Manufacturing Co. Inc.
QUEEN ANNE - Candy - Hershey Chocolate USA
QUEEN ANNE - Flatware - Kirk & Matz Ltd.
QUEEN ANNE - Flatware - Wallace International Silversmiths, Inc.
QUEEN ANNE - Health care products ☆ - Sunrise Medical
QUEEN ANNE - House furnishings ☆ - Gaylan Industries Inc.
QUEEN ANNE - Kitchen and bathroom cabinets - IXL Furniture Co. Inc.
QUEEN ANNE - Lamps ☆ - Lamplight Farms, Inc.
QUEEN ANNE - Maraschino cherries - Gray & Co.
QUEEN ANNE - Mayonnaise ☆ - Boykin & Southern Wholesale Grocers Inc.
QUEEN ANNE - Shampoos - Uncle Sam Chemical Co., Inc.
QUEEN ANNE - Vegetables—canned - Nature's Pride Inc.
QUEEN ANNE'S LACE - Yarn - Henry's Attic
QUEEN B - Apparel and accessories ☆ - Spartan Brands, Inc.
QUEEN B - Brushes—paint - Imperial Paint Applicators Ltd.
QUEEN B - File folders ☆ - Hedges Manufacturing Co.
QUEEN BEE - Fabrics - Gretchen Bellinger Inc.
QUEEN BEE - Golfing equipment - Golfsmith International Inc.
QUEEN BEE - Golfing equipment ☆ - Square Two Golf
QUEEN BEE - Toys—models - Cox Products Inc.
QUEEN BERGAMOT - Hair care products - J. Strickland & Co.
QUEEN BUZZY BEE - Toys - Fisher-Price, Inc.
QUEEN CASUALS - Apparel—women's - Queen Casuals Inc.
QUEEN CAT - Footwear—athletic - Puma Inc.
QUEEN ELIZABETH - Christmas tree ornaments - Cracker Box Inc.
QUEEN ELIZABETH - Dolls ☆ - Effanbee Doll Corp.
QUEEN ELIZABETH 2 - Glassware—household - Cunard Line Limited
QUEEN ELIZABETH I - Flatware - Towle Manufacturing Co.
QUEEN FARMS - Milk - Queens Farms Dairy Inc.
QUEEN GLAZE - Finishing agents - Sterling-Clark-Lurton Corp.
QUEEN HELENE - Hair care products - General Therapeutics Inc.
QUEEN HELENE - Hair care products - Para Laboratories Inc.
QUEEN HELENE SKIN THERAPY - Skin care products - Para Laboratories Inc.
QUEEN JANE'S VERSION - Calendars - Dallas Emporia Press
QUEEN-KRAFT - Cabinets - Rosebud Manufacturing Co.
QUEEN KRISTINA - Meat products—canned - M.H. Greenebaum Inc.
QUEEN LACE - Glassware—household - Queen Lace Co.
QUEEN LOUISE - Tableware—china ☆ - Villeroy and Boch Tableware Ltd.
QUEEN MERRY - Toys - Aqua-Leisure Industries, Inc.
QUEEN O MAT - Door mats - A & A Line & Wire Corp.
QUEEN OF AUSTRALIA - Seafood products—fresh or frozen - GE Consultants
QUEEN OF BEAUTY - Cosmetics - Elysee Scientific Cosmetic Co.
QUEEN OF DIAMONDS - Apparel—women's - Lily of France Inc.
QUEEN OF DIAMONDS - Jewelry ☆ - Hirsch Speidel Inc.
QUEEN OF DIAMONDS - Wallpaper ☆ - Gilford Corp.
QUEEN OF HEARTS - Dolls ☆ - Effanbee Doll Corp.
QUEEN OF HEARTS - Flowers, plants, and seeds - White Swan, Ltd.
QUEEN OF HEARTS - Food products - Wally Sea Products Corp.
QUEEN OF HEARTS - Giftware - Gessner Products Co. Inc.
QUEEN OF MY HEART - Candy - Brown & Haley
QUEEN OF NIGHTS - Apparel—women's - Wasatch Import Co.
QUEEN OF SCOT - Food products ☆ - Midland Grocery Co.
QUEEN OF THE OCEAN - Food products - Ocean-Wide Food Industries Inc.
QUEEN O'HEARTS - Shortening - Patrick Cudahy Inc.
QUEEN QUALITY - Candy - Keppel's Inc.
QUEEN QUALITY - Jewelry ☆ - Fantasy Diamond Corp.
QUEEN QUALITY - Nuts—salted, roasted, cooked, or canned - Lancaster Nut Co. Inc.
QUEEN QUALITY - Women's shoes - Interco Inc.
QUEEN SHEBRA - Apparel and accessories - She Bra Brassiere Co.
QUEEN STEEL - Knives—pocket - Queen Cutlery Co.
QUEEN VICTORIA - Christmas tree ornaments - Cracker Box Inc.
QUEEN VICTORIA - Dishes—china - Martin's Herend Imports Inc.
QUEENCRAFTS - Glassware—household - Queen Lace Co.
QUEENELLA - Food products - M & P Foods Co., Inc.
QUEENELLA - Meat products—pork - M & P Chitlin Co., Inc.
QUEENIE & WINKLE - Apparel - Daggar Group, Ltd.
QUEENMATIC - Watches - Movado Time Corp.
QUEENS - Bedding—linen - Tara Handcrafts
QUEEN'S - Dinnerware—glass - Andrew D. Darvas Inc.
QUEENS - Giftware - Norcrest China Co.
QUEEN'S - Hair curlers - Capitol Novelty Co.
QUEENS - Soap pads ☆ - American Steel Wool Manufacturing Co. Inc.
QUEENS AID - Electrical equipment ☆ - Toastmaster Inc.
QUEENS APPLE - Confections - Janet E. Ecker

QUEENS ART - Iron products - Queens Art Pewter Ltd.
QUEEN'S BIRD - Dishes—earthenware - Royal China & Porcelain Companies Inc.
QUEEN'S BISCUITS - Cookies ☆ - Jaret Specialties Inc.
QUEENS CHINA - Dinnerware - Cuthbertson Imports Inc.
QUEEN'S CHOICE - Cooking equipment—household - New Era Co.
QUEEN'S CHOICE - Ice cream - International Dairy Queen Inc.
QUEEN'S CHOICE - Tea, coffee, and sugar - Golden Crown International
QUEEN'S CHOICE, THE - Paper—tissue - Busy Bee Candles Ltd.
QUEENS COVE - Floor coverings—carpet and rugs - Evans-Black Carpet Mills
QUEENS DELIGHT - Water—distilled ☆ - Absopure Water Co.
QUEEN'S DELITE - Food products - Spice King Corp.
QUEEN'S GARDEN - Floor coverings - Mannington Resilient Floors
QUEEN'S GARDEN - Tableware—china ☆ - Lenox, Inc.
QUEENS GARDEN - Wallpaper - Lin-Gor Wallcoverings
QUEENS GATE - Dinnerware—glass ☆ - Royal China & Porcelain Companies Inc.
QUEEN'S GRANT - Floor coverings - Mannington Resilient Floors
QUEENS GUARD - Furniture ☆ - Bassett Furniture Industries, Inc.
QUEEN'S HIDDEN GARDEN - Earthenware - Portmeirion USA
QUEENS HOUSE - Publisher's imprints - Amereon Ltd.
QUEEN'S LACE - Dinnerware ☆ - Corning Inc.
QUEEN'S LINEN - Tablecloths - Cascade Fibers Co.
QUEENS LOUNGE - Motor vehicles—motor homes ☆ - Honey Recreational Vehicles Inc.
QUEEN'S METAL - Giftware ☆ - Hampshire Pewter Co.
QUEENS OF DIAMONDS - Hair care products - Willat Co.
QUEENS PEARLS - Vitamins and nutritional supplements - Royal Kingdom Enterprises Inc.
QUEEN'S PLAIN - Dinnerware—glass - Waterford Wedgewood USA, Inc.
QUEENS PLATE - Horseshoes - Thoro'bred Racing Plate Co., Inc.
QUEEN'S PRIDE - Juices - Niagara Trading Co. Inc.
QUEEN'S RING - Christmas tree ornaments - Cracker Box Inc.
QUEEN'S ROSE - Dishes—china ☆ - WMF/USA
QUEEN'S SECRET - Skin care products - Maria Janina, Inc.
QUEENS TASTE - Butter - Hunter, Walton and Co. Inc.
QUEENS TREASURE - Floor coverings—carpet and rugs - Queen Carpet Corp.
QUEEN'S TREASURE - Floor coverings—carpet and rugs ☆ - Galaxy Carpet Mills Inc.
QUEEN'S WARE - Earthenware - Waterford Wedgewood USA, Inc.
QUEENSBORO - Cigarettes - Virginia Tobacco Co.
QUEENSBORO - Furniture—wood ☆ - Ficks Reed Co. Inc.
QUEENSBOUGS - Motor vehicles—motor homes ☆ - Honey Recreational Vehicles Inc.
QUEENSBRIDGE - Furniture - Taylor-Ramsey Corp.
QUEENSBURY - Apparel—children's - Palmetto Garment Co. Inc.
QUEENSBURY - Floor coverings - Mannington Resilient Floors
QUEENSBURY - Tables—wood - Mersman Furniture Co.
QUEENSBURY FOR LITTLE QUEENS - Apparel—children's - Palmetto Garment Co. Inc.
QUEENSDOWN - Mattresses ☆ - Kingsdown, Inc.
QUEENSGRANT - Floor coverings—carpet and rugs ☆ - Fieldturf & Carpet Inc.
QUEENSTOWN - Vegetables—canned - S.E.W. Friel
QUEENSWOOD - Cabinets - H.J. Scheirich Co.
QUEER CREEK - Abrasive products - Norton Co.
QUEER GEAR - Apparel - Gary David Johnson
QUEER SPORTS - Apparel and accessories - Gary David Johnson
QUEEZ-EEZ - Vitamins and nutritional supplements - Tishcon Corp.
QUELAN - Health care products - Halsey Drug Co. Inc.
QUELIDRINE - Cough medicines - Abbott Laboratories
QUELL - Pet products - Mardel Laboratories, Inc.
QUELL FIRE - Health care products - East Earth Herb Inc.
QUELQUES FLEURS - Perfumes - Houbigant, Inc.
QUELTUSS - Pharmaceutical preparations - Forest Pharmaceuticals Inc.
QUENCH - Beverages—carbonated - Monarch Co., Inc.
QUENCH - Chewing gum - Mueller Sports Medicine Inc.
QUENCH - Hair care products - Tressa, Inc.
QUENCH-O - Fruit drinks—bottled or canned - Griffin Co.
QUENCH YOUR THIRST FOR GOOD - Beverages—carbonated - World of Peace, LLC
QUENCHED - Apparel - At Last Sportswear Inc.
QUENCHER - Hair care products - Moore Beauty Inc.
QUENCHER SMOOTHIES - Fruit drinks—bottled or canned - Trimurti, Inc.
QUENCHER TO GO - Food products - Kraft Food Ingredients Corp.
QUENCHETTE - Beverages ☆ - Labatt Importers Inc.

☆ = Now out of production

QUENCHY - Beverages - Ohio Beverage Systems
QUENCHY SWEET - Beverages - Ohio Beverage Systems
QUENTIN AQUATIC - Pet products - Quentin Aquatics Inc.
QUENTIN SMYTHE - Coats - Galix Shops Inc.
QUERCETIN - Vitamins and nutritional supplements - Miles Inc.
QUERCETO - Wines ☆ - Prestige Wine Imports Corp.
QUERCETTI - Activity sets, toys - International Playthings Inc.
QUERCI-GEL - Vitamins and nutritional supplements - Tishcon Corp.
QUERIES N THEORIES - Games - Wff'n Proof Learning Games Associates
QUERVCETIN NETTLE LIQUID - Highland Laboratories
QUERY GEN - Computer software - Flynt Systems Corp.
QUERY/XPRESS - Computer software - Relational Data Services Inc.
QUESISIMO - Cheese - Kraft Foods, Inc.
QUESITAS - Tortillas - Tampa Maid Seafoods, Inc.
QUESO LOCO - Food products - Jardine's Texas Foods
QUESO RICO - Cheese - Durrett Cheese Sales
QUESOS LA RICURA - Cheese - Quesos La Ricura, Ltd
QUEST - Apparel and accessories - Adidas USA Inc.
QUEST - Archery equipment ☆ - Martin Archery Inc.
QUEST - Boats - Glen-L Marine Designs
QUEST - Boats–canoes - Kenner Manufacturing Co. Inc.
QUEST - Boats–motor - Four Winns Inc.
QUEST - Bowling balls - Ken's Bowling Supplies
QUEST - Cabinets - Crystal Cabinet Works Inc.
QUEST - Computer software - Allen Communication Inc.
QUEST - Computer software - Deneb Robotics, Inc.
QUEST - Computer software - Gupta Technologies Inc.
QUEST - Computer software - Quickturn Design Systems, Inc.
QUEST - Deodorants–personal ☆ - Richardson-Vicks USA
QUEST - Floor coverings–carpet and rugs - Collins & Aikman Corp.
QUEST - Floor coverings–carpet and rugs - Alexander Smith Carpets
QUEST - Golfing equipment - New Logic Custom Golf Inc.
QUEST - Hair care products - European Tanning Systems Inc.
QUEST - Helmets–athletic - Bell Sports Corp.
QUEST - Machinery - Windsor Industries, Inc.
QUEST - Motor vehicles–automobiles - Nissan Motor Corp. USA
QUEST - Occasional furniture ☆ - JDI Group, Inc.
QUEST - Paper - Simpson Paper Co.
QUEST - Paper–bond - Fox River Paper Co.
QUEST - Rackets–racquetball - Head Sports USA
QUEST - Rackets–tennis - Estusa Corp.
QUEST - Rings–jewelry - Artcarved Inc.
QUEST - Ships–sailing vessels - Prout USA
QUEST - Stoves–wood-burning - Pyro Industries, Inc.
QUEST - Tiles–ceramic ☆ - American Olean Tile Co.
QUEST - Totebags - Jinwoong Inc.
QUEST - Transformers–signaling - Harris Corp.
QUEST - Veterinary pharmaceutical preparations - American Cyanamid Co.
QUEST - Video production - Zenger-Miller, Inc.
QUEST - Vitamins and nutritional supplements ☆ - Optimal Nutrients
QUEST - Watches - Bella Time Corp.
QUEST - Water–bottled or canned - Joseph E. Seagram & Sons, Inc.
QUEST - Wheelchairs - Everest and Jennings International Ltd.
QUEST 2000 - Educational materials - Addison-Wesley Publishing Co.
QUEST ADVANTAGE - Hair care products - European Tanning Systems Inc.
QUEST AMERICA - Apparel and accessories - Howard Bliss
QUEST BOOKS - Publisher's imprints - Theosophical Publishing House
QUEST CASE MANAGEMENT SYSTEM - Computer software - Gottlieb & Wertz, Inc.
QUEST DESIGNS - Bathroom accessories ☆ - Ransburg Accessories Inc.
QUEST ELECTRONICS - Hearing-aid product - American Overseas Trading Corp.
QUEST FOR CAMELOT - Footwear - S. Goldberg and Co. Inc.
QUEST FOR CAMELOT - Video games - Titus Software Corp.
QUEST FOR FIRE - Spices and extracts - Calido Chile Traders Systems, Inc.
QUEST FOR GLORY SHADOWS OF DARKNESS - Video games - Sierra On-Line, Inc.
QUEST FOR THE DRAGON STAR - Toys - Bandai America Inc.
QUEST FOR THE DUNGEONMASTER - Games ☆ - Tsr, Inc.
QUEST FOR THE IDEAL MATE - Games - Avalon Hill Game Co.
QUEST FOR THE RINGS, THE - Toys–electronic ☆ - Philips Consumer Electronics Co.
QUEST OF THE AVATAR - Video games - Origin Systems, Inc.
QUEST OF THE SPACE BEAGLE - Games ☆ - Avalon Hill Game Co.
QUEST PACK - Games - Milton Bradley Co.
QUEST Q - Video production - Zenger-Miller, Inc.

QUESTACOPIA - Games - Anema & Assoc.
QUESTAR - Golfing equipment - Aldila, Inc.
QUESTAR - Hearing aids - Innovative Technology Sciences, Inc.
QUESTAR - Musical instruments - Marching Music Ltd.
QUESTAR - Searchlights - Havis-Shields Equipment Corp.
QUESTAR - Telescopes - Questar Corp.
QUESTAR MISSION - Recording label - Questar Video, Inc.
QUESTED - Audio equipment - AKG Acoustics Inc.
QUESTILLO - Games - Tomy America, Inc.
QUESTION OF GRAVITY - Games ☆ - Mayfair Games, Inc.
QUESTION OF SCRUPLES, A - Games ☆ - Milton Bradley Co.
QUESTOCK IMAGE SEARCH & COMP SYSTEM - Compact discs–prerecorded - Westlight
QUESTRAN - Pharmaceutical preparations - Bristol-Myers Squibb Co.
QUESTRON - Publisher's imprints - Price Stern Sloan Inc.
QUESTUS - Surgical instruments - Wright Medical Technology, Inc.
QUETICO - Boats–canoes - Alumacraft Boat Co.
QUETZAL - Pet products - Quetzal Imports Ltd.
QUEUE MATE PLUS - Audio equipment - Telequest Inc.
QUEUE PLUS - Audio equipment ☆ - Telequest Inc.
QUEUE UP - Recording label - Dennis Alan Yurich
QUEVCETIN/NETTLE PLUS - Vitamins and nutritional supplements - Highland Laboratories
QUEZEL - Food products - Ronald E. Ryan
QUEZON - Cordage and twine ☆ - Winchester-Auburn Mills Inc.
QUI-A-ZONE - Pharmaceutical preparations ☆ - Walker Corp. & Co. Inc.
QUI-KE - Hardware ☆ - Ambassador Industries
QUI-KURE - Pickles - Pikle-Rite Co. Inc.
QUIAGEL - Pharmaceutical preparations - Rugby Laboratories Inc.
QUIAGEN - Pharmaceutical preparations - Goldline Laboratories, Inc.
QUIATEX - Pharmaceutical preparations ☆ - Veratex Group
QUIBELL - Water–bottled or canned - Quibell Corp.
QUIBELL APPALACHIAN PREMIUM SODA - Beverages–carbonated - Quibell Corp.
QUIBRON - Pharmaceutical preparations - Bristol-Myers Squibb Co.
QUIC - Computer software - QMS, Inc.
QUIC-AN-EZY - Security product - Ingram Manufacturing Co.
QUIC-KLEEN - Office supplies - Alvin and Co. Inc.
QUIC KUTTER - Electrical equipment ☆ - Goldblatt Tool Co.
QUIC LIGHT - Lighting equipment - Barnegat Light
QUIC MOUNT - Frames–picture - Nu-Dell Plastics Corp.
QUIC 'N EASY - Automotive parts and accessories - DMI, Inc.
QUIC-RIP - Computer peripheral equipment - QMS, Inc.
QUICAMP - Trailers–travel - Quicamp
QUICARD - Cardboard - Moore Business Forms, Inc.
QUICHE PUFF - Food products - New England Dairy Foods
QUICHOTTE - Wines - Carl Doumani
QUICK - Automotive parts and accessories - Quick Cable Corp.
QUICK - Bakery products - Healthy Oven, Inc.
QUICK - Computer software - Microsoft Corp.
QUICK - Deodorants–personal ☆ - Scherer Laboratories Inc.
QUICK - Easels - The Tiffen Co.
QUICK - Fishing tackle ☆ - Gladding Braided Products Inc.
QUICK - Food products - Paris Food Corp.
QUICK - Housewares ☆ - Spectrum Razor Tools
QUICK! - Pharmaceutical preparations - Dow B. Hickam Inc.
QUICK - Spices and extracts - Aldo's Spices
QUICK-2-GRO - Flowers, plants, and seeds - J. & L. Adikes Inc.
QUICK/2 INSTALL - Computer software - Parallel Storage Solutions, Inc.
QUICK-15 - Varnishes - Mantrose-Haeuser Co. Inc.
QUICK-ABLE - Epoxy - Martin Carbone Inc.
QUICK ACCESS - Publisher's imprints - Research and Education Assn.
QUICK ACTION - Drafting supplies - Alvin and Co. Inc.
QUICK-AIR - Health care products - Medi Inc.
QUICK & EASY - Aircraft–balloons - Anagram International, Inc.
QUICK AND EASY - Caulking compounds - Gibson-Homans Co. (Sealant Technology)
QUICK & EASY - Kitchen appliances - Vaughan Manufacturing Co. Inc.
QUICK & EASY - Patterns–clothing - Mccall Pattern Co.
QUICK & EASY - Pizza-crust mix - American Home Food Products Inc.
QUICK & EASY - Soups–mixes - Goodman
QUICK & EASY WASH - Cleaning preparations - Champions Choice Inc.
QUICK & HOT - Garbage disposal units–household - Anaheim Manufacturing Co.
QUICK & HOT - Water heaters–household - Masco Building Products Corp.
QUICK & NATURAL - Soups–mixes - Spice Hunter

☆ = Now out of production

QUICK & SURE - Diagnostic apparatus - Abacus Diagnostics
QUICK ANSWER - Banks–commercial - First of America Bank Corp.
QUICK ART - Advertising posters - Wheeler Arts
QUICK ART - Computer software - Micrografx, Inc.
QUICK BAGEL - Bagels - Daily Bread Co. Inc.
QUICK BAKE - Kitchen utensils–enameled - Wecolite Co. Inc.
QUICK BAT - Sporting goods - Lan-Cor, Inc.
QUICK-BILT - Shelving units–metal - Frick-Gallagher Manufacturing Co.
QUICK BIND - Binders - Spiral Binding Co. Inc.
QUICK BITE - Hardware - Harry J. Molligan
QUICK BITES - Meat products–poultry - Sara Lee Corp.
QUICK BLUE - Cosmetics - Cosmair Inc.
QUICK BOND - Adhesives and sealants - Ohio Sealants Inc.
QUICK BREW - Coffee makers–electric - Mr. Coffee, Inc.
QUICK-CABLE - Cables - Quick Cable Corp.
QUICK CARE - Pharmaceutical preparations - Ciba-Geigy Corp.
QUICK CASE - Luggage - Ronde
QUICK CELLS PLUGS - Flowers, plants, and seeds - Ulery Greenhouse Co.
QUICK CHAIR - Furniture - Allsteel, Inc.
QUICK CHANGE - Abrasive products - Allway Tools Inc.
QUICK CHANGE - Books–blank - 20th Century Plastics
QUICK-CHANGE - Electrical equipment - Woodhead Industries, Inc.
QUICK CHANGE - Fishing tackle - Gregory L. Pauley
QUICK CHANGE - Holsters - American Sales & Manufacturing Co.
QUICK CHANGE - Knives–hunting ☆ - Hunt Manufacturing Co.
QUICK CHANGE - Manicure preparations ☆ - Avon Products, Inc.
QUICK CHANGE - Paint sprayers - ASM Co.
QUICK-CHANGE - Plastics–laminated ☆ - Plaskolite Inc.
QUICK CHANGE - Trumpets - Miracle Music
QUICK CHANGE 3 IN 1 - Health care products - Sunrise Medical
QUICK CHANGE CABLE - Eyeglasses - Marchon and Marcolin Eyewear Inc.
QUICK CHANGE CRYSTAL CLEAN - Pet products - Longlife Pet Products
QUICK CHARGER - Battery chargers - Kim Laube & Co. Inc.
QUICK:CHAT - Computer software - Don Johnston Inc.
QUICK CHECK - Computer software - CAP Automation
QUICK CHECKERS - Games - Amerigames International Corp.
QUICK CHEF - Cookware - Regal Ware, Inc.
QUICK CHEFS - Cooking utensils–glass - Regal Ware, Inc.
QUICK CHESS - Games - Amerigames International Corp.
QUICK CHIC - See **KOUNTRY KLASSIC**
QUICK CHILL - Insulating materials - Sierra Housewares, Inc.
QUICK CLAMP - Electrical equipment - General Electric Co.
QUICK/CLAMP - Electrical equipment - Pass & Seymour, Inc.
QUICK CLAMP - Tools–power-driven - Black & Decker Corp.
QUICK CLAMP - Wheelchairs - Adaptive Engineering Lab Inc.
QUICK CLASSICS - Sauces - McCormick & Co., Inc.
QUICK CLEAN - Pet products - Vo-Toys Inc.
QUICK CLEANSE - Laxatives - McZand Herbal, Inc.
QUICK-CLEAR - Water purification systems - Penn-Plax, Inc.
QUICK-CLIP - Scissors–hand-operated - Wiss-Cooper Tools
QUICK CLIP - Wigs - Revlon General Wig Manufacturers, Inc.
QUICK CLIP MANTLES - Lanterns–kerosene - Warkinz Industries, Inc.
QUICK COAT - Shortening - Bunge Foods Corp.
QUICK COIF - Hair care products - John Frieda, Inc.
QUICK COMPRESSION - Electrical equipment - Quick Cable Corp.
QUICK CONNECT - Flowers, plants, and seeds ☆ - Security Products Co.
QUICK-CONNECT - Medical and surgical apparatus - Linvatec Corp.
QUICK CONTRACT - Wallpaper - Levwall Inc.
QUICK CONTRACT - Wallpaper - Walldesigns
QUICK CONTRACT V - Wallpaper - Advance Wallcoverings
QUICK CONTRACT II - Wallpaper - Levwall Inc.
QUICK COOL - Air conditioning equipment - Dometic Corp.
QUICK-CORE - Medical apparatus - Cook Imaging Corp.
QUICK COTE+ - Electrical equipment - Quick Cable Corp.
QUICK COURT - Sporting goods - Lifetime Products, Inc.
QUICK COVER - Games - Joyce A. Dibblee
QUICK-CRACKLE - Hobby kits - Duncan Enterprises
QUICK CRUST - Pies–frozen - Crackin Good Bakers Inc.
QUICK CUISINE - Frozen entrees - Pritikin Longevity Center
QUICK CURE - Epoxy resin - System Three Resins, Inc.
QUICK CURE - Hobby kits ☆ - Crown Art Products
QUICK CURE - Veterinary pharmaceutical preparations - Aquarium Products Inc.
QUICK CURL - Dolls - Mattel, Inc.
QUICK-CUT - Cutlery - Scott Fetzer Co.
QUICK CUT - Saws–power - Wellington Leisure Products, Inc.

QUICK DELIGHT - Food products - Stegner Food Products Co.
QUICK DESIGNER KIT - Computer software - Parsons Technology, Inc.
QUICK-DIET - Health care products ☆ - Republic Drug Co. Inc.
QUICK DIP - Household product - American Home Products Corp.
QUICK DRAW - Caulking compounds - Gibson-Homans Co. (Sealant Technology)
QUICK-DRAW - Electronic equipment ☆ - K & H Products Ltd.
QUICK-DRAW - Hydraulic hand punch - Greenlee Textron Inc.
QUICK DRAW - Paper - National Printfast
QUICK-DRAW - Pet products - Penn-Plax, Inc.
QUICK DRAW - Prophylactics - RPS Investments
QUICK DRAW - Toys - Mattel, Inc.
QUICK/DRIVER 6 - Tools–boring - Quick Drive USA Inc.
QUICK/DRIVER 8 - Drills–electric - Quick Drive USA Inc.
QUICK/DRIVER 10 - Drills–electric - Quick Drive USA Inc.
QUICK DRY - Nail care products - Revlon-Realistic Professional Products Inc.
QUICK-DRY - Office supplies - Louis Melind Co.
QUICK DRY - Paints ☆ - Finnaren & Haley Inc.
QUICK DRY - Towels - Q.B. Enterprises, Inc.
QUICK DRY - Varnishes - McCloskey Corp.
QUICK DUMP - Photographic equipment ☆ - Leedal Inc.
QUICK-E-POLE - Electrical equipment - Wiremold Co.
QUICK-EDGE - Tools–hand-operated - Michael R. Owens
QUICK EGG - Egg product - Pureggs Brands, Inc.
QUICK/ENTRY - Electrical equipment - Pass & Seymour, Inc.
QUICK-FENCE - Sporting goods - Sport Supply Group, Inc.
QUICK-FIL - Adhesives and sealants - Porter Paint Co.
QUICK-FILL - Dental equipment - Js Dental Manufacturing, Inc.
QUICK FIND - Office supplies - A.I.P. Products, Inc.
QUICK FINISH - Floor coating applicators - Wilen Companies, Inc.
QUICK FINISH - Hair care products ☆ - Avon Products, Inc.
QUICK-FINISH - Photographic equipment - Eastman Kodak Co.
QUICK-FIRE - Toys–automobiles - Mattel, Inc.
QUICK-FIT - Diapers–disposable - Weyerhaeuser Co.
QUICK-FIT - Doors - Therma-Tru Corp.
QUICK-FIT - Ducts–metal - Nordfab Systems, Inc.
QUICK FIT - Electronic equipment - Galileo Corp.
QUICK FIT - Pet products - Four Paws Products Ltd.
QUICK-FIT - Pet products ☆ - Lazy Pet Products
QUICK-FIT - Plastics - Kelly Klosure Systems
QUICK FIX - Appliance parts - General Electric Co.
QUICK FIX - Food products ☆ - VIP Sales Co. Inc.
QUICK FIX - Golf clubs - Founders Club Golf Co.
QUICK FIX - Hair care products - Hair Research X Inc.
QUICK FIX - Hoses - Melnor Inc.
QUICK FIX - Musical instrument accessories ☆ - Deg Music Products Inc.
QUICK FIX - Photographic equipment - Edwal Scientific Products Corp.
QUICK FIX - Sporting goods - Surfco Hawaii Inc.
QUICK FLICK - Games - Rafferty Enterprises, Inc.
QUICK-FLICK - Knives–hunting - Colonial Knife Co. Inc.
QUICK-FLO - Water heaters–household - Mor-Flo Industries Inc.
QUICK FLO - Water heaters–household - S.A.B.H. U.S. Water Heaters
QUICK FLOOR & WALL PATCH - Concrete products - Camp Co. Inc.
QUICK-FORM - Cartons–paperboard - Rand-Whitney Robertson
QUICK FOX - Dolls - Georgetown Collection, Inc.
QUICK FOX BOOKS - Publisher's imprints - Putnam Publishing Group
QUICK FRAME - Computer software - Mitek Systems, Inc.
QUICK FREEZE - Kitchen appliances - Sunbeam-Oster Household Products
QUICK FX - Computer software - Mitek Systems, Inc.
QUICK GAIN - Vitamins and nutritional supplements - York Barbell Co., Inc.
QUICK GAMES - Games - Amerigames International Corp.
QUICK GATHER - Lace ☆ - Narrow Fabric Industries Inc.
QUICK GEL - Adhesives and sealants - Loctite Corp.
QUICK GRAB - Cement - Continental Brands Inc.
QUICK GRID - Automotive parts and accessories ☆ - Loctite Corp.
QUICK GRIP - Antennas - Allen Telecom Group, Inc.
QUICK GRIP - Crutches - Tubular Fabricators Industry, Inc.
QUICK GRIP - Footwear - Mason Shoe Manufacturing Co.
QUICK GRIP - Tape–adhesive - Conso Products Co.
QUICK-GRIP - Tools - American Tool Companies Inc.
QUICK-HARNESS - Cables - Quick Cable Corp.
QUICK HATCH - Motor vehicle parts and accessories - Design Automotive Group, Inc.
QUICK-HEAT - Electrical equipment - Quick Cable Corp.
QUICK HEAT - Hair care products - Belson Products
QUICK HEAT - Hair curlers - Windmere Corp.

☆ = Now out of production

QUICK HEAT - Health care products - Medi Inc.

QUICK HEAT 8 - Skin care products ☆ - Salon Designs Products

QUICK HEAT JR. - Health care products - Medi Inc.

QUICK HIT - Fungicides ☆ - Hickory Industries, Inc.

QUICK HITCH SYSTEMS - Automotive parts and accessories - Unlimited Solutions Inc.

QUICK HOLD - Electrical equipment - Quick Cable Corp.

QUICK-HOLD - Fabrics - E Z International, Inc.

QUICK HOLD - Hair care products - Paul Mazzotta Inc.

QUICK HOOD - Golfing equipment - Wilson Sporting Goods Co.

QUICK HOOK - Luggage - Samsonite Corp.

QUICK ICE - Health care products - Medi Inc.

QUICK ICE JR. - Health care products - Medi Inc.

QUICK ID - Telephone apparatus - SNI Innovation Inc.

QUICK INC - Inks - Parker Pen USA

QUICK INSIGHT - Computer software - Business Resource Software, Inc.

QUICK-JOB - Adhesives and sealants - Continental Brands Inc.

QUICK JOHN - Deodorizers - Ryter Corp.

QUICK-KALS - Decals and transfers - Max C's Ceramic & Craft

QUICK KILL - Deodorants–personal - Buck Ridge Outdoors Inc.

QUICK-KILL - Pet products - Farnam Cos. Inc.

QUICK-KLAMP - Drafting supplies - Alvin and Co. Inc.

QUICK-KLEEN - Drains ☆ - Reflexx Plastics Inc.

QUICK KLEEN - Vacuum cleaners and accessories - The Eureka Co.

QUICK KLIP - Microphones ☆ - Music People Inc.

QUICK-KOATER - Paint rollers ☆ - Wooster Brush Co.

QUICK LABEL - Computer software - Astro-Med Inc.

QUICK LATCH - Awnings - Denver Tent Co.

QUICK LATCH - Hobby kits - Wellington Leisure Products, Inc.

QUICK LAWN - Flowers, plants, and seeds - Garfield Williamson, Inc.

QUICK-LETTER - Paper–carbon - Dennison National Co.

QUICK LIFO - Computer software - Chrome Data Corp.

QUICK LIFT - Cleaning preparations - Ramsey Co.

QUICK LIFT - Pharmaceutical preparations - D & E Pharmaceuticals, Inc.

QUICK LIFT - Skin-care productss - Estee Lauder Inc.

QUICK-LINK - Cables - Quick Cable Corp.

QUICK-LITE - Photographic equipment ☆ - Yashica Inc.

QUICK-LOAD - Envelopes - Astro-Valcour, Inc.

QUICK LOAF - Breads–mixes - Daily Bread Co. Inc.

QUICK LOCK - Tape–adhesive - Conso Products Co.

QUICK MAID - Food products - Pet Inc.

QUICK MAIL AOCE - Computer software ☆ - CE Software, Inc.

QUICK MAIL MHS - Computer software ☆ - CE Software, Inc.

QUICK MAILER - Office supplies - Transkrit

QUICK MASK - Tape–masking - Diversified Dynamics Corp.

QUICK MASTER - Games ☆ - Learning Games Inc.

QUICK MATH - Recording label - Hasinger Co.

QUICK MEAL - Food products - Hormel Foods Corp.

QUICK METAL - Adhesives and sealants ☆ - Loctite Corp.

QUICK MILL - Kitchen appliances - Salton/Maxim Housewares, Inc.

QUICK MIST - Hair curlers ☆ - Sunbeam-Oster Household Products

QUICK MIST - Nozzles - Spraying Systems Co.

QUICK MITT - Computer peripheral equipment - STASH, Inc.

QUICK MIX - Cosmetics ☆ - Duart Industries Ltd.

QUICK MIX - Food processors - Sunbeam-Oster Household Products

QUICK-MIX - Food products ☆ - Grain Processing Corp.

QUICK MIX - Machinery - Paulsen & Roles Laboratories

QUICK-MIX - Water colors - Rich Art Color Co., Inc.

QUICK MOUNT - Guitars ☆ - Dimarzio, Inc.

QUICK-MOUNT - Lighting fixtures - Swivelier Co. Inc.

QUICK MOUNT PRO - Guitars - Dimarzio, Inc.

QUICK MUFFIN - Breads–mixes - Daily Bread Co. Inc.

QUICK MUZZLE - Pet products - Four Flags Over Aspen Inc.

QUICK N BRITE - Cleaning preparations - Quick 'n Brite, Inc.

QUICK 'N BUTTERY - Food products - Pitsweet Inc.

QUICK 'N CHEESY - Food products - Pitsweet Inc.

QUICK 'N EASY - Adhesives and sealants - Loctite Corp.

QUICK 'N EASY - Closet organizers - Hirsh Co.

QUICK N' EASY - Computer software - Play-Rite Software Inc.

QUICK N' EASY - Egg substitutes - Olson Farms Inc. (Liquid Egg Div.)

QUICK 'N EASY - Enamels - Sherwin-Williams Automotive Finishes Corp.

QUICK 'N EASY - Glue–household or industrial ☆ - S.A. Maxwell Co.

QUICK N' EASY - Grass seed mixture - Advance Seed Co.

QUICK 'N' EASY - Hobby kits - Sign of the Sunflower

QUICK N EASY - Plumbing fixtures–metal - Jameco Industries, Inc.

QUICK 'N' GENTLE - Cosmetics - Ardell International Inc.

QUICK 'N HEARTY - Food products ☆ - General Mills, Inc.

QUICK 'N SAUCY - Fruits and vegetables - Pitsweet Inc.

QUICK 'N TENDER - Noodles ☆ - Nissin Foods USA Co. Inc.

QUICK 'N THICK - Cleaning preparations - Bio-Dex Laboratories

QUICK NET - Netting - Dennco, Inc.

QUICK-NETS - Pet products - Penn-Plax, Inc.

QUICK-NOTES LEARNING SYSTEM, THE - Publisher's imprints - 21st Century Learning Products

QUICK-ON - Artificial fingernails ☆ - Cosrich Inc.

QUICK-ON - Tripods–photographic ☆ - QuickSet International Inc.

QUICK PAINTER - Paint sprayers - Rich Art Color Co., Inc.

QUICK PARCHISI - Games - Amerigames International Corp.

QUICK PASTE - Paint rollers - E-Z Paintr Corp.

QUICK PEP - Vitamins and nutritional supplements - Thompson Medical Co., Inc.

QUICK PICK - Musical instruments - Martin D. Silverman

QUICK PICK - Office supplies - Martin Yale Industries, Inc.

QUICK PICK - Skin care products - Plasto Tech Co. International

QUICK PILAF MIX - Rice ☆ - Fantastic Foods Inc.

QUICK PLUG - Cement - Bondex International Inc.

QUICK PLUG - Lamps - Magnetek, Inc.

QUICK POST - Cement - Set Consumer Products Inc.

QUICK PREP - Blenders - Cuisinart Inc.

QUICK PREP - Gelatin - Vyse Gelatin Co.

QUICK PREP - Tools - Baker Brush Co. Inc.

QUICK-PRO - Varnishes - Allpro Corp.

QUICK QUART - Antifreeze - BASF Corp.

QUICK QUENCH - Hardware - Empire Mercantile Corp.

QUICK QUERY - Computer software - Computer Education Services, Inc.

QUICK QUERY! - Computer software - Computer Education Services, Inc.

QUICK QUESTION - Electronic equipment - Survey Technologies, Inc.

QUICK QUIPS - Trophies–precious metal - Russ Berrie and Co., Inc.

QUICK RAIL - Metal railings ☆ - American General Products Inc.

QUICK RAY-NGE PLUS - Archery equipment - Martin Archery Inc.

QUICK RECIPE - Salad dressings–bottled - T. Marzetti Co.

QUICK RECOVERY - Exercising equipment - Quick Innovations Ltd.

QUICK RECOVERY - Health care products - Pharmaceutical Innovations

QUICK RECOVERY REHYD - Skin care products - Jason Natural Products, Inc.

QUICK REFERENCE ATLAS - Computer software - Rand McNally & Co.

QUICK REGISTER - Computer software - CAP Automation

QUICK RELIEF - Pet products - Elexis Corp.

QUICK REPAIR NUMBERS - Stencils - Stahls' Inc.

QUICK RESCUE - Door openers–electronic ☆ - John Sterling Corp.

QUICK RESTART - Computer software - Powerpro Software, Inc.

QUICK RETRAC - Automotive parts and accessories ☆ - Kodiak Components, Inc.

QUICK REVIEW - Publisher's imprints - Cliff's Notes, Inc.

QUICK-RIG - Cables - MacWhyte Co.

QUICK RIG - Hooks - Quick Rig Corp.

QUICK-RIG - Wire products - Amsted Industries Inc.

QUICK-RISE - Yeast - Universal Foods Corp.

QUICK RIVETS - Brass products - Berman Leather Co. Inc.

QUICK ROAST - Kitchen utensils–enameled - Wecolite Co. Inc.

QUICK ROLLER - Brushes–paint - Diversified Dynamics Corp.

QUICK SCENT - Health care products - Odorite International Inc.

QUICK SCOOP - Kitchen utensils–aluminum - Blitz Manufacturing Co., Inc.

QUICK SCRAPER - Tools–machine - Diversified Dynamics Corp.

QUICK SCRUB - Automotive parts and accessories - Turtle Wax, Inc.

QUICK SEAL - Adhesives and sealants ☆ - Loctite Corp.

QUICK-SEAL - Finishing agents - Lenmar Inc.

QUICK-SEAL - Tape–adhesive - Butler Paper Co.

QUICK-SEAL - Transistors ☆ - Murray Corp.

QUICK SECRETS - Food products - Taj Gourmet Foods

QUICK-SERT - Fasteners–snap - Yardley Products Corp.

QUICK SERVE - Pastries - Sovex Foods, Inc.

QUICK-SET - Finishing agents - Farwest Paint Manufacturing Co. Inc.

QUICK-SET - Fireplaces - Dyna Corp.

QUICK SET - Skin care products - Freeman Cosmetics Corp.

QUICK SET - Sporting goods - Kellwood Co.

QUICK SET - Sporting goods - Outaboundz USA, Inc.

QUICK SET - Steel products - Ashley Aluminum, Inc.

QUICK-SET - Tripods–photographic - QuickSet International Inc.

QUICK SET 404 - Adhesives and sealants - Loctite Corp.

QUICK SET JET - Pumps - Marley Pump Co.

QUICK SHAKE - Housewares - Tupperware Co.

QUICK SHAPE - Skin care products - Paul Mazzotta Inc.
QUICK SHIFT - Bicycle parts and accessories - Sram Corp.
QUICK SHIFT - Bicycles ☆ - Roadmaster Corp.
QUICK-SHINE - Cleaning preparations–household - J. Goddard & Sons
QUICK SHINE - Waxes–sealing - Holloway House, Inc.
QUICK SHIP - Window coverings - Kenney Manufacturing Co.
QUICK SHOCK TABLETS - Water treating compounds - Great Lakes
   Biochemical Co., Inc.
QUICK SHOOTER - Cameras ☆ - Olympus America Inc.
QUICK SHOT - Games - Stuart Entertainment, Inc.
QUICK SHOT HOCKEY - Games ☆ - CBS Toys
QUICK-SIGN - Decals and transfers - P-T Templet Co. Inc.
QUICK SILK - Nail care products - Worldwide Cosmetics
QUICK SILVER - Ammunition - Daisy Manufacturing Co.
QUICK SILVER - Arcade games - Playfair Shuffleboard Co., Inc.
QUICK-SILVER - Archery equipment - Martin Archery Inc.
QUICK SILVER - Floor coverings–carpet and rugs ☆ - Calladium & Marglen
QUICK SILVER - Hair care products ☆ - Gabel's Cosmetics Inc.
QUICK SILVER FLAIR - Pens ☆ - Paper Mate Co.
QUICK SILVERS - Toys - Tonka Corp.
QUICK SLAM - Beverages - Pepsico, Inc.
QUICK-SLIDE - Backpacks - Coleman Co., Inc.
QUICK SLIP - Silicone spray - Contact Industries Inc.
QUICK SNAP - Cameras - Fuji Photo Film USA Inc.
QUICK SNAP - Hearing and face protection ☆ - Sellstrom Manufacturing Co.
QUICK SNAP - Plumbing fixtures - Masco Corp. (Plumbing Products Div.)
QUICK-SNAP KEYRING, THE - Safety products - Civilian Defense, Inc.
QUICK SOLDER - Solder - Loctite Corp.
QUICK SOLUTION - Paints - Bruning Paint Co.
QUICK SOLUTION - Paints - Kyanize Paint Co.
QUICK SORB - Hardware - Excel-Mineral Co. Inc.
QUICK-SPLICE - Construction equipment - Alcan Aluminum Corp. Alcan
   Building Products Div.
QUICK SPROUT - Flowers, plants, and seeds - D. Landreth Seed Co.
QUICK STAND - Christmas tree stands - Emsco Inc.
QUICK START - Animal feeds - Camp-Cap Products
QUICK START - Aquariums–household - Marineland Aquarium Products
QUICK START - Batteries - Exide Corp.
QUICK START - Chemical preparations - Monson Companies, Inc.
QUICK-START - Lighters ☆ - Kenro Inc.
QUICK START - Power supplies - DN Labs Inc.
QUICK START - Research–educational - P.F. Collier L.P.
QUICK START - Tape recorders–video - Akai America Ltd.
QUICK START GROWER - Veterinary pharmaceutical preparations - Moorman
   Manufacturing Co.
QUICK START PRESTARTER - Vitamins and nutritional supplements -
   Moorman Manufacturing Co.
QUICK START STARTER - Veterinary pharmaceutical preparations - Moorman
   Manufacturing Co.
QUICK-STEP - Sporting goods - Marty Gilman Inc.
QUICK STEP - Toys - Tonka Corp.
QUICK STEP - Vitamins and nutritional supplements - D'Anconia Shipley Corp.
QUICK-STEP FLOOR - Floor coverings - Courey International (USA) Inc.
QUICK-STICK - Adhesives and sealants - Evans Adhesive Corp.
QUICK STICK - Adhesives and sealants - Vibe Records Inc.
QUICK-STICK - Adhesives and sealants ☆ - Bemiss-Jason Corp.
QUICK STICK - Cosmetics - Ardell International Inc.
QUICK STICK - Measuring instruments - Davis & Box Manufacturing Co.
QUICK-STICK - Padding–foam ☆ - Astro-Valcour, Inc.
QUICK STIK - Frames–picture - Hunt Manufacturing Co.
QUICK STIR - Dinners–frozen - Kraft Foods, Inc.
QUICK-STORE - Office accessories - Acco World Corp.
QUICK STORE - Refrigerators - General Electric Co.
QUICK STRAW - Agricultural products - Stacey Farms, Inc.
QUICK-STRETCH - Fabrics - QST Industries, Inc.
QUICK STRIKE - Toys–guns - Tonka Corp.
QUICK STRIP - Display cases–plastic - Fiskars Inc.
QUICK STRIP - Paint removers - Bix Manufacturing Co. Inc.
QUICK STROKES API - Computer software - Mitek Systems, Inc.
QUICK STUDY - Publisher's imprints - Barcharts, Inc.
QUICK SUGAR - Sugar - Savannah Foods and Industries Inc.
QUICK SWEEP - Brooms - Kellogg Brush Manufacturing Co.
QUICK SWIM - Swimming pools - Muskin Leisure Products Inc.
QUICK SWITCH - Beauty shops - Amekor Industries
QUICK TABS - Vitamins and nutritional supplements - BNG Enterprises, Inc.
QUICK-TAC-TOE - Games - Amerigames International Corp.

QUICK TACK - Glue–household or industrial - Continental Brands Inc.
QUICK TAG - Identification tags - Quick-Tag, Inc.
QUICK-TAG - Machinery - Axxess Technologies Inc.
QUICK TAKES - Food products - Publix Super Markets, Inc.
QUICK TAN - Hair care products - Palm Beach Beauty Products
QUICK TAP - Electrical equipment - Wiremold Co.
QUICK TEMP - Dryers–hair - Helene Curtis Industries Inc.
QUICK TENT - Tents - Quick Tent, Inc.
QUICK THAW - Kitchen appliances - Nordic Ware
QUICK THAW 2000 - Trays - American Direct Inc.
QUICK THAW MCSTRAW - Ice cream - Roney-Oatman Inc.
QUICK THROTTLE - Notebooks and notepads - Paisano Publications, Inc.
QUICK TIE - Paper - First Brands Properties Inc.
QUICK TIME - Cleaning preparations - W.W. Grainger, Inc.
QUICK TIP KIT, THE - Nail care products - Sogo Inc.
QUICK TIPS - Advertising agencies - GTE Directories Corp.
QUICK TIPS - Publisher's imprints - International Data Group, Inc.
QUICK-TITE - Garden equipment - Handy Things
QUICK TITE - Glue–household or industrial - Loctite Corp.
QUICK TRIK - Toys–automobiles - Mattel, Inc.
QUICK-TRIM - Christmas tree lights - General Enterprises Inc.
QUICK TRIM - Dietary supplement - Quick Trim Clinic of Louisiana, Inc.
QUICK TRIM - Garden equipment - Sears, Roebuck and Co.
QUICK-TRIP - Luggage - Goodhope Bags Industries
QUICK-TURBO - Automotive parts and accessories - Gale Banks Engineering
QUICK-TURF - Flowers, plants, and seeds - NK Lawn & Garden Co.
QUICK-TWIST - Brushes - Mill Rose Co.
QUICK UP - Vacuum cleaners and accessories - The Eureka Co.
QUICK-WAY - Hardware - Miller Utility Service Inc.
QUICK-WAY - Mops - W.E. Kautenberg Co.
QUICK WHIP - Housewares - Hutzler Manufacturing Co.
QUICK WHISKERS - Wigs ☆ - Prince Matchabelli
QUICK WIT - Games - Petermark Inc.
QUICK WIZ - Calculators - Sun Television and Appliances Inc.
QUICK WORD - Games - Smethport Specialty Co.
QUICK WRAP - Bags–plastic - International Designs, Inc.
QUICK WRAP - Coin wrapper - Nadex Industries Inc.
QUICK-WRAP - Hair care products - Gro-Mar Industries Inc.
QUICK-X - Enamels - Steelcote Manufacturing Corp.
QUICK-ZAP - Paints - Ponderosa Paint Manufacturing Co. Inc.
QUICKACCESS - See EN ROUTE
QUICKACCESS - Computer software - Now Software, Inc.
QUICKACCESS Q - Computer software - Boston Technology Inc.
QUICKAIR-5 - Oxygen tents - National Draeger, Inc.
QUICKAIR-10 - Oxygen tents - National Draeger, Inc.
QUICKAPP - Computer software - Digital Communications Associates, Inc.
QUICKBASE - Computer software - Sofdesign Corp.
QUICKBOOKS PRO - Computer software - Intuit Inc.
QUICKBRACKETS - Garment hangers - Rubbermaid Inc.
QUICKBUILD - Vitamins and nutritional supplements - Cybergenics Corproation
QUICKCAM - Computer peripheral equipment - T-Tech, Inc.
QUICKCAPS - Pharmaceutical preparations - Block Drug Co., Inc.
QUICKCAPTION - Computer software - WGBH Educational Foundation
QUICKCAPTURE - Computers - Data Translation, Inc.
QUICKCAR - Coils–ignition - Esoteric Audio USA Inc.
QUICKCAST - Medical apparatus - Landec Corp.
QUICKCHANGE - Automatic changemaking machine - Caesars Atlantic City
QUICKCOAT - Paints ☆ - Watson-Standard Co.
QUICKCOATE - Asphalt felts and coatings - Andek Corp.
QUICKCOATE - Finishing agents - Building Protective Industries
QUICKCODE PRO - Computer software - Natural Intelligence, Inc.
QUICKCONNECT - Computer storage devices–magnetic - Mobiledigital Inc.
QUICKCONTACT - Computer software - Now Software, Inc.
QUICKCOOK - Stoves - White Consolidated Industries, Inc.
QUICKCOVER - Motor vehicle parts and accessories - James P. Wright
QUICKCRATE - Office supplies - Rubbermaid Inc.
QUICKCURE - Dental equipment - Poly-Optical Products, Inc.
QUICKCUTTER - Electrical equipment - Quick Cable Corp.
QUICKDATE - Computer software - Power Up Software Corp.
QUICKDAY - Computer software - Now Software, Inc.
QUICKDISC - Computer software - Interactive Picture Systems, Inc.
QUICKDISK - Computer software ☆ - Symmetry Corp.
QUICKDRAW - Computer software - Apple Computer Inc.
QUICKDRAW - Sporting goods - Encon Safety Products Inc.
QUICKDRAWS - Apparel and accessories - J. Goodman Enterprises
QUICKEDGE - Marine rigging - The Standard Products Co.

QUICKEE - Battery chargers - Dynamic Classics Ltd.
QUICKEE DEFROSTER GUN - Windshields–glass - Dynamic Classics Ltd.
QUICKEN - Computer software - Intuit Inc.
QUICKEN - Computer software - Parsons Technology, Inc.
QUICKEN EASY - Food products - Gold Kist Inc.
QUICKER CLICKER - Pencils - Pentel of America, Ltd.
QUICKER UNSTUFFER, THE - Bags - Hold It Products Corp.
QUICKERASE - Erasers ☆ - Empire Berol USA
QUICKESCAPE - Ladders–metal - HMP Industries, Inc.
QUICKEYS - Computer software - CE Software, Inc.
QUICKFIN - Finishing agents - Daly's Inc.
QUICKFINGER - Gloves - Quickfinger, Inc.
QUICKFIT - Marine engine parts - Brunswick Corp.
QUICKFLASH - Computer software - ADM Consulting Services, Inc.
QUICKFLASH - Medical apparatus - Arrow International Investment Corp.
QUICKFLIP VOLLEYBALL - Games ☆ - CBS Toys
QUICKGELS - Pharmaceutical preparations - Block Drug Co., Inc.
QUICKGRASS - Blankets - American Excelsior Co.
QUICKGRILL - Beef - Conagra, Inc.
QUICKGUIDE - Computer software - Intuit Inc.
QUICKHELP PRO - Computer software - Natural Intelligence, Inc.
QUICKHOOK - Luggage ☆ - Lark Luggage Co. Inc.
QUICKI-NOTE - Stationery - Dennison National Co.
QUICKICK - Battery chargers ☆ - Acme Electric Corp.
QUICKICK - Food products - Cramer Products Inc.
QUICKIE - Artists' materials - Bee Paper Co. Inc.
QUICKIE - Fishing lures - B-17 Fly Tackle Ltd.
QUICKIE - Fishing tackle - Area Rule Engineering Inc.
QUICKIE - Health care products - Sunrise Medical Inc.
QUICKIE - Metals - American Fasteners Corp.
QUICKIE - Mops - Quickie Manufacturing Corp.
QUICKIE - Wheelchairs - Quickie Designs Inc.
QUICKIE 2 - Wheelchairs - Quickie Designs Inc.
QUICKIE 2HP - Wheelchairs - Quickie Designs Inc.
QUICKIE ANGLE, THE - Measuring instruments - Quick Time Quilts
QUICKIE EX - Wheelchairs - Quickie Designs Inc.
QUICKIE GP - Wheelchairs - Quickie Designs Inc.
QUICKIE GPS - Wheelchairs - Quickie Designs Inc.
QUICKIE GPS TI - Wheelchairs - Quickie Designs Inc.
QUICKIE GPV - Wheelchairs - Quickie Designs Inc.
QUICKIE KANGAROO ECOLOGY PACKAGE - Educational materials - Innovative Learning International
QUICKIE KANGAROO PAINT BOOK - Educational materials - Innovative Learning International
QUICKIE KIDZ - Wheelchairs - Quickie Designs Inc.
QUICKIE LK - Wheelchairs - Quickie Designs Inc.
QUICKIE LX - Wheelchairs - Quickie Designs Inc.
QUICKIE P100 - Wheelchairs - Quickie Designs Inc.
QUICKIE P110 - Wheelchairs - Quickie Designs Inc.
QUICKIE P190 - Wheelchairs - Quickie Designs Inc.
QUICKIE P200 - Wheelchairs - Quickie Designs Inc.
QUICKIE P210 - Wheelchairs - Quickie Designs Inc.
QUICKIE P210 WITH PRS - Wheelchairs - Quickie Designs Inc.
QUICKIE P300 - Wheelchairs - Quickie Designs Inc.
QUICKIE P320 - Wheelchairs - Quickie Designs Inc.
QUICKIE Q10 - Wheelchairs - Quickie Designs Inc.
QUICKIE RECLINER - Wheelchairs - Quickie Designs Inc.
QUICKIE REVOLUTION - Wheelchairs - Quickie Designs Inc.
QUICKIE RX - Wheelchairs - Quickie Designs Inc.
QUICKIE SPONGE IN THE JAR - Nail care products - Raymac Corp. Hair & Skin Technology
QUICKIE T45 - Wheelchairs - Quickie Designs Inc.
QUICKIE TI - Wheelchairs - Quickie Designs Inc.
QUICKIE TRIUMPH - Wheelchairs - Quickie Designs Inc.
QUICKIES - Games - Universal Manufacturing Co., Inc.
QUICKILL - Insecticides - Warren Chemical Products Co.
QUICKITS - Hobby kits - Eastern Wire Products Co.
QUICKJACK - Jacks–hydraulic - Cepco Tool Co.
QUICKJET - Nozzles - Spraying Systems Co.
QUICKLAN - Computer software - Simple Connections Co.
QUICKLATCH - Motor vehicle parts and accessories ☆ - National Cycle Inc.
QUICKLEAD - Publisher's imprints - United Methodist Publishing House
QUICKLETS - Analgesics - Bristol-Myers Squibb Co.
QUICKLIB - Computer software - Adaptive Solutions, Inc.
QUICKLIGHTS - Lighting fixtures - Thomas Lighting (Accent Division)
QUICKLINE - Amplifiers - Quickline Products

QUICKLINE - Apparel and accessories - Del Mar Race Management, Inc.
QUICKLINE - Drains - Johnson & Johnson
QUICKLINER - Automotive parts and accessories - James P. Wright
QUICKLINK - Hardware - Wilcoxon Research, Inc.
QUICKLINK - Telephone accessories - Fiber Plus International
QUICKLINK - Wheelchairs - Adaptive Engineering Lab Inc.
QUICKLINK GOLD - Computer software - Smith Micro Software, Inc.
QUICKLOAD - File folders - K & M Co.
QUICKLOADER - Computer software - Reasonable Solutions, Inc.
QUICKMAIL - Computer software - CE Software, Inc.
QUICKMAIL PRO - Computer software - CE Software, Inc.
QUICKMAIL PRO SERVER - Computer software - CE Software, Inc.
QUICKMASH - Potato flakes - J.R. Simplot Co.
QUICKMASK - Safety products - Fume Free, Inc.
QUICKMATE - Telephone accessories - Fiber Plus International
QUICKMIKE - Meters–electric - MTI Corp.
QUICKMIST - Yarn - Brunswick Yarns
QUICKMOUNT - Fixtures - Cami Research Inc.
QUICK'N CREAMY - Cereal ☆ - Pacific Grain Products, Inc.
QUICK'N EASY - Sausages - Habbersett Bros. Inc.
QUICK'N' STURDY - Shelving units–wood - Hirsh Co.
QUICK'N'EASY - Irons–electric - Black & Decker Corp.
QUICKOMB - Skin care products - Headmasters International
QUICKONE - Computer software - Shoestring Engineering, Inc.
QUICKONNECT - Photographic equipment - Sima Products Corp.
QUICKPACK - Electronic equipment - Active Control Experts, Inc.
QUICKPAD - Computer software - Now Software, Inc.
QUICKPAK - Computer software - Crescent Software, Inc.
QUICKPANEL - Computers–mainframe - Total Control Products, Inc.
QUICKPLAN - Office accessories - Corporate Events Organization
QUICKPOCKETS - File folders - Rubbermaid Inc.
QUICKPOINT - Toys - Coloron Industries
QUICKPORT - Electrical equipment - Leviton Manufacturing Co., Inc.
QUICKPRICE - Computer software - Consolidated Rail Corp.
QUICKPRINT - Computer software - Motorola, Inc. (Land Mobile Products Sector)
QUICKPRINT - Paper - Fay Paper Products Inc.
QUICKPUNCH - Giftware ☆ - Cronar Ltd.
QUICKRING - Computer software - Apple Computer Inc.
QUICKSAND - Apparel and accessories - Quicksand Inc.
QUICKSAND - Chewing gum - Fleer Corp.
QUICKSAND - Filters–water - Aquarium Systems, Inc.
QUICKSAND - Games - Tonka Corp.
QUICKSAND - Tools–power-driven - Porter-Cable Corp.
QUICKSCORE DELUXE - Computer software - Dr. T's Music Software Inc.
QUICKSCORE PROFESSIONAL - Computer software - Dr. T's Music Software Inc.
QUICKSCRUB - Soap - Stahmer Weston Scientific
QUICKSEAL - Hair care products - Scruples Professional Salon Products, Inc.
QUICKSEARCH - Computer software - Datadisc, Inc.
QUICKSEARCH - Computer software - SourceView Software International
QUICKSECURE - Electric lighting equipment - Toro Co.
QUICKSET - Clocks ☆ - General Time Corp. (Westclox/Seth Thomas Div.)
QUICKSET - Motor vehicle parts and accessories ☆ - National Cycle Inc.
QUICKSET II - Saws–power - Delta International Machinery Corp.
QUICKSHIP - Pillows - Pacific Coast Feather Co.
QUICKSHOT - Computer software - Bondwell Industrial Co. Inc.
QUICKSHOT - Saws–power - L.S. Starrett Co.
QUICKSHOT - Telephone accessories - Fiber Plus International
QUICKSILVER - Christmas tree ornaments - Cracker Box Inc.
QUICKSILVER - Film - Autotype Americas, Inc.
QUICKSILVER - Finishing agents - Building Protective Industries
QUICKSILVER - Floor coverings - Mannington Mills, Inc.
QUICKSILVER - Machine parts - Hein-Werner Corp.
QUICKSILVER - Motor vehicle parts and accessories ☆ - Bell Sports Corp.
QUICKSILVER - Motor vehicles–automobiles - Zimmer Motor Cars Corp.
QUICKSILVER - Needles–sewing - Coats and Clark Inc.
QUICKSILVER - Packaging–paper - Sealed Air Corp.
QUICKSILVER - Paints ☆ - Andek Corp.
QUICKSILVER - Pens - Gillette Co.
QUICKSILVER - Recording label - Increase Inc.
QUICKSILVER - Sporting goods - Powell Skateboards
QUICKSILVER CLASSIC - Key rings - Bob Murphy Foundation
QUICKSILVER GOSPEL - Recording label - Increase Inc.
QUICKSILVER JAZZ - Recording label - Increase Inc.
QUICKSLICE - Computer software - Stratasys, Inc.

☆ = Now out of production

QUICKSNAP - File folders - Rubbermaid Inc.
QUICKSPOOL - Computer software - Pixel Science Inc.
QUICKSTACK - Trays - Rubbermaid Inc.
QUICKSTAND - Folding work bench - Ryobi America Corp.
QUICKSTART - Computer software - Xerox Corp.
QUICKSTART FOR DATA ENTRY - Computer software - American Management Systems, Inc.
QUICKSTER - Office supplies - Bates Manufacturing Co.
QUICKSTICK - Foam rubber - Alimed, Inc.
QUICKSTICK - Orthopedic products - Smith & Nephew Inc. (Rehabilitation Div.)
QUICKSTICK - Sporting goods ☆ - Dalco Athletic Lettering Inc.
QUICKSTOCK - Computer software - Wordstock, Inc.
QUICKSTOP - Brakes–electromagnetic - Stihl Inc.
QUICKSTRAW - Cups–plastic - Playtex Beauty Care, Inc.
QUICKSTROKES - Computer software - HNC Inc.
QUICKSTYLER - Printers–computer - Destiny Technology Corp.
QUICKSUCCESS - Video production - Pacifica Data Services, Inc.
QUICKSURVEY - Computer software - Granite Communications, Inc.
QUICKSWITCH - Integrated circuits - Quality Semiconductor Inc.
QUICKSWITCH - Lamp bulbs - Emergi-Lite, Inc.
QUICKSYNC - Computer software - Linkpro Inc.
QUICKTAKE - Computer peripheral equipment - Apple Computer Inc.
QUICKTAKE 150 - Cameras - Apple Computer Inc.
QUICKTEST - Electrical equipment - Synergy Microwave Corp.
QUICKTEST - Moisture analyzers - Acrowood Corp.
QUICKTESTS - Computer software - Seven Hills Software
QUICKTIME - Computer software - Apple Computer Inc.
QUICKTITE - Adhesives and sealants - Loctite Corp.
QUICKTOUCH - Telescopes - Northern Telecom, Inc.
QUICKTRIM - Motor vehicle parts and accessories - James P. Wright
QUICKTUNE - Communications equipment - Alliedsignal Inc.
QUICKUP - Computer software - Greg Merriman
QUICKVERSE - Computer software - Parsons Technology, Inc.
QUICKVHDL - Computer software - Mentor Graphics Corp.
QUICKVIEW - Publisher's imprints - National Computer Systems, Inc.
QUICKVUE - Humphrey Systems
QUICKVUE - Computer software - Optical Radiation Corp.
QUICKVUE - Diagnostic apparatus - Quidel Corp.
QUICKVUE IN-LINE - Diagnostic apparatus - Quidel Corp.
QUICKWAY - Mops ☆ - Helen Keller Services for the Blind
QUICKWAY RECORDING - Recording label - Revonah Records
QUICKWEAVE - Hair care products - Morris-Flamingo Inc.
QUICKWRAP - Health care products - Cramer Products Inc.
QUICKWRAP - Medical apparatus - Carolon Co.
QUICKWRAPS - Paper products - Procter & Gamble Co.
QUICKXPENSE - Computer software - Portable Software Corp.
QUICKZOOM - Computer software - Intuit Inc.
QUICMATH - Computer software - Fava Control Systems, Inc.
QUICPLOT - Computer software - QMS, Inc.
QUICROFF - Computer software - QMS, Inc.
QUICSHINE 99 - Cleaning preparations - Jackson Marketing, Inc.
QUICU TARP - Automotive parts and accessories - Zamzow Manufacturing Co. Inc.
QUIDE - Pharmaceutical preparations - Marion Merrell Dow
QUIEN SABE DOS LENGUAS VALE POR DOS. - Recording label - Hampton-Brown Co., Inc.
QUIESCENT - Mattresses ☆ - E & S Vinyl Manufacturing Inc.
QUIESS - Pharmaceutical preparations - Forest Pharmaceuticals Inc.
QUIET - Air conditioning equipment - Quiet Automatic Burner Corp.
QUIET - Water treating compounds - Aquacide
QUIET-1 - Antennas - Antenna Co.
QUIET BOOK - Toys - Snugli
QUIET BREEZE - Fans–electric - Hunter Fan Co.
QUIET-CLOTH - Backpacks - Outdoor Recreation Group
QUIET CONTEMPLATIVE - Health care products - East Earth Herb Inc.
QUIET-COR - Floor coverings - Tarkett, Inc.
QUIET CUSHION - Archery equipment - Saunders Archery Co.
QUIET DAY - Vitamins and nutritional supplements - Naturalife Corp.
QUIET-DOWN - Plugs–ear - Flents Products Co. Inc.
QUIET DRIVE - Racks - Sharper Image Corp.
QUIET DRIVE, THE - Golf carts - Club Car, Inc.
QUIET ELEGANCE - Dinnerware–glass - Mt. Clemens Pottery Co.
QUIET FLEX - Shoes - Clinic Shoe Co.
QUIET FLO - Pumps - Pets Pacifica Inc.
QUIET FORCE - Fans–electric ☆ - Howard Industries Inc.
QUIET-GLIDE - Doors–garage - Stanley Works

QUIET HOUSE - Pipes–cast iron - Charlotte Pipe and Foundry Co.
QUIET INDULGENCE - Bakery products - Kathleen's Bake Shop, Inc.
QUIET INTERLUDE - Floor coverings–carpet and rugs - Cabin Crafts Carpets
QUIET KLEEN - Vacuum cleaners and accessories - The Eureka Co.
QUIET-LINE - Plugs–ear ☆ - Glendale Protective Technologies Inc.
QUIET-LITE - Glass–safety - Buchmin Industries
QUIET MACHINE - Amplifiers - First & Co.
QUIET MOMENT - Floor coverings–carpet and rugs ☆ - Downs Carpet Co. Inc.
QUIET MOMENTS - Apparel–women's - Wal-Mart Stores Inc.
QUIET MOMENTS - Teas - Seelect, Inc.
QUIET NIGHT - Mattresses - E & S Vinyl Manufacturing Inc.
QUIET NIGHT - Vitamins and nutritional supplements - Naturalife Corp.
QUIET NIGHT III - Mattresses - E & S Vinyl Manufacturing Inc.
QUIET NIGHTS - Anti-snoring device - Marc S. Bernstein
QUIET NIGHTS - Floor coverings–carpet and rugs - Monticello Carpet Mills
QUIET NITE - Pharmaceutical preparations ☆ - Morton Grove Pharmaceuticals
QUIET ONE - Aquarium accessories - Rainbow Lifegard Aquarium Products
QUIET-PAK - Industrial machinery - Elgin Sweeper Co.
QUIET PANEL - Tiles–ceiling - PCI Industries Inc.
QUIET! PLEASE - Plugs–ear - Flents Products Co. Inc.
QUIET PLUS - Air conditioning equipment - Warren Manufacturing Co., Inc.
QUIET PRO - Dryers–hair - Windmere Corp.
QUIET RIDE - Wagons–children's - Little Tikes Co.
QUIET RIDER - Motors–outboard - Outboard Marine Corp.
QUIET RUNNER - Mats - E.S. Robbins Corp.
QUIET SENSOR - Fans–electric - Progressive Dynamics, Inc.
QUIET SOUND - Audio equipment - Astounding Technologies
QUIET THOUGHTS - Greeting cards - American Greetings Corp.
QUIET THUNDER - Vibrators - Global Manufacturing, Inc.
QUIET TIME - Musical instrument accessories - Burgett, Inc.
QUIET-TIME - Pet products ☆ - Flexi-Mat Corp.
QUIET TIME ELITE - Infant product - Cosco, Inc.
QUIET TIMES - Novelty items - Quiet Times
QUIET TOUCH - Floor coverings–carpet and rugs - Tuftex Carpet Mills, Inc.
QUIET TOUCH - Hair care products - Clairol Inc.
QUIET WORLD - Pharmaceutical preparations - Whitehall Laboratories
QUIET ZONE - Automotive parts and accessories - American Terminal Supply Co., Inc.
QUIET ZONE - Exhaust systems–motor vehicle - Marine Exhaust Systems, Inc.
QUIET ZONE - Windows - Reynolds Metals Co.
QUIETAIRE - Air conditioning equipment - General Electric Co.
QUIETBAC - Floor coverings - Mannington Resilient Floors
QUIETCABLE - Electronics equipment ☆ - Audix Corp. of America
QUIETCOIL - Medical apparatus - Baxter International Inc.
QUIETEX - Tranquilizers - Farnam Cos. Inc.
QUIETFLEX - Mats - Arden Architectural Specialties, Inc.
QUIETFLITE - Lawn mowers - Outboard Marine Corp.
QUIETKEY - Computers–personal - Dell Computer Corp.
QUIETLINE - Connectors–electrical - Bostwick, Inc.
QUIETLINE - Printers–computer - Software Systems Technology, Inc.
QUIETLINE - Telephones–cellular - Sanyo Fisher (USA) Corp.
QUIETLITE - Lighting equipment - Designs for Vision, Inc.
QUIETMAN - Electronic equipment - Innovative Logic Systems, Inc.
QUIETMAN PLUS - Plugs–ear - Innovative Logic Systems, Inc.
QUIETMASTER - Air conditioning equipment - Friedrich Air Conditioning Co.
QUIETONE - Audio equipment - Meteor Light & Sound Co.
QUIETTEST - Fans–electric - Nutone Inc.
QUIETUDE - Pharmaceutical preparations - Boiron Inc.
QUIETWRITER - Printers–computer - International Business Machines Corp.
QUIETZONE - Insulating materials - Owens Corning
QUIGLEY - Toys–stuffed ☆ - Gund, Inc.
QUIGLEY'S ORCHARD DELUXE-APPLESAUCES 100% NATURAL - Fruits–canned - Quigley's Orchard
QUIJOTE - Dry sausage - Elore Enterprises, Inc.
QUIK - Cleaning preparations - Stearns Packaging Corp.
QUIK - Cocoa–powders or mixes - Nestle Beverage Co.
QUIK - Glue–household or industrial - Slomons Laboratories Inc.
QUIK - Housewares - Ironees Co.
QUIK - Laboratory apparatus - Leco Corp.
QUIK - Paper–gift wrap - Gift Wrap Co.
QUIK - Video games - Titus Software Corp.
QUIK-ALIGN - Motor vehicle parts and accessories - Boler Co.
QUIK-ALIGN - Signs - W.H. Brady Co.
QUIK & CLEAR - Finishing agents - Sterling-Clark-Lurton Corp.

☆ = Now out of production

QUIK-BANDS - Bandages ☆ - Rexall Nutritional Products Inc.
QUIK BLOK - Sunblocks - Sun Pharmaceuticals Corp.
QUIK BOX - Lighting fixtures - Eclipse Manufacturing Co.
QUIK BRIGHT - Floor waxes - Color Tile Ceramic Manufacturing Co.
QUIK-BROOM - Vacuum cleaners and accessories - The Hoover Co.
QUIK BRUSH - Toothbrushes - Pro Care Industries Ltd.
QUIK-CALC - Computer peripheral equipment - American Technical Ceramics Corp.
QUIK CALL - Telephone apparatus - Metro-Tel Corp.
QUIK-CARE - Hair care products - Helene Curtis Industries Inc.
QUIK-CHANGE - Mops - Golden Star Inc.
QUIK CHANGE - Tools–power-driven - Foredom Electric Co.
QUIK CHARGE - Veterinary pharmaceutical preparations - Farnam Cos. Inc.
QUIK CHECK - Sporting goods - Douglas L. Gearhart
QUIK-CHEK - Automotive parts and accessories - Alert Industries
QUIK-CHEK - Key rings ☆ - AC International
QUIK CIRCUIT - Computer software - Bishop Graphics Inc.
QUIK-CLIK - Toys–electronic - Tyco Toys
QUIK-CLOSE - Pet products - Caribsea Inc.
QUIK-CLOT - Veterinary medical equipment ☆ - Farnam Cos. Inc.
QUIK COLOR - Paints ☆ - Seymour of Sycamore Inc.
QUIK-COMM - Communications equipment–satellite - General Electric Co.
QUIK-COURSE - Navigational instruments - Bayfront Industries
QUIK COVER - Automotive parts and accessories ☆ - Fibre Glass-Evercoat Co. Inc.
QUIK-CRACKLE - Paints - Duncan Enterprises
QUIK-CRYLIC - Turpentine - Sterling-Clark-Lurton Corp.
QUIK CUT - Hams - Fischer Packing Co.
QUIK-DIALER - Stationery - Projectapix-II
QUIK-DIP LASHTITE - Cosmetics - Ardell International Inc.
QUIK DIR - Cosmetics - Morris-Flamingo Inc.
QUIK DRIVER - Tools–power-driven - Quik Drive USA Inc.
QUIK-EM - Health care products - Mark One Healthcare Products Inc.
QUIK FENCE - Sporting goods - J.A. Cissel Manufacturing Co.
QUIK FILL - Cleaning preparations - Ecolab Inc.
QUIK FIRE - Kilns - Paragon Industries Inc.
QUIK-FIT - Bathroom fixtures - Shower-Rite Corp.
QUIK-FIT - Lamp bulbs–fluorescent - Duro-Test Corp.
QUIK FIT - Nail-care products - Cosmar Corp.
QUIK-FIT - Plugs–ear - Outdoor Optics, Inc.
QUIK-FIX - Dental equipment - Brimms Inc.
QUIK-FIX - Mortars–clay - Custom Building Products
QUIK FIX - Nail care products - Entrecap Corp.
QUIK-FIX - Tires–bicycles ☆ - Raleigh USA Bicycle Co.
QUIK FLEX - Floor coverings–tile - Tec Inc.
QUIK FLOOR - Plumbing fixtures–metal - Bel-Aire Sales Corp.
QUIK FLOORS - Floor coverings ☆ - Tarkett, Inc.
QUIK FLOSS - Dental equipment - U.S. Floss, Inc.
QUIK-FROST - Plastics–laminated ☆ - Mactac Inc. (Packaging Closures Systems Div.)
QUIK GLAZE - Nail care products - Arthur Matney Co., Inc.
QUIK-GO - Machine parts - Fenner Drives
QUIK-GRAM - Electronic equipment - General Electric Co.
QUIK-HEAT - Water heaters–household - Quiet Automatic Burner Corp.
QUIK-HELP - Veterinary medical equipment ☆ - Farnam Cos. Inc.
QUIK-HIT - Fishing lures - Uniscope, Inc.
QUIK HOOK - Drapery hardware - Kirsch Co.
QUIK-I-POXY - Epoxy - Leech Products Inc.
QUIK-JET - Paint sprayers ☆ - Wooster Brush Co.
QUIK-K'-NECT - Hardware - H.B. Sherman Manufacturing Co.
QUIK KARVE - Housewares - Douglas/Quikut
QUIK KIT - Tools–hand-operated - Auto Glass Specialists, Inc.
QUIK-KOTE - Adhesives and sealants ☆ - GS Roofing Products Co.
QUIK-KUT - Tools–garden - Wallace Manufacturing Corp.
QUIK-LABELS - Labels–paper - W.H. Brady Co.
QUIK-LANCE - Electronic equipment - Heraeus Electro-Nite Co.
QUIK-LIFT - Pens ☆ - Charvoz
QUIK-LINE - Office supplies - W.H. Brady Co.
QUIK LOAD - Photographic equipment - Hudson Photographic Industries Inc.
QUIK LOCK - Electronic equipment - Hudson Photographic Industries Inc.
QUIK LOCK - Photo albums - Holson Co.
QUIK-LOK - Boxes ☆ - Jacob North Printing Co. Inc.
QUIK-LOK - Electrical equipment - Milwaukee Electric Tool Corp.
QUIK-LOK - Handles–wood - Wooster Brush Co.
QUIK-LOK - Mops - Golden Star Inc.
QUIK LOK - Music stands - Music Industries Inc.

QUIK-LOK - Shelving units–metal - Richards-Wilcox Manufacturing Co.
QUIK LOOK VEHICLE STATUS - Computer software - Data View, Inc.
QUIK MAGIC - Polishes - Turtle Wax, Inc.
QUIK-MASKS - Tape–masking - W.H. Brady Co.
QUIK MENU III - Computer software - Neosoft Corp.
QUIK-MIX - Tools - Marshalltown Trowel Co.
QUIK-MOUNT - Marine rigging - Ben-Wa International Inc.
QUIK-N EZY - Housewares - Centsable Toys Inc.
QUIK 'N PERMANENT - Epoxy ☆ - Polymeric Systems, Inc.
QUIK ORANGE PEEL - Citrus-fruit peeler - Intromark Inc.
QUIK OUT - Cleaning preparations ☆ - Magic American Corp.
QUIK-PATCH - Hardware - Quik-Tape
QUIK-PICK - Gaskets - J.A. Sexauer, Inc.
QUIK-PICKET - Hardware - Aluminum Hardgoods Inc.
QUIK/PIK - Cabinets ☆ - Akro-Mils Inc.
QUIK-PIK - Toothpicks - Bravo International Corp.
QUIK-POP - Housewares - Douglas/Quikut
QUIK-PREP - Dental compounds ☆ - Endovations Inc.
QUIK-R - Insulating materials–foam - Celotex Corp.
QUIK-SAN - Cleaning preparations - PLC
QUIK-SEPT - Cleaning preparations - Bausch & Lomb Inc.
QUIK SET - Anchors - Jilson Corp.
QUIK-SET - Anchors - Tie Down, Inc.
QUIK SHINE - Nail-care products - Cosmar Corp.
QUIK SHINE - Scouring pads - Cadie Products Corp.
QUIK-SNAP - Gutters–plastic - Ronald L. Sweers
QUIK-SNAP - Office supplies ☆ - Cardinal Products
QUIK SNIP - Scissors–hand-operated - Jilson Corp.
QUIK-SOLV - Cleaning preparations–household - Colgate-Palmolive Co.
QUIK SPLICE - Photographic equipment - Hudson Photographic Industries Inc.
QUIK SPRAY - Paints - Sheffield Bronze Paint Corp.
QUIK-SPRAY - Stationery - Diagraph Corp.
QUIK START - Fireplace logs–treated - Duraflame, Inc.
QUIK STEP - Seats–automobile - Kolcraft Enterprises, Inc.
QUIK STICK - Electronic equipment - Hudson Photographic Industries Inc.
QUIK STIK - Boats - H.K.S. Tool Products Co.
QUIK STIK - Computer software - Briggs Medical Services, Inc.
QUIK-STIK - Decals and transfers - E-Z Industries Inc.
QUIK STIK - Floor coverings - National Floor Products Co., Inc.
QUIK STIK - Machine parts - Zebco Corp.
QUIK STIK - Musical instrument accessories - Quik Stik Corp.
QUIK-STIK - Sporting goods - AC International
QUIK-STIX - Exercise equipment - Innovative Training Products, Inc.
QUIK-STOP - Clamps–surgical - Thomas Ladisch Associates
QUIK STOP - Vitamins and nutritional supplements - Re-Vita Manufacturing Co., Inc.
QUIK-STRIP - Concrete products - Lite-Form, Inc.
QUIK STRIPE - Paints - Pioneer Manufacturing Co.
QUIK STRIPER - Machinery - Pioneer Manufacturing Co.
QUIK-STRIPPER - Tools–hand-operated - Marking Systems International Ltd.
QUIK-TAK - Wire products ☆ - Phifer Wire Products Inc.
QUIK TAKES - Hair care products - Revlon Consumer Products Corp.
QUIK TALK - Computer software - Spectrum Universal
QUIK TAP - Thermometers - Heraeus Electro-Nite Co.
QUIK-TAPE - Hardware - Quik-Tape
QUIK TAPE - Tape–adhesive - H.A. Milton Corp.
QUIK THREAD - Machine parts - Great Mountain West Supply
QUIK TIES - Hardware - Sea Ties Inc.
QUIK-TITE - Hardware - H.B. Sherman Manufacturing Co.
QUIK-TRAC - Electronics equipment - RTI Research Technology International
QUIK-TRED - Paints - Muralo Co. Inc.
QUIK-VAC BY CADILLAC - Vacuum cleaners and accessories - Clements National Co.
QUIK-WALL - Paints - Dunn Edwards Corp.
QUIK WINK - Motor vehicle parts and accessories - BASF Corp.
QUIKALUMINUM - Epoxy - Polymeric Systems, Inc.
QUIKAVA SPECIALTY COFFEES BY CHOCK FULLO'NUTS - Coffee - Quikava, Inc.
QUIKCOPPER - Epoxy - Polymeric Systems, Inc.
QUIKDRAFT - Computer software - Daniel G. Wendin
QUIKDRAW - Hardware ☆ - Quik-Tape
QUIKFDDI - Computer hardware - Xlnt, Inc.
QUIKFICHE - Computer software - Eagle Systems Technology, Inc.
QUIKFILE - Nail-care products - Cosmar Corp.
QUIKFIND - Diagnostic apparatus - Mainstream Engineering Corp.
QUIKFIT - Health care products - Guardian Products Inc.

☆ = Now out of production

QUIKFLIK - Advertising agencies - Showcard LLC
QUIKGRIP - Handles–rubber - Rubbermaid Inc.
QUIKHINGE - Pipes - Quikcoup, Inc.
QUIKI CORRESPONDENCE - Postcards - Q-Time Art Studio
QUIKIT - Screws - Olympic Manufacturing Group, Inc.
QUIKK - Hair care products - Hayashi for Hair Inc.
QUIKLUG - Tools - Mainstream Engineering Corp.
QUIK'N TASTY - Food products - Quiktrip Corp.
QUIKNET - Computer software - Bergen Brunswig Corp.
QUIKPLASTIK - Epoxy - Polymeric Systems, Inc.
QUIKPLATE - Computer software - Varitronic Systems, Inc.
QUIKPOINT - Touch screen input devices - MicroTouch Systems Inc.
QUIKQUITZ - Vitamins and nutritional supplements - Global Health & Wellness
QUIKRETE - Cement - Package Pavement Co. Inc.
QUIKRETE - Concrete products - Gibraltar National Corp.
QUIKRETE - Concrete–mixture - Quikrete Cos.
QUIKROK - Concrete products - Fosroc Inc.
QUIKRULER - Electronic equipment - Gtco Corp.
QUIKSAND - Filters–water - Bio-Con Labs, Inc.
QUIKSET - Building materials - For Better Living, Inc.
QUIKSET - Piano tuning-pin tightener - American Piano Supply Co.
QUIKSILVER - Sunglasses - Quiksilver, Inc.
QUIKSITE - Computer software - Moffet, Larson & Johnson, Inc.
QUIKSPOUT - Bathroom fixtures - Alsons Corp.
QUIKSTART - Fireplace equipment - Duraflame, Inc.
QUIKSTART - Marine rigging - Outboard Marine Corp.
QUIKSTIK - Tape–adhesive - Gould Packaging Inc.
QUIKSTORE - Cooking equipment–household - Dazey Corp.
QUIKSTORE - Racks - Jarke Corp.
QUIKSTRIP - Screws - Quik Drive USA Inc.
QUIKTAC - Adhesives and sealants - Adhesive Products, Inc.
QUIKTAC - Medical apparatus - Del Mar Avionics
QUIKTAPE - Office accessories - Inventure Development Corp.
QUIKTHANE - Enamels - Bruning Paint Co.
QUIKTIER - Racks - Jarke Corp.
QUIKTRAK - Computer software - Softool Corp.
QUIKTREE - Racks - Jarke Corp.
QUIKTUNE - Archery equipment - New Archery Products Corp.
QUIKTYPE - Transfer lettering - Graphic Media
QUIKUT - Cutlery - Douglas/Quikut
QUIKWALL - Cement - Quikrete Cos.
QUIKWATER - Heating equipment - Webco Industries, Inc.
QUIKWELD - Epoxy ☆ - Polymeric Systems, Inc.
QUIKWOOD - Epoxy - Polymeric Systems, Inc.
QUILCEDA CREEK - Wines - Quilceda Creek Vintners
QUILIGOTTI - Floor covering - Quiligotti Inc.
QUILITE - Building materials - Rodman W. Kotter
QUILL - Cigars ☆ - General Cigar Co., Inc.
QUILL - Pens - Quill Co. Inc.
QUILL - Thread - United Thread Mills Corp.
QUILL 500 - Pens - Quill Co. Inc.
QUILL ART - Pens - Quill Co. Inc.
QUILLCALF - Footwear - Acme Boot Co., Inc.
QUILLETTE - Pens - Reliance Pen & Pencil Corp.
QUILLION - Pillows - Upper Limits, Inc.
QUILLOW - Quilt and pillow in one - Intromark Inc.
QUILT - Dinnerware - Corning Inc.
QUILT - Paper–gift wrap - Patchwork Graphics Inc.
QUILT - Stationery - Pine Tree Farm
QUILT AMERICANA - Dinnerware - Mesa International
QUILT COLLECTION, THE - Jewelry - Gumuchdjian Fils Ltd.
QUILT DIGEST PRESS, THE - Publisher's imprints - NTC Contemporary Publishing Group
QUILT LABELS - Labels–fabric - JHB International Inc.
QUILT-LOC - Mattresses - Spring Air Bedding Inc.
QUILT 'N' TUCK - Hobby kits ☆ - Flora Craft Inc.
QUILT-O'DREAMS - Mattresses - Paramount Industrial Companies Inc.
QUILT-O'PEDK - Mattresses - Paramount Industrial Companies Inc.
QUILT/PATTERN WATE - Fabrics - June Tailor Inc.
QUILT PRESERVES - Quilts - Thimbleberries, Inc.
QUILT PUFF - Pet products - O'Donnell Industries Inc.
QUILT-RAP - Sandwich wrap - James River Corp.
QUILT SHOP SERIES, THE - Publisher's imprints - Martingale & Co.
QUILT SHOPPE - Wallpaper - Preferred Prints
QUILT-TECH - Respirators - Uvex Safety LLC
QUILTA-FILL - Bats–baseball - Jen Cel Lite Corp.

QUILTCRAFT - Bedding–linen - Quiltcraft Industries, Inc.
QUILTEASE - Toys - Nanci Industries
QUILTEC - Cleaning equipment - Contec, Inc.
QUILTED CLOSET, THE - Quilts - Quilted Closet
QUILTED NORTHERN - Paper–toilet - James River Corp.
QUILTED NORTHERN ULTRA - Paper–toilet - James River Corp.
QUILTED NORTHERN WET OR DRY - Paper–toilet - James River Corp.
QUILTED QUICK PICKER-UPPER!, THE - Paper–toweling - Procter & Gamble Co.
QUILTER - Amplifiers ☆ - QSC Audio Products Inc.
QUILTERS DELIGHT - Pins–safety - Star Tech
QUILTER'S FRIEND - Sewing machines–household - VWS Inc.
QUILTER'S KANDI - Apparel and accessories - Streamline Industries, Inc.
QUILTER'S SECRET - Patterns–clothing - Freudenberg Nonwovens Apparel Division
QUILTER'S SQUARE 'N PRESS - Fabrics - June Tailor Inc.
QUILTEX - Infant product ☆ - Pyramid Handbags Inc.
QUILTIE PET BED - Pet products - O'Donnell Industries Inc.
QUILTIES - Hobby kits - Dimensions, Inc.
QUILTING BEE - Furniture–wood - Turney's Wood Shop
QUILTING BEE - Quilting supplies ☆ - American Fiber Industries Corp.
QUILTING MATE - Fabrics - June Tailor Inc.
QUILTING ROUNDS - Fabrics–quilted - Gibbs Manufacturing Co.
QUILTINGS - Dinnerware–glass - Dansk International Designs, Ltd.
QUILTOG - Apparel and accessories - RefrigiWear Inc.
QUILTORAMA - Mattresses - Bemco Associates, Inc.
QUILTZORB - Cleaning equipment - Contec, Inc.
QUIMPER - Dinnerware–glass - Quimper Faience Inc.
QUIMPER - Wallpaper ☆ - Sandpiper Studios
QUIN B STRONG-25 - Vitamins and nutritional supplements - Freeda Vitamins Inc.
QUIN CAL PLUS - Vitamins and nutritional supplements - Nutritional Research Associates Inc.
QUIN-CIN - Pharmaceutical preparations - Rex Research Laboratories
QUIN-CIP - Lubricant - Coltec Industries Inc.
QUINA LA ROUXHE - Pharmaceutical preparations - Vartex Pharmaceuticals Inc.
QUINABEER - Beverages–carbonated - Cawy Bottling Co., Inc.
QUINALAN - Pharmaceutical preparations - Lannett Co. Inc.
QUINAMINE - Hair care products - Caruso International, Inc.
QUINAMINOPH - Pharmaceutical preparations - Goldline Laboratories, Inc.
QUINAMM - Pharmaceutical preparations - Marion Merrell Dow
QUINCAPS - Pharmaceutical preparations - Nutritional Research Associates Inc.
QUINCE & CROSSWELLE - Apparel and accessories ☆ - Edison Brothers Stores, Inc.
QUINCY - Cabinets ☆ - American Woodmark Corp.
QUINCY DRAGON - Swimming pools ☆ - Utikem Products
QUINCY HONEY BEAR - Toys–stuffed - Russ Berrie and Co., Inc.
QUINCY MARKET - Liquors - White Rock Distilleries Inc.
QUINCY QUEEN - Fruits and vegetables - Grigg and Sons
QUINCY SLATE - Floor coverings–tile - Kentile Floors Inc.
QUINCY SQUARE - Floor coverings–carpet and rugs ☆ - Evans-Black Carpet Mills
QUINCY'S SIZZLIN' STRIP - Meat products–beef - Quincy's Restaurants, Inc.
QUINDAN - Pharmaceutical preparations ☆ - Danbury Pharmacal Inc.
QUINDETTES - Pharmaceutical preparations - Rugby Laboratories Inc.
QUINE - Pharmaceutical preparations ☆ - Solvay Pharmaceuticals Inc.
QUINELLA - Floor coverings–carpet and rugs ☆ - Galaxy Carpet Mills Inc.
QUINELLA - Paneling - International Paper (Decorative Products Division)
QUINETAS - Pharmaceutical preparations ☆ - U.S. Ethicals Inc.
QUINEX - Aquatic pharmacuetical preparations ☆ - Aquatronics-Filtronics
QUINIBID - See QUINALAN
QUINIDINE M.B. - Pharmaceutical preparations ☆ - Solvay Pharmaceuticals Inc.
QUINJIN - Beverages–carbonated - V. & E. Kohnstamm Inc.
QUINJIN QUININE - Beverages–carbonated - V. & E. Kohnstamm Inc.
QUINK - Inks - Parker Pen USA
QUINLAN - Pretzels - Borden, Inc.
QUINLAN - Pretzels - Quinlan Pretzel Co.
QUINLAND - Food products - Maloney Seafood Corp.
QUINN - Popcorn - Quinn Popcorn Co. Inc.
QUINN'S - Wine coolers - Guild Wineries
QUINN'S COOLER - Wine coolers - Guild Wineries
QUINN'S HTF MEDIUM - Diagnostic substances - Patrick Quinn
QUINOA - Food products - Eden Foods, Inc.

☆ = Now out of production

QUINOFORM - Antibiotics ☆ - C&M Pharmacal, Inc.
QUINOIDAL, THE - Wigs - Penthouse for Men
QUINORA - Pharmaceutical preparations ☆ - Key Pharmaceuticals Inc.
QUINSANA - Deodorants–personal - Mennen Co.
QUINSTAR - Trailers–travel ☆ - Coachmen Industries, Inc.
QUINSULEX - Aquatic pharmaceutical preparations ☆ - Aquatronics-Filtronics
QUINSYN - Lubricants - Coltec Industries Inc.
QUINSYN-F - Lubricants - Coltec Industries Inc.
QUINT-ART - Puzzles - Kadon Enterprises Inc.
QUINT-MATE - Games - Kadon Enterprises Inc.
QUINT QUOTES - Greeting cards - Kadon Enterprises Inc.
QUINTA DA ALORNA - Wines ☆ - Admiral Wine Merchants
QUINTA DA FOLGOROSA - Wines - Admiral Wine Merchants
QUINTA DA NOVAL - Wines ☆ - Diamond Wine Merchants
QUINTA DE LA ROSA - Wines - Dreyfus Ashby Inc.
QUINTA DE LA ROSA - Wines ☆ - Admiral Wine Merchants
QUINTA DE LUOU - Wines - Admiral Wine Merchants
QUINTA DE NOVAL - Wines ☆ - European Beverage Co., Inc.
QUINTA DE PANCAS - Wines - Admiral Wine Merchants
QUINTA DE PARROTES - Wines - Admiral Wine Merchants
QUINTA DO BAIRRO FALCAO - Wines - Admiral Wine Merchants
QUINTA DO COTTA - Wines - Las Vinas Winery Inc.
QUINTA DO NOVAL - Wines - William Grant & Sons, Inc.
QUINTA DO SERRADO - Wines - Admiral Wine Merchants
QUINTA ESSENTIA - Health care products - Norimoor Co.
QUINTA ESSENTIAL - Food products - Cuisine Perel Corp.
QUINTA-PLY - Cooking equipment–household - Vita Craft Corp.
QUINTABS - Vitamins and nutritional supplements - Freeda Vitamins Inc.
QUINTABS-M - Vitamins and nutritional supplements - Freeda Vitamins Inc.
QUINTACHEX - Games - Kadon Enterprises Inc.
QUINTAHEDRON - Games - Gamescience
QUINTARI PRINCESS, THE - Diamond jewelry - Merit Diamond Corp.
QUINTASPHERE - Contact lenses - R & D Ophthalmics Corp.
QUINTECH - Lubricants ☆ - Proton Engineering Inc.
QUINTEK - Computer software - Quintek Electronics, Inc.
QUINTEL - Watches - Genender International, Inc.
QUINTELLE - Hair care products - Beauty Brands Group
QUINTESS - Pharmaceutical preparations ☆ - Eli Lilly and Co.
QUINTESSA - Wines - Franciscan Vineyards, Inc.
QUINTESSENCE - Bedding–linen - Springs Industries, Inc.
QUINTESSENCE - Fish–fresh or frozen - L & L Packing Co.
QUINTESSENCE - Floor coverings–carpet and rugs - Collins & Aikman Corp.
QUINTESSENCE - Girdles - Character Foundations Inc.
QUINTESSENCE - Paper–gift wrap ☆ - Stephen Lawrence Co.
QUINTESSENCE - Recording label - Counter Culture
QUINTESSENCE - Rings–jewelry - Artcarved Inc.
QUINTESSENCE - Vitamins and nutritional supplements - Pure-Gar
QUINTESSENCE - Wallcoverings - WallCapers Ltd.
QUINTESSENCE - Wallpaper - Sunnyside Prints
QUINTESSENCE BOOKS - Publisher's imprints - Quintessence Publishing Co. Inc.
QUINTESSENT - Mattresses ☆ - E & S Vinyl Manufacturing Inc.
QUINTESSENTIAL GROUNDS - Wallpaper - Christopher Hyland
QUINTESSENTIAL WINDBREAKER - Jackets - Horace Small Apparel Co.
QUINTEST - Electromedical apparatus - Miles Inc.
QUINTET - Candles ☆ - Eastern Seaboard Products Inc.
QUINTET - Computer software - Quintet, Inc.
QUINTET - Dinnerware ☆ - Corning Inc.
QUINTET - Dishwashing compounds - Puritan-Churchill Chemical Co.
QUINTETTE - Giftware - Gorham Inc.
QUINTEX EAR CLEAR - Pet products - Nutritional Research Associates Inc.
QUINTEX SORE HOCK SALVE - Pet products - Nutritional Research Associates Inc.
QUINTICARE - Disinfectants - Schroer Manufacturing Co.
QUINTILLION - Wallpaper - Capital Carousel Inc.
QUINTILLIONS - Games - Kadon Enterprises Inc.
QUINTINIC - Pharmaceutical preparations ☆ - Vangard Labs Inc.
QUINTOMINOES - Games - Kadon Enterprises Inc.
QUINTON 20/20 - Medical apparatus - Quinton Instrument Co.
QUINTON HAZELL - Automotive parts and accessories - Echlin Inc.
QUINTREX - Pet products ☆ - Nutritional Research Associates Inc.
QUINTREX 2 PIECE PELLET FEEDER - Pet products - Nutritional Research Associates Inc.
QUINTREX 3 PIECE AVIARY FEEDER - Pet products - Nutritional Research Associates Inc.

QUINTREX BIRDIE BANQUET - Pet products - Nutritional Research Associates Inc.
QUINTREX BIRDIE DELICER - Pet products - Nutritional Research Associates Inc.
QUINTREX BIRDIE SULFA DROPS - Pet products - Nutritional Research Associates Inc.
QUINTREX BIRDIEMYCIN - Pet products - Nutritional Research Associates Inc.
QUINTREX MIGHTY MITE FOOT & LEG SALVE - Pet products - Nutritional Research Associates Inc.
QUINTREX NESTING FOOD - Pet products - Nutritional Research Associates Inc.
QUINTREX REDAXANTHON - Pet products - Nutritional Research Associates Inc.
QUINTREX SEED KLEEN - Seed recycler - Nutritional Research Associates Inc.
QUINTRIX - Electronic equipment - Panasonic Co.
QUINTROL - Health care products ☆ - Fox Pharmacal Inc.
QUINTS - Dolls - Tyco Toys
QUINTS - Footwear - Martin Diament Import Corp.
QUINTUPLE ROPE - Jewelry - OroAmerica Inc.
QUINTUS - Computer software - Quintus Computer Systems Inc.
QUIP - Computer software - Cheyenne AC Corp.
QUIP QUBES - Games ☆ - Milton Bradley Co.
QUIPHILE - Pharmaceutical preparations - Geneva Generics Inc.
QUIPS - Greeting cards - Current, Inc.
QUIPS AND QUOTES - Games - Talicor Inc.
QUIRST - Lemonade ☆ - Dr. Pepper/Seven Up, Inc.
QUISP - Cereal - Quaker Oats Co.
QUISQUEYA STAR QUALITY FOODS - Food products - Quisqueya Quality Foods, Inc.
QUISTGAARDS - Dinnerware–glass - Dansk International Designs, Ltd.
QUIT - Pharmaceutical preparations ☆ - Pharm-A-Lab
QUIT IT - Women's shoes and hosiery - Midwest Independent Retailers Inc.
QUIT LITE - Window shades ☆ - C-Mor Co.
QUIT-N-TIME - Paint and wallpaper cleaners - Parks Corp.
QUITEQUIET - Telephones - At&T Corp.
QUITTIN' TIME - Beverages–malt - Quiktrip Corp.
QUIVER - Computer software - Advertainment Software, Inc.
QUIVER & QUAKE - Apparel and accessories - Greg and Rhonda Lloyd Enterprises, Inc.
QUIVER JIG - Fishing lures - Lindy Little Joe Inc.
QUIVER LIPS - Pizza and pizza sauce - Cousins Foods Ltd.
QUIVER LIPS - Pizzas–frozen - Paisano Food Products Inc.
QUIVERALL - Novelty items - Russ Berrie and Co., Inc.
QUIVERS - Archery equipment - Martin Archery Inc.
QUIX - Automotive parts and accessories ☆ - Household Research Corp.
QUIX - Bicycle accessories - Edward H. Levine
QUIX - Video games - Nintendo of America Inc.
QUIX-FIX - Measuring instruments - Glass Inc.
QUIX-IT - Detergents ☆ - Household Research Corp.
QUIX STIX - Baton and stick sets - 4 Fun Industries, Inc.
QUIZ - Computer software - SourceView Software International
QUIZ - Thread - Cincinnati Thread Co.
QUIZ CONTROL - Computer software - Quick Study Software Inc.
QUIZ KID - Calculators ☆ - National Semiconductor Corp.
QUIZ KIDS - Computer software - WizardWorks Group Inc.
QUIZ-N-LEARN - Games - AGC, Inc.
QUIZ-WHIZ - Toys–electronic - Hasbro, Inc.
QUIZAM - Computer software - Electronic Arts Inc.
QUIZMASTER - Computer software - SourceView Software International
QUIZZARD - Games - Random House, Inc.
QUIZZER - Electronics equipment - Quizzer Ltd.
QULAIFIER - Golfing equipment - Allied Golf Co.
QUNCK - Games - William Dawes
QUODDY - Footwear - Dunham Boot Makers
QUODIBET - Microscopes - Swift Instruments, Inc.
QUODMASTER - Microscopes - Swift Instruments, Inc.
QUOIN IMAGES - Greeting cards - Steven R. Miller
QUONG HOP - Food products - Quong Hop & Co.
QUOROM - Furniture - Masco Corp.
QUORUM - Building materials - Entol Industries Inc.
QUORUM - Floor coverings–carpet and rugs ☆ - Masland Corp.
QUORUM - Furniture - Pavilion/Sunburst Furniture
QUORUM - Glass–illuminating - Davoil, Inc.
QUORUM - Perfumes - Puig of Barcelona Inc.

☆ = Now out of production

QUORUM COLLECTION, THE - Office furniture–wood - Riverside Furniture Corp.

QUORUM INTERNATIONAL - Lighting fixtures - Davoil, Inc.

QUORUM KNOWLEDGE - Computer software - Quorum Litigation Services, Inc.

QUOT-A-CARDS - Greeting cards ☆ - Stevenson Industries Inc.

QUOTA ADVISOR - Computer software - W. Quinn Associates, Inc.

QUOTABLE - Cups–plastic - Russ Berrie and Co., Inc.

QUOTABLE CROAKS - Patterns–clothing - Ann's Cottage

QUOTABLE EXPRESSIONS - Banners - Trend Enterprises, Inc.

QUOTABLES - Novelty items - West Coast Wood Specialties

QUOTABLES - Posters - Stevenson Industries Inc.

QUOTABLES - Publisher's imprints - Advantage/Aurora Publications

QUOTAGRAPHS - Greeting cards - Happiness Inc.

QUOTANE - Pharmaceutical preparations ☆ - SmithKline Beecham Consumer Healthcare

QUOTATION - Floor coverings–carpet and rugs ☆ - Karastan-Bigelow Inc.

QUOTATIONS - Furniture - National/Mt. Airy Furniture

QUOTATIONS - Greeting cards - American Greetings Corp.

QUOTAVITES - Vitamins and nutritional supplements - Vita-Fore Products Co.

QUOTCHART - Computer software - Quotron Systems Inc.

QUOTE-A-PAGE - Publisher's imprints - Andrews and McMeel

QUOTE BOOK - Trading cards and stamps - Upper Deck Co.

QUOTE UNQUOTE - Games - Winslow Games

QUOTE UNQUOTE - Games - Paul R. Winslow

QUOTECALC - Computer software - Raychem Corp.

QUOTEMARKS - Greeting cards - Renaissance Greeting Cards Inc.

QUOTES - Underwear and nightwear - Henson-Kickernick Inc.

QUOTES PLUS - Computer software - Gary B. Lyben

QUOTEWIN - Computer software - Polydyne Development Corp.

QUOTRON - Computers–personal - Quotron Systems Inc.

QUOTRON 800 - Computer software - Quotron Systems Inc.

QUOTRON 1000 - Computer software - Quotron Systems Inc.

QUOTRON ADVANTAGE AE - Computer software - Quotron Systems Inc.

QUOTRON F/X TRADER - Computer software - Quotron Systems Inc.

QUOTRON HORIZON - Computer software - Quotron Systems Inc.

QUPIX - Amplifiers - Vital Communications

QURVE - Fabrics ☆ - Vanity Fair Mills Inc.

QV-10 - Cameras - Casio, Inc.

QV20/20 - Wood products - Owens Forest Products Co.

QVET - Containers–plastic - Prismasystems Corp.

QVO - Oils–lubricating ☆ - BP America Inc.

QVS - Computers - Quality Value Service, Inc.

QWE QUALITY WATER ENGINEERING - Water purification systems - Quality Water Engineering, Inc.

QWICK KURB - Safety products - Cloverleaf Corp.

QWICK WRAPS - Shoe accessories - Zack'z Products, Inc.

QWICKFLIP - Lenses–photographic - Lenmar Enterprises, Inc.

QWICKIE, THE - Lenses–photographic - Lenmar Enterprises, Inc.

QWIK-BOOT - Tubes–plastic - Jack Pittman & Associates Inc.

QWIK CRUST - Paper products - James River Paper Co., Inc.

QWIK DRAIN - Drains - South Pacific Associates

QWIK-FIT SYRINGE - Medical apparatus - Medrad, Inc.

QWIK FIX - Tire inflators ☆ - Demert & Dougherty, Inc.

QWIK-GARD - Circuit breakers ☆ - Square D Co.

QWIK JON - Pumps - Zoeller Co.

QWIK-K-NECT - Plumbing fixtures–metal - Anderson Copper & Brass

QWIK-KLEEN - Paper–toweling - Buffington

QWIK KRISP - Vegetables–frozen - Stilwell Foods

QWIK-LASER - Footwear - Chippewa Shoe Co.

QWIK PLUG - Surfboards - Qwik Hawaii International Ltd.

QWIK RELEASE - Truck trailer parts - Binkley Co.

QWIK-SANE - Games - Wff'n Proof Learning Games Associates

QWIK SHOT - Cleaning preparations - Medwill Chemical Inc.

QWIK SILVER - Carburetors - Rivera Engineering, Inc.

QWIK SILVER II - Motorcycle parts and accessories - Moultrie Capital International, Inc.

QWIK SILVER II - Motorcycle parts and accessories - Moultrie Capital International, Inc.

QWIK SINK - Tapered leader - Outdoor Technologies Group

QWIK SWITCH - Computers - Western Telematic Inc.

QWIK-TIES - Garden equipment ☆ - Vaughan products

QWIK TRAC - Air purification systems - Simco

QWIK-TUNE - Musical instrument accessories - Evets Corp.

QWIK-WASH - Hand cleanser - Perio Products

QWIK WAVE - Plastics film - James River Paper Co., Inc.

QWIKBOOST - Chemical preparations - Mainstream Engineering Corp.

QWIKCHECK - Chemical preparations - Mainstream Engineering Corp.

QWIKDRY - Cleaning preparations–carpet and rug - Kleenrite Chemical Inc.

QWIKEE QUIVERS - Archery equipment - Archer Sports Inc.

QWIKINJECTOR - Chemical preparations - Mainstream Engineering Corp.

QWIKLATCH - Deadbolt locks - Jojack Industries

QWIK'N LEAN - Meat products–poultry - Zacky Foods Co. (Los Angeles Div.)

QWIKSET - Meters–electric - Brendres, Inc.

QWIKSHARE - Computers - Western Telematic Inc.

QWIKSHOT - Chemical preparations - Mainstream Engineering Corp.

QWINK - Games ☆ - Milton Bradley Co.

QWIP - Food products - Avoset Food Corp.

QWIZZ - Computer software - KMSystems, Inc.

Q.WORKS - Computer software - James C. Ballway

QWS - Windshields–glass - Globe-Amerada Glass Co.

QX-10 - Computers–personal ☆ - Epson America, Inc.

QYX - Typewriters - Exxon Corp.

☆ = Now out of production

R

Addresses and phone numbers for the companies cited in the brands below
are available in the Company Listings section immediately following the brands listings.

R - Apparel - Streamline Fashion Inc.
R - Apparel and accessories - Ripon College
R - Apparel–women's - Ratt
R - Beverages - Randall's Food Markets Inc.
R - Calculators - Cadabra CCS J.V.
R - Chemicals - Ricca Chemical Co.
R - China - Rego China/THC Systems
R - Computer chips - Rambus Inc.
R - Jewelry - Reese Corp.
R - Jewelry - Rego Manufacturing Co. Inc.
R - Jewelry - Rogallo Foundation, Inc.
R - Jewelry–precious - Arbel Jewelry Corp.
R+ - Lamps–ultraviolet - Puretan International Inc.
R - Lighting fixtures - Harris Industries
R - Lighting fixtures–stage ☆ - Ranging Inc.
R - Mattresses - Restonic Inc.
R - Medical apparatus - Ryder International Corp.
R - Prophylactics - LRC North America, Inc.
R - Spices and extracts - Reynoso Bros. International
R - Valves–industrial - Ring-O Valve Corp.
R - Veils - Washington Millinery Supply, Inc.
R-7 - Pet products - Rich Health
R-7M - Veterinary pharmaceutical preparations - Rich Health
R-10 - Paint rollers - Wagner Spray Tech Corp.
R-10 BMX - Bicycles ☆ - Raleigh USA Bicycle Co.
R-22 - Beer - The Stroh Brewery Co.
R-35 - Adhesives and sealants - Roman Adhesives, Inc.
R-100 - Floor coverings ☆ - Tarkett, Inc.
R-105 - Pigments - Radiant Color Div.
R-106 - Pigments - Radiant Color Div.
R-130 - Electronic equipment - AudioControl
R-301 - Pens - Zebra Pen Corp.
R-2000 - Aluminum plate - Reynolds Metals Co.
R-A-CAP - Brackets - Susan Kennedy
R. A. MEINEL - Musical instrument accessories - M & M Distributing Co.
R. & A. COLLECTIONS - Apparel–women's - R. & A. Collections Inc.
R. & B. LANXNER - Liquors - Crown Capital USA Inc.
R & B ROOM & BOARD - Apparel and accessories - Ian Forman
R & C - Health care products - Reed & Carnrick
R & D - Liquors - Leonard Kreusch, Inc.
R & D - Vitamins and nutritional supplements - R & D Laboratories Inc.
R & D DECISION ADVISOR - Computer software - IDS Partners
R & D PROJECT ANALYST - Computer software - IDS Partners
R & F - Pasta - Borden, Inc.
R & F PIGMENT STICKS - Paints–artists' - R & F Encaustics
R & H - Fruit drinks–bottled or canned ☆ - Bunge Foods Corp.
R. & J. COOK - Wines - R. & J. Cook
R & K - Apparel–women's - Jonathan Logan Inc.
R & K ORIGINALS - Apparel–women's - R & K Originals
R & L TABS - Archery equipment - Bear Archery Inc.
R. & M. - Coin purses ☆ - Mautner Co. Inc.
R & M - Signs - National Sales Co.
R & M EVENINGS BY KAREN KWONG - Apparel–women's - R & M Richards, Inc.
R & M. KAUFMAN - Apparel–women's - Russ Togs Inc.
R & M RICHARDS - Apparel and accessories - R & M Richards, Inc.

R & M RICHARDS BY KAREN KWONG - Apparel–women's - R & M Richards, Inc.
R & M RICHARDS EVENINGS BY KAREN KWONG - Apparel–women's - R & M Richards, Inc.
R & O - Seafood products–fresh or frozen - Harrison Pierce & Co. Inc.
R & R - Food products ☆ - Pet Inc.
R & R - Frozen foods - Ocean Duke Corp.
R & R - Furniture–upholstered - August Inc.
R & R - Luggage - R & R Holdings, Inc.
R & R - Recording label - Factory Beat Records Inc.
R & R - Vitamins and nutritional supplements - Amrion, Inc.
R & R - Wood products - R & R Woodworking
R & R FARMS - Seeds–salted, roasted, cooked, or canned - R & R Farms of West MI, Inc.
R & S - Doors–screen - R & S Manufacturing Inc.
R & S - Jewelry - Richards & Sargent Inc.
R & W PARADE - Food products - Chef Italia Inc.
R. B. RICE - Food products - Sara Lee Corp.
R-BAG - Luggage - Brad Markoff Industries Inc.
R:BASE 3.1 - Computer software - Microrim Inc.
R-BEM RESULTS-BASED EDUCATION MODEL - Computer software - Educational Vistas, Inc.
R BEST - Fruits and vegetables - Reimer Farms, Inc.
R-BTEX - Pumps - Gas Research Institute
R/C FLYER - Toys–models - Cox Products Inc.
R/C TURBO SPORTS CAR - Toys - Tomy America, Inc.
R+/CHANGE ACCUM - Computer software - BMC Software, Inc.
R-CLASSICS - Apparel and accessories - R-Stuff Inc.
R-CON - Pipes - Reflange, Inc.
R-CONTROL - Insulating materials - AFM Corp.
R-D - Chemical preparations - Hercules Chemical Co. Inc.
R-D-S RADIO DATA SYSTEM - Radio communications equipment - National Association of Broadcasters
R DE CHATEAU RIEUSSEC - Wines - Seagram's Chateau & Estate Wines Co.
R-DOR - Doors–metal - Acorn Window Systems Inc.
R. E. BRUNE - Musical instruments - Luthier Brune
R E C A P - Hats - Take the Lead Inc.
R-E-D-LINE - Water purification systems - Ecowater Systems, Inc.
R-EDMS - Computer software - Radian Corp.
R-EXPO - Perfumes - R. Expo (USA) Ltd.
R-F - Noodles - Borden Pasta Group
R F PUNCH - Audio equipment - Rockford Corp.
R-FACTOR - Insulating materials–foam - Georgia-Pacific Corp.
R-FDMS - Computer software - Radian Corp.
R. G. ABERNETHY - Shoes - R.G. Abernethy Industries Inc.
R GEAR - Sporting goods - Rossignol Ski Co., Inc.
R-GEL - Pharmaceutical preparations - Healthline Laboratories, Inc.
R-GEN - Shampoos - Owen/Galderma Laboratories Inc.
R-GENE - Pharmaceutical preparations - Kabi Pharmacia Inc.
R-GUARD - Plaster–wallboard - Georgia-Pacific Corp.
R. H. PHILLIPS VINEYARD - Wines - R.H. Phillips Vineyard Inc.
R HANAUER - Men's accessories - R. Hanauer
R I V E N - Computer software - Cyan, Inc.
R-J - Amplifiers - British Industries Co.
R. J. HODGES - Beverages–alcohol - Black Prince Distillery, Inc.
R JOEY RICHI - Apparel–men's - Joseph Roshan and J.R. Enterprises

☆ = Now out of production

R. JOHNS - Jewelry - CJC Holdings, Inc.
R-K - Valves - Ruggles-Klingemann Manufacturing Co.
R-KIVE - File folders - Fellowes Manufacturing Co.
R L - Lamp bulbs - Regency Lighting, Inc.
R. L. DRAKE - Electronic equipment - R.L. Drake Co.
R. L. RICHARD - Apparel and accessories - Briggs New York Corp.
R. L. SODER & SONS - Syrup - R.L. Soder & Sons
R. L. WINSTON - Sporting goods - R.L. Winston Co. Inc.
R-LINE - Food products - JMS Specialty Foods Inc.
R-LITE - Bodyboards - Earth & Ocean Sports, Inc.
R. LOPEZ DE HEREDIA - Wines - Admiral Wine Merchants
R-M - Recording label - R-M Records
R MAR COAT - Building materials - Bunker Industries, Inc.
R. MARTEGANI - Shoes - Roger & Barbara Bowman
R-MER PAK - Sterilizing chambers - Riley Medical Inc.
R. MICHAEL ALAN - Apparel—men's - Craftex Creations Inc.
R/MNOS - Computer software - Racotek, Inc.
R. MORGAN - Giftware - R. Morgan Imports Inc.
R/O - Pottery - Rubens Originals
R-O-M - Musical instrument accessories ☆ - Reed-O-Matic Inc.
R ORTECH - Agricultural chemicals - Rosen's Inc.
R-P - Ammunition - Remington Arms Co., Inc.
R. P. SCHERER - Sporting goods ☆ - Rothco Inc.
R PET 2 - Pet shops - Durable Ralph, Inc.
R. PHILLIPS - Belts - Refil Accessories Inc.
R PRO - Nail care products - Revlon Consumer Products Corp.
R REDSHIRT - Apparel—men's - Fast Clothing, Inc.
R RELATIVITY - Recording label - Relativity Records, Inc.
R+/RESOURCE MAXIMIZER - Computer software - BMC Software, Inc.
R REUNION - Apparel—men's - Seattle Pacific Industries, Inc.
R REVELATION RECORDS - Recording label - Revelation Records
R RICCIO - Apparel and accessories - Metro Knitting Corp.
R RILLION - Musical instruments - Huhhot Sigma Reed-Instrument Co.
R-RMB - Gas machinery - Radian Corp.
R. ROCASSEL - Beverages—alcohol ☆ - Diamond Wine Merchants
R ROTONDO PRECAST - Concrete products - Oldcastle Precast, Inc.
R ROUGH USA - Apparel—men's - L.S.Y. Trade, Inc.
R RUSS - Apparel and accessories - L.C. Licensing, Inc.
R RUSSELL ATHLETIC - Bags—canvas - Russell Corp.
R/S REACT - Computer software - Stanford Technologies Inc.
R. SCHNABL - Violins - Boosey & Hawkes Buffet Crampon USA
R:SCOPE - Computer software - Microrim Inc.
R-SERIES - Generators - Kohler Co.
R-SERIES - Ramps - Montgomery Kone Inc.
R/STIK - Tape—adhesive - Rogers Corp.
R-STIM - Health care products - American Imex
R/T - Audio equipment - Elm Street Industries, Inc.
R-T-U - Paints - Nu-Brite Chemical Co. Inc.
R. TOURNIER - Wines - Paterno Imports, Ltd.
R-TRACK - Computer software - Management Science Associates, Inc.
R/TRU - Aircraft - Leland Electrosystems, Inc.
R. USSIAN CLASS - Shoes—tap - T-Bis Co.
R-V-F GOURMET - Teas - River Valley Foods Inc.
R. W. KNUDSEN - Juices - Knudsen & Sons Inc.
R. W. SNYDER - Beverages - R.W. Snyder Co.
R. W. WEBB - Wines - R.W. Webb Winery
R-WAY - Apparel and accessories - Fleet Street Ltd.
R-WRAP - Insulating materials - Anthony Industries Inc.
R1 2 RESULTS FIRST CHANGE SECOND - Publisher's imprints - Executive Edge, Inc.
R2 - Pizzas—frozen - Sabatasso Foods Inc.
R2-D2 - Apparel and accessories - Lucasfilm Ltd.
R2-D2 - Toys—stuffed - Kenner Products
R2L - Apparel and accessories - R2L, Inc.
R3 FACTOR - Skin care products - Aloe Vera of America, Inc.
R4 SCHOOL HOUSE REASON-THINKING SQUARES - Board games - Alvin F. Polan
R4X - Drill bits - Relton Corp.
R55 - Cleaning preparations - HMK Stone Care System
R63 - Cleaning preparations - HMK Stone Care System
R80 - Cleaning preparations - HMK Stone Care System
R91 - Computer software - General Automation Inc.
R4200 - Computer peripheral equipment - Mips Technologies, Inc.
R4400 - Computer hardware - Mips Technologies, Inc.
R8000 - Computer hardware - Mips Technologies, Inc.
R10000 - Computer hardware - Mips Technologies, Inc.

RA - Food products - Red Arrow Products Co., Inc.
RA - Pharmaceutical preparations - Medco Lab Inc.
RA - Solar energy collectors - Gary R. Gustafson
RA POLY - Apparel and accessories - Research Associates Inc.
RA RA RECORDS - Recording label - Ra Ra Records, Inc.
RA SPES - Vitamins and nutritional supplements - International Medical Research, Inc.
RA2 - Cables - Conquest Sound Inc.
RAA - Computer peripheral equipment - International Business Machines Corp.
RAB - Lighting fixtures - RAB Electric
RABAJA, BARBARESCO RISERVA - Wines - Kobrand Corp.
RABANA - Crocheted and knitted items - Great American Industries Inc. (Robby Len Fashions Divison.)
RABAT - Floor coverings—carpet and rugs - Couristan Inc.
RABBET SYSTEM, THE - Apparel and accessories - Woolrich Woolen Mills Inc.
RABBIT - Alarm systems—burglar - Gemini Industries, Inc.
RABBIT - Bicycles - Columbia Manufacturing Inc.
RABBIT - Motor vehicles—automobiles ☆ - Volkswagen of America Inc.
RABBIT - Thread - New Bedford Thread Co. Inc.
RABBIT BOOSTER 16 - Animal feeds - Bluebonnet Milling Co.
RABBIT CAPTAIN - Skin care products - Takara Belmont USA, Inc.
RABBIT EAR - Antennas—satellite - James E. Robinson
RABBIT EAR - Cleaning supplies - American Textile Products Co.
RABBIT EARS - Publisher's imprints - Picture Book Studio
RABBIT EARS - Recording label - Windham Hill Productions Inc.
RABBIT FOOT - Fishing lures - Hildebrandt Corp.
RABBIT GARD - Nurseries and garden stores - Gilbert and Bennett Manufacturing Co.
RABBIT GLO - Animal feeds - Manna Pro Corp.
RABBIT-IN-HAT - Brushes—paint ☆ - Wooster Brush Co.
RABBIT MAGIC - Pet products ☆ - Bluebonnet Milling Co.
RABBIT OF APPROVAL BERNIE - Macaroni - Annie's Homegrown, Inc.
RABBIT PATCH - Housewares - Shafford Co. Inc.
RABBIT RATION 15 - Animal feeds - Bluebonnet Milling Co.
RABBIT RID - Pesticides—household ☆ - ARI
RABBIT SKINS - T-shirts—men's - Midstates Sportswear
RABBITATS - Pet products - Next to Nature
RABBITS FOOT - Hosiery ☆ - Chipman-Union Inc.
RABBITS RAFFERTY - Greeting cards ☆ - Comicana Inc.
RABBITS, ROBOTS AND A MONKEY - Computer software - Hartley Courseware Inc.
RABDOMUN - Vaccines - Pitman-Moore, Inc.
RABDOMUN - Veterinary pharmaceutical preparations - Schering-Plough Animal Health
RABELL - Jewelry - Ram Jewelry Co.
RABGUARD - Veterinary pharmaceutical preparations - SmithKline Beecham Animal Health Products
RABOT - Washers—metal - Elco Industries, Inc.
RABURN - Washing machine parts - Ecolab Inc.
RAC - Animal feed - Cooperative Research Farms
RAC - Cleaning equipment - Kinetronics Corp.
RAC - Electronic equipment - Rite Autotronics Corp.
RAC - Recording label - Resource Associates Corp.
RACA-LERT - Computer software - Storage Solutions, Inc.
RACA-RAY - Computer peripherals - Storage Solutions, Inc.
RACAL - Television equipment - Television Equipment Associates
RACAL-DECCA - Nautical instruments - Racal-Datacom, Inc.
RACCO HOO - Cereal - Wholly Cow Foods
RACCON CHANCELLOR - Wines ☆ - Bully Hill Vineyards, Inc.
RACCOON - Kites ☆ - Hi-Flier Manufacturing Co.
RACCOON - Metals - Three R Technologies, Inc.
RACE - Computers - Mercury Computer Systems Inc.
RACE - Furniture - Haworth, Inc.
RACE-2-WIN - Toys - Tonka Corp.
RACE 13 - Animal feeds - Farmers Feed Mill Inc.
RACE ACE - Toys—automobiles - Mattel, Inc.
RACE & TRAIL - Dog food - Inorex Inc.
RACE BAIT 308 - Toys—automobiles - Mattel, Inc.
RACE CAR - Candy - Superior Fruit & Confections
RACE CAR RIG - Toys - Fisher-Price, Inc.
RACE CAR 'RITHMETIC - Computer software - Unicorn Software
RACE CERTIFIED - Bicycles - Columbia Manufacturing Inc.
RACE CERTIFIED - Computers - Mercury Computer Systems Inc.
RACE CITY USA - Decals and transfers - Mooresville Chamber of Commerce
RACE DAY - Decals and transfers - Commercial Screen Print, Inc.

☆ = Now out of production

RACE FOR THE WEST - Computer software - Hartley Courseware Inc.
RACE IN A CASE - Toys–automobiles - Lewis Galoob Toys, Inc.
RACE-KLEEN - Office supplies - Alvin and Co. Inc.
RACE 'N SHOW - Toys–automobiles - Mattel, Inc.
RACE NUT - Apparel and accessories - Faskartoonz, Inc.
RACE-PAK - Electrical equipment - Electri-Cable Assemblies, Inc.
RACE PROMOTIONS - Trading cards and stamps - Race Promotions, Inc.
RACE-SCAN - Radios and radio equipment - William W. Garrett, III
RACE SERIES MULTIPORT - Computers - Mercury Computer Systems Inc.
RACE SERIES VANTAGERT - Computers - Mercury Computer Systems Inc.
RACE SPEED - Watches - Race Speed
RACE TEAM GRIPPERS - Toy racing set - Intex Recreation Corp.
RACE TEAM PIT CREW - Toys - Mattel, Inc.
RACE TEAM SERIES - Toys–automobiles - Mattel, Inc.
RACE THE CLOCK - Computer software - Mind Play
RACE THRU SPACE - Games - Hasbro, Inc.
RACE TRAKKER - Electronic equipment - Arm Research, Inc.
RACE-TRAX - Computer software - Trilix, Inc.
RACE TRUCK SERIES - Toys–automobiles - Mattel, Inc.
RACECRAFT SUSPENSION - Motor vehicle parts and accessories - Stephen M. Saleen
RACEDAY EMBROIDERY - Apparel and accessories - RT Marketing Ltd.
RACEL & HENRI - Meat products–poultry - Made in France
RACEMAKER - Computer software - A-Loop Offroads
RACEME - Dinnerware–glass - Nikko Ceramics Inc.
RACER - Apparel and accessories ☆ - Skea Ltd.
RACER - Catheters - Leocor, Inc.
RACER - Hardware - C. Itoh Building Products
RACER - Sporting goods ☆ - Allsop, Inc.
RACER BOY - Apparel and accessories - Steve William Smith
RACER CHASER - Apparel–children's - Ski-Time Corp.
RACER-SPACER - Sporting goods - Ski Accessories Co.
RACER TED - Apparel and accessories - Vermont Teddy Bear Co., Inc.
RACER X - Apparel and accessories - Speed Racer Enterprises, Inc.
RACERASE - Paper–bond - Southworth Co.
RACERBLADE - Skates–roller ☆ - Rollerblade, Inc.
RACEREADY - Apparel and accessories - Gerald L. Hans
RACEREADY - Computers - Mercury Computer Systems Inc.
RACERMATE - Bicycles ☆ - Racer-Mate, Inc.
RACERS - Apparel and accessories - Alison's Pop Inc.
RACERS - Shoes - R. Josephs Sportswear, Inc.
RACER'S BLEND - Coffee - House of Coffee
RACER'S CHOICE - Pet products - The Crab Connection
RACER'S CHOICE - Trading cards and stamps - Pinnacle Brands, Inc.
RACERS EDGE - Bicycles - Otasco
RACERS EDGE - Bottles–plastic - Specialized Bicycle Components, Inc.
RACER'S EDGE - Wheels - Thomas Lowe Ventures, Inc.
RACESTAR - Motor vehicle parts and accessories - Bell Sports Corp.
RACET - Pharmaceutical preparations ☆ - Lemmon Co.
RACETEC - Data loggers - Timothy J. Duffy
RACETECH - Goggles–underwater - TYR Sport, Inc.
RACETRAC - Electronic equipment - Electronic Industries Corp.
RACETRAC - Gasoline - Racetrac Petroleum Inc.
RACETRACK - Computers - Mercury Computer Systems Inc.
RACETRAX - Electrical equipment - Data Broadcasting Corp.
RACETRAY - Trays - Mono-Systems, Inc.
RACEWARE - Computers - Mercury Computer Systems Inc.
RACEWAY - Gasoline - Racetrac Petroleum Inc.
RACEWAY READY - Computers - Mercury Computer Systems Inc.
RACEWIRES - Electronic equipment - Quickcar, Inc.
RACHAEL - Watches - Elgin Watch Co.
RACHEL - Toys - Cap Toys, Inc.
RACHEL - Toys - Tonka Corp.
RACHEL PERRY - Cosmetics - Rachel Perry, Inc.
RACHEL'S BEST - Frozen foods - Lewin Group, Inc.
RACHEL'S BROWNIES - Food products ☆ - Goodmark Foods, Inc.
RACHEL'S GARDEN - Stoneware dinnerware - Iron Mountain Stoneware Inc.
RACHEL'S LACE - Bedding–linen - Dan River Inc.
RACIN' - Apparel and accessories - Accurate Sales Co.
RACIN' HOPPERS - Toys–electronic - Tyco Toys
RACIN' J - Toys - Tonka Corp.
RACIN' RAGS - Fabrics - Kris Kozdras
RACINE - Clocks ☆ - Smith Time Inc.
RACINE - Dinnerware–glass ☆ - WMF/USA
RACING - Floor coverings–carpet and rugs ☆ - Regal Rugs Inc.
RACING - Ophthalmic goods - Foremost Optical Products

RACING BEAT - Machine parts - Racing Beat, Inc.
RACING BUG, THE - Publisher's imprints - Windward Directional Marketing
RACING CHAMPIONS - Toys–automobiles - Racing Champions Inc.
RACING CLUB - Perfumes - Jean Philippe Fragrances, Inc.
RACING DESTRUCTION SET - Computer software - Electronic Arts Inc.
RACING DYNAMICS - Automotive parts and accessories - Electrodyne, Inc.
RACING FORMULA - Oils–lubricating - Kent Oil Co., Inc.
RACING GREEN - Flowers, plants, and seeds - Seaboard Seed Co.
RACING HOT - Kites - Hi-Flier Manufacturing Co.
RACING MACHINES - Greeting cards ☆ - Thought Factory
RACING METALS SERIES - Toys - Mattel, Inc.
RACING PINS - Pins–jewelry - Imprinted Products Corp.
RACING PRO - Bicycles - Roadmaster Corp.
RACING RASCALS - Toys–automobiles - Russ Berrie and Co., Inc.
RACING RIGS - Toys–automobiles ☆ - CBS Toys
RACING SILKS - Lipsticks ☆ - Noxell Corp.
RACING SINGLE - Boats–canoes - Howmar Boat Corp.
RACING STROLLER - Strollers–baby - Racing Strollers Inc.
RACING TECHNIUM - Bicycles ☆ - Raleigh USA Bicycle Co.
RACING TOUGH - Batteries - Ford Motor Co.
RACING WITH WINROSS - Games - Winross Co., Inc.
RACK & STACK - Furniture - H. Wilson Co.
RACK ATTACK - Veterinary nutritional supplements - Sugar Creek Outfitters, Inc.
RACK 'EM - Apparel and accessories - J.D.B. Inc.
RACK 'M - Racks - Denpak Building Products, Inc.
RACK 'N ROAST - Pans - E-Z-Por Corp.
RACK-O - Games - Milton Bradley Co.
RACK-O-RIB-B-Q - Food products ☆ - Pierre Frozen Foods Inc.
RACK O'PORK - Food products - Pierce Foods Corp.
RACK-PACK - Audio equipment - Thermodyne International Ltd.
RACK PACK - Oven racks - Alternative Pioneering Systems Inc.
RACK THE KNIFE - Cutlery ☆ - Lifetime Hoan Corp.
RACK-UP - Sporting goods - Pamir Engineering
RACK-UP - Veterinary pharmaceutical preparations - Matthew Newman
RACKDRAWER - Electronic equipment - Efxx Products Co.
RACKET GUARD - Sporting goods - Unique Sports Products Inc.
RACKET RUBBER - Sporting goods - Unique Sports Products Inc.
RACKETOTE - Sporting goods - Bag Co.
RACKMASTER - Aluminum products - Hollaender Manufacturing Co.
RACKMASTER - Computers - Electronic Technology Services, Inc.
RACKMATE - Bicycles - Rackmate Inc.
RACKMOBILE - Electric lighting equipment - Dextrite, Inc.
RACK'N ROLL TOOL CADDY & ORGANIZER - Tools–garden - Uniontools, Inc.
RACKRAISER - Furniture - Rackraiser, Inc.
RACKRIDER - Amplifiers - Furman Sound, Inc.
RACKSHELF - Electronic equipment - Efxx Products Co.
RACKTALKER - Computer hardware - Multi-Tech Systems, Inc.
RACMAX - Electrical surge protectors - Panamax
RACO - Boxes–switch - Hubbell Inc.
RACO - Hobby kits - Rose Art Industries, Inc.
RACO - Steel products - Hubbell Electrical Products
RACON - Pens - Racon Manufacturing Co. Inc.
RACOON - Stuffed toy with fragrance ☆ - Cosrich Inc.
RACORN - Meat extracts - Famous Brands
RACORN - Meat extracts - John Morrell & Co.
RACQ-O-CHET - Games - Carrom Co.
RACQUET BALL SAVER - Sporting goods - Gexco Enterprises
RACQUET BRA, THE - Apparel stores–sports - Formfit Rogers
RACQUET B.U.M. - Apparel–men's - Chauvin International Ltd.
RACQUET CLUB - Apparel–men's - Hartmarx Corp.
RACQUET CLUB - Apparel–men's - Jaymar-Ruby Inc.
RACQUET CLUB - Colognes ☆ - Mem Co., Inc.
RACQUET GUARD - See ON-GUARD
RACQUET MITTEN - Sporting goods - Mary H. Leavell
RACQUET PACK - Bags–duffel - Ektelon
RACQUETBALLER - Gloves - Ektelon
RACQUETEERS - Sporting goods ☆ - Tumi Luggage, Inc.
R.A.C.S. - Pet products - Ridglan Animal Care Systems
RACTER - Computer software - Mindscape Software Inc.
RACYCLE - Bicycles - Columbia Manufacturing Inc.
RAD - Bicycles - Kent International Inc.
RAD - Bicycles - Roadmaster Corp.
RAD - Computer software - Adobe Systems Inc.
RAD BALL - Sporting goods - N.S.G. Marketing Corp.

RAD BOARD - Scooters–children's - Edward N. Horton II
RAD CADDY - School supplies - Leelo Industries, Inc.
RAD CITY - Apparel and accessories - Rad City
RAD DOG - Office supplies - Mead Corp.
RAD DSP - Electronic equipment - Fostex Corp. of America
RAD GUY - Clothing - NGN Inc.
RAD PAD - Bicycles - Hunt-Wilde Corp.
RAD-PAK - Integrated circuits - Space Electronics, Inc.
RAD RAG - Apparel and accessories - Fetish Group, Inc.
RAD RAPS - Pet collars and leashes - Reflex Corp.
RAD REX - Scooters–children's - Edward N. Horton II
RAD REX R - Scooters–children's - Edward N. Horton II
RAD RIDERS - Three-wheel-vehicle set - Intex Recreation Corp.
RAD RODS - Toys - Tonka Corp.
RAD SLIDE - Bicycles - Hunt-Wilde Corp.
RAD STYLIN - Bicycles - Kent International Inc.
R.A.D. SYSTEMS AGGRESSOR - Safety products - Rape Aggression Defense Systems, Inc.
RAD-TASTIC RACER - Bicycles - Columbia Manufacturing Inc.
RAD, THE - Sporting goods - Wellington Leisure Products, Inc.
RAD WAVE - Jewelry - Phillips International Jewelry & Souvenirs Inc.
RADAEX - Chemical preparations - Etrac Inc.
RADALERT - Measuring instruments - International Medcom, Inc.
RADAN - Cough medicines - Summa Pharmaceutical Laboratories Inc.
RADAR - Bicycles ☆ - Murray, Inc.
RADAR - Computer software - Onsi Corp.
R.A.D.A.R. - Electronic equipment - APA Systems
RADAR - Erasers - Alvin and Co. Inc.
RADAR - Golfing equipment - Ben Hogan Co.
RADAR - Lanterns–electric - Burgess Inc.
RADAR - Lighting fixtures - Timely Products
RA'DAR - Pesticides–agricultural - Allanco
RADAR BALL - Toys ☆ - Revell-Monogram, Inc.
RADAR EYE - Radar detectors ☆ - Whistler Acquistion Corp.
RADAR INTERCEPT - Communications equipment–microwave - Leisure Time Development Corp.
RADAR MISSION - Video games - Nintendo of America Inc.
RADAR RANGER - Toys–automobiles - Mattel, Inc.
RADAR REINDEER - Toys–stuffed - Russ Berrie and Co., Inc.
RADAR SENTRY - Radar systems and equipment - Radatron Corp.
RADARANGE - Ovens–microwave - Amana Refrigeration Inc.
RADARANGE PLUS - Housewares - Amana Refrigeration Inc.
RADARSOFT - Computer software - PCI Remote Sensing Corp.
RADART - Darts and dart games - Dart Mart Inc.
RADARWARE - Housewares ☆ - Amana Refrigeration Inc.
RADASSIST - Medical apparatus - Diacor Inc.
RADAX - Amplifiers ☆ - Electro-Voice, Inc.
RADAX - Computer software - Radax Surveys Co.
RADBERRY - Candy - Nabisco Brands Inc.
RADCAL - Ionizing radiation measurement device - Radcal Corp.
RADCAM - Video equipment - Kevin Dole
RADCLIFFE - Apparel–women's - Kellwood Co.
RADCLIFFE - Bathroom fixtures - Crane Plumbing/Fiat Products
RADCLIFFE - Floor coverings–carpet and rugs ☆ - Atlas Carpet Mills Inc.
RADCLIFFE BY SAG HARBOR - Apparel and accessories - Kellwood Co.
RADCON - Adhesives and sealants - Amteco, Inc.
RADDECAY - Computer software - Framateme Technologies, Inc.
RADDIO - Computer software - Perot Systems Corp.
RADEGAST - Body assemblies–aircraft - Stanley Stawski Distributing Co.
RADELL - Erasers ☆ - Staedtler, Inc.
RADEMAKER - Candy - H. Hamstra & Co.
RADENSKA - Water–mineral - Stanley Stawski Distributing Co.
RADER MASTERPIECE - Golfing equipment - Robert Milton Renegar
RADETT - Erasers - Staedtler, Inc.
RADFORD - Clocks ☆ - Ridgeway Clock Co.
RADI-AIRE - Fans–electric ☆ - Middleby Cooking Systems Group
RADIAC - Electronics equipment - Bulbman Inc.
RADIAC - Grinders - Radiac Abrasives, Inc.
RADIAC - Tools - Klein & Co.
RADIAL - Building materials–concrete - Structural Block Systems, Inc.
RADIAL - Floor coverings–tile - Flexco Co.
RADIAL - Footwear–athletic - Head Sports USA
RADIAL - Golfing equipment ☆ - Ben Hogan Co.
RADIAL - Heating equipment - Mastex Industries, Inc.
RADIAL - Watchbands–base metal - Hirsch Speidel Inc.
RADIAL 500 - Footwear–athletic - Head Sports USA

RADIAL BRIDGE SYSTEM - Musical instruments - Peavey Electronics Corp.
RADIAL EXPRESS - Footwear–athletic - Head Sports USA
RADIAL GRAPHITE - Fishing rod, now out of production - Outdoor Technologies Group
RADIAL JAW - Forceps–medical - Boston Scientific Corp.
RADIAL MASTER - Shock absorbers–motor vehicle - Bridgestone/Firestone, Inc.
RADIAL-MATIC - Shock absorbers–motor vehicle ☆ - Monroe Auto Equipment Co.
RADIAL ROVER - Tires - Dunlop Tire Corp.
RADIAL ST - Tires - General Tire, Inc.
RADIAL TWISTER - Tires - Pos-A-Traction, Inc.
RADIALS - Footwear–men's ☆ - Rockport Co. Inc.
RADIALS - Percussion mallets - American Drum
RADIALUX - Wallpaper ☆ - Walldesigns
RADIAN - Lenses–optical - Tele Vue Optics Inc.
RADIAN CORPORATION - Electrical testing instruments - Radian Corp.
RADIANCE - Cabinets - Nutone Inc.
RADIANCE - Cabinets–wood - Decora
RADIANCE - Candlesticks ☆ - Lenox Crystal, Inc.
RADIANCE - Christmas tree ornaments - Cracker Box Inc.
RADIANCE - Clocks - General Time Corp. (Westclox/Seth Thomas Div.)
RADIANCE - Comforters - Pacific Coast Feather Co.
RADIANCE - Dishes–china - Viletta China Co.
RADIANCE - Drinkware - Indiana Glass Co.
RADIANCE - Floor coverings–carpet and rugs ☆ - Regal Rugs Inc.
RADIANCE - Furniture - Thomasville Furniture Industries Inc.
RADIANCE - Giftware - Sasaki
RADIANCE - Glass–leaded - Seneca Glass Co.
RADIANCE - Glassware–household - Crisa Corp.
RADIANCE - Glassware–household ☆ - National Housewares
RADIANCE - Hair care products - European Tanning Systems Inc.
RADIANCE - Heating equipment - E & S Vinyl Manufacturing Inc.
RADIANCE - Pet products - Best n' Show Pet Products Inc.
RADIANCE - Rings–jewelry - Artcarved Inc.
RADIANCE - Shampoos - Nickers International Ltd.
RADIANCE - Stationery ☆ - Mead Corp.
RADIANCE - Stoves–gas - Vermont Castings, Inc.
RADIANCE - Tiles–ceramic ☆ - American Olean Tile Co.
RADIANCE - Video equipment - Compression Labs, Inc.
RADIANCE - Wallpaper - Pantasote Inc. (Wallcovering Div.)
RADIANCE & POWER ACTION CARDS - Greeting cards - Brightwork Advertising & Training Inc.
RADIANCE ANGELS - Giftware - Fenton Art Glass Co.
RADIANCE BY WASHINGTON MILLINERY - Wedding gowns - Washington Millinery Supply, Inc.
RADIANCE II - Floor coverings–carpet and rugs ☆ - Galaxy Carpet Mills Inc.
RADIANCE WHITE & BRITE - Pet products - Best n' Show Pet Products Inc.
RADIANCY - Rings–jewelry - Artcarved Inc.
RADIANT - Bait - Siberian Salmon Egg Co.
RADIANT - Bathroom cleaner - American Home Products Corp.
RADIANT - Boilers–gas - Burnham Corp.
RADIANT - Candy - Peerless Confection Co.
RADIANT - Chemical preparations - Bio-Rad Laboratories, Inc.
RADIANT - Cosmetics - Beauty Selectives, Inc.
RADIANT - Dinnerware–glass ☆ - Nikko Ceramics Inc.
RADIANT - Lamps - Philips Lighting Co.
RADIANT - Mirrors - Downey Glass
RADIANT - Nibs–pen - Radiant Pen Corp.
RADIANT - Pencils ☆ - Faber-Castell Corp.
RADIANT - Pet products - Rolf C. Hagen (USA) Corp.
RADIANT - Pigments - Radiant Color Div.
RADIANT - Publisher's imprints - Advent Books Inc.
RADIANT - Thread - Imperial Threads Inc.
RADIANT - Toilets–enameled - Kohler Co.
RADIANT - Watches ☆ - SMH (US) Inc.
RADIANT ACCENTS - Candles - Wal-Mart Stores Inc.
RADIANT CHARM - Floor coverings–carpet and rugs - Mohawk Carpet Corp.
RADIANT CHROME - Paints - OEM Paints, Inc.
RADIANT DAWN - Floor coverings–carpet and rugs ☆ - Karastan-Bigelow Inc.
RADIANT ENERGY FORCES - Water purification systems - B & L Businesses, Inc. (Water Savers Worldwide)
RADIANT FLAME - Heaters–space - Desa International, Inc.
RADIANT GLO - Hair care products - Palm Beach Beauty Products
RADIANT GLOW - Floor coverings–carpet and rugs ☆ - Downs Carpet Co. Inc.

☆ = Now out of production

RADIANT HAIR - Hair care products - Perfectly Beautiful, Inc.
RADIANT II - Weather tracking equipment ☆ - Maximum Inc.
RADIANT IN RED - Dolls - Mattel, Inc.
RADIANT JEL - Floor waxes - Uncle Sam Chemical Co., Inc.
RADIANT MUSIC - Recording label - Gospel Publishing House
RADIANT OPALESCENTS - Lipsticks - Del Pharmaceuticals, Inc.
RADIANT PLUS - Pet products - Rolf C. Hagen (USA) Corp.
RADIANT RAINBOW - Key rings - Wald Designs Acrylic Idea Factory
RADIANT RED SPUR - Trees - Columbia Basin Nursery
RADIANT REFLECTION - Frames–picture - Sangray Corp.
RADIANT RIPPLES - Cosmetics - Andre Fantasies Inc.
RADIANT ROCK - Sporting goods - Basins Inc.
RADIANT ROPE - Jewelry–precious - Leach & Garner Co.
RADIANT ROSE - Cosmetics ☆ - Honey & Spice Toiletries
RADIANT RUNKEL - Fruits and vegetables - Joan L. Runkel
RADIANT SECURITY - Brassieres (Bras) - Youthcraft-Charmfit
RADIANT SKIN - Skin care products - Perfectly Beautiful, Inc.
RADIANT STAR - Floor coverings–carpet and rugs ☆ - Karastan-Bigelow Inc.
RADIANT SUNPANELS - Heaters - Marley Electric
RADIANT VELVET - Floor coverings–carpet and rugs - Queen Carpet Corp.
RADIANTFIRES - Gas machinery ☆ - Humphrey Products Co.
RADIANTLINE - Paper - Mead Corp.
RADIANTLY RED - Hair coloring preparations - Clairol Inc.
RADIANTS - Hair care products - Andre Fantasies Inc.
RADIATION PAGER - Radioactive diagnostic substances - Sensor Technology Engineering, Inc.
RADIATION PAGER-S - Radioactive diagnostic substances - Sensor Technology Engineering, Inc.
RADIATOR - Brushes–paint - Corona Brushes Inc.
RADIATOR MUSCLE - Fuel additives - Engine Muscle
RADICAL - Bicycles - Columbia Manufacturing Inc.
RADICAL - Golfing equipment - Square Two Golf
RADICAL FOR CHRIST - Apparel and accessories - Frederick Hammond
RADICAL FRUIT - Beverages - Pepsi-Cola Co.
RADICAL NATURE - Apparel and accessories - Printworks Inc.
RADICAL RAVIOLI - Frozen foods - Flagship Foods Inc.
RADICAL RESCUE - Video games - Konami (America) Inc.
RADICAL RIDER - Bicycles - Columbia Manufacturing Inc.
RADICAL ROOTS - Potato chips - Radical Roots, LLC
RADICAL SOLARNAIL - Cosmetics - Creative Nail Design, Inc.
RADICAL ZONE - Bicycles - Columbia Manufacturing Inc.
RADICALEN - Skin care products - Lendan USA Co.
RADICALLY COOL - Apparel and accessories - James S. Tomaszewski Sr.
RADICARE - Vitamins and nutritional supplements - Ayurvedic Concepts Ltd.
RADICASTER - Guitars - Zion Guitar Technology
RADICH'S - Food products - Radich's
RADICOOL - Fruit pops–frozen - Sherwood Brands, Inc.
RADICOOL - Sporting goods - Wellington Leisure Products, Inc.
RADIENCE - Greeting cards - Regency Thermographers Inc.
RADIENT - Hearing aids - Telex Communications, Inc.
RADIKAL RECORDS - Recording label - Radikal Records
RADIO AAHS - Broadcasting stations–radio ☆ - Harmoney Holdings Inc.
RADIO AMATEUR CALLBOOK - Publisher's imprints - Watson-Guptill Publications
RADIO BASEBALL - Computer software ☆ - Electronic Arts Inc.
RADIO BOY - Radios - Nintendo of America Inc.
RADIO CITY - Floor coverings–tile - Interface, Inc.
RADIO-CROS - Hearing aids - Audiotone, Inc.
RADIO EQUIPPED - Toys–trains - Digitrax, Inc.
RADIO FENCE - Pet products - Radio Fence Corp.
RADIO FIJI - Wallets - Raisin Co., Inc.
RADIO FLYER - Wagons–children's - Radio Flyer Inc.
RADIO FLYER RODEO - Wagons–children's - Radio Flyer Inc.
RADIO FLYER TOWN & COUNTRY - Wagons–children's - Radio Flyer Inc.
RADIO FREE - Apparel - John Quill Entertainment, Inc.
RADIO GIRL - Perfume and powder ☆ - Benjamin Ansehl Co.
RADIO INFO - Communications equipment - Michael Dumke
RADIO JOE - Recording label - Joe C. Brown
RADIO KING - Drums–musical instruments - Gibson Guitar Corp.
RADIO KING - Drums–musical instruments - HSS Inc.
RADIO LINE - Wagons–children's - Radio Flyer Inc.
RADIO LONDON - Apparel and accessories - A.L.T. Sportswear Inc.
RADIO MAP - Maps - Riconstabob's Co.
RADIO MUTE - Musical instrument accessories ☆ - Carpenter Co.
RADIO SHACK - Computer software - Tandy Corp.

RADIO SHACK SPACE PATROL - Radios–citizens' band - Technology Properties, Inc.
RADIO TRIUNFO LDA - Recording label ☆ - Penco Industries Inc.
RADIO-TYME - Footwear–men's - L.B. Evans' Son Co.
RADIO WAVES - Bicycles ☆ - Huffy Corp.
RADIOACTIVE - Recording label - MCA Universal Studios
RADIOCOM - Communications equipment–mobile - Telex Communications, Inc.
RADIOEAR - Hearing aids - Radioear Corp.
RADIOGOLD - Medical apparatus - Candela Laser Corp.
RADIOLA - Recording label - Radiola/Sandy Hook Records
RADIOLITE - Pencils ☆ - Empire Berol USA
RADIOLOGY ONLINE - Computer software - Computer Activity Center, Inc.
RADIOPLOT - Drafting supplies - Koh-I-Noor, Inc.
RADIOPRINT - Computer software - Alps Electric (USA), Inc.
RADIOREAD - Computer software - M & FC Holding Co., Inc.
RADIOWARE - Radio communications equipment - Motorola, Inc. (Land Mobile Products Sector)
RADIOZONE - Apparel and accessories - Capital Kids' Radio Co.
RADIOZONE THE KIDS' STATION - T-shirts–men's - Capital Kids' Radio Co.
RADIS - Computer software - Kositzky and Associates Inc.
RADIS - Liquors ☆ - Distillerie Stock USA Ltd.
RADISH - Computer hardware and Computer software - Radish Communications Systems Inc.
RADISSON HOTELS INTERNATIONAL - Hotel-motel franchise - Radisson Hotels International Inc.
RADISSON II - Furniture ☆ - Bassett Furniture Industries, Inc.
RADIUS - Computer peripheral equipment - Radius Inc.
RADIUS - Electric lighting equipment - Genlyte Group Inc.
RADIUS - Floor coverings–carpet and rugs - Bloomsburg Carpet Industries
RADIUS - Furniture - Ethan Allen, Inc.
RADIUS - Golfing equipment - Golfsmith International Inc.
RADIUS - Luggage - Airway Industries, Inc.
RADIUS - Mattresses - Easyrest Inc.
RADIUS - Medical apparatus - General Electric Co.
RADIUS - Radio communications equipment - Motorola, Inc. (Land Mobile Products Sector)
RADIUS - Toothbrushes - Radius Corp.
RADIUS - Wheelchairs - Fortress Inc.
RADIUS/GRANOBLE BORDER - Floor coverings–carpet and rugs - Bloomsburg Carpet Industries
RADIUS P110 - Radios - Motorola, Inc. (Land Mobile Products Sector)
RADIUS SQUARE - Desks - Domore/DO3
RADIX - Bicycles ☆ - Raleigh USA Bicycle Co.
RADJAH - Mats–grass, reed, and jute - Gloria of America Inc.
RADJO'S BAGWARE - Apparel and accessories - Radjo's Bagware
RADKO - Christmas tree ornaments - Christopher Radko
RADNAI - Skin care products - Macsil Inc. (Balmex Div.)
RADNEE - Crocheted and knitted items - Ohio Knitting Mills Inc.
RADNOR - Floor coverings–carpet and rugs ☆ - Downs Carpet Co. Inc.
RADNOR PRESS - Publisher's imprints - Ideals Publications Inc.
RADO - Watches - SMH (US) Inc.
RADOX - Health care products - Sara Lee Corp.
RADPATH - Computer software - Corporate Computing, Inc.
RADSKULLS APPAREL INC. - Apparel and accessories - Radskuls Apparel Inc.
RADSOK - Electrical equipment - Konnektech
RADSPEAK - Computer software - Compuspeak Laboratories, Inc.
RADSTAR - Radio communications equipment - Science Applications International Corp.
RADSTAT - Computers and software - Dimensional Medicine, Inc.
RADSTATION - Computer software - Clinical Information Advantages, Inc.
RADWARE - Frames–eyeglass - Whole Systems Design, Inc.
RADWOOD - Floor coverings - Radiation Technology Inc.
RAE - Jewelry - Merry-Lee Rae
RAE ASSIST - Computer software - Rae Technology, Inc.
RAE SPORT - Apparel - Raewiks, Inc.
RAEFORD - Fabrics - Burlington Industries, Inc.
RAEHS - Golfing equipment - Kiser Corp.
RAELDINE - Pet products - Rael Co.
RAELMYCIN - Pet products - Rael Co.
RAEMON BECCA - Cosmetics - Morris-Flamingo Inc.
RAEMON BELLA - Cosmetics - Morris-Flamingo Inc.
RAENA MORGAN'S BODY RESCUE! - Vitamins and nutritional supplements - Swanson Health Products, Inc.
RAF - Computer hardware - R & R Manufacturing Co. Inc.

☆ = Now out of production

RAFA - Hair-care products - Rafaela Horta
RAFAEL - Ophthalmic goods ☆ - Luxottica
RAFAEL DE LA TORRE - Footwear–men's - Delta Shoe Group
RAFAEL GONZALEZ - Cigars - Villco Imports Inc.
RAFAEL MENDEZ - Music–sheet - Koff Music Co.
RAFAEL SANCHEZ - Jewelry - Rafael Sanchez Designs Ltd.
RAFAELIAN LINE - Jewelry - Cinerama Jewelry Inc.
RAFAEL'S Y MARIA'S - Corn chips - Grande Foods, Inc.
RAFCO - Fruits–frozen ☆ - Ranson Fruit Co. Inc.
RAFF - Recording label - Musimex Inc.
RAFFAELLA D'AREZZO - Footwear - Raffaella D'Arezzo
RAFFAELLO - Wallcoverings - Cork Products Co. Inc.
RAFFAELO - Leather - Max Wiener & Co., Inc.
RAFFERTY - Apparel–women's - J.C. Penney Co., Inc.
RAFFETO - Desserts - T. Marzetti Co.
RAFFETTO - Food products - Romanoff International Inc.
RAFFIA ACCENTS - Craft supplies - Plaid Enterprises, Inc.
RAFFIA FLOWERS - Craft supplies - Milton Bradley Co.
RAFFINE - Wallpaper - Camelot Design Studios
RAFFINEE - Perfumes - Houbigant, Inc.
RAFFLES - Candy - Creative Confection Concepts, Inc.
RAFFLES - Chocolate candy ☆ - Chipurnoi Inc.
RAFFLES - Cigarettes - Philip Morris Companies Inc.
RAFFLES - Dinnerware–glass ☆ - Royal China & Porcelain Companies Inc.
RAFFLES - Toys–stuffed - Davis Brothers & Madison Ltd.
RAFFLES COLLECTION - Furniture - Carl Levine
RAFFLESPORT - Apparel–men's - Kayser-Roth Corp.
RAFFLESWEAR - Apparel–men's - Kayser-Roth Corp.
RAFFO - Beverages–malt - Monarch Wine Co.
RAFFONE - Wigs - Pete Raffa Inc.
RAFFY I & P - Pet products ☆ - Sera Aquaristik USA Inc.
RAFI - Ophthalmic goods - Swank Optical
RAFINA - Lenses–optical - National Optical Co.
RAFINET - Fabrics ☆ - Vanity Fair Mills Inc.
RAFT-R-MATE - Building materials - UC Industries, Inc.
RAG BABY - Infant apparel - Rag Baby Newport
RAG MAT - Mat boards - Crescent Cardboard Co.
RAG MOP JUNGLE KIDS - Toys–stuffed - Davis Brothers & Madison Ltd.
RAG-MOP KIDS - Dolls ☆ - Davis Brothers & Madison Ltd.
RAG POETS - Apparel and accessories - Transcolor Corp.
RAG TIME - Floor coverings–carpet and rugs ☆ - Regal Rugs Inc.
RAGA MUFFINS - Corn–flour or meal - Wilkins-Rogers Inc.
RAGAMUFFIN RACCOON - Toys–stuffed ☆ - Dakin Inc.
RAGAMUFFIN TEDDY BEARS - Toys–stuffed - Dan-Dee International Ltd.
RAGAMUFFINS - Decals and transfers - Darrow Production Co., Inc.
RAGAMUFFINS - Dolls - Carol Buehner
RAGAMUFFINS - Dolls ☆ - Effanbee Doll Corp.
RAGBALL - Mallets–wood - Ideas That Sell Inc.
RAGBUNNIES - Apparel–children's - Connie Bereny
RAGCOTE - Artists' materials - Andrews/Nelson/Whitehead
RAGE - Amplifiers–musical instrument - Peavey Electronics Corp.
RAGE - Archery equipment - Martin Archery Inc.
RAGE - Automotive parts and accessories - Fibre Glass-Evercoat Co. Inc.
RAGE - Boats - Boston Whaler, Inc.
RAGE - Card game - International Games
RAGE - Games ☆ - Tappe Brothers
RAGE - House furnishings - Gear Holdings, Inc.
RAGE - Skin care products - California SunCare, Inc.
RAGE AGAINST THE MACHINE - Recording label - Rage Against the Machine
RAGE 'N THE CAGE - Game machines - H. Betti Industries, Inc.
RAGE RECORDS - Recording label - Rage Records Inc.
RAGE, THE - Bicycles - Kent International Inc.
RAGG BONES - Pet products - Pearson Industries Inc.
RAGG MAPPS - T-shirts–men's - R. Dwayne Goodson
RAGG WOOL - Slippers - Acorn
RAGGAMUFFIN ORIGINALS - Apparel and accessories - Raggamuffin
  Originals
RAGGED MOUNTAIN PINTO BEANS - Fruits and vegetables - Delta Potato
  Growers Cooperative Association
RAGGEDY ANDY - Dolls - Knickerbocker Toy Co. Inc.
RAGGEDY ANN - Bath product ☆ - Cosrich Inc.
RAGGEDY ANN - Dolls - Knickerbocker Toy Co. Inc.
RAGGEDY ANN - Fruits–canned ☆ - Certified Grocers Midwest Inc.
RAGGEDY ANN & ANDY - Dolls - Applause, Inc.
RAGGEDY ANN AND ANDY - Dolls - Playskool, Inc.

RAGGEDY ANN AND ANDY - Frames–eyeglass - Denver International
  Eyewear Inc.
RAGGEDY ANN & ANDY - Lamps ☆ - Dolly, Inc.
RAGGEDY ANN & ANDY - Puzzles - Milton Bradley Co.
RAGGEDY ANN & ANDY - Talking clock ☆ - Janex Corp.
RAGGEDY ANN AND ANDY - Toys - Toy Works, Inc.
RAGGEDY ANN AND RAGGEDY ANDY - Stationery - Creative Learning
  Products Inc.
RAGGEDY ANN 'N ANDY - Pottery ☆ - Rubens Originals
RAGGEDY ANN PERFUME MATE - Doll with cologne ☆ - Cosrich Inc.
RAGGEDY ANN'S EASTER PARADE - Hobby kits - Hinkle Easter Products
RAGGEDY RIPE - Food products - Cherokee Products Co.
RAGGIES - Towels - Knomark, Inc.
RAGGLE RACCOON - Toys–stuffed ☆ - Dakin Inc.
RAGGY CLOTH - Fabrics - Dan River Inc.
RAGIN' CAJUN - Spices and extracts - Stache Foods
RAGIN' CAJUNS - Apparel and accessories - University of Southwestern
  Louisiana
RAGIN' RED - Liquors - Allen's Ltd.
RAGING - Food products - Allied Old English, Inc.
RAGING BULLSEYE - Darts and dart games - Dart Mart Inc.
RAGING FIGHTER - Computer software ☆ - Konami (America) Inc.
RAGING RED - Cosmetics - Elizabeth Arden Inc.
RAGING RIVERS - Radios - Raging Rivers Waterpark, Inc.
RAGING STEEL - Steel products - Public Communications Services
RAGING VOLCANO - Bicycles ☆ - Huffy Corp.
RAGNET - Computer software - Robert S. Sloat
RAGNO - Tiles–ceramic - United Ceramic Tile Corp.
RAGNO - Tiles–terrazzo - Imperial Tile and Marble Corp.
RAGO - Girdles - Rago Foundations Inc. LLC
RAGO OF NEW YORK - Underwear and nightwear - Rago Foundations Inc.
  LLC
RAGOLDS - Candy ☆ - Ragold Inc.
RAGOZZINO'S - Pasta - J. Ragozzino & Son Inc.
RAGS - Animal feeds - Bush Brothers and Co.
RAGS - Toys–stuffed ☆ - Gund, Inc.
RAGS TO RICHES - Christmas tree ornaments - Cracker Box Inc.
RAGS TO RICHES - Computer programs - Interplay Productions
RAGS UNLIMITED - Men's sportswear - Stanley A. Levine, Inc.
RAGSTON - Artists' materials - Andrews/Nelson/Whitehead
RAGTIME - Candy - Pangburn Candy Co.
RAGTIME - Floor coverings–carpet and rugs ☆ - Trans-Ocean Import Co. Inc.
RAGTIME - Recording label - Janscobey Hot Jazz
RAGTIME - Toys - Azrak-Hamway International, Inc.
RAGTIME RED - Lipsticks - Honey & Spice Toiletries
RAGTIME ROSE - Cosmetics - Flori Roberts Inc.
RAGU - Tomato pastes and sauces - Van Den Bergh Foods Co.
RAGU BEEF TONIGHT - Food products - Van Den Bergh Foods Co.
RAGU CHICKEN TONIGHT - Tomato pastes and sauces - Van Den Bergh
  Foods Co.
RAGU CHUNKY GARDENSTYLE - Spaghetti sauces - Van Den Bergh Foods
  Co.
RAGU OLD WORLD STYLE - Spaghetti sauces - Van Den Bergh Foods Co.
RAGU RECIPE SELECTION - Pasta - Conopco, Inc.
RAH-RAH - Shoes - Gotham Shoe Manufacturing Co.
RAHCO - Water purification systems - Rahco Environmental Services
RAICHLE - Boots - Raichle Molitor USA, Inc.
RAID - Insecticides - S.C. Johnson & Son, Inc.
RAID - Pharmaceutical preparations ☆ - Richards Pharmaceutical Co.
RAID 10 PERFORMANCE MANAGER - Computer software ☆ - ECCS, Inc.
RAID FLEA KILLER PLUS - Pesticides–household - S.C. Johnson & Son, Inc.
RAID LITE - Computer storage devices - Andataco
RAID MAX - Insecticides - S.C. Johnson & Son, Inc.
RAID ON BUNGELING BAY - Computer software ☆ - Broderbund Software,
  Inc.
RAID READY - Computer peripheral equipment - Dataram Corp.
RAID UNSCENTED - Insecticides - S.C. Johnson & Son, Inc.
RAID YARD GUARD - Insecticides - S.C. Johnson & Son, Inc.
RAIDBANK - Computer hardware - Micronet Technology, Inc.
RAIDER - Bicycles - Columbia Manufacturing Inc.
RAIDER - Bicycles ☆ - Raleigh USA Bicycle Co.
RAIDER - Boats–motor ☆ - Cobia Boat Co.
RAIDER - Boats–motor ☆ - Commander Marine
RAIDER - Boats–motor ☆ - Rinker Boat Co. Inc.
RAIDER - Boats–motor ☆ - Trojan Yacht
RAIDER - Fishing lures - Raider Tackle Manufacturing Co.

☆ = Now out of production

RAIDER - Frames—eyeglass ✩ - Universal/Univis Inc.
RAIDER - Golfing equipment - Slotline Golf
RAIDER - Motor vehicles—trucks ✩ - Chrysler Corp. (Dodge Truck Div.)
RAIDERS OF IRONROCK, THE - Games ✩ - Mayfair Games, Inc.
RAIDION - Computer peripheral equipment - Micropolis Corp.
RAIDRUNNER - Computer hardware - Bering Technology, Inc.
RAIDTEC - Electronic equipment - Raidtec Corp.
RAIDWARE - Computer software - Micropolis Corp.
RAIKES - Toys—stuffed ✩ - Applause, Inc.
RAIL - Vegetables—canned - EFCO Importers
RAIL BARON - Games - Avalon Hill Game Co.
RAIL CITY - Apparel and accessories - Alliance Gaming Corp.
RAIL-EASY - Rails—aluminum ✩ - Morgan Products Ltd.
RAIL KING - Toys—trains ✩ - Life-Like Products Inc.
RAIL LIFE - Railings—wood - Action Sales & Marketing, Inc.
RAIL MASTER - Antennas - Wintenna Inc.
RAIL MASTER - Toys—trains - Life-Like Products Inc.
RAIL N RACK - Motor vehicle parts and accessories - Technic Tool Corp.
RAIL PAK - Cases—musical instrument - Distex Corp.
RAIL PRO - Railings—wood - L.J. Smith Co., Inc.
RAIL RIDER - Toys—trains - Life-Like Products Inc.
RAIL RIDER SYSTEM - Toys ✩ - Playskool, Inc.
RAIL RUNNER - Toys—trains - Mattel, Inc.
RAIL, THE - Apparel and accessories - Nordstrom, Inc.
RAIL ZIP - Cleaning preparations - Pacer Technology
RAILBENCH - Chairs—wood - Cassco Products Inc.
RAILCARD - Postcards ✩ - Wm. K. Walthers Inc.
RAILCOST - Computer software - Martin and Associates, Inc.
RAILFAST - Rails—steel - Kerr-McGee Chemical Corp.
RAILGUARD - Railings—metal - Garlock Equipment Co.
RAILING JIG - Railings—metal - Railing Jigs, Inc.
RAILMASTER - Lubricating systems—locomotive - Whitmore Manufacturing Co.
RAILMASTER 72 - Toys—electronic - Tyco Toys
RAILMASTER 102 - Toys—electronic - Tyco Toys
RAILMAX - Computer software - Softronics, Inc.
RAILPLEX - Paints - Strathmore Products, Inc.
RAILPOWER - Toys—trains - MRC
RAILROAD - Boots - Railroad Sock, Inc.
RAILROAD - Card game - The Game Works, Inc.
RAILROAD - Watches ✩ - Toastmaster Inc.
RAILROAD BARON'S BED, THE - Beds—metal - M. Craig Cabinetmaker
RAILROAD MILLS MACCOBOY - Snuff - American Maize-Products Co.
RAILROAD SOCK AN AMERICAN TRADITION SINCE 1901, THE - Socks - Railroad Sock, Inc.
RAILROAD SOCK, THE - Socks - Leininger Mills Inc.
RAILSIM - Computer software - LS Transit Systems, Inc.
RAILSPORT - Apparel—men's - Nordstrom, Inc.
RAILTITE - Lighting fixtures - Guth Lighting
RAILTRAC YARDMASTER - Computer software - Bourque Data Systems, Inc.
RAILWAY EXPRESS - Sweatshirts - RSA Express Inc.
RAIMA DATABASE MANAGER - Computer software - Raima Corp.
RAIMAT ESTATE - Wines - Codorniu USA Inc.
RAIMIS - Computer software - National Specialty Services, Inc.
RAIMUNDO - Guitars ✩ - Music Imports Ltd.
RAIN - Colognes - A.K.A. Saunders, Inc.
RAIN - Detergents ✩ - Blue Cross Laboratories Inc.
RAIN - Glass products - AFG Industries Inc. (Glass Group Div.)
RAIN-A-WAY - Umbrellas - Elizabeth Leather Bags
RAIN AWAY - Cleaning preparations—household - Kafko International Ltd.
RAIN BARREL - Fabric softeners - S.C. Johnson & Son, Inc.
RAIN BARREL - Furniture ✩ - Gem Manufacturing Corp.
RAIN BELT - Sprinklers—lawn - Newell Stamping Manufacturing Corp.
RAIN BIRD - Sprinklers—lawn - Rain Bird National Sales Corp.
RAIN-BLO - Chewing gum - Leaf, Inc.
RAIN-BLO BOOM BOX - Chewing gum - Leaf, Inc.
RAIN-BLO BUBBLE GUM CD PLAYER - Chewing gum - Leaf, Inc.
RAIN-BLO SOUR FRUIT - Chewing gum - Leaf, Inc.
RAIN-BLOK - Waterproofing compounds - Sterling-Clark-Lurton Corp.
RAIN-BOW - Archery equipment ✩ - Bear Archery Inc.
RAIN BOW - Floor coverings—carpet and rugs ✩ - Quaker Inc.
RAIN BREAKER - Umbrellas ✩ - L.P. Henryson Co. Inc.
RAIN-CAP - Automotive parts and accessories - Rain-Cap, Inc.
RAIN CHASER - Apparel and accessories - Durlacher & Co., Inc.
RAIN CLEAR - Cleaning preparations—window - Amsoil, Inc.
RAIN-COTE - Veterinary pharmaceutical preparations - Evergreen Mills Inc.

RAIN-COTE MINERALS - Animal feed supplements - Evergreen Mills Inc.
RAIN CREME - Skin care products - K'Arsan Corp.
RAIN CRYSTAL - Water purification systems - Scientific Glass
RAIN CUPS - Downspouts - Peter C. Edmondson
RAIN DANCE - Floor coverings—carpet and rugs ✩ - Masland Corp.
RAIN DANCE - Rings—jewelry - Artcarved Inc.
RAIN DANCE - Umbrellas - English Mist Ltd.
RAIN DASHER - Hair care products - Andre Fantasies Inc.
RAIN DATE - Hair care products - Andre Fantasies Inc.
RAIN DATE - Sprinklers—lawn - L.R. Nelson Corp.
RAIN DATES - Footwear - Valley Lane Industries Co.
RAIN DEARS - Apparel—men's - Norcross Footwear, Inc.
RAIN DRAIN - Downspouts - Chapiewsky's Inc.
RAIN DRAIN - Drains - Aco Polymer Products Inc.
RAIN DROPS - Wallpaper - Carlton-Metro Wallcoverings
RAIN ESSENTIALS, THE - Umbrellas - Shedrain Corp.
RAIN FAST - Chemical preparations - Conklin Co., Inc.
RAIN-FOLD - Umbrellas - AAA Umbrella Co.
RAIN FOREST - Pet collars - Leatherite-Nylorite Manufacturing Inc.
RAIN FOREST - Recording label - BGM Records
RAIN FOREST - Rings—jewelry - Artcarved Inc.
RAIN FOREST - Stationery - Natural Products Corp.
RAIN FOREST AQUACULTURE PRODUCTS, INC. - Fish—fresh or frozen - Rain Forest Aquaculture Products, Inc.
RAIN FOREST CHEW - Candy - Ben and Jerry's Homemade, Inc.
RAIN FOREST CRUNCH - Ice cream - Ben and Jerry's Homemade, Inc.
RAIN FRESH - Skin care products - Aldi Inc.
RAIN FRESH - Water—bottled or canned - Rain Fresh Water Co.
RAIN-GAITOR - Sprinklers—lawn - H.B. Sherman Manufacturing Co.
RAIN GARDE - Umbrellas - Hollander Umbrellas
RAIN GARDE - Umbrellas - Stapo Industries Inc.
RAIN GEAR - Sprinklers—lawn - L.R. Nelson Corp.
RAIN GLORY - Hair care products - Andre Fantasies Inc.
RAIN-GUARD - Paints - Atlas Chemical Co.
RAIN JET - Sprinklers—lawn - Hardie-Toro Irrigation
RAIN KING - Sprinklers—lawn - Aircap Industries Corp.
RAIN KLEEN - Fabrics - Weblon Inc.
RAIN-KOTE - Automotive parts and accessories - Tuff-Kote Dinol Inc.
RAIN LILY - Shaving preparations - S.C. Johnson & Son, Inc.
RAIN MACHINE - Sprinklers—lawn - La Fayette Brass Co. Inc.
RAIN MAGIC - Hair care products - Andre Fantasies Inc.
RAIN MAKERS, THE - Umbrellas - Gila Products LLC
RAIN MASTER - Gutters—plastic - Bemis Manufacturing Co.
RAIN MASTER - Irrigation equipment - Rain Master Irrigation Systems, Inc.
RAIN MASTER - Waterproof outerwear - Magid Manufacturing Co. Inc.
RAIN MISTER - Sprinklers—lawn - Raindrip, Inc.
RAIN-NO-STAIN - Draperies - Rockland Industries Inc.
RAIN ON IT - Automotive parts and accessories - Perry E. Hubbs
RAIN PATCH - Asphalt mastic roof sealant - Henry Co.
RAIN PRIME - Primers - Temple-Inland Forest Products Corp.
RAIN 'R SHINE - Games - KWG
RAIN RAIDER - Apparel—athletic ✩ - Cooper Sportswear Manufacturing Co., Inc.
RAIN RAMBLER - Hair care products - Andre Fantasies Inc.
RAIN ROLLS RIGHT OFF - Apparel and accessories - Totes, Inc.
RAIN RUN - Garden equipment - Presto Products Co.
RAIN RUNNER - Hair care products - Andre Fantasies Inc.
RAIN SAFE - Fans—electric - Fasco Industries Inc. (Consumer Products Div.)
RAIN SHOT - Hoses - L.R. Nelson Corp.
RAIN SKIPPER - Hair care products - Andre Fantasies Inc.
RAIN SOFT - Water purification systems - RainSoft Water Conditioning Co.
RAIN SONG - Floor coverings—carpet and rugs ✩ - Galaxy Carpet Mills Inc.
RAIN SONG - Guitars - Kuau Technology, Ltd.
RAIN SPA - Shower rods - Shower Spa USA, LLC
RAIN SPRAY - Garden equipment ✩ - Thompson Manufacturing Co.
RAIN SPRAY HOSE NOZZLE - Nozzles - Thompson Manufacturing Co.
RAIN STAIN - Stains - United Gilsonite Laboratories
RAIN-TITE - Adhesives and sealants - Royal Lustre Brands
RAIN TRAIN - Sprinklers—lawn - L.R. Nelson Corp.
RAIN TURF - Chemical preparations - Southwest Feed Product, Inc.
RAIN VISOR - Hair care products - Andre Fantasies Inc.
RAIN WAND - Garden equipment - Dramm Corp.
RAIN-X - Windshields—glass - Unelko Corp.
RAINBAR - Bar fixtures—metal - Kallista Inc.
RAINBAR - Soap - Neutrogena Corp.
RAINBATH - Skin care products - Neutrogena Corp.

RAINBEAUS - Dolls ☆ - Uneeda Doll Co., Inc.
RAINBERRY - Furniture ☆ - Singer Furniture Co.
RAINBERRY FARMS - Juices - Florida Bottling Inc.
RAINBIRD - Recording label - Cimirron/Rainbird Records
RAINBLOSSOM - Toiletries - Les Parfums De Dana, Inc.
RAINBO - Awnings, outdoor curtains - T.J. Bottom Industries Inc. (Rainbo Awning Systems Div.)
RAINBO - Bakery products - Campbell Taggart Inc.
RAINBO - Mops ☆ - Golden Star Inc.
RAINBO BRIDE - Brooms - Hamburg Broom Works Inc.
RAINBO ROCK STICKS - Candy - Murray-Allen International Inc.
RAINBO SHADE - Grass seed - Kellogg Inc.
RAINBOW - Bathroom fixtures - American Standard Inc.
RAINBOW - Beds–wood - Classic Corp.
RAINBOW - Bicycles - Roadmaster Corp.
RAINBOW - Brooms - Lighthouse Industries
RAINBOW - Brushes–paint - Wooster Brush Co.
RAINBOW - Candles - American Candle Co. Inc.
RAINBOW - Candy - Leaf, Inc.
RAINBOW - Computers–personal - Digital Equipment Corp.
RAINBOW - Confections - Thos. D. Richardson Co.
RAINBOW - Dehumidifiers - Maid-o-Mist
RAINBOW - Deodorizers ☆ - Car-Freshner Corp.
RAINBOW - Dinnerware–glass - Nikko Ceramics Inc.
RAINBOW - Dinnerware–glass - Sango Co. Ltd. (Sango USA Div.)
RAINBOW - Dinnerware–glass ☆ - Iris Arc Crystal Inc.
RAINBOW - Electrical equipment - Aura Ceramics, Inc.
RAINBOW - Electronic equipment - Educational Insights, Inc.
RAINBOW - Fabrics–broadcloth - Desire Mills Co. Inc.
RAINBOW - Fabrics–broadcloth - Foss Manufacturing Co., Inc.
RAINBOW - Fabrics–chenille - Mangelsen's (VDI)
RAINBOW - Fireplace equipment - Hearth Craft
RAINBOW - Floor coverings - American Floor Products Co. Inc.
RAINBOW - Floor coverings–carpet and rugs - Masterpiece Finishing Co.
RAINBOW - Food products - Pies Inc.
RAINBOW - Food products - Rainbow Natural Foods
RAINBOW - Footwear - Rainbow Sandals & Shoes Inc.
RAINBOW - Frames–eyeglass ☆ - Universal/Univis Inc.
RAINBOW - Fruit drinks–bottled or canned - Anita Spring Water Co.
RAINBOW - Fruits–canned - Fleming Companies, Inc.
RAINBOW - Furniture - Little Tikes Co.
RAINBOW - Glass–leaded - Noritake Co. Inc.
RAINBOW - Gloves - Jomac Products Inc.
RAINBOW - Golfing equipment - Rainbow Sports
RAINBOW - Greeting cards - Regency Thermographers Inc.
RAINBOW - Kites - Llumar Star Kites Inc.
RAINBOW - Lamps - Rainbow Products Co.
RAINBOW - Lenses–optical - International Space Optics
RAINBEAUS - Marking paints - Rainbow Technology Corp.
RAINBOW - Medical apparatus - Biolog, Inc.
RAINBOW - Mops ☆ - Winchester-Auburn Mills Inc.
RAINBOW - Mortars–clay ☆ - DCS Color & Supply Co. Inc.
RAINBOW - Packaging–paper - C.L. Downey Co.
RAINBOW - Paper ☆ - Hunt Manufacturing Co.
RAINBOW - Paper ☆ - Mead Corp.
RAINBOW - Paper–construction - Bemiss-Jason Corp.
RAINBOW - Pasta - Borden, Inc.
RAINBOW - Pet products - Feller Stone Inc.
RAINBOW - Photographic equipment ☆ - R.T.S. Inc.
RAINBOW - Pigments - Empire Blended Products Co.
RAINBOW - Popcorn - Royal Palm Co., Inc.
RAINBOW - Rings–jewelry - Artcarved Inc.
RAINBOW - Skin care products - Rainbow Research Corp.
RAINBOW - Snuff - Conwood Co. L.P.
RAINBOW - Sporting goods - Habitat Rods
RAINBOW - Sporting goods ☆ - Hedstrom Corp.
RAINBOW - Staplers ☆ - Markwell Manufacturing Co. Inc.
RAINBOW - Teas - Eastern Shore Tea Co.
RAINBOW - Towels ☆ - Mount Vernon Mills Inc.
RAINBOW - Toys–marbles - Al Sandberg
RAINBOW - Umbrellas - Shedrain Corp.
RAINBOW - Upholstery leather - American Leather Manufacturing Co.
RAINBOW - Vacuum cleaners and accessories - Rexair, Inc.
RAINBOW - Vacuum cleaners and accessories - Rexair Manufacturing Inc.
RAINBOW - Wallets, etc. - Inner World Inc.
RAINBOW - Wallpaper ☆ - Priss Prints Inc.

RAINBOW - Water–bottled or canned - Rainbow Water Service
RAINBOW - Waterproof outerwear - Capitol Novelty Co.
RAINBOW - Yardsticks ☆ - L.S. Starrett Co. Inc. (Consumer Products Div.)
RAINBOW 100B - Computers–personal - Digital Equipment Corp.
RAINBOW ALLIE - Apparel and accessories - Allison Manufacturing Co.
RAINBOW & STARS - Wallpaper ☆ - Priss Prints Inc.
RAINBOW ART - Glass–stained - Rainbow Art Glass
RAINBOW BABIES - Figurines - Willitts Design International, Inc.
RAINBOW BAGS - Paper - Bemiss-Jason Corp.
RAINBOW BEAR - Toys–stuffed ☆ - Fun World Inc.
RAINBOW BEND - Playground equipment - Miracle Recreation Equipment Co.
RAINBOW BLUE - Kitchenware–china - H. Wittur & Co.
RAINBOW BODY BUTTER - Skin care products - Rainbow Research Corp.
RAINBOW BRIDGE - Playing cards - Frances Neumann
RAINBOW BRIGHTS - Brushes–hair - I. Sekine Co. Inc.
RAINBOW BRITE - Bathroom accessories ☆ - Tsumura International Inc.
RAINBOW BRITE - Cereal - Ralston Purina Co.
RAINBOW BRITE - Dishes–plastic - Deka Plastics Inc.
RAINBOW BRITE - Games ☆ - Ben Cooper Inc.
RAINBOW BRITE - Radios ☆ - ERTL Co., Inc.
RAINBOW BRITE - Toys ☆ - Coloron Industries
RAINBOW BUNNY - Chocolate candy - Superior Fruit & Confections
RAINBOW BUNNY - Toys–stuffed - Russ Berrie and Co., Inc.
RAINBOW CANDLE DROPS - Candles - Columbia Wax Products Inc.
RAINBOW CANES - Candy - Bobs Candies Inc.
RAINBOW CAY - Wallpaper - Seabrook Wallcoverings, Inc.
RAINBOW CHASER - Photo albums - Lisa Frank, Inc.
RAINBOW CHIPS DELUXE - Cookies - Keebler Co.
RAINBOW CIRCUS ARTS - Exercising equipment ☆ - Jugglebug
RAINBOW CLOWN - Toys–stuffed ☆ - Dakin Inc.
RAINBOW CLOWN AROUND - Novelty items - Cathay International
RAINBOW COCKTAIL - Juices - Pyramid Juice Co.
RAINBOW COCOA LITE - Cake decorating compound - Grace Cocoa Associates, L.P.
RAINBOW COCONUT - Candy - Atkinson Candy Co.
RAINBOW COLLECTION - Flatware ☆ - National Housewares
RAINBOW COLOR - Bird feeds - Petland, Inc.
RAINBOW COLORS - Dyes–food - Spearhead Industries Inc.
RAINBOW COLORS - Novelty items - Paper Magic Group Inc.
RAINBOW CONNECTION - Bicycles - Columbia Manufacturing Inc.
RAINBOW CORAL - Pet products - Ed Stubinger Co.
RAINBOW COVE - Floor coverings¬carpet and rugs ☆ - Karastan-Bigelow Inc.
RAINBOW CRAFT - Fabrics–broadcloth - Foss Manufacturing Co., Inc.
RAINBOW CRAFTS - Toys - Tonka Corp.
RAINBOW DELITE - Doughnuts–mixes - Dawn Food Products Inc.
RAINBOW DROPS - Dyes–food - Spearhead Industries Inc.
RAINBOW EDGE - Frames–eyeglass - Hoya Corp. USA
RAINBOW EXACT - Animal feeds - Kaytee Products Inc.
RAINBOW EYES - Skin care products ☆ - Victoria Vogue, Inc.
RAINBOW FAIRY TALES - Clocks - Bulova Corp.
RAINBOW FARMS - Eggs - Almark Inc.
RAINBOW FARMS - Food products - Amende and Schultz
RAINBOW FARMS - Food products - Mountain Springs of Oregon
RAINBOW FELT STICK-ONS - Stickers - Foss Manufacturing Co., Inc.
RAINBOW FLOWER - Candles ☆ - Will & Baumer, Inc.
RAINBOW FRENCH CLAY - Cosmetics - Rainbow Research Corp.
RAINBOW FRIENDS - Toys–stuffed - Mark Andrew Steiner
RAINBOW GARNET - Jewelry - Rainbow Garnet Inc.
RAINBOW GEMS - Pet products - Now Pet Products
RAINBOW GOLDEN - Cosmetics - Rainbow Research Corp.
RAINBOW GOLF EQUIPMENT - Golfing equipment - Rainbow Sports
RAINBOW HEARTS - Kites - Gayla Industries Inc.
RAINBOW HERBMETIC - Hair care products ☆ - Rainbow Research Corp.
RAINBOW IRIDESCENT - Glassware–household - Federal Glass
RAINBOW JO - Apparel–women's - Michael J. Thornton and Ba Aye Rajan Partnership
RAINBOW KRAFT - Paper - Bemiss-Jason Corp.
RAINBOW LIGHT - Toys ☆ - Imperial Toy Corp.
RAINBOW LIGHT - Vitamins and nutritional supplements - Rainbow Light Nutritional Systems, Inc.
RAINBOW LIGHT, THE - Lamps - Rainbow Light Co.
RAINBOW LINKY HEARTS - Toys–stuffed - Gund, Inc.
RAINBOW LITE - Candles - Empire Manufacturing Co.
RAINBOW MACHINE - Toys - Mars, Inc.
RAINBOW MAKERS - Prisms–optical - Silver Deer Ltd.
RAINBOW MAX - Games - Recycled Paper Products, Inc.

☆ = Now out of production

RAINBOW MIST - Servingware - Indiana Glass Co.
RAINBOW MOUNTAIN - Cribs–wood - Rainbow Mountain, Inc.
RAINBOW MUFFLER - Automotive parts and accessories - Muffler Man Inc.
RAINBOW MULCH COLORANT - Dyes–synthetic - Fecon, Inc.
RAINBOW OILS - Health care products - Essential Oil Co.
RAINBOW PACK - Toys - Tonka Corp.
RAINBOW PAK - Plastics - Alta Industries Inc.
RAINBOW PARFAIT - Bath scents ☆ - Coty Inc.
RAINBOW PARFAIT - Dolls ☆ - Effanbee Doll Corp.
RAINBOW PENS - Office supplies - Alwin Products
RAINBOW PILLAR - Flowers, plants, and seeds - Herman Losely & Son, Inc.
RAINBOW PINWHEEL POPS - Candy - Gladstone Candies
RAINBOW POPS - Candy - Day Spring Enterprises Inc.
RAINBOW PRINCESS - Jewelry - Baby Gold Jewelry, Inc.
RAINBOW PROJECTORS - Lasers - Laser Fantasy International, Inc.
RAINBOW PUPPY - Toys–stuffed - Russ Berrie and Co., Inc.
RAINBOW RABBIT - Candy ☆ - R.M. Palmer Co.
RAINBOW RACER - Toys–stuffed - Gund, Inc.
RAINBOW RAPTURE - Candy ☆ - That's My Favorite Inc.
RAINBOW REAM - Paper–tissue - Crystal Tissue Co. Inc.
RAINBOW REFLECTION - Jewelry - Russ Berrie and Co., Inc.
RAINBOW RINGS - Toys - Tonka Corp.
RAINBOW ROAMERS - Candy - Klein Chocolate Co.
RAINBOW ROCK - Apparel and accessories - John Orr
RAINBOW ROCK - Pet products - Feller Stone Inc.
RAINBOW ROCK - Pet products - Tetra Sales USA
RAINBOW ROCKER - Furniture ☆ - Gem Manufacturing Corp.
RAINBOW RODS - Curling irons–electric - Argonaut Specialties Inc.
RAINBOW ROPES - Candy - Uniconfis Corp.
RAINBOW RUN - Wines - Chateau Benoit Winery
RAINBOW SHERBET - Baskets–wood ☆ - Royal Cathay Trading Co.
RAINBOW SIGNATURE - Mats - Matworks
RAINBOW SPIRITS - Beverages–alcohol - Marie Brizard Wines & Spirits, USA
RAINBOW SPORTS - Shampoos ☆ - Rainbow Research Corp.
RAINBOW SPRINGS - Seafood products–fresh or frozen - Idaho Trout Processors Co.
RAINBOW SQUIRTER - Toys–guns - Imperial Toy Corp.
RAINBOW STAMPER - Rings–jewelry - Mattel, Inc.
RAINBOW STRESS REDUCTION - Film–motion picture - Sam & Venu. a Partnership, Inc.
RAINBOW STYLIST - Mats–rattan - Golden Star Inc.
RAINBOW, THE - Giftware - Faroy Sales
RAINBOW THOUGHTS - Greeting cards - American Greetings Corp.
RAINBOW TIMBER - Games - Cactus Services, Inc.
RAINBOW TIPS - Combs - American Greetings Corp.
RAINBOW TOPPERS - Confections - Signature Brands, LLC
RAINBOW TURF - Flowers, plants, and seeds - Seed Corp. of America
RAINBOW TWEEDS - Floor coverings–carpet and rugs ☆ - American Excelsior Co.
RAINBOW TWIRLS - Macaroni ☆ - Pastamania
RAINBOW TWIRLS - Novelty items ☆ - Easter Unltd. Inc.
RAINBOW TWIST STICKS - Candy - Atkinson Candy Co.
RAINBOW TWISTS - Macaroni ☆ - Golden Grain Co.
RAINBOW WEAVE - Pet products - Mustang Products, Inc.
RAINBOW WHIPS - Paints–artists' ☆ - Duncan Enterprises
RAINBOW WRAP - Infant product - Leachco Inc.
RAINBOW ZOO - Wood products ☆ - Royal Cathay Trading Co.
RAINBOWARD - Greeting cards - Royal Stationery Co.
RAINBOWMATE - Vacuum cleaners and accessories - Rexair, Inc.
RAINBOWRAPS - Novelty items - T & T Industries Inc.
RAINBOWRIDER - Frames–eyeglass ☆ - Universal/Univis Inc.
RAINBOWS - Fabrics - Guilford Mills, Inc.
RAINBOW'S END - Floor coverings–carpet and rugs ☆ - Lees Carpets
RAINBOW'S END - Floor coverings–carpet and rugs ☆ - Masland Corp.
RAINBOWS END - Wallpaper ☆ - David & Dash
RAINBOWSTAR - Vans–conversion - Legacy Conversions, Inc.
RAINBOY - Hoses - L.R. Nelson Corp.
RAINCHECK - Sealing compounds - Stewart-Hall Chemical Corp.
RAINCHECKS - Bathroom accessories - Waterware Inc.
RAINCLIFF - Floor coverings–carpet and rugs ☆ - World Carpets, Inc.
RAINCOAT - Paints - Morwear Paint Co.
RAINCOAT - Waterproofing compounds - Kop-Coat, Inc.
RAINCOTE - Adhesives and sealants ☆ - Edison Brothers Stores, Inc.
RAINCROSS - Beverages–malt - Riverside Brewing Co.
RAINDANCE - Bicycles - Huffy Corp.
RAINDANCE - Cleaning preparations ∑ Armor All Products Corp.

RAINDANCE - Fountains ☆ - Valley View Specialties Co.
RAINDANCER - Bathroom fixtures - Tradewind Industries Inc.
RAINDEARS - Waterproof footwear - Kaysam Corp. of America
RAINDOME - Shower stalls–metal - Kallista Inc.
RAINDRI - Waterproof outerwear - Goorin Bros. Inc.
RAINDRIP - Sprinklers–lawn - Raindrip, Inc.
RAINDROP - Bathroom accessories - Wilardy Originals Inc.
RAINDROP - Deodorizers - Stewart-Hall Chemical Corp.
RAINDROP - Shower stalls–metal - Kohler Co.
RAINDROP - Water–bottled or canned - Vital Living Products Inc.
RAINDROP SHOPPE, THE - Water–bottled or canned - Vital Living Products Inc.
RAINDROPS - Bathing suits - Ocean Pool Co.
RAINDROPS - Christmas tree ornaments - Cracker Box Inc.
RAINDROPS - Dolls ☆ - Uneeda Doll Co., Inc.
RAINDROPS - Fabrics–tapestry ☆ - Columbus Coated Fabrics Co.
RAINDROPS - House furnishings - Kellwood Co.
RAINER - Flatware - Washington Forge Inc.
RAINER IMPORTS - Wood products - Weyerhaeuser Co.
RAINERI - Food products - Bel Canto Fancy Foods Ltd.
RAINFAIR - Waterproof outerwear - Rainfair, Inc.
RAINFALL - Greeting cards - Rainfall Inc.
RAINFALL - Honey ☆ - Rainbow Natural Foods
RAINFIGHTER - Antennas–satellite - Pro Brand International, Inc.
RAINFOREST - Christmas tree ornaments - Enchanted Gold, Inc.
RAINFOREST - Cookies - Heaven Scent Natural Foods
RAINFOREST - Floor coverings–tile - Interface, Inc.
RAINFOREST - Honey - Natural Nectar Corp.
RAINFOREST - Skin care products - Rachel Perry, Inc.
RAINFOREST - Wallpaper ☆ - Three Sisters Studio
RAINFOREST BLEND - Coffee - Frontier Cooperative Herbs
RAINFOREST CRUNCH - Snack foods - The Rainforest Co.
RAINFOREST ENERGY BAGEL - Bagels - New York Bagel Factory
RAINFOREST FARMS - Fruits–dried - U.S. Organic Fruit Co.
RAINFOREST FRIENDS - Cosmetics - International Beauty Network, Inc.
RAINFOREST GRANOLA - Granola bars - Rainforest Products, Inc.
RAINFOREST NUT - See SAVE THE FOREST NUT
RAINFOREST RARITIES - Frozen foods - Howler Products, Inc.
RAINFOREST REMEDIES - Pharmaceutical preparations - Rainforest Remedies
RAINFOREST REMEDIES IX CHEL MAYAN GODDESS OF HEALING - Pharmaceutical preparations - Rainforest Remedies
RAINFOREST RICE PUDDIN' - Pet food - Judee K. Creations, Inc. (Crazy Corn Division)
RAINFOREST RICE PUDDIN' - Pet products - Crazy Corn
RAINFOREST TROLLS - Dolls - Imagi-Toy Group Inc.
RAINFRESH - Disinfectants - Think Medical, Inc.
RAINGAMERS - Jackets - Ram Golf Corp.
RAINGARD - Apparel and accessories - Stearns Manufacturing Co.
RAINGEAR - Umbrellas - Rajkumar C. Khubani
RAINGER - Sprinklers–lawn - H.B. Sherman Manufacturing Co.
RAINGO - Gutters–plastic - Genova Products Inc.
RAINGUARD - Apparel and accessories - Vallen Safety Supply Co.
RAINGUARD - Automotive parts and accessories - Trico Products Corp.
RAINHANDLER - Gutters–plastic - Savetime Corp.
RAINIER - Bakery products - Rainier Natural Foods
RAINIER - Beverages–malt - Rainier Brewing Co.
RAINIER - Beverages–malt - The Stroh Brewery Co.
RAINIER - Frames–eyeglass - U.S. Optical Frame Co.
RAINIER - Giftware - Simon Golub & Sons Inc.
RAINIER - Office furniture–wood - Joyce International Inc.
RAINIER ALE - Beverages–malt - The Stroh Brewery Co.
RAINIER DRAFT LIGHT - Beverages–malt - The Stroh Brewery Co.
RAINIER DRY - Beverages–malt - The Stroh Brewery Co.
RAINIER HONEY WHEAT - Beverages–malt - The Stroh Brewery Co.
RAINIER ICE - Beverages–malt - The Stroh Brewery Co.
RAINIER L.A. - Beverages–malt - Rainier Brewing Co.
RAINIER LIGHT - Beverages–malt - Rainier Brewing Co.
RAINIER LIGHT - Beverages–malt - The Stroh Brewery Co.
RAINIER LIGHT ICE - Beverages–malt - The Stroh Brewery Co.
RAINIER PEAKS - Beverages–malt - Rainier Brewing Co.
RAINIER YAKIMA RED - Beverages–malt - The Stroh Brewery Co.
RAINLOCK - Aluminum products - Reynolds Metals Co.
RAINMAKER - Computer software ☆ - Queue Inc.
RAINMAKER - Toys–models ☆ - Estes Industries
RAINMAKER - Veterinary medical equipment - Farnam Cos. Inc.

RAINMAKER COLLECTION, THE - Business stationery - All-State International, Inc.
RAINMAN PLUS - Computer software - America Online, Inc.
RAINOLDI - Wines - C. Daniele & Co., Inc.
RAINPROOF - Roofing materials - Protecto Wrap Co.
RAINPULSE - Sprinklers–lawn - L.R. Nelson Corp.
RAINSCAPES - Sprinklers–lawn - L.R. Nelson Corp.
RAINSENSOR - Sprinklers–lawn - Rainmatic Corp.
RAINSHAKER - Umbrellas - Jenuine Performance International, Inc.
RAINSHIELD - Fabrics–polypropylene - Reeves Brothers Inc.
RAINSHIELD - Snowblowers ☆ - CRC Chemicals USA/Siloo
RAINSHOWER - Sprinklers–lawn - L.R. Nelson Corp.
RAINSILK - Health care products ☆ - Shaklee Corp.
RAINSOFT - Filters–industrial - RainSoft Water Conditioning Co.
RAINSONG - Pipes–iron - Hoechst Celanese Corp.
RAINSTOPPERS - Umbrellas - World Import Co., Inc.
RAINSTORM - Bathroom fixtures - Frank M. Baroudi
RAINSWEET - Water–bottled or canned ☆ - Universal Beverages, Inc.
RAINSWIRL - Sprinklers–lawn - L.R. Nelson Corp.
RAINTIGHT - Chemical preparations - Sealoflex Inc.
RAINTITE - Adhesives and sealants - Leech Products Inc.
RAINTITE - Paints - Dozier & Gay Paint Co.
RAINTREE - Cabinets ☆ - Karman Kitchens Inc.
RAINTREE - Frames–eyeglass - Pathway Optical Prods.
RAINTREE - Skin care products - Richardson-Vicks USA
RAINTREE DESIGNS/CAMEO - Wallpaper - Bart Klion & Associates Inc.
RAINVUE - Glass cleaner - Sunshire Manufacturing
RAINWALKERS - Pet products - Doggie-Sox Manufacturing Co.
RAINWATER - Hair care products - Levlab, Inc.
RAINWAVE - Sprinklers–lawn ☆ - Melnor Inc.
RAINY DAY - Flowers, plants, and seeds - Seed Corp. of America
RAINY DAY FOODS - Food products - Rainy Day Foods
RAINY DAY FUN - Computer software ☆ - Penny & Giles Data Systems
RAINY DAY RED - Lipsticks ☆ - Honey & Spice Toiletries
RAIS - Computer peripheral equipment - On-Demand Technologies, Inc.
RAISE-N-TILT - Projection screens ☆ - Brandons Inc.
RAISE PH - Chemical preparations - Wardley Corp.
RAISE THE BAR - Beverages - Coca-Cola Co.
RAISE THE TITANIC - Games - Brown and Bigelow Inc.
RAISED A - Doughnuts–mixes - Dawn Food Products Inc.
RAISED IN THE SUN - Wallpaper ☆ - Marburg Wallcoverings Inc.
RAISED PANEL - Cabinets - Scott Manufacturing, Inc.
RAISER'S EDGE, THE - Computer software - Blackbaud, Inc.
RAISIN BRAN - Cereal - New Morning
RAISIN BRAN-FLAX/OMEGA3 - Cereal - New Morn, Inc.
RAISIN' CANE - Oats–rolled or meal - National Oats Co. Inc.
RAISIN DIPS - Candy - Nabisco Brands Co.
RAISIN GRAHAM MUESLI - Cereal - Breadshop's Natural Foods
RAISIN LIFE - Cereal ☆ - Quaker Oats Co.
RAISIN MANIA - Snack foods - American Grains
RAISIN NUT BRAN - Cereal - General Mills, Inc.
RAISIN NUT JOYS - Nuts–candied - Glico Harmony Foods Corp.
RAISIN OATIES - Cookies ☆ - Nanak's Gourmet Cookies
RAISIN RUCKUS - Cookies ☆ - Keebler Co.
RAISIN SESAME CHEW - Food products - Honeypot Treats
RAISIN SQUARES - Cereal - Kellogg Co.
RAISINETS - Candy - Nestle USA
RAISING CANES - Canes - Raising Canes, LLC
RAISINLAND - Raisins - Sunshine Raisin Corp.
RAISINMATE - Juices - David Michael & Co.
RAISINOATS - Cereal - National Oats Co. Inc.
RAISINS - Bathing suits - Raisin Co., Inc.
RAISINS RICE & RYE - Cereal ☆ - Kellogg Co.
RAISINUTS - Snack foods - National Raisin Co.
RAISSA - Jewelry - Raissa Corp.
RAIT - Video tapes–blank - Madison L. Kilpatrick
RAITEK - Watches ☆ - Helbros International
RAIZOFF - Paint removers - United Gilsonite Laboratories
RAIZOR - Toys - Tonka Corp.
RAJ MAHAL - Breads - Omega Foods, Inc.
RAJA - Cigarettes - James B. Russell Inc.
RAJA - Floor coverings–carpet and rugs - Gloria of America Inc.
RAJA - Floor coverings–carpet and rugs ☆ - Trans-Ocean Import Co. Inc.
RAJA PASTELS - Floor coverings–carpet and rugs ☆ - Interloom Ltd.
RAJAH - Boats–motor - Seajay Boats Inc.
RAJAH - Erasers ☆ - Bright Boy Abrasives

RAJAH - File folders ☆ - File-A-Dex Inc.
RAJAH - Tiles–ceramic ☆ - Latco Products
RAJAH CUSTOM - Boats–motor - Seajay Boats Inc.
RAJAN - Cleaning preparations - Rajan Paul
RAJOC - Hair care products - Rajoc International
RAK-IT - Pet products - Aaronco Grooming Products
RAK-ITEER - Pet products - Aaronco Grooming Products
RAKASHAN - Fabrics - Dan River Inc.
RAKE - Footwear–athletic ☆ - Nike, Inc.
RAKE - Frames–eyeglass - Zylo Ware Corp.
RAKE - Hair care products - Major International Inc.
RAKE-AWAY - Garden equipment - Geo. W. McGuire Co. Inc.
RAKE-INVERTER - Farm machinery - Pequea Machine Inc.
RAKE MASTER - Razors - C.A. Daniels & Co.
RAKE MATE - Tools–garden - Emsco Inc.
RAKE-N-HOE - Tools - Granberg International
RAKE THAT SWEEPS, THE - Tools–garden - Uniontools, Inc.
RAKE, THE - Golfing equipment - Northwestern Golf Co.
RAKE, THE - Bicycle parts and accessories - Scott USA Inc.
RAKER III - Saws–chain - Homelite, Inc.
RAKE'S PROGRESS, THE - Recording label - Rake's Progress, Inc.
RAKIBOONE - Toys–stuffed ☆ - Gund, Inc.
RAKKASAH - Dance studios - Shirley A. De Vine
RAKKRATE - Electronic equipment - Efxx Products Co.
RAKKS - Shelving units–metal - Rangine Corp.
RAKU - Nail care products ☆ - Peau Corp.
RAL - Recording label - Rush Associated Labels, Inc.
RALCO - Watches - Movado Time Corp.
RALEIGH - Bicycles - Raleigh USA Bicycle Co.
RALEIGH - Cabinets ☆ - Marsh Furniture Co.
RALEIGH - Cigarettes - Brown & Williamson Tobacco Corp.
RALEIGH - Floor coverings - Congoleum Corp.
RALEIGH - Furniture ☆ - Universal Flooring
RALEIGH - Paints - Wyckoff Paint & Wallpaper Co.
RALEIGH - Tableware–china ☆ - Lenox, Inc.
RALEIGH - Thread - Elmore-Pisgah, Inc.
RALEIGH BICYCLES - Bicycles - Derby Cycle Corp.
RALEIGH COURT - Furniture - Vaughan Furniture Co. Inc.
RALEIGH ENTERPRISES - Women's apparel and handbags - Raleigh Enterprises
RALEIGH LIGHTS - Cigarettes - Brown & Williamson Tobacco Corp.
RALI - Computer software - Smith Advanced Technology, Inc.
RALIENT - Footwear - Vans, Inc.
RALLEE - Coats - PD Fashions, Inc.
RALLINER SCULPTURE - Statuary ☆ - Ideal Originals
RALLO MARSALA - Wines - Banfi Vintners
RALLY - Aircraft–balloons - Raven Industries Inc.
RALLY - Catheters - Scimed Life Systems, Inc.
RALLY - Cleaning preparations - Armor All Products Corp.
RALLY! - Computer software - Attachmate Corp.
RALLY - Flashlights ☆ - Wonder Corp. of America
RALLY - Floor coverings–carpet and rugs - Barrett Carpet Mills Inc.
RALLY - Floor coverings–carpet and rugs - Dan River Inc.
RALLY - Floor coverings–carpet and rugs - Philadelphia Carpets
RALLY - Flowers, plants, and seeds - Panamerican Seed
RALLY - Furniture - Collingwood Furniture
RALLY - Lawn mowers - White Consolidated Industries, Inc.
RALLY - Luggage ☆ - American Tourister, Inc.
RALLY - Motor vehicle dealers - General Motors Corp.
RALLY - Pens - Gillette Co.
RALLY - Shoes–athletic ☆ - Brookfield Athletic Co. Inc.
RALLY - Sporting goods - Ashaway Line & Twine Manufacturing Co.
RALLY - Vacuum cleaners and accessories - The Eureka Co.
RALLY - Vitamins and nutritional supplements - Paonia Enterprises, Inc.
RALLY - Watches - Viva Time Corp.
RALLY-20 - Veterinary pharmaceutical preparations - Vedco, Inc.
RALLY 24 - Bicycles - Raleigh USA Bicycle Co.
RALLY/ALL-SPORTS - Shoes–athletic ☆ - Brookfield Athletic Co. Inc.
RALLY/BOBBY ORR - Skates–ice ☆ - Brookfield Athletic Co. Inc.
RALLY GYM - Finishing agents - Hillyard Enterprises, Inc.
RALLY KING - Trailers–travel ☆ - Shasta Industries Inc.
RALLY RACKS - Bicycle parts and accessories - Rally Racks (Division of GNI)
RALLY RAGS - Flags - Concepts, Inc.
RALLY STRIPE - Amplifiers ☆ - International Music Corp.
RALLY SUPER-GRIP - Automotive parts and accessories - Rally Manufacturing, Inc.

☆ = Now out of production

RALLY TILE - Tile and mats - Matworks
RALLYBALL - Sporting goods - General Sportcraft Co. Ltd.
RALLYE - Binoculars - Pioneer Marketing & Research, Inc.
RALLYE - Oils–lubricating - Petroleum Packers, Inc.
RALLYE - Tires - Uniroyal Goodrich Tire Co.
RALLYE - Watches - Hampden Corp.
RALLYE 280 - Tires - Uniroyal Goodrich Tire Co.
RALLYE 340 - Tires - Uniroyal Goodrich Tire Co.
RALLYE GT - Tires - Uniroyal Goodrich Tire Co.
RALLYE GTI - Motor vehicles–automobiles - Volkswagen of America Inc.
RALLYE HP - Tires - Uniroyal Goodrich Tire Co.
RALLY'S - Fast-food franchise - Rally's, Inc.
RALPH - Apparel–women's - Polo Ralph Lauren Corp.
RALPH - Recording label - T.E.C. Tones/Ralph Records
RALPH KRAMDEN - Dolls ☆ - Effanbee Doll Corp.
RALPH LAUREN - Apparel and accessories - Polo Ralph Lauren Corp.
RALPH LAUREN - Boots ☆ - Acme Boot Co., Inc.
RALPH LAUREN - Cosmetics - Cosmair Inc.
RALPH LAUREN - Furniture - West Point-Pepperell Inc.
RALPH LAUREN - Hats - Hat Attack, Inc.
RALPH LAUREN - Hosiery–women's - Hot Sox Co. Inc. Ralph Lauren Hosiery Div.
RALPH LAUREN - Paints - Polo Ralph Lauren, LP
RALPH LAUREN - Shirts - Morgan Shirt Corp.
RALPH LAUREN - Sunglasses - Optique du Monde Ltd.
RALPH LAUREN - Wallpaper ☆ - Motif Designs, Inc.
RALPH LAUREN FLORAL COLLECTION - Wallpaper - Capital Carousel Inc.
RALPH LAUREN HOME COLLECTION - Wallpaper - Capital Carousel Inc.
RALPH LAUREN SHIRTINGS & STRIPES - Wallpaper - Capital Carousel Inc.
RALPH LAUREN STRIPES & TARTANS - Wallpaper ☆ - Motif Designs, Inc.
RALPH #MARLIN - Apparel–men's - Ralph Marlin & Co., Inc.
RALPH MONTENERO FOR BLANCHE - Apparel–women's ☆ - Blanche
RALPH RALPH LAUREN - Apparel–women's - Polo Ralph Lauren Corp.
RALPH SNART - Publisher's imprints - Caputo Publishing Inc.
RALPHIE - Fruits and vegetables - Legumbres San Francisco Spr-Rl
RALPHIE - Toys–stuffed ☆ - Dakin Inc.
RALPHIE'S - Pet food - Bel Air Food Technology Corp.
RALPH'S - Fruit and vegetable markets ☆ - Sundquist Fruit & Cold Storage
RALPH'S - Snuff - American Maize-Products Co.
RALPH'S - Spices and extracts - Ralph's Foods Co.
RALPHS CALIFORNIA BEEF - Meat products–beef - Ralphs Grocery Co.
RALPH'S PREMIUM - Spices and extracts - Ralph's Foods Co.
RALPHY RACCOON - Puppets - Dakin Inc.
RALSTON - Pet products - Ralston Purina Co.
RALSTON BLEND - Animal feeds - Ralston Purina Co.
RALSTON FOODS - Cereal - Ralston Foods, Inc.
RALSTON PARK - Floor coverings ☆ - Congoleum Corp.
RALSTON-PURINA - Food products - Ralston Purina Co.
RALSTON RATIONS - Animal feeds - Ralston Purina Co.
RALSTON STAX - Crackers - Ralston Purina Co.
RAM - Amplifiers–radio - Semita Corp.
RAM - Batteries ☆ - Rayovac Corp.
RAM - Bicycles - Columbia Manufacturing Inc.
RAM - Chemical preparations - Ram Chemical & Supply, Inc.
RAM - Dropcloths - Olympic General Corp.
RAM - Electrical equipment - Ram Products, Inc.
RAM! - Games ☆ - Avalon Hill Game Co.
RAM - Golfing equipment - Ram Golf Corp.
RAM - Motor vehicles–trucks - Chrysler Corp. (Dodge Truck Div.)
RAM - Office furniture–metal ☆ - Martin Industries, Inc.
RAM - Ophthalmic goods - Embassy Creations Inc.
RAM - Pharmaceutical preparations ☆ - Scrip-Physician Supply Co.
RAM - Polyethylene tubing - Netafim Irrigation, Inc.
RAM - Rackets–racquetball ☆ - Right Gard Corp.
RAM 50 - Motor vehicles–trucks ☆ - Chrysler Corp. (Dodge Truck Div.)
RAM 5000 - Motor vehicle parts and accessories ☆ - Carefree of Colorado
RAM-CHAMBER - Manifolds–motor vehicle - James J. Feuling
RAM COACH - Vans–conversion - Kentron Motor Coach Inc.
RAM FIST - Toys - Tonka Corp.
RAM-FLO - Automotive parts and accessories ☆ - Edelbrock Corp.
RAM-FLX - Knapsacks - Coleman Co., Inc.
RAM-GARD - Pipes–plastic - Ramco Manufacturing Co., Inc.
RAM I - Flowers, plants, and seeds - Jacklin Seed
RAM-IE NOVELTYWARE - Computer software - Arieu Productions
RAM INDUCTION - Computer peripheral equipment - Digital Audio Labs, Inc.
RAM JET - Bicycles - Columbia Manufacturing Inc.

RAM JET - Firearms, accessories, and parts - Beeman Precision Airguns
RAM-JET - Ophthalmic goods - Embassy Creations Inc.
RAM-JET - Soldering equipment - Controls Corp. of America
RAM LABS - Tubes–vacuum - GNP Audio Video Inc.
RAM MAN - Toys - Mattel, Inc.
RAM MISER - Motor vehicles–trucks ☆ - Chrysler Corp. (Dodge Truck Div.)
RAM OUT - Drains - Ramco Chemical Inc.
RAM POINT - Firearms, accessories, and parts - Beeman Precision Airguns
RAM RECORDS - Recording label - Warwick Productions, Inc.
RAM-ROD - Bicycles ☆ - Murray, Inc.
RAM RODS - Toys–automobiles - Nylint Toy Corp.
RAM SHOCK - Watches - Timex Corp.
RAM-TIP - Drill bits - Relton Corp.
RAM TOUGH - Gloves - Hawk Enterprises, Inc.
RAM TOUR - Golfing equipment - Ram Golf Corp.
RAM VAN - Motor vehicles–trucks - Chrysler Corp. (Dodge Truck Div.)
RAM WAGON - Motor vehicles–trucks - Chrysler Corp. (Dodge Truck Div.)
RAM-X - Boats–canoes - Coleman Co., Inc.
RAMA - Incense ☆ - Genie Co. Inc.
RAMA - Pasta - Crystal Food Import Corp.
RAMA LEOPARD - Toys–stuffed ☆ - Dakin Inc.
RAMACS - Computer software - Microwave Networks, Inc.
RAMADA - Mobile homes - Skyline Corp.
RAMADA - Trailers–travel - Apache
RAMADA HOTELS - Hotels and motels - Ramada International Hotels & Resorts
RAMADA INNS - Hotels and motels - Ramada International Hotels & Resorts
RAMADA RENAISSANCE HOTELS - Hotels and motels - Ramada International Hotels & Resorts
RAMAGON - Toys ☆ - Bachmann Industries Inc.
RAMANI - Apparel and accessories - Fashion Boom Inc.
RAMANTADINE - Pharmaceutical preparations - Hoffmann-La Roche Inc.
RAMAR - Apparel–men's - Oxford Industries, Inc.
RAMAS - Computer software - Applied Biomathematics
RAMAZZOTTI - Beverages–alcohol - Laird and Co.
RAMBIT - Drill bits ☆ - ITW Ramset/Red Head
RAMBLER - Bicycles - Columbia Manufacturing Inc.
RAMBLER - Knapsacks - Coleman Co., Inc.
RAMBLER - Leather gloves - Boss Manufacturing Co.
RAMBLER - Motor vehicles ☆ - DaimlerChrysler
RAMBLER - Recording label ☆ - Arhoolie Productions Inc.
RAMBLER - Thread - Threads USA Div.
RAMBLER - Watches - Hampden Corp.
RAMBLER DELUXE - Bicycles - Columbia Manufacturing Inc.
RAMBLER ROSE - Glassware–household ☆ - Lotus Glass Co.
RAMBLERS - Women's shoes ☆ - Consolidated Shoe Co., Inc.
RAMBLIN - Recording label ☆ - Rounder Records Corp.
RAMBLIN ROOT BEER - Beverages–carbonated - Coca-Cola Co.
RAMBLIN ROSE - Wines - Foxwood Wine Cellars
RAMBLIN' WRECKER - Toys–automobiles ☆ - Mattel, Inc.
RAMBLING ROSE - Christmas tree ornaments - Cracker Box Inc.
RAMBLING ROSE - Dishes–china - Viletta China Co.
RAMBLING ROSE - Floor coverings–carpet and rugs - Callaway Carpets
RAMBLING ROSE - Veal - Food Animal Concerns Trust
RAMBO - Archery equipment ☆ - Hoyt
RAMBO - Shoes ☆ - Sidney Rich Associates Inc.
RAMBO BLACK FLAK - Chewing gum ☆ - Amurol Confections Co.
RAMBO: FIRST BLOOD PART II - Computer software - Mindscape Software Inc.
RAMBOL - Cheese ☆ - Bongrain Cheese USA
RAMBOUILLET - Apparel and accessories - AAA Uniforms, Inc.
RAMCHARGER - Motor vehicles–automobiles - DaimlerChrysler
RAMCHECK - Electronic equipment - Innoventions, Inc.
RAMCO - Automotive parts and accessories - Sealed Power Technology
RAMCO - Office supplies - Seminole Paper & Printing Co.
RAMDRILL - Self-drilling anchors ☆ - ITW Ramset/Red Head
RAMEKINS - Dinnerware–glass - Prolon Dinnerware
RAMEN PRIDE - Soups–mixes - Sanwa Foods Inc.
RAMEN PRIDE GOLD - Soups–mixes - Sanwa Foods Inc.
RAMEN SOUP IN A CUP - Soups–mixes - Sanwa Foods Inc.
RAMER - Sporting goods - Ramer Products, Ltd.
RAMERO - Boats–motor ☆ - Rinker Boat Co. Inc.
RAMESES II - Cigarettes - G.A. Georgopulo & Co. Inc.
RAMI - Antennas - R.A. Miller, Industries, Inc.
RAMIAH RECORDS - Recording label - Virgil Hensley Publications
RAMIK - Rodenticides - Hacco, Inc./Loveland Industries, Inc.

☆ = Now out of production

RAMIK BAR BAIT - Rodenticides - Hacco, Inc./Loveland Industries, Inc.
RAMIK MINI BARS - Rodenticides - Hacco, Inc./Loveland Industries, Inc.
RAMIK MOUSER - Rodenticides - Hacco, Inc./Loveland Industries, Inc.
RAMILOSA - Water–mineral - Firesteed Corp.
RAMIREZ - Guitars ☆ - Dauphin Co.
RAMIREZ & FERAUD - Chili–canned - Pet Inc.
RAMJET - Toys–models ☆ - Estes Industries
RAMLINE - Guns - Blount International, Inc. (Sporting Equipment Group)
RAMM STYLES - Uniforms–tailored - Ramm Styles Inc.
RAMM STYLES, INC. - Apparel and accessories - Ramm Styles Inc.
RAMO-O-PINE - Cleaning preparations - Ramco Chemical Inc.
RAMODI'S - Bedding–linen - Ramodi's
RAMODS - Pipes–tobacco - Ramodi's
RAMOLITE - Paints ☆ - Verflex Co. Inc.
RAMON ALLONES - Cigars - Avanti Cigar Co.
RAMONA - Flatware - Yamazaki Tableware Inc.
RAMONA - Food products - Markel-Johnson Poultry Co.
RAMONA - Frames–eyeglass ☆ - Universal/Univis Inc.
RAMONA - Glass–leaded - Seneca Glass Co.
RAMONA - Rings–jewelry - Artcarved Inc.
RAMONA - Water–bottled or canned - Famous Ramona Water Inc.
RAMONA GOLD ACCENT - Flatware - Yamazaki Tableware Inc.
RAMONA GOLD/BLACK - Flatware - Yamazaki Tableware Inc.
RAMONA WAY - Floor coverings–carpet and rugs ☆ - Hollytex Carpet Mills Inc.
RAMONA'S LOVE CHARM STRING - Musical instrument accessories - Max Roisman
RAMON'S - Pharmaceutical preparations - Brown Manufacturing Co.
RAMONT'S - Hobby kits - Mangelsen's (VDI)
RAMP FEET - Rubber anti-slip device - Universal Industrial Products Co.
RAMP-KING - Sporting goods - Cut 'n Jump Ski Corp.
RAMP SYSTEMS - Ramps - Ramp Systems, Inc.
RAMP TRACK - Ramps - Core Industries, Inc.
RAMP TRACK - Steel traction plates - Universal Industrial Products Co.
RAMPAGE - Apparel and accessories - Rampage Clothing Co.
RAMPAGE - Bathing suits - Authentic Fitness Corp.
RAMPAGE - Bicycles ☆ - Kent International Inc.
RAMPAGE - Boats - Glen-L Marine Designs
RAMPAGE - Eyeglasses - Art-Craft Optical Co.
RAMPAGE - Floor coverings–carpet and rugs ☆ - Calladium & Marglen
RAMPAGE - Motor vehicles–trucks ☆ - Chrysler Corp. (Dodge Truck Div.)
RAMPAGE - Rodenticides - Motomco Ltd.
RAMPAGE - Toys–models - Estes Industries
RAMPAGE 2.2 - Motor vehicles–trucks ☆ - Chrysler Corp. (Dodge Truck Div.)
RAMPAR - Bicycles ☆ - Raleigh USA Bicycle Co.
RAMPART - Alarm systems–burglar - Rampart Corp.
RAMPART - Medical apparatus - Rampart Glove Co., Inc.
RAMPART - Ophthalmic goods - Foremost Optical Products
RAMPART - Recording label - Gordo Enterprises
RAMPART - Shingles ☆ - Manville/Schuller
RAMPART - Thread - Threads USA Div.
RAMPARTS - Pumps - Gorman-Rupp Co.
RAMPBALL - Games - Way to Play, Inc.
RAMPED EDGE - Mats - Tenex Corp.
RAMPER - Concrete products - Precast Reddi-Ramp, Inc.
RAMPLUS - Computer software - Forefront/Allmciro, Inc.
RAMPMASTER - Electrical equipment - Evenheat Kiln, Inc.
RAMPON - Health care products - Kendall Co.
RAMPRO - Trash compactors–household - Marathon Equipment Co.
RAMPWAY - Aircraft - Ramp International, Inc.
RAMROD - Apparel and accessories ☆ - Wonderknit
RAMROD - Cigars - Avanti Cigar Co.
RAMROD - Ophthalmic goods - Foremost Optical Products
RAMROD - Vitamins and nutritional supplements - Church and Dwight Co. Inc.
RAMROD COMPETITION 4 - Automotive parts and accessories ☆ - Hurst Performance Inc.
RAMS - Furniture - Robert A.M. Stern Architects
RAMS - Spectrometers - Marquette Electronics, Inc.
RAM'S HEAD - Paints ☆ - Verflex Co. Inc.
RAM'S HORN - Bicycles - Schwinn Cycling & Fitness Inc.
RAM'S HORN - Tobacco products - Scott Tobacco Co.
RAMSA - Amplifiers–musical instrument - Panasonic Co.
RAMSAVER - Computer software - DP-Tek, Inc.
RAMSDELL'S - Sulfides ☆ - E. Fougera & Co. Inc.
RAMSEN - Frames–eyeglass ☆ - Universal/Univis Inc.
RAMSES - Floor coverings–carpet and rugs ☆ - Foreign Accents

RAMSES - Prophylactics - London International U.S. Holdings
RAMSES - Prophylactics - Schmid Laboratories
RAMSES EXTRA - Prophylactics - London International U.S. Holdings
RAMSES EXTRA - Prophylactics - Schmid Laboratories
RAMSES PERSONAL SPERMICIDAL LUBRICANT - Lubricants - London International U.S. Holdings
RAMSES SENSITOL - Prophylactics - London International U.S. Holdings
RAMSES ULTRA - Prophylactics - London International U.S. Holdings
RAMSET - Powder tools and fastening systems - ITW Ramset/Red Head
RAMSEY - Toys–stuffed ☆ - Gund, Inc.
RAMSEY CREATED CLASSICS - Jewelry - RGI, Inc.
RAMSGATE - Floor coverings–carpet and rugs - Collins & Aikman Corp.
RAMSGATE - Floor coverings–carpet and rugs - Patcraft Mills Inc.
RAMSGATE PARK - Floor coverings–carpet and rugs ☆ - Lees Carpets
RAMSHORN - Varnishes ☆ - Valspar Corp.
RAMSS - Computer software - Ramss, Inc.
RAMSTEEL - Computer software - Ram Analysis, LLC
RAMTRON - Integrated circuits - Ramtron International Corp.
RAMU - Frames–eyeglass - May Optical Co. Inc.
RAMUC - Paints - Republic Powdered Metals, Inc.
RAN 64/25 - Modems - Multipoint Networks, Inc.
RANAE'S - Glue–household or industrial - Utah Craft & Floral Supply
RANALLY - Maps ☆ - Rand McNally & Co.
RANAREX - Industrial machinery ☆ - Permutit Co. Inc.
RANAX - Electric lighting equipment - Lutron Electronics Co., Inc.
RANBO - Recording label - Destiny Records
RANCAN - Cymbals - LP Music Group
RANCE - Ophthalmic goods - Embassy Creations Inc.
RANCH - Cabinets ☆ - Haas Cabinet Co. Inc.
RANCH - Floor coverings - Bruce Hardwood Floors
RANCH - Meat products–beef - Thompson Packers Inc.
RANCH BRAND - Meat products - John Morrell & Co.
RANCH BURGER - Hamburger - American Ideas Inc.
RANCH-COTE - Paints - Martin Paint Stores
RANCH COUNTRY - Furniture ☆ - A. Brandt Co. Inc.
RANCH FLAVORED - Tortillas - Guiltless Gourmet, Inc.
RANCH FRIES - Potato chips - Borden, Inc.
RANCH GIRL - Candy - Pangburn Candy Co.
RANCH HAND - Animal feeds - Purina Mills, Inc.
RANCH HAND - Bumpers–motor vehicle - C.P.M. Inc.
RANCH HAND - Meat products–beef - Ranch Hand Foods Inc.
RANCH HAND - Paints - Ponderosa Paint Manufacturing Co. Inc.
RANCH HAND - Pumps ☆ - Simer Pump Co.
RANCH HOUSE - Cutlery - Washington Forge Inc.
RANCH HOUSE - Food products - Old Ranchers Canning Co. Inc.
RANCH HOUSE - Food products ☆ - Universal Frozen Foods Co.
RANCH HOUSE - Meat products–beef - K-Bob's USA, Inc.
RANCH HOUSE - Paints - Lightning Adhesives
RANCH HOUSE - Salt - United Salt Corp.
RANCH KING - Saddles - Livestock Supply Co., Inc.
RANCH LIFE - Paints ☆ - Sinclair Paint Co.
RANCH MASTER - Metals - Behlen Manufacturing Co.
RANCH OAK - Furniture - A. Brandt Co. Inc.
RANCH OVEN - Food products - Golden Pantry West Inc.
RANCH PAL - Footwear - Southern Leather & Shoe Co.
RANCH RED - Paints - Morris Paint & Varnish Co.
RANCH RHYTHM - Candy - Pangburn Candy Co.
RANCH-SKOS - Ophthalmic goods - Embassy Creations Inc.
RANCH SLIMS - Vegetables–frozen ☆ - J.R. Simplot Co.
RANCH STYLE - Canned foods - American Home Food Products Inc.
RANCH, THE - Pizzas–frozen - Snappy Tomato Pizza Co.
RANCH WAGON - Foil–aluminum - Trinidad/Benham Holding Co.
RANCH WAGON - Food products - Landshire Food Service Inc.
RANCH WAGON - Trailers–travel - Franklin Coach Co.
RANCHAND - Trailers–horse - Wegner Manufacturing Inc.
RANCHCRAFT - Apparel and accessories - J.C. Penney Co., Inc.
RANCHER - Boots - Nocona Boot Co. Inc.
RANCHER - Building materials - Behlen Manufacturing Co.
RANCHER - Cabinets - Imperial Cabinet Co. Inc.
RANCHER - Doors–garage - Clopay Millwork
RANCHER - Guitars ☆ - Fred Gretsch Enterprises
RANCHER - Ladders–metal - John S. Tilley Ladders Co. Inc.
RANCHER - Lawn mowers - Alamo Group
RANCHERO - Apparel and accessories - Movses Ourfalian
RANCHERO - Floor coverings - Mannington Resilient Floors
RANCHERO - Floor coverings ☆ - Congoleum Corp.

☆ = Now out of production

RANCHERO - Floor coverings–carpet and rugs - Mohawk Carpet Corp.
RANCHERO - Food products - Campbell Soup Co.
RANCHERO - Frames–eyeglass - Liberty Optical Manufacturing Co.
RANCHERO - Mail boxes - Steel City Corp.
RANCHERO - Manufactured homes - Redman Industries, Inc.
RANCHERO - Motor vehicles–automobiles ☆ - Ford Motor Co.
RANCHERO - Paints - Jones Blair Co.
RANCHERO - Recording label - Musimex Inc.
RANCHERO - Sauces - Otto Knuper
RANCHERO GRANDE - Manufactured homes - Redman Industries, Inc.
RANCHER'S BRAND - Flowers, plants, and seeds - Missouri Southern Seed Corp.
RANCHER'S CHOICE - Animal feeds - Bluebonnet Milling Co.
RANCHER'S CHOICE - Salad dressings–bottled - Kraft Foods, Inc.
RANCHETTES - Sausages ☆ - Schweigert Foods
RANCHGUARD - Siding–metal - Georgia-Pacific Corp.
RANCHMASTER - Building materials - Behlen Manufacturing Co.
RANCHO - Cigars - A.J. Golden Inc.
RANCHO - Paints - Dunn Edwards Corp.
RANCHO - Trailers–travel - Rancho Trailers Inc.
RANCHO - Watches - North American Watch Corp.
RANCHO CALIFORNIA - Fruits and vegetables - Dole Citrus
RANCHO DE PHILO - Beverages–alcohol - Rancho de Philo
RANCHO DEL MAR - Food products - Richard A. Shaw Inc.
RANCHO DEL SOL - Tortillas - Mexpro Foods, Inc.
RANCHO DELUXE - Apparel - Calor Apparel Group International Corp.
RANCHO DOLORES - Fruits–dried - Roberts Fig Co.
RANCHO EL RAE - Trailers–travel - Rancho Trailers Inc.
RANCHO FIESTA - Food products - Richard A. Shaw Inc.
RANCHO HUES - Finishing agents - Dunn Edwards Corp.
RANCHO SAN JULIAN - Beef - James Poett
RANCHO SAN PABLO - Fruit and vegetable markets - PGL Produce, Inc.
RANCHO SANTA FE - Apparel–men's - Stage II Apparel Corp.
RANCHO SISQUOC - Wines - Rancho Sisquoc Winery
RANCHO TEMECULA - Wines ☆ - Mount Palomar Winery Inc.
RANCHO TIERRA VINEYARDS - Wines - Sabrina Importers Ltd.
RANCHTILE - Floor coverings - Congoleum Corp.
RANCHTONE - Paints - Mautz Paint Co.
RANCHWOOD - Siding–insulating - Bird Inc.
RANCHWOOD - Varnishes - Olympic Paint & Varnish Co.
RANCO - Timers–appliance - Robertshaw Controls Co.
RANCOR - Toys - Lucasfilm Ltd.
RAND - Medical apparatus - Luminaud Inc.
RAND MCNALLY - Maps - Natural Color Cards Co.
RAND MCNALLY & CO. - Publisher's imprints - Rand McNally & Co.
RAND MCNALLY MAP PUZZLES - Puzzles - Milton Bradley Co.
RAND-O-PLATE - Paints - Randolph Products Co.
RAND-O-POLY - Paints - Randolph Products Co.
RANDA - Clothing ☆ - Randa Corp.
RANDACRYL - Paints - Randolph Products Co.
RANDALL - Amplifiers–musical instrument - Washburn International
RANDALL - Door frames - Randall Manufacturing Co.
RANDALL - Food products - Randall Food Products Inc.
RANDALL MONROE - Wines - Codera Wine Group
RANDALL'S - See MR. NEATS
RANDALL'S - Food products - Randall's Food Markets Inc.
RANDALL'S - Meat - Levy Food Service L.P.
RANDAN - Recording label - Daran Records
RANDAX - Electronic equipment - GAF Corp.
R&B LIVE - Apparel and accessories - R & B Live, Inc.
R&D - Boats - Rudy G. Dickinson
R&D RACING PRODUCTS U.S.A. - Motor vehicle parts and accessories - Rudy G. Dickinson
RANDERSACKER - Beverages–malt ☆ - Pabst Brewing Co.
RANDINO - Fabrics - Dan River Inc.
RANDIX - Electronic equipment - Randix Industries Inc.
R&M MATERIALS HANDLING INC. - Cranes - R & M Materials Handling, Inc.
RANDMARK - Maps ☆ - Rand McNally & Co.
R&O - Seafood products–fresh or frozen - Darik Enterprises Inc.
RANDOLPH - Furniture - Boling Co.
RANDOLPH - Paints - California Hardware Co.
RANDOLPH - Socks ☆ - Leininger Mills Inc.
RANDOLPH AQUA-LAC - Paints - Randolph Products Co.
RANDOM - Clocks ☆ - General Time Corp. (Westclox/Seth Thomas Div.)
RANDOM - Frames–eyeglass - Liberty Optical Manufacturing Co.
RANDOM - Recording label - Random Enterprises Inc.

RANDOM CRICKET - Electronic dart game - Medalist Marketing Corp.
RANDOM FIELDS - Floor coverings - Mannington Resilient Floors
RANDOM GEAR - Apparel and accessories - R & S Marketing
RANDOM HOUSE - Publisher's imprints - Random House, Inc.
RANDOM HOUSE AUDIOBOOKS - Recording label - Random House Audio Publishing Inc.
RANDOM HOUSE CHILDREN'S M-E-D-I-A - Computer software - Random House, Inc.
RANDOM HOUSE ELECTRONIC PUBLISHING - Compact discs–prerecorded - Random House, Inc.
RANDOM HOUSE ENCYCLOPEDIA - Computer software - Microlytics Inc.
RANDOM HOUSE MASTERPIECE CROSSWORDS - Publisher's imprints - Random House, Inc.
RANDOM HOUSE PROOFREADER - Computer software - Digital Marketing Corp.
RANDOM KRINKLE - Wallpaper - Wolf-Gordon Inc.
RANDOM LEAVES - Dishes–china - Taylor, Smith & Taylor Co.
RANDOM MARBLES - Floor coverings–tile ☆ - Kentile Floors Inc.
RANDOM MOUNT - Frames–picture - C.R. Gibson Co.
RANDOM PLANK - Floor coverings - Azrock Commercial Flooring
RANDOM RIB - Wallpaper - Capital Carousel Inc.
RANDOM ROSE - Floor coverings ☆ - Congoleum Corp.
RANDOM SNOWBOARDS - Snowboards - Random Snowboards
RANDOM WEAVE - Stationery ☆ - Berkshire Stationery Inc.
RANDOMIZER, THE - Publisher's imprints - Reader's Digest Association, Inc.
RANDONEE - Bicycles - REI
RANDOR - Bicycles - Rand International, Inc.
RANDSFJORD - Glassware–household ☆ - Kuhn Concepts
RANDY - Dolls - Horsman
RANDY - Toys–stuffed - Russ Berrie and Co., Inc.
RANDY RACCOON - Toys–stuffed - Russ Berrie and Co., Inc.
RANDY RICK - Hair care products - R & R International Corp.
RANDY WITH LOVE - Clothing - L'Koral Inc.
RANDY'S - Meat products–beef - Ranch Hand Foods Inc.
RANDY'S FAVORITE - Rice ☆ - Falcon Rice Mill Inc.
RANETITE - Paints - Ranetite Manufacturing Co. Inc.
RANEWARE - Computer software - Rane Corp.
RANEY FLEXION - Health care products - Camp, Inc.
RANEY RECORDS - Recording label - Raney Records, Inc.
RANFAC - Medical apparatus - Ranfac Corp.
RANG - Candy - H. Hamstra & Co.
RANGAIRE - Stoves - Rangaire
RANGE - Footwear - Olem Shoe Corp.
RANGE - Meat products–pork - Hormel Foods Corp.
RANGE 1 - Games - Gamescience
RANGE B BREEDER - Animal feeds - Bluebonnet Milling Co.
RANGE BOSS - Automotive parts and accessories - Range Boss, LLC
RANGE BOSS - Electronic equipment - Astro-Med Inc.
RANGE BRAND - Grass seed - Olds Seed Co.
RANGE BUSTER - Recording label - Stardust/Wizard/Doss Records
RANGE EXTENDER - Radios–citizens' band - Royal Sound Co. Inc.
RANGE EXTENDO - Antennas - Wintenna Inc.
RANGE-FINDER - Golfing equipment ☆ - Double Products Co.
RANGE KLEEN - Pans - Range Kleen Manufacturing Inc.
RANGE MASTER - Antennas - Wintenna Inc.
RANGE MATE - Golfing equipment - Western Golf Inc.
RANGE MODIFIER - Animal feeds - Texas Farm Products Co.
RANGE POLE - Tools - David White Inc.
RANGE PRO - Cooking utensils–aluminum ☆ - Himark Enterprises Inc.
RANGE PUP - Dog food - Hubbard Milling Co. (Landon Div.)
RANGE RIDER - Tires - Goodyear Tire & Rubber Co.
RANGE RIFLE - Guns–BB - Daisy Manufacturing Co.
RANGE RINGS - Jewelry - William J. Cronin Goldsmith Ltd.
RANGE ROVER - Motor vehicles–all-terrain - Land Rover North America Inc.
RANGE RUNNER - Bicycles - Roadmaster Corp.
RANGE STAR - Animal feeds - Texas Farm Products Co.
RANGE-TO-TABLE - Cooking utensils–aluminum - Revere Ware Corp.
RANGE TOP-TWO - Cooking equipment–household - R & M Hydrotherm
RANGE TOPPERS - Cookware, servingware, storage containers ☆ - Corning Inc.
RANGELEY - Footwear ☆ - G.H. Bass and Co.
RANGEMASTER - Binoculars ☆ - Bausch & Lomb Inc.
RANGEMASTER - Guns - Remington Arms Co., Inc.
RANGEMASTER - Sporting goods - Blount International, Inc. (Sporting Equipment Group)
RANGEMATIC - Lighting equipment–aircraft - Ranging Inc.

☆ = Now out of production

RANGEN - Fertilizers - Rangen, Inc.
RANGER - See **REGENCY R/S**
RANGER - Ammunition - Olin Corp. (Winchester Div.)
RANGER - Apparel and accessories - Irina Stuart
RANGER - Ashtrays–glass - Ashtray Specialty Co./Marion Products Co.
RANGER - Boats ☆ - Alumitech Inc.
RANGER - Boats–motor ☆ - Cobia Boat Co.
RANGER - Boats–motor ☆ - Marathon Boat Group, Inc.
RANGER - Cigars - General Cigar Co., Inc.
RANGER - Computer software - Graymark International, Inc.
RANGER - Drafting supplies - Mayline/Hamilton
RANGER - Electrical equipment - Thomas & Betts Holdings, Inc.
RANGER - Fabrics - Uniroyal Engineered Products
RANGER - Firearms, accessories, and parts - Welsh Sporting Goods Corp.
  (Boyt Div.)
RANGER - Floor coverings–carpet and rugs - Masterpiece Finishing Co.
RANGER - Gloves - Knoxville Glove Co.
RANGER - Health care products - Ranger All Season Corp.
RANGER - Heating equipment - Suburban Manufacturing Co.
RANGER - Knives–pocket - Colonial Knife Co. Inc.
RANGER - Lighting fixtures - Kenall Manufacturing Co.
RANGER - Microphones - Shure Brothers, Inc.
RANGER - Mops - Piedmont Mop Co.
RANGER - Motor vehicle parts and accessories - Seats Inc.
RANGER - Motor vehicles–trucks - Ford Motor Co.
RANGER - Motorcycles ☆ - Suzuki of America Automotive Corp.
RANGER - Paint sprayers - Speeflo Manufacturing Corp.
RANGER - Paints - Jones Blair Co.
RANGER - Pencil sharpeners ☆ - Hunt Manufacturing Co.
RANGER - Pet products - Reflex Corp.
RANGER - Pork - AMK for Service
RANGER - Projectiles–mortar ☆ - Nationwide Sound Distributors
RANGER - Radar systems and equipment - Crown Plastics Inc.
RANGER - Recording label - Forrest Green Enterprises Inc.
RANGER - Roofing materials - Texas Aluminum Industries Inc.
RANGER - Shelving units–metal ☆ - Frontier Storage Systems Inc.
RANGER - Shoes ☆ - Endicott Johnson Corp.
RANGER - Sporting goods - Shakespeare Fishing Tackle
RANGER - Stoves ☆ - Rangaire
RANGER - Telephones - At&T Corp.
RANGER - Telescopes - Tele Vue Optics Inc.
RANGER - Tools - Railway Handle Corp.
RANGER - Tools - Swan Handle Corp.
RANGER - Toys–models ☆ - Estes Industries
RANGER - Trading cards and stamps - Malibu Comics Entertainment, Inc.
RANGER - Trailers–travel - Apache
RANGER - Truck cabs - Ranger Industries
RANGER - Trumpets ☆ - Deg Music Products Inc.
RANGER - Vacuum cleaners and accessories–commercial - Baracuda
  International Corp.
RANGER - Wallets ☆ - Westerman Manufacturing Co. Inc.
RANGER - Watches - Bulova Corp.
RANGER - Watches - Rolex Watch USA, Inc.
RANGER - Windshield frames–motor vehicle ☆ - National Cycle Inc.
RANGER II - Boats–motor ☆ - Marathon Boat Group, Inc.
RANGER ATV - Toys - Tyco Toys
RANGER BASS - Boats - Ranger Boat Co.
RANGER II - Floor coverings–carpet and rugs - Trend Carpet
RANGER LONGHORN - Knives–hunting - Colonial Knife Co. Inc.
RANGER LUKE'S - Barbecue sauce - Jardine's Texas Foods
RANGER MARK I - Binoculars ☆ - Swift Instruments, Inc.
RANGER OF ARKANSAS - Boats–motor - Ranger Boat Co.
RANGER RICK - Recording label - Trudy Corp.
RANGER RIVERBOAT - Sporting goods - Avon Marine
RANGER ROO GLOBAL GEOGRAPHIC EXPLORER - Video production -
  Joseph David Olmstead
RANGER SPREADER - Ammunition - Olin Corp. (Winchester Div.)
RANGER, THE - Ophthalmic goods - Chums Ltd.
RANGER TOWER PLUS - Toys - Newco, Inc.
RANGERTONE - Electronic equipment - Rangertone Research Inc.
RANGERVISION - Video tapes–blank - Rangertone Research Inc.
RANGESTAR - Navigational instruments - Arthur R. Dennis
RANGETOP - Cereal - Homestead Mills
RANGEWAY GOLF - Golf courses - Rangeway Golf, Ltd.
RANGING - Lighting equipment–aircraft - Ranging Inc.
RANGLES - Corn kernels - Cornnuts Inc.

RANGO - Toys–guns - Mattel, Inc.
RANGONI - Footwear - Wolff Shoe Co.
RANGOON - Fabrics - Dan River Inc.
RANGOON - Floor coverings–carpet and rugs - Milliken & Co. Inc.
RANGR - Radios - General Electric Co.
RANI - Frames–eyeglass - May Optical Co. Inc.
RANI - Incense ☆ - Genie Co. Inc.
RANIER - Footwear–athletic - New Balance Athletic Shoe, Inc.
RANIER - Tents - Puget Sound Tent and Awning
RANIR - Dental equipment - Ranir Corp.
RANK - Electronic equipment - Brimar Inc.
RANK ONE R - Apparel–athletic - Clothes Unlimited, Inc.
RANMARU - Dinnerware ☆ - Sakura Inc.
RANOSAURS - Toys - Proll Toy Co.
RANSBURG - Bathroom accessories - Ransburg Accessories Inc.
RANSBURG JR. - Bathroom accessories ☆ - Ransburg Accessories Inc.
RANSOM - Checkbooks - Checks in the Mail, Inc.
RANSOM - Frames–eyeglass ☆ - Universal/Univis Inc.
RANSOM - Recording label - R & R Productions
RANSOME GREEN'S - Food products - Jardine's Texas Foods
RANSOMES - Lawn mowers - Ransomes-Cushman-Ryan
RANT AND RAVE - Jewelry - Amigos Associates, Inc.
RANTEX - Sanitary napkins - Clinipad Corp.
RANTHANE - Paints - Randolph Products Co.
RANWOOD - Recording label - Welk Music Group
RAO - Musical instrument accessories - William Lewis & Son
RAO GOLD LABEL - Musical instrument accessories - William Lewis & Son
RAOIATORE - Food products ☆ - Golden Whisk Pasta Partners
RAP - Fishing lures - Normark Corp.
RAP - Latex - Dow Chemical Co.
RAP - Recording label - Daran Records
RAP-A-LOT - Recording label - Priority Records
RAP-A-PAK - Backpacks - Rap.A.Pak
RAP-A-TAP - Toys–musical - Little Tikes Co.
RAP ALLSTARS - Apparel and accessories - Michael Wilkerson Jones
RAP ATTACK - Recording label - Aroun' Town Productions Inc.
RAP CAP - Motor vehicle parts and accessories - Steven R. Morvay
RAP DRY - Nail care products - E.O.H. Industries, Inc.
RAP GATOR - Machinery - Gentec Equipment Co.
RAP SNACKS - Potato chips - Rap Snacks, Inc.
RAP STIK - Nail care products - E.O.H. Industries, Inc.
RAP, THE - Nail care products - E.O.H. Industries, Inc.
RAP WITH THE FACTS - Recording label - Twin Sisters Productions
RAP-WRAP - Apparel and accessories - J.M. Marketing & Advertising Group
RAPA - Sausages - Jones Dairy Farm
RAPADURA - Sugar–granulated, refined, or powdered ☆ - Terra Prima, Inc.
RAPALA - Fishing lures - Normark Corp.
RAPALA HUSKY - Fishing lures - Normark Corp.
RAPALA MINNOW SPOON - Fishing lures - Normark Corp.
RAPALLO - Dishes–china - Pasmantier Co. Inc.
RAPAMUNE - Pharmaceutical preparations - American Home Products Corp.
RAPAZZINI - Food products - Rapazzini Winery
RAPCO - Audio equipment - Rapco International
RAPCO - Sporting goods - Rapco
RAPCOLITE - Audio equipment ☆ - Rapco International
RAPELLI - Sausages - Made in France
RAPHAEL - Footwear - New York Transit, Inc.
RAPHAEL - Jewelry - R.N. Koch Inc.
RAPHAEL - Toys - Playmates World Wide Inc.
RAPHAEL - Wallpaper - Koroseal Wallcoverings
RAPHAEL R FLUTEMAKERS - Flutes - Custom Music Co.
RAPHAEL SARTI - Footwear–women's - Imxco Sales Inc.
RAPHON - Antiseptics ☆ - Nephron Pharmaceuticals
RAPI-DRIV - Screwdrivers - Klein Tools Inc.
RAPI-JECT - Medical apparatus - DBL Inc.
RAPICO - Paints ☆ - Impervious Paint Industries Ltd.
RAPID - Concrete–mixture - L.D. Sterns Corp.
RAPID - Hair care products - Roux Laboratories, Inc.
RAPID - Inks ☆ - C.H. Hanson Co.
RAPID - Wire products - Rapid Tag & Wire Co.
RAPID ACTION - Furniture - Action Industries Inc.
RAPID-BREW - Coffee makers–electric - Tops Manufacturing Co. Inc.
RAPID C - Medical apparatus - Smith & Nephew Richards, Inc.
RAPID CACHE - Computer software - Far Stone Technology Inc.
RAPID CASTER - Fishing tackle ☆ - Gladding Braided Products Inc.
RAPID CHANGE - Game machines - Grand Casinos Inc.

☆ = Now out of production

RAPID CHANGE - Knives - Ten Pak Manufacturing Co.

RAPID CHANGE - Recording label - Creative Breakthroughs, Inc.

RAPID CHANGE TECHNOLOGIES - Tape players–video - Creative Breakthroughs, Inc.

RAPID CHART - Medical forms - Pain Specialist, Inc.

RAPID-CLEAR - Ophthalmic goods ☆ - Sellstrom Manufacturing Co.

RAPID CURE - Adhesives and coatings - American Synthetics Co.

RAPID DATABASES - Computer software - Evans & Sutherland Computer Corp.

RAPID DEPLOYMENT FORCE - Toy action figures and acessories - In Time Products Co., Ltd.

RAPID DISPATCH COLLECTION - Furniture–upholstered - Hickory Hill Furniture Corp.

RAPID DRY - Chemical preparations - Pro's Choice Products, Inc.

RAPID-DRY - Diapers–disposable - Confab, Inc.

RAPID DRY - Enamels - PJH Brands

RAPID EIDMS - Computer software - Westinghouse Electric Corp.

RAPID EXFOLIATOR - Skin-care products - Murad Skin Research Laboratories, Inc.

RAPID FILER - Computer software - Novell, Inc.

RAPID FILL - Packaging–paper - Sealed Air Corp.

RAPID FIRE - Spark plugs - General Motors Corp.

RAPID FLOOR - Floor coverings - W.R. Grace & Co.

RAPID FLUSH - Automotive repair shops - Gold Eagle Co.

RAPID-FOAM - Medical apparatus - Soule Medical, Inc.

RAPID FOAM - Splints - Cramer Products Inc.

RAPID FOODS - Food products - Max Bauer Meat Packer Inc.

RAPID-GRO - Fertilizers - Chevron Chemical Co.

RAPID GROOM - Pet products - Electric Cleaner Co.

RAPID-HEAT - Heaters–gas - Holmes Products, Corp.

RAPID/HOS - Computer software - Information Management Corp.

RAPID KILL - Insecticides - Environmental Chemicals Group, Inc.

RAPID LOAD DISPENSING SYSTEMS - Containers - Profitime, Inc.

RAPID MIST - Air purification systems - Holmes Products, Corp.

RAPID OBJECT APPLICATION DEVELOPMENT - Computer software - Ontos, Inc,

RAPID-ONE - Battery chargers - General Electric Co.

RAPID-PAK - Hardware - Ideal Industries Inc.

RAPID PATCH - Chemical preparations - Polymer Engineering Corp.

RAPID-PC - Computer software - Olsen Computer Systems, Inc.

RAPID/PIC - Computer software - Concurrent Technologies Corp.

RAPID/POS - Computer software - Information Management Corp.

RAPID-PRO SERIES - Machinery - Ashby Cross Co., Inc.

RAPID-RATE - Swimming pools ☆ - E-Z Clor Systems

RAPID RE - Computer software - Gateway Information Services, Inc.

RAPID REORG - Computer software - Platinum Technology, Inc.

RAPID REPAIR - Toys - Tonka Corp.

RAPID RESPONSE MANUFACTURING CLIENT/SERVER - Computer software - ProfitKey International Inc.

RAPID RIGHT - Catheters - Schneider (USA) Inc.

RAPID RIVER - Footwear - Bee-Gee Shoe Corp

RAPID ROCK - Concrete products - Tamms Industries Co.

RAPID SET - Artists' medium - Binney & Smith Inc.

RAPID SHAVE - See **PALMOLIVE RAPID SHAVE**

RAPID SHIP - Forklifts - Hoist Liftruck, Manufacturing, Inc.

RAPID SHOT SLAM SET - Toys–automobiles - Matchbox Toys USA

RAPID-SOLV - Vitamins and nutritional supplements - Tishcon Corp.

RAPID-SORB - Machine parts - Dri-Steem Humidifier Co.

RAPID SQL - Computer software - Embarcadero Technologies, Inc.

RAPID STICK - Labels–gummed - Grand Rapids Label Co.

RAPID STRIP - Paint removers ☆ - Waterlox Coatings Corp.

RAPID-TACH - Hitches–trailer - M.J. Electric, Inc.

RAPID TAP - Lubricating oils - Relton Corp.

RAPID TENSION BOLT - Nuts and bolts - NSS Industries

RAPID THAW - Deicing fluid - Robert P. Arnold & Associates, Inc.

RAPID TRANSIT - Frames–eyeglass ☆ - Universal/Univis Inc.

RAPID VUE - Prophylactics - Ansell Inc. (Personal Products Div.)

RAPID WRAP - Bandages - Hydro-Med Products, Inc.

RAPIDAN RIVER - Beverages–alcohol - Omni Services, Inc.

RAPIDAN RIVER VINEYARDS - Wines - Rapidan River Vineyards

RAPIDASE - Yeast - Gist-Brocades Food Ingredients Inc.

RAPIDCAD - Computer terminals - Intel Corp.

RAPIDCD - Computer software - Insignia Solutions Inc.

RAPIDCHECK - Computer software - Rapidforms, Inc.

RAPIDCUT - Saw blades - Credo Co.

RAPIDE - Bicycles ☆ - Raleigh USA Bicycle Co.

RAPIDE-O-MATIC - Ophthalmic goods ☆ - Riviera Trading, Inc.

RAPIDESIGN - Office supplies - Empire Berol USA

RAPIDESIGN CIRCLEOMETER - Measuring instruments - Empire Berol USA

RAPIDEX - Adhesives and sealants - H.B. Fuller Co. (North American Adhesives, Sealants and Coatings Group)

RAPIDFIRE - Audio equipment - Afterburner Industries

RAPIDFIRE - Barbecue and grill accessories - Weber-Stephen Products Co.

RAPIDFIRE - Computer programs - Rapidfire Software, Inc.

RAPIDFIRE - Surgical supplies - C. R. Bard, Inc.

RAPIDISPLAY - Artists' materials ☆ - Graphic Products Corp.

RAPIDKEY LIBRARY - Computer software - i.d. Centric

RAPIDKEY LIBRARY - Computer software - Postalsoft, a Firstlogic Technology

RAPIDLOCK - Binders ☆ - Stationers Loose Leaf Co.

RAPIDO - Cosmetics - Spornette International, Inc.

RAPIDO! - Diagnostic substances - Fry Laboratories, Inc.

RAPIDO - Recording label - International Record Corp.

RAPIDO-EZE - Cleaning preparations - Koh-I-Noor, Inc.

RAPIDO-PAQUE - Inks ☆ - Koh-I-Noor, Inc.

RAPIDOBALL - Pens ☆ - Koh-I-Noor, Inc.

RAPIDOGRAPH - Pens–fountain - Koh-I-Noor, Inc.

RAPIDOGUIDE - Publisher's imprints ☆ - Koh-I-Noor, Inc.

RAPIDOMAT - Inks–drawing - Koh-I-Noor, Inc.

RAPIDOMATIC - Pencils - Koh-I-Noor, Inc.

RAPIDOMETRIC - Publisher's imprints ☆ - Koh-I-Noor, Inc.

RAPIDOPLOT - Artists' materials ☆ - Koh-I-Noor, Inc.

RAPIDPRINT - Calendars - Rapidprint Inc.

RAPIDRAW - Inks - Koh-I-Noor, Inc.

RAPIDREAMER - Power drill bits - SDI Operating Partners

RAPIDREPORT - Computer software - Raosoft, Inc.

RAPIDRIBBONS - Ribbons - Plank's Printing Service Inc.

RAPIDRISE - Yeast - Nabisco Foods Group

RAPIDRY - Skin care products - Opi Products, Inc.

RAPIDS - Bicycles - Huffy Corp.

RAPIDS - Frames–eyeglass ☆ - Universal/Univis Inc.

RAPIDS - Jewelry - Major League Soccer, LLC

RAPIDSCENE - Computer software - Evans & Sutherland Computer Corp.

RAPIDSOLVE - Vitamins and nutritional supplements - Makers of Kal, Inc.

RAPIDSTEEL - Steel products - DTM Corp.

RAPIDTECH - Computer training software - Tech-Ease Corp.

RAPIDTOOL - Computer software - DTM Corp.

RAPIDTRAK - Computer software - Insignia Solutions Inc.

RAPIDTRAK - Machinery - Dana Corp.

RAPIDTRANSIT - Medical apparatus - Cordis Corp.

RAPIDTURF - Flowers, plants, and seeds - Rapid Turf, Inc.

RAPIDUCTION - Machinery - Teledyne Landis Machine

RAPIDVUE - Diagnostic apparatus - Quidel Corp.

RAPIDWAY - Bathroom fixtures - Crane Plumbing/Fiat Products

RAPIDWELL - Kit comprising reagents - United States Biochemical Corp.

RAPIER - Frames–eyeglass - Zylo Ware Corp.

RAPIERS - Cigar boxes–wood - Consolidated Cigar Corp.

RAPINOVET - Veterinary pharmaceutical preparations - Schering-Plough Animal Health

RAPISEAL - Surgical supplies - Fusion Medical Technologies, Inc.

RAPITEST - Garden equipment - Luster Leaf Products Inc.

RAPITEST - Meters–electric - AMI Medical Electronics Inc.

RAPITYPE-N - Stencils - Mason Marking Systems Corp.

RAPIZZI'S - Apparel and accessories - Skip's Cutting, Inc.

RAPLAST - Pet collars - Three Horsemen Inc.

RAPLON - Abrasive products - Norton Co.

RAPLUST - Pet products - J.M. Saddler, Inc.

RAPONEX - Pesticides–agricultural ☆ - Hydroponic Chemical Co. Inc.

RAPP STYLE - Apparel and accessories ☆ - Richard A. Leslie Co. Inc.

RAPP STYLE INTERNATIONAL - Apparel and accessories - Rapp Style, Inc.

RAPPAHANNOCK - Food products - Carmine Foods Inc.

RAPPALO - Floor coverings ☆ - Tarkett, Inc.

RAPPEE - Snuff ☆ - Byfield Snuff Co.

RAPPEL - Ophthalmic goods ☆ - Styl-Rite Optical Manufacturing Co., Inc.

RAPPER BY THE SEA ENTERPRISES, THE - Scuba diving equipment - RCM Enterprises Ltd.

RAPPER, THE - Novelty items - Joe Rapp Inc.

RAPPERS - Apparel and accessories ☆ - Washington Manufacturing Co.

RAPPERS - Hair care products - DMC Corp.

RAPPIN' RASPBERRY - Candy - Spangler Candy Co.

RAPPIN' ROCKIN' - Dolls - Mattel, Inc.

RAPPIN' SANTA - Toys–stuffed - Great American Fun Corp.

RAPPORT - Bathtubs–enameled - Kohler Co.

RAPPORT - Cabinets ☆ - Aristokraft, Inc.
RAPPORT - Computer software - Clarity Software, Inc.
RAPPORT - Furniture ☆ - Lane Co. Inc.
RAPPORT - Games - Jeffrey C. Lee
RAPPORT - Games - Rapport Enterprises Inc.
RAPPORT - Golfing equipment - Rapport Composites, USA, Inc.
RAPPORT II - Wallpaper - Glidden Co.
RAPRENCH - Wrenches - Ridge Tool Co.
RAPS - Prophylactics - LRC North America, Inc.
RAPSCALLIONS - Apparel–children's - Petals, Inc.
RAPSODIA - Recording label ☆ - Penco Industries Inc.
RAPTOR - Alarm systems–burglar - Vehicle Security Electronics, Inc.
RAPTOR - Computer software - Raptor Systems, Inc.
RAPTOR - Guitars - Peavey Electronics Corp.
RAPTOR - Hardware - Utility Composites, Inc.
RAPTOR - Knives–pocket ☆ - United Cutlery Corp.
RAPTOR - Pesticides–household - American Cyanamid Co.
RAPTOR - Watches - Accusplit Inc.
RAPTOR BITES - Candy - Amblin' Entertainment, Inc.
RAPTOR RAVIOLI - Preserved foods–prepackaged - Conagra, Inc.
RAPTOR SYSTEMS - Computer software - Raptor Systems, Inc.
RAPTOR SYSTEMS INCORPORATED - Computer software - Raptor Systems, Inc.
RAPTORGEAR - Apparel–athletic - Raptor Graphics
RAPTURE - Clocks - General Time Corp. (Westclox/Seth Thomas Div.)
RAPTURE - Dinnerware–glass - Nikko Ceramics Inc.
RAPTURE - Floor coverings–carpet and rugs ☆ - World Carpets, Inc.
RAPTURE - Frames–eyeglass ☆ - May Optical Co. Inc.
RAPTURE - Glassware–household ☆ - Lenox Crystal, Inc.
RAPTURE - Musical instruments - Ronald S. Bienstock
RAPTURE - Perfumes - Victoria's Secret Stores, Inc.
RAPTURE - Socks - Leininger Mills Inc.
RAPTURE - Tableware–china ☆ - Lenox, Inc.
RAPTURE - Vitamins and nutritional supplements - Robert Kessler
RAPTURE RECORDS - Recording label - Lifeblood Productions Inc.
RAPTURE ROMANCE - Publisher's imprints - Penguin USA
RAPUNZEL - Cookies ☆ - Edward & Sons Trading Co., Inc.
RAPUNZEL - Dolls - Effanbee Doll Corp.
RAPUNZEL 1-PLY - Yarn - Henry's Attic
RAPUNZEL 2-PLY - Yarn - Henry's Attic
RAPZ - Ophthalmic goods - Karlen Manufacturing, Inc.
RAQUEL - Cosmetics - Rixima Inc.
RAQUEL - Eyeglasses - Art-Craft Optical Co.
RAQUEL - Floor coverings–carpet and rugs - Mohawk Industries Inc.
RAQUEL - Glassware–household ☆ - Crystal Clear Importing Co. Inc.
RAQUEL - Toys - Tonka Corp.
RAQUELLE - Skin care products - Rixima Inc.
RAQUEL'S COLLECTION - Pillows ☆ - J. Kenneth Zahn
RAQUETTE - Lacquers - Raquette Sales Division Inc.
RAR - Film - Eastman Kodak Co.
RARAM - Computer software - At&T Corp.
RARE - Video games - Rare Coin-It Inc.
RARE AIR - Publisher's imprints - Rare Air, Ltd.
RARE ANTIQUE - Liquors - Four Roses Distillers Co.
RARE ATTRACTION - Floor coverings–carpet and rugs - Trend Carpet
RARE BITS - Figurines - Aus-Ben Studios
RARE BREED - Caps–baseball - Sports Access/America
RARE BREED - Pet food - Amway Corp.
RARE BREW - Men's apparel - Pacific Sunwear of California Inc.
RARE EARTH - Recording label - Motown Record Co. L.P.
RARE EARTH - Stationery - Nicole Rae Winston
RARE EARTH MEDICAL - Medical equipment - Rare Earth Medical, Inc.
RARE EDITION - Frames–eyeglass - Liberty Optical Manufacturing Co.
RARE EDITIONS - Apparel–women's - Rare Editions
RARE ELEGANCE - Floor coverings–carpet and rugs ☆ - Customweave Carpets Inc.
RARE ELEGANCE - Floor coverings–carpet and rugs ☆ - World Carpets, Inc.
RARE ESSENCE - Floor coverings–carpet and rugs - Calladium & Marglen
RARE FIND - Floor coverings–carpet and rugs - Masland Corp.
RARE FOOTAGE - Hosiery - Keepers International
RARE FORM - Floor coverings–carpet and rugs - Lees Carpets
RARE GOLD - Skin care products - Avon Products, Inc.
RARE GROOVE - Apparel–children's - Frances Lam Inc.
RARE HARVEST - Rice - Gourmet House Inc.
RARE JEWELS - Nail care products ☆ - Noxell Corp.
RARE MOMENT - Floor coverings–carpet and rugs ☆ - Walter Carpet Mills

RARE MOMENTS - Floor coverings–carpet and rugs - Tuftex Carpet Mills, Inc.
RARE MUSK - Colognes - Revlon Consumer Products Corp.
RARE PEARL - Frames–eyeglass ☆ - Universal/Univis Inc.
R.A.R.E. PLANET FOUNDATION - Clothing - Tad C. Hogenson
RARE PLANT RARE EARTH - Greeting cards - Wolf Lodge Illustrations & Map Co.
RARE SENSATION - Floor coverings–carpet and rugs - Cabin Crafts Carpets
RARE SPIRIT - Floor coverings–carpet and rugs - Queen Carpet Corp.
RARE SPLENDOUR - Floor coverings–carpet and rugs - Gulistan Carpet Inc.
RARE VISION - Floor coverings–carpet and rugs - Lees Carpets
RARE WOODS - Frames–picture - Rare Woods Inc.
RAREBIT - Spices and extracts - Herbert Marmorek & Son, Inc.
RAREBITS - Figurines - Aus-Ben Studios
RARESCOT - Beverages–alcohol - Kentucky Brands of California Inc.
RARITAN - Artists' materials - Hunt Manufacturing Co.
RARITIME - Marine rigging ☆ - Raritan Engineering Co. Inc.
RARITY - Floor coverings–carpet and rugs ☆ - Columbus Mills, Inc.
RARK - Toys ☆ - Those Characters from Cleveland, Inc.
RAS SPORTS - Apparel–athletic - Ras Kids, LLC
RASABLE - Paper–bond ☆ - Parsons Paper Co.
RASBERRY PUREE - Bathroom accessories - Kohler Co.
RASCAL - Bicycles - Klein Bicycle Corp.
RASCAL - Boats–pontoons - Rebel Industries Inc.
RASCAL - Cat food ☆ - Agway Country Foods Inc.
RASCAL - Clippers–barber ☆ - Sunbeam-Oster Household Products
RASCAL - Computer software - Software Connections
RASCAL - Eyeglasses - Art-Craft Optical Co.
RASCAL - Hardware - Atlas Copco Electric Tools Inc.
RASCAL - Motor vehicles–personnel carriers - Electric Mobility Corp.
RASCAL - Musical instrument accessories - Roberto Ciarfella Inc.
RASCAL - Recording label - Pandisc Records
RASCAL - Ships–sailing vessels - Ray Greene Industries
RASCAL - Toys ☆ - Collier-Keyworth Inc.
RASCAL - Toys–models ☆ - Estes Industries
RASCAL - Vitamins and nutritional supplements - Kroeger Herb Products Co. Inc.
RASCAL CONVERTABLE - Scooters–motorized - Electric Mobility Corp.
RASCALS - Candy ☆ - American Chicle Co.
RASCALS - Greeting cards - Specialty Sales Inc.
RASCALS - Puzzles ☆ - Western Publishing Co., Inc.
RASCALS - Recording label - Young Rascals
RASCO - Pens–fountain - Premec USA Inc.
RASE-RITE - Paper–bond - Byron Weston Div.
RASER-PEN - Pens - Micropoint Inc.
RASEZPRESS - Computer hardware - Multi-Tech Systems, Inc.
RASH-BAN - Diapers–cloth ☆ - Salk Co. Inc.
RASHELL - Cosmetics - Rashell Cosmetics, Inc.
RASHELLA - Nightgowns - Shelly Kaye Designs, Inc.
RASHI - Wines - Royal Wine Corp.
RASHID RADAR - Radar systems and equipment - Vehicle Radar Safety Systems Inc.
RASHTI & RASHTI - Apparel–children's - H. J. Rashti & Co., Inc.
RASHTI BABI! - Apparel–children's - H. J. Rashti & Co., Inc.
R.A.S.K. - Educational materials - Leona Campbell
RASKANDO - Skin care products - D'Franssia Corp.
RASKAS - Candy - Square Shooter Candy Co.
RASKAS - Cheese - Raskas Foods, Inc.
RASMUSSEN - Barbecues and grills ☆ - Rasmussen Iron Works Inc.
RASMUSSEN - Liquors - Paramount Distillers Inc.
RASOLA - Cigars - H.L. Neff & Co. Inc.
RASOLLI - Footwear - Rasolli Footwear Corp.
RASP - Agricultural machinery - Byron Enterprises, Inc.
RASPBERRIES AND BLACKBERRIES - Candy - Ferrara Pan Candy Co., Inc.
RASPBERRY - Perfumes - Tennessee Gold Inc.
RASPBERRY BEATER - Sporting goods - Trace Athletic Corp.
RASPBERRY BOUQUET - Skin care products - Maybelline Co.
RASPBERRY BOUQUET - Skin care products - Maybelline Intermediate Co.
RASPBERRY BROWN ALE - Beverages–malt - Table Bluff Brewing, Inc.
RASPBERRY BUDS - Candy - Wilson Candy Co.
RASPBERRY BURMESE - Glassware–household ☆ - Fenton Art Glass Co.
RASPBERRY DELIGHT - Lipsticks ☆ - Tinkerbell
RASPBERRY FLOAT - Christmas tree ornaments - Cracker Box Inc.
RASPBERRY HARMONY - Lipstick and nail polish ☆ - Cosrich Inc.
RASPBERRY/LEMON SPLITS - Candy - Nabisco Holdings Corp.
RASPBERRY 'N CREAM - Food products - Breadshop's Natural Foods
RASPBERRY NEWTONS - Cookies - Nabisco Foods Group

☆ = Now out of production

RASPBERRY PASSION - Fruit drinks–bottled or canned - Chiquita Brands, Inc.

RASPBERRY PATCH - Sporting goods - Trace Athletic Corp.

RASPBERRY PATCH - Teas–herbal - Celestial Seasonings, Inc.

RASPBERRY PEARL - Skin care products - St. Ives Laboratories, Inc.

RASPBERRY PSYCHIC LEMONADE - Beverages - Coca-Cola Co.

RASPBERRY RAVES - Candy - Nellson Candies Inc.

RASPBERRY RIDGE - Beverages–alcohol - Joseph E. Seagram & Sons, Inc.

RASPBERRY ROYALE - Juices - Snapple Beverage Corp.

RASPBERRY ROYALE - Teas - R.C. Bigelow, Inc.

RASPBERRY RUSH - Chewing gum ☆ - Warner-Lambert Co.

RASPBERRY SNAP - Candy ☆ - Swizzels Matlow (USA) Ltd.

RASPBERRY SPLASH - Pretzels - Pretzelmaker, Inc.

RASPBERRY SUPREME - Rouges ☆ - Elysee Scientific Cosmetic Co.

RASPBERRY WHEAT - Beverages–malt - Oxford Brewing Co.

RASPBERRY ZINGER - Teas–herbal - Celestial Seasonings, Inc.

RASPINI - Handbags ☆ - Footwear Express, Ltd.

RASPY GLASS - Sporting goods - William T. White, Jr.

RASPY SPACER - Sporting goods ☆ - Penn's Woods Products Inc.

RASS-MA-TAZZ - Pens - Gillette Co.

RASSIC ROCKERS - Rocking chairs - Daryl J. Brummer

RASTA TIMES - Apparel and accessories - Richard Jones

RASTAN - Video games ☆ - Taito America Corp.

RASTATION - Computer software - Image Systems Technology, Inc.

RASTERFLASH - Computer hardware - Connectware, Inc.

RASTERMASTER - Thermal plotters - Calcomp Inc.

RASTEROPS - Computer software - Rasterops Corp.

RASTERPLUS - Computer software - Graphx, Inc.

RASTERPRESS - Computer hardware - Connectware, Inc.

RASTRAC - Computer software - Jeff Manning

RASTRELLO - Hair care products - Nino Originals

RASTRONICS - Hearing aids - Harc Mercantile Ltd.

RAT - Surfboards - Jeff Battisti

RAT III - Sporting goods ☆ - Powell Skateboards

RAT-A-PULT - Toys - Mattel, Inc.

RAT-A-WAY - Ultrasonic rodent-control device - Jormax Inc.

RAT-B-GON - Rodenticides ☆ - Chevron Chemical Co.

RAT BEACH RED ALE - Beverages–malt - Manhattan Beach Brewing Co.

RAT BONES - Sporting goods - Powell Skateboards

RAT CAFETERIA - Rodenticides - Solvit Inc.

RAT DOOM - Rodenticides ☆ - Fairfax Biological Laboratory

RAT FINK - Toys - Tonka Corp.

RAT FINKIE - Fishing lures - Den Manufacturing Co.

RAT GUARD - Pet products - Ginger, Inc.

RAT KING - Toys - Playmates World Wide Inc.

RAT-NIP - Rodenticides ☆ - Roccorp, Inc.

RAT-NO-MORE - Traps–animal - Control Pak Inc.

RAT-NOTS - Rodenticides - Nott Manufacturing Co. Inc.

RAT NUTS - Sporting goods - Powell Skateboards

RAT-O-MICE - Rodenticides - Mackwin Co.

RAT PACK - Candy - Farley Candy Co.

RAT PINKIE - Fishing lures - Den Manufacturing Co.

RAT REAPER - Rodenticides - Flow-Eze Co.

RAT TRICK - Apparel and accessories - James J. Balboni

RATAN - Paper–waxed - Salinas Valley Wax Paper Co. Inc.

RATCATCHER - Apparel–athletic - H.I.S. Sportswear

RATCH-TECH - Footwear - Jack Schwartz Shoes, Inc.

RATE/DTECT P T - Measuring instruments - H.L. Ledeen Associates

RATE FLOW - Intravenous apparatus - Mcgaw, Inc.

RATED X - Underwear and nightwear - Maidenform Inc.

RATELCO - Electrical equipment - Ratelco, Inc.

RATEMASTER - Computer software - DXI Inc.

RATEX - Rodenticides - United Industries Corp.

RATGEN - Veterinary pharmaceutical preparations - Agritech Laboratories, Inc.

RATH - Meats–luncheon - John Morrell & Co.

RATH BLACK HAWK - Bacon - Famous Brands

RATH BLACK HAWK - Meat extracts - John Morrell & Co.

RATHBONE - Brushes–paint - Winsor & Newton

RATHLIN - Computer software - William H. Amacher

RATHMORE - Flatware - Reed and Barton Corp.

RATINGS GAME, THE - Toys - Tonka Corp.

RATINOLIN INLAID - Office supplies - Artistic Office Products

RATIO - Furniture - Cramer Inc.

RATIOARC - Switches–power - Atto Instruments, Inc.

RATIODRINE - Pharmaceutical preparations ☆ - Lexis Laboratories Inc.

RATION - Dog food - Jim Dandy Co.

RATIONAL APEX - Computer software - Rational

RATIONAL SOFTWARE CORPORATION - Computer software - Rational Software Corp.

RATIONAL SYSTEMS - Computer software - Rational

RATITE ADVANTAGE - Animal feed supplements - American Superior Feeds, Inc.

RATITE ADVANTAGE - Animal feeds - Bluebonnet Milling Co.

RATITE BASIC - Animal feeds - Bluebonnet Milling Co.

RATITE FARE - Pet products - Reliable Protein Products

RATITE FAST FINISH - Animal feeds - Bluebonnet Milling Co.

RATITE MESH - Fencing–chain link - Wescal Industries, Inc.

RATITE PREMIUM - Animal feeds - Bluebonnet Milling Co.

RATITE REGIMEN - Pet products ☆ - Nutritional Research Associates Inc.

RATITE SUPER-START - Animal feeds - Bluebonnet Milling Co.

RATITE THERAPY - Animal feeds - Bluebonnet Milling Co.

RAT'L-BOB - Sporting goods - Plastilite Corp.

RATL R - Fishing lures - Bomber Bait Co.

RATLURE - Insecticides - Green Light Co.

RATMOBILE - Toys–automobiles - Mattel, Inc.

RATOREX - Rodenticides - Mackwin Co.

RATRID - Veterinary pharmaceutical preparations ☆ - Vineland Laboratories Inc.

RATS - Telephones - ImagineNation

RATS, THE - Audio equipment - Pro-Co. Sound Co. Inc.

RATSTAURANT - Rodenticides ☆ - LiphaTech Inc.

RATTAN - Blinds–vertical - Tontine/VyTech Industries Inc.

RATTAN - Floor coverings–carpet and rugs - Masterpiece Finishing Co.

RATTAN - Ophthalmic goods - Foremost Optical Products

RATTL 'N RAP - See RATTLIN' RAPALA

RATTLE BACK - Fishing lures - Lunker Lure Products, Inc.

RATTLE BALL - Toys - Fisher-Price, Inc.

RATTLE DEVLE - Fishing lures - Eppinger Manufacturing Co.

RATTLE ON WHEELS - Toys - Gerber Products Co.

RATTLE ROUSER - Toys - Tot Inc.

RATTLE SCRAPE - Sporting goods - Ole Time Woodsman

RATTLE TOT - Fishing lures - Storm Manufacturing Co.

RATTLELEG - Fishing lures - Rippler Lures Corp.

RATTLER - Alarm systems - Directed Electronics, Inc.

RATTLER - Darts and dart games - Dart Mart Inc.

RATTLER - Eyeglasses - Crews, Inc.

RATTLER - Gocarts - Manco Products, Inc.

RATTLER - Health care products ☆ - CTS Laboratories Inc.

RATTLER - Musical instrument accessories - Pro-Mark Corp.

RATTLER - Recording label - Sarg Recording Co.

RATTLER - Toys–guns - Tonka Corp.

RATTLER, THE - Electronic equipment - DB Products Inc.

RATTLERS - Snake-proof chaps - Thomaston Mills Inc.

RATTLESNAKE - Alarm systems - Directed Electronics, Inc.

RATTLESNAKE EGGS - Novelty items ☆ - Stevenson Industries Inc.

RATTLETAIL - Fishing lures - Buchanan Fishing Industries

RATTLIN - Fishing tackle - South Bend Sporting Goods Inc.

RATTLIN' RABBIT - Toys–stuffed ☆ - Fun World Inc.

RATTLIN' RAPALA - Fishing lures - Normark Corp.

RATTLIN' RIG - Fishing lures - Lindy Little Joe Inc.

RATTLIN' ROGUE - Fishing tackle - Smithwick Lures, Inc.

RATTLIN' SKIRT - Fishing lures - Blue Fox Tackle Co.

RATTLOR - Toys - Mattel, Inc.

RATTLY CARS - Toys–automobiles - Montgomery Schoolhouse

RATTMATT - Notebooks and notepads - Williams Industries, Inc.

RATZ - Skin care products - Henry Beauty Imports Inc.

RAUCHBIER - Beverages–alcohol - Merchant du Vin Corp.

RAUCHENFEL & STEINBIER - Beverages–malt ☆ - HDT Importers Inc.

RAUDILAN PB - Pharmaceutical preparations - Lannett Co. Inc.

RAUDIREX - Pharmaceutical preparations ☆ - Rex Research Laboratories

RAUDIXIN - Pharmaceutical preparations - Bristol-Myers Squibb Co.

RAUL - Musical instruments - Midwest Musical Instrument Co.

RAULAND - Electronic equipment - Rauland-Borg Corp.

RAULAND TRACER - Electronic equipment - Rauland-Borg Corp.

RAULFIA - Pharmaceutical preparations ☆ - JMI-Canton Pharmaceuticals

RAUNEED - Pharmaceutical preparations - Hanlon Drug Products

RAUSCHERT - Novelty items - Biedermann & Sons Inc.

RAUSERP - Pharmaceutical preparations - Bio-Factor Laboratories

RAUSERPIN - Tranquilizers ☆ - Ferndale Laboratories, Inc.

RAUTENSIN - Pharmaceutical preparations - Dorsey Laboratories

RAUTRAX - Pharmaceutical preparations - Bristol-Myers Squibb Co.

RAUTRAX-N - Pharmaceutical preparations - Bristol-Myers Squibb Co.

☆ = Now out of production

RAUVAL - Pharmaceutical preparations ☆ - Pal-Pak Inc.
RAUVERID - Pharmaceutical preparations - Forest Pharmaceuticals Inc.
RAUWESLIN - Pharmaceutical preparations - Wesley Pharmacal Co. Inc.
RAUWOLFEMMS - Pharmaceutical preparations ☆ - C.O. Truxton Inc.
RAUZIDE - Pharmaceutical preparations - Bristol-Myers Squibb Co.
RAV - Leather goods - Clark Leather Products Inc.
RAVAGE - Publisher's imprints ☆ - Marvel Entertainment Group, Inc.
RAVAT - Wines - Bully Hill Vineyards, Inc.
RAVE - Cabinet-lining paper ☆ - U.S. Household Products Co.
RAVE - Cushions - Jay Medical Ltd.
RAVE - Flowers, plants, and seeds - Abbott & Cobb Inc.
RAVE - Hair care products - Chesebrough-Pond's USA Co.
RAVE - Hair care products - Fromm Industries
RAVE - Housewares - Athena Products Corp.
RAVE - Plates–paper - Fonda Group, Inc.
RAVE! - Publisher's imprints - Copley Press, Inc.
RAVE - Recording label - Random Enterprises Inc.
RAVE - Salads–prepackaged - TKO Farms, Inc.
RAVE - Shoes - Viner Brothers Inc.
RAVE - Underwear and nightwear - Bestform Foundations, Inc.
RAVE ALL IN ONE - Hair care products - Conopco, Inc.
RAVE MICROSPRAY - Hair care products - Chesebrough-Pond's USA Co.
RAVE NOTICE - Frames–eyeglass ☆ - Universal/Univis Inc.
RAVE REVIEW - Wallpaper - Carlton-Metro Wallcoverings
RAVE REVIEWS - Apparel and accessories - Montgomery Ward & Co. Inc.
RAVE REVIEWS - Food products - Margaret Van Der Blom Sapp
RAVE REVIEWS II - Wallpaper - Essex Wallcoveringss
RAVE REVIEWS III - Wallpaper - Essex Wallcoveringss
RAVE REVUE - Popcorn - Jasper Foods, Inc.
RAVE SOFT PERM - Hair care products - Chesebrough-Pond's USA Co.
RAVE SPOT PERM - Hair care products - Chesebrough-Pond's USA Co.
RAVEEN - Hair care products - Supreme Beauty Products Co.
RAVEL - Jewelry - Ravel Inc.
RAVEL - Lighters - Colibri Inc.
RAVELLE SQUARE - Floor coverings - Mannington Resilient Floors
RAVELLO BEVERLY HILLS - Jewelry - Amkor Pacific
RAVEN - Apparel and accessories - Raven Industries Inc.
RAVEN - Bicycles - Cannondale Corp.
RAVEN - Bicycles - Huffy Corp.
RAVEN - Blinds–venetian ☆ - Hunter Douglas, Inc.
RAVEN - Boats - Glen-L Marine Designs
RAVEN - Cigarettes - Commonwealth Brands, Inc.
RAVEN - Coatings - Raven Management Services, Inc.
RAVEN - Cutlery ☆ - United Cutlery Corp.
RAVEN - Electronic equipment - William T. Van Pelt, III
RAVEN - Electronics equipment ☆ - AVL
RAVEN - Golfing equipment - Raven Golf Services, Inc.
RAVEN - Ledgers - ACCO USA, Inc.
RAVEN - Motor vehicles–motor homes - Forest River, Inc.
RAVEN - Ophthalmic goods - Embassy Creations Inc.
RAVEN - Paint sprayers - Binks Manufacturing Co.
RAVEN - Paper–carbon ☆ - Buckeye Business Products Inc.
RAVEN - Projection screens - Raven Screen Corp.
RAVEN - Ships–sailing vessels - Cape Cod Shipbuilding Co.
RAVEN - Sunglasses - Arnet, Inc.
RAVEN - Toy - Tonka Corp.
RAVEN - Toys–models ☆ - Estes Industries
RAVEN - Trailers–truck ☆ - Sun-Lite Inc.
RAVEN B-40 AMP - Amplifiers - PRO Manufacturing
RAVEN BEACH - Pet products - Novalek, Inc.
RAVEN BLACK - Floor coverings - Southern Aggregates
RAVEN SOFTWARE - Computer peripheral equipment - Raven Software Corp.
RAVEN STUDIOS LTD. - Boxes - Fagan International
RAVENA - Ophthalmic goods ☆ - Luxottica
RAVENLOFT - Games - Tsr, Inc.
RAVENNA - Floor coverings - Mannington Resilient Floors
RAVENNA - Floor coverings–carpet and rugs - Eligere Carpets
RAVENNA - Giftware - Van Dow-Fenton Inc.
RAVENNA - Shoes ☆ - Allen-Edmonds Shoe Corp.
RAVENNA - Tableware–china ☆ - Villeroy and Boch Tableware Ltd.
RAVENNA WALL - Wallpaper - Blumenthal
RAVENSBURGER - Games - International Playthings Inc.
RAVENSCROFT - Floor coverings ☆ - Tarkett, Inc.
RAVENSWOOD - Shirts - Ravenswood Winery, Inc.
RAVENSWOOD - Stationery ☆ - Superior Marking Equipment Co.
RAVENWOOD - Floor coverings–carpet and rugs ☆ - Masland Corp.

RAVENWOOD - Manufactured homes - Redman Industries, Inc.
RAVENWOOD - Pencils - Reliance Pen & Pencil Corp.
RAVENWOOD BY RAIKES - Figurines - Robert Raikes
RAVER - Books–comic - Malibu Comics Entertainment, Inc.
RAVI - Food products - Sea Greene Co.
RAVIA - Dinnerware–glass ☆ - Crystal Clear Importing Co. Inc.
RAVICO - Candy ☆ - Jaret Specialties Inc.
RAVINA - Sinks–metal - Kohler Co.
RAVIOLETTES - Ravioli–canned ☆ - Nestle USA
RAVIOLI KITCHEN - Food products - Ravioli Kitchen Inc.
RAVIOLI REDS - Food products - Golden Whisk Pasta Partners
RAVIOLOS - Dog food - Vitakraft Pet Products Co., Inc.
RAVISHING - Floor coverings - Aladdin Mills, Inc.
RAVISHING - Floor coverings–carpet and rugs - Ashley Commercial Carpets
RAVISHING RASBERRY - Salad dressings–bottled ☆ - Santa Barbara Olive Co.
RAVISHING RED - Lipsticks - Lancome
RAVISSANT - Fabrics - Vanity Fair Mills Inc.
RAVIVETT - Hair care products - Framesi USA/Roffler Industries Inc.
RAW - Jewelry - Slam Associates
RAW-BONE - Pet food and toys - Items Inc.
RAW COLOR - Cosmetics - Pentech International Inc.
RAW EDGE - Apparel - Shah Safari, Inc.
RAW ENERGY - Vitamins and nutritional supplements - Premier One Products, Inc.
RAW STEEL - Weightlifting equipment - NBG International, Inc.
RAW TESTOSTEROL - Health care products - Nature Health
RAW TRACK RECORDS - Recording label - Raw Track Records Inc.
RAW VIBES - Apparel and accessories - Fresh Jive Manufacturing, Inc.
RAWCLIFFE - Figurines - Rawcliffe Corp.
RAWHIDE - Adhesives and sealants - Puritan-Churchill Chemical Co.
RAWHIDE - Apparel and accessories - Empire Manufacturing Co.
RAWHIDE - Apparel–men's - Brill Bros. Inc.
RAWHIDE - Envelopes - Niagara Envelope Co., Inc.
RAWHIDE - Guns ☆ - Crosman Corp.
RAWHIDE - Knives–hunting - Queen Cutlery Co.
RAWHIDE - Mops - Piedmont Mop Co.
RAWHIDE - Tires - Goodyear Tire & Rubber Co.
RAWHIDE - Trailers–travel ☆ - Custom Campers Inc.
RAWHIDE - Vegetables–frozen - Norpac Services, Inc.
RAWHIDE BAKERY - Pet products - Novapet, Inc.
RAWHIDE BARGAIN BITES - Pet treats - HTZ Investment Corp.
RAWHIDE DINO-KOOKIES - Pet products - Ethical Products Inc.
RAWHIDE EXPRESS - Pet products - Lennox International Inc.
RAWHIDE FARMS - Pet products ☆ - Novapet, Inc.
RAWHIDE RANCH - Pet products - Novapet, Inc.
RAWHYDE FRONTIER - Leather - United American Sales, Inc.
RAWL - Fruits and vegetables - Walter P. Rawl & Sons
RAWL-BOLT - Anchors - Rawlplug Co., Inc.
RAWL-DRIVE - Anchors - Rawlplug Co., Inc.
RAWL-STUD - Anchors - Rawlplug Co., Inc.
RAWLINGS - Sporting goods - Rawlings Sporting Goods Co., Inc.
RAWLINGS - Watches - Bulova Corp.
RAWLITE - Fasteners–hook and eye - Rawlplug Co., Inc.
RAWLPLUG - Fasteners–hook and eye - Rawlplug Co., Inc.
RAWLY - Anchors - Rawlplug Co., Inc.
RAWN - Cleaning preparations - Rawn Co., Inc.
RAWSILQUE - Fabrics–silk - Collins & Aikman Corp.
RAWSKIN - Leather goods - Prime Tanning Co., Inc.
RAWSON ASSOCIATES - Publisher's imprints - MacMillan Publishing Co. Inc.
RAXMANAGER - Computer software - Raxco Software Inc.
RAY - Frames–eyeglass - Rozin Optical Export Corp.
RAY - Transmitting apparatus–radio - Raytheon Co.
RAY 250 - Navigational instruments - Raytheon Co.
RAY ALLEN'S - Pet products - Ray Allen Manufacturing Co. Inc.
RAY & ED'S TACKY-TACKLE CO. - Fishing tackle - Tacky-Tackle Co.
RAY-AWAY - Nail care products - Onyx Corp.
RAY BAN - Ophthalmic goods - Bausch & Lomb Inc.
RAY-BAN CATS - Eyeglasses - Bausch & Lomb Inc.
RAY BAN XRAYS SERIOUS SPORTS SUNGLASSES - Sunglasses - Bausch & Lomb Inc.
RAY-BAR - Paints - Toledo Paint & Chemical Co.
RAY BLOCK - Sunblocks ☆ - Del-Ray Labs, Inc.
RAY-BRITE - Thread - United Thread Mills Corp.
RAY COOK - Golf putters - Ray Cook Co.
RAY-CORE - Building materials–concrete - Ray-Core

☆ = Now out of production

RAY-DF - Navigational instruments - Raytheon Co.
RAY FLOYD - Shoes ✩ - Endicott Johnson Corp.
RAY GLO - Yarn ✩ - Lily Craft Products
RAY JEFFERSON - Navigational instruments - Ray Jefferson
RAY-LAST - Thread - United Thread Mills Corp.
RAY-LINE - Searchlights - ITT Jabsco
RAY-LITE - Eyeglasses ✩ - Bausch & Lomb Inc.
RAY-O-KOOL - Fabrics–rayon ✩ - Dan River Inc.
RAY O LITE - Warning reflector - Pac-Tec Inc.
RAY-O-MATIC - Bells and chimes - Effron Sales
RAY-O-VAC - Batteries - Rothco Inc.
RAY PARKINS - Musical instruments - E.K. Blessing Co. Inc.
RAY PROOF SOUND SHIELD - Construction equipment - Shielding Systems
    Corp. (Ray Proof Div.)
RAY-RITE - Illuminated clipboards - J and R Film Co. Inc.
RAY SCOTT REEL GOOD - Relishes - Ray W. Scott, Jr.
RAY STRAUSS UNLIMITED - Apparel and accessories - Ray Strauss
    Unlimited Inc.
RAY-TEC - Heaters–gas - Sun Technology Corp.
RAYA SYSTEMS - Computer software - Raya Systems, Inc.
RAYADA - Apparel–athletic - Union Bay Sportswear Ltd.
RAYBAKE - Enamels ✩ - PPG Industries, Inc.
RAYBAKE PLASTOX - Enamels ✩ - PPG Industries, Inc.
RAYBAR - Gun sights - Ithaca Gun Co. Inc.
RAYBERN OLD FASHIONED - Meat products - Raybern Foods, Inc.
RAYBESTOS - Automotive parts and accessories - Echlin Inc.
RAYBESTOS - Brake parts - Raybestos/Brake Parts Inc.
RAYBURST - Photographic equipment - SP Systems/Saratons
RAYCAL - Paints - Impervious Paint Industries Ltd.
RAYCAPS - Vitamins and nutritional supplements - Ray Drug Co.
RAYCINE - Clippers–barber - Sunbeam-Oster Household Products
RAYCLIC - Connectors–electrical - Raychem Corp.
RAYCO - Sporting goods - Georgia's Tennis
RAYCO JR. - Sporting goods - Georgia's Tennis
RAYCOM - Transmitting apparatus–radio - Raytheon Co.
RAYCRON - Paints ✩ - PPG Industries, Inc.
RAYCRYL - Lacquers - R and A Coatings. Inc.
RAYDERM - Health care products ✩ - Organics Corp. of America (Ambix
    Laboratories Div.)
RAYDULGLO - Paints - Impervious Paint Industries Ltd.
RAYELLA - Yarn - National Spinning Co., Inc.
RAYE'S - Finishing agents - Deep Flex Plastic Molds Inc.
RAYE'S WOOD TONES - Finishing agents - Deep Flex Plastic Molds Inc.
RAYETTE - Hair care products - Faberge Co.
RAYEX - Sunglasses ✩ - Rayex Corp.
RAYGAMES - Computer software - Raihan U. Haque
RAYGEE - Paints - Impervious Paint Industries Ltd.
RAYGLO - Enamels - Impervious Paint Industries Ltd.
RAYKO CLIMAX - Cosmetics - Morris-Flamingo Inc.
RAYLAN - Computers–mainframe - Raylan Corp.
RAYLOR - Golfing equipment - Taylor Made Golf Co. Inc.
RAYLUSTRE - Paints - Impervious Paint Industries Ltd.
RAYMASTER - Computer software - Lighting Sciences Inc.
RAYMO - Thread - Belding Heminway Co. Inc.
RAYMO - Wheelchairs - Raymo Products Inc.
RAYMODES - Apparel–women's - Raymodes Inc.
RAYMOLD - Brake parts - Raybestos/Brake Parts Inc.
RAYMOND - Skin care products - Raymond Industries
RAYMOND - Wines - Raymond Vineyard and Cellar Inc.
RAYMOND DRAGON - Apparel–men's - Neo-Century Designs Ltd.
RAYMOND E. FEIST'S RIFTWAR LEGACY - Computer software - Dynamix,
    Inc.
RAYMOND HALPERN - Apparel–women's - Movie Star Lingerie
RAYMOND WEIL - Watches - Seville Watch Corp.
RAYMOND'S ORIGINAL ALL NATURAL BREW - Soft drinks - Refreshawaii,
    Inc.
RAYMOR'S - Skin care products - Graymor Chemical Co., Inc.
RAYNAL VSOP - Brandy - Shaw-Ross International Importers
RAYNAUD & CIE. - Dinnerware–glass - Ceralene Inc.
RAYNE - Water–mineral - Rayne Water Systems
RAYNET - Computer software - Raynet Corp.
RAYNOR - Doors–garage ✩ - Raynor Manufacturing Co.
RAYNOR SAFETY SENTINEL - Garage door openers - Raynor Manufacturing
    Co.
RAYNOR SAFETY SURE - Automatic garage door controller - Raynor
    Manufacturing Co.

RAYNOX - Cameras ✩ - Edixa Camera Co.
RAYNTYTE - Fabrics - Manart-Hirsch Co. Inc.
RAYO DE SOL - Food products - Wilson Products Co. Inc.
RAYOGLOS - Enamels ✩ - California Products Corp.
RAYON - Skin care products ✩ - Hess Hair Milk Laboratories Inc.
RAYON CHENILLE 1000 - Yarn - Henry's Attic
RAYON CHENILLE 1300 - Yarn - Henry's Attic
RAYON D'OR - Wines - Calvaresi Winery
RAYONETTE - Yarn - Melrose Yarn Co. Inc.
RAYONICA - Fabrics - Infinite Textile, Inc.
RAYOS - Floor coverings–carpet and rugs ✩ - Eurotex Inc.
RAYOVAC - Batteries - Marathon Projects
RAYOVAC - Batteries - Rayovac Corp.
RAY'S - Chili–canned - Kelly Food Products Inc.
RAY'S - Tortillas ✩ - Barbara's Bakery, Inc.
RAY'S OINTMENT - Pharmaceutical preparations - Heritage Store Inc.
RAY'S READERS - Educational materials - Outside the Box, Inc.
RAYSATIN - Paints - Impervious Paint Industries Ltd.
RAYSEAL - Paints - Impervious Paint Industries Ltd.
RAYSOL - Heating equipment - Raychem Corp.
RAYSON - Cosmetics - Morris-Flamingo Inc.
RAYSPUN - Thread - United Thread Mills Corp.
RAYTEX - Paints - Impervious Paint Industries Ltd.
RAYTEX - Tires ✩ - Bridgestone/Firestone, Inc.
RAYTHEON - Navigational instruments - Raytheon Co.
RAYTREX - Photographic equipment - Eastman Kodak Co.
RAYVE-FLOOR - Sealing compounds - Analab Inc.
RAYVEL - Paints - Impervious Paint Industries Ltd.
RAYVELENE - Paper - Marquardt and Co. Inc.
RAYVELVA - Paints - Impervious Paint Industries Ltd.
RAYVELVET - Paints - Impervious Paint Industries Ltd.
RAZ - Goggles–safety - Parmelee Industries, Inc.
RAZ - Goggles–safety - U.S. Safety Corp.
RAZ ATTACK - Shirts - J.C. Penney Co., Inc.
RAZ-MA-TAZ - Hair care products - Helene Curtis Industries Inc.
RAZA - Apparel and accessories - Urn Co.
RAZBARI RAZZLE - See **RED RASBERRY RAZZLE**
RAZCAL - Water–bottled or canned - Razcal Corp.
RAZER - Posters - Aegis Entertainment, Inc.
RAZERBACK - Toys - Tonka Corp.
RAZOR - Computer software - Tower Concepts, Inc.
RAZOR - Machine tools ✩ - Cincinnati Machine
RAZOR & TIE - Recording label - Razor & Tie Entertainment LLC
RAZOR & TIE - Recording label - Razor & Tie Music
RAZOR BACK - Antennas - Valor Enterprises, Inc.
RAZOR-BACK - Garden equipment - Union Fork and Hoe Co.
RAZOR BACK - Pickles ✩ - Green Bay Foods Co.
RAZOR-BACK - Shovels - Union Tools, Inc.
RAZOR-BACK - Tools–garden - Uniontools, Inc.
RAZOR BAUL - Leather goods - Korchmar Case Co.
RAZOR BLADES - Eyeglasses - Oakley, Inc.
RAZOR BLADES - Tools–machine - Flexovit USA Inc.
RAZOR/CARTRIDGE - Razors–electric - American Safety Razor Co.
RAZOR-COMB - Razors - Nino Originals
RAZOR CREPE - Fabrics–rayon - Euro American Textiles Corp.
RAZOR CUT - Scissors–hand-operated - Select Brands
RAZOR EDGE - Recording label - Razor & Tie Music
RAZOR EDGE GOLD - Scissors–hand-operated - F.W. Engels Inc.
RAZOR GLIDE - Shave cream - Harbert S. Gregory
RAZOR LOGIC - Computer hardware - Razorlogic Systems
RAZOR POINT - Pens - Pilot Pen Corp. of America
RAZOR POINT II - Pens - Pilot Pen Corp. of America
RAZOR SET - Machinery - Marquip, Inc.
RAZOR SHARP - Tools–hand-operated - Pacific Saw and Knife Co.
RAZOR-SPIKE - Security barriers - William Henry Mincher
RAZORBACK - Leather goods - Korchmar Case Co.
RAZORBEAST - Toys–guns - Tonka Corp.
RAZORCLAW - Toys - Hasbro, Inc.
RAZORETTE - Scissors–hand-operated - Select Brands
RAZORFORM - Tools - James J. Gardner
RAZORHEAD - Archery equipment - Bear Archery Inc.
RAZORHOOK - Knives–hunting - Paul Meeks
RAZORLINE - Books–comic ✩ - Marvel Entertainment Group, Inc.
RAZORMATE - Razors–electric - Philips Electronics North America Corp.
RAZZ - Signs - Fasteners for Retail, Inc.
RAZZ MA TAZZ - Candy ✩ - Hoody Corp.

RAZZ M'TAZ - Socks - TGC INC.
RAZZ-PIZZAZ - Salad dressing ☆ - American Spoon Foods Inc.
RAZZA - Hot tubs–fiberglass ☆ - Jacuzzi Inc.
RAZZBERRY CUSHION - Novelty items - S.S. Adams Co.
RAZZCALS - Toys–stuffed - Matchbox Toys USA
RAZZI - Automotive parts and accessories - Razzi Corp.
RAZZI-GRIP - Automotive parts and accessories - Razzi Corp.
RAZZIES - Socks - TGC INC.
RAZZLE - Apparel and accessories ☆ - Kellwood Co.
RAZZLE - Confections - Flurry International, Inc.
RAZZLE DAZZLE - Bicycles - Columbia Manufacturing Inc.
RAZZLE DAZZLE - Bicycles - Roadmaster Corp.
RAZZLE DAZZLE - Cleaning preparations - Robarb Inc.
RAZZLE DAZZLE - Computer software - Road Scholar, Inc.
RAZZLE DAZZLE - Paper products - Giordano Art, Ltd.
RAZZLE DAZZLE - Tea - Boston Tea Co.
RAZZLE-DAZZLE 6 - Yarn - Rainbow Gallery, Inc.
RAZZLE DAZZLE EYES - Cosmetics ☆ - Avon Products, Inc.
RAZZLE DAZZLE PENGUIN - Toys–stuffed ☆ - Dakin Inc.
RAZZLE PARTY LIGHTS - Electric lighting equipment - Noma International, Inc.
RAZZLEBERRI - Flowers, plants, and seeds - Monrovia Nursery Co.
RAZZLEBERRY - Juices - Knudsen & Sons Inc.
RAZZLES - Chewing gum - Fleer Corp.
RAZZLES - Toys–stuffed ☆ - Gund, Inc.
RAZZLES FANTASY FRUITS - Candy - Fleer Corp.
RAZZMATAZZ - Beverages–alcohol - Jim Beam Brands Co.
RAZZMATAZZ - Christmas tree ornaments - Cracker Box Inc.
RAZZM'TAZ - Ophthalmic goods - Foremost Optical Products
RAZZY - Apparel and accessories - International News, Inc.
RAZZY RASPBERRY - Yogurt - Kraft Foods, Inc.
RAZZZLEBERRY - Kitchen appliances ☆ - Sunbeam-Oster Household Products
RB - Horse riding equipment - Reinsman Equestrian Products, Inc.
RB - Jewelry - Robert A. Baum Corp.
RB - Jewelry - Rene Bargueiras, Inc.
RB - Skates–roller - Rollerball International Inc.
RB - Skin care products - Royal Bodycare, Inc.
RB - Valves - Terra Universal, Inc.
RB 350 - Golfing equipment - Pinseeker Golf Corp.
RB CONTRACT - Furniture - Russ Bassett Co.
R.B. EYES - Eyeglasses - Dioptics Medical Products, Inc.
R.B. FIGUREPLANE - Apparel and accessories - Figureplane
RB-I - Jewelry - General Electric Co.
R.B. RICE - Dips–sour cream based - Saramar Corp.
RB67 PRO-SD - Cameras - Mamiya America Corp.
RBC - Health care products - Physician Engineered Products
RBC - Skin care products - Royal Bodycare, Inc.
RBC PLUS - Pharmaceutical preparations ☆ - Saron Pharmacal Corp.
RBF - Recording label ☆ - Rounder Records Corp.
RBH - Sound equipment - West American Corp.
RBI - Drill bits - Rockbit International, Inc.
RBI AMERICAN PIE - Pies–frozen - Brinkley Woods Enterprises, Inc.
RBJ PUTT MASTER - Golfing equipment - RBJ Products, Inc.
R.B.N.Y.C. - Apparel–women's - Twin Era Ltd.
RBRC - Batteries - Rechargeable Battery Recycling Corp.
RBRC RBRC NI-CD - Batteries - Rechargeable Battery Recycling Corp.
RC - Automotive parts and accessories - Leach Co.
RC - Chewing gum ☆ - Amurol Confections Co.
R.C. - Hair care products ☆ - Cassidy Inc.
RC - Jewelry - Renaissance Creations Ltd.
RC - Recording label ☆ - Roadrunner Records, Inc.
RC - Skates–roller - RC Sports Inc.
RC 3 - Cleaning preparations - Minne Jet Inc.
RC 100 - Beverages–carbonated - Royal Crown Cola Co.
RC-100 - Photographic equipment ☆ - Olympus America Inc.
RC COLA - Beverages–carbonated - Royal Crown Cola Co.
RC COLA - Chewing gum ☆ - Amurol Confections Co.
RC COMMANDER - Toys–models - Cox Products Inc.
R.C. HYDRAULIC - Paints - Paint Equipment People
RC-II - Identification jewelry - Jacoby-Bender Inc.
RC/MIGRATOR - Computer software - Platinum Technology, Inc.
RC PERFORMANCE SERIES - Publisher's imprints - Kalmbach Publishing Co.
RC/QUERY - Computer software - Platinum Technology, Inc.
R.C. RADSKATE - Skateboards - Matchbox Toys USA
RC RAUSCH COMPANY - Greeting cards - Rausch Co.

R.C. RIPSKATE - Skateboards - Matchbox Toys USA
RC/SECURE - Computer storage devices–magnetic - Platinum Technology, Inc.
R.C. SHOCKER - Toys–automobiles - Mattel, Inc.
R.C. STANLEY - Socks - Sockyard Co. Inc.
RC TIMER - Electronic equipment - The Fogmaster Corp.
RC/UPDATE - Computer software - Platinum Technology, Inc.
RC2 - Bicycles - Emhart Industries Inc.
RC2 - Computer software - RSA Data Security, Inc.
RC4 - Computer software - RSA Data Security, Inc.
RC5 PLUS - Cleaning preparations - Stanton Magnetics Inc.
RCA - Recording label - RCA Records
RCA - Televisions - General Electric Co.
RCAI - Orthopedic products - Restorative Care of America Inc.
RCBS - Firearms, accessories, and parts - Blount International, Inc. (Sporting Equipment Group)
RCBS POW'R PULL - Firearms, accessories, and parts - Blount International, Inc. (Sporting Equipment Group)
RCC RUTHERFORD - Cheese - American Soco Inc.
R.C.D. - Tiles–ceramic - Roope Corp.
RCD PLATFORM - Computer software - Cellular Technical Services Inc.
RCF - Electronic equipment - EAW
RCH 90 - Golf clubs - Callaway Golf Co.
RCI - Hearing aids ☆ - United Hearing Systems Inc.
RCI - Motor vehicle parts and accessories - Racer Components, Inc.
RCI - Recording label - RCI Records
RCI ATHLETIC EQUIPMENT INC. - Apparel–athletic - Madeira Enterprises Inc.
RCI COATINGS - Paints ☆ - KCI Coatings, Inc.
RCII - Paper–photographic - Eastman Kodak Co.
RCL - Remote control devices - Poof Toy Products, Inc.
RCL-3000 - Lighting equipment - E-Z Sales & Manufacturing, Inc.
R.C.M. - Footwear ☆ - Conjac Inc.
RCMA - Cosmetics - Research Council of Make-Up Artists Inc.
RCMS - Publisher's imprints - Radian Corp.
RCMS ENVIRONMENT - Computer software - TJC Distributing, Inc.
RCMS RENTAL CONTROL MANAGEMENT SYSTEM - Computer software - Discount Computer Rent, Inc.
RCN 1000 - Electrical equipment - General Electric Co.
RCOT - Tires - Bridgestone/Firestone, Inc.
RCP - Computer software - Information Retrieval Companies Inc.
RCP - Recording label - Rustron Music Productions
RCR - Glassware–household - Royal Crystal Rock Inc.
RCR - Key rings - Richard Childress Racing Enterprises, Inc.
RCR COFFEE CO. - Coffee - Brisk Coffee Co.
RCS - Audio equipment - RCS Audio International Inc.
RCS - Computer software - Rhodes Computer Services, Inc.
R.C.S. - Hair care products - House of Winslow
RCS NEWSLINK - Computer software - Radio Computing Services, Inc.
RCS-RUDDER CONTRO SYSTEM - Computer software - Thrustmaster, Inc.
RCVDS - Electronics equipment - Barco Inc.
RCW - Dishes–wood ☆ - Richmond Cedar Works Manufacturing Corp.
RCX - Tires - Michelin Tire Corp.
RD - Flatware - Faramarzipour USA, Inc.
RD - Golfing equipment - MacGregor Golf Co.
RD - Hair coloring preparations - L.T. Laboratories
R.D. - Prophylactics - Finley Co.
RD 90 - Rust removers - Sprayway Inc.
RD-2000 - Concrete–ready-mix - Dolese Bros. Co.
RD ZINS - Bags–duffel - Jack D. Linscott
RDA - Health care products - Lewis Laboratories International Ltd.
RDA BASICS - Vitamins and nutritional supplements - Amrion, Inc.
R.D.A. COMPLETE - Vitamins and nutritional supplements ☆ - Solaray
RDC - Amusement rides - Ride Development Co.
RDC - Coffee - Donovan Coffee Co., Inc.
RDE - Novelty items - RDE Imports
RDIS - Computer software - PC-Plus Communications Lp
RDR - Jewelry - M. & J. Grosbard, Inc.
RDRAM - Computer peripheral equipment - Rambus Inc.
RDS - Furniture - MG Taylor Corp.
RE - Apparel - Shah Safari, Inc.
RE - Jewelry–precious - OE Design Inc.
RE - Recording label - Jazz Composer's Orchestra Association Inc.
RE-AZO - Pharmaceutical preparations - Reese Chemical Co.
RE-BAND - Medical apparatus - Sports Therapy Services, Inc.
RE BOND - Hair care products - Paula Payne Products Co. Inc.

☆ = Now out of production

RE-CIRK-IT - Circuit breakers - Heinemann Electric Co.
RE-COMM - Office supplies - Georgia-Pacific Corp.
RE-CORD-IT - Ledgers ☆ - Master-Craft Corp.
RE-CRETE - Cement - Dayton Superior Corp.
RE-ECCO - Giftwrap - James River Corp.
RE-ED - Health care products ☆ - Chattanooga Group, Inc.
RE-ENTRY - Recording label - Jazz Composer's Orchestra Association Inc.
RE-ESTRUCTURE - Skin care products - Sara Lee Corp.
RE-FIX - Photographic equipment - 21st Century Environmental Management, Inc.
RE-FLEX - Belts–industrial - Sayre Enterprises Inc.
RE:FLEX - Dyes–synthetic - Matsui International Co., Inc.
RE-FLEX CLEAR - Electrodes - Uni-Patch
RE-FLEX VSP - Prosthetic devices - Flex-Foot Inc.
RE-FLX - Veterinary nutritional supplements - Classic Care Products, Inc.
RE-FREEZER - Instrument panels–aircraft - L.N. Gordon Design, Inc.
RE-FRESH - Swimming pools ☆ - E-Z Clor Systems
RE: GENERATION - Glass products - Design Ideas Ltd.
RE GENESIS - Computer software ☆ - PCI Remote Sensing Corp.
RE-GLASS-IT - Chemical preparations ☆ - Woolsey Marine Industries
RE. GRAPH - Reproportioning/resizing pantograph - Graphicraft
RE-INK-IT - Ink - Ink-Rol Products, Inc.
RE-JOYCE - Food products ☆ - Scrivner, Inc.
RE-JUV-NAL - Disinfectants - Hillyard Enterprises, Inc.
RE-JUV-NAL 165 - Disinfectants - Hillyard Enterprises, Inc.
RE KOLLECTION - Apparel–women's - Jonathan Logan Inc.
RE-LACKS - Hair care products - Paul Brown Salon & Spa
RE-LOAD - Pharmaceutical preparations - Bricker Laboratories
RE/LOCATE - Computer software - Realty Information Tracking Services, Inc.
RE:MARK - Computer software - Software Partners, Inc.
RE-MARK-A-CHART - Office supplies - Ghent Manufacturing Inc.
RE-MARKABLES - Office supplies ☆ - Trend Enterprises, Inc.
RE-MED - Bags–duffel - Tough Traveler Inc.
RE NATURE - Paper–toilet - Lenaco Corp.
RE-NATURED - Vitamins and nutritional supplements - Grow Co. Inc.
RE/NEPH - Vitamins and nutritional supplements - Nutra/Balance Products
RE-NEU CREATIONS - Skin care products - CRH International Inc.
RE-NEW-COAT - Paints - Devoe & Raynolds Co.
RE/NEW4U - Golf carts - RE/NEW4U
RE-NU - Chemical preparations - Kolene Corp.
RE-NU - Varnish, spar ☆ - Atlantic Varnish & Paint Co. Inc.
RE-NU HOOD - Dryers–hair - Postcraft Co.
RE-NU-LAC - Enamels ☆ - Devoe & Raynolds Co.
RE-NU-LITE - Enamels ☆ - North Jersey Paint Co. Inc.
RE-NU-SPAR - Varnish ☆ - Atlantic Varnish & Paint Co. Inc.
RE-NUTRIV - Skin care products - Estee Lauder Inc.
RE-NUTRIV PLUS - Skin care products - Estee Lauder Inc.
RE-O-HIST - Pharmaceutical preparations - Quaker City Pharmacal Co.
RE-O-LAX - Health care products ☆ - CTS Laboratories Inc.
RE-O-VITE - Pharmaceutical preparations - Quaker City Pharmacal Co.
RE-PEEL - Rubber cement - Dap Products Inc.
RE-PEETER - Bacon - Peet Packing Co.
RE-PHOTOGRAPHY SCREEN - Projection screens - SP Systems/Saratons
RE-PLY - Electrodes - Uni-Patch
RE-POPS - Automotive parts and accessories - Clark Industries Inc.
RE-RITE - Paper - Fay Paper Products Inc.
RE-RITE - Ribbons–inked - Smith Corona Corp.
RE-RUN - Office supplies - Georgia-Pacific Corp.
RE-SEAL - Adhesives and sealants ☆ - Reardon Products
RE-SERP-ES - Pharmaceutical preparations ☆ - Hyrex Pharmaceuticals
RE:SOLVE - Computer software - PCS Health Systems Inc.
R.E. SPORT - Outerwear - Fleet Street Ltd.
RE-STIX - Stickers and decals - Mantae America Inc.
RE-TECH - Machinery - Enviroquip Systems, Inc.
RE:THINK - Motion picture distributors–prerecorded - Andrea Ashworth
RE-TRAX - Feather dusters - Texas Feathers Inc.
RE-TRED - Footwear - Hawe Yue Inc.
RE-TYPE - Office supplies - Lee Products Co.
RE UNION - Apparel–men's - Seattle Pacific Industries, Inc. (UNIONBAY Sportswear)
RE-USE-A-LOPE, THE - Envelopes - Earth Class Mail Co.
RE-USE-IT RAIN-BLO - Chewing gum - Leaf, Inc.
RE-UZA-FRESH - Fabrics–nylon - Southco, Inc.
RE-VITA TRIM - Vitamins and nutritional supplements - Re-Vita Manufacturing Co., Inc.
RE-VOLT - Toys - Tonka Corp.

RE-WHITE - Correction fluid - Steig Products
REA-LO - Skin care products - Whorton Pharmaceuticals Inc.
REA-LO 30 - Skin care products - Dermco Labs, Inc.
REA-LO LOTION - Skin care products - Dermco Labs, Inc.
REABAN'S - Restaurants–fast food - Reaban's Inc.
REABILANT - Vitamins and nutritional supplements - O'Brien
REACH - Apparel–athletic - Fuqua Industries Inc.
REACH - Balls ☆ - Rubber Queen
REACH - Fungicides - ISK Biosciences Corp.
REACH - Toothbrushes - Johnson & Johnson
REACH FOR A RIVER - Beverages–malt - CRB Co.
REACH FOR THE PEAK - Beverages - Swiss Natural Foods, Inc.
REACH FOR THE STARS - Computer software - Electronic Arts Inc.
REACH FOR THE STARS. .AFFIRMATIONS FOR KIDS! - Games - Karen Rossman
REACH IT - Tools–hand-operated ☆ - G.T. Water Products Inc.
REACH-MASTER - Poles–wood - E-Z Paintr Corp.
REACH OUT - Telephones - At&T Corp.
REACH WONDERGRIP - Toothbrushes - Johnson & Johnson
REACHALL HOUSEMATE - Housewares - Mar-Cat, Co.
REACHER - Paint rollers and sleeves - Corona Brushes Inc.
REACHER CREATURE, THE - Cleaning preparations ☆ - Swiss-Tex Inc.
REACHING MINDS - Recording label - All Kinds of Minds
REACHING RECORDS - Recording label - John Paul Redmon
REACHOUT - Computer software - Ocean Isle Software
REACT - Athletic footwear - Converse Inc.
REACT - Paints - OEM Paints, Inc.
REACT - Smoke alarms ☆ - Jameson Home Products Inc.
R.E.A.C.T. - Sporting goods - True-Titan, Inc.
REACT-A-PACK - Epoxy - Nd Industries, Inc.
REACTION - Bowling balls - DBA Products Co.
REACTION - Golfing equipment - Dunlop Maxfli Sports Corp.
REACTION ACTION - Video production - American Chemical Society
REACTION BALL - Exercising equipment - Kytec Innovative Sports Equipment
REACTION BELT - Exercising equipment - Kytec Innovative Sports Equipment
REACTION BLOCK - Jewelry accessories - Fashion Solutions USA Inc.
REACTION COACH - Computer software - Innovative Training Products, Inc.
REACTION PLUS - Polishes - Advanced Polishing Products
REACTION-TIME - Carburetors - Gg 300, Inc.
REACTIONARM - Machinery - Columbus Mckinnon Corp.
REACTIONS - Apparel - Graphic Prints Inc.
REACTIVATED ENERGY - Batteries - MOCON/Modern Controls, Inc.
REACTIVATOR-BLENDER - Housewares - Jetco Inc.
REACTOPOL - Eyeglasses ☆ - International Tropic-Cal Inc. (I SKI Div.)
REACTOR - Computer software - Reactor Inc.
REACTOR - Guitars - Peavey Electronics Corp.
REACTOR - Wheelchairs - Everest and Jennings International Ltd.
REACTS - Concrete products - Conspec Marketing & Manufacturing Co. Inc.
REACTS HMA - Paving materials–concrete - Reclaim, Inc.
REACTS IP - Paving materials–concrete - Reclaim, Inc.
READ - Salads–prepackaged - Joan of Arc Co.
READ - Vegetables–canned - Chiquita Processed Food, LLC
READ A MAT EAT AND LEARN - Placemats - Straight Edge Inc.
READ-A-RAMA - Computer software - Unicorn Software
READ-A-RHYME - Publisher's imprints - Creative Teaching Press
READ A RUG - Floor coverings–carpet and rugs ☆ - Straight Edge Inc.
READ ALL ABOUT ME - Artists' materials - Panline USA, Inc.
READ AND PRAY - See FRANCISCAN HERALD PRESS
READ AND PRAY - Publisher's imprints ☆ - Franciscan Press
READ & RHYME - Computer software - Unicorn Software
READ AROUND - Games ☆ - Teaching Concepts Inc.
READ-EM-RITE - Golf-putting accessories - Kensington Group
READ HEAD - Hair care products - Mehaz International, Inc.
READ ME FIRST - Publisher's imprint - CompuAdd Computer Corp.
READ MY CHARMS! - Jewelry - Read My Charms
READ-N-FEED - Agricultural machinery - Micro Chemical, Inc.
READ 'N ROLL - Computer software ☆ - Knowledge Adventure
READ-N-SAVE - Coupons - Discount Services, Inc.
READ: READ, EXPLORE, AND DEVELOP - Publisher's imprints - Oddo Publishing Inc.
READ-RITE - Computer peripheral equipment - Read-Rite Corp.
READ TO DISCOVER - Video production - Meredith Corp.
READABILITY ANALYSIS - Computer software - Gamco Industries Inc.
READABILITY ESTIMATOR - Computer programming services - Berta-Max Inc.
READABLE STORIES - Computer software - Laureate Learning Systems Inc.

☆ = Now out of production

READBOURNE - Furniture - National/Mt. Airy Furniture
READEASY - Reading aid - Eagle Marketing
READER - Frames—eyeglass - Rozin Optical Export Corp.
READER - Lamps - General Electric Co.
READER LIGHT - Lamps - General Electric Co.
READER RABBIT - Computer software - The Learning Co., Inc.
READER RABBIT 2 - Computer software - The Learning Co., Inc.
READER RABBIT 3 - Computer software - The Learning Co., Inc.
READER RABBITS READY FOR LETTERS - Computer software ☆ - The Learning Co., Inc.
READER RESPONSE - Paper—writing - Kurtz Bros. Inc.
READER, THE - Computer programming services - Berta-Max Inc.
READERCLEANER; - Cleaning preparations - Visa International Service Association
READERS - Computer hardware - Proprietary Controls Systems Corp.
READER'S CHOICE - Eyeglasses - AAI/ACCESSORIES Associates Inc.
READER'S DIGEST - Games ☆ - Milton Bradley Co.
READER'S DIGEST - Recording label - Delta Entertainment Corp.
READER'S GUIDE - Magazines - Farrar, Straus and Giroux Inc.
READER'S WINDOW - Book ends - Howell Design, Inc.
READERZ - Eyeglasses - Sunglass Designs, Inc.
READI-BAKE - Bakery products—frozen - Readi-Bake Inc.
READI-BAND - Bandages ☆ - Parke-Davis
READI-FLEX - Bandages - Professional Medical Products, Inc.
READI-PADS - Gauze—surgical ☆ - Parke-Davis
READI-PATCHES - Bandages ☆ - Parke-Davis
READI-SPOTS - Bandages ☆ - Parke-Davis
READI-WRAP - Bandages ☆ - Parke-Davis
READIJET - Dental equipment ☆ - Parke-Davis
READIKWIK - Skin care products - Becky Lynn Co.
READING - Kitchen cabinets—metal - American Woodmark Corp.
READING - Knives—carving - Sterling G. Withers
READING - Photographic equipment - Eastman Kodak Co.
READING ACCELERATOR - Automated reading-aid - Alexander Simpson Associates, Inc.
READING AND ME - Computer software ☆ - Knowledge Adventure
READING AND WRITING CONNECTION - Computer software - Hartley Courseware Inc.
READING AROUND WORDS - Computer software - Instructional/ Communications Technology Inc.
READING BLASTER - Computer software - Knowledge Adventure
READING BLASTER JR. - Computer software ☆ - Knowledge Adventure
READING BUILDS A STRONG MIND - Bookmarks - Donald A. Kinkeade
READING CARNIVAL, THE - Computer software - Digital Theater, Inc.
READING COMPREHENSION - Computer software - Optimum Resource, Inc.
READING COMPREHENSION—FAMOUS PEOPLE - Computer software - Optimum Resource, Inc.
READING COMPREHENSION—GEOGRAPHY - Computer software - Optimum Resource, Inc.
READING COMPREHENSION—HISTORY - Computer software - Optimum Resource, Inc.
READING COMPREHENSION—OLYMPICS - Computer software - Optimum Resource, Inc.
READING COMPREHENSION—SCIENCE - Computer software - Optimum Resource, Inc.
READING COMPREHENSION—SPORTS - Computer software - Optimum Resource, Inc.
READING EASE - Furniture - Creative Industries
READING EDGE, THE - Electronic equipment - Xerox Corp.
READING EXPLORATIONS - Publisher's imprints - Globe Fearon Inc.
READING EYE - Electronic equipment ☆ - Steck-Vaughn/EDL
READING FOR POWER - Publisher's imprints - Better Reading Program, Inc.
READING FOR SUCCESSFUL LIVING - Computer software - Gamco Industries Inc.
READING GLASSES - Frames—eyeglass - Rozin Optical Export Corp.
READING LIBRARY - Electronic equipment - Texas Instruments Inc.
READING MACHINE, THE - Computer software - Southwest Edpsych Services Inc.
READING PILLOW - Pillows - Pillowtex Corp.
READING PLUS - Research—educational - P.F. Collier L.P.
READING PROFESSOR - Computer software - ARTSCI Inc.
READING READINESS - Computer software - Orange Cherry Software
READING WB FAMILY ENTERTAINMENT - Books—comic - Time Warner Entertainment Co., L.P.
READING WITH PRECISION - Computer software - Krell Software Corp.

READING, WRITING, AND RUMINATING - Educational materials - Mary Ann Coscarelli
READIROPE - Sealing devices - Fredericseal, Inc.
READITUFTS - Cotton—balls ☆ - Parke-Davis
READIVAC - Vacuum cleaners and accessories - Douglas/Quikut
READMAN - Computers - Sherwin M. Borsuk
READMASTER - Electrical equipment - Master Meter, Inc.
READMATE - Computer software - Steven Behunin
READ'N PLAY - Publisher's imprints - Rainfall Inc.
READOUT - Computer software - Berkeley Speech Technologies Inc.
READWARE - Computer hardware - Management Information Technologies, Inc.
READY! - Computer software ☆ - Symantec Corp.
READY - Computers - NEC Technologies, Inc.
READY 35 - Cameras - Vivitar Corp.
READY-BEAD - Wood products - Georgia-Pacific Corp.
READY BRU - Beverages - Cookbook Brands, Inc.
READY-BRUSH - Giftware - Prime Protection Inc.
READY BRUSH - Toothbrushes - Robert Golden
READY-CAP - Motor vehicle parts and accessories - Reading Body Works, Inc.
READY/CLAD - Cables - Coleman Cable Systems, Inc.
READY COOKED - Food products ☆ - Golden Grain Co.
READY-COVE - Floor coverings ☆ - Johnsonite Flooring Products
READY CRISP - Bacon - SHK Foods, Inc.
READY CRUST - Bakery products - Keebler Co.
READY-CUT - Vegetables—canned - S & W Fine Foods, Inc.
READY-CUT CATERING CHEESES - Cheese puffs - Schreiber Foods, Inc.
READY DOOR - Glass products - Fimbel Door Corp.
READY DOUGH - Breads—frozen - Bridgford Foods Corp.
READY EDITOR - Computer storage devices - Courseware Development Corp.
READY-FIT - Footwear - Elan-Polo, Inc.
READY FLOW - Pens - National Sales Co.
READY-FOLD - Doors—metal - Besam Inc.
READY FOR SCHOOL - Computer software ☆ - Knowledge Adventure
READY-FOR-USE - Health care products - Calley and Currier Co. Inc.
READY GOURMET - Sauces - Grand Gourmet Specialties, Inc.
READY GROUND - Tofu - Tree of Life, Inc.
READY IN 3 MINUTES! - Charcoal - Charcoal Master International Inc.
READY IN RED - Dolls - Mattel, Inc.
READY-LAID - Flooring—hardwood - Joinery Co.
READY LETTERS - Office supplies - Trend Enterprises, Inc.
READY-LIT - Trees—artificial - FFSC, Inc.
READY-LITE - Lighting equipment - BRK Electronics Inc.
READY-MADE - Frames—picture - MCS Industries Inc.
READY MAID - Paints - Eaglo Paint & Varnish Corp.
READY MEAL - Food products - Bernard Fine Foods Inc.
READY MIX - Chemical preparations - Georgia-Pacific Corp.
READY-MOUNT - Photographic equipment - Eastman Kodak Co.
READY-MUFF - Belts—apparel - Howard S. Leight and Associates, Inc.
READY NET GO - Computer software - NetFRAME Systems Inc.
READY PAC - Fruits and vegetables - Ready Pac Produce, Inc.
READY PAK - Doors—wood - Steves & Sons, Inc.
READY PAK - Food products ☆ - Galaxy Food Brokers
READY PATCH - Plaster—wallboard - Mantrose-Haeuser Co. Inc.
READY PATCH LITE - Plaster—wallboard - Mantrose-Haeuser Co. Inc.
READY-PLAQUE - Chemical preparations - Novagen, Inc.
READY POP 4 PACK - Popcorn ☆ - Weaver Popcorn Co. Inc.
READY RACER - Juvenile wheelchairs - Tumble Forms, Inc.
READY RECORD - Calendars ☆ - Hoyle Products
READY RECYCLER - Containers - Rev-A-Shelf, Inc.
READY REMEDIES - Analgesics - CVC Specialties
READY RESCUE - Radios—citizens' band - Midland International Corp.
READY RESERVE - Pumps - Sta-Rite Industries Inc.
READY REST HEEL REST - Electrical equipment - Black & Decker Corp.
READY RING - Jewelry - Craftstones Inc.
READY RISER - Check valves - Grinnell Corp.
READY ROAD REPAIR - Asphalt patching compound - Ready Road Repair, Inc.
READY-ROLLER - Giftware - Prime Protection Inc.
READY-RULED - Artists' materials - Hunt Manufacturing Co.
READY SAFE, THE - Safes - Secure Safes, Inc.
READY SCENT GO - Air fresheners - New Ideas International, Inc.
READY SERIES - Computer software - Courseware Development Corp.
READY SET - Hair care products - Dena Corp.
READY SET GO - Apparel and accessories ☆ - Health-Tex Inc.
READY-SET-GO - Infant product ☆ - Ming Ta Supply

☆ = Now out of production

READY, SET, READ WITH BANANAS AND JACK - Computer programs - Bright Star Technology Inc.

READY SET SHOW! - Display cases–plastic - Expostar Displays, Inc.

READY! SET! SPAGHETTI! - Games - Milton Bradley Co.

READY-SET-STAMP! - Office supplies - All Night Media, Inc.

READY SHELF - Shelving units–metal - Dorfile Manufacturing Co.

READY SNAX - Food products - Ready Pac Produce, Inc.

READY SPAGHETTI - Pasta - Pizza Inn, Inc.

READY STEPS - Stools–metal - Ever-Ready Appliance Manufacturing Co.

READY-STICK - Floor coverings–tile - Sears, Roebuck and Co.

READY SYSTEM - Medical apparatus - Baxter International Inc.

READY TO BLEND - Beverages - SJ's Foods, Inc.

READY-TO-DRINK - Weight-reducing aid - Slim Fast Foods Co.

READY TO EAT NO PRESERVATIVES - Food products - Fresh Western Marketing Inc.

READY TO FLY - Toys - Centuri Corp.

READY TO GO - Computer software - B & N Companies, Inc.

READY-TO-GO - Rope - Wellington Leisure Products, Inc.

READY TO LINE - Brake parts - Import Brake Co.

READY TO ROLL - Automotive repair shops–tires - Tire Discounters, Inc.

READY-TO-ROLL - Carts - A-Bee Syndicate Inc.

READY-TO-ROLL - Packaging–paper - Sealed Air Corp.

READY-TO-SERVE - Puddings–canned ☆ - General Mills, Inc.

READY TO WEAR - Apparel and accessories - Sr Holdings, Inc.

READY-TO-WEAR - Computer software - Hewlett-Packard Co.

READY TO WEAR - Shampoos - John Frieda, Inc.

READY TO WIND DOWN - Men's apparel - Spiegel, Inc.

READYBUILT - Fireplaces - Readybuilt Products Co.

READYBUILT FIREPLACE MANTELS - Fireplace equipment - Readybuilt Products Co.

READYFLAME - Fireplace logs–treated - Readybuilt Products Co.

READYGLOW - Fireplace logs–treated ☆ - Readybuilt Products Co.

READYLINK - Computer hardware - Compex, Inc.

READYMATIC - Photographic equipment - Eastman Kodak Co.

READYPAK - Computer software - Ready-To-Run Software, Inc.

READYPRICE - Computer software - Me Licensing Corp.

READYPRINT - Photographic equipment - Eastman Kodak Co.

READYRITER - Pens - Jos. Lipic Pen Co.

READYROAST CHICKEN - Seasonings - Lynch Supply Inc.

READYRUN - Chemical preparations - Novagen, Inc.

READYSCSI - Computer hardware - Adaptec, Inc.

READYSET - Medical apparatus - Medisystems Corp.

READYSETGO - Computer software - Manhattan Graphics Corp.

READYSETGROW! - Computer software - Atlantis Software Co.

READY.SET.READ - Electronic equipment - Texas Instruments Inc.

READYSETS - Computer software - Viewpoint Datalabs International, Inc.

READYSHIFT I - Computers - Evaluation Systems Inc.

READYTAPE - Computer software ☆ - Compex, Inc.

READYTOGO - Computer software - Elise Dorsey

READYWRITE - Paper–writing - Kurtz Bros. Inc.

REAGLE - Artists' materials - Eagle Supply Co.

REAL - Cigarettes ☆ - R.J. Reynolds Tobacco Co.

REAL - Computer software - Financial Technologies International LP

REAL - Deodorants–personal - Mennen Co.

REAL - Food products - Axelrod Distributors

REAL - Motor vehicle parts and accessories - Boubin Tire Co.

REAL - Trailers–horse - Real Trailers Inc.

REAL - Video games - Matsushita Electric Corp. of America

REAL 3D - Computer hardware - Martin Marietta Corp.

REAL A-PEEL - Household cleaner - Sysco Corp.

REAL-ACTION - Games - Real Action Games Inc.

REAL ACTION POP UPS - Trading cards and stamps - Up Front Sports and Entertainment, Inc.

REAL ADVANTAGE - Computer software - Real Advantage

REAL AIR - Shoe accessories - Brell Mar Products, Inc.

REAL ALOE VERA - Aloe vera juices - Real Aloe Co.

REAL BAGELS - Bagels - 1st National Bagel Co.

REAL BINGO - Games ☆ - Milton Bradley Co.

REAL BODIES. REAL SOLUTIONS. - Bathing suits - Patricia Byrnes Kane

REAL BODY - Hair care products ☆ - Demert & Dougherty, Inc.

REAL BOUT FATAL FURY - Game machines - Snk Corp. of America

REAL BOXER - Apparel and accessories - Catco, Inc.

REAL BRICK - Bricks - U.S. Brick Inc. (Real Brick Products Group)

REAL BUGS - Sporting goods - Empire Industries

REAL CARDS - Greeting cards ☆ - Z-Barten Productions

REAL CHEESECAKE! - Ice cream - Dreyer's Grand Ice Cream, Inc.

REAL CHINA TEA - Teas - Jianlibao America Ltd.

REAL CLOTHES - Apparel–women's - Saks Fifth Avenue

REAL COMFORT - Apparel and accessories - Chadwick's of Boston, Ltd.

REAL COMPANHIA VELHA - Wines - Admiral Wine Merchants

REAL-CORD - Elastic - Southern Webbing Mills, Inc.

REAL CRAW - Fish attractant - Riverside Lures

REAL DECOY, THE - Decoys - A & M Waterfowl Inc.

REAL DESSERTS - Gelatin - Lakeview Farms, Inc.

REAL EASY - Cleaning preparations - United Industries Corp.

REAL ELEGANCE - Dolls - Mattel, Inc.

REAL ENCHILADA, THE - Apparel and accessories - DF & R Restaurants, Inc.

REAL ESTATE ANALYZER - Computer software - HowardSoft

REAL ESTATE COMPUTER STORE, THE - Computer stores - Enterprise Business Solutions Corp.

REAL ESTATE EDUCATION COMPANY - Publisher's imprints - Dearborn Financial Publishing, Inc.

REAL ESTATE LAWYER - Computer storage devices - Z-Law Software, Inc.

REAL ESTATE MASTER - Calculators - Calculated Industries, Inc.

REAL ESTATE PARTNER - Computer software - Robust Software

REAL ESTATE TAXBUSTER, THE - Instructional audio and video tapes - Property Tax Reduction Services Inc.

REAL ESTATEMENT - Computer software - Municipal Management Associates, Inc.

REAL-EYES - Lenses–optical - Great Lakes Coating Laboratory, Inc.

REAL FAST - Food products - Southwest Soyfoods

REAL FEEL - Musical instrument accessories - HQ Percussion Products

REAL FEEL - Toys - Aviva Sport Inc.

REAL FIRM INSTRUCTORS - Video production - Firm Inc.

REAL FLAME - Fireplace equipment - Rasmussen Iron Works Inc.

REAL FOOD FOR THE IDEAL DOG - Dog food - Inorex Inc.

REAL FORMS - Computer software - Performance, Inc.

REAL FRESH - Disinfectants - United Industries Corp.

REAL FRESH - Food products - Real Fresh, Inc.

REAL FRIENDS - T-shirts–men's - Real Friends, Inc.

REAL FRUIT - Food processors - Wapato Fruit Products Inc.

REAL FRUIT - Food products - Boston Brands, Inc.

REAL FRUIT JUICE! GREAT FRUIT TASTE! - Candy - Mars, Inc.

REAL FYRE - Fireplace equipment - Robert H. Peterson Co.

REAL GEESE - Waterfowl decoys - Orchard Enterprises Inc.

REAL GENIUS - Computer software - Knowledge Based Systems, Inc.

REAL GHOSTBUSTERS, THE - Dolls - Kenner Products

REAL GHOSTBUSTERS, THE - Games ☆ - Milton Bradley Co.

REAL GHOSTBUSTERS, THE - Apparel–children's ☆ - Tsumura International Inc.

REAL GIRL - Lipsticks - Sterling Winthrop Inc.

REAL GOLD - Fruit drinks–bottled or canned ☆ - Coca-Cola Co.

REAL-GOOD - Tomato pastes and sauces - Persian Delight Inc.

REAL GRAPE - Juices ☆ - Keystone Food Products

REAL-GRASS - Health care products - Agri-Tech Inc.

REAL HEALTH - Vitamins and nutritional supplements - Real Health Laboratories LLC

REAL HERB - Teas–herbal ☆ - Traditional Medicinals, Inc.

REAL HIDES - Footwear - Acme Boot Co., Inc.

REAL HOME-STYLE GOODNESS - Frozen foods - Barber Foods

REAL KIDS - Dolls - Mary Flack

REAL KIDS REAL SCIENCE - Publisher's imprints - Thames and Hudson Inc.

REAL LEAF - Lard - Patrick Cudahy Inc.

REAL LIFE - Apparel and accessories - Certified Fashion Guild Inc.

REAL LIFE - Greeting cards - Big Bear Enterprises, Inc.

REAL LIFE COUPONS - Greeting cards - Banki Co.

REAL LIFE DOODLES - Publisher's imprints - Banki Co.

REAL LIFE RESEARCH - Health care products - Energen Products Inc.

REAL-LITE - Motor vehicles - Juno Industries Inc.

REAL-LITE - Trailers–travel - MPP International, Inc.

REAL/MAX - Electronic equipment - Modular Computer Systems Inc.

REAL MCCOY - Apparel and accessories - Warnaco Inc.

REAL MCCOY - Automotive parts and accessories - Allied Plastics

REAL MCCOY - Pharmaceutical preparations - McCoy's Products Inc.

REAL MCCOY PEN, THE - Electronic equipment - Elegant Ideas

REAL MCCOY, THE - Saw blades - M.K. Morse Co.

REAL MCCOY, THE - Meat extracts - Real McCoy Meat Corp.

REAL MEN - Toys - Mattel, Inc.

REAL MILK OTNEVA CREAMER - Cream - Otneva Corp.

REAL MILK POWDERED CREAMER, THE - Cream - Otneva Corp.

REAL MOTHER GOOSE, THE - Giftware - Roman, Inc.

REAL MOUNTAIN ALE - Beverages–malt - El Dorado Brewing Co.

REAL MOVES BABY - Dolls - Meritus Industries, Inc.
REAL/NET - Computer hardware - Modcomp/Cerplex L.P.
REAL NICE - Paper–tissue - Stephen Lawrence Co.
REAL NUMBERS - Games - Wff'n Proof Learning Games Associates
REAL OCEAN - Pet products ☆ - Catalina Water Co.
REAL PANCREATIN X5 - Vitamins and nutritional supplements ☆ - Ethical Nutrients
REAL PICTURE ATLAS, THE - Computer storage devices–optical - Now What Software
REAL PINE - Cleaning preparations - White Cap Inc.
REAL POO - Hair care products ☆ - Baumgarten's
REAL POWER - Computer software - Land Management Systems, Inc.
REAL* PRO - Jeans–men's - Sun Apparel, Inc.
REAL PRO - Sporting goods - Porter Athletic Equipment Co.
REAL PURITY - Cleaning preparations - Cosmedic Concepts, Inc.
REAL-Q - Musical instrument accessories - Sabine Musical Manufacturing Co. Inc.
REAL RACERS - Toys - Tonka Corp.
REAL RED - Fruit drinks–bottled or canned - Nestle Beverage Co.
REAL RED - Lumber - Cascade Pole and Lumber Co.
REAL REDS - Hair care products - Clairol Inc.
REAL RIDER - Toys–automobiles - Nationsbank of North Carolina, N.A.
REAL RIDERS - Toys–automobiles - Mattel, Inc.
REAL ROAST - Peanut butter - Safeway Stores Inc.
REAL ROMANCE - Perfumes - Colgate-Palmolive Co.
REAL RUBY - Glassware–household ☆ - Pilgrim Glass Corp.
REAL SALT - Salt - Redmond Clay & Salt Co.
REAL SANGRIA - Wines - Shaw-Ross International Importers
REAL SCRAPE - Sporting goods - Wellington Leisure Products, Inc.
REAL SEAL - Adhesives and sealants - Miller Purcell Co.
REAL SEAL - Sealing compounds - Phelps Industrial Products, Inc.
REAL SERIES, THE - Computer software - CEI Communications, Inc.
REAL SHAPES - Underwear and nightwear - Claxton Manufacturing Co. Inc.
REAL SOLUTIONS FOR REAL LIFE - Consulting services - Homeamerican Credit, Inc.
REAL SOUNDS COMBAT GEAR - Toys - Larami Limited, Inc.
REAL SOUNDS RANCH RIDERS - Toys - Larami Limited, Inc.
REAL SOUTHERN - Fruits and vegetables ☆ - McMullen Food Bank Inc.
REAL/STAR - Electronic equipment - Modular Computer Systems Inc.
REAL STEEL - Shoes - H.H. Brown Shoe Co., Inc.
REAL STUFF, THE - Toys - Imperial Toy Corp.
REAL SUPER DRY - Deodorants–personal - Mennen Co.
REAL TECH - Toys–guns - Diversified Specialists, Inc.
REAL TEXANS EAT BROCCOLI! - Music–sheet - Carol E. Goodell
REAL TEXAS - Paper products ☆ - The Salgo Corp.
REAL TEXAS - Seasonings - The Salgo Corp.
REAL-TIME WEATHER NETWORK, THE - Computer hardware - International Weather Network
REAL-TITE - Housewares - Ever Tite Plugs, Inc.
REAL-TONE - Oil stain - Iowa Paint Manufacturing Co. Inc.
REAL TORINO - Pasta - La Pace Imports
REAL TRIM - Food products - Richard A. Shaw Inc.
REAL TUBE OVERDRIVE - Guitars ☆ - Chandler Industries
REAL TUF - Bags–trash - Arrow Industries, Inc.
REAL TUF - Office supplies - Swansea Manufacturing Co., Inc.
REAL-TUFF - Adhesives and sealants - Hercules Chemical Co. Inc.
REAL VALU - Bakery products–frozen - Herold & Miller Inc.
REAL VERMONT HONEY - Honey - Uncle Dave's Kitchen
REAL VOLUME - Shampoos - Redmond Products, Inc.
REAL WALL - Clocks - Zelco Industries, Inc.
REAL WHEELS - Recording label - Atlantic Recording Corp.
REAL WHIP - Desserts - Presto Food Products, Inc.
REAL WHITE PAGES, THE - Telephone directories - Bellsouth Corp.
REAL-WOOD - Wood products - Star Bronze Co. Inc.
REAL WOOD COLLECTION - Floor coverings–tile - Robbins Interior Surface Inc.
REAL WORLD - Recording label - Virgin Records
REAL YO-YOS, THE - Toys - Jim Simon
REALAIDE - Computer software - Rocky Mountain Software Corp.
REALASAURUS - Educational materials - Linda L. Rosen
REALAUDIO - Computer peripheral equipment - Progressive Networks, Inc.
REALAUDIO PLAYER - Computer software - Progressive Networks, Inc.
REALCALC - Computer software - Integrated Equity Planning
REALDREAM - Recording label - Darksilver Records & Filmworks Inc.
REALE BRAND - Cheese - A & J Cheese Co., Inc.
REALEAN - Hams - Patrick Cudahy Inc.

REALEARTH - Maps - British Technology Group USA, Inc.
REALEMON - Juices - Borden, Inc.
REALEMON - Lemonade - Realemon Foods
REALFIG - Juices ☆ - Realemon Foods
REALFORM - Foundation garments–women's - Merit Foundations Inc.
REALFRUIT COMPANY, THE - Cheese - Boston Brands, Inc.
REALHIDES - Boots - Acme Boot Co., Inc.
REALIFE - Recording label - Cultural Designs
REALIFE MINIATURES - Hobby kits - Scientific Models Inc.
REALIMAGE - Field glasses - Cabela's Inc.
REALIME - Juices - Borden, Inc.
REALIME - Juices - Realemon Foods
REALISTIC - Cosmetics - Ilona, Inc.
REALISTIC - Electronic equipment - Tandy Corp.
REALISTIC - Hair care products - Revlon Consumer Products Corp.
REALISTIC - Novelty items - Health Devices Corp.
REALISTIC EXCLUSIVES - Hair care products - Roux Laboratories, Inc.
REALISTIC RACING COLORS, INC. - Paints - Realistic Racing Colors, Inc.
REALISTIC RETIREMENT ANSWERS - Computer storage devices–magnetic - Scanner Software Systems, Inc.
REALITE - Bratwurst, sausage - Abbyland Processing
REALITE - Lamps - Angelo Brothers Co.
REALITE PLUS - Automotive parts and accessories - Western Aggregates, Inc.
REALITES - Footwear–women's - Oomphies Inc.
REALITI - Work benches - Shure Manufacturing Corp.
REALITIES - Perfumes ☆ - Labelon Corp.
REALITIES BY LIZ CLAIBORNE - Perfumes - Liz Claiborne Inc.
REALITY - Computer software - Kinetic Systems Corp.
REALITY - Heaters–space - Martin Industries, Inc.
REALITY - Mirrors - Metropolitan Mirror & Glass Co. Inc.
REALITY - Optical machinery - Stereomedia, Inc.
REALITY - Snowboards - Chris S. Graham
REALITY CHECK - Computer software - Ventana Systems, Inc.
REALITY INTERACTIVE - Computer software - Reality Interactive, Inc.
REALITY ROCKET - Video games - Alternate Worlds Technology Inc.
REALITY UNIT CONCEPT - Recording label - Jazz Composer's Orchestra Association Inc.
REALKWIK - Computer software - Dexter Savoy
REALLUSIONS - Wigs and hair pieces - Taylormade Hair Replacement
REALLY - Apparel and accessories ☆ - Glamorise Foundations Inc.
REALLY CREAMY - Health care products - Millhopper Marketing Inc.
REALLY DATING - Toys–electronic - Tiger Electronics, Inc.
REALLY GARLICKY - Olive oil - Golden Whisk Pasta Partners
REALLY LIVING ROOM, THE - Furniture - Bean Station Furniture Factory Inc.
REALLY NATURALS - Snack foods - Farley Candy Co.
REALLY RANCH - Nuts–salted, roasted, cooked, or canned ☆ - Sonne Laboratories
REALLY RAW - Honey - Really Raw Honey Co.
REALLY READING - Publisher's imprint - SBF Services Inc.
REALLY, REALLY, REALLY LOVE GOLF - Jewelry - United States Golf Association
REALLY RED - Lipsticks ☆ - Honey & Spice Toiletries
REALLY RESTRICTED SHELL - Computer software - Unitech/Raxco, Inc.
REALLY RUDE - Dolls - Mattel, Inc.
REALLY WOOLLY - Greeting cards - David C. Cook Publishing Co.
REALM - Colognes - Erox Corp.
REALM OF IMPOSSIBILITY - Computer software ☆ - Electronic Arts Inc.
REALMS OF AKANIA-SHADOWS OVER RIVA - Computer software - Sir-Tech Software, Inc.
REALMS OF ARKANIA - Computer software - Sir-Tech Software, Inc.
REALOCK - Fencing–chain link ☆ - CF and I Steel L.P.
REALOGIC - Computer software - Realogic, Inc.
REALONDA - Tiles–ceramic - Matrix Trading Co.
REALPORT - Computer software - Digi International, Inc.
REALPRUNE - Juices ☆ - Realemon Foods
REALPURE - Fruit juices - Network Group
REALPURE - Water–bottled or canned - Network Group
REALSAFE - Safes - Realsafe Security Systems, Inc.
REALTIME - Recording label - Miller & Kreisel Sound Corp.
REALTIME - Watches ☆ - Realtime Corp.
REALTIME ASSOCIATES, INC. - Computer software - Realtime Associates, Inc.
REALTIME VISION - Computer software - Laboratory Technologies Corp.
REALTOR - Collective membership mark - National Association of Realtors
REALTOUR - Computer software - Fantam Technologies
REALTREE - Apparel and accessories - Hunter's Specialties, Inc.

☆ = Now out of production

REALTREE - Firearms, accessories, and parts - Spartan-Realtree Products, Inc.

REALTREE ALL-PURPOSE - Firearms, accessories, and parts - Spartan-Realtree Products, Inc.

REALTUF - Bags–trash - United Plastic Films, Inc.

REALTY CHECK - Computer software - Title Office, Inc.

REALTY EYES - Computer software - Infocode Corp.

REALTY SHOP, THE - Real estate agencies - Realty Shop, Inc.

REALUBE - Lubricants - Lamson Oil Co.

REALWIN - Computer software - Myers Computing Solutions, Inc.

REALWORLD - Computer software - RealWorld Corp.

REALX BABY - Toys–stuffed - Jolly U.S.A., Inc.

REALYS - Nail care products - Realys, Inc.

REAM-DRIVER - Screw drivers - Diversified Research Inc.

REAM-N-KLEAN - Pipe cleaners - Bryn Mawr Smokers Sundries Inc.

REAMES - Food products - Reames Foods Inc.

REAMZALL - Pipes–tobacco ☆ - S.M. Frank & Co. Inc. (Kaywoodie-Yello-Bole-Medico)

REAPER - Toys - Tonka Corp.

REAPERS ROOST - Apparel and accessories - Brad Brophy

REAPING LIZARD RAZOR - Razors - C.A. Daniels & Co.

REAR FLEX BARS - Sporting goods - O'Brien International

REAR GEAR - Apparel and accessories - Edison Brothers Stores, Inc.

REAR GEAR - Furniture–public buildings - Robert A. Forcier and Marsha M. Forcier Partnership

REAR ROLL RETURN - Tarpaulins - Shur-Co Inc.

REAR VIEW - Calendars - Landmark General Corp.

REAR VIEWS - Underwear and nightwear - Intimate Visions Inc.

REAR WINDOW - Ophthalmic apparatus - WGBH Educational Foundation

REARS - Snack foods - Reser's Fine Foods Inc.

REASON - Computer software - CLM Technologies, Ltd.

REASON FOR WRITING, A - Educational materials - Concerned Group, Inc.

REASON, THE - Golfing equipment - Mizuno Corp. of America

REASON WHY, THE - Publisher's imprints ☆ - Harper Junior Books Group

REASONABLE SOLUTIONS - Computer games - Reasonable Solutions, Inc.

REASONS BY TRANSWALL - Partitions–wood - Transwall Corp.

REATTA - Motor vehicles–automobiles - General Motors Corp. (Buick Motor Div.)

REATTA - Strollers–baby - Century Products Co.

REAU GRANDE - Beverages–alcohol - Cameron Craig Ltd.

REAVITA - Pharmaceutical preparations - Reaco Products Inc.

REAVO - Skin care products - Reliv' International, Inc.

REAX - Frames–eyeglass - Sport Logix, Inc.

REB - Containers–plastic - Landmark Plastic Corp.

REBA - Amplifiers - Mason Electronics, Inc.

REBA - Apparel–women's - Rebecca Lamaka

REBA - Novelty items - Reba Mcentire

REBAG - Bags - Earthly Matters Inc.

REBAR - Gloves ☆ - Distributors Service Corp.

REBARK - Pet products - Classic Products

REBECCA - Dolls - Uneeda Doll Co., Inc.

REBECCA - Frames–eyeglass - U.S. Optical Frame Co.

REBECCA - Recording label - GP Records & Tapes

REBECCA DANIELS - Footwear - Rebecca Daniels

REBECCA MOORE - Leather goods - Olivet International Inc.

REBECCA MOSS - Pens - Rebecca Moss Ltd.

REBECCA OF SUNNYBROOK FARM - Dolls ☆ - Effanbee Doll Corp.

REBECCA ROSE - Clothing - RSK Industries, Inc.

REBECCA SMITH DESIGNS - Candy - Rebecca Smith Designs

REBECCA'S GARDEN - Apparel stores–women's - Hearst Corp.

REBEKAH'S - Jams and jellies ☆ - Silver Foods Corp.

REBEL - Bicycles - Columbia Manufacturing Inc.

REBEL - Bicycles ☆ - Muskin Leisure Products Inc.

REBEL - Boats - Glen-L Marine Designs

REBEL - Boats - National Rebel Class Association

REBEL - Boats–motor - Lund Boat Co.

REBEL - Boats–motor - Plastics Research and Development Co.

REBEL - Boats–motor ☆ - Forester Boats Inc.

REBEL - Boats–motor ☆ - Rinker Boat Co. Inc.

REBEL - Clocks - General Time Corp. (Westclox/Seth Thomas Div.)

REBEL - Colognes - Protex

REBEL - Doors–garage ☆ - Raynor Manufacturing Co.

REBEL - Electric guitars ☆ - International Music Corp.

REBEL - Gasoline ☆ - Texas City Refining Inc.

REBEL - Heaters–space - Dri-Eaz Products, Inc.

REBEL - Heating equipment - Emerson Electric Co.

REBEL - Meat products–beef - Suzanna's Kitchen Inc.

REBEL - Motor vehicles ☆ - DaimlerChrysler

REBEL - Ships–sailing vessels - Ray Greene Industries

REBEL - Thread ☆ - American & Efird, Inc.

REBEL - Toys–automobiles - Maisto International, Inc.

REBEL - Watches - Elgin Watch Co.

REBEL 16 - Boats–canoes ☆ - Sawyer Composite Products

REBEL ASSAULT - Computer software - Lucasarts Entertainment Co.

REBEL BLUE - Apparel–children's - Cradle Togs, Inc.

REBEL BREAD - Breads–mixes ☆ - Wind & Willow, LLC

REBEL COMMANDO - Toys - Lucasfilm Ltd.

REBEL ELECTRONICS - Audio equipment - Rebel Electronics Inc.

REBEL-ETTE - Apparel–children's - Robert Mulder

REBEL KIDS - Apparel–children's - Maria Howard

REBEL RECORDS - Recording label - County Records

REBEL ROCK - Recording label - Baddest of the Bad Posse Records

REBEL, THE - Tools–hand-operated - Woodstock International, Inc.

REBEL-X - Apparel and accessories - Mark V. Martocci

REBEL YELL - Beverages–alcohol - Schenley Industries Inc.

REBEL YELL - Liquors - United Distillers Manufacturing, Inc.

REBELLIOUS - Apparel–children's - Robert Mulder

REBELS - Footwear - Eyal Balle

REBELS - Toys ☆ - Intex Recreation Corp.

REBELS RAGE - Dressing gowns - York East Merchandise, Inc.

REBELS UNLV - Apparel–athletic - University of Nevada, Las Vegas

REBER - Candy - Morris National Inc.

REBER - Canned vegetables - Aunt Nellie's Farm Kitchens Inc.

REBER - Confections - George C. Brown's Biscuits & Confections

REBIRTH - Recording label - Rebirth Inc./Wenha Productions

REBIS - Computer software - Rebis

REBLADE - Health care products - Cutlery Associates Inc.

REBOOT - Lunch boxes - Thermos Co.

REBOOT - Shoes ☆ - S. Goldberg and Co. Inc.

REBORN - Starch–laundry - American Belt Co.

REBORN - Vitamins and nutritional supplements ☆ - Pharmavite Corp.

REBOUND - Bandages–orthopedic - Tecnol Medical Products, Inc.

REBOUND - Computer hardware - Teltrust, Inc.

REBOUND - Fabrics - Leucadia, Inc.

REBOUND - Fertilizers - International Soil Systems, Inc.

REBOUND - Firefighting suits - Lion Apparel, Inc.

REBOUND - Games - CBS Toys

REBOUND - Golfing equipment - Rebound Systems Inc.

REBOUND - Hair care products - Golden Sun Vitamins

REBOUND - Health care products - East Earth Herb Inc.

REBOUND - Recording label - Polygram Records, Inc.

REBOUND - Sporting goods - Christy Co.

REBOUND - Toys - Tyco Industries, Inc.

REBOUND - Trading cards and stamps - Treat Entertainment, Inc.

REBOUND 3 - Veterinary nutritional supplements - Oralx Corp.

REBOUND BOARD - Exercising equipment ☆ - Gerstung/Gym-Thing Inc.

REBOUND STRIP - Electrical testing instruments - H+W Test Products

REBOUNDER - Basketball shoes ☆ - Jaclar

REBOUNDER - Games - Ziffco

REBOUNDER - Sporting goods ☆ - L.A. Steelcraft Products Inc.

REBOUNDER, THE - Hoses - Marigold Marketing

REBUILDER - Vitamins and nutritional supplements - Kroeger Herb Products Co. Inc.

REC - Apparel and accessories - Worldwide Creations, Inc.

REC RACER - Exercising equipment ☆ - Little River Marine Co.

REC ROOM - Floor coverings–carpet and rugs - Porter Carpet Mills Inc.

REC-TECH - Asphalt felts and coatings - Maintenance Inc.

RECALL - Clocks - General Time Corp. (Westclox/Seth Thomas Div.)

RECALL - Computer software - Re:Claim, Inc.

RECALL - Vitamins and nutritional supplements - Shaperite Concepts, Ltd.

RECALLIT - Computer software - HPS Software, Inc.

RECAMIER - Vegetables–canned - Recamier Inc.

RECAP - Computer software - Structured Solutions, Inc.

RECAPTURE THE TRADITION - Apparel–athletic - L & W Partnership

RECEBRAL F - Vitamins and nutritional supplements - Benard Industries Inc.

RECEIPT-IT - Computer software - Tax Compliance Management

RECEIPT RITE - Office supplies - Reynolds and Reynolds Co.

RECEPTION - Clocks ☆ - General Time Corp. (Westclox/Seth Thomas Div.)

RECEPTION - Wines ☆ - Bardenheier Wine Cellars

RECEPTIVE - Floor coverings–carpet and rugs ☆ - Walter Carpet Mills

RECEPTOR - Golfing equipment - Aldila, Inc.

RECEPTOR - Watches - AT & E Corp.

RECESSION JEWELRY - Jewelry - Just A Little Stock Co., Inc.

RECHARGE - Juices - Knudsen & Sons Inc.

RECHARGEABLE LIGHTING FLASHLIGHTS & LANTERNS - Flashlights - Garrity Industries

RECHARGEABLES - Hearing aids - Magnatone Hearing Aid Corp.

RECHARGING COMPLEX - Vitamins and nutritional supplements - Nioxin Research Laboratories Inc.

RECIOTO DELLA VALPOICELLA AMARONE CLASSICO SUPERIORE - Wines ☆ - Kobrand Corp.

RECIP-EASE - Corn–flour or meal - Martha White Foods Inc.

RECIPE - Clocks ☆ - General Time Corp. (Westclox/Seth Thomas Div.)

RECIPE - Dog food - Heinz Pet Products Co.

RECIPE - Flour–blended - Stevens Industries Inc.

RECIPE - Mayonnaise - Autry Greer and Sons Inc.

RECIPE - Seafood products–canned or cured ☆ - Peter Pan Seafoods, Inc.

RECIPE BLEND - Cheese - Sargento Cheese Co. Inc.

RECIPE BLEND - Food products - Rathdowney

RECIPE BOOK - Dairy products - Mid-America Dairymen Inc. Southern Div.

RECIPE CHOICE - Frozen foods - Sysco Corp.

RECIPE EXPRESS - Computer software - Pinpoint Publishing

RECIPE FOR PAINTING - Hobby kits - Aleene's

RECIPE GREETINGS - Greeting cards - Continnuus

RECIPE MANAGER, THE - Computer software - Truly Friendly Software, Inc.

RECIPE MEXICANA - Food products - Saramar Corp.

RECIPE READY - Pork - Wilson Foods Corp.

RECIPE ROSTER - Computer software - E-8 Publications, Inc.

RECIPE SAUCES - Food products - General Mills, Inc.

RECIPE SECRETS - Seasonings - Lipton Investments, Inc.

RECIPE STYLE - Sour cream - Old Home Foods Inc.

RECIPE WIZARD - Computer software - Microblast Software

RECIPES-AT-A-GLANCE - Boxes ☆ - Plants-at-a-Glance Corp.

RECIPES FOR LIFE - Publisher's imprint - Cy Decosse Inc.

RECIPES OF AMERICA - Paper products - Sargento Inc.

RECIPRO-SAW - Saws–power - S-B Power Tool Co.

RECIRC - Pumps - Laing Thermotech Inc.

RECITAL - Recording label - Music and Arts Programs of America Inc.

RECITAL TIME - Dolls ☆ - Effanbee Doll Corp.

RECKLESS ATTITUDE - Apparel and accessories - Phillip J. Frasch

RECKLESS ROCKY ROAD - Confections - Weight Watchers International, Inc.

RECKONING - Computer software - David J. Brown

RECLAIM - See REISSUE

RECLAIM 100 - Bags–trash - Chelsea Industries Inc.

RECLAIMER - Heating equipment ☆ - Heat Controller Inc.

RECLINA CHAIR - Recliners - Stratford Co.

RECLINA-GLIDER - Furniture–upholstered - La-Z-Boy Chair Co.

RECLINA-REST - Recliners - La-Z-Boy Chair Co.

RECLINA-ROCKER - Rocking chairs - La-Z-Boy Chair Co.

RECLINA-WAY - Recliners - La-Z-Boy Chair Co.

RECLINE N' LIFT - Chairs–upholstered - Sci-O-Tech Inc.

RECLINERMATES - Furniture - Lane Co. Inc.

RECO - Compressors–refrigeration - York International Corp.

RECO - Figurines - Reco International Corp.

RECO ANGEL COLLECTION - Figurines - Reco International Corp.

RECO CLOWN COLLECTION - Figurines - Reco International Corp.

RECO COLLECTION - Giftware - Reco International Corp.

RECO GOURMET - Kitchenware–earthenware - Reco International Corp.

RECO KALEIDOSCOPE COLLECTION - Giftware - Reco International Corp.

RECO RADI-AIRE - Fans–electric ☆ - Middleby Cooking Systems Group

RECOATIT - Finishing agents - Marine Development & Research Corp.

RECOFEN CAPS - Pharmaceutical preparations - Reese Chemical Co.

RECOFEN-D - Pharmaceutical preparations - Reese Chemical Co.

RECOGNITION - Clocks - General Time Corp. (Westclox/Seth Thomas Div.)

RECOGNITION - Floor coverings–carpet and rugs ☆ - Callaway Carpets

RECOGNITIONS - Publisher's imprints - Crossroad

RECOGNIZER - Computer software - Information & Graphics Systems Inc.

RECOGNIZING FULL SENTENCES - Computer software ☆ - Right on Programs

RECOGNIZING NOUNS - Computer software - Right on Programs

RECOGNIZING VERBS - Computer software - Right on Programs

RECOIL - Apparel and accessories - James and Edwin's T's

RECOIL PADS - Firearms, accessories, and parts - Armsport Inc.

RECOILER - Motor vehicle parts and accessories - Joseph Callavini

RECOILER, THE - Tools–hand-operated - Newborn Brothers & Co., Inc.

RECOLLECTION - Dinnerware–glass - Federal Glass

RECOLLECTION - Paper - Simpson Paper Co.

RECOLLECTION - Pressed glassware - Indiana Glass Co.

RECOLLECTIONS - Burial caskets - Batesville Casket Co., Inc.

RECOLLECTIONS - Chimes ☆ - Nutone Inc.

RECOLLECTIONS - Fabrics - Motif Designs, Inc.

RECOLLECTIONS - Floor coverings–carpet and rugs ☆ - Zenith Carpets

RECOLLECTIONS - Greeting cards ☆ - American Greetings Corp.

RECOLLECTIONS - House furnishings - Lexington Furniture Industries, Inc.

RECOLLECTIONS - Trays ☆ - Giordano Art, Ltd.

RECOLLECTIONS BY CLARK GOFF - Frames–picture - Distinctive Design

RECOLLECTIONS BY LIGHTPOST - Statuary–wood - Lightpost Group, Inc.

RECOLLECTIONS OF PARIS - Christmas tree ornaments - Cracker Box Inc.

RECOMBINANT SPREAD SPECTRUM - Transmitting apparatus–radio - Digital Wireless Corp.

RECOMBIVAX HB - Pharmaceutical preparations - Merck & Co., Inc. (Merck Research Laboratories)

RECOMMENDATION - Floor coverings–carpet and rugs ☆ - Walter Carpet Mills

RECOMMENDED - Recording label - Jazz Composer's Orchestra Association Inc.

RECOMPUTE - Computer peripheral equipment - Recompute! Corp.

RECON - Computer software ☆ - Popular Programs Inc.

RECON - Medical apparatus - Editek, Inc.

RECON - Remote control devices - Perry Tritech, Inc.

RECON 50 - Pet products - Aquatronics-Filtronics

RECONPLUS - Medical apparatus - Baxter International Inc.

RECONSTITUBE - Pharmaceutical preparations - Apothecary Products, Inc.

RECONSTIVE PAC - Hair care products - For Perms Only Inc.

RECONSTRUCT - Hair care products - Scruples Professional Salon Products, Inc.

RECONSTRUCTIONIST PRESS - Publisher's imprints - Hebrew Publishing Co.

RECONSTRUCTIVE - Hair care products - Gefden International Inc.

RECONSTRUCTOR - Hair care products - Gefden International Inc.

RECONSTRUCTOR - Shampoos - Cheveux Inc.

RECOPY - Paper–writing - Champion International Corp.

RECOR - Measuring instruments - Reynolds Equipment Co.

RECOR - Paperboard–corrugated - Menasha Corp.

RECOR - Water purification systems - Terra Group, Inc.

RECORD - Fishing lines ☆ - Cortland Line Co., Inc.

RECORD - Frames–picture - S & W Framing Supplies Inc.

RECORD - Thread - A. Lewis Thread Co. Inc.

RECORD - Wheelchairs - Everest and Jennings International Ltd.

RECORD - Wheelchairs - Medical Composite Technology

RECORD & PLAYBACK - Toys - Fisher-Price, Inc.

RECORD BOND - Cigars ☆ - H.L. Neff & Co. Inc.

RECORD BREAKER - Apparel and accessories - Pep Motif, Inc.

RECORD BREAKER - Cigar boxes–wood - Consolidated Cigar Corp.

RECORD BREAKERS - Toys - Tonka Corp.

RECORD BREAKERS - Toys–automobiles - Hasbro, Inc.

RECORD COLLECTION - Lipsticks ☆ - Honey & Spice Toiletries

RECORD CO. OF THE SOUTH - Recording label - Record Co. of the South

RECORD EXPRESS - Dictating machines - Dictaphone Corp.

RECORD-EZE - Office supplies - Ekonomik Systems

RECORD-FLOW - File folders ☆ - Watson Industries Inc.

RECORD KEEPER'S DELIGHT - Notebooks and notepads - People Systems Inc.

RECORD MASTERS - Recording label - Terock Records

RECORD-O-SYNC - Electronic equipment - T.M. Visual Industries Inc.

RECORD SETTERS - Fishing lures - L & S Bait Co. Inc.

RECORD SETTERS - Magnets - C.M. Paula Co.

RECORD SLUTS - Recording label - Jazz Composer's Orchestra Association Inc.

RECORDAK - Photographic equipment - Eastman Kodak Co.

RECORDATE - Photographic equipment - SP Systems/Saratons

RECORDER - Electronic equipment repair shops ☆ - Hydrolab Corp.

RECORDER - Office supplies ☆ - Faber-Castell Corp.

RECORDER - Paper - Esleeck Manufacturing Co., Inc.

RECORDER - Thermometers - Popper & Sons Inc.

RECORDEX - Office supplies - Victor Systems & Equipment Co.

RECORDINE - Paper - Esleeck Manufacturing Co., Inc.

RECORDING COOPERATIVE - Recording label - S.W. & A. Associates Co.

RECORDING SESSION - Computer software - Midisoft Corp.

RECORDLINK - Computer software - American Management Systems, Inc.

RECORDMASTER - Electronic equipment - Dukane Corp.

RECORDPLATE - Telephone directories - Rediform

RECORDS MANAGEMENT CONTROL - Computer software - Right on Programs

RECORDSTAR - Computer software - I-Net, Inc.

☆ = Now out of production

RECORDVIEW - Computer software - Moore Business Forms, Inc.
RECORT PLUS - Pharmaceutical preparations - Reese Chemical Co.
RECOTON - Converters–electric - Recoton Corp.
RECOUP - Hair care products - ABBA Products Inc.
RECOUP - Vitamins and nutritional supplements - Protech Nutritionals, Inc.
RECOUPAERATOR - Exchangers–heat - Stirling Technology Inc.
RECOUVRER - Hair care products - Peter Hantz Co.
RECOVER - Cosmetics ☆ - Del Pharmaceuticals, Inc.
RECOVER - Facsimile equipment - Appleton Papers Inc.
RECOVER - Pharmaceutical preparations ☆ - Bricker Laboratories
RECOVERY - Orthopedic products - Biomet, Inc.
RECOVERY GEAR USA - Motor vehicles - Recovery Gear USA
RECOVERY POWER FOODS - Vitamins and nutritional supplements - Great Circles, Inc.
RECOVERY RECYCLED - Envelopes - Western States Envelope Co.
RECOVERYPAK - Refrigerant recovery units - York International Corp.
RECREATION - Apparel–women's - Koret of California, Inc.
RECREATION - Hair care products - Helene Curtis Industries Inc.
RECREATIONAL WOODCRAFT - Wood products - Channel Craft
RECRON - Film ☆ - E.I. Dupont de Nemours and Co.
RECRUIT - Jackets - Horace Small Apparel Co.
RECRUITER - Toys–models ☆ - Estes Industries
RECRUITER, THE - Computer software - Micromax, Inc.
RECT - Tomar Electronics Inc.
RECTACAINE - Pharmaceutical preparations - Reese Chemical Co.
RECTAGENE - Pharmaceutical preparations - Pfeiffer Pharmaceuticals Inc.
RECTAL AID - Pharmaceutical preparations - Republic Drug Co. Inc.
RECTALAD - Medical apparatus ☆ - Wallace Laboratories
RECTALGAN - Pharmaceutical preparations ☆ - Wyeth-Ayerst Laboratories
RECTANGLESPRAY - Garden equipment - Thompson Manufacturing Co.
RECTANGULAR SOLID-CORE - Cables - Tara Labs, Inc.
RECTIFY - Hair care products - Concentrics Inc.
RECTIGRAPH - Paper - Xerox Corp.
RECTITE - Adhesives and sealants - Pacer Technology
RECTOLINE - Pharmaceutical preparations - Luyties Pharmacal Co.
RECTOR - Insulation board - Rector Mineral Trading Corp.
RECTOR INFAL - Insulation board - Rector Mineral Trading Corp.
RECTOR SEEK - Cement - Rectorseal Corp.
RECTOR SHIELD - Glue–household or industrial - Rectorseal Corp.
RECTORKLEEN - Soap - Rectorseal Corp.
RECTORSCALE - Chemical preparations - Rectorseal Corp.
RECTORSEAL AIR-LOCK - Adhesives and sealants - Rectorseal Corp.
RECTORSEAL ARCTIC - Cement - Rectorseal Corp.
RECTORSEAL AT-33 - Adhesives and sealants - Rectorseal Corp.
RECTORSEAL GOLD - Cement - Rectorseal Corp.
RECTORSEAL HOT - Cement - Rectorseal Corp.
RECTORSEAL NO. 5 - Chemical preparations - Rectorseal Corp.
RECTORSEAL NO. 9 - Chemical preparations - Rectorseal Corp.
RECTORSEAL T PLUS 2 - Chemical preparations - Rectorseal Corp.
RECTORSEAL TRU-BLU - Chemical preparations - Rectorseal Corp.
RECTORSLIKKK - Chemical preparations - Rectorseal Corp.
RECTORY - Floor coverings–carpet and rugs - Porter Carpet Mills Inc.
RECTOSAN - Pharmaceutical preparations - Herb Products Co.
RECUPERATION - Skin care products - Ilona, Inc.
RECUR - Shampoos ☆ - Scandinavian Natural Health & Beauty Products, Inc.
RECVEONICS UNDERWATER PLATFORM - Sporting goods - Recreonics, Inc.
RECWEAR - Shirts - Munsingwear, Inc.
RECYCLABIN - Bags–plastic - Marino Technologies, Inc.
RECYCLASAURUS - Containers - Douglas Brian Drysdale
RECYCLE! - Apparel and accessories - Quad/Graphics, Inc.
RECYCLE 1 - Bags–trash - North American Plastics Corp.
RECYCLE AMERICA - Adhesives - Power Poxy Adhesives, Inc.
RECYCLE DRAINER CONTAINER - Automotive parts and accessories - Geo Plastics, Inc.
RECYCLE REX - Posters - State of California Dept. of Conservation
RECYCLE-SAC - Health care products - Millhopper Marketing Inc.
RECYCLE WEAR - Apparel and accessories - Recycle Wear, Inc.
RECYCLEAR - Plastics film - Arkwright Inc.
RECYCLED - Recording label - Jazz Composer's Orchestra Association Inc.
RECYCLED DEERFIELD - Paper - Canson-Talens Inc.
RECYCLED PAPER GREETINGS - Greeting cards - Recycled Paper Products, Inc.
RECYCLED ROADSIDE - Bird feeds - Forest Time Products Inc.
RECYCLED SCOTTIES - Facial tissues - Scott Paper Co.
RECYCLED TEENAGER - Novelty items - Trisar Inc.

RECYCLED TRASH COMPANY, THE - Shirts - Monica St. Marie Tognoli
RECYCLED UNIVERSAL HEAVYWEIGHT - Paper - Canson-Talens Inc.
RECYCLEPAK - Bottles–glass - Drug Plastic and Glass Co.
RECYCLER - Antifreeze - Kleer Flo Co. Inc.
RECYCLER - Lawn mowers - Toro Co.
RECYCLERS' TEAM, THE - Brushes ☆ - Flo-Pac Corp.
RECYCLESTER - Chemical preparations - Waste Alternatives, Inc.
RECYCLETTE - Trash organizers - Pro-Mart International
RECYCLING ORGANIZERS - Containers - Tavens Industries Inc.
RECYCLIPS - Paper clips - Noesting Inc.
RECYCLITE - Containers - E.S. Robbins Corp.
RECYCLYING LOGIC - Computer software ☆ - Sunburst Communications, Inc.
RECYCOOL - Shirts - Peter A. Kasprzak
RECYGULLS, THE - Stationery and greetings cards - Sandra Ames
RECYKLEEN - Cleaning preparations–household - Twin Rivers Technologies, L.P.
RED - Balls - Diamond Baseball Co., Inc.
RED - Cat food ☆ - Agway Country Foods Inc.
RED - Cleaning preparations - Isotech Laboratories Manufacturing Inc.
RED - Colognes - Giorgio Beverly Hills
RED - Sunglasses ☆ - Oakley, Inc.
RED - Tools–hand-operated - Burton Corp.
RED - Toys - Jim Henson Productions, Inc.
RED 1 - Beverages–carbonated - Allied Beverage
RED-1 - Crocheted and knitted items - Veratec
RED 2 - Toiletries - Giorgio Beverly Hills, Inc.
RED A FEEDS - Animal feeds - Agri-Dealers Supply Co., Inc.
RED ADAIR - Apparel and accessories - Adair Enterprises, Inc.
RED ALERT - Alarm systems - Beaumont Products, Inc.
RED ALERT - Cleaning preparations - Harris Research, Inc.
RED ALERT - Game machines - Sigma Game Inc.
RED ALERT - Tape–adhesive - Central Products Co.
RED ALERT - Toys–models ☆ - Estes Industries
RED & WHITE - Food containers - Federated Foods Inc.
RED & WHITE - Turkeys - Watson Quality Foods Inc.
RED APPLE - Beverages–carbonated - Shasta Beverages, Inc.
RED APPLE - Kitchenware–earthenware - Watt Pottery Co.
RED APPLE ORCHARD - Fruit drinks–bottled or canned - Johanna Foods, Inc.
RED ARROW - Fruits and vegetables - Shafer Lake Fruit Inc.
RED ARROW - Health care products - Summa Pharmaceutical Laboratories Inc.
RED ASS - Beverages–malt - County Cork, Inc.
RED BAG - Pet products - Mardel Laboratories, Inc.
RED BAG - Pet products - USA-Petrx
RED BALL - Apparel–athletic - Red Ball Corp.
RED BALL - Footwear - La Crosse Footwear, Inc.
RED BALL - Footwear - Norcross Footwear, Inc.
RED BALL BY LACROSSE - Footwear - La Crosse Footwear, Inc.
RED BALL JETS - Footwear–children's - Servus Footwear Co.
RED BALLOON - Novelty items - Red Balloon Co., Inc.
RED BAND - Dinnerware–glass ☆ - Lenox, Inc.
RED BAND - Erasers ☆ - Empire Berol USA
RED BAND - Flour–blended - General Mills, Inc.
RED BAND - Licorice - Holland-American Importing Co. Inc.
RED BAND STICK - Candy - Moretz Candy Co. Inc.
RED BANDANNA - Beverages–carbonated - J.R. Gonzalez Corp.
RED BANK CLOTHING CO. - Jackets - Turnkey Consultants Ltd.
RED BANMER - Tools - Allied Wholesale Inc.
RED BAR - Batteries - Exide Corp.
RED BAR - Paper ☆ - Mead Corp.
RED BARN - Recording label - Goldust Records Co.
RED BARON - Computer software - Sierra Merger Corp.
RED BARON - Food products - Tony's Pizza Service
RED BARON - Hair care products - Select Brands
RED BARON - Kites - North Pacific Products Inc.
RED BARON BROWN - Cosmetics ☆ - Noxell Corp.
RED BARON OVENSTUFFS - Frozen foods - Schwan's Sales Enterprises, Inc.
RED BARON ULTIMATE DEEP DISH - Pizzas–mixes - Schwan's Sales Enterprises, Inc.
RED BARONS - Drums–musical instruments ☆ - J.D. Calato Manufacturing Inc.
RED BARONS - Novelty items - Multi-Purpose Stadium Authority of Lackawanna County
RED BARRICADES - Games - Avalon Hill Game Co.
RED BEANS - Recording label - Red Beans Records

RED BEAR - Amplifiers - Gibson Guitar Corp.
RED BEAR - Apparel and accessories - Red Bear Clothing, Inc.
RED BEAR - Cleaning preparations - SCI Scandicrafts Inc.
RED BELL - Beverages–malt - Red Bell Brewing Co.
RED BERRY - Beverages - Sundor Brands Inc.
RED BIRD - Bicycles - Columbia Manufacturing Inc.
RED BIRD - Candy - Piedmont Candy Co.
RED BIRD - Cereal ☆ - Organic Milling
RED BIRD - Gasoline - Tosco Corp.
RED BIRD - Recording label - GP Records & Tapes
RED BIRD - Shoes - Carolina Shoe Co.
RED BIRD - Vegetables–canned - Agland Inc. (Bean Div.)
RED BITES - Candy - American Licorice Co.
RED BONE ALLEY - Apparel - Barth, Inc.
RED BONES - Footwear - Shoe Show, Inc.
RED BOY - Cheese - Darigold, Inc.
RED BOY - Fruits and vegetables - Sundance Fruit Inc.
RED BOY - Mustard - Clements Food Co. Inc.
RED BRANCH - Video production - Red Branch Productions, Ltd.
RED BRAND - Fencing–steel - Keystone Steel & Wire Co.
RED BRAND - Wire products - Keystone Consolidated Industries, Inc.
RED BRICK ALE - Apparel and accessories - Bricktown Brewery
RED BRICK SYSTEMS - Computer software - Applications Design Inc.
RED BRUSH - Paints - Kansas Paint & Color Co.
RED BUD - Food products ☆ - Hale-Halsell Co.
RED BUD - Thread - Cincinnati Thread Co.
RED BUD TWIST - Tobacco products ☆ - Scott Tobacco Co.
RED BUG - Food products - Blum & Bergeron Inc.
RED BULL - Beverages–malt - The Stroh Brewery Co.
RED BUSH - Teas - Seelect, Inc.
RED CALLIOPE - Wallpaper ☆ - Imperial Wallcoverings, Inc.
RED CANYON - Bicycles - Dynacraft Industries Inc.
RED CAP - Erasers ☆ - Faber-Castell Corp.
RED CAP - Fire extinguishers - Kidde Safety
RED CAP BAJA WHIPS - Automotive parts and accessories ☆ - R & R Sales
RED CARNIVAL - Glassware–household - Fenton Art Glass Co.
RED CARPET - Fruits and vegetables ☆ - Idaho Fruit Sales Inc.
RED CEDAR - Floor coverings - Southern Aggregates
RED CENTER - Saw blades - Simonds Industries Inc.
RED CHEEK - Food products - Cadbury Beverages Inc.
RED CHIEF - Animal feeds ☆ - Foster Canning Inc.
RED CHIEF - Food products - Hudson River Fruit Distributors
RED CHIEF - Handles–wood ☆ - Hartwell Brothers Handle Co.
RED CHIPS - Snack foods - Garden of Eatin', Inc.
RED CIRCLE - Coffee - Great Atlantic & Pacific Tea Co., Inc.
RED CLOUD - Beef jerky - Caldaho Bros. Inc.
RED CLOVER - Wheat–flour or meal - Pillsbury Co.
RED-COAT - Pottery products - Duncan Enterprises
RED CODE - Communications equipment–mobile ☆ - Mid-West Electronics Inc.
RED COON - Chewing tobacco - Conwood Co. L.P.
RED COOPER - Fruits and vegetables - Standex International Corp.
RED COTE - Toothpaste - John O.Butler Co.
RED COW - Cheese - Wisconsin Corp.
RED CRANE TEAS - Teas–herbal - Stephanie Klausner
RED CROSS - Footwear–women's - United States Shoe Corp.
RED CROSS - Health care products - Johnson & Johnson
RED CROSS - Health care products - Mentholatum Co.
RED CROSS - Macaroni - Red Cross Macaroni Co.
RED CROSS - Mattresses - Southern Cross Industries Inc.
RED CROSS - Pasta - Borden, Inc.
RED CROSS - Salt - Akzo America Inc.
RED CROSS - Snuff ☆ - Byfield Snuff Co.
RED CROSS - Vegetables–canned - Furman Foods, Inc.
RED CROSS NURSE - Disinfectants - J. Hubbard Co. Inc.
RED CROSS NURSE - Disinfectants - Sunpoint Products, Inc.
RED CROWN - Gasoline ☆ - Amoco Oil Co.
RED CROWN - Paper ☆ - Ampad Corp.
RED CROWN - Shortening ☆ - CPC International Inc.
RED CROWN - Thread - Cincinnati Thread Co.
RED-CYCLER - Machinery ☆ - Simplicity Manufacturing Inc.
RED-D-BELLS - Bells and chimes - Durbin Industries
RED-D-GRAB - Hooks - Durbin Industries
RED D PULLER - Trailers–truck - Durbin Industries
RED DAGGER - Beverages–alcohol - Canandaigua Wine Co. Inc.
RED DAWN - Fireworks - American Promotional Events, Inc.

RED DECIBEL - Recording label - Twin/Tone Records Inc.
RED DEK - Fasteners–hook and eye - Rawlplug Co., Inc.
RED DELICIOUS - Teas–herbal - Stash Tea Co.
RED DEMON - Mufflers ☆ - International Parts Corp.
RED DEVIL - Brushes - Red Devil Inc.
RED DEVIL - Crackers - Pet Inc.
RED DEVIL - Garden equipment - Precision Products Inc.
RED DEVIL - Hair care products - Fromm Industries
RED DEVIL - Kites ☆ - Hi-Flier Manufacturing Co.
RED DEVIL - Lighter fluid - Red Devil Products Inc.
RED DEVIL - Liqueurs - Jenkins Spirits Corp., Ltd.
RED DEVIL - Lye - Boyle-Midway
RED DEVIL - Safety products - Meeco Manufacturing Co.
RED DEVIL - Varnishes - Red Devil Paints
RED DEVIL - Vegetable sauces - Trappey's Fine Foods Inc.
RED DEVIL SNACKERS - Food products - Pet Inc.
RED DEVIL SPINNER - Fishing lures - Lindy Little Joe Inc.
RED DIAMOND - Coffee - Donovan Coffee Co., Inc.
RED DIAMOND - Food products - Oriental Trading Co., Inc.
RED DIAMOND - Fruits and vegetables ☆ - Diamond Fruit Growers
RED DIAMOND - Gasoline - Tenneco Oil Co.
RED DIAMOND - Welding equipment - Praxair Distributors
RED DIAMOND ULTRA BLEND - Coffee - Donovan Coffee Co., Inc.
RED-DICULOUS ON THE BEACH - Beverages–alcohol - Mango Bottling, Inc.
RED DOG - Beer - Miller Brewing Co.
RED DOG - Recording label - Len Monahan Productions
RED DOG - Watches - Bloomfield International Inc.
RED DOG EXPRESS - Recording label ☆ - Ripete Music Group
RED DOOR - Colognes - Elizabeth Arden Inc.
RED DOT - Balls - Worth Inc.
RED DOT - Beverages–malt ☆ - Eastern Brewing Corp.
RED DOT - Cigars - National Cigar Corp.
RED DOT - Health care products - Guardian Products Inc.
RED DOT - Printing trades machinery - Roller Technology, Inc.
RED DOT - Recording label - Marullo Productions Inc.
RED DOT - Thermometers ☆ - Popper & Sons Inc.
RED DOT - Tires–motorcycle ☆ - Hi-Point Racing Products
RED DOT ARTAR - Lenses–photographic ☆ - Schneider Optics, Inc.
RED DRAGON - Meat products–beef - Curtice-Burns Meat Snacks Inc.
RED DRAGON - Trailers–travel - Flame Engineering Inc.
RED DRAGON - Vegetable sauces ☆ - Trappey's Fine Foods Inc.
RED DRAGON LEISURE - Garden equipment - Flame Engineering Inc.
RED DRAGON OF KRYNN - Games - Tsr, Inc.
RED-E-CLEEN - Cleaning preparations - L.D. Sterns Corp.
RED-E-HEAT - Housewares - JMK International, Inc.
RED E MADE - Breads–mixes - Concord Foods Inc.
RED-E-STRIP - Artists' materials - Vogart Crafts Corp.
RED EAGLE - Bicycles - Columbia Manufacturing Inc.
RED EAGLE - Markers–felt-tip ☆ - Red Eagle Industries
RED EAGLE TRADING CO - Shirts - Russell Corp.
RED EAGLE TRADING CO. - Apparel–athletic - Cross Creek Apparel Inc.
RED END - Rulers–wood - Lufkin Rule Co.
RED END - Saw blades - Simonds Industries Inc.
RED ENGINE - Snack foods ☆ - McCleary Inc.
RED EPOXY - Epoxy - Highside Chemicals Inc.
RED-ETS - Candy - American Licorice Co.
RED EXPRESS - Cigarettes - Philip Morris Companies Inc.
RED EYE - Alarm systems ☆ - SecurityLink from Ameritech
RED EYE - Beverages–alcohol - Brazos Country Foods
RED EYE - Cleaning preparations - W.W. Grainger, Inc.
RED EYE - Fishing lures ☆ - Eppinger Manufacturing Co.
RED EYE - Men's knitwear - Marc D. Sales Corp.
RED EYE - Toys ☆ - Sun Products Corp. (Wellington)
RED EYE NICKELS - Game machines - Universal Distributing of Nevada, Inc.
RED EYE WIGGLER - Fishing lures - Eppinger Manufacturing Co.
RED FACIAL SPONGE - Cosmetics - Karlen Manufacturing, Inc.
RED FALCON - Bicycles - Columbia Manufacturing Inc.
RED FIBER - Envelopes - Quality Park Products Co.
RED FIGURES - Apparel and accessories - Dennis Lodes
RED FIRE - Sporting goods ☆ - Gold Eagle/Arnold Palmer
RED FLAME - Food products - Chiquita Brands, Inc.
RED FLAME - Food products ☆ - California & Washington Co.
RED FLAME PREMIUM DIESEL - Fuel additives - Central Oil & Supply Corp.
RED FLANNEL FACTORY - Pajamas–women's - Red Flannel Factory
RED FLYER - Wagons–children's - Radio Flyer Inc.
RED FONCE - Cosmetics - Lancome

☆ = Now out of production

RED FOOT - Skin care products - Red Foot Products Co. Inc.
RED FOR MEN - Colognes - Giorgio Beverly Hills
RED FOX - Audio equipment - Red Fox Enterprises Inc.
RED FOX - Bicycles - Columbia Manufacturing Inc.
RED FOX - Crock pots ☆ - Wonderknit
RED FOX - Food products - Red Fox Salsa Co., Inc.
RED FOX - Hair care products - Majestic Drug Co., Inc.
RED FOX - Lipsticks - Lancome
RED FOX - Sleeping bags - Coleman Co., Inc.
RED FOX - Sporting goods - FTM Sports
RED FOX - Sporting goods - Wellington Leisure Products, Inc.
RED FOX - Tobacco - Conwood Co. L.P.
RED FOX, THE - Wallpaper - Taylor Wallcoverings Inc.
RED GATE - Fruits–canned - Big Star Food Stores
RED GEL - Pet products - Trophy Animal Health Care
RED GLOW - Tools ☆ - Chapiewsky's Inc.
RED-GLUC - Chemical preparations - Research Organics, Inc.
RED-GO FLEX - Machine parts - Fenner Drives
RED GOAT - Garbage disposal units–commercial - Standex International Corp.
RED GOLD - Tomato pastes and sauces - Red Gold Inc.
RED GOOSE - Shoes - Interco Inc.
RED GUN - Educational materials - Armament Systems and Procedures, Inc.
RED HAND - Boat-bottom coating - Interlux Yacht Finishes
RED HAND - Thread - Blue Mountain Industries, Inc.
RED HAND SWISS - Teas–herbal - Wunderlich-Diez Corp.
RED HAT - Oils–lubricating - Quincy Oil Inc.
RED HAVEN - Preserves - American Spoon Foods Inc.
RED HAWK - Apparel and accessories - Williamson-Dickie Manufacturing Co.
RED HAWK - Electronic equipment - Lindale Industries, Inc.
RED HAWK - Golfing equipment - Besco USA
RED HAWK - Shovels ☆ - Union Fork and Hoe Co.
RED HAWK PRODUCTIONS - Video production - Red Hawk Productions
RED HEAD - Ammunition ☆ - Montgomery Ward & Co. Inc.
RED HEAD - Anchors, fasteners, tools - ITW Ramset/Red Head
RED HEAD - Life preservers - Red Head Brand Corp.
RED HEAD - Lubricants - Ashland Oil, Inc.
RED HEAD - Shoe stretchers - Rochester Shoe Tree Co. Inc.
RED HEADS - Giftware ☆ - Goebel of North America
RED HEART - Pet products ☆ - John Morrell & Co.
RED HEART - Rope - Hooven Allison
RED HEART - Yarn - Coats and Clark Inc.
RED HED - Gasoline - Red Hed Oil Co. Inc.
RED HILL - Food products - Whitfield Foods, Inc.
RED HILL VINEYARD - Wines ☆ - Sebastiani Vineyards, Inc.
RED HILLS VINEYARDS - Wines ☆ - Duck-Pond Cellars
RED HOOK - Brooms - Lighthouse Industries
RED HOOK ESB - Shirts - Redhook Ale Brewery, Inc.
RED HORSE - Apparel and accessories - Russ Togs Inc.
RED HORSE - Game machines - New Gaming Systems
RED HORSE - Health care products - East Earth Herb Inc.
RED HORSE - Recording label - Red Horse Productions/Revolver Records
RED HORSE - Tobacco–chewing or smoking - Swedish Math North America Inc.
RED HOT - Cleaning preparations - Auto Wax Co., Inc.
RED HOT - Firearms, accessories, and parts - Modern Muzzle Loading, Inc.
RED HOT - Golfing equipment - AJ Tech, Inc.
RED HOT - Ladies clothing - Red Hot, Inc.
RED HOT - Lotions - Cramer Products Inc.
RED HOT - Paints - Sheffield Bronze Paint Corp.
RED HOT & BLUE - Barbecue sauce - Red Hot & Blue Restaurants, Inc.
RED HOT BLUES - Snack foods - Garden of Eatin', Inc.
RED HOT CHILE POPPERS - Fruits and vegetables - Anchor Food Products, Inc.
RED HOT DOLLARS - Candy - Henry Heide, Inc.
RED HOT ICE - Video equipment - New Gaming Systems
RED HOT LASTING - Nail care products ☆ - Monteil Paris
RED HOT MAMA'S - Candy - Fine Candy Co.
RED HOT SUMMER NIGHTS - Beverages–carbonated - Coca-Cola Co.
RED HOT TAPE - Tape–adhesive - Seam Master Industry
RED HOTS - Candy - Ferrara Pan Candy Co., Inc.
RED HOTS - Saunas - Miller Sausage Co. Inc.
RED HOUSE - Recording label - Red House Records Inc.
RED I - Apparel–athletic - Aileen Inc.
RED-I-HOT - Heating equipment ☆ - Bradford-White Corp.
RED-I-TUTOR - Electronic equipment - Dukane Corp.

RED INJUN - Bicycles - Columbia Manufacturing Inc.
RED-JACKET - Motor vehicle parts and accessories - Morse Controls
RED JACKET - Socks - Seneca Knitting Mills Corp.
RED JUICE - Tobacco–chewing or smoking - Brown & Williamson Tobacco Corp.
RED KAP - Uniforms–tailored - Red Kap
RED KNIGHT - Handles–wood - Hartwell Brothers Handle Co.
RED-KOTE - Adhesives and sealants - Damon Industries, Inc.
RED L - Food products - Red L Foods Inc.
RED L - Smokestacks - Trifoods International, Inc.
RED LABEL - Apparel–children's - Sara Lee Knit Products Inc.
RED LABEL - Brooms - O-Cedar/Vining Household Products Co.
RED LABEL - Deodorizers - Fragra-Matics Manufacturing Co. Inc.
RED LABEL - Food products ☆ - Gol-Pak Corp.
RED LABEL - Musical instrument accessories - Super-Sensitive Musical String Co.
RED LABEL - Paper - A.B. Dick Co.
RED LABEL - Shotguns ☆ - Sturm, Ruger & Co., Inc.
RED LACES - Candy - American Licorice Co.
RED LACQUER - Tableware–china ☆ - Lenox, Inc.
RED LADY - Fruits and vegetables - Coast Citrus Distributors, Inc.
RED LADY 21 - Wines - Monarch Wine Co. of Georgia
RED LADY ALE - Beverages–malt - Crested Butte Brewery & Pub
RED LANTERN - Pizzas–frozen ☆ - JMS Specialty Foods Inc.
RED LEAF - Cheese - Swissrose International Inc.
RED LETTER - Apparel and accessories - Recipro, Inc.
RED LIGHTNING - Sauces - Rowena's Gourmet Foods Inc.
RED LIGHTNING - Toys - Saban Entertainment, Inc.
RED LINE - Audio equipment - Misco/Minneapolis Speaker Co.
RED LINE - Fire extinguishers - Ansul, Inc.
RED LINE - Glassware–scientific - Corning Inc.
RED LINE - Heating pads–electric - Sunbeam-Oster Household Products
RED LINE - Lubricants ☆ - Unocal Corp.
RED-LINE - Mattresses - Englander Co. Inc.
RED LINE - Soft drink - Shico, Inc.
RED LINE RACING - Trading cards - TV Sports Mailbag, Inc.
RED LINE SERIES/PRO-PLATES - Electric lighting equipment - Jackson Deerfield Manufacturing Corp.
RED LINE VITAMINS - Vitamins and nutritional supplements - Cernitin America Inc.
RED LION - Apparel–women's - Queen Casuals Inc.
RED LION - Bicycles - Columbia Manufacturing Inc.
RED LION - Canvas–artists' - Fredrix Artist Canvas Inc.
RED LION - Cigarettes - P.T.C. Brands, Inc.
RED LION GAMES - Games - Red Lion Corp.
RED LION INN COLLECTION - Furniture–factory ☆ - Clayton Marcus Co. Inc.
RED-LIT - Lighting equipment ☆ - Siemens Components Inc. (Optoelectronics Div.)
RED LOBSTER - Apparel stores–sports ☆ - Terramar Sports Worldwide, Ltd.
RED LODGE - Food products - Red Lodge Canning Co.
RED LOGS - Candy - American Licorice Co.
RED MAGMA - Vitamins and nutritional supplements - Green Foods
RED MAN - Apparel and accessories - P.T.C. Brands, Inc.
RED MAN - Tobacco–chewing or smoking - Swedish Math North America Inc.
RED MAN GOLDEN BLEND - Tobacco–chewing or smoking - Swedish Math North America Inc.
RED MAN SELECT - Tobacco–chewing or smoking - Swedish Math North America Inc.
RED MARK - Recording label - QCA Inc.
RED MARQ - Apparel and accessories - Red Marq Ltd. Inc.
RED MAX - Toys–models ☆ - Estes Industries
RED MILL - Novelty items - Red Mill Manufacturing Inc.
RED MILL FARMS - Cakes - Red Mill Farms Inc.
RED MITTEN - Food products - Coloma Frozen Foods Inc.
RED MONEY AUTHENTIC RUSSIAN RUBLES - Novelty items - Liberty Trading Co., Inc.
RED MOON - Apparel and accessories - Precision Fabrics Group, Inc.
RED MOUNTAIN LAUREL - Wines - Chateau Morrisette, Inc.
RED NECTAR - Beverages–malt - Humboldt Brewing Co.
RED NECTAR ALE - Beverages–malt - Humboldt Brewing Co.
RED NINJA, THE - Toys - Hasbro, Inc.
RED NOVA - Chemical preparations - Novagen, Inc.
RED NU STAIN - Enamels ☆ - Devoe & Raynolds Co.
RED-O-RAY - Musical instrument accessories ☆ - J. D'Addario & Co. Inc.
RED OR DEAD - Shoes - Omni Footwear, Inc.
RED-OUT - Photographic equipment - Argraph Corp. (Samigon Div.)

☆ = Now out of production

RED OUT - Shampoos - Colorful Products Corp.

RED OUTER - Soldering investment - Leo's Products Inc.

RED OVAL FARMS - Crackers ☆ - Tidelands Sales Co. Inc.

RED OWL - Food products ☆ - Super Valu Inc.

RED OXX MFG. INC. - Sporting goods - Red Oxx Manufacturing, Inc.

RED PAIL - Fruits–canned - Johnson-Middleby Co. (Karp's Manufactured Products Div.)

RED PAJAMAS - Recording label - Al Bunetta Management

RED PASSION - Cosmetics - Concept II Cosmetics, Inc.

RED PEARL - Herbal products - Celestine Health, Inc.

RED PELICAN - Mustard - Red Pelican Food Products

RED PIG - Beverages–malt - Cabo Distributing Co., Inc.

RED PLANET - Apparel and accessories - Virtual World Entertainment

RED POWER - Cleaning preparations - Production Car Care Products, Inc.

RED PRIDE - Salmon–smoked, salted, dried, or pickled - North Pacific Seafoods

RED PRIDE - Tobacco–chewing or smoking - P.T.C. Brands, Inc.

RED QUILT - Wallpaper ☆ - Imperial Wallcoverings, Inc.

RED RAIDER - Bicycles - Columbia Manufacturing Inc.

RED RAMBLER - Salmon–smoked, salted, dried, or pickled - Trident Seafoods Corp.

RED RANGER - Games - Saban Entertainment, Inc.

RED RASBERRY RAZZLE - Food products - Golden Whisk Pasta Partners

RED RED SAUCE - Sauces - Johnny Rockets Licensing Corp.

RED RED SODA - Beverages–carbonated ☆ - Monarch Co., Inc.

RED REVENGE - Toys - Tonka Corp.

RED RHINO WAX AND DETERGENTS FOR AUTOS - Cleaning preparations - Barton Lockhart

RED RHINOCEROS - Apparel and accessories - Rhinoceros Sportswear Inc.

RED RIBBON - Colognes - Ventresca Ltd.

RED RIBBON - Food products - Pine Manor, Inc.

RED RIBBON - Fruits and vegetables - Oregon Prune Exchange

RED RIBBON - Fruits and vegetables - Snokist Growers

RED RIBBON BLEND - Coffee - Frontier Cooperative Herbs

RED RIBBON ORNAMENTS - Christmas tree ornaments - Myron Mix

RED RIDER - Bicycles - Columbia Manufacturing Inc.

RED RIDGE - Bicycles - Dynacraft Industries Inc.

RED RIDGE ALE - Beverages–malt - Rainbow Ridge Brewing Co., Inc.

RED RIDGE MOUNTAIN OUTFITTERS - Apparel and accessories - T.P. Saddle Blanket & Trading Inc.

RED RING - Food products ☆ - Curtice-Burns Foods, Inc.

RED RING - Rubber–synthetic ☆ - Dykema Rubber Band Co.

RED RING ROCKER RATTLE - Toys - Fisher-Price, Inc.

RED RIPE - Food products - Pet Inc.

RED RIVER - Cereal - Mille Lacs Wild Rice Co.

RED RIVER - Golfing equipment - Golfsmith International Inc.

RED RIVER HONEY BROWN ALE - Beverages–malt - The Stroh Brewery Co.

RED RIVER KNIVES - Knives - Cold Steel Inc.

RED RIVER PEBBLE - Pet products - National Display Materials

RED RIVER SUNFLOWER WHEAT - Beverages–malt - The Stroh Brewery Co.

RED RIVER VALLEY - Beverages–malt - The Stroh Brewery Co.

RED ROBE - Food products - General Grocer Co.

RED ROCK - Beverages–carbonated - Universal Flavor USA

RED ROCK - Beverages–malt - Miller Brewing Co.

RED ROCK - Bicycles - Huffy Corp.

RED ROCK - Recording label ☆ - Ozark Opry Records

RED ROCK COFFEE COMPANY - Coffee - Red Rock Coffee Co.

RED ROCK TERRACE - Wines - Diamond Creek Vineyards

RED ROCKER - Bicycles, bicycle racks, bicycle saddles, etc. - Steady State Inc.

RED ROCKER - Toys–stuffed ☆ - Gund, Inc.

RED ROCKERS - Automotive parts and accessories - Edelbrock Corp.

RED ROCKET - Boats–motor ☆ - Hobie Cat Co.

RED ROCKET - Wines - Monarch Wine Co. of Georgia

RED ROCKETS - Sausages - Roger Wood Foods, Inc.

RED ROOF INN - Hotels and motels - Red Roof Inns Inc.

RED ROOST - Beverages–malt - La Jolla Brewing Co.

RED ROOSTER - Beverages–malt - Hope Brewing Corp.

RED ROOSTER - Cheese - Churny Co., Inc.

RED ROOSTER - Dinnerware–glass ☆ - Metlox Pottery Shoppe

RED ROOSTER - Food products - Bruce Foods Corp.

RED ROOSTER - Food products - A. Levy & J. Zentner Co.

RED ROOSTER - Vitamins and nutritional supplements - Old 97 Co.

RED ROOSTER - Wines - Monarch Wine Co. of Georgia

RED ROOSTER VITES - Vitamins and nutritional supplements - Dixon-Shane Inc.

RED ROOT - Pipes–tobacco - S.M. Frank & Co. Inc. (Kaywoodie-Yello-Bole-Medico)

RED ROPE - File folders - National Fiberstok Corp.

RED ROPES - Candy - American Licorice Co.

RED ROSE - Animal feeds - Manna Pro Corp.

RED ROSE - Cigars - United States Tobacco Co.

RED ROSE - Flour–blended - Central Milling Co.

RED ROSE - Fruits–pickled or brined - R.C. McAteer Co.

RED ROSE - Iced tea–bottled or canned ☆ - Pokka, Inc.

RED ROSE - Meat products–canned - Detroit City Dairy Inc.

RED ROSE - Teas - Redco Foods Inc.

RED ROSE - Vegetables–dried - Arrow Industries, Inc.

RED ROSE BRAND - Rice - M.I.M.T. Corp. of USA

RED ROSEMINI - Flowers, plants, and seeds - J. Benjamin Williams

RED ROVER - Apparel and accessories ☆ - Nitches, Inc.

RED RUBY - Office supplies - Alvin and Co. Inc.

RED RUBY - Vegetables–dried - Sun Gems

RED RUNG - Ladders–metal - St. Pierre Manufacturing Corp.

RED RUNNER - Crocheted and knitted items - Veratec

RED RYDER - Rifles–pneumatic - Red Ryder Enterprises, Inc.

RED RYDER - Shock absorbers–motor vehicle - Gabriel Ride Control Products Div.

RED RYDER - Toys–guns - Daisy Manufacturing Co.

RED RYDER GAS - Shock absorbers–motor vehicle - Gabriel Ride Control Products Div.

RED SAIL - Food products - OSR Enterprises, Inc.

RED SAIL - Seafood products–canned or cured ☆ - Lyon Food Products Inc.

RED SAIL SPORTSWEAR - Clothing - Watersports Administration Inc.

RED SATIN - Lipsticks - Lancome

RED SATIN GLASS - Glassware–household - Nourot Glass Studio

RED SAVINA HABANERO - Vegetable sauces - GNS Spices Inc.

RED SEA - Recording label - The SOAR Corp.

RED SEAL - Checkbooks - Forest Products Charcoal Co.

RED SEAL - Cigars - United States Tobacco Co.

RED SEAL - Electronic equipment - Thomson Consumer Electronics, Inc.

RED SEAL - Food products - Comly-Flanigen Co. Inc.

RED SEAL - Food products - Pitsweet Inc.

RED SEAL - Food products - Valley Distributing Co.

RED SEAL - Gaskets - Apache Mills Inc.

RED SEAL - Gloves ☆ - Boss Manufacturing Co.

RED SEAL - Laces–boot and shoe ☆ - St. Louis Braid Co.

RED SEAL - Lubricants ☆ - Ashland Oil, Inc.

RED SEAL - Pumps–vacuum - Edson Corp.

RED SEAL - Recording label - RCA Records

RED SENTRY - Padding–foam ☆ - Elkay Products Co. Inc.

RED SETTER - Handbags - Marilee Pearson

RED SHEEP - Cheese - Wisconsin Corp.

RED SHOES - Dolls ☆ - Effanbee Doll Corp.

RED SKY - Apparel and accessories ☆ - Edison Brothers Stores, Inc.

RED SNAP - Apparel–men's - Morgan Manufacturing Co., Inc.

RED SNAPPER - Binders - Dennison National Co.

RED SNAPPER - Cooking equipment–household ☆ - LazyMan, Inc.

RED SNAP'R - Electric-fence product - North Central Plastics Inc.

RED SPOT - Food products ☆ - Agripac, Inc.

RED SPOT - Polishing rouge - Red Spot Paint & Varnish Co., Inc.

RED STAR - Diapers–cloth - Gerber Products Co.

RED STAR - Food products - Universal Foods Corp.

RED STAR - Rope - Hooven Allison

RED STAR PLUS - Food products - Universal Foods Corp.

RED STEEL - Games - Tsr, Inc.

RED STEER CASCADE - Gloves - Red Steer Glove Co.

RED STINGER - Beverages–alcohol - William Grant & Sons, Inc.

RED STONE - Footwear - Elan-Polo, Inc.

RED STORM RISING - Computer software ☆ - Microprose Software, Inc.

RED STREAK - Saw blades - Simonds Industries Inc.

RED STREAK - Tape–adhesive - Brown-Bridge Industries

RED STRIKER AV - Toys–automobiles - Saban Entertainment, Inc.

RED STRIPE - Brushes–paint ☆ - PPG Industries, Inc.

RED-STROKE - Pottery products - Duncan Enterprises

RED STROKES ENTERTAINMENT - Video production - Red Strokes Entertainment, Inc.

RED SUEDE - Erasers ☆ - Bright Boy Abrasives

RED SWAN - Agricultural products - Hilton Gibson and Miller Inc.

RED TAB - Adhesives and sealants - Phil Marano Inc.

☆ = Now out of production

RED TAB - Apparel - Levi Strauss & Co.
RED TAG - Food products ☆ - Dole Food Co., Inc.
RED TAG - Gypsum products - Georgia-Pacific Corp.
RED TAIL - Apparel and accessories - Demco Group
RED TAIL - Beverages–malt ☆ - Mendocino Brewing Co., Inc.
RED TAIL ALE - Beverages–malt - Mendocino Brewing Co., Inc.
RED TANG - File folders - Simonds Industries Inc.
RED TEE, THE - Apparel and accessories - Matthew H. Jacobs
RED THE ROCK AGAINST DRUGS - Novelty items - Mitchener & Upton Games, Inc.
RED THUNDER - Cleaning preparations - Malco Products, Inc.
RED TIDE - Apparel–men's - Merchandising & Marketing Specialists, Inc.
RED-TOP - Paper ☆ - Paper Products Inc.
RED TOP - Plaster–wallboard - United States Gypsum Co.
RED TOP - Snuff - Byfield Snuff Co.
RED TOP - Socks - Seneca Knitting Mills Corp.
RED TOP - Steel products - Keystone Steel & Wire Co.
RED TOP - Thread - Cincinnati Thread Co.
RED TRACTOR - Food products - Andrew J. Stoloff
RED TREASURE - Fruits and vegetables - Pandol Brothers Inc.
RED TULIP - Candy - Beatrice Cos. Inc.
RED TURTLE BRAND - Apparel and accessories - Viewpoint International, Inc.
RED TWILIGHT - Dolls - Tonka Corp.
RED TWIST - Candy - American Licorice Co.
RED UNION - Erasers ☆ - Faber-Castell Corp.
RED VELVET - Lipsticks ☆ - Elysee Scientific Cosmetic Co.
RED VELVET - Musical instrument accessories - Dimarzio, Inc.
RED VINES - Candy - American Licorice Co.
RED VINES BELLY BUSTER FAT FREE - Candy - American Licorice Co.
RED VUE - Thermometers - Popper & Sons Inc.
RED WAGON - Coffee ☆ - Boyd Coffee Co.
RED WAGON - Fruits and vegetables - Bristol AG Partners
RED WAGON PRESCHOOL - Publisher's imprints - Harcourt Brace & Co.
RED WAVES - Seafood products–fresh or frozen - New England Fish Co.
RED WHIPS - Candy - American Licorice Co.
RED WHITE & BLUE - Beverages–malt - The Stroh Brewery Co.
RED WHITE & BLUE LIGHT - Beverages–malt - The Stroh Brewery Co.
RED WHITE & YOU - Toys - Tonka Corp.
RED-WHITE-BLUE - Work clothes - Key Industries, Inc.
RED WING - Boots - Red Wing Shoe Co. Inc.
RED WING - Food products - Red Wing Co., Inc.
RED-WING - Paving materials–concrete - Package Pavement Co. Inc.
RED WING R FACTORS - Footwear - Red Wing Shoe Co. Inc.
RED WINGS FOR WOMEN - Boots - Red Wing Shoe Co. Inc.
RED WOLF - Beverages–malt - Anheuser-Busch Companies Inc.
RED WOLF - Darts and dart games - Dart World Inc.
RED WOLF LAGER - Beverages–malt - Anheuser-Busch Companies Inc.
RED WONG - Apparel and accessories - Sie P. Teo
RED ZINGER - Teas–herbal - Celestial Seasonings, Inc.
RED ZONE - Apparel–athletic - Nancy Kahn Designs, Inc.
RED ZONE - Beverages - Coca-Cola Co.
RED ZONE - Trading cards and stamps - Collision, Inc.
REDACON DX PEDIATRIC - Pharmaceutical preparations - Reese Chemical Co.
REDAELLI - Apparel–men's - G. Maestrelli Corp.
REDAVERDE - Fruits and vegetables - Gourmet Veg-Paq, Inc.
REDBAND - Licorice - Westdale Foods Co.
REDBIRD - Meat products–canned - Bryan Foods, Inc.
REDBIRD - Trailers–truck ☆ - Sun-Lite Inc.
REDBOOK - Publisher's imprints - Hearst Corp.
REDBOOK GIFTS & ACCESSORIES - Toys - National Florist Directory, Inc.
REDBOOK TECHNOLOGIES - Computer hardware - Redbook Technologies, Inc.
REDCO - Eyeglasses - Richard S. Redles
REDCOAT - Beverages–alcohol - Hiram Walker & Sons, Inc.
REDCOLITE - Insulating materials - Redco II
REDCREST - Manufactured homes - Redman Industries, Inc.
REDCREST - Sporting goods - Avon Marine
REDD - Food products - Givaudan Roure
REDDEN-BUDDERS - Popcorn ☆ - Hunt-Wesson, Inc.
REDDI - Computer software - General Power Systems, Inc.
REDDI EDDI - Artists' materials - James K. Benton
REDDI-EGG - Egg substitutes - Nulaid Foods Inc.
REDDI ETCH - Artists' materials - Plaid Enterprises, Inc.
REDDI-FORM - Building materials–concrete - Reddi-Form
REDDI-FRISKET - Paper–kraft - Vogart Crafts Corp.

REDDI INVOICE - Computer software - Neetlok Inc.
REDDI-MAID - Fruits–canned - Cherry Central Cooperative Inc.
REDDI-PORT - Containers–paper - Reddi-Pac, Inc.
REDDI-SLIDE - Medical apparatus - Learning Things Inc.
REDDI SPONGW - Food products - Foremost Farms USA
REDDI-STARCH - Starch–laundry ☆ - Dowbrands L.P.
REDDI-TO-USE - Food products - L. Karp & Sons, Inc.
REDDI WIP - Food products ☆ - Hunt-Wesson, Inc.
REDDING - Clocks ☆ - General Time Corp. (Westclox/Seth Thomas Div.)
REDDING RIDGE FARMS - Tomato pastes and sauces - Van Den Bergh Foods Co.
REDDY - Erasers ☆ - Faber-Castell Corp.
REDDY FRIES - Frozen foods - Reddy-Raw, Inc.
REDDY GLAZE - Pies–fresh - Concord Foods Inc.
REDDY HEATER - Heaters–space - Desa International, Inc.
REDDY ICE - Food products - Southland Corp.
REDDY LEMON - Juices - Concord Foods Inc.
REDDY MIX 23 - Inks - Radiant Color Div.
REDDY TEDDY - T-shirts–men's - Pic-Mount Corp.
REDDY VEGGIES - Vegetables–frozen - Reddy-Raw, Inc.
REDEEMED - Hats - Sara Blumenstein
REDEEMER - Toys - TMP International, Inc.
REDEFINING SKIN CARE - Skin care preparations - Bio-Tonique International, Inc.
REDEMPTION CENTER - Vending machine parts - Smart Industries Corp.
REDENBUDDERS - Popcorn - Conagra, Inc.
REDERM - Skin care products - Co-Med Pharmaceuticals, Inc.
REDEX - Particle board - Louisiana-Pacific Corp.
REDEYE - Recording label - Redeye Records
REDFEATHER - Snowshoes - Redfeather Design Inc.
REDFERN - Sausages - Redfern Foods Corp.
REDFIELD - Rifles - Redfield Co.
REDFIELD ESD - Telescopes - Redfield Co.
REDFORD CLOTHING CO. - Apparel and accessories - Stanley H. Shindler
REDGARD - Paints ☆ - Stoner Inc.
REDGLO - Animal feeds - Farnam Cos. Inc.
REDGLO-ADE - Pet products - Farnam Cos. Inc.
REDHAWK - Revolvers - Sturm, Ruger & Co., Inc.
REDHAWK COFFEES - Coffee - Dispenser Juice Inc.
REDHEAD - Electronic equipment ☆ - AVES Audio Visual Systems Inc.
REDHEAD - Pet products - Mr. Mutt Pet Products Inc.
REDHEAD - Water heaters–household - Alpha Western Corp.
REDHEAD DIGGER - Post hole diggers–hand-operated - Don Savage Co. Inc.
REDHEADS - Computer software - Redheads Software, Inc.
REDHIDE - Envelopes - Alvah Bushnell Co.
REDHOOK - Fish - Redhook Fisheries
REDHOOK RYE - Beverages–malt - Leavenworth Brewery Pub and Restaurant
REDHOT! - Sugar–granulated, refined, or powdered - Durkee French Foods
REDHOTS - Cooking equipment–commercial - Metal Masters Foodservice Equipment Co., Inc.
REDI - Computer software - Spear, Leeds & Kellogg
REDI - Office supplies ☆ - Brown and Bigelow Inc.
REDI - Pet products - Gimborn U.S., Inc.
REDI-ASEPTI - Health care products ☆ - Graham-Field Inc.
REDI-BANDAGE - Bandages - Professional Medical Products, Inc.
REDI-BEVEL - Lumber - Forest Products Group, Inc.
REDI-BITS - Tool bits ☆ - ITW Ramset/Red Head
REDI-BLEND - Paints - Adelphi Coatings Co.
REDI-BOLT - Hardware - Medalist Industries Inc.
REDI-BREADER - Breads–mixes - DCA Food Industries, Inc.
REDI-CAL - Decals and transfers - Ever-Ready Label Corp.
REDI CAT GRASS - Cat food - Gimborn U.S., Inc.
REDI CEL - Vegetables–canned - Redi Foods
REDI-CHEK - Thermometers - Maverick Industries, Inc.
REDI-CHEM - Epoxy fastening system ☆ - ITW Ramset/Red Head
REDI-CLEAN - Stain removers - Nice-Pak Products, Inc.
REDI-CLENE - Cleaning preparations - Windsor Wax Co. Inc.
REDI COMBONE - Dog food - Gimborn U.S., Inc.
REDI-COTTA - Cheese - Losurdo Foods, Inc.
REDI-COVER - Binders ☆ - ACCO USA, Inc.
REDI-CUT - Hobby kits ☆ - Crafters
REDI-CUT - Paper–sand ☆ - Carborundum Abrasives North America
REDI-CUTS - Lumber - Georgia-Pacific Corp.
REDI-DATES - Dates - California Redi-Date Co.
REDI-DRILL - Hammers ☆ - ITW Ramset/Red Head

☆ = Now out of production

REDI-DRIVE - Hammer drive tool ☆ - ITW Ramset/Red Head
REDI-EARTH - Garden equipment - W.R. Grace & Co.
REDI-FICHE - Microfiche equipment ☆ - ACCO USA, Inc.
REDI-FILE - File folders ☆ - Kardex Systems, Inc.
REDI-FINISH - Paper–sand ☆ - Carborundum Abrasives North America
REDI-FIT - Toiletries - Fort Howard Corp.
REDI FLAT - Hair care products - H.L.C. Distributors Inc.
REDI-FLITE - Toys–models - Comet Montrose Ltd.
REDI-FLOW - Spices and extracts - Wixon-Fontarome, Inc.
REDI FOLD - Hair care products - H.L.C. Distributors Inc.
REDI FOLD - Paper–toilet - Colora Henna
REDI FOODS - Vegetables–canned - A. Duda & Sons, Inc.
REDI GARLIC - Vitamins and nutritional supplements - Nature's Products Inc.
REDI-GRIP - Binders ☆ - ACCO USA, Inc.
REDI-GROUT - Mortars–clay ☆ - Custom Building Products
REDI-GUARD - Labels–paper - Ever-Ready Label Corp.
REDI-HIT - Nail anchors ☆ - ITW Ramset/Red Head
REDI-HOOK - Drapery hardware - Kirsch Co.
REDI-KLEEN - Cleaning preparations - Kleer Flo Co. Inc.
REDI-KWIK - Meat products–beef - Colonial Beef Co.
REDI-LETTER - Paper - Rediform
REDI LITE - Lighting equipment - General Cable Corp.
REDI-LUG - Hardware ☆ - Vance Industries Inc.
REDI-MADE - Ammonia ☆ - Keller Food Products Co.
REDI-MADE - Vegetables–dried - Gilroy Foods Inc.
REDI-MAG - Magnetic tape–blank - Richards Distributing, Inc.
REDI-MARK - Hardware stores ☆ - Gilbert and Bennett Manufacturing Co.
REDI-MARK - Markers–felt-tip - Dixon Ticonderoga Co.
REDI-MAT - Mats–grass, reed, and jute ☆ - Stu-Art Supplies Inc.
REDI-MEM - Notebooks and notepads - Redi-Record Industries
REDI-MIX - Cleaning preparations–window ☆ - Gold Eagle Co.
REDI-MIX BLOX-FILL - Blocks–concrete - Proko Industries Inc.
REDI MOUNT - Adhesives and sealants - C-Line Products, Inc.
REDI-NIPS - Rodenticides - Roccorp, Inc.
REDI-OFF - Nail care products ☆ - Nice-Pak Products, Inc.
REDI-PAC - Lumber - Forest Products Group, Inc.
REDI-PAK - Veterinary nutritional supplements - Manna Pro Corp.
REDI-PIERCE - Nuts and bolts - MacLean-Fogg Co.
REDI-PLUG - Connectors–electrical - Zenith Electronics Corp.
REDI-PREP - Food products - Richard A. Shaw Inc.
REDI PREP - Pharmaceutical preparations - Nice-Pak Products, Inc.
REDI-PRONGS - Jewelry - Droste's Jewelry Shoppes, Inc.
REDI-RAC - Racks - JDM Products
REDI-RAMP - Building materials–concrete - Reading Precast, Inc.
REDI RELIEF - Pharmaceutical preparations - Marigny Corp.
REDI RIBS - Meat products–beef - Gorges Foodservice, Inc.
REDI-RIDER - Seats–automobile - Kolcraft Enterprises, Inc.
REDI-RITE - Office supplies - Saunders Manufacturing Co. Inc.
REDI ROAST - Beef - Emmber Foods, Inc.
REDI-RUN - Bottling machinery - Plant Services Corp.
REDI-SAND - Paper–sand ☆ - Carborundum Abrasives North America
REDI-SEAL - Envelopes - Quality Park Products Co.
REDI-SELECTS - Lumber - Forest Products Group, Inc.
REDI-SEP - Health care products - Sellstrom Manufacturing Co.
REDI-SERVE - Food products - On-Cor Frozen Foods, Inc.
REDI-SERVE LITTLE REDI - Meat products - On-Cor Frozen Foods, Inc.
REDI-SET - Tiles–ceramic ☆ - American Olean Tile Co.
REDI SHADE - Window accessories - Shades Unlimited, Inc.
REDI-SHARP - Markers–felt-tip - Dixon Ticonderoga Co.
REDI-SHINE - Shoe polish ☆ - Nice-Pak Products, Inc.
REDI-SHUTTER - Shutters–wood - Maywood Inc.
REDI-SPACK - Caulking compounds - Elmer's Products, Inc.
REDI-SPACK LITE - Caulking compounds - Elmer's Products, Inc.
REDI SPOT - Mirrors - Burco, Inc.
REDI-SPOT - Paints - Pratt & Lambert United, Inc.
REDI-SPUDS - Food products - Redi-Spuds of America
REDI-STICK - Labels–paper - Ever-Ready Label Corp.
REDI-STIK - Hardware - Trim-Lok Inc.
REDI-STIX - Paper–gummed - Standard Publishing Co.
REDI-STRIP - Envelopes - Quality Park Products Co.
REDI-TAC - Envelopes - Quality Park Products Co.
REDI-TEMP - Dental compounds - Jan S. Stahl
REDI-TEMP - Kitchen utensils–aluminum ☆ - Hy Cite Corp.
REDI-TEMP - Thermometers - Trademark Corp.
REDI-TIE - Rope - Wellington Leisure Products, Inc.
REDI-TILT - Tripods–photographic - Davis & Sanford Co. Inc.

REDI-TO-BAKE - Food products - Dimitria Delights Inc.
REDI-2-EAT - Prepared vegetables - Redi-2-Eat
REDI-TOGGLE - Screw anchor ☆ - ITW Ramset/Red Head
REDI-TRIM - Lumber - Forest Products Group, Inc.
REDI-TRIP - Envelopes - Quality Park Products Co.
REDI-TWIST-TIE - Rope - Wellington Leisure Products, Inc.
REDI-VERT - Emulsifiers - Wilbur-Ellis Co.
REDI-WRAP - Flower-pot covers - Ivex Corp.
REDICABLE - Cameras–video - Jasco Products Co. Inc.
REDICARD - Computer hardware - DATA RACE Inc.
REDICUT - Meat products–beef - Colonial Beef Co.
REDIEYE - Ultrasonic scanning devices - Advanced Control Technology, Inc.
REDIFFUSION - Recording label ☆ - Telemark Dance Records
REDIFLEX - Door frames - Dunbarton Corp.
REDIFONE - Communications equipment–marine - Telcom Inc.
REDIFORM - Paper - Rediform
REDIFRAME - Door frames - Dunbarton Corp.
REDIKEEPER - Office supplies - Rediform
REDIMESH - Bandages - MB Products Ltd.
REDIMODEM - Modems - DATA RACE Inc.
REDINGTON - Pens - Sanford Corp.
REDINOTE - Paper - Rediform
REDIPRINT - Stamps–hand - Louis Melind Co.
REDIQUIK - Food products - Standard Foods Inc.
REDIRECTOR/IX - Computer software - Micro Computer Systems, Inc.
REDISAVER - Office supplies - Rediform
REDISCOVER - Computer software - Edunetics Corp.
REDISCOVER - Skin care products - Jafra Cosmetics Inc.
REDISCOVER AN ANCIENT PLEASURE - Coffee ☆ - Continental Coffee Products Co.
REDISCOVER SERIES - Computer software - Edunetics Corp.
REDISEAT - Toilet seats - Kohler Co.
REDISOL - Tar ☆ - Merck & Co., Inc. (Merck Research Laboratories)
REDITEMP-C - Health care products - Wyeth-Ayerst Laboratories
REDITEMP-H - Health care products - Wyeth-Ayerst Laboratories
REDITEST - Lighting equipment - Bodine Co. Inc.
REDITRUK - Motor vehicle parts and accessories - Texas Saddlebags, Inc.
REDITYPE - Paper - Rediform
REDI+WASH - Washcloths - Dove Medical, Inc.
REDIWOOD - Wood products ☆ - Windsor Mill
REDKEN - Hair care products - Redken Laboratories, Inc.
REDKOTE - Paints ☆ - Stoner Inc.
REDLAND - Wines - Sokol Blosser Winery
REDLEFSEN - Frankfurters - Kreiner Imports
REDLEY - Scuba diving equipment - Thomas Simon, Inc.
REDLEYFINS - Sporting goods - Thomas Simon, Inc.
REDLINE - Bicycles - Seattle Bike Supply, Inc.
REDLINE - Computer software and hardware - DSP Technology Inc.
REDLINE - Games ☆ - Kenner Products
REDLINE - Gasoline - Quiktrip Corp.
REDLINE - Rackets–racquetball - Head Sports USA
REDLINER - Toys–automobiles - Mattel, Inc.
REDMAN - Guns - Macho Products Inc.
REDMAN - Manufactured homes - Redman Industries, Inc.
REDMAR - Food products ☆ - Darik Enterprises Inc.
REDMARQUETTE - Rubber-stamp inks - Irwin-Hodson Co.
REDMON - Bathroom accessories - W.C. Redmon Co.
REDMOND AUSSIE - Hair care products - Redmond Products, Inc.
REDMOND CLAY - Pharmaceutical preparations - Redmond Clay & Salt Co.
REDNECK - Beverages–malt - Fischer Brewing Co., Inc.
REDNECK CORNER WINCHESTER, OKLAHOMA - Apparel and accessories - Redneck Corner, Ltd.
REDNECK HEAVEN - Video production - Bethany Bultman
REDNECK JEANS - Apparel and accessories - Redneck Jeans, Built In The U.S. of A.
REDNECK TECH - Fishing tackle - Reef Runner Tackle Co.
REDO2XY - Disinfectants - Bioxy, Inc.
REDONDO - Benches–metal ☆ - Artesian Industries
REDONDO - Fabrics - Dan River Inc.
REDOUBT BAY - Salmon–smoked, salted, dried, or pickled - Tidewater Packing Co.
REDOUT - Salt - Akzo America Inc.
REDOX - Paper–sand - Spirakut Products
REDPACK - Food products - Tri Valley Growers, Inc.
REDRAW - Lubricants - Franklin Oil Corp.
REDROPO - Office supplies - Barkley Filing Supplies

☆ = Now out of production

RED'S - Food products - Lucca Packing Co. of California Inc.
REDSAND - Apparel and accessories - Redsand Inc.
REDSAND - Balls - Wilson Sporting Goods Co.
REDSHIRT - Apparel–men's - Fast Clothing, Inc.
REDSKIN - Airports - Milton Bradley Co.
REDSTAR - Televisions, microwave ovens, etc. - Borlas Sales Corp.
REDSTONE - Sandwiches–prepackaged - Golden Valley Farms Commodity Group, Inc.
REDSTRIPE - Pipes–plastic - Chevron Chemical Co.
REDUCE-AMINE - Vitamins and nutritional supplements - Michigan Pharmaceutical
REDUCE-ME - Skin care products - Sara Lee Corp.
REDUCE PH - Water treating compounds - Wardley Corp.
REDUCED FAT SOUR CREAM & ONION CHIPS & TWISTS - Snack foods - Gardetto's
REDUCED SODIUM NATURAL TAMARI - Soy sauce - San-J International Inc.
REDUCEOMATIC - Girdles - Preferred Foundations
REDUCINE - Pharmaceutical preparations ☆ - D'Franssia Corp.
REDUCINE - Veterinary pharmaceutical preparations - Farnam Cos. Inc.
REDUCING STRESS CREATES SUCCESS - Publisher's imprints - Lewis Publishing
REDUCOL - Veterinary medicine ☆ - American Equine Products Inc.
REDUCTO - Paints - X-I-M Products Inc.
REDUSOL - Chemical preparations ☆ - Woolsey Marine Industries
REDWOLF - Computer software - Redwolf Industries, Inc.
REDWOOD - Bicycles - Marin Mountain Bikes, Inc.
REDWOOD - Computer hardware - Redwood Design Automation, Inc.
REDWOOD - Gloves–rubber - Malaytex USA Inc.
REDWOOD - Manufactured homes - Redman Industries, Inc.
REDWOOD - Recording label - Redwood Cultural Work
REDWOOD - Snuff - American Maize-Products Co.
REDWOOD - Tobacco products - Swisher International, Inc.
REDWOOD - Trailers–travel - Leader Enterprises
REDWOOD & ROSS - Apparel–women's - Gilmore Brothers, Inc.
REDWOOD CANYON CELLARS - Wines - Calafia Wines
REDWOOD COAST - Wines ☆ - Franciscan Vineyards, Inc.
REDWOOD DESIGN A FENCE - Paper - California Redwood Association
REDWOOD DESIGN AUTOMATION - Computer hardware - Redwood Design Automation, Inc.
REDWOOD EMPIRE - Fresh fruits - Redwood Empire Packaging, Inc.
REDWOOD GROVE - Wines - European Beverage Co., Inc.
REDWOOD GROVE - Wines ☆ - Maison Jomere Ltd.
REDWOOD INN - Fruits–candied - Redwood Food Packing Co.
REDWOOD MANOR - Manufactured homes - Redman Industries, Inc.
REDWOOD TRAIL - Wines - Sterling Vineyards, Inc.
REDWOOD VALLEY CELLARS - Wines ☆ - Weibel Vineyards
REDWOODIZER - Finishing agents ☆ - Demert & Dougherty, Inc.
REDWOODS - Shoes - M.X.J. Enterprises, Inc.
REDY COAT - Roofing compound - Henry Co.
REDY MASTIC - Adhesives and sealants - A.Z. Bogert Co.
REEBARK - Pet products ☆ - Flexi-Mat Corp.
REEBOK - Athletic shoes - Reebok International Ltd.
REEBOK - Eyeglasses ☆ - Ambassador Eyewear Group
REEBOK - Gloves - Fabry Glove & Mitten Co.
REEBOK BODY MILL - Exercising equipment - Reebok/CCS Fitness
REEBOK BODY PEAK - Exercising equipment - Reebok/CCS Fitness
REEBOK BODY PLUS - Exercising equipment - Reebok/CCS Fitness
REEBOK BODY ROCKER - Exercising equipment - Reebok/CCS Fitness
REEBOK BODY STRENGTH - Exercising equipment - Reebok/CCS Fitness
REEBOK BODY TREK - Exercising equipment - Reebok/CCS Fitness
REEBOK STEP - Video tapes–blank - Fit Net
REEC-EZ - Diagnostic apparatus - Instrumentation Northwest, Inc.
REECE'S - Food products - Reece Foods Inc.
REED - Apparel–athletic - Reed Manufacturing Co. Inc.
REED - Reference books, online databases - Reed Reference Publishing
REED - Wines - Calera Wine Co.
REED & BARTON - Jewelry - Reed and Barton Corp.
REED & RIBBON - Flatware - Wallace International Silversmiths, Inc.
REED & SEDGE PEAT - Garden equipment ☆ - Hyper-Humus Co.
REED BOOKS - Publisher's imprints - Addison House Interiors Inc.
REED CANDLES - Candles - Reed Candle Co.
REED-O-MATIC - Musical instrument accessories ☆ - Reed-O-Matic Inc.
REED-O-METER - Musical instrument accessories - French American Reeds Manufacturing
REED-PAK - Musical instrument accessories ☆ - Selmer Co. Inc.
REED-RUSH - Cleaning preparations - G. Leblanc Corp.

REED ST. JAMES - Apparel and accessories - Haggar Corp.
REED ST. JAMES - Apparel and accessories - Wemco, Inc.
REED ST. JAMES - Apparel–men's - Host Apparel Inc.
REED ST. JAMES - Uniforms–academic ☆ - Jockey International, Inc.
REED STARLINE - Greeting cards - Paramount Cards Inc.
REEDFLEX - Uniforms–tailored - Reed Manufacturing Co. Inc.
REEDMAN SELECT CERTIFIED - Motor vehicles–automobiles - Reedman Chevrolet, Inc.
REEDPRODUCTIONS - Stationery - Reedproductions
REEDS - Candy - Amurol Confections Co.
REED'S - Candy - Clark Gum Co.
REEDS - Floor coverings–carpet and rugs - Robertex Associates Inc.
REED'S - Paper–cloth-lined ☆ - Creative Expressions Group
REED'S - Pet products - Tetra Sales USA
REED'S CROSSING - Apparel and accessories - Reed Manufacturing Co. Inc.
REEDS TEA DROPS - Candy - Amurol Confections Co.
REEDSBURG VALLEY - Vegetables–canned - Reedsburg Foods Corp.
REEDSTORAGE - Musical instrument accessories ☆ - Rico International
REEDWOOD - Novelty items ☆ - Reed Candle Co.
REEECHIT - Paint rollers - Corona Brushes Inc.
REEF - Bowls - Svend Jensen of Denmark Inc.
REEF - Glassware–household - Crystal Clear Importing Co. Inc.
REEF BRAZIL - Bags–duffel - South Cone, Inc.
REEF BUILDER - Pet products - Seachem Laboratories
REEF CALCIUM - Pet products - Seachem Laboratories
REEF CARE - Water treating compounds - Aquarium Pharmaceuticals, inc.
REEF COMPLETE - Pet products - Seachem Laboratories
REEF CRUISER - Boats–motor - Robert L. Golobic
REEF CRYSTALS - Salt - Aquarium Systems, Inc.
REEF EVOLUTION - Water treating compounds - Aquarium Systems, Inc.
REEF FLECTIONS - Aquarium accessories - Blue Ribbon Pet Products, Inc.
REEF GEAR - Watches - Timex Corp.
REEF IODIDE - Pet products - Seachem Laboratories
REEF NUTRIENT - Aquarium accessories - Kordon
REEF NUTRIENT - Aquarium accessories - Novalek, Inc.
REEF PLUS - Pet products - Seachem Laboratories
REEF RAIDER - Toys - Mattel, Inc.
REEF READY - Pet products - Oceanic Systems, Inc.
REEF SALT - Pet products - Seachem Laboratories
REEF STANTIUM - Pet products - Seachem Laboratories
REEF STATUS: CALCIUM - Pet products - Seachem Laboratories
REEF STATUS: STRONTIUM & MAGNESIUM - Pet products - Seachem Laboratories
REEFAWAY - Boats - Metalmast Marine
REEFER - Yarn - Dixie Yarns, Inc.
REEFER-GALLER - Housewares - Willert Home Products, Inc.
REEFLECTIONS - Aquarium accessories - Blue Ribbon Pet Products, Inc.
REEFORMS - Aquariums–household ☆ - Aquarium Systems, Inc.
REEFPACK - Pet products - Seachem Laboratories
REEFRUNNER - Sporting goods - Marine Sports Designs, Inc.
REEFTAINER - Refrigerated cargo containers - Reefco Manufacturing Corp.
REEL 1 - Recording label - Reel-1-Records Inc.
REEL A CORD - Electrical equipment - General Cable Corp.
REEL APPEAL - Puzzles - Compu-Tech Consulting Services, Inc.
REEL BANK - Film - Compco Photographic/Goldberg Bros.
REEL BUDDY - Sporting goods - Advanced Boat Products Inc.
REEL CAR COVER - Automotive parts and accessories - Chadamy Corp.
REEL COLLECTIBLES - Containers - Promotional Management Group, Inc.
REEL-DEAL - Machinery - Reel-Neat Systems, Inc.
REEL DETECTIVES - Game machines - Atlantic City Coin & Slot Service Co., Inc.
REEL DRAG UNLIMITED ANGLING NETWORK - Apparel and accessories - Reel Drag, Ltd.
REEL E-Z - Dollies and hand-trucks - CW Communications
REEL EASY - Garden equipment - Ames Lawn & Garden Tool Co.
REEL EASY - Garden equipment - Weatherly Consumer Products, Inc.
REEL 'EM IN - Game machines - WMS Gaming Inc.
REEL GEMS - Game machines - Bally Gaming International, Inc.
REEL-IDENT - Labels–paper ☆ - Litton Industrial Automation Systems
REEL JAVA - Coffee - Sony Theatre Management Corp.
REEL-KING - Construction machinery - Southern Machinery Co.
REEL LEADER, THE - Hoses - Hannay Reels
REEL LOVE - Greeting cards - J.S. English Co.
REEL-NEAT - Measuring instruments ☆ - Reel-Neat Systems, Inc.
REEL-O-MATIC - Machinery - Reel-Neat Systems, Inc.
REEL-PAK - Tape recorders–reels - Plastic Reel Corp. of America

---

☆ = Now out of production

REEL QUICK - Garden equipment - Reel Quick Inc.
REEL RAIN - Agricultural machinery - Amadas Industries, Inc.
REEL RITER - Pens ☆ - Park Sherman
REEL SCHPEEL - Games - Game Geste, Inc.
REEL SCRUBBER - Sporting goods - Birchwood Casey
REEL TECH - Fishing tackle - Reel Tech
REEL-TITE WIRE - Wire - Kermco-Dehaai, Inc.
REEL TOTE - Tools–garden - Melnor Inc.
REEL TREATS - Candy and pastries - Edible Arts Inc.
REEL WOMEN FLY FISHING ADVENTURES - Apparel and accessories - Reel Women, Inc.
REELCRAFT - Springs–mechanical - Reelcraft Industries, Inc.
REELECT - Medical apparatus - Dornier Medical Systems, Inc.
REELEEL - Fishing lures - Creme Lure Co.
REELEEL II - Fishing lures - Creme Lure Co.
REELER DEALER - Electronics equipment - Marty Bahn & Co.
REELI-KLEAN - Melting preparations - American Colloid Co.
REELIN' ROADSTER - Toys–automobiles - Mattel, Inc.
REELL - Hinges - Reell Precision Manufacturing Corp.
REELMOBILE - Furniture - Wallach & Associates Inc.
REELO - Gasoline - Mobil Oil Corp.
REELRITE - Photographic equipment - Testrite Instrument Co. Inc.
REELSMOKE - Cellulosic food casings - Viskase Corp.
REELSWINGER - Hoses - Melnor Inc.
REELTENDER - Meat products - GFI America, Inc.
REELWHEEL - Hoses ☆ - Melnor Inc.
REELX - Rustproofing compounds - Corrosion Technologies, Corp.
REELY - Candy - Alottafun, Inc.
REEMSTMA - Cigarettes - G.A. Georgopulo & Co. Inc.
REEMSTMA ERNTE - Cigarettes - G.A. Georgopulo & Co. Inc.
REENO - Cleaning preparations ☆ - Reen'o Corp.
REESE - Food products - World Finer Foods, Inc.
REESE - Locks–padlocks - Waterbury Lock & Specialty Co.
REESE BRAKEMAN TRAILER HITCHES AND TOWING ACCESSORIES - Brake parts - Reese Products, Inc.
REESE CANNONBALL - Olives–canned - World Finer Foods, Inc.
REESE WAY - Floor coverings ☆ - Tarkett, Inc.
REESE'S - Candy - Hershey Chocolate USA
REESE'S - Candy bars - H.B. Reese Candy Co.
REESE'S - Peanut butter - Homestead, Inc.
REESE'S - Stencils - C.H. Hanson Co.
REESE'S COOKIES IN PEANUT BUTTER CUPS - Candy - Hershey Chocolate USA
REESE'S PEANUT BUTTER PUFFS - Cereal - General Mills, Inc.
REESE'S PIECES - Candy - H.B. Reese Candy Co.
REESE'S PINWORM - Pharmaceutical preparations - Reese Chemical Co.
REEVA - Floor coverings–carpet and rugs ☆ - Regal Rugs Inc.
REEVAIR - Waterproofing compounds ☆ - Reeves Brothers Inc.
REEVES - Artists' supply stores - Brittoys
REEVES RACK - Display cases–metal - Dennis Reeves, Inc.
REEVESELECT - Food products ☆ - Durkee French Foods
REEVESHED - Fabrics–polypropylene - Reeves Brothers Inc.
REEVESLINE - Toys–models ☆ - Reeves International, Inc.
REEVETECH - Roofing materials–slate - Reeves Brothers Inc.
REF - Tools ☆ - Reliable Finishing Products, Inc.
REF - Yarn - Fibers and Fabrics of Georgia Inc.
REF BOP BAG-40, THE - Vinyl - Phun from Phoenix! Inc.
REF/OX - Medical apparatus - Baxter International Inc.
REFCON - Gasoline ☆ - Lehigh Portland Cement Co.
REFENESEN - Pharmaceutical preparations - Reese Chemical Co.
REFENESEN PLUS - Pharmaceutical preparations - Reese Chemical Co.
REFERENCE BOOK II, A - Wallpaper - Jack Denst Designs
REFERENCE FOR THE REST OF US!, A - Publisher's imprints - International Data Group, Inc.
REFERENCE MANAGER - Computer software - Delaware Licensing Corp.
REFERENCE OPAQUE - Paper–writing - P.H. Glatfelter Co.
REFERENCE RECORDINGS - Recording label - Reference Recordings Ltd.
REFERENCES FOR THE REST OF US - Publisher's imprints - International Data Group, Inc.
REFERRAL - Computer software - Geoaccess, Inc.
REFFMASTER - Cameras - Pioneer Marketing & Research, Inc.
REFIL-A-LITE - Lighters - Ronson Consumer Products Corp.
REFILL INK SYSTEM - Office supplies - Repeat-O-Type Manufacturing Corp.
REFINE - Surgical instruments - Boehringer Mannheim Corp.
REFINED WALLS - Wallpaper ☆ - H & S Sales Inc.
REFINED WALLS II - Wallpaper ☆ - H & S Sales Inc.

REFINED WALLS III - Wallpaper ☆ - H & S Sales Inc.
REFINED WALLS IV - Wallpaper - Capital Carousel Inc.
REFINED WALLS IV - Wallpaper ☆ - H & S Sales Inc.
REFINEMENTS - Refillable lipstick - Coty Inc.
REFINEMENTS - Wallpaper ☆ - Sandpiper Studios
REFINEMENTS - Wallpaper ☆ - Wallquest, Inc.
REFINEMENTS II - Wallpaper ☆ - Sandpiper Studios
REFLECT - Fixtures–plastic ☆ - Advanced Technology Inc.
REFLECT A COAT - Adhesives and sealants - Moc Products Co., Inc.
REFLECT-A-DOME - Mirrors - Fred Silver and Co. Inc.
REFLECT A LITE - Lighting equipment–automotive - George F. Stowe, Jr.
REFLECT DECOR - Mirrors - National Products Inc.
REFLECT-O-GRAF - Games ☆ - Tappe Brothers
REFLECT-O-TRIM - Novelty items–stitched ☆ - Best Emblem & Insignia Co. Inc.
REFLECT REFLECT GAME CORPORATION - Games - Reflect Game
REFLECTA - Photographic equipment - Bogen Photo Corp.
REFLECTA - Skin care products - Texas Pharmacal Co.
REFLECTA - Tiles–ceramic ☆ - American Olean Tile Co.
REFLECTA-DANA - Pet products - Doggone Pet Products
REFLECTA-LIFE - Pet products - Penn-Plax, Inc.
REFLECTAROUND - Photographic equipment - SP Systems/Saratons
REFLECTATRANS - Film - O'Donnell Corp.
REFLECTION - See **GRAPHICS CONVERTER GOLD**
REFLECTION - Colognes - Mastey De Paris
REFLECTION - Dishes–china - Pickard Inc.
REFLECTION - Doors–storm - Canyon Creek Cabinet Co.
REFLECTION - Enamels - Gray Seal Paint Manufacturing Co. Inc.
REFLECTION - Floor coverings - Congoleum Corp.
REFLECTION - Floor coverings–carpet and rugs ☆ - American Carpet Mills
REFLECTION - Motor vehicles–motor homes - Forest River, Inc.
REFLECTION - Prosthetic apparatus - Freeman Manufacturing Co.
REFLECTION - Thread - Perfect Thread Co. Inc.
REFLECTION - Trailers–travel - Fleetwood Enterprises, Inc.
REFLECTION - Yarn ☆ - Caron International Inc.
REFLECTION 22 - Floor waxes - Nyco Products Co.
REFLECTION 2000 - Office supplies - Rubbermaid Office Products Inc.
REFLECTION COLLECTION - Containers - Amlings Flowerland
REFLECTION COLLECTION - Mirrors - Home Advantage Inc.
REFLECTION CREAM - Furniture polish - Black's Products of High Point Inc.
REFLECTION FREE - Eyeglasses - Essilor of America, Inc.
REFLECTION NETWORK - Computer software - Walker Richer and Quinn Inc.
REFLECTION OF PERFECTION - Audio equipment - Disc Manufacturing Inc.
REFLECTION SYSTEMS - Computer storage devices–optical - Reflection Systems Inc.
REFLECTION TO GO - Computer software - Walker Richer and Quinn Inc.
REFLECTIONS - Aluminum compounds ☆ - Regal Ware, Inc.
REFLECTIONS - Apparel–women's - NCC Industries, Inc.
REFLECTIONS - Bathroom accessories - Continental/SiLite International Inc.
REFLECTIONS - Bathroom accessories - Wilardy Originals Inc.
REFLECTIONS - Bathroom accessories ☆ - Zenith Products Corp.
REFLECTIONS - Bathroom fixtures - Artesian Industries
REFLECTIONS - Bathroom fixtures - D.M.A. Enterprises, Inc.
REFLECTIONS - Bedding–linen - Dan River Inc.
REFLECTIONS - Cabinets - Nutone Inc.
REFLECTIONS - Cameras - Eastman Kodak Co.
REFLECTIONS - Chemical preparations - Grow Group, Inc.
REFLECTIONS - Christmas tree ornaments - Cracker Box Inc.
REFLECTIONS - Cleaning preparations–household - Conklin Co., Inc.
REFLECTIONS - Clocks - General Time Corp. (Westclox/Seth Thomas Div.)
REFLECTIONS - Containers–plastic - Ivex Coated Products Corp.
REFLECTIONS - Dinnerware–glass - Crystal Clear Importing Co. Inc.
REFLECTIONS - Dinnerware–glass - Franciscan by Johnson Brothers, USA, Inc.
REFLECTIONS - Dishes–earthenware - Mug Shanty
REFLECTIONS - Fabrics - Astrup Co.
REFLECTIONS - Fabrics - Uniroyal Engineered Products
REFLECTIONS - Faucets - Chicago Faucet Co.
REFLECTIONS - Finishing agents ☆ - Pioneer/Eclipse Corp.
REFLECTIONS - Floor coverings–carpet and rugs - Calladium & Marglen
REFLECTIONS - Floor coverings–carpet and rugs - Criterion Mills Inc.
REFLECTIONS - Floor coverings–carpet and rugs - Ebsco Carpet Mills
REFLECTIONS - Floor coverings–carpet and rugs - Lotus Carpets
REFLECTIONS - Floor coverings–carpet and rugs - Patcraft Mills Inc.
REFLECTIONS - Floor coverings–carpet and rugs - Porter Carpet Mills Inc.
REFLECTIONS - Floor coverings–carpet and rugs - Regal Rugs Inc.

☆ = Now out of production

REFLECTIONS - Floor coverings–carpet and rugs ☆ - Burtco Enterprises Inc.
REFLECTIONS - Floor coverings–carpet and rugs ☆ - Couristan Inc.
REFLECTIONS - Floor coverings–carpet and rugs ☆ - Downs Carpet Co. Inc.
REFLECTIONS - Floor coverings–carpet and rugs ☆ - Galaxy Carpet Mills Inc.
REFLECTIONS - Frames–picture - Two's Co. Inc.
REFLECTIONS - Furniture - Norwalk Furniture Corp.
REFLECTIONS - Furniture - Universal Flooring
REFLECTIONS - Furniture ☆ - Bassett Furniture Industries, Inc.
REFLECTIONS - Furniture ☆ - Bernhardt Industries
REFLECTIONS - Furniture ☆ - Hammary Furniture Co. Inc.
REFLECTIONS - Garden furniture–rattan - Lloyd/Flanders Industries
REFLECTIONS - Glassware–household - Svend Jensen of Denmark Inc.
REFLECTIONS - Greeting cards - American Greetings Corp.
REFLECTIONS - Hardware - Marley Mouldings Inc.
REFLECTIONS - Jewelry ☆ - Hirsch Speidel Inc.
REFLECTIONS - Liners and covers–Swimming pool - Doughboy Recreational Inc.
REFLECTIONS - Novelty items–paper - Antioch Publishing Co.
REFLECTIONS - Paper–gift wrap - CPS Corp.
REFLECTIONS - Polishing cloths - Mothers Polishes Waxes Cleaners
REFLECTIONS - Publisher's imprints - Warner Press, Inc.
REFLECTIONS - Railings–wood ☆ - Pawling Corp. (Standard Products Div.)
REFLECTIONS - Recording label - Counter Culture
REFLECTIONS - Recording label - Integrity Music, Inc.
REFLECTIONS - Rings–jewelry ☆ - Artcarved Inc.
REFLECTIONS - Shampoos - Marianna Imports, Inc.
REFLECTIONS - Shoes ☆ - Sidney Rich Associates Inc.
REFLECTIONS - Skin care products - Warner-Lambert Co.
REFLECTIONS - Tiles–ceramic - Dal-Tile Corp.
REFLECTIONS - Tiles–ceramic ☆ - Wenczel Tile Co.
REFLECTIONS - Vases ☆ - Lenox Crystal, Inc.
REFLECTIONS - Wallpaper - Kingfisher Wallcoverings
REFLECTIONS - Wallpaper - Koroseal Wallcoverings
REFLECTIONS - Wallpaper - Winfield Design Associates, Inc.
REFLECTIONS - Wallpaper ☆ - Gilford Corp.
REFLECTIONS - Wigs - Revlon General Wig Manufacturers, Inc.
REFLECTIONS - Window coverings ☆ - Hunter Douglas, Inc.
REFLECTIONS - Window shades - Quakermaid Products
REFLECTIONS 6 - Wallpaper ☆ - Kingfisher Wallcoverings
REFLECTIONS BY HAGGAR - Apparel and accessories ☆ - Haggar Corp.
REFLECTIONS COLLECTION - Furniture–factory ☆ - Clayton Marcus Co. Inc.
REFLECTIONS II - Luggage - American Tourister, Inc.
REFLECTIONS III - Wallpaper ☆ - Kingfisher Wallcoverings
REFLECTIONS IN RED - Dolls - Mattel, Inc.
REFLECTIONS OF BEAUTY - Calendars ☆ - Amcal Inc.
REFLECTIONS OF NATURE - Figurines - Mangelsen's (VDI)
REFLECTIONS OF THE HEART - Cups–plastic - Russ Berrie and Co., Inc.
REFLECTIVE - Floor coverings–carpet and rugs - Downs Carpet Co. Inc.
REFLECTIVE EDGE - Window shades - Lee N. Ryden
REFLECTIVE MEMORY - Computer software - Encore Computer U.S., Inc.
REFLECTIVES - Reflective letters and numbers - Cole Consumer Products Inc.
REFLECTIX - Paper - Printmark Industries Inc.
REFLECTO - Pet products - Leather Brothers Inc.
REFLECTO - Pet products - Molor Products Co.
REFLECTO - Toys ☆ - Tedco Inc.
REFLECTO WEB - Craft supplies - C.M. Offray & Son Inc.
REFLECTOR - Cymbals - Paiste America, Inc.
REFLECTOR - Fabrics - Kappler Safety Group
REFLECTOR - Reflectors–optical - Precise International/Wenger
REFLECTOR PHOTOFLOOD - Floodlights - General Electric Co.
REFLECTOR PHOTOSPOT - Lamps - General Electric Co.
REFLECTORIBBON - Craft supplies - C.M. Offray & Son Inc.
REFLECTRON - Video equipment - Kenneth A. Jamieson
REFLEKTA - Paints ☆ - Coronado Paint Co.
REFLEX - Bats–baseball - Easton Aluminum Inc.
REFLEX - Cabinets - Midmark Corp.
REFLEX - Computer software - Borland International, Inc.
REFLEX - Containers–shipping - North America Packaging Corp.
REFLEX - Coveralls - Kimberly-Clark Corp.
REFLEX - Cushions - Foamex
REFLEX - Electrodes - Uni-Patch
REFLEX - Exercising equipment - American Athletic Inc.
REFLEX - Exercising equipment - Christy Co.
REFLEX - Film - Chromaline Corp.
REFLEX - Frames–eyeglass - Universal/Univis Inc.
REFLEX - Pagers - Motorola, Inc.

REFLEX - Projectors–photographic - Rollei of America Inc.
REFLEX - Soccer equipment - Brine Inc.
REFLEX - Sporting goods - Wilson Sporting Goods Co.
REFLEX - Surgical instruments - Richard-Allan Medical Industries, Inc.
REFLEX - Toys - Tonka Corp.
REFLEX - Welding equipment - Uvex Safety LLC
REFLEX 4000 - Projection screens ☆ - Draper Shade and Screen Co. Inc.
REFLEX CLEAR - Electrodes - Uni-Patch
REFLEX COIL - Mattresses - Ohio Mattress Co.
REFLEX MID PLUS - Sporting goods ☆ - Gold Eagle/Arnold Palmer
REFLEX ROLLER - Massage products - Kinsei Shiatsu, Inc.
REFLEX SUPER - Cleaning preparations–window - Malter International Corp.
REFLEX TANTONE - Electrodes - Uni-Patch
REFLEX, THE - Mats - Roope Corp.
REFLEXION - Underwear and nightwear - NCC Industries, Inc.
REFLEXITE REFLECTIVE VINYL - Signs - Sign-Up Corp.
REFLEXLITE - Cables - Loos and Co. Inc.
REFLEXSTONE - Tiles–ceramic - Kowa Texas Inc.
REFLEXX - Boats - Bayliner Marine Corp.
REFLITE - Glass–flat - Orient Glass Inc.
REFLITE - Insulating materials - Refractory Technology, Inc.
REFLUX - Home-health-care products - Ivex Corp.
REFLUX REDUCER - Health care products - Physician Engineered Products
REFLUX SPECIALIST, THE - Pharmaceutical preparations - Smithkline Beecham Corp.
REFLXBOARD - Hockey equipment - Robert D. Montgomery
REFORM - Fabrics - Interface, Inc.
REFORM - Hair care products - Form-U-La-Hair Co.
REFORM - Pens - Reform Writing Instruments
REFORM GREESE - Skin care products - Hanah Beauty & Health Inc.
REFORM SET - Skin care products - Hanah Beauty & Health Inc.
REFORMER - Office supplies - Alvin and Co. Inc.
REFORMULYZER - Scientific apparatus - AC Analytical Controls, Inc.
REFOSCO ALFRESCO - Wines - Monterey Winery
REFRACTIONS - Floor coverings–carpet and rugs ☆ - Karastan-Bigelow Inc.
REFRACTIONS - Plastics–laminated - Formica Corp.
REFRAMERICA - Glass products - Reframerica, Inc.
REFRESH - Deodorizers - Coast Distribution System
REFRESH - Deodorizers - Pine Glo Products Inc.
REFRESH - Deodorizers - Unique Sports Products Inc.
REFRESH - Diapers–disposable ☆ - Whitestone Products Inc.
REFRESH - Juices ☆ - Stokely USA, Inc.
REFRESH - Ophthalmic goods - Allergan, Inc.
REFRESH - Pet products - Bramton Co.
REFRESH - Shampoos ☆ - Oxyfresh Worldwide, Inc.
REFRESH - Vitamins and nutritional supplements - Solaray
REFRESH - Vitamins and nutritional supplements ☆ - Rose International
REFRESH-A-BASEMENT - Oils–vulcanized - Enviro-Dynamics Inc.
REFRESH-A-CLOSET - Deodorizers - Enviro-Dynamics Inc.
REFRESH-A-FRIG - Oils–vulcanized - Enviro-Dynamics Inc.
REFRESH-AIRE - Air purification systems - Pollenex Corp.
REFRESH-IT - Deodorizers - Promaster
REFRESH-KNIT - Knitting machines - Peter Freund Knitting Mills
REFRESH PLUS - Ophthalmic goods - Allergan, Inc.
REFRESH P.M. - Ophthalmic goods - Allergan, Inc.
REFRESHA COLADA LITE COLADA MIXA - Food products - Andre Prost Inc.
REFRESHENAIR - Deodorizers - Surco Products Inc.
REFRESHENERS - Deodorizers - Reckitt & Colman, Inc.
REFRESHER - Cups–paper - Westvaco Corp.
REFRESHER - Towels - Chicopee
REFRESHING - Wallpaper ☆ - W.H.S. Lloyd
REFRESHMENT ZONE - Beverages–carbonated - Pepsico, Inc.
REFRESHMINT - Veterinary pharmaceutical preparations - W.F. Young, Inc.
REFRIED ICE CREAM - Recording label - Refried Ice Cream Band
REFRIGEMATE STORAGE CONTAINERS - Containers - Unity Plastics, Inc.
REFRIGERANT JOURNAL SOFTWARE - Computer software - Environmental Support Solutions, Inc.
REFRIGERATOR ART - Artists' materials ☆ - Refrigerator Art
REFRIGERATOR-FRESH - Seafoods - Product Possibilities, Inc.
REFRIGERATOR MAGNET - Magnets - Carl Seeger Henry and Steven Toce Partnership
REFRIGERATOR MAGNET POUCH, THE - Magnets - Great Graphic Originals
REFRIGERATOR ODOR KLEEN - Cleaning preparations - G.G. Bean Inc.
REFRIGERWRITER - Magnets - A & W Products Co., Inc.
REFRIGICOAT - Apparel and accessories - RefrigiWear Inc.
REFRIGIWEAR - Apparel and accessories - RefrigiWear Inc.

REFRIGUE - Apparel and accessories - RefrigiWear Inc.
REFUSE TO LOSE - Apparel and accessories - Hyden Corp.
REG FINDER, THE - Computer software - Contour Software Inc.
REG-U-TEMP - Health care products - Medi Inc.
REGA - Audio equipment - Import Audio
REGAIN - Vitamins and nutritional supplements - Nellson Candies Inc.
REGAL - Aluminum compounds - Regal Ware, Inc.
REGAL - Beverages–carbonated - Florida Brewing Co.
REGAL - Bicycles - Trailmate Inc.
REGAL - Boats–motor - Regal Marine Industries Inc.
REGAL - Bookcases–metal - Lundia
REGAL - Books–blank - Acme Graphics Inc.
REGAL - Brushes–paint - Corona Brushes Inc.
REGAL - Brushes–paint ☆ - PPG Industries, Inc.
REGAL - Building materials - Texas Aluminum Industries Inc.
REGAL - Cabinets - Quality Cabinets
REGAL - Cabinets ☆ - Diamond Cabinets
REGAL - Chemical preparations - South Central Pool Supply
REGAL - Cleaning preparation - Regal Supply Inc.
REGAL - Clocks ☆ - Ridgeway Clock Co.
REGAL - Computer software - Regal Electronics, Inc.
REGAL - Computers–personal - Micro Express Inc.
REGAL - Curtain rods - Kenney Manufacturing Co.
REGAL - Dishes–china - Pasmantier Co. Inc.
REGAL - Dog food - H.E. Butt Grocery Co.
REGAL - Dolls - Cardinal Inc.
REGAL - Drafting supplies ☆ - Mayline/Hamilton
REGAL - Drums–musical instruments - J.D. Calato Manufacturing Inc.
REGAL - Easels - Anco Wood Specialties Inc.
REGAL - Electronics equipment - Marty Bahn & Co.
REGAL - Fabrics - Handler Textile Corp.
REGAL - Firearms, accessories, and parts - Welsh Sporting Goods Corp. (Boyt Div.)
REGAL - Fireplace equipment - Thermo-Rite Manufacturing Co.
REGAL - Fireplace screens - Jack-Post Corp.
REGAL - Flatware - The Dirilyte Line
REGAL - Flatware - Majestic Silver Co.
REGAL - Floor coverings - Congoleum Corp.
REGAL - Floor coverings–carpet and rugs - Blue Ridge Carpet Mills
REGAL - Floor coverings–carpet and rugs ☆ - Regal Rugs Inc.
REGAL - Florists - Denver Wholesale Florists
REGAL - Food products - Camino Real Foods
REGAL - Footwear - Brown Shoe Co.
REGAL - Frames–picture - Engineered Products Co.
REGAL - Frosting ☆ - Signature Brands, LLC
REGAL - Furniture - Weiman Co.
REGAL - Grass seed - International Seeds, Inc.
REGAL - Guitars ☆ - International Music Corp.
REGAL - Ladders–metal - Davidson Ladders Inc.
REGAL - Latex - Columbia Paint Co.
REGAL - Machinery - Franklin Imprinting Machines
REGAL - Mobile homes ☆ - Kit Manufacturing Co.
REGAL - Motor vehicle parts and accessories - Leer Inc.
REGAL - Motor vehicles–automobiles - General Motors Corp. (Buick Motor Div.)
REGAL - Neckties ☆ - MMG Corp.
REGAL - Occasional furniture ☆ - JDI Group, Inc.
REGAL - Office supplies - R.A. Stewart Superior
REGAL - Paints - Benjamin Moore & Co.
REGAL - Pencils ☆ - Empire Berol USA
REGAL - Pillows - Encore Products Inc.
REGAL - Pipes–tobacco - Dr. Grabow Pre-Smoked Pipes Inc.
REGAL - Plumbing fixtures - Sloan Valve Co.
REGAL - Preserved foods–canned - Grocers Supply Co.
REGAL - Printing trades machinery - Vidac
REGAL - Recording label - Rashid Sales Co.
REGAL - Rice - Cormier Rice Milling Co. Inc.
REGAL - Rifles - Redfield Co.
REGAL - Rope - Wellington Leisure Products, Inc.
REGAL - Sausages - Redfern Foods Corp.
REGAL - Shelving units–metal - Tennsco Corp.
REGAL - Skin care products - Imperial Inc.
REGAL - Staplers - Stanley-Bostitch Inc.
REGAL - Strollers–baby - Century Products Co.
REGAL - Tables–metal - Alvin and Co. Inc.
REGAL - Telephones - At&T Corp.

REGAL - Tiles–ceramic - Huntington/Pacific Ceramics Inc.
REGAL - Wallpaper - Southland Wallcoverings
REGAL - Watchbands–base metal - Regal Industries, Inc.
REGAL - Wigs - Helene Curtis Industries Inc.
REGAL - Windows–screen ☆ - MW Manufacturers, Inc.
REGAL - Wood products - Gossen Corp.
REGAL - Yarn - Regal Manufacturing Co., Inc.
REGAL 8 INN - Hotels and motels - Motel 6 Corp.
REGAL 2000 - Copper compounds - Regal Ware, Inc.
REGAL-ADE - Pharmaceutical preparations ☆ - Regal Laboratories Inc.
REGAL AFFAIR - Floor coverings–carpet and rugs - Mohawk Carpet Corp.
REGAL-AIRE - Luggage - United States Luggage Corp.
REGAL-AIRE - Mats - Ludlow Composites Corp.
REGAL-AIRE II - Luggage - United States Luggage Corp.
REGAL-AX - Pharmaceutical preparations ☆ - Regal Laboratories Inc.
REGAL BAY - Floor coverings–carpet and rugs ☆ - Hollytex Carpet Mills Inc.
REGAL-BID - Pharmaceutical preparations ☆ - Regal Laboratories Inc.
REGAL BLUE - Floor coverings–tile - ECC International
REGAL BRAU - Beverages–malt - Joseph Huber Brewing Co., Inc.
REGAL BROWN - Hair coloring preparations - Helene Curtis Industries Inc.
REGAL CASINO - Cigars - Gesty Trading & Manufacturing Corp.
REGAL CHEF - Meat products–beef - Julian Freirich Food
REGAL CLASSIC - Floor coverings–carpet and rugs ☆ - Gulistan Carpet Inc.
REGAL CLASSIC - Furniture - Good Value Furniture Corp.
REGAL COLLECTION - Glassware–household - Grainware Co.
REGAL COLLECTION - Wallpaper ☆ - Wall Fabrics Inc.
REGAL COTE - Paints ☆ - Nelson Roanoke Corp.
REGAL CREST - Floor coverings ☆ - Congoleum Corp.
REGAL CREST - Potato flakes - Oregon Potato Co.
REGAL CROWN - Candy - Shaffer, Clark & Co. Inc.
REGAL CROWN - Confections - Callard & Bowser USA Inc.
REGAL CROWN - Hams - M.H. Greenebaum Inc.
REGAL CROWN COLLECTION, THE - Pillows - Pillowtex Corp.
REGAL DRIVER - Seat covers - Regal Shearing
REGAL ELEGANCE - Floor coverings–carpet and rugs - Galaxy Carpet Mills Inc.
REGAL FIRST COAT - Paints - Benjamin Moore & Co.
REGAL-FLUR - Pharmaceutical preparations ☆ - Regal Laboratories Inc.
REGAL FLYER - Seat covers - Regal Shearing
REGAL GOLD - Sporting goods ☆ - Daiwa Corp.
REGAL GRAND NATIONAL - Motor vehicles–automobiles ☆ - General Motors Corp. (Buick Motor Div.)
REGAL HEIRLOOM - Dolls ☆ - Effanbee Doll Corp.
REGAL-HIST - Pharmaceutical preparations ☆ - Regal Laboratories Inc.
REGAL HOSTESS - Poultry feeds - Armour Swift-Eckrich
REGAL HOUSE - Furniture–upholstered - American TV & Appliance of Madison, Inc.
REGAL II - Watchbands–base metal - Regal Industries, Inc.
REGAL ISLE - Coffee - Berkshire Ltd.
REGAL LIMITED - Motor vehicles–automobiles - General Motors Corp. (Buick Motor Div.)
REGAL MANOR - Bakery products ☆ - Flowers Industries Inc.
REGAL MANOR - Flatware ☆ - National Housewares
REGAL MANOR - Furniture - Bassett Furniture Industries, Inc.
REGAL MANOR - Tableware–plastic ☆ - Robinson Knife & Fiddlers Plastics
REGAL-NATAL - Pharmaceutical preparations ☆ - Regal Laboratories Inc.
REGAL PLAZA - Floor coverings–carpet and rugs ☆ - Cumberland Mills Inc.
REGAL POINT - Floor coverings–carpet and rugs - Karastan-Bigelow Inc.
REGAL POLARIS - Tiles–ceramic ☆ - Wenczel Tile Co.
REGAL RABBIT - Toys–stuffed - Dakin Inc.
REGAL READERS - Eyeglasses ☆ - Cable Car Eyeware
REGAL RED - Food products - C.M. Holtzinger Fruit Co. Inc.
REGAL REFLECTIONS - Dolls - Mattel, Inc.
REGAL REPRODUCTIONS - Silver antique reproductions - Corbell & Co.
REGAL RIB - Wood products - American Building Components Co.
REGAL RIDER - Saddle cloths - Regal Shearing
REGAL ROSES - Dolls - Seymour Mann Inc.
REGAL ROW - Floor coverings–carpet and rugs - Queen Carpet Corp.
REGAL SELECT - Beverages–malt - General Brewing Co.
REGAL SELECT - Beverages–malt - S & P Co.
REGAL SHEEN - Paints - Natcol Crafts & Hobbies
REGAL SPLENDOR - Floor coverings–carpet and rugs - Karastan-Bigelow Inc.
REGAL SPLENDOR - Floor coverings–carpet and rugs ☆ - Royalweve Carpet Mills
REGAL SPUN - Floor coverings–carpet and rugs ☆ - Regal Rugs Inc.

☆ = Now out of production

REGAL SQUARE - Floor coverings - Congoleum Corp.
REGAL STRIKE - Sporting goods ☆ - Daiwa Corp.
REGAL STRIPE - Floor coverings ☆ - Pawling Corp. (Standard Products Div.)
REGAL STRIPES - Wallpaper ☆ - Paneling Instructions (Paneling Div.)
REGAL SUPREME - Copper compounds ☆ - Regal Ware, Inc.
REGAL-TAPP - Pharmaceutical preparations ☆ - Regal Laboratories Inc.
REGAL TIP - Cigars ☆ - Phillies Cigar Co.
REGAL TIP - Drums—musical instruments - J.D. Calato Manufacturing Inc.
REGAL TOUCH - Floor coverings—carpet and rugs - Coronet Carpets Inc.
REGAL TOUCH - Floor coverings—carpet and rugs ☆ - Regal Rugs Inc.
REGAL TRADITION - Copper compounds ☆ - Regal Ware, Inc.
REGAL TRIBUTE - Floor coverings—carpet and rugs ☆ - Patcraft Mills Inc.
REGAL VELOUR - Seat covers - Saddleman, Inc.
REGAL VELVET - Floor coverings—carpet and rugs - Alexander Smith Carpets
REGAL WHITE - Mops ☆ - Helen Keller Services for the Blind
REGALCYCLE - Exercising equipment - Battle Creek Equipment Co.
REGALE - Lighting fixtures - Angelo Brothers Co.
REGALEMESH - Apparel and accessories - La Regale Ltd.
REGALETTO - Floor coverings—carpet and rugs ☆ - Regal Rugs Inc.
REGALFLEX D.I. - Springs—furniture - Hickory Springs Manufacturing Co.
REGALIA - Floor coverings—carpet and rugs - Durkan Patterned Carpets
REGALIA - Meat products—beef - Farmland Foods, Inc.
REGALIA - Rings—jewelry - Artcarved Inc.
REGALIA - Trailers—travel ☆ - Serro Travel Trailer Co. Inc.
REGALIA - Wallpaper ☆ - Gilford Corp.
REGALIA - Yarn - Regal Manufacturing Co., Inc.
REGALIA BY ALEXANDER JULIAN - Apparel—men's - Alexander Julian Inc.
REGALIA COURT - Flatware ☆ - Gorham Inc.
REGALIA COURT LAPIS - Tableware—china - Gorham Inc.
REGALIA COURT TEAL - Tableware—china - Gorham Inc.
REGALIA ROYALE - Wallpaper ☆ - Royaleigh Designs Ltd.
REGALIS - Wallpaper - Wallpaper Imports Inc.
REGALIS COURT - Wallpaper - Import Ltd.
REGALIS COURT - Wallpaper - United Wallcoverings
REGALITE - Doors—glass ☆ - Taylor Building Products Co.
REGALITE - Jewelry - Ringold's Inc.
REGALO - Mexican handcrafts ☆ - Jacaman Gift Co. Inc.
REGALSAUNA - Exercising equipment - Battle Creek Equipment Co.
REGALWOOD - Floor coverings ☆ - Congoleum Corp.
REGAN COMPANY, THE - Motion picture distributors—prerecorded - Regan Co.
REGANE - Fuel additives - Pennzoil Co. (Gumout Div.)
REGANES - Medical apparatus - N.I.T., Inc.
REGARD - Furniture polish and wax - S.C. Johnson & Son, Inc.
REGARD - Lubricants - Gard Corp.
REGARD - Ophthalmic goods - Foremost Optical Products
REGARD - Washboards - Kimberly-Clark Corp.
REGARD RING, THE - Rings—jewelry - Daniel R. Gorman
REGATTA - Apparel—men's - Cavaliero Cravats
REGATTA - Bicycles ☆ - Huffy Corp.
REGATTA - Computer storage devices ☆ - Amherst International Enterprises Co.
REGATTA - Dinnerware - Denby USA Limited
REGATTA - Dinnerware—glass ☆ - Nikko Ceramics Inc.
REGATTA - Dishes—china ☆ - Gorham Inc.
REGATTA - Exercising equipment - Little River Marine Co.
REGATTA - Floor coverings - Mannington Resilient Floors
REGATTA - Floor coverings—carpet and rugs ☆ - Cabin Crafts Carpets
REGATTA - Floor coverings—carpet and rugs ☆ - Kelly Group Inc.
REGATTA - Floor coverings—carpet and rugs ☆ - Regal Rugs Inc.
REGATTA - Games - Avalon Hill Game Co.
REGATTA - Perfumes - Parfums Givenchy, Inc.
REGATTA - Sporting goods ☆ - Battle Creek Equipment Co.
REGATTA - Teas - Eastern Shore Tea Co.
REGATTA - Tiles—ceramic - Monarch Tile Inc.
REGATTA - Watches - Bulova Corp.
REGATTA - Watches - Telux-Pioneer Inc.
REGATTA BALTOPLATE - Boat-bottom coating - Interlux Yacht Finishes
REGATTA PLUS 5 - Varnish - Interlux Yacht Finishes
REGATTA SPORT - Duffle bag - Regatta Licensing
REGATTA YACHT FABRICS - Fabrics - Weblon Inc.
REGE RESERVE - Wines - Diamond Oaks Vineyard
REGEL - Colognes - Tristar Corp.
REGENA - Brushes—paint ☆ - PPG Industries, Inc.
REGENAL - Hair care products - Wella Corp. (Consumer Products Div.)
REGENAVITE - Vitamins and nutritional supplements - Oxford Laboratories Inc.

REGENCE - Flatware - Couzon USA
REGENCE - Furniture - National/Mt. Airy Furniture
REGENCE - Perfumes - Anjac Inc.
REGENCE - Seafood products—canned or cured - Gourmand Inc.
REGENCY - Agricultural products - Vigoro Industries, Inc.
REGENCY - Alarm systems - Stevens Industries Inc.
REGENCY - Apparel and accessories - Host Apparel Inc.
REGENCY - Appliance parts - Uniden America Corp.
REGENCY - Audio equipment ☆ - Electro-Voice, Inc.
REGENCY - Bathroom accessories - Franklin Brass Manufacturing Co.
REGENCY - Bathtubs—enameled - Novi American Inc.
REGENCY - Beverages—alcohol - Kasser Laird Distilling Co.
REGENCY - Bicycles - Ross Bicycles USA, Ltd.
REGENCY - Blankets - Molly Roberts & Co. Inc.
REGENCY - Blinds—vertical - Royal Shutters Inc.
REGENCY - Boats—motor - Glassmaster Co.
REGENCY - Boats—motor - Godfrey Marine Co.
REGENCY - Boats—motor ☆ - Harris-Kayot Inc.
REGENCY - Boats—motor ☆ - Regal Marine Industries Inc.
REGENCY - Cabinets - H.J. Scheirich Co.
REGENCY - Cabinets - Schrock
REGENCY - Cabinets ☆ - Medallion Kitchens of Minnesota Inc.
REGENCY - Cabinets—wood - Parcraft Distinctive Cabinetry
REGENCY - Cameras - Keystone Camera Corp.
REGENCY - Ceiling panels ☆ - Conwed Plastics
REGENCY - Chairs—plastic - Alladin Plastics Inc.
REGENCY - Christmas tree lights ☆ - Noma International, Inc.
REGENCY - Christmas tree ornaments - Cracker Box Inc.
REGENCY - Clocks - Ridgeway Clock Co.
REGENCY - Cooking utensils—aluminum ☆ - Revere Ware Corp.
REGENCY - Desk sets - Stanton's Quills
REGENCY - Desserts - Regency Creative Foods
REGENCY - Dinnerware—glass ☆ - WMF/USA
REGENCY - Dishes—china - Royal China & Porcelain Companies Inc.
REGENCY - Dishes—china - Waterford Wedgwood USA, Inc.
REGENCY - Dishes—earthenware ☆ - Homer Laughlin China Co.
REGENCY - Dolls - Regency, Inc.
REGENCY - Doors—storm ☆ - Gerkin Windows & Doors
REGENCY - Doors—wood ☆ - Peachtree Doors and Windows Inc.
REGENCY - Doors—wood ☆ - Raynor Manufacturing Co.
REGENCY - Drinkware - Corbell & Co.
REGENCY - Fabrics - E.R. Moore Co.
REGENCY - Fabrics ☆ - Emmess Fabrics Corp.
REGENCY - Fans—electric - Tacony Corp.
REGENCY - Faucets - Kallista Inc.
REGENCY - Fireplaces ☆ - Majestic Co.
REGENCY - Floor coverings - Tarkett, Inc.
REGENCY - Floor coverings ☆ - Bruce Hardwood Floors
REGENCY - Floor coverings—carpet and rugs - Galaxy Carpet Mills Inc.
REGENCY - Floor coverings—carpet and rugs - Providence Rug Co.
REGENCY - Floor coverings—carpet and rugs - Robertex Associates Inc.
REGENCY - Floor coverings—carpet and rugs - Stephen-Leedom Carpet Co.
REGENCY - Floor coverings—carpet and rugs ☆ - Regal Rugs Inc.
REGENCY - Food processors - Sunbeam-Oster Household Products
REGENCY - Food products - Concord Foods Inc.
REGENCY - Fudge - Dawn Food Products Inc.
REGENCY - Giftware ☆ - Gorham Inc.
REGENCY - Glass—leaded - Seneca Glass Co.
REGENCY - Glassware—household - ACC
REGENCY - Greeting cards ☆ - Century Engraving & Embossing Co.
REGENCY - Guns ☆ - Weatherby Inc.
REGENCY - Gutters—plastic - Genova Products Inc.
REGENCY - Health care products - Omron Healthcare, Inc.
REGENCY - Juices - Borden, Inc.
REGENCY - Kitchen, vanity, and bathroom cabinets - IXL Furniture Co. Inc.
REGENCY - Lamps - Kaadan Ltd.
REGENCY - Lighters - Colibri Inc.
REGENCY - Mail boxes - Steel City Corp.
REGENCY - Manufactured homes - Redman Industries, Inc.
REGENCY - Motor vehicles—motor homes - Barth Inc.
REGENCY - Occasional tables ☆ - JDI Group, Inc.
REGENCY - Office supplies ☆ - Bates Manufacturing Co.
REGENCY - Padding—foam ☆ - Foamex LP
REGENCY - Paints - Devoe & Raynolds Co.
REGENCY - Paints—artists' - Winsor & Newton
REGENCY - Pans - Denby USA Limited

REGENCY - Paper–writing - Mead Corp.
REGENCY - Pens - Service Merchandise Co., Inc.
REGENCY - Plywood - Plywood & Panels Inc.
REGENCY - Pressed glassware - Indiana Glass Co.
REGENCY - Pressure sprayers and sprinklers ☆ - Amerace Electronic Components
REGENCY - Shelving units–wood - Naomi Gale Wall Systems
REGENCY - Sporting goods - J.A. Cissel Manufacturing Co.
REGENCY - Sprinklers–lawn - Melnor Inc.
REGENCY - Stationery - Regency Thermographers Inc.
REGENCY - Strollers–baby - Graco Children's Products
REGENCY - Sunglasses - Cliff Weil, Inc.
REGENCY - Thread - Imperial Threads Inc.
REGENCY - Tiles–ceramic - Dal-Tile Corp.
REGENCY - Tires - Bridgestone/Firestone, Inc.
REGENCY - Towels - Best Manufacturing Inc.
REGENCY - Trailers–travel ☆ - Shasta Industries Inc.
REGENCY - Vacuum cleaners and accessories ☆ - Bissell Inc.
REGENCY - Video production - Thomas Nelson, Inc.
REGENCY - Wallpaper - Southland Wallcoverings
REGENCY - Wallpaper - Warner Co.
REGENCY - Watches - Bulova Corp.
REGENCY - Watches - Helbros International
REGENCY - Watches - Nicolet International Inc.
REGENCY - Watches ☆ - SMH (US) Inc.
REGENCY 30 - Tires - Bridgestone/Firestone, Inc.
REGENCY BLACK - Tableware–china - Lenox, Inc.
REGENCY BLUE - Roofing materials–clay - Maruhachi Ceramics of America, Inc.
REGENCY BY SMITH - Glassware–household ☆ - L.E. Smith Glass Co.
REGENCY CIRCLE - Apparel and accessories - Breton Industries
REGENCY COLLECTION - Cooking utensils–stoneware - A.D. Johnson Engraving Co.
REGENCY COLLECTION - Faucets - Elkay Manufacturing Co.
REGENCY COLLECTION - Shoes - Genesco Inc.
REGENCY/CORE - Thread - Imperial Threads Inc.
REGENCY ENTERTAINMENT - Recording label - Thomas Nelson, Inc.
REGENCY GOLD - Brushes–paint - Winsor & Newton
REGENCY GREETINGS - Greeting cards - Regency-Sonnell Greetings Inc.
REGENCY GROUP - Handbags - Marilyn USA
REGENCY INN - House furnishings - Lea Industries Inc.
REGENCY MANOR - House furnishings ☆ - Florida Furniture Industries Inc.
REGENCY OAK - Furniture - Bassett Furniture Industries, Inc.
REGENCY PARK - Floor coverings–carpet and rugs ☆ - Hollytex Carpet Mills Inc.
REGENCY PLACE - Floor coverings–carpet and rugs ☆ - Customweave Carpets Inc.
REGENCY PLACE - Floor coverings–carpet and rugs ☆ - World Carpets, Inc.
REGENCY PLACE - Furniture ☆ - Lane Co. Inc.
REGENCY R/S - Wood products ☆ - Raynor Manufacturing Co.
REGENCY RED - Nail care products - Noxell Corp.
REGENCY REFERENCE LIBRARY - Publisher's imprints ☆ - Zondervan Publishing House
REGENCY ROSE - Christmas tree ornaments - Cracker Box Inc.
REGENCY ROW - Floor coverings–carpet and rugs - Criterion Mills Inc.
REGENCY SQUARE - Floor coverings - Congoleum Corp.
REGENCY SQUARE - Floor coverings–carpet and rugs - Cabin Crafts Carpets
REGENCY SQUARE - Furniture - Bassett Furniture Industries, Inc.
REGENCY STYLES LTD. - Coats - Regal Garment Corp.
REGENCY, THE - Display cases–wood - Expostar Displays, Inc.
REGENCY TWEED - Seat covers - Saddleman, Inc.
REGENCY WOOD SERIES - Siding - Amcraft Building Products Co., Inc.
REGENERATION - Desk sets - Newell Office Products
REGENERATION - Notebooks and notepads - Norcom Inc.
REGENERATION - Toners - Genicom Corp.
REGENERATOR - Garden equipment - Evergreen International, Inc.
REGENERON - Battery - Baar Products
REGENERON - Pharmaceutical preparations - Regeneron Pharmaceuticals Inc.
REGENIX HAIR RETENTION SYSTEM - Hair care products - Pure Balance, Inc.
REGENRX - Pharmaceutical preparations - Apex Energetics, Inc.
REGENT - Apparel–women's - Russ Togs Inc.
REGENT - Automotive parts and accessories - Lancaster Colony Automotive Group
REGENT - Bathroom fixtures - Foremost International Trading Inc.
REGENT - Boats–motor ☆ - Rinker Boat Co. Inc.

REGENT - Brushes–paint - Corona Brushes Inc.
REGENT - Chairs–upholstered - HON Industries Inc.
REGENT - Cheese - Zausner Foods Corp.
REGENT - Daters, inks, numberers - Consolidated Stamp Manufacturing Co. Inc.
REGENT - Desks ☆ - Northwest Metal Products Co.
REGENT - Dishwashing compounds - Ecolab Inc.
REGENT - Doors - United Dominion Industries, Inc.
REGENT - Doors–glass - Robertson-Ceco Corp.
REGENT - Duplicating machines - Eastman Kodak Co.
REGENT - Fabrics - Gretchen Bellinger Inc.
REGENT - Fabrics ☆ - Springs Industries, Inc.
REGENT - Fans–electric - Nutone Inc.
REGENT - Filters–air - Aquaria Inc.
REGENT - Floor coverings–carpet and rugs - Atlas Carpet Mills Inc.
REGENT - Floor coverings–carpet and rugs ☆ - Ebsco Carpet Mills
REGENT - Footwear–athletic - E.S. Originals, Inc.
REGENT - Fruits and vegetables - Saticoy Lemon Association
REGENT - Furniture - Domore/DO3
REGENT - Furniture - Weiman Co.
REGENT - Glassware–household ☆ - Lancaster Colony Corp.
REGENT - Glassware–household ☆ - Lotus Glass Co.
REGENT - Goggles–safety - Ektelon
REGENT - Greeting cards - Warner Press, Inc.
REGENT - Guitars - K & K Musical Instrument Co. Inc.
REGENT - Handles–wood - Fleischmann Handle Co.
REGENT - Hardware - Shepherd Products U.S. Inc.
REGENT - Lighting equipment - Regent Lighting Corp. (Consumer Products Div.)
REGENT - Luggage - Samsonite Corp.
REGENT - Mops ☆ - Helen Keller Services for the Blind
REGENT - Motor vehicles–motor homes ☆ - Commodore Corp.
REGENT - Musical instruments - Boosey & Hawkes Buffet Crampon USA
REGENT - Pipes–tobacco ☆ - S.M. Frank & Co. Inc. (Kaywoodie-Yello-Bole-Medico)
REGENT - Radios - Lenoxx Electronics Corp.
REGENT - Rice - Southern Seasonings Inc.
REGENT - Saddles - Libertyville Saddle Shop, Inc.
REGENT - Sporting goods - Regent Sports Corp.
REGENT - Tape recorders–cassette ☆ - Lanier Voice Products
REGENT - Towels - Monarch Towel Co.
REGENT - Tuxedos ☆ - After Six Inc.
REGENT - Watches - Global Sales, Ltd.
REGENT 12XX - Monocalcium phosphate food additive - Rhone-Poulenc Specialty Chemicals Co.
REGENT 32 - Floor coverings–carpet and rugs - Eagle Carpets Inc.
REGENT COLLECTION - Infant product - Dundee Mills, Inc.
REGENT COLLECTION - Office furniture–wood - Hon Co.
REGENT COLLECTION - Wallpaper ☆ - Sandpiper Studios
REGENT COURT - Floor coverings ☆ - Congoleum Corp.
REGENT COURT - Furniture ☆ - Hooker Furniture Corp.
REGENT CUT - Jewelry - Suberi Brothers, Inc.
REGENT GALLERY - Housewares - Regent Gallery, Inc.
REGENT HALL - Furniture ☆ - Bernhardt Industries
REGENT-RETRO - Doors–metal - United Dominion Industries, Inc.
REGENT ROSE - Tools ☆ - Regent Sheffield, Ltd.
REGENT-SHEFFIELD - Tools - Regent Sheffield, Ltd.
REGENT SPECIAL - Thread ☆ - United Thread Mills Corp.
REGENT SWORDS - Cutlery ☆ - Regent Sheffield, Ltd.
REGENTS COLLEGE - Pens - University of the State of New York
REGENTS PARK - Floor coverings–carpet and rugs ☆ - Walter Carpet Mills
REGENT'S PARK - Furniture - Tomlinson of High Point Inc.
REGENTS ROW - Floor coverings–carpet and rugs - Karastan-Bigelow Inc.
REGENTS ROW - Wallpaper - Parkview Designs
REGENTS ROW HIGHLIGHTS - Floor coverings–carpet and rugs - Karastan-Bigelow Inc.
REGENTS STRIPE - Floor coverings–carpet and rugs - Karastan-Bigelow Inc.
REGGAE - Sporting goods - Wellington Leisure Products, Inc.
REGGAE BY DLR - Footwear - Fred E. Goldstein
REGGAE RASPBERRY - Frozen yogurt - Alta-Dena Certified Dairy, Inc.
REGGAE RHYTHMS - Floor coverings–carpet and rugs - Lotus Carpets
REGGIE - Candy - Nabisco Foods Group
REGGIE - Electrical equipment - Bee-Tek Ltd.
REGGIE - Toys - Animal Fair Inc.
REGGIE BAR - Candy - D.L. Clark Candy Co.
REGGIE'S - Cat food - Moran Foods, Inc.

☆ = Now out of production

REGGIE'S - Desserts - Regency Creative Foods

REGGIE'S - Food products - Regency Creative Foods

REGGIO EMELIA - Tables–wood - Angeles Group, Inc.

REGIDE - Hair care products - Mastey De Paris

REGIME - Furniture ✫ - Bassett Furniture Industries, Inc.

REGIME - Recording label ✫ - Arcade Record Co./Arzee Record Co.

REGIMED - Charts - M M & K, Inc.

REGIMENT - Floor coverings–carpet and rugs - Blue Ridge Carpet Mills

REGIMENT - Floor coverings–carpet and rugs - Criterion Mills Inc.

REGIMENT - Furniture ✫ - Henredon Furniture Industries Inc.

REGIMENT - Lighting fixtures - Hubbell Lighting, Inc. (Lighting Div.)

REGIMENT - Luggage ✫ - Samsonite Corp.

REGIMENT - Wallpaper - Koroseal Wallcoverings

REGIMENT - Watches - Precise International/Wenger

REGIMENT LITE - Wallpaper - Koroseal Wallcoverings

REGIMENTAL - Floor coverings–carpet and rugs - J and J Industries Inc.

REGIMENTAL - Jewelry - Jacoby-Bender Inc.

REGIMENTAL DRUM - Glassware–household - Ceraglass Inc.

REGIMENTAL RIB - Floor coverings–carpet and rugs ✫ - Downs Carpet Co. Inc.

REGIMENTAL STRIPES - Bathing suits - Catalina

REGIMIN - Vitamins and nutritional supplements - Pharmavite Corp.

REGINA - Apparel and accessories ✫ - Regina Products Inc.

REGINA - Boots - Regina Imports

REGINA - Carpet cleaning equipment - Regina Co.

REGINA - Clocks - General Time Corp. (Westclox/Seth Thomas Div.)

REGINA - Frames–eyeglass - U.S. Optical Frame Co.

REGINA - Glassware–household ✫ - Lotus Glass Co.

REGINA - Glassware–household ✫ - Oneida Ltd.

REGINA - Honey - New Horizon

REGINA - Musical instrument accessories - E. & O. Mari Inc.

REGINA - Sporting goods - American Sports Inc.

REGINA - Vacuum cleaners and accessories - Regina Co.

REGINA - Vinegar - Nabisco Foods Group

REGINA - Wines - Regina Wine Co.

REGINA CHAIN - Motorcycle chains - Cosmopolitan Motors Inc.

REGINA NUT PRODUCTS CORP. - Nuts–salted, roasted, cooked, or canned - Regina Nut Products Corp.

REGINA PORTER - Apparel and accessories - Porter House Ltd.

REGINA UNICORN - Toys–stuffed - Russ Berrie and Co., Inc.

REGINA WHITE - Kitchenware–china - H. Wittur & Co.

REGINE - Flatware - Reed and Barton Corp.

REGINE - Flowers, plants, and seeds - Kimbrew-Walter Roses

REGIONAL-PASTA - Noodles - Mrs. Grass

REGIS - Floor coverings–carpet and rugs ✫ - Columbus Mills, Inc.

REGIS - Milk - Regis Milk Co. Inc.

REGIS - Shampoos - Regis Corp.

REGIS FRENCH EXTRA VIRGIN OLIVE OIL - Oils–edible - Europa Foods Ltd.

REGIS HALL - Frames–picture ✫ - Richard-Stephen Co.

REGIS R - Bicycles - Rebike, Inc.

REGISTER - Colognes - Brandy Harvest

REGISTERED TRADITIONS - Jewelry - CJC Holdings, Inc.

REGISTRAR - Wallets - Prince Gardner Inc.

REGISTRAR'S OFFICE - Computer software - Blackbaud, Inc.

REGISTRY - Bedding–linen - Springs Industries, Inc.

REGISTRY - Doors–wood - Pease Industries, Inc.

REGISTRY - Furniture - Henredon Furniture Industries Inc.

REGISTRY - Furniture ✫ - Bassett Furniture Industries, Inc.

REGISTRY - Furniture ✫ - Bernhardt Industries

REGISTRY - Shirts - Pennshire Shirt Corp.

REGITINE - Pharmaceutical preparations - Ciba-Geigy Corp.

REGI$TORE - Computer software - LDI Corp.

REGMANAGER - Computer software - A & M Software, Inc.

REGO - Electronic equipment ✫ - Harcourt General, Inc.

REGO - Recording label - Rego Irish Records, Tapes & Videos

REGOHM - Electrical equipment - Electric Regulator Corp.

REGONOL - Pharmaceutical preparations - Organon Inc.

REGPLU$ - Computer software - Innovative Banking Technologies, Inc.

REGRANEX - Pharmaceutical preparations - Johnson & Johnson

REGROTON - Pharmaceutical preparations - Rhone-Poulenc Rorer Pharmaceuticals Inc.

REGU LAX - Candy - American Chewing Gum Inc.

REGUCIL - Laxatives - Nature's Herbs

REGULACE - Pharmaceutical preparations - Republic Drug Co. Inc.

REGULAR - Cigarette holders - S.M. Frank & Co. Inc. (Kaywoodie-Yello-Bole-Medico)

REGULAR - Trailers–travel - Adams Vacation Trailer Manufacturing Inc.

REGULAR PASSAGE - Health care products - East Earth Herb Inc.

REGULAR POT - Soups–mixes - Mrs. Grass

REGULARITEA - Teas - Natureworks Inc.

REGULATE - Agricultural machinery - Agri Beef Co.

REGULATOR - Drums–musical instruments - Aquarian Accessories Corp.

REGULATOR - Exercising equipment - Goodyear Tire & Rubber Co.

REGULATOR - Housewares - Fort Howard Corp.

REGULATOR-2 - Clocks ✫ - General Time Corp. (Westclox/Seth Thomas Div.)

REGULATORS - Health care products - Aloe Farms

REGULATORY COMPLIANCE KITS - Educational materials - Marcom Group, Ltd.

REGULAX - Pharmaceutical preparations - Republic Drug Co. Inc.

REGULOID - Pharmaceutical preparations - Rugby Laboratories Inc.

REGULUS - Bicycles ✫ - Murray, Inc.

REGUPOL - Floor coverings - Dodge-Regupol Inc.

REGUTOL - Laxatives - Schering-Plough Healthcare Products

REGWARE - Computer software - Thibault Associates

REH - Video production - Warner Bros. Publications

REHA - Brassieres (Bras) ✫ - Elegante Foundations Inc.

REHAB - Medical apparatus - Carolon Co.

REHAB 3 - Braces–orthopedic - Orthopedic Technology, Inc.

REHAB REACHER - Reaching aids - CME Medical Equipment Corp.

REHABILITECH - Wheelchairs - Rehab Designs of America, Inc.

REHABSTATION - Computer software - Clinical Information Advantages, Inc.

REI - Lamps - Natalie Lamp and Shade Corp.

R.E.I. - Sporting goods - Recreational Equipment Inc.

REI-GEN - Vitamins and nutritional supplements - Gourmet Mushrooms Inc.

REIBER - Soups–canned - B. Westergaard & Co. Inc.

REICH-O-BOND - Adhesives and sealants - Reichhold Chemicals, Inc.

REICH-O-MELT - Adhesives and sealants - Reichhold Chemicals, Inc.

REICH STUFF, THE - Games - Avalon Hill Game Co.

REICHARDT IMPERIAL - Meat products–poultry - Reichardt Duck Farm, Inc.

REICHELBRAU - Beverages–alcohol - Best Brands Inc.

REICHMAN - Fireplace equipment - Reichman Inc.

REICH'S - Food products - A. Reich & Sons Inc.

REICHSGRAF VON KESSELSTATT - Wines - Seagram's Chateau & Estate Wines Co.

REID TOOL SUPPLY COMPANY - Hardware - Reid Tool Supply Co.

REIDAMINE - Pharmaceutical preparations ✫ - Solvay Pharmaceuticals Inc.

REID'S - Ice cream ✫ - Borden, Inc.

REIGHNOR - Toys - Tonka Corp.

REIGN GEAR - Umbrellas - Prince Gardner Inc.

REIGNING CATS & DOGS - Pet products - Lock Agency, Inc.

REIKO - Dryers–hair ✫ - Burmax Co. Inc.

REIL ROCK - Building materials - Larry Armstrong

REILLY - Apparel and accessories - Richard C. Reilly

REIMA - Apparel and accessories - S.U.I. Trading Co.

REIN - Accordions - Newark Musical Merchandise Co.

REIN & RIDE - Veterinary pharmaceutical preparations - Destron/IDI, Inc.

REIN CAT - Pet products - Compass Marketing

REINBECK FARMS - Fruits and vegetables - Reinbeck Canning Co.

REINDEER CHOW - Novelty items - Dilijan Products Inc.

REINDEER FEED - Novelty items - Four Score Inc.

REINDEER FOOD - Novelty items - Patty Collins Proctor

REINDEER GAMES - Games - Joyful Noise

REINDEER HOUSE - Novelty items - Anita Beck Cards & Such Inc.

REINDEER PIES - Novelty items - Tom and Sally's Handmade Chocolates, Inc.

REINDEER RANCH - Wines - Round Hill Winery

REINDEER RUN - Figurines - May Department Stores Co.

REINE DE DIJON - Condiments, olives - International Marketing Services Inc.

REINER - Numbering machine - Automated Marking Inc.

REINER STIRRUP - Medical apparatus - Irvin J. Reiner

REINFORCER - Hair care products - P.S. Pibbs Inc.

REINFORCER - Office supplies - Alvin and Co. Inc.

REINHART DETERGENT SERVICES - Cleaning preparations - Reinhart Institutional Foods Inc.

REINHART HARVEST PRIDE - Oils–edible - Reinhart Institutional Foods Inc.

REINHART INSTITUTIONAL - Meat products–beef - Melson Meat Co. Inc.

REINHOLD - Meat products–dried - Reinhold Sausage Co.

REINHOLD & TIMKO - Meat products–dried - American Food Co. Inc.

REINHOLD SCHNABL - Musical instruments - Boosey & Hawkes Buffet Crampon USA

REINHOLDS - Ice cream - Reinhold Ice Cream

✫ = Now out of production

REINHOLD'S FINEST - Ice cream - Reinhold Ice Cream
REINLOCK - Gloves - 49626 New York, Inc.
REINOSA - Cigars - G.A. Georgopulo & Co. Inc.
REINSUL - Insulating materials - Manville/Schuller
REINVERTING OPERATING LENS SYSTEM - Lenses–optical - Volk Optical, Inc.
REIS - Wines - Reis Winery
REISHI EXTRACT - Vitamins and nutritional supplements - Vitamin Research Products Inc.
REISHI MUSHROOM - Health care products - East Earth Herb Inc.
REISHI MUSHROOM SUPREME - Vitamins and nutritional supplements - Planetary Formulas
REISHI-POWER - Vitamins ☆ - Nature's Herbs
REISING'S - Bakery products - Leidenheimer Baking Co.
REISPORT - Sporting goods ☆ - Continental Sports Supply Inc.
REISSUE - Paper–bond - Esleeck Manufacturing Co., Inc.
REITCOMP - Publisher's imprints - Lyons, Benenson & Co. Inc.
REITER - Recording label - Spindletop Records Inc.
REITER DAIRY - Milk - Reiter Dairy Inc.
REITHRITOL - Pharmaceutical preparations ☆ - JMI-Canton Pharmaceuticals
REITZ - Honey ☆ - Sioux Honey Association
REIZART - Giftware ☆ - Gorham Inc.
REJECTOR - Basketball shoes ☆ - Jaclar
REJEX-IT - Chemical preparations - PMC, Inc.
REJOICE - Occasional tables ☆ - JDI Group, Inc.
REJOICE - Publisher's imprints - Publishing House of the Evangelical Lutheran Church in America
REJOICE - Soap - Procter & Gamble Co.
REJOICE - Vitamins and nutritional supplements - Tishcon Corp.
REJOICE! - Women's apparel - Interco Inc.
REJOYN - Prosthetic apparatus - Gain, Inc.
REJUV-A-NAIL - Cosmetics - Dobre Products Inc.
REJUV-A-PERM - Hair care products - Nexxus Products Co.
REJUVA NAIL - Cosmetics ☆ - Alleghany Pharmacal Corp.
REJUVA TILE - Cleaning preparations ☆ - JTM Products Inc.
REJUVANATION - Games - NCC Games
REJUVATONE - Skin care products - Posner Laboratories Inc.
REJUVE - Skin care products - S.A.N. Associates, Inc.
REJUVENATE - Hair care products - Rejuvenate Products, Inc.
REJUVENATION - Health care products - CC Pollen Co.
REJUVENATIVE FOODS - Food products - Deer Garden Foods-Rejuvenative Foods
REJUVENE - Skin care products - Mastey De Paris
REJUVENETICS - Video production - Longevity International, Ltd.
REJUVENIQUE - Skin care products - George E. Springer Jr.
REJUVESOL - Pharmaceutical preparations - Cytosol Laboratories, Inc.
REJUVETOL - Pharmaceutical preparations - Vita Plus Industries Inc.
REJUVEX - Health care products - Sunsource Health Products Inc.
REJUVIA - Skin care products - Del Pharmaceuticals, Inc.
REJUVILIFE - Vitamins and nutritional supplements - Herseth & Herseth, Inc.
REJUVION 200 - Vitamins and nutritional supplements - Source Naturals
REK-O-KUT - Electronic equipment ☆ - Broadcast Electronics, Inc.
REKA - Dust cloth - Reka Merz Cleaning Systems, Inc.
REKA - Recording label - Rains Recording Co.
REKOLLECTION - Apparel and accessories - United Merchants and Manufacturers Inc.
REKONGA - Drums–musical instruments - Enrique Weidmann
REL - Audio equipment - Sumiko Inc.
REL-EEZE - Pharmaceutical preparations - Rel-Eeze/JDM Enterprises
REL-PLAZ - Varnishes - Akzo America Inc.
REL-STONE - Paints - Akzo Coatings Inc.
REL-VAR - Varnishes - Akzo America Inc.
RELA - Analgesics - Schering-Plough Healthcare Products
RELAGESIC - Pharmaceutical preparations - International Ethical Labs., Inc.
RELAIS - Sweaters - Melcon Design
RELATIN - Pharmaceutical preparations ☆ - Scrip-Physician Supply Co.
RELATIONAL DATABASE HOME IMPROVEMENTS - Computer software - Scarborough Enterprises, Inc.
RELATIONS TECHNOLOGY - Computers - Ingres Corp.
RELATIONSHIP MANAGEMENT SYSTEM - Computer software - Fairfield Management Resources Inc.
RELATIVE TIME - Watches - Largely Literary Designs, Inc.
RELATIVITY - Computer software - Liant Software Corp.
RELATIVITY - Recording label - Relativity/Combat/In-Effect
RELATIVITY - Recording label - Relativity Records, Inc.
RELAWN - Flowers, plants, and seeds - Wood Recycling, Inc.

RELAX - Chemical preparations - N. Jonas and Co. Inc.
RELAX - Medical apparatus - Jones-Zylon Co.
RELAX - Mops - Southern Technologies, Inc.
RELAX - Vitamins and nutritional supplements - Unipro Inc.
RELAX-A-BAC - Cushions - Commander-Omni Co. Inc.
RELAX-A-CLINER - Furniture - Barfield Furniture Inc.
RELAX A MOMMY - Recording label - Manali-Leonardo Productions
RELAX-A-PEDIC - Furniture - Barfield Furniture Inc.
RELAX-A-PEDIC - Pillows - Better Sleep, Inc.
RELAX ALARM - Clocks ☆ - General Time Corp. (Westclox/Seth Thomas Div.)
RELAX AMERICA - Apparel and accessories - Relax America, Inc.
RELAX AND GLOW - Hair care products - Keystone Laboratories Inc.
RELAX & REFRESH - Candles - Dial Corp.
RELAX & SLEEP - Health care products - Futurebiotics
RELAX-CINCH - Medical apparatus - Nelkin/Piper Health Products
RELAX ERGONOMIC ARM - Furniture - JSJ Seating Corp.
RELAX-HER - Electronic equipment - Matsushita Electric Corp. of America
RELAX-IN-SOUTE - Recording label - Rashid Sales Co.
RELAX. IT'S RHEEM - Air conditioning equipment - Rheem Manufacturing Co.
RELAX-N-SLEEP - Pillows - Better Sleep, Inc.
RELAX-O-MATIC - Furniture - Barfield Furniture Inc.
RELAXADON - Pharmaceutical preparations - Geneva Generics Inc.
RELAXAGENT - Pharmaceutical preparations - Longevity Pure Medicine
RELAXAMIDE - Pharmaceutical preparations ☆ - C.O. Truxton Inc.
RELAXATION IN A BAG - Apparel and accessories - Jerome Cutting Corp.
RELAXED & SOFT - Brushes–hair - I. Sekine Co. Inc.
RELAXED CHOICES - Apparel and accessories - Wal-Mart Stores Inc.
RELAXED ENERGY - Vitamins and nutritional supplements - Tea Garden Products, Inc.
RELAXED RIDER - Jeans–men's - Lee Apparel Co. Inc.
RELAXED WANDERER - Health care products - East Earth Herb Inc.
RELAXERS - Sandals - Okabashi US Corp.
RELAXING - Teas–herbal - San Francisco Herb & Natural Food Co.
RELAXING RETREAT - Bath salts - Jason Natural Products, Inc.
RELAXO SAFE SLEEP - Pharmaceutical preparations - Brenner Pharmacal Co./Pharma Kwik
RELAXOMAT - Health care products - FutureMed America Inc.
RELAXON - Musical instrument accessories ☆ - Carpenter Co.
RELAXOR - Health care products - India Ink
RELAY - Desks - Herman Miller, Inc.
RELAY 220 - Floor coverings–carpet and rugs ☆ - Olympic Carpets Inc.
RELAY BATONS - Sporting goods - Dacon Manufacturing
RELAY / ON-THE-GO - Computer software - Relay Technology, Inc.
RELCO RESOURCES - Real estate agencies - Regal Quad, Inc.
RELEAD - Lead products - Marine Development & Research Corp.
RELEAF - Pharmaceutical preparations - Biochemics, Inc.
RELEAF - Pharmaceutical preparations - Lake Consumer Products
RELEAS-O-WAX - Hobby kits - Barker Enterprises Inc.
RELEASE - Boats–motor - Custom Marine
RELEASE - Chemical preparations - Aqua Clear Industries Inc.
RELEASE - Housewares ☆ - Blue Cross Laboratories Inc.
RELEASE - Pharmaceutical preparations - Lujafe Caribe Inc.
RELEASE - Recording label - Release Records
RELEASE - Skin care products - Paul Mazzotta Inc.
RELEASE - Yarn - Dixie Yarns, Inc.
RELEASE AID - Archery equipment - Saunders Archery Co.
RELEASE ALIVE - Aquarium accessories - Aquaculture Aquavet
RELEASE ALIVE! - Aquarium accessories - Sportfishing Aquavet
RELEASE ALIVE! - Water treating compounds - Novalek, Inc.
RELEASE AND PAINT - Lubricants - Stoner Inc.
RELEASE ASSURED - Health care products - Leiner Health Products Inc.
RELEASE THE BEAST - Apparel and accessories - Kenneth A. Livingston
RELEASESTRIP - Envelopes–paper - International Envelope Co.
RELENTLESS - Drain pipe cleaners - King of All Manufacturing, Inc.
RELENTLESS - Saws–power - Euro Tool, Inc.
RELEVANT - Apparel and accessories - Painted Lady
RELEVANT - Chimes ☆ - Nutone Inc.
RELEVE - Tables–wood - Berco Tableworks
RELI-A-TEMP - Cabinets - Prince Castle Inc.
RELI-O-BOND - Rubber cement - W.J. Ruscoe Co.
RELIABILITY - Floor coverings–carpet and rugs ☆ - Lees Carpets
RELIABILITY-BASED MAINTENANCE - Computer software - Computational Systems Inc.
RELIABILT - Windows–storm - LF Corp.
RELIABLE - Bags–trash - Mead Corp.
RELIABLE - Binders - Boorum & Pease Co.

☆ = Now out of production

RELIABLE - Cranes - United States Monorail Corp.
RELIABLE - Electrical equipment - MacLean-Fogg Co.
RELIABLE - Floor coverings–carpet and rugs - Karastan-Bigelow Inc.
RELIABLE - Flour–blended - ConAgra Grain Co.
RELIABLE - Food products ☆ - Hygrade Food Products Corp.
RELIABLE - Office equipment - Reliable Office Systems and Supplies, Inc.
RELIABLE - Varnishes ☆ - Reliable Finishing Products, Inc.
RELIABLE ELECTRIC - Electronic equipment - Reltec Corp.
RELIABLE FURNITURE - Furniture - Reliable Furniture Co., Inc.
RELIABLE HEAT - Camping products - Reliable Heat Products, Inc.
RELIABLE OUTERWEAR - Apparel and accessories - Wippette International, Inc.
RELIABOND - Custom Building Products
RELIADET - Electronic equipment - Ensign-Bickford Industries Inc.
RELIAHESIVE - Health care products ☆ - C.R. Bard, Inc.
RELIALINE - Health care products ☆ - C.R. Bard, Inc.
RELIANCE - Automotive parts and accessories - Warren Distribution, Inc.
RELIANCE - Bakery mixes - Westco Products Inc.
RELIANCE - Blotting paper - James River Corp.
RELIANCE - Cases–cigar - Vigilant Inc.
RELIANCE - Electronics equipment - Reliance Plastics & Packaging
RELIANCE - Fireplace equipment ☆ - Hearth Craft
RELIANCE - Flags - Annin and Co.
RELIANCE - Floor coverings–carpet and rugs - Blue Ridge Carpet Mills
RELIANCE - Floor coverings–carpet and rugs - J and J Industries Inc.
RELIANCE - Floor coverings–carpet and rugs - Richmond Carpet Mills
RELIANCE - Floor coverings–carpet and rugs - Tuftex Carpet Mills, Inc.
RELIANCE - Floor coverings–carpet and rugs ☆ - Southern Carpet Mills
RELIANCE - Fuses - Brush Fuses Inc.
RELIANCE - Hones - Perfecto Products Co.
RELIANCE - Medical apparatus - Uromed Corp.
RELIANCE - Orthopedic products - Howmedica Inc.
RELIANCE - Paints - Reliance Paint Co. Inc.
RELIANCE - Pencils - Reliance Pen & Pencil Corp.
RELIANCE - Pet products - Prevue Metal Products Inc.
RELIANCE - Ribbons–inked ☆ - Curtis-Young Corp.
RELIANCE - Siding - Owens Corning
RELIANCE - Sporting goods - Rothco Inc.
RELIANCE - Stoves - Vermont Castings, Inc.
RELIANCE - Toiletries ☆ - Absorbent Web Engineering
RELIANCE - Watches - Croton Watch Co., Inc.
RELIANCE II - Floor coverings–carpet and rugs - J and J Industries Inc.
RELIANCE TRADING CORP. - Flowers–artificial - Harold-Lawrence Associates Inc.
RELIANT - Batteries - Concorde Battery Corp.
RELIANT - Boats - Glen-L Marine Designs
RELIANT - Floor coverings–carpet and rugs - Hollytex Carpet Mills Inc.
RELIANT - Motor vehicles–automobiles ☆ - Chrysler Corp. (Chrysler-Plymouth Div.)
RELIANT - Respirators - AirSep Corp.
RELIANT - Safety products - Reliant Technologies, Inc.
RELIANT - Toys–models - Estes Industries
RELIANT CHARGER - Medical apparatus - Allan J. Walling
RELIANT-ONE - Pumps–water - Campbell Group (Wayne Home Equipment Div.)
RELIANT VCD - Medical apparatus - Allan J. Walling
RELIANTT - Floor coverings ☆ - Tarkett, Inc.
RELIASEAL - Health care products - C.R. Bard, Inc.
RELIC - Guitars - Fender Musical Instruments
RELIC - Leather goods - Fossil, Inc.
RELIC - Recording label - Relic Record Productions Inc.
RELIEF - See RELIEF VASCULAR
RELIEF - Cosmetics - Shiseido Cosmetics (America) Ltd.
RELIEF - Floor coverings ☆ - Tarkett, Inc.
RELIEF - Health care products ☆ - Nova Health Systems Inc.
RELIEF - Ophthalmic goods - Allergan, Inc.
RELIEF - Veterinary pharmaceutical preparations - DVM Pharmaceuticals, Inc.
RELIEF-BAND - Medical device - Maven Labs, Inc.
RELIEF BEYOND RELIEF - Apparel and accessories - Glamorise Foundations Inc.
RELIEF GRAIN - Pipes–tobacco - S.M. Frank & Co. Inc. (Kaywoodie-Yello-Bole-Medico)
RELIEF-O-CHROME - Posters - Dye-A-Photo Inc.
RELIEF PAK - Sporting goods - Fabrication Enterprises
RELIEF PLUS - Health care products - Kmart Corp.
RELIEF PLUS - Hydrogen peroxide - Kmart Properties, Inc.

RELIEF VASCULAR - Socks - Jobst Institute Inc.
RELIEV-01 - Pharmaceuticals - Rexall Sundown, Inc.
RELIEVE - Analgesics - Johnson & Johnson
RELIEVE - Microwave components - Vesture Corp.
RELIEVER, THE - Massage products - Robert B. Taylor
RELIEVERS - Shoe insoles - Aearo Co.
RELIGION - Apparel and accessories - Woodhouse Apparel, Inc.
RELIGION AND POLITICS - Publisher's imprints - Syracuse University Press
RELIGION SAUCE - Sauces - Larry N. Stouffer
RELINER MSP - Cement - Standard Cement Materials, Inc.
RELISHI ROYALE - Health care products - Natrol, Inc.
RELISYS - Computer peripheral equipment - Relisys
RELIV - Cosmetics - Reliv' International, Inc.
RELIV HEALTHY - Food products - Reliv' International, Inc.
RELLIM - Apparel–children's - Buster Brown Apparel Inc.
RELM - Radios - RELM Communications Inc.
RELM PLUS - Radios - RELM Communications Inc.
RELOC - Bags–plastic - Fantapak International Corp.
RELOMS - Apparel–women's - Smoler Bros. Inc.
RELOPLEX - Musical instrument accessories - Rico International
RELOSMART - Computer software - Right Choice, Inc.
RELOTRAC - Construction equipment rental services - Sir Friendly, Ltd.
RELPO - Garden equipment - Reliable Glassware & Pottery Co.
RELSKA - Vodka - Heublein, Inc.
RELTON - Saws–power - Relton Corp.
RELTORK - Motors - Tridelta Industries, Inc.
RELUCI - Lighting fixtures - Swivelier Co. Inc.
RELY - Chemical preparations ☆ - Stoner Inc.
RELY - Tampons - Procter & Gamble Co.
RELY-ON - Caulking compounds - Dap Products Inc.
RELY-ON - Floor coverings–carpet and rugs - Ludlow Composites Corp.
RELY ON THE TIGER - Gasoline - Exxon Corp.
REM - Cough medicines - Alvin Last Inc.
REM - Exercising equipment - Marcy Fitness Products
REM - Lubricating oils - Remington Arms Co., Inc.
REM - Medical apparatus - Valleylab Inc.
REM - Tool boxes ☆ - Remline Co.
REM-BRITE - Paper - Riverside Paper Corp.
REM GARSON - Apparel and accessories - Garson International Inc.
REM PRO - Tool boxes - Remline Co.
REM-STIK - Labels–paper - Kardex Systems, Inc.
REM-STOR - Computer hardware - Removable Media Solutions, Inc.
REM-UMC - Ammunition - Remington Arms Co., Inc.
REM XQL - Tool boxes - Remline Co.
REMA RESERVE - Fish–canned or cured - Rema Food, Inc.
REMAGON - Games - Miller Board Design
REMAGON - Games - Marvin L. Miller
REMAILER - Business forms - Moore Business Forms, Inc.
REMAIN SOFT - Gloves - Netz Glove & Mitten Co.
REMAKE - Apparel and accessories - Daniel Venissac
REMAK'S - Cosmetics - L.A. Remaks International Inc.
REMAN - Motor vehicles–buses - Dial Corp.
REMAN RECYCLE SAVE THE EARTH - Motor vehicle parts and accessories - Springfield Remanufacturing Corp.
REMARCABLE - Tools - Eraser Co. Inc.
REMARCABLE - Tools–power-driven - Remarcable Co., Inc.
REMARK-A-BULL - Games - Custom Manufacturing, Inc.
REMARK-A-LABEL - Labels–paper - Don Bredesen
REMARKABLE - Cleaning preparations - Heat Co.
REMARKABLE - Lanterns–electric ☆ - Zelco Industries, Inc.
REMARKABLE - Towels - Sears, Roebuck and Co.
REMARKABLES - Apparel–children's - Sara Lee Knit Products Inc.
REMARKABLES - Bulletin boards–cork ☆ - Creative Expressions Group
REMARKABOARD - Bulletin boards–wood - Marsh Chalkboard Co.
REMARQUE - Apparel–women's ☆ - Barbizon Lingerie
REMARQUE - Skin care products - Carolyn Price
REMATCH - Apparel–women's - Blue Isle of California
REMBRANDT - Antennas - Recoton Corp.
REMBRANDT - Artists' materials ☆ - M. Grumbacher Inc.
REMBRANDT - Brushes–hair - Select Brands
REMBRANDT - Computer software - DG/Systems
REMBRANDT - Cups–paper ☆ - Creative Expressions Group
REMBRANDT - Fabrics - Vertilux-Louverlux Corp.
REMBRANDT - File folders - Angler's Roslyn Group Ltd.
REMBRANDT - Fishing lures - Den Manufacturing Co.
REMBRANDT - Floor coverings ☆ - Congoleum Corp.

☆ = Now out of production

REMBRANDT - Floor coverings–carpet and rugs - Barrett Carpet Mills Inc.
REMBRANDT - Glassware–household - Crisa Corp.
REMBRANDT - Glassware–household ☆ - Spiegelau Inc.
REMBRANDT - Hams - New York Commodities Corp.
REMBRANDT - Jewelry - Bijouterie Inc.
REMBRANDT - Jewelry - K & M Associates
REMBRANDT - Lamps - Rembrandt Lamps
REMBRANDT - Paints–artists' - Canson-Talens Inc.
REMBRANDT - Photo albums - Rembrandt Photo Services
REMBRANDT - Pipes - National Briar Pipe Co.
REMBRANDT - Toothbrushes - Den-Mat Corp.
REMBRANDT DAZZLING WHITE - Toothpaste - Den-Mat Corp.
REMBRANDT GEL PLUS - Toothpaste - Den-Mat Corp.
REMBRANDT LAMPS - Lamps - Harris Industries
REMBRANDT MASTERPIECE - Lamps - Rembrandt Lamps
REMBRANDT MINT - Toothpaste - Den-Mat Corp.
REMBRANDT ORIGINAL - Toothpaste - Den-Mat Corp.
REMBRANDT TILES - Tiles–ceramic - Promise House Products, Inc.
REMBRANDTS OF CRYSTAL - Glassware–household - Queen Lace Co.
REMCO - Hardware ☆ - Robert E. Miller & Co. Inc.
REMCO - Toys - Azrak-Hamway International, Inc.
REMCRAFT - Lighting equipment - Remcraft Lighting Products
REMDVER-P - Seat belts - William Hudson & Associates
REMEDE - Skin care products - L'anza Research International
REMEDERM - Skin care products - Mana Products, Inc.
REMEDY - Water purification systems - Apollo Corp.
REMEDY-ONE ROTOCLAVE - Medical apparatus - Tempico, Inc.
REMEGEL - Antacids - Warner-Lambert Co.
REMEMBEAR - Toys–stuffed - Joan E. Graham
REMEMBER - Computer peripheral equipment - Compton's NewMedia
REMEMBER RING - Jewelry - Plainville Stock Co.
REMEMBER THE ALAMO - Games ☆ - Tsr, Inc.
REMEMBER THE DAY BOUQUET - T-shirts–men's - Kelly Products
Unlimited, Inc.
REMEMBER THE MAGIC - Jewelry - Kirk's Folly, Inc.
REMEMBER WHEN - Bags - Howard Decorative Packaging Inc.
REMEMBER WHEN - Christmas tree ornaments - Cracker Box Inc.
REMEMBER WHEN - Greeting cards - American Greetings Corp.
REMEMBERED DREAMS BY LOUISE POMMINVILLE - Frames–picture -
Distinctive Design
REMEMBERING - Floor coverings–carpet and rugs - Monticello Carpet Mills
REMEMBERING RAINBOWS - Apparel and accessories - Sally Moors
REMEMBRANCE - Bedding–linen - Dan River Inc.
REMEMBRANCE - Brassieres (Bras) - Warnaco Inc.
REMEMBRANCE - Candy - Miss Saylor's Candies
REMEMBRANCE - Dishes–china ☆ - Pickard Inc.
REMEMBRANCE - Fabrics–tapestry - Comark Wallcoverings
REMEMBRANCE - Floor coverings–carpet and rugs ☆ - Downs Carpet Co.
Inc.
REMEMBRANCE - Furniture ☆ - Bassett Furniture Industries, Inc.
REMEMBRANCE - Glass–leaded - Seneca Glass Co.
REMEMBRANCE - Tableware–china ☆ - Pfaltzgraff Investment Co.
REMEMBRANCE CARDS - Greeting cards - Clark Imports Inc.
REMEMBRANCE MEMORIAL - Pet products - Hoegh Industries Inc.
REMEMBRANCE PECAN PERKS - Candy - Zachary Confections Inc.
REMEMBRANCES - House furnishings ☆ - Lea Industries Inc.
REMEMBRANCES - Wallpaper ☆ - Thomas Strahan Wallcoverings
REMEMBRANCES OF CHILDHOOD - Figurines - Unicover Corp.
REMEMO - Office supplies ☆ - Park Sherman
REMEMORY - Computer peripheral equipment - Rememory Corp.
REMEX - Computer hardware - Removable Media Solutions, Inc.
REMF - Meters–electric - S.M.C. Technologies Int.
REMFORM - Screws - Research Engineering & Manufacturing Inc.
REMI-CLAEYS - Juvenile product - International Imports
REMICI - Cosmetics - Naissance, Inc.
REMIFERRUN - Vitamins and nutritional supplements - Enzymatic Therapy,
Inc.
REMIN - Luggage - Remin Laboratories, Inc. (Kart-a-Bag Div.)
REMIND - Computer software - Cognitive Systems Inc.
REMINDERPRO - Computer software - Crystal Software, Inc.
REMINGTON - Apparel stores–sports - Co. Store
REMINGTON - Chairs–wood - Hon Co.
REMINGTON - Floor coverings–carpet and rugs - Blue Ridge Carpet Mills
REMINGTON - Floor coverings–carpet and rugs ☆ - Len Dal Carpets
REMINGTON - Frames–eyeglass ☆ - Universal/Univis Inc.
REMINGTON - Furniture ☆ - Stanley Furniture Co. Inc.

REMINGTON - Guns - Remington Arms Co., Inc.
REMINGTON - Housewares - Remington Products Co.
REMINGTON - Neckties - Remington Apparel Co. Inc.
REMINGTON - Plugs–electric - Remington Arms Co., Inc.
REMINGTON - Recording label ☆ - American Tape Corp.
REMINGTON - Saws–chain - Desa International, Inc.
REMINGTON - Tires - Dunlop Tire Corp.
REMINGTON - Typewriters - Morse Typewriter Co. Inc.
REMINGTON - Window coverings - Remington Building Products
REMINGTON 1858 - Guns - Euroarms of America
REMINGTON EXPRESS SET - Curling irons–electric - Remington Products
Co.
REMINGTON FIELDMASTER - Telescopes - Remington Arms Co., Inc.
REMINGTON GROOMING - Electrical equipment - Remington Products Co.
REMINGTON RAND - Office supplies ☆ - Pennbarr Corp.
REMINGTON ROSE - Wallpaper ☆ - Three Sisters Studio
REMINGTON TARGETMASTER - Telescopes - Remington Arms Co., Inc.
REMINISCE BOOKS - Publisher's imprints - Reiman Publications, LP
REMINISCENCE - Furniture - Bassett Furniture Industries, Inc.
REMINISCENCE - Furniture ☆ - Stanley Furniture Co. Inc.
REMINISCENCE - Wallcovering ☆ - Fashon Wallcoverings
REMINISCENCE - Wallpaper - Winfield Design Associates, Inc.
REMINISCENCE BINGO - Health care products - Maddak Inc.
REMIRA - Apparel–children's ☆ - William Carter Co.
REMISAR - Pharmaceutical preparations - Upjohn Co.
REMIX - Tires - Michelin Tire Corp.
REMLE - Musical instrument accessories - Remle Musical Products Inc.
REMLEY'S - Food products - Remley Orchards Corp.
REMLIF - Computer software - Electric Power Research Institute Inc.
REMLINE - Spades - Remline Co.
REMNANT HOUSE - Apparel–women's ☆ - Bobbie Brooks Inc.
REMO - Plumbing fixtures - Cherne Industries Inc.
REMO - Wines - Southwest Distributing Inc.
REMO USA SPORTMALLET - Mallets–rubber - Remo, Inc.
REMO USA SPORTSTIX - Musical instrument accessories - Remo, Inc.
REMODELER SERIES AKER, THE - Hardware - Aker Plastics Co. Inc.
REMODELINE - Bathroom fixtures - Lasco Products Group
REMOISSENET PERE ET FILS - Wines - Classic Wine Imports Inc.
REMOLDINE - Skin care products - Dorothy Gray Cosmetics Ltd.
REMOND - Infant product - Handy Chair Corp.
REMOND FOR BABIES - Infant product - Handy Chair Corp.
REMOSAN - Seasonings - Herb Products Co.
REMOTE COMMAND - Telephone apparatus ☆ - Nutone Inc.
REMOTE COMMAND - Toys - Azrak-Hamway International, Inc.
REMOTE COMMANDER - Electronic equipment - Sony Corp. of America
REMOTE CONTROL - Diaries - Cullman Ventures Inc.
REMOTE CONTROL - Games ☆ - Pressman Toy Corp.
REMOTE GUARD - Remote control devices - Simtec Products, Inc.
REMOTE GUARD - Television equipment - Andrew I. Schacher
REMOTE IDEA - Remote control cover - AMS Design
REMOTE INTELLIGENT DISTRIBUTION ELEMENTSUPPORT - Software -
Raynet Corp.
REMOTE/IX - Computer software - Micro Computer Systems, Inc.
REMOTE MAN - Apparel and accessories - Sammie L. Stinson, Jr.
REMOTE NEST - Furniture - Alex T. Wilkey Jr.
REMOTE OFFICE - Computer software - Stampede Technologies, Inc.
REMOTE OFFICE GOLD - Computer software - Stampede Technologies, Inc.
REMOTE PICS - Electronic equipment - Presearch Inc.
REMOTE PLAY - Computers - Mercury Computer Systems Inc.
REMOTE RECEIVER - Telephone devices and light signals for the deaf -
American Communications Corp.
REMOTE RETRIEVER - Housewares ☆ - Blue Ridge International Products
Co., Inc.
REMOTE TOTE - Housewares - Remote-Tote, Inc.
REMOTECOLLABORATION - Furniture - MG Taylor Corp.
REMOTECONTROL/2 - Computer software - Compuware Corp.
REMOTENT - Computer software - Seattle Lab, Inc.
REMOTEPOINT - Computer hardware - Interlink Electronics, Inc.
REMOTESHADOW - Computer software - ASCI
REMOTETEAM - Computer software - Scopus Technology, Inc.
REMOTEVISION - Computer software - Token Technology Inc.
REMOV-O-DINE - Stain removers - Walter G. Legge Co., Inc.
REMOV-Z-IT - Paint removers - Standard Brands Paint Co.
REMOVA-BELL - Musical instrument accessories ☆ - Selmer Co. Inc.
REMOVABLE PROJECT ENVIRONMENT - Computer hardware - Fostex Corp.
of America

☆ = Now out of production

REMOVABLES - Footwear - E.S. Originals, Inc.

REMOVAL MADE EASY - Cleaning preparations - Motsenbocker Aedvanced Developments, Inc.

REMOVATRON - Cosmetics - Removatron International

REMOVE - Shampoos ☆ - KMS Research Inc.

REMOVE-A-SEAL - Caulking compounds ☆ - Dap Products Inc.

REMOVE-A-SOUND - Radios - Caltex Manufacturing Distributing Inc.

REMOVE ALL - Hair care products - Tressa, Inc.

REMOVE & CUT - Staple removers - Ace Fastener

REMOVE-IT - Computer software - Software Syndicate, Inc.

REMOVER - Cosmetics ☆ - Para Laboratories Inc.

REMP - Floor coverings - Tek Stil Concepts Inc.

REMP - Floor coverings–tile - Remp

REMRAIL - Computer hardware - Removable Media Solutions, Inc.

REMSED - Antihistamine preparations - Du Pont Pharmaceuticals

REMSEM PRESS - Publisher's imprints - Chemical Publishing Co. Inc.

REMSERVE - Computer software - Rememory Corp.

REMSITE - Computer software - Tempfunds America, Inc.

REMSTAR - Health care products - Respironics, Inc.

REMTEK - Insulating materials ☆ - Raynet Corp.

REMUDA RANCH - Recording label - Remuda Ranch

REMULAR-S - Pharmaceutical preparations - International Ethical Labs

REMUS - Butter - Michigan Milk Producers Association

REMY GAUTHIER - Beverages–alcohol - Maison Portier & Fils

REMY MARTIN - Wines - Remy Martin Amerique Inc.

REMY PANNIER - Wines ☆ - Cannon Wines Ltd.

REN - Regulators–automotive - Power Plus Corp.

REN - Toys - Hanna-Barbera Productions, Inc.

REN & STIMPY - Candy - Topps Co., Inc.

REN & STIMPY SHOW - Prepackaged sound recordings - Viacom International Inc.

REN & STIMPY SHOW, THE - Novelty items - Viacom International Inc.

REN MAUR - Publisher's imprints - Factory Beat Records Inc.

REN-O-THIN - Agricultural machinery - Ransomes-Cushman-Ryan

REN-O-VATE - Herbicides ☆ - J. & L. Adikes Inc.

REN ROME - Recording label - Factory Beat Records Inc.

RENA ROWAN - Apparel–women's ☆ - Jones Apparel Group Inc.

RENAC - Cosmetics - Morris-Flamingo Inc.

RENACARB - Aquariums–household - Rena Corp.

RENACOR - Aquariums–household - Rena Corp.

RENAFLO - Hemofiltration apparatus - Minntech Corp.

RENAHERB - Vitamins and nutritional supplements ☆ - J.R. Carlson Laboratories Inc.

RENAIS - Glass products - Glass Inc.

RENAISSANCE - Artists' materials - CSI Creations de France

RENAISSANCE - Audio equipment - GNP Audio Video Inc.

RENAISSANCE - Banjos - OME Co. Inc.

RENAISSANCE - Bathroom fixtures - Crane Plumbing/Fiat Products

RENAISSANCE - Bathroom fixtures ☆ - Melard Manufacturing Corp.

RENAISSANCE - Cabinets - Les-Care Kitchens Inc.

RENAISSANCE - Calendars - Success Business Industries, Inc.

RENAISSANCE - Chessboards ☆ - Milton Bradley Co.

RENAISSANCE - Computer software - Digital Equipment Corp.

RENAISSANCE - Computer software - Eastman Kodak Co.

RENAISSANCE - Doors–wood - Maywood Inc.

RENAISSANCE - Faucets - Chicago Faucet Co.

RENAISSANCE - Floor coverings - Congoleum Corp.

RENAISSANCE - Floor coverings - Mannington Resilient Floors

RENAISSANCE - Floor coverings–carpet and rugs - Durkan Patterned Carpets

RENAISSANCE - Floor coverings–carpet and rugs - Olympic Carpets Inc.

RENAISSANCE - Floor coverings–carpet and rugs - Providence Rug Co.

RENAISSANCE - Floor coverings–carpet and rugs - Remp

RENAISSANCE - Foil–aluminum - Highland Supply Corp.

RENAISSANCE - Frames–eyeglass - Ambassador Eyewear Group

RENAISSANCE - Frames–picture - Terragrafics Inc.

RENAISSANCE - Furniture - Arbek Furniture Manufacturing Inc.

RENAISSANCE - Furniture - Columbia Manufacturing Inc.

RENAISSANCE - Furniture - Stanley Furniture Co. Inc.

RENAISSANCE - Furniture ☆ - Bassett Furniture Industries, Inc.

RENAISSANCE - Giftware ☆ - Kraftware Corp. (Morgan Div.)

RENAISSANCE - Giftware ☆ - L.E. Smith Glass Co.

RENAISSANCE - Glassware–household ☆ - Lenox Crystal, Inc.

RENAISSANCE - Glassware–household ☆ - Lotus Glass Co.

RENAISSANCE - Greeting cards - Renaissance Greeting Cards Inc.

RENAISSANCE - Hair care products - Waverly Beauty Products

RENAISSANCE - Jewelry - L G Imports Manufacturing Co.

RENAISSANCE - Laboratory apparatus - E.I. Dupont de Nemours and Co.

RENAISSANCE - Leather goods - Hugo Bosca Co., Inc.

RENAISSANCE - Luggage - American Flyer

RENAISSANCE - Motor vehicles–buses - Motor Coach Industries, Inc.

RENAISSANCE - Musical instruments - Getzen Co.

RENAISSANCE - Occasional furniture - American Furniture Co. Inc.

RENAISSANCE - Office supplies ☆ - JM Co.

RENAISSANCE - Paper - Light Impressions Corp.

RENAISSANCE - Paper - Precision Coatings, Inc.

RENAISSANCE - Pottery ☆ - Doranne

RENAISSANCE - Recording label - Everest Record Group

RENAISSANCE - Rings–jewelry - L & M Castings Inc.

RENAISSANCE - Skin care products - J.A. Fleuridas Co.

RENAISSANCE - Skin care products - Nexxus Products Co.

RENAISSANCE - Sporting goods - Hueblers Industries

RENAISSANCE - Tea kettles–nonelectric - Metro/Thebe, Inc.

RENAISSANCE - Telescopes - Tele Vue Optics Inc.

RENAISSANCE - Thread - Sew-Art International

RENAISSANCE - Tiles–ceramic - KPT Inc.

RENAISSANCE - Tiles–ceramic - Monarch Tile Inc.

RENAISSANCE - Tiles–ceramic ☆ - American Olean Tile Co.

RENAISSANCE - Wainscotting - Georgia-Pacific Corp.

RENAISSANCE - Wallpaper - Winfield Design Associates, Inc.

RENAISSANCE - Watches - Accutime Watch Corp.

RENAISSANCE - Watches ☆ - SMH (US) Inc.

RENAISSANCE - Windows–storm - Duo-Temp

RENAISSANCE ANGEL COLLECTION - Christmas tree ornaments - Lenox, Inc.

RENAISSANCE COLLECTION - Dishes–earthenware - Denby USA Limited

RENAISSANCE COLLECTION - Wallcovering - C/S Group/DecoGard Products

RENAISSANCE COMMANDER - Aircraft–airplanes - Twin Commander Aircraft Corp.

RENAISSANCE CS - Computer software - Ross Systems Inc.

RENAISSANCE FAIR - Wallpaper ☆ - Heritage House Designs

RENAISSANCE II - Floor coverings–carpet and rugs ☆ - Galaxy Carpet Mills Inc.

RENAISSANCE NATIVITY - Figurines - Flambro Imports, Inc.

RENAISSANCE OF ENGLISH EMBOSSING - Wallpaper - Patterson Piazza

RENAISSANCE PASTRIES - Bakery products - Renaissance Pastries, Inc.

RENAL LINK - Computer software - Baxter International Inc.

RENALCAL - Vitamins and nutritional supplements - Clintec Nutrition Co.

RENALDO'S - Food products - Quality Products International Corp.

RENALGIN - Pharmaceutical preparations - Glaxo Wellcome Inc.

RENALOG - Computer storage devices–magnetic - Minntech Corp.

RENAN - Shampoos - Renan Beauty Products, Inc.

RENARD - Bassoons - Fox Products Corp.

RENARD - Liquors - M.S. Walker Inc./Seacoast

RENARD ROUGE FONCE - Handbags - Ok J. Lee

RENA'S - Vegetables–canned - Haddon House Food Products Inc.

RENASINE - Aquariums–household - Rena Corp.

RENASPOT - Pet products - Rena Corp.

RENASSANCE - Golfing equipment - Renaissance Golf Products, Inc.

RENATA - Garages - Overhead Door Corp.

RENATA - Glassware–household ☆ - Crisa Corp.

RENATA BORSETTI - Apparel and accessories - Soley Ltd.

RENATA, THE - Doors–vinyl - Overhead Door Corp.

RENATE WHITE - Kitchenware–china - H. Wittur & Co.

RENATO - Footwear - Southern Leather & Shoe Co.

RENATO COLLEZIONE - Apparel–men's - Yavoy, Inc.

RENATO RATTI - Wines - Paterno Imports, Ltd.

RENATORE - Cosmetics - Renbow International Ltd. USA

RENATROPHIN PMG - Vitamins and nutritional supplements - Standard Process Inc.

RENATURE - Packaging–foam - Mason Box Co. Inc.

RENAULT - Motor vehicles - Renault Inc.

RENAULT - Wines - Renault Winery

RENCH - Apparel and accessories - Rench

RENCO - Garden equipment - L.J. Rench & Co.

RENCOLOR - Cosmetics - Renbow International Ltd. USA

RENDEE - Recording label - True Records Inc.

RENDELL - Napkins–paper ☆ - Royal Imprints Corp.

RENDER A REVELATION - Computer software - Intergraph Corp.

RENDER RITE - Decals and transfers ☆ - Magic Touch/Pacific Airbrush

RENDERDOG - Computer software - Lamb & Co., Inc.

RENDERINGS - Floor coverings–carpet and rugs - Eagle Carpets Inc.

RENDERINGS - Floor coverings–carpet and rugs ☆ - J and J Industries Inc.

☆ = Now out of production

RENDEROC - Mortars–clay - Fosroc Inc.
RENDERPRINT - Computer software - Insight Development Corp.
RENDES VOUS - Candy - Morris National Inc.
RENDEVOUS - Drums–musical instruments ☆ - Grossman Music Corp.
RENDEW - Hair care products - Renbow International Ltd. USA
RENDEZ-VOUS - Lipsticks - Lancome
RENDEZ-VOUS - Telescopes - Northern Telecom, Inc.
RENDEZVOUS - Christmas tree ornaments - Cracker Box Inc.
RENDEZVOUS - Computer software - Encyclopaedia Britannica Inc.
RENDEZVOUS - Dinnerware–glass - Nikko Ceramics Inc.
RENDEZVOUS - Floor coverings–carpet and rugs ☆ - Helios Carpets
RENDEZVOUS - Floor coverings–carpet and rugs ☆ - Downs Carpet Co. Inc.
RENDEZVOUS - Garden furniture - Winston Furniture Co. Inc.
RENDEZVOUS - Luggage - Airway Industries, Inc.
RENDEZVOUS - Meat products–dried - Samuel R. Penrod
RENDEZVOUS - Occasional tables ☆ - JDI Group, Inc.
RENDEZVOUS - Role-playing game - Stratton & Co. Inc.
RENDEZVOUS - Slacks–men's - Glen Oaks Industries Inc.
RENDEZVOUS - Tableware–china - Lenox, Inc.
RENDEZVOUS - Underwear and nightwear - Maidenform Inc.
RENDEZVOUS - Water treating compounds - Great Lakes Biochemical Co., Inc.
RENDEZVOUS - Wines - Yakima River Winery Inc.
RENDEZVOUS SHIMMERS - Underwear and nightwear - Maidenform Inc.
RENDITION - Floor coverings–carpet and rugs ☆ - Zenith Carpets
RENDITIONS - Greeting cards - Renditions
RENDITIONS INTERNATIONAL FINE FRAGRANCES - Perfumes - Renditions International Ltd.
RENDOLITE - Fiberglass panels - Auburn Plastic Engineering
RENE - Apparel and accessories - Dutchess Lingerie
RENE - Cosmetics - Kresco
RENE - Neckties - Salem Neckwear Corp.
RENE BARBIER - Wines - Freixenet USA
RENE BEAUCHAMPS - Toys - Tonka Corp.
RENE BOULAY - Wines - European Beverage Co., Inc.
RENE DUBARRY - Beverages–alcohol - Wine Imports Ltd.
RENE DUMONT - Musical instruments ☆ - St. Louis Music Supply Co.
RENE GUINOT - Skin care products - Francosmetics International Inc.
RENE JUNOT - Wines - Sunbelt Beverage Corp.
RENE LORENZ - Musical instruments - Newark Musical Merchandise Co.
RENE OF PARIS - Wigs - Rene of Paris Inc.
RENE PICOT - Cheese - Dairy Fresh Products Co.
RENE SCHMIDT - Wines - Classic Wine Imports Inc.
RENEE - Dolls - Justin Products, Inc.
RENEE - Dolls ☆ - R. William Gilbert Associates Inc.
RENEE - Hair care products - Nutrine Ltd.
RENEE - Vegetables–canned - A. Sargenti Co. Inc.
RENEE ANN - Girdles - Character Foundations Inc.
RENEE AWAY - Footwear - Ocean's Edge Inc.
RENEE BARBIER - Wines - Logret Import & Export Co.
RENEE MACEE - Hair care products - Nutrine Ltd.
RENEE'S GOURMET GOODIES - Vegetable sauces - Gourmet Goodies, Inc.
RENEGADE - Antennas - Wintenna Inc.
RENEGADE - Bicycles - Roadmaster Corp.
RENEGADE - Boats - Glen-L Marine Designs
RENEGADE - Boats - Zodiac of North America
RENEGADE - Boats–motor ☆ - Lund Boat Co.
RENEGADE - Boats–motor ☆ - Marathon Boat Group, Inc.
RENEGADE - Cleaning preparations - W.W. Grainger, Inc.
RENEGADE - Computer software - General Signal Corp.
RENEGADE - Darts and dart games - Dart World Inc.
RENEGADE - Firearms, accessories, and parts - Welsh Sporting Goods Corp. (Boyt Div.)
RENEGADE - Fishing tackle - Wal-Mart Stores Inc.
RENEGADE - Goggles–safety - Parmelee Industries, Inc.
RENEGADE - Goggles–safety - U.S. Safety Corp.
RENEGADE - Golfing equipment - Spalding & Evenflo Companies, Inc.
RENEGADE - Lawn mowers - WW Grinder Corp.
RENEGADE - Leather - Horween Leather Co.
RENEGADE - Luggage - Airway Industries, Inc.
RENEGADE - Propellers - Outboard Marine Corp.
RENEGADE - Pumps - Marley Pump Co.
RENEGADE - Rifles ☆ - Thompson/Center Arms
RENEGADE - Skates–roller - Seneca Sports, Inc.
RENEGADE - Statuary - Service Merchandise Co., Inc.
RENEGADE - Video games - Taito America Corp.

RENEGADE - Watches ☆ - Swiss Army Brands, Ltd.
RENEGADE - Weightlifting equipment - Ektelon
RENEGADE JR. LACROSSE SET - Sporting goods - Seneca Sports, Inc.
RENEGADE PADDLE BALL - Sporting goods - Seneca Sports, Inc.
RENEGADES - Tobacco–chewing or smoking - Swedish Math North America Inc.
RENEGADES - Toy vehicles - Intex Recreation Corp.
RENERGIE - Skin care products - Lancome
RENETTE - Apparel–women's - Renette Foundations Corp.
RENEW - Computer peripheral equipment - Eden Systems Corp.
RENEW - Paper–gift wrap - CPS Corp.
RENEW - Pet products - Seachem Laboratories
RENEW - Prosthetic apparatus - Coloplast Corp.
RENEW-A-NAIL - Cosmetics - Sally Hansen
RENEW A PERM - Hair care products - Del Pharmaceuticals, Inc.
RENEW-ALL - Paints ☆ - Wescon Products Co.
RENEW ANTIQUE - Paper–book - Central National-Gottesman Inc.
RENEW PET RECYCLED POLYESTER CARPETS FOR THE FUTURE FOR THE GOOD OF YOUR HOME & - Floor coverings–carpet and rugs - Shaw Industries Inc.
RENEW-POINT - Pencils ☆ - Faber-Castell Corp.
RENEWAL - Batteries - Rayovac Corp.
RENEWAL - Hair care products - Scruples Professional Salon Products, Inc.
RENEWAL! - Recording label - Integrity Music, Inc.
RENEWAL - Skin care products - Giovanni Cosmetics Inc.
RENEWED - Motor vehicle parts and accessories - Navistar International Transportation Corp.
RENEWZ - Cleaning preparations - Stewart-Hall Chemical Corp.
RENFREW - Tape–adhesive - Montreal Hockey Co.
RENFRO - Socks - Renfro Corp.
RENFRO VALLEY - Sportswear, novelty buttons, etc. - Entertainment Center Inc.
RENGO - Girdles - Crown Foundations Inc.
RENIES - Baskets–wood - Root Candle Co.
RENMAGIC - Hair care products - Renbow International Ltd. USA
RENNER DAVIS - Giftware - Billy Penn Corp.
RENNER-DAVIS - Stationery - Renner-Davis Co.
RENNER DAVIS BY CONTEMPO - Dishes–paper - Penn Corp.
RENNER DAVIS BY CONTEMPO - Paper–gift wrap - Renner-Davis Co.
RENNEW - Disinfectants - Alcide Corp.
RENNIE - Dinnerware–glass - Cyclamen Studio
RENNIE - Food products - Sara Lee Corp.
RENNIE - Wallcoverings - Ben Rose Ltd.
RENNIN - Pharmaceutical preparations - City Chemical Corp.
RENNINGTON - Cabinets - Aristokraft, Inc.
RENO - Bicycles ☆ - Huffy Corp.
RENO - Cigar boxes–wood ☆ - Consolidated Cigar Corp.
RENO - Cigarettes - Darcon International Corp.
RENO - Computer peripheral equipment - Media Vision Technology Inc.
RENO - Fabrics - Vertilux-Louverlux Inc.
RENO - Floor coverings–carpet and rugs ☆ - Galaxy Carpet Mills Inc.
RENO-30 - Pharmaceutical preparations - Bracco Diagnostics, Inc.
RENO-60 - Pharmaceutical preparations - Bracco Diagnostics, Inc.
RENO 400 - Amplifiers–musical instrument - Peavey Electronics Corp.
RENO-FLUSH - Vitamins and nutritional supplements - Tishcon Corp.
RENO-KENO - Games ☆ - Milton Bradley Co.
RENO-M - Pharmaceutical preparations - Bristol-Myers Squibb Co.
RENO-SED - Pharmaceutical preparations - Vita Elixir Co. Inc.
RENOGEN - Pharmaceutical preparations - Tishcon Corp.
RENOGRAFIN - Pharmaceutical preparations - Bristol-Myers Squibb Co.
RENOIR - Artists' materials - M. Grumbacher Inc.
RENOIR - Brushes–paint - Pratt & Lambert, Inc.
RENOIR - Floor coverings - Mannington Resilient Floors
RENOIR - Floor coverings–carpet and rugs ☆ - Columbus Mills, Inc.
RENOIR - Floor coverings–carpet and rugs ☆ - Lees Carpets
RENOIR COLLECTION - Bakery products - Morris National, Inc.
RENOIR IMPRESSIONISTS SOCIETY - Housewares - Terry Arts International, Inc.
RENOK - Medical apparatus - Baxter International Inc.
RENOLUX - Infant product - David Tzabar
RENOMA - Leather goods - Senix Group
RENOQUID - Pharmaceutical preparations ☆ - Glenwood LLC
RENOVA - Skin care products - Johnson & Johnson
RENOVAIRE - Agricultural machinery - Ransomes-Cushman-Ryan
RENOVATOR - Cleaning preparations - Dura Seal
RENOVATOR - Cleaning preparations - Hillyard Enterprises, Inc.

☆ = Now out of production

RENOVATOR - Foundation garments–women's - Strouse, Adler Co.
RENOVATOR SERIES - Electric lighting equipment - Solar Kinetics, Inc.
RENOVET - Ice chests–foam ☆ - Care-Tech Laboratories Inc.
RENOVEX - Electronic equipment - Neumade Products Corp.
RENOVEX - Tires - Michelin Tire Corp.
RENOVIST - Pharmaceutical preparations - Bristol-Myers Squibb Co.
RENOVUE - Pharmaceutical preparations - Bristol-Myers Squibb Co.
RENOWN - Amplifiers–musical instrument - Peavey Electronics Corp.
RENOWN - Animal feeds - Hubbard Milling Co.
RENOWN - Chocolate candy - Sweet Candy Co.
RENOWN - Floor coverings - Congoleum Corp.
RENOWN - Floor coverings–carpet and rugs - Patcraft Mills Inc.
RENOWN - Floor coverings–carpet and rugs ☆ - Ebsco Carpet Mills
RENOWN - Food products - Knapp-Sherrill Co.
RENOWN - Sporting goods - Victor Sports
RENOWN 112 - Amplifiers–musical instrument - Peavey Electronics Corp.
RENOWNED - Floor coverings–carpet and rugs ☆ - Hollytex Carpet Mills Inc.
RENSET - Hair care products - Renbow International Ltd. USA
RENSHAW - Frosting ☆ - Signature Brands, LLC
RENSHENFENGWANGJIANG - Vitamins and nutritional supplements - Fmali
   Herb Co.
RENT - Greeting cards - Julie Larson
RENT-A-PET - Pet products - A.C. Industries
RENTAISSANCE - Computer software - Rentaissance Marketing, Inc.
RENTAL ONLY - Footwear - James R. Moyle
RENTAR - Automotive parts and accessories - Lee Ratner
RENTER FRIENDLY - Shower stalls–plastic - Alsons Corp.
RENTHERMAL - Hair care products - Renbow International Ltd. USA
RENTON WESTERN WEAR - Apparel and accessories - Renton Western
   Wear, Inc.
RENU - Cleaning preparations - Bausch & Lomb Inc.
RENU - Cosmetics ☆ - M.L. Campbell Co.
RENU - Pipeline transportation - Nicor Technologies Inc.
RENU - Skin care products - Vitamin Research Products Inc.
RENU-A-GLO - Finishing agents ☆ - Ziebart International Corp.
RENU-A-SHINE - Finishing agents - Ziebart International Corp.
RENU II SKIN CARE - Skin care products - Vitamin Research Products Inc.
RENU TRAVELLER - Pharmaceutical preparations - Bausch & Lomb Inc.
RENUIT - Skin care products ☆ - Palm Beach Beauty Products
RENUIT - Varnishes ☆ - KCI Coatings, Inc.
RENULUSTER - Paints - Dozier & Gay Paint Co.
RENUWELL - Well restorer and rejuvenator - Vibe Records Inc.
RENUZIT - Deodorizers - Drackett Co.
RENUZIT ELECTRIC LONGLAST - Electrical equipment - Dial Corp.
RENUZIT LONGLAST - Air freshener cartidges - Drackett Co.
RENUZIT LONGLAST - Deodorizers - Dial Corp.
RENUZIT NEW NATURALS - Deodorizers - Dial Corp.
RENUZIT ROOMATE - Deodorizers - Drackett Co.
RENWICK - Product description unknown - Renwick du Canada Inc.
RENWOOD - Wines - Renwood Winery, Inc.
RENWOOD - Wood products - Grand Rapids Dowel Works Inc.
RENY PICOT - Cheese ☆ - Dan Carter Inc.
RENZ-E-Z - Cleaning preparations - Remwood Products Co. Inc.
RENZO - Rum - Italian and French Wine Co. of Buffalo Inc.
REO - Computer storage devices ☆ - Pinnacle Micro, Inc.
REO - Jeans–men's - Alberto Btesh
REO - Jewelry - REO Co.
REO TAHITI - Recording label - Criterion Music Corp.
REO VIKING - Tools - Bloomfield Manufacturing Co.
REOKID - Jewelry ☆ - REO Co.
REOMAR - Photographic equipment - Eastman Kodak Co.
REOMUNE - Veterinary pharmaceutical preparations - Biomune Co.
REON RAINSTORM - Cleaning preparations - K & W Products
REOPRO - Pharmaceutical preparations - Eli Lilly and Co.
REOTEK - Giftware ☆ - REO Co.
REP - Modems - Lacerte Software Corp.
REP - Ophthalmic goods - Foremost Optical Products
REP - Pet products - Nekton USA Inc.
REP-D-CHLOR - Pet products - Aquatronics-Filtronics
REP ESTRA - Pharmaceutical preparations ☆ - Central Pharmaceutical Inc.
REP-PRED 40 - Pharmaceutical preparations - Central Pharmaceutical Inc.
REP-PRED 80 - Pharmaceutical preparations - Central Pharmaceutical Inc.
REP RINSE - Veterinary pharmaceutical preparations - Cal-Tex Naturals, Inc.
REP TEST - Pharmaceutical preparations ☆ - Central Pharmaceutical Inc.
REPACCS - Telephone apparatus - Remote Switch Systems, Inc.
REPACKING YOUR BAGS - Pudding pops–frozen - Taking Charge, Inc.

REPACORP LABEL PRODUCTS R - Office supplies - Repacorp, Inc.
REPAIR - Hair care products ☆ - KMS Research Inc.
REPAIRIT QUICK - Epoxy - Polymeric Systems, Inc.
REPAIRMAN IN A KIT - Chemical preparations - Coldweld Corp.
REPAIRSOURCE - Computer software - Cooperative Computing, Inc.
REPAIRSTIK - Adhesives and sealants - Accumetric, Inc.
REPALLOY - Electrical equipment - Repco, Inc.
REPAN - Health care products - Everett Laboratories Inc.
REPARTEE - Bathtubs–enameled - Kohler Co.
REPCO - Sporting goods - Communications Sales Co.
REPCO - Vitamins and nutritional supplements - McShares, Inc.
REPCON - Framing supplies - Repcon International, Inc.
REPEAT-CORDER - Electronic equipment ☆ - Canon USA, Inc.
REPEAT-O-TYPE - Office supplies - Repeat-O-Type Manufacturing Corp.
REPEAT PATTERNS - Wallpaper - Jack Denst Designs
REPEAT PERFORMANCE - Paper - PM Co. (Office Products Div.)
REPEAT PERFORMANCE - Wallpaper - Galaxie Handprints
REPEATA - Pencils - Accutec Inc.
REPEATER - Ammunition ☆ - Olin Corp. (Winchester Div.)
REPEATER - Cameras - Amglo-Kemlite
REPEATER - Garden equipment - Union Fork and Hoe Co.
REPEATER - Lenses–photographic - SP Systems/Saratons
REPEATER - Ophthalmic goods - Foremost Optical Products
REPEATER - Projectors–photographic - Eiki International Inc.
#REPEATER, THE - Tools - LRH Enterprises Inc.
REPEATIER - Guns–BB - Crosman Corp.
REPECHAGE - Skin care products - Repechage
REPEEL - Varnish removers - C.B. Dolge Co.
REPEL - Floor waxes - Uncle Sam Chemical Co., Inc.
REPEL - Pet products - Farnam Cos. Inc.
REPEL - Pet products - Security Product Co.
REPEL - Pharmaceutical preparations - Wisconsin Pharmacal Co. Inc.
REPEL - Repellent - Security Products Co.
REPEL - Skin care products ☆ - Divajex
REPEL - Stucco - Highland Stucco and Lime Products, Inc.
REPEL-A-CIDE - Veterinary pharmaceutical preparations - Happy Jack, Inc.
REPEL-ALL - Pet products ☆ - St. Aubrey
REPEL-X - Fly sprays - Farnam Cos. Inc.
REPEL-X R.T.U. - Fly sprays - Farnam Cos. Inc.
REPELL - Coatings - Pleko Products, Inc.
REPELLENT - Pet products - HTZ Investment Corp.
REPELLO PRODUCTS - Insecticides - Carl J. Abraham
REPEN VK - Pharmaceutical preparations ☆ - Solvay Pharmaceuticals Inc.
REPENDO - Health care products - Halsom Home Care
REPERTOIRE - Computer software - Control Data Systems Inc.
REPERTOIRE - Ophthalmic goods - Foremost Optical Products
REPERTOIRE - Recording label - Sonic Arts Corp.
REPETABS - Pharmaceutical preparations - Schering-Plough Healthcare
   Products
REPETOIRE - Tableware–china ☆ - Lenox, Inc.
REPETTO - Bird cages - Active Pet Supplies
REPEYOUNG - Cosmetics - Green Foods
REPHENYL CAPS - Pharmaceutical preparations - Reese Chemical Co.
REPIDERM - Pet products - Biochemics, Inc.
REPIGLICAN - Toys–stuffed - Warthog Productions, Ltd.
REPIPET - Measuring and dispensing pumps - Labindustries Inc.
REPL - Computer software - At&T Corp.
REPLA-K - Gutters–plastic - Genova Products Inc.
REPLACE - Apparel–men's - Silenzio Sportswear, Inc.
REPLACE - Capes–fur - Sterling-Clark-Lurton Corp.
REPLACE - Dental equipment - Steri-Oss, Inc.
REPLACE - Doors–metal - Pease Industries, Inc.
REPLACE - Hair care products - KMS Research Inc.
REPLACEMATS - Mats - Copquin Murphy Inc.
REPLACER - Lighting equipment - General Electric Co.
REPLASTEC - Plastics - Replastec, Inc.
REPLAY - Chewing gum ☆ - Planters LifeSavers Co.
REPLAY - Electronic equipment - Daktronics Inc.
REPLAY - Hair care products - Dellaria International Inc.
REPLAY - Paper–writing - Champion International Corp.
REPLENADERM - Cosmetics - Andrew Jergens Co.
REPLENIDERM - Skin care products - Andrew Jergens Co.
REPLENISH - Computer software - R.L. Miley Systems, Inc.
REPLENISH - Hair care products - Faberge Co.
REPLENISH - Vitamins and nutritional supplements - Leiner Health Products
   Inc.

☆ = Now out of production

REPLENISHING - Cosmetics - Noxell Corp.

REPLENISHING BODY MOISTURIZER - Skin care products - Aveda Corp.

REPLENS - Pharmaceutical preparations - Warner-Wellcome

REPLI-KEY - Locks–padlocks - ILCO Unican Corp.

REPLI-PAC - Patches, insignia, and emblems ☆ - Best Emblem & Insignia Co. Inc.

REPLICA - Audio equipment - Telex Communications, Inc.

REPLICA - Clocks ☆ - General Time Corp. (Westclox/Seth Thomas Div.)

REPLICA - Doors–glass - Crestline

REPLICA - Hair care products - Nexxus Products Co.

REPLICARE - Bandages - Smith and Nephew United Inc.

REPLICAS 1800 - Furniture - Thomasville Furniture Industries Inc.

REPLICAS & RARITIES - Housewares - Valleau Brass Foundry

REPLICATECH - Laboratory apparatus - Replicatech, Inc.

REPLICATION SERVER - Computer software - Sybase, Inc.

REPLIGEN - Pharmaceutical preparations - Repligen Corp.

REPLIGRAPH - Canvas art reproductions - CRA Production Lab Co.

REPLIQUE - Colognes - Frances Denney

REPLIQUE - Floor coverings–carpet and rugs ☆ - Olympic Carpets Inc.

REPLIX - Computer software - Samsung Software America Inc.

REPLOGLE - Globes - Replogle Globes Inc.

REPLY - Electronic equipment - Fleetwood Furniture Co.

REPMATE - Computer software - Budgetext Corp.

REPMGR - Computer software - DataSolve Business Systems Inc.

REPO CORT - Pharmaceutical preparations ☆ - R.A. McNeil Co.

REPOGEST - Veterinary pharmaceutical preparations ☆ - Schering-Plough Animal Health

REPOISE - Pharmaceutical preparations ☆ - A.H. Robins Co. Inc.

REPOM CF - Health care products - Everett Laboratories Inc.

REPONDRE 20 - Hair coloring preparations - Stylors Inc.

REPORT - Paper - Saxon Paper Co.

REPORT BINDER, THE - Binders ☆ - Samsill Corp.

REPORT CARD - Computer software - W. Christopher Musselwhite

REPORT CARD II - Computer software - Quality Computers and Applications

REPORT EXPRESS - Computer software - Sears Payment Systems, Inc.

REPORT MASTER - Computer software - Codemaster Corp.

REPORT RIGHT - Computer software - NCH Promotional Services, Inc.

REPORT STYLER - Computer software - Alpha Software Corp.

REPORTER - Computer software ☆ - Hydrolab Corp.

REPORTER - Men's apparel - Laurentian Group

REPORTFOLIO - File folders - Angler's Roslyn Group Ltd.

REPORTFOLIO - File folders - Vocational Research Inst.

REPORTLINK - Computer software - Paychex, Inc.

REPORTMATE - Computer software - McGraw-Hill Companies, Inc.

REPORTMATE - Computer software - Watersoft Development Co.

REPORTSMITH - Computer software - Indigo Software Corp.

REPORTVIEW - Computer software - Xpoint Corp.

REPORTXTENDER - Computer peripheral equipment - OTG Software

REPOSANS-10 - Pharmaceutical preparations - Wesley Pharmacal Co. Inc.

REPOSE - Pillows - Kohler Co.

REPOTEST - Veterinary pharmaceutical preparations ☆ - Schering-Plough Animal Health

REPOUSSE - Flatware - Kirk Stieff Co.

REPOUSSE - Frames–picture - Terragrafics Inc.

REPOWER - Oils–lubricating - Repower Automotive Products Inc.

REPP LTD. - Apparel and accessories - Edison Brothers Stores, Inc.

REPRESENTATIONS - Computer software - Carl E. Hewitt

REPRIEVE - Pharmaceutical preparations - Mayer Laboratories, Inc.

REPRISE - Furniture ☆ - Bassett Furniture Industries, Inc.

REPRISE - Paper products - Georgia-Pacific Corp.

REPRISE - Paperboard - Fiber Mark, Inc.

REPRISE - Recording label - Warner Bros. Records Inc.

REPRISE - Wallpaper - Sunnyside Prints

REPRO - Playground equipment - BCI Burke Co., Inc.

REPRO-TRAN - Electronic equipment - Transilwrap Co., Inc.

REPROBENCH - Electronic equipment ☆ - Leedal Inc.

REPROBOND - Imaging material - Graphic Technology Inc.

REPROBOX - Photographic equipment ☆ - Leedal Inc.

REPROCAD EXPRESS - Computer software - Reprocad, Inc.

REPRODUCTA - Greeting cards - Reproducta Co., Inc.

REPROLITH - Film - Anitec Image Corp.

REPROMAX - Photographic equipment ☆ - International Paper Co.

REPROMOUNT - Plastic film - Mactac Inc. (Packaging Closures Systems Div.)

REPRONAR - Electronic equipment - Honeywell Inc.

REPRONET - Computer software - Repronet, Inc.

REPRORISK - Computer diskettes–blank - Micromedex, Inc.

REPRORUBBER - Surgical supplies - Flexbar Machine Corp.

REPROSERVER - Computer software - Repronet, Inc.

REPROSTAND - Photographic equipment - Leedal Inc.

REPROVIT - Photographic equipment - Leica USA Inc.

REPS - Gloves–leather - Concertina Group, Inc.

REPSILON - Computer software - R.J. Reynolds Tobacco Co.

REPSOLVE - Computer software - DataSolve Business Systems Inc.

REPTA-SUN - Lighting equipment - Fluker Farms Inc.

REPTARIUM - Pet shops - Apogee Enterprises Inc.

REPTECH - Pressure gauges - Cato Western, Inc.

REPTI CAGE - Pet products - Zoo Med Laboratories, Inc.

REPTI-CAVE - Pet products - Zoo Med Laboratories, Inc.

REPTI FLORA - Pet products - Zoo Med Laboratories, Inc.

REPTI GEAR - Pet products - Petland, Inc.

REPTI HAMMOCK - Pet products - Zoo Med Laboratories, Inc.

REPTI MANIA - Pet products - Zoo Med Laboratories, Inc.

REPTI-OASIS - Pet products - Zoo Med Laboratories, Inc.

REPTI-SCOOP - Pet products - Four Paws Products Ltd.

REPTICARE - Pet products - Zoo Med Laboratories, Inc.

REPTILE - Cleaning preparations - L & A, Inc.

REPTILE - Recording label - Reptile Records

REPTILE BELT HARNESS - Pet products - R.A.F. Trading Inc.

REPTILE CAFE - Pet products - Blue Ribbon Pet Products, Inc.

REPTILE-FARE - Pet products - Reliable Protein Products

REPTILE FOUNTAIN - Pet products - Molor Products Co.

REPTILE HABITATS - Cages–wire ☆ - Pets International, Ltd.

REPTILE HEAT MATS - Pet products - Kane Manufacturing Co.

REPTILE NOSE GARD - Pet products - R.A.F. Trading Inc.

REPTILE RATION - Animal feed supplements - Michele T. Emmons

REPTILE RITERS - Pens - Moon Products, Inc.

REPTILE SHOULDER REVERSE SADDLE - Pet products - R.A.F. Trading Inc.

REPTILE T.E.N. - Pet food - Wardley Corp.

REPTILELITE - Lamps - Angelo Brothers Co.

REPTILIA - Wallpaper ☆ - Fidelity Industries, Inc.

REPTILIAN - Cases–eyeglass - California Optical Leather Inc.

REPTILIAN OASIS - Pet products - Reptilia

REPTILIBOTS - Toys - Trendmasters, Inc.

REPTILIN - Pet products ☆ - Sera Aquaristik USA Inc.

REPTILITE - Lamps - Sperti Sunlamp

REPTITHERM UTH - Pet products - Zoo Med Laboratories, Inc.

REPTIVITE - Veterinary pharmaceutical preparations - Zoo Med Laboratories, Inc.

REPTO-SEAL - Pet products - Tetra Sales USA

REPTO-STAT - Pet products ☆ - Tetra Sales USA

REPTOCAL - Pet products - Tetra Sales USA

REPTOHEAT - Pet products - Tetra Sales USA

REPTOMIN - Pet products - Tetra Sales USA

REPTON - Computer software - Sirius Software Development Inc.

REPTOSOL - Pet products - Tetra Sales USA

REPTOVIT - Pet products - Tetra Sales USA

REPUBLIC - Bond paper - Copco Papers Inc.

REPUBLIC - Daters and numberers - Consolidated Stamp Manufacturing Co. Inc.

REPUBLIC - Driveway sealer, etc. - Continental Materials Co.

REPUBLIC - Flags - Annin and Co.

REPUBLIC - Furnaces–industrial ☆ - Arrowhead Environmental Control

REPUBLIC - Hardware - Blaine Window Hardware Inc.

REPUBLIC - Heating equipment ☆ - Bradford-White Corp.

REPUBLIC - Lawn mower - American Lawn Mower Co.

REPUBLIC - Navigational instruments - Esterline Technologies Corp.

REPUBLIC - Sinks–metal - Federal Home Products

REPUBLIC - Stoves–wood-burning - Vogelzang International Corp.

REPUBLIC - Tableware–china - Lenox, Inc.

REPUBLIC - Tires - Kelly-Springfield Tire Co.

REPUBLIC - Tires - Lee Tire & Rubber Co.

REPUBLIC 54 - Gypsum products - Republic Gypsum Co.

REPUBLIC DRUG - Pharmaceutical preparations - Republic Drug Co. Inc.

REPUBLIC MOLDING - Containers–plastic - Lawnware Products, Inc.

REPUBLIC OF ROME - Games - Avalon Hill Game Co.

REPUBLIC OF TEA, THE - Art prints and related products - Republic of Tea, Inc.

REPUBLIC OF TEXAS, THE - Wines - Republic of Texas Restaurant, Inc.

REPUBLIC PAINTS - Paints - Spectra-Tone Paint Corp.

REPUBLIC SEATING - Seats–automobile - AIC Corp.

REPUBLOCRAT - Games - Arthur M. Youngblood

REPUTAIN - Chemical preparations - Zeneca Inc.

REPUTATION - Fruits–pickled or brined - National Fruit Product Co., Inc.

REPUTATION - Shirts - United Pacific Apparel (USA), Inc.

REPUTATIONS - Apparel and accessories - U.P.A. Licensing Inc.

REQL - Computer software - Burl Software Laboratories, Inc.

REQUA - Health care products ☆ - Requa Manufacturing Co. Inc.

REQUEST - Computer software - General Re Corp.

REQUEST - Employment agencies–temporary help - Request, Inc.

REQUEST - Floor coverings–carpet and rugs ☆ - Galaxy Carpet Mills Inc.

REQUEST - Medical instruments - Merit Medical Systems Inc.

REQUEST - Toothbrushes - Larmax Products Inc.

REQUEST A DOCUMENT - Computer software - Mdl Information Systems, Inc.

REQUEST PACK - Cereal ☆ - Kellogg Co.

REQUESTLINK - Computer software - Datastream Systems Inc.

REQUIN 3 - Dietary food, vitamin, and mineral supplements - Nutrition for Life International, Inc.

REQUIREMENTS MANAGER, THE - Computer software - Computer Training Services

REQUIREMENTS WOMAN - Apparel and accessories - Itemeyes Inc.

REQUISITE - Skin care products - Swank Inc.

REQUISITE TECHNOLOGY - Electronic equipment - Requisite Technology, Inc.

REQUISITION - Paper–writing - Butler Paper Co.

RER - Recording label - Cuneiform Records

REREDOS - Sporting goods - Tom Donohoe & Co. Ltd.

REROOF - Roofing materials–clay ☆ - Master's Choice Inc.

RERUN - Apparel and accessories - Leon Seltzer

RES-CUE - Health care products - Ambu Inc.

RES-FELT - Paper–tar - Georgia-Pacific Corp.

RES-N-GEL - Paints–artists' - Martin F. Weber Co.

RES-N-GLAS - Chemical preparations - Woolsey Marine Industries

RES-N-TILL - Computer software - Kansas State University

RES OFF - Health care products - Pharmaceutical Innovations

RES OXIDE - Brake pads - Brake Maker, Inc.

RES-Q - Aquatic pharmacuetical preparations ☆ - Aquatronics-Filtronics

RES-Q - Pet products - Best n' Show Pet Products Inc.

RES-Q - Pharmaceutical preparations - Boyle & Co.

RES-Q 1000 - Vitamins and nutritional supplements - Res-Q International

RES-Q-JACK - Jacks–hydraulic - Cepco Tool Co.

RESA - Pharmaceutical preparations - Vita Elixir Co. Inc.

RESAID - Pharmaceutical preparations - Geneva Generics Inc.

RESCAPS D.M. - Pharmaceutical preparations - Geneva Generics Inc.

RESCHS PILSENER - Beverages–malt - Mission Imports Inc.

RESCINEMMS - Pharmaceutical preparations ☆ - C.O. Truxton Inc.

RESCLOR - Pharmaceutical preparations - Dunhall Pharmaceuticals Inc.

RESCO - Dog food - Tecla Co. Inc.

RESCO - Jewelry - Ring Specialty Co.

RESCOLOR - Hair care products ☆ - Thomas & Thompson Co. Inc.

RESCON - Prescription drug ☆ - Ion Laboratories Inc.

RESCRIPTOR - Pharmaceutical preparations - Upjohn Co.

RESCU - Alarm systems ☆ - Allen Telecom Group, Inc.

RESCUE - Abrasive products - Minnesota Mining & Manufacturing Co.

RESCUE - Brooms ☆ - Emsco Inc.

RESCUE - Health care products - Esteem Products Ltd.

RESCUE - Pesticides–household - Sterling International, Inc.

RESCUE - Vitamins and nutritional supplements - Guardian Royalty Corp.

RESCUE 1 - Toys ☆ - Placo Products Co.

RESCUE 4X4 - Bicycles ☆ - Huffy Corp.

RESCUE 911 - Apparel and accessories - CBS Inc.

RESCUE AIR SYSTEM - Air conditioning equipment - Rescue Air Systems, Inc.

RESCUE ALIVE - Life preservers - Robert C. Beer

RESCUE & RESTORE - Dental compounds - Rescue & Restore

RESCUE DATA RECOVERY SOFTWARE - Computer software - Allmicro, Inc.

RESCUE DIVISION - Toys ☆ - Jak-Pak Inc.

RESCUE HEROES - Toys - Fisher-Price, Inc.

RESCUE-IES - Computer software - GTE Government Information Services Inc.

RESCUE II-E - Flowers, plants, and seeds - Jacklin Seed

RESCUE-LURE - Fishing tackle ☆ - Church Tackle Co.

RESCUE OLLIE NORTH - Games - Gamescience

RESCUE ON FRACTALUS - Video games - Lucasfilm Ltd.

RESCUE ONE - Boats - Anthony P. Lumpkin

RESCUE PHONE - Amplifiers - Rescue Phone, Inc.

RESCUE RAKE - Hair care products - Rescue Marketing Group

RESCUE RANGER - Toys–automobiles - Mattel, Inc.

RESCUE REMEDY - Health care products - Ellon Bach USA Inc.

RESCUE ROVER - Bathroom accessories ☆ - Blue Ridge International Products Co., Inc.

RESCUE SPINE BOARD - Swimming pools - Recreonics, Inc.

RESCUE THE WORLD - Handbags - Lantis Corp.

RESCUE TUBE - Swimming pools - Recreonics, Inc.

RESCUE TUBE II - Swimming pools - Recreonics, Inc.

RESCUE TUBE III - Swimming pools - Recreonics, Inc.

RESCUE WRAP - Medical apparatus - Robert Alan Ricketts

RESCUED PAPERS - Paper - Overly Publishing Co. Inc.

RESCUER - Communications equipment–microwave - Pollenex Corp.

RESCUEWARE - Computer software - Seer Technologies, Inc.

RESCUMATIC - Safety products - D B Industries, Inc.

RESEAL - Fluid dispensing containers - Reseal International L.P.

RESEARCH - Audio equipment ☆ - Teledyne Acoustic Research

RESEARCH - Paper–bond - Byron Weston Div.

RESEARCH ASSISTANT1 - Computer software - Vitale Software Group

RESEARCH BANK, THE - Computer storage devices–optical - Securities Data Licensing Corp.

RESEARCH COLLECTION - Steel products - Kewaunee Scientific Corp.

RESEARCHIT - Computer software ☆ - Right on Programs

RESEARCHSTATION - Computer software - Helix Systems Inc.

RESEARCHWARE - Computer software - Cast, Inc.

RESEDIT - Computer software - Apple Computer Inc.

RESEEDIT - Flowers, plants, and seeds - Ed Hume Seeds Inc.

RESELLER'S SOURCE FOR CONNECTIVITY, THE - Catalogs - Black Box Corp.

RESERCEN - Pharmaceutical preparations ☆ - Central Pharmaceutical Inc.

RESERPAL - Pharmaceutical preparations - Bio-Factor Laboratories

RESERPANEED - Pharmaceutical preparations - Hanlon Drug Products

RESERPATABS - Pharmaceutical preparations ☆ - Saron Pharmacal Corp.

RESERPOID - Pharmaceutical preparations ☆ - Upjohn Co.

RESER'S - Food products - Reser's Fine Foods Inc.

RESER'S BULL-WHIP - Snack foods ☆ - Reser's Fine Foods Inc.

RESER'S EL MUCHACHO - Food products - Reser's Fine Foods Inc.

RESERV - Bricks - North American Refractories Co.

RESERVATUM - Wines ☆ - Diamond Wine Merchants

RESERVE - Apparel and accessories - Fashion Avenue Knits Inc. and John Finch, Jr. Partnership

RESERVE - Barbecue sauce - Sysco Corp.

RESERVE - Frames–eyeglass - Tura LP

RESERVE - Inks–duplicating ☆ - Pelikan, Inc.

RESERVE - Mattresses - King Koil Licensing Co., Inc.

RESERVE CABERNET SAUVIGNON - Wines - Trefethen Vineyards Winery Inc.

RESERVE HARVEST - Food products - Norm Thompson Outfitters, Inc.

RESERVE RIESLING & GEWURZTRAMINER - Wines ☆ - Kobrand Corp.

RESERVE SAINT-MARC - Wines ☆ - Maison Jomere Ltd.

RESERVE START - Batteries - Exide Corp.

RESERVE WINES - Wines - IDV Wines (Beaulieu Vineyard)

RESERVED SEAT - Apparel–children's - Jay-Zee Inc.

RESERVETRAC - Computer software - Summit Associates, Inc.

RESERVOIR - Apparel–men's - Jeetish Imports Inc.

RESGRAM - Computer peripheral equipment - Reservoir Characterization Research Andconsulting, Inc.

RESHAPE FORMULA, THE - Vitamins and nutritional supplements - Body Wise International, Inc.

RESI-BOND - Resins–polymer - Georgia-Pacific Corp.

RESI-CAT - Resins–polymer - Georgia-Pacific Corp.

RESI-FLAKE - Resins–polymer - Georgia-Pacific Corp.

RESI-GROW - Fertilizers - Georgia-Pacific Corp.

RESI-LAM - Resins–synthetic - Georgia-Pacific Corp.

RESI-MAT - Resins–polymer - Georgia-Pacific Corp.

RESI-MIX - Adhesives and sealants - Georgia-Pacific Corp.

RESI-PATCH - Adhesives and sealants - Georgia-Pacific Corp.

RESI-SEAL - Resins–polymer - Georgia-Pacific Corp.

RESI-SET - Resins–polymer - Georgia-Pacific Corp.

RESI-SHELL - Resins–polymer - Georgia-Pacific Corp.

RESI-STRAN - Resins–polymer - Georgia-Pacific Corp.

RESI-VAT - Resins–polymer - Georgia-Pacific Corp.

RESIDENCE - Floor coverings ☆ - Azrock Commercial Flooring

RESIDENCY - Motor vehicles–motor homes - Thor Tech, Inc.

RESIDENT - Health care products - Omron Healthcare, Inc.

RESIDENT COMMANDER - Computer software - Eastman Kodak Co.

RESIDENT EXPERT - Computer software - SourceView Software International

RESIDENTIAL - Manufactured homes - Redman Industries, Inc.

RESIDENTIAL APPRAISER, THE - Computer software - Software for Real Estate Professionals, Inc.

RESIDONT - Adhesives and sealants - Penthouse for Men

RESIGLAS - Fiberboard ☆ - Fibre Glass-Evercoat Co. Inc.
RESILIENCE - Computer peripheral equipment - Resilience Corp.
RESILIENCE - Hosiery–women's - Sara Lee Corp.
RESILIENCE - Recording label - ODR Inc.
RESILIENCE - Skin care products - Estee Lauder Inc.
RESILIENCE - Vitamins and nutritional supplements - Marine Biotherapies
RESILIENT - Computer hardware - Resilience Corp.
RESILIO - Apparel and accessories - Wemco, Inc.
RESILIO SPORT - Apparel and accessories - Wemco, Inc.
RESILITE - Sporting goods - Nichols Wrestling Products Inc.
RESILOY - Shutters–wood - U.S. Polymers, Inc.
RESIN - Giftware - Christhomas Corp.
RESIN/COAT - Paint rollers - Wooster Brush Co.
RESIN-CRETE - Paints - Penn Crete Products Co. Inc.
RESIN-FIVE - Solder - Kester Solder Co.
RESIN-LOC - Fabrics - Clark-Schwebel Fiber Glass Corp.
RESIN-MATE - Water treating compounds - Spectrum Labs, Inc.
RESIN-NU - Outdoor furniture cleaner - Keromate Products Inc.
RESIN-TITE - Plywood - Roseburg Forest Products Co.
RESIN-TONE - Paints - Penn Crete Products Co. Inc.
RESINAL - Pet products - Aquatronics-Filtronics
RESINALL - Abrasive products - Norton Co.
RESINAM - Pet products - Aquatronics-Filtronics
RESINATOR, THE - Shirts - Michael Faliero
RESINCO - Pet products - Aquatronics-Filtronics
RESINCORE - Particle board - Rodman Industries Inc.
RESINDEK - Paneling - Johnson-Doppler Lumber
RESINEATER - Cleaning preparations - Finger Lakes Chemicals, Inc.
RESINGARD - Salt - Akzo America Inc.
RESINITE - Film - Borden, Inc.
RESINITE - Pet products - Aquatronics-Filtronics
RESINITE - Plastics film - AEP Industries, Inc.
RESINIZED - Abrasive products - Norton Co.
RESINOL - Adhesives and sealants - Loctite Corp.
RESINOL - Soap - Mentholatum Co.
RESINPLEX - Wallcovering - The Creative Edge, Inc.
RESINSEAL - Paints - Dunn Edwards Corp.
RESINTECH - Chemical preparations - Resintech, Inc.
RESINTONE - Paints ☆ - Montgomery Ward & Co. Inc.
RESINWEAVE - Furniture - Brown Jordan Co.
RESIST - Apparel and accessories - P M Product Marketing
RESIST - Health care products - Pacific BioLogic Inc.
RESIST-A-BALL - Exercising equipment - Michael P. Morris
RESIST-LITE - Glass–safety - Buchmin Industries
RESISTA-CRETE - Paints - Waterlox Coatings Corp.
RESISTAL - Belts–apparel - Humphrey's Inc.
RESISTAL - Watches - Croton Watch Co., Inc.
RESISTALL - Paper - L.L. Brown Paper Co.
RESISTANCE - Recording label - Jazz Composer's Orchestra Association Inc.
RESISTANCE PLUS - Health care products - Life Force Nutrition
RESISTAT - Fabrics–nylon - BASF Corp.
RESISTER, THE - Floor coverings–carpet and rugs ☆ - Karastan-Bigelow Inc.
RESISTEX - Medical apparatus - Mercury Enterprises, Inc.
RESISTEX - Wallcovering - Parex, Inc.
RESISTICK - Surgical supplies - Aaron Medical Industries, Inc.
RESISTIGEN - Vitamins and nutritional supplements - Murdock
  Pharmaceuticals, Inc.
RESISTITE - Varnishes - Commercial Chemical Co. Inc.
RESISTO - Floor waxes - Uncle Sam Chemical Co., Inc.
RESISTO - Neckties - Resisto Tie Makers
RESISTO - Paper–photographic - Eastman Kodak Co.
RESISTO - Thread - Signal Thread Co. Inc.
RESISTOL - Buckles - Hat Brands, Inc.
RESISTOL - Hats - Resistol Hats
RESISTOL - Paints ☆ - Valspar Corp.
RESISTON - Pharmaceutical preparations - Consolidated Midland Corp.
RESISTORM - Paints ☆ - Empire State Varnish Co.
RESISTORUST - Paints - Pettit Paint Co. Inc.
RESISTOVAR - Vases - Lilly Co.
RESISTOX - Paints - Standard T Chemical Co. Inc.
RESIWELD - Sealing compounds ☆ - Tec Inc.
RESIZE - Computer software - Blue Sky Software Corp.
RESIZOLE - Pet products - Virbac, Inc.
RESLO - Microphones ☆ - Ercona Corp.
RESLOOM - Chemical preparations ☆ - Monsanto Co.
RESMASTER - Computer software - Reservation Technologies, Inc.

RESN-X II - Floor coating - Rock-Tred Corp.
RES'N'WOOD - Tables–wood ☆ - Classic Plaques Inc.
RESO II - Musical instrument accessories ☆ - G. Leblanc Corp.
RESO CHAMBER - Musical instrument accessories - Otto Link Inc.
RESO-PAD - Musical instrument accessories - United Musical Instruments USA
  Inc.
RESO-SPECIAL - Musical instrument accessories ☆ - G. Leblanc Corp.
RESO-TONE - Banjos ☆ - International Music Corp.
RESO-TONE - Clarinets - G. Leblanc Corp.
RESOCOR - Plywood ☆ - Harbor Sales Co.
RESOFLO - Air purification systems - United Dominion Industries, Inc.
RESOL - Chemical preparations - Wyeth-Ayerst Laboratories
RESOLITE - Paints - Farwest Paint Manufacturing Co. Inc.
RESOLUT - Sutures - W.L. Gore & Associates, Inc.
RESOLUTE - Binders ☆ - ACCO USA, Inc.
RESOLUTE - Colognes - Ritornelle Inc.
RESOLUTE - Ledgers - Brown-Bridge Industries
RESOLUTE - Lighting fixtures - Manifesto Corp.
RESOLUTE ACCLAIM - Stoves–wood-burning - Vermont Castings, Inc.
RESOLUTION - Computer software - Mediation Solutions, Inc.
RESOLUTION - Floor coverings - Mannington Mills, Inc.
RESOLUTION - Floor coverings - Mannington Resilient Floors
RESOLUTION - Floor coverings - Monticello Carpet Mills
RESOLUTION III - Fabrics–terrycloth ☆ - Guilford Mills, Inc.
RESOLVE - Carpet cleaning brush - Sterling Winthrop Inc.
RESOLVE - Cleaning preparations–carpet and rug - D-Con Co. Inc.
RESOLVE - Cleaning preparations–carpet and rug - Linden Corp.
RESOLVE - Computer software - Da Vinci Systems, Inc.
RESOLVE - Hair care products - Joico Laboratories, Inc.
RESOLVE - Herbicides - American Cyanamid Co.
RESOLVE - Ophthalmic goods - Allergan, Inc.
RESOLVE 828 - Vitamins and nutritional supplements - Vita Source, Inc.
RESOLVER - Computer software - Burleigh Instruments, Inc.
RESOMAX - Lenses–photographic - SP Systems/Saratons
RESONANCE - Computer software - Thru-Put Technology
RESONANS - Musical instrument accessories - Metropolitan Music Co.
RESONANT - Telephones - Resonant Communications Corp.
RESONATE - Computer software - Resonate Inc.
RESONEX - Imaging equipment - Resonex Inc.
RESONITE - Clarinets ☆ - Selmer Co. Inc.
RESORABOND - Resins–polymer - Georgia-Pacific Corp.
RESORB - Degreasing solvents ☆ - KC Products, Inc. (Sharon D. Spence)
RESORCIPHEN - Chemical preparations - Indspec Chemical Corp.
RESORCITATE - Skin care products - Schieffelin & Co. (Pharmaceutical
  Laboratories Div.)
RESORSABOND - Adhesives and sealants - Georgia-Pacific Resins, Inc.
RESORT - Trailers–travel ☆ - Fleetwood Enterprises, Inc.
RESORT '83 - Cosmetics - Alexandra De Markoff, Ltd.
RESORT LINE HAWAII - Apparel and accessories - Aloha Candle
  Manufacturing Co. Inc.
RESORT RECORDS - Recording label - Resort Records Inc.
RESORT SPA - Shower stalls–metal - Fan-Fi International Inc.
RESORTER - Boats–motor - Century Boat Co.
RESORTER - Boats–motor ☆ - Alumacraft Boat Co.
RESORTER - Eyeglasses - Art-Craft Optical Co.
RESORTER BARGE - Boats–motor ☆ - Hewes Marine Co.
RESORTWEAVE - Apparel and accessories - Palm Beach Co., Inc.
RESOUND - Electrical testing instruments - Resound Corp.
RESOUNDER - Amplifiers–musical instrument - Pacific Music Supply Co.
RESOURCE - Consulting services - Source Marketing, Inc.
RESOURCE - Floor coverings–carpet and rugs - Philadelphia Carpets
RESOURCE - Paper products - Georgia-Pacific Corp.
RESOURCE - Paper–writing - Gilbert Paper Co.
RESOURCE - Vitamins and nutritional supplements - Novartis Nutrition Corp.
RESOURCE - Wallpaper ☆ - Bolta Wallcoverings
RESOURCE 28 - Wallpaper - Glidden Co.
RESOURCE 1000 - Wallpaper - Glidden Co.
RESOURCE-FUL - Bags–paper - Viva Specialty Food Brokerage Inc.
RESOURCE GATEWAY - Computer software - Universal Data Solutions, Inc.
RESOURCE PRO - Computer software - Prentice-Hall, Inc.
RESOURCES CONSERVATION - Bathroom fixtures - Resources Park
RESPAHERB - Vitamins and nutritional supplements ☆ - J.R. Carlson
  Laboratories Inc.
RESPAIRE - Pharmaceutical preparations - Laser Inc.
RESPALOR - Nutritional suuplement - Mead Johnson & Co.
RESPECT - Compressors - American Standard Inc.

☆ = Now out of production

RESPECT - Jewelry - Jenai Lane
RESPECT - Recording label - Fantasy Inc.
RESPECT YOUR ELDERS - Greeting cards - Susan B. Licata
RESPECTEE - Skin care products - Lancome
RESPI-SED - Pharmaceutical preparations ☆ - Vortech Pharmaceuticals
RESPICARE - Vitamins and nutritional supplements - Ayurvedic Concepts Ltd.
RESPIFLOW - Pharmaceutical preparations - Respiflow, Inc.
RESPINOL - Pharmaceutical preparations - Misemer Pharmaceuticals Inc.
RESPIRADYNE - Health care products - Sherwood Medical Co.
RESPIRAR 02 - Skin care products - Revlon Consumer Products Corp.
RESPIRATION LONG - Medical apparatus - Nellcor Puritan Bennett
RESPIRATION SIMULATOR - Medical apparatus - Nellcor Puritan Bennett
RESPIRATOR - Cushions—foam ☆ - Hi-Life Rubber Inc.
RESPIRATORY PROTECTOR - Air purification systems - Mst, Inc.
RESPIRGARD - Health care products - Marquest Medical Products Inc.
RESPITE - Pharmaceutical preparations - Durham Pharmacal Corp.
RESPITE - Pharmaceutical preparations - Stiefel Laboratories, Inc.
RESPLENDENCE - Flatware - Wallace International Silversmiths, Inc.
RESPLEX - Vitamins and nutritional supplements - Amrion, Inc.
RESPOMUNE-CP - Veterinary pharmaceutical preparations - Oxford Veterinary Laboratories, Inc.
RESPONADEX - Electronic equipment - T.M. Visual Industries Inc.
RESPOND - Animal feeds - Agway Country Foods Inc.
RESPOND - Computer software - Infection Control and Prevention Analysts, Inc.
RESPOND - Cushions - Leucadia, Inc.
RESPOND - Shampoos - Colgate-Palmolive Co.
RESPOND - Vitamins and nutritional supplements - J.R. Carlson Laboratories Inc.
RESPOND AGRILABS - Veterinary pharmaceutical preparations - Agri Laboratories, Ltd.
RESPOND II - Health care products - Medtronic Nortech
RESPOND SELECT - Health care products - Medtronic Nortech
RESPONDOR - Electronics equipment - MPC Educational Systems Inc.
RESPONSE - Chairs—wood - Krueger International, Inc.
RESPONSE - Clocks - General Time Corp. (Westclox/Seth Thomas Div.)
RESPONSE - Eyeglasses - Art-Craft Optical Co.
RESPONSE - Floor coverings ☆ - Tarkett, Inc.
RESPONSE - Floor coverings—carpet and rugs - Calladium & Marglen
RESPONSE - Floor coverings—carpet and rugs - Regal Rugs Inc.
RESPONSE - Food products - Central Soya Co. Inc.
RESPONSE - Medical apparatus - Mentor Corp.
RESPONSE - Sporting goods - Prince Manufacturing Inc.
RESPONSE-A-MATIC - Electronics equipment - Instructional Industries Inc.
RESPONSE FORMULA FP - Pet food - Iams Co.
RESPONSE PACK - First aid kits - Butterworth Health Corp.
RESPONSECHECK - Checkbooks - Attitude Measurement Corp.
RESPONSER - Electronics equipment - GEL Systems Inc.
RESPONSEWARE - Computer peripheral equipment - Computer Site Technologies, Inc.
RESPONSIBLE CHOICE - Fruits and vegetables - Stemilt Growers, Inc.
RESPONSIVE - Smoke detectors - Figgie International Inc.
RESPONSIVE TIME LOGGER - Computer software - Alan Macy
RESPONSYN - Machine parts - Quincy Technologies Inc.
RESPOSABLE - Medical apparatus - King Systems Corp.
RESPOUSSE - Floor coverings ☆ - Kentile Floors Inc.
RESQME - Computer software - Saami J. Shaibani
RESQUE - Hair-care products - Costec 20 Inc.
RESQUE EXTRA - Hair conditioner - Costec 20 Inc.
RESS - Wines - Beer Import Co.
REST - Watches - Power of Rest Unlimited
REST-A-PHONE - Telephone accessories - Rest-a-Phone Corp.
REST-ALL - Chairs—metal - Ohio Chair Co.
REST ASSURED - Chairs—upholstered - Franklin Corp.
REST ASSURED - Fabrics - Rockland Industries Inc.
REST ASSURED - Infant product - Gerry Baby Products Co.
REST ASSURED - Pharmaceutical preparations - Dener Management Inc.
REST ASSURED - Pillows - Kimberly-Clark Corp.
REST ASSURED - Sanitary paper - Rochester Midland Corp.
REST-BAK - Binders - Boorum & Pease Co.
REST EASY - Pharmaceutical preparations - Walgreen Co.
REST-I-FILM - Office supplies ☆ - JM Co.
REST-IT - Folding chairs - Donald F. Gray
REST MATE - Medical apparatus - Encore Products Inc.
REST 'N' SHAVE - Bathroom fixtures - Betzy A. Soma
REST PROTECTOR - Mattress pads - Chatham Manufacturing Co.

REST-Q - Toys - Tonka Corp.
REST-RITE - Frames—eyeglass - J.I. Morris Co.
REST SECURE - Mattress pads - Chatham Manufacturing Co.
REST SMART - Mattress pads - Chatham Manufacturing Co.
REST TECHNOLOGIES - Diagnostic apparatus - Jerald H. Simmons
REST WARMER - Mattress pads - Chatham Manufacturing Co.
RESTABOUTS - Shoes - Lowell Shoe, Inc.
RESTACK EM - Puzzles - Parris Manufacturing Co.
RESTART - Envelopes - International Paper Co.
RESTAURANT BASICS - Computer software - Aureflam Corp.
RESTAURANT EXPRESS - Computer software - Systems Software Resource, Inc.
RESTAURANT RECIPE - Salad dressings—bottled - Nalley's Fine Foods
RESTAURANT ROW - Food products - Sea Snack Foods Inc.
RESTAURANT, THE - Apparel and accessories - 23 Food, Inc.
RESTCUE CC - Medical apparatus - SSI Medical Services, Inc.
RESTEX - Health care products ☆ - Republic Drug Co. Inc.
RESTFUL - Vitamins and nutritional supplements - Amrion, Inc.
RESTICKABLES - Games - Colorforms
RESTIES - Paper - Fay Paper Products Inc.
RESTING ON THE WINDS - Wallpaper - Jack Denst Designs
RESTING ROTIFERS - Pet shops - Florida Aqua Farms Inc.
RESTITUTION - Recording label - New View Publications, Inc.
RESTLESS - Apparel and accessories - Restless USA Inc.
RESTLESS - Floor coverings—carpet and rugs ☆ - Walter Carpet Mills
RESTLESS - Lenses—optical - Ditto Industries Inc.
RESTLESS - Recording label - Enigma Entertainment
RESTLESS HEART - Apparel—women's - Roland Kosser
RESTLITE - Eyeglasses - Art-Craft Optical Co.
RESTO - Furniture—wood ☆ - Flanders Industries Inc.
RESTO-CRETE - Waterproofing compounds - Western Waterproofing Co. Inc.
RESTOCRAT - Recliners - Ethan Allen, Inc.
RESTOL - Pharmaceutical preparations - Biosante Distributors Inc.
RESTON - Furniture ☆ - Keller Manufacturing Co.
RESTON LLOYD - Kitchen utensils—aluminum - Reston Lloyd Ltd.
RESTONIC - Mattresses - Restonic Inc.
RESTONIC MATTRESSES - Mattresses - Restonic Corp.
RESTOPHEN - Pharmaceutical preparations ☆ - P.J. Noyes Co., Inc.
RESTOR - Hair care products - Buty-Wave Products Co., Inc.
RESTOR - Milk—canned or powdered - Express Foods Co. Inc.
RESTOR-A-FINISH - Furniture polish and wax - Howard Products
RESTOR-A-FLOOR - Floor waxes - Sanitek Products Inc.
RESTOR-A-GLOSS - Cleaning preparations - W.W. Grainger, Inc.
RESTORA - Hair care products - Roux Laboratories, Inc.
RESTORATION - Computer software - Environmental Research Institute of Michigan
RESTORATION - Floor coverings - Applied Radiant Energy Corp.
RESTORATION - Siding—metal - Wolverine Technologies
RESTORATION DETAILS - Siding—insulating ☆ - Wolverine Technologies
RESTORATION PAVERS - Floor coverings—tile ☆ - Kepcor, Inc./SSI Tiles
RESTORATION PORTFOLIO - Siding—insulating - Wolverine Technologies
RESTORE - Cleaning preparations - Great Lakes Biochemical Co., Inc.
RESTORE - Dentifrices - Lifecore Biomedical, Inc.
RESTORE - Mattress pads - Bio Clinic Corp.
RESTORE - Paper—construction - NCR Corp.
RESTORE - Paper—writing - P.H. Glatfelter Co.
RESTORE - Pharmaceutical preparations - Inagra Co.
RESTORE - Skin care products - Elementals Skin Care, LLC
RESTORE - Sporting goods - Unique Sports Products Inc.
RESTORE 4 - Cleaning preparations - Sirius Products, Inc.
RESTORE PAC - Finishing agents - PortionPac Chemical Corp.
RESTORE THE EARTH - Detergents - Laurie J. Brown
RESTORE-X - Paints - Forrest Paint Co.
RESTORE YOUR WOOD FLOOR - Floor waxes ☆ - Klean-Strip
RESTORED BALANCE - Vitamins and nutritional supplements - Marine Biotherapies
RESTORIL - Pharmaceutical preparations - Sandoz Pharmaceuticals Corp.
RESTPLANT - Dental compounds - Imtec Corp.
RESTRAC ENTERPRISE - Computer software - Microtrac Systems, Inc.
RESTRAN - Pharmaceutical preparations ☆ - Jones Medical Industries, Inc. (Medical Div.)
RESTRICTED - Apparel—women's - Way to Go Sportswear, Inc.
RESTRICTED CALORIE FORMULA - Dog food - Iams Co.
RESTROSPECT - Furniture ☆ - Singer Furniture Co.
RESTRUCTURE - Shampoos - Care-Tech Laboratories Inc.
RESTSAFE - Pillows - Pacific Coast Feather Co.

☆ = Now out of production

RESTWELL - Apparel and accessories - Sleepwear Inc.

RESTWELL - Pet products - Flexi-Mat Corp.

RESU-RITER - Computer software ☆ - Cambridge Educational

RESUCT NET/SERVER SOFTWARE - Computer software - Dawning Technologies Inc.

RESULIN - Antibiotics - Schieffelin & Co. (Pharmaceutical Laboratories Div.)

RESULTANTE - Skin care products - Christian Dior Perfumes Corp.

RESULTS - Apparel and accessories ☆ - Edison Brothers Stores, Inc.

RESULTS - Frames–eyeglass - May Optical Co. Inc.

RESULTS - Skin care products - Revlon Consumer Products Corp.

RESUMAIL - Computer software - Opportunity Network, Inc.

RESUME - Notebooks and notepads - Riverside Paper Corp.

RESUME REVOLUTION - Computer software - Cambridge Educational

RESUMEMANAGER - Computer software - JWT Specialized Communications, Inc.

RESUMES & MORE - Computer software - Parsons Technology, Inc.

RESURFIX - Skin care products - Topix Pharmaceuticals, Inc.

RESURGE - Machine parts - Power Sentry, Inc.

RESURRECTION - Health care products - Life-Renewal Inc.

RESVERAMAX - Vitamins and nutritional supplements - International Health Products, Inc.

R.E.T. - Skin care products - Palm Beach Beauty Products

RETABLO - Nativities - La Casa De Carlo

RETACS - Publisher's imprints - Transamerica Corp.

RETAIL - Computer software - Seaport Software

RETAIL EXPRESS - Computer storage devices–magnetic - Advanced Cybernetics, Inc.

RETAIL LINK - Computer software - Wal-Mart Stores Inc.

RETAIL SOLUTION, THE - Computer software - Northwest Network Solutions, Inc.

RETAIN - Cosmetics - Ray Hayes Inc.

RETAIN - Dentifrices - Colgate-Palmolive Co.

RETAINER FRESH - Cleaning preparations - Orthodontic Care Corp.

RETAINING COMPOUND 609 - Adhesives and sealants - Loctite Corp.

RETAINING COMPOUND 620 - Adhesives and sealants - Loctite Corp.

RETAINING COMPOUND 635 - Adhesives and sealants - Loctite Corp.

RETAINING COMPOUND 640 - Adhesives and sealants - Loctite Corp.

RETAINING COMPOUND 642 - Adhesives and sealants - Loctite Corp.

RETAINING COMPOUND 675 - Adhesives and sealants - Loctite Corp.

RETAINING COMPOUND 680 - Adhesives and sealants - Loctite Corp.

RETAR - Electronic equipment - Apollo Audiovisual Div.

RETARD - Cleaning preparations–carpet and rug - Imperial Manufacturing Co. Inc.

RETARD-DOX - Pharmaceutical preparations - Rowpar Pharmaceuticals, Inc.

RETARD-X - Paints - Benjamin Moore & Co.

RETARDO - Paints - Benjamin Moore & Co.

RETCH-A-RAT TOMCAT - Toys ☆ - Those Characters from Cleveland, Inc.

RETCO - Thread - Threads USA Div.

RETCO - Waterproof outerwear ☆ - American Camper

RETE - Frames–eyeglass ☆ - Universal/Univis Inc.

RETEC - Electronics equipment - RTI Research Technology International

RETECTRON - Electronics equipment - RTI Research Technology International

RETENTION - Floor coverings–carpet and rugs - Burtco Enterprises Inc.

RETET - Pharmaceutical preparations ☆ - Solvay Pharmaceuticals Inc.

RETEX - Hair care products - Nutrine Ltd.

RETHMEYER - Coffee - Rethmeyer Coffee Co.

RETIBOL - Vitamins and nutritional supplements - Atletika Inc.

RETICULEX - Pharmaceutical preparations - Eli Lilly and Co.

RETICULOGEN - Pharmaceutical preparations - Eli Lilly and Co.

RETICULON - Fabrics–broadcloth - Chicopee

RETICULOSE - Pharmaceutical preparations - Advanced Viral Research Corp.

RETIN-A - Pharmaceutical preparations - Ortho Pharmaceutical Corp.

RETINA - Cameras - Eastman Kodak Co.

RETINA - Footwear - USA Retina Inc.

RETINAX - Lubricants - Shell Oil Co.

RETINETTE - Cameras - Eastman Kodak Co.

RETINOL - Sothys USA Inc.

RETINOL - Skin care products - Fanie International

RETINOL GLOW - Skin care products - Forever Young Inc.

RETINY A - Vitamins and nutritional supplements - Health Products Corp.

RETIRE! - Computer software - New World Software Inc.

RETIRE ASAP - Retirement-planning software - Calypso Software Corp.

RETIRE WITH $1 MILLION DOLLARS - Computer software - Elaine Zimmerman

RETIREMENT GROUP, THE - Consulting services - Retirement Group

RETIREMENT MATTERS - Advertising agencies - Massachusetts Mutual Life Insurance Co.

RETKI - Computer software - Liikkuva Systems International, Inc.

RETOLD CLASSIC NOVEL - Publisher's imprints - Perfection Learning Corp.

RETOLD TALES - Publisher's imprints - Perfection Learning Corp.

RETO'S RIG - Fishing lures - Fred Arbogast Co. Inc.

RETOUCH - Computer hardware - Carlton International Corp.

RETRAC - Floor coverings–carpet and rugs - Carter Carpets

RETRAC-DOR - Hardware - Hettich America L.P.

RETRACT-A-LEASH - Pet products ☆ - Johnson Pet-Dor Inc.

RETRACT-O-MATIC - Extension cords - Pacific Electricord Co.

RETRACT-O-VISORS - Visors - Hot Top Cap Co., Inc.

RETRACTA-BELT - Traffic and crowd control systems - Visiontran Corp.

RETRACTABLE - Knives–pocket - Allway Tools Inc.

RETRACTABLE - Shoes–athletic - Retractable, Inc.

RETRACTABLE LIP BRUSH - Cosmetics - Karlen Manufacturing, Inc.

RETRACTION - Pens - Pentech International Inc.

RETRACTO - Luggage - United States Luggage Corp.

RETRACTO - Pens - Pentech International Inc.

RETRACTOR - Shaving preparations ☆ - Schick/Wilkinson

RETRACTOR BOUNCE-FREE DARTS - Darts and dart games - Dart Mart Inc.

RETRAN - Transmissions–motor vehicle - General Motors Corp.

RETRAX - Medical equipment - Syringe Concepts Corp.

RETRE-GEL - Pharmaceutical preparations - Triton Consumer Products, Inc.

RETREAD - Toys - Tonka Corp.

RETREADS - Shoes - Benjamin Shir Inc.

RETRIEVA - Fabrics–polyester - Global Green, Inc.

RETRIEVE IT! - Computer programs - Claris Corp.

RETRIEVE-MC - Computer software - IMRS Operations Inc.

RETRIEVER - Computer software - Burns & McDonnell Waste Consultants, Inc.

RETRIEVER - Electronic equipment - ESM International Inc.

RETRIEVER - Electronics equipment - Isco Inc.

RETRIEVER - Pet food - Tractor Supply Co.

RETRIEVER PALETTE - Computer programs - Target Development

RETRIKE - Three-wheeled bicycle - Rebike, Inc.

RETRIX - Apparel and accessories - Coastal Entertainment, Inc.

RETRO - Apparel–women's - Nanwani International Ltd.

RETRO - Beverages - American Beverage Corp.

RETRO - Clocks ☆ - General Time Corp. (Westclox/Seth Thomas Div.)

RETRO - Dinnerware–glass - Arita Sales Co. Inc.

RETRO - Fabrics - Interface, Inc.

RETRO - Furniture - Pavilion/Sunburst Furniture

RETRO - Glass products - Durand International

RETRO - Pencils - Staedtler, Inc.

RETRO - Recording label - Jazz Composer's Orchestra Association Inc.

RETRO - Slacks–men's - Kalikow Bros. Inc.

RETRO - Sporting goods - Retrosports, Inc.

RETRO - Sporting goods - Sports Replay, Inc.

RETRO - Sunglasses - Style Eyes of California

RETRO - Video equipment - Draper Shade and Screen Co. Inc.

RETRO-ACTIVE - Apparel and accessories - Baron Group Ltd.

RETRO-CLAR - Water purification systems - Parkson Corp.

RETRO DAMASK - Wallpaper - Maya Romanoff Corp.

RETRO-FIT - Electrical equipment - Quick Cable Corp.

RETRO LEAGUE SPORT - Apparel and accessories - L & L Manufacturing Co.

RETRO LITE - Lighters–cigarette - Scripto-Tokai Corp.

RETRO-MATIC - Electronic equipment - Telex Communications, Inc.

RETRO PARTS - Musical instrument accessories - Kaman Music Corp.

RETRO PHONE - Telephones - Planned Technologies Ltd.

RETRO 0.5 - Pencils - Staedtler, Inc.

RETRO-R - Roofing materials - NCI Building Systems, Inc.

RETRO SPORTS - Sporting goods - Sports Replay, Inc.

RETRO-STOP - Brackets - Willard S. Norton

RETRO-TECH - Doors–metal - United Dominion Industries, Inc.

RETRO-TECH SYSTEM - Doors–metal - United Dominion Industries, Inc.

RETRO-TIE - Building materials–concrete - AA Wire Products Co.

RETRO-TREM - Guitars - Allparts

RETRO VINTAGE FOOTBALL - Soccer equipment - Classico Sports USA

RETROACTIVE - Recording label - Ripete Music Group

RETROFIT - Sporting goods - Allsop, Inc.

RETROFLEX SYSTEM - Footwear - United States Shoe Corp.

RETROFOCUS - Lenses–photographic ☆ - Edixa Camera Co.

RETROGLO - Yarn - Metlon Corp.

RETROGRADE - Apparel and accessories - Marble Sportswear, Inc.

RETROGUARD - Valves - Quest Medical Inc.

RETROKIT - Clutches–industrial - Logan Clutch Corp.

☆ = Now out of production

RETROKIT - Lighting fixtures ☆ - Hubbell Lighting, Inc. (Lighting Div.)
RETRONEU - Giftware - Excel Cutlery Inc.
RETROPAK - Lighting fixtures - Hubbell Lighting, Inc. (Lighting Div.)
RETROPHANE - Electrical equipment - Rhone-Poulenc Inc.
RETROSET - Doors—metal - United Dominion Industries, Inc.
RETROSPEC - Safety products - Willson/Dalloz Safety
RETROSPECT - Apparel and accessories - Monaco Apparel Inc.
RETROSPECT VIII - Wallcoverings ☆ - Louis W. Bowen
RETROSPECTIVES: ANNE - Furniture ☆ - Mersman Furniture Co.
RETROSPECTIVES: ELIZABETH - Furniture ☆ - Mersman Furniture Co.
RETROSPECTIVES: VICTORIA - Furniture ☆ - Mersman Furniture Co.
RETROTECH - Automotive parts and accessories - Stephen Demosthenes
RETROVIR - Pharmaceutical preparations - Burroughs Wellcome Co.
RETROVIVAL - Apparel and accessories - Shannon Dockery Bakos
RETROWEAR - Dresses—women's - Fritzi California
RETT - Ophthalmic goods - Styl-Rite Optical Manufacturing Co., Inc.
RETTERER - Tools—hand-operated - Claridon Tool & Die, Inc.
RETURN OF THE INVADERS - Video games - Taito America Corp.
RETURN OF THE JEDI - Kites ☆ - Spectra Star Kites
RETURN OF THE JEDI - Toys - Lucasfilm Ltd.
RETURN OF THE NATIVE - Stationery - Jill Ann Maeder
RETURN OF THE WITCH LORD - Games - Hasbro, Inc.
RETURN OF WERDNA - Computer software - Sir-Tech Software, Inc.
RETURN TO ATLANTIS - Computer software - Electronic Arts Inc.
RETURN TO ELEGANCE - Floor coverings—carpet and rugs - Lees Carpets
RETURN TO ELEGANCE - Wallpaper - Sterling Prints
RETURN TO NATURE - Apparel and accessories - Miss Erika, Inc.
RETURN TO THE MOON - Computer software - Lunacorp, Inc. (DBA)
RETURN TO THE MOON - Computer storage devices—optical - Lunar Eclipse Software
RETURN TO ZORK - Video games - Activision, Inc.
RETURNELOPE - Envelopes - Mail-Well Envelope
RETURNET - Computer software - Jenware, Inc.
RETZLAFF RULER - Surgical instruments - Alcon Laboratories, Inc.
REUBENISSIMO - Sandwiches—prepackaged ☆ - Swissrose International Inc.
REUBENS - Flowers, plants, and seeds - Jacklin Seed
REUBENS - Meats—luncheon - Dairy Fresh Products Co.
REUGE - Music boxes ☆ - Alice Sturzinger Ltd.
REUMA-RUB - Pharmaceutical preparations ☆ - Durham's Products Co.
REUMALATE - Pharmaceutical preparations ☆ - U.S. Ethicals Inc.
REUMASAN OLYMPIC PLUS - Pharmaceutical preparations - Vartex Pharmaceuticals Inc.
REUMATON - Pharmaceutical preparations - Wampole Laboratories Div.
REUNION - Eyeglasses - Art-Craft Optical Co.
REUNION - Floor coverings - Bruce Hardwood Floors
REUNION - Furniture ☆ - Tell City Chair Co.
REUNION - Orthopedic products - Smith & Nephew Richards, Inc.
REUNION - Recording label - Word, Inc.
REUNION BLUES - Leather goods - Reunion Blues Corp.
REUNION FEATURE STRIPS - Floor coverings - Bruce Hardwood Floors
REUNION FOODS - Seasonings - Ken Young Food Distributors, Inc.
REUP - Recording label - Third Story Recording Inc.
REUSABLE DISPOSABLE - Dishes—plastic - Solo Cup Co.
REUSABLE GROCERY BAG, THE - Bags—canvas - SeaGroup Marketing Co.
REUSABLE LUNCH BOX SYSTEM - Lunch boxes - Thermos Co.
REUSCH - Apparel and accessories - Hart Ski Manufacturing Co.
REUSCHE COLORS - Dinnerware—glass - Reusche & Co.
REUSE-A-FAX - Paper - Multicomp, Inc.
REUSEABLES - Cooking equipment—household - Nordic Ware
REUSSNER COLLECTION - Statuary - Actuelle Products Inc.
REUTER - Soap - Lanman & Kemp-Barclay & Co. Inc.
REUTER BARRY - Soap - Lanman & Kemp-Barclay & Co. Inc.
REUTER MANUFACTURING - Centrifuges—industrial - Green Isle Environmental Services, Inc.
REUZIT - Office supplies - Effron Sales
REV - Beverages—carbonated - Eon Foods America, Inc.
REV - Paints ☆ - Valspar Corp.
REV - Vitamins and nutritional supplements - Enrich International, Inc.
REV-ALERT - Health care products - Tishcon Corp.
REV DUST - Chemical preparations - Milwhite, Inc.
REV-GLOW - Paints ☆ - Valspar Corp.
REV-MASONRY - Paints ☆ - Valspar Corp.
REV 'N ROCKET - Toys - Mattel, Inc.
REV PAD - Sporting goods - Cycle Products Co.
REV-SATIN - Paints ☆ - Valspar Corp.
REV-SEAL - Paints ☆ - Valspar Corp.

REV-SHIELD - Paints ☆ - Valspar Corp.
REV-TAR - Tar-based roof cements - Pioneer Manufacturing Co.
REV-UP - Computer storage devices ☆ - MDY Advanced Technologies, Inc.
REV UP - Hair coloring preparations - Revlon Consumer Products Corp.
REV X - Video games - Midway Manufacturing Co.
REVA - Ophthalmic goods ☆ - Luxottica
REVA - Rackets—racquetball - Ektelon
REVA TCD TRAFFIC CONTROL DEVICES - Lighting equipment - Reva Plastics Corp.
REVAC - Garden equipment - Roto-Hoe Co.
REVAL - Cigarettes - G.A. Georgopulo & Co. Inc.
REVAN - Musical instruments - J.M. Sahlein Music Co. Inc.
REVASC - Pharmaceutical preparations - Ciba-Geigy Corp.
REVCO - Novelty items - Revco D.S., Inc.
REVE - Lipsticks - Lancome
REVEAL - Apparel—women's ☆ - Berlei USA
REVEAL - Computer peripheral equipment - Reveal Computer Products, Inc.
REVEAL - Dental equipment - Welch Allyn, Inc.
REVEAL - Leak-detection systems - UVP Inc.
REVEAL - Tables—wood - Fixtures Furniture
REVEAL - Tape—adhesive - Kendall Co.
REVEAL - Window coverings - Duratex Inc.
REVEILLE - Floor coverings—carpet and rugs - Coronet Carpets Inc.
REVEILLE - Lime and gypsum ☆ - AMPEL Corp.
REVEILLON - Wallcoverings - Laura Ashley
REVEINA - Tiles—ceramic - Kowa Texas Inc.
REVEL - Beverages—carbonated - Ginger's Kitchen, LLC
REVEL - Floor coverings—carpet and rugs - Masterpiece Finishing Co.
REVEL - Floor coverings—carpet and rugs ☆ - Patcraft Mills Inc.
REVEL - Frames—picture ☆ - Gallery Revel
REVELATION - Apparel stores—lingerie - Goddess Bra
REVELATION - Dentifrices - Alvin Last Inc.
REVELATION - Fireplace doors and screens ☆ - Thomas Industries Inc.
REVELATION - Floor coverings—carpet and rugs - Mohawk Carpet Corp.
REVELATION - Floor coverings—carpet and rugs ☆ - Galaxy Carpet Mills Inc.
REVELATION - Guitars - HSS Inc.
REVELATION - Health care products - REVELATION LLC
REVELATION - Musical instrument accessories ☆ - Herco Products
REVELATION - Recording label - Survivor Records/Dream Makers Inc.
REVELATION - Sporting goods - Western Auto Supply Co.
REVELATION - Tobacco products - House of Windsor Inc.
REVELATION - Vinegar - H.N. Crosby Co.
REVELATION - Window shades - Draper Shade and Screen Co. Inc.
REVELATIONS - Wallpaper - Regency Mills Inc.
REVELATIONS - Wallpaper ☆ - Rigo Wallcoverings Inc.
REVELATOR - Fishing lures ☆ - Church Tackle Co.
REVELEE - Beverages—carbonated - Ginger's Kitchen, LLC
REVELL - Toys—models - Revell-Monogram, Inc.
REVELL BOOKS - Publisher's imprints - Fleming H. Revell Co.
REVELL BOOKS - Publisher's imprints ☆ - Zondervan Publishing House
REVELLE - Drums—musical instruments - Pacific Music Supply Co.
REVELRY - Fabrics - Greenwood Mills Inc.
REV'EM UP RACERS - Toys—automobiles - Buddy L Inc.
REVENESCENCE - Skin care products - Charles of the Ritz Group Ltd.
REVENGE - Apparel and accessories - Pier Connection
REVENGE - Athletic shoes - Converse Inc.
REVENGE - Cleaning preparations - Roxide International, Inc.
REVENGE - Eyeglasses - Ken Wilson
REVENGE - Frames—eyeglass ☆ - Universal/Univis Inc.
REVENGE - Powerboat ☆ - Boston Whaler, Inc.
REVENGE - Sunglasses - Gatorz Sport Optiks
REVENGE CARDS - Greeting cards - Palm Projects Inc.
REVENGE CUDDY - Powerboat ☆ - Boston Whaler, Inc.
REVENGE DEEP-FREEZE - Irons—electric - Roxide International, Inc.
REVENGE EXTERMINATORS - Irons—electric - Roxide International, Inc.
REVENGE MOLE & GOPHER BOIT - Traps—animal - Roxide International, Inc.
REVENGE MOLE TRAPS - Traps—animal - Roxide International, Inc.
REVENGE OF DOK - Video games - Taito America Corp.
REVENGE OF DRANCON - Games - Sega of America, Inc.
REVENGE OF THE PHARAOH - Games - Mattel, Inc.
REVENGE - RODENT SMOKE BOMBS - Traps—animal - Roxide International, Inc.
REVENGE SHIRTMAKERS - Apparel and accessories ☆ - Pier Connection
REVENGER - Alarm systems—burglar - Directed Electronics, Inc.
REVENGER - Fishing lures - Patriot Lure Manufacturing

☆ = Now out of production

REVENGER LT - Tires–automobile - Jetzon/Telstar Tire
REVENGER METRIC HR - Tires–automobile ✩ - Jetzon/Telstar Tire
REVENGER RV - Tires - Jetzon/Telstar Tire
REVENGER SR - Tires–automobile - Jetzon/Telstar Tire
REVENGER-VR - Tires–automobile - Jetzon/Telstar Tire
REVENNA - Giftware ✩ - Gorham Inc.
REVENT - Computer software - Commsoft
REVENUE - Frames–eyeglass - Zylo Ware Corp.
REVENUEWATCH - Computer software - MCIS, Inc.
REVERE - Bicycles - Columbia Manufacturing Inc.
REVERE - Cutlery ✩ - Regent Sheffield, Ltd.
REVERE - Dishes–china ✩ - WMF/USA
REVERE - Fireplace equipment - Thermo-Rite Manufacturing Co.
REVERE - Food products ✩ - Associated Food Stores Inc.
REVERE - Globes ✩ - Replogle Globes Inc.
REVERE - Ice making machinery - Nicola, Gudbranson, and Cooper
REVERE - Musical instrument accessories - Multivox/Sorkin Music Co. Inc.
REVERE - Musical instruments - Entertainment Music Marketing Corp.
REVERE - Ophthalmic goods - Foremost Optical Products
REVERE - Pet products - Revere Manufacturing
REVERE - Recording label - Revere Records
REVERE - Rubber–molded - Ring King Visibles, Inc.
REVERE - Siding–metal - Alcan Aluminum Corp. Alcan Building Products Div.
REVERE - Sinks - Revere Sink Corp.
REVERE - Tape–adhesive - Plymouth Rubber Co., Inc.
REVERE - Trailers–travel - Coachmen Industries, Inc.
REVERE - Trailers–travel ✩ - Shasta Industries Inc.
REVERE - Veterinary pharmaceutical preparations - Petco Animal Supplies, Inc.
REVERE BRAND - Bakery products - G & S Metal Products Co., Inc.
REVERE NON-STICK SPECTRUM - Cooking utensils–aluminum - Revere Ware Corp.
REVERE WARE - Cooking utensils–aluminum - Revere Ware Corp.
REVERE WARE - Metal cleaners and polishes - Copper Clad Products Inc.
REVERE WARE GALAXY - Cooking utensils–aluminum ✩ - Revere Ware Corp.
REVERE WARE NEPTUNE - Cooking utensils–aluminum ✩ - Revere Ware Corp.
REVEREND HORTON HEAT - Apparel and accessories - Jim Heath
REVERIE - Floor coverings–carpet and rugs - Sweetwater Carpet Corp.
REVERIE - Frames–eyeglass - Zylo Ware Corp.
REVERIE - Luggage - Airway Industries, Inc.
REVERIE - Tableware–china - Lenox, Inc.
REVERIES - Toilets–enameled - Kohler Co.
REVERS-A-CORE - Air conditioning equipment - Metal Industries Inc.
REVERS-A-FAN - Fans–electric - Vegetable Factory, Inc. (Sunbeam Structures Div.)
REVERS-A-MAT - Mat boards - Callen Photo Mount Corp.
REVERSA - Pharmaceutical preparations - Tri Hawk Corp.
REVERSA-GARB - Uniforms–tailored - Angelica Uniform Group
REVERSAFLOW - Pet products - Aquatronics-Filtronics
REVERSALATED - Doors–metal - Insulated Structures, Inc.
REVERSAMAT - Mats - Interstate Mat & Rubber
REVERSATILE - Games ✩ - Learning Games Inc.
REVERSE 911 - Computer hardware - Unique Solutions, Inc.
REVERSE-A-CLEAN - Paint sprayers - Graco Inc.
REVERSE-A-LOG - Heating equipment - Shenandoah Manufacturing Co., Inc.
REVERSE-A-MATIC-SPLIT - Heat pumps - Heat Controller Inc.
REVERSE-A-SHELF - Hardware - National Lock Cabinet Hardware
REVERSE-A-SKETCH - Toys - Ohio Art Co.
REVERSE-A-SKETCH - Toys - Allen D. West
REVERSE BRAKE CASTERS - Office supplies - Master Caster Co.
REVERSE COMPLEX AM - Skin care products - Physicians Select Inc.
REVERSE EM - Puzzles - Parris Manufacturing Co.
REVERSE GRAIN - Apparel–athletic - Can Am Textiles Inc.
REVERSE JAM - Toy action figures - Tonka Corp.
REVERSE PENSION PLAN - Publisher's imprints - RDU Publications
REVERSE SUNBURST PATTERN - Rackets–racquetball - Spalding & Evenflo Companies, Inc.
REVERSE THE CURSE - Apparel and accessories - Howard Shear
REVERSE WEAVE - Apparel and accessories - Champion Products Inc.
REVERSIBLE - Cabinets - Nutone Inc.
REVERSIBLE - Dryers–hair ✩ - Sunbeam-Oster Household Products
REVERSIBLE URSULA - Games - Franklin Merchandising Co.
REVERSIBLES - Toys–automobiles - Lewis Galoob Toys, Inc.
REVERSION - Skin care products - James S. Beckman, Jr.

REVERSION RESISTANT - Hair care products - Alberto-Culver Co.
REVERSO - Watches - Jaeger-Le Coultre SA
REVERSOL - Pharmaceutical preparations - Organon Inc.
REVERZIPLES - Dolls - Mattel, Inc.
REVEX - Pharmaceutical preparations - Ohmeda Pharmaceutical Products Division Inc.
REVFORM 360 - Hardware - Predator Industries, Inc.
REVIA - Pharmaceutical preparations - Dupont Merck Pharmaceutical Co.
REVIEW - Computer software - General Electric Co.
REVIEW AND EXPOSITOR - Publisher's imprints - Review and Expositor, Inc.
REVIEW BY BAXTER - Apparel and accessories - Baxter International, Ltd.
REVIEWARE - Computer software - Princeton Review Management Corp.
REVIEWER - Eyeglasses - Martin-Copeland Eyewear Corp.
REVILLE - Shaving preparations - Jean Alexander Cosmetics, Inc.
REVILLON - Sunglasses - L'Amy Inc.
REVIS - Tape recorders - Compco Photographic/Goldberg Bros.
REVISE - Hair care products - Paul Mazzotta Inc.
REVISIONS - Apparel and accessories - Leo Burnett Co. Worldwide Inc.
REVISIONS - Eyeglasses - Cable Car Eyeware
REVISIONS - Office furniture ✩ - La-Z-Boy Chair Co.
REVISO - Computer software - Informative Graphics Corp.
REVITA - Skin care products - Chasalco Inc.
REVITAE - Skin care products - Helga Van Dyke Skin Care
REVITAL EYES - Pharmaceutical preparations - American Hygienic Laboratories Inc.
REVITAL EYES - Skin care products - Fanie International
REVITAL ICE - Pharmaceutical preparations - Clear Mountain Products, Inc.
REVITALEX - Hair care products - Luster Products, Inc.
REVITALISANT CONCENTRE - Skin care products - Ella Bache Inc.
REVITALIZER - Cleaning preparations - CMC Inc.
REVITALIZER - Coatings - APT Advanced Polymer Technology Corp.
REVITALIZER - Hair care products - Cheveux Inc.
REVITALIZER - Health care products ✩ - Sunrise Medical (Respiratory Products Division)
REVITALIZER - Vitamins and nutritional supplements - Mayor Pharmaceutical Laboratories
REVITALIZER SOFT-START - Health care products ✩ - Sunrise Medical (Respiratory Products Division)
REVITALIZING - Cosmetics - Maybelline Co.
REVITALIZING FACE COLLECTION - Cosmetics - Maybelline Co.
REVITALIZING FOOTBATH - Skin care products - Schering-Plough Healthcare Products
REVITALIZING LIP INDULGENCE - Cosmetics - Maybelline Co.
REVIVAL - Doors - ODL, Inc.
REVIVAL - Faucets - Kohler Co.
REVIVAL - Wallpaper - The Creative Edge, Inc.
REVIVAL - Window frames - Georgia-Pacific Corp.
REVIVALS - Furniture - Vincent J. Grechen, Jr.
REVIVANAIL - Cosmetics - European Touch Co.
REVIVANAIL + COLOR - Cosmetics - European Touch Co.
REVIVASOME - Skin care products - Reviva Laboratories
REVIVE - Cleaning preparations - Bemis Co. Inc.
REVIVE - Cleaning preparations ✩ - Acton Technologies Inc.
REVIVE - Cleaning preparations ✩ - D.I.Y. Products
REVIVE - Hair care products - Helene Curtis Industries Inc.
REVIVE - Hair care products - Rescue Marketing Group
REVIVE - Leather tanning and finishing - Chicago Sole Leather Distributors Inc.
REVIVE - Napkins–paper - Shaw's Supermarkets, Inc.
REVIVE - Shoe polish - Wolverine World Wide, Inc.
REVIVEX - Hair care products - Helene Curtis Industries Inc.
REVIVIT - See **DOBRE PROTEAN**
REVIVO - Hair care products - Nino Originals
REVIVO - Health care products ✩ - Woltra Corp.
REVIVOR - Hair care products - Hairtech International Inc.
REVLON - Hair care products - Revlon General Wig Manufacturers, Inc.
REVLON - Skin care products - Revlon Consumer Products Corp.
REVLON ALTERNATIVE HAIR - Wigs - Revlon General Wig Manufacturers, Inc.
REVLON DIRECTIONS - Wigs - Revlon General Wig Manufacturers, Inc.
REVLON HAIR MAGIC - Wigs - Revlon General Wig Manufacturers, Inc.
REVLON INSPIRATIONS - Wigs - Revlon General Wig Manufacturers, Inc.
REVLON LENGTHWISE - Cosmetics - Revlon Consumer Products Corp.
REVLON LUSTERIZER - Hair care products - Revlon Consumer Products Corp.
REVLON QUICKCLIP - Wigs - Revlon General Wig Manufacturers, Inc.
REVLON REFLECTIONS - Wigs - Revlon General Wig Manufacturers, Inc.

✩ = Now out of production

REVLON REFLECTIONS PLUS - Wigs - Revlon General Wig Manufacturers, Inc.

REVLON RESULTS - Skin care products - Revlon Consumer Products Corp.

REVLON SHADINGS - Hair coloring preparations - Revlon Consumer Products Corp.

REVLON SKIN THERAPY - Skin care products - Revlon Consumer Products Corp.

REVLON STRONG COLOR - Nail care products - Revlon Consumer Products Corp.

REVMAN - Ceramic products - Revman Industries, Inc.

REVO - Jackets - Revo, Inc.

REVO - Medical supplies - Linvatec Corp.

REVO - Performance sunglasses - Revo Sunglasses Inc.

REVO-FILE - File folders ☆ - Mosler Inc.

REVOLT ON ANTARES - Games ☆ - Tsr, Inc.

REVOLUTION - Amplifiers–musical instrument - Peavey Electronics Corp.

REVOLUTION - Boilers–gas - Burnham Corp.

REVOLUTION - Colognes - Brandy Harvest

REVOLUTION - Computer peripheral equipment - Amistar Corp.

REVOLUTION - Counter tops–plastic - Formica Corp.

REVOLUTION - Darts and dart games - Dart Mart Inc.

REVOLUTION - Flashlights - Streamlight, Inc.

REVOLUTION - Flowers, plants, and seeds - Williams Lawn Seed, Inc.

REVOLUTION - Hair care products - Helene Curtis Industries Inc.

REVOLUTION - Recording label - Ichiban Records, Inc.

REVOLUTION - Recording label - Laffitte Entertainment Division, Inc.

REVOLUTION - Science kits - Carlisle Corp.

REVOLUTION - Solar energy collectors - Fafco Inc.

REVOLUTION '76 - Computer peripheral equipment - Compton's NewMedia

REVOLUTION 200 - Bicycles ☆ - Huffy Corp.

REVOLUTION BY VOIT - Balls - Voit Corp.

REVOLUTION X - Toys - Midway Manufacturing Co.

REVOLUTIONARY - Lenses–optical - Ditto Industries Inc.

REVOLUTIONARY RASPBERRY - Water–bottled or canned - Sparkling American

REVOLUTIONARY RECORDS - Apparel - Eddie Laster

REVOLVE-R - Prefabricated buildings–metal - Universal Building Concepts, Inc.

REVOLVER - Audio speakers - Southern Audio Services Inc.

REVOLVER - Motor vehicles–trucks - Capitol Tool and Die Co.

REVOLVER - Office supplies - Bates Manufacturing Co.

REVOLVER - Recording label - Red Horse Productions/Revolver Records

REVOLVER - Toys - Mattel, Inc.

REVOLVER, THE - Hair care products - Helene Curtis Industries Inc.

REVOLVING WORLD 7 - Games ☆ - Pal Productions Inc.

REVOLVO - Optical services ☆ - Carpenter Co.

REVONAH - Recording label - Revonah Records

REVS - Pharmaceutical preparations ☆ - Vitarine Pharmaceuticals Inc.

REVTECH - Motor vehicle parts and accessories - Custom Chrome, Inc.

REVTECH 2 - Motorcycle parts and accessories - Custom Chrome, Inc.

REVUE - Ditto Industries Inc.

REVUE - Glassware–household - Oneida Ltd.

REVUE - Paper–writing - Monadnock Paper Mills Inc.

REVUE PC 100 - Paper–writing - Monadnock Paper Mills Inc.

REWARD - Dog food - Heinz Pet Products Co.

REWARD - Eyeglasses - Art-Craft Optical Co.

REWARD - Floor coverings–carpet and rugs - Barrett Carpet Mills Inc.

REWARD - Fruits and vegetables - Sunland Packing House Co.

REWARD - Paints ☆ - American Art Clay Co. Inc.

REWARD - Publisher's imprints - Prentice-Hall, Inc.

REWARD MASK - Paints–artists' - American Art Clay Co. Inc.

REWARD POCKET - Tobacco - American Tobacco Co.

REWARD SUPERPREMIUM - Dog food - Heinz Pet Products Co.

REWARDING - Floor coverings–carpet and rugs - Mattel Carpet & Rug Inc.

REWARDS - Belts–apparel - Humphrey's Inc.

REWATER - Irrigation equipment - Rewater Systems, Inc.

REWIND - Apparel and accessories - Joel Auerbach

REWINDS - Paper–gift wrap - Paper Factory of Wisconsin, Inc.

REWIPAC - Packaging–paper - Rewipac Holding Inc.

REWORD - Computer software - Expert Designware, Inc.

REWORD - Games - Kopptronix Co.

REWRITE - Paper ☆ - Rite-Made Paper Converters Inc.

REX - Automotive parts and accessories - Stant Corp.

REX - Bicycles - Columbia Manufacturing Inc.

REX - Daters and numberers - Consolidated Stamp Manufacturing Co. Inc.

REX - Dog food - Specialty Feeds Inc.

REX - Fishing lures - Weezel Bait Co.

REX - Food products - Bar S Food Co. Inc.

REX - Food products - Cudahy Co.

REX - Hair care products - Major/Advance International

REX - Hair care products - William Marvy Co., Inc.

REX - Machine parts - Rex Gauge Co., Inc.

REX - Machine parts - Rexnord Corp.

REX - Meat products–poultry - Hubbard Milling Co.

REX - Musical instruments ☆ - Fred Gretsch Enterprises

REX - Pins - American Pin & Fastener Corp.

REX - Pins–straight - Eliscu & Co. Inc.

REX - Seafood products–fresh or frozen ☆ - King Oscar Inc.

REX - Sporting goods - Exel Marketing Inc.

REX - Thread - Premier Thread Co.

REX - Tiles–ceramic - Federal Tile Imports Inc.

REX - Tiles–terrazzo - Imperial Tile and Marble Corp.

REX - Twine - John Rauschenberger Co.

REX - Veterinary pharmaceutical preparations - Viobin U.S.A.

REX - Vinegar ☆ - Rex Vinegar Co.

REX-A-HIST - Pharmaceutical preparations - C.S. Ruckstuhl Co. Inc.

REX-A-VIM - Pharmaceutical preparations - C.S. Ruckstuhl Co. Inc.

REX-AIR BAIT AERATORS - Aquarium accessories - Rex-Air, Inc.

REX & COMPANY - Apparel–children's - Spencer's Inc.

REX & COMPANY - Apparel–children's - Spencer's Inc. of Mount Airy, North Carolina

REX EDGE - Computer software - GE Capital Mortgage Services, Inc.

REX EME CREAM - Skin care products - Brun Laboratories

REX-ESTRIN - Pharmaceutical preparations ☆ - Rex Research Laboratories

REX GOLDEN NUGGETS - Dog food - Specialty Feeds Inc.

REX LESTER - Apparel–women's - NUB, Inc.

REX MAGRELINK - Couplings - Rexnord Corp.

REX MARK-IT - Map tacks - American Pin & Fastener Corp.

REX OMEGA - Couplings - Rexnord Corp.

REX-ROYAL - Accordions - Fred Gretsch Enterprises

REX ROYALE - Vegetables–canned - Reich Mushrooms Inc.

REX TECHT - Apparel and accessories - Front Corp.

REX-TON - Denture cleaners ☆ - Gena Laboratories Inc.

REXA - Ophthalmic goods ☆ - Luxottica

REXADAN - Health care products - Revlon Consumer Products Corp.

REXAIR - Vacuum cleaners and accessories - Rexair Manufacturing Inc.

REXALAC - Pharmaceutical preparations - Rex Research Laboratories

REXALL - Pharmaceutical preparations - Rexall Nutritional Products Inc.

REXALL MANAGED CARE - Pharmaceutical preparations - Rexall Sundown, Inc.

REXALL SHOWCASE INTERNATIONAL - Vitamins and nutritional supplements - Rexall Sundown, Inc.

REXATOL - Pharmaceutical preparations ☆ - Rex Research Laboratories

REXCILLIN - Pharmaceutical preparations - C.S. Ruckstuhl Co. Inc.

REXCOAT - Plastics–laminated - Rexam Graphics Inc.

REXCRAFT - Bugles - Buglecraft Inc.

REXEL - Staples - ACCO USA, Inc.

REXELL - Resins–polyethylene - Rexene Corp.

REXENAMINE - Pharmaceutical preparations ☆ - Rex Research Laboratories

REXFORD - Leather goods - Ricardo Beverly Hills

REXHAM PRESENTATION - Paper–coated - Rexham Graphics Inc.

REXIGEN - Prescription drug ☆ - Ion Laboratories Inc.

REXIUS - Recording label - Sunny Day Productions Inc.

REXOCAPS - Pharmaceutical preparations ☆ - Rex Research Laboratories

REXOLATE - Pharmaceutical preparations - Hyrex Pharmaceuticals

REXON - Computer hardware - Wangtek Inc.

REXONE - Pharmaceutical preparations ☆ - Pacific Mineral Industries

REXPOINT - Floor coverings–carpet and rugs - Karastan-Bigelow Inc.

REXTAB - Shingles–asphalt or tar ☆ - Flintkote Co.

REXTAB - Shingles–asphalt or tar ☆ - GS Roofing Products Co.

REXTON - Hearing aids - Rexton Inc.

REXWELL - Aquarium accessories - Rex-Air, Inc.

REXWRITER - Office machines ☆ - Alpha Microsystems

REY - Ophthalmic goods - Swank Optical

REY - Tools–jewelers - Swest Inc.

REY DEL MUNDO - Cigars ☆ - Danby-Palicio

REY DEL NORTE - Fish–canned or cured - Corte & Co.

REY WEST - Cigars - G.W. Van Slyke & Horton

REYBIER - Cheese - Arthur Schuman Inc.

REYBURN - Labels–paper - Printed Systems

REYMAG - Wire - Reynolds Metals Co.

REYMONDON - Window shades - Metro Mills Inc.

REYMOND'S - Bakery products - SB Royalty Co. Inc.
REYMONT - Frames–eyeglass ☆ - Universal/Univis Inc.
REYNAC - Beverages–alcohol - Peartree Imports Inc.
REYNAL & CO. - Publisher's imprints ☆ - William Morrow and Co. Inc.
REYNEA BLACK & WHITE - Teas - Southern Tea Co.
REYNELLE - Yarn ☆ - JCA, Inc.
REYNO - Cigarettes - R.J. Reynolds Tobacco Co.
REYNOGUARD - Gutters–metal - Reynolds Metals Co.
REYNOLDS - Barbecue sauce - Reynolds Sugar Bush Inc.
REYNOLDS - Dishes–earthenware ☆ - Royal China & Porcelain Companies Inc.
REYNOLDS - Hardware - Blaine Window Hardware Inc.
REYNOLDS - Hats - Paramount Headwear, Inc.
REYNOLDS - Hobby kits - JCA, Inc.
REYNOLDS - Tires - Reynolds Tire and Rubber Corp.
REYNOLDS - Windows–storm - Reynolds Metals Co.
REYNOLDS AMERICAN CLASSIC - Vinyl siding - Reynolds Metals Co.
REYNOLDS & REYNOLDS - Paper - Reynolds and Reynolds Co.
REYNOLDS COMBINE - Water treating compounds - Reynolds Water Conditioning Co.
REYNOLDS NATURAL LEAF - Tobacco products - R.J. Reynolds Tobacco Co.
REYNOLDS SUN CURED - Cigarettes - R.J. Reynolds Tobacco Co.
REYNOLDS WRAP - Foil–aluminum - Reynolds Metals Co.
REYNOLITE - Aluminum compounds - Reynolds Metals Co.
REZ - Adhesives and sealants - PPG Industries, Inc.
REZ - Paints - PPG Architectural Finishes, Inc.
REZ-CAST - Mats - Rez-Tech Industrial Services
REZAMID - Skin care products - Summers Laboratories Inc.
REZAYEH - Food products - Nicola International, Inc.
REZI-WAX - Floor waxes - Red Spot Paint & Varnish Co., Inc.
REZIDE - Pharmaceutical preparations ☆ - Edwards Pharmaceuticals, Inc.
REZISTANCE, THE - T-shirts - Kathryn H. Kendrick
REZISTOR - Saw blades - Sandvik Saws & Tools
REZOOM - Vitamins and nutritional supplements - Shaperite Concepts, Ltd.
REZROK - Building materials–concrete - Ellisor & Associates Inc.
REZTEMP - Wood products - Georgia-Pacific Corp.
REZTORE - Plastics–laminated - Desco Industries Inc.
REZULT - Herbicides - BASF Corp.
REZUMAR - Fish–canned or cured - Joseph Caragol Inc.
REZWOOD - Adhesives and sealants - Imperial Adhesives Inc.
R.F. - Food products - Beatrice Cos. Inc.
RF - Screws - Rocknel Fastener, Inc.
RF - Transceivers - Ace Antenna Co.
RF-AUDIENCE! - Communications equipment - Motorola, Inc. (Land Mobile Products Sector)
RF-CONDUCTOR! - Communications equipment - Motorola, Inc. (Land Mobile Products Sector)
RF MICRO DEVICES - Electronic equipment - RF Micro Devices, Inc.
RF MODIFICATION - Flutes - Raymond Fabrizio
RF PASSPORT - Communications equipment - Palomar Technologies Corp.
RF RANGE FURNITURE - Furniture - Range Furniture, Inc.
RF VALVE - Valves - RF Technologies, Inc.
R.F.C. - Fruits and vegetables - Regal Fruit Cooperative
RFC - Fruits–frozen ☆ - Ranson Fruit Co. Inc.
RFI - Insulating materials - Recycled Fibre Industries, Inc.
RFMS - Computer software - RFMS Inc.
RFS - Computer peripheral equipment - Radio Frequency Systems, Inc.
RFS - Computer software - Information Retrieval Companies Inc.
RFS - Jewelry - R.F. Simmons Co.
RFS 2035 - Electronic equipment - Eastman Kodak Co.
RFT - Vinyl - Superior American Plastics Co.
RFX - Cable connectors - Amphenol Corp.
RG - Jewelry - Ruben's Jewelry Manufacturing
RG - Plaster - W.R. Grace & Co.
RG-1 - Pliers ☆ - ACCO USA, Inc.
R.G. DUN - Cigars - National Cigar Corp.
RG NEW YORK - Apparel–women's - Russ Togs Inc.
R.G. RAY - Metal clamps - R.G. Ray Corp.
RGA - Leather goods - RGA Accessories Inc.
RGA CALROSE - Rice - Rice Growers of California
RGB RECORDS - Recording label - Hearts of Space Inc.
RGB/VIDEOLINK - Computer peripheral equipment - RGB Spectrum
RGC - Jewelry - Ridco Inc.
RGF HOME PURE - Air purification systems - RGF 03 Systems, Inc.
RGI - Jewelry - Ru-Gem International Corp.

RGM - Pocket watches - Roland Murphy
RGS - Apparel–women's - Russ Togs Inc.
RGS - Computer software - National Council on Compensation Insurance, Inc.
RG'S RG'S - Meat products - Huisken Meat Center, Inc.
RGVS - Jewelry - Richard Glatter, Inc.
R.H. - Cosmetics - RH Cosmetics Corp.
RH - Fans–exhaust - Rahn Industries, Inc.
RH - Men's apparel - R. Hanauer
R.H. FORSCHNER - Cutlery - Forschner Group Inc.
R.H. FORSCHNER - Cutlery - Swiss Army Brands, Ltd.
RHAGS INTERNATIONALE - Shirts - Rhags Internationale
RHANE - Audio equipment - Saul Mineroff Electronics Inc.
RHAPSBERRY IN BLUE - Candy - That's My Favorite Inc.
RHAPSODIE - Cosmetics - Lancome
RHAPSODIE - Soap - Frances Denney
RHAPSODY - Biscuits - Bahlsen Inc.
RHAPSODY - Bottles–glass - Demptos Glass Corp.
RHAPSODY - Cabinets - Aristokraft, Inc.
RHAPSODY - Chimes ☆ - J.W. Stannard Co.
RHAPSODY - China black tea - Galaxy Tea Corp.
RHAPSODY - Christmas tree ornaments - Cracker Box Inc.
RHAPSODY - Dinnerware–glass ☆ - Nikko Ceramics Inc.
RHAPSODY - Dinnerware–glass ☆ - Royal China & Porcelain Companies Inc.
RHAPSODY - Dishes–china - Taylor, Smith & Taylor Co.
RHAPSODY - Electronic equipment - Alaron Inc.
RHAPSODY - Flatware ☆ - Couzon USA
RHAPSODY - Floor coverings - Mannington Resilient Floors
RHAPSODY - Floor coverings–carpet and rugs - Carpet Crafts Inc.
RHAPSODY - Floor coverings–carpet and rugs - Conquest Carpet Mills Inc.
RHAPSODY - Floor coverings–carpet and rugs - Philadelphia Carpets
RHAPSODY - Floor coverings–carpet and rugs - S and S Mills Inc.
RHAPSODY - Floor coverings–carpet and rugs ☆ - Downs Carpet Co. Inc.
RHAPSODY - Floor coverings–carpet and rugs ☆ - Galaxy Carpet Mills Inc.
RHAPSODY - Floor coverings–carpet and rugs ☆ - Trans-Ocean Import Co. Inc.
RHAPSODY - Furniture - Weiman Co.
RHAPSODY - Furniture ☆ - Hammary Furniture Co. Inc.
RHAPSODY - Glassware–household ☆ - Lotus Glass Co.
RHAPSODY - Hair care products - Helene Curtis Industries Inc.
RHAPSODY - Hair care products - Wella Corp. (Consumer Products Div.)
RHAPSODY - Harmonicas - Hohner Inc.
RHAPSODY - Hearing aids - Beltone Electronics Corp.
RHAPSODY - Home health care products - Arjo Manufacturing Co.
RHAPSODY - Luggage - Samsonite Corp.
RHAPSODY - Paper–gift wrap ☆ - Papercraft Corp.
RHAPSODY - Prosthetic apparatus - Freeman Manufacturing Co.
RHAPSODY - Recording label - Executive Suite Records
RHAPSODY - Rings–jewelry - Artcarved Inc.
RHAPSODY - Shoes - Shoe Masters Inc.
RHAPSODY - Stationery - PPC, Inc.
RHAPSODY - Watches - Bulova Corp.
RHAPSODY - Yarn ☆ - National Spinning Co., Inc.
RHAPSODY IN BLUE - Dolls ☆ - Effanbee Doll Corp.
RHAPSODY IN COLOR - Wallpaper - Advent Industries Inc.
RHAPSODY IN COLOR - Wallpaper - Capital Carousel Inc.
RHAPSODY IN GOLD - Rings–jewelry ☆ - Artcarved Inc.
RHAPSODY IN HUES - Wallpaper - Manhattan Creations Ltd.
RHAPSODY IN HUES - Wallpaper - Michele Wallpaper Inc.
RHAPSODY IN RED - Wines ☆ - Shenandoah Vineyards
RHAPSODY IN ROSE - Dinnerware–glass ☆ - WMF/USA
RHAPSODY IN SILK - Wallpaper - Vymura
RHB FORMULA - Pet products - RHB Enterprises
RHEA - Floor coverings–carpet and rugs - Masland Corp.
RHEA - Frames–eyeglass - Pathway Optical Prods.
RHEABAN - Pharmaceutical preparations - Pfizer Inc.
RHEEM - Air conditioning equipment - Rheem Manufacturing Co.
RHEEM - RUUD UNIVERSAL - Water heaters–household - Rheem Manufacturing Co.
RHEI-MINT - Pharmaceutical preparations ☆ - JMI-Canton Pharmaceuticals
RHEILA PEARLS - Candy - Haram-Christensen Corp.
RHEIN RIVER NYMPH - Wines - Lohmiller Wine Distributors
RHEINART ESTATE - Wines - H. Schmitt Soehne, Inc.
RHEINBERG - Wines - Frank Sutton & Co.
RHEINFEST - Wines ☆ - Louis Glunz Inc.
RHEINGAU - Wines - Beer Import Co.
RHEINGOLD - Beverages–malt - The Stroh Brewery Co.

☆ = Now out of production

RHEINGOLD - Harmonicas - Hohner Inc.
RHEINGOLD LIGHT - Beverages–malt - The Stroh Brewery Co.
RHEINLAENDER - Wines - Lohmiller Wine Distributors
RHEINLANDER - Beverages–malt - Rainier Brewing Co.
RHEINLANDER - Beverages–malt - The Stroh Brewery Co.
RHEINLANDER - Cheese - Beaverton Foods
RHEMU - Pharmaceutical preparations - Ratite Products, Inc.
RHEOBUILD - Concrete–mixture - Master Builders Inc.
RHEOCELL - Concrete–mixture - Master Builders Inc.
RHEOCRETE - Concrete–mixture - Master Builders Inc.
RHEOLATE - Lubricants - Rheox, Inc.
RHEOMAC - Concrete–mixture - Master Builders Inc.
RHEOMAC SF - Concrete–mixture - Master Builders Inc.
RHEOMET - Solder - Kester Solder Co.
RHEOMIX - Concrete–mixture - Master Builders Inc.
RHEOTRACK - Computer software - Hertzler Systems Inc.
RHEOVAC - Electronic equipment - Intek, Inc.
RHESONATIV - Pharmaceutical preparations - Kabi Pharmacia Inc.
RHETOREX - Circuit boards - VMX Inc.
RHEUMAQUIK - Pharmaceutical preparations - Schering-Plough Healthcare
Products
RHEUMARTH - Pharmaceutical ☆ - Iodent Co.
RHEUMATEX - Pharmaceutical preparations - Wampole Laboratories Div.
RHEUMIXX - Health care products - Pharma Botanixx
RHEUMIXX - Pharmaceutical preparations - Botanixx, Inc.
RHI - Apparel and accessories - Roller Hockey International
RHI RHI ENTERTAINMENT, INC. - Recording label - RHI Entertainment, Inc.
RHIANNA - Floor coverings–carpet and rugs - Masland Corp.
RHINALL - Pharmaceutical preparations - Schering-Plough Healthcare
Products
RHINE - Hardware - Harloc, Inc.
RHINE BEAR - Wine ☆ - Charles Jacquin et Compagnie Inc.
RHINE HARVEST - Cereal ☆ - Liberty Richter Inc.
RHINE VALLEY - Pumpernickel bread - Iversen Baking Co.
RHINEGAL - Wines - Old Europe Inc.
RHINEHESSEN - Beverages–alcohol - Old Europe Inc.
RHINELANDER - Beverages–malt - Joseph Huber Brewing Co., Inc.
RHINELANDER - Boots ☆ - Etonic Inc.
RHINELANDER BOCK - Beverages–malt - Joseph Huber Brewing Co., Inc.
RHINESTONE - Floor coverings–carpet and rugs ☆ - Barrett Carpet Mills Inc.
RHINESTONES - Greeting cards - Renaissance Greeting Cards Inc.
RHINEX D-LAY - Pharmaceutical preparations ☆ - Lemmon Co.
RHINICOMP JR. - Pharmaceutical preparations ☆ - JMI-Canton
Pharmaceuticals
RHINIHAB JR. - Pharmaceutical preparations ☆ - JMI-Canton Pharmaceuticals
RHINITISAN - Pharmaceutical preparations - Bioforce of America Ltd.
RHINO - Apparel and accessories - Adtees Corp.
RHINO - Automotive parts and accessories - Miti Manufacturing Co., Inc.
RHINO - Bicycles - Dynacraft Industries, Inc.
RHINO - Books–blank - Running Rhino & Co.
RHINO - Cases–camera - Innovative Manufacturing Corp.
RHINO - Cases–camera - Kiwi
RHINO - Cases–musical instrument - Mechanical Music Corp.
RHINO - Chairs–folding - Cramer Inc.
RHINO - Fishing rods - Zebco Corp.
RHINO - Guns - Rhino Gun Cases Inc.
RHINO - Hammers - A to Z Tool, Inc.
RHINO - Motor vehicle parts and accessories - Alejandro R. Gonzalez Pasos
RHINO - Mufflers–motor vehicle - International Parts Corp.
RHINO - Musical instrument accessories ☆ - David Wexler & Co.
RHINO - Oils–lubricating - Conklin Co., Inc.
RHINO - Paper - Smurfit Newsprint Corp. (Cladwood Div.)
RHINO - Recording label - Capitol-EMI Music Inc.
RHINO - Recording label - Rhino Records, Inc.
RHINO - Toys - Tonka Corp.
RHINO - Tractors - Rhino International, Inc.
RHINO - Valves - Rhino Valves Worldwide, Inc.
RHINO - Windows - Gerkin Windows & Doors
RHINO BAR - Confections - Famous Pacific Dessert Co.
RHINO CHASERS - Beverages–malt - Rhino Chasers
RHINO CLOTH - Fabrics - Pacific Trail, Inc.
RHINO-FLEX - Office supplies ☆ - Esselte Corp.
RHINO-FLEX - Rope - Wellington Leisure Products, Inc.
RHINO-HIDE - Extension cords - Pacific Electricord Co.
RHINO HIDE - Fishing tackle - Zebco Corp.
RHINO KNIFE SHARPENER - Knife sharpeners - Rhino Industries

RHINO MAT - Motor vehicles–trucks - Superior Industries International, Inc.
RHINO NEW ARTISTS - Recording label - Rhino Inc.
RHINO PAD II - Office supplies - Artistic Office Products
RHINO PERFORMANCE MUFFLERS - Mufflers–motor vehicle - Midas
International Corp.
RHINO POWER - Heating equipment - Smith Corp.
RHINO-POWER - Rope - Wellington Leisure Products, Inc.
RHINO-PRENE - Hardware - Woodward-Wanger Co.
RHINO ROPES - Rope - Wellington Leisure Products, Inc.
RHINO RUBBER - Pet products - T.F.H. Publications, Inc.
RHINO TOUGH - Fishing rods - Zebco Corp.
RHINO-TUFF - Plastics film - Trans Consolidated Distributors, Inc.
RHINO USA - Abrasive products - Realys, Inc.
RHINO WRAP - Hockey equipment - Bending Branches
RHINO-X INDUSTRIES - Bags–plastic - High-D Acquisition Corp.
RHINOBAR - Lathes - Lexair, Inc.
RHINOBOND - Adhesives and sealants - Olympic Manufacturing Group, Inc.
RHINOCAPS - Health care products - Ferndale Laboratories, Inc.
RHINOGEN - Veterinary pharmaceutical preparations - Oxford Veterinary
Laboratories, Inc.
RHINOGESIC - Pharmaceutical preparations - Pal-Pak Inc.
RHINOGESIC GG - Pharmaceutical preparations ☆ - Pal-Pak Inc.
RHINOHIDE - Vinyl - Kimberly-Clark Corp.
RHINOLIN - Desk sets - Artistic Office Products
RHINOLIN SELECT - Office supplies - Artistic Office Products
RHINOPOWER - Electrical surge protectors - SL Waber Inc.
RHINORB - Toys - Mattel, Inc.
RHINOSEAL - Adhesives and sealants - Future 500
RHINOSOFT - Computer software - Rhino Diagnostics, Inc.
RHINOTEK - Magnetic tape–blank - Gerald Chamales Corp.
RHINOX SHIELD - Galvanized fasteners - Bontel Fastener Corp.
RHINSPEC - Pharmaceutical preparations ☆ - Lemmon Co.
RHIP - Checkbooks - Nationsbank Corp.
RHM DOCKWEAR - Apparel–men's - R.H. Macy & Co.
RHO - Ophthalmic goods ☆ - Luxottica
RHODA - Frames–eyeglass - Zylo Ware Corp.
RHODA LEE - Apparel–women's - Rhoda Lee, Inc.
RHODA +LYNNE - Apparel–women's - Swell Fashion, Inc.
RHODA SODA - Dolls - Mattel, Inc.
RHODE ISLAND - Frames–eyeglass ☆ - Universal/Univis Inc.
RHODEN - Tires - Rhoton Corp.
RHODENOL - Fertilizers - Pharmline, Inc.
RHODES - Furniture - Rhodes Inc.
RHODES - Musical instruments - Rolandcorp US
RHODES - Pianos ☆ - Fender Musical Instruments
RHODES 18 - Ships–sailing vessels - Cape Cod Shipbuilding Co.
RHODES 19 - Boats - Stuart Marine
RHODES 22 - Ships–sailing vessels - General Boats Corp.
RHODES AMERICAN - Steel wool - Rhodes Co.
RHODES/AMERICAN - Steel-wool pads - American Steel Wool Manufacturing
Co. Inc.
RHODES BAKE-N-SERV - Breads–frozen - Rhodes International, Inc.
RHODES MAKES THE MEAL - Bakery products - Moraine Co.
RHODES STUDIOS - Christmas tree ornaments - Rhodes Studios Ltd.
RHODESIAN CAMO - Apparel and accessories - Moteng International, Inc.
RHODESTER - Sporting goods - Bell Sports Corp.
RHODEX - Electronic equipment - Enthone-OMI
RHODIA - Frames–eyeglass - Zylo Ware Corp.
RHODIA - Notebooks and notepads - Alvin and Co. Inc.
RHODIGEM - Jewelry - Goodman & Co.
RHODIGOLD - Wallpaper - Goodman & Co.
RHODIUM - Pharmaceutical preparations - City Chemical Corp.
RHODODENDRON - Paper - Strathmore Paper Co.
RHODORA - Tableware–china ☆ - Lenox, Inc.
RHODOS - Dinnerware–glass ☆ - WMF/USA
RHODOS - Rings–jewelry - Artcarved Inc.
RHOM-ANTICS - Toys - Kadon Enterprises Inc.
RHOMBO MAGNETIC BLOCKS - Toys - Michael S. Longuet-Higgins
RHOMBS - Floor coverings - Harris-Tarkett, Inc.
RHOMBUS - Chairs–stacking - Fixtures Furniture
RHONDA HARNESS - Apparel–women's - Shady Grove Inc.
RHONDO - Chairs–wood - Joyce International Inc.
RHONE - Frames–eyeglass ☆ - Universal/Univis Inc.
RHONE ESTATES - Beverages–alcohol - World Shippers & Importers
RHS - Fire extinguishers - Figgie International Inc.

☆ = Now out of production

RHU-B-PAK - Fruits and vegetables ☆ - Washington Rhubarb Growers Association

RHUBRUM LILY - Dinnerware–glass - Nikko Ceramics Inc.

RHULI - Analgesics - Rydelle Laboratories Inc.

RHULI BITE-AID - Skin care products - S.C. Johnson & Son, Inc.

RHULIGEL - Skin care products - S.C. Johnson & Son, Inc.

RHULISPRAY - Skin care products - S.C. Johnson & Son, Inc.

RHUM BARBANCOURT - Rum - Carillon Importers Ltd.

RHUM BARBANCOURT - Rum - Monsieur Henri Wines Ltd.

RHUM SAINT JAMES - Beverages–alcohol - Cointreau America Inc.

RHUMBA - Fabrics - Gretchen Bellinger Inc.

RHUMBA - Yarn ☆ - William Unger & Co. Inc.

RHUMBA RUM - Food products - L. Karp & Sons, Inc.

RHUS-ALL - Pharmaceutical preparations - Barry Laboratories Inc.

RHUS TOX - Pharmaceutical preparations ☆ - Lemmon Co.

RHUS TOX. 4X - Homeopathic remedies - Washington Homeopathic Products

RHUSIGEN - Veterinary pharmaceutical preparations - Schering-Plough Animal Health

RHUSTICON - Poison-ivy and poison-oak treatment - American Pharmaceutical Co.

RHV - Ventilation equipment - Seiho International, Inc.

RHY - Eyeglasses - Martin-Copeland Eyewear Corp.

RHYMATION - Games - Jjags Inc.

RHYME - Floor coverings–carpet and rugs ☆ - Royalweve Carpet Mills

RHYME IN TIME, A - Games - Jill Renee Lenhart

RHYME TIME - Apparel–children's - Rahmey International Inc.

RHYMES - Apparel–women's - Cabrais Inc.

RHYMES & 'NYMS - Toys - Joan Carolyn Berry

RHYMEWIZARD - Computer software - Wing and a Prayer Software, Inc.

RHYMING NOTEBOOK - Computer software - First Byte Inc.

RHYTHM - Bedding–linen - Dan River Inc.

RHYTHM - Computer software - 12 Technologies, Inc.

RHYTHM - Costumes - Victoria's Dance-Theatrical Supply

RHYTHM - Dinnerware–glass ☆ - Homer Laughlin China Co.

RHYTHM - Frames–eyeglass - Pathway Optical Prods.

RHYTHM - Golfing equipment - Ram Golf Corp.

RHYTHM - Incense - Excelsior Incense Works

RHYTHM - Recording label - Terock Records

RHYTHM ACCENT - Leotards - Donna S. Turner

RHYTHM ACE - Musical instruments - Multivox/Sorkin Music Co. Inc.

RHYTHM AND BLUE - Cosmetics - Elizabeth Arden Inc.

RHYTHM AND BLUE - Recording label - Donna Douglas

RHYTHM AND BLUES - Harmonicas - Hohner Inc.

RHYTHM & CRUISE - Bags - Ronald H. Usem

RHYTHM GOLD - Glassware–household - Lenox, Inc.

RHYTHM MAKER - Musical instruments ☆ - Fred Gretsch Enterprises

RHYTHM PLATINUM - Glassware–household - Lenox, Inc.

RHYTHM SAFARI - Recording label - Hilton Rosenthal Music, Inc.

RHYTHM SAFARI - Recording label - Priority Records

RHYTHM SKATEBOARDS - Skateboards - Planet Earth Skateboards, Inc.

RHYTHM TRIBE - Recording label - Thomas Guzman-Sanchez

RHYTHMICS - Dinnerware–glass - Nikko Ceramics Inc.

RHYTHMLITE - Lighting fixtures - Peavey Electronics Corp.

RHYTHMPAK - Audio equipment - George Timothy O'Farrell

RHYTHMS PRODUCTIONS - Recording label - Rhythms Productions

RI - Ceramic products and rugs - Revman Industries, Inc.

R.I. - Food products - John Sexton and Co.

RI - Rackets–tennis ☆ - Rackets International (Racket Sports Div.)

RI MID PRO - Rackets–tennis ☆ - Rackets International (Racket Sports Div.)

RIA - Electrical equipment - G.O. Aeurofiamma, Inc.

RIA - Prophylactics - Line One Laboratories

RIA TERRA - Apparel and accessories - Partners in Progress Inc.

RIADA - Skin care products - Riada Cosmetics Corp.

RIAENVIA - Cardboard - Ria Telecommunications, Inc.

RIALTA - Motor vehicles–motor homes - Winnebago Industries, Inc.

RIALTA - Whirlpools - Jacuzzi Inc.

RIALTO - Bedding–linen - Dan River Inc.

RIALTO - Breads - Rialto Breadsticks Inc.

RIALTO - Dinnerware–glass ☆ - WMF/USA

RIALTO - Floor coverings - Mannington Resilient Floors

RIALTO - Frames–eyeglass - Zylo Ware Corp.

RIALTO - Glassware–household - Spiegelau Inc.

RIALTO - Hams - Jack Greenberg Inc.

RIALTO - Macaroni ☆ - Cumberland Macaroni Manufacturing Co.

RIALTO - Recording label - CA-Song Music

RIALTO - Toilets–enameled - Kohler Co.

RIALTO DROPS - Candy ☆ - Maillard Corp.

RIALTO, THE - Electronic equipment - AudioControl

RIANA ROUGE - Computer storage devices–optical - Konami (America) Inc.

RIASOL - Health care products ☆ - Blair Laboratories Inc.

RIATA - Cigars - Te-Amo

RIATA - Frames–eyeglass - Zylo Ware Corp.

R.I.B. - Sporting goods - Avon Marine

RIB-A-TAC - Cement - Bridgestone/Firestone, Inc.

RIB-B-Q - Meat products–pork - Pierre Frozen Foods Inc.

RIB-BIT - Screw drivers - Credo Co.

RIB BONE - Skateboards - Powell Skateboards

RIB CAGE - Bicycle parts and accessories - Specialized Bicycle Components, Inc.

RIB CAGE - Wet suits–rubber - O'Neill, Inc.

RIB CORD - Floor coverings–carpet and rugs - Trend Carpet

RIB FLAIR - Lenses–optical - Kelley & Hueber

RIB-FLEX - Window shades - Allied Extrusions

RIB-IT - Barbecue sauce - Ruthie's Cafe

RIB-IT! - Craft supplies - Minnetonka Mills Inc.

RIB-LITE - Sporting goods - Bike Athletic Co.

RIB-O-MATIC - Computer software - Valis Group

RIB-STEP - Mats - Proffitt Manufacturing Co.

RIB STICKERS - Food products ☆ - Stow-A-Way Industries

RIB-TICKLER, THE - Food products - Mustards Corp.

RIB TICKLERS - Food products ☆ - Denny's Inc.

RIB-TICKLERS - Greeting cards ☆ - Amberley Greeting Card Co.

RIB TICKLIN' - Cheese ☆ - Heluva Good Cheese Inc.

RIB-TITE - Weather stripping - Caldwell Manufacturing Co.

RIB-TRED - Mats - Proffitt Manufacturing Co.

RIBAC - Floor coverings ☆ - Harris-Tarkett, Inc.

RIBB-ON-TEX PLUS - Fabrics–tapestry ☆ - Combeau Industries

RIBBAND - Hobby kits - Finish Line, Inc.

RIBBED WHITES - Underwear and nightwear - Fruit of the Loom Inc.

RIBBER, THE - Crocheted and knitted items ☆ - Puritan Sportswear Corp.

RIBBI RABBIT - Toys–stuffed - Russ Berrie and Co., Inc.

RIBBIT RACIN - Game machines - Lazer-Tron Corp.

RIBBIT-RIBITT - Apparel–children's - Jane Colby Inc.

RIBBITT - Giftware ☆ - Doranne

RIBBITT - Toys–stuffed ☆ - Gund, Inc.

RIBBON - Boxes - Traditions Press Inc.

RIBBON - Frames–eyeglass - Liberty Optical Manufacturing Co.

RIBBON - Pencils ☆ - Faber-Castell Corp.

RIBBON - Publisher's imprints - Penguin USA

RIBBON BOUQUET - Dinnerware ☆ - Corning Inc.

RIBBON CANDY - Christmas tree ornaments - Cracker Box Inc.

RIBBON CANE - Syrup - Food Products Inc.

RIBBON CONNECTIONS - Ribbons - Ribbon Connections, Inc.

RIBBON CURL - Cooking utensils–enameled ☆ - General Housewares Corp.

RIBBON DAISY - Bedding–linen - Dan River Inc.

RIBBON DANCER - Frames–picture - Terragrafics Inc.

RIBBON DANCER - Toys - Shoot the Moon Products, Inc.

RIBBON DOPE - Tape–adhesive ☆ - Permacel

RIBBON EDGE - Flatware - Gorham Inc.

RIBBON EDGE II - Flatware ☆ - Gorham Inc.

RIBBON FLOW - Hand held food dispensers - Stull Closure Technologies, Inc.

RIBBON MAGIC - Ribbons - Ribbon Magic, Inc.

RIBBON MISER - Printers–computer - Avery Dennison Corp.

RIBBON OF LOVE - Rings–jewelry - Artcarved Inc.

RIBBON REED - Flatware ☆ - Kirk Stieff Co.

RIBBON ROPE - Jewelry - Aurafin Corp.

RIBBON SERIES - Benches–metal - Victor Stanley, Inc.

RIBBON SILK - Wallpaper - Koroseal Wallcoverings

RIBBON SONNET - Bedding–linen - Dan River Inc.

RIBBON, THE - Ribbons–inked - Curtis-Young Corp.

RIBBON WIRE - Apparel–women's - Exquisite Form Industries

RIBBONETTE - Ribbons ☆ - CPS Corp.

RIBBONPOINT - Yarn - Tracy Wallace Mabry

RIBBONS - Fashion Ribbon Co. Inc.

RIBBONS - Curling irons–electric - Helen of Troy Corp.

RIBBONS - Floor coverings–carpet and rugs - Langhorne Carpet Co. Inc.

RIBBONS - Ribbons–inked - Design Circle Ltd.

RIBBONS - Toys–stuffed - Jared D. Lee Studio Inc.

RIBBONS AND BOWS - Blouses–women's - Kellwood Co.

RIBBONS AND BOWS - Dinnerware–glass ☆ - Royal China & Porcelain Companies Inc.

RIBBONS AND BOWS - Wallpaper - Sanitas Wallcoverings

RIBBONS & CLOVERS - Bedding–linen - Dan River Inc.
RIBBONS & HEARTS - Shoes–athletic - Stride Rite Corp.
RIBBONS & ROSES - Dinnerware–glass - Royal China & Porcelain Companies Inc.
RIBBONS AND ROSES - Jams and jellies - Knott's Berry Farm
RIBBONS & ROSES - Toys - Mattel, Inc.
RIBBONS & ROSES - Wallpaper ☆ - Andover Wallcovering
RIBBONS & ROSES II - Wallpaper ☆ - Andover Wallcovering
RIBBONS & WAVES - Skin care products - Brocato International
RIBBONS OF COLOUR - Glassware–household - Owens-Illinois Inc. (Libbey Div.)
RIBBONZ - Ribbons ☆ - Z-Barten Productions
RIBCAGE - Toys - Tonka Corp.
RIBCORD - Wallcovering ☆ - Technique Textiles Inc.
RIBCUTS - Food products - Universal Frozen Foods Co.
RIBE - Glassware–household - Dansk International Designs, Ltd.
RIBENA - Juices ☆ - Gilway Co. Ltd.
RIBERA DEL DUERO - Wines - European Beverage Co., Inc.
RIBEZZO - Wines - Tempo Imports Ltd.
RIBGRIPPER - Tires–bicycles ☆ - Carlisle Tire & Rubber Co.
RIBLINE - Doors–garage - McKee Door, Inc.
RIBO-2 - Vitamins and nutritional supplements - Tyson & Associates, Inc.
RIBOFLEX - Vitamins and nutritional supplements - Great Life Laboratories Inc.
RIBOMINS WITH RNA - Great Life Laboratories Inc.
RIBOZIME - Pharmaceutical preparations - Wesley Pharmacal Co. Inc.
RIBOZYME PHARMACEUTICALS INCORPORATED - Pharmaceutical preparations - Ribozyme Pharmaceuticals Inc.
RIBRONS - Footwear–women's - Argyris Inc.
RIBTEX - Floor coverings–carpet and rugs - Panelfold Inc.
RIBZ - Dog food - Ralston Purina Co.
RIC - Audio equipment - Rickenbacker International Corp.
RIC - Catheter - Arrow International Investment Corp.
RIC COUNTER DUSTER - Brooms - Lighthouse Industries
RIC SHA - Food products - Richard A. Shaw Inc.
RICA CIDRA - Cider - Napa Valley Wines
RICA MALT TONIC - Beverages–carbonated - Cawy Bottling Co., Inc.
RICARD INC. - Apparel and accessories - Charles Richard, III
RICARDO - Frames–eyeglass ☆ - Universal/Univis Inc.
RICARDO - Meat products–beef - Imperial Commodities Corp.
RICARDO - Musical instruments - Tilben Co.
RICARDO - Snack foods - Millner Trading Co. Inc.
RICARDO'S - Food products - Mexican Food Manufacturing of Omaha Inc.
RICARE - Recording label - Carrie Records
RICASOLI - Wines - Seagram's Chateau & Estate Wines Co.
RICCADONNA - Wines ☆ - Francis A. Bonanno, Inc.
RICCAR - Sewing machines–household - Riccar America Co.
RICCAR - Sewing machines–household - Tacony Corp.
RICCARDI - Wines - M.S. Walker Inc./Seacoast
RICCARDO FALCHINI VERNACCIA - Wines - William Grant & Sons, Inc.
RICCHETTI - Tiles–terrazzo - Imperial Tile and Marble Corp.
RICCI - Flatware - Argentieri (USA) Inc.
RICCIARDI - Ice cream - Borden, Inc.
RICCIARELLI - Food products - Bel Canto Fancy Foods Ltd.
RICCIONE - Apparel–women's - Wide Pacific Development, Inc.
RICCIONE - Yarn ☆ - William Unger & Co. Inc.
RICCO - Apparel and accessories - Ricco A. Richardson
RICE - Food products - Rice Food Markets, Inc.
RICE - Napkins–paper - Freund-Mayer & Co. Inc.
RICE - Thread - A.H. Rice Co.
RICE-A-RONI - Food products - Golden Grain Co.
RICE ACCENTS - Frozen foods - Pillsbury Co.
RICE & SHINE - Cereal - Arrowhead Mills, Inc.
RICE AUDIO - Video tapes–blank - Robert Carl Rice
RICE BAGGER, THE - Craft supplies - Rose Manufacturing
RICE BITES - Snack foods - American Grains
RICE BRAN OPTIONS - Cereal - Ralston Purina Co.
RICE BUBBLES - Cereal ☆ - Kellogg Co.
RICE BURNER - Apparel - Allen S. Guilmette
RICE CHEX - Cereal - Ralston Purina Co.
RICE CREAM - Cereal - Southern Brown Rice
RICE CURL - Snack foods - Energy Food Factory Inc.
RICE DREAM - Food products - Imagine Foods Inc.
RICE DRILL - Machinery - Robroy Industries, Inc.
RICE FRYS - Food products - American Frozen Foods Inc.
RICE GOURMET - Frozen foods - O.R.A. Corp.
RICE HONEYS - Food products - Nabisco Foods Group

RICE IN AN INSTANT - Rice - Uncle Ben's, Inc.
RICE KRISPIES - Cereal - Kellogg Co.
RICE KRISPIES TREATS - Snack foods - Kellogg Co.
RICE 'N EASY - Rice - Riceland Foods, Inc.
RICE N' GRAVY - Recording label - Bobby C. Guidry
RICE NECTAR - Syrup - T & A Gourmet
RICE NESS - Food products - Fearn Natural Foods, Division of Modernproducts, Inc.
RICE ORIGINALS - Food products - Green Giant Co.
RICE PAPER - Frames–picture - Framemica Co.
RICE PAPER - Wallpaper - Capital Carousel Inc.
RICE PARISIENNE - Rice ☆ - Persian Delight Inc.
RICE PLANTERS - Hammocks - Pawleys Island Rope Hammock
RICE RIVER - Cereal - Homestead Mills
RICE RIVER FARMS - Rice - Chieftain Wild Rice Co.
RICE ROAD, THE - Meat-based entrees, sauces - MCC Foods America, Inc.
RICE SLICE - Food products - Galaxy Foods Co.
RICE SNAPS - Crackers ☆ - Edward & Sons Trading Co., Inc.
RICE SNAX - Rice - Amsnack, Inc.
RICE SWEETIES - Candy - T & A Gourmet
RICE THINS - Snack foods - Sesmark Foods Inc.
RICE TOPPER - Meat sauces ☆ - Nalley's Fine Foods
RICE TWICE - Cereal - U.S. Mills, Inc.
RICELAND - Rice - Riceland Foods, Inc.
RICELAND PERFECTION - Rice - Riceland Foods, Inc.
RICEMAN - Cooking equipment–household - Chung Yuan Chang
RICE'S - Juices - Rice Juice Co.
RICE'S BEST - Tobacco products - Scott Tobacco Co.
RICESELECT - Rice - Ricetec, Inc.
RICESWEET - Desserts - Charity's Food
RICEWRAP - Pipes - Robroy Industries, Inc.
RICH - Bakery products ☆ - FoodSalesWest Inc.
RICH - Beverages ☆ - Escalon Frozen Foods
RICH - Frames–eyeglass - Hudson Optical Corp.
RICH - Gasoline - Rich Oil Inc.
RICH - Ladders–metal - Rich Ladder Co.
RICH - Lipsticks ☆ - Honey & Spice Toiletries
RICH ACRAL - Water colors - Rich Art Color Co., Inc.
RICH & BITCHY - Apparel and accessories - Bette Appel Inc.
RICH & CHUNKY - Yogurt–frozen - General Mills, Inc.
RICH AND FAMOUS - Cosmetics - Revlon Consumer Products Corp.
RICH & LASTING - Lipsticks - Circle of Beauty, Inc.
RICH & NATURAL - Hair coloring preparations - Aminco Inc.
RICH AND QUICK - Food products ☆ - Merkt Cheese Co., Inc.
RICH & QUICK MICRO-SAUCE - Sauces - Merkt Cheese Co., Inc.
RICH & RARE - Whiskey - Hiram Walker & Sons, Inc.
RICH & SINFUL - Cookies - Best Maid Cookie Co.
RICH AND TANGY - Food products - Curtice-Burns Foods, Inc.
RICH & ZESTY - Juices - Wagner Excello Foods Inc.
RICH ART - Paints–artists' - Rich Art Color Co., Inc.
RICH BICH - Candy bars - Rich Bich Biplane Co.
RICH-BRIGHT - Plastics - Richards Distributing, Inc.
RICH BROOK - Food products - Oscar Mayer Foods Corp.
RICH-CAL - Plastics - Richards Distributing, Inc.
RICH-CAST - Plastics - Richards Distributing, Inc.
RICH CHOCOLATE OVALTINE - Vitamins and nutritional supplements - Himmel Nutrition Inc.
RICH COLOR - Cosmetics - Max Factor & Co.
RICH CRAFT - Mobile homes - Oakwood Homes Corp.
RICH-CRAFT - Paints - Rich Art Color Co., Inc.
RICH-CRYL - Paints - Rich Art Color Co., Inc.
RICH DARK HONEYDEW - Tobacco products - Faber, Coe & Gregg Inc.
RICH-DIPT - Chocolate candy - Laymon Candy Co. Inc.
RICH E - Skin care products - Marlyn Co. Inc.
RICH EARTH - Pancakes–mixes - Fearn Natural Foods, Division of Modernproducts, Inc.
RICH FARMER POOR FARMER - Games - McJay Game Co.
RICH GEL - Paints - Rich Art Color Co., Inc.
RICH GIRL - Apparel and accessories ☆ - Warnaco Inc.
RICH GLO - Paints - Rich Art Color Co., Inc.
RICH-GLO-ACRAL - Paints - Rich Art Color Co., Inc.
RICH GRAIN - Bakery products ☆ - Flowers Industries Inc.
RICH HARVEST - Juices - Rich Harvest Juice Co.
RICH HEALTH - Hair care products - Gimborn U.S., Inc.
RICH HEALTH - Pet products - Rich Health
RICH IN ALL - Flour–blended - Langlois Flour Co.

☆ = Now out of production

RICH LIFE - Shampoos ☆ - Noxell Corp.
RICH LIGHTS - Cigarettes - Brown & Williamson Tobacco Corp.
RICH LINE - Boats - Richland Diversified Industries, Inc.
RICH LINE - Boats–motor - Rich Line
RICH-LITE - Eyeglasses - Art-Craft Optical Co.
RICH LOOK - Juices–frozen - Tropicana Products, Inc.
RICH LUX - Paints - M.A. Bruder & Sons Inc.
RICH MOUNTAIN - Barbecues and grills - Real Ideas Inc.
RICH 'N CHOCOLATE - Beverages–malt - Kelley-Clarke Co.
RICH 'N CINNAMON - Rolls - Interstate Brands Corp.
RICH 'N CREAMY - Cosmetics ☆ - Bonne Bell, Inc.
RICH 'N CREAMY - Puddings–canned - Knouse Foods Cooperative, Inc.
RICH 'N CREAMY - Soups–mixes ☆ - Sanwa Foods Inc.
RICH 'N CREMEY - Food products ☆ - Orth Co. (Bruce)
RICH 'N EASY - Frosting ☆ - Pillsbury Co.
RICH 'N EGG - Salad dressings–bottled - Miami Margarine Co. Inc.
RICH-N-FIBER - Juices - Knudsen & Sons Inc.
RICH N' FREE - Ice cream - Nouvelle Ice Cream Corp.
RICH 'N GENTLE - Cosmetics - Maybelline Co.
RICH-N-LOVELY - Cosmetics - Gera Dist. Inc.
RICH N NATURAL - Ice cream ☆ - Knudsen Dairy Products
RICH 'N NATURAL - Skin care products ☆ - Worldwide Cosmetics
RICH N' READY - Fruit drinks–bottled or canned - Everfresh Beverages, Inc.
RICH 'N RED - Food products - Gilroy Energy Co.
RICH 'N ROBUST - Teas ☆ - Romanoff International Inc.
RICH N' SLIM - Ice cream - Nouvelle Ice Cream Corp.
RICH 'N TENDER - Flour–blended ☆ - Orth Co. (Bruce)
RICH PLAN - Food products - Rich Plan Corp.
RICH PLAN - Food products ☆ - Cap's Italian Foods Inc.
RICH-R GOLD - Insulating materials - Schuller International, Inc.
RICH-R PLUS - Insulating materials - Schuller International, Inc.
RICH RAGS - Apparel–children's - Lilliana Zevallos
RICH REWARD - Floor coverings–carpet and rugs - Evans-Black Carpet Mills
RICH, RICH COLOURS - Cosmetics - Flori Roberts Inc.
RICH RUBY ACCENT - Glass products - Westmoreland Glass Co.
RICH SPLENDOR - Nail care products ☆ - Shiseido Cosmetics (America) Ltd.
RICH STAIN - Craft supplies - Rich Art Color Co., Inc.
RICH-SUEDE - Fabrics - Charles W. Fifield, Jr. Co., Inc.
RICH-TEX - Wallpaper - Royson's Corp.
RICH TRADITION - Floor coverings–carpet and rugs - Calladium & Marglen
RICH TRADITIONS - Bakery products - Campbell Taggart Inc.
RICH TRADITIONS - Coffee - Starbucks Corp.
RICH-WALL - Wallpaper - Royson's Corp.
RICHARD - Gold products - Richard Associates Inc.
RICHARD - Photographic equipment - Richard Manufacturing Co.
RICHARD - Toys–stuffed ☆ - Gund, Inc.
RICHARD - Toys–stuffed ☆ - Russ Berrie and Co., Inc.
RICHARD ADLAI - Wines - Hilton Commercial Group Inc.
RICHARD BERNARD - Fabrics - Richard Bernard Fabrics
RICHARD BERNARDI - Handbags - Regal Bag Corp.
RICHARD BIGELOW - Skin care products - H.B. Accessories
RICHARD BISHOP, LTD. - Office supplies ☆ - H.C. Meyers Co.
RICHARD CARUSO - Hair care products - Caruso International, Inc.
RICHARD CARUSO - Skin care products - Celeste Co. Inc.
RICHARD CARUSO PRO SET 30 - Hair care products - Celeste Co. Inc.
RICHARD COCCO SIGNATURE - Musical instrument accessories - E. & O. Mari Inc.
RICHARD CUNEO - Wines ☆ - Sebastiani Vineyards, Inc.
RICHARD DAYHOFF - Apparel–women's - Richard Dayhoff Designs Inc.
RICHARD DE BAS - Paper - Arjo Wiggins USA
RICHARD DUFFY - Footwear - ISC International Inc.
RICHARD FRERES - Liquors - Crestfield Importers Ltd.
RICHARD HARTWICH - Cosmetics - Richard Hartwik Inc.
RICHARD JUDSON ZOLAN COLLECTION - Giftware - Roman, Inc.
RICHARD LANG - Apparel and accessories - Elizabeth Terrell Designs Ltd.
RICHARD MARSHALL - Apparel–women's - Tumbleweeds from the West Inc.
RICHARD MEIER - Flatware - Reed and Barton Corp.
RICHARD MICHAELS - Wines - San Francisco Wine Exchange
RICHARD PETTY - Toys - ERTL Co., Inc.
RICHARD PETTY CHALLENGE - Toys–electronic - Tyco Toys
RICHARD ROYCE COLLECTION - Footwear - New York City Shoes Inc.
RICHARD SCARRY - Toys–stuffed - Toy Works, Inc.
RICHARD SCARRY'S BEST READERS EVER - Publisher's imprints - Western Publishing Co., Inc.
RICHARD SCOTT - Apparel–men's - Swank Inc.
RICHARD SIMMONS - Backpacks - Richard Simmons

RICHARD SIMMON'S - Salad dressings–bottled ☆ - Chelten House Products Inc.
RICHARD STEIN - Hair care products - Richard Stein Hair Care Products Inc.
RICHARD TYLER - Apparel and accessories - Tyler Trafficant, Inc.
RICHARD WALLICH SPORT - Apparel and accessories - Rainbow Licensing Group, Inc.
RICHARD WILTON COLLECTIONS, THE - Metals - Wilton Co.
RICHARD'S - Beverages–alcohol - Canandaigua Wine Co. Inc.
RICHARDS - Wines - Tenner Brothers Inc.
RICHARDS & SARGENT - Jewelry - Richards & Sargent Inc.
RICHARD'S GOURMET COFFEE - Coffee - Richard's of Chestnut Hill, Inc.
RICHARD'S SPECIAL VERMONT PIZZA R.S.V.P. - Pizza and related food products - R.S.V.P.
RICHARD'S WILD IRISH ROSE - Beverages–alcohol - Canandaigua Wine Co. Inc.
RICHARD'S WILD IRISH ROSE - Wines - Tenner Brothers Inc.
RICHARDSON - Candy - Thos. D. Richardson Co.
RICHARDSON - Frames–eyeglass ☆ - Universal/Univis Inc.
RICHARDSON - Recording label - Richardson Records
RICHARDSON - Syrup - Richardson-T Foods Corp.
RICHARDSON & ROBBINS - Desserts - Pet Inc.
RICHARDSON BAY SPRAY - Sunblocks - California North
RICHARDSON COUNTY - Furniture ☆ - Singer Furniture Co.
RICHARDSON (RACE) RAPID ACCESS COSTESTIMATING SPREADSHEET SYSTEM, THE - Computer software - Richardson Engineering Services, Inc.
RICHARDSON VINEYARDS - Wing assemblies–aircraft - Richardson Vineyards
RICHCO HI-TECH - Hoses - Richco Plastic Co.
RICHCRAFT - Sporting goods - Richcraft Inc.
RICHELIEU - Brandy - Kentucky Brands of California Inc.
RICHELIEU - Dishes–china ☆ - WMF/USA
RICHELIEU - Food products - CPC Best Foods
RICHELIEU - Frames–eyeglass - May Optical Co. Inc.
RICHELIEU - Fruits and vegetables - Richelieu Trading Co.
RICHELIEU - Jewelry - Richelieu Corp.
RICHELIEU COURT - Tableware–china - Lenox, Inc.
RICHELIEU LACE - Scarves - American Trading Co.
RICHES OF THE WORLD - Wallpaper ☆ - Capital Carousel Inc.
RICHEWOOD - Wood products - Boling Co.
RICHFIELD - Flatware - Utica Cutlery Co.
RICHFIELD - Frames–eyeglass - Zylo Ware Corp.
RICHFIELD - Mobile homes - Oakwood Homes Corp.
RICHFIELD - Pickles - W.B. Roddenbery Co., Inc.
RICHFIELD - Ships - Lewmar Marine Inc.
RICHFOOD - Food products - Richfood, Inc.
RICHGLOSS - Paper - Mead Corp.
RICHHEIMER - Coffee - Richheimer Coffee Co.
RICHIE - Pharmaceutical preparations ☆ - Richie Pharmacal Co. Inc.
RICHIE RICH - Games ☆ - Milton Bradley Co.
RICHIMAGE - Computer software - Crandell Group, Inc.
RICHINELLO - Sausages - Aladdin Marketing Sales
RICHISTINE DH - Health care products ☆ - Halsey Drug Co. Inc.
RICHLAC - Pet products ☆ - Rich Health
RICHLAND - Cigarettes - Brown & Williamson Tobacco Corp.
RICHLAND - Floor coverings - Tarkett, Inc.
RICHLAND - Footwear ☆ - H.H. Brown Shoe Co., Inc.
RICHLAND - Fruits and vegetables - Richland Sales Co.
RICHLAND - House furnishings - Lea Industries Inc.
RICHLAND LIGHTS 25S - Cigarettes - Brown & Williamson Tobacco Corp.
RICHLANDS - Food products - Rogers Foods Inc.
RICHLEIGH - Floor coverings–carpet and rugs - Gulistan Carpet Inc.
RICHLEIGH - Floor coverings–carpet and rugs ☆ - Karastan-Bigelow Inc.
RICHLIFE - Vitamins and nutritional supplements - ICN Pharmaceuticals Inc.
RICHLOFT - Fabrics–polyester - E.R. Carpenter Co.
RICHLY BLENDED - Bakery products - Parco Foods, Inc.
RICHLY DESERVED - Cakes - Green County of Wisconsin
RICHLY DESERVED STORYBOOK - Bakery products ☆ - Green County of Wisconsin
RICHLYN - Antacids - Global Pharmaceutical Corp.
RICHMAID - Ice cream - San Francisco Ice Cream Co.
RICHMAN'S - Ice cream - Richman Ice Cream Co.
RICHMARK - Handbags - Richmark International Corp.
RICHMARK - Hosiery ☆ - McCubbin Hosiery Inc.
RICHMARK - Labels–paper - Richmark Co.
RICHMOND - Cabinets - American Woodmark Corp.
RICHMOND - Clocks ☆ - General Time Corp. (Westclox/Seth Thomas Div.)

☆ = Now out of production

RICHMOND - Colognes - KLR Products, Inc.
RICHMOND - Cribs–metal - Evenflo Juvenile Furniture Co.
RICHMOND - Dinnerware–glass ☆ - Royal China & Porcelain Companies Inc.
RICHMOND - Dishes–china - Pickard Inc.
RICHMOND - Dolls ☆ - Effanbee Doll Corp.
RICHMOND - Door frames - Richmond Frame Co. Inc.
RICHMOND - Floor coverings–carpet and rugs ☆ - Cumberland Mills Inc.
RICHMOND - Floor coverings–carpet and rugs ☆ - Richmond Carpet Mills
RICHMOND - Flowers, plants, and seeds - Jonathan Green, Inc.
RICHMOND - Furniture - Haworth, Inc.
RICHMOND - Furniture ☆ - Athens Furniture Industries Inc.
RICHMOND - Furniture ☆ - Bassett Furniture Industries, Inc.
RICHMOND - Kitchen and bathroom cabinets - IXL Furniture Co. Inc.
RICHMOND - Luggage - American Tourister, Inc.
RICHMOND - Printing paper - James River Corp.
RICHMOND - Recording label - Highland Music Inc.
RICHMOND - Shoes ☆ - Allen-Edmonds Shoe Corp.
RICHMOND - Water heaters–household - Richmond Water Heaters
RICHMOND - Wood products ☆ - Lami Wood Products Inc.
RICHMOND 5 SPEED - Automotive parts and accessories - Hurst Performance Inc.
RICHMOND BLENDER'S CHOICE - Tobacco–chewing or smoking - Sterling Tobacco Co.
RICHMOND HALL - Footwear–men's - JBI, Inc.
RICHMOND HILL - Cabinets - Belwood Inc.
RICHMOND HILL - Floor coverings - Mannington Resilient Floors
RICHMOND OAK FROST - Cabinets and cabinet accessories - IXL Furniture Co. Inc.
RICHMOND PARK - Floor coverings–carpet and rugs ☆ - Walter Carpet Mills
RICHMOND WHITE - Dishes–china - Waterford Wedgwood USA, Inc.
RICHMUND - Polish, etc ☆ - Cook and Dunn Paint Corp.
RICH'N CHEWY - Cookies - Frito-Lay, Inc.
RICH'N'CREAMY - Cocoa–powders or mixes - Nestle Beverage Co.
RICH'S - Coffee, tea, milk - Ireland Coffee and Tea Inc.
RICH'S - Meat products–poultry ☆ - Louis Rich Co.
RICH'S - Pastries - Rich Products Corp.
RICH'S GRAND AMERICAN - Pies–fresh - Rich Products Corp.
RICH'S HOME BAKE SHOPPE - Cookies - Rich Products Corp.
RICH'S MIXES - Food products - Rich Products Corp.
RICH'S READY DELI SET TO GO - Meat products–beef - Rich Products Corp.
RICH'S SMOKEHOUSE - Food products - Rich Products Corp.
RICHSTONE - Concrete products - SES Ltd.
RICHTER - Food products ☆ - Liberty Richter Inc.
RICHTER - Machine parts - ITT Industries, Inc.
RICHTER - Seafood products–canned or cured - Haram-Christensen Corp.
RICHTER SCALE - Electronic equipment - AudioControl
RICHTERS - Vinegar - Specialty Brands Inc.
RICHTER'S POTATO STARCH - Starch–edible - Europa Foods Ltd.
RICHTEX - Shortening - Humko Products
RICHTHOFEN'S WAR - Games - Avalon Hill Game Co.
RICHTON - Apparel–men's - Richton International Corp.
RICHVALE - Fruits and vegetables - Wapato Fruit Products Inc.
RICHVIEW - Window coverings - Tehdex Corp.
RICHWHIP - Whipped topping–frozen - Rich Products Corp.
RICHWICH - Snack foods ☆ - Glenn Foods Inc.
RICHWOOD - Bathroom fixtures ☆ - Artesian Industries
RICHWOOD - Briefcases ☆ - Salzburg Creations Inc.
RICHWOOD - Cabinets–wood ☆ - Kitchen Kompact Inc.
RICHWOOD - Chimes ☆ - Nutone Inc.
RICHWOOD - Clocks ☆ - General Time Corp. (Westclox/Seth Thomas Div.)
RICHWOOD - Fans–electric - Classic Concepts Inc.
RICHWOOD - Paints - Blue Ribbon Paint Co.
RICHWOOD - Plastics - Richwood Building Products, Inc.
RICHWOOD II - Cabinets–wood - Kitchen Kompact Inc.
RICHY KREME - Doughnuts - Richy Kreme Products, Inc.
RICK - Food products - Dole Food Co., Inc.
RICK - Ophthalmic goods - Rozin Optical Export Corp.
RICK DERRINGER - Guitars ☆ - Dimarzio, Inc.
RICK HACKER'S CELEBRITY CARDS - Greeting cards - Rick Hacker's Celebrity Cards
RICK OF CALIFORNIA - Fruits and vegetables - Dole Fresh Vegetables Inc.
RICK RACK - Racks - Oakwood Manufacturing Co.
RICK ROYCE - Barbecue sauce - Royce Foods
RICKENBACKER - Guitars - Rickenbacker International Corp.
RICKENBACKER - Motor vehicles ☆ - Rickenbacker Motor Co.

RICKEY'S WORLD FAMOUS SAUCE - Chili sauce - Rickey's Commissary Inc.
RICKI - Vegetables–canned - Heskett Foods
RICKIE FREEMAN - Apparel–women's - Rickie Freeman, Ltd.
RICKMAN - Motorcycles ☆ - Target Motorsports
RICKS - Apparel and accessories ☆ - Ramstar Mills, Inc.
RICK'S - Spices and extracts - C & D Flavor Co.
RICKSHAW - Exercising equipment - Columbia Medical Manufacturing
RICKY - Dolls - Mattel, Inc.
RICKY! - Recording label - Slamdek/Scramdown
RICKY RACCOON - Toys–stuffed - Russ Berrie and Co., Inc.
RICKY RACQUET - Apparel and accessories - Levi & Freeman
RICKY RACQUET RR - Apparel and accessories - Levi & Freeman
RICKY RATTLER PET SNAKE - Candy - Herman Goelitz Candy Co., Inc.
RICO - Fishing lures - JEF International Inc.
RICO - Frames–eyeglass - U.S. Optical Frame Co.
RICO - Musical instrument accessories - Rico International
RICO - Novelty items ☆ - Jobar International Inc./Bibi Products
RICO - Pottery ☆ - Rubens Originals
RICO - Recording label - Combo Records
RICO - Sewing machines–household - Fleur De Paris
RICO - Shoes - Record Industrial Co.
RICO-MIA - Cheese - Great Lakes Cheese Co., Inc.
RICO-PLEX - Musical instrument accessories ☆ - Rico International
RICO ROYAL - Musical instrument accessories - Rico International
RICOCHET - Computer software - Metricom Inc. (Wireless Services Div.)
RICOCHET - Floor coverings–carpet and rugs ☆ - Regal Rugs Inc.
RICOCHET - Toys–automobiles - Tonka Corp.
RICOCHET RAIL - Games - Products Co., Inc.
RICOCHET RUBBER CHECKS - Novelty items - Ricochet Inc.
RICOH - Photocopy machines - RICOH Corp.
RICOLA - Cough drops - Prince of Peace Enterprises Inc.
RICOLA - Cough drops - Ricola Inc.
RICON - Elevators - Ricon Corp.
RID - Pharmaceutical preparations - Pfizer Inc.
RID-A-CRITTER - Fly swatters - Reaver, Carol
RID-A-FOAM - Pet products - Lake Products Co. Inc.
RID A GUM - Cleaning preparations - Rid-A-Gum, Inc.
RID-A-MILL - Insecticides - Ciba-Geigy Corp.
RID-A-PAIN - Pharmaceutical preparations ☆ - Pfeiffer Pharmaceuticals Inc.
RID-DECUBE - Mattresses - Med-E-Care, Inc.
RID ICE - Salt - B.C.A. Products
RID-ICH - Aquarium accessories - Kordon
RID-ICH + - Aquarium accessories - Kordon
RID-ICH - Aquarium accessories - Novalek, Inc.
RID IT - Cleaning preparations–household - Polyjohn Enterprises Corp.
RID-ITCH - Footcare products - Thomas & Thompson Co. Inc.
RID-JID - Ironing boards ☆ - Seymour Housewares Corp.
RID-MAX - Flypaper - Ken-Car International
RID-MITE - Pet products - Tetra Sales USA
RID-O-FOG - Eyeglasses ☆ - Lensco Products
RID-O-GERM - Disinfectants - Uncle Sam Chemical Co., Inc.
RID ROSES - Flowers, plants, and seeds - Equiflor Corp.
RID ROT - Pet products - Tetra Sales USA
RID SKID - Paints ☆ - Kelly-Moore Paint Co. Inc.
RID WORM - Pet products - Tetra Sales USA
RID-X - Cleaning preparations–household - D-Con Co. Inc.
RIDALL-ZINC - Rodenticides ☆ - LiphaTech Inc.
RIDDELL - Bags–duffel - Riddell, Inc.
RIDDLE - Apparel and accessories ☆ - Warnaco Inc.
RIDDLE - Paper cups - James River Corp.
RIDDLER, THE - Publisher's imprints - DC Comics
RIDDLES - Apparel–athletic - Nazareth Kentury Mills
RIDDLES & RICHES - Games - Frank Dilorenzo
RIDE - Sporting goods - Ride Snowboard Co.
RIDE-A-WAY - Toys ☆ - Sun Products Corp. (Wellington)
RIDE-AIRE - Aerators, now out of production - Ransomes-Cushman-Ryan
RIDE ALONG CARRIER - Infant product - Fisher-Price, Inc.
RIDE & REST - Strollers–baby - Jolly Jumper Inc.
RIDE-EEZ - Shoe accessories - Hemp's Co.
RIDE 'EM RACERS - Toys–stuffed - Fun World Inc.
RIDE FOR THE BRAND - Apparel and accessories - Sports Apparel Marketing, Inc.
RIDE HARD - T-shirts–men's - Destinee' Eploriums
RIDE-LITE - Health care products ☆ - Invacare Corp.
RIDE MASTER - Shock absorbers–motor vehicle - Bridgestone/Firestone, Inc.
RIDE 'N HIDE - Toys ☆ - Creative Playthings Ltd.

☆ = Now out of production

RIDE N RUN - Infant product - Tri Industries, Inc.
RIDE ON - Bicycle parts and accessories - W.L. Gore & Associates, Inc.
RIDE-ON RALLY - Toys - Fisher-Price, Inc.
RIDE RITE - Bicycles ☆ - Graber Products, Inc.
RIDE-RITE - Springs–mechanical - Bridgestone/Firestone, Inc.
RIDE RITE - Strollers–baby - Pansy Ellen Products, Inc.
RIDE SAFE - Helmets–athletic - Ride Safe Inc.
RIDE SCIENCE TECHNOLOGY - Apparel and accessories - Sport USA, Inc.
RIDE THE CREST OF QUALITY! - Veterinary medical equipment - Devon-Aire, Inc.
RIDE THE RODS - Games ☆ - Carrom Co.
RIDE THE WAVES - Ships–patrol boats ☆ - Kinco International Inc.
RIDE2 - Bicycle parts and accessories - Prism Designs, Inc.
RIDEAU - Boats–motor ☆ - Rinker Boat Co. Inc.
RIDEAU - Window shades ☆ - Verosol
RIDELASTIC - Land vehicle parts - Ridewell Corp.
RIDEM - Toys - Empire of Carolina Inc.
RIDERRISER - Exercising equipment - Healthrider, Inc.
RIDERS - Apparel–athletic - H.D. Lee Co., Inc.
RIDERS - Jeans–men's - Lee Apparel Co. Inc.
RIDERS CHOICE - Apparel and accessories - Executive Apparel, Inc.
RIDERS OF THE SILVER SCREEN - Cutlery - Smoky Mountain Knife Works
RIDERS R - Apparel and accessories - H.D. Lee Co., Inc.
RIDERWARE MOTORCYCLE APPAREL - Apparel and accessories - Mid-USA Cycle Parts, Inc.
RIDG-A-DIZED - Staircases–metal - Quaker Plastic Corp.
RIDGE - Boots - Ridge Sports Inc.
RIDGE - Floor coverings–carpet and rugs ☆ - Regal Rugs Inc.
RIDGE - Packaging–paper ☆ - Astro-Valcour, Inc.
RIDGE - Tiles–concrete - Blue Ridge Talc Co. Inc.
RIDGE - Wines - Ridge Vineyards Inc.
RIDGE CREEK - Apparel and accessories - St. Lolly International Inc.
RIDGE-FLOW - Aluminum products - N.H. Rudeen Co.
RIDGE HAWK - Toys–models - Cox Products Inc.
RIDGE MANAGER - Agricultural machinery - Acra-Plant, Inc.
RIDGE MASTER - Ventilation equipment - Mid-America Building Products Corp.
RIDGE REST - Padding–foam - Cascade Designs, Inc.
RIDGE RIDERS - Toy cycles - Intex Recreation Corp.
RIDGE ROVER - Knapsacks - Coleman Co., Inc.
RIDGE RUNNER - Bicycles - Columbia Manufacturing Inc.
RIDGE RUNNER - Brushes–hair - Spornette International, Inc.
RIDGE RUNNER - Ventilation equipment - Leslie-Locke, Inc.
RIDGE UNIVENT - Ventilation equipment - Air Vent Inc.
RIDGE VENT - Ventilation equipment - Leigh
RIDGECREST - Floor coverings–carpet and rugs - Hollytex Carpet Mills Inc.
RIDGECREST - Furniture - Mersman Furniture Co.
RIDGECREST - Swimming pools ☆ - Doughboy Recreational Inc.
RIDGECREST CELLARS - Wines - Giumarra Vineyards
RIDGEDALE - Floor coverings–carpet and rugs - Karastan-Bigelow Inc.
RIDGEDLE - Manufactured homes - Redman Industries, Inc.
RIDGEE-FOAM - Fishing lures - Thomas and Thomas Rodmakers Inc.
RIDGEFIELD - Clocks ☆ - General Time Corp. (Westclox/Seth Thomas Div.)
RIDGEFIELD - Desks - Hon Co.
RIDGEFIELD - Floor coverings–carpet and rugs - Bloomsburg Carpet Industries
RIDGEFIELD - Furniture ☆ - Bassett Furniture Industries, Inc.
RIDGEFOAM - Packaging–foam ☆ - Astro-Valcour, Inc.
RIDGEGROOVE - Hardware ☆ - Masonite Corp.
RIDGELAND - Guitars ☆ - Fred Gretsch Enterprises
RIDGELAND - Recording label - Madison Station Productions
RIDGELIGHT - Glass products - Lasco Products Group
RIDGELINE - Coats - Eddie Bauer Inc.
RIDGELINE - Golfing equipment - Sun Mountain Sports, Inc.
RIDGELINE - Hardware ☆ - Masonite Corp.
RIDGELINE - Roofing materials–slate - Ondura Inc.
RIDGEMONT - Floor coverings - Mannington Resilient Floors
RIDGEMONT - Wallpaper - Koroseal Wallcoverings
RIDGEMOUNT - Floor coverings - Mannington Resilient Floors
RIDGERUNNER - Antennas ☆ - Firestik Antenna Co.
RIDGERUNNER - Recording label - Ridge Runner
RIDGES - Underwear and nightwear ☆ - Henson-Kickernick Inc.
RIDGESIDE STRIP - Floor coverings - Bruce Hardwood Floors
RIDGETEX - Roofing materials - GAF Corp.
RIDGEVIEW - Socks - Ridgeview Inc.
RIDGEVIEW FARMS OF WISCONSIN - Cheese ☆ - DMV USA Inc.
RIDGEWAY - Clocks ☆ - Ridgeway Clock Co.

RIDGEWAY - Floor coverings - Tarkett, Inc.
RIDGEWAY - Floor coverings–carpet and rugs ☆ - Regal Rugs Inc.
RIDGEWAY - Jewelry - Jacoby-Bender Inc.
RIDGEWAY - Sporting goods - Kellwood Co.
RIDGEWAY BY KELTY - Sporting goods - Kellwood Co.
RIDGEWOOD - Blackboards–slate ☆ - Anco Wood Specialties Inc.
RIDGEWOOD - Blinds–venetian - Kenney Manufacturing Co.
RIDGEWOOD - Blinds–venetian - Spring Window Fashions Division, Inc.
RIDGEWOOD - Burial caskets - Batesville Casket Co., Inc.
RIDGEWOOD - Cabinets - Dewils Industries Inc.
RIDGEWOOD - Cabinets ☆ - Medallion Kitchens of Minnesota Inc.
RIDGEWOOD - Doors–glass ☆ - Malta Co.
RIDGEWOOD - Floor coverings - Bruce Hardwood Floors
RIDGEWOOD - Furniture ☆ - Hooker Furniture Corp.
RIDGEWOOD - Recording label - Gallery II Records Inc.
RIDGEWOOD - Siding–insulating - Amerimark Building Products, Inc.
RIDGI-HIDE - Metal finishing equipment - Goettl's Metal Products Co.
RIDGID - Hardware - Emerson Electric Co.
RIDGID - Tools - Ridge Tool Co.
RIDGID-KOLLMANN - Drain pipe cleaners - Ridge Tool Co.
RIDGIES - Potato chips - Wise Foods
RIDGLASS - Shingles - Ridglass Shingles Manufacturing Co., Inc.
RIDGOLATOR - Ventilation equipment - Klauer Manufacturing Co.
RIDGWAYS - Teas ☆ - Chase Collection, Inc.
RIDING A BICYCLE SHOULDN'T BE HARD - Bicycle parts and accessories - Serfus, Inc.
RIDING ACADEMY - Publisher's imprints - Random House, Inc.
RIDING HIGH - Apparel–men's - Resource Fashions Inc.
RIDING ON THE EDGE - Apparel and accessories - Eric W. Brothers
RIDLEN - Adhesives and sealants - Ridlen Manufacturing Inc.
RIDLEN PRO SENIOR - Craft supplies - Ridlen Manufacturing Inc.
RIDLEY PARK - Floor coverings ☆ - Tarkett, Inc.
RIDLEY'S - Food products - Ridley's Original Muffin Chips Co.
RIDLEYS - Jams and jellies ☆ - Chase Collection, Inc.
RIDOMIL GOLD - Fungicides - Ciba-Geigy Corp.
RIDWAX - Hearing aids - Oto-Med Technologies, Inc.
RIEBECK-ROMONTA - Waxes–sealing - Strohmeyer and Arpe Co.
RIEDEL - Glassware–household - Riedel Crystal of America Inc.
RIEDL - Clarinets - Ideal Musical Merchandise Co.
RIEGEL - Apparel–children's ☆ - Mount Vernon Mills Inc.
RIEGELEIN - Food products - George C. Brown's Biscuits & Confections
RIEGER KLOSS - Pianos - Hanseatic Overseas Trading Inc.
RIEMERSCHMID - Beverages–alcohol - Dieter Steinmann Inc.
RIES - Photographic equipment - Ries Industries Inc.
RIESBECK'S - Teas - Riesbeck Food Markets Inc.
RIESEN CHOCOLATE CHEW - Chocolate candy - Storck USA L.P.
RIETVELD USA - Apparel and accessories - Rick Rietveld
RIF - Balls–baseball - Worth Inc.
RIFA LITES - Lighting equipment - Lowel-Light Manufacturing Inc.
RIFA TRI LITEBAG - Cases–camera - Lowel-Light Manufacturing Inc.
RIFADIN - Antibiotics - Marion Merrell Dow
RIFAMATE - Pharmaceutical preparations - Marion Merrell Dow
RIFEAL - Computer software - Mnemonic Systems Inc.
RIFFELS COFFEE - Coffee - Riffel's Coffee Co.
RIFFS - Musical instrument accessories - Dunlop Manufacturing, Inc.
RIFLE - Cleaning preparations–household - Puritan-Churchill Chemical Co.
RIFLE - Golfing equipment - Brunswick Corp.
RIFLEMAN - Knives - Tru-Balance Knife Co.
RIFLEPAL - Cabinets–wood - Palmer Metal Products Inc.
RIFOCIN - Antibiotics - Marion Merrell Dow
RIFT - Recording label - Jazz Composer's Orchestra Association Inc.
RIFT LORDS - Games - Flying Buffalo Inc.
RIFTS - Toys - Kevin Siembieda
RIG LUBE - Lubricants - Navtec Inc.
RIG-MASTER - Hardware - Caldwell Group, Inc.
RIG-RAP - Tape–adhesive - Navtec Inc.
RIG RAP - Tape–masking - Navtec Inc.
RIG TO KILL - Apparel and accessories - Richard V. Tibbetts
RIG WRECKER - Toys–automobiles - Mattel, Inc.
RIGA ACCESSORIES - Apparel and accessories ☆ - TGL Corp.
RIGA BY TRAFALGAR - Leather goods - TGL Corp.
RIGA-PLEAT - Filters–air - Farr Co.
RIGAFLEX - Combines–agricultural - Rigaflex, Inc.
RIGAFLO - Filters–air - Farr Co.
RIGALYA - Vodka - Latvijas Balzams Distillery
RIGATTI - Apparel and accessories - Italian Suits Inc.

☆ = Now out of production

RIGAUD - Perfumes - FMG/Tsumara Medical

RIGBLOC - Metals - Rigbloc Enterprises Inc.

RIGBY - Electronics equipment - RTI Research Technology International

RIGEL - Fabrics - Scan Lines Inc.

RIGEL - Musical instruments - Peter Langdell

RIGEL 3 - Toys—models ☆ - Estes Industries

RIGGED RESULTS - Games ☆ - Mayfair Games, Inc.

RIGGER - Tools - Columbus Mckinnon Corp.

RIGGER'S - Bags ☆ - Byer of Maine

RIGGERSTIK - Fishing tackle ☆ - Fenwick

RIGGERTONE - Artists' materials ☆ - Robert Simmons Inc.

RIGHT - Pet products - Farmland Industries Inc.

RIGHT AMOUNT, THE - Vitamins and nutritional supplements - APIC USA, Inc.

RIGHT ANGLE - Golfing equipment - James J. Manley

RIGHT ANGLE, THE - Prisms—optical - Tedco Inc.

RIGHT AT HOME - Wallpaper ☆ - Pantasote Inc. (Wallcovering Div.)

RIGHT-AWAY - Food products - Right-Away Foods Corp.

RIGHT BACK - Hair care products - Lustrasilk Corp. of America Inc.

RIGHT BURGER - Vegetables—frozen - Mud Pie Frozen Foods, Inc.

RIGHT CHOICE - Apparel—women's - Bonanza Sportswear Inc.

RIGHT CHOICE - Bags—trash - Avantage Group Inc.

RIGHT CHOICE - Food products ☆ - Super Valu Inc.

RIGHT CHOICE - Paint rollers ☆ - Wooster Brush Co.

RIGHT CHOICE A.M. - Vitamins and nutritional supplements - Body Wise International, Inc.

RIGHT CHOICE P.M. - Vitamins and nutritional supplements - Body Wise International, Inc.

RIGHT COLORS, THE - Wallpaper - Snap & Sell Corp.

RIGHT CONNECTION - Identification jewelry - Jacoby-Bender Inc.

RIGHT CONNECTION, THE - Apparel—women's - Tamara Epstein

RIGHT CONTACTS, THE - Sockets—electric - Johnstech International Corp.

RIGHT CONTAINER PRODUCTS, THE - Catalogs - Barrel Accessories and Supply Co. Inc.

RIGHT CORNER - Linen - Bentley Bedding

RIGHT COURSE - Dinners—frozen ☆ - Stouffer Foods Corp.

RIGHT CUT - Tobacco—chewing or smoking - United States Tobacco Co.

RIGHT DRESS - Fertilizers - MacAndrews and Forbes Corp.

RIGHT DRESS - Hosiery - Wolverine World Wide, Inc.

RIGHT EGG, THE - Egg product - Pureggs Brands, Inc.

RIGHT FIRST CHOICE, THE - Computer software - Manzanita Software Systems

RIGHT FOR LUNCH - Food products ☆ - Pillsbury Co.

RIGHT FROM THE START - Batteries - GNB Inc. (Automotive Battery Div.)

RIGHT FROM THE START - Paints - Zehrung Corp.

RIGHT-GARD - Sporting goods - Right Gard Corp.

RIGHT GUARD - Deodorants—personal - Gillette Co.

RIGHT HEIGHT - High chairs - Lisco, Inc.

RIGHT IMAGE - Uniforms—tailored ☆ - Riverside Manufacturing Co.

RIGHT IMAGES, THE - Computer peripheral equipment - Norstrilia Software Inc.

RIGHT INGREDIENTS ARE RIGHT INSIDE!, THE - Soups—mixes - Hormel Foods Corp.

RIGHT KIND - Dental equipment - John O.Butler Co.

RIGHT LINES - Wallpaper ☆ - Pickhardt & Siebert USA Inc.

RIGHT LINES II - Wallpaper - Bayview Wallcoverings

RIGHT LINK, THE - Golfing equipment - Golf Training Systems, Inc.

RIGHT MOVE, THE - Publisher's imprints - Jayne B. Knox

RIGHT MOVES - Apparel—men's - Santana Ltd.

RIGHT NOW - Hair care products - Giovanni Cosmetics Inc.

RIGHT OFF THE BAT - Games - Grand Slam Baseball Corp.

RIGHT ON - All-occasion cards ☆ - Regency Thermographers Inc.

RIGHT ON - Cleaning preparations ☆ - Calgon Vestal Laboratories

RIGHT ON - Farm machinery - Spyker Spreader Works

RIGHT ON - Hair care products - Lustrasilk Corp. of America Inc.

RIGHT-ON - Skin care products - Waverly Beauty Products

RIGHT-ON - Varnishes - Aleene's

RIGHT ON RED BEST ON BLACK - Wax removers - Egl 1, Inc.

RIGHT ON SIGHT - Eyeglasses - F. Steven Schneider

RIGHT REASONS - Floor coverings—carpet and rugs ☆ - Lees Carpets

RIGHT RECOMMENDATION WRITER, THE - Computer software - Cambridge Educational

RIGHT RIBBON SYSTEM - Ribbons—inked - Smith Corona Corp.

RIGHT SITE, THE - Computer software - Easy Analytic Software

RIGHT START - Cereal ☆ - U.S. Mills, Inc.

RIGHT START - Fertilizers - Treessentials Co.

RIGHT STEP - Sandals - Genki USA

RIGHT STEP, THE - Veterinary pharmaceutical preparations - Life Data Labs, Inc.

RIGHT STUFF - Kites - Hi-Flier Manufacturing Co.

RIGHT STUFF, THE - Floor coverings—carpet and rugs - Ashley Commercial Carpets

RIGHT STUFF, THE - Apparel and accessories - Avirex Ltd.

RIGHT STUFF, THE - Chemical preparations - Larry J. Bloom

RIGHT STUFF, THE - Popcorn - Curtice-Burns Foods, Inc.

RIGHT STUFF!, THE - Chemical preparations - Graphic Technologies, Inc.

RIGHT STUFF, THE - Popcorn - Nalley's Fine Foods

RIGHT STUFF, THE - Wallpaper ☆ - Pantasote Inc. (Wallcovering Div.)

RIGHT STUFF, THE - Wallcoverings - Ben Rose Ltd.

RIGHT SUPPORT FOR YOU - Apparel—women's - NCC Industries, Inc.

RIGHT THERE - Darts and dart games - Emersome

RIGHT TIGHT, THE - Apparel and accessories - Impromptu Productions Inc.

RIGHT TOUCH - Computer peripheral equipment - NMB Technologies Inc. (Hi-Tek Div.)

RIGHT TOUCH - Fabrics—tapestry ☆ - Coloroll Inc.

RIGHT TRACKS, THE - Music recorders - MMO Music Group Inc.

RIGHT WAY TEE - Sporting goods - Schutt Manufacturing Co.

RIGHT WAY TO WATER, THE - Hoses - Aquapore Moisture Systems, Inc.

RIGHTAPE - Tape measures - The Right Tape Co.

RIGHTEOUS RAGS - Shirts - Righteous Rags Inc.

RIGHTO - Vegetables—canned - Reinbeck Canning Co.

RIGHTOUT - Cleaning preparations—carpet and rug - Outright Industries, Inc.

RIGHTRAC - Medical equipment - Exonix Research Corp.

RIGHTS ON! - Computer software - SKP Book Consultants Inc.

RIGHTSHAPE - Biscuits - Campbell Taggart Inc.

RIGHTWEIGH - Scales—bathroom - Metro Corp.

RIGHTWRITER - Computer software - Que Software

RIGI - Candy - Jacques F. Weber Co.

RIGI-BUMP - Ferroalloys - Rigidized Metals Corp.

RIGI-FLEX - Electrical equipment - Westinghouse Electric Corp.

RIGI-KON - Filters—air - Air Kontrol Inc.

RIGID - Electrical equipment - GB Electrical Inc.

RIGID - Knives - United Cutlery Corp.

RIGID BRITE - Plastics—laminated - Cooley Sign Systems, Inc.

RIGID CLAMPS - Clamps—metal - Sign-Up Corp.

RIGID DOOR - Construction equipment - Heartland Industries, Inc.

RIGID GAS - Ophthalmic goods - Blairex Laboratories, Inc.

RIGID RIB - Roofing materials—clay - WCI Steel Inc.

RIGID ROLL - Roofing materials - Trimline Building Products

RIGID TIE - Construction equipment - Simpson Strong-Tie Co., Inc.

RIGID UNI-BODY DESIGN - Chairs—wood - La-Z-Boy Chair Co.

RIGID-WRAP - Artists' materials - Activa Products Inc.

RIGIDAC - Adhesives and sealants - Bogert Plastics Inc.

RIGIDAIR - Artists' materials - Gilman Brothers Co.

RIGIDBILT - Sporting goods - Schutt Manufacturing Co.

RIGIDENT - Denture materials - Carter-Wallace, Inc.

RIGIDEX - Building materials - Fibergrate Composite Structures

RIGIDFRAME - Insulating materials - Defender Inc.

RIGIDLITE - Pipe couplings - Grinnell Corp.

RIGIDLOK - Plumbing fixtures - Grinnell Corp.

RIGIDUCT - Glass—flat ☆ - PPG Industries, Inc.

RIGIDWARE - Plates—paper - Premier Industries Inc.

RIGIFLEX - Plastics - L.J. Van Dyke

RIGITRODE - Electrodes - Environmental Elements Corp.

RIGMAROLE - Colognes ☆ - Avon Products, Inc.

RIG'N - Fishing tackle - Owner American Corp.

RIGNES SPECIAL - Beverages—alcohol - Heaven Hill Distilleries, Inc.

RIGO - Insecticides - Rigo Co.

RIGO ARTECH II - Wallpaper ☆ - Rigo Wallcoverings Inc.

RIGO CONTRACT VOL. III - Wallpaper - Rigo Wallcoverings Inc.

RIGO CUSTOM BORDERS - Wallpaper - Rigo Wallcoverings Inc.

RIGO GROUNDS - Wallpaper - Rigo Wallcoverings Inc.

RIGO HEAVYWIEGHT - Wallpaper - Rigo Wallcoverings Inc.

RIGO SPORT R1/15 - Apparel and accessories - Rigo Enterprises

RIGO TECH - Wallpaper - Rigo Wallcoverings Inc.

RIGO TEXTURES - Wallpaper - Rigo Wallcoverings Inc.

RIGO TEXTURES II - Wallpaper - Rigo Wallcoverings Inc.

RIGO TEXTURES PLUS - Wallpaper - Rigo Wallcoverings Inc.

RIGOL - Fruits and vegetables ☆ - Marglo Products Corp.

RIGOLESTER CLOWN - Toys—stuffed - Russ Berrie and Co., Inc.

RIGOLETTO - Cigars - J.C. Newman Cigar Co.

RIGOLETTO - Tomato pastes and sauces - Lico Brands, Inc.

RIGOLETTO BLACK MAGIC - Cigars ☆ - J.C. Newman Cigar Co.

☆ = Now out of production

RIGOR MOTOR - Toys - Mattel, Inc.
RIGO'S BEST - Insecticides - Rigo Co.
RIGSCAN - Pharmaceutical preparations - Neoprobe Corp.
RIGULATOR - Calculators - Cadabra CCS J.V.
RIISE - Cabinets - James G. Riise
RIJELO'S - Pizzas–frozen - Nation Pizza Products L.P.
RIJKDOM - Cigars - Gesty Trading & Manufacturing Corp.
RIJKS MUSEUM HOLLAND - Postcards ☆ - Fotofolio Inc.
RIK RAK - Cosmetics ☆ - Renbow International Ltd. USA
RIK SHA - Food products - Treasure Isle Inc.
RIKALOFF - Vodka - Majestic Distilling Co.
RIKSHA RUNNER - Exercise apparatus - Solomon Wroclawsky
RIKY WAX - Cosmetics - Worldwide Cosmetics
RIL-SWEET - Sweeteners–artificial ☆ - Schering-Plough Healthcare Products
RILA - Olives–pickled or brined - Euro International
RILEY - Golfing equipment - John Riley Golf Inc.
RILEY ACCESS - CRIBS - Cribs–metal - HARD Manufacturing Co. Inc.
RILEY'S - Publisher's imprints - Riley Electric Log, Inc.
RILEY'S COFFEE & FUDGE - Food products - Thomas & Riley Coffee, Ltd.
RILLET - Floor coverings ☆ - Tarkett, Inc.
RILUX - Hair care products - Lever Brothers Co. Inc.
RIM - Deicing equipment–aircraft - Revere Products
RIM - Orthopedic head controls - International Medical Core
RIM - Recording label - Urgent! Records
RIM BENDER - Apparel and accessories - Michael Wilkerson Jones
RIM-FIRE - Apparel and accessories - St. Lolly International Inc.
RIM HANGER - Action figures and accessories - Tonka Corp.
RIM LIFE - Chemical preparations - Fuller Brothers, Inc.
RIM RAGE - Sporting goods - Guy Wells & Co., Inc.
RIM RAKE - Auto parts - Delta Cycle Corp.
RIM ROCKA - Apparel stores–men's - Tunee Apparel Inc.
RIM RODS - Bicycles - Wheelsmith Fabrications Inc.
RIM SHAKER - Balls–basketball - Hutch Sports USA Inc.
RIMA - Rice - Connell Co.
RIMA GREENBERG - Chessboards - Rima Greenberg
RIMACTANE - Antibiotics - Ciba-Geigy Corp.
RIMAI - Tiles–ceramic ☆ - Mediterranean Exports
RIMANTO - Vodka - Dieter Steinmann Inc.
RIMAR - Window frames - Rimar Inc.
RIMBALL - Sporting goods - Rimball Marketing and Development, Inc.
RIMFIL - Plastic materials - Rimpac International Co.
RIMFIRE - Ammunition - Blount International, Inc. (Sporting Equipment Group)
RIMFIRE - Tires - Dunlop Tire Corp.
RIMFLY - Fishing reels - Cortland Line Co., Inc.
RIMINI - Floor coverings–tile ☆ - Kentile Floors Inc.
RIMINI - Housewares - Himark Enterprises Inc.
RIMLINE - Frames–eyeglass - Hudson Optical Corp.
RIMMER - Chase Collection, Inc.
RIMMS RESOURCES IN MOTION MANAGEMENT SYSTEM - Computer software - Lightstone Group, Inc.
RIMOWA - Photographic equipment - H.P. Marketing Corp.
RIMROCK - Fruits and vegetables ☆ - Marley Orchards Corp.
RIMROCK - Rifles - Pacific Research Laboratories, Inc.
RIMROCK - Tiles–ceramic - R.L. Mueller
RIMS - Motor vehicle parts and accessories - Purecussion Inc.
RIMSKIN - Chemical preparations - Recticel North America, Inc.
RIMULA - Oils–lubricating - Shell Oil Co.
RIMWRAP - Tape–adhesive - RND Co.
RIN-T - Computers - Mercury Computer Systems Inc.
RINADE-B.I.D. - Pharmaceutical preparations - Econo Med Pharmaceuticals Inc.
RINALDI - Shoes ☆ - Schwartz & Benjamin Inc.
RINALDO ROSSELLI - Footwear - Shuman Shoe Co. Inc.
RINASCIMUTO - Wallpaper - Blumenthal
RINCONADA - Fruits and vegetables ☆ - Marglo Products Corp.
RINE - Jewelry - W. Rinegold Inc.
RINEK - Rope ☆ - Waterbury Rope Mills
RING - Candy ☆ - Topps Co., Inc.
RING - Containers–plastic - Ring Can Corp.
RING 5 - Pet products - Vo-Toys Inc.
RING-A-BELL - Balls–basketball - Logan Electric Specialty Manufacturing Co.
RING-A-DINGS - Toys–stuffed - Gund, Inc.
RING-A-ROUND - Underwear and nightwear - Bestform Foundations, Inc.
RING-A-TOY - Toys - Gerber Products Co.
RING A WISH - Paper products - Associated Network Inc.
RING & PETAL - Glass products - Westmoreland Glass Co.

RING AROUND THE MOON - Christmas tree ornaments - Cracker Box Inc.
RING AROUND THE NOSY - Games - Pressman Toy Corp.
RING AROUND THE TREE - Pet products - Four Paws Products Ltd.
RING-BARB - Hardware - Hillwood Manufacturing Co.
RING BEAD - Handbags - Lumured Corp.
RING BEARER - Games - Gamescience
RING BOLT - Locks–door - Exit Security, Inc.
RING-DEX - Index cards - Dennison National Co.
RING DING - Cakes - Drake Bakeries, Inc.
RING-FLO - Catheters - Tyco International Ltd.
RING-FREE - Oils–lubricating - MacMillan Ring-Free Oil Co. Inc.
RING HANGER - Craft supplies - Ziabicki Import Co.
RING KIDS, THE - Sporting goods - London Publishing Co.
RING KING - Office furniture–wood - Ring King Visibles, Inc.
RING KLIPS - Paper clips - Baumgarten's
RING LEADER - Floor coverings - Durable Corp.
RING LEADER - Onions - Delicious Foods Co.
RING LOC - Tools–hand-operated - William Kenneth Hagerty
RING MASTER - Machinery - Porta-Nails, Inc.
RING MASTER - Mats - Superior Manufacturing Group/Notrax Floor Matting
RING-O - Valves–industrial - Ring-O Valve Corp.
RING-O-DOUGH - Games - Rowland Specialty Co.
RING O' FRIENDS - Dolls - Mattel, Inc.
RING O LITE - Lamp bulbs–fluorescent - Angelo Brothers Co.
RING-O-ROUND KEYS - Toys–stuffed ☆ - Gund, Inc.
RING OUT - Cleaning preparations–household - International Trading Hawaii, Inc.
RING-PEN - Health care products - Maddak Inc.
RING POP - Candy - Topps Co., Inc.
RING QUEST - Video games - Origin Systems, Inc.
RING RAIDERS - Toys ☆ - Those Characters from Cleveland, Inc.
RING RAT - Apparel and accessories - Gym Rat, Inc.
RING ROOST - Craft supplies - Pepperell Braiding Co. Inc.
RING-SEAL - Lubricants - Shaler Co.
RING SLIPPER - Skin care products - Walbak International Marketing, Ltd.
RING-THE-DATE - Paper–gummed ☆ - Park Sherman
RING THING - Games - Julian M. Tindall
RING TOSS - Toys ☆ - Lauri Inc.
RING TUF PAK - Containers–plastic - Ring Can Corp.
RING TUFF - Paper - Xerox Corp.
RING-VENT - Tiles–ceiling - Artcrest Products Co. Inc.
RINGA-MAJIGS - Construction toys - James Industries, Inc.
RINGALERT - Medical apparatus - E.P.S., Inc.
RINGBUILDER - Computer peripheral equipment - 3Com Corp.
RINGCENTRAL - Computer software - Ring Zero Systems, Inc.
RINGDIRECTOR - Electronic equipment - Lynx Automation Inc.
RINGER - Fertilizers - Ringer Corp.
RINGER - Golfing equipment ☆ - James E. Corbett
RINGER - Musical instruments ☆ - Selmer Co. Inc.
RINGER - Pizzas–frozen - Grande Cheese Co.
RINGER - Shirts - Sara Lee Knit Products Inc.
RINGER - Work clothes - H.W. Carter & Sons Inc.
RINGERS - Food products - Stello Foods, Inc.
RINGFOLIO - Binders - Dennison National Co.
RINGLET - Brassieres (Bras) ☆ - Lovable Co.
RINGLETTS - Vegetables–frozen - Norpac Services, Inc.
RINGLINE - Paper–writing - Kurtz Bros. Inc.
RINGLOK - Filters–water - Jacuzzi Brothers
RINGLORDS - Collector cards - Players International Ltd.
RINGLUBE - Bearings–industrial - Tribology Systems, Inc.
RINGMAKER - Onions - Eisenberg Co.
RINGMASTER - Computer software - Livestock Marketing Services Corp.
RINGMASTER - Floor coverings–carpet and rugs - Cabin Crafts Carpets
RINGMASTER - Projectors–photographic - Eiki International Inc.
RINGNES - Beverages–malt - Heaven Hill Distilleries, Inc.
RINGO - Apparel and accessories - Haselson International Trading, Inc.
RINGO - Shoes–athletic - Coast Shoes Inc.
RINGO - Toys ☆ - Esquire Novelty Corp.
RINGO DOG - Toys–stuffed - Gund, Inc.
RINGO RATTLE - Toys–stuffed - Gund, Inc.
RINGS - Footwear - Angel-Etts of California, Inc.
RINGS & THINGS - Jewelry - Ullenberg Corp.
RINGS OF REFLECTION - Jewelry–precious - Rings of Reflection LLC
RINGS OF ROYALTY - Rings–jewelry ☆ - Artcarved Inc.
RINGS ON YOUR FINGERS - Candy - Ce De Candy Inc.
RINGSBY - Toys–automobiles - Toy Truck Lines, Inc.

☆ = Now out of production

RINGSDORF HEALTH CONCEPTS - Vitamins and nutritional supplements ☆ - Ringsdorf Research, L.L.C.

RINGSIDE TRADING CARDS - Trading cards and stamps - International Sports Collectibles Inc.

RINGSPUN - Yarn - Parkdale Mills, Inc.

RINGTALES - Toys - Price Stern Sloan Inc.

RINGTHING - Tools–hand-operated - Ringthing of California

RINGZ - Snack foods - Borden, Inc.

RINI'S - Wines - Rini Wine Co.

RINK-LEADER - Skates–ice - Gotham Shoe Manufacturing Co.

RINK RAT - Apparel and accessories - Gym Rat, Inc.

RINKER - Boats–motor - Rinker Boat Co. Inc.

RINKMASTER QUAD - Skates–roller - Seneca Sports, Inc.

RINKY DINK - Jewelry - Rinky Dink Co., Inc.

RINKY DINK - Novelty items - S.J. Miller Co.

RINKY DINKS - Candy - Willy Wonka Brands

RINO MARTINENEGO - Wines - Tyfield Importers

RINOSAN - Herbal products - Jose M. Gonzalez-Blanco

RINS-NO-MORE - Cleaning preparations - Multi-Care Corp.

RINSA RAMA - Hair care products - Fleetwood Co.

RINSE - Plumbing fixtures–metal ☆ - Moen Inc.

RINSE-A-WAY - Cleaning preparations ☆ - Duchess Royale Inc.

RINSE-AID - Cleaning preparations - Well-Flow Technologies, Inc.

RINSE AWAY - Hair care products - Alberto-Culver Co.

RINSE AWAY - Paint removers ☆ - Klean-Strip

RINSE CONTROL - Hair care products - Pro Design International, Inc.

RINSE DRY - Rinse additives for dishwashers - Ecolab Inc.

RINSE ENHANCERS - Dishwashing compounds - Benckiser Consumer Products Inc.

RINSE FREE - Cleaning preparations–carpet and rug - Promaster

RINSE KLEEN - Paint and wallpaper cleaners - Sterling-Clark-Lurton Corp.

RINSE N SET - Cosmetics - Johnson Products Co., Inc.

RINSE 'N TONE - Skin care products - Moore Beauty Inc.

RINSE N VAC - Cleaning equipment - Blue Lustre, LLC

RINSE NO MORE - Brushes - Pro Sales Industries, Inc.

RINSE NO MORE - Shampoos - King Research, Inc.

RINSE ROYAL - Hair care products - Nicole Research Inc.

RINSE-TO-CLEAN - Vaporizers - Duracraft Corp.

RINSE WELL - Housewares - Techniplas Inc.

RINSENVAC - Carpet-cleaning system - Blue Lustre, LLC

RINSO - Detergents - Lever Brothers Co. Inc.

RINX, THE - Apparel and accessories - Rinx

RINZ-FREE - Cleaning preparations–household - Harley Chemicals

RINZA - Skin care products - Hanah Beauty & Health Inc.

RIO - Accordions - Excelsior Accordions Inc.

RIO - Aquarium accessories - Technological Aquatic Associated Manufacturing

RIO - Brushes–paint ☆ - PPG Industries, Inc.

RIO - Chairs–upholstered - Fixtures Furniture

RIO - Cigarettes - Philip Morris Companies Inc.

RIO - Electronics equipment - Specialix, Inc.

RIO - Fabrics - Vertilux-Louverlux Inc.

RIO - Fans–electric - Dennis Bearden

RIO - Flatware ☆ - Couzon USA

RIO - Floor coverings–carpet and rugs - Couristan Inc.

RIO - Floor coverings–carpet and rugs - Mohawk Carpet Corp.

RIO - Floor coverings–carpet and rugs - World Carpets, Inc.

RIO - Floor coverings–carpet and rugs ☆ - Trans-Ocean Import Co. Inc.

RIO - Flowers, plants, and seeds - Olsen-Fennell Seeds, Inc.

RIO - Footwear - Her-Man Imports Inc.

RIO - Frames–eyeglass - U.S. Optical Frame Co.

RIO - Glassware–household - Owens-Illinois Inc. (Libbey Div.)

RIO - Plumbing fixtures - National Fiber Glass Products

RIO - Syrup - Rio Syrup Co. Inc.

RIO - Tote bags - American Flyer

RIO - Wigs ☆ - Paula Young

RIO - Yarn - Henry's Attic

RIO BEACH COLLECTION - Chairs–folding - All-Luminum Products Inc.

RIO BLAST - Toys - Mattel, Inc.

RIO BRAVO - Apparel - Prestige Apparel, Inc.

RIO BRAVO - House furnishings ☆ - Florida Furniture Industries Inc.

RIO BREEZE - Water–mineral ☆ - Golden Brands Marketing

RIO CS - Lighting fixtures - Gesing International Inc.

RIO DE JANEIRO - Luggage ☆ - Universal Trav-ler Inc.

RIO DE ORO - Bakery products - Clements Food Co. Inc.

RIO DIABLO - Food products - Rio Diablo

RIO D'ORO - Food products - Tropicana Products, Inc.

RIO GOLD - Beverages - Fantasy Blankebaer

RIO GOLD - Fruit drinks–bottled or canned - Smith's Dairy Products Co.

RIO GRANDE - Apparel and accessories - J.C. Penney Co., Inc.

RIO GRANDE - Beverages–alcohol - Mccormick Distilling Co., Inc.

RIO GRANDE - Cement - Rio Grande Portland Cement Corp.

RIO GRANDE - Cigars - Gesty Trading & Manufacturing Corp.

RIO GRANDE - Floor coverings–carpet and rugs - Mattel Carpet & Rug Inc.

RIO GRANDE - Furniture - Dinaire Corp.

RIO GRANDE - Furniture ☆ - Bean Station Furniture Factory Inc.

RIO GRANDE - Luggage - York Partners, L.P.

RIO GRANDE - Shingles - U.S. Intec, Inc.

RIO GRANDE - Shrimp–fresh or frozen - Morgan City Freezer & Cold Storage Inc.

RIO GRANDE - Skin care products - Great American Health Foods

RIO GRANDE - Trailers–travel ☆ - Fleetwood Enterprises, Inc.

RIO GRANDE - Wallpaper ☆ - Wolf-Gordon Inc.

RIO GRANDE BREWING - Beverages–malt - Rio Grande Brewing Co.

RIO GRANDE STONEWARE - Candles - Rio Grande Stoneware, Inc.

RIO GRANDE VALLEY WHITEWINGS - Apparel and accessories - Texas Professional Baseball, Inc.

RIO GRANT - Crackers - Vista Bakery, Inc.

RIO LADY - Apparel and accessories - Robar Distributing Co., Inc.

RIO LOBO RANCHWEAR - Clothing - Donald Matthew Daley

RIO LOCO - Apparel and accessories - Sea World, Inc.

RIO LUNA - Chile peppers, jalapeno peppers - Border Foods Inc.

RIO NEGRO ARGENTINA - Beverages–alcohol - Tosi Vintners International

RIO PARROT - Toys–stuffed ☆ - Dakin Inc.

RIO QUEST - Chemical preparations - Rio Linda Chemical Co., Inc.

RIO RATZ - Apparel and accessories - Robar Distributing Co., Inc.

RIO RICO - Fishing tackle - JEF International Inc.

RIO SELECT JAZZ - Musical instrument accessories - Rico International

RIO SUNWEAR - Shoes - R. Josephs Sportswear, Inc.

RIO SYRUP - Syrup - C.R. Frank Popcorn & Supply Co.

RIO VALLEY - Vegetables–canned - Rio Valley Canning Co., Inc.

RIO VIEJO - Wines ☆ - Domecq Importers Inc.

RIOBIN-50 - Pharmaceutical preparations ☆ - Pasadena Research Laboratories, Inc.

RIOJA - Wines - Commercial Office of Spain

RIOJANO - Sausages - S. Abuin Packing Inc.

RIOKA - Cameras and accessories - Aimex Camera Inc.

RIOPAN - Antacids - Whitehall Laboratories

RIOPAN PLUS - Antacids - Whitehall Laboratories

RIOPAN PLUS 2 - Antacids - Whitehall Laboratories

RIOS DE ORO - Coffee - Welker Brothers Marketing, Inc.

RIOS OF MERCEDES - Boots - Rios of Mercedes Handmade Boots

RIOT EXTINGUISHER, THE - Alarms–personal - Defense Technology Corp. of America

RIOTGLAS - Glass–flat - Guardian Industries Corp.

RIOTGUARD - Glass products - Laminated Glass Corp.

RIOTSHIELD - Glass–safety ☆ - Laminated Glass Corp.

RIP - Apparel and accessories - LFP Inc.

RIP - Athletic supporters - Custom Support Corp.

R.I.P. - Golfing equipment ☆ - Progear, Inc.

R.I.P. - Skateboards - Powell Skateboards

RIP - Toys–electronic - Sounds Fun, Inc.

RIP & CLIP - Paper bags - Union Camp Corp. (Fine Paper Division)

RIP AND RAM - Tools–hand-operated - Newtron Products

RIP CITY - Coffee - Boyd Coffee Co.

RIP CURL - Bicycles - Dynacraft Industries Inc.

RIP-IT-UP - Apparel and accessories - Vincent Esposito

RIP KIT - Apparel and accessories - W.L. Gore & Associates, Inc.

RIP-L - Potato chips - Old Dutch Foods, Inc.

RIP 'N RAIN - Containers - Avantech Resource Center, Inc.

RIP N RUN - Hooks - A Ripping Success, Inc.

RIP OFF - Apparel and accessories - Thomas B. Bluemel

RIP OFFS - Apparel and accessories - Brennan Johnston

RIP-OFF'S - Footwear - Sunbelt Footwear Corp.

RIP-OFFS - Paper - Riverside Paper Corp.

RIP-OFFS - Sporting goods - Regal Industries, Inc.

RIP-OPE - Envelopes - Tension Envelope Corp.

RIP RAT - Toys–automobiles - Mattel, Inc.

RIP RIDER - Apparel and accessories - Pacific Sunwear of California Inc.

RIP-ROARING MACARONI & BEEF - Food products - Conagra, Inc.

RIP ROAR'N - Soups–canned - Buckeye Beans & Herbs, Inc.

RIP ROCKETS - Darts and dart games - Tonka Corp.

RIP SAW - Toys–guns - Tonka Corp.

☆ = Now out of production

RIP-SCREEN - Machine parts - Williams Patent Crusher & Pulverizer Co.
RIP SHAD - Fishing lures - Bomber Bait Co.
RIP STOP GRID - Hair care products - Andre Fantasies Inc.
RIP TIDE - Fishing lures - Classic Fishing Products, Inc.
RIP TIDE - Seafood products–fresh or frozen - Gorton Group
RIP-TIE - Cables - Effron Sales
RIP VAN WINKLE - Mattresses - Aireloom Bedding Co.
RIP-WHILE-PRINT - Computer software - Electronics for Imaging, Inc.
RIPA - Bicycle parts and accessories ☆ - Joseph Caragol Inc.
RIPARO - Hair care products - Modafini Inc.
RIPAVERINE - Pharmaceutical preparations - Pharmics Inc.
RIPCORD - Toys ☆ - Ray Plastic Inc.
RIPE - Nail care products - Ripe, Inc.
RIPE WHEAT - Melamine product - Boonton Molding Co. Inc.
RIPENSA - Containers–metal - Liberty Richter Inc.
RIPIT - Apparel–athletic - William R. Ackerman
RIPLETS - Snack foods ☆ - Sunshine Biscuits, Inc.
RIPLEY - Wines - Schloss Doepken Winery
RIPLEY BELIEVE IT OR NOT VEGETABLE SEEDS - Flowers, plants, and seeds - Grace's Gardens, Inc.
RIPLEY'S BELIEVE IT OR NOT! - Computer software - Ripley Entertainment Inc.
RIPLEY'S BELIEVE IT OR NOT - Flowers, plants, and seeds - Page Seed Co.
RIPLEY'S BELIEVE IT OR NOT - Games ☆ - Milton Bradley Co.
R.I.P.'N RIC - Fishing lures - All Outdoor Marketing, Inc.
RIPON ATHLETIC - Apparel stores–sports - Ripon Awardjackets, Inc.
RIPOSTE - Computer peripheral equipment - Escher Group, Ltd.
RIPPED FAST - Vitamins and nutritional supplements - Dener Management Inc.
RIPPED FORCE - Vitamins and nutritional supplements - American Body Building Products, Inc.
RIPPED FUEL - Vitamins and nutritional supplements - Twinlab
RIPPEN - Computer software - Orincon Corp.
RIPPER - Child's pedal car - Radio Flyer Inc.
RIPPER - Games ☆ - Avalon Hill Game Co.
RIPPER - Machine tools - Valenite Inc.
RIPPER - Toys - Wham-O Manufacturing Co.
RIPPERS - Shoes - KangaROOS USA Inc.
RIPPIN' CHIPS - Cookies - Ripon Foods, Inc.
RIPPIN' GOOD - Cookies - Ripon Foods, Inc.
RIPPIN RATLER - Flags - Plastics Research and Development Co.
RIPPLBED - Alternating-pressure beds - International Medical Core
RIPPLE - Wines ☆ - Ernest and Julio Gallo Winery
RIPPLE CRISP - Cereal - General Mills, Inc.
RIPPLE DIPPLES - Potato chips ☆ - Super Valu Inc.
RIPPLE STRIPPER - Power transformers - Ultravolt, Inc.
RIPPLE THRU - Computer software - Digital Software, Inc.
RIPPLE TOP - Water heaters–household - Central Boiler, Inc.
RIPPLEFLEX - Building materials - Intalite International, NV
RIPPLEFOLD - Drapery hardware - Kirsch Co.
RIPPER LURES - Fishing lures - Rippler Lures Corp.
RIPPLES - Aluminum foil wrap - Highland Supply Corp.
RIPPLES - Floor coverings–carpet and rugs - Regal Rugs Inc.
RIPPLES - House furnishings - Dan River Inc.
RIPPLES - Snack foods ☆ - Anheuser-Busch Companies Inc.
RIPPLES ON THE WATER - Christmas tree ornaments - Cracker Box Inc.
RIPPLESOUND - Corrugated aluminum - Intalite International, NV
RIPPLESPUN - Fabrics - Dan River Inc.
RIPPLING WINDS - Floor coverings–carpet and rugs - Masterpiece Finishing Co.
RIPPLIN'S - Potato chips ☆ - Keebler Co.
RIPRO JR. - Duplicating machines - RICOH Corp.
RIPSAW - Recording label - Ripsaw Record Co.
RIPSAW - Toy vehicle - Tonka Corp.
RIPSPINNER - See **RIPSTINGER**
RIPSTER - Toys - Mattel, Inc.
RIPSTICK - Fishing lures - Reef Runner Tackle Co.
RIPSTINGER - Toys - Mattel, Inc.
RIPSTINGER - Toys ☆ - Wham-O Manufacturing Co.
RIPSTIXX - Golfing equipment - SPL International, Inc.
RIPSTOP - Tarpaulins - R.E. Peacock Co./Southwestern Cordage Co.
RIPTIDE - Books–comic - Rob Liefeld, Inc.
RIPTIDE - Colognes - Lady in Red, Ltd.
RIPTIDE - Fabrics - Rosebar Textile Co.
RIPTIDE - Floor coverings–carpet and rugs ☆ - Quaker Inc.
RIPTIDE - Motors–outboard - Classic Manufacturing Co., Inc.

RIPTIDE - Recording label - Ripete Music Group
RIPTIDE - Vertical blinds - Atlantic Venetian Blind & Drapery Co.
RIPTILE - Toys–automobiles - Mattel, Inc.
RIPTRON - Ships–patrol boats - Sub-4 Inc.
RIPWARE - Computer software - Imageworx Corp.
RIS - Boats–liferafts - Boat Saver
RIS-GAY - Novelty items - Barnhart Industries Inc.
RISC86 - Computer hardware - Nexgen Microsystems
RISE - Apparel and accessories - Farook I. Hameed
RISE - Computer integrated systems design services - Rise Int'l., Inc.
RISE - Fish food - Agway Country Foods Inc.
RISE - Rope - Wellington Leisure Products, Inc.
RISE - Shaving preparations - Carter-Wallace, Inc.
RISE AND DECLINE OF THE THIRD REICH - Games - Avalon Hill Game Co.
RISE & SHINE - Dolls - Mattel, Inc.
RISE AND SHINE - Recording label - McCain Brothers, Inc.
RISE & SHINE - Vitamins and nutritional supplements - Vitamin Research Products Inc.
RISE & SHINE - Wallpaper - Hunting Valley Prints
RISE 'N DINE - Chairs–plastic ☆ - Century Products Co.
RISE N' SHINE - Fruits and vegetables - William E. Meek
RISE N' SHINE - Hair care products - Garcoa Labs/Vitamin Classics
RISE 'N SHINE - Housewares - Shafford Co. Inc.
RISE 'N SHINE - Pharmaceutical preparations - Victor Drug Corp.
RISE 'N STRETCH - Underwear and nightwear - Youthcraft-Charmfit
RISE 'N STRIDE - Underwear and nightwear - Youthcraft-Charmfit
RISE OF THE TRIAD - Computer software - Apogee Software Ltd.
RISE SUPER GEL - Shaving preparations - Carter-Wallace, Inc.
RISER BY MOEN - Faucets - Moen Inc.
RISER-GARD - Pipes - Lamson & Sessions Co.
RISER VISOR - Vacuum cleaners and accessories - The Eureka Co.
RISERIA D'ITALIA - Rice - Dean & Deluca Inc.
RISERS - Frozen foods - Schwan's Sales Enterprises, Inc.
RISETTES - Diapers–disposable - Weyerhaeuser Co.
RISI - Snack foods - Crispy Snacks
RISING - Paper ☆ - Fox River Paper Co.
RISING BARRIER PAPER - Paperboard - Rising Paper, Division of Fox River Paper Co.
RISING CONSERVATION BOARD - Paperboard - Rising Paper, Division of Fox River Paper Co.
RISING MUSEUM BOARD - Paperboard - Rising Paper, Division of Fox River Paper Co.
RISING SON HEALTH PRODUCTS - Vitamins and nutritional supplements - Rising Son Health Products, Inc.
RISING STAR - Apparel stores–lingerie - Formflex Foundations Inc.
RISING STAR - Recording label - Parr-X Corp.
RISING STAR - Sporting goods - O'Brien International
RISING STAR - Trading cards and stamps - Fleer Corp.
RISING STAR RITA - Wines - Steak & Ale Corp.
RISING SUN - Food products - Rising Sun Farms, Inc.
RISING SUN - Furniture - Singer Furniture Co.
RISING SUN - Recording label - Scene Productions/Purple Haze Music
RISING SUN FARM - Food products - Rising Sun Farms, Inc.
RISING TIDE - Floor coverings–carpet and rugs - Gulistan Carpet Inc.
RISING TIDE - Food products - Rising Tide Natural Foods, Inc.
RISING WAVE - Computer software - Rising Wave
R.I.S.K. - Apparel and accessories - BUM International Inc.
RISK - Games - Parker Brothers
R.I.S.K. EQUIPMENT - Apparel and accessories - BUM International Inc.
RISK INSIGHTS - Computer software - Learning Insights, LLC
RISK IT! - Skateboards - Risk It, Inc.
RISK MAP - Cantor and Co.
R.I.S.K. WEAR - Apparel and accessories - Chauvin International Ltd.
RISKIT - Computer software - Atlantic Richfield Co.
RISKLINK - Computer software - Risk Management Solutions, Inc.
RISKMONITOR - Computer software - Axiom Software Laboratories, Inc.
RISKVIEW - Computer software - Palisade Corp.
RISLEY - Water–mineral - Risley Cold Springs
RISLONE - Lubricants - Shaler Co.
RISMAVAC-CR6 - Veterinary pharmaceutical preparations - Intervet, Inc.
RISOM/BURR - Tables–wood ☆ - Howe Furniture Corp.
RISOMATIC - Tripods–photographic - SP Systems/Saratons
RISPERDAL - Antipsychotic - Janssen Pharmaceutica Inc.
RISQUE - Apparel–women's - Hossana Corp.
RISQUE - Brassieres (Bras) - Bi-Flex International
RISQUE - Footwear ☆ - Brown Shoe Co.

☆ = Now out of production

RISQUETTES - Greeting cards - House of Oz
RIST - Furniture - K.M.L. Industries
RISTADYL - Pharmaceutical preparations ☆ - Wendt-Bristol Co.
RISTALARM - Watches - Gruen Marketing Corp.
RISTCURVE - Watches - Gruen Marketing Corp.
RISTINE - Skin care products - Colorado Medical Center, P.C.
RISTO - File folders - Risto Inc.
RISTOCETIN - Pharmaceutical preparations ☆ - Cutter Laboratories
RISTSIDE - Watches - Gruen Marketing Corp.
RISVOLD'S - Salads–prepackaged - Risvold's Inc.
RIT - Dyes–household - CPC International Inc.
RIT-A-WEED - Weed-control blankets - Atlantic Construction Fabrics, Inc.
RITA - Computer software - Computer Science Innovations, Inc.
RITA - Oils–edible - Rosa Food Products Co.
RITA BONITA - Dolls - Mattel, Inc.
RITA COLLECTION - Apparel–women's - Kyounghee Lee
RITA MILDRED - Apparel–women's - Rita Mildred Inc.
RITA MILLER'S - Honey - Miller's Honey Co.
RITALIN - Pharmaceutical preparations - Ciba-Geigy Corp.
RITALIN SR - Pharmaceutical preparations - Ciba-Geigy Corp.
RITA'S OLD FASHIONED CUSTARD - Custard–frozen - Rita's Water Ice, Inc.
RITAVENA 5 - Cosmetics - R.I.T.A. Corp.
RITCHEY - Bicycles - Ritchey Design Inc.
RITCHIE - Water dispensers - Ritchie Industries, Inc.
RITCHIE CREEK - Wines - Ritchie Creek Vineyards
RITCHIE SWIMWEAR - Bathing suits - Double J of Broward Inc.
RITE - Forms–preprinted - Dress Rite Forms
RITE ACROSS - Office supplies - Esselte Corp.
RITE & BRITE - Cleaning preparations–household - US Foodservice
RITE-ANGLE - Office supplies - Smead Manufacturing Co.
RITE ANGULATOR - Educational materials - R.L.S. Enterprises, Inc.
RITE-BRAN - Rice ☆ - Uncle Ben's, Inc.
RITE CUP - Housewares - Allrite Sheet Metal Inc.
RITE DIET - Food products - Bakers Franchise Corp.
RITE DOWN - Binders - Boorum & Pease Co.
RITE DOWN - Binders - Esselte Corp.
RITE-EASE - Paper - Dennison National Co.
RITE FORM - Apparel–women's - Lane Bryant, Inc.
RITE GLUE - Adhesive for moisteners and gluers ☆ - Better Packages
RITE GRADE - Food products ☆ - Blue Star Growers Inc.
RITE-HITE - Building materials - Rite-Hite Corp.
RITE-HITE - Chairs–wood - Dependable Manufacturing Co.
RITE HITE - Golfing equipment - Plawood Mormac Corp.
RITE-HITE - Medical apparatus - Hill Rom, Inc.
RITE-HITE - Toys ☆ - Today's Kids Inc.
RITE-IN - Golfing equipment - Golfco, Inc.
RITE KIND - Condiments ☆ - Rite Kind Products
RITE KOTE - Paints - MCI Quality Coatings
RITE LIFE - Vitamins and nutritional supplements - Nima Products Inc.
RITE-LIFE - Vitamins and nutritional supplements - Shaperite Concepts, Ltd.
RITE LINE - Paper–rolls ☆ - Rite-Made Paper Converters Inc.
RITE-LITE - Lighting fixtures - Bayco Products Inc.
RITE LITE ROUNDS - Crackers - Barbara's Bakery, Inc.
RITE LOK - Adhesives and sealants - Chemence, Inc.
RITE-N-RACE - Office supplies - Stempel Manufacturing Co.
RITE O GRAPH - Office supplies ☆ - Blue Ribbon Pen & Pencil Co. Inc.
RITE-O-MATIC - Pens ☆ - Universal Fountain Pen & Pencil Co.
RITE OF SPRING - Glassware–household ☆ - Crisa Corp.
RITE-OFF - Cleaning preparations - Rite-Off Inc.
RITE-ON - Oils–lubricating - Conklin Co., Inc.
RITE-OUT - Ribbons ☆ - Eaton Allen Ko-Rec-Type Corp.
RITE PAD - Computer software - JFK Associates Inc.
RITE POINT - Desk sets - Souvenir Inc.
RITE RANCH - Food products - Meat Factory Inc.
RITE-SCALE - Toys ☆ - Today's Kids Inc.
RITE-SIZE - Aquariums–household - Marineland Aquarium Products
RITE SOURCE, THE - Cleaning preparations - Grow Group, Inc.
RITE START - Food products - Conagra, Inc.
RITE-TEMP - Faucets - Kohler Co.
RITE TURNS - Recording label - Maxx Records
RITE-TYPE - Wire and metal products - Rite-Hite Corp.
RITE-TYPE-SNAP - Office supplies - Miami Systems Corp.
RITE-WAY - Balls–basketball - Roy G. Williams
RITEBRITE - Chalk - Quartet Manufacturing Co.
RITEIT - Thread ☆ - SCT Yarns Inc.
RITENAP - Napkins–paper - Fort Howard Corp.

RITEPOINT - Pens - Ritepoint Inc.
RITER'S COPI - Paper–carbon ☆ - Leedall Products Manufacturing Co.
RITETRAX - Toys–trains - Mike's Train House, Inc.
RITEWELL - Crayons ☆ - Walbuck Crayon Co., Inc.
RITI - Recording label - Jazz Composer's Orchestra Association Inc.
RITMIESTER - Cigars - James B. Russell Inc.
RITO - Oils–edible - Rito Partnership
RITS - Heat exchangers - L & M Radiator Inc.
RITTEN HOUSE - Chimes ☆ - Fasco Industries Inc. (Consumer Products Div.)
RITTENHOUSE - Floor coverings–carpet and rugs ☆ - Downs Carpet Co. Inc.
RITTENHOUSE - Floor coverings–carpet and rugs ☆ - Regal Rugs Inc.
RITTENHOUSE - Luggage ☆ - Gateway Travelware
RITTENHOUSE - Wallpaper - J. Chesterfield Studio
RITTENHOUSE SQUARE - Dinnerware–glass ☆ - Lenox, Inc.
RITTENHOUSE SQUARE - Furniture - Henredon Furniture Industries Inc.
RITTER - Chocolate candy - FCW Imports
RITTER - Chocolate candy - Haram-Christensen Corp.
RITTER - Food products ☆ - Curtice-Burns Foods, Inc.
RITTER CELLARS - Wines - Codera Wine Group
RITTER KRAFT BORN - Beverages–malt ☆ - Acme Food Specialties Inc.
RITTER SPORT - Confections - Kreiner Imports
RITTERBRAU - Beverages–malt - Acme Food Specialties Inc.
RITTERGOLD - Coffee ☆ - Reco International Corp.
RITTOS - Beverages–alcohol ☆ - Distributors & Condal Imports
RITTS - Furniture - Ritts Co. (Astrolite Div.)
RITUAL - Perfumes ☆ - Charles of the Ritz Group Ltd.
RITUAL QUILTS - Fabrics - Martha McDonell
RITUALS - Sunglasses - Bausch & Lomb Inc.
RITUALS - Toiletries ☆ - Smith & Vandiver, Inc.
RITUEL DE BAIN - Skin care products - Frances Denney
RITZ - Brushes–paint - Rubberset Co.
RITZ - Christmas tree ornaments - Cracker Box Inc.
RITZ - Cigarettes - R.J. Reynolds Tobacco Co.
RITZ - Crackers - Nabisco Foods Group
RITZ - Flatware - Washington Forge Inc.
RITZ - Glassware–household ☆ - Crisa Corp.
RITZ - Housewares - John Ritzenthaler Co.
RITZ - Housewares - Shen Manufacturing Co. Inc.
RITZ - Nail care products - Rudolph International, Inc.
RITZ - Occasional tables - JDI Group, Inc.
RITZ - Ophthalmic goods - Rozin Optical Export Corp.
RITZ - Paper ☆ - Plainwell Tissue
RITZ - Perfumes - Charles of the Ritz Group Ltd.
RITZ - Shoes - Allen-Edmonds Shoe Corp.
RITZ AIR CRISPS - Snack foods - Nabisco Foods Group
RITZ ARK - Crackers - Nabisco Holdings Corp.
RITZ BITS - Crackers - Nabisco Foods Group
RITZ CLASSIC - Colognes - Charles of the Ritz Group Ltd.
RITZ GLAZE - Floor coverings - Tarkett, Inc.
RITZ LA GRAND - Skin care products - Rudolph International, Inc.
RITZ NEW YORK - Skin care products - Rudolph International, Inc.
RITZ OF PARIS - Robes - Russell-Newman, Inc.
RITZ ROYALE - Skin care products - Rudolph International, Inc.
RITZ SNACK MIX - Crackers - Nabisco Foods Group
RITZ SPREADABLES - Crackers - Nabisco Foods Group
RITZ, THE - Wallpaper - Carlton-Metro Wallcoverings
RITZ TIPS - Nail care products - Rudolph International, Inc.
RITZEE - Gloves - Wells Lamont Corp.
RITZY - Floor coverings–carpet and rugs - Burtco Enterprises Inc.
RITZY - Floor coverings–carpet and rugs - Mohawk Carpet Corp.
RITZY - Floor coverings–carpet and rugs ☆ - Whitecrest Carpet Mills
RITZY MITSY - Dolls - Mattel, Inc.
RITZY RICES - Rice - Wildwood Creations
RITZY'S - Apparel and accessories - G.D.R. Franchisee Association, Inc.
RIUNITE - Wines - Banfi Vintners
RIVA - Cabinets - Keller Kitchen Cabinets Southern Inc.
RIVA - Glassware–household - Crystal Clear Importing Co. Inc.
RIVA - Motor vehicles - Yamaha Motor Corp. USA
RIVA - Skin care products - Riva International (Professional Products Div.)
RIVA - Whirlpools - Jacuzzi Inc.
RIVA BY CONAIR - Telephones - Conair Corp.
RIVA RANCH - Wines - Wente Bros.
RIVA SILK - Apparel and accessories - Brigata International, Inc.
RIVAL - Dog food - Armour Swift-Eckrich
RIVAL - Dog food - Strongheart Products, Inc.
RIVAL - Dryers–hair - Ross Sales Co.

RIVAL - Hand daters - Consolidated Stamp Manufacturing Co. Inc.
RIVAL - Jeans–women's - Debra Salerno
RIVAL - Kitchen appliances - Rival Manufacturing Co.
RIVAL - Mattresses - Simmons USA
RIVAL - Oils–lubricating - USA Petroleum Corp.
RIVAL - Pencils - National Pen & Pencil Co.
RIVAL - Rackets–racquetball - Lisco, Inc.
RIVAL - Surfboards ☆ - Earth & Ocean Sports, Inc.
RIVAL - Thread - A. Lewis Thread Co. Inc.
RIVAL REALMS - Computer software - Titus Software Corp.
RIVAL SELECT - Kitchen appliances - Rival Co.
RIVARD'S MOTHER'S PENDANT - Jewelry - Rivard's Fine Jewelry, Inc.
RIVAR'S - Costumes - Rivar's Custom Show Apparel Inc.
RIVCO - Uniforms–tailored - Riverside Manufacturing Co.
RIVCO PERFIT - Work clothes - Riverside Manufacturing Co.
RIVE GAUCHE - Perfumes - Yves St. Laurent Parfum Corp.
RIVER - Cigarettes - R.J. Reynolds Tobacco Co.
RIVER - Floor coverings–carpet and rugs ☆ - Regal Rugs Inc.
RIVER - Rice - Riviana Foods Inc.
RIVER & PIKE - Bags–duffel - Pacific Market, Inc.
RIVER BANK - Food products - The Rainforest Co.
RIVER BEND - Wines - Davis Bynum Winery
RIVER BIRCH - Apparel and accessories - Glenn Farms, Inc.
RIVER BLUE - Cosmetics - Lancome
RIVER BOTTOMS - Apparel–men's - Williamson-Dickie Manufacturing Co.
RIVER BRAND - Apparel and accessories - Cluett, Peabody & Co.
RIVER BROWN RICE - Rice - Riviana Foods Inc.
RIVER CATCH - Seafood products–fresh or frozen - Sysco Corp.
RIVER CITY - Jeans–men's - Klayman Pants Co.
RIVER CITY - Protective wear - Shelby Group International, Inc.
RIVER COUNTRY - Wines - Montelle Winery
RIVER COUNTRY - Wines ☆ - Wollersheim Winery, Inc.
RIVER CREST - Furniture - River Oaks Furniture, Inc.
RIVER FALLS - Sinks–metal - Kohler Co.
RIVER FALLS - Wines - European Beverage Co., Inc.
RIVER GAMBLER - Game tables - IGT - North America
RIVER GEMS - Jewelry - Rio Grande Albuquerque, Inc.
RIVER GRIPPERS - Boots - Danner Shoe Manufacturing Co.
RIVER GROVE - Fruit - Florida Fresh
RIVER GUIDE - Boats–fishing - Klamath Boat Co. Inc.
RIVER HAWK - Boats - Southeastern Boat and Fiberglass
RIVER HAZE - Christmas tree ornaments - Cracker Box Inc.
RIVER HILLS - Cheese - Dan Carter Inc.
RIVER HOUSE - Home furnishings - Weilwood Industries Inc.
RIVER JACK - Boots - JBI, Inc.
RIVER JON - Boats - O.M.C. Aluminum Boat Group
RIVER LEAF - Paper products - Paper Conversions Inc.
RIVER MASTER - Sporting goods - Lindy Little Joe Inc.
RIVER MUSIC - Recording label - River Music
RIVER OAKS - Dishes–china - Viletta China Co.
RIVER OAKS - Wallpaper - Seabrook Wallcoverings, Inc.
RIVER OAKS - Wines ☆ - Clos du Bois Wines
RIVER OF DREAMS - Beverages - Bunge Foods Corp.
RIVER OF LIFE - Vitamins and nutritional supplements - Planetary Formulas
RIVER OTTER - Boats–pontoons - Water Otter, Inc.
RIVER PORT - Apparel–women's - Richman Gordman Stores Inc.
RIVER PRIDE - Fruits and vegetables - DNE World Fruit Sales
RIVER QUEEN - Nuts–salted, roasted, cooked, or canned - Leavitt Corp.
RIVER RAID - Computer software - Activision, Inc.
RIVER RANCH ANGEL HAIR SLAW - Coleslaw - Fresh Western Marketing Inc.
RIVER RAT - Boats - Glen-L Marine Designs
RIVER RAT - Sport tubes - Intex Recreation Corp.
RIVER RIBS - Fabrics - Dan River Inc.
RIVER ROAD - Furniture - Vaughan Furniture Co. Inc.
RIVER ROAD - Seasonings - Bolner's Fiesta Products, Inc.
RIVER ROAD VINEYARDS - Wines - River Road Vineyards
RIVER ROCK - Tiles–ceramic ☆ - Terra Green Ceramics, Inc.
RIVER RUBBER - Shoe soles - Deckers Outdoor Corp.
RIVER RUN - Dog food - Stevens Industries Inc.
RIVER RUN - Floor coverings–carpet and rugs - Mohawk Industries Inc.
RIVER RUN - Wines - River Run Vintners
RIVER RUNNER - Boats–motor - Hewes Marine Co.
RIVER RUNNER - Sporting goods - Outdoor Technologies Group
RIVER RUNNERS - Boats - Valco Aluminum Boats
RIVER SHARPE - Apparel–men's - River Sharpe, Inc.

RIVER SPIRIT - Footwear - E.S. Originals, Inc.
RIVER SPORT - Footwear - E.S. Originals, Inc.
RIVER STREET SWEETS - Candy - Pam Strickland
RIVER TEST - Apparel and accessories - Finish Line, Inc.
RIVER TRADER - Apparel and accessories - Frederick Atkins, Inc.
RIVER TREK - Apparel - Rainforest Inc.
RIVER TUBE - Sporting goods - Coleman Co., Inc.
RIVER VALLEY - Fruits–frozen - Valley Packers Inc.
RIVER VALLEY - Wines - Moyer Vineyards Inc.
RIVERA - Projectors–photographic - Brumberger Co. Inc.
RIVERA - Wines - Paterno Imports, Ltd.
RIVERA ENGINEERING - Motorcycle parts and accessories - Rivera Engineering, Inc.
RIVERBEND - Apparel and accessories - Rocking Horse Industries, Inc.
RIVERBEND - Floor coverings–carpet and rugs ☆ - Criterion Mills Inc.
RIVERBEND - Furniture - Pilliod Co.
RIVERBIRCH - Prefabricated buildings–wood - Champion Enterprises Inc.
RIVERBOAT - Colognes - Brandy Harvest
RIVERBOAT - Computer software - Step 1 Systems Corp.
RIVERBOAT GAMBLER - Dolls ☆ - Effanbee Doll Corp.
RIVERBREEZE - Fabrics - Dan River Inc.
RIVERBY - Floor coverings ☆ - Tarkett, Inc.
RIVERCITY PRESS - Publisher's imprints - Amereon Ltd.
RIVERCLUB - Fabrics - Dan River Inc.
RIVERCOOL - Fabrics - Dan River Inc.
RIVERCREST - Fabrics - Dan River Inc.
RIVERDALE - Dinnerware–glass ☆ - Royal China & Porcelain Companies Inc.
RIVERDALE - Tableware–china - Lenox, Inc.
RIVERDALE PRIDE INSIDE - Beverages–carbonated - East Coast Properties Corp.
RIVERDOGS - Balls–baseball - South Carolina Baseball Club, L.P.
RIVERGATE FARMS - Fruits and vegetables - Graziano Produce Co.
RIVERGATE FARMS - Wallpaper - Seabrook Wallcoverings, Inc.
RIVERGLEN CELLARS - Wines - Pellegrini Bros. Wines Inc.
RIVERHALL - Wood products - Georgia-Pacific Corp.
RIVERHEAD - Publisher's imprints - Putnam Berkley Group, Inc.
RIVERHILL USA - Toys–stuffed - DCN Industries Inc.
RIVERIA - Flatware - Couzon USA
RIVERIA - Hardware - National Lock Hardware
RIVERIZED - Fabrics - Dan River Inc.
RIVERJONS - Boats–skiffs ☆ - C-G Industries Inc.
RIVERKNIT - Fabrics - Dan River Inc.
RIVERKNOLL - Trailers–travel - Fleetwood Enterprises, Inc.
RIVERLEAF - Paper - PCI Paper Conversions, Inc.
RIVERLIN - Fabrics ☆ - Dan River Inc.
RIVERLON - Fabrics - Dan River Inc.
RIVERMONT - Floor coverings–carpet and rugs - Customweave Carpets Inc.
RIVERMONT - Furniture - Mersman Furniture Co.
RIVERPRESS - Fabrics - Dan River Inc.
RIVERSET - Fabrics - Dan River Inc.
RIVERSHELL - Exercising equipment - Little River Marine Co.
RIVERSIDE - Animal feeds - Terra Chemicals International
RIVERSIDE - Fabrics - Dan River Inc.
RIVERSIDE - Floor coverings - Bruce Hardwood Floors
RIVERSIDE - Flowers, plants, and seeds - Terra International, Inc.
RIVERSIDE - Furniture - Riverside Furniture Corp.
RIVERSIDE - Golfing equipment - Golfsmith International Inc.
RIVERSIDE - Meat products–poultry - Stevens Industries Inc.
RIVERSIDE - Paper–construction - Riverside Paper Corp.
RIVERSIDE - Phonographs - Fantasy Inc.
RIVERSIDE - Seafood products–fresh or frozen - Morgan City Freezer & Cold Storage Inc.
RIVERSIDE - Seafood products–fresh or frozen - Riverside Seafoods Inc.
RIVERSIDE - Uniforms–tailored - Riverside Manufacturing Co.
RIVERSIDE - Watches - Elgin Watch Co.
RIVERSIDE BREWING CO. - Glassware–household - Riverside Brewing Co.
RIVERSIDE DRIVE - Dinnerware–glass ☆ - Lenox, Inc.
RIVERSIDE DRIVE - Floor coverings–carpet and rugs ☆ - Hollytex Carpet Mills Inc.
RIVERSIDE GRANTS - Computer software - Riverside Software, Inc.
RIVERSIDE MASTERBILT - Uniforms–tailored - Riverside Manufacturing Co.
RIVERSIDE PUBLISHING CO., THE - Publisher's imprints - Houghton Mifflin Co.
RIVERSIDE VINEYARD - Wines - House of Burgundy Inc.
RIVERSIDE VINEYARDS - Wines - L. Foppiano Wine Co.
RIVERSONG - Publisher's imprints ☆ - Zondervan Publishing House

☆ = Now out of production

RIVERSTONE - Wines - J. Lohr Winery
RIVERSTONES - Lamps - Griffin Design
RIVERTON - Cabinets ☆ - Grandview Products Co.
RIVERTON - Cement - Riverton Corp.
RIVERTON - Floor coverings—carpet and rugs - Whitecrest Carpet Mills
RIVERTOOLS - Boating equipment and accessories - Michael L. Fentress
RIVERTOWN RED - Wines - Minnesota Winegrowers Cooperative
RIVERVIEW - Bedding—linen - Dan River Inc.
RIVERVIEW - Computer peripheral equipment - Advanced Computer Communications
RIVERVIEW - Manufactured homes - Redman Industries, Inc.
RIVERVIEW - Recording label - Rockland Records
RIVERWALK - Floor coverings—carpet and rugs ☆ - Whitecrest Carpet Mills
RIVERWALK - Wallpaper ☆ - Pickhardt & Siebert USA Inc.
RIVERWOOD - Floor coverings—carpet and rugs - Cabin Crafts Carpets
RIVERWOOD - Machinery - Riverwood International Corp.
RIVES - Artists' materials - Andrews/Nelson/Whitehead
RIVES BFK - Paper - Canson-Talens Inc.
RIVET - Computer storage devices - Time Warner Interactive Group
RIVET-ALL - Rivets—metal ☆ - Marson Creative Fastener Group
RIVET LOCK - Binders - Loose Leaf House
RIVET-RAX - Shelving units—metal - Storex Division
RIVETRITE - Shelving units—metal - Penco Products Div.
RIVETS - Flatware - Anacapa Corp.
RIVETS - Sunglasses ☆ - Corning Inc.
RIVETZ OF BOSTON - Neckties - Global Neckwear Marketing Inc.
RIVIERA - See PACIFIC REEF
RIVIERA - Accordions ☆ - Fred Gretsch Enterprises
RIVIERA - Air conditioning equipment - Carrier Corp.
RIVIERA - Bicycles - Ross Bicycles USA, Ltd.
RIVIERA - Blankets—electric ☆ - Sunbeam-Oster Household Products
RIVIERA - Boats - Glen-L Marine Designs
RIVIERA - Boats—motor - Ebbtide Corp.
RIVIERA - Boats—motor - Midwestern Industries Corp.
RIVIERA - Boats—motor ☆ - Century Boat Co.
RIVIERA - Boats—motor ☆ - Stamas Yacht Inc.
RIVIERA - Cabinets - Riviera Cabinets Inc.
RIVIERA - Cigarettes - American Tobacco Co.
RIVIERA - Cigarettes - Commonwealth Brands, Inc.
RIVIERA - Dishes—china - Pasmantier Co. Inc.
RIVIERA - Doors—glass - Yale Ogron Manufacturing Co. Inc.
RIVIERA - Electronic equipment - Compco Photographic/Goldberg Bros.
RIVIERA - Fabrics - Dan River Inc.
RIVIERA - Floor coverings - Mannington Resilient Floors
RIVIERA - Floor coverings—carpet and rugs - Coronet Carpets Inc.
RIVIERA - Floor coverings—carpet and rugs - Playfield International Inc.
RIVIERA - Floor coverings—carpet and rugs ☆ - Cactus Mat Manufacturing Co.
RIVIERA - Food products - Lucca Packing Co. of California Inc.
RIVIERA - Giftware ☆ - Gorham Inc.
RIVIERA - Glass—leaded - Seneca Glass Co.
RIVIERA - Glassware—household - Crystal Clear Importing Co. Inc.
RIVIERA - Hair care products - Monte Carlo Hairpiece Co.
RIVIERA - Hair coloring preparations - Helene Curtis Industries Inc.
RIVIERA - Heat pumps - Aqua Cal, Inc.
RIVIERA - Leather goods - St. Thomas Inc.
RIVIERA - Lighting fixtures - Angelo Brothers Co.
RIVIERA - Manufactured homes - Redman Industries, Inc.
RIVIERA - Mattresses - Montgomery Ward & Co. Inc.
RIVIERA - Motor vehicle parts and accessories - Cricket Camper Manufacturing Co.
RIVIERA - Motor vehicles—automobiles - General Motors Corp. (Buick Motor Div.)
RIVIERA - Pasta - Riviera Ravioli Inc.
RIVIERA - Pens ☆ - Faber-Castell Corp.
RIVIERA - Pipes—tobacco - Dr. Grabow Pre-Smoked Pipes Inc.
RIVIERA - Pizzas—mixes ☆ - Dadco Food Products Inc.
RIVIERA - Recording label - Cadet Records Inc.
RIVIERA - Soups—canned - Curtice-Burns Foods, Inc.
RIVIERA - Tableware—china - Villeroy and Boch Tableware Ltd.
RIVIERA - Trailers—travel ☆ - Hop-Cap Inc.
RIVIERA - Underwear and nightwear - Bestform Foundations, Inc.
RIVIERA - Wallpaper - Sunnyside Prints
RIVIERA - Wallpaper ☆ - Wallprints
RIVIERA - Wallpaper ☆ - Wolf-Gordon Inc.
RIVIERA - Window coverings - Levolor Inc.
RIVIERA - Yarn - Henry's Attic

RIVIERA CLASSIX - Sunglasses - Riviera Trading, Inc.
RIVIERA COLLECTION - Daily planners, address books, etc. - Arcata Graphics Co. Arcata Graphics Book Group
RIVIERA COLLECTION - Wallpaper - K.M.L. Industries
RIVIERA COLLECTIONS - Sunglasses - Riviera Trading, Inc.
RIVIERA CONVERTIBLES - Furniture stores - Riviera Convertibles Inc.
RIVIERA CRUISER - Boats—pontoons - Riviera Cruiser
RIVIERA MIMOSA MIST - Sachets - Andre Richard
RIVIERA OPTIX - Sunglasses - Riviera Trading, Inc.
RIVIERA TRUNKS - Luggage - Mercury Luggage Manufacturing Co.
RIVIERA-WESTERN BARBECUE - Chili—canned - Riviera Foods
RIVIERA XIV - Wallpaper - Sunnyside Prints
RIVIERA XV - Wallpaper - Sunnyside Prints
RIVIERA XVI - Wallpaper - Sunnyside Prints
RIVIERE - Furniture ☆ - Bassett Furniture Industries, Inc.
RIVIT - Glue—household or industrial - H. Behlen & Bro. Inc.
RIVITON - Toys—erector sets ☆ - Parker Brothers
RIVNUT - Tools - B.F. Goodrich Co.
RIVOIRE & CARRET - Pasta - ABA Management & Development Inc.
RIVOLI - Draperies - Maya Romanoff Corp.
RIVOLI - Floor coverings—carpet and rugs ☆ - Masland Corp.
RIVULET - Water filtering unit - Rival Co.
RIX - Pharmaceutical preparations ☆ - Household Research Corp.
RIXSON - Hardware - Yale Security Inc.
RIZ - Lubricants - Shaler Co.
RIZ LA CROIX - Cigarette papers - American Tobacco Co.
RIZCOUS - Rice ☆ - Wehah Farm, Inc.
RIZLA CADET - Cigarette holders - Gesty Trading & Manufacturing Corp.
RIZLA LUXURY - Cigarette holders - Gesty Trading & Manufacturing Corp.
RIZLA SUPER EXPRESS - Cigarette holders - Gesty Trading & Manufacturing Corp.
RIZLE - Paper—cigarette - Robert Burton Associates Ltd.
RIZZA PIZZA - See THE ORIGINAL RICE CRUST PIZZA
RIZZI - Socks - Garment Group of California
RIZZOLI - Recording label ☆ - Rizzoli International Publications Inc.
RIZZOLI INTERNATIONAL PUBLICATIONS INC. - Publisher's imprints - Rizzoli International Publications Inc.
RIZZOLI/NEW YORK - Publisher's imprints - Rizzoli International Publications Inc.
RIZZONI - Shirts - 88 International, Inc.
RIZZO'S - Food products - Lucy's Foods
RIZZO'S MALABAR INN - Pasta - Mary Frances Defabo
RJ - Apparel—athletic - RJ Cycle Wear Inc.
R.J. & CO. - Apparel—women's - Robert Baker
RJ & S - Jewelry - Jensen & Sons Inc.
R.J. GOLD - Tobacco products - R.J. Reynolds Tobacco Co.
R.J. STEVENS - Apparel—women's - Private Label International Ltd.
RJ VISTA - Connectors—electrical - Amphenol Corp.
RJA - Sprayers - Roto-Jet of America Co., Inc.
RJB DESIGNS - Dolls - Rhonda Brennan
RJD - Recording label - RJD Records
RJG - Watches - RJG Photo Retouching
RJP - Electrical equipment - RJP Electronics, Inc.
RJPLUS - Office furniture—metal - Rosejohnson
RJ'S - Juices - Bakerview Farms
RJS - Perfumes - RJS Inc.
RK - Hair care products - Redken Laboratories, Inc.
RK - Publisher's imprints - Masquerade Books, Inc.
RK BOOK - Publisher's imprints - Progressive Awareness Research, Inc.
RK MASTER - Computer peripheral equipment - Master Healthcare Systems, LLC
RK ROYAL KENT - Dinnerware - Namor International Corp.
RK TAILORING - Apparel—men's - Ruth's Custom Sewing
RKAZITELI - Wines - McGregor Vineyard Winery
RKINET - Computer software ☆ - CONDUIT
RKO - Blank audio tapes ☆ - American Sound & Video
RKO COLORCHROME - Blank video tapes ☆ - American Sound & Video
RL - Jewelry - Ronald Litoff Ltd.
RL - Roofing materials—clay - Triangle Metal and Manufacturing Inc.
RL 2000 - Luggage and furniture - Polo Ralph Lauren Corp.
RL FLO-MASTER - Sprayers - Root-Lowell Manufacturing Co.
RLI - Jewelry - Perfect Time, Inc.
RLI 55 - Contact lenses - RLI Vision Corp.
RLIMS-LITE - Computer software - Westinghouse Hanford Co.
RLN - Computer software - Digital Communications Associates, Inc.
RLR - Detergents - Cadie Products Corp.

☆ = Now out of production

RLR INDUSTRIES, INC. - Electric lighting equipment - RLR Industries, Inc.
RLT - Flooring–hardwood - Overseas Hardwoods Co.
RLX 1.6 - Lenses–optical - Signet Armorlite, Inc.
RLXLITE - Lenses–optical - Signet Armorlite, Inc.
RLXPLUS - Lenses–optical - Signet Armorlite, Inc.
RM - Advertising agencies - Massachusetts Mutual Life Insurance Co.
RM - Briquettes - Robert Mondavi Winery
RM - Food products - Richwood Meat Co., Inc.
RM - Metals - Rarities Mint Inc.
RM - Printed materials - Resort Maps, Inc.
R.M. - Recording label - Cheetah Records Inc.
R.M. - Recording label - Terock Records
RM 6400 - Rifles - Redfield Co.
RM CANINE PARVO XL - Veterinary nutritional supplements - Rhone Merieux, Inc.
RM/CODEBENCH - Computer software - Ryan McFarland Corp.
RM/GRAFS - Computer software - Ryan McFarland Corp.
RM/PANELS - Computer software - Ryan McFarland Corp.
RM QUIGG'S - Food products - Conrad Rice Mill Inc.
RM RETIREMENT MATTERS - Advertising agencies - Massachusetts Mutual Life Insurance Co.
RM ROADMASTER FLEET - Computer hardware - P.G. Technologies Inc.
RM STYLE - Apparel and accessories - Ralph Marlin & Co., Inc.
RM ZZ - Sprinklers–lawn - Rainmatic Corp.
RMA - Sporting goods - Pompanette Inc.
RMAX - Radio communications equipment - Kenneth Dean Stephens
RMB - Computer software - Hewlett-Packard Co.
RMC - Bicycles - Bicycle Import Group Inc.
RMC - Lighting fixtures - Sterling Reflector & Manufacturing Co.
RMC-270 - Golfing equipment - Golfsmith International Inc.
RMD - Tiles–ceramic - Capitol Tile Import Co.
RME HAWK - Irrigation equipment - Rain Master Irrigation Systems, Inc.
RME SENTAR - Irrigation equipment - Rain Master Irrigation Systems, Inc.
RMI - Pianos - Allen Organ Co.
RMLA - Women's and children's clothing - RMLA, Inc.
RMOVE GEAR/LOOK - Sporting goods - Bell Sports Corp.
RMP - Educational materials - Team Labs Corp.
RMR PLUS - Apparel and accessories - United Merchants and Manufacturers Inc.
RMS - Brandy - Remy Martin Amerique Inc.
RMS - Computer software - Heart Watchers International Inc.
RMS - Electronic equipment - MBT International, Inc.
RMS - Electronic equipment - RMS Electronics, Inc.
RMS - Pharmaceutical preparations - Upsher-Smith Laboratories, Inc.
RMX - Bicycles - Roadmaster Corp.
RMZ - Automotive parts and accessories - RMZ, Inc.
RN CLOTH - Fabrics - Dan River Inc.
RNA - Vitamins and nutritional supplements - Great Life Laboratories Inc.
RNA-BC - Vitamins and nutritional supplements - Great Life Laboratories Inc.
RNA TACK - Laboratory apparatus - Biotecx Laboratories, Inc.
RNASE AWAY - Cleaning preparations - Molecular Bio-Products, Inc.
RNM - Jewelry - Michaud Co. Inc.
RN'R REST AND RELAX - Vitamins and nutritional supplements - Vitamin Shoppe Industries Inc.
RNSTAT - Computer software - Community Health Computing, Inc.
RNT - Jewelry - Roniet Creations Inc.
RO - Jewelry - Rose Anderson
RO-AMPEN - Pharmaceutical preparations ☆ - Solvay Pharmaceuticals Inc.
RO-BEE - Apparel–children's - Rhobbe Inc.
RO-BILE - Pharmaceutical preparations ☆ - Solvay Pharmaceuticals Inc.
RO-BRICK - Bricks - Ro-Tile Inc.
RO-CABLE - Cables - Kevlin Corp.
RO-CILLIN VK - Pharmaceutical preparations ☆ - Solvay Pharmaceuticals Inc.
RO-CYCLINE - Pharmaceutical preparations ☆ - Solvay Pharmaceuticals Inc.
RO-DENT - Rodenticides - Mackwin Co.
RO-DO-RID - Rodenticide - Atlas Chemical Corp.
RO-DOLLS - Dolls - Rosaylia Wilson
R.O. DRINKING WATER 'N ICE - Ice - WNI Acquisition Corp.
RO-FEDRIN - Cold remedies - Robinson Laboratories Inc.
RO-FLO - Benches–wood - Rowe-Reilly Corp.
RO-GON - Pesticides–household - Environmental Pesticide Investment Corp.
RO-GUN - Toys–guns - Mattel, Inc.
RO-HIST - Antihistamine preparations - Robinson Laboratories Inc.
RO-KEY - Tools–hand-operated - Ro-Key Corp., Inc.
RO-PON - Enamels - Rodda Paint Co.
RO-SHAM-BO - Apparel and accessories - Lora M. Flamme

RO-STONE - Floor coverings–tile - Ro-Tile Inc.
RO TAB - Recording label - Marullo Productions Inc.
RO-TABS - Pharmaceutical preparations ☆ - Solvay Pharmaceuticals Inc.
RO-TEL - Cheese - Borden, Inc.
RO-TILE - Floor coverings–tile - Ro-Tile Inc.
RO-TRIM - Exercising equipment - Battle Creek Equipment Co.
RO-ZIA - Meat products–beef ☆ - Rosina Food Products Inc.
RO3000 - Electrical equipment - Rogers Corp.
RO4000 - Electronic equipment - Rogers Corp.
ROACH ATTACK - Insecticides ☆ - Reuter Manufacturing inc.
ROACH-AWAY - Insecticides - Willert Home Products, Inc.
ROACH DESTROYER - Insecticides - Bacon Products Corp.
ROACH DOOM - Insecticides ☆ - Fairfax Biological Laboratory
ROACH ENDER - Poison–roach - Boyle-Midway
ROACH ERASE - Insecticides - Lynwood Laboratories, Inc.
ROACH GEAR - Apparel - Cockroach International Inc.
ROACH PLUS - Insecticides - Rogers Consumer Products
ROACH-PRUFE - Pesticides–household - Copper Brite, Inc.
ROACH REAPER - Rodenticides - Flow-Eze Co.
ROACH RIDD - Insecticides - Enforcer Products Inc.
ROACH SNAX - Insecticides - Roach Busters Inc.
ROACH STOP - Insecticides - Abepco Manufacturing Co.
ROACH TERMINATOR - Insecticides - Farnam Cos. Inc.
ROAD - Audio equipment - Rickenbacker International Corp.
ROAD - Bicycles - Raleigh USA Bicycle Co.
R.O.A.D. - Computer software - Ontos, Inc,
ROAD - Recording label - Darva Records
ROAD - Recording label - Music Services of America
ROAD AMERICA - Automotive parts and accessories ☆ - Wells Manufacturing Corp.
ROAD & RAIL - Toys–electronic ☆ - Tyco Toys
ROAD ATLANTA - Apparel and accessories - Road Atlanta, Ltd.
ROAD BINDER - Chemical preparations - Georgia-Pacific Corp.
ROAD BLASTERS - Toys–automobiles - Matchbox Toys USA
ROAD BLOCK - Bicycles - Dynacraft Industries Inc.
ROAD BONES - Skates–roller - Powell Skateboards
ROAD BOSS - Cases–musical instrument - Humes & Berg Manufacturing Co. Inc.
ROAD BOX - Tool boxes - Stack-On Products Co.
ROAD BUILDER - Toys - Tyco Toys
ROAD BURNERS - Toys–automobiles - Imperial Toy Corp.
ROAD CHAMP - Tires - Kumho USA Inc.
ROAD CLIMBER - Bicycles ☆ - Kent International Inc.
ROAD CONSTRUCTION AHEAD - Recording label - Fred Levine Productions
ROAD CONSTRUCTION AHEAD - Toys–automobiles - ERTL Co., Inc.
ROAD DOG - Beverages–malt - Broadway Brewing Co.
ROAD EAGLE - Electronic equipment - Bob Bartlett & Associates Inc.
ROAD EATERS JUST FOR KIDS - Toys–automobiles - Majorette Toys (U.S.) Inc.
ROAD FLIPPER - Toys–automobiles - Mattel, Inc.
ROAD GANG - Automotive parts and accessories - Delco Remy America, Inc.
ROAD GRIPPER - Bicycles - Ross Bicycles USA, Ltd.
ROAD GRIPPER - Tires - Carlisle Tire & Rubber Co.
ROAD GUARD - Tires - Montgomery Ward & Co. Inc.
ROAD HAWKS - Toys–automobiles - Mattel, Inc.
ROAD HEAT - Bicycles - Kent International Inc.
ROAD HEAT - Toys–automobiles - Hasbro, Inc.
ROAD HOG - Antennas - Valor Enterprises, Inc.
ROAD HOG - Trays ☆ - Blue Ridge International Products Co., Inc.
ROAD KILL - Cleaning preparations - Ch2o International
ROAD KILL - Dried meats - Caldaho Bros. Inc.
ROAD KILL - Toys–automobiles - Mattel, Inc.
ROAD-KILL CRITTERS - Candy - Peter N. Gammelgard
ROAD KING - Batteries - Exide Corp.
ROAD KING - Cleaning preparations - United Industries Corp.
ROAD KING - Sandwiches–prepackaged - H-D Michigan, Inc.
ROAD KING - Tires - Bridgestone/Firestone, Inc.
ROAD KINGS - Toys–automobiles - Imperial Toy Corp.
ROAD LOAD - Motor vehicle parts and accessories - Smith Engineering & Machine Co., Inc.
ROAD MASTER - Automotive parts and accessories - SDI Operating Partners
ROAD MINER - Road construction machinery - Trencor, Inc.
ROAD OF LIFE, THE - Diaries - Richard N. Loyd
ROAD PATROL - Electronic equipment - Tandy Corp.
ROAD PATROL XK - Electronic equipment - Tandy Corp.
ROAD PETS - Candy ☆ - Trolli, Inc.

☆ = Now out of production

ROAD PIRATE - Toys–automobiles - Mattel, Inc.

ROAD PRIDE - Automotive parts and accessories - Road Pride

ROAD PRO - Chemical preparations - Midwest Industrial Supply, Inc.

ROAD RACER - Games ☆ - Avalon Hill Game Co.

ROAD-RACKS - Automotive parts and accessories ☆ - Macklanburg-Duncan Co.

ROAD RAD - Bicycles - Roadmaster Corp.

ROAD RAGE - Video production - Konami (America) Inc.

ROAD RAGS - Apparel and accessories - Maurices Inc.

ROAD RALLY - Game machines - Atlantic City Coin & Slot Service Co., Inc.

ROAD RANGER - Toys - Tonka Corp.

ROAD RANGER - Trailers–travel - Kit Manufacturing Co.

ROAD RANGER ELITE - Trailers–travel - Kit Manufacturing Co.

ROAD RANGER ESPRE - Motor vehicles–motor homes ☆ - Kit Manufacturing Co.

ROAD RASH RELIEF - First aid kits - Chris Weld

ROAD RAT - Toys–automobiles - Mattel, Inc.

ROAD RECORDER - Recording label - Prima Facie, Inc.

ROAD RIDER - Skateboards - Santa Cruz Skateboards

ROAD RIPPER - Toys - Tonka Corp.

ROAD ROCKERS - Loudspeakers - International Jensen Inc.

ROAD ROLLER - Toys–automobiles - Mattel, Inc.

ROAD RULES - Glassware–household - Viacom International Inc.

ROAD-RUNNER - Automotive parts and accessories ☆ - Goerlich's

ROAD RUNNER - Bicycles - Columbia Manufacturing Inc.

ROAD RUNNER - Computer software - Road Runner Medical, Inc.

ROAD RUNNER - Exercising equipment - Battle Creek Equipment Co.

ROAD RUNNER - Motor vehicles–automobiles ☆ - Chrysler Corp. (Chrysler-Plymouth Div.)

ROAD RUNNER - Trailers–horse - Wegner Manufacturing Inc.

ROAD RUNNER - Vitamins and nutritional supplements - The Lifestar Millennium, Inc.

ROAD RUNNER TRACKER - Circular saw blades - United States Saw Corp.

ROAD SCAN - Automotive parts and accessories - Moto Mirror, Inc.

ROAD SCHOLAR - Games ☆ - Century Products Co.

ROAD SENTRY - Valves - Sauer Inc.

ROAD SHOW - Video games - Williams Electronics Games, Inc.

ROAD SHOW OFFS - Decals and transfers - Paper Magic Group Inc.

ROAD SHOW, THE - Antennas–satellite - Frank Carlson

ROAD SIDE RALPH'S CARCASS COOKIES - Bakery products - Tsunami Wave, Inc.

ROAD STAR - Antennas - Winegard Co.

ROAD STAR - Athletic footwear - Converse Inc.

ROAD TALK - Posters - Road Talk, Inc.

ROAD TAMER - Tires - Montgomery Ward & Co. Inc.

ROAD TAPES - Recording label - Takilma East Productions

ROAD TECH - Bicycles - Kent International Inc.

ROAD THUNDER - Audio equipment - MTX

ROAD THUNDER PRO - Audio equipment - MTX

ROAD TO BETTER HEALTH, THE - Dinners–frozen - MCC Foods America, Inc.

ROAD TO HANA - Wallpaper - K.M.L. Industries

ROAD TO HANA - Wallpaper - Textile Wallcoverings International Ltd.

ROAD TO OPTIMISM, THE - Publisher's imprints - JM Perry Corp.

ROAD TO THE TOP - Computer software - Mindscape Software Inc.

ROAD TO THE WHITE HOUSE - Games - Mayfair Games, Inc.

ROAD TOAD - Motorcycles ☆ - Pabatco

ROAD TORCH - Toys–automobiles - Mattel, Inc.

ROAD-TOUGH PICKUPS - Toys - Tonka Corp.

ROAD TRAIL - Tires - Carlisle Tire & Rubber Co.

ROAD TRIP - Wallpaper - Chapters Wallcoverings

ROAD TRIP ADVENTURES - Publisher's imprints - Prima Communications, Inc.

ROAD VAC - Toys - Mattel, Inc.

ROAD VISION - Defrosters–motor vehicle - Anthony B.J. Eoga

ROAD WARRIOR - Bicycles - Dynacraft Industries Inc.

ROAD WARRIOR - Computers - Computer Products Plus, Inc.

ROAD WARRIOR - Wallets - Craft Billfold Corp.

ROAD WARRIOR-GLOVES - Gloves - Knoxville Glove Co.

ROAD WARRIOR PRODUCTS GLOBAL CONNECTIVITY - Connectors–electronic - Computer Products Plus, Inc.

ROAD WARRIOR TTR - Electronic equipment - Measurements Dynamics, LLC

ROAD WARRIOR'S COMPANION - Recording label - Insight Producers, Inc.

ROAD WARS - Toys - Mattel, Inc.

ROAD WHIZ - Maps - LDT Inc.

ROAD-WOOD - Amplifiers - Electro-Voice, Inc.

ROAD WRITER - Publisher's imprints - Riverside Paper Corp.

ROADBUDDY - Electrical equipment - McLaughlin Electronics Inc.

ROADCRAFT - Motor vehicle parts and accessories - Saddleman, Inc.

ROADFLIGHT - Aerodynamic vehicle panels - Roadflight, Inc.

ROADHANDLER - Tires - Sears, Roebuck and Co.

ROADHAWK - Batteries - Douglas Battery Manufacturing Co.

ROADHAWK - Machinery - Toro Co.

ROADHAWK - Motorcycles - Emgo International Ltd.

ROADHOUSE - Barbecue sauce - Roadhouse, Inc.

ROADHOUSE JEANS - Apparel and accessories - 3 X Lucky Inc.

ROADHOUSE RED - Wines - Breitenbach Wine Cellars

ROADHOUSE RIBS - Preserved foods–prepackaged - Leadbelly's Inc.

ROADHUGGER - Bicycles - Ross Bicycles USA, Ltd.

ROADIE - Cases–musical instrument - Hybrid Cases

ROADIE - Housewares - Pat Traegde

ROADIE RENCH - Tools–hand-operated - S. Ross Jennings

ROADKILL - Apparel and accessories - Fiskars Inc.

ROADKILL - Electronic equipment - AAMP of Florida, Inc.

ROADKILL CAFE - Film–motion picture - Backstreet Tees

ROADKILL COOKING - Publisher's imprints ☆ - United Cutlery Corp.

ROADMAP - Jeans–men's - Road Map Ltd.

ROADMASTER - Bicycles - Roadmaster Corp.

ROADMASTER - Gloves–work - Magid Manufacturing Co. Inc.

ROADMASTER - Motor vehicles–automobiles - General Motors Corp. (Buick Motor Div.)

ROADMASTER - Motor vehicles–motor homes ☆ - Shasta Industries Inc.

ROADMASTER - Radar systems and equipment - Royal Sound Co. Inc.

ROADMASTER - Tires - Cooper Tire & Rubber Co.

ROADMASTER JR. - Bicycles - Roadmaster Corp.

ROADMASTER SNAKES - Cables - Pro-Co. Sound Co. Inc.

ROADMASTER USA - Bicycles - Roadmaster Corp.

ROADMATE - Ice chests–plastic - Igloo Products Corp.

ROADMATES - Automotive parts and accessories - Goerlich's

ROADMATES - Brake parts - AP Parts

ROADMOCS - Footwear - H.H. Brown Shoe Co., Inc.

ROADMUSIC - Recording label - Thomasfilms, Inc.

ROADNODE - Computer software - Techsmith Corp.

ROADNOTES - Computer software - KCH Computer Systems, Inc.

ROADPAL - Antennas - Firestik Antenna Co.

ROADPRO - Motor vehicle parts and accessories - Seats Inc.

ROADPRO - Radios–citizens' band - D.A.S. Distributors, Inc.

ROADRACER - Bicycles - Ross Bicycles USA, Ltd.

ROADRACER - Recording label ☆ - Roadrunner Records, Inc.

ROADREP - Computer software - DataSolve Business Systems Inc.

ROADRUNNER - Antennas ☆ - Firestik Antenna Co.

ROADRUNNER - Cases–musical instrument - Pignose Industries

ROADRUNNER - Cases–musical instrument - Roadrunner Cases Inc.

ROADRUNNER - Computer peripheral equipment - Colourcomp Corp.

ROADRUNNER - Computers–personal ☆ - Micro Express Inc.

ROADRUNNER - Containers–metal - Steel City Corp.

ROADRUNNER - Floor coverings–carpet and rugs - Newport Carpet Mills Inc.

ROADRUNNER - Garden equipment - McCulloch Corp.

ROADRUNNER - Home-health-care products - Independent Mobility Systems Inc.

ROADRUNNER - Machinery - Liquid Control Corp.

ROADRUNNER - Needlework stands and frames - American Crewel & Canvas Studio

ROADRUNNER - Tape measures - Keson Industries Inc.

ROADRUNNER - Trailers–travel - Arizona Roadrunner RV

ROADRUNNER - Trailers–truck ☆ - Sun-Lite Inc.

ROADRUNNER TRACKER - Saw blades ☆ - Oldham Saw Co., Inc.

ROADSEARCH - Computer software - Columbia Software

ROADSEARCH PLUS - Computer software - Columbia Software

ROADSHOW - Cameras–video - Sound & Video Systems, Inc.

ROADSHOW - Recording label - Roadshow Music Corp.

ROADSHOW QUICKMAPS - Computer peripheral equipment - Roadshow International, Inc.

ROADSIDE - Apparel–men's - Route 66, LP

ROADSIDE - Food products - Gilbert-Robinson Inc.

ROADSIDE ATTRACTION - Flowers, plants, and seeds - White Swan, Ltd.

ROADSIDE CAFE - Egg entrees - Morrison Restaurants Inc.

ROADSIDE FARMS - Food products ☆ - Sanofi Bio-Industries Inc.

ROADSIDE GEOLOGY - Publisher's imprints - Mountain Press Publishing Co.

ROADSIDE HISTORY - Publisher's imprints - Mountain Press Publishing Co.

ROADSTER - Automotive parts and accessories - Igloo Products Corp.

ROADSTER - Fabrics - Gretchen Bellinger Inc.

ROADSTER - Footwear–athletic - L.A. Gear, Inc.
ROADSTER - Furniture - Little Tikes Co.
ROADSTER - Infant product - Century Products Co.
ROADSTER - Motorcycles ☆ - Harley-Davidson, Inc.
ROADSTERS 99 - Video games - Titus Software Corp.
ROADSTONE - Footwear - JBI, Inc.
ROADTECH - Computer storage devices - Touchstone Software Corp.
ROADTUFF - Brake parts - Alliedsignal Inc.
ROADWARE - Publisher's imprints - Paisano Publications, Inc.
ROADWARRIOR - Shock absorbers–motor vehicle - Northern Automotive Corp.
ROADWORK - Sporting goods - Hillerich & Bradsby Co.
ROADWORKS - Cordage and twine ☆ - Suzuki Corp.
ROAM - Apparel and accessories - Apparel Industries International, Inc.
ROAM-ABOUT - Pet products - Four Paws Products Ltd.
ROAM ALONE - Apparel and accessories - Tire Mart, Inc.
ROAMABOUT - Computer peripheral equipment - Digital Equipment Corp.
ROAMER - Boats–motor ☆ - Chris Craft Boats
ROAMER - Fabrics - Greenwood Mills Inc.
ROAMER - Footwear ☆ - Sebago Inc.
ROAMER - Trailers–travel - Snowy Mountain Recreational Products
ROAMER - Vacuum cleaners and accessories–commercial ☆ - Advance Machine Co.
ROAMERS - Candy - Klein Chocolate Co.
ROAN MOUNTAIN - Stoneware dinnerware - Iron Mountain Stoneware Inc.
ROANOKE - Dishes–china ☆ - Royal China & Porcelain Companies Inc.
ROANOKE - Flatware - Royal Silver Manufacturing Co. Inc.
ROANOKE - Floor coverings–carpet and rugs ☆ - Atlas Carpet Mills Inc.
ROANOKE - Floor coverings–carpet and rugs ☆ - Colonial Mills Inc.
ROANOKE - Giftware - Gorham Inc.
ROANOKE - Moldings–plaster of paris - Roanoke Moulding Design
ROANOKE - Shoes ☆ - Allen-Edmonds Shoe Corp.
ROANOKE - Trailers–travel ☆ - Fleetwood Enterprises, Inc.
ROANOKE - Weather tracking equipment ☆ - Bausch & Lomb Inc.
ROAR - Paper–toweling - Kimberly-Clark Corp.
ROAR-HIDE - Pet food - T.F.H. Publications, Inc.
ROAR-HIDE - Pet products - Nylabone Products
ROAR MOWER - Toys - Steven Manufacturing Co.
ROAR U.S.A. - Apparel and accessories - Roar USA
ROARER - Toys–automobiles - Mattel, Inc.
ROARIN' TIGER RIDER - Toys–automobiles - CBS Toys
ROARING 20'S - Hosiery–men's - Clovermere Sales Corp.
ROARING 20'S - Jewelry ☆ - Hobe Cie. Ltd.
ROARING 20'S - Pianos - Universal Player Piano Co.
ROARING 20'S - Teas ☆ - Alvita Products Co.
ROARING CAMP - Apparel and accessories ☆ - Edison Brothers Stores, Inc.
ROARING DIESEL - Toys–trains - Life-Like Products Inc.
ROARING FIRE ENGINE - Toys - Clover Toys, Inc.
ROARING MOUSE ENTERTAINMENT, INC. - Computer software - Roaring Mouse Entertainment, Inc.
ROARING RACERS - Toy automobiles - Racing Champions Inc.
ROARING RIVER - Upholstered furniture - River Oaks Furniture, Inc.
ROARING ROADSTERS - Toys ☆ - Henry Gordy International Inc.
ROARING SPRING - Notebooks and notepads - Roaring Spring Blank Book Co.
ROARING SPRING - Water–bottled or canned - Roaring Spring Bottling
ROARING THUNDER - Toys - Tonka Corp.
ROARING TWENTIES - Wallpaper ☆ - ICI Americas Inc.
ROARY - Recording label - Home Sweet Home Educational Media Co.
ROARY - Stationery - Lisa Frank, Inc.
ROARY LION - Puppets - Dakin Inc.
ROAST - Recording label ☆ - Ray Lawrence Ltd.
ROAST-AIR - Cooking equipment–household - Metal Ware Corp.
ROAST AIR OVEN - Ovens–roaster - Metal Ware Corp.
ROAST OF OLD NEW YORK, A - Coffee - Noah's New York Bagels, Inc.
ROAST RESSLER - Kitchen utensils–aluminum - Niblack
ROAST-RITE - Meat products–poultry - Norbest Inc.
ROASTAROMA - Teas–herbal - Celestial Seasonings, Inc.
ROASTED 7-GRAIN - Cereal - Cream of the West
ROASTED 'N READY - Meat products–poultry - Conagra, Inc.
ROASTED RED PEPPER SALSA - Sauces - Guiltless Gourmet, Inc.
ROASTED TOM - Turkeys - Cooper's Turkey Place, Inc.
ROASTERE - Coffee - Treasure Valley Coffee, Inc.
ROASTER'S CHOICE - Coffee - Compass Foods Inc.
ROASTERS COFFEE & TEA COMPANY - Coffee - Roasters
ROASTERS DOWNTOWN GRIND - Coffee - Roasters

ROASTERY - Meat products–poultry - Hester Industries, Inc.
ROASTIES - Sausages - Rudolph Frey Inc.
ROASTIN' BAGS - Cooking equipment–household - Durkee French Foods
ROASTMASTER - Mobile grill and concessionaire - Born Free Motorcoach Div.
ROASTMASTER'S COLLECTION - Coffee - Saramar Corp.
ROAST'N BAG - Spices and extracts - Burns Philp Food Inc.
ROASTWELL - Pans ☆ - General Housewares Corp.
ROATAN - Pens - Roatan International Corp.
ROB - Dolls - Hasbro, Inc.
ROB - Ophthalmic goods - Rozin Optical Export Corp.
ROB-BART - Toys - Tonka Corp.
ROB-RIC - Mayonnaise - Robert Arranaga & Co.
ROB ROSKOPP - Skateboards - Santa Cruz Skateboards
ROB ROY - Apparel–children's - Garan, Inc.
ROB ROY - Boats - Glen-L Marine Designs
ROB ROY - Boats - Marine Concepts
ROB ROY - Tobacco–chewing or smoking - Amar Blends Co.
ROB SCOT KNITTING MILLS - Apparel and accessories - Thurman Manufacturing Co.
ROBACIDE - Water treating compounds - Robarb Inc.
ROBAIRES BEST - Salad dressings–bottled ☆ - Sweet Adelaide Enterprises
ROBALATE - Antacids ☆ - A.H. Robins Co. Inc.
ROBALD - Apparel and accessories - Bayliner Marine Corp.
ROBAMATE - Tranquilizers - Robinson Laboratories Inc.
ROBAMOX - Pharmaceutical preparations ☆ - A.H. Robins Co. Inc.
ROBART - Toys–models - Robart Manufacturing Inc.
ROBATA - Snack foods ☆ - Great Eastern Sun Trading Co. Inc.
ROBATHOL - Skin care products - Pharmaceutical Specialties, Inc.
ROBB ROSS - Food products - Sunstar Foods Inc.
ROBBA - Beverages–alcohol - M.S. Walker Inc./Seacoast
ROBBE - Imitation fur ☆ - Ivy International Ltd.
ROBBIA ELEGANTE - Pottery ☆ - Rubens Originals
ROBBIE RABBIT - Pet products ☆ - Flexi-Mat Corp.
ROBBIE RIVERS - Apparel–women's ☆ - Bobbie Brooks Inc.
ROBBIE'S - Food products - R/R International Marketing Services
ROBBINS - Floor coverings - Cincinnati Floor Co. Inc.
ROBBINS - Floor coverings - Robbins Inc.
ROBBINS - Recording label - Robbins Entertainment LLC
ROBBINS - Thread - Belding Heminway Co. Inc.
ROBBINS WOLFE - Advertising agencies - Robbins Wolfe Inc.
ROBBI'S FRIENDS - Magnets - Rainfall Inc.
ROBBY LEN - Bathing suits - Great American Industries Inc. (Robby Len Fashions Divison.)
ROBBY THE MOUSE - Computer software ☆ - Ventura Educational Systems
ROBBY'S - Bowling balls - Ebonite International, Inc.
ROBBY'S PANCAKE MIX - Pancakes–mixes - H & J Marketing, Inc.
ROBE CORPORATION OF AMERICA - Robes - Harwood Companies Inc.
ROBE SPINNING - Games - Twinson Co.
ROBER POWELL - Figurines - Robert Powell Association
ROBERK - Automotive parts and accessories - Stant Corp.
ROBERN - Cabinets–metal - Sylvania Territories, Inc.
ROBERT ALISON - Wines - Estate William Baccala
ROBERT ALLEN - Fabric stores - Ametex/Robert Allen Contract Fabrics
ROBERT ALLEN - Fabrics ☆ - Masco Corp.
ROBERT AMERIGO - Apparel–men's - R.A. Ltd.
ROBERT AMERIGO - Apparel–men's - Sero Co., Inc.
ROBERT BESTIEN - Handbags - Robert Bestien
ROBERT BOSCH - Automotive parts and accessories - Robert Bosch Corp.
ROBERT BRENT CO. - Artists' materials - Creek-Turn Inc. (Ceramic Supply Div.)
ROBERT BURNS - Cigars - General Cigar Co., Inc.
ROBERT CHAMBERS - Lamps - J. Kenneth Zahn
ROBERT COMSTOCK +OESTE - Apparel–women's - Comstock Load Inc.
ROBERT CORR - Soft drinks - Corr's Natural Beverages Inc.
ROBERT CRAIG - Hair care products - Color by Robert Craig Hair, Inc.
ROBERT CROWDER - Wallpaper ☆ - Robert Crowder & Co.
ROBERT DE LANZA - Hair care products - L'anza Research International
ROBERT F. CLARK - Jewelry - William O. DeLillo and Robert F. Clark Partnership
ROBERT FRIEDEL - Food products - George C. Brown's Biscuits & Confections
ROBERT HAVILAND & C. PARLON - Dinnerware–glass - Lalique North America
ROBERT JOHN SPORTS - Apparel–women's - Kellwood Co.
ROBERT JOHNSON - Shirts - Willis B. Brumfield
ROBERT KAUFMAN - Posters - Silver Visions Publishing Co.

☆ = Now out of production

ROBERT KEENAN - Wines - Robert Keenan Winery

ROBERT L. #CRAGER & CO. - Publisher's imprints - Pelican Publishing Co. Inc.

ROBERT LATOUR - Frames–eyeglass - National Vision Associates, Ltd.

ROBERT LAWRENCE - Apparel and accessories - Gottschalks Inc.

ROBERT LEDOUX - Wines ✩ - Alimar & Cie. Inc.

ROBERT LEE MORRIS - Flatware - Reed and Barton Corp.

ROBERT LONGSTAFF - Puzzles - Kingdom Puzzles

ROBERT MARTEL - Musical instruments - Hershman Musical Instrument

ROBERT-MICHELE LOIRE - Wines - Parliament Import Co.

ROBERT MONDAVI - Wines - Robert Mondavi Winery

ROBERT NELSON - Posters ✩ - Icart Vendor Graphics Inc.

ROBERT ORIGINALS - Jewelry - Jewelry Fashions Inc.

ROBERT PEPI - Wines - Kendall Jackson Winery, Ltd.

ROBERT PEPI WINERY - Wines - Robert Pepi Winery

ROBERT POWELL DESIGNS - Jewelry - Robert Powell Association

ROBERT POWERS - Dresses–women's ✩ - Sweetwater Hosiery Mills Inc.

ROBERT R. HARVEY - Jewelry - Nusantara Inc.

ROBERT ROSE - Jewelry - Robert Rose

ROBERT ROSE - Jewelry–costume - Jewelry Fashions Inc.

ROBERT ROTHSCHILD - Chocolate - Rothschild Berry Farm, Inc.

ROBERT SCHAFER - Apparel–men's ✩ - Burma-Bibas, Inc.

ROBERT SCOTT - Apparel–women's - Robert Scott Inc.

ROBERT SCOTT LTD. - Apparel and accessories - Kellwood Co.

ROBERT SERAFINI - Shirts - Capital Mercury Shirt Corp.

ROBERT SPOONER GALERIE - Frames–picture - Robert Spooner Galerie

ROBERT STEMMLER - Wines - Buena Vista Winery, Inc.

ROBERT STEMMLER WINERY - Wines - Buena Vista Winery, Inc.

ROBERT +STEMMLER WINERY - Wines - Robert Stemmler Winery

ROBERT STEVENS - Office supplies ✩ - Faber-Castell Corp.

ROBERT STOCK - Apparel and accessories - Oxford Industries, Inc.

ROBERT STOCK - Apparel–men's ✩ - West Mill Clothes Inc.

ROBERT STOCK - Neckties ✩ - Remington Apparel Co. Inc.

ROBERT TERRY - Apparel and accessories - Kellwood Co.

ROBERT TERRY - Apparel–women's - Robert Scott Ltd. Inc.

ROBERT THIBAUD - Musical instruments - Enzo Pizzi

ROBERT TRENT +JONES - Apparel and accessories - Robert Trent Jones

ROBERT TRENT JONES - Apparel and accessories - Robert Trent Jones

ROBERT URIST RETINOL EXTRA - Health care products - Urist Cosmetics USA Inc.

ROBERT VENTURI - Flatware - Reed and Barton Corp.

ROBERT YOUNG - Wines ✩ - Belvedere Winery

ROBERTA - Apparel and accessories - Breton Industries

ROBERTA - Skin care products - IDG-International Designers Group Inc.

ROBERTA'S - Deodorizers - Roberta's, Inc.

ROBERTO - Food products - Tosi Trading Co.

ROBERTO - Glassware–household - ACC

ROBERTO - Musical instruments - Roberto Ciarfella Inc.

ROBERTO CAPUCCI - Frames–eyeglass - Euro-Frames Inc.

ROBERTO CASTELLANI - Wines - Tyfield Importers

ROBERTO CHILLINI - Shoes - Globe Footwear Corp.

ROBERTO GUCCI'S - Liquors - Fred Bofird Co.

ROBERTO MORELLI - Sunglasses - Bonneau Co.

ROBERTO VIANNI - Footwear - Neiman Marcus Co.

ROBERTO VICCI - Jewelry - David Geoffrey Accessories

ROBERTO'S - Tomato pastes and sauces ✩ - Roberts Bros. Inc.

ROBERTS - Candlesticks - Roberts Colonial House Inc.

ROBERT'S - Cookies - Barbara Dee Bakery (Div. of President Baking)

ROBERTS - Dairy products - Roberts Dairy Co.

ROBERTS - Food products ✩ - Walden Farms, Inc.

ROBERTS - Fruit drinks–bottled or canned - Natural Juice Manufacturing Co.

ROBERTS - Fruits–dried - Roberts Fig Co.

ROBERTS - Knives - Perfection Tip Co.

ROBERTS - Mayonnaise - Double Lucky Corp.

ROBERTS - Shoes ✩ - Roberts

ROBERTS - Skin care products - The Roberts Group

ROBERTS - Skin care products - Roberts Research Laboratories, Inc.

ROBERTS 4 POINT - Novelty items - Roberts Colonial House Inc.

ROBERT'S AMERICAN GOURMET - Snack foods - Robert's American Gourmet

ROBERTS CUSTOM SOFTWARE - Computer peripheral equipment - Ken Roberts

ROBERTS FOLD - Doors–metal - Dap Products Inc.

ROBERTS GORDON - Heaters–gas - Roberts-Gordon, Inc.

ROBERTS HOMETOWN - Milk - Roberts Hometown Dairy

ROBERTSHAW - Controls–heating systems - Robertshaw Controls Co.

ROBERTSON - Draperies - Robertson Factories Inc.

ROBERTSON - Musical instruments - Roberto Ciarfella Inc.

ROBERTSON - Tiles–ceramic ✩ - Maxsam Sales, Inc.

ROBERTSON Q - Building materials–concrete - Robertson-Ceco Corp.

ROBES OF FAITH - Apparel and accessories - Danielle Designs

ROBESON - Cutlery - Robeson Industries

ROBESON SHUR EDGE - Knives–pocket - Queen Cutlery Co.

ROBI - Toilets–portable - Aerobic Systems Ltd.

ROBIC - Watches - Marshall-Browning International Corp.

ROBICON THE SINE OF QUALITY - Electronic equipment - Halmar Robicon Group, Inc.

ROBIE - Brackets - Frank Lloyd Wright Foundation

ROBIE - Electronic equipment - Tandy Corp.

ROBIKS - Shoes–athletic ✩ - Titleist & Foot-Joy Worldwide

ROBIN - Bicycles - Ross Bicycles USA, Ltd.

ROBIN - Books–comic - DC Comics

ROBIN - Rings–jewelry - Artcarved Inc.

ROBIN & HER MUSICAL ROCKING CHAIR - Dolls - Goldberger Doll Manufacture Co.

ROBIN & ME - Apparel and accessories ✩ - Regent International Corp.

ROBIN COURT - Floor coverings - Tarkett, Inc.

ROBIN EGGS - Candy - Leaf, Inc.

ROBIN GAYLE GIRL - Apparel–women's - Eber International

ROBIN HOOD - Archery equipment - Woodcraft Equipment Co.

ROBIN HOOD - Bicycles ✩ - Raleigh USA Bicycle Co.

ROBIN HOOD - Cookies - General Mills, Inc.

ROBIN HOOD - Dolls ✩ - Effanbee Doll Corp.

ROBIN HOOD - Fans–exhaust - Duralast Products

ROBIN HOOD - Flour, baking mixes, cereal - International Multifoods Corp.

ROBIN HOOD - Games ✩ - Parker Brothers

ROBIN HOOD - Gin - Beaver Wine Co.

ROBIN HOOD - Handles–wood - Hartwell Brothers Handle Co.

ROBIN HOOD - Recording label - Cadet Records Inc.

ROBIN RAINBOW - Novelty items - Easter Unltd. Inc.

ROBIN REED - Crackers ✩ - British American Imports

ROBIN ROSE - Snack foods - Robin Rose America, Inc.

ROBIN WHITE - Perfumes ✩ - Vi-Jon Laboratories, Inc.

ROBINETTE - Wines - Laureate Imports Co.

ROBINETTS - Vitamins and nutritional supplements - Wesley Pharmacal Co. Inc.

ROBINHOOD - Archery equipment ✩ - The Coleman Co.

ROBINHOOD - Window frames ✩ - Biltbest Windows

ROBINHOODS - Pet products - RobinHoods

ROBINS - Electronic equipment - Benjamin Electroproducts Inc. (Robins Div.)

ROBINS ISLAND - Seafood products–fresh or frozen - George Braun Oyster Co. Inc.

ROBIN'S NEST - Pies–frozen - Robin's Nest, Inc.

ROBINSEWN - Thread - Belding Heminway Co. Inc.

ROBINSON - Analgesics - Robinson Laboratories Inc.

ROBINSON - Bicycles - GT Bicycles Inc.

ROBINSON - Cutlery - Robinson Knife Manufacturing Co., Inc.

ROBINSON - Ice cream - Robinson Dairy Inc.

ROBINSON - Seafood products–canned or cured ✩ - Robinson Canning Co. Inc.

ROBINSON COLLECTION, THE - Jewelry - Sterling Inc.

ROBINSON CRUSOE - Product description unknown - C.F. Sauer Co.

ROBINSON GARLIC - Fruits and vegetables - Robison Ranch

ROBINSON RACING - Bicycles - GT Bicycles Inc.

ROBINSON RANCH SHALLOTS - Fruits and vegetables - Robison Ranch

ROBINSON REMINDERS - Photo albums - Heritage Springfield Inc.

ROBINSON'S - Barbecue sauce - Robinson's Barbecue Sauce

ROBINSON'S - Thread - Belding Heminway Co. Inc.

ROBINSVILLE - Bedding–linen - Dan River Inc.

ROBISON RANCH - Fruits and vegetables - Robison Ranch

ROBITUSSETS - Cough drops - A.H. Robins Co. Inc.

ROBITUSSIN - Cough medicines - A.H. Robins Co. Inc.

ROBITUSSIN LIQUID CENTER - Cough drops - A.H. Robins Co. Inc.

ROBITUSSIN LIQUIGELS - Cough medicines - A.H. Robins Co. Inc.

ROBITUSSIN NIGHTTIME RELIEF - Cold remedies - A.H. Robins Co. Inc.

ROBITUSSIN PEDIATRIC - Cough medicines - A.H. Robins Co. Inc.

ROBLEE - Footwear ✩ - Brown Shoe Co.

ROBO ARMY - Video games - Snk Corp. of America

ROBO-CART - Golf carts - Theima Technology

ROBO-DOOR - Vending machines - Vendo Co.

ROBO FORCE - Toys–stuffed - CBS Toys

ROBO-GOLF - Games - Rowland Development Corp.

✩ = Now out of production

ROBO-LASH - Compressors - Diesel Engine Retarders, Inc.
ROBO-PUNKS - Games - Gamescience
ROBO ROADIE - Electrical equipment - Gibson Strings & Accessories
ROBO-SPLAT - Apparel and accessories - RPB Inc.
ROBO SURFER - Surfboards - Surftek Inc.
ROBO VIAL - Vials–glass - Kimble Glass, Inc.
ROBO-WALL - Portable partition - Brewster Corp.
ROBOBLASTER - Toy glove - Talk to Me Products, Inc.
ROBOCAP - Alarm systems - Minerva Industries, Ltd.
ROBOCOP - Toys–stuffed - Kenner Products
ROBOCOP 2 - Candy - Topps Co., Inc.
ROBOCRANE - Cranes - National Institute of Standards & Technology
ROBOFLEX - Exercising equipment - Lucian Randolph
ROBOGIE - Recording label ☆ - Music for Little People
ROBOHELP - Computer software - Blue Sky Software Corp.
ROBOKENT - Floor cleaning equipment - Kent Co.
ROBOKID - Watches and clocks - Ruby International, Inc.
ROBOLABE - Labeling machinery - GSMA Systems, Inc.
ROBOLINKS - Toys–erector sets ☆ - Revell-Monogram, Inc.
ROBOMATH - Computer software - Mind Play
ROBOMOR - Computer software - Heroix Corp.
ROBOPONG - Sporting goods - Joseph E. Newgarden, Jr.
ROBOQUEST - Computer peripheral equipment - Philips Electronics North America Corp.
ROBORALLY - Games - Wizards of the Coast, Inc.
ROBOSECT - Toys - Saban Entertainment, Inc.
ROBOT - Adhesives and sealants - Adhesive Tapes International, Inc.
ROBOT - Locks–door - Burle Industries Inc. (Robot Div.)
ROBOT - Photographic equipment - Heitz Service Corp.
ROBOT ODYSSEY - Computer software ☆ - Gessler Publishing Co., Inc.
ROBOT ODYSSEY I - Computer software ☆ - The Learning Co., Inc.
ROBOT RASCALS - Computer software ☆ - Electronic Arts Inc.
ROBOT RECORDER - Cameras - Heitz Service Corp.
ROBOT ROYAL - Cameras - Heitz Service Corp.
ROBOT STAR - Cameras - Heitz Service Corp.
ROBOT SURVEILLANCE - Cameras - Heitz Service Corp.
ROBOT TANK - Computer software - Activision, Inc.
ROBOT WARRIORS - Toys - Azrak-Hamway International, Inc.
ROBOT WARS - Chewing gum ☆ - Fleer Corp.
ROBOTARM II - Actuators–pneumatic - Bettis Corp.
ROBOTECH - Hats ☆ - Arlington Hat Co. Inc.
ROBOTECH DEFENDERS - Toys ☆ - Revell-Monogram, Inc.
ROBOTECH INSECTOIDS - Toys ☆ - Revell-Monogram, Inc.
ROBOTHAND - Health care products ☆ - Intercontinental Enterprises Ltd.
ROBOTIC ARSENAL MOBILIZER - Toys–automobiles - Saban Entertainment, Inc.
ROBOTICS PRESS - Embossing plates - Dilithium Press
ROBOTIX - Toys - DGI/Buki
ROBOTIX - Toys - Learning Curve Toys, LLC
ROBOTIX - Toys–erector sets ☆ - Milton Bradley Co.
ROBOTIX-ARGUS - Toys–erector sets ☆ - Milton Bradley Co.
ROBOTIX-BOLTAR - Toys–erector sets ☆ - Milton Bradley Co.
ROBOTIX-RAYNOR - Toys–erector sets ☆ - Milton Bradley Co.
ROBOTIX-STEGORR - Toys–erector sets ☆ - Milton Bradley Co.
ROBOTIX-TARGON - Toys–erector sets ☆ - Milton Bradley Co.
ROBOTIX-TYRANNIX - Toys–erector sets ☆ - Milton Bradley Co.
ROBOTIX-VENTURAK - Toys–erector sets ☆ - Milton Bradley Co.
ROBOTIX-VORTREK - Toys–erector sets ☆ - Milton Bradley Co.
ROBOTIX-XANOX - Toys–erector sets ☆ - Milton Bradley Co.
ROBOTIX-ZORDAK - Toys–erector sets ☆ - Milton Bradley Co.
ROBOTMAN - Games ☆ - Ben Cooper Inc.
ROBOTMAN - Games ☆ - Parker Brothers
ROBOTMAN & FRIENDS - Toys - Kenner Products
ROBOTPRO - Motoman, Inc.
ROBOTREK - Video games - Enix America Corp.
ROBOTS, LASERS & GALAXIES - Toys ☆ - Imperial Toy Corp.
ROBOTS OF DAWN - Computer software - Epyx Inc.
ROBOTWAR - Computer software - Muse Software
ROBSAN GOLF - Golfing equipment - Robsan Corp.
ROBSON - Figurines ☆ - Goebel of North America
ROBSPUN - Thread - Belding Heminway Co. Inc.
ROBT BURNS - Blankets - Molly Roberts & Co. Inc.
ROBTEX - Thread - Belding Heminway Co. Inc.
ROBTFLEX - Appliance parts - Robert Manufacturing Co.
ROBUST - Breads ☆ - Natural Ovens of Manitowoc Inc.
ROBUST - Cleaning preparations–household - Puritan-Churchill Chemical Co.

ROBUST - Floor coverings ☆ - Durable Corp.
ROBUSTO - Cigars - Tropical Tobacco
ROBUSTO REJECTS - Cigars - Phillips & King Cigar, Inc.
ROBUSTURN - Machine tools - Okuma America
ROBY - Recording label - Robert Pakter
ROBYN - Dolls ☆ - Effanbee Doll Corp.
ROBYN JOYCE - Skin care products - Kathryn Joyce Feldman
ROBYN-LYN CREATIONS - Handbags - Jaclyn, Inc.
ROC - Medical apparatus - Innovasive Devices, Inc.
ROC-EDGE - Circular saw blades - U.S. Lawn Products, Inc.
ROC LOC - Bicycle parts and accessories - Giro Sport Design
ROC-LON - Draperies ☆ - Rockland Industries Inc.
ROC-LON DESIGNER - Draperies ☆ - Rockland Industries Inc.
ROC-MO - Exercising equipment - Rocky Mountain Gym Equipment Co. Inc.
ROC-N-EDGE - Artists' materials - Graphic-Standard Instruments Co.
ROC ST. ANDRE - Wines - World Wide Wine and Spirits Inc.
ROC-SEAL - Enamels ☆ - Waterlox Coatings Corp.
ROC-SET - Coatings - La Habra Products, Inc.
ROC THERAPEUTIC - Cosmetics ☆ - Dermik Laboratories Inc.
ROCA - Candy - Brown & Haley
ROCA - Ceramic tile - Interceramic Inc.
ROCA - Dinnerware - Standex International Corp.
ROCA - Dishes–china - H.F. Coors China Co.
ROCA BARS - Chocolate candy - Brown & Haley
ROCA BITS - Candy - Brown & Haley
ROCA NUGGETS - Candy - Brown & Haley
ROCAILLE - Yarn ☆ - Joseph Galler Inc.
ROCALTROL - Pharmaceutical preparations - Roche Laboratories
ROCAR - Wines - Shaw-Ross International Importers
ROCC - Adhesives and sealants - Man-Gill Chemical Co.
ROCCA - Cameras ☆ - Reeves Photo Sales Inc.
ROCCA - Food products ☆ - Dean & Deluca Inc.
ROCCA BELLA - Food products - Lindsay International
ROCCA DELLE MACIE CHIANTI CLASSICO - Wines - Palm Bay Imports, Inc.
ROCCAL - Veterinary pharmaceutical preparations - Winthrop Pharmaceuticals
ROCCAMATIC - Cameras ☆ - Reeves Photo Sales Inc.
ROCCI RUMANI - Handbags - Ronett Trading, Inc.
ROCCO - Meat products–poultry - Rocco Turkeys Inc.
ROCCO - Toys–stuffed ☆ - Russ Berrie and Co., Inc.
ROCCO BARACCO JEANS - Perfumes ☆ - Classic Fragrances Ltd.
ROCCO BARACCO TRE - Perfumes ☆ - Classic Fragrances Ltd.
ROCCO'S - Pita chips - Pletzel Corp.
ROCEPHIN - Antibiotics - Roche Laboratories
ROCES - Sporting goods - Revue International
ROCHAMBEAU - Floor coverings - Mannington Resilient Floors
ROCHAMBEAU - Furniture - Collingwood Furniture
ROCHE - Floor coverings–carpet and rugs - Patcraft Mills Inc.
ROCHE - Fruits and vegetables ☆ - Roche Fruit Co. Inc.
ROCHE - Pharmaceutical preparations - Hoffmann-La Roche Inc.
ROCHE-BOBOIS - Furniture - Roche-Bobois USA
ROCHE HARBOR - Paper products - Roche Harbor L.P.
ROCHE-THOMAS - Musical instrument accessories - Roche-Thomas Co.
ROCHELLE - Computer hardware - Rochelle Communications, Inc.
ROCHELLE - Cordials - Paramount Distillers Inc.
ROCHELLE - Floor coverings–carpet and rugs ☆ - Evans-Black Carpet Mills
ROCHELLE - Furniture - Rochelle Furniture Manufacturing Co.
ROCHELLE - Jewelry ☆ - K & M Associates
ROCHELLE - Toilets–enameled - Kohler Co.
ROCHE'S EMBROCATION - Pharmaceutical preparations ☆ - Consolidated Midland Corp.
ROCHESTER - Beverages–carbonated - A and W Brands Inc.
ROCHESTER - Clocks ☆ - General Time Corp. (Westclox/Seth Thomas Div.)
ROCHESTER - Office supplies - Yawman and Erbe of California Corp.
ROCHESTER MEDICAL - Catheters - Rochester Medical Corp.
ROCHESTER MODULAR - Beds–wood - Floatation Systems Inc.
ROCHESTER RED WINGS - Decals and transfers - Rochester Community Baseball, Inc.
ROCHIOLI VINEYARDS - Wines - Paterno Imports, Ltd.
ROCK - Beverages–malt - Latrobe Brewing Co.
ROCK - Computer software - Carnegie Group Inc.
ROCK - Musical instrument accessories - Gibson Strings & Accessories
ROCK-A-BILLY - Recording label - Terock Records
ROCK-A-BYE BABY - Audio equipment - Great American Audio Corp.
ROCK-A-BYE BEAR - Infant product - Rock-A-Bye Baby Inc.
ROCK-A-BYE BEAR - Toys–stuffed - Dakin Inc.
ROCK-A-BYE BUNNY - Infant product - Rock-A-Bye Baby Inc.

☆ = Now out of production

ROCK-A-BYE COLLECTION, THE - Recording label - Child's Gift of Lullabyes
ROCK-A-BYE EYES - Toys–stuffed ☆ - CBS Toys
ROCK-A-BYE PONY - Toys - Mattel, Inc.
ROCK-A-BYE WAY - Frames–picture - Papel Freelance, Inc.
ROCK-A-CHAIR - Chairs–wood - Master Woodcraft Inc.
ROCK-A-CRIB - Springs–furniture - N.K.R. Precision Manufacturing Corp.
ROCK-A-DOODLE - Computer software - Capstone Software
ROCK-A-DRI - Apparel–children's ☆ - Pioneer Industrial Products Co.
ROCK-A-NASH-A-BILLY - Recording label - Terock Records
ROCK-A-PEAL-BAND - Greeting cards - A + A
ROCK-A-STACK - Toys - Fisher-Price, Inc.
ROCK ALLOY - Nuts and bolts - Rockford Products Corp. (International Group)
ROCK & MINERAL HUNT - Toys - Uncle Milton Industries Inc.
ROCK AND ROLL HALL OF FAME - Novelty items–glass - Rock and Roll Hall of Fame Foundation Inc.
ROCK & SOUL ORCHESTRA, THE - Recording label ☆ - MBM Productions Int'l, Inc.
ROCK BANDS - Jewelry - Squire Boone Caverns, Inc.
ROCK BINOC - Binoculars - Tasco Sales, Inc.
ROCK BLOCK - Guitars - Allparts
ROCK BOARD - Nuts and bolts - Elco Industries, Inc.
ROCK BOCK - Beverages–malt - Latrobe Brewing Co.
ROCK BOSS - Machinery - W.S. Tyler, Inc.
ROCK BROOK - Beverages–alcohol ☆ - Safeway Stores Inc.
ROCK-BUILT - Printing trades machinery - K-Cor, Inc.
ROCK BUSTER - Toys–automobiles - Mattel, Inc.
ROCK CARBIDE - Saws–power - Black & Decker Corp.
ROCK CITY - Jewelry–precious - Roussels
ROCK CITY - Novelty items - See Rock City, Inc.
ROCK CLAW - Hooks - William S. Eirich
ROCK CLIMBER - Bicycles - Roadmaster Corp.
ROCK CREEK - Bicycles ☆ - Huffy Corp.
ROCK CREEK TECHNOLOGIES - Computer software - Rock Creek Technologies, Inc.
ROCK CREST - Water–bottled or canned ☆ - Sparkletts Water Co.
ROCK DOG BRAND - Apparel and accessories - Andiamo, Inc.
ROCK EATER - Machinery - Portec Inc.
ROCK 'EM SOCK 'EM - Toys - Tyco Toys
ROCK EMBASSY - Apparel and accessories - Rock Embassy Inc.
ROCK EXPRESS - Chewing gum ☆ - Amurol Confections Co.
ROCK EXPRESS, THE - Toys–trains - Life-Like Products Inc.
ROCK FACE - Ceiling tile ☆ - Conwed Plastics
ROCK-FLY - Shoes - Jiun Tay USA Corp.
ROCK GARDEN - Floor coverings - Congoleum Corp.
ROCK GARDEN - Garden equipment ☆ - South Bend Toy Manufacturing Co.
ROCK GLEN - Floor coverings - Congoleum Corp.
ROCK HARBOR - Boats–fishing - Estero Bay Investors, Inc.
ROCK HARD - Waxes–sealing ☆ - Golden Star Inc.
ROCK HILL FARMS SINGLE BARREL - Beverages–alcohol - Sazerac Co. Inc.
ROCK HOCKEY - Posters - New York Islanders Hockey Club L.P.
ROCK HOG - Drills–electric ☆ - Rock Hog Rock Drilling Products USA
ROCK ICE - Beverages–malt ☆ - Labatt Importers Inc.
ROCK ICE - Skates–roller - K-2 Corp.
ROCK ISLAND - Apparel and accessories - Rock Island Inc.
ROCK ISLAND - Recording label - All Star Promotions
ROCK ISLAND EXPRESS - Toys–electronic - Tyco Toys
ROCK-IT - Exercising equipment - Pro-Tec Inc.
ROCK-IT CARGO - Apparel - Rock-it Cargo USA Inc.
ROCK-IT COMIX - Apparel and accessories - International Strategic Marketing, Inc.
ROCK-IT STROBE - Toys - SLM Inc.
ROCK-KNIT - Coats–men's ☆ - Goodstein Bros. & Co. Inc.
ROCK KNOWLEDGE - Apparel and accessories - R Designs
ROCK KRITTERS - Jewelry - B.G. Mudd, Ltd.
ROCK LIGHT - Beverages–malt - Latrobe Brewing Co.
ROCK ME - Toys - Roadmaster Corp.
ROCK MIRACLE - Paint and varnish removers - Pyrock Chemical Corp.
ROCK 'N ALGIE - Toys - May Optical Co. Inc.
ROCK N' BOLT - Computer software - Activision, Inc.
ROCK 'N BOUNCE - Infant product - Graco Children's Products
ROCK 'N CUDDLE - Infant product - Graco Children's Products
ROCK 'N JOCK - Apparel and accessories - Viacom International Inc.
ROCK 'N LEARN - Recording label - Rock 'N Learn Inc.
ROCK 'N PLAY - Dolls - Mattel, Inc.
ROCK 'N RAP - Toys - Mattel, Inc.

ROCK 'N READ - Recording label - Rock 'N Learn Inc.
ROCK 'N RIDE - Toys - Kolcraft Enterprises, Inc.
ROCK-N-ROLL - Bicycles - Burley Design Cooperative
ROCK-N-ROLL - Fireworks - Ingram Enterprises, Inc.
ROCK 'N ROLL - Game - Pitco Manufacturing
ROCK 'N ROLL - Recording label - Scotti Brothers Records Inc.
ROCK 'N ROLL - Toys - Shelcore Inc.
ROCK 'N ROLL - Underwear and nightwear - Bestform Foundations, Inc.
ROCK N' ROLL - Watches - Western Watches International
ROCK 'N ROLL CHEWS - Candy - Confex Inc.
ROCK 'N' ROLL DANCERS - Novelty items ☆ - Jobar International Inc./Bibi Products
ROCK 'N' ROLL EGGS - Novelty items ☆ - Easter Unltd. Inc.
ROCK N ROLL RACING - Computer software - Interplay Productions
ROCK N ROLL REUNION 55 - Coats - Rock Roll Reunion Inc.
ROCK N ROLL SUPERSTAR - Games - Dersom/Scott Productions
ROCK N ROLLER - Strollers–baby - Cosco, Inc.
ROCK-N-ROLLER - Toys ☆ - Wonderline
ROCK 'N RYE - Beverages–carbonated - Faygo Beverages, Inc.
ROCK 'N SLEEP - Beds–wood ☆ - Century Products Co.
ROCK 'N' WHISTLE - Candy ☆ - Glenn Confections Inc.
ROCK 'N WRITE - Pens - Pentel of America, Ltd.
ROCK NARLIES - Toys - Tonka Corp.
ROCK OF BOSTON, THE - Broadcasting stations–radio - Infinity Broadcasting Corp.
ROCK ON - Bicycles - Kent International Inc.
ROCK-OUT! - Tools–garden - Dry-Tab Package Sealer Co.
ROCK PAK - Beverages - White Rock Products Corp.
ROCK POINT - Sporting goods - Rock Point Outfitters
ROCK POP - Beverages - White Rock Products Corp.
ROCK POT - Toys - Tonka Corp.
ROCK POWER - Bicycles ☆ - Huffy Corp.
ROCK-POWER - Cleaning preparations - Rock-Tred Corp.
ROCK-R-ROLL - Infant product - Sandbox Industries
ROCK-R-SEEL - Electrical equipment - A.P.M. Hexseal Corp.
ROCK RADIO - Radios ☆ - Sun Coast Merchandise Corp.
ROCK RIB - Fabrics - Greenwood Mills Inc.
ROCK RIB - Tools ☆ - Goldblatt Tool Co.
ROCK RIPPER - Augers - Pengo Industries, Inc.
ROCK RIVER - Footwear - Home Court International, Ltd.
ROCK ROLLER - Toys - Tonka Corp.
ROCK ROSE - Wines - Cronin Vineyards
ROCK-RUNNER - Fishing tackle - Northland Fishing Tackle, Inc.
ROCK SAW - Saws–hand-operated - Designit Corp.
ROCK-SHAKES - Siding–insulating ☆ - Manville/Schuller
ROCK SHOT - Toys - Tonka Corp.
ROCK SHOX - Apparel and accessories - Rockshox, Inc.
ROCK SLIDE PIE - Bakery products - Gourmet Concepts International, Inc.
ROCK SOCKS - Athletic footwear - Five Ten
ROCK SOLID TIME - Watches - Cooper & Co., Inc.
ROCK SPRING - Water–bottled or canned - Rock Spring Water Co.
ROCK STAR - Footwear - Trico International Inc.
ROCK STAR CONCERT - Trading cards and stamps ☆ - Amurol Confections Co.
ROCK STEADY - Pet products - Northeastern Products Corp.
ROCK-TEX - Siding–insulating ☆ - Aluminum Co. of America
ROCK, THE - Balls–basketball - Anaconda Sports, Inc.
ROCK, THE - Work benches - Production Industries Inc.
ROCK THE VOTE - Educational materials - Rock the Vote Education Fund
ROCK THE WORLD SOUTH PACIFIC - Apparel and accessories - Save Our World Inc.
ROCK TORQUE - Mining vehicle axles - Wagner Mining and Construction Equipment Co.
ROCK TOUGH - Automotive parts and accessories - Wagner Mining and Construction Equipment Co.
ROCK TRAIL - Bicycles ☆ - Huffy Corp.
ROCK TRAX - Musical instrument accessories - Hal Leonard Corp.
ROCK U - Clothing - H.H. Cutler Co.
ROCK VALLEY - Paints - Rock Paint & Chemical Co.
ROCK-WALL - Paints - Washington Paint Products
ROCKABEAR CHAIR - Rocking chairs - Flexible Flyer Co.
ROCK.A.DOODLE COLORING BOOK - Computer software - Capstone Software
ROCKAFLAGE - Apparel and accessories - Scott E. Anderson
ROCKAPETTA - Toys ☆ - Marlon Creations
ROCKAS - Percussion instrument - Robert Feldman

☆ = Now out of production

ROCKASAURUS REX - Toys - Tonka Corp.
ROCKAWAY TOWNSQUARE - Banks–commercial - CPI-Rockaway Townsquare Corp.
ROCKBEAT - Recording label - Westwood Entertainment Group
ROCKBOTTOM - Publisher's imprints ☆ - Bandanna Books
ROCKBRIDGE - Clocks - Ridgeway Clock Co.
ROCKBRIDGE - Floor coverings–carpet and rugs ☆ - Lees Carpets
ROCKBRIDGE - Furniture–upholstered ☆ - Webb Furniture Enterprises Inc.
ROCKCLASS - Computer software - Schlumberger Technology Corp.
ROCKCOTE - Cookware - West Bend Co.
ROCKCOTE - Paints - Valspar Corp.
ROCKEATER - Saws–hand-operated - Takagi Tools, Inc.
ROCKEFELLER CENTER - Novelty items - Rockefeller Group, Inc.
ROCKER FLARES - Rocker panels guards - Craig Rasmussen Enterprises
ROCKER GARD - Paints - Minnesota Mining & Manufacturing Co.
ROCKER STOPPER - Anchors - Davis Instruments Corp.
ROCKER WEAR - Apparel–athletic - Dangerous Design
ROCKERPEDAL - Bicycle parts and accessories - Dana P Hervig
ROCKERPEDALS - Exercising equipment - RockerPedal, Inc.
ROCKERS - Cookies - Nabisco Foods Group
ROCKERS - Musical instrument accessories ☆ - Selmer Co. Inc.
ROCKET - Ammunition - Remington Arms Co., Inc.
ROCKET - Bats–baseball - Baum Research and Development Co.
ROCKET - Boats–motor - Rinker Boat Co.
ROCKET - Computer software - Rocket Software Inc.
ROCKET - Floor coverings ☆ - Congoleum Corp.
ROCKET - Footwear–athletic - American Athletic Shoe Co.
ROCKET - Footwear–athletic - Puma Inc.
ROCKET - Game tables - American International Shuffleboard Corp.
ROCKET - Guitars ☆ - International Music Corp.
ROCKET - Hardware - Alumatic Corp. of America
ROCKET - Hardware ☆ - Hettich America L.P.
ROCKET - Hardware ☆ - True Temper Hardware Co.
ROCKET - Ice cream - Eskimo Pie Corp.
ROCKET - Kites - Llumar Star Kites Inc.
ROCKET - Lighting fixtures - Swivelier Co. Inc.
ROCKET - Medical apparatus - Rocket USA, Ltd.
ROCKET - Ophthalmic goods - Revlon Consumer Products Corp.
ROCKET - Paper–carbon ☆ - Eaton Allen Ko-Rec-Type Corp.
ROCKET - Pet products - Rapid Electric/R & R Manufacturing
ROCKET - Pipes–tobacco - Bradberry Briar Pipe Corp.
ROCKET - Projection screens - Brumberger Co. Inc.
ROCKET - Recording label - MCA Universal Studios
ROCKET - Rope ☆ - Crow Rope Industries LLC
ROCKET - Sporting goods - Windsurfing International Inc.
ROCKET - Tools - Tilden-Rocket Tool Co.
ROCKET - Toys - Sky-Way Products
ROCKET - Toys–stuffed ☆ - Gund, Inc.
ROCKET - Trays - D.C. Electronic Industries, Inc.
ROCKET - Varnishes - Jones Blair Co.
ROCKET - Watches - Bulova Corp.
ROCKET - Wines - Monarch Wine Co. of Georgia
ROCKET 500 - Toys–automobiles - Thomas Lowe Ventures, Inc.
ROCKET AEROHEADS - Archery equipment - Rocket Aerohead Corp.
ROCKET DOG - Shoes - Sbicca of California
ROCKET EAGLE - Machine tools - B & J Manufacturing Co., Inc.
ROCKET FUEL - Herbal products - Oakmont Investments Co.
ROCKET KNIGHT ADVENTURES - Computer software ☆ - Konami (America) Inc.
ROCKET-LINE - Calendars - Goes Lithographing Co.
ROCKET MAN - Fireworks - China Pyrotechnics, Inc.
ROCKET ONE - Boats–motor ☆ - Monark Boat Co.
ROCKET POPS - Candy ☆ - Casanova Chocolate Co.
ROCKET PRO BULLET - Toys - Marvlee Inc.
ROCKET RANGERS - Games - Gamescience
ROCKET RELEASE - Lubricants - Stoner Inc.
ROCKET RIDER - Playground equipment ☆ - Hedstrom Corp.
ROCKET ROLLERS - Toys - Tyco Toys
ROCKET SCIENCE - Apparel–children's - Montgomery Ward & Co. Inc.
ROCKET SCIENCE - Electronic equipment - Rocket Science, Ltd.
ROCKET SERIES - Bobsleds and toboggans - Paris Co. Inc.
ROCKET-SHIP - Cleaning preparations - Tuway American Group
ROCKET SHOT - Toys–automobiles - Mattel, Inc.
ROCKET-SHUTE - Toys ☆ - Princess Soft Toys
ROCKET STANDER, THE - Health care products - Mulholland Positioning Systems Inc.

ROCKETANK - Toys–automobiles - Mattel, Inc.
ROCKETCHIP - Integrated circuits - Western Digital Corp.
ROCKETEER - Candy - Topps Co., Inc.
ROCKETKNIGHT - Computer software ☆ - Konami (America) Inc.
ROCKETRY - Floor coverings–carpet and rugs - Roxbury Carpet Co.
ROCKETS - Trading cards and stamps - Rocket Ball, Ltd.
ROCKETSTORM - Games - Tonka Corp.
ROCKETTES - Dolls - Rockefeller Group, Inc.
ROCKETTES - Floor coverings ☆ - Congoleum Corp.
ROCKFACE - Suspended-ceiling panels ☆ - Conwed Plastics
ROCKFALL - Water dispensers - Jandy Industries, Inc.
ROCKFORD - Cabinets - Imperial Cabinet Co. Inc.
ROCKFORD - Computer software - First Star Software Inc.
ROCKFORD - Fasteners–snap - Rockford Products Corp. (International Group)
ROCKFORD - Floor coverings–carpet and rugs - Blue Ridge Carpet Mills
ROCKFORD - Floor coverings–carpet and rugs ☆ - Dorsett Carpet Mills Inc.
ROCKFORD - Tiles–ceramic - KPT Inc.
ROCKFORD - Tomato pastes and sauces ☆ - Fremont Co.
ROCKFORD - Watches - Bennett Brothers Inc.
ROCKFORD-FOSGATE - Audio equipment - Rockford Fosgate
ROCKFORD MACHINE TOOL - Machine tools - Devlieg-Bullard Services Group
ROCKFORDE - Cabinets ☆ - Dura-Craft Kitchens
ROCKGARDS - Rock-group trading cards - Brockum Co.
ROCKHARD - Varnishes - H. Behlen & Bro. Inc.
ROCKIES - Key chains, money clips, and trophies - Colorado Baseball Partnership 1993, Ltd.
ROCKIES WORLD BRAND - Apparel and accessories - Miller International Inc.
ROCKIN' ABC'S - Soups–canned ☆ - Fantastic Foods Inc.
ROCKIN' BROWN - Lipsticks ☆ - Honey & Spice Toiletries
ROCKIN HORSE - Musical instrument accessories - St. Louis Music Supply Co.
ROCKIN' HORSE - Musical instrument accessories - SLM Marketplace
ROCKIN' PENGUIN - Bedding–linen - Dan River Inc.
ROCKIN POCKETS - Infant product - Leachco Inc.
ROCKIN POPPIN - Toys ☆ - Libby Lee Toys Inc.
ROCKIN' RABBITS - Candy - R.M. Palmer Co.
ROCKIN' RADIO - Toys - Playskool, Inc.
ROCKIN' RED PUNCHER - Fruit drinks–bottled or canned - General Mills, Inc.
ROCKIN ROBIN - Recording label - Ripete Music Group
ROCKIN' ROBOT - Tape players - Kid Designs Inc.
ROCKIN' RUINS - Pet products - Penn-Plax, Inc.
ROCKIN SANDI - Dolls ☆ - Totsy Manufacturing Co., Inc.
ROCKING FRIEND - Toys - Gerber Products Co.
ROCKING HORSE - Clocks - General Time Corp. (Westclox/Seth Thomas Div.)
ROCKING HORSE - Recording label - New Renaissance Records
ROCKING K - Meat products–canned - Stagg Foods, Inc.
ROCKING K - Shirts - Kennington Limited Inc.
ROCKING LOAFER - Recliners ☆ - Flexsteel Industries Inc.
ROCKING PET - Toys–stuffed - Fun World Inc.
ROCKING PONY - Toys - Fisher-Price, Inc.
ROCKING PUPPY - Toys - Fisher-Price, Inc.
ROCKING RACKETS - Toy stores - Walt Disney Co.
ROCKING TOYS OF AMERICA - Ride-on rocking toys - Rocking Toys of America Inc.
ROCKINGHAM - Dinnerware–glass ☆ - Royal China & Porcelain Companies Inc.
ROCKINGHAM - Food processors - Wampler Foods Inc.
ROCKINGHAM - Furniture - Universal Flooring
ROCKINGHAM - Furniture–wood - Merillat Industries, Inc.
ROCKIT - Exercising equipment - Soloflex, Inc.
ROCKIT - Recording label - Rockit Records Inc.
ROCKITE - Cement - Hartline Products Co. Inc.
ROCKITY ROLLERS - Toys - Mattel, Inc.
ROCKLAND - Audio equipment - Rockland Scientific Corp.
ROCKLAND - Blinds–venetian - Alamo Distributors
ROCKLAND - Food products - Rockland Provision Co.
ROCKLAND - Recording label - Dharma Records
ROCKLAND HARBOR COLLECTION, THE - Tables–wood - Moosehead Manufacturing Co.
ROCKLAND TOOL CO. - Tools - Ocean State Jobbers, Inc.
ROCKLATH - Plaster–wallboard - United States Gypsum Co.
ROCKLEDGE - Furniture - Ashley Furniture Industries, Inc.
ROCKLEDGE SPORT - Apparel and accessories - Regatta Licensing
ROCKLINE - Paper ☆ - Rockline Industries Inc.

☆ = Now out of production

ROCKLORDS - Toys - Tonka Corp.

ROCKLYN HOUSE - Cakes ☆ - Kitty Koehler's Kitchens

ROCKMAN - Amplifiers ☆ - Scholz Research & Development, Inc.

ROCKMEADOW PRINTS - Wallpaper ☆ - Newmarket Designs Ltd.

ROCKMOC - Footwear - H.H. Brown Shoe Co., Inc.

ROCKMOUNT - Apparel and accessories - Rockmount Ranch Wear
Manufacturing Co.

ROCKMOUNT - Electronic equipment - Efxx Products Co.

ROCKMOUNT RANCH WEAR - Apparel—men's - Rockmount Ranch Wear
Manufacturing Co.

ROCK'N CHARITY - Apparel and accessories - T.J. Martell Foundation

ROCKOLA - Furniture ☆ - Bassett Furniture Industries, Inc.

ROCKOUSTICS - Amplifiers - GNP Audio Video Inc.

ROCKPILE, THE - Apparel and accessories - Colorado Baseball Partnership
1993, Ltd.

ROCKPIX - Guitars - Lulirama International, Inc.

ROCKPORT - Floor coverings—carpet and rugs - Trans-Ocean Import Co. Inc.

ROCKPORT - Footwear - Rockport Co. Inc.

ROCKPORT - Furniture ☆ - Bassett Furniture Industries, Inc.

ROCKPORT, THE - Sinks—porcelain ☆ - Jameco Industries, Inc.

ROCKPRO - Computer software - Resources Engineering Systems, Inc.

ROCKQUEST - Exercising equipment - Rockquest Co.

ROCKRIDGE - Floor coverings ☆ - Congoleum Corp.

ROCKRIDGE - Ice cream - Dreyer's Grand Ice Cream, Inc.

ROCKS - Ball bearings - Rollerblade, Inc.

ROCKS & BUGS & THINGS - Toys—stuffed - CBS Toys

ROCKSAFE - Novelty items ☆ - OWI, Inc.

ROCKSAND - Stationery - Past-Time Greetings by Rocksand, Ltd.

ROCKSCAPES - Fountains - Brigitte Pottery

ROCKSLIDE - Bicycles - Huffy Corp.

ROCKSON - Audio equipment - MBT International, Inc.

ROCKSTAR-16 - Electrical equipment - Alta Research Corp.

ROCKSTEADY - Toys - Playmates World Wide Inc,

ROCKSTOP - Musical instrument accessories - E. Rockowitz Rockstop

ROCKTEX - Paints - Cyclart Inc.

ROCKVILLE - Furniture ☆ - Bassett Furniture Industries, Inc.

ROCKWARE - Decals and transfers - Krimson Corp.

ROCKWELD CTM - Epoxy coatings ☆ - Fosroc Inc.

ROCKWELL - Figurines ☆ - Gorham Inc.

ROCKWELL - Floor coverings—carpet and rugs - Barrett Carpet Mills Inc.

ROCKWELL - Identification tags - Rockwell Shops Ltd.

ROCKWELL HEIRLOOM SANTA COLLECTION, THE - Glassware—
household - Norman Rockwell Gallery, Ltd.

ROCKWELL PINK - Stone products - Rockwell Granite Co.

ROCKWELL WHITE - Stone products - Rockwell Granite Co.

ROCKWELL'S HOME TOWN - Novelty items - Norman Rockwell Gallery, Ltd.

ROCKWERKS - Bicycle parts and accessories - J & B Importers, Inc.

ROCKWOOD - Guitars - HSS Inc.

ROCKWOOD - Trailers—travel - Forest River, Inc.

ROCKWOOD - Wallpaper ☆ - Singer Wallcoverings, Inc.

ROCKWOOD - Water—bottled or canned - Rockwood Spring Water Co.

ROCKWOOD COLLECTION - Furniture - Moosehead Manufacturing Co.

ROCKWOOD E Z WALL - Concrete products - Rockwood Retaining Walls, Inc.

ROCKWOOL - Insulating materials - Rockwool Industries Inc.

ROCKY - Binoculars - Pioneer Marketing & Research, Inc.

ROCKY - Fishing lures - Harrison-Hoge Industries Inc.

ROCKY - Motor vehicles ☆ - Daihatsu America Inc.

ROCKY - Ophthalmic goods - Rozin Optical Export Corp.

ROCKY - Scooters—children's - Peg Perego USA Inc.

ROCKY - Toys - Hasbro, Inc.

ROCKY 911 SERIES - Boots - Rocky Shoes & Boots, Inc.

ROCKY & BULLWINKLE - Footwear - S. Goldberg and Co. Inc.

ROCKY & BULLWINKLE - Toys ☆ - Mighty Star Inc. (Special Effects Div.)

ROCKY AND BULLWINKLE AND FRIENDS - Greeting cards - Ward
Productions, Inc.

ROCKY & BULLWINKLE PRESTO-SPARKLE PAINTS - Paint sets—hobby ☆
- Kenner Products

ROCKY BAY - Food products - Slade Gorton and Co. Inc.

ROCKY BOOTS - Boots - Rocky Shoes & Boots, Inc.

ROCKY BOPPERS - Boxing mitts ☆ - Intex Recreation Corp.

ROCKY COAST - Floor coverings - Mannington Resilient Floors

ROCKY CREEK - Furniture ☆ - Bassett Furniture Industries, Inc.

ROCKY CREEK - Siding—insulating ☆ - Union Camp Corp. (Fine Paper
Division)

ROCKY FACE - Floor coverings—carpet and rugs - Barrett Carpet Mills Inc.

ROCKY FISHING - Footwear - Rocky Shoes & Boots, Inc.

ROCKY III - Bop bags ☆ - Intex Recreation Corp.

ROCKY MALLOW - Candy - Russell Stover Candies, Inc.

ROCKY MOUNTAIN - Agricultural products - Art Morgan

ROCKY MOUNTAIN - Archery equipment - Archer Sports Inc.

ROCKY MOUNTAIN - Popcorn - Stock Popcorn Co. Inc.

ROCKY MOUNTAIN - Sporting goods - Orvis Co., Inc.

ROCKY MOUNTAIN - Sporting goods - Craig Steichen

ROCKY MOUNTAIN - Trailers—travel - Clay Camper Co. Inc.

ROCKY MOUNTAIN - Water—bottled or canned - Rocky Mountain Water

ROCKY MOUNTAIN BAGEL CO. - Food products - Rocky Mountain Bagel
Co., Inc.

ROCKY MOUNTAIN BLEND - Coffee - Arabica Inc.

ROCKY MOUNTAIN CHOCOLATE FACTORY - Chocolate candy - Rocky
Mountain Chocolate Factory, Inc.

ROCKY MOUNTAIN CLOTHING CO - Apparel and accessories - Miller
International Inc.

ROCKY MOUNTAIN EXPRESS - Toys—trains ☆ - Wm. K. Walthers Inc.

ROCKY MOUNTAIN FARMS - Ice cream - Snelgrove Ice Cream, Inc.

ROCKY MOUNTAIN GLOW - Trees - J. Frank Schmidt & Son Co.

ROCKY MOUNTAIN GOLD - Fishing tackle - Don-Rich Co. Inc.

ROCKY MOUNTAIN HIGH - Fireworks - Ingram Enterprises, Inc.

ROCKY MOUNTAIN HIGH - Jams and jellies - Mountain Maid Gourmet Jelly

ROCKY MOUNTAIN KING - Snowmobiles - Polaris Industries Partners LP

ROCKY MOUNTAIN LEGEND, THE - Beverages—malt ☆ - Adolph Coors Co.

ROCKY MOUNTAIN PROGRAMMING & COMPUTING PLUS PLUS -
Computers - RMPC++

ROCKY MOUNTAIN RAINBOW - Jams and jellies - Mountain Maid Gourmet
Jelly

ROCKY MOUNTAIN RAM - Computer hardware - Rocky Mountain Ram, LLC

ROCKY MOUNTAIN RANGE - Stoves—gas - R.M. Range and Co., Inc.

ROCKY MOUNTAIN RECORDS MANAGERS - Paper products - RMRM, Inc.

ROCKY MOUNTAIN ROAD - Desserts - Boulder Brownie Co.

ROCKY MOUNTAIN SAFE - Safes - Rocky Mountain Safe, Inc.

ROCKY MOUNTAIN SEASONS - Seasonings - Rocky Mountain Seasons, Inc.

ROCKY MOUNTAIN SOFTWOOD SHAVINGS - Wood products - Teton Forest
Products, LLC

ROCKY MOUNTAIN SPLENDOR - Flowers, plants, and seeds - J. Frank
Schmidt & Son Co.

ROCKY MOUNTAIN SUNSHINE - Jams and jellies - Mountain Maid Gourmet
Jelly

ROCKY MOUNTAIN TOY COMPANY - Toys - The Rocky Mountain Int'l
Trading Co.

ROCKY MTN. MUD - Bakery products - Our Name is Mud, Inc.

ROCKY PATH - Ice cream - Baskin-Robbins USA Co.

ROCKY POINT PRESERVE - Amusement parks - Sea World, Inc.

ROCKY RACOON - Toys - Tonka Corp.

ROCKY RIDGE - Bicycle - Marin Mountain Bikes, Inc.

ROCKY ROAD - Candy - Annabelle Candy Co. Inc.

ROCKY ROAD - Toys—stuffed - Russ Berrie and Co., Inc.

ROCKY ROADS - Footwear - Volpe Shoe Co.

ROCKY SAFARI - Footwear - Rocky Shoes & Boots, Inc.

ROCKY STALKERS - Footwear - Rocky Shoes & Boots, Inc.

ROCKY STRIDERS - Footwear - Rocky Shoes & Boots, Inc.

ROCKY SUPPORT SYSTEMS - Footwear - Rocky Shoes & Boots, Inc.

ROCKY THE DOLPHIN - Bookmarks - Nicholas James Lee

ROCKY TOP - Treated lumber and millwork - Rocky Top Wood Preservers Inc.

ROCKY TOP FARMS - Chocolate candy - Rocky Top Farms

ROCKY WALKING - Footwear - Rocky Shoes & Boots, Inc.

ROCKY'S - Nuts—salted, roasted, cooked, or canned - Rocky Peanut Co., Inc.

ROCKY'S BOOTS - Computer software ☆ - Gessler Publishing Co., Inc.

ROCKY'S BOOTS - Computer software ☆ - The Learning Co., Inc.

ROCKY'S CHOICE - Food products ☆ - Losurdo Foods, Inc.

ROCKY'S REPLAY A GAME ARCADE - Video equipment - Rocky's Replay
Inc.

ROCO - Coffee - Sellurs, Inc.

ROCO - Hardware ☆ - Bondex International Inc.

ROCO BALM - Lip balms - Roosa & Ratliff Drug Co.

ROCOCO - Flatware ☆ - Henriksen Imports Inc.

ROCORE - Motor vehicle parts and accessories - Rocore Industries, Inc.

ROCSPORTS - Footwear - Rockport Co. Inc.

ROCSUEDE - Finishing agents - Rock Paint & Chemical Co.

ROCUT - Hardware - Rothenberger USA, Inc.

ROD & GUN - Footwear—men's - C.O. Lynch Enterprises, Inc.

ROD BLANKET - Sporting goods ☆ - Rod Caddy Industries

ROD BUCKLE - Buckles - Indiana Mills & Manufacturing, Inc.

ROD CADDY - Sporting goods ☆ - Rod Caddy Industries

ROD GILBERT'S HOCKEY - Games ☆ - A.R.C. Toys Inc.
ROD LAVER - Apparel–athletic ☆ - Warnaco Inc.
ROD LAVER'S PRO TENNIS - Games ☆ - A.R.C. Toys Inc.
ROD-MATE - Fishing tackle ☆ - Hypark Specialty Co., Inc.
ROD MINDER - Sporting goods - Magic Products, Inc.
ROD POCKET - Fishing rods - Sound Inventions, Inc.
ROD-RAK - Fishing tackle ☆ - National Manufacturing Co.
RODAGON - Photographic equipment - H.P. Marketing Corp.
RODAGON-G - Photographic equipment - H.P. Marketing Corp.
RODAGON-WA - Photographic equipment - H.P. Marketing Corp.
RODALE - Publisher's imprints - National Plan Service
RODALE PRESS - Publisher's imprints - Rodale Press, Inc.
RODAN - Toys - Toho Co., Ltd.
RODANIA - Watches - Rodania Watch Co. Inc.
RODBUCKLE - Hardware - Indiana Marine Co. (Indiana Mills & Manufacturing)
RODCO - Flour–blended ☆ - Stevens Industries Inc.
RODDA - Candy - Rodda Candy Co.
RODDENBERY'S - Food products - W.B. Roddenbery Co., Inc.
RODDY BOY - Food products - J.M. Rodriguez & Co. Inc.
RODE DOG RECORDS - Recording label - Reunion Records
RODE RIDER - Amusement rides - S & S Power, Inc.
RODE WALKER - Apparel and accessories - Sidran, Inc.
RODEHEAVER - Recording label - Word, Inc.
RODEK - Car stereo equipment - Rodek, Inc.
RODELL - Jewelry - Rodell Manufacturing Co.
RODELLE - Toilets–enameled - Kohler Co.
RODENSTOCK - Photographic equipment - H.P. Marketing Corp.
RODENT ROUTER - See **RAT-A-WAY**
RODEO - Apparel–men's ☆ - Sedgefield Sportswear Co.
RODEO - Bathing suits - Ocean Pool Co.
RODEO - Beverages–carbonated - Ginger Group, Ltd.
RODEO - Bicycles - Columbia Manufacturing Inc.
RODEO - Fruits and vegetables ☆ - Columbia Fruit Packers Inc.
RODEO - Herbicides - Monsanto Co.
RODEO - Leather goods - Rodeo Leather Goods Co. Inc.
RODEO - Meat products–beef - John Morrell & Co.
RODEO - Medical apparatus - Occunomix International Inc.
RODEO - Motor vehicles–automobiles - American Isuzu Motors Inc.
RODEO - Pet products - Interwood Corp.
RODEO - Root beer–bottled or canned - Amazing Beverages, Inc.
RODEO - Watches - Majesti Watch Co. Inc.
RODEO DRIVE - Apparel–children's - Rodeo Drive, Inc.
RODEO DRIVE - Boots - Durango Boot Co. Inc.
RODEO DRIVE - Fabrics–tapestry ☆ - Coloroll Inc.
RODEO DRIVE - Floor coverings–carpet and rugs - Mohawk Industries Inc.
RODEO DRIVE - Floor coverings–carpet and rugs ☆ - Hollytex Carpet Mills Inc.
RODEO DRIVE - Wallpaper - Frankford Wallcoverings Inc.
RODEO LEGENDS - Jackets - Westark Garment Manufacturing, Inc.
RODEO MILE - Jewelry - Harry Winston, Inc.
RODEO MOUNTAIN - Amusement rides - Universal Recreation Co., Inc.
RODEO RAGS - Apparel and accessories - Rodeo Rags Inc.
RODEO RIG - Toys - Fisher-Price, Inc.
RODEO ROCKY - Playground equipment ☆ - Miracle Recreation Equipment Co.
RODEO ROMANCE - Toys - Tonka Corp.
RODEO ROSE - Toys - Tonka Corp.
RODEO ROUGH - Apparel and accessories - GWB, Inc.
RODEO STOUT - Beverages–malt - Crested Butte Brewery & Pub
RODEO ZONE - Shirts - M & F Western Products, Inc.
RODERICH PAESOLD - Musical instruments - Boosey & Hawkes Buffet Crampon USA
RODEWAY - Floor coverings ☆ - Tarkett, Inc.
RODEWAY INNS - Hotels and motels - Choice Hotels International Inc.
RODEX - Pharmaceutical preparations - Legere Pharmaceuticals Inc.
RODEX - Rodenticides - Hacco, Inc./Loveland Industries, Inc.
RODEX BLOX - Rodenticides - Hacco, Inc./Loveland Industries, Inc.
RODGER DODGER - Toys–automobiles - Mattel, Inc.
RODGERS - Organs–musical instrument - Rodgers Instrument Corp.
RODGERS AND HAMMERSTEIN R&H - Apparel and accessories - Rodgers Family Partnership
RODGERS AND HAMMERSTEIN RH - Dolls - Executor of the Estate of Oscar Hammerstein II
RODI - Engines–internal combustion - Rodi Power Systems, Inc.
RODIAL - Wicker, rattan - Kaju Kencana Fortuna
RODIER - Scarves ☆ - Jewel Case Inc.

RODIN - Apparel and accessories - Rodin Fashion Jeans
RODIN - Apparel–women's - Camille Claudel Corp.
RODINAL - Photographic equipment - Miles Inc. (Agfa Div.)
RODINAX - Photographic equipment ☆ - Miles Inc. (Agfa Div.)
RODINVENTION - Greeting cards - Robert Rodin
RODLITE - Wheel rims–motor vehicle - Weld Racing, Inc.
RODMATE - Fishing tackle - Rodmate
RODNEY - Toys–stuffed ☆ - Gund, Inc.
RODNEY RACCOON - Paper–writing - Premier Agendas, Inc.
RODNEY RACCOON - Puppets - Dakin Inc.
RODNEY STRONG - Wines - Klein Foods, Inc.
RODNEY STRONG - Wines - Rodney Strong Vineyards
RODO - Novelty items - Rodo Inc.
RODO OF ITALY - Handbags - Lisette Handbags Ltd.
RODOLFO - Ophthalmic goods - Rozin Optical Export Corp.
RODOLFO VALENTINO - Footwear ☆ - Olem Shoe Corp.
RODON - Fishing-rod cases - Cortland Line Co., Inc.
RODOS - Yarn ☆ - JCA, Inc.
ROD'R CHART MATE - Tubes–plastic - Beckson Marine Inc.
RODRAK - Racks - John D. Pruit
RODREX - Fishing rods - Rodrex, Inc.
RODRIGUEZ - Food products - Rodriguez Foods Inc.
RODRIGUEZ - Skateboards ☆ - Powell Skateboards
RODRUNNER - Cables–steel - General Wire Spring Co.
ROD'S - Dairy products - Ryan Foods Co.
ROD'S - Food products - Rod's Food Products Inc.
ROD'S - Whipped topping–frozen - Campbell Taggart Inc.
RODSTER - Automotive parts and accessories - Henry M. Caroselli
RODWARE - Automotive parts and accessories ☆ - Echlin Inc.
RODZILLA - Toys–automobiles - Mattel, Inc.
ROEBUCKS - Apparel and accessories - Sears, Roebuck and Co.
ROEDERER ESTATE - Wines - Roederer U.S. Marketing Inc.
ROEHLEN - Machinery - Standex International Corp.
ROENISCH - Pianos - Hanseatic Overseas Trading Inc.
ROENITZ - Footwear - H.C. Roenitz Co. Inc.
ROESCH - Cooking utensils–cast iron ☆ - Roesch Inc.
ROESCH CENTURY III - Fireplaces ☆ - Roesch Inc.
ROEVE - Watches - Scott Resources
ROEZIT - Pharmaceutical preparations - Lusal Enterprises, Inc.
ROFERON-A - Pharmaceutical preparations - Roche Laboratories
ROFFE - Ski suits–women's - Roffe Inc.
ROFFE 360 - Apparel–athletic - Roffe Inc.
ROFFLER - Hair care products - Framesi USA/Roffler Industries Inc.
ROFFLER BLUE - Hair care products - Framesi USA/Roffler Industries Inc.
ROFFLER GOLD - Hair care products - Framesi USA/Roffler Industries Inc.
ROFLARE - Tools - Rothenberger USA, Inc.
ROFONICS - Audio equipment - Rogers Foam Corp.
ROFREN - Brake pads - Rofren Disc Brake, Inc.
ROFROST - Tools - Rothenberger USA, Inc.
ROGAINE - Pharmaceutical preparations - Upjohn Co.
ROGASKA - Glassware–household - Miller-Rogaska Inc.
ROGEL - Bakery products - Fenwick Enterprises, Inc.
ROGENIC - Pharmaceutical preparations - Forest Pharmaceuticals Inc.
ROGER - Frames–eyeglass - Rozin Optical Export Corp.
ROGER - Ophthalmic goods ☆ - Luxottica
ROGER CAPRON - Tiles–ceramic - Amsterdam Corp.
ROGER DUNSTAN - Apparel–men's - Central-Samuels Inc.
ROGER HONG - Food products - American Specialty Foods Inc.
ROGER HONG - Food products ☆ - PFP Speciality Foods Inc.
ROGER LATHAM - Sporting goods ☆ - Penn's Woods Products Inc.
ROGER LUGUET - Wines - Rolar Imports Ltd.
ROGER PARA - Brushes–hair ☆ - Major International Inc.
ROGER RABBIT - Toys - Playskool, Inc.
ROGER RACCOON - Toys–stuffed ☆ - Dakin Inc.
ROGERS - Electronic equipment ☆ - Philips Electronics North America Corp.
ROGERS - Food products - Speaco Foods Inc.
ROGERS - Musical instruments - Fender Musical Instruments
ROGERS - Pens - Newell Office Products
ROGERS - Potato flakes - Rogers Foods Inc.
ROGER'S - Seasonings - Serv-Quick Foods
ROGERS & SPENCER - Guns - Euroarms of America
ROGERS BY ONEIDA - Flatware - Oneida Ltd.
ROGERS CO. - Pans ☆ - Stanley Roberts, Inc.
ROGERS LOUISIANA - Seasonings - Speaco Foods Inc.
ROGERS MAJESTIC - Radios ☆ - Philips Electronics North America Corp.
ROGERS RECORDS - Office supplies ☆ - Newell Office Products

☆ = Now out of production

ROGERS' ROWDIES - Statuary - Edward L. Rogers
ROGERS ROYAL - Meat products–poultry - B.C. Rogers Food Service, Inc.
ROGESIC - Pharmaceutical preparations - Rotex Pharmaceuticals Inc.
ROGET - Apparel–children's - Roget Industries Ltd.
ROGET'S 21ST CENTURY THESAURUS - Publisher's imprints - Thomas Nelson, Inc.
'ROGIES - Food products - Ateeco, Inc.
ROGONAR - Photographic equipment - H.P. Marketing Corp.
ROGONAR-S - Photographic equipment - H.P. Marketing Corp.
ROGUE - Amplifiers–musical instrument ☆ - Fred Gretsch Enterprises
ROGUE - Apparel–athletic - Match Play of Pinehurst
ROGUE - Bicycles - Columbia Manufacturing Inc.
ROGUE - Boats–canoes - Black River Canoes
ROGUE - Boats–motor ☆ - Cruisers
ROGUE - Boats–motor ☆ - Marathon Boat Group, Inc.
ROGUE - Frames–eyeglass ☆ - Universal/Univis Inc.
ROGUE - Guitars - Alembic Inc.
ROGUE - Jewelry ☆ - Anson Inc.
ROGUE - Pens ☆ - Faber-Castell Corp.
ROGUE - Pipes–tobacco ☆ - S.M. Frank & Co. Inc. (Kaywoodie-Yello-Bole-Medico)
ROGUE - Recording label - Jazz Composer's Orchestra Association Inc.
ROGUE - Recording label - Rogue Enterprises, Inc.
ROGUE - Sporting goods - Ektelon
ROGUE - Toys–models ☆ - Estes Industries
ROGUE AMERICAN AMBER ALE - Beverages–malt - Rogue Ales
ROGUE ARTISAN LAGER - Beverages–malt - Rogue Ales
ROGUE BRUTAL BITTER ALE - Beverages–malt - Rogue Ales
ROGUE DEAD GUY ALE - Beverages–malt - Rogue Ales
ROGUE DRY HOP RED - Beverages–malt - Rogue Ales
ROGUE HALFE-E-WEIZEN ALE - Beverages–malt - Rogue Ales
ROGUE HAZELNUT BROWN NECTAR ALE - Beverages–malt - Rogue Ales
ROGUE HONEY CREAM ALE - Beverages–malt - Rogue Ales
ROGUE I2PA ALE - Beverages–malt - Rogue Ales
ROGUE II - Fabrics - Uniroyal Engineered Products
ROGUE MAIERBOCK ALE - Beverages–malt - Rogue Ales
ROGUE MCROGUE SCOTCH ALE - Beverages–malt - Rogue Ales
ROGUE MEXICALI ROGUE ALE - Beverages–malt - Rogue Ales
ROGUE MOCHA PORTER - Beverages–malt - Rogue Ales
ROGUE MOGUL ALE - Beverages–malt - Rogue Ales
ROGUE OLD CRUSTACEAN ALE - Beverages–malt - Rogue Ales
ROGUE OREGON GOLDEN ALE - Beverages–malt - Rogue Ales
ROGUE RIVER - Footwear - Wolverine World Wide, Inc.
ROGUE RIVER - Fruits–canned - Rogue River Packing Corp.
ROGUE RUNNER - See RIVER RUNNER
ROGUE ST. ROGUE RED ALE - Beverages–malt - Rogue Ales
ROGUE SANTA'S PRIVATE PARTY RESERVE ALE - Beverages–malt - Rogue Ales
ROGUE SHAKESPEARE STOUT - Beverages–malt - Rogue Ales
ROGUE SMOKE ALE - Beverages–malt - Rogue Ales
ROGUE, THE - Synthesizers–musical instrument ☆ - EJE Research Corp.
ROGUE WILD IRISH ROGUE ALE - Beverages–malt - Rogue Ales
ROGUE YOUNGER'S SPECIAL BITTER ALE - Beverages–malt - Rogue Ales
ROHM & HAAS - Insecticides - Rohm and Haas Co.
ROHN - Communications equipment–mobile - UNR-Rohn
ROHNER - Socks - Kenko International Inc.
ROHO - Cushions - Roho, Inc.
ROHO - Golfing equipment - Taylor Made Golf Co. Inc.
ROHO - Wines - Monarch Wine Co. of Georgia
ROHTSTEIN - Fruits and vegetables - Orchard Foods
ROI - Archery equipment - Saunders Archery Co.
ROI BUILDER - Computer software - National Education Training Group, Inc.
ROI DU SOLIEL - Frames–eyeglass - Hudson Optical Corp.
ROICO - Ammonia ☆ - Mid-America Chemical Inc.
ROILGARD - Filters–fuel - MJR Industries, Inc.
ROINCERI - Olive oil - Bel Canto Fancy Foods Ltd.
ROINCO - Disc brake pads - Roinco Manufacturing Co. Inc.
ROIR - Recording label - Jazz Composer's Orchestra Association Inc.
ROIS DROIS - Liquors - Crestfield Importers Ltd.
ROISSY - Bathroom fixtures ☆ - Crane Plumbing/Fiat Products
ROITAN - Cigar boxes–wood - Consolidated Cigar Corp.
ROJEIRO - Wines - Admiral Wine Merchants
ROJO MONTANA - Wines - Joseph E. Seagram & Sons, Inc.
ROJO, THE RED LOBSTER - Greeting cards - A + A
ROJON BIJA SUPREMO - Spices and extracts - La Flor Products Co., Inc.
ROJO'S - Food products ☆ - Chilay Foods Corp.

ROK AXE - Guitars - Music Industries Inc.
ROK-LOK - Paints - Key Laboratories Inc.
ROK-N-ROLL - Sporting goods - Hoag-Co.
ROK-RAP - Tape–adhesive - Andek Corp.
ROK SAK - Cases–musical instrument - Music Industries Inc.
ROKAN - Security systems - Rokan Corp.
ROKEACH - Food products - I. Rokeach and Sons Inc.
ROKINON - Photographic equipment - Rokina International Inc.
ROKK - Sporting goods - Kellwood Co.
ROKK STEADY - Recording label - Rokk Steady Records
ROKKO - Floor coverings - Toli International
ROKKOR - Lenses–photographic ☆ - Minolta Corp.
ROKON - Motor vehicles–motor homes - Rokon International, Inc.
ROKON TRAIL BREAKER - Motor vehicles–motor homes - Rokon International, Inc.
ROK'T DEVLET - Fishing lures - Eppinger Manufacturing Co.
ROKUNAR - Lenses–photographic - Aetna Optix Inc.
ROL-A-BALL - Games - Master Woodcraft Inc.
ROL-A-CIZER - Exercising equipment - GB & Associates,Inc.
ROL-A-KOTE - Paints - Remien & Kuhnert Co.
ROL-A-RAMP - Paint rollers - Arsco International Inc.
ROL-A-STOR - Containers - U-Neeks Products Inc.
ROL-BRUSH - Paint rollers - Rol-Brush Manufacturing, Div. (Michigan Brush Mfg. Co., Inc.)
ROL-DEK - Floor coverings - Pawling Corp. (Standard Products Div.)
ROL-DEX - Filing cabinets–metal - Watson Industries Inc.
ROL EZE - Paints - MCI Quality Coatings
ROL GLO - Paints - MCI Quality Coatings
ROL HIDE - Paints - MCI Quality Coatings
ROL-IT - Games - Master Woodcraft Inc.
ROL-KLIPPIES - Hair curlers - Capitol Novelty Co.
ROL-LABELS - Office supplies - Esselte Corp.
ROL LATEX - Paints - MCI Quality Coatings
ROL-LUX - Window shades - Vertilux-Louverlux Inc.
ROL-LUX-ROLLER SHADE FABRIC - Fabrics - Vertilux-Louverlux Inc.
ROL-O-FLEXOR - Massage products - John A. Oseka
ROL-R-LIFT - Hardware stores ☆ - Wynco Products
ROL-RULER - Rulers–wood - Rol-Ruler Co.
ROL-THREAD - Hardware - Hillwood Manufacturing Co.
ROLADEN - Shutters–wood - Environmental Seal & Security
ROLAIDS - Candy - American Chicle Co.
ROLAMECH - Pens - Rolamech Inc.
ROLAND - Apparel–men's ☆ - Cavaliero Cravats
ROLAND - Beverages–malt ☆ - Dribeck Importers, Inc.
ROLAND - Bicycles - Roland Distributing
ROLAND - Food products - American Roland Food Corp.
ROLAND - Musical instruments - Rolandcorp US
ROLAND DELUXE - Doughnuts–mixes - Roland Industries Inc.
ROLAND RYE - Breads–mixes - Roland Industries Inc.
ROLAND STAR - Shrimp–fresh or frozen - Mat Roland Seafood Co.
ROLAND WHEAT - Breads–mixes - Roland Industries Inc.
ROLANDBREAD - Breads–mixes - Roland Industries Inc.
ROLANE - Hosiery - Kayser-Roth Corp.
ROLATAPE - Measuring instruments - Rolatape Corp.
ROLATAPE MEASURING SYSTEMS - Measuring instruments - Rolatape Corp.
ROLATH - Plastics - Bedford Industries, Inc.
ROLATUSS - Cough medicines - Robinson Laboratories Inc.
ROLD GOLD - Pretzels - Frito-Lay, Inc.
ROLDIP - Scoops - Zeroll Co.
ROLE AIDS - Games - Mayfair Games, Inc.
ROLE STUDY TAPES MG - Recording label - Martha Gerhart
ROLEE - Hair care products - M & R Distributors, Inc.
ROLENE - Ophthalmic goods ☆ - Luxottica
ROLEOVERS - Children's costumes - Environments, Inc.
ROLEPLAYER - Games - Steve Jackson Games Inc.
ROLET - Potato sticks - Rolet
ROLETO - Apparel–athletic - Sepp Sport Inc.
ROLEX - Watches - Rolex Watch USA, Inc.
ROLEX DAYTONA - Watches - Rolex Watch USA, Inc.
ROLEXEN - Cough medicines - Robinson Laboratories Inc.
ROLEXUS - Switches–electric - Judco Manufacturing Inc.
ROLEZE - Shoe polish - Chicago Sole Leather Distributors Inc.
ROLF - Bicycle parts and accessories - Rolf Dietrich
ROLFE - Trailers–boat - Kilbourn Machine Co. Inc.
ROLFE ART - Flowers, plants, and seeds - Puiforcat

☆ = Now out of production

ROLFS - Belts–apparel - Amity Leather Products Co.

ROLFS - Leather goods - Rolfs Leather Products

ROLFS BRASS KEYWARE - Key rings - AR Accessories Group Inc.

ROLFS DESIGNER COLLECTION - Leather goods ☆ - Rolfs Leather Products

ROLFS LITES - Wallets - AR Accessories Group Inc.

ROLICE - Cookies - Kalar International, Inc.

ROLL-A-BAG - Pet products - Penn-Plax, Inc.

ROLL-A-BALL - Writing product - Island Pen Manufacturing Corp.

ROLL-A-CART - Machinery - S. Morantz Inc.

ROLL-A-CHART - Nautical instruments ☆ - Fred Silver and Co. Inc.

ROLL-A-COLOR - Paints ☆ - Shiva Inc.

ROLL-A-DOOR - Doors–garage ☆ - McKee Door, Inc.

ROLL-A-FINISH - Tools–machine - Cogsdill Tool Products, Inc.

ROLL-A-FLEX - Shutters–metal - Folding Shutter Corp.

ROLL-A-FLOW - Kilns - Swindell-Dressler International Co.

ROLL-A-GLIDE - Office supplies - Esselte Corp.

ROLL-A-GYM - Exercising equipment - Life Improvement, Inc.

ROLL-A-LOG - Fireplace equipment ☆ - Trepte Wire and Metal Works

ROLL-A-MAGIC - Food products machinery - R. Foster Enterprises

ROLL A PAR - Games ☆ - Milton Bradley Co.

ROLL-A-PILLA - Toys - Tyco Toys

ROLL-A-ROD - Drapery hardware - Young Ideas Inc.

ROLL A ROUNDS - Toys - Fisher-Price, Inc.

ROLL-A-SCENE - Paper - Penn-Plax, Inc.

ROLL-A-SIGN - Blinds–venetian - International Mercantile Industries, Inc.

ROLL A' SKETCH - Dispenser for drawing paper - Mead Corp.

ROLL-A-TAN - Sunblocks - Ledimar Inc.

ROLL-A-TEMP - Curling irons–electric - Helene Curtis Industries Inc.

ROLL-A-TEX - Adhesives and sealants - Gamma Laboratories Inc.

ROLL-A-WAY - Conveyors - Roll-A-Way Conveyors, Inc.

ROLL-A-WAY BEDS - Mattresses - High Point Bedding, Inc.

ROLL A WAY DERBY - Toys - Tyco Toys

ROLL-A-WET - Mops - Rubbermaid Commercial Products Inc.

ROLL-ACOUSTIC - Adhesives and sealants - Gamma Laboratories Inc.

ROLL-ACOUSTIC - Computers–personal ☆ - Hamilton Sorter Co. Inc.

ROLL AID - Health care products - Stand Aid of Iowa Inc.

ROLL-AID - Medical apparatus - Spenco Medical Corp.

ROLL-AIR - Compressors–air - Illinois Fastening Systems

ROLL ALONG BRIGHTS - Toys–stuffed ☆ - Gund, Inc.

ROLL ALONG PUZZLE TRAIN - Toys–trains - Mattel, Inc.

ROLL & SET - Hair care products - A.W. Curtis Laboratories, Inc.

ROLL AROUND CLOWN - Toys ☆ - Playskool, Inc.

ROLL-AROUND SOUND - Audio equipment - Califone International Inc.

ROLL-AROUNDS - Office supplies - Master Caster Co.

ROLL-AROUNDS TRAVEL WHEELS - Wheels - Master Caster Co.

ROLL AWAY - Boats–liferafts - Avon Marine

ROLL-AWAY - Exercising equipment - Battle Creek Equipment Co.

ROLL-AWAY - Luggage - United States Luggage Corp.

ROLL AWAY - Paint rollers - Wagner Spray Tech Corp.

ROLL-AWAY - Pet products ☆ - Petland, Inc.

ROLL-BABY - Golfing equipment - Peter L. Minotti Enterprises

ROLL-BOND - Electronic equipment ☆ - Olin Corp.

ROLL CALL - Pet products - Pet Medic Corp.

ROLL CONTROL - Automotive parts and accessories - Hurst Performance Inc.

ROLL CONTROL - Boats - Comfort Afloat

ROLL CONTROL - Brackets - East Coast Plastics Inc.

ROLL CONTROL - Brakes–bicycle - Rollerwear, Inc.

ROLL-DEX - Floor coverings ☆ - Pawling Corp. (Standard Products Div.)

ROLL-DRI - Printing trades machinery - Research, Inc.

ROLL-EEZ - Bearings–industrial - Roll-Eez Inc.

ROLL-ETTE - Stencils - Ideal Stencil Machine and Tape Co.

ROLL-EZ - Projectors–photographic ☆ - Logan Electric Specialty Manufacturing Co.

ROLL-EZE - Housewares ☆ - Home Equipment Manufacturing Co.

ROLL EZE - Stencils - Ideal Stencil Machine and Tape Co.

ROLL-IN - Golfing equipment - Kenneth Smith Inc.

ROLL KING - Golf carts ☆ - Ajay Leisure Products Inc.

ROLL-KLEEN - Apparel and accessories - Laidlaw Corp.

ROLL KLEEN - Machine parts - Uniwave, Inc.

ROLL MATRIX - Welding equipment - Alloy Rods Global, Inc.

ROLL MEMO - Paper–gummed - Park Sherman

ROLL 'N CUT - Toys - Tonka Corp.

ROLL-N-FOLD - Soccer equipment - Sport Supply Group, Inc.

ROLL 'N GLUE - Adhesives and sealants - Pentel of America, Ltd.

ROLL N GO - Patching compounds - Metalcrete Industries Inc.

ROLL N LOCK - Automotive parts and accessories - Toppertown Inc.

ROLL N LOCK - Truck bed cover - Roll-N-Lock Corp.

ROLL-N-PAINT - Toys - Lepage's, Inc.

ROLL 'N RAK - Computer peripheral equipment - Hunt Holdings, Inc.

ROLL 'N RATTLE SHAKER - Toys - Hasbro, Inc.

ROLL N' RIDER - Toys ☆ - Those Characters from Cleveland, Inc.

ROLL-N'-SET - Construction equipment - Sico Inc.

ROLL 'N STACK - Toys - Mattel, Inc.

ROLL-N-TILT - Projection screens - Brandons Inc.

ROLL-NIX - Marine rigging ☆ - Hyde Products Inc.

ROLL-O-BAG - Bags–plastic - Sidney Plastics, Inc.

ROLL-O-MATIC - Luggage ☆ - Hartmann Luggage Co.

ROLL-O-MATIC - Mops - M.B. Walton, Inc.

ROLL-O-RULER - Drafting supplies - China Palace Enterprise Co.

ROLL-O-VEND - Trailers–travel - Trailer Craft

ROLL-O-WRINGER - Mops - M.B. Walton, Inc.

ROLL-ON - Fly sprays - Farnam Cos. Inc.

ROLL-ON - Inks - Sanford Corp.

ROLL-ON - Pigments–paint - Gamma Laboratories Inc.

ROLL-OUT - Appliance parts - Dial Industries Inc.

ROLL-OUT - Filing cabinets–metal - Supreme Equipment & Systems Corp.

ROLL OUT - Plant growth regulators - Griffin Corp.

ROLL OVER RUBEN - Sandwiches–prepackaged ☆ - Little Lady Foods Inc.

ROLL PATROL - Toys–automobiles - Mattel, Inc.

ROLL PEN - Office supplies - American Tombow Inc.

ROLL PEN JR. - Office supplies - American Tombow Inc.

ROLL PEN SR. - Office supplies ☆ - American Tombow Inc.

ROLL PLEAT - Drapery hardware ☆ - Spring Window Fashions Division, Inc.

ROLL-POD - Photographic equipment - Frank R. Ward

ROLL-QUICK - Electronic equipment ☆ - EDCON Publishing

ROLL-RITE - Tarpaulins - Roll Rite Corp.

ROLL RITE - Tobacco products ☆ - House of Edgeworth

ROLL SQUEEZE - Inks - Ideal Stencil Machine and Tape Co.

ROLL/STOR - Tubes–plastic - Fellowes Manufacturing Co.

ROLL, THE - Snack foods - Farley Candy Co.

ROLL-TOP - Containers - Alvin and Co. Inc.

ROLL-TOP - Hot tubs–plastic ☆ - Coleman Spas

ROLL-UM - Games - GRG Co.

ROLL-UP - Medical apparatus - Home Care Products Inc.

ROLL-UP, THE - Computer peripheral equipment - Gtco Corp.

ROLL-UPS - Exercising equipment - Jeffrey Landers

ROLL USA - Skates–roller - First Team Sports, Inc.

ROLL-VENT - Roofing materials - Celotex Corp.

ROLL VENT - Roofing materials - Benjamin Obdyke Inc.

ROLL VENT 2 - Roofing materials ☆ - Benjamin Obdyke Inc.

ROLL X - Bags–trash - Pitt Plastic Inc.

ROLL-X - Pet products - Stromberg's Chicks & Pets Ltd.

ROLLA PINS - Hair care products ☆ - N.B. Cohen Co.

ROLLABALL - Exercising equipment - Fabrication Enterprises

ROLLABIND - Office machines - Rollabind, Inc.

ROLLABOUT - Luggage - NLDA Associates, Inc.

ROLLACAP - Hair care products - N. Seligman Co.

ROLLADUFFLE - Bags–duffel - Orvis Co., Inc.

ROLLAFLEX - Display cases–plastic - Expostar Displays, Inc.

ROLLAFLOR - Floor topping, glaze, primer, etc. - Construction Adhesives Co.

ROLLAGE - Cosmetics - Spornette International, Inc.

ROLLAGRAPH - Roller stamp - Clearsnap, Inc.

ROLLAIRE - Lawn mowers - Ransomes-Cushman-Ryan

ROLLAKANS - Floor coverings–carpet and rugs - Capel, Inc.

ROLLARAMA - Perfumes - Andre Richard

ROLLASUM - Toys ☆ - Knight Toy & Novelty Corp.

ROLLAWAY - Hardware ☆ - Frantz Manufacturing Co.

ROLLAWORD - Toys ☆ - Knight Toy & Novelty Corp.

ROLLBAR - Footwear - New Balance Athletic Shoe, Inc.

ROLLBAR STABILITY SYSTEM - Footwear - New Balance Athletic Shoe, Inc.

ROLLDOR - Paper–toilet - Clark Paper Converting Corp.

ROLLE - Frames–eyeglass ☆ - Universal/Univis Inc.

ROLLED EDGE - Holsters - American Sales & Manufacturing Co.

ROLLEI - Photographic equipment ☆ - H.P. Marketing Corp.

ROLLEI 6000 - Cameras ☆ - H.P. Marketing Corp.

ROLLEICORD - Photographic equipment - Rollei of America Inc.

ROLLEIFLEX - Cameras ☆ - H.P. Marketing Corp.

ROLLEIMAR - Photographic equipment - Rollei of America Inc.

ROLLEIMAT - Photographic equipment - Rollei of America Inc.

ROLLEIVISION - Projectors–photographic ☆ - H.P. Marketing Corp.

ROLLER - Sporting goods - Britton of Southport Inc.

☆ = Now out of production

ROLLER-ACTION - Publisher's imprints - Lo Duca Bros. Musical Instruments Inc.

ROLLER AIDS - Hair care products ☆ - Willat Co.

ROLLER BABY - Dolls - Tyco Toys

ROLLER BACK - Massage products - Mary J. Durand

ROLLER BALL - Pens - Sanford Corp.

ROLLER BALL PENS - Pens - Quill Co. Inc.

ROLLER B.U.M. - Apparel—men's - Chauvin International Ltd.

ROLLER COASTER - Games - Tonka Corp.

ROLLER COASTER - Games ☆ - Milton Bradley Co.

ROLLER COASTER - Mops - Crystal Lake Manufacturing, Inc.

ROLLER COASTER - Vending machines - Thaitalian Vending & Manufacturing Co.

ROLLER COASTERS - Pasta - American Home Food Products Inc.

ROLLER COATER - Tools - Martin Carbone Inc.

ROLLER COVER KEEPER - Paint rollers - Aqua-Tainer Co.

ROLLER CURLS - Hair care products - Conair Corp.

ROLLER DERBY - Floor coverings—carpet and rugs ☆ - Len Dal Carpets

ROLLER DERBY - Skates—roller - Roller Derby Skate Corp.

ROLLER DOODLE - Pens - Tulip Productions

ROLLER GRILL - Food products - Alex Foods, Inc.

ROLLER GRIP - Chains - St. Pierre Manufacturing Corp.

ROLLER HOCKEY INTERNATIONAL - Apparel and accessories - Roller Hockey International

ROLLER JENI WINGS - Ships—sailing vessels - Britton of Southport Inc.

ROLLER KING - Sliding windows - International Aluminum Corp.

ROLLER-KLEEN - Paint and wallpaper cleaners - Sterling-Clark-Lurton Corp.

ROLLER-MATES - Window shades - Ellery Products Manufacturing Co., Inc.

ROLLER PERM - Hair care products - Gillette Co.

ROLLER POP - Candy - Topps Co., Inc.

ROLLER PRO - Skates—roller - Roller Pro International Corp.

ROLLER QUEEN - Sliding windows - International Aluminum Corp.

ROLLER RACER - Chewing gum - Amurol Confections Co.

ROLLER ROO - Advertising agencies - Roller Skating Rink Operators Association

ROLLER-SEAL - Film - Emerald Film Systems

ROLLER SLIDE - Toys ☆ - American Toy & Furniture Co.

ROLLER-STAY - Boats - Mariner Co.

ROLLER STOP - Skates—roller - Rollerstop Inc.

ROLLER TECH - Skates—roller - National Sporting Goods Corp.

ROLLER TILT - Windows - Caldwell Manufacturing Co.

ROLLER-VAC - Vacuum cleaners and accessories - Roller-Vac Co.

ROLLER WAVE - Exercising equipment ☆ - Gerstung/Gym-Thing Inc.

ROLLER WRAP - Sporting goods - Chisco, Inc.

ROLLERAMIC - Projection screens - Draper Shade and Screen Co. Inc.

ROLLERBABY - Jogging stroller - Tri Industries, Inc.

ROLLERBALL - Shirts - Rollerball International Inc.

ROLLERBALL PLOTTER PENS - Drafting supplies - Koh-I-Noor, Inc.

ROLLERBLADE - Apparel—athletic - Rollerblade, Inc.

ROLLERBLADE FUN SNACKS - Snack foods - General Mills, Inc.

ROLLERBOARD - Skateboards - Rollerboard International, LLC

ROLLERBONES - Skates—roller - Powell Skateboards

ROLLERBUG - Tools - Goldblatt Tool Co.

ROLLERCOASTER - Paint rollers - Acca-Mark

ROLLERCOASTER, THE - Office supplies - Dri Mark Products, Inc.

ROLLERCOAT - Paints - Triangle Coatings Inc.

ROLLERETTE - Cosmetics ☆ - Marianna Imports, Inc.

ROLL'ERG - Wheelbarrows - Roll'erg North America, Inc.

ROLLERGLIDE - Drapery hardware ☆ - Kenney Manufacturing Co.

ROLLERHOCKEY GEAR BAG - Bags - Zepter Sports International

ROLLERLINER - Pens - Empire Berol USA

ROLLERMAGIC - Stamps—hand - Tara Toy Corp.

ROLLERMARK - Pens - Union Pen Co.

ROLLERS - Dog food ☆ - Mardel Laboratories, Inc.

ROLLERS - Pet products - USA-Petrx

ROLLERS BY BAKER - Brushes—paint - Baker Brush Co. Inc.

ROLLERS EDGE - Skates—roller - National Sporting Goods Corp.

ROLLERS, THE - Luggage - Paragon Luggage, Inc.

ROLLERSKI - Roller skates - Perry-Time International

ROLLERSTICK - Pens - Gillette Co.

ROLLERVIEW - Window shades - Eli Custom Window Treatment, Ltd.

ROLLERWALL - Paint rollers - Rollerwall Inc.

ROLLERZ - Skating rinks—roller - Canstar Sports USA

ROLLEX MARK II - Structural clay - Rollex Corp.

ROLLICKIN' ROLLERS - Toys - Mattel, Inc.

ROLLIEVER - Medical apparatus - L.C. Liming & Sons, Inc.

ROLLIN COMB, THE - Hair care products - Helene Curtis Industries Inc.

ROLLIN DEEP - Shirts - Olaes Enterprises Inc.

ROLLING ACTION - Pet products - Willinger Bros., Inc.

ROLLING AND LEARNING - Games - Creative Enterprises Inc.

ROLLING BOMBER - Drums—musical instruments ☆ - HSS Inc.

ROLLING ESTATES - Furniture - Bassett Furniture Industries, Inc.

ROLLING HILLS - Floor coverings—carpet and rugs - Kelly Group Inc.

ROLLING HILLS - Floor coverings—carpet and rugs ☆ - Royalweve Carpet Mills

ROLLING HILLS VINEYARDS - Wines - Rolling Hills Vineyards

ROLLING MEADOW - Ice cream - Jack & Jill Ice Cream Co.

ROLLING ROCK - Beverages—malt - Latrobe Brewing Co.

ROLLING ROCK BOCK - Beverages—malt - Latrobe Brewing Co.

ROLLING ROCK LIGHT - Beverages—malt - Latrobe Brewing Co.

ROLLING ROCK LITE - Beverages—malt - Labatt Importers Inc.

ROLLING ROCK PREMIUM - Beverages—malt - Labatt Importers Inc.

ROLLING ROCK PREMIUM - Beverages—malt - Latrobe Brewing Co.

ROLLING ROOF, THE - Awnings - Rainbow Awnings

ROLLING RUBBER - Paints - Pergament Home Centers Inc.

ROLLING SPRINGS - Water—bottled or canned - Clear Springs Limited, Inc.

ROLLING STOCK - Furniture - J. & D. Brauner Inc.

ROLLING STONE - Tiles—ceramic - KPT Inc.

ROLLING STONES - Hobby kits - Natural Science Industries, Ltd.

ROLLING STONES - Neckties - Ralph Marlin & Co., Inc.

ROLLING STONES - Recording label - Atlantic Records

ROLLING STRONG A TRUCKER'S GYM - Sports clubs - Rolling Strong Co., Inc.

ROLLING THUNDER - Fireworks - B.J. Alan Co. Inc.

ROLLING VINEYARDS FARM WINERY - Wines - Rolling Vineyards Farm Winery

ROLLING WEST - Food products - Western Farmers Association

ROLLINS - Alarm systems - Rollins Protective Services

ROLLINS - Recording label - CA-Song Music

ROLLINS - Transmissions—motor vehicle - Carlyle Johnson Machine Co.

ROLLIT - Cigarettes ☆ - Robert Burton Associates Ltd.

ROLLMA - Paper cutters - Kreonite Inc.

ROLLMASTER - Hitches—trailer - Lyle L. Cattau

ROLLMASTER - Office supplies - Mayer Manufacturing Corp.

ROLLO-RULER - Office supplies - Alvin and Co. Inc.

ROLLOBACK - Window shades - Kwik-Affix Products

ROLLOMETER - Skates—roller - Fariel Enterprises, Inc.

ROLLOSCOPE - Medical apparatus - Siemens Medical Systems, Inc.

ROLLOTRONIC - Cosmetics - RBI Distributors

ROLLOUT - Bags—duffel - Ektelon

ROLLOUT - Sporting goods - Voit Corp.

ROLLOUT BLEU - Balls - Voit Corp.

ROLLOUTS - Paper products - Lisa Frank, Inc.

ROLLOVER - Games - Enginuity

ROLLOVER - Pet products - Dog's Life Inc.

ROLLOVERS - Food products - Saramar Corp.

ROLLPAK - Bags—trash - Rollpak Corp.

ROLLPIN - Hardware ☆ - MacLean-ESNA

ROLLPRUF - Gloves—safety - Mapa Pioneer Corp.

ROLLRECEIVE - Computer software - Automation, Inc.

ROLLRITE - Photographic equipment - Testrite Instrument Co. Inc.

ROLLS - Eyeglasses - Martin-Copeland Eyewear Corp.

ROLLS - Musical instrument accessories - CTC Music Inc.

ROLLS BATTERY ENGINEERING - Batteries - Rolls Battery Engineering, Ltd.

ROLLS INTERNATIONAL - Trailers—travel ☆ - Carriage, Inc.

ROLLS ROLLER - Adhesives and sealants ☆ - Arsco International Inc.

ROLLS ROSS - Bicycles - Ross Bicycles USA, Ltd.

ROLLS-ROYCE - Motor vehicles—automobiles - Rolls-Royce Motors Inc.

ROLLSHARP ! - Knife blades - Fiskars Inc.

ROLLSTAR - Window shades - Castec Window Shading Inc.

ROLLSTONE - Apparel and accessories - Rollstone International Hats Co.

ROLLSTOP - Ships—sailing vessels - Lewmar Marine Inc.

ROLLTEK - Paper—rolls - Unisource Brands, Inc.

ROLLTOP 100 - Computer peripheral equipment - MicroComputer Accessories Inc.

ROLLUP - Computer software - MediaPlan, Inc.

ROLLWICH - Sandwiches—prepackaged - Sandwich Specialists, Inc.

ROLLY - Toys—stuffed - Russ Berrie and Co., Inc.

ROLLY-O'S - Dog food - Horton Co., Inc.

ROLLY'S PIZZA STIX - Frozen pizza - Rolly's Convenient Foods, Inc.

ROLMARK - Varnishes - Marsh Co.

ROLMFAX - Facsimile equipment - Rolm Co.

ROLMFAX/PC - Computer software - Rolm Co.
ROLO - Candy - Hershey Chocolate USA
ROLO LATCH - Fencing–gates and posts - Master Halco Inc.
ROLO THE BEAR - Furniture–children's - Maze Inc.
ROLOCOLOR - Markers–felt-tip - Life Lines Manufacturing
ROLODEX - Office supplies - Newell Office Products
ROLODEX - Office supplies - Rolodex Corp.
ROLODEX LIVE! - Computer software - DacEasy Inc.
ROLODEX NECESSITIES - Office supplies - Newell Office Products
ROLODEX PETITE - Office supplies - Rolodex Corp.
ROLODEX SYSTEM, THE - Office supplies - Rolodex Corp.
ROLODEX-V-FILE - Office supplies - Rolodex Corp.
ROLODEX VIP - Office supplies - Rolodex Corp.
ROLOFF - Hardware - Roloff Manufacturing Corp.
ROLOMAT - Floor coverings - American Floor Products Co. Inc.
ROLOMATIC BINGO - Games ☆ - Milton Bradley Co.
ROLOMATIC CONTROL - Office supplies ☆ - Rolodex Corp.
ROLOO HELP OFFICE - Computer software - Blue Sky Software Corp.
ROLOO HTML - Computer software - Blue Sky Software Corp.
ROLOTAPE - Hardware - Elyria Fence & Implement Co. Inc.
ROLOX - Antacids ☆ - Pure Pack Inc.
ROLSAFE - Shutters–metal - Bruce Hoovis
ROLSCREEN - Doors–glass ☆ - Pella Corp.
ROLTRONIC PRO - Razors–electric - Parks Products Inc.
ROLUX - Enamels - Rodda Paint Co.
ROLY BIN - Office supplies - Alvin and Co. Inc.
ROLY-POLY - Candy ☆ - R.M. Palmer Co.
ROLY POLY - Flowers, plants, and seeds - W. Atlee Burpee and Co.
ROLY POLY - Glassware–household - Anchor Hocking Glass, Inc.
ROLY POLY - Glassware–household - Federal Glass
ROLY-POLY - Marine rigging - W.H. Salisbury & Co.
ROLY POLY - Yarn - William Unger & Co. Inc.
ROLY POLY COW - Toys–stuffed ☆ - Gund, Inc.
ROLY POLY PUTTY - Toys ☆ - Imperial Toy Corp.
ROLY POLY SANTA - Toys–stuffed ☆ - Gund, Inc.
ROLY POLY SNOWMAN - Toys–stuffed ☆ - Gund, Inc.
ROLY POLYS - Toys - Alvimar Manufacturing Co. Inc.
ROLY RACCOON - Toys - Fisher-Price, Inc.
ROLY SPORT HEATHERTONES - Yarn - William Unger & Co. Inc.
ROLYAN - Orthopedic products - Smith & Nephew Inc. (Rehabilitation Div.)
ROLYAN ALIGNRITE - Splints - Smith & Nephew Inc. (Rehabilitation Div.)
ROLYAN AQUAFORM - Splints - Smith & Nephew Inc. (Rehabilitation Div.)
ROLYAN CARVE-IT - Splints - Smith & Nephew Inc. (Rehabilitation Div.)
ROLYAN DURA GEL - Splints - Smith & Nephew Inc. (Rehabilitation Div.)
ROLYAN DYTRO - Orthopedic products - Smith & Nephew Inc. (Rehabilitation Div.)
ROLYAN KUSHIONSPLINT - Orthopedic products - Smith & Nephew Inc. (Rehabilitation Div.)
ROLYAN NEOZIP - Splints - Smith & Nephew Inc. (Rehabilitation Div.)
ROLYAN PROGRESSIVE - Elastomers - Smith & Nephew Inc. (Rehabilitation Div.)
ROLYAN R-LITE - Elastomers - Smith & Nephew Inc. (Rehabilitation Div.)
ROLYAN SOF-STRETCH - Splints - Smith & Nephew Inc. (Rehabilitation Div.)
ROLYAN TAP - Splints - Smith & Nephew Inc. (Rehabilitation Div.)
ROLYAN WORKHARD - Splints - Smith & Nephew Inc. (Rehabilitation Div.)
ROM - Health care products ☆ - Sammons Preston
ROM - Recording label - ROM Records
ROM DANCE, THE - Recording label - Patricia Yu
ROM-TECH - Computers - Adam Michael Sacks
ROMA - Air conditioning equipment - Roma Industries, Inc.
ROMA - Artists' materials - Sculpture House Inc.
ROMA - Bathroom fixtures and fittings - American Standard Inc.
ROMA - Colognes - Procter & Gamble Co.
ROMA - Dolls ☆ - Effanbee Doll Corp.
ROMA - Food products - Dicrasto Dairy & Food Products Inc.
ROMA - Footwear - Leo's Dancewear, Inc.
ROMA - Furniture - Landes Manufacturing Co.
ROMA - Furniture–children's ☆ - Child Craft Industries Inc.
ROMA - Glassware–household ☆ - Avitra Corp.
ROMA - Luggage ☆ - Montgomery Ward & Co. Inc.
ROMA - Mushrooms - Giorgio Foods Inc.
ROMA - Musical instruments - Eastern Music Co.
ROMA - Paper - Fabriano America Inc.
ROMA - Paper ☆ - Rockline Industries Inc.
ROMA - Pasta - Hershey Pasta Group
ROMA - Pet products ☆ - Aqua Stock/Petcetera Inc.

ROMA - Pizzas–mixes - Dadco Food Products Inc.
ROMA - Soccer balls - Audero Sports Supply
ROMA - Tiles–ceramic - Dal-Tile Corp.
ROMA - Violins - Ideal Musical Merchandise Co.
ROMA - Watchbands–base metal ☆ - Roma Industries
ROMA - Wigs ☆ - Paula Young
ROMA - Window coverings - Vertilux-Louverlux Inc.
ROMA - Wines - Guild Wineries
ROMA DI CALIFORNIA - Wines - Guild Wineries
ROMA FAMILY STYLE - Pizzas–mixes ☆ - Dadco Food Products Inc.
ROMA KIDS - Backpacks - Romar International Corp.
ROMA-NOL - Antiseptic - Jamol Laboratories Inc.
ROMA ORIGINAL STYLE - Pizzas–frozen - Dadco Food Products Inc.
ROMA-REX - Vinegar ☆ - Rex Vinegar Co.
ROMA RIVIERA - Pizzas–mixes ☆ - Dadco Food Products Inc.
ROMA VINO D'UVA - Wines - Guild Wineries
ROMABLOK JR. - Staplers - Salco, Inc.
ROMABLOK SR. - Staplers - Salco, Inc.
ROMAC REPORT - Publisher's imprints - Romac Report Public Opinion Guides, Inc.
ROMADE - Prescription drug - American Pharmaceutical Co.
ROMAGNA - Wallpaper ☆ - Osborne & Little
ROMAGORA - Crocheted and knitted items - Towne & King Inc.
ROMAIN BRAUDE - Musical instruments - Ernest Deffner Inc.
ROMAINE - Frames–eyeglass - Zylo Ware Corp.
ROMALANG - Staplers - Salco, Inc.
ROMALON - Hosiery - Virginia Maid Hosiery Mills Inc.
ROMAN - Bathroom fixtures - Kohler Co.
ROMAN - Cabinets - Superior Woodwork Inc.
ROMAN - Cereal - Roman Meal Co.
ROMAN - Floor coverings ☆ - Azrock Commercial Flooring
ROMAN - Jewelry - Roman Co.
ROMAN - Leather goods - Shin's Trading Co.
ROMAN - Paper - Parsons Paper Co.
ROMAN - Recording label - CA-Song Music
ROMAN - Sausages - Formico Food Co.
ROMAN - Tiles–ceramic ☆ - Boiardi Products Corp.
ROMAN ACCENT - Floor coverings ☆ - Tarkett, Inc.
ROMAN-ADE LYTES - Beverages ☆ - Country Springs Beverage Co.
ROMAN ANTIQUE - Dinnerware–plastic - Annieglass
ROMAN ARC - Hammocks - The HammockSource
ROMAN BAR, THE - Fruits–candied - Beverly Productions
ROMAN BATH OIL - Skin care products - M.C. Products Ltd.
ROMAN CARBIDE - Tools–hand-operated - Woodstock International, Inc.
ROMAN CLASSIC - Tiles–ceramic ☆ - American Marazzi Tile, Inc.
ROMAN COBBLE - Stone products - Concrete Stone & Tile Corp.
ROMAN ELEGANCE - Floor coverings ☆ - Congoleum Corp.
ROMAN EMPIRE: THE FALL OF ROME, THE - Computer software - Electronic Courseware Systems Inc.
ROMAN-FINGERS - Food products - Pierce Foods Corp.
ROMAN FORUM - Floor coverings - Mannington Resilient Floors
ROMAN HARNESS - Pet products - Leatherite-Nylorite Manufacturing Inc.
ROMAN HOLIDAY - Apparel and accessories ☆ - Glamorise Foundations Inc.
ROMAN HOLIDAY - Christmas tree ornaments - Cracker Box Inc.
ROMAN HOLIDAY - Eyeglasses - Art-Craft Optical Co.
ROMAN HOLIDAY - Tomato pastes and sauces - Stanislaus Food Products Co.
ROMAN HOLIDAY - Watches - Hampden Corp.
ROMAN LIGHT - Breads–mixes - Roman Meal Co.
ROMAN MEAL - Cereal - Roman Meal Co.
ROMAN MEAL - Waffles–frozen - Pet Inc.
ROMAN-NAPOLEON ERA - Games - Classic Games Co. Inc.
ROMAN NUMERALS - Computer software - Orange Cherry Software
ROMAN SPA - Skin care products ☆ - ABRA Inc.
ROMAN SPRINGS - Water–bottled or canned - Beverage America, Inc.
ROMAN SQUARE - Floor coverings - Mannington Resilient Floors
ROMAN STRIPE - Hosiery–women's ☆ - Alba-Waldensian, Inc.
ROMAN TELLER - Musical instruments - Ideal Musical Merchandise Co.
ROMAN TELLER - Musical instruments - St. Louis Music Supply Co.
ROMAN VILLA CLASSIC - Salad dressing - Genfood Inc.
ROMAN WALK - Floor coverings ☆ - Congoleum Corp.
ROMAN WALL - Wallpaper - Blumenthal
ROMAN WAY - Floor coverings ☆ - Congoleum Corp.
ROMANAIRE - Floor coverings - Congoleum Corp.
ROMANCE - Apparel–women's - Lily of France Inc.
ROMANCE - Christmas tree ornaments - Cracker Box Inc.

☆ = Now out of production

ROMANCE - Clocks - General Time Corp. (Westclox/Seth Thomas Div.)
ROMANCE - Computer software - Philip B. Payne and Nancy C. Payne
ROMANCE - Cutlery ☆ - Lifetime Hoan Corp.
ROMANCE - Dinnerware - Corning Inc.
ROMANCE - Fabrics - Dan River Inc.
ROMANCE - Flatware - Dansk International Designs, Ltd.
ROMANCE - Floor coverings—carpet and rugs - Calladium & Marglen
ROMANCE - Footwear—women's - Hawaii Shoe Co.
ROMANCE - Frames—eyeglass - May Optical Co. Inc.
ROMANCE - Glassware—household ☆ - Lenox Crystal, Inc.
ROMANCE - Glassware—household ☆ - Lotus Glass Co.
ROMANCE - Mattresses - King Koil Licensing Co., Inc.
ROMANCE - Rings—jewelry - Artcarved Inc.
ROMANCE - Skin care products - Veeco Manufacturing Co.
ROMANCE - Tiles—ceramic ☆ - American Marazzi Tile, Inc.
ROMANCE - Wallpaper - Cynthia Gibson Inc.
ROMANCE ALIVE - Recording label - Beverly R. Blonstein
ROMANCE BY KEN CORNET - Earthenware - Porta
ROMANCE BY REUGE - Music boxes - Alice Sturzinger Ltd.
ROMANCE CAKES - Bakery products - Campbell Taggart Inc.
ROMANCE COLORS - Lipsticks - Schering-Plough Healthcare Products
ROMANCE DU JOUR - Apparel—women's - Romance Du Jour, Inc.
ROMANCE IN BLACK - Publisher's imprints - Marron Publishers Inc.
ROMANCE OF FLOWERS BY GARY BUKOVNIK - Dinnerware—glass ☆ - Block China Co.
ROMANCE OF THE SEA - Flatware - Wallace International Silversmiths, Inc.
ROMANCE ON A SHOESTRING - Game - NJS Enterprises
ROMANCE TESTER - Novelty items - Adams Apple Distributing L.P.
ROMANCE WITH FRANCE - Wallcovering - Wall Trends, Inc.
ROMANEE CONTI - Wines - Wilson Daniels Ltd.
ROMANELLI - Shoes - World Import Co. Inc.
ROMANELLI - Toys—guns - Victor M. Bulgarelli Associates Inc.
ROMANESQUE - Floor coverings - Congoleum Corp.
ROMANESQUE - Floor coverings—carpet and rugs - J.L. Benson Co.
ROMANESQUE - Floor coverings—carpet and rugs - World Carpets, Inc.
ROMANESQUE - Floor coverings—carpet and rugs ☆ - Masland Corp.
ROMANESQUE - Mirrors ☆ - Bassett Furniture Industries, Inc.
ROMANESQUE - Wallpaper - Textile Wallcoverings International Ltd.
ROMANESQUE COLUMN - Candles ☆ - Will & Baumer, Inc.
ROMANETTE - Window shades - Kirsch Co.
ROMANI - Apparel—men's - Supreme International Corp.
ROMANIAN - Floor coverings—carpet and rugs ☆ - Capel, Inc.
ROMANIAN FORMULA 3 - Health care products - Health Products Corp.
ROMANINA - Vegetables—canned - J.M. Rodriguez & Co. Inc.
ROMANO - Breads—frozen ☆ - April Hill Inc.
ROMANO - Cigars ☆ - General Cigar Co., Inc.
ROMANO - Colognes ☆ - Key West Aloe Inc.
ROMANO - Wines - Gibson Wine Co.
ROMANO-CHIK - Food products - Pierce Foods Corp.
ROMANO COLLECTION - Furniture ☆ - Evenflo Juvenile Furniture Co.
ROMANOFF - Caviar - Romanoff International Inc.
ROMANOFF COLLECTION, THE - Jewelry - Hunting World, Inc.
ROMANOFF R - Caviar - T. Marzetti Co.
ROMANOFF RUSSIAN - Teas - Romanoff International Inc.
ROMANOFF VINYL - Wallpaper - Maya Romanoff Corp.
ROMANTASY - Adult games - Robert L. Meliodon
ROMANTEX - Adhesives and sealants - Vitricon
ROMANTIC - Computer software - Philip B. Payne and Nancy C. Payne
ROMANTIC - Wallpaper ☆ - Kingfisher Wallcoverings
ROMANTIC CONDOM ROSE - Prophylactics - Richard A. Porraro
ROMANTIC COUNTRY BERRIES AND BLOSSOMS - Glassware—household ☆ - Fenton Art Glass Co.
ROMANTIC ENCOUNTERS - Computer software - Spectrum Universal
ROMANTIC EXPRESSIONS - Jewelry - Valuevision International, Inc.
ROMANTIC FANTASY - Brassieres (Bras) - Vanity Fair Mills Inc.
ROMANTIC FANTASY - Wallcoverings - Beverly Stevens Ltd.
ROMANTIC GARDEN - Flowers, plants, and seeds - Applewood Seed & Garden Group
ROMANTIC GARDEN - Skin care products - Natural Body Bath Aroma Art
ROMANTIC ILLUSIONS - Perfumes - Jean Philippe Fragrances, Inc.
ROMANTIC JEWELS - Floor coverings - Aladdin Mills, Inc.
ROMANTIC LEGENDS - Wallpaper ☆ - Legend Wallcoverings
ROMANTIC MOODS - Toiletries - Montgomery Ward & Co. Inc.
ROMANTIC REFLECTIONS - Greeting cards - American Greetings Corp.
ROMANTIC RENDEZVOUS - Bath salts - Jason Natural Products, Inc.
ROMANTIC ROSE - Deodorants—personal - Mennen Co.

ROMANTIC ROSE BRIDE - Dolls - Mattel, Inc.
ROMANTIC SENSATIONS! - Games - Games Partnership Ltd., Inc.
ROMANTIC SPLENDOUR - Jewelry - Avon Products, Inc.
ROMANTIC TAPESTRIES - Wallpaper ☆ - Bob Mitchell Designs
ROMANTIC TRADITIONAL I - Wallpaper ☆ - J. Josephson, Inc.
ROMANTIC WEDDING - Dolls - Mattel, Inc.
ROMANTICA - Frames—eyeglass - Zylo Ware Corp.
ROMANTICA - Giftware ☆ - Rubens Originals
ROMANTICA - Glassware—household ☆ - Lancaster Colony Corp.
ROMANTICA - Health care products - Smith & Vandiver, Inc.
ROMANTICA - Pudding pops—frozen ☆ - Conopco, Inc.
ROMANTICA - Tableware—china - Villeroy and Boch Tableware Ltd.
ROMANTICA - Wallpaper - Advance Wallcoverings
ROMANTICA - Wallpaper ☆ - Southport
ROMANTICALLY INCLINED - Wallpaper - Wallcoverings Unlimited Inc.
ROMANTICALLY YOURS - Wallpaper - Bayview Wallcoverings
ROMANTICO - Copper compounds ☆ - Regal Ware, Inc.
ROMANTICS - Floor coverings—carpet and rugs - Mohawk Carpet Corp.
ROMANTICS - Greeting cards and calendars - Weedn Design Ltd.
ROMANTICS - Jewelry ☆ - Hirsch Speidel Inc.
ROMANTICS - Wallpaper - Palette Prints Inc.
ROMANTICS BY PLAYBOY - Apparel and accessories - Playboy Enterprises, Inc.
ROMANTICS, THE - Dinnerware—glass - Franciscan by Johnson Brothers, USA, Inc.
ROMANTIGUE - Wallpaper - Capital Carousel Inc.
ROMANTIQUE - Bathroom fixtures - Alsons Corp.
ROMANTIQUE - Floor coverings—carpet and rugs - Mohawk Industries Inc.
ROMANTIQUE - Glassware—household - Durand International
ROMANTIQUE - Glassware—household - Gorham Inc.
ROMANTIQUE - Jewelry ☆ - Hirsch Speidel Inc.
ROMANTIQUE - Wallpaper - Wall Fabrics Inc.
ROMANTIQUE BATH - Bath salts - Romantique Inspirations
ROMANTIQUE GOLD - Glassware—household - Gorham Inc.
ROMANY - Dishes—earthenware - Denby USA Limited
ROMANZA - Floor coverings—carpet and rugs - Whitecrest Carpet Mills
ROMANZA - Olive oil - Pompeian Inc.
ROMANZA - Whirlpool baths - American Standard Inc.
ROMARK - Paints ☆ - Glidden Co.
ROMAROUND - Handbags - Romar International Corp.
ROMA'S BY LEO - Apparel and accessories ☆ - Leo's Dancewear, Inc.
ROMATE CREAM - Beverages—alcohol - Shaw-Ross International Importers
ROMATEX - Wallpaper - Walldesigns
ROMAY - Food products - Knapp-Sherrill Co.
ROMAY - Skin-care products - Bannis Products
ROMAZINE - Pharmaceutical preparations - Wesley Pharmacal Co. Inc.
ROMBAUER VINEYARDS - Wines - Rombauer Vineyards
ROMBIX - Puzzles - Kadon Enterprises Inc.
ROMBIX JR. - Puzzles - Kadon Enterprises Inc.
ROME - Luggage - Jinwoong Inc.
ROME TUSS DM - Cough syrup - American Pharmaceutical Co.
ROMEO - Beverages—alcohol - David Sherman Corp.
ROMEO - Cigars ☆ - General Cigar Co., Inc.
ROMEO - Confections - Bahlsen Inc.
ROMEO - Floor coverings—carpet and rugs ☆ - Regal Rugs Inc.
ROMEO - Fruit and vegetable markets - Frigid Food Products Inc.
ROMEO - Nail care products - Orly International Inc.
ROMEO & GIULIETTA - Cookies ☆ - Liberty Richter Inc.
ROMEO BEAR - Toys—stuffed ☆ - Fun World Inc.
ROMEO E. GIULLIETTA - Desserts - Bell'amore Imports Inc.
ROMEO GIGLI - Collar buttons - H. Alpert and Co.
ROMEO GIGLI - ITALY - Eyeglasses ☆ - Private Eyes Sunglass Corp.
ROMEO GIGLI PER UOMO - Collar buttons - H. Alpert and Co.
ROMEO PITTI - Neckwear, belts - Nova Imports Inc.
ROMEO ROMA - Handbags - Y & S Handbag Inc.
ROMEO TIGER - Toys—stuffed - Russ Berrie and Co., Inc.
ROMEO VALLI MADE IN ITALY - Footwear—women's - Fe. Ma. Inc.
ROMEO'S EXOTIC PEANUT PUNCH - Beverages - Norbert B. Powell
ROMER - Helmets—athletic ☆ - Phoenix Products Inc.
ROMER - Measuring instruments - Romer, Inc.
ROMER - Measuring instruments - Romer Supratech Inc.
ROMERINA - Cough medicines ☆ - D'Franssia Corp.
ROMERJOPF - Cooking utensils—stoneware - McLendon Co.
ROMERTOPF - Kitchenware—earthenware - Reco International Corp.
ROMET FILTER - Medical apparatus - Luminaud Inc.
ROMEX - Decongestant - American Pharmaceutical Co.

☆ = Now out of production

ROMEX - Staples - Hillwood Manufacturing Co.
ROMEX - Wire–insulated - General Cable Corp.
ROMFH - Apparel and accessories - Laura Frances Romfh
ROMGUARD - Envelopes ☆ - National Church Supply Co. Inc.
ROMI-KON - Water purification systems - Koch Membrane Systems, Inc.
ROMIC - Bicycles - Romic Cycle Co.
ROMILAR AC - Cough medicines - Scot-Tussin Pharmacal Co.
ROMILLE - Crocheted and knitted items ☆ - Roosevelt Mills Inc.
ROMM - Toys - Mattel, Inc.
ROMMCO - Machinery - Red Oaks Mill Machine Corp.
ROMMEL BATTLES FOR TOBRUK - Computer software - Electronic Arts Inc.
ROMMY - Hair care products - Rommy Hunt Revson
ROMNEE - Medical apparatus - Michelle Fontana
ROMNEY - Artists' materials ☆ - M. Grumbacher Inc.
ROMNEY - Dishes–earthenware ☆ - Royal China & Porcelain Companies Inc.
ROMNIBUS - Compact discs–prerecorded - Largely Literary Designs, Inc.
ROMO - Chairs–upholstered - Fixtures Furniture
ROMO - Notebooks and notepads - Romo Paper Products Corp.
ROMONA - Eggs - Dairy Fresh Products Corp.
ROMONA - Recording label - Jody Record Corp.
ROMONTA - Waxes–sealing - Strohmeyer and Arpe Co.
ROMP-A-ROUND - Apparel–children's - Gerber Products Co.
ROMP-A-ROUND - Apparel–children's ☆ - Kent Inc.
ROMP-ON - Adhesives and sealants - Puritan-Churchill Chemical Co.
ROMPAX - Containers - David Greene
ROMPER - Toys–automobiles - Commonwealth Inc.
ROMPER ROOM'S I LOVE MY ALPHABET - Computer software - First Star Software Inc.
ROMPER STOMPERS - Toys - Playskool, Inc.
ROMPERS - Diapers–disposable - Whitestone Products Inc.
ROMPING RASCAL PUP - Toys–stuffed - Dakin Inc.
ROMPING RASCAL SIAMESE - Toys–stuffed - Dakin Inc.
ROMULATOR - Computer software ☆ - Onset Computer Corp.
ROMULUS - Shoes–athletic - Reebok International Ltd.
ROMUNDA - Eyeglasses - Martin-Copeland Eyewear Corp.
ROMUNDA - Watchbands–base metal - Hirsch Speidel Inc.
ROMWEBER - Furniture - Romweber Co.
ROMY BERLIN - Apparel and accessories ☆ - Kellwood Co.
RON & ASSOCIATES - Mats - Ron & Associates Inc.
RON-ART - Paints–artists' - T.J. Ronan Paint Corp.
RON BERMUDEZ - Beverages–alcohol - Laird and Co.
RON BOCOY - Rum - David Sherman Corp.
RON BOTRAN - Rum - Shaw-Ross International Importers
RON CHERESKIN - Apparel and accessories - Cluett, Peabody & Co.
RON COPA - Rum - Paramount Distillers Inc.
RON CORADO - Rum - M.S. Walker Inc./Seacoast
RON DE VU - Flatware - Towle Manufacturing Co.
RON DEL BARRILITO - Rum - Sazerac Co. Inc.
RON-GLO - Paints - T.J. Ronan Paint Corp.
RON JON SURF SHOP - Apparel–athletic - Ron Jon Surf Shop
R.O.N. KITS - First aid kits - Airline Textile Manufacturing Co.
RON-KOTE - Paints - T.J. Ronan Paint Corp.
RON MARNO - Rum - M.S. Walker Inc./Seacoast
RON MATUSALEM - Beverages–alcohol - Ron Matusalem Co.
RON MERITO - Rum - Jim Beam Brands Co.
RON PABLO - Rum - Montebello Brands, Inc.
RON PATALBA - Rum - Sazerac Co. Inc.
RON RIO - Rum - Mccormick Distilling Co., Inc.
RON ROBERTO - Rum - M.S. Walker Inc./Seacoast
RON-SON - Mushrooms - Ron Son Foods, Inc.
RON SON - Vegetables–canned - Ron Son Foods, Inc.
RON TRIGO - Rum - M.S. Walker Inc./Seacoast
RON VEGA - Rum - East-West Distributing Co.
RON VICARO - Rum - American Stores Co.
RON VIEJO DE CALDAS - Rum - Shaw-Ross International Importers
RON VIRGIN - Rum - White Rock Distilleries Inc.
RONA - Pigments - EM Industries, Inc.
RONALD CHARLES - Window coverings - Norman Lacoff & Associates Inc.
RONALD FELDMAN - Recording label - Jazz Composer's Orchestra Association Inc.
RONALD KOLODZIE FOR EYEFUL - Lingerie, loungewear - Boutique Loungewear Inc.
RONALD LOUIS - Luggage - Atchison Products, Inc.
RONALD MCDONALD - Bird feeds - Charlie's Woodshop
RONAMEL SPEED FINISH - Paints - T.J. Ronan Paint Corp.
RONAN & KUNZL - Sporting goods - Basketball Products International Inc.

RONARTE AUTOTRENDS - Publisher's imprints - SCP Records
RONARTE PUBLICATIONS(ASCAP) - Publisher's imprints - SCP Records
RONAS - Food products - I. Rokeach and Sons Inc.
RONASE - Pharmaceutical preparations ☆ - Solvay Pharmaceuticals Inc.
RONAY - Apparel and accessories - Ronay Inc.
RONAY - Frames–eyeglass - May Optical Co. Inc.
RONCALLI - Musical instrument accessories - David Wexler & Co.
RONCO - Footwear - Ron London Associates
RONCO - Pasta - Borden, Inc.
RONCO - Spaghetti - Ronco Enterprises Inc.
RONCOCO - Beverages–alcohol - Ron Matusalem Co.
RONCOLAC - Lacquers ☆ - T.J. Ronan Paint Corp.
RONCOTE - Paper - Permalin Products Co.
RONDALYN - Plumbing fixtures - American Standard Inc.
RONDEAU - Floor coverings–carpet and rugs - Karastan-Bigelow Inc.
RONDEAU - Floor coverings–carpet and rugs ☆ - World Carpets, Inc.
RONDEAU - Pet products - Rolf C. Hagen (USA) Corp.
RONDEAU - Underwear and nightwear - NCC Industries, Inc.
RONDEAU DE CHAMPAGNE - Dairy products ☆ - Besnier USA, Inc.
RONDEC - Cough medicines - Ross Laboratories
RONDEL - Jewelry - Magnolia Diamonds Inc.
RONDEL - Wines - Guinness Import Co.
RONDELAY - Brassieres (Bras) - Bi-Flex International
RONDELAY - Cosmetics - Kaemark Inc.
RONDELAY - Frames–eyeglass - May Optical Co. Inc.
RONDELE - Cheese - Tony Ingoglia Salami and Cheese Co. Inc.
RONDELE - Housewares - Basic Line, Inc.
RONDELET - Furniture ☆ - Stanley Furniture Co. Inc.
RONDELITTLER - Food products - Tyson Foods Inc.
RONDELLE - Candlesticks ☆ - Lenox Crystal, Inc.
RONDELLE - Dishes–china ☆ - Gorham Inc.
RONDELLE - Flatware ☆ - Anacapa Corp.
RONDELLE - Floor coverings ☆ - Congoleum Corp.
RONDIAZ - Rum - Rondiaz Rum Co.
RONDINAX - Tanks–photographic ☆ - Heitz Service Corp.
RONDINI - Accordions ☆ - Grossman Music Corp.
RONDISSE - Cosmetics - Luzier Personalized Cosmetics, Inc.
RONDO - See ROMO
RONDO - Boxes–paperboard - Mason Box Co. Inc.
RONDO - Brushes–hair ☆ - Nino Originals
RONDO - Desks ☆ - Domore/DO3
RONDO - Dinnerware–glass - Cyclamen Studio
RONDO - Dishes–earthenware - Denby USA Limited
RONDO - Fabrics–cotton ☆ - J.C. Penney Co., Inc.
RONDO - Floor coverings ☆ - Azrock Commercial Flooring
RONDO - Lenses–optical - National Optical Co.
RONDO - Tables–wood ☆ - Howe Furniture Corp.
RONDO - Tableware–china ☆ - Villeroy and Boch Tableware Ltd.
RONDO-SPHERE - Cosmetics - Diane Products Inc.
RONDOMYCIN - Antibiotics ☆ - Wallace Laboratories
RONDOS - Ice cream - Dove International
RONDURE - Dinnerware–glass - Sango Co. Ltd. (Sango USA Div.)
RONDURE - Furniture ☆ - Bassett Furniture Industries, Inc.
RONEL - Jewelry - Ullenberg Corp.
RONETT RR NEW YORK - Handbags - Ronnet Trading Inc.
RONEY - Yogurt - Roney-Oatman Inc.
RONEY'S PREMIUM - Ice cream - Roney-Oatman Inc.
RONFORD - Pianos - Ford Piano Supply Co.
RONI-MAC - Pasta - American Beauty Macaroni
RONI WERNER - Frames–picture ☆ - Werner Co.
RONIACOL - Diuretics - Roche Laboratories
RONICA - Watches - E & T Inc.
RONIGEN - Pharmaceutical preparations ☆ - Goldline Laboratories, Inc.
RONII - Cigarette lighters - Ronson Consumer Products Corp.
RONIN - Publisher's imprints - Ronin Publishing, Inc.
RONIN PUBLISHING INC. - Publisher's imprints - Ronin Publishing, Inc.
RONIN WARRIORS - Toys - Playmates World Wide Inc.
RONIUM - Pharmaceutical preparations ☆ - Pasadena Research Laboratories, Inc.
RONIWOK - Apparel and accessories - Roni E. Doyon
RONK - Sporting goods - Mattel, Inc.
RONLEE - Apparel and accessories - Ronlee Apparel Co.
RONLUCK - Floor coverings–linoleum - Lucky America Inc.
RONMAR - Shirts - Ronmar Industrial
RONN - Labels–paper - Sue Records Inc.
RONNI - Girdles - Crown Foundations Inc.

☆ = Now out of production

RONNI NICOLE - Apparel–women's - Ronni Nicole II, Inc.
RONNIE A. - Apparel–women's - Ronnie A. Corp.
RONNIE DA VINCI - Jewelry - Ronnie DaVinci Inc.
RONNIE JANA - Apparel–children's - House of Ronnie, Inc.
RONNIE RABBIT - Candy ☆ - Keppel's Inc.
RONNIE SELLERS' - Calendars - Ronnie Sellers Productions
RONNIE TATE'S DETAILS 37 - Hair care products - Ronnie Tate
RONNIE TOGS - Apparel–children's - House of Ronnie, Inc.
RONNING - Giftware - Baekgaard Ltd.
RONNINGS - Inks ☆ - Charvoz
RONNOCO - Coffee - Ronnoco Coffee Co.
RONNY LEE - Music–sheet - Sunrise Publishing Co. Inc.
RONNYBROOK FARM DAIRY - Dairy products - Ronnybrook Farm Dairy
RONRICO - Rum - House of Seagram
RONRICO - Rum - Jim Beam Brands Co.
RONSARD - Underwear and nightwear ☆ - M.A. Rabinowitz Corp.
RONSO - Thread - Blue Mountain Industries, Inc.
RONSON - Lighters - Ronson Consumer Products Corp.
RONSONOL - Lighter fluid - Ronson Consumer Products Corp.
RONTANA - Glassware–household - Hillside House of Originals
RONTINI - Apparel–women's - Kay Windsor Inc.
RONVET - Pharmaceutical preparations - Armenpharm Ltd.
RONZONI - Dairy products - Homestead, Inc.
RONZONI - Food products - Ronzoni Foods Inc.
RONZONI - Pasta - Hershey Pasta Group
RONZONI SPAGHETTI AND ALFREDO SAUCE MIXES - Sauces - Williams Foods, Inc.
ROO - Bicycles - Columbia Manufacturing Inc.
ROO - Toys - Tonka Corp.
ROO BOARD - Emery products - Creative Nail Design, Inc.
ROO RA MADE IN U.S.A. - Apparel–men's - Zam Clothing Co.
ROOD BLAUW - Cigars - Gesty Trading & Manufacturing Corp.
ROOF-AID - Roofing materials - MSA Sales Group, Inc.
ROOF AMERICA PLUS - Adhesives and sealants ☆ - Master's Choice Inc.
ROOF BLANKET - Insulating materials - Tremco Inc.
ROOF CEMENT - Cement - Black Swan Manufacturing Co.
ROOF FIX - Adhesives and sealants - Monsey Products Co.
ROOF GARD - Tape–adhesive - Metallized Products Inc.
ROOF GENERAL - Roofing materials - Neyra Industries, Inc.
ROOF GUARD - Coatings - Tresco Paint Co. Inc.
ROOF-KOTE - Paints - Tuff-Kote Co. Inc.
ROOF-LIGHT - Windows–storm - APC Corp.
ROOF MAP - Computer software - Professional Service Industries Inc.
ROOF MASTIC - Coatings - Somay Products Inc.
ROOF PLATE - Paints - Bruning Paint Co.
ROOF PREP - Coatings - Tresco Paint Co. Inc.
ROOF-PRIME - Paints - Permite Corp.
ROOF PRO - Automotive parts and accessories ☆ - Macklanburg-Duncan Co.
ROOF PROOF - Paints - Gibson-Homans Co.
ROOF RENEW - Paints - Coronado Paint Co.
ROOF REPAIR - Adhesives and sealants - Macco Adhesives
ROOF RESCUE SYSTEM - Roofing materials ☆ - Gardner Asphalt Corp.
ROOF WINDOW - Windows–plastic - Natural Skylights Inc.
ROOFAB - Waterproofing compounds - Andek Corp.
ROOFCALC SOFTWARE ESTMASTER - Computer software - Merik Marketing, Inc.
ROOFD-X - Waterproofing compounds - Andek Corp.
ROOFD-X GOLD - Waterproofing compounds - Andek Corp.
ROOFD-X RAC - Waterproofing compounds - Andek Corp.
ROOFDEX - Adhesives and sealants - Plastics & Resins Ltd.
ROOFER - Roofing materials–clay ☆ - Stuhr Enterprises Inc.
ROOFERS PRIDE - Building materials - Brewer Co.
ROOFGARD - Paints ☆ - Sampson Coatings Inc.
ROOFGRIP - Roofing materials - Illinois Tool Works Inc.
ROOFKING - Air conditioning equipment ☆ - Nordyne Inc.
ROOFLEX - Adhesives and sealants - Sinclair Paint Co.
ROOFLOCK - Asphalt felts and coatings ☆ - Gibson-Homans Co.
ROOFMAN ROOF MANAGER - Computer software - Crowder & Associates Inc.
ROOFRIDE - Air conditioning equipment - Carrier Corp.
ROOFSAFE - Scaffolds–metal - Gary W. Eisenmenger
ROOFSCAPE - Shingles–asphalt or tar - Bird Inc.
ROOK - Games - Parker Brothers
ROOKE - Medical apparatus - Osborn Medical Corp.
ROOKIE - Bicycles ☆ - J.C. Penney Co., Inc.
ROOKIE - Pitching machine - Grand Slam USA

ROOKIE - Skating rinks–roller ☆ - National Sporting Goods Corp.
ROOKIE CUBE - Trading card holder - ANCO Collector Supplies, Inc.
ROOKIE EXCHANGE - Trading cards and stamps - Upper Deck Co.
ROOKIE FORCE - Trading cards and stamps - Upper Deck Co.
ROOKIE GARDENER, THE - Broadcasting stations–television - Spartan Communications, Inc.
ROOKIE IDOLS - Trading cards - Score Group, Inc.
ROOKIE ROLL CALL - Trading cards and stamps - Pinnacle Brands, Inc.
ROOKIE SENSATIONS - Trading cards and stamps - Fleer Corp.
ROOKIES CLASSIC - Fruits–dried - Joe V. Hernandez
ROOM 13 - Apparel and accessories - Kim Doran
ROOM AT THE TOP - Wallpaper ☆ - Newmarket Designs Ltd.
ROOM BY ROOM - Apparel and accessories - Sherwin-Williams Automotive Finishes Corp.
ROOM DEFENDER - Novelty items - Happiness Express Inc.
ROOM DESIGNER, THE - Craft supplies - Room Designer
ROOM GROOM - Paints - Mantrose-Haeuser Co. Inc.
ROOM MAKERS, THE - Furniture - Sico Inc.
ROOM MATE - Lighting fixtures - Swivelier Co. Inc.
ROOM MATES - Floor coverings - York Wall Coverings Inc.
ROOM MATES FOR KIDS - Wallpaper - York Wall Coverings Inc.
ROOM PERFUME - Deodorizers - Bernard Cappelli Inc.
ROOM PLANNER - Wallpaper ☆ - Imperial Wallcoverings, Inc.
ROOM READY - Audio equipment - Sneak*eex Inc.
ROOM SAVER - Recliners - Flexsteel Industries Inc.
ROOM SCENTER - Incense - Potpourri Designs
ROOM SCENTERS - Candles - Carolina Designs Ltd.
ROOM SCENTERS - Novelty items - Biedermann & Sons Inc.
ROOM SERVICE - Audio equipment - Recoton Corp.
ROOM SERVICE - Coffee makers–electric ☆ - Sunbeam-Oster Household Products
ROOM SERVICE - Floor coverings–carpet and rugs - Kelly Group Inc.
ROOM TO GROW - Wallpaper ☆ - Kingfisher Wallcoverings
ROOM TO GROW II - Wallpaper ☆ - Kingfisher Wallcoverings
ROOM TO ROOM - Wallpaper - Kenneth McDonald Designs
ROOM TUNES - Audio equipment - GNP Audio Video Inc.
ROOM VIEWER - Computer software - Timesaver Software
ROOM-WARE - Shelving units–wood - Kason Merchandising Fixtures Inc.
ROOM WITH A VIEW, A - Compact discs–prerecorded - Shore Bets Inc.
ROOMAIR - Filters–air - Airflow Systems, Inc.
ROOMAKER - Porch enclosure system ☆ - Continental Aluminum Products Co. Inc.
ROOMANCE - Cleaning preparations ☆ - Demert & Dougherty, Inc.
ROOMANTICS - Wallpaper - Capital Carousel Inc.
ROOMARANG - Boomerangs - Ozwest Imports, Inc.
ROOMASTER - Tents ☆ - Colorado Tent Co.
ROOMATE - Health care products ☆ - Sunrise Medical
ROOMATE III - Oxygen ☆ - Cryogenic Associates Inc.
ROOMATES - Furniture - Ethan Allen, Inc.
ROOMIDIFIER - Housewares - Edwards Creative Products, Inc.
ROOMIES, THE - Toys - Shelly Adventures
ROOMMATE - Electronic equipment - AVL
ROOMMATE - Floor coverings–carpet and rugs - Burtco Enterprises Inc.
ROOMMATE - Heat pumps - Climate Master, Inc.
ROOMMATE - Lighting fixtures - Point Electric
ROOMMATE 60 - Air freshener - Dial Corp.
ROOMS IN BLOOM - Wallcovering - Gencorp Inc.
ROOMSTRETCHER - Lenses ☆ - Buhl Optical Co.
ROOMTOONS - Recording label - Blue Flame Records
ROOMTOP - Air conditioning equipment - Carrier Corp.
ROOMWORKS - Furniture - Rubbermaid Inc.
ROONEY DOG - Greeting cards - Rooney Dog Productions, Inc.
ROOOOFUS THE ROLLER ROO - Advertising agencies - Roller Skating Rink Operators Association
ROOPIE - Paperboard - Rupaco Paper Corp.
ROOPSTER ROUX - Apparel and accessories - Lavaille Metoyer
ROOS - Footwear–athletic - KangaROOS USA Inc.
ROOSA INVERT-A-FORKS - Forklifts - GLR Enterprizes, Inc.
ROOSEVELT - Mattresses - Simmons USA
ROOSEVELT BEARS - Figurines - Schmid Inc.
ROOSKIN - Footwear–athletic - KangaROOS USA Inc.
ROOSTCELL - Containers - Biopore, Inc.
ROOSTER - Motor vehicle parts and accessories ☆ - Bell Sports Corp.
ROOSTER - Musical instruments ☆ - Vic Firth Inc.
ROOSTER - Neckties - Rooster Inc.
ROOSTER - Tobacco–chewing or smoking - United States Tobacco Co.

☆ = Now out of production

ROOSTER - Tool belts - Rooster Products International, Inc.

ROOSTER BLUES - Recording label - Rooster Blues Records

ROOSTER BODY TECH - Medical apparatus - Rooster Products International, Inc.

ROOSTER CONVERTIBLE - Neckties ☆ - Global Neckwear Marketing Inc.

ROOSTER EYE - Fishing lures - Yakima Bait Co.

ROOSTER PRODUCTS - Tool boxes - Rooster Products International, Inc.

ROOSTER-SPUR - Fishing nets - Four Rivers Tackle Co.

ROOSTER TAIL - Fishing lures - Yakima Bait Co.

ROOSTERKNIT - Apparel and accessories - Rooster Inc.

ROOSTERS - Beverages–carbonated - Western Syrup Co.

ROOT - Candles - Root Candle Co.

ROOT 66 - Beverages–carbonated ☆ - Anheuser-Busch Companies Inc.

ROOT AWAY - Root destroyer - Vibe Records Inc.

ROOT BEER KEGS - Candy ☆ - Tootsie Roll Industries, Inc.

ROOT DESTROYER - Plumbing-line cleaner - Jancyn Manufacturing Corp.

ROOT-EATER - Root eliminator ☆ - Coughlan Products Corp.

ROOT FOOD - Vitamins and nutritional supplements - Nutra-Source Corp.

ROOT GOBBLER - Root eliminator - Comstar International Inc. (IPC Div.)

ROOT HOG - Welding equipment - Jay W. Dwight

ROOT LIFT - Hair care products ☆ - St. Ives Laboratories, Inc.

ROOT MASTER B-1 - Chemical preparations - Master Nurserymen's Association

ROOT-N-WRITE - Pencils - WINCRAFT

ROOT-OUT - Chemical preparations ☆ - Elcal Enterprises Ltd.

ROOT STIMULATOR - Hair care products - Urban Laboratories, Inc.

ROOT T TOOT - Candy ☆ - Just Born Inc.

ROOT TO HEALTH - Herbal products - Hsu's Ginseng Enterprises Inc.

ROOTABAGA COUNTRY - Fruits and vegetables - Rootabaga Enterprises Inc.

ROOTBOUND - Games - Locus Games

ROOTBUILDER - Planters - Whitcomb & Stephens

ROOTED IN STRENGTH - Hair care products - Helene Curtis, Inc.

ROOTFEEDER - Garden equipment - Thompson Manufacturing Co.

ROOTI - Beverages–carbonated - Canada Dry Corp.

ROOTIES FAMOUS - Sauces - Rooties Foods International, Inc.

ROOTIN TOOTIN ROSE - Toys - Tonka Corp.

ROOTO - Cleaning preparations - Rooto Corp.

ROOTONE - Fertilizers - Rhone-Poulenc Inc.

ROOTONE - Fertilizers - Security Products Co.

ROOTS - Hair care products - Garcoa Labs/Vitamin Classics

ROOTS & FRUITS - Fruits and vegetables - Roots & Fruits Cooperative Produce

ROOTS II - Computer software ☆ - Commsoft

ROOTS III - Computer software - Commsoft

ROOTS/M - Computer software ☆ - Commsoft

ROOTS OF CANADA - Frames–eyeglass - Carrera Eyewear Corp.

ROOTS OF NATURE - Hair care products - Amethyst Investment Group, Inc.

ROOTS TO HEALTH - Vitamins and nutritional supplements - Roots to Health Inc.

ROOTS WRITER - Computer software - Commsoft

ROOTSHIELD - Fungicides - Bioworks, Inc.

ROOTTRINE - Herbicides ☆ - Applied Biochemists, Inc.

ROOTWARE - Computer software - Lloyd W. Root

ROOVERS - Embossing machines - Star Parts Inc.

ROOZENGAARDE - Flowers, plants, and seeds - Washington Bulb Co. Inc.

ROP-CORD - Tiles–ceramic - Roope Corp.

ROPA - Apparel–women's - Hairston Roberson

ROPE-A-BONE - Pet food - Creative Marketing, Inc.

ROPE-A-RONI - Beef - Taylor Country Farms Ltd.

ROPE COAT - Chemical preparations - Whitmore Manufacturing Co.

ROPE-RENCH - Wrenches - Rumstick Design Group Inc.

ROPE TRICK - Jewelry - Marvella Inc.

ROPE WRANGLER - Rope - Keeper Corp.

ROPER - Dishwashers–household - Whirlpool Properties, Inc.

ROPER - Knives–pocket - Buck Knives, Inc.

ROPER - Pet food and toys - Products Carousel Inc.

ROPER - Prefabricated buildings–metal ☆ - Ropert General Electric

ROPER - Shoes–athletic - Karman Western Apparel

ROPER RANGE GEAR - Coats - Karman Western Apparel

ROPES - Apparel and accessories - D. Frad, Inc.

ROPES - Apparel–athletic - Frozen Ropes Apparel & Equipment

ROPES - Pens - Pentech International Inc.

ROPETEX - Wallcovering - Panelfold Inc.

ROPEZONE - Sporting goods - Oncourt Offcourt, Inc.

ROPITEAU FRERES - Wines - Palm Bay Imports, Inc.

ROPITEAU WINES OF BURGUNDY - Wines - Palm Bay Imports, Inc.

ROPOD - Tripods–photographic - Rose Manufacturing Co.

ROPPE - Floor coverings - Roope Corp.

ROPPONGI - Footwear - Hiraoka New York Corp.

ROPRES - Pharmaceutical preparations - Rotex Pharmaceuticals Inc.

ROPTEX - Envelopes - Western States Envelope Co.

ROPUMP - Drain pipe cleaners - Rothenberger USA, Inc.

ROPURE ST. - Water treatment units - Barnstead Thermolyne Corp.

ROQ AMERICA - Apparel and accessories - John Paul Rock

ROR - Rings–jewelry - Sterling Inc.

RORAX - Automotive parts and accessories - Whittington Chemicals Inc.

ROREX - Hair care products - Revlon Consumer Products Corp.

ROSA - Dinnerware ☆ - Corning Inc.

ROSA - Earthenware - Shafford Co. Inc.

ROSA - Food products - Rosa Food Products Co.

ROSA - Glassware–household ☆ - Crisa Corp.

ROSA - Pens - Rosa Pen Co.

ROSA BELLA - Oils–essential - Royal Country, Inc.

ROSA BLANCA - Food products - Digiorgio

ROSA GALLICA - Dishes–china - Viletta China Co.

ROSA GOLUB ORIGINALS - Novelty items - RDE Imports

ROSA-GRAF - Skin care products ☆ - Nemectron-Belmont Inc.

ROSA GRANDE - Food products - Hormel Foods Corp.

ROSA JANE - Syrup - Cole Brothers Co.

ROSA MARIA - Spices and extracts - Nurita Foods, Inc.

ROSA MOSQUETA - Skin care products - Aubrey Organics, Inc.

ROSA-SPINA - Paper - Fabriano America Inc.

ROSALCO - Furniture - Rosalco Inc.

ROSALEEN - House furnishings - Dan River Inc.

ROSALENE - Glassware–household ☆ - Fenton Art Glass Co.

ROSALIE - Dishes–china - Waterford Wedgewood USA, Inc.

ROSALIND - Pajamas–women's ☆ - J.C. Penney Co., Inc.

ROSALINDA - Flowers, plants, and seeds - Flowerwood Nursery, Inc.

ROSALYNN - Dinnerware ☆ - International China Corp.

ROSAMOND - Dinnerware–glass ☆ - Lenox, Inc.

ROSAMUNDE - Rings–jewelry - Artcarved Inc.

ROSAN - Paints - Talon Paint Inc.

ROSARIO - Slacks–women's - Stanwood Corp.

ROSARIO - Toilets–enameled - Kohler Co.

ROSARITA - Food products - Hunt-Wesson, Inc.

ROSARITA - Food products - Rosarita Mexican Foods Co.

ROSAROMA - Deodorizers ☆ - Car-Freshner Corp.

ROSARY GAME, THE - Games - Family Rosary, Inc.

ROSASPINA - Artists' materials - Andrews/Nelson/Whitehead

ROSBARB - Wines - Breitenbach Wine Cellars

ROSCO - Dog food - Heinz Pet Products Co.

ROSCO - Paints - Rosco Laboratories Inc.

ROSCO - Tools - Vermont American Corp.

ROSCOE'S - Sauces - Roscoe's Inc.

ROSCOGEL - Electronic equipment - Rosco Laboratories Inc.

ROSCOLENE - Electronic equipment - Rosco Laboratories Inc.

ROSCOLUX - Electronic equipment - Rosco Laboratories Inc.

ROSCOSCREEN - Electronic equipment - Rosco Laboratories Inc.

ROSCOTRAN - Electronic equipment - Rosco Laboratories Inc.

ROSE - Candy - Nuts to You

ROSE - Dinnerware ☆ - Corning Inc.

ROSE - Dinnerware–glass - Noritake Co. Inc.

ROSE - Fruits and vegetables - Columbia Fruit Packers Inc.

ROSE - Garden equipment - L. Rose Hardware Inc.

ROSE - Glass products - Westmoreland Glass Co.

ROSE - Glassware–household - Rezler & Howell Co.

ROSE - Glassware–household ☆ - Fenton Art Glass Co.

ROSE - Meat products–beef - Rose Packing Co. Inc.

ROSE - Meat products–canned - Foell Packing Co.

ROSE - Musical instrument accessories - Dimarzio, Inc.

ROSE - Novelty items - Armament Systems and Procedures, Inc.

ROSE - Seafood products–canned or cured - Rose Frozen Shrimp Inc.

ROSE - Sporting goods - Rose Manufacturing Co.

ROSE - Teas - Rose Coffee Co.

ROSE - Wigs - Paula Young

ROSE 1 RAPID ON-SCENE SPECIAL EVENTS VEHICLE - Golf carts - Eugene H. Eskey III

ROSE ACRE FARMS - Eggs - Hansen Egg Co.

ROSE ACRE FARMS - Eggs - Rose Acre Farms, Inc.

ROSE & CROWN - Tobacco products - Brick-Hanauer Co.

ROSE & FLOWER INSECT SPRAY - Insecticides - Security Products Co.

ROSE AND SHORE - Meat products–beef - Rose & Shore Meat Co.

☆ = Now out of production

ROSE ANTIQUA - Glassware—household ☆ - Ceraglass Inc.
ROSE ARBOR - Christmas tree ornaments - Cracker Box Inc.
ROSE ARCADE - Bedding—linen - Dan River Inc.
ROSE ART - Crayons - Rose Art Industries, Inc.
ROSE ART - Toys - Coloron Industries
ROSE ART FUN DOUGH - Toys - Rose Art Industries, Inc.
ROSE BAY - Seafood products—fresh or frozen - Jacques F. Weber Co.
ROSE BENGAL - Pharmaceutical preparations - Akorn Inc.
ROSE BENGAL STRIPS - Ophthalmic goods - Akorn Inc.
ROSE BLANKET - Flowers, plants, and seeds - Bear Creek Gardens, Inc.
ROSE BOUQUET - Dinnerware—glass - Nikko Ceramics Inc.
ROSE BOUQUET - Dinnerware—glass ☆ - Johnson Brothers, USA, Inc.
ROSE BOUQUET - Glassware—household ☆ - Fenton Art Glass Co.
ROSE BOUQUET - Luggage - American Flyer
ROSE BOWL - Games ☆ - Milton Bradley Co.
ROSE BOWLS - Giftware - Fenton Art Glass Co.
ROSE BRAND - Cookies - Tsue Chong Co., Inc.
ROSE BRIDE - Dolls - Mattel, Inc.
ROSE BUD - Chewing tobacco - Conwood Co. L.P.
ROSE BUD - Milk - Rosebud Creamery Inc.
ROSE BUFF - Cosmetics - Lancome
ROSE BURMESE - Glassware—household ☆ - Fenton Art Glass Co.
ROSE CAGE INK, INC. - Children's apparel - Rose Cage Ink, Inc.
ROSE CANTON - House furnishings - McSin Oriental Import Co.
ROSE CHANDAL - Skin care products - European Cosmetics Inc.
ROSE CHINTZ - Dinnerware—glass - Johnson Brothers, USA, Inc.
ROSE CITY - Food products - Bozzuto's Food Services
ROSE CLAY - Hair care products ☆ - Nature de France
ROSE CODORNIU - Wines - Codorniu USA Inc.
ROSE CORSAGE - Glassware—household ☆ - Fenton Art Glass Co.
ROSE COTTAGE - Apparel and accessories - Wal-Mart Stores Inc.
ROSE CRACKERS - Crackers - Prepco
ROSE CREST - Candy ☆ - Log House Foods Inc.
ROSE CROIX - Fruits and vegetables - Comstock Michigan Fruit
ROSE DE CHAUNAC - Wines - Seven Lakes Vineyard
ROSE DE MAI - Perfumes - Revlon Consumer Products Corp.
ROSE DEFENSE - Insecticides - Green Light Co.
ROSE DELICAT - Nail care products - Cosmair Inc.
ROSE DIABLE - Lipsticks - Cosmair Inc.
ROSE D'OR - Nail care products - Cosmair Inc.
ROSE DOUCE - Cosmetics - Lancome
ROSE DUET - Floor coverings—carpet and rugs ☆ - Regal Rugs Inc.
ROSE E. DEE - Craft supplies - Minnetonka Mills Inc.
ROSE-EXPOSED - Cosmetics - Revlon Consumer Products Corp.
ROSE FARM - Food products - F.O. Mitchell & Bro. Inc.
ROSE FEVER - Craft supplies - VIP/VIP Crafts
ROSE FLAMINGO - Cosmetics - Revlon Consumer Products Corp.
ROSE FLEUR - Lipsticks - Cosmair Inc.
ROSE GARD - Garden equipment - Eaton Brothers Corp.
ROSE GARDEN - Dinnerware—glass - Block China Co.
ROSE GARDEN - Floor coverings—carpet and rugs ☆ - Capel, Inc.
ROSE GARDEN - Flowers, plants, and seeds - Rose Garden Inc.
ROSE GARDEN - Giftware - Fenton Art Glass Co.
ROSE GARDEN - Glassware—household ☆ - Crystal Clear Importing Co. Inc.
ROSE GARDEN - Housewares ☆ - Schwarz Bros. Plastics
ROSE GARDEN - Teas ☆ - R.C. Bigelow, Inc.
ROSE GARDEN COLLECTION - Lighting fixtures - Angelo Brothers Co.
ROSE GARLAND - Dinnerware—glass ☆ - Franciscan by Johnson Brothers, USA, Inc.
ROSE GLACE - Lipsticks - Lancome
ROSE GOLD - Nail care products - Cosmair Inc.
ROSE GROW - Lawn mowers ☆ - Thompson Manufacturing Co.
ROSE HALL CATHEDRAL - Cabinets - Wellborn Cabinet, Inc.
ROSE HILL - Food products - Rose Hill Poultry Corp.
ROSE HILL - Herbal products - St. John's Herb Garden Inc.
ROSE HILL - Wine - Royal Imports
ROSE HILL BOOKS - Publisher's imprints - Fordham University Press
ROSE HILL LINEN COMPANY, THE - Linen - Rose Hill Linen Co.
ROSE INDIEN - Cosmetics - Lancome
ROSE IRISEE - Cosmetics - Lancome
ROSE IS A ROSE, A - Posters ☆ - Edward Weston Fine Arts
ROSE JOHNSON - Office furniture—wood - La-Z-Boy Chair Co.
ROSE JOLIE - Lipsticks - Lancome
ROSE LAKE - Cutlery ☆ - Lifetime Hoan Corp.
ROSE LEAF - Insecticides - Black Leaf Products Co.

ROSE-LEE BEVERLY HILLS INTERCHANGEABLE HEEL - Footwear—women's - Lewis International Importing/Exporting, Inc.
ROSE LU - Nail care products - Starlight Nail Supplies, Inc.
ROSE MANOR - Tableware—china ☆ - Lenox, Inc.
ROSE MANOR COLLECTION - Giftware - Lenox, Inc.
ROSE-MARIE - Apparel stores—lingerie - H.F. Robbins
ROSE MARIE REID - Bathing suits - Jonathan Logan Inc.
ROSE MATE - Fertilizers - Greenview Lawn & Garden Products
ROSE MEDALION - Giftware - Arnart Imports Inc.
ROSE MEDALLION - Wallpaper - Newmarket Designs Ltd.
ROSE MILK - Skin care products - Smithkline Beecham Corp.
ROSE MIST - Bedding—linen - Dan River Inc.
ROSE MITCHAM - Food products - A.M. Todd Co.
ROSE MOFFORD ROSE'S SALSA - Tomato pastes and sauces - S.E.R., Inc.
ROSE NACRE - Lipsticks - Lancome
ROSE OF LOVE - Giftware - Russ Berrie and Co., Inc.
ROSE O'NEILL KEWPIE COLLECTION, THE - Giftware ☆ - Enesco Corp.
ROSE ORGANICS - Fertilizers - Rose Disposal Services, Inc.
ROSE PARADE - Bedding—linen - Dan River Inc.
ROSE PARADE - Giftware - World of Porcelain & Glassware
ROSE PARADE - Video production - Pasadena Tournament of Roses Association
ROSE PECAN - Lipsticks - Cosmair Inc.
ROSE PETAL - Housewares ☆ - Lamplight Farms, Inc.
ROSE PETAL PLACE - Bathroom accessories ☆ - Tsumura International Inc.
ROSE PETAL PLACE - Dishes—plastic - Deka Plastics Inc.
ROSE PETAL PLACE - Games ☆ - Parker Brothers
ROSE PETALS - Perfumes - Heritage Store Inc.
ROSE POINT - Flatware - Wallace International Silversmiths, Inc.
ROSE PORTRAIT - Dinnerware ☆ - Corning Inc.
ROSE POTPOURRI - Nail care products - Cosmair Inc.
ROSE QUARTZ - Glassware—household ☆ - Fenton Art Glass Co.
ROSE QUARTZ - Nail care products - Cosmair Inc.
ROSE QUARTZ - Recording label - Flying Fish Records Inc.
ROSE RECORDS - Recording label - MTS, Inc.
ROSE RIBBON - Floor coverings—carpet and rugs - Trans-Ocean Import Co. Inc.
ROSE SACHET - Dishes—china - Taylor, Smith & Taylor Co.
ROSE SAND - Lipsticks - Lancome
ROSE SILHOUETTE - Silverware - Imperial Schrade Corp.
ROSE SOFT - Skin care products - Helene Curtis Industries Inc.
ROSE SPLENDOR - Dinnerware—glass - Nikko Ceramics Inc.
ROSE STICK - Bacon - Bob Ostrow Co.
ROSE STUDIOS - Computer software - Rose Studios, Inc.
ROSE TIARA - Flatware - Gorham Inc.
ROSE-TONE - Flowers, plants, and seeds - Espoma Co.
ROSE TOTINO'S - Pasta ☆ - Pillsbury Co.
ROSE TRELLIS - Dinnerware ☆ - Corning Inc.
ROSE VALLEY - Skin care products - Rose Valley Laboratories, Inc.
ROSE VINE - Frames—picture - Terragrafics Inc.
ROSE VISOR - Apparel—women's - Upper Crust by Miss Cynthia, Inc.
ROSE-X - Cleaning preparations—household - Desoto, Inc.
ROSEANNA - Dinnerware—glass - Crystal Clear Importing Co. Inc.
ROSEANNE - Floor coverings—carpet and rugs - Regal Rugs Inc.
ROSEANNE & TOM'S BIG FOOD DINER - Apparel and accessories - Thomas D. Arnold
ROSEART - Paints—artists' - Rose Art Industries, Inc.
ROSEBEARY - Toys—stuffed ☆ - Gund, Inc.
ROSEBLOSSOM - Dinnerware ☆ - Corning Inc.
ROSEBLUSH - Food products - World West Sales
ROSEBROOK - Cabinets—wood - Edgewater Cabinets
ROSEBUD - Agricultural products - Mulch Manufacturing, Inc.
ROSEBUD - Bedding—linen - Marcus Bros. Crib Products Inc.
ROSEBUD - Bicycles - Roadmaster Corp.
ROSEBUD - Computer software - Magee Enterprises, Inc.
ROSEBUD - Cosmetics - Lancome
ROSEBUD - Dolls - Mattel, Inc.
ROSEBUD - Floor coverings—carpet and rugs ☆ - Regal Rugs Inc.
ROSEBUD - Food products - Beatrice Cos. Inc.
ROSEBUD - Glassware—household ☆ - Knobler International Ltd.
ROSEBUD - Greeting cards - Norcross Inc.
ROSEBUD CHINTZ - Dishes—earthenware ☆ - Royal China & Porcelain Companies Inc.
ROSEBUD COLLECTION - Giftware ☆ - Himark Enterprises Inc.
ROSEBUD MINTS - Candy ☆ - Russell Stover Candies, Inc.
ROSEBUD PIGGY - Toys—stuffed - Russ Berrie and Co., Inc.

☆ = Now out of production

ROSEBUDS - Hobby kits - Fashion Ribbon Co. Inc.
ROSEBUGGY - Juvenile product - Par Industries, Inc.
ROSEBURG - Lumber - Woodex Lumber Corp.
ROSECLIFF - Floor coverings–carpet and rugs ☆ - Trans-Ocean Import Co. Inc.
ROSECLIFF - Giftware ☆ - Gorham Inc.
ROSECRAFT KIDS - Jewelry - Hanover Advisors, Inc.
ROSECRANS - Floor coverings ☆ - Tarkett, Inc.
ROSECREST - Jewelry - Magnolia Diamonds Inc.
ROSEDALE - Food products - Seneca Foods Corp.
ROSEDALE - Glassware–household ☆ - Lotus Glass Co.
ROSEDUST - Cosmetics - Merle Norman Cosmetics
ROSEFRUIT - Vegetables–canned ☆ - Lyons Canning Co. Inc.
ROSEHALL - Cabinets - Wellborn Cabinet, Inc.
ROSEHALL - Floor coverings - Mannington Resilient Floors
ROSEHART - Vegetables–canned - Elgin Canning Co.
ROSEL YARN - Yarn - Roselon Industries, Inc.
ROSELAND - Flatware - Reed and Barton Corp.
ROSELAND - Glassware–household - Owens-Illinois Inc. (Libbey Div.)
ROSELANE - Figurines - Roselane Pottery
ROSELAWN - Agricultural products ☆ - Mulch Manufacturing, Inc.
ROSELEA - Floor coverings - Mannington Resilient Floors
ROSELI - Food products - JP Foodservice, Inc.
ROSELLE - Olive oil ☆ - Liberty Richter Inc.
ROSELYN - Tableware–china ☆ - Lenox, Inc.
ROSEMAR - Giftware ☆ - Towle Silversmiths
ROSEMARIE - Dinnerware ☆ - Corning Inc.
ROSEMARIE BEAR - Toys–stuffed - Dakin Inc.
ROSEMARY - Floor coverings–carpet and rugs ☆ - Regal Rugs Inc.
ROSEMARY - Toys–stuffed ☆ - Gund, Inc.
ROSEMARY FOR REMEMBRANCE - Sachets - Rosemary Co., Inc.
ROSEMARY HILL FARM - Teas - Eastern Shore Tea Co.
ROSEMARY PLUS - Vitamins and nutritional supplements - Kroeger Herb Products Co. Inc.
ROSEMARY WAKE-UP LOVE MITT - Health care products - Elizabeth Van Buren Aromatherapy
ROSEMARY'S - Candy - Rosemary Candy Co.
ROSEMEAD - Publisher's imprints ☆ - Zondervan Publishing House
ROSEMEADE - Dishes–china - Waterford Wedgewood USA, Inc.
ROSEMETIC - Skin-care products - Carechem Corp.
ROSEMONT - Bedding–linen - Dan River Inc.
ROSEMONT - Floor coverings - Mannington Resilient Floors
ROSEMONT - Floor coverings–carpet and rugs - Barrett Carpet Mills Inc.
ROSEMONT - Floor coverings–carpet and rugs - Quaker Inc.
ROSEMONT - Floor coverings–carpet and rugs ☆ - Regal Rugs Inc.
ROSEMONT - Furniture ☆ - Hammary Furniture Co. Inc.
ROSEMONT - Tableware–china ☆ - Lenox, Inc.
ROSEMONT - Wallpaper ☆ - Pickhardt & Siebert USA Inc.
ROSEMONT - Wines - Hammer Co.
ROSEMONT COLLECTION - Wood products - Vermillion Inc.
ROSEMONT SQUARE - Floor coverings - Congoleum Corp.
ROSEMOUNT SYSTEM 3 - Programmable processor - Rosemount Inc.
ROSEN - Candy - E. Rosen Co.
ROSENBERGER'S - Fruit drinks–bottled or canned - Rosenbergers Dairies Inc.
ROSENBLOOM'S - Gelatin - Rosenbloom's
ROSENBLUM CELLARS - Wines - Rosenblum Cellars, Inc.
ROSENE - Glassware–household ☆ - Lotus Glass Co.
ROSENE - Hobby kits - Edna Looney Products
ROSENS - Meat products–beef - G & D Foods Inc.
ROSENTHAL CLASSIC - Glassware–household - Rosenthal USA Ltd.
ROSENTHAL STUDIO-LINIE - Glassware–household - Rosenthal USA Ltd.
ROSENVOLD - Ophthalmic goods - Sparta Surgical
ROSEOX - Herbal products - Hauser Chemical Research, Inc.
ROSEOX660 - Spices and extracts - Hauser Chemical Research, Inc.
ROSEPOINTE - Tableware–china - Lenox, Inc.
ROSEPRIDE - Insecticides - Monsanto Co.
ROSERAIE - Tiles–ceramic ☆ - Monarch Tile Inc.
ROSERED - Spices and extracts - Schoenfeld and Sons Inc.
ROSEROPE - Jewelry - OroAmerica Inc.
ROSE'S - Beverages - Cadbury Beverages Inc.
ROSES - Clocks - General Time Corp. (Westclox/Seth Thomas Div.)
ROSES - Colognes ☆ - Avon Products, Inc.
ROSES - Floor coverings–carpet and rugs ☆ - Regal Rugs Inc.
ROSES - Flowers–artificial ☆ - Design Circle Ltd.
ROSE'S - Food products - Alpha Sales Inc.

ROSE'S - Juices - Mott's Inc.
ROSE'S - Marmalade - Shaffer, Clark & Co. Inc.
ROSES & BOWS - Glass products - Westmoreland Glass Co.
ROSES AND LACE - Giftware - Russ Berrie and Co., Inc.
ROSES 'N CHOCOLATES - Chocolate candy - Maxfield Candy Co.
ROSES 'N' RIBBONS - Tiles–ceramic - Monarch Tile Inc.
ROSES ON RUBY - Glassware–household - Fenton Art Glass Co.
ROSES REMEMBERED - Jewelry - House of Roses Rosaries
ROSE'S SECRET - Barbecue sauce - D'Forte/La Cantina Brands
ROSETOX - Pesticides–household - Bonide Products, Inc.
ROSETTA - Fans–electric - Fasco Industries Inc. (Consumer Products Div.)
ROSETTA - Musical instruments - Tilben Co.
ROSETTA - Yarn ☆ - Roselon Industries, Inc.
ROSETTE - Dinnerware–glass - Franciscan by Johnson Brothers, USA, Inc.
ROSETTE - Dolls - Mattel, Inc.
ROSETTE - Fabrics - Superior Shade & Blind Co. Inc.
ROSETTE - Floor coverings ☆ - Congoleum Corp.
ROSETTE - Floor coverings–carpet and rugs - Eligere Carpets
ROSETTE - Floor coverings–carpet and rugs ☆ - Daltonian Carpet & Cushion Inc.
ROSETTE - Lipsticks - Lancome
ROSETTES - Pasta - Best Foods/Mueller Co.
ROSETTI - Dinnerware–glass ☆ - Royal China & Porcelain Companies Inc.
ROSETTI - Neckties - Resisto Tie Makers
ROSETTO - Food products - Rosetto Foods Inc.
ROSEWATER BLUSH - Cosmetics - Max Factor & Co.
ROSEWOOD - Computer software - Adobe Systems Inc.
ROSEWOOD - Dishes–wood ☆ - Dansk International Designs, Ltd.
ROSEWOOD - Glassware–household - Wallace International Silversmiths, Inc.
ROSEWOOD - Nail care products - Cosmair Inc.
ROSEWOOD - Pet products - Petberrys
ROSEWOOD - Wallpaper ☆ - Imperial Wallcoverings, Inc.
ROSEWOOD COMBINATIONS - Floor coverings ☆ - Teak International
ROSEWOOD FARMS - Cheese - Rosewood Products Inc.
ROSEWOOD II - Wallpaper ☆ - Imperial Wallcoverings, Inc.
ROSEWOOD MANOR - Toys ☆ - Today's Kids Inc.
ROSEWOOD'S VERY RARE - Whiskey - Old Boone Distillery Co.
ROSEXPRESS - Flowers, plants, and seeds - Rosexpress Inc.
ROSEY KIDS - Apparel–children's - Rosey Kids
ROSEY TOMATO - Apparel–women's - Smiles Fashion Corp.
ROSIE - Dolls - Diversified Specialists, Inc.
ROSIE - Fabrics - Motif Designs, Inc.
ROSIE - Paper–tissue - Atlas Paper Mills, Ltd.
ROSIE - Wallpaper - Capital Carousel Inc.
ROSIE AND THE ROCKERS - Toys ☆ - Imperial Toy Corp.
ROSIE II - Wallpaper - Motif Designs, Inc.
ROSIE O'GRADY - Wines - Bardenheier Wine Cellars
ROSIE THE BRAZILIAN ROSEWOOD NUT - Paints - Performance Coatings Inc.
ROSIEAES ITALIA - Wallpaper - Capital Carousel Inc.
ROSIE'S BABIES - Bedding–linen - Diplomat Corp.
ROSIE'S KIDS - Bedding–linen - Diplomat Corp.
ROSILAND - Recording label - Eucharist Films Distribution
ROSIN X - Soldering equipment - M.W. Dunton Co.
ROSINA - Giftware - Norcrest China Co.
ROSINA - Meat products–beef - Rosina Food Products Inc.
ROSINA - Processed foods - L and S Packing Co., Inc.
ROSINA EST. 1963 - Meat products - Rosina Food Products Inc.
ROSINA LIGHT - Food products - Rosina Food Products Inc.
ROSITA - Cordials - Marie Brizard Wines & Spirits, USA
ROSITA - Dinnerware–glass ☆ - WMF/USA
ROSITA - Paints ☆ - St. Louis Paint Manufacturing Co.
ROSITA - Recording label - Freddie Records
ROSITA SI - Specialty foods–canned ☆ - Ruiz Food Products Inc.
ROSITA SI SUPREME - Specialty foods–canned ☆ - Ruiz Food Products Inc.
ROSITAS COCINA - Soups–canned - Rak Baran Frozen Foods Inc.
ROSKO & ROSKO - Food products ☆ - Old Ranchers Canning Co. Inc.
ROSLYN - Apparel and accessories - Marshall Field's
ROSLYN - Food products - Vanderhorst Cannery
ROSOCO - Valves - Ronald Soroule
ROSOFF - Pickles - Hebrew Foods Inc.
ROSPI - Tools–plumbing - Rothenberger USA, Inc.
ROSS - Abrasive products - Conros Corp.
ROSS - Audio equipment - International Music Corp.
ROSS - Bicycles - Ross Bicycles USA, Ltd.
ROSS - Computers–mainframe - Ross Technology, Inc.

☆ = Now out of production

ROSS - Fertilizers - Weatherly Consumer Products, Inc.
ROSS - Musical instrument accessories - Ross Mallet Instruments Inc.
ROSS - Seafood products–fresh or frozen ☆ - Harrison Pierce & Co. Inc.
ROSS - Thread ☆ - Perfect Thread Co. Inc.
ROSS & CROMARTY - Apparel and accessories - TMG Corp.
ROSS APOLLO - Bicycles - Ross Bicycles USA, Ltd.
ROSS BARRACUDA - Bicycles - Ross Bicycles USA, Ltd.
ROSS-COMMON - Water–bottled or canned - Ross-Common Beverage
ROSS-CONES - Sealing devices - American Metal Chemical Corp.
ROSS CONVERTIBLE - Bicycles - Ross Bicycles USA, Ltd.
ROSS EUROPA - Bicycles - Ross Bicycles USA, Ltd.
ROSS EUROSPORT X - Bicycles - Ross Bicycles USA, Ltd.
ROSS GRAN TOUR - Bicycles - Ross Bicycles USA, Ltd.
ROSS-KELLER - Wines - Ross Keller Winery
ROSS MOTO-X-ROSS - Bicycles - Ross Bicycles USA, Ltd.
ROSS NETTING - Fencing–wood - Weatherly Consumer Products, Inc.
ROSS NUT CO. - Edible processed nuts - Ross Nut Co.
ROSS NUTS, THE - Nuts–salted, roasted, cooked, or canned - Ross Nut Co.
ROSS POLOBIKE - Bicycles - Ross Bicycles USA, Ltd.
ROSS PROFESSIONAL - Bicycles - Ross Bicycles USA, Ltd.
ROSS RANCHER - Bicycles - Ross Bicycles USA, Ltd.
ROSS RODEO - Bicycles - Ross Bicycles USA, Ltd.
ROSS ROOT FEEDER - Fertilizers - Weatherly Consumer Products, Inc.
ROSS SUPER - Fertilizers - Ross Daniels Inc.
ROSS SYSTEMS - Electronics equipment - International Music Corp.
ROSS-TEX - Thread ☆ - Perfect Thread Co. Inc.
ROSS WINERY-NAPA VINTNERS - Wines - Napa Valley Wines
ROSSANA - Candy - Perugina Chocolate & Confections Inc.
ROSSANO - Shoes ☆ - Allen-Edmonds Shoe Corp.
ROSSCO - Stationery - H.T. Herbert Co. Inc.
ROSSELLA - Food products - Louis Metafora Co. Inc.
ROSSER - Medical apparatus - Cabot Technology Corp.
ROSSETTE - Cooking utensils–enameled - Denby USA Limited
ROSSETTI'S GARDEN - Wallpaper ☆ - Ashford House
ROSSI - Firearms, accessories, and parts - International Armament Corp.
ROSSI - Luggage - Melissa Designs Inc.
ROSSI - Shoes ☆ - Ennesi Shoe Co. Inc.
ROSSI CUSTOMCRAFT - Footwear ☆ - Schwartz & Benjamin Inc.
ROSSIGNOL - Sporting goods - Rossignol Ski Co., Inc.
ROSSIGNOL ALPINE SYSTEMS - Skis - Rossignol Ski Co., Inc.
ROSSINI - Beverages–alcohol - Castiglione Imports
ROSSINI - Footwear - Olem Shoe Corp.
ROSSINI'S - Pizzas–frozen - Nation Pizza Products L.P.
ROSSINI'S CLASSIC CELLARS - Wines - Wakefern Food Corp.
ROSSI'S - Pasta - Rossi Pasta
ROSSITOP - Skis - Rossignol Ski Co., Inc.
ROSSLARE - Earthenware ☆ - Waterford Wedgewood USA, Inc.
ROSSLER - Dishes–earthenware - Mikasa Co.
ROSSLI - Cigars - James B. Russell Inc.
ROSSMORE - Earthenware ☆ - Waterford Wedgewood USA, Inc.
ROSSMORE - Floor coverings–carpet and rugs - Atlas Carpet Mills Inc.
ROSSMORE PLACE - Floor coverings–carpet and rugs - Atlas Carpet Mills Inc.
ROSSO ANTICO - Beverages–alcohol - Blair Importers Ltd.
ROSSTHERM - Insulating materials - American Metal Chemical Corp.
ROSTOCK - Meat products - White Packing Co., Inc.
ROSTOCK BRAND - Meat products–pork - White Packing Co., Inc.
ROSWELL - Furniture ☆ - Singer Furniture Co.
ROSWELL MANOR - House furnishings - Lexington Furniture Industries, Inc.
ROSY BLUE - Jewelry - Rosy Blue Jewelry Inc.
ROSY CHEEKS - Jams and jellies - Sarabeth's Kitchen
ROSY-GLOW - Cleaning preparations ☆ - Elcal Enterprises Ltd.
ROSY PUMP - Plumbing fixtures–metal - Presto-Tek
ROT-GARD - Paints ☆ - Briner Paint Manufacturing Co. Inc.
ROT HEAD - Watches - Mattel, Inc.
ROT NOT - Adhesives and sealants ☆ - Induron Coatings Inc.
ROT-STOP - Paints - Valspar Corp.
ROT-STOP - Pesticides–household - Bonide Products, Inc.
ROTA 2 - Razors - Philips Electronics North America Corp.
ROTA-BILT - Shelving units–plastic ☆ - Frick-Gallagher Manufacturing Co.
ROTA-CLOSER - Hardware - H.B. Ives
ROTA-CUFF - Exercising equipment - Sport Supply Group, Inc.
ROTA-FLEX - Paper - Rotary Printing Co. Inc.
ROTA LEVELER - Tools–masonry - Marshalltown Trowel Co.
ROTA-MASTER - Tools - Osborn Manufacturing Corp.
ROTA-SEW - Paper - Rotary Printing Co. Inc.

ROTA TECH - Food products - International Specialty Supply
ROTA TRIM - Photographic equipment - Tiffen Manufacturing Corp.
ROTABIN - Bins - Frick-Gallagher Manufacturing Co.
ROTACASE - Revolving bookcases and storage racks - Rotacase Inc.
ROTACATOR - Gauging instruments - Woodstock International, Inc.
ROTADYNE - Plates–plastic - Rotation Dynamics Corp.
ROTALEVELER - Brackets - Marshalltown Trowel Co.
ROTANELLI - Food products - Rotanelli Foods Inc.
ROTANELLI'S - Ravioli–canned - Rotanelli's Authentic Pasta (Div. of Specialty Brands, Inc.)
ROTAR - Toys - Mattel, Inc.
ROTARY - Motorcycles ☆ - Suzuki of America Automotive Corp.
ROTARY - Musical instruments ☆ - St. Louis Music Supply Co.
ROTARY GRIP - Sporting goods - Rotary-Grip Inc.
ROTARY MASSAGE - Hardware ☆ - Hardie-Toro Irrigation
ROTARY MATE - Measuring instruments - Martingale & Co.
ROTARY MOTION PROBE - Educational materials - Team Labs Corp.
ROTARY MOWERS - Lawn mowers - Alamo Industrial
ROTARY RULE - Measuring instruments - Martingale & Co.
ROTARY TOTEM - Recording label - Jazz Composer's Orchestra Association Inc.
ROTARY WET/DRY - Razors–electric - Remington Products Co.
ROTASHIELD - Computer peripheral equipment - American Home Products Corp.
ROTATING TUNNEL OF LITE - Mirrors ☆ - Lava-Simplex Internationale
ROTATION - Games - Ralph J. Oravec
ROTATION RESISTANT - Cables - MacWhyte Co.
ROTATIONS - Hair care products - Conair Corp.
ROTATOR - Insecticides - Mallinckrodt Veterinary, Inc.
ROTATOR, THE - Sporting goods - Italgom-USA
ROTATRACT - Razors ☆ - Philips Electronics North America Corp.
ROTAWAVE - Molding compounds–plastics - Amana Refrigeration Inc.
ROTBART - Shaving preparations - Gillette Co.
ROTEC - Racks - RTC Industries, Inc.
ROTECTIN - Veterinary pharmaceutical preparations - Farnam Cos. Inc.
ROTECTIN 1 - Veterinary pharmaceutical preparations - Farnam Cos. Inc.
ROTECTIN 2 - Veterinary pharmaceutical preparations - Farnam Cos. Inc.
ROTEL - Food products - Knapp-Sherrill Co.
RO*TEL - Tomatoes and chilies - American Home Food Products Inc.
ROTELLA - Oils–lubricating - Shell Oil Co.
ROTELLE - Pasta - Maxfor Foods Inc.
ROTENIER - Jewelry - Rotenier, Ltd.
ROTENONE - Pet products - Goodwinol Products Corp.
ROTEX - Labeling product, envelopes, etc. - International Rotex Inc.
ROTEX - Office supplies ☆ - Esselte Corp.
ROTH - Trees–artificial - Vincent Lippe Co.
ROTH AUDIO/VIDEO LIBRARY - Publisher's imprints ☆ - Roth Publishing Inc.
ROTH-HANDLE - Cigarettes - G.A. Georgopulo & Co. Inc.
ROTH KASE TRADITION - Cheese - Roth Kase USA, Ltd.
ROTH KIRCH - Dolls - Dollsandreams
ROTHAV - Pharmaceutical preparations - Rotex Pharmaceuticals Inc.
ROTHCO - Sporting goods - Rothco Inc.
ROTHKIRCH DOLLS - Toys ☆ - Reeves International, Inc.
ROTHMANS - Cigarettes - House of Edgeworth
ROTHMOUR - Apparel and accessories - Rothmour Investments, Inc.
ROTHSCHILD - Brandy - Paramount Distillers Inc.
ROTHSCHILD - Coats–children's - S. Rothschild & Co., Inc.
ROTHSCHILD - Dishes–china - Martin's Herend Imports Inc.
ROTHSCHILDS - Candy - Warner-Lambert Co.
ROTHSCHILDS - Cigarettes - G.A. Georgopulo & Co. Inc.
ROTHWELL - Sinks–metal ☆ - Artesian Industries
ROTI - T-shirts and sweatshirts - Embarcadero Inn Associates
ROTI EXPRESS - Frozen foods - Natural Life Inc.
ROTI-RICH - Animal feeds - Florida Aqua Farms Inc.
ROTICUL - Garden equipment ☆ - Simplicity Manufacturing Inc.
ROTIGER - Saws–power - Rothenberger USA, Inc.
ROTIM - Plastics film - E.I. Dupont de Nemours and Co.
ROTISSER-EASE - Seasonings - Tone Brothers, Inc.
ROTISSERIE READY - Meat products - Sara Lee Corp.
ROTISSERIE RECIPE - Seasonings - McCormick & Co., Inc.
ROTO - Hardware - Roto Frank of America Inc.
ROTO-7 - Drill bits - National Express, Inc.
ROTO BOSS - Tillers–rotary - White Outdoor Products Inc.
ROTO-BRITE - Cleaning equipment - Chemical Specialties Manufacturing Corp.
ROTO-BUSINESS - Office supplies - Roto Photo Co. Inc.
ROTO-CADDY - Desk sets - Park Sherman

☆ = Now out of production

ROTO-CAM - Surgical supplies - J. Jamner Surgical Instruments, Inc.
ROTO-COAT - Machinery - Lawson Screen Products, Inc.
ROTO-COIL - Electronic equipment - Sony Corp. of America
ROTO-CRIMPER - Tools–plumbing - Hosecomatic
ROTO CUBE - Display cases–metal - Krapf Business Systems, Inc.
ROTO-CUT - Machinery - Raymond Judy Corp.
ROTO DELUXE - Paper - Blandin Paper Co.
ROTO-EDGER - Garden equipment - Ames Lawn & Garden Tool Co.
ROTO-FILE - Office supplies - Chicago Hair Good Inc.
ROTO-FLEX - Tools - Seatek Co. Inc.
ROTO FLO - Painter ☆ - Polaris Industries Partners LP
ROTO-FLOW - Meat grinders - Hollymatic Corp.
ROTO FORGED - Gun barrels - Ithaca Gun Co. Inc.
ROTO-FRYER - Kitchen appliances - DeLonghi America Inc.
ROTO-HAMMER - Drills–electric ☆ - S-B Power Tool Co.
ROTO-HINGE - Hinges - Abra Inc.
ROTO-HOE - Tools–garden - Roto-Hoe Co.
ROTO II - Labeling machinery - Litton Industrial Automation Systems
ROTO KIMCO - Labels–paper ☆ - Litton Industrial Automation Systems
ROTO-KITE KIT - Educational materials ☆ - Twinson Co.
ROTO LOCK - Fasteners–hook and eye - Southtec, Inc.
ROTO-LOK - Surgical supplies - J. Jamner Surgical Instruments, Inc.
ROTO-LOK AWNING - Window frames ☆ - Biltbest Windows
ROTO-LON - Floor coverings - Congoleum Corp.
ROTO-MATIC - Compasses–gyroscopic - Rule Industries, Inc.
ROTO-MATIC - Musical instrument accessories - Grover/Trophy Musical Products Inc.
ROTO-MATIC - Vacuum cleaners and accessories ☆ - The Eureka Co.
ROTO MAZE - Games - Little Harbor Corp.
ROTO-MIX - Mixers–concrete ☆ - Roto-Mix, Inc. (J-STAA Industries, Inc.)
ROTO-MIX-ROUND - Farm machinery - Roto-Mix, Inc. (J-STAA Industries, Inc.)
ROTO-MIXER - Mixers–concrete ☆ - Roto-Mix, Inc. (J-STAA Industries, Inc.)
ROTO-NOTO - Recording label - Target Records
ROTO PHASE - Electrical equipment - Arco Electric Products Corp.
ROTO-PHOTO - Photo albums - Roto Photo Co. Inc.
ROTO-PHOTO - Projectors–photographic ☆ - Tyco Toys
ROTO PUMP - Pumps ☆ - Kleer Flo Co. Inc.
ROTO-RECLAIMER - Machinery - Haahjem North American Inc.
ROTO-ROBOT - Toys - Mattel, Inc.
ROTO-ROD - Controls–heating systems - Cobra Products Inc.
ROTO-SEAL - Plastic security seals - E.J. Brooks Co.
ROTO-SET - Hammers ☆ - S-B Power Tool Co.
ROTO-SHINE - Electrical equipment ☆ - Ronson Consumer Products Corp.
ROTO-SHOW - Electronic equipment - GAF Corp.
ROTO-SHOW - Projectors–photographic ☆ - Tyco Toys
ROTO-SKINNER - Tools - Seatek Co. Inc.
ROTO-SPLIT - Tools - Seatek Co. Inc.
ROTO-SPLIT SUPER - Tools - Seatek Co. Inc.
ROTO-STIK - Industrial machinery - Pemberton, Inc.
ROTO STRIPPER - Paint removers - Miracle Products
ROTO-SWING - Doors–glass - Roto/Swing Inc.
ROTO-TIP - Drums–musical instruments ☆ - Cappella Wood Enterprises
ROTO TOMS - Drums–musical instruments - Remo, Inc.
ROTO-TRAY - Containers - Arthur Brown and Bros. Inc.
ROTO-TWIST - Conveyors - ASGCO Manufacturing Inc.
ROTO-VECTION - Ovens–convection - International Technology, Inc.
ROTO-VENT - Construction equipment ☆ - H.D. Hudson Manufacturing Co.
ROTOBOND - Inks–letterpress - Sun Chemical Corp.
ROTOBRITE - Paper - Madison Paper Industries
ROTOBRUSH - Vacuum cleaners and accessories–commercial - Howard C. Smith, Inc.
ROTOCAST - Boats–pontoons - Rotocast Plastic Products
ROTOCHOK - Motor vehicles - Rotochok Co.
ROTOCHOPPER - Machinery - PCR, Inc.
ROTOCLAVE - Tools–machine - Tempico, Inc.
ROTOCLEAN - Nozzles - Spraying Systems Co.
ROTOCOMP - Adhesives and sealants - Nd Industries, Inc.
ROTOGRAPH - Office accessories - Krapf Business Systems, Inc.
ROTOGRO - Agricultural products - Links Manufacturing, Inc.
ROTOLA - Meat products - John Volpi & Co., Inc.
ROTOMATIC - Musical instrument accessories - Grover Musical Products, Inc.
ROTOMATIC - Projectors–photographic ☆ - H.P. Marketing Corp.
ROTOMATIC - Projectors–photographic ☆ - Tyco Toys
ROTOMATIC - Tools–power-driven - Seatek Co. Inc.
ROTON H HAGER - Hinges - Hager Hinge Co.
ROTONDA - Tableware–china - Villeroy and Boch Tableware Ltd.

ROTOR - Musical instrument accessories - Musichem
ROTOR - Tools–power-driven - Rotor Tool Co.
ROTOR DYNAMICS - Electronics - Rotor Dynamics Americas, Inc.
ROTOR-GRIND - Grinders - Del Zotto Manufacturing
ROTORPRO - Machinery - Gerardo Greinsberger
ROTOSPRAY - Tools–power-driven - Loctite Corp.
ROTOSWITCH - Switches–electric - General Automotive Specialty Co., Inc.
ROTOTRAY - Trays ☆ - GAF Corp.
ROTOTRON - Watches - Elgin Watch Co.
ROTOVIBE - Musical instrument accessories - Dunlop Manufacturing, Inc.
ROTRAC - Tools - Rothenberger USA, Inc.
ROTRING - Artists' materials - Koh-I-Noor, Inc.
ROTRING 600 - Pens ☆ - Koh-I-Noor, Inc.
ROTRING ART PENCIL - Artists' materials - Koh-I-Noor, Inc.
ROTRING ARTIST COLOR - Artists' materials - Koh-I-Noor, Inc.
ROTRING RAPIDOGRAPH - Artists' materials - Koh-I-Noor, Inc.
ROTRING RAPIDOGRAPH F - Drafting supplies - Koh-I-Noor, Inc.
ROTRING RAPIDOLINER - Pens - Koh-I-Noor, Inc.
ROTRON - Aquariums–household - Aquaculture Research/Environmental Associates Inc.
ROTRTWIST - Drill bits - Star Anchors & Fasteners
ROTT FYTER - Paints - McCloskey Corp.
ROTTED WOOD HARDENER - Wood fillers - H.F. Staples & Co. Inc.
ROTTEFELLA - Binding–fabric - Erik Sports Inc.
ROTTEFELLA - Sporting goods - Exel Marketing Inc.
ROTTENKIDS, THE - Dolls - Doll Factory, Inc.
ROTTERDAM SHAG - Tobacco products - Faber, Coe & Gregg Inc.
ROTTICO MILITARY DIVISION - Apparel and accessories - Rothco Inc.
ROTUNDA - Apparel and accessories - Ford Motor Co.
ROTUNDA - Floor coverings - Mannington Resilient Floors
ROTUNDA - Meat products–pork - Rotunda Packing
ROTUNDA - Musical instrument accessories - Excelsior Accordions Inc.
ROUBAIX - Bicycles - Toshoku America Inc.
ROUBI DOUX - Teas - USA Beverage, Inc.
ROUDON-SMITH VINEYARDS - Windshields–plastic - Roudon-Smith Vineyards Inc.
ROUEN - Furniture ☆ - Davis Cabinet Co.
ROUGE - Beverages–alcohol ☆ - White Rock Products Corp.
ROUGE A LEVRES - Lipsticks - Sothys USA Inc.
ROUGE CRISTAL - Lipsticks - Lancome
ROUGE DE COCO - Cosmetics - Chanel Inc.
ROUGE DE ROUGE - Wines ☆ - Calera Wine Co.
ROUGE ET BLEU - Lipsticks - Lucien Lallouz
ROUGE ET NOIR - Cheese - Marin French Cheese Co.
ROUGE ET NOIR - Food products - Dairy Fresh Products Co.
ROUGE EXTREME - Cosmetics - Chanel Inc.
ROUGEON - Wines - Meredith Vineyard
ROUGH AND READY RED - Wines - Nevada City Winery
ROUGH COUNTRY - Tobacco products - Scott Tobacco Co.
ROUGH DIAMOND - Recording label - Gregory John Bernard
ROUGH DIAMOND - Recording label - Survivor Records/Dream Makers Inc.
ROUGH DRESS - Apparel and accessories - M'otto Enterprises, Inc.
ROUGH-HIDE - Pet food - T.F.H. Publications, Inc.
ROUGH-HOUSE - Tool boxes - Disston Co.
ROUGH HOUSE GANG - Footwear - Wolverine World Wide, Inc.
ROUGH 'N READY - Snack foods - Circle K Corp.
ROUGH N' TOUGH - Floor coverings–carpet and rugs ☆ - Prestige Mills Inc.
ROUGH NECK - Batteries - Exide Corp.
ROUGH ON RATS - Rodenticides - Brown Manufacturing Co.
ROUGH PRINT - Decals and transfers ☆ - Sangray Corp.
ROUGH RIDER - Apparel–women's - Circle T Western Wear
ROUGH RIDER - Bicycles - Columbia Manufacturing Inc.
ROUGH RIDER - Floor coverings–carpet and rugs - Blue Ridge Carpet Mills
ROUGH RIDER - Garden equipment - Emsco Inc.
ROUGH RIDER - Gardening accessories - Rubbermaid Inc.
ROUGH RIDER - Golfing equipment - Golfsmith International Inc.
ROUGH RIDER - Prophylactics - Ansell Inc. (Personal Products Div.)
ROUGH RIDER - Snuff - Brown & Williamson Tobacco Corp.
ROUGH-RIDER - Wheelchairs - Kareco International Inc.
ROUGH RIDERS - Bags and brief cases - Global Fashion Accessories, Inc.
ROUGH RIDERS - Candy - Claeys Candy Inc.
ROUGH RIDERS - Toys - Intex Recreation Corp.
ROUGH RYDER - Knives–pocket - Smoky Mountain Knife Works
ROUGH SAWN - Shutters–wood ☆ - Ohline Corp.
ROUGH SERVICE - Electric lighting equipment - Ampac Industries Inc.
ROUGH SHAKE - Aluminum products ☆ - Kaiser Aluminum & Chemical Corp.

☆ = Now out of production

ROUGH SKIN REMOVING CREAM - Skin care products - Schering-Plough Healthcare Products
ROUGH STICK BY HECTOR - Furniture—wood - Hector R. Aguilar
ROUGH STOCK - Headwear - RHE, Inc.
ROUGH STUFF - Plaster—wallboard - Applied Texture Inc.
ROUGH THREADS - Apparel and accessories - Crystal Brands Inc.
ROUGH TOTE - Containers - Rubbermaid Inc.
ROUGH TOUGH - Plumbing fixtures—enameled - Schaul Manufacturing Co.
ROUGH USA - Apparel and accessories - L.S.Y. Trade, Inc.
ROUGH WALL - Resins—acrylic - Stanson Inc. (Dacor Brick Div.)
ROUGH WEATHER RUGGED RELIABLE SUPERIOR OUTDOOR APPAREL - Apparel and accessories - Gant Corp.
ROUGH WRITER - Crayons - Scripto-Tokai Corp.
ROUGHAGE CONVERTER - Pet food - PM AG Products Inc.
ROUGHCUT - Knives ☆ - Camillus Cutlery Co.
ROUGHHOUSE - Floor coverings—carpet and rugs ☆ - Calladium & Marglen
ROUGHIES - Footwear—athletic - Clinic Shoe Co.
ROUGHLYTE - Lighting equipment - Genlyte Group Inc.
ROUGHNECK - Containers—trash - Rubbermaid Inc.
ROUGHNECK - Enamels - Gulf States Paint Co.
ROUGHNECK - Flashlights - Rayovac Corp.
ROUGHNECK - Food containers - Thermos Co.
ROUGHNECK - Hand tools - Olympia Industrial Inc.
ROUGHNECK - Mops - Rubbermaid Cleaning Products Inc.
ROUGHNECKS - Toys - Intex Recreation Corp.
ROUGHTEX - Building materials—asbestos - Champion International Corp.
ROUGHTOTE - Containers - Rubbermaid Inc.
ROUGIE - Food products - Gourmet America
ROUGIE - Meat products—canned - Hansen Caviar Co.
ROUGIE - Meat products—poultry - Made in France
ROULEAU - Floor coverings—tile - Burke Flooring Products
ROULETTE - Glassware—household - Hoya Corp.
ROUND - Cosmetics - Revlon-Realistic Professional Products Inc.
ROUND-A-BOUT - Health care products - Mor-Loc Corp.
ROUND-A-BOUT - Kitchen appliances - Dazey Corp.
ROUND-A-MATIC - Brushes—hair - Magic Distributing Ltd.
ROUND-A-MOUNT - Metals - National Products, Inc.
ROUND-ABOUT - Apparel—women's ☆ - Carmen Foundations Inc.
ROUND ABOUT - Infant product ☆ - Graco Children's Products
ROUND BACK - Lighting fixtures - Swivelier Co. Inc.
ROUND BASS - Musical instrument accessories - Guild Music Corp.
ROUND CRIB, THE - Cribs—wood - Round Crib Co.
ROUND FOUR - Games ☆ - Milton Bradley Co.
ROUND GILT - Pencils ☆ - Faber-Castell Corp.
ROUND HILL - Beverages—alcohol - Round Hill Winery
ROUND HILL - Food processors - Wampler Foods Inc.
ROUND HILL - Turkey products - Round Hill Foods
ROUND HILL VINEYARDS - Wines - Round Hill Winery
ROUND I - Conveyors - Round I, Inc.
ROUND INDERECTOR - Lighting fixtures - Voigt Lighting Industries Inc.
ROUND LITE - Chimes ☆ - Nutone Inc.
ROUND O' BITES - Cakes ☆ - Metz Baking Co.
ROUND RIVER - Recording label ☆ - Alcazar Productions
ROUND ROBIN - Medical apparatus - Ventura Enterprises, Inc.
ROUND STIC - Pens - Bic Corp.
ROUND TABLE - Candy - Tower Candy Co.
ROUND TEA BAGS - Coffee - Tetley Inc.
ROUND-THE-CLOCK - Calendars - Success Business Industries, Inc.
ROUND-THE-CLOCK - Deodorizers - Surco Products Inc.
ROUND THE CLOCK - Floor coverings—carpet and rugs - Kelly Group Inc.
ROUND THE CLOCK - Food products - Hanover Foods Corp.
ROUND THE CLOCK - Hosiery—women's - Danskin, Inc.
ROUND-THE-CLOCK - Skin care products - Goubaud
ROUND-TOP - Nails—horseshoe - National Nail Corp.
ROUND TOP - Windows—storm - Marvin Windows and Doors
ROUND TOWNERS - Unlined leather gloves - Boss Manufacturing Co.
ROUND TRIP - Apparel and accessories - Direct Access International, Inc.
ROUND-TRIP - Envelopes - Tension Envelope Corp.
ROUND UP - Candy - Pangburn Candy Co.
ROUND UP - Floor coverings—carpet and rugs ☆ - Walter Carpet Mills
ROUND UP - Food products - Bar S Food Co. Inc.
ROUND-UP - Health care products - Maddak Inc.
ROUND UP - Pet products - Buckaroo Marine
ROUND UP JELLY - Jams and jellies - Mountain Maid Gourmet Jelly
ROUNDABOUT - Containers—plastic - Romanoff Products Inc.
ROUNDABOUT - Floor coverings—carpet and rugs ☆ - Columbus Mills, Inc.

ROUNDABOUT - Games - Fundex Games, Ltd.
ROUNDABOUT - Glassware—household - Durand International
ROUNDABOUT - Ice chests—plastic - Coleman Co., Inc.
ROUNDABOUT - Playground equipment - Wonderline
ROUNDABOUT - Scrub brushes - Sunshine Industries Inc.
ROUNDABOUTS - Vegetables—frozen ☆ - Lamb-Weston, Inc.
ROUNDBALL UNLIMITED - Apparel—athletic - Greely F. Snowden, Jr.
ROUNDEL - Floor coverings—tile - Johnsonite Flooring Products
ROUNDELS - Games - Thomas C. Lamar
ROUNDER - Brushes—hair - Phillips Brush Corp.
ROUNDER - Recording label - Rounder Records Corp.
ROUNDERS - Cap racks - Bil-Built Manufacturing Co.
ROUNDEZ-VOUS - Underwear and nightwear ☆ - Lovable Co.
ROUNDHOUSE, THE - Automotive repair shops - Roundhouse Inc.
ROUNDOMINOES - Games - Kadon Enterprises Inc.
ROUNDRIVE - Hardware - Illinois Tool Works Inc.
ROUNDSPRAY - Lawn mowers - Thompson Manufacturing Co.
ROUNDTABLE - Greeting cards - American Greetings Corp.
ROUNDTOIT - Balls - James A. Foxx
ROUNDUP - Barbecues and grills ☆ - Shepherd Products U.S. Inc.
ROUNDUP - Floor coverings—carpet and rugs - Concord/Aldon Industries Inc.
ROUNDUP - Food products - Cudahy Co.
ROUNDUP - Herbicides - Monsanto Co.
ROUNDUP HAT CO. - Hats - W. Alboum Hat Co., Inc.
ROUNDUP READY SOYBEANS FOR OVER THE TOPAPPLICATION - Flowers, plants, and seeds - Monsanto Co.
ROUNDUP TIME - Tablecloths - Straubel Paper Co.
ROUNDVENT - Window frames - CW Ohio Inc.
ROUNDY'S - Food products - Midland Grocery Co.
ROUNDY'S - Food products - Roundy's Inc.
ROUNTREE - Meat products—beef - Rountree Packing Co.
ROUSANA PRINTS - Greeting cards - Rousana Cards
ROUSSEAU - Floor coverings—carpet and rugs - Bellbridge Carpets
ROUSSEAU - Floor coverings—carpet and rugs - Evans-Black Carpet Mills
ROUSSETTES - Snack foods - A & A Food Products Corp.
ROUST-A-BOUT - Hosiery ☆ - Wigwam Mills Inc.
ROUSTABOUT - Boats - Glen-L Marine Designs
ROUSTER - Gloves—rubber - Granet Inc.
ROUT-T - Computers - Mercury Computer Systems Inc.
ROUTE 2 - Computer peripheral equipment - Learmonth & Burchette Management Systems, Inc.
ROUTE 9 - Footwear - Nine West Group Inc.
ROUTE 11 - Snack foods - Route 11 Potato Chip Factory
ROUTE 56 - Communications equipment - Sealevel Systems, Inc.
ROUTE 66 - Fabrics - Interface, Inc.
ROUTE 66 - Fruits and vegetables - Cadiz Land Co., Inc.
ROUTE 66 - Luggage - Route 66, Inc.
ROUTE 66 - Trailers - Contract Manufacturer, Inc.
ROUTE 66 FOODS - Seat belts - Gayle Garivaltis, George Garivaltis and Hilary Garivaltis Partnership
ROUTE 66 HIGHWAY LEATHERS - Handbags - Route 66, Inc.
ROUTE 101 - Computer software - Optisys, Inc.
ROUTE A BAGGIES - Stationery - Graphic Center
ROUTE AUTHORITY - Computer peripheral equipment - Structural Instrumentation, Inc.
ROUTE ONE - Apparel—women's - Kay Windsor Inc.
ROUTE ROLLER - Board game - Intromark Inc.
ROUTEFINDER - Computer hardware - Multi-Tech Systems, Inc.
ROUTEFINDER100 - Computer hardware - Multi-Tech Systems, Inc.
ROUTEMASTER - Containers - Mexico Plastic Co.
ROUTEMASTER - Dollies—industrial - Magline Inc.
ROUTEPRO DESIGNER - Computer software - CAPS Logistics, Inc.
ROUTEPRO DISPATCHER - Computer software - CAPS Logistics, Inc.
ROUTEPRO RESIDENTIAL - Computer software - CAPS Logistics, Inc.
ROUTER ART - Computer software - Thermwood Corp.
ROUTER-CIM - Computer software - Bo Fred Diversified, Inc.
ROUTERMATE - Computer hardware - Cray Communications, Inc.
ROUTERPM - Computer software - 3DV Technology, Inc.
ROUTERWARE - Computer software - Routerware, Inc.
ROUTFINDER200 - Computer hardware - Multi-Tech Systems, Inc.
ROUTH'S PRIDE - Seafood products—fresh or frozen ☆ - Ocean Beauty Seafood, Inc.
ROUTLEDGE - Publisher's imprints - Routledge
ROUX - Beverages—alcohol - Rolar Imports Ltd.
ROUX - Hair care products - Roux Laboratories, Inc.
ROUX WHITE - Hair care products - Roux Laboratories, Inc.

☆ = Now out of production

ROVAK - Computer peripheral equipment - Rovak, Inc.
ROVAL MANUFACTURING CORP. - Paints - Ro-Val Manufacturing Corp.
ROVAN - Fruits–dried - Ross Packing Co.
ROVANGNATI PRESCUTTO COTTO - Meat products - Crystal Food Import Corp.
ROVAR - Cupolas - Aluminum Co. of America
ROVEL - Containers–metal - Rovel Co.
ROVEL - Oils–lubricating - Schaeffer Oil Inc.
ROVER - Audio equipment - Rover Enterprises Co. Inc.
ROVER - Electronic equipment - Possibilities Co.
ROVER - Lighters ☆ - Ronson Consumer Products Corp.
ROVER - Medical apparatus - APT Technology, Inc.
ROVER - Motor vehicles–personnel carriers ☆ - Electric Mobility Corp.
ROVER - Motorcycles ☆ - Suzuki of America Automotive Corp.
ROVER - Office supplies - Alvin and Co. Inc.
ROVER - Sporting goods - Avon Marine
ROVER - Wood products ☆ - Grovco Sales Co. Inc.
ROVER BOY - Heaters–space - Spectrum Infrared Inc.
ROVER COOKER - Barbecues and grills - Coast Distribution System
ROVER PLUS NINE - Apparel - James Miller
ROVER ROPE - Pet products - McCarty Manufacturing
ROVERALLS - Pet products - Sirius Co.
ROVERDRILL - Machinery - Adgo, Inc.
ROVERETO DI GAVI - Wines - Kobrand Corp.
ROVEROLLI - Dog food - Ralston Purina Co.
ROVERS - Boats–pontoons ☆ - Valco Aluminum Boats
ROVI - Recording label - Musimex Inc.
ROVIN' WRECKER - Toys - Tonka Corp.
ROVING ROSTRUM - Audio equipment - Perma Power Electronics Inc.
ROVITE - Vitamins and nutritional supplements - Rotex Pharmaceuticals Inc.
ROVNER - Musical instrument accessories - CTC Music Inc.
ROW ALL-STAR WIPERS - Cleaning cloths - Row Clothing Enterprises, Inc.
ROW WING - Rowing oars - Piantedosi Oars
ROWAN - Furniture - Boling Co.
ROWAN - Office supplies - Transilwrap Co., Inc.
ROWASA - Pharmaceutical preparations - Solvay Pharmaceuticals Inc.
ROWBIKE - Bicycles - O.S. Designs, Inc.
ROWBOAT - Fabrics - Gretchen Bellinger Inc.
ROWCO - Electronics equipment - Educational Technology Inc.
ROWDY - Puppets - Rowdy, Inc.
ROWDY - Shoes ☆ - Allen-Edmonds Shoe Corp.
ROWE - Motor vehicle parts and accessories - Rivera Engineering, Inc.
ROWE - Vending machines - Rowe International, Inc.
ROWE 'L-EZY - Lawn mowers - Thompson Manufacturing Co.
ROWELS - Towels - Sara Sue Dix
ROWENA - Recording label - Tiki Enterprises Inc.
ROWENA'S - Bakery products - Rowena's Inc.
ROWENA'S - Food products - Rowena's Gourmet Foods Inc.
ROWENA'S WONDERFUL JAM AND JELLY FACTORY - Cakes–mixes - Rowena's Gourmet Foods Inc.
ROWEX - Exercising equipment - Battle Creek Equipment Co.
ROWGANICS - Health care products ☆ - Aloe Farms
ROWLF - Toys - Jim Henson Productions, Inc.
ROWLOCKS - Boats–canoes - Coleman Co., Inc.
ROWMAN & SCHRAM - Publisher's imprints - Rowman & Littlefield Publishers Inc.
ROWMAX - Exercising equipment ☆ - CSA, Inc.
ROWOCO - Housewares ☆ - Selfix, Inc.
ROWS OF BOWS - Hair curlers - Anne A. Nowlin
ROWSE ORCHARD - Food products - Rowse Inc.
ROX - Cases–camera ☆ - Edixa Camera Co.
ROX-HIDE - Luggage ☆ - Hartmann Luggage Co.
ROX-VAR - Varnishes - Diamond/Kuhn Paint Co.
ROXANN ROUGE - Wines - Schloss Doepken Winery
ROXANNE - Bathing suits - Milady Brassiere & Corset Co., Inc.
ROXANNE - Bathing suits - Roxanne Swim Suits Co. Inc.
ROXANNE - Frames–eyeglass - U.S. Optical Frame Co.
ROXANNE - Telephones - Cathay International
ROXANNE - Watches - Bulova Corp.
ROXANNE ASSOULIN - Jewelry - Maurice Max Inc.
ROXANNE ROLLER - Toys - Mattel, Inc.
ROXBURY - Clocks ☆ - General Time Corp. (Westclox/Seth Thomas Div.)
ROXBURY - Floor coverings - Mannington Resilient Floors
ROXBURY - Wine ☆ - Ingleside Plantation Winery
ROXCEL - Adhesives and sealants ☆ - Roxite Fiberglass
ROXEPOXY - Floor coverings - Roxseal Products

ROXEY - Pet products ☆ - Shurfine International, Inc.
ROXHALL - Clocks - Roxhall Time Corp.
ROXICET - Vitamins and nutritional supplements - Roxane Laboratories Inc.
ROXIE - Blouses–women's ☆ - Shady Grove Inc.
ROXIE RACCOON - Toys–stuffed ☆ - Dakin Inc.
ROXITE - Fiberboard - Roxite Fiberglass
ROXITE BLUBAK - Binding–fabric - Holliston Mills, Inc.
ROXIUM - Cement - Roxite Fiberglass
ROXO - Fly swatters - Roxide International, Inc.
ROXO PAPER CAT - Traps–animal - Roxide International, Inc.
ROXON - Bonding compound - Commercial Chemical Co. Inc.
ROXON - Heating equipment - Roxide International, Inc.
ROXSEAL - Floor slabs–concrete - Roxseal Products
ROXTER POCKET LITE - Lamps - Roxter Lighting
ROXTOWN - Recording label - Bold 1 Records
ROXY - Computer software - Font Bureau
ROXY - Thread - Threads USA Div.
ROXY - Wallpaper - CSE Designs
ROXY - Yarn ☆ - Tahki Imports Ltd.
ROXYD - Pet products ☆ - Sera Aquaristik USA Inc.
ROXY'S WORLD FAMOUS - Syrup - Detroit Popcorn Co.
ROY - Toys–stuffed - Dakin Inc.
ROY - Washing machines–household ☆ - White Consolidated Industries, Inc.
ROY AN GUS' HILLBILLY HOLLENDAISE NOT JUST ANOTHER BARBEQUE SAUCE - Sauces - Roy an Gus' Enterprises
ROY CLARK - Frankfurters - Fanestil Packing
ROY GENE - Wallets - Le Baron Manufacturing Corp.
ROY GONIA - Pet products - Lucky Dog Equipment Inc.
ROY J. MAIER - Musical instrument accessories ☆ - Rico International
ROY SMACK - Fretted instruments ☆ - International Music Corp.
ROYAL - Apparel–athletic - Montreal Hockey Co.
ROYAL - Artists' materials - American Blueprint Co. Inc.
ROYAL - Audio equipment - Saul Mineroff Electronics Inc.
ROYAL - Bathroom fixtures - Melard Manufacturing Corp.
ROYAL - Beef - Formico Food Co.
ROYAL - Bicycles - Columbia Manufacturing Inc.
ROYAL - Blinds–vertical - Royal Shutters Inc.
ROYAL - Boats–motor - Regal Marine Industries Inc.
ROYAL - Chocolate candy - Maxfield Candy Co.
ROYAL - Cigar boxes–wood ☆ - Consolidated Cigar Corp.
ROYAL - Colognes - Tristar Corp.
ROYAL - Curtain rods - Newell Window Furnishing Co.
ROYAL - Dinnerware–glass ☆ - WMF/USA
ROYAL - Doors–metal - Masco Corp.
ROYAL - Drums–musical instruments - MMB Music Inc.
ROYAL - Dryers–hair - Ross Sales Co.
ROYAL - Fishing reels - American Import Co.
ROYAL - Floor coverings - Dexter Corp. (Mercer Plastics Div.)
ROYAL - Floor coverings–carpet and rugs - Edgecrest Carpet Mills
ROYAL - Food products - Elite Mushroom Co., Inc.
ROYAL - Fruits–canned - Oceana Canning Co.
ROYAL - Furniture - Weiman Co.
ROYAL - Game tables - American International Shuffleboard Corp.
ROYAL - Games - Crisloid Inc.
ROYAL - Gelatin - Nabisco Foods Group
ROYAL - Girdles - Bi-Flex International
ROYAL - Glass products ☆ - Royal Products
ROYAL - Hair-care products, bath oils, baby-care product, skin-care product - Benjamin Ansehl Co.
ROYAL - Handbags - Lucerne Time
ROYAL - Hardware - Alumatic Corp. of America
ROYAL - Hardware - Alumax Aluminum Corp.
ROYAL - Health care products ☆ - Desert Health Products, Inc.
ROYAL - Horseshoes - St. Pierre Manufacturing Corp.
ROYAL - Ladders–wood - John S. Tilley Ladders Co. Inc.
ROYAL - Lamps - Royal China Co.
ROYAL - Lighting fixtures - Swivelier Co. Inc.
ROYAL - Manicure sets ☆ - London International U.S. Holdings
ROYAL - Mats - Royal Rubber & Manufacturing Co.
ROYAL - Meat products–poultry - B.C. Rogers Food Service, Inc.
ROYAL - Musical instruments - Tropical Music and Pro Audio
ROYAL - Nozzles - La Fayette Brass Co. Inc.
ROYAL - Office supplies - Bates Manufacturing Co.
ROYAL - Office supplies - Royal Index Tab Co.
ROYAL - Office supplies - Esselte Corp.
ROYAL - Ophthalmic goods - Capo, Inc.

☆ = Now out of production

ROYAL - Paints - Cook and Dunn Paint Corp.
ROYAL - Paints - Our Own Hardware Co.
ROYAL - Paper–gift wrap - Royal Paper Corp.
ROYAL - Pasta - Royal Angelus Macaroni Co.
ROYAL - Pet products - Pet Connection
ROYAL - Photographic equipment - Eastman Kodak Co.
ROYAL - Plumbing fixtures - Sloan Valve Co.
ROYAL - Rice - Basmati Rice Imports Inc.
ROYAL - Salad dressings–bottled - Sigma Quality Foods Corp.
ROYAL - Salmon–smoked, salted, dried, or pickled - North Pacific Seafoods
ROYAL - Seafood products–fresh or frozen - Royal Seafoods Inc.
ROYAL - Skin care products - Hess Hair Milk Laboratories Inc.
ROYAL - Sour cream - Royal Food Products Co.
ROYAL - Sporting goods - Jarvinen USA
ROYAL - T-shirts–men's - Midstates Sportswear
ROYAL - Tools–hand-operated - Royal Merchandise Co.
ROYAL - Toys–stuffed - Jolly U.S.A., Inc.
ROYAL - Trailers - Royal Truck Bodies, Inc.
ROYAL - Trailers–travel - Coachmen Industries, Inc.
ROYAL - Trailers–travel - Franklin Coach Co.
ROYAL - Trailers–travel ☆ - Allen Camper Manufacturing Co. Inc.
ROYAL - Vacuum cleaners and accessories - Royal Appliance Manufacturing Co.
ROYAL - Watches - Elgin Watch Co.
ROYAL - Wire–copper - Triangle Wire & Cable, Inc.
ROYAL - Yeast - Dutch Boy Co.
ROYAL 76 - Gasoline ☆ - Unocal Corp.
ROYAL ACCENT - Floor coverings–carpet and rugs ☆ - Downs Carpet Co. Inc.
ROYAL ACCENTS - Leather goods - Royal Accents, Ltd.
ROYAL ACCESSORIES - Scarves - Specialty Retailers, Inc.
ROYAL ADDERLEY - Glassware–household - Royal Doulton-Somerset UK Ltd.
ROYAL AFFAIR - Floor coverings–carpet and rugs ☆ - Prestige Mills Inc.
ROYAL AGES - Beverages–alcohol - Paddington Corp.
ROYAL AIR - Floor coverings - Mannington Resilient Floors
ROYAL AIRE - Flues ☆ - Malm Fireplaces Inc.
ROYAL ALASKA - Seafood products–fresh or frozen - Ocean Beauty Seafood, Inc.
ROYAL ALASKA - Seafood products–fresh or frozen - Seattle Seafoods Inc.
ROYAL ALBERT - Dinnerware–glass - Royal Doulton-Somerset UK Ltd.
ROYAL ALMOND CRUSH - Skin care products - Goubaud
ROYAL AMBASSADOR - Floor coverings–carpet and rugs - Royal Ambassador Rugs
ROYAL AMERICAN - Cheese - Land O'Lakes Inc.
ROYAL AMERICAN SAPPHIRE - Jewelry - Jewelry by Michael, Inc.
ROYAL AMETHYST - Flowers, plants, and seeds - DeVor Nurseries Inc.
ROYAL & REGAL - Teas - Queen's Empire
ROYAL ANN - Glassware–household - Royal Products
ROYAL ANNE - Furniture ☆ - Keller Manufacturing Co.
ROYAL AOLLANOLIA - Cheese - Webeco Foods Inc.
ROYAL ARCADIA - Floor coverings–carpet and rugs ☆ - Rugby Rugs Inc.
ROYAL ARCHER - Jewelry - Jacoby-Bender Inc.
ROYAL ARMS - Candy - McDonald Candy Co. Inc.
ROYAL ARTIST - Musical instruments - C. Bruno & Son Inc.
ROYAL ARTISTRY - Floor coverings–carpet and rugs ☆ - J and J Industries Inc.
ROYAL ASCOT - Gin - Old Boone Distillery Co.
ROYAL ASCOT - Glassware–household ☆ - National Housewares
ROYAL AUBURN - Cut stone - Cold Spring Granite Co.
ROYAL AUTOLINE - Tools–hand-operated - Royal Merchandise Co.
ROYAL BAMBOO - Flatware - Reed and Barton Corp.
ROYAL BANNER - Cigars - National Cigar Corp.
ROYAL BARD - Sporting goods ☆ - Gold Eagle/Arnold Palmer
ROYAL BASHAR - Floor coverings–carpet and rugs ☆ - Rugby Rugs Inc.
ROYAL BAYREUTH - Kitchenware–china - H. Wittur & Co.
ROYAL BEAUTE E - Skin care products ☆ - Marlyn Co. Inc.
ROYAL BEAUTY - Jewelry - Jacoby-Bender Inc.
ROYAL BEE - Vitamins and nutritional supplements - Natural Organics, Inc.
ROYAL BELGIUM - Coffee - H & H International Co. USA
ROYAL BENGAL - Apparel–men's ☆ - Michaels/Stern & Co. Inc.
ROYAL BEST - Seafood products–fresh or frozen - Royal Seafoods Inc.
ROYAL BLANC - Dishes–china ☆ - Royal China & Porcelain Companies Inc.
ROYAL BLEND - Food products - Ricetec, Inc.
ROYAL BLOSSOM - Food products - Seasia
ROYAL BLUE - Oils–lubricating - Arkla Chemical Corp. (Petroleum Div.)

ROYAL BLUE - Stencils ☆ - Heyer Inc.
ROYAL BLUE CHATEAU - Dishes–china - Tidemark Co.
ROYAL BLUES - Apparel and accessories - G.V. Trademark Investments Ltd.
ROYAL BOHEMIA - Glassware–household - Murmac Importing Corp.
ROYAL BOND - Paints ☆ - Mac-O-Lac Paints Inc.
ROYAL BOTANIX - Flowers–artificial - Magicsilk, Inc.
ROYAL BOUQUET - Floor coverings–carpet and rugs - Rugby Rugs Inc.
ROYAL BRASS - Fireplaces - Preway Industries Inc.
ROYAL BRAZIL - Candy ☆ - Fenn Brothers Inc.
ROYAL BRIGHTON - Glassware ☆ - Indiana Glass Co.
ROYAL BRISTOL - Flatware - Utica Cutlery Co.
ROYAL BUFFET - Flatware - Oneida Ltd.
ROYAL BURGUNDY - Flowers, plants, and seeds - Leo E. Gentry Wholesale Nursery, Inc.
ROYAL BY SIRECO - Hosiery - Blue Heaven Hosiery Co., Inc.
ROYAL CADDEF - Fishing tackle - Fin-Wall Enterprises
ROYAL CALIFORNIA BASMATI - Rice - Wehah Farm, Inc.
ROYAL CALOMARI - Seafood products–fresh or frozen - Royal Seafoods Inc.
ROYAL CAMEO - Floor coverings–carpet and rugs - Gulistan Carpet Inc.
ROYAL CANADIAN - Hams - Suzannah Farms
ROYAL CANADIAN - Tobacco products - Lane Ltd.
ROYAL CANADIAN - Whiskey - Jas. Barclay & Co. Ltd.
ROYAL CAPE - Flowers, plants, and seeds - Monrovia Nursery Co.
ROYAL CAPRI - Boats–houseboats ☆ - Harris-Kayot Inc.
ROYAL CAPTAIN - Pipes–tobacco - Bradberry Briar Pipe Corp.
ROYAL CARLTON - Giftware - Arnart Imports Inc.
ROYAL CAROUSEL - Fireplaces - Malm Fireplaces Inc.
ROYAL CASCADE - Fruits and vegetables - Oregon Cherry Growers, Inc.
ROYAL CASTLE - Floor coverings–carpet and rugs - Lees Carpets
ROYAL CASTLE - Glassware–household - Neuwirth Co.
ROYAL CATHAY - Furniture–wood - Guangdong Enterprises, Inc.
ROYAL CHAIN - Steering mechanisms–motor vehicle - Superior Industries International, Inc.
ROYAL CHAMPION - Jewelry - Jacoby-Bender Inc.
ROYAL CHANG - Floor coverings–carpet and rugs - Rugby Rugs Inc.
ROYAL CHARTER - Furniture - Ethan Allen, Inc.
ROYAL CHARTER - Furniture ☆ - Lane Co. Inc.
ROYAL CHEF - Housewares - Anchor Hocking Glass, Inc.
ROYAL CHERRIES - Candy ☆ - Leaf, Inc.
ROYAL CHERRY - Cabinets–wood ☆ - Kemper
ROYAL CHERRY - Tables - Impact Furniture
ROYAL CHIEFTAIN - Cigars - Malecon Tobacco, LLC
ROYAL CHILD - Apparel–children's - True Silver Corp.
ROYAL CHINA - Dishes–earthenware - Royal China & Porcelain Companies Inc.
ROYAL CHINTZ - Wallpaper ☆ - Andover Wallcovering
ROYAL CHOCOLATE - Cakes - Dinkel's Bakery
ROYAL CHOICE - Agricultural products - Hogan Associates
ROYAL CHOICE - Candy - Bohemian Biscuit Co.
ROYAL CIRCLE - Cigars - A.J. Golden Inc.
ROYAL CLARET - Christmas tree ornaments - Cracker Box Inc.
ROYAL CLASSIC - Towels - Fieldcrest Cannon, Inc.
ROYAL CLIPPER - Watches - Bulova Corp.
ROYAL CLUB - Crocheted and knitted items - Puritan Sportswear Corp.
ROYAL CLUB - Food products - Fairco, Inc.
ROYAL CLUB - Men's apparel - Jekel Inc.
ROYAL CLUB - Mincemeat ☆ - Frigid Food Products Inc.
ROYAL CLUSTERS - Candy - Nabisco Foods Group
ROYAL COACH - Floor coverings–carpet and rugs - Monticello Carpet Mills
ROYAL COACH - Kitchenware–china - Charles Zahn-Import Merchant
ROYAL COACH - Wallpaper ☆ - Imperial Wallcoverings, Inc.
ROYAL COACHMAN - Liquors - Crown Capital USA Inc.
ROYAL COACHMEN - Apparel and accessories ☆ - Levi Strauss & Co. (Accessory Div.)
ROYAL COACHMEN - Health care products - Harvy Surgical Supply Corp.
ROYAL COAT - Artists' materials - Plaid Enterprises, Inc.
ROYAL COAT - Pet products - Bioglan Animal Products Inc.
ROYAL COLA LIGHT - Beverages–carbonated - Royal Crown Cola Co.
ROYAL COLLECTION - Greeting cards ☆ - Paper Magic Group Inc.
ROYAL COLLECTION - Tail assemblies–aircraft - Superior Industries International, Inc.
ROYAL COLLECTION - Wallpaper ☆ - Wall Fabrics Inc.
ROYAL COLLECTION, THE - Enameled ware - British American Imports
ROYAL COLLECTION, THE - Health care products ☆ - Naturade Inc.
ROYAL COLONY - Floor coverings–carpet and rugs - Burlington House Carpets

ROYAL COLUMBIAN - Stationery ☆ - Westvaco Corp.

ROYAL COMFORT - Tobacco products - John Middleton Inc.

ROYAL COMFORT - Underwear and nightwear - J.C. Penney Co., Inc.

ROYAL CONNECTION - Handbags - Holiday Fair, Inc.

ROYAL CONTESSA - Dishes–china ☆ - Gorham Inc.

ROYAL CONTINENTAL BOX COMPANY - Boxes–corrugated paperboard - Royal Continental Box Co.

ROYAL COOK - Kitchen utensils–aluminum - Faramarzipour USA, Inc.

ROYAL COPENHAGEN - Apparel–men's - Swank Inc.

ROYAL COPENHAGEN - Colognes - Tsumura International Inc.

ROYAL COPENHAGEN - Giftware - Royal Copenhagen Porcelain Inc.

ROYAL COPENHAGEN - Giftware - Viking Import House Inc.

ROYAL COTTAGE - Wallpaper ☆ - Eisenhart Wallcoverings Co.

ROYAL COTTAGE 2 - Wallpaper ☆ - Eisenhart Wallcoverings Co.

ROYAL COUNTRY RETREATS - Furniture - Drexel Heritage Furnishings, Inc.

ROYAL COUPLE - Dolls - Mattel, Inc.

ROYAL COURT - Cigars - Lignum-2, Inc.

ROYAL COURT - Floor coverings - Congoleum Corp.

ROYAL COURT - Floor coverings–carpet and rugs - Daltonian Carpet & Cushion Inc.

ROYAL COURT - Floor coverings–carpet and rugs - Queen Carpet Corp.

ROYAL COURT - Floor coverings–carpet and rugs ☆ - Karastan-Bigelow Inc.

ROYAL COURT - Seafood products–fresh or frozen - K & C Food Sales

ROYAL COURT - Towels - Sears, Roebuck and Co.

ROYAL CRAFT - Boats - MCP Inc.

ROYAL CRAFT - Manufactured homes ☆ - Redman Industries, Inc.

ROYAL CREAM KOLA - Beverages–carbonated - Honey Pure Natural Beverages

ROYAL CREATIONS - Audio equipment - Royal Creations Inc.

ROYAL CRESCENT - Wallcovering books - Seabrook Wallcoverings, Inc.

ROYAL CREST - Artists' materials - Hurlock Bros. Co. Inc.

ROYAL CREST - Dishes–china - Richard-Stephen Inc.

ROYAL CREST - Food products ☆ - Interstate Restaurant Supply Co.

ROYAL CREST - Fruits–frozen - Hawthorn Mellody Inc.

ROYAL CREST - Milk - Royal Crest Dairy Inc.

ROYAL CREST - Window shades - John Dixon Inc.

ROYAL CREST BY EVANS - Footwear–men's - L.B. Evans' Son Co.

ROYAL CREST DAIRY - Dairy products - Royal Crest Dairy Inc.

ROYAL CREST WOVEN WOODS - Blinds–venetian - Royal Crest Inc.

ROYAL CROWN - Beverages–carbonated - Royal Crown Cola Co.

ROYAL CROWN - Bicycles - Columbia Manufacturing Inc.

ROYAL CROWN - Figurines - Arnart Imports Inc.

ROYAL CROWN - Hair care products - J. Strickland & Co.

ROYAL CROWN - Jewelry - Jacoby-Bender Inc.

ROYAL CROWN - Leather - Leather Factory Inc.

ROYAL CROWN - Motor vehicles - Superior Industries International, Inc.

ROYAL CROWN COLA - Syrup ☆ - The Atlantic Beverage Group, USA, Inc.

ROYAL CROWN DERBY - Dinnerware–glass - Royal Doulton-Somerset UK Ltd.

ROYAL CROWN DRAFT PREMIUM COLA - Beverages–carbonated - Royal Crown Cola Co.

ROYAL CROWNFORD - Dinnerware–glass ☆ - Crownford Giftware Co. Inc.

ROYAL CRUISER - Luggage - Monarch Luggage Co., Inc.

ROYAL CRYSTAL BY PETROV - Glassware–household - Petrov Enterprises Ltd.

ROYAL CRYSTAL ROCK - Candlesticks ☆ - Biedermann & Sons Inc.

ROYAL CRYSTAL ROCK - Glassware–household - Royal Crystal Rock Inc.

ROYAL CUMBERLAND - Dinnerware–glass ☆ - Royal Copenhagen Porcelain Inc.

ROYAL CUP - Coffee ☆ - Royal Cup, Inc.

ROYAL CUP COFFEE 1896 - Dinnerware - Royal Cup, Inc.

ROYAL CUT - Beef - Blue Diamond Meat Co.

ROYAL CUTHBERTSON - Dinnerware - Cuthbertson Imports Inc.

ROYAL CUTS, THE - Jewelry - Suberi Brothers, Inc.

ROYAL CUTTINGS LTD. - Wallpaper - Snap & Sell Corp.

ROYAL CZAR - Liquors - Frank-Lin Distillers Products

ROYAL DAIM - Wallpaper - Carlton-Metro Wallcoverings

ROYAL DAN - Fabrics - Dan River Inc.

ROYAL DANBY - Marble products - Carl Schilling Stoneworks

ROYAL DANE - Stainless steel ☆ - Latama Inc.

ROYAL DANISH - Glassware–household ☆ - Ceraglass Inc.

ROYAL DANSK - Biscuits - Murray-Allen International Inc.

ROYAL DE NEUVILLE - Wines - Frank Sutton & Co.

ROYAL DELFTWARE - Giftware - Blue Delft Co. Inc.

ROYAL DELICIOUS - Hair-care products ☆ - Benjamin Ansehl Co.

ROYAL DELUXE - Hair care products - Helene Curtis Industries Inc.

ROYAL-DELUXE - Photo albums - Pioneer Photo Albums, Inc.

ROYAL DELUXE - Plates–paper - Beach Products

ROYAL DEVON - Giftware - Gorham Inc.

ROYAL DIADEM - Combs - Cardinal Comb & Brush

ROYAL DIAMOND - Garden equipment - Valley View Specialties Co.

ROYAL DIAMOND - Shelving units–metal - Lee-Rowan Co.

ROYAL DIAMOND CUT - Toiletries, hair-care products - Benjamin Ansehl Co.

ROYAL DIAMOND PLUS - Cooking equipment–household - Regal Ware, Inc.

ROYAL DISTINCTIONS - Mats - Royal Rubber & Manufacturing Co.

ROYAL DOULTON - Giftware - Royal Doulton-Somerset UK Ltd.

ROYAL DOULTON - Telephones - TT Systems Corp.

ROYAL DOULTON - Wallpaper ☆ - James Seeman Studios

ROYAL DOULTON CRYSTAL - Glassware–household - Royal Doulton-Somerset UK Ltd.

ROYAL DOULTON LAMBETHWARE - Glassware–household - Royal Doulton-Somerset UK Ltd.

ROYAL DOULTON PLATES & FIGURINES - Giftware - Viking Import House Inc.

ROYAL DRAGON - Food products - Nabisco Foods Group

ROYAL DRAGOONS - Cigarettes - G.A. Georgopulo & Co. Inc.

ROYAL DUKE - Computer peripheral equipment ☆ - Duchess Royale Inc.

ROYAL DUKE - Pipes–tobacco - Dr. Grabow Pre-Smoked Pipes Inc.

ROYAL DUTCH - Cocoa–powders or mixes - W.L.M. Bensdorp Co.

ROYAL DUTCH - Giftware - Blue Delft Co. Inc.

ROYAL DUTCH - Shrimp–canned or cured ☆ - Eastern Fish Co.

ROYAL DUTCH - Wines - Old Dutch Imports

ROYAL DUX - Giftware - Crystal Clear Importing Co. Inc.

ROYAL DUX - Glassware–household ☆ - Queen Lace Co.

ROYAL DYNASTY - Flatware ☆ - Kirk Stieff Co.

ROYAL DYNASTY - Floor coverings–carpet and rugs - Barrett Carpet Mills Inc.

ROYAL DYNASTY - Floor coverings–carpet and rugs ☆ - Columbus Mills, Inc.

ROYAL EAGLE - Desk sets ☆ - Jesse Jones Box Corp.

ROYAL EAGLE - Dishes–china - Arrow International, Inc.

ROYAL EAGLE - Gasoline - Colonial Oil Industries Inc.

ROYAL EAGLE - Tools–hand-operated - Durall-Eagle Tools

ROYAL-EASY WAY - Tents - Denver Tent Co.

ROYAL EDGE - Roofing materials - Roofing Products International, Inc.

ROYAL EDGE, THE - Glass–flat - Downey Glass

ROYAL EDITION - Floor coverings–carpet and rugs - Bloomsburg Carpet Industries

ROYAL ELECTRIC - Electrical equipment - Triangle Wire & Cable, Inc.

ROYAL ELEGANCE - Fabrics - Decorative Aides Co. Inc.

ROYAL ELEGANCE - Floor coverings - Tarkett, Inc.

ROYAL ELEGANCE - Floor coverings–carpet and rugs - Aldon Industries Inc.

ROYAL ELEGANCE - Floor coverings–carpet and rugs ☆ - Karastan-Bigelow Inc.

ROYAL ELEGANCE - Floor coverings–carpet and rugs ☆ - Lees Carpets

ROYAL ELEGANCE - Towels - Fieldcrest Cannon, Inc.

ROYAL ELEGANCE - Wallpaper ☆ - S.R. Wood Inc.

ROYAL ELITE - Hitches–trailer - Superior Industries International, Inc.

ROYAL EMBROIDERED LACE - Lace - Bischoff Embroidered Lace

ROYAL EMPRESS - Coats–fur - Ronlee Apparel Co.

ROYAL ENDORPHINS 600 - Pharmaceutical preparations - Young Shin Health Corp.

ROYAL ENERGETIC - Mattresses - Royal-Pedic Mattress Manufacturing & Bedding Co.

ROYAL ENFIELD - Exercising equipment - G. Joannou Cycle Co., Inc.

ROYAL ENGLISH - Silver products - Wallace International Silversmiths, Inc.

ROYAL ESSENCE - Skin care products - Advanced Products, Inc.

ROYAL ESSEX - Bicycles - Columbia Manufacturing Inc.

ROYAL ESTATE - Floor coverings–carpet and rugs ☆ - World Carpets, Inc.

ROYAL EXCELLENCY - Floor coverings–carpet and rugs ☆ - Lees Carpets

ROYAL EXPLORERS CORPS - Apparel and accessories - Breier of Amsterdam Inc.

ROYAL FAMILY - Bedding–linen - Fieldcrest Cannon, Inc.

ROYAL FANTASY - Dolls - Brass Key, Inc.

ROYAL FANTASY - Floor coverings–carpet and rugs ☆ - World Carpets, Inc.

ROYAL FASHION - Draperies - Robertson Factories Inc.

ROYAL FASHION - Watches - Elgin Watch Co.

ROYAL FAVOR - Floor coverings–carpet and rugs - Alexander Smith Carpets

ROYAL FEEDS - Animal feeds - Leach Grain & Milling Co., Inc.

ROYAL FELT - Paper ☆ - Wausau Paper Mills Co.

ROYAL FIBER - Paper - Wausau Paper Mills Co.

ROYAL FINISH - Paints ☆ - Valspar Corp.

ROYAL FLANNEL - Apparel–men's - Tropical Garment Manufacturing Co.

☆ = Now out of production

ROYAL FLORAL DISTRIBUTORS, INC. - Florists - Royal Floral Distributors, Inc.

ROYAL FLUSH - Candy - Bohemian Biscuit Co.

ROYAL FLUSH - Cleaning preparations–household - Blue Cross Laboratories Inc.

ROYAL FLUSH - Floor coverings–carpet and rugs - Galaxy Carpet Mills Inc.

ROYAL FLUSH - Food products - SPADA enterprise, ltd.

ROYAL FLUSH - Games - Crisloid Inc.

ROYAL FLUSH FEVER - Games - Autotote Systems, Inc.

ROYAL FLUSHER - Bathroom accessories - G.T. Water Products Inc.

ROYAL FLYER - Bicycles - Columbia Manufacturing Inc.

ROYAL FOAM - Foam rubber - Ocean Foam Inc.

ROYAL FORCE - Vitamins and nutritional supplements - Montana Naturals Int'l. Inc.

ROYAL FOUNTAIN - Trees - J. Frank Schmidt & Son Co.

ROYAL FOX - Lotions - Majestic Drug Co., Inc.

ROYAL FRIEZE - Floor coverings–carpet and rugs - Couristan Inc.

ROYAL FUDGE 'N' CAKE - Food products - American Dairy Queen Corp.

ROYAL GALA BITS - Candy ☆ - F.B. Washburn Candy Corp.

ROYAL GALA BUDS - Candy ☆ - F.B. Washburn Candy Corp.

ROYAL GALLERY - Floor coverings - Congoleum Corp.

ROYAL GALLERY - Frames–picture - Acme Frame Products, Inc.

ROYAL GALLERY - Furniture - American Furniture Co. Inc.

ROYAL GALLERY OF FRAMES - Frames–picture - Acme Frame Products, Inc.

ROYAL-GARD - Building materials - Royston Laboratories, Inc.

ROYAL-GARD - Paints - Graham Paint and Varnish Co.

ROYAL GARDEN - Dinnerware ☆ - Corning Inc.

ROYAL GARDEN - Dinnerware–glass - Royal China & Porcelain Companies Inc.

ROYAL GARDEN - Floor coverings - Congoleum Corp.

ROYAL GARDENS - Clocks - General Time Corp. (Westclox/Seth Thomas Div.)

ROYAL GARDENS - Coffee - Thanksgiving Coffee Co.

ROYAL GARDENS - Wallpaper - Lin-Gor Wallcoverings

ROYAL GARNET - Food products - Norpac Services, Inc.

ROYAL GATE - Vodka - Haas Bros.

ROYAL GEM - Food products - Morgan Foods Inc.

ROYAL GEMS - Watches - Gruen Marketing Corp.

ROYAL GEMS ROLLS - Candy ☆ - Spangler Candy Co.

ROYAL GENT - Umbrellas - AAA Umbrella Co.

ROYAL GENTLEMAN - Beverages–alcohol - Mccormick Distilling Co., Inc.

ROYAL GENTLEMAN - Beverages–alcohol - James A. Robertson Co.

ROYAL GEORGE - Tableware–china - Blue Delft Co. Inc.

ROYAL GIFT - Chocolate candy - Hooper's Chocolates

ROYAL GLEN - Meat products–beef - Prairieland Producers Cooperative

ROYAL GLEN PLAID - Floor coverings–carpet and rugs ☆ - Mohawk Carpet Corp.

ROYAL GLOBE - Fruits and vegetables - Marglo Products Corp.

ROYAL GOLD - Film - Johnson & Johnson

ROYAL GOLD - Fruits and vegetables - Standex International Corp.

ROYAL GOLD - Hair care products ☆ - Willat Co.

ROYAL GOLD - Hams - CKF Foods, Inc.

ROYAL GOLD - Tableware–china ☆ - Villeroy and Boch Tableware Ltd.

ROYAL GOODWAAGEN - Pottery - Blue Delft Co. Inc.

ROYAL GORDEWAAGEN - Giftware - Eastern Shore Trading Co.

ROYAL GRACE - Floor coverings–carpet and rugs ☆ - Lees Carpets

ROYAL GRAHAM - Cookies - Mother's Cake & Cookie Co.

ROYAL GRAIN - Luggage ☆ - Alfred Dunhill of London Inc.

ROYAL GRANDEUR - Giftware ☆ - Gorham Inc.

ROYAL GRANITE - Floor coverings - Toli International

ROYAL GUARD - Automotive parts and accessories - Lancaster Colony Automotive Group

ROYAL GUARD - Bicycles - Columbia Manufacturing Inc.

ROYAL HAEGER - Giftware - Haeger Potteries

ROYAL HAMADAN - Floor coverings–carpet and rugs - Rugby Rugs Inc.

ROYAL HAMPTON BRAND - Meat products - Gerald Koscinski

ROYAL HARVEST FOODS - Frankfurters - Suffield Poultry, Inc.

ROYAL HAWAIIAN - Christmas tree ornaments - Cracker Box Inc.

ROYAL HAWAIIAN - Confections - Hawaiian Plantations Inc.

ROYAL HEART - Jewelry - Jacoby-Bender Inc.

ROYAL HEATHERS - Floor coverings–carpet and rugs ☆ - Criterion Mills Inc.

ROYAL HERBAL - Pet products - Pet Connection

ROYAL HERBAL WORDS - Pet products - Pet Connection

ROYAL HERITAGE - Bedding–linen - Poly-Commodity Corp.

ROYAL HERITAGE - Boats–pontoons - Harris-Kayot Inc.

ROYAL HI-CLAD - Tools - Lufkin Rule Co.

ROYAL HIGHNESS - Brassieres (Bras) ☆ - Marja Foundations

ROYAL HOLIDAY - Trailers–travel ☆ - Holiday Rambler Corp.

ROYAL HOLLAND - Giftware ☆ - Eastern Shore Trading Co.

ROYAL HOLLAND - Twine - Universal Cooperative Inc.

ROYAL HOLLY - Dishes–china - Royal China Co.

ROYAL HONG KONG - Dishes–china - Waterford Wedgewood USA, Inc.

ROYAL HONORS - Floor coverings–carpet and rugs - Roxbury Carpet Co.

ROYAL HOOD - Apparel and accessories - Abe Maya

ROYAL HORTICULTURAL SOCIETY PRINTS - Posters - One-of-a-Kind Workshop

ROYAL HOST - Ice cream - Certified Grocers of California, Ltd.

ROYAL HOST - Wines - Oak Ridge Vineyards

ROYAL HOUSE - Candles - United Trade Consultants, Ltd.

ROYAL HOUSE - Food products - Royal House Food Products Co.

ROYAL HOUSE - Ice cream - Allied Marketing, Inc.

ROYAL HOUSE - Teas - Modern Tea Packers

ROYAL HUNT - Luggage - York Luggage Co.

ROYAL HUNTSMAN - Beverages–alcohol - James A. Robertson Co.

ROYAL HUSSAR - Beverages–alcohol - James A. Robertson Co.

ROYAL I - Trailers–travel - Franklin Coach Co.

ROYAL II - Plumbing fixtures–metal ☆ - Sloan Valve Co.

ROYAL IMPERIAL - Dishes–china - Gorham Inc.

ROYAL IMPERIAL - Floor coverings - American Floor Products Co. Inc.

ROYAL IMPRINTS - Giftware - Royal Imprints Corp.

ROYAL INN - See **CLARION**

ROYAL INTERNATIONAL - Trailers–travel - Carriage, Inc.

ROYAL INVITATION - Dolls - Mattel, Inc.

ROYAL INVITATION - Wallpaper - Mirage Wallcovering Co.

ROYAL ISABELLA - Cosmetics - Sonis Advertising & Public Relations Inc.

ROYAL ISLANDER - Beverages–alcohol - Consolidated Distilled Products Inc.

ROYAL ISLANDER - Paints - Smiland Paint Co.

ROYAL ISLANDS - Beverages–carbonated ☆ - Dr. Pepper/Seven Up, Inc.

ROYAL JAMAICA - Cigar boxes–wood - Consolidated Cigar Corp.

ROYAL JASMINE - Teas ☆ - R.C. Bigelow, Inc.

ROYAL JELLY - Health care products - Above All Health Inc.

ROYAL JELLY ELIXA - Pharmaceutical preparations - Vita Elixir Co. Inc.

ROYAL JEWEL - Food products - Jewel Food Stores Inc.

ROYAL JEWEL - Window shades - C-Mor Co.

ROYAL JEWELS - Jewelry - Royal Silk Products, Inc.

ROYAL JUBILEE - Pottery ☆ - Blue Delft Co. Inc.

ROYAL K-70 - Roofing materials - NCI Building Systems, Inc.

ROYAL K-SHEEN PETS - Toys–stuffed - Kamar International Inc.

ROYAL KAHALA - Floor coverings–carpet and rugs ☆ - Customweave Carpets Inc.

ROYAL KALABAR - Floor coverings–carpet and rugs - Rugby Rugs Inc.

ROYAL KASHMIR - Floor coverings ☆ - Teak International

ROYAL KELLY - Tableware–china - Lenox, Inc.

ROYAL KERRY - Biscuits - Atalanta Corp.

ROYAL KING - Teas–herbal - Herba Natural Products, Inc.

ROYAL KING RECORDS - Music–sheet - Royal King Records

ROYAL KINGSDOWN - Mattresses - Kingsdown, Inc.

ROYAL KONA - Food products - Sara Lee Corp.

ROYAL LA GAR - Vitamins and nutritional supplements - Wellness World, Inc.

ROYAL LABORATORIES - Skin care products - Royal Laboratories Cosmetics

ROYAL LADY - Umbrellas - AAA Umbrella Co.

ROYAL LADY SIGNET - Golfing equipment - Kenneth Smith Inc.

ROYAL LAID - Paper–writing - Wausau Paper Mills Co.

ROYAL LAID TEXT - Paper–bond ☆ - Wausau Paper Mills Co.

ROYAL LANCER - Watches - Bulova Corp.

ROYAL LAPIS - Dishes–china - Waterford Wedgewood USA, Inc.

ROYAL LEERDAM - Giftware - Eastern Shore Trading Co.

ROYAL LEERDAM - Glassware–household ☆ - National Housewares

ROYAL LEGACY - Swimming pools - Lomart Industries

ROYAL LEGEND - Floor coverings–carpet and rugs - Lees Carpets

ROYAL LEGWEAR - Socks - Specialty Retailers, Inc.

ROYAL LEPRECHAUN - Motor vehicles–motor homes - Coachmen Industries, Inc.

ROYAL LILY - Flatware - Gorham Inc.

ROYAL LILY - Toilets–enameled - Kohler Co.

ROYAL LIMITED - Dinnerware - May Department Stores Co.

ROYAL LIMOGE - Wallpaper - Capital Carousel Inc.

ROYAL LIMOGES - Wallpaper - Richard E. Thibaut, Inc.

ROYAL LINE, THE - Lanterns–electric ☆ - Regent Lighting Corp. (Consumer Products Div.)

ROYAL LINEN - Paper - Wausau Paper Mills Co.

ROYAL LINK - Motor vehicles - Superior Industries International, Inc.

ROYAL LION - Bicycles - Columbia Manufacturing Inc.

ROYAL LIQUISOAP - Beauty aids - Benjamin Ansehl Co.

ROYAL LITE - Polishing rouge - Steel Bright Products Co.

ROYAL LITE ROYAL SHIELD - Lighting equipment - Royal Lite Manufacturing and Supply Corp.

ROYAL LOCK - Architectural panels - American Building Components Co.

ROYAL LONDON - Bicycles - Columbia Manufacturing Inc.

ROYAL LOUNGERS - Robes - Royal Robes Inc.

ROYAL LUNCH - Crackers - Nabisco Foods Group

ROYAL LUSTRE - Paints - Royal Lustre Brands

ROYAL LUSTRE - Thread - Threads USA Div.

ROYAL LUSTRE PREMIUM - Adhesives and sealants - Royal Lustre Brands

ROYAL LUXURY - Floor coverings–carpet and rugs - Alexander Smith Carpets

ROYAL LUXURY - Floor coverings–carpet and rugs ☆ - Aldon Industries Inc.

ROYAL MAGIC - Games - Fun, Inc.

ROYAL MAID - Cleaning preparations–household - Royal Maid Association for the Blind Inc.

ROYAL MAID - Dairy products - H.E. Butt Grocery Co.

ROYAL MAID - Footwear–women's ☆ - U.S. Water

ROYAL MAJESTIC - Whiskey - Majestic Distilling Co.

ROYAL MAJESTY - Floor coverings–carpet and rugs ☆ - Karastan-Bigelow Inc.

ROYAL MANDARIN CHOCOLATE - Coffee ☆ - Boyd Coffee Co.

ROYAL MANOR - Bathroom accessories - Popular Club Plan, Inc.

ROYAL MANOR - Floor coverings–carpet and rugs - Gulistan Carpet Inc.

ROYAL MANOR - Floor coverings–carpet and rugs ☆ - Downs Carpet Co. Inc.

ROYAL MANOR - Furniture ☆ - Athens Furniture Industries Inc.

ROYAL MARBLE - Paper–writing - Wausau Paper Mills Co.

ROYAL MARINE - Plywood - Georgia-Pacific Corp.

ROYAL MARK - Bicycles - Bicycle Import Group Inc.

ROYAL MARK - Rubber–molded - M & R Marking Systems, Inc.

ROYAL MARQUIS - Luggage - United States Luggage Corp.

ROYAL MASTER - Pencils - Elgin School Supply Co. Inc.

ROYAL MAX PREMIUM DIESEL - Fuel systems–motor vehicle - Kerr-McGee Chemical Corp.

ROYAL MAXFLI - Balls–golf - Dunlop Maxfli Sports Corp.

ROYAL MEDJOOL - Dates - Royal Medjool Date Gardens

ROYAL MESH - Jewelry - Jacoby-Bender Inc.

ROYAL METALLIC - Paints - DecoArt, Inc.

ROYAL METALLICS - Paints ☆ - DecoArt, Inc.

ROYAL MH-30 - Plant growth regulators - Uniroyal Chemical Co. Inc. (Crop Protection Div.)

ROYAL MILLS - Spices and extracts ☆ - Clawson Co.

ROYAL MISS - Footwear - ISC International Inc.

ROYAL MISTIC - Beverages - Joseph Victori Wines Inc.

ROYAL MOGHREB - Wines - Victoire Imports Co.

ROYAL MONARCH - Floor coverings–carpet and rugs ☆ - Karastan-Bigelow Inc.

ROYAL MONARCH ACCENTS - Floor coverings–carpet and rugs ☆ - Karastan-Bigelow Inc.

ROYAL MOULINE - Thread - Coats and Clark Inc.

ROYAL MUSIC - Recording label - Refuge Music Group

ROYAL MYSTIQUE MIRACLE BEAUTY SOAP - Soap - M & G Trading Co.

ROYAL NATURE - Toiletries, hair-care products - Benjamin Ansehl Co.

ROYAL NETHERLAND - Tableware–china ☆ - Blue Delft Co. Inc.

ROYAL NURSERY, THE - Posters ☆ - One-of-a-Kind Workshop

ROYAL OAK - Charcoal - Royal Oak Enterprises, Inc.

ROYAL OAK - Cutlery ☆ - National Housewares

ROYAL OAK - Flatware ☆ - Anacapa Corp.

ROYAL OAK - Furniture ☆ - Virginia House Furniture Corp.

ROYAL OAK - Handles–wood ☆ - Turner, Day and Woolworth Handle Corp.

ROYAL OAK - House furnishings ☆ - Lea Industries Inc.

ROYAL OAK - Rum - Angostura

ROYAL OAK - Shelving units–wood ☆ - Kirsch Co.

ROYAL OAK - Tables - Impact Furniture

ROYAL OAK PALE ALE - Beverages–malt - Phoenix Imports Ltd.

ROYAL OAK PLUS - Charcoal - Royal Oak Enterprises, Inc.

ROYAL OAK XL100 - Shutters–wood ☆ - Mid-America Building Products Corp.

ROYAL OAKS - Flags - Dettra Flag Co. Inc.

ROYAL OAKS - Furniture - Singer Furniture Co.

ROYAL OAKS - Mobile homes - Kit Manufacturing Co.

ROYAL-ON-TOPS - Candy - Raymond Foods Inc.

ROYAL ONYX - Tableware–china ☆ - Pfaltzgraff Investment Co.

ROYAL OPERTO - Wines - Admiral Wine Merchants

ROYAL OPORTO - Beverages–alcohol ☆ - Nor-Glo Import Co.

ROYAL OPTICAL - Sunglasses - Capo, Inc.

ROYAL ORCHID - Giftware ☆ - Albert E. Price, Inc.

ROYAL OSTRICH - Meat products - Lindwood Farm, Inc.

ROYAL OSTRICH FARM - Meat products - Lindwood Farm, Inc.

ROYAL OVEN - Food products ☆ - The Froz Fruit Co.

ROYAL PACIFIC - Wallpaper - Quality House Inc.

ROYAL PAISLEY - Beverages–alcohol - Joseph E. Seagram & Sons, Inc.

ROYAL PALACE - Wallcoverings - Stretchwall Fabrics Co.

ROYAL PALM - Apparel–men's - Tropical Garment Manufacturing Co.

ROYAL PALM - Manufactured homes ☆ - Redman Industries, Inc.

ROYAL PALM BEACH - Apparel and accessories - Palm Beach Co., Inc.

ROYAL PALMS - Cigars - Faber, Coe & Gregg Inc.

ROYAL PANTRY - Bakery products - Van Den Bergh Foods Co.

ROYAL PARIS - Needles–sewing - Coats and Clark Inc.

ROYAL PARIS - Needlework supplies ☆ - Susan Bates Inc.

ROYAL PARK - Furniture–wood ☆ - Flanders Industries Inc.

ROYAL PARLIAMENT - Clocks ☆ - General Time Corp. (Westclox/Seth Thomas Div.)

ROYAL PASTRY - Desserts - Nabisco Foods Group

ROYAL PASTRY - Flour - Interstate Milling Co.

ROYAL PATENT - Flour–blended ☆ - ConAgra Grain Co.

ROYAL PATRICIAN - Dishes–china - Herman Dodge & Son Inc.

ROYAL PAVILLION - Floor coverings - Mannington Resilient Floors

ROYAL PAVILLION - Furniture - Hammary Furniture Co. Inc.

ROYAL PENNY - Pet products - Rich Health

ROYAL PEONY - Tableware–china ☆ - Lenox, Inc.

ROYAL PERSIAN - Floor coverings–carpet and rugs - Rugby Rugs Inc.

ROYAL PETITE - Apparel–women's - Specialty Retailers, Inc.

ROYAL PICCADILLY - Biscuits ☆ - Commerce Foods Inc.

ROYAL PINE - Cleaning preparations–household - Stanson Corp.

ROYAL PINE - Shelves, magazine racks, curios, etc ☆ - Cornwall Industries Inc.

ROYAL PLANTATION - Coffee - Compass Foods Inc.

ROYAL PLUSH - Floor coverings–carpet and rugs - Alexander Smith Carpets

ROYAL POET - Cigars - A.J. Golden Inc.

ROYAL POINT - Floor coverings–carpet and rugs - Catalina Carpet Mills Inc.

ROYAL POLO SPORTS CLUB - Sport clothing - Sun Queen, Inc.

ROYAL POLY POMPOM - Sporting goods - Valley Decorating Co.

ROYAL POWER MID - Sporting goods ☆ - Gold Eagle/Arnold Palmer

ROYAL PRESTIGE - Kitchen utensils–aluminum - Hy Cite Corp.

ROYAL PRIDE - Floor coverings–carpet and rugs - Lees Carpets

ROYAL PRINCE - Bicycles - Roadmaster Corp.

ROYAL PRINCE - Food products - Joan of Arc Co.

ROYAL PRINCE, THE - Vacuum cleaners and accessories - Royal Appliance Manufacturing Co.

ROYAL PRINCESS - Apparel stores–lingerie - Goddess Bra

ROYAL PRINCESS - Chocolate candy - H & H International Co. USA

ROYAL PRINCESS - Floor coverings–carpet and rugs ☆ - Karastan-Bigelow Inc.

ROYAL PRO - Curling irons–electric - Windmere Corp.

ROYAL PRODUCTS INC. - Vitamins and nutritional supplements - John A Shannon

ROYAL PURPLE - Food products - C.M. Holtzinger Fruit Co. Inc.

ROYAL PURPLE - Lipsticks ☆ - Honey & Spice Toiletries

ROYAL PURPLE - Lubricants - Royal Purple Inc.

ROYAL PURSUIT - Games - Smethport Specialty Co.

ROYAL QUALITY - Tablecloths - Royal Paper Products Inc.

ROYAL QUALITY FOODS - Beef - Royal Quality Foods, Inc.

ROYAL RAJ - Wallpaper - Kirk-Brummel

ROYAL RECIPE - Confections - Crown Candy Corp.

ROYAL RECIPE - Salsa - Regal Crown Corp.

ROYAL RECORDS - Recording label - Royal King Records

ROYAL RED - Food products - Speaco Foods Inc.

ROYAL REMOVER - Contact lenses - Amcon Laboratories, Inc.

ROYAL RICHES - Games - IGT - North America

ROYAL RIO - Vegetables–canned - Knapp-Sherrill Co.

ROYAL ROAD - Floor coverings–carpet and rugs ☆ - Evans-Black Carpet Mills

ROYAL ROAD - Rings–jewelry - Artcarved Inc.

ROYAL ROBBINS - Apparel and accessories - Royal Robbins

ROYAL ROBE, A - Robes - Royal Robes Inc.

ROYAL-ROLL - Wheels - Faultless Caster Co.

ROYAL ROMANCE - Dolls - Mattel, Inc.

☆ = Now out of production

ROYAL ROMANCE - Floor coverings–carpet and rugs - Evans-Black Carpet Mills

ROYAL ROOST - Wallpaper - Royaleigh Designs Ltd.

ROYAL ROPE - Motor vehicle parts and accessories - Superior Industries International, Inc.

ROYAL ROSE - Flatware - Wallace International Silversmiths, Inc.

ROYAL ROSE - Fruits and vegetables - European Vegetable Specialties Farms Inc.

ROYAL ROSE - Stoves–gas - Royal Rose Inc.

ROYAL ROUGE - Dinnerware–glass ✰ - WMF/USA

ROYAL RS STATIONERY - Paper–writing - Taylor Corp.

ROYAL RUBY - Cosmetics - Lancome

ROYAL RUBY - Glassware–household ✰ - Anchor Hocking Glass, Inc.

ROYAL RUBY REDS - Fruits and vegetables - Standex International Corp.

ROYAL RULES - Computer software ✰ - Sunburst Communications, Inc.

ROYAL RUMBLE - Novelty items - Titan Sports, Inc.

ROYAL RUSSETT - Fruits and vegetables ✰ - Western Idaho Potato Processing Co.

ROYAL SABRE - Bicycles - Columbia Manufacturing Inc.

ROYAL SAHARA - Handbags - Samsonite Corp.

ROYAL SALUTE - Floor coverings–carpet and rugs - Barrett Carpet Mills Inc.

ROYAL SALUTE - Liquors - House of Seagram

ROYAL SATIN - Flatware - Wallace International Silversmiths, Inc.

ROYAL SATIN - Pet shops - Dermo Inc.

ROYAL SATIN - Shortening ✰ - Safeway Stores Inc.

ROYAL SAXONY - Floor coverings–carpet and rugs - Couristan Inc.

ROYAL SCARLET - Salad oils - Supreme Oil Co.

ROYAL SCHOONHOVEN - Tableware–earthenware - Blue Delft Co. Inc.

ROYAL SCOT - Bicycles ✰ - Corso Bicycle Distributor Inc.

ROYAL SCOT - Margarine - Miami Margarine Co. Inc.

ROYAL SCOT - Oils–lubricating - MacMillan Ring-Free Oil Co. Inc.

ROYAL SCOT - Projection screens - Brumberger Co. Inc.

ROYAL SCOT - Tobacco–chewing or smoking - G.A. Georgopulo & Co. Inc.

ROYAL SCOTLAND - Cookies - International Multi-Products, Ltd.

ROYAL SEAL - Tires - Uniroyal Goodrich Tire Co.

ROYAL SEAL - Tools–hand-operated - Royal Merchandise Co.

ROYAL SEAL - Wines ✰ - Batavia Wine Cellars Inc.

ROYAL SEASHELL - Jewelry - Jacoby-Bender Inc.

ROYAL SECRET - Perfumes - Monteil Paris

ROYAL SELECT - Coffee - Alliant Foodservice, Inc.

ROYAL SELECT - Fruits–canned - Lakeside Packing Co.

ROYAL SETH - Clocks - General Time Corp. (Westclox/Seth Thomas Div.)

ROYAL SHAH - Floor coverings–carpet and rugs - Roxbury Carpet Co.

ROYAL SHAVE - Hair care products ✰ - J. Strickland & Co.

ROYAL SHEEN - Cleaning preparations - S & S Car Care, Inc.

ROYAL SHELL - Cutlery ✰ - Lifetime Hoan Corp.

ROYAL SHELL - Flatware - Wallace International Silversmiths, Inc.

ROYAL SHIELD - Gloves–rubber - Semantodontics, Inc.

ROYAL SHIELD - Hair care products ✰ - J. Strickland & Co.

ROYAL SHIELD - Shoes ✰ - Endicott Johnson Corp.

ROYAL SIGNET - Golfing equipment - Kenneth Smith Inc.

ROYAL SILK - Fabrics–tapestry - Coloroll Inc.

ROYAL SILK - Paper - Wausau Paper Mills Co.

ROYAL SILK - Perfumes ✰ - Royal Silk Ltd.

ROYAL SILK - Pet products - Virbac, Inc.

ROYAL SILK - Skin care products ✰ - Beehive Botanicals Inc.

ROYAL SILK CLASSICS - Fabrics–tapestry - Coloroll Inc.

ROYAL SILK IV - Fabrics–tapestry - Coloroll Inc.

ROYAL SILK VIGNETTES - Fabrics–tapestry ✰ - Coloroll Inc.

ROYAL SILVER - Men's toiletries ✰ - London International U.S. Holdings

ROYAL SILVER - Pharmaceutical preparations - David Wastchak

ROYAL SKITTLES - Games ✰ - Carrom Co.

ROYAL SMOOTHTEX - Toothpicks - Royal Paper Products Inc.

ROYAL SNACK - Food products ✰ - Vita Food Products, Inc.

ROYAL SNAKE - Jewelry - Jacoby-Bender Inc.

ROYAL SOCIETY - Fabrics - Dan River Inc.

ROYAL SOVEREIGN - Beverages–alcohol - James A. Robertson Co.

ROYAL SOVEREIGN - Floor coverings–carpet and rugs ✰ - Karastan-Bigelow Inc.

ROYAL SOVEREIGN - Shingles–shakes - GAF Corp.

ROYAL SPLENDOR - Christmas tree ornaments - Cracker Box Inc.

ROYAL SPLENDOR - Cosmetics ✰ - Shiseido Cosmetics (America) Ltd.

ROYAL SPLENDOR - Dolls - Mattel, Inc.

ROYAL SPORT - Apparel–women's - Specialty Retailers, Inc.

ROYAL SPORT - Gasoline - Superior Industries International, Inc.

ROYAL SPORT - Skin-care products - Jean Philippe Fragrances, Inc.

ROYAL STAFFORD - Clocks ✰ - General Time Corp. (Westclox/Seth Thomas Div.)

ROYAL STANDARD - Bicycles - Columbia Manufacturing Inc.

ROYAL STAR - Clocks ✰ - General Time Corp. (Westclox/Seth Thomas Div.)

ROYAL STAR - Giftware - North American Foreign Trading Corp.

ROYAL STAR - Rings–jewelry - Artcarved Inc.

ROYAL STATIONERY - Stationery - Taylor Corp.

ROYAL STERLING - Cleaning preparations - Herbert Stanley Co.

ROYAL STERLING - Floor coverings–carpet and rugs ✰ - Lees Carpets

ROYAL STOCK - Toys - Tonka Corp.

ROYAL STOCK XO - Brandy - Disusa Imports Co.

ROYAL STONEGLOW - Floor coverings ✰ - Tarkett, Inc.

ROYAL STRATFORD - Novelty items - Chase Collection, Inc.

ROYAL STREAM - Sporting goods ✰ - Rod Caddy Industries

ROYAL STUART - Wallpaper - Seabrook Wallcoverings, Inc.

ROYAL-SUEDE - Fabrics - Dicey Fabrics, Inc.

ROYAL SUEDE - Floor coverings–carpet and rugs - Couristan Inc.

ROYAL SUITE - Floor coverings–carpet and rugs ✰ - Zenith Carpets

ROYAL SUITE - Wallpaper - Royaleigh Designs Ltd.

ROYAL SULTAN - Floor coverings–carpet and rugs - Rugby Rugs Inc.

ROYAL SUN - Juices - Tropicana Products, Inc.

ROYAL SUPREME - Chocolate candy - Crown Candy Corp.

ROYAL SUPREME - Floor coverings–carpet and rugs ✰ - Lees Carpets

ROYAL SUPREME - Scissors–hand-operated ✰ - National Housewares

ROYAL SWEDEN - Brushes–hair - The Montclair Co.

ROYAL SWEDEN - Caviar - Haram-Christensen Corp.

ROYAL SWIFT WIND - Toys - Mattel, Inc.

ROYAL SYMPHONY - Wallpaper ✰ - Cherry Hill Studio

ROYAL-T - Toys - Tonka Corp.

ROYAL TAFFETA - Floor coverings–carpet and rugs ✰ - Gulistan Carpet Inc.

ROYAL TAPESTRY - Floor coverings–carpet and rugs ✰ - J and J Industries Inc.

ROYAL TAPESTRY - Floor coverings–carpet and rugs ✰ - Karastan-Bigelow Inc.

ROYAL TAPESTRY - Recording label - Diadem Music Group

ROYAL TERRY - Towels - Barth-Dreyfuss of California

ROYAL TERRY OF CALIFORNIA - Towels - Barth-Dreyfuss of California

ROYAL TETTAU - Kitchenware–china - H. Wittur & Co.

ROYAL TEX - Sporting goods ✰ - Gold Eagle/Arnold Palmer

ROYAL TEXT - Paper ✰ - Wausau Paper Mills Co.

ROYAL THREADS - Shirts - Royal Threads

ROYAL THRONE - Dolls - Mattel, Inc.

ROYAL TIGER - Shrimp–fresh or frozen - Suram Trading Corp.

ROYAL TILT - Brooms - Royal Maid Association for the Blind Inc.

ROYAL TOKAJI WINE CO. - Wines - Wilson Daniels Ltd.

ROYAL TONY - Wines ✰ - Delicato Vineyards

ROYAL TOP - Floor coverings–tile ✰ - Halstead International

ROYAL TOUCH - Towels - Fieldcrest Cannon, Inc.

ROYAL TOUR - Luggage - Airway Industries, Inc.

ROYAL TRADITION - Flatware ✰ - Kirk Stieff Co.

ROYAL TRADITION - Floor coverings–carpet and rugs ✰ - Downs Carpet Co. Inc.

ROYAL TRADITIONS FOR THE HOME - Wallpaper - Studio Designs

ROYAL TRAVELER - Trailers–travel ✰ - Coachmen Recreational Vehicle Co.

ROYAL TRAVELLER - Luggage - Samsonite Corp.

ROYAL TREASURE - Floor coverings–carpet and rugs - Lees Carpets

ROYAL TREASURES - Dolls - Adelco International Inc.

ROYAL TREASURES - Herbal products - International Treasure Chest, Inc.

ROYAL TREATMENT - Floor coverings–carpet and rugs - Monticello Carpet Mills

ROYAL TREATMENT - Hair care products - Paula Payne Products Co. Inc.

ROYAL TREATS - Food products - Hilton Commercial Group Inc.

ROYAL TRITON 10-30 - Oils–lubricating ✰ - Unocal Corp.

ROYAL TRIUMPH - Jewelry - Jacoby-Bender Inc.

ROYAL TROPICS - Vitamins and nutritional supplements - Papaya Orchards

ROYAL TWIST - Floor coverings - Durable Corp.

ROYAL VAC - Hair care products - Fromm Industries

ROYAL VALANCE - Window shades - Allied Extrusions

ROYAL VEGA - Flowers, plants, and seeds - Vans, Inc.

ROYAL VELLUM - Stationery ✰ - Pratt & Austin Co.

ROYAL VELOUR - Floor coverings–carpet and rugs - Couristan Inc.

ROYAL VELVET - Floor coverings–carpet and rugs - Calladium & Marglen

ROYAL VELVET - Flowers, plants, and seeds - Conard-Pyle Co.

ROYAL VERMEIL - Jewelry - Diamonique Corp.

ROYAL VET - Pet products - King Pharmaceuticals, Inc.

ROYAL VIENNESE CHOCOLATE - Coffee ✰ - Boyd Coffee Co.

ROYAL VIKING - Cheese - Webeco Foods Inc.
ROYAL VIKING - Floor coverings–carpet and rugs - Galaxy Carpet Mills Inc.
ROYAL VIKING - Tobacco products - Alfred & Christian Petersen U.S. Ltd.
ROYAL VINTAGE - Floor coverings–carpet and rugs - Lees Carpets
ROYAL VINTAGE - Tobacco–chewing or smoking - Amar Blends Co.
ROYAL WARWICK - Giftware ☆ - Treasure Masters
ROYAL WEAR - Apparel and accessories - Specialty Retailers, Inc.
ROYAL WEDDING, A - Computer software - Digital Matrix Corp.
ROYAL WHIP - Whipped topping–frozen - Nabisco Foods Group
ROYAL WILLIAMETTE - Fruits and vegetables - Oregon Cherry Growers, Inc.
ROYAL WIND - Floor coverings–carpet and rugs ☆ - Regal Rugs Inc.
ROYAL WINDSOR - Dinnerware–glass - Royal China & Porcelain Companies Inc.
ROYAL WING - Bird feeds - Agway Country Foods Inc.
ROYAL WOOD - Floor coverings - Congoleum Corp.
ROYAL WOOLYN - Detergents ☆ - Andrew Jergens Co.
ROYAL WORCESTER - Dishes–china - Royal China & Porcelain Companies Inc.
ROYAL WORLD - Floor coverings–carpet and rugs ☆ - World Carpets, Inc.
ROYAL WORLD - Teas - Syrian Bakery Co., Inc.
ROYAL-X - Film - Eastman Kodak Co.
ROYAL XL - Sports rackets and accessories - Victor Sports
ROYAL YACHT BRAID - Rope ☆ - New England Ropes Inc.
ROYAL YACHT MIXTURE - Seat covers - Alfred Dunhill of London Inc.
ROYAL YORK - Bicycles - Columbia Manufacturing Inc.
ROYAL YORK - Coffee - Becharas Coffee Co.
ROYAL ZOO - Stationery - Royal Stationery Co.
ROYALAIRE - Heating equipment - Hart and Cooley Inc.
ROYALAIRE - Jewelry - Farber Corp.
ROYALAX - Floor coverings–carpet and rugs - Couristan Inc.
ROYALCLAD - Wood products ☆ - Masonite Corp.
ROYALCOTE - Wood products ☆ - Masonite Corp.
ROYALCREST - Jewelry - Merit Diamond Corp.
ROYALE - Bicycles ☆ - Kent International Inc.
ROYALE - Cabinets - De Pere Cabinet
ROYALE - Cakes - Godiva Chocolatier
ROYALE - Cookies - Sunshine/Salerno Inc.
ROYALE - Fabrics - Dan River Inc.
ROYALE - Figurines ☆ - Reco International Corp.
ROYALE - Fishing tackle - Fenwick
ROYALE - Floor coverings–carpet and rugs - Patrick Carpet Mills
ROYALE - Folding doors ☆ - American Fold Doors Inc.
ROYALE - Food products - Mexi-Frost Specialties Co.
ROYALE - Fruit drinks–bottled or canned - Prairie Farms Dairy Inc.
ROYALE - Fruits and vegetables ☆ - Sun World International
ROYALE - Furniture - National/Mt. Airy Furniture
ROYALE - Giftware - Pickard Inc.
ROYALE - Glassware–household - Durand International
ROYALE - Manicure preparations - Nailtex Inc.
ROYALE - Motor vehicles–motor homes - Barth Inc.
ROYALE - Paints - Glidden Co.
ROYALE - Paper–writing - School Stationers Corp.
ROYALE - Plumbing fixtures–metal - Speakman Co. (Manufacturing Div.)
ROYALE - Rings–jewelry - Artcarved Inc.
ROYALE - Soybean oil - Catania-Spagna Corp.
ROYALE - Sporting goods - J.A. Cissel Manufacturing Co.
ROYALE - Stoves–wood-burning - Sierra Manufacturing Co. of Virginia
ROYALE - Strollers–baby - Century Products Co.
ROYALE - Toilets–enameled - Kohler Co.
ROYALE - Trailers–travel - Compact Equipment Co.
ROYALE - Trailers–travel ☆ - Fleetwood Enterprises, Inc.
ROYALE - Vans–conversion ☆ - Carriage, Inc.
ROYALE - Wallpaper - Jolie Papier
ROYALE - Yarn ☆ - Joseph Galler Inc.
ROYALE BY LUCIEN PICCARD - Watches - Lucien Piccard/Arnex
ROYALE CORDS - Aprons ☆ - Now Designs
ROYALE CREMES - Ice cream - Bresler's Industries Inc.
ROYALE DAMASK - Wallpaper ☆ - Wallpaper Imports Inc.
ROYALE GERMANIA CRYSTAL - Figurines ☆ - Reco International Corp.
ROYALE GOURMET - Coffee - Compass Foods Inc.
ROYALE GOURMET - Coffee - Great Atlantic & Pacific Tea Co., Inc.
ROYALE INTERNATIONALE - Coffee - Compass Foods Inc.
ROYALE KING BUBBA - Golfing equipment - Special Tee Golf, Inc.
ROYALE LITES - Confections - Bresler's Industries Inc.
ROYALE MADE - Golfing equipment - Special Tee Golf, Inc.
ROYALE MONTAINE - Liqueur - Charles Jacquin et Compagnie Inc.

ROYALE ROYALE - Fabrics - Gretchen Bellinger Inc.
ROYALEAN - Hams - Patrick Cudahy Inc.
ROYALES - Candy - Price Candy Co. Inc.
ROYALESQUE - Floor coverings–carpet and rugs - Cabin Crafts Carpets
ROYALETTE'S - Footwear - Lehigh Safety Shoe Co.
ROYALEX RAIDER - Boats–canoes ☆ - Sawyer Composite Products
ROYALFOLD - Napkins–paper - Wisconsin Tissue Mills Inc.
ROYALGLO - Electronic equipment - Olivetti Office USA, Inc.
ROYALGRIP - Sporting goods ☆ - Georgia's Tennis
ROYALINES - Candy - Alfred D. Co., Inc.
ROYALIST - Cigars ☆ - Phillies Cigar Co.
ROYALIST - Musical instruments ☆ - Armstrong Woodwinds
ROYALIST - Towels - Monarch Towel Co.
ROYALITE - Bicycles - Columbia Manufacturing Inc.
ROYALITE - Jewelry - Tiara Corp.
ROYALITY - Guitars ☆ - Sierra Instrument Co.
ROYALLE - Watches - Helbros International
ROYALLE COLLECTION - Leather goods - Prince Gardner Inc.
ROYALMAID - Mops - Signature Works, Inc.
ROYALMED - Medical apparatus - McKeesson Red Line
ROYALOFT - Pillows - Pacific Coast Feather Co.
ROYALOK - Electrical equipment - Triangle Wire & Cable, Inc.
ROYALPALM - Apparel and accessories - Tropical Sportswear International Corp.
ROYALPRINT - Photographic equipment - Eastman Kodak Co.
ROYALS - Candy - Brach and Brock Confections Inc.
ROYALS - Chocolate candy - Mars, Inc.
ROYALS - Cigars - E. Regensburg & Sons
ROYALS INTERNATIONAL - Trailers–travel - Royals International
ROYALS KAUFFMAN STADIUM - Dinnerware–plastic - Kansas City Royals Baseball Club
ROYALSILK - Flowers–artificial - Pacific Sunshine Enterprises Inc.
ROYALSTOCK - Brandy - Distillerie Stock USA Ltd.
ROYALSTON - Ice cream - Ice Cream Pies, Inc.
ROYALSTONE - Floor coverings–carpet and rugs - Barrett Carpet Mills Inc.
ROYALTE - Manicure preparations - Backscratchers, Inc.
ROYALTEL - Television equipment - Lance Industries
ROYALTILE - Wood products ☆ - Masonite Corp.
ROYALTON - Gloves - Granet Inc.
ROYALTON - Linen - Bibb Co.
ROYALTON - Pipes–tobacco - Dr. Grabow Pre-Smoked Pipes Inc.
ROYALTON SOFTGEL - Vitamins and nutritional supplements - Winning Laboratories Corp.
ROYALTY - See ENCON
ROYALTY - Bedding–linen - Poly-Commodity Corp.
ROYALTY - Cabinets - Kent Moore Cabinets Inc.
ROYALTY - Cabinets - H.J. Scheirich Co.
ROYALTY - Cooking utensils–enameled ☆ - National Housewares
ROYALTY - Floor coverings–carpet and rugs - Trans-Ocean Import Co. Inc.
ROYALTY - Floor coverings–carpet and rugs - Value Carpets Inc.
ROYALTY - Floor coverings–carpet and rugs ☆ - Regal Rugs Inc.
ROYALTY - Food products - United Apple Sales Inc.
ROYALTY - Furniture–upholstered - Imperial of Morristown Inc.
ROYALTY - Games - S.J. Miller Co.
ROYALTY - Hair care products - Brooklyn Mills Inc.
ROYALTY - Mattresses - Sealy Inc.
ROYALTY - Wallcoverings - Ben Rose Ltd.
ROYALTY - Yarn - Dixie Yarns, Inc.
ROYALTY FREE MUSIC - Compact discs–prerecorded - Gary Lamb
ROYALTY HOUSE - Food products - Sunstar Foods Inc.
ROYALTY IN STONE - Stone products - Georgia Marble Co.
ROYALTY VODKA - Vodka ☆ - Carillon Importers Ltd.
ROYALVIEW - Doors–metal ☆ - Better-Bilt Aluminum Products Co.
ROYALWARE - Flatware - Royal Maid Association for the Blind Inc.
ROYALWEAR - Medical apparatus - McKeesson Red Line
ROYALWOOD - Shingles - U.S. Intec, Inc.
ROYALYTE - Lighting fixtures - Hunter Fan Co.
ROYCE - Leather goods - Emporium Leather Co.
ROYCE - Musical instrument accessories - Westheimer Corp.
ROYCE CRAFT - Baskets–wood - Royce Craft Inc.
ROYCE NEW YORK - Hosiery - Grand Union Co.
ROYCE PRO-CUSSION - Musical instrument accessories - Westheimer Corp.
ROYCE-UNION - Sporting goods - Royce-Union Co.
ROYD - Audio equipment - Import Audio
ROYL - Brooms - F.M. Thorpe Manufacturing Co.
ROYL-DERM - Pharmaceutical preparations - Renaissance Pharmaceutical

☆ = Now out of production

ROYLCO - Paper products - Roylco, Inc.
ROYLCO EVERYBODY'S BEAUTIFUL PRODUCTS - Paper products - Roylco, Inc.
ROYLCO KABOODLE - Toys - Roylco, Inc.
ROYLE OF LONDON - Greeting cards - Nu-Art Inc.
ROYLE PUBLICATIONS - Posters - Graphic Arts Unltd. Inc.
ROYMAC - Dinnerware–plastic - Brookpark Plastics Inc.
ROYOX - Cleaning preparations–household ✰ - Royce Chemical Co.
ROY'S ROASTERS - Chicken - Hardee's Food Systems, Inc.
ROYSON'S - Wallpaper - Royson's Corp.
ROYSTON - Sheet metal panels - AWH Corp.
ROZ - Shampoos - Jay Co.
ROZAN - Chocolate candy ✰ - Perrier Group of America Inc.
ROZDALI - Rice - Nile Spice Foods Inc.
ROZES PORTS - Wines - Tyfield Importers
ROZOL - Rodenticides - LiphaTech Inc.
RP - Audio recording products - Recording Products
RP - Electronic equipment ✰ - H. Wilson Co.
RP - Rifles ✰ - Thompson/Center Arms
RP 1.5 - Cosmetics - Reliv' International, Inc.
RP-MYCIN - Pharmaceutical preparations ✰ - Solvay Pharmaceuticals Inc.
RP2100 - Heaters–swimming pool - Raypak Inc.
RPBACCESS - Computer software - Award Software International, Inc.
RPC - Detergents - Rual Products Co.
RPC - Fruits–dried - Ross Packing Co.
R.P.C. - Meat products–poultry - Perdue Farms Inc.
RPC - Rust removers - Castoleum Corp.
RPD 255 - Deodorants–personal - Hill Manufacturing Co. Inc.
RPET2 - Pet products - Durable Ralph, Inc.
RPF - Paper filler - Arcan Inc.
RPG - Vegetables–canned - G & A Produce Sales, Inc.
RPI - Pharmaceutical preparations - Ribozyme Pharmaceuticals Inc.
RPLOT - Computer software - Commsoft
RPM - Apparel–men's - Cluett, Peabody & Co.
RPM - Electrical equipment - PerSeptive Biosystems, Inc.
RPM - Fertilizers - Howard Fertilizer Co., Inc.
RPM - Games ✰ - Milton Bradley Co.
RPM - Hinges - Reell Precision Manufacturing Corp.
R.P.M. - Ophthalmic goods - Foremost Optical Products
RPM - Recording label - Jazz Composer's Orchestra Association Inc.
RPM BEARINGS - Sporting goods - Hyper Corp.
RPM GOLFER - Housewares - RPM Industries, Inc.
RPM GOLFER - Shoe trees - RPM Industries Inc. (Dewitt Plastics Div.)
RPM PLUS - Animal feeds - Moorman Manufacturing Co.
RPM RACERS - Toys - Tonka Corp.
RPM REMOTE PRINT MANAGER - Computer software - Brooks Internet Software, Inc.
RPMS RECYCLED PLASTIC MATERIALS - Benches–plastic - C & M Eagle Inc.
RPS - Photographic equipment - Reeves Photo Sales Inc.
RPS - Video equipment - Draper Shade and Screen Co. Inc.
RPS ACCESS - Computer software - RPS, Inc.
RPS-INTEGRATOR - Computer software - Iowa Computer Resources Inc.
RPS MULTI SHIP - Computer software - RPS, Inc.
RPXPRESS! - Computer software - Culverin Corp.
R.Q. - Vitamins and nutritional supplements - Kroeger Herb Products Co. Inc.
RR - Apparel and accessories - Rampage Clothing Co.
RR - Cleaning preparations - Roebic Laboratories Inc.
RR - Electronic equipment - Poly Products Corp.
RR - Greeting cards - Reproducta Co., Inc.
RR - Jewelry - Rotenier, Ltd.
RR READY RACK - Furniture - Ready Metal Manufacturing Co.
RR ROYAL RECOGNITION, INC. - Awards, plaques and medals - Royal Recognition, Inc.
RR ROYALE REGO - Dishes–china - Rego China/THC Systems
RR ROYCE - Hosiery - Royce Hosiery Mills Inc.
RRC - Rings–jewelry - Robin Ring Corp.
RRI RENT ROLL INC. - Computer software - Rent Roll Inc.
RRIG - Locks–door - Powerbrace Corp.
RRIMGLOS - Chemical preparations ✰ - Nyco Minerals, Inc.
RRL - Apparel and accessories - Polo Ralph Lauren Corp.
RRL RALPH LAUREN EST. 1993 - Apparel and accessories - Polo Ralph Lauren Corp.
RRP - Recording label - Rite Record Productions Inc.
RRR - Electronic equipment - Poly Products Corp.
RRR - Recording label - Jazz Composer's Orchestra Association Inc.

RRROLLING WRRRITER - Pens - Pentel of America, Ltd.
RRRUYCE - Greeting cards ✰ - Great Graphic Originals
RRTI - Air purification systems - Refrigerant Recovery Technologies, Inc.
RRU - Air purification systems - Refrigerant Recovery Technologies, Inc.
RRUFF STUFF - Pet products - Penn-Plax, Inc.
RRW IMPORTS - Glassware–household - Wilson Marketing Concepts
RS - Dinnerware–glass - Rhyne & Son Inc.
RS - Recording label - Jazz Composer's Orchestra Association Inc.
RS - Vacuum cleaners and accessories - The Hoover Co.
RS-1 - Medical equipment - International Rehabilitative Sciences, Inc.
RS 19 - Exercising equipment ✰ - Little River Marine Co.
R.S. & COMPANY - Apparel and accessories - Robert Stock Designs, Inc.
RS R - Motor vehicle parts and accessories - Racing Beat, Inc.
RS1 - Bicycles ✰ - Raleigh USA Bicycle Co.
RS2 - Bicycles ✰ - Raleigh USA Bicycle Co.
RS3 - Bicycles ✰ - Raleigh USA Bicycle Co.
RS3 - Computer peripheral equipment - Oxford Molecular Group
RS4 - Lubricants - National Aerosol Products Co.
RSA - Computer software - R. Scott Associates, Inc.
RSA FAM - Controls–air conditioning systems - RSA
RSACHECK - Computer software - RSA Data Security, Inc.
RSAREF - Computer software - RSA Data Security, Inc.
RSASIGN - Computer software - RSA Data Security, Inc.
RSAT 2000 - Computer software - LCC Inc.
RSB - Boats–motor - RSB Fiberglass Forms Inc.
RSC - Apparel–children's ✰ - Russ Togs Inc.
RSC - Electronic equipment - Radio Systems Corp.
RSC AIR - Cables - Tara Labs, Inc.
RSDL - Radios–citizens' band ✰ - E.F. Johnson Co.
RSI REGULATIONS SYSTEMS, INC. - Computer software - Regulations Systems, Inc.
RSL - Sporting goods - Guterman International Inc.
RSL-200 - Lighting fixtures - Holophane Corp.
RSL-350 - Lighting fixtures - Holophane Corp.
RSL COLLECTION, THE - Apparel–women's - RSL Group
RSN - Fuel systems–aircraft - Stanadyne Automotive Corp.
RSO - Department stores - Recovery Sales Corp.
RSO - Recording label - Polygram Records, Inc.
RSOM - Computer peripheral equipment - Cornerstone Software, Inc.
RSP - Computer peripheral equipment - Mountaingate Data Systems, Inc.
R.S.P. - Fruits and vegetables - J.H. Verbridge & Son Inc.
RSP TECHNOLOGIES - Electrical equipment - Rocktron Corp.
RSR - Computer storage devices - Alliant Techsystems Inc.
RSS - Paper goods - Creative Factory, Inc.
RSS - Telephone apparatus - Remote Switch Systems, Inc.
RSS REMOTE SERVICES SYSTEM - Telephone apparatus - Sparton Corp.
RSSU - Computer software - Computer Aided Systems, Inc.
R.S.T.'S U.S.A. - T-shirts–men's - R.S. Trading Co.
RSU - Apparel and accessories - Ray Strauss Unlimited Inc.
R.S.V. PEN - Novelty items - Agent Andy Inc.
RSVIP - Computer software - Rock Systems, Inc.
RSVP - Cheese - R.S.V.P.
RSVP - Chocolate bars - Hershey Chocolate USA
RSVP - Computer hardware - Gammagraphx, Inc.
R.S.V.P. - Computer software ✰ - Gessler Publishing Co., Inc.
R.S.V.P. - Cream - Tuscan
RSVP - Electronic equipment - B & W Nuclear Technologies, Inc.
R.S.V.P. - Footwear - Trico International Inc.
RSVP - Games ✰ - Milton Bradley Co.
RSVP - Medical apparatus - Marquette Electronics, Inc.
RSVP - Video equipment - MacKenzie Laboratories Inc.
RSVP - Video tapes–blank ✰ - Royal Sound Co. Inc.
RSVP - Wallpaper - Southland Wallcoverings
R.S.V.P. TUSCAN FARMS - Food products - Tuscan
RT - Coffee - Wm. B. Reily & Co. Inc.
RT - Oils–lubricating - Shell Oil Co.
RT - Yarn - Artee Industries, Inc.
RT 510 - Bicycles - Huffy Corp.
RT 516 - Bicycles - Huffy Corp.
RT 520 - Bicycles - Huffy Corp.
RT-2000 - Mattress pads - CH Administration, Inc.
RT/AI - Computer programs - Intellisys, Inc.
RT-BDEXM - Chemical preparations - Restek Corp.
RT-GRAPHICS - Computer software - Farradyne Systems Inc.
RT II - Apparel–women's - Russ Togs Inc.
RT INDUSTRIES - Wire - RT Industries

RT JUNIOR - Tobacco products - Scott Tobacco Co.
RT-OPT - Computer software - Aspen Technology, Inc.
RT STARTER - Deodorizers - Ryter Corp.
RTA - Electronic equipment - Specialix, Inc.
RTA - Optical machinery - Dicon
RTB - Nuts and bolts - NSS Industries
RTBEMCH - Computer software - Wandel & Goltermann Technologies, Inc.
RTC - Chemical preparations - Shipley Co. Inc.
RTC-100 - Computer software - Danka Corp.
RTE.ABOUT - Computer software - Digital Equipment Corp.
RTI - Electronic equipment - RTI Research Technology International
RTK FM - Communications equipment - Accqpoint Communications Corp.
RTLX - X-ray apparatus - Panoramic Corp.
RTMS - Computer hardware - Ace*Comm Corp.
RTO - Vitamins and nutritional supplements - Bob O'Leary Sports Science
RTP - Building materials - Tamko Roofing Products, Inc.
RTP INTERNATIONAL - Recording label - R.T.P. International
RTPM - Computer software - Hilco Technologies, Inc.
RTR - Audio equipment ✰ - RTR Speaker Co.
RTS - Doors–metal - Castlegate Inc.
RTS - Machine parts - Rexnord Corp.
RTS - Rackets–racquetball - Ektelon
RTS-321 - Musical instrument accessories - Efxx Products Co.
RTSIZER - Computer software - Malvern/Insitec, Inc.
R.T.U. - Adhesives and sealants - Brod-Dugan Co./Sherwin Williams Co.
RTUNZIP - Computer software - RT Computer Graphics, Inc.
RTV - Exercising equipment - Marchris, Inc.
RTV - Recording label - Allegiance Records Ltd.
RTV - Trailers - Classic Manufacturing Inc.
RTV BLACK - Silicon products - Fel-Pro Inc.
RTX - Electronic equipment - RTX Corp.
RTZIP - Computer software - RT Computer Graphics, Inc.
RU 2000 - Gasoline - Shell Oil Co.
RU-A-DRON - Pharmaceutical preparations ✰ - Boots Pharmaceuticals Inc.
RU-ANDROSPAN - Pharmaceutical preparations - Boots Pharmaceuticals Inc.
RU-CORT - Pharmaceutical preparations - Boots Pharmaceuticals Inc.
RU-EST - Pharmaceutical preparations - Boots Pharmaceuticals Inc.
RU-HEM - Pharmaceutical preparations ✰ - Boots Pharmaceuticals Inc.
RU-HIST - Pharmaceutical preparations ✰ - Boots Pharmaceuticals Inc.
RU-HY T - Pharmaceutical preparations ✰ - Boots Pharmaceuticals Inc.
RU-K-N - Pharmaceutical preparations ✰ - Boots Pharmaceuticals Inc.
RU-LETS - Pharmaceutical preparations - Rugby Laboratories Inc.
RU-LOR - Pharmaceutical preparations ✰ - Boots Pharmaceuticals Inc.
RU-PHEMMS - Pharmaceutical preparations ✰ - C.O. Truxton Inc.
RU-SPAS - Pharmaceutical preparations ✰ - Boots Pharmaceuticals Inc.
RU-THIOSAL - Pharmaceutical preparations ✰ - Boots Pharmaceuticals Inc.
RU-TUSS - Pharmaceutical preparations - Boots Pharmaceuticals Inc.
RU-TUSS II - Pharmaceutical preparations - Boots Pharmaceuticals Inc.
RU-VERT-M - Pharmaceutical preparations - Solvay Pharmaceuticals Inc.
RUAM - Pharmaceutical preparations - Allen & Associates International, Inc.
RUANA - Knives–hunting - Ruana Knife Works, Inc.
RUB-A-DUB - Markers–felt-tip - Sanford Corp.
RUB A DUB BOOKS - Publisher's imprints - Straight Edge Inc.
RUB-A-DUB DOGGIE - Toys–stuffed - CBS Toys
RUB-A-DUB DOLLY - Toys–stuffed ✰ - CBS Toys
RUB-A-DUB SANTA - Figurines - Telco Creations, Inc.
RUB-A-DUB-TUB - Games ✰ - Tyco Toys
RUB A DUBS - Paper–toweling - Nice-Pak Products, Inc.
RUB-A-ROUNDS - Toys - Fisher-Price, Inc.
RUB AND GO - Analgesics - Aromatique, Inc.
RUB-BERT DUCK - Kites ✰ - Hi-Flier Manufacturing Co.
RUB-BUB - Adhesives and sealants - Ace Rubber Products Inc.
RUB-DOWN - Skin care products - Nutri-West
RUB-HER - Prophylactics - LTC Products, Inc.
RUB-LITE - Office supplies - Alvin and Co. Inc.
RUB 'N BUFF - Paints - American Art Clay Co. Inc.
RUB-N-GLUE - Adhesives and sealants ✰ - Champion International Corp.
RUB 'N PLAY - Games - Colorforms
RUB-NALL - Health care products ✰ - Mackwin Co.
RUB-ONS - Adhesives and sealants - Prestype Inc.
RUB OUT - Cleaning preparations–window - Unger Enterprises Inc.
RUB-OUT - Stain removers - Nala Barry Laboratories
RUB R - Plastisols - Union Ink Co.
RUB-R-COTE - Hardware ✰ - Boatlife Inc.
RUB-R-MOLD - Latex - Deep Flex Plastic Molds Inc.
RUB-R-SHEEN - Paints ✰ - Kelly-Moore Paint Co. Inc.

RUBA-TRON - Floor coverings - American Floor Products Co. Inc.
RUBA-WEEV - Rubber matting ✰ - American Floor Products Co. Inc.
RUBACHEM - Cleaning preparations - Rubacheminc
RUBACORE - Erasers - Dixon Ticonderoga Co.
RUBACORE DUO - Erasers - Dixon Ticonderoga Co.
RUBAIYAT - Watches - Bulova Corp.
RUBAIYAT - Wines - Cakebread Cellars, Inc.
RUBALYNE - Bulletin boards–wood - Adjusta Bulletin Board System Inc.
RUBASHKIN - Meat products - Agriprocessors Inc.
RUBATEX - Sporting goods - B.G. Watersports
RUBAYAT II - Fabrics–broadcloth - Collins & Aikman Corp.
RUBBA - Adhesives and sealants ✰ - Adhesive Products, Inc.
RUBBA-LIFE - Floor coverings–carpet and rugs - Carpet Products Co.
RUBBARIDERS - Toys - Rockler Companies, Inc.
RUBBER ANCHOR - Padding–foam - Jade Industries Inc.
RUBBER BANZ - Eyeglasses ✰ - Style Eyes of California
RUBBER BARON - Pet products - Aaronco Grooming Products
RUBBER BARON - Pet products - Aaronco Pet Products, Inc.
RUBBER BELT - Apparel and accessories - MST Corp.
RUBBER BRUSH - Mats - Superior Manufacturing Group/Notrax Floor Matting
RUBBER-COAT - Paints - California Products Corp.
RUBBER CORE - Fishing tackle - Water Gremlin Co.
RUBBER DUCKY - Audio equipment - Russell Industries Inc.
RUBBER DUFFER STRESS WEDGE - Golfing equipment ✰ - Laid Back Enterprises, Inc.
RUBBER EDGE TRIM - Hardware - Trim-Lok Inc.
RUBBER GRIP - Tools - Fuller Tool Co. Inc.
RUBBER KING - Hoses - Radiator Specialty Co.
RUBBER-LOK - Hardware - Trim-Lok Inc.
RUBBER-LUSTRE - Paints - Miller Paint Co., Inc.
RUBBER-MULE - Hardware ✰ - Deuer Manufacturing Inc.
RUBBER-NECK - Lighting fixtures - Ac-cetera Inc.
RUBBER PARQUETRY - Toys ✰ - Lauri Inc.
RUBBER QUEEN - Housewares - Lancaster Colony Automotive Group
RUBBER RENU - Cleaning preparations - Horizons Marketing Group, Inc.
RUBBER SATIN - Paints - Mautz Paint Co.
RUBBER SCRUBBERS - Automotive parts and accessories ✰ - Turtle Wax, Inc.
RUBBER SCRUBBERS - Sponges - Glit, Inc.
RUBBER-SEAL - Hardware - Trim-Lok Inc.
RUBBER SHARBO - Pens - Zebra Pen Corp.
RUBBER SNUBBER - Hardware ✰ - Deuer Manufacturing Inc.
RUBBER STAMP CENTER - Floor display - All Night Media, Inc.
RUBBER STAMP FACTORY, THE - Stamps–hand - Rubberstampede Partnership
RUBBER STAMP INK - Inks ✰ - Ranger Industries
RUBBER STAMP RANCH - Stamps–hand - Rubber Stamp Ranch
RUBBER TREE - Prophylactics - Global Giggles
RUBBER WRITERS - Writing instruments - Pentech International Inc.
RUBBERCRAFT - Floor coverings ✰ - Azrock Commercial Flooring
RUBBERFLEX - Adhesives and sealants - Republic Powdered Metals, Inc.
RUBBERGARD - Roofing materials–concrete - Bridgestone/Firestone, Inc.
RUBBERHEAD - Erasers ✰ - Faber-Castell Corp.
RUBBERHOG - Tools–machine - L.R. Oliver & Co., Inc.
RUBBERIZE BY CENTURY - Coatings - Century Industries Corp.
RUBBERIZE-IT - Paints - D.I.Y. Products
RUBBERIZER - Chemical preparations - Haz-Mat Response Technologies, Inc.
RUBBERLUX - Foam rubber - A.A.S.R. Inc.
RUBBERMAID - Housewares - Rubbermaid Inc.
RUBBERMAID 2000 - Garden furniture - Rubbermaid-Allibert Inc.
RUBBERNECKS - Condoms - Creative Collections
RUBBERQUEEN - Housewares - Loma/Rubberqueen
RUBBERSEAL - Paints - Smith Paint Products
RUBBERSEAL - Tape–adhesive - L.D. Sterns Corp.
RUBBERSET - Brushes–paint - Rubberset Co.
RUBBING STICK - Burnishing machines - Scratch-Art Co., Inc.
RUBBISH - Apparel and accessories - Nordstrom, Inc.
RUBBIT - Pet products - Beth Byrne
RUBBIT - Veterinary medical equipment - Equipro
RUBBOS - Erasers ✰ - Diener Industries Inc.
RUBE - Toys - Tonka Corp.
RUBELLA-PLUS - Pharmaceutical preparations - Wampole Laboratories Div.
RUBELOGEN - Vaccines ✰ - Parke-Davis
RUBEN M. TEJADA'S SIGNATURE SERIES - Dolls - Sandy Dolls
RUBENS - Artists' materials - M. Grumbacher Inc.
RUBENS ORIGINALS - Pottery - Rubens Originals

✰ = Now out of production

RUBENSTEIN BROS. - Apparel–men's - Rubenstein Bros., Inc.
RUBEROID - Floor coverings ☆ - Tarkett, Inc.
RUBEROID - Roofing materials–clay - GAF Corp.
RUBEROL - Paints ☆ - California Products Corp.
RUBESOL-1000 - Pharmaceutical preparations - Central Pharmaceutical Inc.
RUBETHERM - Analgesics - Claflin Co.
RUBGUM - Erasers - Durasol Drug & Chemical Co.
RUBI - Golfing equipment - Rubi Sports Technology, Inc.
RUBIAFORCE - Health care products ☆ - Bioforce of America Ltd.
RUBICON - Bicycles - Sandpoint Design, Inc.
RUBICON - Candy ☆ - Bortz Chocolate Co.
RUBICON - Lenses–optical - Tasco Sales, Inc.
RUBICON - Wines - Niebaum-Coppola Estate Winery
RUBIDIS ELIXIR - Pharmaceutical preparations - Cincinnati Pharmacal Co.
RUBIE'S - Costumes - Rubie's Costume Co., Inc.
RUBIE'S CLASSIC STORYBOOK CHARACTERS - Costumes - Rubie's Costume Co., Inc.
RUBIES OF BURMA - Christmas tree ornaments - Cracker Box Inc.
RUBIE'S SKULL WARRIORS - Costumes - Rubie's Costume Co., Inc.
RUBIGO - Cosmetics - Rubigo Cosmetics Inc.
RUBIK'S CUBE - Puzzles - CBS Toys
RUBIK'S GAME - Games ☆ - CBS Toys
RUBIK'S MAGIC - Puzzles ☆ - Milton Bradley Co.
RUBIK'S PUZZLES - Puzzles - Oddzon Products, Inc.
RUBIK'S RACE - Games ☆ - CBS Toys
RUBIK'S REVENGE - Games ☆ - CBS Toys
RUBIK'S WORLD - Games ☆ - CBS Toys
RUBINI FRIULI - Beverages–alcohol - Orion Imports Ltd.
RUBINO - Glassware–household ☆ - WMF/USA
RUBINO - Olive oil ☆ - Fred Montesi Super Markets
RUBINSTEIN'S - Salmon–smoked, salted, dried, or pickled - Trident Seafoods Corp.
RUBIO'S - Food products - Rubio's Restaurants Inc.
RUBIS - Nail care products - Cosmair Inc.
RUBKLEEN - Erasers - Faber-Castell Corp.
RUBLE - Gin - M.S. Walker Inc./Seacoast
RUBMAR - Skin care products ☆ - Marlop Pharmaceuticals Inc.
RUB'N'ETCH - Tools - Armour Products
RUBR-MERIC - Roofing materials–slate - Colonial Refining and Chemical Co.
RUBRAMIN - Pharmaceutical preparations - Bristol-Myers Squibb Co.
RUBRAPET - Pharmaceutical preparations - Medco Lab Inc.
RUBRAPLEX - Vitamins and nutritional supplements - Lannett Co. Inc.
RUBRAVITE - Vitamins and nutritional supplements - Lannett Co. Inc.
RUB'RGATE - Handles–rubber - Dare Products Inc.
RUBROBEN-1000 - Pharmaceutical preparations ☆ - Medical Products Panamericana Inc.
RUBSCHLAGER - Breads - Rubschlager Baking Corp.
RUBSTIK - See **STIKKI-WAX**
RUBY - Computer hardware - VLSI Technology, Inc.
RUBY - Dolls ☆ - Effanbee Doll Corp.
RUBY - Floor coverings–carpet and rugs ☆ - Couristan Inc.
RUBY - Flowers, plants, and seeds - Cornell Research Foundation, Inc.
RUBY - Glassware–household - Fenton Art Glass Co.
RUBY - Hair care products - Fromm Industries
RUBY - Office supplies - Faber-Castell Corp.
RUBY - Recording label - Slash Records
RUBY - Toys - Tootsietoy
RUBY - Watches - Elgin Watch Co.
RUBY - Watches - Andre Le Marquand/USA, Inc.
RUBY ANN'S - Cakes and cookies - Parco Foods, Inc.
RUBY BEE - Food products - Beatrice Cos. Inc.
RUBY BEHOLDER - Measuring instruments - Martingale & Co.
RUBY BLUE - Jewelry - J.M.H. Casting Corp.
RUBY CAROUSEL - Frozen foods - Bailey Nurseries, Inc.
RUBY COLLECTION - Candy - Kraft Foods, Inc.
RUBY CONTESSA - Dishes–china ☆ - Gorham Inc.
RUBY CROWN - Glassware–household - Lancaster Colony Corp.
RUBY DOOBIE - Dolls - Mattel, Inc.
RUBY HILL GOLF CLUB - Golfing equipment - Ruby Hill Golf Club LLC
RUBY KIST - Food products - Clement Pappas and Co.
RUBY LTD. - Apparel–men's ☆ - Jaymar-Ruby Inc.
RUBY ON CRYSTAL - Glass products - Westmoreland Glass Co.
RUBY RAISINS - Fruits–dried ☆ - Paradigm Foodworks
RUBY RED - Juices - Ocean Spray Cranberries Inc.
RUBY RED ORANGE JUICE - Beverages - Tropicana Products, Inc.
RUBY RED PASSION - Toys–automobiles - Mattel, Inc.

RUBY RED SQUIRT - Beverages–carbonated - Squirtco
RUBY SEAL - Food products - Paradise Products Corp.
RUBY SLIPPERS - Confections - Famous Pacific Dessert Co.
RUBY STONE - Manicure preparations - ESI Industries Inc.
RUBY-STRENGTH - Incense - Shoyeido Corp.
RUBY SUPERSYSTEM - Computers - Verifone, Inc.
RUBY VIXEN - Wines - Fox Run Vineyards
RUBY WAY - Perfumes - Eurostar Corp.
RUBYFLUID - Adhesives and sealants - Ruby Chemical Co.
RUBYKINS - Greeting cards - Elizabeth A. Gorcey
RUBY'S - Toys - Strombecker Corp.
RUBZ - Erasers - Pentech International Inc.
RUC-DANE - Pharmaceutical preparations ☆ - Boots Pharmaceuticals Inc.
RUC-GESIC - Pharmaceutical preparations ☆ - Boots Pharmaceuticals Inc.
RUCHESSE - Ribbons - Vaban Ribbons International
RUCK-SED - Pharmaceutical preparations ☆ - Boots Pharmaceuticals Inc.
RUCK ZUCK - Bathroom accessories - R-Z Co. of America Inc.
RUCKER - Sport shirts - Canterbury Tales Inc.
RUCK'N BUCK - Hunting equipment - Buck Stop Lure Co., Inc.
RUCRAFTS - Aprons - Ru Crafts
RUDDER PUTTER - Golfing equipment - Ruddr Putter
RUDDERMASTER - Rudders - Raritan Engineering Co. Inc.
RUDDY DUCK - Apparel and accessories - Ruddy Duck Apparel Co. Inc.
RUDE - Cymbals - Paiste America, Inc.
RUDE DOG - Apparel–athletic - Sun Sportswear, Inc.
RUDE DUDES - Chewing gum - World Candies Inc.
RUDI'S - Baked goods - Rudis Bakery
RUDIS - Lubricating oils ☆ - Shell Oil Co.
RUDI'S BAKERY - Bakery products - Lakshmi, Inc.
RUDOLF BUCHNER - Musical instruments - John M. Connolly & Co. Inc.
RUDOLF LESCH FINE ARTS - Posters - Graphic Arts Unltd. Inc.
RUDOLF MEINL - Musical instruments - Custom Music Co.
RUDOLF MULLER - Wines - Palace Brands Co.
RUDOLF STEINER - Publisher's imprints - Garber Communications Inc.
RUDOLFINI - Wines - European Beverage Co., Inc.
RUDOLFO VALENTINO - Footwear–men's - Delta Shoe Group
RUDOLPH - Food products - Beatrice Cos. Inc.
RUDOLPH BUCK BOX - Flowers, plants, and seeds ☆ - Forest Time Products Inc.
RUDOLPH FOODS - Snack foods - Rudolph Foods Co.
RUDOLPH THE RED-NOSED REINDEER - Giftware ☆ - Enesco Corp.
RUDOLPH WURLITZER - Pianos - Wurlitzer Co.
RUDOLPH'S - Cookies ☆ - Haram-Christensen Corp.
RUDOLPH'S BACON SNAPS MICROWAVE PORK RINDS-SNACK FOODS - Pork rinds - Rudolph Foods Co.
RUDS - Apparel and accessories - Ruds, Inc.
RUDY MUCK - Musical instrument accessories - Rudy Muck Musical Instruments
RUDY RABBIT - Confections ☆ - Comet Confectionery Inc.
RUDY T. - Neckties - Rudy T Sales
RUDYBALL - Trading cards and stamps - Rocket Ball, Ltd.
RUDYROO - Recording label - Meritage, Inc.
RUDY'S - Pork rinds - Rudolph Foods Co.
RUDY'S CHEDDAR FRY - Snack foods - Rudolph Foods Co.
RUDY'S FARM - Food products - Rudy's Farm Co.
RUDY'S FARM FINEST QUALITY - Chili–canned - Saramar Corp.
RUDY'S HOT FRY - Snack foods - Rudolph Foods Co.
RUE DE PARC - Apparel–women's - Back in the Black Ltd.
RUE DU REVE - Apparel and accessories - Third Generation Bankers Corp.
RUE ROYALE - Floor coverings–carpet and rugs - Atlas Carpet Mills Inc.
RUE ROYALE - Perfumes - Willem F. Van Calsem, IV
RUE ROYALEG - Footwear ☆ - Margaret Gerald
RUEBAN - Musical instruments - Hyer Percussion Products
RUEDRICH'S RED SEAL ALE - Beverages–malt - North Coast Brewing Co., Inc.
RUEFOOD - Food products - Ruefood, Inc.
RUEVEN - Glassware–household - Nouveau Art Glass Co. Inc.
RUF-KUT - Welding equipment - Alloy Rods Global, Inc.
RUF-N-RED-E - Uniforms–tailored - Red Kap
RUF RIDER - Automotive parts and accessories ☆ - Meguiar's, Inc.
RUF SAWN - Plywood ☆ - Simpson Timber Co.
RUF-TONE - S.M. Frank & Co. Inc. (Kaywoodie-Yello-Bole-Medico)
RUF-X - Siding - Masonite Corp.
RUFCO - Plastics - Raven Industries Inc.
RUFEN - Pharmaceutical preparations - Boots Pharmaceuticals Inc.
RUFF & READY - Pet products - Speedy Pet Tags

RUFF & READY - Toys–electronic - Gay's Pro Rodeo Equipment Co.
RUFF BITES - Pet food - American Health Kennels, Inc.
RUFF-COTE - Paints - Evans Paint
RUFF DEVIL - Golfing equipment - Integra Bank/Pittsburgh
RUFF FIRE - Sporting goods ☆ - Gold Eagle/Arnold Palmer
RUFF GRIP - Metals - BBC Fasteners
RUFF HAUZ - Pet products - Dogloo Inc.
RUFF HAUZ - Pet products - R.C. Steele Co.
RUFF HEWN - Belts–apparel - Gem-Dandy, Inc.
RUFF IN PUFF - Frankfurters wrapped in puff pastry - Cooking Masters
RUFF JEAN - Apparel and accessories - Ruff Hewn, Inc.
RUFF 'N' READY - Mats - U.S. Mat & Rubber Co. Inc.
RUFF N READY - Sporting goods - Chace Leather Products
RUFF 'N REDI - Paper–sand ☆ - Carborundum Abrasives North America
RUFF N' ROLLY - Pet products - Petstuff, Inc.
RUFF N TUFF - Bicycles ☆ - Huffy Corp.
RUFF N TUFF - Fabrics - Dan River Inc.
RUFF-N-TUFF - Machine tools - Fastcut Tool Corp.
RUFF N' TUFF - Mats - Royal Rubber & Manufacturing Co.
RUFF NECKS - Children's shoes - International Seaway Trading Corp.
RUFF-NEX - Screws - Olympic Manufacturing Group, Inc.
RUFF-PAINTER - Paints - Padco Companies, Inc.
RUFF-RIDER - Brushes–paint - H & G Industries
RUFF-RIDER - Golfing equipment - Con-Sole Golf Corp.
RUFF SPUN - Crocheted and knitted items - Garland Knitting Mills
RUFF-STUFF - Adhesives and sealants - Induron Coatings Inc.
RUFF STUFF - Beverages–alcohol - David Briggs Enterprises, Inc.
RUFF STUFF - Pet products - Penn-Plax, Inc.
RUFF-STUFF - Wallpaper ☆ - Walls Alive
RUFF TOYS MIGHTY MARBLE - Pet products - Petco Animal Supplies, Inc.
RUFFDEK - Roofing materials–clay - MacMillan Bloedel Building Materials
RUFFDEK PLUS - Roofing materials–clay - MacMillan Bloedel Building Materials
RUFFELOS - Ice cream ☆ - Thin's Inn Inc.
RUFFERSEAL - Roofing materials–concrete - L.D. Sterns Corp.
RUFFERSEALIT - Roofing materials–concrete - L.D. Sterns Corp.
RUFFHIDES - Shoes ☆ - Endicott Johnson Corp.
RUFFHOUSE - Toys ☆ - Parker Brothers
RUFFIAN - Beverages–malt - Mountain Valley Brewpub, Inc.
RUFFIAN - Bicycles ☆ - Murray, Inc.
RUFFIAN - Floor coverings–carpet and rugs ☆ - Playfield International Inc.
RUFFIAN - Perfumes - Bluegrass Gifts Unlimited, Inc.
RUFFIES - Bags–trash - Carlisle Plastics, Inc.
RUFFIES - Bags–trash - Carlisle Plastics, Inc.
RUFFIES - Candy - McDonald Candy Co. Inc.
RUFFIES COLOR SCENTS - Bags–trash - Carlisle Plastics, Inc.
RUFFIES SURE STRENGTH - Bags–trash - Carlisle Plastics, Inc.
RUFFINO - Wines - Schieffelin and Somerset Co.
RUFFLE BED - Pet products - Flexi-Mat Corp.
RUFFLE BOARD - Paperboard - Wilton Industries, Inc.
RUFFLE EIGHT - Hair care products - Rapparama, Inc.
RUFFLE FUN - Dolls - Mattel, Inc.
RUFFLE PANDA - Toys–stuffed - Russ Berrie and Co., Inc.
RUFFLER - Fishing lures - Fred Arbogast Co. Inc.
RUFFLER - Pet products - Togs for Dogs & Cats
RUFFLER COLLECTION - Apparel and accessories - Rooster Inc.
RUFFLERNIT - Apparel and accessories - Rooster Inc.
RUFFLES - Dolls ☆ - Uneeda Doll Co., Inc.
RUFFLES - Potato chips - Frito-Lay, Inc.
RUFFLES - Yarn ☆ - William Unger & Co. Inc.
RUFFLES & FLOURISHES COLLECTION - Furniture - Pinnacle Furniture Co.
RUFFLES & LACE - Children's clothing patterns - Ruffles & Lace
RUFFLES 'N BOWS - Infant product - Lisco, Inc.
RUFFLES REDUCED FAT - Potato chips - Frito-Lay, Inc.
RUFFLES SILKEN WHISPERS - Skin care products ☆ - Avon Products, Inc.
RUFFLETTE - Draperies ☆ - Drexel House of Draperies
RUFFMEAL - Paper ☆ - J.L. Hammett Co.
RUFFNER'S - Beverages - Ruffner's Inc.
RUFFY - Socks - Leininger Mills Inc.
RUFFY-TUFFY - Fabrics - S.M. Arnold Inc.
RUFIJI - Apparel–children's ☆ - Health-Tex Inc.
RUFOLEX - Pharmaceutical preparations - Lannett Co. Inc.
RUFRIDER - Wood products - Canton Lumber
RUFSTAIN - Paints ☆ - Pratt & Lambert United, Inc.
RUFTUF - Tools - Osborn Manufacturing Corp.
RUFUS - Health care products - ETAC USA Inc.

RUG - Rugbacking - Rug-Hold Co., Inc.
RUG AID - Floor coverings–carpet and rugs - E.R. Carpenter Co.
RUG-AID - Floor coverings–carpet and rugs - Omalon
RUG ANCHOR - Floor coverings–carpet and rugs - Carpet Cushion Corp.
RUG AROMA - Deodorizers - Surco Products Inc.
RUG BOND - Adhesives and sealants ☆ - Continental Brands Inc.
RUG BOSS - Cleaning preparations–carpet and rug - Pullman/Holt Corp.
RUG-BUG KILLER - Insecticides - Four Paws Products Ltd.
RUG-CHEK - Floor coverings–carpet and rugs - No-Muv Corp., Inc.
RUG-CHEK PLUS - Floor coverings–carpet and rugs - No-Muv Corp., Inc.
RUG CLEAN - Cleaning preparations–carpet and rug ☆ - W.J. Hagerty & Sons Ltd. Inc.
RUG CRAFTERS - Floor covering stores - Rug Crafters
RUG DOCTOR EZ-1 MIGHTY PRO - Carpet cleaning equipment - Rug Doctor, L.P.
RUG FRESH - Deodorizers - Airwick Industries
RUG FRESH - Deodorizers - Surco Products Inc.
RUG GRABBER - Floor coverings - Sponge-Cushion Inc.
RUG GRIP - Rugbacking - Cadie Products Corp.
RUG GRIPPER - Floor coverings–carpet and rugs - Carpet Products Co.
RUG GRIPPER - Floor coverings–carpet and rugs - Rugby Rugs Inc.
RUG HUG - Floor coverings–carpet and rugs - Capel, Inc.
RUG HUGGER - Mats - Ludlow Composites Corp.
RUG-HUGGER II - Floor coverings–carpet and rugs - Ludlow Composites Corp.
RUG-IT-'L' - Cleaning preparations–carpet and rug - Certified International
RUG-LOC - Antislip rug treatment - American Non-Slip Products
RUG MATES - Floor coverings–carpet and rugs - Couristan Inc.
RUG MATES II - Floor coverings–carpet and rugs - Couristan Inc.
RUG PATROL - Cleaning preparations–carpet and rug - A.H. Robins Co. Inc.
RUG-PERFECT - Floor coverings–carpet and rugs - John D. Kurtz
RUG RAT - Apparel and accessories - Gym Rat, Inc.
RUG RAT - Health care products - Consumer Care Products, Inc.
RUG ROVER - Cleaning preparations–carpet and rug ☆ - Landa, Inc.
RUG SAVER - Protective mat for under stoves - American Stove Products
RUG SHAMPOO CONCENTRATE - Cleaning preparations–carpet and rug - Analab Inc.
RUG STOP - Floor coverings–carpet and rugs - Superior American Plastics Co.
RUG WALL - Glassware–household - Hillside House of Originals
RUGALA - Pastries - My Mother's Delicacies, Inc.
RUGAMUFFIN - Floor coverings–carpet and rugs - Gayle M. Oberti
RUGATTI - Sunglasses - Euro-Frames Inc.
RUGBY - Apparel and accessories - Arnav Industries Inc.
RUGBY - Apparel and accessories - DeLong Sportswear Inc.
RUGBY - Floor coverings–carpet and rugs - Carpet Cushion Corp.
RUGBY - Furniture - Westinghouse Electric Corp.
RUGBY - Handbags - S.C. Import & Export Ltd.
RUGBY - Motor vehicles ☆ - Durant Motors Inc.
RUGBY - Oils–lubricating - Pennsylvania Petroleum Products Co.
RUGBY II - Flowers, plants, and seeds - Jacklin Seed
RUGBY OUTFITTERS - Apparel stores–sports - Rugged Wear Ltd.
RUGBY OXFORD - Fabrics - Dan River Inc.
RUGBY STRIPES - Fabrics–broadcloth - Desire Mills Co. Inc.
RUGBY...TRY IT - Apparel–athletic - Richard M. Kelly
RUGER - Candy bars - Sherwood Brands, Inc.
RUGER - Firearms, accessories, and parts - Sturm, Ruger & Co., Inc.
RUGER CHEMICAL CO., INC. - Chemical preparations - Ruger Chemical Co., Inc.
RUGER P91DC - Firearms, accessories, and parts - Sturm, Ruger & Co., Inc.
RUGER SPORT - Candy - Sherwood Brands, Inc.
RUGER VAQUERO - Firearms, accessories, and parts ☆ - Sturm, Ruger & Co., Inc.
RUGG - Tools–garden ☆ - Rugg Manufacturing Co. Inc.
RUGG ROAD - Paper - Rugg Road Handmade Paper
RUGGED - Windows–storm - Green Hammer Metal Products Co.
RUGGED BREED, THE - Compressors–air ☆ - Emglo Products L.P. (Emglo Air Compressors)
RUGGED COUNTRY BY CAMPUS - Apparel - Interco Inc.
RUGGED COUNTRY OUTFITTERS - Apparel and accessories - Samsons Inc.
RUGGED DUCKIE - Antennas - Childs Corp.
RUGGED DUTY - Lamp bulbs - Angelo Brothers Co.
RUGGED EXPOSURE - Backpacks - United Merchandising Corp.
RUGGED GEAR - Firearms, accessories, and parts - Aaladin Industries Inc.
RUGGED GEAR - Shoes ☆ - J.C. Penney Co., Inc.
RUGGED LIFE - Floor coverings ☆ - Congoleum Corp.

☆ = Now out of production

RUGGED LITE - Flashlights - Garrity Industries
RUGGED MAX - Apparel and accessories - Rugged Sportswear, Inc.
RUGGED OUTBACK - Athletic shoes - Payless Shoesource Worldwide, Inc.
RUGGED OUTDOORS - Apparel–men's - Alps Sportswear Manufacturing Co.
RUGGED RANGE - Leather - AAI/ACCESSORIES Associates Inc.
RUGGED RED - Floor coverings ✩ - Congoleum Corp.
RUGGED RED - Paint sprayers ✩ - Wooster Brush Co.
RUGGED RIB - Roofing and siding materials - American Building Components Co.
RUGGED RIBS - Apparel–men's - Alps Sportswear Manufacturing Co.
RUGGED ROBERT - Wire products - Wire Products Co. Inc.
RUGGED SHARK - Boots - Rugged Footwear Co.
RUGGED SHUTTERS - Shutters–metal - Green Hammer Metal Products Co.
RUGGED TEE'S - Apparel–athletic - Rugged Sportswear, Inc.
RUGGED TERRAIN - Shirts - Starter Corp.
RUGGED TOOLS - Tools–garden - S & R International Inc.
RUGGED TRAIL - Apparel–men's - Strawbridge & Clothier
RUGGED TRAVELER - Firearms, accessories, and parts - Welsh Sporting Goods Corp. (Boyt Div.)
RUGGED TRAVELER - Luggage - I.J.K. Sales Corp.
RUGGED-WEAR - Apparel and accessories - Dan River Inc.
RUGGED WEST - Candy ✩ - Glade Taffy Town, Inc.
RUGGEDCUT - Oils–lubricating - J.C. Whitlam Manufacturing Co.
RUGGEDWEAR - Floor waxes - Fluoro Plastics Inc.
RUGGER - Apparel and accessories - Palm Beach Co., Inc.
RUGGER - Luggage ✩ - Samsonite Corp.
RUGGER - Yarn - Brunswick Yarns
RUGGIE BEAR - Infant product ✩ - Century Products Co.
RUGGIES - Floor coverings–carpet and rugs ✩ - Colonial Mills Inc.
RUGGIES - Footwear–children's - W.L. Kreider's Sons Manufacturing Co. Inc.
RUGGIETTES - Footwear–children's - W.L. Kreider's Sons Manufacturing Co. Inc.
RUGGLES - Ice cream - Smith's Dairy Products Co.
RUGGLES LOWFAT - Ice cream - Smith's Dairy Products Co.
RUGGLESPUN - Crocheted and knitted items - Garland Knitting Mills
RUGID WEAR - Apparel–athletic - Kenneth D. Fagan
RUGLO - Cleaning preparations–carpet and rug - Analab Inc.
RUGLYDE - Automotive accessories - American Grease Stick Co.
RUGMASTER - Brushes - White Consolidated Industries, Inc.
RUGMASTER - Vacuum cleaners and accessories - Hako Minuteman Inc.
RUGMASTER PLUS - Brushes - White Consolidated Industries, Inc.
RUGMAT - Housewares - Camp Chef
RUGPLAN - Yarn - Brunswick Yarns
RUGRATS - Apparel and accessories - Viacom International Inc.
RUGS AMERICA - Floor coverings–carpet and rugs - Impex
RUGSAFE - Padding–foam - Vantage Industries Inc.
RUGSTER - Machinery ✩ - Pacific Steamex Cleaning System Inc.
RUGTEX - Floor coverings–carpet and rugs - Tack Levye
RUGUERY - Toys ✩ - Cronar Ltd.
RUGULATOR - Vacuum cleaners and accessories - The Eureka Co.
RUHEXATAL - Pharmaceutical preparations ✩ - Lemmon Co.
RUHRGLAS - Glassware–household - St. Gobain International Glassware
RUHRTALER - Breads ✩ - Liberty Richter Inc.
RUIDOSO - Shirts - Blue Bell, Inc.
RUIZ - Frozen foods - Ruiz Food Products Inc.
RUIZ INTERNATIONAL - Dinners–frozen ✩ - Ruiz Food Products Inc.
RUKIN'S - Cleaning preparations - Rukin Industries Inc.
RULAN - Plastics - E.I. Dupont de Nemours and Co.
RULE - Pumps–water - Rule Industries, Inc.
RULE 41 - Tape–adhesive - Central Products Co.
RULE 500 - Pumps–water - Rule Industries, Inc.
RULE-A-MATIC - Pumps - Rule Industries, Inc.
RULE-A-MATIC PLUS - Switches–electric - Rule Industries, Inc.
RULE BENDER, THE - Rulers–metal - Graham Packaging & Design, Inc.
RULE FINDER - Computer software - Regenisys Corp.
RULE PUMP PAK - Pumps - Rule Industries, Inc.
RULEBUILDER - Computer software - RMS Electronic Commerce Systems, Inc.
RULER - Fruits and vegetables - Saticoy Lemon Association
RULERS - Computer software ✩ - DataPak Software Inc.
RULES ARE THE SAME, BUT THE GAME IS DANGEROUSLY DIFFERENT!, THE - Games - Wow Toys, Inc.
RULES OF THE GAME - Apparel–athletic - Ralph Sampson Sportswear, Inc.
RULES OF THE GAME - Games - Poole Enterprises, Inc.
RULES OF THE ROAD - Games ✩ - Cadaco Div.
RULEWARE - Computer software - Price Waterhouse Llp

RULINER - Bearings - Dixon Industries Corp.
RULON - Hosiery - Rudin & Roth Inc.
RULOX - Pharmaceutical preparations - Rugby Laboratories Inc.
RUM & MAPLE - Tobacco products - Lane Ltd.
RUM CURED CROOKS - Cigars ✩ - House of Windsor Inc.
RUM DROP - Liqueurs - Mango Bottling, Inc.
RUM-K - Pharmaceutical preparations - Fleming & Co.
RUM 'N EGG - Hair care products - Para Laboratories Inc.
RUM SWIZZLE - Beverages–alcohol - Holiday Food & Beverage Ltd.
RUMA SWEET - Dog food - Land O'Lakes Inc.
RUMAFIX - Vitamins and nutritional supplements - Kroeger Herb Products Co. Inc.
RUMAKI - Food products - Acme Continental Foods Inc.
RUMAR ORIGINALS - Apparel–men's - Alan Stuart, Inc.
RUMAX - Veterinary nutritional supplements - Agri Beef Co.
RUMBA - Bicycles - Burley Design Cooperative
RUMBA - Cleaning preparations - Vitarroz
RUMBA - Collar buttons - Balenciaga Inc.
RUMBA - Floor coverings ✩ - Tarkett, Inc.
RUMBA - Vegetables–dried - Spokane Seed Co.
RUMBER - Floor coverings - Rumbar Materials Inc.
RUMBLE AND ROAR - Toys–automobiles - Toy Biz, Inc.
RUMBLE SEATS - Apparel–women's ✩ - Wilkins Industries Inc.
RUMBLED - Bricks - Pine Hall Brick Co.
RUMBLES - Beverages ✩ - Wine Group Inc.
RUMBLES - Snack foods ✩ - Frito-Lay, Inc.
RUMBLESTICK - Golfing equipment - Meyer Design Group, Inc.
RUMEN AVAILABLE CARBOHYDRATE - Animal feeds - Cooperative Research Farms
RUMEN AVAILABLE PROTEIN - Animal feeds - Cooperative Research Farms
RUMEX - Rum flavor - American Flavor & Fragrance Corp.
RUMFORD - Baking powder - Rumford Co.
RUMFORD - Lamps ✩ - Tensor Corp.
RUMI K - Games - Cadaco Div.
RUMI-TECH - Veterinary nutritional supplements - Morgan Manufacturing Co., Inc.
RUMICAL - Veterinary pharmaceutical preparations - Griffin Industries Inc.
RUMI'S - Relishes - Rumi Corp.
RUMMIKUB - Games - Pressman Toy Corp.
RUMMY - Beverages–carbonated - Wonder Orange Co.
RUMMY-JACK - Games - Drybranch Inc./Sport Design
RUMMY-O - Games - Cardinal Industries, Inc.
RUMMY Q - Games - Kingstone International Corp.
RUMMY RUMBLE - Board game - International Games
RUMMY Z - Games - Pacific Game Co.
RUMMYNUT - Ice cream - Taste the Tropics, Inc.
RUMOCHA - Candy - Square Shooter Candy Co.
RUMONA - Beverages–alcohol - Carriage House Imports Ltd.
RUMOR - Computer software - D.M. Witte and Associates, Inc.
RUMOR COMP - Sporting goods - O'Brien International
RUMOR PRO - Sporting goods - O'Brien International
RUMORS - Floor coverings–carpet and rugs - Monticello Carpet Mills
RUMORS - Footwear - Southern Shoe Importers Inc.
RUMOURS - Apparel–women's - Lovable Co.
RUMOURS - Watches - Classic Time Watch Co.
RUMP ROOST - Stadium seat - Windy Point Enterprises
RUMPA PAD - Cushions - Rumpa-Pad
RUMPELSTILTSKIN - Recording label - Wood'n Music Inc.
RUMPELSTILTSKIN'S LABYRINTH OF THE LOST - Computer software - Terraglyph Interactive, LP
RUMPLE BEARSKINS - Novelty items ✩ - At the Zoo
RUMPLE MINZE - Beverages–alcohol - Paddington Corp.
RUMPLEFOLK 9 10 11 12 1 2 3 - Figurines - Mary L. Gonzales
RUMPUS ROOM - Toys - Tyco Toys
RUN-A-BOUT - Bicycles - Schwinn Cycling & Fitness Inc.
RUN-ABOUT - Motor vehicles–motor homes ✩ - Mitchell & Sons Inc.
RUN & FLIP OVER - Toys–stuffed ✩ - Fun World Inc.
RUN AND GUN - Games ✩ - Konami (America) Inc.
RUN EMMITT RUN - Apparel–athletic - Emmitt, Inc.
RUN FOR COVER - Apparel–women's - J.C. Penney Co., Inc.
RUN FOR IT - Computer software ✩ - Optimum Resource, Inc.
RUN FOR THE MONEY - Computer software - Voyager Software Corp.
RUN KARDS - Pet products - Barkleigh Productions, Inc.
RUN-N-CHUTE - Sporting goods - Strength Systems, Inc.
RUN 'N GUN - See **RUN 'N SLAM**
RUN 'N SLAM - Basketball shoes - Converse Inc.

RUN REPAIR - Hosiery–women's ☆ - Tulip Productions
RUN-RITE - Cleaning preparations - Calidad Auto Tech Products, Inc.
RUN ROADER - Motor vehicle parts and accessories - Rivera Engineering, Inc.
RUN THE GAUNTLET - Toys–automobiles - Matchbox Toys USA
RUN TIME - Computer software - Vertex Industries Inc.
RUN WITH THE PACK - Apparel and accessories - Anheuser-Busch Companies Inc.
RUNA/TAB - Paper - Mead Corp.
RUNABOUT - Audio equipment - Boston Acoustics Inc.
RUNABOUT - Fabrics - Gretchen Bellinger Inc.
RUNABOUT - Motor vehicles - Ransomes-Cushman-Ryan
RUNABOUT - Motor vehicles - Sunline Coach Co.
RUNABOUT - Skin care products - Golden Door Skin Care
RUNABOUT - Strollers–baby - Runabout Strollers
RUNABOUT - Televisions ☆ - Philips Consumer Electronics Co.
RUNABOUT - Vacuum cleaners and accessories - The Hoover Co.
RUNABOUT - Wheelchairs - MUL Acquisition Corp. II
RUNABOUT BALL - Pet products - Pets International, Ltd.
RUNABOUT II - Strollers–baby - Aprica Kassai USA Inc.
RUNABOUTS - Slacks–women's - Henry I. Siegel Co. Inc.
RUNABOUT'S - Socks - Sockyard Co. Inc.
RUNAROUNDS - Apparel–women's - Wal-Mart Stores Inc.
RUNAWAY - Bicycles - Roadmaster Corp.
RUNAWAY - Perfumes - Eurostar Corp.
RUNAWAYS - Luggage - Welsh Sporting Goods Corp. (Boyt Div.)
RUNBALL - Footwear - Fila USA, Inc.
RUNE - Novelty items - Flying Buffalo Inc.
RUNE - Recording label - Cleverland Records
RUNEL - Spices and extracts - Holland-American Importing Co. Inc.
RUNEQUEST - Games - Avalon Hill Game Co.
RUNES OF VIRTUE - Toys - Origin Systems, Inc.
RUNFREE - Health care products - Traco Laboratories Inc.
RUNG REST - Shelving units–wood ☆ - Howard Manufacturing Co.
RUNGELBLUMENSALBE - Pharmaceutical preparations - Merz Apothecary Inc.
RUNNER - Trailers–travel ☆ - Jayco Inc.
RUNNER, THE - Apparel–athletic - Howe K. Sipes Co.
RUNNER UP - Apparel and accessories - American Argo Corp.
RUNNERS' COMFORT - Shoe accessories - Frelonic/Division of Dertek Corp.
RUNNERS LUBE - Health care products - Mueller Sports Medicine Inc.
RUNNER'S RUB - Skin care products ☆ - Texas Best Unlimited, LP
RUNNERS' SHIELD - Vitamins and nutritional supplements - Source Naturals
RUNNER'S WEDGE - Shoe accessories ☆ - Schering-Plough Healthcare Products
RUNNER'S WORLD MARATHON - Games ☆ - T.J. Bohme
RUNNIN' COOL - Containers–insulated - Virginia H. Fitzgerald
RUNNIN' WILD - Apparel and accessories - Magnificient Wonders
RUNNING BRA, THE - Apparel–athletic - Formfit Rogers
RUNNING BROOK - Apparel and accessories - Ida M. Long
RUNNING BRUTE - Bicycles - Ross Bicycles USA, Ltd.
RUNNING FREE - Dolls - CPG Products Corp.
RUNNING MATE - Calendars - Day Runner, Inc.
RUNNING PROGRAM, THE - Computer software - Meca Software, Inc.
RUNNING RHINO - Giftware - Running Rhino & Co.
RUNNING SQUARE - Exercising equipment - Gerstung/Gym-Thing Inc.
RUNNING SQUIRREL - Artists' materials ☆ - Riebe's Artist Materials Inc.
RUNNING WATER - Bottles–plastic - Douglas L. Allen
RUNNYMEADE BLUE - Dishes–china - Waterford Wedgewood USA, Inc.
RUNPOOL - Exercising equipment - AquaCiser Inc.
RUNS ON NEXTSTEP - Computer software - Next Computer, Inc.
RUNSTIK - Suntan lotions - Sports Cosmetics Co. Ltd.
RUNT SPOOK - Fishing lures - James Heddon's Sons
RUNTS - Candy - Willy Wonka Brands
RUNWALK - Footwear - Nike, Inc.
RUNWAY - Fruits and vegetables - Farmington Packing Co., Inc.
RUNWAY - Salt - Vigoro Industries, Inc.
RUNWAY I - Apparel and accessories - M. Serman & Co. Inc.
RUNWAY ROUTER - Electrical equipment - B-Line Systems, Inc.
RUNWELL - Hardware ☆ - Frantz Manufacturing Co.
RUOK - Apparel and accessories - Goodview Enterprises, Ltd.
RUPERT RACCOON - Toys–stuffed - Dakin Inc.
RUPP - Cheese - Swissrose International Inc.
RUPTURE EASER - Medical apparatus - Nelkin/Piper Health Products
RURAL CONTEMPORARY - Mailboxes - Babco
RURAL CROSSING COLLECTION - Furniture - Brady Furniture Co. Inc.
RURAL HALL PINE COLLECTION - Furniture - Brady Furniture Co. Inc.

RURAL OAK COLLECTION - Furniture - Brady Furniture Co. Inc.
RURAL RETREAT - Decorative accessories - Shenandoah Designs International Inc.
RURAL RETREAT - Furniture ☆ - Universal Flooring
RURAL RETRET - Furniture - Vaughan Furniture Co. Inc.
RURAL RHYTHM - Recording label - Rural Rhythm Records
RURAL ROUTE 1 - Popcorn - Trelay Farms, Inc.
RUS-ETTES - Food products - Universal Frozen Foods Co.
RUS IDA - Food products ☆ - Universal Frozen Foods Co.
RUS-KIL - Paints - Mobile Paint Manufacturing Co.
RUS-SPARK - Wines - Rus-Spark American-Hungarian Trading Limited Liability Co.
RUS-TIQUE - Bricks - Miami Brick & Stone Co.
RUSA - Software - Cascade Marketing Associates
RUSALKA - Glassware–household - Rusalka, Inc.
RUSCALE - Water treating compounds - Sherwood Laboratories Inc.
RUSCOE - Adhesives and sealants - W.J. Ruscoe Co.
RUSE IT! A GAME OF CHANCE AND WIT. - Games - Bellrose Inc.
RUSFRE - Rustproofing compounds - 3 B Products Co. Inc.
RUSH - Apparel–athletic - NGN Inc.
RUSH! - Computer peripheral equipment - Microdoctor
RUSH - Computer software - Concept Automation Inc.
RUSH - Honey - Alveole Foods
RUSH - Shoes - Famolare Inc.
RUSH - Soft drinks ☆ - Corr's Natural Beverages Inc.
RUSH - Tools - Eraser Co. Inc.
RUSH HOUR - Shoes - Edison Brothers Stores, Inc.
RUSH HOUR EXPRESS - Shoes ☆ - Edison Brothers Stores, Inc.
RUSH HOUR RALLY - Computer software - Gamco Industries Inc.
RUSH HOUR RECIPE - Publisher's imprints - Pillsbury Co.
RUSHING - Wines - Winery Rushing
RUSHMAN - Window shades ☆ - Rushman Magnolia Shutters
RUSHMORE - Food products - Federal Beef Processors South
RUSHMORE - Kitchen cabinets–metal - American Woodmark Corp.
RUSHMORE - Skin care products ☆ - Delta Industries International, Inc.
RUSHMORE - Water–bottled or canned - Sodak Distributing Co.
RUSHMORE COLLECTION - Furniture ☆ - Southern Furniture Co. of Conover
RUSHPLUSH - Dolls - Natalie F. Lederman
RUSHTON - Boats–canoes ☆ - Old Town Canoe Co.
RUSK - Hair care products - Rusk Inc.
RUSKI - Beverages–malt ☆ - Blair Importers Ltd.
RUSKO - Landscaping products - Rusko Inc.
RUSON - Gloves - Rubin Gloves Inc.
RUSS - Apparel–women's - Russ Togs Inc.
RUSS - Frames–eyeglass - Rozin Optical Export Corp.
RUSS - Toys - Ja-Ru Inc.
RUSS CLASSIC - Apparel and accessories - L.C. Licensing, Inc.
RUSS GIRL - Apparel–children's - Russ Togs Inc.
RUSS KALVIN - Hair care products - Consumer Products Association Distributors
RUSS ORIGINAL SPORT COMPANY - Jeans–women's - L.C. Licensing, Inc.
RUSS PETITE - Apparel–women's - Russ Togs Inc.
RUSS SIGNATURE - Apparel and accessories - L.C. Licensing, Inc.
RUSS STUDIO - Apparel and accessories - Russ Togs Inc.
RUSS TEEN - Apparel–athletic - Russ Togs Inc.
RUSS TOGS - Apparel–athletic - Russ Togs Inc.
RUSSCAN - Communications equipment–mobile ☆ - Russell Industries Inc.
RUSSE - Cookies - Sunshine/Salerno Inc.
RUSSE MOLNAR & MOSER - Colognes - Szablya Consultants, Inc.
RUSSELL - Apparel–athletic - Russell Athletic Div.
RUSSELL - Cutlery - Russell Harrington Cutlery, Inc.
RUSSELL - Moccasins - W.C. Russell Moccasin Co.
RUSSELL - Ophthalmic goods ☆ - Luxottica
RUSSELL - Socks - Russell National Sport Socks
RUSSELL ALLIGATOR - Knives–putty - Russell Harrington Cutlery, Inc.
RUSSELL ATHLETIC R GET TOUGH - Bags–duffel - Russell Corp.
RUSSELL GREEN RIVER - Cutlery - Russell Harrington Cutlery, Inc.
RUSSELL INTERNATIONAL - Cutlery - Russell Harrington Cutlery, Inc.
RUSSELL OPTIMIST - Boats–dinghies ☆ - Russell Sailboats Inc.
RUSSELL STOVER - Candy - Russell Stover Candies, Inc.
RUSSELL TRUST UNIVERSE - Recording label - Frank Russell Co.
RUSSELL'S - Vinegar - Clements Food Co. Inc.
RUSSER - Meat products - Russer Foods
RUSSER LIGHT - Meats–luncheon - Russer Foods
RUSSER LIL' SALT LOW FAT - Frankfurters ☆ - Russer Foods
RUSSER SELF-SERVE DELI - Meats–luncheon - Russer Foods

☆ = Now out of production

RUSSET - Dishes—earthenware - Denby USA Limited

RUSSET - Erasers ☆ - Bright Boy Abrasives

RUSSET BROWN - Dinnerware—glass - Franciscan by Johnson Brothers, USA, Inc.

RUSSET KING - Fruits and vegetables - Skone & Connors Produce Inc.

RUSSET WIND - Cosmetics - Almay Inc.

RUSSETT BLOSSOMS - Dinnerware—glass ☆ - Lenox, Inc.

RUSSIAN CAMPAIGN - Games - Avalon Hill Game Co.

RUSSIAN CARAVAN - Teas - Eastern Shore Tea Co.

RUSSIAN CARAVAN - Teas - Grace Tea Co. Ltd.

RUSSIAN COLLECTION - Furniture - John Widdicomb Co.

RUSSIAN DISK, THE - Computer software - Queue Inc.

RUSSIAN DRESSING - Wallpaper - Aresda Design Associates

RUSSIAN HOOK - Fishing tackle - Best Tackle Manufacturing Co.

RUSSIAN LEATHER - Colognes - Schnapp Enterprises Inc.

RUSSIAN RIVER - Wines - Belvedere Winery

RUSSIAN ROULETTE - Game machines - Emil Tavinsky

RUSSIAN-SLAVIC LEGACY, THE - Figurines - Asian-Slavic Legacy,Inc.

RUSSIAN TEACUP - Toilets—enameled - Kohler Co.

RUSSIAN: THE EASY WAY - Computer software ☆ - Gessler Publishing Co., Inc.

RUSSIAN TOY MUSEUM COLLECTION - Toys - Schylling Associates Inc.

RUSSIAN TREASURES - Jewelry - Russian Treasures, Inc.

RUSSIE - Apparel—athletic - Russ Togs Inc.

RUSSIYA - Vodka - Savco Importers

RUSSO - Pasta - Gooch Foods Inc.

RUSSOFF - Vodka - Paramount Distillers Inc.

RUSSOUND - Audio equipment - Russound/FMP, Inc.

RUST-A-HOY - Rust removers - Travaco Laboratories Inc.

RUST-AWAY - Cleaning preparations—carpet and rug - Uncle Sam Chemical Co., Inc.

RUST AWAY - Penetrating oil - Contact Industries Inc.

RUST AWAY - Rust removers - Marine Development & Research Corp.

RUST BARRIER - Adhesives and sealants - Griot's Garage

RUST BEATER - Paints - Dutch Boy Group

RUST BOMB - Oils—lubricating - Conklin Co., Inc.

RUST BREAKER - Oils—lubricating - Sherwin-Williams Automotive Finishes Corp.

RUST-BUSTER - Bicycles - Technical Packaging Corp.

RUST BUSTER - Rust removers - Markal Co.

RUST BUSTER - Rust removers - Mt. Hood Chemical Corp.

RUST-BUSTER - Water treating compounds ☆ - Elcal Enterprises Ltd.

RUST BUSTR - Cleaning preparations - Core Products Co., Inc.

RUST CHECK - Paints - Pen Paints Inc.

RUST CHEM - Paints ☆ - Devoe & Raynolds Co.

RUST COP - Lubricants - Carwell Products, Inc.

RUST CRAFT - Greeting cards - American Greetings Corp.

RUST-CRAFTS - Paints - Nu-Brite Chemical Co. Inc.

RUST CURB - Rust removers - Chase Products Co.

RUST CURE - Cleaning preparations—household - Win-Chekd Inc.

RUST-CURE - Paints - L.D. Sterns Corp.

RUST DESTROYER - Paints - Advanced Protective Products Inc.

RUST-E-RACE - Paints - Commercial Chemical Co. Inc.

RUST EATER - Automotive parts and accessories - Turtle Wax, Inc.

RUST ELIMINATOR - Sealing compounds - Ziebart International Corp.

RUST-ERASER - Cleaner for rusted metals - Coricone Corp.

RUST-FIX - Rust removers - DIMC, Inc.

RUST-FIX - Rust removers - Krylon/Dupli-Color

RUST-GONE - Paints - Sigma Coatings USA BV.

RUST GUARD - Cleaning preparations - Whink Products Co.

RUST GUARD - Paints - Standard Brands Paint Co.

RUST GUN, THE - Stain removers - Fast Industries, Inc.

RUST HALT - Paints - Sinclair Paint Co.

RUST INHIBITING PRIMER - Paints - Master's Choice Inc.

RUST JELLY - Antirust product ☆ - Devcon Consumer Products (ITW Devcon)

RUST-KILL - Enamels - Dean and Barry Co.

RUST-KILL-PAINTS - Paints - Mac-O-Lac Paints Inc.

RUST KING - Paints - Suntec Paint Inc.

RUST KNOCK OUT - Paints - Advanced Protective Products Inc.

RUST KNOCKOUT - Primers - Layton Industries

RUST KUTTER - Rust removers - Klean-Strip

RUST MAGIC - Paints - Krylon/Dupli-Color

RUST-MATE - Paints - Zynolyte Products Co.

RUST MISER - Sealing compounds - Monsey Products Co.

RUST-MUVER - Cleaning preparations—carpet and rug - Imperial Manufacturing Co. Inc.

RUST NIP - Rust removers ☆ - Roccorp, Inc.

RUST NO MORE - Paints - Masury Paint Co.

RUST-NOT - Paints - Jones Blair Co.

RUST NOT - Paints - Plasti-Kote Co. Inc.

RUST-O-CRYLIC - Finishing agents - Rust-Oleum Corp.

RUST-O-LASTIC - Paints - M.A. Bruder & Sons Inc.

RUST-O-LOID - Paints ☆ - H. Behlen & Bro. Inc.

RUST-O-MATIC - Rust removers - Emerald Labs, Inc.

RUST-O-THANE - Finishing agents - Rust-Oleum Corp.

RUST-OFF - Pigments—paint - Garon Products Inc.

RUST OFF - Rust removers - Conklin Co., Inc.

RUST-OLEUM - Finishing agents - Rust-Oleum Corp.

RUST OUT - Fiberboard ☆ - Fibre Glass-Evercoat Co. Inc.

RUST-PLEX - Paints - California Products Corp.

RUST RAIDER - Paints - Colonial Refining and Chemical Co.

RUST RAZOR - Rust removers - Rust-Oleum Corp.

RUST REFORMER - Rust removers - Rust-Oleum Corp.

RUST-RESISTOR - Rust removers - Farwest Paint Manufacturing Co. Inc.

RUST-RID - Paints - Jones Blair Co.

RUST RINSE - Rust removers - Dampney Co., Inc.

RUST RUSTLER - Paints - Automatic Construction Co.

RUST-SCAT - Coatings - Coronado Paint Co.

RUST-SCREEN - Paints - Porter Paint Co.

RUST-SELE - Finishing agents - Waterlox Coatings Corp.

RUST SOLVER - Paints - Krylon/Dupli-Color

RUST STOP - Paints - Frazee Paint

RUST TOUGH - Enamels - Krylon/Dupli-Color

RUST ZAPPER - Rust removers - Pro Power, Inc.

RUSTAID - Cleaning preparations - Marinize Products Corp.

RUSTALLOY - Paints - Tresco Paint Co. Inc.

RUSTALOY - Enamels - Pratt & Lambert United, Inc.

RUSTALOY - Paints - Fulton Co.

RUSTBOND - Primers - Carboline Co.

RUSTCHEM - Paints - Growco Aerosol

RUSTCOTE - Rustproofing compounds - Garon Products Inc.

RUSTED EDGES - Automotive parts and accessories ☆ - Marson Creative Fastener Group

RUSTED ROOT - Apparel and accessories - Touchy Pegg

RUSTERMINATOR ELECTRONIC RUST CONTROL - Electrical equipment - Stevens Car Care Products

RUSTEX - Paints - Valspar Corp.

RUSTGO - Work benches - Nelson King Inc.

RUSTGUARD - Paints - Wattyl Paint Corp.

RUSTHEADS - Hats - H & E Products

RUSTIC - Blinds—vertical - Ultra Vertical Blinds Inc.

RUSTIC - Fencing—wood - Coastal Lumber Co.

RUSTIC - Floor coverings ☆ - Harris-Tarkett, Inc.

RUSTIC - Frames—eyeglass - Zylo Ware Corp.

RUSTIC - Fruits and vegetables - Comstock Michigan Fruit

RUSTIC - Hobby kits ☆ - Craft World International Inc.

RUSTIC - Paints - Frazee Paint

RUSTIC - Pet products - American Cat Emporium

RUSTIC - Shingles—asphalt or tar ☆ - Celotex Corp.

RUSTIC - Tiles—ceramic - Buchtal USA

RUSTIC - Tiles—ceramic - Dal-Tile Corp.

RUSTIC - Varnishes - Perry & Derrick Co.

RUSTIC ACRES - Furniture ☆ - Bassett Furniture Industries, Inc.

RUSTIC BEIGE GRAPE - Pottery ☆ - Rubens Originals

RUSTIC BERBER - Floor coverings—carpet and rugs ☆ - Downs Carpet Co. Inc.

RUSTIC CHARM - Clocks - General Time Corp. (Westclox/Seth Thomas Div.)

RUSTIC CLASS II - Floor coverings—carpet and rugs - Evans-Black Carpet Mills

RUSTIC CLAY - Floor coverings—tile - Kentile Floors Inc.

RUSTIC PLAYARD - Pet products - American Cat Emporium

RUSTIC RAMPART - Shingles ☆ - Manville/Schuller

RUSTIC SHINGLE - Aluminum products ☆ - Kaiser Aluminum & Chemical Corp.

RUSTIC STONE - Floor coverings - Kentile Floors Inc.

RUSTIC STONE II - Floor coverings—tile - Kentile Floors Inc.

RUSTIC TONE - Finishing agents - Davis Paint Co.

RUSTIC TONE - Paints - Kwal-Howells Inc.

RUSTIC TONE - Stain - C.M. Athey Paint Co.

RUSTIC WOOD - Varnishes - Kwal-Howells Inc.

RUSTIC WOOD LATH ART - Toys ☆ - Coloron Industries

RUSTICA BRUN - Tiles—ceramic ☆ - Monarch Tile Inc.

RUSTICA VACCARI - Tiles–ceramic ☆ - Monarch Tile Inc.
RUSTICANA - Calendars - Goes Lithographing Co.
RUSTICANA - Frames–eyeglass - Zylo Ware Corp.
RUSTICANA - Wood products - Weyerhaeuser Co.
RUSTICIDE - Rust removers - Skybryte Co.
RUSTICO - Cheese - Sini Fulvi USA Inc.
RUSTICO - Floor coverings–carpet and rugs - V & B Carpet
RUSTICTONE - Paints - Vogel Paint and Wax Co., Inc.
RUSTICWOOD - Paints - Sophir Morris Paint
RUSTIK - Candles - Design Ideas Ltd.
RUSTIQUE - Apparel–men's - Rustic River Ltd.
RUSTIQUE - Paints ☆ - Colony Paints Div.
RUSTIQUE - Recording label - Band Box Record Co.
RUSTITE - Paints - T.J. Ronan Paint Corp.
RUSTIVER - Wallpaper - 3-G Mermet Inc.
RUSTLER - Apparel and accessories - Wrangler Apparel Co.
RUSTLER - Apparel and accessories - Wrangler Co.
RUSTLER - Musical instrument accessories - Roberto Ciarfella Inc.
RUSTLER - Ophthalmic goods - Embassy Creations Inc.
RUSTLER - Trailers–travel ☆ - Mitchell & Sons Inc.
RUSTLER - Watches - Delta Impex Watch Corp.
RUSTLERS - Cigar boxes–wood - Consolidated Cigar Corp.
RUSTLER'S - Snack foods - Frito-Lay, Inc.
RUSTLESS ONE, THE - Containers–insulated ☆ - Aladdin Industries, Inc.
RUSTLOK - Adhesives and sealants - Pettit Paint Co. Inc.
RUSTMASTER PRO - Paints - Glidden Co.
RUSTO - Homeopathic remedies - Washington Homeopathic Products
RUSTOFLEX - Enamels ☆ - KCI Coatings, Inc.
RUSTOP - Paints ☆ - Mac-O-Lac Paints Inc.
RUSTPLATE - Paints - KCI Coatings, Inc.
RUSTPROOF - Shower stalls–plastic - Plaskolite Inc.
RUSTREAT - Paints - Nowstar
RUSTRIPPER - Rust removers - Oakite Products, Inc.
RUSTRON - Recording label - Rustron Music Productions
RUSTWIZ - Paints - OEM Paints, Inc.
RUSTY - Candy ☆ - R.M. Palmer Co.
RUSTY - Ophthalmic goods ☆ - Luxottica
RUSTY - Pet products - Strongheart Products, Inc.
RUSTY - Toys–stuffed - Russ Berrie and Co., Inc.
RUSTY AND ROSY - Video production - Waterford Institute Inc.
RUSTY-DUCK - Oils–lubricating - Hydra-Tone Chemicals, Inc.
RUSTY SCUPPER - Restaurants–fast food - Nestle USA
RUSTY STAUB'S LE GRAND ORANGE - Beverages–alcohol - Le Grand Orange, Inc.
RUSTY WALLACE - Sunglasses - Rusty Wallace, Inc.
RUSTY'S - Beverages–malt - Brinker Restaurant Corp.
RUSTY'S ROAD KNIGHT AMBER - Beverages–malt - Brinker Restaurant Corp.
RUSU - Wallpaper - Enterprise Wallcoverings Inc.
RUT-N-POUR - Medical apparatus - Instruments for Research and Industry, I2R Inc.
RUTABAGA - Recording label - Old Homestead Record Co.
RUTDOG - Recording label - Jazz Composer's Orchestra Association Inc.
RUTGERS - Floor coverings ☆ - Arthur J. Beacom & Co.
RUTGERS - Lenses–optical - Ditto Industries Inc.
RUTGERS UNIVERSITY PRESS - Publisher's imprints - Rutgers University Press
RUTH - Eyeglasses - Art-Craft Optical Co.
RUTH - Mail boxes - Gordon Associates
RUTH ANNE - Hosiery - Kayser-Roth Corp.
RUTH HUKING - Giftware - Ruth Huking
RUTH HUNT'S - Candy - Ruth Hunt Candy Co.
RUTH NORMAN - Apparel–women's - Ruth Civic
RUTH OF CAROLINA - Apparel–children's - Young Generations, Inc.
RUTH ORIGINALS - Dresses–women's - Young Generations, Inc.
RUTH SCHARF - Apparel–children's - Bryan Industries, Inc.
RUTHAL/CIDE - Antiseptics - Ruthal Industries Inc.
RUTHERFORD - Cutlery ☆ - Lifetime Hoan Corp.
RUTHERFORD - Toys–stuffed - Russ Berrie and Co., Inc.
RUTHERFORD BRICK - Floor coverings ☆ - Azrock Commercial Flooring
RUTHERFORD ESTATE CELLARS - Wines - Heublein, Inc.
RUTHERFORD HILL WINERY - Wines - Rutherford Hill Winery
RUTHERFORD RANCH - Wine - Round Hill Winery
RUTHERFORD RECYCLES - Pens - Environmental Management Consultants Inc.
RUTHERFORD RESERVE - Wines - Cakebread Cellars, Inc.

RUTHERFORD VINEYARDS - Wines - Bronco Wine Co.
RUTHERFORD VINTNERS - Wines - Rutherford Vintners Inc.
RUTHIE - Dolls - Horsman
RUTHIE JOY & TAD - Giftware ☆ - Brushcreek Creative Co.
RUTHIES - Vegetables–frozen - Ruthies Foods, Inc.
RUTHIE'S RIB-IT - Barbecue sauce - Fire Mountain Enterprises
RUTHLESS - Cleaning preparations - W.W. Grainger, Inc.
RUTHLESS - Recording label - Big Money Inc.
RUTHLESS - Wire–barbed - Keystone Steel & Wire Co.
RUTH'S - Cookies ☆ - Archway Cookie Inc.
RUTH'S CUSTOM SEWING - Apparel–women's - Ruth's Custom Sewing
RUTI - Frames–eyeglass ☆ - Universal/Univis Inc.
RUTIN - Health care products - Above All Health Inc.
RUTIPLEN-C - Pharmaceutical preparations - Medical Products Panamericana Inc.
RUTLAND - Cabinets - Merillat Industries, Inc.
RUTLAND - Caulking compounds - Rutland Products
RUTLAND - Clocks ☆ - General Time Corp. (Westclox/Seth Thomas Div.)
RUTLAND SLATE - Floor coverings–tile ☆ - Kentile Floors Inc.
RUTLEDGE - Apparel stores–lingerie ☆ - Formfit Rogers
RUTLEDGE - Bicycles - Columbia Manufacturing Inc.
RUTLEDGE - Furniture ☆ - Bassett Furniture Industries, Inc.
RUTLEDGE - Rings–jewelry ☆ - Artcarved Inc.
RUTLEDGE - Tableware–china - Lenox, Inc.
RUTMONT - Stationery ☆ - Tuttle Law Print Inc.
RUTTERS - Milk - Rutter Brothers Dairy Inc.
RUUD - Air conditioning equipment - Rheem Manufacturing Co.
RUVEA - Fabrics–nylon ☆ - E.I. Dupont de Nemours and Co.
RUXTON - Playing cards ☆ - United States Playing Card Co.
RUXTON - Watches - Bulova Corp.
RUXXAC - Photographic equipment - American Photographic Instrument Co.
R.V. - Apparel–men's - U.O.D., Inc.
RV - Maps - American Map Corp.
RV - Skin care products ☆ - Center Laboratories/Hermal Dermatology Group
RV AIDE - Portable-toilet treatment ☆ - Vibe Records Inc.
RV MAGIC - Cleaning preparations - Perfection Polishers, Inc.
RV PABA - Suntan lotions ☆ - ICN Pharmaceuticals Inc.
RV PAQUE - Suntan lotions - ICN Pharmaceuticals Inc.
RV PELLENT - Suntan lotions ☆ - ICN Pharmaceuticals Inc.
RV PLUS - Suntan lotions ☆ - ICN Pharmaceuticals Inc.
RV POWER SHOWER TOTE - Handbags - Sharon Enterprises
RV-SOFT - Facial tissues - Sealand Technology, Inc.
RV-TRINE - Chemical preparations - Applied Biochemists, Inc.
RV TWO-WAY - Awnings–metal - Francis L. Struben
RV3 - Lawn and garden hose ☆ - Amerace Electronic Components
RVF HONDA - Computer software ☆ - Microprose Software, Inc.
RVG - Diamond powder - General Electric Co.
RVIEW - Computer software - Legent Corp.
RVISION - Housewares - Rvision, Inc.
RVL - Jewelry - Ravel Inc.
RVP - Recording label - Rustron Music Productions
RVP - Suntan lotions ☆ - ICN Pharmaceuticals Inc.
RVR'S CHOICE - Cleaning preparations - Autre Products, Ltd.
R.V.S. - Amplifiers–musical instrument - Woodwind & Brasswind
RW - Awnings ☆ - Carefree of Colorado
RW - Jewelry - Richards and West, Inc.
RW CHANG - Frames–picture - Flashco
RW LIMITED EDITIONS - Dishes–china - Royal China & Porcelain Companies Inc.
R.W. SMITHS PIG WINGS - Pork - R & S Meats, Inc.
R.W. ZANT CO. DELIZOUS FARMS - Meat products–beef - R.W. Zant Co.
RW2000 - Computer software - Passport Software, Inc.
RWH - Jewelry - Mark A. Ryan
RWP - Giftware - Wilton Co.
RWR - Jewelry - Rubin & Co.
RX - Firearms, accessories, and parts - Beeman Precision Airguns
RX - Headphones - Westone Laboratories Inc.
RX - Health care products - Essex Medical Products
RX - Inks - Genicom Corp.
RX - Machinery ☆ - RX Honing Machine Corp.
RX - Ribbons–inked - GENICOM Corp.
RX - Shampoos - Chasalco Inc.
RX-7 - Motor vehicles–automobiles - Mazda Motor of America Inc.
RX 7000 - Gloves - Climax Clothing Industries, Inc.
RX ALERT - Health care products - Rx Systems International
RX DME II - Health care products - P.C. Solutions

☆ = Now out of production

RX ELIPSE - Medical apparatus - Advanced Cardiovascular Systems, Inc.

RX FOR GREAT NAILS - Manicure preparations - Del Pharmaceuticals, Inc.

RX FOR HAIR & HANDS - Skin care products - Consumer Products Association Distributors

RX FOR HEALTH - Pharmaceutical preparations - Global Source Management & Consulting, Inc.

RX HONING MACHINE - Medical apparatus - RX Honing Machine Corp.

RX LABEL ALERT - Stickers - Julius L. Brodsky

RX MARINE - Pharmaceutical preparations - Hawaiian Marine Imports Inc.

RX MARXMARK - Greeting cards - Mark Boulos

RX, MRX - Controls–heating systems - Surface Combustion, Inc.

RX PLUS - Nuts–salted, roasted, cooked, or canned - Robert Industries Inc.

RX REGISTER - Thermometers ☆ - Trademark Corp.

RX ROCKER - Health care products - Rx Rocker Corp.

RX2000 - Computer software - Melville Corp.

RXGOLD - Vitamins and nutritional supplements - Sports One, Inc.

RXLIFE - Vitamins and nutritional supplements - Transamerica Mailings, Inc.

RXMATES - Cordage and twine - J & B Associates

RXP - Ammunition - Remington Arms Co., Inc.

RXP - Fuel additives - RxP Products Inc.

RXPERTISE - Computer software - Summit Care Corp.

RXPO - Electrical equipment - Controlled Power Corp.

RXSERVER - Computer software - Comcotec, Inc.

RXSTAT - Computer software - Community Health Computing, Inc.

RXSUMMARY - Computer software - American Drug Stores, Inc.

RXV-BP-1 - Veterinary medicine - Walco International, Inc.

RY - Jewelry - Ryan Gems, Inc.

RY-AL - Hair care products - Ry-Al Beauty Corp.

RY-FLA-VOR - Rye–flour or meal - Nabisco Foods Group

RY-KA - Paints ☆ - Hampton Paint Manufacturing Co.

RY-PAGE - Electronic equipment ☆ - D'San Corp.

RY ZING - Spices and extracts - Crompton & Knowles Corp.

RYAN - Agricultural machinery - Ransomes-Cushman-Ryan

RYAN - Brushes–paint - Corona Brushes Inc.

RYAN - Dolls - Mattel, Inc.

RYAN - Frames–eyeglass - U.S. Optical Frame Co.

RYAN - Sour cream - Ryan Foods Co.

RYAN STEELE - Toys - Saban Entertainment, Inc.

RYAN ZZIPPER - Apparel and accessories - Zzip Designs

RYANS CREME - Beverages–alcohol - White Rock Distilleries Inc.

RYBACK - Hair care products - Quirino Miranda

RYBA'S MACKINAC ISLAND - Ice cream - London's Farm Dairy, Inc.

RYBO - Yeast - Gilette Food Flavorings Inc.

RYBOVICH - Sporting goods - Spencer Boat Co.

RYCOM - Meters and test equipment - Rycom Instruments, Inc.

RYCOTIN - Prescription drug ☆ - IDE-Interstate Inc.

RYD-ALL - Pet products - P.M. Pet Products

RYDAL - Floor coverings–carpet and rugs - Downs Carpet Co. Inc.

RYDER CUP - Sportswear and sporting goods - Professional Golfers' Association of America

RYDER CUP II - Golfing equipment - Tommy Armour Golf Co.

RYDIAMIN - Pharmaceutical preparations ☆ - Schwarz Pharma

RYDS - Boats–motor - Outboard Marine Corp.

RYE - Frames–eyeglass - Zylo Ware Corp.

RYE - Recording label - Jewel Records

RYE CHIPS - Snack foods ☆ - General Mills, Inc.

RYE CREEK - Apparel and accessories - Garan Services Corp.

RYE DATE MUESLI - Cereal - Breadshop's Natural Foods

RYE-OLA - Pumpernickel and black bread - Iversen Baking Co.

RYELAND - Floor coverings–carpet and rugs - Tuftex Carpet Mills, Inc.

RYG - Navigational instruments - Russell Sailboats Inc.

RYGJA - Yarn - William Unger & Co. Inc.

RYKA - Cases–camera - Ryka Associates, Inc.

RYKA - Photographic equipment - Saul Bower Inc.

RYKO ANALOGUE - Recording label - Rykodisc Inc.

RYKO VISION - Recording label - Rykodisc Inc.

RYKODISC - Recording label - Rykodisc Inc.

RYKOFF INTERNATIONAL - Food products - US Foodservice

RYKOFF SEXTON CONNOISSEUR ALAMO ZESTFUL - Seasonings - Rykoff-Sexton, Inc.

RYKOFF SEXTON CURE SUPREME - Hams - Rykoff-Sexton, Inc.

RYKOFF SEXTON FLAV-R-MATE - Shortening - Rykoff-Sexton, Inc.

RYKOFF SEXTON GOLDEN EXTENDA FRY - Shortening - Rykoff-Sexton, Inc.

RYKOFF-SEXTON INTERNATIONAL - Food products - US Foodservice

RYKOFF SEXTON NATURE'S BEGINNINGS - Water–bottled or canned - Rykoff-Sexton, Inc.

RYKOFF SEXTON OLD FASHIONED COUNTRY KETTLE - Preserved foods–canned - Rykoff-Sexton, Inc.

RYKOFF SEXTON PAN REDDY - Bacon - Rykoff-Sexton, Inc.

RYKOFF SEXTON PREMIUM PAK - Beverages - Rykoff-Sexton, Inc.

RYKOFF SEXTON TROPICAL BREEZE - Teas - Rykoff-Sexton, Inc.

RYKRISP - Crackers - Ralston Purina Co.

RYLER STYLERS - Hair care products - Ry-Al Beauty Corp.

RYLON - Paints - Touraine Paints Inc.

RYMED - Pharmaceutical preparations - Edwards Pharmaceuticals, Inc.

RYMED-JR - Pharmaceutical preparations ☆ - Edwards Pharmaceuticals, Inc.

RYMED-TR - Pharmaceutical preparations - Edwards Pharmaceuticals, Inc.

RYNA - Antihistamine preparations - Wallace Laboratories

RYNA-C - Pharmaceutical preparations - Wallace Laboratories

RYNA-CX - Pharmaceutical preparations - Wallace Laboratories

RYNA-TUSSADINE - Antihistamine preparations ☆ - Wallace Laboratories

RYNAFORM - Building materials - Fibergrate Composite Structures

RYNAL - Pharmaceutical preparations ☆ - Blaine Co. Inc.

RYNALON - Paints - Touraine Paints Inc.

RYNATAN - Antihistamine preparations - Wallace Laboratories

RYNATAN-S - Pharmaceutical preparations - Wallace Laboratories

RYNATUSS - Antihistamine preparations - Wallace Laboratories

RYNO - Artists' materials - Gilman Brothers Co.

RYNO-SPAR - Varnishes ☆ - Pratt & Lambert United, Inc.

RYNO-TAR - Epoxy - Pratt & Lambert United, Inc.

RYNO-THANE - Enamels - Pratt & Lambert United, Inc.

RYNOLITE - Finishing agents - Farwest Paint Manufacturing Co. Inc.

RYNOSEAL - Adhesives and sealants ☆ - Pratt & Lambert United, Inc.

RYO FILTERMATIC - Cigarette filters ☆ - Sutliff Tobacco Co.

RYOBI - Fishing tackle - Ryobi America Corp.

RYOBI DOORMAN - Door openers–electronic - Ryobi America Corp.

RYON - Saddles - Luskey's Western Stores, Inc.

RYPLEX - Paints - Touraine Paints Inc.

RYTHM - Furniture ☆ - Bassett Furniture Industries, Inc.

RYTHROSITE - Pharmaceutical preparations ☆ - Xttrium Laboratories Inc.

RYTHYM STRIDE - Apparel–women's - Cupid Foundations Inc.

RYTRON-B - Pharmaceutical preparations - Wesley Pharmacal Co. Inc.

RYVITA - Crackers - Peacock Foods Inc.

RYZA-GESIC - Pharmaceutical preparations - Dade Pharmaceuticals Inc.

RZ - Recording label - Flat Town Music Co.

RZ67 PROII - Cameras - Mamiya America Corp.